SWANN
AUCTIONS

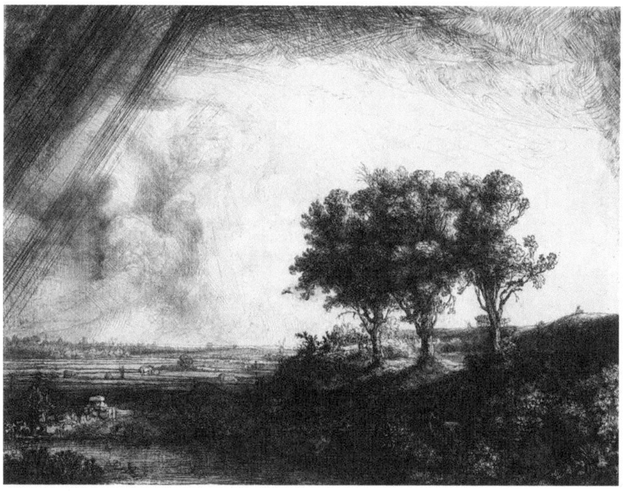

Rembrandt,
The Three Trees,
etching, engraving
and drypoint, 1643,
sold on
November 6, 2003
for $164,750.

Beggarstaff Brothers,
A Trip to Chinatown,
color lithograph poster,
London, 1894, sold on May
10, 2004 for an artists'
record $43,700.

Carleton Watkins album,
Yo-Semite Valley,
with 51 albumen prints,
San Francisco, 1863, sold on
May 20, 2004
for $115,000.

19th & 20th Century Photographs
Inquiries: Daile Kaplan • dkaplan@swanngalleries.com • 212-254-4710, ext 21

Prints & Drawings
Inquiries: Todd Weyman • tweyman@swanngalleries.com • 212-254-4710, ext 32

Vintage Posters
Inquiries: Nicholas D. Lowry • nlowry@swanngalleries.com • 212-254-4710, ext 53

Catalogues and complete auction schedule online at www.swanngalleries.com.

AUTOGRAPHS
BOOKS/MANUSCRIPTS
MAPS/ATLASES
PHOTOGRAPHS
POSTERS
WORKS OF ART ON PAPER

Swann Galleries, Inc.
104 East 25th Street, New York, NY 10010
212 254 4710 Fax: 212 979 1017

IAO

Hislop's
Art Sales Index

2005

36th annual edition

August 2003 to August 2004

Hislop's
Art Sales Index

2005

36th annual edition

August 2003 to August 2004

for

Oil Paintings, Works on Paper, Miniatures, Prints, Photographs and Sculpture

Edited by
Duncan Hislop

Published by

Art Sales Index Ltd
194 Thorpe Lea Road, Egham, Surrey, TW20 8HA, England

ISBN 0 903872 81 1

Published, computer composition and typeset by
Art Sales Index Ltd
194 Thorpe Lea Road, Egham, Surrey TW20 8HA, England
Tel: ++ 44 (0) 1784 451145 Fax: ++ 44 (0) 1784 451144
Email: info@art-sales-index.com Internet: www.art-sales-index.com

Printed and bound by
Polestar
Exeter,Devon

Contents

Contents

INTRODUCTION
The Art Sales Index contains the price and details of Oil Paintings, Watercolours, Drawings, Miniatures, Prints and Sculpture sold at public auction around the world during the twelve month period of the international auction season, from August in one year until August in the following year. The works of 40,000 Old Master, 19th Century, Modern and Contemporary artists are represented. ASI records in the region of 140,000 sale results each season and handles around 3,000 catalogues from 450 different auctioneers. Sale prices are listed in ascending order. For each artist, Oil Paintings are given first, followed by Prints, Sculpture, Miniatures, Works on Paper which includes crayon, drawings, gouache, pastel, pencil, watercolour and mixed media ending with Photographs.

Starting Price
Items for the different media qualify for entry when they exceed a certain "starting" price. Over the years, starting prices have been adjusted to take inflation into account. Currently these are £250/$400/400 Euro for Oil Paintings and Works on Paper. £1000/$1500/1500 Euro for Miniatures and Sculpture. £2000/$3000/3000 Euro for Prints and Photographs. £5000/$7000/7000 Euro for the categories 'after', 'circle', 'style', 'follower', 'studio' and for Schools of a country.

Sources of information
Over the last thirty six years ASI has gained considerable experience in accurately extracting information from auction catalogues, price lists and other information provided by auctioneers. Each catalogue is processed by at least six trained personnel. However, ASI cannot be held responsible for errors unwittingly made, nor for unknowingly reproducing incorrect information. ASI cannot vouch for the authenticity of pictures recorded. Here we must rely on the reputation and integrity of the auctioneer. The price a picture reaches at auction can be influenced by many factors, condition, subject matter and size are just a few. We recommend that the reader makes a thorough research when buying and selling at auction, consulting reference books and obtaining advice from experienced sources.

"Bought-in" pictures
Pictures offered for sale at auction usually have a "reserve" placed on them by the owner in order that they should not be sold at a price, which he considers to be below their real value.The Auction House may provide estimates as a guide to the potential buyer. If the bidding does not reach the reserve, the pictures are deemed to have been unsold. These lots are known as "bought-in". ASI does not record "bought-in" works. The majority of auctioneers exclude these "bought-in" prices from their price lists. However, there might be occasions when a "bought-in" price is inadvertently included. If any price is of particular importance to a subscriber, then he would be advised to check directly with the auctioneer.

Prices, buyer's premium and exchange rates
ASI does not include the Buyer's Premium. The price recorded is the "hammer" price, which is the value called out at auction and at which the item is "knocked down" to the bidder. Buyer's and seller's premiums can vary between auction houses, in recent years prices over a certain value attract different rates. The following example for Sotheby's is 19.5% on the first £70,000 or $100,000 and 10% on the remainder. Local taxes may also need to be taken into consideration. During the course of the auction season, all entries to the ASI Data Bank are made at the weekly exchange rate applicable to the date of the sale.

Presentation of artists' names
The convention adopted by ASI in the presentation of artists' names is to show the surname first, followed by the forenames, followed by the "de", "de la", "van" and "von" etc. Hence, Sir Anthony van Dyck is listed as "DYCK, Sir Anthony van." Le Corbusier is shown as "CORBUSIER, le". An exception is made where the "de", etc is embedded in the name, for example: Anne Louis Girodet de Roucy Trioson is shown as "GIRODET DE ROUCY TRIOSON, Anne Louis". Where the qualifications "after", "circle", "attrib", "studio" and "style" are used, they are shown after the name. A picture catalogued as "Style of Abraham Calraet" is shown as "CALRAET, Abraham (style)".

Wherever possible, ASI uses the name given by the auctioneer in the sale catalogue. Obvious spelling mistakes are corrected but other changes are kept to a minimum. However, in some instances, and especially with Old Masters, it is necessary to adopt standardisatio, (there are 15 ways of spelling Bartholomew in European language. Also, the presentation of an artist's name is not uniform throughout the world. But there are certain "conventions" which responsible auctioneers follow.

Average Weekly exchange rates to the Pound Sterling over the past five seasons

Country and Currency Code	Auction Season 2003/2004	2002/2003	2001/2002	2000/2001	1999/2000
Australia (A.D)	2.44	2.70	2.75	2.72	2.54
Austria (A.S)	-	-	22.17	22.44	21.99
Belgium (B.FR)	-	-	65.00	65.80	64.46
Brazil (B.R)	5.46	-	-	-	-
Canada (C.D)	2.34	2.39	2.28	2.20	2.33
Czech Republic (C.KR)	47.16	47.03	51.28	56.61	57.71
Denmark (D.KR)	10.86	11.21	13.15	12.16	11.90
Eire (E.P)	-	-	1.26	1.28	1.25
Europe (Euro)	1.46	1.51	1.6	1.6	-
Finland (F.M)	-	-	9.58	9.69	9.48
France (F.FR)	-	-	10.57	10.69	10.49
Germany (DM)	-	-	3.15	3.19	3.12
Greece (G.D)	-	-	549.11	554.78	545.66
Hong Kong (HK.D)	13.60	12.43	11.34	11.26	12.34
Hungary (H.F)	375.80	370.33	396.52	418.04	-
Italy (I.L)	-	-	3120.28	3158.42	3094.08
Mexico (M.P)	19.44	16.52	13.56	13.60	15.01
Netherlands (D.FL)	-	-	3.55	3.59	3.51
New Zealand (NZ.D)	2.77	3.03	3.32	3.44	3.19
Norway (N.KR)	12.17	11.46	12.49	13.15	13.09
Poland (P.Z)	6.79	6.29	5.98	6.12	6.65
Singapore (S.D)	3.00	2.79	2.62	2.55	2.69
Slovakia (SL.K)	59.57	60.06	-	-	-
South Africa (SA.R)	11.95	14.07	14.85	11.14	10.14
Spain (S.P)	-	-	268.12	271.40	265.85
Sweden (S.KR)	13.29	13.81	14.89	14.41	13.58
Switzerland (S.FR)	2.27	2.23	2.36	2.49	2.53
Taiwan (T.D)	-	54.93	50.058	46.07	51.32
USA (US.D)	1.75	1.59	1.45	1.44	1.58

Note 1: Exchange rates used throughout the year are those applicable to the date of the sale.
Note 2: Sales in Argentina, Guatemala, Israel, Morocco, Russia, Uruguay and Venezuela are recorded in US Dollars.
Note 3: Since 2002, Austria, Belgium, Eire, Finland, France, Germany, Greece, Italy, Netherlands, Portugal and Spain are recorded in Euros.

These conventions are best illustrated by quoting directly from a Christie's catalogue:

a) a work catalogued with the name(s) or recognised designation of an artist, without qualification, is in our opinion a work by the artist;

b) in other cases, in our opinion, the following expressions, with the following meanings are used:

attributed to probably a work by the artist in whole or in part (ASI use "attrib");
studio of a work by an unknown hand in the studio of the artist which may or may not have been executed under the artist's direction (ASI use "studio");
circle of a work by an (as yet) unidentified but distinct hand, closely associated with the named artist but not necessarily his pupil (ASI use "circle");
style/follower of a work by a painter working in the artist's style, contemporary or nearly contemporary, but not neccessarily his pupil (ASI use "style");
manner of a work executed in the artist's style but of a later date (ASI use "style");
after a copy (of any date) of a known work of the artist (ASI use "after").

Note also the views on signatures as recorded in Sotheby's catalogues:

a) references to signature, inscription, dates refer to the present state of the work;

b) the term "bears a signature" and/or "date" and/or "inscription" means that in our opinion the artist's name and/or date and/or inscription have been added by another hand;

c) the term "signed" and/or "dated" and/or "inscribed" means that in our opinion the signature and/or date and/or inscription are from the hand of the artist.

Medium and dimensions

All pictures listed are oil on canvas unless otherwise stated. Sales in other media follow afterwards. The measurements of pictures are "height by width" and measurements of 3-dimensional pieces are "height by width by depth".

Abbreviations

Abbreviations used in the index include:

attrib = attributed to	exhib = exhibited	pat = patina
b/w = black and white	f = foundry	prov = provenance
bears sig = bears signature	fl = flourished	/R = illustrated in catalogue
C = Century	htd = heightened	rec = rectangular
c. = circa	i = inscribed	rem = remains of
chk = chalk	in = inches	s = signed
chl = charcoal	incl = including	sig = signature
cm = centimetres	indis = indistinct	snr = senior
col = colour	init = initials	st = stamped
d = dated	jnr = junior	W/C = watercolour
dr = drawing	lit = literature	? = unknown dates and nationality of artist
est = estimate	mono = monogram	# = lot number
exec = executed	num = number	

How to read an entry:

LEEUW, Adrian de (1859-1926) Belgian

£1389 $2333 €2500 Horse drawn carriage in winter (67x107cm-26x42in) s.d. 5-Mar-3 Koller, Zurich #6483/R est:2500-3500 (S.FR 3500)

LEEUW, Adrian de	artist's name
(1859-1926) Belgian	artist's dates of birth and death and nationality
£1389 $2333 €2500	hammer price realised in Pounds Sterling, US Dollars and Euro
Horse drawn carriage in winter	title or description of picture
(67x107cm-26x42in)	dimensions, height by width in centimetres & inches
s.d.	signed and dated
5-Mar-3	date of auction
Koller, Zurich	auctioneer's name and place of sale
#6483/R	lot number and reproduced in the sale catalogue
est:2500-3500	low and high estimate in currency of sale
(S.FR 3500)	currency of sale and local price

INTRODUCTION

Le volume d'Art Sales Index (Répertoire des Ventes d'Oeuvres d'Art) donnent le prix et les détails relatifs à des peintures à l'huile, aquarelles, dessins, estampes et sculptures vendus aux enchères dans le monde entier au cours des douze mois écoulés-du mois d'août au mois de juillet de l'année suivante. Nous appelons cette période la "saison de ventes". Dans ces deux volumes figurent quelques 40,000 Maitres anciens, artistes du 19ème siècle, artistes modernes et contemporains. Chaque saison, L'ASI traite plus de 140,000 résultats de ventes et dispose de 3,000 catalogues de vente provenant de 450 commissaires-priseurs différents.Les oeuvres en tous genres peuvent être répertoriées lorsque leur prix initial dépasse un certain seuil. Au fil des ans, les prix initiaux ont été relevés pour tenir compte de l'inflation. Les niveaux de prix pour la saison figurent à la page des sous-titres du chapitre approprié. Les Prix de vente sont répertoriés par ordre croissant. Pour chaque artiste, les peintures à l'huile figurent en première place, suivies des aquarelles, dessins, miniatures et des sculptures. Chacune des techniques est differenciées par sections.

Sources d'Information

Le Répertoire est compilé à partir de catalogues, de listes de prix et autres informations fournies par les commissaires-priseurs. L'ASI recueille les informations avec le plus grand soin. Toutefois, l'ASI ne peut être tenu responsable des erreurs accidentelles ni de la reproduction involontaire d'informations erronnées. L'ASI ne peut pas garantir l'authenticité des tableaux répertoriés. La réputation et l'intégrité du commissaire-priseur en sont le meilleur garant.

Tableaux "rachetés" (ou "Invendus")

Le propriétaire d'un tableau mis aux enchères place généralement une "réserve" sur ce tableau pour éviter qu'il ne soit vendu à un prix qu'il considère inférieur à sa valeur réelle. Si les enchères n'atteignent pas ce niveau, on considère que le tableau n'a pas été vendu. En Angleterre, ces articles sont appelés "Rachetés" (ou Invendus) L'ASI ne répertorie que les ventes réelles: les prix "rachetés" ne sont pas enregistrés. La plupart des commissaires-priseurs principaux ne font pas figurer les prix "rachetés" sur leurs listes de prix. Il peut cependant arriver que des commissaires-priseurs fassent figurer ces prix "rachetés" sur leurs listes. L'ASI n'est pas toujours à même de faire la distinction. Lorsqu'un prix spécifique est d'une importance capitale il est conseillé de procéder à une vérification auprès des commissaires-priseurs eux-mêmes.

Prix, taux de change et commission

Le prix indiqué par l'ASI est, dans tous les cas, le prix "du marteau" celui qui est atteint lors des enchères et auquel l'oeuvre est adjugée à l'enchérisseur. Dans la plupart des pays, l'acheteur doit s'attendre à payer des frais supplémentaires de 5 à 15%. Au Royaume-Uni, ces frais sont appelés "Buyer's Premium" (Commission). Cette commission n'est pas comprise dans le prix indiqué. Les impôts locaux ou nationaux, les commissions ne sont pas non plus ajoutés au prix indiqué. Lorsqu'une "paire" de tableaux a été vendue, le prix s'entend pour la paire, et non pour chacun des tableaux.

Présentation du nom des artistes

L'ASI a convenu de présenter le nom des artistes en faisant figurer d'abord le nom de famille, puis les prénoms, puis les particules "de", "de la", "van", "von", etc. Ainsi, Sir Anthony van Dyck figure sous "DYCK, Sir Anthony van". Le Corbusier figure sous "CORBUSIER, le". Une exception est faite lorsque le "de" etc fait partie intégrante du nom, par exemple: Anne Louis Girodet de Roucy Trioson figure sous "GIROUDET DE ROUCY TRIOSON, Anne Louis". Lorsque les termes "d'apres", "cercle de", "attrib", "atelier de" et "style" sont utilisés, ils viennent après le nom. Un tableau répertorié "Style d'Abraham Calraet" figure sous "CALRAET, Abraham (style)". Dans toute la mesure du possible, l'ASI utilise le nom donné par le commissaire-priseur dans le catalogue de vente. Les fautes trop évidentes sont rectifiées, mais on limite autant que possible les autres modifications. Pourtant, dans certains cas - tout particulièrement avec les maîtres anciens - il convient d'adopter un nom standard (le nom Bartholomew revêt quinze orthographes différentes dans les langues européennes!) De plus, la présentation du nom d'un artiste n'est pas uniforme dans le monde entier. Mais il existe certaines "conventions" que les commissaires-priseurs sérieux suivent généralement. Le plus simple est de citer directement un catalogue de Christie's:

a) Une oeuvre cataloguée avec le(s) nom(s) ou la désignation, reconnue d'un artiste, sans autre qualificatif, est selon nous l'oeuvre de cet artiste.

b) Dans les autres cas, on utilise les expressions suivantes, qui signifient:

attribué à	Selon nous, probablement une oeuvre de l'artiste en totalité ou en partie (l'ASI utilise "attrib")
atelier de	Selon nous, une oeuvre exécutée dans l'atelier de l'artiste, et peut-être supervisée par lui (l'ASI utilise "studio")
cercle de	Selon nous, une oeuvre de la période de l'artiste et témoignant de son influence (l'ASI utilise "circle")
dans le style de	Selon nous, une oeuvre exécutée dans le style de l'artiste, mais pas nécessairement par un élève (l'ASI utilise "style")
a la manière de	Selon nous, une oeuvre exécutée dans le style de l'artiste, mais à une date ultérieure (l'ASI utilise "style")
d'après	Selon nous, une copie (date quelconque) d'une oeuvre de l'artiste (l'ASI utilise "after")

Noter également le point de vue sur la signature tel qu'il figure sur les catalogues de Sotheby's:

a) Les références à la signature, à l'inspection et aux dates visent l'état actuel de l'oeuvre.

b) Le terme porte une "signature" et/ou une "date" et/ou une "inscription" signifie que, selon nous, le nom de l'artiste et/ou la date et/ou l'inscription ont été ajoutés par une autre main.

c) Le terme "signé" et/ou "daté" et/ou "inscrit" signifie que, selon nous, la signature et/ou la date et/ou l'inscription sont de la main de l'artiste.

Types d'oeuvres et dimentions

Chaque artiste à sa section. Il y à la section huile qui figure toujours en première place, puis la section aquarelle, dessin, miniature et aussi la section sculpture. Les dimensions des tableaux s'entendent "hauteur x largeur" et les dimensions des pièces tridimentionnelles s'entendent "hauteur x largeur x profondeur".

Abréviations

Les abréviations utilisées dans le Répertoire sont:

attrib = attribué à	exhib = exposer	pat = patiné
b/w = noir et blanc	f = la fonderie	prov = provenance
bears sig = porte signature	fl = fleuri	/R = illustré sur catalogue
C = siècle	htd = rehaussé	rec = rectangulaire
c. = environ	i = inscrit	rem = rappeler de
chk = craiel	ins = les pouces	s = signé
chl = fusain	incl = inclus	sig = signature
cm = centimètres	indis = illisible	snr = senior
col = couleur	inits = initiales	st = porte un cachet
d = daté	jnr = junior	W/C = aquarelle
dr = dessin	lit = litérature	# = numero de lot
est = estimation	mono = monogramme	(?) = nationalité et dates de l'artiste inconnues
exec = realiser	num = numero	

Comment lire une entrée

ADNET, Françoise (1924-) French

£674 $1025 €1200 La poupée à la pendule Louis XVI (45x54cm-18x21in) s. 6-Nov-3 Beaussant & Lefevre, Paris #72

ADNET, Françoise	Nom et prénom de l'artiste
(1924-) French	Nationalité de l'artiste: Dates de naissance et décès
£674 $1025 €1200	Prix obtenu en livres, dollars et en Euro
La poupée à la pendule Louis XVI	Titre ou description du tableau
(45x54cm - 18x21in)	Dimensions, hauteur par largeur, en cms et pouces
s.	Signé
6-Nov-3	Date de la vente aux enchères
Beaussant & Lefevre, Paris	Commissaires-priseurs
#72	No de lot du tableau

EINLEITUNG
Die Art Sales Index enthalten Preise und Details über Ölgemälde, Aquarelle, Zeichnungen, Miniaturen, Druckgraphiken und Skulpturen, die auf weltweiten, öffentlichen Auktionen während der 12- monatigen Auktionssaison (von August eines Jahres bis August des nächsten Jahres) verkauft wurden. Werke von etwa 40.000 Künstlern, dazu zählen alte Meister, die Künstler des 19. Jahrhundert sowie moderne und zeitgenössische Künstler, sind in beiden Bänden aufgeführt. Art Sales Index bearbeitet jede Saison etwa 140.000 Verkaufsergebnisse aus über 3,000 Katalogen von 450 verschiedenen Auktionatoren. Verkaufspreise stehen in aufsteigender Reihenfolge. Für jeden Künstler werden zuerst Ölgemälde augeführt, gefolgt von Druckgraphiken, Skulpturen, Miniaturen und Werken auf Papier, die Kreide, Zeichenstift, Gouache, Bleistift, Aquarelle und gemischte Medien enthalten.

PREISGRENZE
Die Kunstobjekte der verschiedenen Medien kommen dann für eine Eintragung in Frage, wenn sie über einer bestimmten Preisgrenze liegen. Um den Inflationsfaktor zu berücksichtigen, hat sich diese Grenze über die Jahre hin verändert. Momentan ist der Limitpreis 400 Euro für Ölgemälde und Aquarelle, 1.500 Euro für Skulpturen und Miniaturen, 7.000 Euro für die Kategorien "Nach, Umkreis, Art, Studio", Schule eines Landes oder Druckgraphiken.

VERÄNDERUNGEN FÜR DIESE JAHRESAUSGABE
In der diesjährigen Ausgabe gab es ein paar Veränderungen. In jeder Saison erhält ASI mehr Kunstkataloge von einer grösseren Anzahl von Auktionshäuser. Um diese erhöhte Anzahl von Eintragungen zu erfassen, haben wir die Dimensionen des Buches vergrössert. Das verbeserte Seitenformat macht Eintragungen leichter lesbar. Art Sales Index führt ein sehr straffes Produktionsprogramm, sodass wir bereits vier Wochen nach Ende der Auktionssaison in Druck gehen können. Aus diesem Grund ist der Art Sales Index zu Beginn der neuen Saison erhältlich. Da manche Auktionshäuser ihre Kataloge und Preislisten nicht rechtzeitig senden oder Nachfragen nicht termingerecht beantwortet können, schliessen wir in der diesjährigen Ausgabe solche Verkäufe von der vorhergehenden Saison mit ein.

BEZUGSQUELLEN FÜR INFORMATIONEN
Unsere vierzigjährige Erfahrung ermöglicht es us, detailierte und exakte Informationen aus Katalogen, Preislisten und anderen Informationsquellen von Autionatoren zu entnehmen. Jeder Katalog wird von mindestens sechs geschulten Mitarbeitern bearbeitet. Allerdings kann Art Sakes Index keine Verantwortung oder Haftung für Fehler oder falsche Information, die unbewusst abgedruckt worden sind, übernehmen. Art Sales Index übernimmt keine Garantie für die Echtheit der aufgeführten Bilder. Wir verlassen uns auf den Ruf und die Integrität des Auktionators. Der Preis, der für ein Bild bei der Auktion erreicht wird, hängt von vielen Faktoren ab. Zustand, Thema und Grösse sind nur ein paar. Wir empfehlen dem Leser vor Kauf und Verkauf durch Auktionen genaue Nachforschungen anzustellen, Nachschlagwerke einzusehen und Rat von erfahrenen Quellen zu beziehen.

UNVERKAUFTE LOSE
Gemälde, die auf Auktionen zum Verkauf angeboten werden, sind vom Besitzter gewöhnlich mit einen 'Niedrigstpreis' eingereicht worden, damit sie nicht zu einem Preis verkauft werden, der zu tief unter dem tatsächlichen Wert liegt. Das Auktionshaus kann eine Schätzung als Richtlinie für den Käufer erstellen. Wird dieser Limitpreis beim Bieten nicht erreicht, so werden diese Lose als nicht verkauft betrachtet und als 'bought-in' beschrieben, die von ASI nicht verzeichnet werden. Obwohl die meisten Auktionshäuser die unverkauften Lose nicht in ihre Preislisten einschliessen, könnte es jedoch vorkommen, dass ein 'bought-in' Preis unabsichtlich aufgeführt worden ist. Müssten Sie über einen gewissen Preis absolute Sicherheit haben, raten wir Ihnen, direkt beim Auktionator nachzufragen.

PREISE, KÄUFERPRÄMIE UND WECHSELKURSE
Die von Art Sales Index aufgeführten Preise enthalten keine Käuferprämie. Der angegebene Preis ist der Zuschlagspreis, also der Preis, der auf der Auktion ausgerufen wird und zu dem der Gegenstand dem Bieter zugeschlagen wird. Käufer- und Verkäuferprämien sind von Auktionshaus zu Auktionshaus verschieden. Sotheby's z.B. berechnet 19.5% für die ersten UK£70,000 oder $100,000 und 10% für den restlichen Betrag. Örtliche Steuern sollten ebenfalls in Erwägung gezogen werden. Während der Auktionssaison werden alle Eintragungen in der Art Sales Index Data Bank mit der wöchentlichen Umtauschrate aufgeführt, die für das Datum des Verkaufs in Frage kommt.

SCHREIBUNG DER NAMEN DER KÜNSTLER
Die Reihenfolge, in der die Namen der Künstler aufgeführt sind, ist so angeordnet, dass der Familienname zuerst, dann Vorname(n) und dahinter "de", "de la", "van" und "von" etc. stehen. Somit findet man Sir Anthony van Dyck als "DYCK, Sir Anthony van". Le Corbusier ist als "CORBUSIER, le" angegeben. Eine Ausnahme wird gemacht, wenn "de" zwischen den Namen steht, z.B. Anne Louis Girodet de Roucy Trioson wird dann als "GIRODET DE ROUCY TRIOSON, Anne Louis" aufgefuehrt. Wenn nähere Bestimmungen angegeben sind, wie "after", "circle", "attrib", "studio", stehen diese nach dem Namen. Ein Gemälde, das als "Style of Abraham Calraet" katalogisiert ist, findet man als "CALRAET, Abraham (style)".

Wo möglich, verwendet Art Sales Index den Namen, der vom Auktionator im Verkaufskatalog angegeben ist. Eindeutige Schreibfehler werden berichtigt. Andere Änderungen sind auf ein Minimum beschränkt. In manchen Fällen, besonders bei alten Meistern, ist es notwendig, eine Vereinheitlichung vorzunehmen (in den europäischen Sprachen gibt es 15 verschiedene Möglichkeiten Bartholomew zu schreiben). Hinzu kommt, dass die Namensschreibung eines Künstlers weltweit nicht universal ist. Es bestehen jedoch gewisse Richtlinien, an die sich viele Auktionatoren halten. Als bestes Beispiel geben wir einige Katalogauszüge von Christie's an:

a) Ein Werk, das mit dem Namen, bzw. den Namen oder mit dem Erkennungszeichen eines Künstlers aufgeführt ist, aber keine nähere Beschreibung hat, ist unserer Meinung nach ein Werk dieses Künstlers.

b) In anderen Fällen werden unserer Meinung nach folgende Ausdrücke mit folgenden Bedeutungen verwendet:

attributed to — Wahrscheinlich ein ganz oder zum Teil vom Künstler ausgeführtes Werk (Art Sales Index verwendet die Bezeichnung "attrib")

studio of	Ein Werk von unbekannter Hand, das im Studio des Künstlers mit oder ohne dessen Aufsicht entstanden ist. (Art Sales Index verwendet die Bezeichnung "studio")
circle of	Ein Werk einer (bisher) unbekannten Hand, welches unter dem Einfluss des Künstlers entstand, aber nicht unbedingt von einem seiner Schüler stammt. (Art Sales Index verwendet die Bezeichnung "circle")
style of *follower of*	Ein Werk eines Malers, der im Stil des Künstlers arbeitet, zeitgenössisch oder fast zeitgenössisch, aber nicht unbedingt sein Schüler war. (Art Sales Index verwendet die Bezeichnung "style")
manner of	Ein Werk ausgeführt im Stil des Künstlers, aber zu einem späteren Zeitpunkt. (Art Sales Index verwendet die Bezeichnung "style")
after	Eine Reproduktion (beliebiges Datum) eines Werkes des Künstlers. (Art Sales Index verwendet die Bezeichnung "after")

Bitte nehmen Sie auch die Anmerkung im Sotheby's Katalog zur Kenntnis:
a) Bemerkungen über die Unterschrift, Inschrift und Daten beziehen sich auf den gegenwärtigen Zustand des Werkes.
b) Die Bezeichnung "bears signature" (trägt Unterschrift) und/oder "date" (Datum) und/oder "inscription" (Inschrift), bedeutet unserer Meinung nach, dass die Unterschrift, und/oder Datum, und/oder Inschrift von anderer Hand hinzugefügt wurde.
c) Die Bezeichnung "signed" (unterschrieben), und/oder "date" (Datum) und/oder "inscribed" (Inschrift) bedeutet unserer Meinung nach, dass die Unterschrift, und/oder Datum, und/oder Inschrift von der Hand des Künstlers sind.

ABKÜRZUNGEN

Zu den in diesem Index verwendeten Abkürzungen gehören:

attrib = zugeschrieben
b/w = schwarz/weiss
bears sig = trägt Unterschrift
C = Jahrhundert
c = circa
chk = Kreide
chl = Kohle
cm = Zentimeter
col = Farbe
d = datiert
dr = Zeichnung
est = Schätzung
exec = ausgeführt
exhib = ausgestellt
f = Giesserei
fl = tätig
htd = gehöht
i = mit Inschrift
in = Zoll
incl = einschliesslich
indis = undeutlich
init = Initiale
jnr = Junior
lit = Literatur
mono = Monogramm
num = Nummer
pat = Patina
prov = Herkunft
/R = illustriert
rec = rechteckig
rem = Überreste
s = unterschrieben
sig = Unterschrift
snr = Senior
st = gestempelt
W/C = Aquarell
? = unbekannte Daten und Nationalität des Künstlers
= Katalog Nummer

Medien und Masse

Falls nicht anders angegeben, fallen die aufgeführten Gemälde in die Kategorie Öl auf Leinwand. Verkäufe in anderen Medien folgen anschliessend. Bildermasse sind in Höhe mal Breite angegeben. Die Masse von dreidimensionalen Werken sind in Höhe mal Breite mal Tiefe dargestellt.

WIE VERSTEHT MAN EINE EINTRAGUNG

LEEUW, Adrian de (19th C) Belgian
£1389 $2333 €2500 Horse drawn carriage in winter (67x107cm - 26x42in) s. 5-Mar-3 Koller, Zuerich #6483/R est: 2500-3500 (S.FR 3500)

LEEUW, Adrian de	Name des Künstlers
(19th C) Belgian	Geburts- und Todesjahr des Künstlers und Nationalität
£1389 $2333 €2500	erzielter Preis in Pounds Sterling, US Dollars and Euro
(67x107cm 26x42in)	Grösse, Höhe mal Breite in Zentimeter und Zoll
s.	unterschrieben
5-Mar-3	Tag der Auktion
Koller, Zurich	Name des Auktionators und Verkaufsort
# 6483	Katalognummer des Bildes
R	Reproduziert im Verkaufskatalog
est. 2500-3500	Niedriger und Hoher Schätzwert
(S.FR 3500)	Währung des Verkaufs
	Erzielter örtlicher Verkaufspreis

THE £1,000,000 CLUB

for artists whose work has sold for over £1 million during the 2003/2004 season

AVERCAMP, Hendrick (1585-1634) Dutch

£4,305,556	$7,750,000	€6,286,112	Winter scene. 22-Jan-4 Sotheby's, New York

BACON, Francis (1909-1992) British

£2,500,000	$4,550,000	€3,650,000	Study for Pope VI. 5-Feb-4 Sotheby's, London
£2,100,000	$3,864,000	€3,066,000	Three studies of Isabel Rawsthorne. 24-Jun-4 Christie's, London
£2,035,928	$3,400,000	€2,972,455	Three studies for portrait of Lucian Freud. 12-Nov-3 Sotheby's, New York
£1,400,000	$2,576,000	€2,044,000	Study for self portrait. 23-Jun-4 Sotheby's, London

BALEN, Hendrik van and BRUEGHEL, Jan (elder) (17th C) Flemish

£1,100,000	$1,903,000	€1,606,000	Virgin and Child with the infant Saint John the Baptist. 10-Dec-3 Christie's, London

BALTHUS (1908-2001) French

£1,899,441	$3,400,000	€2,773,184	Golden afternoon. 6-May-4 Sotheby's, New York
£1,800,000	$3,276,000	€2,628,000	Nu aux bras leves. 3-Feb-4 Sotheby's, London

BASQUIAT, Jean Michel (1960-1988) American

£2,455,090	$4,100,000	€3,584,431	Untitled - two heads on gold. 12-Nov-3 Sotheby's, New York
£2,200,000	$4,048,000	€3,212,000	Untitled. 23-Jun-4 Sotheby's, London
£1,061,453	$1,900,000	€1,549,721	Low pressure zone. 12-May-4 Sotheby's, New York
£1,005,587	$1,800,000	€1,468,157	Blue heads. 13-May-4 Phillips, New York

BAZILLE, Jean-Frederic (1841-1870) French

£2,653,631	$4,750,000	€3,874,301	Pots de fleurs. 5-May-4 Sotheby's, New York

BECKMANN, Max (1884-1950) German

£1,350,000	$2,470,500	€1,971,000	Woman with flowers. 2-Feb-4 Christie's, London
£1,229,050	$2,200,000	€1,794,413	Reclining nude sharply foreshortened. 6-May-4 Sotheby's, New York

BIERSTADT, Albert (1830-1902) American/German

£3,720,930	$6,400,000	€5,432,558	Yosemite valley. 3-Dec-3 Sotheby's, New York

BLAKE, William (1757-1827) British

£1,955,307	$3,500,000	€2,854,748	Good and evil angels struggling for possession of a child. 5-May-4 Sotheby's, New York

BOSSCHAERT, Ambrosius (elder) (1573-1621) Flemish

£1,578,947	$2,905,263	€2,400,000	Still life with bouquet of roses, tulips in roemer. 25-Jun-4 Piasa, Paris

BRAQUE, Georges (1882-1963) French

£1,061,453	$1,900,000	€1,549,721	Paysage de l'Estaque. 6-May-4 Sotheby's, New York
£1,061,453	$1,900,000	€1,549,721	Femme a la guitare. 6-May-4 Sotheby's, New York

BRUEGHEL, Pieter (younger) (1564-1637) Flemish

£1,150,000	$2,104,500	€1,679,000	Birdtrap. 7-Jul-4 Christie's, London

CAILLEBOTTE, Gustave (1848-1894) French

£3,529,412	$6,000,000	€5,152,942	Chemin montant. 4-Nov-3 Christie's, Rockefeller NY

CALDER, Alexander (1898-1976) American

£3,113,773	$5,200,000	€4,546,109	Untitled. 11-Nov-3 Christie's, Rockefeller NY
£1,396,648	$2,500,000	€2,039,106	Small crinkly. 12-May-4 Sotheby's, New York

CATTELAN, Maurizo (1960-) Italian

£1,033,520	$1,850,000	€1,508,939	Ballad of Trotsky. 12-May-4 Sotheby's, New York

CEZANNE, Paul (1839-1906) French

£4,588,235	$7,800,000	€6,698,823	Nature morte, pommes et poires. 5-Nov-3 Sotheby's, New York
£4,000,000	$7,320,000	€5,840,000	Grand bouquet de fleurs. 2-Feb-4 Christie's, London

CHIRICO, Giorgio de (1888-1978) Italian

£3,575,419	$6,400,000	€5,220,112	Great methaphysic. 4-May-4 Christie's, Rockefeller NY

CLOSE, Chuck (1940-) American

£1,396,648	$2,500,000	€2,039,106	Gwynne. 11-May-4 Christie's, Rockefeller NY

DADDI, Bernardo (1312-1350) Italian

£1,400,000	$2,562,000	€2,044,000	Coronation of the Vergin. 7-Jul-4 Sotheby's, London

DANLOUX, Henri Pierre (1753-1809) French

£1,229,050	$2,200,000	€1,794,413	Baron de Besenval. 27-May-4 Sotheby's, New York

DEGAS, Edgar (1834-1917) French

£4,500,000	$8,190,000	€6,570,000	Petite danseuse de quatorze ans. 3-Feb-4 Sotheby's, London
£3,700,000	$6,734,000	€5,402,000	Chevaux de courses. 21-Jun-4 Sotheby's, London
£2,178,771	$3,900,000	€3,181,006	Promenade des chevaux. 5-May-4 Sotheby's, New York
£2,178,771	$3,900,000	€3,181,006	Avant la course. 5-May-4 Sotheby's, New York

DIEBENKORN, Richard (1922-1993) American

£1,061,453	$1,900,000	€1,549,721	Ocean Park 73. 11-May-4 Christie's, Rockefeller NY

DONGEN, Kees van (1877-1968) French/Dutch

£1,300,000	$2,379,000	€1,898,000	Danseuse aux bijoux. 2-Feb-4 Christie's, London

DUBUFFET, Jean (1901-1985) French
£1,731,844 $3,100,000 €2,528,492 Vache tachetee. 11-May-4 Christie's, Rockefeller NY
£1,061,453 $1,900,000 €1,549,721 Cow with the beautiful muzzle. 12-May-4 Sotheby's, New York

DUFY, Raoul (1877-1953) French
£1,564,246 $2,800,000 €2,283,799 Fete a Sainte-Adresse. 5-May-4 Sotheby's, New York

FEININGER, Lyonel (1871-1956) American/German
£2,200,000 $4,026,000 €3,212,000 Newspaper readers II. 2-Feb-4 Christie's, London

FREUD, Lucian (1922-) British/German
£1,850,000 $3,367,000 €2,701,000 Factory in North London. 4-Feb-4 Christie's, London
£1,500,000 $2,760,000 €2,190,000 Painter, redheaded man no.II. 23-Jun-4 Sotheby's, London

GAINSBOROUGH, Thomas (1727-1788) British
£1,650,000 $2,805,000 €2,409,000 Portrait of Richard Tickell, wearing a brown coat. 27-Nov-3 Sotheby's, London

GEROME, Jean Léon (1824-1904) French
£1,700,000 $3,094,000 €2,482,000 La grande piscine a Brusa. 15-Jun-4 Sotheby's, London

GIACOMETTI, Alberto (1901-1966) Swiss
£5,058,824 $8,600,000 €7,385,883 Grande femme debout IV. 5-Nov-3 Sotheby's, New York
£1,700,000 $3,094,000 €2,482,000 Femme debout. 3-Feb-4 Sotheby's, London
£1,700,000 $3,128,000 €2,482,000 Femme de Venise VII. 22-Jun-4 Christie's, London
£1,235,294 $2,100,000 €1,803,529 Buste de Diego. 4-Nov-3 Christie's, Rockefeller NY

GOGH, Vincent van (1853-1890) Dutch
£6,176,471 $10,500,000 €9,017,648 L'allee des alyscamps. 4-Nov-3 Christie's, Rockefeller NY
£5,411,765 $9,200,000 €7,901,177 La moisson en Provence. 5-Nov-3 Sotheby's, New York
£4,600,000 $8,372,000 €6,716,000 Deux crabes. 21-Jun-4 Sotheby's, London
£4,352,941 $7,400,000 €6,355,294 Le pont de Langlois a Arles. 4-Nov-3 Christie's, Rockefeller NY
£2,294,118 $3,900,000 €3,349,412 Nature morte, branche d'amandier. 4-Nov-3 Christie's, Rockefeller NY

GRIS, Juan (1887-1927) Spanish
£3,687,151 $6,600,000 €5,383,240 Console de marbre. 6-May-4 Sotheby's, New York

HARTLEY, Marsden (1877-1943) American
£1,220,930 $2,100,000 €1,782,558 Storm down Pine Point Way, Old Orchard Beach. 3-Dec-3 Sotheby's, New York

HOCKNEY, David (1937-) British
£1,257,485 $2,100,000 €1,835,928 Portrait of Nick Wilder. 12-Nov-3 Sotheby's, New York

HOMER, Winslow (1836-1910) American
£1,193,182 $2,100,000 €1,742,046 Farmer with a pitchfork. 18-May-4 Christie's, Rockefeller NY

HOOCH, Pieter de (1629-1681) Dutch
£1,100,000 $2,013,000 €1,606,000 Card players at table. 7-Jul-4 Sotheby's, London

HUYSUM, Jan van (1682-1749) Dutch
£4,400,000 $7,612,000 €6,424,000 Still life of fruit in a basket with flowers and other fruit all upon a marble ledge. 11-Dec-3 Sotheby's, London
£2,700,000 $4,671,000 €3,942,000 Still life of flowers in a terracotta vase upon a marble ledge before a niche. 11-Dec-3 Sotheby's, London

JAWLENSKY, Alexej von (1864-1941) Russian
£4,352,941 $7,400,000 €6,355,294 Schokko - Schokko mit tellerhut. 5-Nov-3 Sotheby's, New York

JIN KUN and LIANG SHIZHENG (17/18th C) Chinese
£1,671,408 $3,008,535 €2,440,256 Emperor Qianlong's review of the Grand Parade of Troops. 26-Apr-4 Christie's, Hong Kong

JOHNS, Jasper (1930-) American
£2,814,371 $4,700,000 €4,108,982 Grey Numbers. 11-Nov-3 Christie's, Rockefeller NY
£1,564,246 $2,800,000 €2,283,799 Corpse and mirror. 12-May-4 Sotheby's, New York

KANDINSKY, Wassily (1866-1944) Russian
£2,700,000 $4,968,000 €3,942,000 Mountainous landscape. 22-Jun-4 Christie's, London

KELLY, Ellsworth (1923-) American
£1,452,514 $2,600,000 €2,120,670 Chatham XIII - yellow red. 12-May-4 Sotheby's, New York

KLIMT, Gustav (1862-1918) Austrian
£15,294,118 $26,000,000 €22,329,412 Landhaus am Attersee. 5-Nov-3 Sotheby's, New York
£1,800,000 $3,276,000 €2,628,000 Farmhouse with birch trees. 21-Jun-4 Sotheby's, London

KLINE, Franz (1910-1962) American
£1,197,605 $2,000,000 €1,748,503 Rue. 11-Nov-3 Christie's, Rockefeller NY
£1,017,964 $1,700,000 €1,486,227 Four Square. 11-Nov-3 Christie's, Rockefeller NY

KOONING, Willem de (1904-1997) American/Dutch
£5,988,024 $10,000,000 €8,742,515 Spike's folly I. 12-Nov-3 Sotheby's, New York
£1,976,048 $3,300,000 €2,885,030 Untitled XVII. 11-Nov-3 Christie's, Rockefeller NY
£1,731,844 $3,100,000 €2,528,492 Standing figure. 11-May-4 Christie's, Rockefeller NY
£1,284,916 $2,300,000 €1,875,977 Porch in a landscape. 11-May-4 Christie's, Rockefeller NY

KOONS, Jeff (1955-) American
£2,737,430 $4,900,000 €3,996,648 Jim Beam JB Turner train. 11-May-4 Christie's, Rockefeller NY
£1,077,844 $1,800,000 €1,573,652 Lifeboat. 11-Nov-3 Christie's, Rockefeller NY

KRASNER, Lee (1908-1984) American
£1,017,964 $1,700,000 €1,486,227 Celebration. 11-Nov-3 Christie's, Rockefeller NY

LEGER, Fernand (1881-1955) French
£11,764,707 $20,000,000 €17,176,472 La femme en rouge et vert. 4-Nov-3 Christie's, Rockefeller NY
£1,229,050 $2,200,000 €1,794,413 Deux femmes a l'enfant. 4-May-4 Christie's, Rockefeller NY

LEMPICKA, Tamara de (1898-1980) Polish
£2,290,503 $4,100,000 €3,344,134 Portrait de Mrs Bush. 4-May-4 Christie's, Rockefeller NY

LICHTENSTEIN, Roy (1923-1997) American
£2,541,900 $4,550,000 €3,711,174 Step-on can with leg. 12-May-4 Sotheby's, New York
£1,137,725 $1,900,000 €1,661,079 Woman, sunlight, moonlight. 12-Nov-3 Sotheby's, New York

LIEVENS, Jan (1607-1674) Dutch
£1,650,000 $3,019,500 €2,409,000 Tronie. 7-Jul-4 Sotheby's, London
£1,016,484 $1,850,000 €1,484,067 Portrait of a boy in Persian dress. 17-Jun-4 Christie's, Rockefeller NY

MACKE, August (1887-1914) German
£1,500,000 $2,730,000 €2,190,000 Woman bathing. Pierrot with dancing couple. 21-Jun-4 Sotheby's, London

MANET, Edouard (1832-1883) French
£13,128,493 $23,500,000 €19,167,600 Courses au Bois de Boulogne. 5-May-4 Sotheby's, New York

MANTUA SCHOOL, 15th C
£6,200,000 $10,726,001 €9,052,000 Mars, Venus, Cupid and Vulcan. 11-Dec-3 Christie's, London

MARDEN, Brice (1938-) American
£1,317,365 $2,200,000 €1,923,353 10 dialog 2. 12-Nov-3 Sotheby's, New York

MARINI, Marino (1901-1980) Italian
£1,600,000 $2,672,000 €2,336,000 Rider. 20-Oct-3 Sotheby's, London
£1,100,000 $2,024,000 €1,606,000 Rider. 22-Jun-4 Christie's, London

MARTIN, Agnes (1912-) American/Canadian
£1,377,246 $2,300,000 €2,010,779 Leaves. 12-Nov-3 Sotheby's, New York

MATISSE, Henri (1869-1954) French
£5,900,000 $10,856,001 €8,614,000 Odalisque au fauteuil noir. 22-Jun-4 Christie's, London
£2,200,000 $4,004,000 €3,212,000 Torse nu, bras leves. 21-Jun-4 Sotheby's, London
£1,284,916 $2,300,000 €1,875,977 Les quatre rosaces aux motifs bleus. 6-May-4 Sotheby's, New York

MEIFREN Y ROIG, Eliseo (1859-1940) Spanish
£5,033,557 $9,362,417 €7,500,000 My garden. 2-Mar-4 Ansorena, Madrid

MELENDEZ, Luis (1716-1780) Italian
£2,000,000 $3,600,000 €2,920,000 Arbutus berries on a plate, apples, a wood barrel and bread rolls on a wooden table. 23-Jan-4 Christie's, Rockefeller NY
£1,000,000 $1,730,000 €1,460,000 Pears on a plate, a melon and a decorated Manises jar with plums on a wooden ledge. 10-Dec-3 Christie's, London

MIGNON, Abraham (1640-1679) German
£1,450,000 $2,508,500 €2,117,000 Still life of roses, poppies and other flowers, blackberries and redcurrants and insects. 10-Dec-3 Bonhams, New Bond Street

MILLAIS, Sir John Everett (1829-1896) British
£1,000,000 $1,820,000 €1,460,000 Cherry ripe. 1-Jul-4 Sotheby's, London

MIRO, Joan (1893-1983) Spanish
£2,681,564 $4,800,000 €3,915,083 Rouge, bleu et bel espoir. 4-May-4 Christie's, Rockefeller NY

MODIGLIANI, Amedeo (1884-1920) Italian
£14,117,648 $24,000,000 €20,611,766 Nu couche - sur le cote gauche. 4-Nov-3 Christie's, Rockefeller NY
£5,500,000 $10,010,001 €8,030,000 Garcon a la veste bleue. 21-Jun-4 Sotheby's, London
£1,400,000 $2,548,000 €2,044,000 Christina. 21-Jun-4 Bonhams, New Bond Street

MONDRIAN, Piet (1872-1944) Dutch
£1,675,978 $3,000,000 €2,446,928 Composition in blue. yellow. red and grey. 4-May-4 Christie's, Rockefeller NY
£1,450,000 $2,668,000 €2,117,000 Composition II, with red in a square. 22-Jun-4 Christie's, London

MONET, Claude (1840-1926) French
£8,379,889 $15,000,000 €12,234,638 Bassin aux nympheas. 6-May-4 Sotheby's, New York
£5,470,588 $9,300,000 €7,987,058 Nympheas. 5-Nov-3 Sotheby's, New York
£3,750,000 $6,825,000 €5,475,000 Nympheas. 21-Jun-4 Sotheby's, London
£2,450,000 $4,459,000 €3,577,000 Vetheuil. 3-Feb-4 Sotheby's, London
£2,350,000 $4,324,000 €3,431,000 Plage de Juan-les-Pins. 22-Jun-4 Christie's, London
£2,234,637 $4,000,000 €3,262,570 Bateaux sur le Galet. 5-May-4 Sotheby's, New York
£2,176,471 $3,700,000 €3,177,648 Nympheas. 4-Nov-3 Christie's, Rockefeller NY
£2,011,173 $3,600,000 €2,936,313 Paysage de printemps a Giverny. 4-May-4 Christie's, Rockefeller NY
£1,173,184 $2,100,000 €1,712,849 La Seine en crue a Vetheuil. 4-May-4 Christie's, Rockefeller NY
£1,100,000 $2,002,000 €1,606,000 Iris. 21-Jun-4 Sotheby's, London
£1,000,000 $1,700,000 €1,460,000 Le train a jeufosse. 5-Nov-3 Sotheby's, New York

MOORE, Henry O M (1898-1986) British
£3,235,294 $5,500,000 €4,723,529 Three piece reclining figure, draped. 4-Nov-3 Christie's, Rockefeller NY

MORAN, Thomas (1837-1926) American
£2,352,941 $4,400,000 €3,435,294 Mist in the Yellowstone. 24-Jul-4 Coeur d'Alene, Hayden

MUNNINGS, Sir Alfred (1878-1959) British
£3,910,615 $7,000,000 €5,709,498 The Red Prince Mare. 5-May-4 Sotheby's, New York
£1,350,000 $2,295,000 €1,971,000 Early morning on the Manton Downs. 27-Nov-3 Sotheby's, London

NEWMAN, Barnett (1905-1970) American
£1,976,048 $3,300,000 €2,885,030 White fire I. 12-Nov-3 Sotheby's, New York

PASCALI, Pino (1935-1968) Italian
£1,400,000 $2,338,000 €2,044,000 Cannone semovente. 21-Oct-3 Christie's, London

PEALE, Charles Willson (1741-1827) American
£3,125,000 $5,500,000 €4,562,500 George Washington. 18-May-4 Christie's, Rockefeller NY

PICASSO, Pablo (1881-1973) Spanish
£51,955,308 $93,000,000 €75,854,750 Garcon a la pipe. 5-May-4 Sotheby's, New York
£7,374,302 $13,200,000 €10,766,481 Sauvetage. 6-May-4 Sotheby's, New York
£5,865,922 $10,500,000 €8,564,246 Nu accroupi. 6-May-4 Sotheby's, New York
£5,117,647 $8,700,000 €7,471,765 Nu couche. 5-Nov-3 Sotheby's, New York
£4,550,000 $8,281,000 €6,643,000 Femme couchee a la meche blonde. 21-Jun-4 Sotheby's, London
£3,407,821 $6,100,000 €4,975,419 Plante de tomate. 5-May-4 Sotheby's, New York
£2,764,706 $4,700,000 €4,036,471 Femme endormie. 5-Nov-3 Sotheby's, New York
£2,500,000 $4,575,000 €3,650,000 Buste de femme. 2-Feb-4 Christie's, London
£2,200,000 $4,004,000 €3,212,000 Femme assise au chapeau de paille. 3-Feb-4 Sotheby's, London
£2,200,000 $4,004,000 €3,212,000 Mousquetaire et nu couche. 3-Feb-4 Sotheby's, London
£2,122,905 $3,800,000 €3,099,441 Femme assise. 6-May-4 Sotheby's, New York
£2,117,647 $3,600,000 €3,091,765 Personnage a la pipe. 5-Nov-3 Sotheby's, New York
£2,000,000 $3,640,000 €2,920,000 Carafe et plante de tomate. 21-Jun-4 Sotheby's, London
£1,600,000 $2,928,000 €2,336,000 Guitare sur tapis rouge. 2-Feb-4 Christie's, London
£1,340,782 $2,400,000 €1,957,542 Femme assise dans un fauteuil. 4-May-4 Christie's, Rockefeller NY
£1,284,916 $2,300,000 €1,875,977 Nature morte a la cafetiere. 6-May-4 Sotheby's, New York
£1,235,294 $2,100,000 €1,803,529 La mandoliniste assise. 5-Nov-3 Sotheby's, New York
£1,058,824 $1,800,000 €1,545,883 Nu assis. 5-Nov-3 Sotheby's, New York
£1,033,520 $1,850,000 €1,508,939 Peintre et modele. 4-May-4 Christie's, Rockefeller NY
£1,005,587 $1,800,000 €1,468,157 Bouteille de Malaga. 4-May-4 Christie's, Rockefeller NY
£1,000,000 $1,820,000 €1,460,000 Tete de femme. 21-Jun-4 Sotheby's, London

PISSARRO, Camille (1830-1903) French
£1,176,471 $2,000,000 €1,717,648 Paysage a osny pres de L'Abreuvoir. 5-Nov-3 Sotheby's, New York

POLLOCK, Jackson (1912-1956) American
£5,810,056 $10,400,000 €8,482,682 Number 12. 11-May-4 Christie's, Rockefeller NY

PRENDERGAST, Maurice (1859-1924) American
£1,079,546 $1,900,000 €1,576,137 Courtyard, West End library, Boston. 18-May-4 Christie's, Rockefeller NY

RAUSCHENBERG, Robert (1925-) American
£1,452,514 $2,600,000 €2,120,670 Monk. 11-May-4 Christie's, Rockefeller NY

REDON, Odilon (1840-1916) French
£1,899,441 $3,400,000 €2,773,184 Vase au guerrier japonais. 4-May-4 Christie's, Rockefeller NY

RENOIR, Pierre Auguste (1841-1919) French
£3,600,000 $6,552,000 €5,256,000 Jeune femme se baignant. 21-Jun-4 Sotheby's, London
£2,737,430 $4,900,000 €3,996,648 Jeunes filles aux lilas. 6-May-4 Sotheby's, New York

REYNOLDS, Sir Joshua (1723-1792) British
£3,000,000 $5,460,000 €4,380,000 Portrait of Mrs Baldwin. 1-Jul-4 Sotheby's, London
£1,150,000 $1,955,000 €1,679,000 Portrait of Miss Hickey. 27-Nov-3 Sotheby's, London

RICHTER, Gerhard (1932-) German
£2,035,928 $3,400,000 €2,972,455 Zwei kerzen - two candles. 12-Nov-3 Sotheby's, New York
£1,843,576 $3,300,000 €2,691,621 4096 Farben. 11-May-4 Christie's, Rockefeller NY
£1,117,319 $2,000,000 €1,631,286 Bottle with apple. 12-May-4 Sotheby's, New York
£1,005,587 $1,800,000 €1,468,157 Wolken. 11-May-4 Christie's, Rockefeller NY

ROSSETTI, Dante Gabriel (1828-1882) British
£1,300,000 $2,392,000 €1,898,000 Pandora. 9-Jun-4 Christie's, London

ROTHKO, Mark (1903-1970) American
£4,730,539 $7,900,000 €6,906,587 No.8 - white stripe. 12-Nov-3 Sotheby's, New York
£4,469,274 $8,000,000 €6,525,140 No 15. 11-May-4 Christie's, Rockefeller NY
£3,832,336 $6,400,000 €5,595,211 Untitled. 11-Nov-3 Christie's, Rockefeller NY

RUBENS, Sir Peter Paul (1577-1640) Flemish
£2,200,000 $4,026,000 €3,212,000 Night scene with old lady holding basket and candle. 7-Jul-4 Sotheby's, London

RUSCHA, Edward (1937-) American

£1,787,710	$3,200,000	€2,610,057	Damage. 11-May-4 Christie's, Rockefeller NY
£1,017,964	$1,700,000	€1,486,227	Not only securing the last letter but damaging it as well, boss. 12-Nov-3 Sotheby's, New York

SARGENT, John Singer (1856-1925) British/American

£4,460,228	$7,850,000	€6,511,933	Robert Louis Stevenson and his wife. 19-May-4 Sotheby's, New York
£2,840,909	$5,000,000	€4,147,727	Venetian Loggia. 19-May-4 Sotheby's, New York
£1,363,636	$2,400,000	€1,990,909	Madame Roger-Jourdain. 19-May-4 Sotheby's, New York

SCHIELE, Egon (1890-1918) Austrian

£1,700,000	$3,094,000	€2,482,000	Lovers. 21-Jun-4 Sotheby's, London
£1,350,000	$2,457,000	€1,971,000	Girl with green pinafore. 3-Feb-4 Sotheby's, London
£1,200,000	$2,184,000	€1,752,000	Reclining woman in yellow dress. 21-Jun-4 Sotheby's, London

SIGNAC, Paul (1863-1935) French

£1,550,000	$2,852,000	€2,263,000	Balises, Saint-Briac. 22-Jun-4 Christie's, London

SIGNORINI, Telemaco (1835-1901) Italian

£2,500,000	$4,250,000	€3,650,000	Tow-path. 18-Nov-3 Sotheby's, London

SISLEY, Alfred (1839-1899) French

£1,400,000	$2,548,000	€2,044,000	Route a Louveciennes. 21-Jun-4 Sotheby's, London
£1,300,000	$2,379,000	€1,898,000	Route de Marly-le-Roi. 2-Feb-4 Christie's, London

SMITH, David (1906-1965) American

£1,508,380	$2,700,000	€2,202,235	Untitled. 12-May-4 Sotheby's, New York

SOROLLA Y BASTIDA, Joaquin (1863-1923) Spanish

£3,300,000	$5,610,000	€4,818,000	Bathing time. 18-Nov-3 Sotheby's, London

SOUTINE, Chaim (1893-1943) Russian

£1,200,000	$2,184,000	€1,752,000	Femme entrant dan sl'eau. 21-Jun-4 Sotheby's, London

SPENCER, Sir Stanley (1891-1959) British

£1,100,000	$2,013,000	€1,606,000	Christ preaching at Cookham Regatta; listening from punts. 2-Jun-4 Sotheby's, London

STAEL, Nicolas de (1914-1955) French

£1,150,000	$2,093,000	€1,679,000	Mediterranee. 5-Feb-4 Sotheby's, London

STILL, Clyfford (1904-1980) American

£1,564,246	$2,800,000	€2,283,799	1960-F. 12-May-4 Sotheby's, New York
£1,017,964	$1,700,000	€1,486,227	1945-R. 11-Nov-3 Christie's, Rockefeller NY

TITIAN (c.1488-1576) Italian

£1,952,055	$3,318,493	€2,850,000	Saint Mary Magdalene. 9-Nov-3 Finarte, Venice

TURNER, Joseph Mallord William (1775-1851) British

£2,200,000	$4,004,000	€3,212,000	Fort Vimieux. 1-Jul-4 Sotheby's, London

TWOMBLY, Cy (1928-) American

£1,452,514	$2,600,000	€2,120,670	Untitled - Bolsena. 12-May-4 Sotheby's, New York

VERMEER OF DELFT, Jan (1632-1675) Dutch

£14,500,000	$26,535,000	€21,170,000	Young woman seated at virginals. 7-Jul-4 Sotheby's, London

WARHOL, Andy (1928-1987) American

£3,463,687	$6,200,000	€5,056,983	Self portrait. 11-May-4 Christie's, Rockefeller NY
£3,351,956	$6,000,000	€4,893,856	Large flowers. 11-May-4 Christie's, Rockefeller NY
£1,675,978	$3,000,000	€2,446,928	Single Elvis. 11-May-4 Christie's, Rockefeller NY
£1,452,514	$2,600,000	€2,120,670	Last Supper. 12-May-4 Sotheby's, New York
£1,197,605	$2,000,000	€1,748,503	Details of the last supper. 12-Nov-3 Sotheby's, New York
£1,197,605	$2,000,000	€1,748,503	Oxidation painting. 12-Nov-3 Sotheby's, New York
£1,005,587	$1,800,000	€1,468,157	Campbell's soup can - Clam Chowder Manhatten style. 12-May-4 Sotheby's, New York

ZOCCHI, Giuseppe (1711-1767) Italian

£1,150,000	$1,989,500	€1,679,000	Florence, view of the Piazza della Signoria and figures gathered round a puppet show. 11-Dec-3 Sotheby's, London

These 194 sales account for £550,909,179 - $973,796,211 of the total market turnover

AUCTION SEASON ANALYSIS

These tables have been compiled from sale results recorded by Art Sales Index Ltd for the 2003/2004 auction season
154,049 entries were made for 45,132 artists,
3,020 auction catalogues were received from 519 auction houses,
turnover recorded was £1.87 billion, $3.30 billion.
Total number of entries in this edition - 166,407.

Sales by Nationality of Artist or Sculptor

Country	Lots sold	UK £(m)	US $(m)
American	20,215	349.62	611.45
Australia/New Zealand	5,728	31.34	54.35
Austria	3,677	48.62	85.39
British	25,870	176.76	311.96
Belgium	5,302	27.33	48.74
Canada	3,238	17.84	31.30
Flemish	1,338	30.65	54.57
France	22,990	375.17	666.57
Germany	10,980	93.75	165.73
Netherlands	6,902	113.32	200.35
Hungary	1,299	7.53	13.21
Italy	12,172	183.29	322.30
Israel	473	2.44	4.29
Oriental	2,393	42.81	75.06
Poland	827	5.98	10.59
Russia	2,805	48.34	85.47
Scandinavia	10,122	40.86	71.83
South Africa	697	1.26	2.20
South America	2,690	27.52	48.55
Spain/Portugal	5,239	185.52	330.59
Switzerland	3,335	34.96	61.63

Number of Works Sold by Medium in Sterling Price Bands

	Works on Paper	Oils	Sculpture	Miniatures	Prints
less than 1,000	20,874	34,361	253	6	12
1,000 - 4,999	15,391	36,120	4,215	356	3,714
5,000 - 9,999	3,084	9,543	1,138	97	1,157
10,000 - 24,999	2,462	7,757	1,063	55	670
25,000 - 49,999	765	3,138	426	16	157
50,000 - 99,999	380	1,569	255	4	36
100,000 - 249,999	234	1,022	164	1	17
250,000 - 499,999	77	350	49	-	2
500,000 - 999,999	20	166	18	-	2
Over £1 million	22	155	18	-	1

Value of Works Sold by Medium in Sterling Price Bands

(figures are in Million Pounds)

	Works on Paper	Oils	Sculpture	Miniatures	Prints
less than 1,000	10.90	18.63	0.22	0.01	0.01
1,000 - 4,999	33.92	82.96	9.93	0.84	10.75
5,000 - 9,999	21.34	66.30	8.02	0.66	7.84
10,000 - 24,999	37.78	120.28	16.41	0.84	9.74
25,000 - 49,999	25.83	107.97	14.66	0.50	5.20
50,000 - 99,999	25.99	107.34	17.62	0.24	2.36
100,000 - 249,999	35.36	158.22	24.51	0.11	2.53
250,000 - 499,999	26.57	121.03	16.43	-	0.63
500,000 - 999,999	14.56	112.51	11.20	-	1.14
Over £1 million	46.39	464.18	41.46	-	1.95

Number of Works Sold by Medium in US Dollar Price Bands

	Works on Paper	Oils	Sculpture	Miniatures	Prints
less than 1,000	12,908	20,038	8	-	8
1,000 - 4,999	19,488	40,146	3,186	249	2,014
5,000 - 9,999	4,602	12,485	1,496	142	1,987
10,000 - 24,999	3,519	10,885	1,423	91	1,237
25,000 - 49,999	1,506	4,978	649	37	355
50,000 - 99,999	643	2,810	394	12	118
100,000 - 249,999	401	1,612	275	4	36
250,000 - 499,999	142	636	96	-	9
500,000 - 999,999	59	310	43	-	2
Over $1 million	41	281	29	-	2

Value of Works Sold by Medium in US Dollar Price Bands

(figures are in Million Dollars)

	Works on Paper	Oils	Sculpture	Miniatures	Prints
less than 1,000	8.63	13.58	0.01	-	0.1
1,000 - 4,999	44.98	97.01	9.43	0.75	7.80
5,000 - 9,999	32.14	88.08	10.43	1.03	13.71
10,000 - 24,999	54.94	169.13	22.61	1.37	18.61
25,000 - 49,999	52.33	173.33	22.60	1.25	11.91
50,000 - 99,999	44.14	194.64	27.15	0.75	7.79
100,000 - 249,999	60.70	246.04	41.97	0.53	5.16
250,000 - 499,999	48.66	221.36	32.58	-	3.05
500,000 - 999,999	39.17	213.03	29.33	-	1.68
Over $1 million	106.21	985.27	85.50	-	4.59

SALES BY COUNTRY

Country	Lots sold	Local Currency (m)	UK £(m)	US $(m)
Argentina US$	558	5.58	3.09	5.58
Australia	4,689	70.71	28.70	49.81
Austria	3,429	26.94	18.38	32.12
Belgium	4,942	17.10	11.69	20.57
Brazil	149	6.90	1.26	2.26
Canada	3,829	34.56	14.75	25.84
Czech Republic	291	21.81	0.46	0.81
Denmark	4,469	173.36	15.93	28.08
Eire	2,328	13.38	9.17	16.05
Finland	1,513	9.05	6.20	10.86
France	18,971	182.26	122.97	218.74
Germany	11,295	73.54	50.17	88.23
Hong Kong	950	385.97	28.35	49.55
Hungary	712	1,940.95	5.16	8.96
Israel US$	307	1.89	1.11	1.89
Italy	8,690	99.93	68.12	119.75
Mexico	97	4.58	0.24	0.41
Netherlands	4,877	39.91	27.16	47.58
New Zealand	1,393	13.61	4.93	8.53
Norway	1,189	49.46	4.12	7.20
Poland	553	11.20	1.79	3.13
Portugal	33	0.10	0.07	0.12
Russia US$	206	0.40	0.22	0.40
Singapore	368	14.74	4.94	8.65
South Africa	871	18.46	1.57	2.73
Spain	3,010	24.03	16.34	29.18
Sweden	4,036	286.90	21.47	37.61
Switzerland	4,583	70.56	31.01	55.04
United Kingdom	33,666	549.74	549.74	984.81
Uruguay US$	432	2.01	1.16	2.01
USA	30,398	1,436.97	821.45	1,436.97
Venezuela US$	519	1.55	0.89	1.55

Auction house, date, catalogue title and reference code

Please note, the absence of a catalogue indicates that no fine art was sold

AB Stockholms Auktionsverk, Stockholm - Sweden
5 Nov 3 Modern Art
3 Dec 3 Fine Art
27 Apr 4 Modern Art
26 May 4 Fine Art

Abell Auction Company, Los Angeles - USA
16 May 4 Fine Art

Adjug'art, Brest, - France
4 Nov 3 Asian Art
16 Dec 3 Fine Art
22 Jun 4 Asian Art & Paintings

Agra, Warsaw - Poland
17 Sep 3 Engravings & Sketches by Polish Artists
2 Oct 3 Polish Art
15 Oct 3 Polish Art
19 Oct 3 19th & 20th Century Polish & European Art
16 Nov 3 20th Century Fine Art
19 Nov 3 Polish Art
4 Dec 3 Polish Art
10 Dec 3 Polish Art
14 Dec 3 19th & 20th Century Polish Art
14 Mar 4 19th & 20th Century Polish & European Paintings
4 Apr 4 20th Century Art
6 May 4 Polish Contemporary Art
23 May 4 19th & 20th Century Polish & European Paintings
27 May 4 Polish Drawings & Graphics
20 Jun 4 Modern & Contemporary Art

Alderfer's, Hatfield, PA - USA
10 Sep 3 Fine Art
10 Dec 3 Fine Art
3 Mar 4 Fine Art
9 Jun 4 Fine Art

Allgauer Auktionshaus, Kempten - Germany
6 Nov 3 Autumn Fine Art Auction
8 Jan 4 Winter Fine Art Auction
22 Apr 4 Spring Fine Art Auction
8 Jul 4 Summer Fine Art Auction - S39

Altermann Galleries, Santa Fe, NM - USA
22 Aug 3 Indian Market Last Call Auction
19 Sep 3 Stan Davis & Kim MacKey collection
1 Nov 3 Paintings & Fine Art
15 May 4 Spring Auction

Altus, Berlin - Germany
22 Aug 3 Fine Art - No.162
19 Sep 3 Fine Art - No.163
17 Oct 3 Fine Art - No.164
14 Nov 3 Fine Art - No.165
12 Dec 3 Fine Art - No.166
30 Jan 4 Fine Art - No.167
27 Feb 4 Fine Art - No.168
26 Mar 4 Fine Art - No.169
23 Apr 4 Fine Art - No.170
28 May 4 Fine Art - No.171
25 Jun 4 Fine Art - No.172
23 Jul 4 Fine Art - No.173

Amberes, Antwerp - Belgium
6 Oct 3 Fine Art
1 Dec 3 Fine Art
9 Feb 4 Fine Art
22 Mar 4 Fine Art
10 May 4 Fine Art
14 Jun 4 Fine Art

Ambrose, Loughton - UK
6 Nov 3 Fine Art
10 Dec 3 Fine Art
29 Jan 4 Fine Art
26 Feb 4 Fine Art

Amersham Auction Rooms, Amersham - UK
7 Aug 3 Fine Art
4 Sep 3 Fine Art
2 Oct 3 Fine Art
5 Feb 4 Fine Art
4 Mar 4 Fine Art
1 Apr 4 Fine Art
6 May 4 Fine Art
3 Jun 4 Fine Art

Anaf, Lyon - France
19 Oct 3 Old Masters & Modern Art
30 Nov 3 20th Century Art Nouveau
8 Feb 4 17th, 18th & 19th Century Art
28 Mar 4 18th & 19th Century Art
6 Jun 4 Old Masters and Works of Art

Anderson & Garland, Newcastle - UK
23 Sep 3 Fine Art incl. Paintings
9 Dec 3 Fine Art incl. Paintings
23 Mar 4 Fine Art incl. Paintings
29 Jun 4 Fine Art incl. Paintings

Andrew Hartley, Ilkley - UK
13 Aug 3 Fine Art
8 Oct 3 Fine Art
3 Dec 3 Fine Art
12 Feb 4 Fine Art
7 Apr 4 Fine Art
16 Jun 4 Fine Art

Andrew Smith, Winchester - UK
30 Sep 3 Fine Art
2 Dec 3 Fine Art

Ansorena, Madrid - Spain
30 Sep 3 Fine Art Part I - No.256
1 Oct 3 Fine Art Part II - No.256
4 Nov 3 Fine Art - No.257
15 Dec 3 Fine Art - No.258
26 Jan 4 Fine Art - No.259
2 Mar 4 Fine Art - No.260
14 Apr 4 Fine Art - No.261

Anthemion, Cardiff - UK
17 Mar 4 Fine Art
21 Jul 4 Fine Art - No.65

Arnold, Frankfurt - Germany
6 Sep 3 Fine Art
22 Nov 3 Fine Art
29 Nov 3 Modern & Contemporary Art
6 Mar 4 Fine Art
5 Jun 4 Fine Art

Arroyo, Buenos Aires - Argentina
30 Mar 4 Paintings - No.52
4 May 4 Paintings - No.53
11 May 4 Paintings - No.54
1 Jun 4 Paintings - No.55
29 Jun 4 Paintings - No.56
5 Jul 4 Paintings No.57

Artcurial Briest, Paris - France
21 Oct 3 Collection of Bruno Mouron
21 Oct 3 Modern & Contemporary Art
8 Dec 3 Modern Art
9 Dec 3 Modern Art - Part II
9 Dec 3 Avant-gardes - 1945 to the Present
9 Dec 3 Contemporary Art
10 Dec 3 Photographs
16 Dec 3 Old Masters & Fine Art
16 Dec 3 Collection of Professor Philippe Dahhan
1 Mar 4 Prints
2 Mar 4 Modern Art
3 Mar 4 Abstract & Contemporary Art - Atelier Germain
8 Mar 4 The Estate of Mrs V - with Bailly-Pommery
27 Apr 4 Modern Art
28 Apr 4 Contemporary Art
7 Jun 4 Modern Art - Part I
7 Jun 4 Collection of Mr X, 17 Drawings from 1909 1926
8 Jun 4 Contemporary Art - Part I
8 Jun 4 Modern Art - Part II
9 Jun 4 Contemporary Art - Part II
9 Jun 4 Brut Art
10 Jun 4 Photographs
15 Jun 4 Old Master Paintings & Furniture
28 Jun 4 Automobilia & Maritime

7 Jul 4 Modern Art, Contemporary Prints & Abstract Art

Arte Maya, - Guatemala
5 Dec 3 Fine Art

Arthur James, Delray Beach, FL - USA
9 Sep 3 Fine Art
9 Dec 3 Fine Art
20 Jan 4 Fine Art
24 Feb 4 Fine Art
23 Mar 4 Fine Art
20 Apr 4 Fine Art
18 May 4 Fine Art

Artus Associes, Paris - France
30 Oct 3 Fine Art
12 Dec 3 Fine Art

Aspire, Cleveland, OH - USA
12 Sep 3 Fine Art
14 Nov 3 Fine Art
16 Jan 4 Fine Art
19 Mar 4 Fine Art
28 May 4 Fine Art

Auction Maastricht, Maastricht - Netherlands
10 Oct 3 October Online Auction
3 Dec 3 December Online Auction
4 Mar 4 March Online Auction

Auctions by the Bay, - USA
9 Aug 3 Fine Art
13 Sep 3 Fine Art
11 Oct 3 Fine Art
8 Nov 3 Fine Art
20 Nov 3 Fine Art
13 Dec 3 Fine Art
10 Jan 4 Fine Art
7 Feb 4 Fine Art
13 Mar 4 Fine Art
10 Apr 4 Fine Art
8 May 4 Fine Art
8 Jun 4 Fine Art
10 Jul 4 Fine Art

Auktion Burkard, Luzern - Switzerland
22 Nov 3 20th Century Art - Nr.56

Auktionhaus Geble, Radolfzell - Germany
8 Nov 3 Fine Art - No.66
27 Mar 4 Fine Art - No.67
3 Jul 4 Fine Art - No.68

Auktionhaus Georg Rehm, Augsburg - Germany
13 Feb 4 Fine Art - No.185
26 Mar 4 Fine Art - No.186
30 Apr 4 Fine Art - No.187

Auktionhaus Zofingen, Zofingen - Switzerland
28 Nov 3 Fine Art - No.30
4 Jun 4 Fine Art - No.31

Australian Art Auctions, Sydney - Australia
28 Jun 4 Australian & International Paintings - No.122

Babuino, Rome - Italy
18 Nov 3 Modern & Contemporary Art
1 Dec 3 Contents of a Neapolitan Villa
4 Mar 4 100 Works by Mario Sironi and Francesco de Martino's Collection
30 Mar 4 Modern & Contemporary Art
13 May 4 Paintings & Furniture from a Milan Apartment
22 Jun 4 Paintings & Decorative Arts

Badum, Bamberg - Germany
3 Apr 4 Fine Art - No.32
3 Jul 4 Modern Art & Old Masters - No.33

Bailly Pommery, Paris - France
15 Dec 3 Old Masters & Drawings, Prints & Ceramics
9 Apr 4 Succession of Mme V

Bamfords, Derby - UK
9 Sep 3 Fine Art
2 Mar 4 Fine Art

Barridoff Galleries, Portland, ME - USA
8 Aug 3 Fine American & European Art

Bassenge, Berlin - Germany
27 Nov 3 Art of 15th - 19th Centuries - No.82
27 Nov 3 Uncommon Prints - No.82
28 Nov 3 Photographs - No.82
28 Nov 3 Decorative Graphics - No.82
29 Nov 3 20th Century Art - No.82
13 May 4 15th to 19th Century Art - No.83
14 May 4 15th to 19th Century Prints and Drawings - No.83
15 May 4 20th Century Art - No.83
11 Jun 4 Photographs - No.83

Bearnes, Exeter - UK
18 Sep 3 Fine Art - EX159
14 Oct 3 Fine Art - SE33
28 Oct 3 Fine Art - EX161
18 Nov 3 Fine Art - EX162
9 Dec 3 Fine Art - No.EX163
13 Jan 4 Fine Art - EX164
2 Mar 4 Spring Sale - SE34
16 Mar 4 Fine Art - EX167
22 Mar 4 Fine Art - SF11
6 Apr 4 Fine Art - EX168
27 Apr 4 Fine Art - EX169
8 Jun 4 Fine Art - EX171
6 Jul 4 Fine Art - SE35
20 Jul 4 Fine Art - EX173

Beaussant & Lefevre, Paris - France
10 Oct 3 19th & 20th Century Photography
5 Nov 3 Old Masters & Fine Art
3 Dec 3 Modern Art, Art Nouveau & Art Deco
10 Dec 3 Important Paintings & Works of Art
11 Feb 4 Prints, Drawings, Paintings & Sculptures
19 Mar 4 Old Masters & Fine Art
28 Apr 4 Paintings & Decorative Art
27 May 4 Asian Art - with Thierry Portier
9 Jun 4 Paintings & Fine Art
16 Jun 4 Paintings & Fine Art
2 Jul 4 Manuscripts, Books & Photographs

Beeston Castle Salerooms, Tarporley - UK
29 Jun 4 Fine Art

Behringer, Furth - Germany
17 Oct 3 Fine Art - No.20
14 May 4 Fine Art - No.21

Ben-Ami, Tivoli - Israel
1 Dec 3 Paintings
1 Jan 4 Paintings
1 Feb 4 Paintings
1 Mar 4 Paintings
1 Apr 4 Paintings
1 May 4 Paintings
1 Jun 4 Paintings
1 Jul 4 Paintings

Bergmann, Erlangen - Germany
25 Oct 3 Fine Art - No.72
20 Mar 4 Fine Art - No.73
19 Jun 4 Summer Auction

Berlinghof, Heidelberg - Germany
17 Oct 3 Fine Art - No.102
12 Dec 3 Fine Art - No.103

Bernaerts, Antwerp - Belgium
15 Sep 3 Art & Antiques - No.76
20 Oct 3 Romantic & Modern Masters - No.77
17 Nov 3 Ancient & Romantic Art - No.79
15 Dec 3 Fine Art - No.80
8 Mar 4 Arts & Antiques - No.81
26 Apr 4 Arts & Antiques - No.83
24 May 4 Art & Antiques - No.84
21 Jun 4 Art & Antiques - No.85

Beurret, Zurich - Switzerland
17 May 4 Paintings from a Private Collection

Biddle & Webb, Birmingham - UK
4 Sep 3 Fine Art - No.3269
2 Oct 3 Fine Art - No.3279
17 Oct 3 Fine Art
6 Nov 3 Fine Art - No.3292
4 Dec 3 Fine Art - No.3306
5 Feb 4 Fine Art - No.3326
1 Apr 4 Fine Art - No.3349
6 May 4 Fine Art - No.3363

Bigwood, Stratford upon Avon - UK
26 Sep 3 Fine Art
28 Nov 3 Fine Art

19 Dec 3 Fine Art
26 Mar 4 Fine Art
30 Apr 4 Fine Art
28 May 4 Fine Art
25 Jun 4 Fine Art
30 Jul 4 Fine Art

Binoche, Orleans - France
25 Oct 3 Fine Art - with Ghislain de Maredsous
20 Mar 4 Fine Art
19 Jun 4 Fine Art

Binoche, Paris - France
13 Nov 3 Animal Paintings
11 Dec 3 Succession of Madame B
24 Mar 4 Modern Paintings
2 Jul 4 Sculptures, Modern & Contemporary Art

Blanchet, Paris - France
30 Sep 3 Modern Paintings & Prints
6 Oct 3 Modern Art
28 Nov 3 Modern & Contemporary Art
3 Dec 3 Paintings & Works of Art
15 Mar 4 Modern & Contemporary Art
26 May 4 19th Century Paintings, Old Masters & Drawings
15 Jun 4 Modern Paintings & Sculptures

Blomqvist, Oslo - Norway
24 Sep 3 Schoyen Collection - No.4
13 Oct 3 Autumn Auction - No.5
8 Dec 3 Christmas Auction - No.6
22 Mar 4 Paintings & Decorative Arts - No.1
7 Jun 4 Paintings & Fine Art - No.2

Blomqvist Lysaker, Oslo, Oslo - Norway
25 Aug 3 Fine Art - No.26
22 Sep 3 Fine Art - No.27
20 Oct 3 Fine Art - No.28
17 Nov 3 Fine Art - No.29
13 Dec 3 Christmas Auction - No.30
2 Feb 4 Fine Art - No.31
29 Mar 4 Fine Art - No.2
14 Jun 4 Fine Art - No.3404

Bloomsbury, London - UK
21 May 4 19th & 20th Century Photographs - No.488
27 May 4 Prints, Drawings, Maps & Atlases - No.489
2 Jul 4 Modern & Contemporary Prints & Drawings - No.493

Bloss, Merzhausen - Germany
6 Oct 3 Fine Art
8 Dec 3 Fine Art
29 Mar 4 Fine Art
28 Jun 4 Fine Art

Bolland & Marotz, Bremen - Germany
26 Sep 3 Fine Art - No.119
5 Dec 3 Fine Art - No.120
28 Feb 4 Estate of Borgward - No.550
26 Mar 4 Fine Art - No.121
18 Jun 4 Fine Art - No.122

Bolsa de Arte, Rio de Janeiro - Brazil
27 Apr 4 Fine Art
6 Jul 4 Fine Art

Bonhams, Bath - UK
20 Oct 3 Pictures - No.10564
1 Dec 3 Paintings & Works on Paper - No.10570
16 Feb 4 Pictures - No.10364
29 Mar 4 Paintings & Works on Paper - No.11117
24 May 4 County Sale - No.11123
14 Jun 4 Pictures - No.11125
21 Jun 4 Wales & the West Country - No.10566
26 Jul 4 Paintings & Works on Paper - No.11131

Bonhams, Bury St Edmunds - UK
3 Sep 3 The Athenaeum Sale - No.10521
10 Dec 3 The Athenaeum Sale - No.10647
7 Apr 4 The Athenaeum Sale - No.10949
23 Jun 4 The Athenaeum Sale - No.10950

Bonhams, Chester - UK
1 Sep 3 County Sale - No.10436 & 10437
23 Sep 3 Paintings & Prints - No.10440
29 Oct 3 The Chester Sale - No.10444
22 Nov 3 Contents of Mobberley Hall - No.10731
2 Feb 4 County Sale, Silver & Pictures - No.10716 & 10717
17 Mar 4 The Chester Sale - No.10721,10722 & 107233
6 Apr 4 Maps, Prints, Paintings & Silver - No.10725
19 Apr 4 Sporting Memorabilia - No.10726
27 Apr 4 Applied Arts & Sculptures - No.10728
8 Jun 4 Maps, Prints, Paintings & Silver - No.10969
14 Jul 4 The Chester Sale - No.10974, 10975 & 10976

Bonhams, Edinburgh - UK
21 Aug 3 The Scottish Sale - No.10198
18 Sep 3 Art & Antiques - No.10216
16 Oct 3 19th & 20th Century Pictures & Prints - No.10218
23 Oct 3 Art & Antiques - No.10665
13 Nov 3 Art & Antiques - No.10656
4 Dec 3 Fine Paintings - No.10652
18 Dec 3 Art & Antiques - No.10657
29 Jan 4 Art & Antiques - No.10899
25 Mar 4 Art & Antiques - No.10904
8 Apr 4 19th & 20th Century Pictures & Prints - No.10905
22 Apr 4 Art & Antiques - No.10906
6 May 4 Design 1860 to Present - No.10907
20 May 4 Art & Antiques - No.10908
11 Jun 4 Furniture, Clocks & Works of Art - No.10910
22 Jul 4 Art & Antiques - No.10912

Bonhams, Ipswich - UK
12 Aug 3 County Sale - No.10520
16 Sep 3 County Sale - No.10643
14 Oct 3 County Sale - No.10644
11 Nov 3 County Sale - No.10645
2 Dec 3 County Sale - No.10646
13 Jan 4 County Sale - No.10953
20 Apr 4 County Sale - No.10956
11 May 4 County Sale - No.10957
8 Jun 4 County Sale - No.10958

Bonhams, Knightsbridge - UK
5 Sep 3 Automobilia - No.10628 - Chichester
9 Sep 3 British & Continental Oil Paintings - No.10346
16 Sep 3 Modern Paintings - No.10354
23 Sep 3 British and Continental Paintings - No.10350
1 Oct 3 Marine Paintings - No.10305 & 10581
7 Oct 3 British & Continental Paintings - No.10358
14 Oct 3 British & Continental Paintings - No.10366
21 Oct 3 Modern Paintings & Sculpture - No.10363
11 Nov 3 British & Continental Oil Paintings - No.10379
18 Nov 3 Vision 21 - Paintings, Sculptures & Works on Paper - No.10397 - Brompton Room
25 Nov 3 British & Continental Paintings - No.10391 - Brompton Road
3 Dec 3 Sporting Paintings - No.10580
9 Dec 3 Old Master Drawings - No.10747
13 Jan 4 British & Continental Oil Paintings - No.10771
20 Jan 4 Modern Paintings - 10735
27 Jan 4 British & Continental Paintings - No.10767
10 Feb 4 British & Continental Oil Paintings - No.10933
17 Feb 4 Modern Paintings incl. Studio Sale of Hans Schwarz - No.10934
9 Mar 4 British & Continental Art - No.11161
16 Mar 4 Vision 21 - No.11098
23 Mar 4 British & Continental Paintings - No.11173
31 Mar 4 The Sporting Sale - No.11109
6 Apr 4 British & Continental Oil Paintings - No.11287
27 Apr 4 Modern Paintings - No.11170
11 May 4 British & Continental Oil Paintings - No.11337
18 May 4 Modern Paintings - No.11334
25 May 4 British & Continental Paintings - No.11339
8 Jun 4 British & Continental Art - No.11340
15 Jun 4 Modern Paintings - No.11341
22 Jun 4 British and Continental Paintings - No.11342
29 Jun 4 Fine Art - No.10832
6 Jul 4 British & Continental Oil Paintings - No.11343
7 Jul 4 Old Master Drawings - No.11184
13 Jul 4 Vision 21 - No.11344
13 Jul 4 Rock & Roll Memorabilia - No.11289
17 Jul 4 Traditional Rivercraft & Maritime - No.10820 - Henley-on-Thames
28 Jul 4 Sporting & Ornithological Paintings - No.11345

Bonhams, Knowle - UK
5 Aug 3 County Sale - No.10461
2 Sep 3 County Sale - No. 10462
16 Sep 3 Paintings & Works of Art - No.10464
28 Oct 3 County Sale - No.10469
25 Nov 3 Paintings incl. Works by Snaffles - No.10473

10 Feb 4 County Sale - No.11055
24 Feb 4 Paintings, Works of Art & Furniture - No.11056
9 Mar 4 County Sale - No.11059
27 Apr 4 Paintings incl. Works by Snaffles - No.11064
18 May 4 County Sale - No.11065
8 Jun 4 County Sale - No.11067
29 Jun 4 Paintings, Furniture & Works of Art - No.11069

Bonhams, Leeds - UK
9 Sep 3 County Sale - No.10416
23 Sep 3 Modern & Contemporary Pictures - No.10417
18 Nov 3 Yorkshire and 19th & 20th Century Paintings - No.10422
2 Dec 3 Fine Art - No.10423
17 Dec 3 Picture Sale - No.11097
20 Jan 4 Paintings & Prints - No.10844
16 Mar 4 Fine Art - No.10881
20 Apr 4 County Sale incl. Paintings & Prints - No.10882
15 Jun 4 Modern & Contemporary Paintings - No.10886

Bonhams, New Bond Street, London - UK
16 Sep 3 Marine Pictures - No.10191
7 Oct 3 Portrait Miniatures & Silhouettes - No.10534
14 Oct 3 Caricatures - No.10532
22 Oct 3 Modern & Contemporary Art - No.10429
29 Oct 3 Old Master Paintings - No.10457
4 Nov 3 Travel & Topographical Pictures - No.10486
4 Nov 3 Fine British & Continental Watercolours & Drawings - No.10505
18 Nov 3 Fine Portrait Miniatures - No.10578
19 Nov 3 19th Century Paintings - No.10340
1 Dec 3 Prints - No.10619
2 Dec 3 20th Century British Art - No.10535
10 Dec 3 Old Master Paintings & Drawings - No.10616
16 Dec 3 The Greek Sale - No.10584
3 Feb 4 Portrait Miniatures & Silhouettes - No.11186
17 Feb 4 Marine Paintings - No.10693
9 Mar 4 British & Continental Drawings & Watercolours - No.10765
16 Mar 4 20th Century British Art - No.10890
23 Mar 4 19th Century Paintings - No.10810
29 Mar 4 Old Master & Modern Prints - No.11049
21 Apr 4 Old Master Paintings - No.10946
22 Apr 4 The Albion Collection of Portrait Miniatures - No.11185
26 Apr 4 Automobilia - No.11092 - RAF Museum, Hendon
27 Apr 4 Travel & Topographical Pictures - No.10766
29 Apr 4 Islamic & Indian Art - No.10814
11 May 4 The Greek Sale - No.11197
13 May 4 Design 1860-1945 - No.10826
18 May 4 Photographs - No.11255
8 Jun 4 Fine British & Continental Watercolours & Drawings - No.11269
8 Jun 4 Asian Art incl. Sculptures - No.10781
15 Jun 4 20th Century British Art - No.11171
16 Jun 4 19th Century Paintings - No.11280
19 Jun 4 Automobilia - No.11237 - Boughton House
21 Jun 4 Modern & Contemporary Art - No.11174
24 Jun 4 Fine Portrait Miniatures - No.11052
25 Jun 4 Goodwood Festival of Speed - No.11094 - Goodwood House
28 Jun 4 Old Master & Modern Prints - No.11050
7 Jul 4 Old Master Paintings - No.10948
15 Jul 4 Natural History Books & Watercolours - No.11388
21 Jul 4 The Contents of Marwell House - No.11355

Bonhams, Oxford - UK
2 Sep 3 Paintings, Furniture & Works of Art - No.10518
4 Nov 3 County Sale - No.10776
9 Dec 3 Paintings, Furniture & Works of Art - No.10683
13 Jan 4 County Sale - No.10853
3 Feb 4 County Sale - No.10995
2 Mar 4 County Sale - No.10996
16 Mar 4 Paintings, Furniture & Works of Art - No.10997
30 Mar 4 County Sale - No.10999
15 Jun 4 Paintings & Fine Art - No.11005

Bonhams, Par - UK
4 Sep 3 Fine Art - No.10272
4 Dec 3 Fine Art - No.10276
4 Mar 4 Fine Art - No.11023
3 Jun 4 Fine Art - No.11027

Bonhams & Brooks, Mundford - UK
22 Mar 4 The Contents of the Old Rectory, Banningham - No.11166

Bonhams & Butterfields, Los Angeles, CA - USA
24 Aug 3 Sunset Estate Auction
28 Sep 3 Sunset Estate Auction - With Bonhams
19 Oct 3 Sunset Estate Auction
9 Nov 3 20th Century Furniture, Decorative Arts & Fine Art - No.7464N & 7468K
9 Nov 3 Modern, Contemporary & Latin American Fine Art - No.7470U
16 Nov 3 Sunset Estate Auction - No.7484T
18 Jan 4 Sunset Estate Auction - No.7500T
8 Feb 4 Revival of the Centuries - No.7503G
22 Feb 4 Sunset Estate Auction - No.7505T
21 Mar 4 Sunset Estate Auction - No.7517T
18 Apr 4 Sunset Estate Auction - No.7524T
2 May 4 Modern, Contemporary & Latin American Art - No.7529U
23 May 4 Sunset Estate Auction - No.7532T
13 Jun 4 Sunset Estate Auction - No.7540T
20 Jun 4 Furniture & Decorative Arts - No.7543V
27 Jun 4 20th Century Furniture & Decorative Arts - No.7535N/7550K
18 Jul 4 Sunset Estate Auction - No.7553T

Bonhams & Butterfields, San Francisco, CA - USA
1 Aug 3 Nautical Items - 7455M - Newport, RI
1 Aug 3 Automobilia Sale - 7451M - Newport, Ri
17 Aug 3 SoMa Estate Auction
21 Sep 3 SoMa Estate Auction - With Bonhams
30 Sep 3 Fine Asian Works Of Art
14 Oct 3 Fine Art - Hans Ricter Sale
21 Oct 3 Fine Prints & Photographs
26 Oct 3 SoMa Estate Auction
4 Nov 3 Fine Asian Works of Art - No.7474O
19 Nov 3 European Paintings - No.7476P
10 Dec 3 California & American Paintings & Sculpture - No.7479D - With Bonhams
25 Jan 4 SoMa Estate Auction - No.7502F
29 Feb 4 SoMa Estate Auction - No.7509F
15 Mar 4 European & American Furniture & Decorative Art - No.7512G
16 Mar 4 Marine Art - No.7523X
28 Mar 4 SoMa Estate Auction - No.7520F
30 Mar 4 Dogs in Art - No.10497
6 Apr 4 Asian Decorative Arts - No.7531O
6 Apr 4 Important Collection of Prints by Hiroshi Yoshida - No.7549O
19 Apr 4 Prints & Photographs - No.7525K
25 Apr 4 SoMa Estate Auction - No.7527F
2 May 4 Estate of Francoise Hermann - No.7533G - Brookline, Massachusetts
10 May 4 Asian Works of Art - No.75360
18 May 4 European Paintings - No.7534P
23 May 4 SoMa Estate Auction - No.7539F
7 Jun 4 American & European Furniture & Works of Art - No.7452G
8 Jun 4 Californian & American Sculptures & Paintings - No.7544D
14 Jun 4 Ethnographic Works of Art - No.7546E
27 Jun 4 Soma Estate Auction - No.7541F
25 Jul 4 Soma Estate Auction

Bonhams & James Adam, Dublin - Eire
10 Dec 3 Important Irish Art - No.3069

Bonhams, Brooks & Langlois, Jersey - UK
17 Sep 3 Selected Antiques & Works of Art - No.10615

Bonhams, West Country, Honiton - UK
25 Mar 4 Fine Art - No.11153

Boos Gallery, Troy, MI - USA
10 Dec 3 Fine Paintings & Decorative Art - No.239

Boscher, Cherbourg - France
11 Aug 3 Paintings
24 Nov 3 Paintings
19 Apr 4 Paintings

Bracketts, Tunbridge Wells - UK
12 Sep 3 Fine Art
30 Oct 3 Fine Art
19 Nov 3 Fine Art
12 Dec 3 Fine Art
13 Feb 4 Fine Art
2 Apr 4 Fine Art

21 May 4 Fine Art

Bretagne Encheres, Saint Malo - France
17 Apr 4 Fine Art

Brightwells, Leominster - UK
20 Aug 3 Fine Art
17 Sep 3 Fine Art
15 Oct 3 Fine Art
5 Nov 3 Fine Art
3 Dec 3 Fine Art
14 Jan 4 Fine Art
4 Feb 4 Fine Art
3 Mar 4 Fine Art
31 Mar 4 Fine Art
21 Apr 4 Fine Art
16 Jun 4 Fine Art
14 Jul 4 Fine Art

Brissoneau, France - France
12 May 4 Sculptures, Drawings, Autographs & Books

Bristol Auction Rooms, Bristol - UK
2 Sep 3 Antique & Decorative Items
30 Sep 3 Antique & Decorative Items
4 Nov 3 Antique & Decorative Items
9 Dec 3 Antique & Decorative items
27 Jan 4 Antique & Decorative Sale
2 Mar 4 Antique & Decorative Items
6 Apr 4 Antique & Decorative Items

Brunk, Ashville, NC - USA
6 Sep 3 Fine Art
3 Jan 4 Fine Art
21 Feb 4 Fine Art
10 Apr 4 Fine Art
29 May 4 Fine Art
17 Jul 4 Fine Art

Bruton Knowles, Cheltenham - UK
21 Oct 3 Fine Art
11 Dec 3 Fine Art
26 Feb 4 Fine Art

Bukowskis, Stockholm - Sweden
4 Nov 3 Modern Art - No.529
2 Dec 3 International Autumn Auction - No.530
26 Apr 4 Modern & Contemporary Art & Design - No.531
25 May 4 International Auction - No.532

Bukowskis & Horhammer, Helsinki - Finland
21 Sep 3 Fine Art - No.110
26 Oct 3 Fine Art - No.111
29 Nov 3 International Autumn Auction - No.112
8 Feb 4 Fine Art - No.113
7 Mar 4 Fine Art - No.114
8 May 4 Fine Art - No.115
9 Jun 4 Fine Art - No.116

Bunch, Chadds Ford, PA - USA
20 Apr 4 Fine Art

Bunte, Elgin, IL - USA
20 Sep 3 Fine Art

Byrne's, Chester - UK
23 Jun 4 Fine Art

C & K, Leipzig - Germany
26 Jun 4 Fine Art - No.1

CRN Auctions, Cambridge, MA - USA
16 Nov 3 European & American Art
10 Jan 4 Fine Art
16 May 4 Fine Art

Cabral Moncada Leiloes, Lisbon - Portugal
31 May 4 Fine Art - No.65

Caddigan, Hanover, MA - USA
19 Apr 4 Holiday Estates Auction

Calmels Cohen, Paris - France
27 Nov 3 Modern Paintings
2 Dec 3 Modern & Contemporary Art
21 Mar 4 Contemporary & Surrealist Art
21 Mar 4 Modern Art
4 May 4 Modern & Contemporary Art
22 Jun 4 Collection Banque Sudameris
30 Jun 4 Modern & Contemporary Art

Camard, Paris - France
16 Oct 3 Decorative Art of the 20th Century
20 Nov 3 Paintings & Fine Art
1 Dec 3 Modern Art & Sculptures
14 May 4 Art Nouveau & Art Deco
19 May 4 19th & 20th Century Russian Works of Art
8 Jun 4 Decorative Arts
10 Jun 4 Modern Art
15 Jun 4 Design

Cambi, Genoa - Italy
24 Sep 3 Fine Art
18 Nov 3 Marine Art - No.39
19 Nov 3 20th Century Fine Art - No.40
26 Feb 4 Antiques - No.42

Campo, Vlaamse Kaai, Antwerp - Belgium
21 Oct 3 Fine Art - No.57
9 Dec 3 Fine Art - No.58
30 Mar 4 Fine Art - No.59
27 Apr 4 Modern & Contemporary Art - No.60
8 Jul 4 Paintings & Antiques - No.61

Campo & Campo, Grote Steenweg, Antwerp - Belgium
21 Oct 3 Modern Art - No.54
2 Dec 3 Classic Sale - No.55
30 Mar 4 Classic Sale - No.56
27 Apr 4 Modern Art - No.57
25 May 4 Classic Sale - No.58

Cannon & Cannon, Pietermaritzburg - South Africa
24 Feb 4 Fine Art
30 Mar 4 Fine Art
25 May 4 Fine Art

Canterbury Auction Galleries, Canterbury - UK
12 Aug 3 Fine Art
14 Oct 3 Fine Art
29 Nov 3 Fine Art
2 Dec 3 Fine Art
24 Feb 4 Fine Art
20 Apr 4 Fine Art
15 Jun 4 Fine Art

Capes Dunn, Manchester - UK
16 Sep 3 Oil Paintings & Watercolours
16 Dec 3 Oil Paintings, Watercolours & Drawings
9 Mar 4 Oil Paintings, Watercolours & Prints
6 Apr 4 Oil Paintings, Watercolours and Prints
15 Jun 4 Oil Paintings, Watercolours and Prints
29 Jun 4 Oil Paintings, Watercolours & Drawings

Carlsen Gallery, Greenville - USA
28 Sep 3 Fine Art
29 Nov 3 Fine Art
18 Jan 4 Fine Art
28 Mar 4 Fine Art

Castellana, Madrid - Spain
11 Nov 3 Paintings - No.222
10 Dec 3 Paintings - No.227
14 Jan 4 Paintings - No.232

Chambelland & Giafferi, Paris - France
9 Dec 3 Old Masters & Modern Art
25 May 4 Old Masters & Modern Art

Charbonneaux, Paris - France
29 Sep 3 Paintings & Fine Art
19 Oct 3 Modern & Contemporary Art
17 Nov 3 Modern & Primitive Art
15 Dec 3 Modern & Contemporary Art
13 Feb 4 Fine Art
28 Apr 4 Modern Art
18 Jun 4 Modern & Contemporary Art

Charles Ross, - UK
22 Apr 4 Fine Art

Charlton Hall, Columbia, SC - USA
27 Sep 3 Southern Estates Auction
13 Dec 3 Southern Estates Auction
3 Apr 4 Southern Estates Auction
19 Jun 4 Southern Estates Auction
20 Jun 4 Southern Estates Auction

Charterhouse, Sherborne - UK
23 Apr 4 Fine Art
16 Jul 4 Books, Pictures & Prints

Chassaing Rivet, Toulouse - France
12 Nov 3 Paintings & Decorative Arts
22 Jun 4 Works by the Sculptor E H Duler
22 Jun 4 19th & 20th Century Paintings

Chayette & Cheval, Paris - France
25 Jan 4 Modern Paintings
17 May 4 Atelier of Paul Ackerman & Paris School

Cheffins, Cambridge - UK
10 Sep 3 Fine Art & Antiques
22 Oct 3 Fine Art & Antiques
3 Dec 3 Fine Art & Antiques
11 Feb 4 Fine Art & Antiques
10 Mar 4 Fine Art & Antiques
21 Apr 4 Fine Art & Antiques
23 Jun 4 Fine Art & Antiques
7 Jul 4 Books & Prints

Chenu & Scrive, Lyon - France
20 Apr 4 Modern Paintings
25 Apr 4 Fine Art
29 Jun 4 Fine Paintings

Chochon-Barre & Allardi, Paris - France
5 Dec 3 Old Masters, Modern Art & Sculptures
16 Mar 4 Corsia Gilbert & Kotik Pravoslav
12 May 4 Contemporary Art

Christie's, Amsterdam (Euro) - Netherlands
2 Sep 3 Pictures, Watercolours & Drawings - No.2593
28 Oct 3 19th Century European Art - No.2602
5 Nov 3 Old Master Pictures & Drawings - No.2604
18 Nov 3 20th Century Decorative Arts - No.2606
25 Nov 3 20th Century Art - No.2607
10 Dec 3 European Noble House Sale - No.2610
3 Feb 4 Pictures, Watercolours & Drawings - No.2613
16 Mar 4 Indonesian Art - No.2616
30 Mar 4 European Furniture, Sculpture & Works of Art - No.2618
21 Apr 4 19th Century European Art - No.2620
17 May 4 Old Master Paintings - No.2623
9 Jun 4 20th Century Art incl. Belgian Art - No.2626
15 Jun 4 20th Century Decorative Arts - No.2627
22 Jun 4 Pictures, Watercolours & Drawings - No.2628
1 Jul 4 Collection of the Late Mrs Doodeheefver-Toonen - No.2647

Christie's, Hong Kong
26 Oct 3 Southeast Asian Pictures - No.2147
26 Oct 3 Fine Modern & Contemporary Chinese Paintings - No.2150
26 Oct 3 20th Century Chinese Art - No.2148
26 Oct 3 Fine Classical Chinese Paintings & Calligraphy - No.2151
27 Oct 3 Chinese Ceramics & Works of Art Part I & II - No.2152
25 Apr 4 Southeast Asian & 20th Century Indian Pictures - No.2160
25 Apr 4 20th Century Chinese Art - No.2161
25 Apr 4 Fine Classical Chinese Paintings & Calligraphy - No.2163
25 Apr 4 Fine Modern and Contemporary Chinese Painting - No.2162
26 Apr 4 Imperial Sale - Fine Chinese Ceramics & Works of Art - No.2165

Christie's, London - UK
24 Sep 3 Art of India - No.6807
24 Sep 3 Exploration & Travel - No.9694
25 Sep 3 Exploration & Travel - No.6808
21 Oct 3 Italian Sale - 20th Century Art - No.6757
22 Oct 3 Post War and Contemporary Art - No.6758
29 Oct 3 Old Master Pictures - No.6817
30 Oct 3 The Scottish Sale - No.6834 - Edinburgh
12 Nov 3 Japanese Art & Design - No.6820
20 Nov 3 British Art On Paper - No.6825
21 Nov 3 20th Century British Art - No.6826
25 Nov 3 British Pictures 1500-1850 & Victorian Pictures - No.6829 & 6866
25 Nov 3 Important Russian Art - No.6827
26 Nov 3 Important British & Irish Art - No.6831
2 Dec 3 Old Master, Modern & Contemporary Prints - No.6833
3 Dec 3 19th Century European Art - No.6759
9 Dec 3 Portrait Miniatures - No.6816
10 Dec 3 Old Master Pictures - No.6837
11 Dec 3 Important European Furniture, Sculpture & Works of Art - No.6839
2 Feb 4 The Art of the Surreal - No.6870
2 Feb 4 Impressionist & Modern Art - Evening Sale - No.6882
3 Feb 4 Impressionist & Modern Art - Day Sale - No.6883
4 Feb 4 Post-War & Contemporary Art - Evening Sale - No.6885
5 Feb 4 Impressionist & Modern Works on Paper - No.6884
5 Feb 4 Post-War & Contemporary Art - Day Sale - No.6886
4 Mar 4 Collection de Madame X - No.6806
8 Mar 4 Art for Life
7 Apr 4 The Quentin Keynes Collection - No.6890
8 Apr 4 The Quentin Keynes Collection - Part III - No.6890
21 Apr 4 Old Master Pictures - No.6893
27 Apr 4 Islamic Art - No.6895
14 May 4 Irish Art incl. the William and Joan Roth Collection - No.6899
18 May 4 Important Daguerrotypes by Joseph Philibert Girault de Prangey - No.6978
19 May 4 Photographs - No.6900
21 May 4 Sporting Art - No.6902
25 May 4 Portrait Miniatures - No.6903
3 Jun 4 British Works on Paper - No.6906
4 Jun 4 20th Century British - No.6907
9 Jun 4 Important Irish & British Art - No.6911
10 Jun 4 Furniture, Decorative Arts & Sculpture - No.6912
11 Jun 4 British Pictures - No.6908
11 Jun 4 Victorian Pictures incl John Schaeffer Collection of Sculpture - No.6909
17 Jun 4 19th Century European Art - No.6916
21 Jun 4 Chirk Castle - No.7000 - Chirk Castle
22 Jun 4 Impressionist & Modern Art - Evening Sale - No.6919
23 Jun 4 Impressionist & Modern Art - Day Sale - No.6921
24 Jun 4 Impressionist & Modern Works on Paper - No.6922
24 Jun 4 Post-War & Contemporary Art - Evening Sale - No.6923
25 Jun 4 Post-War & Contemporary Art - Day Sale - No.6924
30 Jun 4 Old Master & Modern Prints - No.6920
6 Jul 4 Old Master & 19th Century Drawings - No.6926
7 Jul 4 Old Master Paintings - No.6979

Christie's, Los Angeles, CA - USA
29 Oct 3 California, Western & American Drawings, Drawings & Sculpture - No.1293
28 Apr 4 California, Western & American Paintings, Drawings & Sculptures - No.1393

Christie's, Melbourne - Australia
25 Nov 3 Australian, International & Contemporary Paintings - No.1043
30 Mar 4 Decorative Arts - No.1049
3 May 4 Australian, International & Contemporary Paintings - No.1048

Christie's, Milan - Italy
24 Nov 3 Modern & Contemporary Art - No.2434
4 Dec 3 Furniture & Works of Art - No.2435
24 May 4 Modern & Contemporary Art - No.2445

Christie's, Paris - France
30 Sep 3 Paintings & Fine Art - No.5062
21 Oct 3 Flammarion Collection - No.5074
5 Nov 3 Asian Art & Fine Art - No.5063
26 Nov 3 20th Century Decorative Arts - No.5064
2 Dec 3 Collection of Baron Hottinguer - No.5075
8 Dec 3 Paintings & Fine Art - No.5073
16 Dec 3 Paintings & Fine Art - No.5070
17 Dec 3 19th Century Drawings - No.5047
18 Mar 4 Old Master & 19th Century Drawings - No.5082
22 Apr 4 Fine Art - No.5083
29 Apr 4 Daniel Filipacchi's Library - Part I - No.5059
11 May 4 Interior Decorations - No.5103
18 May 4 20th Century Decorative Arts - No.5097
26 May 4 Impressionist & Contemporary Art - No.5096
27 May 4 Madame Bernheim's Collection - No.5104
10 Jun 4 Latin American Art - No.5106
24 Jun 4 Old Master & 19th Century Paintings - No.5087

Christie's, Rockefeller, NY - USA
23 Sep 3 Post-War & Contemporary Art - No.1269
24 Sep 3 Prints & Multiples - No.1263
25 Sep 3 Impressionist & Modern Art - No.1271
30 Sep 3 The House Sale - No.1273
9 Oct 3 Fine American Paintings - No.1276
20 Oct 3 Photographs - No.1287
21 Oct 3 Important Silver & Russian Works of Art - No.1286
28 Oct 3 19th Century Sculpture & Works of Art - No.1291
29 Oct 3 19th Century European Art - No.1290
4 Nov 3 Prints & Multiples - No.1292

4 Nov 3 Impressionist & Modern Art - Evening Sale - No.1299
5 Nov 3 Impressionist & Modern Art & Works of Paper - No.1300
11 Nov 3 Post War & Contemporary Art - No.1301
11 Nov 3 Dorothy C. Miller Collection - No.1400
12 Nov 3 Post War & Contemporary Art - Morning Session - No.1302
12 Nov 3 Post-War & Contemporary Art - Afternoon Session - No.1303
18 Nov 3 Latin American Art - No.1304
25 Nov 3 The Russell B. Aitken Collection - No.1329
2 Dec 3 The House Sale - No.1308
4 Dec 3 Important American Paintings, Drawings & Sculptures - No.1309
5 Dec 3 Sporting Art - No.1312
17 Dec 3 Playboy at 50 - No.1325
12 Jan 4 American Indian Art - No.1332
14 Jan 4 The House Sale - No.1333
22 Jan 4 Old Master & 19th Century Drawings - No.1340
23 Jan 4 Old Master Paintings - No.1331
4 Feb 4 The House Sale - No.1342
10 Feb 4 Maritime - No.1401
12 Feb 4 Prints & Multiples - No.1344
17 Feb 4 Photographs - No.1345
25 Feb 4 Impressionist & Modern Art - No.1347
3 Mar 4 House Sale - No.1349
9 Mar 4 Fine 20th Century Decorative Arts - No.1350
11 Mar 4 Fine American Paintings, Drawings & Sculpture - No.1351
23 Mar 4 Japanese & Korean Art - No.1353
24 Mar 4 Chinese Works of Art - No.1354
25 Mar 4 Indian & Southeast Asian Art - No.1355
30 Mar 4 The House Sale - No.1356
22 Apr 4 19th Century European Art - No.1364
23 Apr 4 19th Century Furniture & Sculpture, incl Collection of Sir Gilbert - No.1365
27 Apr 4 Photographs - No.1367
28 Apr 4 Prints & Multiples - No.1368
4 May 4 Impressionist & Modern Art - Evening Sale - No.1370
5 May 4 Impressionist & Modern Works on Paper - No.1371
11 May 4 Post-War & Contemporary Art - Evening Sale - No.1373
12 May 4 Post-War & Contemporary Art - Morning Session - No.1374
12 May 4 Post-War & Contemporary Art - Afternoon Session - No.1375
18 May 4 Important American Art - No.1377
3 Jun 4 The Doris Duke Collection - No.1455
15 Jun 4 Important 20th Century Decorative Arts - No.1385
16 Jun 4 Wayne LaPoe Collection of Oceanliner Memorabilia & Art - No.1469
17 Jun 4 Old Master Paintings - No.1380
13 Jul 4 The House Sale - No.1396
29 Jul 4 Maritime - No.1398

Christie's, Rome - Italy

11 Dec 3 19th Century Art - No.2439
17 Dec 3 Old Master Paintings & Drawings - No.2440
10 Jun 4 19th Century Art - No.2448
16 Jun 4 Old Master Pictures & Drawings - No.2451

Christie's, South Kensington - UK

28 Aug 3 British & Continental Pictures & Works on Paper - No.9674
4 Sep 3 British & Victorian Pictures - No.9678
11 Sep 3 Impressionist, Modern & Post-War Art - No.9686
18 Sep 3 19th Century European Art - No.9692
26 Sep 3 Old Master Pictures - No.9695
8 Oct 3 At Home - Decorative Objects & Pictures - No.9704/06
15 Oct 3 Art Deco - No.9718
15 Oct 3 Art Nouveau - No.9778
16 Oct 3 British Art On Paper - No.9712
16 Oct 3 Twentieth Century British Art - No.9714
17 Oct 3 Indian & Islamic Works of Art & 20th Century Indian Paintings - No.9713
30 Oct 3 20th Century Prints - No.9721
31 Oct 3 Old Master Pictures - No.9725
6 Nov 3 British & Continental Pictures & Works on Paper - No.9730
13 Nov 3 British & Victorian Pictures - No.9737
13 Nov 3 Lalique Glass & 20th Century European Sculpture - No.9736
14 Nov 3 Chinese Ceramics & Works of Art - No.9731
18 Nov 3 19th & 20th Century Photographs - No.9740
19 Nov 3 Maritime Models & Maritime & Naval Battles - No.9743 & 9744
27 Nov 3 Sporting Art & Dogs - No.9751
2 Dec 3 Portrait Miniatures - No.9754 & 9755
3 Dec 3 20th Century British Art - No.9756
3 Dec 3 British & Continental Watercolours - No.9757
4 Dec 3 Japanese & Asian Decorative Arts - No.9758
4 Dec 3 19th Century European Art - No.9746
11 Dec 3 Impressionist, Modern & Post War Art - No.9759
12 Dec 3 Old Master Pictures & Drawings - No.9768
15 Jan 4 British & Continental Pictures - At Home - No.9795 & 9796
19 Feb 4 British & Continental Pictures - No.9980
27 Feb 4 Old Master Pictures - No.9871
4 Mar 4 British & Victorian Paintings, incl. Scottish Paintings - No.9984
11 Mar 4 20th Century British Art - No.9932
16 Mar 4 Portrait Miniatures, Objects of Vertu & Silver - At Home - No.9802
18 Mar 4 British & Continental Pictures - At Home - No.9806
25 Mar 4 British & Continental Watercolours - No.9811
25 Mar 4 19th Century European Art - No.9810
1 Apr 4 Impressionist & Modern Pictures - No.9814
1 Apr 4 Contemporary & Post-War Art - No.9815
8 Apr 4 British & Continental Pictures - No.9818
21 Apr 4 Art Nouveau & Art Deco - No.9828
21 Apr 4 Pipewell Hall, Northamptonshire & Bostock House - No.9826
22 Apr 4 Art Nouveau & Art Deco - No.9829
23 Apr 4 Old Master Pictures - No.9830
29 Apr 4 British & Continental Pictures - No.9833
29 Apr 4 Travel & Natural History - No.9834
30 Apr 4 Indian & Islamic Works of Art - No.9835
13 May 4 20th Century European Sculpture & Lalique Glass - No.9843 & 9845
13 May 4 Asian Decorative Arts - No.9842
14 May 4 The Irish Sale & 20th Century British Art - No.9846
19 May 4 Furniture & Decorative Arts incl. Pictures - No.9849 & 9850
26 May 4 Maritime - No.9855 & 9856
27 May 4 British & Victorian Paintings - No.9857
3 Jun 4 Prints & Multiples - No.9844
10 Jun 4 Sporting Art & Dogs - No.9864
16 Jun 4 19th Century European Art - No.9866
30 Jun 4 Pop Art - No.5521
1 Jul 4 20th Century British Art - No.9876
1 Jul 4 British & Continental Watercolours incl. Original Illustrations - No.9877
9 Jul 4 Old Master Pictures - No.9884
13 Jul 4 At Home Week - Portrait Miniatures - No.9885
14 Jul 4 At Home Week - No.9887 & 9889

Christie's, Sydney - Australia

26 Aug 3 Australian, & International Paintings - No.1041
27 Aug 3 The BHP Billiton Collection of Australian Art - No.1041
15 May 4 The Collection of John Schaeffer at Rona - No.1052

Christie's, Tel Aviv - Israel

2 Oct 3 19th & 20th Century Art - The Tel Aviv Sale - No.1001

Christie's, Zurich - Switzerland

29 Sep 3 Swiss Art - No.1313
7 Jun 4 Swiss Art - No.1317

Christopher Matthews, Harrogate - UK

7 May 4 Fine Art

Chrystals Auctions, Isle of Man - UK

30 Oct 3 Paintings, Watercolours & Prints
31 Oct 3 Oil Paintings & Watercolours
5 Dec 3 Fine Art & Antiques
7 May 4 Fine Art & Antiques

Clarke Gammon, Guildford - UK

9 Dec 3 Fine Art
24 Feb 4 Fine Art
20 Apr 4 Fine Art

Claude Aguttes, Neuilly-sur-Seine - France

6 Oct 3 The World of Benjamin Rabier
15 Oct 3 Paintings & Fine Art
20 Nov 3 Modern & Contemporary Art
27 Nov 3 Art Nouveau & Art Deco
2 Dec 3 19th & 20th Century Paintings
8 Dec 3 Old Masters & Fine Art

16 Dec 3 19th & 20th Century Modern & Oriental Paintings
4 Mar 4 Works on Paper
9 Apr 4 19th Century, Oriental & Modern Paintings
27 Apr 4 Art Nouveau & Art Deco
29 Apr 4 Modern Paintings & Sculpture
11 Jun 4 19th & 20th Century French, European & Islamic Art
15 Jun 4 Old Masters & Works of Art

Claude Boisgirard, Paris - France
14 Nov 3 Art Nouveau & Art Deco
17 Nov 3 School of Paris, Poland, Russia, & Central Europe
23 Nov 3 Marine Art
10 Dec 3 Modern Paintings
15 Mar 4 Parisian School
19 Mar 4 Oriental Art
21 Mar 4 Marine Art
24 Mar 4 Old Master Paintings & Drawings
5 May 4 Art Nouveau and Art Deco
16 Jun 4 Paris School
24 Jun 4 Old Master Paintings & Drawings

Clevedon Salerooms, Clevendon - UK
25 Sep 3 Fine Art
27 Nov 3 Fine Art
4 Mar 4 Fine Art
17 Jun 4 Fine Art

Cobbs, Peterborough, NH - USA
3 Jan 4 Fine Art
10 Apr 4 Fine Art

Coeur d'Alene, Hayden, ID - USA
24 Jul 4 Fine 19th & 20th Century Western, Wildlife & Sporting Art

Collins, Kennebunk, ME - USA
3 Jan 4 19th & 20th Century American Paintings
24 Apr 4 Fine Art

Compagnie Marocaine des Objets d'Art, Casablanca - Morocco
20 Sep 3 Oriental & Contemporary Art - Casablanca

Cornette de St.Cyr, Paris - France
11 Oct 3 Contemporary Art
25 Oct 3 Modern & Contemporary Art
23 Nov 3 Succession of Christian de Rabaudy
8 Dec 3 Paintings & Fine Art
18 Dec 3 Modern & Contemporary Art
25 Jan 4 Avant-Garde
2 Feb 4 Design
21 Feb 4 Modern & Contemporary Art & Prints
29 Mar 4 Contemporary Art
24 Apr 4 Modern & Contemporary Art
9 Jun 4 Primitive & Asian Arts
14 Jun 4 Paintings & Art Deco
29 Jun 4 Contemporary Art

Coutau Begarie, Paris - France
29 Sep 3 Hunting Art
7 Nov 3 Equestrian Art
21 Nov 3 Paintings & Fine Art
1 Dec 3 Paintings & Fine Art
3 Dec 3 Hunting Art
1 Mar 4 Hunting Art
2 Apr 4 Sporting Art
5 May 4 19th & 20th Century Modern Paintings
12 May 4 Sporting Art
9 Jul 4 Drawings by Germaine Bouret & Fine Art

Credit Municipal, Paris - France
23 Oct 3 Fine Art
1 Apr 4 Fine Art
24 Jun 4 Paintings & Sculptures

Crow, Dorking - UK
28 Apr 4 Fine Art

Cumbria Auction Rooms, Carlisle - UK
7 Jun 4 Important Antiques & Works of Art

Daguerre, Paris - France
26 Nov 3 Fine Art
26 Mar 4 Fine Art - No.18
25 Jun 4 Fine Art - No.19 - with Brissonneau

Dales, Durban - South Africa
8 Jun 4 Fine Art
6 Jul 4 Fine Art

Dallas Auction Gallery, Texas - USA
14 Jan 4 Fine Art
25 Feb 4 Fine Art
14 Apr 4 Fine Art
13 May 4 Fine Art
14 Jul 4 Fine Art

Dan Ripley, Indianapolis - USA
7 Feb 4 Fine Art
6 Mar 4 Fine Art
3 Apr 4 Fine Art
1 May 4 Fine Art
5 Jun 4 Fine Art
1 Jul 4 Fine Art

Daniel Cooney, Brooklyn - USA
19 Apr 4 Fine Art Online Auction
30 Jun 4 Fine Art

Daniel Herry, Beaune - France
19 Oct 3 Fine Art
25 Apr 4 Fine Art - No.1006

David Dike, Dallas, TX - USA
18 Oct 3 Texan Art

David Duggleby, Scarborough - UK
9 Sep 3 The Whitby Picture Sale
6 Oct 3 Fine Art
1 Dec 3 Fine Art
23 Feb 4 Fine Art
30 Mar 4 The Whitby Picture Sale
17 May 4 Fine Art

David Kahn, Paris - France
7 Nov 3 Islamic, Maritime & Cruiseliner Art
29 Apr 4 Fine Art & Paintings

David Lay, Penzance - UK
14 Oct 3 Fine Art
10 Feb 4 Fine Art
20 May 4 Fine Art
4 Jun 4 Fine Art
15 Jun 4 Fine Art - P004

David Rago, Lambertville, NJ - USA
25 Oct 3 Modern Art & Design
13 Feb 4 Estate Auction
3 Apr 4 Modern Art
24 Apr 4 The Brutten-Herrick Collection of Contemporary Art
11 Jun 4 Estate Auction

Dawo, Saarbrucken - Germany
8 May 4 Fine Art - No.139
9 Jul 4 Fine Art - No.141

De Veres Art Auctions, Dublin - Eire
23 Sep 3 Irish Art
25 Nov 3 Irish Art
30 Mar 4 Irish Art
22 Jun 4 Irish Art

De Vuyst, Lokeren - Belgium
11 Oct 3 Impressionist, Modern Art & Old Masters - No.119
13 Dec 3 Impressionist, Modern Art & Old Masters - No.120
13 Mar 4 Impressionist, Modern Art & Old Masters - No.121
15 May 4 Modern Art - No.122

De Zwann, Amsterdam - Netherlands
17 Mar 4 Fine Art

DeFina, Austinburg, OH - USA
13 Mar 4 Fine Art - With Rachel Davis

Deauville, Deauville - France
22 Aug 3 19th & 20th Century Art
29 Aug 3 Sporting Art

Deburaux, Boulogne - France
5 Apr 4 Fine Art
17 Apr 4 Fine Art

Dee Atkinson & Harrison, Driffield - UK
1 Aug 3 Fine Art
26 Sep 3 Fine Art
21 Nov 3 Fine Art
5 Mar 4 Fine Art
30 Apr 4 Fine Art

Della Rocca, Torino - Italy
1 Oct 3 19th & 20th Century Paintings & Sculptures
28 Oct 3 16th, 17th & 18th Century Paintings & Furniture

8 Jun 4 Fine Art

Delorme & Bocage, Paris - France
17 Nov 3 Drawings & Paintings
17 Dec 3 Drawings & Paintings

Delvaux, Paris - France
19 Dec 3 Old Masters, Modern Art & Fine Art
30 Jun 4 19th Century & Modern Paintings

Desmond Judd, Cranbrook - UK
7 Sep 3 Fine Art
21 Sep 3 Fine Art
19 Oct 3 Fine Art
16 Nov 3 Fine Art
14 Dec 3 Fine Art
11 Jan 4 Fine Art
25 Jan 4 Fine Art
21 Mar 4 Fine Art

Deutscher-Menzies, Malvern - Australia
2 Sep 3 Australian & International Fine Art
26 Nov 3 Australian & International Fine Art - No.23
10 Mar 4 Australian & International Fine Art - No.24
16 Jun 4 Fine Art - No.25

Dianous, Marseille - France
25 Oct 3 Paintings

Dickins, Middle Claydon - UK
9 Jan 4 Fine Art
20 Feb 4 Fine Art
12 Mar 4 Fine Art
17 Apr 4 Pictures
12 Jun 4 Summer Picture Sale

Dickinson, Davy & Markham, Brigg - UK
28 Oct 3 Fine Art
10 Feb 4 Fine Art
2 Jun 4 Fine Art

Digard, Paris - France
22 Mar 4 Old Masters & Modern Drawings

Dominic Winter, Swindon - UK
22 Jul 4 British & Continental Watercolours & Oil Paintings

Dorotheum, Graz - Austria
25 Sep 3 Austrian Artists of 19th & 20th Centuries
4 Dec 3 Art & Antiques
22 Apr 4 Styrian Art
27 May 4 Art & Antiques

Dorotheum, Klagenfurt - Austria
19 Nov 3 Art & Antiques
19 May 4 Art & Antiques

Dorotheum, Linz - Austria
27 Nov 3 Art & Antiques
13 May 4 Art & Antiques

Dorotheum, Prague - Czech Republic
4 Oct 3 Art & Antiques
29 Nov 3 Art & Antiques
6 Mar 4 Art & Antiques
22 May 4 Art & Antiques

Dorotheum, Salzburg - Austria
2 Oct 3 Modern Graphic Art
15 Oct 3 Fine Art
16 Oct 3 Modern & Contemporary Art
20 Nov 3 Christmas Auction
5 Feb 4 Sculptures
5 Mar 4 Paintings from the Blaas Collection
7 Apr 4 Easter Auction
9 Jun 4 Modern & Contemporary Art

Dorotheum, Vienna - Austria
10 Sep 3 Fine Art from Seehotel Werzer Wallerwirt - Portschach
15 Sep 3 Art Nouveau & Art Works of 20th century
16 Sep 3 Modern Graphics
30 Sep 3 Sculptures - No.2035
30 Sep 3 Old Master Drawings, Prints to 1900, Watercolours & Miniatures - No.2034
1 Oct 3 Old Masters - No.2036
14 Oct 3 20th Century Art - Nr.2038
15 Oct 3 Fine Art - Special Auction - No.78 - Wr. Neustadt
28 Oct 3 20th Century Oil Paintings & Watercolours - No.2039
5 Nov 3 Charity Auction - Caritas Hospiz
11 Nov 3 Modern Prints
12 Nov 3 Design
24 Nov 3 19th Century Paintings & Watercolours
25 Nov 3 Jugendstil & Art Nouveau
26 Nov 3 Modern & Contemporary Art - No.2042
5 Dec 3 Antiques - No.2044
10 Dec 3 19th Century Paintings & Watercolours - No.2045
19 Dec 3 20th Century Art - No.2046
27 Jan 4 20th Century Paintings
9 Feb 4 Modern Graphics
24 Feb 4 Oil Paintings & Watercolours
8 Mar 4 Art Nouveau & Art Deco
9 Mar 4 20th Century Art
17 Mar 4 Fine Art - No.79 - Wr. Neustadt
24 Mar 4 Old Master Paintings
25 Mar 4 Sculpture
26 Mar 4 Master Drawings, Prints before 1900, Watercolours & Miniatures
26 Mar 4 Furniture & Decorative Arts
8 Apr 4 19th Century Paintings & Watercolours
16 Apr 4 Asian Art
21 Apr 4 20th Century Art
29 Apr 4 Imperial Court Memorabilia
25 May 4 Modern & Contemporary Art
26 May 4 20th Century Art Nouveau
27 May 4 19th Century Art
9 Jun 4 Modern Graphics
16 Jun 4 Old Master Paintings
21 Jun 4 19th Century Paintings

Douglas, South Deerfield, MA - USA
15 Aug 3 Fine Art
14 Nov 3 Fine Art
2 Apr 4 Fine Art
7 May 4 Fine Art

Doutrebente, Paris - France
28 Nov 3 Old Masters, Modern Art & Fine Art
7 Apr 4 Paintings & Drawings
25 Jun 4 Fine Art

Doyle, New York, NY - USA
21 Aug 3 End of Summer Sale, including Paintings - No.0308211
24 Sep 3 19th & 20th Century Decorative Arts - No.03BE03
22 Oct 3 Old Master Paintings & Drawings - No.03CN03
5 Nov 3 At Home, including Paintings - No.03FD11
11 Nov 3 Old Master, Modern & Contemporary Prints - No.03BP02
18 Nov 3 American Furniture & Decorative Arts - No.03AM02
3 Dec 3 Modern, Contemporary, European & American Art - No.03PT02
8 Jan 4 Furniture & Paintings - No.04FD01
21 Jan 4 Old Master Paintings & Drawings - No.04CN01
10 Feb 4 Dogs in Art - No.04DG01
25 Feb 4 19th & 20th Century Decorative Arts - No.04BE01
10 Mar 4 Paintings, Furniture & Decorations - No.04FD03
25 Mar 4 Paintings, Furniture & Decorations - No.04FD04
27 Apr 4 Furniture & Decorative Arts - No.04AM01
4 May 4 Old Master, Modern & Contemporary Prints - No.04BP01
6 May 4 Modern & European Art - No.04PT01
19 May 4 Old Master Paintings & Drawings - No.04CN2
26 May 4 American Art - No.04PT02
9 Jun 4 Belle Epoque - No.04BE02
23 Jun 4 Paintings, Furniture & Decorations - No.04FD05
15 Jul 4 Paintings, Furniture & Decorations - No.04FD06

Dr Fritz Nagel, Leipzig - Germany
11 Oct 3 Fine Art - No.14
2 Apr 4 Decorative Arts - No.15L

Dr Fritz Nagel, Stuttgart - Germany
25 Sep 3 Fine Art - No.389
27 Sep 3 Modern Art - No.25M
29 Sep 3 Fine Art - No.62
7 Nov 3 Asian Art - China, Tibet, Southwest Asia - No.26A
8 Nov 3 Asian Art - Korea & Japan - No.26A
11 Dec 3 Art & Antiques - No.390
15 Dec 3 Collectables - No.63V
25 Mar 4 Art & Antiques - No.391
29 Mar 4 Collectables - No.64V
30 Apr 4 Modern Art - No.26M
21 May 4 Asian Art - No.27A
22 May 4 Asian Art - No.27A
22 May 4 Asian Art - No.27A
24 Jun 4 Art & Antiques - No.392
28 Jun 4 Collectables - No.65V

Dr Lehr, Berlin - Germany
25 Oct 3 Paintings & Works of Art - No.17
24 Apr 4 Paintings & Works of Art - No.18

Dr Sturies, Dusseldorf - Germany
15 May 4 Modern & Contemporary Art - No.11

Dreweatt Neate, Newbury - UK
24 Sep 3 Pictures & Books - No.12241/2/3
4 Nov 3 Affordable Pictures - No.12273
28 Jan 4 Pictures & Books
7 Apr 4 Affordable Pictures
11 May 4 Antique & Decorative Items - Bristol Auction Rooms
19 May 4 Pictures & Books - No.12394
28 May 4 Gallery Sale - Honiton
15 Jun 4 Fine Art - Bristol Salerooms
9 Jul 4 Fine Art - Tunbridge Wells
20 Jul 4 Fine Art - Bristol Salerooms
30 Jul 4 Gallery Sale - Honiton

Drouot Estimations, Paris - France
14 Nov 3 Paintings & Fine Art
28 Nov 3 20th Century Decorative Arts, Modern Paintings & Prints
30 Apr 4 Art Nouveau & Art Deco

Du Mouchelle, Detroit, MI - USA
15 Aug 3 Fine Art
19 Sep 3 Fine Art
17 Oct 3 Fine Art
25 Oct 3 Fine Art
14 Nov 3 Fine Art
12 Dec 3 Fine Art
9 Jan 4 Fine Art
13 Feb 4 Fine Art
12 Mar 4 Fine Art
16 Apr 4 Fine Art
24 Apr 4 Fine Art
14 May 4 Fine Art
11 Jun 4 Fine Art
19 Jun 4 Contemporary Graphics
9 Jul 4 Fine Art

Duke & Son, Dorchester - UK
30 Oct 3 Fine Art
11 Mar 4 Fine Art
8 Jul 4 Fine Art

Dunbar Sloane, Auckland - New Zealand
20 Aug 3 Fine Art
3 Dec 3 Fine Art
28 Apr 4 Fine Art

Dunbar Sloane, Wellington - New Zealand
27 Aug 3 Fine Art
26 Nov 3 Fine Art
12 May 4 Fine Art

Duran, Madrid - Spain
23 Sep 3 Paintings & Fine Art - No.385
20 Oct 3 Paintings & Fine Art - No.386
17 Nov 3 Paintings & Fine Art - No.387
16 Dec 3 Paintings & Fine Art - No.388
26 Jan 4 Paintings & Fine Art - No.389
24 Feb 4 Paintings & Fine Art - No.390
22 Mar 4 Paintings & Fine Art - No.391
27 Apr 4 Paintings & Fine Art - No.392
25 May 4 Paintings & Fine Art - No.393
22 Jun 4 Paintings & Fine Art - No.395
12 Jul 4 Paintings & Fine Art - No.396

E & Eve, Paris - France
24 Nov 3 Garden & Country Items
4 Dec 3 Miniatures
22 Mar 4 Garden & Country Items
3 Jun 4 Paintings & Prints

ELR Auctions, Sheffield - UK
12 Sep 3 Fine Art
5 Dec 3 Fine Art
26 Mar 4 Fine Art

Edgar Horn, Eastbourne - UK
10 Sep 3 Fine Art
29 Oct 3 Fine Art
10 Dec 3 Fine Art

Eldred, East Dennis, MA - USA
7 Aug 3 Fine Art - EUR03
20 Aug 3 Prints of Paul Jacoulet - JAC03
21 Nov 3 Americana & Marine Art - FAM03
12 Dec 3 Fine Art - WFDA03
24 Mar 4 Antiques & Decorative Arts - No.388
2 Apr 4 Americana - SPAM04
14 May 4 Fine & Decorative Art - SPSP04
29 Jul 4 Marine & Export Art

Eric Pillon, Calais - France
9 Nov 3 Paintings & Sculptures
14 Dec 3 Paintings, Sculptures & Tapestries
14 Mar 4 19th Century, Impressionist, Modern Paintings & Sculptures
30 May 4 Paintings & Sculpture - Le Touquet
4 Jul 4 19th Century, Post-Impressionist & Modern Paintings

Everard, Savannah - USA
7 Jun 4 Fine Art

Ewbank, Woking - UK
2 Oct 3 Fine Art
11 Dec 3 Fine Art
11 Mar 4 Fine Art
24 Jun 4 Fine Art

Falk & Falk, Zurich - Switzerland
28 Nov 3 Books & Fine Art - No.10
12 Jun 4 Rare Books and Art - No.11

Fallon, Copake, NY - USA
30 Aug 3 Americana
1 Jan 4 Fine Art
27 Mar 4 Americana
15 May 4 Americana
17 Jul 4 Americana

Farsetti, Prato - Italy
7 Nov 3 Fine Art - No.119
14 Nov 3 Fine Art - No.120
28 Nov 3 Modern & Contemporary Art incl. Photographs - No.121-I
29 Nov 3 Modern Art - No.121-II
27 Mar 4 Old Master Paintings & Furniture - No.122
2 Apr 4 Tuscan Art & 19th Century Paintings - No.123
28 May 4 Modern & Contemporary Art - No.124-I
29 May 4 Modern Art - No.124-II
11 Jun 4 Paintings, Sculptures, Design & Prints - No.125

Feletin, Provins - France
26 Oct 3 Fine Art
7 Dec 3 Fine Art
1 Feb 4 Fine Art
14 Mar 4 Fine Art
16 May 4 Fine Art
27 Jun 4 Fine Art
25 Jul 4 Fine Art

Fellows & Sons, Birmingham - UK
7 Oct 3 Paintings, Prints & Decorative Pictures
17 Feb 4 Paintings & Prints
18 May 4 Paintings & Prints

Fenner & Co, Tavistock - UK
27 Oct 3 Fine Art
15 Feb 4 The Works of Robert O Lenkiewicz

Ferri, Paris - France
10 Dec 3 Old Masters & Modern Art & Sculptures
3 Mar 4 19th Century & Modern Paintings

Finan Watkins & Co, Mere - UK
4 Oct 3 Fine Art
12 Jun 4 Antiques & Works of Art incl Tribal Art

Finarte, Venice - Italy
19 Sep 3 Fine Art - 03VEG4
20 Sep 3 Fine Art - 03VEG3
21 Sep 3 Old Masters - 03VEG1
21 Sep 3 Fine Art - 03VEG3
7 Nov 3 Italian Furniture & Works of Art - 03VEH1
8 Nov 3 San Gregorio Abbey - Fine Art & Sculptures - 03VEH2
9 Nov 3 San Gregorio Abbey - Rare Old Masters - 03VEH3
12 Dec 3 Furniture & Sculptures - 03VEI1
13 Dec 3 Old Masters & Fine Art - 03VEI2
14 Dec 3 Rare Old Masters - 03VEI3
14 Dec 3 Four Paintings from a Private Collection - 03VEI4
28 Feb 4 Fine Art - 04VEA2
29 Feb 4 Old Masters & Rare Paintings - 04VEA3
29 Feb 4 Italian & European Furniture & Works of Art - 04VEA1
28 Mar 4 35 Works by Virgilio Guidi - No.1237

2 May 4 Paintings & Sculptures - 04VEB2
3 Jul 4 Fine Art
4 Jul 4 Old Master Paintings - 04VED2
4 Jul 4 Furniture & Decorative Arts

Finarte Semenzato, Milan - Italy
14 Oct 3 19th Century Paintings - No.1214
22 Oct 3 Old Master Paintings - No.1221 - Via Manzoni
23 Oct 3 Furniture & Paintings - No.1219
19 Nov 3 Etchings, Prints & Drawings - No.1224
20 Nov 3 Modern & Contemporary Art - No.1225
9 Dec 3 19th Century Paintings - No.1226
16 Dec 3 Modern & Contemporary Art - No.1229 - Via Manzoni
16 Dec 3 Modern & Contemporary Art - No.1230
17 Dec 3 Furniture & Paintings - No.1231
17 Dec 3 Contents of a Milan Apartment - No.1232
16 Mar 4 Modern & Contemporary Art - No.1236
16 Mar 4 Watercolours, Paintings & Sculptures - No.1235
31 Mar 4 Furniture, Paintings & Works of Art - No.1241
21 Apr 4 Books & Graphic Arts - No.1243
12 May 4 Important Old Master Paintings - No.1245
25 May 4 19th Century Paintings - No.1248
8 Jun 4 Modern & Contemporary Art - No.1250
8 Jun 4 Works on Paper & Sculpture under 2000 Euros - No.1249
17 Jun 4 Old Masters & Furniture - No.1252

Finarte Semenzato, Rome - Italy
14 Oct 3 Paintings & Fine Art - No.1216
14 Oct 3 Fine Art - No.1215
15 Oct 3 Paintings, Sculptures & Fine Art - No.1218
13 Nov 3 Modern & Contemporary Art - No.1222
10 Dec 3 Old Master & 19th Century Paintings - No.1227
24 Mar 4 Paintings, Fine Art & Furniture - No.1238
24 Mar 4 Furniture & Paintings - No.1239
24 Mar 4 An Important Painting by Carlo Dolci - No.1238
24 Mar 4 Fourteen 19th Century Paintings from a Noble Roman Family - No.1238
22 Apr 4 Modern & Contemporary Art - No.1244
17 May 4 Furniture & Important Decorative Arts - No.1246
17 May 4 19th Century Old Masters - No.1247
22 Jun 4 Furniture & Old Master Paintings - No.1253
23 Jun 4 19th Century Paintings - No.1254

Frank Peege, Freiburg - Germany
1 Apr 4 Fine Art - No.106
17 Jun 4 Fine Art -catalogue on web from 02 Jun 04 - No.107

Fraysse, Paris - France
21 Oct 3 Old Masters, Modern Art & Fine Art
3 Dec 3 Modern & Decorative Art
3 Mar 4 Fine Art
7 Apr 4 Fine Art

Freeman Fine Arts, Philadelphia, PA - USA
19 Sep 3 Tri-Annual Paintings Sale - No.1181
7 Dec 3 Fine Paintings and Sculpture - No.1187
23 Jan 4 Paintings - No.1191
6 Feb 4 Fine Art - No.1192
22 Feb 4 Private Painting Collection - No.1193
20 Mar 4 English & Continental Fine Art - No.1194
2 Apr 4 Ti-Annual Paintings - No.1193A
24 Apr 4 Americana - No.1195
25 Jun 4 Tri Annual Painting Sale - No.1202
27 Jun 4 American & European Paintings - No.1203

G.E. Sworder & Son, Stansted - UK
9 Sep 3 Fine Art
21 Oct 3 Fine Art
2 Dec 3 Fine Art
3 Feb 4 Fine Art
13 Feb 4 Artists For All
30 Mar 4 Fine Art
25 May 4 Fine Art
20 Jul 4 Fine Art

Galeria y Remates, Montevideo - Uruguay
1 Sep 3 Paintings - No.29
7 Oct 3 National Paintings - No.32
20 Nov 3 National Paintings - No.35
25 Nov 3 National & International Paintings
15 Dec 3 Important Paintings - No.38
5 Jan 4 Important Paintings - No.39
22 Feb 4 National & International Paintings - No.42
22 Jun 4 National & International Paintings - No.50

Galerie Dobiaschofsky, Bern - Switzerland
5 Nov 3 Fine Art - No.97
7 Nov 3 Swiss Art - No.97-II
12 May 4 Paintings & Decorative Arts - No.98
14 May 4 Swiss Art - No.98

Galerie Fischer, Luzern - Switzerland
19 Nov 3 Art Auction - No.387
16 Jun 4 Fine Art - No.389

Galerie Gloggner, Luzern - Switzerland
15 Nov 3 Old & Modern Art
22 May 4 Old Master & Modern Art

Galerie Koller, Geneva - Switzerland
16 Nov 3 Fine Art - GE35

Galerie Koller, Zurich - Switzerland
19 Sep 3 Old Master & 19th Century Paintings - A126/2 - Koller West
19 Sep 3 Fine Art - A126/1
1 Dec 3 Fine Art - W199 - Koller West Auctions
2 Dec 3 International Modern & Swiss Art - Z15
3 Dec 3 Fine Art - A127
25 Mar 4 Col Iseli-Mooser - S102
26 Mar 4 19th Century paintings & Old Masters - A128/2
23 Jun 4 Modern Swiss Art - Z16

Galerie Kornfeld, Bern - Switzerland
17 Jun 4 Drawings, Old Masters and Graphics - No.232
17 Jun 4 Collection of Heumann Chemnitz - No.233
17 Jun 4 19th & 20th Century Art - No.234
18 Jun 4 19th & 20th Century Art - No.234

Galerie Moderne, Brussels - Belgium
26 Aug 3 Paintings & Fine Art - No.0308
23 Sep 3 Antiques, Paintings & Fine Art - No.0309
21 Oct 3 Fine Art - No.0310
18 Nov 3 Fine Art - No.0311
16 Dec 3 Fine Art - No.0312
20 Jan 4 Fine Art - No.0401
17 Feb 4 Fine Art - No.0402
23 Mar 4 Fine Art - No.0403
20 Apr 4 Fine Art - No.0404
18 May 4 Fine Art - No.0405
15 Jun 4 Fine Art - No.0406

Galerie Stuker, Bern - Switzerland
13 May 4 Spring Auction

Galerie du Rhone, Sion - Switzerland
12 Dec 3 International & Swiss Art - No.24 & 25
5 Jun 4 Paintings & Fine Art

Galleria Pace, Milan - Italy
13 Nov 3 Modern & Contemporary Art - No.59
11 Mar 4 Modern & Contemporary Art - No.60
10 Jun 4 Modern & Contemporary Art - No.61

Galleria Pananti, Florence - Italy
22 May 4 Modern & Contemporary Art - No.25
17 Jun 4 Modern & Contemporary Art - No.26

Galleria Rosenberg, Milan - Italy
7 Nov 3 Modern & Contemporary Art - No.13
6 Feb 4 Modern & Contemporary Art - No.14

Gardiner & Houlgate, Corsham - UK
12 Sep 3 Fine Art
12 Nov 3 Fine Art
7 Apr 4 Fine Art
20 May 4 Fine Art

George Kidner, Lymington - UK
1 Oct 3 Fine Art
7 Jan 4 Fine Art
28 Apr 4 Fine Art
7 Jul 4 Fine Art & Paintings

Gerard, Besancon - France
8 Nov 3 Paintings
31 Jan 4 Paintings
3 Apr 4 Paintings
19 Jun 4 Fine Art

Germann, Zurich - Switzerland
25 Nov 3 Paintings, Sculptures, Prints & Photographs - No.2302
8 Jun 4 Paintings & Fine Art - No.2401

Gildings, Market Harborough - UK
2 Sep 3 Fine Art

21 Oct 3 Fine Art
6 Jan 4 Fine Art
16 Mar 4 Fine Art
25 May 4 Fine Art

Gioffredo, Nice - France
20 Nov 3 Fine Art
30 Mar 4 Fine Art
29 Jun 4 Fine Art
20 Jul 4 Fine Art

Giraudeau, Tours - France
27 Oct 3 Paintings & Fine Art
16 Feb 4 Paintings & Fine Art
3 May 4 Paintings & Fine Art
10 May 4 19th Century & Modern Paintings

Glerum, Amsterdam - Netherlands
29 Sep 3 Fine Art - No.246
20 Oct 3 19th & 20th Century Oils, Watercolours & Fine Art - No.247
24 Nov 3 Modern Paintings & Fine Art - No.252
8 Dec 3 Art from The Haag - 1800-2000 - No.253
29 Mar 4 Works on Paper - No.257
19 Apr 4 19th & 20th Century Art - No.258
17 May 4 Old Master Paintings - No.260
7 Jun 4 Modern & Present Day Paintings, Drawings & Graphics - No.262
22 Jun 4 Art & Antiques - No.263

Glerum, Singapore
3 Apr 4 Asian Pictures & Fine Art - No.SPA003 - with Larasati

Goldings, Grantham - UK
18 Sep 3 Fine Art
4 Feb 4 Fine Art
5 May 4 Fine Art

Goodman, Sydney - Australia
27 Oct 3 14th Sydney National Art Auction
28 Oct 3 Affordable Paintings
29 Mar 4 15th Sydney National Art Auction - with Bonhams
31 Mar 4 Affordable Art - With Bonhams
20 Jul 4 16th Sydney National Art Auction
21 Jul 4 Affordable Art

Gorringes, Bexhill on Sea - UK
16 Sep 3 Fine Art
16 Dec 3 Fine Art
3 Feb 4 Fine Art
4 May 4 Fine Art
27 Jul 4 Fine Art

Gorringes, Lewes - UK
9 Sep 3 Fine Art
21 Oct 3 Fine Art
2 Dec 3 Fine Art
27 Jan 4 Fine Art
9 Mar 4 Fine Art
29 Apr 4 Fine Art
8 Jun 4 Fine Art
22 Jul 4 Fine Art

Gorringes, Worthing - UK
25 Sep 3 Antiques and Fine Art
20 Nov 3 Antiques and Fine Art
5 Feb 4 Antiques and Fine Art
15 Apr 4 Antiques & Fine Art
17 Jun 4 Antiques & Fine Art

Goteborgs Auktionsverk, Goteborg - Sweden
25 Apr 4 Quality Auction

Grant, Worcester - UK
25 Sep 3 Transport Collectables Sale
30 Oct 3 Autumn Fine Art Auction
19 Feb 4 Fine Art
13 May 4 Fine Art

Greenslade Hunt, Taunton - UK
9 Oct 3 Fine Art
27 Nov 3 Fine Art

Grev Wedels Plass, Oslo - Norway
19 Nov 3 Modern Auction
19 Nov 3 Munch Auction
16 Dec 3 Christmas Auction
25 May 4 Classic & Modern Art
10 Jun 4 Summer Auction

Grogan & Co, Dedham, MA - USA
21 Sep 3 American & European Paintings, American & European Paintings - N0.93
7 Dec 3 American & European Paintings & 18th & 19th Century Decorations - No.94
29 Feb 4 Fine Art - No.95
2 May 4 Fine Art - No.96

Gros & Delettrez, Paris - France
5 Dec 3 Old Masters, Modern Art, Art Nouveau & Art Deco
15 Dec 3 Islamic & Oriental Art
19 Dec 3 Books & Graphic Arts
26 Jan 4 Paintings & Fine Art
15 Mar 4 Oriental Art
5 Jun 4 Paintings & Prints, Magic & Illusionism
14 Jun 4 Orientalist Paintings

Hagelstam, Helsinki - Finland
18 Sep 3 Fine Art - No.97
23 Oct 3 Fine Art - No.98
13 Dec 3 Fine Art
25 Mar 4 Paintings & Fine Art
15 May 4 International Auction

Hales, Newton Abbot - UK
25 Feb 4 Fine Art
28 Apr 4 Fine Art

Halls, Shrewsbury - UK
12 Sep 3 Fine Art
8 Oct 3 Ludford House Sale
22 Oct 3 Fine Art
12 Nov 3 Fine Art
12 Dec 3 Affordable Pictures
13 Feb 4 Affordable Pictures
28 Apr 4 Paintings, Silver & Jewellery - No.5018
11 Jun 4 Affordable Pictures

Hamilton Osborne King, Dublin - Eire
28 Sep 3 House Clearance Auction - No.7212
25 Nov 3 Contents of Lissadell House - With Christie's
31 May 4 Irish Art
17 Jun 4 Furniture & Fine Art - No.7208

Hampton & Littlewood, Exeter - UK
29 Oct 3 Fine Art
28 Jan 4 Fine Art
28 Apr 4 Fine Art
19 May 4 Fine Art
28 Jul 4 Fine Art

Hamptons, Godalming - UK
26 Nov 3 Oil Paintings, Watercolours & Prints
10 Dec 3 Fine Art
24 Mar 4 Spring Fine Art Sale
1 May 4 Fine Art
22 Jun 4 Fine Art - Marlborough
6 Jul 4 Fine Art

Hans Stahl, Hamburg - Germany
11 Oct 3 Fine Art
14 Feb 4 Fine Art
3 Apr 4 Fine Art
19 Jun 4 Fine Art

Hans Stahl, Toestorf - Germany
30 Aug 3 Fine Art
8 Nov 3 Fine Art
6 Dec 3 Paintings & Prints
8 May 4 Fine Art

Hans Widmer, St Gallen - Switzerland
24 Oct 3 Important Paintings - No.231
18 Nov 3 Fine Art - No.232

Hartung & Hartung, Munich - Germany
4 Nov 3 Manuscripts, Autographs & Graphics - No.108
4 May 4 Manuscripts, Autographs & Prints - No.109

Harvey Clar, Oakland, CA - USA
23 Aug 3 Fine Art
20 Sep 3 Fall Auction
18 Oct 3 Fine Art
15 Nov 3 Fine Art
6 Dec 3 Fine Art
10 Jan 4 Fine Art
7 Feb 4 Fine Art
6 Mar 4 Fine Art
3 Apr 4 Fine Art

1 May 4 Fine Art
22 May 4 Fine Art
19 Jun 4 Fine Art

Hassfurther, Vienna - Austria
25 Nov 3 Modern & Classic Art - No.36
27 May 4 Paintings & Fine Art - No.37

Hauswedell & Nolte, Hamburg - Germany
2 Dec 3 Modern Art - No.375
3 Dec 3 Art after 1945 - No.376
10 Jun 4 Modern Art - No.378
11 Jun 4 Contemporary Art - No.380
11 Jun 4 Paintings & Drawings 1400-1800 - No.379

Heffel, Vancouver - Canada
30 Aug 3 Fine Art
4 Sep 3 Fine Art - On-line
2 Oct 3 Fine European & American Art - On-line
6 Nov 3 Fine Canadian & Irish Art - On-line
27 Nov 3 Fine Canadian Art Auction - Toronto
8 Jan 4 International & Canadian Works on Paper - On-line
5 Feb 4 Fine Canadian Art - On-line
4 Mar 4 Contemporary American, European & Canadian Art - On-line
1 Apr 4 International Art - On-line
6 May 4 Fine Canadian Art - On-line
27 May 4 Fine Canadian Art - On-line
3 Jun 4 Paintings - On-line
1 Jul 4 American, Canadian & European Art - On-line

Henry Adams, Chichester - UK
17 Sep 3 Fine Art
28 Oct 3 Fine Art
28 Jan 4 Fine Art
27 Apr 4 Fine Art
27 Jul 4 Fine Art

Herr, Cologne - Germany
25 Oct 3 Fine Art - No.52
27 Mar 4 Fine Art - No.53

Hindemae, Ullerslev - Denmark
9 Aug 3 Paintings & Works Of Art - No.15
28 Sep 3 Paintings & Works Of Art - No.16

Hindman Galleries, Chicago, IL - USA
7 Dec 3 Fine Art
15 Dec 3 Contemporary Art
25 Jan 4 Fine Art
21 Mar 4 Fine Art
25 Apr 4 Fine Art
23 May 4 18th and 19th Century American and European Paintings
27 Jun 4 Fine Art
10 Jul 4 Fine Art

Hobbs Parker, Ashford - UK
6 Nov 3 Antiques & Fine Art
4 Dec 3 Antiques & Fine Art
4 Mar 4 Antiques & Fine Art
15 Apr 4 Antiques & Fine Art
22 Jul 4 Fine Art

Hodgins, Calgary - Canada
17 Nov 3 Fine Art
1 Jun 4 Paintings & Fine Art

Hogben, Folkestone - UK
6 Sep 3 Fine Art
27 Sep 3 Fine Art
18 Oct 3 Fine Art
13 Dec 3 Fine Art
14 Feb 4 Fine Art
27 Mar 4 Fine Art

Holloways, Banbury - UK
16 Sep 3 Fine Art
4 Nov 3 Fine Art
27 Jan 4 Fine Art
27 Apr 4 Antique & Fine Art
8 Jun 4 Fine Art
20 Jul 4 Fine Art

Honiton Galleries, Honiton - UK
5 Sep 3 Fine Art
23 Oct 3 Fine Art
5 Dec 3 Fine Art
6 Feb 4 Fine Art
16 Apr 4 Fine Art

Horta, Brussels - Belgium
15 Sep 3 Fine Art
13 Oct 3 Fine Art
10 Nov 3 Fine Art
8 Dec 3 Fine Art
19 Jan 4 Fine Art
16 Feb 4 Fine Art
15 Mar 4 Fine Art
19 Apr 4 Fine Art
10 May 4 Fine Art
14 Jun 4 Fine Art

Hotel Des Ventes Mosan, Liege - Belgium
15 Oct 3 Antiques & Fine Art
10 Dec 3 Antiques & Fine Art
17 Mar 4 Antiques & Fine Art
16 Jun 4 Antiques & Fine Art

Hotel de Ventes Vanderkindere, Brussels - Belgium
9 Sep 3 Paintings & Fine Art
14 Oct 3 Paintings & Fine Art
18 Nov 3 Paintings & Fine Art
18 Nov 3 Belgian Army Club Sale
9 Dec 3 Paintings & Fine Art
13 Jan 4 Paintings & Fine Art
17 Feb 4 Paintings & Fine Art
16 Mar 4 Paintings & Fine Art
11 May 4 Paintings & Fine Art
15 Jun 4 Paintings & Fine Art

Hotel des Ventes de Vienne, Vienne - France
24 Apr 4 Fine Art

Hugo Ruef, Munich - Germany
5 Nov 3 Old & Modern Art - No.498
10 Dec 3 Old & Modern Art - No.499
24 Mar 4 Paintings & Decorative Arts - No.500
16 Jun 4 Old Masters & Modern Art - No.501

Hutchinson, Boroughbridge - UK
20 Apr 4 Fine Art

Ibbett Mosely, Sevenoaks - UK
22 Oct 3 Fine Art
28 Jan 4 Fine Art

Il Ponte, Milan - Italy
28 Oct 3 Fine Art - No.196
29 Oct 3 Fine Art - No.196
17 Dec 3 Paintings & Decorative Arts - No.197
24 Mar 4 Books, Paintings & Furniture - No.199
19 May 4 Furniture & Decorative Arts - No.200
12 Jul 4 Paintings & Fine Art - No.201

Illustration House, New York, NY - USA
15 Nov 3 Illustrative Paintings & Drawings
26 Feb 4 Porch Auction XV
15 May 4 Illustration Art

Imberdis, Pont-Audemer - France
19 Oct 3 Sculpture & Decorative Arts
20 Jun 4 Fine Art

International Art Centre, Auckland - New Zealand
27 Nov 3 Fine Art
7 Dec 3 Collectable Art
25 Mar 4 Paintings & Fine Art
4 Apr 4 Collectable Art

Jackson's, Cedar Falls, IA - USA
24 Sep 3 Fine Art
22 Nov 3 American & European Fine Art
12 Mar 4 Fine Art
19 Jun 4 Americana & Fine Art

Jacobs & Hunt, Petersfield - UK
8 Aug 3 Fine Art
12 Sep 3 Fine Art

James Adam, Dublin - Eire
26 Aug 3 Contemporary & Modern Art - No.4045
10 Sep 3 Paintings & Decorative Arts & Furniture - No.8081
24 Sep 3 Irish Art - No.3068
26 Nov 3 Fine Period Furniture, Paintings & Decorative Arts - No.8082
16 Dec 3 Contemporary & Modern Art - No.4046
16 Dec 3 The Max Maccabe Studio Sale - No.4047
10 Mar 4 Period Furniture, Paintings & Decorative Arts - No.8083
31 Mar 4 Irish Art - No.3070

20 Apr 4 Contemporary & Modern Art - No.4048
19 May 4 Furniture, Paintings & Decorative Arts - No.8084
26 May 4 Important Irish Art - No.8084 - With Bonhams
15 Jun 4 Modern & Contemporary Art
13 Jul 4 Fine Art

James Julia, Fairfield, ME - USA
20 Aug 3 Fine Art
8 Jan 4 English & European Paintings
16 Apr 4 Spring Antique & Fine Art Auction

James Thompson, Kirby Lonsdale - UK
17 Sep 3 19th & 20th Century Watercolours, Oils & Prints
19 Nov 3 19th & 20th Century Paintings
21 Jan 4 Oil Paintings & Watercolours
17 Mar 4 Oil Paintings & Watercolours
19 May 4 Oil Paintings & Watercolours

Jeffery Burchard, St Pertersberg, FL - USA
17 Aug 3 Estate Antiques & Fine Art
20 Sep 3 Estate Antiques & Fine Art
19 Oct 3 Estate Antiques & Fine Art
24 Jan 4 Estate Antiques & Fine Art
21 Feb 4 Estate Antiques & Fine Art
21 Mar 4 Estate Antiques & Fine Art
18 Apr 4 Estate Antiques & Fine Art
15 May 4 Estate Antiques & Fine Art
19 Jun 4 Estate Antiques & Fine Art

Jim Railton, Alnwick - UK
8 Nov 3 Fine Art
17 Apr 4 Estate Auction - No.42
30 Jul 4 Fine Art - Gosforth Racecourse

Joel, Victoria - Australia
13 Oct 3 Fine Art - Spring Auction
7 Dec 3 Christmas Auction - XMAS03
5 Feb 4 Fine Art - No.5132
1 Apr 4 Fine Art - No.5140
10 May 4 Fine Art - Autumn Auction
3 Jun 4 Fine Art - No.5148
27 Jun 4 Fine Art
1 Jul 4 Fine Art - No.5152

Johan Sebok, Bamberg - Germany
8 May 4 Fine Art - No.79

John Bellman, Billingshurst - UK
21 Jan 4 Fine Art
18 Feb 4 Fine Art
17 Mar 4 Fine Art
21 Apr 4 Fine Art
19 May 4 Fine Art
14 Jul 4 Fine Art

John Moran, Pasadena, CA - USA
18 Nov 3 California & American Paintings
17 Feb 4 California & American Paintings
15 Jun 4 California & American Paintings

John Nicholson, Haslemere - UK
11 Sep 3 Fine Art
23 Sep 3 Oil Paintings, Watercolours, Prints & Engravings
28 Sep 3 Contemporary & Post War Russian Paintings
5 Nov 3 Fine Art
17 Dec 3 Contemporary Russian Paintings
18 Dec 3 Fine Art
4 Feb 4 Fine Art
17 Mar 4 Fine Art
5 May 4 Fine Art
5 May 4 Russian Paintings
16 Jun 4 Fine Art
21 Jul 4 Fine Art
21 Jul 4 Russian Paintings

John Ross & Co, Belfast - N.Ireland
10 Sep 3 James Stanley Prosser Collection
1 Oct 3 Irish Paintings
3 Dec 3 Irish Paintings
3 Mar 4 Irish Paintings
11 Mar 4 Fine Art
2 Jun 4 Irish Paintings - No.44

John Taylors, Louth - UK
11 Nov 3 Fine Art
6 Jul 4 Fine Art

Joron-Derem, Paris - France
24 Mar 4 Paintings, Drawings & Fine Art

16 May 4 Chateau de Vitry-La-Ville Contents
28 Jun 4 Fine Art

Joyner Waddington, Toronto - Canada
2 Dec 3 Canadian Art
1 Jun 4 Canadian Art

Karl & Faber, Munich - Germany
25 May 4 Fine Art - No.206

Karlheinz Kaupp, Staufen - Germany
19 Sep 3 Art & Antiques
25 Mar 4 Art & Antiques
12 Jun 4 Art & Antiques

Karrenbauer, Konstanz - Germany
26 Mar 4 Fine Art - No.195
26 Jun 4 Fine Art & Varia - No.197

Kenneth Van Blarcom, South Natick, MA - USA
8 Nov 3 Annual Fall Auction
2 May 4 Fine Art

Ketterer, Hamburg - Germany
24 Oct 3 Old Masters & Modern Art - No.283
26 Mar 4 Old & Modern Art & Maritime Art - No.286

Ketterer, Munich - Germany
5 Dec 3 Classics Of The 20th Century & Munich School - No.285
5 Dec 3 Fine Art-Informal - No.285
14 May 4 Classics of the 20th Century & Munich School - No.290
14 May 4 Special Auction Bauhaus - No.290
14 May 4 German Avant-Garde - No.290

Keys, Aylsham - UK
15 Aug 3 Pictures
17 Oct 3 Pictures
5 Dec 3 Pictures
13 Feb 4 Pictures
30 Mar 4 Pictures
16 Apr 4 Pictures
11 Jun 4 Pictures

Kieselbach, Budapest - Hungary
4 Oct 3 Fine Art
12 Dec 3 Winter Sale
28 Apr 4 Fine Paintings - No.25

Klefisch, Cologne - Germany
19 Jun 4 Fine Art - No. 80

Kohn, Paris - France
14 Nov 3 Old Masters & Works of Art
24 Nov 3 17th, 18th & 19th Century Fine Art
15 Dec 3 Modern Paintings & Sculptures
28 Apr 4 Fine Art
5 Jul 4 Important Paintings
6 Jul 4 Furniture & Fine Art

Kunsthallen, Copenhagen - Denmark
17 Sep 3 International Auction - No.540
26 Nov 3 Modern Art - No.541
2 Dec 3 Paintings & Works of Art - No.541
25 Feb 4 International Auction - No.542

L & B, Essen-Ruutenscheid - Germany
27 Mar 4 Paintings - No.36

Lacy Scott, Bury St Edmunds - UK
20 Sep 3 Fine Art
20 Mar 4 Fine Art
19 Jun 4 Fine Art

Lambrays, Wadebridge - UK
31 Dec 3 Fine Art

Lane, Penzance - UK
2 Oct 3 Pictures & prints
11 Dec 3 Fine Art
26 Feb 4 Important Pictures
3 Jun 4 Pictures & Prints

Lawrences, Bletchingley - UK
16 Sep 3 Fine Art
28 Oct 3 Fine Art
9 Dec 3 Fine Art
3 Feb 4 Fine Art
16 Mar 4 Fine Art
27 Apr 4 Fine Art
8 Jun 4 Fine Art
20 Jun 4 Fine Art

Lawrences, Crewkerne - UK
16 Oct 3 Fine Art
14 Jan 4 Fine Art
22 Apr 4 Fine Art
8 Jul 4 Fine Art

Lawson Menzies, Sydney - Australia
26 Aug 3 Australian Paintings - No.3661
29 Oct 3 Fine Australian & International Art - No.3671
19 Dec 3 Fine Art - No.7333
23 Jan 4 Fine Art - No.7336
27 Feb 4 Fine Art - No.7342
26 Mar 4 General Sale incl. Paintings - No.7347
30 Mar 4 Estate of Chandler Coventry - No.3700
3 May 4 International Decorative Arts - No.3691
25 May 4 Aboriginal Art - No.3696
28 May 4 General Sale incl. Paintings - No.7361
25 Jun 4 General Sale incl. Paintings - No.7369
23 Jul 4 General Sale incl. Paintings - No. 7374
25 Jul 4 Priestley Collection - No.3711

Le Mouel, Paris - France
13 May 4 Photographs
5 Jul 4 Modern & Contemporary Art

Le Roux & Morel, Paris - France
7 Apr 4 Ateliers Istrati & Dumitresco
9 Jun 4 17th & 19th Century Paintings

Lempertz, Cologne - Germany
31 Oct 3 Photographs - No.844
14 Nov 3 Fine Art - No.845
15 Nov 3 Old Masters, Drawings & Sculptures - No.846
26 Nov 3 Modern Art - No.847
27 Nov 3 Contemporary Art - No.849
5 Dec 3 Asian Art - No.850
13 Dec 3 Old Masters, 19th Century, Modern & Contemporary Art - No.851
8 May 4 Photographs - No.854
21 May 4 Decorative Arts - No.855
22 May 4 Old Master Paintings - No.856
4 Jun 4 Contemporary Art - No.858
5 Jun 4 Modern Art - No.859

Lesieur & Le Bars, Le Havre - France
26 Oct 3 Paintings, Marine Art & Fine Art
11 Nov 3 Paintings & Fine Art
7 Dec 3 Paintings & Fine Art
8 Feb 4 180 Russian Paintings
7 Mar 4 Paintings, Sculptures and Works of Art

Levis, Calgary - Canada
5 Oct 3 Fine Art
23 Nov 3 Fine Art
18 Apr 4 Fine Art

Libert, Castor, Paris - France
12 Dec 3 Paintings & Fine Art
28 Jan 4 Paintings & Fine Art
7 Apr 4 Succession Amodio

Lilla Bukowskis, Stockholm - Sweden
25 Aug 3 Fine Art - No.154
29 Sep 3 Fine Art - No.155
15 Dec 3 Fine Art - No.156
26 Jan 4 Fine Art - No.157
14 Jun 4 Fine Art - No.159

Lincoln, Orange, NJ - USA
16 Sep 3 Fine Art
11 Nov 3 Fine Art
16 Dec 3 Fine Art

Livinec, Gaudcheau & Jezequel, Rennes Cedex - France
7 Oct 3 Paintings & Fine Art
7 Dec 3 Paintings & Fine Art
21 Feb 4 Paintings & Fine Art - Saint-Malo
7 Mar 4 Paintings & Fine Art
17 Apr 4 Paintings & Fine Art - Saint-Malo
8 Jun 4 Paintings & Fine Art
14 Jul 4 Fine Art & Paintings - Saint-Malo

Locati, Maple Glen - USA
25 Apr 4 Fine Art Online Auction

Locke & England, Leamington Spa - UK
4 Sep 3 Collectors' Items
2 Oct 3 Collectors' Items
30 Oct 3 Collectors' Items
4 Dec 3 Collectors' Items
29 Jan 4 Fine Art
26 Feb 4 Fine Art
25 Mar 4 Fine Art
22 Apr 4 Fine Art
24 Jun 4 Fine Art
29 Jul 4 Fine Art

Lombrail & Teucquam, Paris - France
5 Oct 3 Paintings & Fine Art
21 Nov 3 Sculptures & 19th Century & Modern Paintings
29 Mar 4 Paintings, Prints & Works of Art
16 May 4 Paintings & Fine Art
13 Jun 4 Paintings, Prints & Works of Art

Lots Road Auctions, London - UK
3 Aug 3 Fine Antiques, Objets d'Art, & Paintings - No.853
10 Aug 3 Fine Art - No.854
17 Aug 3 Fine Art - No.855
7 Sep 3 Fine Art - No.858
14 Sep 3 Fine Art - No.859
21 Sep 3 Fine Art - No.860
28 Sep 3 Fine Art - No.861
5 Oct 3 Fine Art - No.862
12 Oct 3 Fine Art - No.863
2 Nov 3 Fine Art - No.866
9 Nov 3 Fine Art - No.867
16 Nov 3 Fine Art - No.868
23 Nov 3 Fine Art - No.869
30 Nov 3 Fine Art - No.870
7 Dec 3 Fine Art - No.871
4 Jan 4 Fine Art - No.873
11 Jan 4 Fine Art - No.874
18 Jan 4 Fine Art - No.875
1 Feb 4 Fine Art - No.877
8 Feb 4 Fine Art - No.878
15 Feb 4 Fine Art - No.879
22 Feb 4 Fine Art - No.880
7 Mar 4 Fine Art - No.882
21 Mar 4 Fine Art - No.884
28 Mar 4 Fine Art - No.885
4 Apr 4 Fine Art - No.886
18 Apr 4 Fine Art - No.887
2 May 4 Fine Art - No.889
30 May 4 Fine Art - No.893
6 Jun 4 Fine Art - No.894
13 Jun 4 Fine Art - No.895
20 Jun 4 Russian Impressionist Art - No.896
4 Jul 4 Fine Art - No.898
18 Jul 4 Fine Art - No.900
25 Jul 4 Fine Art - No.901

Louis C. Morton, Lomas Virreyes - Mexico
24 Sep 3 Antiques - No.320
29 Oct 3 Fine Art of Mexico & Europe - No.324
30 Oct 3 Modern & Contemporary Art - No.325
9 Dec 3 Modern & Contemporary Art - No.329
27 Jan 4 Decorative Arts incl. Paintings - No.331
24 Feb 4 19th Century European Art - No.332
25 Mar 4 Prints & Paintings - No.336
31 Mar 4 Antiques - No.338

Louis Taylor, Stoke on Trent - UK
16 Sep 3 Pictures
9 Dec 3 Oil Paintings & Watercolours
8 Mar 4 Fine Art
14 Jun 4 Fine Art

Lyon & Turnbull, Edinburgh - UK
16 Oct 3 Pictures - No.76
11 Dec 3 Fine Paintings - No.82
19 Feb 4 Jewellery & Paintings - No.85 & 86
21 Apr 4 Fine Art - No.89
28 May 4 Fine Paintings - No.92
10 Jun 4 Pictures - No.94
12 Jul 4 Golf, Fishing & Sporting Memorabilia - No.96
21 Jul 4 Contents of Jordanstone - No.98 - Jordanstone

Maigret, Paris - France
5 Dec 3 19th & 20th Century Paintings, Art Nouveau & Art Deco
10 Dec 3 Paintings & Fine Art
17 Mar 4 19th Century & Old Master Drawings
7 Apr 4 Art Nouveau Art Deco
11 Jun 4 Paintings & Fine Art

23 Jun 4 Paintings & Art Nouveau
6 Jul 4 Art Nouveau & Art Deco

Mallams, Cheltenham - UK
18 Sep 3 Fine Art
16 Oct 3 Fine Art
20 Nov 3 Fine Art
8 Jan 4 Fine Art
26 Feb 4 Fine Art
25 Mar 4 Fine Art
22 Apr 4 Fine Art
27 May 4 Fine Art
22 Jul 4 Fine Art

Mallams, Oxford - UK
27 Aug 3 Fine Art - BH270803
3 Oct 3 Oil Paintings & Watercolours
29 Oct 3 Fine Art
26 Nov 3 Fine Art
19 Dec 3 Fine Art
28 Jan 4 Fine Art
25 Feb 4 Irish, Scottish & Welsh Paintings
3 Mar 4 Fine Art
7 May 4 Pictures & Books
26 May 4 Fine Art
28 Jul 4 Pictures

Marie & Robert, Paris - France
5 Apr 4 Paintings, Drawings & Modern Sculptures
17 May 4 Oriental Art
17 Jun 4 Fine Art

Martel Maides, Guernsey - UK
25 Nov 3 Fine Art - No.80237
1 Apr 4 Fine Art - No.802008
22 Jul 4 Fine Art - No.802009

Martinot & Savignat, Pontoise - France
13 Dec 3 Paintings, Prints, Sculptures & Ceramics

Matthew's, Lake Oswego - USA
16 Mar 4 Fine Paintings

Maynards, Vancouver - Canada
16 Sep 3 Canadian & International Art
19 Nov 3 Contemporary Art
9 Dec 3 Antiques, Fine Art & Jewellery

Mealy's, Castlecomer - Eire
28 Oct 3 Fine Art
18 Nov 3 Fine Art
23 Mar 4 Fine Art
22 Jun 4 Fine Art

Meeting Art, Vercelli - Italy
6 Sep 3 Modern & Contemporary Art - No.520
18 Oct 3 Modern & Contemporary Art - No.522
1 Nov 3 20th Century Paintings - No.523
14 Feb 4 Furniture & Works of Art - No.531
13 Mar 4 Modern & Contemporary Art - No.533
1 May 4 19th & 20th Century Art - No.536
30 May 4 100 Artists for a Collection - No.538
12 Jun 4 Modern & Contemporary Art - No.540

Mehlis, Plauen - Germany
21 May 4 Fine Art - No.34

Mellors & Kirk, Nottingham - UK
25 Sep 3 Fine Art
4 Dec 3 Fine Art
5 Feb 4 Fine Art
22 Apr 4 Fine Art
1 Jul 4 Fine Art

Mervyn Carey, Cranbrook - UK
26 Nov 3 Fine Art
30 Jun 4 Fine Art

Michael Zeller, Lindau - Germany
9 Oct 3 International Bodensee Art Auction - No.78
5 Dec 3 International Bodensee Art Auction - No.79
6 May 4 International Bodensee Art Auction - No.80
25 Jun 4 International Bodensee Art Auction - No.81

Millon & Associes, Paris - France
26 Sep 3 Old Masters & Modern Art
1 Oct 3 Modern & Contemporary Art
14 Oct 3 Atelier of Germaine Nordmann
20 Nov 3 Hunting Art & Historic Souvenirs
25 Nov 3 Art Nouveau, Art Deco
27 Nov 3 Modern & Contemporary Paintings & Sculptures
1 Dec 3 Old Masters & Works of Art
10 Dec 3 Art Nouveau, Art Deco
2 Feb 4 Modern Art & 20th Century Decorative Art
19 Mar 4 Modern & Contemporary Art
30 Mar 4 16th -20th Century Paintings & Drawings
1 Apr 4 Collection of Monsieur V
26 Apr 4 Contemporary Russian Paintings
7 May 4 Modern & Contemporary Art
12 May 4 Photographs
23 Jun 4 Paintings & Fine Art
25 Jun 4 Fine Paintings
29 Jun 4 Art Nouveau & Art Deco
5 Jul 4 Paintings

Mitchells, Cockermouth - UK
2 Oct 3 Fine Art
11 Dec 3 Fine Art
4 Mar 4 Fine Art
13 May 4 Fine Art
15 Jul 4 Fine Art

MonsAntic, Mons-Maisieres - Belgium
28 Mar 4 Fine Art
16 May 4 Fine Art
4 Jul 4 Fine Art

Moore Allen and Innocent, Cirencester - UK
5 Sep 3 Sporting Sale
31 Oct 3 Picture Sale
28 Nov 3 Fine Art
12 Dec 3 Fine Art
5 Mar 4 Fine Art
2 Apr 4 Picture Sale
18 Jun 4 Fine Art
9 Jul 4 Fine Art

Morphets, Harrogate - UK
11 Sep 3 Fine Art
27 Nov 3 Fine Art
11 Mar 4 Fine Art
10 Jun 4 Fine Art

Mu Terem Galeria, Budapest - Hungary
16 Apr 4 Paintings - No.16

Muizon & Le Coent, Senlis - France
16 Nov 3 Paintings & Fine Art
21 Mar 4 Paintings & Fine Art

Mullucks Wells, Essex - UK
22 Mar 4 Fine Art & Antiques
12 Jul 4 Fine Art

Museumsbygningen, Kobenhavn - Denmark
3 Sep 3 Fine Art - No.27
3 Dec 3 Fine Art - No.29
25 Feb 4 Fine Art - No.30
7 Jun 4 Fine Art - No.32

Nadeau, Windsor, CT - USA
20 Sep 3 Fine Art
11 Oct 3 Fine Art
1 Jan 4 Fine Art
3 Apr 4 Fine Art

Naon & Cia, Buenos Aires - Argentina
3 Dec 3 Important Paintings

Neal & Fletcher, Woodbridge - UK
3 Dec 3 Fine Art
17 Mar 4 Fine Art
30 Jun 4 Fine Art

Neal Auction Company, New Orleans, LA - USA
2 Aug 3 Summer Estates Auction
4 Oct 3 Louisiana Purchase Auction
6 Dec 3 Holiday Estates Auction
7 Feb 4 Winter Estates Auction
3 Apr 4 Spring Estates Auction
5 Jun 4 Late Spring Estates Auction

Neales, Nottingham - UK
7 Aug 3 Fine Art
2 Oct 3 Fine Art
16 Oct 3 Fine Art
11 Dec 3 Fine Art
18 Mar 4 Fine Art - AE045
10 Jun 4 Fine Art - AE047

Neret-Minet, Paris - France
15 Oct 3 Paintings & Fine Art
29 Nov 3 Youth Art
10 Dec 3 Paintings & Fine Art
31 Jan 4 Marine Art
26 Mar 4 Old Masters & Modern Paintings
3 Apr 4 Young Contemporary Creation
3 Jul 4 Maritime
5 Jul 4 Paintings & Works of Art

Neumeister, Munich - Germany
24 Sep 3 Fine Art - No.321
25 Sep 3 Fine Art - No.148
22 Oct 3 Fine Art - No.149
13 Nov 3 20th Century Art - No.34
3 Dec 3 Fine Art - No.322
4 Dec 3 Fine Art - No.150
4 Feb 4 Varia Auction - No.151
17 Mar 4 Paintings & Decorative Arts - No.323
18 Mar 4 Fine Art - No.152
21 Apr 4 Fine Art - No.153
13 May 4 Modern Art - No.35
30 Jun 4 Fine Art - No.324
1 Jul 4 Varia Auction - V154

New Orleans Auction, Louisiana, LA - USA
20 Sep 3 Fine Art - No.0305
22 Nov 3 Fine Art No.0306
17 Jan 4 Fine Art - No.0401
27 Mar 4 Fine Art - No.0402
22 May 4 Fine Art - No.0403
17 Jul 4 Fine Art - No.0404

Nigel Ward, Hereford - UK
18 Oct 3 Fine Art
15 Nov 3 Fine Art
13 Dec 3 Fine Art
31 Jan 4 Fine Art
21 Feb 4 Fine Art

North East Auctions, Portsmouth, NH - USA
1 Aug 3 Fine Art
3 Aug 3 Collection of Cora & Benjamin Ginsburg
31 Oct 3 Fine Art
6 Mar 4 Collection of Colonial Williamsburg
21 May 4 Fine Art

O'Gallerie, Portland, OR - USA
18 Aug 3 Furniture & Decorative Arts
22 Sep 3 Furniture & Decorative Arts
27 Oct 3 Furniture & Decorative Arts
1 Dec 3 Furniture & Decorative Arts
19 Jan 4 Furniture & Decorative Arts
23 Feb 4 The McFarlane Estate Auction
29 Mar 4 Furniture & Decorative Arts
3 May 4 Furniture & Decorative Arts
7 Jun 4 Furniture & Decorative Arts

Oger, Dumont, Paris - France
3 Dec 3 Paintings & Fine Art
19 Mar 4 Paintings & Fine Art
9 Jun 4 Paintings & Fine Art

Olivers, Sudbury - UK
18 Sep 3 Fine Art
11 Dec 3 Fine Art
1 Apr 4 Fine Art
24 Jun 4 Fine Art

Osenat, Fontainebleau - France
7 Dec 3 19th Century Paintings: Barbizon School
31 Jan 4 Sale Empire
29 Feb 4 Decorative Arts
16 May 4 Modern Paintings
6 Jun 4 Barbizon School

Outer Cape Auctions, Provincetown - USA
9 Nov 3 Fine Art
3 Jan 4 Fine Art
15 Feb 4 Fine Art
3 Apr 4 Fine Art
17 Jul 4 Fine Art

Outhwaite & Litherland, Liverpool - UK
25 Nov 3 Fine Art
26 May 4 Fine Art

Page, Batavia, NY - USA
6 Mar 4 Fine Art

Palais de Beaux Arts, Brussels - Belgium
9 Sep 3 Fine Art
7 Oct 3 Fine Art
1 Dec 3 Fine Art
3 Dec 3 Fine Art
30 Mar 4 Fine Art
25 May 4 Fine Art
7 Jun 4 Belgian Art
22 Jun 4 Fine Art

Pandolfini, Florence - Italy
7 Oct 3 Fine Art
26 Nov 3 Modern & Contemporary Art, Italian Design 1940-1990
9 Dec 3 19th & 20th Century Paintings
29 Mar 4 Furniture & Paintings
21 Jun 4 19th & 20th Century Art
29 Jun 4 Villa Clementina: Property of Mauro Forghieri

Patersons, Paisley - UK
17 Feb 4 Fine Art
18 May 4 Fine Art

Paul Beighton, Thurcroft - UK
31 Aug 3 Fine Art
7 Mar 4 Fine Art

Paul Kieffer, Pforzheim - Germany
6 Feb 4 Old Masters & Contemporary Art - No.52
7 May 4 Old Masters & Modern Art - No.53

Peron, Melun - France
19 Oct 3 Fine Art

Peschetau-Badin Godeau & Leroy, Paris - France
18 Mar 4 Old Masters & Modern Drawings & Sculptures

Peter Francis, Carmarthen - UK
9 Sep 3 Fine Art
21 Oct 3 Fine Art
2 Dec 3 Fine Art
27 Jan 4 Fine Art
9 Mar 4 Fine Art
27 Apr 4 Fine Art
8 Jun 4 Fine Art
20 Jul 4 Fine Art

Peter Webb, Newmarket - New Zealand
12 Aug 3 Affordable Art - No.255
20 Aug 3 DB Breweries Collection - No.873
23 Sep 3 Fine New Zealand Paintings & Decorative Arts - No.256
4 Nov 3 Affordable Art - No.257
9 Dec 3 Fine Paintings & Decorative Arts - No.258
24 Feb 4 Affordable Fine Art - No.259
30 Mar 4 Fine Art - No.260
11 May 4 Affordable Art - No.261
29 Jun 4 Fine Paintings, Jewellery & Works of Art - No.262

Peter Wilson, Nantwich - UK
24 Sep 3 Fine Art
26 Nov 3 Fine Art
18 Feb 4 Fine Art
28 Apr 4 Fine Art
6 Jul 4 Fine Art

Philippe Schuler, Zurich - Switzerland
16 Sep 3 Fine Art - No.90
8 Dec 3 Fine Art - No.91
22 Mar 4 Fine Art - No.92
14 Jun 4 Fine Art - No.93

Phillips, New York, NY - USA
16 Oct 3 Joshua P. Smith Collection of Photographs - NY040303
17 Oct 3 Photographs - NY040403
30 Oct 3 American Art - NY030203
13 Nov 3 Contemporary Art - Part I - NY010303
14 Nov 3 Contemporary Art - Part II - NY010403
8 Dec 3 20th & 21st Century Design Art - NY050403
10 Dec 3 Contemporary Art - NY010503
22 Apr 4 A Century of Fine Photographs, 1840's - 1940's Part I - NY040104
23 Apr 4 A Century of Fine Photographs, 1840's - 1940's Part II - NY040204
24 Apr 4 Photographs Part II - NY040304
13 May 4 Contemporary Art Part 1 - NY010104
14 May 4 Contemporary Art Part 2 - NY010204
10 Jun 4 20-21st Century Design Art

10 Jun 4 Contemporary Art

Piasa, Paris - France
6 Nov 3 Prints
14 Nov 3 Oriental Art
21 Nov 3 20th Century Photographs, Sculptures & Fine Art
4 Dec 3 Succession of Annie Ronchese
8 Dec 3 Paintings, Drawings & Fine Art
10 Dec 3 Old Drawings & Sketches
11 Dec 3 Prints
12 Dec 3 Paintings & Sculptures of 19th & 20th Centuries
17 Dec 3 Old Masters
19 Dec 3 Fine Art
28 Jan 4 Art Nouveau, Art Deco
12 Mar 4 Asian Art
19 Mar 4 19th & 20th Century Drawings
23 Mar 4 Art Nouveau
26 Mar 4 Old Master Paintings & Fine Art
1 Apr 4 Letters, Manuscripts & Historical Documents
7 Apr 4 Paintings & Sculptures of 19th & 20th Centuries
29 Apr 4 Old Master & Modern Prints
14 May 4 Photographs from the Collection of Auguste Salzmann
9 Jun 4 Collection Bernadac
10 Jun 4 Prints
11 Jun 4 Art Nouveau & Art Deco
16 Jun 4 19th & 20th Century Drawings
18 Jun 4 19th & 20th Century Drawings, Paintings & Sculptures
23 Jun 4 Succession of Mr & Mrs Pierre Sommer
25 Jun 4 Important Old Master Paintings
30 Jun 4 Fine Art

Pierre Berge, Paris - France
13 Oct 3 Old Masters & Modern Art
5 Nov 3 Design - Serge Manzon
18 Nov 3 Modern Art
25 Nov 3 Modern Paintings - Geneva
26 Nov 3 20th Century Decorative Arts
19 Dec 3 Old Masters, Primitive & Fine Art
26 Mar 4 Old Masters, Miniatures & Fine Art
16 Apr 4 Sculptures
16 Apr 4 Modern & Contemporary Art
13 May 4 19th & 20th Century Art
4 Jun 4 Paintings & Fine Art from a Flat in Neuilly-sur-Seine
11 Jun 4 Prints & Paintings
30 Jun 4 Old Masters, Miniatures & Works of Art

Pinneys, Montreal - Canada
9 Dec 3 Canadian & European Art

Pook & Pook, Downingtown, PA - USA
20 Sep 3 Fine Art
6 Dec 3 Fine Art
10 Jan 4 Fine Art
20 Mar 4 Fine Art
21 May 4 Fine Art
22 May 4 The Collection of George & Mae Crittenton

Porro, Milan - Italy
15 Nov 3 Old Masters & Fine Art - No.3
16 Dec 3 Modern & Contemporary Works of Art - No.4
25 Feb 4 Old Masters - No.6
25 Feb 4 19th Century Paintings - No.5
27 Apr 4 Old Masters & Works of Art - No.7
26 May 4 Old Master Paintings - No.8
14 Jun 4 Modern & Contemporary Art - No.9

Quinn's, Falls Church - USA
6 Sep 3 Fine Art
1 Jan 4 Fine Art
16 Feb 4 Fine Art

Quittenbaum, Hamburg - Germany
13 Sep 3 Paintings & Fine Art - No.37
6 Dec 3 Old Masters & 19th Century Paintings - No.41
28 Feb 4 Paintings & Fine Art - No.42
19 Jun 4 Paintings & Fine Art - No.45

Quittenbaum, Munich - Germany
8 Nov 3 Jugendstil & Art Deco - No.39
24 Apr 4 Art Nouveau, Art Deco - No.43

Rabourdin & Choppin de Janvry, Paris - France
26 Sep 3 19th & 20th Century Paintings
15 Oct 3 19th & 20th Century Paintings & Fine Art
19 Oct 3 Oriental Art
28 Oct 3 19th & 20th Century Sculptures
5 Nov 3 19th & 20th Century Paintings & Works of Art
6 Nov 3 Atelier of Jules-Alexis Muenier
12 Dec 3 Old Masters, Ceramics & Sculptures
14 Dec 3 Modern & Contemporary Prints & Paintings
17 Dec 3 Paintings, Art Nouveau, Art Deco & Fine Art

Rachel Davis, Shaker Heights, OH - USA
25 Oct 3 Works of Art on Paper
20 Mar 4 Prints & Drawings
19 Jun 4 Works on Paper

Rasmussen, Copenhagen - Denmark
2 Sep 3 International Paintings & Works of Art - No.724
7 Oct 3 Modern Art & Design - No.726
2 Dec 3 International Industrial Art - No.727
9 Dec 3 International Art - No.727
24 Feb 4 International Auction - No.729
2 Mar 4 International Paintings & Works of Art - No.729
29 Mar 4 Erik Olesen's Collection - No.731
29 Mar 4 Modern Art - No.731
2 Jun 4 Works of Art - No.732
9 Jun 4 Paintings, Drawings & Prints - No.732

Rasmussen, Havnen, Copenhagen - Denmark
30 Aug 3 Paintings & Works Of Art - No.36
27 Sep 3 Paintings & Works Of Art - No.37
25 Oct 3 Paintings & Works Of Art - No.38
29 Nov 3 Paintings & Works Of Art - No.39
7 Feb 4 Paintings & Works of Art - No.41
24 Apr 4 Paintings & Works of Art - No.42
19 Jun 4 Paintings & Works of Art - No.44

Rasmussen, Vejle - Denmark
4 Aug 3 Paintings & Works Of Art - No.89
22 Sep 3 Paintings & Works Of Art - No.90
10 Nov 3 Paintings & Works Of Art - No.91
12 Jan 4 Fine Art - No.93
15 Mar 4 Fine Art & Design - No.94
10 May 4 Paintings & Works of Art - No.96

Reiner Dannenberg, Berlin - Germany
27 Sep 3 Art & Antiques - No.91
6 Dec 3 Art & Antiques - No.92
27 Mar 4 Art & Antiques - No.93
19 Jun 4 Art & Antiques - No.94

Reiss & Sohn, Konigstein - Germany
21 Nov 3 Old & New Art - No.92
24 Apr 4 Paintings & Fine Art - No.94

Remi Ader, Paris - France
10 Dec 3 Fine Art

Renaud, Paris - France
17 Oct 3 Succession of Suzanne Levina - with Giquello
6 Dec 3 Photographs, Drawings & Collages - with Giquello
12 Dec 3 Ancient & Modern Paintings - with Giquello
15 May 4 International Surrealism - with Giquello
16 Jun 4 19th Century & Modern Paintings & Prints - With Giquello

Renault-Aubry, Pontivy - France
16 May 4 Fine Art

Rendalls, Ashburton - UK
14 Aug 3 Fine Art
18 Sep 3 Fine Art
16 Oct 3 Fine Art
13 Nov 3 Fine Art
11 Dec 3 Fine Art
22 Jan 4 Fine Art
19 Feb 4 19th & 20th Century Paintings
15 Apr 4 Works by Robert O Lenkiewicz
13 May 4 Fine Art
15 Jul 4 Fine Art

Ribeyre & Baron, Paris - France
22 Oct 3 Graphic Arts
19 Mar 4 Fine Art & Paintings
22 Jun 4 Paintings & Decorative Arts

Richard Opfer, Timonium, MD - USA
18 Mar 4 Private Collection of James L Kochan

Richardson & Smith, Whitby - UK
21 Aug 3 Fine Art
12 Sep 3 Fine Art
10 Oct 3 Fine Art
30 Oct 3 Fine Art

4 Dec 3 Fine Art
19 Feb 4 Fine Art
15 Apr 4 Fine Art
20 May 4 Fine Art
15 Jul 4 Fine Art

Rieber Auktionhaus, Stuttgart - Germany
18 Sep 3 Fine Art
26 Apr 4 Fine Art

Rieunier, Paris - France
1 Dec 3 Old Masters & Drawings, Modern Art
8 Mar 4 Modern Paintings
29 Mar 4 Succession of Madame H, Monsieur D & Monsieur G
4 Jun 4 Modern Paintings - Atelier Marcel Valentin
23 Jun 4 Old Master Paintings & Drawings

Ritchie, Toronto - Canada
15 Sep 3 Studio of late Harold Town - No.697.1
23 Sep 3 Canadian Art - No.697.2
28 Oct 3 Fine Art - No.699.4
2 Dec 3 European & American Art - No.703
24 Feb 4 Decorative Art - No.709
2 Mar 4 Canadian Art - No.710
4 May 4 European & American Art - No.714
15 Jun 4 Decorative Arts - No.717

Robin & Fattori, Granville - France
31 Jan 4 Maritime
1 Feb 4 Furniture & Decorative Arts

Rogeon, Paris - France
17 May 4 Haitian Paintings

Rogers Jones, Clwyd - UK
27 Sep 3 Welsh Fine Art
30 Sep 3 Fine Art
27 Jan 4 Fine Art
24 Feb 4 Fine Art
30 Mar 4 Fine Art
24 Apr 4 Welsh Fine Art

Roland's, New York - USA
11 May 4 Fine Art

Rosebery Fine Art, London - UK
12 Aug 3 Fine Art
16 Sep 3 Fine Art
14 Oct 3 Fine Art
11 Nov 3 Fine Art
9 Dec 3 Fine Art
20 Jan 4 Fine Art
17 Feb 4 Fine Art
23 Mar 4 Fine Art
20 Apr 4 Fine Art
18 May 4 Fine Art
15 Jun 4 Fine Art
13 Jul 4 Fine Art

Rossini, Paris - France
8 Dec 3 Fine Art From a Castle
10 Dec 3 Art of 19th & 20th Century
17 Jan 4 Atelier Suzanne Kaehrling
13 Feb 4 Succession Madame B
21 Mar 4 Sporting Art
30 Mar 4 Pierre Miquel Collection
2 Apr 4 Contents of a Castle
15 Jun 4 19th & 20th Century Paintings, Prints & Sculptures
25 Jun 4 Fine Art from Maitre B Apartment in Avenue d'Eylau
28 Jun 4 Paintings & Fine Art

Rouillac, Paris - France
4 Jan 4 Sculpture & Furniture
11 Jan 4 The Davignon Succession
18 Apr 4 Collection Wilder Burnap
6 Jun 4 Contents of the Orangerie of Cheverny

Rowley, Little Downham Ely - UK
9 Sep 3 Fine Art
4 Nov 3 Fine Art
24 Feb 4 Fine Art
20 Apr 4 Fine Art
29 Jun 4 Fine Art

Rupert Toovey, Washington - UK
13 Aug 3 Fine Art
8 Oct 3 Fine Art
5 Nov 3 Fine Art
10 Dec 3 Christmas Sale
21 Jan 4 Fine Art
18 Feb 4 Fine Art
17 Mar 4 Fine Art
21 Apr 4 Fine Art
19 May 4 Fine Art
16 Jun 4 Fine Art
14 Jul 4 Fine Art

Saint Hippolyte, Montreal - Canada
26 Aug 3 Fine Art
15 Dec 3 Fine Art
27 Jan 4 Canadian & International Art - Ritz-Carlton

Salle des ventes Pillet, Lyons la foret - France
12 Oct 3 Paintings & Fine Art
30 Nov 3 Paintings & Fine Art
4 Apr 4 Paintings & Fine Art
20 Jun 4 Atelier Jean Mayodon

Sant Agostino, Turin - Italy
20 Oct 3 Old Master & Modern Art - No.83
17 Nov 3 Modern & Contemporary Art - No.84
22 Mar 4 Furniture & Paintings - No.85
14 Jun 4 Paintings & Furniture - No.86

Santa Fe Art, Santa Fe, NM - USA
1 Nov 3 Fine Art

Scarborough Perry Fine Arts, Hove - UK
18 Sep 3 Fine Art
11 Dec 3 Fine Art
25 Mar 4 Fine Art
13 May 4 Fine Art
24 Jun 4 Fine Art

Schloss Ahlden, Ahlden - Germany
19 Sep 3 Fine Art - No.122
28 Nov 3 Fine Art - No.123
8 May 4 Antiques & Modern Art - No.125
14 May 4 Fine Art - No.125

Schopmann, Hamburg - Germany
6 Sep 3 Fine Art
4 Dec 3 Fine Art
28 Apr 4 Fine Art

Schrager Galleries, Milwaukee, WI - USA
27 Oct 3 Fine Art - No.167
26 Jan 4 Fine Art - No.168
26 Apr 4 Fine Art - No.169
19 Jul 4 Fine Art - No.170

Segre, Madrid - Spain
16 Sep 3 Paintings - No.17
28 Oct 3 Paintings - No.18
29 Oct 3 Decorative Art - No.18
16 Dec 3 Paintings - No.19
3 Feb 4 Paintings - No.20
4 Feb 4 Decorative Art - No.20
30 Mar 4 Paintings - No.21
31 Mar 4 Decorative Art - No.21
18 May 4 Paintings - No.22
19 May 4 Furniture & Decorative Arts - No.22
29 Jun 4 Paintings - No.23

Selkirks, St Louis, MO - USA
13 Sep 3 Autumn Gallery - 03SEPG
7 Nov 3 20th Century Design & Fine Art
6 Dec 3 Winter Gallery - No.03DECG
20 Mar 4 Paintings & Decorative Arts
22 May 4 20th Century Design & Fine Art
26 Jun 4 Summer Fine Art Auction - 04JUNG

Semenzato, Florence - Italy
26 May 4 Furniture & Fine Art from a Lucchesia Villa
27 May 4 Furniture & Paintings

Shannon's, Milford, CT - USA
23 Oct 3 Fine Paintings
6 May 4 Fine Paintings

Shapes, Edinburgh - UK
2 Aug 3 Paintings & Fine Art - No.83
6 Sep 3 The Contents of Glencruitten House - No.84
11 Oct 3 Paintings & Fine Art - No.85
8 Nov 3 Paintings & Fine Art - No.86
6 Dec 3 Paintings & Fine Art - No.87
31 Jan 4 Paintings & Fine Art - No.88
6 Mar 4 Paintings & Fine Art - No.89

3 Apr 4 Paintings & Fine Art - No.90
1 May 4 Paintings & Fine Art - No.91
5 Jun 4 Paintings & Fine Art
3 Jul 4 Paintings & Fine Art

Shapiro, Sydney - Australia
1 Sep 3 Spring Traditional - No.7
10 Dec 3 Australian & International Art - No.8
21 Jul 4 Modern, Contemporary & Aboriginal Art - No.10

Shelley, Hendersonville, NC - USA
21 Nov 3 Premier Auction

Shishkin Gallery, Moscow - Russia
27 Mar 4 Russian Art - Neglinnaya ul 29/14
24 Apr 4 Russian Old Masters - Neglinnaya ul 29/14
29 May 4 Russian Art

Sigalas, Stuttgart - Germany
19 Sep 3 Fine Art - No.93
29 Nov 3 Fine Art - No.94
3 Feb 4 Fine Art & Tribal Art - No.95
27 Mar 4 Fine Art - No.96
22 May 4 Miscellaneous & Tribal Art - No.97

Simpson's, Houston, TX - USA
28 Sep 3 Fine Art
16 Nov 3 Fine Art

Skinner, Bolton, MA - USA
10 Aug 3 Country Americana - No.2207
26 Feb 4 Discovery - No.2229
18 Mar 4 Discovery - No.2233

Skinner, Boston, MA - USA
12 Sep 3 American & European Paintings & Prints - No.2210
4 Oct 3 European Furniture & Decorative Arts - No.2223
1 Nov 3 American Furniture & Decorative Arts - No.2241
21 Nov 3 American & European Paintings - No.2220
6 Dec 3 20th Century Furniture & Decorative Arts - No.2213
24 Jan 4 Fine Art - No.2222
22 Feb 4 American Furniture & Decorative Art - No.2230
5 Mar 4 American & European Paintings & Prints - No.2232
24 Apr 4 European Furniture & Decorative Arts - No.2234
14 May 4 American & European Paintings - No.2236
6 Jun 4 American Furniture & Decorative Arts - No.2242
19 Jun 4 20th Century Decorative Arts
17 Jul 4 European & Asian Furniture & Decorative Arts - No.2246

Sloans & Kenyon, Bethseda - USA
20 Sep 3 Fine Art - No.2
15 Nov 3 Estate Sale - No.3
13 Dec 3 Fine Art - No.4
7 Feb 4 Estate Auction - No.5
20 Mar 4 Fine Art - No.6
7 May 4 Fine Art - No.7
26 Jun 4 Decorative Arts - No.8
31 Jul 4 Summer Celebration Auction - No.9

Slotin Folk Art, Buford - USA
15 Nov 3 Folk Art
24 Apr 4 Folk Art

Sotheby's, Amsterdam - Netherlands
22 Sep 3 Estate of Late Princess Lilian of Belgium - AM0896
29 Sep 3 Arcade Auction: Paintings - AM0897
7 Oct 3 European Furniture, Sculpture & Good Decorations - AM0894
21 Oct 3 Important 19th Century Paintings - AM0900
4 Nov 3 Old Master Paintings - AM0902
4 Nov 3 Old Master Drawings - AM0903
2 Dec 3 Modern & Contemporary Art - AM0909
3 Dec 3 Prints & Photographs - AM0909
7 Dec 3 Silver, Jewelry & Paintings - AM0911 - Arcade Sale
15 Mar 4 18th, 19th & 20th Century Paintings - AM0916
6 Apr 4 European Furniture, Sculpture and Works of Art - AM0910
20 Apr 4 19th Century European Paintings - AM0920
5 May 4 The Von Galen Collection - AM0928
9 May 4 Paul de Grande Restoration Project - AM0937
18 May 4 Old Master Paintings - AM0923
19 May 4 The Unicorno Collection - Old Master Drawings - AM0944
7 Jun 4 20th Century Decorative Arts & Design - AM0926
8 Jun 4 Modern & Contemporary Art - AM0925
22 Jun 4 European Furniture, Sculpture & Works of Art - AM0927
28 Jun 4 Paintings & Watercolours - AM0929

Sotheby's, Billingshurst - UK
25 May 4 Sculpture & Architectural Items - B04880

Sotheby's, Hong Kong
26 Oct 3 Fine Chinese Ceramics & Works of Art - HK0197
27 Oct 3 Fine Chinese Paintings - HK0198
25 Apr 4 Emperor & Scholar - HK0202
26 Apr 4 Fine Chinese Paintings - HK0204

Sotheby's, London - UK
27 Aug 3 Scottish & Sporting Pictures & Sculpture - L03621 - Gleneagles Hotel
30 Sep 3 Elton John & His London Lifestyle - L03503
6 Oct 3 Warhol & The Pop Generation - L03162
14 Oct 3 The Travel Sale - L03622
14 Oct 3 Fawley House Sale - L03504 - Oxfordshire
15 Oct 3 Arts of the Islamic World - L03221
20 Oct 3 20th Century Italian Art - L03624
21 Oct 3 Impressionist & Modern Art - L03007
21 Oct 3 Contemporary Art - L03024
28 Oct 3 European Sculpture & Works of Art 900-1900 - L03232
29 Oct 3 The Haute Epoque Sale - L03626
12 Nov 3 Fine Chinese Ceramics & Works of Art - L03211
13 Nov 3 Natural History, Travel, Atlases & Maps - L03625
18 Nov 3 19th Century European Paintings incl. Spanish Painting 1850-1930 - L03103
18 Nov 3 The Greek Sale - L03104
19 Nov 3 Russian Pictures - L03112
20 Nov 3 Important Silver, Gold Boxes and Faberge - L03768
27 Nov 3 British Pictures - L03124
27 Nov 3 Important British Pictures - L03123
2 Dec 3 The Marine Sale - L03856
3 Dec 3 Modern British and Irish Art - L03141
4 Dec 3 Old Master, Modern & Contemporary Prints - L03163
11 Dec 3 Old Master Paintings - Parts I & II - L03033
11 Dec 3 English literature, History, Children's Books & Illustrations - L03409
12 Dec 3 European Sculptures & Works of Art 900-1900 - L03233
12 Dec 3 Treasures from the Rothschild Collection - L03506
3 Feb 4 Surrealist Art - L04005
3 Feb 4 German & Austrian Art - L04004
3 Feb 4 Impressionist & Modern Art - Evening Sale - L04002
4 Feb 4 Impressionist & Modern Works on Paper - L04006
4 Feb 4 Impressionist & Modern Art - Day Sale - L04003
5 Feb 4 Contemporary Art - Evening Sale - L04020
6 Feb 4 Contemporary Art - Day Sale - L04021
26 Mar 4 The British Sale - L04120
19 Apr 4 Scottish Pictures - L04130 - Hopetoun House, Edinburgh
21 Apr 4 European Sculpture & Works of Art 900-1900 - L04230
22 Apr 4 Old Master Paintings - L04030
28 Apr 4 Islamic Works of Art - L04220
6 May 4 Contemporary Asian Art - L04751
13 May 4 The Irish Sale - L04620
13 May 4 Natural History, Travel, Atlases & Maps - L04401
26 May 4 Russian Pictures - L04110
27 May 4 Important Silver & Portrait Miniatures - L04765
2 Jun 4 Modern British & Irish Art - L04140
8 Jun 4 Japanese Prints - L04753
9 Jun 4 Japanese & Korean Works of Art - L04752
9 Jun 4 Fine Chinese Ceramics & Works of Art - L04210
15 Jun 4 19th Century European Paintings & Oriental Art - L04100
21 Jun 4 Impressionist & Modern Art - Evening Sale - L04007
22 Jun 4 Impressionist & Modern Art - Day Sale - L04008
22 Jun 4 Impressionist & Modern Works on Paper - L04010
23 Jun 4 Contemporary Art - Evening Sale - L04022
24 Jun 4 Contemporary Art - Day - L04023
1 Jul 4 Old Master, Modern & Contemporary Prints - L04160
1 Jul 4 Important British Pictures - L04121
1 Jul 4 The British Sale - L04122
7 Jul 4 Old Master Paintings Part I - L04031
8 Jul 4 Old Master Paintings - Part II - L04032
8 Jul 4 English Literature, History, Illustrations & Photographs - L04407
8 Jul 4 Old Master Drawings - L04040
9 Jul 4 European Sculpture & Works of Art, 900-1900 - L04231

Sotheby's, Melbourne - Australia
24 Nov 3 Fine Australian & International Paintings - AU0676
15 Mar 4 The WMC Collection of Australian Contemporary Art - AU0677
4 May 4 Fine Australian Art - AU0679

17 May 4 Estate of the Late John Kenny - AU0678
19 May 4 Decorative Arts - AU0680
26 Jul 4 Aboriginal Art - AU0681

Sotheby's, Milan - Italy

21 Oct 3 Paintings & Fine Art from the Estate of a Milanese Lady - MI0225
12 Nov 3 Fine Art - MI224
25 Nov 3 Modern & Contemporary Art - MI0219
2 Dec 3 Old Master Paintings - MI0220
10 Dec 3 19th Century Paintings - MI0222
18 May 4 Contents from a House in Farnese Square - MI0239
25 May 4 Modern & Contemporary Art - MI0228
1 Jun 4 Old Master Paintings - MI0229
8 Jun 4 19th Century Paintings - MI0230
15 Jun 4 Furniture, Works of Art, Ceramics & Silver - MI0232
22 Jun 4 Books, Prints & Gouaches - MI0227

Sotheby's, New York, NY - USA

10 Sep 3 Arcade Furniture, Decorative Arts & Carpets - N01735
7 Oct 3 European & American Paintings, Drawings & Sculpture - N01732 - With Arcade
17 Oct 3 Photographs - N07925
18 Oct 3 Decorative Arts from the Collection of Carter Burden - N07937
20 Oct 3 English Furniture, Ceramics & Decorations - N07927
28 Oct 3 19th Century European Art - N07930
31 Oct 3 Prints - N07931
5 Nov 3 Impressionist & Modern Art - Part I - N07934
6 Nov 3 Impressionist & Modern Art - Part II - N07936
12 Nov 3 Contemporary Art- Evening Sale - N07938
13 Nov 3 Contemporary Art - Morning Sale - N07940
13 Nov 3 Contemporary Art - Afternoon Sale - N07940
19 Nov 3 Latin American Art - N07944
3 Dec 3 American Paintings, Drawings & Sculpture - N07950
11 Dec 3 The Collecting Eye of Seymour Stein - N07933
12 Dec 3 Joop Collection of 20th Century Decorative Works of Art - N07943
13 Dec 3 20th Century Decorative Works - N07947
19 Dec 3 Arcade - Paintings - N01734
15 Jan 4 Important Americana - N07959
16 Jan 4 American Folk Portraits & Furniture - Collection Egan - N07960
17 Jan 4 Collection of Alice & Murray Braunfeld - N07961
21 Jan 4 Old Master Drawings - N07963
21 Jan 4 Arcade - Old Master & 19th Century European Paintings - N01736
22 Jan 4 Important Old Master Paintings - N07965
22 Jan 4 Old Master Paintings - N07965
10 Feb 4 Arcade Auction - N01037
11 Feb 4 Impressionist & Modern Art - N07968
12 Feb 4 Modern & Contemporary Art - N01738
11 Mar 4 20th Century Decorative Arts - N07971
18 Mar 4 Israeli & International Art - N07973
18 Mar 4 Important Judaica - N07969
23 Mar 4 Chinese Works of Art - N07974
24 Mar 4 Indian & Southeast Asian Art - N07975
30 Mar 4 Arcade - Furniture & Decorative Works of Art - N01739
31 Mar 4 Arcade - American Art - N01740
7 Apr 4 English Country House - N07979
16 Apr 4 French & Continental Decorative Arts - N07976
23 Apr 4 19th Century Art - N07984
23 Apr 4 Russian Art - N07985
27 Apr 4 Important Photographs from a Private Collection - N07986
28 Apr 4 Gordon Bennett Collection of Carleton Watkins Photographs of Yosemite - N07966
28 Apr 4 Photographs - N07987
30 Apr 4 Prints - N07988
5 May 4 The Greentree Foundation : Impressionist & Modern Art - NY7989
6 May 4 Impressionist & Modern Art - Day Sale - N07991
6 May 4 Impressionist & Modern Art - Evening Sale - N07990
12 May 4 Contemporary Art - Evening Sale - N07993
13 May 4 Contemporary Art - Morning Sale - N07995
13 May 4 Contemporary Art - Afternoon Sale - N07995
18 May 4 Decorative Works of Art from the Greentree Foundation - N07992
19 May 4 American Art incl. Property from the Greentree Foundation - N07997
26 May 4 Latin American Art - N08001
27 May 4 Old Master Paintings - N08002
27 May 4 British & Sporting Paintings - N07964
10 Jun 4 Estate of Katharine Hepburn - N08004
16 Jun 4 Furniture & Decorative Arts - N01742
22 Jun 4 Important Americana - N07998
24 Jun 4 American Indian Art incl. Property from the Estate of Paul Peralta-Ramos - N08042
29 Jun 4 Old Master & Contemporary Paintings - Arcade Auction - N01743
15 Jul 4 Arcade Furniture & Decorations - N01751

Sotheby's, Olympia - UK

9 Sep 3 Fine Decorative Art & Design From 1870 - W03812
10 Sep 3 Modern British Paintings - W03711
11 Sep 3 The Football Sale - W03844
18 Sep 3 Paintings & Drawings From The Studio of Robert Lenkiewicz - W03723 - With Bearne's
1 Oct 3 19th Century Paintings - W03712
2 Oct 3 Silver, Miniatures, Vertu & European Ceramics - W03769
14 Oct 3 European Furniture, Bronzes & Rugs - W03784
22 Oct 3 Impressionist & Modern Art - W03716
30 Oct 3 Old Master Paintings - W03714
12 Nov 3 19th Century Paintings - W03718
13 Nov 3 Fine Chinese Works of Art - W03754
18 Nov 3 The Welsh & Oak Sale - W03786
19 Nov 3 The Sporting Sale - W03855
19 Nov 3 Photographs - W03722
20 Nov 3 Russian Works of Art, Faberge & Icons - W03831
25 Nov 3 Decorative Arts & Design from 1870 - W03813
26 Nov 3 Modern British Paintings - W03717
2 Dec 3 Interior Decorator - W03854
9 Dec 3 Old Master Paintings - W03719
11 Dec 3 Fine Japanese & Chinese Works of Art - W03757
18 Dec 3 Silver, Miniatures & Vertu - W03770
13 Jan 4 Furniture & Interior Decorator - W04775
21 Jan 4 British & Continental Pictures - W04700
4 Feb 4 Contemporary Art - W04701
11 Feb 4 Modern British & Irish Art - W04702
17 Feb 4 Furniture & Interior Decorator - W04850
24 Feb 4 Decorative Arts - W04810
10 Mar 4 British & Continental Pictures - W04703
24 Mar 4 Impressionist & Modern Art - W04704
6 Apr 4 Furniture & Interior Decorator - W04777
7 Apr 4 Chinese & Japanese Works of Art - W04750
20 Apr 4 Old Master Drawings - W04720
20 Apr 4 Old Master Paintings - W04705
10 May 4 The Greek Sale - W04852
11 May 4 Menuhin Sale - W04874
19 May 4 Modern British & Irish Art - W04706
26 May 4 British & Continental Pictures - W04707
3 Jun 4 Decorative Arts & Design from 1870 - W04811
15 Jun 4 Furniture & Interior Decorator incl 19th Century Bronzes - W04853
24 Jun 4 Contemporary Art - W04709
29 Jun 4 European Ceramics, Glass, Silver & Vertu - W04860
6 Jul 4 Old Master Paintings - W04710
13 Jul 4 Furniture & Interior Decorator - W04854
14 Jul 4 British & Continental Pictures - W04711
22 Jul 4 The Keil Sale - W04872

Sotheby's, Paris - France

2 Oct 3 The Didier Kahn-Sriber Collection - PF3026
15 Oct 3 Collection of Mrs Barbara Piasecka Johnson - PF3023
6 Nov 3 Furniture, Works of Art, Paintings & Drawings - PF3010
18 Nov 3 20th Century Decorative Arts - PF3009
25 Nov 3 The Collection of Hugette Beres - PF3018
2 Dec 3 Empire Sale - PF3014
15 Dec 3 Furniture & Works of Art - PF3013
31 Mar 4 Spring Sale - Furniture & Works of Art - PF4002
29 Apr 4 Collection of Sculptures - PF4018
17 May 4 20th Century Decorative Arts - PF4004
27 May 4 Pop Around - Collection Pierre Lescure - PF4021
23 Jun 4 Old Master & 19th Century Paintings & Drawings - PF4010
23 Jun 4 Important Furniture & Decorative Arts - PF4009
29 Jun 4 Franco Cesari's Collection of Sculptures & Paintings - PF4019
18 Jul 4 The Secret Garden of Marianne et Pierre Nahon - Part II - PF4098 - Vence

Sotheby's, Singapore

12 Oct 3 South East Asian Paintings - SG7016
4 Apr 4 South East Asian Paintings - SG7017

Sotheby's, Sydney - Australia
25 Aug 3 Important Paintings From The Collection of John Schaeffer - AU0673
25 Aug 3 Fine Australian Paintings - AU0673

Sotheby's, Toronto - Canada
18 Nov 3 Important Canadian Art - TO0702 - With Ritchies
31 May 4 Important Canadian Art - No.716 - with Ritchies

Sotheby's, Zurich - Switzerland
9 Dec 3 Swiss Art - ZH0307
26 May 4 Swiss Art - ZH0404

South Bay Auctions, Long Island, NY - USA
4 Oct 3 Fine Art
6 Dec 3 Fine Art
31 Jan 4 Fine Art
3 Apr 4 Fine Art
12 May 4 Fine Art - On-line

St-Germain-en-Laye, Saint Germain en Laye - France
12 Oct 3 Paintings & Sculptures
19 Oct 3 Paintings & Sculptures
14 Dec 3 Paintings & Sculptures
14 Mar 4 Paintings & Sculptures
21 Mar 4 Paintings & Sculptures
4 Apr 4 Paintings & Sculptures
19 Jun 4 Paintings & Sculpture

Stadion, Trieste - Italy
10 Oct 3 Maritime & Austrian Art
3 Dec 3 19th & 20th Century Art
20 Feb 4 Paintings & Decorative Arts
12 May 4 19th & 20th Century Art
18 Jun 4 Paintings & Prints

Stephan Welz & Co, Johannesburg - South Africa
20 Oct 3 Paintings, Watercolours, Sculpture & Prints - SA0310 - With Sothebys
4 Nov 3 Decorative & Fine Arts - SA0311
10 Nov 3 Decorative Arts & Collector's Items - SA0312
3 Dec 3 The Collection of the late M E C Hurvitz - SA0314 - With Sotheby's
30 Mar 4 Decorative & Fine Arts - SA0402 - With Sotheby's
31 May 4 South African, British & Continental Fine Art - SA0405

Subastas Odalys, Caracas - Venezuela
21 Sep 3 Venezuelan Masters - No.88
28 Sep 3 Contemporary Art - No.89
19 Oct 3 Venezuelan Art - No.90
23 Nov 3 Venezuelan Artists - No.93
7 Dec 3 Contemporary Art - No.94
14 Mar 4 Venezuelan Old Masters - No.95
28 Mar 4 Venezuelan Masters - No.96
25 Apr 4 Venezuelan Art - No.97
21 Jun 4 Venezuelan Art - No.98
27 Jun 4 Contemporary Art - No.99

Susanin's, Chicago, IL - USA
6 Sep 3 Fine Art - No.191
14 Sep 3 Fine Art - No.4
20 Sep 3 Fine Art - No.193
4 Oct 3 Fine Art - No.195
19 Oct 3 Fine Art - No.5
25 Oct 3 Fine Art - No.198
1 Nov 3 Fine Art - No.199
7 Dec 3 Fine Art - No.6
13 Dec 3 Fine Art - No.204
10 Jan 4 Fine Art - Sale 10
17 Jan 4 Fine Art - No.11
24 Jan 4 Fine Art - No.207
21 Feb 4 Fine Art - No.209
6 Mar 4 Fine Art - No.210
13 Mar 4 Fine Art - No.9
3 Apr 4 Fine Art - No.212
1 May 4 Fine Art - No.214
8 May 4 Fine Art - No.10
15 May 4 Fine Art - No.215
5 Jun 4 Fine Art - No.18
12 Jun 4 Fine Art - No.217
26 Jun 4 Fine Art - No.11
10 Jul 4 Fine Art - No.218
17 Jul 4 Fine Art - No.20
24 Jul 4 Fine Art - No.219

Swann Galleries, New York, NY - USA
18 Sep 3 19th & 20th Century Prints & Drawings - No.1976
25 Sep 3 The Work Of Al Hirschfeld - No.1977
21 Oct 3 Important 19th & 20th Century Photographs - No.1981
6 Nov 3 100 Important Old Master Prints - No.1983
6 Nov 3 Old Master Through Contemporary Prints - No.1983
21 Nov 3 Contemporary Art - No.1987
9 Dec 3 Photographic Literature & Photographs - No.1989
22 Jan 4 Prints & Drawings (Discovery Sale) - No.1993
29 Jan 4 Old Master Drawings - No.1994
17 Feb 4 100 Fine Photographs - No.1996
2 Mar 4 19th & 20th Century Prints & Drawings - No.1999
6 May 4 Old Master Through Contemporary Prints - No.2005
6 May 4 100 Important Old Master Prints - No.2005
20 May 4 Photographs - No.2007
10 Jun 4 American Watercolours & Drawings - No.2009

Tajan, Paris (Euro) - France
5 Aug 3 Modern & Contemporary Art
24 Sep 3 Haute Epoque
10 Oct 3 19th & 20th Century Photographs
17 Oct 3 Old Masters
5 Nov 3 Decorative Arts of 20th Century
6 Nov 3 Drawings 1500-1900
17 Nov 3 19th Century Paintings, Drawings & Sculptures
19 Nov 3 20th Century Paintings, Drawings & Sculptures
24 Nov 3 Decorative Art - No.3419
25 Nov 3 Contemporary Art - No.3402
25 Nov 3 Asian Art - No.3413
28 Nov 3 Prints - No.3366
3 Dec 3 19th & 20th Century Paintings & Sculptures, Works on Paper - No.3400
8 Dec 3 Graphic Art, Oriental & Islamic Art - No.3384
17 Dec 3 18th & 19th Century Decorative Art - No.3389 - Four Seasons Hotel
18 Dec 3 Impressionist & Modern Paintings & Sculptures - No.3401
18 Dec 3 Old Masters Paintings - No.3429
21 Jan 4 Jewish Art - No.4411
3 Mar 4 19th & 20th Century Paintings, Drawings & Sculptures - No.4417
4 Mar 4 20th Century Decorative Arts - No.4421
5 Mar 4 Haute Epoque - No.4400
17 Mar 4 1500-1900 Drawings - No.4407
17 Mar 4 20th Century Decorative - No.4425
24 Mar 4 Old Master Paintings - No.4404
31 Mar 4 Prints - No.4408
7 Apr 4 Charity Sale to Help Victims of Al-Hoceima Earthquake - No.4474
26 Apr 4 19th & 20th Century Paintings & Sculptures - No.4415
30 Apr 4 19th Century Paintings & Sculptures - No.4405
18 May 4 Contemporary Art - No.4433
27 May 4 20th Century Decorative Arts - No.4436
3 Jun 4 Oriental Arts & Orientalist Paintings - No.4437
7 Jun 4 Photographs - No.4434
9 Jun 4 Impressionist & Modern Paintings & Sculptures - No.4440
11 Jun 4 Asian Art - No.4482
14 Jun 4 19th & 20th Century Art - No.4476
16 Jun 4 Fine Art - No.4439
21 Jun 4 Old Master Paintings - No.4466
24 Jun 4 Old Master Paintings - No.4459
25 Jun 4 20th Century Decorative Arts - No.4443
7 Jul 4 18th & 19th Century Works of Art - No.4448

Tamlyn, Bridgewater - UK
24 Apr 4 Fine Art

Tayler & Fletcher, Bourton on the Water - UK
26 Oct 3 Fine Art
24 Feb 4 Fine Art

Teitgen, Nancy - France
12 Oct 3 Old Masters & Modern Art
30 Nov 3 Paintings & Fine Art
6 Dec 3 Atelier of Mme Nicole Gauthier
1 Feb 4 Paintings & Fine Art
21 Mar 4 Art Nouveau & Art Deco
27 Jun 4 Paintings & Fine Art

Tennants, Leyburn - UK
19 Nov 3 Autumn Sale
21 Apr 4 Spring Sale
22 Jul 4 Decorative Arts incl. Paintings

Themis, Brussels - Belgium
4 Nov 3 Fine Art

Thierry & Lannon, Brest - France
21 Oct 3 Paintings & Fine Art
21 Dec 3 Prints, Sculptures & Paintings
24 Feb 4 Paintings & Fine Art
16 May 4 Paintings of the Brittany School
25 May 4 Works of Art by Maurice Leonard & Georges Lacombe
24 Jul 4 Paintings & Fine Art

Thomas Adams, Dublin - Eire
26 Aug 3 Fine Art

Thomaston Place, Thomaston, ME - USA
27 Sep 3 Boothbay onsite
28 Nov 3 Fine Art
28 Feb 4 Estate Auction
1 May 4 Fine Art
24 Jul 4 Damariscotta Onsite

Thomson Roddick & Medcalfe (C), Carlisle - UK
27 Feb 4 Fine Art

Thomson Roddick & Medcalfe (E), Edinburgh - UK
10 Nov 3 Fine Art
29 Mar 4 Fine Art

Thos Mawer, Lincoln - UK
27 Mar 4 Fine Art
26 Jun 4 Fine Art

Tiffin King & Nicholson, Carlisle - UK
24 Nov 3 Important Antiques & Works of Art

Touati, Paris - France
13 Dec 3 Fine Art

Treadway Gallery, Cincinnati, OH - USA
7 Sep 3 20th Century Art & Design
7 Dec 3 20th Century Art & Design
7 Mar 4 20th Century Art & Design
23 May 4 20th Century Art & Design
5 Jun 4 Decorative Arts featuring Rookwood

Trembath Welch, Great Dunmow - UK
17 Nov 3 Fine Art

Tring Auctions, Tring - UK
30 Jan 4 Fine Art
26 Mar 4 Fine Art
28 May 4 Fine Art
23 Jul 4 Fine Art

Tuttarte, Carpi - Italy
7 Nov 3 19th & 20th Century Art
4 Jun 4 Modern & Contemporary Art

Uppsala Auktionskammare, Uppsala - Sweden
12 Oct 3 Decorative Arts
7 Dec 3 Fine Art
29 Feb 4 Decorative Arts
28 May 4 Fine Art

Van Ham, Cologne - Germany
30 Oct 3 Photography - No.228
20 Nov 3 Old Masters - No.229
4 Dec 3 Modern & Contemporary Art - No.230
1 Apr 4 Fine Art - No.231
14 May 4 Photographs - No.232
15 May 4 Modern & Contemporary Art - No.233
1 Jul 4 Fine Art - No.234

Venator & Hansten, Cologne - Germany
26 Sep 3 Books, Prints & Drawings - No.90
26 Mar 4 Books, Prints & Graphics - No.91/II

Vendu Notarishuis, Rotterdam - Netherlands
11 Nov 3 Paintings & Fine Art
11 May 4 Paintings & Fine Art - No.220

Vendue Huis, Gravenhage - Netherlands
10 Oct 3 Fine Art
5 Nov 3 Fine Art
4 Dec 3 Fine Art
30 Jun 4 Fine Art

Versailles Encheres, Versailles - France
9 Nov 3 Old Masters & Modern Art
14 Dec 3 Abstract & Contemporary Art
29 Feb 4 Modern & Contemporary Paintings & Prints
28 Mar 4 Paintings & Furniture
25 Apr 4 Contemporary & Abstract Art

20 Jun 4 Paintings & Fine Art
27 Jun 4 Paintings
25 Jul 4 Paintings & Fine Art

Villa Grisebach, Berlin - Germany
27 Nov 3 Photographs - No.111
28 Nov 3 Selected Works of Art - No.112
29 Nov 3 19th & 20th Century Art - No.113
29 Nov 3 Third Floor - Fine Art - No.114
10 Jun 4 Photographs - No.115
11 Jun 4 Collection of Claudia von Schilling - No.116
11 Jun 4 Selected Works of Art - No.117
12 Jun 4 19th & 20th Century Art - No.118
12 Jun 4 Third Floor - No.119

Von Zezschwitz, Munich - Germany
14 Nov 3 Art Nouveau & Art Deco - No.16
15 Nov 3 19th & 20th Century Art - No.17
14 May 4 19th & 20th Century Art - No.20
25 Jun 4 Modern Art & Design - No.21

Waddingtons, Toronto - Canada
16 Oct 3 Old Master, 19th & 20th Century Prints
3 Nov 3 Inuit Art
17 Nov 3 British, European & American Art
18 Nov 3 Decorative Arts
22 Mar 4 20th Century Decorative Arts
26 Apr 4 Inuit Art
14 Jun 4 European & American Art
15 Jun 4 Decorative Arts

Walker's, Ottawa - Canada
21 Nov 3 Fine Paintings & Decorative Art
9 Jun 4 Fine Paintings & Decorative Art

Watson's, Christchurch - New Zealand
9 Sep 3 Fine Art
9 Mar 4 Fine Art
11 May 4 Fine Art
13 Jul 4 Fine Art

Weidler, Nurnberg - Germany
11 Sep 3 Fine Art - No.830
20 Nov 3 Fine Art - No.850
5 Dec 3 Fine Art - No.855
12 Feb 4 Fine Art - No.870
27 Feb 4 Fine Art - No.875
22 Apr 4 Fine Art - No.890
1 Jul 4 Fine Art - No.910
16 Jul 4 Fine Art - No.915

Wendl, Rudolstadt - Germany
5 Sep 3 Fine Art - No.46
28 Nov 3 Fine Art - No.47
5 Mar 4 Fine Art - No.48
11 Jun 4 Fine Art - No.49

Weschler, Washington, DC - USA
12 Sep 3 Property from Estate of Ella Poe Burling - No.1270
13 Sep 3 Fine Art & 20th Century Decorative Arts - No.1267/1268
13 Dec 3 American & European Fine Art - No.1272
21 Feb 4 European & American Furniture & Decorative Arts - No.1274
23 Apr 4 Property from the Estate of Ella Poe Burling - No.1277
24 Apr 4 Fine Art & 20th Century Decorative Art - No.1276
22 May 4 European, American & Asian Art - No.1278

Whyte's, Dublin - Eire
16 Sep 3 Irish Art
18 Nov 3 Irish Art
17 Feb 4 Irish Art
27 Apr 4 Irish Art

Wiener Kunst Auktionen, Vienna - Austria
23 Sep 3 Fine Art - No.46
28 Oct 3 Fine Art - No.47
27 Nov 3 Art Nouveau - No.48
28 Nov 3 Contemporary Paintings & Old Masters - No.48
28 Apr 4 Contemporary Paintings & Art - No.49
22 Jun 4 Art & Antiques - No.50

Wilkinson, Doncaster - UK
28 Sep 3 Fine Art
23 Nov 3 Fine Art
29 Feb 4 Fine Art
25 Apr 4 Fine Art
20 Jun 4 Fine Art

William A Smith, - USA
1 Sep 3 Fine Art
28 Feb 4 Fine Art
14 Mar 4 Fine Art
31 May 4 Memorial Day Auction

William Jenack, Chester, NY - USA
24 Aug 3 Fine Art
21 Sep 3 Fine Art
19 Oct 3 Fine Art
16 Nov 3 Fine Art
7 Dec 3 Fine Art
11 Jan 4 Fine Art
8 Feb 4 Fine Art
7 Mar 4 Fine Art
2 May 4 Fine Art
23 May 4 Fine Art
13 Jun 4 Fine Art
18 Jul 4 Fine Art

Windibank, Dorking - UK
13 Sep 3 Fine Art
18 Oct 3 Fine Art
7 Feb 4 Fine Art
24 Apr 4 Fine Art incl Pictures
5 Jun 4 Fine Art
10 Jul 4 Fine Art

Wingetts, Wrexham - UK
3 Sep 3 Fine Art
22 Oct 3 Fine Art
10 Dec 3 Fine Art
21 Apr 4 Fine Art
9 Jun 4 Fine Art

Winter Associates, Plainville, CT - USA
8 Sep 3 Fine Art
15 Dec 3 Fine Art
19 Jan 4 Fine Art
23 Feb 4 Fine Art
26 Apr 4 Fine Art
24 May 4 Fine Art
21 Jun 4 Fine Art
19 Jul 4 Fine Art

Winterberg, Heidelberg - Germany
10 Oct 3 15th-20th Century Art - No.67
2 Apr 4 Fine Art - No.68

Wintertons, Lichfield - UK
28 Jan 4 Fine Art

Wolf's, New York - USA
16 Jun 4 Paintings

Woodwards, Cork - Eire
24 Sep 3 Fine Art
22 Oct 3 Fine Art
28 Jan 4 Fine Art
11 Feb 4 Fine Art

Woolley & Wallis, Salisbury - UK
2 Sep 3 20th Century Decorative Art
16 Sep 3 English & Continental Furniture & Works Of Art
1 Oct 3 Books, Prints, Oil Paintings & Watercolours
4 Nov 3 Paintings & Fine Art
13 Jan 4 Paintings & Fine Art
16 Mar 4 Works of Art
7 Apr 4 Paintings, Books & Prints
28 Apr 4 Clarice Cliff & Art Deco
18 May 4 Contents of Ashley Manor, Kings Somborne, Hampshire

Wotton Auction Rooms, Wotton-under-Edge - UK
24 Feb 4 Fine Art
23 Mar 4 Fine Art
20 Apr 4 Fine Art
18 May 4 Fine Art

Wright, Chicago, IL - USA
14 Sep 3 Modernist 20
9 Nov 3 Modern & Contemporary Art
28 Mar 4 Modern Design
16 May 4 Modern & Contemporary Art
6 Jun 4 Modernist 20th Century

York Town, York, PA - USA
26 Sep 3 Fine Art
12 Dec 3 Fine Art

Zadick, Uberlingen - Germany
12 Mar 4 Fine Art

Zurichsee Auktionen, Erlenbach - Switzerland
31 Mar 4 Paintings

other American Auctioneer
23 Mar 4 Fine Art - Elders Antiques
16 Apr 4 20th Century American Realism - American Auctions & Appraisal
20 May 4 Fine & Decorative Art - Ruggiero Associates
6 Jun 4 Asian Art - Phoenix Fine Art
14 Jul 4 Fine Art - Litchfield

other British Auctioneer
30 Dec 3 Fine Art - Wotton Auction Rooms
13 Jan 4 Fine Art - Philip Laney
23 Jan 4 Fine Art - Charterhouse Auctioneers
24 Jan 4 Fine Art - Tamlyn & Son
25 Feb 4 Fine Art - Richard Winterton
10 Mar 4 Fine Art - Abbots Auction Rooms
3 Apr 4 Fine Art - Ramsay Cornish Auctioneers
5 Apr 4 Fine Art - Cato Crane & Company
19 Apr 4 Fine Art - Jack Dudgeon
28 Apr 4 Fine Art - Robert Bell & Company
1 May 4 Fine Art - Henry Holden
5 May 4 Fine Art - Denham's
8 May 4 Fine Art - Morris Bricknell
22 May 4 Fine Art - Greenwich Auction Partnership
26 Jun 4 Fine Art - Addisons
28 Jun 4 Fine Art - Jack Dudgeon

other European Auctioneer
15 May 4 Fine Art - Vichy Encheres, Guy Laurent
16 May 4 Fine Art - Valoir-Blois
20 Jul 4 Fine Art - B Vassy & P Jalenques

Number of sales covered in this edition - 3020

CROSS REFERENCES

There are many cases where an artist is more widely known by some cognomen instead of his original name. The most obvious examples are Rembrandt and El Greco, whose real names are, respectively, Rembrandt Harmensz van Rijn and Domenikos Theotokopoulos. A list of these 'common names' is given below and appear in this edition.

A

ADAM, Victor Charles Edouard see ADAM, Edouard (jnr)
AGUILELLA, Henri see CUECO, Henri
ALDINE, Marc see BOUVARD, Antoine
ALDINI, Casimiro *see* TOMBA, Casimiro
ALKEN, Samuel Henry *see* ALKEN, Henry (jnr)
ALLEGRI, Antonio *see* CORREGGIO
ALSTON, Abbey *see* ALTSON, Abbey
ALVAREZ DE SOTOMAYOR, Fernando *see* SOTOMAYOR Y ZARAGOZA, Fernando
ANDERSSON, Gustaf Albert *see* ALBERT, Gustaf
APPIAN, Jacques Barthelemy *see* APPIAN, Adolphe
ARANDA, Jose Jimenez *see* JIMENEZ Y ARANDA, Jose
ARDEN, Edward *see* TUCKER, Edward
ARTVELT, Andries van *see* EERTVELT, Andries van
ARZADUN, Carmelo de *see* CARMELO DE ARZADUN

B

BACCHIACA, Francesco *see* UBERTINI, Francesco
BACICCIA *see* GAULLI, Giovanni Battista
BADGER, Clarissa W *see* MUNGER, Clarissa
BADURA, Faye Swengel *see* SWENGEL, Faye
BAGNACAVALLO, Bartolomeo (elder) *see* RAMENGHI, Bartolomeo (elder)
BAKSCHEJEFF, Wassily N *see* BAKSHEEV, Vasily
BARBARELLI, Giorgio *see* GIORGIONE
BARBATELLI, Bernardino *see* POCCETTI, Bernardino
BARBIERI, Giovanni Francesco *see* GUERCINO, Giovanni Francesco
BARRAUD-PELLET, Jeanne *see* JANEBE
BASALDELLA, Afro *see* AFRO
BASALDELLA, Mirko *see* MIRKO
BAUMANN, Elisabeth Jerichau *see* JERICHAU-BAUMANN, Elisabeth
BAUMGÄRTNER, Adolf *see* STOILOFF, Constantin
BEATTIE-BROWN, William *see* BROWN, William Beattie
BEDOLI, Girolamo Francesco *see* MAZZOLA, Girolamo Bedoli
BELIN, Jean *see* FONTENAY, Jean Baptiste Belin de
BERG, Franciscus Johannes Gysbertus van den *see* JOHFRA
BERRETTINI, Pietro da *see* CORTONA, Pietro da
BERTOLETTI, Marcelli *see* PASQUAROSA
BEURDEN, Alexander F W E *see* SCHOONHOVEN VAN BEURDEN, Alexander Franciscus van
BEVERLOO, Cornelis Guillaume *see* CORNEILLE
BIANCA, Angelo dell'Oca *see* DALL`OCA BIANCA, Angelo
BILEVELT, Giovanni *see* BILIVERTI, Giovanni
BISSCHOP, Suze *see* ROBERTSON, Suze
BLEULER, Louis *see* BLEULER, Johann Ludwig
BOLOGNE, Jean de *see* GIAMBOLOGNA
BOLTON-JONES, Hugh *see* JONES, Hugh Bolton
BOOGAARD, Willem Johan *see* BOOGAARD, Willem Jacobus
BORCH, Gerard ter *see* TERBORCH, Gerard
BORTOLUZZI, Bianco Pietro *see* BIANCO, Pieretto
BOSSCHAERT, Thomas *see* WILLEBOIRTS, Thomas
BOUVARD, Antoine Joseph *see* BOUVARD, Joseph Antoine
BOUVIER, Agnes Rose *see* NICHOLL, Agnes Rose
BRAUER, Arik *see* BRAUER, Erich
BREANSKI, Alfred de (jnr) *see* BREANSKI, Alfred Fontville de
BREMEN, Meyer von *see* MEYER VON BREMEN, Johann Georg
BRENNERSTEIN-WICHERA, Raimund Ritter von *see* WICHERA, Raimund von
BRINCK, H A *see* BJULF, Soren Christian
BROWN, Hugh Boycott *see* BOYCOTT-BROWN, Hugh
BUONAMICO, Agostino *see* TASSI, Agostino

C

CAFISSA, Nicolo *see* CASISSA, Nicola
CALIARI, Paolo *see* VERONESE, Paolo
CALISTO DA LODI *see* PIAZZA, Calisto
CANAL, Antonio *see* CANALETTO
CANLASSI, Guido *see* CAGNACCI, Guido
CAPPONI, Raffaelo de *see* GARBO, Raffaellino del
CARLOS-REYMOND *see* REYMOND, Carlos
CARMICHAEL, Herbert *see* SCHMALZ, Herbert Gustave
CASENTINO, Jacopo del *see* LANDINI, Jacopo
CATALA, Luis Alvarez *see* ALVAREZ CATALA, Luis
CATE, Ten *see* TEN CATE
CECCO BRAVO *see* MONTELATICI, Francesco
CELIS, Perez *see* PEREZ CELIS
CERANO *see* CRESPI, Giovanni Battista
CERMAK, Jaroslav *see* CZERMAK, Jaroslav
CEULEN, Cornelis Janssens van *see* JONSON, Cornelis
CHANA ORLOFF *see* ORLOFF, Chana
CHANG YU *see* SAN-YU
CHICHKINE, Ivan Ivanovitch *see* SHISHKIN, Ivan Ivanovich
CIGOLI, Ludovico *see* CARDI, Lodovico
CIHLARZ, Wolfgang *see* SALOME
CLARK OF GREENOCK, William *see* CLARK, William
CLARK, Joseph Dixon (snr) *see* CLARK, Dixon
CLAUDE LORRAIN *see* GELLEE, Claude
CLAVEL, Marie Joseph Leon *see* IWILL, Joseph
CLEMENT, Marcel *see* MARCEL-CLEMENT, Amedee Julien
CLEMENT-SERVEAU *see* SERVEAU, Clement
COECKE, Pieter van Aelst *see* AELST, Pieter Coecke van
COLEMAN, Helen Cordelia *see* ANGELL, Helen Cordelia
COLOMBO, Luigi *see* FILLIA
COLYER, Edwaert *see* COLLIER, Evert
CONRAD-KICKERT *see* KICKERT, Conrad
CORDINGLEY, Georges Ricard *see* RICARD-CORDINGLEY, Georges
CORMIER, Joseph Descomps *see* DESCOMPS, Joe
CORNEILLE DE GROUX, Henri Jules Charles *see* GROUX, Henry de
CORTESE, Guglielmo *see* COURTOIS, Guillaume
COSSINGTON-SMITH, Grace *see* SMITH, Grace Cossington
COSTER, Anne Vallayer *see* VALLAYER-COSTER, Anne
COUVER, Jan van *see* KOEKKOEK, Hermanus (jnr)
CRIVELLONE, Angelo Maria *see* CRIVELLI, Angelo Maria

D

D'ALIGNY, Theodore Caruelle *see* CARUELLE D`ALIGNY, Theodore
D'ARPINO *see* CESARI, Giuseppe
D'ERRICO, Antonio *see* TANZIO DA VARALLO, Antonio d`Enrico
DAVIS, Val *see* DAVIS, J Valentine
DAWIDI *see* DJULWARAK, Dawidi
DECAUX, Vicomtesse Iphigenie *see* MILET-MOREAU, Iphigenie
DEFOREST, Roy *see* FOREST, Roy de
DEGRAIN, Antonio Munoz *see* MUNOZ-DEGRAIN, Antoine
DEHAVEN, Franklin *see* HAVEN, Franklin de
DELAROCHE, Hippolyte *see* DELAROCHE, Paul
DESFILLES, Charles *see* BEGO, Charles
DESMET, Leon *see* SMET, Leon de
DJURIC, Miodrag *see* DADO, Miodrag Djuric
DODERHULTARN *see* PETERSSON, Axel
DOMENICO, Ridolfi di *see* GHIRLANDAIO, Ridolfo
DONAU, Erich Josef *see* DOGARTH, Erich Josef
DREYFUSS, Marcel *see* DYF, Marcel
DRULMAN, Marinus Johannes *see* JONGERE, Marinus de
DUBOIS DRAHONET, Alexandre Jean *see* DRAHONET, Alexandre Jean Dubois
DUBOURG, Victoria *see* FANTIN-LATOUR, Victoria
DUMARESQ, Armand *see* ARMAND-DUMARESQ, Edouard Charles

E

EKMAN, Marie Louise *see* BERGENSTRAHLE, Marie Louise de Geer
EMPOLI, Jacopo da *see* CHIMENTI, Jacopo
ERLER, Erich *see* ERLER-SAMADEN, Erich

F

FERNANDI, Francesco *see* IMPERIALI, Francesco
FIKRET MOUALLA *see* MOUALLA, Fikret
FIORI, Mario da *see* NUZZI, Mario

FIRMIN-GIRARD *see* GIRARD, Marie Firmin
FLETCHER, Edward Henry Eugene *see* FLETCHER, Edwin
FLORES, Pancho *see* FLORES, Francisco
FORTESCUE-BRICKDALE, Eleanor *see* BRICKDALE, Eleanor Fortesque
FOURNIER, Gabriel Francisque Alexis *see* GABRIEL-FOURNIER
FRANCK, Pauwels/Pauvels or FRANCESCHI, Paolo *see* FIAMMINGO, Paolo
FRANCOIS, Gustave *see* BARRAUD, Gustave Francois
FRANK-BOGGS *see* BOGGS, Frank Myers
FRANKY BOY *see* SEVEHON, Francky Boy
FRASER, Garden William *see* GARDEN, William Fraser
FRECHOU, Charles *see* FRECHON, Charles
FRERE, Theodore *see* FRERE, Charles Theodore
FRIIS-NYBO, Poul *see* NYBOE, Friis

G

GALGARIO, Fra *see* GHISLANDI, Vittore
GALVAN, Jesus Guerrero *see* GUERRERO GALVAN, Jesus
GARCIA-TELLA, Jose *see* TELLA, Jose Garcia
GASSEL, Lucas van *see* HELMONT, Lucas van Gassel
GEGO *see* GOLDSCHMIDT, Gertrudis
GEISEL, Theodor S *see* SEUSS, Dr
GERSHOV, Solomon Moiseevich *see* GUERTCHOV, Solomon
GHERARDO DI JACOPO STARNINA *see* STARNINA, Gherardo
GHIDONI, Matteo *see* PITOCCHI, Matteo de
GHIRLANDAIO, Michele di Ridolfo del *see* TOSINI, Michele
GINDERTAEL, Emile van *see* MILO, Jean
GONZALEZ DE LA SERNA, Ismael *see* SERNA, Ismael de la
GRAZIA, Leonardo *see* LEONARDO DA PISTOIA
GREVENBROECK, Charles Laurent *see* GREVENBROECK, Orazio
GRONINGEN, Jan Swart van *see* SWART VAN GRONINGEN, Jan
GROSS, Valentine *see* HUGO, Valentine
GUDIN, Herminie *see* GUDIN, Henriette
GUGGENHEIM, Willy *see* VARLIN
GUIARD, Adelaide Labille *see* LABILLE-GUIARD, Madame Adelaide
GUIDI, Giovanni (elder) *see* SCHEGGIA, Giovanni di Ser Giovanni
GUN, Karl Federovich *see* HUNS, Karlis Fridikh

H

HAARLEM, Cornelis Cornelisz van *see* CORNELISZ, Cornelis van Haarlem
HACHT/HAECHT, Tobias van *see* VERHAECHT, Tobias
HAHN, William *see* HAHN, Karl Wilhelm
HALFORD, Constance *see* REA, Constance
HANSEN, Adolf Heinrich Claus *see* HEINRICH-HANSEN, Adolf
HARTUNG, Julius *see* REICHERT, Carl
HASLEHURST, Ernest William *see* HAZELHUST, Ernest William
HAYNES-WILLIAMS, John *see* WILLIAMS, John Haynes
HEGG, Teresa Maria *see* LANDERSET, Theresa Maria de
HENRY, David Reid *see* REID-HENRY, David M
HIEPES, Tomas *see* YEPES, Tomas
HIRSCH-PAULI, Hanna *see* PAULI, Hanna
HOFFMANN, Kurt R *see* SONDERBORG, Kurt R H
HOHENBERG, Josef Wagner *see* WAGNER-HOHENBERG, Josef
HOLLYER, William Perring *see* HOLLYER, W P
HOOD, George Percy Jacomb *see* JACOMB-HOOD, George Percy
HOYNCK VAN PAPENDRECHT, Jan *see* PAPENDRECHT, Jan Hoynck van
HUGUE, Manuel Martinez *see* MANOLO
HUNTLY, Nancy *see* SHEPPARD, Nancy
HYATT, Anna Vaughn *see* HUNTINGTON, Anna Hyatt

I

IMOLA, Innocenzo *see* FRANCUCCI, Innocenzo
INNOCENTI, Battista degli *see* NALDINI, Giovan Battista
ISUPOV, Aleksei Vladimirovich *see* ISSUPOFF, Alessio
IVANOVITCH, Paul *see* JOANOVITCH, Paul

J

JACKSON, Harriett A E *see* BROWNING, Harriett A E
JACOPO di Rossello *see* FRANCHI, Rossello di Jacopo
JAMES, Willy *see* ROCHAT, Willy
JEANNERET, Charles Edouard *see* CORBUSIER, le
JEGOROV, Andrei A *see* YEGOROV, Andrei
JONES, Allan Gwynne *see* GWYNNE-JONES, Allan
JONES, Joseph John *see* JONES, Joe
JUANES, JUAN DE *see* MASIP, Vicente Juan

K

KABEL, Adrian van der *see* CABEL, Adrian van der
KAISERMANN, Francois *see* KEISERMANN, Franz
KALRAET, Abraham van *see* CALRAET, Abraham van
KAVANAUGH, Marion *see* WACHTEL, Marion K
KEILHAU, Bernhard *see* KEIL, Bernhard
KEMPF VON HARTENKAMPF, Gottlieb Theodor *see* HARTENKAMPF, Gottlieb Theodor Kempf von
KERCKHOVEN, Jacob van de *see* CASTELLO, Jacopo da
KEUNINCK, Kerstiaen de (elder) *see* KONINCK, Kerstiaen de (elder)
KEY SATO *see* SATO, Key
KIKOINE, Jacob *see* YANKEL, Jacques
KINNAIRD, Francis Joseph *see* KINNAIRD, Wiggs
KISELEV, Alexandre Alexandrovitch *see* KISSELEOV, Alexandre Alexandrovitch
KLEIN, Frits *see* KLEIN, Friedrich Franz
KLOCKER, David *see* EHRENSTRAHL, David Klocker von
KLOSSOWSKI, Balthasar *see* BALTHUS
KNIGHTON-HAMMOND, Arthur Henry *see* HAMMOND, Arthur Henry Knighton
KOEKKOEK, Hermanus (jnr) *see* COUVER, Jan van
KOLLER, Johann Rudolf *see* KOLLER, Rudolf
KOMAROMI-KATZ, Endre *see* KACZ, Endre Komaromi
KORFF, Alexander Hugo Bakker *see* BAKKER-KORFF, Alexander Hugo
KOUDRIACHOV, Ivan A *see* KUDRIASHEV, Ivan
KOUYOUMOJIAN, Elvire *see* JAN, Elvire
KOWALSKI-WIERUSZ, Alfred von *see* WIERUSZ-KOWALSKI, Alfred von
KRUSEMAN VAN ELTEN, Hendrik Dirk *see* ELTEN, Hendrik Dirk Kruseman van
KABEL, Adrian van der *see* CABEL, Adrian van der
KAISERMANN, Francois *see* KEISERMANN, Franz
KALRAET, Abraham van *see* CALRAET, Abraham van
KAVANAUGH, Marion *see* WACHTEL, Marion K
KEILHAU, Bernhard *see* KEIL, Bernhard
KEMPF VON HARTENKAMPF, Gottlieb Theodor *see* HARTENKAMPF, Gottlieb Theodor Kempf von
KERCKHOVEN, Jacob van de *see* CASTELLO, Jacopo da
KEUNINCK, Kerstiaen de (elder) *see* KONINCK, Kerstiaen de (elder)
KEY SATO *see* SATO, Key
KIKOINE, Jacob *see* YANKEL, Jacques
KINNAIRD, Francis Joseph *see* KINNAIRD, Wiggs
KISELEV, Alexandre Alexandrovitch *see* KISSELEOV, Alexandre Alexandrovitch
KLEIN, Frits *see* KLEIN, Friedrich Franz
KLOCKER, David *see* EHRENSTRAHL, David Klocker von
KLOSSOWSKI, Balthasar *see* BALTHUS
KNIGHTON-HAMMOND, Arthur Henry *see* HAMMOND, Arthur Henry Knighton
KOEKKOEK, Hermanus (jnr) *see* COUVER, Jan van
KOLLER, Johann Rudolf *see* KOLLER, Rudolf
KOMAROMI-KATZ, Endre *see* KACZ, Endre Komaromi
KORFF, Alexander Hugo Bakker *see* BAKKER-KORFF, Alexander Hugo
KOUDRIACHOV, Ivan A *see* KUDRIASHEV, Ivan
KOUYOUMOJIAN, Elvire *see* JAN, Elvire
KOWALSKI-WIERUSZ, Alfred von *see* WIERUSZ-KOWALSKI, Alfred von
KRUSEMAN VAN ELTEN, Hendrik Dirk *see* ELTEN, Hendrik Dirk Kruseman van

L

LAMBERT, Louis Eugene *see* LAMBERT, Eugene
LAMEN, Jasper van der *see* LAANEN, Jasper van der
LAPIRA *see* PIRA, la
LARSEN, Carl Frederick Emanuel *see* LARSEN, Emanuel
LASSALLE, Louis Simon *see* CABAILLOT, Louis Simon
LAVREINCE, Nicolas (younger) *see* LAFRENSEN, Nicolas (younger)
LEAL, Juan de Valdes *see* VALDES LEAL, Juan de
LECLERC, Sebastien Jacques *see* LECLERC DES GOBELINS, Sebastian
LEDUC, Victor Viollet *see* VIOLLET LE DUC, Victor

M

N

O

P

R

S

T

U

V

W

X

Y

Z

Index
to
International Auction Sales for the 2003/2004 Season

STARTING PRICES

Oil Paintings & Works on Paper

£250 - $400 - 400 Euro

Miniatures & Sculpture

£1,000 - $1,500 - 1,500 Euro

Prints & Photographs

£2,000 - $3,000 - 3,000 Euro

Regional "schools"

£5,000 - $7,000 - 7,000 Euro

A S (?) ?
£14231 $24477 €20777 View of Kronstadt (72x88cm-28x35in) init.d.1842. 2-Dec-3 Bukowskis, Stockholm #436/R est:100000-125000 (S.KR 185000)

AABY, S (20th C) Danish?
£774 $1214 €1130 Young woman on beach (49x73cm-19x29in) s. 30-Aug-3 Rasmussen, Havnen #2250 (D.KR 8300)

AACHEN, Hans von (1552-1616) German
Works on paper
£455 $800 €664 Resurrection (29x21cm-11x8in) pen brown ink col wash oval. 19-May-4 Doyle, New York #6014/R

AADNES, Peder Pedersen (1739-1792) Norwegian
£14932 $24339 €21651 Portraits of Maren Christine and Gierttru Maria - both wives of Vicar P C Holbye (72x60cm-28x24in) s.i.verso pair. 24-Sep-3 Blomqvist, Oslo #99/R est:200000-250000 (N.KR 175000)

AAE, Arvid (1877-1913) Swedish
£406 $689 €593 Two girls on bathing bridge (42x57cm-17x22in) s. 10-Nov-3 Rasmussen, Vejle #219/R (D.KR 4400)

AAGAARD, C F (1833-1895) Danish
£290 $518 €423 Landscape from Aebelo (39x53cm-15x21in) s.i.d.10 maj 1889. 10-May-4 Rasmussen, Vejle #92/R (D.KR 3200)
£355 $561 €515 Spring day by cabin in woods (22x35cm-9x14in) s. 2-Sep-3 Rasmussen, Copenhagen #1910/R (D.KR 3800)
£539 $1003 €787 Wooden house painted red behind pine trees in landscape (62x42cm-24x17in) s. 2-Mar-4 Rasmussen, Copenhagen #1401/R (D.KR 6000)
£841 $1329 €1219 River through woods (40x29cm-16x11in) s.d.1890. 2-Sep-3 Rasmussen, Copenhagen #1751/R (D.KR 9000)

AAGAARD, Carl Frederic (1833-1895) Danish
£332 $538 €485 Bird on overturned beech tree (28x35cm-11x14in) s. 9-Aug-3 Hindemae, Ullerslev #99/R (D.KR 3500)
£802 $1500 €1203 Extensive coastal landscape with shipping beyond (34x45cm-13x18in) s. 25-Jul-4 Bonhams & Butterfields, San Francisco #6040/R est:2000-3000
£905 $1511 €1321 Untitled - fishing from the dock (53x80cm-21x31in) s.indis d. 17-Nov-3 Hodgins, Calgary #44/R est:2500-3000 (C.D 2000)
£2686 $4915 €3922 Sailing vessel off the northern coast of Kronborg (44x80cm-17x31in) s. 9-Jun-4 Rasmussen, Copenhagen #1681/R est:30000 (D.KR 30000)
£4328 $8007 €6319 Wooded landscape with waterway and fisherman in rowing boat (106x74cm-42x29in) s.d.1885. 15-Mar-4 Rasmussen, Vejle #23/R est:20000 (D.KR 48000)
£4492 $8356 €6558 View of the Bay of Naples from an Italian villa (51x45cm-20x18in) s.indis.d.1889. 2-Mar-4 Rasmussen, Copenhagen #1282/R est:50000 (D.KR 50000)
£7289 $13266 €10934 View towards Bay of Naples from a loggia (57x85cm-22x33in) s.d.1873. 19-Jun-4 Rasmussen, Havnen #2062/R est:20000-30000 (D.KR 82000)
£8953 $16383 €13071 Landscape from Jaegersborg Dyrehave (110x162cm-43x64in) s.d.1857 exhib.prov. 9-Jun-4 Rasmussen, Copenhagen #1680/R est:125000-150000 (D.KR 100000)

AAGAARD, Martin (1863-1913) Norwegian
£256 $409 €371 Seascape (51x75cm-20x30in) s. 22-Sep-3 Blomqvist, Lysaker #1346 (N.KR 3000)
£451 $754 €650 Fishing boat by the coast (42x60cm-17x24in) s. 26-Oct-3 Bukowskis, Helsinki #543/R
£1000 $1730 €1460 The pilot boat coming towards land (20x84cm-8x33in) s. panel. 13-Dec-3 Blomqvist, Lysaker #1419/R est:6000-8000 (N.KR 11500)

AALTO, Ilmari (1891-1934) Finnish
£369 $687 €550 Landscape (40x49cm-16x19in) s.d.19 exhib.prov. 7-Mar-4 Bukowskis, Helsinki #281/R
£465 $744 €660 Still life (46x55cm-18x22in) s. 18-Sep-3 Hagelstam, Helsinki #843
£699 $1189 €1000 Rain clouds (40x50cm-16x20in) s.d.20 board. 29-Nov-3 Bukowskis, Helsinki #26/R
£704 $1127 €1000 Still life of bottles (46x38cm-18x15in) s. 21-Sep-3 Bukowskis, Helsinki #301/R

AALTONA, Veikko (1910-1990) Finnish
£629 $1070 €900 Flowers in vase (82x65cm-32x26in) s.d.47. 29-Nov-3 Bukowskis, Helsinki #261/R
£979 $1664 €1400 Light in the window (94x120cm-37x47in) s.d.1945 canvas on board exhib. 29-Nov-3 Bukowskis, Helsinki #248/R

AALTONEN, Waino (1894-1966) Finnish
£533 $955 €800 Calf (47x57cm-19x22in) s.d.1930. 15-May-4 Hagelstam, Helsinki #155/R
£669 $1070 €950 Woman (40x34cm-16x13in) s.d.1924 exhib. 18-Sep-3 Hagelstam, Helsinki #807
£3287 $5587 €4700 Evening landscape, February (48x40cm-19x16in) s. board exhib. 29-Nov-3 Bukowskis, Helsinki #38/R est:4000-4500
Sculpture
£1067 $1909 €1600 Dancing shadow (58x45cm-23x18in) s. pat.bronze exec.c.1958 lit. 15-May-4 Hagelstam, Helsinki #2/R est:1600
£1081 $1935 €1600 Musica (19cm-7in) s.d.1927 bronze. 8-May-4 Bukowskis, Helsinki #18/R est:1000-1200
£1533 $2821 €2300 Woman kneeling (60cm-24in) s.d.1910 bronze. 9-Jun-4 Bukowskis, Helsinki #316/R est:2000
£1892 $3386 €2800 Guardian angel (41cm-16in) s. bronze. 8-May-4 Bukowskis, Helsinki #4/R
£2162 $3870 €3200 Sorrow (21cm-8in) s. bronze. 8-May-4 Bukowskis, Helsinki #13/R est:1000-1500
£3333 $5967 €5000 The javelin thrower (97x130cm-38x51in) s.num.3/8 bronze exec.c.1948. 15-May-4 Hagelstam, Helsinki #1/R est:6000
£5282 $9137 €7500 Sisters (56cm-22in) s.d.1945 black granite lit. 13-Dec-3 Hagelstam, Helsinki #1/R est:7000

AALUND, Martin (1967-) Swedish
£1051 $1893 €1534 Marvel (122x122cm-48x48in) s.d.2002 verso prov. 26-Apr-4 Bukowskis, Stockholm #503/R (S.KR 14500)

AAMOT, Paul Coucheron (?) Norwegian
£391 $677 €571 The pilot boat coming in (55x78cm-22x31in) s. panel. 13-Dec-3 Blomqvist, Lysaker #1420 (N.KR 4500)

AAMUND, Susanne (1943-) Danish
£323 $548 €472 House with figures (125x80cm-49x31in) s.d.83 exhib. 10-Nov-3 Rasmussen, Vejle #607/R (D.KR 3500)

AARNIO, Eero (20th C) Finnish
Sculpture
£1700 $3094 €2550 Glove chair (127x107cm-50x42in) enamelled steel plastic upholstery lit. 30-Jun-4 Christie's, Kensington #76/R est:1800-2200

AARON, Joseph (1959-) American
£604 $1100 €882 Sunset (20x25cm-8x10in) s. i.v panel. 15-Jun-4 John Moran, Pasadena #170a
£604 $1100 €882 Coastal landscape (23x30cm-9x12in) s. panel. 15-Jun-4 John Moran, Pasadena #170
£604 $1100 €882 Goleta Beach II (23x30cm-9x12in) s. panel. 15-Jun-4 John Moran, Pasadena #169
£706 $1200 €1031 Afternoon at the lake (23x30cm-9x12in) s. i.verso birch panel. 18-Nov-3 John Moran, Pasadena #148a
£741 $1400 €1082 Montecito coastal (28x36cm-11x14in) s. panel. 17-Feb-4 John Moran, Pasadena #160/R est:1500-2000
£765 $1300 €1117 Goleta beach (30x41cm-12x16in) s. i.verso birch panel. 18-Nov-3 John Moran, Pasadena #148
£952 $1800 €1390 Houses in coastal landscape - Corona del Mar (30x41cm-12x16in) s. i. verso panel. 17-Feb-4 John Moran, Pasadena #159/R est:1500-2000
£1058 $2000 €1545 Coastal landscape - Refugio State Beach (28x36cm-11x14in) s. i. verso panel. 17-Feb-4 John Moran, Pasadena #160a/R est:1200-1800
£1059 $1800 €1546 Montecito coastal (61x76cm-24x30in) s. birch panel. 18-Nov-3 John Moran, Pasadena #147 est:2500-4000
£1190 $2250 €1737 Lake Casitas sunset (41x51cm-16x20in) i. verso panel. 17-Feb-4 John Moran, Pasadena #120a/R est:1800-2500

AAS, Nils (1933-) Norwegian
Sculpture
£1173 $2159 €1713 Henrik Ibsen (45cm-18in) brown pat.bronze. 29-Mar-4 Rasmussen, Copenhagen #450/R est:15000-18000 (D.KR 13000)

AAS, Walther (1928-1990) Norwegian
£325 $598 €488 Mountain landscape, Grindafjellet. s. 14-Jun-4 Blomqvist, Lysaker #1004/R (N.KR 4000)

AASLING, Lennart (1921-1966) Swedish
£319 $574 €479 Still life (76x80cm-30x31in) s. panel. 25-Apr-4 Goteborg Auktionsverk, Sweden #380/R (S.KR 4400)

ABA-NOVAK, Vilmos (1894-1941) Hungarian
£223 $400 €326 Rural landscape with cattle crossing a river (61x30cm-24x12in) s.verso pressboard. 20-Mar-4 Selkirks, St. Louis #515
£4344 $7211 €6342 Autumn forest (69x55cm-27x22in) s. 4-Oct-3 Kieselbach, Budapest #100/R (H.F 1600000)
£4543 $8041 €6633 Woman in red (65x50cm-26x20in) painted c.1925. 28-Apr-4 Kieselbach, Budapest #91/R (H.F 1700000)
£5000 $9100 €7300 Peasants (35x35cm-14x14in) s. tempera board prov. 15-Jun-4 Sotheby's, London #78/R est:5000-7000
£7377 $13353 €10770 In the inn (62x52cm-24x20in) s. tempera. 16-Apr-4 Mu Terem Galeria, Budapest #14/R (H.F 2800000)
£9773 $16224 €14269 In the market place (64x53cm-25x21in) s. tempera board. 4-Oct-3 Kieselbach, Budapest #161/R (H.F 3600000)
£16033 $28379 €23408 Transylvanian village (61x70cm-24x28in) s.d.35 tempera board. 28-Apr-4 Kieselbach, Budapest #146/R (H.F 6000000)
£33930 $58699 €49538 Trattoria (79x94cm-31x37in) 12-Dec-3 Kieselbach, Budapest #223/R (H.F 13000000)
£38007 $63092 €55490 On the field (61x95cm-24x37in) s. 4-Oct-3 Kieselbach, Budapest #129/R (H.F 14000000)
Works on paper
£3207 $5676 €4682 Felsobanya (35x50cm-14x20in) s.i.d.26 indian ink. 28-Apr-4 Kieselbach, Budapest #110/R (H.F 1200000)
£3265 $6008 €4767 Circus performers (30x46cm-12x18in) s. W/C. 29-Mar-4 Goodman, Sydney #123/R est:1200-1800 (A.D 8000)

ABADES, Juan Martinez (1862-1920) Spanish
£3947 $7145 €6000 Shipwreck (60x98cm-24x39in) s. 14-Apr-4 Ansorena, Madrid #164/R est:6000
£9155 $16021 €13000 Sailing boat on the Abra (60x86cm-24x34in) s.d.1908. 16-Dec-3 Segre, Madrid #97/R est:10000
£10870 $17826 €15000 Bajamar (60x100cm-24x39in) s.d.1893. 27-May-3 Durán, Madrid #168/R est:9000

ABADIA, Juan de la (1473-1496) Spanish
£50000 $90000 €73000 Archangel Michael (146x79cm-57x31in) panel. 21-Apr-4 Christie's, London #60/R est:20000-30000

ABADIE, Jean (20th C) French
£270 $484 €400 Jeune fille au bouquet et a l'enfant (81x65cm-32x26in) s. 10-May-4 Giraudeau, Tours #91

£297 $532 €440 Toilette apres le bain (54x65cm-21x26in) s. 10-May-4 Giraudeau, Tours #93
£338 $605 €500 Vie silencieuse (54x65cm-21x26in) s. 10-May-4 Giraudeau, Tours #92
£432 $774 €640 Fin des vendanges (54x65cm-21x26in) s. 10-May-4 Giraudeau, Tours #94

ABADIE-LANDEL, Pierre (1896-1972) French
£396 $649 €550 Marine (50x61cm-20x24in) s.i.d.32. 3-Jun-3 Livinec, Gaudcheau & Jezequel, Rennes #59

ABAKANOWICZ, Magdalena (1930-) Polish
Works on paper
£1034 $1728 €1500 Vision 1 (48x72cm-19x28in) s.d.1997 ink wash. 16-Nov-3 Agra, Warsaw #3/R est:400

ABATE, Goffredo de (1849-1932) Italian
£483 $801 €700 Landscape near Biella (27x37cm-11x15in) s.d.1931 board. 1-Oct-3 Della Rocca, Turin #18/R
£759 $1259 €1100 Little tailor (19x32cm-7x13in) s. 1-Oct-3 Della Rocca, Turin #287/R

ABATE, Teonesto de (1898-1981) Italian
£345 $572 €500 Corn field (60x40cm-24x16in) s. 1-Oct-3 Della Rocca, Turin #255/R
£414 $687 €600 Landscape (49x60cm-19x24in) s.d.951 board. 1-Oct-3 Della Rocca, Turin #248/R
£483 $801 €700 San Giorio, Val Susa (50x70cm-20x28in) s.d.961. 1-Oct-3 Della Rocca, Turin #291/R
£521 $885 €750 Still life with bird (100x50cm-39x20in) s. 1-Nov-3 Meeting Art, Vercelli #397/R
£667 $1227 €1000 Flowers (70x5cm-28x2in) s. s.verso. 14-Jun-4 Sant Agostino, Torino #157/R
£745 $1244 €1050 Elsa (80x50cm-31x20in) s.d.1967. 20-Oct-3 Sant Agostino, Torino #147/R
Works on paper
£345 $572 €500 Seascape (35x45cm-14x18in) s.d.951 W/C cardboard. 1-Oct-3 Della Rocca, Turin #112/R

ABATTUCI, Pierre (1871-1942) Belgian
£500 $920 €750 Jardin dans toute sa splendeur (43x59cm-17x23in) s. 14-Jun-4 Horta, Bruxelles #219
£728 $1326 €1100 Paysage maritime (55x90cm-22x35in) s. 15-Jun-4 Galerie Moderne, Brussels #251/R

ABBASI, Shaykh (fl.1650-1683) Persian
Works on paper
£30000 $53100 €43800 Tambur player (35x22cm-14x9in) i. pen wash htd gold. 27-Apr-4 Christie's, London #84/R est:15000-20000

ABBATI, Giuseppe (1836-1868) Italian
£26667 $48267 €40000 Bay in Castiglioncello (15x20cm-6x8in) init. board lit. 2-Apr-4 Farsetti, Prato #582/R est:40000-45000

ABBATI, Giuseppe (attrib) (1836-1868) Italian
£467 $845 €700 Tuscan landscape with farm (20x30cm-8x12in) i.verso board. 30-Mar-4 Babuino, Rome #391/R

ABBATT, Agnes Dean (1847-1917) American
Works on paper
£248 $400 €362 Otter cliffs (23x33cm-9x13in) s. W/C. 20-Aug-3 James Julia, Fairfield #1696/R

ABBE, Salomon van (1883-?) Dutch/British
Works on paper
£250 $448 €365 An Ostende fisherman (39x30cm-15x12in) s. W/C. 25-May-4 Bonhams, Knightsbridge #185/R
£380 $680 €555 Dawn, a languid stretch (60x34cm-24x13in) s. W/C bodycol. 25-May-4 Bonhams, Knightsbridge #209/R

ABBEMA, Louise (1858-1927) French
£359 $600 €524 Jeune femme (23x15cm-9x6in) s. panel. 11-Oct-3 Auctions by the Bay, Alameda #1696/R

ABBETT, Robert Kennedy (1926-) American
£12291 $22000 €17945 Bob Whites and pointer (58x91cm-23x36in) board. 15-May-4 Altermann Galleries, Santa Fe #163/R

ABBEY, Edwin Austin (1852-1911) American
£1582 $2500 €2310 Lancelot and Guenevere (48x38cm-19x15in) s. panel oval. 7-Sep-3 Treadway Gallery, Cincinnati #537/R est:3000-5000
£107345 $190000 €156724 Dance of the troubadors (40x103cm-16x41in) s.i.d.1897 oil gold gilt. 2-May-4 Bonhams & Butterfields, San Francisco #1160/R est:30000-50000
Works on paper
£401 $750 €585 Seated young woman reading (13x13cm-5x5in) pen ink. 26-Feb-4 Illustration House, New York #1
£1617 $2700 €2361 Trumpeters heralding the birth of Jesus Christ (48x36cm-19x14in) s.d.1899 pen ink. 15-Nov-3 Illustration House, New York #28/R est:3000-5000

ABBO, Jussuf (?) ?
Works on paper
£347 $624 €520 Female nude (48x34cm-19x13in) s.i.d. chk htd red board. 24-Apr-4 Dr Lehr, Berlin #2/R
£367 $660 €550 Girl's head (37x22cm-15x9in) s. w/C. 24-Apr-4 Dr Lehr, Berlin #1/R

ABBOT, Agnes Anne (1897-1992) American
£265 $475 €387 Hillside landscape (20x26cm-8x10in) i.verso board prov. 14-May-4 Skinner, Boston #167/R
£363 $650 €530 On the coast (20x25cm-8x10in) board prov. 14-May-4 Skinner, Boston #169/R
Works on paper
£195 $350 €285 Western mountain landscape (37x54cm-15x21in) s. W/C prov. 14-May-4 Skinner, Boston #170/R
£220 $350 €321 High water (54x36cm-21x14in) s. W/C. 12-Sep-3 Skinner, Boston #444/R
£391 $700 €571 At the shore, Florida (35x55cm-14x22in) W/C prov. 14-May-4 Skinner, Boston #279/R
£435 $700 €635 Ogunquit beach (38x58cm-15x23in) W/C double-sided. 20-Aug-3 James Julia, Fairfield #1617/R
£503 $900 €734 Dockside, Menemsha (37x54cm-15x21in) s. W/C prov. 14-May-4 Skinner, Boston #262/R

ABBOTT, Berenice (1898-1991) American
Photographs
£1693 $3200 €2472 Herald Square (16x17cm-6x7in) i. verso silver print. 17-Feb-4 Swann Galleries, New York #64a/R est:4000-5000
£1695 $3000 €2475 Chicken market, 55 Hester Street, 1937 (24x19cm-9x7in) i.d.verso gelatin silver print prov.lit. 27-Apr-4 Christie's, Rockefeller NY #30/R est:3000-5000
£1796 $3000 €2622 Steel arch (21x16cm-8x6in) s.i.verso gelatin silver print lit. 16-Oct-3 Phillips, New York #92/R est:6000-8000
£1946 $3250 €2841 Newsstand, East 32nd Street and Third Avenue (46x58cm-18x23in) s.num.37/40 photo exec.1935 printed later. 17-Oct-3 Sotheby's, New York #206/R est:3000-5000
£2111 $3800 €3082 Newsstand (20x25cm-8x10in) i.verso gelatin silver print lit. 23-Apr-4 Phillips, New York #75/R est:3000-5000
£2373 $4200 €3465 Lamport Export Company, 507 Broadway, 1935 (18x24cm-7x9in) i.d. gelatin silver print. 27-Apr-4 Christie's, Rockefeller NY #31/R est:5000-7000
£2695 $4500 €3935 New York at night (35x27cm-14x11in) s. photo exec.1932 printed later prov. 17-Oct-3 Sotheby's, New York #205/R est:4000-6000
£2695 $4500 €3935 New York at night (24x19cm-9x7in) s. gelatin silver print exec.1936 printed c.1970 prov.lit. 20-Oct-3 Christie's, Rockefeller NY #46/R est:4000-6000
£3069 $5800 €4481 New York at night (35x27cm-14x11in) silver print. 17-Feb-4 Swann Galleries, New York #44/R est:6000-9000
£3107 $5500 €4536 El, second and third avenue lines, Bowery and Division Streets, Manhattan (59x47cm-23x19in) s.num.37/40 photo printed 1982. 28-Apr-4 Sotheby's, New York #124/R est:3000-5000
£3107 $5500 €4536 Warehouse, Water and Dock Streets, Brooklyn (71x91cm-28x36in) s.num.2/24 photo printed later prov. 28-Apr-4 Sotheby's, New York #130/R est:5000-7000
£3234 $5400 €4722 Jean Cocteau with mask (11x16cm-4x6in) silver print. 21-Oct-3 Swann Galleries, New York #99/R est:6000-9000
£3333 $6000 €4866 Cliff and Ferry Street (22x8cm-9x3in) i.d.1935 gelatin silver print prov.lit. 23-Apr-4 Phillips, New York #3/R est:6000-8000
£3390 $6000 €4949 Advertisements, East Houston Street and 2nd Ave, Northeast corner (19x24cm-7x9in) s. photo. 28-Apr-4 Sotheby's, New York #126/R est:5000-7000
£3497 $5944 €5000 East Broadway No 294, Manhattan (24x19cm-9x7in) i.d. verso silver gelatin lit.exhib. 27-Nov-3 Villa Grisebach, Berlin #1100/R est:5000-7000
£4000 $7360 €6000 Broadway and Exchange Place (49x13cm-19x5in) s. i. verso silver gelatin board lit.exhib. 10-Jun-4 Villa Grisebach, Berlin #1000/R est:4500-5500
£4067 $7279 €6100 Buildings in New York (25x20cm-10x8in) s. silver print. 13-May-4 Le Mouel, Paris #111 est:5000-6000
£4192 $7000 €6120 Under the El at the Battery (15x23cm-6x9in) s. gelatin silver print lit. 20-Oct-3 Christie's, Rockefeller NY #3/R est:4000-6000
£4520 $8000 €6599 Greenwich village images (46x59cm-18x23in) s. photos 1936 and c.1950 printed later two prov. 28-Apr-4 Sotheby's, New York #128/R est:6000-9000
£4790 $8000 €6993 Portrait of Eugene Atget (24x18cm-9x7in) s. photo exec.c.1925 printed c.1930. 17-Oct-3 Sotheby's, New York #195/R est:5000-7000
£4790 $8000 €6993 Exchange place (49x12cm-19x5in) s. photo exec.1933 printed later. 17-Oct-3 Sotheby's, New York #204/R est:5000-7000
£5085 $9000 €7424 Industrial images (67x90cm-26x35in) s.num.8/24 and 11/24 photos 1935 and 1958/printed later two prov. 28-Apr-4 Sotheby's, New York #122/R est:5000-7000
£5085 $9000 €7424 Manhattan bridge (58x47cm-23x19in) s.num.37/40 photo printed 1982. 28-Apr-4 Sotheby's, New York #125/R est:3000-5000
£5085 $9000 €7424 Pennsylvania station interior (94x74cm-37x29in) s.num.5/24 photo exec.c.1934 printed later prov. 28-Apr-4 Sotheby's, New York #131/R est:5000-7000
£5367 $9500 €7836 New York at night (57x46cm-22x18in) s. photo printed later prov. 28-Apr-4 Sotheby's, New York #123/R est:7000-10000
£5988 $10000 €8742 New York at night (59x47cm-23x19in) s. photo exec.1932 printed later prov. 17-Oct-3 Sotheby's, New York #128/R est:6000-9000
£7345 $13000 €10724 New York at night (33x27cm-13x11in) s. photo. 28-Apr-4 Sotheby's, New York #127/R est:6000-9000
£11976 $20000 €17485 El, second and third avenue lines, Hanover Square and Pearl Street (46x36cm-18x14in) s.i.d.1936 photo. 17-Oct-3 Sotheby's, New York #207/R est:10000-15000

ABBOTT, Clem (1939-1989) Australian?
Works on paper
£329 $596 €480 Central Australia. W/C. 1-Apr-4 Joel, Victoria #119 (A.D 800)

ABBOTT, Douglas (1948-) Australian
Works on paper
£471 $842 €688 Untitled (48x35cm-19x14in) s. W/C canvasboard exec 1998 prov. 25-May-4 Lawson Menzies, Sydney #109/R (A.D 1200)
£510 $913 €745 Untitled (48x35cm-19x14in) s. W/C canvasboard exec 1998 prov. 25-May-4 Lawson Menzies, Sydney #108/R (A.D 1300)

ABBOTT, John White (1763-1851) British
Works on paper
£312 $550 €456 Dormition of the Virgin (48x46cm-19x18in) pencil. 28-May-4 Aspire, Cleveland #109/R
£3800 $6460 €5548 On the Warren near Dawlish, Devon (22x40cm-9x16in) s.verso pen ink W/C on two joined sheet. 27-Nov-3 Sotheby's, London #256/R est:3000-5000
£4500 $8235 €6570 River near Hawthornden, Devon (49x41cm-19x16in) i.d.1791 pen brown grey ink W/C five joined sheets prov. 3-Jun-4 Christie's, London #54/R est:5000-8000
£4800 $8784 €7008 Near Roslyn Castle, Edinburgh (24x19cm-9x7in) s.i.d.1791 pencil brown ink W/C prov. 3-Jun-4 Christie's, London #53/R est:4000-6000
£16000 $27200 €23360 Peamore, Devon (45x57cm-18x22in) s.d.1799 pencil pen blk in, W/C on seven sheets of paper prov. 20-Nov-3 Christie's, London #58/R est:18000-25000

ABBOTT, John White (attrib) (1763-1851) British
Works on paper
£300 $537 €438 Coastal town (11x18cm-4x7in) black ink W/C. 18-Mar-4 Christie's, Kensington #738/R

ABBOTT, Lemuel Francis (1760-1803) British
£8500 $15640 €12410 Portrait of a young boy in a brown coat and breeches, holding a skipping rope, in a landscape (63x76cm-25x30in) prov. 11-Jun-4 Christie's, London #31/R est:5000-8000

ABBOTT, Lemuel Francis (attrib) (1760-1803) British
£1100 $2013 €1606 Portrait of a gentleman wearing a brown coat (75x62cm-30x24in) 6-Jul-4 Bonhams, Knightsbridge #82/R est:500-700

ABBOTT, Yarnell (1870-1938) American
£2907 $5000 €4244 Stone houses (76x91cm-30x36in) s. s.i.d.32 verso. 7-Dec-3 Freeman, Philadelphia #133 est:5000-8000
Works on paper
£284 $475 €415 Beached boats, Cassis (25x20cm-10x8in) s. gouache exhib. 20-Jun-3 Freeman, Philadelphia #70/R

ABBOUD, Chafik (1926-) Lebanese
£268 $502 €400 Carnet d'Aout (24x35cm-9x14in) s.d.Aout 61 distemper canvas on cardboard prov. 29-Feb-4 Versailles Encheres #195
£738 $1307 €1100 Composition no 134 (113x83cm-44x33in) s.d.1962 s.i.d.verso distemper paper on panel. 28-Apr-4 Charbonneaux, Paris #98 est:800-1000
£1000 $1770 €1460 La lucarne a Callas. Abstract (24x27cm-9x11in) s.d.77 canvas on board two. 29-Apr-4 Bonhams, New Bond Street #552/R est:1000-1500
£1049 $1783 €1500 Tendres galipettes (54x81cm-21x32in) s. s.i.d.1979 verso. 28-Nov-3 Drouot Estimations, Paris #214
£1259 $2140 €1800 Composition (99x64cm-39x25in) s. panel painted 1959 exhib. 28-Nov-3 Drouot Estimations, Paris #209/R est:1500-2000
£1399 $2378 €2000 Devoir de vacances II (61x50cm-24x20in) s. s.i.d.1978 verso. 28-Nov-3 Drouot Estimations, Paris #212 est:600-800
£1538 $2615 €2200 Shapes II (65x92cm-26x36in) s. s.i.d.1975 verso. 28-Nov-3 Drouot Estimations, Paris #215 est:800-1100
£1875 $2963 €2700 Bruxelles (73x92cm-29x36in) s.d.1957 prov. 27-Apr-3 Versailles Encheres #9
£1958 $3329 €2800 Retour (73x60cm-29x24in) s. s.i.verso. 28-Nov-3 Drouot Estimations, Paris #213 est:800-1000
£2098 $3566 €3000 Allegory (180x200cm-71x79in) s. i.d.1985 verso. 28-Nov-3 Drouot Estimations, Paris #217 est:2000-2500
£2098 $3566 €3000 Opale (97x130cm-38x51in) s. s.i.d.1975 verso. 28-Nov-3 Drouot Estimations, Paris #216/R est:2500-3000
£2797 $4755 €4000 Composition (95x129cm-37x51in) s.d.1960 s.d.verso. 28-Nov-3 Drouot Estimations, Paris #210 est:1500-2000
£2937 $4993 €4200 Composition (130x97cm-51x38in) s. s.d.1960 verso exhib. 28-Nov-3 Drouot Estimations, Paris #211/R est:2000-2500
£4000 $7080 €5840 La broderie chinoise (90x71cm-35x28in) s. s.d.85 verso exhib. 29-Apr-4 Bonhams, New Bond Street #551/R est:4000-6000
£4895 $8322 €7000 Room I (160x160cm-63x63in) s. s.i.d.1987 verso tempera. 28-Nov-3 Drouot Estimations, Paris #218 est:2000-2500
£7000 $12390 €10220 Gestes I (158x143cm-62x56in) s.i. oil pencil newspaper on canvas prov. 29-Apr-4 Bonhams, New Bond Street #553/R est:7000-10000
Works on paper
£345 $638 €500 Composition (20x33cm-8x13in) s.d.aout 61 gouache mixed media. 13-Feb-4 Charbonneaux, Paris #32

ABBRESCIA, Joe (1936-) American
£12032 $22500 €17567 Follow the trail (76x132cm-30x52in) s. 24-Jul-4 Coeur d'Alene, Hayden #36/R est:15000-25000

ABDULLA, Ian (1947-) Australian
£1079 $1802 €1619 Untitled (60x91cm-24x36in) s.d.1999 acrylic. 27-Oct-3 Goodman, Sydney #39/R (A.D 2600)
Works on paper
£1198 $2073 €1749 Untitled, setting snares along the fence to catch a kangaroo (56x76cm-22x30in) s.i. synthetic polymer paint. 10-Dec-3 Shapiro, Sydney #135 est:3000-5000 (A.D 2815)
£1545 $2441 €2240 Swapping tins of bully beef for local food (56x76cm-22x30in) s.d.7/3/94 synthetic polymer paint prov. 28-Jul-3 Sotheby's, Paddington #510/R est:2500-4000 (A.D 3800)
£1702 $2945 €2485 Untitled, when we had filled the bags with peas (56x76cm-22x30in) s.i. synthetic polymer paint. 10-Dec-3 Shapiro, Sydney #137/R est:3000-5000 (A.D 4000)
£1829 $2890 €2652 Shooting kungari, swans (57x76cm-22x30in) s.d.7/3/94 sp. prov. 28-Jul-3 Sotheby's, Paddington #509/R est:2500-4000 (A.D 4500)
£1875 $3506 €2813 Untitled (56x76cm-22x30in) s.i. synthetic polymer exec. c.1993. 21-Jul-4 Shapiro, Sydney #133/R est:4500-6000 (A.D 4800)
£2128 $3681 €3107 Untitled, when we used to go camping down near Gerard Mission (56x76cm-22x30in) s.i. synthetic polymer paint. 10-Dec-3 Shapiro, Sydney #136/R est:3000-5000 (A.D 5000)
£3252 $5138 €4715 Walking home with the sheep's head (76x102cm-30x40in) s. synthetic polymer paint canvas prov. 28-Jul-3 Sotheby's, Paddington #511/R est:2500-3500 (A.D 8000)
£5285 $8350 €7663 Pelicans at Katarapko (121x151cm-48x59in) s. synthetic polymer paint canvas prov.exhib. 28-Jul-3 Sotheby's, Paddington #189/R est:8000-12000 (A.D 13000)
£5285 $8350 €7663 Loading bales of Lucerne (122x153cm-48x60in) s. synthetic polymer paint canvas prov.exhib. 28-Jul-3 Sotheby's, Paddington #190/R est:5000-8000 (A.D 13000)

ABDULLAH, R Basoeki (1915-1993) Javanese
£2941 $5324 €4294 Flowers (75x100cm-30x39in) s. 3-Apr-4 Glerum, Singapore #74/R est:11000-15000 (S.D 9000)
£5208 $8698 €7604 Nude (76x100cm-30x39in) s. 12-Oct-3 Sotheby's, Singapore #150/R est:18000-28000 (S.D 15000)
£6159 $9547 €8992 Sleeping beauty (65x130cm-26x51in) s.d.9/3/1969. 6-Oct-2 Sotheby's, Singapore #160/R est:12000-15000 (S.D 17000)
£7843 $14196 €11451 Picturesque (75x100cm-30x39in) s. i.verso. 3-Apr-4 Glerum, Singapore #10/R est:12000-16000 (S.D 24000)
£12043 $19269 €17583 Kerbau (80x120cm-31x47in) s.d.57. 18-May-3 Sotheby's, Singapore #158/R est:20000-30000 (S.D 33600)

ABDULLAH, Sudjono (1911-1991) Javanese
£612 $1096 €900 Cloth market (60x101cm-24x40in) s. 16-Mar-4 Christie's, Amsterdam #57/R
£1156 $2070 €1700 Market stall under a flamboyant tree (78x100cm-31x39in) s. 16-Mar-4 Christie's, Amsterdam #60/R est:1800-2200

ABDULLAH, Suriosubroto (1878-1941) Javanese
£3080 $4774 €4497 Forest landscape (60x100cm-24x39in) s. 6-Oct-2 Sotheby's, Singapore #143/R est:3000-4000 (S.D 8500)

ABEELE, Jodocus Sebastian van den (1797-1855) Belgian
Works on paper
£1000 $1730 €1460 View of Rome from the terrace of the Villa Medici (13x20cm-5x8in) s.i.d.1830 pencil W/C gum arabic. 12-Dec-3 Christie's, Kensington #557/R est:1000-1500

ABEELE, Remy van den (1918-1995) Belgian
£586 $1084 €850 L'equilibre (90x70cm-35x28in) s. 16-Feb-4 Horta, Bruxelles #66

ABEILLE, Jacques (1906-) French
£441 $750 €644 Still life with bread, cheese and eggs (53x38cm-21x15in) s.d.50 prov. 22-Nov-3 Jackson's, Cedar Falls #399/R

ABEL, Philippe (20th C) ?
Sculpture
£1325 $2477 €2000 Femme assise. bronze exec.1930. 20-Jul-4 other European Auctioneer #199

ABEL-TRUCHET (1857-1918) French
£4610 $7699 €6500 L'omnibus sur le boulevard de Clichy (23x36cm-9x14in) s.i. i.verso panel. 20-Jun-3 Drouot Estimations, Paris #99/R est:2000-3000
£4830 $8500 €7052 Victorian ladies lounging in folding chairs in a lush garden (33x41cm-13x16in) s. panel. 28-May-4 Aspire, Cleveland #21/R est:10000-15000

ABELARDI, Angelo (attrib) (1883-1969) Italian
£1447 $2663 €2200 Portrait of small child in red clothing (49x54cm-19x21in) s. 24-Jun-4 Dr Fritz Nagel, Stuttgart #689/R est:900

ABELENDA, Manuel (1889-1957) Spanish
£3020 $5346 €4500 Betanzos seen from Peirao (38x45cm-15x18in) s. board lit. 27-Apr-4 Durán, Madrid #696/R est:2500
£3636 $6073 €5200 Paisaje con puente en ruinas y gallinas (76x54cm-30x21in) s. 24-Jun-3 Segre, Madrid #289/R est:5200
£7383 $13215 €11000 Landscape (58x70cm-23x28in) s. s.i.verso lit. 25-May-4 Durán, Madrid #156/R est:6000
£20134 $37450 €30000 Fair (60x94cm-24x37in) s. s.i.verso. 2-Mar-4 Ansorena, Madrid #65/R est:30000
Works on paper
£352 $609 €500 Dallas and Alabama (19x34cm-7x13in) s. ink. 15-Dec-3 Ansorena, Madrid #198/R

ABELING, Johan (1953-) Dutch
£816 $1486 €1200 Dijk bij electra - landscape with fence (30x35cm-12x14in) s.d. masonite prov. 3-Feb-4 Christie's, Amsterdam #554 est:500-700

ABELLO PRAT, Joan (1922-) Spanish
£966 $1738 €1400 Autumnal landscape (46x55cm-18x22in) s.d.73. 26-Jan-4 Durán, Madrid #125/R
£1479 $2588 €2100 View of Villafranca (46x38cm-18x15in) s.d.45. 16-Dec-3 Durán, Madrid #97/R
£2632 $4763 €4000 Landscape with river and women (65x81cm-26x32in) s.d.46. 14-Apr-4 Ansorena, Madrid #284/R est:4000
£4027 $7490 €6000 Landscape with figures. s. 2-Mar-4 Ansorena, Madrid #836/R est:6000
£6806 $11229 €9800 Flowers (66x110cm-26x43in) s. s.i.verso. 2-Jul-3 Ansorena, Madrid #852/R

ABELOOS, Victor (1881-1965) Belgian
£278 $453 €400 Vaches a Knokke (43x66cm-17x26in) s. 23-Sep-3 Galerie Moderne, Brussels #871/R

£288	$489	€420	Elegante a la mantille (50x40cm-20x16in) s.d.1918 panel. 10-Nov-3 Horta, Bruxelles #350
£319	$533	€450	Les pensees (50x60cm-20x24in) s. 17-Jun-3 Galerie Moderne, Brussels #389
£347	$552	€500	Fillette et singe (60x45cm-24x18in) s. panel. 9-Sep-3 Vanderkindere, Brussels #25
£552	$1021	€800	Vase fleuri (92x70cm-36x28in) s. 19-Jan-4 Horta, Bruxelles #387
£552	$1021	€800	Complicite (134x91cm-53x36in) s. 16-Feb-4 Horta, Bruxelles #89

ABELS, Jacobus Theodorus (1803-1866) Dutch

£3667	$6600	€5500	Moonlit beach with fishermen at work (11x15cm-4x6in) s. panel. 21-Apr-4 Christie's, Amsterdam #78/R est:1500-2000

ABELS, Jacobus Theodorus (attrib) (1803-1866) Dutch

£1156	$2105	€1700	Moonlit river landscape (29x37cm-11x15in) panel. 3-Feb-4 Christie's, Amsterdam #66/R est:1200-1600

ABEND, Harry (1937-) Venezuelan/Polish

Sculpture

£957	$1560	€1397	Untitled (60x12x18cm-24x5x7in) s.verso bronze exec.1984. 20-Jul-3 Subastas Odalys, Caracas #82

ABERCROMBIE, Gertrude (1909-1977) American

£1747	$3250	€2551	The Countess Nerona (20x25cm-8x10in) masonite. 5-Mar-4 Skinner, Boston #424/R est:2000-3000
£2049	$3750	€2992	Grey house (8x10cm-3x4in) s.d.1945 ms. 5-Jun-4 Treadway Gallery, Cincinnati #690/R est:2500-3500
£3294	$5500	€4809	Self portrait (65x48cm-26x19in) s. board. 19-Oct-3 Bonhams & Butterfields, Los Angeles #7071 est:1500-2000
£3763	$7000	€5494	Queen (10x13cm-4x5in) s.d.1954 board. 7-Mar-4 Treadway Gallery, Cincinnati #696/R est:4000-6000
£3825	$7000	€5585	Green house (10x13cm-4x5in) s.d.1945 masonite. 5-Jun-4 Treadway Gallery, Cincinnati #691/R est:3000-5000
£4918	$9000	€7180	Sunset (20x25cm-8x10in) s.d.1954 board. 5-Jun-4 Treadway Gallery, Cincinnati #689/R est:4000-6000
£9827	$17000	€14347	Self portrait (61x86cm-24x34in) s.d.53 exhib. 15-Dec-3 Hindman, Chicago #1/R est:5000-7000

ABERDAM, Alfred (1894-1963) Polish

£280	$468	€409	Maternite (67x33cm-26x13in) s. board prov. 21-Oct-3 Bonhams, Knightsbridge #21/R
£414	$691	€600	La danse (60x50cm-24x20in) s.d.1957 verso. 17-Nov-3 Claude Boisgirard, Paris #1/R
£426	$711	€600	Nature morte aux instruments de musique (42x61cm-17x24in) s. 19-Jun-3 Millon & Associes, Paris #216
£500	$835	€730	Performers on a trapeze (65x81cm-26x32in) s.d.1957 verso prov. 21-Oct-3 Bonhams, Knightsbridge #57/R
£1656	$3013	€2500	Cavaliers mystiques (130x162cm-51x64in) s. 16-Jun-4 Claude Boisgirard, Paris #13/R est:2500-3000

ABERG, Emil (1864-1940) Swedish

£671	$1234	€1007	Summer Sunday in Djurgarden (70x95cm-28x37in) s. 14-Jun-4 Lilla Bukowskis, Stockholm #56 (S.KR 9200)

ABERG, Pelle (1909-1964) Swedish

£508	$914	€762	Cafe interior with figures (75x60cm-30x24in) s.d.49 panel. 25-Apr-4 Goteborg Auktionsverk, Sweden #365/R (S.KR 7000)
£513	$908	€749	Southern town scene (62x40cm-24x16in) indis sig.i. 27-Apr-4 AB Stockholms Auktionsverk #870/R (S.KR 7000)
£802	$1475	€1203	By the nesting-box (36x44cm-14x17in) s. panel. 14-Jun-4 Lilla Bukowskis, Stockholm #58/R (S.KR 11000)
£901	$1622	€1315	Clown (46x38cm-18x15in) s. panel. 26-Jan-4 Lilla Bukowskis, Stockholm #190 (S.KR 12000)
£1015	$1827	€1482	The waiter (61x50cm-24x20in) s. panel. 26-Apr-4 Bukowskis, Stockholm #183/R (S.KR 14000)
£1172	$2075	€1711	Woman at table in cafe (33x24cm-13x9in) s. panel. 27-Apr-4 AB Stockholms Auktionsverk #694/R est:18000-20000 (S.KR 16000)
£1190	$1940	€1737	Clown playing the cello (35x27cm-14x11in) s. panel. 29-Sep-3 Lilla Bukowskis, Stockholm #340 est:10000-12000 (S.KR 15500)
£1190	$1940	€1737	Clown (46x38cm-18x15in) s. panel. 29-Sep-3 Lilla Bukowskis, Stockholm #575 est:8000-10000 (S.KR 15500)
£1197	$2154	€1748	Girl seated at a bar (68x58cm-27x23in) s. 26-Apr-4 Bukowskis, Stockholm #184/R est:15000-20000 (S.KR 16500)
£1267	$2066	€1850	Italian town scene (121x123cm-48x48in) s. panel. 29-Sep-3 Lilla Bukowskis, Stockholm #1 est:20000-25000 (S.KR 16500)
£1284	$2183	€1875	The dance restaurant (58x44cm-23x17in) s. panel. 4-Nov-3 Bukowskis, Stockholm #118/R est:15000-20000 (S.KR 17000)
£1465	$2593	€2139	Friend of the birds (73x60cm-29x24in) s. panel exhib. 27-Apr-4 AB Stockholms Auktionsverk #748/R est:20000-25000 (S.KR 20000)
£1511	$2568	€2206	Ladies at cafe (42x33cm-17x13in) s. panel. 4-Nov-3 Bukowskis, Stockholm #117a/R est:20000-25000 (S.KR 20000)
£1511	$2568	€2206	Woman wearing yellow coat smoking cigar (41x33cm-16x13in) s. panel. 5-Nov-3 AB Stockholms Auktionsverk #639/R est:20000-25000 (S.KR 20000)
£1737	$2953	€2536	Clown (46x38cm-18x15in) s. panel. 5-Nov-3 AB Stockholms Auktionsverk #638/R est:25000-30000 (S.KR 23000)
£1737	$2953	€2536	Girl wearing white hat (38x46cm-15x18in) s. panel. 5-Nov-3 AB Stockholms Auktionsverk #747/R est:20000-25000 (S.KR 23000)
£1905	$3371	€2781	The red hat (33x24cm-13x9in) s. panel. 27-Apr-4 AB Stockholms Auktionsverk #747/R est:12000-15000 (S.KR 26000)
£3097	$5264	€4522	Girl at table in cafe (61x50cm-24x20in) s. 5-Nov-3 AB Stockholms Auktionsverk #889/R est:20000-25000 (S.KR 41000)

ABERLI, Johann Ludwig (1723-1786) Swiss

Works on paper

£345	$617	€504	Weissenauw (26x37cm-10x15in) i. W/C. 12-May-4 Dobiaschofsky, Bern #1209/R (S.FR 800)

ABIDINE, Dino (1913-) French

£4070	$7000	€5942	Harbor scene (130x96cm-51x38in) s.verso prov. 3-Dec-3 Doyle, New York #78/R est:1200-1600
£4564	$8078	€6800	Composition (89x116cm-35x46in) s. prov. 28-Apr-4 Artcurial Briest, Paris #304/R est:3000-3500

ABILDGAARD, Nicolai Abraham (1743-1809) Danish

Works on paper

£394	$677	€575	Nude youth and other nudes (11x20cm-4x8in) pencil sketch. 3-Dec-3 Museumsbygningen, Copenhagen #136 (D.KR 4200)
£467	$738	€677	Figure composition with two figures playing lyres with cupid (21x17cm-8x7in) init. pen pencil prov. 2-Sep-3 Rasmussen, Copenhagen #2017/R (D.KR 5000)
£473	$818	€691	Male model (21x13cm-8x5in) pencil study prov. 9-Dec-3 Rasmussen, Copenhagen #1334/R (D.KR 5000)
£890	$1531	€1299	Study of Cupid with lyre (16x16cm-6x6in) s.i. ink. 3-Dec-3 Museumsbygningen, Copenhagen #138 (D.KR 9500)

ABILDGAARD, Nicolai Abraham (attrib) (1743-1809) Danish

£2079	$3597	€3035	Richard III dashing up from his bed, scared after the vision (38x29cm-15x11in) 9-Dec-3 Rasmussen, Copenhagen #1335/R est:15000-25000 (D.KR 22000)

Works on paper

£1701	$3044	€2500	Une vieille femme tenant une quenouille s'adressant a une jeune femme (13x17cm-5x7in) i. pen brown ink wash prov. 19-Mar-4 Piasa, Paris #197/R est:2500

ABLETT, William Albert (1877-1937) French

£1241	$2297	€1800	Sisters (92x65cm-36x26in) s. 19-Jan-4 Horta, Bruxelles #89 est:2000-3000

Works on paper

£805	$1297	€1200	Femme a son miroir (65x50cm-26x20in) s. pastel. 23-Feb-3 St-Germain-en-Laye Encheres #79/R
£1338	$2221	€1900	La reparatin et le raccord. s.i.d.1929 exhib.lit. 15-Jun-3 Artcurial Briest, Paris #78/R est:1500-2500

ABRAAMYAN, Artashes (1921-) Armenian

£450	$819	€657	Market Scene (57x80cm-22x31in) s. painted c.1970. 20-Jun-4 Lots Road Auctions, London #368/R

ABRAHAM, Friedrich (20th C) German

£541	$968	€800	Spring landscape (61x81cm-24x32in) 6-May-4 Michael Zeller, Lindau #562/R

ABRAHAMS, Ivor (1935-) British

£580	$1044	€847	Untitled (101x76cm-40x30in) s.d.75 mixed media prov. 26-Apr-4 Bukowskis, Stockholm #510/R (S.KR 8000)

Works on paper

£326	$587	€476	Study for suburban shrub I (66x60cm-26x24in) s.d.72 mixed media collage prov. 26-Apr-4 Bukowskis, Stockholm #509/R (S.KR 4500)
£363	$653	€530	Untitled (59x34cm-23x13in) s.d.April 71 mixed media diptych prov. 26-Apr-4 Bukowskis, Stockholm #508/R (S.KR 5000)

ABRAHAMSEN, Emil (1875-1964) Norwegian

£270	$496	€394	Evening sky (28x50cm-11x20in) s. 29-Mar-4 Blomqvist, Lysaker #1001/R (N.KR 3400)

ABRAHAMSON, Ola (1883-1980) Norwegian

£690	$1269	€1007	From Kabelvaag, Landligge (66x77cm-26x30in) s. exhib. 29-Mar-4 Blomqvist, Lysaker #1002 (N.KR 8700)

ABRAHAMSSON, Anette (1954-) Swedish

£264	$449	€385	Exterior II (97x130cm-38x51in) s.d.85 verso. 4-Nov-3 Bukowskis, Stockholm #602/R (S.KR 3500)
£1319	$2334	€1926	Untitled (190x205cm-75x81in) s.d.1985 verso. 27-Apr-4 AB Stockholms Auktionsverk #1108/R est:10000-15000 (S.KR 18000)

ABRAMOVICH, Pinchas (1909-1986) ?

£1995	$3650	€2913	Still life with fruits by an open window (70x49cm-28x19in) s. 1-Jun-4 Ben-Ami, Tel Aviv #4888/R est:4000-5000

ABRAMOVICZ, Leon (1880-1978) Austrian

£567	$1043	€850	Female nude (86x61cm-34x24in) paper on board. 9-Jun-4 Dorotheum, Salzburg #579/R

ABRAMOVITZ, Albert (1879-1963) American/Russian

£700	$1253	€1022	Busy street in a Continental town (62x47cm-24x19in) s. board. 26-May-4 Sotheby's, Olympia #296/R

ABRAMOWICZ, Bronislaw van (1837-1912) Polish

£2013	$3564	€3000	Squadron commander on horseback (48x38cm-19x15in) s.d.1871 panel. 29-Apr-4 Dorotheum, Vienna #198/R est:2000-3000

ABRAMOWICZ, Leo (1889-1978) Russian

£274	$466	€400	Man's portrait (62x42cm-24x17in) board. 5-Nov-3 Hugo Ruef, Munich #1235
£300	$552	€450	Woman sewing (32x24cm-13x9in) paper. 9-Jun-4 Dorotheum, Salzburg #577/R
£667	$1227	€1000	Houses (29x39cm-11x15in) bears i. board. 9-Jun-4 Dorotheum, Salzburg #621/R
£694	$1132	€1000	Vase of flowers (78x54cm-31x21in) mono. 23-Sep-3 Wiener Kunst Auktionen, Vienna #84/R

£800 $1440 €1200 Still life with flowers and fruit (57x43cm-22x17in) 21-Apr-4 Dorotheum, Vienna #120/R
£867 $1560 €1300 Still life with flowers and fruit (67x56cm-26x22in) masonite. 21-Apr-4 Dorotheum, Vienna #117/R
£1034 $1893 €1500 Flowers (62x44cm-24x17in) board. 27-Jan-4 Dorotheum, Vienna #136/R est:1500-1800
£1316 $2421 €2000 Flowers and fruit (63x44cm-25x17in) board. 22-Jun-4 Wiener Kunst Auktionen, Vienna #172/R est:1000

ABRATE, Angelo (1900-1985) Italian
£400 $736 €600 Snow (45x55cm-18x22in) s. 14-Jun-4 Sant Agostino, Torino #199/R
£952 $1705 €1400 Snow in Charousse (46x55cm-18x22in) s. 22-Mar-4 Sant Agostino, Torino #64/R

ABREU, Antonio (1890-1962) Portuguese
£470 $841 €700 Calm waters, Paio Pires (48x61cm-19x24in) s. board. 31-May-4 Cabral Moncada Leiloes, Lisbon #239/R

ABREU, Mario (1919-1993) Venezuelan
£449 $750 €656 Figure (61x49cm-24x19in) s. masonite. 19-Oct-3 Subastas Odalys, Caracas #59/R
£897 $1615 €1310 Nude (65x43cm-26x17in) s. masonite. 25-Apr-4 Subastas Odalys, Caracas #67/R
£1141 $1940 €1666 Yare Devil (71x51cm-28x20in) s. masonite painted 1961. 23-Nov-3 Subastas Odalys, Caracas #83/R
£1316 $2395 €1974 Untitled (69x47cm-27x19in) s. cardboard. 21-Jun-4 Subastas Odalys, Caracas #65/R
Sculpture
£3434 $6250 €5151 Magic thing (47x47x7cm-19x19x3in) s. acrylic metal panel exec.1970. 21-Jun-4 Subastas Odalys, Caracas #97/R
Works on paper
£242 $445 €353 Untitled (30x20cm-12x8in) s. mixed media card. 28-Mar-4 Subastas Odalys, Caracas #119
£516 $950 €774 Figure (35x52cm-14x20in) s. mixed media exec.1956. 27-Jun-4 Subastas Odalys, Caracas #32
£1133 $2085 €1700 Woman (70x49cm-28x19in) s. mixed media paper on panel exec.1986. 27-Jun-4 Subastas Odalys, Caracas #13/R
£6453 $10970 €9421 Magical object (63x42cm-25x17in) s. mixed media card exec.1970. 23-Nov-3 Subastas Odalys, Caracas #144/R est:12000

ABRIL, Ben (1923-1995) American
£688 $1300 €1004 Farm and horses in rolling Calif landscape (61x91cm-24x36in) s. prov. 17-Feb-4 John Moran, Pasadena #152/R

ABSOLON, John (1815-1895) British
Works on paper
£250 $450 €365 Landscape with harvesters resting. Man seated asleep (16x24cm-6x9in) W/C double-sided prov. 21-Jan-4 Doyle, New York #13
£280 $529 €409 Mother and child in an interior by a fire (33x43cm-13x17in) s. W/C. 19-Feb-4 Richardson & Smith, Whitby #358
£3000 $5490 €4380 Reapers at rest (28x37cm-11x15in) s. W/C. 7-Apr-4 Woolley & Wallis, Salisbury #174/R est:3000-3500

ABSOLON, Kurt (1925-1958) Austrian
Works on paper
£1611 $2883 €2400 Bird (32x48cm-13x19in) s.d.1955 pen brush Indian ink prov. 25-May-4 Dorotheum, Vienna #221/R est:2600-3400
£1958 $3329 €2800 Landscape (43x30cm-17x12in) s.d.1950 mixed media. 28-Nov-3 Wiener Kunst Auktionen, Vienna #606/R est:1000-2000
£3356 $6007 €5000 Wild cat with raised hand (39x57cm-15x22in) s.d.1953 pen Indian ink wash. 25-May-4 Dorotheum, Vienna #220/R est:5000-7000
£3497 $5944 €5000 Don Quixote (35x47cm-14x19in) s.d.1961 mixed media. 28-Nov-3 Wiener Kunst Auktionen, Vienna #607/R est:2000-4000
£3846 $6538 €5500 Pittoresk (43x30cm-17x12in) s.i.d.1951 pen Indian ink W/C. 26-Nov-3 Dorotheum, Vienna #186/R est:5000-7000

ABT, Otto (1903-1982) Swiss
£1042 $1740 €1500 Portrait de femme (41x33cm-16x13in) s. 21-Oct-3 Artcurial Briest, Paris #214b/R est:1800-2200

ACCARDI, Carla (1924-) Italian
£669 $1111 €950 Nerorosso (15x10cm-6x4in) s. tempera paper. 14-Jun-3 Meeting Art, Vercelli #511
£1014 $1664 €1400 Untitled (46x63cm-18x25in) s.d.64 tempera paper pair. 27-May-3 Sotheby's, Milan #212 est:1000-1500
£1087 $1783 €1500 Composition (25x35cm-10x14in) s. tempera paper. 29-May-3 Galleria Pace, Milan #70/R est:2000
£1304 $2139 €1800 Untitled (24x32cm-9x13in) s.d.2000 verso tempera paper. 30-May-3 Farsetti, Prato #24/R
£1304 $2139 €1800 Untitled (35x51cm-14x20in) s.d.1986 tempera on wall paper. 30-May-3 Farsetti, Prato #45/R
£1304 $2139 €1800 Untitled (35x51cm-14x20in) s.d.86 tempera on wall paper. 30-May-3 Farsetti, Prato #267/R
£1667 $2633 €2400 Purple and green (20x30cm-8x12in) vinyl. 6-Sep-3 Meeting Art, Vercelli #345 est:2000
£2013 $3725 €3000 Green, pink (38x57cm-15x22in) s. s.i.verso tempera paper painted 1990. 11-Mar-4 Galleria Pace, Milan #86/R est:3300-4300
£3521 $5845 €5000 White black (50x70cm-20x28in) s.i.d.2002 verso vinyl canvas. 14-Jun-3 Meeting Art, Vercelli #73/R est:5000
£3846 $6538 €5500 Untitled (66x86cm-26x34in) s.d.88 s.i.d.verso prov. 25-Nov-3 Sotheby's, Milan #13/R est:4000-6000
£4161 $7448 €6200 Untitled (50x70cm-20x28in) s.d.2000 vinyl exhib.lit. 28-May-4 Farsetti, Prato #332/R est:4000-5000
£5405 $9514 €8000 Two sectors (50x40cm-20x16in) s.d.97 s.i.d.verso prov. 24-May-4 Christie's, Milan #110/R est:2500-3500
£6522 $10696 €9000 Joyful colours (100x130cm-39x51in) s.d.1990 s.i.d.verso vinyl prov.lit. 27-May-3 Sotheby's, Milan #1/R est:8000-10000
£6643 $11294 €9500 Composition 313 (70x50cm-28x20in) s.d.1962 tempera casein. 26-Nov-3 Pandolfini, Florence #68/R est:10000-12000
£7047 $12614 €10500 Orange, green, purple (70x90cm-28x35in) s.d.1992 s.i.d.verso vinyl lit. 30-May-4 Meeting Art, Vercelli #18 est:8000
£7383 $13215 €11000 Planet (48x67cm-19x26in) s.d.59 tempera casein paper on canvas lit. 28-May-4 Farsetti, Prato #270/R est:9000-11000
£8966 $14972 €13000 Negative (40x60cm-16x24in) s. painted 1956 vinyl. 14-Nov-3 Farsetti, Prato #301/R est:5500-6500
Works on paper
£397 $723 €600 Untitled (24x33cm-9x13in) s. mixed media. 17-Jun-4 Galleria Pananti, Florence #547/R
£690 $1152 €1000 Composition (24x34cm-9x13in) s.d.1993. 17-Nov-3 Sant Agostino, Torino #47/R
£3221 $5766 €4800 Red-black (50x40cm-20x16in) s.d.1997 casein on canvas. 28-May-4 Farsetti, Prato #315/R est:3600-4000
£3803 $6313 €5400 Composition (35x48cm-14x19in) s.d.1951 s.verso W/C cardboard on canvas. 14-Jun-3 Meeting Art, Vercelli #345/R est:4000

ACCONCI, Vito (1940-) American
Photographs
£8451 $14620 €12000 My turn (50x99cm-20x39in) s.i.d.1970 photograph pastel graffiti in 4 parts prov. 9-Dec-3 Artcurial Briest, Paris #437/R est:8000-12000
£11500 $20930 €16790 Two point piece (129x104cm-51x41in) s.i.d.Aug 3 1969 i.verso gelatin silver prints 2 in 5 parts prov. 6-Feb-4 Sotheby's, London #125/R est:8000-12000
Works on paper
£1611 $2900 €2352 Diagram for Instant house (16x20cm-6x8in) init.i.d.1980 ink graphite diptych prov. 24-Apr-4 David Rago, Lambertville #17/R est:400-600

ACEBAL Y DIGORAS, Arturo (1912-1978) Argentinian
£493 $863 €700 Valley (45x53cm-18x21in) s.d.51. 16-Dec-3 Durán, Madrid #651/R

ACERBI, Ezechiele (1850-1920) Italian
£704 $1218 €1000 Seamstress (16x10cm-6x4in) cardboard on canvas lit. 10-Dec-3 Sotheby's, Milan #41/R

ACERBI, Mario (1887-?) Italian
£530 $964 €800 Portrait of woman (63x47cm-25x19in) s. board oval. 17-Jun-4 Finarte Semenzato, Milan #315

ACEVEDO, Miguel (1947-) Spanish
£638 $1066 €900 Cliffs in La Coruna (30x60cm-12x24in) s. 20-Oct-3 Durán, Madrid #212/R

ACEVES, Tomas (19th C) Spanish
£4255 $7106 €6000 L'Alcazar, Seville (80x61cm-31x24in) s.i.d.91. 16-Jun-3 Gros & Delettrez, Paris #449/R est:4500-6000

ACHA, Juan Antonio de (1908-) Spanish?
£319 $533 €450 Barcos (81x100cm-32x39in) s. 23-Jun-3 Durán, Madrid #666/R

ACHARD, Jean Alexis (1807-1884) French
£1600 $2912 €2400 Summer landscape (15x24cm-6x9in) s. panel. 1-Jul-4 Van Ham, Cologne #1190/R est:900

ACHEFF, William (1947-) American
£10056 $18000 €14682 Pot Person (28x41cm-11x16in) 15-May-4 Altermann Galleries, Santa Fe #127/R
£16760 $30000 €24470 From earlier days (84x76cm-33x30in) 15-May-4 Altermann Galleries, Santa Fe #128/R
£20053 $37500 €29277 Blue is the night (61x56cm-24x22in) s. 24-Jul-4 Coeur d'Alene, Hayden #47/R est:25000-30000
£20053 $37500 €29277 Zuni medicine (66x76cm-26x30in) s. prov. 24-Jul-4 Coeur d'Alene, Hayden #155/R est:30000-50000
£29412 $50000 €42942 Yesterday (66x117cm-26x46in) 1-Nov-3 Altermann Galleries, Santa Fe #91

ACHEN, Georg (1860-1912) Danish
£302 $541 €441 From Frederiksberg Garden (25x34cm-10x13in) s.d.86. 12-Jan-4 Rasmussen, Vejle #453 (D.KR 3200)
£403 $726 €588 Portrait of Erik Skram (69x49cm-27x19in) s.d.90 panel. 24-Apr-4 Rasmussen, Havnen #2018 (D.KR 4500)
£841 $1329 €1219 Peasant girl in beech wood in sunshine (46x50cm-18x20in) s. exhib. 2-Sep-3 Rasmussen, Copenhagen #1660/R (D.KR 9000)
£4196 $7007 €6000 Young woman reading in sunny interior (58x66cm-23x26in) s.d.96. 28-Jun-3 Bolland & Marotz, Bremen #608/R est:4900

ACHENBACH, Andreas (1815-1910) German
£851 $1523 €1242 Southern village with figures by mountain lake (40x54cm-16x21in) s.d.1846. 12-Jan-4 Rasmussen, Vejle #429/R (D.KR 9000)
£1724 $2879 €2500 Storm off Dutch coast (14x18cm-6x7in) s.d.99 panel. 15-Nov-3 Lempertz, Koln #1571/R est:2500
£1806 $2943 €2600 River landscape (27x41cm-11x16in) s. panel. 24-Sep-3 Neumeister, Munich #378/R est:2000
£2450 $4460 €3700 Departing fishermen on a stormy day (26x36cm-10x14in) s.d.1870 board. 18-Jun-4 Bolland & Marotz, Bremen #573/R est:2900
£2817 $4873 €4000 Landscape with farmstead in trees (21x15cm-8x6in) s. panel. 13-Dec-3 Lempertz, Koln #1/R est:3000
£3919 $6897 €5800 Scillian coast (26x37cm-10x15in) mono. 22-May-4 Lempertz, Koln #1475/R est:3000
£8028 $12924 €11721 Dutch harbour scene in moonlight (84x105cm-33x41in) s.d.71. 25-Aug-3 Lilla Bukowskis, Stockholm #579 est:25000-30000 (S.KR 105000)

Works on paper
£6294 $10699 €9000 Camp San Rocco (70x56cm-28x22in) mono. W/C gouache. 20-Nov-3 Van Ham, Cologne #1450/R est:7500

ACHENBACH, Andreas (attrib) (1815-1910) German
£318 $525 €461 Untitled, ships passing lighthouse, coming into harbour at dusk (53x38cm-21x15in) init.d.1887. 7-Jul-3 Schrager Galleries, Milwaukee #1558
£4161 $7740 €6200 Winter landscape with horse-drawn sleigh (56x100cm-22x39in) mono.d.1855. 5-Mar-4 Wendl, Rudolstadt #3550/R est:5800

ACHENBACH, Oswald (1827-1905) German
£1333 $2427 €2000 Study of a hilly landscape (17x33cm-7x13in) s.d.1848 canvas on board. 1-Jul-4 Van Ham, Cologne #1191/R est:1500
£2013 $3745 €3000 Above the Bay of Naples in evening (60x46cm-24x18in) 6-Mar-4 Arnold, Frankfurt #679 est:6000
£3200 $5792 €4800 Fisherwomen on southern Italian coast (24x22cm-9x9in) s. 1-Apr-4 Van Ham, Cologne #1268/R est:4600
£3356 $6174 €5000 Evening grape harvest by Italian mountain lake (48x62cm-19x24in) s. 26-Mar-4 Bolland & Marotz, Bremen #478/R est:9000
£4161 $7656 €6200 Campagna farmstead (50x40cm-20x16in) s. 26-Mar-4 Bolland & Marotz, Bremen #479/R est:2000
£10490 $17832 €15000 Fishing boats returning home on Amalfi coast (41x33cm-16x13in) s. 20-Nov-3 Van Ham, Cologne #1452/R est:6200
£18000 $33120 €27000 Waterfall with two bathers (32x26cm-13x10in) s.d.1851. 12-Jun-4 Villa Grisebach, Berlin #100/R est:9000-12000
Works on paper
£533 $965 €800 Two herders in autumn sun (13x20cm-5x8in) s. W/C. 1-Apr-4 Van Ham, Cologne #1266

ACHENBACH, Rosa (1817-?) German
Works on paper
£369 $679 €550 Romantic landscape in the Campagna (32x53cm-13x21in) s.d.1833 mixed media. 24-Mar-4 Hugo Ruef, Munich #1169

ACHER, Ernest (1890-?) Czechoslovakian
£861 $1567 €1300 Vue de Cassis (60x73cm-24x29in) s. 16-Jun-4 Claude Boisgirard, Paris #17

ACHILLES, Ferdinand (attrib) (?) German?
£1200 $2220 €1752 Landscape, believed to be Altona, Hamburg (74x94cm-29x37in) 10-Feb-4 Bonhams, Knightsbridge #75/R est:1000-1500

ACHINI, Angelo (1850-1930) Italian
£4072 $6516 €5945 Church interior with family (85x121cm-33x48in) s. 16-Sep-3 Philippe Schuler, Zurich #3300/R est:6000-8000 (S.FR 9000)
£8145 $13032 €11892 Christening (116x97cm-46x38in) s. 16-Sep-3 Philippe Schuler, Zurich #3301/R est:6000-8000 (S.FR 18000)
Works on paper
£933 $1717 €1400 Portrait de jeune fille (48x41cm-19x16in) s. W/C. 9-Jun-4 Oger, Dumont, Paris #42
£1057 $1659 €1543 Admiration (89x92cm-35x36in) s. W/C hardboard. 1-Sep-3 Shapiro, Sydney #340/R est:2500-3500 (A.D 2600)

ACHT, René-Charles (1920-) Swiss
£189 $325 €276 Tourbillon jaune (74x91cm-29x36in) s.i.d.1960 verso. 7-Dec-3 Treadway Gallery, Cincinnati #726/R
£400 $652 €584 Study in oil, blue and grey (89x114cm-35x45in) s.d.1959 prov. 23-Sep-3 John Nicholson, Haslemere #169

ACKE, Johan Axel Gustaf (1859-1924) Swedish
£3846 $6615 €5615 Coastal landscape from Lerici Bay, Italy (83x121cm-33x48in) s.d.1900. 3-Dec-3 AB Stockholms Auktionsverk #2242/R est:30000-35000 (S.KR 50000)
£6358 $11000 €9283 Leander's body washed ashore (120x178cm-47x70in) indis sig.d.1884 prov.exhib. 11-Dec-3 Sotheby's, New York #151/R est:7000-9000

ACKEIN, Marcelle (1882-1952) French
Works on paper
£268 $497 €400 Marocaines assises (13x16cm-5x6in) chl pastel exhib. 15-Mar-4 Gros & Delettrez, Paris #98/R
£1678 $3104 €2500 Flutiste Marocain (62x48cm-24x19in) s. chl. 15-Mar-4 Gros & Delettrez, Paris #96/R est:2500-3500

ACKER, Florimond van (1858-1940) Belgian
£699 $1189 €1000 Portrait d'un homme et d'une femme (70x57cm-28x22in) pair. 1-Dec-3 Amberes, Antwerp #358
Works on paper
£441 $700 €644 With mother (36x56cm-14x22in) s.i. W/C gouache. 12-Sep-3 Skinner, Boston #231/R

ACKER, Johannes Baptista van (1794-1863) Flemish
Works on paper
£223 $373 €323 Portrait d'homme (15x11cm-6x4in) s. W/C oval. 17-Jun-3 Pinneys, Montreal #75 (C.D 500)

ACKERBERG, A (19th C) Danish?
£561 $886 €813 Epiphyllum hybridum (31x23cm-12x9in) s.d.1881. 2-Sep-3 Rasmussen, Copenhagen #1716/R (D.KR 6000)

ACKERMAN, Paul (1908-1981) French
£267 $477 €400 Dans la synagogue (116x146cm-46x57in) st.sig. 17-May-4 Chayette & Cheval, Paris #24
£267 $477 €400 Main de Dieu (125x205cm-49x81in) s. i.verso. 17-May-4 Chayette & Cheval, Paris #52/R
£276 $497 €400 Quete de l'Absolu (55x69cm-22x27in) s. paper on panel. 25-Jan-4 Chayette & Cheval, Paris #110
£345 $621 €500 Jour se leve (100x68cm-39x27in) s. paper on panel. 25-Jan-4 Chayette & Cheval, Paris #109
£347 $621 €520 Voyage (81x100cm-32x39in) st.sig. 17-May-4 Chayette & Cheval, Paris #83/R
£362 $666 €550 Composition (65x54cm-26x21in) s. 27-Jun-4 Versailles Encheres #3
£367 $656 €550 Abstract (92x155cm-36x61in) st.sig. 17-May-4 Chayette & Cheval, Paris #31
£413 $740 €620 Paysage de glace (98x130cm-39x51in) st.sig. 17-May-4 Chayette & Cheval, Paris #74/R
£433 $776 €650 Paysage de montagne (116x146cm-46x57in) st.sig. 17-May-4 Chayette & Cheval, Paris #82
£533 $955 €800 Abstract (83x205cm-33x81in) s. 17-May-4 Chayette & Cheval, Paris #29/R
£552 $993 €800 Decouverte d'un autre monde (64x100cm-25x39in) s. paper on panel. 25-Jan-4 Chayette & Cheval, Paris #108
£733 $1313 €1100 Phare. Soleil levant (72x100cm-28x39in) st.sig. pair. 17-May-4 Chayette & Cheval, Paris #91
£769 $1308 €1100 Portrait d'homme (37x26cm-15x10in) s. panel. 27-Nov-3 Calmels Cohen, Paris #58/R
£800 $1472 €1200 Paysage (65x81cm-26x32in) st.sig. prov. 9-Jun-4 Beaussant & Lefèvre, Paris #94/R
Works on paper
£243 $406 €350 Batisseurs (45x49cm-18x19in) s. gouache. 21-Oct-3 Artcurial Briest, Paris #315

ACKERMAN, Robert (20th C) American?
£189 $350 €276 Untitled (305x183cm-120x72in) 18-Jan-4 Bonhams & Butterfields, Los Angeles #7039/R

ACKERMANN, Franz (1963-) German
£98000 $178360 €143080 Untitled - mental map, Evasion III (280x285cm-110x112in) s.i.d.96 verso prov. 4-Feb-4 Christie's, London #1/R est:35000-45000

ACKERMANN, Gerald (1876-1960) British
Works on paper
£300 $546 €438 Sienna (24x35cm-9x14in) s. i.verso pen ink W/C prov.exhib. 15-Jun-4 Rosebery Fine Art, London #500
£340 $609 €496 Haymaking with cathedral beyond (23x38cm-9x15in) s. W/C. 13-May-4 Mitchells, Cockermouth #1010
£400 $736 €584 Cloud over a North Norfolk estuary (9x12cm-4x5in) s. W/C. 11-Jun-4 Keys, Aylsham #561
£410 $705 €599 Open landscape with figures in chalk pit (30x48cm-12x19in) W/C. 5-Dec-3 Keys, Aylsham #561
£420 $777 €613 Castle in a landscape (17x24cm-7x9in) s. W/C over pencil. 14-Jan-4 Lawrence, Crewkerne #1351
£650 $1190 €949 Still life of white anemones in a vase (29x23cm-11x9in) s. W/C pencil. 7-Apr-4 Woolley & Wallis, Salisbury #57/R
£700 $1106 €1015 Cley mill, Norfolk (23x35cm-9x14in) s. W/C. 3-Sep-3 Bonhams, Bury St Edmunds #328
£750 $1290 €1095 Sailing at Blakeney (24x36cm-9x14in) s. W/C prov. 7-Dec-3 Lots Road Auctions, London #352
£800 $1376 €1168 Boats at Blakeney, Norfolk (23x36cm-9x14in) s. W/C. 5-Dec-3 Keys, Aylsham #562/R
£800 $1464 €1168 Still life of primulas in a vase (29x23cm-11x9in) s. W/C pencil. 7-Apr-4 Woolley & Wallis, Salisbury #56/R
£850 $1556 €1241 Still life of roses in a vase (24x24cm-9x9in) s. W/C pencil. 7-Apr-4 Woolley & Wallis, Salisbury #59/R
£850 $1556 €1241 Still life of white primulas in a vase (25x22cm-10x9in) s. W/C pencil. 7-Apr-4 Woolley & Wallis, Salisbury #60/R
£1400 $2590 €2044 Boats on an estuary (17x24cm-7x9in) s. W/C pencil. 14-Jan-4 Lawrence, Crewkerne #1352/R est:500-700
£1500 $2745 €2190 Still life of anemones in a blue and white jug (32x29cm-13x11in) s. W/C pencil. 7-Apr-4 Woolley & Wallis, Salisbury #58/R est:800-1200
£1500 $2685 €2190 Woodbridge Suffolk (23x36cm-9x14in) s. W/C. 7-May-4 Mallams, Oxford #239/R est:1500-2000
£1700 $3043 €2482 Woodbridge the Quay (23x36cm-9x14in) s. W/C. 7-May-4 Mallams, Oxford #240/R est:1500-2000
£1700 $3043 €2482 Blakeney Regatta. High water - Overy Staithe (23x35cm-9x14in) s. pencil W/C pair prov. 26-May-4 Christie's, Kensington #483/R est:700-900
£1900 $3534 €2774 Gloucester Cathedral (24x35cm-9x14in) s. W/C exhib. 2-Mar-4 Bearnes, Exeter #324/R est:600-800

ACKERMANN, Johann Adam (1780-1853) German
Works on paper
£2465 $4264 €3500 Paysage animes (29x45cm-11x18in) s.d.1799 W/C black crayon pair. 12-Dec-3 Renaud, Paris #122/R est:3000

ACKERMANN, Marguerite (1900-1990) Swiss
£262 $477 €383 Winter landscape (27x22cm-11x9in) s. i.verso cardboard. 16-Jun-4 Fischer, Luzern #2001 (S.FR 600)

ACKERMANN, Max (1887-1975) German
£1342 $2376 €2000 Untitled (48x15cm-19x6in) s.d. pastel. 30-Apr-4 Dr Fritz Nagel, Stuttgart #717/R est:2000
£1528 $2551 €2200 Abstract composition (19x10cm-7x4in) mono.d. pastel. 24-Oct-3 Ketterer, Hamburg #257/R est:3500-3700
£1867 $3379 €2800 Composition (38x56cm-15x22in) i. 2-Apr-4 Dr Fritz Nagel, Leipzig #4020/R est:3200
£2083 $3479 €3000 Untitled - composition with figure (24x33cm-9x13in) oil tempera. 25-Oct-3 Dr Lehr, Berlin #2/R est:6000
£2292 $3735 €3300 Colour composition (65x50cm-26x20in) i. stretcher. 27-Sep-3 Dr Fritz Nagel, Stuttgart #9452/R est:5000

£2333	$4270	€3500	Blue (24x400cm-9x157in) s.i.d. verso oil tempera board prov. 5-Jun-4 Lempertz, Koln #562/R est:4000-5000
£2400	$4392	€3600	Untersee (24x34cm-9x13in) s. oil tempera board prov. 5-Jun-4 Lempertz, Koln #561/R est:4000-5000
£2400	$4392	€3600	Improvisation on orange (22x31cm-9x12in) s.i.d. verso oil tempera prov. 5-Jun-4 Lempertz, Koln #563/R est:4000-5000
£2667	$4800	€4000	Composition (24x20cm-9x8in) s.d.1953 verso pastel chk on panel. 26-Apr-4 Rieber, Stuttgart #1153/R est:4950
£2667	$4773	€4000	Composition in blue (48x31cm-19x12in) s.d.2.7.65 s.d. verso oil chk scratched board prov. 14-May-4 Ketterer, Munich #257/R est:5000-6000
£2917	$4813	€4200	Composition (50x32cm-20x13in) s.d.73. 5-Jul-3 Geble, Radolfzell #440/R est:4200
£3472	$5729	€5000	Untersee on autumn morning (51x72cm-20x28in) s. i.d.1942 verso board. 5-Jul-3 Geble, Radolfzell #439/R est:5800
£4000	$7360	€6000	Studio scene (22x32cm-9x13in) s.i.d.1946 paper on cardboard prov. 12-Jun-4 Villa Grisebach, Berlin #333/R est:4500-6000
£6335	$10769	€9249	Vertical movement (54x38cm-21x15in) s.d.49 i.verso board prov. 22-Nov-3 Burkhard, Luzern #113/R est:15000-18000 (S.FR 14000)
£8145	$13846	€11892	America (55x37cm-22x15in) s.d.1951 verso canvas on board. 22-Nov-3 Burkhard, Luzern #112/R est:15000-18000 (S.FR 18000)
£9028	$15076	€13000	Untitled - couple in street (88x44cm-35x17in) s.d. stretcher oil tempera. 25-Oct-3 Dr Lehr, Berlin #1/R est:9000
£11189	$19021	€16000	Picture 31/1950 (64x53cm-25x21in) s.d.1950 i. verso panel. 29-Nov-3 Arnold, Frankfurt #7/R est:6000
Works on paper			
£347	$566	€500	Composition in black (31x24cm-12x9in) s.d.1945 chk typing paper. 27-Sep-3 Dr Fritz Nagel, Stuttgart #9022/R
£360	$590	€500	Geometric composition (25x16cm-10x6in) s.d. s.i.d. verso graphite. 4-Jun-3 Ketterer, Hamburg #116/R
£890	$1514	€1300	Bathers (25x18cm-10x7in) mono.d.39 chl. 8-Nov-3 Geble, Radolfzell #809/R
£909	$1564	€1300	Untitled (50x32cm-20x13in) s.d.1973 i.verso chk. 4-Dec-3 Van Ham, Cologne #3/R
£1141	$2019	€1700	Composition in blue (49x31cm-19x12in) s.d.29.III.62 pastel. 30-Apr-4 Dr Fritz Nagel, Stuttgart #714/R est:3000
£1208	$2138	€1800	Untitled (21x24cm-8x9in) s.d. pastel. 30-Apr-4 Dr Fritz Nagel, Stuttgart #716/R est:3300
£1333	$2400	€2000	Untitled (31x48cm-12x19in) s.d.1974 pastel. 26-Apr-4 Rieber, Stuttgart #1156/R est:2950
£1549	$2479	€2200	Untitled (28x22cm-11x9in) s.d.1957 pastel. 18-Sep-3 Rieber, Stuttgart #972/R est:2980
£1867	$3416	€2800	Abstract composition (24x15cm-9x6in) s.d.54 pastel chk. 5-Jun-4 Lempertz, Koln #564/R est:2500
£1879	$3364	€2800	Untitled (16x25cm-6x10in) s.i.d.1947 verso mixed media. 25-May-4 Karl & Faber, Munich #188/R est:3600
£1944	$3169	€2800	Composition in blue (32x24cm-13x9in) s.d.1973 pastel. 27-Sep-3 Dr Fritz Nagel, Stuttgart #9450/R est:2800
£2000	$3600	€3000	Untitled (25x17cm-10x7in) pastel. 26-Apr-4 Rieber, Stuttgart #1155/R est:2980
£2083	$3396	€3000	Composition (50x35cm-20x14in) s.d.1983 pastel. 27-Sep-3 Dr Fritz Nagel, Stuttgart #9451/R est:2400
£2333	$4177	€3500	Country dance - stained glass project (26x17cm-10x7in) mono. col chk transparent paper prov. 14-May-4 Ketterer, Munich #215/R est:3500-4500
£2349	$4322	€3500	Figures (26x17cm-10x7in) mono. col pastel chk parchment. 26-Mar-4 Ketterer, Hamburg #283/R est:3500-4000
£2708	$4415	€3900	Composition in blue (31x48cm-12x19in) s.d.1972 pastel. 27-Sep-3 Dr Fritz Nagel, Stuttgart #9453/R est:3200
£2740	$4658	€4000	To peace (49x31cm-19x12in) s.d.58 pastel. 8-Nov-3 Geble, Radolfzell #752/R est:4000
£2797	$4811	€4000	Musicians (25x16cm-10x6in) col pastel chk prov. 5-Dec-3 Ketterer, Munich #75/R est:3500-4500

ACKERMANN, Otto (1872-1953) German

£278	$458	€400	Moonlit meadow (45x60cm-18x24in) s. 5-Jul-3 Geble, Radolfzell #442

ACKERMANN, Peter (1934-) German

£559	$951	€800	Towers and roofs (79x59cm-31x23in) s. i.d. 1964. 29-Nov-3 Arnold, Frankfurt #2/R
£909	$1545	€1300	Palazzo (36x35cm-14x14in) s.d.68. 29-Nov-3 Bassenge, Berlin #6602
£1690	$2924	€2400	Composition (75x80cm-30x31in) s.d.69. 13-Dec-3 Lempertz, Koln #107/R est:1500
£2238	$3804	€3200	Theatre (100x90cm-39x35in) s.d.67. 29-Nov-3 Bassenge, Berlin #6601/R est:3500

ACKERMANN, Thomas (1952-) Canadian?

£361	$672	€527	Man practising yoga (137x81cm-54x32in) s.i.d.1999 verso. 2-Mar-4 Ritchie, Toronto #201/R (C.D 900)

ACLAND, Henry Wentworth Dyke (1815-1900) British

Works on paper			
£1342	$2403	€2000	Upper lake of Killarney. Cashel Co. Tipperary. castle of Glenquin, Co. Limerick (27x35cm-11x14in) s.i.d.1842 pen ink W/C set of three. 26-May-4 James Adam, Dublin #20/R est:2000-3000

ACLE, Rosa (1916-1990) Uruguayan

£588	$1000	€858	Composition 56 (52x45cm-20x18in) s.d.89. 25-Nov-3 Galeria y Remates, Montevideo #75/R

ACOSTA LEON, Angel (1932-1964) Cuban

£7986	$13337	€11500	L'horloge (100x82cm-39x32in) s. i.verso panel. 23-Oct-3 Credit Municipal, Paris #78/R est:4000-5000
£13966	$25000	€20390	Horloge (100x82cm-39x32in) s. plywood. 26-May-4 Sotheby's, New York #156/R est:15000-20000
Works on paper			
£1119	$1924	€1600	Hammock (57x75cm-22x30in) s.d.1963 i.verso mixed media ink pencil chl prov. 4-Dec-3 Van Ham, Cologne #291/R est:1600

ACRAMAN, William Henry (fl.1856-1868) British

Works on paper			
£950	$1549	€1378	White cockatoo perched on a tea chest (32x27cm-13x11in) s.d.Nov 24 1852 verso W/C htd. prov. 21-Jul-3 Sotheby's, London #826

ACS, Agostos (1889-1947) Hungarian

£490	$817	€700	Chatting in the village (60x80cm-24x31in) 10-Oct-3 Stadion, Trieste #229
£559	$934	€800	Extensive landscape with figures (75x100cm-30x39in) 10-Oct-3 Stadion, Trieste #230/R
£1389	$2361	€2000	Summer's day in peasant garden (80x133cm-31x52in) s. 28-Oct-3 Dorotheum, Vienna #156 est:2200-2600

ACS, Joe (1936-) Canadian

£215	$359	€314	Hillard grain elevators (23x40cm-9x16in) s.i.d.1972 board. 17-Nov-3 Hodgins, Calgary #260/R (C.D 475)
£260	$476	€380	Elevator in Southern Alberta (30x40cm-12x16in) s.i. acrylic board. 1-Jun-4 Hodgins, Calgary #1/R (C.D 650)

ACTON, Arlo (1933-) American

Sculpture			
£5000	$9000	€7300	Untitled (111cm-44in) wood shoe stretcher. 25-Apr-4 Bonhams & Butterfields, San Francisco #5646/R est:800-1200

ADAM, Albrecht (1786-1862) German

£1119	$1924	€1600	Hungarian horse rider with horse dealer in front of a farm building (9cm-4in circular) s. i.verso copper. 3-Dec-3 Neumeister, Munich #521/R est:900
£19444	$33056	€28000	Spanish riding school (43x49cm-17x19in) s.d.1856 prov. 28-Oct-3 Wiener Kunst Auktionen, Vienna #34/R est:5000-10000
£38000	$69160	€55480	Two Arabian stallions and other horses in an extensive landscape (81x114cm-32x45in) s.d.1816 prov. 15-Jun-4 Sotheby's, London #23/R est:40000-60000
Works on paper			
£32168	$55329	€46000	Battles scenes from the Russian campaign of 1812 (21x29cm-8x11in) five s. W/C ten. 3-Dec-3 Neumeister, Munich #364/R est:22000

ADAM, Benno (1812-1892) German

£993	$1658	€1400	Hunting dog with puppies (15x21cm-6x8in) panel. 17-Oct-3 Berlinghof, Heidelberg #924/R
£1486	$2750	€2170	End of the fox hunt (97x124cm-38x49in) s. d.1860. 15-Jul-4 Sotheby's, New York #74/R est:4000-6000
£3846	$6538	€5500	Portrait of horse in desert (38x48cm-15x19in) mono.d.1854. 24-Nov-3 Dorotheum, Vienna #56/R est:4000-4500
£5667	$10200	€8500	Stable friends (80x107cm-31x42in) s.d.1860 lit. 22-Apr-4 Allgauer, Kempten #3459/R est:9800

ADAM, E (19/20th C) French

£423	$778	€635	Crown Prince Olav (60x92cm-24x36in) s. 14-Jun-4 Blomqvist, Lysaker #1006/R (N.KR 5200)
£1645	$2977	€2500	Portrait du navire Georges Flemming (61x92cm-24x36in) s.d.1902. 19-Apr-4 Boscher, Cherbourg #713/R est:2500-3000

ADAM, Edmond Victor Charles (1868-1938) French

£900	$1440	€1314	The steam and sail ship Cyrus (62x92cm-24x36in) s.d.1899. 16-Sep-3 Rosebery Fine Art, London #485/R
£1357	$2267	€1981	The Milwaukie (62x92cm-24x36in) s.d.1899. 17-Nov-3 Waddingtons, Toronto #200/R est:3000-5000 (C.D 3000)
£9016	$16500	€13524	American bark Guy G Goss (61x91cm-24x36in) s. 29-Jul-4 Eldred, East Dennis #288/R est:10000-12000

ADAM, Edmond Victor Charles (attrib) (1868-1938) French

£524	$964	€765	Seascape (50x69cm-20x27in) s. 14-Jun-4 Philippe Schuler, Zurich #5800 (S.FR 1200)

ADAM, Edouard (1847-1929) French

£482	$883	€704	The regatta (18x35cm-7x14in) s. 2-Feb-4 Blomqvist, Lysaker #1002/R (N.KR 6000)
£945	$1635	€1380	Danish steam ship at sea (48x87cm-19x34in) s.d.1876. 9-Dec-3 Rasmussen, Copenhagen #1485/R (D.KR 10000)
£1200	$2196	€1752	Steam ship on squally seas (61x91cm-24x36in) s.d.1878. 9-Jul-4 Dreweatt Neate, Newbury #403/R est:500-700
£1453	$2500	€2121	Steamship - Wallace D Noyes (58x91cm-23x36in) s.d.1919. 7-Dec-3 Freeman, Philadelphia #31 est:2500-4000
£1500	$2685	€2190	Belgian steamer Cervantes running out of Le Havre (61x91cm-24x36in) s.i.d.1905. 26-May-4 Christie's, Kensington #530/R est:2000-4000
£1667	$2783	€2400	Hirondelle de la mer (61x41cm-24x16in) s.d.1904. 26-Oct-3 Lesieur & Le Bars, Le Havre #89
£1678	$2853	€2400	Mixte ville de St Nicolas (60x92cm-24x36in) s.d.1901. 24-Nov-3 Boscher, Cherbourg #738/R est:2300-3000
£1958	$3329	€2800	German Emperor, navire sous voile au large d'une cote (62x90cm-24x35in) s.d.1876. 23-Nov-3 Claude Boisgirard, Paris #198 est:3000-4000
£2200	$3740	€3212	American clipper being towed into Le Havre (60x91cm-24x36in) s.i.d.1872. 19-Nov-3 Christie's, Kensington #580/R
£2459	$4500	€3590	Cerastes off a point of land (62x91cm-24x36in) s.d.1877. 29-Jul-4 Christie's, Rockefeller NY #261/R est:6000-8000
£2639	$4407	€3800	Le France (60x92cm-24x36in) painted 1912. 26-Oct-3 Lesieur & Le Bars, Le Havre #108
£2793	$5000	€4078	British Barque - Argosy outward bound under full sail (61x91cm-24x36in) s.i.d.1889 prov. 16-Mar-4 Bonhams & Butterfields, San Francisco #6153/R est:3000-5000
£2797	$4755	€4000	Navire de guerre de la marine Haitienne (41x62cm-16x24in) s.d.1886. 23-Nov-3 Claude Boisgirard, Paris #197/R est:4500-6000

ADAM, Edouard (attrib) (1847-1929) French

£1536	$2750	€2243	British Barque - Adelaide running through a gale under reduced sail (61x91cm-24x36in) 16-Mar-4 Bonhams & Butterfields, San Francisco #6149/R est:3000-5000

ADAM, Emil (1843-1924) German

£833	$1317	€1200	Foxhunt (26x36cm-10x14in) s.d.1875 board lit. 19-Sep-3 Schloss Ahlden, Ahlden #1551/R
£5628	$10074	€8217	Portrait of the horse, Rother Stadl and his trainer, John Reeves (72x92cm-28x36in) s.i.d.09. 22-Mar-4 Philippe Schuler, Zurich #4441/R est:4000-6000 (S.FR 13000)
£22535	$36056	€32000	Horses, Indienne, Conception, Chelsea and Awor (44x54cm-17x21in) one s.d.1884 two s.d.1885 one s.d.1886 four. 22-Sep-3 Sotheby's, Amsterdam #262/R est:40000-60000

Works on paper

£252	$403	€350	Etude de cheval, Flair (22x30cm-9x12in) s.i.d.1906 blk crayon htd white chk. 16-May-3 Tajan, Paris #211

ADAM, Eugen (1817-1880) German

£764	$1245	€1100	Roccoco rider with two horses and dog (19x25cm-7x10in) s.i.d.1864 board. 24-Sep-3 Neumeister, Munich #380/R

Works on paper

£2533	$4611	€3800	View of Salzburg (20x30cm-8x12in) i.d.1837 verso W/C lit. 3-Jul-4 Badum, Bamberg #137/R est:4450

ADAM, Franz (1815-1886) German

£22222	$40000	€32444	Stable lad (77x103cm-30x41in) s.d.1860 prov. 23-Apr-4 Sotheby's, New York #36/R est:40000-60000

Works on paper

£300	$540	€450	Horse (22x28cm-9x11in) s. pencil. 24-Apr-4 Reiss & Sohn, Konigstein #5459/R

ADAM, Heinrich (1787-1862) German

Works on paper

£2013	$3705	€3000	Lake Como with Torno (55x71cm-22x28in) s.d.1832 W/C lit. 24-Mar-4 Hugo Ruef, Munich #1170/R est:3000

ADAM, Henri (1864-1917) French

Works on paper

£563	$1025	€850	La chasse a courre (64x90cm-25x35in) s.d.1907 W/C. 16-Jun-4 Renaud, Paris #38/R

ADAM, Joseph Denovan (1842-1896) British

£360	$659	€526	Highland mother (31x46cm-12x18in) sold with two letters. 6-Apr-4 Bonhams, Knightsbridge #39/R
£1050	$1817	€1533	Cattle in a barn (41x61cm-16x24in) s. 10-Dec-3 Bonhams, Bury St Edmunds #578/R est:600-900
£1600	$2864	€2336	Bringing in the herd (50x74cm-20x29in) s. 26-May-4 Sotheby's, Olympia #213/R est:1500-2000
£2800	$5152	€4088	Driving home (70x109cm-28x43in) 11-Jun-4 Christie's, London #195/R est:3000-5000

Works on paper

£2800	$4396	€4060	Island herd (35x50cm-14x20in) s.d.1896 W/C. 27-Aug-3 Sotheby's, London #973/R est:1000-1500

ADAM, Joseph Denovan (jnr) (?-c.1935) British

£3784	$7000	€5525	Confidences - two west highland terriers (38x48cm-15x19in) s.d.19 panel exhib. 10-Feb-4 Doyle, New York #232/R est:3000-5000

ADAM, Julius I (1826-1874) German

Works on paper

£278	$464	€400	Peasant interior (13x17cm-5x7in) s.d. W/C over pencil. 24-Oct-3 Ketterer, Hamburg #121/R

ADAM, Julius II (1852-1913) German

£2639	$4301	€3800	White cat (33x48cm-13x19in) s.d.26.VI.91. 25-Sep-3 Dr Fritz Nagel, Stuttgart #1322/R est:4000
£4491	$7500	€6557	Blue bow (14x20cm-6x8in) s. panel. 7-Oct-3 Sotheby's, New York #121 est:12000-18000
£4491	$7500	€6557	Little fighters (15x20cm-6x8in) s. panel. 7-Oct-3 Sotheby's, New York #125 est:12000-18000
£5430	$9231	€7928	Boy with three cats (19x15cm-7x6in) s.d.1884 panel. 19-Nov-3 Fischer, Luzern #1197/R est:12000-15000 (S.FR 12000)
£12500	$20375	€18000	Five kittens playing in basket (31x46cm-12x18in) s. 24-Sep-3 Neumeister, Munich #381/R est:25000
£16783	$28867	€24000	Five kittens in a basket (23x34cm-9x13in) s. 3-Dec-3 Neumeister, Munich #522/R est:19000

Works on paper

£600	$1074	€900	Study of kitten (8x7cm-3x3in) s.d.15 II 96 pencil. 13-May-4 Bassenge, Berlin #5510/R

ADAM, Luitpold (elder) (1888-1950) German

£267	$488	€400	Farmer with draught-horse in a summer field (74x117cm-29x46in) s.d.1923. 5-Jun-4 Arnold, Frankfurt #523/R
£486	$812	€700	Hay harvest (50x70cm-20x28in) s.d.1940 board lit. 25-Oct-3 Bergmann, Erlangen #957/R

ADAM, Otto (1901-1973) German

£1042	$1719	€1500	Still life with basket, fruit, fish and bottles (50x60cm-20x24in) s. 5-Jul-3 Geble, Radolfzell #444/R est:750

Works on paper

£342	$582	€500	Bodensee landscape (42x54cm-17x21in) s. gouache A/C. 8-Nov-3 Geble, Radolfzell #811/R

ADAM, Patrick William (1854-1929) British

£550	$919	€803	Church in the snow (72x96cm-28x38in) s. 16-Oct-3 Christie's, Kensington #328
£1736	$2760	€2500	Winter, a study (19x35cm-7x14in) canvasboard. 10-Sep-3 James Adam, Dublin #45 est:2200-2800
£2500	$4300	€3650	In the Garden, the Knoll, North Berwick (50x67cm-20x26in) s.prov. 4-Dec-3 Bonhams, Edinburgh #83/R est:6000-8000
£3500	$6335	€5110	Old water pump (35x26cm-14x10in) s. panel. 19-Apr-4 Sotheby's, London #80/R est:3000-4000
£7500	$13425	€10950	The orange room (61x46cm-24x18in) s.d.1923. 28-May-4 Lyon & Turnbull, Edinburgh #86/R est:2000-3000
£45000	$81450	€65700	Study, Ardilea, North Berwick (92x68cm-36x27in) s.d.1917. 19-Apr-4 Sotheby's, London #82/R est:50000-70000

Works on paper

£320	$550	€467	Continental garden (39x27cm-15x11in) s. W/C. 4-Dec-3 Bonhams, Edinburgh #75

ADAM, Richard Benno (1873-1937) German

£3667	$6637	€5500	Woman on horse (56x70cm-22x28in) s.d.1912. 1-Apr-4 Van Ham, Cologne #1272/R est:5000

ADAM, Richard Benno (attrib) (1873-1937) German

£671	$1235	€1000	Oberammergau (45x60cm-18x24in) 24-Mar-4 Hugo Ruef, Munich #915

ADAM, Victor Edouard (19/20th C) French?

£3077	$5231	€4400	The Paolo T sailing (61x91cm-24x36in) s.i.d.1900. 18-Nov-3 Cambi, Genoa #421/R est:3500-4500

ADAM, William (1846-1931) American

£250	$400	€365	Campbell House, Saratoga. s. canvasboard. 20-Sep-3 Harvey Clar, Oakland #1329
£1176	$2000	€1717	Monterey coastal (30x38cm-12x15in) s. canvasboard prov. 18-Nov-3 John Moran, Pasadena #198 est:1500-2000
£1923	$3500	€2808	Gate in flower garden (25x30cm-10x12in) s. canvasboard prov. 15-Jun-4 John Moran, Pasadena #20 est:3000-4000

ADAMETZ, Heinrich Emil (1884-1971) German

£389	$724	€580	Boat builders at work (84x111cm-33x44in) s.d.54 i.verso. 5-Mar-4 Wendl, Rudolstadt #3551/R
£524	$902	€750	Rower (72x99cm-28x39in) s.d.1931. 4-Dec-3 Van Ham, Cologne #4

ADAMI, Franco (1933-) Italian

Sculpture

£2703	$4757	€4000	Rhinoceros (50x24x22cm-20x9x9in) s. base black marble exec 1983 prov.lit. 18-May-4 Tajan, Paris #97/R est:4000-5000

ADAMI, Valerio (1935-) Italian

£2797	$4755	€4000	Police notice (49x63cm-19x25in) s.d.1973 tempera card. 20-Nov-3 Finarte Semenzato, Milan #219/R est:8000-8500
£3041	$5351	€4500	Structure for figure (60x50cm-24x20in) s.i.verso prov. 24-May-4 Christie's, Milan #178/R est:5000-7000
£3793	$6069	€5500	Chevalier a la rose (60x50cm-24x20in) s.i.verso acrylic. 13-Mar-3 Galleria Pace, Milan #151/R est:7200-9200
£3931	$6565	€5700	Untitled (73x92cm-29x36in) s.i.d.1964. 17-Nov-3 Sant Agostino, Torino #294/R est:5000-6000
£5000	$9100	€7300	Soweto - the beginning of the end (90x67cm-35x26in) s.stretcher s.i.verso acrylic painted 1993 prov. 4-Feb-4 Sotheby's, Olympia #224/R est:3000-4000
£5282	$8768	€7500	Untitled (73x91cm-29x36in) s.verso acrylic. 11-Jun-3 Finarte Semenzato, Milan #582/R
£5369	$9933	€8000	Study for Red Cross (50x61cm-20x24in) s.i.verso acrylic painted 1998. 11-Mar-4 Galleria Pace, Milan #126/R est:11000-14000
£5594	$9510	€8000	Figure (92x73cm-36x29in) s.d.64 prov. 20-Nov-3 Finarte Semenzato, Milan #227/R est:4000-5000
£5705	$10097	€8500	Valmy (146x66cm-57x26in) i. s.i.verso acrylic painted 1989 prov. 28-Apr-4 Artcurial Briest, Paris #393/R est:10000-12000
£6040	$10812	€9000	Centaure (81x60cm-32x24in) s.i.verso. 30-May-4 Meeting Art, Vercelli #48 est:9000
£6333	$11400	€9500	Camel (81x100cm-32x39in) s.i. acrylic. 24-Apr-4 Cornette de St.Cyr, Paris #416/R est:10000-12000
£6711	$12013	€10000	Crash on the corner (73x92cm-29x36in) s. i.d.65 prov. 25-May-4 Sotheby's, Milan #165/R est:10000-15000
£7042	$12183	€10000	Relax (73x92cm-29x36in) s.i.d.1966 verso. 14-Dec-3 Versailles Encheres #164/R est:12000-15000
£8123	$14946	€11860	Le retour du fils prodigue (198x147cm-78x58in) init. s.verso. 29-Mar-4 Rasmussen, Copenhagen #156/R est:125000-150000 (D.KR 90000)
£8667	$15947	€13000	Great Moghul (97x74cm-38x29in) s. painted 1994 lit. 12-Jun-4 Meeting Art, Vercelli #390/R est:10000
£9091	$15182	€13000	Study for pornography scene (81x65cm-32x26in) s.i.d.1966-67 verso prov. 29-Jun-3 Versailles Encheres #168/R
£9091	$15455	€13000	La visite (98x129cm-39x51in) s.i.verso acrylic prov. 25-Nov-3 Tajan, Paris #78/R est:10000-12000
£9155	$16021	€13000	North South (130x97cm-51x38in) s.i.d.72 verso acrylic prov. 16-Dec-3 Porro, Milan #38/R est:10000-12000
£9790	$16643	€14000	Apres-midi d'un faune (129x97cm-51x38in) s.i.verso acrylic prov. 25-Nov-3 Tajan, Paris #79/R est:10000-12000
£11888	$20210	€17000	Gym (81x64cm-32x25in) s.i.d.1968 verso acrylic. 20-Nov-3 Finarte Semenzato, Milan #222/R est:7000-8000
£15000	$27300	€21900	Angelus (147x198cm-58x78in) s.i.d.28.5.78 and 28.9.78 verso acrylic prov.exhib. 6-Feb-4 Sotheby's, London #219/R est:15000-20000
£19580	$32699	€28000	La Domenica di Amburgo (198x147cm-78x58in) s.i.d.17/08/71-1/9/71 verso prov.exhib. 11-Oct-3 Cornette de St.Cyr, Paris #26/R est:20000-30000
£23611	$38958	€34000	La piscina (195x130cm-77x51in) s.i.d.18-2-66 verso prov. 2-Jul-3 Cornette de St.Cyr, Paris #121/R est:35000-40000

Works on paper

£352	$616	€500	Nineteen September (47x66cm-19x26in) s.d.1962 wax crayon tempera. 16-Dec-3 Finarte Semenzato, Milan #144/R
£542	$996	€791	Sunset (47x35cm-19x14in) s.d.2.2.84 pencil. 29-Mar-4 Rasmussen, Copenhagen #363/R (D.KR 6000)
£652	$1070	€900	Interior (36x45cm-14x18in) s.i.d.60 graphite tempera prov. 27-May-3 Sotheby's, Milan #2
£1056	$1754	€1500	La Valle del Petrolio (48x66cm-19x26in) s.d.1963 mixed media. 14-Jun-3 Meeting Art, Vercelli #69/R est:1500
£1208	$2162	€1800	Show (49x67cm-19x26in) s.i.d.61 pencil. 25-May-4 Sotheby's, Milan #103 est:1500
£1333	$2440	€2000	Il cane (35x47cm-14x19in) s.d.7/9/70 crayon. 7-Jun-4 Palais de Beaux Arts, Brussels #147 est:600-800
£2028	$3488	€2900	Sans titre (73x53cm-29x21in) s.d.1977 W/C prov. 3-Dec-3 Fraysse & Associes, Paris #100/R est:3000-3800
£2897	$4837	€4200	Tennis players (76x56cm-30x22in) s. gouache card. 13-Nov-3 Galleria Pace, Milan #64/R est:6200
£12319	$20203	€17000	Mirage (114x146cm-45x57in) s.i.d.65 verso liquitex on canvas prov. 27-May-3 Sotheby's, Milan #295/R est:18000-25000

ADAMS, Ansel (1902-1984) American

Photographs

£1657	$3000	€2419	Western landscape with triple rock formation (38x48cm-15x19in) s.num.V/1 77/110 black white photograph. 3-Apr-4 David Rago, Lambertville #103/R est:900-1400
£1693	$3200	€2472	Grass and pool (18x23cm-7x9in) s. gelatin silver print executed 1935. 17-Feb-4 Christie's, Rockefeller NY #121/R est:3000-5000
£1796	$3000	€2622	Snow in orchard, Yosemite Valley (37x48cm-15x19in) s. gelatin silver print exec.1947/1970. 21-Oct-3 Bonhams & Butterfields, San Francisco #1478/R
£1852	$3500	€2704	White Mountains, from the Buttermilk Country (19x24cm-7x9in) s. i.verso gelatin silver print. 17-Feb-4 Christie's, Rockefeller NY #122/R est:2000-3000
£1916	$3200	€2797	Dune, White Sands National Monument, New Mexico (34x26cm-13x10in) s. i.verso gelatin silver print exec.c.1942 printed c.1980 lit. 20-Oct-3 Christie's, Rockefeller NY #269/R est:4000-6000
£2096	$3500	€3060	Old Faithful Geyser, Yellowstone National Park, Wyoming (25x18cm-10x7in) s. gelatin silver print exec.1942-1970. 21-Oct-3 Bonhams & Butterfields, San Francisco #1477/R
£2096	$3500	€3060	Cathedral Peak and lake, Yosemite National Park, California (18x24cm-7x9in) s. gelatin silver print exec.c.1960/1963 prov.lit. 20-Oct-3 Christie's, Rockefeller NY #266/R est:3000-5000
£2147	$3800	€3135	Yosemite Falls (24x18cm-9x7in) s.i. gelatin silver print executed c.1950. 27-Apr-4 Christie's, Rockefeller NY #7/R est:2000-3000
£2210	$4000	€3227	Mt Lyell and Mt Macclure, Yosemite National Park (20x25cm-8x10in) s.num.15 gelatin silver print exec.c.1936/1970s. 19-Apr-4 Bonhams & Butterfields, San Francisco #345/R est:3000-5000
£2246	$3750	€3279	Cloud, hill, Philmont (24x34cm-9x13in) s. photo exec.c.1960 prov. 17-Oct-3 Sotheby's, New York #18/R est:3000-5000
£2395	$4000	€3497	Upper Yosemite falls, spring (25x19cm-10x7in) s. num.13 verso photo exec.c.1940 printed later. 17-Oct-3 Sotheby's, New York #6/R est:5000-7000
£2395	$4000	€3497	Hulls, San Francisco, California (26x33cm-10x13in) s. gelatin silver print board exec. c.1932 prov. 17-Oct-3 Phillips, New York #151/R est:4000-6000
£2486	$4500	€3630	Moon and half dome (25x19cm-10x7in) s. num.76 verso gelatin silver print 1960/printed later. 19-Apr-4 Bonhams & Butterfields, San Francisco #346/R est:3000-5000
£2529	$4300	€3692	Barn and fence, Cape Cod (51x66cm-20x26in) s. photograph. 21-Nov-3 Eldred, East Dennis #806/R est:1500-2500
£2624	$4750	€3831	Factory interior (48x38cm-19x15in) s.num.V/10 black white photograph. 3-Apr-4 David Rago, Lambertville #102/R est:1200-1800
£2695	$4500	€3935	El capitan, winter (24x19cm-9x7in) s. num.17 verso photo exec.c.1940 printed later. 17-Oct-3 Sotheby's, New York #8/R est:5000-7000
£2844	$4750	€4152	Oakland harbour (22x16cm-9x6in) s. photo exec.c.1930. 17-Oct-3 Sotheby's, New York #26/R est:8000-12000
£2955	$5200	€4314	Bridal falls, Yosemite (48x38cm-19x15in) silver print. 20-May-4 Swann Galleries, New York #420/R est:4000-5000
£3293	$5500	€4808	Snow scene in Yosemite (16x23cm-6x9in) s. photo exec.c.1948-49 exhib. 17-Oct-3 Sotheby's, New York #27/R est:6000-9000
£3293	$5500	€4808	Snowy road in Yosemite (16x23cm-6x9in) s. s.i.verso photo exec.c.1948-49 exhib. 17-Oct-3 Sotheby's, New York #29/R est:6000-9000
£3593	$6000	€5246	Golden Gate before the bridge (15x23cm-6x9in) s.d.1932 photo lit. 17-Oct-3 Sotheby's, New York #22/R est:10000-15000
£3593	$6000	€5246	Golden Gate, San Francisco (17x23cm-7x9in) s. i.verso photo lit. 17-Oct-3 Sotheby's, New York #23/R est:10000-20000
£3593	$6000	€5246	Dawn, autumn, Great Smokey Mountains National Park, Tennessee (49x35cm-19x14in) s. i.d.1948 verso gelatin silver print. 20-Oct-3 Christie's, Rockefeller NY #267/R est:5000-7000
£3593	$6000	€5246	Banner Peak, Thousand Island Lake (14x20cm-6x8in) s.i. parmelian print exec.1923 lit. 20-Oct-3 Christie's, Rockefeller NY #270/R est:4000-6000
£3892	$6500	€5682	Redwoods, Bull Creek Flat, northern California (39x47cm-15x19in) s. i.d.verso gelatin silver print exec.c.1960-1970 lit. 20-Oct-3 Christie's, Rockefeller NY #265/R est:6000-8000
£3955	$7000	€5774	Moon and half dome (25x19cm-10x7in) s. num.12 verso photo printed later. 28-Apr-4 Sotheby's, New York #77/R est:5000-7000
£3955	$7000	€5774	Cemetery statue and oil derricks, Long Beach, California (38x47cm-15x19in) s.num.81/115 st.verso photo printed 1976 prov. 28-Apr-4 Sotheby's, New York #84/R est:5000-7000
£3977	$7000	€5806	Grand Teton from Jackson Lake (29x22cm-11x9in) with sig.i.verso silver print. 20-May-4 Swann Galleries, New York #409/R est:8000-12000
£4072	$6801	€5945	Aspens, Northern New Mexico (39x49cm-15x19in) silver gelatin board prov.lit. 24-Jun-3 Germann, Zurich #701/R est:10000-15000 (S.FR 9000)
£4192	$7000	€6120	Merced river cliffs, autumn, Yosemite valley, California (40x49cm-16x19in) s. studio st.i.d.verso photo board exec.c.1939 printed later. 17-Oct-3 Sotheby's, New York #13/R est:8000-12000
£4444	$8000	€6488	Grand Teton and Snake River, Wyoming (25x33cm-10x13in) s. gelatin silver print exec.c.1960. 24-Apr-4 Collins, Maine #4/R est:5000-7000
£4491	$7500	€6557	El Capitan, sunrise, Yosemite (39x32cm-15x13in) s. i.d.1968 verso gelatin silver print prov.lit. 21-Oct-3 Bonhams & Butterfields, San Francisco #1479/R
£4491	$7500	€6557	Sundown, the Pacific (47x37cm-19x15in) s. studio st.i.d.1953 verso photo printed later. 17-Oct-3 Sotheby's, New York #10/R est:5000-7000
£4491	$7500	€6557	Old Faithful, Yellowstone National Park (25x17cm-10x7in) s. studio st.i.verso photo exec.1942 printed later. 17-Oct-3 Sotheby's, New York #12/R est:4000-6000
£5090	$8500	€7431	Moon and half dome (25x19cm-10x7in) s. num.12 verso photo board exec.1960 printed later. 17-Oct-3 Sotheby's, New York #16/R est:5000-7000
£6215	$11000	€9074	Sand dunes, sunrise, Death Valley National Monument, California (48x36cm-19x14in) s. i.d.1948 verso photo printed later. 28-Apr-4 Sotheby's, New York #80/R est:10000-15000
£6215	$11000	€9074	Selected images (24x29cm-9x11in) s. photo three printed 1948-1963 prov. 28-Apr-4 Sotheby's, New York #148/R est:7000-10000
£7186	$12000	€10492	Mt Williamson, Sierra Nevada from Owens Valley, California (35x46cm-14x18in) s. i.d.1944 verso gelatin silver print. 20-Oct-3 Christie's, Rockefeller NY #268/R est:8000-10000
£7784	$13000	€11365	Aspens, northern New Mexico (39x49cm-15x19in) s. studio st.i.d.1958 verso photo printed later prov. 17-Oct-3 Sotheby's, New York #5/R est:12000-18000
£7784	$13000	€11365	Sand dunes, sunrise, Death Valley National Monument, California (48x36cm-19x14in) s. studio st.i.d.1948 verso photo printed later. 17-Oct-3 Sotheby's, New York #17/R est:10000-15000
£7910	$14000	€11549	Icicles at the Awahnee Hotel (23x18cm-9x7in) photo board exec.c.1930 prov. 28-Apr-4 Sotheby's, New York #81/R est:10000-15000
£7910	$14000	€11549	Sierra Nevada, Mount Williamson from Manzanar, CA (38x48cm-15x19in) s.i.d.1970 gelatin silver print. 27-Apr-4 Christie's, Rockefeller NY #2/R est:8000-10000
£8523	$15000	€12444	Grand Teton and the Snake River (39x48cm-15x19in) with sig.i.d.1942 verso silver print. 20-May-4 Swann Galleries, New York #401/R est:18000-22000
£8982	$15000	€13114	Aspens, northern New Mexico (38x48cm-15x19in) s. i.d.1958 verso gelatin silver print printed c.1970 prov.lit. 20-Oct-3 Christie's, Rockefeller NY #262/R est:12000-18000
£9040	$16000	€13198	Tetons and the Snake River, Grand Teton National Park, Wyoming (27x34cm-11x13in) s.i.d.1942 gelatin silver print lit. 27-Apr-4 Christie's, Rockefeller NY #4/R est:15000-20000
£9659	$17000	€14102	Thundercloud, Lake Tahoe (49x39cm-19x15in) with sig. silver print. 20-May-4 Swann Galleries, New York #402/R est:8000-12000
£10169	$18000	€14847	Aspen, Northern New Mexico (39x49cm-15x19in) s.i.d.1978 gelatin silver print lit. 27-Apr-4 Christie's, Rockefeller NY #1/R est:12000-18000
£11377	$19000	€16610	Meyer's Ranch, Sierra Nevada (17x23cm-7x9in) s. photo exec.c.1930. 17-Oct-3 Sotheby's, New York #24/R est:10000-20000
£12429	$22000	€18146	The Tetons and the Snake River, Grand Teton National Park, Wyoming (39x48cm-15x19in) s. i.d.1942 verso photo printed c.1969 prov. 28-Apr-4 Sotheby's, New York #79/R est:18000-22000
£12429	$22000	€18146	Monolith, the face of Half Dome, Yosemite National Park, California (49x37cm-19x15in) s. i.d.1927 verso photo printed 1979. 28-Apr-4 Sotheby's, New York #82/R est:12000-18000
£12429	$22000	€18146	Winter sunrise, Sierra Nevada from Lone Pine (37x50cm-15x20in) s. i.d.verso photo printed April 1978 prov. 28-Apr-4 Sotheby's, New York #86/R est:18000-22000
£13174	$22000	€19234	Moonrise, Hernandez, New Mexico (38x49cm-15x19in) s. studio st.i.verso photo board exec.1941 printed c.1960. 17-Oct-3 Sotheby's, New York #15/R est:25000-35000
£14371	$24000	€20982	Moonrise, Hernandez, New Mexico (39x48cm-15x19in) s. i.d.1941/1970s verso gelatin silver print prov.lit. 20-Oct-3 Christie's, Rockefeller NY #38/R est:25000-35000
£15569	$26000	€22731	Clearing winter storm (40x49cm-16x19in) s. studio st.i.d.1944 verso photo printed later. 17-Oct-3 Sotheby's, New York #7/R est:20000-30000
£17964	$30000	€26227	The Tetons and the Snake River, Grand Teton National Park, Wyoming (39x48cm-15x19in) s. studio st.i.d.1942 verso photo printed later. 17-Oct-3 Sotheby's, New York #11/R est:18000-22000
£18563	$31000	€27102	Moon and half dome, Yosemite Valley (49x38cm-19x15in) s. studio.i.verso photo board printed c.1969. 17-Oct-3 Sotheby's, New York #124/R est:20000-30000
£19760	$33000	€28850	Winter sunrise, Sierra Nevada from Lone Pine (43x58cm-17x23in) s.i.d.1944 photo printed c.1979 prov. 17-Oct-3 Sotheby's, New York #121/R est:15000-25000
£19774	$35000	€28870	Clearing winter storm, Yosemite Valley, 1944 (39x49cm-15x19in) s.i. gelatin silver print. 27-Apr-4 Christie's, Rockefeller NY #5/R est:20000-30000
£20339	$36000	€29695	Georgia O'Keeffe and Orville Cox, Canyon de Chelly (25x34cm-10x13in) s. i.d.1937 photo printed c.1976. 28-Apr-4 Sotheby's, New York #78/R est:6000-8000
£20958	$35000	€30599	Portfolio VI (39x49cm-15x19in) s.num. gelatin silver print 10 folio clamshell box lit. 20-Oct-3 Christie's, Rockefeller NY #261/R est:30000-40000
£22599	$40000	€32995	Moonrise, Hernandez, New Mexico (38x49cm-15x19in) s.i.d.1970 gelatin silver print lit. 27-Apr-4 Christie's, Rockefeller NY #3/R est:25000-35000
£24859	$44000	€36294	Portfolio VII (49x39cm-19x15in) s.num. gelatin silver prints one Polaroid set of 12. 28-Apr-4 Sotheby's, New York #83/R est:40000-60000
£28144	$47000	€41090	Portfolio three, Yosemite valley. s.num i.verso photos edition of 208 sixteen portfolio. 17-Oct-3 Sotheby's, New York #19/R est:50000-70000
£40719	$68000	€59450	Tetons and Snake River, Grand Teton National Park, Wyoming (48x59cm-19x23in) s.i.d.1942 verso gelatin silver print printed c.1970 lit. 20-Oct-3 Christie's, Rockefeller NY #271/R est:40000-60000
£41916	$70000	€61197	Rose and driftwood (19x24cm-7x9in) s. photo exec.c.1932 lit. 17-Oct-3 Sotheby's, New York #21/R est:30000-50000

ADAMS, Bernard (fl.1916-1939) British

£1250	$2125	€1825	Kensington Gardens, study of figures seated under parasols in woodlands (70x91cm-28x36in) s.i.verso. 31-Oct-3 Moore Allen & Innocent, Cirencester #771/R est:500-800
£1600	$2672	€2336	Chelsea fruit shop (81x86cm-32x34in) s. prov.exhib. 16-Oct-3 Christie's, Kensington #441/R est:800-1200

ADAMS, C J (1857-1931) British

Works on paper

£330	$584	€482	Milking time (13x28cm-5x11in) s. 30-Apr-4 Dee Atkinson & Harrison, Driffield #797/R

ADAMS, Charles James (1857-1931) British

£300	$501	€438	King Richards III's body being returned to Leicester (61x91cm-24x36in) s. canvas on board. 13-Nov-3 Christie's, Kensington #290/R
£1000	$1800	€1460	In the meadows (25x35cm-10x14in) s. i.verso. 21-Apr-4 Tennants, Leyburn #1129 est:1000-1200

£1800 $3294 €2628 Cows reclining in meadow with stream and trees beyond (60x49cm-24x19in) s. 6-Jul-4 Peter Wilson, Nantwich #1/R est:1500-2000
£1900 $3287 €2774 Pastoral scene with cattle resting by a stream (41x61cm-16x24in) s. 14-Dec-3 Desmond Judd, Cranbrook #1078
£2900 $5278 €4234 Milking time (39x54cm-15x21in) s. 5-Feb-4 Mellors & Kirk, Nottingham #533/R est:2000-2500
Works on paper
£320 $525 €467 Farmyard with haystack and feeding ducks (24x16cm-9x6in) s.d.1887 W/C. 3-Jun-3 Fellows & Sons, Birmingham #45/R
£420 $769 €613 Farmyard scene with ducks in foreground, hay-cart beyond (17x24cm-7x9in) s.d.1882 W/C. 6-Jul-4 Peter Wilson, Nantwich #47/R
£580 $1061 €847 Return of the fishing fleet, Whitby (35x53cm-14x21in) s.d.1885 W/C htd bodycol scratching out exhib. 6-Jul-4 Peter Wilson, Nantwich #48/R
£650 $1053 €949 Farmyard with woman feeding hens (36x53cm-14x21in) s. W/C. 31-Jul-3 Biddle & Webb, Birmingham #910

ADAMS, Charles James (attrib) (1857-1931) British
Works on paper
£360 $576 €526 Cattle on a highland shore (17x15cm-7x6in) s. W/C. 16-Sep-3 Rosebery Fine Art, London #413/R

ADAMS, Charles Partridge (1858-1942) American
£1872 $3500 €2733 Riverbed in drought (30x41cm-12x16in) s. canvasboard prov. 24-Jul-4 Coeur d'Alene, Hayden #267/R est:5000-7500
£2406 $4500 €3513 Mountainous landscape with stream (25x36cm-10x14in) s. prov. 24-Jul-4 Coeur d'Alene, Hayden #38/R est:4000-6000
£3297 $6000 €4814 View of the Rockies (23x31cm-9x12in) s.d.1896. 29-Jun-4 Sotheby's, New York #259/R est:2000-3000
£8556 $16000 €12492 Tetons and Mount Moran (46x91cm-18x36in) s. prov. 24-Jul-4 Coeur d'Alene, Hayden #24/R est:15000-25000
£11173 $20000 €16313 Desert mountains, sunset (51x76cm-20x30in) s. 14-May-4 Skinner, Boston #85/R est:1000-1500
Works on paper
£852 $1500 €1244 Longs peak and meeker, Estes Park Colorado (15x20cm-6x8in) s. i.verso W/C cardboard. 18-May-4 Arthur James, Florida #124 est:800-1200
£1337 $2500 €1952 Lake and snow-capped mountain (13x20cm-5x8in) s. W/C prov. 24-Jul-4 Coeur d'Alene, Hayden #266/R est:2000-3000
£1498 $2500 €2187 Dusk near Denver, Colorado (25x38cm-10x15in) s. i.verso W/C gouache prov. 23-Oct-3 Shannon's, Milford #156/R est:2000-3000
£1514 $2800 €2210 Mountain range landscape (41x51cm-16x20in) s. W/C gouache board. 13-Mar-4 Susanin's, Chicago #6090/R est:600-800
£1604 $3000 €2342 Reflections (20x28cm-8x11in) s. gouache prov. 24-Jul-4 Coeur d'Alene, Hayden #265/R est:4000-6000
£1912 $3250 €2792 Long's Peak (13x20cm-5x8in) s.d.1896 W/C prov.lit. 1-Nov-3 Santa Fe Art, Santa Fe #111/R est:2000-3000
£2059 $3500 €3006 Near the New Mexico, Colorado border (18x25cm-7x10in) s.d.99 W/C prov.lit. 1-Nov-3 Santa Fe Art, Santa Fe #110/R est:2500-3500
£2540 $4750 €3708 Evening under crescent moon (18x25cm-7x10in) s. gouache prov. 24-Jul-4 Coeur d'Alene, Hayden #268/R est:3000-5000

ADAMS, Charles Partridge (attrib) (1858-1942) American
£503 $900 €734 Seascape (25x36cm-10x14in) bears sig. 21-Mar-4 Bonhams & Butterfields, Los Angeles #7318/R est:600-800

ADAMS, Clinton (1918-) American
£659 $1100 €962 Untitled (127x178cm-50x70in) s.d.67 s.i.d.verso. 19-Oct-3 Bonhams & Butterfields, Los Angeles #7016

ADAMS, James E (19th C) British
£550 $985 €803 On the Barmouth road. Old lock, near Chiddingfold (25x36cm-10x14in) one s. pair. 18-Mar-4 Christie's, Kensington #551/R

ADAMS, James Frederick (1914-1984) British
Works on paper
£260 $442 €380 Dartmouth, Devon (36x62cm-14x24in) s. W/C. 4-Nov-3 Dreweatt Neate, Newbury #40

ADAMS, James L (fl.1874-1890) British
£300 $477 €438 Rocky riverbank in wooded countryside (60x90cm-24x35in) s. 18-Mar-3 Anderson & Garland, Newcastle #426/R

ADAMS, Jay (20th C) American
£269 $450 €393 Brief stop over (28x81cm-11x32in) board. 15-Nov-3 Slotin Folk Art, Buford #521/R
£299 $500 €437 Landfill entrepreneur (25x122cm-10x48in) board. 15-Nov-3 Slotin Folk Art, Buford #524/R

ADAMS, Jean (1899-1970) Dutch
£833 $1317 €1200 Self portrait (122x60cm-48x24in) s.i.d.21 Maaet 1933. 2-Sep-3 Christie's, Amsterdam #376/R est:1000-1500
£2361 $3849 €3400 Man sitting (111x151cm-44x59in) s.d.1931 s.i.d.verso. 29-Sep-3 Sotheby's, Amsterdam #337/R

ADAMS, John Clayton (1840-1906) British
£900 $1494 €1314 Faggott gatherer and a dog near a cottage (46x76cm-18x30in) s. 1-Oct-3 Woolley & Wallis, Salisbury #199/R
£2600 $4732 €3796 Near Ripley, Surrey (30x45cm-12x18in) s. 16-Jun-4 Bonhams, New Bond Street #37/R est:1500-2000

ADAMS, John Clayton (attrib) (1840-1906) British
£320 $534 €467 Sheep by gorse bush on heath (29x47cm-11x19in) indis.sig. 16-Oct-3 Lawrence, Crewkerne #740

ADAMS, John Quincy (1874-1933) Austrian
£385 $700 €562 Portrait of a lady (41x38cm-16x15in) s.d.1924. 7-Feb-4 Sloans & Kenyon, Bethesda #1305/R

ADAMS, Lilian (fl.1892-1911) British
£201 $373 €293 Landscape (61x51cm-24x20in) s. 2-Mar-4 Ritchie, Toronto #99/R (C.D 500)

ADAMS, Mark (1925-) American
Works on paper
£235 $400 €343 Jo's flowers (35x26cm-14x10in) s.d.78 W/C prov. 9-Nov-3 Bonhams & Butterfields, Los Angeles #4036/R

ADAMS, Maud (19th C) British?
Works on paper
£1600 $2672 €2336 Collector's home (44x30cm-17x12in) s. pencil W/C bodycol prov. 16-Oct-3 Christie's, Kensington #138/R est:1800-2500

ADAMS, Norman (20th C) American
£294 $500 €429 Whitetail deer, winter scene (25x20cm-10x8in) s. prov. 21-Nov-3 Skinner, Boston #340/R

ADAMS, Norman (1927-) British
£420 $785 €613 Tall trees (19x11cm-7x4in) s.d.55 board. 25-Feb-4 Mallams, Oxford #368
Works on paper
£300 $552 €438 Sunflowers with insects (142x203cm-56x80in) init.d.85 i.verso mixed media. 23-Mar-4 Rosebery Fine Art, London #893
£800 $1488 €1168 Daily apocalypse. W/C gouache. 8-Mar-4 Christie's, London #4

ADAMS, René (20th C) ?
£532 $984 €798 Abstract (52x42cm-20x17in) s.d.2001 oil on paper. 13-Jul-4 Watson's, Christchurch #71/R est:2000-3500 (NZ.D 1500)

ADAMS, Robert (1917-) British
Photographs
£2667 $4800 €3894 Concrete and ice, Missouri River, Clay County, South Dakota (17x22cm-7x9in) s.i. num.verso gelatin silver print. 23-Apr-4 Phillips, New York #267/R est:6000-8000
£6111 $11000 €8922 Untitled (12x15cm-5x6in) gelatin silver print mounted on board prov. 23-Apr-4 Phillips, New York #46/R est:6000-8000
£10169 $18000 €14847 Colorado Springs (15x15cm-6x6in) s.i.d.1974 verso photo prov. 28-Apr-4 Sotheby's, New York #163/R est:3000-5000
Sculpture
£1272 $2200 €1857 Link (25cm-10in) num.1/6 lacquered bronze prov. 15-Dec-3 Hindman, Chicago #56/R est:800-1000

ADAMS, Wayman (1883-1959) American
£497 $900 €726 Doctor Fraser (127x102cm-50x40in) s.verso. 14-Apr-4 Dallas Auction Gallery, Dallas #323/R
£1744 $3000 €2546 Affinities (132x102cm-52x40in) s. 6-Dec-3 Neal Auction Company, New Orleans #564/R est:3000-5000
£2335 $4250 €3409 Remains of the Portfolio Club supper (71x86cm-28x34in) s.d.1917 prov. 7-Feb-4 Neal Auction Company, New Orleans #450/R est:6000-9000
£3313 $5500 €4837 Prima Donna (38x30cm-15x12in) s. wood panel. 4-Oct-3 Neal Auction Company, New Orleans #556/R est:5000-7000

ADAMS, William Dacres (1864-1951) British
£2000 $3260 €2920 Double portraits of young girls seated beneath a tree in parkland (68x144cm-27x57in) s.d.1904. 25-Sep-3 Mellors & Kirk, Nottingham #766/R est:800-1200

ADAMS-ACTON, John (1831-1910) British
Sculpture
£3400 $6222 €4964 Bust of Pharaoh's daughter (178cm-70in) s.i.d.1863 white marble tapering pillar. 10-Jun-4 Neales, Nottingham #850 est:2000-4000

ADAMSKI, Derek (1967-) Polish
£1138 $2094 €1707 Goddess of Hunting (140x100cm-55x39in) s. 14-Jun-4 Blomqvist, Lysaker #1007/R est:15000-20000 (N.KR 14000)

ADAMSKI, Hans Peter (1947-) German?
£594 $1010 €850 Untitled (115x160cm-45x63in) s.d.97 verso. 27-Nov-3 Lempertz, Koln #1/R

ADAMSON, Dorothy (?-1934) British
£9200 $15640 €13432 Summer sewing (46x51cm-18x20in) s. 30-Oct-3 Christie's, London #187/R est:3000-5000

ADAMSON, Harry Curieux (1916-) American
£9239 $17000 €13489 Ducks in flight (61x91cm-24x36in) s.d.1979 board prov. 8-Jun-4 Bonhams & Butterfields, San Francisco #4147/R est:3000-5000

ADAMSON, Robert and HILL, David Octavius (19th C) British
Photographs
£1916 $3200 €2797 Marquis of Northampton (19x13cm-7x5in) salted paper print. 21-Oct-3 Swann Galleries, New York #2/R est:3000-4000

£2036 $3400 €2973 Dr Forbes, Glasgow (19x14cm-7x6in) salted paper print. 21-Oct-3 Swann Galleries, New York #1/R est:2000-3000

ADAN, Louis Émile (1839-1937) French
£262 $477 €383 On the shores of the lake (24x33cm-9x13in) s. paper on canvas prov. 16-Jun-4 Fischer, Luzern #2004/R (S.FR 600)
£786 $1431 €1148 Washerwoman at the lakeside (25x33cm-10x13in) s. prov. 16-Jun-4 Fischer, Luzern #2005/R (S.FR 1800)
Works on paper
£423 $731 €600 Enfant en costume traditional breton (29x19cm-11x7in) s.i. W/C traces blk crayon. 10-Dec-3 Piasa, Paris #132
£1197 $2071 €1700 Une semeuse (62x48cm-24x19in) chl. 10-Dec-3 Piasa, Paris #131/R est:1500
£1761 $3046 €2500 L'heure de la soupe (64x48cm-25x19in) chl white chk grey paper. 10-Dec-3 Piasa, Paris #134/R est:1500
£2041 $3653 €3000 Fontaine dans un parc. Pavillon dans un parc (26x35cm-10x14in) s. W/C pair. 19-Mar-4 Piasa, Paris #170/R est:2000

ADCOCK, J Wilton (1863-1930) British
£540 $880 €788 Mother, baby, child and dog resting by a stream (30x60cm-12x24in) 28-Sep-3 Wilkinson, Doncaster #295/R

ADDAMS, Charles (1912-1988) American
Works on paper
£2374 $4250 €3466 Cannibal returns home after a day in the jungle (33x36cm-13x14in) s. pen ink wash en grisaille. 15-May-4 Illustration House, New York #133/R est:4000-6000
£4190 $7500 €6117 Giant prehistoric bird carrying off hunter, bird sanctuary (43x33cm-17x13in) s. W/C. 15-May-4 Illustration House, New York #132/R est:8000-12000
£4790 $8000 €6993 Man and pet dragon return from the newsstand (23x25cm-9x10in) s. ink wash. 15-Nov-3 Illustration House, New York #45/R est:5000-8000

ADDE, Per (1926-) Norwegian
£545 $1002 €818 House among trees (84x106cm-33x42in) s. sold with two drawings of dog in one frame. 14-Jun-4 Blomqvist, Lysaker #1008 (N.KR 6700)

ADDERTON, Charles William (1866-?) British
Works on paper
£280 $445 €406 Pony and figures working on the beach (24x35cm-9x14in) s. W/C. 9-Sep-3 David Duggleby, Scarborough #165
£380 $692 €555 Fishing boats before Holy Island (28x36cm-11x14in) s. W/C. 15-Jun-4 David Lay, Penzance #65
£450 $828 €657 Sorting the nets, with anchored boats (23x34cm-9x13in) s. W/C. 10-Jun-4 Morphets, Harrogate #538/R

ADDEY, Joseph Poole (1852-1922) Irish
£2254 $3606 €3200 County Wexford cabin (61x46cm-24x18in) s.d.1906. 16-Sep-3 Whyte's, Dublin #161/R est:2000-3000
Works on paper
£347 $566 €500 Shallows of the Lee, near Cork (26x37cm-10x15in) s.d.1914 W/C. 24-Sep-3 James Adam, Dublin #20/R
£1690 $2704 €2400 Irish homestead (33x15cm-13x6in) s.d.1890 W/C prov. 16-Sep-3 Whyte's, Dublin #88/R est:1800-2200

ADDISON, Robert (1924-) American
Works on paper
£625 $1100 €913 Barn in winter (46x64cm-18x25in) s. gouache. 23-May-4 Hindman, Chicago #1017/R est:1000-2000

ADDISON, William Grylls (?-1904) British
Works on paper
£280 $456 €409 River landscape (48x76cm-19x30in) s.d.1880 W/C bodycol. 24-Sep-3 Dreweatt Neate, Newbury #43
£340 $622 €496 Lily pond (48x76cm-19x30in) s.d.1880 W/C. 27-Jan-4 Bonhams, Knightsbridge #175/R

ADELANTADO ENFEDAQUE, Felix (1911-2001) Spanish
£414 $745 €600 Frozen worlds (60x73cm-24x29in) s. 26-Jan-4 Durán, Madrid #52/R
£471 $772 €650 Mundos Helados (60x73cm-24x29in) s. s.i.d.1973. 27-May-3 Durán, Madrid #72/R

ADEMOLLO, Carlo (1825-1911) Italian
£9155 $15838 €13000 Genre scene (131x90cm-52x35in) s. 9-Dec-3 Pandolfini, Florence #221/R est:13000-13500

ADEMOLLO, Luigi (1764-1849) Italian
£18000 $32400 €27000 Scene from literature (69x102cm-27x40in) tempera paper on canvas set of 4. 21-Apr-4 Finarte Semenzato, Milan #551/R est:25000-27000
Works on paper
£3169 $5261 €4500 Bucolic scene (38x38cm-15x15in) s.d.1839 wash cardboard. 11-Jul-3 Finarte, Venice #527/R

ADEYEV, Sergei (1949-) Russian
£250 $438 €365 Winter in the country (69x59cm-27x23in) s. 17-Dec-3 John Nicholson, Haslemere #84
£604 $1130 €900 Winter in the village (45x59cm-18x23in) s. 24-Feb-4 Durán, Madrid #712/R

ADI, Yuswantoro (1966-) Indonesian?
£1720 $2753 €2511 Kami hanya bisa gigit jari (100x100cm-39x39in) s.d.2003 s.i.d.2003 verso acrylic. 18-May-3 Sotheby's, Singapore #191/R est:4000-6000 (S.D 4800)

ADLEN, Michel (1899-1980) Russian
£336 $621 €500 Nature morte aux poires (36x46cm-14x18in) s. 15-Mar-4 Claude Boisgirard, Paris #1/R
£537 $983 €800 Environs de Juan-Les-Pins (55x65cm-22x26in) s. i. verso. 7-Jul-4 Artcurial Briest, Paris #97
£563 $1025 €850 La rue de Breuil (55x45cm-22x18in) s.d.1955. 16-Jun-4 Claude Boisgirard, Paris #18/R
£604 $1105 €900 Riviere de Yerres (46x61cm-18x24in) s. i.d.1956 verso. 7-Jul-4 Artcurial Briest, Paris #98

ADLER DE DANZIG, Salomon (attrib) (1630-1709) German
£2113 $3655 €3000 Portrait of a man (45x32cm-18x13in) 11-Dec-3 Dr Fritz Nagel, Stuttgart #438/R est:4000

ADLER, Edmund (1871-1957) German
£1793 $3317 €2600 Siblings (38x31cm-15x12in) s. 12-Feb-4 Weidler, Nurnberg #319/R est:1500
£2035 $3500 €2971 Coasting (69x81cm-27x32in) s. 7-Dec-3 Freeman, Philadelphia #18 est:4000-6000
£4027 $7128 €6000 Two children (53x41cm-21x16in) s. panel. 28-Apr-4 Wiener Kunst Auktionen, Vienna #35/R est:5000-10000
£4196 $7217 €6000 Three children enjoying the snow (68x55cm-27x22in) s. 3-Dec-3 Neumeister, Munich #524/R est:3000
£4360 $7500 €6366 Grandfather's favorite (68x55cm-27x22in) s. 3-Dec-3 Doyle, New York #108/R est:10000-15000
£9341 $17000 €13638 Dressing up a little doll (58x69cm-23x27in) s. 29-Jun-4 Sotheby's, New York #113/R est:10000-15000
£9500 $17100 €13870 Flowers for grandmother (55x68cm-22x27in) s. 21-Jan-4 Sotheby's, Olympia #436/R est:6000-8000

ADLER, Jankel (1895-1949) Polish
£1676 $3000 €2447 Cosmological eye (26x34cm-10x13in) estate st.verso board prov. 18-Mar-4 Sotheby's, New York #114/R est:4000-6000
£2514 $4500 €3670 Still life (23x32cm-9x13in) s.i. oil sand panel. 18-Mar-4 Sotheby's, New York #113/R est:4000-6000
£4400 $8052 €6600 Abstract still life (54x65cm-21x26in) i. verso oil sand prov.exhib. 5-Jun-4 Lempertz, Koln #566/R est:6000
Works on paper
£600 $1002 €876 Standing figure (10x11cm-4x4in) i.verso pen ink. 21-Oct-3 Bonhams, Knightsbridge #6/R
£838 $1500 €1223 Seated nude (31x23cm-12x9in) i.verso ink W/C prov. 18-Mar-4 Sotheby's, New York #115/R est:2000-3000
£1047 $1800 €1529 Figure seated at a table with book (20x23cm-8x9in) s. ink W/C crayon exec 1946 prov. 7-Dec-3 Freeman, Philadelphia #53 est:1000-1500
£1397 $2500 €2040 Seated man (78x57cm-31x22in) s. brown ink prov. 18-Mar-4 Sotheby's, New York #116/R est:3000-5000
£4800 $8496 €7008 Still life of flower in a blue and white vase (64x48cm-25x19in) s.d.29 mixed media on board. 27-Apr-4 Bonhams, Knightsbridge #142/R est:2000-3000
£4895 $8420 €7000 Flowers in jug (63x49cm-25x19in) s. mixed media. 2-Dec-3 Hauswedell & Nolte, Hamburg #1/R est:5000

ADLER, Jules (1865-1952) French
£400 $728 €584 Figures in a park (64x53cm-25x21in) s. 16-Jun-4 Andrew Hartley, Ilkley #1038
£612 $1096 €900 Gardien de moutons a Etaples (54x65cm-21x26in) s.i.d.1901. 18-Mar-4 Peschetau-Badin Godeau & Leroy, Paris #21
£612 $1096 €900 Haleur (50x40cm-20x16in) s.i. board. 18-Mar-4 Peschetau-Badin Godeau & Leroy, Paris #22

ADLER, Leo (1897-) Austrian
£433 $776 €650 Kremsmauer (33x44cm-13x17in) s.d.1944 board. 13-May-4 Dorotheum, Linz #505/R

ADLER, Rose (1892-1969) French
Works on paper
£3444 $6302 €5200 Projet de reliure (14x22cm-6x9in) s. collage mixed media board. 9-Apr-4 Bailly Pommery, Paris #86/R est:3000-5000

ADLER, Salomon (attrib) (18th C) German
£658 $1211 €1000 Portrait of a man - possibly self portrait (45x32cm-18x13in) 24-Jun-4 Dr Fritz Nagel, Stuttgart #665/R

ADLINGTON, Mark (1965-) British
£500 $880 €730 Bull (46x61cm-18x24in) init. board. 18-May-4 Woolley & Wallis, Salisbury #243/R
Works on paper
£440 $774 €642 Torro (28x36cm-11x14in) s. mixed media. 18-May-4 Woolley & Wallis, Salisbury #236/R
£500 $880 €730 Siesta (29x42cm-11x17in) chl conte. 18-May-4 Woolley & Wallis, Salisbury #176/R
£1100 $1936 €1606 Three calves (60x72cm-24x28in) chl conte. 18-May-4 Woolley & Wallis, Salisbury #217/R est:300-500
£1200 $2112 €1752 Tight turn (28x37cm-11x15in) init. mixed media. 18-May-4 Woolley & Wallis, Salisbury #237/R est:200-300

ADLOFF, Karl (1819-1863) German
£872 $1605 €1300 Snowy Dutch coast (31x47cm-12x19in) s. lit. 25-Mar-4 Karlheinz Kaupp, Staufen #2326/R

ADNAMS, Marion (fl.1927-1935) British
£400 $688 €584 Shells (64x63cm-25x25in) s. board. 4-Dec-3 Mellors & Kirk, Nottingham #914/R

£650	$1170	€949	Green knots or frogs of Sark (31x26cm-12x10in) s. s.i.verso tempera. 22-Apr-4 Mellors & Kirk, Nottingham #1019/R
£1200	$2124	€1752	Les Sardiniers (52x71cm-20x28in) s. board. 27-Apr-4 Bonhams, Knowle #148 est:150-200

Works on paper

£320	$576	€467	Tower of the cathedral church of All Saints Derby (21x13cm-8x5in) s. pencil wash. 22-Apr-4 Mellors & Kirk, Nottingham #1023

ADNET, Françoise (1924-) French

£733	$1313	€1100	La pie morte (100x81cm-39x32in) s. 16-May-4 Feletin, Province #123
£1667	$3033	€2500	Fillette au chapeau (150x74cm-59x29in) s.d.1958. 30-Jun-4 Delvaux, Paris #61/R est:1800-2500

ADNET, Jacques (1900-1984) French

Sculpture

£6578	$11774	€9800	Le tango (35cm-14in) s. wood. 27-May-4 Tajan, Paris #98/R est:3000-4000

ADNEY, Noel (1878-1965) British

£550	$968	€803	Still life of two jugs with tulips and daffodils and pansy in a pot to the side (54x62cm-21x24in) s. 19-May-4 Christie's, Kensington #697/R

ADOLFS, Gerard Pieter (1897-1968) Dutch

£417	$658	€600	Composition (30x40cm-12x16in) board. 2-Sep-3 Christie's, Amsterdam #456
£1046	$1893	€1527	Woman (40x30cm-16x12in) s. 4-Apr-4 Sotheby's, Singapore #6/R est:2000-3000 (S.D 3200)
£1049	$1751	€1500	Algerian street scene (40x50cm-16x20in) s. triplex. 30-Jun-3 Sotheby's, Amsterdam #435/R
£1361	$2435	€2000	People working a field (30x40cm-12x16in) s.d. panel. 16-Mar-4 Christie's, Amsterdam #48/R est:1200-1600
£1505	$2409	€2197	Straatje in Arabische Wyk (40x30cm-16x12in) s.d.33 i.d.33 verso. 18-May-3 Sotheby's, Singapore #34/R est:2000-3000 (S.D 4200)
£1644	$2795	€2400	Indian village (29x39cm-11x15in) s. i.verso panel. 5-Nov-3 Vendue Huis, Gravenhage #542/R est:2200-2600
£1736	$2899	€2535	Octhendlicht (30x40cm-12x16in) s.d.32. 12-Oct-3 Sotheby's, Singapore #45/R est:5000-7000 (S.D 5000)
£1849	$3329	€2700	Jalan dessa (30x40cm-12x16in) s.i.verso panel. 25-Apr-4 Christie's, Hong Kong #502/R est:30000-50000 (HK.D 26000)
£2587	$4399	€3700	Fiesta di Redentore in Venice (60x80cm-24x31in) s. 20-Nov-3 Van Ham, Cologne #1456/R est:1200
£3125	$5219	€4563	Japanese Pagoda (80x60cm-31x24in) s. board. 12-Oct-3 Sotheby's, Singapore #41/R est:6000-8000 (S.D 9000)
£3656	$5849	€5338	Market. Nude (30x41cm-12x16in) pair. 18-May-3 Sotheby's, Singapore #45/R est:2500-3500 (S.D 10200)
£4301	$6882	€6279	Pemandangan di Modjo-Agung (28x38cm-11x15in) s. canvas on board. 18-May-3 Sotheby's, Singapore #31/R est:10000-12000 (S.D 12000)
£4575	$8281	€6680	Market (30x40cm-12x16in) s.d.68 board. 4-Apr-4 Sotheby's, Singapore #41/R est:5000-7000 (S.D 14000)
£6159	$9547	€8992	Market (60x80cm-24x31in) s. 6-Oct-2 Sotheby's, Singapore #30/R est:6000-8000 (S.D 17000)
£9266	$15475	€13528	Planting rice (60x80cm-24x31in) s. 26-Oct-3 Christie's, Hong Kong #5/R est:38000-45000 (HK.D 120000)
£10884	$19483	€16000	Legong dancer, Bali (50x40cm-20x16in) s. s.i.d.verso. 16-Mar-4 Christie's, Amsterdam #72/R est:3000-5000

Works on paper

£1020	$1827	€1500	Street vendor (62x42cm-24x17in) s.d.56 gouache W/C. 16-Mar-4 Christie's, Amsterdam #101 est:1200-1600

ADOLPHE, Albert Jean (1865-1940) American

£389	$650	€568	Nude model (46x30cm-18x12in) s.i.d. 20-Jun-3 Freeman, Philadelphia #96/R
£1304	$2400	€1904	Nude model (46x30cm-18x12in) s.i. 25-Jun-4 Freeman, Philadelphia #295/R est:600-800

ADOMEIT, George G (1879-1967) American

£509	$850	€743	Under the bridge (18x25cm-7x10in) s. canvasboard. 25-Oct-3 Rachel Davis, Shaker Heights #38/R
£649	$1200	€948	Impressionistic landscape (51x41cm-20x16in) 18-Jan-4 Carlsen Gallery, Greenville #540/R

ADRIAENSSEN, Alexander (1587-1661) Flemish

£1189	$2045	€1700	Nature morte au gibier (42x52cm-17x20in) panel. 2-Dec-3 Campo & Campo, Antwerp #1 est:1750-2250
£2600	$4680	€3796	Still life of fish on a wooden table (25x36cm-10x14in) s.d.1643 panel prov. 20-Apr-4 Sotheby's, Olympia #296/R est:2000-3000
£3103	$5152	€4500	Birds (19x25cm-7x10in) s.d.1647. 30-Sep-3 Ansorena, Madrid #26/R est:4500
£20548	$34932	€30000	Still life with fish, bread and flowers (44x56cm-17x22in) copper. 4-Nov-3 Ansorena, Madrid #98/R est:30000

ADRIAENSSEN, Alexander (attrib) (1587-1661) Flemish

£4444	$8000	€6488	Still life of ham on a pewter plate and other objects (35x55cm-14x22in) s.i. panel. 21-Jan-4 Sotheby's, New York #65/R est:8000-12000
£7237	$13316	€11000	Still life with oysters and eggs (59x102cm-23x40in) panel prov. 24-Jun-4 Christie's, Paris #24/R est:10000-15000

ADRIAENSSEN, Vincent (1595-1675) Flemish

£5298	$9642	€8000	Orazio Coclite defending the bridge over the Tiber (72x100cm-28x39in) oval. 16-Jun-4 Christie's, Rome #428/R est:8000-10000

ADRIAN, Marc (1930-) Austrian

£2098	$3566	€3000	Untitled (174x75cm-69x30in) s.verso. 28-Nov-3 Wiener Kunst Auktionen, Vienna #623/R est:1200-3000

ADRIAN-NILSSON, Gosta (1884-1965) Swedish

£2462	$4234	€3595	Water butt (41x34cm-16x13in) mono. panel. 7-Dec-3 Uppsala Auktionskammare, Uppsala #212/R est:15000-20000 (S.KR 32000)
£4641	$8354	€6776	Battle for life (112x203cm-44x80in) study painted 1923. 26-Apr-4 Bukowskis, Stockholm #150/R est:60000-80000 (S.KR 64000)
£5287	$8988	€7719	Gold trees and new houses (48x56cm-19x22in) init. cardboard exhib. 4-Nov-3 Bukowskis, Stockholm #150/R est:80000-100000 (S.KR 70000)
£6042	$10272	€8821	The siding (55x45cm-22x18in) init. panel. 4-Nov-3 Bukowskis, Stockholm #146/R est:60000-80000 (S.KR 80000)
£12085	$20544	€17644	Looping the Loop (50x26cm-20x10in) s. panel lit. 5-Nov-3 AB Stockholms Auktionsverk #720/R est:200000-250000 (S.KR 160000)
£14141	$25453	€20646	The indian (51x38cm-20x15in) s. paper on panel. 26-Apr-4 Bukowskis, Stockholm #152a/R est:150000-175000 (S.KR 195000)
£14503	$26106	€21174	La femme et la vase au fleurs (61x49cm-24x19in) init. d.1923 verso prov. 26-Apr-4 Bukowskis, Stockholm #10/R est:200000-250000 (S.KR 200000)
£44562	$75755	€65061	Circus (86x70cm-34x28in) mono. painted c.1920-1922 exhib. 4-Nov-3 Bukowskis, Stockholm #41/R est:500000-700000 (S.KR 590000)
£47861	$86149	€69877	The canal-lock, Borensberg (56x48cm-22x19in) s. painted 1915 prov.lit. 26-Apr-4 Bukowskis, Stockholm #78/R est:250000-300000 (S.KR 660000)

Works on paper

£500	$860	€730	Crescendo (25x22cm-10x9in) mono.d.1913 Indian ink htd white. 7-Dec-3 Uppsala Auktionskammare, Uppsala #214/R (S.KR 6500)
£510	$939	€765	Absent milk allowance (24x30cm-9x12in) s. d.1946 verso gouache prov. 14-Jun-4 Lilla Bukowskis, Stockholm #924 (S.KR 7000)
£650	$1046	€949	The pumpkin is bewitched (30x22cm-12x9in) s. i.verso gouache. 25-Aug-3 Lilla Bukowskis, Stockholm #523 (S.KR 8500)
£680	$1156	€993	Surrealistic landscape (26x21cm-10x8in) init. W/C exec.c.1940. 4-Nov-3 Bukowskis, Stockholm #40/R (S.KR 9000)
£1095	$1862	€1599	Die Katze (22x19cm-9x7in) init. W/C exec.c.1914. 4-Nov-3 Bukowskis, Stockholm #36/R (S.KR 14500)
£1218	$2106	€1778	Flag of distress (28x21cm-11x8in) s.d.52 mixed media. 15-Dec-3 Lilla Bukowskis, Stockholm #733 est:5000-6000 (S.KR 15500)
£1378	$2480	€2012	The waterfall (71x50cm-28x20in) init. mixed media. 26-Apr-4 Bukowskis, Stockholm #72/R est:25000-30000 (S.KR 19000)
£1450	$2611	€2117	Robbers on the cross (40x50cm-16x20in) s.d.38 gouache. 26-Apr-4 Bukowskis, Stockholm #73/R est:20000-25000 (S.KR 20000)
£1737	$2953	€2536	Black ellipse (24x35cm-9x14in) init.d.54 gouache prov. 5-Nov-3 AB Stockholms Auktionsverk #646/R est:8000-10000 (S.KR 23000)
£1737	$2953	€2536	Cowboy (48x38cm-19x15in) i. W/C exhib. 4-Nov-3 Bukowskis, Stockholm #149/R est:20000-25000 (S.KR 23000)
£2393	$4307	€3494	By the duck pond. Sketch (32x22cm-13x9in) s. W/C chk double-sided exec.c.1928-30. 26-Apr-4 Bukowskis, Stockholm #77/R est:25000-30000 (S.KR 33000)
£2492	$4237	€3638	The motor cyclist (33x19cm-13x7in) s. W/C htd white. 5-Nov-3 AB Stockholms Auktionsverk #766/R est:15000-20000 (S.KR 33000)
£2870	$4879	€4190	A cigar shop (21x14cm-8x6in) init.i. mixed media prov. 4-Nov-3 Bukowskis, Stockholm #37/R est:20000-25000 (S.KR 38000)
£3021	$5136	€4411	Cockerel (49x34cm-19x13in) s.d.1958 gouache exhib. 5-Nov-3 AB Stockholms Auktionsverk #765 est:40000-45000 (S.KR 40000)
£3021	$5136	€4411	Street lamps (27x44cm-11x17in) init. gouache W/C. 4-Nov-3 Bukowskis, Stockholm #147/R est:20000-25000 (S.KR 40000)
£4061	$7310	€5929	After the fishing (46x34cm-18x13in) init.d.38 gouache W/C exhib. 26-Apr-4 Bukowskis, Stockholm #71/R est:45000-50000 (S.KR 56000)
£4396	$7780	€6418	The old town (49x34cm-19x13in) s. gouache panel. 27-Apr-4 AB Stockholms Auktionsverk #648/R est:30000-40000 (S.KR 60000)

ADRIANI, Camillo (20th C) American

£5183	$8500	€7515	New England town with harbour in the background (71x84cm-28x33in) s. 4-Jun-3 Alderfer's, Hatfield #273/R est:4000-6000

ADRION, Lucien (1889-1953) French

£1333	$2440	€2000	Paris, Place de Ste Marie Madeleine (55x65cm-22x26in) s. prov. 5-Jun-4 Lempertz, Koln #568/R est:3200
£1399	$2378	€2000	Mediterranean coast (60x73cm-24x29in) s.d.37 prov. 26-Nov-3 Lempertz, Koln #555/R est:3500
£1405	$2600	€2051	Sur la place a Deauville (38x46cm-15x18in) s. 13-Jul-4 Christie's, Rockefeller NY #184/R est:1000-1500
£1467	$2625	€2200	Trees in bloom in the suburbs - La belle St Cloud (60x74cm-24x29in) s. 13-May-4 Neumeister, Munich #273/R est:1800-2000
£1472	$2400	€2149	La plage a Trouville (50x65cm-20x26in) s.indis.i. 25-Sep-3 Christie's, Rockefeller NY #541/R est:3000-5000
£1620	$2689	€2300	Place de la Bourse animee (73x92cm-29x36in) s. 16-Jun-3 E & Eve, Paris #93/R
£2113	$3655	€3000	Un jardin (89x116cm-35x46in) s. 12-Dec-3 Piasa, Paris #137 est:3000-3500
£2600	$4342	€3796	Les Champs Elysees (65x81cm-26x32in) s.i.stretcher. 22-Oct-3 Sotheby's, Olympia #95/R est:3000-4000
£2761	$4500	€4031	Bievres, la gare (54x65cm-21x26in) s.i.d.26. 25-Sep-3 Christie's, Rockefeller NY #526/R est:4000-6000
£2838	$4996	€4143	Le Jardin des Tuileries (60x73cm-24x29in) s. prov. 22-May-4 Galerie Gloggner, Luzern #1/R est:3800-4500 (S.FR 6500)
£3944	$6823	€5600	Notre Dame and Augustin quayside (55x45cm-22x18in) s. panel prov. 13-Dec-3 Lempertz, Koln #274/R est:3000
£4895	$8322	€7000	Seine with The Louvre (65x81cm-26x32in) s.d.25 prov. 26-Nov-3 Lempertz, Koln #554/R est:10000

ADSETT, Sandy (20th C) New Zealander

£1273	$1998	€1846	Whakakohore, protest (98x98cm-39x39in) s.i.d.1981 verso acrylic board. 27-Aug-3 Dunbar Sloane, Wellington #32/R est:2500-4000 (NZ.D 3500)

ADUATZ, Fritz (1907-) Polish

£1608	$2734	€2300	Composition (58x78cm-23x31in) s.verso. 28-Nov-3 Wiener Kunst Auktionen, Vienna #497/R est:3000-7000

Works on paper

£1127	$1870	€1600	Mask play (29x45cm-11x18in) s. W/C. 12-Jun-3 Dorotheum, Graz #107/R

ADZAK, Roy (1927-1987) British

£2200	$4048	€3212	Hollow cast of man and woman (100x99cm-39x39in) s.d.66 verso oil canvas plaster casts. 24-Jun-4 Sotheby's, Olympia #589/R est:800-1200

AELST, Pieter Coecke van (1502-1550) Flemish

£39726	$67534	€58000	Christ and his Disciples on their way to Emmaus (68x87cm-27x34in) panel prov.exhib.lit. 4-Nov-3 Sotheby's, Amsterdam #48/R est:40000-60000
£100000	$173000	€146000	Adoration of the Magi. Saint Joseph. Balthasar (119x164cm-47x65in) oak panel triptych prov.lit. 11-Dec-3 Sotheby's, London #5/R est:100000-150000
£120000	$207600	€175200	Saint Martin dividing his cloak (97x68cm-38x27in) panel prov.lit. 11-Dec-3 Sotheby's, London #4/R est:50000-70000

AELST, Pieter Coecke van (attrib) (1502-1550) Flemish

£15789	$29053	€24000	Holy Family in interior (108x72cm-43x28in) panel. 22-Jun-4 Palais de Beaux Arts, Brussels #159/R est:30000-40000

AELST, Pieter Coecke van (circle) (1502-1550) Flemish

£5500	$10065	€8030	Madonna and Child in river landscape (96x61cm-38x24in) panel shaped top. 9-Jul-4 Christie's, Kensington #8/R est:6000-8000
£15385	$26462	€22000	Adoration of the Magi, shepherds, circumcision of Christ (91x112cm-36x44in) panel triptych. 3-Dec-3 Neumeister, Munich #459/R est:28000

Works on paper

£7500	$13725	€10950	Roman battle scene (25x20cm-10x8in) bears init. pen blk ink htd white prov. 8-Jul-4 Sotheby's, London #67/R est:8000-12000

AELST, Pieter Coecke van (studio) (1502-1550) Flemish

£15000	$25950	€21900	Madonna and Child with a donor (59x41cm-23x16in) panel shaped top prov. 10-Dec-3 Bonhams, New Bond Street #109/R est:15000-20000

AELST, Pieter Coecke van (style) (1502-1550) Flemish

£15000	$27450	€21900	Biblical scenes (91x104cm-36x41in) panel arched top triptych prov. 8-Jul-4 Sotheby's, London #107/R est:20000-30000

AELST, Willem van (1626-1683) Dutch

£67568	$120946	€100000	Still life with grapes, peach, cabbage-white, dragon-fly, snail and fly (33x28cm-13x11in) s.d.1665 prov. 5-May-4 Sotheby's, Amsterdam #288/R est:50000-70000

AELST, Willem van (attrib) (1626-1683) Dutch

£20833	$34375	€30000	Still life of fruit including grapes, peaches and cherries (47x62cm-19x24in) prov. 3-Jul-3 Van Ham, Cologne #950/R est:40000

AELST, Willem van (studio) (1626-1683) Dutch

£10000	$17300	€14600	Still life of peaches on a pewter plate, grapes, and nuts on a red cloth (64x52cm-25x20in) s. 11-Dec-3 Sotheby's, London #168a/R est:10000-15000

AEPPLI, Eva (1925-) French

£18349	$30642	€26606	Au revoir (130x195cm-51x77in) s.i.d.1962 verso exhib. 19-Jun-3 Kornfeld, Bern #151/R est:17500 (S.FR 40000)

Works on paper

£4585	$8345	€6694	Sphinx (94x41cm-37x16in) s. chl wash. 17-Jun-4 Kornfeld, Bern #152/R est:10000 (S.FR 10500)
£5459	$9934	€7970	La vue - lunettes (73x39cm-29x15in) s. chl wash htd white. 17-Jun-4 Kornfeld, Bern #151/R est:10000 (S.FR 12500)
£6114	$11127	€8926	Marguerite (34x18cm-13x7in) chl 7 in one frame. 17-Jun-4 Kornfeld, Bern #153/R est:10000 (S.FR 14000)

AERNI, Franz Theodor (1853-1918) German

£961	$1720	€1403	Children playing (72x56cm-28x22in) s.i.d.1897. 26-May-4 Sotheby's, Zurich #15/R est:2000-3000 (S.FR 2200)
£1739	$3183	€2539	Evening scene in a fishing village near Naples (74x41cm-29x16in) 4-Jun-4 Zofingen, Switzerland #2733 est:5500 (S.FR 4000)
£1810	$3077	€2643	Family of herders in the Campagna (34x49cm-13x19in) s. 28-Nov-3 Zofingen, Switzerland #2450/R est:5500 (S.FR 4000)
£5000	$8950	€7300	Italian peasants on the way to the market (115x71cm-45x28in) s.i. 26-May-4 Sotheby's, Olympia #266/R est:5000-7000
£11000	$20020	€16500	Paysages italiens (60x44cm-24x17in) s.i.d.98 pair. 29-Jun-4 Chenu & Scrive, Lyon #1/R est:12000-15000
£13000	$21710	€18980	Angriff auf eine karavane - attack on a caravan (72x151cm-28x59in) s. 14-Oct-3 Sotheby's, London #95/R est:10000-15000
£21333	$38827	€32000	View of the Forum in Rome (77x151cm-30x59in) s.d.80. 1-Jul-4 Van Ham, Cologne #1194/R est:35000

AERS, Marguerite (1918-1995) Belgian

£302	$562	€450	Mother and child (80x75cm-31x30in) s. 8-Mar-4 Bernaerts, Antwerp #763/R
£317	$587	€460	Elegante a l'ombrelle (55x46cm-22x18in) s. 19-Jan-4 Horta, Bruxelles #349
£364	$663	€550	Mere et enfant dans un jardin (55x45cm-22x18in) s. 15-Jun-4 Galerie Moderne, Brussels #203/R
£420	$701	€600	Elegante a l'opera (55x46cm-22x18in) s. 13-Oct-3 Horta, Bruxelles #435
£448	$829	€650	Elegante dans un parc (55x46cm-22x18in) s. 19-Jan-4 Horta, Bruxelles #350
£563	$907	€800	Jeune femme (55x46cm-22x18in) s. 11-May-3 Versailles Encheres #95
£594	$1022	€850	Elegantes en promenade (51x61cm-20x24in) s. 8-Dec-3 Horta, Bruxelles #350

AERTS, Dick (1956-) Dutch

Sculpture

£1467	$2699	€2200	Poezie (62cm-24in) s. brown pat bronze marble base conceived 1995 prov. 9-Jun-4 Christie's, Amsterdam #258/R est:2500-3500

AERTSEN, Pieter (1507-1575) Dutch

£22000	$40260	€32120	Kitchen maid in interior (170x83cm-67x33in) d.1569 panel prov. 8-Jul-4 Sotheby's, London #257/R est:20000-30000

AERTSEN, Pieter (attrib) (1507-1575) Dutch

£2778	$4417	€4000	Golgotha (83x64cm-33x25in) panel. 9-Sep-3 Vanderkindere, Brussels #90

AERTSEN, Pieter (circle) (1507-1575) Dutch

£5405	$9514	€8000	Christ and the woman taken in adultery (100x139cm-39x55in) i. panel. 18-May-4 Sotheby's, Amsterdam #34/R est:8000-12000

AERTTINGER, Carl August (1803-1876) German

£5556	$10000	€8112	Great stone mill on a river with mounted tradesmen (87x117cm-34x46in) s. prov. 22-Apr-4 Christie's, Rockefeller NY #24/R est:15000-20000

AESCHBACHER, Arthur (1923-) Swiss

£738	$1381	€1100	Sans titre (131x96cm-52x38in) s.i.d.1989 verso acrylic paper on canvas prov. 29-Feb-4 Versailles Encheres #197
£772	$1443	€1150	Sans titre (130x96cm-51x38in) s.d.1980 verso acrylic paper on canvas prov. 29-Feb-4 Versailles Encheres #196/R
£1678	$2970	€2500	Parole d'ecailles (55x46cm-22x18in) s.d.1962 s.i.verso decoupage canvas. 28-Apr-4 Artcurial Briest, Paris #375a/R est:2800-3200

Works on paper

£563	$975	€800	Sans titre (65x50cm-26x20in) s. collage cardboard prov. 14-Dec-3 Versailles Encheres #184/R
£634	$1096	€900	Sans titre (65x50cm-26x20in) s. collage cardboard prov. 14-Dec-3 Versailles Encheres #185/R
£658	$1211	€1000	Brule-Divague (29x21cm-11x8in) s. s.i.d.1962 verso torn posters. 27-Jun-4 Versailles Encheres #160/R
£667	$1200	€1000	Untitled (57x49cm-22x19in) s.d.1964 collage cardboard prov. 25-Apr-4 Versailles Encheres #194
£733	$1320	€1100	Untitled (55x41cm-22x16in) s.d.1968 collage cardboard prov. 25-Apr-4 Versailles Encheres #197
£764	$1276	€1100	Sans titre (37x680cm-15x268in) mono. s.d.1961 verso pieces of wood on board prov. 21-Oct-3 Artcurial Briest, Paris #550/R
£775	$1340	€1100	Oblitere - o, l'omega rayon violet de ses yeux (130x97cm-51x38in) s. s.d.1982 verso collage canvas prov. 14-Dec-3 Versailles Encheres #183/R
£804	$1343	€1150	Untitled (195x130cm-77x51in) s. collage on canvas prov. 29-Jun-3 Versailles Encheres #178/R
£839	$1401	€1200	Theatre dechire (65x50cm-26x20in) s. collage cardboard prov. 29-Jun-3 Versailles Encheres #177/R
£867	$1560	€1300	Voyelle Venus devorante (70x31cm-28x12in) s. s.i.verso torn posters exec.1961. 25-Apr-4 Versailles Encheres #162
£1079	$1770	€1500	L'alphabet s'enlise (53x41cm-21x16in) s. s.i.d.1962 verso collage wood. 6-Jun-3 David Kahn, Paris #26 est:1200-1400
£1232	$2132	€1750	Mot cle en paradis capitonne (40x31cm-16x12in) s.d.1960 i.verso torn poster on canvas. 14-Dec-3 Versailles Encheres #182/R est:1200-1500
£1259	$2102	€1800	Untitled (44x59cm-17x23in) s.d.1965 collage cardboard. 29-Jun-3 Versailles Encheres #189/R
£1667	$2633	€2400	Asperges de la trinite (55x45cm-22x18in) s.d.1961 s.i.d.verso torn posters. 27-Apr-3 Versailles Encheres #88
£2708	$4279	€3900	Composition (87x38cm-34x15in) s.d.1963 torn posters panel. 27-Apr-3 Versailles Encheres #89

AESCHBACHER, Hans (1906-) Swiss

Sculpture

£7424	$13288	€10839	Relief (49x43x4cm-19x17x2in) mono.d.1969 verso bronze three. 26-May-4 Sotheby's, Zurich #157/R est:8000-12000 (S.FR 17000)

AESCHER, H (?) ?

Works on paper

£909	$1627	€1327	Oriental interior (66x49cm-26x19in) s. 22-Mar-4 Philippe Schuler, Zurich #6332 (S.FR 2100)

AFFANDI (1907-1990) Indonesian

£2899	$4493	€4233	Lobsters (32x62cm-13x24in) s. 6-Oct-2 Sotheby's, Singapore #172/R est:8000-10000 (S.D 8000)
£7483	$13395	€11000	Grand Canyon I (53x84cm-21x33in) mono.d.1958. 16-Mar-4 Christie's, Amsterdam #136/R est:12000-16000
£7971	$12355	€11638	Portrait of former Brazilian ambassador's wife, Ruth Leao (129x97cm-51x38in) s.d.1964. 6-Oct-2 Sotheby's, Singapore #117/R est:20000-30000 (S.D 22000)
£10000	$18100	€14600	Rice fields (76x99cm-30x39in) mono.d.1956. 1-Apr-4 Christie's, Kensington #133/R est:10000-15000
£11380	$20484	€16615	Javanese boat (46x64cm-18x25in) mono.d.1970. 25-Apr-4 Christie's, Hong Kong #563/R est:120000-200000 (HK.D 160000)
£13514	$24324	€19730	Bull-cart in the field (58x98cm-23x39in) mono.d.1970. 25-Apr-4 Christie's, Hong Kong #564/R est:120000-200000 (HK.D 190000)
£13889	$23194	€20278	Sunflowers (80x100cm-31x39in) s.d.1970. 12-Oct-3 Sotheby's, Singapore #123/R est:30000-50000 (S.D 40000)
£13889	$23194	€20278	Boats (99x129cm-39x51in) s.d.1978 s.i.verso. 12-Oct-3 Sotheby's, Singapore #126/R est:40000-60000 (S.D 40000)
£14583	$24354	€21291	Snow in Swiss Alps (100x130cm-39x51in) s.d.1972. 12-Oct-3 Sotheby's, Singapore #122/R est:30000-40000 (S.D 42000)
£22569	$37691	€32951	Meluku Sawah (99x130cm-39x51in) s.d.1986. 12-Oct-3 Sotheby's, Singapore #125/R est:40000-60000 (S.D 65000)
£23551	$36504	€34384	Ipanema beach (81x100cm-32x39in) s.d.1966. 6-Oct-2 Sotheby's, Singapore #111/R est:30000-40000 (S.D 65000)
£23611	$39431	€34472	Self Portrait (55x48cm-22x19in) s.i.d.60 prov. 12-Oct-3 Sotheby's, Singapore #138/R est:38000-48000 (S.D 68000)
£24510	$44363	€35785	Feeding frenzy (100x130cm-39x51in) mono.d.1963 prov. 3-Apr-4 Glerum, Singapore #75/R est:70000-90000 (S.D 75000)
£25806	$41290	€37677	Kapal (130x150cm-51x59in) s.d.1983. 18-May-3 Sotheby's, Singapore #142/R est:35000-45000 (S.D 72000)
£26144	$47320	€38170	Potret Nenek (128x97cm-50x38in) init.d.1978 i.verso. 3-Apr-4 Glerum, Singapore #65/R est:34000-44000 (S.D 80000)
£27174	$42120	€39674	Sunflowers (100x137cm-39x54in) s.d.1964 exhib. 6-Oct-2 Sotheby's, Singapore #112/R est:35000-45000 (S.D 75000)
£27778	$46389	€40556	Sleep (95x170cm-37x67in) s.d.1964. 12-Oct-3 Sotheby's, Singapore #129/R est:80000-120000 (S.D 80000)
£27778	$50278	€40556	Pohon Kelapa dan Matahari (130x150cm-51x59in) init.d.96 lit. 3-Apr-4 Glerum, Singapore #28/R est:60000-80000 (S.D 85000)

£28986	$44928	€42320	Fishing boats (120x136cm-47x54in) s.d.1984. 6-Oct-2 Sotheby's, Singapore #157/R est:40000-60000 (S.D 80000)
£29344	$49004	€42842	Jago - cockfight (100x121cm-39x48in) init.d.1967. 26-Oct-3 Christie's, Hong Kong #51/R est:200000-300000 (HK.D 380000)
£29412	$53235	€42942	Rumah gadang (99x128cm-39x50in) s.d.1977. 4-Apr-4 Sotheby's, Singapore #128/R est:40000-60000 (S.D 90000)
£30108	$48172	€43958	Bunga kana (115x145cm-45x57in) s.d.1984. 18-May-3 Sotheby's, Singapore #143/R est:40000-60000 (S.D 84000)
£31046	$56193	€45327	Nude (75x140cm-30x55in) s.d.1966 prov. 4-Apr-4 Sotheby's, Singapore #129/R est:80000-120000 (S.D 95000)
£32258	$51613	€47097	Bedroom scene (98x136cm-39x54in) s.d.1971. 18-May-3 Sotheby's, Singapore #140/R est:40000-60000 (S.D 90000)
£32680	$59150	€47713	Leak (143x117cm-56x46in) s.d.1979. 4-Apr-4 Sotheby's, Singapore #155/R est:100000-120000 (S.D 100000)
£35948	$65065	€52484	Penjual bebek (160x100cm-63x39in) s.d.1969. 4-Apr-4 Sotheby's, Singapore #126/R est:60000-80000 (S.D 110000)
£36559	$58495	€53376	Penari legong kipas merah (128x97cm-50x38in) s.d.1979. 18-May-3 Sotheby's, Singapore #137/R est:50000-70000 (S.D 102000)
£36559	$58495	€53376	Fighting dogs (104x125cm-41x49in) s.d.1960 lit. 18-May-3 Sotheby's, Singapore #141/R est:60000-80000 (S.D 102000)
£39118	$70413	€57112	Man with a rooster (97x131cm-38x52in) mono.d.1975 prov. 25-Apr-4 Christie's, Hong Kong #591/R est:280000-400000 (HK.D 550000)
£39216	$70980	€57255	Self portrait and masks (140x120cm-55x47in) s.d.1964. 4-Apr-4 Sotheby's, Singapore #127/R est:75000-95000 (S.D 120000)
£43478	$67391	€63478	Snow over Ohio (98x127cm-39x50in) s.d.1962 exhib. 6-Oct-2 Sotheby's, Singapore #115/R est:35000-45000 (S.D 120000)
£45139	$75382	€65903	Bertarung (110x140cm-43x55in) s.d.1965 lit. 12-Oct-3 Sotheby's, Singapore #127/R est:70000-90000 (S.D 130000)
£45752	$82810	€66798	Market (93x120cm-37x47in) s. lit. 4-Apr-4 Sotheby's, Singapore #154/R est:140000-160000 (S.D 140000)
£46259	$82803	€68000	Eiffel Tower, Paris (70x50cm-28x20in) mono. indis d. 16-Mar-4 Christie's, Amsterdam #137/R est:12000-16000
£51613	$82581	€75355	Waringin tree (90x143cm-35x56in) s.d.1969 lit. 18-May-3 Sotheby's, Singapore #135/R est:45000-65000 (S.D 144000)
£61776	$103166	€90193	Self portrait (120x97cm-47x38in) init.d.1968. 26-Oct-3 Christie's, Hong Kong #96/R est:250000-350000 (HK.D 800000)
£62092	$112386	€90654	Lelaki dengan Ayam Jantan (119x138cm-47x54in) init.d.1964. 3-Apr-4 Glerum, Singapore #35/R est:80000-110000 (S.D 190000)
£68817	$110108	€100473	Man and cockerel (130x98cm-51x39in) s.d.1965 prov. 18-May-3 Sotheby's, Singapore #138/R est:60000-80000 (S.D 192000)
£68841	$106703	€100508	Self portrait with the artist's wife (107x81cm-42x32in) s.i.d.1952 exhib. 6-Oct-2 Sotheby's, Singapore #113/R est:70000-90000 (S.D 190000)
£71124	$128023	€103841	Balinese girl and child with offerings (130x102cm-51x40in) mono.d.1965. 25-Apr-4 Christie's, Hong Kong #590/R est:480000-650000 (HK.D 1000000)
£73118	$116989	€106752	Eiffel tower (125x100cm-49x39in) s.d.1977. 18-May-3 Sotheby's, Singapore #136/R est:60000-80000 (S.D 204000)
£76389	$127569	€111528	Self portrait (129x99cm-51x39in) s.d.1975. 12-Oct-3 Sotheby's, Singapore #128/R est:120000-180000 (S.D 220000)
£90323	$144516	€131872	Self portrait (130x95cm-51x37in) s.d.1975. 18-May-3 Sotheby's, Singapore #139/R est:60000-80000 (S.D 252000)
£92664	$154749	€135289	Two Balines girls with offerings (135x112cm-53x44in) init.i.d.1956 prov. 26-Oct-3 Christie's, Hong Kong #97/R est:320000-600000 (HK.D 1200000)
£108108	$180541	€157838	Drinking tuak (98x167cm-39x66in) init.d.1968. 26-Oct-3 Christie's, Hong Kong #95/R est:220000-320000 (HK.D 1400000)
£112319	$174094	€163986	Strip-tease in Baltimore (101x122cm-40x48in) s.d.1962 exhib. 6-Oct-2 Sotheby's, Singapore #114/R (S.D 310000)
£114379	$207026	€166993	Minum tauk (95x128cm-37x50in) s.d.1969. 4-Apr-4 Sotheby's, Singapore #130/R est:80000-100000 (S.D 350000)
£170697	$307255	€249218	Pohon beringin - banyan tree (154x137cm-61x54in) mono.d.1968. 25-Apr-4 Christie's, Hong Kong #589/R est:450000-650000 (HK.D 2400000)
£184922	$332859	€269986	View of Manhattan from Brooklyn Bridge (76x122cm-30x48in) mono.d.1962 prov. 25-Apr-4 Christie's, Hong Kong #592/R est:380000-550000 (HK.D 2600000)
Works on paper			
£5435	$8424	€7935	Self portraits (55x55cm-22x22in) s. ink. 6-Oct-2 Sotheby's, Singapore #144/R est:5000-7000 (S.D 15000)
£10417	$17396	€15209	Female Nude (46x58cm-18x23in) s.d.1949 mixed media. 12-Oct-3 Sotheby's, Singapore #134/R est:30000-40000 (S.D 30000)
£15625	$26094	€22813	Self portrait (134x49cm-53x19in) s.i. mixed media. 12-Oct-3 Sotheby's, Singapore #133/R est:38000-48000 (S.D 45000)

AFFLECK, Andrew F (fl.1910-1935) British

£600	$1110	€876	Belinzona, Italy (51x64cm-20x25in) s. tempera. 9-Mar-4 Gorringes, Lewes #2027
£1192	$2170	€1800	River landscape (51x76cm-20x30in) s.verso. 18-Jun-4 Bolland & Marotz, Bremen #574/R est:870

AFFLECK, William (1869-1909) British

Works on paper			
£580	$1003	€847	Tranquil wooded river landscapes (22x31cm-9x12in) s.d.1922 W/C pair. 9-Dec-3 Rosebery Fine Art, London #582/R
£735	$1352	€1073	Woman with doves (45x31cm-18x12in) s. W/C. 29-Mar-4 Goodman, Sydney #131/R (A.D 1800)

AFFORTUNATI, Aldo (1906-) Italian

£231	$400	€337	Ballerinas on stage in long dresses (30x41cm-12x16in) s. 10-Dec-3 Boos Gallery, Michigan #530/R
£231	$400	€337	Ballerinas on stage in long dresses (30x41cm-12x16in) s. 10-Dec-3 Boos Gallery, Michigan #531/R
£291	$530	€440	Old wall and countryside (35x50cm-14x20in) s. s.i.verso board. 17-Jun-4 Galleria Pananti, Florence #596/R
£1517	$2534	€2200	Campment by the sea (33x62cm-13x24in) s. board. 14-Nov-3 Farsetti, Prato #534/R est:2000-2500

AFONSO, Nadir (1920-) Portuguese

£2759	$4579	€4000	Untitled (73x64cm-29x25in) s.d.46. 1-Oct-3 Ansorena, Madrid #579/R est:4000

AFRICANO, Nicholas (1948-) American

£659	$1200	€962	Study for Grandmother (51x40cm-20x16in) s.i.d.1984 verso acrylic fabric diptych. 29-Jun-4 Sotheby's, New York #603/R est:2000-3000
Works on paper			
£381	$700	€556	Camille with a hat (51x36cm-20x14in) init.i.d.1989 verso wax mortar dye linen prov. 25-Jun-4 Freeman, Philadelphia #253/R

AFRO (1912-1976) Italian

£6711	$12013	€10000	Composition (59x49cm-23x19in) tempera paper on canvas. 30-May-4 Meeting Art, Vercelli #36 est:10000
£9459	$16649	€14000	Composition (48x66cm-19x26in) s.d.52 tempera pastel paper prov. 24-May-4 Christie's, Milan #249/R est:20000-30000
£13768	$22580	€19000	Untitled (70x100cm-28x39in) s. tempera mixed media card prov. 27-May-3 Sotheby's, Milan #193/R est:12000-15000
£15385	$26154	€22000	Still life with ninepin (40x51cm-16x20in) s.d.41 prov.exhib.lit. 25-Nov-3 Sotheby's, Milan #204/R est:18000-22000
£52448	$89161	€75000	Portrait of Turcato (62x73cm-24x29in) s.d.942 exhib.lit. 25-Nov-3 Sotheby's, Milan #226/R est:75000-90000
£53333	$96000	€80000	Turtle (35x52cm-14x20in) s.d.66 exhib.lit. 22-Apr-4 Finarte Semenzato, Rome #348/R est:30000-35000
£65000	$108550	€94900	Composizione (50x60cm-20x24in) s.d.58 prov.exhib.lit. 21-Oct-3 Christie's, London #25/R est:30000-40000
£126667	$233067	€190000	Tiresia (145x100cm-57x39in) s.d.75 exhib.lit. 8-Jun-4 Finarte Semenzato, Milan #458/R est:190000-210000
£270000	$450900	€394200	La scheggia (92x150cm-36x59in) s.d.56 prov.exhib.lit. 21-Oct-3 Christie's, London #20/R est:180000-240000
£286713	$487413	€410000	Prisons (87x129cm-34x51in) s.d.58 oil mixed media prov.exhib.lit. 25-Nov-3 Sotheby's, Milan #216/R est:170000-250000
Prints			
£2657	$4517	€3800	Totem (64x79cm-25x31in) s. eau forte exhib.lit. 24-Nov-3 Christie's, Milan #13/R est:1800-2200
Works on paper			
£2685	$4805	€4000	Composition (24x33cm-9x13in) pencil pastel W/C exec.c.1952. 25-May-4 Sotheby's, Milan #102/R est:4000
£4483	$7486	€6500	Study for 'Season in the West' (10x15cm-4x6in) s.d.56 W/C. 13-Nov-3 Finarte Semenzato, Rome #216/R est:3800-4500
£11888	$20210	€17000	Summer in the allotment (57x43cm-22x17in) s.d.55 chl. 25-Nov-3 Sotheby's, Milan #222/R est:18000-22000
£11972	$19873	€17000	Small uncovered canvas (15x23cm-6x9in) s.d.69 mixed media on canvas. 13-Jun-3 Farsetti, Prato #317/R est:18000
£14085	$23380	€20000	Untitled (56x43cm-22x17in) mixed media card. 11-Jun-3 Finarte Semenzato, Milan #567/R est:22000
£21127	$36972	€30000	Untitled (50x71cm-20x28in) s.d.67 mixed media paper on canvas. 16-Dec-3 Porro, Milan #30/R est:40000-45000
£27972	$47552	€40000	Newspaper 64-3 (60x85cm-24x33in) s.d.64 s.i.d.on stretcher mixed media paper on canvas exhib. 29-Nov-3 Farsetti, Prato #475/R est:30000-35000
£48322	$86497	€72000	Bitter source (30x50cm-12x20in) s.d.58 mixed media board exhib.lit. 25-May-4 Sotheby's, Milan #273/R est:50000-70000
£50000	$88000	€74000	Re-consruction and peace (37x100cm-15x39in) s.d.54 mixed media masonite lit. 24-May-4 Christie's, Milan #346/R est:60000-80000
£52448	$89161	€75000	Beautiful bride (104x155cm-41x61in) s. s.i.d.1966 verso mixed media paper on canvas lit. 29-Nov-3 Farsetti, Prato #477/R est:60000-70000

AFSARY, Cyrus (1940-) American

£1366	$2200	€1981	Apache man (14x11cm-6x4in) 22-Aug-3 Altermann Galleries, Santa Fe #110
£1615	$2600	€2342	Green valley (16x12cm-6x5in) 22-Aug-3 Altermann Galleries, Santa Fe #111
£2941	$5000	€4294	Afternoon rest (38x76cm-15x30in) 1-Nov-3 Altermann Galleries, Santa Fe #161
£5000	$8500	€7300	Face to face (36x71cm-14x28in) oil on linen. 1-Nov-3 Altermann Galleries, Santa Fe #178
£5587	$10000	€8157	Distant view (61x91cm-24x36in) 15-May-4 Altermann Galleries, Santa Fe #176/R
£8380	$15000	€12235	Contemplation (76x61cm-30x24in) 15-May-4 Altermann Galleries, Santa Fe #21/R

AGADATI, Baruch (20th C) ?

Works on paper			
£304	$550	€444	Dancer (50x35cm-20x14in) s. mixed media cardboard. 1-Apr-4 Ben-Ami, Tel Aviv #4735/R

AGAFONOV, Evgeniy Andreievich (1879-c.1956) Russian

£1156	$2000	€1688	Pink Orchard (69x61cm-27x24in) s. 10-Dec-3 Bonhams & Butterfields, San Francisco #6062/R est:3000-5000

AGAM, Yaacov (1928-) Israeli

£2168	$3685	€3100	Untitled - changing colours (46x70cm-18x28in) s.i.d.1973 verso acrylic board prov.exhib. 27-Nov-3 Lempertz, Koln #2/R est:2500
£2941	$5000	€4294	Stand still (112x112cm-44x44in) s.i.d.70 verso. 9-Nov-3 Bonhams & Butterfields, Los Angeles #4080/R est:4000-6000
£5369	$9987	€8000	Composition (20x40cm-8x16in) s.d.1951 isorel. 3-Mar-4 Tajan, Paris #137/R est:12000-15000
£8430	$14500	€12308	Structure couleurs (33x33cm-13x13in) s.i.d.1973-74 oil on corrugated metal prov. 3-Dec-3 Doyle, New York #48/R est:14000-18000
£8939	$16000	€13051	Image mage (56x56cm-22x22in) oil corrugated metal canvas covered panel. 6-May-4 Doyle, New York #83/R est:10000-15000
Sculpture			
£1223	$2250	€1786	Andromedar - Modular spaceograph (48x48x7cm-19x19x3in) s. polymorph col serigraph folded pvc lit. 8-Jun-4 Germann, Zurich #12/R est:1800-2200 (S.FR 2800)
£1448	$2462	€2114	Untitled (66x65x7cm-26x26x3in) s. polymorph col serigraph on folded PVC. 25-Nov-3 Germann, Zurich #141/R est:3000-4000 (S.FR 3200)
£1497	$2500	€2186	Rotating sculpture (61x60cm-24x24in) s.d.1974 num.5/4 polished bronze. 7-Oct-3 Sotheby's, New York #389 est:2000-3000
£1810	$3023	€2643	Agamorama (28x32x12cm-11x13x5in) s. plastic pvc col serigraph lit. 24-Jun-3 Germann, Zurich #30/R est:5000-6000 (S.FR 4000)
£1921	$3535	€2805	Tower (87x22x22cm-34x9x9in) s. polymorph serigraph plastic. 8-Jun-4 Germann, Zurich #13/R est:4000-5000 (S.FR 4400)
£1991	$3385	€2907	Untitled (92x91x7cm-36x36x3in) s. polymorph col serigraph on folded PVC. 25-Nov-3 Germann, Zurich #140/R est:4000-5000 (S.FR 4400)
£2620	$4821	€3825	Space divider (22x18x7cm-9x7x3in) s.i. silvered brass. 8-Jun-4 Germann, Zurich #63/R est:6000-8000 (S.FR 6000)

£2800 $5068 €4088 Touch me (46x23x42cm-18x9x17in) s. chrome plated steel cast c.1970 lit. 1-Apr-4 Christie's, Kensington #216/R est:2000-3000
£8054 $14255 €12000 Pleine ocrhestration 4 themes contrepoints (9x12cm-4x5in) s.i.d.1962 verso relief metal paint on panel prov.exhib. 28-Apr-4 Artcurial Briest, Paris #336/R est:12000-15000
Works on paper
£720 $1310 €1080 Untitled (35x40cm-14x16in) s. mixed media. 21-Jun-4 Subastas Odalys, Caracas #21

AGAR, Eileen (1899-1991) British
£280 $482 €409 Watch (61x46cm-24x18in) s. acrylic prov. 3-Dec-3 Christie's, Kensington #763/R
£700 $1295 €1022 Animal (25x35cm-10x14in) s. s.d.1967. 11-Mar-4 Christie's, Kensington #234/R
£1500 $2640 €2190 Sunburst (41x30cm-16x12in) oil col crayon pencil paperboard. 19-May-4 Sotheby's, Olympia #306/R est:1500-2000
£1900 $3458 €2774 Two figures (22x17cm-9x7in) s. oil collage. 15-Jun-4 Bonhams, New Bond Street #85/R est:800-1200
£2800 $5180 €4088 Untitled (102x126cm-40x50in) s. s.d.1973 verso. 13-Jul-4 Bonhams, Knightsbridge #2/R est:3000-5000
Works on paper
£280 $504 €409 Collection of shells (23x15cm-9x6in) s. pen gouache. 20-Jan-4 Bonhams, Knightsbridge #108
£800 $1360 €1168 Return of Nautilus (22x29cm-9x11in) s.d.1983 i.verso W/C gouache felt-tip pen pencil prov. 26-Nov-3 Sotheby's, Olympia #183/R
£900 $1530 €1314 Sunburst (42x29cm-17x11in) mixed media board. 26-Nov-3 Hamptons Fine Art, Godalming #141
£2000 $3580 €2920 Abstract composition with fish (54x36cm-21x14in) s. W/C gouache. 16-Mar-4 Bonhams, New Bond Street #103/R est:1200-1800
£2000 $3580 €2920 Surrealist head (60x39cm-24x15in) pencil gouache oil prov. 14-May-4 Christie's, Kensington #633/R est:2000-3000

AGASSE, Jacques Laurent (1767-1849) Swiss
£25862 $46293 €37759 Milking time or visit to the farm (60x50cm-24x20in) mono. prov.lit. 17-May-4 Beurret, Zurich #4/R est:60000-80000 (S.FR 60000)
£63953 $110000 €93371 Portrait of Lord Rivers with two greyhounds (107x91cm-42x36in) painted c.1825 prov.exhib. 5-Dec-3 Christie's, Rockefeller NY #14/R est:120000-180000
Works on paper
£2632 $4395 €3843 Caleche tiree par quatre chevaux (22x26cm-9x10in) dr. exec.c.1825. 16-Nov-3 Koller, Geneva #1238 est:7000-9000 (S.FR 6000)
£5000 $9000 €7300 Study of a saddled horse held by a man at the bridle (19x26cm-7x10in) red chk oil paint. 21-Jan-4 Sotheby's, New York #144/R est:8000-12000

AGASSE, Jacques Laurent (attrib) (1767-1849) Swiss
£1584 $2692 €2313 Study of brown horse (42x51cm-17x20in) paper on board. 19-Nov-3 Fischer, Luzern #1071/R est:3500-5000 (S.FR 3500)

AGASSE, Jacques Laurent (circle) (1767-1849) Swiss
£12000 $21120 €17520 Bay racehorse held by a trainer in a landscape with jockey and other figures (75x100cm-30x39in) prov. 21-May-4 Christie's, London #81/R est:7000-10000

AGATHON, Leonard (1841-?) French
Sculpture
£3067 $5551 €4600 Female figure (25cm-10in) s. verso bronze lit. 1-Apr-4 Van Ham, Cologne #1112/R est:2800

AGAUD, Tjov (20th C) ?
Sculpture
£3843 $6418 €5611 Mother and child (100x93x54cm-39x37x21in) s. bronze. 13-Oct-3 Blomqvist, Oslo #346/R est:50000-70000 (N.KR 45000)

AGAZZI, Carlo (1870-1922) Italian
£347 $573 €500 On the Navigli (60x100cm-24x39in) s.i.d.1895. 1-Jul-3 Il Ponte, Milan #467

AGAZZI, Rinaldo (1857-1939) Italian
Works on paper
£395 $726 €600 Seated peasant (32x26cm-13x10in) s.d.95 chl lead. 23-Jun-4 Finarte Semenzato, Rome #6/R
£1678 $3003 €2500 Face of woman (69x49cm-27x19in) s.d.1922 W/C pastel card. 25-May-4 Finarte Semenzato, Milan #146/R est:2000-2500
£1901 $3289 €2700 Face of woman (69x49cm-27x19in) s.d.1922 pastel W/C card. 9-Dec-3 Finarte Semenzato, Milan #57/R est:2000-2500

AGERBEEK, Ernst C L (20th C) Dutch
£9266 $15475 €13528 Chinese district in oil Batavia (62x80cm-24x31in) s. painted c.1926 prov.lit. 26-Oct-3 Christie's, Hong Kong #17/R est:140000-160000 (HK.D 120000)

AGERSNAP, Hans (1857-1925) Danish
£362 $648 €529 Winter landscape (53x79cm-21x31in) s. 10-May-4 Rasmussen, Vejle #201/R (D.KR 4000)
£478 $775 €693 Landscape from old Vinding near Vejle (58x89cm-23x35in) s.d.1899. 4-Aug-3 Rasmussen, Vejle #301/R (D.KR 5000)
£897 $1641 €1300 Extensive landscape (86x125cm-34x49in) s. 27-Jan-4 Dorotheum, Vienna #26/R

AGGER, Knud (1895-1973) Danish
£398 $637 €577 Summer day with fishing boat on the way to harbour (68x78cm-27x31in) s. 17-Sep-3 Kunsthallen, Copenhagen #240 (D.KR 4200)
£474 $758 €687 Interior scene with woman (66x72cm-26x28in) s. 17-Sep-3 Kunsthallen, Copenhagen #236/R (D.KR 5000)

AGGETT, Lionel (1938-) British
Works on paper
£440 $695 €642 Summer, St James (53x74cm-21x29in) s. pastel exhib. 5-Sep-3 Honiton Galleries, Honiton #25/R

AGGHAZY, Gyula (1850-1919) Hungarian
£802 $1419 €1171 One Hundred Acre wood (28x35cm-11x14in) s. cardboard. 28-Apr-4 Kieselbach, Budapest #71/R (H.F 300000)

AGGIAQ, George (1917-) North American
Sculpture
£950 $1700 €1387 Eskimo with canoe and paddle (30x18x8cm-12x7x3in) s.i. ivory green soapstone exec.c.1950 prov. 7-May-4 Sloans & Kenyon, Bethesda #57/R est:2200-2600

AGHAJANIAN, Sophie (20th C) Irish?
£338 $592 €480 Shape of light (52x60cm-20x24in) init. 16-Dec-3 James Adam, Dublin #9/R

AGLIETTI, Romeo (19/20th C) Italian
£1333 $2453 €2000 Paysage de Kabylie (32x42cm-13x17in) s. panel. 14-Jun-4 Gros & Delettrez, Paris #460/R est:2000-3000
£3191 $5330 €4500 Koubba surplombant la baie (55x80cm-22x31in) s.d.1933 panel. 16-Jun-3 Gros & Delettrez, Paris #253/R est:4000-5000

AGLIO, Agostino (1777-1857) Italian
£660 $1208 €964 Holy Family (35x45cm-14x18in) s.d.1848 board. 7-Apr-4 Bonhams, Bury St Edmunds #436/R
£3191 $5649 €4659 View over Heidelberg (156x207cm-61x81in) s.d.1840. 28-Apr-4 Dunbar Sloane, Auckland #50/R est:12000-15000 (NZ.D 9000)
Works on paper
£550 $985 €803 Portraits of Lord Castelreagh and William Carr, Viscount Beresford (39x32cm-15x13in) indis.sig.i. pencil chk pair. 14-May-4 Christie's, Kensington #301/R
£1250 $2325 €1825 Portrait of Sir Walter Scott (39x31cm-15x12in) pencil chk sold with two other sketches by same hand. 4-Mar-4 Christie's, Kensington #14/R est:800-1200
£2600 $4654 €3796 Portrait of Thomas Moore (37x32cm-15x13in) i. pencil white chk. 14-May-4 Christie's, Kensington #302/R est:700-900

AGNETTI, Vincenzo (1926-1981) Italian
£13423 $24027 €20000 Copy from reality (80x118cm-31x46in) s. i.d.71 verso acrylic felt board on plexiglas prov. 25-May-4 Sotheby's, Milan #155/R est:2000-2500
Photographs
£5369 $9611 €8000 Four evangelists (41x51cm-16x20in) s.d.73 photograph on card exec.1973. 28-May-4 Farsetti, Prato #280/R est:4000-5000
£6000 $10020 €8760 Semiosi (25x35cm-10x14in) s.i.d.1970 verso photo print prov. 21-Oct-3 Christie's, London #55/R est:4000-6000
Works on paper
£1972 $3273 €2800 Changeable (50x60cm-20x24in) s.d.1967 verso painted wood. 11-Jun-3 Finarte Semenzato, Milan #602/R
£2667 $4853 €4000 Tears (100x72cm-39x28in) s.d.1978 mixed media. 12-Jul-4 Il Ponte, Milan #981 est:4200-4400
£4000 $7280 €6000 Composition (73x51cm-29x20in) s.d.1975 mixed media photograph. 12-Jul-4 Il Ponte, Milan #975 est:5000-6000
£5000 $9200 €7500 Cable, telephone, cable (45x104cm-18x41in) s.i.d.73 mixed media board prov. 14-Jun-4 Porro, Milan #51/R est:7000-8000
£5634 $9352 €8000 Quando mi vidi non c'ero - When I saw myself I was not there (62x60cm-24x24in) s.i.d.1971 verso felt board exhib. 11-Jun-3 Finarte Semenzato, Milan #603/R
£7200 $12024 €10512 Ritratto d'uomo (70x84cm-28x33in) s.d.1972 verso spray paint plywood steel perspex box prov.exhib. 21-Oct-3 Christie's, London #57/R est:6000-8000

AGNINI, Aldo (1935-) Italian
Works on paper
£333 $613 €500 Only appearances (124x102cm-49x40in) s.d.1995 mixed media collage on canvas. 12-Jun-4 Meeting Art, Vercelli #826

AGOSTINELLI, Antonio (18th C) Italian
Sculpture
£4800 $8736 €7200 Untitled (52cm-20in) stone. 3-Jul-4 Finarte, Venice #254a/R est:7000-8000

AGOSTINELLI, Mario (1915-) Brazilian
£759 $1267 €1100 By the Seine (52x64cm-20x25in) s. board. 9-Jul-3 Hugo Ruef, Munich #57

AGOSTINI, Guido (19th C) Italian
£344 $550 €502 Alpine valley landscape (58x48cm-23x19in) s. 20-Sep-3 Jeffery Burchard, Florida #33/R
£377 $640 €550 Landscape with fox (63x42cm-25x17in) 7-Nov-3 Farsetti, Prato #279
£400 $736 €584 Castiglione del Lago (16x11cm-6x4in) s.d.1880 board. 29-Mar-4 Bonhams, Bath #72/R
£950 $1748 €1387 Alpine landscape with town on a mountain above a lake (38x30cm-15x12in) 24-Jun-4 Ewbank, Send #574/R
£1549 $2494 €2200 Vedute dell'Africo vecchio (35x19cm-14x7in) three. 8-May-3 Farsetti, Prato #425 est:1800-2200
£2000 $3680 €2920 Capriccio of the Roma campagna (21x26cm-8x10in) s. board oval. 25-Mar-4 Christie's, Kensington #96/R est:2000-3000
£2837 $4738 €4000 View of Certaldo (43x32cm-17x13in) s. i.verso. 14-Oct-3 Finarte Semenzato, Milan #90/R est:4000

AGOSTINI, Max Michel (1914-1997) French
£517 $859 €750 Bouquet de fleurs (61x46cm-24x18in) s. 30-Sep-3 Blanchet, Paris #241/R
£738 $1307 €1100 Champ de lavande (38x55cm-15x22in) s. 29-Apr-4 Claude Aguttes, Neuilly #63

AGOSTINI, Peter (1913-) American
Sculpture
£2235 $4000 €3263 Saracen II 1215 AD (74x66cm-29x26in) s.d.1960 num.1/3 prov.exhib.lit. 16-May-4 Wright, Chicago #357/R est:1000-1500

AGOSTINI, Tony (1916-1990) Italian
£208 $381 €304 Nature morte au crabe (46x38cm-18x15in) 27-Jan-4 Iegor de Saint Hippolyte, Montreal #39 (C.D 500)
£671 $1248 €1000 La chaise fleurie (22x12cm-9x5in) s. pair. 3-Mar-4 Ferri, Paris #153
Works on paper
£377 $640 €550 Nature morte a la theiere (27x20cm-11x8in) s. gouache. 9-Nov-3 Eric Pillon, Calais #243/R

AGRASOT Y JUAN, Joaquim (1837-1919) Spanish
£1092 $1987 €1594 Spanish peasant (34x18cm-13x7in) s. panel. 16-Jun-4 Fischer, Luzern #1139/R est:2500-2700 (S.FR 2500)
£1585 $2741 €2250 Donkey (25x25cm-10x10in) s. 10-Dec-3 Castellana, Madrid #209/R est:2000
£4861 $7924 €7000 Embroidering (24x16cm-9x6in) s. board. 23-Sep-3 Durán, Madrid #196/R est:5500
£7692 $12846 €11000 Portrait of woman (24x19cm-9x7in) s. board. 30-Jun-3 Ansorena, Madrid #333/R est:4800
£11348 $18950 €16000 Valencian woman playing the guitar (91x51cm-36x20in) s. exhib.lit. 20-Oct-3 Durán, Madrid #120/R
Works on paper
£216 $400 €315 Venice (23x13cm-9x5in) s. W/C. 13-Mar-4 Susanin's, Chicago #6195/R

AGRESTI, Livio (attrib) (1508-1580) Italian
Works on paper
£420 $756 €613 Last supper (10x14cm-4x6in) black chk prov. 20-Apr-4 Sotheby's, Olympia #32/R

AGRESTI, R (19th C) French
£829 $1500 €1210 Good book (34x43cm-13x17in) s. 30-Mar-4 Christie's, Rockefeller NY #80/R est:2000-3000

AGRICOLA, Carl Joseph (1779-1852) German
£3356 $5940 €5000 Scene from Sappho from Franz Grillparzer (72x65cm-28x26in) s.d.818 verso. 28-Apr-4 Wiener Kunst Auktionen, Vienna #10/R est:5000-10000

AGRICOLA, Carl Joseph (attrib) (1779-1852) German
£1958 $3329 €2800 Venus and little Cupid (113x92cm-44x36in) 28-Nov-3 Wiener Kunst Auktionen, Vienna #412/R est:2000-6000
£5034 $9262 €7500 Cupid and Psyche (113x92cm-44x36in) 24-Mar-4 Dorotheum, Vienna #247/R est:6000-7000

AGRICOLA, Christoph Ludwig (1667-1719) German
£6207 $10366 €9000 Landscape with travellers. Landscape with riders (16x22cm-6x9in) tempera paper pair exhib. 12-Nov-3 Sotheby's, Milan #105/R est:8000-12000
Works on paper
£2500 $4500 €3650 Red fronted parakeet (28x20cm-11x8in) i.verso bodycol. 22-Jan-4 Christie's, Rockefeller NY #201/R est:2000-3000

AGRICOLA, Christoph Ludwig (attrib) (1667-1719) German
Works on paper
£8000 $14400 €11680 River landscapes with figures (15x19cm-6x7in) gouache paper on card set of eight varying sizes. 21-Apr-4 Bonhams, New Bond Street #86/R est:4000-6000

AGRICOLA, Rudolf Alexander (1912-) Russian
Sculpture
£1818 $3091 €2600 Girl (61cm-24in) s. bronze Cast.Noack, Berlin. 29-Nov-3 Arnold, Frankfurt #9/R est:1400
£2483 $4146 €3600 Nude boy (61cm-24in) i. brown pat bronze Cast H Noack. 13-Nov-3 Neumeister, Munich #187/R est:4000-4200

AGTHE, Curt (1862-1943) German
£367 $667 €550 Farmer's wife with umbrella in front of farmhouse (21x31cm-8x12in) s.d.92 i.verso. 1-Jul-4 Neumeister, Munich #2647

AGUADO, Carlos (1936-) Spanish
£395 $714 €600 Landscape with trees (45x38cm-18x15in) s.d.81. 14-Apr-4 Ansorena, Madrid #192/R
£1208 $2259 €1800 Old door (38x46cm-15x18in) s. i.verso. 24-Feb-4 Durán, Madrid #1/R est:500

AGUAYO, Fermin (1926-1977) Spanish
£2133 $3861 €3200 Self-portrait (35x27cm-14x11in) s.verso canvas on board prov. 30-Mar-4 Segre, Madrid #234/R est:750
£3521 $5634 €5000 Man seen from the back (46x33cm-18x13in) s.verso board. 16-Sep-3 Segre, Madrid #129/R est:2500

AGUEDA DE LA PISA (1942-) Spanish
£493 $908 €750 Composition (100x100cm-39x39in) s.d.72. 22-Jun-4 Durán, Madrid #94/R
£493 $908 €750 Composition (100x100cm-39x39in) s.d.72. 22-Jun-4 Durán, Madrid #93/R

AGUELI, Ivan (1869-1917) Swedish
£3846 $6615 €5615 Portrait of girl (23x19cm-9x7in) exhib.prov. 2-Dec-3 Bukowskis, Stockholm #10/R est:40000-50000 (S.KR 50000)
£4923 $8468 €7188 Nature morte (25x32cm-10x13in) canvas on panel prov.exhib.lit. 2-Dec-3 Bukowskis, Stockholm #8/R est:80000-100000 (S.KR 64000)
£15385 $26462 €22462 Woman in profile, possibly Madame Huot (54x46cm-21x18in) canvas on panel. 2-Dec-3 Bukowskis, Stockholm #9/R est:80000-100000 (S.KR 200000)
£23651 $42336 €34530 Evening (41x20cm-16x8in) i.d.1937 verso canvas on panel prov.exhib.lit. 25-May-4 Bukowskis, Stockholm #6/R est:200000-220000 (S.KR 320000)
£24231 $41677 €35377 Landscape with brook (18x23cm-7x9in) i. canvas on panel prov.exhib.lit. 2-Dec-3 Bukowskis, Stockholm #11/R est:225000-250000 (S.KR 315000)
Works on paper
£654 $1125 €955 Female study (30x23cm-12x9in) st.sig. pencil double-sided. 7-Dec-3 Uppsala Auktionskammare, Uppsala #155/R (S.KR 8500)

AGUERO, Carlos (20th C) Argentinian
£824 $1500 €1203 Dream protector. Tales (33x24cm-13x9in) i.d.1979 verso tempera paper pair. 5-Jul-4 Arroyo, Buenos Aires #63/R est:1500
Works on paper
£1093 $2000 €1596 Dialogue (24x33cm-9x13in) mixed media. 1-Jun-4 Arroyo, Buenos Aires #23

AGUIAR, Jose (1895-?) Spanish
£3172 $5266 €4600 Don Quixote and Sancho (94x67cm-37x26in) s. board. 1-Oct-3 Ansorena, Madrid #584/R est:3800
£3521 $6162 €5000 Nude (92x62cm-36x24in) s. double-sided. 16-Dec-3 Durán, Madrid #163/R est:4750
£13194 $20979 €19000 Crucifixion (200x156cm-79x61in) s.d.964 prov.lit. 29-Apr-3 Durán, Madrid #159/R est:18000

AGUIARI, Tito (1834-1908) Italian
Works on paper
£839 $1443 €1200 Lunch time (65x47cm-26x19in) s. W/C. 3-Dec-3 Stadion, Trieste #1152/R

AGUILAR ALCUAZ, Federico (1932-) Philippino
£2581 $4129 €3768 Yellow still life (92x73cm-36x29in) s.i.d.1963 verso prov. 18-May-3 Sotheby's, Singapore #96/R est:6000-8000 (S.D 7200)
£3871 $6194 €5652 Still life with fruits and flowers (66x80cm-26x31in) s. s.d.1960 prov. 18-May-3 Sotheby's, Singapore #95/R est:6000-8000 (S.D 10800)
£4623 $8321 €6750 Tap room (54x71cm-21x28in) s.i.d.81. 25-Apr-4 Christie's, Hong Kong #545/R est:55000-70000 (HK.D 65000)
£11380 $20484 €16615 Panoramic view of Manila (100x300cm-39x118in) s.d.1977. 25-Apr-4 Christie's, Hong Kong #562/R est:150000-200000 (HK.D 160000)

AGUILAR DE LA RUA, Ildefonso (1945-) Spanish
Works on paper
£1377 $2258 €1900 Fragmentos de lava 5 (90x110cm-35x43in) s. s.i.d.1997 verso mixed media panel. 27-May-3 Durán, Madrid #77/R est:1900

AGUILAR MORE, Ramon (1924-) Spanish
£1250 $2063 €1800 Monumental, Barcelona (49x32cm-19x13in) s. s.i.verso board. 2-Jul-3 Ansorena, Madrid #930/R

AGUILO, Miguel (1928-) Spanish
£458 $792 €650 Flagellation (141x105cm-56x41in) s.d.1945. 15-Dec-3 Ansorena, Madrid #67/R

AGUIRRE Y ORTEGUI, Philippe (1961-) ?
Sculpture
£1389 $2319 €2000 Hombre (46cm-18in) s.d.1988 bronze. 21-Oct-3 Campo, Vlaamse Kaai #350 est:2000-2300

AGUIRRE, Ignacio (1900-1990) Mexican
£10667 $19627 €16000 Self-portrait (64x49cm-25x19in) s.d.1943 cardboard prov. 10-Jun-4 Christie's, Paris #27/R est:8000-10000

AGUIRRE, Luis Fernando (1935-) Spanish
£282 $487 €400 Female nude and gentleman (81x100cm-32x39in) s. s.d.1968 verso. 15-Dec-3 Ansorena, Madrid #989/R
£282 $487 €400 Vertical going on on horizontal (81x100cm-32x39in) s. s.d.1968 verso. 15-Dec-3 Ansorena, Madrid #1014/R
£401 $694 €570 Cold clothes to remember (120x100cm-47x39in) s. s.d.1969 verso. 15-Dec-3 Ansorena, Madrid #1004/R
£414 $745 €600 Going out for dinner (100x81cm-39x32in) s. 26-Jan-4 Ansorena, Madrid #868/R
£448 $807 €650 Embracing (97x130cm-38x51in) s. s.i.d.1966-67 verso. 26-Jan-4 Ansorena, Madrid #935/R
£486 $802 €700 Relax (90x70cm-35x28in) s. s.i.d.64 verso. 2-Jul-3 Ansorena, Madrid #946/R
£514 $873 €750 Combined forms (90x80cm-35x31in) s. sid.1970 verso. 4-Nov-3 Ansorena, Madrid #888/R
£556 $917 €800 Don Carnal and Lady Cuaresma (100x81cm-39x32in) s.i.d.1968 verso. 2-Jul-3 Ansorena, Madrid #910/R

£556 $917 €800 Blue man (100x81cm-39x32in) s. s.i.d.1967 verso. 2-Jul-3 Ansorena, Madrid #1028/R
£567 $919 €800 Formas en evolucion (100x81cm-39x32in) s. s.i.d.1970 verso. 20-May-3 Ansorena, Madrid #277/R
£685 $1164 €1000 Right now (130x81cm-51x32in) s. sid.1966 verso. 4-Nov-3 Ansorena, Madrid #1004/R
£922 $1494 €1300 Paraiso limitado (90x81cm-35x32in) lit. 20-May-3 Ansorena, Madrid #296/R

AGUNA, Encarnacion (?) Spanish
£293 $489 €425 Market (38x46cm-15x18in) s. 17-Nov-3 Durán, Madrid #628/R

AGUZZI, Fabio (1953-) Italian
£1000 $1840 €1500 Bread (45x60cm-18x24in) s.i.verso. 12-Jun-4 Meeting Art, Vercelli #387/R est:1500

AH, Quah (?) ?
Works on paper
£1766 $3250 €2578 Buffalo Dance (46x41cm-18x16in) gouache. 24-Jun-4 Sotheby's, New York #206/R est:1500-2000

AHL, C F (20th C) ?
£325 $601 €475 The entrance to Gudhjem Harbour (31x45cm-12x18in) s. 15-Mar-4 Rasmussen, Vejle #137 (D.KR 3600)

AHL, Henry Hammond (1869-1953) American
£252 $450 €368 Springfield autumn (25x39cm-10x15in) s. 14-May-4 Skinner, Boston #188/R
£484 $900 €707 Webester (20x25cm-8x10in) s. i.verso canvasboard. 5-Mar-4 Skinner, Boston #433/R
£3106 $5000 €4535 Apple blossom hillside (51x66cm-20x26in) s. 20-Aug-3 James Julia, Fairfield #1414/R est:5000-7000

AHLBERG, Arvid Magnus (1851-1932) Swedish
£399 $718 €599 Seascape with sailing vessel (38x54cm-15x21in) s. 25-Apr-4 Goteborg Auktionsverk, Sweden #166/R (S.KR 5500)

AHLBERG, Johan (1752-1813) Swedish
£1344 $2419 €1962 Female nude - Amphrition (145x112cm-57x44in) after van Loo. 24-Apr-4 Rasmussen, Havnen #2273/R est:10000 (D.KR 15000)

AHLBERG, John (1881-?) Swedish
£296 $529 €432 Boulevard Edgar Quinet, Paris (35x27cm-14x11in) s. d.1913 verso panel. 28-May-4 Uppsala Auktionskammare, Uppsala #238/R (S.KR 4000)

AHLBERG, Ole (1949-) Danish
£717 $1290 €1047 Composition (81x100cm-32x39in) s.d.1986. 24-Apr-4 Rasmussen, Havnen #4100/R (D.KR 8000)

AHLERS-HESTERMANN, Friedrich (1883-1973) German
£1678 $2970 €2500 Portrait of woman from Brockmann family, Hamburg (72x56cm-28x22in) s.d.1923. 28-Apr-4 Schopman, Hamburg #596/R est:3500
£6711 $12349 €10000 Window in Paris (92x73cm-36x29in) s.d.1912. 24-Mar-4 Hugo Ruef, Munich #1204/R est:8000
£17114 $31490 €25500 White bridge (54x66cm-21x26in) s.d. prov. 26-Mar-4 Ketterer, Hamburg #291/R est:10000-12000
£23333 $42700 €35000 Young men in garden pavilion (100x120cm-39x47in) s.d.1904 prov.exhib.lit. 5-Jun-4 Lempertz, Koln #569/R est:15000-18000

AHLGRENSSON, Bjorn (1872-1918) Swedish
£1256 $2249 €1834 Spring landscape (24x25cm-9x10in) s.d.91. 26-May-4 AB Stockholms Auktionsverk #2344/R est:20000-25000 (S.KR 17000)

AHLMANN, Marie (1889-1985) Danish
£327 $517 €474 Convalescent. Sketch of woman with jug (50x73cm-20x29in) double-sided exhib. 2-Sep-3 Rasmussen, Copenhagen #2005/R (D.KR 3500)

AHLSTEDT, Fredrik (1839-1901) Finnish
£1042 $1740 €1500 Moonlight (26x17cm-10x7in) s. 23-Oct-3 Hagelstam, Helsinki #1010 est:2500
£1486 $2661 €2200 Summer evening at Aaland (33x41cm-13x16in) s.d.83. 8-May-4 Bukowskis, Helsinki #99/R est:2500-3000
£2657 $4517 €3800 Evening in the skerries (23x17cm-9x7in) s.d.1885 board. 29-Nov-3 Bukowskis, Helsinki #80/R est:1700-2200
£3916 $6657 €5600 Hakkapelit - man wearing armoured helmet (67x48cm-26x19in) s.d.67 exhib. 29-Nov-3 Bukowskis, Helsinki #57/R est:5000-6000
£4932 $8829 €7300 Evening light (47x39cm-19x15in) s. 8-May-4 Bukowskis, Helsinki #77/R est:5000-6000
Prints
£7432 $13304 €11000 Fetching water one winter evening (68x122cm-27x48in) s.d.75. 8-May-4 Bukowskis, Helsinki #58/R est:12000-15000

AHLSTEDT, Nina (1853-1907) Finnish
£2113 $3655 €3000 Mattila farm (32x44cm-13x17in) s.d.1890. 13-Dec-3 Hagelstam, Helsinki #92/R est:3500

AHMED, Sheikh (20th C) Indian?
Works on paper
£550 $875 €803 Leaders use Shell (34x64cm-13x25in) gouache pencil. 10-Sep-3 Sotheby's, Olympia #76/R

AHRENDT, William (1933-) American?
£2159 $3800 €3152 Grand Canyon (79x58cm-31x23in) s. prov. 23-May-4 Hindman, Chicago #144/R est:1000-1500

AHRENDTS, Carl Eduard (1822-1898) Dutch
£355 $650 €518 Quiet afternoon, figures on a sailboat (15x22cm-6x9in) s. 10-Jul-4 Auctions by the Bay, Alameda #429/R
£1497 $2724 €2200 On the beach (13x16cm-5x6in) s. panel. 3-Feb-4 Christie's, Amsterdam #127/R est:600-800
£1842 $3389 €2800 Fisherfolk by a village on the Dutch coast (28x42cm-11x17in) s. panel. 22-Jun-4 Christie's, Amsterdam #1/R est:2000-3000
£2800 $5040 €4200 Skaters on a frozen waterway (40x31cm-16x12in) s. panel oval. 20-Apr-4 Sotheby's, Amsterdam #8/R est:3000-5000

AHRENDTS, Leopold (19th C) German
Photographs
£2517 $4280 €3600 Berlin castle from the Lustgarten (19x23cm-7x9in) i. gold toned albumen lit. 28-Nov-3 Bassenge, Berlin #4001/R est:2000

AHRENS, Carl Henry von (1863-1936) Canadian
£293 $497 €428 Sunny forest glade (39x30cm-15x12in) s. 21-Nov-3 Walker's, Ottawa #90/R (C.D 650)
£1013 $1723 €1479 Woodland and Aspen (46x69cm-18x27in) s. 21-Nov-3 Walker's, Ottawa #89/R est:1200-1600 (C.D 2250)

AHSMANN, J (20th C) ?
£1188 $1900 €1734 Lavish tabletop still life (89x130cm-35x51in) s.d.1916 s.i.verso. 19-Sep-3 Freeman, Philadelphia #78/R est:1000-1500

AHTELA, H (1881-1968) Finnish
£2013 $3745 €3000 Landscape from Tornedalen (67x77cm-26x30in) s.d.52 i.verso. 7-Mar-4 Bukowskis, Helsinki #283/R est:1800

AHTOLA, Taisto (1917-2000) Finnish
£1049 $1783 €1500 Concentration upon the stage (24x19cm-9x7in) s. board. 29-Nov-3 Bukowskis, Helsinki #249/R est:1000-1200

AHUATZI, Armando (1950-) Mexican
£263 $448 €384 Still life with vegetables (20x25cm-8x10in) s.d.1989. 30-Oct-3 Louis Morton, Mexico #152 (M.P 5000)

AID, George-Charles (1872-1938) American
£722 $1300 €1054 Portrait of a young woman wearing a blue dress and fur trimmed hat (67x54cm-26x21in) s. canvas on board. 24-Apr-4 Weschler, Washington #631/R

AIGAI, Takahisa (attrib) (1796-1843) Japanese
Works on paper
£350 $601 €500 Coastal landscape with mountains in background (125x44cm-49x17in) s. ink col hanging scroll. 5-Dec-3 Lempertz, Koln #767/R

AIGEN, Karl (1685-1762) Austrian
£2013 $3705 €3000 Landscape with ruins, waterfall and figures (69x54cm-27x21in) 24-Mar-4 Dorotheum, Vienna #262/R est:2000-3000

AIGNER, Eduard (1903-1978) German
£403 $741 €600 Woman (40x50cm-16x20in) s. 24-Mar-4 Hugo Ruef, Munich #1206
£1208 $2223 €1800 Mother and children (106x140cm-42x55in) s. 24-Mar-4 Hugo Ruef, Munich #1205/R est:1800

AIGNER, Fritz (1930-) Austrian
Works on paper
£400 $716 €600 Curious onlookers (21x29cm-8x11in) s. Indian ink. 13-May-4 Dorotheum, Linz #602/R
£467 $835 €700 Great welcome (21x29cm-8x11in) s.d.65 Indian ink. 13-May-4 Dorotheum, Linz #603/R
£769 $1308 €1100 Erotic double picture (36x50cm-14x20in) s.d.1993 mixed media. 27-Nov-3 Dorotheum, Linz #608

AIKEN, Gayleen (20th C) American
Works on paper
£222 $400 €324 Back side of a saw mill (33x41cm-13x16in) crayon. 24-Apr-4 Slotin Folk Art, Buford #765/R
£299 $500 €437 My Rambilli cousins music parade (36x43cm-14x17in) crayon prov. 15-Nov-3 Slotin Folk Art, Buford #469/R

AIKMAN, William (attrib) (1682-1731) British
£1200 $2148 €1752 Portrait of a gentleman (73x61cm-29x24in) painted oval. 26-May-4 Sotheby's, Olympia #10/R est:1500-2000

AILLAUD, Gilles (1928-) French
£21053 $38737 €32000 Ours polaire (200x150cm-79x59in) s.d.1975 verso prov. 27-Jun-4 Versailles Encheres #134/R est:25000-30000
£26056 $45077 €37000 Mangoustes dans la nuit (195x130cm-77x51in) s.d.1976 verso prov.exhib.lit. 14-Dec-3 Versailles Encheres #165/R est:22000-25000

AIME, Andre Louis (19th C) French

£1972	$3273	€2800	Effet de lumiere a travers bois (36x55cm-14x22in) s. 15-Jun-3 Peron, Melun #162a

AIME, Tino (1931-) Italian

£267	$491	€400	Rural houses (50x70cm-20x28in) s.d.1969 board. 12-Jun-4 Meeting Art, Vercelli #149
£567	$1043	€850	Rye fields (60x80cm-24x31in) s.d.1967 board. 12-Jun-4 Meeting Art, Vercelli #530
£748	$1339	€1100	Winter in Bastia (60x80cm-24x31in) s.d1973 masonite. 22-Mar-4 Sant Agostino, Torino #354/R

AIMETTI, Carlo (1901-) Italian

£235	$432	€350	Wooded landscape (50x70cm-20x28in) s.d.944 board. 24-Mar-4 Il Ponte, Milan #657/R
£377	$588	€550	Valley amongst rocks (80x60cm-31x24in) s.d. i.verso board. 8-Apr-3 Il Ponte, Milan #489

AIMONE, Nino (1932-) Italian

£340	$609	€500	Window (50x35cm-20x14in) s. s.i.d.1963-64 on stretcher exhib. 22-Mar-4 Sant Agostino, Torino #387/R

AINI, Philippe (attrib) (20th C) French

£2465	$4264	€3500	Le ramasseur (89x51cm-35x20in) s. s.i.d.1983 verso. 14-Dec-3 Versailles Encheres #224 est:2500-3000

AINSLEY, Dennis (1880-1952) French

£201	$375	€293	Flower market, Belgium (51x66cm-20x26in) s. 29-Feb-4 Bonhams & Butterfields, San Francisco #4580
£444	$800	€648	Market scene (61x91cm-24x36in) s. 20-Apr-4 Arthur James, Florida #137/R

AINSLEY, Samuel James (1806-1874) British

£750	$1403	€1125	Ruins at Paestum (19x33cm-7x13in) init.i.d.1852. 26-Jul-4 Bonhams, Bath #58/R
£6500	$11635	€9490	Classical figures in an extensive Italianate landscape (120x162cm-47x64in) 26-May-4 Sotheby's, Olympia #68/R est:4000-6000

AISTROP, E (19/20th C) British

£1550	$2635	€2263	Jack russell. Manchester terrier. Bull terrier (25x30cm-10x12in) two s. set of three. 27-Nov-3 Christie's, Kensington #295/R est:1000-1500

AISTROP, Edward (19/20th C) British

£1216	$2250	€1775	Head of smooth fox terrier. Head of wirehaired fox terrier (23x23cm-9x9in) one init. board two. 10-Feb-4 Doyle, New York #184/R est:1500-2500
£2027	$3750	€2959	Head of wirehaired fox terrier. Head of cairn terrier (23x23cm-9x9in) one init. board two. 10-Feb-4 Doyle, New York #186/R est:1500-2500

AITCHISON, Craigie (1926-) British

£3200	$5920	€4672	African boy with rose, flowers and budgies (30x23cm-12x9in) oil collage on board painted 1969-70 prov.lit. 11-Mar-4 Christie's, Kensington #334/R est:3000-5000
£6000	$10320	€8760	Portrait of Nelson Woo (30x25cm-12x10in) s.d.1994 overlap prov. 3-Dec-3 Sotheby's, London #99/R est:6000-8000

AITCHISON, Craigie (attrib) (1926-) British

£320	$592	€467	Still life with blue vase and red bowl (24x25cm-9x10in) board. 10-Mar-4 Cheffins, Cambridge #53/R

AITKEN, Annie Laurie Crawford (20th C) American

Sculpture

£88235	$150000	€128823	Woman holding dolphin (180cm-71in) st.f.Scoma i. bronze. 25-Nov-3 Christie's, Rockefeller NY #194/R est:15000-25000

AITKEN, Doug (20th C) American

Photographs

£7186	$12000	€10492	Conspiracy (122x122cm-48x48in) c-print plexiglas edition 3 of 10 prov. 13-Nov-3 Sotheby's, New York #466/R est:8000-12000
£8000	$14720	€11680	Over the ocean (167x122cm-66x48in) s.verso c-print mounted on plexiglass prov.lit. 25-Jun-4 Christie's, London #223/R est:8000-12000
£17964	$30000	€26227	Mirror (51x63cm-20x25in) each init.num.2/2 verso cibachrome prints eleven exec 1998 prov. 12-Nov-3 Christie's, Rockefeller NY #536/R est:60000-80000
£22455	$37500	€32784	Two second separation (48x237cm-19x93in) c.-print plexiglas two parts edition 3 of 5 prov. 13-Nov-3 Sotheby's, New York #467/R est:2000-30000

Sculpture

£53073	$95000	€77487	Electric Earth. s.i.d.1999 cav plastic laser disc cx encoded audio prov.exhib.lit. 13-May-4 Phillips, New York #5/R est:100000-150000

AITKEN, Gladys (fl.1915-1920) British

Works on paper

£520	$894	€759	Collecting the lobster pots (25x33cm-10x13in) s. W/C. 5-Dec-3 Chrystals Auctions, Isle of Man #225/R

AITKEN, James (fl.1880-1935) British

Works on paper

£380	$680	€555	Going out for the night (33x48cm-13x19in) s. i.verso pencil W/C. 26-May-4 Christie's, Kensington #434/R
£520	$868	€759	Seascape. W/C. 13-Nov-3 Bonhams, Edinburgh #344
£550	$985	€803	Sunlit seas (33x23cm-13x9in) s. W/C exhib. 7-May-4 Chrystals Auctions, Isle of Man #258

AITKEN, James A (1846-1897) British

£420	$722	€613	Holy loch (26x43cm-10x17in) s.d.74. 6-Dec-3 Shapes, Edinburgh #424

Works on paper

£363	$668	€530	In Mid Atlantic (35x50cm-14x20in) s. W/C. 9-Jun-4 Walker's, Ottawa #356/R (C.D 900)

AITKEN, John Ernest (1881-1957) British

Works on paper

£1000	$1720	€1460	Dutch canal scene (33x48cm-13x19in) s. W/C. 5-Dec-3 Chrystals Auctions, Isle of Man #247/R est:1000-1500
£1200	$2220	€1752	East Linton, Fife (19x52cm-7x20in) W/C. 14-Jul-4 Bonhams, Chester #350 est:700-900
£1450	$2465	€2117	Towing in trawlers, Lowestoft (36x44cm-14x17in) s. W/C. 29-Oct-3 Bonhams, Chester #362 est:600-800
£2016	$3710	€2943	The inner harbour, Port St Mary (35x49cm-14x19in) s.i. W/C. 9-Jun-4 Walker's, Ottawa #355/R est:2000-2500 (C.D 5000)
£3200	$5088	€4640	Fishing boats by the quayside. s. W/C. 9-Sep-3 David Duggleby, Scarborough #218 est:700-1000
£3200	$5760	€4672	Harbour scene (48x73cm-19x29in) s. W/C. 21-Jan-4 Sotheby's, Olympia #239/R est:800-1200

AIVAZOVSKY, I K (1817-1900) Russian

Works on paper

£2457	$4251	€3587	Harbour town, possibly Theodosia (21x29cm-8x11in) s. sepia gouache. 9-Dec-3 Rasmussen, Copenhagen #1732/R est:25000 (D.KR 26000)

AIVAZOVSKY, Ivan Konstantinovich (1817-1900) Russian

£4029	$7372	€5882	Rough seas (28x37cm-11x15in) s.d.1879 oil W/C. 9-Jun-4 Rasmussen, Copenhagen #1621/R est:6000-8000 (D.KR 45000)
£6579	$12105	€10000	Lakeside scene, early morning, with fishing boats landing (20x27cm-8x11in) s. 25-Jun-4 Michael Zeller, Lindau #520/R est:9000
£8879	$14028	€12963	Figures in punt by coast, moonlit night (12x14cm-5x6in) s. prov. 2-Sep-3 Rasmussen, Copenhagen #1646/R est:10000-15000 (D.KR 95000)
£9000	$15300	€13140	Ship by the shore (8x10cm-3x4in) init. s.d.1887 verso panel. 19-Nov-3 Sotheby's, London #42/R est:3000-5000
£9868	$18158	€15000	Warship on the Black Sea (20x27cm-8x11in) s. 25-Jun-4 Michael Zeller, Lindau #521/R est:9000
£23611	$38486	€34000	Three master under cloudy skies in stormy sea (19x24cm-7x9in) s.d.1873. 25-Sep-3 Dr Fritz Nagel, Stuttgart #1321/R est:15000
£26000	$44200	€37960	Nice (16x13cm-6x5in) s.d.1896 s.i.d.verso panel. 19-Nov-3 Sotheby's, London #38/R est:10000-15000
£30000	$51000	€45000	Boats in a bay (20x27cm-8x11in) s.indis.d. 25-Nov-3 Christie's, London #127/R est:10000-15000
£38000	$64600	€55480	Swimmers off the beach of Theodosia (17x26cm-7x10in) s.d.1873 lit. 19-Nov-3 Sotheby's, London #41/R est:15000-20000
£40000	$68000	€60000	Seascape with boat (21x27cm-8x11in) s.indis.d. 25-Nov-3 Christie's, London #115/R est:12000-18000
£45000	$76500	€65700	Black sea coast at night (27x20cm-11x8in) init. board. 19-Nov-3 Sotheby's, London #37/R est:8000-12000
£50000	$85000	€73000	Sailing boat off Yalta, Ayu Dag beyond (24x39cm-9x15in) s.d.1893 lit. 19-Nov-3 Sotheby's, London #44/R est:30000-40000
£50000	$85000	€75000	Coastal landscape (19x27cm-7x11in) s. 25-Nov-3 Christie's, London #114/R est:12000-18000
£55000	$98450	€80300	View of Ischia (23x29cm-9x11in) s.d.1872 s.d.verso. 26-May-4 Sotheby's, London #57/R est:25000-30000
£55000	$98450	€80300	Ayu-dag (20x25cm-8x10in) s. indis d. 26-May-4 Sotheby's, London #61/R est:20000-30000
£55000	$98450	€80300	Storm (34x27cm-13x11in) s.d.1881 s.i.verso canvas on board. 26-May-4 Sotheby's, London #63/R est:30000-40000
£57692	$90000	€	View from seashore of Venice at sunset (30x38cm-12x15in) s.cyrillic d.1867 prov. 11-Apr-3 Christie's, Rockefeller NY #6/R est:30000-50000
£58000	$105560	€84680	Ships at sea by moonlight (25x19cm-10x7in) s.i. board. 16-Jun-4 Bonhams, New Bond Street #23/R est:15000-20000
£60000	$102000	€90000	Ship in rough seas (47x40cm-19x16in) s.d.89. 25-Nov-3 Christie's, London #126/R est:15000-20000
£66163	$114461	€96598	Seascape with sailing ship in a calm (26x40cm-10x16in) s.d.1887. 9-Dec-3 Rasmussen, Copenhagen #1290/R est:200000-250000 (D.KR 700000)
£66901	$117077	€95000	Voiliers a l'entree de la Corne d'Or (58x88cm-23x35in) s. prov. 16-Dec-3 Claude Aguttes, Neuilly #81/R est:30000-40000
£75000	$134250	€109500	Shipwreck (23x34cm-9x13in) indis sig. exhib.lit. 26-May-4 Sotheby's, London #56/R est:30000-40000
£95000	$161500	€138700	Arrival of the Russian Ship in Constantinople (32x43cm-13x17in) s.d.1880. 19-Nov-3 Sotheby's, London #40/R est:80000-120000
£130000	$232700	€189800	View of the Crimea (25x36cm-10x14in) s. i.verso exhib.lit. 26-May-4 Sotheby's, London #60/R est:45000-60000
£130000	$232700	€189800	Shipping on a moonlit coast (25x32cm-10x13in) s. exhib.lit. 26-May-4 Sotheby's, London #62/R est:45000-60000
£200000	$358000	€292000	Survivor (59x95cm-23x37in) s.d.1888. 26-May-4 Sotheby's, London #65/R est:80000-120000
£200000	$358000	€292000	Black Sea (89x131cm-35x52in) s.d.1889. 26-May-4 Sotheby's, London #64/R est:100000-150000
£200000	$358000	€292000	Firing of the Turkish fleet by Kanaris in 1822 (124x90cm-49x35in) s.d.1892. 26-May-4 Sotheby's, London #67/R est:150000-200000
£220000	$374000	€321200	Sailing boat at sunset flying the Russian tricolour (85x68cm-33x27in) s.d.1883 oval lit. 19-Nov-3 Sotheby's, London #39/R est:70000-90000
£270589	$460000	€395060	Panorama of St. Petersburg as seen from the River Neva (61x92cm-24x36in) s.d.1875. 19-Nov-3 Bonhams & Butterfields, San Francisco #88/R
£370000	$662300	€540200	View of Yalta (52x78cm-20x31in) s.d.1867 s.d.verso exhib.lit. 26-May-4 Sotheby's, London #66/R est:250000-350000
£520000	$884000	€759200	Sunset over the Golden Horn (120x167cm-47x66in) s.d.1866 prov.lit. 19-Nov-3 Sotheby's, London #45/R est:400000-500000
£520000	$884000	€759200	Ship moored off the coast, Constantinople (109x158cm-43x62in) s.d.1874 prov. 19-Nov-3 Sotheby's, London #46/R est:280000-350000
£533333	$960000	€778666	Survivors (198x268cm-78x106in) s.d.1878 s.d.verso prov. 23-Apr-4 Sotheby's, New York #38/R est:800000-1200000
£650000	$1105000	€975000	View of Constantinople (121x195cm-48x77in) s.d.1852. 25-Nov-3 Christie's, London #116/R est:240000-280000

Works on paper

£2414 $4466 €3500 Ships off Black Sea coast (20x28cm-8x11in) s. cyrillic wash Indian ink prov. 14-Feb-4 Hans Stahl, Hamburg #116/R est:3000
£3500 $5950 €5250 Seascape (15x11cm-6x4in) s. pencil htd white cardboard. 25-Nov-3 Christie's, London #125/R est:3500-4500
£4167 $6500 € Sketches of boats at harbour (24x31cm-9x12in) one s.cyrillic d.1843 pencil two. 11-Apr-3 Christie's, Rockefeller NY #14/R est:6000-8000
£8000 $13600 €11680 Boat at sea (20x27cm-8x11in) s.d.1878 pencil htd crayon. 19-Nov-3 Sotheby's, London #43/R est:3000-5000
£10000 $17900 €14600 Ship on the ocean (12x20cm-5x8in) s.d.1880 graphite pencil. 26-May-4 Sotheby's, London #59/R est:3000-5000
£22000 $39380 €32120 Coastal scene with windmill (20x29cm-8x11in) s.d.1891 graphite pencil scratching paper peel on board. 26-May-4 Sotheby's, London #58/R est:7000-9000
£70000 $119000 €105000 Italian coast (28x45cm-11x18in) s.d.1842 gouache cardboard on panel prov.exhib. 25-Nov-3 Christie's, London #113/R est:25000-35000

AIVAZOVSKY, Ivan Konstantinovich (attrib) (1817-1900) Russian

£1148 $2100 €1676 Marine landscape (12x17cm-5x7in) bears init. oil wood. 1-Feb-4 Ben-Ami, Tel Aviv #4650/R est:3000-4000
£2923 $5028 €4268 Coastal landscape with French two-masted schooner (28x36cm-11x14in) 3-Dec-3 AB Stockholms Auktionsverk #2652/R est:15000-20000 (S.KR 38000)
£5369 $9879 €8000 Sailing ship in stormy sea (25x16cm-10x6in) s.cyrillic board. 25-Mar-4 Dr Fritz Nagel, Stuttgart #689/R est:7000
£33108 $58270 €49000 View of Feodosia, sunset (72x110cm-28x43in) lit. 19-May-4 Camard, Paris #114/R est:60000-80000

AIVAZOVSKY, Ivan Konstantinovich (school) (1817-1900) Russian

£5594 $9510 €8000 Two master in the Bay of Ayu Dag in the Crimea (50x71cm-20x28in) 24-Nov-3 Dorotheum, Vienna #147/R est:10000-12000

AIVAZOVSKY, Ivan Konstantinovich (studio) (1817-1900) Russian

£2647 $4500 €3865 Ship on rough seas under a threatening sky (34x49cm-13x19in) bears sig. 19-Nov-3 Bonhams & Butterfields, San Francisco #89/R

AIVAZOVSKY, Ivan Konstantinovich (style) (1817-1900) Russian

£5814 $10000 €8488 Moonlit harbour scene (43x74cm-17x29in) bears sig.d. 7-Dec-3 Freeman, Philadelphia #32 est:3000-5000
£6040 $10812 €9000 Wreck on a rocky coast in moonlight (61x85cm-24x33in) 27-May-4 Dorotheum, Vienna #203/R est:6000-8000

AIZELIN, Eugène (1821-1902) French

Sculpture

£1049 $1783 €1500 Bohemienne assise a la mandoline (53cm-21in) s.st.f.F. Barbedienne medaille pat bronze. 1-Dec-3 Rieunier, Paris #22 est:1300
£1074 $1901 €1600 Femme assise (51cm-20in) s.i. pat bronze. 29-Apr-4 Sotheby's, Paris #192/R est:2000-3000
£1136 $2000 €1659 Bust of a woman with kerchief hat and cross necklace (58x28cm-23x11in) s. marble marble base. 1-Jan-4 Quinn's, Falls Church #258/R
£1400 $2618 €2100 Seated young girl (53cm-21in) s. pat bronze. 21-Jul-4 John Nicholson, Haslemere #852
£2414 $4031 €3500 Judith (62x24x22cm-24x9x9in) pat bronze. 11-Jul-3 Rabourdin & Choppin de Janvry, Paris #150/R
£3020 $5346 €4500 Femme a la lampe a huile (85cm-33in) s.st.f.Barbedienne pat bronze. 30-Apr-4 Tajan, Paris #40/R est:5000-6000
£5000 $8650 €7300 Nymphe de Diane (95cm-37in) s.num.116 brown pat bronze st.f.F.Barbedienne. 12-Dec-3 Sotheby's, London #250/R est:5000-7000

AIZPIRI, Paul (1919-) French

£1271 $2161 €1856 Head of a Clown (42x33cm-17x13in) s. sold with exhibition poster print by artist prov. 24-Nov-3 Sotheby's, Melbourne #349/R est:4000-6000 (A.D 3000)
£2155 $3858 €3146 Clown (46x38cm-18x15in) s.d.1955 prov. 13-May-4 Pierre Berge, Paris #64/R est:5000-6000 (S.FR 5000)
£2961 $5447 €4500 Grand Canal (94x68cm-37x27in) s. 22-Jun-4 Ribeyre & Baron, Paris #65/R est:6000-8000
£5638 $10091 €8400 Vase de fleurs (55x46cm-22x18in) s. 30-May-4 Eric Pillon, Calais #215/R
£5906 $10572 €8800 Clown (43x34cm-17x13in) s. painted 1955 prov.exhib. 26-May-4 Christie's, Paris #58/R est:8000-12000
£6176 $10500 €9017 Jeune garcon (53x38cm-21x15in) s. 7-Nov-3 Selkirks, St. Louis #588/R est:4000-5000
£7000 $11690 €10220 Nature morte au compotier (75x106cm-30x42in) s. prov. 21-Oct-3 Sotheby's, London #157/R est:8000-12000
£7328 $12237 €10699 Flowers in a blue vase (72x58cm-28x23in) s. 20-Oct-3 Stephan Welz, Johannesburg #216/R est:60000-90000 (SA.R 85000)
£9202 $15000 €13435 Le violiniste (81x53cm-32x21in) s. 25-Sep-3 Christie's, Rockefeller NY #601/R est:15000-20000
£9816 $16000 €14331 Nature morte avec fleurs (74x51cm-29x20in) s. prov. 25-Sep-3 Christie's, Rockefeller NY #560/R est:18000-22000
£17178 $28000 €25080 Fleurs dans bleu vase (73x60cm-29x24in) s. 25-Sep-3 Christie's, Rockefeller NY #557/R est:18000-25000

Works on paper

£260 $416 €380 French river with barge at quayside near bridge and buildings (36x48cm-14x19in) s. W/C pen. 18-Sep-3 Olivers, Sudbury #131/R

AJDUKIEWICZ, Thaddeus von (1852-1916) Polish

£3642 $6629 €5500 Portrait of the Princess Fedoras of Sachsen-Meiningen on horseback (112x90cm-44x35in) s.d.1899. 16-Jun-4 Hugo Ruef, Munich #919/R est:5000
£4167 $6875 €6000 Arrival of horse drawn sledge (56x100cm-22x39in) s.d.1883. 2-Jul-3 Neumeister, Munich #602/R est:4000
£8321 $14395 €12149 Horse rider firing pistol (55x90cm-22x35in) s. painted c.1900. 14-Dec-3 Agra, Warsaw #19/R est:55000 (P.Z 55000)
£13013 $22902 €18999 Wooded landscape with figures (43x88cm-17x35in) painted 1876. 23-May-4 Agra, Warsaw #6/R (P.Z 92000)

AJMONE, Giuseppe (1923-) Italian

£1056 $1849 €1500 Nude in the studio (55x46cm-22x18in) s.d.1971 prov. 17-Dec-3 Il Ponte, Milan #1125 est:1800-2000
£1333 $2453 €2000 Nude (73x50cm-29x20in) s.d.1961 i.verso. 14-Jun-4 Sant Agostino, Torino #341/R est:2000-2500
£1408 $2338 €2000 Little nude and window (73x60cm-29x24in) s.d.69 i.d.verso. 11-Jun-3 Finarte Semenzato, Milan #722/R
£1497 $2679 €2200 In the shade (73x92cm-29x36in) s. i.d.1987 verso. 16-Mar-4 Finarte Semenzato, Milan #41/R est:1700
£1678 $2853 €2400 Untitled (55x45cm-22x18in) s. 24-Nov-3 Christie's, Milan #212/R
£1818 $3091 €2600 Untitled (55x46cm-22x18in) s. 24-Nov-3 Christie's, Milan #214/R est:1200-1600
£2319 $3803 €3200 Wood (73x60cm-29x24in) s.d.58 s.i.d.verso prov. 27-May-3 Sotheby's, Milan #7/R est:4000
£2899 $4754 €4000 Still life of fruit (46x61cm-18x24in) s. s.i.d.1953 verso prov. 27-May-3 Sotheby's, Milan #6/R est:4000

Works on paper

£306 $548 €450 Reclining female nude (33x41cm-13x16in) s. W/C card. 16-Mar-4 Finarte Semenzato, Milan #42
£347 $549 €500 Flowers (50x35cm-20x14in) pastel card. 6-Sep-3 Meeting Art, Vercelli #389
£733 $1349 €1100 Landscape (24x34cm-9x13in) s. W/C sold with pastel by A Forgioli. 10-Jun-4 Galleria Pace, Milan #43/R

AJMONE, Lidio (1884-1945) Italian

£909 $1518 €1300 Termitarium (22x27cm-9x11in) board exhib.lit. 26-Jun-3 Sant Agostino, Torino #67/R
£1342 $2376 €2000 Pallanza (23x33cm-9x13in) s.i.d.1910 cardboard. 1-May-4 Meeting Art, Vercelli #361 est:1500
£1678 $2970 €2500 Afternoon in Andezeno (35x45cm-14x18in) s. i.verso cardboard. 1-May-4 Meeting Art, Vercelli #168 est:2500
£2378 $3971 €3400 Sun on Mount Blanc (24x33cm-9x13in) s.d.1936 board. 26-Jun-3 Sant Agostino, Torino #74/R
£2695 $4501 €3800 Costantinoples (27x35cm-11x14in) s. board. 20-Oct-3 Sant Agostino, Torino #280/R est:4500
£6690 $11574 €9500 On the beach (48x32cm-19x13in) s.d.1922 board. 11-Dec-3 Christie's, Rome #143/R est:4500-5500

AKAJ, Fujio (1945-) Indonesian

Works on paper

£367 $656 €550 Untitled (70x99cm-28x39in) s. W/C. 15-May-4 Van Ham, Cologne #400

AKED, Aleen (1907-2003) Canadian

£203 $345 €296 Lake Louise. 28-Oct-3 Ritchie, Toronto #2188 (C.D 450)
£216 $352 €315 Dredging Sarasota (30x41cm-12x16in) s. i.verso canvasboard prov. 23-Sep-3 Ritchie, Toronto #98 (C.D 475)
£225 $383 €329 Doorway of Sarasota County Courthouse. 28-Oct-3 Ritchie, Toronto #2193 (C.D 500)
£227 $370 €331 On the beach (23x30cm-9x12in) s.verso panel prov. 23-Sep-3 Ritchie, Toronto #91/R (C.D 500)
£241 $448 €352 Still life of a cabbage (41x51cm-16x20in) estate st.verso prov. 2-Mar-4 Ritchie, Toronto #103 (C.D 600)
£250 $408 €365 White house (30x41cm-12x16in) s. s.d.1936 verso canvasboard prov. 23-Sep-3 Ritchie, Toronto #96 (C.D 550)
£261 $486 €381 Backyard (49x41cm-19x16in) estate st.verso prov. 2-Mar-4 Ritchie, Toronto #105 (C.D 650)
£321 $598 €469 Portrait of a woman (66x74cm-26x29in) s. prov. 2-Mar-4 Ritchie, Toronto #102/R (C.D 800)
£321 $598 €469 House building (30x41cm-12x16in) s. canvasboard prov. 2-Mar-4 Ritchie, Toronto #106/R (C.D 800)
£341 $556 €498 House in Sarasota (41x51cm-16x20in) s. s.i.verso prov. 23-Sep-3 Ritchie, Toronto #100/R (C.D 750)
£361 $672 €527 Still life with green apples (41x51cm-16x20in) s. prov. 2-Mar-4 Ritchie, Toronto #107/R (C.D 900)
£409 $667 €597 Under the banyan tree (41x51cm-16x20in) s. s.i.verso prov.exhib. 23-Sep-3 Ritchie, Toronto #101/R est:600-800 (C.D 900)
£442 $822 €645 Portrait of a woman with a bowl of apples (76x63cm-30x25in) s. prov. 2-Mar-4 Ritchie, Toronto #101/R (C.D 1100)
£455 $741 €664 Sunny myakka (76x91cm-30x36in) s. s.i.d.1938 verso prov. 23-Sep-3 Ritchie, Toronto #90/R est:1200-1800 (C.D 1000)
£500 $815 €730 By the open window (63x76cm-25x30in) s. s.i.d.1940 verso exhib. 23-Sep-3 Ritchie, Toronto #89/R est:1000-1500 (C.D 1100)
£500 $815 €730 Portrait of Pinkie (50x40cm-20x16in) s. s.i.verso prov. 23-Sep-3 Ritchie, Toronto #94/R est:700-900 (C.D 1100)
£522 $971 €762 Fish houses, Hog Creek, Sarasota (35x51cm-14x20in) s.d.1936 prov. 2-Mar-4 Ritchie, Toronto #109/R (C.D 1300)
£773 $1260 €1129 In my garden (40x30cm-16x12in) s. canvasboard prov. 23-Sep-3 Ritchie, Toronto #99 (C.D 1700)
£1205 $2241 €1759 Possibly, under the banyan tree (51x41cm-20x16in) s.d.36 prov. 2-Mar-4 Ritchie, Toronto #100/R est:700-900 (C.D 3000)
£1364 $2223 €1991 Studio still life (51x63cm-20x25in) s. prov. 23-Sep-3 Ritchie, Toronto #95/R est:600-800 (C.D 3000)
£1365 $2540 €1993 Mellow myakka (76x91cm-30x36in) s. prov. 2-Mar-4 Ritchie, Toronto #108/R est:1200-1800 (C.D 3400)
£1526 $2839 €2228 Apprentice pillars courtyard, Ringling Museum of Art, Sarasota, Florida (61x46cm-24x18in) s. canvasboard prov. 2-Mar-4 Ritchie, Toronto #104/R est:600-800 (C.D 3800)

AKEEAKTASHUK (1898-1954) North American

Sculpture

£1351 $2297 €1972 Inuit hunter fighting a polar bear (25cm-10in) dark green soapstone base exec.c.1950. 3-Nov-3 Waddingtons, Toronto #141/R est:3000-5000 (C.D 3000)
£1712 $2910 €2500 Inuit hunter pulling in his kill (13cm-5in) marbled green soapstone hide. 3-Nov-3 Waddingtons, Toronto #151/R est:2000-2500 (C.D 3800)

AKELEY, Carl Ethan (1864-1926) American

Sculpture

£119186 $205000 €174012 Wounded comrade (30cm-12in) i.numA-3 dark brown pat. bronze prov. 3-Dec-3 Sotheby's, New York #134/R est:30000-50000

AKEMARR, Rosie Morton (20th C) Australian
Works on paper
£706 $1264 €1031 Bush Medicine (121x91cm-48x36in) synthetic polymer paint linen exec 2003 prov. 25-May-4 Lawson Menzies, Sydney #234/R (A.D 1800)

AKEN, Jan van (18th C) Flemish
£2095 $3686 €3100 Mountain landscape with two riders (22x30cm-9x12in) mono. panel prov. 22-May-4 Lempertz, Koln #1000/R est:2000

AKEN, Josef van (c.1709-1749) Flemish
£3167 $5068 €4624 Elegant figures at quayside fish market (39x53cm-15x21in) copper. 19-Sep-3 Koller, Zurich #3048/R est:8000-12000 (S.FR 7000)

AKERBLOM, Rudolf (1849-1925) Finnish
£528 $845 €750 Waiting (29x21cm-11x8in) s.d.84. 21-Sep-3 Bukowskis, Helsinki #498/R

AKERMAN, Jim (20th C) Canadian
£240 $439 €350 Carstairs, Alberta (30x25cm-12x10in) s.i.d.2003 acrylic board. 1-Jun-4 Hodgins, Calgary #258/R (C.D 600)
£249 $416 €364 Winter in Ryley, Alberta (30x20cm-12x8in) s.i.d.2001 acrylic on board. 17-Nov-3 Hodgins, Calgary #278/R (C.D 550)

AKERS, Vivian Milner (1886-1966) American
£1022 $1900 €1492 Impressionist landscape with pond and buildings (38x51cm-15x20in) s.d.1914. 3-Mar-4 Alderfer's, Hatfield #437/R est:1000-1500
£1285 $2300 €1876 Niesen and the little church at Einigen on the shore of Lake of Thun (30x35cm-12x14in) s.d.1939 i.verso board. 14-May-4 Skinner, Boston #304/R est:1000-1500
£4012 $6500 €5817 Pennesseewasse (61x79cm-24x31in) s.d.1956. 8-Aug-3 Barridorf, Portland #199/R est:5000-7000

AKERSTROM, Jonas (attrib) (1759-1795) Swedish
£1077 $1852 €1572 Hercules and Omphale (66x58cm-26x23in) 2-Dec-3 Bukowskis, Stockholm #317/R (S.KR 14000)
£1996 $3572 €2914 Apollo and the Nine Muses at Parnassos (30x107cm-12x42in) en grisaille paper. 26-May-4 AB Stockholms Auktionsverk #2136/R est:10000-12000 (S.KR 27000)

AKESUK, Latcholassie (1919-) North American
Sculpture
£901 $1532 €1315 Seal and a bird (20cm-8in) mottled green soapstone. 3-Nov-3 Waddingtons, Toronto #313/R est:2500-3500 (C.D 2000)
£1351 $2297 €1972 Seal shaman (38cm-15in) s. mottled green soapstone. 3-Nov-3 Waddingtons, Toronto #324/R est:4000-6000 (C.D 3000)
£3153 $5360 €4603 Two birds (66cm-26in) marbled white soapstone. 3-Nov-3 Waddingtons, Toronto #338/R est:8000-10000 (C.D 7000)
£7207 $12252 €10522 Spirit owl (49cm-19in) mottled white soapstone exec.c.1974. 3-Nov-3 Waddingtons, Toronto #333/R est:10000-15000 (C.D 16000)

AKI, Said (1926-) Lebanese
Works on paper
£2400 $4248 €3504 Nude red (79x59cm-31x23in) s.d.82 mixed media on board. 29-Apr-4 Bonhams, New Bond Street #562/R est:2000-3000

AKKERINGA, Johannes Evert (younger) (1894-?) Dutch
£833 $1317 €1200 White lilacs and pink carnations (37x26cm-15x10in) s.d.1928 s.verso. 2-Sep-3 Christie's, Amsterdam #202 est:700-900

AKKERINGA, Johannes Evert Hendrik (1861-1942) Dutch
£699 $1168 €1000 Stable interior (37x56cm-15x22in) s. panel. 30-Jun-3 Sotheby's, Amsterdam #94
£2667 $4800 €4000 Chrysanthemums in a vase (42x32cm-17x13in) 20-Apr-4 Sotheby's, Amsterdam #95/R est:2000-4000
£3750 $6000 €5475 Domestic scene in courtyard, mother and child with hens and chicks (36x36cm-14x14in) s.d.1904 canvas on board. 20-Sep-3 Jeffery Burchard, Florida #24/R
£5556 $10000 €8112 Landscape with girl on road, Scheveningen (28x41cm-11x16in) s. oak panel. 24-Apr-4 Rasmussen, Havnen #2088/R est:8000-12000 (D.KR 62000)
£6667 $12000 €10000 Mother and child picking flowers (22x48cm-9x19in) s. panel prov. 20-Apr-4 Sotheby's, Amsterdam #206/R est:12000-18000
£11333 $20400 €17000 Little friends (15x22cm-6x9in) s. panel. 21-Apr-4 Christie's, Amsterdam #113/R est:8000-12000
£15278 $25972 €22000 Lathyrus, sweetpea in a vase (44x32cm-17x13in) s. s.i.d.1937 verso i.stretcher. 28-Oct-3 Christie's, Amsterdam #185/R est:7000-9000
£18667 $33600 €28000 Afternoon tea (17x24cm-7x9in) s. panel. 21-Apr-4 Christie's, Amsterdam #86/R est:10000-15000
£56667 $102000 €85000 Children playing on the beach (46x66cm-18x26in) s. 20-Apr-4 Sotheby's, Amsterdam #196/R est:35000-45000
Works on paper
£1447 $2620 €2200 Spring (25x33cm-10x13in) s. W/C prov. 19-Apr-4 Glerum, Amsterdam #122/R est:1500-2000
£4167 $7083 €6000 Playing in the dunes (18x25cm-7x10in) s. blk chk W/C htd white. 28-Oct-3 Christie's, Amsterdam #120/R est:3000-5000

AKKERMAN, Ben (1920-) Dutch
£3333 $6133 €5000 Untitled (35x38cm-14x15in) canavs on board prov. 9-Jun-4 Christie's, Amsterdam #367/R est:5000-7000
£3333 $6133 €5000 Untitled (41x41cm-16x16in) canvas on board prov. 9-Jun-4 Christie's, Amsterdam #368/R est:5000-7000

AKKERMAN, Philip (1957-) American
£900 $1656 €1314 Self portrait no 49 (27x25cm-11x10in) s.d.2000 board prov. 24-Jun-4 Sotheby's, Olympia #415/R est:1000-1500
£900 $1656 €1314 Self portrait no 113 (27x25cm-11x10in) init.d.1999 board prov. 24-Jun-4 Sotheby's, Olympia #417/R est:1000-1500
£1800 $3312 €2628 Self portrait no 39 (27x25cm-11x10in) init.d.1999 board prov. 24-Jun-4 Sotheby's, Olympia #416/R est:1000-1500
£4000 $7360 €6000 Selfportrait (40x34cm-16x13in) each s. two d.1989 board three. 8-Jun-4 Sotheby's, Amsterdam #149/R est:6000-8000

AKKERSDIJK, Jacob (1815-1862) Dutch
£1329 $2259 €1900 Le bon buveur (26x22cm-10x9in) mono.d.1839 panel. 18-Nov-3 Vanderkindere, Brussels #34 est:2000-3000

AKKERSDIJK, Jacob (attrib) (1815-1862) Dutch
£658 $1191 €1000 A mother given her newborn at her birth (63x49cm-25x19in) panel. 19-Apr-4 Glerum, Amsterdam #89/R

AKMEN, Daniele (1945-) ?
£423 $731 €600 Match de rugby (130x97cm-51x38in) s. acrylic painted 1972 prov. 9-Dec-3 Artcurial Briest, Paris #486

AKOPIAN, Georges (1912-) Russian
£537 $993 €800 Paysage de Haute Provence (53x65cm-21x26in) s. 15-Mar-4 Claude Boisgirard, Paris #3
£671 $1242 €1000 Nature morte aux feuilles de vigne (73x60cm-29x24in) s. 15-Mar-4 Claude Boisgirard, Paris #5
£772 $1428 €1150 La route de Digne (46x55cm-18x22in) s. 15-Mar-4 Claude Boisgirard, Paris #2/R
£940 $1738 €1400 Nature morte aux branches d'olivier (60x73cm-24x29in) s. 15-Mar-4 Claude Boisgirard, Paris #4

AKPALIAPIK, Manasie (1955-) North American
Sculpture
£826 $1488 €1206 Inuit woman's face with inset eyes, other side with an Inukshuk (56cm-22in) whalebone. 26-Apr-4 Waddingtons, Toronto #133/R est:1800-2000 (C.D 2000)
£901 $1532 €1315 Shaman and whale with teeth, and Inuit drum dancer (42cm-17in) weathered whalebone double-sided. 3-Nov-3 Waddingtons, Toronto #415/R est:2500-3500 (C.D 2000)
£1074 $1934 €1568 Musk of ox with inset horns and eyes (43cm-17in) weathered whalebone. 26-Apr-4 Waddingtons, Toronto #151/R est:2500-3500 (C.D 2600)
£1405 $2529 €2051 Skull and vertebrae (28cm-11in) s. whalebone. 26-Apr-4 Waddingtons, Toronto #499/R est:700-1000 (C.D 3400)
£1441 $2450 €2104 Spirit seals, walrus and shaman totem (63cm-25in) weathered whalebone red stone base. 3-Nov-3 Waddingtons, Toronto #411/R est:2500-3500 (C.D 3200)
£1983 $3570 €2895 Owl with inset eyes and buffalo horns (38cm-15in) s. green pink marble. 26-Apr-4 Waddingtons, Toronto #496/R est:3500-4500 (C.D 4800)

AKRITHAKIS, Alexis (1939-) Greek
£32000 $54400 €46720 Jugement premier (110x146cm-43x57in) s.i.d.71 tempera prov.exhib.lit. 18-Nov-3 Sotheby's, London #46/R est:20000-30000
Sculpture
£22000 $39380 €32120 Suitcases (86x136cm-34x54in) s.verso mixed media wood exec c.1973-75 prov. 10-May-4 Sotheby's, Olympia #34/R est:18000-25000
Works on paper
£5000 $8500 €7300 Construction (82x72cm-32x28in) s.d.1984 verso mixed media on wood prov.exhib.lit. 18-Nov-3 Sotheby's, London #52/R est:5000-7000
£5000 $8950 €7300 Wooden construction (51x32cm-20x13in) s.i.d.83 verso mixed media panel prov. 10-May-4 Sotheby's, Olympia #71/R est:5000-7000
£8000 $14320 €11680 Construction (70x90cm-28x35in) s.d.84 verso mixed media wood prov.lit. 10-May-4 Sotheby's, Olympia #72/R est:8000-12000
£12500 $21250 €18250 Airplane with clouds (62x53cm-24x21in) s.d.84 verso mixed media on wood prov.exhib.lit. 18-Nov-3 Sotheby's, London #45/R est:8000-12000

AL-KAABI, Saadi (1937-) Iraqi
Works on paper
£600 $1062 €876 Figure with horse (30x36cm-12x14in) s.d.1977 W/C. 29-Apr-4 Bonhams, New Bond Street #582/R

AL-RAWI, Nuri (1925-) Iraqi
Works on paper
£500 $885 €730 Two figures with bird. Naourah (28x34cm-11x13in) s.d.1993 W/C gouache two. 29-Apr-4 Bonhams, New Bond Street #581/R

AL-ZIBAWI, Mahmoud (1962-) Lebanese
Works on paper
£1100 $1947 €1606 Face. Standing nude (97x57cm-38x22in) s.d.88 one s.d.81 mixed media one oil. 29-Apr-4 Bonhams, New Bond Street #564/R est:1000-1500

ALACRUN, F (19th C) ?
£919 $1700 €1342 Over the fence (33x48cm-13x19in) s. 10-Feb-4 Doyle, New York #231/R est:2500-3500

ALAMON, Gustavo (1935-) South American
£529 $900 €772 Robots II (116x89cm-46x35in) s.d.76. 25-Nov-3 Galeria y Remates, Montevideo #94
£824 $1400 €1203 Robots (142x195cm-56x77in) s.d.77. 25-Nov-3 Galeria y Remates, Montevideo #93/R
Works on paper
£324 $550 €473 Robots (45x56cm-18x22in) s.d.80 mixed media. 25-Nov-3 Galeria y Remates, Montevideo #99

ALANKO, Aarne (1896-1968) Finnish
£634 $1014 €900 Still life (34x108cm-13x43in) s. 18-Sep-3 Hagelstam, Helsinki #1037

ALANKO, Uuno (1878-1964) Finnish
£338 $541 €480 Gladiolus (81x65cm-32x26in) s.d.1939. 21-Sep-3 Bukowskis, Helsinki #306/R
£408 $654 €580 Summer's day (66x81cm-26x32in) s. 21-Sep-3 Bukowskis, Helsinki #307/R

ALAPHILIPPE, Camille (20th C) French
Sculpture
£824 $1400 €1203 Nude dancer (41cm-16in) s. brown pat. bronze executed c.1928. 22-Nov-3 Jackson's, Cedar Falls #192/R est:1500-2500

ALAPOTI, Matti (1934-) Finnish
Works on paper
£322 $599 €480 An ordinary story (75x53cm-30x21in) s.d.83 mixed media. 7-Mar-4 Bukowskis, Helsinki #285/R

ALARCON, Felix (19th C) Spanish
£379 $630 €550 Stroll (35x19cm-14x7in) s. board. 1-Oct-3 Della Rocca, Turin #284/R
£578 $1052 €850 Beach with girl (36x45cm-14x18in) s.d.1889. 3-Feb-4 Segre, Madrid #15/R
£1507 $2562 €2200 Modiste sur les boulevards (35x19cm-14x7in) s. panel. 9-Nov-3 Eric Pillon, Calais #54/R
£1507 $2562 €2200 Parisienne, Place de la Bastille (35x19cm-14x7in) s. panel. 9-Nov-3 Eric Pillon, Calais #53/R

ALARCON, Jose (19th C) Spanish
£1087 $1783 €1500 Maja (42x28cm-17x11in) s.d.90. 27-May-3 Durán, Madrid #191/R est:1000
£2465 $4264 €3500 Spanish beauty (90x65cm-35x26in) s. 15-Dec-3 Ansorena, Madrid #342/R est:3500
£3448 $5759 €5000 Elegant ladies (60x49cm-24x19in) s. 17-Nov-3 Durán, Madrid #219/R est:4000

ALARCON, Jose Maria (19th C) Spanish
£1745 $3089 €2600 Flamenco dancer from Madrid (100x66cm-39x26in) s. 28-Apr-4 Schopman, Hamburg #451/R est:1800

ALATERRE, Louis Georges (20th C) French
£278 $458 €400 Lac Chambon (65x54cm-26x21in) s. oval. 3-Jul-3 Claude Aguttes, Neuilly #8

ALAUX, Gustave (1887-1965) French
£966 $1767 €1400 La promenade du soir (26x34cm-10x13in) panel. 31-Jan-4 Gerard, Besancon #23
£2069 $3786 €3000 Le vaisseau, Le Dragon en mer (50x65cm-20x26in) s. 31-Jan-4 Gerard, Besancon #24
£2246 $3750 €3279 Bay of Goree (38x56cm-15x22in) s. 7-Oct-3 Sotheby's, New York #94 est:3000-5000

ALAUX, Jean Pierre (1925-) French
£300 $501 €438 L'attente (59x37cm-23x15in) s.i.verso prov. 14-Oct-3 Sotheby's, London #528
£400 $668 €584 Les baux de Provence (40x35cm-16x14in) s.i.d.1957 verso board. 14-Oct-3 Sotheby's, London #527
£500 $835 €730 Dryade (58x37cm-23x15in) s. 14-Oct-3 Sotheby's, London #533
£500 $835 €730 L'habillage (52x44cm-20x17in) s. i.d.1957 verso board. 14-Oct-3 Sotheby's, London #532
£500 $835 €730 La danceuse de l'isle de St. Marguerite pres Cannes (63x91cm-25x36in) s. i.verso. 14-Oct-3 Sotheby's, London #535
£592 $1089 €900 La naissance d'Aphrodite (65x81cm-26x32in) s. 23-Jun-4 Maigret, Paris #99
£700 $1169 €1022 La bonne de mer (26x21cm-10x8in) s. 14-Oct-3 Sotheby's, London #525
£800 $1336 €1168 Sleeping woman below a tree (20x25cm-8x10in) s. 14-Oct-3 Sotheby's, London #534
£800 $1336 €1168 L'aurore (21x16cm-8x6in) s. i.d.1961 verso board. 14-Oct-3 Sotheby's, London #536
£900 $1503 €1314 Coastal scene (58x80cm-23x31in) s. 14-Oct-3 Sotheby's, London #529/R est:400-600
£979 $1635 €1400 Le songe (56x118cm-22x46in) s. panel. 13-Oct-3 Horta, Bruxelles #56
£1000 $1670 €1460 Mermaid's vision (62x72cm-24x28in) s. 14-Oct-3 Sotheby's, London #523/R est:400-600
£1200 $2004 €1752 La femme en bouquet de soleil (72x52cm-28x20in) s. board. 14-Oct-3 Sotheby's, London #530/R est:800-1200
£1400 $2338 €2044 Woman wearing hats (91x71cm-36x28in) s. 14-Oct-3 Sotheby's, London #524/R est:400-600

ALAUZET, Jean (20th C) French
£1399 $2336 €2000 Girl with apple (61x46cm-24x18in) s. canvas on board. 11-Oct-3 Hans Stahl, Hamburg #47/R est:1200
£1399 $2336 €2000 Two seamstresses! (49x60cm-19x24in) s. canvasboard. 11-Oct-3 Hans Stahl, Hamburg #48/R est:1400

ALBANI, Francesco (1578-1660) Italian
£7778 $14000 €11356 Assumption of the Virgin (50x38cm-20x15in) copper. 22-Jan-4 Sotheby's, New York #232/R est:15000-20000

ALBANI, Francesco (attrib) (1578-1660) Italian
£4964 $8291 €7000 Deux anges (72x78cm-28x31in) oval. 17-Oct-3 Tajan, Paris #36/R est:8000-10000

ALBANI, Francesco (circle) (1578-1660) Italian
£18462 $31754 €26955 Venus with doves (138x93cm-54x37in) 2-Dec-3 Bukowskis, Stockholm #335/R est:150000-200000 (S.KR 240000)
£28000 $50400 €40880 Venus at the forge of Vulcan. Toilet of Venus. Venus and Adonis. Diana's nymphs (52cm-20in circular) copper set of four. 21-Apr-4 Christie's, London #82/R est:15000-20000

ALBANO, Sergio (1939-) Italian
£340 $609 €500 Pope (35x29cm-14x11in) s.d.1971 i.verso cardboard exhib. 22-Mar-4 Sant Agostino, Torino #390/R
£414 $687 €600 Beautiful (30x30cm-12x12in) board. 1-Oct-3 Della Rocca, Turin #49/R
£467 $859 €700 Black cat (25x30cm-10x12in) s. oil acrylic board painted 1986. 14-Jun-4 Sant Agostino, Torino #356/R
£476 $852 €700 Winter landscape (30x30cm-12x12in) s. board painted 1993. 22-Mar-4 Sant Agostino, Torino #371/R
£533 $981 €800 Card queen (40x40cm-16x16in) s. i.d.1990 verso board. 14-Jun-4 Sant Agostino, Torino #357/R
£667 $1227 €1000 Methaphysical interior (77x62cm-30x24in) s.d.1973 board. 14-Jun-4 Sant Agostino, Torino #358/R
£748 $1339 €1100 Sweet France (24x18cm-9x7in) s.d.1985 board. 22-Mar-4 Sant Agostino, Torino #392/R

ALBEEL, Jan van den (20th C) ?
£267 $491 €400 Vii mini diotiima (30x30cm-12x12in) s.i.d.1967 verso acrylic. 12-Jun-4 Meeting Art, Vercelli #759

ALBERCA, Gabriel (1934-) Spanish
£500 $900 €730 Roses (38x28cm-15x11in) i.verso board prov. 21-Apr-4 Cheffins, Cambridge #518/R

ALBERICI, Augusto (1846-?) Italian
£2200 $4070 €3212 On the terrace (30x49cm-12x19in) s.i. 14-Jul-4 Sotheby's, Olympia #210/R est:2000-3000

ALBEROLA, Jean Michel (1953-) French
Works on paper
£1049 $1783 €1500 Melampus II (137x133cm-54x52in) s.i.d.1982 pastel. 18-Nov-3 Pierre Berge, Paris #14/R est:1500-2000
£1538 $2646 €2200 Melanitas (150x150cm-59x59in) s.d.1981 pastel prov. 3-Dec-3 Tajan, Paris #478/R est:3000-4000
£1806 $3016 €2600 Miroir (93x64cm-37x25in) s.d.89 mixed media prov. 21-Oct-3 Artcurial Briest, Paris #619/R est:3000-4000
£3221 $5927 €4800 Voyage en Espagne II (150x101cm-59x40in) s.d.1989 gouache prov.exhib. 29-Mar-4 Cornette de St.Cyr, Paris #88/R est:6000-8000
£4930 $8627 €7000 Peintre et son modele (147x122cm-58x48in) s.d.1981 chl sanguine pastel gouache. 18-Dec-3 Cornette de St.Cyr, Paris #154/R est:5000-6000
£5333 $9600 €8000 Avispoda (150x295cm-59x116in) s.d.1985 pastel paper on panel prov. 25-Apr-4 Versailles Encheres #216 est:6000-8000
£5467 $9949 €8200 Sticte II (136x150cm-54x59in) s.i.d.1983 mixed media prov. 2-Jul-4 Binoche, Paris #9/R est:10000-12000
£6081 $10703 €9000 Trois etoiles (148x88cm-58x35in) mixed media canvas on panel exec with J Le Gac F Rouan prov. 18-May-4 Tajan, Paris #130/R est:10000-12000

ALBERS, Josef (1888-1976) American
£4000 $6920 €5840 Homage to the square, orange, brown (29x29cm-11x11in) card painted c.1960-65. 11-Dec-3 Christie's, Kensington #216/R est:4000-6000
£7000 $12110 €10220 Homage to the square, brown, grey, green (29x29cm-11x11in) card painted c.1960-65. 11-Dec-3 Christie's, Kensington #215/R est:5000-7000
£8500 $13515 €12325 Homage to the square - blue, green (29x29cm-11x11in) oil on card. 11-Sep-3 Christie's, Kensington #189/R est:5000-7000
£9000 $15570 €13140 Homage to the square, black, grey (30x30cm-12x12in) card painted c.1960-65. 11-Dec-3 Christie's, Kensington #218/R est:5000-7000
£9500 $15105 €13775 Homage to the square - yellow, brown (29x29cm-11x11in) oil on card. 11-Sep-3 Christie's, Kensington #188/R est:5000-7000
£9500 $16435 €13870 Homage to the square, orange, peach, yellow (29x29cm-11x11in) card painted c.1960-65. 11-Dec-3 Christie's, Kensington #217/R est:5000-7000
£13000 $20670 €18850 Homage to the square - lime, grey, green (30x30cm-12x12in) oil on card. 11-Sep-3 Christie's, Kensington #183/R est:5000-7000
£13000 $20670 €18850 Homage to the square - black, grey, brown (30x30cm-12x12in) oil on card. 11-Sep-3 Christie's, Kensington #184/R est:5000-7000
£17164 $29694 €25059 Reddish and grey and cobalt green and cadmium green (40x40cm-16x16in) mono.d.1958 oil pavatex prov. 9-Dec-3 Peter Webb, Auckland #86/R est:30000-50000 (NZ.D 46000)
£20958 $35000 €30599 Study for homage to the square, geocentric (81x81cm-32x32in) mono.d.65 s.i.d.1965 verso masonite prov.exhib. 13-Nov-3 Sotheby's, New York #228/R est:50000-70000
£22000 $40040 €32120 Study for Homage to the Square - Mild Signal (45x45cm-18x18in) mono.d.66 s.i.d.verso masonite prov. 5-Feb-4 Christie's, London #167/R est:22000-25000
£23944 $41423 €34000 Desert glow II (61x61cm-24x24in) mono.d.71 i. verso panel. 13-Dec-3 Lempertz, Koln #108/R est:20000-25000
£27536 $45159 €38000 Homage to the square; enduring (58x58cm-23x23in) s.d.58 i.d.verso prov. 27-May-3 Sotheby's, Amsterdam #437/R est:30000-40000
£27933 $50000 €40782 Pueblo (42x57cm-17x22in) mono.d.47 paper on board on masonite prov. 13-May-4 Sotheby's, New York #131/R est:20000-30000
£28000 $51520 €40880 Study for homage to the square, Negev (61x61cm-24x24in) mono.d.63 oil on masonite prov. 25-Jun-4 Christie's, London #174/R est:25000-35000
£30000 $55200 €43800 Study for homage to the square (50x50cm-20x20in) mono.d.61 oil on aluminium prov. 25-Jun-4 Christie's, London #175/R est:35000-45000
£36000 $66240 €52560 Study for homage to the square (46x46cm-18x18in) mono.d.72 i. verso masonite prov.exhib. 24-Jun-4 Sotheby's, London #139/R est:15000-20000
£50000 $91000 €73000 Study for homage to the square, awaiting (61x61cm-24x24in) mono.d.62 i.d.1962 verso masonite prov. 6-Feb-4 Sotheby's, London #118/R est:40000-60000

£50898 $85000 €74311 Homage to the square, quiet question (102x102cm-40x40in) s.i.d.1958 verso masonite prov. 13-Nov-3 Sotheby's, New York #225/R est:120000-180000
£55866 $100000 €81564 Hommage to the square - engaged (76x76cm-30x30in) mono.d.58 s.i.d.verso masonite prov.lit. 13-May-4 Sotheby's, New York #175/R est:80000-120000
£56886 $95000 €83054 White Facade (71x102cm-28x40in) mono.d.60 s.i.d.verso masonite prov.exhib. 12-Nov-3 Christie's, Rockefeller NY #302/R est:100000-150000
£75000 $136500 €109500 Homage to the square, auriferous (81x81cm-32x32in) mono.d.55 s.i.d.verso masonite prov.exhib. 4-Feb-4 Christie's, London #12/R est:40000-60000
£77844 $130000 €113652 Homage to the square, proposed (102x102cm-40x40in) mono.i.d.1966 masonite prov. 13-Nov-3 Phillips, New York #31/R est:120000-180000
£86858 $147659 €126813 Homage to the Square - Ripening (121x121cm-48x48in) s.d.1967 verso panel prov. 5-Nov-3 AB Stockholms Auktionsverk #1161/R est:1200000-1500000 (S.KR 1150000)
£110000 $200200 €160600 Study for homage to the square, floating aura (101x101cm-40x40in) mono.d.67 s.i.d.verso masonite prov.exhib. 4-Feb-4 Christie's, London #34/R est:60000-80000
£160000 $267200 €233600 Study for homage to the square, shaded shade (102x102cm-40x40in) mono.d.63 s.i.d.1963 verso masonite prov. 22-Oct-3 Christie's, London #72/R est:60000-70000
£160000 $294400 €233600 Homage to the square - expectant (102x102cm-40x40in) mono. s.i.d.58 verso masonite prov. 23-Jun-4 Sotheby's, London #30/R est:100000-150000
£173184 $310000 €252849 Homage to the square - Grisaille with Gold (122x122cm-48x48in) mono.d.61 s.i.d.verso masonite prov.exhib. 11-May-4 Christie's, Rockefeller NY #13/R est:150000-200000
£191617 $320000 €279761 Homage to the Square - Stage Light (122x122cm-48x48in) mono.d.66 s.i.d. verso masonite prov. 11-Nov-3 Christie's, Rockefeller NY #11/R est:150000-250000

Photographs
£10778 $18000 €15736 Bruno and Schirfa Caneresi, Ascona (22x15cm-9x6in) i.d.1930 photo collage silver gelatin print board prov.lit. 17-Oct-3 Phillips, New York #60/R est:20000-30000

Prints
£2177 $3897 €3200 SP-XI (63x63cm-25x25in) init.d.67 num.97/125 col lithograph. 16-Mar-4 Finarte Semenzato, Milan #40/R est:2000
£11176 $19000 €16317 Homage to the square (55x55cm-22x22in) screenprint set of 10. 31-Oct-3 Sotheby's, New York #492/R
£12333 $22077 €18500 Homage to the square (35x35cm-14x14in) s.i.d. col silkscreen portfolio of 10 prov. 14-May-4 Ketterer, Munich #282/R est:9000-12000
£29944 $53000 €43718 SP, homage to the square (63x63cm-25x25in) s.i.d.num. col screenprint set of twelve album. 28-Apr-4 Christie's, Rockefeller NY #253/R est:15000-20000

Works on paper
£2432 $4500 €3551 Structured constellation (43x56cm-17x22in) pencil India ink graph paper exec c.1958 prov. 13-Jul-4 Christie's, Rockefeller NY #16/R est:2000-3000
£2688 $5000 €3924 K-32 (20x28cm-8x11in) init.d.1956 pen ink. 2-Mar-4 Swann Galleries, New York #2/R est:5000-8000

ALBERS, Josef (attrib) (1888-1976) American
£486 $900 €710 Deep (81x81cm-32x32in) acrylic panel. 13-Mar-4 DeFina, Austinburg #880/R
£1189 $2200 €1736 Morning (102x102cm-40x40in) acrylic panel. 13-Mar-4 DeFina, Austinburg #812 est:300-500

ALBERS, Josef (studio) (1888-1976) American
Photographs
£2448 $4161 €3500 Josef Albers (34x29cm-13x11in) photogram gelatin silver. 28-Nov-3 Bassenge, Berlin #4112/R est:1600

ALBERT, Ernest (1857-1946) American
£3226 $6000 €4710 The day's end (50x60cm-20x24in) s.d.1937 i.verso. 5-Mar-4 Skinner, Boston #493/R est:6000-8000

ALBERT, Ernest (1900-1976) Belgian
£1000 $1800 €1500 Reclining nude (65x80cm-26x31in) s. 26-Apr-4 Bernaerts, Antwerp #584/R est:1500-1750

ALBERT, Ernest (fl.1890s) British
Works on paper
£300 $555 €438 Running before the wind (28x36cm-11x14in) s. W/C. 9-Mar-4 Gorringes, Lewes #2157

ALBERT, Friedrich Wilhelm Ferdinand Theodor (1822-?) German
£2980 $5454 €4500 Evening lake landscape with fishermen (68x105cm-27x41in) s. 8-Apr-4 Dorotheum, Vienna #41/R est:3800-4200

ALBERT, Gustaf (1866-1905) Swedish
£887 $1588 €1295 Hon Fleurs Harbour in moonlight (45x55cm-18x22in) s.d.97 panel exhib. 26-May-4 AB Stockholms Auktionsverk #2090/R (S.KR 12000)
£2615 $4498 €3818 Peniche dans une ecluse (54x73cm-21x29in) s. 2-Dec-3 Bukowskis, Stockholm #88/R est:20000-25000 (S.KR 34000)

ALBERT, Jos (1886-1981) Belgian
£533 $955 €800 Pharmacy (39x24cm-15x9in) s. 15-May-4 De Vuyst, Lokeren #2/R
£660 $1049 €950 Nature morte a l'attrape mouches (26x22cm-10x9in) s. panel sold with a document. 15-Sep-3 Horta, Bruxelles #31
£872 $1614 €1300 The eggs (40x55cm-16x22in) s.d.1923. 13-Mar-4 De Vuyst, Lokeren #2/R
£2414 $4466 €3500 Les charmes (71x80cm-28x31in) s. exhib. 13-Jan-4 Vanderkindere, Brussels #7/R est:1500-2000
£4690 $8676 €6800 Paysage avenue Montjoie (54x43cm-21x17in) s.d.1912 exhib. 13-Jan-4 Vanderkindere, Brussels #105 est:2000-3000
£5172 $9569 €7500 Trompe-l'oeil (60x46cm-24x18in) s. 19-Jan-4 Horta, Bruxelles #182/R est:10000-12000
Works on paper
£276 $510 €400 Autoportrait (44x30cm-17x12in) s.d.1918 dr. 13-Jan-4 Vanderkindere, Brussels #24
£4552 $8421 €6600 Femme en bleu dans la cuisine (80x61cm-31x24in) s.d.1914 W/C exhib. 13-Jan-4 Vanderkindere, Brussels #110 est:2500-4000

ALBERT, Jos (attrib) (1886-1981) Belgian
£397 $723 €600 Le potager de la maison du pecheur (66x90cm-26x35in) 15-Jun-4 Vanderkindere, Brussels #14

ALBERT, Karl (1911-) American
£403 $750 €588 Desert scene (51x61cm-20x24in) s. painted c.1940. 7-Mar-4 Treadway Gallery, Cincinnati #624/R

ALBERT-LASARD, Loulou (1891-1969) German
Works on paper
£517 $864 €750 La lune a Cannes (25x34cm-10x13in) s.d.1939 i.verso W/C pen paper on paper. 13-Nov-3 Neumeister, Munich #234/R

ALBERT-LEFEUVRE, Louis Étienne Marie (19th C) French
Sculpture
£2973 $5232 €4400 Mere et enfant (98cm-39in) s. pat bronze. 18-May-4 Galerie Moderne, Brussels #1519/R est:3500-4500
£4930 $8627 €7000 Les fondeurs moyen-age (48cm-19in) s. pewter bronze Cast Siot lit. 16-Dec-3 Artcurial Briest, Paris #50/R est:7000-10000

ALBERTI, Cherubino (1553-1615) Italian
Works on paper
£1300 $2249 €1898 Study for the figure of Atlante (14x8cm-6x3in) pen brown ink over red chk. 9-Dec-3 Bonhams, Knightsbridge #14/R est:1500-2000

ALBERTI, Durante (1538-1613) Italian
£2416 $4446 €3600 Martyrdom of Saint Andrew (94x70cm-37x28in) lit. 29-Mar-4 Pandolfini, Florence #631/R est:4000

ALBERTI, Giovanni (1558-1601) Italian
£1690 $2806 €2400 Figures going to church in the snow (97x150cm-38x59in) s. 16-Jun-3 Dorotheum, Vienna #239/R est:2400-2800

ALBERTI, Giuseppe Vizzotto (1862-1931) Italian
£5500 $10010 €8030 Road home at dusk (89x61cm-35x24in) s. canvas on board. 16-Jun-4 Christie's, Kensington #117/R est:4000-6000
Works on paper
£600 $1020 €876 Paying homage at the lagoon shrine, Venice (51x34cm-20x13in) s.i.d.1898 pencil W/C bodycol. 6-Nov-3 Christie's, Kensington #970/R
£850 $1564 €1241 View of a Venetian street (33x17cm-13x7in) s. bodycol. 23-Mar-4 Bonhams, Knightsbridge #178/R

ALBERTINI, Oreste (1887-1953) Italian
£1733 $3189 €2600 Vase with white lilies (44x35cm-17x14in) s. paper on board. 8-Jun-4 Sotheby's, Milan #104/R est:1000-2000
£3521 $6092 €5000 Lugano Lake (39x49cm-15x19in) s. i.verso board painted 1931. 10-Dec-3 Sotheby's, Milan #63/R est:5000-7000
£3767 $5877 €5500 Landscape in the morning (45x68cm-18x27in) s. board. 8-Apr-3 Il Ponte, Milan #574/R
£4965 $8291 €7000 Winter landscape (60x80cm-24x31in) s.d.1939. 14-Oct-3 Finarte Semenzato, Milan #183/R

ALBERTIS, Sebastiano de (1828-1897) Italian
£4667 $8587 €7000 Horses (33x43cm-13x17in) s. 10-Jun-4 Christie's, Rome #193/R est:7000-10000
£8156 $13621 €11500 Battle (15x29cm-6x11in) s. board prov. 14-Oct-3 Finarte Semenzato, Milan #202/R est:13000
Works on paper
£845 $1462 €1200 Soldier and horse (10x8cm-4x3in) s. W/C. 9-Dec-3 Finarte Semenzato, Milan #143

ALBERTO, Pietro (1929-) Italian
£1007 $1862 €1500 Mazes (80x70cm-31x28in) s.d.1990 acrylic lit. 13-Mar-4 Meeting Art, Vercelli #84 est:1500

ALBERTS, Jacob (1860-1941) German
£800 $1448 €1200 Norwegian landscape with snow covered peaks (49x68cm-19x27in) s. canvas on board. 3-Apr-4 Hans Stahl, Hamburg #1/R
£1712 $2911 €2500 Misty mudflats (46x71cm-18x28in) s. 8-Nov-3 Hans Stahl, Toestorf #51/R est:3500

ALBERTS, Tom (1962-) Australian
£1220 $1915 €1769 Untitled (91x107cm-36x42in) s.d.1994 linen prov. 26-Aug-3 Christie's, Sydney #290/R est:3000-5000 (A.D 3000)
Works on paper
£486 $782 €710 Self portrait in black (68x49cm-27x19in) s.d.1992 chl conte prov.exhib. 25-Aug-3 Sotheby's, Paddington #231/R est:1200-1800 (A.D 1200)

ALBERTS, Willem Jacobus (1912-) Dutch
£250 $430 €365 Windmill beside a lake (28x38cm-11x15in) s. prov. 5-Dec-3 Keys, Aylsham #651
£250 $430 €365 Quiet evening drink (28x38cm-11x15in) s. prov. 5-Dec-3 Keys, Aylsham #652
£333 $607 €500 Brook by the Veluwe, near Nykerk (38x58cm-15x23in) s. 30-Jun-4 Vendue Huis, Gravenhage #123/R

£350 $602 €511 Summer sailing (38x46cm-15x18in) s. prov. 5-Dec-3 Keys, Aylsham #653/R
£350 $602 €511 River scene, Central Holland (38x46cm-15x18in) s. prov. 5-Dec-3 Keys, Aylsham #654
£548 $932 €800 Along the Ijssel (59x99cm-23x39in) s. 5-Nov-3 Vendue Huis, Gravenhage #270/R
£616 $1048 €900 Cows watering (39x59cm-15x23in) s. 5-Nov-3 Vendue Huis, Gravenhage #271/R

ALBERTSEN, Andreas Marius Valdemar (1868-1954) Danish
£2209 $3800 €3225 Harbour scene with ships by the docks (81x117cm-32x46in) s.d.99. 6-Dec-3 Pook & Pook, Downington #98/R est:1500-2500

ALBIERI, Gino (1881-1949) Italian
£940 $1729 €1400 Scanno (80x60cm-31x24in) s. i.d.1928 verso. 24-Mar-4 Il Ponte, Milan #642/R est:1000-1200

ALBINET, Jean Paul (1954-) French
£599 $1048 €850 Bonheur (33x46cm-13x18in) s.i.d.1990 acrylic ink serigraph. 18-Dec-3 Cornette de St.Cyr, Paris #91/R
£739 $1294 €1050 Reve promis (33x46cm-13x18in) s.i.d.1990 acrylic ink serigraph. 18-Dec-3 Cornette de St.Cyr, Paris #90/R

ALBINO, Luca (1884-1952) Italian
£1284 $2259 €1900 Coast near Amalfi (41x54cm-16x21in) s. card. 19-May-4 Il Ponte, Milan #1043 est:1200-1300

ALBINSON, Dewey Ernest (1898-1971) American
£518 $850 €751 Hay bales (48x69cm-19x27in) s. painted c.1935. 7-Jun-3 Treadway Gallery, Cincinnati #1486
Works on paper
£219 $400 €320 Street scene (41x51cm-16x20in) s. pastel executed c.1940. 5-Jun-4 Treadway Gallery, Cincinnati #724/R

ALBISETTI, Natale (19/20th C) Swiss
£1477 $2746 €2200 La famille reunie autour du puits (73x92cm-29x36in) s. 7-Mar-4 Lesieur & Le Bars, Le Havre #1/R

ALBITZ, Richard (20th C) German
£287 $479 €410 Winter scene (74x96cm-29x38in) s. s.i. verso panel. 28-Jun-3 Dannenberg, Berlin #646/R
£699 $1189 €1000 Yellow house (38x36cm-15x14in) s. i.d.1931 verso canvas on board. 26-Nov-3 Lempertz, Koln #556/R

ALBIZU, Enrique (1926-) Spanish
Works on paper
£493 $863 €700 Forms (48x27cm-19x11in) s.d.1973 pastel. 16-Dec-3 Durán, Madrid #650/R

ALBOTTO, Francesco (1722-1758) Italian
£119718 $198732 €170000 Cannaregio Canal with view of Ponte delle Guglie (61x101cm-24x40in) lit. 11-Jul-3 Finarte, Venice #534/R est:100000-140000

ALBRECHT, Balthasar Augustin (attrib) (1687-1765) German
£938 $1500 €1369 Monk with book (64x76cm-25x30in) i.d.1720. 20-Sep-3 Sloans & Kenyon, Bethesda #1154/R est:1750-2250

ALBRECHT, Carl (1862-1926) German
£278 $453 €400 Peasant sat on bench smoking pipe (86x65cm-34x26in) s. i. verso. 27-Sep-3 Dannenberg, Berlin #517/R
£738 $1358 €1100 Pipe smoker outside farmstead (87x64cm-34x25in) s. i. verso. 26-Mar-4 Bolland & Marotz, Bremen #480/R
£1192 $2170 €1800 Spring bouquet of flowers (36x30cm-14x12in) s. 18-Jun-4 Bolland & Marotz, Bremen #576/R est:2200

ALBRECHT, Gretchen (1943-) New Zealander
£346 $619 €505 Forest and waterfalls (29x42cm-11x17in) s.i.d.86 oil stick collage paper. 12-May-4 Dunbar Sloane, Wellington #136 est:1500-2500 (NZ.D 1000)
£1730 $3097 €2526 Untitled pastel hemisphere (150x300cm-59x118in) s.d.58 acrylic shaped canvass in two parts. 12-May-4 Dunbar Sloane, Wellington #35/R est:10000-18000 (NZ.D 5000)
£6993 $12727 €10210 Garden no.16 (144x104cm-57x41in) s.d.1971 acrylic. 29-Jun-4 Peter Webb, Auckland #70/R est:20000-30000 (NZ.D 20000)
Works on paper
£435 $739 €635 Autumnal 2 (10x15cm-4x6in) s.i.d.1997 W/C. 4-Nov-3 Peter Webb, Auckland #83/R est:1000-1500 (NZ.D 1200)
£502 $863 €733 Abstract fish (49x66cm-19x26in) s.d.1958 mixed media. 7-Dec-3 International Art Centre, Auckland #336 (NZ.D 1350)
£725 $1167 €1059 Study for a painting - after Zeshin (57x76cm-22x30in) s.d.83 W/C. 20-Aug-3 Dunbar Sloane, Auckland #29/R est:2000-4000 (NZ.D 2000)
£944 $1718 €1378 Study for large hemisphere (57x75cm-22x30in) s.i.d.1984 W/C. 29-Jun-4 Peter Webb, Auckland #179/R est:3500-4500 (NZ.D 2700)
£1715 $2795 €2504 Study for mysteries/correspondences (56x76cm-22x30in) s.i.d.1983 W/C. 23-Sep-3 Peter Webb, Auckland #9/R est:4000-6000 (NZ.D 4750)
£2256 $3835 €3294 Fragment with shadow (44x84cm-17x33in) s.d.1989 mixed media canvas. 27-Nov-3 International Art Centre, Auckland #48/R est:4500-6500 (NZ.D 6000)
£3091 $4853 €4482 Crossbow (105x74cm-41x29in) s.i.d.1975 W/C. 27-Aug-3 Dunbar Sloane, Wellington #21/R est:9000-14000 (NZ.D 8500)

ALBRICI, Enrico (1714-1775) Italian
Works on paper
£789 $1453 €1200 Three satyrical figures (19x19cm-7x7in) pen ink W/C. 22-Jun-4 Sotheby's, Milan #125/R

ALBRIGHT, Adam Emory (1862-1957) American
£645 $1200 €942 Yellow roses (33x46cm-13x18in) s. painted c.1930. 7-Mar-4 Treadway Gallery, Cincinnati #610/R est:1500-2000
£659 $1100 €962 Figures in a barn (61x51cm-24x20in) s. 26-Oct-3 Bonhams & Butterfields, San Francisco #6516/R
£1266 $2000 €1848 Figures along the coast (51x66cm-20x26in) s. 7-Sep-3 Treadway Gallery, Cincinnati #591/R est:5000-7000
£1916 $3200 €2797 In the fields (65x92cm-26x36in) oil pencil. 9-Oct-3 Christie's, Rockefeller NY #63/R est:4000-6000
£3495 $6500 €5103 Figure along the coast (51x66cm-20x26in) s. painted c.1920. 7-Mar-4 Treadway Gallery, Cincinnati #567/R est:4000-6000
£5028 $9000 €7341 Two boys on lane going fishing (64x46cm-25x18in) s.d.1900 prov. 20-Mar-4 Sloans & Kenyon, Bethesda #1205/R est:6000-8000

ALBRIGHT, Gertrude Partington (1883-1959) American
£11561 $20000 €16879 Actress - Elise Schuyler (117x91cm-46x36in) s. prov. 10-Dec-3 Bonhams & Butterfields, San Francisco #6278/R est:6000-8000

ALBRIGHT, Henry James (1887-1951) American
£315 $500 €460 Laguna Beach (14x17cm-6x7in) s. canvas on board. 12-Sep-3 Skinner, Boston #511/R
£407 $700 €594 Rocky landscape (28x36cm-11x14in) s.verso canvas on board painted c.1920. 7-Dec-3 Treadway Gallery, Cincinnati #583/R
£409 $650 €597 Laguna coast, California (14x18cm-6x7in) s. canvas on board. 12-Sep-3 Skinner, Boston #509/R
£409 $650 €597 Mountain vista (28x36cm-11x14in) s. canvasboard. 4-May-3 William Jenack, New York #356
£629 $1000 €918 Retrean Rocks, Laguna beach, California (23x30cm-9x12in) s.i.d.1922 canvasboard. 4-May-3 William Jenack, New York #68

ALBRIGHT, Lloyd (1896-1950) American
£2994 $5000 €4371 Chimayo, New Mexico (61x46cm-24x18in) board. 18-Oct-3 David Dike, Dallas #170/R est:4000-6000

ALBRIGHT, Malvin Marr (1897-1983) American
£2246 $3750 €3279 Incoming tide, Maine (91x114cm-36x45in) s. prov.exhib.lit. 7-Oct-3 Sotheby's, New York #228 est:1000-2000

ALBUTT, Virginia (20th C) British?
£300 $555 €438 Fatma laying the table, Tangier (44x44cm-17x17in) s.d.2003 canvasboard. 13-Feb-4 Sworder & Son, Bishops Stortford #121/R

ALCAHUD, Gloria (1937-) Spanish
£272 $495 €400 Mars, step 11 (50x60cm-20x24in) s.i.verso board. 3-Feb-4 Segre, Madrid #249/R

ALCALA, Antonio (20th C) Spanish
£448 $749 €650 Gypsy (136x67cm-54x26in) s. 17-Nov-3 Durán, Madrid #1247/R

ALCALAY, Albert (1917-) American
Works on paper
£222 $400 €324 Summer at the pond (6x8cm-2x3in) s.d.1973 W/C gouache prov. 24-Apr-4 David Rago, Lambertville #9/R

ALCALDE, Juan (1918-) Spanish
£845 $1479 €1200 Family (22x30cm-9x12in) s. board. 16-Dec-3 Durán, Madrid #610/R
£1702 $2757 €2400 Plaza of the Victoria, Paris (54x65cm-21x26in) s. 20-May-3 Ansorena, Madrid #304/R est:2000
Works on paper
£867 $1577 €1300 Five houses (36x50cm-14x20in) s. W/C gouache pencil prov. 29-Jun-4 Segre, Madrid #226/R

ALCANTARA, Antonio (1918-) Venezuelan
£449 $835 €656 Caracas (47x38cm-19x15in) s. masonite. 14-Mar-4 Subastas Odalys, Caracas #23/R
£452 $700 €660 Greek coast (50x65cm-20x26in) s. 29-Sep-2 Subastas Odalys, Caracas #14/R
£602 $1095 €903 Seascape (32x45cm-13x18in) s. 21-Jun-4 Subastas Odalys, Caracas #118/R
£610 $1000 €891 Landscape (40x35cm-16x14in) s. painted 1951. 1-Jun-3 Subastas Odalys, Caracas #124

ALCANTARA, Miguel (20th C) Venezuelan
£433 $780 €632 Landscape (69x149cm-27x59in) s. painted 1988. 25-Apr-4 Subastas Odalys, Caracas #121

ALCERRECA Y COMONFORT, Ignacio (19th C) Mexican
£6322 $10748 €9230 Church of the Sad Night (102x69cm-40x27in) s.d.1889. 29-Oct-3 Louis Morton, Mexico #42/R est:130000-150000 (M.P 120000)

ALCIATI, Ambrogio (1878-1929) Italian
£922 $1540 €1300 Leda (39x30cm-15x12in) s. board lit. 20-Oct-3 Sant Agostino, Torino #90/R
£1818 $3036 €2600 Nude on the sofa (55x50cm-22x20in) s. 26-Jun-3 Sant Agostino, Torino #282/R est:2000-2500
£2083 $3542 €3000 Nude on the sofa (55x50cm-22x20in) s. 1-Nov-3 Meeting Art, Vercelli #398/R est:3000

ALCIATI, Evangelina Gemma (1883-1959) Italian

£694	$1181	€1000	Sun in the valley (48x34cm-19x13in) s. cardboard. 1-Nov-3 Meeting Art, Vercelli #321/R

ALCOLEA, Carlos (1949-1992) Spanish

£7432	$13081	€11000	Drunk (99x69cm-39x27in) i. oil acrylic wax crayon painted 1988 prov. 18-May-4 Segre, Madrid #160/R est:9000

ALCOPLEY, Lewin (1910-1992) American

Works on paper

£299	$500	€437	Untitled (25x14cm-10x6in) s.d.1953 ink. 11-Nov-3 Christie's, Rockefeller NY #114/R

ALCORLO BARRERA, Manuel (1935-) Spanish

£1702	$2757	€2400	Sacred Family (57x40cm-22x16in) s.d.59 panel. 20-May-3 Ansorena, Madrid #330/R est:2400
£2553	$4136	€3600	Ropa tendida (50x110cm-20x43in) s.d.59. 20-May-3 Ansorena, Madrid #310/R est:3600
£4605	$8336	€7000	Surrealist composition with figures (162x130cm-64x51in) s.d.90. 14-Apr-4 Ansorena, Madrid #279/R est:7000

Works on paper

£280	$510	€420	Young girl in profile (20x13cm-8x5in) s. pencil sanguine. 29-Jun-4 Segre, Madrid #295/R
£329	$605	€500	Girl in yellow (65x50cm-26x20in) s.d.1962 pastel. 22-Jun-4 Durán, Madrid #78/R

ALDEGREVER, Heinrich (1502-1558) German

Prints

£4803	$8742	€7012	Martin Luther. copperplate. 17-Jun-4 Kornfeld, Bern #1/R est:12500 (S.FR 11000)

ALDENRATH, Heinrich Jakob (1775-1844) German

Miniatures

£1757	$3092	€2600	Portrait of Luise Furstin Radziwill as a bride (8cm-3in circular) gouache ivory. 21-May-4 Lempertz, Koln #566/R est:1500

ALDERSON, Dorothy Margaret (1900-1992) British

Works on paper

£300	$501	€438	Farmer and shire horses harvesting in a coastal landscape (8x25cm-3x10in) s.d.1988 W/C. 10-Oct-3 Richardson & Smith, Whitby #127
£450	$752	€657	Fox Hounds at Hunt kennels (8x13cm-3x5in) s. W/C. 10-Oct-3 Richardson & Smith, Whitby #116/R

ALDERSON, Dorothy Margaret and Elizabeth Mary (20th C) British

£520	$827	€759	Cattle at a riverside (25x35cm-10x14in) s.d.1959. 18-Mar-3 Anderson & Garland, Newcastle #194
£650	$1034	€949	Garsby Grange (12x18cm-5x7in) s.i.d.1926. 18-Mar-3 Anderson & Garland, Newcastle #198
£650	$1170	€949	The Eiger, Monch and Jungfrau from Schynige Platte, Switzerland (46x56cm-18x22in) s.d.1969 i.verso canvasboard. 21-Apr-4 Tennants, Leyburn #1231
£660	$1049	€964	Rabbits in a hutch (26x32cm-10x13in) s.d.1921. 18-Mar-3 Anderson & Garland, Newcastle #193/R
£1150	$1829	€1679	Montage of animal studies (9x14cm-4x6in) s. some i. 8 mounted together. 18-Mar-3 Anderson & Garland, Newcastle #196/R est:400-700

Works on paper

£420	$756	€613	Study of the horse Green Label (20x25cm-8x10in) s.d.1959 pencil W/C scratching out. 21-Apr-4 Tennants, Leyburn #981
£430	$774	€628	Study of a hunter standing in a landscape (18x26cm-7x10in) s.d.1968 pencil W/C. 21-Apr-4 Tennants, Leyburn #984
£700	$1260	€1022	Study of three spaniels on a heather-clad moor, mountains beyond (17x24cm-7x9in) s.d.1982 pencil W/C. 21-Apr-4 Tennants, Leyburn #982/R
£750	$1193	€1095	Montage of landscape, flower and animal studies (10x13cm-4x5in) s.d.1924 W/C eight mounted together. 18-Mar-3 Anderson & Garland, Newcastle #197
£2000	$3400	€2920	Moorland ponies (34x57cm-13x22in) s.i.d.1970 pencil W/C. 19-Nov-3 Tennants, Leyburn #912/R est:1500-2500

ALDIN, Cecil (1870-1935) British

£520	$868	€759	Bit of still life (37x30cm-15x12in) 12-Nov-3 Sotheby's, Olympia #98/R
£1300	$2171	€1898	Reflection (50x35cm-20x14in) s. 12-Nov-3 Sotheby's, Olympia #97/R est:1000-1500

Works on paper

£280	$512	€409	Toast (21x24cm-8x9in) s. crayon htd white. 27-Jan-4 Bonhams, Knightsbridge #173/R
£450	$752	€657	Huntsman approaching a ditch, hounds in the distance (13x18cm-5x7in) s. pen ink W/C on ivorine. 9-Oct-3 Greenslade Hunt, Taunton #575/R
£450	$842	€657	Hunt returning home, sun setting in the distance (13x18cm-5x7in) s. pen ink wash ivorine. 22-Jul-4 Tennants, Leyburn #679
£500	$920	€730	Terrier pup (12x12cm-5x5in) s. ink W/C on tiles sold with companion two. 14-Jun-4 Bonhams, Bath #31
£822	$1397	€1200	Zoo study (32x22cm-13x9in) s. wash prov. 5-Nov-3 Beaussant & Lefèvre, Paris #57/R
£950	$1511	€1387	Study of a highland terrier (10x13cm-4x5in) s. pen ink ivorine. 9-Sep-3 Gorringes, Lewes #1827/R
£1096	$1863	€1600	Dog jumping on owner (37x27cm-15x11in) s.i.d.1905 chl dr htd col. 5-Nov-3 Beaussant & Lefèvre, Paris #58/R
£1200	$2208	€1752	Come hup! I say, you hugly beast (46x28cm-18x11in) s. pen ink W/C lit. 10-Jun-4 Christie's, Kensington #139/R est:2500-3500
£1230	$1992	€1796	Paddy and friends (25x22cm-10x9in) i. mixed media prov. 30-Jul-3 Goodman, Sydney #197/R est:1200-1800 (A.D 3000)
£1250	$2013	€1813	Rotund huntsman with horse at the edge of a field (46x28cm-18x11in) s. W/C. 15-Aug-3 Keys, Aylsham #514/R est:1250-1500
£1250	$2038	€1825	Buy from the farmer (24x21cm-9x8in) s. i.verso pen ink pencil. 24-Sep-3 Dreweatt Neate, Newbury #74/R est:1000-1500
£2000	$3400	€2920	Scottie (10x12cm-4x5in) s. pencil pen ink col chk. 27-Nov-3 Christie's, Kensington #309/R est:2000-3000
£2000	$3740	€2920	Study of two pug pups, seated (30x31cm-12x12in) s. chl pastel. 22-Jul-4 Tennants, Leyburn #691 est:500-700
£2400	$4320	€3504	Study of a resting terrier (9x12cm-4x5in) s. pencil chl wash ivorine. 21-Apr-4 Tennants, Leyburn #987/R est:400-600
£4000	$7200	€5840	Turpin and friends on sofa (25x41cm-10x16in) s. crayon pastel. 21-Apr-4 Brightwells, Leominster #736/R est:4000-6000

ALDOR, Janos Laszlo (1895-?) Hungarian

£279	$500	€407	Young girl in national costume (79x58cm-31x23in) s. 20-Mar-4 Sloans & Kenyon, Bethesda #1163/R

ALDRICH, Clarence Nelson (1893-1953) American

Works on paper

£305	$500	€442	Industrial scene (46x64cm-18x25in) s. W/C board exec.c.1935. 7-Jun-3 Treadway Gallery, Cincinnati #1477
£381	$625	€552	Farm scene (48x64cm-19x25in) s. W/C exec.c.1935. 7-Jun-3 Treadway Gallery, Cincinnati #1479

ALDRICH, George Ames (1872-1941) American

£682	$1200	€996	Autumn landscape (41x36cm-16x14in) s. board painted c.1900. 23-May-4 Treadway Gallery, Cincinnati #574/R
£1297	$2400	€1894	Early morning (46x61cm-18x24in) s. 13-Mar-4 Susanin's, Chicago #6050/R est:1200-2000
£1647	$2750	€2405	Rockport (61x76cm-24x30in) s.d.1914. 16-Nov-3 CRN Auctions, Cambridge #27/R
£3352	$6000	€5028	Cottage by the river (91x76cm-36x30in) s. 16-May-4 Abell, Los Angeles #430/R
£4190	$7500	€6117	Brittany village scene from the river (64x76cm-25x30in) s. 15-May-4 Jeffery Burchard, Florida #195
£9302	$16000	€13581	Old water mill in Normandy (76x91cm-30x36in) s. painted c.1915. 7-Dec-3 Treadway Gallery, Cincinnati #564/R est:12000-16000
£11976	$20000	€17485	River in winter (81x91cm-32x36in) s. 9-Oct-3 Christie's, Rockefeller NY #47/R est:6000-8000

ALDRIDGE, Frederick James (1850-1933) British

£550	$946	€803	Fishing boats entering harbour (23x30cm-9x12in) 2-Dec-3 Gorringes, Lewes #2275
£1350	$2322	€1971	Fishing boats at sea (25x36cm-10x14in) s. pair. 2-Dec-3 Gorringes, Lewes #2272/R est:1500-2000
£1600	$2768	€2336	Shipping off Shoreham harbour (25x36cm-10x14in) s. 14-Dec-3 Desmond Judd, Cranbrook #1034
£1600	$2768	€2336	Shoreham fishing boats and other shipping (25x36cm-10x14in) s. 14-Dec-3 Desmond Judd, Cranbrook #1035
£3700	$5957	€5365	Near Dordrecht, Holland (51x76cm-20x30in) s.d.1889 i.verso. 23-Feb-3 Desmond Judd, Cranbrook #1021

Works on paper

£260	$481	€380	Chichester Harbour (8x18cm-3x7in) s. W/C. 13-Feb-4 Keys, Aylsham #539/R
£280	$512	€409	Strong breeze (26x38cm-10x15in) s. W/C. 27-Jan-4 Bonhams, Knightsbridge #86
£360	$612	€526	On the Thames (22x13cm-9x5in) s.i. W/C. 28-Oct-3 Bearnes, Exeter #727
£360	$601	€526	Pyramids at Gizeh (20x27cm-8x11in) s.i. W/C. 12-Nov-3 Sotheby's, Olympia #27/R
£360	$673	€526	Fishing boats off a coastline (14x22cm-6x9in) s. pencil W/C. 22-Jul-4 Tennants, Leyburn #648
£400	$636	€584	Venetian fishing fleet at sunset (18x38cm-7x15in) s. W/C. 12-Sep-3 Gardiner & Houlgate, Bath #50/R
£400	$716	€584	Fishing boats in Venice (21x27cm-8x11in) s. W/C. 16-Mar-4 Bonhams, Oxford #44/R
£425	$731	€621	Dutch shipping (20x15cm-8x6in) s.i. W/C. 5-Dec-3 Keys, Aylsham #448
£520	$884	€759	Fishing boats and other shipping by a quayside (26x37cm-10x15in) s. pencil W/C. 19-Nov-3 Tennants, Leyburn #878
£520	$931	€759	Morning after the adur (36x40cm-14x16in) s. W/C. 16-Mar-4 Bonhams, Oxford #38
£520	$957	€759	Fishing boats in the Venetian lagoon (21x27cm-8x11in) s. W/C. 23-Mar-4 Bonhams, Knightsbridge #21/R
£650	$1053	€943	On the Thames (38x55cm-15x22in) s.i. W/C. 30-Jul-3 Hamptons Fine Art, Godalming #55
£750	$1373	€1095	Sailing back into harbour. Reefed sails in a swell (31x47cm-12x19in) s. W/C pair. 27-Jan-4 Bonhams, Knightsbridge #309/R
£840	$1512	€1226	The Grand Canal, Venice (23x28cm-9x11in) s. 24-Jan-4 British Auctioneer #275
£870	$1601	€1270	Shoreham trawlers (53x36cm-21x14in) W/C. 27-Mar-4 Hogben, Folkstone #117/R
£920	$1582	€1343	Venezia (25x37cm-10x15in) s.i. W/C. 2-Dec-3 Sotheby's, London #95/R
£950	$1748	€1387	Double-master in choppy seas (25x36cm-10x14in) s. W/C. 23-Mar-4 Bonhams, Knightsbridge #74/R
£980	$1735	€1431	Off Shoreham Harbour (36x53cm-14x21in) s.d.17 W/C. 29-Apr-4 Gorringes, Lewes #2517
£1070	$1969	€1562	Basham. s.d.1917 W/C. 27-Mar-4 Hogben, Folkstone #118/R est:400-600
£1200	$2268	€1752	Setting Off (36x53cm-14x21in) s. W/C htd white. 17-Feb-4 Bonhams, New Bond Street #26/R est:700-900
£1250	$1975	€1825	On the Adur (35x53cm-14x21in) s.i. W/C. 23-Jul-3 Hampton & Littlewood, Exeter #410/R est:1200-1500
£1384	$2478	€2021	Fishing trawlers at the dock (50x75cm-20x30in) s. W/C. 11-May-4 Watson's, Christchurch #32/R est:1500-2500 (NZ.D 4000)
£1450	$2335	€2103	Fully rigged brigantine tacking to starboard on choppy sea (36x53cm-14x21in) s. W/C exec.c.1880. 23-Feb-3 Desmond Judd, Cranbrook #1028
£1500	$2805	€2190	Kingston Quays. Shoreham Harbour (37x54cm-15x21in) s.i. pencil W/C pair. 22-Jul-4 Tennants, Leyburn #647/R est:1000-1500
£1800	$2808	€2610	Barque and other craft off Newhaven (36x53cm-14x21in) s.d.1917 W/C. 20-Oct-2 Desmond Judd, Cranbrook #801
£2900	$4611	€4205	Shipping entering the river Dart, Devon (51x71cm-20x28in) s. W/C exec.c.1890-1900. 23-Mar-3 Desmond Judd, Cranbrook #1021

ALDRIDGE, John Arthur Malcolm (1905-1984) British

£340	$629	€496	Temple of Antoninus and Faustina, Rome, Sept 1957 (25x34cm-10x13in) s.d.57 board. 14-Jan-4 Lawrence, Crewkerne #1434
£360	$634	€526	Teatro di Marcello San Nicola in Carcere (19x37cm-7x15in) init.d.66 board. 18-May-4 Woolley & Wallis, Salisbury #11/R
£380	$673	€555	Still life in grey vase (31x31cm-12x12in) s.d.58 board. 27-Apr-4 Bonhams, Knightsbridge #104/R
£800	$1456	€1168	Wagon and Dovecote (23x56cm-9x22in) 15-Jun-4 Bonhams, Knightsbridge #232/R
£800	$1408	€1168	Still life, Bologna rolls (26x35cm-10x14in) s.d.1968 board. 18-May-4 Woolley & Wallis, Salisbury #52/R
£850	$1343	€1233	Place yard, Great Bardfield, February 1956 (41x56cm-16x22in) s. s.i.d.verso board. 3-Sep-3 Bonhams, Bury St Edmunds #394/R
£960	$1690	€1402	Still life with roses in a glass vase (40x35cm-16x14in) s.d.59. 18-May-4 Woolley & Wallis, Salisbury #55/R
£1150	$2024	€1679	Cathay quinces and christmas roses (45x56cm-18x22in) exhib. 18-May-4 Woolley & Wallis, Salisbury #28/R est:400-600

Works on paper

£300	$501	€438	Charles II Street, London (24x34cm-9x13in) init.i.d.16.8.44 W/C prov. 21-Oct-3 Bonhams, Knightsbridge #105/R
£300	$528	€438	Forecourt of a church, Naples (37x26cm-15x10in) s.d.1945 pencil wash. 18-May-4 Woolley & Wallis, Salisbury #251/R
£450	$792	€657	Piazza Trevi (20x25cm-8x10in) s.i.d.29/30 Sept 57 ink wash. 18-May-4 Bonhams, Knightsbridge #206/R
£620	$1147	€905	Convent of S. Maria in Campitelli, Rome (37x56cm-15x22in) s.i.d.1951 W/C pencil. 14-Jan-4 Lawrence, Crewkerne #1354
£1000	$1760	€1460	Florence, summer, bathers in the Arno (23x30cm-9x12in) s.i.d.1945 W/C. 18-May-4 Woolley & Wallis, Salisbury #281/R est:300-500

ALDWINCKLE, Eric (1909-1980) Canadian/British

£1171	$1991	€1710	Skier (27x34cm-11x13in) s.d.1942 board. 23-Nov-3 Levis, Calgary #1/R est:2800-3000 (C.D 2600)

ALECHINSKY, Pierre (1927-) Belgian

£8741	$14860	€12500	Composition (37x46cm-15x18in) s.d.56. 28-Nov-3 Drouot Estimations, Paris #206 est:8000-10000
£11268	$19493	€16000	Faire mouche (98x66cm-39x26in) s.d.1973 s.i.d.1973 verso acrylic paper on canvas. 13-Dec-3 De Vuyst, Lokeren #508/R est:14000-16000
£11806	$18653	€17000	Pieces rares (65x52cm-26x20in) s. s.i.d.1988 verso paper on canvas. 27-Apr-3 Versailles Encheres #34
£15000	$27300	€21900	Laine vierge (146x123cm-57x48in) s.d.1999 s.i.d.stretcher acrylic paper on canvas prov. 5-Feb-4 Christie's, London #152/R est:12000-15000
£17483	$29720	€25000	Duo final (73x60cm-29x24in) s. s.d.VIII 62 verso s.i.d.stretcher prov. 25-Nov-3 Christie's, Amsterdam #265/R est:30000-50000
£17840	$29793	€26046	Rosiere Republicaine (100x77cm-39x30in) s. s.i.d.1974 verso paper on canvas exhib.prov. 7-Oct-3 Rasmussen, Copenhagen #29/R est:200000-250000 (D.KR 190000)
£18681	$33066	€27274	Composition (96x95cm-38x37in) s.d.1986 paper on canvas prov. 27-Apr-4 AB Stockholms Auktionsverk #1184/R est:150000-200000 (S.KR 255000)
£19719	$34113	€28000	Trois poles (46x56cm-18x22in) s. s.i.d.1957 verso prov. 9-Dec-3 Artcurial Briest, Paris #405/R est:22000-26000
£23466	$43177	€34260	Du bout des doigts (65x54cm-26x21in) s. s.d.1966 verso. 29-Mar-4 Rasmussen, Copenhagen #104/R est:150000 (D.KR 260000)
£23649	$41622	€35000	Envoie de disparition (215x88cm-85x35in) s.d.1980 acrylic eau-forte prov. 18-May-4 Tajan, Paris #105/R est:40000-45000
£26057	$45078	€37000	Montezuma (94x94cm-37x37in) s. s.i.d.2000 verso acrylic prov.exhib.lit. 9-Dec-3 Artcurial Briest, Paris #406/R est:4000-60000
£28986	$47536	€40000	Before Mexico (100x153cm-39x60in) s. acrylic paper on card on canvas painted 1965 prov.exhib. 27-May-3 Sotheby's, Amsterdam #410/R est:40000-60000
£34742	$58019	€50723	Couple en laine naturelle (100x152cm-39x60in) s. s.d.1977 verso paper on canvas prov. 7-Oct-3 Rasmussen, Copenhagen #43/R est:400000 (D.KR 370000)
£38000	$69920	€55480	Rumeur publique (120x147cm-47x58in) s. s.i.d.1964 verso prov.exhib. 24-Jun-4 Sotheby's, London #211/R est:35000-45000
£40000	$72800	€58400	Le bleu du vent (137x127cm-54x50in) s. s.i.d.1966 verso prov.exhib. 6-Feb-4 Sotheby's, London #206/R est:50000-70000
£50000	$91000	€73000	Les douceurs de l'enfer (137x133cm-54x52in) s. s.i.d.1964 verso prov.exhib. 6-Feb-4 Sotheby's, London #201/R est:70000-100000

Prints

£2000	$3580	€3000	L'envie de partir (83x97cm-33x38in) s.i.d.1989 num.27/99 col etching. 15-May-4 De Vuyst, Lokeren #5 est:3300-3600
£2013	$3725	€3000	L'envie de partir (83x97cm-33x38in) s.i.d.1989 num.5/99 etching. 13-Mar-4 De Vuyst, Lokeren #8/R est:3300-3600
£3379	$6048	€5000	Reponse muette (181x90cm-71x35in) s.d.1988 col aquatint. 4-May-4 Calmels Cohen, Paris #21 est:5000-5500
£4196	$7217	€6000	Horloger (98x60cm-39x24in) s.i.d.1975 handcoloured etching paper on card. 2-Dec-3 Sotheby's, Amsterdam #307/R est:5000-7000
£5000	$9200	€7500	Untitled (98x60cm-39x24in) s.d.1975 aquatint W/C prov. 9-Jun-4 Christie's, Amsterdam #316/R est:6000-8000

Sculpture

£2685	$4966	€4000	Totems (23x10cm-9x4in) s. num.74/150 pol bronze st.f.A Valsuani two. 13-Mar-4 De Vuyst, Lokeren #3/R est:4000-5000
£11513	$21184	€17500	Pied des stalles (51x50x50cm-20x20x20in) s. num.4/8 pat bronze Cast Blanchet. 27-Jun-4 Versailles Encheres #147/R est:18000-20000

Works on paper

£671	$1248	€1000	Papier de famille (20x26cm-8x10in) s.i.d.30.VIII.1970 Indian ink. 3-Mar-4 Artcurial Briest, Paris #300
£972	$1624	€1400	Sans titre (18x24cm-7x9in) s.d.1966 ink. 25-Oct-3 Cornette de St.Cyr, Paris #558/R
£972	$1624	€1400	Sans titre (19x30cm-7x12in) s.d.VII-1966 ink. 25-Oct-3 Cornette de St.Cyr, Paris #559/R
£1033	$1725	€1508	Figure composition (26x42cm-10x17in) s.d.1961 Indian ink. 7-Oct-3 Rasmussen, Copenhagen #11/R (D.KR 11000)
£1165	$1829	€1701	Composition with figure (20x16cm-8x6in) s.d.1978 W/C. 30-Aug-3 Rasmussen, Havnen #4360 est:3000-4000 (D.KR 12500)
£1267	$2318	€1900	Composition (39x26cm-15x10in) s.d.1978 india ink. 7-Jun-4 Palais de Beaux Arts, Brussels #149/R est:2000-3000
£1270	$2159	€1854	Composition - Flora Danica (36x22cm-14x9in) s.d.1988 W/C on etching. 26-Nov-3 Kunsthallen, Copenhagen #5/R est:15000 (D.KR 13500)
£1382	$2350	€2018	Composition with snake and tree (43x27cm-17x11in) s.d.1972 W/C. 10-Nov-3 Rasmussen, Vejle #557/R est:18000-20000 (D.KR 15000)
£1408	$2352	€2056	Figure composition (25x38cm-10x15in) s.d.61 Indian ink. 7-Oct-3 Rasmussen, Copenhagen #9/R est:10000 (D.KR 15000)
£1514	$2800	€2210	Tramways d'Odessa (34x52cm-13x20in) s.d.1991 India ink gouache printed paper on paper prov. 13-Jul-4 Christie's, Rockefeller NY #5/R est:2000-3000
£1659	$2654	€2406	Figure composition (26x21cm-10x8in) s.d.1977 Indian ink exhib. 17-Sep-3 Kunsthallen, Copenhagen #5/R est:20000 (D.KR 17500)
£1698	$2751	€2479	Untitled (37x23cm-15x9in) s.d.1976 gouache INdian ink. 24-May-3 Burkhard, Luzern #141/R est:3500-4000 (S.FR 3600)
£1748	$2972	€2500	Head (15x20cm-6x8in) s.d.23 07 1988 blk brown ink. 25-Nov-3 Christie's, Amsterdam #113/R est:2500-3500
£1818	$3036	€2600	Accordionist (31x23cm-12x9in) s.d.48 collage prov.exhib. 11-Oct-3 De Vuyst, Lokeren #3/R est:1500-2000
£1818	$3091	€2600	Two figures (19x14cm-7x6in) s.d.23 juillet 1988 blk brown ink. 25-Nov-3 Christie's, Amsterdam #58/R est:2500-3500
£2083	$3292	€3000	Composition (37x23cm-15x9in) s.d.1994 W/C. 27-Apr-3 Versailles Encheres #17
£2308	$3854	€3300	Toujours plus haut: on dit ca (39x25cm-15x10in) s.i.d.62 Chinese ink. 29-Jun-3 Versailles Encheres #36/R
£2527	$4650	€3689	Article suivis sur aquarellade (62x92cm-24x36in) s.d.1978 W/C on aquatint. 29-Mar-4 Rasmussen, Copenhagen #103/R est:20000 (D.KR 28000)
£2797	$4671	€4000	Composition (99x60cm-39x24in) s.i.d.1975 Indian ink pencil col etching. 11-Oct-3 De Vuyst, Lokeren #491/R est:4000-5000
£2797	$4811	€4000	Enghien (17x24cm-7x9in) s.d.1977 W/C ink mixed media. 2-Dec-3 Sotheby's, Amsterdam #296/R est:4000-6000
£3568	$5959	€5209	Zizanie (43x27cm-17x11in) s.d.72 W/C exhib. 7-Oct-3 Rasmussen, Copenhagen #54/R est:20000-25000 (D.KR 38000)
£3784	$7000	€5525	Ressorts IV (49x60cm-19x24in) s.d.1987 India ink rubbings Japan paper prov. 12-Feb-4 Sotheby's, New York #256/R est:10000-15000
£4332	$7971	€6325	Autour de chute (59x98cm-23x39in) s.d.1979 num.14/60 W/C aquatint. 29-Mar-4 Rasmussen, Copenhagen #127/R est:45000 (D.KR 48000)
£6434	$10937	€9200	Composition (62x91cm-24x36in) s.d.1973 W/C Japan paper. 25-Nov-3 Christie's, Amsterdam #279/R est:10000-15000
£6993	$11678	€10000	Fleur (97x59cm-38x23in) s. W/C aquatint prov. 11-Oct-3 Cornette de St.Cyr, Paris #76/R est:10000-12000
£12081	$22349	€18000	Composition (96x64cm-38x25in) s.i.d.1973 W/C. 13-Mar-4 De Vuyst, Lokeren #495/R est:16000-20000
£19580	$32699	€28000	Traite des excitants IV modernes (136x75cm-54x30in) s.d.1990 Chinese ink mixed media paper on canvas. 29-Jun-3 Versailles Encheres #121

ALEGIANI, Francesco (19/20th C) Italian

£538	$1000	€785	Trompe l'oeil (50x35cm-20x14in) s.i. prov. 5-Mar-4 Skinner, Boston #361/R

ALEGRE, Agustin (1936-) Spanish

£436	$816	€650	Open orange (33x41cm-13x16in) s.d.2002 board s.i.d.verso. 24-Feb-4 Durán, Madrid #3/R
£759	$1366	€1100	Common people (73x50cm-29x20in) s. 26-Jan-4 Ansorena, Madrid #259/R

ALEJANDRO, Ramon (1943-) Cuban

£500	$910	€730	Sirene (55x40cm-22x16in) s.i.d.67 verso canvas on board prov. 4-Feb-4 Sotheby's, Olympia #186/R
£1081	$2043	€1600	Le mal du pays (101x82cm-40x32in) s.i.d.1969 verso. 21-Feb-4 Cornette de St.Cyr, Paris #229/R est:2000-3000
£2027	$3831	€3000	Le silentiare (130x97cm-51x38in) s.i.d.oct/nov 1968 verso prov. 21-Feb-4 Cornette de St.Cyr, Paris #230/R est:3000-3500

ALEMANNO, Pietro (c.1430-c.1497) Austrian

£140000	$256200	€204400	Madonna and Child with two angels (105x51cm-41x20in) s.d.1488 gold ground panel prov.exhib.lit. 7-Jul-4 Christie's, London #12/R est:40000-60000

ALENZA Y NIETO, Leonardo (1807-1845) Spanish

£1724	$2879	€2500	Untitled (37x26cm-15x10in) 11-Nov-3 Castellana, Madrid #152/R est:2500
£25000	$45250	€38000	Fight over a guitar (46x61cm-18x24in) s.d.1843. 14-Apr-4 Ansorena, Madrid #156/R est:36000

Works on paper

£377	$640	€550	Scene from the Don Quixote (28x47cm-11x19in) wash. 4-Nov-3 Ansorena, Madrid #413/R

ALESSANDRI, Lorenzo (1927-2000) Italian

£476	$852	€700	Karla 2 (50x40cm-20x16in) s.d.1963. 22-Mar-4 Sant Agostino, Torino #391/R

ALEX, Kosta (1925-) American

Sculpture

£1013	$1600	€1479	Man with hat (69x43cm-27x17in) i.d.1963 num.3/6 bronze Cast Susse. 27-Jul-3 Bonhams & Butterfields, Los Angeles #7030/R est:1200-1600

ALEXANDER OF TUNIS, Earl (1891-1969) ?

£750	$1388	€1095	Palace of Queluz, Portugal (45x61cm-18x24in) s. i. board. 11-Mar-4 Christie's, Kensington #85/R est:400-600
£1900	$3515	€2774	Lake Como (56x46cm-22x18in) s.d.1945 s.i.d.verso lit. 11-Mar-4 Christie's, Kensington #86/R est:700-1000

ALEXANDER, Clifford Grear (1870-1954) American

£254	$450	€371	Moss covered rocks (51x61cm-20x24in) s. 2-May-4 Grogan, Boston #72/R
£267	$425	€390	Trout brook, Francois NH (56x46cm-22x18in) s. 12-Sep-3 Skinner, Boston #412/R
£335	$600	€489	River landscape with trees on far bank (51x33cm-20x13in) s.d.99. 11-May-4 Roland's, New York #473260/R

ALEXANDER, Cosmo (attrib) (1724-1772) British

£3600	$6480	€5256	Portrait of a gentleman (75x61cm-30x24in) 21-Jan-4 Sotheby's, Olympia #36/R est:400-600

ALEXANDER, David (20th C) British?

£915	$1637	€1336	Three plus inventions (148x170cm-58x67in) s.d.1987 i.verso acrylic. 6-May-4 Heffel, Vancouver #1/R est:2000-3000 (C.D 2250)
£1451	$2467	€2118	Boggy boogie (170x150cm-67x59in) s.d.1983 acrylic prov. 6-Nov-3 Heffel, Vancouver #1/R est:2000-3000 (C.D 3250)

ALEXANDER, Douglas (1871-1945) British

£507	$932	€770	Lake and mountain view (35x51cm-14x20in) s. canvasboard. 22-Jun-4 De Veres Art Auctions, Dublin #165
£526	$968	€800	In County Kerry (40x50cm-16x20in) s. i.verso canvasboard. 22-Jun-4 De Veres Art Auctions, Dublin #151
£583	$1056	€875	Connemara lake (40x50cm-16x20in) s.i.verso canvasboard. 30-Mar-4 De Veres Art Auctions, Dublin #195/R
£667	$1207	€1000	Among the Connemara mountains (50x59cm-20x23in) s.i.verso canvasboard. 30-Mar-4 De Veres Art Auctions, Dublin #247/R
£733	$1327	€1100	Among the Kerry hills (50x59cm-20x23in) s.i.verso canvasboard. 30-Mar-4 De Veres Art Auctions, Dublin #196/R
£769	$1308	€1100	Connemara landscape (39x50cm-15x20in) s. canvasboard. 25-Nov-3 De Veres Art Auctions, Dublin #4/R est:900-1200
£839	$1427	€1200	Evening light (40x50cm-16x20in) s.i.verso. 25-Nov-3 De Veres Art Auctions, Dublin #164/R est:800-1200
£987	$1816	€1500	Near Louisburg, Connemara. Near Recess, Connemara (20x36cm-8x14in) s.i.verso pair. 22-Jun-4 Mealy's, Castlecomer #126/R est:600-900
£1184	$2179	€1800	Landscape (49x60cm-19x24in) s. canvas on board. 22-Jun-4 De Veres Art Auctions, Dublin #172b est:1400-1800
£1333	$2413	€2000	Turf stacks, Connemara (30x30cm-12x12in) s.i. 30-Mar-4 De Veres Art Auctions, Dublin #123/R est:2000-3000
£2200	$3982	€3300	Evening, Connemara (24x34cm-9x13in) s. canvasboard. 31-Mar-4 James Adam, Dublin #15/R est:2500-3500
£3667	$6637	€5500	Lake and mountain landscape, west of ireland (39x44cm-15x17in) s. 31-Mar-4 James Adam, Dublin #27/R est:3000-4000
£3916	$6657	€5600	Sun burst, west of Ireland (76x91cm-30x36in) s. 18-Nov-3 Whyte's, Dublin #105/R est:4000-6000
Works on paper			
£280	$456	€406	Connemara landscape (27x38cm-11x15in) s. W/C. 23-Sep-3 Bonhams, Knightsbridge #175/R
£336	$601	€500	West of Ireland landscape (24x34cm-9x13in) s. W/C. 31-May-4 Hamilton Osborne King, Dublin #110
£336	$601	€500	At Ballinahinch, Connemara (17x26cm-7x10in) s. W/C. 31-May-4 Hamilton Osborne King, Dublin #216/R
£433	$784	€650	Sunset, Connemara (25x35cm-10x14in) s. W/C prov. 31-Mar-4 James Adam, Dublin #119/R
£503	$901	€750	Cottage in mountain landscape (21x28cm-8x11in) s. W/C. 26-May-4 James Adam, Dublin #187/R
£503	$901	€750	Antrim coast (22x28cm-9x11in) s. W/C. 31-May-4 Hamilton Osborne King, Dublin #126/R
£507	$932	€770	On Lough Anure (26x37cm-10x15in) s. W/C. 22-Jun-4 De Veres Art Auctions, Dublin #195/R
£537	$961	€800	Spring landscape, Connemara (27x29cm-11x11in) s. W/C. 31-May-4 Hamilton Osborne King, Dublin #136/R
£574	$1085	€850	Looking towards Delphi, Connemara (38x53cm-15x21in) s. i.verso W/C prov. 17-Feb-4 Whyte's, Dublin #170/R
£600	$1086	€900	Quiet day, Connemara (26x36cm-10x14in) s. W/C. 30-Mar-4 De Veres Art Auctions, Dublin #180/R
£638	$1141	€950	Turf stacks, Ireland (37x53cm-15x21in) s. W/C. 26-May-4 James Adam, Dublin #197/R
£660	$1075	€950	Sunset at recess Connemara (25x36cm-10x14in) s. i.verso W/C. 28-Sep-3 Hamilton Osborne King, Dublin #141
£720	$1202	€1051	Evening light on the bog at Cashel na Gor, Co Donegal. i.verso W/C. 15-Nov-3 Nigel Ward, Hereford #1428/R
£800	$1448	€1200	Road to Leenane, Connemara (25x37cm-10x15in) s.i.verso W/C. 31-Mar-4 James Adam, Dublin #25/R
£833	$1358	€1200	Evening lights Connemara (25x36cm-10x14in) s. W/C. 28-Sep-3 Hamilton Osborne King, Dublin #139 est:400-600
£868	$1415	€1250	Ballynakill Bay, Connemara (37x52cm-15x20in) s. W/C. 24-Sep-3 James Adam, Dublin #149/R est:800-1200
£900	$1530	€1314	Among the Twelve Pins, Connemara (37x52cm-15x20in) s. W/C. 29-Oct-3 Edgar Horn, Eastbourne #341
£933	$1689	€1400	Near Crolly, Co Donegal (25x36cm-10x14in) s.i.verso W/C. 31-Mar-4 James Adam, Dublin #108/R
£1000	$1810	€1500	Turf stacks in mountain landscape (36x51cm-14x20in) s. W/C. 31-Mar-4 James Adam, Dublin #24/R est:1200-1800
£1200	$2172	€1800	Lake and mountain landscape (37x52cm-15x20in) s. W/C. 31-Mar-4 James Adam, Dublin #157/R est:1000-1500
£1620	$2802	€2300	Bog landscape (25x37cm-10x15in) s. W/C sold with 3 others by the same hand. 10-Dec-3 Bonhams & James Adam, Dublin #192/R est:1500-2000
£1745	$3089	€2600	Turf stacks in the west of Ireland (25x37cm-10x15in) s. W/C pair. 27-Apr-4 Whyte's, Dublin #216/R est:1500-2000
£2083	$3396	€3000	In the Black Valley, Co Kerry. Near Glenleigh, Co. Kerry (37x52cm-15x20in) s. i.verso W/C pair. 28-Sep-3 Hamilton Osborne King, Dublin #238/R est:1500-2000

ALEXANDER, Edwin (1870-1926) British

£380	$646	€555	Wild flowers (18x34cm-7x13in) init. board. 10-Nov-3 Thomson Roddick & Medcalf, Edinburgh #249/R
Works on paper			
£260	$465	€380	Sweet peas (30x15cm-12x6in) pencil drawing. 7-May-4 Chrystals Auctions, Isle of Man #217
£400	$640	€584	Bluebells (20x10cm-8x4in) init.d.97 W/C. 15-May-3 Bonhams, Edinburgh #366
£500	$900	€730	Puerta del vina alhambra (53x36cm-21x14in) init.i.d.04 gouache. 22-Apr-4 Bonhams, Edinburgh #326
£800	$1336	€1168	Grasses. Yellow buds (32x16cm-13x6in) init. gouache two. 16-Oct-3 Bonhams, Edinburgh #153
£800	$1384	€1168	Hawkweed seeds dispersing (24x15cm-9x6in) mono.d.1903 W/C. 11-Dec-3 Lyon & Turnbull, Edinburgh #61/R
£800	$1384	€1168	Spider and reeds (32x17cm-13x7in) mono. W/C. 11-Dec-3 Lyon & Turnbull, Edinburgh #62/R

ALEXANDER, Francis (1800-1880) American

Works on paper			
£387	$700	€565	Portrait of Parker C Chandler (69x53cm-27x21in) s. W/C oval. 16-Apr-4 James Julia, Fairfield #783/R

ALEXANDER, Jean (1911-1994) British

£275	$509	€402	Walton on the Naze (30x35cm-12x14in) s. board. 13-Feb-4 Sworder & Son, Bishops Stortford #26/R

ALEXANDER, John (fl.1710-1757) British

£600	$1020	€876	Portrait of a lady, thought to be a daughter of the Duke of Gordon (75x61cm-30x24in) 8-Nov-3 Shapes, Edinburgh #416/R

ALEXANDER, John (1945-) American

£12291	$22000	€17945	Saskwatch in the Bois de Boulogne (229x254cm-90x100in) s. s.i.d.1-86 verso prov. 13-May-4 Sotheby's, New York #469/R est:12000-18000
Works on paper			
£649	$1200	€974	The Piney Woods (36x48cm-14x19in) s.d.66 W/C. 17-Jul-4 New Orleans Auction, New Orleans #874/R

ALEXANDER, Keith (1946-) South African

£560	$936	€818	Marsh mist (55x75cm-22x30in) s. 20-Oct-3 Stephan Welz, Johannesburg #261/R est:7000-10000 (SA.R 6500)
£2586	$4319	€3776	Optimist (44x63cm-17x25in) s. i.verso canvas on board. 20-Oct-3 Stephan Welz, Johannesburg #262/R est:7000-10000 (SA.R 30000)

ALEXANDER, Larn (20th C) British?

Works on paper			
£700	$1190	€1022	Still life with flowers in a vase (51x40cm-20x16in) s. pastel. 4-Nov-3 Dreweatt Neate, Newbury #59
£900	$1530	€1314	Still life with flowers in a vase (43x54cm-17x21in) s.d.1947 pastel. 4-Nov-3 Dreweatt Neate, Newbury #58

ALEXANDER, Lena (fl.1905-1936) British

Works on paper			
£700	$1127	€1015	Freesias (53x60cm-21x24in) s. pastel. 21-Aug-3 Bonhams, Edinburgh #1207/R
£900	$1674	€1314	Still life with tulips (46x36cm-18x14in) s.d.1948 pastel prov. 4-Mar-4 Christie's, Kensington #177/R

ALEXANDER, Peter (1939-) American

£2260	$4000	€3300	Ice III (152x168cm-60x66in) init.d.89 acrylic. 2-May-4 Bonhams & Butterfields, Los Angeles #3088/R est:4000-6000

ALEXANDER, Robert L (1840-1923) British

£950	$1758	€1387	Dog studies - Terriers (15x10cm-6x4in) s. two. 13-Feb-4 Keys, Aylsham #734/R
£4324	$8000	€6313	Setters resting (18x33cm-7x13in) mono. canvas on panel. 10-Feb-4 Doyle, New York #239/R est:6000-8000
£18000	$28260	€26100	Orphans (140x102cm-55x40in) s. board exhib. 27-Aug-3 Sotheby's, London #992/R est:4000-6000

ALEXANDRAKIS, Alexandros (1913-1968) Greek

£4500	$8055	€6570	Diana (67x130cm-26x51in) s.d.1950 prov. 10-May-4 Sotheby's, Olympia #147/R est:5000-7000
Works on paper			
£1300	$2327	€1898	Battle scene (24x34cm-9x13in) s.d.80 pen ink prov. 10-May-4 Sotheby's, Olympia #125/R est:1000-1500

ALEXANDRIS, Sandro de (1939-) ?

£671	$1100	€980	Ripertizione ortogonale B1 (40x40cm-16x16in) s.i.d.1968-1972 verso card on board prov. 28-May-3 Sotheby's, Amsterdam #116/R

ALEXANDROVNA, Grand Duchess Olga (1882-1960) Russian

£444	$809	€666	Farmyard with geese (36x47cm-14x19in) s. canvas on panel. 19-Jun-4 Rasmussen, Havnen #2111/R (D.KR 5000)
£622	$1132	€933	Landscape from Aldershvile Park in Bagsvaerd (33x41cm-13x16in) s. 19-Jun-4 Rasmussen, Havnen #2276 (D.KR 7000)
£711	$1294	€1067	Autumn landscape in the birch wood (51x61cm-20x24in) s. canvas on panel. 19-Jun-4 Rasmussen, Havnen #2112/R (D.KR 8000)
£1096	$1897	€1600	Spring landscape with sunshine (46x38cm-18x15in) s. 9-Dec-3 Rasmussen, Copenhagen #1705/R (D.KR 11600)
£2430	$3839	€3524	Potted plants on the artist's window ledge (32x48cm-13x19in) s. 2-Sep-3 Rasmussen, Copenhagen #1723/R est:10000-12000 (D.KR 26000)
Works on paper			
£280	$443	€406	Spring flowers (17x13cm-7x5in) s. W/C. 2-Sep-3 Rasmussen, Copenhagen #2016/R (D.KR 3000)
£358	$655	€523	Anemones and other spring flowers (10x14cm-4x6in) s. W/C. 9-Jun-4 Rasmussen, Copenhagen #2025 (D.KR 4000)
£701	$1107	€1016	Lilacs in vase (17x14cm-7x6in) s. W/C. 2-Sep-3 Rasmussen, Copenhagen #1721/R (D.KR 7500)
£935	$1477	€1356	Window ledge with potted plants (11x13cm-4x5in) s. W/C. 2-Sep-3 Rasmussen, Copenhagen #1724/R (D.KR 10000)
£1443	$2669	€2107	Interior scene with table set for dinner and flowers in vase (36x31cm-14x12in) s. W/C exhib. 15-Mar-4 Rasmussen, Vejle #207/R est:15000 (D.KR 16000)
£1611	$2949	€2352	Cyclamens on window ledge (32x36cm-13x14in) s. W/C prov. 9-Jun-4 Rasmussen, Copenhagen #1628/R est:10000-15000 (D.KR 18000)
£2149	$3932	€3138	At the table (32x36cm-13x14in) s. W/C prov. 9-Jun-4 Rasmussen, Copenhagen #1629/R est:12000-18000 (D.KR 24000)
£2686	$4915	€3922	Guarding the table (32x36cm-13x14in) s. W/C exhib.prov. 9-Jun-4 Rasmussen, Copenhagen #1627/R est:15000-20000 (D.KR 30000)
£2754	$4516	€3800	Still life (30x37cm-12x15in) s. W/C. 27-May-3 Beaussant & Lefèvre, Paris #327/R est:1500-1800
£3500	$5950	€5110	Interior with vase of flowers (27x36cm-11x14in) s. gouache ink. 19-Nov-3 Sotheby's, London #100/R est:3500-4500

ALEXEEV, Nikolai (1813-1880) Russian

£3200	$5728	€4672	Portrait of a lady in a fur shawl (74x60cm-29x24in) s. 26-May-4 Sotheby's, Olympia #361/R est:3000-5000

ALFANO, Carlo (1932-) Italian

£1486	$2616	€2200	Untitled (170cm-67in circular) s.d.70 verso oil collage board. 24-May-4 Christie's, Milan #79/R est:2500-3500
Works on paper			
£1056	$1754	€1500	Frammenti di un autoritratto anonimo N 51 (31x40cm-12x16in) s.i.d.1971 material collage. 13-Jun-3 Hauswedell & Nolte, Hamburg #509/R est:1800

ALFELT, Else (1910-1975) Danish

£316	$581	€461	Still life of yellow flowers and fruit (54x43cm-21x17in) s.d.36. 29-Mar-4 Rasmussen, Copenhagen #456 (D.KR 3500)
Works on paper			
£361	$675	€527	March mountains (22x28cm-9x11in) s.d.3/9.46 crayon prov. 25-Feb-4 Kunsthallen, Copenhagen #112/R (D.KR 4000)
£847	$1439	€1237	Mountains (28x45cm-11x18in) s.d.41 W/C. 26-Nov-3 Kunsthallen, Copenhagen #15/R (D.KR 9000)
£993	$1827	€1450	Mountain tops (48x31cm-19x12in) s.d.55 W/C pencil exhib. 29-Mar-4 Rasmussen, Copenhagen #340/R (D.KR 11000)
£1706	$2730	€2474	The mountains and room 5 (31x48cm-12x19in) s.i.d.Dec.71 W/C prov. 17-Sep-3 Kunsthallen, Copenhagen #39/R est:18000 (D.KR 18000)

ALFELT, Vibeke (1934-1999) Danish

£316	$591	€461	The park's blue horses (76x56cm-30x22in) mono.d.1982 s.verso. 25-Feb-4 Museumsbygningen, Copenhagen #43 (D.KR 3500)
£344	$616	€502	The forest's blue horses (100x136cm-39x54in) mono. s.d.1978 verso. 10-May-4 Rasmussen, Vejle #557 (D.KR 3800)

ALFIERI, Attilio (1904-1992) Italian

£300	$552	€450	Still life (25x35cm-10x14in) s. s.d.80. 10-Jun-4 Galleria Pace, Milan #12/R
£333	$613	€500	Still life (40x50cm-16x20in) s. 12-Jun-4 Meeting Art, Vercelli #211/R
£333	$613	€500	Still life (30x40cm-12x16in) s.d.1980 verso. 12-Jun-4 Meeting Art, Vercelli #553/R
£367	$675	€550	Still life (40x50cm-16x20in) s. d.1951 verso. 14-Jun-4 Sant Agostino, Torino #168/R
£451	$713	€650	Basket with cabbage (60x50cm-24x20in) painted 1968. 6-Sep-3 Meeting Art, Vercelli #624
£471	$772	€650	Composition (44x52cm-17x20in) s. 29-May-3 Galleria Pace, Milan #15/R
£1081	$1903	€1600	Hieroglyphics (60x45cm-24x18in) s.d.941. 19-May-4 Il Ponte, Milan #1107 est:900-1000
£1701	$3044	€2500	Factories (74x119cm-29x47in) s. 16-Mar-4 Finarte Semenzato, Milan #373/R est:3000

ALFONS, Sven (1918-1996) Swedish

£440	$778	€642	Halcyone - composition (81x60cm-32x24in) s.d.51 exhib. 27-Apr-4 AB Stockholms Auktionsverk #680/R (S.KR 6000)
£733	$1297	€1070	Initials (100x81cm-39x32in) s.d.66 exhib. 27-Apr-4 AB Stockholms Auktionsverk #679/R (S.KR 10000)

ALFONSO, Carlos (20th C) South American?

£6857	$12000	€10011	Murano waters (154x110cm-61x43in) s.d.87 s.i.verso acrylic burlap prov. 19-Dec-3 Sotheby's, New York #1181/R est:10000-15000

ALFONZO, Carlos Jose (1950-1991) Cuban

£17647	$30000	€25765	Sin Titulo (213x213cm-84x84in) acrylic painted c.1990 prov. 19-Nov-3 Sotheby's, New York #158/R est:30000-35000

ALFORD, John (?) British

£310	$515	€453	Falmouth Regatta (30x60cm-12x24in) s.d.1999 board. 2-Oct-3 Lane, Penzance #81

ALFREDSON, Albert (20th C) American

£323	$600	€472	Snowy stream (61x71cm-24x28in) s. painted c.1950. 7-Mar-4 Treadway Gallery, Cincinnati #543/R

ALFREE, Bernard (?) British

£520	$957	€759	Still life of flowers in a bronze urn (35x30cm-14x12in) s. 10-Jun-4 Lyon & Turnbull, Edinburgh #85

ALFSEN, John Martin (1902-1971) Canadian

£321	$511	€469	Portrait of boy (39x31cm-15x12in) s. 15-Sep-3 Ritchie, Toronto #57/R (C.D 700)

ALFVEN, Hugo (1872-1960) Swedish

Works on paper			
£786	$1359	€1148	Coastal landscape, Southern Italy (24x34cm-9x13in) s.d.okt.1924. 15-Dec-3 Lilla Bukowskis, Stockholm #279 (S.KR 10000)

ALGARDI, Alessandro (1602-1654) Italian

£2349	$4205	€3500	Beyond his words (70x100cm-28x39in) s.i.d.1998 verso oil acrylic. 25-May-4 Sotheby's, Milan #214/R est:2500-3000
Works on paper			
£4000	$7320	€5840	Rest on the flight into Egypt, with kneeling angel presenting flowers (19x23cm-7x9in) black chk. 6-Jul-4 Christie's, London #50/R est:4000-6000
£28169	$49296	€40000	Une allegorie de la Religion, tenant une croix et un calice (11x8cm-4x3in) col chk pen brown ink wash prov. 17-Dec-3 Christie's, Paris #7/R est:40000-60000

ALGMINAS, Arvydas (20th C) ?

£341	$600	€498	Still life (48x58cm-19x23in) s. masonite painted 1991. 23-May-4 Hindman, Chicago #1021/R
£341	$600	€498	Still life (51x74cm-20x29in) s. 23-May-4 Hindman, Chicago #1022/R

ALGMINOWICZ, Paula (20th C) American

£411	$650	€600	Carousel (30x61cm-12x24in) s. board. 7-Sep-3 Treadway Gallery, Cincinnati #725/R

ALHILALI, Neda (1938-) American

Works on paper			
£294	$550	€429	Burning bush (122x91cm-48x36in) s.d.80 mixed media metal prov. 29-Feb-4 Bonhams & Butterfields, San Francisco #4595

ALI, Mihr (attrib) (19th C) Persian

£450000	$796500	€657000	Portrait of Abbas Mirza (199x96cm-78x38in) 27-Apr-4 Christie's, London #112/R est:200000-300000

ALI, Mihr (studio) (19th C) Persian

£150000	$265500	€219000	Portrait of Hasan Ali Mirza Shuja Al-Saltana (176x99cm-69x39in) i. 27-Apr-4 Christie's, London #113/R est:120000-160000
£160000	$283200	€233600	Portrait of Shayka Ali Mirza (172x97cm-68x38in) 27-Apr-4 Christie's, London #114/R est:100000-150000

ALI, Rachid Ben (20th C) ?

£559	$951	€800	I'm 12 (120x120cm-47x47in) s.d.2001 verso. 24-Nov-3 Glerum, Amsterdam #213/R

ALIBASYAH, Abas (1928-) Javanese

£1667	$2583	€2434	Three figures (59x80cm-23x31in) s.d.1962 exhib. 6-Oct-2 Sotheby's, Singapore #128/R est:4500-6500 (S.D 4600)
£2355	$3650	€3438	Horse (50x65cm-20x26in) s.d.62. 6-Oct-2 Sotheby's, Singapore #137/R est:4000-6000 (S.D 6500)
£2536	$3931	€3703	Self portrait (61x51cm-24x20in) s. sold with oils by DJAYA, SUHADI, ZAINI four. 6-Oct-2 Sotheby's, Singapore #122/R est:7000-10000 (S.D 7000)

ALIBERTI, Dino (1935-) Italian

£333	$613	€500	Still life (30x40cm-12x16in) s. board painted 1978. 12-Jun-4 Meeting Art, Vercelli #671/R
£333	$613	€500	View of Peroldrado (40x40cm-16x16in) s. painted 1995 lit. 12-Jun-4 Meeting Art, Vercelli #905/R
£336	$594	€500	Hilly landscape (40x50cm-16x20in) s. s.i.d.2000 verso lit. 1-May-4 Meeting Art, Vercelli #12
£336	$594	€500	Summer in Strada Mont Cervet (50x40cm-20x16in) s. s.i.d.1992 verso. 1-May-4 Meeting Art, Vercelli #70
£336	$594	€500	Susa Valley (35x25cm-14x10in) s. painted 1996 lit. 1-May-4 Meeting Art, Vercelli #136
£336	$594	€500	Winter in Susa Valley (25x35cm-10x14in) s. 1-May-4 Meeting Art, Vercelli #162
£336	$594	€500	Landscape (60x50cm-24x20in) s. s.verso. 1-May-4 Meeting Art, Vercelli #293
£336	$594	€500	Combe di Mattie, Susa Valley (40x30cm-16x12in) s. s.i.d.1987 verso lit. 1-May-4 Meeting Art, Vercelli #388
£336	$594	€500	Summer in the hills (40x40cm-16x16in) s. s.i.d.2000 verso. 1-May-4 Meeting Art, Vercelli #402
£369	$653	€550	Landscape (50x60cm-20x24in) s. s.verso lit. 1-May-4 Meeting Art, Vercelli #302
£694	$1181	€1000	Autumn in Novaretto (70x50cm-28x20in) s. lit. 1-Nov-3 Meeting Art, Vercelli #96/R

ALIKATUKTUK, Ananaisie (1944-) North American

Works on paper			
£1532	$2604	€2237	Taleelayu and family (42x61cm-17x24in) stencil. 3-Nov-3 Waddingtons, Toronto #268/R est:1000-1500 (C.D 3400)

ALINARI, Luca (1943-) Italian

£347	$549	€500	Untitled (15cm-6in circular) canvas on board. 6-Sep-3 Meeting Art, Vercelli #718
£379	$633	€550	Early periods (39cm-15in circular) s. i.verso board. 17-Nov-3 Sant Agostino, Torino #71/R
£458	$760	€650	Colline (19x19cm-7x7in) s. canvas on panel round. 14-Jun-3 Meeting Art, Vercelli #290
£458	$760	€650	Untitled (47x67cm-19x26in) s. tempera paper on canvas. 14-Jun-3 Meeting Art, Vercelli #516
£500	$920	€750	Untitled (45x35cm-18x14in) s. 12-Jun-4 Meeting Art, Vercelli #666/R
£537	$993	€800	Untitled (10x59cm-4x23in) s. canvas on board. 13-Mar-4 Meeting Art, Vercelli #441
£570	$1055	€850	Untitled (29x33cm-11x13in) s. canvas on board. 13-Mar-4 Meeting Art, Vercelli #171
£728	$1326	€1100	Landscape (50x50cm-20x20in) s. painted 1994. 17-Jun-4 Galleria Pananti, Florence #468/R
£728	$1326	€1100	Given life (29x19cm-11x7in) s. acrylic painted 2001. 17-Jun-4 Galleria Pananti, Florence #534/R
£775	$1286	€1100	Paesaggio fantastico (24x34cm-9x13in) s. canvas on panel. 14-Jun-3 Meeting Art, Vercelli #564
£800	$1472	€1200	Landscape (58x58cm-23x23in) s.d.93 acrylic pastel. 11-Jun-4 Farsetti, Prato #203/R
£1007	$1862	€1500	Landscape (40x50cm-16x20in) s. 13-Mar-4 Meeting Art, Vercelli #86 est:1500
£1133	$2085	€1700	Untitled (58x58cm-23x23in) s. canvas on board. 12-Jun-4 Meeting Art, Vercelli #242/R est:1000
£1250	$1975	€1800	Untitled. canvas on board. 6-Sep-3 Meeting Art, Vercelli #692 est:1500

£1268 $2104 €1800 Palm tree by the sea (50x50cm-20x20in) s.i. oil col crayon. 13-Jun-3 Farsetti, Prato #482/R
£1370 $2329 €2000 Landscape (60cm-24in circular) s. oil acrylic board. 7-Nov-3 Galleria Rosenberg, Milan #42/R est:2000
£1655 $2648 €2400 Landscape (60cm-24in circular) s. 13-Mar-3 Galleria Pace, Milan #144/R est:2800-3500
£1733 $3137 €2600 Red field (70x70cm-28x28in) s. acrylic canvas on board exhib.lit. 2-Apr-4 Farsetti, Prato #211/R est:2600-2900
£1733 $3189 €2600 Composition (44x64cm-17x25in) s. canvas on board. 10-Jun-4 Galleria Pace, Milan #162/R est:4000
£2517 $4280 €3600 House in the wood (58x91cm-23x36in) s. oil pencil canvas on board. 28-Nov-3 Farsetti, Prato #92/R est:3500-4500
£3691 $6607 €5500 Landscape (150cm-59in circular) acrylic canvas on board. 28-May-4 Farsetti, Prato #207/R est:4500-5500
£4167 $6583 €6000 From the nest it's asking glasses of powder (130x130cm-51x51in) oil mixed media canvas on board painted 1995. 6-Sep-3 Meeting Art, Vercelli #742 est:6000
£4362 $7809 €6500 Chosen male (120x120cm-47x47in) s. oil mixed media canvas on board exhib.lit. 30-May-4 Meeting Art, Vercelli #79 est:5000
£4930 $8183 €7000 Il Maschio Prescelto (120x120cm-47x47in) s. oil mixed media canvas on panel. 14-Jun-3 Meeting Art, Vercelli #115/R est:5000

Works on paper
£420 $701 €600 Two figures (75x56cm-30x22in) s. W/C. 26-Jun-3 Sant Agostino, Torino #168/R
£600 $1104 €900 Landscape (50x60cm-20x24in) s. mixed media card. 12-Jun-4 Meeting Art, Vercelli #293/R
£1056 $1754 €1500 Paesaggio fantastico (50x60cm-20x24in) s. mixed media cardboard. 14-Jun-3 Meeting Art, Vercelli #554/R est:1500
£1467 $2699 €2200 Back to a broken dream (60x60cm-24x24in) s. mixed media canvas on board exec.1996 lit. 12-Jun-4 Meeting Art, Vercelli #610/R est:1000
£2230 $3924 €3300 Landscape (69x69cm-27x27in) s.d.1997 mixed media on canvas. 22-May-4 Galleria Pananti, Florence #378/R est:3000-3500

ALIOTH, Max (1883-1968) Swiss

Works on paper
£431 $772 €629 Sunny alpine landscape in autumn (36x49cm-14x19in) s.d.1922 W/C. 12-May-4 Dobiaschofsky, Bern #3401 (S.FR 1000)

ALIOTO, Massimiliano (1972-) Italian

£1074 $1987 €1600 Suburbs (60x50cm-24x20in) s.d.1999 s.i.d.verso. 13-Mar-4 Meeting Art, Vercelli #148 est:500
£2133 $3925 €3200 Other directions (100x150cm-39x59in) s.d.2002 s.i.d.verso. 12-Jun-4 Meeting Art, Vercelli #127/R est:2000

ALISERIS, Carlos (20th C) Uruguayan

£635 $1200 €927 Wood at night (73x93cm-29x37in) s. s.i.d.1962 verso. 22-Feb-4 Galeria y Remates, Montevideo #81/R

ALISON, David (1882-1955) British

£300 $540 €438 Portrait of a girl (60x50cm-24x20in) s. 22-Apr-4 Bonhams, Edinburgh #319
£320 $512 €467 Portrait of James Weir. 18-Sep-3 Bonhams, Edinburgh #319
£360 $580 €522 Portrait of the artist brother (75x62cm-30x24in) s. 21-Aug-3 Bonhams, Edinburgh #1068
£380 $608 €555 Portrait of William Meiklem, with a newspaper (115x90cm-45x35in) s. 18-Sep-3 Bonhams, Edinburgh #396
£450 $725 €653 Infant in a white gown (50x29cm-20x11in) s. 21-Aug-3 Bonhams, Edinburgh #1067
£1200 $1932 €1740 Summer (61x51cm-24x20in) s. 21-Aug-3 Bonhams, Edinburgh #1066/R est:1000-1500
£2100 $3381 €3045 Still life of dahlias. s. canvasboard. 21-Aug-3 Bonhams, Edinburgh #1069/R
£2300 $3703 €3335 Reclining nude (44x59cm-17x23in) s. canvasboard. 21-Aug-3 Bonhams, Edinburgh #1071/R est:800-1200
£3700 $6771 €5402 Portrait of a lady, seated at a piano, thought to be Catherine Fountain (81x91cm-32x36in) s. prov. 28-Jan-4 Dreweatt Neate, Newbury #106/R est:800-1200

ALISON, Henry Young (1889-1972) British

£1000 $1790 €1460 A deserted beach (36x46cm-14x18in) s. panel. 28-May-4 Lyon & Turnbull, Edinburgh #68 est:1000-1500

ALISON, Thomas (fl.1880-1914) British

£650 $1118 €949 On the west coast, Scotland (76x127cm-30x50in) s. indis d. 2-Dec-3 Sotheby's, London #108/R

ALIVEZ (19/20th C) ?

£2371 $4244 €3462 North African market (22x70cm-9x28in) s. 12-May-4 Dobiaschofsky, Bern #301/R est:3000 (S.FR 5500)

ALIX, Yves (1890-1969) French

£533 $965 €800 Paysage (48x55cm-19x22in) s. painted c.1920. 5-Apr-4 Marie & Robert, Paris #1
£534 $960 €800 Rouge et bleu (60x81cm-24x32in) s. painted 1963. 26-Apr-4 Tajan, Paris #202

ALIZIER, Andre G (1897-?) French

£594 $950 €867 Lucienne (71x61cm-28x24in) s. exhib. 20-Sep-3 Bunte, Elgin #1267

ALKE, Elizabeth Heil (1877-1938) American

£610 $1000 €885 Rolling hills. Flowering tree (5x6cm-2x2in) one s. board painted c.1925 pair. 7-Jun-3 Treadway Gallery, Cincinnati #1442

ALKEMA, Wobbe (1900-1984) Dutch

Works on paper
£2667 $4907 €4000 Design for linocut (40x28cm-16x11in) init.d.26 W/C pencil prov.exhib. 8-Jun-4 Sotheby's, Amsterdam #221/R est:4000-6000

ALKEN, Henry (19th C) British

Works on paper
£380 $703 €555 Gig with three figures up an extensive landscape beyond (18x23cm-7x9in) s. W/C bodycol. 11-Mar-4 Duke & Son, Dorchester #129/R
£440 $748 €642 Hunt in full chase (13x23cm-5x9in) s. W/C. 29-Oct-3 Mallams, Oxford #690/R
£480 $888 €701 Huntsman and hounds (15x23cm-6x9in) s. W/C bodycol pair. 11-Mar-4 Duke & Son, Dorchester #128/R
£560 $969 €818 Fox hunting scenes (13x18cm-5x7in) both s. W/C htd white pair. 11-Dec-3 Neales, Nottingham #544
£750 $1403 €1095 Carriage ride (28x22cm-11x9in) s. W/C oval. 21-Jul-4 Lyon & Turnbull, Edinburgh #121/R
£4200 $7854 €6132 The Meet (24x32cm-9x13in) s. W/C sold with two other hunting scenes three. 21-Jul-4 Lyon & Turnbull, Edinburgh #120/R est:2000-3000

ALKEN, Henry (attrib) (19th C) British

£1486 $2750 €2170 Waiting for master (20x30cm-8x12in) bears sig. board. 10-Feb-4 Doyle, New York #208/R est:1500-2500

ALKEN, Henry (jnr) (1810-1894) British

£550 $995 €803 Over the ditch! (22x29cm-9x11in) 31-Mar-4 Bonhams, Knightsbridge #78/R
£669 $1157 €950 Huntsman on horseback jumping a fence (30x40cm-12x16in) s. 10-Dec-3 Christie's, Amsterdam #868/R
£8500 $15640 €12410 Passing the hunt (46x76cm-18x30in) s. panel. 23-Mar-4 Bonhams, New Bond Street #39/R est:3000-5000

ALKEN, Henry (jnr-attrib) (1810-1894) British

£1207 $2160 €1762 Riders by fence with dog pack. Riders hunting with dogs (21x28cm-8x11in) i. panel pair. 12-May-4 Dobiaschofsky, Bern #302/R est:3000 (S.FR 2800)
£1667 $3000 €2434 Fighting cocks (24x18cm-9x7in) pair prov. 23-Jan-4 Christie's, Rockefeller NY #122/R est:2000-3000

ALKEN, Henry (snr) (1785-1851) British

£1374 $2500 €2006 York-London coach (30x45cm-12x18in) s. panel. 29-Jun-4 Sotheby's, New York #170/R est:4000-6000
£1600 $2944 €2336 In full cry (29x39cm-11x15in) s. board prov. 10-Jun-4 Christie's, Kensington #44/R est:1500-2000
£2793 $5000 €4078 Racehorse in loose box (35x46cm-14x18in) s. panel prov. 27-May-4 Sotheby's, New York #205/R est:5000-7000
£3352 $6000 €4894 Shooting party in the Scottish highlands (33x61cm-13x24in) prov. 27-May-4 Sotheby's, New York #204/R est:6000-8000
£8197 $15000 €11968 End of the run (46x62cm-18x24in) s. prov. 3-Jun-4 Christie's, Rockefeller NY #436/R est:15000-20000
£26667 $48000 €38934 Madman, a birchen cock (69x55cm-27x22in) i. prov.exhib. 23-Jan-4 Christie's, Rockefeller NY #123/R est:8000-12000
£29330 $52500 €42822 Meet. Drawing cover. Full cry. Death (28x37cm-11x15in) s. set of 4 prov. 27-May-4 Sotheby's, New York #233/R est:40000-60000

Works on paper
£248 $400 €362 On point (15x20cm-6x8in) s. W/C graphite. 20-Aug-3 James Julia, Fairfield #638/R
£550 $1029 €825 Chase (20x30cm-8x12in) W/C prov. 21-Jul-4 John Nicholson, Haslemere #47
£694 $1132 €1000 Horsemen (23x37cm-9x15in) s. W/C over pencil. 25-Sep-3 Dr Fritz Nagel, Stuttgart #1133/R
£2500 $4600 €3650 Hacking to the meet. Approaching the fence. Over the fence. Trotting on (23x33cm-9x13in) one s. pencil wash set of four. 10-Jun-4 Christie's, Kensington #36/R est:3000-4000

ALKEN, Henry (snr-attrib) (1785-1851) British

£889 $1600 €1298 Fighting cock in a landscape (30x36cm-12x14in) board prov. 23-Jan-4 Christie's, Rockefeller NY #121/R est:2000-3000
£4469 $8000 €6525 Dover to London coach (33x41cm-13x16in) panel. 27-May-4 Sotheby's, New York #203/R est:8000-10000

Works on paper
£412 $700 €602 On the scent (27x37cm-11x15in) s.i. graphite W/C prov. 21-Nov-3 Skinner, Boston #219/R

ALKEN, Henry (snr-circle) (1785-1851) British

£7558 $13000 €11035 Finish (65x91cm-26x36in) prov. 5-Dec-3 Christie's, Rockefeller NY #11/R est:12000-18000

ALKEN, S (?) British

£1111 $1889 €1600 Two greyhounds following a hare (31x39cm-12x15in) 28-Oct-3 Mealy's, Castlecomer #480

ALKEN, Samuel (jnr) (1784-1825) British

£4500 $7650 €6570 Racehorse with a spaniel (63x76cm-25x30in) s.d.1807. 27-Nov-3 Christie's, Kensington #50/R est:5000-8000
£9497 $17000 €13866 Tally-ho (61x79cm-24x31in) s.d.1809. 27-May-4 Sotheby's, New York #229/R est:10000-12000

Works on paper
£991 $1775 €1447 Three jockeys at the start (28x45cm-11x18in) s. pencil w/C. 12-May-4 Dobiaschofsky, Bern #303/R est:2200 (S.FR 2300)

ALKEN, Samuel (jnr-attrib) (1784-1825) British

Works on paper
£382 $650 €558 Grey and bay stallions fighting (22x27cm-9x11in) s.d.Jun 1815 graphite W/C. 21-Nov-3 Skinner, Boston #221/R est:300-500

ALKEN, Samuel (snr-attrib) (1756-1815) British
£2410 $4000 €3519 Fighting game cocks (43x58cm-17x23in) s.d.1791 tin. 4-Oct-3 Neal Auction Company, New Orleans #372/R est:2500-3500

ALLAIS, Pierre (?-1782) French
£2797 $4755 €4000 Portrait de jeune femme tenant un eventail (74x59cm-29x23in) 30-Nov-3 Salle des ventes Pillet, Lyon la Foret #111 est:4000-6000

ALLAIS, Pierre (attrib) (?-1782) French
£5102 $9133 €7500 Portrait de mere et fille (98x80cm-39x31in) 19-Mar-4 Beaussant & Lefèvre, Paris #69/R est:6000-8000

ALLAN, Archibald Russell Watson (1878-1959) British
Works on paper
£350 $557 €511 West coast (37x54cm-15x21in) s. pastel. 10-Sep-3 Sotheby's, Olympia #155/R
£750 $1343 €1095 Blossom in a blue and white vase (55x66cm-22x26in) s. pastel. 28-May-4 Lyon & Turnbull, Edinburgh #6

ALLAN, James (19th C) British?
£300 $489 €438 Interior, man with lion's head, other figures asleep (122x122cm-48x48in) part collage. 23-Sep-3 John Nicholson, Haslemere #183/R

ALLAN, Jesse (1936-) American
Works on paper
£588 $1000 €858 Untitled (33x51cm-13x20in) s.d.1964 W/C. 9-Nov-3 Wright, Chicago #419 est:1200-1500
£978 $1800 €1467 Whale's path and the swan's road (56x41cm-22x16in) s.d.Nov 1984 W/C mixed media. 8-Jun-4 Auctions by the Bay, Alameda #1125/R

ALLAN, R (?) British
£600 $1020 €876 Nuneham near Oxford. Iffley Mill, near Oxford (44x61cm-17x24in) s. pair. 26-Nov-3 Hamptons Fine Art, Godalming #216
£900 $1548 €1314 Windsor Castle and Hambledon Mill (41x61cm-16x24in) s. 2-Dec-3 Gorringes, Lewes #2379

ALLAN, Robert Weir (1852-1942) British
£320 $534 €467 Fishing boats (28x41cm-11x16in) s. prov. 17-Oct-3 Keys, Aylsham #710
£720 $1202 €1051 In harbour (34x53cm-13x21in) s. 19-Jun-3 Bonhams, Edinburgh #307
£1200 $1884 €1740 Path through the cornfields (38x53cm-15x21in) s. 27-Aug-3 Sotheby's, London #1115/R est:1500-2000
£1550 $2480 €2263 Schooner moored, Venice (44x58cm-17x23in) s. 18-Sep-3 Bonhams, Edinburgh #348/R est:800-1200
£1800 $3312 €2628 Scottish fishing village with ducks in foreground (38x53cm-15x21in) s.d.1895 panel. 8-Jun-4 Gorringes, Lewes #2069/R est:2000-3000
£2000 $3620 €2920 At Nikko, Japan (51x35cm-20x14in) s.i.d.1907 W/C prov. 19-Apr-4 Sotheby's, London #38/R est:2000-3000
£4800 $8016 €7008 Ebbing tide (84x118cm-33x46in) s. exhib. 16-Oct-3 Bonhams, Edinburgh #134/R est:4000-6000
Works on paper
£350 $571 €511 Old arch at Cho Yung Kuan, Nankou Pass (25x36cm-10x14in) s. W/C. 23-Sep-3 John Nicholson, Haslemere #85
£444 $816 €648 Mother and child homeward bound (30x48cm-12x19in) s. W/C. 14-Jun-4 Waddingtons, Toronto #180/R est:1000-1500 (C.D 1100)
£450 $819 €657 Damascus Gate, Jerusalem (51x35cm-20x14in) s. pencil W/C. 1-Jul-4 Christie's, Kensington #383/R
£470 $752 €686 Ramsgate (39x56cm-15x22in) s. W/C. 18-Sep-3 Bonhams, Edinburgh #304
£500 $835 €730 Sheep grazing, Catacol, Arran (35x52cm-14x20in) s. W/C. 16-Oct-3 Lyon & Turnbull, Edinburgh #89
£550 $919 €803 Rye (51x36cm-20x14in) s. W/C. 16-Oct-3 Lyon & Turnbull, Edinburgh #123
£600 $1098 €876 Iford Bridge near Christchurch (34x51cm-13x20in) s. W/C. 29-Jan-4 Bonhams, Edinburgh #340
£700 $1323 €1022 Island of May (37x51cm-15x20in) s.i.d.1880 W/C. 19-Feb-4 Lyon & Turnbull, Edinburgh #109
£800 $1336 €1168 East Coast harbour scene (35x51cm-14x20in) s.d.1922 W/C. 16-Oct-3 Lyon & Turnbull, Edinburgh #60
£850 $1420 €1241 Fishing Boats, Wick (37x52cm-15x20in) s. W/C. 16-Oct-3 Lyon & Turnbull, Edinburgh #2
£1100 $1903 €1606 Children on a country path near Montrose (28x44cm-11x17in) s. W/C. 11-Dec-3 Lyon & Turnbull, Edinburgh #63/R est:800-1200
£1100 $2013 €1606 View down a Dutch canal (35x51cm-14x20in) s. W/C. 27-Jan-4 Bonhams, Knightsbridge #166/R est:1000-1500
£1342 $2470 €2000 London Street scene with figures (52x36cm-20x14in) s.d.1926 W/C. 23-Mar-4 Mealy's, Castlecomer #1084/R est:500-800
£1600 $2768 €2336 Fishing boats in the lagoon, Venice (47x64cm-19x25in) s.d.1881 W/C. 11-Dec-3 Lyon & Turnbull, Edinburgh #6/R est:1000-1500
£3000 $5430 €4380 Entrance to the temple at Nikko, Japan (51x35cm-20x14in) s.i.d.1907 W/C prov. 19-Apr-4 Sotheby's, London #37/R est:2000-3000
£3800 $6308 €5548 Sorting the catch, St Ives harbour (33x50cm-13x20in) s. W/C. 2-Oct-3 Lane, Penzance #110/R est:2500-3000

ALLAN, Sir William (1782-1850) British
£10000 $15700 €14500 Ballad of old Robin Gray (65x92cm-26x36in) s.d.1826 exhib. 27-Aug-3 Sotheby's, London #902/R est:10000-15000

ALLARD, Therese (20th C) Canadian?
£226 $355 €330 Femme en manteau d'hiver (106x79cm-42x31in) s.d.fev.1938 board. 26-Aug-3 Iegor de Saint Hippolyte, Montreal #47 (C.D 500)

ALLARD-L'OLIVIER, Fernand (1883-1933) Belgian
£284 $474 €400 Vue de ville en Hollande (35x27cm-14x11in) s. cardboard. 17-Jun-3 Vanderkindere, Brussels #102
£1047 $1800 €1529 Surprised by a little Satyr (119x79cm-47x31in) s.d.23 oval. 6-Dec-3 Neal Auction Company, New Orleans #988/R est:2000-3000
£1119 $1902 €1600 Fleuve au Congo. Scene animee au Congo (35x26cm-14x10in) s. panel. 18-Nov-3 Vanderkindere, Brussels #234 est:400-600
£1267 $2267 €1900 Fair in the Congo (26x35cm-10x14in) s. panel. 15-May-4 De Vuyst, Lokeren #10/R est:700-1000
£1457 $2652 €2200 Nanga (36x27cm-14x11in) s. panel. 15-Jun-4 Galerie Moderne, Brussels #325/R est:300-400
£2517 $4280 €3600 Ferme ensoleillee (92x64cm-36x25in) s. panel. 1-Dec-3 Palais de Beaux Arts, Brussels #17/R est:1000-1500

ALLASON, Silvio (1845-1912) Italian
£350 $584 €500 Undergrowth (19x30cm-7x12in) prov. 26-Jun-3 Sant Agostino, Torino #37/R

ALLAVENA, Luigi (?) Italian?
Works on paper
£360 $662 €526 High Bordighera, Genoa, a courtyard scene (40x23cm-16x9in) s. W/C. 26-Mar-4 Bigwood, Stratford on Avon #292

ALLBON, Charles Frederick (1856-1926) British
Works on paper
£280 $512 €409 Harvest lunch (29x44cm-11x17in) s.d.82 W/C. 27-Jan-4 Bristol Auction Rooms #598/R
£300 $501 €438 Babbacombe, Devon (22x47cm-9x19in) s.i.d.96 W/C htd white. 14-Oct-3 Bearnes, Exeter #348
£300 $549 €438 Extensive river landscape (21x64cm-8x25in) mono. W/C. 7-Apr-4 Dreweatt Neate, Newbury #59
£300 $561 €450 Fishing boats off the coast (23x48cm-9x19in) s. W/C. 22-Jul-4 Gorringes, Lewes #2012
£311 $557 €454 Country lane with windmill (37x66cm-15x26in) mono.i. W/C. 12-May-4 Dunbar Sloane, Wellington #106 (NZ.D 900)
£350 $644 €511 Fishermen at Exmouth, Devon (27x47cm-11x19in) s. W/C. 22-Jun-4 Bonhams, Knightsbridge #31/R
£360 $580 €522 Fishing boats making for the mouth of the Scheldt (23x48cm-9x19in) s. W/C. 15-Aug-3 Keys, Aylsham #532/R
£360 $601 €526 Runswick Bay (23x36cm-9x14in) s.i. grisaille htd white. 10-Oct-3 Richardson & Smith, Whitby #111/R

ALLCOT, John (1888-1973) Australian
£306 $511 €444 Cottage in the hills, Burragate NSW (19x24cm-7x9in) s. board. 13-Jul-3 James Lawson, Sydney #477 est:650-750 (A.D 750)
£800 $1432 €1168 Blue Star Line's New Zealand Star leaving Sydney (41x51cm-16x20in) s. canvasboard. 26-May-4 Christie's, Kensington #523/R
£1000 $1790 €1460 Blue Star Line's Queensland Star in Sydney harbour (51x61cm-20x24in) s. canvasboard. 26-May-4 Christie's, Kensington #524a/R est:1500-2500
£1074 $2009 €1611 Taranaki (30x34cm-12x13in) s. board. 20-Jul-4 Goodman, Sydney #102/R est:2000-3000 (A.D 2750)
£1885 $3054 €2752 Boat Harbinger (49x60cm-19x24in) s. board prov. 30-Jul-3 Goodman, Sydney #106/R est:3000-4000 (A.D 4600)
£2075 $3465 €3113 Loch Etive (51x61cm-20x24in) s. canvas on board. 27-Oct-3 Goodman, Sydney #176/R est:4500-6500 (A.D 5000)
Works on paper
£389 $650 €568 RMS Ventura (30x46cm-12x18in) s.i.d.1913 gouache board. 20-Jun-3 Freeman, Philadelphia #36/R
£656 $1062 €958 Macquarie (25x35cm-10x14in) s.i.d.1932 gouache W/C. 30-Jul-3 Goodman, Sydney #107/R (A.D 1600)

ALLCOT, John (attrib) (1888-1973) Australian
£380 $695 €555 British three master off Sydney Heads (51x61cm-20x24in) s. canvasboard. 8-Apr-4 Christie's, Kensington #160

ALLEAUME, Ludovic (1859-?) French
£1676 $3000 €2447 Views of the Holy Land (18x36cm-7x14in) s.i. panel pair. 18-Mar-4 Sotheby's, New York #269/R est:3000-5000

ALLEBE, Augustus (1838-1927) Dutch
£7639 $12757 €11000 Buurtpaatje (81x63cm-32x25in) mono.d.69 panel prov.exhib. 21-Oct-3 Sotheby's, Amsterdam #3/R est:7000-9000
Works on paper
£403 $745 €600 Portrait of an elegant lady (35x48cm-14x19in) s.d.1903. 15-Mar-4 Sotheby's, Amsterdam #52/R

ALLEGRAIN, Christophe Gabriel (attrib) (1710-1795) French
£9507 $16637 €13500 Moise sauve des eaux (5x115cm-2x45in) 17-Dec-3 Piasa, Paris #72/R est:10000-12000

ALLEGRAIN, Étienne (1653-1736) French
£15000 $27000 €21900 Extensive river landscape with peasants on a path (96x135cm-38x53in) 21-Apr-4 Christie's, London #65/R est:10000-15000

ALLEGRE, Raymond (1857-1933) French
£845 $1513 €1200 Bord de riviere (21x27cm-8x11in) s.i. panel. 11-Jan-4 Rouillac, Vendome #301

ALLEGRINI, Francesco (1587-1663) Italian
Works on paper
£300 $519 €438 Horseman and soldiers approaching a town, with dead man and crows (27x20cm-11x8in) i.verso pen brown ink wash prov. 12-Dec-3 Christie's, Kensington #347
£1000 $1730 €1460 God the Father, with the Dove of the Holy Spirit (19x16cm-7x6in) red chk. 12-Dec-3 Christie's, Kensington #346/R est:1000-2000

£1749	$3200	€2554	Seated male angel (24x17cm-9x7in) red chk. 29-Jan-4 Swann Galleries, New York #68/R est:2000-3000
£2000	$3460	€2920	Crucifixion with the Virgin, Mary Magdalen and Saint John (20x15cm-8x6in) red chk red wash prov. 12-Dec-3 Christie's, Kensington #348/R est:600-800

ALLEGRINI, Francesco (attrib) (1587-1663) Italian

Works on paper			
£1200	$2160	€1752	Triumphal arch (33x15cm-13x6in) i. pen brown ink wash black chk. 20-Apr-4 Sotheby's, Olympia #49/R est:600-800

ALLEMAND, Hector (1809-1886) French

£1600	$2912	€2400	Troupeau a l'etang (34x56cm-13x22in) s.d.1856. 29-Jun-4 Chenu & Scrive, Lyon #3/R est:2500-3500

ALLEN, Cecil (20th C) American

Works on paper			
£320	$550	€467	Portrait of a woman (66x53cm-26x21in) s. W/C exec.c.1940. 7-Dec-3 Treadway Gallery, Cincinnati #687/R

ALLEN, Charles Curtis (1886-1950) American

£435	$800	€635	Two trees (28x38cm-11x15in) s. board. 25-Jun-4 Freeman, Philadelphia #125/R
£621	$1000	€907	Sunset Ogunquit, Maine (23x28cm-9x11in) s. board. 20-Aug-3 James Julia, Fairfield #1386/R
£1173	$1900	€1701	Mount Monadnock in winter (43x58cm-17x23in) 26-Jul-3 Thomaston Place, Thomaston #119/R
£1453	$2600	€2121	Vermont winter landscape. s. 31-May-4 William A Smith, Plainfield #7/R
£1832	$2950	€2675	Mount Monadnock, NH (94x104cm-37x41in) prov. 20-Aug-3 James Julia, Fairfield #1385/R est:4000-6000

ALLEN, Daphne (1899-?) British

Works on paper			
£1150	$2093	€1679	Fairies among bluebells and primroses (25x21cm-10x8in) s. W/C htd white over traces pencil. 29-Jun-4 Bonhams, Knowle #40 est:300-500

ALLEN, Davida (1951-) Australian

£2510	$4041	€3665	Troll lover (97x97cm-38x38in) s.i.d.Jan 1989 verso prov. 25-Aug-3 Sotheby's, Paddington #373/R est:6000-10000 (A.D 6200)
£5691	$8935	€8252	Father and baby (119x100cm-47x39in) s.i.d.1984 verso prov. 26-Aug-3 Christie's, Sydney #91/R est:8000-15000 (A.D 14000)

ALLEN, Douglas (1935-) American

£432	$800	€631	Bear. Woodcock (28x33cm-11x13in) s. one masonite one board two. 10-Feb-4 Doyle, New York #113/R

ALLEN, George B (?) Australian?

Works on paper			
£1186	$2017	€1732	View of Melbourne from Hawthorn (17x46cm-7x18in) W/C gouache. 24-Nov-3 Sotheby's, Melbourne #220/R est:1000-2000 (A.D 2800)

ALLEN, Greg (1958-) Australian

Works on paper			
£305	$479	€442	Australian landscape (62x86cm-24x34in) s.d.85 W/C. 26-Aug-3 Lawson Menzies, Sydney #27 (A.D 750)

ALLEN, Harry Epworth (1894-1958) British

£380	$692	€570	Landscape with ruins at Kildonan, Isle of Arran (24x36cm-9x14in) tempera. 20-Jun-4 Wilkinson, Doncaster #310
£1900	$3230	€2774	Quarry (32x47cm-13x19in) s. tempera prov. 18-Nov-3 Bonhams, Leeds #126/R est:1500-2000
£2083	$3396	€3000	Street scene with three women (21x17cm-8x7in) s. card. 24-Sep-3 James Adam, Dublin #108/R est:3000-4000
£3500	$6370	€5110	Farmyard (33x49cm-13x19in) s. tempera. 15-Jun-4 Bonhams, Leeds #41/R est:3500-4000
£4306	$7018	€6200	West of Ireland village with donkey and figures (24x34cm-9x13in) s. card. 24-Sep-3 James Adam, Dublin #107/R est:4000-6000
£4400	$6996	€6424	Irish landscape (55x66cm-22x26in) s. tempera board. 10-Sep-3 Sotheby's, Olympia #165/R est:4000-6000
£5800	$9860	€8468	Haddon Hall, Derbyshire (49x60cm-19x24in) s. canvasboard. 21-Nov-3 Christie's, London #8/R est:5000-8000
£10000	$16300	€14500	Figure group looking out to sea on a southern Irish coast (38x54cm-15x21in) s. tempera. 23-Sep-3 Bonhams, Leeds #179/R est:10000-12000
£12000	$19560	€17400	Air-raid shelter (49x61cm-19x24in) s. tempera. 23-Sep-3 Bonhams, Leeds #178/R est:12000-15000
£13487	$24816	€20500	On the soap box (51x61cm-20x24in) s. tempera board. 22-Jun-4 De Veres Art Auctions, Dublin #99/R est:20000-25000
Works on paper			
£250	$410	€365	Connemara village (20x25cm-8x10in) s. pencil W/C wash. 4-Jun-3 John Ross, Belfast #164
£310	$515	€453	Thatched farmhouse above a valley (17x24cm-7x9in) s. W/C. 2-Oct-3 Lane, Penzance #139
£520	$884	€759	Near Buxton (48x33cm-19x13in) pastel prov. 18-Nov-3 Bonhams, Leeds #128
£520	$884	€759	Longshaw pool, Derbyshire (22x32cm-9x13in) s. pastel. 18-Nov-3 Bonhams, Leeds #134/R
£580	$986	€847	Portrait of Lucy, the artist's wife (36x25cm-14x10in) s. pencil W/C. 18-Nov-3 Bonhams, Leeds #127/R
£1100	$2002	€1606	Bridge (33x47cm-13x19in) s. gouache bodycol. 15-Jun-4 Bonhams, Leeds #42/R
£3826	$6848	€5700	Lusk village (28x36cm-11x14in) s. pastel. 26-May-4 James Adam, Dublin #95/R est:4000-6000

ALLEN, J D (1851-1947) American

£1766	$3250	€2578	Scouting the herd (91x71cm-36x28in) 24-Jun-4 Sotheby's, New York #167/R est:3000-5000

ALLEN, John Howard (1866-1935) American

£349	$600	€510	Country road (46x61cm-18x24in) s. 7-Dec-3 Grogan, Boston #63/R

ALLEN, John Whitacre (fl.1886-1901) British

£3448	$6379	€5000	Landscape with lake and figures (102x129cm-40x51in) s.d.1878. 14-Feb-4 Meeting Art, Vercelli #221/R est:5000

ALLEN, Joseph (1770-1839) British

£450	$765	€657	Portrait of Reverend Whitehall Davies (100x81cm-39x32in) s.d.1799. 4-Nov-3 Woolley & Wallis, Salisbury #156/R

ALLEN, Joseph William (1803-1852) British

£650	$1086	€949	On the Welsh coast, Bangor (47x61cm-19x24in) prov. 13-Nov-3 Christie's, Kensington #87/R
Works on paper			
£280	$482	€409	Cutting reeds (18x34cm-7x13in) s.d.1840 pencil W/C. 3-Dec-3 Christie's, Kensington #191

ALLEN, Junius (1898-1962) American

£1657	$3000	€2419	East river fog (20x25cm-8x10in) s. s.i.verso acrylic canvas on board prov. 31-Mar-4 Sotheby's, New York #35/R est:2000-3000
£3824	$6500	€5583	Sunlight and shadow (61x74cm-24x29in) s. i.d.1947v. prov. 21-Nov-3 Skinner, Boston #497/R est:2000-4000
Works on paper			
£217	$400	€317	House by the sea (48x66cm-19x26in) s. W/C. 26-Jun-4 Susanin's, Chicago #6056/R

ALLEN, Thomas (1849-1924) American

£190	$350	€277	Cows in a meadow, building and trees in background (30x43cm-12x17in) board. 9-Jun-4 Alderfer's, Hatfield #385/R
£226	$400	€330	Summer landscape with barn (30x46cm-12x18in) estate st.verso panel. 1-May-4 Thomaston Place, Thomaston #296/R
£242	$450	€353	Sketch of Stephen S Fitzgerald playing a flute (28x18cm-11x7in) s.d.1884 canvas on board. 6-Mar-4 North East Auctions, Portsmouth #1073
£282	$500	€412	Sand dunes by the sea, probably Cape Cod (25x13cm-10x5in) estate st.verso. 1-May-4 Thomaston Place, Thomaston #358/R
£282	$500	€412	Man on a horse and woman in cart with thatched roof house at end of path (30x46cm-12x18in) estate st.verso. 1-May-4 Thomaston Place, Thomaston #359/R
£282	$500	€412	Two figures in a summer landscape, probably Massachusetts (20x46cm-8x18in) estate st.verso. 1-May-4 Thomaston Place, Thomaston #378/R
£283	$500	€413	Fall scene of stacked cornstalks with stormy sky, probably Grt Barrington (23x36cm-9x14in) estate st.verso. 1-May-4 Thomaston Place, Thomaston #368/R
£339	$600	€495	Two steer among mountain laurel, probably Mount Wachusetts (30x46cm-12x18in) estate st.verso. 1-May-4 Thomaston Place, Thomaston #129/R
£339	$600	€495	Yearling cow under fall trees (30x46cm-12x18in) s.verso panel. 1-May-4 Thomaston Place, Thomaston #259/R
£339	$600	€495	Cows grazing in a summer pasture (30x46cm-12x18in) estate st.verso panel. 1-May-4 Thomaston Place, Thomaston #298/R
£339	$600	€495	Hillside landscape with approaching storm, Texas (30x46cm-12x18in) estate st.verso panel. 1-May-4 Thomaston Place, Thomaston #333/R
£346	$550	€505	Blue skies (46x61cm-18x24in) s.d.1911. 12-Sep-3 Skinner, Boston #422/R
£395	$700	€577	Pool in the woods (48x66cm-19x26in) s. canvasboard. 1-May-4 Thomaston Place, Thomaston #84/R
£395	$700	€577	Fall wood scene with brown horse and blue cart near split rail fence (28x46cm-11x18in) s. panel. 1-May-4 Thomaston Place, Thomaston #319/R
£395	$700	€577	Broadside view of a sheep in summer grass (28x41cm-11x16in) estate st.verso panel. 1-May-4 Thomaston Place, Thomaston #369/R
£395	$700	€577	Four brown cattle in landscape (30x46cm-12x18in) s. board. 1-May-4 Thomaston Place, Thomaston #383/R
£452	$800	€660	Mare with foal feeding, probably Cape Cod (30x46cm-12x18in) estate st.verso. 1-May-4 Thomaston Place, Thomaston #119/R
£452	$800	€660	Deserted, ancient hillside graveyard (30x36cm-12x14in) s.i. panel. 1-May-4 Thomaston Place, Thomaston #257/R
£452	$800	€660	Single figure seated by the seashore (30x46cm-12x18in) d.2/4/1889 estate st.verso. 1-May-4 Thomaston Place, Thomaston #331/R
£537	$950	€784	Full standing black and white cow with bell (28x36cm-11x14in) estate st.verso panel. 1-May-4 Thomaston Place, Thomaston #391/R
£765	$1300	€1117	Cows in a forest glade (66x99cm-26x39in) s. 21-Nov-3 Eldred, East Dennis #882/R est:2000-3000
£960	$1700	€1402	Rooster studies (20x15cm-8x6in) estate st.verso panel pine four. 1-May-4 Thomaston Place, Thomaston #82/R
£1022	$1900	€1492	Landscape with prominent sky (41x61cm-16x24in) s.d.1911. 3-Mar-4 Alderfer's, Hatfield #439 est.600-800
£1469	$2600	€2145	Rooster studies (20x15cm-8x6in) estate st.verso panel on Cuban cigar box lids four. 1-May-4 Thomaston Place, Thomaston #79/R
£1469	$2600	€2145	Four horses by a stream in Texas (30x48cm-12x19in) estate st.verso panel. 1-May-4 Thomaston Place, Thomaston #258/R
Works on paper			
£282	$500	€412	Herd of black faced Suffolk sheep on grassy hillside (23x43cm-9x17in) s. 1-May-4 Thomaston Place, Thomaston #203/R
£339	$600	€495	Two steer on a mountain laurel path, probably near Provincetown, Mass (318x48cm-125x19in) indis.sig.verso W/C. 1-May-4 Thomaston Place, Thomaston #123/R
£508	$900	€742	Mare with foal feeding (38x56cm-15x22in) s. W/C gouache. 1-May-4 Thomaston Place, Thomaston #124/R

ALLEN, William Sullivant Vanderbilt (1860-1931) American

£6486	$12000	€9470	In the music room with daffodils (55x46cm-22x18in) s.i. prov. 11-Mar-4 Christie's, Rockefeller NY #27/R est:12000-18000
£56886	$95000	€83054	Evening by the lake (60x58cm-24x23in) s.d.1887 prov.exhib.lit. 9-Oct-3 Christie's, Rockefeller NY #30/R est:20000-30000

ALLENBACH, Jean Claude (1947-) French

£517 $926 €755 Bouquet (80x80cm-31x31in) s. i. verso acrylic. 12-May-4 Dobiaschofsky, Bern #3402/R (S.FR 1200)

ALLER, Gonzalo (1973-) Spanish

£671 $1201 €1000 At the window (65x100cm-26x39in) s. 25-May-4 Durán, Madrid #173/R
£884 $1583 €1300 Smoking by the window (89x116cm-35x46in) s. 22-Mar-4 Durán, Madrid #136/R

ALLERSTON, John Taylor (fl.c.1900) British

£500 $795 €725 Quayside with warehouses and boats (20x30cm-8x12in) s.d.1890. 9-Sep-3 David Duggleby, Scarborough #272
£700 $1260 €1022 The Herbert, a three-masted barque of Boston ashore at Flamborough Head (34x45cm-13x18in) s.i.d.1870. 21-Apr-4 Tennants, Leyburn #1108

ALLIMANDI, Enrico (1910-1984) Italian

£347 $590 €500 Landscape (38x46cm-15x18in) s.d.1952 board double-sided. 1-Nov-3 Meeting Art, Vercelli #20
£408 $731 €600 Mount of Cappuccini (24x19cm-9x7in) s.d.1945 cardboard. 22-Mar-4 Sant Agostino, Torino #376/R
£667 $1227 €1000 Woman (70x50cm-28x20in) s.d.1959 cardboard on canvas exhib. 14-Jun-4 Sant Agostino, Torino #360/R
£816 $1461 €1200 Woman resting (45x32cm-18x13in) s.d.1966 cardboard on canvas. 22-Mar-4 Sant Agostino, Torino #508/R
£1517 $2534 €2200 Still life (39x46cm-15x18in) s. cardboard. 17-Nov-3 Sant Agostino, Torino #103/R
Works on paper
£510 $913 €750 Nude and rider (48x34cm-19x13in) s. pastel prov. 22-Mar-4 Sant Agostino, Torino #375/R

ALLINGHAM, Helen (1848-1926) British

Works on paper
£750 $1320 €1095 The Shrubbery (24x17cm-9x7in) s.d.1873 W/C. 19-May-4 Dreweatt Neate, Newbury #4/R
£1400 $2324 €2044 Rose Arch (9x15cm-4x6in) s. W/C. 1-Oct-3 Sotheby's, Olympia #102/R est:1000-1500
£2000 $3700 €2920 Vegetable stall (13x10cm-5x4in) s. W/C. 9-Mar-4 Bonhams, New Bond Street #94/R est:2000-3000
£2400 $4416 €3504 Campiello delle Steppe, Venice (24x17cm-9x7in) s. W/C prov. 8-Jun-4 Bonhams, New Bond Street #86/R est:800-1200
£2700 $5049 €3942 Goose girl (21x16cm-8x6in) s. W/C. 20-Jul-4 Sworder & Son, Bishops Stortford #704/R est:2500-3000
£9400 $15698 €13724 Spring time (23x18cm-9x7in) s. W/C. 12-Nov-3 Sotheby's, Olympia #100/R est:6000-8000
£10000 $18300 €14600 At West Hagbourne, Berks (19x27cm-7x11in) s. pencil W/C gum arabic scratching out prov.exhib.lit. 3-Jun-4 Christie's, London #19/R est:8000-12000
£10000 $18400 €14600 Cottage near Blackdown, Sussex (24x34cm-9x13in) s. W/C prov.exhib.lit. 8-Jun-4 Bonhams, New Bond Street #80/R est:10000-15000
£10000 $18400 €14600 Cottage near Freshwater, Isle of Wight (30x37cm-12x15in) s. W/C. 8-Jun-4 Bonhams, New Bond Street #81/R est:10000-15000
£10319 $16820 €15066 Cottage at Grayswood (23x23cm-9x9in) s. W/C. 17-Jul-3 Naón & Cia, Buenos Aires #10/R
£11000 $18700 €16060 Surrey Cottage (19x15cm-7x6in) s. pencil W/C gum arabic htd bodycol scratching out prov. 20-Nov-3 Christie's, London #106/R est:8000-12000
£11000 $18370 €16060 Old Surrey cottage (29x39cm-11x15in) s. W/C. 12-Nov-3 Sotheby's, Olympia #54/R est:10000-15000
£11000 $20350 €16060 Fiddler (27x25cm-11x10in) s. i.verso W/C prov.exhib.lit. 9-Mar-4 Bonhams, New Bond Street #90/R est:8000-12000
£11000 $20130 €16060 At Wroughton, Wiltshire (24x30cm-9x12in) s. i. verso pencil W/C htd bodycol scratching out exhib. 3-Jun-4 Christie's, London #180/R est:12000-18000
£11500 $19205 €16790 West Tarring (46x37cm-18x15in) s. W/C lit. 12-Nov-3 Sotheby's, Olympia #101/R est:10000-15000
£12500 $23000 €18250 Vine cottage (23x18cm-9x7in) s. W/C exhib.lit. 8-Jun-4 Bonhams, New Bond Street #78/R est:12000-18000
£14000 $23800 €20440 Farringford, Isle of Wight (31x24cm-12x9in) s. i.mount pencil W/C prov. 19-Nov-3 Tennants, Leyburn #997/R est:15000-20000
£14000 $25900 €20440 Thatched cottage with figures (26x35cm-10x14in) s. W/C lit. 9-Mar-4 Bonhams, New Bond Street #89/R est:12000-18000
£14000 $25620 €20440 On the Brook Road, near Witley (26x21cm-10x8in) s. pencil W/C scratching out prov.exhib.lit. 3-Jun-4 Christie's, London #179/R est:15000-20000
£16500 $27555 €24090 Old farm (32x42cm-13x17in) s. W/C prov. 12-Nov-3 Sotheby's, Olympia #55/R est:15000-25000
£19000 $34960 €27740 The cradle (23x19cm-9x7in) s. W/C prov.exhib.lit. 8-Jun-4 Bonhams, New Bond Street #79/R est:10000-15000
£20000 $33400 €29200 Old Surrey cottage (36x48cm-14x19in) s. W/C lit. 12-Nov-3 Sotheby's, Olympia #99/R est:20000-30000
£21000 $38850 €30660 Near Hambledon (29x38cm-11x15in) s. W/C prov.exhib.lit. 9-Mar-4 Bonhams, New Bond Street #88/R est:15000-20000

ALLINGHAM, Helen (attrib) (1848-1926) British

Works on paper
£400 $644 €580 Studies of chickens (30x20cm-12x8in) i. pencil seven on one leaf. 13-Aug-3 Rupert Toovey, Partridge Green #12/R

ALLINSON, Adrian (1890-1959) British

£600 $1080 €876 Mer de Glace (65x92cm-26x36in) s. 20-Jan-4 Bonhams, Knightsbridge #172
£650 $1203 €949 Brickworks (36x38cm-14x15in) s. 13-Feb-4 Keys, Aylsham #897
£1600 $2672 €2336 Derelict clay pit, Cornwall (56x81cm-22x32in) s. board exhib. 16-Oct-3 Christie's, Kensington #461/R est:1500-2000
£1600 $2672 €2336 Giant sunflowers (82x66cm-32x26in) s. 16-Oct-3 Christie's, Kensington #684 est:1000-1500
£3600 $6336 €5256 Landscape with blossoms (66x91cm-26x36in) 19-May-4 Sotheby's, Olympia #147/R est:4000-6000
Works on paper
£440 $814 €642 Paysage Lagaure (28x37cm-11x15in) s.d.24 pastel. 16-Feb-4 Bonhams, Bath #65
£450 $797 €657 Continental landscape with houses (40x30cm-16x12in) s.d.23 pastel. 27-Apr-4 Bonhams, Knightsbridge #245
£480 $782 €701 Boy with donkey (28x37cm-11x15in) i. pastel prov. 24-Sep-3 Dreweatt Neate, Newbury #78

ALLINSON, Garlies W (fl.1930) British

Works on paper
£950 $1710 €1387 Storm of Loch Inge (48x71cm-19x28in) s. gouache. 22-Apr-4 Mellors & Kirk, Nottingham #995/R

ALLIOT, Lucien Charles Edouard (1877-1967) French

Sculpture
£5800 $9454 €8468 Dancing Lady (39cm-15in) ivory gilt bronze white veined blk marble base. 28-Sep-3 Wilkinson, Doncaster #31/R

ALLIRAND, Renaud (20th C) French

£658 $1211 €1000 Composition (41x33cm-16x13in) s.d.2003 acrylic. 27-Jun-4 Versailles Encheres #193/R
Works on paper
£317 $548 €450 Composition (65x50cm-26x20in) s.d.2001 Chinese ink acrylic. 14-Dec-3 Versailles Encheres #221/R
£387 $670 €550 Untitled (50x65cm-20x26in) s.d.2002 Chinese ink chl. 9-Dec-3 Artcurial Briest, Paris #557

ALLISON, Roy (?) British?

£650 $1229 €949 La loge (102x76cm-40x30in) s. after Pierre Auguste Renoir. 19-Feb-4 Christie's, Kensington #41/R

ALLOM, Thomas (1804-1872) British

Works on paper
£400 $740 €584 St Maclou, Rouen (18x13cm-7x5in) s. sepia. 9-Mar-4 Bonhams, Knightsbridge #56/R
£400 $736 €584 Busy Darlington Road with St Cuthbert's church in the distance (10x15cm-4x6in) s. pencil brown wash htd white. 25-Mar-4 Christie's, Kensington #21/R
£550 $1012 €803 Verney Park. Fairlawn (8x12cm-3x5in) W/C pair. 22-Jun-4 Bonhams, Knightsbridge #6/R

ALLONGE, Auguste (1833-1898) French

Works on paper
£426 $689 €600 Les bles. s. W/C. 24-May-3 Martinot & Savignat, Pontoise #144
£524 $876 €750 Paysage (34x51cm-13x20in) s. W/C. 25-Jun-3 Maigret, Paris #31
£559 $934 €800 Bord de riviere (34x51cm-13x20in) W/C. 25-Jun-3 Maigret, Paris #30
£638 $1034 €900 Sous bois a Fontainebleau (27x39cm-11x15in) W/C. 24-May-3 Martinot & Savignat, Pontoise #145
£667 $1213 €1000 Chemin a Barbizon (33x51cm-13x20in) s. W/C. 5-Jul-4 Neret-Minet, Paris #34b
£704 $1218 €1000 Paysage Mediterraneen (46x74cm-18x29in) s. W/C. 13-Dec-3 Martinot & Savignat, Pontoise #201
£816 $1461 €1200 Vue d'un etang (26x55cm-10x22in) s.d.1869 pierre noire stumping out scratching beige paper. 17-Mar-4 Tajan, Paris #143
£1206 $1953 €1700 Sous bois (78x56cm-31x22in) s. W/C. 24-May-3 Martinot & Savignat, Pontoise #146 est:1700-1800
£1232 $2020 €1700 Rochers a Fontainebleau (57x77cm-22x30in) s. W/C. 11-May-3 Osenat, Fontainebleau #1 est:1500-1800
£1957 $3209 €2700 Les bouleaux pres de la riviere (78x56cm-31x22in) s. W/C. 11-May-3 Osenat, Fontainebleau #2 est:2500-2800

ALLORI, Alessandro (1535-1607) Italian

£52778 $95000 €77056 Dead Christ attended by two angels (45x39cm-18x15in) copper prov.exhib.lit. 22-Jan-4 Sotheby's, New York #17/R est:70000-90000

ALLORI, Alessandro (attrib) (1535-1607) Italian

£1447 $2663 €2200 Portrait of gentleman (5x4cm-2x2in) copper oval. 25-Jun-4 Piasa, Paris #58 est:2000-3000
£20979 $35035 €30000 Portrait of Annibale Caro (46x31cm-18x12in) i.verso board. 7-Oct-3 Pandolfini, Florence #620/R est:35000-45000

ALLORI, Alessandro (circle) (1535-1607) Italian

£25862 $47586 €37759 Portrait of a woman (93x74cm-37x29in) prov.lit. 26-Mar-4 Koller, Zurich #3014/R est:25000-35000 (S.FR 60000)

ALLOSIA, Giuseppe (1910-1983) Italian

£1399 $2378 €2000 Untitled (49x70cm-19x28in) sold with mixed media by S Dangelo. 25-Nov-3 Sotheby's, Milan #52 est:1000-1500
£1486 $2616 €2200 Destruction (80x67cm-31x26in) s.d.1952 oil enamel lit. 22-May-4 Galleria Pananti, Florence #416/R est:2200-2500

ALLOU, Gilles (1670-1751) French

Works on paper
£1523 $2772 €2300 Portrait de Madame de Monsaux tenant une quenouille (29x21cm-11x8in) i. sanguine prov. 16-Jun-4 Piasa, Paris #113 est:2500

ALLOUARD, Henri (1844-1929) French

Sculpture
£1453 $2600 €2121 Napoleon (38cm-15in) s.st.f.Societe des Bronzes brown pat bronze marble pedestal. 20-Mar-4 Freeman, Philadelphia #726/R est:1500-2500

ALLSTON, Washington (1779-1843) American
£8824 $15000 €12883 Landscape (33x30cm-13x12in) painted c.1830. 30-Oct-3 Phillips, New York #1/R est:7000-10000

ALLUAUD, Eugène (1866-1947) French
£2368 $4358 €3600 Les roches rouges (58x75cm-23x30in) s. 23-Jun-4 Maigret, Paris #22/R est:2500-3000
£4217 $7000 €6157 Pont sur la Creuse (81x99cm-32x39in) s. s.i.stretcher. 4-Oct-3 Neal Auction Company, New Orleans #263/R est:7000-10000

ALMA-TADEMA, Lady Laura (1852-1909) British
£4113 $6664 €5800 Portrait of a young girl (110x60cm-43x24in) s. 20-May-3 Ansorena, Madrid #107/R est:5800

ALMA-TADEMA, Sir Lawrence (1836-1912) British
£1667 $3000 €2500 Man looking up (39x32cm-15x13in) s.i.d.1856 panel. 21-Apr-4 Christie's, Amsterdam #134/R est:2500-3500
£11000 $20240 €16060 Figures on the terrace by the Acropolis (20x41cm-8x16in) s. panel prov.exhib.lit. 26-Mar-4 Sotheby's, London #67/R est:10000-15000
£11500 $19550 €16790 Una Carita (11x8cm-4x3in) s.i. board prov.exhib.lit. 25-Nov-3 Christie's, London #151/R est:8000-12000
£44118 $75000 €64412 Thou rose of all roses (43x28cm-17x11in) s.d.OpCCLXXII prov.exhib.lit. 28-Oct-3 Sotheby's, New York #73/R est:100000-150000
£86705 $150000 €126589 Catullus reading his poems at Lesbia's House (39x48cm-15x19in) s.d.70 panel prov.exhib.lit. 11-Dec-3 Sotheby's, New York #90/R est:150000-200000
£411765 $700000 €601177 Melody on a Mediterranean terrace (46x66cm-18x26in) s.i. panel prov.lit. 28-Oct-3 Sotheby's, New York #68/R est:300000-400000

ALMARAZ, Carlos (1941-1989) ?
Works on paper
£807 $1300 €1178 Moonlight beach (49x63cm-19x25in) s.d.84 pastel. 17-Aug-3 Bonhams & Butterfields, San Francisco #5841

ALMEIDA, Alvaro Duarte de (1909-1972) Portuguese
£1342 $2403 €2000 Peasant woman (35x50cm-14x20in) s. board. 31-May-4 Cabral Moncada Leiloes, Lisbon #223/R est:1200-1800

ALMEIDA, Jorge de (20th C) Portuguese
£1007 $1802 €1500 Painting (90x150cm-35x59in) s. painted 1970. 31-May-4 Cabral Moncada Leiloes, Lisbon #242/R est:1500-2250

ALMELA, Fernando (1943-) Spanish
£408 $743 €600 Still life (73x60cm-29x24in) s.d.1985 s.d.verso prov.exhib. 3-Feb-4 Segre, Madrid #333/R

ALMGREN, Gosta (1888-?) Swedish
Sculpture
£1478 $2646 €2158 Standing female nude (96cm-38in) s. green pat.bronze Cast Otto Meyers. 26-May-4 AB Stockholms Auktionsverk #2229/R est:20000-25000 (S.KR 20000)

ALMON, Leroy (1938-1997) American
Sculpture
£2335 $3900 €3409 Slave ships coming to America (58x61cm-23x24in) paint wood. 15-Nov-3 Slotin Folk Art, Buford #312/R est:1000-2000

ALMOND, Darren (1971-) British
Sculpture
£10180 $17000 €14863 Alfred (114x22x1cm-45x9x0in) painted aluminum edition 1 of 2 prov. 13-Nov-3 Sotheby's, New York #465/R est:7000-10000

ALOISE (1886-1964) Swiss
Works on paper
£10204 $18266 €15000 Untitled (98x73cm-39x29in) crayon pastel collage craft paper sketch verso double-sided exhib. 21-Mar-4 Calmels Cohen, Paris #46/R est:15000-20000
£14336 $24657 €20500 Untitled (65x23cm-26x9in) i. pastel crayon double-sided exhib. 2-Dec-3 Calmels Cohen, Paris #63/R est:15000-20000

ALONSO ALONSO (20th C) Spanish
£390 $651 €550 Woman and bowl of fruit (120x98cm-47x39in) s. 23-Jun-3 Durán, Madrid #700/R

ALONSO ALONSO, Francisco (1930-) Spanish
£310 $515 €450 Bridge (58x78cm-23x31in) 1-Oct-3 Ansorena, Madrid #609/R
£375 $619 €540 Seascape (60x80cm-24x31in) s. 2-Jul-3 Ansorena, Madrid #904/R
£377 $640 €550 Nature bleue (66x83cm-26x33in) s. sid.1961 verso. 4-Nov-3 Ansorena, Madrid #961/R
£461 $834 €700 Still life in blue and red (80x100cm-31x39in) s. 14-Apr-4 Ansorena, Madrid #294/R
£483 $869 €700 Rocio by the window (100x81cm-39x32in) s. s.i.verso. 26-Jan-4 Ansorena, Madrid #157/R
£986 $1706 €1400 Regatta (70x102cm-28x40in) s. 15-Dec-3 Ansorena, Madrid #1006/R

ALONSO PALACIOS, Vicente (1955-) Spanish
Works on paper
£306 $548 €450 Robots restorer (39x29cm-15x11in) s. W/C. 22-Mar-4 Durán, Madrid #6/R
£335 $585 €475 Young poet (35x27cm-14x11in) s. W/C. 16-Dec-3 Durán, Madrid #19/R
£352 $616 €500 Head of Arab (35x27cm-14x11in) s. W/C. 16-Dec-3 Durán, Madrid #20/R

ALONSO, Carlos (1929-) Argentinian
£3017 $5400 €4405 Red nude (60x35cm-24x14in) 11-May-4 Arroyo, Buenos Aires #2
£3571 $6500 €5214 Nude (51x66cm-20x26in) s. cardboard. 29-Jun-4 Arroyo, Buenos Aires #103/R est:6500
£7143 $13000 €10429 Study of Caravaggio (70x100cm-28x39in) s.i.d.76 tempera paper on board. 29-Jun-4 Arroyo, Buenos Aires #70/R est:4000
£8242 $15000 €12033 Landscape (100x100cm-39x39in) s.d.81. 5-Jul-4 Arroyo, Buenos Aires #81/R est:15000
£10440 $19000 €15242 Still life (92x113cm-36x44in) s.d.63. 29-Jun-4 Arroyo, Buenos Aires #90/R est:15000
£20765 $38000 €30317 Village (150x100cm-59x39in) cardboard. 1-Jun-4 Arroyo, Buenos Aires #69
Works on paper
£385 $700 €562 Golden foot (35x23cm-14x9in) s.d.51 ink. 5-Jul-4 Arroyo, Buenos Aires #99/R
£934 $1700 €1364 Exterminator (36x49cm-14x19in) s.d.66 ink. 5-Jul-4 Arroyo, Buenos Aires #42/R est:1100
£1117 $2000 €1631 Letter (27x34cm-11x13in) ink pencil. 11-May-4 Arroyo, Buenos Aires #1
£1326 $2400 €1936 Young woman (72x40cm-28x16in) sepia ink. 30-Mar-4 Arroyo, Buenos Aires #104
£1538 $2800 €2245 Theatre (33x25cm-13x10in) s. mixed media. 5-Jul-4 Arroyo, Buenos Aires #57/R est:1400
£3716 $6800 €5425 Three graces (35x49cm-14x19in) mixed media collage. 1-Jun-4 Arroyo, Buenos Aires #97
£6630 $12000 €9680 Run (70x100cm-28x39in) ink. 30-Mar-4 Arroyo, Buenos Aires #89
£8101 $14500 €11827 Composition in blue (57x77cm-22x30in) s.d.57 mixed media. 4-May-4 Arroyo, Buenos Aires #65/R est:7000
£8380 $15000 €12235 Anatomy lesson (50x70cm-20x28in) s.d.70 ink. 4-May-4 Arroyo, Buenos Aires #46/R est:2400

ALONSO, F (20th C) Philippino
£1156 $2070 €1700 Noblemen in the garden (42x50cm-17x20in) s. 22-Mar-4 Durán, Madrid #641/R est:1200

ALONSO, Rafael (1924-1995) Spanish
Works on paper
£390 $632 €550 Vista de Pueblo (49x67cm-19x26in) s.d.1946 W/C. 20-May-3 Ansorena, Madrid #982

ALONSO, Raul (20th C) Argentinian
Works on paper
£5304 $9600 €7744 Fruit and pots. Letter (50x65cm-20x26in) pastel cardboard pair. 30-Mar-4 Arroyo, Buenos Aires #25

ALONSO-PEREZ, Carlos (19/20th C) Spanish
£1133 $2051 €1700 Love declaration (79x66cm-31x26in) s. 30-Mar-4 Segre, Madrid #26/R est:1500

ALONSO-PEREZ, Mariano (1858-1914) Spanish
£4500 $8280 €6570 Toledo (35x61cm-14x24in) s.i.d.73 panel. 25-Mar-4 Christie's, Kensington #157/R est:5000-7000
Works on paper
£931 $1546 €1350 Gallant scene (32x23cm-13x9in) s. W/C. 30-Sep-3 Ansorena, Madrid #7/R

ALONZI, Robert (1953-) Belgian
£567 $948 €800 La peur (141x136cm-56x54in) s. 15-Oct-3 Hotel des Ventes Mosan, Brussels #260

ALONZO PEREZ, Carlos (19/20th C) Spanish
£1475 $2700 €2154 Scissors grinder (71x58cm-28x23in) s. 5-Jun-4 Treadway Gallery, Cincinnati #551/R est:2000-4000

ALONZO, D (20th C) French
Sculpture
£4832 $8553 €7200 Esclave attachee (28cm-11in) s. pat bronze ivory. 30-Apr-4 Drouot Estimations, Paris #11/R est:1200-1500

ALONZO, Dominique de (19/20th C) French
Sculpture
£1111 $2044 €1665 French noblewoman. s. bronze ivory. 8-Jun-4 Della Rocca, Turin #282/R est:1300-1600
£1379 $2152 €2000 Figure of a lady holding a ribboned staff (30cm-12in) incised sig. bronze. 1-Aug-2 Joel, Victoria #493 est:2000-2500 (A.D 4000)
£2800 $5152 €4200 Enchainee (26cm-10in) s. golden pat bronze ivory. 9-Jun-4 Beaussant & Lefèvre, Paris #265/R est:1800-2000
£3733 $6795 €5600 Guerrier Renaissance (60cm-24in) s.d.1907 pat bronze white marble. 30-Jun-4 Delvaux, Paris #64/R est:3000-4000

ALORDA Y PEREZ, Ramon (1848-1899) Spanish
Works on paper
£319 $543 €460 Seascape with boats (55x76cm-22x30in) s. W/C. 28-Oct-3 Segre, Madrid #17/R

ALOTT, R (19/20th C) ?
£1711 $3147 €2600 Coastal landscape (16x35cm-6x14in) s. board. 23-Jun-4 Finarte Semenzato, Rome #87/R est:3000-3500

ALOTT, Robert (1850-1910) Austrian
£574 $930 €832 Girl with pigeons, ruins and palace in background (39x26cm-15x10in) s,. 4-Aug-3 Rasmussen, Vejle #360/R (D.KR 6000)
£1200 $2160 €1800 Lively square in Northern Italian village (48x32cm-19x13in) s.d.1908. 26-Apr-4 Rieber, Stuttgart #864/R est:1980
£1389 $2264 €2000 Naples (20x46cm-8x18in) s. masonite. 23-Sep-3 Wiener Kunst Auktionen, Vienna #7/R est:1500-2000
£1527 $2841 €2229 Town by river, mountains in background (31x57cm-12x22in) s.d.1880 panel. 2-Mar-4 Rasmussen, Copenhagen #1345/R est:10000 (D.KR 17000)
£1528 $2521 €2200 Southern Italian landscape (31x57cm-12x22in) s. panel. 3-Jul-3 Van Ham, Cologne #1045/R est:2200
£1867 $3397 €2800 Park in Rome with figures (102x73cm-40x29in) s.d.1902. 30-Jun-4 Neumeister, Munich #494/R est:3000
£1958 $3329 €2800 Southern landscape with Italian woman (68x55cm-27x22in) s.d.1904. 24-Nov-3 Dorotheum, Vienna #220/R est:3000-3600
£2083 $3479 €3000 Southern coastal city (87x50cm-34x20in) s.d.1902 panel lit. double-sided. 25-Oct-3 Bergmann, Erlangen #945/R est:2500
£3056 $5042 €4400 Southern Italian coastal village (55x68cm-22x27in) s.d.1895. 3-Jul-3 Van Ham, Cologne #1046/R est:4500
£4027 $7208 €6000 Fishing in the Bay of Naples (58x89cm-23x35in) s.d.1880. 27-May-4 Dorotheum, Vienna #229/R est:6000-8000
£4196 $7133 €6000 Naples (48x74cm-19x29in) s.d.1901. 24-Nov-3 Dorotheum, Vienna #13/R est:6000-7000
£7692 $13077 €11000 Women selling flowers on the Via Appia (73x100cm-29x39in) s. 24-Nov-3 Dorotheum, Vienna #136/R est:3400-4000

ALOTT, Rudolf (attrib) (19th C) French
£750 $1275 €1095 Peasants and figures on a street (29x46cm-11x18in) indis.sig. 26-Nov-3 Hamptons Fine Art, Godalming #132a

ALPER, Nathalie (20th C) American
£301 $550 €452 Bright passage (137x1300cm-54x512in) s.i.d.1982 verso. 31-Jul-4 Sloans & Kenyon, Bethesda #292/R

ALPERT, Alexander (1896-?) American?
£375 $600 €548 Abstract (61x41cm-24x16in) s. board. 21-Sep-3 William Jenack, New York #260

ALPUY, Julio (1919-) Uruguayan
£2683 $4400 €3917 Composition Zepellin (46x38cm-18x15in) s.d.50 cardboard. 3-Jun-3 Galeria y Remates, Montevideo #74
£4667 $8587 €7000 Homme et cheval (35x43cm-14x17in) s. cardboard. 9-Jun-4 Tajan, Paris #28/R est:8000-10000
£5588 $9500 €8158 El arbol de la vida (122x96cm-48x38in) s.d.75 prov. 19-Nov-3 Sotheby's, New York #140/R est:10000-15000
£8696 $16000 €12696 Town (64x84cm-25x33in) prov. 22-Jun-4 Galeria y Remates, Montevideo #98/R est:18000-20000
£10294 $17500 €15029 Composition with figures (82x121cm-32x48in) s.d.1950 exhib. 25-Nov-3 Galeria y Remates, Montevideo #52/R
£15363 $27500 €22430 Untitled (80x50cm-31x20in) s.d.50 board. 26-May-4 Sotheby's, New York #16/R est:20000-25000

ALS, Peder (1725-1776) Danish
£14178 $24527 €20700 Princess Louise with dog at her side (77x62cm-30x24in) prov. 9-Dec-3 Rasmussen, Copenhagen #1209/R est:100000-125000 (D.KR 150000)

ALS, Peder (attrib) (1725-1776) Danish
£1890 $3270 €2759 Knight of the Grand Cross (79x62cm-31x24in) 9-Dec-3 Rasmussen, Copenhagen #1379/R est:25000 (D.KR 20000)

ALSINA, J (19/20th C) French
£994 $1600 €1451 Game of billiards (33x46cm-13x18in) s. 14-Jan-4 Christie's, Rockefeller NY #8/R est:1500-2000
£4305 $7877 €6500 L'oasis (37x53cm-15x21in) s. 9-Apr-4 Claude Aguttes, Neuilly #123/R est:6000-8000

ALSINA, Jacques (19/20th C) French
£3741 $6697 €5500 Campement pres de l riviere (43x58cm-17x23in) s. canvas on panel. 21-Mar-4 St-Germain-en-Laye Encheres #30/R est:4500-5000

ALSINA, Jose (19/20th C) ?
£1141 $2019 €1700 Palm reading (50x66cm-20x26in) s. 27-Apr-4 Durán, Madrid #192/R est:1700
£10000 $18301 €15000 La vie au bord de l'Oued (54x74cm-21x29in) s. 3-Jun-4 Tajan, Paris #213/R est:15000-18000
£10638 $17766 €15000 Famille de nomades (46x61cm-18x24in) s. 16-Jun-3 Gros & Delettrez, Paris #96/R est:10000-15000

ALSLOOT, Denis van (c.1570-1628) Dutch
£54667 $97853 €82000 Extensive winter river landscape with the Flight into Egypt (50x64cm-20x25in) panel prov.exhib. 17-May-4 Christie's, Amsterdam #73/R est:80000-120000
Works on paper
£3500 $6405 €5110 Heavily wooded landscape with a distant castle by a stream (22x34cm-9x13in) bears attrib pen brown ink brown blue wash prov. 8-Jul-4 Sotheby's, London #18/R est:4000-6000

ALSLOOT, Denis van (circle) (c.1570-1628) Dutch
£6993 $12028 €10000 La conversion de Saint Hubert (39x31cm-15x12in) copper. 3-Dec-3 Palais de Beaux Arts, Brussels #678/R est:10000-13000

ALSOP, Adele (20th C) American
£300 $537 €438 West Cardinal Point of the Eagle (127x152cm-50x60in) s.d.82. 18-Mar-4 Christie's, Kensington #686/R

ALSTON, Edward Constable (?-1939) British
£750 $1388 €1095 Pan and Syrinx (127x60cm-50x24in) s. 13-Jan-4 Bonhams, Knightsbridge #324/R

ALSTON, Frederick Cornelius (1895-?) American
£782 $1400 €1142 Knight shift (91x71cm-36x28in) one i.d.1920 verso one s. i.verso one oil one W/C gouache board 2. 7-May-4 Sloans & Kenyon, Bethesda #1623/R

ALT, Duane (1935-) American
£3727 $6000 €5404 L'apres-midi a Portofino (76x127cm-30x50in) 22-Aug-3 Altermann Galleries, Santa Fe #158

ALT, Franz (1821-1914) Austrian
£2148 $3844 €3200 Peasants in a winter landscape (22x28cm-9x11in) s.d.1840. 27-May-4 Dorotheum, Vienna #144/R est:3000-3500
Works on paper
£276 $458 €400 Portrait of young woman in chair (17x13cm-7x5in) s.d.27 Juli 1847 W/C pencil. 30-Sep-3 Dorotheum, Vienna #140/R
£347 $549 €500 Rocky coastal landscape (18x24cm-7x9in) s. W/C. 5-Sep-3 Wendl, Rudolstadt #3252/R
£490 $832 €700 Jungfrau from Interlaken (19x27cm-7x11in) s.i.d. W/C board. 21-Nov-3 Reiss & Sohn, Konigstein #161/R
£946 $1693 €1400 Living room. Dining room (25x32cm-10x13in) s.d.1892 W/C pair. 6-May-4 Michael Zeller, Lindau #565/R
£1379 $2290 €2000 Schloss Klehsheim near Salzburg (24x34cm-9x13in) s.d.1884 W/C. 30-Sep-3 Dorotheum, Vienna #233/R est:4000-4500
£1655 $2748 €2400 Vegetable market outside Como Cathedral (19x17cm-7x7in) s.d.Juli 1884 W/C. 30-Sep-3 Dorotheum, Vienna #222/R est:2400-2600
£2013 $3604 €3000 Naples, Castelmare (23x32cm-9x13in) s.i.d.853 W/C. 27-May-4 Hassfurther, Vienna #30/R est:3000-4000
£2282 $4199 €3400 Jungfrau from Interlaken (19x28cm-7x11in) s.d.1867 W/C. 26-Mar-4 Dorotheum, Vienna #186/R est:2000-2500
£3056 $5042 €4400 Rusian city - possibly Moscow (41x58cm-16x23in) s.d.1855 W/C htd white gold. 2-Jul-3 Neumeister, Munich #435/R est:3000
£3448 $5724 €5000 Aachen Munster with Palace Chapel (35x34cm-14x13in) s.i.d.30.Juni 1881 W/C. 30-Sep-3 Dorotheum, Vienna #232/R est:4000-4500
£3691 $6534 €5500 Hofburg (14x23cm-6x9in) s.d.1894 W/C prov. 28-Apr-4 Wiener Kunst Auktionen, Vienna #21/R est:5500-12000
£3793 $6297 €5500 Regensburg (25x35cm-10x14in) s.i.d.1881 W/C. 30-Sep-3 Dorotheum, Vienna #234/R est:5000-5500

ALT, Jacob (1789-1872) German
£4110 $6411 €6000 Mountain stream (27x34cm-11x13in) s. panel. 10-Apr-3 Weidler, Nurnberg #302/R est:10000
£4545 $7727 €6500 Entrance to Noonberg convent in Salzburg (30x23cm-12x9in) s.d.1850. 24-Nov-3 Dorotheum, Vienna #71/R est:7000-9000
Works on paper
£2500 $4125 €3600 Rider with dog in Upper Austrian landscape (22x19cm-9x7in) s.d.1854 W/C over pencil htd white. 2-Jul-3 Neumeister, Munich #436/R est:2200
£2715 $4507 €3964 Main square of Kassa, Kosice (15x20cm-6x8in) s. W/C. 4-Oct-3 Kieselbach, Budapest #59/R (H.F 1000000)

ALT, Otmar (1940-) German
£322 $547 €460 Woodland scene (70x50cm-28x20in) s.d.60. 28-Nov-3 Wendl, Rudolstadt #3904/R
£1181 $1972 €1700 Colourful cow IV (50x40cm-20x16in) s.d. s.i.d. verso acrylic panel. 25-Oct-3 Dr Lehr, Berlin #12/R est:2000
£1224 $2080 €1750 Dracula (65x54cm-26x21in) s.d. i. stretcher. 29-Nov-3 Bassenge, Berlin #6603/R est:2500
£1333 $2440 €2000 Untitled - portrait (76x57cm-30x22in) s.d.89 acrylic board prov.lit. 4-Jun-4 Lempertz, Koln #4/R est:2000
£1620 $2802 €2300 Enchanted professor (80x60cm-31x24in) s.d.68 s.i. stretcher acrylic. 13-Dec-3 Lempertz, Koln #109/R est:3000
£2098 $3566 €3000 Swan fairy and colourful dog (80x56cm-31x22in) s.d.1966 s.i. stretcher. 27-Nov-3 Lempertz, Koln #7/R est:3500-4000
Sculpture
£1818 $3091 €2600 Sledge people (57x63x67cm-22x25x26in) s.d.69 brown gold pat.bronze exhib.lit. 27-Nov-3 Lempertz, Koln #6/R est:3000-4000
Works on paper
£629 $1083 €900 Moon over (41x32cm-16x13in) s.i.d.1975 gouache pencil. 4-Dec-3 Van Ham, Cologne #7

ALT, Rudolf von (1812-1905) Austrian
£2550 $4693 €3800 Troppau (12x19cm-5x7in) s.i. W/C. 26-Mar-4 Dorotheum, Vienna #176/R est:6000-8000
£21477 $38013 €32000 Reichenau (21x30cm-8x12in) s.i.d.8.Juni 876 W/C. 28-Apr-4 Wiener Kunst Auktionen, Vienna #22/R est:35000-50000
Works on paper
£537 $988 €800 Regensburg (31x23cm-12x9in) s.i. pencil sketch verso. 26-Mar-4 Dorotheum, Vienna #67/R
£556 $928 €800 Tower (17x6cm-7x2in) s.i. pencil board. 24-Oct-3 Ketterer, Hamburg #41/R
£4310 $7931 €6293 Tomb of Friedrich III in St Stephen's Cathedral, Vienna (33x45cm-13x18in) s.d.852 gouache. 26-Mar-4 Koller, Zurich #3128/R est:10000-15000 (S.FR 10000)

£6897	$12689	€10070	Livadia, Castle, on the Crimea (26x39cm-10x15in) s.i. W/C. 26-Mar-4 Koller, Zurich #3130/R est:15000-25000 (S.FR 16000)
£7639	$12986	€11000	Interior of Palais Windisch Graetz (23x30cm-9x12in) s.d.1848 W/C prov. 28-Oct-3 Wiener Kunst Auktionen, Vienna #31/R est:7000-12000
£13889	$23611	€20000	Schloss Chotzen (37x54cm-15x21in) s.i.d.884 w/C. 28-Oct-3 Wiener Kunst Auktionen, Vienna #33/R est:15000-50000
£13889	$23611	€20000	Interior in Palais Windisch Graetz (24x32cm-9x13in) s.d.1848 W/C prov. 28-Oct-3 Wiener Kunst Auktionen, Vienna #32/R est:7000-12000
£21477	$38013	€32000	Prague Cathedral (15x21cm-6x8in) s.d.1839 i. verso W/C prov. 28-Apr-4 Wiener Kunst Auktionen, Vienna #23/R est:22000-50000
£22819	$41987	€34000	Vienna (19x28cm-7x11in) s.d.1885 W/C. 26-Mar-4 Dorotheum, Vienna #190/R est:30000-35000
£23490	$41577	€35000	Town with figures and horse drawn carriages (14x21cm-6x8in) s.d.859 prov. 28-Apr-4 Wiener Kunst Auktionen, Vienna #19/R est:22000-50000
£25000	$45500	€36500	St Mark's Venice (28x39cm-11x15in) s. pencil W/C htd white. 17-Jun-4 Christie's, London #91/R est:30000-40000
£26207	$43503	€38000	Nerva Forum in Rome (38x45cm-15x18in) s.d.7.Dezember 865 W/C lit.exhib. 30-Sep-3 Dorotheum, Vienna #241/R est:35000-40000
£39860	$67762	€57000	View of Stephansdom (20x12cm-8x5in) s.d.1847 W/C. 25-Nov-3 Hassfurther, Vienna #14/R est:55000-60000
£111111	$188889	€160000	Street (37x51cm-15x20in) s.d.887 W/C paper/board. 28-Oct-3 Wiener Kunst Auktionen, Vienna #30/R est:80000-250000

ALT, Rudolf von (attrib) (1812-1905) Austrian

Works on paper

£671	$1235	€1000	Country house on a tributary of the Dona (30x45cm-12x18in) s.i. W/C on pencil. 26-Mar-4 Bolland & Marotz, Bremen #389/R
£8725	$15617	€13000	Moon lake (24x33cm-9x13in) i.d.19.Sept 1849 W/C. 27-May-4 Dorotheum, Graz #91/R est:600

ALT, Theodor (1846-1937) Austrian

£1944	$3169	€2800	Still life with grapes, apples, pears and nuts (32x39cm-13x15in) s. prov. 24-Sep-3 Neumeister, Munich #383/R est:4000

ALTAMIRANO, Arturo Pacheco (1905-) Chilean

£455	$800	€664	Fishing boats (45x61cm-18x24in) s. prov. 5-Jan-4 Galeria y Remates, Montevideo #95/R
£682	$1200	€996	Marina, Chile (64x91cm-25x36in) s. painted c.1960. 23-May-4 Treadway Gallery, Cincinnati #590/R
£898	$1500	€1311	Seascape (53x66cm-21x26in) s. painted 1971. 13-Jul-3 Subastas Odalys, Caracas #54 est:5000
£2725	$4550	€3979	Fishermen (60x73cm-24x29in) s. 13-Jul-3 Subastas Odalys, Caracas #93/R est:5000

ALTAMURA, Jean (1852-1878) Greek

£6500	$11635	€9490	Sailing off the coast (22x29cm-9x11in) s. paper on board prov. 10-May-4 Sotheby's, Olympia #161/R est:3000-5000

ALTAMURA, Jean (attrib) (1852-1878) Greek

£5200	$9100	€7592	After the storm (38x55cm-15x22in) s. 16-Dec-3 Bonhams, New Bond Street #68/R est:3000-5000

ALTAMURA, Saverio (1826-1897) Italian

£2465	$4264	€3500	Nelson reading (29x22cm-11x9in) s.i.verso. 11-Dec-3 Christie's, Rome #94/R est:2000-3000
£2587	$4399	€3700	Portrait of Garibaldi (46x66cm-18x26in) s. i.d.1890 verso lit. 28-Nov-3 Schloss Ahlden, Ahlden #1426/R est:2800

ALTDORFER, Albrecht (circle) (1480-1538) German

£22000	$37400	€32120	Portrait of a cleric holding a book (35x26cm-14x10in) i.verso panel prov.exhib.lit. 29-Oct-3 Christie's, London #48/R est:15000-25000

ALTEN, Mathias Joseph (1871-1938) German

£516	$950	€753	Landscape with a house (20x25cm-8x10in) s. board. 26-Jun-4 Susanin's, Chicago #6040/R
£806	$1500	€1177	Autumn landscape (28x33cm-11x13in) s.d.1900. 3-Mar-4 Christie's, Rockefeller NY #40/R est:1200-1800
£1132	$1800	€1653	Landscape with herd of sheep (29x42cm-11x17in) s. canvas on panel. 13-Sep-3 Weschler, Washington #762/R est:1000-1500
£1163	$2000	€1698	Fire of fall (35x40cm-14x16in) s. canvas on masonite painted c.1905. 3-Dec-3 Doyle, New York #200/R est:5000-7000
£1384	$2200	€2021	Katwick (30x42cm-12x17in) s.i. canvas on panel. 13-Sep-3 Weschler, Washington #763/R est:1000-1500
£1397	$2500	€2040	Loading the boat (46x61cm-18x24in) indis.sig. 8-Jan-4 James Julia, Fairfield #733/R est:4000-6000
£1429	$2700	€2086	Two plough horses in rolling terrain (23x30cm-9x12in) s.d.1913 canvas on board. 21-Feb-4 Brunk, Ashville #539/R est:500-1000
£1657	$3000	€2419	Rocky shore, Saugatuck (33x23cm-13x9in) board painted c.1913. 16-Apr-4 Du Mouchelle, Detroit #2076/R est:2500-3500
£1761	$2800	€2571	Washerwoman beside a cottage (30x44cm-12x17in) s.i. canvas on panel. 13-Sep-3 Weschler, Washington #764/R est:1000-1500
£1795	$3250	€2621	Little Dutch girl (30x41cm-12x16in) s. board. 16-Apr-4 James Julia, Fairfield #664/R est:3000-5000
£2516	$4000	€3673	Valencia (30x45cm-12x18in) s.i.d.1912 canvas on panel. 13-Sep-3 Weschler, Washington #761/R est:1000-1500
£4233	$8000	€6180	Shore scene with two oxen pulling boat (30x43cm-12x17in) s. canvasboard. 21-Feb-4 Brunk, Ashville #288/R est:2000-4000
£8982	$15000	€13114	Woods with stream (76x97cm-30x38in) 17-Oct-3 Du Mouchelle, Detroit #2012/R est:15000-20000

ALTENBOURG, Gerhard (1926-1989) German

Works on paper

£1806	$3015	€2600	The smile (28x31cm-11x12in) s.mono.i.d. W/C lithographic chk ochre pencil. 25-Oct-3 Dr Lehr, Berlin #13/R est:3000
£2667	$4800	€4000	Gerhard Ernst (200x160cm-79x63in) mono. W/C litho. 24-Apr-4 Dr Lehr, Berlin #11/R est:6000
£2958	$4910	€4200	Hill of heads (21x15cm-8x6in) mono. s.i.d.1971 verso W/C. 13-Jun-3 Hauswedell & Nolte, Hamburg #511/R est:3000
£3000	$5370	€4500	Stripped glance (64x26cm-25x10in) s.d. i. verso W/C on pencil pastel. 15-May-4 Dr Sturies, Dusseldorf #1/R
£8333	$15250	€12500	Composition (67x49cm-26x19in) s.d.1988 pastel W/C gouache graphite chk chl sepia pencil. 4-Jun-4 Lempertz, Koln #7/R est:12000

ALTENKIRCH, Otto (1875-1945) German

£470	$832	€700	Winter landscape (46x58cm-18x23in) s. 30-Apr-4 Dr Fritz Nagel, Stuttgart #23/R
£833	$1392	€1200	Landscape with stream (58x79cm-23x31in) s.d.1928. 22-Oct-3 Neumeister, Munich #663/R
£1115	$1996	€1650	Landscape with pond and mill (68x80cm-27x31in) s. 6-May-4 Michael Zeller, Lindau #566/R est:900
£1319	$2203	€1900	Timbered houses under trees (86x85cm-34x33in) s. 22-Oct-3 Neumeister, Munich #662/R est:1200

ALTENKOPF, Joseph (1818-1855) Austrian

£455	$773	€650	Arcadian landscape with temple ruins and lovers (38x51cm-15x20in) s.d.1854. 29-Nov-3 Sigalas, Stuttgart #264/R

ALTERMANN, Horst (1925-1978) German

£403	$741	€600	Lake Garda in sunshine (80x100cm-31x39in) s. 25-Mar-4 Karlheinz Kaupp, Staufen #2330/R
£436	$811	€650	Interior celebration scene in a large ballroom (70x100cm-28x39in) s. i.verso. 5-Mar-4 Wendl, Rudolstadt #3554/R
£621	$1148	€900	Fox hunt (68x98cm-27x39in) s. 12-Feb-4 Weidler, Nurnberg #4505/R

ALTHAUS, Fritz (fl.1881-1914) British

Works on paper

£250	$425	€365	Oyster catchers on the shore (24x42cm-9x17in) s. W/C. 25-Nov-3 Bonhams, Knowle #151
£340	$578	€496	Fishing boats in calm waters (29x44cm-11x17in) s.d.1900 W/C. 25-Nov-3 Bonhams, Knowle #164
£350	$595	€511	Kirkstall Abbey, during snow storm, March (30x44cm-12x17in) s.i. pencil W/C. 19-Nov-3 Tennants, Leyburn #889
£400	$736	€584	Shepherd driving his flock through a town (25x36cm-10x14in) s.d.1902 pencil W/C. 25-Mar-4 Christie's, Kensington #133/R

ALTHERR, Paul (1870-1928) Swiss

£452	$769	€660	Two nude boys in summer landscape (81x60cm-32x24in) mono. 28-Nov-3 Zofingen, Switzerland #2887/R (S.FR 1000)

ALTIDOR, Alfred (?) Haitian

£299	$475	€437	Ball at Sans Souci Palace (50x60cm-20x24in) s. masonite prov. 13-Sep-3 Weschler, Washington #718/R

ALTINK, Jan (1885-1975) Dutch

£1224	$2229	€1800	Still life with anemones in a bottle (40x30cm-16x12in) s.d.40. 3-Feb-4 Christie's, Amsterdam #436/R est:2000-3000
£3000	$5490	€4500	Gronings landscape with a horse in front of a farm (48x59cm-19x23in) s.d.45. 7-Jun-4 Glerum, Amsterdam #110/R est:8000-12000
£3000	$5490	€4500	Farmer in front of his farm in a Gronings landscape (59x79cm-23x31in) s.d.40. 7-Jun-4 Glerum, Amsterdam #114/R est:9000-12000
£6993	$11888	€10000	Farmyard with haystack (50x60cm-20x24in) s.d.40 prov. 25-Nov-3 Christie's, Amsterdam #164/R est:6000-8000

Works on paper

£612	$1114	€900	Farmyard (30x47cm-12x19in) s.d.47 black chk W/C. 3-Feb-4 Christie's, Amsterdam #438
£6333	$11653	€9500	Portrait of Hendrick Werkman (40x30cm-16x12in) waxpaint prov. 8-Jun-4 Sotheby's, Amsterdam #183/R est:8000-12000
£13333	$24533	€20000	Sunflowers in a vase (60x54cm-24x21in) s.d.27 wax paint canvas. 9-Jun-4 Christie's, Amsterdam #201/R est:20000-25000

ALTMAN, Dirk Gerardus (1839-1896) Dutch

£952	$1705	€1400	Indonesian landscape with horse and dog (34x45cm-13x18in) s.d.2/87. 16-Mar-4 Christie's, Amsterdam #7/R est:800-1200

ALTMANN, Alexandre (1885-1950) Russian

£2000	$3400	€2920	River bank (71x58cm-28x23in) s. 19-Nov-3 Sotheby's, London #112/R est:2000-3000
£2600	$4576	€3796	Still life of red flowers (25x28cm-10x11in) s. board. 18-May-4 Bonhams, Knightsbridge #183/R est:400-600
£2857	$5114	€4200	Le sous-bois (50x65cm-20x26in) s.d.1909. 19-Mar-4 Ribeyre & Baron, Paris #76 est:600-800
£3378	$5946	€5000	Landscape (73x59cm-29x23in) s. 19-May-4 Camard, Paris #38 est:5000-7000
£3649	$6750	€5328	Coastal scene with mountains and village (46x71cm-18x28in) s. 17-Jan-4 New Orleans Auction, New Orleans #511/R est:2000-4000
£3800	$6916	€5700	Massif de fleurs (46x55cm-18x22in) s. 4-Jul-4 Eric Pillon, Calais #223/R
£4800	$8592	€7008	Mother with her children (45x27cm-18x11in) s.d.1907. 26-May-4 Sotheby's, Olympia #371/R est:2000-3000
£4930	$8528	€7000	Jetee de fleurs (55x37cm-22x15in) s. 14-Dec-3 Eric Pillon, Calais #130/R
£4967	$9040	€7500	Sous bois (46x61cm-18x24in) 16-Jun-4 Claude Boisgirard, Paris #19/R est:8000-9000
£5667	$10313	€8500	Still life with summer flowers (50x61cm-20x24in) s. oval. 1-Jul-4 Van Ham, Cologne #1196/R est:1800
£6500	$11635	€9490	Vase of flowers (65x50cm-26x20in) s.i. 26-May-4 Sotheby's, Olympia #434/R est:2000-3000
£6897	$12414	€10000	Allee dans la foret (81x60cm-32x24in) s. 25-Jan-4 Chayette & Cheval, Paris #174/R est:4500-5000
£6954	$12656	€10500	Bercy quays (54x65cm-21x26in) s.d.1909. 15-Jun-4 Rossini, Paris #60/R est:4000-6000
£7000	$12530	€10220	Autumn trees on the riverbank (38x55cm-15x22in) s. 26-May-4 Sotheby's, London #184/R est:7000-9000
£7047	$13037	€10500	Moret sur Loing (46x61cm-18x24in) s. 15-Mar-4 Claude Boisgirard, Paris #6/R est:4000-4500

£7383 $13732 €11000 La mer (54x65cm-21x26in) s. prov. 2-Mar-4 Artcurial Briest, Paris #158/R est:4000-5000
£7500 $12750 €10950 Flower arrangement in a ceramic jug (55x38cm-22x15in) s. 19-Nov-3 Sotheby's, London #228/R est:3000-4000
£7778 $14000 €11356 Spring landscape (54x74cm-21x29in) s. 23-Apr-4 Sotheby's, New York #57/R est:15000-20000
£9000 $15300 €13140 The Bridge (71x58cm-28x23in) s. 19-Nov-3 Sotheby's, London #110/R est:3000-5000
£9000 $16110 €13500 Bouquet de fleurs sauvages (65x50cm-26x20in) s. 17-May-4 Chayette & Cheval, Paris #131/R est:6000-8000
£9061 $16037 €13500 Paysage a la riviere, le barrage (61x81cm-24x32in) s. 27-Apr-4 Artcurial Briest, Paris #144/R est:8000-10000
£9091 $15636 €13000 Bord d'etang (73x60cm-29x24in) s. 3-Dec-3 Tajan, Paris #367 est:3000-5000
£9239 $16537 €13489 Garden in full bloom (73x60cm-29x24in) s. 28-May-4 Uppsala Auktionskammare, Uppsala #180/R est:15000-18000 (S.KR 125000)
£9272 $16874 €14000 Two trees by the water (61x50cm-24x20in) s. 15-Jun-4 Rossini, Paris #63/R est:2500-3500
£9333 $16707 €14000 House by the river (50x61cm-20x24in) s. painted 1911. 17-May-4 Chayette & Cheval, Paris #141/R est:7000-9000
£10526 $19368 €16000 Vue de Bosphore (55x46cm-22x18in) s. panel. 28-Jun-4 Joron-Derem, Paris #116/R est:5000-6000
£11000 $18700 €16060 River landscape (81x65cm-32x26in) s. 19-Nov-3 Sotheby's, London #109/R est:5000-7000
£11000 $18700 €16060 Bridge over the canal (62x50cm-24x20in) s. 19-Nov-3 Sotheby's, London #111/R est:4000-5000
£11000 $18700 €16060 Rushes by the river (65x81cm-26x32in) s. 19-Nov-3 Sotheby's, London #127/R est:4000-5000
£11379 $20483 €16500 Paysage de neige (100x171cm-39x67in) s. 25-Jan-4 Chayette & Cheval, Paris #177/R est:5000-6000
£11921 $21695 €18000 Washerwomen at the river (65x54cm-26x21in) s. 15-Jun-4 Rossini, Paris #61/R est:3000-4000
£13000 $23270 €18980 Autumn landscape (53x73cm-21x29in) s. 26-May-4 Sotheby's, Olympia #394/R est:3000-5000
£13333 $24000 €20000 Ferme au bord d'un canal (40x70cm-16x28in) s. 26-Apr-4 Tajan, Paris #125/R est:3500-4500
£14000 $23800 €20440 Mountain village in autumn (66x81cm-26x32in) s. 19-Nov-3 Sotheby's, London #113/R est:3000-4000
£14000 $23800 €20440 Landscape in the South of France (57x73cm-22x29in) s. 19-Nov-3 Sotheby's, London #122/R est:3000-4000
£14615 $25138 €21338 Le bateau de Sainte Maxime (73x60cm-29x24in) s. i.verso. 3-Dec-3 AB Stockholms Auktionsverk #2593/R est:75000-100000 (S.KR 190000)
£15000 $26850 €21900 In the valley of Saint Germain (54x65cm-21x26in) s. 26-May-4 Sotheby's, London #177/R est:8000-12000
£15000 $26850 €21900 Riverside landscape (65x81cm-26x32in) s. 26-May-4 Sotheby's, Olympia #484/R est:4000-6000
£15172 $27310 €22000 Paysage (50x61cm-20x24in) s. 25-Jan-4 Chayette & Cheval, Paris #168/R est:4500-5000
£16000 $28640 €23360 Trees in snow (81x60cm-32x24in) s. 26-May-4 Sotheby's, London #173/R est:6000-8000
£17000 $28900 €24820 Winter landscape (81x81cm-32x32in) s. 19-Nov-3 Sotheby's, London #108/R est:4000-5000
£17000 $30430 €24820 By the river (73x53cm-29x21in) s. 26-May-4 Sotheby's, London #174/R est:7000-9000
£17000 $30430 €24820 Village on the Canal (73x92cm-29x36in) s. 26-May-4 Sotheby's, London #178/R est:8000-12000
£17219 $31338 €26000 Garden in bloom (54x65cm-21x26in) s.d.1930. 15-Jun-4 Rossini, Paris #62/R est:3000-4000
£18000 $32220 €26280 Composition with flowers by a window (50x65cm-20x26in) s.d.1909. 26-May-4 Sotheby's, London #180/R est:7000-9000
£20000 $34000 €29200 Villa with red shutters (92x73cm-36x29in) s. 19-Nov-3 Sotheby's, London #130/R est:5000-7000
£20000 $35800 €29200 By the river (65x81cm-26x32in) s. 26-May-4 Sotheby's, London #185/R est:6000-8000
£20000 $35800 €29200 Villa, Paris (51x42cm-20x17in) s.i.d.1907. 26-May-4 Sotheby's, London #181/R est:8000-12000
£20833 $37500 €30416 Port du midi avec fleurs et bateaux (81x101cm-32x40in) s. 23-Apr-4 Sotheby's, New York #55/R est:15000-20000
£22000 $37400 €32120 Garden path in autumn (90x72cm-35x28in) s. 19-Nov-3 Sotheby's, London #129/R est:8000-12000
£23611 $42500 €34472 Landscape by the water's edge (73x51cm-29x20in) s. 23-Apr-4 Sotheby's, New York #56/R est:18000-25000
£24000 $42960 €35040 Snowy landscape (100x172cm-39x68in) s. 26-May-4 Sotheby's, London #183/R est:10000-15000
£26000 $46540 €37960 Rocky shore (98x146cm-39x57in) s.d.1913. 26-May-4 Sotheby's, London #175/R est:8000-12000
£60000 $107400 €87600 Tree by the lake in winter (116x87cm-46x34in) s. 26-May-4 Sotheby's, London #179/R est:6000-8000
Works on paper
£476 $852 €700 Portrait de jeune femme de profil (50x30cm-20x12in) s. pastel. 19-Mar-4 Ribeyre & Baron, Paris #77
£1267 $2267 €1900 Bouquet (41x36cm-16x14in) s. W/C. 17-May-4 Chayette & Cheval, Paris #132 est:2000-2500

ALTMANN, Anton (younger) (1808-1871) Austrian
£662 $1212 €1000 Wash day behind house (39x31cm-15x12in) s.d.837 panel. 8-Apr-4 Dorotheum, Vienna #126
Works on paper
£805 $1482 €1200 Organ grinder (42x32cm-17x13in) s.d.862 W/C. 26-Mar-4 Dorotheum, Vienna #192/R

ALTMANN, Gerard (1877-1940) Dutch
£413 $739 €603 River landscape with figure loading a barge (44x70cm-17x28in) s. 31-May-4 Stephan Welz, Johannesburg #67 (SA.R 5000)
£658 $1191 €1000 Cows in the meadow with willows on the left along the canal (30x45cm-12x18in) s. 19-Apr-4 Glerum, Amsterdam #202/R
£1275 $2359 €1900 Milking time (40x60cm-16x24in) s. sold with a landscape by Willem Noordijk. 15-Mar-4 Sotheby's, Amsterdam #122/R est:1000-1500

ALTMANN, Nathan (1889-1970) Israeli
£15000 $25950 €21900 Portrait of a woman holding red roses (89x69cm-35x27in) s.d.1922 prov. 11-Dec-3 Christie's, Kensington #54/R est:3000-5000

ALTMANN, Nathan (attrib) (1889-1970) Israeli
Works on paper
£604 $1100 €882 Man with hat (43x33cm-17x13in) chl. 8-Feb-4 William Jenack, New York #320/R

ALTMANN, Sybrand (1822-1890) Dutch
£759 $1267 €1100 Saleswoman at the door (24x20cm-9x8in) s. panel. 11-Nov-3 Vendu Notarishuis, Rotterdam #149

ALTOMONTE, Martino (1657-1745) Italian
£8000 $13840 €11680 Holy Family (99x73cm-39x29in) painted oval. 10-Dec-3 Bonhams, New Bond Street #41/R est:6000-8000
Works on paper
£400 $716 €600 Study of three putti (20x30cm-8x12in) i. chk. 13-May-4 Bassenge, Berlin #5350/R

ALTON, Lois (1894-1972) Austrian
£326 $597 €476 Summer flowers (60x50cm-24x20in) s. board. 4-Jun-4 Zofingen, Switzerland #2414 (S.FR 750)
£800 $1472 €1200 Oberinntal (50x49cm-20x19in) s. board. 9-Jun-4 Dorotheum, Salzburg #609/R

ALTOON, John (1925-1969) American
Works on paper
£552 $1000 €806 Untitled (76x102cm-30x40in) s.d.67 ink paper board. 18-Apr-4 Bonhams & Butterfields, Los Angeles #7095 est:1500-2000
£1130 $2000 €1650 Untitled (76x102cm-30x40in) s.indis.d.6 ink. 2-May-4 Bonhams & Butterfields, Los Angeles #3058/R est:2000-4000

ALTRUI, E (attrib) (19th C) ?
£4469 $8000 €6525 Sorrento (74x112cm-29x44in) i.d.18. 14-May-4 Skinner, Boston #141/R est:5500-6500

ALTSON, Abbey (1864-c.1949) British
£1500 $2550 €2190 Portrait of a young girl in a blue dress (61x51cm-24x20in) s. prov. 19-Nov-3 Tennants, Leyburn #1177/R est:1000-1500
£4000 $6800 €5840 Cool reception (87x112cm-34x44in) s.d.1902. 19-Nov-3 Bonhams, New Bond Street #75/R est:6000-8000

ALTSTADT, Wagner (?) ?
£733 $1333 €1070 Cardinal at his writing desk (38x55cm-15x22in) s. 7-Feb-4 Rasmussen, Havnen #2182/R (D.KR 8000)

ALVAR, Sunol (1935-) Spanish
£775 $1340 €1100 L'assiette de poisson (39x89cm-15x35in) s. 13-Dec-3 Touati, Paris #18/R
£810 $1401 €1150 L'eglise (46x55cm-18x22in) s. s.d.1964 verso. 13-Dec-3 Touati, Paris #17/R
£845 $1462 €1200 Flamenco (55x46cm-22x18in) s. 13-Dec-3 Touati, Paris #16/R
£870 $1600 €1270 Grupo de amistad (130x89cm-51x35in) s. s.i.verso prov. 25-Mar-4 Doyle, New York #83/R est:1200-1600
£880 $1523 €1250 Visage (33x56cm-13x22in) s. 13-Dec-3 Touati, Paris #15/R
£973 $1800 €1421 Nature morte au candelabre (81x51cm-32x20in) s. s.d.62 verso prov. 12-Feb-4 Sotheby's, New York #85/R est:2000-3000
£1092 $1888 €1550 Menine au pigeon (50x61cm-20x24in) s. 13-Dec-3 Touati, Paris #14/R est:1500
£1156 $2070 €1700 Face (33x55cm-13x22in) s. 22-Mar-4 Durán, Madrid #138/R est:1300
£1162 $2010 €1650 Fleurs et cerises (61x50cm-24x20in) s. s.i.d.janvier 1963 verso. 13-Dec-3 Touati, Paris #12/R est:1500
£1162 $2010 €1650 Femme a la colombe (81x60cm-32x24in) s. s.d.68-69 verso. 13-Dec-3 Touati, Paris #13/R est:1500
£1224 $2192 €1800 Dish with fish (39x89cm-15x35in) s. 22-Mar-4 Durán, Madrid #137/R est:1500

ALVARADO, Hugo (1948-) Canadian
Works on paper
£260 $476 €380 Cityscape (48x56cm-19x22in) s.d.1997 mixed media collage. 1-Jun-4 Hodgins, Calgary #158/R (C.D 650)

ALVAREZ AYLLON, Emilio (19/20th C) Spanish
£352 $616 €500 Landscape in Granada (45x25cm-18x10in) s. 16-Dec-3 Durán, Madrid #35/R
£423 $731 €600 Rural landscape (16x29cm-6x11in) s. 15-Dec-3 Ansorena, Madrid #269/R
£582 $990 €850 Seascape (11x21cm-4x8in) s. board. 4-Nov-3 Ansorena, Madrid #335/R
£616 $1048 €900 Beduins (12x21cm-5x8in) s. 4-Nov-3 Ansorena, Madrid #368/R
£1585 $2773 €2250 Horse race (35x80cm-14x31in) s. 16-Dec-3 Durán, Madrid #131/R
£1596 $2665 €2250 Seascape (21x36cm-8x14in) s. 20-Oct-3 Durán, Madrid #96/R

ALVAREZ BASSO, Dario (1968-) Venezuelan
£1818 $3036 €2600 Untitled (100x170cm-39x67in) s.i.d.9.1992 verso oil glaze mixed media canvas. 24-Jun-3 Segre, Madrid #151/R est:1800

ALVAREZ BRAVO, Manuel (1902-2002) Mexican

Photographs

£1795 $3250 €2621 Urinating boy (24x17cm-9x7in) s. platinum print 1927/1980 prov. 19-Apr-4 Bonhams & Butterfields, San Francisco #369/R est:1200-1800
£1795 $3250 €2621 La desuendada (22x16cm-9x6in) s. platinum print 1938/printed later. 19-Apr-4 Bonhams & Butterfields, San Francisco #371/R est:2000-3000
£1795 $3250 €2621 A fish called sword (23x18cm-9x7in) s.verso gelatin silver print 1944/1970. 19-Apr-4 Bonhams & Butterfields, San Francisco #373/R est:2000-3000
£1808 $3200 €2640 Nino Orinando, 1927 (23x16cm-9x6in) s. platinum print lit. 27-Apr-4 Christie's, Rockefeller NY #87 est:4000-6000
£1932 $3400 €2821 Techos de Usila (30x39cm-12x15in) with sig. silver print. 20-May-4 Swann Galleries, New York #433/R est:5000-7000
£1933 $3500 €2822 Retrato de lo eterno (22x18cm-9x7in) s. platinum print 1935/1970. 19-Apr-4 Bonhams & Butterfields, San Francisco #370/R est:3000-5000
£2000 $3580 €3000 Dancers' daughter (24x17cm-9x7in) mono. silver print lit. 13-May-4 Le Mouel, Paris #123/R est:3000-3500
£2147 $3800 €3135 Obrero en Huelga, Asesinado, 1934 (19x25cm-7x10in) s.i. gelatin silver print lit. 27-Apr-4 Christie's, Rockefeller NY #85/R est:5000-7000
£2328 $4400 €3399 Retrato de lo eterno (24x19cm-9x7in) s. verso silver print. 17-Feb-4 Swann Galleries, New York #58/R est:3500-4500
£2401 $4250 €3505 El umbral (24x19cm-9x7in) s.i.num.verso photo printed later prov. 28-Apr-4 Sotheby's, New York #143/R est:5000-7000
£2624 $4750 €3831 La buena fama durmiendo (18x24cm-7x9in) s.verso gelatin silver print 1938/printed later lit. 19-Apr-4 Bonhams & Butterfields, San Francisco #372/R est:3000-5000
£2667 $4773 €4000 Buena Fama (24x18cm-9x7in) s.verso silver print. 13-May-4 Le Mouel, Paris #122/R est:3500-4500
£2695 $4500 €3935 Little horse on ice-cream cart (12x16cm-5x6in) s.i. platinum print exec.1930 printed c.1970. 20-Oct-3 Christie's, Rockefeller NY #56/R est:5000-7000
£2778 $5000 €4056 El ensueno (24x18cm-9x7in) s. gelatin silver print on board prov.lit. 23-Apr-4 Phillips, New York #121/R est:6000-8000
£2800 $4760 €4088 El trapo negro- black cloth (24x18cm-9x7in) init.verso gelatin silver print. 18-Nov-3 Christie's, Kensington #166/R est:2000-3000
£2844 $4750 €4152 Espejo negro (33x25cm-13x10in) s.i.verso photo exec.1947 printed later prov. 17-Oct-3 Sotheby's, New York #140/R est:1500-2500
£3293 $5500 €4808 Good reputation sleeping (19x25cm-7x10in) s.num.34/75 i.verso gelatin silver print exec.1939/1974 lit. 20-Oct-3 Christie's, Rockefeller NY #55/R est:4000-6000
£3439 $6500 €5021 Magueyes Heridos (29x37cm-11x15in) s. i. verso silver print. 17-Feb-4 Swann Galleries, New York #76/R est:6000-8000
£3672 $6500 €5361 Selected images (19x24cm-7x9in) one s.num.ac/v one s.i.verso photo 2 printed later prov. 28-Apr-4 Sotheby's, New York #142/R est:5000-7000
£3889 $7000 €5678 Obstracles (19x24cm-7x9in) s. gelatin silver print prov.lit. 23-Apr-4 Phillips, New York #202/R est:7000-10000
£3892 $6500 €5682 La buena fama durmiendo (18x24cm-7x9in) s.i.verso photo exec.1938 printed later. 17-Oct-3 Sotheby's, New York #214/R est:5000-7000
£3955 $7000 €5774 La buena fama durmiendo (17x24cm-7x9in) s.i.verso photo printed later. 28-Apr-4 Sotheby's, New York #141/R est:5000-7000
£3955 $7000 €5774 Sed publica, 1934 (24x19cm-9x7in) s.i.d.1934 num.19/75 gelatin silver print lit. 27-Apr-4 Christie's, Rockefeller NY #86/R est:5000-7000
£4000 $7200 €5840 Good reputation sleeping (18x24cm-7x9in) s. gelatin silver print prov.lit. 23-Apr-4 Phillips, New York #204/R est:6000-8000
£4192 $7000 €6120 Two nudes (18x25cm-7x10in) s. gelatin silver print set of 2 lit. 16-Oct-3 Phillips, New York #76/R est:6000-8000
£11377 $19000 €16610 Untitled (25x20cm-10x8in) s.i. gelatin silver print set of 4 lit. 16-Oct-3 Phillips, New York #74/R est:10000-15000
£13772 $23000 €20107 Mexico (15x24cm-6x9in) s.i.verso gelatin silver print lit. 16-Oct-3 Phillips, New York #73/R est:15000-20000
£15569 $26000 €22731 Self-portrait (25x20cm-10x8in) s.i. gelatin silver print setof 7 lit. 16-Oct-3 Phillips, New York #75/R est:15000-20000
£19162 $32000 €27977 Untitled (24x19cm-9x7in) s. fourteen i. num.20/100 verso gelatin silver print 15 folio box. 20-Oct-3 Christie's, Rockefeller NY #54/R est:30000-40000
£21557 $36000 €31473 Eight nudes (24x19cm-9x7in) s.i. gelatin silver print set of 8 lit. 16-Oct-3 Phillips, New York #79/R est:18000-22000
£24859 $44000 €36294 Fifteen photographs (23x18cm-9x7in) s.num.53/75 photo exec.1929-72 printed 1974 fifteen folio. 28-Apr-4 Sotheby's, New York #191/R est:30000-50000
£33333 $60000 €48666 Striking worker (19x24cm-7x9in) s. gelatin silver print prov.lit. 23-Apr-4 Phillips, New York #36/R est:30000-50000
£47904 $80000 €69940 Untitled (19x24cm-7x9in) s.i.versogelatin silver prints set of 10 one platinum print lit. 16-Oct-3 Phillips, New York #78/R est:20000-24000

ALVAREZ CATALA, Luis (1836-1901) Spanish

£1200 $2220 €1752 Admiring cupid and Psyche (18x13cm-7x5in) s. oil paper on panel prov. 15-Jan-4 Christie's, Kensington #724/R est:1000-1500
£13986 $23357 €20000 Opinion exchange (57x83cm-22x33in) s.i. 30-Jun-3 Ansorena, Madrid #345/R est:18000
£65972 $107535 €95000 Great wedding (67x121cm-26x48in) s. 23-Sep-3 Durán, Madrid #200/R est:95000

ALVAREZ DE LUGO, Luis (20th C) Venezuelan

£266 $495 €388 Woman (50x40cm-20x16in) s. painted 1982. 14-Mar-4 Subastas Odalys, Caracas #63

ALVAREZ DE SOTOMAYOR, Maria Rosario (1921-) Spanish

£276 $500 €420 Urban view with figures (49x39cm-19x15in) s. cardboard. 14-Apr-4 Ansorena, Madrid #13/R
£567 $948 €800 Market in San Ildefonso Square (50x64cm-20x25in) s. board. 20-Oct-3 Durán, Madrid #204/R
£1181 $1924 €1700 Museum of El Prado (73x92cm-29x36in) s. 16-Jul-3 Durán, Madrid #106/R est:1600
£3947 $7263 €6000 Wedding reception (106x131cm-42x52in) s.d.2003. 22-Jun-4 Durán, Madrid #662/R est:6000

ALVAREZ DIAZ, Emilio (1879-1952) Argentinian

£1310 $2188 €1900 Battle (27x53cm-11x21in) s. board. 17-Nov-3 Durán, Madrid #197/R est:1900

ALVAREZ FERNANDEZ, Jose (19th C) Spanish

£1510 $2809 €2250 Bandits (45x71cm-18x28in) s. 2-Mar-4 Ansorena, Madrid #321/R est:2250
£2113 $3655 €3000 Bandits (45x71cm-18x28in) s. 15-Dec-3 Ansorena, Madrid #52/R est:3000

ALVAREZ SALES, Cruz (1904-1947) Venezuelan

£281 $470 €410 Seascape (35x45cm-14x18in) s. cardboard. 13-Jul-3 Subastas Odalys, Caracas #57

ALVAREZ, A A (20th C) Venezuelan?

£1150 $1875 €1679 Creole bowls (41x50cm-16x20in) s. painted 1987. 28-Sep-3 Subastas Odalys, Caracas #103

ALVAREZ, L (19th C) ?

£8108 $14514 €12000 Gallant couple (44x33cm-17x13in) 10-May-4 Amberes, Antwerp #238

ALVAREZ, Mabel (1891-1985) American

£523 $900 €764 Waiting donkey (41x33cm-16x13in) s. i.verso. 7-Dec-3 Grogan, Boston #68/R
£1719 $2750 €2510 Ode to Goya (127x155cm-50x61in) s. 18-May-3 Auctions by the Bay, Alameda #1102/R
£4046 $7000 €5907 Nude on chaise (51x41cm-20x16in) s. i.verso canvasboard. 10-Dec-3 Bonhams & Butterfields, San Francisco #6282/R est:7000-10000
£5978 $11000 €8728 Nude by a doorway (61x35cm-24x14in) s. canvasboard. 8-Jun-4 Bonhams & Butterfields, San Francisco #4368/R est:3000-5000

ALVAREZ, Manuel Angel (19/20th C) Spanish

£1119 $1869 €1600 Lady with shawl (59x46cm-23x18in) s. 30-Jun-3 Ansorena, Madrid #305/R

ALVAREZ, Xavier (1949-) ?

Sculpture

£1208 $2162 €1800 Plenitude (75cm-30in) s. num.1/6 pat bronze. 30-May-4 Eric Pillon, Calais #307/R

ALVAREZ-SALA, Ventura (1871-?) Spanish

Works on paper

£532 $888 €750 Aldea de Asturias (16x25cm-6x10in) s. W/C. 23-Jun-3 Durán, Madrid #56/R

ALVEAR, Gerardo de (1887-1964) Spanish

£559 $1012 €850 Rio de la Plata, Buenos Aires (19x23cm-7x9in) s. board. 14-Apr-4 Ansorena, Madrid #25/R
£940 $1748 €1400 Still life (38x46cm-15x18in) s. canvas on cardboard. 2-Mar-4 Ansorena, Madrid #10/R
£6897 $11448 €10000 Boys playing cards (88x68cm-35x27in) s. 30-Sep-3 Ansorena, Madrid #84/R est:10000

ALVIANI, Getulio (1939-) Italian

£1141 $2042 €1700 Surface (18x18cm-7x7in) s.i.d.1972-86 verso aluminium. 30-May-4 Meeting Art, Vercelli #14 est:1500
£1399 $2378 €2000 Colours (44x43cm-17x17in) s.i.verso paper on board prov. 25-Nov-3 Sotheby's, Milan #11/R est:2000-3000

Sculpture

£1007 $1862 €1500 Study for surface (19x19cm-7x7in) s.i.d.1996 verso aluminium. 13-Mar-4 Meeting Art, Vercelli #388 est:1500
£1067 $1963 €1600 Surface (18x181cm-7x71in) s.i.d.1972 verso aluminium. 12-Jun-4 Meeting Art, Vercelli #500/R est:1500
£1098 $1800 €1603 Superficie a testura vibratile (10x10cm-4x4in) s.i.d.1966 verso aluminium on wood prov. 28-May-3 Sotheby's, Amsterdam #1/R est:1000-1200
£1533 $2821 €2300 Surface (21x36cm-8x14in) s.i.d.1975 verso. 12-Jun-4 Meeting Art, Vercelli #842/R est:1500
£2797 $4755 €4000 Surface (36x36cm-14x14in) s.i.verso aluminium board prov. 25-Nov-3 Sotheby's, Milan #10/R est:3000-4000
£3169 $5261 €4500 Shape 5 (42x73cm-17x29in) s. s.i.verso aluminium relief. 11-Jun-3 Finarte Semenzato, Milan #571/R
£3636 $6182 €5200 Untitled (54x54cm-21x21in) s.i.d.1996 verso aluminium. 24-Nov-3 Christie's, Milan #86/R est:3000-4000
£4027 $7208 €6000 Surface (36x36cm-14x14in) s.i. aluminium board prov. 25-May-4 Sotheby's, Milan #192/R est:3000-4000
£4268 $7000 €6231 Superficie a testura vibratile (72x18cm-28x7in) s.i. verso aluminium on panel prov. 28-May-3 Sotheby's, Amsterdam #9/R est:4000-5000
£4469 $8000 €6525 Ohne titel (70x70cm-28x28in) s.verso aluminum on wood panel exec.c.1970-75 prov. 14-May-4 Phillips, New York #287 est:4000-6000
£4749 $8500 €6934 Ohne titel, 71041 (71x71cm-28x28in) s.verso aluminum white laminant wood panel prov. 14-May-4 Phillips, New York #292/R est:3000-4000
£5467 $10059 €8200 N.0014 (70x70cm-28x28in) s.i.verso aluminium prov. 14-Jun-4 Porro, Milan #53/R est:6000-8000
£6711 $12013 €10000 Surface (70x70cm-28x28in) s.i. steel aluminium board. 25-May-4 Sotheby's, Milan #189/R est:8000-10000

Works on paper

£2550 $4565 €3800 Colous (39x38cm-15x15in) s.i.verso mixed media paper on board exec.1974 prov. 25-May-4 Sotheby's, Milan #193/R est:2000-3000

ALYS, Francis (1959-) Belgian

£10000 $18200 €14600 Sillones (54x36cm-21x14in) oil encaustic fabric on wood exec c.1985 prov. 5-Feb-4 Christie's, London #222/R est:10000-15000
£11173 $20000 €16313 The loser, the winter (27x45cm-11x18in) st.artist seal oil graphite collage postcard painted c.1998 prov. 14-May-4 Phillips, New York #101/R est:8000-12000
£15000 $27600 €21900 Fairy tales (36x42cm-14x17in) s.d.1988 oil oilstick on sewn canvas exhib. 25-Jun-4 Christie's, London #261/R est:15000-22000
£15642 $28000 €22837 Desk (19x24cm-7x9in) s.d.1993 verso oil masking tape panel prov.exhib. 12-May-4 Christie's, Rockefeller NY #315/R est:20000-30000
£15951 $26000 €23288 Sin titulo, paisaje Urbano (13x17cm-5x7in) s.d.1996 verso canvas on panel exhib. 23-Sep-3 Christie's, Rockefeller NY #75/R est:5000-7000
£17877 $32000 €26100 Two beds (14x18cm-6x7in) s.d.1995 verso canvas on masonite prov.exhib. 12-May-4 Christie's, Rockefeller NY #314/R est:20000-30000
£25140 $45000 €36704 Cat no 2 (61x72cm-24x28in) i. s.d.1994 verso one tin wood stretcher bars 2 parts prov.exhib. 13-May-4 Sotheby's, New York #376/R est:40000-60000

£26000 $47320 €37960 Study for the Blue Ship (29x34cm-11x13in) i.d.1933 verso oil clock mechanism canvas on board prov. 5-Feb-4 Christie's, London #221/R est:15000-20000
£36810 $60000 €53743 Corona. two s.i.d.1995-6 verso 1 panel 2 oil on aluminum triptych prov. 23-Sep-3 Christie's, Rockefeller NY #73/R est:25000-35000
£39106 $70000 €57095 Untitled, man/woman with shoe on the head (20x18cm-8x7in) one s.d.1995 verso one oil wax one acrylic sheet metal two prov. 12-May-4 Christie's, Rockefeller NY #313/R est:50000-70000
£60000 $110400 €87600 Untitled (138x117cm-54x46in) s.i. oil mixed media set of four different sizes prov.exhib. 23-Jun-4 Sotheby's, London #38/R est:60000-80000
£83832 $140000 €122395 Untitled, hands on white (17x12cm-7x5in) oil wood tin two parts exec.c.1994 prov. 13-Nov-3 Sotheby's, New York #473/R est:50000-70000
£95808 $160000 €139880 Untitled (119x92cm-47x36in) s.d.1996 verso enamel sheet metal and oil on canvas seven prov. 12-Nov-3 Christie's, Rockefeller NY #508/R est:40000-60000
Sculpture
£19553 $35000 €28547 Untitled - dog''s house (140x85x120cm-55x33x47in) wood metal plastic fabric electric lamp glass executed 1984. 13-May-4 Phillips, New York #56/R est:40000-60000
Works on paper
£10056 $18000 €14682 Untitled woman pouring (30x23cm-12x9in) pencil acrylic vellum three parts exec 1998 prov. 13-May-4 Sotheby's, New York #350/R est:18000-25000

AMADIO, Vittorio (1934-) Italian
£414 $691 €600 Mask (40x30cm-16x12in) s. s.i.d.98 verso acrylic. 14-Nov-3 Farsetti, Prato #72/R

AMADORI, Giuliano (1893-1972) Italian
£2027 $3162 €3000 View of lake (50x52cm-20x20in) 30-Mar-3 Adma, Formigine #698 est:600-800
£2095 $3268 €3100 View of mountains (73x91cm-29x36in) 30-Mar-3 Adma, Formigine #686 est:800-1000
£2162 $3373 €3200 Fishermen on riverbank (50x53cm-20x21in) 30-Mar-3 Adma, Formigine #695 est:600-800
£5405 $8432 €8000 View of village (116x200cm-46x79in) 30-Mar-3 Adma, Formigine #747 est:1500-1800

AMAGULA, Nandjiwarra (c.1926-1989) Australian
Works on paper
£650 $1021 €943 Untitled (63x36cm-25x14in) natural pigments bark. 27-Aug-3 Christie's, Sydney #766 est:500-800 (A.D 1600)
£650 $1021 €943 Untitled (37x63cm-15x25in) natural pigments bark. 27-Aug-3 Christie's, Sydney #769 est:500-800 (A.D 1600)
£813 $1276 €1179 Untitled (66x39cm-26x15in) natural pigments bark. 27-Aug-3 Christie's, Sydney #768 est:500-800 (A.D 2000)
£1953 $3652 €2930 Spirits of the morning star dancing in the daylight (42x49cm-17x19in) earth pigments eucalyptus bark prov. 26-Jul-4 Sotheby's, Melbourne #42/R est:3000-5000 (A.D 5000)

AMAGULA, Nandjiwarra (attrib) (c.1926-1989) Australian
Works on paper
£3906 $7305 €5859 Creation of the Milky Way (41x41cm-16x16in) earth pigments eucalyptus bark exec.c.1960 prov. 26-Jul-4 Sotheby's, Melbourne #41/R est:3000-5000 (A.D 10000)

AMAN-JEAN, Edmond François (1860-1935) French
£27273 $46909 €39000 Miss Ella Carmichael (75x61cm-30x24in) s.d.1905 cardboard lit. 3-Dec-3 Oger, Dumont, Paris #2 est:10000-15000
Works on paper
£338 $605 €500 Les oiseaux (47x63cm-19x25in) s.i. chl. 7-May-4 Millon & Associes, Paris #84
£777 $1391 €1150 Etude de jeune femme a la tresse (54x44cm-21x17in) s. graphite. 7-May-4 Millon & Associes, Paris #83/R
£805 $1425 €1200 Portrait au vase bleu (40x32cm-16x13in) s.i. pastel board. 27-Apr-4 Artcurial Briest, Paris #1/R

AMAND, Jacques François (1730-1769) French
£1905 $3410 €2800 Le galant jardinier (32x56cm-13x22in) s. red chk. 18-Mar-4 Christie's, Paris #134/R est:3000-5000

AMANN, Carl (1908-1971) German
£5333 $9813 €8000 Self portrait (55x41cm-22x16in) s.i.d.1937 panel. 12-Jun-4 Villa Grisebach, Berlin #247/R est:8000-10000

AMARAL, Jim (1933-) American
Works on paper
£637 $1000 €930 Three old pieces of fruit (56x65cm-22x26in) s. collage on panel exec.1980. 23-Nov-2 Subastas Odalys, Caracas #10/R

AMARAL, Kate (20th C) British?
£300 $543 €438 Market scene (84x70cm-33x28in) s.d.58. 30-Mar-4 Sworder & Son, Bishops Stortford #556/R

AMAROTICO, Joseph (20th C) American
£236 $425 €345 Composition (15x15cm-6x6in) s.d.68 acrylic board. 23-Jan-4 Freeman, Philadelphia #253/R
£250 $400 €365 Space dream I (25x18cm-10x7in) acrylic board prov. 19-Sep-3 Freeman, Philadelphia #103/R
Works on paper
£217 $400 €317 Building (56x43cm-22x17in) s.d.63 gouache. 25-Jun-4 Freeman, Philadelphia #43/R

AMAT, Jose (1883-?) Spanish
£411 $699 €600 Landscape with houses (14x22cm-6x9in) s. cardboard. 4-Nov-3 Ansorena, Madrid #327/R

AMATO, Orazio (1884-1952) Italian
£4133 $7605 €6200 Vase of flowers (80x60cm-31x24in) s. 14-Jun-4 Sant Agostino, Torino #293/R est:2300-2800
£7000 $12880 €10500 Bread (168x149cm-66x59in) s. 10-Jun-4 Christie's, Rome #141/R est:2000-2400

AMATRUDA, Marilyn (1947-) ?
£522 $903 €762 Still life of bowl of fruit and vase (100x92cm-39x36in) s. 13-Dec-3 Blomqvist, Lysaker #1002/R (N.KR 6000)
£739 $1279 €1079 Still life of flowers in vase (115x100cm-45x39in) s. 13-Dec-3 Blomqvist, Lysaker #1001 (N.KR 8500)

AMAURY-DUVAL, Eugène Emmanuel (1808-1885) French
Works on paper
£4895 $8420 €7000 Portrait en buste de Valentine Delessert (67x50cm-26x20in) pastel pierre noire chk. 8-Dec-3 Christie's, Paris #34/R est:800-1200

AMBERG, Wilhelm (1822-1899) German
£872 $1605 €1300 Young woman sitting under tree (62x47cm-24x19in) s.i.d.1870 lit. 25-Mar-4 Karlheinz Kaupp, Staufen #2331/R
£4000 $7280 €5840 Distant thoughts (83x63cm-33x25in) s. 16-Jun-4 Bonhams, New Bond Street #20/R est:4000-6000

AMBILLE, Paul (1930-) French
£300 $552 €450 Le bateau blanc (50x73cm-20x29in) s.d.1985 i.verso. 14-Jun-4 Tajan, Paris #214
£694 $1132 €1000 Les coloquintes (54x65cm-21x26in) s.d.95 s.i.verso. 26-Sep-3 Rabourdin & Choppin de Janvry, Paris #10

AMBLER, Christopher Gifford (1886-?) British
Works on paper
£1243 $2250 €1815 Solo performance (31x48cm-12x19in) s. W/C gouache. 30-Mar-4 Bonhams & Butterfields, San Francisco #146/R est:2500-3500

AMBRASATH, Franz (20th C) American/German
£707 $1300 €1032 Fishing and sail boats under sunset sky (71x81cm-28x32in) s. prov. 29-Mar-4 O'Gallerie, Oregon #781/R

AMBROGIANI, Pierre (1907-1985) French
£1207 $2209 €1750 Bouquet de fleurs (65x52cm-26x20in) s. panel. 1-Feb-4 Feletin, Province #108
£1333 $2413 €2000 Le vieil amandier (60x73cm-24x29in) s. 30-Mar-4 Gioffredo, Nice #340
£1333 $2453 €2000 Le Col de Mougnes (60x81cm-24x32in) s. i. verso. 11-Jun-4 Hauswedell & Nolte, Hamburg #1107/R est:3000
£1667 $3033 €2500 Arlesienne (100x50cm-39x20in) s. 4-Jul-4 Eric Pillon, Calais #264/R
£1761 $2923 €2500 Le Champs (61x81cm-24x32in) s. 14-Jun-3 Meeting Art, Vercelli #317/R est:2500
£1800 $3258 €2700 Chevaux en Camargue (54x65cm-21x26in) s. 1-Apr-4 Credit Municipal, Paris #64 est:1500-2000
£1888 $3210 €2700 Paris, la Place de l'Opera (73x54cm-29x21in) s.d.1958. 28-Nov-3 Blanchet, Paris #175 est:3000-4000
£2000 $3660 €3000 Toreadors (92x73cm-36x29in) prov. 6-Jun-4 Rouillac, Vendome #35
£2067 $3720 €3100 Assemblee de femmes (65x92cm-26x36in) s. 26-Apr-4 Tajan, Paris #159/R est:2400-3000
£2324 $4020 €3300 Vase de fleurs (46x38cm-18x15in) s. panel. 14-Dec-3 Eric Pillon, Calais #261/R
£2368 $4358 €3600 Nu de dos (92x73cm-36x29in) s. 28-Jun-4 Joron-Derem, Paris #242/R est:3000-4000
£2378 $4042 €3400 Phare de la vieille couronne (60x73cm-24x29in) s. i.verso. 28-Nov-3 Drouot Estimations, Paris #202 est:3500-4000
£2606 $4508 €3700 Maestros (65x54cm-26x21in) s.i.d.1962 verso. 14-Dec-3 Eric Pillon, Calais #262/R
£2667 $4853 €4000 Phare de la vieille couronne (60x73cm-24x29in) s. i.verso. 4-Jul-4 Eric Pillon, Calais #288/R
£2759 $4966 €4000 Scene champetre (60x73cm-24x29in) s. 25-Jan-4 Chayette & Cheval, Paris #256/R est:3500-4500
£2778 $4639 €4000 Fruits a la cruche blanche (65x92cm-26x36in) s. i.verso. 25-Oct-3 Cornette de St.Cyr, Paris #373/R est:4000-5000
£2917 $4871 €4200 Chevriere (73x54cm-29x21in) s. 25-Oct-3 Dianous, Marseille #400
£2980 $5454 €4500 Still life of a bouquet of flowers (54x81cm-21x32in) s.d.1953. 7-Apr-4 Piasa, Paris #184/R est:3000-4000
£4167 $6958 €6000 Cueillette des lavandes (60x81cm-24x32in) s. 25-Oct-3 Dianous, Marseille #405
£5034 $9363 €7500 Moment de tendresse (61x38cm-24x15in) s. 2-Mar-4 Artcurial Briest, Paris #234/R est:2000-2500
Works on paper
£282 $487 €400 Deposition de croix (35x27cm-14x11in) s. gouache. 12-Dec-3 Piasa, Paris #192
£317 $548 €450 Personnages (31x23cm-12x9in) s. gouache. 12-Dec-3 Piasa, Paris #191
£420 $722 €600 Lamontagne (39x49cm-15x19in) s. gouache. 3-Dec-3 Tajan, Paris #134
£454 $782 €650 La fenaison (39x49cm-15x19in) s. gouache. 3-Dec-3 Tajan, Paris #133/R
£872 $1614 €1300 Fenaison (39x49cm-15x19in) s. gouache. 14-Mar-4 St-Germain-en-Laye Encheres #166/R
£1172 $2110 €1700 Personnages (52x40cm-20x16in) s. crayon. 25-Jan-4 Chayette & Cheval, Paris #273 est:300-400

AMBROGIO DI BALDESE (attrib) (1352-1429) Italian
£78873 $138028 €112000 Madonna and Child (59x37cm-23x15in) board. 17-Dec-3 Christie's, Rome #426/R est:10000-15000

AMBROSE, Charles E (fl.1824-1848) British
£3000 $5010 €4380 Portrait of an officer of the 12th Royal Lancers, Prince of Wales (89x70cm-35x28in) s.verso lit. 14-Oct-3 Sotheby's, London #483/R est:3000-4000

AMBROSE, John (?) British
£250 $418 €365 Harbour (28x38cm-11x15in) s. board. 14-Oct-3 David Lay, Penzance #425
£250 $455 €365 Cornish harbour (46x36cm-18x14in) s. board. 15-Jun-4 David Lay, Penzance #560
£260 $434 €380 Morning light (33x38cm-13x15in) s. 17-Oct-3 Keys, Aylsham #332
£260 $476 €380 Beach scene (29x39cm-11x15in) s. board. 3-Jun-4 Lane, Penzance #151
£270 $451 €394 Venice (33x38cm-13x15in) s. 14-Oct-3 David Lay, Penzance #480
£280 $510 €409 Boats at Gweek (51x61cm-20x24in) s. 15-Jun-4 David Lay, Penzance #647
£320 $534 €467 Low tide, St. Ives (51x61cm-20x24in) s. 14-Oct-3 David Lay, Penzance #473
£380 $692 €555 St. Ives (40x35cm-16x14in) s. board. 21-Jun-4 Bonhams, Bath #418
£480 $874 €701 East Looe (61x76cm-24x30in) s. 15-Jun-4 David Lay, Penzance #639
£500 $835 €730 Polpero (56x48cm-22x19in) s. 17-Oct-3 Keys, Aylsham #334/R
£680 $1272 €993 St Ives harbour (65x90cm-26x35in) s. 26-Feb-4 Lane, Penzance #156
£850 $1335 €1233 Vessels at low tide, Looe, Cornwall (91x102cm-36x40in) s. 28-Aug-3 Christie's, Kensington #314/R

AMBROSE, Lester J (1879-?) American
£1714 $3000 €2502 Artist's studio (61x76cm-24x30in) s. 19-Dec-3 Sotheby's, New York #1139/R est:3000-5000

AMEGLIO, Mario (1897-1970) French
£331 $619 €500 Val de Grace. masonite. 20-Jul-4 other European Auctioneer #125
£433 $797 €650 Vue de Martigues depuis le port (28x36cm-11x14in) s. panel. 14-Jun-4 Cornette de St.Cyr, Paris #65
£493 $799 €700 Marche aux fleurs a la Madeleine a Paris (24x33cm-9x13in) s. panel. 11-Aug-3 Boscher, Cherbourg #780/R
£500 $920 €750 Vue du Pont-Neuf (38x55cm-15x22in) s. 14-Jun-4 Cornette de St.Cyr, Paris #64
£556 $928 €800 Place de l'Opera (46x55cm-18x22in) s. 21-Oct-3 Galerie Moderne, Brussels #311/R
£633 $1153 €950 Paris, les quais (16x24cm-6x9in) s. panel. 4-Jul-4 Eric Pillon, Calais #189/R
£634 $1020 €900 Bastia, old harbour (46x55cm-18x22in) s. 11-May-3 Versailles Encheres #96/R
£667 $1213 €1000 Port de la Rochelle (46x55cm-18x22in) s. 4-Jul-4 Eric Pillon, Calais #188/R
£680 $1218 €1000 Place Clichy (38x46cm-15x18in) s. s.d.1949 verso. 19-Mar-4 Ribeyre & Baron, Paris #86
£920 $1500 €1343 Montmartre et Sacre-Coeur (46x55cm-18x22in) s.i. 25-Sep-3 Christie's, Rockefeller NY #547/R est:1500-2000
£1074 $1987 €1600 Paris, marche aux fleurs (24x33cm-9x13in) s. panel. 14-Mar-4 Eric Pillon, Calais #128/R
£1597 $2667 €2300 Boulevard Saint-Denis (33x55cm-13x22in) s. 25-Oct-3 Dianous, Marseille #371
£2359 $3916 €3350 Rouen (60x73cm-24x29in) s.i.d. 16-Jun-3 E & Eve, Paris #100/R

AMELIN, Albin (1902-1975) Swedish
£466 $751 €680 Composition (63x49cm-25x19in) s.i. paper on board. 25-Aug-3 Lilla Bukowskis, Stockholm #125 (S.KR 6100)
£2175 $3916 €3176 Young woman with bouquet of flowers (92x73cm-36x29in) s.d.52. 26-Apr-4 Bukowskis, Stockholm #93/R est:35000-40000 (S.KR 30000)
£2551 $4694 €3827 Vase with amaryllis (90x100cm-35x39in) s.d.41. 14-Jun-4 Lilla Bukowskis, Stockholm #581 est:40000-50000 (S.KR 35000)
£3692 $6351 €5390 Still life of flowers in vase (78x61cm-31x24in) s.d.48 panel. 7-Dec-3 Uppsala Auktionskammare, Uppsala #255/R est:50000-60000 (S.KR 48000)
£5589 $9502 €8160 Still life of flowers (100x81cm-39x32in) s.d.58. 4-Nov-3 Bukowskis, Stockholm #138/R est:80000-100000 (S.KR 74000)
£5801 $10442 €8469 Still life of flowers (94x74cm-37x29in) s. 26-Apr-4 Bukowskis, Stockholm #91/R est:100000-125000 (S.KR 80000)
£5913 $10584 €8633 Still life of flowers (93x75cm-37x30in) s. 28-May-4 Uppsala Auktionskammare, Uppsala #280/R est:80000-100000 (S.KR 80000)
£6344 $10785 €9262 Still life of flowers (100x81cm-39x32in) s.d.59. 5-Nov-3 AB Stockholms Auktionsverk #772/R est:60000-80000 (S.KR 84000)
£7402 $12583 €10807 Torrent in the mountains (110x130cm-43x51in) s. 4-Nov-3 Bukowskis, Stockholm #140/R est:100000-125000 (S.KR 98000)
Works on paper
£615 $1058 €898 Young girl with red tulips (71x54cm-28x21in) s.d.48 gouache. 7-Dec-3 Uppsala Auktionskammare, Uppsala #253/R (S.KR 8000)
£1378 $2480 €2012 Still life of flowers (75x52cm-30x20in) s.d.51 mixed media. 26-Apr-4 Bukowskis, Stockholm #167/R est:25000-30000 (S.KR 19000)
£1450 $2611 €2117 Bouquet of flowers in blue vase (55x47cm-22x19in) s.d.33 gouache exhib. 26-Apr-4 Bukowskis, Stockholm #168/R est:25000-30000 (S.KR 20000)
£1538 $2646 €2245 Still life of flowers with orange background (98x69cm-39x27in) s.d.48 gouache. 7-Dec-3 Uppsala Auktionskammare, Uppsala #259/R est:20000-25000 (S.KR 20000)
£1767 $2879 €2580 Still life of flowers (72x59cm-28x23in) s.d.31 mixed media. 29-Sep-3 Lilla Bukowskis, Stockholm #497 est:15000-20000 (S.KR 23000)
£2103 $3785 €3070 Hydrangea in white vase (71x56cm-28x22in) s.d.40 mixed media. 26-Apr-4 Bukowskis, Stockholm #92/R est:40000-50000 (S.KR 29000)
£2271 $4020 €3316 Flowers (74x60cm-29x24in) s.d.30 mixed media panel. 27-Apr-4 AB Stockholms Auktionsverk #866/R est:30000-35000 (S.KR 31000)

AMEN, Irving (1918-) American?
Sculpture
£2500 $4250 €3650 Untitled (38x13cm-15x5in) s. bronze. 9-Nov-3 Wright, Chicago #149 est:5000-7000

AMEN, Jeanne (1863-1923) French
£431 $772 €629 Still life (39x32cm-15x13in) s.d.1890 paper on board. 12-May-4 Dobiaschofsky, Bern #305/R (S.FR 1000)

AMEN, Woody van (1936-) Dutch
Works on paper
£345 $576 €500 Postcard (45x66cm-18x26in) s.d.1980 collage. 11-Nov-3 Vendu Notarishuis, Rotterdam #76/R

AMENDOLA, G B (1848-1887) Italian
Sculpture
£3099 $5144 €4400 Lucy (52cm-20in) s.i.d.1882 pat bronze. 11-Jun-3 Christie's, Rome #9/R est:2000-2500

AMENOFF, Gregory (1948-) American
£556 $1000 €812 Untitled (23x24cm-9x9in) oil paper. 24-Apr-4 David Rago, Lambertville #187/R
£2844 $4750 €4152 Groundswell (229x229cm-90x90in) s.i.d.3/85 verso prov. 7-Oct-3 Sotheby's, New York #359 est:4000-6000

AMER, Ghada (1963-) Egyptian
£7667 $13953 €11500 So close (100x50cm-39x20in) s.d.1992 acrylic thread prov. 29-Jun-4 Cornette de St.Cyr, Paris #181/R est:10000-15000

AMER, Lluis (1943-) Spanish
£399 $654 €550 Port of Amsterdam (35x75cm-14x30in) s. 27-May-3 Durán, Madrid #745/R

AMERICAN PRIMITIVE SCHOOL
£5000 $8500 €7300 Portrait of child seated in chair and holding spray of flowers (66x56cm-26x22in) 31-Oct-3 North East Auctions, Portsmouth #1836

AMERICAN SCHOOL
£3784 $7000 €5525 Portrait of two sisters in pink dresses, with roses and their pet dog (62x72cm-24x28in) painted c.1830. 15-Jan-4 Sotheby's, New York #302/R est:7000-10000
£9259 $15000 €13518 Portrait of Sarah Behnam (86x84cm-34x33in) prov.lit.exhib. 1-Aug-3 North East Auctions, Portsmouth #715/R est:8000-12000
£11111 $18000 €16222 Three young children (112x97cm-44x38in) 1-Aug-3 North East Auctions, Portsmouth #718/R est:15000-20000
£14198 $23000 €20729 New England couple (76x64cm-30x25in) panel pair. 1-Aug-3 North East Auctions, Portsmouth #834/R
£17901 $29000 €26135 Town green with three meeting houses (86x124cm-34x49in) 1-Aug-3 North East Auctions, Portsmouth #912/R
Sculpture
£20062 $32500 €29291 Indian squaw (160cm-63in) 1-Aug-3 North East Auctions, Portsmouth #814/R est:10000-15000
Works on paper
£21196 $39000 €30946 Residence of Mary Wakeman (66x97cm-26x38in) dr. 28-Mar-4 Carlsen Gallery, Greenville #443/R

AMERICAN SCHOOL, 18th C
£5960 $10907 €9000 La vierge entouree de saints (55x39cm-22x15in) panel. 7-Apr-4 Libert, Castor, Paris #6 est:1200-1500
£37634 $70000 €54946 Portraits of Mary Jarvis and Captain Phineas Stone (69x46cm-27x18in) paper on canvas painted c.1796 pair prov.exhib. 6-Mar-4 North East Auctions, Portsmouth #444/R est:20000-30000

AMERICAN SCHOOL, 18th/19th C
£5376 $10000 €7849 Floral still life (81x107cm-32x42in) 6-Mar-4 Harvey Clar, Oakland #1583

AMERICAN SCHOOL, 19th C
£2415 $4250 €3526 Portrait of the Evans, sister (91x76cm-36x30in) 18-May-4 Arthur James, Florida #123/R est:4000-6000
£3529 $6000 €5152 American steamboat (76x127cm-30x50in) s. 1-Nov-3 Skinner, Boston #138/R est:3000-6000
£3784 $7000 €5525 Portraits of Dr and Mrs Joseph (75x60cm-30x24in) pair painted c.1820. 15-Jan-4 Sotheby's, New York #310/R est:6000-10000
£3804 $7000 €5554 Three children with straw hat and dog (133x117cm-52x46in) painted c.1845. 22-Jun-4 Sotheby's, New York #177/R est:6000-8000
£3804 $7000 €5554 Portrait of a little girl (114x76cm-45x30in) painted c.1870 prov. 8-Jun-4 Bonhams & Butterfields, San Francisco #4000/R est:3000-5000
£3911 $7000 €6566 Portrait of Mary Margaret Green, daughter of Capt John Green Jr (76x61cm-30x24in) 20-Mar-4 Pook & Pook, Downington #443/R est:4000-6000
£4076 $7500 €5951 Vermont landscape (53x80cm-21x31in) init. i. stretcher. 27-Jun-4 Freeman, Philadelphia #84/R est:1500-2500
£4088 $6500 €5968 Child in a red dress holding a cart and whip (91x66cm-36x26in) 10-Sep-3 Sotheby's, New York #373/R est:3000-4000
£4099 $7500 €5985 Little girl on a pink dress holding her doll (91x74cm-36x29in) 6-Jun-4 Skinner, Boston #353 est:4000-6000
£4324 $8000 €6313 Portrait of a young child in a yellow dress, seated on a red chair (65x55cm-26x22in) painted c.1830. 15-Jan-4 Sotheby's, New York #332/R est:4000-6000
£4396 $8000 €6418 Portrait of a young girl holding a rattle (91x76cm-36x30in) 7-Feb-4 Neal Auction Company, New Orleans #998/R est:5000-7000

£4469 $8000 €7504 Portrait of Samuel Keen Ashton as a young boy with his dog (152x97cm-60x38in) painted c.1830. 20-Mar-4 Pook & Pook, Downington #97/R est:5000-7000
£4595 $8500 €6709 Portrait of Charles Augustus Mack and his pet squirrel (64x51cm-25x20in) painted c.1825 prov. 15-Jan-4 Sotheby's, New York #301/R est:6000-10000
£4595 $8500 €6709 Hunter in snow shoes (28x23cm-11x9in) 13-Mar-4 DeFina, Austinburg #538/R est:600-900
£4749 $8500 €7973 Portrait of Harriett Burr Ashton as a young girl with flowers (152x97cm-60x38in) painted c.1830. 20-Mar-4 Pook & Pook, Downington #99/R est:5000-7000
£5346 $8500 €7805 The Mr. and Mrs. E. Grove Lawrence family (76x124cm-30x49in) two attached panels painted c.1835. 13-Sep-3 Selkirks, St. Louis #41/R est:7000-9000
£5523 $9500 €8064 Lady at piano (114x76cm-45x30in) 7-Dec-3 Freeman, Philadelphia #119 est:2000-3000
£5525 $10000 €8067 Barrel of cheer (62x51cm-24x20in) 31-Mar-4 Sotheby's, New York #61/R est:3000-5000
£5679 $9200 €8235 Still life (44x29cm-17x11in) board. 8-Aug-3 Barridorf, Portland #63/R est:4000-6000
£6145 $11000 €10318 Portrait of a young girl (89x71cm-35x28in) painted c.1835. 20-Mar-4 Pook & Pook, Downington #123/R est:3500-4500
£6349 $12000 €9270 Double portrait of two boys (36x30cm-14x12in) 21-Feb-4 Weschler, Washington #237 est:1000-1500
£6593 $12000 €9626 Ellsley (61x82cm-24x32in) 29-Jun-4 Sotheby's, New York #200/R est:4000-6000
£7325 $11500 €10695 Portrait of Wm Henry Spooner and sister Elizabeth. 1-Sep-3 William A Smith, Plainfield #18/R
£7514 $13000 €10970 Switzer's Camp (23x41cm-9x16in) indis.mono.i.d.1887 paper on board prov. 10-Dec-3 Bonhams & Butterfields, San Francisco #6139/R est:3000-5000
£7568 $14000 €11049 Civil war scene around a campfire (52x72cm-20x28in) 17-Jan-4 Sotheby's, New York #1212/R est:3000-5000
£9189 $17000 €13416 Portrait of George Washington (74x61cm-29x24in) prov. 15-Jan-4 Sotheby's, New York #321/R est:5000-10000
£10383 $19000 €15159 Portrait of three children in an interior (86x69cm-34x27in) 6-Jun-4 Skinner, Boston #26/R est:15000-25000
£12579 $20000 €18365 Child in a red dress with her dog (61x71cm-24x28in) panel. 10-Sep-3 Sotheby's, New York #418/R est:3500-4500
£15924 $25000 €23249 Harborscape with ships including large sailing ship and sidewheeler (33x46cm-13x18in) 30-Aug-3 Fallon, Copake #23 est:1000-1500
£16393 $30000 €23934 Portrait of Louise Hyde as a young child (76x64cm-30x25in) prov. 6-Jun-4 Skinner, Boston #179/R est:12000-15000
£16484 $30000 €24067 Portrait of Harriet Buckney Withers Gassoway (76x61cm-30x24in) sold with gold ring worn by the sitter prov. 7-Feb-4 Sloans & Kenyon, Bethesda #1307/R est:3000-5000
£16667 $31000 €24334 Portrait of Robert Fulton (76x64cm-30x25in) prov.exhib.lit. 6-Mar-4 North East Auctions, Portsmouth #410/R est:10000-15000
£17196 $32500 €25106 Portrait of Achsah E M Connelly age 9 (147x107cm-58x42in) prov. 22-Feb-4 Skinner, Boston #149/R est:15000-25000
£18919 $35000 €27622 Young mother and her child (18x23cm-7x9in) painted c.1820 prov. 15-Jan-4 Sotheby's, New York #299/R est:5000-7000
£20270 $37500 €29594 Portrait of a dark haired rosy cheeked young lad wearing gold watch chain (74x61cm-29x24in) painted c.1835. 17-Jan-4 Sotheby's, New York #1201/R est:25000-35000
£20667 $36993 €31000 Docks (120x200cm-47x79in) indis.sig. 16-May-4 Joron-Derem, Paris #121/R est:30000
£70270 $130000 €102594 Village of Gulph Mills, Pennsylvania (88x134cm-35x53in) painted c.1820 prov. 15-Jan-4 Sotheby's, New York #314/R est:20000-30000

Photographs
£5090 $8500 €7431 Mercantile building with freight cars. daguerreotype cased exec.c.1850. 17-Oct-3 Sotheby's, New York #97/R est:3000-5000
£5389 $9000 €7868 Ship at sea. daguerreotype cased exec.c.1850. 17-Oct-3 Sotheby's, New York #96/R est:4000-6000
£6587 $11000 €9617 Young woman at a melodian. hand-tinted daguerreotype cased exec.c.1850. 17-Oct-3 Sotheby's, New York #39/R est:8000-12000
£7186 $12000 €10492 Franklin Palmer, Sonora, Cal. daguerreotype cased. 17-Oct-3 Sotheby's, New York #51/R est:3000-5000
£8383 $14000 €12239 Chess set in front of a painted portrait of a girl. Two young girls. one i.d.1853 hand-tinted daguerreotype cased pair lit. 17-Oct-3 Sotheby's, New York #99/R est:4000-6000
£8982 $15000 €13114 Pianist. hand-tinted daguerreotype cased exec.c.1850 prov. 17-Oct-3 Sotheby's, New York #50/R est:25000-35000
£8995 $17000 €13133 Dentist resting hand on false teeth with instruments in case. half plate daguerreotype. 17-Feb-4 Swann Galleries, New York #1/R est:15000-25000

Sculpture
£4261 $7500 €6221 Carousel horse (132x147cm-52x58in) carved wood. 18-May-4 Sotheby's, New York #176/R est:12000-18000
£7386 $13000 €10784 Ships figurehead (127cm-50in) carved wood on rockwork base. 18-May-4 Sotheby's, New York #107/R est:8000-12000
£8108 $15000 €11838 Bust of a gentleman (44cm-17in) carved walnut. 17-Jan-4 Sotheby's, New York #1214/R est:15000-20000
£18466 $32500 €26960 Eagle (94x91cm-37x36in) carved painted gilded. 18-May-4 Sotheby's, New York #13/R est:12000-18000
£39773 $70000 €58069 Indian chief (188cm-74in) wood cigar store figure prov. 18-May-4 Sotheby's, New York #186/R est:12000-18000
£119318 $210000 €174204 Eagle (101x180cm-40x71in) gilded zinc. 18-May-4 Sotheby's, New York #15/R est:7000-9000

Miniatures
£4261 $7500 €6221 Farm in Germantown near the banks of the river Schuylkill (5cm-2in) oil sepia on ivory. 21-May-4 Pook & Pook, Downington #243/R est:2000-2500

Works on paper
£3243 $6000 €4735 Sacred to the memory of Thomas Lothrop (41x52cm-16x20in) W/C pen ink. 17-Jan-4 Sotheby's, New York #1275/R est:3000-5000
£3804 $7000 €5554 Goddess of Liberty (59x38cm-23x15in) W/C pen ink exec.c.1820. 22-Jun-4 Sotheby's, New York #201/R est:5000-8000
£3824 $6500 €5583 Portrait of a girl holding flowers (38x30cm-15x12in) gouache graphite. 1-Nov-3 Skinner, Boston #206/R est:1000-1500
£5689 $9500 €8306 Still life with watermelon (37x50cm-15x20in) W/C prov.lit. 11-Nov-3 Christie's, Rockefeller NY #208/R est:3000-5000
£6349 $12000 €9270 Memorial (38x53cm-15x21in) i. W/C. 22-Feb-4 Skinner, Boston #183/R est:4000-6000
£13800 $22080 €20148 Great Salt Lake City, America (43x56cm-17x22in) W/C bodycol. 20-Sep-3 Lacy Scott, Bury St.Edmunds #440/R

AMERICAN SCHOOL, 19th/20th C
£5435 $10000 €7935 Return of the gulls (61x79cm-24x31in) 10-Jun-4 Sotheby's, New York #502/R est:1000-1500

AMERICAN SCHOOL, 20th C
£3408 $6100 €4976 Five Pound Island, Gloucester harbour (51x61cm-20x24in) indis.sig. 8-Jan-4 James Julia, Fairfield #657/R est:3500-4500
£6522 $12000 €9522 Children playing in the shallows (45x55cm-18x22in) prov. 8-Jun-4 Bonhams & Butterfields, San Francisco #4062/R est:3000-5000

Sculpture
£7558 $13000 €11035 Life size portrait of a gentleman wearing frock coat, holding hat and gloves (180cm-71in) dark brown pat bronze circular wooden base on casters prov. 7-Dec-3 Freeman, Philadelphia #105 est:5000-8000

Works on paper
£3533 $6500 €5158 Fenwick, Old Saybrook, Connecticut (41x51cm-16x20in) init.i.d.1976 sold with painting by C J Nicholas. 10-Jun-4 Sotheby's, New York #566/R est:1500-2000

AMERICO, Pedro (19th C) Brazilian
Works on paper
£1282 $2269 €1923 On an expedition (20x28cm-8x11in) s.d.1858 W/C. 27-Apr-4 Bolsa de Arte, Rio de Janeiro #10/R (B.R 7000)
£1374 $2514 €2061 Model (62x49cm-24x19in) s.i.d.1861 chl. 6-Jul-4 Bolsa de Arte, Rio de Janeiro #1/R (B.R 7500)

AMERLING, Friedrich von (1803-1887) Austrian
£1745 $3123 €2600 Self portrait (72x58cm-28x23in) 27-May-4 Dorotheum, Vienna #105/R est:5000-6000
£3147 $5350 €4500 Portrait of Christoph Heinrich Bialo-Blockly (71x58cm-28x23in) s.d.1856. 24-Nov-3 Dorotheum, Vienna #70/R est:4500-5500
£3759 $6277 €5300 La veuve (59x72cm-23x28in) s. 20-Oct-3 Bernaerts, Antwerp #270/R est:1500-2000

Works on paper
£1141 $2042 €1700 Reclining girl with handkerchief on the sofa (19x14cm-7x6in) pen wash htd white. 27-May-4 Hassfurther, Vienna #31 est:1500-2000
£2238 $3804 €3200 Love-sick girl with music book (17x13cm-7x5in) pencil ink brush wash. 25-Nov-3 Hassfurther, Vienna #17/R est:2000-2500

AMERLING, Friedrich von (attrib) (1803-1887) Austrian
£1656 $3013 €2500 Biedermeier portrait of children (46x37cm-18x15in) 19-Jun-4 Bergmann, Erlangen #790 est:2500
£1761 $3046 €2500 Portrait of a young lady with crown of flowers in her hair (42x37cm-17x15in) board. 10-Dec-3 Dorotheum, Vienna #227/R est:2500-3000

AMERONGEN, Friedrich Freiherr von (1878-?) German
£267 $491 €400 Sunny autumn landscape in a mountain valley (76x51cm-30x20in) s. 11-Jun-4 Wendl, Rudolstadt #3906/R

AMES, Arthur Forbes (1906-1975) American
£201 $375 €293 High Sierras (46x61cm-18x24in) s. canvasboard. 29-Feb-4 Bonhams & Butterfields, San Francisco #4554

AMES, Blanche (1878-1969) American
£315 $500 €460 Table top still life with flowers, microscope and book (102x71cm-40x28in) s.on stretcher. 12-Sep-3 Skinner, Boston #337/R

AMES, Ezra (1768-1836) American
£1324 $2250 €1933 Portrait of a young woman with dark curls seated beside a column in classical scroll arm chair (81x69cm-32x27in) lit. 31-Oct-3 North East Auctions, Portsmouth #1737

AMES, Joseph Alexander (attrib) (1816-1872) American
£629 $1000 €918 Portrait of a young woman (53x43cm-21x17in) s.d.1869. 13-Sep-3 Selkirks, St. Louis #44

AMESEDER, Eduard (1856-1938) Austrian
£347 $566 €500 Southern harbour landscape (68x59cm-27x23in) s. 23-Sep-3 Wiener Kunst Auktionen, Vienna #110/R
£538 $926 €785 Summer landscape with cattle (40x56cm-16x22in) s.d.1896. 2-Dec-3 Bukowskis, Stockholm #274/R (S.KR 7000)
£1300 $2366 €1898 Sestri levante, Italy (39x51cm-15x20in) s. 16-Jun-4 Christie's, Kensington #124/R est:400-600

AMEZAGA, Rafael (1928-) Spanish
£379 $683 €550 Picasso, genius (60x72cm-24x28in) s.i. 26-Jan-4 Durán, Madrid #122/R

AMICIS, Cristoforo de (1902-1987) Italian
£1159 $1901 €1600 Homage to Cimabue (70x31cm-28x12in) s. tempera chl paper on board set of 4 prov.exhib. 27-May-3 Sotheby's, Milan #52
£1268 $2104 €1800 Natura morta coi melograni (40x60cm-16x24in) s. s.i.verso. 14-Jun-3 Meeting Art, Vercelli #185/R est:1500
£1333 $2453 €2000 Nude (50x40cm-20x16in) s. painted 1978. 8-Jun-4 Finarte Semenzato, Milan #206/R est:2000-2500
£1467 $2699 €2200 Still life with jugs (30x40cm-12x16in) s. cardboard on canvas prov. 8-Jun-4 Finarte Semenzato, Milan #105/R est:1000-1500

AMICONI, Bernardo (19th C) Italian
£2000 $3640 €2920 Arranging flowers on the balcony (142x112cm-56x44in) s.d.1874. 16-Jun-4 Christie's, Kensington #133/R est:2500-3500

AMIET, Cuno (1868-1961) Swiss

£3664	$6558	€5349	Spring landscape (30x40cm-12x16in) mono.d.31. 13-May-4 Stuker, Bern #14/R est:6000-8000 (S.FR 8500)
£4698	$8409	€7000	Portrait of Beata Ambrosi (65x54cm-26x21in) mono.d.51 panel prov. 25-May-4 Dorotheum, Vienna #52/R est:10000-15000
£5263	$9684	€7684	Still life with vase of flowers and sculpture (32x41cm-13x16in) mono.d.46 masonite. 23-Jun-4 Koller, Zurich #3056/R est:12000-18000 (S.FR 12000)
£5830	$9502	€8512	Female nude before red apple harvest (29x22cm-11x9in) mono.d.12 W/C. 29-Sep-3 Christie's, Zurich #57/R est:10000-12000 (S.FR 13000)
£6787	$11742	€9909	Capolago (22x28cm-9x11in) mono.d.1910 pencil col pencil W/C. 9-Dec-3 Sotheby's, Zurich #34/R est:10000-15000 (S.FR 15000)
£7692	$12846	€11230	Flowers in vase (22x16cm-9x6in) mono.d.1949 panel prov. 24-Jun-3 Germann, Zurich #59/R est:8000-10000 (S.FR 17000)
£7692	$13077	€11230	Still life with bust and porcelain box (33x42cm-13x17in) mono.d.1941. 28-Nov-3 Zofingen, Switzerland #2888/R est:20000 (S.FR 17000)
£7759	$13888	€11328	Roses (41x33cm-16x13in) mono.d.43. 13-May-4 Stuker, Bern #12/R est:18000-25000 (S.FR 18000)
£8072	$13157	€11785	Early spring (55x46cm-22x18in) mono.d.6.Marz 53 masonite. 29-Sep-3 Christie's, Zurich #73/R est:18000-25000 (S.FR 18000)
£8621	$15431	€12587	Portrait of Frau Amiet (60x54cm-24x21in) mono.i. panel. 14-May-4 Dobiaschofsky, Bern #125/R est:19000 (S.FR 20000)
£9052	$16203	€13216	Meadow with trees and houses (65x54cm-26x21in) mono.d.57. 14-May-4 Dobiaschofsky, Bern #120/R est:26000 (S.FR 21000)
£9565	$17504	€13965	Garden (73x60cm-29x24in) mono. masonite. 7-Jun-4 Christie's, Zurich #67/R est:18000-25000 (S.FR 22000)
£9910	$17045	€14469	Still life with carnations (37x45cm-15x18in) mono.d.60 prov. 2-Dec-3 Koller, Zurich #3033/R est:16000-34000 (S.FR 22000)
£10917	$19541	€15939	Pont Royal (55x46cm-22x18in) mono.d.1933. 26-May-4 Sotheby's, Zurich #77/R est:25000-35000 (S.FR 25000)
£11790	$21105	€17213	Garden (55x33cm-22x13in) mono.d.1940 prov. 26-May-4 Sotheby's, Zurich #139/R est:20000-30000 (S.FR 27000)
£13100	$23450	€19126	Frau Amiet with bunch of flowers (70x38cm-28x15in) mono.d.1921. 26-May-4 Sotheby's, Zurich #66/R est:35000-45000 (S.FR 30000)
£13575	$23077	€19820	Oschwand (54x65cm-21x26in) mono.d.1940 i.d. verso prov.exhib. 28-Nov-3 Zofingen, Switzerland #2890/R est:38000 (S.FR 30000)
£13913	$25461	€20313	Summer meadow with trees (50x73cm-20x29in) mono.d.40. 7-Jun-4 Christie's, Zurich #68/R est:30000-50000 (S.FR 32000)
£15766	$27117	€23018	Early spring with tree (54x45cm-21x18in) mono.d.1943 prov.exhib. 2-Dec-3 Koller, Zurich #3023/R est:35000-45000 (S.FR 35000)
£16055	$26812	€23280	Bouquet de fleurs (30x24cm-12x9in) mono.d. cardboard. 21-Jun-3 Galerie du Rhone, Sion #460/R est:25000-35000 (S.FR 35000)
£26009	$43435	€37973	Woman painting (60x55cm-24x22in) mono. i. stretcher. 24-Oct-3 Hans Widmer, St Gallen #22/R est:18000-32000 (S.FR 58000)
£34934	$62533	€51004	Summer garden in Oschwand (93x73cm-37x29in) mono.d.1934 s.i.d.1934 verso. 26-May-4 Sotheby's, Zurich #78/R est:80000-120000 (S.FR 80000)
£38462	$61538	€56155	Bretonne en adoration (54x45cm-21x18in) mono.d.1893 board prov. 16-Sep-3 Philippe Schuler, Zurich #3220/R est:15000-20000 (S.FR 85000)
£51570	$84058	€75292	Lake Thun with Niesen (66x86cm-26x34in) mono.d.31 prov.exhib.lit. 29-Sep-3 Christie's, Zurich #71/R est:70000-90000 (S.FR 115000)
£71749	$116951	€104754	Winter landscape (91x98cm-36x39in) mono.d.28. 29-Sep-3 Christie's, Zurich #31/R est:130000-150000 (S.FR 160000)

Works on paper

£362	$615	€529	Standing male figure (46x36cm-18x14in) mono. Indian ink. 18-Nov-3 Hans Widmer, St Gallen #1001/R (S.FR 800)
£498	$846	€727	Animal study: cow's head (16x14cm-6x6in) chl. 18-Nov-3 Hans Widmer, St Gallen #1002 (S.FR 1100)
£517	$926	€755	Young woman (20x17cm-8x7in) mono. chl. 12-May-4 Dobiaschofsky, Bern #1342 (S.FR 1200)
£529	$899	€772	Girl playing cello (22x16cm-9x6in) mono. pencil Indian ink. 5-Nov-3 Dobiaschofsky, Bern #1412/R (S.FR 1200)
£571	$914	€828	Horse sketch (16x20cm-6x8in) mono. Indian ink. 15-May-3 Stuker, Bern #1035 (S.FR 1200)
£679	$1133	€991	Study for crossing in Lyss (18x11cm-7x4in) mono. pencil. 24-Jun-3 Germann, Zurich #901 est:1000-1300 (S.FR 1500)
£948	$1697	€1384	Landscape near Interlaken (18x28cm-7x11in) mono.d.43 pencil. 14-May-4 Dobiaschofsky, Bern #121/R est:3000 (S.FR 2200)
£963	$1609	€1396	Standing nude girl with long hair (48x34cm-19x13in) mono. chl pencil wash. 19-Jun-3 Kornfeld, Bern #158 (S.FR 2100)
£1273	$2113	€1846	Le concert (17x24cm-7x9in) s.i.d.1922 W/C prov. 13-Jun-3 Zofingen, Switzerland #2765/R est:4000 (S.FR 2800)
£1391	$2546	€2031	Study of apple pickers (25x20cm-10x8in) mono. pencil prov. 7-Jun-4 Christie's, Zurich #71/R est:3000-5000 (S.FR 3200)
£1468	$2451	€2129	Young woman wearing necklace (24x19cm-9x7in) mono. pastel. 19-Jun-3 Kornfeld, Bern #157 est:4000 (S.FR 3200)
£1478	$2705	€2158	Study of Der Jungbrunnen (49x36cm-19x14in) mono.d.15 ink prov. 7-Jun-4 Christie's, Zurich #72/R est:2500-3500 (S.FR 3400)
£1681	$3009	€2454	Mother and child in landscape (13x9cm-5x4in) mono.d.97 pencil. 14-May-4 Dobiaschofsky, Bern #123/R est:2800 (S.FR 3900)
£1743	$2911	€2527	Flowers (25x22cm-10x9in) mono.d.57 W/C. 19-Jun-3 Kornfeld, Bern #160 est:3000 (S.FR 3800)
£1762	$2996	€2573	Fruit harvest (18x10cm-7x4in) mono.d.14 pencil. 7-Nov-3 Dobiaschofsky, Bern #69/R est:2000 (S.FR 4000)
£3139	$5117	€4583	Coastal landscape (18x25cm-7x10in) mono.d.1892 W/C. 29-Sep-3 Christie's, Zurich #28/R est:7000-9000 (S.FR 7000)
£3139	$5117	€4583	Hellsau in spring (27x18cm-11x7in) mono. W/C. 29-Sep-3 Christie's, Zurich #53/R est:7000-9000 (S.FR 7000)
£3587	$5848	€5237	Coastal landscape (17x26cm-7x10in) mono.d.93 W/C study verso. 29-Sep-3 Christie's, Zurich #30/R est:7000-9000 (S.FR 8000)
£3587	$5848	€5237	Nude with red fruit harvest behind (18x12cm-7x5in) mono.d.11 W/C. 29-Sep-3 Christie's, Zurich #58/R est:7000-9000 (S.FR 8000)
£3812	$6213	€5566	Study for 'Youth spring' (35x49cm-14x19in) mono.d.15 chl over W/C. 29-Sep-3 Christie's, Zurich #44/R est:7000-9000 (S.FR 8500)
£5381	$8771	€7856	Coastal landscape (18x25cm-7x10in) mono.d.1892 W/C. 29-Sep-3 Christie's, Zurich #29/R est:7000-9000 (S.FR 12000)
£6881	$11491	€9977	Clarens on Lake Geneva (23x29cm-9x11in) mono.d.07 i. verso W/C over pencil. 19-Jun-3 Kornfeld, Bern #156 est:15000 (S.FR 15000)
£9170	$16415	€13388	Landscape near Hellsau (22x30cm-9x12in) momno.i.d.1896 W/C. 26-May-4 Sotheby's, Zurich #75/R est:8000-12000 (S.FR 21000)
£10917	$19541	€15939	Still life of flowers, carnations in a yellow vase (37x31cm-15x12in) mono.d.1943 gouache prov. 26-May-4 Sotheby's, Zurich #138/R est:25000-30000 (S.FR 25000)
£16157	$28921	€23589	Oschwand (29x23cm-11x9in) mono.d.1912 pencil W/C exhib. 26-May-4 Sotheby's, Zurich #45/R est:14000-18000 (S.FR 37000)

AMIGONI, Jacopo (1675-1752) Italian

£46980	$87852	€70000	Zephirus and Cloris (61x104cm-24x41in) prov. 25-Feb-4 Porro, Milan #14/R est:50000

AMIGONI, Jacopo (attrib) (1675-1752) Italian

£1631	$2725	€2300	Venus et Adonis (28x34cm-11x13in) panel. 17-Oct-3 Tajan, Paris #20 est:1500-2000
£8380	$15000	€12235	Portrait of Maria Anna Joseph Charlotte, born Princess von Pfalzsulzbach (128x103cm-50x41in) 27-May-4 Sotheby's, New York #51/R est:20000-30000

AMIGONI, Jacopo (style) (1675-1752) Italian

£5500	$9900	€8030	Flora (51x44cm-20x17in) 20-Apr-4 Sotheby's, Olympia #344/R est:2000-3000

AMIOT, Patrick and LAUREN, Brigitte (20th C) Canadian

Sculpture

£1667	$2733	€2434	Ken Dryden, Montreal Canadiens goalie (76x25x30cm-30x10x12in) d.2003 num.1/1 epoxy steel clay. 28-May-3 Maynards, Vancouver #51/R est:5000-6000 (C.D 3750)

AMIR OF KARRAYA, Shaikh Muhammad (fl.1820-1840) Indian

Works on paper

£14000	$22820	€20440	Bay horse standing with a groom (41x56cm-16x22in) i.d.1842 pencil W/C gum arabic htd white. 24-Sep-3 Christie's, London #140/R est:15000-20000

AMIR OF KARRAYA, Shaikh Muhammad (studio) (fl.1820-1840) Indian

Works on paper

£7000	$11410	€10220	White stallion with a groom. Bay horse with groom (13x20cm-5x8in) both i. pencil W/C gum arabic htd white two. 24-Sep-3 Christie's, London #146/R est:3000-5000

AMISANI, Giuseppe (1881-1941) Italian

£1538	$2569	€2200	Still life with flowers (52x64cm-20x25in) s. 24-Jun-3 Finarte Semenzato, Rome #131/R
£4167	$7083	€6000	Street in Sibi Okba (65x46cm-26x18in) s. board. 28-Oct-3 Il Ponte, Milan #283/R
£5667	$10143	€8500	Portrait of woman (85x60cm-33x24in) s. 13-May-4 Babuino, Rome #570/R est:1500-2000

AMITOOK, Isaac (1916-) North American

Sculpture

£1892	$3216	€2762	Mother holding a knife, a child in her amaut (13cm-5in) mottled green soapstone antler. 3-Nov-3 Waddingtons, Toronto #184/R est:2500-3500 (C.D 4200)

AMITTU, Davidiluak Alasua (1910-1976) North American

Sculpture

£811	$1378	€1184	Priest with clasped hands (13cm-5in) s. mottled dark soapstone. 3-Nov-3 Waddingtons, Toronto #87/R est:500-700 (C.D 1800)
£2162	$3676	€3157	Inuit woman holding a fish, her child in an amaut (25cm-10in) s. mottled grey soapstone. 3-Nov-3 Waddingtons, Toronto #84/R est:3000-5000 (C.D 4800)

AMMIRATO, Domenico (1833-?) Italian

£340	$568	€496	Boat off the Italian coast (14x9cm-6x4in) s.d.87 oil on card. 11-Nov-3 Bonhams, Knightsbridge #186/R
£750	$1275	€1095	Temple of Venere a Boya, Italy (11x14cm-4x6in) s. i.verso panel oval. 6-Nov-3 Christie's, Kensington #857/R

AMODIO, Giulio (1868-?) Italian

£2155	$3858	€3146	Children making music (86x65cm-34x26in) s. 12-May-4 Dobiaschofsky, Bern #306/R est:6000 (S.FR 5000)

AMODIO, M (19th C) Italian

Sculpture

£1351	$2500	€1972	Seated Mercury (79cm-31in) s. golden brown pat bronze after the antique. 15-Jul-4 Sotheby's, New York #253/R est:2500-3500

AMOR, Rick (1948-) Australian

£1957	$3327	€2857	Dog (25x30cm-10x12in) s.d.89 i.d.verso. 26-Nov-3 Deutscher-Menzies, Melbourne #71/R est:3500-5500 (A.D 4600)
£2043	$3472	€2983	Broken Ship (56x66cm-22x26in) s.d.84 i.d.verso. 26-Nov-3 Deutscher-Menzies, Melbourne #202/R est:5000-7000 (A.D 4800)
£5106	$8681	€7455	The dream (54x69cm-21x27in) s.d.90 s.i.d.90 verso prov. 25-Nov-3 Christie's, Melbourne #112/R est:12000-18000 (A.D 12000)
£5285	$8297	€7663	Across the city (57x81cm-22x32in) s.d.95 i.d.May 95 verso prov.exhib. 26-Aug-3 Christie's, Sydney #55/R est:12000-15000 (A.D 13000)
£9924	$18061	€14489	Afternoon by the sea (66x81cm-26x32in) s.d.2003 i.d.verso. 16-Jun-4 Deutscher-Menzies, Melbourne #11/R est:15000-20000 (A.D 26000)
£10744	$19876	€15686	Out to sea (151x196cm-59x77in) s.d.91 s.i.d.Dec 90-Jan 91 verso prov.exhib. 15-Mar-4 Sotheby's, Melbourne #1/R est:25000-35000 (A.D 26000)
£15447	$24252	€22398	Still life in an empty factory (146x196cm-57x77in) s.d.95 i.d.June 95 verso prov.exhib.lit. 27-Aug-3 Christie's, Sydney #522/R est:30000-40000 (A.D 38000)
£18033	$28492	€26328	The city 6am (129x162cm-51x64in) s.d.90 d.i.Dec 89 verso prov.exhib. 2-Sep-3 Deutscher-Menzies, Melbourne #23/R est:20000-30000 (A.D 44000)
£20661	$38223	€30165	Sea (129x198cm-51x78in) s.d.89 s.i.d.verso prov.exhib. 15-Mar-4 Sotheby's, Melbourne #45/R est:25000-35000 (A.D 50000)

Works on paper

£528	$829	€766	Building (27x37cm-11x15in) s.d.17/9/96 gouache. 27-Aug-3 Christie's, Sydney #519 est:700-1000 (A.D 1300)
£610	$957	€885	Study for still life in old factory (55x74cm-22x29in) s.d.18/9/95 chl prov.exhib. 27-Aug-3 Christie's, Sydney #656 est:900-1200 (A.D 1500)
£725	$1320	€1059	Study for an afternoon in an arcade (16x29cm-6x11in) s.d.97 gouache. 16-Jun-4 Deutscher-Menzies, Melbourne #400/R est:1500-2000 (A.D 1900)

£785 $1452 €1146 Fitzroy Garden (54x75cm-21x30in) s.d.13.7.93 chl prov. 15-Mar-4 Sotheby's, Melbourne #204 est:700-900 (A.D 1900)
£853 $1340 €1237 House near the sea (58x78cm-23x31in) s.d.27/3/97 chl prov.exhib. 27-Aug-3 Christie's, Sydney #564 est:1000-1500 (A.D 2100)
£909 $1682 €1327 Bull and blossom (37x73cm-15x29in) s.d.28.5.92 pastel prov. 15-Mar-4 Sotheby's, Melbourne #126/R est:2500-3500 (A.D 2200)
£1983 $3669 €2895 Coastal panorama and cloud (13x74cm-5x29in) pastel gouache prov. 15-Mar-4 Sotheby's, Melbourne #107/R est:1800-2500 (A.D 4800)
£2273 $4205 €3319 Study for the ramp (55x74cm-22x29in) s. indis d.1992 gouache prov. 15-Mar-4 Sotheby's, Melbourne #119/R est:4000-6000 (A.D 5500)

AMORELLY, Pietro de (19th C) Italian
£820 $1517 €1197 Grand canal, Venice. View in Amsterdam (15x30cm-6x12in) s.i.verso pair. 14-Jan-4 Lawrence, Crewkerne #1402/R

AMORGASTI, Antonio (1880-1942) Italian
Sculpture
£1034 $1728 €1500 Deux chats devorant des poissons (15x20cm-6x8in) s.d.1916 num.45 brown pat bronze. 17-Nov-3 Bernaerts, Antwerp #25/R est:740-1000
£1611 $2980 €2400 Chamelier accompagne de ses chiens (59x60cm-23x24in) s.st.f.Bellens brown pat bronze marble socle. 15-Mar-4 Horta, Bruxelles #153 est:2000-3000

AMOROSI, Antonio (1660-1736) Italian
£1761 $3081 €2500 Jeune fille jouant au tambourin (42x33cm-17x13in) 17-Dec-3 Piasa, Paris #66/R est:4000-6000
£2698 $4964 €4100 La lecon de couture (36x49cm-14x19in) 22-Jun-4 Calmels Cohen, Paris #19/R est:1200-1500
£6000 $10920 €9000 Country concert (35x43cm-14x17in) 30-Jun-4 Neumeister, Munich #480/R est:9000

AMOROSI, Antonio (attrib) (1660-1736) Italian
£1600 $2992 €2336 Seamstress (42x33cm-17x13in) 27-Feb-4 Christie's, Kensington #208/R est:600-800
£2500 $4500 €3650 Portrait of a child (41x32cm-16x13in) 21-Jan-4 Sotheby's, New York #109/R est:4000-6000
£5500 $9900 €8030 Peasant selling pigeons. Peasant buying grapes (12x18cm-5x7in) copper pair prov. 23-Apr-4 Christie's, Kensington #251/R est:6000-8000

AMORSOLO, Fernando (1892-1972) Philippino
£4118 $7000 €6012 Tribal girl in dress (48x33cm-19x13in) s.d.1935 board prov. 9-Nov-3 Bonhams & Butterfields, Los Angeles #4134/R est:6000-8000
£5797 $8986 €8464 Hemp weavers (30x41cm-12x16in) s.d.1960 canvas on board. 6-Oct-2 Sotheby's, Singapore #80/R est:15000-20000 (S.D 16000)
£6950 $11606 €10147 Still life of tropical fruits (33x41cm-13x16in) s.i.d.1928 board. 26-Oct-3 Christie's, Hong Kong #33/R est:80000-100000 (HK.D 90000)
£7971 $12355 €11638 Tropical landscape (66x51cm-26x20in) s.d.1970 prov. 6-Oct-2 Sotheby's, Singapore #72/R est:2000-28000 (S.D 22000)
£8170 $14788 €11928 Man with cockerel (33x41cm-13x16in) s.d.1932 canvas on board. 4-Apr-4 Sotheby's, Singapore #104/R est:20000-30000 (S.D 25000)
£8500 $15045 €12410 Portrait of a Filipino man (48x37cm-19x15in) s. board. 27-Apr-4 Bonhams, New Bond Street #32/R est:10000-15000
£9266 $15475 €13528 Tropical lagoon (33x24cm-13x9in) s.d.1923 panel. 26-Oct-3 Christie's, Hong Kong #27/R est:100000-200000 (HK.D 120000)
£9420 $14601 €13753 Bonca boats (40x51cm-16x20in) s.d.1958. 6-Oct-2 Sotheby's, Singapore #89/R est:22000-28000 (S.D 26000)
£9804 $17745 €14314 Man with cockerel (38x48cm-15x19in) s.d.1938 canvas on board. 4-Apr-4 Sotheby's, Singapore #103/R est:30000-40000 (S.D 30000)
£11950 $19000 €17447 Rice planting (68x99cm-27x39in) s.d.1960. 12-Sep-3 Skinner, Boston #529a/R
£12429 $22000 €18146 Portrait of a lady (41x33cm-16x13in) s.d.1939 board sold with a companion. 2-May-4 Bonhams & Butterfields, Los Angeles #3094/R est:10000-15000
£14706 $26618 €21471 Planting rice (50x64cm-20x25in) s. 4-Apr-4 Sotheby's, Singapore #100/R est:45000-65000 (S.D 45000)
£15000 $25500 €21900 Midday rest (56x76cm-22x30in) s.d.1957. 4-Nov-3 Bonhams, New Bond Street #38/R est:20000-30000
£15217 $23587 €22217 Mount Arayat (36x49cm-14x19in) s.d.1931 canvas on board prov. 6-Oct-2 Sotheby's, Singapore #71/R est:30000-35000 (S.D 42000)
£15217 $23587 €22217 Harvest time (51x66cm-20x26in) s.d.1952. 6-Oct-2 Sotheby's, Singapore #76/R est:30000-40000 (S.D 42000)
£15647 $28165 €22845 Market scene (61x84cm-24x33in) s.d.1959 prov. 25-Apr-4 Christie's, Hong Kong #561/R est:200000-280000 (HK.D 220000)
£15686 $28392 €22902 Bathing by the stream (80x57cm-31x22in) s.d.57. 4-Apr-4 Sotheby's, Singapore #106/R est:48000-68000 (S.D 48000)
£16667 $27833 €24334 Winnowing rice (56x71cm-22x28in) s.d.1950. 12-Oct-3 Sotheby's, Singapore #80/R est:35000-55000 (S.D 48000)
£17391 $26957 €25391 Resting under the mango tree (56x71cm-22x28in) s.d.1953. 6-Oct-2 Sotheby's, Singapore #77/R est:30000-45000 (S.D 48000)
£17974 $32533 €26242 Harvest (59x85cm-23x33in) s.d.1960. 4-Apr-4 Sotheby's, Singapore #101/R est:50000-70000 (S.D 55000)
£20290 $31449 €29623 Tinkling dance (61x86cm-24x34in) s.d.1964. 6-Oct-2 Sotheby's, Singapore #73/R est:30000-40000 (S.D 56000)
£22569 $37691 €32951 Sunset (71x101cm-28x40in) s.d.1959. 12-Oct-3 Sotheby's, Singapore #75/R est:65000-85000 (S.D 65000)
£25806 $41290 €37677 Igorots (51x66cm-20x26in) s.d.1936 canvas on board. 18-May-3 Sotheby's, Singapore #75/R est:35000-55000 (S.D 72000)
£25806 $41290 €37677 Man with rooster (40x52cm-16x20in) s.d.1933 canvas on board. 18-May-3 Sotheby's, Singapore #82/R est:40000-60000 (S.D 72000)
£26389 $44069 €38528 Under the mango tree (63x89cm-25x35in) s.d.1948. 12-Oct-3 Sotheby's, Singapore #79/R est:45000-65000 (S.D 76000)
£29412 $53235 €42942 Transplanting rice (75x99cm-30x39in) s.d.1954. 4-Apr-4 Sotheby's, Singapore #102/R est:65000-85000 (S.D 90000)
£29412 $53235 €42942 Cockfight (62x85cm-24x33in) s.d.1949 canvas on board. 4-Apr-4 Sotheby's, Singapore #105/R est:40000-60000 (S.D 90000)
£30108 $48172 €43958 Igorot fire dance (61x76cm-24x30in) s.d.1948. 18-May-3 Sotheby's, Singapore #77/R est:45000-65000 (S.D 84000)
£39216 $70980 €57255 Princess Urduja (61x87cm-24x34in) s.d.1959. 4-Apr-4 Sotheby's, Singapore #107/R est:50000-70000 (S.D 120000)
£47312 $75699 €69076 Mango harvest (51x65cm-20x26in) s.d.1939 canvas on board. 18-May-3 Sotheby's, Singapore #83/R est:50000-70000 (S.D 132000)
£52083 $86979 €76041 By the stream (121x99cm-48x39in) s.d.1949. 12-Oct-3 Sotheby's, Singapore #76/R est:150000-250000 (S.D 150000)

AMOS, Imre (1907-1945) Hungarian
Works on paper
£748 $1324 €1092 In Russia (37x29cm-15x11in) indian ink. 28-Apr-4 Kieselbach, Budapest #87/R (H.F 280000)
£1449 $2623 €2116 Self portrait with angel (35x30cm-14x12in) s. ink paper on card. 16-Apr-4 Mu Terem Galeria, Budapest #7/R (H.F 550000)
£1697 $2935 €2478 Garden of memories (45x59cm-18x23in) W/C. 12-Dec-3 Kieselbach, Budapest #67/R (H.F 650000)

AMPENBERGER, Stefan (1908-1983) South African
£248 $443 €362 Extensive landscape (49x59cm-19x23in) s. canvas on board. 31-May-4 Stephan Welz, Johannesburg #143 (SA.R 3000)
£276 $461 €403 High veld landscape (39x49cm-15x19in) s. board. 20-Oct-3 Stephan Welz, Johannesburg #647 est:2000-3000 (SA.R 3200)
£345 $576 €504 Mountains landscape (34x43cm-13x17in) s. board. 20-Oct-3 Stephan Welz, Johannesburg #793 est:2800-3600 (SA.R 4000)

AMSHEWITZ, John Henry (1882-1942) British
£345 $576 €504 Figures and musicians outside a cape farmhouse (45x34cm-18x13in) s.i.verso board. 20-Oct-3 Stephan Welz, Johannesburg #527 est:3000-5000 (SA.R 4000)
£470 $799 €686 Horse drawn buggy arriving at a cape farmhouse (54x44cm-21x17in) s. 4-Nov-3 Stephan Welz, Johannesburg #677 est:3000-5000 (SA.R 5500)
£504 $913 €736 Still life of two Japanese figurines and a floral arrangement (25x46cm-10x18in) s. 30-Mar-4 Stephan Welz, Johannesburg #521 est:3000-5000 (SA.R 6000)
£726 $1235 €1060 Landing of Van Riebeeck (51x32cm-20x13in) s. s.i.d.1941 verso board. 4-Nov-3 Stephan Welz, Johannesburg #602/R est:3000-5000 (SA.R 8500)

AMSTEL, T van (20th C) Dutch
£299 $500 €437 Canal scene (58x58cm-23x23in) s. masonite oval. 20-Jun-3 Freeman, Philadelphia #189/R

AMUNDARAIN, Susana (20th C) South American
£235 $405 €343 Untitled (49x90cm-19x35in) s.verso acrylic painted 1986. 7-Dec-3 Subastas Odalys, Caracas #130

AMUS, Eugenio (1834-1899) Italian/French
£761 $1371 €1142 Seascape with lifeboat in rough weather (30x46cm-12x18in) s. 25-Apr-4 Goteborg Auktionsverk, Sweden #164/R (S.KR 10500)

ANACKER, Jean (1878-1955) German
£822 $1397 €1200 Spring in mountain landscape (70x59cm-28x23in) s. board. 5-Nov-3 Hugo Ruef, Munich #919

ANANNY, Terry (1956-) Canadian
£362 $605 €529 Collecting the sap (30x40cm-12x16in) s. acrylic. 17-Nov-3 Hodgins, Calgary #179/R (C.D 800)
£600 $1098 €876 Winter play (75x90cm-30x35in) s.i. acrylic. 1-Jun-4 Hodgins, Calgary #284/R (C.D 1500)

ANASTASI, Auguste (1820-1889) French
£1200 $2172 €1800 Apremont (22x30cm-9x12in) exhib.lit. 30-Mar-4 Rossini, Paris #278/R est:1800-2500
£1370 $2151 €2000 Basse-cour de plein air (20x36cm-8x14in) indis.sig.d.1861 panel. 20-Apr-3 Deauville, France #57/R est:1500-2000
£1399 $2406 €2000 Femme sur le chemin du village (46x37cm-18x15in) s. 7-Dec-3 Osenat, Fontainebleau #110 est:1800-2000
£1400 $2562 €2100 Grands arbres (27x20cm-11x8in) st.init.verso panel. 6-Jun-4 Osenat, Fontainebleau #34/R est:3000-3500
£2533 $4585 €3800 Rochers et mer bleue a Douarnenez, Bretagne (23x37cm-9x15in) lit. 30-Mar-4 Rossini, Paris #274/R est:3000-5000
£2800 $5124 €4200 Cottage (38x64cm-15x25in) s.d.1850. 6-Jun-4 Osenat, Fontainebleau #33/R est:5000-5500
£3133 $5671 €4700 Terrasse de couvent en Italie (38x69cm-15x27in) studio st. panel. 31-Mar-4 Sotheby's, Paris #101/R est:4000-6000
Works on paper
£300 $543 €450 Falaise d'Etretat (27x37cm-11x15in) st.mono.i.indis.d.8 juillet 47 pen black ink wash. 30-Mar-4 Rossini, Paris #275/R
£714 $1279 €1050 Bords de riviere a Bougival (30x45cm-12x18in) s.i. pen W/C gouache. 19-Mar-4 Millon & Associes, Paris #42/R
£1333 $2413 €2000 Moissonneuse-retour des champs (27x18cm-11x7in) mono. exhib.lit. 30-Mar-4 Rossini, Paris #277/R est:1500-2500

ANASTASI, William (1933-) American
Works on paper
£1111 $2000 €1622 Untitled (7x11cm-3x4in) s. graphite. 24-Apr-4 David Rago, Lambertville #366/R est:200-400

ANBURY, Sir Thomas (18/19th C) British
Works on paper
£3000 $4890 €4380 North East View of Hyderabad, on the Musi river (25x64cm-10x25in) i. pencil pen grey ink W/C prov.exhib. 24-Sep-3 Christie's, London #29/R est:3000-5000

ANCELET, Gabriel Auguste (19th C) French
Works on paper
£267 $491 €400 Plafond a caissons (48x83cm-19x33in) W/C htd gouache. 9-Jun-4 Le Roux & Morel, Paris #11
£433 $797 €650 Projet de restauration d'un chateau (49x68cm-19x27in) s. W/C. 9-Jun-4 Le Roux & Morel, Paris #12
£567 $1043 €850 Interieur de Saint Pierre de Rome (24x17cm-9x7in) s.d.1852 W/C. 9-Jun-4 Le Roux & Morel, Paris #15
£2133 $3925 €3200 Vues d'Italie et de Grece dont Pompei. Villa d'Este et Athens (10x19cm-4x7in) s.d.1853 W/C five. 9-Jun-4 Le Roux & Morel, Paris #10/R est:1200-1500

ANCELIN, Charles (20th C) French
£430 $760 €640 Attelage sur plage (43x55cm-17x22in) s. 3-May-4 Giraudeau, Tours #31

ANCELLET, Émile (19/20th C) French
£676 $1277 €1000 Bord de mer (43x61cm-17x24in) s.d.1901. 21-Feb-4 Livinec, Gaudcheau & Jezequel, Rennes #106

ANCELOT, Marguerite Virginie (1792-1875) French
£4276 $7868 €6500 Henri IV et Catherine de Medicis (74x101cm-29x40in) bears sig.d.1819 exhib. 23-Jun-4 Sotheby's, Paris #67/R est:20000-30000

ANCHER, Anna (1859-1935) Danish
£2559 $4095 €3736 Interior scene with young Skagen girl sewing (44x38cm-17x15in) indis.init. panel. 22-Sep-3 Rasmussen, Vejle #133/R est:30000-40000 (D.KR 27000)
£13744 $21991 €20066 Interior scene with man mending socks (37x47cm-15x19in) s. exhib. 22-Sep-3 Rasmussen, Vejle #135/R est:150000 (D.KR 145000)
£41588 $71947 €60718 The artist's mother Ane Hedvig Brondum seated at writing desk (45x53cm-18x21in) s.d.1910 exhib. 9-Dec-3 Rasmussen, Copenhagen #1276/R est:300000-350000 (D.KR 440000)
Works on paper
£284 $491 €415 Morning coffee in the garden (11x14cm-4x6in) init.i. pencil. 9-Dec-3 Rasmussen, Copenhagen #1720 (D.KR 3000)

ANCHER, Helga (attrib) (1883-1964) Danish
£276 $470 €403 Chickens by railings (28x35cm-11x14in) init. 10-Nov-3 Rasmussen, Vejle #118/R (D.KR 3000)

ANCHER, Michael (1849-1927) Danish
£701 $1107 €1016 Fisherman seen from behind (28x14cm-11x6in) 2-Sep-3 Rasmussen, Copenhagen #1889 (D.KR 7500)
£1244 $2115 €1816 Interior scene with seated fisherman (50x37cm-20x15in) s.d.81. 10-Nov-3 Rasmussen, Vejle #267/R est:15000-20000 (D.KR 13500)
£1584 $2487 €2313 Portrait of the sculptor Rudolph Tegner at Skagen (37x29cm-15x11in) init.i.d.1907. 30-Aug-3 Rasmussen, Havnen #2213/R est:10000-15000 (D.KR 17000)
£1611 $2949 €2352 Sunset over Brovandene south of Skagen (29x40cm-11x16in) init. 9-Jun-4 Rasmussen, Copenhagen #1833/R est:12000-15000 (D.KR 18000)
£1848 $2957 €2698 Interior scene with mother feeding her child (44x36cm-17x14in) mono. 22-Sep-3 Rasmussen, Vejle #132/R est:20000 (D.KR 19500)
£1970 $3604 €2876 Skagen fisherman (41x30cm-16x12in) init.d.25. 9-Jun-4 Rasmussen, Copenhagen #1794/R est:25000 (D.KR 22000)
£2074 $3837 €3028 Portrait of fisherman (35x29cm-14x11in) init.d.15. 15-Mar-4 Rasmussen, Vejle #78/R est:20000-25000 (D.KR 23000)
£2686 $4915 €3922 Skagen fisherman (35x25cm-14x10in) init. prov. 9-Jun-4 Rasmussen, Copenhagen #1793/R est:10000-15000 (D.KR 30000)
£2857 $4857 €4171 Interior scene with the fisherman Ole Svendsen by window (56x45cm-22x18in) init.d.05 exhib. 10-Nov-3 Rasmussen, Vejle #264/R est:30000-40000 (D.KR 31000)
£2857 $4857 €4171 Portrait of a fisherman with sou'wester (41x31cm-16x12in) init.d.17 panel. 10-Nov-3 Rasmussen, Vejle #265/R est:35000 (D.KR 31000)
£3000 $5520 €4380 Fisherman in the evening sun, Skagen (39x32cm-15x13in) s. 23-Mar-4 Bonhams, New Bond Street #27/R est:3000-5000
£3044 $5570 €4444 Evening at Skagen Strand with fishermen catching eel (34x59cm-13x23in) init.d.20. 9-Jun-4 Rasmussen, Copenhagen #1784/R est:25000-35000 (D.KR 34000)
£3200 $5888 €4672 Entrance to the artist's house at Skagen (58x43cm-23x17in) init. 23-Mar-4 Bonhams, New Bond Street #25/R est:4000-6000
£3214 $5560 €4692 Bearded man with straw hat (40x30cm-16x12in) init.indis.d.13 or 18 i.verso. 9-Dec-3 Rasmussen, Copenhagen #1539/R est:15000-20000 (D.KR 34000)
£3953 $7353 €5771 Seagulls at Skagen Sonderstrand (70x97cm-28x38in) s. 2-Mar-4 Rasmussen, Copenhagen #1420/R est:40000 (D.KR 44000)
£5551 $10158 €8104 The garden at Michael and Anna Ancher's house at Markvej, Skagen (59x43cm-23x17in) init. 9-Jun-4 Rasmussen, Copenhagen #1792/R est:75000 (D.KR 62000)
£5607 $8860 €8130 Young girl - Marie harvesting at Skagen (95x80cm-37x31in) init.d.04 exhib.prov. 2-Sep-3 Rasmussen, Copenhagen #1513/R est:50000-75000 (D.KR 60000)
£6542 $10336 €9486 Young girl reading (47x62cm-19x24in) init. exhib. 2-Sep-3 Rasmussen, Copenhagen #1504/R est:100000 (D.KR 70000)
£6616 $11446 €9659 Fisher family at sunset (54x64cm-21x25in) init.d.10. 9-Dec-3 Rasmussen, Copenhagen #1271/R est:50000-75000 (D.KR 70000)
£8057 $14745 €11763 Two fishermen wearing oil skins looking out of window (54x48cm-21x19in) init.d.15 prov. 9-Jun-4 Rasmussen, Copenhagen #1475/R est:100000-125000 (D.KR 90000)
£9569 $15502 €13875 Fishermen in sunshine at Skagen Strand (44x65cm-17x26in) init.d.92. 4-Aug-3 Rasmussen, Vejle #2/R est:125000-150000 (D.KR 100000)
£10821 $20018 €15799 Young mother holding baby (54x49cm-21x19in) init.d.13 prov. 15-Mar-4 Rasmussen, Vejle #63/R est:125000-150000 (D.KR 120000)
£12287 $21257 €17939 After bonfire night - fishermen enjoying the late afternoon sunshine (40x73cm-16x29in) init.d.02. 9-Dec-3 Rasmussen, Copenhagen #1268/R est:100000-125000 (D.KR 130000)
£19766 $36766 €28858 Anna Ancher seated in chair wearing black dress (88x68cm-35x27in) prov. 2-Mar-4 Rasmussen, Copenhagen #1267/R est:75000-125000 (D.KR 220000)
£34026 $58866 €49678 Two friends - Skagen fishermen Niels Ottesen and Peter Rontved (69x111cm-27x44in) s.i.d.99 exhib. 9-Dec-3 Rasmussen, Copenhagen #1277/R est:400000 (D.KR 360000)
£41479 $76736 €60559 Anna, Michael and Helga Ancher seated at breakfast table, Markvejen, Skagen (94x82cm-37x32in) s.d.20 exhib. 15-Mar-4 Rasmussen, Vejle #66/R est:400000 (D.KR 460000)
£53908 $100270 €78706 Winding wool - Maren Sofie Olsen and a small boy (107x143cm-42x56in) s.d.1887 exhib.prov. 2-Mar-4 Rasmussen, Copenhagen #1248/R est:500000-600000 (D.KR 600000)
Prints
£8531 $13649 €12455 Fisherman and boy at Skagen Strand (56x71cm-22x28in) s.d.1884. 22-Sep-3 Rasmussen, Vejle #136/R est:100000 (D.KR 90000)
Works on paper
£622 $1008 €902 Portrait of fisherman (17x15cm-7x6in) pencil. 4-Aug-3 Rasmussen, Vejle #6/R (D.KR 6500)
£1229 $2126 €1794 Skagen fisherman Old Svendsen (28x22cm-11x9in) s. pencil prov. 9-Dec-3 Rasmussen, Copenhagen #1729 est:5000 (D.KR 13000)

ANCIAUX, Germaine (?) ?
£533 $965 €800 Mere et enfant (60x40cm-24x16in) s. 30-Mar-4 Palais de Beaux Arts, Brussels #459

ANDENMATTEN, Leo (1922-1979) Swiss
£1982 $3370 €2894 City in red (73x100cm-29x39in) s. 7-Nov-3 Dobiaschofsky, Bern #227/R est:4500 (S.FR 4500)

ANDER, Ture (1881-1959) Swedish
£1231 $2117 €1797 The yellow house (42x54cm-17x21in) s.d.16. 3-Dec-3 AB Stockholms Auktionsverk #2240/R est:12000-15000 (S.KR 16000)

ANDERBERG, Niklas (1950-) Danish
£564 $960 €823 Composition (155x100cm-61x39in) 26-Nov-3 Kunsthallen, Copenhagen #106 (D.KR 6000)
£564 $960 €823 Composition (155x100cm-61x39in) 26-Nov-3 Kunsthallen, Copenhagen #112/R (D.KR 6000)

ANDERBOUHR, Paul-Jean (1909-) French
£367 $667 €550 Quai de Seine (54x45cm-21x18in) s. 29-Jun-4 Chenu & Scrive, Lyon #4
£1006 $1800 €1469 Dimanche matin place de la Concorde. s.i. 13-May-4 Dallas Auction Gallery, Dallas #204/R est:2000-4000

ANDERLECHT, Engelbert van (1918-1961) Belgian
Works on paper
£1184 $2143 €1800 Composition (99x70cm-39x28in) Indian ink. 19-Apr-4 Horta, Bruxelles #48 est:1500-1800

ANDERSEN, Asger (1908-1980) Danish
£766 $1240 €1111 Spring - composition with figures moving (122x120cm-48x47in) s.d.78. 4-Aug-3 Rasmussen, Vejle #674/R (D.KR 8000)

ANDERSEN, Carl Ferdinand (1846-1913) Danish
£1050 $1711 €1533 Father looking after the children (53x55cm-21x22in) s.d.1874. 27-Sep-3 Rasmussen, Havnen #2132/R (D.KR 11200)

ANDERSEN, Cilius (1865-1913) Danish
£561 $886 €813 Small girl greeting harvester returning home, Jyllinge (77x97cm-30x38in) s.d.1899. 2-Sep-3 Rasmussen, Copenhagen #1688/R (D.KR 6000)
£1963 $3101 €2846 The young model in the studio (138x103cm-54x41in) s.d.1911. 2-Sep-3 Rasmussen, Copenhagen #1701/R est:15000 (D.KR 21000)
£4412 $7500 €6442 Arranging the flowers (76x63cm-30x25in) s.d.1895. 29-Oct-3 Christie's, Rockefeller NY #15/R est:8000-12000

ANDERSEN, Gunnar Aagaard (1919-1982) Danish
£1557 $2833 €2273 Composition (46x61cm-18x24in) 7-Feb-4 Rasmussen, Havnen #4233 est:1000 (D.KR 17000)

ANDERSEN, Ib (1884-1943) Danish
£332 $531 €485 Adam and Eve (43x55cm-17x22in) init. 22-Sep-3 Rasmussen, Vejle #723/R (D.KR 3500)
£341 $546 €498 Adam and Eve (109x149cm-43x59in) 22-Sep-3 Rasmussen, Vejle #732/R (D.KR 3600)
£711 $1137 €1038 Abraham and Isaac (150x200cm-59x79in) s. 22-Sep-3 Rasmussen, Vejle #722/R (D.KR 7500)
£853 $1365 €1245 Stormy seas with mermaids on cliffs (99x120cm-39x47in) s. 22-Sep-3 Rasmussen, Vejle #731/R (D.KR 9000)
Works on paper
£1625 $2989 €2373 Cat seated on window ledge (56x78cm-22x31in) s.d.35 Indian ink W/C pencil exhib.prov. 29-Mar-4 Rasmussen, Copenhagen #538/R est:5000 (D.KR 18000)

ANDERSEN, Johan Vilhelm (1892-1971) Danish
£271 $506 €396 Study from near Avignon (50x43cm-20x17in) init. exhib. 25-Feb-4 Museumsbygningen, Copenhagen #40 (D.KR 3000)

ANDERSEN, Julius (19th C) Danish
£2489 $4530 €3734 Fjord landscape from Greenland with women in boat (27x94cm-11x37in) s. 19-Jun-4 Rasmussen, Havnen #2130/R est:4000-6000 (D.KR 28000)
£2507 $4587 €3660 Three Eskimos fishing from rocks (48x42cm-19x17in) s. 9-Jun-4 Rasmussen, Copenhagen #1779/R est:10000 (D.KR 28000)

ANDERSEN, Mogens (1916-2003) Danish
£1223 $2079 €1786 Composition (55x46cm-22x18in) init. 26-Nov-3 Kunsthallen, Copenhagen #114/R est:10000 (D.KR 13000)
£1896 $3033 €2768 Composition (73x60cm-29x24in) init. painted c.1980 exhib. 22-Sep-3 Rasmussen, Vejle #639/R est:20000 (D.KR 20000)
£2916 $4958 €4257 Composition (146x114cm-57x45in) s.d.1992 verso. 26-Nov-3 Kunsthallen, Copenhagen #30/R est:30000 (D.KR 31000)
Works on paper
£470 $800 €686 Composition (66x50cm-26x20in) init.d.April 70 W/C. 26-Nov-3 Kunsthallen, Copenhagen #18 (D.KR 5000)

ANDERSEN, Mogens S (1909-2002) Danish
£271 $486 €396 Coastal landscape with lighthouse (80x105cm-31x41in) s. 10-May-4 Rasmussen, Vejle #688/R (D.KR 3000)
£281 $469 €410 Landscape from Store Klit near Blaavandshuk (85x140cm-33x55in) s. 25-Oct-3 Rasmussen, Havnen #4010 (D.KR 3000)

£361 $664 €527 Wooded landscape (81x70cm-32x28in) s.d.c.1941 verso. 29-Mar-4 Rasmussen, Copenhagen #551 (D.KR 4000)
£433 $810 €632 Evening landscape (70x90cm-28x35in) s.d.34 verso. 25-Feb-4 Kunsthallen, Copenhagen #7 (D.KR 4800)
£474 $769 €692 After sunset, Kerteminde (79x100cm-31x39in) s. 9-Aug-3 Hindemae, Ullerslev #1084/R (D.KR 5000)

ANDERSEN, Niels (1924-) Danish
£1067 $1941 €1600 Portrait of Grethe (61x47cm-24x19in) mono.d.56 i.verso. 3-Jul-4 Badum, Bamberg #65/R est:2400

ANDERSEN, Nils Severin (1897-1972) South African
£474 $792 €692 Cape farmhouse (60x90cm-24x35in) s. board. 20-Oct-3 Stephan Welz, Johannesburg #778 est:3500-5000 (SA.R 5500)

ANDERSEN, Robin Christian (1890-1969) Austrian
£2098 $3566 €3000 Still life (76x98cm-30x39in) mono. 28-Nov-3 Wiener Kunst Auktionen, Vienna #495/R est:3000-5000
£4196 $7133 €6000 Still life (58x74cm-23x29in) prov.lit. 25-Nov-3 Hassfurther, Vienna #18/R est:4000-4500
Works on paper
£333 $600 €500 Cyclamen (60x47cm-24x19in) s. pencil W/C double-sided. 21-Apr-4 Dorotheum, Vienna #154/R
£367 $675 €550 Cyclamen (45x30cm-18x12in) s. pencil W/C. 9-Jun-4 Dorotheum, Salzburg #804/R
£533 $960 €800 Stork and tortoise (62x38cm-24x15in) s. mixed media. 21-Apr-4 Dorotheum, Vienna #152/R
£986 $1725 €1400 Still life with plant and fruits (35x50cm-14x20in) mono. W/C gouache. 19-Dec-3 Dorotheum, Vienna #156/R

ANDERSEN, Roy H (1930-) American
£3073 $5500 €4487 Long hunt (30x23cm-12x9in) 15-May-4 Altermann Galleries, Santa Fe #37/R
£16201 $29000 €23653 Horse and the lion (91x66cm-36x26in) 15-May-4 Altermann Galleries, Santa Fe #130/R
£20053 $37500 €29277 Learnin the ropes (76x102cm-30x40in) s. prov.exhib.lit. 24-Jul-4 Coeur d'Alene, Hayden #240/R est:30000-40000
£23464 $42000 €34257 When ponies dance (102x76cm-40x30in) 15-May-4 Altermann Galleries, Santa Fe #39/R
£25401 $47500 €37085 This one will care for you (61x76cm-24x30in) prov.lit. 24-Jul-4 Coeur d'Alene, Hayden #130/R est:20000-30000

ANDERSEN, Soren (1926-) Danish
£360 $576 €526 Street on the west coast (82x94cm-32x37in) init.d.60 exhib. 22-Sep-3 Rasmussen, Vejle #590 (D.KR 3800)

ANDERSEN, Wilhelm (1867-1945) Danish
£473 $818 €691 Still life of flowers plate and statuette on table (73x62cm-29x24in) s. 9-Dec-3 Rasmussen, Copenhagen #1583/R (D.KR 5000)

ANDERSEN-LUNDBY, Anders (1841-1923) Danish
£531 $967 €775 Fjord landscape with farmer ploughing his field (19x36cm-7x14in) s.d.1876. 7-Feb-4 Rasmussen, Havnen #2202 (D.KR 5800)
£541 $1001 €790 Seascape with man-o-war off the coast (17x25cm-7x10in) s. 15-Mar-4 Rasmussen, Vejle #155/R (D.KR 6000)
£625 $1019 €900 Fishing boats at anchor (31x40cm-12x16in) s.i. verso canvas on board. 26-Sep-3 Bolland & Marotz, Bremen #486/R
£632 $1023 €916 Winter landscape with buildings (40x56cm-16x22in) s. 4-Aug-3 Rasmussen, Vejle #343/R (D.KR 6600)
£797 $1370 €1164 Winter landscape with man walking with his dog, Sollerod (19x26cm-7x10in) s.d.1874. 3-Dec-3 Museumsbygningen, Copenhagen #188/R (D.KR 8500)
£984 $1810 €1476 Summer landscape with bridge across river (28x40cm-11x16in) s. 14-Jun-4 Lilla Bukowskis, Stockholm #835 (S.KR 13500)
£1000 $1820 €1500 Winter landscape with deer (96x71cm-38x28in) s.d.1888. 1-Jul-4 Van Ham, Cologne #1197/R est:3500
£1164 $2130 €1699 Landscape from Langelinie. Approaching thunder storm (27x37cm-11x15in) i.verso pair painted c.1870. 9-Jun-4 Rasmussen, Copenhagen #1751/R est:10000 (D.KR 13000)
£1342 $2470 €2000 Horse drawn peasant cart in winter landscape (44x62cm-17x24in) s. board on panel. 25-Mar-4 Dr Fritz Nagel, Stuttgart #691/R est:2500
£1944 $3169 €2800 Winter landscape lit by afternoon sun (76x114cm-30x45in) s. 25-Sep-3 Dr Fritz Nagel, Stuttgart #1324/R est:2800
£1977 $3677 €2886 Winter landscape (24x37cm-9x15in) s.d.1876. 2-Mar-4 Rasmussen, Copenhagen #1255/R est:25000 (D.KR 22000)
£2200 $4070 €3212 Frozen pond. Bringing in the firewood (30x42cm-12x17in) s.d.1872 pair. 10-Mar-4 Sotheby's, Olympia #244/R est:1500-2000
£2238 $4096 €3267 Morning, tending the cows (48x65cm-19x26in) s. 9-Jun-4 Rasmussen, Copenhagen #1743/R est:30000-40000 (D.KR 25000)
£2238 $4096 €3267 Winter's day at the outskirts of wood (30x42cm-12x17in) s.d.1872. 9-Jun-4 Rasmussen, Copenhagen #1752/R est:25000 (D.KR 25000)
£2238 $4096 €3267 Thatched house on the outskirts of wood (30x42cm-12x17in) s.d.1872. 9-Jun-4 Rasmussen, Copenhagen #1755/R est:25000 (D.KR 25000)
£2517 $4280 €3600 Sailing ships off coast (35x63cm-14x25in) s. 24-Nov-3 Dorotheum, Vienna #59/R est:3600-4000
£3125 $5094 €4500 Munich street (64x54cm-25x21in) s.d.91. 26-Sep-3 Bolland & Marotz, Bremen #485/R est:3800
£3592 $6214 €5244 Winter landscape with small boy on country road (32x42cm-13x17in) s.indis.d.1873 or 1878. 9-Dec-3 Rasmussen, Copenhagen #1387/R est:25000 (D.KR 38000)
£5047 $7974 €7318 Winter's day in the wood with man walking his dog (55x44cm-22x17in) s.d.1874. 2-Sep-3 Rasmussen, Copenhagen #1800/R est:25000 (D.KR 54000)
£6289 $11698 €9182 River in winter landscape, German Alps behind (70x87cm-28x34in) s. 2-Mar-4 Rasmussen, Copenhagen #1254/R est:75000 (D.KR 70000)
£8086 $15040 €11806 Winter's day with trees in sunshine (69x96cm-27x38in) s.d.1874. 2-Mar-4 Rasmussen, Copenhagen #1222/R est:25000-35000 (D.KR 90000)
£8953 $16383 €13071 Oxen and cart by Himmelbjerg Islands (81x126cm-32x50in) s.d.1879 exhib.prov. 9-Jun-4 Rasmussen, Copenhagen #1702/R est:100000-125000 (D.KR 100000)

ANDERSKOW, John (1927-) Danish
£307 $567 €448 Green landscape with white flowers (81x98cm-32x39in) s. 15-Mar-4 Rasmussen, Vejle #678/R (D.KR 3400)

ANDERSON, Blair (?) British?
£900 $1503 €1314 Peat cutting (144x179cm-57x70in) s.verso. 11-Oct-3 Shapes, Edinburgh #326

ANDERSON, Charles Goldsborough (1865-1936) British
£616 $992 €899 Sir Henry Irving as Hamlet (141x82cm-56x32in) 12-Aug-3 Peter Webb, Auckland #116 (NZ.D 1700)
£2865 $5243 €4183 Portrait of lady on terrace with borzoi (220x110cm-87x43in) s.d.1901. 9-Jun-4 Rasmussen, Copenhagen #1592/R est:25000-30000 (D.KR 32000)

ANDERSON, Clayton (1964-) Canadian
£1351 $2297 €1972 View of Link Island (61x76cm-24x30in) s.d.2003 s.i.verso acrylic board. 27-Nov-3 Heffel, Vancouver #165/R est:2500-4500 (C.D 3000)
£2846 $5093 €4155 Between the trees (50x121cm-20x48in) s.d.2004 i.verso acrylic board. 27-May-4 Heffel, Vancouver #201/R est:4000-5000 (C.D 7000)
£2928 $4977 €4275 Near Seymour Narrows (61x101cm-24x40in) s.d.2003 s.i.verso acrylic board. 27-Nov-3 Heffel, Vancouver #167/R est:4000-5000 (C.D 6500)
£3252 $5821 €4748 Buttle Lake at dusk (71x81cm-28x32in) s.d.2001 i.verso acrylic board. 27-May-4 Heffel, Vancouver #153/R est:3500-4500 (C.D 8000)
£4065 $7276 €5935 Melting snow on the bluff (61x76cm-24x30in) s.d.2004 i.verso acrylic board. 27-May-4 Heffel, Vancouver #151/R est:4000-5000 (C.D 10000)

ANDERSON, Douglas (1934-) British
£270 $478 €394 Tethered owl (40x25cm-16x10in) s. panel. 2-May-4 Lots Road Auctions, London #370

ANDERSON, Edward Enoch (1878-1961) British
Works on paper
£400 $688 €584 Whitby harbour (33x20cm-13x8in) s. W/C. 4-Dec-3 Richardson & Smith, Whitby #423/R

ANDERSON, Emily (19th C) British?
Works on paper
£300 $480 €438 Ploughing scene with two shire horses and farmhand (33x48cm-13x19in) s.d.1890 W/C. 16-Sep-3 Gorringes, Bexhill #1691

ANDERSON, Guy Irving (1906-1998) American
£983 $1700 €1435 Man over sharp sea. Two floating figures (18x107cm-7x42in) s. one d.78 oil paper pair. 13-Dec-3 Sloans & Kenyon, Bethesda #507/R est:400-500

ANDERSON, Harold (1894-1973) American
£1955 $3500 €2854 House call (79x97cm-31x38in) s. 26-May-4 Doyle, New York #151/R est:2000-4000

ANDERSON, J (?) ?
£2000 $3580 €2920 Lost in thought (51x41cm-20x16in) s. 27-May-4 Christie's, Kensington #276/R est:3000-5000

ANDERSON, James (1813-1899) ?
£1679 $3056 €2451 Goldminer (76x63cm-30x25in) 16-Jun-4 Deutscher-Menzies, Melbourne #258/R est:5000-7500 (A.D 4400)
Photographs
£5594 $9510 €8000 The Forum Romanum and Temple of Saturn (76x99cm-30x39in) gold toned albumen lit. 28-Nov-3 Bassenge, Berlin #4004/R est:9000

ANDERSON, James Bell (1886-1938) British
£260 $478 €380 Portrait of a gentleman, wearing a bow tie, seated (104x76cm-41x30in) s.d.1914. 24-Jun-4 Ewbank, Send #568/R

ANDERSON, John (19th C) British
£700 $1267 €1022 Rocket (139x130cm-55x51in) s.i.d.verso. 31-Mar-4 Goodman, Sydney #272 (A.D 1700)
£1772 $2800 €2587 Interior (51x61cm-20x24in) s. 7-Sep-3 Treadway Gallery, Cincinnati #696/R est:2000-3000
£2033 $3191 €2948 Adelphi (179x200cm-70x79in) s.d.95 i.d.1995 stretcher linen prov. 27-Aug-3 Christie's, Sydney #688/R est:2500-4500 (A.D 5000)
£2236 $3510 €3242 Through red hill (169x195cm-67x77in) s.i.d.1995 verso prov.exhib. 27-Aug-3 Christie's, Sydney #741/R est:2000-4000 (A.D 5500)
£6073 $9777 €8867 Summer (205x230cm-81x91in) s.d.03 linen canvas. 25-Aug-3 Sotheby's, Paddington #446/R est:7000-9000 (A.D 15000)

ANDERSON, John MacVicar (1835-1915) British
£45000 $76500 €65700 View of Westminster from the Thames (91x182cm-36x72in) s.d.1878. 25-Nov-3 Christie's, London #154/R est:50000-80000

ANDERSON, John Stewart (20th C) British
Works on paper
£6500 $10335 €9490 Design for the motorists prefer Shell poster (27x48cm-11x19in) s.d.35 gouache sold with a design by another hand lit. 10-Sep-3 Sotheby's, Olympia #83/R est:400-600

ANDERSON, Kathleen Winifred (1878-1968) South African
£248 $443 €362 Johannesburg Art Gallery, Joubert Park (58x48cm-23x19in) 31-May-4 Stephan Welz, Johannesburg #258 (SA.R 3000)

ANDERSON, Laura (20th C) American
£255 $400 €372 Pears and red paper (30x30cm-12x12in) s. 20-Apr-3 Outer Cape Auctions, Provincetown #31/R
£478 $750 €698 Red and green Adirondack chairs (76x61cm-30x24in) s. 20-Apr-3 Outer Cape Auctions, Provincetown #78/R
£1622 $3000 €2368 Three boats (91x112cm-36x44in) s. 17-Jul-4 Outer Cape Auctions, Provincetown #80/R

ANDERSON, Oscar (1873-1953) American
£240 $450 €350 Wintertime (20x28cm-8x11in) s. i.d.Feb 10 1932 verso. 29-Feb-4 Grogan, Boston #70/R
£6707 $11000 €9725 Home harbor (81x71cm-32x28in) s. i.verso prov. 31-May-3 Brunk, Ashville #35/R est:1500-2500

ANDERSON, Robert (1842-1885) British
Works on paper
£250 $465 €365 Trawlers entering harbour (25x40cm-10x16in) s. W/C scratching out. 2-Mar-4 Bearnes, Exeter #376
£300 $552 €438 Waiting for a nibble (15x22cm-6x9in) s. W/C. 23-Jun-4 Cheffins, Cambridge #452/R
£330 $600 €482 Montiome on the beach (15x28cm-6x11in) s.d.1869 pencil W/C gouache prov. 7-Feb-4 Neal Auction Company, New Orleans #94
£360 $623 €526 Wanderers, Brittany (75x52cm-30x20in) s.d.1883 W/C. 10-Dec-3 Bonhams, Bury St Edmunds #539
£452 $750 €660 Near Montiome on the beach (15x28cm-6x11in) s.d.1869 pencil W/C gouache. 4-Oct-3 Neal Auction Company, New Orleans #259/R
£700 $1281 €1022 Unloading the grain cart (35x51cm-14x20in) s.d.1876 W/C. 28-Jan-4 Hampton & Littlewood, Exeter #386/R

ANDERSON, Sophie (1823-1903) British
£4500 $8280 €6570 Young flower girl (47x37cm-19x15in) init. board. 23-Mar-4 Bonhams, New Bond Street #68/R est:4000-6000
£11000 $20240 €16060 Initials (53x43cm-21x17in) s. prov. 11-Jun-4 Christie's, London #109/R est:6000-10000
£12500 $23000 €18250 Hanging the garland (31x37cm-12x15in) 26-Mar-4 Sotheby's, London #73/R est:10000-15000
£16000 $29440 €23360 Reading time (43x53cm-17x21in) s. 11-Jun-4 Christie's, London #108/R est:7000-10000
£48000 $81600 €70080 Cheat (51x61cm-20x24in) s. prov. 27-Nov-3 Sotheby's, London #337/R est:12000-18000

ANDERSON, Stanley (1884-1966) British
Works on paper
£350 $627 €511 The chaff-cutter (17x15cm-7x6in) s.i. pencil. 25-May-4 Bonhams, Knightsbridge #56/R
£450 $765 €657 Hazy winter morning (22x31cm-9x12in) s. W/C over pencil. 1-Dec-3 Bonhams, Bath #50/R
£1000 $1720 €1460 In the shade, cattle and horse resting under a spreading tree (23x30cm-9x12in) s. W/C. 5-Dec-3 Keys, Aylsham #431 est:1000-1500

ANDERSON, Walter Inglis (1903-1965) American
£45181 $75000 €65964 Study for the mural Southern History and Life (86x91cm-34x36in) plywood panel on masonite prov. 4-Oct-3 Neal Auction Company, New Orleans #545/R est:30000-50000
£84302 $145000 €123081 Study for the mural of the History of the South (51x152cm-20x60in) wood prov. 6-Dec-3 Neal Auction Company, New Orleans #582/R est:20000-30000
Works on paper
£1024 $1700 €1495 Cat (28x20cm-11x8in) i. ink. 4-Oct-3 Neal Auction Company, New Orleans #547/R est:1500-2500
£3614 $6000 €5276 Bird with iris (28x20cm-11x8in) i. W/C prov. 4-Oct-3 Neal Auction Company, New Orleans #548/R est:6000-9000
£4070 $7000 €5942 Grapefruit grove (20x28cm-8x11in) i. W/C prov. 6-Dec-3 Neal Auction Company, New Orleans #588/R est:7000-10000
£4518 $7500 €6596 Trees (20x28cm-8x11in) W/C prov. 4-Oct-3 Neal Auction Company, New Orleans #546/R est:7000-10000
£5523 $9500 €8064 Two reclining tigers (20x28cm-8x11in) W/C. 6-Dec-3 Neal Auction Company, New Orleans #589/R est:4000-6000
£6395 $11000 €9337 Rice birds on Horn Island (20x28cm-8x11in) W/C. 6-Dec-3 Neal Auction Company, New Orleans #583/R est:7000-10000
£10843 $18000 €15831 Horn Island (20x84cm-8x33in) W/C triptych prov. 4-Oct-3 Neal Auction Company, New Orleans #549/R est:12000-18000

ANDERSON, Will (fl.1880-1895) British
£300 $555 €438 Mother and child on a track beside a farmstead, an extensive landscape (20x53cm-8x21in) s. W/C htd white. 11-Mar-4 Duke & Son, Dorchester #68/R
£1379 $2552 €2000 Paysage anime (15x30cm-6x12in) series of four. 13-Jan-4 Vanderkindere, Brussels #179 est:2000-3000
£1600 $2672 €2336 Kentish farm (56x93cm-22x37in) s. 13-Nov-3 Christie's, Kensington #127 est:800-1200

ANDERSON, William (1757-1837) British
£1600 $2656 €2336 Provisioning the fleet (36x48cm-14x19in) s.d.1807 panel. 1-Oct-3 Bonhams, Knightsbridge #147/R est:300-500
£3000 $5160 €4380 Shipping off the Dutch coast (11x16cm-4x6in) one s.d.1895 panel pair. 2-Dec-3 Sotheby's, London #9/R est:3000-5000
£3600 $6588 €5256 Dawlish - an extensive coastal scene (22x29cm-9x11in) panel prov. 6-Jul-4 Bearnes, Exeter #496/R est:1500-2000
£4500 $7200 €6570 Bell Inn, Erith, Kent (25x36cm-10x14in) panel. 16-Sep-3 Bonhams, New Bond Street #42/R est:5000-7000
£7000 $12530 €10220 Three-master and other ships on the Thames at Millwall with moored colliers (67x94cm-26x37in) s. 26-May-4 Christie's, Kensington #584/R est:6000-8000
£9730 $18000 €14206 Dutch warship and merchantmen in an estuary, and figures on the shore (45x61cm-18x24in) indis.sig.d.1795 prov. 10-Feb-4 Christie's, Rockefeller NY #162/R est:20000-30000
£23000 $42320 €33580 A 47 gun third rate in three position off Table Bay, Cape of Good Hope (84x130cm-33x51in) with sig.d.1790. 11-Jun-4 Christie's, London #48/R est:12000-18000
Works on paper
£3200 $5728 €4672 Anchorage at Spithead (21x30cm-8x12in) s. blk ink W/C prov. 26-May-4 Christie's, Kensington #373/R est:2000-3000

ANDERSON, William (attrib) (1757-1837) British
£1600 $2720 €2336 Dutch barges (17x23cm-7x9in) s.d.1805 panel pair. 19-Nov-3 Christie's, Kensington #450/R
Works on paper
£1500 $2370 €2175 Shipping in a calm sea (21x30cm-8x12in) W/C prov. 3-Sep-3 Bonhams, Bury St Edmunds #327/R est:800-1200

ANDERSSON, Allan (1904-1979) Swedish
£305 $548 €458 Bird of prey (80x100cm-31x39in) s. 25-Apr-4 Goteborg Auktionsverk, Sweden #417/R (S.KR 4200)

ANDERSSON, Lars (1957-) Swedish
£1172 $2075 €1711 Woman and stone (130x110cm-51x43in) init.d.90 exhib. 27-Apr-4 AB Stockholms Auktionsverk #1045/R est:8000-10000 (S.KR 16000)

ANDERSSON, Lolle (1907-) Swedish
£276 $496 €414 Garden with flowers (46x55cm-18x22in) s. panel. 25-Apr-4 Goteborg Auktionsverk, Sweden #382/R (S.KR 3800)

ANDERSSON, Marten (1934-) Swedish
Works on paper
£788 $1419 €1150 With horse and cart (26x34cm-10x13in) s. W/C. 26-Jan-4 Lilla Bukowskis, Stockholm #735 (S.KR 10500)
£1099 $1945 €1605 Lots of timber and moonlight (150x113cm-59x44in) s.d.1958 mixed media panel prov. 27-Apr-4 AB Stockholms Auktionsverk #873/R est:20000-25000 (S.KR 15000)
£4079 $6934 €5955 Fantasy landscape with figures at dusk (46x127cm-18x50in) mixed media panel painted c.1960. 5-Nov-3 AB Stockholms Auktionsverk #641/R est:40000-60000 (S.KR 54000)
£15106 $25680 €22055 Composition with bomber plane in fantasy landscape (70x99cm-28x39in) s.d.1959 mixed media canvas. 5-Nov-3 AB Stockholms Auktionsverk #640/R est:60000-80000 (S.KR 200000)

ANDERSSON, Mats Olof (attrib) (19th C) Swedish
£566 $911 €826 Ninewe den store stad (81x103cm-32x41in) cardboard. 25-Aug-3 Lilla Bukowskis, Stockholm #666 (S.KR 7400)

ANDERSSON, Nils (1817-1865) Swedish
£1700 $3043 €2482 Sleigh ride on the ice (52x67cm-20x26in) s.d.1858. 25-May-4 Bukowskis, Stockholm #128/R est:20000-25000 (S.KR 23000)

ANDERSSON, Oscar (1877-1906) Swedish
£1330 $2381 €1942 Visiting the blacksmith's (59x89cm-23x35in) s.d.1865. 26-May-4 AB Stockholms Auktionsverk #2172/R est:18000-20000 (S.KR 18000)
Works on paper
£292 $536 €438 Officers running amok (18x27cm-7x11in) init. Indian ink wash. 14-Jun-4 Lilla Bukowskis, Stockholm #538 (S.KR 4000)
£802 $1475 €1203 Damascus - caricature of August Strindberg (22x25cm-9x10in) init. Indian ink. 14-Jun-4 Lilla Bukowskis, Stockholm #529 (S.KR 11000)

ANDERSSON, Torsten (1926-) Swedish
£2564 $4538 €3743 Composition with blue background (42x42cm-17x17in) indis sig.d.66. 27-Apr-4 AB Stockholms Auktionsverk #1004/R est:35000-40000 (S.KR 35000)
£10989 $19451 €16044 Sunset (70x131cm-28x52in) s.d.61 lit. 27-Apr-4 AB Stockholms Auktionsverk #1003/R est:150000 (S.KR 150000)
£11329 $19260 €16540 Skvader - composition (126x96cm-50x38in) s.d.58. 5-Nov-3 AB Stockholms Auktionsverk #1042/R est:150000-175000 (S.KR 150000)

ANDOE, Joe (1955-) American
£703 $1300 €1026 Holly Branch (51x75cm-20x30in) s. prov. 13-Jul-4 Christie's, Rockefeller NY #151/R est:800-1200
£4790 $8000 €6993 Untitled, rose (102x122cm-40x48in) s. linen prov. 13-Nov-3 Sotheby's, New York #598/R est:5000-7000

ANDOLFATTO, Natalino (1933-) Italian
Sculpture
£1342 $2403 €2000 Untitled (56x50cm-22x20in) black marble exec.1974 prov. 25-May-4 Sotheby's, Milan #105 est:400

ANDORFF, Paul (1849-?) German
£563 $975 €800 Market scene in German town (19x13cm-7x5in) s. board. 10-Dec-3 Dorotheum, Vienna #37/R

ANDRADA, Elsa (1920-) Uruguayan
£345 $576 €500 Untitled (30x40cm-12x16in) s. cardboard. 11-Nov-3 Castellana, Madrid #1/R
£414 $691 €600 Untitled (40x50cm-16x20in) s. cardboard. 11-Nov-3 Castellana, Madrid #2/R
£414 $691 €600 Untitled (54x42cm-21x17in) s. cardboard. 11-Nov-3 Castellana, Madrid #38/R
£414 $691 €600 Untitled (38x48cm-15x19in) s. cardboard. 11-Nov-3 Castellana, Madrid #183/R

ANDRADA, Jose de (20th C) ?
£8392 $14014 €12000 Les deux amies (130x130cm-51x51in) s.d.1921. 24-Jun-3 Millon & Associes, Paris #6/R est:12000-15000

ANDRAE, Elisabeth (1876-1945) German
£417 $658 €600 Summer flowers (73x64cm-29x25in) s. 6-Sep-3 Schopman, Hamburg #780/R
£594 $1010 €850 River landscape with harbour (74x94cm-29x37in) s. 20-Nov-3 Van Ham, Cologne #1462
£1259 $2140 €1800 Lakeside scene (77x95cm-30x37in) s.d.1926 board lit. 28-Nov-3 Schloss Ahlden, Ahlden #1606/R

ANDRE, Albert (1869-1954) French
£993 $1808 €1500 Coin de jardin (26x35cm-10x14in) s. canvas on cardboard. 15-Jun-4 Rossini, Paris #34/R est:1400-2000
£2778 $4639 €4000 Young woman on garden bench (30x26cm-12x10in) s. 24-Oct-3 Ketterer, Hamburg #259/R est:5000-6000
£2973 $5500 €4341 Corbeille de fruits, vase de fleurs (38x46cm-15x18in) s. panel. 13-Jul-4 Christie's, Rockefeller NY #176/R est:4000-6000
£3198 $5500 €4669 Route d'Orsan Yard (30x53cm-12x21in) s. prov. 7-Dec-3 Freeman, Philadelphia #68 est:3000-5000
£3879 $6944 €5663 Coin de table, pire dans une assiette (29x40cm-11x16in) st.sig. canvas on board. 12-May-4 Dobiaschofsky, Bern #307/R est:12000 (S.FR 9000)
£4000 $7400 €5800 Environ d'Aix-en-Provence (35x49cm-14x19in) s. prov. 13-Feb-4 Rossini, Paris #27/R est:4000-5000
£4121 $7500 €6017 Paysage Provencal (55x66cm-22x26in) s. 29-Jun-4 Sotheby's, New York #336/R est:10000-15000
£5307 $9500 €7748 Vue de Laudun (29x64cm-11x25in) s. 6-May-4 Sotheby's, New York #426/R est:10000-15000
£5348 $10000 €7808 Nature morte avec coings et raisins (26x45cm-10x18in) s. painted c.1910. 25-Feb-4 Christie's, Rockefeller NY #22/R est:9000-12000
£6000 $11040 €8760 Femmes cueillant des fruits (46x55cm-18x22in) s. board painted 1908. 24-Mar-4 Sotheby's, Olympia #50/R est:8000-10000
£6000 $11040 €8760 Jeune fille a la fenetre devant le jardin (73x60cm-29x24in) s. 24-Mar-4 Sotheby's, Olympia #60/R est:8000-10000
£7000 $12880 €10220 Femme lisant (55x46cm-22x18in) s. prov. 22-Jun-4 Sotheby's, London #247/R est:7000-10000
£7042 $12183 €10000 Atelier (81x65cm-32x26in) s. 9-Dec-3 Artcurial Briest, Paris #225/R est:7000-8000
£8276 $15310 €12000 Corbeille de fruits (59x46cm-23x18in) pair prov. 13-Feb-4 Rossini, Paris #22/R est:4000-5000
£9000 $15030 €13140 Femme lisant a la terrasse - Mme Frantz Jourdain (43x50cm-17x20in) s. oil on card painted 1917 prov. 21-Oct-3 Sotheby's, London #126/R est:9000-12000
£9000 $16380 €13140 Fruits, pichet et pain (46x55cm-18x22in) s. painted 1935 prov.exhib. 3-Feb-4 Christie's, London #193/R est:10000-15000
£10115 $18814 €15070 Bouquet de roses et digitales (65x51cm-26x20in) bears st.sig. prov. 3-Mar-4 Tajan, Paris #53/R est:3500-4500
£12500 $20875 €18250 Cuisine (39x54cm-15x21in) s. 22-Oct-3 Sotheby's, Olympia #33/R est:8000-12000
£15000 $25050 €21900 Zinnias, fond bleu (65x54cm-26x21in) s. painted 1926 prov. 22-Oct-3 Sotheby's, Olympia #41/R est:10000-15000
£15363 $27500 €22430 L'atelier de l'artiste (81x65cm-32x26in) s. 6-May-4 Sotheby's, New York #451/R est:18000-25000
£16000 $29440 €24000 Le cafe parisien (39x58cm-15x23in) s. 11-Jun-4 Claude Aguttes, Neuilly #181/R est:10000-12000
£16000 $29440 €23360 Boulevard de Clichy (27x24cm-11x9in) s. board painted 1925 prov. 23-Jun-4 Christie's, London #159/R est:12000-15000
£16760 $30000 €24470 Still life (50x61cm-20x24in) st.sig. prov. 6-May-4 Sotheby's, New York #436/R est:20000-30000
£18156 $32500 €26508 Vue de Laudun (50x85cm-20x33in) s. prov. 6-May-4 Sotheby's, New York #424/R est:10000-20000
£20667 $38027 €31000 En terrasse l'ete (39x58cm-15x23in) s. 11-Jun-4 Claude Aguttes, Neuilly #182/R est:10000-12000
£27941 $47500 €40794 Plage du grau du roi (54x65cm-21x26in) s. prov. 6-Nov-3 Sotheby's, New York #155/R est:30000-40000

ANDRE, Albert (attrib) (1869-1954) French
£1088 $1948 €1600 Still life of flowers (32x41cm-13x16in) s. board on panel lit. 20-Mar-4 Bergmann, Erlangen #1146 est:1600

ANDRE, Carl (1935-) American
Sculpture
£61453 $110000 €89721 Angle - element series (122x91x30cm-48x36x12in) wood 2 timbers exec 1971 prov.exhib.lit. 12-May-4 Sotheby's, New York #51/R est:100000-150000
£70000 $128800 €102200 Pair (31x30x91cm-12x12x36in) western red cedar wood in six units executed 1980 prov.exhib.lit. 24-Jun-4 Christie's, London #21/R est:60000-80000
£71856 $120000 €104910 Arcata Five (122x91x91cm-48x36x36in) western red cedar timbers exec 1983 prov.exhib. 12-Nov-3 Christie's, Rockefeller NY #596/R est:100000-150000
£131737 $220000 €192336 Field (1x107x109cm-0x42x43in) ceramic magnets 630 units prov.exhib.lit. 13-Nov-3 Sotheby's, New York #123/R est:60000-80000

ANDRE, Charles Hippolyte (1850-?) French
£650 $1190 €949 Dusk in the meadow (38x61cm-15x24in) s. 8-Apr-4 Christie's, Kensington #73/R

ANDRE, Edmond (?-1877) French
£800 $1328 €1168 Connoisseur (46x30cm-18x12in) s.d.72. 1-Oct-3 Sotheby's, Olympia #248/R
£978 $1800 €1428 The graffitist (18x8cm-7x3in) s. panel. 25-Jun-4 Freeman, Philadelphia #189/R est:800-1200

ANDRE, Jules (1807-1869) French
£1773 $3050 €2589 Scene de farme (38x46cm-15x18in) s. 3-Dec-3 Naón & Cia, Buenos Aires #38/R est:1200-1500

ANDREA DI NERI (14th C) Italian
£20690 $38069 €30207 The last supper (37x47cm-15x19in) tempera gold panel prov.lit. 26-Mar-4 Koller, Zurich #3007/R est:30000-50000 (S.FR 48000)

ANDREA, Cornelis (1914-) Dutch
£274 $466 €400 Figures with stone bottles (40x29cm-16x11in) s. 5-Nov-3 Vendue Huis, Gravenhage #436/R
£377 $640 €550 Chip cafe (28x39cm-11x15in) s. 5-Nov-3 Vendue Huis, Gravenhage #437
£385 $662 €550 Still life of flowers with view of park (40x20cm-16x8in) s. panel. 8-Dec-3 Glerum, Amsterdam #348/R
£500 $915 €750 The dancers (29x39cm-11x15in) s. canvas on board. 7-Jun-4 Glerum, Amsterdam #329/R
£526 $968 €800 Winter landscape with rainstorm (53x70cm-21x28in) s. s.i. on stretcher. 22-Jun-4 Christie's, Amsterdam #604/R
£629 $1051 €900 Dye (41x31cm-16x12in) s.i.verso. 30-Jun-3 Sotheby's, Amsterdam #488
£664 $1110 €950 Opposite the artist's studio (52x70cm-20x28in) s.d.1944. 30-Jun-3 Sotheby's, Amsterdam #353
£959 $1630 €1400 Red church, Chocula, Mexico (52x70cm-20x28in) s. 5-Nov-3 Vendue Huis, Gravenhage #438/R
£1042 $1646 €1500 Bed of Frederic Mistral (40x50cm-16x20in) s. canvas on panel. 26-Apr-3 Auction Maastricht #14/R est:1500-2000
£1507 $2562 €2200 Blindman's bluff (39x49cm-15x19in) s. 5-Nov-3 Vendue Huis, Gravenhage #437a/R est:1000-1500
£1678 $2887 €2400 View of Westland from the studio of the artist (52x70cm-20x28in) s.d.44. 8-Dec-3 Glerum, Amsterdam #135/R est:2500-3000
Works on paper
£411 $699 €600 Landscape with boat in a bottle in the foreground (46x62cm-18x24in) s. W/C. 5-Nov-3 Vendue Huis, Gravenhage #435/R

ANDREA, John de (1941-) American
Sculpture
£12570 $22500 €18352 Standing woman with grey eyes (165x47x18cm-65x19x7in) fibreglass polychromed polyester hair exec 1976 prov. 13-May-4 Sotheby's, New York #228/R est:18000-25000
£25449 $42500 €37156 Two young women nude (76x154x61cm-30x61x24in) fiberglass polychromed polyester hair two parts prov.exhib. 13-Nov-3 Sotheby's, New York #218/R est:20000-30000
£25767 $42000 €37620 Giamella (147x122x58cm-58x48x23in) fibreglass polychromed polyester hair two wood bases prov. 23-Sep-3 Christie's, Rockefeller NY #140/R est:20000-30000
£40268 $72081 €60000 Girl with clasped hands (159x40x38cm-63x16x15in) glass fibre polychrome polyester hair exec. 1984 prov.exhib. 27-May-4 Sotheby's, Paris #264/R est:20000-30000

ANDREA, Pat (1942-) Dutch
£3333 $6133 €5000 The wind (100x135cm-39x53in) s.d.1983 s.i.d.stretcher prov. 9-Jun-4 Christie's, Amsterdam #113/R est:5000-7000
Works on paper
£267 $480 €400 Untitled (22x25cm-9x10in) s.d.1976 ink dr. 25-Apr-4 Versailles Encheres #229
£560 $963 €800 Personnages (42x21cm-17x8in) s. mixed media. 3-Dec-3 Tajan, Paris #488
£789 $1453 €1200 Poete Jean-P Montant l'escalier (34x38cm-13x15in) s.d.1987 s.i.d. verso mixed media collage wood. 28-Jun-4 Joron-Derem, Paris #191
£810 $1401 €1150 Able-bodied woman. Modern art (50x65cm-20x26in) s.i.d.1982 W/C pencil two. 13-Dec-3 De Vuyst, Lokeren #8

ANDREAE, Tobias (1823-1873) German
£396 $674 €578 Portrait of bearded man (14x14cm-6x6in) mono. panel. 5-Nov-3 Dobiaschofsky, Bern #308/R (S.FR 900)
£5333 $9707 €8000 Moonlit night on Capri (88x145cm-35x57in) s.d.1865. 30-Jun-4 Neumeister, Munich #495/R est:10000

ANDREASSON, Folke (1902-1948) Swedish
£261 $470 €392 Model (42x33cm-17x13in) s. 25-Apr-4 Goteborg Auktionsverk, Sweden #323/R (S.KR 3600)
£464 $835 €696 Portrait of a friend, Sven-Olof (37x30cm-15x12in) s. 25-Apr-4 Goteborg Auktionsverk, Sweden #320/R (S.KR 6400)
£1245 $2204 €1818 The red cottage (61x67cm-24x26in) s.d.35. 27-Apr-4 AB Stockholms Auktionsverk #899/R est:12000-15000 (S.KR 17000)
£1246 $2119 €1819 Two trees (65x54cm-26x21in) s. panel. 4-Nov-3 Bukowskis, Stockholm #18/R est:15000-18000 (S.KR 16500)
£1360 $2311 €1986 Potted plant by window (42x30cm-17x12in) s. canvas on panel. 4-Nov-3 Bukowskis, Stockholm #98/R est:12000-15000 (S.KR 18000)
£1885 $3394 €2752 Landscape from the west coast (27x35cm-11x14in) s. 26-Apr-4 Bukowskis, Stockholm #146/R est:12000-15000 (S.KR 26000)
£2266 $3852 €3308 Beach huts and fishing boat (65x54cm-26x21in) s,. 4-Nov-3 Bukowskis, Stockholm #97/R est:30000-35000 (S.KR 30000)
£2341 $3980 €3418 Boat on river (35x43cm-14x17in) s. canvas on panel. 4-Nov-3 Bukowskis, Stockholm #99/R est:18000-20000 (S.KR 31000)
£2719 $4622 €3970 Summer evening in Haga (55x61cm-22x24in) s.d.34 panel. 4-Nov-3 Bukowskis, Stockholm #96/R est:35000-40000 (S.KR 36000)

ANDREENKO, Mikhail (1895-1982) Russian
£6000 $10740 €8760 Still life with pipe, playing cards and musk (46x55cm-18x22in) s.d.35. 26-May-4 Sotheby's, London #161/R est:6000-8000

ANDREES, Gerhard (1936-) German?
£417 $696 €600 Delineation I (100x160cm-39x63in) s.d. i. stretcher oil pencil. 24-Oct-3 Ketterer, Hamburg #598/R

ANDREEV, J D (19th C) Russian
£1791 $3277 €2615 Snow storm in forest (32x53cm-13x21in) s. 9-Jun-4 Rasmussen, Copenhagen #1615/R est:5000 (D.KR 20000)

ANDREEW, Igor (1932-) Russian
£333 $613 €500 L'excentrique (205x207cm-81x81in) s. 10-Jun-4 Camard, Paris #204/R

ANDREINI, Ferdinando (1843-?) Italian
Sculpture
£21277 $35532 €30000 Psyche et cupidon (215cm-85in) s. white marble green marble column exec.c.1880. 17-Jun-3 Christie's, Paris #94/R est:15000-30000

ANDREIS, Alex de (19/20th C) Belgian
£595 $1100 €869 Cavalier with gloved hand holding a cane (81x64cm-32x25in) s. 16-Feb-4 Quinn's, Falls Church #462/R
£750 $1275 €1095 Drinking cavalier (53x31cm-21x12in) s. canvas on board. 18-Nov-3 Bonhams, Leeds #180a/R
£800 $1480 €1168 Cavaliere holding a sword (81x66cm-32x26in) s. 14-Jul-4 Sotheby's, Olympia #199/R
£905 $1511 €1321 Cavalier with his rifle (81x65cm-32x26in) s. prov. 17-Nov-3 Waddingtons, Toronto #31/R est:1500-2000 (C.D 2000)
£1000 $1660 €1460 Cavalier (81x65cm-32x26in) 2-Oct-3 Heffel, Vancouver #2 (C.D 2250)
£1467 $2655 €2200 Triumphant chef (64x79cm-25x31in) s. prov. 30-Mar-4 De Veres Art Auctions, Dublin #258 est:2000-3000
£2232 $3839 €3259 A friendly drink (47x55cm-19x22in) s.d.1922 prov. 2-Dec-3 Ritchie, Toronto #49/R est:2000-4000 (C.D 5000)

ANDREIS, Alex de (attrib) (19/20th C) Belgian
£321 $600 €482 Portrait of a cavalier (74x61cm-29x24in) 25-Jul-4 Bonhams & Butterfields, San Francisco #6033/R

ANDREOLI, Attilio (1877-1950) Italian
Works on paper
£458 $760 €650 Il bacio (57x78cm-22x31in) s. pastel cardboard. 11-Jun-3 Christie's, Rome #87

ANDREONI, Orazio (19th C) Italian
Sculpture
£14706 $25000 €21471 Suzanne after her bath (224cm-88in) s. marble sold with base. 28-Oct-3 Christie's, Rockefeller NY #133/R est:15000-25000

ANDREOTTI, F (1847-1930) Italian
£1000 $1820 €1500 Romantic scene (50x39cm-20x15in) s. 3-Jul-4 Badum, Bamberg #320/R est:2200

ANDREOTTI, Federico (1847-1930) Italian
£669 $1158 €950 Hen (8x13cm-3x5in) s. board. 9-Dec-3 Pandolfini, Florence #251
£1377 $2258 €1900 Village (15x9cm-6x4in) s. board. 29-May-3 Galleria Pace, Milan #95/R est:2800
£11151 $18288 €15500 Musical intermezzo (92x137cm-36x54in) s. 10-Jun-3 Pandolfini, Florence #106/R est:20000-25000
£12000 $21840 €17520 Flowers for music (65x49cm-26x19in) s. prov. 15-Jun-4 Sotheby's, London #206/R est:12000-18000
£23529 $40000 €34352 Visit to the studio (75x59cm-30x23in) s. 29-Oct-3 Christie's, Rockefeller NY #218/R est:40000-60000

ANDRES, Richard (20th C) American
£220 $350 €321 New plans (122x147cm-48x58in) s. 12-Sep-3 Aspire, Cleveland #94

ANDRESEN, Jens Christian (1865-1949) Swedish
£853 $1424 €1245 Neptunus (314x164cm-124x65in) s. 12-Oct-3 Uppsala Auktionskammare, Uppsala #150 (S.KR 11000)

ANDREU, Mariano (1888-1976) Spanish
£8235 $14000 €12023 Surreal composition (35x48cm-14x19in) s.d.40 board. 9-Nov-3 Bonhams & Butterfields, Los Angeles #4020/R
£14000 $25760 €20440 Bstinadoes (44x56cm-17x22in) s.d.Juillet 34 board prov. 24-Mar-4 Sotheby's, Olympia #85/R est:10000-15000
Works on paper
£320 $573 €467 Musician (43x23cm-17x9in) pencil. 5-May-4 British Auctioneer #808
£415 $693 €623 Fete musicale dans un jardin (31x47cm-12x19in) s.d.36 pencil. 27-Oct-3 Goodman, Sydney #226/R (A.D 1000)
£1667 $3033 €2500 Musiciennes (30x41cm-12x16in) s.d.1923 pastel htd white. 30-Jun-4 Delvaux, Paris #53/R est:1000-1500
£2000 $3640 €3000 Bathers (40x60cm-16x24in) s.d.1926 crayon htd gouache. 30-Jun-4 Delvaux, Paris #54/R est:1000-1500

ANDREU, Teodoro (1870-1934) Spanish
£1053 $1905 €1600 Immaculate Conception (151x86cm-59x34in) prov. 14-Apr-4 Ansorena, Madrid #124/R est:1500

ANDREW, Keith (1947-) British
Works on paper
£280 $512 €409 Caernarvon Castle (13x20cm-5x8in) s.d.1976 W/C. 6-Jul-4 Peter Wilson, Nantwich #84/R

ANDREWS, Ambrose (1824-1859) American
£1584 $2645 €2313 Untitled - mount of the Holy Cross (95x63cm-37x25in) s. 17-Nov-3 Hodgins, Calgary #90/R est:3500-4500 (C.D 3500)

ANDREWS, Benny (1930-) American
£3125 $5500 €4563 Animal study num 5 (30x43cm-12x17in) s. s.i.d.1964 verso. 23-May-4 Treadway Gallery, Cincinnati #673/R est:3000-5000
£4088 $6500 €5968 Covetousness (61x46cm-24x18in) s. s.d.64 verso oil masonite masonite. 12-Sep-3 Skinner, Boston #545/R
Sculpture
£1027 $1900 €1499 Capital (137cm-54in) s. painted cardboard plaster base. 17-Jul-4 Susanin's, Chicago #5018/R est:200-400
Works on paper
£543 $1000 €793 Lines (46x30cm-18x12in) s.d.June 25 1975 mixed media collage pen ink. 10-Jun-4 Swann Galleries, New York #3/R

ANDREWS, Edith Alice (fl.1900-1940) British
Works on paper
£320 $534 €467 Summer garden in full bloom (24x19cm-9x7in) s. W/C. 9-Jul-3 Peter Wilson, Nantwich #73

ANDREWS, George H (1816-1898) British
£600 $1116 €876 Excitement was too much! (46x61cm-18x24in) s. 4-Mar-4 Christie's, Kensington #643/R
£850 $1420 €1241 Portrait of a lady, and her admirer (45x34cm-18x13in) 7-Oct-3 Bonhams, Knightsbridge #157/R
£1374 $2500 €2006 Scene Champetre (64x76cm-25x30in) 7-Feb-4 Sloans & Kenyon, Bethesda #1271/R est:2000-2500
£2473 $4500 €3611 Les plaisirs du bal (84x124cm-33x49in) s. prov. 29-Jun-4 Sotheby's, New York #159/R est:5000-7000
Works on paper
£260 $413 €377 Estuary scene with beached fishing vessel (16x24cm-6x9in) W/C. 9-Sep-3 David Duggleby, Scarborough #197
£400 $704 €584 Estuary scene (16x23cm-6x9in) W/C. 19-May-4 John Bellman, Billingshurst #1840/R
£1800 $3222 €2628 Paddle tug guiding a merchantman into a harbour, probably Dover (68x117cm-27x46in) s. W/C. 17-Mar-4 Bonhams, Chester #381/R est:2000-3000

ANDREWS, George H (attrib) (1816-1898) British
Works on paper
£235 $425 €343 Marine scene (23x30cm-9x12in) W/C. 14-Apr-4 Dallas Auction Gallery, Dallas #390

ANDREWS, Henry (19th C) British
£950 $1587 €1387 Billet-doux (76x64cm-30x25in) s. 13-Nov-3 Christie's, Kensington #304/R
£7000 $12880 €10220 Proposal. Scandal (37x31cm-15x12in) s.d.1853 panel pair. 11-Jun-4 Christie's, London #203/R est:8000-12000

ANDREWS, Leonard Gordon (1885-1960) British
£260 $460 €380 Angler on a riverbank with Chantonbury Ring beyond (40x52cm-16x20in) s. 27-Apr-4 Bonhams, Knightsbridge #127/R

ANDREWS, Michael (1928-) British
£44000 $75680 €64240 Untitled (211x211cm-83x83in) acrylic wash linen prov.lit. 3-Dec-3 Sotheby's, London #82/R est:10000-15000

ANDREWS, Samuel (c.1767-1807) British
Miniatures
£1500 $2595 €2190 Gentleman in brown coat (7cm-3in) init.d.1798 oval. 9-Dec-3 Christie's, London #165/R est:1500-2500
Works on paper
£650 $1086 €949 Portrait of gentleman said to be Mr John Wilton (7x6cm-3x2in) s.d.1804 en grisaille. 14-Oct-3 Bearnes, Exeter #301/R

ANDREWS, Sybil (1898-1992) British
Prints
£1524 $2728 €2225 Plough (30x34cm-12x13in) s.i. num.11/60 col linocut exec. 1961 prov.lit. 27-May-4 Heffel, Vancouver #119/R est:2500-3500 (C.D 3750)
£1697 $2834 €2478 Plough (29x33cm-11x13in) s.i. two col linocut. 17-Nov-3 Hodgins, Calgary #174/R est:3000-4000 (C.D 3750)
£2036 $3400 €2973 Tumulus (29x21cm-11x8in) s.i. col linocut. 17-Nov-3 Hodgins, Calgary #283/R est:5000-6000 (C.D 4500)
£2066 $3657 €3016 Trackway (33x20cm-13x8in) s.num.22/60 col linocut. 3-May-4 Christie's, Melbourne #134/R est:5000-7000 (A.D 5000)
£2236 $4002 €3265 Gypsies (27x30cm-11x12in) s.i. num.37/60 col linocut exec. 1939 prov.lit. 27-May-4 Heffel, Vancouver #117/R est:4000-5000 (C.D 5500)
£2893 $5351 €4224 Steeplechasing (17x26cm-7x10in) s.num.5/60 colour linocut. 10-Mar-4 Deutscher-Menzies, Melbourne #142/R est:8000-10000 (A.D 7000)
£3000 $5160 €4380 Market day (28x34cm-11x13in) s.i.num.33/60 col linocut. 4-Dec-3 Sotheby's, London #134/R est:3000-4000
£3470 $6384 €5066 Mowers (29x35cm-11x14in) s.num.4/6 woodblock print lit. 29-Mar-4 Goodman, Sydney #119/R est:8000-12000 (A.D 8500)
£3988 $6500 €5822 Windmill (38x26cm-15x10in) s.i. linocut executed 1933. 24-Sep-3 Christie's, Rockefeller NY #49/R est:1800-2200
£4065 $7276 €5935 Steeplechasing (18x27cm-7x11in) s.i.num.7/60 linocut prov. 31-May-4 Sotheby's, Toronto #88/R est:7000-9000 (C.D 10000)
£5405 $9189 €7891 In full cry (28x41cm-11x16in) s.i. num.46/50 col linocut executed 1931 exhib.lit. 27-Nov-3 Heffel, Vancouver #11/R est:4000-6000 (C.D 12000)
£6383 $10851 €9319 Football (25x32cm-10x13in) s.num.41/60 linocut. 25-Nov-3 Christie's, Melbourne #93/R est:8000-12000 (A.D 15000)
Works on paper
£290 $493 €423 Head of a young man (33x22cm-13x9in) s. chk pastel prov. 6-Nov-3 Heffel, Vancouver #3/R (C.D 650)

ANDREWS, Thomas (19th C) British

£280	$493	€409	Favourite toy (35x28cm-14x11in) board. 19-May-4 Christie's, Kensington #602/R

ANDREWS, Walter (?) British

£231	$425	€337	Seascape with crashing waves (23x30cm-9x12in) s.d.53 board. 9-Jun-4 Alderfer's, Hatfield #386

ANDREWS, William (1840-1927) Australian

£1779	$3184	€2597	On the Nepean River, New South Wales (67x118cm-26x46in) s.d.1866. 15-May-4 Christie's, Sydney #391/R est:1500-2500 (A.D 4500)

ANDREY-PREVOST, Fernand (1890-1961) French

£276	$505	€400	La ruelle (46x38cm-18x15in) s. canvas on cardboard. 2-Feb-4 Millon & Associes, Paris #177/R
£310	$568	€450	Les musiciens (73x60cm-29x24in) s. 2-Feb-4 Millon & Associes, Paris #222/R
£345	$631	€500	Nature morte (61x50cm-24x20in) s. 2-Feb-4 Millon & Associes, Paris #129/R
£345	$631	€500	La zone (46x65cm-18x26in) s.d.1942. 2-Feb-4 Millon & Associes, Paris #185
£345	$631	€500	Deux clowns (81x45cm-32x18in) s. 2-Feb-4 Millon & Associes, Paris #221
£379	$694	€550	Au port (60x50cm-24x20in) s. 2-Feb-4 Millon & Associes, Paris #194
£414	$757	€600	Devant le miroir. 2-Feb-4 Millon & Associes, Paris #214
£759	$1388	€1100	Camp de Gitans ou Les derniers Romanichels (60x80cm-24x31in) s. 2-Feb-4 Millon & Associes, Paris #187/R
£828	$1514	€1200	Avant d'embarquer (46x37cm-18x15in) s. 2-Feb-4 Millon & Associes, Paris #193/R
£862	$1578	€1250	La foire (38x46cm-15x18in) s.verso. 2-Feb-4 Millon & Associes, Paris #224/R
£966	$1767	€1400	Le cirque (73x100cm-29x39in) s. exhib. 2-Feb-4 Millon & Associes, Paris #223/R
£1241	$2272	€1800	Un coin de port, le Distract (89x130cm-35x51in) s.d.1928. 2-Feb-4 Millon & Associes, Paris #195/R

ANDRI, Ferdinand (1871-1956) Austrian

£1678	$2970	€2500	Mountain landscape (32x48cm-13x19in) s. board prov. 28-Apr-4 Wiener Kunst Auktionen, Vienna #87/R est:2200-5000

ANDRIANOV, P N (1916-1996) Russian

£245	$450	€358	Sketch for the painting of Chrushev and cosmonauts (39x50cm-15x20in) cardboard painted 1960's. 27-Mar-4 Shishkin Gallery, Moscow #7/R
£268	$480	€391	On a sunny beach (35x49cm-14x19in) cardboard painted 1960. 29-May-4 Shishkin Gallery, Moscow #46/R
£272	$500	€397	Mooring (35x50cm-14x20in) cardboard painted 1950's. 27-Mar-4 Shishkin Gallery, Moscow #6/R
£299	$550	€437	Girl in the sun (31x31cm-12x12in) cardboard painted 1950's. 27-Mar-4 Shishkin Gallery, Moscow #8/R
£299	$550	€437	Fishermen (35x51cm-14x20in) cardboard painted 1950's. 27-Mar-4 Shishkin Gallery, Moscow #9/R
£307	$550	€448	Kakhovka on construction (36x50cm-14x20in) cardboard painted 1960's. 29-May-4 Shishkin Gallery, Moscow #45/R
£326	$600	€476	Bank (25x34cm-10x13in) cardboard painted 1950's. 27-Mar-4 Shishkin Gallery, Moscow #4/R
£335	$600	€489	On the banks of the Dnepr (42x70cm-17x28in) cardboard painted 1960's. 29-May-4 Shishkin Gallery, Moscow #42/R
£359	$660	€524	After the cloud burst, Crimea (57x50cm-22x20in) cardboard painted 1950's. 27-Mar-4 Shishkin Gallery, Moscow #12/R
£380	$700	€555	The lilac bouquet (56x49cm-22x19in) painted 1940's. 27-Mar-4 Shishkin Gallery, Moscow #11/R
£389	$700	€568	Slava Vederskiy (102x74cm-40x29in) oil on cardboard. 24-Apr-4 Shishkin Gallery, Moscow #48/R
£556	$1000	€812	Landing stage, Gurzuf (109x50cm-43x20in) oil on cardboard. 24-Apr-4 Shishkin Gallery, Moscow #47/R est:3000-4000
£598	$1100	€873	Isakiev Cathedral (25x35cm-10x14in) cardboard painted 1950's. 27-Mar-4 Shishkin Gallery, Moscow #5/R
£726	$1300	€1060	Winter (59x72cm-23x28in) cardboard painted 1960's. 29-May-4 Shishkin Gallery, Moscow #44/R
£726	$1300	€1060	Lilac (50x70cm-20x28in) cardboard painted 1960's. 29-May-4 Shishkin Gallery, Moscow #48/R
£778	$1400	€1136	Cherries in winter (67x63cm-26x25in) oil on paper. 24-Apr-4 Shishkin Gallery, Moscow #49/R est:2000-2500
£950	$1700	€1387	Our house (81x79cm-32x31in) cardboard painted 1960's. 29-May-4 Shishkin Gallery, Moscow #43/R est:2500-3500
£1556	$2800	€2272	Children with mushrooms (67x78cm-26x31in) oil on plywood. 24-Apr-4 Shishkin Gallery, Moscow #46/R est:5000-6000

ANDRIES, Alex de (19/20th C) Belgian?

£740	$1169	€1073	Cavalier (81x65cm-32x26in) s.d.1925. 3-Sep-3 Bonhams, Bury St Edmunds #395

ANDRIESSE, Erik (1957-1993) Dutch?

Works on paper

£1678	$2853	€2400	Amaryllis and butterfly (40x50cm-16x20in) s.d.92 mixed media. 24-Nov-3 Glerum, Amsterdam #285/R est:2000-4000

ANDRIESSEN, Alexander (attrib) (17th C) Dutch

£2252	$4098	€3400	Nature morte au chat (41x53cm-16x21in) panel. 16-Jun-4 Hotel des Ventes Mosan, Brussels #131/R est:3000-4000

ANDRIESSEN, Anthony (1746-1813) Dutch

Works on paper

£328	$600	€479	Cows grazing near a wooded landscape (16x20cm-6x8in) s.verso brush black ink gray wash. 29-Jan-4 Swann Galleries, New York #193/R
£541	$951	€800	Landscape with figures and a dog (16x11cm-6x4in) s.verso pen grey ink wash prov. 19-May-4 Sotheby's, Amsterdam #258/R
£1486	$2616	€2200	Cottage near a country road (12x14cm-5x6in) s.i.verso W/C black chk prov. 19-May-4 Sotheby's, Amsterdam #308/R est:1000-1500

ANDRIESSEN, Christiaan (1775-1846) Dutch

Works on paper

£3243	$5708	€4800	Man with a violin standing in front of a cabinet (18x26cm-7x10in) i. bears sig.verso pen black ink grey wash black chk prov. 19-May-4 Sotheby's, Amsterdam #334/R est:1000-1500
£6419	$11297	€9500	Arrival of a crate of paintings addressed to J Andriessen (18x26cm-7x10in) i. pen grey ink wash W/C prov.exhib.lit. 19-May-4 Sotheby's, Amsterdam #335/R est:1500-2000

ANDRIEU, Pierre (1821-1892) French

£4085	$7148	€5800	Combat de cavaliers (38x46cm-15x18in) prov. 16-Dec-3 Claude Aguttes, Neuilly #58/R est:8000-10000

Works on paper

£400	$728	€600	Mort de Marc-Aurele (24x32cm-9x13in) crayon prov. 30-Jun-4 Delvaux, Paris #118

ANDRIEU, Pierre (attrib) (1821-1892) French

Works on paper

£1119	$1902	€1600	Charge de cavaliers (24x36cm-9x14in) pen dr. 21-Nov-3 Coutau Begarie, Paris #107 est:150-200

ANDRIEUX, Clement-Auguste (1829-1880) French

£2852	$4934	€4050	Le wagon, scene animee (46x61cm-18x24in) s. 13-Dec-3 Martinot & Savignat, Pontoise #209/R est:3500-4000

Works on paper

£412	$750	€602	Cavalry in Battle (22x34cm-9x13in) pencil. 4-Feb-4 Christie's, Rockefeller NY #130/R

ANDRIUOLI, Mimmo (1946-) Italian

£282	$521	€420	Along the river (50x50cm-20x20in) s. s.i.verso. 13-Mar-4 Meeting Art, Vercelli #158
£333	$613	€500	Before the concert (70x50cm-28x20in) s. s.i.verso. 12-Jun-4 Meeting Art, Vercelli #145/R
£333	$613	€500	Rest (70x50cm-28x20in) s. s.i.verso painted 2002. 12-Jun-4 Meeting Art, Vercelli #575/R

ANDRIZ, Rudolph (19/20th C) Dutch

£745	$1200	€1088	Farewell (56x69cm-22x27in) s. 24-Feb-3 O'Gallerie, Oregon #862/R

ANDROUSOW, Vadime (1895-1975) Russian

Sculpture

£1533	$2821	€2300	Rider (49cm-19in) terracotta. 11-Jun-4 Piasa, Paris #13/R est:2500-3000
£9396	$16819	€14000	Femme a sa toilette (43x32x19cm-17x13x7in) s.d.47 terracotta. 27-May-4 Tajan, Paris #153/R est:7000-8000

ANDRUS, Vera (1896-1979) American

Works on paper

£430	$800	€628	Harlem River Bridge (45x56cm-18x22in) s.d.1936 W/C. 2-Mar-4 Swann Galleries, New York #15/R est:1000-1500

ANDRUZ, Chanti (?) American?

£193	$350	€282	Tugboat and ships in a harbour (56x71cm-22x28in) s.d.53 canvasboard. 18-Apr-4 Bonhams & Butterfields, Los Angeles #7055

ANDRYCHIEWICZ, Zygmunt (1861-1943) Polish

£3438	$5741	€5019	At a cafe table (77x57cm-30x22in) s.d.91. 19-Oct-3 Agra, Warsaw #19/R est:16000 (P.Z 22000)

ANELAY, Henry (1817-1883) British

Works on paper

£330	$600	€482	English Coast (23x53cm-9x21in) pencil W/C. 7-Feb-4 Neal Auction Company, New Orleans #653/R

ANESI, Paolo (1697-1773) Italian

£10440	$19000	€15242	Classical figures conversing on the banks of a river (61x48cm-24x19in) 17-Jun-4 Christie's, Rockefeller NY #70/R est:6000-8000
£10811	$19027	€16000	Coastal landscape (22x30cm-9x12in) 18-May-4 Sotheby's, Milan #532/R est:8000-12000
£22069	$36855	€32000	River landscapes with anglers and ruins (14x16cm-6x6in) board pair prov. 12-Nov-3 Sotheby's, Milan #163/R est:15000-20000
£27586	$46069	€40000	River landscapes in the Roman countryside (20x32cm-8x13in) pair. 12-Nov-3 Sotheby's, Milan #164/R est:25000-35000
£40000	$69200	€58400	Castel Sant Angelo and the Tiber with fishermen. Tiber and Ponte Rotto, Rome (46x97cm-18x38in) pair prov. 10-Dec-3 Bonhams, New Bond Street #26/R est:40000-60000
£57432	$101081	€85000	River landscape. Roman countryside (35x77cm-14x30in) pair. 18-May-4 Sotheby's, Milan #511/R est:25000-35000

ANESI, Paolo (circle) (1697-1773) Italian

£17568	$30919	€26000	Coastal landscapes (35x78cm-14x31in) pair. 18-May-4 Sotheby's, Milan #512/R est:10000-15000

ANESI, Paolo (style) (1697-1773) Italian

£10135	$17838	€15000	River landscapes with boats (48x38cm-19x15in) pair. 18-May-4 Sotheby's, Milan #160/R est:8000-12000

ANFRIE, Charles (1833-?) French

Sculpture			
£1284	$2298	€1900	Ramasseuse de coquillages (63cm-25in) s. brown pat bronze. 10-May-4 Horta, Bruxelles #290 est:1000-1500

ANG KIUKOK (1931-) Philippino

£2581	$4129	€3768	Fish (36x23cm-14x9in) s.d.76 canvas on board. 18-May-3 Sotheby's, Singapore #66/R est:6000-8000 (S.D 7200)
£5208	$8698	€7604	Roosters (72x47cm-28x19in) s.d.66 tempera paper lit. 12-Oct-3 Sotheby's, Singapore #63/R est:15000-20000 (S.D 15000)
Works on paper			
£6022	$9634	€8792	Rooster (74x48cm-29x19in) s.d.66 mixed media. 18-May-3 Sotheby's, Singapore #59/R est:15000-20000 (S.D 16800)

ANGAS, George French (1822-1886) British

Works on paper			
£55970	$96828	€81716	Apihai Te Kawau, Principal Chief of Ngati Whatua and his nephew (29x22cm-11x9in) i. W/C htd white. 9-Dec-3 Peter Webb, Auckland #46/R est:150000-200000 (NZ.D 150000)

ANGE, N (?) ?

£1127	$1949	€1600	Navires dans la Tempete (35x65cm-14x26in) s.d.1878. 14-Dec-3 St-Germain-en-Laye Encheres #35 est:1500

ANGEL, Rifka (1899-?) American/Russian

£223	$400	€326	Still life in green (39x20cm-15x8in) s.d.1975 panel prov. 14-May-4 Skinner, Boston #379/R
Works on paper			
£223	$400	€326	Pink carnations (47x35cm-19x14in) s.d.1965 i.verso mixed media oil panel prov. 14-May-4 Skinner, Boston #350/R
£269	$500	€393	Spring bouquet before a blue background (48x33cm-19x13in) s.d.1964 mm oil panel prov. 5-Mar-4 Skinner, Boston #380/R
£299	$475	€437	Bouquet of autumn flowers (49x36cm-19x14in) s.d.1973 mixed media oil panel prov. 12-Sep-3 Skinner, Boston #371/R
£503	$800	€734	Full bloom (51x41cm-20x16in) s.d.1968 mixed media oil panel prov. 12-Sep-3 Skinner, Boston #369/R

ANGELI, Eduard (1942-) Austrian

£3191	$5330	€4500	Hiding place (110x140cm-43x55in) s.d.74 acrylic exhib. 14-Oct-3 Dorotheum, Vienna #241/R est:4000-7000

ANGELI, Filippo (1600-1640) Italian

£40845	$70662	€58000	Bearing the Cross (43x61cm-17x24in) copper. 11-Dec-3 Binoche, Paris #25/R est:60000-70000

ANGELI, Filippo (attrib) (1600-1640) Italian

Works on paper			
£400	$692	€584	Two standing figures (15x14cm-6x6in) i.verso pen brown ink. 12-Dec-3 Christie's, Kensington #366/R
£800	$1464	€1168	Bugler about to mount his horse (18x14cm-7x6in) pen ink wash sold with another. 7-Jul-4 Bonhams, Knightsbridge #75a/R
£3289	$6053	€5000	Study of two figures (21x16cm-8x6in) pencil lead prov. 22-Jun-4 Sotheby's, Milan #19/R est:3500-4500

ANGELI, Franco (1935-1988) Italian

£336	$621	€500	Half dollar (70x70cm-28x28in) s.verso paint. 13-Mar-4 Meeting Art, Vercelli #20
£353	$554	€550	Half dollar (30x30cm-12x12in) enamel. 22-Nov-2 Galleria Pananti, Florence #1
£528	$877	€750	Cactus (80x60cm-31x24in) s.verso enamel. 14-Jun-3 Meeting Art, Vercelli #82/R
£533	$981	€800	G Franchetti (60x80cm-24x31in) s.i.verso enamel painted 1984. 12-Jun-4 Meeting Art, Vercelli #290/R
£567	$1043	€850	Untitled (60x80cm-24x31in) s.verso enamel. 12-Jun-4 Meeting Art, Vercelli #694/R
£616	$1048	€900	Female wolf (50x70cm-20x28in) s.i.d.1975 verso. 7-Nov-3 Tuttarte, Modena #708
£652	$1070	€900	Untitled (43x65cm-17x26in) s.i. acrylic mixed media paper prov. 27-May-3 Sotheby's, Milan #9
£685	$1164	€1000	Half dollar (70x120cm-28x47in) s. enamel painted 1985. 7-Nov-3 Galleria Rosenberg, Milan #115/R
£694	$1097	€1000	Obelisks (100x80cm-39x31in) enamel. 6-Sep-3 Meeting Art, Vercelli #332
£699	$1189	€1000	Roman eagle (70x120cm-28x47in) enamel. 19-Nov-3 Cambi, Genoa #490/R
£704	$1169	€1000	Obelisco (100x80cm-39x31in) s.i.verso enamel. 14-Jun-3 Meeting Art, Vercelli #306/R
£704	$1169	€1000	Untitled (80x100cm-31x39in) s.verso enamel exec 1980. 14-Jun-3 Meeting Art, Vercelli #590/R
£733	$1349	€1100	For Tano (100x60cm-39x24in) s.i.verso enamel painted 1982. 12-Jun-4 Meeting Art, Vercelli #114/R
£733	$1349	€1100	Seascape (60x80cm-24x31in) s.i. acrylic painted 1984. 12-Jun-4 Meeting Art, Vercelli #807/R
£775	$1286	€1100	Obelisco (110x60cm-43x24in) s.i.verso enamel. 14-Jun-3 Meeting Art, Vercelli #358/R est:1000
£775	$1286	€1100	Cuneo (90x90cm-35x35in) s.i.verso enamel painted 1980. 14-Jun-3 Meeting Art, Vercelli #571/R
£805	$1498	€1200	Eagles (100x70cm-39x28in) s. enamel card. 4-Mar-4 Babuino, Rome #415
£867	$1595	€1300	Half dollar (70x120cm-28x47in) s.verso enamel painted 1988. 12-Jun-4 Meeting Art, Vercelli #448/R
£897	$1434	€1300	Toy (60x80cm-24x31in) s.i.verso enamel. 13-Mar-3 Galleria Pace, Milan #17/R est:1500-2000
£909	$1545	€1300	Half dollar (70x120cm-28x47in) enamel painted 1985. 19-Nov-3 Cambi, Genoa #491/R
£933	$1680	€1400	Puppet (100x60cm-39x24in) s.verso acrylic enamel. 22-Apr-4 Finarte Semenzato, Rome #336 est:1400-1600
£942	$1545	€1300	Untitled (70x100cm-28x39in) s.d.68 acrylic collage card prov. 27-May-3 Sotheby's, Milan #10 est:1500
£966	$1612	€1400	Wave (70x70cm-28x28in) s.verso acrylic. 13-Nov-3 Finarte Semenzato, Rome #254 est:1100-1300
£966	$1545	€1400	Obelisk (80x60cm-31x24in) s.i.verso enamel painted c.1980. 13-Mar-3 Galleria Pace, Milan #115/R est:1700-2200
£986	$1637	€1400	Homage to Giorgio Franchetti (80x100cm-31x39in) s.i.verso enamel lit. 13-Jun-3 Farsetti, Prato #203/R
£1000	$1840	€1500	Adrianopoli (120x90cm-47x35in) s.i.verso enamel. 12-Jun-4 Meeting Art, Vercelli #100/R est:1000
£1007	$1862	€1500	Yellow (80x100cm-31x39in) s.i.verso enamel painted 1986. 13-Mar-4 Meeting Art, Vercelli #101 est:1000
£1007	$1862	€1500	Night scene (130x100cm-51x39in) s.i.verso enamel painted 1986 lit. 13-Mar-4 Meeting Art, Vercelli #117 est:1500
£1014	$1784	€1500	Untitled (100x100cm-39x39in) s. acrylic painted c.1975. 24-May-4 Christie's, Milan #53 est:1500-2000
£1034	$1655	€1500	Geometrie (80x60cm-31x24in) s.i.verso enamel painted c.1980. 13-Mar-3 Galleria Pace, Milan #59/R est:1700-2200
£1067	$1963	€1600	Symbol (60x70cm-24x28in) s.i.verso enamel. 8-Jun-4 Finarte Semenzato, Milan #50/R est:1500-2000
£1067	$1963	€1600	Half dollar (130x100cm-51x39in) enamel painted 1982 lit. 12-Jun-4 Meeting Art, Vercelli #471/R est:1500
£1067	$1963	€1600	G. Cromo (130x100cm-51x39in) s.i.verso enamel painted 1988 lit. 12-Jun-4 Meeting Art, Vercelli #726/R est:1500
£1074	$1987	€1600	Obelisk (130x100cm-51x39in) s.i.verso enamel painted 1986. 13-Mar-4 Meeting Art, Vercelli #399 est:1500
£1074	$1922	€1600	Adrianopoli (100x60cm-39x24in) s.i. verso enamel painted 1986. 28-May-4 Farsetti, Prato #33/R est:1600-1900
£1088	$1948	€1600	Landscape (100x80cm-39x31in) s. enamel prov. 16-Mar-4 Finarte Semenzato, Milan #43/R est:1300
£1103	$1843	€1600	Toy (130x100cm-51x39in) s.verso enamel lit. 14-Nov-3 Farsetti, Prato #222/R est:1600-1900
£1111	$1756	€1600	Eastern (60x80cm-24x31in) enamel. 6-Sep-3 Meeting Art, Vercelli #318 est:750
£1172	$1958	€1700	Horizon (80x60cm-31x24in) s.verso acrylic. 13-Nov-3 Finarte Semenzato, Rome #235 est:1200-1500
£1181	$1865	€1700	Victory (120x100cm-47x39in) enamel. 6-Sep-3 Meeting Art, Vercelli #543 est:1500
£1200	$2208	€1800	Red car (100x60cm-39x24in) s.i.verso enamel painted 1984. 8-Jun-4 Finarte Semenzato, Milan #51/R est:1500-2000
£1224	$2192	€1800	Detail (70x120cm-28x47in) s.i.verso enamel painted 1983. 16-Mar-4 Finarte Semenzato, Milan #345/R est:1200
£1242	$2297	€1850	Eastern (100x60cm-39x24in) s.i.verso enamel painted 1983. 13-Mar-4 Meeting Art, Vercelli #380 est:1000
£1252	$2128	€1790	Adrianopoli (60x80cm-24x31in) s.i.verso enamel prov. 18-Nov-3 Babuino, Rome #322/R est:800-1200
£1259	$2140	€1800	Oriental (80x60cm-31x24in) s.i.verso enamel. 20-Nov-3 Finarte Semenzato, Milan #2/R est:1600-2200
£1329	$2259	€1900	American eagle (69x120cm-27x47in) i.verso enamel painted 1984. 28-Nov-3 Farsetti, Prato #32/R est:1400-1700
£1345	$2152	€1950	Gold silver (70x120cm-28x47in) s.i.verso enamel. 13-Mar-3 Galleria Pace, Milan #28/R est:1800-2400
£1370	$2329	€2000	Roman eagle (60x80cm-24x31in) s.verso enamel painted 1974. 7-Nov-3 Galleria Rosenberg, Milan #28/R est:2000
£1379	$2303	€2000	Half dollar (70x70cm-28x28in) s.verso acrylic pair. 13-Nov-3 Finarte Semenzato, Rome #288 est:1200-1500
£1467	$2699	€2200	Souvenir (99x89cm-39x35in) s.verso acrylic painted 1986 prov. 8-Jun-4 Finarte Semenzato, Milan #303/R est:2000-3000
£1622	$2854	€2400	Untitled (70x100cm-28x39in) s. painted c.1973 prov. 24-May-4 Christie's, Milan #186/R est:2000-3000
£1689	$2973	€2500	Half dollar (100x100cm-39x39in) s.verso enamel prov. 24-May-4 Christie's, Milan #103/R est:2000-3000
£1736	$2743	€2500	Landscape in Sicily (130x160cm-51x63in) enamel. 6-Sep-3 Meeting Art, Vercelli #553 est:2500
£2029	$3328	€2800	Untitled (100x70cm-39x28in) s.d.66 enamel card pair. 27-May-3 Sotheby's, Milan #8
£2042	$3390	€2900	Paesaggio, prima meta anni 70 (60x80cm-24x31in) s. s.i.verso enamel. 14-Jun-3 Meeting Art, Vercelli #77/R est:1000
£2042	$3390	€2900	Orizzonte (130x160cm-51x63in) s.i. enamel. 14-Jun-3 Meeting Art, Vercelli #104/R est:2500
£2069	$3455	€3000	Half dollar (100x100cm-39x39in) enamel exhib. 17-Nov-3 Sant Agostino, Torino #288/R est:3000-4000
£2098	$3566	€3000	Half dollar (100x130cm-39x51in) s. enamel prov. 24-Nov-3 Christie's, Milan #182/R est:3000-4000
£2148	$3995	€3200	Two empires (70x100cm-28x39in) i. oil wax crayon W/C card on canvas. 4-Mar-4 Babuino, Rome #116 est:1000-1500
£2685	$4805	€4000	Explosion (160x170cm-63x67in) s.i.verso enamel painted 1974. 28-May-4 Farsetti, Prato #240/R est:3900-4300
£2703	$4757	€4000	Of America (50x70cm-20x28in) s.i.verso acrylic prov. 24-May-4 Christie's, Milan #181/R est:5000-8000
Works on paper			
£483	$772	€700	Lupa Capitolina (70x100cm-28x39in) s. mixed media. 13-Mar-3 Galleria Pace, Milan #2/R
£816	$1461	€1200	Study for half dollar (35x35cm-14x14in) s.verso. 16-Mar-4 Finarte Semenzato, Milan #343/R
£933	$1680	€1400	Maradona (40x30cm-16x12in) s.verso collage enamel on canvas. 22-Apr-4 Finarte Semenzato, Rome #277 est:700-900
£1020	$1827	€1500	Half dollar (71x120cm-28x47in) s.verso. 16-Mar-4 Finarte Semenzato, Milan #342/R est:900
£1067	$1963	€1600	Souvenir (100x130cm-39x51in) s.i.verso enamel painted 1986. 12-Jun-4 Meeting Art, Vercelli #857/R est:1500
£1333	$2400	€2000	Moravia (70x100cm-28x39in) s. mixed media paper on canvas. 22-Apr-4 Finarte Semenzato, Rome #114/R est:1600-2000
£1351	$2378	€2000	Sabaudia (130x100cm-51x39in) s.i.verso enamel. 24-May-4 Christie's, Milan #86/R est:2000-3000

£2517 $4280 €3600 Big black painting (52x77cm-20x30in) s.d.1964 mixed media paper on canvas. 20-Nov-3 Finarte Semenzato, Milan #30/R est:3800-4000

ANGELI, Heinrich von (1840-1924) Austrian
£319 $508 €460 Portrait de femme (63x47cm-25x19in) s.d.1882. 9-Sep-3 Palais de Beaux Arts, Brussels #290
£625 $1063 €900 Portrait of woman wearing pearl necklace (70x55cm-28x22in) s.d.1918 panel. 28-Oct-3 Dorotheum, Vienna #127/R
£2740 $4658 €4000 Portrait de femme a la robe rouge (69x39cm-27x15in) s. panel. 6-Nov-3 Sotheby's, Paris #42/R est:4000-6000

ANGELINI, Tito (1806-1878) Italian
Sculpture
£2800 $5124 €4088 Bust of bejewelled lady (69cm-27in) s.d.1870 marble. 9-Jul-4 Sotheby's, London #113/R est:3000-5000

ANGELIS, D de (19th C) Italian
£5000 $9100 €7300 Young aristocrats (55x75cm-22x30in) s.i.d.1875. 16-Jun-4 Christie's, Kensington #100/R est:5000-7000

ANGELIS, G de (?) ?
Works on paper
£3500 $5950 €5110 Kolokotronis recruiting at Corfu. Kolokotronis fleeing to safety (25x35cm-10x14in) s.i.d.1838 pencil wash bodycol pair. 18-Nov-3 Sotheby's, London #78/R est:2000-3000

ANGELIS, Luigi de (1881-?) Italian
£671 $1248 €1000 Little village square (40x48cm-16x19in) s.d.1955 tempera board. 4-Mar-4 Babuino, Rome #509

ANGELIS, Salvatore de (1856-?) Italian
Works on paper
£642 $1149 €950 SS Mazeppa, Capt W B Brown crossing the Bay of Biscay (65x92cm-26x36in) s.i. lit. 8-May-4 Schloss Ahlden, Ahlden #760/R

ANGERER, Max (1877-1955) Swiss
£629 $1070 €900 Summer mountain landscape (54x68cm-21x27in) s.d.1907. 20-Nov-3 Dorotheum, Salzburg #209/R
£1399 $2378 €2000 High mountain pasture in early summer (38x52cm-15x20in) s. 20-Nov-3 Dorotheum, Salzburg #212/R est:2000-2800

ANGERER, Walter Andreas (younger) (1940-) German
£874 $1460 €1250 Portrait before landscape (47x37cm-19x15in) s.d.1974 board. 27-Jun-3 Michael Zeller, Lindau #718/R

ANGERMAYER, Johann Adalbert (1674-c.1740) German
£58190 $107069 €84957 Flowers in stone alcove (17x13cm-7x5in) s.d.1719 copper prov.lit. 26-Mar-4 Koller, Zurich #3022/R est:50000-70000 (S.FR 135000)

ANGES, Charles des (fl.1870-1910) French
£8500 $14450 €12410 Portrait of William Henry, Rowland Edward and Frederick John Cooper (142x114cm-56x45in) 19-Nov-3 Tennants, Leyburn #1180/R est:6000-10000

ANGHIK, Abraham Apakark (1951-) North American
Sculpture
£1892 $3216 €2762 Bird and her young (44cm-17in) mottled green soapstone. 3-Nov-3 Waddingtons, Toronto #422/R est:2500-3500 (C.D 4200)

ANGIER, W Donald (20th C) British
Works on paper
£300 $549 €438 Matt Cockings Corner, St Ives (44x36cm-17x14in) s. gouache. 3-Jun-4 Lane, Penzance #172
£320 $586 €467 St Ives, Cornwall, the harbour (42x36cm-17x14in) s. gouache. 3-Jun-4 Lane, Penzance #173
£360 $659 €526 Old timers, St Ives, going out (43x36cm-17x14in) s. gouache. 3-Jun-4 Lane, Penzance #174

ANGILLIS, Pieter (1685-1734) Flemish
£3352 $6000 €4894 Country folk eating and dancing outside tavern (60x97cm-24x38in) s.d.1726 prov. 27-May-4 Sotheby's, New York #224/R est:6000-8000

ANGKAMA, Secadipraja (1913-) Indonesian
£1307 $2366 €1908 Still life (70x60cm-28x24in) s.d.14.8.83. 4-Apr-4 Sotheby's, Singapore #141/R est:4000-6000 (S.D 4000)
£2536 $3931 €3703 Kebun Kubis di Tamgkuban Perahu (65x80cm-26x31in) s.d.69. 6-Oct-2 Sotheby's, Singapore #164/R est:7000-9000 (S.D 7000)

ANGLADA-CAMARASA, Herman (1873-1959) Spanish
£486 $773 €700 View of village (55x46cm-22x18in) s. 9-Sep-3 Vanderkindere, Brussels #77
£36184 $66579 €55000 Belles de nuit (19x13cm-7x5in) s.i. board. 22-Jun-4 Durán, Madrid #211/R est:18000
£37931 $63345 €55000 Montserrat mountains (52x61cm-20x24in) s. 17-Nov-3 Durán, Madrid #241/R est:18000
£120000 $204000 €175200 Vase of flowers (82x82cm-32x32in) s. prov.exhib.lit. 18-Nov-3 Sotheby's, London #233/R
£520000 $884000 €759200 Pink puss (104x191cm-41x75in) s. prov.exhib.lit. 18-Nov-3 Sotheby's, London #224/R

ANGLADA-CAMARASA, Herman (attrib) (1873-1959) Spanish
£2113 $3507 €3000 Still life with teapot (46x43cm-18x17in) s. 11-Jun-3 Christie's, Rome #102/R est:1500-2000

ANGLADA-PINTO, Luis (1873-1946) Spanish
£674 $1125 €950 Jeune femme aux boucles d'argent (41x33cm-16x13in) s. 16-Jun-3 Gros & Delettrez, Paris #232

ANGLADE (19/20th C) French
£1049 $1804 €1500 Paysage au bruyere. 5-Dec-3 Gros & Delettrez, Paris #77a est:1200-2000

ANGLADE, Gaston (1854-1927) French
£423 $756 €600 Paysage de montagne (53x63cm-21x25in) s. 11-Jan-4 Rouillac, Vendome #303
£517 $926 €755 Farmstead in sunshine (32x46cm-13x18in) s.d.1898. 12-May-4 Dobiaschofsky, Bern #308/R (S.FR 1200)
£833 $1392 €1200 Paysage ensoleille (54x73cm-21x29in) s.d.1903. 21-Oct-3 Campo & Campo, Antwerp #3
£1100 $1837 €1606 View down to the lake at dusk (51x64cm-20x25in) s. 8-Oct-3 Christie's, Kensington #795/R est:1000-1500
£1268 $2218 €1800 Paysage de bruyeres (65x54cm-26x21in) s. 17-Dec-3 Rabourdin & Choppin de Janvry, Paris #44/R est:1800-2200

ANGLADE, Henri Vincent (1876-1956) French
£2000 $3580 €3000 Reclining woman (60x80cm-24x31in) s. oval. 13-May-4 Babuino, Rome #535/R est:800-1200

ANGLES (?) French
Sculpture
£1608 $2734 €2300 Bust of a woman (47cm-19in) s. white marble. 18-Nov-3 Mealy's, Castlecomer #201/R est:2300-2600

ANGLO-CHINESE SCHOOL, 19th C
£3631 $6500 €5301 British Brig - Sarah under full sail in Far Eastern Waters bound for America (46x58cm-18x23in) 16-Mar-4 Bonhams & Butterfields, San Francisco #6156/R est:4000-6000
Works on paper
£26000 $48100 €37960 Flowers and associated fauna. pencil W/C 49 album. 15-Jul-4 Bonhams, New Bond Street #1/R est:20000-30000

ANGLO-DUTCH SCHOOL, 17th C
£6500 $11050 €9490 Portrait of a young girl in a white dress trimmed with crimson ribbons, dog by her side (107x84cm-42x33in) prov. 25-Nov-3 Christie's, London #1/R est:3000-5000

ANGLO-FLEMISH SCHOOL, 17th C
£13000 $23660 €18980 Carriage and six outriders and sportsmen on a country road (102x145cm-40x57in) 21-Jun-4 Christie's, London #38/R est:10000-15000
Sculpture
£14000 $25060 €20440 Orpheus charming the beasts (81x74cm-32x29in) walnut carved panel. 11-May-4 Sotheby's, Olympia #420/R est:6000-8000

ANGMA, Josephie (1905-) North American
Sculpture
£901 $1532 €1315 Mother with her child in her amaut (24cm-9in) s. mottled grey soapstone exec.c.1965. 3-Nov-3 Waddingtons, Toronto #420/R est:1500-2500 (C.D 2000)

ANGOLO DEL MORO, Battista (attrib) (1514-1575) Italian
Works on paper
£1361 $2435 €2000 Le concours de Pan et d'Apollon (28x42cm-11x17in) indigo wash pen brown ink. 19-Mar-4 Piasa, Paris #4/R est:2000-2500

ANGQVIST, Olle (1922-) Swedish
£330 $584 €482 Copse II (38x33cm-15x13in) init.d.79 acrylic canvas on panel. 27-Apr-4 AB Stockholms Auktionsverk #987/R (S.KR 4500)

ANGRAND, Charles (1854-1926) French
£11000 $20240 €16060 Petit port (46x55cm-18x22in) s. prov. 22-Jun-4 Sotheby's, London #131/R est:12000-15000
£90000 $165600 €131400 Gardeur de dindons (55x46cm-22x18in) s.d.1881 prov.exhib.lit. 22-Jun-4 Sotheby's, London #148/R est:50000-70000

ANGUHADLUQ, Luke (1895-1982) North American
Works on paper
£383 $651 €559 Untitled, arctic animals (51x66cm-20x26in) col pencil. 3-Nov-3 Waddingtons, Toronto #203/R (C.D 850)

ANGUIANO, Raul (1915-) Mexican
Works on paper
£307 $500 €448 Carnaval en Huejotzingo (51x66cm-20x26in) s.d.1930 W/C laid paper. 28-Sep-3 Simpson's, Houston #175a/R
£508 $900 €742 Woman seated on a box, holding a vase (49x70cm-19x28in) s.d.76 pastel crayon. 2-May-4 Bonhams & Butterfields, Los Angeles #3111/R

£1714	$3000	€2502	Pescaderes (70x50cm-28x20in) s.d.61 gouache prov. 19-Dec-3 Sotheby's, New York #1163/R est:5000-7000

ANGUIER, Michel and GARNIER, Pierre (after) (17th C) French

Sculpture			
£27972	$48112	€40000	Figures of Amphitrite and Bacchus (38cm-15in) brown green pat bronze htd base bronze prov.lit. 2-Dec-3 Christie's, Paris #712/R est:12000-18000

ANGUS, Rita (1908-1970) New Zealander

£3460	$6194	€5052	Lights and roofs, Oaklet Street, London (27x29cm-11x11in) s.i.verso acrylic board. 12-May-4 Dunbar Sloane, Wellington #25/R est:7500-15000 (NZ.D 10000)
£15734	$28636	€22972	Rape paddock - Hawkes Bay landscape (29x39cm-11x15in) s. i.verso hardboard. 29-Jun-4 Peter Webb, Auckland #56/R est:45000-65000 (NZ.D 45000)
Works on paper			
£554	$991	€809	St. Pancras Station, London (12x20cm-5x8in) s. ink executed c.1960. 12-May-4 Dunbar Sloane, Wellington #24/R est:800-1600 (NZ.D 1600)
£1736	$2760	€2535	Rock at waikanae (24x22cm-9x9in) s.d.1951 W/C. 1-May-3 Dunbar Sloane, Wellington #57/R est:5000-7000 (NZ.D 5000)
£2180	$3902	€3183	Botanical study of kowhai flowers (14x12cm-6x5in) s. W/C. 12-May-4 Dunbar Sloane, Wellington #23/R est:8000-12000 (NZ.D 6300)
£2612	$4519	€3814	Portrait of Tilli Frankel (42x30cm-17x12in) s.d.1939 pencil. 9-Dec-3 Peter Webb, Auckland #25/R est:7000-10000 (NZ.D 7000)
£8000	$12560	€11600	Irises (27x38cm-11x15in) s.verso W/C prov. 27-Aug-3 Dunbar Sloane, Wellington #30/R est:24000-30000 (NZ.D 22000)

ANGYALFFY, Erzsebet (19th C) Hungarian

£490	$817	€700	Bathers (60x75cm-24x30in) 10-Oct-3 Stadion, Trieste #130/R

ANH QUAN (1962-) Vietnamese

£2257	$3769	€3295	Girl with birdcage (100x80cm-39x31in) s. 12-Oct-3 Sotheby's, Singapore #116/R est:4000-6000 (S.D 6500)

ANISFELD, Boris (1878-1973) Russian

£9302	$16000	€13581	Snow maiden (64x76cm-25x30in) s.d.1921 board. 3-Dec-3 Doyle, New York #74/R est:2500-3500
£20000	$34000	€29200	Interior with woman and fruit (64x50cm-25x20in) s. 19-Nov-3 Sotheby's, London #226/R est:7000-9000
£22222	$40000	€32444	Circus (115x92cm-45x36in) 23-Apr-4 Sotheby's, New York #77/R est:40000-60000
£24000	$42960	€35040	Northern mystery (64x76cm-25x30in) s.d.1921 gouache on board. 26-May-4 Sotheby's, London #279/R est:12000-18000
£25000	$42500	€36500	Past Glory (90x102cm-35x40in) s.d.1953. 19-Nov-3 Sotheby's, London #214/R est:25000-35000
£30556	$55000	€44612	Elegy (152x127cm-60x50in) s.d.1939 i.verso. 23-Apr-4 Sotheby's, New York #75/R est:60000-80000
£32000	$54400	€46720	Al Fresco reverie (114x91cm-45x36in) s. 19-Nov-3 Sotheby's, London #229/R est:30000-40000
£38000	$68020	€55480	Floral arrangement in a ceramic jug (102x89cm-40x35in) s.d.1947. 26-May-4 Sotheby's, London #281/R est:25000-35000
£38889	$70000	€56778	Still life with daisies (96x76cm-38x30in) s. 23-Apr-4 Sotheby's, New York #76/R est:35000-45000
£45000	$76500	€65700	Contrast (92x119cm-36x47in) s. 19-Nov-3 Sotheby's, London #230/R est:45000-65000
Works on paper			
£2162	$3805	€3200	Projet de costume (40x30cm-16x12in) s. gouache. 19-May-4 Camard, Paris #30 est:3000-4000
£4444	$8000	€6488	Stage set for curtain, palace at night, the bluebird (55x65cm-22x26in) s.i. gouache exhib. 23-Apr-4 Sotheby's, New York #114/R est:8000-12000

ANIVITTI, Filippo (1876 1955) Italian

£704	$1218	€1000	Farm (35x45cm-14x18in) s. board. 11-Dec-3 Christie's, Rome #3
£1800	$3096	€2628	Campo dei Fiori, Roma (26x50cm-10x20in) s. 4-Dec-3 Christie's, Kensington #36/R est:2000-3000
£1831	$3168	€2600	The Appia (33x60cm-13x24in) s. 10-Dec-3 Finarte Semenzato, Rome #274 est:2800-3200
£2113	$3655	€3000	Landscape (30x40cm-12x16in) s. board sold with another. 11-Dec-3 Christie's, Rome #20 est:1300-1800
Works on paper			
£604	$1069	€900	Summer bloom (29x46cm-11x18in) s. W/C. 1-May-4 Meeting Art, Vercelli #234
£1243	$2250	€1815	Cardinal having tea (48x33cm-19x13in) W/C. 16-Apr-4 Du Mouchelle, Detroit #2080/R est:1500-2500
£1250	$2300	€1900	The Appia (30x36cm-12x14in) s. W/C. 23-Jun-4 Finarte Semenzato, Rome #31/R est:1500-1700
£1690	$2924	€2400	The Tiber in Fiumicino (35x60cm-14x24in) s. W/C card lit. 11-Dec-3 Christie's, Rome #21/R est:1800
£1972	$3411	€2800	Spring in the fields (35x62cm-14x24in) s. W/C card. 11-Dec-3 Christie's, Rome #23/R est:2300-2800
£2254	$3899	€3200	Roman countryside (40x60cm-16x24in) s. W/C pair. 10-Dec-3 Sotheby's, Milan #22/R est:800-1200

ANJOS, Armando (?) ?

Works on paper			
£325	$543	€475	Nude (48x64cm-19x25in) s. col chks. 20-Jun-3 Chrystals Auctions, Isle of Man #243/R

ANKARCRONA, Alexis (1825-1901) Swedish

£407	$728	€594	Country girl with cows by brook (62x41cm-24x16in) s.d.86. 28-May-4 Uppsala Auktionskammare, Uppsala #123/R (S.KR 5500)
£1538	$2615	€2200	Fishermen in rowing boats in fjord landscape (72x107cm-28x42in) s.d.86. 29-Nov-3 Bukowskis, Helsinki #358/R est:1800-2000
£3154	$5425	€4605	Caravan with camels (46x76cm-18x30in) prov. 2-Dec-3 Bukowskis, Stockholm #99/R est:25000-30000 (S.KR 41000)
£6462	$11114	€9435	Desert landscape with figures and camels (89x147cm-35x58in) s.d.1873. 2-Dec-3 Bukowskis, Stockholm #98/R est:40000-50000 (S.KR 84000)

ANKARCRONA, Alexis (attrib) (1825-1901) Swedish

£430	$701	€628	Queen Marie Antoinette (71x58cm-28x23in) i.verso. 29-Sep-3 Lilla Bukowskis, Stockholm #244 (S.KR 5600)

ANKARCRONA, Gustaf (1869-1933) Swedish

£1183	$2117	€1727	Farm in winter (43x66cm-17x26in) s.d.1905. 26-May-4 AB Stockholms Auktionsverk #2212/R est:8000-10000 (S.KR 16000)
Works on paper			
£1231	$2117	€1797	Winter landscape from Skansen with girl on skies and horses (58x45cm-23x18in) s.d.1901 mixed media lit. 3-Dec-3 AB Stockholms Auktionsverk #2451/R est:16000-18000 (S.KR 16000)

ANKARCRONA, Henrik (1831-1917) Swedish

£768	$1252	€1121	Oriental desert scene (32x23cm-13x9in) s. panel. 29-Sep-3 Lilla Bukowskis, Stockholm #146 (S.KR 10000)
£9333	$16707	€14000	Assalt (74x126cm-29x50in) s.d.74. 17-May-4 Finarte Semenzato, Rome #86/R est:18000-20000

ANKELEN, Eugen (1858-1942) German

£1528	$2490	€2200	Beach life on edge of fishing village (66x103cm-26x41in) s.i. 25-Sep-3 Dr Fritz Nagel, Stuttgart #1323/R est:1900

ANKENY, John Sites (1870-1946) American

£254	$425	€371	Crecy en Brie (38x56cm-15x22in) s.i.d.93. 13-Jul-3 Butterfields, San Francisco #2031/R

ANKER, Albert (1831-1910) Swiss

£11189	$19245	€16000	At the blacksmith's (48x42cm-19x17in) s. 3-Dec-3 Neumeister, Munich #526/R est:11000
£11312	$18100	€16516	Portrait of toddler with rattle (20x20cm-8x8in) s.d.28.Sept.1878. 19-Sep-3 Koller, Zurich #3076/R est:25000-35000 (S.FR 25000)
£94828	$174483	€138449	Portrait of a girl (41x32cm-16x13in) s. prov.exhib.lit. 26-Mar-4 Koller, Zurich #3084/R est:200000-300000 (S.FR 220000)
£167401	$284582	€244405	First steps (66x36cm-26x14in) s. prov.exhib.lit. 7-Nov-3 Dobiaschofsky, Bern #54/R (S.FR 380000)
£224138	$401207	€327241	Still life with wine bottle, glass and bread rolls (51x43cm-20x17in) s. prov.lit.exhib. 17-May-4 Beurret, Zurich #31/R est:200000-300000 (S.FR 520000)
£224138	$401207	€327241	Bathers (64x123cm-25x48in) s.d. prov.exhib. 17-May-4 Beurret, Zurich #32/R est:500000-700000 (S.FR 520000)
£262009	$468996	€382533	Siblings Zaeslin I (55x80cm-22x31in) s. prov.exhib.lit. 26-May-4 Sotheby's, Zurich #11/R est:600000-800000 (S.FR 600000)
£302691	$493386	€441929	Still life with coffee and potatoes (51x42cm-20x17in) s. prov.exhib.lit. 29-Sep-3 Christie's, Zurich #14/R est:300000-400000 (S.FR 675000)
£302691	$493386	€441929	Still life: upper class tea (51x42cm-20x17in) s. prov.exhib.lit. 29-Sep-3 Christie's, Zurich #15/R est:300000-400000 (S.FR 675000)
Works on paper			
£452	$769	€660	Seated woman writing (11x17cm-4x7in) pencil double-sided. 18-Nov-3 Hans Widmer, St Gallen #1003 (S.FR 1000)
£573	$974	€837	Girl eating soup (25x31cm-10x12in) chl. 5-Nov-3 Dobiaschofsky, Bern #1086 (S.FR 1300)
£749	$1273	€1094	Young girl knitting (30x22cm-12x9in) chl. 7-Nov-3 Dobiaschofsky, Bern #58/R (S.FR 1700)
£917	$1532	€1330	Peasant sitting at table (12x18cm-5x7in) Indian ink. 23-Jun-3 Philippe Schuler, Zurich #3870 (S.FR 2000)
£1193	$1992	€1730	Peasant woman drinking coffee (34x25cm-13x10in) pencil parchment. 23-Jun-3 Philippe Schuler, Zurich #3871/R est:1800-2400 (S.FR 2600)
£1193	$1992	€1730	House study (21x26cm-8x10in) s.d.1892 pencil W/C. 23-Jun-3 Philippe Schuler, Zurich #3873 est:2000-2500 (S.FR 2600)
£1293	$2315	€1888	Seated woman peeling vegetables (24x32cm-9x13in) pencil. 14-May-4 Dobiaschofsky, Bern #49/R est:3500 (S.FR 3000)
£1293	$2315	€1888	Portrait of peasant girl (36x25cm-14x10in) chl double-sided. 13-May-4 Stuker, Bern #17/R est:2500-3000 (S.FR 3000)
£1591	$2641	€2307	Boy writing (14x17cm-6x7in) Indian ink pencil i. verso. 13-Jun-3 Zofingen, Switzerland #2768/R est:4500 (S.FR 3500)
£1965	$3576	€2869	Boy writing at table (28x42cm-11x17in) chk exhib. double-sided. 17-Jun-4 Kornfeld, Bern #158 est:7500 (S.FR 4500)
£2814	$5037	€4108	Municipal scribe (43x40cm-17x16in) chl board prov. 22-Mar-4 Philippe Schuler, Zurich #4301/R est:4000-5300 (S.FR 6500)
£3846	$6615	€5500	Landscape with lake and mountains in background (17x25cm-7x10in) s. W/C. 3-Dec-3 Neumeister, Munich #368/R est:3500
£6550	$11725	€9563	Two men drinking schnaps (59x90cm-23x35in) chl chk lit. 26-May-4 Sotheby's, Zurich #16/R est:10000-15000 (S.FR 15000)
£7860	$14070	€11476	Blond girl knitting (18x16cm-7x6in) col pencil W/C prov.exhib. 26-May-4 Sotheby's, Zurich #7/R est:5000-8000 (S.FR 18000)
£15217	$27848	€22217	Grandfather with pipe (35x26cm-14x10in) s.d.1903 W/C over pen. 7-Jun-4 Christie's, Zurich #8/R est:40000-60000 (S.FR 35000)
£15948	$28547	€23284	Peasant with pipe (34x24cm-13x9in) s.d.1909 W/C over pencil. 14-May-4 Dobiaschofsky, Bern #60/R est:36000 (S.FR 37000)
£17181	$29207	€25084	Portrait of young woman with hair in plait (39x31cm-15x12in) s. chl. 7-Nov-3 Dobiaschofsky, Bern #65/R est:18000 (S.FR 39000)
£19565	$35804	€28565	Grandmother with coffee (35x25cm-14x10in) s.d.1904 W/C. 7-Jun-4 Christie's, Zurich #7/R est:40000-60000 (S.FR 45000)
£19824	$33700	€28943	Grandmother preparing beans (33x24cm-13x9in) s.d.1908 w/C. 7-Nov-3 Dobiaschofsky, Bern #61/R est:45000 (S.FR 45000)
£21552	$38578	€31466	Convalescing by the oven (24x34cm-9x13in) s.d.1907 W/C. 14-May-4 Dobiaschofsky, Bern #52/R est:50000 (S.FR 50000)
£25551	$43436	€37304	Blonde haired girl reading book at table (34x24cm-13x9in) s.i.d.1908 W/C. 7-Nov-3 Dobiaschofsky, Bern #57/R est:65000 (S.FR 58000)
£27273	$48818	€39819	Girl putting flowers in vase (35x25cm-14x10in) s.d. exhib.prov. 22-Mar-4 Philippe Schuler, Zurich #4303/R est:33000-46200 (S.FR 63000)
£39130	$71609	€57130	Boy writing (35x24cm-14x9in) s.d.1902 W/C prov. 7-Jun-4 Christie's, Zurich #10/R est:90000-120000 (S.FR 90000)
£41485	$74258	€60568	Interior by lamplight (32x23cm-13x9in) s. pencil W/C. 26-May-4 Sotheby's, Zurich #5/R est:30000-40000 (S.FR 95000)

ANKER, Herman Wedel (1845-1895) Norwegian

£634	$1167	€926	Landscape from Gudvangen in Sogne (23x17cm-9x7in) s. panel. 29-Mar-4 Blomqvist, Lysaker #1005/R (N.KR 8000)

£650 $1197 €975 Women by woodland road (31x24cm-12x9in) s. 14-Jun-4 Blomqvist, Lysaker #1015 (N.KR 8000)
£2836 $4905 €4141 Wooded landscape from Bogstad, near Christiania (34x26cm-13x10in) s.d.85 panel. 9-Dec-3 Rasmussen, Copenhagen #1679/R est:20000 (D.KR 30000)

ANNA, Margit (1913-1991) Hungarian
£2898 $5246 €4231 Beata (35x25cm-14x10in) s. 16-Apr-4 Mu Terem Galeria, Budapest #15/R (H.F 1100000)

ANNAERT, J P (19th C) American
£4918 $9000 €7180 Boy with geese (127x91cm-50x36in) s. 10-Apr-4 Brunk, Ashville #690/R est:600-1200

ANNALY, Mme (1855-?) French
£1467 $2684 €2200 Peintre a Fontainebleau, auto-portrait (66x94cm-26x37in) s. painted c.1885. 6-Jun-4 Osenat, Fontainebleau #115/R est:2500-3000

ANNAN, Thomas (1828-1887) British
Photographs
£30556 $55000 €44612 Old closes and streets of Glasgow (20x32cm-8x13in) carbon prints album of 40. 22-Apr-4 Phillips, New York #21/R est:70000-100000

ANNENKOFF, Yuri (1889-1974) Russian
£4698 $8644 €7000 Still life with playing cards, pipe, wine bottle, glass (40x35cm-16x14in) s. lit. 25-Mar-4 Karlheinz Kaupp, Staufen #2332/R est:250
£24000 $42960 €35040 Villas by the river (65x91cm-26x36in) s. 26-May-4 Sotheby's, London #151/R est:18000-25000
£32000 $57280 €46720 French landscape (66x92cm-26x36in) s. 26-May-4 Sotheby's, London #150/R est:18000-25000
£36000 $64440 €52560 Portrait of Rene Guerra (81x65cm-32x26in) s. 26-May-4 Sotheby's, London #152/R est:20000-30000
Works on paper
£310 $515 €450 Dancer (28x20cm-11x8in) s. chl htd W/C. 6-Oct-3 Blanchet, Paris #255
£310 $515 €450 Two men (36x26cm-14x10in) s. chl. 6-Oct-3 Blanchet, Paris #257
£345 $572 €500 Young lady (36x25cm-14x10in) chl Chinese ink htd gouache. 6-Oct-3 Blanchet, Paris #256/R
£556 $1000 €812 City landscape 2 (19x14cm-7x6in) pencil. 24-Apr-4 Shishkin Gallery, Moscow #23/R est:1500-2000
£662 $1205 €1000 Femme au miroir (36x26cm-14x10in) mono. pen india ink. 15-Jun-4 Blanchet, Paris #146/R
£676 $1189 €1000 Etudes de nu (21x26cm-8x10in) mono.d.50 pen ink. 19-May-4 Camard, Paris #8
£793 $1317 €1150 Spanish dancer (48x32cm-19x13in) s. gouache chl. 6-Oct-3 Blanchet, Paris #251
£793 $1317 €1150 Spanish dancer (49x32cm-19x13in) s. gouache chl. 6-Oct-3 Blanchet, Paris #252/R
£833 $1500 €1216 City landscape 4 (18x13cm-7x5in) pencil. 24-Apr-4 Shishkin Gallery, Moscow #24/R est:1500-2000
£931 $1546 €1350 Couple de danseurs (42x26cm-17x10in) s. graphite. 6-Oct-3 Blanchet, Paris #258/R
£2000 $3400 €2920 Still life with basket of flowers (48x63cm-19x25in) s. ink htd gouache. 19-Nov-3 Sotheby's, London #178/R est:2000-3000
£4800 $8160 €7008 Three costume designs (48x32cm-19x13in) two s. one init. ink pencil W/C gouache one htd. gold paint three. 19-Nov-3 Sotheby's, London #192/R est:2000-3000
£5500 $9350 €8030 Still life with ceramic vase and pear (65x50cm-26x20in) s. gouache prov. 19-Nov-3 Sotheby's, London #212/R est:4000-6000
£8000 $14720 €11680 Untitled (31x26cm-12x10in) s.d.1920 wood collage W/C pencil metal wire board prov.exhib. 24-Jun-4 Christie's, London #366/R est:8000-12000
£28000 $50960 €40880 Portrait of Daniel Geccen (44x38cm-17x15in) s.d.1922 i.verso W/C pen ink prov. 21-Jun-4 Bonhams, New Bond Street #19/R est:30000-40000

ANNESLEY, Jennifer (20th C) Canadian
Works on paper
£400 $732 €584 October coulee (34x53cm-13x21in) s.i.d.1997 W/C. 1-Jun-4 Hodgins, Calgary #43/R (C.D 1000)

ANNIGONI, Pietro (1910-1988) Italian
£1056 $1754 €1500 Paesaggio nel verde (13x18cm-5x7in) s.verso cardboard. 14-Jun-3 Meeting Art, Vercelli #684/R est:1500
£1500 $2655 €2190 Portrait of a lady (60x48cm-24x19in) panel. 27-Apr-4 Bonhams, Knightsbridge #221/R est:1200-1500
£2000 $3680 €3000 Landscape (18x27cm-7x11in) s. cardboard. 11-Jun-4 Farsetti, Prato #500/R est:2700-3000
£2013 $3725 €3000 Landscape (17x26cm-7x10in) s. card. 11-Mar-4 Galleria Pace, Milan #26 est:2800-3600
£2394 $4142 €3400 London (20x24cm-8x9in) s.d.LXIX. 9-Dec-3 Pandolfini, Florence #390/R est:2800-3000
£4698 $8691 €7000 Miglianino (30x40cm-12x16in) s.i. cardboard on canvas. 13-Mar-4 Meeting Art, Vercelli #226 est:7000
£5705 $10554 €8500 Landscape (30x40cm-12x16in) s. cardboard on canvas. 11-Mar-4 Galleria Pace, Milan #147/R est:8300-10500
Works on paper
£347 $549 €500 Landscape (22x15cm-9x6in) Chinese ink. 6-Sep-3 Meeting Art, Vercelli #386
£420 $764 €613 Female nude on a divan (36x54cm-14x21in) s.d.1969 red grey chk. 29-Jun-4 Anderson & Garland, Newcastle #167
£500 $850 €730 Study of mans face (15x10cm-6x4in) s.i.d.XXI-II-LXXVI sanguine. 29-Oct-3 Hampton & Littlewood, Exeter #490/R
£500 $920 €750 Face (15x10cm-6x4in) s. sanguine. 12-Jun-4 Meeting Art, Vercelli #209/R
£667 $1227 €1000 Face (20x15cm-8x6in) s. sanguine. 12-Jun-4 Meeting Art, Vercelli #604/R
£694 $1097 €1000 Face (20x15cm-8x6in) sanguine card. 6-Sep-3 Meeting Art, Vercelli #528
£699 $1189 €1000 Suzanne and the elderly. London (19x24cm-7x9in) s.i.d.MCMXXXII Chinese ink W/C prov. two. 25-Nov-3 Sotheby's, Milan #133/R
£699 $1189 €1000 Self-portrait. Landscape (9x14cm-4x6in) s. Chinese ink card two. 25-Nov-3 Sotheby's, Milan #144/R
£935 $1534 €1300 Portrait of Emilio Martelli (29x20cm-11x8in) s.i. sanguine. 10-Jun-3 Pandolfini, Florence #379 est:600-800
£1042 $1646 €1500 Face (20x14cm-8x6in) sanguine card. 6-Sep-3 Meeting Art, Vercelli #645 est:1000
£1119 $1902 €1600 Portrait of lady. Fisherman. Landscape (23x32cm-9x13in) s. felt-tip pen one double-sided set of 3. 25-Nov-3 Sotheby's, Milan #105 est:800-1000
£1133 $2085 €1700 Nude (38x23cm-15x9in) s. W/C prov. 8-Jun-4 Finarte Semenzato, Milan #52/R est:500-700
£1172 $1958 €1700 Face of old man (19x14cm-7x6in) s. sanguine wash card. 14-Nov-3 Farsetti, Prato #77/R est:1600-1900
£1342 $2483 €2000 Face (28x19cm-11x7in) s. sanguine. 11-Mar-4 Galleria Pace, Milan #25/R est:2300-3000
£1477 $2732 €2200 Figure (30x20cm-12x8in) s. sanguine. 11-Mar-4 Galleria Pace, Milan #101/R est:2500-3000
£1479 $2558 €2100 Group in Iceland (38x54cm-15x21in) s.i. pastel. 9-Dec-3 Pandolfini, Florence #327/R est:1300-1400
£1517 $2534 €2200 Face of old man (28x19cm-11x7in) s. sanguine wash card. 14-Nov-3 Farsetti, Prato #216/R est:2100-2500
£1620 $2802 €2300 View of the Arno (36x51cm-14x20in) s.d.1962 Chinese ink W/C. 9-Dec-3 Pandolfini, Florence #94/R est:600-700
£1667 $2733 €2300 Face (30x20cm-12x8in) s. sanguine. 29-May-3 Galleria Pace, Milan #128/R est:4800
£1739 $2852 €2400 Bathers. Sunday trip (16x32cm-6x13in) s.i.d.MCMXXXI Chinese ink W/C prov. two. 27-May-3 Sotheby's, Milan #11 est:2000

ANNOIS, Leonard Lloyd (1906-1966) Australian
Works on paper
£246 $388 €359 Boats, Mornington (25x35cm-10x14in) s.d.44 w/C. 2-Sep-3 Deutscher-Menzies, Melbourne #364/R (A.D 600)
£369 $583 €539 Approaching storm, Flinders (26x37cm-10x15in) s.d.44 W/C. 2-Sep-3 Deutscher-Menzies, Melbourne #365/R (A.D 900)

ANNOVI, Nereo (1908-1981) Italian
£647 $1062 €900 Portrait of woman (60x48cm-24x19in) 5-Jun-3 Adma, Formigine #749

ANONYMOUS
£193182 $340000 €282046 Painter standing beside a canvas depicting Cupid (114x94cm-45x37in) 21-May-4 North East Auctions, Portsmouth #1487/R
Sculpture
£9756 $15415 €14146 Tiwi ceremonial spearhead dance wand with face (76cm-30in) black resin col ochre. 28-Jul-3 Sotheby's, Paddington #141/R est:4000-6000 (A.D 24000)
£10811 $18054 €15784 Mencari kutu - catching lice (126x76cm-50x30in) resin. 26-Oct-3 Christie's, Hong Kong #73/R est:38000-45000 (HK.D 140000)
£13581 $24580 €19828 Cylindrical sculpture (184x40x20cm-72x16x8in) sheet metal plywood spray paint. 30-Mar-4 Lawson Menzies, Sydney #320 est:300-500 (A.D 33000)
£17045 $30000 €24886 Alexander the Great, bust of soldier in military garb (122x76x36cm-48x30x14in) bronze marble. 3-Jan-4 Brunk, Ashville #157/R est:5000-10000
£23239 $40204 €33000 Hercule combattant l'hydre de Lerne (215cm-85in) bronze Cast Rudier. 10-Dec-3 Ferri, Paris #204/R est:25000-30000

ANONYMOUS (11/13th C)
Works on paper
£14225 $25605 €20769 Five ducks (25x92cm-10x36in) scroll ink colour on silk. 26-Apr-4 Christie's, Hong Kong #949/R est:100000-150000 (HK.D 200000)

ANONYMOUS (15th/16th C)
Works on paper
£13514 $24324 €19730 Travels of Emperor Mu of the Zhou Dynasty (52x473cm-20x186in) bears sig. Zhao Boqu col ink gold handscroll silk. 25-Apr-4 Christie's, Hong Kong #310/R est:40000-50000 (HK.D 190000)

ANONYMOUS, 17th C
£5656 $9050 €8258 Portrait of young woman from Spiring family (199x106cm-78x42in) d.1615. 16-Sep-3 Philippe Schuler, Zurich #3305/R est:8000-10000 (S.FR 12500)
£6040 $11114 €9000 The martyrdom of St Peter (65x50cm-26x20in) i. copper. 27-Mar-4 Geble, Radolfzell #698/R est:2800
£12676 $20408 €18000 Ritratto di uomo con cappello e mantello (86x63cm-34x25in) i. verso. 8-May-3 Farsetti, Prato #656/R est:12000-15000
£15436 $28403 €23000 Still life with jug, large glass, plates with prawns (56x76cm-22x30in) panel. 27-Mar-4 Geble, Radolfzell #706/R est:4000
Works on paper
£10326 $19000 €15076 Scenes from the Tale of Genji (69x363cm-27x143in) ink gold leaf eight panel screen. 23-Mar-4 Christie's, Rockefeller NY #67/R est:7000-9000
£17391 $32000 €25391 Cherry blossom viewing at Mount Yoshino (102x267cm-40x105in) ink silver gold leaf six panel screen. 23-Mar-4 Christie's, Rockefeller NY #71/R est:35000-45000
£152174 $280000 €222174 Scenes in and around Osaka (88x356cm-35x140in) ink gold leaf pair eight panel screens. 23-Mar-4 Christie's, Rockefeller NY #70/R est:120000-180000

ANONYMOUS (18th C)
£10769 $18523 €15723 Fox in the poultry yard (116x170cm-46x67in) 7-Dec-3 Uppsala Auktionskammare, Uppsala #25/R est:20000-25000 (S.KR 140000)
£20946 $37493 €31000 St Katharina (128x97cm-50x38in) 8-May-4 Dawo, Saarbrucken #4/R est:2000
£23529 $40000 €34352 El milagro (65x93cm-26x37in) i. painted c.1777 prov.exhib.lit. 19-Nov-3 Sotheby's, New York #70/R est:30000-40000
£24434 $39095 €35674 Murder of Ceasar (148x211cm-58x83in) 16-Sep-3 Philippe Schuler, Zurich #3307/R est:8000-12000 (S.FR 54000)
£52308 $89969 €76370 Danae and the Gold Rain (130x180cm-51x71in) bears sig.d.1704. 7-Dec-3 Uppsala Auktionskammare, Uppsala #1/R est:20000-25000 (S.KR 680000)
Works on paper
£7240 $11584 €10570 Italian river landscape with figures (32x46cm-13x18in) gouache. 16-Sep-3 Philippe Schuler, Zurich #5853 est:1400-1800 (S.FR 16000)

£12637 $23126 €18956 Opening ceremony of the Portao do Passeio Publico (24x45cm-9x18in) gouache. 6-Jul-4 Bolsa de Arte, Rio de Janeiro #54/R (B.R 69000)
£462304 $832148 €674964 Imperial Autumn Hunt at Mulan (50cm-20in) handscroll ink colour on silk. 26-Apr-4 Christie's, Hong Kong #985/R est:4000000-6000000 (HK.D 6500000)

ANONYMOUS (19th C)
£6875 $11000 €10038 Promenade scene of woman and child and a young black boy in a top hat (79x64cm-31x25in) 20-Sep-3 Pook & Pook, Downington #261a/R est:1000-1500
£10227 $18000 €14931 Portrait of Jane Clarissa Walton, Morganton, North Carolina (76x64cm-30x25in) prov. 3-Jan-4 Brunk, Ashville #448/R est:4000-8000
£11972 $20711 €17000 The old city of Turku (53x68cm-21x27in) 13-Dec-3 Hagelstam, Helsinki #58/R est:8500
£19595 $34486 €29000 Portrait of bearded man (38x32cm-15x13in) 24-May-4 Bernaerts, Antwerp #372/R est:1000-1250
£22059 $37500 €32206 Puerto de Mazatlan (42x67cm-17x26in) 19-Nov-3 Sotheby's, New York #83/R est:18000-22000
Photographs
£13559 $24000 €19796 Young boy with black family. ambrotype exec.c.1860. 28-Apr-4 Sotheby's, New York #98/R est:5000-7000
Sculpture
£11246 $19344 €16419 Morian figures (205cm-81in) painted wood pair. 2-Dec-3 Rasmussen, Copenhagen #791/R est:100000-125000 (D.KR 120000)

ANONYMOUS (20th C)
£11034 $20193 €16000 Little oriental boy in dress uniform (152x90cm-60x35in) i. i. verso. 27-Jan-4 Dorotheum, Vienna #11/R est:1200-1800

ANOUSH, Rahnarvardkar (20th C) ?
£393 $625 €570 Lady with gentleman and scowling woman (97x48cm-38x19in) s. canvas on board. 12-Sep-3 Aspire, Cleveland #82

ANQUETIN, Louis (1861-1932) French
£1400 $2534 €2100 Femme nue souriante (90x72cm-35x28in) s.d.1892 pastel three sheets on canvas. 30-Mar-4 Rossini, Paris #341/R est:2000-3000

ANRAEDT, Pieter van (?-1678) Dutch
£3500 $5950 €5110 Portrait of a lady wearing a pearl necklace (108x78cm-43x31in) s. 31-Oct-3 Christie's, Kensington #44/R est:2000-3000

ANREITER, Alois von (1803-1882) Austrian
Works on paper
£570 $1010 €850 Kaiser Ferdinand I and his wife (30x26cm-12x10in) s. W/C oval. 29-Apr-4 Dorotheum, Vienna #52/R

ANRROY, Anton van (1870-1949) Dutch
£800 $1408 €1168 West Indian harbour. Figure in a West Indian harbour (24x33cm-9x13in) indis i. panel pair. 19-May-4 Christie's, Kensington #752/R

ANSCOMBE, Robert (fl.1950s) British
£380 $699 €555 French design, with V Gardner up (51x60cm-20x24in) s.i. 10-Jun-4 Christie's, Kensington #203/R

ANSDELL, Richard (1815-1885) British
£1000 $1700 €1460 Stalking in the highlands (27x42cm-11x17in) s.d.1860. 19-Nov-3 Sotheby's, Olympia #43/R est:1000-1500
£1600 $2656 €2336 Fox and a dead pheasant (31x49cm-12x19in) init.d.1871 prov.exhib. 1-Oct-3 Woolley & Wallis, Salisbury #206/R est:800-1200
£1854 $3375 €2800 Two dogs in a landscape with a lake in background (22x34cm-9x13in) s.d.1869 panel. 19-Jun-4 Hans Stahl, Hamburg #7/R est:3500
£3727 $6000 €5441 Queen Victoria and Prince Albert with children and attendants setting off for the hunt (68x89cm-27x35in) s.d.86. 14-Jan-4 Christie's, Rockefeller NY #53/R est:8000-12000
£8000 $14080 €11680 English Setter with a pheasant (68x51cm-27x20in) init.d.1866 prov. 21-May-4 Christie's, London #44/R est:8000-12000
£8500 $14450 €12410 Charles, 2nd earl of Talbot on a dark bay hunter, with his greyhounds Top and Tabinet (49x64cm-19x25in) s.d.1840. 25-Nov-3 Christie's, London #70/R est:8000-12000
£58000 $91060 €84100 Sheep gathering in Glen Spean (91x191cm-36x75in) s. exhib. 27-Aug-3 Sotheby's, London #1178/R est:70000-100000
£100000 $157000 €145000 Crossing the burn (86x166cm-34x65in) s.d.1863 prov. 27-Aug-3 Sotheby's, London #1179/R est:100000-150000

ANSDELL, Richard (style) (1815-1885) British
£7800 $14430 €11388 Successful shoot (112x138cm-44x54in) 10-Feb-4 Bonhams, Knightsbridge #268/R est:5000-7000

ANSEELE, Frans (1819-?) Belgian
£379 $683 €550 Portrait de l'architecte Sutton (117x87cm-46x34in) s. 20-Jan-4 Galerie Moderne, Brussels #287

ANSEN-HOFMANN, E (19/20th C) German
£2000 $3700 €2920 Chase (73x99cm-29x39in) s. 10-Mar-4 Sotheby's, Olympia #309/R est:2000-3000
£2241 $4012 €3272 Le butin (89x124cm-35x49in) s. 17-May-4 Beurret, Zurich #19/R est:6000-8000 (S.FR 5200)
£3893 $7162 €5800 Slave trader (89x124cm-35x49in) s. prov. 26-Mar-4 Ketterer, Hamburg #170/R est:5000-6000

ANSHUTZ, Thomas Pollock (1851-1912) American
Works on paper
£234 $425 €342 Embracing women (61x46cm-24x18in) chl. 8-Feb-4 William Jenack, New York #124/R

ANSINGH, Lizzy (1875-1959) Dutch
£521 $823 €750 Portrait of the sculptor George Petel, wearing a black waistcoat and cloak (60x45cm-24x18in) after Sir Anthony van Dyck prov. 2-Sep-3 Christie's, Amsterdam #7/R
£1088 $1981 €1600 Delightful dolls (27x19cm-11x7in) s. canvas on panel. 3-Feb-4 Christie's, Amsterdam #162 est:600-800
£2721 $4952 €4000 New baby (79x67cm-31x26in) init. 3-Feb-4 Christie's, Amsterdam #163/R est:1500-2000
£4667 $8400 €7000 Oudewijvenmolen - old ladies in a carriage (102x164cm-40x65in) 20-Apr-4 Sotheby's, Amsterdam #123/R est:8000-12000
£22667 $40800 €34000 Awaken (142x134cm-56x53in) s.d.1915 s.i.verso prov.exhib.lit. 21-Apr-4 Christie's, Amsterdam #158/R est:25000-35000

ANSPACH, Henri (20th C) Belgian
£517 $864 €750 Ne debout (55x35cm-22x14in) s.d.1928. 17-Nov-3 Claude Boisgirard, Paris #3/R

ANTAKOLSKY, Mark Matveievich (1843-1902) Russian
Sculpture
£16667 $30000 €24334 Mephistopheles (89cm-35in) s. bronze. 23-Apr-4 Sotheby's, New York #42/R est:30000-40000
£26000 $44200 €39000 Mephistopheles (84cm-33in) s. pat bronze. 25-Nov-3 Christie's, London #154/R est:25000-35000

ANTEN, Djef (1851-1913) Belgian
£759 $1403 €1100 Bouleaux sur fond de meules (113x70cm-44x28in) 19-Jan-4 Horta, Bruxelles #461

ANTEQUERA, Isidro (1926-) Spanish
£362 $594 €500 Bodegon dorado (47x60cm-19x24in) s. s.i.verso. 27-May-3 Durán, Madrid #625/R

ANTES, Horst (1936-) German
£4422 $7916 €6500 Untitled (40x30cm-16x12in) s.i.d.3.3.74 verso prov. 21-Mar-4 Calmels Cohen, Paris #99/R est:6000-8000
£12667 $23307 €19000 Red figure (60x40cm-24x16in) i.d.1970/71/73 verso. 11-Jun-4 Villa Grisebach, Berlin #1608/R est:14000-18000
£20979 $36084 €30000 Figure with large bird (59x76cm-23x30in) s. s.i.d.1963 verso acrylic plywood prov.exhib. 5-Dec-3 Ketterer, Munich #162/R est:30000-40000
£37333 $68693 €56000 Untitled (92x62cm-36x24in) s.d.61 tempera col crayon chl paper. 11-Jun-4 Villa Grisebach, Berlin #1606/R est:14000-18000
Prints
£4545 $7818 €6500 Large figure of head with five eyes (96x68cm-38x27in) s. aquatec chl pencil black oil crayon prov. 5-Dec-3 Ketterer, Munich #166/R est:8500-9500
Sculpture
£2000 $3620 €2920 Kopf (43x44x13cm-17x17x5in) with sig.num.780/1000 steel executed 1977. 1-Apr-4 Christie's, Kensington #258/R est:2000-3000
£2098 $3566 €3000 Figure 1000 (221cm-87in) s. num.163/1000 iron exec.1987. 25-Nov-3 Sotheby's, Milan #119/R est:2000-3000
£3061 $5480 €4500 Sculpture (204cm-80in) metal. 19-Mar-4 Millon & Associes, Paris #168/R est:3000-4000
£4366 $7554 €6200 Head (45x44x13cm-18x17x5in) st.sig.i. rust pat.steel prov. 13-Dec-3 Lempertz, Koln #276/R est:3000
Works on paper
£1000 $1840 €1500 Lovers (17x20cm-7x8in) s. i.d. verso. 11-Jun-4 Hauswedell & Nolte, Hamburg #1108/R est:1500
£1119 $1937 €1634 Nude lady with red cap (30x25cm-12x10in) s.d.1966 W/C prov. 9-Dec-3 Peter Webb, Auckland #91/R est:3000-4000 (NZ.D 3000)
£1467 $2699 €2200 Composition (32x40cm-13x16in) s. pastel gouache prov. 9-Jun-4 Christie's, Amsterdam #184/R est:1800-2200
£2333 $4177 €3500 Figure (31x52cm-12x20in) s.i.d. W/C prov. 14-May-4 Ketterer, Munich #304/R est:3800-4800
£2333 $4293 €3500 Figure with raised arms (32x40cm-13x16in) s. col chk chl pigment. 12-Jun-4 Villa Grisebach, Berlin #362/R est:4000-5000
£2333 $4293 €3500 Composition (75x53cm-30x21in) s.d.1961 ink w, graphite chk. 11-Jun-4 Villa Grisebach, Berlin #1607/R est:5000-7000
£8451 $14028 €12000 Head (70x60cm-28x24in) s.i.d.1967 verso aquatec canvas. 13-Jun-3 Hauswedell & Nolte, Hamburg #519/R est:18000
£15000 $27600 €21900 Kauernde figur (120x100cm-47x39in) s.i.d.1973 verso aquatec canvas prov.exhib. 24-Jun-4 Sotheby's, London #221/R est:15000-20000
£24000 $42960 €36000 Yellow figure blue (130x80cm-51x31in) s.i.d. verso aquatec prov.exhib. 14-May-4 Ketterer, Munich #272/R est:28000-35000
£25352 $42085 €36000 Blue picture for Terres des Hommes (70x60cm-28x24in) s.i.d.1970 verso aquatic canvas. 13-Jun-3 Hauswedell & Nolte, Hamburg #520/R est:40000

ANTHONIS, Victor (19/20th C) Belgian?
£380 $673 €555 Interior scene with a woman seated at a table making lace (39x40cm-15x16in) s. board. 28-Apr-4 Peter Wilson, Nantwich #100

ANTHONISSEN, Hendrick van (1606-?) Dutch
£7534 $12808 €11000 Fishermen in a rowing boat and sailing vessels in a choppy sea (26x40cm-10x16in) indis.mono. panel prov.exhib. 4-Nov-3 Sotheby's, Amsterdam #59/R est:10000-15000

ANTHONY, Carol (1943-) American?
£299 $550 €437 New Mexico courtyard, noon (28x28cm-11x11in) s.i.d.1984 oil col pastel paper. 10-Jun-4 Swann Galleries, New York #4/R

ANTHOONS, Willy (1911-1983) Belgian
Works on paper
£302 $535 €450 Composition (35x26cm-14x10in) s.d.1961 gouache. 27-Apr-4 Campo, Vlaamse Kaai #302

ANTOINE, Marguerite (1907-1989) ?
£308 $514 €440 Ballerine lacant ses chaussons (34x25cm-13x10in) s. panel. 13-Oct-3 Horta, Bruxelles #457
£486 $773 €700 Jeune femme nue allongee (87x101cm-34x40in) s. 15-Sep-3 Horta, Bruxelles #465
£521 $870 €750 Etrille (54x44cm-21x17in) s. 21-Oct-3 Galerie Moderne, Brussels #290/R

ANTOINE, Otto (1865-1951) German
£280 $467 €400 Dresden (13x18cm-5x7in) s. board. 28-Jun-3 Dannenberg, Berlin #648/R
£333 $610 €500 Bend in the river with cargo boat and mountain (64x86cm-25x34in) s.d.1901. 5-Jun-4 Arnold, Frankfurt #524/R
£1757 $3092 €2600 Berlin, view of cathedral and castle bridge (24x31cm-9x12in) s. board. 22-May-4 Lempertz, Koln #1476/R est:1500
£2917 $4813 €4200 Berlin (73x95cm-29x37in) s. 3-Jul-3 Van Ham, Cologne #1049 est:1200

ANTOMMARCHI, Francois (1780-1838) Italian
Sculpture
£1103 $2019 €1600 Masque mortuaire de l'Empereur Napoleon 1er (34cm-13in) brown pat bronze Cast Richard et Quesnel. 31-Jan-4 Gerard, Besancon #239

ANTON, Francois (1944-) French?
£302 $535 €450 La fil a la patte (33x41cm-13x16in) s. 29-Apr-4 Claude Aguttes, Neuilly #98
£728 $1326 €1100 Trois personnages assis (54x68cm-21x27in) s. panel. 20-Jun-4 Salle des ventes Pillet, Lyon la Foret #3/R

ANTON, Werner (1902-1976) German
£490 $842 €700 Hamburg docks (60x80cm-24x31in) s.i. 4-Dec-3 Schopman, Hamburg #760/R

ANTONI, Janine (1964-) American
Photographs
£53892 $90000 €78682 Mom and Dad (61x51cm-24x20in) c-print three parts edition 3 of 6 prov.exhib.lit. 13-Nov-3 Sotheby's, New York #409/R est:70000-100000

ANTONI, Louis Ferdinand (1872-1940) French
£1067 $1963 €1600 Labours en bord de mer (57x73cm-22x29in) s. cardboard. 8-Jun-4 Livinec, Gaudcheau & Jezequel, Rennes #135/R
£1986 $3316 €2800 Cavalier sur un marche (86x100cm-34x39in) s. 16-Jun-3 Gros & Delettrez, Paris #276/R est:2500-3500
£2908 $4856 €4100 Depart du cavalier (92x72cm-36x28in) s.d.90 panel. 19-Oct-3 Rabourdin & Choppin de Janvry, Paris #20/R est:4500-5300
£3380 $5848 €4800 Halte pres du temple de Djelila (76x94cm-30x37in) s.d.1931. 15-Dec-3 Gros & Delettrez, Paris #406/R est:3500-4500

ANTONIO DA PESARO, Giovanni (15th C) Italian
£22000 $40260 €32120 Angel of the annunciation. Virgin annunciate (39x30cm-15x12in) i. gold ground panel for an altarpiece two prov. 7-Jul-4 Christie's, London #11/R est:25000-35000

ANTONIO DA VITERBO (attrib) (15th C) Italian
£2837 $4738 €4000 Madonna with baby (26x35cm-10x14in) panel. 18-Jun-3 Christie's, Rome #361 est:4000-6000

ANTONIO DELLA CATENA (circle) (fl.1531-1543) Italian
£4237 $7500 €6186 Ave Maria (208x130cm-82x51in) panel. 2-May-4 Bonhams & Butterfields, San Francisco #1015/R est:3000-5000

ANTONIO, Cristobal de (19th C) Spanish
£272 $487 €400 Flowers (35x27cm-14x11in) s. cardboard. 22-Mar-4 Durán, Madrid #111/R
£272 $487 €400 Flowers (35x27cm-14x11in) s. cardboard. 22-Mar-4 Durán, Madrid #110/R

ANTONIO, Pietro (17th C) Italian?
Works on paper
£600 $1110 €876 Allegory of the House of Bourbon (36x22cm-14x9in) indis sig. gouache. 14-Jan-4 Lawrence, Crewkerne #1304

ANTONISSEN, Henri Joseph (1737-1794) Flemish
£898 $1500 €1311 Landscape (27x38cm-11x15in) s. panel. 20-Oct-3 Sotheby's, New York #167/R est:3000-5000
£12000 $21960 €17520 Peasants with a cattle in an open landscape (78x108cm-31x43in) s.d.1778. 6-Jul-4 Sotheby's, Olympia #588/R est:8000-12000

ANTONOV, Fedor (1904-1994) Russian
£978 $1800 €1428 Winter forest scene (90x120cm-35x47in) painted 1950's. 27-Mar-4 Shishkin Gallery, Moscow #57/R est:4000-5000
£2624 $4750 €3831 In the studio (71x92cm-28x36in) s. 30-Mar-4 Bonhams & Butterfields, San Francisco #138/R est:4000-6000

ANTONY, George Wilfred (1800-1860) British
£1500 $2745 €2190 Departure (49x90cm-19x35in) i. 6-Jul-4 Bonhams, Knightsbridge #110a/R est:1500-2000

ANTRAL, Louis Robert (1895-1940) French
£899 $1475 €1250 L'Ile aux cygnes (33x41cm-13x16in) s.d.1932 verso cardboard. 6-Jun-3 Chochon-Barre & Allardi, Paris #20/R
Works on paper
£385 $642 €550 Voiles bleues (26x45cm-10x18in) s.d.1933 W/C. 27-Jun-3 Doutrebente, Paris #41/R
£1126 $2060 €1700 Peniches (30x41cm-12x16in) s.i. W/C ink. 7-Apr-4 Doutrebente, Paris #27/R est:800

ANTRO, Alexandre van (19th C) Belgian?
£528 $950 €771 Return from the hunt (53x41cm-21x16in) s.d.1866 panel. 23-Jan-4 Freeman, Philadelphia #185/R

ANTUM, Aert van (17th C) Dutch
£29801 $54536 €45000 Marines aux vaisseaux hollandais (44x98cm-17x39in) panel four. 7-Apr-4 Libert, Castor, Paris #28/R est:50000-70000

ANTUM, Aert van (attrib) (17th C) Dutch
£3497 $6014 €5000 Paysage cotier avec nombreux voiliers (33x41cm-13x16in) copper. 3-Dec-3 Palais de Beaux Arts, Brussels #679/R est:5000-7000

ANTWERP SCHOOL (16th C) Flemish
£6960 $12041 €10162 Holy Family with a view of Antwerp Cathedral beyond, seen from the south (108x72cm-43x28in) panel. 9-Dec-3 Sotheby's, Olympia #301/R est:6000-8000
£7800 $13494 €11388 Adoration of the Magi. Saint Francis receiving the Stigmata. Saint Jerome in Penitence (60x38cm-24x15in) panel triptych. 9-Dec-3 Sotheby's, Olympia #318/R est:3000-4000
£8000 $14400 €11680 The Last Supper (105x168cm-41x66in) panel. 22-Apr-4 Sotheby's, London #43/R est:8000-12000
£8609 $15755 €13000 Altar piece (32x12cm-13x5in) panel triptych. 7-Apr-4 Dorotheum, Salzburg #6/R est:13000-15000
£9589 $16301 €14000 Adoration of the Magi (66x49cm-26x19in) panel. 4-Nov-3 Sotheby's, Amsterdam #43/R est:12000-18000
£17568 $30919 €26000 Christ on the cross with Mary, Mary Magdalen and John (88cm-35in) triptych panel prov. 22-May-4 Lempertz, Koln #1001/R est:30000
£72222 $130000 €105444 Holy Family. Saint Catherine of Alexandria. Saint Barbra (22x24cm-9x9in) panel triptych prov.exhib. 23-Jan-4 Christie's, Rockefeller NY #16/R est:70000-100000

ANTWERP SCHOOL (17th C) Flemish
£5946 $11000 €8681 Adam and Eve in the garden of Eden (26x38cm-10x15in) panel. 17-Jan-4 Sotheby's, New York #1123/R est:4000-6000
£11486 $20216 €17000 Orpheus searching Eurydice in the underworld (64x79cm-25x31in) 18-May-4 Sotheby's, Amsterdam #49/R est:5000-7000

ANUSZKIEWICZ, Richard (1930-) American
£2162 $4000 €3157 Wind's Eye (61x61cm-24x24in) s.d.1965 liquitex board prov. 13-Jul-4 Christie's, Rockefeller NY #13/R est:2000-3000
£2432 $4500 €3551 Sunbow (40x40cm-16x16in) s.d.1968 acrylic panel prov. 12-Feb-4 Sotheby's, New York #182/R est:2000-3000
£6145 $11000 €8972 Union of the four (132x127cm-52x50in) prov. 14-May-4 Skinner, Boston #394/R est:5000-7000

ANWAR, Ahmad Zakii (1955-) Malaysian
£1390 $2321 €2029 Still life (69x69cm-27x27in) s. 26-Oct-3 Christie's, Hong Kong #87/R est:12000-16000 (HK.D 18000)
£1458 $2435 €2129 Still life (68x69cm-27x27in) s.d.00. 12-Oct-3 Sotheby's, Singapore #85/R est:3000-4000 (S.D 4200)
£1467 $2450 €2142 Still life (69x69cm-27x27in) s. 26-Oct-3 Christie's, Hong Kong #86/R est:12000-16000 (HK.D 19000)
£1699 $2837 €2481 Still life (69x69cm-27x27in) s. 26-Oct-3 Christie's, Hong Kong #85/R est:12000-16000 (HK.D 22000)

ANZALONE, Chuck (20th C) American
£202 $375 €295 Water and sky (61x76cm-24x30in) s. 17-Jul-4 Outer Cape Auctions, Provincetown #1a/R
£255 $400 €372 UU Church, Provincetown (36x28cm-14x11in) s. board. 20-Apr-3 Outer Cape Auctions, Provincetown #62
£294 $500 €429 Morning light (46x36cm-18x14in) s. board. 9-Nov-3 Outer Cape Auctions, Provincetown #96/R
£297 $550 €434 Water lilies (76x61cm-30x24in) s. 15-Feb-4 Outer Cape Auctions, Provincetown #65/R
£317 $575 €463 Home Port Lane (61x91cm-24x36in) s.d.2000. 3-Apr-4 Outer Cape Auctions, Provincetown #77/R
£456 $825 €666 Summer garden (61x76cm-24x30in) s. 3-Apr-4 Outer Cape Auctions, Provincetown #53/R
£483 $850 €705 Sunset (76x61cm-30x24in) s. 3-Jan-4 Outer Cape Auctions, Provincetown #95/R
£552 $900 €806 Twilight (76x61cm-30x24in) s. board. 19-Jul-3 Outer Cape Auctions, Provincetown #48/R

ANZINGER, Siegfried (1953-) Austrian
£420 $713 €600 Untitled (63x48cm-25x19in) s.d.24.4.84 acrylic Indian ink prov. 27-Nov-3 Lempertz, Koln #12/R
£1074 $1976 €1600 Figures (80x57cm-31x22in) s.d. acrylic. 26-Mar-4 Ketterer, Hamburg #293/R est:1500-2000
£1223 $2250 €1786 Untitled (70x50cm-28x20in) s.d.1989 verso prov. 8-Jun-4 Germann, Zurich #102/R est:3000-5000 (S.FR 2800)
£1379 $2524 €2000 Untitled (57x40cm-22x16in) s.d.82 acrylic. 27-Jan-4 Dorotheum, Vienna #242/R est:2200-3000
£1462 $2369 €2135 Untitled (62x48cm-24x19in) s. prov. 24-May-3 Burkhard, Luzern #66/R est:1500-2000 (S.FR 3100)
£8333 $14167 €12000 Untitled. s.d.81 s.d.81 verso acrylic. 28-Oct-3 Wiener Kunst Auktionen, Vienna #290/R est:16000-25000

£15278	$25972	€22000	Untitled (150x100cm-59x39in) s.i.d.1988 verso egg tempera exhib. 28-Oct-3 Wiener Kunst Auktionen, Vienna #286/R est:20000-30000
£17361	$29514	€25000	Moor (200x140cm-79x55in) s.d.11/83 verso acrylic cotton exhib.lit. 28-Oct-3 Wiener Kunst Auktionen, Vienna #282/R est:20000-25000
Sculpture			
£2183	$4017	€3187	Dog on head (200x24x41cm-79x9x16in) board bamboo canes wire plaster prov. 8-Jun-4 Germann, Zurich #101/R est:8000-12000 (S.FR 5000)
Works on paper			
£352	$616	€500	Nude Karin (40x51cm-16x20in) s.i.d.1978 pen ink. 19-Dec-3 Dorotheum, Vienna #323/R
£355	$592	€500	Christ before Pilate (22x31cm-9x12in) s.d.Okt.76 Indian ink. 14-Oct-3 Dorotheum, Vienna #231/R
£423	$701	€600	Untitled (59x41cm-23x16in) s. s.d.1982 verso gouache. 13-Jun-3 Hauswedell & Nolte, Hamburg #532/R
£467	$840	€700	Untitled (31x47cm-12x19in) mono. w/C. 21-Apr-4 Dorotheum, Vienna #246/R
£467	$840	€700	Kater Carlo (23x24cm-9x9in) s.i.d.7.11.76 W/C. 21-Apr-4 Dorotheum, Vienna #247/R
£496	$829	€700	Crucified figure (35x26cm-14x10in) s.d.7.1.76 pencil. 14-Oct-3 Dorotheum, Vienna #232/R
£638	$1180	€950	Untitled (35x46cm-14x18in) s.d.10.82 gouache oil chk. 9-Mar-4 Dorotheum, Vienna #220/R
£704	$1232	€1000	Untitled (85x41cm-33x16in) s.d.85 gouache. 19-Dec-3 Dorotheum, Vienna #378/R
£830	$1527	€1212	Untitled (61x43cm-24x17in) s.d.1981 mixed media prov. 8-Jun-4 Germann, Zurich #755 (S.FR 1900)
£839	$1427	€1200	Untitled (41x29cm-16x11in) s.d.83 gouache graphite col pen three. 27-Nov-3 Lempertz, Koln #11/R est:1000-1200
£933	$1680	€1400	Seated figure (29x40cm-11x16in) s.d.01 W/C pencil col pen board. 21-Apr-4 Dorotheum, Vienna #292/R
£987	$1816	€1500	Untitled (53x94cm-21x37in) s.d.1983 mixed media. 22-Jun-4 Wiener Kunst Auktionen, Vienna #397/R est:1500
£1049	$1783	€1500	Giraffe and tree-top (30x41cm-12x16in) s.d.97 W/C pencil. 27-Nov-3 Dorotheum, Linz #632/R est:1600-2000
£1189	$2021	€1700	The clown and the girl (34x39cm-13x15in) s. mixed media. 26-Nov-3 Dorotheum, Vienna #267/R est:1800-2200
£1678	$2970	€2500	Untitled (97x69cm-38x27in) s.d. mixed media. 28-Apr-4 Wiener Kunst Auktionen, Vienna #276/R est:2500-4500
£1879	$3326	€2800	Untitled (95x68cm-37x27in) s.d. mixed media. 28-Apr-4 Wiener Kunst Auktionen, Vienna #277/R est:2500-4500
£2238	$3804	€3200	Untitled (70x50cm-28x20in) s.d.1978/1979 mixed media. 28-Nov-3 Wiener Kunst Auktionen, Vienna #703/R est:3000-4000

ANZINGER, Siegfried and NAGEL, Daniel (20th C) Austrian

£313	$522	€450	Utnitled (89x70cm-35x28in) s.d. acrylic tempera. 24-Oct-3 Ketterer, Hamburg #602/R
£313	$522	€450	Untitled (90x70cm-35x28in) s.d. acrylic tempera. 24-Oct-3 Ketterer, Hamburg #601/R
£313	$522	€450	Untitled (90x69cm-35x27in) s.d. bears i. acrylic tempera. 24-Oct-3 Ketterer, Hamburg #603/R

APARICIO Y INGLADA, Jose (c.1770-1838) Spanish

£5801	$10500	€8469	Ferdinand VII, King of Spain (130x104cm-51x41in) painted c.1820. 3-Apr-4 Neal Auction Company, New Orleans #594/R est:3000-5000

APATFALVI, Czeme J (?) Hungarian

£267	$500	€390	Parlor (61x91cm-24x36in) s. 25-Feb-4 Doyle, New York #25/R
£337	$550	€492	Still life of books and spectacles (51x61cm-20x24in) s. 27-Sep-3 Charlton Hall, Columbia #112

APELLANIZ, Jesus (1898-1969) Spanish

£2349	$4205	€3500	Village (23x28cm-9x11in) s. board. 25-May-4 Durán, Madrid #165/R est:1200

APIN, Mochtar (1923-1994) Indonesian

£3472	$5799	€5069	Woman under the sun (115x80cm-45x31in) s.d.1964. 12-Oct-3 Sotheby's, Singapore #175/R est:8000-15000 (S.D 10000)

APOL, Armand-Adrien-Marie (1879-1950) Belgian

£267	$480	€400	Moored fishing sloops (55x65cm-22x26in) s. 26-Apr-4 Bernaerts, Antwerp #295/R
£267	$477	€400	Ruelle animee (24x33cm-9x13in) s. panel. 11-May-4 Vanderkindere, Brussels #32
£267	$491	€400	Arriere de ferme (42x50cm-17x20in) s. 14-Jun-4 Horta, Bruxelles #232
£400	$720	€600	Nu de dos (50x42cm-20x17in) s. 20-Apr-4 Galerie Moderne, Brussels #360/R
£617	$1048	€901	Cornfield in summer (50x60cm-20x24in) s.d.1919 bears i. 5-Nov-3 Dobiaschofsky, Bern #309/R (S.FR 1400)
£621	$1148	€900	Etang a Ohain (50x60cm-20x24in) s. 19-Jan-4 Horta, Bruxelles #21
£621	$1037	€900	Harbour (127x152cm-50x60in) s. lit. 12-Jul-3 Bergmann, Erlangen #676/R
£650	$1164	€949	Water lilies on a lake (50x61cm-20x24in) s. 18-Mar-4 Christie's, Kensington #513/R
£800	$1448	€1200	Vue de ferme. s. 30-Mar-4 Palais de Beaux Arts, Brussels #473
£833	$1325	€1200	Peniche amarree (50x60cm-20x24in) s. 15-Sep-3 Horta, Bruxelles #197
£909	$1518	€1300	Vue de ferme. s. 7-Oct-3 Palais de Beaux Arts, Brussels #528
£1241	$2073	€1800	Harbour entrance (83x103cm-33x41in) s.d.1910. 11-Nov-3 Vendu Notarishuis, Rotterdam #148 est:2000-3000
£1325	$2411	€2000	Corn field in summer (50x60cm-20x24in) s.d.1919. 21-Jun-4 Dorotheum, Vienna #85/R est:2400-2800
£1471	$2750	€2148	Village on the water (51x61cm-20x24in) s. 25-Feb-4 Dallas Auction Gallery, Dallas #66/R est:3000-5000

APOL, Louis (1850-1936) Dutch

£1986	$3316	€2800	The ferry (35x50cm-14x20in) s. canvas on panel. 20-Oct-3 Glerum, Amsterdam #67/R est:3000-5000
£3333	$6000	€5000	Late afternoon in winter (34x50cm-13x20in) s. 20-Apr-4 Sotheby's, Amsterdam #105/R est:6000-8000
£5667	$10200	€8500	Figures in a winter landscape at dusk (31x23cm-12x9in) s. panel prov. 20-Apr-4 Sotheby's, Amsterdam #137/R est:5000-7000
£6250	$10438	€9000	Wintry road along a waterway (20x26cm-8x10in) s. board prov. 21-Oct-3 Sotheby's, Amsterdam #156/R est:10000-15000
£7237	$13099	€11000	Wintry canal with draught horse along the tow-path (34x49cm-13x19in) s. 19-Apr-4 Glerum, Amsterdam #115/R est:8000-12000
£10000	$18000	€15000	By the canal in winter at dusk (27x42cm-11x17in) s. panel. 21-Apr-4 Christie's, Amsterdam #103/R est:12000-16000
£10417	$17396	€15000	Wooded landscape at dusk (80x131cm-31x52in) s.d.81. 21-Oct-3 Sotheby's, Amsterdam #252/R est:15000-20000
£11111	$18556	€16000	Wood gatherers in the Haages Bos in winter (71x97cm-28x38in) s. 21-Oct-3 Sotheby's, Amsterdam #247/R est:20000-30000
£13158	$23816	€20000	A sleigh in a forest of The Hague (40x60cm-16x24in) s. 19-Apr-4 Glerum, Amsterdam #104/R est:12000-16000
£13357	$22973	€19100	Winter scene with moored flat-bottom boats (45x60cm-18x24in) s. 8-Dec-3 Glerum, Amsterdam #36/R est:17000-24000
£13889	$23611	€20000	Late afternoon in winter (40x50cm-16x20in) s. 28-Oct-3 Christie's, Amsterdam #132a/R est:12000-16000
£31250	$52187	€45000	Winter on the Oude Scheveningseweg, The Hague (72x92cm-28x36in) s. prov. 21-Oct-3 Sotheby's, Amsterdam #244/R est:40000-60000
Works on paper			
£664	$1143	€950	Stormy weather at sea (15x22cm-6x9in) s. gouache. 7-Dec-3 Sotheby's, Amsterdam #589
£1164	$1979	€1700	Canal in winter (9x16cm-4x6in) s. gouache. 5-Nov-3 Vendue Huis, Gravenhage #130 est:900-1200
£1667	$2783	€2400	Mallejan in the snow (10x13cm-4x5in) s. black chk W/C htd white. 21-Oct-3 Sotheby's, Amsterdam #105/R est:1000-1500
£3333	$6000	€5000	Crossing a bridge in winter (15x19cm-6x7in) s. pencil bodycol. 21-Apr-4 Christie's, Amsterdam #88/R est:2000-3000
£3667	$6600	€5500	Wood gatherers on a country lane in winter (34x52cm-13x20in) s. W/C. 20-Apr-4 Sotheby's, Amsterdam #129/R est:6000-8000
£4651	$8000	€6790	Woman along a country road in winter (42x54cm-17x21in) s. W/C gouache. 3-Dec-3 Doyle, New York #100/R est:4000-6000

APONOVICH, James (1948-) American?

Works on paper			
£968	$1800	€1413	A walk on the wall with A J L (52x34cm-20x13in) graphite. 5-Mar-4 Skinner, Boston #587/R est:1200-1800
£1529	$2600	€2232	Portrait of Deborah (81x59cm-32x23in) mono. graphite. 21-Nov-3 Skinner, Boston #427/R est:1800-2200

APOSTOLI, Gigorii (1897-1930) Rumanian

£1517	$2534	€2200	Jeux dans le sous-bois. Promenade en voiture a cheval (54x73cm-21x29in) s.verso double-sided. 17-Nov-3 Claude Boisgirard, Paris #5/R est:2500-3000

APPEL, Charles P (1857-1928) American

£540	$950	€788	Harbour scene (23x30cm-9x12in) s.d.1921. 23-May-4 Treadway Gallery, Cincinnati #529/R
£1180	$1900	€1711	Evening sunset landscape, New Jersey country village (30x41cm-12x16in) s. 17-Aug-3 Jeffery Burchard, Florida #34
£1188	$1900	€1734	Landscape with stream (28x41cm-11x16in) s. 20-Sep-3 Pook & Pook, Downington #522/R est:2000-2500
£1776	$3250	€2593	Reflections at sunset (30x46cm-12x18in) s. painted c.1910. 5-Jun-4 Treadway Gallery, Cincinnati #618/R est:4000-6000
£2174	$4000	€3174	Evening glow (30x40cm-12x16in) s. 8-Jun-4 Bonhams & Butterfields, San Francisco #4040/R est:3000-5000
£2273	$4000	€3319	Quiet brook (36x51cm-14x20in) s. i.stretcher painted c.1910. 23-May-4 Treadway Gallery, Cincinnati #540/R est:3000-4000
£3073	$5500	€4487	Quiet day on the coast (51x76cm-20x30in) s. prov. 6-May-4 Shannon's, Milford #182/R est:4000-6000
£3073	$5500	€4487	Fishing in a creek (36x51cm-14x20in) s. prov. 6-May-4 Shannon's, Milford #250/R est:3000-5000
£3352	$6000	€4894	Tending the herd by the river (36x51cm-14x20in) s.d.1927 prov. 6-May-4 Shannon's, Milford #230/R est:3000-5000
£4790	$8000	€6993	Rowing on a river (51x76cm-20x30in) s.d.1927 masonite prov. 23-Oct-3 Shannon's, Milford #29/R est:2500-3500

APPEL, Karel (1921-) Dutch

£1088	$1981	€1600	Farmer (113x79cm-44x31in) s. painted 1944. 3-Feb-4 Christie's, Amsterdam #542 est:1000-1500
£1131	$1957	€1651	Composition (37x26cm-15x10in) s.d.82 acrylic paper. 12-Dec-3 Galerie du Rhone, Sion #203/R est:3500-4500 (S.FR 2500)
£1357	$2348	€1981	Composition (36x25cm-14x10in) s.d.82 acrylic paper. 12-Dec-3 Galerie du Rhone, Sion #202/R est:3500-4500 (S.FR 3000)
£1403	$2427	€2048	Composition (36x26cm-14x10in) s.d.82 acrylic paper. 12-Dec-3 Galerie du Rhone, Sion #201/R est:3500-4500 (S.FR 3100)
£2303	$4237	€3500	Chrysanthemums in a vase (40x30cm-16x12in) s.d.40. 22-Jun-4 Christie's, Amsterdam #475/R est:2000-3000
£3607	$6673	€5266	Composition (50x60cm-20x24in) s.d.75 paper on canvas. 15-Mar-4 Rasmussen, Vejle #502/R est:30000-40000 (D.KR 40000)
£3625	$6163	€5293	Untitled (32x28cm-13x11in) s. acrylic cardboard. 5-Nov-3 AB Stockholms Auktionsverk #1118/R est:40000-50000 (S.KR 48000)
£4000	$7360	€6000	Chat (51x67cm-20x26in) s. acrylic paper on canvas painted c.1970-75. 9-Jun-4 Artcurial Briest, Paris #422/R est:6000-8000
£4333	$7973	€6500	Figure (76x50cm-30x20in) s. acrylic col crayons paper on canvas exec 1981 prov. 8-Jun-4 Sotheby's, Amsterdam #264/R est:3000-4000
£4895	$8420	€7000	Untitled (65x50cm-26x20in) s.d.83 acrylic waxed crayon paper on card. 2-Dec-3 Sotheby's, Amsterdam #312/R est:5000-7000
£4923	$8468	€7188	Composition with head (75x55cm-30x22in) s. paper on canvas. 7-Dec-3 Uppsala Auktionskammare, Uppsala #298/R est:40000-50000 (S.KR 64000)
£5287	$8988	€7719	Untitled (50x50cm-20x20in) s. acrylic paper. 5-Nov-3 AB Stockholms Auktionsverk #1139/R est:25000-30000 (S.KR 70000)
£5287	$8988	€7719	Untitled (74x53cm-29x21in) s. acrylic over col serigraph on canvas. 5-Nov-3 AB Stockholms Auktionsverk #1144/R est:80000-100000 (S.KR 70000)
£5667	$10427	€8500	Untitled (76x91cm-30x36in) s.d.75 acrylic paper prov. 9-Jun-4 Christie's, Amsterdam #311/R est:6000-8000
£5667	$10427	€8500	La chanson de la voix interieur (89x117cm-35x46in) s.d.80 acrylic paper lit. 9-Jun-4 Christie's, Amsterdam #320/R est:6000-8000
£6335	$10769	€9249	Personnage (100x80cm-39x31in) s.d.1991 exhib.lit. 25-Nov-3 Germann, Zurich #17/R est:15000-20000 (S.FR 14000)

£6486	$12000	€9470	Head (25x20cm-10x8in) s. painted 1976 prov. 12-Feb-4 Sotheby's, New York #119/R est:4000-6000
£6667	$12267	€10000	Enfant avec trotinette (37x22cm-15x9in) s. s.i.verso. 12-Jun-4 Meeting Art, Vercelli #851/R est:10000
£6993	$12028	€10000	Boogschutter (40x50cm-16x20in) s. 2-Dec-3 Sotheby's, Amsterdam #156/R est:10000-15000
£7143	$13000	€10429	Once I was the sun (56x76cm-22x30in) s.d.78 acrylic on paper prov. 29-Jun-4 Sotheby's, New York #501/R est:7000-10000
£7333	$13493	€11000	Horseback rider (50x40cm-20x16in) s. painted c.1987-88 prov. 9-Jun-4 Christie's, Amsterdam #314/R est:8000-12000
£7517	$13831	€11200	Tete (77x56cm-30x22in) s. acrylic paper on canvas painted c.1984 prov. 24-Mar-4 Joron-Derem, Paris #127/R est:15000-18000
£7692	$13077	€11000	Untitled (58x81cm-23x32in) s.d.1970 acrylic card on canvas. 26-Nov-3 Pandolfini, Florence #146/R est:11000-13000
£7746	$13401	€11000	Sans titre (71x53cm-28x21in) s. acrylic paper. 14-Dec-3 Versailles Encheres #136/R est:12000-15000
£8000	$14720	€12000	Tete (24x19cm-9x7in) s. painted 1967 prov.exhib. 9-Jun-4 Christie's, Amsterdam #306/R est:12000-16000
£8000	$14720	€12000	Boogschutter (50x40cm-20x16in) s. prov. 9-Jun-4 Christie's, Amsterdam #307/R est:8000-12000
£8333	$13917	€12000	Deux figures (51x69cm-20x27in) s. acrylic paper. 21-Oct-3 Campo, Vlaamse Kaai #352/R est:9000-11000
£8392	$14266	€12000	Le Petit Bonhomme II (64x45cm-25x18in) s. oil wooden relief painted 1985 exhib. 25-Nov-3 Christie's, Amsterdam #271/R est:10000-15000
£9000	$16560	€13500	Untitled (46x27cm-18x11in) s. painted 1976-1977 prov. 9-Jun-4 Artcurial Briest, Paris #421/R est:15000-20000
£9091	$15455	€13000	Untitled (75x57cm-30x22in) s. acrylic card on board. 24-Nov-3 Christie's, Milan #224/R est:10000-15000
£9878	$16792	€14422	Composition (27x25cm-11x10in) s.d.57 oil gouache paper exhib.prov. 26-Nov-3 Kunsthallen, Copenhagen #21/R est:100000 (D.KR 105000)
£10000	$18400	€15000	Deux personnages (76x76cm-30x30in) s. prov. 9-Jun-4 Christie's, Amsterdam #313/R est:15000-20000
£10067	$18523	€15000	Deux tetes (89x120cm-35x47in) s. acrylic paper on canvas painted c.1980. 24-Mar-4 Joron-Derem, Paris #129 est:15000-18000
£10329	$17249	€15080	Figure composition on blue background (68x84cm-27x33in) s.d.1973 acrylic paper on canvas. 7-Oct-3 Rasmussen, Copenhagen #69/R est:125000 (D.KR 110000)
£10500	$19320	€15330	Phantoms in the night (75x102cm-30x40in) s.d.57 i.verso oil W/C wax crayon on cardboard. 25-Jun-4 Christie's, London #141/R est:12000-16000
£10855	$19648	€16500	Figure (66x50cm-26x20in) s.d.77 oil wood. 14-Apr-4 Ansorena, Madrid #275/R est:16500
£11329	$19260	€16540	Indien (93x74cm-37x29in) s. d.1981 verso acrylic panel. 5-Nov-3 AB Stockholms Auktionsverk #1111/R est:100000-125000 (S.KR 150000)
£11656	$19000	€17018	Tete (73x60cm-29x24in) s.d.68 acrylic prov. 23-Sep-3 Christie's, Rockefeller NY #102/R est:15000-20000
£12575	$21000	€18360	Big head (61x46cm-24x18in) s. prov. 13-Nov-3 Sotheby's, New York #237/R est:12000-18000
£13043	$21391	€18000	Face (112x77cm-44x30in) s. paper on canvas. 27-May-3 Sotheby's, Amsterdam #411/R est:18000-25000
£13287	$22587	€19000	Three heads (65x81cm-26x32in) s. painted 1960 prov. 25-Nov-3 Christie's, Amsterdam #260/R est:15000-20000
£13287	$22587	€19000	Landscape (40x50cm-16x20in) s. painted c.1976. 25-Nov-3 Christie's, Amsterdam #266/R est:15000-20000
£13986	$23357	€20000	Head (116x89cm-46x35in) s. acrylic exhib.lit. 11-Oct-3 De Vuyst, Lokeren #496/R est:19000-22000
£14803	$27237	€22500	Whole family together (50x70cm-20x28in) s.d.1971 s.i.d. verso prov. 28-Jun-4 Joron-Derem, Paris #188/R est:25000-30000
£15278	$24139	€22000	Figure (61x38cm-24x15in) painted 1971. 6-Sep-3 Meeting Art, Vercelli #617 est:20000
£19162	$32000	€27977	Spacious Persons (89x116cm-35x46in) s.d.72 acrylic prov. 12-Nov-3 Christie's, Rockefeller NY #417/R est:40000-60000
£19905	$31848	€28862	Figure composition (70x100cm-28x39in) s.d.63 paper on canvas. 17-Sep-3 Kunsthallen, Copenhagen #23/R est:225000 (D.KR 210000)
£20000	$33400	€29200	Image (100x82cm-39x32in) s. prov. 22-Oct-3 Christie's, London #17/R est:20000-30000
£22378	$38042	€32000	Untitled (60x90cm-24x35in) s.d.71. 25-Nov-3 Sotheby's, Milan #219/R est:15000-20000
£23952	$40000	€34970	Space Animals (118x147cm-46x58in) s.d.70 acrylic prov.exhib. 12-Nov-3 Christie's, Rockefeller NY #416/R est:40000-60000
£24000	$44160	€35040	Tete problematique (72x56cm-28x22in) s. exec 1967 prov. 24-Jun-4 Sotheby's, London #210/R est:20000-30000
£24000	$44160	€35040	Untitled (90x60cm-35x24in) s. painted c.1975 prov. 24-Jun-4 Sotheby's, London #213/R est:18000-25000
£24658	$41918	€36000	Untitled (45x54cm-18x21in) s.d.55. 4-Nov-3 Ansorena, Madrid #920/R est:36000
£25333	$46613	€38000	Some of my friends (60x120cm-24x47in) s. exec c.1967 prov. 8-Jun-4 Sotheby's, Amsterdam #88/R est:40000-60000
£25449	$42500	€37156	Two people (127x152cm-50x60in) s.d.72 i.stretcher canvas on wood. 13-Nov-3 Sotheby's, New York #238/R est:50000-70000
£30000	$54600	€43800	Magical figure (244x193cm-96x76in) s. acrylic prov.exhib.lit. 6-Feb-4 Sotheby's, London #215/R est:30000-40000
£31469	$53497	€45000	Woman and bird (130x97cm-51x38in) s.d.1972 painted wooden relief prov. 25-Nov-3 Christie's, Amsterdam #250/R est:50000-70000
£34000	$62560	€49640	Big herd in the fallen city (122x183cm-48x72in) s. painted 1989 prov. 24-Jun-4 Sotheby's, London #214/R est:20000-30000
£35000	$58450	€51100	Untitled (129x89cm-51x35in) s.d.68 prov.exhib. 21-Oct-3 Sotheby's, London #403/R est:20000-30000
£37559	$62723	€54836	Les amoureux tristes (81x116cm-32x46in) s. painted 1961 exhib.prov. 7-Oct-3 Rasmussen, Copenhagen #28/R est:400000 (D.KR 400000)
£39000	$65130	€56940	Flamme Riante (116x88cm-46x35in) s.d.59 i.stretcher prov.exhib. 21-Oct-3 Sotheby's, London #408/R est:35000-45000
£44693	$80000	€65252	Face (102x76cm-40x30in) s. i.d.1971 stretcher prov.exhib. 13-May-4 Sotheby's, New York #210/R est:30000-40000
£45000	$82800	€65700	Zingende vogel (150x150cm-59x59in) s.d.75 i.stretcher prov. 25-Jun-4 Christie's, London #143/R est:30000-40000
£46667	$85867	€70000	Figure (41x33cm-16x13in) s.d.51 prov. 9-Jun-4 Christie's, Amsterdam #321/R est:70000-90000
£60000	$110400	€90000	Screaming animal (110x140cm-43x55in) s.d.54. 9-Jun-4 Christie's, Amsterdam #328/R est:90000-120000
£60000	$110400	€87600	Head carrier (131x97cm-52x38in) s. painted 1954 prov.lit. 24-Jun-4 Sotheby's, London #212/R est:60000-80000
£69930	$118881	€100000	Les campagnards (81x180cm-32x71in) s.d.1973 tryptich prov. 25-Nov-3 Christie's, Amsterdam #268/R est:60000-80000
£70000	$128800	€102200	Explosive Landscape (130x162cm-51x64in) s.d.59 prov. 24-Jun-4 Sotheby's, London #208/R est:40000-60000
£73333	$134933	€110000	Mating animals (88x110cm-35x43in) s.d.52 exhib.lit. 8-Jun-4 Sotheby's, Amsterdam #84/R est:100000-150000
£90909	$154545	€130000	L'oiseau en chase (130x195cm-51x77in) s.d.61 i.stretcher prov.exhib. 25-Nov-3 Christie's, Amsterdam #269/R est:90000-120000
£340000	$625600	€496400	L'exode le monde floral (129x210cm-51x83in) s.d.53 prov.exhib. 24-Jun-4 Christie's, London #13/R est:250000-350000
Prints			
£3333	$5567	€4800	Oiseau (76x56cm-30x22in) s.d.59 serigraph htd gouache col wax pastels. 21-Oct-3 Artcurial Briest, Paris #638c est:1500-1800
Sculpture			
£1245	$2204	€1818	Figure composition (63x63cm-25x25in) s.d.76 num.29/99 multiple polychrome ceramic tondo. 27-Apr-4 AB Stockholms Auktionsverk #1176/R est:15000-20000 (S.KR 17000)
£1500	$2715	€2190	Jumping fox with green virgin (51x61cm-20x24in) s.num.39/50 verso oil wood relief. 1-Apr-4 Christie's, Kensington #221/R est:2000-3000
£1818	$3127	€2600	Clown (48cm-19in) i.d.77 num.136/300 painted wood. 2-Dec-3 Sotheby's, Amsterdam #328/R est:2500-3500
£2206	$3750	€3221	Couple (45x63cm-18x25in) s. painted wood. 31-Oct-3 Sotheby's, New York #495/R
£2899	$4754	€4000	Untitled (34x34cm-13x13in) s.d.76 num.2/6 painted glazed plate in plexiglass box. 27-May-3 Sotheby's, Amsterdam #415/R est:4000-6000
£4706	$8000	€6871	Close together (77cm-30in) s. painted wood. 31-Oct-3 Sotheby's, New York #496/R
£5435	$8913	€7500	Untitled (34x34cm-13x13in) s.d.77 num.1/6 paint glazed plate plexiglass box lit. 27-May-3 Sotheby's, Amsterdam #414/R est:4000-6000
£7143	$13000	€10429	Horseman (120x89x40cm-47x35x16in) s.d.78 num.3/8 painted wood. 29-Jun-4 Sotheby's, New York #500/R est:6000-9000
£7246	$11884	€10000	Figure (65cm-26in) s. glazed ceramic one of one exec.1973 prov.lit. 27-May-3 Sotheby's, Amsterdam #420/R est:10000-15000
£8042	$13430	€11500	Oiseau (82x82x82cm-32x32x32in) s. num.II/IV wood relief. 7-Oct-3 Livinec, Gaudcheau & Jezequel, Rennes #156
£10000	$16700	€14600	Olifant (64x48x37cm-25x19x15in) s.d.1950 num.2/6 painted bronze lit. 21-Oct-3 Sotheby's, London #402/R est:10000-15000
£29167	$48125	€42000	L'enfant hussard (132x84x12cm-52x33x5in) s.d. num.5/6 painted bronze Cast Bocquel lit. 2-Jul-3 Cornette de St.Cyr, Paris #45/R est:40000-50000
£40000	$72800	€58400	Le homme avec chapeau comme le ciel (275x115x48cm-108x45x19in) s.d.1966 verso oil wood prov.lit. 6-Feb-4 Sotheby's, London #214/R est:25000-35000
Works on paper			
£629	$1070	€900	Composition (40x56cm-16x22in) s.d.47 gouache. 1-Dec-3 Palais de Beaux Arts, Brussels #166a
£738	$1321	€1100	Dimanche (22x34cm-9x13in) s.d.84 gouache collage on photograph lit. 26-May-4 Christie's, Paris #125/R
£940	$1682	€1400	Jogging de King Kong (35x27cm-14x11in) s.d.84 gouache collage over photograph lit. 26-May-4 Christie's, Paris #124/R
£1074	$1922	€1600	Babel-Babylone (33x35cm-13x14in) gouache collage over photograph exec.1984 lit. 26-May-4 Christie's, Paris #126/R est:1500-2000
£1149	$2022	€1700	Portrait (23x17cm-9x7in) s.d.1988 felt pen prov. 18-May-4 Tajan, Paris #102/R est:1200-1500
£1267	$2318	€1900	Man with hat (30x24cm-12x9in) s. gouache pastel. 7-Jun-4 Glerum, Amsterdam #389/R est:1800-2200
£1745	$3123	€2600	Avenue (42x35cm-17x14in) s.d.84 gouache collage over photograph lit. 26-May-4 Christie's, Paris #123/R est:1500-2000
£1846	$3175	€2695	Composition with head (32x24cm-13x9in) s. gouache. 7-Dec-3 Uppsala Auktionskammare, Uppsala #299/R est:20000-25000 (S.KR 24000)
£2081	$3828	€3100	Composition (32x25cm-13x10in) s.d.1980 gouache. 24-Mar-4 Joron-Derem, Paris #130/R est:3500-4000
£2133	$3861	€3200	Personnage (75x55cm-30x22in) s.d.1983 gouache ink. 1-Apr-4 Credit Municipal, Paris #29 est:3000-4000
£2454	$4000	€3583	Looking like birds (57x76cm-22x30in) s. crayon prov.lit. 23-Sep-3 Christie's, Rockefeller NY #100/R est:5000-7000
£3200	$5088	€4640	Big bird looking for me (58x74cm-23x29in) s. wax crayon. 11-Sep-3 Christie's, Kensington #177/R est:2500-3500
£3226	$6000	€4710	Figural composition (55x76cm-22x30in) s.d.55 gouache prov. 5-Mar-4 Skinner, Boston #614/R est:12000-14000
£3357	$5706	€4800	Two figures (30x40cm-12x16in) s.d.92 wax crayons W/C. 25-Nov-3 Christie's, Amsterdam #86/R est:5000-7000
£4000	$7280	€5840	Untitled (51x65cm-20x26in) s. pastel prov. 6-Feb-4 Sotheby's, London #210/R est:4000-6000
£4061	$7310	€5929	Untitled (33x29cm-13x11in) s. mixed media. 26-Apr-4 Bukowskis, Stockholm #252a/R est:50000-60000 (S.KR 56000)
£4196	$7217	€6000	Untitled (50x64cm-20x25in) s.d.58 gouache chk. 4-Dec-3 Van Ham, Cologne #8/R est:7000
£4200	$6678	€6090	Good morning (58x76cm-23x30in) s.d.69 wax crayon. 11-Sep-3 Christie's, Kensington #179/R est:2500-3500
£4420	$8000	€6453	Untitled, two heads (124x64cm-49x25in) s. gouache. 18-Apr-4 Jeffery Burchard, Florida #152/R
£4667	$8587	€7000	Creatures of the sea (34x24cm-13x9in) s.d.54 go blk ink. 9-Jun-4 Christie's, Amsterdam #317/R est:2500-3500
£5333	$9813	€8000	Figures (54x67cm-21x26in) s.d.1972 mixed media card on canvas. 12-Jun-4 Meeting Art, Vercelli #492/R est:7000
£5797	$9507	€8000	Untitled (68x83cm-27x33in) s.d.74 gouache black chk. 27-May-3 Sotheby's, Amsterdam #412/R est:8000-12000
£5828	$9500	€8509	Bird sitting on my head (57x76cm-22x30in) s.d.69 col crayon prov.lit. 23-Sep-3 Christie's, Rockefeller NY #105/R est:6000-8000
£6000	$11040	€9000	Birds (55x77cm-22x30in) s.d.55 go pastel. 9-Jun-4 Christie's, Amsterdam #309/R est:10000-15000
£6466	$10797	€9440	Untitled (77x57cm-30x22in) s.d.60 mixed media prov. 20-Oct-3 Stephan Welz, Johannesburg #217/R est:80000-100000 (SA.R 75000)
£6466	$10797	€9440	Untitled (77x56cm-30x22in) s.d.60 mixed media prov. 20-Oct-3 Stephan Welz, Johannesburg #218/R est:80000-100000 (SA.R 75000)
£6587	$11000	€9617	Deux personnages (50x64cm-20x25in) s.d.58 gouache oilstick. 7-Oct-3 Sotheby's, New York #416 est:10000-15000
£6606	$11825	€9645	Head of a man (49x49cm-19x19in) s. mixed media paper foil. 31-May-4 Stephan Welz, Johannesburg #460/R est:25000-35000 (SA.R 80000)
£6993	$12028	€10000	Untitled (25x20cm-10x8in) s.i.d.48 gouache W/C ink crayon. 2-Dec-3 Sotheby's, Amsterdam #144/R est:10000-12000
£7000	$13020	€10220	Animals and birds, abstract (48x64cm-19x25in) W/C. 7-Mar-4 Paul Beighton, Rotherham #498 est:2000-3500
£7704	$13097	€11248	Untitled (65x81cm-26x32in) s.d.74 mixed media. 4-Nov-3 Bukowskis, Stockholm #284/R est:60000-80000 (S.KR 102000)
£7975	$13000	€11644	Walking and talking together (57x76cm-22x30in) s.d.69 col crayon prov.lit. 23-Sep-3 Christie's, Rockefeller NY #104/R est:6000-8000
£8000	$14560	€11680	Red figure (77x55cm-30x22in) s.d.59 s.i.d. verso gouache prov. 5-Feb-4 Christie's, London #144/R est:9000-12000
£8000	$14560	€11680	Vol d'oiseaux (50x64cm-20x25in) s.d.58 i.verso gouache W/C col chks prov. 5-Feb-4 Christie's, London #146/R est:8000-12000
£14000	$25480	€20440	Shenandoah Forest (90x120cm-35x47in) s.d.1961 s.i.d. verso gouache wax crayon prov. 5-Feb-4 Christie's, London #145/R est:10000-15000
£17483	$30070	€25000	Figuur mit oorbellen (51x39cm-20x15in) s.d.53 gouache black chk crayon prov. 2-Dec-3 Sotheby's, Amsterdam #134/R est:20000-30000
£31469	$54126	€45000	Vragende kinderen (49x65cm-19x26in) s.d.49 col crayons. 2-Dec-3 Sotheby's, Amsterdam #131/R est:50000-70000

APPEL, Karel (attrib) (1921-) Dutch
£408 $750 €596 Abstract portrayal suggesting a knight in armour (53x84cm-21x33in) s. prov. 29-Mar-4 O'Gallerie, Oregon #794/R

APPEL, Kevin (1967-) American
£5828 $9500 €8509 Storage blue 2 (141x152cm-56x60in) s.i.d. 2 verso acrylic oil canvas on panel prov. 23-Sep-3 Christie's, Rockefeller NY #83/R est:10000-15000
£19461 $32500 €28413 Red house study (62x76cm-24x30in) acrylic paper eight parts prov. 13-Nov-3 Sotheby's, New York #469/R est:15000-20000

APPELT, Dieter (1935-) German
Photographs
£3593 $6000 €5246 The mark on the mirror breathing makes (30x40cm-12x16in) s.i.d.1977 verso gelatin silver print lit. 17-Oct-3 Phillips, New York #69/R est:4000-6000

APPERLEY, George Owen Wynne (1884-1960) British
£2276 $3778 €3300 Centaure (43x33cm-17x13in) s. d.1944 verso. 30-Sep-3 Ansorena, Madrid #110/R est:2200
£2900 $5278 €4234 Spanish gypsy, Granada (46x39cm-18x15in) s. prov. 1-Jul-4 Christie's, Kensington #107/R est:1000-1500
Works on paper
£322 $537 €460 Woman (15x10cm-6x4in) s. pencil dr. 30-Jun-3 Ansorena, Madrid #119/R
£400 $716 €584 Spanish street scene (25x35cm-10x14in) s.d.1911 W/C. 25-May-4 Sworder & Son, Bishops Stortford #432/R
£500 $930 €730 Low tide on windy day (25x34cm-10x13in) s.d.1913 W/C. 2-Mar-4 Bearnes, Exeter #334/R
£674 $1125 €950 Cordoba, Espagne (13x10cm-5x4in) s. W/C. 19-Jun-3 Millon & Associes, Paris #225/R
£820 $1296 €1189 Venice (35x24cm-14x9in) s. W/C bodycol. 3-Sep-3 Bonhams, Bury St Edmunds #353/R
£1050 $1754 €1533 Spanish scene, men riding a donkey (25x15cm-10x6in) s. W/C. 18-Jun-3 John Nicholson, Haslemere #594 est:300-500
£1081 $1903 €1600 Portrait of boy (34x24cm-13x9in) s.d.1949 wash pastel. 18-May-4 Segre, Madrid #68/R est:1300
£1449 $2377 €2000 Tetuan (23x16cm-9x6in) s. W/C. 27-May-3 Durán, Madrid #192/R est:1000
£2168 $3620 €3100 View of Granada (25x17cm-10x7in) s.d.1923 W/C. 30-Jun-3 Ansorena, Madrid #28/R

APPERT, G (19th C) French
£1400 $2226 €2030 Figures around a table with a song bird (97x127cm-38x50in) s. 9-Sep-3 Bonhams, Knightsbridge #72/R est:500-800

APPIA, Beatrice (20th C) Swiss
£317 $555 €450 Maisons dans la campagne (22x26cm-9x10in) s. panel. 21-Dec-3 Thierry & Lannon, Brest #269
£1067 $1909 €1600 Bateaux a Sete (38x46cm-15x18in) s. 16-May-4 Thierry & Lannon, Brest #281 est:800-1000

APPIAN, Adolphe (1818-1898) French
£1701 $3044 €2500 Jeune garcon et son chien au bord de la riviere (32x55cm-13x22in) s. 19-Mar-4 Millon & Associes, Paris #41/R est:1500-2000
£1733 $3137 €2600 La briqueterie (22x26cm-9x10in) s. panel exhib.lit. 30-Mar-4 Rossini, Paris #273/R est:1000-1500
£1879 $3495 €2800 Paysage au pecheur (30x50cm-12x20in) s. 3-Mar-4 Ferri, Paris #150 est:3000-3500
£1879 $3364 €2800 Bord de mer a Roquebrune (25x41cm-10x16in) s. painted 1884. 26-May-4 Blanchet, Paris #191/R est:1000-1200
£1940 $3569 €2832 Lake Geneva (39x30cm-15x12in) s. prov. 26-Mar-4 Koller, Zurich #3097/R est:3500-5500 (S.FR 4500)
£2041 $3714 €3000 Martigues (19x33cm-7x13in) s.i. 8-Feb-4 Anaf, Lyon #74 est:3000-3200
£3067 $5551 €4600 Harbour on southern French coast (30x56cm-12x22in) s. 1-Apr-4 Van Ham, Cologne #1275/R est:3400
£3623 $5942 €5000 Le ruisseau a Roussillon dit la Roche Appian (43x75cm-17x30in) s.d. i.verso exhib. 11-May-3 Osenat, Fontainebleau #30/R est:5000
£4196 $7217 €6000 Calanque dans le Midi (34x62cm-13x24in) s.i.d.1876. 7-Dec-3 Osenat, Fontainebleau #185/R est:6500-7000
£5352 $8885 €7600 Pique-nique en foret (38x63cm-15x25in) s. 15-Jun-3 Peron, Melun #118
£7692 $13231 €11000 La calanque de Sormiou (33x52cm-13x20in) s. 7-Dec-3 Osenat, Fontainebleau #184 est:10000-12000
Works on paper
£400 $728 €600 Pecheur au bord de l'etang (31x44cm-12x17in) s. chl dr. 29-Jun-4 Chenu & Scrive, Lyon #6/R
£914 $1617 €1360 Ruisseau dans un sous-bois (50x38cm-20x15in) s. dr htd white. 30-Apr-4 Tajan, Paris #129/R est:700-900

APPIAN, Louis (1862-1896) French
£667 $1213 €1000 Terrasse au soleil (26x46cm-10x18in) s. 29-Jun-4 Chenu & Scrive, Lyon #9
£1053 $1937 €1600 Chaumiere (28x39cm-11x15in) s. canvas on panel. 23-Jun-4 Maigret, Paris #66/R est:600-1000
£1736 $2951 €2500 La cascade (27x23cm-11x9in) s. 30-Oct-3 Artus Associes, Paris #4/R est:1000-2500
£4014 $6663 €5700 Pecheurs et baigneurs sur la plage de Cotte (32x55cm-13x22in) s. 15-Jun-3 Peron, Melun #115

APPIANI, Andrea (1754-1817) Italian
£7778 $14000 €11356 Olympus (29x60cm-11x24in) 22-Jan-4 Sotheby's, New York #271/R est:15000-20000
£15000 $27450 €21900 Saint John the Baptist on rock. Christ Child seated in landscape reading (60x45cm-24x18in) s.d.1797 panel pair prov. 8-Jul-4 Sotheby's, London #336/R est:15000-20000
£373626 $680000 €545494 Portrait of Napoleon Bonaparte, holding a sabre (99x81cm-39x32in) prov.exhib.lit. 17-Jun-4 Christie's, Rockefeller NY #29/R est:100000-150000
Works on paper
£629 $1070 €900 Portrait of Costanzino (11x9cm-4x4in) i. pen ink. 19-Nov-3 Finarte Semenzato, Milan #503/R
£2000 $3660 €2920 Saint Matthew holding a book seated on a cloud surrounded by angels (42x33cm-17x13in) black chk. 6-Jul-4 Christie's, London #92/R est:1000-1500

APPIANI, Andrea (younger) (1817-1865) Italian
£4167 $7083 €6000 Portrait of girl (81x62cm-32x24in) s.d.1854. 1-Nov-3 Meeting Art, Vercelli #329/R est:3000

APPLEBEE, Frank Woodbury (1902-) American
£324 $600 €473 Woman reading a newspaper (51x41cm-20x16in) s. prov. 15-Jul-4 Sotheby's, New York #83/R

APPLEBEE, Leonard (1914-) British
£250 $443 €365 Still life a bearded bust sculpture and apples (69x49cm-27x19in) s.d.47. 28-Apr-4 Peter Wilson, Nantwich #68

APPLEBY, Theodore (1923-) American
£1141 $2019 €1700 Sold (162x130cm-64x51in) s. 27-Apr-4 Campo & Campo, Antwerp #3/R est:1250-1750

APPLEGATE, Frank (1882-1934) American
Works on paper
£2059 $3500 €3006 Pueblo village (18x23cm-7x9in) s. W/C prov.lit. 1-Nov-3 Santa Fe Art, Santa Fe #152/R est:4000-6000

APPLETON, Jean (1911-) Australian
£307 $485 €448 Seated nude (48x32cm-19x13in) s. paper prov.exhib. 2-Sep-3 Deutscher-Menzies, Melbourne #374/R (A.D 750)
£345 $538 €500 Boys playing (25x30cm-10x12in) s. board. 1-Aug-2 Joel, Victoria #197 est:1000-1500 (A.D 1000)
£1803 $2849 €2632 Landscape (45x61cm-18x24in) s. board prov. 2-Sep-3 Deutscher-Menzies, Melbourne #287/R est:4000-6000 (A.D 4400)

APPLEYARD, Frederick (1874-1963) British
£600 $1122 €900 Spanish square (70x91cm-28x36in) s. 21-Jul-4 Anthemion, Cardiff #603/R

APPLEYARD, Joseph (1908-1960) British
£360 $612 €526 Crown point in Leeds (24x63cm-9x25in) s. board. 18-Nov-3 Bonhams, Leeds #149
Works on paper
£760 $1269 €1110 Airedale beagles moving off from the Royalty Inn, Otley Chevin (38x51cm-15x20in) s. W/C. 8-Oct-3 Andrew Hartley, Ilkley #1099
£1000 $1720 €1460 Bramham Moor open race (31x46cm-12x18in) s.d.57 i.verso board. 3-Dec-3 Bonhams, Knightsbridge #126 est:800-1200

APRILE, Vincenzo (20th C) Italian
£450 $707 €653 Casolare (56x47cm-22x19in) s. i.verso. 28-Aug-3 Christie's, Kensington #227/R

APSHOVEN, Thomas van (1622-1664) Flemish
£6993 $12028 €10000 La danse des paysans devant l'auberge, le ville d'Anvers sur l'arrier-plan (48x64cm-19x25in) panel. 3-Dec-3 Palais de Beaux Arts, Brussels #682/R est:9000-12000

APSHOVEN, Thomas van (attrib) (1622-1664) Flemish
£631 $1085 €921 Gallant scene (32x24cm-13x9in) panel. 8-Dec-3 Philippe Schuler, Zurich #5823 (S.FR 1400)
£700 $1211 €1022 Bagpipe player in a landscape (29x37cm-11x15in) mono. panel. 12-Dec-3 Christie's, Kensington #52/R

APSHOVEN, Thomas van (studio) (1622-1664) Flemish
£6028 $10067 €8500 Interieur de medecin (41x54cm-16x21in) panel. 15-Oct-3 Rabourdin & Choppin de Janvry, Paris #39/R est:5000-6000

APSITIS, Aleksander Petrovic (1880-1944) Russian
Works on paper
£1500 $2550 €2190 Devilish Nymph (45x32cm-18x13in) s.d.1936 W/C gouache over pencil. 19-Nov-3 Sotheby's, London #190/R est:2000-3000

APT, Charles (1933-) American
£543 $1000 €793 Paddock business (20x25cm-8x10in) s. paper exhib. 25-Jun-4 Freeman, Philadelphia #234/R

APUATIMI, Declan (1930-1985) Australian
Sculpture
£1328 $2484 €1992 Bima (43cm-17in) earth pigments ironwood exec.c.1980 prov. 26-Jul-4 Sotheby's, Melbourne #55/R est:3000-4000 (A.D 3400)
£1406 $2630 €2109 Bima (48cm-19in) earth pigments ironwood exec.c.1980. 26-Jul-4 Sotheby's, Melbourne #56/R est:3000-5000 (A.D 3600)
£2539 $4748 €3809 Tiwi Pukumani pole (218cm-86in) earth pigments ironwood exec.c.1978 prov. 26-Jul-4 Sotheby's, Melbourne #227/R est:8000-12000 (A.D 6500)
£4472 $7065 €6484 Pelican (61cm-24in) earth pigments hardwood exec.c.1972 prov.exhib.lit. 28-Jul-3 Sotheby's, Paddington #247/R est:3000-5000 (A.D 11000)

APUATIMI, Jean Baptiste (1940-2002) Australian
£1570 $2905 €2292 Kulama (199x120cm-78x47in) natural earth pigments synthetic binder on canvas painted 2000. 15-Mar-4 Sotheby's, Melbourne #36 est:3000-5000 (A.D 3800)
Works on paper
£273 $511 €410 Jilamara, sacred body painting (76x57cm-30x22in) s.v pigment exec. 1998 prov. 21-Jul-4 Shapiro, Sydney #7/R (A.D 700)
£313 $584 €468 Jilamara, sacred body painting (76x57cm-30x22in) pigment prov. 21-Jul-4 Shapiro, Sydney #9/R (A.D 800)
£352 $657 €528 Jilamara, sacred body painting (76x57cm-30x22in) pigment prov. 21-Jul-4 Shapiro, Sydney #8/R (A.D 900)
£391 $730 €587 Jilamara, sacred body painting (76x57cm-30x22in) s.verso pigment exec. 1998 prov. 21-Jul-4 Shapiro, Sydney #6/R (A.D 1000)
£1094 $2045 €1641 Minga (115x53cm-45x21in) pigment exec. c.2000 prov. 21-Jul-4 Shapiro, Sydney #5/R est:3000-5000 (A.D 2800)
£1098 $1965 €1603 Jilamarra (114x53cm-45x21in) natural earth pigments canvas exec 2003. 25-May-4 Lawson Menzies, Sydney #243/R est:2500-3000 (A.D 2800)
£1176 $2106 €1717 Pandanus Mats (76x27cm-30x11in) natural earth pigments arches paper exec 2002 prov. 25-May-4 Lawson Menzies, Sydney #244/R est:1800-2200 (A.D 3000)
£1255 $2246 €1832 Parmajini (77x76cm-30x30in) natural earth pigments canvas exec 2002 prov. 25-May-4 Lawson Menzies, Sydney #246/R est:3500-4500 (A.D 3200)

APWERLA, Michelle Holmes (20th C) Australian
Works on paper
£1176 $2106 €1717 Countryside (91x121cm-36x48in) synthetic polymer paint linen exec 2002 prov. 25-May-4 Lawson Menzies, Sydney #233/R est:3500-4500 (A.D 3000)

AQIGAAQ, Mathew (1940-) North American
Sculpture
£1171 $1991 €1710 Two musk ox, the face of a shaman emerging from them (33cm-13in) s. mottled dark soapstone. 3-Nov-3 Waddingtons, Toronto #164/R est:2500-3500 (C.D 2600)
£1712 $2910 €2500 Polar bear holding a caribou head with antlers (28cm-11in) s. mottled grey soapstone. 3-Nov-3 Waddingtons, Toronto #725 est:2000-2500 (C.D 3800)

AQUINO, Luis (1895-1968) Argentinian
£8380 $15000 €12235 Red ground (50x70cm-20x28in) s.d.67 cardboard. 4-May-4 Arroyo, Buenos Aires #93/R est:14000
£9836 $18000 €14361 Stream (70x90cm-28x35in) 1-Jun-4 Arroyo, Buenos Aires #61

ARA, Birgitta (20th C) Finnish
Sculpture
£1149 $2056 €1700 Yoga (8cm-3in) s.num.7/12 polished bronze. 8-May-4 Bukowskis, Helsinki #230/R est:800-1000

ARA, Krishna Hawlaji (1914-1985) Indian
Works on paper
£750 $1253 €1095 Still life (56x39cm-22x15in) s. pencil gouache. 17-Oct-3 Christie's, Kensington #518/R

ARADA, Mario (1894-?) Italian
£426 $711 €600 Rice field in April (40x50cm-16x20in) s. board. 20-Oct-3 Sant Agostino, Torino #19/R

ARAEZ, Luciano (20th C) Spanish
£355 $592 €500 Fishermen (65x81cm-26x32in) s. 20-Oct-3 Durán, Madrid #611/R

ARAKI KAMPO (1831-1915) Japanese
Works on paper
£436 $781 €650 Untitled (26x35cm-10x14in) s. ink. 27-May-4 Beaussant & Lefèvre, Paris #282

ARAKI, Nobuyoshi (1940-) Japanese
Photographs
£2013 $3705 €3000 Tokyomania (60x75cm-24x30in) s.verso gelatin silver print exec 2000 prov.exhib. 29-Mar-4 Cornette de St.Cyr, Paris #101/R est:3000-5000
£2601 $4500 €3797 From suicide Tokyo (78x106cm-31x42in) s.verso cibachrome exec.1998-2002 prov. 10-Dec-3 Phillips, New York #604/R est:3000-4000
£3000 $5100 €4380 Untitled from colorscapes (61x51cm-24x20in) cibachrome plexiglas. 18-Nov-3 Christie's, Kensington #219/R est:3000-5000
£3333 $6000 €5000 Nu au canape (40x32cm-16x13in) s.verso silver print. 24-Apr-4 Cornette de St.Cyr, Paris #420/R est:5000

ARALOV, Vladimir (1893-1972) Russian
£17000 $28900 €24820 Transporting the prisoner, Red Square, Moscow (130x160cm-51x63in) s.i.d.33. 19-Nov-3 Sotheby's, London #83/R est:6000-8000

ARAPOFF, Alexis (1904-1948) Russian
£500 $850 €730 Small fire (46x51cm-18x20in) s. 21-Nov-3 Skinner, Boston #581/R est:300-500
£6500 $11635 €9490 Artist's children in Walcott Garden, 1937 (48x61cm-19x24in) s. exhib. 26-May-4 Sotheby's, London #201/R est:7000-9000
£15000 $25500 €21900 Circus Act (60x73cm-24x29in) s.d.28. 19-Nov-3 Sotheby's, London #193/R est:15000-20000
£26000 $46540 €37960 Flower seller (60x81cm-24x32in) s.d.28. 26-May-4 Sotheby's, London #202/R est:15000-20000
Works on paper
£235 $400 €343 In the garden (45x30cm-18x12in) s. W/C. 21-Nov-3 Skinner, Boston #407/R

ARATYM, Hubert (1936-2000) German
£1477 $2732 €2200 Untitled (60x60cm-24x24in) s.d.1969. 9-Mar-4 Dorotheum, Vienna #139/R est:2600-3400
£2013 $3604 €3000 Heraldism Onirique (54x81cm-21x32in) s.d.1961 i. stretcher. 25-May-4 Dorotheum, Vienna #259/R est:2800-3600
Works on paper
£604 $1117 €900 Untitled (34x35cm-13x14in) s.d.98 W/C. 9-Mar-4 Dorotheum, Vienna #238/R
£633 $1140 €950 Untitled (25x28cm-10x11in) s.d.1977 W/C. 21-Apr-4 Dorotheum, Vienna #236/R
£828 $1514 €1200 Untitled (26x49cm-10x19in) s. pencil W/C prov. 27-Jan-4 Dorotheum, Vienna #195/R
£1333 $2400 €2000 Untitled (25x37cm-10x15in) s.d.1981 W/C. 21-Apr-4 Dorotheum, Vienna #296/R est:1200-1800

ARBESSER-RASTBURG, Assinta von (1884-?) Austrian
£826 $1379 €1198 Still life of flowers (75x64cm-30x25in) s. 23-Jun-3 Philippe Schuler, Zurich #3556 (S.FR 1800)

ARBO, Peter Nicolai (1831-1892) Norwegian
£1053 $1695 €1537 On the mountain road (22x31cm-9x12in) s. board. 13-Oct-3 Joel, Victoria #249/R est:2000-4000 (A.D 2600)

ARBORELIUS, Olof (1842-1915) Swedish
£272 $495 €400 Summer landscape (75x115cm-30x45in) s. 8-Feb-4 Bukowskis, Helsinki #488/R
£423 $728 €618 Seagulls on beach (69x116cm-27x46in) s. 7-Dec-3 Uppsala Auktionskammare, Uppsala #196 (S.KR 5500)
£569 $1046 €854 Boy wearing red jacket (53x43cm-21x17in) s.d.1864. 14-Jun-4 Lilla Bukowskis, Stockholm #221 (S.KR 7800)
£1478 $2646 €2158 Country girl with goats (48x76cm-19x30in) s.d.1883. 25-May-4 Bukowskis, Stockholm #143/R est:20000-25000 (S.KR 20000)
£1626 $2911 €2374 Lake landscape with woman by red cottage (85x125cm-33x49in) s. 25-May-4 Bukowskis, Stockholm #142/R est:30000-40000 (S.KR 22000)
£1848 $3307 €2698 Summer landscape with milkmaid and cattle (70x106cm-28x42in) s. 25-May-4 Bukowskis, Stockholm #144/R est:25000-30000 (S.KR 25000)
£12308 $21169 €17970 Wedding in Dalarna (81x122cm-32x48in) s. 2-Dec-3 Bukowskis, Stockholm #122/R est:125000-150000 (S.KR 160000)

ARBOTONI, Bartolomeo (1594-1676) Italian
£29371 $49049 €42000 Kitchen interior (94x126cm-37x50in) lit. 7-Oct-3 Pandolfini, Florence #594/R est:36000-40000

ARBUCKLE, George Franklin (1909-2001) Canadian
£223 $384 €326 Poplars (30x40cm-12x16in) s. board painted 1937. 2-Dec-3 Joyner Waddington, Toronto #408 (C.D 500)
£340 $622 €496 September morning (25x30cm-10x12in) s. canvas on board prov. 1-Jun-4 Joyner Waddington, Toronto #447 (C.D 850)
£1600 $2928 €2336 Northern lumbering town, Haliburton (50x60cm-20x24in) s. board. 1-Jun-4 Joyner Waddington, Toronto #42/R est:3000-4000 (C.D 4000)

ARBUS, Andre (1903-1969) French
Sculpture
£2657 $4517 €3800 Tete de jeune fille (33cm-13in) s.st.f.C. Valsuani black pat bronze marble slab socle. 24-Nov-3 Tajan, Paris #103/R est:4000-5000
£4196 $7133 €6000 Acteon (40x10x10cm-16x4x4in) s.num.5/8 gilt bronze marble socle st.f.Fonderies de la Plaine. 24-Nov-3 Tajan, Paris #104/R est:6000-8000
£4895 $8420 €7000 Femme au miroir (26cm-10in) mono. gilt pat bronze. 3-Dec-3 Fraysse & Associes, Paris #85/R est:4000-6000
£6944 $11319 €10000 Buste d'Acteon (114cm-45in) num.EA III/IV mat gold pat bronze Cast Coubertin. 18-Jul-3 Pierre Berge, Paris #102 est:10000-150000
£12588 $21399 €18000 Musique (92cm-36in) s.st.f. num.3/8 pat bronze prov.exhib.lit. 19-Nov-3 Tajan, Paris #40/R est:12000-15000

ARBUS, Diane (1923-1971) American
Photographs
£1796 $3000 €2622 Girl in stormcoat, NYC (21x14cm-8x6in) i.verso num.3 gelatin silver print exec.1960 one of 75 prov. 17-Oct-3 Phillips, New York #109/R est:3000-4000
£1796 $3000 €2622 Three-legged man, NYC (14x20cm-6x8in) i.verso num.3 gelatin silver print exec.1961 one of 75 prov. 17-Oct-3 Phillips, New York #110/R est:3000-4000
£1796 $3000 €2622 Women on a sun deck, Coney Island, NY (13x19cm-5x7in) i.verso num.2 gelatin silver print exec.1960 one of 75 prov. 17-Oct-3 Phillips, New York #111/R est:3000-4000
£1944 $3500 €2838 Window in her bedroom (36x36cm-14x14in) s.num.19/75 gelatin silver print prov.lit. 23-Apr-4 Phillips, New York #158/R est:4000-6000
£1944 $3500 €2838 Norman Mailer at home, Brooklyn, NY (37x37cm-15x15in) s.num.,24/75 gelatin silver print prov.lit. 23-Apr-4 Phillips, New York #159/R est:4000-6000
£1944 $3500 €2838 Jorge Luis Borges in Central Park, N.Y.C (36x37cm-14x15in) s.num.12/75 gelatin silver print prov.lit. 23-Apr-4 Phillips, New York #160/R est:3000-5000
£2667 $4800 €3894 Girl in a coat lying on her bed, N.Y.Composition (36x36cm-14x14in) s.num.11/75 verso gelatin silver print prov.lit. 23-Apr-4 Phillips, New York #157/R est:4000-6000
£3056 $5500 €4462 South Bay Singles, couple on a chaise lounge (35x36cm-14x14in) s.verso gelatin silver print prov.lit. 23-Apr-4 Phillips, New York #156/R est:4000-6000
£3892 $6500 €5682 Wax museum axe murderer, Coney Island, New York (25x17cm-10x7in) s.num.645-8-1U-114 st.verso photo printed c.1960-61. 17-Oct-3 Sotheby's, New York #264/R est:8000-12000
£4696 $8500 €6856 Untitled, 3 (38x38cm-15x15in) s.i.d.num.58/75 verso gelatin silver print 1970-71. 19-Apr-4 Bonhams & Butterfields, San Francisco #350/R est:3000-5000
£4889 $8800 €7138 Young couple on a bench in Washington Square Park, N.Y.C (37x37cm-15x15in) s.num.10/75 gelatin silver print prov.lit. 23-Apr-4 Phillips, New York #155/R est:4000-6000

£5248 $9500 €7662 Girl in a party dress, NYC (37x36cm-15x14in) s.i.d.num.21/75 gelatin silver print 1962/printed later. 19-Apr-4 Bonhams & Butterfields, San Francisco #348/R est:2000-4000
£5556 $10000 €8112 Husband and wife in the woods at a nudist camp, N.J 1963 (39x37cm-15x15in) s.i. gelatin silver print prov.lit. 23-Apr-4 Phillips, New York #50/R est:25000-35000
£6780 $12000 €9899 Young waitress at a nudist camp, N.J, 1963 (8x7cm-3x3in) s.i.d. gelatin silver print executed c.1967 prov.lit. 27-Apr-4 Christie's, Rockefeller NY #232/R est:15000-20000
£7500 $13725 €10950 Two ladies at the automat NYC (51x41cm-20x16in) s.i.d.num.52/75 verso silver print 1966 printed later. 8-Jul-4 Sotheby's, London #426/R est:5500-8500
£7735 $14000 €11293 Russian midget friends in living room on 100th St, NYC (37x37cm-15x15in) bears another sig.i.d. num.38/75 verso gelatin print 1963/1972. 19-Apr-4 Bonhams & Butterfields, San Francisco #349/R est:3000-5000
£10169 $18000 €14847 Topless dancer in her dressing room, San Francisco, Cal, 1968 (35x35cm-14x14in) s.i.d. gelatin silver print. 27-Apr-4 Christie's, Rockefeller NY #350/R est:15000-20000
£10180 $17000 €14863 Patriotic young man with flag (37x37cm-15x15in) s.i.d.1967 num.47/75 verso gelatin silver print lit. 20-Oct-3 Christie's, Rockefeller NY #148/R est:8000-10000
£11299 $20000 €16497 Waitress, nudist camp, New Jersey (6x6cm-2x2in) s.i.d.1963 verso photo printed c.1967 sold with envelope prov.lit. 28-Apr-4 Sotheby's, New York #228/R est:20000-30000
£11976 $20000 €17485 Circus fat lady and her dog, Troubles (20x19cm-8x7in) i. gelatin silver print exec.1964 lit. 17-Oct-3 Phillips, New York #63/R est:20000-30000
£12575 $21000 €18360 Girl with a beehive hairdo, NYC (24x22cm-9x9in) i.verso gelatin silver print exec.1965 prov.exhib. 17-Oct-3 Phillips, New York #45/R est:25000-35000
£31073 $55000 €45367 Child with a toy hand grenade in Central Park, N.Y.C (37x36cm-15x14in) s.i.d. num.29/75 gelatin silver print executed c.1962. 27-Apr-4 Christie's, Rockefeller NY #348/R est:25000-35000
£34132 $57000 €49833 Girl in a watchcap, NYC (35x27cm-14x11in) i.verso gelatin silver print exec.1965 prov. 17-Oct-3 Phillips, New York #46/R est:30000-50000
£47904 $80000 €69940 A castle in Disneyland, CA (35x27cm-14x11in) i. gelatin silver print exec.1962 prov.lit. 17-Oct-3 Phillips, New York #49/R est:50000-70000
£48023 $85000 €70114 Waitress, nudist camp (26x25cm-10x10in) s.i. s.i.d.1963 verso photo printed c.1967prov.lit. 28-Apr-4 Sotheby's, New York #227/R est:60000-80000
£74850 $125000 €109281 Xmas tree in a living room in Levittown, LI (35x27cm-14x11in) i. gelatin silver print exec.1963 prov.lit. 17-Oct-3 Phillips, New York #48/R est:60000-90000
£84746 $150000 €123729 Family on their lawn one Sunday in Westchester, N Y (26x26cm-10x10in) bears another sig. photo printed 1968-1970 prov.lit. 27-Apr-4 Sotheby's, New York #12/R est:80000-120000
£94444 $170000 €137888 Young man in curlers at home on west 20th Street, N.Y.C, 1966 (39x38cm-15x15in) i. num.4642-1-6u-1620 verso gelatin silver print prov.lit. 23-Apr-4 Phillips, New York #51/R est:100000-150000
£215569 $360000 €314731 Box of ten photographs (36x36cm-14x14in) num.15/50 gelatin silver print plexiglass box ten prov.lit. 17-Oct-3 Phillips, New York #47/R est:90000-120000
£237288 $420000 €346440 Identical twins, Cathleen and Colleen, Roselle, N J (37x37cm-15x15in) s.i.d.1967 verso photo prov.lit. 27-Apr-4 Sotheby's, New York #11/R est:250000-350000

ARBUS, Diane and SELKIRK, Neil (20th C) American

Photographs
£2395 $4000 €3497 Untitled, 5 (38x37cm-15x15in) s.i.d.1970-71 num.3/75 st.verso photo printed later prov. 17-Oct-3 Sotheby's, New York #272/R est:4000-6000
£5090 $8500 €7431 Child crying, N J (36x37cm-14x15in) s.i.d.1967 num.26/75 st.verso photo printed later. 17-Oct-3 Sotheby's, New York #265/R est:5000-7000
£9581 $16000 €13988 King and queen of a senior citizens dance, NYC (37x37cm-15x15in) s.i.d.1970 num.33/50 st.verso photo prov. 17-Oct-3 Sotheby's, New York #269/R est:5000-8000
£11377 $19000 €16610 Xmas tree in a living room in Levittown, L I (37x37cm-15x15in) s.i.d.1963 num.47/50 st.verso photo prov. 17-Oct-3 Sotheby's, New York #270/R est:7000-10000
£12575 $21000 €18360 Junior Interstate Ballroom dance champions, Yonkers, NY (38x37cm-15x15in) s.i.d.1962 num.45/75 st.verso photo printed later. 17-Oct-3 Sotheby's, New York #271/R est:10000-15000
£13559 $24000 €19796 Jewish giant at home with his parents in the Bronx, NY (38x38cm-15x15in) s.i.d.1970 num.33/50 photo. 28-Apr-4 Sotheby's, New York #232/R est:25000-35000
£15819 $28000 €23096 Russian midget friends in a living room on 100th St, NYC (38x38cm-15x15in) s.i.d.num.48/75 photo printed 1972 prov. 28-Apr-4 Sotheby's, New York #162/R est:7000-10000
£16168 $27000 €23605 Family on their lawn one Sunday in Westchester, N Y (37x38cm-15x15in) s.i.d.1968 num.37/50 st.verso photo prov. 17-Oct-3 Sotheby's, New York #266/R est:10000-15000
£18563 $31000 €27102 Child with toy hand grenade in Central Park, NYC (37x37cm-15x15in) s.i.d.1962 num.25/75 st.verso photo printed later prov. 17-Oct-3 Sotheby's, New York #268/R est:25000-35000

ARBY, Luca (20th C) French?

Works on paper
£704 $1141 €1000 Composition (100x73cm-39x29in) mixed media. 5-Aug-3 Tajan, Paris #81/R

ARCANGELO (1956-) Italian

£1600 $2944 €2400 Mystery room (85x68cm-33x27in) s.d.1998 oil mixed media. 12-Jun-4 Meeting Art, Vercelli #837/R est:2000
Works on paper
£503 $931 €750 Away from the wheat (28x41cm-11x16in) s.d.1002 pastel chl cardboard. 13-Mar-4 Meeting Art, Vercelli #36
£1397 $2571 €2040 Untitled (113x100cm-44x39in) s.d.1991 mono.d. verso prov. 8-Jun-4 Germann, Zurich #112/R est:3000-4000 (S.FR 3200)

ARCANGELO, Exposito (20th C) Italian

Works on paper
£1719 $2923 €2510 South (173x100cm-68x39in) s.i.d.1985 verso mixed media collage prov. 25-Nov-3 Germann, Zurich #23/R est:3500-4500 (S.FR 3800)

ARCHER, Charles (1855-1931) British

£700 $1169 €1022 Plums and an apple, on a mossy bank (25x30cm-10x12in) s. 13-Nov-3 Christie's, Kensington #358/R
£1700 $3162 €2482 Still life study of ripe fruit (50x60cm-20x24in) s. 2-Mar-4 Bamfords, Derby #449 est:1500-2000
£1800 $3240 €2628 Still life with apples, plums and grapes on a woodland bank (19x24cm-7x9in) s. 22-Apr-4 Mellors & Kirk, Nottingham #1131/R est:2000-2500
£2800 $5040 €4088 Still life with primroses, apple blossom and bird's nest on a woodland bank (49x59cm-19x23in) s. 22-Apr-4 Mellors & Kirk, Nottingham #1124/R est:3000-4000

ARCHER, James (1823-1904) British

£898 $1500 €1311 Centaurs (81x13cm-32x5in) s.d.1890 panel part of a collection of 45 prov.lit. 7-Oct-3 Sotheby's, New York #138 est:6000-8000
£7500 $12900 €10950 Young Bacchus riding on a leopard (125x91cm-49x36in) exhib. 4-Dec-3 Bonhams, Edinburgh #107/R est:8000-12000

ARCHER, Patrick (20th C) American

£278 $500 €406 Montmartre Paris (23x15cm-9x6in) s. masonite prov. 20-Apr-4 Arthur James, Florida #22/R

ARCHINTI, Ettore (1878-1944) Italian

Sculpture
£4225 $7310 €6000 Little sister (30cm-12in) s.d.1912 bronze. 10-Dec-3 Sotheby's, Milan #148/R est:1800-2500

ARCHIPENKO, Alexander (1887-1964) American/Russian

Sculpture
£10490 $17832 €15000 Abstract woman figure (37cm-15in) s.d.1913 bronze marble base. 29-Nov-3 Bukowskis, Helsinki #312/R est:15000-18000
£17568 $32500 €25649 Fiancee (51cm-20in) i. num.2 baked clay prov.lit. 11-Feb-4 Sotheby's, New York #39/R est:35000-45000
£19553 $35000 €28547 Torso (60cm-24in) s.d.1948 num.4/12F green blue pat bronze st.f.Modern Art prov. 5-May-4 Christie's, Rockefeller NY #328/R est:40000-60000
£19553 $35000 €28547 Small reclining figure (32cm-13in) i.d.1913 num.8/12 green brown pat bronze prov.lit. 6-May-4 Sotheby's, New York #328/R est:35000-45000
£32402 $58000 €47307 Madonna (62cm-24in) s. verso white marble exec 1936 prov.lit. 5-May-4 Christie's, Rockefeller NY #296/R est:50000-70000
£45000 $81900 €65700 Flat torso (36cm-14in) i. polished nickel silver bronze cast c.1936 prov.lit. 4-Feb-4 Sotheby's, London #290/R est:35000-45000
£94972 $170000 €138659 Woman combing her hair (62cm-24in) s.d.1915 num.6 green brown pat bronze prov.lit. 5-May-4 Christie's, Rockefeller NY #292/R est:200000-300000
£164706 $280000 €240471 Dancers, Version 3 (62cm-24in) s.i.d.1912 num.3/8 gold pat bronze conceived 1912 prov.exhib.lit. 5-Nov-3 Christie's, Rockefeller NY #268/R est:250000-350000
£241176 $410000 €352117 Gruppe - feminine solitude (77cm-30in) s. white marble conceived 1912 prov.exhib.lit. 4-Nov-3 Christie's, Rockefeller NY #30/R est:400000-600000
Works on paper
£3125 $5219 €4500 Nu en gris, etude (57x30cm-22x12in) s. lead pencil ink. 21-Oct-3 Artcurial Briest, Paris #99/R est:5000-7000
£4861 $8118 €7000 Grand nu a la chevelure, etude (57x35cm-22x14in) s. col crayons. 21-Oct-3 Artcurial Briest, Paris #97/R est:6000-8000
£5369 $9503 €8000 Femme debout (57x34cm-22x13in) s. gouache ink wash col crayon. 27-Apr-4 Artcurial Briest, Paris #93/R est:800-12000
£8681 $14497 €12500 Nu en bleu, etude (57x35cm-22x14in) s. col crayons. 21-Oct-3 Artcurial Briest, Paris #98/R est:5000-7000

ARCHULETA, Felipe (1910-1991) American

Sculpture
£1198 $2000 €1749 Giraffe (66x36x13cm-26x14x5in) s.i.d.1974 paint wood string prov. 15-Nov-3 Slotin Folk Art, Buford #216/R est:500-1000

ARCIERI, Charles F (1885-1945) American

£1890 $3250 €2759 Girl with her dog (37x40cm-15x16in) s. canvas on board prov. 3-Dec-3 Doyle, New York #232/R est:5000-7000

ARCIMBOLDO, Giuseppe (attrib) (1527-1593) Italian

Works on paper
£2632 $4842 €4000 Study (10x7cm-4x3in) pen ink W/C over pencil. 22-Jun-4 Sotheby's, Milan #12/R est:2000-3000

ARCIMBOLDO, Giuseppe (style) (1527-1593) Italian

£10000 $18000 €14600 Anthropomorphic landscape (100x79cm-39x31in) prov. 23-Jan-4 Christie's, Rockefeller NY #158/R est:7000-10000
£10769 $18523 €15723 The shell woman (39x40cm-15x16in) panel. 3-Dec-3 AB Stockholms Auktionsverk #2717/R est:35000-40000 (S.KR 140000)
£23077 $42000 €33692 Four anthropomorphic heads, allegories of Water, Earth, Fire and Air (19x15cm-7x6in) copper set of four. 17-Jun-4 Christie's, Rockefeller NY #6/R est:30000-50000

ARCT, Eugeniusz (1899-1974) Polish

Works on paper
£738 $1381 €1100 New York at night (30x37cm-12x15in) s.d.1949 gouache oil paper on panel. 28-Feb-4 Bolland & Marotz, Bremen #299/R

ARDEN, Charlotte Leonie (1859-1904) Belgian

£667 $1227 €1000 Enfants se baignant (19x24cm-7x9in) s. panel. 14-Jun-4 Horta, Bruxelles #287
£1027 $1747 €1500 Ramasseurs defaines (40x60cm-16x24in) s. 10-Nov-3 Horta, Bruxelles #352

ARDEN, Henri (1858-1917) Belgian
£420 $722 €600 Bateaux de peche dans le port (27x40cm-11x16in) s. panel. 2-Dec-3 Campo & Campo, Antwerp #6
£428 $774 €650 Coucher de soleil sur le port de peche (60x72cm-24x28in) s. 19-Apr-4 Horta, Bruxelles #21
£490 $817 €700 Paysage enneige anime (35x27cm-14x11in) s. 13-Oct-3 Horta, Bruxelles #312
£595 $1100 €869 Marine landscape (38x66cm-15x26in) s. 14-Jan-4 Dallas Auction Gallery, Dallas #408/R est:1500-2500
£600 $1074 €900 River scene with boat on the bank (36x17cm-14x7in) s. panel. 15-May-4 De Vuyst, Lokeren #12
£674 $1125 €950 Marine en Hollande (24x40cm-9x16in) s. panel. 17-Jun-3 Vanderkindere, Brussels #101
£805 $1490 €1200 Barques de peche au clair de lune (40x32cm-16x13in) s. panel. 15-Mar-4 Horta, Bruxelles #185
£909 $1564 €1300 Bateaux au port (60x40cm-24x16in) s. 2-Dec-3 Campo & Campo, Antwerp #8/R
£1119 $1924 €1600 Decharge de la cargaison (40x60cm-16x24in) s. 2-Dec-3 Campo & Campo, Antwerp #7/R est:1400-1800
£2416 $4470 €3600 Barque de peche et vapeur dans un estuaire (70x100cm-28x39in) s. 15-Mar-4 Horta, Bruxelles #184 est:4000-5000

ARDEN-QUIN, Carmelo (1913-) Uruguayan
£19553 $35000 €28547 Aris (61x49cm-24x19in) s.i.d.49 verso board prov.exhib. 26-May-4 Sotheby's, New York #50/R est:15000-20000
Works on paper
£592 $1089 €900 Composition (17x24cm-7x9in) s.d.1958 mixed media collage cardboard. 27-Jun-4 Versailles Encheres #10
£733 $1341 €1100 Abstract (63x38cm-25x15in) s.i.d.1976 W/C mixed media. 6-Jul-4 Bolsa de Arte, Rio de Janeiro #91/R (B.R 4000)
£769 $1285 €1100 Composition (20x20cm-8x8in) mono. mixed media cardboard. 29-Jun-3 Versailles Encheres #43/R
£921 $1695 €1400 Composition (20x23cm-8x9in) s.d.1969 ink collage prov. 27-Jun-4 Versailles Encheres #29/R
£1053 $1937 €1600 Composition (24x32cm-9x13in) s.d.1961 mixed media collage cardboard prov. 27-Jun-4 Versailles Encheres #28/R est:1200-1500
£1250 $1975 €1800 Composition (24x31cm-9x12in) s.d.1960 collage cardboard prov. 27-Apr-3 Versailles Encheres #28
£1408 $2437 €2000 Composition (33x24cm-13x9in) s.d.1969 mixed media collage. 14-Dec-3 Versailles Encheres #38/R est:1500-2000

ARDENTI DE FAENZA, Alexandre (1530-1595) Italian
Works on paper
£2400 $4320 €3504 Female allegorical figure with putti bearing symbols. Head of putto (25x22cm-10x9in) s. pen brown ink double-sided. 20-Apr-4 Sotheby's, Olympia #14/R est:1000-1500

ARDISSONE, Yolande (1872-?) French
£284 $474 €400 Nature morte au bouquet de fleurs (65x50cm-26x20in) s. 14-Oct-3 Millon & Associes, Paris #102
£324 $550 €473 Le bono (33x41cm-13x16in) s. 5-Nov-3 Doyle, New York #6/R
£408 $750 €596 Jardin Normand (30x30cm-12x12in) s. i.stretcher. 25-Mar-4 Doyle, New York #3/R
£559 $1000 €816 Fleurs et fruits (91x71cm-36x28in) s. i. stretcher. 8-Jan-4 Doyle, New York #3/R
£598 $1100 €873 Sur la plage (51x61cm-20x24in) s. 9-Jun-4 Doyle, New York #3004
£761 $1400 €1111 Chateau Breton et Bles (51x61cm-20x24in) s. 9-Jun-4 Doyle, New York #3005
£824 $1400 €1203 Saint Matine (51x51cm-20x20in) s. 5-Nov-3 Doyle, New York #7/R est:1000-1500
£852 $1500 €1244 Les vignes a lorgnes (33x41cm-13x16in) s. prov. 18-May-4 Arthur James, Florida #154 est:1200-1600
£870 $1600 €1270 Bateaux a doeloin (81x81cm-32x32in) s. i.stretcher. 25-Mar-4 Doyle, New York #4/R est:3000-4000
£870 $1600 €1270 Aout en Bretagne (81x81cm-32x32in) s. i.stretcher. 25-Mar-4 Doyle, New York #5/R est:3000-4000
£870 $1600 €1270 Les iris (91x74cm-36x29in) s. 9-Jun-4 Doyle, New York #3003 est:3000-4000
£872 $1500 €1273 Le port de palais (73x92cm-29x36in) s. i.stretcher. 3-Dec-3 Doyle, New York #151/R est:3000-5000
£872 $1500 €1273 Les tamarys (73x60cm-29x24in) s. i.stretcher. 3-Dec-3 Doyle, New York #152/R est:2500-3500
£1104 $1800 €1612 Arbres fruitiers (81x99cm-32x39in) s. 24-Sep-3 Doyle, New York #2 est:3000-5000
£1166 $1900 €1702 L'aubere des ajoine (51x51cm-20x20in) s. 24-Sep-3 Doyle, New York #3 est:2000-3000
£1471 $2500 €2148 Flowers in the country (99x99cm-39x39in) s. 5-Nov-3 Doyle, New York #5/R est:3000-5000

ARDIZZONE, Edward (1900-1979) British
Works on paper
£300 $546 €438 Model resting (9x14cm-4x6in) init. pencil. 15-Jun-4 Bonhams, Knightsbridge #125
£400 $728 €584 Gossip in the sun (21x17cm-8x7in) init. pen blk ink prov.exhib. 1-Jul-4 Christie's, Kensington #1/R
£470 $799 €686 Illustration to Shakespeare's King Lear (9x15cm-4x6in) s. pencil ink. 27-Nov-3 Greenslade Hunt, Taunton #988/R
£550 $1001 €803 Manner Makyth Man (12x16cm-5x6in) s. pen black ink prov.exhib. 1-Jul-4 Christie's, Kensington #3/R
£850 $1445 €1241 Evening (24x18cm-9x7in) init. pen ink. 27-Nov-3 Greenslade Hunt, Taunton #989/R
£1100 $1870 €1606 Hippies in the garden of Guggenheim Museum, Venice (19x28cm-7x11in) init. W/C pen ink. 1-Dec-3 Bonhams, Bath #53/R est:800-1200
£2200 $3740 €3212 In a public house (18x19cm-7x7in) s.i. pen ink exhib. 27-Nov-3 Greenslade Hunt, Taunton #990/R est:800-1200
£2300 $4209 €3358 Bathing in Antibes (19x25cm-7x10in) init. blk ink W/C prov.exhib. 3-Jun-4 Christie's, London #217/R est:1500-2500

ARDON, Mordecai (1896-1992) Israeli
£26506 $44000 €38699 Fields in the Emek (55x46cm-22x18in) s.d.64 prov.exhib.lit. 2-Oct-3 Christie's, Tel Aviv #81/R est:45000-65000
£27933 $50000 €40782 Flowers (56x46cm-22x18in) s.d.55 i.d.55 verso masonite. 18-Mar-4 Sotheby's, New York #12/R est:50000-70000
£36313 $65000 €53017 Portrait of a young woman (73x60cm-29x24in) s. s.d.77 stretcher. 18-Mar-4 Sotheby's, New York #25/R est:50000-70000
£39106 $70000 €57095 Fish and the moon (46x55cm-18x22in) s. s.i.stretcher painted c.1950. 18-Mar-4 Sotheby's, New York #11/R est:50000-70000
£55866 $100000 €81564 From the old city (92x65cm-36x26in) s. s.i.d.1968 stretcher prov.lit. 18-Mar-4 Sotheby's, New York #26/R est:90000-120000
£57229 $95000 €83554 Bloom and Sign (159x128cm-63x50in) s.d.70 s.i.d.verso exhib.lit. 2-Oct-3 Christie's, Tel Aviv #83/R est:120000-160000

ARDUINO, Giovanni Maria (?-1647) Italian
£5208 $8698 €7500 Esther and Assuerus (48x62cm-19x24in) 22-Oct-3 Finarte Semenzato, Milan #57/R est:6000-8000

ARDUINO, Nicola (1887-1974) Italian
£336 $594 €500 Young woman (44x34cm-17x13in) s. canvas on cardboard. 1-May-4 Meeting Art, Vercelli #394

ARELLANO, Juan (1888-1960) Philippino
£3871 $6194 €5652 Moro vintas (40x48cm-16x19in) s.d.59 board. 18-May-3 Sotheby's, Singapore #67/R est:10000-15000 (S.D 10800)

ARELLANO, Juan de (1614-1676) Spanish
£15278 $24903 €22000 Still life of flowers in glass vase (65x52cm-26x20in) prov. 25-Sep-3 Dr Fritz Nagel, Stuttgart #1210/R est:35000

ARELLANO, Juan de (after) (1614-1676) Spanish
£1053 $1758 €1537 Still life of flowers (80x63cm-31x25in) prov. 15-Nov-3 Galerie Gloggner, Luzern #26/R est:1200-1500 (S.FR 2400)

ARELLANO, Juan de (style) (1614-1676) Spanish
£11034 $18428 €16000 Still lives with flowers (49x66cm-19x26in) pair. 12-Nov-3 Sotheby's, Milan #117/R est:10000-15000

AREN, Olof (1918-) Swedish
£401 $738 €602 View of Stockholm (62x80cm-24x31in) s. 14-Jun-4 Lilla Bukowskis, Stockholm #662 (S.KR 5500)

ARENBURG, Mark von (20th C) ?
Works on paper
£671 $1201 €1000 Untitled (77x41cm-30x16in) s. gouache. 27-May-4 Sotheby's, Paris #95/R

ARENDS, Jan (1738-1805) Dutch
Works on paper
£1701 $3044 €2500 Popperoeden-Ambacht (20x31cm-8x12in) s.d.1772 pen ink wash pierre noire prov. 19-Mar-4 Beaussant & Lefèvre, Paris #25/R est:2200-2500

ARENDS, Karl Oskar (1863-1932) German
£400 $732 €584 Figures walking by a church in an alpine landscape (56x61cm-22x24in) s. board. 8-Apr-4 Christie's, Kensington #197/R

ARENDS, Lodewyk Hendrik (1817-1873) Dutch
£851 $1421 €1200 Horses drinking at the water trough (22x28cm-9x11in) s. panel. 20-Oct-3 Glerum, Amsterdam #44/R

ARENIUS, Olof (1701-1766) Swedish
£9427 $16308 €13763 Portrait of Queen Lovisa Ulrika (138x109cm-54x43in) 15-Dec-3 Lilla Bukowskis, Stockholm #775/R est:150000-200000 (S.KR 120000)

ARENIUS, Olof (attrib) (1701-1766) Swedish
£769 $1323 €1123 Portrait of Professor Jonas Meldercreutz (80x66cm-31x26in) 7-Dec-3 Uppsala Auktionskammare, Uppsala #51/R (S.KR 10000)

ARENO, Joseph R (1950-) American
£317 $575 €463 Miam canal, Miami Arizona (28x36cm-11x14in) s. board. 18-Apr-4 Bonhams & Butterfields, Los Angeles #7005/R
£370 $700 €540 Fiesta, Santa Barbara courthouse (35x50cm-14x20in) s. panel. 22-Feb-4 Bonhams & Butterfields, Los Angeles #7002
£1087 $2000 €1587 East Beach, Santa Barbara (30x43cm-12x17in) s. i.d.2002 verso masonite. 8-Jun-4 Bonhams & Butterfields, San Francisco #4389/R est:3000-5000
£3468 $6000 €5063 East Beach Volleyball, Santa Barbara (33x47cm-13x19in) s.i.verso masonite. 10-Dec-3 Bonhams & Butterfields, San Francisco #6338/R est:3000-5000

ARENTZ, Josef M (1903-1969) American
£351 $650 €512 Seascape (61x91cm-24x36in) s. 13-Mar-4 DeFina, Austinburg #800a/R

ARENYS, Ricardo (1914-) Spanish
£682 $1174 €996 Three white horses (72x90cm-28x35in) s. 3-Dec-3 Stephan Welz, Johannesburg #6 est:7000-10000 (SA.R 7500)
£1100 $1870 €1606 Five bay horses (69x160cm-27x63in) s. 19-Nov-3 Sotheby's, Olympia #132/R est:600-900

ARESTE, Guillermo (20th C) Spanish
£352 $616 €500 Grapes harvest (93x73cm-37x29in) s.i.d.1938 verso after Goya. 16-Dec-3 Durán, Madrid #1176/R

ARETUSI, Cesare (after) (1549-1612) Italian
£8633 $14158 €12000 Portrait of Ranuccio I Farnese (86x67cm-34x26in) prov. 4-Jun-3 Sotheby's, Milan #80/R est:3000-4000

AREVALO, Xavier (20th C) Mexican
£2286 $4000 €3338 Banistas (161x20cm-63x8in) s.i.d.90. 19-Dec-3 Sotheby's, New York #1193/R est:6000-8000

ARGIMON, Daniel (1929-1996) Spanish
£884 $1610 €1300 Untitled (81x65cm-32x26in) s.d.1992 oil collage. 3-Feb-4 Segre, Madrid #220/R
£2211 $4024 €3250 Cosmonaute (100x81cm-39x32in) painted 1965 exhib.lit. 3-Feb-4 Segre, Madrid #325/R est:3250

ARGOV, Michael (1920-) Israeli
£336 $601 €500 Composition (27x35cm-11x14in) s.d.58 s.verso. 25-May-4 Chambelland & Giafferi, Paris #89/R
£1745 $3123 €2600 Femme attablee (65x50cm-26x20in) s. painted c.1950. 25-May-4 Chambelland & Giafferi, Paris #90/R est:3000-4000
£2198 $4000 €3209 Boats in the harbour (51x63cm-20x25in) s.d.55 s.verso. 29-Jun-4 Sotheby's, New York #406/R est:4000-6000
Works on paper
£268 $481 €400 La terrasse (35x50cm-14x20in) s.i.d.47 W/C graphite. 25-May-4 Chambelland & Giafferi, Paris #91/R

ARGUELLO, Miguel Angel (1941-) Spanish
£604 $1130 €900 Young man with hat (92x74cm-36x29in) s.d.69. 24-Feb-4 Durán, Madrid #693/R
Works on paper
£845 $1352 €1200 Flowers (90x69cm-35x27in) s.d.1978 pastel pencil cardboard prov. 16-Sep-3 Segre, Madrid #157/R

ARGUTINSKY, Elisabeth (20th C) German?
£1250 $2088 €1800 Still life with jug (74x61cm-29x24in) s.d.1932. 25-Oct-3 Dr Lehr, Berlin #51/R est:2400

ARGYROS, Otto H (1884-1963) Greek
£5822 $9082 €8500 Couple reading newspaper (127x107cm-50x42in) s. 10-Apr-3 Weidler, Nurnberg #6502/R est:2000

ARGYROS, Oumbertos (1877-1963) Greek
£868 $1415 €1250 Dog with red ribbon (46x32cm-18x13in) s.d.44 board. 24-Sep-3 Neumeister, Munich #384/R
£1379 $2469 €2013 Mykonos (24x34cm-9x13in) s. board. 12-May-4 Dobiaschofsky, Bern #314/R est:4800 (S.FR 3200)
£2000 $3580 €2920 Red ribbon (46x32cm-18x13in) s. board. 10-May-4 Sotheby's, Olympia #133/R est:1800-2500
£3400 $6086 €4964 Still life of flowers in a vase (75x55cm-30x22in) s. prov. 11-May-4 Bonhams, New Bond Street #54/R est:2500-3500
£4000 $7160 €5840 Fishing boats by a jetty (36x50cm-14x20in) s. board. 10-May-4 Sotheby's, Olympia #127/R est:4000-6000
£4500 $8055 €6570 Returning from the quarry (50x69cm-20x27in) paper. 10-May-4 Sotheby's, Olympia #138/R est:5000-7000
£5000 $8950 €7300 View of Mykonos (50x70cm-20x28in) hardboard prov.exhib. 11-May-4 Bonhams, New Bond Street #48/R est:4500-6000
£9500 $17005 €13870 Lecture (131x111cm-52x44in) s. 10-May-4 Sotheby's, Olympia #167/R est:6000-8000
£13000 $22750 €18980 Couple of young shepherds in the fields (100x125cm-39x49in) s. 16-Dec-3 Bonhams, New Bond Street #34/R est:10000-15000

ARIAS, Francisco (1912-1977) Spanish
£2746 $4394 €3900 Woman bathing (92x73cm-36x29in) s. lit. 16-Sep-3 Segre, Madrid #123/R est:4800
Works on paper
£361 $650 €527 Portrait of two girls (46x41cm-18x16in) s. mixed media. 20-Jan-4 Arthur James, Florida #16

ARICO, Rodolfo (1930-2002) Italian
£433 $797 €650 Nude (48x58cm-19x23in) s.d.1958. 10-Jun-4 Galleria Pace, Milan #6/R
£1745 $3123 €2600 Radioactive (120x80cm-47x31in) s.d.1973 on stretcher i.verso acrylic canvas on board prov. 25-May-4 Sotheby's, Milan #173/R est:1500-2000
£3800 $6878 €5700 Orpheus geometry (118x200cm-46x79in) s.d.72 verso acrylic lit. 2-Apr-4 Farsetti, Prato #240/R est:3600-4000
£3846 $6538 €5500 Perspective (250x390cm-98x154in) s.d.1973 verso acrylic canvas on board prov. 24-Nov-3 Christie's, Milan #30 est:3000-4000
Works on paper
£507 $832 €700 White relief (70x100cm-28x39in) s.d.67 mixed media. 27-May-3 Il Ponte, Milan #418
£570 $1055 €850 Plan C-Y (70x100cm-28x39in) s.i. mixed media cardboard prov. 11-Mar-4 Galleria Pace, Milan #3/R
£699 $1189 €1000 Prism and collimating lenses didactically (71x100cm-28x39in) s.d.1965 W/C oil pencil sold with one by A Carena. 25-Nov-3 Sotheby's, Milan #156/R
£839 $1427 €1200 Untitled (50x70cm-20x28in) s.d.85 mixed media card pair. 24-Nov-3 Christie's, Milan #56/R
£2113 $3697 €3000 Sensus (76x123cm-30x48in) s.d.89 mixed media on canvas. 16-Dec-3 Finarte Semenzato, Milan #247/R est:2700
£2238 $3804 €3200 Untitled (70x100cm-28x39in) s.d.71 collage spray paint pen set of 3. 24-Nov-3 Christie's, Milan #58/R est:2000-3000

ARIELI, Mordecai (1909-1993) Polish
£412 $700 €602 Still life (51x71cm-20x28in) s. cardboard on board painted 1960's. 1-Dec-3 Ben-Ami, Tel Aviv #4304/R
Works on paper
£230 $420 €336 Still life with fruit (34x48cm-13x19in) s.d.1947 gouache. 1-Feb-4 Ben-Ami, Tel Aviv #4646/R

ARIENTI, Stefano (1961-) Italian
Sculpture
£2819 $5046 €4200 Big snake (11x20x13cm-4x8x5in) s.d.1987 cut and folded book. 25-May-4 Sotheby's, Milan #225/R est:2000-3000
£3521 $6162 €5000 Turbin (33x15x33cm-13x6x13in) folded train timetable. 16-Dec-3 Finarte Semenzato, Milan #212/R est:2400
Works on paper
£2148 $3844 €3200 Cloud (47x84cm-19x33in) folded and glued paper exec.1988. 25-May-4 Sotheby's, Milan #226/R est:2000-3000

ARIF, Ahmad (20th C) Indonesian?
£543 $842 €793 Boats (47x68cm-19x27in) s.d.67. 6-Oct-2 Sotheby's, Singapore #129/R (S.D 1500)

ARIFIEN, Nief (1955-) Indonesian?
£2124 $3845 €3101 Will you merry me (70x60cm-28x24in) s.d.2000 s.d.verso. 4-Apr-4 Sotheby's, Singapore #175/R est:4000-6000 (S.D 6500)
£2151 $3441 €3140 Berhias (80x76cm-31x30in) s.d.88. 18-May-3 Sotheby's, Singapore #176/R est:5000-7000 (S.D 6000)
£2941 $5324 €4294 Mambo 5 (60x70cm-24x28in) s.d.2002 s.i.d.verso. 4-Apr-4 Sotheby's, Singapore #174/R est:5000-7000 (S.D 9000)
£2941 $5324 €4294 Dinner (80x70cm-31x28in) s.d.2002 s.i.d.verso. 4-Apr-4 Sotheby's, Singapore #173/R est:4000-6000 (S.D 9000)
£3441 $5505 €5024 By the beach (60x70cm-24x28in) s.d.96. 18-May-3 Sotheby's, Singapore #175/R est:600-8000 (S.D 9600)
£3442 $5335 €5025 Never let a day pass by (80x70cm-31x28in) s.d.98 s.i.d.1988 verso. 6-Oct-2 Sotheby's, Singapore #176/R est:6000-8000 (S.D 9500)
£5208 $8698 €7604 Come closer to me (90x79cm-35x31in) s.d.2002 s.i.d.verso. 12-Oct-3 Sotheby's, Singapore #156/R est:9000-12000 (S.D 15000)

ARIGLIANO, Giuseppe (1917-) Italian
£496 $829 €700 Coastal view, Genoa Nervi (30x40cm-12x16in) s. board. 14-Oct-3 Finarte Semenzato, Milan #12
£1611 $3012 €2400 Coastal view (40x50cm-16x20in) 26-Feb-4 Cambi, Genoa #473/R est:600-700

ARIJAC, Henry Jacques (1941-) Haitian
£195 $350 €285 Celebration (60x75cm-24x30in) s. i.verso tooling. 14-May-4 Skinner, Boston #407/R

ARIKHA, Avigdor (1929-) Israeli
£1117 $2000 €1631 Untitled (25x20cm-10x8in) s. board. 16-May-4 Wright, Chicago #209/R est:4000-6000
£1676 $3000 €2447 Sacrifice of Isaac (38x46cm-15x18in) s. s.i.d.1955 verso. 18-Mar-4 Sotheby's, New York #35/R est:5000-7000
£1972 $3411 €2800 La danse (14x18cm-6x7in) s.d.1952 panel. 12-Dec-3 Piasa, Paris #220/R est:1500-2000
£2034 $3600 €2970 Figures in a street in Jerusalem (22x27cm-9x11in) s.d.1957. 1-May-4 Ben-Ami, Tel Aviv #4818/R est:6000-8000
£2254 $3899 €3200 Paysage nordique (27x16cm-11x6in) s.d.1956. 12-Dec-3 Piasa, Paris #219/R est:2000-3000
£4670 $8500 €6818 La tour de Babel (65x81cm-26x32in) s.d.1957 s.i.d.verso. 29-Jun-4 Sotheby's, New York #404/R est:7000-9000
£5495 $10000 €8023 L'expulsion du paradis (91x72cm-36x28in) s.d.1957 i.d.verso. 29-Jun-4 Sotheby's, New York #405/R est:8000-10000
£19553 $35000 €28547 Ritual objects (54x81cm-21x32in) s.d.23 VII 95 verso prov. 18-Mar-4 Sotheby's, New York #44/R est:40000-60000
£23743 $42500 €34665 Saint Emillion (65x100cm-26x39in) s.d.24 VII 97 verso. 18-Mar-4 Sotheby's, New York #56/R est:50000-70000
Works on paper
£302 $561 €450 Etude pour un portrait de Mr David de R. Etude de tete (65x50cm-26x20in) s.d.55 chl double-sided. 3-Mar-4 Artcurial Briest, Paris #302
£302 $561 €450 Composition (26x16cm-10x6in) s.d.60 W/C ink prov. 3-Mar-4 Artcurial Briest, Paris #303
£423 $731 €600 Crucifixion. s.d.1957 ink. 12-Dec-3 Piasa, Paris #227
£762 $1386 €1150 Promenade (51x45cm-20x18in) s.d.1955 sanguine dr. 15-Jun-4 Rossini, Paris #180/R
£958 $1600 €1399 Abstract composition (64x50cm-25x20in) s.d.58 W/C. 7-Oct-3 Sotheby's, New York #361 est:2500-3500
£993 $1808 €1500 Untitled (63x48cm-25x19in) s.d.1959 chl. 15-Jun-4 Rossini, Paris #181 est:1000-1200

ARIOLA, Fortunato (1827-1872) American
£4360 $7500 €6366 Twilight in the tropics (90x122cm-35x48in) s. 3-Dec-3 Doyle, New York #248/R est:8000-12000

ARIS, Fred (20th C) British
£400 $668 €584 Merry-go-round (56x66cm-22x26in) s. board. 21-Oct-3 Bonhams, Knightsbridge #91/R

ARJONA, Francisco (1944-) Spanish
£281 $477 €410 Little gypsies, Almeria (46x37cm-18x15in) sid.73 verso board. 4-Nov-3 Ansorena, Madrid #872/R
£377 $640 €550 Fontan Square, Oviedo (50x60cm-20x24in) s.d. s.d.73 verso board. 4-Nov-3 Ansorena, Madrid #994/R
£870 $1426 €1200 Landscape (27x36cm-11x14in) s.d.8 mayo 1982 verso panel. 27-May-3 Durán, Madrid #21/R

£890 $1514 €1300 Peasants (135x120cm-53x47in) s.d.1973. 4-Nov-3 Ansorena, Madrid #401 est:500

ARKACOF, D (20th C) Russian?
Works on paper
£1796 $3000 €2622 Riding the plains with Borzois (71x99cm-28x39in) s. W/C. 16-Nov-3 Simpson's, Houston #144a/R

ARKHIPOV, Abram (1862-1930) Russian
£11111 $20000 €16222 Northern landscape (34x47cm-13x19in) indis sig. canvas on board prov. 23-Apr-4 Sotheby's, New York #33/R est:15000-20000
£17000 $28900 €25500 Portrait of peasant woman (78x61cm-31x24in) s.d.1917. 25-Nov-3 Christie's, London #140/R est:10000-15000
£102564 $160000 € Russian peasant drinking tea (141x106cm-56x42in) s.d.1917. 11-Apr-3 Christie's, Rockefeller NY #26/R est:70000-100000
£133333 $240000 €194666 Portrait of a Russian peasant girl (105x81cm-41x32in) s. prov. 23-Apr-4 Sotheby's, New York #22/R est:200000-300000
Works on paper
£979 $1536 €1429 Russian farmers making music and dancing (42x64cm-17x25in) mono. i.verso gouache. 30-Aug-3 Rasmussen, Havnen #2167 (D.KR 10500)

ARKLEY, Howard (1951-1999) Australian
£2893 $5120 €4224 House (25x20cm-10x8in) s.d.97 acrylic paper prov. 3-May-4 Christie's, Melbourne #81/R est:8000-10000 (A.D 7000)
£4527 $8193 €6609 Organic model G (211x162cm-83x64in) s.d.76 acrylic. 30-Mar-4 Lawson Menzies, Sydney #156/R est:12000-15000 (A.D 11000)
Works on paper
£1447 $2459 €2113 House (28x22cm-11x9in) s.d.87 synthetic polymer paint photocopy prov. 26-Nov-3 Deutscher-Menzies, Melbourne #67/R est:4000-6000 (A.D 3400)
£1532 $2604 €2237 Californian bungalow (27x31cm-11x12in) s.d.87 W/C synthetic polymer paint photocopy prov. 26-Nov-3 Deutscher-Menzies, Melbourne #54/R est:4000-6000 (A.D 3600)
£2254 $3562 €3291 Home (29x21cm-11x8in) s.d.94 s.d.1994 verso synthetic polymer paint prov. 2-Sep-3 Deutscher-Menzies, Melbourne #15/R est:4000-6000 (A.D 5500)
£3099 $5733 €4525 Family house, suburban exterior (72x107cm-28x42in) s.d.93 W/C screenprint. 10-Mar-4 Deutscher-Menzies, Melbourne #187a/R est:9000-12000 (A.D 7500)
£7438 $13760 €10859 Front gate and home (76x55cm-30x22in) s.d.97 synthetic polymer. 10-Mar-4 Deutscher-Menzies, Melbourne #192/R est:22000-28000 (A.D 18000)
£9312 $14992 €13596 Figurative (200x120cm-79x47in) s.d.1981 i.verso synthetic polymer paint canvas prov.exhib. 25-Aug-3 Sotheby's, Paddington #147/R est:20000-30000 (A.D 23000)
£9917 $18347 €14479 Suburban house (74x54cm-29x21in) synthetic polymer. 10-Mar-4 Deutscher-Menzies, Melbourne #160/R est:22000-28000 (A.D 24000)
£19835 $36694 €28959 Girl in a car (122x122cm-48x48in) synthetic polymer executed c.1976-77 prov. 10-Mar-4 Deutscher-Menzies, Melbourne #44/R est:60000-80000 (A.D 48000)
£24809 $45153 €36221 Houses with tree (175x135cm-69x53in) s. i.d.1996 verso synthetic polymer on canvas. 16-Jun-4 Deutscher-Menzies, Melbourne #91/R est:50000-60000 (A.D 65000)
£39634 $70945 €57866 Psychedelic head (175x135cm-69x53in) synthetic polymer canvas exec 1990 exhib.lit. 4-May-4 Sotheby's, Melbourne #32/R est:70000-100000 (A.D 97500)

ARLAUD, Jacques Antoine (1668-1746) Swiss
Miniatures
£6800 $11560 €9928 Grand Dauphin de France (6cm-2in) W/C oval. 18-Nov-3 Bonhams, New Bond Street #21/R est:3000-5000

ARLAUD-JURINE, Louis Ami (attrib) (1751-1829) Swiss
Miniatures
£1500 $2550 €2190 Gentleman with blue coat with red collar (6cm-2in) gold frame oval. 18-Nov-3 Bonhams, New Bond Street #121/R est:1500-2000
Works on paper
£766 $1317 €1118 Portrait of a boy (16x14cm-6x6in) chk grisaille. 8-Dec-3 Philippe Schuler, Zurich #4194/R (S.FR 1700)

ARLETT, Johann (?) American?
£398 $725 €581 Genre, Europe (66x51cm-26x20in) s. 7-Feb-4 Dan Ripley, Indianapolis #18

ARLINGSSON, Erling (1904-1982) Swedish
£443 $794 €647 Southern landscape with palms (41x56cm-16x22in) mono. paper on panel. 28-May-4 Uppsala Auktionskammare, Uppsala #294 (S.KR 6000)
£481 $885 €722 Early spring in Vaagaa (56x68cm-22x27in) s.i.d.1965. 14-Jun-4 Lilla Bukowskis, Stockholm #103 (S.KR 6600)
£591 $1058 €863 Coastal landscape with breakers (36x46cm-14x18in) mono. panel. 28-May-4 Uppsala Auktionskammare, Uppsala #293/R (S.KR 8000)
£665 $1191 €971 Autumn landscape (41x55cm-16x22in) mono. tempera panel. 28-May-4 Uppsala Auktionskammare, Uppsala #295/R (S.KR 9000)
£761 $1371 €1142 Lake landscape (38x43cm-15x17in) s. i.d.1935 verso. 25-Apr-4 Goteborg Auktionsverk, Sweden #313/R (S.KR 10500)
£870 $1566 €1270 Red house by woodland road (35x40cm-14x16in) init. cardboard. 26-Apr-4 Bukowskis, Stockholm #39/R (S.KR 12000)
£879 $1556 €1283 Autumn landscape with waterway (50x61cm-20x24in) init. 27-Apr-4 AB Stockholms Auktionsverk #653/R (S.KR 12000)
£906 $1632 €1323 Rapids (51x55cm-20x22in) init. 26-Apr-4 Bukowskis, Stockholm #37/R (S.KR 12500)
£952 $1686 €1390 Landscape view of blue fjord (50x61cm-20x24in) init. 27-Apr-4 AB Stockholms Auktionsverk #900/R (S.KR 13000)
£1088 $1958 €1632 Landscape view towards the valley (50x62cm-20x24in) init. 25-Apr-4 Goteborg Auktionsverk, Sweden #398/R est:18000 (S.KR 15000)
£1154 $1985 €1685 October - river and brown wood (46x55cm-18x22in) mono. panel. 7-Dec-3 Uppsala Auktionskammare, Uppsala #265/R est:10000-12000 (S.KR 15000)
£1218 $2106 €1778 Blue landscape (46x55cm-18x22in) s. panel. 15-Dec-3 Lilla Bukowskis, Stockholm #550 est:15000 (S.KR 15500)
£1257 $2174 €1835 Landscape with small cottage (38x46cm-15x18in) s. panel. 15-Dec-3 Lilla Bukowskis, Stockholm #560 est:8000-10000 (S.KR 16000)
£1478 $2646 €2158 Figures in town (50x60cm-20x24in) mono. panel. 28-May-4 Uppsala Auktionskammare, Uppsala #292/R est:12000-15000 (S.KR 20000)
£1523 $2741 €2224 Landscape with brook (55x65cm-22x26in) init. 26-Apr-4 Bukowskis, Stockholm #38/R est:12000-15000 (S.KR 21000)
Works on paper
£739 $1323 €1079 Still life of flowers in vase (48x38cm-19x15in) mono. gouache. 28-May-4 Uppsala Auktionskammare, Uppsala #291/R (S.KR 10000)

ARMAJANI, Siah (1939-) American
£778 $1400 €1136 Notations on reading room num 2 (32x29cm-13x11in) paint balsa wood cardboard collage three parts prov. 24-Apr-4 David Rago, Lambertville #296/R
Sculpture
£1333 $2400 €1946 Louis Kahn lecture room for the Fleisher Art memorial (9x17x30cm-4x7x12in) i. paint balsa wood plexiglass exhib. 24-Apr-4 David Rago, Lambertville #536/R est:2000-3000

ARMAN, Fernandez (1928-) American/French
£528 $924 €750 Cosusopa (42x59cm-17x23in) s. s.i.d.1967 verso. 16-Dec-3 Durán, Madrid #56/R
£586 $979 €850 Figures (37x23cm-15x9in) s. tempera paper on board painted 1969. 17-Nov-3 Sant Agostino, Torino #188/R
£2238 $3849 €3200 Composition (76x100cm-30x39in) s. panel painted c.1954. 4-Dec-3 Piasa, Paris #92/R est:3000-4000
£2550 $4565 €3800 Figures (28x24cm-11x9in) s. oil card on board prov. 25-May-4 Sotheby's, Milan #204/R est:1500-2000
£3333 $6000 €5000 Composition abstraite (35x22cm-14x9in) s. panel prov. 25-Apr-4 Versailles Encheres #159 est:3500-4500
£3333 $6133 €5000 Untitled (40x30cm-16x12in) s. painted 2002 canvas on board. 10-Jun-4 Galleria Pace, Milan #132/R est:8000
£3500 $6335 €5110 Les pinces (125x95cm-49x37in) s. ink executed c.1978. 1-Apr-4 Christie's, Kensington #211/R est:2000-3000
£6711 $12416 €10000 Untitled (81x60cm-32x24in) s. paint dispensers exec.2003. 13-Mar-4 Meeting Art, Vercelli #357 est:10000
£6711 $12013 €10000 La chance des neophytes (86x54cm-34x21in) s. panel prov. 25-May-4 Dorotheum, Vienna #411/R est:11000-13000
£9500 $17480 €13870 Untitled (81x61cm-32x24in) s.overlap acrylic paint tubes. 24-Jun-4 Sotheby's, Olympia #487/R est:6000-8000
£10067 $18624 €15000 Untitled (102x81cm-40x32in) s. canvas on board painted 2003. 13-Mar-4 Meeting Art, Vercelli #127 est:10000
£11409 $20195 €17000 Autumn in Connecticut (100x80cm-39x31in) s. tubes of green acrylic paint on canvas on panel prov. 28-Apr-4 Artcurial Briest, Paris #352/R est:15000-20000
£13000 $23920 €18980 Cyclo futurism (110x141cm-43x56in) s. acrylic paintbrushes bicycle parts canvas on panel prov. 24-Jun-4 Sotheby's, London #265/R est:15000-20000
£13380 $22211 €19000 Untitled (100x81cm-39x32in) s. oil acrylic pieces of violin canvas on panel. 14-Jun-3 Meeting Art, Vercelli #120/R est:15000
£13986 $24056 €20000 Untitled (216x221cm-85x87in) i.overlap oil paintbrushes canvas on panel painted 1987. 2-Dec-3 Sotheby's, Amsterdam #188/R est:18000-25000
£15278 $24139 €22000 Untitled (134x102cm-53x40in) acrylic guitar canvas on board. 6-Sep-3 Meeting Art, Vercelli #616 est:16000
£15333 $28367 €23000 Violon menagere (89x56cm-35x22in) s. wood violin plexiglas exec.1973 prov. 18-Jul-4 Sotheby's, Paris #201/R est:15000-20000
£17000 $31280 €24820 Monochrome accumulation no.6 - no.7 - no.18 (41x30cm-16x12in) each s. verso acrylic paint tubes exec 1988 three prov.lit. 24-Jun-4 Sotheby's, London #157/R est:8000-12000
£22000 $36740 €32120 Les chapeaux de max gritt (162x130cm-64x51in) s.d.65 prov.lit. 21-Oct-3 Sotheby's, London #354/R est:15000-20000
Prints
£2448 $4210 €3500 Eaux thermales (30x22cm-12x9in) s.d.56 col ink stamps exhib. 4-Dec-3 Piasa, Paris #74/R est:2500-3000
Sculpture
£865 $1600 €1263 Double Chassis (29cm-11in) s. num.113/140 bronze incl base cast Bocquel. 13-Jul-4 Christie's, Rockefeller NY #54/R est:3000-5000
£1000 $1840 €1460 Apollo decoupe (35cm-14in) s.num.18/99 bronze st.f.Bocquel. 24-Jun-4 Sotheby's, Olympia #501/R est:1000-1500
£1049 $1783 €1500 Waiting to exhale (45x25x7cm-18x10x3in) s.i. cigars is plexiglass box. 26-Nov-3 Dorotheum, Vienna #331/R est:2000-3000
£1049 $1804 €1500 Ordures au naturel (18cm-7in) s. scrap jar edition 71/150. 4-Dec-3 Piasa, Paris #52/R est:300-400
£1119 $1902 €1600 Violin (53cm-21in) s. bronze burnt wood in perspex incl perspex base. 25-Nov-3 Christie's, Amsterdam #156/R est:1500-2000
£1133 $1926 €1654 Untitled (65x54cm-26x21in) s.num.48/100 putty spades red paint plexiglass. 4-Nov-3 Bukowskis, Stockholm #560/R est:20000-25000 (S.KR 15000)
£1305 $2350 €1905 Vital (33cm-13in) s.num.7/100 dark pat.bronze Cast Bocqual. 26-Apr-4 Bukowskis, Stockholm #584/R est:20000-25000 (S.KR 18000)
£1333 $2453 €2000 Venus (33cm-13in) s.st.f. Bocquel num.55/100 brown pat. bronze incl. base. 9-Jun-4 Christie's, Amsterdam #285/R est:2000-3000
£1333 $2453 €2000 Dolls (41x31x7cm-16x12x3in) s. num.88/100 dolls plexiglas. 12-Jun-4 Meeting Art, Vercelli #97/R est:2000
£1333 $2467 €2000 Chaise violoncelle (84x41x38cm-33x16x15in) s. num.112/1800 pat bronze cushion exec.1993 prov. 18-Jul-4 Sotheby's, Paris #208/R est:2000-2500
£1344 $2365 €1962 Violin (58x21cm-23x8in) s. brass. 23-May-4 Agra, Warsaw #23/R (P.Z 9500)
£1408 $2338 €2000 Passe temps (40x40cm-16x16in) s. various objects plexiglass exec 1971. 14-Jun-3 Meeting Art, Vercelli #546/R est:2000
£1448 $2419 €2100 Trumpet (54cm-21in) s. bronze. 14-Nov-3 Farsetti, Prato #14/R est:900-1200
£1465 $2593 €2139 Accumulation de rasoirs electriques (40x25x40cm-16x10x16in) El apparatus plexibox. 27-Apr-4 AB Stockholms Auktionsverk #1159/R est:20000-30000 (S.KR 20000)
£1467 $2625 €2200 Violene (31x16x10cm-12x6x4in) i. bronze. 15-May-4 Van Ham, Cologne #411/R est:2400
£1467 $2625 €2200 Saxo (29x10x19cm-11x4x7in) i. polished bronze. 15-May-4 Van Ham, Cologne #412/R est:2200
£1476 $2613 €2200 Telephones (13x24x23cm-5x9x9in) s. num.6/150 two bronze telephones. 28-Apr-4 Artcurial Briest, Paris #378 est:1500-2000
£1477 $2732 €2200 Waiting to exhale (45x25x7cm-18x10x3in) s.i. num.17/100 cigarettes plexiglas. 9-Mar-4 Dorotheum, Vienna #231/R est:2000-3000
£1538 $2615 €2200 Accumulation de papier (64x40x10cm-25x16x4in) s. num.27/100 plexiglas paper. 24-Nov-3 Christie's, Milan #109/R est:1500-2000
£1612 $2853 €2354 Violins (37cm-15in) s. metal plastic incl.wood socle. 27-Apr-4 AB Stockholms Auktionsverk #1162/R est:12000-15000 (S.KR 22000)

£1667	$3083	€2500	Chaise violoncelle (84x41x38cm-33x16x15in) s. num.143/1800 pat bronze cushion exec.1993 prov. 18-Jul-4 Sotheby's, Paris #210/R est:2000-2500
£1667	$3083	€2500	Chaise violoncelle (84x41x38cm-33x16x15in) s. num.140/1800 pat bronze cushion exec.1993 prov. 18-Jul-4 Sotheby's, Paris #207/R est:2000-2500
£1667	$3083	€2500	Chaise violoncelle (84x41x38cm-33x16x15in) s. num.138/1800 pat bronze cushion exec.1993 prov. 18-Jul-4 Sotheby's, Paris #205/R est:2000-2500
£1667	$3083	€2500	Chaise violoncelle (84x41x38cm-33x16x15in) s. num.139/1800 pat bronze cushion exec.1993 prov. 18-Jul-4 Sotheby's, Paris #206/R est:2000-2500
£1668	$3002	€2435	Venus aux petits cuiliers (46cm-18in) s.num.88/100 gold pat.bronze stainless steel incl.marble socle. 26-Apr-4 Bukowskis, Stockholm #582/R est:15000-18000 (S.KR 23000)
£1689	$2973	€2500	Knives (50x36x27cm-20x14x11in) s.i. knives. 22-May-4 Galleria Pananti, Florence #490/R est:2500-3000
£1733	$3207	€2600	Chaise violoncelle (84x41x38cm-33x16x15in) s. num.142/1800 pat bronze cushion exec.1993 prov. 18-Jul-4 Sotheby's, Paris #209/R est:2000-2500
£1736	$2743	€2500	Violin (62x21x24cm-24x8x9in) bronze. 6-Sep-3 Meeting Art, Vercelli #89 est:2500
£1748	$3007	€2500	Trompette (54cm-21in) s.i. decoupe soude bronze one from edition of 100. 2-Dec-3 Calmels Cohen, Paris #87/R est:3000-4000
£1765	$3000	€2577	Slice of liberty (75cm-30in) st.sig. pat bronze. 31-Oct-3 Sotheby's, New York #498/R
£1800	$3114	€2628	Violon decoupe (56cm-22in) s.num.97/100 gold pat bronze. 11-Dec-3 Christie's, Kensington #267/R est:2000-3000
£1800	$3312	€2628	Telephones (13x25cm-5x10in) s.num.18/150 bronze st.f. two in four parts. 24-Jun-4 Sotheby's, Olympia #503/R est:2000-3000
£1813	$3082	€2647	Untitled (65x44cm-26x17in) s.num.36/100 paint brushes blue paint plexiglass. 4-Nov-3 Bukowskis, Stockholm #561/R est:15000-20000 (S.KR 24000)
£1813	$3263	€2647	Le tombeau Paganini (56cm-22in) s.num.31/150 gold pat.bronze marble socle. 26-Apr-4 Bukowskis, Stockholm #585/R est:25000-30000 (S.KR 25000)
£1818	$3127	€2600	Le reveil (10x10x6cm-4x4x2in) s.d.71 plexiglas exhib. 4-Dec-3 Piasa, Paris #42/R est:1500-2000
£1867	$3435	€2800	Candy (33x27x8cm-13x11x3in) s.i. plastic doll legs perspex box with lithograph by same artist. 8-Jun-4 Sotheby's, Amsterdam #291/R est:3000-4000
£1888	$3210	€2756	Au coeur de la musique (43cm-17in) s.num.10/100 polished and pat.bronze incl.socle. 5-Nov-3 AB Stockholms Auktionsverk #1126/R est:30000-35000 (S.KR 25000)
£1892	$3329	€2800	Secret de la musique (74cm-29in) s. num.25/99 brown pat bronze f.Bocquel. 18-May-4 Tajan, Paris #169/R est:3000-4000
£1972	$3411	€2800	Archers en Menorah (43x48cm-17x19in) s. num.11/50 brown pat bronze Cast Bocquel. 15-Dec-3 Charbonneaux, Paris #271/R est:1500-2000
£2000	$3640	€2920	Venus and trombones (48cm-19in) s.d num.99/100 green pat bronze gold. 4-Feb-4 Sotheby's, Olympia #165/R est:2000-3000
£2000	$3680	€2920	Venus aux horloges (46cm-18in) s.num.1/100 bronze sold with base. 24-Jun-4 Sotheby's, Olympia #500/R est:2000-3000
£2083	$3479	€3000	Colere de violon (58x25x8cm-23x10x3in) s.i. impression in copper illumintated in box prov. 21-Oct-3 Artcurial Briest, Paris #530/R est:3000-4000
£2095	$3959	€3100	Traite de violon (37cm-15in) s. gilt pat bronze edition of 75. 21-Feb-4 Cornette de St.Cyr, Paris #234/R est:3000-3500
£2098	$3608	€3000	Violons decoupes (53cm-21in) s.num.105 and 106 gilt bronze 2 violins in 4 pieces Cast Valsuani. 4-Dec-3 Piasa, Paris #76/R est:3000-4000
£2133	$3926	€3200	Colere blanche (63x52x20cm-25x20x8in) s. num.135/150 painted resin prov. 9-Jun-4 Artcurial Briest, Paris #483/R est:1500-2000
£2148	$3952	€3200	Venus aux cors de chasse (56x17x15cm-22x7x6in) s. num.94/100 bronze. 24-Mar-4 Joron-Derem, Paris #110/R est:5000-6000
£2148	$3844	€3200	Violons miniatures (22x15x3cm-9x6x1in) s. num.23/75 bronze resin plexiglas prov. 26-May-4 Christie's, Paris #122/R est:2500-3500
£2158	$3540	€3000	Periwinkle blue (32x26x6cm-13x10x2in) s.i. verso tubes of col paint gouache. 4-Jun-3 Ketterer, Hamburg #131/R est:3000-4000
£2245	$4018	€3300	Venus and watches (55cm-22in) s. num.78/100 bronze watches. 16-Mar-4 Finarte Semenzato, Milan #48 est:2400
£2292	$3735	€3300	Inclusion de tubes de coleurs dans resine (64x29cm-25x11in) s.i. mixed media tubes of colour acrylic plexiglas. 27-Sep-3 Dr Fritz Nagel, Stuttgart #9454/R est:2400
£2308	$3969	€3300	La danse du feu (54cm-21in) num.68/100 violin in plexiglass executed 1998. 2-Dec-3 Sotheby's, Amsterdam #327/R est:4000-6000
£2321	$4177	€3389	Untitled (74cm-29in) s.num.8/100 green pat.bronze. 26-Apr-4 Bukowskis, Stockholm #581/R est:40000-45000 (S.KR 32000)
£2349	$4322	€3500	Coeur du probleme (42x16x13cm-17x6x5in) s. num.20/99 pat bronze f.Bocquel. 24-Mar-4 Joron-Derem, Paris #112 est:5000-5500
£2381	$4262	€3500	Pair of violins (53cm-21in) num.96/150 two violins gilt pat bronze cire perdue Valsuani. 19-Mar-4 Millon & Associes, Paris #196/R est:2500-3000
£2416	$4446	€3600	Inclusion de poupees (31x41x6cm-12x16x2in) s.num.83/100 multiple. 28-Mar-4 Anaf, Lyon #18/R est:3500-4000
£2439	$4000	€3561	Poubelles (71x51x12cm-28x20x5in) paper in plexiglass frame on wooden base prov.exhib. 28-May-3 Sotheby's, Amsterdam #79/R est:4000-5000
£2467	$4440	€3700	Venus decoupee (50cm-20in) s. num.42/100 pat bronze Cast Barelier. 24-Apr-4 Cornette de St.Cyr, Paris #422/R est:4000
£2533	$4535	€3800	J (49x12x3cm-19x5x1in) s. brushes resin acrylic box. 15-May-4 Van Ham, Cologne #410/R est:2900
£2600	$4784	€3796	Accumulation de Chupa-Chups (41x30cm-16x12in) s. lillipops plexiglas edition of 50. 24-Jun-4 Sotheby's, Olympia #494/R est:2000-3000
£2620	$4821	€3825	Accumulation de spatules (77x55x20cm-30x22x8in) s. spatula col plastic. 8-Jun-4 Germann, Zurich #151/R est:7000-9000 (S.FR 6000)
£2635	$4980	€3900	Venus aux cuilleres (56x15cm-22x6in) s.num.30/100 gilt pat bronze silver metal. 21-Feb-4 Cornette de St.Cyr, Paris #239 est:4500-5000
£2667	$4773	€4000	Violin (64x20cm-25x8in) s. brown pat bronze one of 100 lit. 15-May-4 De Vuyst, Lokeren #602/R est:5000-6000
£2685	$4805	€4000	Saxophone (25x25cm-10x10in) s. num.24/60 bronze nichel exec.1997. 30-May-4 Meeting Art, Vercelli #7 est:4000
£2690	$4303	€3900	Untitled (41x30x3cm-16x12x1in) s. collection of screws under plexiglass edn 56/100. 13-Mar-3 Galleria Pace, Milan #89/R est:4500-5400
£2690	$4303	€3900	Untitled (40x29x5cm-16x11x2in) s.i. coloured tubes under plexiglass exec 70-80. 13-Mar-3 Galleria Pace, Milan #93/R est:4500-6000
£2703	$5108	€4000	Venus aux couteaux (58x15cm-23x6in) s.num.29/100 gilt pat bronze silver metal. 21-Feb-4 Cornette de St.Cyr, Paris #238 est:4000-4500
£2715	$4615	€3964	Accumulation de spatules (77x55x20cm-30x22x8in) s. spatulas col plexiglas. 25-Nov-3 Germann, Zurich #6/R est:8000-10000 (S.FR 6000)
£2721	$4871	€4000	Saxophone (80cm-31in) s. bronze. 16-Mar-4 Finarte Semenzato, Milan #47 est:2400
£2770	$5236	€4100	Chevalet de violon (49cm-19in) s.num.15/10 violin plexiglas. 21-Feb-4 Cornette de St.Cyr, Paris #233/R est:2500-3000
£2778	$4639	€4000	Shoes (33x46x8cm-13x18x3in) s.num.23/100 verso cut shoes plexiglas wood paint. 25-Oct-3 Cornette de St.Cyr, Paris #136 est:3500-4000
£2778	$4639	€4000	Tea for two (35x33x18cm-14x13x7in) s.num.EA polished bronze wood marble base prov. 21-Oct-3 Artcurial Briest, Paris #553/R est:6000-8000
£2797	$4811	€4000	Full-up (7x27cm-3x11in) s.d.67-68-85 boites invitations four in plexiglas. 4-Dec-3 Piasa, Paris #27/R est:4000-6000
£2800	$5012	€4088	Statue of Liberty (74cm-29in) s.num.68/100 green pat bronze. 16-Mar-4 Bonhams, Knightsbridge #6/R est:3000-5000
£2819	$5187	€4200	Zingaro (36x14x42cm-14x6x17in) s. num.17/99 pat bronze Cast f.Bocquel. 24-Mar-4 Joron-Derem, Paris #111/R est:5000-5500
£2870	$4879	€4190	Violin brisee (63cm-25in) s.num.72/100 gold pat.bronze on stone socle. 4-Nov-3 Bukowskis, Stockholm #652/R est:40000-50000 (S.KR 38000)
£2973	$5232	€4400	Venus with clocks (56x16x17cm-22x6x7in) s.i. mixed media num.6/20. 22-May-4 Galleria Pananti, Florence #501/R est:2500-3000
£3000	$5520	€4380	Violin (64cm-25in) s.num.XXI/XXX polished bronze sold with base. 24-Jun-4 Sotheby's, Olympia #502/R est:3000-4000
£3000	$5460	€4500	Inclusion de montre (5x2x1cm-2x1x0in) st.sig. num.1/1 gold resin. 29-Jun-4 Cornette de St.Cyr, Paris #64/R est:5000-6000
£3000	$5460	€4500	Accumulation de voitures miniatures (30x22x7cm-12x9x3in) s. model cars resin. 29-Jun-4 Cornette de St.Cyr, Paris #77/R est:6000-8000
£3077	$5231	€4400	Accumulation (18x14x4cm-7x6x2in) s.d.1970 cigarette packets cigarette ends paper plastic. 24-Nov-3 Christie's, Milan #153/R est:4000-6000
£3087	$5681	€4600	Togo (34x126x100cm-13x50x39in) s.num.13-T-04 multiple table edition of 60. 28-Mar-4 Anaf, Lyon #19/R est:4500-5000
£3169	$5482	€4500	Violin (64x20cm-25x8in) s. polished bronze marble base one of 30 lit. 13-Dec-3 De Vuyst, Lokeren #513/R est:5000-6000
£3194	$5335	€4600	Inclusion de cigares (40x24x7cm-16x9x3in) s.num.22/100 cigars resin. 25-Oct-3 Cornette de St.Cyr, Paris #133/R est:4500-5000
£3356	$6208	€5000	Violin (64x20cm-25x8in) s. brown pat bronze marble base one of 100 lit. 13-Mar-4 De Vuyst, Lokeren #577/R est:5000-6000
£3357	$5706	€4800	Chaise (80x50cm-31x20in) s.num. bronze Cast Regis Bocquel. 27-Nov-3 Calmels Cohen, Paris #112/R est:6000-8000
£3378	$6385	€5000	Inclusion de cigares (40x24x7cm-16x9x3in) s.num.53/100 cigars resin. 21-Feb-4 Cornette de St.Cyr, Paris #236/R est:4500-5000
£3497	$6014	€5000	Rouages de montres (10x15cm-4x6in) s.d.61 watch parts box. 4-Dec-3 Piasa, Paris #13/R est:2000-3000
£3500	$6370	€5110	Accumulation of tees (91x60cm-36x24in) s. golf tees in resin plexi-glass exec 1988. 4-Feb-4 Sotheby's, Olympia #162/R est:2000-3000
£3521	$6092	€5000	Pizzicato (57cm-22in) st.sig.i. gold pat.bronze prov. 13-Dec-3 Lempertz, Koln #277/R est:2000
£3623	$5942	€5000	Cubist violin (65cm-26in) s. num.65/100 pat bronze exec.2002. 29-May-3 Galleria Pace, Milan #120/R est:8000
£3636	$6073	€5200	Accumulation de pinceaux (66x67x18cm-26x26x7in) s. brushes. 11-Oct-3 Cornette de St.Cyr, Paris #34/R est:4000-5000
£3716	$6541	€5500	Violin (73x40x15cm-29x16x6in) s.i. num.8/100 violin. 22-May-4 Galleria Pananti, Florence #491/R est:2000-3000
£3846	$6423	€5500	Violin (64x20cm-25x8in) brown pat bronze incl. marble base. 11-Oct-3 De Vuyst, Lokeren #571/R est:5000-6000
£4000	$7280	€5840	Violin (58cm-23in) s.i. num.3/20 polished bronze exec 2001. 4-Feb-4 Sotheby's, Olympia #164/R est:3000-5000
£4000	$7360	€5840	Violin (56cm-22in) s.i.num.10/10 polished bronze sold with base. 24-Jun-4 Sotheby's, Olympia #490/R est:3000-4000
£4167	$6958	€6000	Mooncrescent (42x62x33cm-17x24x13in) i. bronze. 25-Oct-3 Cornette de St.Cyr, Paris #567/R est:6000-8000
£4167	$6583	€6000	Colere de violon (24x18cm-9x7in) violin on canvas. 6-Sep-3 Meeting Art, Vercelli #348 est:5000
£4225	$7310	€6000	Statue de la liberte (77x25x18cm-30x10x7in) s.num.AP 2/2 green pat soldered bronze prov. 14-Dec-3 Versailles Encheres #177/R est:7000-8000
£4333	$7973	€6500	Violon bleu 4. violin paint prov. 11-Jun-4 Claude Aguttes, Neuilly #202/R est:8000-10000
£4336	$7457	€6200	Pour Fahri avec communion plastique (25x25cm-10x10in) s.i. decoupage plexiglas. 4-Dec-3 Piasa, Paris #49/R est:2000-3000
£4362	$8027	€6500	Violon (72cm-28in) s.num.III/XXX multiple gilt pat bronze marble socle. 28-Mar-4 Anaf, Lyon #47/R est:7000-8000
£4545	$7818	€6500	Le cendrier de fahri (65x71cm-26x28in) cendrier fige resin white panel. 4-Dec-3 Piasa, Paris #28/R est:6000-8000
£4600	$8372	€6716	Violin (58cm-23in) s.i. num.9/20 blk brown pat bronze gold exec 2001. 4-Feb-4 Sotheby's, Olympia #161/R est:3000-5000
£4601	$7500	€6717	Nice, accumulation (96x58cm-38x23in) brass latches exec.c.1980-85. 23-Sep-3 Christie's, Rockefeller NY #180/R est:3000-5000
£4667	$8633	€7000	Uncomfortable (88x56x46cm-35x22x18in) s.st.f.Bocquel num.5/8 pat bronze exec.1984 prov. 18-Jul-4 Sotheby's, Paris #176/R est:8000-10000
£5000	$9250	€7500	S F chair (88x54x43cm-35x21x17in) s.st.f.Bocquel num.5/8 pat bronze exec.1984 prov. 18-Jul-4 Sotheby's, Paris #177/R est:8000-10000
£5245	$9021	€7500	Hygiene de la vision (48x26x27cm-19x10x11in) s.i.d.1960 assemblage vision instrument wood. 4-Dec-3 Piasa, Paris #39/R est:12000-15000
£5944	$10224	€8500	Portrait de famille (90x60x30cm-35x24x12in) s.i.d.1961-65 verso padlocks resin iron bowl chain board prov.lit. 4-Dec-3 Piasa, Paris #43/R est:8000-10000
£6000	$11100	€9000	Open space (182x90x46cm-72x35x18in) s.st.f.Bocquel num.5/8 pat bronze exec.1984 prov.exhib.lit. 18-Jul-4 Sotheby's, Paris #171/R est:10000-15000
£6133	$11224	€9200	Violon decoupee, hommage a Klein (66cm-26in) s. num.VI/IX violin pigment plexiglass. 6-Jun-4 Anaf, Lyon #310/R est:9000-10000
£6294	$10510	€9000	Accumulation de clefs (80x60x6cm-31x24x2in) s. keys plexiglas. 11-Oct-3 Cornette de St.Cyr, Paris #28/R est:12000-15000
£6500	$11830	€9490	U. (79x67x15cm-31x26x6in) paint brushes canvas in perspex exec 1989 exhib. 4-Feb-4 Sotheby's, Olympia #159/R est:3500-4500
£6500	$11765	€9490	Accumulation de pics (89x35x32cm-35x14x13in) welded iron cast 1979 prov. 1-Apr-4 Christie's, Kensington #212/R est:6000-8000
£6579	$12105	€9605	Violon coupe, EA 1/2 (67x25x10cm-26x10x4in) s. gold pat bronze sold with base. 23-Jun-4 Koller, Zurich #3204/R est:12000-18000 (S.FR 15000)
£6667	$12333	€10000	One day in Amsterdam (88x58x60cm-35x23x24in) s.st.f.Bocquel num.7/8 pat bronze exec.1984 prov. 18-Jul-4 Sotheby's, Paris #179/R est:10000-15000
£6993	$12028	€10000	Montres gousset et divers (32x20cm-13x8in) s.i. watch pieces plexiglas exec.c.1973. 4-Dec-3 Piasa, Paris #12/R est:6000-8000
£7000	$11130	€10150	Sans titre (70x50x45cm-28x20x18in) s. brown pat. bronze prov. 11-Sep-3 Christie's, Kensington #249/R est:5000-7000
£7000	$11130	€10150	Sans titre (69x50x45cm-27x20x18in) s. brown pat. bronze prov. 11-Sep-3 Christie's, Kensington #250/R est:5000-7000
£7000	$12950	€10500	Pompei's syndrome (88x58x65cm-35x23x26in) s.st.f.Bocquel num.8/8 pat bronze exec.1984 prov. 18-Jul-4 Sotheby's, Paris #178/R est:10000-15000
£7047	$12966	€10500	Togo (38x121x121cm-15x48x48in) s. ink serigraph on glass on table base exec 1997. 29-Mar-4 Cornette de St.Cyr, Paris #84/R est:10000-12000
£7483	$13395	€11000	Menagere (89x56x29cm-35x22x11in) s. pieces of violin in plexiglass. 19-Mar-4 Millon & Associes, Paris #195 est:6000-8000
£7586	$12138	€11000	Untitled (61x49x12cm-24x19x5in) s. trumpet on canvas oil exec 2002. 13-Mar-3 Galleria Pace, Milan #138/R est:11000-15000
£8000	$13360	€11680	Accumalation brisee (70x90x8cm-28x35x3in) s. broken plates plexiglas box prov. 22-Oct-3 Christie's, London #27/R est:8000-12000
£8367	$14978	€12300	Accumulation of ancient spears (76x28cm-30x11in) s.d.70 ancient bronze spears in plexiglass. 19-Mar-4 Millon & Associes, Paris #197/R est:6000-8000
£8392	$14266	€12000	Untitled (30x12x10cm-12x5x4in) s. napkin ring wooden box plexiglas prov. 25-Nov-3 Sotheby's, Milan #162/R est:13000-18000
£8562	$14555	€12500	Tubes and instruments (60x80cm-24x31in) s. oil tubes instrument. 7-Nov-3 Galleria Rosenberg, Milan #34/R est:12500
£8725	$16141	€13000	Composition (81x60x6cm-32x24x2in) s. painted violin oil canvas on board. 11-Mar-4 Galleria Pace, Milan #143/R est:16000-20000

£8725	$16141	€13000	Accumulation (80x60x6cm-31x24x2in) s. col tubes oil on canvas exec.2002. 11-Mar-4 Galleria Pace, Milan #145/R est:15000-19000
£8725	$15617	€13000	Untitled (128x36x3cm-50x14x1in) nails in 3 parts exec.1965 lit. 26-May-4 Christie's, Paris #83/R est:2000-3000
£8725	$15617	€13000	Puristic monochrome (114x78cm-45x31in) s. tubes of colour acrylic plexiglas. 25-May-4 Dorotheum, Vienna #410/R est:14000-16000
£8741	$15035	€12500	Roulements (27x34cm-11x13in) s.i.d.1960 stainless steel ballbearings canvas bag. 4-Dec-3 Piasa, Paris #11/R est:6000-8000
£9333	$17267	€14000	Horizontal catastrophe (101x140x66cm-40x55x26in) s.st.f.Bocquel num.5/8 pat bronze exec.1984 prov. 18-Jul-4 Sotheby's, Paris #175/R est:15000-20000
£9333	$16987	€14000	Untitled (101x41x41cm-40x16x16in) s. tubes acrylic plexiglas prov. 29-Jun-4 Cornette de St.Cyr, Paris #81/R est:15000-18000
£9427	$16969	€13763	Untitled (63x32x6cm-25x13x2in) s. violin in plexiglass. 26-Apr-4 Bukowskis, Stockholm #473/R est:80000-100000 (S.KR 130000)
£9500	$17480	€13870	Pour ma Jolie - guitar (94x46x15cm-37x18x6in) s. num. EA 2/2 bronze exec 1982 prov. 24-Jun-4 Sotheby's, London #255/R est:8000-12000
£9507	$16447	€13500	Accumulation de cles (45x39x53cm-18x15x21in) s.d.78 steel wood. 15-Dec-3 Marc Kohn, Paris #120/R est:12000-15000
£9790	$17621	€14293	Colour tubes (102x82x5cm-40x32x2in) s. assemblage canvas on panel in plexiglass. 26-Apr-4 Bukowskis, Stockholm #569/R est:60000-80000 (S.KR 135000)
£10000	$16700	€14500	Untitled (81x60x3cm-32x24x1in) s. violin oil on canvas exec.2003. 13-Nov-3 Galleria Pace, Milan #127/R est:16500
£10000	$18400	€14600	Accumulation of telephones (69x59x54cm-27x23x21in) bolted telephone receivers on wood base executed 1979 prov.exhib. 25-Jun-4 Christie's, London #134/R est:9000-12000
£10000	$18300	€15000	Sodage decoupee (85cm-33in) s. num.24/99 golden pat bronze exec. 2003. 6-Jun-4 Anaf, Lyon #311/R est:7000-8000
£10000	$18400	€15000	Untitled (73x54cm-29x21in) s. saxophone clarinet on painted canvas exec.2001. 12-Jun-4 Meeting Art, Vercelli #749/R est:10000
£10000	$18500	€15000	Grandfather's incineration (225x45x25cm-89x18x10in) s.st.f.Bocquel num.6/8 pat bronze exec.1984. 18-Jul-4 Sotheby's, Paris #173/R est:18000-25000
£10000	$18200	€14600	Accumulations de voilons decoupes (81x50cm-32x20in) s. fragmented violins plexiglas prov. 21-Jun-4 Bonhams, New Bond Street #85/R est:10000-15000
£10169	$18000	€14847	Hommage a Yves Klein (66x32x22cm-26x13x9in) s.num.32/99 col pigment violins plexiglas three. 28-Apr-4 Christie's, Rockefeller NY #255/R est:15000-20000
£10333	$18497	€15500	Razor blades (102x102cm-40x40in) s. razor blades. 16-May-4 Lombrail & Teucquam, Paris #185/R
£10490	$17833	€15000	Togo (121x121x38cm-48x48x15in) s. col ink serigraph inkwells panel glass table edition of 60. 25-Nov-3 Tajan, Paris #28/R est:10000-12000
£10490	$18042	€15000	Gutenberg (43x59x16cm-17x23x6in) s.d.70 typewriter pieces coffrage plexiglas. 4-Dec-3 Piasa, Paris #10/R est:8000-10000
£10667	$19413	€16000	Hommage a Yves Klein (66x32x21cm-26x13x8in) s. resin pigment. 29-Jun-4 Cornette de St.Cyr, Paris #154/R est:15000-20000
£10778	$18000	€15736	Hommage a Yves Klein (66x32x21cm-26x13x8in) s.num.26/99 pigment violins plexiglas three parts. 13-Nov-3 Sotheby's, New York #245/R est:12000-18000
£11173	$20000	€16313	Untitled, chanukka (40x66x60cm-16x26x24in) brass cast edition of nine prov. 14-May-4 Phillips, New York #264/R est:20000-30000
£11189	$19245	€16000	Sans titre (80x40x5cm-31x16x2in) s.d.1965 broken burnt violin plexiglas exhib. 4-Dec-3 Piasa, Paris #79/R est:12000-18000
£11888	$19853	€17000	Prisonnier cubiste (72x27x20cm-28x11x8in) s.num.1/2 gold pat bronze violin Cast Bocquel lit. 11-Oct-3 Cornette de St.Cyr, Paris #35/R est:12000-15000
£12000	$19080	€17400	Hommage a Yves Klein (66x32x21cm-26x13x8in) s.num.36/99 pigment on three violins in plexiglass. 11-Sep-3 Christie's, Kensington #251/R est:12000-18000
£12000	$21840	€17520	Hommage a Yves Klein (66x32x21cm-26x13x8in) i. num.10/99 pigment three violins in plexiglass exec 1992. 5-Feb-4 Christie's, London #158/R est:12000-16000
£12000	$21720	€17520	Colere de violon (90x58cm-35x23in) s. broken violins in plexiglass executed 1980 prov. 1-Apr-4 Christie's, Kensington #213/R est:4000-6000
£12000	$22080	€17520	Fragments selon les quantes (160x120x12cm-63x47x5in) s. chinese porcelain fragments in polyester resin prov. 24-Jun-4 Sotheby's, London #259/R est:10000-15000
£12195	$20000	€17805	Memorial Buffalo Bill (19x15x16cm-7x6x6in) s. paper targets in cube-shaped glass on wood base prov.exhib.lit. 28-May-3 Sotheby's, Amsterdam #81/R est:20000-25000
£12587	$21021	€18000	Colere d'acordeon (120x120x20cm-47x47x8in) accordion pieces plexiglas lit. 11-Oct-3 Cornette de St.Cyr, Paris #29/R est:25000-30000
£13194	$20847	€19000	Table basse aux violons (50x100x90cm-20x39x35in) s. num.EA1/2 welded bronzeviolins prov. 27-Apr-3 Versailles Encheres #97
£13287	$22189	€19000	40 kilos de non ferreux (100x50x12cm-39x20x5in) s. metal taps plexiglas lit. 11-Oct-3 Cornette de St.Cyr, Paris #79/R est:18000-22000
£13333	$24267	€20000	Violoncelles (73x106x106cm-29x42x42in) s. num.2/8 pat bronze glass lit. 29-Jun-4 Cornette de St.Cyr, Paris #72/R est:22000-25000
£13423	$24027	€20000	Violon japonais (25x25x25cm-10x10x10in) s.d.67 plastic violin prov.lit. 26-May-4 Christie's, Paris #84/R est:2500-3000
£13497	$22000	€19706	10,000 razor blades (190x190cm-75x75in) metal razor blades resin plexiglas prov.exhib. 23-Sep-3 Christie's, Rockefeller NY #186/R est:20000-30000
£13986	$24056	€20000	Poubelle organique, trash mash (45x45x20cm-18x18x8in) organic scrap plexiglas exhib. 4-Dec-3 Piasa, Paris #82/R est:6000-8000
£14000	$22260	€20300	Cello (120x120cm-47x47in) s.num.2/8 gold pat. wood bronze. 11-Sep-3 Christie's, Kensington #241/R est:15000-20000
£14000	$25760	€20440	Untitled (75x23x8cm-30x9x3in) s.d.67 broken violin resin plexiglas prov. 24-Jun-4 Sotheby's, London #264/R est:8000-12000
£14336	$24657	€20500	Successive et langoureuse (100x81cm-39x32in) s.i.d.1966 verso statue pieces black wood panel prov.exhib.lit. 4-Dec-3 Piasa, Paris #30/R est:15000-20000
£14371	$24000	€20982	Austerlitz's Sky (183x269cm-72x106in) sliced violins bows acrylic diptych canvas prov.exhib. 12-Nov-3 Christie's, Rockefeller NY #420/R est:30000-40000
£14667	$26987	€22000	La cote de Vailly (100x81cm-39x32in) s.i. paint tubes violin parts on canvas exec 1990. 8-Jun-4 Sotheby's, Amsterdam #128/R est:25000-35000
£14685	$25259	€21000	Poignard et lances (69x29cm-27x11in) s. bronze daggers plexiglas. 4-Dec-3 Piasa, Paris #88/R est:12000-15000
£14970	$25000	€21856	Violin table base (39x117x103cm-15x46x41in) s.num.1/2 welded gold pat bronze st.f. prov. 13-Nov-3 Sotheby's, New York #242/R est:30000-40000
£15000	$27300	€21900	A chacun son du (150x120x12cm-59x47x5in) s. Chinese porcelain fragments resin plexiglas prov. 6-Feb-4 Sotheby's, London #228/R est:10000-15000
£15000	$27150	€21900	La femme markee (84x35x48cm-33x14x19in) encased polyester resin exec 1995 prov. 1-Apr-4 Christie's, Kensington #217/R est:8000-12000
£15385	$25692	€22000	Five o'clock tea (103x50x45cm-41x20x18in) s.num.4/8 green pat bronze metal argente Cast Art Bonvicini lit. 11-Oct-3 Cornette de St.Cyr, Paris #30/R est:20000-30000
£15436	$27322	€23000	Soleil bleu (120x90x12cm-47x35x5in) s. fragments Chinese porcelain in resin exec 1989 prov.exhib. 28-Apr-4 Artcurial Briest, Paris #351/R est:15000-20000
£16000	$29440	€23360	Successivement - Arman's orchestra (129x86x53cm-51x34x21in) incised sig.num.5/8 welded bronze cellos prov.exhib.lit. 25-Jun-4 Christie's, London #137/R est:12000-15000
£16667	$30333	€25000	Shoes (141x110x9cm-56x43x4in) s. shoes plexiglas prov. 29-Jun-4 Cornette de St.Cyr, Paris #54/R est:25000-30000
£16783	$28867	€24000	Humour noir (84x29x7cm-33x11x3in) s.d.66 burnt violin plexiglas. 4-Dec-3 Piasa, Paris #78/R est:12000-18000
£17450	$31235	€26000	Brume orange (160x120x9cm-63x47x4in) paint pots mixed media plexiglas exec.1969 prov. 25-May-4 Sotheby's, Milan #199/R est:20000-25000
£17483	$30070	€25000	Sans titre (59x59x12cm-23x23x5in) s.i.d.68 compressed col tubes 4 plaques 5 butterfly screws. 4-Dec-3 Piasa, Paris #83/R est:10000-15000
£18000	$33300	€27000	Table saxo et violoncelle (50x98x70cm-20x39x28in) s.st.f.Bocquel num.8/8 bronze glass exec.1996 prov. 18-Jul-4 Sotheby's, Paris #200/R est:15000-18000
£18531	$30948	€26500	Accumulation de tubes (152x122cm-60x48in) s.verso paint tubes on canvas. 11-Oct-3 Cornette de St.Cyr, Paris #33/R est:25000-30000
£18792	$33261	€28000	Colere de violon (74x45cm-29x18in) s.d.71 broken violin in plexiglass. 28-Apr-4 Artcurial Briest, Paris #361/R est:25000-30000
£20270	$38311	€30000	Hommage a Yves Klein (66x32x21cm-26x13x8in) s. multiple resin pigment edition of 99. 21-Feb-4 Cornette de St.Cyr, Paris #240/R est:15000-20000
£20280	$34881	€29000	It works (127x80cm-50x31in) s. i.verso metal prisms plastic prov.exhib.lit. 4-Dec-3 Piasa, Paris #57/R est:25000-35000
£20979	$36084	€30000	Sans titre (65x153cm-26x60in) s.d.62 paint cut statue black panel wood lit. 4-Dec-3 Piasa, Paris #89/R est:15000-20000
£20980	$35665	€30000	Black Indian invasion (148x183x5cm-58x72x2in) s. black col Indian ink bottle polyester plexiglas prov.exhib.lit. 25-Nov-3 Tajan, Paris #26/R est:28000-32000
£22028	$36787	€31500	Venus aux pinceaux (42x55x57cm-17x22x22in) s. num.1/4 pat bronze lit. 29-Jun-3 Versailles Encheres #185/R
£23077	$39692	€33000	Clic-clac rate (80x100cm-31x39in) s.d.1963 photo soufflet fragments wood panel prov.exhib.lit. 4-Dec-3 Piasa, Paris #14/R est:18000-22000
£23776	$40895	€34000	La fin des traditions (200x160cm-79x63in) s. broken clock pieces plexiglas prov. 4-Dec-3 Piasa, Paris #23/R est:40000-60000
£24476	$40874	€35000	Venus aux telephones (160x58x12cm-63x23x5in) s. dark pat bronze silver edition of 8 lit. 11-Oct-3 Cornette de St.Cyr, Paris #31/R est:35000-40000
£24476	$40874	€35000	Sided (122x70x26cm-48x28x10in) s. gold pat bronze violoncelle edition of 8 lit. 11-Oct-3 Cornette de St.Cyr, Paris #38/R est:35000-45000
£24667	$45387	€37000	Diana, Noli me Tangere (178x80x50cm-70x31x20in) s. num.EA 3/3 cut soldered bronze Cast Bocquel prov.lit. 8-Jun-4 Artcurial Briest, Paris #236a/R est:40000-50000
£25001	$44001	€37000	U. (180x55cm-71x22in) collection medical ampoules in plastic exec 1962 prov.lit. 18-May-4 Tajan, Paris #76/R est:40000-50000
£25694	$42910	€37000	Venus au violon (149x80x30cm-59x31x12in) s. green pat bronze violin edition of 8. 25-Oct-3 Cornette de St.Cyr, Paris #572/R est:35000-40000
£26536	$47500	€38743	Violin table (74x152x71cm-29x60x28in) sig. bronze glass top exec 2000 prov. 13-May-4 Sotheby's, New York #208/R est:30000-40000
£26667	$49333	€40000	Tous azimuts (200x130x120cm-79x51x47in) welded iron exec.1980 prov.exhib.lit. 18-Jul-4 Sotheby's, Paris #153/R est:40000-60000
£26667	$49333	€40000	Feu Louis XV (89x122x68cm-35x48x27in) s.d.85 num.5/8 pat bronze prov.exhib.lit. 18-Jul-4 Sotheby's, Paris #266/R est:40000-60000
£27972	$46713	€40000	Prisonnier, violoncelle (130x80x130cm-51x31x51in) s.num.2/2 gold pat bronze violoncelle. 11-Oct-3 Cornette de St.Cyr, Paris #36/R est:40000-50000
£28000	$51800	€42000	Table violoncelles (70x85x90cm-28x33x35in) s.st.f.Bocquel num.4/8 bronze glass exec.1993 prov. 18-Jul-4 Sotheby's, Paris #211/R est:25000-35000
£32000	$59200	€48000	Renault Osaka 17 (240x240cm-94x94in) air filters plexiglas exec.1969 prov.exhib. 18-Jul-4 Sotheby's, Paris #258/R est:50000-70000
£34965	$60140	€50000	Miles Davis fossili (175x116cm-69x46in) trumpet pieces concrete prov.exhib. 4-Dec-3 Piasa, Paris #19/R est:40000-60000
£37583	$69154	€56000	Vibrations (187x163cm-74x64in) s. watch parts in resin exec 1972 exhib. 29-Mar-4 Cornette de St.Cyr, Paris #114/R est:45000-50000
£38462	$66154	€55000	La mort d'Arlequin (120x90cm-47x35in) s.d.1962 smashed guitar wood panel prov.exhib.lit. 4-Dec-3 Piasa, Paris #31/R est:15000-20000
£42667	$78933	€64000	Icones (190x160x17cm-75x63x7in) wood copper exec.1996 prov.exhib. 18-Jul-4 Sotheby's, Paris #257/R est:60000-80000
£43357	$74573	€62000	Contrebasse (200x160cm-79x63in) broken burnt double bass coffrage plexiglas. 4-Dec-3 Piasa, Paris #51/R est:40000-60000
£43624	$78087	€65000	Cimabue (200x159x22cm-79x63x9in) s.d.70 resin polyester tar cello. 26-May-4 Christie's, Paris #85/R est:40000-60000
£55944	$96224	€80000	End of romanticism (173x121cm-68x48in) s. broken guitars coffrage black wood box prov.exhib. 4-Dec-3 Piasa, Paris #47/R est:40000-60000
£71856	$120000	€104910	Counterpoint for cellos (396x142x117cm-156x56x46in) cast welded bronze prov. 13-Nov-3 Sotheby's, New York #243/R est:100000-150000
£80000	$148000	€120000	Turbeau (350x250cm-138x98in) bronze exec.1987 prov.exhib.lit. 18-Jul-4 Sotheby's, Paris #152/R est:120000-150000
Works on paper			
£747	$1323	€1091	Sliced Arman paint box (90x70cm-35x28in) s. collage with black background. 27-Apr-4 AB Stockholms Auktionsverk #1160/R (S.KR 10200)
£755	$1284	€1102	Calligraphie de violon (43x31cm-17x12in) s.d.1970 Indian ink prov. 5-Nov-3 AB Stockholms Auktionsverk #1131/R (S.KR 10000)
£769	$1323	€1100	Iris (13x16cm-5x6in) collage green cardboard. 4-Dec-3 Piasa, Paris #66/R
£805	$1498	€1200	Cachet (18x12cm-7x5in) s. ink executed 1958 lit. 3-Mar-4 Tajan, Paris #212/R
£903	$1507	€1300	Violons (48x31cm-19x12in) s.i. Indian ink prov. 21-Oct-3 Artcurial Briest, Paris #532 est:800-1200
£1111	$1855	€1600	Sans titre (61x46cm-24x18in) s.i.d.68 Indian ink glycerol. 21-Oct-3 Artcurial Briest, Paris #597 est:1000-1500
£1111	$1855	€1600	Sans titre (61x50cm-24x20in) s.d.68 blk Indian ink. 21-Oct-3 Artcurial Briest, Paris #599 est:1000-1500
£1111	$1855	€1600	Sans titre (61x50cm-24x20in) s.d.68 gouache glycerol paint. 21-Oct-3 Artcurial Briest, Paris #601 est:1000-1500
£1111	$1855	€1600	Sans titre (57x47cm-22x19in) s.dd.68 blk Indian ink. 21-Oct-3 Artcurial Briest, Paris #602/R est:1000-1500
£1200	$2208	€1800	Toucher (20x26cm-8x10in) s. mixed media exec.1998. 12-Jun-4 Meeting Art, Vercelli #350/R est:1500
£1250	$2088	€1800	26 tubes et coulures (61x50cm-24x20in) s.d.68 Indian ink paint glycerol. 21-Oct-3 Artcurial Briest, Paris #598 est:1200-1500
£1389	$2320	€2000	Marteaux (65x50cm-26x20in) s. Indian ink W/C. 21-Oct-3 Artcurial Briest, Paris #590/R est:1500-2000
£1554	$2937	€2300	Explosion (49x65cm-19x26in) s. mixed media collage. 21-Feb-4 Cornette de St.Cyr, Paris #241 est:2500-3000
£1596	$2666	€2300	Sans titre (61x50cm-24x20in) s.d.68 Indian ink silver spray. 21-Oct-3 Artcurial Briest, Paris #600/R est:1200-1500
£1736	$2899	€2500	5 Violons en noir et blanc (64x48cm-25x19in) s.i.d.69 Indian ink gouache. 21-Oct-3 Artcurial Briest, Paris #603 est:1500-2000
£1806	$3016	€2600	Sans titre (60x48cm-24x19in) s.d.69 Indian ink glycerol. 21-Oct-3 Artcurial Briest, Paris #604 est:1500-2000
£1829	$3000	€2670	Calligraphie de violon (34x54cm-13x21in) s. ink printed music paper prov.exhib. 28-May-3 Sotheby's, Amsterdam #152/R est:3000-4000
£2000	$3680	€3000	Composition (41x29cm-16x11in) s. gouache exec.2002. 12-Jun-4 Meeting Art, Vercelli #850/R est:3000
£2013	$3685	€3000	Pinces (65x50cm-26x20in) s. gouache ink crayon Canson paper exec 1976. 7-Jul-4 Artcurial Briest, Paris #208 est:1500-2000
£2081	$3476	€3038	Sans titre (63x48cm-25x19in) s.d.1963 mixed media prov. 24-Jun-3 Germann, Zurich #6/R est:2300-3500 (S.FR 4600)

£2083	$3479	€3000	7 violons (74x54cm-29x21in) s. Indian ink ink wash. 21-Oct-3 Artcurial Briest, Paris #605/R est:1000-1500
£2238	$3849	€3200	Allure d'objects (104x72cm-41x28in) s.d.60 ink paper on cardboard. 4-Dec-3 Piasa, Paris #55/R est:3500-4000
£2639	$4407	€3800	Sans titre (75x109cm-30x43in) s. Indian ink gouache. 21-Oct-3 Artcurial Briest, Paris #604a est:1000-1500
£2667	$4906	€4000	Coloured tubes (100x100cm-39x39in) s. col tubes in resin exec 1973 prov.lit. 9-Jun-4 Artcurial Briest, Paris #478/R est:25000-30000
£2684	$4751	€4000	Eclisses de violons (64x50cm-25x20in) s.d.71 Indian ink gouache exec 1971. 28-Apr-4 Artcurial Briest, Paris #365/R est:1500-2000
£2800	$5152	€4088	La lune en Rodage (22x21cm-9x8in) s.d.1959 ink g prov. 24-Jun-4 Sotheby's, Olympia #495/R est:2000-3000
£5797	$9507	€8000	Jour et nuit (44x30cm-17x12in) s. d.1996 verso collage paint-tubes oil. 27-May-3 Sotheby's, Amsterdam #423/R est:10000-12000
£7343	$12629	€10500	Cachet (77x54cm-30x21in) s.i.d.verso ink stamp paper on canvas. 4-Dec-3 Piasa, Paris #56/R est:4000-6000
£10140	$17441	€14500	Le manifeste (39x29cm-15x11in) s.d.66 press cuttings plexiglas. 4-Dec-3 Piasa, Paris #1/R est:8000-12000
£13000	$23920	€18980	Untitled (120x90cm-47x35in) s. golf tees polyester resin plexiglass exec 1989 prov. 24-Jun-4 Sotheby's, London #158/R est:8000-12000
£18056	$30153	€26000	Etres de neige (180x210cm-71x83in) s. paint brushes acrylic on double canvas exec 1987-1988 prov. 21-Oct-3 Artcurial Briest, Paris #544/R est:28000-32000
£18182	$31273	€26000	What happened to the flowers (92x92cm-36x36in) s. Andy Warhol lithograph fragments plexiglas prov. 4-Dec-3 Piasa, Paris #40/R est:10000-15000
£25676	$45189	€38000	Untitled (200x30cm-79x12in) s. polishing machine assemblage acrylic canvas on board exec.1988. 22-May-4 Galleria Pananti, Florence #505/R est:17000-19000
£28000	$51520	€42000	Filles de camaret (200x140cm-79x55in) s.d.62 metallic springs on red painted wood prov.exhib.lit. 8-Jun-4 Sotheby's, Amsterdam #99/R est:30000-45000

ARMAN, Leopold (20th C) Venezuelan?

£555	$905	€810	Intimacy (140x100cm-55x39in) s. acrylic painted 1997. 20-Jul-3 Subastas Odalys, Caracas #124

ARMAND-DUMARESQ, Edouard Charles (1826-1895) French

£9869	$18158	€15000	Scene pastorale (220x189cm-87x74in) 24-Jun-4 Tajan, Paris #75/R est:10000-15000

ARMANDO (1929-) Dutch

£1600	$2864	€2400	Untitled (50x65cm-20x26in) s.d.12/53 graphite col chks. 15-May-4 Van Ham, Cologne #413/R est:1000
£2667	$4907	€4000	Fahne - flag (80x100cm-31x39in) i.d.1984 s.i.d.stretcher prov. 9-Jun-4 Christie's, Amsterdam #373/R est:4000-6000
£4000	$7360	€6000	Gefechtsfeld (165x225cm-65x89in) s.i.d.27/10/85 stretcher prov. 9-Jun-4 Christie's, Amsterdam #372/R est:6000-8000
£4367	$8035	€6376	Untitled (92x122cm-36x48in) s.d.1958 verso. 8-Jun-4 Germann, Zurich #115/R est:11000-13000 (S.FR 10000)
£10000	$18400	€15000	Peinture (80x100cm-31x39in) s.d.4/60 verso oil nails prov. 8-Jun-4 Sotheby's, Amsterdam #100/R est:20000-30000
£11189	$19245	€16000	Seestuck (200x200cm-79x79in) s.i.d.1986 stretcher acrylic. 2-Dec-3 Sotheby's, Amsterdam #178/R est:15000-20000
£15385	$26154	€22000	Blue cloud (180x160cm-71x63in) s.d.2002 i.verso lit. 24-Nov-3 Glerum, Amsterdam #284/R est:22000-24000
Sculpture			
£1119	$1902	€1600	Head (13cm-5in) s.d.95 num.2/3 verso bronze conceived 1995 prov.exhib. 25-Nov-3 Christie's, Amsterdam #148/R est:1500-2000
Works on paper			
£2098	$3566	€3000	Untitled - series of six drawings (18x13cm-7x5in) all init.d.81 pencil six. 25-Nov-3 Christie's, Amsterdam #313/R est:2500-3500

ARMAS, Enrico (1957-) Venezuelan

£367	$675	€551	Red wood (81x100cm-32x39in) s. acrylic. 27-Jun-4 Subastas Odalys, Caracas #128
£802	$1460	€1203	Art today (99x140cm-39x55in) s. acrylic painted 2003. 21-Jun-4 Subastas Odalys, Caracas #73
£825	$1345	€1205	Yellow dusk (100x140cm-39x55in) s. acrylic painted 2001. 28-Sep-3 Subastas Odalys, Caracas #27/R
£915	$1665	€1373	Golden blue (130x190cm-51x75in) s. acrylic painted 2003. 21-Jun-4 Subastas Odalys, Caracas #31
£1381	$2375	€2016	Untitled (134x235cm-53x93in) s. 7-Dec-3 Subastas Odalys, Caracas #53

ARMBREST, Duncan (20th C) Canadian

£260	$476	€380	Muskoka (21x26cm-8x10in) s.i. panel prov. 1-Jun-4 Hodgins, Calgary #414/R (C.D 650)

ARMEILLE DEMARLE (20th C) French

£433	$780	€650	Nu allonge au chapeau (46x55cm-18x22in) s.d.1925. 20-Apr-4 Chenu & Scrive, Lyon #72/R

ARMENISE, Raffaello (1852-1925) Italian

£2727	$4691	€3900	Cave by the sea (26x41cm-10x16in) s.i. board. 3-Dec-3 Stadion, Trieste #1110/R est:1000-1500
£9396	$16631	€14000	Back from pasture (64x100cm-25x39in) s. i.verso lit. 1-May-4 Meeting Art, Vercelli #478 est:10000

ARMESTO, Alvarez Primitivo (19th C) Spanish

£2660	$4441	€3750	Young girl (66x50cm-26x20in) s. 23-Jun-3 Durán, Madrid #219/R est:1800
£3014	$5123	€4400	Ducks on pond (86x138cm-34x54in) s. 4-Nov-3 Ansorena, Madrid #48/R est:4400

ARMET Y PORTANEL, Jose (1843-1911) Spanish

£671	$1201	€1000	Landscape (20x32cm-8x13in) s. 25-May-4 Durán, Madrid #638/R
£7919	$14730	€11800	Seascape (68x117cm-27x46in) s. 2-Mar-4 Ansorena, Madrid #73/R est:10800
£8696	$14261	€12000	Coastal landscape (68x117cm-27x46in) s. exhib. 27-May-3 Durán, Madrid #272/R est:10000
£8725	$16228	€13000	Landscape (71x141cm-28x56in) s. 2-Mar-4 Ansorena, Madrid #59/R est:13000
£14384	$24452	€21000	Harbour (65x81cm-26x32in) s. 4-Nov-3 Ansorena, Madrid #355/R est:21000

ARMET, Jose (19th C) Spanish

£751	$1300	€1096	Men at a table (25x36cm-10x14in) s. 10-Dec-3 Alderfer's, Hatfield #289/R est:800-1000

ARMFELT, George (20th C) British?

£280	$518	€409	Group of mice with a truckle of cheese (17x25cm-7x10in) panel prov. 11-Feb-4 Cheffins, Cambridge #445/R

ARMFIELD, Diana (1920-) British

£300	$501	€438	St Julia over the ploughed field (20x25cm-8x10in) init. board. 16-Oct-3 Christie's, Kensington #361
£390	$651	€569	Dog on the shore, Cardigan Bay (18x23cm-7x9in) init. board prov. 14-Oct-3 Rosebery Fine Art, London #452
£500	$920	€730	Vineyard, South of France (18x23cm-7x9in) init. board. 24-Mar-4 Hamptons Fine Art, Godalming #306/R
£600	$1020	€876	Home from the train, Kew (23x28cm-9x11in) init. canvas on board. 26-Nov-3 Hamptons Fine Art, Godalming #154
£600	$1062	€876	French hillside (18x24cm-7x9in) init. canvas on board. 27-Apr-4 Bonhams, Knightsbridge #212/R
£720	$1310	€1051	Barn, Tagliocozzo (26x28cm-10x11in) init. canvas on board prov. 15-Jun-4 Bonhams, Knightsbridge #25/R
£1000	$1820	€1460	St Felix - Lauragais (28x35cm-11x14in) init. board prov. 1-Jul-4 Christie's, Kensington #273/R est:600-800
£1800	$3006	€2628	Primroses from Meifod, north Wales (21x25cm-8x10in) init. i.verso board prov. 16-Oct-3 Christie's, Kensington #358 est:1000-1500
£1800	$3330	€2628	Marigolds with other flowers (30x23cm-12x9in) init. board. 11-Feb-4 Sotheby's, Olympia #196/R est:1500-2000
Works on paper			
£620	$1141	€905	Venice (24x18cm-9x7in) init. pastel. 24-Mar-4 Hamptons Fine Art, Godalming #249/R
£620	$1128	€905	Candles in San Marco (28x23cm-11x9in) pastel. 19-Jun-4 Lacy Scott, Bury St.Edmunds #381/R

ARMFIELD, Edward (19th C) British

£290	$493	€423	Puppies at play in a hay barn (90x69cm-35x27in) s. 4-Nov-3 Peter Webb, Auckland #235/R (NZ.D 800)
£300	$546	€438	Gun dog with a partridge (28x38cm-11x15in) s.d.1869. 29-Jun-4 Bonhams, Knowle #94
£308	$524	€450	Hunting dogs with game (89x70cm-35x28in) s. 4-Nov-3 Peter Webb, Auckland #232/R (NZ.D 850)
£360	$619	€526	Terriers rabbiting (30x41cm-12x16in) 2-Dec-3 Gorringes, Lewes #2237
£360	$644	€526	Head of a terrier (20x18cm-8x7in) init. board. 7-May-4 Mallams, Oxford #410
£400	$728	€584	Terriers ratting in a barn (31x41cm-12x16in) s. 1-Jul-4 Mellors & Kirk, Nottingham #771/R
£455	$805	€664	Three terriers with their quarry (39x29cm-15x11in) s. 3-May-4 Lawson Menzies, Sydney #401 (A.D 1100)
£550	$990	€803	Chasing the fox (30x35cm-12x14in) s.d.1851. 21-Jan-4 Sotheby's, Olympia #321/R
£600	$1116	€876	Figures in a river landscape (50x76cm-20x30in) s. 4-Mar-4 Christie's, Kensington #468/R
£600	$1098	€876	An audacious thief (30x40cm-12x16in) s. 8-Apr-4 Christie's, Kensington #139/R
£700	$1288	€1022	Gundogs on the scent. Dogs hunting in shrubland (10x26cm-4x10in) panel pair. 10-Jun-4 Christie's, Kensington #401/R
£900	$1656	€1314	Spaniels flushing a pheasant (30x41cm-12x16in) s. 10-Jun-4 Christie's, Kensington #400/R
£950	$1729	€1387	Terriers in a barn with a caged rat (30x40cm-12x16in) 1-Jul-4 Mellors & Kirk, Nottingham #782/R
£980	$1774	€1431	Terriers around a trapped rat (19x24cm-7x9in) s. pair. 30-Mar-4 Sworder & Son, Bishops Stortford #538/R
£1000	$1870	€1460	Three terriers in a barn, rats in a cage (48x74cm-19x29in) init. 27-Feb-4 Thomson, Roddick & Medcalf, Carlisle #254
£1000	$1810	€1460	Four terriers ratting in a barn (38x28cm-15x11in) s. 16-Apr-4 Keys, Aylsham #746/R est:700-900
£1200	$2208	€1752	Terriers ratting in a barn (49x59cm-19x23in) 10-Jun-4 Christie's, Kensington #368/R est:1500-2000
£1500	$2655	€2190	Day's bag (91x71cm-36x28in) s. 28-Apr-4 Halls, Shrewsbury #493/R est:1500-2000
£1600	$2720	€2336	Terriers ratting. Terriers in a barn (30x41cm-12x16in) s. pair. 27-Nov-3 Christie's, Kensington #315/R est:1500-2000
£1800	$3312	€2628	Rat trap. Hot pot (41x61cm-16x24in) s. pair. 10-Jun-4 Christie's, Kensington #369/R est:2000-3000
£1900	$3496	€2774	Terriers at a rabbit hole. Terriers ratting in a barn (51x76cm-20x30in) s. pair. 10-Jun-4 Christie's, Kensington #389/R est:2000-3000
£2700	$4968	€3942	In a stable. At the end of the day (41x61cm-16x24in) s. pair. 24-Mar-4 Hamptons Fine Art, Godalming #311/R

ARMFIELD, Edward (attrib) (19th C) British

£500	$885	€730	Four terriers in a cottage interior (49x60cm-19x24in) 28-Apr-4 Peter Wilson, Nantwich #79
£989	$1800	€1444	Drunken dog (46x36cm-18x14in) indis.i. 7-Feb-4 Neal Auction Company, New Orleans #473/R est:2500-3500

ARMFIELD, G (fl.1840-1875) British

£2300	$4209	€3358	Terriers in a barn, one looking down a rat hole, other lying on a barrel (28x38cm-11x15in) s. 28-Jan-4 Wintertons, Lichfield #388 est:1500-2500

ARMFIELD, George (fl.1840-1875) British

£280	$501	€420	Three Fox-Terriers playing with mouse (30x40cm-12x16in) 11-May-4 Christie's, Paris #213/R
£320	$573	€467	Angler in a river landscape (18x25cm-7x10in) s. 18-Mar-4 Christie's, Kensington #572/R
£420	$664	€609	Terriers ratting (17x22cm-7x9in) s. board. 24-Jul-3 Lawrence, Crewkerne #942

£450	$752	€657	Fox watching rabbits (52x61cm-20x24in) 11-Nov-3 Bonhams, Knightsbridge #188/R
£500	$860	€730	Terriers on a rabbit warren (14x19cm-6x7in) s.d.1854 board. 4-Dec-3 Mellors & Kirk, Nottingham #946
£520	$832	€759	Woodland scene with fox and two terrier dogs (30x38cm-12x15in) s. 8-Jan-3 Biddle & Webb, Birmingham #853
£549	$1000	€824	Two terriers in a barn waiting at a rat hole (28x38cm-11x15in) s. 16-Jun-4 Wolf's, New York #487279/R
£600	$948	€870	Off the Isle of Wight (20x30cm-8x12in) s. i.verso. 4-Sep-3 Christie's, Kensington #195/R
£676	$1251	€987	Landscape with horses and pigeons (55x76cm-22x30in) s. 15-Mar-4 Rasmussen, Vejle #114 (D.KR 7500)
£750	$1380	€1095	Gone to ground (15x20cm-6x8in) s. 10-Jun-4 Christie's, Kensington #384/R
£800	$1472	€1168	Three hungry terriers waiting by a bowl (31x41cm-12x16in) s. 10-Jun-4 Christie's, Kensington #417
£898	$1671	€1311	Dogs on their own in the workshop (51x61cm-20x24in) s. 2-Mar-4 Rasmussen, Copenhagen #1604/R (D.KR 10000)
£900	$1530	€1314	Terriers ratting (25x30cm-10x12in) s. 27-Nov-3 Christie's, Kensington #314/R
£950	$1748	€1387	Terriers ratting in a barn. Terriers at a rabbit hole (15x20cm-6x8in) board pair. 10-Jun-4 Christie's, Kensington #388/R
£1100	$1892	€1606	Terriers ratting in a barn (64x76cm-25x30in) s. 2-Dec-3 Gorringes, Lewes #2377/R est:1000-1500
£1200	$2244	€1752	Two spaniels flushing a cock pheasant from the undergrowth (31x36cm-12x14in) 22-Jul-4 Tennants, Leyburn #858 est:1200-1400
£1300	$2392	€1898	Bounty the flirt, two terriers and a spaniel at play (29x35cm-11x14in) s.i.d.1871 prov. 29-Mar-4 Thomson Roddick & Medcalf, Edinburgh #211 est:1000-1500
£1357	$2267	€1981	Terriers ratting (50x61cm-20x24in) s. 17-Nov-3 Waddingtons, Toronto #105/R est:2000-3000 (C.D 3000)
£1381	$2500	€2016	Hot on his heels (25x30cm-10x12in) 30-Mar-4 Bonhams & Butterfields, San Francisco #42/R est:2500-3500
£1486	$2750	€2170	Terriers ratting (30x41cm-12x16in) one s. pair. 10-Feb-4 Sotheby's, New York #249/R est:1500-2500
£1550	$2449	€2263	Patiently waiting, two terriers in a landscape (48x73cm-19x29in) s. 23-Jul-3 Hampton & Littlewood, Exeter #451/R est:600-800
£1863	$3000	€2720	Flushing the pheasant (46x61cm-18x24in) s. stretcher. 20-Aug-3 James Julia, Fairfield #637/R est:4000-8000
£1900	$3496	€2774	Hounds and terriers in a baronial hall (71x91cm-28x36in) 10-Jun-4 Christie's, Kensington #367/R est:2000-3000
£1934	$3500	€2824	Dogs hunting pheasant (46x61cm-18x24in) s,. 3-Apr-4 Neal Auction Company, New Orleans #602/R est:5000-8000
£2179	$3900	€3181	Horse, dogs and game fowl (64x76cm-25x30in) s. 16-May-4 CRN Auctions, Cambridge #53/R
£2200	$3938	€3212	Gamekeeper's dog (43x53cm-17x21in) s.d.1867. 26-May-4 Sotheby's, Olympia #109/R est:800-1200
£2210	$4000	€3227	Terriers approaching a fox in a wooded landscape (51x61cm-20x24in) s.d.1865. 30-Mar-4 Bonhams & Butterfields, San Francisco #34/R est:3800-4500
£2400	$4368	€3504	Cottage interior with terriers, and caged rabbit (23x30cm-9x12in) s. 4-Feb-4 Goldings, Lincolnshire #491/R
£2432	$4500	€3551	Terriers ratting (46x61cm-18x24in) s. bears d.188. 10-Feb-4 Doyle, New York #200/R est:3000-5000
£2700	$4266	€3915	Gundogs resting (14x19cm-6x7in) s. board. 24-Jul-3 Lawrence, Crewkerne #944/R est:800-1200
£2762	$5000	€4033	Waiting to go out. Cornered (51x51cm-20x20in) pair. 30-Mar-4 Bonhams & Butterfields, San Francisco #49/R est:5500-8000
£3867	$7000	€5646	Spaniels putting up pheasant (41x56cm-16x22in) 30-Mar-4 Bonhams & Butterfields, San Francisco #43/R est:5500-7500
£3867	$7000	€5646	Good companions (23x30cm-9x12in) s.d.1864. 30-Mar-4 Bonhams & Butterfields, San Francisco #52/R est:4500-6000
£4143	$7500	€6049	Manchester terrier in a landscape (65x78cm-26x31in) 30-Mar-4 Bonhams & Butterfields, San Francisco #35/R est:6000-8000
£4143	$7500	€6049	Sportsman's companions (41x53cm-16x21in) s. 30-Mar-4 Bonhams & Butterfields, San Francisco #45/R est:6500-8000

ARMFIELD, George (attrib) (fl.1840-1875) British

£310	$570	€453	Terriers in a barn near upturned bucket (21x29cm-8x11in) board. 24-Jun-4 Olivers, Sudbury #119/R
£600	$1020	€876	Terriers chasing a rabbit (22x27cm-9x11in) canvas on board. 27-Nov-3 Christie's, Kensington #312/R
£815	$1500	€1190	Three terriers ratting (41x61cm-16x24in) s. 25-Jun-4 Freeman, Philadelphia #317/R est:1000-1500
£850	$1352	€1241	Two terriers chasing a rabbit (24x29cm-9x11in) 18-Mar-3 Anderson & Garland, Newcastle #554/R
£1156	$1999	€1688	Resting before the hunt (70x91cm-28x36in) 9-Dec-3 Pinneys, Montreal #53/R est:3000-4000 (C.D 2600)
£1500	$2790	€2190	Spaniels in interior with brace of pheasant (34x44cm-13x17in) 2-Mar-4 Bearnes, Exeter #406/R est:800-1200
£2000	$3440	€2920	Foxterriers in the stable (49x61cm-19x24in) s. 3-Dec-3 AB Stockholms Auktionsverk #2539/R est:18000-20000 (S.KR 26000)

ARMFIELD, Maxwell (1882-1972) British

£4624	$8000	€6751	Oedipus and the sphinx (34x24cm-13x9in) tempera board. 11-Dec-3 Sotheby's, New York #1/R est:8000-12000
£56000	$92960	€81760	Madison Square Park, New York (86x76cm-34x30in) mono.i. lit. 30-Sep-3 Sotheby's, London #352/R est:25000-35000
Works on paper			
£400	$692	€584	Hips in a Jar (30x25cm-12x10in) pencil W/C. 10-Dec-3 Bonhams, Bury St Edmunds #540/R
£700	$1113	€1022	Seeds, study for a still life (28x23cm-11x9in) i. pencil W/C pair exhib. 10-Sep-3 Sotheby's, Olympia #132/R

ARMFIELD, Stuart (1916-2000) British

£270	$483	€394	Impressionist Cornish landscape with daffodils in the foreground (42x74cm-17x29in) s. board. 16-Mar-4 Gildings, Market Harborough #462
£400	$732	€584	Still life for the Sixties (49x90cm-19x35in) s. egg tempera panel. 7-Apr-4 Woolley & Wallis, Salisbury #331/R
£400	$732	€584	Mushrooms (30x90cm-12x35in) s. board prov. 7-Jul-4 Cheffins, Cambridge #127
£520	$884	€759	Sea shore still life no 9 (49x75cm-19x30in) s. tempera board. 25-Nov-3 Bonhams, Knowle #219
£660	$1122	€964	Gulls on a harbour wall (49x75cm-19x30in) s. tempera board. 25-Nov-3 Bonhams, Knowle #220
£2700	$5022	€3942	Cornish farm, ducks and waterwheel (45x59cm-18x23in) s. tempera board. 2-Mar-4 Bearnes, Exeter #325/R est:1000-1500
Works on paper			
£600	$1092	€876	Arum lilies by a window (72x48cm-28x19in) s. W/C. 15-Jun-4 Bonhams, Knightsbridge #80/R

ARMIN, Emil (1883-1971) American

£588	$1000	€858	Still life of flowers (51x41cm-20x16in) s.d.1927 exhib. 22-Nov-3 Jackson's, Cedar Falls #91/R est:500-700

ARMINGTON, Frank Milton (1876-1941) Canadian

£1250	$2150	€1825	Southern part of Jerusalem from the Mount of Olives (32x40cm-13x16in) s.d.1938. 2-Dec-3 Joyner Waddington, Toronto #373/R est:2000-3000 (C.D 2800)
£1250	$2150	€1825	Beside Galillee, Palestine (32x40cm-13x16in) s.d.1938. 2-Dec-3 Joyner Waddington, Toronto #374/R est:2000-3000 (C.D 2800)
£2000	$3660	€2920	Jardin du Luxembourg, Paris (22x27cm-9x11in) s.d.1923 panel. 1-Jun-4 Joyner Waddington, Toronto #495 est:2500-3500 (C.D 5000)
£2000	$3660	€2920	Les Roches, St Jean Du Doight (49x60cm-19x24in) s.d.1918 prov. 1-Jun-4 Hodgins, Calgary #317/R est:4000-5000 (C.D 5000)
£3000	$5490	€4380	Montmartre (60x45cm-24x18in) s. prov. 1-Jun-4 Joyner Waddington, Toronto #233/R est:8000-10000 (C.D 7500)
£4491	$7500	€6557	Church of Christ Congregational, Milford, Connecticut (76x107cm-30x42in) s.d.1940 s.i.verso. 23-Oct-3 Shannon's, Milford #237/R est:3000-5000
£5645	$10387	€8242	Church of Christ Congregational, Milford, Connecticut (76x106cm-30x42in) s. s.i.verso. 9-Jun-4 Walker's, Ottawa #78/R est:20000-30000 (C.D 14000)

ARMITAGE, Kenneth (1916-2002) British

Sculpture			
£2300	$4186	€3358	Daydream (28cm-11in) plastic exec. 1973. 15-Jun-4 Bonhams, New Bond Street #117/R est:2500-3500
£2800	$4816	€4088	Day dream (28cm-11in) i. plastic wood sold with box. 3-Dec-3 Christie's, Kensington #768/R est:2500-3500
£2800	$5180	€4088	Day dream (28cm-11in) plastic wood. 11-Mar-4 Christie's, Kensington #204/R est:1500-2000
£4500	$8235	€6570	Prophet (32cm-13in) init.d.1962 num2/6 brown pat. bronze lit. 4-Jun-4 Christie's, London #142/R est:5000-8000
£5000	$8600	€7300	Girl without a face (38cm-15in) init. black pat bronze. 2-Dec-3 Bonhams, New Bond Street #179/R est:3000-5000
£5405	$10000	€7891	Mother and Child (22cm-9in) dark brown pat bronze marble plinth Cast 1953. 12-Feb-4 Sotheby's, New York #136/R est:5000-7000
£7500	$12900	€10950	Sprawling woman (59cm-23in) init. d.69 num 5/6 golden pat bronze. 2-Dec-3 Bonhams, New Bond Street #180/R est:6000-8000
£8725	$15443	€13000	Tall oak (75x43x30cm-30x17x12in) mono.d.1980 brown green pat bronze. 28-Apr-4 Artcurial Briest, Paris #307/R est:15000-20000
£10811	$20000	€15784	Family going for a walk (27cm-11in) black matte pat bronze marble plinth exec c.1953. 12-Feb-4 Sotheby's, New York #135/R est:8000-12000
£11000	$18700	€16060	Little monitor (31cm-12in) light brown pat. bronze conceived 1961 lit. 21-Nov-3 Christie's, London #156/R est:8000-12000
£22000	$37400	€32120	Sybil - second version (101cm-40in) init.verso dark gold pat. bronze conceived 1961 prov.exhib.lit. 21-Nov-3 Christie's, London #160/R est:15000-20000
£24000	$40800	€35040	Model for the Krefeld Monument no.2 (35cm-14in) init.num.2 black pat. bronze conceived 1956 prov. 21-Nov-3 Christie's, London #155/R est:20000-30000
£34000	$62220	€49640	Standing figure (107cm-42in) init. brown green pat. bronze st.f.Guss Noack lit. 4-Jun-4 Christie's, London #138/R est:12000-18000
Works on paper			
£1020	$1827	€1500	Untitled (40x48cm-16x19in) mono.d.49 ink prov. 21-Mar-4 Calmels Cohen, Paris #107/R est:400-600

ARMLEDER, John M (1948-) Swiss

£400	$720	€600	Untitled (30x29cm-12x11in) s.d.1992 mixed media fabric. 24-Apr-4 Cornette de St.Cyr, Paris #428
£1630	$3000	€2445	Untitled, no 57 (100x81cm-39x32in) s.d.1986 verso reactive metallic paint prov. 10-Jun-4 Phillips, New York #460/R est:4000-6000
£2283	$4200	€3425	Untitled, no 47 (100x81cm-39x32in) s.d.1986 verso prov. 10-Jun-4 Phillips, New York #457/R est:4000-6000
£4825	$8877	€7045	Untitled (73x60cm-29x24in) s. dispersion pencil varnish exhib. 23-Jun-4 Koller, Zurich #3090 est:2500-3500 (S.FR 11000)
£5307	$9500	€7748	Untitled (195x130cm-77x51in) s.d.1986 verso acrylic prov.exhib. 14-May-4 Phillips, New York #333/R est:6000-8000
£5600	$10248	€8400	Untitled (73x60cm-29x24in) s.d.1982 verso exhib.lit. 4-Jun-4 Lempertz, Koln #19/R est:2500
Sculpture			
£33520	$60000	€48939	Untitled. twelve disco balls electric motor spotlights prov.exhib. 14-May-4 Phillips, New York #193/R est:40000-60000
Works on paper			
£390	$651	€566	Untitled (36x48cm-14x19in) s. verso collage. 23-Jun-3 Philippe Schuler, Zurich #2012 (S.FR 850)
£1140	$2098	€1664	Untitled (74x51cm-29x20in) mono.d.79 W/C col pencil silk-paper prov. 23-Jun-4 Koller, Zurich #3139/R est:300-500 (S.FR 2600)
£2632	$4842	€3843	Untitled (35x41cm-14x16in) mono.d.78 mixed media collage wrapping paper prov. 23-Jun-4 Koller, Zurich #3091 est:300-500 (S.FR 6000)

ARMODIO (1938-) Italian

£10563	$17535	€15000	Romeo (50x70cm-20x28in) s. tempera panel. 14-Jun-3 Meeting Art, Vercelli #229/R est:10000

ARMOUR, George Denholm (1864-1949) British

£1050	$1754	€1533	Portrait of a skewbald in a landscape (43x51cm-17x20in) s. 9-Oct-3 Greenslade Hunt, Taunton #492/R est:500-800
Works on paper			
£280	$476	€409	Struggling through the mud (12x26cm-5x10in) init. chk. 27-Nov-3 Christie's, Kensington #40/R
£1000	$1840	€1460	Derby, 1921 (39x31cm-15x12in) s.i.d.1821 monochrome wash htd white. 10-Jun-4 Christie's, Kensington #161/R est:500-700

ARMOUR, Mary (1902-2000) British

£2200	$4092	€3212	Early spring near Arisaig (61x69cm-24x27in) s.d.70. 4-Mar-4 Christie's, Kensington #227/R est:2500-3500

£2400	$3864	€3480	Gateside, Kilbarchan (36x56cm-14x22in) s.d.58 board. 21-Aug-3 Bonhams, Edinburgh #1130/R est:2000-3000
£4000	$6280	€5800	Still life with red tulips (51x60cm-20x24in) s.d.72. 27-Aug-3 Sotheby's, London #1057/R est:5000-7000
£6500	$10465	€9425	Mixed pansies (45x29cm-18x11in) s.d.1977. 21-Aug-3 Bonhams, Edinburgh #1129/R est:3000-5000
£6500	$11765	€9490	Sunset on the Clyde (63x76cm-25x30in) s. exhib. 19-Apr-4 Sotheby's, London #144/R est:4000-6000
£7600	$12236	€11020	Flowers with two white roses (64x54cm-25x21in) s.d.72. 21-Aug-3 Bonhams, Edinburgh #1203/R est:8000-12000
£8200	$15006	€11972	Flowers with tulips (50x40cm-20x16in) s.d.1982 board. 8-Apr-4 Bonhams, Edinburgh #31/R est:7000-10000
£10500	$16485	€15225	Still life with Christmas roses (51x60cm-20x24in) s.d.1985. 27-Aug-3 Sotheby's, London #1058/R est:5000-7000
£14000	$21980	€20300	Still life with black tulips (76x61cm-30x24in) s.d.48 prov. 27-Aug-3 Sotheby's, London #1055/R est:8000-12000
£17500	$28175	€25375	Still life with vine leaves (75x75cm-30x30in) s.d.1981 exhib. 21-Aug-3 Bonhams, Edinburgh #1128/R est:15000-20000

Works on paper

£380	$699	€555	Gardening (37x53cm-15x21in) s.d.54 chl wash. 23-Mar-4 Rosebery Fine Art, London #888
£420	$756	€613	Morning Loch Broom (26x46cm-10x18in) s.d.75 pastel. 22-Apr-4 Bonhams, Edinburgh #341
£440	$761	€642	Snow near bridge Weir (30x55cm-12x22in) s. i.verso W/C. 9-Dec-3 Anderson & Garland, Newcastle #151
£1450	$2494	€2117	Gourds on a plate (52x65cm-20x26in) s.d.59 ink W/C gouache. 4-Dec-3 Bonhams, Edinburgh #69/R est:1500-1800
£3000	$5430	€4380	Gourds on a plate (52x65cm-20x26in) s.d.59 W/C pen ink. 19-Apr-4 Sotheby's, London #140/R est:3000-4000
£3400	$5780	€4964	Autumn leaves and Petunias (52x34cm-20x13in) s.d.1984 pastel buff paper. 30-Oct-3 Christie's, London #154/R est:2500-3500

ARMS, John Taylor (1887-1953) American

Prints

£1963	$3200	€2866	Venetian filigree (37x49cm-15x19in) s.i.d.1931 etching wove paper. 24-Sep-3 Christie's, Rockefeller NY #3/R est:2500-3500
£2016	$3750	€2943	Cobwebs (24x19cm-9x7in) s.i. etching exec. 1921 one of 75 prov. 5-Mar-4 Skinner, Boston #7/R est:1200-1800

Works on paper

£376	$700	€549	Chapelle St Ave-en-Bas. Mexican church (17x19cm-7x7in) s. graphite two prov. 5-Mar-4 Skinner, Boston #507/R

ARMSTEAD, Henry Hugh (1828-1905) British

Sculpture

£12000	$22080	€17520	St. Michael and serpent of Satan dismayed (94cm-37in) brown pat. bronze prov.lit. 11-Jun-4 Christie's, London #87/R est:7000-10000

ARMSTRONG, Alixe Jean Shearer (1894-?) British

Works on paper

£260	$473	€380	Untitled (43x61cm-17x24in) mixed media. 15-Jun-4 David Lay, Penzance #304

ARMSTRONG, Amos Lee (1899-?) American

£470	$850	€686	Louisiana Road (53x69cm-21x27in) s.i. board exhib. 3-Apr-4 Neal Auction Company, New Orleans #887

ARMSTRONG, Arthur (1924-1996) Irish

£537	$961	€800	Autumn landscape (29x22cm-11x9in) s. i.verso board. 31-May-4 Hamilton Osborne King, Dublin #104/R
£733	$1327	€1100	Scrubland by the sea (14x19cm-6x7in) s. board. 31-Mar-4 James Adam, Dublin #114/R
£1200	$2112	€1752	Inishmore (25x34cm-10x13in) s. board prov. 19-May-4 Sotheby's, Olympia #319/R est:600-800
£1900	$3173	€2774	Two fields and island (51x61cm-20x24in) board prov. 16-Oct-3 Christie's, Kensington #480/R est:800-1200
£2282	$4039	€3400	Still life with bronze head (58x75cm-23x30in) board prov. 27-Apr-4 Whyte's, Dublin #75/R est:3000-4000
£2400	$4392	€3504	Promontory, Connemara (61x50cm-24x20in) s. board. 2-Jun-4 John Ross, Belfast #146 est:2500-2750
£2800	$5068	€4200	Black rocks (91x76cm-36x30in) s. board prov. 31-Mar-4 James Adam, Dublin #78/R est:3000-5000
£2800	$5068	€4200	Light over Inishlacken (39x50cm-15x20in) board prov. 31-Mar-4 James Adam, Dublin #103/R est:3000-5000

Works on paper

£474	$872	€720	Coastal landscape (23x52cm-9x20in) s.i. W/C. 22-Jun-4 De Veres Art Auctions, Dublin #4/R
£1074	$1901	€1600	Kitchen interior with view of courtyard and pump (36x28cm-14x11in) s. wax crayon pencil prov. 27-Apr-4 Whyte's, Dublin #3/R est:1500-2000
£1409	$2523	€2100	Soft day (30x52cm-12x20in) s. mixed media prov. 26-May-4 James Adam, Dublin #58/R est:2000-3000
£2013	$3604	€3000	Figures in a coastal landscape (49x40cm-19x16in) s. mixed media collage. 26-May-4 James Adam, Dublin #55/R est:3000-4000

ARMSTRONG, Carolyn Faught (1910-) American

Works on paper

£417	$750	€609	Blue nymphs (53x71cm-21x28in) s.d.1948 gouache exhib. 23-Jan-4 Freeman, Philadelphia #57/R

ARMSTRONG, Geoffrey (20th C) South African?

£268	$461	€391	Skywalk, Baffin Island (147x118cm-58x46in) s. 2-Dec-3 Joyner Waddington, Toronto #395 (C.D 600)

ARMSTRONG, Ian (1923-) Australian

£255	$434	€372	Seated nude and dog (76x56cm-30x22in) s.d.81. 26-Nov-3 Deutscher-Menzies, Melbourne #242/R (A.D 600)
£319	$543	€466	Nude and Nundah rug (146x96cm-57x38in) s.d.66 i.d.1965 stretcher. 25-Nov-3 Christie's, Melbourne #173/R (A.D 750)
£344	$554	€502	Mill Road (76x55cm-30x22in) s.d.92 bears i.verso. 25-Aug-3 Sotheby's, Paddington #254/R (A.D 850)
£351	$621	€512	Blue nude (103x70cm-41x28in) s.d.72 i.d.1972 verso. 3-May-4 Christie's, Melbourne #347/R (A.D 850)
£410	$647	€599	Figures (61x51cm-24x20in) s.d.79. 2-Sep-3 Deutscher-Menzies, Melbourne #320/R (A.D 1000)
£455	$841	€664	Burnt tree, Anglesea (81x101cm-32x40in) s.d.92. 15-Mar-4 Sotheby's, Melbourne #27 est:2000-3000 (A.D 1100)
£620	$1097	€905	Mimi Liang (162x129cm-64x51in) s.d.75 i.d.1975 stretcher. 3-May-4 Christie's, Melbourne #317/R (A.D 1500)
£851	$1447	€1242	Sketch for Piano Bar Castros (45x56cm-18x22in) s.d.89 i.stretcher verso exhib. 26-Nov-3 Deutscher-Menzies, Melbourne #237/R (A.D 2000)

ARMSTRONG, John (1893-1973) British

Works on paper

£320	$554	€467	Infra-red photography, from Achievements for an Industry (10x17cm-4x7in) i.verso pen black ink over print. 9-Dec-3 Rosebery Fine Art, London #713
£480	$830	€701	Inert gases, from Achievements of an Industry (34x50cm-13x20in) black col chk prov. 9-Dec-3 Rosebery Fine Art, London #710/R
£750	$1290	€1095	Surreal landscape (16x22cm-6x9in) init. pencil W/C col chk. 3-Dec-3 Christie's, Kensington #692/R

ARMSTRONG, Robert (1953-) Irish

£867	$1560	€1300	Bright bank reflection (80x70cm-31x28in) s.i.d.96 verso. 20-Apr-4 James Adam, Dublin #40/R
£1000	$1800	€1500	White day (112x97cm-44x38in) s.i.d.94/95. 20-Apr-4 James Adam, Dublin #143/R est:1500-2000
£1622	$3065	€2400	Wicklow crucible (122x142cm-48x56in) si.d.1991 verso. 17-Feb-4 Whyte's, Dublin #105/R est:2000-3000

ARMSTRONG, Rolf (1881-1960) American

Works on paper

£1283	$2400	€1873	Portrait of a dark haired beauty (56x43cm-22x17in) s. pastel exec.c.1940. 26-Feb-4 Illustration House, New York #7 est:2500-4000
£2685	$4805	€4000	From Hawai (79x65cm-31x26in) s. pastel. 27-May-4 Sotheby's, Paris #94/R est:4000-6000
£4564	$8169	€6800	The red angel (102x74cm-40x29in) s. pastel cardboard exec. c.1950 lit. 27-May-4 Sotheby's, Paris #93/R est:4000-6000

ARMSTRONG, William (1822-1914) Canadian/Irish

Works on paper

£268	$461	€391	Landscape with canoe (16x23cm-6x9in) W/C. 2-Dec-3 Joyner Waddington, Toronto #407 (C.D 600)
£343	$630	€501	Indians by Table Rock, Niagara Falls (15x21cm-6x8in) s.d.1852 W/C. 9-Jun-4 Walker's, Ottawa #122/R (C.D 850)
£813	$1455	€1187	Lake Mutinadinadad, North Shore, Lake Huron (39x53cm-15x21in) bears sig W/C. 31-May-4 Sotheby's, Toronto #83/R est:3000-4000 (C.D 2000)
£1964	$3379	€2867	With the Wolseley Expedition (16x39cm-6x15in) s.d.69 W/C. 2-Dec-3 Joyner Waddington, Toronto #131/R est:3000-4000 (C.D 4400)

ARMSTRONG, William Weaver (1862-1906) American

£1279	$2200	€1867	Mountain lake (46x61cm-18x24in) s. board. 6-Dec-3 Selkirks, St. Louis #175/R est:2000-3000
£1553	$2500	€2267	Sierra Peaks, a snow-capped mountain landscape (56x91cm-22x36in) s. 20-Jan-3 O'Gallerie, Oregon #826/R est:2500-3500

ARNAIZ, Doroteo (1936-) Spanish

£310	$559	€450	Shapes (55x46cm-22x18in) s. d.64 verso. 26-Jan-4 Durán, Madrid #54/R

ARNAL, François (1924-) French

£473	$846	€700	Pompei (73x92cm-29x36in) s.d.56 prov.exhib. 4-May-4 Calmels Cohen, Paris #181
£489	$842	€700	Le retour a Pirasca (100x81cm-39x32in) s.i.d.1986. 3-Dec-3 Tajan, Paris #469/R
£567	$1014	€850	Nemo (65x81cm-26x32in) s.d.55 s.i.d.55 verso prov.exhib. 15-May-4 De Vuyst, Lokeren #14
£608	$1089	€900	Untitled (73x54cm-29x21in) s.d.50 i.verso prov. 4-May-4 Calmels Cohen, Paris #186 est:1500-2000
£1074	$1997	€1600	Mutants (100x81cm-39x32in) s.i.d.1961 verso. 3-Mar-4 Tajan, Paris #220 est:1500-2000
£1579	$2905	€2400	Untitled (73x53cm-29x21in) s.d.1950 panel prov. 27-Jun-4 Versailles Encheres #42/R est:2000-3000
£1611	$2851	€2400	Composition abstraite (49x58cm-19x23in) s.d.51. 28-Apr-4 Artcurial Briest, Paris #265/R est:2000-2500
£2465	$4264	€3500	L'epreuve de la soif (89x116cm-35x46in) s.d.1955 s.i.d.verso exhib. 14-Dec-3 Versailles Encheres #68/R est:5000-6000
£2500	$4600	€3800	Pompei (73x92cm-29x36in) s.d.1956 s.i.d.verso prov.exhib. 27-Jun-4 Versailles Encheres #60/R est:2500-3000
£3662	$6335	€5200	Composition (120x134cm-47x53in) s.d.1951 prov. 9-Dec-3 Artcurial Briest, Paris #492/R est:3000-4000

Works on paper

£267	$491	€400	Cherie et le soleil (12x32cm-5x13in) s.d.52 gouache paper on canvas. 13-Jun-4 Lombrail & Teucquam, Paris #134/R
£400	$720	€600	Composition (48x63cm-19x25in) s. ink wash. 24-Apr-4 Cornette de St.Cyr, Paris #429/R
£658	$1211	€1000	Composition (45x54cm-18x21in) s.d.1975 pastel W/C ink. 27-Jun-4 Versailles Encheres #61/R

ARNASUNGAAQ, Barnabus (1924-) North American

Sculpture

£811	$1378	€1184	Musk ox (38cm-15in) s. mottled grey soapstone. 3-Nov-3 Waddingtons, Toronto #165/R est:1500-2000 (C.D 1800)

£901 $1532 €1315 Inuit hunter holding a knife (30cm-12in) dark soapstone ivory. 3-Nov-3 Waddingtons, Toronto #180/R est:2000-3000 (C.D 2000)
£1532 $2604 €2237 Seated Inuit woman (23cm-9in) s. mottled dark soapstone. 3-Nov-3 Waddingtons, Toronto #159/R est:3000-5000 (C.D 3400)
£1532 $2604 €2237 Inuit mother and her children (30cm-12in) s. mottled dark soapstone. 3-Nov-3 Waddingtons, Toronto #176/R est:2500-3500 (C.D 3400)
£1712 $2910 €2500 Inuit woman (38cm-15in) mottled dark grey soapstone. 3-Nov-3 Waddingtons, Toronto #168/R est:1500-2000 (C.D 3800)

ARNAUD, Dominique (20th C) French
Works on paper
£400 $724 €600 Sans titre (130x97cm-51x38in) mono. mixed media. 3-Apr-4 Neret-Minet, Paris #78

ARNAUD, Giovanni (1829-1869) Italian
£2310 $3835 €3350 Reclining female nude (70x128cm-28x50in) s.d.1915. 1-Oct-3 Della Rocca, Turin #229/R est:4000-5000

ARNAUD, Marcel (1877-1956) French
£1146 $1914 €1650 Personnage devant le mas (22x41cm-9x16in) s. 25-Oct-3 Dianous, Marseille #389
£1944 $3247 €2800 Glaieuls (73x60cm-29x24in) s. 25-Oct-3 Dianous, Marseille #403

ARNAUD, Pierre Francis (20th C) French
Works on paper
£400 $728 €600 Monotype au virement de bord (29x23cm-11x9in) s.d.92 W/C. 3-Jul-4 Neret-Minet, Paris #187/R

ARNAY, L R (?) ?
£1341 $2172 €1944 Interior (25x30cm-10x12in) s. panel. 31-Jul-3 International Art Centre, Auckland #170/R est:1800-2500 (NZ.D 3700)

ARNDT, Mina (?) ?
Works on paper
£761 $1363 €1111 Isolated gate (23x15cm-9x6in) s. W/C. 12-May-4 Dunbar Sloane, Wellington #8 est:1000-2000 (NZ.D 2200)

ARNEGGER, Alois (1879-1967) Austrian
£319 $533 €450 Pancorto (59x100cm-23x39in) s. 16-Oct-3 Dorotheum, Salzburg #604/R
£403 $742 €588 Winter in the Alps (61x91cm-24x36in) s. 14-Jun-4 Waddingtons, Toronto #29/R est:1500-2000 (C.D 1000)
£444 $816 €648 Alpine village in the snow (41x59cm-16x23in) s. 14-Jun-4 Waddingtons, Toronto #30/R est:1000-1500 (C.D 1100)
£500 $900 €750 Alpenglow (60x80cm-24x31in) s. 21-Apr-4 Dorotheum, Vienna #88
£549 $1000 €802 Alpine village scene (69x99cm-27x39in) s. 19-Jun-4 Jeffery Burchard, Florida #72
£567 $1014 €850 Autumn (43x53cm-17x21in) s. lit. 14-May-4 Schloss Ahlden, Ahlden #2829/R
£567 $1014 €850 Farmstead in spring (42x53cm-17x21in) s. lit. 14-May-4 Schloss Ahlden, Ahlden #2828/R
£625 $981 €900 Landscape (74x99cm-29x39in) s. 30-Aug-3 Hans Stahl, Toestorf #5/R
£694 $1132 €1000 Winter walk (68x48cm-27x19in) s. 23-Sep-3 Wiener Kunst Auktionen, Vienna #124/R
£694 $1132 €1000 Spring landscape (68x48cm-27x19in) s. 23-Sep-3 Wiener Kunst Auktionen, Vienna #125/R
£709 $1184 €1000 Winter landscape with evening sun (51x76cm-20x30in) s. 16-Oct-3 Dorotheum, Salzburg #603/R
£719 $1337 €1050 Field landscape with houses, figures and goats (42x80cm-17x31in) s. panel. 2-Mar-4 Rasmussen, Copenhagen #1611/R (D.KR 8000)
£764 $1260 €1100 On the Riviera (80x80cm-31x31in) s. 3-Jul-3 Van Ham, Cologne #1051/R
£764 $1245 €1100 Alpine peaks on winter evening (69x100cm-27x39in) s. i. verso panel. 24-Sep-3 Neumeister, Munich #386/R
£764 $1245 €1100 Zill valley on winter evening (75x80cm-30x31in) s. i. verso panel. 24-Sep-3 Neumeister, Munich #387
£819 $1466 €1196 Autumn landscape with pond in front of farmstead (74x100cm-29x39in) s. 13-May-4 Stuker, Bern #19/R est:1800-2200 (S.FR 1900)
£845 $1479 €1200 Mountain village (62x92cm-24x36in) s. 19-Dec-3 Dorotheum, Vienna #121/R
£979 $1664 €1400 Farmstead in spring (42x53cm-17x21in) s. 20-Nov-3 Dorotheum, Salzburg #214/R
£1067 $1909 €1600 Venice in moonlight (76x101cm-30x40in) s. 15-May-4 Hagelstam, Helsinki #49/R est:2500
£1078 $1800 €1574 Hoch Koenig (61x86cm-24x34in) s. canvas on masonite. 7-Oct-3 Sotheby's, New York #148 est:2000-3000
£1117 $2000 €1631 Autumn landscape with bridge and peasants (76x104cm-30x41in) s. 8-May-4 Susanin's, Chicago #6053/R est:2400-3400
£1197 $2095 €1700 Winter evening with Alps in background (70x100cm-28x39in) s. 19-Dec-3 Dorotheum, Vienna #88/R est:1500-2000
£1200 $1884 €1740 Villas on the edge of Lake Como (69x99cm-27x39in) s. board. 28-Aug-3 Christie's, Kensington #230/R est:1500-2000
£1268 $2218 €1800 Winter in Gastein (61x92cm-24x36in) s. 19-Dec-3 Dorotheum, Vienna #75/R est:1800-2400
£1275 $2334 €1900 Capri, view from Sorrent (61x80cm-24x31in) s. lit. 8-Jul-4 Allgauer, Kempten #2046/R est:1900
£1300 $2067 €1885 Italian coastal landscape (90x125cm-35x49in) s. 9-Sep-3 Bonhams, Knightsbridge #77/R est:600-800
£1357 $2267 €1981 Capri (69x99cm-27x39in) s. canvas on masonite prov. 17-Nov-3 Waddingtons, Toronto #26/R est:1500-2500 (C.D 3000)
£1400 $2548 €2100 Winter landscape with Wilde Kaiser mountains in evening (70x99cm-28x39in) s. 30-Jun-4 Neumeister, Munich #496/R
£1502 $2703 €2193 Italian coastal landscape (88x123cm-35x48in) s. 26-Jan-4 Lilla Bukowskis, Stockholm #768 est:35000-40000 (S.KR 20000)
£1538 $2646 €2200 Alpine glow in Gasteinertal (59x80cm-23x31in) s. 4-Dec-3 Dorotheum, Graz #1/R est:1100
£1736 $2865 €2500 Coastal landscape near Sorrento (70x100cm-28x39in) 3-Jul-3 Van Ham, Cologne #1052/R est:2400
£1745 $3123 €2600 Coast of Capri (70x100cm-28x39in) s. 27-May-4 Dorotheum, Graz #3/R est:1100
£1748 $2972 €2500 Ligurian coast (70x100cm-28x39in) s. 20-Nov-3 Van Ham, Cologne #1463/R est:2800
£1988 $3500 €2902 Italian waterside village with figures (79x109cm-31x43in) s. 23-May-4 Bonhams & Butterfields, Los Angeles #7044/R
£2500 $4600 €3650 Springtime in the orchard (73x100cm-29x39in) s. 25-Mar-4 Christie's, Kensington #179/R est:3000-5000
£2800 $5152 €4088 Sorrento (70x101cm-28x40in) s. 25-Mar-4 Christie's, Kensington #142/R est:3000-5000
£3000 $4800 €4350 Winter woodland landscape (70x100cm-28x39in) s. 18-Sep-3 Christie's, Kensington #62/R est:3000-5000
£3265 $5845 €4800 Sorrento coast (90x125cm-35x49in) s. 17-Mar-4 Neumeister, Munich #395/R est:3000
£3333 $5433 €4800 Bay of Naples with Vesuvius (70x100cm-28x39in) s. 24-Sep-3 Neumeister, Munich #385a/R est:3800
£3500 $6440 €5110 Bernina mountain range, Italy (71x100cm-28x39in) s. 25-Mar-4 Christie's, Kensington #180/R est:3000-5000

ARNEGGER, August (20th C) Austrian
£1700 $2839 €2482 St Martin, Tennengebirge, Salzburg (61x92cm-24x36in) s. sold with a companion. 7-Oct-3 Bonhams, Knightsbridge #249/R est:1000-1500

ARNEGGER, Georg (1901-) Austrian
£1399 $2406 €2000 Spring in Taormina (60x100cm-24x39in) s. 6-Dec-3 Hans Stahl, Toestorf #2/R est:2400

ARNEGGER, Gottfried (1905-) Austrian
£452 $769 €660 Amalfi coast (57x79cm-22x31in) s. 28-Nov-3 Zofingen, Switzerland #2542 (S.FR 1000)
£809 $1400 €1181 Amalfi Way, Italy (61x91cm-24x36in) 12-Dec-3 Du Mouchelle, Detroit #2024/R
£948 $1697 €1384 Sorrento peninsula (57x79cm-22x31in) s. 12-May-4 Dobiaschofsky, Bern #315/R est:1900 (S.FR 2200)
£1129 $2077 €1648 Coastal scene, Italy (69x99cm-27x39in) s. 14-Jun-4 Waddingtons, Toronto #33/R est:3000-3500 (C.D 2800)
£1800 $3312 €2628 Taormina (60x100cm-24x39in) s.i. 25-Mar-4 Christie's, Kensington #143/R est:2000-3000

ARNELL, Maj (1910-) Swedish
£276 $496 €414 The tree trunk (57x52cm-22x20in) init. 25-Apr-4 Goteborg Auktionsverk, Sweden #301/R (S.KR 3800)

ARNESEN, Vilhelm (1865-1948) Danish
£271 $500 €396 Seascape with sailing vessels (30x44cm-12x17in) s.d.1920. 15-Mar-4 Rasmussen, Vejle #95 (D.KR 3000)
£297 $481 €431 Landscape with windmills and sailing vessel on canal (32x43cm-13x17in) s.d.1915. 4-Aug-3 Rasmussen, Vejle #51/R (D.KR 3100)
£356 $594 €520 Coastal landscape with sailing vessels off Hven (30x44cm-12x17in) s.d.1926. 25-Oct-3 Rasmussen, Havnen #2597/R (D.KR 3800)
£383 $620 €555 Steam ship Annam and other vessels on the Chinese Sea (45x71cm-18x28in) s.i.d.jan.20/1899. 4-Aug-3 Rasmussen, Vejle #47/R (D.KR 4000)
£387 $658 €565 Seascape with sailing boats (37x48cm-15x19in) s.d.1938. 10-Nov-3 Rasmussen, Vejle #316/R (D.KR 4200)
£485 $883 €708 Several vessels in the channel between Snekkersten and Helsingborg (32x52cm-13x20in) s.d.1922. 7-Feb-4 Rasmussen, Havnen #2305 (D.KR 5300)
£489 $832 €714 Ship's portrait of Freya af Thisted (60x77cm-24x30in) s.d.1879. 29-Nov-3 Rasmussen, Havnen #2034/R (D.KR 5200)
£507 $862 €740 The barque Thorvaldsen off Kronborg (50x75cm-20x30in) s.d.1932. 10-Nov-3 Rasmussen, Vejle #299/R (D.KR 5500)
£655 $1095 €956 Seascape with many vessels (52x78cm-20x31in) s.d.1918. 25-Oct-3 Rasmussen, Havnen #2550/R (D.KR 7000)
£655 $1095 €956 Seascape with sailing vessels off the coast (48x76cm-19x30in) s.d.1936. 25-Oct-3 Rasmussen, Havnen #2601 (D.KR 7000)
£674 $1214 €1011 Harbour view with boats (27x44cm-11x17in) s.d.1894. 25-Apr-4 Goteborg Auktionsverk, Sweden #182/R (S.KR 9300)
£689 $1116 €999 Seascape with sailing vessels at Sundet (52x75cm-20x30in) s.d.1929. 4-Aug-3 Rasmussen, Vejle #46/R (D.KR 7200)
£701 $1107 €1016 Seascape with sailing boats (46x72cm-18x28in) s.d.1918. 2-Sep-3 Rasmussen, Copenhagen #1624/R (D.KR 7500)
£762 $1371 €1113 Seascape with sailing ship off coast line (53x76cm-21x30in) s.d.1920. 24-Apr-4 Rasmussen, Havnen #2111/R (D.KR 8500)
£843 $1407 €1231 Ship's portrait of Betty of Frederikshavn (46x70cm-18x28in) i. 25-Oct-3 Rasmussen, Havnen #2646/R (D.KR 9000)
£851 $1472 €1242 Steamship off the coast at Aandalsnaes (45x71cm-18x28in) s.i.d.12 juli 1910. 9-Dec-3 Rasmussen, Copenhagen #1517/R (D.KR 9000)
£873 $1414 €1275 Seascape with sailing boat (74x103cm-29x41in) s.d.1919. 9-Aug-3 Hindemae, Ullerslev #257/R (D.KR 9200)
£895 $1638 €1307 Boys bathing from rocks (28x44cm-11x17in) s.i.d.15.8.1913. 9-Jun-4 Rasmussen, Copenhagen #1976/R (D.KR 10000)
£898 $1671 €1311 Seascape with vessels in fresh breeze (45x72cm-18x28in) s.d.90. 2-Mar-4 Rasmussen, Copenhagen #1447/R (D.KR 10000)
£900 $1431 €1305 Merchantman Swordfish off Copenhagen (47x73cm-19x29in) s.d.1938. 9-Sep-3 Sworder & Son, Bishops Stortford #397/R
£933 $1699 €1400 View of Dragor Harbour (32x48cm-13x19in) s.i.d.1894. 19-Jun-4 Rasmussen, Havnen #2350/R (D.KR 10500)
£988 $1838 €1442 Fishing boat off Gilleleje Harbour (45x72cm-18x28in) s.d.1914. 2-Mar-4 Rasmussen, Copenhagen #1405/R (D.KR 11000)
£1970 $3604 €2876 Seascape with boats in Copenhagen Harbour (80x120cm-31x47in) s.d.1939. 7-Jun-4 Museumsbygningen, Copenhagen #153/R est:25000 (D.KR 22000)
£2000 $3440 €2920 Shipping off the Danish Coast (51x75cm-20x30in) s.d.1929. 2-Dec-3 Sotheby's, London #55/R est:2000-3000
£2516 $4679 €3673 Sailing vessels on calm seas (45x61cm-18x24in) s.d.1914. 2-Mar-4 Rasmussen, Copenhagen #1243/R est:7000-10000 (D.KR 28000)

ARNESON, Robert (1930-1992) American
Works on paper
£7186 $12000 €10492 Prone (75x105cm-30x41in) s. conte crayon oilstick oil pastel prov.exhib. 7-Oct-3 Sotheby's, New York #369 est:3000-5000
£19117 $32500 €27911 Nite wolf (114x274cm-45x108in) s.d.1987 chl acrylic graphite prov. 9-Nov-3 Bonhams & Butterfields, Los Angeles #4060/R est:15000-20000

ARNEST, Bernard Patrick (1917-1986) American

£1497 $2500 €2186 Man in orange (112x97cm-44x38in) s.d.51 prov.exhib. 23-Oct-3 Shannon's, Milford #196/R est:2000-3000

ARNEZ, Helmut (20th C) Austrian?

£315 $535 €450 Landscape (67x85cm-26x33in) s.d.62 panel. 27-Nov-3 Dorotheum, Linz #479/R

ARNHEIM, Clara (1865-1943) German

£1049 $1804 €1500 Country harbour (47x70cm-19x28in) s. board. 6-Dec-3 Hans Stahl, Toestorf #65/R est:1400

ARNING, Eddie (1898-1992) American

Works on paper

£599 $1000 €875 People in a bedroom (56x71cm-22x28in) crayon posterboard. 15-Nov-3 Slotin Folk Art, Buford #215/R

£694 $1250 €1013 Three purple figures (56x71cm-22x28in) crayon crapas on pasteboard. 24-Apr-4 Slotin Folk Art, Buford #350/R est:3000-4000

£833 $1500 €1216 Abstract boat (41x56cm-16x22in) crayon crapas. 24-Apr-4 Slotin Folk Art, Buford #351/R est:3000-4000

£898 $1500 €1311 Man in white suit (56x71cm-22x28in) crayon poster. 15-Nov-3 Slotin Folk Art, Buford #214/R est:1000-2000

£1111 $2000 €1622 You better believe it (51x64cm-20x25in) crayon. 24-Apr-4 Slotin Folk Art, Buford #349/R est:3000-5000

£1611 $2900 €2352 Take a puff its spring time (51x64cm-20x25in) crayon on poster. 24-Apr-4 Slotin Folk Art, Buford #348/R est:3000-5000

ARNITZ, Rick (20th C) ?

£1117 $1900 €1631 Untitled (61x61cm-24x24in) init.d.94 verso oil enamel prov. 9-Nov-3 Bonhams & Butterfields, Los Angeles #4078/R est:3000-5000

ARNO, Peter (1904-1968) American

Works on paper

£1033 $1900 €1508 Then it's moved and seconded that the compulsory retirement age be advanced to 95 (41x30cm-16x12in) s. ink wash on board prov. 23-Jun-4 Doyle, New York #5005/R est:1200-1800

£2695 $4500 €3935 Could you direct me to the Bear Mountain Nudist Camp (46x33cm-18x13in) s. chl wash oval lit. 15-Nov-3 Illustration House, New York #43/R est:3500-5000

£2695 $4500 €3935 O K, cut 'er hard (41x36cm-16x14in) s. chl wash lit. 15-Nov-3 Illustration House, New York #44/R est:4000-6000

ARNOLD, Carl Johann (1829-1916) German

£909 $1564 €1300 Mishap (31x23cm-12x9in) s. 3-Dec-3 Neumeister, Munich #527/R

ARNOLD, Carl Johann (attrib) (1829-1916) German

£927 $1687 €1400 Soldier sleeping on guard duty (25x22cm-10x9in) s. copper. 19-Jun-4 Hans Stahl, Hamburg #11/R

ARNOLD, Christian (1889-1960) German

£295 $543 €440 Farmstead on moorland (23x28cm-9x11in) mono. board. 26-Mar-4 Bolland & Marotz, Bremen #310/R

£336 $617 €500 Evening on the moor (29x38cm-11x15in) mono. W/C. 26-Mar-4 Bolland & Marotz, Bremen #309/R

£367 $660 €550 Fire lilies (60x44cm-24x17in) mono. W/C tempera board. 24-Apr-4 Dr Lehr, Berlin #38/R

£432 $708 €600 Dusk (56x40cm-22x16in) mono.d. W/C. 4-Jun-3 Ketterer, Hamburg #134/R

£433 $780 €650 Winter evening (37x52cm-15x20in) mono. tempera board. 24-Apr-4 Dr Lehr, Berlin #37/R

£467 $840 €700 Winter meadows (37x52cm-15x20in) mono. board. 24-Apr-4 Dr Lehr, Berlin #36/R

£2000 $3580 €3000 Self - me (52x39cm-20x15in) mono. Indian ink brush prov. 14-May-4 Ketterer, Munich #1/R est:1000-2000

Works on paper

£278 $453 €400 Landscape with farmstead near Bremen (43x57cm-17x22in) mono. W/C. 26-Sep-3 Bolland & Marotz, Bremen #292

£347 $566 €500 Bridge in Bremen (36x29cm-14x11in) mono. W/C. 26-Sep-3 Bolland & Marotz, Bremen #288/R

£486 $792 €700 Landscape after the rain (38x53cm-15x21in) mono. 26-Sep-3 Bolland & Marotz, Bremen #291

£625 $1044 €900 By the cathedral (55x40cm-22x16in) mono. W/C. 24-Oct-3 Ketterer, Hamburg #609/R

£733 $1313 €1100 Forest clearing (53x37cm-21x15in) mono.d.27 W/C. 15-May-4 Van Ham, Cologne #414

£833 $1358 €1200 Path through hilly landscape (44x58cm-17x23in) mono. W/C. 26-Sep-3 Bolland & Marotz, Bremen #290/R

£867 $1551 €1300 Mountain landscape (52x33cm-20x13in) mono.d.29 W/C. 15-May-4 Van Ham, Cologne #416/R

£903 $1472 €1300 Hilly fields on autumn evening (44x58cm-17x23in) mono. W/C. 26-Sep-3 Bolland & Marotz, Bremen #289/R

£1181 $1972 €1700 Houses in the suburbs (40x54cm-16x21in) mono.d. w/C. 24-Oct-3 Ketterer, Hamburg #262/R est:1800-1900

ARNOLD, Edward (1824-1866) American/German

£3500 $6265 €5110 American three-master Sarah G Hyde off a lighthouse (74x91cm-29x36in) s.d.1861. 26-May-4 Christie's, Kensington #618/R est:3000-5000

ARNOLD, Eve (1913-) American

Photographs

£2300 $3910 €3358 Marilyn Monroe resting before giving her speech, Bement, Illinois (18x27cm-7x11in) s.i. pigment transfer print exec.1955 printed later lit. 19-Nov-3 Sotheby's, Olympia #190/R est:300-500

£2500 $4250 €3650 Marilyn Monroe on the set of the Misfits, Nevada (27x40cm-11x16in) silver print exec.1960 printed later prov. 19-Nov-3 Sotheby's, Olympia #192/R est:1600-1800

ARNOLD, Georg Johann (20th C) ?

£677 $1233 €988 Sea landscape (65x75cm-26x30in) s. 20-Jun-4 Agra, Warsaw #1/R (P.Z 4700)

ARNOLD, George (1753-1806) British

Works on paper

£280 $510 €409 Homeward bound, a clipper (36x51cm-14x20in) s.d.1914 W/C bodycol. 15-Jun-4 David Lay, Penzance #657

ARNOLD, Gerhard (1938-) German

£590 $974 €850 Summer idyll (70x90cm-28x35in) s. 3-Jul-3 Van Ham, Cologne #1053

ARNOLD, Graham (1932-) British

£4200 $7224 €6132 Beethoven's Triple Concerto (71x71cm-28x28in) s. board. 2-Dec-3 Bonhams, New Bond Street #193/R est:2000-3000

ARNOLD, Henry (19/20th C) ?

Sculpture

£1631 $2643 €2300 Femme a la lyre (80x22x22cm-31x9x9in) s.st.f.Colin brown pat bronze exec.c.1920. 24-May-3 Martinot & Savignat, Pontoise #87/R est:2500-3000

ARNOLD, Marion (1947-) South African

Works on paper

£248 $443 €362 Still life with a tonga stool and a jar (56x77cm-22x30in) s.d.85 W/C over pencil. 31-May-4 Stephan Welz, Johannesburg #185 (SA.R 3000)

ARNOLD, Patience (fl.1925-1939) British

Works on paper

£260 $481 €380 Punch and Judy show (30x43cm-12x17in) s. W/C. 14-Jul-4 Bonhams, Chester #357

ARNOLD, Phyllis (1938-) British

Works on paper

£300 $492 €438 Farmyard boss (7x10cm-3x4in) s. gouache vellum. 4-Jun-3 John Ross, Belfast #20

£300 $492 €438 Newcomer (7x10cm-3x4in) s. gouache vellum. 4-Jun-3 John Ross, Belfast #21

ARNOLD, Ralph Moffett (1928-) American

£529 $900 €772 Here is still (74x58cm-29x23in) s. oil acrylic collage prov. 9-Nov-3 Wright, Chicago #410

ARNOLD-LUDSTECK, Cornelia (20th C) German

£559 $1029 €850 Fence (50x50cm-20x20in) s.d.97 verso calico. 25-Jun-4 Von Zezschwitz, Munich #373/R

£559 $1029 €850 Summer (50x50cm-20x20in) s.d.97 verso calico. 25-Jun-4 Von Zezschwitz, Munich #374/R

ARNOLDI, Charles (1946-) American

Sculpture

£2973 $5500 €4341 Untitled (50x69cm-20x27in) s.d.1986 verso painted wood construction plywood prov. 13-Jul-4 Christie's, Rockefeller NY #26/R est:3000-5000

ARNOLDI, Nag (1928-) Swiss

Sculpture

£1638 $2932 €2391 Seated horse (19cm-7in) mono.i. brown pat.bronze. 12-May-4 Dobiaschofsky, Bern #2505 est:4000 (S.FR 3800)

ARNOLDI, Per (1941-) Danish

£662 $1184 €967 Still life of bowls (100x100cm-39x39in) s. 12-Jan-4 Rasmussen, Vejle #616/R (D.KR 7000)

£767 $1435 €1120 Compositions (45x30cm-18x12in) s.d.91 three. 25-Feb-4 Kunsthallen, Copenhagen #87/R (D.KR 8500)

£1087 $1946 €1587 Composition with bowler hats (120x120cm-47x47in) s.d.77 verso. 12-Jan-4 Rasmussen, Vejle #617/R (D.KR 11500)

ARNOULD, Reynold (1919-1980) French

Sculpture

£1958 $3270 €2800 S 47 (18x43cm-7x17in) mono. num.1/4 polished bronze lit. 11-Oct-3 De Vuyst, Lokeren #12/R est:1700-1900

Works on paper

£420 $713 €600 Abstract composition (55x44cm-22x17in) s. gouache. 24-Nov-3 Glerum, Amsterdam #260/R

ARNOUX, Michel (1833-1877) French

£1176 $1965 €1717 Cold hands (21x15cm-8x6in) s. panel prov. 17-Nov-3 Waddingtons, Toronto #193/R est:2000-3000 (C.D 2600)

£3200 $5728 €4672 Helping Hand (38x28cm-15x11in) s. panel. 7-May-4 Mallams, Oxford #401/R est:2000-3000

ARNTZEN, Henry (1885-1957) Norwegian
£313 $542 €457 House with fence (49x56cm-19x22in) s. 13-Dec-3 Blomqvist, Lysaker #1005 (N.KR 3600)

ARNTZENIUS, Elise Claudine (1902-1982) Dutch
£1027 $1747 €1500 Roses in a white vase (36x29cm-14x11in) s. board. 5-Nov-3 Vendue Huis, Gravenhage #328/R est:300-400
£2098 $3608 €3000 Still life of flowers (25x35cm-10x14in) s. panel. 8-Dec-3 Glerum, Amsterdam #249/R est:1800-2200
Works on paper
£342 $582 €500 Roses in white jug (48x36cm-19x14in) s. W/C. 5-Nov-3 Vendue Huis, Gravenhage #329/R

ARNTZENIUS, Floris (1864-1925) Dutch
£1319 $2085 €1900 By a stream (52x31cm-20x12in) s. canvas on panel. 2-Sep-3 Christie's, Amsterdam #204/R est:1800-2200
£17333 $31200 €26000 Huurrijtuigen (39x59cm-15x23in) s. panel painted c.1895 exhib. 21-Apr-4 Christie's, Amsterdam #122/R est:30000-50000
£17881 $32543 €27000 Marche anime (26x46cm-10x18in) s. painted c.1900. 15-Jun-4 Vanderkindere, Brussels #125/R est:6000-8000
£36667 $66000 €55000 Figures on the Noordeinde, The Hague (65x83cm-26x33in) s. prov. 20-Apr-4 Sotheby's, Amsterdam #202/R est:60000-80000
£43056 $71903 €62000 Spuistraat in the Hague (50x73cm-20x29in) prov. 21-Oct-3 Sotheby's, Amsterdam #239/R est:50000-70000
Works on paper
£972 $1536 €1400 Small street in a Dutch town (19x13cm-7x5in) indis sig. chl bodycol W/C. 2-Sep-3 Christie's, Amsterdam #212 est:500-700
£2778 $4639 €4000 Moored boats in Scheveningen (14x20cm-6x8in) s. s.d.1924 verso W/C black chk htd white. 21-Oct-3 Sotheby's, Amsterdam #137/R est:4000-6000
£4110 $6986 €6000 Street in Amsterdam (18x12cm-7x5in) s. chl W/C. 5-Nov-3 Vendue Huis, Gravenhage #125/R est:2000-3000
£4861 $8264 €7000 Painter Carl August Breitenstein at work (34x44cm-13x17in) s. W/C bodycol htd white prov. 28-Oct-3 Christie's, Amsterdam #163/R est:7000-9000
£6250 $10625 €9000 Busy street in the Hague (12x9cm-5x4in) s. pencil W/C gouache blk chk htd white cardboard exhib. 28-Oct-3 Christie's, Amsterdam #169/R est:6000-8000
£6667 $12000 €10000 Busy street, The Hague (20x13cm-8x5in) s. W/C htd white. 20-Apr-4 Sotheby's, Amsterdam #210/R est:7000-9000
£7333 $13200 €11000 Figures on the beach, Scheveningen (12x19cm-5x7in) s. W/C pencil htd white. 20-Apr-4 Sotheby's, Amsterdam #133/R est:6000-8000
£10000 $18000 €15000 Sluice in Nieuwveen (52x73cm-20x29in) s. black chk W/C htd white exhib. 21-Apr-4 Christie's, Amsterdam #132/R est:15000-20000
£10140 $17441 €14500 Two horses in the winter cold (37x49cm-15x19in) s. gouache prov.exhib.lit. 8-Dec-3 Glerum, Amsterdam #34/R est:12000-15000
£13333 $24000 €20000 Figures on the Brouwersgracht, The Hague (42x30cm-17x12in) s. pencil W/C bodycol prov. 21-Apr-4 Christie's, Amsterdam #129/R est:20000-30000
£19444 $33056 €28000 Barge with flowers moored at the Smitswater, The Hague (38x55cm-15x22in) s. pencil W/C htd white prov.exhib. 28-Oct-3 Christie's, Amsterdam #183/R est:15000-20000
£21333 $38400 €32000 Figures on the Noordeinde, The Hague (47x54cm-19x21in) s. W/C. 20-Apr-4 Sotheby's, Amsterdam #214/R est:15000-25000

ARNTZENIUS, Paul (1883-1965) Dutch
£377 $640 €550 Still life with lemons (34x46cm-13x18in) s. 5-Nov-3 Vendue Huis, Gravenhage #327
£490 $842 €700 Still life with stone jug and bowl with fruit (46x38cm-18x15in) s. 8-Dec-3 Glerum, Amsterdam #75/R
£816 $1486 €1200 Sea (36x50cm-14x20in) s. 3-Feb-4 Christie's, Amsterdam #275 est:600-800
£921 $1695 €1400 Ocean view (38x55cm-15x22in) s. 28-Jun-4 Sotheby's, Amsterdam #137/R
Works on paper
£336 $617 €500 Moored boats by a saw-mill (30x40cm-12x16in) s.d.1907 black chk. 29-Mar-4 Glerum, Amsterdam #44

ARNULPHY, Claude (attrib) (1697-1786) French
£2381 $4262 €3500 Portrait de Madame de Barrigue de Fontainieu (112x94cm-44x37in) 19-Mar-4 Beaussant & Lefèvre, Paris #66/R est:4000-5000

AROCH, Arieh (1908-1974) Russian
£18156 $32500 €26508 Girl returning from school (69x90cm-27x35in) s.i.d.1956 prov.exhib.lit. 18-Mar-4 Sotheby's, New York #24/R est:30000-40000
£24096 $40000 €35180 Sign (42x57cm-17x22in) s.indis.d. i.verso painted 1960s prov.exhib. 2-Oct-3 Christie's, Tel Aviv #86/R est:40000-60000
Works on paper
£6627 $11000 €9675 Untitled (31x24cm-12x9in) s. gouache wax crayon chl pen ink pencil exec 1965 exhib. 2-Oct-3 Christie's, Tel Aviv #103/R est:9000-12000

AROE, Jacob Andreas (1803-1870) Danish
Works on paper
£937 $1528 €1368 Landscape with houses, Frederikshaab in Greenland (22x33cm-9x13in) W/C. 27-Sep-3 Rasmussen, Havnen #3050/R (D.KR 10000)
£5867 $10677 €8801 The Colony Frederikshaab in Greenland, 1843 (34x46cm-13x18in) W/C. 19-Jun-4 Rasmussen, Havnen #2292/R est:30000-35000 (D.KR 66000)

ARON, Remy (1952-) French
£1329 $2259 €1900 Le modele dans l'atelier (73x60cm-29x24in) s. 27-Nov-3 Calmels Cohen, Paris #71/R est:1700-1900

ARONSON, David (1923-) American
Sculpture
£1250 $2275 €1825 Standing woman (170cm-67in) bronze. 4-Feb-4 Sotheby's, Olympia #105b/R est:800-1200

ARONSON, Naoum (1872-1943) Russian
Sculpture
£24000 $43200 €35040 Lovers (153x57cm-60x22in) s.d.20 white marble wood stand lit. 21-Apr-4 Sotheby's, London #154/R est:12000-18000

ARONSON, Naoum (attrib) (1872-1943) Russian
Sculpture
£3991 $7144 €5827 Seated girl (24cm-9in) s. carved polished red marble. 26-May-4 AB Stockholms Auktionsverk #2477/R est:4000-5000 (S.KR 54000)

ARONSON-LILJEGRAL, Martin (1869-?) Danish
Works on paper
£284 $455 €415 Small boy seated on bench (97x63cm-38x25in) s.d.1899 pastel. 22-Sep-3 Rasmussen, Vejle #28/R (D.KR 3000)

AROSENIUS, Ivar (1878-1909) Swedish
Works on paper
£480 $860 €701 Spying on the lovers (14x20cm-6x8in) mono.d.02 mixed media. 28-May-4 Uppsala Auktionskammare, Uppsala #174/R (S.KR 6500)
£517 $926 €755 Portrait of man (29x22cm-11x9in) mono.d.03 mixed media. 28-May-4 Uppsala Auktionskammare, Uppsala #171/R (S.KR 7000)
£1035 $1852 €1511 In the pup (14x17cm-6x7in) init.d.1900 W/C. 25-May-4 Bukowskis, Stockholm #24/R (S.KR 14000)
£1154 $1985 €1685 Ball game, Normandy (28x44cm-11x17in) init.d.03 W/C exhib.lit. 2-Dec-3 Bukowskis, Stockholm #45/R est:10000-12000 (S.KR 15000)
£1192 $2051 €1740 An art performance (14x13cm-6x5in) init.d.97 mixed media. 2-Dec-3 Bukowskis, Stockholm #44/R est:8000-10000 (S.KR 15500)
£1615 $2778 €2358 The Viking (20x16cm-8x6in) init.d.05 mixed media. 2-Dec-3 Bukowskis, Stockholm #43/R est:12000-15000 (S.KR 21000)
£2143 $3837 €3129 Self-portrait with beer and sandwich (20x19cm-8x7in) init.d.01 W/C. 25-May-4 Bukowskis, Stockholm #23/R est:15000-18000 (S.KR 29000)
£2462 $4234 €3595 Midsummer (111x161cm-44x63in) init.d.02 W/C. 3-Dec-3 AB Stockholms Auktionsverk #2483/R est:35000-40000 (S.KR 32000)

AROSTEGUI, Alejandro (1935-) Nicaraguan
£172 $286 €249 Petroglifos (195x40cm-77x16in) s.d.1974 plywood. 12-Jun-3 Louis Morton, Mexico #101 est:2100-2500 (M.P 3000)
£229 $381 €332 Petroglifos (60x122cm-24x48in) s.d.1974 wood. 12-Jun-3 Louis Morton, Mexico #102/R est:2100-2500 (M.P 4000)
£287 $476 €416 Still life V (214x84cm-84x33in) s.d.1974 oil collage plywood. 12-Jun-3 Louis Morton, Mexico #99/R est:2000-3000 (M.P 5000)
£402 $667 €583 Ruinas de Managua (181x161cm-71x63in) s.d.1977 oil collage plywood. 12-Jun-3 Louis Morton, Mexico #120/R est:3000-4000 (M.P 7000)
£430 $714 €624 Diosa de la fertilidad (137x112cm-54x44in) s.d.1966 oil collage plywood. 12-Jun-3 Louis Morton, Mexico #113/R est:4000-6000 (M.P 7500)
Works on paper
£184 $305 €267 Paisaje lunar (45x75cm-18x30in) s.d.1980 mixed media. 12-Jun-3 Louis Morton, Mexico #125 est:2000-3000 (M.P 3200)
£488 $810 €708 Nocturno con dos figuras (130x179cm-51x70in) s.d.1997 mixed media collage. 12-Jun-3 Louis Morton, Mexico #124/R est:3000-4000 (M.P 8500)

AROSTEGUI, Juan de (1899-1988) Spanish
£301 $512 €440 Basque figure (56x44cm-22x17in) s. board. 4-Nov-3 Ansorena, Madrid #378/R
£342 $582 €500 Basque fisherman (55x46cm-22x18in) s. 4-Nov-3 Ansorena, Madrid #399/R
£342 $582 €500 Basque fishermen (55x46cm-22x18in) s. 4-Nov-3 Ansorena, Madrid #876/R
£369 $687 €550 Fishermen (81x64cm-32x25in) s. 2-Mar-4 Ansorena, Madrid #322/R

ARP, Carl (1867-1913) German
£385 $654 €550 Sandy area in mountains (14x21cm-6x8in) s. board. 21-Nov-3 Reiss & Sohn, Konigstein #1/R

ARP, Jean (1887-1966) French
£23077 $39692 €33000 Constellation (61x48cm-24x19in) paint relief cardboard exhib.lit. 2-Dec-3 Calmels Cohen, Paris #62/R est:25000-30000
£550000 $1012000 €803000 Cravates et tete (105x135cm-41x53in) s.verso panel painted 1927 prov.exhib.lit. 22-Jun-4 Christie's, London #32/R est:250000-350000
Prints
£2038 $3750 €2975 Composition (56x76cm-22x30in) s. lithograph executed c.1960. 28-Mar-4 Wright, Chicago #567/R est:1500-2000
£2657 $4571 €3800 Paolo and Francesca (17x12cm-7x5in) s. woodcut. 2-Dec-3 Hauswedell & Nolte, Hamburg #4/R est:3800
Sculpture
£1130 $2000 €1650 Amega dans l'omega (27x27cm-11x11in) wood suede box. 2-May-4 Bonhams & Butterfields, Los Angeles #3028/R est:3000-5000
£1600 $2864 €2400 Homme vue par une fleur (10x11x8cm-4x4x3in) bronze prov. 14-May-4 Ketterer, Munich #220/R est:2000-2400
£2029 $3328 €2800 Homme vu par une fleur (10x11cm-4x4in) bronze one of c.400 exec.1958 lit. 27-May-3 Sotheby's, Amsterdam #385/R est:1200-1600
£2238 $3849 €3200 Composition (10x11x8cm-4x4x3in) bronze. 2-Dec-3 Hauswedell & Nolte, Hamburg #3/R est:1800
£3889 $7000 €5678 Relief concret S (53x20cm-21x8in) s. num.2/5 bronze on aluminium prov. 20-Jan-4 Arthur James, Florida #109
£4645 $8500 €6782 Soleil (15x3x15cm-6x1x6in) st.sig.num.6 black pat bronze edition of 8 exec.c.1965. 6-Jun-4 Wright, Chicago #359/R est:5000-7000
£4813 $9000 €7027 Untitled (29x29cm-11x11in) s. num.1/5 polished bronze prov. 25-Feb-4 Christie's, Rockefeller NY #114/R est:8000-12000
£5946 $11000 €8681 Buste silvestre (14cm-6in) i.num.5 5/10 polished bronze prov.lit. 11-Feb-4 Sotheby's, New York #43/R est:12000-18000
£6987 $12716 €10201 Decoupage 25 (41x26cm-16x10in) s. num.1/5 bronze exec. 1962 prov. 18-Jun-4 Kornfeld, Bern #5/R est:15000 (S.FR 16000)

£6993	$12028	€10000	Untitled (50x50cm-20x20in) s.num.4/5 verso duralumin. 2-Dec-3 Calmels Cohen, Paris #70/R est:10000-12000
£7143	$13000	€10429	Buste silvestre (14cm-6in) i.num.7/10 polished bronze conceived 1963 lit. 29-Jun-4 Sotheby's, New York #354/R est:10000-15000
£7175	$11695	€10476	Configuration. Formes preadamites (27x26cm-11x10in) wood relief prov.lit. 29-Sep-3 Christie's, Zurich #103/R est:10000-15000 (S.FR 16000)
£8500	$15640	€12410	Relief Architectonique Vegetal (39x26cm-15x10in) i. num.3/5 verso bronze cast 1959 edn of 5 prov.lit. 22-Jun-4 Sotheby's, London #296/R est:6000-8000
£11765	$20000	€17177	Sculpture mythique (30cm-12in) st.init. polished copper conceived 1949 edn of 5 prov.lit. 6-Nov-3 Sotheby's, New York #297/R est:25000-35000
£19214	$34969	€28052	Untitled (59x60cm-23x24in) painted wood relief exec. 1963 prov.lit. 18-Jun-4 Kornfeld, Bern #6/R est:30000 (S.FR 44000)
£20690	$34552	€30000	Petit theatre (110x68x18cm-43x27x7in) num.4/5 bronze exhib.lit. 17-Nov-3 Sant Agostino, Torino #293/R est:23000-26000
£21678	$37287	€31000	Bonhomme (96x38x12cm-38x15x5in) brass edition 2 of 5 exhib.lit. 2-Dec-3 Calmels Cohen, Paris #61/R est:15000-20000
£22346	$40000	€32625	Couronne chantante (48x49cm-19x19in) wood exec 1966 prov.lit. 6-May-4 Sotheby's, New York #406/R est:25000-35000
£33557	$61745	€50000	Dream figure (31x18x10cm-12x7x4in) white marble steel base exec 1942 prov.exhib.lit. 29-Mar-4 Cornette de St.Cyr, Paris #24/R est:60000-80000
£38235	$65000	€55823	S'accroupissant (54cm-21in) brown pat bronze conceived 1960 prov.lit. 5-Nov-3 Christie's, Rockefeller NY #350/R est:50000-70000
£40000	$73600	€58400	Couple (56x69cm-22x27in) wood relief cloth exec 1945 prov.exhib.lit. 22-Jun-4 Sotheby's, London #193/R est:40000-60000
£41176	$70000	€60117	Sculpture Mediterraneene I (61cm-24in) white marble conceived and exec 1941 lit. 6-Nov-3 Sotheby's, New York #234/R est:60000-80000
£43296	$77500	€63212	Entre feuille et oiseau (63cm-25in) brown pat bronze excl base conceived 1959 prov.exhib.lit. 6-May-4 Sotheby's, New York #331/R est:70000-90000
£65000	$119600	€94900	Sculpture et voussures (61x80cm-24x31in) painted wood relief exec 1957 edn of 2 prov.lit. 22-Jun-4 Sotheby's, London #199/R est:40000-60000
£67039	$120000	€97877	Sculpture Mediterreenne II (40cm-16in) mono. num.1/5 st.f.Susse brown pat bronze conceived 1942 lit. 6-May-4 Sotheby's, New York #375/R est:30000-40000
£88235	$150000	€128823	Assis (29x44x18cm-11x17x7in) limestone exec 1937 prov.exhib.lit. 6-Nov-3 Sotheby's, New York #296/R est:100000-150000
£89385	$160000	€130502	Trois bourgeons (51cm-20in) mono. num.II/III brown pat bronze conceived 1957 prov.exhib.lit. 6-May-4 Sotheby's, New York #336/R est:50000-70000
£100000	$182000	€146000	Daphne I (121cm-48in) green pat bronze one of three conceived 1955 prov.exhib.lit. 3-Feb-4 Christie's, London #237/R est:100000-150000
£155000	$285200	€226300	Torse-fruit (75cm-30in) num.III/V bronze st.f.Georges Rudier lit. 22-Jun-4 Sotheby's, London #299/R est:80000-120000
£350000	$640500	€511000	Configuration (70x55cm-28x22in) painted wood relife executed 1932 prov.exhib.lit. 2-Feb-4 Christie's, London #54/R est:150000-200000
£411765	$700000	€601177	Meudon Venus (190cm-75in) num.I polished gold pat. st.f.Susse executed 1956 prov.exhib.lit. 5-Nov-3 Sotheby's, New York #55/R est:600000-800000
Works on paper			
£183	$306	€265	Composition (29x21cm-11x8in) s. brush Indian ink prov. 19-Jun-3 Kornfeld, Bern #170 (S.FR 400)
£764	$1276	€1100	Arp par Michel Seuphor (21x18cm-8x7in) s. graphite. 25-Oct-3 Cornette de St.Cyr, Paris #575/R
£1101	$1839	€1596	Figure (37x27cm-15x11in) s. pencil. 19-Jun-3 Kornfeld, Bern #172 est:4000 (S.FR 2400)
£1485	$2732	€2168	Composition (33x23cm-13x9in) s. W/C on col woodcut lit. 8-Jun-4 Germann, Zurich #128/R est:3500-4500 (S.FR 3400)
£1748	$3007	€2500	Untitled (18x22cm-7x9in) s. collage prov.exhib. 2-Dec-3 Calmels Cohen, Paris #36/R est:1500-2000
£2937	$5052	€4200	Untitled (13x13cm-5x5in) collage. 2-Dec-3 Calmels Cohen, Paris #35/R est:1500-2000
£3020	$5406	€4500	Untitled (31x17cm-12x7in) s. d.66 verso pencil W/C prov. 25-May-4 Sotheby's, Milan #7/R est:3000
£3303	$5516	€4789	Untitled (45x31cm-18x12in) s. chl on W/C exhib. 19-Jun-3 Kornfeld, Bern #173/R est:7500 (S.FR 7200)
£3636	$6255	€5200	Untitled (26x20cm-10x8in) s.indis.i. Indian ink tracing paper. 2-Dec-3 Calmels Cohen, Paris #37/R est:3000-4000
£3636	$6255	€5200	Untitled (27x20cm-11x8in) Indian ink. 2-Dec-3 Calmels Cohen, Paris #38/R est:3000-4000
£3846	$6615	€5500	Untitled (30x44cm-12x17in) chl pastel. 2-Dec-3 Calmels Cohen, Paris #39/R est:4000-5000
£4698	$8409	€7000	Constellation (29x21cm-11x8in) s.d.43 graphite. 27-May-4 Christie's, Paris #142/R est:10000-15000
£4737	$8716	€7200	Composition (31x46cm-12x18in) W/C crayon. 24-Jun-4 Credit Municipal, Paris #33/R est:6500-8000
£5430	$9231	€7928	Face landscape (34x24cm-13x9in) s. W/C pencil exec. c.1960. 22-Nov-3 Burkhard, Luzern #120/R est:12000-14000 (S.FR 12000)
£5459	$9934	€7970	Collage aux formes standardisee (44x26cm-17x10in) s. frottage collage drawing prov. 17-Jun-4 Kornfeld, Bern #162/R est:10000 (S.FR 12500)
£6000	$11040	€8760	Sur une pointe (16x18cm-6x7in) s. collage exec.1959 prov. 22-Jun-4 Sotheby's, London #511/R est:7000-9000
£6135	$10000	€8957	Composition noire et grise (25x22cm-10x9in) s. chl paper collage paper on board prov. 25-Sep-3 Christie's, Rockefeller NY #610/R est:3000-5000
£7823	$14003	€11500	Alchimie optique (51x38cm-20x15in) s. crayon exec 1961 prov.exhib.lit. 21-Mar-4 Calmels Cohen, Paris #42/R est:12000-15000
£8257	$13789	€11973	T Gaston Puel (65x50cm-26x20in) s.i. gouache. 19-Jun-3 Kornfeld, Bern #174/R est:20000 (S.FR 18000)
£24667	$44893	€37000	Two flowers (56x71cm-22x28in) s. verso cut board paint prov.exhib.lit. 30-Jun-4 Calmels Cohen, Paris #63/R est:40000-50000

ARPA Y PEREA, Jose (attrib) (1860-1952) Spanish

£391	$700	€571	Portrait of a lady in white manila. i. 13-May-4 Dallas Auction Gallery, Dallas #191/R

ARPA, Jose (1860-1952) Spanish

£369	$661	€550	Procession (9x15cm-4x6in) s. board. 25-May-4 Durán, Madrid #159/R
£403	$721	€600	Toledo (9x15cm-4x6in) s. board. 25-May-4 Durán, Madrid #160/R

ARPAD, Romek (1883-1960) Hungarian

£378	$684	€552	Still life with pots and bottles (48x59cm-19x23in) s. 30-Mar-4 Stephan Welz, Johannesburg #165 est:2000-3000 (SA.R 4500)

ARPKE, Otto (1886-1943) German

£1000	$1830	€1500	Bacchanal (76x90cm-30x35in) s.d.1917 after J Jordaens. 5-Jun-4 Arnold, Frankfurt #525/R est:2000

ARPS, Bernardus (1865-1938) Dutch

£268	$499	€400	Woman gathering wood on forest path (40x60cm-16x24in) s. 4-Mar-4 Auction Maastricht #1131/R

ARRANZ BRAVO, Eduard (1941-) Spanish

£810	$1296	€1150	Bala-cab (50x50cm-20x20in) s.d.1968 s.i.d.verso prov.lit. 16-Sep-3 Segre, Madrid #153/R
£1361	$2476	€2000	Woman and head of man (61x50cm-24x20in) s. s.i.d.1967 verso lit. 3-Feb-4 Segre, Madrid #308/R est:1400
Works on paper			
£590	$1003	€850	Red landscape (50x65cm-20x26in) s.d.1971 gouache board. 28-Oct-3 Segre, Madrid #307/R

ARREDONDO Y CALMACHE, Ricardo (1850-1911) Spanish

£7895	$14526	€12000	Virgin Path, Toledo (46x84cm-18x33in) 22-Jun-4 Durán, Madrid #209/R est:4500
£8844	$15830	€13000	Toledo (75x54cm-30x21in) s. 22-Mar-4 Durán, Madrid #219/R est:4250
£9420	$15449	€13000	Camino de la Virgen, Toledo (46x84cm-18x33in) 27-May-3 Durán, Madrid #261/R est:7500
£10526	$19368	€16000	River Tajo (85x58cm-33x23in) s. 22-Jun-4 Durán, Madrid #210/R est:6000
£11111	$18111	€16000	Rocky landscape (46x86cm-18x34in) s. 23-Sep-3 Durán, Madrid #185/R est:14000
£11806	$19243	€17000	Patio with pots (49x70cm-19x28in) s. 23-Sep-3 Durán, Madrid #184/R est:14000
£13043	$21391	€18000	En el patio del cigarral (46x86cm-18x34in) s. 27-May-3 Durán, Madrid #260/R est:10000
£13194	$21507	€19000	River Tajo (85x58cm-33x23in) s. 23-Sep-3 Durán, Madrid #186/R est:18000
£18116	$29710	€25000	Panoramica de Toledo (52x76cm-20x30in) s. 27-May-3 Durán, Madrid #259/R est:25000

ARREGUI, Romana (1875-1932) French

£867	$1569	€1300	Old man smoking cigar (27x22cm-11x9in) s. board. 30-Mar-4 Segre, Madrid #106/R
£867	$1569	€1300	Old man with hat and pipe (27x22cm-11x9in) s. board. 30-Mar-4 Segre, Madrid #107/R
£952	$1733	€1400	Couple de pecheurs (27x21cm-11x8in) s. panel pair. 8-Feb-4 Anaf, Lyon #75 est:1400-1800
£1000	$1820	€1500	Ancianos (38x61cm-15x24in) s. 29-Jun-4 Segre, Madrid #28/R est:1500
£1419	$2497	€2100	Philosopher with book (64x54cm-25x21in) s. i.verso. 18-May-4 Segre, Madrid #40/R est:2100
£1419	$2497	€2100	Philosopher (64x54cm-25x21in) s. i.verso. 18-May-4 Segre, Madrid #41/R est:2100

ARRESSE (fl.1790-1800) French

Miniatures			
£2400	$4152	€3504	Young officer in green coat with silver buttons and silver epaulette (6cm-2in circular) s. silver-gilt frame. 9-Dec-3 Christie's, London #91/R est:1000-1500

ARRIETA, Virgilio (20th C) Venezuelan?

£456	$720	€666	Pulling the nets (110x130cm-43x51in) s. painted 1999. 1-Dec-2 Subastas Odalys, Caracas #96/R

ARRIGONI, Antonio (attrib) (1664-c.1730) Italian

£4577	$8011	€6500	Jefte meeting his daughter (112x159cm-44x63in) 17-Dec-3 Christie's, Rome #457/R est:5000-7000

ARRIGONI-NERI, Jean Francois (1937-) Italian?

Works on paper			
£302	$562	€450	Voilier (50x34cm-20x13in) s. W/C. 7-Mar-4 Lesieur & Le Bars, Le Havre #174
£317	$513	€450	Voilier anglais (46x34cm-18x13in) s. W/C. 11-Aug-3 Boscher, Cherbourg #790
£347	$580	€500	Canot de peche (50x35cm-20x14in) s. W/C. 26-Oct-3 Lesieur & Le Bars, Le Havre #117

ARROWSMITH, Sue (1968-) British

Works on paper			
£500	$910	€730	Untitled (56x76cm-22x30in) pencil acrylic. 21-Jun-4 Bonhams, New Bond Street #109/R
£650	$1183	€949	Untitled (56x76cm-22x30in) pencil ink. 21-Jun-4 Bonhams, New Bond Street #108/R

ARROWSMITH, Thomas (18/19th C) British

Miniatures			
£1700	$3128	€2482	Young boy, with long blond hair, wearing a scarlet coat (2cm-1in) s.d.1797 verso gold frame prov.exhib. 24-Jun-4 Bonhams, New Bond Street #87/R est:700-900

ARROYO, Edouard (1937-) Spanish

£2667	$4853	€4000	Butterfly's corrida (46x55cm-18x22in) s.d.1960 oil collage prov. 29-Jun-4 Cornette de St.Cyr, Paris #85/R est:4000-5000
£3000	$5460	€4500	Warrior (66x102cm-26x40in) s.d.1960 verso prov. 29-Jun-4 Cornette de St.Cyr, Paris #86/R est:4000-5000
£4514	$7448	€6500	Sans titre (96x78cm-38x31in) s. painted c.1970 prov. 2-Jul-3 Cornette de St.Cyr, Paris #124/R est:10000-12000
£6897	$12414	€10000	Landscape and figure (34x82cm-13x32in) s.d.1985 canvas on board. 26-Jan-4 Ansorena, Madrid #897/R est:10000
£7746	$13556	€11000	Parmi les peintres (74x54cm-29x21in) s. oil gouache paper. 18-Dec-3 Cornette de St.Cyr, Paris #118/R est:12000-15000
£8000	$14720	€12000	Yellow (73x60cm-29x24in) s. s.i.verso prov. 14-Jun-4 Porro, Milan #46/R est:11000-13000

£8667 $15773 €13000 Carmen Amaya - Waldorf Astoria (45x61cm-18x24in) s.d.1989 oil gouache collage paper prov.exhib.lit. 29-Jun-4 Segre, Madrid #175/R est:6600
£11016 $19498 €16415 Pont d'Arcole (250x200cm-98x79in) s.d.65 prov. 28-Apr-4 Artcurial Briest, Paris #396/R est:1000-15000
£19014 $33275 €27000 Parmi les peintres (54x73cm-21x29in) s. oil gouache paper. 18-Dec-3 Cornette de St.Cyr, Paris #119/R est:18000-20000
£27113 $47447 €38500 Parmi les peintes - Churchill peintre (92x73cm-36x29in) s.d.1969 s.i.d.verso. 18-Dec-3 Cornette de St.Cyr, Paris #117/R est:40000-50000
Sculpture
£1000 $1840 €1500 Churchill painter (43x43cm-17x17in) painted ceramic exec.1973. 14-Jun-4 Sant Agostino, Torino #376/R est:1500-2000
£1972 $3411 €2800 Martirio (38x21x27cm-15x8x11in) s.num.6/9 steel aluminium. 14-Dec-3 Versailles Encheres #171/R est:2500-3000
Works on paper
£1000 $1670 €1460 Tanger (33x57cm-13x22in) s.i.d.1985 collage pencil grey pastel prov. 22-Oct-3 Bonhams, New Bond Street #92/R est:1000-1500
£1275 $2346 €1900 Reflexions sur l'exil, Sevilla-Franfurt/Main. s.i.d.1978 col crayon cardboard prov. 24-Mar-4 Binoche, Paris #104/R est:1000-1500
£2000 $3640 €3000 Pez (34x45cm-13x18in) s.i.d.1989 gouache wash collage card on panel. 29-Jun-4 Segre, Madrid #174/R est:3000
£2113 $3655 €3000 Jean Charles de Castelbajac en ramoneur (102x66cm-40x26in) s.i.d.1982 graphite wax crayon. 14-Dec-3 Versailles Encheres #170/R est:2500-3000
£2113 $3697 €3000 Serie - Saul Steinberg dans le desert (50x54cm-20x21in) s.d.1972 gouache collage paper on canvas prov. 18-Dec-3 Cornette de St.Cyr, Paris #124/R est:3000-4000
£2639 $4407 €3800 Reflexions sur l'exile (40x60cm-16x24in) s.i.d.1978 wax crayon, col pencil gouache prov. 21-Oct-3 Christie's, Paris #122/R est:2000-3000
£3221 $5766 €4800 Composition (46x56cm-18x22in) s.i.d.74 verso collage on sand paper exhib. 25-May-4 Sotheby's, Milan #219/R est:3500-4000
£3239 $5669 €4600 Three figures (32x27cm-13x11in) s.d.1983 W/C gouache prov.exhib. 16-Dec-3 Segre, Madrid #151/R est:4000
£3521 $6092 €5000 Tina (66x50cm-26x20in) s.d.1972 s.i.d.verso col crayon prov. 9-Dec-3 Artcurial Briest, Paris #383/R est:4000-6000
£3873 $6778 €5500 Homme au chapeau rouge (52x40cm-20x16in) s.d.1982 gouache W/C lead pencil. 18-Dec-3 Cornette de St.Cyr, Paris #123/R est:2500-4000
£4200 $7014 €6132 Ramoneur XIII (102x73cm-40x29in) s.d.1979 pencil chl crayon prov. 22-Oct-3 Bonhams, New Bond Street #91/R est:3000-4000
£4730 $8324 €7000 Man with hat (78x56cm-31x22in) s. mixed media paper on canvas. 19-May-4 Il Ponte, Milan #1126 est:5000-6000
£5245 $8759 €7500 Portrait d'acteur (64x49cm-25x19in) s.d.1975 pastel prov. 11-Oct-3 De Vuyst, Lokeren #492/R est:8500-10000
£5986 $10475 €8500 Red Flag (100x70cm-39x28in) s.d.1968 s.i.verso gouache paper on canvas. 18-Dec-3 Cornette de St.Cyr, Paris #125/R est:4000-6000
£7113 $12447 €10100 Le Pont d'Arcole (100x70cm-39x28in) s.i.d.1961 mixed media board on canvas. 18-Dec-3 Cornette de St.Cyr, Paris #126/R est:5000-7000

ARRUE Y VALLE, Jose (1885-1977) Spanish
Works on paper
£6993 $11678 €10000 Popular dance in Orozco (33x24cm-13x9in) s. W/C. 30-Jun-3 Ansorena, Madrid #42/R est:9000

ARRUE, Ramiro (1892-1971) Spanish
£4437 $8075 €6700 Cote basque (36x44cm-14x17in) s. 20-Jun-4 Salle des ventes Pillet, Lyon la Foret #7/R est:8000-10000
£9220 $15397 €13000 Le ronde basque (32x40cm-13x16in) s. panel. 19-Jun-3 Millon & Associes, Paris #232/R est:2000-3000
£22297 $39912 €33000 Paysage du Pays Basque (50x60cm-20x24in) s.i.d.21 panel prov. 5-May-4 Coutau Begarie, Paris #56/R est:8000-12000
Works on paper
£1225 $2230 €1850 La rencontre devant le village (22x30cm-9x12in) s. gouache. 20-Jun-4 Salle des ventes Pillet, Lyon la Foret #4/R est:1800-2000
£1258 $2290 €1900 La parade (20x26cm-8x10in) s. gouache. 20-Jun-4 Salle des ventes Pillet, Lyon la Foret #6/R est:1800-2000
£1267 $2293 €1900 Basque devant un village (26x16cm-10x6in) s. gouache. 4-Apr-4 Salle des ventes Pillet, Lyon la Foret #2/R est:1500-2000
£1656 $3013 €2500 Danse basque devant un village (21x28cm-8x11in) s. gouache. 20-Jun-4 Salle des ventes Pillet, Lyon la Foret #5/R est:1800-2000
£1833 $3318 €2750 Couple basque et boeufs devant un village (20x22cm-8x9in) s. gouache. 4-Apr-4 Salle des ventes Pillet, Lyon la Foret #3/R est:1500-2000
£1993 $3328 €2850 Basque figures playing cards (26x32cm-10x13in) s. mixed media. 30-Jun-3 Ansorena, Madrid #234/R

ARSENIUS, John (1818-1903) Swedish
£435 $784 €635 Study of a dog (27x19cm-11x7in) s. panel. 26-Jan-4 Lilla Bukowskis, Stockholm #35 (S.KR 5800)
£480 $860 €701 Haymaking (23x26cm-9x10in) s. 26-May-4 AB Stockholms Auktionsverk #2160/R (S.KR 6500)
£2143 $3837 €3129 Hussar on horseback (54x43cm-21x17in) s. 25-May-4 Bukowskis, Stockholm #238/R est:20000-25000 (S.KR 29000)
£3077 $5292 €4492 Stable interior with horse (75x92cm-30x36in) s.d.1854. 3-Dec-3 AB Stockholms Auktionsverk #2389/R est:12000-15000 (S.KR 40000)
£11154 $19185 €16285 Stable boy with horses (113x150cm-44x59in) s. prov.lit. 2-Dec-3 Bukowskis, Stockholm #147/R est:80000-100000 (S.KR 145000)

ARSENIUS, Karl Georg (1855-1908) Swedish
£2000 $3440 €2920 Woman on horseback and dog in landscape (60x50cm-24x20in) s.d.1895 exhib. 7-Dec-3 Uppsala Auktionskammare, Uppsala #165/R est:15000-20000 (S.KR 26000)

ARSENIUS, Sam (1857-1912) Swedish
£352 $566 €514 Horse in meadow (46x52cm-18x20in) s. 25-Aug-3 Lilla Bukowskis, Stockholm #439 (S.KR 4600)

ARSLAN, Yuksel (20th C) French?
Works on paper
£1701 $3044 €2500 Portrait of Edouard Roditi (51x40cm-20x16in) s.i.d.1964 col crayons pastel. 21-Mar-4 Calmels Cohen, Paris #73 est:800-1000

ARSON, Alphonse Alexandre (1822-c.1880) French
Sculpture
£1491 $2400 €2177 Standing bull (27cm-11in) i. bronze. 14-Jan-4 Christie's, Rockefeller NY #307/R est:2000-3000
£1988 $3200 €2902 Standing bull (27cm-11in) i. bronze. 14-Jan-4 Christie's, Rockefeller NY #306/R est:2000-3000

ART, Berthe (1857-1934) Belgian
Works on paper
£789 $1453 €1200 Vase, fleurs et potirons (55x75cm-22x30in) s. pastel. 22-Jun-4 Palais de Beaux Arts, Brussels #193/R
£940 $1738 €1400 Bouquet de roses (80x60cm-31x24in) s. pastel gouache. 15-Mar-4 Horta, Bruxelles #187
£1342 $2483 €2000 Still life with yellow roses (75x65cm-30x26in) s. pastel paper on canvas. 13-Mar-4 De Vuyst, Lokeren #13/R est:2200-2600
£1447 $2663 €2200 Bouquet de fleurs (81x65cm-32x26in) s. pastel. 22-Jun-4 Palais de Beaux Arts, Brussels #192/R est:1000-1500
£2368 $4358 €3600 Quatre perroquets (81x68cm-32x27in) s. pastel. 22-Jun-4 Palais de Beaux Arts, Brussels #191/R est:1800-2400

ARTAN, Louis (1837-1890) Belgian
£541 $1022 €800 Marine (39x54cm-15x21in) s. 17-Feb-4 Vanderkindere, Brussels #48
£625 $994 €900 Voilier en Mer du Nord (18x26cm-7x10in) s. 15-Sep-3 Horta, Bruxelles #356
£979 $1635 €1400 Voiliers en mer du Nord (29x62cm-11x24in) s. 13-Oct-3 Horta, Bruxelles #241
£1370 $2329 €2000 Vue de l'Escaut (26x50cm-10x20in) s. 10-Nov-3 Horta, Bruxelles #320
£1656 $3013 €2500 Mer agitee au crepuscule (101x150cm-40x59in) s. 15-Jun-4 Vanderkindere, Brussels #16 est:1500-2000
£1733 $3172 €2600 Bateaux de peche en mer (33x63cm-13x25in) s. 7-Jun-4 Palais de Beaux Arts, Brussels #226/R est:2500-3500
£1972 $3411 €2800 Retour des pecheurs (23x50cm-9x20in) s. 9-Dec-3 Vanderkindere, Brussels #136 est:1300-1600
£2028 $3387 €2900 Les preparatifs de la barque de peche (43x63cm-17x25in) s. 13-Oct-3 Horta, Bruxelles #240/R est:2000-3000

ARTAN, Louis (attrib) (1837-1890) Belgian
£8333 $13250 €12000 Le phare de Nieuport (101x70cm-40x28in) prov. 9-Sep-3 Palais de Beaux Arts, Brussels #194 est:300-450

ARTARIO, Charles (19th C) Italian
£1117 $2000 €1631 Courting scene (24x19cm-9x7in) 9-Jan-4 Du Mouchelle, Detroit #2002/R est:2000-4000

ARTAUD, William (1763-1823) British
£250 $418 €365 Tobit drawing away the evil spirit (21x38cm-8x15in) i.verso panel. 13-Nov-3 Christie's, Kensington #306/R

ARTEAGA Y ALFARO, Matias (1630-1703) Spanish
£4545 $7591 €6500 Biblical scene (147x93cm-58x37in) s. 30-Jun-3 Ansorena, Madrid #171/R

ARTEMOFF, Georges (1892-1965) Russian
£2185 $3977 €3300 Nature morte aux fleurs et fruits (65x46cm-26x18in) s. 16-Jun-4 Claude Boisgirard, Paris #20/R est:3000-3500
£9396 $17289 €14000 Lapon en vetement traditionnel portant un arc et une biche sur ses epaules (125x87cm-49x34in) s. stained carved wood panel. 26-Mar-4 Neret-Minet, Paris #48/R est:15000
Sculpture
£9790 $16643 €14000 Femme ailee (139x59cm-55x23in) s. polished wood relief. 24-Nov-3 Tajan, Paris #37/R est:15000-18000
Works on paper
£319 $504 €450 Man with guitar (43x33cm-17x13in) s. W/C. 24-Jul-3 Claude Boisgirard, Paris #48/R

ARTENS, Peter von (1937-) Colombian
£9412 $16000 €13742 Still life (91x91cm-36x36in) s. 19-Nov-3 Sotheby's, New York #179/R est:20000-25000
£10615 $19000 €15498 Untitled (101x101cm-40x40in) s. painted 2000. 26-May-4 Sotheby's, New York #150/R est:25000-30000

ARTER, Charles John (1860-1923) American
£2402 $4371 €3507 The turkey girl (38x53cm-15x21in) s.d.1898. 16-Jun-4 Fischer, Luzern #1113/R est:4500-5500 (S.FR 5500)
£2609 $4200 €3809 Flower seller in Venice (81x129cm-32x51in) s. 14-Jan-4 Christie's, Rockefeller NY #1/R est:4000-6000

ARTIGUE, Jack (20th C) French
£268 $491 €400 Bretonnes dans un interior (44x35cm-17x14in) s. isorel. 7-Jul-4 Artcurial Briest, Paris #74

ARTIOLI, Bruno (1943-2000) Italian
£282 $468 €400 Barca sulla spiaggia (40x40cm-16x16in) s. oil sand panel. 14-Jun-3 Meeting Art, Vercelli #376
£317 $526 €450 Le Barche a Vela (35x50cm-14x20in) s. oil sand panel. 14-Jun-3 Meeting Art, Vercelli #636
£333 $613 €500 Cabins on the beach (30x50cm-12x20in) s. oil sand board. 12-Jun-4 Meeting Art, Vercelli #688/R
£336 $621 €500 Beached boat (50x50cm-20x20in) s. oil sand board. 13-Mar-4 Meeting Art, Vercelli #243

£367	$675	€550	Beached boats (50x60cm-20x24in) s. oil sand board. 12-Jun-4 Meeting Art, Vercelli #294/R
£367	$675	€550	Girl on bike (70x50cm-28x20in) s. s.verso. 12-Jun-4 Meeting Art, Vercelli #514
£367	$675	€550	Beach (40x50cm-16x20in) s. s.verso oil sand board lit. 12-Jun-4 Meeting Art, Vercelli #586/R
£500	$920	€750	Beach (50x70cm-20x28in) s. s.verso oil sand lit. 12-Jun-4 Meeting Art, Vercelli #193/R
£500	$920	€750	Windy day (60x80cm-24x31in) s. oil sand. 12-Jun-4 Meeting Art, Vercelli #566/R
£503	$931	€750	Parasols (60x90cm-24x35in) s. s.verso oil mixed media board painted 2000. 13-Mar-4 Meeting Art, Vercelli #190
£503	$931	€750	Beached boats (70x80cm-28x31in) s.s.verso oil sand board. 13-Mar-4 Meeting Art, Vercelli #234
£667	$1227	€1000	Boat and parasol (80x110cm-31x43in) s. oil sand board. 12-Jun-4 Meeting Art, Vercelli #974/R
£772	$1428	€1150	Sailing boats in the silence (40x70cm-16x28in) s. s.i.d.verso oil sand board lit. 13-Mar-4 Meeting Art, Vercelli #528

ARTS, Alexis (1940-) Canadian

£222	$384	€324	Rue Sherbrooke et Bishop, Montreal (61x46cm-24x18in) s. s.i.d.88 verso. 9-Dec-3 Pinneys, Montreal #177 (C.D 500)

ARTS, Dorus (1901-1961) Dutch

£748	$1362	€1100	Waterlillies in a forest pond (70x60cm-28x24in) s. 3-Feb-4 Christie's, Amsterdam #208 est:800-1200
£893	$1536	€1304	Gathering firewood (51x71cm-20x28in) s. 2-Dec-3 Joyner Waddington, Toronto #344/R est:2000-3000 (C.D 2000)

ARTSCHWAGER, Richard (1923-) American

£9000	$15030	€13140	Weaving 11 (54x63cm-21x25in) s.d.70 verso acrylic celotex prov. 22-Oct-3 Christie's, London #79/R est:10000-15000
£14970	$25000	€21856	Untitled (126x64cm-50x25in) acrylic celotex wood mirror painted c.1980 prov. 13-Nov-3 Sotheby's, New York #567/R est:20000-30000
£20000	$36400	€29200	Descent of Zed (142x107cm-56x42in) acrylic celotex exec 1989 prov.exhib. 5-Feb-4 Christie's, London #190/R est:10000-15000
£28000	$46760	€40880	Tree of life (134x89cm-53x35in) acrylic celotex prov. 22-Oct-3 Christie's, London #82/R est:20000-30000
£36313	$65000	€53017	Porch (103x125cm-41x49in) acrylic celotex painted 1971 prov. 13-May-4 Sotheby's, New York #225/R est:50000-70000
Sculpture			
£2119	$3750	€3094	Book (13x51x30cm-5x20x12in) s.num.5 formica on wood. 30-Apr-4 Sotheby's, New York #301/R est:2500-3500
£6704	$12000	€9788	Pregunta II (75x28x5cm-30x11x2in) s.i.d.83 num.3/6 verso oil shellac wood two parts prov.exhib. 12-May-4 Christie's, Rockefeller NY #483/R est:10000-15000
£7186	$12000	€10492	D W II (161x79x55cm-63x31x22in) plywood pine hardware prov. 13-Nov-3 Sotheby's, New York #568/R est:12000-18000
£7186	$12000	€10492	Untitled - cross sculpture (116x106x81cm-46x42x32in) s.d.1994 wood metal fasteners sold with pen dr. same subject. 14-Nov-3 Phillips, New York #170/R est:20000-30000
£20134	$37047	€30000	Instrument (150x60x30cm-59x24x12in) s.i.d.1990 base wood formica prov. 29-Mar-4 Cornette de St.Cyr, Paris #55/R est:30000-40000
Works on paper			
£313	$509	€450	Berlin - sun - rise (10x15cm-4x6in) s.d.1990 Indian ink board. 27-Sep-3 Dr Fritz Nagel, Stuttgart #9030/R
£2198	$4000	€3209	Volcano III (48x63cm-19x25in) s.d.82 chl prov. 29-Jun-4 Sotheby's, New York #529/R est:6000-8000

ARTUS, Charles (1897-1978) French

Sculpture			
£1361	$2163	€2000	Ours (11x19cm-4x7in) s. laster prov. 23-Mar-3 Salle des ventes Pillet, Lyon la Foret #141
£1429	$2271	€2100	Panthere (11x17cm-4x7in) s. plaster prov. 23-Mar-3 Salle des ventes Pillet, Lyon la Foret #140
£1633	$2596	€2400	Taureau (16x23cm-6x9in) s. plaster prov. 23-Mar-3 Salle des ventes Pillet, Lyon la Foret #146
£1701	$2704	€2500	Antilope (22cm-9in) s. plaster prov. 23-Mar-3 Salle des ventes Pillet, Lyon la Foret #144
£2109	$3353	€3100	Coq (33x22cm-13x9in) s.plaster. 23-Mar-3 Salle des ventes Pillet, Lyon la Foret #139
£2318	$4219	€3500	Antilope couchee (13x24cm-5x9in) s.i. pat bronze marble base Cast Valsuani. 20-Jun-4 Salle des ventes Pillet, Lyon la Foret #164/R est:3500-4000
£2721	$4327	€4000	Levrier (21x31cm-8x12in) s. black pat bronze. 23-Mar-3 Salle des ventes Pillet, Lyon la Foret #134
£2721	$4327	€4000	Vache (27x44cm-11x17in) s. plaster prov. 23-Mar-3 Salle des ventes Pillet, Lyon la Foret #138
£2721	$4327	€4000	Brocard (16x32cm-6x13in) s. plaster prov. 23-Mar-3 Salle des ventes Pillet, Lyon la Foret #145
£2789	$4435	€4100	Caniche royal (18x18cm-7x7in) s. clay prov. 23-Mar-3 Salle des ventes Pillet, Lyon la Foret #147
£3061	$4867	€4500	Pigeon (32x13cm-13x5in) s. black pat bronze. 23-Mar-3 Salle des ventes Pillet, Lyon la Foret #135
£3401	$5408	€5000	Truie (28x50cm-11x20in) s. plaster. 23-Mar-3 Salle des ventes Pillet, Lyon la Foret #137
£3741	$5949	€5500	Chien couche (9x34cm-4x13in) s. brown pat bronze. 23-Mar-3 Salle des ventes Pillet, Lyon la Foret #136
£10408	$16549	€15300	Corbeau (35x32cm-14x13in) s. black pat bronze. 23-Mar-3 Salle des ventes Pillet, Lyon la Foret #133
£10544	$16765	€15500	Poule sultane (42x44cm-17x17in) s.st.f.Valsuani black pat bronze. 23-Mar-3 Salle des ventes Pillet, Lyon la Foret #132
£17007	$27041	€25000	Ibis rouges (50x67cm-20x26in) s. brown pat bronze prov. 23-Mar-3 Salle des ventes Pillet, Lyon la Foret #131 est:18000

ARTUS, Walter (1873-1945) German

Works on paper			
£369	$687	€550	View of Rochlitz Castle (45x54cm-18x21in) s.d.1923 W/C. 5-Mar-4 Wendl, Rudolstadt #3559/R

ARTYMOWSKI, Roman (1919-1993) Polish

£777	$1406	€1166	Landscape (70x100cm-28x39in) s.d.58. 4-Apr-4 Agra, Warsaw #16/R (P.Z 5500)

ARTZ, Constant (1870-1951) Dutch

£272	$495	€400	Duck family (18x24cm-7x9in) s. plywood. 3-Feb-4 Christie's, Amsterdam #180
£395	$726	€600	Going for a swim (18x24cm-7x9in) s. plywood. 22-Jun-4 Christie's, Amsterdam #196/R
£699	$1203	€1000	Ducks near the waterside (12x18cm-5x7in) s. panel. 7-Dec-3 Sotheby's, Amsterdam #634/R
£789	$1453	€1200	Ducks by the waterside (24x30cm-9x12in) s. plywood. 22-Jun-4 Christie's, Amsterdam #187/R
£789	$1453	€1200	Ducks with their ducklings near the waterfront (18x24cm-7x9in) s. panel. 28-Jun-4 Sotheby's, Amsterdam #31/R
£1141	$2111	€1700	Duck with her ducklings near the waterfront (15x28cm-6x11in) s. panel. 15-Mar-4 Sotheby's, Amsterdam #91/R est:1200-1800
£1233	$2096	€1800	Ducks at the edge of the water (17x24cm-7x9in) s. panel. 5-Nov-3 Vendue Huis, Gravenhage #131/R est:1500-2000
£1250	$2300	€1900	Ducks and ducklings in a meadow (23x32cm-9x13in) s. panel. 22-Jun-4 Christie's, Amsterdam #254/R est:1200-1600
£1275	$2359	€1900	Duck with her ducklings near birch trees (24x18cm-9x7in) s. panel. 15-Mar-4 Sotheby's, Amsterdam #93/R est:1500-2500
£1301	$2212	€1900	Ducks at the edge of the water (17x23cm-7x9in) s. panel. 5-Nov-3 Vendue Huis, Gravenhage #132/R est:1750-2000
£1316	$2421	€2000	Duck with ducklings near the waterside (17x22cm-7x9in) s. panel. 28-Jun-4 Sotheby's, Amsterdam #67/R est:2000-3000
£1333	$2387	€2000	Duck family by the water edge (39x48cm-15x19in) s. 11-May-4 Vendu Notarishuis, Rotterdam #49/R est:1500-2000
£1447	$2663	€2200	Duck with ducklings in a landscape (30x40cm-12x16in) s. panel. 28-Jun-4 Sotheby's, Amsterdam #64/R est:2000-3000
£1477	$2717	€2200	Duck with ducklings in stream (29x40cm-11x16in) s. panel lit. 25-Mar-4 Karlheinz Kaupp, Staufen #2340/R est:1700
£1667	$2717	€2400	Duck with her ducklings on the riverbank (18x24cm-7x9in) s. panel. 29-Sep-3 Sotheby's, Amsterdam #127/R
£1905	$3467	€2800	Taking the brood water (25x30cm-10x12in) s. 3-Feb-4 Christie's, Amsterdam #189/R est:2000-3000
£1905	$3467	€2800	Ducks by the waterside (47x39cm-19x15in) s. plywood. 3-Feb-4 Christie's, Amsterdam #274/R est:3000-5000
£1958	$3368	€2800	Duck family (60x100cm-24x39in) s. 8-Dec-3 Glerum, Amsterdam #72/R est:3500-5000
£2177	$3962	€3200	First swim (40x50cm-16x20in) s. plywood. 3-Feb-4 Christie's, Amsterdam #276/R est:2500-3500
£2303	$4168	€3500	Duck family (50x40cm-20x16in) s. 19-Apr-4 Glerum, Amsterdam #231/R est:3500-4000
£3000	$5520	€4380	Ducks and ducklings on a river bank (40x81cm-16x32in) s. 25-Mar-4 Christie's, Kensington #172/R est:3000-5000
£6000	$11100	€8760	First swim (55x85cm-22x33in) s. 14-Jul-4 Sotheby's, Olympia #181/R est:2000-3000
Works on paper			
£483	$806	€700	Ducks at the edge of the ditch (23x32cm-9x13in) s. W/C. 11-Nov-3 Vendu Notarishuis, Rotterdam #51

ARTZ, David Adolf Constant (1837-1890) Dutch

£1860	$3200	€2716	Family meal (56x71cm-22x28in) s. 2-Dec-3 Christie's, Rockefeller NY #40/R est:4000-6000
£2857	$5200	€4200	Return of the flock (30x13cm-12x5in) s. panel prov. 3-Feb-4 Christie's, Amsterdam #143/R est:3000-5000
Works on paper			
£1300	$2249	€1898	Minding the baby (55x43cm-22x17in) s. W/C. 11-Dec-3 Lyon & Turnbull, Edinburgh #34/R est:1000-1500
£2333	$4200	€3500	Before supper (65x89cm-26x35in) s. chl black chk prov.exhib.lit. 21-Apr-4 Christie's, Amsterdam #101/R est:3000-5000

ASCH, Pieter Jansz van (1603-1678) Dutch

£2432	$4281	€3600	Trees along canal (29x36cm-11x14in) panel. 22-May-4 Lempertz, Koln #1004/R est:4500
£3000	$5370	€4500	Figures in landscape with river (71x91cm-28x36in) init. board. 12-May-4 Finarte Semenzato, Milan #79/R est:5000-7000
£3017	$5552	€4405	Landscape with shepherd and fishermen (48x66cm-19x26in) mono. panel prov. 26-Mar-4 Koller, Zurich #3031/R est:10000-14000 (S.FR 7000)
£6400	$11712	€9344	Wooded river landscape (48x66cm-19x26in) s. panel prov. 9-Jul-4 Christie's, Kensington #30/R est:5000-7000
£8000	$14640	€11680	River landscape with hawking party (42x63cm-17x25in) init. panel prov. 8-Jul-4 Sotheby's, London #292/R est:8000-12000
£9396	$17289	€14000	Wooded river landscape with anglers (64x46cm-25x18in) mono. panel. 24-Mar-4 Dorotheum, Vienna #178/R est:10000-15000

ASCH, Pieter Jansz van (attrib) (1603-1678) Dutch

£2917	$4608	€4200	River landscape with a merchant selling his wares beneath a straw canopy by a grotto (56x88cm-22x35in) init. panel. 2-Sep-3 Christie's, Amsterdam #39/R est:3000-5000

ASCHENBACH, Ernst (1872-1954) Norwegian

£267	$446	€390	Mill by waterfall (50x80cm-20x31in) s. 17-Nov-3 Blomqvist, Lysaker #1007 (N.KR 3200)
£275	$460	€402	Dairy farm by fjord (50x81cm-20x32in) s. 20-Oct-3 Blomqvist, Lysaker #1016 (N.KR 3200)
£313	$542	€457	Winter landscape with snow (70x100cm-28x39in) s. 13-Dec-3 Blomqvist, Lysaker #1007 (N.KR 3600)
£350	$585	€511	Winter landscape (49x74cm-19x29in) s. 17-Nov-3 Blomqvist, Lysaker #1009 (N.KR 4200)
£361	$604	€527	Mountain pasture (70x100cm-28x39in) s. 20-Oct-3 Blomqvist, Lysaker #1014 (N.KR 4200)
£361	$604	€527	Dairy farm in the mountains (78x101cm-31x40in) s. 20-Oct-3 Blomqvist, Lysaker #1015/R (N.KR 4200)
£365	$632	€533	Black-cocks displaying (60x80cm-24x31in) s. 13-Dec-3 Blomqvist, Lysaker #1006 (N.KR 4200)
£406	$674	€589	Winter landscape (65x105cm-26x41in) s. 16-Jun-3 Blomqvist, Lysaker #1002 (N.KR 4700)
£585	$942	€854	Capercaillie on tree trunk (100x73cm-39x29in) s. 25-Aug-3 Blomqvist, Lysaker #1007 (N.KR 6800)

£602 $970 €879 Cattle grazing (73x102cm-29x40in) s. 25-Aug-3 Blomqvist, Lysaker #1006 (N.KR 7000)

ASCHENBRENNER, Lennart (1943-) Swedish
£659 $1167 €962 The handle (65x81cm-26x32in) s.d.82. 27-Apr-4 AB Stockholms Auktionsverk #947/R (S.KR 9000)
£659 $1167 €962 Putty spade (73x60cm-29x24in) s.d.80. 27-Apr-4 AB Stockholms Auktionsverk #1128/R (S.KR 9000)

ASDRUBALI, Gianni (1955-) Italian
£267 $491 €400 Untitled (67x50cm-26x20in) s.d.1993 verso acrylic canvas on cardboard. 12-Jun-4 Meeting Art, Vercelli #713
£570 $1055 €850 Black and white (70x55cm-28x22in) s.d.1988 verso. 13-Mar-4 Meeting Art, Vercelli #16
£632 $1056 €915 Untitled (70x50cm-28x20in) s.d.1988. 13-Nov-3 Galleria Pace, Milan #29/R
£845 $1403 €1200 Composition (100x70cm-39x28in) s.d.1990 enamel. 14-Jun-3 Meeting Art, Vercelli #109/R est:1000
Works on paper
£267 $491 €400 Untitled (70x50cm-28x20in) s.d.1993 verso mixed media canvas on cardboard. 12-Jun-4 Meeting Art, Vercelli #7

ASENDORPF, Bartold (1888-1946) German
Works on paper
£315 $535 €450 Extensive landscape (31x24cm-12x9in) mono.d.1940 mixed media. 28-Nov-3 Wendl, Rudolstadt #3908/R

ASHBAUGH, Dennis (1946-) American
Works on paper
£1486 $2750 €2170 Untitled (91x104cm-36x41in) s.d.91 W/C prov. 12-Feb-4 Sotheby's, New York #347/R est:4000-6000
£1486 $2750 €2170 Untitled (91x104cm-36x41in) s.d.94 W/C prov. 12-Feb-4 Sotheby's, New York #348/R est:4000-6000

ASHBURNER, William F (fl.1900-1932) British
Works on paper
£1500 $2700 €2190 Playtime. Clematis (59x24cm-23x9in) s. pencil W/C htd white pair. 22-Apr-4 Mellors & Kirk, Nottingham #1036/R est:2500-3000

ASHBY, Henry (fl.1794-1855) British
£3000 $5010 €4380 Portrait of an officer mounted on his charger (56x46cm-22x18in) s. exhib. 14-Oct-3 Sotheby's, London #491 est:2000-3000

ASHBY, Robert (19th C) British
Works on paper
£620 $1054 €905 Hard times (30cm-12in circular) s.d.1872 W/C. 30-Oct-3 Locke & England, Leamington Spa #214/R

ASHBY, Steve (1904-1980) American
Sculpture
£1611 $2900 €2352 Nude (28x15cm-11x6in) painted wood construction prov. 24-Apr-4 Slotin Folk Art, Buford #384/R est:1000-2000

ASHEVAK, Karoo (1940-1974) North American
Sculpture
£1532 $2604 €2237 Bird (15cm-6in) weathered whalebone. 3-Nov-3 Waddingtons, Toronto #659/R est:1500-2000 (C.D 3400)
£2027 $3446 €2959 Bird (43cm-17in) weathered whalebone exec.c.1970. 3-Nov-3 Waddingtons, Toronto #397/R est:3000-5000 (C.D 4500)
£4505 $7658 €6577 Inuit figure with an inset eye (36cm-14in) whalebone base. 3-Nov-3 Waddingtons, Toronto #386/R est:15000-20000 (C.D 10000)
£6757 $11486 €9865 Standing Inuit (33cm-13in) weathered whalebone. 3-Nov-3 Waddingtons, Toronto #390/R est:15000-20000 (C.D 15000)
Works on paper
£811 $1378 €1184 Colourful owl (51x66cm-20x26in) s. felt tip exec.c.1969. 3-Nov-3 Waddingtons, Toronto #207/R est:2000-2500 (C.D 1800)

ASHEVAK, Kenojuak (1927-) North American
Sculpture
£1532 $2604 €2237 Bird with upswept wings (51cm-20in) s. mottled green soapstone. 3-Nov-3 Waddingtons, Toronto #329a/R est:3500-4500 (C.D 3400)
Works on paper
£221 $411 €323 Untitled (50x66cm-20x26in) sig.syllabics felt marker. 2-Mar-4 Ritchie, Toronto #222/R (C.D 550)
£631 $1072 €921 Owl and bears (56x76cm-22x30in) s. felt tip. 3-Nov-3 Waddingtons, Toronto #265a/R (C.D 1400)
£676 $1149 €987 Birds over the sun (33x51cm-13x20in) sealskin stencil. 3-Nov-3 Waddingtons, Toronto #286/R (C.D 1500)
£991 $1685 €1447 Dark owl (56x76cm-22x30in) s. felt tip exec.c.1969. 3-Nov-3 Waddingtons, Toronto #206/R est:1500-2000 (C.D 2200)
£4054 $6892 €5919 Hare spirits (48x61cm-19x24in) skin stencil. 3-Nov-3 Waddingtons, Toronto #283/R est:4000-6000 (C.D 9000)

ASHEVAK, Tommy (1931-) North American
Sculpture
£1171 $1991 €1710 Inuit hunter with teeth holding a harpoon and knife (30cm-12in) weathered whalebone antler wood base. 3-Nov-3 Waddingtons, Toronto #660 est:1500-2000 (C.D 2600)

ASHFORD, William (1746-1824) British
£17000 $30430 €24820 Wooded landscape, with figures and livestock on a path and ruins beyond (53x75cm-21x30in) s.d.1809 prov.lit. 14-May-4 Christie's, London #23/R est:10000-15000
£115000 $195500 €167900 Prospect of Belan House, Ballitore, County Kildare (153x243cm-60x96in) 27-Nov-3 Sotheby's, London #185/R est:60000-80000

ASHINWELL, Reginald (19/20th C) British?
Works on paper
£460 $837 €672 Cattle in a river and mountain landscape. s.d. 6-Feb-4 Honiton Galleries, Honiton #338

ASHLEY, Clifford Warren (1881-1947) American
£273 $500 €410 Whaling scene (20x13cm-8x5in) unfinished. 29-Jul-4 Eldred, East Dennis #296/R

ASHLEY, Frank N (1920-) American
£331 $600 €483 Three jockeys in locker room (28x36cm-11x14in) masonite. 16-Apr-4 American Auctioneer #11/R

ASHOONA, Kaka (1928-) North American
Sculpture
£811 $1378 €1184 Seal (37x30x30cm-15x12x12in) s.d.1995 green serpentine stone prov. 27-Nov-3 Heffel, Vancouver #141 est:2000-2500 (C.D 1800)
£811 $1378 €1184 Owl (30cm-12in) s. marbled green soapstone. 3-Nov-3 Waddingtons, Toronto #628/R est:1800-2000 (C.D 1800)
£1712 $2910 €2500 Seated polar bear (48cm-19in) s. white stone. 3-Nov-3 Waddingtons, Toronto #111/R est:3500-4500 (C.D 3800)
£1802 $3063 €2631 Sedna (53cm-21in) s. marbled white stone. 3-Nov-3 Waddingtons, Toronto #103/R est:4000-6000 (C.D 4000)
£2928 $4977 €4275 Crouching Inuit figure (48cm-19in) s. marbled white stone. 3-Nov-3 Waddingtons, Toronto #104/R est:4000-6000 (C.D 6500)

ASHOONA, Kiawak (1933-) North American
Sculpture
£1689 $2871 €2466 Inuit hunter holding a harpoon and line (25cm-10in) i. mottled green soapstone hide exec.c.1968. 3-Nov-3 Waddingtons, Toronto #316/R (C.D 3750)
£2432 $4135 €3551 Inuk lifting a seal flipper with a bird perched on his head (56cm-22in) marbled dark soapstone. 3-Nov-3 Waddingtons, Toronto #88/R est:4000-6000 (C.D 5400)
£3604 $6126 €5262 Wind blown running Inuk (51cm-20in) s. marbled green soapstone. 3-Nov-3 Waddingtons, Toronto #89/R est:4000-6000 (C.D 8000)

ASHOONA, Napachie (20th C) North American
Sculpture
£901 $1532 €1315 Inuit mother with child sharing her amautik (39cm-15in) mottled green soapstone. 21-Nov-3 Walker's, Ottawa #150/R est:1800-2400 (C.D 2000)

ASHOONA, Pitseolak (1925-) North American
Prints
£2072 $3523 €3025 Playing kickball with demons (47x60cm-19x24in) num.15/50 stonecut. 3-Nov-3 Waddingtons, Toronto #285/R est:2000-3000 (C.D 4600)
Works on paper
£248 $421 €362 Arctic camp scene (7x58cm-3x23in) s. felt tip exec.c.1969. 3-Nov-3 Waddingtons, Toronto #211/R (C.D 550)
£338 $574 €493 Hunter in kayak (66x51cm-26x20in) s. felt tip exec.c.1969. 3-Nov-3 Waddingtons, Toronto #213/R (C.D 750)
£450 $766 €657 Inuit woman with bird (61x48cm-24x19in) s. felt tip exec.c.1969. 3-Nov-3 Waddingtons, Toronto #205/R (C.D 1000)
£495 $842 €723 Inuit family in umiak (51x66cm-20x26in) s. felt tip exec.c.1969. 3-Nov-3 Waddingtons, Toronto #214/R (C.D 1100)
£11712 $19910 €17100 Untitled (43x36cm-17x14in) col felt tip twenty-seven album. 3-Nov-3 Waddingtons, Toronto #217/R est:24000-28000 (C.D 26000)

ASHTON, Ethel V (20th C) American
£1105 $1900 €1613 Early snow in old Philadelphia (64x76cm-25x30in) s.verso. 7-Dec-3 Freeman, Philadelphia #209 est:1200-1800
£2907 $5000 €4244 Cotton Candy vendors (102x61cm-40x24in) s.verso i.st.stretcher. 7-Dec-3 Freeman, Philadelphia #205 est:1200-1800
Works on paper
£598 $1100 €873 At the seashore (20x28cm-8x11in) pastel pencil. 25-Jun-4 Freeman, Philadelphia #95/R
£815 $1500 €1190 Gathering for July fourth celebration (20x28cm-8x11in) pastel pencil. 25-Jun-4 Freeman, Philadelphia #88/R est:1000-1500

ASHTON, Federico (1840-1904) Italian
£1842 $3389 €2800 Upper Italian river landscape with houses and sailing boats (35x55cm-14x22in) s.d.1881. 24-Jun-4 Dr Fritz Nagel, Stuttgart #686/R est:1100

ASHTON, J (jnr) (?) British?
£1400 $2240 €2044 Sporting dog and terrier (23x28cm-9x11in) s. board. 16-Sep-3 Holloways, Banbury #302/R est:400-450

ASHTON, Julian Howard (1877-1964) Australian
£250 $418 €365 Australian landscape (41x46cm-16x18in) s. 14-Oct-3 David Lay, Penzance #42

ASHTON, Sir John William (1881-1963) Australian/British

£346	$543	€502	Point Marie, Paris (37x54cm-15x21in) s. 26-Aug-3 Lawson Menzies, Sydney #363 (A.D 850)
£407	$700	€594	Maiden tending to her goat in a mountain landscape (48x33cm-19x13in) s. panel. 7-Dec-3 Hindman, Chicago #772/R
£697	$1101	€1018	Moored ships, Sidney harbour (24x33cm-9x13in) s.d.08 canvas on board prov. 2-Sep-3 Deutscher-Menzies, Melbourne #297/R est:2000-3000 (A.D 1700)
£779	$1230	€1137	Sydney harbour (35x44cm-14x17in) s. canvas on board prov. 2-Sep-3 Deutscher-Menzies, Melbourne #296/R est:2500-4000 (A.D 1900)
£813	$1276	€1187	Glitter, Sydney harbour (26x38cm-10x15in) s. board. 1-Sep-3 Shapiro, Sydney #315 (A.D 2000)
£813	$1455	€1187	View across the bay (35x43cm-14x17in) s. board. 10-May-4 Joel, Victoria #414 est:2000-3000 (A.D 2000)
£826	$1405	€1239	Windsor landscape (35x45cm-14x18in) canvas on board. 28-Oct-3 Goodman, Sydney #268/R (A.D 2000)
£1236	$1941	€1792	Australian, British coastal scene, Sydney (36x44cm-14x17in) s.d.1940 board prov. 27-Aug-3 Dunbar Sloane, Wellington #75/R est:3000-5000 (NZ.D 3400)
£1423	$2233	€2063	NSW coast at Narremburn (50x60cm-20x24in) s.d.1950. 26-Aug-3 Christie's, Sydney #319 est:3500-5000 (A.D 3500)
£1423	$2233	€2063	Landscape (52x63cm-20x25in) s. 26-Aug-3 Christie's, Sydney #329/R est:3500-5000 (A.D 3500)
£1527	$2779	€2229	Luxembourg Gardens, Paris (34x43cm-13x17in) i.verso canvas on board. 16-Jun-4 Deutscher-Menzies, Melbourne #428/R est:3000-5000 (A.D 4000)
£1780	$3025	€2599	Louvre (36x44cm-14x17in) s. board prov. 24-Nov-3 Sotheby's, Melbourne #192/R est:4000-6000 (A.D 4200)
£1780	$3025	€2599	Circular Quay (24x32cm-9x13in) indis.s.d. canvas on card. 24-Nov-3 Sotheby's, Melbourne #250/R est:2500-3500 (A.D 4200)
£1829	$3275	€2670	Canal Walk (28x38cm-11x15in) s. board. 10-May-4 Joel, Victoria #300 est:2500-3500 (A.D 4500)
£2441	$4566	€3662	Golden Glitter Sydney harbour (50x50cm-20x20in) s. 20-Jul-4 Goodman, Sydney #18/R est:5000-7000 (A.D 6250)
£2863	$5210	€4180	House boats, The Spit, Sydney Harbour (37x45cm-15x18in) s.d.1937 i.verso. 16-Jun-4 Deutscher-Menzies, Melbourne #267/R est:7000-9000 (A.D 7500)
£2905	$4851	€4358	Afternoon glitter (46x61cm-18x24in) s. i.verso. 27-Oct-3 Goodman, Sydney #177/R est:7000-10000 (A.D 7000)
£4545	$8409	€6636	On the Seine (61x81cm-24x32in) s. canvas on board painted c.1936 prov. 10-Mar-4 Deutscher-Menzies, Melbourne #67/R est:10000-15000 (A.D 11000)
Works on paper			
£452	$750	€655	Sailing ship. s. W/C. 14-Jun-3 Fallon, Copake #174/R

ASHTON, William (18th C) British

£350	$595	€511	Still life of roses in a green vase (30x25cm-12x10in) s. board. 19-Nov-3 Tennants, Leyburn #1220
£1822	$2933	€2660	In the Luxembourg gardens, Paris (44x59cm-17x23in) s.d.1926. 13-Oct-3 Joel, Victoria #239/R est:3000-3500 (A.D 4500)
£2947	$5275	€4303	Morning, Mosman, Sydney Harbour (49x59cm-19x23in) s. painted c.1940. 10-May-4 Joel, Victoria #196/R est:6000-8000 (A.D 7250)
Works on paper			
£313	$538	€457	Surrey landscape (32x44cm-13x17in) s. gouache prov. 2-Dec-3 Ritchie, Toronto #36/R (C.D 700)
£480	$859	€701	Feluccas on the Nile at dusk (16x29cm-6x11in) mono. W/C. 26-May-4 Christie's, Kensington #419/R
£850	$1420	€1241	Feluccas on the Nile by moonlight (37x55cm-15x22in) s. W/C bodycol. 16-Oct-3 Christie's, Kensington #147/R

ASINS RODRIGUEZ, Elena (1940-) Spanish

Works on paper			
£839	$1401	€1200	Utseski 5 (78x99cm-31x39in) s.i.d.18 octubre 1980 Indian ink. 24-Jun-3 Segre, Madrid #128/R

ASIS, Antonio (1932-) Argentinian

Sculpture			
£976	$1600	€1425	Vibration continue (62x31x11cm-24x12x4in) s.i.d.1961 metal oil wood prov. 28-May-3 Sotheby's, Amsterdam #39/R est:1000-1500

ASKELAND, Unni (1962-) Norwegian

£1761	$3153	€2571	Munch adoption - Salome (135x145cm-53x57in) s.verso. 22-Mar-4 Blomqvist, Oslo #641/R est:18000-22000 (N.KR 22000)

ASKENAZY, Maurice (1888-1961) American

£1553	$2500	€2252	Gathering flowers along a path (74x60cm-29x24in) s. 24-Aug-3 Bonhams & Butterfields, Los Angeles #7002a est:2000-3000
£7065	$13000	€10315	Deep in thought (50x61cm-20x24in) s. 8-Jun-4 Bonhams & Butterfields, San Francisco #4360/R est:5000-7000

ASKEVOLD, Anders Monsen (1834-1900) Norwegian

£732	$1346	€1098	Young man with straps (34x11cm-13x4in) s. panel. 14-Jun-4 Blomqvist, Lysaker #1022/R (N.KR 9000)
£1103	$1843	€1600	River in hilly landscape (36x48cm-14x19in) s.d.1899. 15-Nov-3 Lempertz, Koln #1577/R est:3000
£1288	$2253	€1880	Milkmaid and cattle at watering place (76x69cm-30x27in) s.i. 16-Dec-3 Grev Wedels Plass, Oslo #341/R est:20000-30000 (N.KR 15000)
£1707	$3141	€2561	Landscape from the West coast (48x81cm-19x32in) s. 14-Jun-4 Blomqvist, Lysaker #1017/R est:25000-30000 (N.KR 21000)
£1946	$3113	€2841	Norwegian fjord landscape (35x53cm-14x21in) s.d.1895. 16-Sep-3 Philippe Schuler, Zurich #3314/R est:2000-2500 (S.FR 4300)
£2000	$3680	€2920	Journey home (58x42cm-23x17in) s.d.1899. 25-Mar-4 Christie's, Kensington #176/R est:3000-5000
£2202	$3942	€3215	Cow by watering place (57x40cm-22x16in) s.d.1886. 25-May-4 Grev Wedels Plass, Oslo #2/R est:30000-40000 (N.KR 27000)
£2897	$4578	€4201	Der Sorfjord in Hardanger Norwegen (53x82cm-21x32in) s.d.1890. 2-Sep-3 Rasmussen, Copenhagen #1529/R est:30000 (D.KR 31000)
£3581	$6553	€5228	Norwegian fjord landscape with small boats by village (52x83cm-20x33in) s.d.1888. 9-Jun-4 Rasmussen, Copenhagen #1842/R est:30000 (D.KR 40000)
£3777	$6609	€5514	Fjord landscape with church and village (33x42cm-13x17in) s.d.1891. 16-Dec-3 Grev Wedels Plass, Oslo #342/R est:40000-60000 (N.KR 44000)
£4323	$7739	€6312	Cattle at the watering place (55x76cm-22x30in) s.d.1898 exhib. 22-Mar-4 Blomqvist, Oslo #344/R est:60000-80000 (N.KR 54000)
£5963	$10256	€8706	Landscape from Ullensvang (57x91cm-22x36in) s.d.1894 i.stretcher. 8-Dec-3 Blomqvist, Oslo #435/R est:90000-110000 (N.KR 70000)

ASKEW, Victor (1909-) British

£298	$542	€450	War time shipping in a harbour, probably Brixham (49x60cm-19x24in) s. 17-Jun-4 Hamilton Osborne King, Dublin #164

ASKNASY, Isaac Lvovich (1856-1902) Russian

Works on paper			
£1806	$2943	€2600	Fire in the Shtetl (45x59cm-18x23in) s.d.1881 pastel W/C. 29-Sep-3 Sotheby's, Amsterdam #58/R

ASLAN (20th C) French?

Sculpture			
£1514	$2513	€2150	Jeune femme au tablier l'arriere denude (67cm-26in) s. brown pat. 16-Jun-3 E & Eve, Paris #109
£1585	$2630	€2250	Jeune femme assise sur un tronc (47cm-19in) s.num.2/8 brown black pat. 16-Jun-3 E & Eve, Paris #110

ASLUND, Acke (1881-1958) Swedish

£315	$568	€460	Barn interior with cows (51x60cm-20x24in) s.indis.d. 26-Jan-4 Lilla Bukowskis, Stockholm #247 (S.KR 4200)
£739	$1323	€1079	Riding the horses home (38x47cm-15x19in) init.i.d.1931 canvas on panel. 25-May-4 Bukowskis, Stockholm #223/R (S.KR 10000)
£1423	$2448	€2078	Horses in green summer meadow (37x44cm-15x17in) s.d.1951 panel. 3-Dec-3 AB Stockholms Auktionsverk #2320/R est:20000-25000 (S.KR 18500)
£2882	$5160	€4208	Galloping horses (61x75cm-24x30in) init.d.aug.1944. 25-May-4 Bukowskis, Stockholm #222/R est:40000-50000 (S.KR 39000)
Works on paper			
£466	$858	€699	Horses (46x62cm-18x24in) s.i.d.1940 mixed media. 14-Jun-4 Lilla Bukowskis, Stockholm #55 (S.KR 6400)
£538	$876	€785	Man with horse (48x60cm-19x24in) s.d.maj 1911 chl. 29-Sep-3 Lilla Bukowskis, Stockholm #518 (S.KR 7000)

ASLUND, Kjell (1948-) Swedish

£1319	$2334	€1926	Untitled (98x124cm-39x49in) s.d.1988 verso acrylic tempera panel prov. 27-Apr-4 AB Stockholms Auktionsverk #937/R est:12000-15000 (S.KR 18000)

ASOMA, Tudashi (20th C) Japanese

£1250	$2200	€1825	Black bathing suit (119x104cm-47x41in) s.i.d.1967. 23-May-4 Treadway Gallery, Cincinnati #717/R est:1500-2500

ASPA, Rosario (19th C) British

Works on paper			
£550	$935	€803	Petit Bot Bay, Guersney (23x35cm-9x14in) s.i. W/C. 25-Nov-3 Martel Maides, Guernsey #174

ASPDEN, David (1935-) Australian

£413	$702	€620	Tropical cyclone (89x69cm-35x27in) i.d.95 verso paper. 28-Oct-3 Goodman, Sydney #493 (A.D 1000)
£820	$1328	€1197	Rosellas at Canyonleigh (81x71cm-32x28in) board. 30-Jul-3 Goodman, Sydney #59/R (A.D 2000)
£2686	$4969	€3922	Flora and fauna (161x363cm-63x143in) s.d.87 i.verso. 15-Mar-4 Sotheby's, Melbourne #12/R est:6000-8000 (A.D 6500)
£3719	$6322	€5430	Centrepiece II (15x212cm-6x83in) s.i.verso acrylic prov. 29-Oct-3 Lawson Menzies, Sydney #142/R est:3000-5000 (A.D 9000)
£5106	$8834	€7455	Fishing on the Hawkesbury (152x244cm-60x96in) s.i.d.1995 verso. 10-Dec-3 Shapiro, Sydney #23/R est:12000-18000 (A.D 12000)
Works on paper			
£1025	$1619	€1497	New York roof series (101x75cm-40x30in) s.i.d.80 verso synthetic polymer. 2-Sep-3 Deutscher-Menzies, Melbourne #215/R est:2500-3500 (A.D 2500)
£1065	$1683	€1555	New York roof series (100x76cm-39x30in) s.i.d.80 verso synthetic polymer. 2-Sep-3 Deutscher-Menzies, Melbourne #216/R est:2500-3500 (A.D 2600)
£1229	$1942	€1794	New York roof series (100x76cm-39x30in) s.i.d.80 verso synthetic polymer canvas. 2-Sep-3 Deutscher-Menzies, Melbourne #255/R est:2500-3500 (A.D 3000)

ASPE, Renee (1922-1969) French

Works on paper			
£634	$1096	€900	Petit village mediterraneen (55x60cm-22x24in) s. gouache. 14-Dec-3 Eric Pillon, Calais #223/R

ASPELL, Peter (1918-) Canadian

£595	$1100	€869	Ancient landscape with green head (168x198cm-66x78in) s.d.89 prov. 10-Feb-4 Sotheby's, New York #273
£643	$1195	€939	Ancient Burial XI (25x35cm-10x14in) s.d.1988 paper on board prov. 4-Mar-4 Heffel, Vancouver #1/R (C.D 1600)
£800	$1464	€1168	Door of Islam (180x120cm-71x47in) s.d.1976 i.verso prov. 3-Jun-4 Heffel, Vancouver #2/R est:1000-1500 (C.D 2000)
£2410	$4482	€3519	Ancient landscape with green head (167x198cm-66x78in) s.d.1989 prov. 4-Mar-4 Heffel, Vancouver #2/R est:3000-4000 (C.D 6000)

ASPERTINI, Amico (1474-1552) Italian

Works on paper			
£1104	$1800	€1612	Portrait of a muscular arm (13x18cm-5x7in) s. pen ink paper laid to paper. 27-Sep-3 Charlton Hall, Columbia #582/R est:3000-5000

ASPETTATI, Antonio Mario (?) Italian?

£845	$1462	€1200	Before going out (49x34cm-19x13in) s. card. 9-Dec-3 Pandolfini, Florence #342/R

£845 $1462 €1200 Tights (49x34cm-19x13in) s. card. 9-Dec-3 Pandolfini, Florence #341/R

ASPETTI, Tiziano (studio) (c.1565-1607) Italian
Sculpture
£14000 $24220 €20440 Apollo and Venus (46cm-18in) greenish brown pat. pair lit. 11-Dec-3 Christie's, London #26/R est:15000-25000

ASPEVIG, Clyde (1951-) American
£34759 $65000 €50748 Beartooth Lake (76x102cm-30x40in) s. 24-Jul-4 Coeur d'Alene, Hayden #131/R est:30000-50000

ASPINALL, Michael (20th C) Australian
Works on paper
£706 $1264 €1031 Dog Fence (91x244cm-36x96in) s. verso natural earth pigments linen exec 2000. 25-May-4 Lawson Menzies, Sydney #195/R (A.D 1800)

ASPINWALL, Reginald (1858-1921) British
£450 $810 €657 Woodland stream with a waterfall and rocks in the foreground (47x62cm-19x24in) s.d.1883. 21-Apr-4 Tennants, Leyburn #1167
£700 $1120 €1015 Oxcliffe on the Lune estuary (0x45cm-0x18in) s. 17-Sep-3 James Thompson, Kirby Lonsdale #96/R
Works on paper
£300 $501 €438 River landscape with bridge (35x25cm-14x10in) s. W/C htd white. 7-Oct-3 Fellows & Sons, Birmingham #437

ASPLUND, Nils (1874-1958) Swedish
£574 $1085 €850 Putto on dolphin (63x55cm-25x22in) s. oval. 20-Feb-4 Stadion, Trieste #314/R

ASSAR, Nasser (1928-) Iranian
£379 $633 €550 Composition (100x81cm-39x32in) s.d.1962. 17-Nov-3 Charbonneaux, Paris #192

ASSCHE, Henri van (1774-1841) Belgian
£1333 $2387 €2000 Farmer woman and children in a hilly landscape with houses and church (35x48cm-14x19in) mono. panel. 14-May-4 Behringer, Furth #1687/R est:2500

ASSCHE, van (?) Belgian?
£1333 $2453 €2000 Conversation devant une procession (58x78cm-23x31in) s. panel. 14-Jun-4 Horta, Bruxelles #101 est:2500-3500

ASSE, Genevieve (1923-) French
£375 $627 €548 Composition (35x27cm-14x11in) s. 17-Nov-3 Blomqvist, Lysaker #1011 (N.KR 4500)
£1549 $2680 €2200 Untitled (16x22cm-6x9in) s.d.83 verso acrylic prov. 9-Dec-3 Artcurial Briest, Paris #506/R est:1000-1200
£2632 $4842 €4000 Composition (65x81cm-26x32in) s. s.d.1965 verso prov. 27-Jun-4 Versailles Encheres #66/R est:4000-5000
Works on paper
£991 $1705 €1447 Objets (47x64cm-19x25in) s. gouache. 8-Dec-3 Philippe Schuler, Zurich #3004 (S.FR 2200)

ASSELBERGS, Alphonse (1839-1916) Belgian
£530 $964 €800 Couche de soleil en Ardennes (31x38cm-12x15in) panel. 16-Jun-4 Hotel des Ventes Mosan, Brussels #163
£743 $1405 €1100 Paysage au moulin a vent (28x42cm-11x17in) s. panel. 17-Feb-4 Vanderkindere, Brussels #518
£1034 $1728 €1500 Village sous la neige (38x64cm-15x25in) s. 12-Nov-3 Chassaing Rivet, Toulouse #130
£1733 $3137 €2600 Paysage avec vache et bergere (30x46cm-12x18in) s. panel. 30-Mar-4 Campo & Campo, Antwerp #4/R est:2000-4000

ASSELBERGS, Gustave (1938-1967) Dutch
£4000 $7360 €6000 Victory 1945 (120x90cm-47x35in) s.d.64 verso i. stretcher oil collage cloth prov. 9-Jun-4 Christie's, Amsterdam #351/R est:7000-9000
Works on paper
£525 $876 €750 Untitled (48x64cm-19x25in) s.d.63 collage. 30-Jun-3 Sotheby's, Amsterdam #469/R
£867 $1595 €1300 Untitled (32x34cm-13x13in) s. gouache collage painted c.1961. 9-Jun-4 Christie's, Amsterdam #352/R

ASSELBERGS, Jan (1937-) Dutch
Works on paper
£1259 $2102 €1800 Reclining nude (48x63cm-19x25in) s. chk. 30-Jun-3 Sotheby's, Amsterdam #249/R

ASSELIN, Maurice (1882-1947) French
£318 $528 €461 Anemones (51x38cm-20x15in) s.i.d.1911 verso. 13-Jun-3 Zofingen, Switzerland #2410/R (S.FR 700)
£364 $663 €550 Vase de fleurs (35x27cm-14x11in) s. 18-Jun-4 Piasa, Paris #116
£364 $663 €550 Bouquet d'anemones (46x37cm-18x15in) s. panel. 18-Jun-4 Piasa, Paris #118
£400 $716 €600 Vase de fleurs (81x54cm-32x21in) s. 12-May-4 Brissoneau, France #51
£403 $749 €600 La Place du Carrousel (24x33cm-9x13in) s. isorel exhib. 3-Mar-4 Ferri, Paris #306
£470 $864 €700 Bouquet of flowers (81x54cm-32x21in) s. 24-Mar-4 Joron-Derem, Paris #73
£1079 $1770 €1500 Femme a la chemise rose (93x73cm-37x29in) s. 3-Jun-3 Livinec, Gaudcheau & Jezequel, Rennes #101/R
Works on paper
£296 $518 €420 Barques sous voiles pres de la jetee (23x31cm-9x12in) s. W/C. 21-Dec-3 Thierry & Lannon, Brest #217

ASSELYN, Jan (1610-1652) Dutch
£28966 $48372 €42000 Rome, the Tiber (51x63cm-20x25in) prov. 12-Nov-3 Sotheby's, Milan #113/R est:30000-40000
Works on paper
£959 $1630 €1400 Rider, with figures and dogs on a path by an arched entrance (20x32cm-8x13in) i. black chk grey wash htd white. 4-Nov-3 Sotheby's, Amsterdam #103/R

ASSELYN, Jan (attrib) (1610-1652) Dutch
£1611 $2949 €2352 Pastoral scene with ruins, cattle and figures (50x66cm-20x26in) 7-Jun-4 Museumsbygningen, Copenhagen #109/R est:20000-25000 (D.KR 18000)
Works on paper
£701 $1107 €1016 Landscape with fishermen, riders and animals (40x56cm-16x22in) chl. 2-Sep-3 Rasmussen, Copenhagen #2031/R (D.KR 7500)

ASSELYN, Jan (circle) (1610-1652) Dutch
£6000 $10920 €8760 Packhorse in a courtyard (20x25cm-8x10in) i. panel. 21-Jun-4 Christie's, London #72/R est:5000-8000

ASSELYN, Jan (school) (1610-1652) Dutch
£7895 $14526 €12000 Port mediterraneen (70x95cm-28x37in) 23-Jun-4 Rieunier, Paris #27/R est:6000-8000

ASSENBAUM, Fanny (1848-1901) German
£1745 $3263 €2600 Wooded coastline (85x112cm-33x44in) s. 24-Feb-4 Dorotheum, Vienna #18/R est:2600-2800
£1745 $3263 €2600 Flock of sheep by stream (85x114cm-33x45in) mono. 24-Feb-4 Dorotheum, Vienna #17/R est:2600-2800

ASSENDELFT, Cornelis van (1870-1945) Dutch
£417 $679 €600 A forest, Groesbeek (79x74cm-31x29in) s. 29-Sep-3 Sotheby's, Amsterdam #350

ASSERETO, Giovacchino (1600-1649) Italian
£46309 $86597 €69000 Allegory of Foolish Love (98x115cm-39x45in) 25-Feb-4 Porro, Milan #44/R est:66000

ASSERETO, Giovacchino (attrib) (1600-1649) Italian
£4667 $8447 €7000 Abraham blessing Izaac (104x144cm-41x57in) 30-Mar-4 Babuino, Rome #38/R est:7000

ASSUS, Armand Jacques (1892-1977) French
£728 $1362 €1100 Paris le Cafe de la Grotte (60x50cm-24x20in) s. 20-Jul-4 Gioffredo, Nice #16/R

ASSUS, Armand Jacques (attrib) (1892-1977) French
£966 $1613 €1400 Voiliers a Cannes (45x55cm-18x22in) bears sig. cardboard. 17-Nov-3 Tajan, Paris #165/R est:1500-2000

AST, Balthasar van der (1590-1656) Dutch
£55000 $95150 €80300 Still life with roses, tulip, iris and other flowers in roemer on stone ledge (25x19cm-10x7in) remains of sig. copper prov. 11-Dec-3 Sotheby's, London #55/R est:60000-80000

AST, Balthasar van der (circle) (1590-1656) Dutch
£4469 $8000 €6525 Still life with iris, tulip, rose and other flowers in glass vase (30x22cm-12x9in) copper. 27-May-4 Sotheby's, New York #25/R est:6000-8000

AST, Balthasar van der (style) (1590-1656) Dutch
£5333 $9547 €8000 Still life of flowers (41x31cm-16x12in) board. 12-May-4 Finarte Semenzato, Milan #51/R est:8000-12000

ASTERIADIS, Agenor (1898-1977) Greek
£7000 $11900 €10220 Shipyard (73x101cm-29x40in) s.d.71 s.i.d.1971 verso egg tempera canvas on board. 18-Nov-3 Sotheby's, London #34/R est:7000-10000
£15000 $25500 €21900 Virgin of the Hill (110x92cm-43x36in) s.d.74 tempera board exhib. 18-Nov-3 Sotheby's, London #35/R est:15000-20000
£20000 $35800 €29200 Pilgrims at Prodomos Monastery (90x124cm-35x49in) s.d.1953 egg tempera board exhib. 10-May-4 Sotheby's, Olympia #57/R est:8000-12000
Works on paper
£2000 $3400 €2920 Vase of flowers (62x48cm-24x19in) s. W/C pencil. 18-Nov-3 Sotheby's, London #130/R est:2000-3000

ASTI, Angelo (1847-1903) French
£419 $700 €612 Girl with red hair (25x18cm-10x7in) board. 17-Oct-3 Du Mouchelle, Detroit #2084/R
£736 $1200 €1075 Auburn haired beauty (41x30cm-16x12in) s. 24-Sep-3 Doyle, New York #4
£1389 $2361 €2000 Une belle fille (46x33cm-18x13in) s. 28-Oct-3 Christie's, Amsterdam #63/R est:2000-3000
£1676 $3000 €2447 Portrait of a redhead (46x32cm-18x13in) s. prov. 14-May-4 Skinner, Boston #317/R est:3000-5000

ASTLEY, John (1730-1787) British
£6000 $11040 €8760 Portrait of a gentleman, standing, wearing red military dress (105x89cm-41x35in) canvas on board. 26-Mar-4 Sotheby's, London #11/R est:6000-8000

ASTOIN, Marie (1924-) French
£959 $1630 €1400 Troubadours (61x50cm-24x20in) s. 9-Nov-3 Eric Pillon, Calais #238/R

ASTROM, Werner (1885-1979) Finnish
£413 $761 €620 Italian town (65x55cm-26x22in) s.d.1924. 9-Jun-4 Bukowskis, Helsinki #581/R
£486 $812 €700 Cows (55x64cm-22x25in) s.d.1916. 23-Oct-3 Hagelstam, Helsinki #910
£604 $1111 €900 Garden (44x50cm-17x20in) s.d.1918. 25-Mar-4 Hagelstam, Helsinki #1027
£639 $1067 €920 Rambling rose (55x46cm-22x18in) s.d.1911. 26-Oct-3 Bukowskis, Helsinki #542/R
£729 $1218 €1050 Still life (82x60cm-32x24in) s. 23-Oct-3 Hagelstam, Helsinki #913
£2465 $4264 €3500 Garden (50x46cm-20x18in) s.d.1911. 13-Dec-3 Hagelstam, Helsinki #157/R est:1500

ASTRUP, Nikolai (1880-1928) Norwegian
£22764 $41659 €33235 One night in July at 2 am. (50x70cm-20x28in) s. 7-Jun-4 Blomqvist, Oslo #366a/R (N.KR 280000)
Prints
£5204 $9315 €7598 Returning home from harvesting (15x22cm-6x9in) s. hand col woodcut. 22-Mar-4 Blomqvist, Oslo #385/R est:60000-80000 (N.KR 65000)
£13821 $25293 €20179 Moon in May (19x25cm-7x10in) s. hand col woodcut lit. 7-Jun-4 Blomqvist, Oslo #394/R est:150000-170000 (N.KR 170000)

ASTUDIN, Nicolai (1848-1925) German
£1572 $2861 €2295 Mountain landscape with alpine huts (84x130cm-33x51in) s.d.1878. 16-Jun-4 Fischer, Luzern #1231/R est:3000-4000 (S.FR 3600)
£1633 $2922 €2400 Farmstead by river, possible Mosel (28x46cm-11x18in) s. 17-Mar-4 Neumeister, Munich #396/R est:2500

ASUNTA, Heikki (1904-1959) Finnish
£537 $988 €800 Ylojarvi (35x45cm-14x18in) s.d.1946 exhib. 25-Mar-4 Hagelstam, Helsinki #1077
£577 $1062 €860 Ylojarvi (35x45cm-14x18in) s.d.1946 exhib. 25-Mar-4 Hagelstam, Helsinki #1078

ASVERI, Gianfranco (1948-) Italian
Works on paper
£906 $1676 €1350 Circus in the fields (50x50cm-20x20in) s.i.d.1999 verso mixed media board. 13-Mar-4 Meeting Art, Vercelli #79

ASZTALOS, Gyula (?) ?
£839 $1401 €1200 Female nude (72x97cm-28x38in) 10-Oct-3 Stadion, Trieste #160/R

ATALAYA, Enrique (1851-1914) Spanish
£479 $815 €700 Path and statue (11x7cm-4x3in) s. cardboard. 4-Nov-3 Ansorena, Madrid #373/R
£537 $993 €800 Bord de riviere (7x11cm-3x4in) s. paper. 14-Mar-4 Eric Pillon, Calais #41/R
£634 $1096 €900 Caleche (7x11cm-3x4in) s. paper. 14-Dec-3 St-Germain-en-Laye Encheres #42
£839 $1401 €1200 Caleche (7x11cm-3x4in) s. cardboard. 29-Jun-3 Eric Pillon, Calais #77/R
£1334 $2400 €2000 Partie de campagne (14x22cm-6x9in) s.d.1907 panel. 26-Apr-4 Tajan, Paris #118/R est:2000-2500
£2113 $3655 €3000 Hure de la fermeture (10x16cm-4x6in) s. panel. 14-Dec-3 Eric Pillon, Calais #44/R

ATAMIAN, Charles Garabed (1872-1947) Turkish
£987 $1816 €1500 Anemones dans un vase (46x55cm-18x22in) s. 25-Jun-4 Daguerre, Paris #164/R est:1500-1800
£5102 $9133 €7500 Sur les remparts Saint Gilles (39x46cm-15x18in) s.i. 19-Mar-4 Millon & Associes, Paris #92/R est:6000-8000
£6500 $11700 €9490 Girl in the surf (66x82cm-26x32in) s. 20-Jan-4 Bonhams, Knightsbridge #4/R est:2000-3000
£10915 $18884 €15500 Enfants jouant au bord de mer (73x93cm-29x37in) s. 10-Dec-3 Millon & Associes, Paris #57/R est:8000-10000

ATCHEALAK, Davie (1947-) North American
Sculpture
£4054 $6892 €5919 Inuit drummer dancing on the back of a polar bear (71cm-28in) s. weathered whalebone. 3-Nov-3 Waddingtons, Toronto #54/R est:7000-10000 (C.D 9000)

ATCHUGARRY, Pablo (1954-) Uruguayan
Sculpture
£43333 $79733 €65000 Life's force (207x31x26cm-81x12x10in) pink marble exec.2003 exhib. 10-Jun-4 Christie's, Paris #75/R est:24000-28000

ATGET, Eugène (1857-1927) French
Photographs
£1693 $3200 €2472 Passage des 2 Pavillons, 6 rue Beaujolais, Paris (22x18cm-9x7in) i.verso albumen print. 17-Feb-4 Christie's, Rockefeller NY #20/R est:3000-5000
£1796 $3000 €2622 Interior, Rue de Romainville (22x18cm-9x7in) i.num.742 and 2 verso albumen print. 17-Oct-3 Sotheby's, New York #199/R est:4000-6000
£1808 $3200 €2640 Marche des patriarchs (21x17cm-8x7in) i.num.3800 verso gold toned alumen print. 27-Apr-4 Christie's, Rockefeller NY #110/R est:4000-6000
£1900 $3345 €2850 Versailles, Maison close (18x22cm-7x9in) i.num.1015 verso albumen print prov. 21-May-4 Bloomsbury, London #60/R est:3000-5000
£2000 $3520 €3000 Versailles, maison close, Petite Place (23x18cm-9x7in) st.i.num.11 verso toned gelatin silver print prov. 21-May-4 Bloomsbury, London #59/R est:5000-8000
£2096 $3500 €3060 Impasse Barbette (21x17cm-8x7in) i.num.3024 verso albumen print exec.c.1898 prov. 20-Oct-3 Christie's, Rockefeller NY #33/R est:5000-7000
£2222 $4000 €3244 Fontaine charlemagne, Reu Charlemagne, Paris (22x17cm-9x7in) i.num.3964 albumen print. 23-Apr-4 Phillips, New York #93/R est:7000-10000
£2515 $4200 €3672 Hotel D'Argenson, rue de Grenelle 101 (22x18cm-9x7in) num.5469 verso albumen print executed c.1907. 21-Oct-3 Swann Galleries, New York #57/R est:3000-4000
£2778 $4722 €4000 Hotel St Anne, Paris (22x18cm-9x7in) i. verso albumin. 31-Oct-3 Lempertz, Koln #53/R est:5000
£3593 $6000 €5246 Grand trianon (17x21cm-7x8in) s.i.num.1223 albumen print exec.c.1920. 17-Oct-3 Sotheby's, New York #198/R est:4000-6000
£4500 $7920 €6570 Versailles (22x18cm-9x7in) i.num.69 verso albumen print. 19-May-4 Christie's, London #117/R est:3000-5000
£5988 $10000 €8742 Le colleur d'affiches, Saint-Germain-des-Pres (17x22cm-7x9in) i.verso albumen print exec.May 1898 prov.lit. 17-Oct-3 Phillips, New York #125/R est:10000-15000
£8475 $15000 €12374 Boulevard de Bonne-Nouvelle (18x23cm-7x9in) i.num.6679 st.verso printing-out-paper print. 28-Apr-4 Sotheby's, New York #106/R est:10000-15000

ATILA (1931-1987) French
£1361 $2436 €2000 Untitled (114x146cm-45x57in) s.d.75 prov. 21-Mar-4 Calmels Cohen, Paris #109/R est:1000-1200
Works on paper
£816 $1461 €1200 Untitled (62x90cm-24x35in) s.i.d.74 W/C prov. 21-Mar-4 Calmels Cohen, Paris #108/R

ATILA, Ede Kardy (1931-1987) French
£733 $1342 €1100 La scene (130x97cm-51x38in) s.d.68. 7-Jun-4 Palais de Beaux Arts, Brussels #329/R
£1333 $2440 €2000 Un appetit d'empereur (195x195cm-77x77in) s.d.1969. 7-Jun-4 Palais de Beaux Arts, Brussels #150/R est:2000-3000

ATKINS, Albert Henry (1899-1951) American
Sculpture
£5946 $11000 €8681 Sea goddess (41cm-16in) green brown pat bronze. 11-Mar-4 Christie's, Rockefeller NY #31/R est:6000-8000

ATKINS, Anna (1799-1871) ?
Photographs
£5367 $9500 €7836 Poa aquatica (34x24cm-13x9in) i. cyanotype photogram exec.c.1850 prov.exhib. 28-Apr-4 Sotheby's, New York #100/R est:8000-12000
£6215 $11000 €9074 New Zealand (35x25cm-14x10in) i. cyanotype photogram exec.c.1850 prov. 28-Apr-4 Sotheby's, New York #99/R est:8000-12000
£6780 $12000 €9899 Blechnum boreale (34x24cm-13x9in) i. cyanotype photogram exec.c.1850 prov.lit. 28-Apr-4 Sotheby's, New York #102/R est:8000-12000
£13559 $24000 €19796 South America (35x25cm-14x10in) i. cyanotype photogram exec.c.1850 prov.exhib. 28-Apr-4 Sotheby's, New York #101/R est:12000-18000
£200000 $352000 €292000 British algae (25x21cm-10x8in) photograph pair prov.lit. 19-May-4 Christie's, London #48/R est:200000-300000

ATKINS, Catherine J (fl.1880-1916) British
Works on paper
£520 $962 €759 Fond memories (71x53cm-28x21in) s. W/C. 9-Mar-4 Bonhams, Knightsbridge #75/R
£1200 $2208 €1752 Chums (53x35cm-21x14in) s. W/C bodycol exhib. 8-Jun-4 Bonhams, New Bond Street #115/R est:1000-1500

ATKINS, Caven (1907-) Canadian
£2236 $4002 €3265 York mills treescape (68x96cm-27x38in) s.d.37 i.verso prov.exhib. 31-May-4 Sotheby's, Toronto #33/R est:6000-8000 (C.D 5500)
£9146 $16372 €13353 Hockey melee (91x107cm-36x42in) s.i.d.41 i.verso prov.exhib. 31-May-4 Sotheby's, Toronto #35/R est:7000-10000 (C.D 22500)
Works on paper
£261 $486 €381 Back lane, Walnut Street, Winnipeg, Manitoba (26x20cm-10x8in) s.d.28 pencil prov. 2-Mar-4 Ritchie, Toronto #142/R (C.D 650)
£803 $1494 €1172 Trees in spring (25x35cm-10x14in) s.d.1928 i.verso W/C prov. 2-Mar-4 Ritchie, Toronto #140/R est:600-800 (C.D 2000)
£884 $1643 €1291 Hogs hollow (28x35cm-11x14in) s.d.36 W/C prov. 2-Mar-4 Ritchie, Toronto #139/R est:600-800 (C.D 2200)
£964 $1793 €1407 Green house (18x25cm-7x10in) s.d.28 i.verso W/C prov. 2-Mar-4 Ritchie, Toronto #141/R est:500-700 (C.D 2400)
£1446 $2689 €2111 Exploration of nature's abstract forms (39x57cm-15x22in) s.d.37 s.d.August 28th 1937 W/C prov. 2-Mar-4 Ritchie, Toronto #143/R est:1200-1600 (C.D 3600)

ATKINS, David (1910-) American
£280 $493 €409 Sauveterre, France, early morning (19x27cm-7x11in) s.verso board. 18-May-4 Woolley & Wallis, Salisbury #10/R
£300 $528 €438 Afternoon landscape (30x52cm-12x20in) board. 18-May-4 Woolley & Wallis, Salisbury #9/R
£380 $669 €555 Lake at Gravetye Manor (28x30cm-11x12in) board. 18-May-4 Woolley & Wallis, Salisbury #96/R
£580 $1021 €847 Landscape, Send (53x55cm-21x22in) s.verso board. 18-May-4 Woolley & Wallis, Salisbury #210/R
£740 $1302 €1080 Th sea, winter (37x38cm-15x15in) s.i.verso board. 18-May-4 Woolley & Wallis, Salisbury #201/R

ATKINS, Samuel (fl.1787-1808) British

Works on paper			
£340	$564	€496	Royal Navy frigate, revenue cutter and other vessels off Osborne House (26x39cm-10x15in) W/C. 6-Oct-3 David Duggleby, Scarborough #247
£480	$859	€701	Crowded brig in a cracking breeze (11x16cm-4x6in) s. grey in, W/C. 26-May-4 Christie's, Kensington #383/R
£500	$895	€730	English man-o-war leaving port (12x18cm-5x7in) blk in, W/C. 26-May-4 Christie's, Kensington #374/R
£520	$848	€759	Men-of-war and other distant vessels before a storm with choppy waters (17x19cm-7x7in) W/C. 26-Sep-3 Bigwood, Stratford on Avon #406
£600	$1116	€876	British Indiaman (11x16cm-4x6in) s. monochrome wash. 2-Mar-4 Bearnes, Exeter #301/R
£1000	$1830	€1460	Victualling the fleet (10x30cm-4x12in) s. W/C over pencil prov. 8-Jul-4 Duke & Son, Dorchester #58/R est:300-600
£1800	$3402	€2628	Shipping scenes (11x16cm-4x6in) all s. pen ink W/C four. 17-Feb-4 Bonhams, New Bond Street #43/R est:800-1200
£1850	$3441	€2701	British man-o-war and other vessels offshore (28x39cm-11x15in) s. W/C. 2-Mar-4 Bearnes, Exeter #302/R est:1000-1500

ATKINS, W E (1842-1910) British

Works on paper			
£1650	$2739	€2409	Shipping in Portsmouth harbour, three-decker man-of-war and other shipping (33x71cm-13x28in) s.d.1908 W/C. 4-Oct-3 Finan Watkins & Co, Mere #146/R

ATKINS, William Edward (1842-1910) British

£235	$425	€343	Sailing vessels at sea (30x41cm-12x16in) s.d.1803. 3-Apr-4 Charlton Hall, Columbia #155/R
Works on paper			
£400	$640	€584	H M Brig Persian running in full sail after battle (28x40cm-11x16in) s.i. pen ink W/C. 16-Sep-3 Rosebery Fine Art, London #588/R
£700	$1281	€1022	Steam and sail surrounding a hulk (41x58cm-16x23in) s. W/C bodycol htd white. 7-Apr-4 Bonhams, Bury St Edmunds #395
£950	$1587	€1387	Portsmouth Harbour (27x45cm-11x18in) s.d.1865 W/C. 14-Oct-3 Bearnes, Exeter #324/R

ATKINSON (?) British

£449	$836	€656	Still life of dead birds, letter and jug (61x51cm-24x20in) s.d.1879. 2-Mar-4 Rasmussen, Copenhagen #1226/R (D.KR 5000)

ATKINSON, Amy B (1859-1916) British

£1100	$1947	€1606	Woman mending the nets (20x25cm-8x10in) mono. 27-Apr-4 Bonhams, Knightsbridge #6/R est:500-700

ATKINSON, Esmond (20th C) New Zealander

Works on paper			
£277	$496	€404	Kapiti Island (24x43cm-9x17in) init.d.17.2.27 W/C. 12-May-4 Dunbar Sloane, Wellington #127/R (NZ.D 800)

ATKINSON, George (19/20th C) British

Works on paper			
£929	$1700	€1356	Illinois skyscraper (89x64cm-35x25in) pastel. 10-Jul-4 Hindman, Chicago #17/R est:300-500
£1132	$1800	€1653	Fall Ridge Pass (91x163cm-36x64in) pastel. 14-Sep-3 Susanin's, Chicago #6011/R est:1000-1500
£1384	$2200	€2021	West of Raymond (38x91cm-15x36in) pastel. 14-Sep-3 Susanin's, Chicago #6022/R est:700-900
£1639	$3000	€2393	East of Eden (64x89cm-25x35in) pastel. 10-Jul-4 Hindman, Chicago #18/R est:500-700
£1761	$2800	€2571	East of Illiopolis (61x127cm-24x50in) pastel. 14-Sep-3 Susanin's, Chicago #6021/R est:700-900

ATKINSON, George Mounsey Wheatley (1806-1884) British

£3103	$5741	€4500	Sirius in rough sea (60x87cm-24x34in) 11-Feb-4 Woodwards, Cork #20/R est:1000-1500
£4000	$6800	€5840	Entrance to Rio de Janeiro, Brazil (69x103cm-27x41in) s. exhib. 4-Nov-3 Bonhams, New Bond Street #163/R est:4000-6000
£6000	$10200	€8760	Merchantmen (61x91cm-24x36in) s.d.1872. 19-Nov-3 Christie's, Kensington #474/R
£12973	$24000	€18941	Armed British brig becalmed in the approaches to Rio de Janeiro, Brazil (61x89cm-24x35in) s.d.1844 prov. 10-Feb-4 Christie's, Rockefeller NY #232/R est:20000-30000
£13380	$23148	€19000	Paddler steamer, Ocean, passing Roche's Point, Cork harbour (66x99cm-26x39in) s.d.1841. 10-Dec-3 Bonhams & James Adam, Dublin #7/R est:20000-25000

ATKINSON, H (19/20th C) British

£4200	$7728	€6132	Prize winning red-brown cock. Prize winning brown-red hen (35x30cm-14x12in) s.i. pair. 10-Jun-4 Christie's, Kensington #251/R est:1500-2000

ATKINSON, John (1863-1924) British

£480	$763	€701	Shire horse in a stable (39x56cm-15x22in) s. 18-Mar-3 Anderson & Garland, Newcastle #360
£540	$859	€788	Farm labourers building a haystack with horse-cart and poultry in foreground (24x35cm-9x14in) s. 18-Mar-3 Anderson & Garland, Newcastle #359
£600	$954	€876	Horse-drawn harrow (22x31cm-9x12in) s. 18-Mar-3 Anderson & Garland, Newcastle #361/R
£1000	$1660	€1460	Working in the field (30x40cm-12x16in) 1-Oct-3 Sotheby's, Olympia #83/R est:1000-1500
£1600	$2880	€2336	Picking potatoes (30x40cm-12x16in) s. i.verso canvasboard. 21-Apr-4 Tennants, Leyburn #1173/R est:1200-1500
£4600	$8280	€6716	Farmer seated on a harrow being pulled by three shire horses (102x152cm-40x60in) s. 21-Apr-4 Tennants, Leyburn #1174/R est:2500-3000
Works on paper			
£560	$913	€818	Potato pickers and a horse-cart in a field (49x60cm-19x24in) s.d.1920 W/C. 23-Sep-3 Anderson & Garland, Newcastle #294/R
£600	$1110	€876	Gypsy caravans and horses (15x34cm-6x13in) s. W/C. 14-Jul-4 Sotheby's, Olympia #96/R
£620	$1128	€905	Tuppence - Portrait of a dog (32x41cm-13x16in) s.i.d.11.09 W/C. 29-Jun-4 Anderson & Garland, Newcastle #256
£650	$1086	€949	At Sedgefield Races (33x51cm-13x20in) W/C prov. 10-Oct-3 Richardson & Smith, Whitby #104/R
£680	$1176	€993	Yorkshire quarry, draught horses feeding (15x23cm-6x9in) s. W/C. 9-Dec-3 Anderson & Garland, Newcastle #341
£680	$1244	€993	Ploughman and team (33x49cm-13x19in) W/C. 1-Jun-4 Hodgins, Calgary #300/R (C.D 1700)
£780	$1271	€1139	Rotten Row, Hyde Park, London (34x49cm-13x19in) W/C. 23-Sep-3 Anderson & Garland, Newcastle #295a
£1000	$1630	€1460	Farm workers stacking corn onto a horse-cart (23x33cm-9x13in) s. W/C. 23-Sep-3 Anderson & Garland, Newcastle #296/R
£1050	$1911	€1533	Corn Harvest, North Yorkshire (20x29cm-8x11in) s. W/C. 29-Jun-4 Anderson & Garland, Newcastle #257 est:450-750
£1100	$1749	€1595	Horses and hounds passing dales farmhouse (22x27cm-9x11in) s. W/C. 9-Sep-3 David Duggleby, Scarborough #211/R est:1000-1500
£1360	$2489	€1986	Ploughman and team (38x55cm-15x22in) s. W/C. 1-Jun-4 Hodgins, Calgary #301/R est:1200-1800 (C.D 3400)
£1800	$3366	€2628	Cottage at Hinderwell, lady feeding chickens in a sunlit garden (27x38cm-11x15in) s. pencil W/C. 22-Jul-4 Tennants, Leyburn #744/R est:1400-1600
£1900	$3591	€2774	Fishmarket, North Shields (22x31cm-9x12in) s. W/C. 18-Feb-4 Peter Wilson, Nantwich #68
£2000	$3400	€2920	Plough horses. Harvest (28x38cm-11x15in) s. W/C pair. 25-Nov-3 Bonhams, Knightsbridge #68/R est:2000-3000
£2000	$3600	€2920	Ploughing in springtime (45x60cm-18x24in) s.i. pencil W/C htd white. 21-Apr-4 Tennants, Leyburn #1057/R est:2000-2500
£2000	$3680	€2920	Riders in rotten row, Hyde Park (19x26cm-7x10in) s.i.d.7.3.11 pencil W/C htd white. 8-Jun-4 Holloways, Banbury #252/R est:400-600
£2400	$4368	€3504	Cow Hill, October fair (46x61cm-18x24in) s.i.d.1907 pencil W/C. 15-Jun-4 Bonhams, Leeds #164/R est:1600-2400
£2500	$4550	€3650	Gypsy caravans at a northern horse fair (36x52cm-14x20in) s. W/C. 29-Jun-4 Anderson & Garland, Newcastle #258/R est:2500-4500
£3400	$6188	€4964	Durham coast beach scene with figures in Edwardian dress (26x35cm-10x14in) s. W/C. 29-Jun-4 Anderson & Garland, Newcastle #259/R est:2500-4000
£5000	$8650	€7300	Yarm Horse Fair with gypsy horse traders and caravans (39x32cm-15x13in) s. W/C. 9-Dec-3 Anderson & Garland, Newcastle #342/R est:1500-2500

ATKINSON, John (attrib) (1863-1924) British

£550	$919	€803	Showing shire horses (33x43cm-13x17in) 10-Oct-3 Richardson & Smith, Whitby #96/R

ATKINSON, John Augustus (1775-1833) British

£800	$1440	€1168	Ambush (61x50cm-24x20in) i.verso panel. 21-Jan-4 Sotheby's, Olympia #82/R
Works on paper			
£350	$585	€511	Don Quixote and Sancho Panza (16x22cm-6x9in) W/C. 14-Oct-3 Bonhams, Knightsbridge #52/R

ATKINSON, John Gunson (fl.1849-1885) British

£380	$623	€555	On the Greta, Yorkshire, an angler on the rocky river bank (30x41cm-12x16in) s.d.1878. 29-May-3 Neales, Nottingham #804/R
£520	$868	€759	Longshaw Moor. Derbyshire cottage near Frogatt Edge (25x45cm-10x18in) mono. s.i.verso pair. 20-Oct-3 Bonhams, Bath #2
£900	$1458	€1305	On the Kent, near Kendale. On a river (25x46cm-10x18in) s. i.verso pair. 30-Jul-3 Hamptons Fine Art, Godalming #273/R

ATKINSON, Robert (1863-1896) British

£2500	$3975	€3625	On the Hawkesbury River, New South Wales (41x56cm-16x22in) s.d.1889 i.verso. 9-Sep-3 Bonhams, Knightsbridge #174/R est:1000-1500

ATKINSON, W (?) British?

£1600	$2608	€2336	Shipping off the coast (75x126cm-30x50in) s. 25-Sep-3 Mellors & Kirk, Nottingham #764/R est:800-1200

ATKINSON, William Edwin (1862-1926) Canadian

£290	$499	€423	Early autumn day (35x30cm-14x12in) s.d.1904. 2-Dec-3 Joyner Waddington, Toronto #513 (C.D 650)
£300	$549	€438	Muskoka scene (23x38cm-9x15in) s.d.1918 board. 3-Jun-4 Heffel, Vancouver #4/R (C.D 750)
£313	$538	€457	Wooded country lane (26x21cm-10x8in) s.d.96 board. 2-Dec-3 Joyner Waddington, Toronto #443 (C.D 700)
£440	$805	€642	Canal boat below the bridge (24x31cm-9x12in) s.d.1925 board. 1-Jun-4 Joyner Waddington, Toronto #378/R (C.D 1100)
£444	$816	€648	Luxembourg Gardens (24x31cm-9x12in) s.d.1923. 9-Jun-4 Walker's, Ottawa #136/R (C.D 1100)
£520	$952	€759	Old Mill (22x27cm-9x11in) s.d.96 canvas on board. 1-Jun-4 Joyner Waddington, Toronto #520 (C.D 1300)
£610	$1091	€891	Fontainebleu (30x43cm-12x17in) s.i.d.1893. 27-May-4 Heffel, Vancouver #100/R (C.D 1500)
£640	$1171	€934	Woman walking along a quiet street (35x26cm-14x10in) s. board. 1-Jun-4 Joyner Waddington, Toronto #335/R (C.D 1600)
£679	$1133	€991	Untitled - spring thaw (43x33cm-17x13in) s. 17-Nov-3 Hodgins, Calgary #351 est:2000-2500 (C.D 1500)
£682	$1111	€996	Early autumn day. Fontainbleu (35x31cm-14x12in) s.d.1904 s.d.verso pair. 23-Sep-3 Ritchie, Toronto #76/R est:2000-3000 (C.D 1500)
£720	$1318	€1051	Country House (21x26cm-8x10in) s.d.96 panel oil sketch of a stream verso double-sided. 1-Jun-4 Joyner Waddington, Toronto #400/R est:800-1200 (C.D 1800)
£785	$1421	€1146	Through the woods (53x51cm-21x20in) s.d.1925. 18-Apr-4 Levis, Calgary #1/R est:2500-3000 (C.D 1900)
£880	$1610	€1285	Street Market, Pont Aven, France (25x32cm-10x13in) s.d.1921 canvas on board prov. 1-Jun-4 Joyner Waddington, Toronto #195/R est:2000-3000 (C.D 2200)
£1120	$2050	€1635	Market, Concarneau, France (24x32cm-9x13in) s.d.1918 panel prov. 1-Jun-4 Joyner Waddington, Toronto #136/R est:2000-3000 (C.D 2800)
£1210	$2226	€1767	Pont Avon market (20x25cm-8x10in) 9-Jun-4 Walker's, Ottawa #134/R est:700-1000 (C.D 3000)
Works on paper			
£200	$366	€292	Path leading to the forest (23x15cm-9x6in) s.d.1895 W/C. 1-Jun-4 Hodgins, Calgary #448/R (C.D 500)

£262 $482 €383 English cottage, evening (30x47cm-12x19in) s.d.1924 W/C. 9-Jun-4 Walker's, Ottawa #135/R (C.D 650)
£282 $519 €412 Forest stream, Devon (28x38cm-11x15in) s.d.1924 W/C. 9-Jun-4 Walker's, Ottawa #132/R (C.D 700)
£302 $556 €441 Polperro, Cornwall (39x28cm-15x11in) s.d.1923 W/C. 9-Jun-4 Walker's, Ottawa #131/R (C.D 750)
£321 $598 €469 Moonlight, near the canal, Tavistock (38x56cm-15x22in) s.d.1910 W/C. 2-Mar-4 Ritchie, Toronto #43/R (C.D 800)

ATKYNS, Edwin (19th C) British
£300 $501 €438 Landscape with sheep and figures on a path by a farm (127x76cm-50x30in) s.d.1880. 11-Jul-3 Jim Railton, Durham #382a/R

ATL, Dr (1875-1964) Mexican
£27933 $50000 €40782 Self-portrait in mountainous landscape (51x41cm-20x16in) s.d.1960 paper on board prov. 26-May-4 Sotheby's, New York #33/R est:50000-70000
Works on paper
£964 $1533 €1407 Volcano with smoke (31x46cm-12x18in) s. chl. 29-Apr-3 Louis Morton, Mexico #104/R est:30000-40000 (M.P 16000)

ATLAN, Jean (1913-1960) French
£13100 $24105 €19126 Sans titre (49x73cm-19x29in) s.d.1958 lit. 8-Jun-4 Germann, Zurich #29/R est:35000-40000 (S.FR 30000)
£13889 $23194 €20000 Jardins de carthage (44x38cm-17x15in) s.d.54 s.i.verso lit. 21-Oct-3 Artcurial Briest, Paris #389/R est:25000-30000
£16107 $28832 €24000 Untitled (46x55cm-18x22in) s. lit. 26-May-4 Christie's, Paris #64/R est:28000-32000
£17958 $31067 €25500 Sans titre (80x65cm-31x26in) s. panel prov. 12-Dec-3 Artus Associes, Paris #160
£18000 $30060 €26280 Untitled (81x54cm-32x21in) s. painted 1959 prov.lit. 21-Oct-3 Sotheby's, London #392/R est:12000-18000
£18056 $30153 €26000 Sans titre (73x50cm-29x20in) s. lit. 21-Oct-3 Artcurial Briest, Paris #387/R est:23000-25000
£18666 $34346 €28000 Gardien du seuil (50x73cm-20x29in) s.d.59 i. verso prov.lit. 8-Jun-4 Artcurial Briest, Paris #205/R est:30000-40000
£18667 $34347 €28000 Byzance II (50x73cm-20x29in) s.d.58 i.verso prov.exhib.lit. 9-Jun-4 Christie's, Amsterdam #305/R est:25000-35000
£19581 $33287 €28000 Sans titre (72x49cm-28x19in) s.d.1959 prov.exhib.lit. 25-Nov-3 Tajan, Paris #12/R est:30000-35000
£20333 $36600 €30500 Untitled (73x50cm-29x20in) s. prov.lit. 25-Apr-4 Versailles Encheres #82 est:30000-35000
£20775 $35940 €29500 Sans titre (38x61cm-15x24in) s.d.1958 prov.lit. 14-Dec-3 Versailles Encheres #127/R est:30000-35000
£32168 $55329 €46000 Hejaz (60x92cm-24x36in) s.d.58 i.verso lit. 2-Dec-3 Calmels Cohen, Paris #76/R est:50000-60000
£35000 $63700 €51100 Untitled (130x81cm-51x32in) s. burlap painted 1958 prov.lit. 5-Feb-4 Christie's, London #116/R est:40000-60000
£36111 $59583 €52000 Sans titre (93x60cm-37x24in) s. prov.lit. 2-Jul-3 Cornette de St.Cyr, Paris #21/R est:55000-66000
£36364 $61820 €52000 Arjouna (116x81cm-46x32in) s.d.1958 prov.exhib.lit. 25-Nov-3 Tajan, Paris #10/R est:40000-45000
£45000 $81900 €65700 Untitled (92x60cm-36x24in) s. prov.lit. 6-Feb-4 Sotheby's, London #177/R est:30000-40000
£46853 $78245 €67000 Untitled (100x65cm-39x26in) s.d.1956. 29-Jun-3 Versailles Encheres #106/R
£49306 $77903 €71000 Mukden (130x81cm-51x32in) s.d.1958 s.i.d.verso prov.exhib.lit. 27-Apr-3 Versailles Encheres #33
£52448 $87587 €75000 Untitled (81x130cm-32x51in) s. prov.lit. 29-Jun-3 Versailles Encheres #82/R
Works on paper
£426 $711 €600 Composition (27x20cm-11x8in) s.d.56 pastel. 14-Oct-3 Millon & Associes, Paris #98
£3005 $5018 €4387 Figure composition (64x48cm-25x19in) s. pastel exhib. 7-Oct-3 Rasmussen, Copenhagen #1/R est:40000-60000 (D.KR 32000)
£3267 $5880 €4900 Composition (44x53cm-17x21in) s.d.1956 pastel. 24-Apr-4 Cornette de St.Cyr, Paris #430/R est:6000-8000
£3379 $6048 €5000 Untitled (24x31cm-9x12in) s. pastel. 4-May-4 Calmels Cohen, Paris #164/R est:5000-6000
£3394 $5667 €4955 Morocco (23x31cm-9x12in) s. s.i. verso pastel chk prov.lit. 24-Jun-3 Germann, Zurich #37/R est:8000-10000 (S.FR 7500)
£4161 $7657 €6200 Untitled (63x45cm-25x18in) s.i. pastel chk chl mixed media exec 1957 lit. 29-Mar-4 Cornette de St.Cyr, Paris #16/R est:4000-5000
£4422 $7031 €6500 L'oiseau de barbarie (50x65cm-20x26in) s.d.1952 pastel board prov.exhib.lit. 23-Mar-3 Mercier & Cie, Lille #292/R est:7000-8000
£5594 $9622 €8000 Composition (27x37cm-11x15in) s.d.52 pastel. 4-Dec-3 Piasa, Paris #91/R est:6000-8000
£6389 $10094 €9200 Untitled (31x23cm-12x9in) s.d.1953 pastel prov.lit. 27-Apr-3 Versailles Encheres #52
£8784 $15460 €13000 Untitled (50x65cm-20x26in) s.d.1952 pastel board prov.lit. 18-May-4 Tajan, Paris #40/R est:15000-18000

ATROSHENKO, Viacheslav (1935-1994) Oriental
£1800 $3312 €2700 White light II (122x152cm-48x60in) s.i.d.1983 verso acrylic. 24-Jun-4 Sotheby's, Olympia #521/R est:2000-3000

ATTANASIO, Natale (1846-1924) Italian
£2800 $5152 €4200 Painer (35x24cm-14x9in) init. board. 10-Jun-4 Christie's, Rome #82/R est:3700-3900

ATTAR, Alain (1957-) Canadian
£270 $459 €394 Untitled (122x152cm-48x60in) s.verso. 19-Nov-3 Maynards, Vancouver #81b (C.D 600)

ATTAR, Suad (1942-) Iraqi
£2600 $4602 €3796 Midsummer dreaming (15x20cm-6x8in) s.d.1991 board set of three. 29-Apr-4 Bonhams, New Bond Street #579/R est:1800-2400

ATTARDI, Massimo (1961-) Italian
Photographs
£1067 $1963 €1600 Untitled (105x105cm-41x41in) s.verso photograph on board exec.2004. 12-Jun-4 Meeting Art, Vercelli #736/R est:1000
£1400 $2576 €2100 Untitled (150x112cm-59x44in) s.verso photograph exec.2004. 12-Jun-4 Meeting Art, Vercelli #123/R est:1500

ATTARDI, Ugo (1923-) Italian
£1538 $2615 €2200 Along the Tiber (35x50cm-14x20in) s. 24-Nov-3 Christie's, Milan #102 est:2500-3000
£1622 $2854 €2400 Bridge on the Tiber (30x40cm-12x16in) s. acrylic oil paper. 22-May-4 Galleria Pananti, Florence #405/R est:2000-2500
£1678 $2853 €2400 Nude (70x50cm-28x20in) s.d.940 s.verso. 24-Nov-3 Christie's, Milan #163/R est:3500-5000
£1867 $3435 €2800 Along the Tiber (35x50cm-14x20in) s. 12-Jun-4 Meeting Art, Vercelli #718/R est:2000
£2345 $3916 €3400 The Tiber in Rome (50x70cm-20x28in) s.d.969. 14-Nov-3 Farsetti, Prato #323/R est:3400-3900
£2657 $4517 €3800 Interior with fish and vase of flowers (40x50cm-16x20in) s. 24-Nov-3 Christie's, Milan #114/R est:3000-4000
£3020 $5617 €4500 Woman at seaside (100x70cm-39x28in) s.d.1963 tempera W/C pencil card. 4-Mar-4 Babuino, Rome #65 est:3000-4000
£4333 $7800 €6500 Figures on the road (70x95cm-28x37in) s. painted 1960. 22-Apr-4 Finarte Semenzato, Rome #245/R est:5500-6500
£6933 $12480 €10400 Bridge on the Tiber (82x101cm-32x40in) s. painted 1962. 22-Apr-4 Finarte Semenzato, Rome #319/R est:6000-7000
Works on paper
£667 $1200 €1000 Killing (120x100cm-47x39in) s.i.d.963 mixed media paper on canvas. 22-Apr-4 Finarte Semenzato, Rome #358/R
£1533 $2775 €2300 Compliments (90x61cm-35x24in) s.d.960 hydropaint exhib.lit. 2-Apr-4 Farsetti, Prato #167/R est:1600-1900

ATTENDU, Antoine Ferdinand (19th C) French
£793 $1348 €1158 Still life with lobster and gherkins in glass (14x23cm-6x9in) s. panel. 5-Nov-3 Dobiaschofsky, Bern #314/R (S.FR 1800)

ATTENHOFER, August (1828-1862) German
£348 $637 €508 Raphael Sanzio Urbino (54x45cm-21x18in) s.i.d.1849. 4-Jun-4 Zofingen, Switzerland #2320 (S.FR 800)

ATTERSEE, Christian Ludwig (1940-) Austrian
£905 $1511 €1321 Chock's coming! (87x62cm-34x24in) s.i.d.1982 acrylic. 24-Jun-3 Germann, Zurich #121/R (S.FR 2000)
£1831 $3204 €2600 Keil komm (87x62cm-34x24in) s.i.d.82 acrylic lacq casein col chk col pencil pencil chl board. 19-Dec-3 Dorotheum, Vienna #372/R est:4000-6000
£1986 $3316 €2800 Weather duet (62x44cm-24x17in) s.i. acrylic mixed media board. 16-Oct-3 Dorotheum, Salzburg #740/R est:2200-3200
£2113 $3697 €3000 Cat's piano (63x44cm-25x17in) s.i.d.92 acrylic lacq casein col chk col pencil pencil chl board. 19-Dec-3 Dorotheum, Vienna #427/R est:3600-4500
£2238 $3849 €3200 Luftikus (85x110cm-33x43in) s.d.1983 s.i.d.verso prov. 3-Dec-3 Tajan, Paris #482 est:2000-3000
£2517 $4280 €3600 Boy will be ball (63x44cm-25x17in) s.i. acrylic varnish casein col chk pencil. 26-Nov-3 Dorotheum, Vienna #308/R est:3400-5000
£2837 $4738 €4000 Composition (84x59cm-33x23in) s.i.d.84 s.i.d. verso acrylic varnish casein col chk col pencil chl. 14-Oct-3 Dorotheum, Vienna #279/R est:4500-6500
£3191 $5330 €4500 Composition (58x83cm-23x33in) s.i.d.67 s.d.78 acrylic varnish casein col chk pencil chl board. 14-Oct-3 Dorotheum, Vienna #236/R est:5000-7000
£10738 $19221 €16000 German sail (107x82cm-42x32in) s.i.d.82/84 s.i.d. verso acrylic varnish prov.exhib. 25-May-4 Dorotheum, Vienna #379/R est:18000-22000
Works on paper
£543 $907 €793 Composition (43x31cm-17x12in) s.i.d.1978 mixed media. 24-Jun-3 Germann, Zurich #140/R (S.FR 1200)
£1176 $1965 €1717 Flower eggs (62x44cm-24x17in) s.i.d.1979 mixed media. 24-Jun-3 Germann, Zurich #119 est:2500-3000 (S.FR 2600)
£1176 $1965 €1717 Twilight in Sbrinz with flesh (44x62cm-17x24in) s.i.d.1974 mixed media. 24-Jun-3 Germann, Zurich #141/R est:2500-3000 (S.FR 2600)
£1268 $2218 €1800 Christmas room (31x21cm-12x8in) s.i. mixed media. 19-Dec-3 Dorotheum, Vienna #420/R est:1800-2200
£1316 $2421 €2000 Die Pferdin sehnt - The female horse saw (44x31cm-17x12in) s.i. mixed media. 22-Jun-4 Wiener Kunst Auktionen, Vienna #425/R est:2000
£1342 $2376 €2000 Magpies (62x43cm-24x17in) s.i.d. mixed meida lit. 28-Apr-4 Wiener Kunst Auktionen, Vienna #249/R est:2000-4000
£1357 $2267 €1981 Evening fruit (62x87cm-24x34in) s.i.d.1978 mixed media acrylic. 24-Jun-3 Germann, Zurich #120/R est:3500-4500 (S.FR 3000)
£1549 $2572 €2200 Harvest (43x31cm-17x12in) s.d.92 mixed media. 12-Jun-3 Dorotheum, Graz #127/R
£3356 $5940 €5000 Composition (59x86cm-23x34in) s.d. mixed media board lit. 28-Apr-4 Wiener Kunst Auktionen, Vienna #267/R est:5000-8000

ATTESLANDER, Sofie-Zo (1874-?) Polish
£390 $632 €550 Portrait of young beauty wearing large hat (80x72cm-31x28in) s.d.1905 lit. 23-May-3 Karlheinz Kaupp, Staufen #1923/R
£570 $1061 €850 Woman wearing hat (70x60cm-28x24in) s.d.1905. 6-Mar-4 Arnold, Frankfurt #684/R
£638 $1173 €950 Woman's portrait (95x70cm-37x28in) s.d.1915. 27-Mar-4 L & B, Essen #57/R

ATTWELL, Mabel Lucie (1879-1964) British
Works on paper
£300 $528 €438 Ooops, too late! - little girl crying after having just cut off her pony tail (18x23cm-7x9in) s. W/C htd white. 18-May-4 Fellows & Sons, Birmingham #223/R
£1000 $1840 €1460 Don't mind the blackouts, you can always stay the night (18x11cm-7x4in) W/C bodycol prov. 8-Jun-4 Bonhams, New Bond Street #141/R est:800-1000
£1100 $1980 €1606 Just one bite, Hovis, your baker bakes it (73x56cm-29x22in) s. crayon W/C. 21-Jan-4 Sotheby's, Olympia #252/R est:500-700
£1200 $2208 €1752 Who's afraid of the rain (17x12cm-7x5in) s.i. W/C prov. 8-Jun-4 Bonhams, New Bond Street #140/R est:800-1000
£3200 $5888 €4672 Fairies and pixies at play by moonlight (50x35cm-20x14in) s. W/C. 8-Jun-4 Bonhams, New Bond Street #139/R est:3000-5000

ATTWOOD, Thomas Reginald (1865-1926) New Zealander
£326 $525 €476 River landscape (90x60cm-35x24in) s. 12-Aug-3 Peter Webb, Auckland #35 (NZ.D 900)
£543 $875 €793 Wanganui River (88x57cm-35x22in) s. 20-Aug-3 Dunbar Sloane, Auckland #120/R est:1800-2500 (NZ.D 1500)

ATWATER and PARSONS (20th C) American?
Prints
£2305 $3849 €3250 New York and Brooklyn (59x84cm-23x33in) col lithograph. 23-Jun-3 Durán, Madrid #712/R

ATWOOD, J (19/20th C) British?
£3600 $6588 €5256 Still lifes with various flowers in bronze urns (76x63cm-30x25in) s. canvas on board pair. 6-Jul-4 Sotheby's, Olympia #597/R est:800-1200

ATWOOD, Robert (1892-?) American
£1217 $2300 €1777 Rural landscape with farm buildings, possibly Tennessee (76x91cm-30x36in) s. 21-Feb-4 Brunk, Ashville #642/R est:500-1000

ATYEO, Brian (1950-) Canadian
Works on paper
£360 $613 €526 Morning glow (57x76cm-22x30in) s. W/C prov. 23-Nov-3 Levis, Calgary #4/R (C.D 800)

AUBE, Paul (1837-1916) French
Sculpture
£2069 $3455 €3000 Le serment (82x20x28cm-32x8x11in) s.st.f.A.A. Hebrard brown pat bronze. 17-Nov-3 Tajan, Paris #90/R est:3500-4000

AUBERJONOIS, René (1872-1957) Swiss
£3664 $6558 €5349 Pecheur au bord du lac (36x46cm-14x18in) s. 14-May-4 Dobiaschofsky, Bern #116/R est:12000 (S.FR 8500)
£8297 $14852 €12114 Dompteuse (54x46cm-21x18in) s. canvas on board exhib.lit. 26-May-4 Sotheby's, Zurich #122/R est:15000-20000 (S.FR 19000)
£19651 $35175 €28690 Picador Renverse (40x50cm-16x20in) s.d.1942 prov.exhib.lit. 26-May-4 Sotheby's, Zurich #119/R est:14000-18000 (S.FR 45000)
Works on paper
£259 $463 €378 Femme accroupie dans un champ (15x16cm-6x6in) s. Indian ink wash. 12-May-4 Dobiaschofsky, Bern #1371 (S.FR 600)
£279 $494 €407 Gens pauvres (22x18cm-9x7in) s.i.d.42 ink pencil. 12-Jun-4 Falk & Falk, Zurich #795 (S.FR 650)
£459 $766 €666 Lute playing harlequin (32x23cm-13x9in) Indian ink. 19-Jun-3 Kornfeld, Bern #192 (S.FR 1000)
£563 $1007 €822 Woman hanging out washing (25x16cm-10x6in) s. pencil. 22-Mar-4 Philippe Schuler, Zurich #4140 (S.FR 1300)
£563 $1007 €822 Le peintre et son modele (45x32cm-18x13in) s. sepia Indian ink lit. 22-Mar-4 Philippe Schuler, Zurich #4141/R (S.FR 1300)
£742 $1329 €1083 La vie de chateau (14x17cm-6x7in) mono.i. pencil col pencil. 26-May-4 Sotheby's, Zurich #89/R est:1500-2000 (S.FR 1700)
£1147 $1915 €1663 Le Dandy (33x24cm-13x9in) mono. pencil. 19-Jun-3 Kornfeld, Bern #193 est:2500 (S.FR 2500)
£1834 $3283 €2678 Les deux baigneuses (26x18cm-10x7in) s. pencil. 26-May-4 Sotheby's, Zurich #93/R est:1800-2500 (S.FR 4200)
£2358 $4221 €3443 Le salut de l'ecuyere (25x18cm-10x7in) s. pencil lit. 26-May-4 Sotheby's, Zurich #90/R est:2000-3000 (S.FR 5400)

AUBERT, Georges (1886-1961) Swiss
£1034 $1852 €1510 Figure in boat (65x100cm-26x39in) s. exhib. 12-May-4 Dobiaschofsky, Bern #318 est:1200 (S.FR 2400)

AUBERT, H (19th C) French
£661 $1123 €965 Still life with grapes, apple and jug (38x46cm-15x18in) s. 5-Nov-3 Dobiaschofsky, Bern #315/R (S.FR 1500)
£705 $1198 €1029 Still life with berries, greengages and brass pot (38x46cm-15x18in) s. 5-Nov-3 Dobiaschofsky, Bern #316/R (S.FR 1600)

AUBERT, William (1856-1942) Swiss
£500 $830 €725 Female nude in boudoir (83x130cm-33x51in) s. 13-Jun-3 Zofingen, Switzerland #2772/R (S.FR 1100)

AUBERTIN, Bernard (1934-) French
£1216 $2141 €1800 Serviette rouge (64x49cm-25x19in) red serviette and oil board. 18-May-4 Tajan, Paris #112/R est:1200-1500
£1678 $2803 €2400 Disque clou (100x100cm-39x39in) s.i.d.1967-76 verso paint nails panel prov. 29-Jun-3 Versailles Encheres #207/R
Sculpture
£1216 $2141 €1800 Dessin de feu circulaire (90x90cm-35x35in) s.i.d.1974 verso burnt matches aluminium under plexiglass prov. 18-May-4 Tajan, Paris #111/R est:2000-3000
£3354 $5500 €4897 Point rouge (8x8x8cm-3x3x3in) oil nails wood prov.exhib. 28-May-3 Sotheby's, Amsterdam #40/R est:2000-3000
Works on paper
£322 $602 €480 Rouge (40x26cm-16x10in) s.i.d.1976 pencil. 29-Feb-4 Versailles Encheres #201
£915 $1500 €1336 Dessin de feu (42x36cm-17x14in) s.i.d.1973 verso burned matches on cardboard prov.exhib. 28-May-3 Sotheby's, Amsterdam #163/R est:1500-2000
£1087 $1783 €1500 Dessin de feu circulaire (65x50cm-26x20in) s.i.d.1973 burnt matches on wood prov. 27-May-3 Sotheby's, Amsterdam #446/R est:1500-2000
£3354 $5500 €4897 Clous 61 no 23 (19x25cm-7x10in) s.i.d.61 verso nails oil wood prov.exhib. 28-May-3 Sotheby's, Amsterdam #16/R est:5000-7000

AUBERY, Jean (1880-?) French
£300 $501 €438 Route de printemps (33x41cm-13x16in) s. 21-Oct-3 Bonhams, Knightsbridge #19/R

AUBLET, Albert (1851-1938) French
£400 $736 €600 La Baie de Naples (35x26cm-14x10in) s.i. exhib. 14-Jun-4 Tajan, Paris #85
£671 $1229 €980 Two Arabs by fountain in Cairo (46x33cm-18x13in) s.i.d.1880. 9-Jun-4 Rasmussen, Copenhagen #1907/R (D.KR 7500)
£861 $1395 €1248 Southern scene with church and houses (61x46cm-24x18in) s. 4-Aug-3 Rasmussen, Vejle #414/R (D.KR 9000)
£1678 $3104 €2500 Matmassy, femmes Tunisiennes sous la tente (19x27cm-7x11in) s.i. cardboard. 15-Mar-4 Gros & Delettrez, Paris #145/R est:2500-3000
£1761 $3046 €2500 Ruelle a Tunis (35x27cm-14x11in) s. cardboard. 15-Dec-3 Gros & Delettrez, Paris #404/R est:2500-4000
£10000 $18200 €14600 Jeune tunisienne (130x83cm-51x33in) s.indis.d.1902 prov. 15-Jun-4 Sotheby's, London #128/R est:12000-18000
£23611 $42500 €34472 Artist (23x31cm-9x12in) s.d.1880 panel. 23-Apr-4 Sotheby's, New York #89/R est:15000-20000

AUBREY, Christopher (19th C) New Zealander
Works on paper
£625 $994 €913 Rabbitors hut (16x28cm-6x11in) s.d.1883 W/C. 1-May-3 Dunbar Sloane, Wellington #41/R est:2500-3500 (NZ.D 1800)
£2076 $3716 €3031 Campfire beside lake (24x35cm-9x14in) s.d.05 W/C. 12-May-4 Dunbar Sloane, Wellington #26/R est:8000-12000 (NZ.D 6000)

AUBREY, Jean (1880-?) French
£400 $668 €584 Rue du carpentra (38x46cm-15x18in) s. 21-Oct-3 Bonhams, Knightsbridge #16/R

AUBRIET, Claude (c.1665-1742) French
Works on paper
£417 $750 €609 Two studies of an exotic fruits, a cross section, and three seeds (31x45cm-12x18in) i. bodycol vellum. 22-Jan-4 Christie's, Rockefeller NY #257/R
£2759 $4607 €4000 Corneille noire albinos (38x29cm-15x11in) W/C gouache black crayon brush col ink vellum or possibly studio. 13-Nov-3 Binoche, Paris #25/R est:1500

AUBRY, Émile (1880-1964) French
£1189 $1985 €1700 Femme berbere (55x46cm-22x18in) s. paper on canvas. 7-Oct-3 Livinec, Gaudcheau & Jezequel, Rennes #101a/R
Works on paper
£2148 $3973 €3200 Jeune fille du Sud (44x37cm-17x15in) s. pastel chl. 15-Mar-4 Gros & Delettrez, Paris #245/R est:1500-2000

AUBRY, Étienne (1745-1781) French
£2817 $4676 €4000 La bonne mere (21x27cm-8x11in) panel. 13-Jun-3 Renaud, Paris #13/R est:4000-6000
£20000 $36600 €29200 Sleeping boy (48x39cm-19x15in) s.d.1773 oval prov. 8-Jul-4 Sotheby's, London #174/R est:20000-30000

AUBRY, Étienne (attrib) (1745-1781) French
£1119 $1924 €1600 Une jeune mere et son enfant (37x27cm-15x11in) paper on canvas. 8-Dec-3 Piasa, Paris #4 est:2000-2500
Works on paper
£500 $865 €730 Bust of a girl in a bonnet, lace-making (25x16cm-10x6in) col chk grey wash. 9-Dec-3 Bonhams, Knightsbridge #2/R

AUBRY, Louis François (1767-1851) French
Miniatures
£1800 $3114 €2628 Young lady (7cm-3in) gilt-metal frame oval. 9-Dec-3 Christie's, London #195/R est:2000-3000
£2690 $4922 €3900 Jeune fille portant un sabre d'officiersuperieur (9x7cm-4x3in) s. sculpted brass surround wood frame oval. 31-Jan-4 Osenat, Fontainebleau #604

AUBURTIN, Jean François (1866-1930) French
£4296 $7518 €6100 Les pins en bord de mer (52x74cm-20x29in) board prov. 21-Dec-3 Thierry & Lannon, Brest #123/R est:4800-5200
Works on paper
£1192 $2229 €1800 Les trois voiliers et la balise rouge (36x62cm-14x24in) mono. W/C gouache. 24-Jul-4 Thierry & Lannon, Brest #91/R est:1500-2000
£1333 $2387 €2000 Belle-Ile-en-Mer, voilier au Domois (31x50cm-12x20in) mono. gouache. 16-May-4 Thierry & Lannon, Brest #80/R est:1800-2000
£1733 $3103 €2600 Bretagne, Erquy (30x75cm-12x30in) gouache prov. 16-May-4 Thierry & Lannon, Brest #82/R est:2500-3000
£2833 $5072 €4250 Belle-Ile-en-Mer, Coucher de soleil a Goulphar (31x50cm-12x20in) mono. gouache. 16-May-4 Thierry & Lannon, Brest #81/R est:2000-2500

AUDEBES, René (20th C) French?
£1329 $2285 €1900 Personnages (108x208cm-43x82in) s. oil paper on canvas. 5-Dec-3 Chochon-Barre & Allardi, Paris #15/R est:1400-1800

AUDETTE, Yvonne (1930-) Australian
£7287 $11733 €10639 Archimedes notebook (91x120cm-36x47in) s.d.68 i.verso prov.exhib. 25-Aug-3 Sotheby's, Paddington #142/R est:12000-15000 (A.D 18000)
£12195 $21829 €17805 Fog lights in the bay (76x91cm-30x36in) s.i.d.1968/69 verso prov. 4-May-4 Sotheby's, Melbourne #35/R est:30000-40000 (A.D 30000)
£32389 $52146 €47288 Cantata no.16 (100x85cm-39x33in) s.d.1958 i.verso plywood panel prov.exhib.lit. 25-Aug-3 Sotheby's, Paddington #114/R est:30000-50000 (A.D 80000)

AUDIFFRED, Edouard (1818-1861) French

£2333	$4177	€3500	Paysage a la cascade en Italie (66x86cm-26x34in) s.d.1850. 16-May-4 Joron-Derem, Paris #41/R est:4000-6000

AUDRAN, Claude III (attrib) (1658-1734) French

£87912	$160000	€128352	Alegories of the months of the year, figures of Gods (239x57cm-94x22in) canvas on panel set of six. 17-Jun-4 Christie's, Rockefeller NY #47/R est:200000-250000

AUDUBON, John James (1785-1851) American/French

Prints

£1848	$3400	€2698	Wild turkey (99x66cm-39x26in) offset lithograph. 27-Mar-4 New Orleans Auction, New Orleans #729 est:1200-1800
£1946	$3600	€2841	Fish crow (97x64cm-38x25in) engraving hand col. 17-Jul-4 New Orleans Auction, New Orleans #777/R est:4000-7000
£1981	$3250	€2872	Summer or Wood Duck from birds of America (97x61cm-38x24in) chromolithograph. 4-Jun-3 Alderfer's, Hatfield #264 est:400-600
£2235	$4000	€3263	Finch (51x30cm-20x12in) col etching aquatint wove paper. 20-Mar-4 Sloans & Kenyon, Bethesda #314/R est:2000-2500
£2401	$4250	€3505	Yellow breasted chat (64x51cm-25x20in) num.28 hand col lithograph. 1-May-4 Thomaston Place, Thomaston #98/R
£2542	$4500	€3711	Carolina parrots (99x66cm-39x26in) chromolithograph on chipboard exec.c.1900. 1-May-4 Thomaston Place, Thomaston #99a/R
£7062	$12500	€10311	Mockingbird and rattlesnake (84x58cm-33x23in) num.5 hand col lithograph. 1-May-4 Thomaston Place, Thomaston #99/R

Works on paper

£22099	$40000	€32265	Portrait of Captain Gilbert Morris (25x20cm-10x8in) s.d.1821 black chk. 3-Apr-4 Neal Auction Company, New Orleans #434/R est:15000-25000

AUDUBON, John James (after) (1785-1851) American/French

Prints

£3243	$6000	€4735	Glossy ibis (53x66cm-21x26in) hand colored etching. 15-Jan-4 Sotheby's, New York #174/R est:6000-8000
£3514	$6500	€5130	Snow goose (55x91cm-22x36in) hand colored aquatint. 15-Jan-4 Sotheby's, New York #173/R est:6000-7000
£3514	$6500	€5130	Blue winged teal (37x52cm-15x20in) hand colored etching aquatint. 15-Jan-4 Sotheby's, New York #171/R est:7000-8000
£3804	$7000	€5554	White-headed eagle (65x98cm-26x39in) col engraving aquatint. 22-Jun-4 Sotheby's, New York #30/R est:4000-6000
£4076	$7500	€5951	White-headed eagle (66x98cm-26x39in) col engraving aquatint. 22-Jun-4 Sotheby's, New York #31 est:6000-8000
£4348	$8000	€6348	Red-shouldered hawk (99x67cm-39x26in) col engraving aquatint. 22-Jun-4 Sotheby's, New York #39/R est:8000-12000
£4620	$8500	€6745	Great horned owl (98x65cm-39x26in) col engraving aquatint. 22-Jun-4 Sotheby's, New York #41/R est:7000-9000
£5163	$9500	€7538	Ruffed grouse (65x99cm-26x39in) col engraving aquatint. 22-Jun-4 Sotheby's, New York #34/R est:10000-15000
£5405	$10000	€7891	White headed pigeon (64x53cm-25x21in) hand colored etching. 15-Jan-4 Sotheby's, New York #164/R est:12000-14000
£5435	$10000	€7935	Mocking bird (84x60cm-33x24in) col engraving aquatint. 22-Jun-4 Sotheby's, New York #26/R est:8000-12000
£5435	$10000	€7935	Passenger pigeon (98x65cm-39x26in) col engraving aquatint. 22-Jun-4 Sotheby's, New York #42/R est:10000-15000
£5435	$10000	€7935	Meadow lark (97x65cm-38x26in) col engraving aquatint. 22-Jun-4 Sotheby's, New York #60/R est:15000-20000
£5523	$9500	€8064	Blue jay (79x53cm-31x21in) num.21 col engraving. 6-Dec-3 Neal Auction Company, New Orleans #472/R est:9000-12000
£5978	$11000	€8728	Carolina turtle dove (98x65cm-39x26in) col engraving aquatint. 22-Jun-4 Sotheby's, New York #24/R est:8000-10000
£7609	$14000	€11109	Ivory-billed woodpecker (99x65cm-39x26in) col engraving aquatint. 22-Jun-4 Sotheby's, New York #43 est:20000-30000
£7609	$14000	€11109	Fish hawk (98x65cm-39x26in) col engraving aquatint. 22-Jun-4 Sotheby's, New York #49/R est:15000-20000
£10326	$19000	€15076	Virginian partridge (65x99cm 26x39in) col engraving aquatint. 22-Jun-4 Sotheby's, New York #47/R est:15000-20000
£10870	$20000	€15870	Great American hen and young (64x97cm-25x38in) col etching engraving. 22-Jun-4 Sotheby's, New York #22/R est:25000-30000
£11413	$21000	€16663	Snowy owl (89x58cm-35x23in) col engraving aquatint. 22-Jun-4 Sotheby's, New York #55/R est:30000-50000
£11957	$22000	€17457	Carolina parrot (84x60cm-33x24in) col engraving aquatint. 22-Jun-4 Sotheby's, New York #28/R est:30000-50000
£11957	$22000	€17457	Ivory-billed woodpecker (100x68cm-39x27in) col engraving aquatint. 22-Jun-4 Sotheby's, New York #44/R est:30000-50000
£27027	$50000	€39459	American white pelican (89x60cm-35x24in) hand colored etching aquatint. 15-Jan-4 Sotheby's, New York #170/R est:60000-80000
£27174	$50000	€39674	Great American cock male (99x65cm-39x26in) col engraving. 22-Jun-4 Sotheby's, New York #21/R est:30000-50000
£33967	$62500	€49592	Snowy owl (89x57cm-35x22in) col engraving aquatint. 22-Jun-4 Sotheby's, New York #56/R est:80000-120000

AUDY, Jonny (19th C) French

Works on paper

£426	$689	€600	La halte du chasseur (17x21cm-7x8in) s.d.1849 W/C pen black ink. 21-May-3 Daguerre, Paris #88
£426	$689	€600	Chasseur sur son cheval (17x22cm-7x9in) s. W/C. 21-May-3 Daguerre, Paris #89
£426	$689	€600	Jockey a cheval (14x21cm-6x8in) s. W/C. 21-May-3 Daguerre, Paris #91
£507	$832	€700	Cavalier (15x10cm-6x4in) s. W/C gouache. 28-May-3 Coutau Begarie, Paris #324/R

AUER, Grigor (1882-1967) Finnish

£268	$499	€400	Italian landscape (51x41cm-20x16in) s.d.54. 7-Mar-4 Bukowskis, Helsinki #287/R
£282	$519	€420	Hostorar (50x38cm-20x15in) s. 25-Mar-4 Hagelstam, Helsinki #805
£333	$607	€490	Fishing boats (40x51cm-16x20in) s.i.d.55. 8-Feb-4 Bukowskis, Helsinki #310/R
£340	$619	€500	Landscape from Capri (51x40cm-20x16in) s.i.d.57. 8-Feb-4 Bukowskis, Helsinki #309/R
£503	$926	€750	Lilacs (41x51cm-16x20in) s.i.d.1930. 25-Mar-4 Hagelstam, Helsinki #996
£559	$951	€800	Flowers in vase (46x60cm-18x24in) s.d.1947. 29-Nov-3 Bukowskis, Helsinki #82/R

AUERBACH, Arnold (1898-1978) British

Works on paper

£1300	$2236	€1898	Mornington Crescent (22x22cm-9x9in) pencil chalk. 2-Dec-3 Bonhams, New Bond Street #172/R est:800-1200
£4000	$6880	€5840	Mornington Crescent (21x22cm-8x9in) pencil crayon. 2-Dec-3 Bonhams, New Bond Street #171/R est:800-1200

AUERBACH, Frank (1931-) British/German

£27000	$49680	€39420	St Paul's building site, winter (81x122cm-32x48in) board painted c.1955 prov.lit. 24-Jun-4 Sotheby's, London #244/R est:30000-40000
£28000	$50680	€40880	Oxford Street building site (51x35cm-20x14in) painted c.1958 prov.exhib. 1-Apr-4 Christie's, Kensington #299/R est:15000-20000
£30000	$50100	€43800	Reclining figure of Jym (41x51cm-16x20in) painted 1985 prov. 21-Oct-3 Sotheby's, London #416/R est:30000-40000
£38000	$69920	€55480	J Y M seated III (40x30cm-16x12in) painted 1989 prov. 24-Jun-4 Sotheby's, London #242/R est:28000-35000
£58000	$106140	€84680	Seated model in Studio IV (30x15cm-12x6in) board painted 1964 prov.lit. 4-Jun-4 Christie's, London #96/R est:40000-60000
£65000	$118950	€94900	Head of Paula Eyles (70x61cm-28x24in) painted 1969 prov.exhib.lit. 4-Jun-4 Christie's, London #97/R est:40000-60000
£75000	$125250	€109500	From the studio (46x46cm-18x18in) board painted 1992-3 prov. 21-Oct-3 Sotheby's, London #412/R est:50000-70000
£140000	$254800	€204400	Head of J.Y.M. II (62x66cm-24x26in) painted 1986 prov.exhib. 5-Feb-4 Sotheby's, London #15/R est:60000-80000
£150000	$255000	€219000	E.O.W looking into fire II (46x41cm-18x16in) board double-sided painted 1962 prov.exhib.lit. 21-Nov-3 Christie's, London #153/R est:50000-80000
£220000	$404800	€321200	To the studios II (35x63cm-14x25in) painted 1983 prov.exhib. 23-Jun-4 Sotheby's, London #5/R est:70000-90000
£310000	$570400	€452600	Head of J.Y.M II (66x61cm-26x24in) s. painted 1984-85 prov.exhib.lit. 23-Jun-4 Sotheby's, London #3/R est:60000-80000

Prints

£3200	$5856	€4672	Lucien Freud (15x14cm-6x6in) s.i.d.1981 num.13/50 grey black tone etching. 3-Jun-4 Christie's, Kensington #309/R est:800-1200

Works on paper

£2600	$4784	€3796	Primrose Hill (23x28cm-9x11in) pencil paper on board prov. 24-Jun-4 Sotheby's, Olympia #476/R est:1000-1500
£3200	$5344	€4672	Study for Primrose Hill (21x29cm-8x11in) pen black ink felt tip pen prov. 16-Oct-3 Christie's, Kensington #691/R est:1500-2000
£3600	$6588	€5256	Primrose Hill (24x30cm-9x12in) black crayon oil prov. 4-Jun-4 Christie's, London #95a/R est:4000-6000
£8500	$15640	€12410	Untitled (46x48cm-18x19in) s.d.1954 verso pastel chl double-sided prov. 24-Jun-4 Sotheby's, London #243/R est:6000-8000

AUERBACH-LEVY, William (1889-1964) American

£190	$350	€277	Nude (25x30cm-10x12in) s. board exhib. 25-Jun-4 Freeman, Philadelphia #190/R
£219	$400	€320	White horse (51x61cm-20x24in) 5-Jun-4 Neal Auction Company, New Orleans #425
£281	$450	€410	Seated worker (122x99cm-48x39in) s. 17-May-3 Bunte, Elgin #1209
£375	$600	€548	Old timer (130x104cm-51x41in) s. 17-May-3 Bunte, Elgin #1208
£438	$700	€639	Nudes (102x81cm-40x32in) 17-May-3 Bunte, Elgin #1207
£2813	$4500	€4107	Artist and model (127x102cm-50x40in) init. 17-May-3 Bunte, Elgin #1205 est:1500-2500
£2813	$4500	€4107	Reclining nude (102x127cm-40x50in) s.d.1934. 17-May-3 Bunte, Elgin #1206 est:1000-1500
£4218	$6750	€6158	Interior scene with women looking at artwork (102x127cm-40x50in) s. 17-May-3 Bunte, Elgin #1204 est:2000-3000

AUFRAY, Joseph (1836-?) French

£1500	$2685	€2190	Basket of cherries (35x25cm-14x10in) s. panel. 18-Mar-4 Christie's, Kensington #723/R est:1200-1800
£7000	$12950	€10220	Little helpers (27x21cm-11x8in) s. board pair. 14-Jul-4 Sotheby's, Olympia #183/R est:3000-5000

AUGE, Philippe (1935-) French

£231	$400	€337	Still life of fruit (36x61cm-14x24in) s. 13-Dec-3 Susanin's, Chicago #5025/R
£294	$500	€429	Still life of fruit (28x36cm-11x14in) s. 7-Nov-3 Selkirks, St. Louis #590
£374	$700	€546	Loving wind (46x56cm-18x22in) s. prov. 24-Feb-4 Arthur James, Florida #234
£531	$950	€775	Basket of fruit (99x99cm-39x39in) s. 20-Mar-4 Selkirks, St. Louis #533/R

AUGSBOURG, Geo (1902-1974) Swiss

Works on paper

£413	$689	€599	C F Ramuz et Auberjonois (26x20cm-10x8in) s.i.d. ink. 21-Jun-3 Galerie du Rhone, Sion #310/R (S.FR 900)

AUGUSTE, Benito (20th C) Haitian

£546	$1000	€797	Figures walking in a square (40x51cm-16x20in) s.d.73 board. 3-Jun-4 Christie's, Rockefeller NY #1118/R est:500-700
£546	$1000	€797	Town scene (51x41cm-20x16in) s.d.Auguste 73 board. 3-Jun-4 Christie's, Rockefeller NY #1119/R est:500-700

AUGUSTE, Jules Robert (attrib) (1789-1850) French

£400	$724	€600	Portrait presume du Comte Demetrius Palatiano (16x12cm-6x5in) oil paper on cardboard. 30-Mar-4 Rossini, Paris #666
£467	$845	€700	Souliote au fusil, portrait presume du Comte Demetrius Palatiano (40x32cm-16x13in) 30-Mar-4 Rossini, Paris #664

£1000	$1810	€1500	Paysage aux deux arbres (20x26cm-8x10in) cardboard. 30-Mar-4 Rossini, Paris #669 est:600-1000
£2467	$4465	€3700	Tete d'Africain (41x32cm-16x13in) exhib. 30-Mar-4 Rossini, Paris #667 est:300-500

Works on paper

£333	$603	€500	Oriental dans un interieur (18x13cm-7x5in) W/C gouache. 30-Mar-4 Rossini, Paris #668
£1200	$2172	€1800	Personnage en costume Souliote, portrait presume du Comte Palatiano (19x13cm-7x5in) W/C gouache. 30-Mar-4 Rossini, Paris #662/R est:300-500

AUGUSTIN, Edgar (1936-) German?

Works on paper

£296	$491	€420	Untitled (70x49cm-28x19in) s.i.d.1980 pencil collage. 13-Jun-3 Hauswedell & Nolte, Hamburg #535/R

AUGUSTIN, Jean Baptiste Jacques (1759-1832) French

Miniatures

£2148	$3952	€3200	Un homme de qualite en redingote bleue, gilet et cravate blancs (6x5cm-2x2in) oval gold plated frame lit. 26-Mar-4 Pierre Berge, Paris #92/R est:2000-3000
£2800	$4648	€4088	Portrait of a gentleman wearing a black coat (6cm-2in) silver gilt frame shield shaped prov. 2-Oct-3 Sotheby's, Olympia #18/R est:3000-4000
£20000	$34600	€29200	Librarian Maret (6cm-2in circular) s.d.1792. 9-Dec-3 Christie's, London #156/R est:6000-8000

AUGUSTIN, Ludwig (1882-1960) Austrian?

£500	$785	€725	In the harem (79x90cm-31x35in) s. board. 28-Aug-3 Christie's, Kensington #253/R

AUGUSTIN, Pauline (1781-1865) French

Miniatures

£2500	$4475	€3650	Young gentleman called Victor Jean Baptiste Simon Jacquinot of Pamplona (12cm-5in) s.d.1824 gilt metal foliate rec.black wood frame. 25-May-4 Christie's, London #190/R est:1800-2200

AUGUSTINER, Werner (1922-1986) Austrian

£367	$660	€550	City (55x35cm-22x14in) s.d.67 panel. 22-Apr-4 Dorotheum, Graz #2
£567	$1020	€850	Girl in the street (78x54cm-31x21in) 22-Apr-4 Dorotheum, Graz #1/R
£775	$1286	€1100	Mallorca (46x54cm-18x21in) s. 12-Jun-3 Dorotheum, Graz #1/R

Works on paper

£302	$541	€450	Red light scene (38x30cm-15x12in) s. W/C. 27-May-4 Dorotheum, Graz #93/R
£528	$877	€750	Mallorca (25x32cm-10x13in) s.d.79 W/C. 12-Jun-3 Dorotheum, Graz #108/R

AUGUSTINER, Werner (attrib) (1922-1986) Austrian

£417	$663	€600	Street scene (54x78cm-21x31in) s. 10-Sep-3 Dorotheum, Vienna #107

AUGUSTINO, L (19th C) ?

£1000	$1790	€1460	Madonna and child (53x36cm-21x14in) s.d.1874 verso. 7-May-4 Chrystals Auctions, Isle of Man #211 est:1100-1500

AUGUSTINUS, Z (1973-) American?

£811	$1500	€1184	Couples (89x69cm-35x27in) s. board exhib. 13-Mar-4 Susanin's, Chicago #6049/R est:4000-6000

AUGUSTSON, Goran (1936-) Finnish

£313	$522	€450	Lonely (50x75cm-20x30in) s.d.99 acrylic. 26-Oct-3 Bukowskis, Helsinki #292/R
£326	$545	€470	Mean time (40x45cm-16x18in) s. acrylic. 26-Oct-3 Bukowskis, Helsinki #287/R
£369	$687	€550	Shore for boats (40x52cm-16x20in) s.d.98 acrylic. 7-Mar-4 Bukowskis, Helsinki #292/R
£469	$854	€690	G-major, A-minor (60x65cm-24x26in) s.d.96 acrylic. 8-Feb-4 Bukowskis, Helsinki #313/R
£479	$800	€690	Nature's embrace (70x80cm-28x31in) s.d.97 acrylic. 26-Oct-3 Bukowskis, Helsinki #289/R
£585	$1065	€860	Home evening (74x63cm-29x25in) s.d.95 acrylic. 8-Feb-4 Bukowskis, Helsinki #317/R
£634	$1096	€900	Pythagorean -composition (70x80cm-28x31in) s.d.1998 acrylic board. 13-Dec-3 Hagelstam, Helsinki #191/R
£1419	$2540	€2100	Composition (60x69cm-24x27in) s. 8-May-4 Bukowskis, Helsinki #238/R est:1800-2200

Works on paper

£295	$549	€440	Happiness Bridge (30x45cm-12x18in) s.d.93 gouache. 7-Mar-4 Bukowskis, Helsinki #291/R
£483	$889	€720	Untitled (78x60cm-31x24in) s.d.1993 gouache. 25-Mar-4 Hagelstam, Helsinki #974

AUJAME, Jean (1905-1965) French

£1200	$2172	€1800	Paysan et village (60x73cm-24x29in) s. 4-Apr-4 Salle des ventes Pillet, Lyon la Foret #1/R est:250-300

Works on paper

£467	$854	€700	Projet pour le paquebot France, appartement Bourbonais (47x61cm-19x24in) s.i.d.61 gouache. 6-Jun-4 Anaf, Lyon #312
£724	$1332	€1100	Femmes (49x54cm-19x21in) s.d.1964 W/C. 28-Jun-4 Joron-Derem, Paris #237

AULD, James Muir (1879-1942) Australian

£574	$906	€838	Summer, Dee Why (35x46cm-14x18in) s. exhib. 2-Sep-3 Deutscher-Menzies, Melbourne #353/R est:1500-2500 (A.D 1400)
£785	$1335	€1146	Moonrise (24x29cm-9x11in) s. canvasboard. 29-Oct-3 Lawson Menzies, Sydney #102/R est:1000-1250 (A.D 1900)

AULIE, Reidar (1904-1977) Norwegian

£687	$1202	€1003	Children and dachshund in the studio (46x55cm-18x22in) panel. 16-Dec-3 Grev Wedels Plass, Oslo #131/R (N.KR 8000)
£2121	$3796	€3097	The shipyard workers are arriving (37x49cm-15x19in) s. s.i. verso panel. 25-May-4 Grev Wedels Plass, Oslo #78/R est:15000-20000 (N.KR 26000)

Works on paper

£804	$1471	€1174	Building workers (50x76cm-20x30in) s. gouache. 2-Feb-4 Blomqvist, Lysaker #1012/R (N.KR 10000)

AULT, George C (1891-1948) American

£90909	$160000	€132727	Hunter's return (51x41cm-20x16in) s.d.43 prov. 19-May-4 Sotheby's, New York #143/R est:125000-175000
£100543	$185000	€146793	View from Brooklyn (45x54cm-18x21in) s.d.27 prov. 8-Jun-4 Bonhams & Butterfields, San Francisco #4105/R est:30000-50000

Works on paper

£307	$550	€448	Red barn, winter (18x28cm-7x11in) s. W/C gouache. 11-Jan-4 William Jenack, New York #248
£978	$1800	€1428	Reclining female nude (33x41cm-13x16in) s.d.1927 pencil. 10-Jun-4 Swann Galleries, New York #5/R est:2500-3500
£3261	$6000	€4761	Tree study (38x27cm-15x11in) s.d.23 pencil. 8-Jun-4 Bonhams & Butterfields, San Francisco #4103/R est:3000-5000

AUMONIER, James (1832-1911) British

£2800	$5012	€4088	Okehampton Cattle, Dartmoor (54x146cm-21x57in) s.d.1871 exhib. 26-May-4 Sotheby's, Olympia #168/R est:3000-5000

Works on paper

£411	$699	€600	Arrivee au village (15x26cm-6x10in) s. mixed media. 10-Nov-3 Horta, Bruxelles #222
£700	$1141	€1015	Brighton (17x24cm-7x9in) s.i.d.1896 W/C. 23-Sep-3 Bonhams, Knightsbridge #22/R
£800	$1296	€1160	Walberswick (23x80cm-9x31in) s.d.78 W/C. 30-Jul-3 Hamptons Fine Art, Godalming #101

AUMONIER, John S (20th C) British

£400	$716	€584	Grey day (18x25cm-7x10in) s. 18-Mar-4 Christie's, Kensington #537/R

AUPILLARDJUK, Mariano (1923-) North American

Sculpture

£811	$1378	€1184	Standing goose (18cm-7in) i. weathered whalebone. 3-Nov-3 Waddingtons, Toronto #226/R est:600-900 (C.D 1800)

AURELI, Giuseppe (1858-1929) Italian

£1007	$1802	€1500	Village with figures (26x21cm-10x8in) s.d.1895 board. 25-May-4 Finarte Semenzato, Milan #105/R est:1200-1400

Works on paper

£976	$1600	€1415	Evening at Lepezzia (61x97cm-24x38in) s. i.verso W/C. 31-May-3 Brunk, Ashville #108/R est:2000-4000

AURORA, Mario (20th C) American?

Sculpture

£2640	$4250	€3854	Dancing ballerina (198cm-78in) s. bronze. 15-Aug-3 Du Mouchelle, Detroit #2010/R est:3000-5000

AUSBORN, Gerhard (1933-) German

£664	$1143	€950	Composition (60x81cm-24x32in) s. d.1959 verso. 6-Dec-3 Hans Stahl, Toestorf #98/R

AUSLEGER, Rudolf (1897-1974) German

Works on paper

£805	$1442	€1200	Still life with blue glass (33x30cm-13x12in) mono.d.21 W/C pencil. 25-May-4 Karl & Faber, Munich #193/R

AUSSANDON, Hippolyte (1836-?) French

Works on paper

£452	$724	€655	Aurora (21x14cm-8x6in) s. pencil. 15-May-3 Stuker, Bern #1042 (S.FR 950)

AUSTEN, Alexander (fl.1891-1909) British

£350	$595	€511	Sportman's toast (41x61cm-16x24in) s. 27-Nov-3 Christie's, Kensington #18
£1041	$1738	€1520	The cellist (48x31cm-19x12in) s. 17-Nov-3 Waddingtons, Toronto #97 est:1500-2000 (C.D 2300)

AUSTEN, John (1886-1948) British

£430	$701	€628	Steam train crossing Victoria Bridge on the Severn Valley Railway (102x76cm-40x30in) s. 25-Sep-3 Grant, Worcester #112/R

AUSTEN, Winifred (1876-1964) British

£260	$465	€380	Mallard in flight (22x28cm-9x11in) mono.i. 16-Mar-4 Gildings, Market Harborough #417

Works on paper
£550 $985 €803 Foraging party, birds on sand dunes (34x45cm-13x18in) mono. W/C. 16-Mar-4 Bonhams, Oxford #43

AUSTIN, Alexander (fl.1891-1909) British
£699 $1189 €1000 Appraiser (39x60cm-15x24in) s. 26-Nov-3 James Adam, Dublin #49/R
£850 $1547 €1241 Conversation pieces. s. painted c.1910 pair. 16-Jun-4 Brightwells, Leominster #875/R

AUSTIN, C (?) ?
£1329 $2300 €1940 Woman on bridge (76x64cm-30x25in) s.d.1876. 13-Dec-3 Charlton Hall, Columbia #79y/R est:800-1200

AUSTIN, Cary (20th C) American
£569 $950 €831 The storm (48x86cm-19x34in) s. acrylic. 11-Oct-3 Nadeau, Windsor #211/R

AUSTIN, Darrel (1907-1994) American
£243 $450 €355 Dark lady (61x51cm-24x20in) s.d.52 prov. 10-Mar-4 Doyle, New York #62/R
£528 $850 €771 Young beast in a marsh (30x41cm-12x16in) s.d.1968. 22-Feb-3 Bunte, Elgin #1165

AUSTIN, Larry (20th C) American
Works on paper
£565 $1050 €825 Model wearing early Miriam Haskell necklace and bracelet by Frank Hess (20x25cm-8x10in) W/C board exec.c.1940. 6-Mar-4 Dan Ripley, Indianapolis #136
£565 $1050 €825 Model wearing Miriam Haskell cluster clip and bracelet by Frank Hess (20x25cm-8x10in) W/C gouache board exec.c.1940. 6-Mar-4 Dan Ripley, Indianapolis #137

AUSTIN, Robert Sargent (1895-1973) British
Works on paper
£360 $634 €526 Sleeping mother and child and a baby in a waiting room (52x42cm-20x17in) studio st. black chk ink squared transfer. 19-May-4 Sotheby's, Olympia #10/R
£360 $634 €526 Miss Barbara Harris (46x58cm-18x23in) s.d.1943 chl exhib. 19-May-4 Sotheby's, Olympia #42/R
£680 $1197 €993 Peasant woman resting her load (36x30cm-14x12in) s. indis d. W/C pencil gouache exhib. 19-May-4 Sotheby's, Olympia #1/R
£700 $1232 €1022 Ling (23x24cm-9x9in) studio st. black chk two. 19-May-4 Sotheby's, Olympia #17/R
£750 $1320 €1095 Night scene, mother at bedside. Mother and cradle (43x34cm-17x13in) W/C gouache two exhib. 19-May-4 Sotheby's, Olympia #20/R
£780 $1373 €1139 Seated female nude, arms raised. Nude and Ling (37x29cm-15x11in) s.d.1934 col chk two. 19-May-4 Sotheby's, Olympia #49/R
£800 $1408 €1168 Clare seated on a chaise longue (56x45cm-22x18in) s.d.1938 chl exhib. 19-May-4 Sotheby's, Olympia #30/R
£850 $1496 €1241 Child kissing mother (33x24cm-13x9in) chl red chk sold with two others by same hand. 19-May-4 Sotheby's, Olympia #29/R
£1200 $2112 €1752 Burnham Overy, Staithe (22x26cm-9x10in) s. W/C pencil set of four. 19-May-4 Sotheby's, Olympia #11/R est:500-700
£1200 $2112 €1752 After the bath. Reading on blue sofa (41x28cm-16x11in) W/C ink two. 19-May-4 Sotheby's, Olympia #19/R est:500-700
£1200 $2184 €1800 Ballerina (45x63cm-18x25in) s.d.1936 W/C pencil pen ink. 2-Jul-4 Bloomsbury, London #48/R est:2000-3000
£1300 $2288 €1898 Rachel (23x21cm-9x8in) init.d.5 Jan 1942 red chk two. 19-May-4 Sotheby's, Olympia #14/R est:800-1200
£1950 $3432 €2847 Toil (39x35cm-15x14in) s. W/C gouache exhib. 19-May-4 Sotheby's, Olympia #2/R est:800-1200

AUSTIN, Samuel (1796-1834) British
Works on paper
£460 $782 €672 Keniworth Castle (28x41cm-11x16in) W/C. 29-Oct-3 Bonhams, Chester #412
£500 $860 €730 Extensive harvesting scene with mountain background (30x48cm-12x19in) s. W/C. 5-Dec-3 Keys, Aylsham #442/R
£850 $1572 €1241 Loading the boats in Liverpool harbour (14x22cm-6x9in) exhib. W/C sold with two others three prov. 10-Mar-4 Sotheby's, Olympia #133/R est:800-1200
£1400 $2380 €2044 Beach scene at sunset with figures, horse and dog (55x89cm-22x35in) s.d.1821 pencil W/C exhib. 19-Nov-3 Tennants, Leyburn #859 est:1200-1500

AUSTRIAN SCHOOL, 16th C
£6993 $11888 €10000 Joachim's sacrifice at the Temple of Jerusalem (109x78cm-43x31in) 20-Nov-3 Dorotheum, Salzburg #18/R est:20000-30000

AUSTRIAN SCHOOL, 17th C
£4698 $8691 €7000 Eastern figures near a classical ruin (114x78cm-45x31in) 15-Mar-4 Sotheby's, Amsterdam #11/R est:2000-3000
£14765 $27168 €22000 Battle scene from the Austrian Turkish wars (73x136cm-29x54in) prov. 24-Mar-4 Dorotheum, Vienna #423/R est:10000-15000

AUSTRIAN SCHOOL, 18th C
£14865 $26162 €22000 Historical scene with a young man holding the hand of a bearded man (92x74cm-36x29in) prov. 18-May-4 Sotheby's, Amsterdam #47/R est:5000-7000
£20000 $34600 €29200 Extensive battlefield with a cavalry skirmish in the foreground (146x242cm-57x95in) 10-Dec-3 Bonhams, New Bond Street #47/R est:10000-15000
Sculpture
£10884 $19483 €16000 Crucifixion (54cm-21in) brown pat.bronze wooden socle. 17-Mar-4 Neumeister, Munich #183/R est:2000
£23529 $40000 €34352 Stag (132x150x76cm-52x59x30in) wood prov. 25-Nov-3 Christie's, Rockefeller NY #212/R est:30000-50000
£30986 $54225 €44000 Allegory of Spring (261cm-103in) carved wood. 16-Dec-3 Christie's, Paris #248/R est:15000-20000

AUSTRIAN SCHOOL, 19th C
£22000 $40040 €32120 View of Constantinople (91x122cm-36x48in) painted c.1830 prov. 15-Jun-4 Sotheby's, London #138/R est:15000-20000

AUSTRIAN SCHOOL, 19th/20th C
£11842 $21789 €18000 Meerschaum (126x63cm-50x25in) indis.s. 22-Jun-4 Wiener Kunst Auktionen, Vienna #201/R est:3000
Sculpture
£5556 $10000 €8112 Oriental merchant (48cm-19in) i. cold paint bronze lamp st.f.Bergman. 22-Apr-4 Christie's, Rockefeller NY #207/R est:10000-15000
£5556 $10000 €8112 Prayer (74cm-29in) st.f.Bergman cold paint col glass brown pat bronze lamp. 22-Apr-4 Christie's, Rockefeller NY #209/R est:10000-15000
£7778 $14000 €11356 At the well (70cm-28in) i. cold painted brown pat bronze col glass lamp st.f.Bergman. 22-Apr-4 Christie's, Rockefeller NY #208/R est:15000-20000
£11667 $21000 €17034 Oriental beauty sailing on a barge (46cm-18in) i. cold paint bronze lamp st.f.Bergman. 22-Apr-4 Christie's, Rockefeller NY #206/R est:12000-18000

AUSTRIAN, Ben (1870-1921) American
£1136 $2000 €1659 Florida landscape (33x25cm-13x10in) s. i.verso board. 21-May-4 Pook & Pook, Downington #94/R est:3000-3500
£1628 $2800 €2377 Summer landscape of poplar grove (25x30cm-10x12in) s. exhib. 6-Dec-3 Pook & Pook, Downington #131/R est:2500-3500
£5313 $8500 €7757 Landscape (48x69cm-19x27in) s.i.d.1916. 20-Sep-3 Pook & Pook, Downington #499/R est:7000-10000
£10465 $18000 €15279 Eight chicks surrounding one chick standing on a flowerpot (36x28cm-14x11in) s. 6-Dec-3 Pook & Pook, Downington #130/R est:6000-9000
£23864 $42000 €34841 Scene of a hen and her 11 chicks, with empty shells (51x66cm-20x26in) s. 21-May-4 Pook & Pook, Downington #202/R est:25000-35000

AUTERE, Hannes (1888-1967) Finnish
Sculpture
£1757 $3145 €2600 Madonna and Child (40cm-16in) s.d.42 bronze lit. 8-May-4 Bukowskis, Helsinki #27/R est:2500-3000
£1933 $3461 €2900 The preacher Moses gets water from the rock (20x29cm-8x11in) s.d.1924 wood relief. 15-May-4 Hagelstam, Helsinki #23/R est:2800
£4324 $7741 €6400 Girl (62cm-24in) s.d.1940 bronze lit. 8-May-4 Bukowskis, Helsinki #19/R est:4000-6000
£5405 $9676 €8000 Abraham and Isaac (57cm-22in) s.d.1936 painted wood exhib.lit. 8-May-4 Bukowskis, Helsinki #2/R

AUTHOUART, Daniel (1943-) French
Works on paper
£1206 $2013 €1700 Nounours Travolta (38x28cm-15x11in) s.d.12/95 mixed media. 19-Oct-3 Imberdis, Pont Audemer #53

AUTISSIER, Louis Marie (1772-1830) French
Miniatures
£5500 $9845 €8030 Hebe and the Eagle, standing in a cloud (11x8cm-4x3in) s.d.1811 scrolling gilt wood frame rec. 25-May-4 Christie's, London #226/R est:3000-5000
£8500 $14705 €12410 Francois Charles Joseph Bonaparte, King of Rome (8cm-3in) s.d.1817 oval prov.lit. 9-Dec-3 Christie's, London #206/R est:6000-8000

AUTORINO, Anthony (1937-) American
£295 $550 €431 Beach scene with figures (76x61cm-30x24in) s. 3-Mar-4 Alderfer's, Hatfield #376/R

AUVIGNE, Jean (after) (20th C) French
Prints
£4372 $8000 €6383 Bord de Normandie, Espostion Internationale Paris (99x65cm-39x26in) col lithograph exhib. 29-Jul-4 Christie's, Rockefeller NY #216/R est:6000-8000

AUVRAY, Felix (1800-1833) French
£400 $720 €600 Mise au tombeau (65x49cm-26x19in) s.d.1824. 25-Apr-4 Daniel Herry, Beaune #97

AUZOU, Pauline (1775-1835) French
Works on paper
£317 $548 €450 Diane and Callisto (27x39cm-11x15in) blk crayon white chk blue paper oval. 10-Dec-3 Piasa, Paris #122
£360 $576 €500 Portrait de jeune femme, les cheveux detaches (54x42cm-21x17in) chl white chk sanguine. 16-May-3 Tajan, Paris #44

AUZOU, Pauline (attrib) (1775-1835) French
Works on paper
£324 $531 €450 Portrait de femme. Etude d'apres l'Antique (39x33cm-15x13in) pierre noire estompe sanguine double-sided. 6-Jun-3 Maigret, Paris #58/R

AVALOS, Juan de (1911-) Spanish
Sculpture
£1135 $1895 €1600 Women seated (48cm-19in) pat bronze blk marble base. 23-Jun-3 Durán, Madrid #1480/R est:1000

AVANZI, Vittorio (1850-1910) Italian
£1338 $2315 €1900 Rural path (42x28cm-17x11in) s.d.1897. 9-Dec-3 Finarte Semenzato, Milan #134/R est:600-700

AVATANEO, Miguel (20th C) Venezuelan?

£1588	$2700	€2318	Nude (70x150cm-28x59in) s. painted 1991-92. 23-Nov-3 Subastas Odalys, Caracas #152/R est:4000

AVEDON, Richard (1923-) American

Photographs

£1796	$3000	€2622	Andy Warhol, artist, New York City (25x20cm-10x8in) s.i.d.1969/71 gelatin silver print. 21-Oct-3 Bonhams & Butterfields, San Francisco #1498/R
£2275	$3800	€3322	June Leaf, sculptress, Mabou Mines, Nova Scotia, July 17 (24x19cm-9x7in) s.i.d.1975 num.3 of 50 verso gelatin silver print exhib.lit. 20-Oct-3 Christie's, Rockefeller NY #203/R est:4000-6000
£5682	$10000	€8296	Judy Garland (19x24cm-7x9in) with sig. silver print. 20-May-4 Swann Galleries, New York #445/R est:12000-18000
£11377	$19000	€16610	Dovima with elephants, evening dress by Dior, Cirque d'Hiver, Paris (25x19cm-10x7in) s.num.12/100 photo exec.1955 printed later. 17-Oct-3 Sotheby's, New York #246/R est:12000-18000
£15569	$26000	€22731	Lauren Hutton, Great Exuma, the Bahamas (45x46cm-18x18in) s.num.18/50 gelatin silver print exec.1968 lit. 20-Oct-3 Christie's, Rockefeller NY #85/R est:15000-20000
£22754	$38000	€33221	Dovima and the elephants, dress by Dior, Cirque d'Hiver, Paris (129x103cm-51x41in) s.num.1/50 gelatin silver print exec.1955 prov.lit. 20-Oct-3 Christie's, Rockefeller NY #84/R est:35000-45000

AVELLINO, Onofrio (circle) (1674-1741) Italian

£7914	$12978	€11000	Holy Family (100x75cm-39x30in) 4-Jun-3 Ketterer, Hamburg #33/R est:12000-14000

AVENALI, Marcello (1912-1981) Italian

£338	$595	€500	Composition. s. 22-May-4 Galleria Pananti, Florence #311/R
£966	$1612	€1400	Still life (36x27cm-14x11in) s. board. 13-Nov-3 Finarte Semenzato, Rome #302 est:800-1200
£1000	$1800	€1500	Roman cathedral (80x90cm-31x35in) s.s.i.verso. 22-Apr-4 Finarte Semenzato, Rome #186 est:1500-2000

AVENDANO FERNANDEZ, Donato (1840-) Spanish

£940	$1682	€1400	Bridge in Alcantara (27x34cm-11x13in) s. cardboard. 25-May-4 Durán, Madrid #103/R

AVENDANO, Serafin de (1838-1916) Spanish

£9524	$17048	€14000	Washerwomen (102x62cm-40x24in) s. 22-Mar-4 Durán, Madrid #244/R est:12000
£10738	$20081	€16000	Garden in Galicia (88x54cm-35x21in) s. 24-Feb-4 Durán, Madrid #245/R est:12000
£10738	$19007	€16000	Summer in the French Pyrenees (70x110cm-28x43in) s. 27-Apr-4 Durán, Madrid #189/R est:16000
£13423	$23758	€20000	Landscape with peasant woman (55x110cm-22x43in) s.d.1904. 27-Apr-4 Durán, Madrid #188/R est:18000
£36913	$69027	€55000	June in the Pyrenees (80x120cm-31x47in) s. 24-Feb-4 Durán, Madrid #256/R est:22500

AVENDANO, Teodomiro (19th C) Spanish

Works on paper

£811	$1427	€1200	Girl at farm (34x24cm-13x9in) s.d.1879 W/C. 18-May-4 Segre, Madrid #15/R

AVERAGE, Joe (20th C) Canadian

£991	$1685	€1447	Bonfire (114cm-45in) s.d.95 verso acrylic on board. 19-Nov-3 Maynards, Vancouver #80 est:2000-3000 (C.D 2200)

AVERCAMP, Hendrick (1585-1634) Dutch

£4305556	$7750000	€6286112	Winter scene (53x94cm-21x37in) mono. panel. 22-Jan-4 Sotheby's, New York #26/R est:4000000-6000000

AVERCAMP, Hendrick (attrib) (1585-1634) Dutch

Works on paper

£2055	$3493	€3000	Man, seen from behind, shearing loose fibres from woven wool (14x9cm-6x4in) i.verso black chk pen ink wash framing lines prov. 5-Nov-3 Christie's, Amsterdam #123/R est:3000-5000
£2361	$4250	€3447	Milkmaid (15x10cm-6x4in) i. pen ink W/C prov.exhib.lit. 21-Jan-4 Sotheby's, New York #74/R est:4000-5000

AVERCAMP, Hendrick (style) (1585-1634) Dutch

£65517	$108759	€95000	Skating pleasures in Dutch village (35x48cm-14x19in) 18th C follower copper prov.exhib. 1-Oct-3 Dorotheum, Vienna #206/R est:25000-35000

AVERIN, Alexandre (1952-) Russian

£250	$408	€365	Girl with a toy boat (24x33cm-9x13in) s. 28-Sep-3 John Nicholson, Haslemere #32
£250	$418	€365	Anastasia (27x35cm-11x14in) s. 13-Jul-3 John Nicholson, Haslemere #62
£250	$448	€365	Young girl painting beside the pond (50x35cm-20x14in) s. 5-May-4 John Nicholson, Haslemere #234
£278	$453	€400	Acariciando al caballo (35x24cm-14x9in) s. 16-Jul-3 Durán, Madrid #639/R
£296	$545	€450	Summer (41x33cm-16x13in) s. 22-Jun-4 Durán, Madrid #688/R
£300	$501	€438	At the seaboard (35x27cm-14x11in) s. 13-Jul-3 John Nicholson, Haslemere #57/R
£300	$537	€438	Artist at the etudes (38x55cm-15x22in) s. 5-May-4 John Nicholson, Haslemere #139
£302	$565	€450	Little dancer (22x70cm-9x28in) s. 24-Feb-4 Durán, Madrid #715
£313	$509	€450	Before the action (33x24cm-13x9in) s. 23-Sep-3 Durán, Madrid #659/R
£325	$582	€475	Children fishing (35x27cm-14x11in) s. 5-May-4 John Nicholson, Haslemere #238/R
£329	$605	€500	Summer (40x50cm-16x20in) s. 22-Jun-4 Durán, Madrid #690/R
£329	$605	€500	In the boat (40x50cm-16x20in) s. 22-Jun-4 Durán, Madrid #693/R
£336	$594	€500	Reading (38x41cm-15x16in) s. 27-Apr-4 Durán, Madrid #706/R
£347	$566	€500	On the canal (50x35cm-20x14in) s. 16-Jul-3 Durán, Madrid #640/R
£350	$571	€511	Sea breakers (35x27cm-14x11in) s. 28-Sep-3 John Nicholson, Haslemere #7
£350	$571	€511	Silfidas (38x55cm-15x22in) s. 28-Sep-3 John Nicholson, Haslemere #81
£350	$613	€511	Nastya on the beach (24x35cm-9x14in) s. 17-Dec-3 John Nicholson, Haslemere #59/R
£350	$585	€511	Anastasia on the beach (27x35cm-11x14in) s. 13-Jul-3 John Nicholson, Haslemere #199/R
£350	$627	€511	Walk by the coast (40x50cm-16x20in) s. 5-May-4 John Nicholson, Haslemere #236/R
£395	$726	€600	Spring day (61x50cm-24x20in) s. 22-Jun-4 Durán, Madrid #689/R
£400	$652	€584	Violin player (41x27cm-16x11in) s. 28-Sep-3 John Nicholson, Haslemere #55/R
£400	$716	€584	On the terrace (61x46cm-24x18in) s. 5-May-4 John Nicholson, Haslemere #53/R
£490	$877	€715	Two girls by the sea (35x27cm-14x11in) s. 5-May-4 John Nicholson, Haslemere #9/R
£521	$828	€750	Junto a la orilla (50x40cm-20x16in) s. 29-Apr-3 Durán, Madrid #795/R
£550	$919	€803	By the lilac tree (61x38cm-24x15in) s. 13-Jul-3 John Nicholson, Haslemere #58/R
£559	$1029	€850	Having tea (61x50cm-24x20in) s. 22-Jun-4 Durán, Madrid #691/R
£567	$948	€800	Strolling in the garden (33x24cm-13x9in) s. 20-Oct-3 Durán, Madrid #697/R
£590	$962	€850	In the garden (60x73cm-24x29in) s. 16-Jul-3 Durán, Madrid #637/R
£590	$962	€850	Young girl with parrots (54x46cm-21x18in) s. 16-Jul-3 Durán, Madrid #638/R
£600	$1002	€876	Walking along the coast of Normandy (36x55cm-14x22in) s. 13-Jul-3 John Nicholson, Haslemere #56/R
£604	$1069	€900	Summer in the fields (38x55cm-15x22in) s. 27-Apr-4 Durán, Madrid #708/R
£604	$1081	€900	Strolling by the river (50x61cm-20x24in) s. 25-May-4 Durán, Madrid #713/R
£638	$1066	€900	Garden with flowers (55x38cm-22x15in) s. 20-Oct-3 Durán, Madrid #696/R
£650	$1216	€975	Summer day (50x61cm-20x24in) s. 21-Jul-4 John Nicholson, Haslemere #435/R
£652	$1070	€900	Paseo en los montes (46x55cm-18x22in) s. 27-May-3 Durán, Madrid #764/R
£660	$1049	€950	The lesson (44x56cm-17x22in) s. 29-Apr-3 Durán, Madrid #796/R
£671	$1255	€1000	Garden in bloom (55x46cm-22x18in) s. 24-Feb-4 Durán, Madrid #713/R
£738	$1381	€1100	Summer day (61x50cm-24x20in) s. 24-Feb-4 Durán, Madrid #714/R
£800	$1496	€1200	Water lilies (50x61cm-20x24in) s. 21-Jul-4 John Nicholson, Haslemere #384/R
£825	$1378	€1205	Seagulls feeding with boats and figures (46x56cm-18x22in) s. 18-Jun-3 John Nicholson, Haslemere #690
£850	$1488	€1241	Artists at work with pretty girl (38x61cm-15x24in) s. 17-Dec-3 John Nicholson, Haslemere #71/R
£900	$1611	€1314	Playing by the sea (38x55cm-15x22in) s. 5-May-4 John Nicholson, Haslemere #104/R
£950	$1549	€1387	At the sands (46x55cm-18x22in) s. 28-Sep-3 John Nicholson, Haslemere #60/R
£950	$1587	€1387	Morning tea (65x54cm-26x21in) s. 13-Jul-3 John Nicholson, Haslemere #53/R
£950	$1701	€1387	At the seaside (46x55cm-18x22in) s. 5-May-4 John Nicholson, Haslemere #144/R
£1050	$1712	€1533	An evening ramble (55x46cm-22x18in) s. 28-Sep-3 John Nicholson, Haslemere #59/R
£1350	$2201	€1971	Blooming meadow (61x46cm-24x18in) s. 28-Sep-3 John Nicholson, Haslemere #165/R
£1400	$2282	€2044	Evening in the boat (46x61cm-18x24in) s. 28-Sep-3 John Nicholson, Haslemere #33/R
£1400	$2618	€2100	On the Black Sea (38x55cm-15x22in) s. 21-Jul-4 John Nicholson, Haslemere #430/R est:1600-1800
£1500	$2505	€2190	Morning ramble by the sea (46x55cm-18x22in) s. 13-Jul-3 John Nicholson, Haslemere #144/R
£2000	$3340	€2920	Unexpected catch (46x61cm-18x24in) s. 13-Jul-3 John Nicholson, Haslemere #145/R

AVERY, Charles (20th C) British

Works on paper

£2400	$4440	€3504	Creation of the Omniverse (60x84cm-24x33in) graphite col pencil paper on board five. 13-Jul-4 Bonhams, Knightsbridge #7/R est:2500-3500

AVERY, March (20th C) American

£694	$1200	€1013	Yellow trees (117x76cm-46x30in) s.d.68 i.d.verso. 13-Dec-3 Weschler, Washington #590
£867	$1500	€1266	Father and mother (122x102cm-48x40in) s.d.62. 13-Dec-3 Weschler, Washington #591 est:1000-1500

AVERY, Milton (1885-1965) American

£1657	$3000	€2419	Fall (10x18cm-4x7in) s.d.1960 i.verso board prov. 31-Mar-4 Sotheby's, New York #21/R est:3000-6000

£5975 $9500 €8724 Afghan (21x16cm-8x6in) s. board. 12-Sep-3 Skinner, Boston #382/R est:8000
£9189 $17000 €13416 Three trees (23x61cm-9x24in) s.d.1955 oil crayon paper on board prov. 11-Mar-4 Christie's, Rockefeller NY #97/R est:7000-10000
£11892 $22000 €17362 Summer's end (46x61cm-18x24in) s.d.1954 oil crayon W/C prov. 11-Mar-4 Christie's, Rockefeller NY #103/R est:15000-25000
£21802 $37500 €31831 Owl (23x13cm-9x5in) s.d.1955 board prov.exhib. 3-Dec-3 Sotheby's, New York #83/R est:12000-18000
£24709 $42500 €36075 Pink jacket (41x30cm-16x12in) s.d.1962 i.verso canvasboard prov. 3-Dec-3 Sotheby's, New York #86/R est:20000-30000
£36932 $65000 €53921 White nude (76x46cm-30x18in) s.d.1945 canvas on board. 18-May-4 Christie's, Rockefeller NY #146/R est:50000-70000
£37791 $65000 €55175 Lone chicken (23x22cm-9x9in) s.d.1954 board prov.exhib. 3-Dec-3 Sotheby's, New York #84/R est:15000-20000
£48295 $85000 €70511 Green pitcher (36x46cm-14x18in) s.d.1949 i.verso canvasboard prov. 19-May-4 Sotheby's, New York #167/R est:70000-90000
£63953 $110000 €93371 Straw hat (91x61cm-36x24in) s.d.1963 canvasboard prov. 4-Dec-3 Christie's, Rockefeller NY #98/R est:80000-120000
£85227 $150000 €124431 Red robe (51x41cm-20x16in) s.d.1953 canvasboard prov. 18-May-4 Christie's, Rockefeller NY #129/R est:60000-80000
£87209 $150000 €127325 Mother and child (61x46cm-24x18in) s. i.verso board prov. 4-Dec-3 Christie's, Rockefeller NY #114/R est:100000-150000
£168605 $290000 €246163 Seascape (58x89cm-23x35in) s.d.1945 prov. 3-Dec-3 Sotheby's, New York #85/R est:250000-350000

Prints

£1613 $3000 €2355 Reclining nude (92x19cm-36x7in) s.d.1941 num.60/100 drypoint. 2-Mar-4 Swann Galleries, New York #24/R est:2000-3000
£1676 $3000 €2447 Child cutting (13x17cm-5x7in) s.i.d.1936 drypoint. 6-May-4 Swann Galleries, New York #384/R est:1500-2500
£1719 $2871 €2510 Reclining nude (9x18cm-4x7in) s.d.1941 num.a/p etching edition of 100 prov. 16-Oct-3 Waddingtons, Toronto #36/R est:1000-1500 (C.D 3800)
£2118 $3600 €3092 Flight (18x23cm-7x9in) s.d.1953 num.1/25 col woodcut. 6-Nov-3 Swann Galleries, New York #487/R est:1500-2500
£2250 $3600 €3285 Standing nude (36x20cm-14x8in) s.d.1941 num.13/60 drypoint. 18-Sep-3 Swann Galleries, New York #31/R est:2000-3000
£2471 $4200 €3608 Nude (9x28cm-4x11in) s.d.1952 num.1/20 col woodcut. 6-Nov-3 Swann Galleries, New York #486/R est:1500-2500
£2941 $5000 €4294 Nude combing hair (22x16cm-9x6in) s.d.1961 num.55/90 drypoint. 6-Nov-3 Swann Galleries, New York #485/R est:2000-3000
£3176 $5400 €4637 Standing nude (36x20cm-14x8in) s.d.1941 num.55/60 drypoint. 6-Nov-3 Swann Galleries, New York #484/R est:2000-3000
£8939 $16000 €13051 Laurels number four (42x33cm-17x13in) drypoint set of five. 6-May-4 Swann Galleries, New York #383/R est:8000-12000

Works on paper

£552 $1000 €806 Winter in Woodstock, New York (43x36cm-17x14in) s. W/C gouache. 16-Apr-4 James Julia, Fairfield #619/R est:4000-6000
£670 $1200 €978 Reclining nude (23x38cm-9x15in) s. pencil. 8-May-4 Susanin's, Chicago #6063/R est:1500-2400
£761 $1400 €1111 Crouching female nude (28x20cm-11x8in) s. pencil. 10-Jun-4 Swann Galleries, New York #6/R
£870 $1600 €1270 Two female nudes at a drawing table (28x20cm-11x8in) s. pencil. 10-Jun-4 Swann Galleries, New York #7/R est:2500-3500
£1676 $3000 €2447 Mother and child (28x20cm-11x8in) s.d.1949 ink. 26-May-4 Doyle, New York #163/R est:4000-6000
£1714 $3000 €2502 Man on a park bench (22x28cm-9x11in) s. pencil. 19-Dec-3 Sotheby's, New York #1039/R est:5000-7000
£1955 $3500 €2854 Harbour (28x20cm-11x8in) s.d.1958 i.verso ink prov. 16-May-4 Wright, Chicago #108/R est:3000-4000
£2000 $3500 €2920 Music maker (28x22cm-11x9in) s.d.1950 i.d.1950 verso flobrush. 19-Dec-3 Sotheby's, New York #1040/R est:2000-3000
£2717 $5000 €3967 Reclining figure (19x26cm-7x10in) s.d.1959 ink prov. 27-Jun-4 Freeman, Philadelphia #134/R est:2000-3000
£2762 $5000 €4033 Fish (9x25cm-4x10in) s.d.1952 crayon. 31-Mar-4 Sotheby's, New York #15/R est:2500-3500
£4286 $7500 €6258 Swimmer asleep (35x43cm-14x17in) s. s.i.d.1957 verso pencil. 19-Dec-3 Sotheby's, New York #1047/R est:3000-5000
£5525 $10000 €8067 Landscape with hills and trees (38x84cm-15x33in) W/C. 16-Apr-4 Du Mouchelle, Detroit #2071/R est:10000-15000
£6044 $11000 €8824 Young girl (43x35cm-17x14in) s.d.1956 i.verso ballpoint pen crayon pencil. 29-Jun-4 Sotheby's, New York #307/R est:8000-12000
£8721 $15000 €12733 Proud hen (43x56cm-17x22in) s.d.1956 i.verso gouache oil crayon prov. 3-Dec-3 Sotheby's, New York #91/R est:15000-25000
£10795 $19000 €15761 Boatyard (30x46cm-12x18in) s. W/C gouache black paper exec c.1932-34 prov. 19-May-4 Sotheby's, New York #170/R est:15000-25000
£10811 $20000 €15784 Afternoon trees (48x63cm-19x25in) s.d.1954 pastel oil crayon. 11-Mar-4 Christie's, Rockefeller NY #104/R est:15000-25000
£12973 $24000 €18941 Divers (46x30cm-18x12in) s. gouache prov. 11-Mar-4 Christie's, Rockefeller NY #99/R est:15000-25000
£17442 $30000 €25465 Hills, New Hampshire (56x76cm-22x30in) s. W/C prov. 3-Dec-3 Sotheby's, New York #87/R est:30000-50000
£22727 $40000 €33181 White caps and mountains (45x60cm-18x24in) s. W/C gouache exec c.1942-45 prov. 18-May-4 Christie's, Rockefeller NY #135/R est:30000-50000
£26163 $45000 €38198 Sally sewing (44x58cm-17x23in) s.d.1959 w pencil prov. 4-Dec-3 Christie's, Rockefeller NY #97/R est:30000-50000
£31250 $55000 €45625 Twosome (28x79cm-11x31in) s.d.1948 i.verso W/C gouache pencil prov. 19-May-4 Sotheby's, New York #172/R est:50000-70000
£37037 $60000 €53704 Stormy sky, stormy sea (56x76cm-22x30in) s. W/C prov.exhib. 8-Aug-3 Barridorf, Portland #177/R est:60000-90000

AVERY, Ralph Hillyer (1906-1976) American

Works on paper

£1344 $2500 €1962 Spring street (20x28cm-8x11in) W/C. 6-Mar-4 Page, Batavia #102
£1613 $3000 €2355 Rochester, Main Street looking west (43x56cm-17x22in) mixed media. 6-Mar-4 Page, Batavia #103

AVERY, Sally Michel (1905-2003) American

£1730 $3200 €2526 Quiet Beach (40x51cm-16x20in) s.i. verso canvasboard prov. 13-Jul-4 Christie's, Rockefeller NY #161/R est:800-1200

Works on paper

£245 $450 €358 Gentleman reading a book (25x18cm-10x7in) s.d.1960 ink prov. 25-Jun-4 Freeman, Philadelphia #8/R

AVIA, Amalia (1930-) Spanish

£1831 $3168 €2600 Shoe shop (22x26cm-9x10in) s. board. 15-Dec-3 Ansorena, Madrid #947/R est:2400
£1974 $3632 €3000 Shelter (49x81cm-19x32in) s. s.i.verso board exhib. 22-Jun-4 Durán, Madrid #156/R est:3000

AVILO, F (19th C) Italian

£4333 $7800 €6500 Venetian vegetable seller (106x53cm-42x21in) s. 21-Apr-4 Christie's, Amsterdam #57/R est:7000-9000

AVNER, Herve (1954-) French?

£1400 $2506 €2100 La route jaune (50x65cm-20x26in) s. acrylic. 16-May-4 Thierry & Lannon, Brest #200c est:2200-2500
£1690 $2958 €2400 Promenade sur le port de Pont-Aven (50x65cm-20x26in) s. acrylic oil pastel. 21-Dec-3 Thierry & Lannon, Brest #372 est:2200-2500

Works on paper

£436 $811 €650 Paysans aux champs (63x49cm-25x19in) s. pastel. 7-Mar-4 Livinec, Gaudcheau & Jezequel, Rennes #20
£600 $1074 €900 Un apres-midi d'ete en Bretagne (23x30cm-9x12in) s. pastel. 16-May-4 Thierry & Lannon, Brest #200
£704 $1232 €1000 Jour de marche (32x40cm-13x16in) s. pastel. 21-Dec-3 Thierry & Lannon, Brest #371

AVOLIO, Eugenio (1876-1929) Italian

Sculpture

£16667 $27167 €24000 Table decoration with Neptune. s. silvered gilded metal. 25-Sep-3 Dr Fritz Nagel, Stuttgart #1539/R

AVONDO, Vittorio (1836-1910) Italian

£1627 $2636 €2295 Landscape (14x36cm-6x14in) board. 21-May-3 Babuino, Rome #229/R
£3333 $5967 €5000 Portraits of the artist's mother and father (98x74cm-39x29in) oval pair prov. 13-May-4 Babuino, Rome #328/R est:4000-5000
£4225 $7014 €6000 Campagna romana (28x43cm-11x17in) s. prov. 11-Jun-3 Christie's, Rome #121/R est:7000-10000

AVONT, Pieter van (attrib) (1600-1632) Flemish

£1399 $2336 €2000 Holy Family (36x30cm-14x12in) panel oval. 29-Jun-3 St-Germain-en-Laye Encheres #2/R
£1631 $2725 €2300 Le repos pendant la fuite en Egypte (36x46cm-14x18in) copper. 17-Oct-3 Tajan, Paris #37 est:2000-3000

AVRAMIDIS, Joannis (1922-) Austrian

Sculpture

£9091 $15455 €13000 Small triassic (18cm-7in) s. black pat.bronze. 29-Nov-3 Villa Grisebach, Berlin #327/R est:10000-15000
£34965 $59441 €50000 Figure II (163cm-64in) s. brown pat.bronze prov. 28-Nov-3 Villa Grisebach, Berlin #84/R est:50000-70000

Works on paper

£400 $720 €600 Female torso (62x44cm-24x17in) s.d. pencil board. 24-Apr-4 Dr Lehr, Berlin #43
£867 $1560 €1300 Figures (50x70cm-20x28in) mono.d.1964 gouache chk board. 24-Apr-4 Dr Lehr, Berlin #42/R
£1500 $2385 €2175 Figurenreihe (51x70cm-20x28in) wax crayon gouache on card. 11-Sep-3 Christie's, Kensington #74/R est:800-1200
£2098 $3566 €3000 Untitled (51x73cm-20x29in) mono.d.64 s.d.1964 verso chk gouache board. 27-Nov-3 Lempertz, Koln #13/R est:1000

AVY, Joseph (1871-?) French

£517 $859 €750 Centaure. s. 1-Oct-3 Millon & Associes, Paris #160
£4706 $8000 €6871 Study for Bal Blanc (38x46cm-15x18in) s. 28-Oct-3 Sotheby's, New York #168/R est:8000-12000

AXELROD, Z (?) Israeli?

£1061 $1900 €1549 Interior of the Spanish Synagogue, Jerusalem (39x49cm-15x19in) s. 18-Mar-4 Sotheby's, New York #262/R est:2000-3000

AXELSON, Axel (1854-1892) Swedish

£692 $1191 €1010 Farm scene at Borgermastaregatan, Stockholm (24x33cm-9x13in) s. 3-Dec-3 AB Stockholms Auktionsverk #2308/R (S.KR 9000)

AXENTOWICZ, Theodor (1859-1938) Polish

£1070 $2000 €1562 Carpathian Highlander (38x28cm-15x11in) s. 25-Feb-4 Doyle, New York #30/R est:3000-5000

Works on paper

£2821 $4401 €4119 Figures in a winter scene (68x49cm-27x19in) s. mixed media pastel W/C cardboard. 30-Mar-3 Agra, Warsaw #19/R est:18000 (P.Z 18000)
£5043 $9179 €7363 Portrait of a woman and dog (67x51cm-26x20in) s. pastel canvas on paper board. 20-Jun-4 Agra, Warsaw #2/R (P.Z 35000)

AXER, Otto (1909-1983) Polish?

£336 $558 €491 Green head (50x39cm-20x15in) cardboard. 2-Oct-3 Agra, Warsaw #30/R (P.Z 2200)
£690 $1152 €1000 Three children with toys (95x125cm-37x49in) s. i.d.1980 verso. 16-Nov-3 Agra, Warsaw #9/R
£847 $1534 €1237 Composition (73x92cm-29x36in) s. 4-Apr-4 Agra, Warsaw #35/R (P.Z 6000)

AXTMANN, Leopold (1700-1748) Czechoslovakian

£4895 $8322 €7000 Still life with game (84x121cm-33x48in) s.d.1744 panel lit. 28-Nov-3 Schloss Ahlden, Ahlden #1385/R est:6800

AY TJOE, Christine (1973-) Indonesian
Works on paper
£1961 $3549 €2863 Alter ego - alter ego (120x100cm-47x39in) s.d.04 s.i.d.2004 verso mixed media canvas. 3-Apr-4 Glerum, Singapore #44/R est:2000-3000 (S.D 6000)

AYALA, Josefa de (1630-1684) Spanish
£50000 $91500 €73000 Pears and marasce cherries in a basket, porcelain bowl, flowers on a partly draped table (78x142cm-31x56in) 7-Jul-4 Christie's, London #72/R est:20000-30000

AYERS, Duffy (20th C) British
£300 $516 €438 Girl in blue, reading (24x29cm-9x11in) s. board prov. 3-Dec-3 Cheffins, Cambridge #658/R

AYLING, George (1887-1960) British
£440 $704 €642 Ulverscroft priory, Leicestershire (41x61cm-16x24in) s. board. 18-Sep-3 Goldings, Lincolnshire #807/R
£950 $1511 €1387 Coastal town (79x59cm-31x23in) s. canvasboard. 10-Sep-3 Sotheby's, Olympia #203/R
£1500 $2580 €2190 Toward Waterloo Bridge (55x74cm-22x29in) board. 2-Dec-3 Sotheby's, London #103/R est:800-1200
Works on paper
£370 $585 €537 Evening harvest scene by English rural hamlet (38x56cm-15x22in) s. W/C. 17-Nov-2 Desmond Judd, Cranbrook #862

AYLLON, Fernando Pascual (1896-1959) Argentinian
£391 $700 €571 Village street (15x22cm-6x9in) board. 11-May-4 Arroyo, Buenos Aires #3
£604 $1100 €882 Landscape (46x36cm-18x14in) s. 5-Jul-4 Arroyo, Buenos Aires #52/R

AYLMER, Thomas Brabazon (1806-c.1856) British
£4000 $7280 €5840 Castle of Ischia, in the Bay of Naples, Mount Vesuvius beyond (75x120cm-30x47in) exhib. 1-Jul-4 Sotheby's, London #146/R est:5000-7000

AYLWARD, James de Vine (fl.1895-1917) British
£400 $668 €584 Hussars on a track (18x13cm-7x5in) s. panel. 13-Nov-3 Christie's, Kensington #325

AYME, Alix (1894-1989) French
£263 $484 €400 Visage (22x16cm-9x6in) graphite dr. 25-Jun-4 Millon & Associes, Paris #156
£387 $670 €550 Femme et paysage (34x19cm-13x7in) s. lacquer panel. 10-Dec-3 Millon & Associes, Paris #357/R
£1126 $2049 €1700 La liseuse pres du village annamite (46x70cm-18x28in) s. lacquer panel. 15-Jun-4 Blanchet, Paris #147/R est:1500-2000

AYON, L (19th C) ?
£2262 $3846 €3303 Madrid (23x50cm-9x20in) s.i.d.Marzo 1803 i.stretcher. 19-Nov-3 Fischer, Luzern #1078/R est:5000-7500 (S.FR 5000)
£2489 $4231 €3634 Madrid (35x61cm-14x24in) s.i. i. stretcher. 19-Nov-3 Fischer, Luzern #1079/R est:6000-8000 (S.FR 5500)

AYOTTE, Leo (1909-1976) Canadian
£1156 $1999 €1688 Au bord du lac (40x20cm-16x8in) s. 15-Dec-3 Iegor de Saint Hippolyte, Montreal #2 (C.D 2600)

AYRES, Donald (20th C) British
£780 $1217 €1139 Hunt crossing a river, possibly in Wales (61x91cm-24x36in) s. 28-Mar-3 Greenslade Hunt, Taunton #500/R

AYRES, Gillian (1930-) British
£2500 $4175 €3650 Tadwalis Island (90cm-35in circular) s.d.82 prov. 16-Oct-3 Christie's, Kensington #720/R est:2000-3000
£4500 $7740 €6570 Bella Donna (137x245cm-54x96in) s.d.66 overlap i.stretcher prov. 3-Dec-3 Sotheby's, London #89/R est:4000-6000
Works on paper
£300 $474 €435 Composition (38x56cm-15x22in) s. col chk exhib. 24-Jul-3 Lawrence, Crewkerne #887/R
£320 $576 €467 Composition (38x56cm-15x22in) s. pencil col chks prov. 20-Jan-4 Bonhams, Knightsbridge #283/R

AYRES, Lily (?-1936) American
£6024 $10000 €8795 Oak Lawn plantation home of Jane and Lt Eli James P Ayres (84x132cm-33x52in) s.d.1868. 4-Oct-3 Neal Auction Company, New Orleans #465/R est:9000-12000

AYRES, Tim (1965-) Dutch?
Works on paper
£290 $475 €400 Study for: What is it that determines (76x56cm-30x22in) s.d.94 s.i.d.1994 on backing felt-tip pen pencil prov. 27-May-3 Sotheby's, Amsterdam #566/R

AYRTON, Michael (1921-1975) British
£1900 $3173 €2774 Owl light (46x56cm-18x22in) s.d.62 i.d.Nov 62 verso oil wax. 16-Oct-3 Christie's, Kensington #687/R est:1000-1500
£2800 $4928 €4088 Barley Matrix (76x126cm-30x50in) s.d.August 65 oil collage. 18-May-4 Bonhams, Knightsbridge #56/R est:1500-2000
£5000 $9100 €7300 Thames foreshore (56x64cm-22x25in) s.d.47 board. 15-Jun-4 Bonhams, Leeds #60/R est:2000-4000
£18000 $32940 €26280 Thunder approaching (84x109cm-33x43in) s.d.1948 i.d.verso prov.exhib.lit. 2-Jun-4 Sotheby's, London #78/R est:20000-30000
Sculpture
£2000 $3400 €2920 Siren (24cm-9in) bronze wooden base one of 9. 26-Nov-3 Sotheby's, Olympia #140/R est:2000-3000
£2400 $4128 €3504 Icarus in flight (14cm-6in) gold pat bronze. 2-Dec-3 Bonhams, New Bond Street #183/R est:1000-1500
£3000 $5460 €4380 Minotaur risen (25cm-10in) bronze. 15-Jun-4 David Lay, Penzance #672/R est:3000-3500
£3500 $6020 €5110 Icarus chained (17cm-7in) num 7/9 brown pat bronze wire. 2-Dec-3 Bonhams, New Bond Street #182/R est:1200-1800
£4000 $7400 €5840 Scavenger II (41cm-16in) num.4/9 brown pat. bronze. 11-Mar-4 Christie's, Kensington #228/R est:2000-3000
£4600 $8096 €6716 Minotaur (38cm-15in) brown pat. bronze slate base prov. 18-May-4 Woolley & Wallis, Salisbury #365/R est:4000-6000
£5800 $10730 €8468 Geode (51cm-20in) num.5/9 bronze perspex rock crystal wooden base. 11-Feb-4 Sotheby's, Olympia #280/R est:2000-3000
£6500 $11895 €9490 Icarus transformed I (61cm-24in) brown pat bronze lit. 4-Jun-4 Christie's, London #141/R est:6000-8000
£6967 $11287 €10172 Figure with a skein 2 (88x18x32cm-35x7x13in) s. num.1/9 bronze prov. 30-Jul-3 Goodman, Sydney #186/R est:12000-18000 (A.D 17000)
£7000 $12740 €10220 Shepherd (91cm-36in) brown pat bronze lit. 1-Jul-4 Christie's, Kensington #206/R est:6000-8000
£7800 $13416 €11388 Couple (22cm-9in) num.5/9 dark brown pat bronze composite base. 3-Dec-3 Sotheby's, London #92/R est:4000-6000
£11000 $20130 €16060 Bone sentinel (94cm-37in) dark brown pat. bronze lit. 4-Jun-4 Christie's, London #139/R est:6000-8000
Works on paper
£500 $910 €730 Contained head II (326x25cm-128x10in) s.i.d.1970 ink exhib. 15-Jun-4 Bonhams, Knightsbridge #177/R
£828 $1531 €1200 Aptera 64. Estuary 4-1-65 (36x54cm-14x21in) both s.d.64 65 double-sided pair. 11-Feb-4 Woodwards, Cork #14/R
£1000 $1720 €1460 Mother and child (46x34cm-18x13in) s.d.56 ink wash. 2-Dec-3 Bonhams, New Bond Street #186/R est:1000-1500
£1700 $2839 €2482 Sea II (50x64cm-20x25in) s.d.60 mixed media collage. 21-Oct-3 Bonhams, Knightsbridge #52/R est:1000-1500
£1700 $2924 €2482 Kouros (76x64cm-30x25in) s.d.30.7.63 collage board. 2-Dec-3 Bonhams, New Bond Street #188/R est:1000-1500
£2200 $3784 €3212 Looking glass (40x50cm-16x20in) s.i.d.15.11.74 ink wash pencil. 2-Dec-3 Bonhams, New Bond Street #185/R est:800-1200
£2500 $4300 €3650 Demeter and Kore (39x49cm-15x19in) s.d.28.11.65 ink wash. 2-Dec-3 Bonhams, New Bond Street #184/R est:1000-1500
£2800 $5180 €4088 Dark Trinity (44x34cm-17x13in) s.i. chl pen ink W/C. 11-Mar-4 Christie's, Kensington #227/R est:2500-3500
£3200 $5920 €4672 Figure under trees (62x46cm-24x18in) s.d.11.11.61 chl. 11-Mar-4 Christie's, Kensington #226/R est:1000-1500

AZAMBRE, Étienne (19/20th C) French
£4839 $9000 €7065 Woman and child reading by lamplight (53x66cm-21x26in) s. 3-Mar-4 Alderfer's, Hatfield #313/R est:1000-1500

AZEGLIO, Massimo de (1798-1866) Italian
Works on paper
£559 $934 €800 Fiumicino (14x22cm-6x9in) i. W/C. 26-Jun-3 Sant Agostino, Torino #17/R

AZEMA, Louis (1876-1963) French
£777 $1391 €1150 Oiseau de feu - au dos Nijinsky (72x48cm-28x19in) s. cardboard. 7-May-4 Millon & Associes, Paris #93/R
£878 $1572 €1300 Soir d'hiver, sur le chassis neige bleue (81x116cm-32x46in) s. 7-May-4 Millon & Associes, Paris #91/R
£912 $1633 €1350 Nu au peignoir (61x50cm-24x20in) s. 7-May-4 Millon & Associes, Paris #92/R

AZIZ, Abdul (1928-2002) Javanese
£2317 $3869 €3383 Pasar - market (44x65cm-17x26in) s. 26-Oct-3 Christie's, Hong Kong #55/R est:22000-32000 (HK.D 30000)
£3243 $5416 €4735 Mother and child (34x29cm-13x11in) s.i.d.1989. 26-Oct-3 Christie's, Hong Kong #54/R est:18000-28000 (HK.D 42000)
£3304 $5617 €4824 Portrait of young woman from Bali (50x40cm-20x16in) s. bears i.d. 5-Nov-3 Dobiaschofsky, Bern #317/R est:6000 (S.FR 7500)
£4247 $7093 €6201 People in front of a house, Bali (35x29cm-14x11in) s. 26-Oct-3 Christie's, Hong Kong #56/R est:22000-32000 (HK.D 55000)
£4514 $7538 €6590 Sayang Anak (50x40cm-20x16in) s.d.1988. 12-Oct-3 Sotheby's, Singapore #153/R est:6000-8000 (S.D 13000)
£11594 $17971 €16927 Reclining nude (75x100cm-30x39in) s.d.1983. 6-Oct-2 Sotheby's, Singapore #159/R est:18000-25000 (S.D 32000)
£17204 $27527 €25118 Dancer (52x126cm-20x50in) s.d.1963. 18-May-3 Sotheby's, Singapore #151/R est:18000-25000 (S.D 48000)
£29344 $49004 €42842 Girl holding an elaborate headdress (93x63cm-37x25in) s.i.d.1986. 26-Oct-3 Christie's, Hong Kong #59/R est:45000-55000 (HK.D 380000)
£71895 $130131 €104967 Blissful family (145x60cm-57x24in) s.d.1995 pair prov. 3-Apr-4 Glerum, Singapore #50/R (S.D 220000)
£81081 $135405 €118378 Berpandangan - loving gaze (145x65cm-57x26in) s.i.d.1987 pair. 26-Oct-3 Christie's, Hong Kong #50/R est:160000-200000 (HK.D 1050000)

AZNARD, Louis (1910-) French?
Works on paper
£423 $731 €600 Femme du Hoggar (33x24cm-13x9in) s. sanguine. 15-Dec-3 Gros & Delettrez, Paris #329

AZOULAY, Jose (1925-) Algerian
Works on paper
£313 $491 €450 Jockey en course (54x44cm-21x17in) s. wash. 29-Aug-3 Deauville, France #83

AZPIROZ, Manuel de (1903-1953) Spanish
£828 $1382 €1200 Fish seller (100x80cm-39x31in) s. 17-Nov-3 Durán, Madrid #175/R

AZUMA, Kengiro (1926-) Japanese
Sculpture
£3221 $5766 €4800 Study for Sion convent (100x45x43cm-39x18x17in) s. bronze prov. 25-May-4 Sotheby's, Milan #178/R est:2000-3000

AZUZ, David (1942-) Israeli
Works on paper
£420 $713 €600 Portrait de femme (15x10cm-6x4in) s. W/C. 27-Nov-3 Calmels Cohen, Paris #97/R

AZZAWI, Dia (1939-) Iraqi
Works on paper
£2200 $3894 €3212 Orange square. Man and bird (28x26cm-11x10in) s.d.73 W/C gouache pen ink two. 29-Apr-4 Bonhams, New Bond Street #583/R est:1500-2000
£3000 $5310 €4380 Calligraphy (89x59cm-35x23in) gouache pen ink pastel. 29-Apr-4 Bonhams, New Bond Street #584/R est:3000-5000

AZZINARI, Franco (1949-) Italian
£367 $675 €550 Farm on the hills (20x30cm-8x12in) s.d.1980. 12-Jun-4 Meeting Art, Vercelli #937/R
£1007 $1862 €1500 Bushes (70x50cm-28x20in) s.d.1975. 13-Mar-4 Meeting Art, Vercelli #206 est:1500
£1056 $1754 €1500 Untitled (40x60cm-16x24in) s.d.1999. 14-Jun-3 Meeting Art, Vercelli #234/R est:1500
£2891 $5262 €4250 Colours of life (60x40cm-24x16in) s. 6-Feb-4 Galleria Rosenberg, Milan #84/R est:3000
£2891 $5262 €4250 Words' nature (60x40cm-24x16in) s. 6-Feb-4 Galleria Rosenberg, Milan #112/R est:3000

AZZOPARDI, Deborah (20th C) ?
£1500 $2775 €2190 Summer (99x99cm-39x39in) acrylic board. 13-Jul-4 Bonhams, Knightsbridge #12/R est:1200-1500
£1600 $2960 €2336 Decisions (80x122cm-31x48in) acrylic board. 13-Jul-4 Bonhams, Knightsbridge #9 est:1200-1800

BAADE, Knud Andreassen (1808-1879) Norwegian
Works on paper
£370 $639 €540 Kaarevig 22 juli 1855 (42x57cm-17x22in) s. pencil wash. 13-Dec-3 Blomqvist, Lysaker #1013 (N.KR 4250)

BAAGOE, Carl (1829-1902) Danish
£536 $868 €777 Coastal landscape from Julebaek (34x42cm-13x17in) mono.d.82. 4-Aug-3 Rasmussen, Vejle #171 (D.KR 5600)
£711 $1137 €1038 Coastal landscape with sailing vessels off town (24x34cm-9x13in) s.d.86. 22-Sep-3 Rasmussen, Vejle #301/R (D.KR 7500)
£1078 $2005 €1574 Sailing vessels off the coast at sunset (25x36cm-10x14in) s.d.1861. 2-Mar-4 Rasmussen, Copenhagen #1437/R est:12000-15000 (D.KR 12000)
£1545 $2580 €2256 Seascape with Man-o-war off the coast (35x53cm-14x21in) s.d.1867. 25-Oct-3 Rasmussen, Havnen #2565/R est:10000 (D.KR 16500)
£1545 $2580 €2256 Seascape with sailing vessels (23x33cm-9x13in) s. 25-Oct-3 Rasmussen, Havnen #2569/R est:6000-8000 (D.KR 16500)
£1611 $2578 €2352 Seascape with sailing vessels off coast (48x73cm-19x29in) s.d.1862. 22-Sep-3 Rasmussen, Vejle #272/R est:15000-20000 (D.KR 17000)
£3022 $5500 €4533 Seascape with many vessels (43x64cm-17x25in) s.d.1875. 19-Jun-4 Rasmussen, Havnen #2046/R est:5000-10000 (D.KR 34000)
£5482 $9484 €8004 Sailing vessels in Sundet off Kronborg (35x58cm-14x23in) s.d.1861. 9-Dec-3 Rasmussen, Copenhagen #1476/R est:35000-40000 (D.KR 58000)

BAAGOE, Carl (attrib) (1829-1902) Danish
£295 $501 €431 Coastal landscape at moonlight (19x27cm-7x11in) init. 10-Nov-3 Rasmussen, Vejle #500 (D.KR 3200)

BAALBAKI, Abdul Hameed (1940-) Lebanese
£1800 $3186 €2628 Cafe scene. Maids on Corniche (97x78cm-38x31in) one s.d.79 one s.d.84 two. 29-Apr-4 Bonhams, New Bond Street #550/R est:2000-3000

BABADIN, V (19/20th C) Russian
£3235 $6016 €4723 Sailing vessels off St Petersburg (44x63cm-17x25in) s. 2-Mar-4 Rasmussen, Copenhagen #1317/R est:4000-6000 (D.KR 36000)

BABB, Stanley Nicholson (19/20th C) British
Sculpture
£1700 $2924 €2482 Maquette for a sculpture of Diana the Huntress (42cm-17in) s.d.1928 terracotta incl. oak base. 4-Dec-3 Mellors & Kirk, Nottingham #1023/R est:600-800
£1800 $3096 €2628 Maquette for a sculpture of two figures (47cm-19in) s.d.1932 terracotta incl. oak base. 4-Dec-3 Mellors & Kirk, Nottingham #1022/R est:500-700

BABBAGE, Herbert Ivan (1875-1916) New Zealander
£420 $697 €613 Beach boats low tide, St Ives harbour (21x28cm-8x11in) s. canvasboard. 2-Oct-3 Lane, Penzance #329
Works on paper
£319 $565 €466 Seascape (25x34cm-10x13in) s. W/C double-sided. 28-Apr-4 Dunbar Sloane, Auckland #274 (NZ.D 900)

BABBERGER, Auguste (1885-1936) German
£961 $1691 €1403 Mountain landscape (51x71cm-20x28in) s.d.16 board prov. 22-May-4 Galerie Gloggner, Luzern #10/R est:1800-2500 (S.FR 2200)
£2193 $3662 €3202 Summer flowers (77x59cm-30x23in) s. i.d.1922 verso board prov. 15-Nov-3 Galerie Gloggner, Luzern #5/R est:4800-5500 (S.FR 5000)
Works on paper
£437 $795 €638 Angel (34x22cm-13x9in) pastel prov. 16-Jun-4 Fischer, Luzern #2714/R (S.FR 1000)
£1579 $2637 €2305 Urn mountains with Scherhorn (47x34cm-19x13in) i. pastel chk prov. 15-Nov-3 Galerie Gloggner, Luzern #6/R est:1400-1600 (S.FR 3600)

BABELAY, Louis (fl.1920-1931) Swiss
£323 $550 €472 Tempting fate, view with a cat (38x55cm-15x22in) s. indis i. 21-Nov-3 Skinner, Boston #36/R

BABITCH, Oleg (?) Russian
£289 $526 €425 Fleurs d'ete. s. 8-Feb-4 Lesieur & Le Bars, Le Havre #81

BABOULENE, Eugène (1905-1994) French
£930 $1600 €1358 Douelan (50x61cm-20x24in) init.i.d.58 verso prov. 3-Dec-3 Doyle, New York #145/R est:3000-5000
£1650 $3003 €2409 Le Repos (46x55cm-18x22in) s. s.i.d.1954 verso prov. 15-Jun-4 Bonhams, Knightsbridge #224/R est:1500-2000
£2600 $4784 €3900 La lessive (50x61cm-20x24in) s. s.i.d.1954 verso. 11-Jun-4 Pierre Berge, Paris #220/R est:2500-3000
£7047 $12966 €10500 Montmartre (89x116cm-35x46in) s. prov. 28-Mar-4 Anaf, Lyon #21/R est:9000-10000
Works on paper
£638 $1066 €900 Jeune femme se coiffant (25x32cm-10x13in) s. W/C. 14-Oct-3 Millon & Associes, Paris #80/R
£845 $1462 €1200 Les Alpilles (32x45cm-13x18in) s. gouache. 10-Dec-3 Remi Ader, Paris #35
£845 $1462 €1200 Les Alpilles (32x45cm-13x18in) s. gouache. 10-Dec-3 Neret-Minet, Paris #35

BABUREN, Dirck van (studio) (17th C) Dutch
£13235 $22500 €19323 Christ carring the cross on the way to Calvary with Saint Veronia offering her veil (193x241cm-76x95in) 19-Nov-3 Bonhams & Butterfields, San Francisco #18/R

BACARDY, Don (1934-) American
Works on paper
£601 $1100 €877 Tom Wudl (61x48cm-24x19in) pencil ink wash. 10-Jul-4 Hindman, Chicago #21/R est:150-250

BACARISAS, Gustavo (19/20th C) Spanish
Works on paper
£1846 $3304 €2750 Woman from Andalucia (60x45cm-24x18in) s. pastel. 25-May-4 Durán, Madrid #138/R est:1200

BACCHI, Cesare (20th C) Italian
£680 $1238 €993 Portrait of a girl holding a bouquet of flowers (100x81cm-39x32in) s.d.1907. 15-Jun-4 Rosebery Fine Art, London #508/R

BACCI, Adolfo (attrib) (1856-1897) Italian
£400 $628 €580 Flower girl (35x25cm-14x10in) s. 28-Aug-3 Christie's, Kensington #61/R

BACCI, Baccio Maria (1888-1974) Italian
£5369 $9611 €8000 Seamstress (73x54cm-29x21in) s. cardboard on board prov.exhib. 25-May-4 Sotheby's, Milan #13/R est:10000

BACCIGALUPPO, Giuseppe (1744-1821) Italian
£76389 $129861 €110000 I dodici mesi dell'anno con i segni dello zodiaco (31x52cm-12x20in) 28-Oct-3 Della Rocca, Turin #353/R est:70000-90000

BACH, Alois (1809-1893) German
£867 $1560 €1300 Return home of the straw ferry (21x20cm-8x8in) s. board. 26-Apr-4 Rieber, Stuttgart #1056/R
£1208 $2223 €1800 Dutch winter landscape with ice skaters (24x35cm-9x14in) mono. panel. 24-Mar-4 Hugo Ruef, Munich #926/R est:800
£1538 $2646 €2200 Horse market in Munich (9cm-4in circular) mono.d.32 i.d.1832 verso metal. 3-Dec-3 Neumeister, Munich #528/R est:900

BACH, Elvira (1951-) German
£880 $1461 €1250 Girl wearing colourful skirt (20x20cm-8x8in) s.d.1978 verso. 13-Jun-3 Hauswedell & Nolte, Hamburg #540/R
£1250 $2088 €1800 At the bar (85x61cm-33x24in) s.d. verso acrylic board. 24-Oct-3 Ketterer, Hamburg #263/R est:1800-2000
£2416 $4518 €3600 Self with two children (120x100cm-47x39in) s.d.1999 verso acrylic. 28-Feb-4 Quittenbaum, Hamburg #79/R est:3000
£5634 $9746 €8000 The cigarette (100x80cm-39x31in) s.i.d.1985 verso acrylic. 13-Dec-3 Lempertz, Koln #111/R est:3000
Works on paper
£647 $1062 €900 Self portrait with child (30x19cm-12x7in) s.d.1994 mixed media board. 4-Jun-3 Ketterer, Hamburg #137/R
£856 $1472 €1250 Woman with large orchid (102x74cm-40x29in) s.d.97 mixed media. 2-Dec-3 Koller, Zurich #3304 est:1200-2000 (S.FR 1900)
£1119 $1902 €1600 Woman with snake (105x78cm-41x31in) s. gouache. 29-Nov-3 Villa Grisebach, Berlin #707/R est:1800-2200
£1333 $2440 €2000 Untitled (30x19cm-12x7in) s.d.90 gouache board three. 4-Jun-4 Lempertz, Koln #20/R est:1500

BACH, Gottlieb Friedrich (1714-1785) German
Works on paper
£2586 $4759 €3776 Emil Leopold August. Friedrich Prince of Sachsen Gotha (25x21cm-10x8in) pastel parchment oval pair. 26-Mar-4 Koller, Zurich #3068/R est:5000-8000 (S.FR 6000)

BACH, Guido (1828-1905) German
Works on paper
£500 $935 €750 Egyptian woman carrying a brace of chickens (54x37cm-21x15in) s.i.d.1876 W/C. 26-Jul-4 Bonhams, Bath #14/R
£2600 $4784 €3796 Poultry market, Cairo (68x109cm-27x43in) s.d.1883 W/C prov.exhib. 23-Mar-4 Rosebery Fine Art, London #831/R est:2000-3000
£5782 $10350 €8500 Alum's day at the Ara Coeli Rome (115x74cm-45x29in) s.d.1881 W/C htd gouache prov.exhib. 17-Mar-4 Maigret, Paris #6/R est:4000-6000

BACHE, Otto (1839-1927) Danish
£376 $677 €549 Summer landscape (17x40cm-7x16in) s. cardboard on canvas. 24-Apr-4 Rasmussen, Havnen #2140/R (D.KR 4200)
£406 $759 €593 Portrait of the dog Fancy Pointer (51x44cm-20x17in) s.d.1913. 25-Feb-4 Museumsbygningen, Copenhagen #165 (D.KR 4500)
£417 $667 €609 White cow seen from behind (79x55cm-31x22in) s. i.stretcher. 22-Sep-3 Rasmussen, Vejle #247/R (D.KR 4400)
£471 $842 €688 Deer resting on woodland (48x63cm-19x25in) s. prov. 10-May-4 Rasmussen, Vejle #279/R (D.KR 5200)
£473 $818 €691 Horse lying down (51x74cm-20x29in) init.d.99 study. 9-Dec-3 Rasmussen, Copenhagen #1594/R (D.KR 5000)
£567 $1015 €828 Woodland glade by Frijsenborg, children by tree in foreground (41x32cm-16x13in) s. 12-Jan-4 Rasmussen, Vejle #76/R (D.KR 6000)
£750 $1350 €1095 On the quayside (28x41cm-11x16in) s.d.1879. 20-Jan-4 Bonhams, Knightsbridge #9/R
£809 $1504 €1181 Gangway by a man-o-war (78x40cm-31x16in) s. 2-Mar-4 Rasmussen, Copenhagen #1438/R (D.KR 9000)
£851 $1523 €1242 Vikings in fight with mermaids (45x51cm-18x20in) s.d.1909. 12-Jan-4 Rasmussen, Vejle #213/R (D.KR 9000)
£902 $1668 €1317 Italian street scene with woman shouting at a vegetable seller with donkey (41x33cm-16x13in) s. 15-Mar-4 Rasmussen, Vejle #55/R (D.KR 10000)
£1200 $2148 €1752 Sondenwinden (61x61cm-24x24in) i. 18-Mar-4 Christie's, Kensington #449/R est:1500-2000
£1253 $2294 €1829 Boy wearing sailor's outfit sitting on garden bench (31x24cm-12x9in) s.i.d.1909 prov. 9-Jun-4 Rasmussen, Copenhagen #1590/R est:15000-20000 (D.KR 14000)
£1512 $2616 €2208 Stone wall (39x29cm-15x11in) s.d.1863 sold with Indian ink landscape. 9-Dec-3 Rasmussen, Copenhagen #1703/R est:4000-6000 (D.KR 16000)
£3044 $5570 €4444 Landscape with children playing and man on horseback (54x75cm-21x30in) s. 9-Jun-4 Rasmussen, Copenhagen #1686/R est:40000 (D.KR 34000)
£5391 $10027 €7871 The King is arriving - scene from the square in front of Ermemitage Palace (67x98cm-26x39in) s. 2-Mar-4 Rasmussen, Copenhagen #1268/R est:60000-100000 (D.KR 60000)
£28751 $53477 €41976 Young girl wearing pink dress holding flowers in her hand (81x56cm-32x22in) s. study painted c.1894 prov. 2-Mar-4 Rasmussen, Copenhagen #1272/R est:75000-125000 (D.KR 320000)
£40431 $75202 €59029 The wild stood still in Frederiksborg old stud farm (165x251cm-65x99in) s.d.1908 exhib.prov. 2-Mar-4 Rasmussen, Copenhagen #1236/R est:500000-700000 (D.KR 450000)
£85049 $155640 €124172 Street scene with figures, Kobmagergade (78x54cm-31x21in) s.d.1893 prov. 9-Jun-4 Rasmussen, Copenhagen #1448/R est:1000000 (D.KR 950000)

BACHELIER, Charles Claude (fl.1834-1852) French
£308 $524 €450 Summer landscape with stream bed (46x65cm-18x26in) s. 5-Nov-3 Dobiaschofsky, Bern #318/R (S.FR 700)

BACHELIN, Auguste (1830-1890) Swiss
£294 $500 €429 Paysage fluvial (24x45cm-9x18in) s.mono. verso. 28-Nov-3 Zofingen, Switzerland #2894 (S.FR 650)
£1145 $1947 €1672 Au lac de Thoune (38x54cm-15x21in) s.i.d.1875 stretcher. 7-Nov-3 Dobiaschofsky, Bern #53/R est:3000 (S.FR 2600)
£1762 $2996 €2573 Conversation before the hunt (62x78cm-24x31in) s. mono. verso. 7-Nov-3 Dobiaschofsky, Bern #5/R est:7500 (S.FR 4000)

BACHELIN, Auguste (attrib) (1830-1890) Swiss
£264 $449 €385 Still life with potatoes, butter and bread (61x50cm-24x20in) i. 5-Nov-3 Dobiaschofsky, Bern #319/R (S.FR 600)

BACHEM, Bele (1916-) German
£664 $1109 €950 Bettina (32x22cm-13x9in) s.d. i. verso tempera. 10-Oct-3 Winterberg, Heidelberg #922/R
Works on paper
£347 $580 €500 Costume sketch (16x25cm-6x10in) s.i. biro Indian ink W/C. 24-Oct-3 Ketterer, Hamburg #614/R
£874 $1460 €1250 Little lion tamer (22x18cm-9x7in) mixed media. 10-Oct-3 Winterberg, Heidelberg #923/R
£955 $1471 €1500 Elisabeth (50x40cm-20x16in) s. i. verso casein panel. 4-Sep-2 Schopman, Hamburg #183/R est:1500
£1329 $2285 €1900 Surreal beach scene (37x47cm-15x19in) s. casein mixed media panel. 4-Dec-3 Schopman, Hamburg #665/R est:600
£1624 $2501 €2550 Artistes and riders (86x49cm-34x19in) s. i. verso casein. 4-Sep-2 Schopman, Hamburg #182/R est:2500

BACHER, Otto Henry (1856-1909) American
£484 $890 €707 Portrait of General John Devereux (45x38cm-18x15in) s.i. prov. 14-Jun-4 Waddingtons, Toronto #2/R est:500-700 (C.D 1200)

BACHIS, Lidia (1969-) Italian
£336 $621 €500 Maddalena 02 stop (70x50cm-28x20in) s.i.d.2003 verso on plotter. 13-Mar-4 Meeting Art, Vercelli #340
£400 $736 €600 Decadent Tokyo (70x70cm-28x28in) s.i.d.2002 acrylic on plotter. 12-Jun-4 Meeting Art, Vercelli #442/R
£433 $797 €650 House red (75x60cm-30x24in) s.i.d.2003 verso acrylic on plotter. 12-Jun-4 Meeting Art, Vercelli #818/R
£467 $859 €700 Purple detail 01 (70x70cm-28x28in) s.i.d.2002 verso acrylic on plotter. 12-Jun-4 Meeting Art, Vercelli #43/R

BACHLER, Josef (1914-1979) Austrian
£302 $541 €450 Untitled (15x21cm-6x8in) s.d.12.10.1972 col pen board prov. 25-May-4 Dorotheum, Vienna #310/R
Works on paper
£268 $481 €400 Flowers (20x15cm-8x6in) s.i.d.2.7.1971 col pen biro prov. 25-May-4 Dorotheum, Vienna #285/R

BACHMANN, A (19/20th C) ?
£2657 $4571 €3800 Sur les bords du Bosphore (73x98cm-29x39in) s. 3-Dec-3 Beaussant & Lefèvre, Paris #22/R est:3000

BACHMANN, Adolphe (19/20th C) Swiss
£3333 $5967 €5000 Vue d'Istambul (45x62cm-18x24in) s. 16-May-4 MonsAntic, Maisieres #373 est:3000-4000

BACHMANN, Alfred (1863-1954) German
Works on paper
£268 $494 €400 North Sea dunes by moonlight (30x48cm-12x19in) s.d.1917 pastel chk. 26-Mar-4 Bolland & Marotz, Bremen #482a/R
£302 $553 €450 Gulls over the stormy sea (26x37cm-10x15in) s.d.1926 i.verso pastel lit. 8-Jul-4 Allgauer, Kempten #1954/R
£1517 $2534 €2200 Morning sun over North Sea (35x43cm-14x17in) s. i. verso pastel. 9-Jul-3 Hugo Ruef, Munich #266/R est:600

BACHMANN, Edwin Karl (1900-1960) Swiss
£262 $482 €383 Bachau on Zurichsee (65x81cm-26x32in) s. i. stretcher. 14-Jun-4 Philippe Schuler, Zurich #5711 (S.FR 600)

BACHMANN, Edwin Paul (1896-1971) Swiss
£478 $875 €698 Swiss mountain village scene (70x60cm-28x24in) s.d.1917. 4-Jun-4 Zofingen, Switzerland #2738/R (S.FR 1100)

BACHMANN, Hans (1852-1917) Swiss
£431 $772 €629 Farmstead (30x45cm-12x18in) mono. canvas on board. 12-May-4 Dobiaschofsky, Bern #319/R (S.FR 1000)
£901 $1550 €1315 Portrait of a girl (44x32cm-17x13in) d.1909 canvas on board. 8-Dec-3 Philippe Schuler, Zurich #3316/R (S.FR 2000)

BACHMANN, Hermann (1922-) German
£699 $1189 €1000 Figurine with raised arms (30x21cm-12x8in) s.d.56. 29-Nov-3 Bassenge, Berlin #6607/R

BACHMANN, Jakob Edwin (1873-1957) Swiss
£271 $462 €396 Alpine scene (65x50cm-26x20in) s.d.1931. 28-Nov-3 Zofingen, Switzerland #2895 (S.FR 600)

BACHMANN, Karl (1874-1924) Hungarian
£395 $715 €577 Oriental still life (15x21cm-6x8in) s. s.verso. 16-Apr-4 Mu Terem Galeria, Budapest #25/R (H.F 150000)

BACHMANN, Otto (1915-1996) Swiss
£588 $1000 €858 Surreal figures (40x40cm-16x16in) s.d.1960 pavatex. 25-Nov-3 Germann, Zurich #97/R (S.FR 1300)
£727 $1207 €1054 Figures by campfire (28x35cm-11x14in) board. 13-Jun-3 Zofingen, Switzerland #2773/R est:1900 (S.FR 1600)
£1055 $1762 €1530 Nirvana (100x61cm-39x24in) s.d. masonite. 23-Jun-3 Philippe Schuler, Zurich #3375 est:2500-3000 (S.FR 2300)
£1835 $3064 €2661 Chicago (90x60cm-35x24in) s. masonite. 23-Jun-3 Philippe Schuler, Zurich #3376/R est:5000-7000 (S.FR 4000)
£2620 $4821 €3825 Femme au chapeau de fleurs (138x59cm-54x23in) s. masonite. 8-Jun-4 Germann, Zurich #1234/R est:6000-8000 (S.FR 6000)

BACHRACH-BAREE, Emmanuel (1863-1943) Austrian
£308 $524 €450 Custom's post by white tower in Rothenburg o/Tauber (26x20cm-10x8in) s. board. 5-Nov-3 Hugo Ruef, Munich #930/R
£1987 $3616 €3000 In the courtyard (53x73cm-21x29in) s. 16-Jun-4 Hugo Ruef, Munich #927/R est:3000

BACHRACH-BAREE, Helmuth (1898-1964) German
£434 $799 €660 Shepherd and sheep in a mountainous landscape (51x69cm-20x27in) s. cardboard. 25-Jun-4 Michael Zeller, Lindau #562/R

BACK, Robert (1922-) British/Australian
£3514 $6500 €5130 USS Franklin, racing schooners and other shipping (73x93cm-29x37in) s. prov. 10-Feb-4 Christie's, Rockefeller NY #241/R est:8000-12000

BACK, Yngve (1904-1990) Finnish
£279 $508 €410 Garden chair (79x65cm-31x26in) s.d.89. 8-Feb-4 Bukowskis, Helsinki #326/R
£347 $580 €500 Archipelago (65x82cm-26x32in) s. 26-Oct-3 Bukowskis, Helsinki #307/R
£676 $1209 €1000 Spring flowers (81x65cm-32x26in) s.d.64. 8-May-4 Bukowskis, Helsinki #241/R

BACKER, Harriet (1845-1932) Norwegian
£44035 $78823 €64291 Interior from Flyen (32x41cm-13x16in) s.i.d.90 prov.exhib.lit. 22-Mar-4 Blomqvist, Oslo #335/R est:500000-600000 (N.KR 550000)

BACKER, Jacob Adriaensz (1608-1651) Dutch
Works on paper
£4082 $7306 €6000 Un portrait d'homme, tenant son manteau (22x19cm-9x7in) i. black white chk prov. 18-Mar-4 Christie's, Paris #194/R est:1000-1500
£6507 $11062 €9500 Study of an elegantly dressed young lady (30x22cm-12x9in) black chk htd white. 4-Nov-3 Sotheby's, Amsterdam #66/R est:15000-20000

BACKER, Jacob Adriaensz (attrib) (1608-1651) Dutch
£4000 $7240 €6000 Bileams donkey (54x71cm-21x28in) mono.d.1638 panel exhib.lit. 1-Apr-4 Van Ham, Cologne #1161/R est:5500

BACKER, Jacob de (1560-c.1590) Flemish
£6993 $12028 €10000 Loth et ses filles (51x66cm-20x26in) panel. 3-Dec-3 Palais de Beaux Arts, Brussels #1251/R est:10000-15000
£9655 $16028 €14000 Virgin and Child with Adam and Eve (77x108cm-30x43in) panel. 1-Oct-3 Dorotheum, Vienna #83/R est:16000-25000
£11268 $19719 €16000 La Vierge et l'enfant Jesus avec l'allegorie de l'amour divin (102x72cm-40x28in) panel. 16-Dec-3 Artcurial Briest, Paris #203/R est:12000-15000
£22000 $39600 €32120 Nativity (108x90cm-43x35in) panel. 22-Apr-4 Sotheby's, London #16/R est:12000-18000

BACKER, Jacob de (circle) (1560-c.1590) Flemish
£15517 $28552 €22655 Fall of Phaeton (45x30cm-18x12in) panel. 26-Mar-4 Koller, Zurich #3027/R est:40000-60000 (S.FR 36000)

BACKEREEL, Jacques (attrib) (17th C) Flemish
£4444 $8000 €6488 Abraham meeting the angels by a village, extensive landscape beyond (69x113cm-27x44in) panel. 21-Jan-4 Sotheby's, New York #83/R est:10000-15000

BACKHAUS, Georg (1870-?) German
£1164 $1979 €1700 Portrait of young woman (67x52cm-26x20in) s.d.1898 s. 6-Nov-3 Allgauer, Kempten #3363/R est:100

BACKHOUSE, John Philamon (1845-1905) New Zealander
£752 $1278 €1098 Kororareka beach. Lake Taupo (16cm-6in circular) oil terracotta plate pair. 27-Nov-3 International Art Centre, Auckland #107/R (NZ.D 2000)

BACKMANSSON, Hugo (1860-1953) Finnish
£282 $451 €400 Fez (33x51cm-13x20in) s. 18-Sep-3 Hagelstam, Helsinki #858/R
£302 $556 €450 Town, Tangier (46x56cm-18x22in) s. 25-Mar-4 Hagelstam, Helsinki #902
£340 $619 €500 Cottage in the skerries (34x43cm-13x17in) s.d.1923. 8-Feb-4 Bukowskis, Helsinki #320/R
£352 $563 €500 Tangier (40x52cm-16x20in) s. 18-Sep-3 Hagelstam, Helsinki #852
£396 $661 €570 Tangier (30x46cm-12x18in) s. 23-Oct-3 Hagelstam, Helsinki #882/R
£403 $741 €600 Tangier (33x53cm-13x21in) s. 25-Mar-4 Hagelstam, Helsinki #967
£458 $732 €650 Bazaar (41x46cm-16x18in) s.d.1920. 18-Sep-3 Hagelstam, Helsinki #920/R
£480 $883 €720 Gallop (36x25cm-14x10in) s.d.1921. 9-Jun-4 Bukowskis, Helsinki #352/R
£533 $955 €800 Street in Fez (56x40cm-22x16in) s.d.1939 cardboard. 15-May-4 Hagelstam, Helsinki #59/R
£541 $968 €800 Sunny day (60x48cm-24x19in) s.i. 8-May-4 Bukowskis, Helsinki #72/R
£671 $1248 €1000 Castle (36x50cm-14x20in) s.d.1923. 7-Mar-4 Bukowskis, Helsinki #295/R
£738 $1358 €1100 Town, Tangier (55x46cm-22x18in) s. 25-Mar-4 Hagelstam, Helsinki #903/R
£1000 $1790 €1500 From Sveaborg (39x49cm-15x19in) s.d.1922 canvas on board. 15-May-4 Hagelstam, Helsinki #60/R est:1200
£1351 $2419 €2000 View from Aabo (38x54cm-15x21in) s.d.1934. 8-May-4 Bukowskis, Helsinki #161/R est:2000-2300
£1400 $2506 €2100 Moroccan dancer (52x30cm-20x12in) s.d.1918. 15-May-4 Hagelstam, Helsinki #57/R est:1800
£2667 $4773 €4000 The Pavillion, Oktoberfest in Munich (47x38cm-19x15in) s.d.1904. 15-May-4 Hagelstam, Helsinki #58/R est:4000
£2887 $4620 €4100 Woman laughing (39x34cm-15x13in) s.d.1913. 18-Sep-3 Hagelstam, Helsinki #819/R est:850
Works on paper
£423 $676 €600 Tangier (33x52cm-13x20in) s.d.1909 W/C. 18-Sep-3 Hagelstam, Helsinki #854/R

BACKOFEN, Hans (circle) (c.1470-1519) German
Sculpture
£25503 $46926 €38000 Bishop (135cm-53in) wood. 24-Mar-4 Hugo Ruef, Munich #1635/R est:10000

BACKSTROM, Barbro (1939-1990) Swedish
Sculpture
£1435 $2440 €2095 Female figure (26x22cm-10x9in) s.indis.d.1981 netting sculpture metal base prov. 4-Nov-3 Bukowskis, Stockholm #563/R est:20000-25000 (S.KR 19000)
£1511 $2568 €2206 Female figure (29x28cm-11x11in) s. netting sculpture metal base. 4-Nov-3 Bukowskis, Stockholm #562/R est:20000-25000 (S.KR 20000)
£2711 $4798 €3958 Pra-Line (38x64x64cm-15x25x25in) iron rope asphalt earth sold with wood socle. 27-Apr-4 AB Stockholms Auktionsverk #1053/R est:40000-50000 (S.KR 37000)
£4532 $7704 €6617 Torso (57x29cm-22x11in) painted netting sculpture prov. 4-Nov-3 Bukowskis, Stockholm #588/R est:50000-60000 (S.KR 60000)
£6647 $11299 €9705 Three bodies (21x26cm-8x10in) s.d.1974 netting sculpture. 4-Nov-3 Bukowskis, Stockholm #594/R est:35000-40000 (S.KR 88000)
£16239 $27606 €23709 Hands (96x92cm-38x36in) netting sculpture. 4-Nov-3 Bukowskis, Stockholm #554/R est:125000-150000 (S.KR 215000)
£27190 $46224 €39697 Icarus (140x210cm-55x83in) s.d.1983 netting sculpture prov.lit. 4-Nov-3 Bukowskis, Stockholm #551/R est:275000-325000 (S.KR 360000)

BACKVIS, François (1857-1926) Belgian
£559 $951 €800 Vase de dahlias. Vase do roses (62x42cm-24x17in) s. pair. 18-Nov-3 Vanderkindere, Brussels #233
£810 $1401 €1150 In the sheep stall (60x91cm-24x36in) s.d.1900. 13-Dec-3 De Vuyst, Lokeren #11/R
£940 $1738 €1400 Sheep and chickens in a stall (33x23cm-13x9in) s. panel. 13-Mar-4 De Vuyst, Lokeren #15/R
£1418 $2369 €2000 Cheval attaque par des chiens (60x80cm-24x31in) s. 17-Jun-3 Galerie Moderne, Brussels #169/R est:2000-3000
£1467 $2640 €2200 Sheep and lambs at the edge of the wood (50x47cm-20x19in) s.d.83. 26-Apr-4 Bernaerts, Antwerp #65/R est:2000-2500
£2533 $4535 €3800 Landscape with cows (60x100cm-24x39in) s.d.1879. 15-May-4 De Vuyst, Lokeren #536/R est:2700-3000
£2837 $4738 €4000 La charrue (60x90cm-24x35in) s. 17-Jun-3 Galerie Moderne, Brussels #354/R est:5000-6000

BACON, Francis (1909-1992) British
£1400000 $2576000 €2044000 Study for self portrait (35x30cm-14x12in) painted 1973 prov.exhib.lit. 23-Jun-4 Sotheby's, London #4/R est:600000-800000
£2035928 $3400000 €2972455 Three studies for portrait of Lucian Freud (35x30cm-14x12in) i.d,1965 verso in three parts. 12-Nov-3 Sotheby's, New York #13/R est:2500000-3500000
£2100000 $3864000 €3066000 Three studies of Isabel Rawsthorne (35x30cm-14x12in) s.i.d.1966 triptych prov.lit. 24-Jun-4 Christie's, London #26/R est:1500000-2000000
£2500000 $4550000 €3650000 Study for Pope VI (152x117cm-60x46in) painted 1961 prov.exhib.lit. 5-Feb-4 Sotheby's, London #16/R est:2800000-3200000
Prints
£1921 $3400 €2805 Untitled - Woodrow Wilson (65x48cm-26x19in) s.i. col etching. 30-Apr-4 Sotheby's, New York #304/R est:4000-6000
£2000 $3440 €2920 Study for a self portrait (84x63cm-33x25in) s.num.41/180 lithograph. 2-Dec-3 Christie's, London #83/R est:1500-2500
£2000 $3640 €2920 Portrait of John Edwards, right panel (61x45cm-24x18in) s.num.116/150 col lithograph. 30-Jun-4 Christie's, London #168/R est:2000-3000
£2000 $3640 €2920 Wrapped telephone (71x56cm-28x22in) s.d.1985 num.86/100 lithograph collage board. 1-Jul-4 Sotheby's, London #323/R est:2500-3000
£2133 $3819 €3200 Tauromachie (169x119cm-67x47in) lithograph. 16-May-4 Osenat, Fontainebleau #1 est:2000-3000
£2147 $3800 €3135 Portrait of John Edwards (65x49cm-26x19in) s.num.98/99 col etching aquatint center panel of triptych. 28-Apr-4 Christie's, Rockefeller NY #257/R est:2500-3500
£2162 $4000 €3157 Right panel of triptych (135x98cm-53x39in) st.sig.num.73/84 col aquatint. 12-Feb-4 Christie's, Rockefeller NY #17/R est:5000-7000
£2193 $4035 €3202 Composition with figure and wash basin (47x36cm-19x14in) s. num.33/100 aquatinta etching. 23-Jun-4 Koller, Zurich #3207/R est:4500-6000 (S.FR 5000)
£2235 $4000 €3263 Etude de corps humain (46x33cm-18x13in) s.num.121/150 col lithograph. 6-May-4 Swann Galleries, New York #386/R est:3000-5000
£2270 $3677 €3200 Imprenta del estudio de Trotsky de Mejico (88x61cm-35x24in) s. num.49/99 engraving. 20-May-3 Ansorena, Madrid #930/R est:2500
£2400 $4368 €3504 Triptych inspired by the Orestia of Aeschylus (54x104cm-21x41in) s.num.57/150 col lithograph after the painting. 1-Jul-4 Sotheby's, London #317/R est:2500-3000
£2400 $4368 €3504 Study for portrait of John Edwards (95x68cm-37x27in) s.num.105/180 col lithograph after the painting. 1-Jul-4 Sotheby's, London #318/R est:2500-3500
£2400 $4368 €3504 William Blake (59x50cm-23x20in) s.i. col lithograph exec.c.1985 after the painting. 1-Jul-4 Sotheby's, London #320/R est:2500-3000
£2588 $4400 €3778 Portrait of Michel Leiris (30x25cm-12x10in) s.i. col etching aquatint. 21-Nov-3 Swann Galleries, New York #9/R est:4000-6000
£2600 $4732 €3796 Study for a portrait of John Edwards (68x50cm-27x20in) s.num.180/180 col lithograph. 30-Jun-4 Christie's, London #169/R est:2000-3000
£2706 $4600 €3951 Figure at a washbasin (47x36cm-19x14in) s.i. col etching aquatint. 21-Nov-3 Swann Galleries, New York #10/R est:6000-9000
£2796 $5200 €4082 Untitled (81x59cm-32x23in) s.num.58/150 offset col lithograph. 2-Mar-4 Swann Galleries, New York #27/R est:4000-6000
£2937 $4993 €4200 Self-portrait (51x93cm-20x37in) s.i. col lithograph. 28-Nov-3 Tajan, Paris #130/R est:3000
£2941 $5000 €4294 Metropolitan triptych (39x30cm-15x12in) s.num.83/99 col aquatint. 21-Nov-3 Swann Galleries, New York #7/R est:4000-6000
£3356 $5940 €5000 Oedipus and the Sphynx (127x90cm-50x35in) s. num.77/150 lithograph exec.1984. 29-Apr-4 David Kahn, Paris #174/R est:5000-6000
£3379 $5946 €5000 Triptych Oresteia of Aeschylus (53x103cm-21x41in) s. num.59/100 col lithograph triptych exec 1981. 18-May-4 Tajan, Paris #164/R est:5000-6000
£3631 $6500 €5301 Metropolitan (39x30cm-15x12in) s.num.9/99 etching aquatint triptych. 6-May-4 Swann Galleries, New York #385/R est:10000-15000
£3691 $6903 €5500 Etude pour le corps humain (45x33cm-18x13in) s. num.3/150 col lithograph. 1-Mar-4 Artcurial Briest, Paris #61/R est:2500
£3691 $6903 €5500 Self-portrait (51x93cm-20x37in) s.i. col lithograph one of 60. 1-Mar-4 Artcurial Briest, Paris #59/R est:3000-4000
£3691 $6755 €5500 Triptyque autoportrait (51x93cm-20x37in) s. col lithograph edn of 60. 7-Jul-4 Artcurial Briest, Paris #190/R est:3000-4000
£3716 $6540 €5500 Oedipe et le Sphinx (126x89cm-50x35in) s. num.42/150 col lithograph exec 1984. 18-May-4 Tajan, Paris #165/R est:5000-6000
£3800 $6916 €5548 Michel Leris, mirroir de la tauromachie, portrait of Michel Leiris (48x36cm-19x14in) s. i.verso col lithograph edition of 155 after the painting. 1-Jul-4 Sotheby's, London #316/R est:2500-3500
£3893 $7279 €5800 Self-portrait. s. print exec.1991. 1-Mar-4 Artcurial Briest, Paris #60 est:3000-4000
£4118 $7000 €6012 Seated figure (134x98cm-53x39in) st.sig. etching aquatint drypoint. 31-Oct-3 Sotheby's, New York #501/R
£4412 $7500 €6442 Metropolitan triptych (39x30cm-15x12in) col aquatint triptych. 31-Oct-3 Sotheby's, New York #500/R
£5226 $9250 €7630 Metropolitan triptych (39x29cm-15x11in) s.num.1974-77 etching aquatint three. 30-Apr-4 Sotheby's, New York #303/R est:9000-12000
£5294 $9000 €7729 Metropolitan triptych (39x30cm-15x12in) s.i. etching aquatint printed on one sheet. 21-Nov-3 Swann Galleries, New York #8/R est:12000-18000
£5298 $9642 €8000 Repons (178x360cm-70x142in) s. col lithograph triptych exec.1989. 15-Jun-4 Rossini, Paris #1/R est:8000-10000
£5406 $9514 €8000 Repons (178x360cm-70x142in) s.i. col lithograph triptych exec 1989 prov. 18-May-4 Tajan, Paris #163/R est:8000-10000
£6333 $11400 €9500 Etude pour auto-portrait (84x63cm-33x25in) s. col lithograph. 24-Apr-4 Cornette de St.Cyr, Paris #29/R est:6000

£6780 $12000 €9899 Study for bullfight no.1 (159x119cm-63x47in) s.num.128/150 col lithograph. 30-Apr-4 Sotheby's, New York #302/R est:8000-10000
£7343 $12629 €10500 Second version du triptyque de 1994, 1998, grand taille (143x106cm-56x42in) s.num.EA col lithograph vellum triptych. 3-Dec-3 Fraysse & Associes, Paris #98/R est:7500-8500

Works on paper
£900 $1638 €1314 Untitled (23x20cm-9x8in) pen ink. 4-Feb-4 Sotheby's, Olympia #37/R

BACON, Henry (1839-1912) American
£3750 $6000 €5475 Mid-afternoon chat (51x71cm-20x28in) s.d.1885. 20-Sep-3 Bunte, Elgin #1414 est:4000-6000

Works on paper
£403 $750 €588 Pulling the boat ashore (34x50cm-13x20in) s.i. graphite W/C. 5-Mar-4 Skinner, Boston #315/R
£495 $852 €723 Sailing boats on the Nile (43x59cm-17x23in) s.d.1907 W/C. 8-Dec-3 Philippe Schuler, Zurich #4195 (S.FR 1100)

BACON, John Henry Frederick (1868-1914) British
Works on paper
£250 $440 €365 Baked potato man (26x38cm-10x15in) s.d.1905 monochrome W/C htd white. 18-May-4 Fellows & Sons, Birmingham #217/R

BACON, Peggy (1895-1987) American
£347 $650 €507 Artists dilemma (13x13cm-5x5in) s.d.69 board prov.exhib. 29-Feb-4 Grogan, Boston #73/R
£773 $1400 €1129 Drunk and disorderly (33x74cm-13x29in) board. 16-Apr-4 American Auctioneer #13/R
£1243 $2250 €1815 Eating between meals (46x58cm-18x23in) panel. 16-Apr-4 American Auctioneer #15/R est:3000-5000

Works on paper
£247 $400 €358 Street sweeper (30x41cm-12x16in) s. dr. prov. 8-Aug-3 Barridorf, Portland #312/R

BACQUE, Daniel Joseph (1874-1947) French
Sculpture
£1192 $2181 €1800 An Amazon (45x58cm-18x23in) s. black pat. bronze. 6-Apr-4 Sotheby's, Olympia #172/R est:1800-2500

BADA SHANREN (1626-1705) Chinese
Works on paper
£26255 $43846 €38332 Narcissus and rock (30x30cm-12x12in) d.1699 ink pair. 26-Oct-3 Christie's, Hong Kong #458/R (HK.D 340000)
£27027 $45135 €39459 Thrush (30x30cm-12x12in) ink pair lit. 26-Oct-3 Christie's, Hong Kong #457/R (HK.D 350000)

BADALOCCHIO, Sisto (attrib) (1581-1647) Italian
£2848 $5183 €4300 Diane (69x72cm-27x28in) 16-Jun-4 Renaud, Paris #9/R est:1500-1800
£7092 $11844 €10000 San Sebastiano curato da Santa Irene (149x227cm-59x89in) 18-Jun-3 Christie's, Rome #441/R est:12000-15000

BADAMI, Andrea (1913-) American
£389 $700 €568 Sunbather reading (71x61cm-28x24in) 24-Apr-4 Slotin Folk Art, Buford #606/R

BADARACCO, Giuseppe (1588-1657) Italian
Works on paper
£371 $630 €530 Saint Simon Stock (24x16cm-9x6in) pen W/C pencil. 19-Nov-3 Finarte Semenzato, Milan #492/R

BADCOCK, Douglas (1922-) New Zealander
£421 $779 €615 Hansens farm, The Remarkables, Queenstown (39x50cm-15x20in) s.d.69 board. 9-Mar-4 Watson's, Christchurch #53 est:400-1000 (NZ.D 1150)
£706 $1215 €1031 Ngatinamae Peak, Eglington Valley (56x70cm-22x28in) s. board. 7-Dec-3 International Art Centre, Auckland #320 (NZ.D 1900)
£1003 $1796 €1464 Sunlight, Dart Valley - Paradise (56x70cm-22x28in) s.d.55 board. 11-May-4 Watson's, Christchurch #4/R (NZ.D 2900)

BADCOCK, John (?) New Zealander?
£440 $813 €642 Northwest change (29x45cm-11x18in) s. acrylic board. 9-Mar-4 Watson's, Christchurch #13/R est:1200-2000 (NZ.D 1200)

Works on paper
£295 $469 €431 Fairylands, Maries garden (54x72cm-21x28in) s. W/C. 1-May-3 Dunbar Sloane, Wellington #381 (NZ.D 850)

BADEN, Karoline Luise von (1723-1783) German
£3394 $5430 €4955 At the bedside of an elegant sick woman (53x43cm-21x17in) panel. 16-Sep-3 Philippe Schuler, Zurich #3315/R est:2000-2500 (S.FR 7500)
£5656 $9050 €8258 Portrait of a man in black coat (17x13cm-7x5in) panel. 16-Sep-3 Philippe Schuler, Zurich #3316/R est:1400-1800 (S.FR 12500)

BADER, Angelica and TANTERL, Dietmar (20th C) German
Photographs
£3200 $5728 €4800 Lecture - Helmut Friedel (132x176cm-52x69in) cibachrome. 13-May-4 Neumeister, Munich #540/R est:1800-2500

BADER, Josef (19th C) German
£594 $993 €850 Christ at the Last Supper (92x76cm-36x30in) s.d.1835. 27-Jun-3 Michael Zeller, Lindau #487/R

BADGER, Joseph (attrib) (1708-1765) American
£2717 $5000 €3967 Portrait of mother and child (126x102cm-50x40in) 27-Jun-4 Freeman, Philadelphia #72/R est:3000-5000
£4372 $8000 €6383 Portrait of Joseph Goldthwaite (58x46cm-23x18in) prov. 6-Jun-4 Skinner, Boston #48/R est:6000-8000
£22727 $42500 €33181 Portrait of an aristocratic lady in gown. painted c.1750. 28-Feb-4 Thomaston Place, Thomaston #25/R

BADGER, Samuel Finley Morse (1873-1919) American
£3784 $7000 €5525 Four-masted schooner, Sarah W Lawrence, in New England waters (66x107cm-26x42in) s.d.94. 10-Feb-4 Christie's, Rockefeller NY #206/R est:8000-12000

BADHAM, Edward Leslie (1873-1944) British
£280 $512 €409 Old Town Hastings (36x23cm-14x9in) s. 27-Jan-4 Gorringes, Lewes #1560

BADHAM, Herbert Edward (1899-1961) Australian
£27893 $47418 €40724 Kings Cross fair (48x38cm-19x15in) s.d.45 composition board exhib. 29-Oct-3 Lawson Menzies, Sydney #37/R est:75000-85000 (A.D 67500)

BADI, Aquiles (1894-1976) Argentinian
£1530 $2800 €2234 Via Appia, Rome (28x41cm-11x16in) tempera cardboard. 1-Jun-4 Arroyo, Buenos Aires #16
£3073 $5500 €4487 Washerwomen's garden (70x50cm-28x20in) s. s.i.d.1970 verso. 4-May-4 Arroyo, Buenos Aires #94/R est:4800

BADIA, Juan (20th C) ?
£806 $1500 €1177 La Guerra (122x61cm-48x24in) d.1970 panel exhib. 6-Mar-4 Harvey Clar, Oakland #1544

BADII, Libero (20th C) Argentinian
Sculpture
£6011 $11000 €8776 Christ (59x17cm-23x7in) bronze. 1-Jun-4 Arroyo, Buenos Aires #35
£9836 $18000 €14361 Study of woman I (54cm-21in) bronze. 1-Jun-4 Arroyo, Buenos Aires #30

Works on paper
£659 $1200 €962 Figure (38x32cm-15x13in) s.d.86 mixed media. 5-Jul-4 Arroyo, Buenos Aires #33/R
£670 $1200 €978 Figure (21x14cm-8x6in) mixed media. 11-May-4 Arroyo, Buenos Aires #5
£782 $1400 €1142 Figures (14x19cm-6x7in) mixed media. 11-May-4 Arroyo, Buenos Aires #6
£1117 $2000 €1631 The bad. 13 April 1991 (31x22cm-12x9in) mixed media pair. 11-May-4 Arroyo, Buenos Aires #4
£1593 $2900 €2326 Figure (37x27cm-15x11in) s.d.1992 mixed media. 5-Jul-4 Arroyo, Buenos Aires #68/R est:2900
£1648 $3000 €2406 Figure (30x22cm-12x9in) s.d.73 mixed media. 29-Jun-4 Arroyo, Buenos Aires #19/R est:2800

BADIN, Pierre Adolphe (1805-1877) French
£5170 $9254 €7600 Chiens devant trophee de chasse (109x131cm-43x52in) 19-Mar-4 Beaussant & Lefèvre, Paris #80/R est:3000-4000

BADIOLA, Txomin (1957-) Spanish
Works on paper
£1224 $2229 €1800 132 (60x85cm-24x33in) s.i.d.1989 ink wash marble powder prov. 3-Feb-4 Segre, Madrid #197/R est:1800

BADMIN, Stanley Roy (1906-1989) British
Works on paper
£850 $1445 €1241 The Beacon (27x40cm-11x16in) s.i. ink W/C exec.1977. 26-Nov-3 Sotheby's, Olympia #59/R
£950 $1615 €1387 Trees at thecastle entrance, Arundel (28x20cm-11x8in) s. W/C exhib. 26-Nov-3 Sotheby's, Olympia #109/R
£1300 $2171 €1898 Long Melford Mill, Suffolk (18x23cm-7x9in) s.i. pencil W/C bodycol prov. 16-Oct-3 Christie's, Kensington #288/R est:1200-1800
£4000 $6360 €5840 Durham from Wharton Park (18x34cm-7x13in) s.i.d.July 1947-Jan.48 pencil W/C prov.exhib. 10-Sep-3 Sotheby's, Olympia #147/R est:3000-5000
£4400 $8008 €6600 Horse barn, Illinois farm (25x25cm-10x10in) s.i.d. W/C pen ink. 2-Jul-4 Bloomsbury, London #51/R est:1500-2000

BADUR, Frank (1944-) German
£604 $1027 €882 Composition (40x60cm-16x24in) s.d.1989 verso prov. 5-Nov-3 AB Stockholms Auktionsverk #1015/R (S.KR 8000)
£793 $1348 €1158 Red monochrome (50x60cm-20x24in) s.d.89 verso. 5-Nov-3 AB Stockholms Auktionsverk #1014/R (S.KR 10500)
£1465 $2593 €2139 Untitled (123x66cm-48x26in) s.d.83 verso diptych prov. 27-Apr-4 AB Stockholms Auktionsverk #1197/R est:25000-30000 (S.KR 20000)

BADURA, Bernard (1896-1986) American
£1890 $3250 €2759 Deep Valley (20x25cm-8x10in) s.i.verso board prov. 7-Dec-3 Freeman, Philadelphia #222 est:800-1200

BAECHLER, Donald (1956-) American
£1437 $2400 €2098 Small red line drawing no.5 (42x35cm-17x14in) init.i.d.91 tempera on paper. 14-Nov-3 Phillips, New York #308/R est:3000-5000

£1437	$2400	€2098	Small red line drawing no.6 (42x35cm-17x14in) init.i.d.91 tempera on paper collage prov. 14-Nov-3 Phillips, New York #309/R est:3000-5000
£1437	$2400	€2098	Small red line drawing no.7 (42x35cm-17x14in) init.i.d.91 tempera paper collage prov. 14-Nov-3 Phillips, New York #311/R est:3000-5000
£1497	$2500	€2186	Small red line drawing no.3 (42x35cm-17x14in) init.i.d.91 tempera paper collage prov. 14-Nov-3 Phillips, New York #310/R est:3000-5000
£3846	$7000	€5615	Untitled - self portrait (43x36cm-17x14in) init.d.87 acrylic. 29-Jun-4 Sotheby's, New York #574/R est:4000-6000
£5495	$10000	€8023	Coney Island (46x46cm-18x18in) init.d.89 i.verso. 29-Jun-4 Sotheby's, New York #572/R est:5000-7000
£6711	$12013	€10000	Don's dilemma II (117x89cm-46x35in) s.i.d.1982 verso enamel paper prov. 27-May-4 Sotheby's, Paris #278/R est:10000-15000
£8383	$14000	€12239	Have a nice life (99x120cm-39x47in) init.i.d.88 verso acrylic canvas collage prov. 13-Nov-3 Sotheby's, New York #604/R est:15000-20000
£9000	$16560	€13140	Untitled (122x122cm-48x48in) s.d.1982 verso acrylic prov. 25-Jun-4 Christie's, London #263/R est:10000-15000
£10778	$18000	€15736	Sunflower (152x152cm-60x60in) init.i.d.97 verso acrylic fabric collage prov. 13-Nov-3 Sotheby's, New York #605/R est:20000-30000
£11500	$19205	€16790	Study for 29 Burton Street no 2 (194x100cm-76x39in) init.d.01 acrylic fabric paper collage paper prov. 22-Oct-3 Christie's, London #78/R est:7000-9000
£12291	$22000	€17945	Thistle 2 (102x101cm-40x40in) s.d.1999 overlap oil acrylic fabric collage prov. 13-May-4 Sotheby's, New York #481/R est:20000-30000
£14525	$26000	€21207	Globe (122x122cm-48x48in) s.i.d.98 verso oil acrylic thread printed fabric collage prov. 13-May-4 Sotheby's, New York #482/R est:25000-35000
£37989	$68000	€55464	Composition with green rabbit (190x190cm-75x75in) init.i.d.92 verso acrylic collage prov. 14-May-4 Phillips, New York #231/R est:40000-60000
£43114	$72000	€62946	Virtues of obesity (282x282cm-111x111in) init.i. verso acrylic oil collage on linen executed 1990 prov.exhib. 13-Nov-3 Phillips, New York #21/R est:40000-60000
Works on paper			
£2333	$4293	€3500	Untitled (123x86cm-48x34in) pencil wax crayon exec. 1979. 12-Jun-4 Villa Grisebach, Berlin #435/R est:3500-4500
£3297	$6000	€4814	Fingers (42x34cm-17x13in) init.d.92 gesso gouache coffee collage prov. 29-Jun-4 Sotheby's, New York #615/R est:4000-6000
£11976	$20000	€17485	Ahmad's flower no 7 (195x104cm-77x41in) init.d.94 gouache printed paper collage. 12-Nov-3 Christie's, Rockefeller NY #620/R est:20000-30000

BAEDER, John (1938-) American

£18792	$33638	€28000	Bells Pond diner (77x92cm-30x36in) s.i.d.90 prov.lit. 27-May-4 Sotheby's, Paris #263/R est:20000-30000
Works on paper			
£3356	$6007	€5000	Wally's diner (43x60cm-17x24in) s.i.d.1982 W/C prov.lit. 27-May-4 Sotheby's, Paris #249/R est:3000-5000
£3892	$6500	€5682	Malaga (47x26cm-19x10in) s.d.76 W/C. 7-Oct-3 Sotheby's, New York #366 est:3000-5000

BAELLIEUR, Cornelis de (attrib) (17th C) Flemish

£1056	$1849	€1500	La nativite (20x14cm-8x6in) copper htd gold. 19-Dec-3 Delvaux, Paris #101/R est:600-800

BAELLIEUR, Cornelis de (elder-attrib) (1607-1671) Flemish

£1056	$1849	€1500	Annonciation (33x23cm-13x9in) copper. 17-Dec-3 Piasa, Paris #2

BAEN, Jan de (1633-1702) Dutch

£8219	$13973	€12000	Portrait of Jan van der Haer. Portrait of Helena van der Haer (122x94cm-48x37in) s. indis d. one indis sig. 5-Nov-3 Christie's, Amsterdam #53/R est:15000-25000

BAER, Fritz (1850-1919) German

£1020	$1827	€1500	Summer landscape with farmsteads (46x56cm-18x22in) s. 17-Mar-4 Neumeister, Munich #397/R est:1200

BAER, Fritz (attrib) (1850-1919) German

£342	$582	€500	Landscape with farmstead (46x31cm-18x12in) i. verso. 5-Nov-3 Hugo Ruef, Munich #927

BAER, Jo (1929-) American

£19162	$32000	€27977	Lavender Wraparound (109x135cm-43x53in) s.d.70-74 verso prov. 12-Nov-3 Christie's, Rockefeller NY #598/R est:20000-30000

BAER, Kurt (1905-?) American

£2249	$4250	€3284	Sanctuary (64x76cm-25x30in) s.d.1948 prov. 17-Feb-4 John Moran, Pasadena #120/R est:2000-3000

BAER, Oswald (1906-1941) Austrian

£470	$832	€700	Flowers in green glass vase (55x75cm-22x30in) s.d.27 double-sided. 28-Apr-4 Schopman, Hamburg #524/R

BAERDEMAEKER, Felix de (1836-1878) Belgian

£1408	$2437	€2000	Dutch village scene (30x42cm-12x17in) s. 10-Dec-3 Dorotheum, Vienna #47/R est:2000-2200

BAERENT, Sophie (19th C) Danish?

Works on paper			
£421	$664	€610	Outskirts of Florence with animals and figures (32x46cm-13x18in) s.i.d.Juni 1831 pencil W/C. 3-Sep-3 Museumsbygningen, Copenhagen #235 (D.KR 4500)

BAERENTZEN, Emilius (1799-1868) Danish

£379	$607	€553	Portrait of Miss Tychsen (35x28cm-14x11in) 22-Sep-3 Rasmussen, Vejle #81/R (D.KR 4000)

BAERTLING, Olle (1911-1981) Swedish

£1378	$2480	€2012	Scinti (50x65cm-20x26in) s. d.1949 verso. 26-Apr-4 Bukowskis, Stockholm #229/R est:25000-30000 (S.KR 19000)
£1465	$2593	€2139	Force Abstraite VII (81x65cm-32x26in) s. d.1946 verso. 27-Apr-4 AB Stockholms Auktionsverk #772/R est:25000-30000 (S.KR 20000)
£1586	$2696	€2316	DERBY I - composition (65x54cm-26x21in) s. d.1947 verso. 5-Nov-3 AB Stockholms Auktionsverk #830/R est:25000-30000 (S.KR 21000)
£10256	$18154	€14974	Theme blanc noir jaune (60x92cm-24x36in) s.i.d.1953 exhib.prov. 27-Apr-4 AB Stockholms Auktionsverk #758/R est:140000-160000 (S.KR 140000)
£12840	$21828	€18746	AIYA - composition (92x60cm-36x24in) s.i.d.1955 prov. 5-Nov-3 AB Stockholms Auktionsverk #799/R est:100000-125000 (S.KR 170000)
£15962	$26657	€23305	Sergai - concrete composition (195x97cm-77x38in) s.d.1962 prov. 7-Oct-3 Rasmussen, Copenhagen #96/R est:150000-200000 (D.KR 170000)
£16239	$27606	€23709	Kiakam - composition (195x97cm-77x38in) s.d.1975 verso. 5-Nov-3 AB Stockholms Auktionsverk #705/R est:200000-225000 (S.KR 215000)
£19637	$33384	€28670	DENI - composition (92x180cm-36x71in) s.d.1960 verso. 5-Nov-3 AB Stockholms Auktionsverk #806/R est:180000-200000 (S.KR 260000)
£21148	$35952	€30876	Neam - composition (92x180cm-36x71in) s.d.1957 verso exhib.prov. 4-Nov-3 Bukowskis, Stockholm #292/R est:275000-300000 (S.KR 280000)
£21978	$38901	€32088	Sergai - composition (195x97cm-77x38in) s.d.1962 verso prov. 27-Apr-4 AB Stockholms Auktionsverk #885/R est:350000-400000 (S.KR 300000)
£22659	$38520	€33082	Arekyram - composition (195x97cm-77x38in) s.d.1964 verso. 4-Nov-3 Bukowskis, Stockholm #294/R est:300000-325000 (S.KR 300000)
£30201	$54060	€45000	Aguibi (180x92cm-71x36in) s.d.1958 verso i.d.on stretcher prov. 25-May-4 Sotheby's, Milan #167/R est:1500-2000
Sculpture			
£9890	$17505	€14439	XU - composition (343cm-135in) indis sig.d.1968 black varnished steel prov.lit. 27-Apr-4 AB Stockholms Auktionsverk #788/R est:125000-150000 (S.KR 135000)

BAERWIND, Rudi (1910-1982) German

£432	$708	€600	Composition (79x63cm-31x25in) s.i.d. board. 4-Jun-3 Ketterer, Hamburg #141/R
£570	$1050	€850	Paysage IV (89x58cm-35x23in) s.i. i.d. verso panel. 26-Mar-4 Bolland & Marotz, Bremen #653/R
£845	$1462	€1200	Untitled (115x90cm-45x35in) s.d.1968. 13-Dec-3 Lempertz, Koln #278/R

BAES, Émile (1879-1954) Belgian

£300	$540	€450	Self portrait (73x50cm-29x20in) s.d.1932. 26-Apr-4 Bernaerts, Antwerp #1135/R
£405	$726	€600	Coucher de soleil sur le monument (60x75cm-24x30in) s. 10-May-4 Horta, Bruxelles #150
£483	$893	€700	Elegante a Rabat, Orientaliste (40x50cm-16x20in) s. panel. 16-Feb-4 Horta, Bruxelles #175
£629	$1070	€900	Nu assis (55x45cm-22x18in) s. 18-Nov-3 Vanderkindere, Brussels #114
£733	$1349	€1100	Elegante de dos se mirant (72x56cm-28x22in) s. 14-Jun-4 Horta, Bruxelles #30
£890	$1514	€1300	Jeune fille au piano (36x28cm-14x11in) s.d.1900 panel. 10-Nov-3 Horta, Bruxelles #327
£897	$1488	€1300	Devant le miroir (100x60cm-39x24in) s. 1-Oct-3 Millon & Associes, Paris #89/R
£933	$1680	€1400	Nu de dos (75x55cm-30x22in) s. indis.d.191. 20-Apr-4 Galerie Moderne, Brussels #381/R est:1200-1600
£1000	$1800	€1500	Reclining nude (45x55cm-18x22in) s. 26-Apr-4 Bernaerts, Antwerp #446 est:1200-1400
£1060	$1928	€1600	Nu au fauteuil (60x50cm-24x20in) s. panel. 15-Jun-4 Vanderkindere, Brussels #88 est:1500-2000
£1149	$2171	€1700	Nu couche (84x103cm-33x41in) s. 17-Feb-4 Vanderkindere, Brussels #20/R est:1200-1800
£1316	$2421	€2000	Marchands ambulants a Venise (150x125cm-59x49in) s.d.1906. 22-Jun-4 Palais de Beaux Arts, Brussels #194/R est:2500-3500
£1389	$2208	€2000	Nu regardant la mer (92x73cm-36x29in) s. 9-Sep-3 Vanderkindere, Brussels #22
£1399	$2378	€2000	Reclining female nude (115x147cm-45x58in) s. i.verso. 24-Nov-3 Glerum, Amsterdam #89/R est:1500-2000
£1538	$2615	€2200	Modele nu dans l'atelier (30x22cm-12x9in) s. cardboard. 1-Dec-3 Palais de Beaux Arts, Brussels #212/R est:500-750
£1678	$2803	€2400	Composition aux fleurs et aux fruits. s.d.1904. 13-Oct-3 Horta, Bruxelles #178 est:1500-1800
£2000	$3640	€3000	Portrait of a young woman and infant (96x76cm-38x30in) 20-Jun-4 Wilkinson, Doncaster #318 est:3000-4500
£2013	$3725	€3000	Nude in front of the mirror (110x76cm-43x30in) s. 13-Mar-4 De Vuyst, Lokeren #540/R est:3000-4000
£2313	$4140	€3400	Femme nue (130x90cm-51x35in) s. 16-Mar-4 Vanderkindere, Brussels #95/R est:1500-2500
£2662	$4259	€3700	Jeune femme nue (140x80cm-55x31in) s.d.1932. 18-May-3 Salle des ventes Pillet, Lyon la Foret #52/R
£3873	$6701	€5500	Interior with standing nude (130x90cm-51x35in) s. 13-Dec-3 De Vuyst, Lokeren #543/R est:5500-6500
£4667	$8400	€7000	Reclining nude (84x150cm-33x59in) s. 26-Apr-4 Bernaerts, Antwerp #139/R est:6600-8000

BAES, Firmin (1874-1945) Belgian

£694	$1104	€1000	Village endormi (43x55cm-17x22in) s. canvas on cardboard. 9-Sep-3 Vanderkindere, Brussels #35/R
£2759	$5103	€4000	Les Iles Borromees (60x90cm-24x35in) s.d.1902. 16-Feb-4 Horta, Bruxelles #174 est:5000-6000
Works on paper			
£278	$453	€400	Massif d'hortensias. s. pastel. 23-Sep-3 Galerie Moderne, Brussels #784
£733	$1313	€1100	Paysage en Ardennes (26x40cm-10x16in) s. pastel. 15-May-4 De Vuyst, Lokeren #17
£1053	$1937	€1600	Letter (50x40cm-20x16in) s. pastel. 22-Jun-4 Palais de Beaux Arts, Brussels #196/R est:2250-3500
£1316	$2421	€2000	Orchids (50x40cm-20x16in) s. pastel. 22-Jun-4 Palais de Beaux Arts, Brussels #195/R est:2500-3500
£1399	$2378	€2000	La robe rose (120x100cm-47x39in) s.d.1943 pastel. 1-Dec-3 Palais de Beaux Arts, Brussels #214/R est:2000-3000
£1500	$2775	€2190	Enigme (70x50cm-28x20in) s.d.1915 i.verso pastel. 14-Jul-4 Sotheby's, Olympia #285/R est:1500-2000
£8671	$14741	€12400	Femme au berceau (57x69cm-22x27in) s. pastel exhib. 1-Dec-3 Palais de Beaux Arts, Brussels #221/R est:3000-4000

BAES, Lionel (1839-1913) Belgian

£317	$587	€460	Elegante au jabot (68x54cm-27x21in) s.d.1874. 19-Jan-4 Horta, Bruxelles #292

£319 $533 €450 Le macon (73x35cm-29x14in) s. 17-Jun-3 Vanderkindere, Brussels #146
£355 $592 €500 Elegante (43x25cm-17x10in) s. 17-Jun-3 Vanderkindere, Brussels #148

BAES, Rachel (1912-1983) Belgian
£500 $900 €750 Vase with flowers (100x80cm-39x31in) s. 26-Apr-4 Bernaerts, Antwerp #402/R
£533 $955 €800 Le miroir d'Alice (70x60cm-28x24in) s. s.i.d.1954 verso. 15-May-4 De Vuyst, Lokeren #18/R
£559 $934 €800 Le parterre (65x54cm-26x21in) s. s.i.verso. 11-Oct-3 De Vuyst, Lokeren #13
£560 $1003 €818 L'abime (81x65cm-32x26in) s. i.d.1956 verso. 12-May-4 Dobiaschofsky, Bern #320 (S.FR 1300)
£1611 $2980 €2400 La nourrice (81x65cm-32x26in) s. s.i.verso. 13-Mar-4 De Vuyst, Lokeren #16/R est:1000-1400
£2400 $4392 €3600 Le faux calcul (146x114cm-57x45in) s.d.1974 verso. 7-Jun-4 Palais de Beaux Arts, Brussels #27/R est:3000-4000

BAESCHLIN, Pierre Laurent (1886-?) French
£1100 $1980 €1606 Jardin (61x50cm-24x20in) s. board. 21-Jan-4 Sotheby's, Olympia #504/R est:800-1200

BAETS, Angelus de (1793-1855) Belgian
£12667 $23180 €19000 Interieur d'eglise (71x54cm-28x21in) s.d.1833 panel. 7-Jun-4 Palais de Beaux Arts, Brussels #240/R est:10000-15000

BAETS, Angelus de (attrib) (1793-1855) Belgian
£1074 $1976 €1600 Dutch landscape with windmill and ferry (37x50cm-15x20in) bears sig. lit. 25-Mar-4 Karlheinz Kaupp, Staufen #2228/R

BAEYENS, Adolf (1886-1969) Belgian
£559 $934 €800 Saint-Michielshelling in Gent under snow (55x75cm-22x30in) s. 11-Oct-3 De Vuyst, Lokeren #14

BAEZA, Manuel (1915-1986) Spanish
£646 $1176 €950 Women in landscape (60x73cm-24x29in) s. 3-Feb-4 Segre, Madrid #124/R
£1897 $3414 €2750 Night scene (89x116cm-35x46in) s. lit. 26-Jan-4 Durán, Madrid #139/R est:2500
Works on paper
£280 $467 €400 Woman with rose (45x31cm-18x12in) s. wash. 30-Jun-3 Ansorena, Madrid #123/R

BAFFIER, Jean Eugene (1851-1921) French
Sculpture
£3191 $5170 €4500 Buste de Girard de Pelleuse de Brener (59cm-23in) s.i.d.1884 terracotta lit. 23-May-3 Sotheby's, Paris #283/R est:4500-6000

BAGAN, W Daniel (1953-) Canadian
£227 $411 €331 Common nocturne no.9 (75x75cm-30x30in) s.i.d.1990 verso prov. 18-Apr-4 Levis, Calgary #414/R (C.D 550)
£227 $411 €331 Common nocturne no.8 (75x75cm-30x30in) s.i.d.1990 verso prov. 18-Apr-4 Levis, Calgary #415/R (C.D 550)

BAGDATOPOULOS, William Spencer (1888-1965) Greek
Works on paper
£420 $659 €609 Street market, Mexico (71x53cm-28x21in) s. pencil W/C bodycol. 28-Aug-3 Christie's, Kensington #486/R
£750 $1275 €1095 Meenakshi Temple, Madurai, India (48x71cm-19x28in) W/C htd white. 4-Nov-3 Bonhams, New Bond Street #64/R
£1333 $2413 €2000 New market in Calcutta (52x74cm-20x29in) i.d.1925 W/C lit. 3-Apr-4 Badum, Bamberg #67/R est:2000

BAGEL, Moses (1908-1995) French
£590 $986 €850 Composition (30x22cm-12x9in) s. oil gouache. 21-Oct-3 Artcurial Briest, Paris #242/R
Works on paper
£382 $638 €550 Composition. Composition with fruit (23x15cm-9x6in) s.i. W/C ink double-sided. 21-Oct-3 Artcurial Briest, Paris #244
£521 $869 €750 Couseuses (54x38cm-21x15in) s. W/C ink. 21-Oct-3 Artcurial Briest, Paris #241/R

BAGETTI, Giuseppe Pietro (attrib) (1764-1831) Italian
Works on paper
£345 $576 €500 Cavaliers dans la tempete (22x30cm-9x12in) bears sig. W/C. 17-Nov-3 Delorme & Bocage, Paris #88/R

BAGG, Henry Howard (1852-1928) American
£238 $440 €347 Landscape with mountains in the background reflecting on a lake (48x74cm-19x29in) s. 16-Jan-4 Aspire, Cleveland #39/R
£750 $1200 €1095 Castle (51x76cm-20x30in) s. 19-Sep-3 Freeman, Philadelphia #152/R est:800-1200

BAGGE, Eva (1871-1964) Swedish
£314 $544 €458 Thinking (38x46cm-15x18in) s. prov. 15-Dec-3 Lilla Bukowskis, Stockholm #865 (S.KR 4000)
£314 $544 €458 Canal view, Venice (35x27cm-14x11in) s.d.03 prov. 15-Dec-3 Lilla Bukowskis, Stockholm #867 (S.KR 4000)
£517 $926 €755 Playing patience - interior (28x25cm-11x10in) s. panel. 26-May-4 AB Stockholms Auktionsverk #2213/R (S.KR 7000)
£846 $1455 €1235 In the kitchen (42x35cm-17x14in) s. 2-Dec-3 Bukowskis, Stockholm #158/R (S.KR 11000)
£2069 $3704 €3021 Still life of fruit, pot and bottle (33x41cm-13x16in) s. prov. 25-May-4 Bukowskis, Stockholm #47/R est:25000-30000 (S.KR 28000)
Works on paper
£415 $676 €606 Coastal landscape (22x29cm-9x11in) s. gouache. 29-Sep-3 Lilla Bukowskis, Stockholm #495 (S.KR 5400)
£660 $1142 €964 Interior scene with old woman (25x21cm-10x8in) s. W/C gouache prov. 15-Dec-3 Lilla Bukowskis, Stockholm #863 (S.KR 8400)
£911 $1676 €1367 Girl from Brittany (22x15cm-9x6in) s. W/C. 14-Jun-4 Lilla Bukowskis, Stockholm #289 (S.KR 12500)

BAGHOT DE LA BERE, Stephen (19/20th C) ?
Works on paper
£360 $673 €540 Bacchic revelry around a binfire (38x28cm-15x11in) s.i.d.1916 W/C. 22-Jul-4 Gorringes, Lewes #1732

BAGLEY, Laurence (20th C) British
£450 $765 €657 Glittering wings, submarine flying boat off Calshot Castle, Southampton (51x74cm-20x29in) s. sold with a print. 26-Nov-3 Hamptons Fine Art, Godalming #153

BAGNOLI, Marco (1949-) Italian
£2013 $3725 €3000 Esotheric (120x160cm-47x63in) s.i.d.1978. 13-Mar-4 Meeting Art, Vercelli #68 est:3000

BAGSHAWE, Joseph Richard (1870-1909) British
£500 $905 €730 Lone vessel (25x36cm-10x14in) board prov. 15-Apr-4 Richardson & Smith, Whitby #102/R
£1300 $2353 €1898 Fishing boat off the Irish Coast (23x33cm-9x13in) board. 15-Apr-4 Richardson & Smith, Whitby #104/R est:600-800
£1500 $2715 €2190 Clippers and other vessels (25x33cm-10x13in) board prov. 15-Apr-4 Richardson & Smith, Whitby #107/R est:400-600
£2200 $3872 €3212 From the East Pier landing, Staithes, towards Cowbar Nab (23x33cm-9x13in) panel prov. 20-May-4 Richardson & Smith, Whitby #673
£2400 $4344 €3504 Racing to market (33x48cm-13x19in) prov.exhib. 15-Apr-4 Richardson & Smith, Whitby #112/R est:800-1200
£3900 $7059 €5694 Fishing cobbles in choppy seas (59x89cm-23x35in) s. 30-Mar-4 David Duggleby, Scarborough #214/R est:1200-1500
£13000 $22100 €18980 Whitby cobbles with figures leaving Staithes (61x91cm-24x36in) s. 18-Nov-3 Bonhams, Leeds #268/R est:5000-7000

BAHAMONDE, Aldo (1963-) Chilean
Works on paper
£775 $1340 €1100 Still life with cigarettes (59x73cm-23x29in) s.d.88 chl dr. 15-Dec-3 Ansorena, Madrid #192/R

BAHIEU, Jules G (19th C) Belgian
£1059 $1800 €1546 Chickens in the barn and outside the coop (37x18cm-15x7in) s. board pair. 20-Nov-3 Auctions by the Bay, Alameda #1008/R

BAHNER, Hermann (1867-1933) German
£800 $1464 €1200 Hay-making at Niederrheim (74x108cm-29x43in) s.i.d.99. 5-Jun-4 Arnold, Frankfurt #527/R

BAHRMANN, Hermann (1874-1941) German
£420 $713 €600 Still life with potatoes and pots (45x62cm-18x24in) s.d.28. 20-Nov-3 Van Ham, Cologne #1466

BAI XUESHI (1915-) Chinese
Works on paper
£1422 $2560 €2076 Lofty peaks (37x44cm-15x17in) s.i.d.1985 ink col. 26-Apr-4 Sotheby's, Hong Kong #597/R est:20000-25000 (HK.D 20000)
£1931 $3224 €2819 Boating (37x44cm-15x17in) s.i.d.1985 ink col gold paper. 27-Oct-3 Sotheby's, Hong Kong #289/R est:20000-30000 (HK.D 25000)

BAIER, Jean (1932-) ?
£586 $1007 €856 Diamond (100x100cm-39x39in) enamel steel. 8-Dec-3 Philippe Schuler, Zurich #3006/R (S.FR 1300)
£1261 $2169 €1841 Etude pour Brasilia (143x44cm-56x17in) enamel steel painted 1983. 8-Dec-3 Philippe Schuler, Zurich #3005 est:3000-4000 (S.FR 2800)
£1310 $2410 €1913 Etude pour Brasilia (52x124cm-20x49in) s.i. s.i.d. stretcher acrylic metal. 8-Jun-4 Germann, Zurich #237 est:2000-3000 (S.FR 3000)

BAIERL, Theodor (1881-1932) German
£1181 $1924 €1700 Amazones resting (36x29cm-14x11in) s. panel. 24-Sep-3 Neumeister, Munich #388/R est:1650

BAIGAI, Totoki (1749-1804) Japanese
Works on paper
£489 $900 €714 Landscape with calligraphy (119x49cm-47x19in) s. ink hanging scroll. 23-Mar-4 Christie's, Rockefeller NY #104/R
£1958 $3368 €2800 Two Chinese walkers in a mountain landscape (134x19cm-53x7in) s.i. ink col hanging scroll. 5-Dec-3 Lempertz, Koln #762/R est:2800

BAIGENT, Richard (19th C) British
£260 $486 €380 Beaufort Tower, and Church of the Hospital of St Cross, near Winchester (8x12cm-3x5in) i.verso board. 25-Feb-4 Mallams, Oxford #390/R

BAIJOT, Leopold M (1936-) French
£4698 $8315 €7000 Le beau tapis du Caire (80x70cm-31x28in) s. lit. 28-Apr-4 Charbonneaux, Paris #102/R est:6000-8000
£5034 $8909 €7500 Venise, perle de lumiere (90x70cm-35x28in) s. lit. 28-Apr-4 Charbonneaux, Paris #103/R est:6000-8000

BAIL, Antoine Jean (1830-1918) French
£2069 $3455 €3000 Joyeux vignerons (36x61cm-14x24in) s.d. 17-Nov-3 Tajan, Paris #93/R est:3000-4000

BAIL, Franck Antoine (1858-1924) French
£7258 $13355 €10597 Still life with melon, grapes, tomatoes, copper pot on a table (157x109cm-62x43in) s.d.97 prov. 14-Jun-4 Waddingtons, Toronto #296/R est:20000-25000 (C.D 18000)

BAIL, J (19th C) British
£9859 $17253 €14000 Scene d'atelier (73x92cm-29x36in) s.d.87. 16-Dec-3 Artcurial Briest, Paris #248/R est:15000-18000

BAIL, Joseph (1862-1921) French
£993 $1808 €1500 Paysanne devant sa chaumiere (41x33cm-16x13in) s. panel. 19-Jun-4 St-Germain-en-Laye Encheres #63/R est:1500-1800
£4636 $8437 €7000 Les lingeres (46x55cm-18x22in) s. 16-Jun-4 Renaud, Paris #36/R est:3500-3800
£5556 $10000 €8112 La pecheuse (56x47cm-22x19in) s. prov. 23-Apr-4 Sotheby's, New York #160/R est:10000-15000
£5682 $10000 €8296 Interior scene with woman in her kitchen (135x99cm-53x39in) s.i. 21-May-4 Pook & Pook, Downington #280/R est:15000-20000
£25000 $42500 €36500 Cuisiner (37x57cm-15x22in) s. 28-Oct-3 Sotheby's, New York #143/R est:20000-30000

BAILEY, Albert E (fl.1890-1904) British
£1250 $2088 €1825 Swans in a reed filled lake with figures on bank (45x60cm-18x24in) s,. 17-Nov-3 Trembath Welch, Great Dunmow #506/R est:1500-2000

BAILEY, Frederick Victor (20th C) British
£280 $468 €406 Still life of roses, tulips, mixed summer blossom and moth on a ledge (41x30cm-16x12in) s.d. 22-Jun-3 Desmond Judd, Cranbrook #1051

BAILEY, Julian (1963-) British
£500 $935 €730 Friends in the pub (13x14cm-5x6in) init. board. 25-Feb-4 Mallams, Oxford #364

BAILEY, Nancy (20th C) British
£350 $585 €511 Mylor Bridge boat yard (51x76cm-20x30in) s. i.verso. 14-Oct-3 David Lay, Penzance #347

BAILEY, Peter J (1951-) British
£300 $537 €438 Jazz theme, Checkerboard Club (80x98cm-31x39in) s.i.verso. 17-May-4 David Duggleby, Scarborough #644/R
£300 $537 €438 International hair stylist (59x45cm-23x18in) s. s.i.verso. 17-May-4 David Duggleby, Scarborough #645/R
£360 $680 €526 Jazz theme, Mr Babalo (80x100cm-31x39in) s.i.verso. 23-Feb-4 David Duggleby, Scarborough #629/R
£400 $756 €584 Pedro Calvi, dirty dancing (80x100cm-31x39in) s.i.verso. 23-Feb-4 David Duggleby, Scarborough #630/R
£720 $1361 €1051 Equine series: Drinkers (59x79cm-23x31in) s. 23-Feb-4 David Duggleby, Scarborough #658/R
£760 $1436 €1110 Equine series: King Arabians (60x81cm-24x32in) s. 23-Feb-4 David Duggleby, Scarborough #659/R

BAILEY, R D (20th C) British
£600 $1062 €876 Summer holiday, figures on a beach (28x38cm-11x15in) mono. oil on paper. 28-Apr-4 Peter Wilson, Nantwich #35

BAILEY, Terry (1937-) British
£1892 $3500 €2762 Work boats racing off Falmouth (52x70cm-20x28in) s. board. 10-Feb-4 Christie's, Rockefeller NY #251/R est:3000-5000

BAILEY, William (1930-) American
Prints
£1647 $2750 €2405 Umbria verde (36x46cm-14x18in) s.d.1996 num.2/50 col aquatint etching. 21-Oct-3 Bonhams & Butterfields, San Francisco #1275/R
Works on paper
£1816 $3250 €2651 Female nudes (38x29cm-15x11in) s.d.1995 graphite two prov. 6-May-4 Doyle, New York #99/R est:1500-2500

BAILLEUX, Cesar (1937-) Belgian
Sculpture
£1000 $1790 €1500 La petite amie du casseur de tetes (130x65cm-51x26in) red copper wood base lit. 15-May-4 De Vuyst, Lokeren #19/R est:1300-1500

BAILLON-VINCENNES, Charles (1878-1932) Swiss
£323 $579 €472 Schloss Colombier (81x65cm-32x26in) s. board. 13-May-4 Stuker, Bern #21/R (S.FR 750)

BAILLY, Adolphe (19th C) French
£2300 $4209 €3358 Parisian river scene (53x81cm-21x32in) s. 7-Apr-4 Gardiner & Houlgate, Bath #354/R est:2500-3750

BAILLY, Alice (1872-1938) Swiss
£4036 $6578 €5893 Scene de rue (27x34cm-11x13in) s. prov. 29-Sep-3 Christie's, Zurich #65/R est:10000-15000 (S.FR 9000)
£8734 $15633 €12752 Femme en rouge (81x65cm-32x26in) s. 26-May-4 Sotheby's, Zurich #123/R est:8000-12000 (S.FR 20000)
Works on paper
£371 $683 €542 Interior with woman knitting (62x46cm-24x18in) s. W/C. 14-Jun-4 Philippe Schuler, Zurich #4104 (S.FR 850)
£6787 $11742 €9909 Concert dans le jardin (83x95cm-33x37in) s. gouache W/C crayon prov. 12-Dec-3 Galerie du Rhone, Sion #628/R est:15000-20000 (S.FR 15000)

BAILLY, David (1584-c.1657) Dutch
Works on paper
£16667 $30000 €24334 Portrait of a young man (13x12cm-5x5in) d.1623 pen brown ink. 21-Jan-4 Sotheby's, New York #56/R est:20000-25000

BAIN, Donald (1904-1979) British
£800 $1488 €1168 Spring flowers in a jug (49x39cm-19x15in) s. canvasboard prov. 4-Mar-4 Christie's, Kensington #176/R
£850 $1522 €1241 Still life of assorted roses (61x51cm-24x20in) s.d.1944 verso. 28-May-4 Lyon & Turnbull, Edinburgh #89/R
£1800 $3060 €2628 Pink and red carnations (61x46cm-24x18in) s.d.1944 verso. 30-Oct-3 Christie's, London #157/R est:2000-3000
£2000 $3220 €2900 Still life and mountain landscape (62x75cm-24x30in) s.d.1943 verso. 21-Aug-3 Bonhams, Edinburgh #1184/R est:2000-3000
Works on paper
£320 $605 €467 French street scene (30x26cm-12x10in) s. pen ink col chk. 19-Feb-4 Lyon & Turnbull, Edinburgh #32
£360 $569 €522 Cagnes sur mer (28x39cm-11x15in) s. mixed media executed 1947. 3-Sep-3 Bonhams, Bury St Edmunds #419
£800 $1512 €1168 Market, Rue La Pic, Paris (45x41cm-18x16in) s. pastel. 19-Feb-4 Lyon & Turnbull, Edinburgh #155

BAINES, Thomas (1820-1875) British
£5000 $8850 €7300 Party attacked by kaffirs between Beaufort and Granhamstown (46x63cm-18x25in) bears i. 27-Apr-4 Bonhams, New Bond Street #97/R est:5000-8000
£20000 $32600 €29200 Death shot (51x66cm-20x26in) s.i. 25-Sep-3 Christie's, London #461/R est:20000-30000
£23529 $42588 €34352 Patrol under the command of Captain Fisher charged in Van Beulen's Hoek, Kat River (43x62cm-17x24in) s.d.1859 i.verso prov. 30-Mar-4 Stephan Welz, Johannesburg #479/R est:250000-300000 (SA.R 280000)
Works on paper
£1800 $3186 €2628 Flood sweeping down the Kuisi River, South West Africa, Christmas Eve 1862 (29x39cm-11x15in) s.d.Dec 24 1862 W/C prov. 27-Apr-4 Bonhams, New Bond Street #98/R est:2000-3000

BAINES, Thomas (attrib) (1820-1875) British
£1800 $3186 €2628 East Indiaman in Table Bay (30x41cm-12x16in) 29-Apr-4 Christie's, Kensington #134/R est:300-500

BAIRD, Annie (1932-1999) New Zealander
Works on paper
£277 $496 €404 From Kelburn Parade (57x75cm-22x30in) s.i.d.1987 W/C. 12-May-4 Dunbar Sloane, Wellington #306 (NZ.D 800)
£278 $442 €406 Towards St. Clair (56x75cm-22x30in) s.d.1984 W/C. 1-May-3 Dunbar Sloane, Wellington #123 (NZ.D 800)
£588 $1053 €858 Red haired girl in black beret (54x74cm-21x29in) s.d.1987 W/C. 12-May-4 Dunbar Sloane, Wellington #607 (NZ.D 1700)
£623 $1152 €910 From my window (55x73cm-22x29in) s.d.80 W/C. 9-Mar-4 Watson's, Christchurch #5 est:1800-3000 (NZ.D 1700)
£745 $1378 €1088 Lyttelton Port (57x77cm-22x30in) s.i.d.1989 W/C. 13-Jul-4 Watson's, Christchurch #9/R (NZ.D 2100)

BAIRD, H (19th C) ?
£1702 $2843 €2400 Scene d'interieur (30x45cm-12x18in) s. 17-Jun-3 Galerie Moderne, Brussels #412/R est:2000-3000

BAIRD, Nathaniel Hughes (1865-c.1930) British
£3600 $5724 €5220 Wind and sun following the plough (61x84cm-24x33in) momo. 9-Sep-3 Bonhams, Knightsbridge #175/R est:1200-1800
Works on paper
£290 $484 €423 Grey tow horse on the Ouse (27x37cm-11x15in) mono. W/C. 20-Oct-3 Bonhams, Bath #78
£480 $874 €701 Controlling the carthorse (20x20cm-8x8in) mono. pencil W/C htd white. 1-Jul-4 Christie's, Kensington #208/R
£605 $1113 €883 Harvest field (27x34cm-11x13in) mono. W/C. 14-Jun-4 Waddingtons, Toronto #92/R est:1500-2500 (C.D 1500)
£800 $1440 €1168 Tow path (29x40cm-11x16in) mono. W/C. 21-Jan-4 Sotheby's, Olympia #227/R
£1200 $2160 €1752 Hay carts (45x49cm-18x19in) mono. W/C over pencil. 21-Jan-4 Sotheby's, Olympia #230/R est:1200-1800
£1500 $2700 €2190 The rest (36x28cm-14x11in) mono. W/C. 21-Jan-4 Sotheby's, Olympia #228/R est:800-1200

BAIRD, William Baptiste (1847-1917) American
£369 $650 €539 Rocky coast (20x15cm-8x6in) s.i. panel painted c.1880. 23-May-4 Treadway Gallery, Cincinnati #507/R
£376 $700 €549 Alpine landscape (56x81cm-22x32in) s. painted c.1880. 7-Mar-4 Treadway Gallery, Cincinnati #520/R
£493 $818 €700 Riviere vers la ville (31x23cm-12x9in) mono. panel. 15-Jun-3 Peron, Melun #244

£667	$1207	€1000	Summer idyll (32x46cm-13x18in) s. 1-Apr-4 Van Ham, Cologne #1277/R
£800	$1280	€1168	Cockerel and chickens (16x22cm-6x9in) s.i.verso board. 17-Sep-3 Bonhams, Brooks & Langlois, Jersey #54/R
£1000	$1800	€1460	Sheep grazing in a field (33x46cm-13x18in) s. 21-Jan-4 Sotheby's, Olympia #351/R est:1000-1500
£1035	$1852	€1511	Landscape with cattle (32x45cm-13x18in) s. 26-May-4 AB Stockholms Auktionsverk #2381/R (S.KR 14000)
£1127	$1870	€1600	Troupeau (33x46cm-13x18in) s. 15-Jun-3 Peron, Melun #213
£1308	$2249	€1910	Landscape with cattle (32x45cm-13x18in) s. 3-Dec-3 AB Stockholms Auktionsverk #2546/R est:15000-20000 (S.KR 17000)
£2095	$3750	€3143	Pastoral landscape (33x46cm-13x18in) s.d.1881 panel. 16-May-4 Abell, Los Angeles #129
£3000	$4890	€4380	Cockerel, hen and chicks in a yard (15x23cm-6x9in) s. panel. 23-Sep-3 John Nicholson, Haslemere #296/R est:1500-3000

BAIRNSFATHER, Bruce (1888-1959) British

£380	$680	€555	Swigging the last drop (51x51cm-20x20in) 7-May-4 Mallams, Oxford #400/R
£480	$859	€701	Wistanstoe Salop (58x48cm-23x19in) s. 7-May-4 Mallams, Oxford #398/R

Works on paper

£400	$736	€584	Telephone trials no 1 (26x17cm-10x7in) s.i. pencil. 22-Jun-4 Bonhams, Knightsbridge #63/R

BAISCH, Hermann (1846-1894) German

£634	$1096	€900	Young bull (25x33cm-10x13in) canvas on board. 11-Dec-3 Dr Fritz Nagel, Stuttgart #508/R
£1690	$2924	€2400	Shepherd in the evening (54x39cm-21x15in) s. canvas on panel. 13-Dec-3 Lempertz, Koln #3/R est:2500
£2113	$3655	€3000	Grassy garden (30x37cm-12x15in) panel. 13-Dec-3 Lempertz, Koln #4/R est:3000
£6000	$10860	€9000	By the water (54x95cm-21x37in) s. 1-Apr-4 Van Ham, Cologne #1277a/R est:10000

BAITLER, Zoma (1908-1994) Uruguayan

£247	$400	€358	Flowers (28x36cm-11x14in) s. 29-Jul-3 Galeria y Remates, Montevideo #137
£259	$420	€376	Cypress trees and the beach (25x26cm-10x10in) s.i.d.1941 panel. 29-Jul-3 Galeria y Remates, Montevideo #39
£397	$750	€580	Pine trees and dunes (80x60cm-31x24in) 22-Feb-4 Galeria y Remates, Montevideo #91/R
£462	$850	€675	Landscape in Aguada (30x40cm-12x16in) s. 22-Jun-4 Galeria y Remates, Montevideo #75/R
£489	$900	€714	Rio Negro Street (39x51cm-15x20in) s. 22-Jun-4 Galeria y Remates, Montevideo #76/R
£588	$1000	€858	Street (45x56cm-18x22in) s. 25-Nov-3 Galeria y Remates, Montevideo #20/R
£588	$1000	€858	Street in Paris (25x30cm-10x12in) s. 25-Nov-3 Galeria y Remates, Montevideo #116/R
£647	$1100	€945	Industrial town (60x80cm-24x31in) s. 25-Nov-3 Galeria y Remates, Montevideo #21/R
£676	$1150	€987	Cabildo, Buenos Aires (26x30cm-10x12in) s. 25-Nov-3 Galeria y Remates, Montevideo #117
£688	$1300	€1004	Punta Ballena (50x60cm-20x24in) s. s.i.d.66 verso. 22-Feb-4 Galeria y Remates, Montevideo #88/R
£756	$1300	€1104	Window on the Seine (79x99cm-31x39in) s.i. painted c.1960. 7-Dec-3 Treadway Gallery, Cincinnati #640/R
£794	$1500	€1159	Peniche (40x50cm-16x20in) s. 22-Feb-4 Galeria y Remates, Montevideo #92/R est:1500
£802	$1300	€1163	Cerrito street (51x61cm-20x24in) s. 29-Jul-3 Galeria y Remates, Montevideo #93/R
£824	$1450	€1203	Factory in Capurro (50x60cm-20x24in) s. 5-Jan-4 Galeria y Remates, Montevideo #90/R
£824	$1450	€1203	Dog and factory (41x50cm-16x20in) s. 5-Jan-4 Galeria y Remates, Montevideo #96/R
£847	$1600	€1237	Punta del Este (50x60cm-20x24in) s. 22-Feb-4 Galeria y Remates, Montevideo #90/R est:3000
£882	$1500	€1288	Summer morning (48x67cm-19x26in) s. 25-Nov-3 Galeria y Remates, Montevideo #19/R
£898	$1500	€1311	Countryside (60x80cm-24x31in) s. s.i.d.1960 verso. 7-Oct-3 Galeria y Remates, Montevideo #103/R
£966	$1700	€1410	River (61x80cm-24x31in) s. s.i.d.1950 verso. 5-Jan-4 Galeria y Remates, Montevideo #89/R est:2500-3200
£1294	$2200	€1889	Medanos street (51x57cm-20x22in) s. 25-Nov-3 Galeria y Remates, Montevideo #160/R
£1358	$2200	€1969	A rugged spot (59x68cm-23x27in) s. s.i.verso. 29-Jul-3 Galeria y Remates, Montevideo #92/R est:2800-3300
£1467	$2700	€2142	Roosevelt Park (70x98cm-28x39in) s. 22-Jun-4 Galeria y Remates, Montevideo #71/R est:4000
£1471	$2500	€2148	Morning fog (50x70cm-20x28in) s. 25-Nov-3 Galeria y Remates, Montevideo #35/R
£1529	$2600	€2232	Avenida de Mayo (75x103cm-30x41in) s.d. 25-Nov-3 Galeria y Remates, Montevideo #130/R
£1588	$2700	€2318	Town street (70x60cm-28x24in) s. 25-Nov-3 Galeria y Remates, Montevideo #132/R
£1647	$2800	€2405	Seascape (50x60cm-20x24in) s. 25-Nov-3 Galeria y Remates, Montevideo #162/R
£1768	$2900	€2581	Saint-Denis (83x57cm-33x22in) s. s.verso. 3-Jun-3 Galeria y Remates, Montevideo #102
£1882	$3200	€2748	Suburbs (64x94cm-25x37in) s. 25-Nov-3 Galeria y Remates, Montevideo #49/R
£1882	$3200	€2748	Mountain village (75x100cm-30x39in) s. 25-Nov-3 Galeria y Remates, Montevideo #48/R
£2096	$3500	€3060	Countryside (80x100cm-31x39in) s. exhib. 7-Oct-3 Galeria y Remates, Montevideo #27/R
£2386	$4200	€3484	Bridge in Paris (60x70cm-24x28in) s. i.d.71 verso. 5-Jan-4 Galeria y Remates, Montevideo #80/R est:4000-5000
£2941	$5000	€4294	The Seine (65x73cm-26x29in) s. 25-Nov-3 Galeria y Remates, Montevideo #161/R
£3059	$5200	€4466	Paris (76x100cm-30x39in) s. 25-Nov-3 Galeria y Remates, Montevideo #47
£4000	$6800	€5840	Autumn sun (77x106cm-30x42in) s.d.1947. 25-Nov-3 Galeria y Remates, Montevideo #131/R
£5059	$8600	€7386	Pont des Invalides (57x74cm-22x29in) s.d.1949. 25-Nov-3 Galeria y Remates, Montevideo #34/R

BAIXERAS Y VERDAGUER, Dionisio (1862-1943) Spanish

Works on paper

£403	$753	€600	Girl with bottles (23x16cm-9x6in) s.d.1905 dr. 24-Feb-4 Durán, Madrid #109/R
£476	$790	€690	Figures on the beach (15x23cm-6x9in) s. pencil dr. 1-Oct-3 Ansorena, Madrid #485/R

BAIXERAS Y VERDAGUER, Dionisio (attrib) (1862-1943) Spanish

£818	$1300	€1194	Fortune teller (63x76cm-25x30in) indis.sig. 12-Sep-3 Skinner, Boston #219/R

BAIZE, Wayne (1943-) American

£1242	$2000	€1801	After the cut, study (23x30cm-9x12in) 22-Aug-3 Altermann Galleries, Santa Fe #94

Works on paper

£373	$600	€541	Tying the knot (38x43cm-15x17in) pencil. 22-Aug-3 Altermann Galleries, Santa Fe #96
£435	$700	€631	Little Indians (33x36cm-13x14in) col pencil. 22-Aug-3 Altermann Galleries, Santa Fe #45
£621	$1000	€900	Longhorn (36x51cm-14x20in) mixed media. 22-Aug-3 Altermann Galleries, Santa Fe #93
£870	$1400	€1262	Patience (28x33cm-11x13in) mixed media. 22-Aug-3 Altermann Galleries, Santa Fe #13
£994	$1600	€1441	Beginning to thaw (25x38cm-10x15in) col pencil. 22-Aug-3 Altermann Galleries, Santa Fe #97

BAJ, Enrico (1924-2003) Italian

£1020	$1827	€1500	Horses (19x64cm-7x25in) board painted 1948. 16-Mar-4 Finarte Semenzato, Milan #54/R est:1000
£1342	$2403	€2000	Study fore canvas (75x47cm-30x19in) s.i.d.1980. 25-May-4 Sotheby's, Milan #183/R est:2000-3000
£1761	$2923	€2500	Vescovo Dupanloux Accademia di Francia (15x14cm-6x6in) s.i.verso oil braiding. 14-Jun-3 Meeting Art, Vercelli #48/R est:2500
£2029	$3328	€2800	Untitled (38x29cm-15x11in) s. cardboard painted 1966 prov. 27-May-3 Sotheby's, Milan #12 est:3000
£3380	$5848	€4800	Zut-Zut (33x40cm-13x16in) s. i.verso oil collage. 13-Dec-3 De Vuyst, Lokeren #494/R est:4000-5000
£3472	$5486	€5000	Pasture (40x31cm-16x12in) acrylic collage panel. 6-Sep-3 Meeting Art, Vercelli #346 est:5000
£3521	$6092	€5000	Personaggio (30x24cm-12x9in) s.d.55 oil collage. 13-Dec-3 De Vuyst, Lokeren #499/R est:3000-4000
£4225	$7394	€6000	Pandione and Zendippe at moonlight (81x91cm-32x36in) s. s.i.verso. 16-Dec-3 Finarte Semenzato, Milan #351/R est:4800-5200
£5072	$8319	€7000	Mountain (50x59cm-20x23in) s. oil fabric collage painted 1958 prov.lit. 27-May-3 Sotheby's, Milan #13/R est:7000
£5556	$8778	€8000	Little totem (61x36cm-24x14in) acrylic on felt painted 1996. 6-Sep-3 Meeting Art, Vercelli #584 est:7000
£5797	$9507	€8000	There rocks were mingling (80x90cm-31x35in) s. s.i.d.57 verso oil tar. 27-May-3 Sotheby's, Milan #14/R est:8000
£7394	$12940	€10500	Head of woman (60x50cm-24x20in) s.d.1957 verso prov. 17-Dec-3 Il Ponte, Milan #1115/R est:9000-10000
£9060	$16218	€13500	Profile (55x46cm-22x18in) s. acrylic collage cottonwool painted 1966 prov.lit. 30-May-4 Meeting Art, Vercelli #44 est:5000
£9396	$16819	€14000	Woman screaming and boar (100x150cm-39x59in) s.d.54 s.i.d.verso prov.lit. 25-May-4 Sotheby's, Milan #41/R est:10000
£10564	$18275	€15000	Portrait (88x68cm-35x27in) painted 1957 prov. 9-Dec-3 Artcurial Briest, Paris #404/R est:8000-12000

Sculpture

£1156	$2070	€1700	Rolling general (62x66cm-24x26in) s.i. doll wood lit. 16-Mar-4 Finarte Semenzato, Milan #57/R est:450
£1538	$2615	€2200	Archeologist (82cm-32in) s.d.1994 num.20/40 bronze marble base. 26-Nov-3 Pandolfini, Florence #171/R
£1565	$2801	€2300	Figure (47cm-19in) metal. 16-Mar-4 Finarte Semenzato, Milan #56/R est:2000
£1972	$3411	€2800	Gourounski mask (52x21x15cm-20x8x6in) s.verso collage wood lit. 14-Dec-3 Versailles Encheres #172/R est:2500-3000
£2254	$3899	€3200	Huwawahumbra (86x40cm-34x16in) s.verso collage wood lit. 14-Dec-3 Versailles Encheres #173/R est:3000-3500
£2817	$4676	€4000	Maschera con doppio fiocco (70x40cm-28x16in) s.verso wood acrylic collage. 14-Jun-3 Meeting Art, Vercelli #297/R est:4000
£3034	$5068	€4400	Hahaubutu (55x33x9cm-22x13x4in) mask exec.1994 exhib. 17-Nov-3 Sant Agostino, Torino #307/R est:2500-3500

Works on paper

£276	$441	€400	Studio per la caccia allo Snark (27x22cm-11x9in) s.d.1986 pencil. 13-Mar-3 Galleria Pace, Milan #21/R
£362	$594	€500	Odradek (25x18cm-10x7in) s. wax crayon. 29-May-3 Galleria Pace, Milan #74/R
£638	$1180	€950	Legnano battle (24x36cm-9x14in) s. Chinese ink. 11-Mar-4 Galleria Pace, Milan #5/R
£664	$1129	€950	Study for fabric (47x33cm-19x13in) s.d.55 mixed media. 26-Nov-3 Pandolfini, Florence #69/R
£962	$1510	€1500	Horatius Nelson Duke of Bronte (80x70cm-31x28in) shell metal assemblage on silk. 22-Nov-2 Galleria Pananti, Florence #15 est:1300-1500
£1000	$1590	€1450	Caesar (34x25cm-13x10in) s. pencil pen ink acrylic double-sided. 11-Sep-3 Christie's, Kensington #220/R est:1200-1800
£1103	$1843	€1600	Decorated (38x30cm-15x12in) s.d.1979 pencil. 13-Nov-3 Galleria Pace, Milan #112/R
£1342	$2483	€2000	Composition (70x70cm-28x28in) mixed media collage. 11-Mar-4 Galleria Pace, Milan #17/R est:2200-3000
£1467	$2669	€2200	Personnage (50x61cm-20x24in) collage pieces of mirror prov. 30-Jun-4 Calmels Cohen, Paris #81/R est:1500-2000
£1993	$3388	€2850	Monument (40x29cm-16x11in) s. collage cardboard prov.lit. 18-Nov-3 Babuino, Rome #407/R est:1000-1500
£3846	$7000	€5615	Head (40x40cm-16x16in) s. mixed media collage prov. 29-Jun-4 Sotheby's, New York #479/R est:3000-5000
£5366	$9659	€7834	Head (42x52cm-17x20in) s. mixed media collage. 26-Apr-4 Bukowskis, Stockholm #252/R est:30000-40000 (S.KR 74000)
£6376	$11413	€9500	Professor Bakey (103x73cm-41x29in) s. s.i.d.68 verso plastic collage on board prov.lit. 25-May-4 Sotheby's, Milan #46/R est:4000

£6667 $12267 €10000 Hug me, I need you (35x45cm-14x18in) s. mixed media on fabric prov. 14-Jun-4 Porro, Milan #43/R est:5400-6400
£6711 $12013 €10000 Two figures (29x34cm-11x13in) s. haberdashery cottonwool exec.1974. 28-May-4 Farsetti, Prato #363/R est:10000-11000
£6803 $12177 €10000 Head (45x53cm-18x21in) s. mixed media on brocade. 16-Mar-4 Finarte Semenzato, Milan #439/R est:11000
£6936 $12000 €10127 She like very much her silk dress (74x91cm-29x36in) s. collage fabric prov. 15-Dec-3 Hindman, Chicago #35/R est:10000-12000
£7000 $12880 €10220 Animal in darkness (49x70cm-19x28in) s. mixed media paper collage exec 1961 prov.exhib.lit. 24-Jun-4 Sotheby's, London #207/R est:6000-8000
£7747 $13402 €11000 Pollock's tie (160x230cm-63x91in) collage vinyl on canvas prov.lit. 9-Dec-3 Artcurial Briest, Paris #512/R est:15000-20000
£8054 $14416 €12000 Attese (40x60cm-16x24in) s. i. stretcher collage metal screws material felt oil prov. 25-May-4 Dorotheum, Vienna #69/R est:12000-14000
£8392 $14266 €12000 Figure (81x61cm-32x24in) s. s.d.1968 verso plastic fabric medal on board prov.exhib.lit. 24-Nov-3 Christie's, Milan #183/R est:12000-16000
£11888 $20210 €17000 Tete de femme (54x65cm-21x26in) s. mixed media fabric exhib.lit. 20-Nov-3 Finarte Semenzato, Milan #229/R est:12000-14000
£12667 $23433 €19000 General (200x150cm-79x59in) i. mosaic exec.1988 prov.exhib. 18-Jul-4 Sotheby's, Paris #236/R est:20000-30000
£15000 $25050 €21900 Generale in pensione con la barba (99x49cm-39x19in) s.d.56 s.i.verso mixed media collage canvas prov.lit. 21-Oct-3 Sotheby's, London #380/R est:15000-20000
£16484 $29176 €24067 Dick de Loney (92x73cm-36x29in) s. mixed media collage painted 1966 prov.lit. 27-Apr-4 AB Stockholms Auktionsverk #1186/R est:225000-250000 (S.KR 225000)

BAJ, Enrico and Andrea (20th C) Italian
Sculpture
£922 $1494 €1300 Ecuba (70cm-28in) s. verso wood. 22-May-3 Stadion, Trieste #223/R est:1200-1600

BAJ, Enrico and KOSTABI, Mark (20th C) Italian/American
Works on paper
£828 $1382 €1200 Ketty (27x24cm-11x9in) s.d.1992 mixed media collage. 13-Nov-3 Galleria Pace, Milan #42/R

BAK, Samuel (1933-) Israeli
£7955 $14000 €11614 Still life with pears (100x81cm-39x32in) s.d.1988. 1-Jan-4 Ben-Ami, Tel Aviv #4398/R est:18000-24000
£18156 $32500 €26508 Surreal landscape (97x146cm-38x57in) s. 18-Mar-4 Sotheby's, New York #21/R est:25000-30000
Sculpture
£1712 $2911 €2500 Oiseau (50x50cm-20x20in) brown pat bronze. 9-Nov-3 Eric Pillon, Calais #276/R
Works on paper
£837 $1423 €1222 Transatlantic in blue (15x24cm-6x9in) s. i. verso gouache. 5-Nov-3 Dobiaschofsky, Bern #320/R (S.FR 1900)

BAKALOWICZ, Ladislaus (1833-1904) Polish
£4200 $7224 €6132 Dinner party (38x61cm-15x24in) s.i. panel. 4-Dec-3 Christie's, Kensington #140/R est:3000-5000
£7801 $13028 €11000 Young girl near a rosebush. s. panel. 20-Oct-3 Bernaerts, Antwerp #20 est:10000-15000
£12222 $22000 €17844 Recital (65x91cm-26x36in) s.i. 22-Apr-4 Christie's, Rockefeller NY #31/R est:30000-40000

BAKALOWICZ, Stephan Wladislawowitsch (1857-1947) Russian
£824 $1500 €1203 Two ladies at the theatre (24x19cm-9x7in) panel. 29-Jun-4 Sotheby's, New York #123/R est:2000-3000
£1989 $3500 €2904 North African coastal landscape with Arabs at a mosque. s.d.1920. 1-Jan-4 Nadeau, Windsor #194/R est:4000-7000
£12667 $23053 €19000 Deux femmes en drapee dans un decor a l'antique (65x47cm-26x19in) s.i.d.1879. 5-Jul-4 Le Mouel, Paris #8/R est:2000-25000
£28000 $50120 €40880 Arabs by the mosque (34x52cm-13x20in) s.d.1920. 26-May-4 Sotheby's, London #88/R est:6000-8000
£40000 $72800 €58400 The letter (45x37cm-18x15in) s.d.MCMXIV panel prov. 15-Jun-4 Sotheby's, London #49/R est:8000-12000

BAKELS, Reinier Sybrand (1873-1956) Dutch
£308 $524 €450 Town view with haulage cart (41x79cm-16x31in) studio st. verso. 5-Nov-3 Vendue Huis, Gravenhage #259
£445 $757 €650 Schevening 11 at the yard (30x42cm-12x17in) s.d.11. 5-Nov-3 Vendue Huis, Gravenhage #263
£514 $873 €750 Brittany landscape with mills (65x100cm-26x39in) 5-Nov-3 Vendue Huis, Gravenhage #262
£559 $934 €800 Sheep in an extensive landscape (65x110cm-26x43in) s. 30-Jun-3 Sotheby's, Amsterdam #268/R
£616 $1048 €900 Village street with haystack and pigeon-house (38x58cm-15x23in) s. 5-Nov-3 Vendue Huis, Gravenhage #260
£753 $1281 €1100 Elburg harbour (41x61cm-16x24in) s.indis.d. studio st. verso. 5-Nov-3 Vendue Huis, Gravenhage #264
£822 $1397 €1200 View of Enkhuizen with camels by night (40x62cm-16x24in) s. studio st. verso. 5-Nov-3 Vendue Huis, Gravenhage #261
£3082 $5240 €4500 Dordrecht in winter (190x131cm-75x52in) s.d.19. 5-Nov-3 Vendue Huis, Gravenhage #129/R est:5000-6000

BAKER (?) ?
£1489 $2487 €2100 Bord de mer anime (56x90cm-22x35in) s.d.72. 17-Jun-3 Vanderkindere, Brussels #199 est:1750-2500

BAKER OF LEAMINGTON, Thomas (1809-1869) British
£2300 $4301 €3358 Cattle resting on a sunlit hillside (20x28cm-8x11in) s.d.1861 panel. 24-Feb-4 Bonhams, Knowle #83/R est:2000-3000
£2661 $4763 €3885 Conway mill (61x48cm-24x19in) s.d.1850. 28-May-4 Uppsala Auktionskammare, Uppsala #139/R est:20000-25000 (S.KR 36000)
£5500 $8690 €7975 Figures by a river with cottages beyond (51x76cm-20x30in) s.d.1846. 4-Sep-3 Christie's, Kensington #134/R est:2000-3000
£6500 $11050 €9490 Stoneleigh Park (51x77cm-20x30in) s.d.1854 i.verso. 27-Nov-3 Sotheby's, London #359/R est:5000-7000
Works on paper
£520 $957 €759 Riverside scene with fishermen and sheep (20x37cm-8x15in) s.d.August 13.1882 W/C. 24-Jun-4 Locke & England, Leamington Spa #173/R
£791 $1250 €1147 Cottages at Thachbrook (18x25cm-7x10in) s. graphite dr. 27-Jul-3 Simpson's, Houston #222
£900 $1422 €1305 Cattle watering near the church, Milverton, Leamington Spa (12x17cm-5x7in) s.d.1859 i.verso W/C pencil. 24-Jul-3 Lawrence, Crewkerne #837
£940 $1758 €1372 Kenilworth Castle. Kenilworth Castle interior (13x17cm-5x7in) one s.d.1837 W/C over pencil pair. 24-Feb-4 Bonhams, Knowle #20
£950 $1739 €1387 Eathorp (24x35cm-9x14in) s.d.June 5th 1856 W/C. 29-Jan-4 Locke & England, Leamington Spa #200/R
£1150 $2116 €1679 Near Offchurch (27x35cm-11x14in) s.d.1862 W/C. 25-Mar-4 Locke & England, Leamington Spa #84/R est:1000-1500

BAKER, Alan Douglas (1914-1987) Australian
£289 $492 €434 Floral still life (38x33cm-15x13in) s. board. 28-Oct-3 Goodman, Sydney #331 (A.D 700)
£529 $830 €767 Untitled - apple blossoms (14x20cm-6x8in) s. board. 26-Aug-3 Lawson Menzies, Sydney #123 est:1500-2000 (A.D 1300)
£621 $968 €900 Helianthus (39x49cm-15x19in) s. board. 1-Aug-2 Joel, Victoria #273 est:1500-2000 (A.D 1800)
£830 $1386 €1245 Camellias (19x24cm-7x9in) s. board. 27-Oct-3 Goodman, Sydney #212/R (A.D 2000)
£870 $1600 €1270 Fallen rose (29x25cm-11x10in) s. i.verso canvasboard. 29-Mar-4 Goodman, Sydney #226/R (A.D 2130)
£894 $1601 €1305 Vase of white flowers (37x48cm-15x19in) s. composition board exhib. 4-May-4 Sotheby's, Melbourne #269 (A.D 2200)
£1245 $2079 €1868 Roses (29x36cm-11x14in) s. board. 27-Oct-3 Goodman, Sydney #215/R est:1800-2500 (A.D 3000)
£1393 $2257 €2034 Still life daisies (39x49cm-15x19in) s. board prov. 30-Jul-3 Goodman, Sydney #102/R est:2000-3000 (A.D 3400)
£1570 $2905 €2292 Camellias in a ginger jar (30x38cm-12x15in) s. board. 10-Mar-4 Deutscher-Menzies, Melbourne #341/R est:4000-6000 (A.D 3800)
£1639 $2656 €2393 Summer flowers (41x51cm-16x20in) s. board. 30-Jul-3 Goodman, Sydney #100/R est:4000-5000 (A.D 4000)
£3719 $6322 €5430 Almond blossom (43x76cm-17x30in) s. board. 29-Oct-3 Lawson Menzies, Sydney #94/R est:3000-5000 (A.D 9000)

BAKER, Christina Asquith (1868-1960) Australian
£1393 $2201 €2034 Sandbank in the Goulburn (92x71cm-36x28in) s. prov.exhib. 2-Sep-3 Deutscher-Menzies, Melbourne #292/R est:4000-6000 (A.D 3400)

BAKER, David C (20th C) American
£223 $400 €326 Fishing (46x61cm-18x24in) s. canvasboard. 14-May-4 Skinner, Boston #193/R

BAKER, Dennis (1951-) Australian
£569 $893 €825 Sirius Cove twilight, Sydney harbour (90x90cm-35x35in) s.i. 27-Aug-3 Christie's, Sydney #796 est:200-400 (A.D 1400)

BAKER, Elisha Taylor (1827-1890) American
£2429 $4250 €3546 Ships in moonlight (46x61cm-18x24in) mono. 19-Dec-3 Sotheby's, New York #1079/R est:4000-6000
£3804 $7000 €5554 Sailing boats at the entrance to a harbour (35x61cm-14x24in) s.indis.d. prov. 8-Jun-4 Bonhams & Butterfields, San Francisco #4015/R est:7000-10000

BAKER, Elisha Taylor (attrib) (1827-1890) American
£4888 $8750 €7136 America's cup trials (66x91cm-26x36in) prov. 11-Jan-4 William Jenack, New York #77 est:8000-12000

BAKER, George Herbert (1878-1943) American
£320 $550 €467 Road along the woods. s. 6-Dec-3 Harvey Clar, Oakland #1363
£645 $1200 €942 Indiana landscape (46x61cm-18x24in) s. painted c.1915. 7-Mar-4 Treadway Gallery, Cincinnati #620/R est:1000-2000
£1453 $2500 €2121 Autumn day (46x51cm-18x20in) s. board painted c.1925. 7-Dec-3 Treadway Gallery, Cincinnati #543/R est:2000-3000

BAKER, Harry (1849-1875) British
Works on paper
£520 $868 €759 Green light that lingers in the West (59x98cm-23x39in) s. W/C exhib. 16-Oct-3 Lyon & Turnbull, Edinburgh #87

BAKER, Kenneth (20th C) South African
£252 $456 €368 Going home (33x45cm-13x18in) s.d.77 board. 30-Mar-4 Stephan Welz, Johannesburg #216 est:900-1200 (SA.R 3000)
£269 $487 €393 Quiet farm road (35x95cm-14x37in) s. board. 30-Mar-4 Stephan Welz, Johannesburg #215 est:1600-2000 (SA.R 3200)
£274 $465 €400 Figures and houses, Bo-kaap (19x41cm-7x16in) s. board. 4-Nov-3 Stephan Welz, Johannesburg #363 est:700-1000 (SA.R 3200)
£319 $578 €466 Malay quarter (60x45cm-24x18in) s. canvas on board. 30-Mar-4 Stephan Welz, Johannesburg #205 est:2500-4000 (SA.R 3800)
£325 $552 €475 Figures in a street, Bo-Kaap (39x56cm-15x22in) s. board. 4-Nov-3 Stephan Welz, Johannesburg #367 est:1600-2000 (SA.R 3800)
£336 $608 €491 Mothers and their children (64x55cm-25x22in) s.d.67. 30-Mar-4 Stephan Welz, Johannesburg #229 est:2500-4000 (SA.R 4000)

BAKER, Oliver (1856-1939) British
£1321 $2365 €1929 Yarn spinning, North Wales (60x100cm-24x39in) s. i. verso. 10-May-4 Joel, Victoria #384 est:1200-1600 (A.D 3250)

BAKER, Ruth Brink (20th C) American
£570 $900 €832 County fair (61x46cm-24x18in) s. board. 7-Sep-3 Treadway Gallery, Cincinnati #749/R

BAKER, Samuel Henry (1824-1909) British
£290 $522 €435 Laren woods in Barroudale (60x100cm-24x39in) s. 25-Apr-4 Goteborg Auktionsverk, Sweden #169/R (S.KR 4000)
£544 $979 €816 The pond at Hampstead (46x78cm-18x31in) s. 25-Apr-4 Goteborg Auktionsverk, Sweden #168/R (S.KR 7500)
£880 $1496 €1285 View near Dolgelly, north Wales (50x75cm-20x30in) s. 1-Dec-3 Bonhams, Bath #104/R
£960 $1786 €1402 Avon near Nafford Mill, a study from nature (19x29cm-7x11in) mono. board pair. 2-Mar-4 Bearnes, Exeter #444/R

BAKER, W G (19th C) Australian
£1021 $1827 €1491 Pelorus River (39x49cm-15x19in) s.i. 11-May-4 Watson's, Christchurch #72/R est:4000-5000 (NZ.D 2950)
Works on paper
£1282 $2372 €1872 Pastoral scene, Wairarapa (36x54cm-14x21in) s.i. W/C. 9-Mar-4 Watson's, Christchurch #45 est:2850-3500 (NZ.D 3500)

BAKER, William (19th C) British
£850 $1471 €1241 Country road on a winter's evening (64x49cm-25x19in) s.d.1908. 9-Dec-3 Anderson & Garland, Newcastle #406/R
Works on paper
£330 $601 €482 Cottages in the snow (40x59cm-16x23in) W/C. 29-Jun-4 Anderson & Garland, Newcastle #201
£520 $848 €759 Caravan in the snow (54x42cm-21x17in) W/C. 23-Sep-3 Anderson & Garland, Newcastle #257/R
£560 $1030 €818 Elderly stick gatherer on a winter path (39x54cm-15x21in) s.d.1910 W/C. 23-Mar-4 Anderson & Garland, Newcastle #151/R
£960 $1565 €1402 Village churchyard on a winter's day (45x70cm-18x28in) s.indis.d. below mount W/C. 23-Sep-3 Anderson & Garland, Newcastle #256/R

BAKER, William Bliss (1859-1886) American
£8602 $16000 €12559 Quiet Pond (51x31cm-20x12in) s. 3-Mar-4 Christie's, Rockefeller NY #5/R est:2000-3000

BAKER, William George (1864-1929) New Zealander
£362 $616 €529 Mt. Ruapehu (75x111cm-30x44in) s.i. 4-Nov-3 Peter Webb, Auckland #6/R est:3000-5000 (NZ.D 1000)
£509 $799 €738 Makara Rock to Mana Island, Cook Strait (44x66cm-17x26in) s.i. 27-Aug-3 Dunbar Sloane, Wellington #122 (NZ.D 1400)
£532 $941 €777 Sailing boat in a landscape (54x80cm-21x31in) s. 28-Apr-4 Dunbar Sloane, Auckland #104/R (NZ.D 1500)
£623 $1115 €910 Near Island bay (60x90cm-24x35in) s.i. 11-May-4 Peter Webb, Auckland #60/R est:2000-3000 (NZ.D 1800)
£725 $1232 €1059 Near Feilding (60x90cm-24x35in) s.i. 4-Nov-3 Peter Webb, Auckland #221 est:3000-4000 (NZ.D 2000)
£946 $1741 €1381 Cargills Cliff, Dunedin (45x70cm-18x28in) s.i. 25-Mar-4 International Art Centre, Auckland #154/R (NZ.D 2650)
£1090 $1853 €1591 Pelorus river (46x68cm-18x27in) s.i. 27-Nov-3 International Art Centre, Auckland #129/R (NZ.D 2900)
£1211 $2168 €1768 Milford Sound (74x109cm-29x43in) s.i. 11-May-4 Peter Webb, Auckland #164/R est:4000-6000 (NZ.D 3500)
£1250 $2025 €1813 Near Wellington (60x90cm-24x35in) s.i. 31-Jul-3 International Art Centre, Auckland #60/R est:4000-6000 (NZ.D 3450)

BAKER, Wright (19th C) British
£19000 $32300 €27740 Anxious moment (91x122cm-36x48in) s.d.94 exhib. 25-Nov-3 Christie's, London #136/R est:6000-10000

BAKER-CLACK, Arthur (1877-1955) Australian
£1581 $2830 €2372 Still life of spring flowers (57x49cm-22x19in) s. board prov. 17-May-4 Sotheby's, Melbourne #583/R est:4000-6000 (A.D 4000)
£2893 $5120 €4224 French house (49x60cm-19x24in) s. board. 3-May-4 Christie's, Melbourne #208/R est:7000-9000 (A.D 7000)
£3099 $5485 €4525 Vase of peonies (45x37cm-18x15in) s. 3-May-4 Christie's, Melbourne #232/R est:5500-7500 (A.D 7500)

BAKERZAH, Wilhelm (20th C) ?
£331 $603 €500 Early morning, O'Connell Bridge (39x50cm-15x20in) s. 15-Jun-4 James Adam, Dublin #163/R
£411 $747 €620 Figure with wolfhounds and terriers (28x39cm-11x15in) s. 15-Jun-4 James Adam, Dublin #154/R

BAKHUYZEN, Alexandre H (1826-1878) Dutch
£567 $948 €800 Forest fen in the evening (21x30cm-8x12in) s.d.70 panel. 20-Oct-3 Glerum, Amsterdam #63
£695 $1266 €1050 Paysage anime a l'etang (25x33cm-10x13in) s. 15-Jun-4 Vanderkindere, Brussels #92
£699 $1203 €1000 Vaches dans un paysage (67x90cm-26x35in) s.d.1873. 2-Dec-3 Campo & Campo, Antwerp #16/R
£839 $1443 €1200 Ferme dans un paysage (67x90cm-26x35in) s.d.1873. 2-Dec-3 Campo & Campo, Antwerp #15/R
£1507 $2562 €2200 Hilly landscape with figures in the foreground (29x43cm-11x17in) s.d.1889 panel. 5-Nov-3 Vendue Huis, Gravenhage #47/R est:2500-3000

BAKHUYZEN, Gerardina Jacoba van de Sande (1826-1895) Dutch
£2741 $4906 €4002 Landscape with houses, town in background (45x60cm-18x24in) s. 12-Jan-4 Rasmussen, Vejle #428/R est:40000 (D.KR 29000)
£19444 $33056 €28000 Pink and white roses (19x28cm-7x11in) s.d.1868 panel. 28-Oct-3 Christie's, Amsterdam #207/R est:20000-30000
Works on paper
£1711 $3147 €2600 Wild flowers and brambles (32x21cm-13x8in) s. pencil W/C. 22-Jun-4 Christie's, Amsterdam #15/R est:700-900
£1711 $3147 €2600 White azalea on a stone (20x31cm-8x12in) s.d.1863 pencil W/C. 22-Jun-4 Christie's, Amsterdam #17/R est:800-1200

BAKHUYZEN, Hendrick van de Sande (1795-1860) Dutch
£3691 $6829 €5500 Cows in a landscape (35x40cm-14x16in) s. panel. 15-Mar-4 Sotheby's, Amsterdam #92/R est:3000-5000
Works on paper
£1944 $3247 €2800 Sorting the catch on Scheveningen Beach (34x31cm-13x12in) s. pen ink wash. 21-Oct-3 Sotheby's, Amsterdam #41/R est:3000-5000

BAKHUYZEN, Julius Jacobus van de Sande (1835-1925) Dutch
£592 $1072 €900 Shepherd and flock near a pen in the evening sun (36x32cm-14x13in) s. canvas on panel. 19-Apr-4 Glerum, Amsterdam #112/R
£709 $1184 €1000 Small lane with farm (42x33cm-17x13in) s. canvas on panel. 20-Oct-3 Glerum, Amsterdam #83/R
£3667 $6600 €5500 Rowing down the river (33x22cm-13x9in) s. canvas on panel prov. 21-Apr-4 Christie's, Amsterdam #106/R est:2500-3500
£4861 $8264 €7000 Heading home, a farm amongst fields (37x58cm-15x23in) s. 28-Oct-3 Christie's, Amsterdam #126/R est:3000-5000
£6711 $12349 €10000 Cattle drinking in pond (104x140cm-41x55in) s. 25-Mar-4 Dr Fritz Nagel, Stuttgart #693/R est:7000
£9333 $16800 €14000 Shepherdess and her flock on a country lane (66x104cm-26x41in) s. indis d. 20-Apr-4 Sotheby's, Amsterdam #217/R est:10000-15000
Works on paper
£347 $549 €500 Women conversing in the dunes (27x39cm-11x15in) s. pencil ink W/C htd white. 2-Sep-3 Christie's, Amsterdam #207
£946 $1665 €1400 Shepherdess with sheep and dog in a hilly wooded landscape (39x56cm-15x22in) W/C black chk prov.exhib. 19-May-4 Sotheby's, Amsterdam #344/R
£1486 $2616 €2200 Two girls on a bleaching field (12x19cm-5x7in) W/C black chk prov.exhib. 19-May-4 Sotheby's, Amsterdam #345/R est:700-900

BAKHUYZEN, L (1631-1708) Dutch
£1300 $2067 €1885 Stormy seas (46x61cm-18x24in) s. panel. 9-Sep-3 David Duggleby, Scarborough #382 est:1500-2000

BAKHUYZEN, Ludolf (1631-1708) Dutch
£1722 $3134 €2600 Fishing boats with approaching storm (59x84cm-23x33in) mono. 18-Jun-4 Bolland & Marotz, Bremen #480/R est:2200
£1918 $3260 €2800 Ship in storm (36x56cm-14x22in) 5-Nov-3 Hugo Ruef, Munich #856 est:2500
£22381 $40958 €32676 Figures and cattle by canal near manor farm (95x130cm-37x51in) s.d.1689. 9-Jun-4 Rasmussen, Copenhagen #1548/R est:250000 (D.KR 250000)
£75000 $137250 €109500 Small Dutch vessels in breezy coastal waters, harbour beyond (73x100cm-29x39in) s. prov.exhib.lit. 7-Jul-4 Sotheby's, London #6/R est:40000-60000
£100000 $186000 €146000 Dutch twenty-gun frigate dismasted in a storm off Enkhuizen (100x128cm-39x50in) prov.lit. 4-Mar-4 Christie's, London #338/R est:20000-40000
Works on paper
£608 $1070 €900 Sea battle (8x12cm-3x5in) pen W/C prov. 22-May-4 Lempertz, Koln #1212/R
£4795 $8151 €7000 Man-of-war on a choppy sea, with figures on a jetty (14x22cm-6x9in) bears mono.d.1699 pen brown ink grey wash prov. 4-Nov-3 Sotheby's, Amsterdam #90/R est:1500-2000
£5000 $9150 €7300 Coastal scene with sailing boats and figures on a beach (17x24cm-7x9in) black lead pen ink wash framing lines. 6-Jul-4 Christie's, London #177/R est:1500-2000

BAKHUYZEN, Ludolf (attrib) (1631-1708) Dutch
£927 $1688 €1400 Marine aux vaisseaux hollandais par temps calme (19x25cm-7x10in) panel. 21-Jun-4 Tajan, Paris #61 est:1500-2000
£3636 $6182 €5200 Le naufrage (89x155cm-35x61in) panel. 18-Nov-3 Vanderkindere, Brussels #160 est:2500-4000
Works on paper
£1000 $1840 €1500 Amsterdam (12x19cm-5x7in) pen brush W/C. 11-Jun-4 Hauswedell & Nolte, Hamburg #804/R est:2000

BAKHUYZEN, Ludolf (style) (1631-1708) Dutch
£11258 $20603 €17000 Navires hollandais pres d'un rivage, par gros temps (66x89cm-26x35in) 7-Apr-4 Libert, Castor, Paris #27/R est:8000-12000

BAKHUYZEN, van de Sande (?) Dutch
£4400 $7480 €6424 Morning environs of the Hague (64x102cm-25x40in) i. 28-Oct-3 Dickinson, Davy & Markham, Brigg #1078 est:2000-3000

BAKKE, Magnus D (20th C) American
£476 $900 €695 Atmospheric river landscape (41x51cm-16x20in) s.d.1922 canvasboard. 17-Feb-4 John Moran, Pasadena #17/R

BAKKER, Antoon (1880-?) Dutch
£329 $595 €500 View of Nicholas Church from the Central Station, Amsterdam (24x30cm-9x12in) s.d.1902 panel. 19-Apr-4 Glerum, Amsterdam #151/R

BAKKER, Frans (1871-1944) Dutch
£290 $484 €420 View of the Tandjong-Priok (26x60cm-10x24in) s. marouflé. 11-Nov-3 Vendu Notarishuis, Rotterdam #31/R

BAKKER, Johannes (1879-1944) Dutch
£400 $728 €600 Fishing port of Ymuiden (40x60cm-16x24in) s. board. 30-Jun-4 Vendue Huis, Gravenhage #625

BAKKER-KORFF, Alexander Hugo (1824-1882) Dutch
£7500 $13800 €10950 Les poissons Chinois (15x12cm-6x5in) s.d.79 panel. 23-Mar-4 Bonhams, New Bond Street #12/R est:8000-12000

Works on paper
£1958 $3368 €2800 Interiors (29x41cm-11x16in) s.d.1873 pen ink three lit. 8-Dec-3 Glerum, Amsterdam #3/R est:3000-5000

BAKOLIN, Nikolai (19th C) Russian
£1600 $2912 €2336 Russian troika (60x78cm-24x31in) s. panel. 16-Jun-4 Christie's, Kensington #206/R est:1000-1500

BAKST, Léon (1866-1924) Russian
£567 $1026 €850 Tete de negre au turban rose (27x22cm-11x9in) cardboard. 5-Apr-4 Marie & Robert, Paris #80/R
Prints
£48000 $81600 €72000 Martyrdom of Saint Sebastian (393x123cm-155x48in) s. lithograph lit. 25-Nov-3 Christie's, London #203/R est:20000-30000
Works on paper
£600 $1092 €876 Nude study (18x11cm-7x4in) init. chl prov. 1-Jul-4 Christie's, Kensington #517/R
£700 $1274 €1022 Nude (22x32cm-9x13in) s. pencil exhib. 21-Jun-4 Bonhams, New Bond Street #47/R
£925 $1600 €1351 Study of a landscape (34x25cm-13x10in) s. pastel. 13-Dec-3 Weschler, Washington #526 est:2000-3000
£993 $1808 €1500 Projet de costume (27x18cm-11x7in) s. gouache. 16-Jun-4 Claude Boisgirard, Paris #21/R est:1500-1800
£1400 $2408 €2044 Costume design, Daphnis et Chloe - Pan (28x23cm-11x9in) s.i.d.1921 pencil W/C. 3-Dec-3 Christie's, Kensington #268/R est:700-900
£2467 $4514 €3700 Costume design for Le martyre de St Sebastien (29x19cm-11x7in) s.i. gouache on pencil htd silver gold prov. 5-Jun-4 Lempertz, Koln #574/R est:4000-5000
£2649 $4821 €4000 Les promeneurs (30x21cm-12x8in) s. graphite W/C. 16-Jun-4 Claude Boisgirard, Paris #22 est:4000-5000
£3000 $5100 €4380 Study of a veiled woman and a dancing boy (27x20cm-11x8in) pencil prov.exhib. 19-Nov-3 Sotheby's, London #180/R est:3000-5000
£3333 $6000 €4866 Sketch for the palace decor (23x21cm-9x8in) s.d.1921 pencil htd white on board prov.exhib. 23-Apr-4 Sotheby's, New York #111/R est:6000-8000
£3600 $6192 €5256 Costume designs (33x23cm-13x9in) one s.i.d.1921 one i. pencil W/C htd silver gold pair prov. 3-Dec-3 Christie's, Kensington #266/R est:3000-5000
£4333 $7843 €6500 Colombine dans la Belle au bois dormant (28x21cm-11x8in) s.d.1921 black crayon W/C gouache prov.exhib. 2-Apr-4 Rossini, Paris #67/R est:3000-4000
£8000 $14320 €11680 Costume design for the shepherdesses in Daphnis and Chloe (26x18cm-10x7in) s.i. gouache over pencil on card. 26-May-4 Sotheby's, London #217/R est:4000-6000
£10795 $19000 €15761 Costume design for femmes du peuple (27x20cm-11x8in) s. gouache pencil gold paint. 18-May-4 Sotheby's, New York #84/R est:12000-18000
£11111 $20000 €16222 Costume design for Helene de sparte (27x15cm-11x6in) st.sig.i. verso mixed media prov. 23-Apr-4 Sotheby's, New York #106/R est:20000-30000
£12162 $21405 €18000 Danseuse au chale (63x42cm-25x17in) s.d.1910 W/C gouache. 19-May-4 Camard, Paris #58 est:15000-18000
£13000 $22100 €18980 Costume design for a page boy for Sleeping Beauty (29x16cm-11x6in) s.d.1916 pencil W/C silver paint prov. 19-Nov-3 Sotheby's, London #173/R est:10000-15000
£13000 $23270 €18980 Costume design for the Fee de Richesse in la Bella au Bois Dormant (27x19cm-11x7in) i. pencil W/C. 26-May-4 Sotheby's, London #216/R est:8000-12000
£19886 $35000 €29034 Costume design for a male Greek dancer in the Bacchanale in Cleopatre (28x22cm-11x9in) s.i.d.1910 gouache pencil silver paint. 18-May-4 Sotheby's, New York #83/R est:15000-20000
£42000 $71400 €61320 Costume design for Ida Rubinstein - Istar (48x31cm-19x12in) s.i. pencil W/C gouache htd gold silver prov.lit. 19-Nov-3 Sotheby's, London #172/R est:20000-30000
£400000 $680000 €584000 Echo Abandonne (66x48cm-26x19in) s.d.1922 W/C over pencil htd gold silver paint prov.exhib. 19-Nov-3 Sotheby's, London #174/R est:60000-80000

BAKST, Léon (attrib) (1866-1924) Russian
Works on paper
£594 $950 €867 Costume design of Nijinsky in Narcisse (25x20cm-10x8in) s.d.1911 W/C. 21-Sep-3 William Jenack, New York #300

BAKSTEEN, Dirk (1886-1971) Dutch
£1215 $2030 €1750 L'orage menacant (30x35cm-12x14in) s.d.1968 verso. 21-Oct-3 Campo, Vlaamse Kaai #356/R est:1250-1500
£3497 $5944 €5000 Fermes sous la neige (60x76cm-24x30in) s.d.1952-1953 verso. 1-Dec-3 Palais de Beaux Arts, Brussels #20/R est:5000-7500

BAL, Gerard (19/20th C) Belgian
£304 $535 €450 Tree landscape at sunset (35x50cm-14x20in) s. 24-May-4 Bernaerts, Antwerp #538/R

BALACA, Jose (1810-1869) Spanish
£1074 $1922 €1600 Still life of flowers (80x64cm-31x25in) s. 25-May-4 Durán, Madrid #684/R est:1200

BALACA, Ricardo (1844-1880) Portuguese
Works on paper
£625 $994 €900 Fifteen portraits of famous people (10x8cm-4x3in) s. chl drawings. 29-Apr-3 Durán, Madrid #26/R

BALAKCHINE, Evgueni (1961-) Russian
£300 $489 €438 Still life with peonies (54x65cm-21x26in) s. 28-Sep-3 John Nicholson, Haslemere #105

BALANDE, Gaston (1880-1971) French
£420 $713 €600 Paysage au pont de chemin de fer. s. 21-Nov-3 Lombrail & Teucquam, Paris #142
£1014 $1814 €1500 Bord de riviere (50x81cm-20x32in) s. paper on canvas. 10-May-4 Giraudeau, Tours #124
£1056 $1827 €1500 Grand arbre au chemin pres d'une riviere (54x65cm-21x26in) s. 10-Dec-3 Rossini, Paris #47/R
£1408 $2437 €2000 Terrace in bloom (60x58cm-24x23in) s. prov.exhib. 10-Dec-3 Finarte Semenzato, Rome #279/R est:2000-2500
£1507 $2562 €2200 Jardin devant la maison (50x65cm-20x26in) s. 9-Nov-3 Eric Pillon, Calais #150/R
£1544 $2763 €2300 Venise (46x55cm-18x22in) s.i.d. 25-May-4 Chambelland & Giafferi, Paris #97/R est:1200-1500
£2185 $3977 €3300 Le port de La Rochelle (46x55cm-18x22in) s. panel. 20-Jun-4 Salle des ventes Pillet, Lyon la Foret #8/R est:1500-1800
£2483 $4146 €3600 Famille de pecheurs (102x131cm-40x52in) s.d.1908. 17-Nov-3 Tajan, Paris #163 est:4000-6000
£2649 $4821 €4000 Marche normand (46x5cm-18x2in) s. cardboard. 16-Jun-4 Renaud, Paris #44/R est:4500-5000
£2657 $4571 €3800 Le port de la Rochelle (50x100cm-20x39in) s. 5-Dec-3 Gros & Delettrez, Paris #83/R est:3000-4000
Works on paper
£280 $476 €400 Paris, la rue Pascal XIII et l'Hopital Broca (22x31cm-9x12in) s. gouache. 28-Nov-3 Blanchet, Paris #113

BALANSINO, Giovanni (1912-1986) Italian
£347 $590 €500 Landscape (50x70cm-20x28in) s. masonite. 1-Nov-3 Meeting Art, Vercelli #5

BALANYA MOIX, Ismael (1921-) Spanish
£355 $574 €500 La Celestina (21x31cm-8x12in) s.d.48 acrylic paper. 20-May-3 Ansorena, Madrid #370/R
£532 $862 €750 Puerto (38x61cm-15x24in) s.d.66. 20-May-3 Ansorena, Madrid #352/R

BALBI, Filippo (1806-1890) Italian
£4930 $8528 €7000 Pilgrim (75x100cm-30x39in) s.i.d.1857. 10-Dec-3 Sotheby's, Milan #25/R est:7000-10000

BALBIANO DI CALCAVAGNO, Eugenio (1816-1872) Italian
Works on paper
£336 $594 €500 View of Siracusa (11x44cm-4x17in) s.i. W/C. 1-May-4 Meeting Art, Vercelli #22

BALCAR, Jiri (1929-1968) Czechoslovakian
£3073 $5224 €4487 Town (75x50cm-30x20in) s.d.57. 29-Nov-3 Dorotheum, Prague #94/R est:80000-120000 (C.KR 140000)
Works on paper
£878 $1493 €1282 Untitled (83x58cm-33x23in) s.d.64 chl pastel cardboard. 29-Nov-3 Dorotheum, Prague #168/R est:40000-60000 (C.KR 40000)

BALCH, Georgia W (1888-?) American
£223 $400 €326 Vermont landscape (56x66cm-22x26in) s. 8-Jan-4 James Julia, Fairfield #1289/R

BALCIAR, Gerald George (1942-) American
Sculpture
£2469 $4000 €3580 Canyon cubs (76cm-30in) bronze. 23-May-3 Altermann Galleries, Santa Fe #215
£3352 $6000 €4894 Above all (91cm-36in) bronze edn of 50. 15-May-4 Altermann Galleries, Santa Fe #159/R

BALDANCOLI, Vittorio (19th C) Italian
£1350 $2200 €1971 Whispered devotion (86x66cm-34x26in) s. 24-Sep-3 Doyle, New York #5/R est:4000-6000

BALDANCOLI, Vittorio (attrib) (19th C) Italian
£4420 $8000 €6453 Flirtation moment (87x67cm-34x26in) s. 30-Mar-4 Christie's, Rockefeller NY #64/R est:8000-12000

BALDASSINI, Guglielmo (1885-1952) Italian
£385 $654 €562 Venice - the Lagoon (16x28cm-6x11in) s. board. 28-Nov-3 Zofingen, Switzerland #2546 (S.FR 850)
£2550 $4565 €3800 Place Ile de Beaute, Nice (44x55cm-17x22in) s. 25-May-4 Finarte Semenzato, Milan #103/R est:4000-5000

BALDASSINI, Guglielmo (attrib) (1885-1952) Italian
£423 $731 €600 Seascape (28x36cm-11x14in) 9-Dec-3 Pandolfini, Florence #248/R

BALDERO, Luigi G (?) ?
£2199 $3672 €3100 Une partie de carte sous la Renaissance (61x73cm-24x29in) s. pair. 20-Jun-3 Drouot Estimations, Paris #77 est:3000-4000

BALDESSARI, John (1931-) American
£20958 $35000 €30599 Blood, for Raymond Carver (127x203cm-50x80in) oil vinyl paint photograph prov. 13-Nov-3 Sotheby's, New York #403/R est:18000-25000
Photographs
£5389 $9000 €7868 Fox, maquette for the elbow series (76x76cm-30x30in) col photo three attached parts prov.exhib. 13-Nov-3 Sotheby's, New York #401/R est:6000-8000
£5389 $9000 €7868 Ass, maquette for the elbow series A2 (76x76cm-30x30in) col photo three attached parts prov.exhib. 13-Nov-3 Sotheby's, New York #402/R est:6000-8000
£19553 $35000 €28547 Oasis (143x361cm-56x142in) hand tinted gelatin silver print board five prov. 12-May-4 Christie's, Rockefeller NY #425/R est:40000-60000
£40223 $72000 €58726 Compositions, dynamic/static, red/green (228x271cm-90x107in) black white photos vinyl paint oil tint two prov. 12-May-4 Christie's, Rockefeller NY #424/R est:50000-70000

Prints

£3073	$5500	€4487	Hog - Maquette for the elbow series A1 (76x76cm-30x30in) folio D process on vinyl inkjet on canvas three parts prov.exhib. 13-May-4 Sotheby's, New York #419/R est:6000-8000
£3464	$6200	€5057	Pig - Maquette for the elbow series A3 (76x76cm-30x30in) folio D process on vinyl inkjet canvas three parts prov.exhib. 13-May-4 Sotheby's, New York #418/R est:6000-8000

Works on paper

£1297	$2400	€1894	Scratch (51x40cm-20x16in) s.d.1996 offset rubber ink over mixed media exhib. 13-Jul-4 Christie's, Rockefeller NY #80/R est:2000-3000

BALDESSARI, Roberto Iras (1894-1965) Italian

£333	$607	€500	Street on the edge of Gardasee (59x49cm-23x19in) s. 1-Jul-4 Weidler, Nurnberg #4504/R
£397	$723	€600	Dutch flower market (40x50cm-16x20in) s. 19-Jun-4 Hans Stahl, Hamburg #15
£397	$723	€600	View of Notre Dame with boats and shoppers in foreground (50x40cm-20x16in) s. 19-Jun-4 Hans Stahl, Hamburg #19
£500	$905	€750	Fishing boats and old houses on the Lagoon near Chioggia (50x70cm-20x28in) s. 3-Apr-4 Hans Stahl, Hamburg #3
£530	$964	€800	Extensive view towards Venice (25x35cm-10x14in) board. 19-Jun-4 Hans Stahl, Hamburg #16/R
£559	$934	€800	Busy Italian coastal town (27x35cm-11x14in) s. 11-Oct-3 Hans Stahl, Hamburg #56
£583	$1061	€880	Landscape with figures near Venice (60x80cm-24x31in) s. i.verso. 19-Jun-4 Hans Stahl, Hamburg #14/R
£583	$1061	€880	Busy scene in Ischia Harbour (60x80cm-24x31in) s. i.verso stretcher. 19-Jun-4 Hans Stahl, Hamburg #18/R
£587	$1062	€880	Venice: busy scene in front of Doges Palace (60x80cm-24x31in) s. 3-Apr-4 Hans Stahl, Hamburg #5
£633	$1146	€950	Houses on Lake Lugano (50x70cm-20x28in) s. i. verso. 3-Apr-4 Hans Stahl, Hamburg #4
£683	$1263	€990	Amalfi (50x70cm-20x28in) s. 14-Feb-4 Hans Stahl, Hamburg #3/R
£733	$1327	€1100	Torbole harbour on Lake Garda (50x60cm-20x24in) s. i. verso. 3-Apr-4 Hans Stahl, Hamburg #7/R
£1259	$2102	€1800	Fishermen hauling in the nets in Bay of Naples (49x69cm-19x27in) bears sig. 11-Oct-3 Hans Stahl, Hamburg #57/R est:1800
£1300	$2353	€1950	Isola Pescatori, Lago Maggiore (50x60cm-20x24in) s. i. verso. 3-Apr-4 Hans Stahl, Hamburg #6/R est:700
£1600	$2944	€2400	Figure reading (21x14cm-8x6in) s. i.verso cardboard prov.lit. 14-Jun-4 Porro, Milan #10/R est:2500-3500
£2966	$5486	€4300	Camogli church on Riviera Ponente (50x70cm-20x28in) s. i. verso. 14-Feb-4 Hans Stahl, Hamburg #2/R est:900
£10490	$17832	€15000	Face decomposition (30x24cm-12x9in) s. cardboard exhib. 25-Nov-3 Sotheby's, Milan #180/R est:15000-20000
£18121	$32436	€27000	Still life with radiator (32x19cm-13x7in) init. oil tempera collage cardboard. 25-May-4 Sotheby's, Milan #233/R est:25000-30000

Works on paper

£9790	$16643	€14000	Dynamism III (47x31cm-19x12in) init. pastel exhib. 25-Nov-3 Sotheby's, Milan #179/R est:10000-15000

BALDI, Lazzaro (1624-1703) Italian

Works on paper

£4722	$8500	€6894	Two putti around an urn (25x17cm-10x7in) black chk pen brown ink wash prov. 22-Jan-4 Christie's, Rockefeller NY #49/R est:5000-8000

BALDO, Luigi (1884-1961) Italian

Works on paper

£344	$550	€502	View in Venice (36x18cm-14x7in) s. W/C. 21-Sep-3 William Jenack, New York #220

BALDOCK, Charles E (fl.1890-1905) British

Works on paper

£320	$595	€467	Autumn wooded landscape with a cock pheasant (23x18cm-9x7in) W/C. 7-Mar-4 Paul Beighton, Rotherham #524

BALDOCK, James Walsham (c.1822-1898) British

£726	$1169	€1060	Still life of birds (37x43cm-15x17in) s.d.1859. 25-Aug-3 Lilla Bukowskis, Stockholm #984 (S.KR 9500)
£9200	$15272	€13432	Foxhounds Richmond, Regulus and Ringwood (43x58cm-17x23in) s.d.1866. 2-Oct-3 Neales, Nottingham #705/R est:3000-5000

BALDUCCI, Giovanni (1560-c.1631) Italian

Works on paper

£2632	$4842	€4000	Scene from John of Austria's life (20x33cm-8x13in) pen ink W/C prov. 22-Jun-4 Sotheby's, Milan #28/R est:4000-6000

BALDUNG GRIEN, Hans (1484-1545) German

Prints

£2267	$4057	€3400	Adam and Eve (25x10cm-10x4in) woodcut. 13-May-4 Bassenge, Berlin #5012/R est:900

BALDUS, Edouard Denis (1813-1882) French

Photographs

£2500	$4500	€3650	Au louvre, Pavillon Richelieu, Paris (45x34cm-18x13in) s.i. num.24 albumen print. 22-Apr-4 Phillips, New York #130/R est:6000-8000
£2797	$4671	€4000	Arles (34x43cm-13x17in) albumen print lit. 10-Oct-3 Tajan, Paris #140/R
£3889	$7000	€5678	Vezelay, porte des catechumenes (28x21cm-11x8in) salt print. 22-Apr-4 Phillips, New York #18/R est:8000-12000

BALDWIN, Andrew (?) American

£475	$750	€694	Hudson River scene with two sloops and a dory in foreground (61x76cm-24x30in) s. 25-Jul-3 Eldred, East Dennis #193/R

BALDWYN, C H C (fl.1887-1912) British

Works on paper

£820	$1484	€1197	Plovers on heathland (24x34cm-9x13in) s. W/C. 1-Apr-4 Martel Maides, Guernsey #263

BALDWYN, Charles H C (fl.1887-1912) British

Works on paper

£780	$1271	€1139	Magpies perched upon apple blossom. Three young warblers (25x35cm-10x14in) both s.d.1903 W/C htd white two. 24-Sep-3 Dreweatt Neate, Newbury #4/R

BALE, Alice Marian Ellen (1875-1955) Australian

£345	$538	€500	Castlemaine Street (19x29cm-7x11in) i. i.verso. 1-Aug-2 Joel, Victoria #282 est:1000-1500 (A.D 1000)

BALE, Charles Thomas (fl.1866-1875) British

£360	$655	€526	Still life of a dove on a table amongst fruit (36x46cm-14x18in) s. 3-Feb-4 Sworder & Son, Bishops Stortford #271/R
£407	$680	€594	Still life of fruit and game on stone ledge (45x35cm-18x14in) s. 17-Nov-3 Waddingtons, Toronto #92/R (C.D 900)
£420	$756	€613	Still life of fruit in a basket on stone ledge (43x33cm-17x13in) mono.d. 20-Apr-4 Clarke Gammon, Guildford #26/R
£500	$835	€730	Grapes, plums, and peaches with a jug on a ledge (35x46cm-14x18in) indis.sig. 13-Nov-3 Christie's, Kensington #369/R
£600	$1002	€876	Grapes, plums, peach and butterfly on a mossy bank (30x41cm-12x16in) mono.d.1871. 13-Nov-3 Christie's, Kensington #370/R
£600	$1074	€876	Still life of fruit on a silver stand, glass goblet and two-handled vase (29x19cm-11x7in) mono. 17-Mar-4 Bonhams, Chester #353
£670	$1200	€1126	Still life with fruit and stein on table (46x36cm-18x14in) s. 20-Mar-4 Pook & Pook, Downington #317/R
£850	$1420	€1241	Fruit and game on a ledge. Tankard with fruit on a ledge (46x35cm-18x14in) s. 13-Nov-3 Christie's, Kensington #368/R
£900	$1431	€1305	Still life with game and fruit (51x76cm-20x30in) s. 9-Sep-3 Bonhams, Knightsbridge #231/R
£932	$1500	€1361	Grapes, plums, peaches, gourd and an elaborate covered compote on table (61x51cm-24x20in) s. indis d. 14-Jan-4 Christie's, Rockefeller NY #71/R est:3000-5000
£1000	$1810	€1460	Still life study of dead duck, fruit and stein on a table (485x742cm-191x292in) s. 16-Apr-4 Keys, Aylsham #710/R est:1000-1500
£1025	$1660	€1497	Still life with fruit, pheasant and salt glaze pitcher (50x75cm-20x30in) s. 30-Jul-3 Goodman, Sydney #199/R (A.D 2500)
£1109	$1984	€1619	Still life of strawberries, grapes and pears (25x30cm-10x12in) s. 26-May-4 AB Stockholms Auktionsverk #2409/R est:18000-20000 (S.KR 15000)
£1200	$2196	€1752	Still life of fruit, birds nest and jug (30x40cm-12x16in) s. sold with a companion. 6-Apr-4 Bonhams, Knightsbridge #77/R est:1000-1500
£1300	$2054	€1885	Grapes and apples on a wooden ledge. Grapes and peaches on a stone ledge (46x36cm-18x14in) s. one d.1888 pair. 4-Sep-3 Christie's, Kensington #317/R est:800-1200
£1300	$2379	€1898	Fruit still life on a stone ledge (35x44cm-14x17in) mono. 1-Feb-4 Lots Road Auctions, London #360 est:600-800
£1900	$3496	€2774	Still life of fruit and vine leaves on a ledge (30x25cm-12x10in) mono. pair. 8-Jun-4 Bonhams, Knightsbridge #339c/R est:800-1200

BALE, Charles Thomas (attrib) (fl.1866-1875) British

£503	$800	€734	Still life with grapes and currants (20x31cm-8x12in) s. 12-Sep-3 Skinner, Boston #217/R
£566	$900	€826	Still life with grapes, plums and strawberries (20x30cm-8x12in) s. 12-Sep-3 Skinner, Boston #215/R

BALE, Edwin (1838-1923) British

Works on paper

£550	$985	€803	Statue of Desideris, the sculptor, looking out over Florence (34x63cm-13x25in) s. W/C. 25-May-4 Bonhams, Knightsbridge #191/R

BALE, John Edward (fl.1856-1859) British

Works on paper

£260	$465	€380	South Creake (36x54cm-14x21in) s.d.1858 W/C htd bodycol. 22-Mar-4 Bonhams & Brooks, Norfolk #160/R
£340	$609	€496	Interior of South Creake Church, Norfolk (71x51cm-28x20in) s.d.1858 W/C. 22-Mar-4 Bonhams & Brooks, Norfolk #159/R

BALE, T C (19th C) British

£1000	$1840	€1460	New toy (15x20cm-6x8in) mono.d.1868. 8-Jun-4 Bonhams, Knightsbridge #194/R est:800-1200

BALE, Thomas Charles (1855-1925) British

£486	$900	€710	Confiscation (23x18cm-9x7in) 10-Mar-4 Doyle, New York #3/R
£500	$925	€730	Still life of a bird, jar, vine leaves and basket of fruit (44x34cm-17x13in) s. 9-Mar-4 Bonhams, Knightsbridge #205/R
£865	$1600	€1263	Still life with game (53x43cm-21x17in) one mono.d.1880 pair. 10-Feb-4 Sotheby's, New York #250/R est:1500-2500

BALEN, Hendrik van (1575-1632) Flemish

£5594	$9510	€8000	Noces de Psyche et l'Amour (46x55cm-18x22in) bears sig panel. 21-Nov-3 Coutau Begarie, Paris #124/R est:12000-15000

BALEN, Hendrik van (circle) (1575-1632) Flemish
£1831 $2930 €2600 Mother of God with Christ child and saints (20x28cm-8x11in) copper. 18-Sep-3 Rieber, Stuttgart #1163/R est:2800
£5245 $9021 €7500 Finding of Moses (134x227cm-53x89in) 2-Dec-3 Sotheby's, Milan #71/R est:5000-7000
£8000 $14640 €12000 Holy Family with Saint JOhn and putti (28x34cm-11x13in) copper. 1-Jun-4 Sotheby's, Milan #75/R est:3000-4000

BALEN, Hendrik van and BRUEGHEL, Jan (elder) (17th C) Flemish
£1100000 $1903000 €1606000 Virgin and Child with the infant Saint John the Baptist (94x72cm-37x28in) panel prov. 10-Dec-3 Christie's, London #20/R est:400000-600000

BALEN, Hendrik van and BRUEGHEL, Jan (elder-style) (17th C) Flemish
£24615 $42338 €35938 In the Garden of Paradise - landscape with figures and exotic animals (62x80cm-24x31in) copper prov. 7-Dec-3 Uppsala Auktionskammare, Uppsala #16/R est:100000-150000 (S.KR 320000)

BALEN, Hendrik van and BRUEGHEL, Jan (younger) (17th C) Flemish
£101399 $172378 €145000 Diana's nymphs after the hunt (58x76cm-23x30in) panel. 29-Nov-3 Bukowskis, Helsinki #386/R est:100000-120000
£163265 $259592 €240000 L'allegorie de la Terre (47x83cm-19x33in) panel. 23-Mar-3 Mercier & Cie, Lille #177/R est:150000-200000

BALEN, Hendrik van and BRUEGHEL, Jan (younger-attrib) (17th C) Flemish
£6711 $12349 €10000 Allegorie de l'ete (51x66cm-20x26in) copper. 24-Mar-4 Tajan, Paris #52/R est:10000-14000

BALEN, Hendrik van and BRUEGHEL, Jan (younger-circle) (17th C) Flemish
£16783 $28867 €24000 Diane chasseresse dans un paysage (70x100cm-28x39in) panel. 3-Dec-3 Palais de Beaux Arts, Brussels #1252/R est:10000-24000

BALEN, Matthys (1684-1766) Flemish
£4895 $8175 €7000 Landscape (12x13cm-5x5in) board prov. 30-Jun-3 Ansorena, Madrid #364/R
£4895 $8175 €7000 Landscape (12x13cm-5x5in) board prov. 30-Jun-3 Ansorena, Madrid #364a/R

BALENGHIEN, Gustave (?-1953) ?
£400 $632 €584 Still life with a vase of roses (46x38cm-18x15in) 27-Apr-3 Wilkinson, Doncaster #304

BALESTRA, Antonio (1666-1740) Italian
£10274 $17466 €15000 Madonna and Child (57x43cm-22x17in) 9-Nov-3 Finarte, Venice #24/R est:14000-18000

BALESTRA, Antonio (attrib) (1666-1740) Italian
£7800 $13260 €11388 Finding moses (122x140cm-48x55in) 31-Oct-3 Christie's, Kensington #145/R est:5000-8000
Works on paper
£1200 $2160 €1752 Virgin and Child in a landscape, other figures, and God the Father above (17x25cm-7x10in) pen brown ink grey wash black chk. 20-Apr-4 Sotheby's, Olympia #33/R est:600-800

BALESTRIERI, Lionello (1872-1958) Italian
£638 $1066 €900 Houses on the Seine (29x42cm-11x17in) s. board. 14-Oct-3 Finarte Semenzato, Milan #124/R
£750 $1328 €1095 In the artist's studio (36x51cm-14x20in) s. board. 29-Apr-4 Christie's, Kensington #199/R
£1690 $2924 €2400 Painter (30x21cm-12x8in) s. card. 9-Dec-3 Pandolfini, Florence #270/R est:1800-2000
£2000 $3680 €3000 Bridge in Paris (46x65cm-18x26in) s. cardboard on canvas. 8-Jun-4 Sotheby's, Milan #72/R est:3000-5000
£2535 $4386 €3600 Evening (45x62cm-18x24in) s. 9-Dec-3 Pandolfini, Florence #263 est:2000-2500
£3297 $6000 €4814 Despair (64x80cm-25x31in) s. prov. 29-Jun-4 Arroyo, Buenos Aires #44/R est:3000

BALESTRINI, Carlo (1868-1923) Italian
£1528 $2597 €2200 Rural path with peasant woman (25x209cm-10x82in) s. cardboard. 29-Oct-3 Il Ponte, Milan #587 est:800-900
£4667 $8587 €7000 Along the path (160x95cm-63x37in) init. 10-Jun-4 Christie's, Rome #199/R est:8000-10000

BALET, Jan (20th C) ?
£284 $522 €415 Circo piccolo di Venezia (50x60cm-20x24in) s. 8-Jun-4 Germann, Zurich #759/R (S.FR 650)

BALFOUR-BROWNE, Vincent (1880-1963) British
Works on paper
£460 $846 €672 Pheasant and duck in a winter landscape (27x42cm-11x17in) init.d.1931 W/C scratching out. 29-Mar-4 Bonhams, Bath #29/R
£1800 $3276 €2628 Stag at Eve has drunk his fill (24x38cm-9x15in) init.d.1907 pencil W/C htd white. 5-Feb-4 Mellors & Kirk, Nottingham #488/R
£3200 $5952 €4672 Then some of them got our wind, deer in a highland landscape (30x46cm-12x18in) init.d.1955 W/C. 4-Mar-4 Mitchells, Cockermouth #794/R est:500-800

BALINK, Hendricus (1882-1963) American
£2284 $3700 €3312 New Mexico autumn (25x30cm-10x12in) 23-May-3 Altermann Galleries, Santa Fe #195
£8824 $15000 €12883 Cowboy (76x61cm-30x24in) s. prov. 1-Nov-3 Santa Fe Art, Santa Fe #221/R est:30000-40000

BALINT, Endre (1914-1986) Hungarian
£13361 $23649 €19507 Continuation (11x90cm-4x35in) s.d.63 panel. 28-Apr-4 Kieselbach, Budapest #138/R (H.F 5000000)

BALINT, Rezso (1885-1945) Hungarian
£10440 $18061 €15242 Nagybanya landscape (78x73cm-31x29in) s. painted c.1908. 12-Dec-3 Kieselbach, Budapest #59/R (H.F 4000000)
Works on paper
£321 $568 €469 Railway station in Brussels (18x26cm-7x10in) s. pastel. 28-Apr-4 Kieselbach, Budapest #11/R (H.F 120000)

BALIRR, Balirr (1905-1977) Australian
Works on paper
£264 $417 €383 Salt water bream (49x51cm-19x20in) earth pigments eucalyptus bark exec.c.1968 prov.exhib.lit. 28-Jul-3 Sotheby's, Paddington #257 (A.D 650)

BALJEU, Joost (1925-1991) Dutch
Works on paper
£2899 $4754 €4000 Untitled (11x20cm-4x8in) s.d.1955 on backing gouache collage card prov. 27-May-3 Sotheby's, Amsterdam #362/R est:4000-6000

BALKA, Miroslaw (1958-) Polish
Sculpture
£2100 $3507 €3066 Untitled (23x20x20cm-9x8x8in) plaster of Paris leather. 22-Oct-3 Christie's, London #134/R est:1500-2500

BALKE, Peder (1804-1887) Norwegian
£21386 $36356 €31224 Mountain landscape (33x25cm-13x10in) s. i.verso panel painted c.1865. 19-Nov-3 Grev Wedels Plass, Oslo #42/R est:150000-200000 (N.KR 250000)
£21951 $40171 €32048 Fjord landscape with steamer (30x42cm-12x17in) s. paper on panel exhib. 7-Jun-4 Blomqvist, Oslo #334/R est:180000-220000 (N.KR 270000)

BALKENHOL, Stephan (1957-) German
£2800 $5124 €4200 Lion - blackboard drawing (185x130cm-73x51in) s.d.1994 verso oil chk varnish panel prov. prov.exhib. 4-Jun-4 Lempertz, Koln #22/R est:4500
Sculpture
£10000 $18400 €15000 Man with red lips (128cm-50in) painted wood exec 1994. 8-Jun-4 Sotheby's, Amsterdam #154/R est:25000-35000
£14371 $24000 €20982 Kopf saule - man head on a column (160x20x35cm-63x8x14in) painted wa-wa wood executed 1993 prov. 14-Nov-3 Phillips, New York #117/R est:25000-35000
£21229 $38000 €30994 Alligator man (99x99x46cm-39x39x18in) oil cedar prov.exhib. 12-May-4 Christie's, Rockefeller NY #324/R est:20000-30000
£29050 $52000 €42413 Drei figurensaulen, manner (162x34x24cm-64x13x9in) acrylic wawa wood three prov. 12-May-4 Christie's, Rockefeller NY #323/R est:60000-80000
£29330 $52500 €42822 Man with bullhead (160x30x20cm-63x12x8in) poplar wood paint exec 1996 prov. 13-May-4 Sotheby's, New York #447/R est:30000-40000
£60976 $95732 €88415 Three chickens on a screw (155x75x80cm-61x30x31in) painted Douglas fir prov.exhib. 26-Aug-3 Christie's, Sydney #104/R est:90000-120000 (A.D 150000)
Works on paper
£313 $561 €470 Tightrope walker (26x42cm-10x17in) s.d. feltpen. 15-May-4 Dr Sturies, Dusseldorf #7/R
£382 $638 €550 Sans titre (20x12cm-8x5in) chl prov. 25-Oct-3 Cornette de St.Cyr, Paris #580

BALL, Alice W (?-1929) American
£919 $1700 €1379 Flower garden outside a shuttered window (89x71cm-35x28in) s. 19-Jul-4 Winter Associates, Plainville #160/R est:500-1000

BALL, Gareth Lloyd (20th C) British
Works on paper
£600 $954 €876 Brian Moore England and Harlequins (49x35cm-19x14in) s.d.92 gouache. 11-Sep-3 Sotheby's, Olympia #102/R

BALL, Henry (fl.1919-1939) British
£1700 $3094 €2482 Nottingham street scenes Theatre Square and Houndsgate (49x39cm-19x15in) one s.d.1929 pair. 5-Feb-4 Mellors & Kirk, Nottingham #588/R est:400-600

BALL, J (19th C) British
£1103 $1843 €1600 East (141x183cm-56x72in) s. tempera collage copper fabric cardboard. 13-Nov-3 Finarte Semenzato, Rome #281/R est:1500-2000

BALL, Pamela Thalben (20th C) British
£400 $736 €584 Back street canal in Venice (40x50cm-16x20in) s. mill board. 23-Mar-4 Anderson & Garland, Newcastle #338/R

BALL, Percival (19th C) British
Sculpture
£5588 $9500 €8158 Captive boatmen (123x39cm-48x15in) s. marble relief prov. 28-Oct-3 Christie's, Rockefeller NY #132/R

BALL, Robert (20th C) American
Sculpture
£1647 $2750 €2405 Outfoxed (69x74x33cm-27x29x13in) num.21/27 bronze. 11-Oct-3 Nadeau, Windsor #129/R est:4500-6000

BALL, Sydney (1933-) Australian
£3306 $5851 €4827 Jacob's room (218x167cm-86x66in) s.i.d.1976 verso acrylic enamel cotton duck prov. 3-May-4 Christie's, Melbourne #221/R est:7000-10000 (A.D 8000)
Works on paper
£420 $764 €613 Putnam Green (57x77cm-22x30in) s. i.d.74 verso synthetic polymer enamel prov. 16-Jun-4 Deutscher-Menzies, Melbourne #604/R est:400-600 (A.D 1100)

BALL, Thomas (1819-1911) American
Sculpture
£11047 $19000 €16129 Napoleon (188x58cm-74x23in) s.d.1856 marble prov. 2-Dec-3 Christie's, Rockefeller NY #563/R est:2500-3500

BALL, Victor (?) ?
£361 $650 €527 Shepherd resting with his flock above a hayfield (61x91cm-24x36in) s. 24-Apr-4 Weschler, Washington #628/R

BALL, Wilfred Williams (1853-1917) British
Works on paper
£250 $448 €365 Figures on a village bridge (14x23cm-6x9in) s.d.85 W/C. 25-May-4 Bonhams, Knightsbridge #158/R
£280 $476 €409 Cleeve Mill, near Windsor (11x20cm-4x8in) s.i.d.86 W/C. 26-Nov-3 Hamptons Fine Art, Godalming #91
£340 $578 €496 From the Riva Degli Schiaboni (28x18cm-11x7in) s.d.87 W/C. 30-Oct-3 Duke & Son, Dorchester #82/R
£500 $850 €730 Itteringham and Sebley Heath, Brockenhurst (16cm-6in) s. W/C pair. 27-Nov-3 Clevedon Sale Rooms #169
£500 $910 €730 The cathedral at Ely enshrouded in mist (16x24cm-6x9in) s.d. pencil W/C scatching out. 1-Jul-4 Christie's, Kensington #139/R
£580 $1061 €847 Landscape at sunset (18x26cm-7x10in) s. W/C. 28-Jan-4 Dreweatt Neate, Newbury #9
£720 $1318 €1051 St Lo (26x19cm-10x7in) s.i.d.1905 W/C. 28-Jan-4 Dreweatt Neate, Newbury #2/R

BALLA, Giacomo (1871-1958) Italian
£3521 $6162 €5000 High tide (27x31cm-11x12in) s. i.verso board. 16-Dec-3 Finarte Semenzato, Milan #323/R est:7800-8200
£3867 $7115 €5800 Vase of flowers (65x56cm-26x22in) s. board. 8-Jun-4 Della Rocca, Turin #274/R est:5000-6000
£12081 $21624 €18000 Portrait of the carpenter (36x28cm-14x11in) s. cardboard. 29-May-4 Farsetti, Prato #519/R est:15000-18000
£12752 $22826 €19000 Geometry (25cm-10in circular) s. cardboard prov.exhib. 25-May-4 Sotheby's, Milan #236/R est:20000-25000
£14000 $25480 €20440 Linee andamentali (15x31cm-6x12in) s.d.14 painted 1926-1928 prov. 3-Feb-4 Christie's, London #229/R est:15000-20000
£16554 $29135 €24500 Portrait of lady (70x45cm-28x18in) s. i.verso. 19-May-4 Il Ponte, Milan #1074 est:25000-30000
£16779 $31208 €25000 Villa Borghese (27x32cm-11x13in) s. s.d.1950 verso board. 4-Mar-4 Babuino, Rome #488 est:8000-12000
£19580 $33287 €28000 Roman figures (24x33cm-9x13in) s. board painted c.1898. 25-Nov-3 Sotheby's, Milan #182/R est:20000-30000
£20979 $35664 €30000 Portrait of Carluccio (61x43cm-24x17in) s. s.i.d.1889 verso lit. 24-Nov-3 Christie's, Milan #298/R est:30000-40000
£20979 $35664 €30000 Speed lines (30x24cm-12x9in) s. tempera paper on cardboard. 29-Nov-3 Farsetti, Prato #459/R est:25000-30000
£22069 $36855 €32000 Study for 'Restless soul' (34x23cm-13x9in) s. canvas on cardboard prov.lit. 13-Nov-3 Finarte Semenzato, Rome #450/R est:35000-38000
£31469 $53497 €45000 Light lines (39x58cm-15x23in) s. board painted 1919 exhib. 29-Nov-3 Farsetti, Prato #458/R est:30000-40000
£34899 $62470 €52000 Trend (44x21cm-17x8in) s. masonite painted c.1925. 29-May-4 Farsetti, Prato #523/R est:50000-60000
£36364 $61818 €52000 Lines (17x25cm-7x10in) s.d.1919 exhib.lit. 24-Nov-3 Christie's, Milan #313/R est:35000-45000
£86957 $142609 €120000 Canto patriottico in piazza di Siena (27x37cm-11x15in) s. panel exhib.lit. 31-May-3 Farsetti, Prato #654/R est:120000-150000
£111888 $190210 €160000 Ballucecolormare (95x211cm-37x83in) s.i. exhib.lit. 20-Nov-3 Finarte Semenzato, Milan #164/R est:100000-130000
£197183 $345070 €280000 Spring fluidity (53x50cm-21x20in) s. painted c.1917 prov.exhib.lit. 16-Dec-3 Porro, Milan #4/R
£202703 $356757 €300000 The strange man's chair. Portrait of woman (55x74cm-22x29in) s. s.i.verso double-sided painted 1929 prov.exhib.lit. 24-May-4 Christie's, Milan #279/R est:200000-300000
£209790 $356643 €300000 Trees and hedge in Villa Borghese (101x101cm-40x40in) s. painted c.1905 prov.exhib. 25-Nov-3 Sotheby's, Milan #185/R est:300000-400000
£314685 $534965 €450000 Colour changing composition (55x76cm-22x30in) s. i.verso oil pencil paper on canvas painted 1912 prov.exhib.lit. 25-Nov-3 Sotheby's, Milan #205/R
Sculpture
£2080 $3537 €2975 Futurist flower (130x110cm-51x43in) painted wood exhib.lit. 18-Nov-3 Babuino, Rome #481/R est:2000-3000
£2933 $5280 €4400 Ecarte (46cm-18in) num.9/9 painted steel plexiglas base prov.exhib.lit. 22-Apr-4 Finarte Semenzato, Rome #261/R est:5000-6000
£6579 $12105 €10000 Siege (61x60x44cm-24x24x17in) painted wood exec.1929 prov.lit. 27-Jun-4 Versailles Encheres #148/R est:10000-12000
Works on paper
£966 $1612 €1400 Trees (17x22cm-7x9in) s. Chinese ink sold with another by G Stradone. 13-Nov-3 Finarte Semenzato, Rome #130 est:1200-1500
£2183 $3974 €3187 Testa (21x19cm-8x7in) s.i. pencil. 17-Jun-4 Kornfeld, Bern #187 est:5000 (S.FR 5000)
£4000 $7360 €6000 Study for sofa (21x33cm-8x13in) s. pencil dr double-sided. 11-Jun-4 Farsetti, Prato #380/R est:6000-8000
£8000 $14720 €11680 Futuristic composition (10x15cm-4x6in) s. verso W/C crayon card recto pen ink verso double-sided prov. 24-Jun-4 Christie's, London #362/R est:8000-12000
£10067 $18020 €15000 Study of bike (13x17cm-5x7in) s. pencil exec.c.1913 exhib. 25-May-4 Sotheby's, Milan #242/R est:15000-20000
£13043 $21391 €18000 Elisabetta (48x32cm-19x13in) s. pastel. 31-May-3 Farsetti, Prato #613/R est:18000-22000
£17483 $29720 €25000 Decorative pattern (23x32cm-9x13in) s. W/C exhib. 29-Nov-3 Farsetti, Prato #457/R est:24000-28000
£19310 $32248 €28000 Portrait of Elisa on the terrace (24x21cm-9x8in) s.i. sanguine prov.lit. 13-Nov-3 Finarte Semenzato, Rome #209/R est:26000-28000
£22819 $40846 €34000 Villa Borghese (15x20cm-6x8in) s.verso pastel cardboard diptych exec.c.1905. 29-May-4 Farsetti, Prato #520/R est:30000-40000

BALLABENE, Rudolf Raimund (1890-1968) Austrian
£845 $1479 €1200 Sunflowers (65x80cm-26x31in) s. 19-Dec-3 Dorotheum, Vienna #146/R

BALLACHEY, Barbara (1949-) Canadian
£528 $946 €771 Along the road near Chain Lake (119x152cm-47x60in) s.d.1991. 6-May-4 Heffel, Vancouver #21/R (C.D 1300)
£537 $972 €784 Ware Ridge, autumn (91x121cm-36x48in) s.d.1981 prov. 18-Apr-4 Levis, Calgary #302/R est:900-1200 (C.D 1300)

BALLAGH, Robert (1943-) Irish
£1007 $1782 €1500 Proposed murals, map series (46x34cm-18x13in) s.i. acrylic board three in one frame prov.lit. 27-Apr-4 Whyte's, Dublin #167/R est:1800-2200
£1611 $2851 €2400 Female landscape (30x18cm-12x7in) s.d.1978 verso prov. 27-Apr-4 Whyte's, Dublin #168/R est:1500-2000
£2027 $3831 €3000 Black and white (51x36cm-20x14in) s.d.1981 verso. 17-Feb-4 Whyte's, Dublin #198/R est:3000-4000
£20979 $35664 €30000 Girl looking at a Patrick Scott (176x176cm-69x69in) s. acrylic. 25-Nov-3 De Veres Art Auctions, Dublin #69/R est:14000-18000
£32000 $57280 €46720 Turkish Bath (122cm-48in circular) s. acrylic after Ingres lit. 13-May-4 Sotheby's, London #109/R est:15000-20000
£64865 $122595 €96000 My studio 1969 (183x244cm-72x96in) s.d.1976 verso oil acrylic prov.exhib.lit. 17-Feb-4 Whyte's, Dublin #93/R est:20000-30000
Prints
£2533 $4585 €3800 World war refugees II (84x77cm-33x30in) s.verso silkscreen print acrylic wood. 30-Mar-4 De Veres Art Auctions, Dublin #127b/R est:4000-6000
Works on paper
£629 $1145 €950 Dolly mixtures 8 (29x35cm-11x14in) collage prov. 15-Jun-4 James Adam, Dublin #172/R
£4000 $7240 €6000 Cecil King box (31x41cm-12x16in) mixed media prov. 31-Mar-4 James Adam, Dublin #70/R est:2000-3000

BALLANTINE, Ian (20th C) British
Sculpture
£1800 $3276 €2700 Sleeping environment (237x104cm-93x41in) lacquered wood settee shelves prov.lit. 30-Jun-4 Christie's, Kensington #26/R est:2000-4000

BALLANTINE, Mary (fl.1920-1939) British
£550 $875 €803 Still life with butterfly and goldfish (71x91cm-28x36in) s. 10-Sep-3 Sotheby's, Olympia #193/R

BALLARD, Brian (1943-) Irish
£550 $902 €803 Hollywood Pier (22x28cm-9x11in) s.d.2002 board. 4-Jun-3 John Ross, Belfast #44
£604 $1081 €900 Sea and rocks - blue (24x34cm-9x13in) s.d.93 i. verso board. 31-May-4 Hamilton Osborne King, Dublin #144/R
£700 $1302 €1022 Still life, blue glass (30x20cm-12x8in) s.d.04 board. 3-Mar-4 John Ross, Belfast #27
£800 $1464 €1168 Colin mountain (30x91cm-12x36in) s.d.97. 2-Jun-4 John Ross, Belfast #204
£1000 $1800 €1460 Flowers reflection (20x15cm-8x6in) s.d.94 board prov. 20-Jan-4 Bonhams, Knightsbridge #78/R est:600-800
£1000 $1860 €1460 Still life (20x25cm-8x10in) s. 3-Mar-4 John Ross, Belfast #45 est:800-1200
£1100 $2046 €1606 Still life, flowers in a jar (35x25cm-14x10in) s.d.2001 board. 3-Mar-4 John Ross, Belfast #96 est:1200-1400
£1259 $2140 €1800 Memento mori (30x41cm-12x16in) s.d.1993. 18-Nov-3 Whyte's, Dublin #231 est:1000-1500
£1300 $2132 €1898 Still life (35x25cm-14x10in) s. 4-Jun-3 John Ross, Belfast #125
£1400 $2408 €2044 Still life, flowers in a white jug (20x30cm-8x12in) s.d.2001 board. 3-Dec-3 John Ross, Belfast #155 est:800-1000
£1477 $2643 €2200 Primroses and Iron - still life (26x35cm-10x14in) s.d.98 i. verso. 31-May-4 Hamilton Osborne King, Dublin #129/R est:1500-2500
£1486 $2809 €2200 Jar and clock (25x36cm-10x14in) s.d.2002 i.verso. 17-Feb-4 Whyte's, Dublin #231/R est:1800-2200
£1500 $2490 €2190 Still life, roses against white (35x25cm-14x10in) s.d.87 board. 1-Oct-3 John Ross, Belfast #124 est:1000-1200
£1600 $2656 €2336 Sea at Ballycastle (61x76cm-24x30in) s.d.85 board. 1-Oct-3 John Ross, Belfast #212 est:1200-1500
£1611 $2883 €2400 Pot of irises and blue jug (39x29cm-15x11in) s.d.2001 board. 26-May-4 James Adam, Dublin #65/R est:2500-3500
£1700 $2822 €2482 Female nude study (40x35cm-16x14in) s.d.2001 board. 1-Oct-3 John Ross, Belfast #25 est:1500-1750
£1800 $2988 €2628 Reflections on the lagoon (25x35cm-10x14in) s.d.2000. 1-Oct-3 John Ross, Belfast #128 est:1500-1800
£2000 $3620 €3000 Books on a table (30x40cm-12x16in) s.d.2003 i.verso. 30-Mar-4 De Veres Art Auctions, Dublin #96/R est:2500-3500
£2027 $3831 €3000 Jug with poppies and daisies (51x41cm-20x16in) s.d.1989. 17-Feb-4 Whyte's, Dublin #195/R est:4000-5000
£2200 $4026 €3212 Female nude study (50x40cm-20x16in) s.d.2003. 2-Jun-4 John Ross, Belfast #159 est:2400-2600
£2230 $4214 €3300 Lagan sunset (61x76cm-24x30in) s.d.1985 board. 17-Feb-4 Whyte's, Dublin #236/R est:2000-3000
£2467 $4465 €3700 Blue vase and bottle (36x26cm-14x10in) s. 30-Mar-4 De Veres Art Auctions, Dublin #105/R est:3000-4000
£2500 $4150 €3650 Blue jug and bottle (61x76cm-24x30in) s.d.96. 1-Oct-3 John Ross, Belfast #154 est:2500-3000
£2535 $4056 €3600 Tulips and daisies (36x25cm-14x10in) s.d.1995. 16-Sep-3 Whyte's, Dublin #208/R est:2500-3500

£2632 $4842 €4000 Still life with irises and bottles (38x61cm-15x24in) s. 22-Jun-4 De Veres Art Auctions, Dublin #115/R est:4000-6000
£2657 $4517 €3800 Daisies and lemon (41x51cm-16x20in) s.d.91 i.verso. 25-Nov-3 De Veres Art Auctions, Dublin #117a/R est:4000-5000
£2703 $5108 €4000 Striped vase with irises (51x41cm-20x16in) s.d.2001. 17-Feb-4 Whyte's, Dublin #190/R est:4000-5000
£2800 $4592 €4088 Still life (50x61cm-20x24in) s.d.89. 4-Jun-3 John Ross, Belfast #146
£3077 $5231 €4400 Still life (51x34cm-20x13in) s.d.2003 canvas on board. 25-Nov-3 De Veres Art Auctions, Dublin #116/R est:3000-4000
£3133 $5671 €4700 Interior (46x59cm-18x23in) s.d.2003. 30-Mar-4 De Veres Art Auctions, Dublin #47/R est:4000-6000
£3200 $5952 €4672 Female nude study (61x45cm-24x18in) s. 3-Mar-4 John Ross, Belfast #30 est:2500-3000
£3217 $5469 €4600 Blue jug and clock (41x51cm-16x20in) s.d.2002 i.verso. 18-Nov-3 Whyte's, Dublin #205/R est:3500-4500
£3380 $5408 €4800 Books and poppies (41x51cm-16x20in) s.d.2000 i.verso. 16-Sep-3 Whyte's, Dublin #216/R est:3500-4500
£3490 $6177 €5200 Reflected still life, blue (61x76cm-24x30in) s.d.1998 i.verso exhib. 27-Apr-4 Whyte's, Dublin #185/R est:4000-6000
£3500 $6510 €5110 Still life (61x76cm-24x30in) s.d.2000. 3-Mar-4 John Ross, Belfast #149 est:3500-4500
£3800 $6802 €5548 Still life with lemons and tulips (61x46cm-24x18in) s.d.93 board. 14-May-4 Christie's, Kensington #398/R est:2500-3500
£3960 $7009 €5900 Boats at Groomsport, Bangor, County Down (61x76cm-24x30in) s.d.2001. 27-Apr-4 Whyte's, Dublin #192/R est:5000-7000
£4200 $7518 €6132 Magnolias in a jug (51x76cm-20x30in) s.d.88 prov. 14-May-4 Christie's, Kensington #397/R est:3000-5000
£4306 $7018 €6200 Model holding leg (40x50cm-16x20in) s.d.1991. 24-Sep-3 James Adam, Dublin #79/R est:4000-6000
Works on paper
£280 $465 €409 Still life (17x12cm-7x5in) s.d.83 W/C. 1-Oct-3 John Ross, Belfast #56
£360 $598 €526 Still life (20x15cm-8x6in) s.d.88 pen ink wash W/C. 1-Oct-3 John Ross, Belfast #197
£380 $623 €555 Still life (20x15cm-8x6in) s.d.88 pen ink dr. 4-Jun-3 John Ross, Belfast #135
£400 $664 €584 Still life (17x12cm-7x5in) s.d.89 W/C. 1-Oct-3 John Ross, Belfast #20

BALLARD, Harry (19/20th C) American
Works on paper
£1437 $2400 €2098 Swat the pest with a thrift stamp (79x71cm-31x28in) s. gouache exec.c.1917. 15-Nov-3 Illustration House, New York #1/R est:2000-4000

BALLARD, Richard (20th C) ?
£320 $586 €467 Streets of Moss Side Manchester (152x132cm-60x52in) s.verso. 6-Apr-4 Capes Dunn, Manchester #847/R

BALLAVOINE, Jules Frederic (1855-1901) French
£900 $1665 €1314 Portrait of a lady (34x26cm-13x10in) s. 14-Jul-4 Sotheby's, Olympia #201/R
£1242 $2309 €1850 Femme a la chevelure rousse (46x38cm-18x15in) s. 7-Mar-4 Lesieur & Le Bars, Le Havre #4/R
£1536 $2750 €2243 Blue lady (46x38cm-18x15in) s. 6-May-4 Doyle, New York #51/R est:2000-3000
£2000 $3340 €2920 Letter (45x37cm-18x15in) s. 7-Oct-3 Bonhams, Knightsbridge #165/R est:2000-3000
£3846 $6615 €5615 La belle rousse (47x38cm-19x15in) s. 3-Dec-3 AB Stockholms Auktionsverk #2624/R est:30000-35000 (S.KR 50000)
£5556 $10000 €8112 Appollon et Daphne (97x131cm-38x52in) s. prov. 22-Apr-4 Christie's, Rockefeller NY #129/R est:12000-18000

BALLE, Mogens (1921-1988) Danish
£491 $800 €717 Untitled (67cm 26in circular) init. s.d.66 verso panel prov. 25-Sep-3 Christie's, Rockefeller NY #630/R
£717 $1290 €1047 Composition (24x33cm-9x13in) init. 24-Apr-4 Rasmussen, Havnen #4158 (D.KR 8000)
£753 $1279 €1099 Composition (34x47cm-13x19in) s.d.88 oil gouache paper. 26-Nov-3 Kunsthallen, Copenhagen #162/R (D.KR 8000)
£800 $1464 €1200 View (18x18cm-7x7in) s.verso. 7-Jun-4 Glerum, Amsterdam #412/R
£861 $1395 €1248 Composition (23x48cm-9x19in) s. s.d.84 verso. 4-Aug-3 Rasmussen, Vejle #539/R (D.KR 9000)
£941 $1599 €1374 Composition (41x33cm-16x13in) init. 26-Nov-3 Kunsthallen, Copenhagen #60/R (D.KR 10000)
£1106 $1880 €1615 Composition (38x46cm-15x18in) INIT. 10-Nov-3 Rasmussen, Vejle #570/R est:15000 (D.KR 12000)
£1317 $2239 €1923 Composition (46x55cm-18x22in) init. 26-Nov-3 Kunsthallen, Copenhagen #6a/R est:15000 (D.KR 14000)
£1444 $2657 €2108 Figure composition (38x46cm-15x18in) init. s.stretcher. 29-Mar-4 Rasmussen, Copenhagen #105/R est:12000-15000 (D.KR 16000)
£1659 $2654 €2422 Composition (46x55cm-18x22in) init. 22-Sep-3 Rasmussen, Vejle #642/R est:20000 (D.KR 17500)
£1715 $3155 €2504 Figure composition (50x61cm-20x24in) init. i.verso. 29-Mar-4 Rasmussen, Copenhagen #314/R est:18000 (D.KR 19000)
£1760 $3291 €2570 Composition (55x65cm-22x26in) init. 25-Feb-4 Kunsthallen, Copenhagen #2/R est:15000 (D.KR 19500)
£2535 $4234 €3701 Between dusk and moon (49x108cm-19x43in) init. diptych with painted canvas between. 7-Oct-3 Rasmussen, Copenhagen #3/R est:15000-20000 (D.KR 27000)
£3944 $6586 €5758 Estuary from Henne beach II (65x92cm-26x36in) init. exhib. 7-Oct-3 Rasmussen, Copenhagen #2/R est:20000-25000 (D.KR 42000)
£4332 $7971 €6325 Figure composition (81x103cm-32x41in) init. 29-Mar-4 Rasmussen, Copenhagen #108/R est:40000 (D.KR 48000)
Works on paper
£469 $867 €685 Composition (32x44cm-13x17in) s. gouache. 15-Mar-4 Rasmussen, Vejle #503/R (D.KR 5200)

BALLE, Mogens and DOTREMONT, Christian (20th C) Danish/Belgian
Works on paper
£1408 $2352 €2056 Ecrit comme ci comme ca (55x74cm-22x29in) s.d.1977 Indian ink exhib. 7-Oct-3 Rasmussen, Copenhagen #10/R est:12000-15000 (D.KR 15000)

BALLE, Otto P (1865-1916) Danish
£267 $485 €401 Farmyard with peasant shifting manure (50x60cm-20x24in) s.d.1899. 19-Jun-4 Rasmussen, Havnen #2275 (D.KR 3000)
£379 $701 €553 Bringing the cows home (57x85cm-22x33in) s.d.1903-04. 15-Mar-4 Rasmussen, Vejle #466/R (D.KR 4200)
£404 $752 €590 Grey day over Bjornehoved, collecting seaweed (50x84cm-20x33in) s. 2-Mar-4 Rasmussen, Copenhagen #1203/R (D.KR 4500)
£516 $923 €753 Autumn landscape with horses and haycart (34x47cm-13x19in) s. exhib. 10-May-4 Rasmussen, Vejle #93/R (D.KR 5700)
£4000 $7400 €5840 Artist's wife in an interior (53x49cm-21x19in) s.d.1907 i.stretcher. 10-Mar-4 Sotheby's, Olympia #306/R est:2500-3500

BALLEN, Roger (1950-) ?
Photographs
£2200 $3740 €3212 Sergeant F de Bruin, Department of Prisons employee (40x40cm-16x16in) s.i.d.verso silver print exec.1992. 19-Nov-3 Sotheby's, Olympia #171/R est:800-1120

BALLENBERGER, Karl (1801-1860) German
£4000 $6680 €5800 St Elisabeth von Thuringen distributing alms (33x27cm-13x11in) mono.d.44 panel prov.lit. 15-Nov-3 Lempertz, Koln #1579/R est:3000

BALLENTYNE, Joyce (c.1920-) American
£2550 $4565 €3800 The guitarist (76x61cm-30x24in) s. painted 1954 lit. 27-May-4 Sotheby's, Paris #97/R est:1500-2000
£4027 $7208 €6000 Gentlemen recycling (77x61cm-30x24in) s. painted 1954 lit. 27-May-4 Sotheby's, Paris #96/R est:800-1000
£4027 $7208 €6000 Thanks for the orchid (76x61cm-30x24in) s. painted 1955 lit. 27-May-4 Sotheby's, Paris #98/R est:1000-1500

BALLERO, Antonio (1864-1932) Italian
£1776 $3268 €2700 Lights in the wood (31x40cm-12x16in) s. board. 23-Jun-4 Finarte Semenzato, Rome #102/R est:1500-1700
Works on paper
£2763 $5084 €4200 Pasture (40x54cm-16x21in) s.d.1928 mixed media cardboard. 23-Jun-4 Finarte Semenzato, Rome #103/R est:2500-2700

BALLESIO, Federico (19th C) Italian
Works on paper
£1739 $2800 €2539 Cardinal's tea-time (53x36cm-21x14in) s.i. pencil W/C. 14-Jan-4 Christie's, Rockefeller NY #9/R est:2000-3000

BALLESIO, Francesco (1860-1923) Italian
Works on paper
£620 $1029 €905 Italian peasant girl (64x47cm-25x19in) s. W/C. 1-Oct-3 Sotheby's, Olympia #222/R

BALLESIO, Giuseppe (?) Italian
£1700 $3009 €2482 Card players (41x58cm-16x23in) s. 29-Apr-4 Gorringes, Lewes #2399 est:1200-1800

BALLESTER, Rosalie (1949-) French
£633 $1140 €950 Composition technique (120x120cm-47x47in) s. 26-Apr-4 Millon & Associes, Paris #154b/R
Works on paper
£467 $845 €700 Mecanique celeste (100x100cm-39x39in) s. mixed media. 3-Apr-4 Neret-Minet, Paris #84
£467 $845 €700 Nouvelle galaxie (100x100cm-39x39in) s. mixed media. 3-Apr-4 Neret-Minet, Paris #231
£490 $832 €700 Galaxie (100x81cm-39x32in) s. mixed media canvas. 29-Nov-3 Neret-Minet, Paris #219
£559 $951 €800 Diagonale 45 (120x120cm-47x47in) s. mixed media canvas. 29-Nov-3 Neret-Minet, Paris #84

BALLHEIM, H (19th C) ?
£1276 $2297 €1863 Portrait of elegant girl (79x63cm-31x25in) s. 26-Jan-4 Lilla Bukowskis, Stockholm #201 est:25000-30000 (S.KR 17000)
£2516 $4000 €3673 Madonna and Child (79x64cm-31x25in) s. 5-May-3 O'Gallerie, Oregon #820/R est:3000-4000

BALLIESTER (19/20th C) Brazilian?
£2381 $4214 €3572 Vapor (32x73cm-13x29in) s.i.d.1908. 27-Apr-4 Bolsa de Arte, Rio de Janeiro #5/R (B.R 13000)

BALLIN, Auguste (1842-?) French
£380 $703 €555 Brent at Brentford (13x22cm-5x9in) s. panel exhib. 14-Jul-4 Christie's, Kensington #956
£703 $1132 €1026 Fishing boats leaving Etaples Harbour (17x29cm-7x11in) s. panel. 25-Aug-3 Lilla Bukowskis, Stockholm #1020 (S.KR 9200)
£1300 $2405 €1898 Harbour view (27x21cm-11x8in) s. panel. 14-Jul-4 Sotheby's, Olympia #221/R est:800-1200

BALLINGALL, Alexander (fl.1880-1910) British
Works on paper
£676 $1149 €987 Active wharf (48x66cm-19x26in) s.d.1895 W/C. 21-Nov-3 Walker's, Ottawa #248/R (C.D 1500)
£700 $1302 €1022 Entrance to the Grand Canal (48x74cm-19x29in) s. W/C. 4-Mar-4 Mitchells, Cockermouth #842/R

£850 $1445 €1241 Shore at Leith (34x52cm-13x20in) s.i. pencil W/C. 19-Nov-3 Tennants, Leyburn #993a
£900 $1503 €1314 Fleet setting sail (46x66cm-18x26in) s.d.1895 W/C. 16-Oct-3 Bonhams, Edinburgh #121/R

BALLINGER, Harry Russell (1892-1994) American
£489 $900 €714 Monhegan fog (51x61cm-20x24in) s. i.stretcher. 23-Jun-4 Doyle, New York #5006/R

BALLUE, Pierre Ernest (1855-1928) French
£282 $468 €400 Maisons pres de la riviere (38x55cm-15x22in) cardboard. 15-Jun-3 Peron, Melun #234
£300 $531 €438 L'arc en ciel (27x35cm-11x14in) s. board. 29-Apr-4 Christie's, Kensington #14
£317 $526 €450 Maisons au bord de la riviere (46x64cm-18x25in) 15-Jun-3 Peron, Melun #235
£738 $1321 €1100 La Ramasseuse de fagots (65x54cm-26x21in) s.d.1881. 25-May-4 Chambelland & Giafferi, Paris #76/R
£795 $1454 €1200 Une Rue a Montreuil-Belay au printemps (27x35cm-11x14in) s. panel. 7-Apr-4 Piasa, Paris #46
£1100 $1837 €1606 Bank of the river (30x41cm-12x16in) s.i.d.1893 prov. 22-Oct-3 Sotheby's, Olympia #24/R est:1000-2000
£1322 $2247 €1930 Sunny river with washerwomen (64x92cm-25x36in) s. 5-Nov-3 Dobiaschofsky, Bern #323/R est:3000 (S.FR 3000)
£1497 $2380 €2200 Village en campagne (50x65cm-20x26in) s. 23-Mar-3 St-Germain-en-Laye Encheres #55/R
£1594 $2614 €2200 Boisiere en foret (65x54cm-26x21in) s. 11-May-3 Osenat, Fontainebleau #219 est:2000-2200
£2667 $4880 €4000 Montigny-sur-Loing (54x73cm-21x29in) s. i.verso. 6-Jun-4 Osenat, Fontainebleau #136/R est:3500-4000

BALLUF, Ernst (1921-) Austrian
Works on paper
£355 $592 €500 Approaching storm (30x40cm-12x16in) s.i.d.76 W/C paper on board. 16-Oct-3 Dorotheum, Salzburg #874/R
£594 $1010 €850 Evening (34x49cm-13x19in) s.i.d.76 mixed media. 27-Nov-3 Dorotheum, Linz #548/R
£600 $1074 €900 Storm over Waxenberg (25x36cm-10x14in) s.d.73 W/C. 13-May-4 Dorotheum, Linz #570/R

BALMER, Barbara (1929-) British
Works on paper
£280 $515 €409 Outlook (30x40cm-12x16in) s. W/C. 29-Mar-4 Thomson Roddick & Medcalf, Edinburgh #222

BALMER, Paul Friedrich Wilhelm (1865-1922) Swiss
£498 $846 €727 Girl with blue bow in hair (55x43cm-22x17in) s.i.d.1911 verso. 28-Nov-3 Zofingen, Switzerland #2902 (S.FR 1100)
£690 $1234 €1007 Hare hunt (47x151cm-19x59in) 12-May-4 Dobiaschofsky, Bern #322/R est:1300 (S.FR 1600)
£3409 $5659 €4943 Sunday idyll (90x61cm-35x24in) s.d.1921. 13-Jun-3 Zofingen, Switzerland #2774/R est:2000 (S.FR 7500)

BALMETTE, Jules Jean (19th C) French
£2533 $4611 €3800 Pierre le Grand sauve par sa mere de la fureur des Strelitz (92x100cm-36x39in) s.i. painted c.1880. 30-Jun-4 Delvaux, Paris #8/R est:2500-3000

BALMFORD, Hurst (1871-1950) British
£530 $991 €774 Island ruins, St. Ives (38x51cm-15x20in) s. canvasboard. 20-Jul-4 Sworder & Son, Bishops Stortford #743/R
£900 $1620 €1314 Boats in the harbour (38x50cm-15x20in) s. board. 20-Jan-4 Bonhams, Knightsbridge #18/R
£1200 $2160 €1752 Polperro village and harbour (58x41cm-23x16in) board. 21-Jan-4 James Thompson, Kirby Lonsdale #36

BALMIGERE, Paul Marcel (20th C) French
£1507 $2562 €2200 Marchande de fleurs (41x33cm-16x13in) s. 9-Nov-3 Eric Pillon, Calais #56/R

BALOGH, Endre Kompoczy (1911-1977) Hungarian
£600 $1074 €876 Vase of summer flowers by an ornamental urn (76x61cm-30x24in) s. 18-Mar-4 Christie's, Kensington #705/R

BALOGHY, George (1950-) New Zealander
£1316 $2237 €1921 Symonds Street (59x84cm-23x33in) s.d.1986. 27-Nov-3 International Art Centre, Auckland #23/R est:4500-6000 (NZ.D 3500)

BALOUZET, Armand Auguste (1858-1905) French
£336 $601 €500 Paysage a la mare (45x65cm-18x26in) s. 26-May-4 Blanchet, Paris #190/R

BALS, Hilaire (1940-) Belgian
£278 $464 €400 Pres de la ferme (18x24cm-7x9in) s. panel. 21-Oct-3 Campo, Vlaamse Kaai #659
£313 $522 €450 Volaille et charrette dans un paysage (18x24cm-7x9in) s. panel. 21-Oct-3 Campo, Vlaamse Kaai #660
£470 $832 €700 Betail dans un paysage (30x40cm-12x16in) s. panel. 27-Apr-4 Campo, Vlaamse Kaai #305
£493 $853 €700 Pres de la mare (35x45cm-14x18in) s. panel. 9-Dec-3 Campo, Vlaamse Kaai #253

BALSAITIS, Jonas (1948-) Australian
Works on paper
£1074 $1988 €1568 K.I.P, number four (142x173cm-56x68in) s.d.1991 i.verso synthetic polymer. 15-Mar-4 Sotheby's, Melbourne #133 est:1000-2000 (A.D 2600)
£1229 $1942 €1794 Imprint image No 15, ashes of Vietnam (122x173cm-48x68in) s.i.d.1990 stretcher synthetic polymer prov.exhib. 2-Sep-3 Deutscher-Menzies, Melbourne #210/R est:2000-3000 (A.D 3000)

BALSAMO, Renato (20th C) Italian
Works on paper
£2797 $4755 €4000 Olive tree in Puglia (50x60cm-20x24in) s. s.i.d.92 verso mixed media on canvas. 28-Nov-3 Farsetti, Prato #309/R est:3500-4500

BALSAMO, Salvatore (1894-1922) Italian
£600 $1074 €900 Cock (63x45cm-25x18in) s. cardboard. 12-May-4 Stadion, Trieste #647/R
£667 $1193 €1000 Pierrot (73x48cm-29x19in) s. cardboard. 12-May-4 Stadion, Trieste #648/R
£1133 $2063 €1700 Girl from Calabria (50x31cm-20x12in) s. i.verso board. 12-Jul-4 Il Ponte, Milan #465
£1267 $2305 €1900 Views of Naples (12x20cm-5x8in) card 4 in one frame. 12-Jul-4 Il Ponte, Milan #407 est:450-500

BALSAMO, Vincenzo (1935-) Italian
£667 $1227 €1000 Untitled (30x24cm-12x9in) s.d.1983. 12-Jun-4 Meeting Art, Vercelli #9
£667 $1227 €1000 Still life (40x50cm-16x20in) s. 12-Jun-4 Meeting Art, Vercelli #739/R
£993 $1808 €1500 Untitled (80x120cm-31x47in) s. painted 1978. 17-Jun-4 Galleria Pananti, Florence #240/R est:800-1000
£1056 $1754 €1500 Paesaggio (34x50cm-13x20in) s.d.1966 verso. 14-Jun-3 Meeting Art, Vercelli #184/R est:1500
£1056 $1754 €1500 Composition (65x50cm-26x20in) s.d.1993 verso board on canvas. 14-Jun-3 Meeting Art, Vercelli #362/R est:1500
£1379 $2303 €2000 Untitled (70x50cm-28x20in) s.d.98 verso. 13-Nov-3 Finarte Semenzato, Rome #255/R est:1800-2400

BALSGAARD, Carl Vilhelm (1812-1893) Danish
£750 $1222 €1095 Still life of fruit and flowers on ledge (24x30cm-9x12in) init.d.1844. 28-Sep-3 Hindemae, Ullerslev #9/R (D.KR 8000)
£1028 $1624 €1491 Apricots on a branch (29x38cm-11x15in) s. 2-Sep-3 Rasmussen, Copenhagen #1570/R (D.KR 11000)

BALSON, Ralph (1890-1964) Australian
£1172 $2191 €1758 Untitled (61x76cm-24x30in) enamel board. 21-Jul-4 Shapiro, Sydney #161/R est:6000-8000 (A.D 3000)
£4029 $7454 €5882 Matter painting (120x90cm-47x35in) s.d.62 i.verso enamel on hardboard prov.exhib. 15-Mar-4 Sotheby's, Melbourne #110/R est:4000-6000 (A.D 9750)
£6967 $11008 €10172 Matter painting (85x116cm-33x46in) s. enamel board prov.exhib. 2-Sep-3 Deutscher-Menzies, Melbourne #74/R est:15000-20000 (A.D 17000)
£12195 $21829 €17805 Constructivist painting (47x60cm-19x24in) card painted c.1942. 4-May-4 Sotheby's, Melbourne #146/R est:20000-30000 (A.D 30000)
Works on paper
£3484 $5505 €5087 Untitled (51x76cm-20x30in) s.d.59 pastel prov.exhib. 2-Sep-3 Deutscher-Menzies, Melbourne #194/R est:5500-7500 (A.D 8500)

BALTARD, Louis Pierre (1764-1846) French
Works on paper
£1987 $3616 €3000 Etude de sculptures antiques dans une cour du Vatican (45x36cm-18x14in) pen wash W/C. 16-Jun-4 Beaussant & Lefèvre, Paris #57/R est:3000-4000
£4966 $8889 €7300 Entree du Louvre (19x14cm-7x6in) W/C pair. 19-Mar-4 Beaussant & Lefèvre, Paris #20/R est:3000-4000

BALTERMANTS, Dmitri (1912-1990) Russian
Photographs
£2260 $4000 €3300 Cosmonaut ahmet Han Syltan (48x58cm-19x23in) gelatin silver print lit. 27-Apr-4 Christie's, Rockefeller NY #264/R est:5000-7000

BALTHUS (1908-2001) French
£54423 $97417 €80000 Les volubilis I (46x55cm-18x22in) s.d.55 prov.exhib.lit. 21-Mar-4 Calmels Cohen, Paris #168/R est:80000-100000
£99548 $169231 €220000 Portrait de Frederique (81x65cm-32x26in) s.d.55 lit. 25-Nov-3 Pierre Berge, Paris #22/R est:200000-300000
£450000 $823500 €657000 Portrait de Rosabianca Skira (61x50cm-24x20in) board painted 1949 prov.exhib.lit. 2-Feb-4 Christie's, London #41/R est:300000-400000
£1800000 $3276000 €2628000 Nu aux bras leves (151x83cm-59x33in) s.d.1951 prov.exhib.lit. 3-Feb-4 Sotheby's, London #48/R est:1800000-2200000
£1899441 $3400000 €2773184 Golden afternoon (200x200cm-79x79in) painted 1957 prov.exhib.lit. 6-May-4 Sotheby's, New York #138/R est:4000000-6000000
Works on paper
£1056 $1828 €1500 Petite figure grotesque (21x16cm-8x6in) Chinese ink prov.exhib.lit. 9-Dec-3 Artcurial Briest, Paris #191 est:1500-2000
£5102 $9133 €7500 Deux personnages dont un allonge sur un banc (22x17cm-9x7in) Indian ink exec. 1924-1925 prov.lit. 21-Mar-4 Calmels Cohen, Paris #158/R est:8000-10000
£5986 $10356 €8500 Etude pour Pont-Neuf (18x22cm-7x9in) col crayon wax crayon double-sided prov.exhib. 9-Dec-3 Artcurial Briest, Paris #192/R est:7000-10000
£14000 $25480 €20440 Double etude pour Japonaise a la table rouge (38x55cm-15x22in) mono.d.64 pencil pen ink wash buff paper prov.lit. 5-Feb-4 Christie's, London #428/R est:15000-20000
£14493 $23768 €20000 Figura in poltrona (39x29cm-15x11in) mono. pencil drawing. 31-May-3 Farsetti, Prato #616/R est:20000-25000
£15000 $27300 €21900 Paysage de Monte Calvello (70x99cm-28x39in) mono. crayon exec 1978 prov.exhib.lit. 5-Feb-4 Christie's, London #427/R est:15000-20000
£16760 $30000 €24470 Etude pour Nu au repos (49x34cm-19x13in) mono.i. W/C pencil exec 1972 prov.exhib.lit. 5-May-4 Christie's, Rockefeller NY #147/R est:30000-40000

£24000	$43680	€35040	Sleeping woman (36x48cm-14x19in) mono.d.82 pencil buff paper prov.lit. 5-Feb-4 Christie's, London #426/R est:30000-40000
£30000	$54600	€43800	Woman sleeping (45x60cm-18x24in) mono. pencil buff paper exec 1948 prov.exhib.lit. 5-Feb-4 Christie's, London #425/R est:25000-35000
£70000	$128800	€102200	Study of Katia reading (38x28cm-15x11in) s. pencil drawn 1968-70 prov.exhib.lit. 24-Jun-4 Christie's, London #444/R est:30000-40000
£125698	$225000	€183519	Nu assis (100x70cm-39x28in) pencil exec 1972 prov.lit. 6-May-4 Sotheby's, New York #391/R est:150000-250000
£180556	$301528	€260000	Etude pour le peintre et son modele (70x100cm-28x39in) mono pencil prov.exhib.lit. 21-Oct-3 Christie's, Paris #79/R est:120000-150000
£216216	$387027	€320000	Etude pour nu au repos (95x68cm-37x27in) s. crayon prov. 5-May-4 Coutau Begarie, Paris #59/R est:120000-150000

BALTZ, Lewis (1945-) American

Photographs			
£3473	$5800	€5071	Laguna Beach, Thanksgiving Day (15x23cm-6x9in) s.i.d.1970 verso gelatin silver print prov. 17-Oct-3 Phillips, New York #25/R est:5000-7000
£8383	$14000	€12239	Candlestick point (20x25cm-8x10in) s.i.d. gelatin silver print chromogenic col print album. 16-Oct-3 Phillips, New York #229/R est:12000-18000

BALUNIN, Mikhail Abramovich (1875-c.1939) Russian

Works on paper			
£2297	$4112	€3400	The pals (29x39cm-11x15in) s. W/C. 8-May-4 Bukowskis, Helsinki #466/R est:2000-2500

BALWE, Arnold (1898-1983) German

£1477	$2613	€2200	Wurburg garden (58x43cm-23x17in) mono. i.d. verso board. 30-Apr-4 Dr Fritz Nagel, Stuttgart #713/R est:1200
£2083	$3479	€3000	Sun over the dunes (66x76cm-26x30in) s.i.d.1938 verso prov. 24-Oct-3 Ketterer, Hamburg #266/R est:3500-4500
£2276	$3801	€3300	In Rhodos (76x100cm-30x39in) s. 13-Nov-3 Neumeister, Munich #238/R est:5000-6000
£2800	$5012	€4200	Summer night (92x60cm-36x24in) s. s.d. verso. 13-May-4 Neumeister, Munich #280/R est:3000-3500
£3103	$5183	€4500	Melting snow (76x100cm-30x39in) s. 13-Nov-3 Neumeister, Munich #239/R est:4000-6000
£3691	$6534	€5500	Garden at dusk (70x100cm-28x39in) s.i.d. verso. 30-Apr-4 Dr Fritz Nagel, Stuttgart #704/R est:7000
£3889	$6494	€5600	Evening on the Zuiderzee (66x86cm-26x34in) s.d. s.i. verso prov. 24-Oct-3 Ketterer, Hamburg #265/R est:6000-7000
£5333	$9547	€8000	Christmas angel (73x93cm-29x37in) s. s.i. verso. 13-May-4 Neumeister, Munich #281/R est:2500-2800
£6111	$9594	€8800	Flower fields in autumn with figures (67x85cm-26x33in) s.d.33 s.i.d. verso. 30-Aug-3 Hans Stahl, Toestorf #56/R est:12000
£7042	$12183	€10000	Southern cafe (76x100cm-30x39in) s. i. verso. 13-Dec-3 Lempertz, Koln #113/R est:4500
£7042	$12183	€10000	Winter night (73x93cm-29x37in) s. s.i. verso exhib. 13-Dec-3 Lempertz, Koln #279/R est:5000-7000
£7383	$13067	€11000	Park with plane trees (70x100cm-28x39in) s. s.i.d. verso. 30-Apr-4 Dr Fritz Nagel, Stuttgart #707/R est:12000
£8000	$14320	€12000	Flowers in jug (66x76cm-26x30in) s. s.i. verso. 13-May-4 Neumeister, Munich #277/R est:12000-14000
£9333	$16707	€14000	Golden bouquet (110x66cm-43x26in) s. s.i. verso. 13-May-4 Neumeister, Munich #279/R est:10000-12000
£9375	$15656	€13500	Garden (85x49cm-33x19in) s. i. verso lit. 25-Oct-3 Bergmann, Erlangen #969/R est:13500
£10345	$17276	€15000	Farmer's garden (85x100cm-33x39in) s. s.i.verso. 13-Nov-3 Neumeister, Munich #237/R est:15000-18000
£17450	$30886	€26000	Country garden (116x81cm-46x32in) s. s.i.d. verso. 30-Apr-4 Dr Fritz Nagel, Stuttgart #703/R est:8000
£27465	$47514	€39000	Summer garden (89x116cm-35x46in) s.i. verso prov. 13-Dec-3 Lempertz, Koln #280/R est:6000-8000

BALWE-STAIMMER, Elisabeth (1896-1973) German

£470	$832	€700	Still life with Christmas angel and apple (66x48cm-26x19in) s.d. W/C. 30-Apr-4 Dr Fritz Nagel, Stuttgart #702/R
Works on paper			
£769	$1285	€1100	Busy Dutch harbour (58x80cm-23x31in) s. W/C gouache. 11-Oct-3 Hans Stahl, Hamburg #6/R
£839	$1401	€1200	Market scene (48x64cm-19x25in) s. W/C gouache lit. 11-Oct-3 Hans Stahl, Hamburg #5/R
£1611	$2851	€2400	Still life with apples (52x69cm-20x27in) s. W/C. 30-Apr-4 Dr Fritz Nagel, Stuttgart #708/R est:800
£1724	$2879	€2500	Tyrol landscape, at Walchsee (57x80cm-22x31in) s. s.i.verso W/C. 13-Nov-3 Neumeister, Munich #241/R est:2800-3000
£2349	$4158	€3500	Interior (56x77cm-22x30in) s. W/C. 30-Apr-4 Dr Fritz Nagel, Stuttgart #712/R est:800

BALZE, Jean Paul Étienne (1815-1884) French

£1761	$3046	€2500	Scene de l'antique (27x39cm-11x15in) paper. 10-Dec-3 Piasa, Paris #114/R est:3000

BALZE, Raymond (1818-1909) French

£3500	$6370	€5110	Water sprites in an Arcadian landscape (114x73cm-45x29in) s.d.1890. 16-Jun-4 Christie's, Kensington #110/R est:3500-4500
Works on paper			
£450	$810	€657	Juliet discovered by Friar Laurence (36x49cm-14x19in) col chk. 20-Apr-4 Sotheby's, Olympia #178/R

BAMA, James E (1926-) American

£1117	$2000	€1631	Scantily clad lounging woman with champagne glasses (10x38cm-4x15in) s. board. 15-May-4 Illustration House, New York #127/R est:2500-4000
£1366	$2200	€1981	Cowboy with saddle (7x7cm-3x3in) board. 22-Aug-3 Altermann Galleries, Santa Fe #138
£2095	$3750	€3059	Transporting a prisoner by camel caravan (36x64cm-14x25in) s. oil sepia tones board. 15-May-4 Illustration House, New York #14/R est:4000-6000
£2174	$3500	€3152	Indian on horse (7x8cm-3x3in) board. 22-Aug-3 Altermann Galleries, Santa Fe #114
£2545	$4250	€3716	Xian in winter (36x76cm-14x30in) s. 11-Oct-3 Nadeau, Windsor #26/R est:15000-22000
£4469	$8000	€6525	Old snow fence (30x51cm-12x20in) board. 15-May-4 Altermann Galleries, Santa Fe #174/R
£5348	$10000	€7808	Lucylie Moon Hall (36x30cm-14x12in) s. board prov. 24-Jul-4 Coeur d'Alene, Hayden #232/R est:10000-20000
Works on paper			
£1118	$1800	€1621	Cowboy with snow shoes (10x11cm-4x4in) pencil. 22-Aug-3 Altermann Galleries, Santa Fe #137

BAMBER, Bessie (fl.1900-1910) British

£480	$888	€701	Two kittens before a vase (16x15cm-6x6in) init. milk glass. 14-Jul-4 Bonhams, Chester #318
£500	$850	€730	Three kittens in a around a basket (17x24cm-7x9in) init. panel. 6-Nov-3 Hobbs Parker, Ashford #721/R
£720	$1289	€1051	Three kittens playing in a basket (17x24cm-7x9in) init.d.07 on milk glass. 17-Mar-4 Bonhams, Chester #232
£800	$1512	€1168	Game of skittles (12x20cm-5x8in) init. oil on opaque glass. 19-Feb-4 Christie's, Kensington #351/R
£850	$1462	€1241	Kittens (15x23cm-6x9in) init.d.04 glass. 4-Dec-3 Richardson & Smith, Whitby #432/R
£880	$1496	€1285	Study of two cats (33x48cm-13x19in) s. mono. 5-Nov-3 Brightwells, Leominster #1001/R
£1000	$1800	€1460	Three kittens by a potted palm (17x23cm-7x9in) s.d. 1905 painted on glass. 21-Apr-4 Cheffins, Cambridge #505/R est:1000-1500
£1100	$1892	€1606	Pug dogs in a basket (15x23cm-6x9in) init.d.1905 milch glass. 3-Dec-3 Neal & Fletcher, Woodbridge #309/R est:200-400
£1100	$2013	€1606	New friend (18x14cm-7x6in) init. board. 8-Apr-4 Christie's, Kensington #143/R est:500-700
£1300	$2327	€1898	Kittens (24x49cm-9x19in) init. panel. 11-May-4 Bonhams, Knightsbridge #186/R est:1500-2000
£1300	$2405	€1898	Three kittens and a porcelain bowl (16x24cm-6x9in) init. milk glass. 14-Jul-4 Bonhams, Chester #317 est:800-1200
£2100	$3927	€3150	Three kittens with a pile of books (19x32cm-7x13in) init. oil milk glass. 26-Jul-4 Bonhams, Bath #22/R est:1000-1500
£2400	$4392	€3504	Kitten in a basket of flowers and kitten sitting on a book by two vases (10x15cm-4x6in) mono. opaline glass pair. 7-Apr-4 Gardiner & Houlgate, Bath #192/R est:1800-2500
Works on paper			
£1300	$2210	€1898	Dandie Dinmonts (20x25cm-8x10in) indis sig.d.1928 W/C on ivorine. 27-Nov-3 Christie's, Kensington #296/R est:600-800

BAMBERGER, Fritz (1814-1873) German

£2587	$4399	€3700	Sierra Nevada (31x42cm-12x17in) s.d.1870 board. 20-Nov-3 Van Ham, Cologne #1469/R est:3000
Works on paper			
£993	$1808	€1500	Country landscape with mountains in the distance (64x104cm-25x41in) s.i.verso chl. 16-Jun-4 Hugo Ruef, Munich #1144/R est:1500

BAMBURY, Stephen (1951-) New Zealander

£643	$1164	€939	Site works set 5 no.16 (73x38cm-29x15in) i. s.d.1981 verso. 30-Mar-4 Peter Webb, Auckland #147/R est:3000-4000 (NZ.D 1800)
£1429	$2586	€2086	Co-ordinates (26x53cm-10x21in) i. s.d.1977-78 verso acrylic. 30-Mar-4 Peter Webb, Auckland #6/R est:4000-6000 (NZ.D 4000)
£1503	$2736	€2194	Avize (50x32cm-20x13in) i.verso acrylic pencil resin. 29-Jun-4 Peter Webb, Auckland #180/R est:2500-3500 (NZ.D 4300)
£4021	$7318	€5871	Also relieve thew heavines of the materials (54x54cm-21x21in) s.i.d.1991 acrylic copper leaf aluminium diptych. 29-Jun-4 Peter Webb, Auckland #21/R est:10000-15000 (NZ.D 11500)
£5776	$9415	€8433	Necessary Connection (107x86cm-42x34in) s.i.d.1998 verso resin acrylic. 23-Sep-3 Peter Webb, Auckland #38/R est:9000-12000 (NZ.D 16000)
Works on paper			
£3571	$6464	€5214	In the direction of metallic organisation (72cm-28in circular) i. s.d.1988-89 stretcher verso mixed media on canvas. 30-Mar-4 Peter Webb, Auckland #59/R est:10000-15000 (NZ.D 10000)
£3571	$6464	€5214	Air is filled with an infinite amount of lines, no.3 (72cm-28in circular) i. s.d.1989 stretcher verso mixed media on can vas. 30-Mar-4 Peter Webb, Auckland #60/R est:10000-15000 (NZ.D 10000)
£5224	$9037	€7627	Sienna XII (50x100cm-20x39in) s.i.d.1996 verso 23K gold schlag metal acrylic aluminium diptych. 9-Dec-3 Peter Webb, Auckland #18/R est:12000-16000 (NZ.D 14000)

BAMFYLDE, Coplestone Warre (1719-1791) British

£3000	$5100	€4380	Extensive Italianate landscape with a herdsman resting in the foreground (57x82cm-22x32in) 27-Nov-3 Sotheby's, London #176/R est:2500-4000
Works on paper			
£900	$1530	€1314	View of Torbay (23x48cm-9x19in) i.verso pen ink w, over pencil htd scratching out prov. 27-Nov-3 Sotheby's, London #248/R
£900	$1530	€1314	View of Southampton (22x42cm-9x17in) i.verso W/C over pencil on two sheet prov. 27-Nov-3 Sotheby's, London #249/R
£900	$1620	€1314	Arcadian landscape with figures and cattle by a stream (42x55cm-17x22in) s.d.1775 W/C htd white prov. 22-Apr-4 Lawrence, Crewkerne #735/R

BANCHIERI, Giuseppe (1927-1994) Italian

£800	$1448	€1200	Landscape (40x40cm-16x16in) s.d.1968 s.i.d.verso. 2-Apr-4 Farsetti, Prato #218

BANCROFT, Elias (?-1924) British

£300	$510	€438	Continental town scene (44x61cm-17x24in) s.i.verso. 22-Nov-3 Bonhams, Chester #340
£550	$946	€803	Sheep grazing in open landscape with mountain background (20x36cm-8x14in) s.d.1879. 5-Dec-3 Keys, Aylsham #703

Works on paper
£300 $567 €438 Alfalfa, Seville (37x27cm-15x11in) s.d.1882 i.verso W/C. 18-Feb-4 Peter Wilson, Nantwich #63
£360 $659 €526 Portrait of a maid before a country house (76x54cm-30x21in) s.d.1878. bodycol. 27-Jan-4 Bonhams, Knightsbridge #75/R
£620 $1054 €905 Boy playing with a boat by stone steps (37x27cm-15x11in) s.d.1890 i.verso W/C. 26-Nov-3 Peter Wilson, Nantwich #119/R

BANCROFT, Milton Herbert (1867-1947) American
Works on paper
£350 $595 €511 St Michael's Mount from the mainland (26x58cm-10x23in) s.i. gouache. 30-Oct-3 Bracketts, Tunbridge Wells #1051/R

BAND, Max (1900-1974) Israeli?
£243 $450 €355 Lost in thought (81x61cm-32x24in) s.d.1932. 15-Jul-4 Doyle, New York #5/R
Works on paper
£559 $934 €800 Interieur d'un temple religieux (49x30cm-19x12in) s.d.35 gouache. 25-Jun-3 Rabourdin & Choppin de Janvry, Paris #88/R

BANDEIRA (1922-1967) Brazilian
£32967 $58352 €49451 Eclipse (46x55cm-18x22in) s.d.1954 s.i.d.verso. 27-Apr-4 Bolsa de Arte, Rio de Janeiro #104/R (B.R 180000)
£39377 $72060 €59066 Night scene (65x162cm-26x64in) s.i.d.1962. 6-Jul-4 Bolsa de Arte, Rio de Janeiro #169/R (B.R 215000)
Works on paper
£1282 $2269 €1923 Landscape (19x14cm-7x6in) s.i.d.1949 W/C. 27-Apr-4 Bolsa de Arte, Rio de Janeiro #105/R (B.R 7000)
£1557 $2755 €2336 Untitled (25x37cm-10x15in) s.d.1959 gouache. 27-Apr-4 Bolsa de Arte, Rio de Janeiro #106/R (B.R 8500)
£16484 $29176 €24726 Untitled (31x124cm-12x49in) s. gouache. 27-Apr-4 Bolsa de Arte, Rio de Janeiro #101/R (B.R 90000)

BANDEIRA, Antonio (1922-1967) Brazilian
Works on paper
£1067 $1963 €1600 Cidade notura (12x14cm-5x6in) s.d.64 gouache W/C prov. 9-Jun-4 Artcurial Briest, Paris #432 est:2000-3000

BANDELLI, Enrico (1941-) Italian
£563 $935 €800 Su e Giu per Settignano (110x110cm-43x43in) s. s.i.verso. 14-Jun-3 Meeting Art, Vercelli #364

BANDI, Hans (1896-1973) Swiss?
£431 $772 €629 Lake Thun (75x100cm-30x39in) s.d.52 i. verso. 12-May-4 Dobiaschofsky, Bern #323/R (S.FR 1000)

BANDINELLI, Baccio (attrib) (1493-1560) Italian
£40000 $73200 €58400 Portrait of the artist, in a black coat (19cm-7in circular) oil on slate prov. 7-Jul-4 Christie's, London #9/R est:20000-30000

BANDO, Toshio (1890-1973) Japanese
£1060 $1928 €1600 Pigeon (24x33cm-9x13in) s. 15-Jun-4 Rossini, Paris #168/R est:800-1200
£1457 $2666 €2200 Roulottes et gitans (29x55cm-11x22in) s. 7-Apr-4 Piasa, Paris #172/R est:2500-3000
£1773 $2961 €2500 Nature morte au guerrier japonais (50x61cm-20x24in) s. 15-Oct-3 Claude Aguttes, Neuilly #3 est:2000-3000
£1879 $3326 €2800 Nature morte aux fruits (24x33cm-9x13in) s. 27-Apr-4 Artcurial Briest, Paris #203/R est:1800-2500
£2113 $3655 €3000 Pigeon (24x33cm-9x13in) s. 14-Dec-3 Eric Pillon, Calais #96/R
£2500 $4475 €3650 Dove (33x46cm-13x18in) s. 6-May-4 Sotheby's, London #63/R est:3000-4000
£5348 $10000 €7808 Femme nue assise (33x41cm-13x16in) s. oil gold silver paint. 25-Feb-4 Christie's, Rockefeller NY #36/R est:5000-7000
Works on paper
£235 $437 €350 Chat assis (23x18cm-9x7in) s. Indian ink ink wash. 2-Mar-4 Artcurial Briest, Paris #94

BANEGAS LISTA, Javier (1974-) Spanish
Works on paper
£483 $869 €700 Galatea (90x95cm-35x37in) s.d.98 mixed media board. 26-Jan-4 Durán, Madrid #74/R

BANG, August (?) Swedish?
£1536 $2504 €2243 Moonlit coastal landscape (86x155cm-34x61in) s. 29-Sep-3 Lilla Bukowskis, Stockholm #571 est:25000-30000 (S.KR 20000)

BANG, Christian (1868-?) Danish
£627 $1147 €915 Woman wearing red dress seated on terrace (139x116cm-55x46in) mono.d.1909. 9-Jun-4 Rasmussen, Copenhagen #1603/R (D.KR 7000)

BANG, Wilhelmine Marie (1848-1932) Danish
£448 $819 €654 Man in his workshop (56x67cm-22x26in) mono.d.95. 9-Jun-4 Rasmussen, Copenhagen #2003/R (D.KR 5000)

BANGALA, England (c.1925-) Australian
Works on paper
£325 $514 €471 Jingubardabiya, triangular pandanus skirts (82x38cm-32x15in) earth pigments eucalyptus bark exec.c.1980. 28-Jul-3 Sotheby's, Paddington #334 (A.D 800)

BANKS, J O (fl.1856-1873) British
£1900 $3534 €2774 Mother's pride (36x30cm-14x12in) s. 4-Mar-4 Christie's, Kensington #617 est:1500-2000
£5864 $9500 €8503 Lazy one (36x46cm-14x18in) s. sold with another. 8-Aug-3 Barridorf, Portland #95/R est:4000-6000
£14000 $25480 €20440 Off to market (64x101cm-25x40in) s. 16-Jun-4 Bonhams, New Bond Street #40/R est:7000-10000

BANKS, Johnny (20th C) American
Works on paper
£222 $400 €324 Adam and Eve (61x86cm-24x34in) col pencil ink. 24-Apr-4 Slotin Folk Art, Buford #634/R
£250 $450 €365 Adam and Eve in the prime of their glory (56x89cm-22x35in) col pencil ink. 24-Apr-4 Slotin Folk Art, Buford #633/R

BANKS, Robert (1911-) British
Works on paper
£850 $1573 €1241 Ponte de Megio, Venice (63x45cm-25x18in) s. W/C prov. 11-Feb-4 Cheffins, Cambridge #402/R
£850 $1522 €1241 Venetian canal (47x65cm-19x26in) s.i. pencil W/C. 14-May-4 Christie's, Kensington #520
£1100 $2035 €1606 S Bartolomeo dell Isola, Rome (66x48cm-26x19in) s.d.1972 W/C prov. 11-Feb-4 Cheffins, Cambridge #401/R est:600-800
£1400 $2590 €2044 Palazzo Stabile, Venice (66x50cm-26x20in) s. W/C prov. 11-Feb-4 Cheffins, Cambridge #403/R est:600-800
£2027 $3750 €2959 Santa Maria dei Mircaoli and Lecce. S Oronzo (71x51cm-28x20in) second s.i. W/C paper on board two prov. 15-Jul-4 Sotheby's, New York #128/R est:1000-1500

BANKS, Thomas J (1828-1896) British
£615 $1100 €898 Landscape with stream and waterfall (51x41cm-20x16in) mono.d.73. 21-Mar-4 Jeffery Burchard, Florida #24/R
£1100 $1837 €1606 Figures conversing by path in rural Yorkshire landscape (20x33cm-8x13in) mono.d.1882. 16-Nov-3 Desmond Judd, Cranbrook #1090

BANNARD, Walter Darby (1931-) American
Works on paper
£958 $1600 €1399 China spring (168x251cm-66x99in) s.indis.i.stretcher alkyd resin canvas prov. 7-Oct-3 Sotheby's, New York #360 est:700-900
£1294 $2200 €1889 Sea of clouds (196x175cm-77x69in) s.i.d.1974 verso alkyd resin. 9-Nov-3 Wright, Chicago #474 est:1000-1500

BANNATYNE, John James (1835-1911) British
£1400 $2338 €2044 Islay from the Kintyre Coast (71x92cm-28x36in) s. 16-Oct-3 Lyon & Turnbull, Edinburgh #133 est:1500-2000
£3000 $5430 €4380 Arran, from Torrisdale, Kintyre (51x76cm-20x30in) s. 19-Apr-4 Sotheby's, London #116/R est:3000-5000
Works on paper
£350 $627 €511 Bury on the Arun (30x48cm-12x19in) s. W/C htd white. 25-May-4 Bonhams, Knightsbridge #8/R

BANNER, A (19th C) ?
£751 $1351 €1096 Country idyll (41x61cm-16x24in) s. s.d.1888. 26-Jan-4 Lilla Bukowskis, Stockholm #131 (S.KR 10000)

BANNER, Alfred (fl.1878-1914) British
£300 $510 €438 Tent near Ingelby (36x61cm-14x24in) s.d.1895 i.d.verso. 30-Oct-3 Duke & Son, Dorchester #191/R
£350 $637 €511 Arley-on-Severn (30x46cm-12x18in) s.i.verso. 15-Jun-4 David Lay, Penzance #242
£750 $1290 €1095 Midday break. Rest by the gate (15x23cm-6x9in) s.d.1887 board pair. 3-Dec-3 Bonhams, Knightsbridge #87/R
£950 $1710 €1387 Derbyshire lane (21x36cm-8x14in) s.d.1901 canvasboard. 22-Apr-4 Mellors & Kirk, Nottingham #1122/R
£950 $1748 €1387 Morning call, family at the door of a thatched cottage with a tradesman (30x51cm-12x20in) s.d.1892 s.i.verso. 10-Jun-4 Morphets, Harrogate #503/R

BANNER, Delmar Harmood (1896-1983) British
Works on paper
£500 $830 €730 Scafell from Hardknott Fell (38x56cm-15x22in) s.d.1935 W/C. 2-Oct-3 Mitchells, Cockermouth #857/R

BANNERMAN, Hamlet (fl.1879-1891) British
£403 $684 €588 Cornish Harbour (35x26cm-14x10in) s.i. artist board. 24-Nov-3 Sotheby's, Melbourne #352 (A.D 950)

BANNINGER, Otto Charles (1897-1973) Swiss
Sculpture
£2533 $4534 €3698 Horse's head (26cm-10in) mono.d.1949/60 bronze. 26-May-4 Sotheby's, Zurich #118/R est:2500-3000 (S.FR 5800)
£2609 $4774 €3809 Female nude walking (63cm-25in) mono.d.1948 bronze prov. 4-Jun-4 Zofingen, Switzerland #2227/R est:6000 (S.FR 6000)
£5677 $10162 €8288 Sitting with scarf (28cm-11in) mono.d.1939 st.f.K Stutz exhib. 26-May-4 Sotheby's, Zurich #51/R est:3000-5000 (S.FR 13000)

BANNINGER, Urs (1950-) Swiss
Works on paper
£317 $538 €463 Herzig (151x219cm-59x86in) s.i.d.1973 verso acrylic. 25-Nov-3 Germann, Zurich #722 (S.FR 700)

BANNISTER, Edward M (1833-1901) American
£23256 $40000 €33954 Figures on a pier at edge of lake (51x76cm-20x30in) s.d. 3. 7-Dec-3 Freeman, Philadelphia #123 est:10000-15000

BANNISTER, Pati (1929-) American
£1639 $3000 €2393 Little girl in the country (79x51cm-31x20in) s. masonite. 5-Jun-4 Neal Auction Company, New Orleans #712/R est:3000-5000
Works on paper
£249 $450 €364 Little girl with pot of flowers (25x18cm-10x7in) s. pastel. 3-Apr-4 Neal Auction Company, New Orleans #917

BANNON, John T (?) ?
£250 $430 €365 Antrim coast near Glenarm (28x93cm-11x37in) s. board. 3-Dec-3 John Ross, Belfast #89
£300 $516 €438 Fishing, Donegal (40x50cm-16x20in) s.d.93 board. 3-Dec-3 John Ross, Belfast #239
£360 $659 €526 Thatch cottage, Co. Antrim (50x76cm-20x30in) s. board. 2-Jun-4 John Ross, Belfast #84

BANTE, Arthur (1887-1951) German
£278 $453 €400 Venice (50x70cm-20x28in) s.d.27 i. verso. 26-Sep-3 Bolland & Marotz, Bremen #633/R

BANTI, Cristiano (1824-1904) Italian
£3380 $5611 €4800 Studio per il ritrovamento del cadavere di Lorenzo de'Medici (39x24cm-15x9in) s. prov.exhib.lit. 11-Jun-3 Christie's, Rome #157/R est:6000-8000
£9732 $18198 €14500 Women chatting (14x10cm-6x4in) board prov.lit. 25-Feb-4 Porro, Milan #8/R est:18000

BANTI, Leon Marcello (1880-?) Italian
£347 $590 €500 Women at the river (31x21cm-12x8in) init. board double-sided. 1-Nov-3 Meeting Art, Vercelli #7

BANTING, John (1902-1970) British
£413 $731 €603 La plante du coeur (57x67cm-22x26in) s.d.1930. 3-May-4 Christie's, Melbourne #210/R (A.D 1000)
£884 $1583 €1300 Untitled (51x40cm-20x16in) traces sig. panel. 21-Mar-4 Calmels Cohen, Paris #71/R est:1500-2000
£1700 $3094 €2482 Ruins and clothes line (51x40cm-20x16in) s.i. stretcher. 1-Jul-4 Christie's, Kensington #370/R est:1000-1500
£11000 $18700 €16060 Abstract masks (84x27cm-33x11in) s.d.1929 two. 21-Nov-3 Christie's, London #66/R est:1000-1500
Works on paper
£280 $484 €409 Abstract composition with flowing forms and bells (33x42cm-13x17in) s.d.1951 gouache. 9-Dec-3 Rosebery Fine Art, London #559/R
£420 $777 €613 Head studies (25x38cm-10x15in) s.d.1928 pen ink. 10-Mar-4 Sotheby's, Olympia #116/R
£600 $1110 €876 Shells and nude (48x56cm-19x22in) s.d.1950 pencil W/C gouache. 11-Mar-4 Christie's, Kensington #304/R
£900 $1530 €1314 Shells (29x39cm-11x15in) s.d.1950 W/C bodycol two. 21-Nov-3 Christie's, London #67/R

BANTING, Sir Frederick Grant (1891-1941) Canadian
£1802 $3063 €2631 Cobalt mine shaft (22x27cm-9x11in) s. panel prov.lit. 21-Nov-3 Walker's, Ottawa #28/R est:5000-7000 (C.D 4000)
£2252 $3829 €3288 Barn, Quebec village (20x25cm-8x10in) i.verso panel prov.exhib. 18-Nov-3 Sotheby's, Toronto #155/R est:3500-4500 (C.D 5000)
£2590 $4403 €3781 Fall landscape (27x34cm-11x13in) s. panel prov. 18-Nov-3 Sotheby's, Toronto #104/R est:6000-8000 (C.D 5750)
£6504 $11642 €9496 Dundas Harbour (19x26cm-7x10in) s. i.d.1927 verso panel prov.exhib. 27-May-4 Heffel, Vancouver #41/R est:9000-12000 (C.D 16000)

BANTLE, Hermann Anton (1872-1930) German
Works on paper
£347 $566 €500 Woman's portrait (27x21cm-11x8in) s.i.d.1908 pastel board. 27-Sep-3 Dr Fritz Nagel, Stuttgart #9033/R

BANTZER, Carl (1857-1941) German
Works on paper
£336 $624 €500 Woodland scene with old beech trees (17x26cm-7x10in) s. W/C. 5-Mar-4 Wendl, Rudolstadt #3567/R

BAPTISTA, Hugo (1935-) Venezuelan
£231 $425 €347 Sunset (46x36cm-18x14in) s. painted 1968. 27-Jun-4 Subastas Odalys, Caracas #31/R
£248 $405 €362 Untitled (173x110cm-68x43in) s. acrylic painted 1965. 20-Jul-3 Subastas Odalys, Caracas #77
£299 $500 €437 Woman (74x61cm-29x24in) s. 19-Oct-3 Subastas Odalys, Caracas #113
£316 $575 €474 Yellow volcano (90x70cm-35x28in) s. painted 1980. 21-Jun-4 Subastas Odalys, Caracas #16
£424 $780 €636 Untitled (172x110cm-68x43in) s. painted 1965. 27-Jun-4 Subastas Odalys, Caracas #70

BAR-EL, Ido (1959-) Israeli
£2095 $3750 €3059 Night in the Kibbutz (152x53cm-60x21in) oil wooden door. 18-Mar-4 Sotheby's, New York #61/R est:4500-5500

BARABAS, Miklos (1810-1898) Hungarian
£1436 $2483 €2097 Man in a fur hat with a cup of coffee (93x72cm-37x28in) s.d.1865 verso after Jan Kupezky. 12-Dec-3 Kieselbach, Budapest #127/R (H.F 550000)
£1765 $2929 €2577 Noble man with golden necklace (31x25cm-12x10in) s.d.1840. 4-Oct-3 Kieselbach, Budapest #146/R (H.F 650000)
£10962 $18964 €16005 Moritz Szitanyi Ulmann, Founder of the Hungarian Trade Bank of Pest (92x73cm-36x29in) s.d.1857. 12-Dec-3 Kieselbach, Budapest #87/R (H.F 4200000)
Works on paper
£1141 $2019 €1700 Erzherzog Albrecht (57x42cm-22x17in) s.d.856 W/C pencil chk. 29-Apr-4 Dorotheum, Vienna #167/R est:1600-2400

BARABINO, Angelo (1883-1950) Italian
£7000 $12880 €10500 Peach trees in Casa Berutti (35x43cm-14x17in) s. board. 14-Jun-4 Sant Agostino, Torino #327/R est:6000-8000
£16779 $30034 €25000 Road to Berutti House (50x61cm-20x24in) s. painted 1938-40. 25-May-4 Finarte Semenzato, Milan #207/R est:15000-16000
£32215 $57664 €48000 Spring in Tortona countryside (70x79cm-28x31in) s. 25-May-4 Finarte Semenzato, Milan #209/R est:30000-33000
Works on paper
£1374 $2500 €2006 Two women reading (72x52cm-28x20in) s. pastel. 29-Jun-4 Sotheby's, New York #378/R est:4000-6000

BARABINO, Nicolo (1832-1891) Italian
£1391 $2531 €2100 La Vierge de l'Annonciation (37x29cm-15x11in) 21-Jun-4 Tajan, Paris #18/R est:2000-3000
£2676 $4442 €3800 La Munificenza (80x63cm-31x25in) trace sig. 11-Jun-3 Christie's, Rome #91/R est:4000-5000

BARAK, William (1824-1903) Australian
Works on paper
£19531 $36523 €29297 Untitled, ceremony (52x52cm-20x20in) earth pigments W/C pencil prov.exhib.lit. 26-Jul-4 Sotheby's, Melbourne #10/R est:50000-80000 (A.D 50000)

BARANOFF-ROSSINE, Vladimir (1888-1942) Russian
£42000 $71400 €61320 Still life with boots (35x50cm-14x20in) s. card prov.exhib. 19-Nov-3 Sotheby's, London #235/R est:15000-20000
£60000 $107400 €87600 Bathers (48x72cm-19x28in) s. lit. 26-May-4 Sotheby's, London #244/R est:60000-80000
£583333 $1050000 €851666 Still life with chair (87x69cm-34x27in) i.d.1911 prov.exhib. 23-Apr-4 Sotheby's, New York #65/R est:300000-400000
Works on paper
£1400 $2506 €2044 Rocky landscape (22x19cm-9x7in) init.i. ink W/C. 26-May-4 Sotheby's, Olympia #421/R est:800-1200
£16000 $28640 €23360 Abstract composition - head of a clown (28x38cm-11x15in) init. W/C board lit. 26-May-4 Sotheby's, London #242/R est:18000-25000

BARANY, Eugene (1912-1979) French
£413 $731 €603 Man painting (38x48cm-15x19in) s. board. 3-May-4 Christie's, Melbourne #369/R (A.D 1000)
£1271 $2008 €1856 Memories of Montmartre (91x107cm-36x42in) 2-Sep-3 Deutscher-Menzies, Melbourne #451/R est:1500-2500 (A.D 3100)
£1322 $2340 €1930 Black cat (121x141cm-48x56in) s.d.75. 3-May-4 Christie's, Melbourne #209/R est:2000-3000 (A.D 3200)

BARATELLA, Paolo (1935-) Italian
£400 $736 €600 Paolo is unhappy even on horseback (100x105cm-39x41in) s.d.1970 s.i.d.verso prov. 8-Jun-4 Finarte Semenzato, Milan #55/R
£400 $736 €600 Putto (60x50cm-24x20in) s.i.d.2004 verso oil mixed media. 12-Jun-4 Meeting Art, Vercelli #25/R
£400 $736 €600 Methaphysical remains (60x50cm-24x20in) s.i.d.2004 oil mixed media. 12-Jun-4 Meeting Art, Vercelli #301/R
£1067 $1963 €1600 Remembering a blue sky (114x146cm-45x57in) s.i.d.1964 oil mixed media collage. 12-Jun-4 Meeting Art, Vercelli #475/R est:1000
£1067 $1963 €1600 Homage to Tancredi (143x170cm-56x67in) s.i.d.1964 oil mixed media collage. 12-Jun-4 Meeting Art, Vercelli #858/R est:1000
Works on paper
£347 $573 €500 Homage to Bacon (50x60cm-20x24in) s.i.d.68 mixed media. 1-Jul-3 Il Ponte, Milan #779

BARBA, Juan (1915-1982) Spanish
£330 $524 €475 La clase de pintura (61x46cm-24x18in) s. 29-Apr-3 Durán, Madrid #16/R
£347 $552 €500 La lectura (61x46cm-24x18in) s. 29-Apr-3 Durán, Madrid #17/R
£987 $1786 €1500 Figures (81x60cm-32x24in) s. lit. 14-Apr-4 Ansorena, Madrid #109/R est:1500

BARBAIX, René (1909-1966) Belgian
£567 $1014 €850 Chez arlequin (60x73cm-24x29in) s.d.46 s.i.d.46 verso exhib. 15-May-4 De Vuyst, Lokeren #20

BARBANCON, Christian (1940-) ?
£324 $531 €450 Page 314B (54x65cm-21x26in) s. s.i.verso prov. 6-Jun-3 David Kahn, Paris #27

BARBANTI, Giuliano (1936-) Italian
£1409 $2523 €2100 SS24C306. SS24C307 (70x70cm-28x28in) s.i.verso acrylic painted 1974 prov. pair. 25-May-4 Sotheby's, Milan #172/R est:200-300

BARBARINI, Emil (1855-1930) Austrian

£1528	$2490	€2200	In the storm waters under bridge (21x26cm-8x10in) s. 24-Sep-3 Neumeister, Munich #389/R est:1800
£2000	$3620	€3000	Post coach on snowy track outside village (53x42cm-21x17in) s. 1-Apr-4 Van Ham, Cologne #1278/R est:1700
£2113	$3655	€3000	Street cafe with flower seller (16x20cm-6x8in) s. panel. 10-Dec-3 Dorotheum, Vienna #233/R est:3400-4000
£2797	$4755	€4000	Florence market (31x21cm-12x8in) s. panel. 28-Nov-3 Wiener Kunst Auktionen, Vienna #436/R est:4000-7000
£3125	$5500	€4563	Flower vendor (20x31cm-8x12in) s. panel. 18-May-4 Bonhams & Butterfields, San Francisco #94/R est:3000-5000
£3497	$5944	€5000	Mountain landscape with figures (73x98cm-29x39in) mono. 24-Nov-3 Dorotheum, Vienna #200/R est:5000-6000
£4167	$6875	€6000	Flower market on Karlsplatz, Vienna (25x39cm-10x15in) s. panel. 2-Jul-3 Neumeister, Munich #604/R est:5000
£4196	$7133	€6000	Market (21x32cm-8x13in) s. panel. 24-Nov-3 Dorotheum, Vienna #124/R est:7000-8000
£4667	$8587	€7000	Le marche aux fleurs a Paris (21x31cm-8x12in) s. panel. 11-Jun-4 Claude Aguttes, Neuilly #20/R est:4000-6000
£6993	$11888	€10000	Woman selling flowers in Vienna (36x58cm-14x23in) s. panel. 24-Nov-3 Dorotheum, Vienna #229/R est:10000-12000

BARBARINI, Emil (attrib) (1855-1930) Austrian

£1127	$1949	€1600	Mountain landscape with farmsteads and figures (75x100cm-30x39in) 11-Dec-3 Dr Fritz Nagel, Stuttgart #510/R est:1800

BARBARINI, Franz (1804-1873) Austrian

£1078	$1929	€1574	Waterfall at Bad Gastein (73x100cm-29x39in) mono.d.866. 12-May-4 Dobiaschofsky, Bern #324/R est:4500 (S.FR 2500)
£1389	$2361	€2000	Untersberg near Salzburg (32x40cm-13x16in) s.d.860 board. 28-Oct-3 Dorotheum, Vienna #94/R est:2600-3000
£1774	$3265	€2590	Couple by tranquil river. Family on a hill side path (39x53cm-15x21in) s.d.1847 panel. 14-Jun-4 Waddingtons, Toronto #34/R est:3000-4000 (C.D 4400)

BARBARINI, Franz (attrib) (1804-1873) Austrian

£611	$1125	€892	Coast with ships, animals and figures (31x41cm-12x16in) mono. 14-Jun-4 Philippe Schuler, Zurich #4256 (S.FR 1400)

BARBARINI, Gustav (1840-1909) Austrian

£775	$1286	€1100	Mountains with mill (35x27cm-14x11in) s. board. 16-Jun-3 Dorotheum, Vienna #91
£2113	$3655	€3000	Traveller resting by a stream (69x55cm-27x22in) s. 10-Dec-3 Dorotheum, Vienna #165/R est:3400-3800

BARBARO, Giovanni (fl.1890-1907) British

Works on paper

£260	$465	€380	Still life of fruit with plate and copper pot (33x79cm-13x31in) s. W/C bodycol htd white. 18-Mar-4 Neales, Nottingham #711
£800	$1432	€1168	Still lifes of fruit (72x34cm-28x13in) s. W/C pair. 25-May-4 Bonhams, Knightsbridge #201/R

BARBASAN, Mariano (1864-1924) Spanish

£2039	$3691	€3100	Rocky landscape (58x40cm-23x16in) board. 14-Apr-4 Ansorena, Madrid #47/R est:2300
£2837	$4596	€4000	Paisaje de Anticoli (14x19cm-6x7in) s.d.28-6-1906. 20-May-3 Ansorena, Madrid #176/R est:3800
£4000	$7160	€5840	Goat herder in a landscape (17x21cm-7x8in) s.i.d.1915. 26-May-4 Sotheby's, Olympia #276/R est:3000-4000
£16000	$29440	€23360	Farmyard scene (18x30cm-7x12in) s.i.d.1906 panel. 25-Mar-4 Christie's, Kensington #152/R est:4000-6000

BARBAUD-KOCK, Marthe Elisabeth (1862-?) French

£682	$1132	€989	Nature morte aux fleurs (50x61cm-20x24in) s. 13-Jun-3 Zofingen, Switzerland #2412/R est:2000 (S.FR 1500)
£8000	$14640	€12000	Bouquet de fleurs dans un panier d'osier (114x140cm-45x55in) s. 6-Jun-4 Anaf, Lyon #37/R est:12000-15000

BARBAZZA, Paolo (18th C) Italian

Works on paper

£4200	$7686	€6300	Ancient Rome (9x14cm-4x6in) s. W/C htd white set of eleven. 6-Jul-4 Christie's, London #89/R est:2000-3000

BARBEAU, Marcel (1925-) Canadian

£446	$768	€651	Tendresse (69x82cm-27x32in) s.d.80 acrylic. 2-Dec-3 Joyner Waddington, Toronto #431 (C.D 1000)
£600	$1098	€876	Reflets printaniers (48x63cm-19x25in) s.d.1989 acrylic paper. 1-Jun-4 Hodgins, Calgary #327/R (C.D 1500)
£1220	$2183	€1781	Neiges eblouies (51x61cm-20x24in) s.d.76 s.i.d.verso acrylic prov. 31-May-4 Sotheby's, Toronto #70/R est:3000-5000 (C.D 3000)

BARBEDIENNE, Ferdinand (1810-1892) French

Sculpture

£1000	$1810	€1500	Lorenzo de Medicis (36cm-14in) s. pat bronze lit. 31-Mar-4 Segre, Madrid #837/R
£1192	$2181	€1800	Minverva (185cm-73in) s. brown pat. bronze. 6-Apr-4 Sotheby's, Amsterdam #284/R est:2000-3000
£1317	$2200	€1923	Boy and fish (38cm-15in) s. bronze. 19-Oct-3 Susanin's, Chicago #6014/R est:2000-4000
£1702	$2843	€2400	Ambroise Pare (49x19x17cm-19x7x7in) s.i. bronze. 20-Oct-3 Sant Agostino, Torino #96/R est:500
£5667	$10370	€8500	La fleuve (63x52cm-25x20in) white marble after Caffieri. 6-Jun-4 Anaf, Lyon #y/R est:8000-10000

BARBEDIENNE, Ferdinand (attrib) (1810-1892) French

Sculpture

£2989	$5500	€4364	Figure of a Bacchante (91cm-36in) s. bronze. 9-Jun-4 Doyle, New York #3266 est:7000-9000

BARBEDIENNE, Ferdinand and GAUTHERIN, Jean (19th C) French

Sculpture

£4861	$8264	€7000	Clotilde de Surville (106cm-42in) s.i. pat bronze lit. 29-Oct-3 Segre, Madrid #675/R est:2900

BARBER, Charles Burton (1845-1894) British

£83333	$150000	€121666	Little baker with her two assistants (71x92cm-28x36in) s.d.1890. 23-Apr-4 Sotheby's, New York #65/R est:180000-220000

BARBER, Joseph Moseley (fl.1858-1889) British

£1276	$2170	€1863	Interior with mother and child (36x46cm-14x18in) s.d.1890. 26-Nov-3 Deutscher-Menzies, Melbourne #284/R est:2500-3500 (A.D 3000)

BARBER, Sam (1943-) American

£4865	$9000	€7298	October morn, bather by the pond (122x152cm-48x60in) s.d.1983 board. 17-Jul-4 Outer Cape Auctions, Provincetown #65/R

BARBER, Thomas (attrib) (1768-1843) British

£300	$501	€438	Portrait of a gentleman (76x61cm-30x24in) 14-Oct-3 David Lay, Penzance #23

BARBERIS, Irene (1953-) Australian

Works on paper

£1322	$2446	€1930	White horse, and I saw heaven opened (243x304cm-96x120in) s.d.1997 i.verso synthetic polymer prov.exhib. 15-Mar-4 Sotheby's, Melbourne #120 est:4000-6000 (A.D 3200)

BARBETTE, Josias (c.1650-1730) Danish

Miniatures

£8000	$14400	€11680	Husband, wife and their three sons (3cm-1in) s.i.d.1698 enamel gold oval five leather case prov.exhib. 22-Apr-4 Bonhams, New Bond Street #18/R est:5000-7000

BARBEY, Valdo (1883-1965) French

£915	$1584	€1300	Square de la place des Vosges (32x40cm-13x16in) s. 10-Dec-3 Ferri, Paris #98/R est:400-450
£1035	$1728	€1500	Le defile de mode (60x73cm-24x29in) s. 17-Nov-3 Tajan, Paris #115/R est:1200-2000

BARBIER, Andre (1883-1970) French

£537	$1004	€800	Sienne (30x40cm-12x16in) s.i.d.1935 oil paper on canvas. 29-Feb-4 Versailles Encheres #105/R
£559	$951	€800	Baie de Villefranche (38x46cm-15x18in) s. cardboard. 28-Nov-3 Blanchet, Paris #65/R est:800-1000
£664	$1129	€950	Les toits de Paris (28x50cm-11x20in) s. 28-Nov-3 Blanchet, Paris #68/R
£805	$1490	€1200	Falaises d'Etretat (50x61cm-20x24in) st.sig. paper on canvas. 14-Mar-4 St-Germain-en-Laye Encheres #91/R
£1918	$3260	€2800	Les inondations (60x73cm-24x29in) s. 5-Nov-3 Rabourdin & Choppin de Janvry, Paris #15/R est:3000-3500
£3800	$6574	€5548	Church on a cliff top, possibly at Varengeville (81x65cm-32x26in) s. 11-Dec-3 Lyon & Turnbull, Edinburgh #51/R est:3000-5000

BARBIER, Antoine (1859-?) French

Works on paper

£674	$1125	€950	Rue Tourbet et Bey, Tunis (38x26cm-15x10in) s. W/C. 16-Jun-3 Gros & Delettrez, Paris #213/R

BARBIER, Georges (1882-1932) French

Works on paper

£276	$458	€400	Femme a la lyre (28x18cm-11x7in) s. pen ink W/C. 6-Oct-3 Blanchet, Paris #213/R
£276	$458	€400	Femme a la tiare (28x18cm-11x7in) s. pen ink. 6-Oct-3 Blanchet, Paris #219
£276	$458	€400	Pretre en toge (29x20cm-11x8in) s. pen ink. 6-Oct-3 Blanchet, Paris #220
£276	$458	€400	Femme en tiare (29x19cm-11x7in) s. pen ink. 6-Oct-3 Blanchet, Paris #221
£276	$458	€400	Femme en tunique (29x19cm-11x7in) s. pen ink. 6-Oct-3 Blanchet, Paris #223
£276	$458	€400	Femme en robe (23x18cm-9x7in) s. pen ink. 6-Oct-3 Blanchet, Paris #225
£380	$635	€555	Hunter (21x15cm-8x6in) s. gouache. 21-Oct-3 Bonhams, Knightsbridge #78/R
£600	$1032	€876	Don Juan aux enfers (12x23cm-5x9in) s.d.1921 pencil black ink W/C lit. 3-Dec-3 Christie's, Kensington #278
£2500	$4600	€3800	Five O'Clock tea (30x24cm-12x9in) s. i. verso W/C Indian ink cream paper on board. 25-Jun-4 Tajan, Paris #7/R est:3000-3500

BARBIER, Jean Jacques le (1738-1826) French

Works on paper

£550	$952	€803	Sacrifice to Venus, vestal virgin sacrificing two doves on an altar (25x19cm-10x7in) pen grey ink bodycol vellum. 12-Dec-3 Christie's, Kensington #486/R
£890	$1513	€1300	Travaux sur une route (60x43cm-24x17in) s.d.1784 pen ink wash. 6-Nov-3 Tajan, Paris #64/R

£1067 $1931 €1600 L'automne, le printemps, l'ete (43x28cm-17x11in) s. black crayon one double-sided three. 30-Mar-4 Rossini, Paris #12/R est:1500-2000
£3846 $6615 €5500 Jeunes femmes apportant des fleurs a une statue de Flore dans un paysage (35x29cm-14x11in) s.d.1773 pen ink W/C. 2-Dec-3 Christie's, Paris #518/R est:2000-3000

BARBIER, Jean Jacques le (attrib) (1738-1826) French
£1800 $2862 €2610 Game of knucklebones (74x60cm-29x24in) 9-Sep-3 Bonhams, Knightsbridge #213/R est:2000-3000

BARBIERI, Contardo (1900-1960) Italian
£1154 $2100 €1685 Young woman reading (79x58cm-31x23in) s. 7-Feb-4 Sloans & Kenyon, Bethesda #1263a/R est:700-1000
Works on paper
£243 $428 €360 View of Bardolino (24x34cm-9x13in) s.i. W/C exec.1946. 19-May-4 Il Ponte, Milan #1396

BARBIERI, Giovanni Battista (after) (c.1580-?) Italian
£5200 $8840 €7592 Persian Sybil (123x92cm-48x36in) 29-Oct-3 Bonhams, New Bond Street #103/R est:1500-2000

BARBIERS, Pieter Pietersz (1749-1842) Dutch
Works on paper
£3056 $5500 €4462 Study of a black parrot on a tree branch (30x24cm-12x9in) W/C gouache. 21-Jan-4 Sotheby's, New York #136/R est:5000-7000

BARBISAN, Giovanni (1914-1988) Italian
£2183 $3493 €3100 Caorle farms (40x69cm-16x27in) s. s.i.verso. 19-Sep-3 Finarte, Venice #460/R
£2817 $4930 €4000 Woman knitting (60x50cm-24x20in) s. s.d.1959 verso. 16-Dec-3 Finarte Semenzato, Milan #86/R est:4000-4400
£3099 $5423 €4400 Cup with pumpkin flowers (30x40cm-12x16in) s.d.1965 board. 16-Dec-3 Finarte Semenzato, Milan #88/R est:4500-5500

BARBOUR, William (20th C) American?
£237 $425 €346 Dogs hunting (51x64cm-20x25in) painted 1916. 11-May-4 Roland's, New York #473280/R

BARBOZA, Diego (1945-) Venezuelan
£363 $675 €530 Nude (45x60cm-18x24in) s. painted 1996. 14-Mar-4 Subastas Odalys, Caracas #8/R

BARBUDO, Salvador Sanchez (1858-1917) Spanish
£524 $892 €750 Etude de fleurs (8x14cm-3x6in) s. panel. 24-Nov-3 E & Eve, Paris #187
£1611 $2964 €2400 Procession (48x35cm-19x14in) s. 24-Mar-4 Il Ponte, Milan #555/R est:2400-2600
£5634 $9746 €8000 Pre-nuptial agreement between Isabelle of Castilla and Alfonso of Aragone (70x90cm-28x35in) s. 10-Dec-3 Finarte Semenzato, Rome #285/R est:8000-10000
£7000 $12740 €10220 First steps (33x43cm-13x17in) s. panel. 17-Jun-4 Christie's, London #96/R est:8000-12000
£22642 $36000 €33057 Story of the golden fleece (41x76cm-16x30in) s.painted 1886. 13-Sep-3 Selkirks, St. Louis #472/R est:20000-30000
£42553 $71064 €60000 Boda Ducal, Venecia (43x72cm-17x28in) s.d.86 panel. 23-Jun-3 Durán, Madrid #236/R est:42500
Works on paper
£621 $1117 €900 Swiss Guard in the Vatican (25x15cm-10x6in) s. W/C. 26-Jan-4 Ansorena, Madrid #296/R

BARCAGLIA, Donato (1849-1930) Italian
Sculpture
£1867 $3435 €2800 Old smoker (38x23x23cm-15x9x9in) s. bronze. 8-Jun-4 Sotheby's, Milan #154/R est:1500-1800
£55336 $99051 €80791 Love blinded (142cm-56in) s. base marble exec 1875 prov.exhib.lit. 15-May-4 Christie's, Sydney #422/R est:100000-150000 (A.D 140000)

BARCALA, Washington (1920-) Uruguayan
Works on paper
£333 $607 €500 Palacios (11x15cm-4x6in) s.i. col pencil exec c.1950. 29-Jun-4 Segre, Madrid #100/R
£4422 $8048 €6500 Composition (54x62cm-21x24in) s. s.verso collage wood threads prov. 3-Feb-4 Segre, Madrid #199/R est:3500

BARCALARIO, A (?) Italian?
£1295 $2124 €1800 Taggia (56x76cm-22x30in) s.d.87. 10-Jun-3 Pandolfini, Florence #114 est:1200-1300

BARCELO, Jose (1923-2002) Spanish
£408 $743 €600 Portrait of woman (39x31cm-15x12in) s.d.1958 board exhib.lit. 3-Feb-4 Segre, Madrid #156/R
£493 $863 €700 Still life (50x68cm-20x27in) s. board lit. 16-Dec-3 Durán, Madrid #655/R

BARCELO, Miguel (1957-) Spanish
£3267 $6011 €4900 Untitled (75x59cm-30x23in) s.d.1987 paper prov. 11-Jun-4 Pierre Berge, Paris #75/R est:6000-8000
£31000 $57040 €45260 Untitled (50x66cm-20x26in) s.d.88 gouache prov. two. 24-Jun-4 Sotheby's, London #287/R est:8000-12000
£35000 $64400 €51100 Muso de Bakono (30x30cm-12x12in) s.i.d.1991 oil sand on canvas prov. 25-Jun-4 Christie's, London #170/R est:20000-30000
£60000 $110400 €87600 Man reading newspaper (100x150cm-39x59in) s.d.XII 83 oil newspaper collage paper on board prov. 25-Jun-4 Christie's, London #173/R est:70000-90000
£65868 $110000 €96167 Submarine (251x148cm-99x58in) s.i.d.2000 verso acrylic oil on canvas prov.exhib.lit. 13-Nov-3 Phillips, New York #33/R est:80000-120000
£100000 $182000 €146000 Cent caps (195x160cm-77x63in) s.i.d.VII.92 verso oil mixed media prov.exhib. 6-Feb-4 Sotheby's, London #192/R est:100000-150000
£450000 $828000 €657000 Pase de Pecho (67x101cm-26x40in) s.i.d.VII 90 oil sand seaweed resin newspaper gauze on canvas. 24-Jun-4 Christie's, London #32/R est:400000-700000
Sculpture
£10615 $19000 €15498 Cap esclafat (47x45x33cm-19x18x13in) i.num. of eight cast bronze prov.exhib. 14-May-4 Phillips, New York #234/R est:15000-20000
£21229 $38000 €30994 Autoportrait sur pichet, self portrait on jug (59x21x30cm-23x8x12in) i.num. of eight bronze prov.exhib. 14-May-4 Phillips, New York #233/R est:20000-30000
Works on paper
£4200 $7644 €6132 El Sahara (31x43cm-12x17in) s.i.d.17.111.88 W/C. 4-Feb-4 Sotheby's, Olympia #5/R est:1800-2200
£90000 $150300 €131400 Pierres-Tetes (175x119cm-69x47in) s.i.d.XI.95 verso mixed media card on canvas prov.exhib. 21-Oct-3 Sotheby's, London #375/R est:90000-120000
£90000 $163800 €131400 Interior Hollandes (130x195cm-51x77in) s.i.d.VII 89 verso mixed media canvas prov.exhib. 5-Feb-4 Sotheby's, London #30/R est:100000-150000
£150000 $273000 €219000 Novelo Mojada (195x300cm-77x118in) s.i.d.XI 85 verso mixed media canvas prov. 5-Feb-4 Sotheby's, London #56/R est:150000-180000
£190000 $349600 €277400 Improvisacio III (194x195cm-76x77in) s.i.d.87 mixed media on canvas prov. 24-Jun-4 Christie's, London #28/R est:220000-280000
£450000 $819000 €657000 En Los Medios (90x92cm-35x36in) s.i.d.VIII.90 verso mixed media canvas prov.lit. 5-Feb-4 Sotheby's, London #53/R est:380000-450000

BARCHUS, Eliza R (1857-1959) American
£367 $650 €536 Mt Hood at sunset (25x30cm-10x12in) s. board. 3-May-4 O'Gallerie, Oregon #69/R
£406 $650 €593 Rooster Rock, Oregon (30x56cm-12x22in) s. 22-Sep-3 O'Gallerie, Oregon #23/R
£516 $950 €753 Mt Hood at noonday (46x56cm-18x22in) s. 29-Mar-4 O'Gallerie, Oregon #109
£537 $950 €784 Three Sister, Oregon at sunset (30x25cm-12x10in) s. i.verso board. 3-May-4 O'Gallerie, Oregon #118/R
£546 $1000 €797 Three sisters (41x61cm-16x24in) s. 7-Jun-4 O'Gallerie, Oregon #701/R est:1500-2000
£615 $1100 €898 Mt Hood, Oregon, mountain, reflective water in foreground (30x46cm-12x18in) s. 16-Mar-4 Matthew's, Oregon #42/R
£683 $1100 €997 Mt Hood at sunset (30x46cm-12x18in) s. 20-Jan-3 O'Gallerie, Oregon #91/R
£706 $1200 €1031 Rooster Rock, Oregon (30x56cm-12x22in) s. 1-Dec-3 O'Gallerie, Oregon #48/R est:700-900
£710 $1300 €1037 Mt. Rainier at noon day (18x33cm-7x13in) s. 7-Jun-4 O'Gallerie, Oregon #68/R est:800-1000
£710 $1300 €1037 Mt. Hood at sunset (25x30cm-10x12in) s. board. 7-Jun-4 O'Gallerie, Oregon #132/R est:1200-1600
£714 $1300 €1042 View of Mt Hood (30x46cm-12x18in) s. prov. 15-Jun-4 John Moran, Pasadena #153
£719 $1200 €1050 Mt Rainier at noonday (56x81cm-22x32in) s. 27-Oct-3 O'Gallerie, Oregon #118/R est:1000-1500
£815 $1500 €1190 Mt Hood at noon day (30x46cm-12x18in) s. canvas on wood. 29-Mar-4 O'Gallerie, Oregon #724/R est:1800-2500
£899 $1700 €1313 Mt Hood at sunset (25x30cm-10x12in) s. panel. 23-Feb-4 O'Gallerie, Oregon #38/R est:1000-1500
£960 $1700 €1402 Entrance to San Francisco, California harbour (36x71cm-14x28in) s. 3-May-4 O'Gallerie, Oregon #719/R est:1200-1800
£1073 $1900 €1567 Mt Hood at sunset (41x61cm-16x24in) s. canvas on masonite. 3-May-4 O'Gallerie, Oregon #200/R est:1500-2000
£1093 $2000 €1596 Mt. Shasta at noon day (56x91cm-22x36in) s. 7-Jun-4 O'Gallerie, Oregon #828/R est:3000-4000
£1412 $2500 €2062 Monterey, California seascape (46x91cm-18x36in) s. 3-May-4 O'Gallerie, Oregon #755/R est:2500-3500
£1503 $2750 €2194 Mt. Hood at sunset (41x56cm-16x22in) s. 7-Jun-4 O'Gallerie, Oregon #799/R est:2500-3500
£1554 $2750 €2269 Three Sisters, Oregon (56x91cm-22x36in) s. 3-May-4 O'Gallerie, Oregon #801/R est:2000-3000
£2186 $4000 €3192 Carter Lake, Oregon (30x91cm-12x36in) 7-Jun-4 O'Gallerie, Oregon #113/R est:2500-3500
£3226 $6000 €4710 Mt Hood (76x127cm-30x50in) s. 5-Mar-4 Skinner, Boston #302/R est:2000-3000
£3438 $5500 €5019 Multnomah Falls, Oregon (56x91cm-22x36in) s. 22-Sep-3 O'Gallerie, Oregon #768/R est:2000-3000
£6417 $12000 €9369 Mt. Shasta at noonday (74x124cm-29x49in) s. board. 24-Jul-4 Coeur d'Alene, Hayden #39/R est:8000-12000

BARCHUS, Eliza R (attrib) (1857-1959) American
£1000 $1600 €1460 Mountain landscape, northern California (81x122cm-32x48in) d.1885 prov. 22-Sep-3 O'Gallerie, Oregon #787/R est:2000-3000

BARCIA, Augusto (1926-) South American
£441 $750 €644 On the mountains (86x130cm-34x51in) s. 25-Nov-3 Galeria y Remates, Montevideo #206/R

BARCLAY, Albert Paterson (1912-1998) British
£550 $974 €803 Leagarth Fetlar Shetland Isles (35x76cm-14x30in) s.d.78 board. 28-Apr-4 Peter Wilson, Nantwich #43
Works on paper
£260 $460 €380 Hunting in Derbyshire (23x32cm-9x13in) s.d.80 W/C. 28-Apr-4 Peter Wilson, Nantwich #129
£380 $673 €555 Hunting in Derbyshire with hounds and huntsmen (47x60cm-19x24in) s.d.78 W/C. 28-Apr-4 Peter Wilson, Nantwich #128

BARCLAY, Edith (?) British
Works on paper
£400 $668 €584 Shepherd with sheep and dog in river (23x33cm-9x13in) s. W/C. 17-Oct-3 Keys, Aylsham #495

BARCLAY, J (?) British
£2000 $3580 €2920 Faggot gatherers. Crossing the river (25x41cm-10x16in) s. pair. 27-May-4 Christie's, Kensington #193/R est:1000-1500

BARCLAY, McClelland (1891-1943) American
£1070 $2000 €1562 Smiling young woman against black background (43x36cm-17x14in) s. board painted c.1930. 26-Feb-4 Illustration House, New York #11 est:3000-4000
£1955 $3500 €2854 Woman turning to smile at man following her (79x46cm-31x18in) s.i. 15-May-4 Illustration House, New York #94/R est:2000-3000
£2953 $5286 €4400 Cinema set (61x81cm-24x32in) s. 27-May-4 Sotheby's, Paris #142/R est:600-800
£5307 $9500 €7748 Smiling young woman skier (102x71cm-40x28in) s. 15-May-4 Illustration House, New York #90/R est:6000-8000
Works on paper
£578 $1000 €844 Bill the hallman (27x21cm-11x8in) s.i.d.Oct 29 1933 pencil. 11-Dec-3 Sotheby's, New York #214/R est:1000-1500
£934 $1700 €1364 Hawaiian dancer, model, young Deena Clark (33x25cm-13x10in) s. gouache sold with maracas and photos prov. 7-Feb-4 Sloans & Kenyon, Bethesda #1304/R est:1800-2200

BARCLAY, R (19/20th C) Irish
Works on paper
£528 $845 €750 Orby, winner of English and Irish dervies (25x30cm-10x12in) s. i.d.1907 verso W/C prov. 16-Sep-3 Whyte's, Dublin #110/R

BARCSAY, Jeno (1900-1998) Hungarian
£1229 $2176 €1794 In a conversation (16x19cm-6x7in) s. oil paper. 28-Apr-4 Kieselbach, Budapest #162/R (H.F 460000)
£2308 $3831 €3370 Composition (40x50cm-16x20in) s. 4-Oct-3 Kieselbach, Budapest #136/R (H.F 850000)
£4216 $7630 €6155 Composition (21x32cm-8x13in) s. panel. 16-Apr-4 Mu Terem Galeria, Budapest #174/R (H.F 1600000)

BARD, James (1815-1897) American
Works on paper
£9317 $15000 €13603 Side wheeler Jesse Hoyt (64x124cm-25x49in) s. W/C. 20-Aug-3 James Julia, Fairfield #587/R est:15000-25000

BARDA, Wally (1956-) Australian
£289 $535 €422 Woronora Spring (213x136cm-84x54in) s.i.verso painted 1987 prov. 15-Mar-4 Sotheby's, Melbourne #232 (A.D 700)

BARDASANO BAOS, Jose (1910-1979) Spanish
£2438 $3851 €3559 Landscape in Mexico (100x120cm-39x47in) s. 24-Jul-3 Louis Morton, Mexico #64/R est:60000 (M.P 40000)
£2624 $4251 €3700 En la ermita de San Antonio (59x45cm-23x18in) s. 20-May-3 Ansorena, Madrid #179/R est:3700

BARDELLINI, Pietro (attrib) (1728-1806) Italian
£1400 $2422 €2044 Saint Charles Borromeo (74x61cm-29x24in) indis.sig.indis.d.1769. 12-Dec-3 Christie's, Kensington #267/R
£14286 $25571 €21000 Groupes de musiciens (33x41cm-13x16in) oval pair. 19-Mar-4 Oger, Dumont, Paris #33/R est:8000-10000

BARDEY, Jeanne (20th C) French
£1562 $2750 €2281 Still life with flowers in a porcelain vase (63x53cm-25x21in) s. 18-May-4 Bonhams & Butterfields, San Francisco #141/R est:3000-5000

BARDI, Luigi (19/20th C) Italian
£5000 $8950 €7300 Madonna della Sedia (71cm-28in circular) s.i.d.1866 verso. 22-Mar-4 Bonhams & Brooks, Norfolk #288/R est:3000-5000

BARDI, Oscar (20th C) Italian
£629 $1083 €900 View of Trieste (60x90cm-24x35in) s. board. 3-Dec-3 Stadion, Trieste #1147/R

BARDILL, Ralph William (1876-1935) British
Works on paper
£250 $458 €365 Late autumn, Bettws-y-coed (24x35cm-9x14in) s. 3-Jun-4 Lane, Penzance #114
£250 $458 €365 Rocks and beeches, Bettws-y-coed (24x35cm-9x14in) s. 3-Jun-4 Lane, Penzance #115/R
£650 $1060 €949 Autumn treescape (46x58cm-18x23in) s. W/C. 27-Sep-3 Rogers Jones, Clwyd #54
£694 $1132 €1000 Rural nature (76x122cm-30x48in) s. W/C. 24-Sep-3 Woodwards, Cork #11
£1489 $2487 €2100 Lady by farm buildings (28x36cm-11x14in) s. W/C. 18-Jun-3 Woodwards, Cork #6
£1489 $2487 €2100 Rural cottage with lady and geese (24x36cm-9x14in) s. W/C. 18-Jun-3 Woodwards, Cork #7
£1700 $3094 €2482 Welsh stream (64x87cm-25x34in) s. pencil W/C gum arabic htd white. 5-Feb-4 Mellors & Kirk, Nottingham #479/R est:800-1200

BARDIN, Jean (attrib) (1732-1809) French
Works on paper
£1733 $3189 €2600 Jeroboam seduit les filles des amalecites (47x63cm-19x25in) i. pen blk ink W/C. 11-Jun-4 Maigret, Paris #11/R est:3000-4000

BARDIN, Jesse Redwin (1923-1997) American
£245 $400 €358 Untitled, pale blue, yellow and white (25x36cm-10x14in) s. 27-Sep-3 Charlton Hall, Columbia #29/R
£291 $475 €425 Bright moment (25x36cm-10x14in) s.i. 27-Sep-3 Charlton Hall, Columbia #27/R
£429 $700 €626 Temple of fragments (30x41cm-12x16in) s.i. 27-Sep-3 Charlton Hall, Columbia #504/R
£491 $800 €717 Untitled, abstract (30x41cm-12x16in) s.d. 27-Sep-3 Charlton Hall, Columbia #501
£1104 $1800 €1612 Untitled, abstract (102x127cm-40x50in) s. 27-Sep-3 Charlton Hall, Columbia #516/R est:2000-3000

BARDONE, Guy (1927-) French
£260 $478 €380 Bouquet a la Chaise (65x92cm-26x36in) s. s.i.d.55 and 56 verso prov. 23-Mar-4 Rosebery Fine Art, London #812
£415 $743 €610 Ruisseau ombre, Jura (56x46cm-22x18in) s. 19-Mar-4 Ribeyre & Baron, Paris #89
£1500 $2760 €2190 Ete a Clerence (81x116cm-32x46in) s. s.i.d.69 verso. 24-Mar-4 Sotheby's, Olympia #88/R est:1000-1500
Works on paper
£276 $510 €400 Troupeau sur la plage, Ceylan (45x60cm-18x24in) s. W/C. 13-Feb-4 Charbonneaux, Paris #33
£420 $701 €600 Maison dans un parc (45x60cm-18x24in) s. W/C. 25-Jun-3 Blanchet, Paris #90/R

BARDOT, Brigitte (20th C) French
Works on paper
£1100 $1936 €1606 Self portrait sketch (65x44cm-26x17in) prov. sold with print. 18-May-4 Woolley & Wallis, Salisbury #274/R est:100-200

BARDRUM, G (19th C) ?
£520 $935 €759 Indian seated smoking pipe by his tent (77x63cm-30x25in) s.d.1878. 24-Apr-4 Rasmussen, Havnen #2208/R (D.KR 5800)

BARDWELL, Thomas (1704-1767) British
£70000 $125300 €102200 Portrait of Ned Baldry's shell horse (183x189cm-72x74in) sold with one volume deer hunting in Norfolk. 22-Mar-4 Bonhams & Brooks, Norfolk #226/R est:4000-6000

BARDWELL, Thomas (attrib) (1704-1767) British
£3200 $5856 €4672 Portrait of Sophia, Countess of Carteret (70x52cm-28x20in) i. 7-Jul-4 Bonhams, New Bond Street #77/R est:2000-3000

BARDWELL, Thomas (style) (1704-1767) British
£18605 $32000 €27163 Court portrait of Thomas, second Earl of Strafford. Portrait of Countess Anne (218x135cm-86x53in) one i. pair. 6-Dec-3 Neal Auction Company, New Orleans #284/R est:10000-20000

BARE, Émile (19th C) French
£492 $900 €718 Parisian street scene near the Arche de Triomphe (25x20cm-10x8in) s. board. 10-Apr-4 Cobbs, Peterborough #59/R

BAREAU, Georges (1866-1931) French
Sculpture
£1316 $2421 €2000 Athlete as blacksmith (95cm-37in) s. dark pat.bronze. 24-Jun-4 Dr Fritz Nagel, Stuttgart #934/R est:2400
£4000 $7560 €5840 Diana the huntress (80cm-31in) s.st.f.F. Barbedienne gilt brown pat bronze. 17-Feb-4 Sotheby's, Olympia #51/R est:4000-6000
£5215 $8500 €7614 Diana riding an eagle (79cm-31in) bronze after George Marie Bareau. 24-Sep-3 Doyle, New York #439 est:4000-6000

BAREN, Johannes Antonius van der (1616-1686) Flemish
£8000 $14320 €12000 Floral garland and cartouche with the Vision of St Ignatius Loyola (64x50cm-25x20in) copper prov. 17-May-4 Christie's, Amsterdam #68/R est:12000-16000

BARENGER, James (jnr) (1780-1831) British
£1243 $2300 €1865 Race horse standing before a fence (53x74cm-21x29in) s. canvas on panel. 14-Jul-4 American Auctioneer #490272/R est:2500-3500

BARENGER, James (jnr-circle) (1780-1831) British
£8743 $16000 €12765 Full cry (65x84cm-26x33in) prov. 3-Jun-4 Christie's, Rockefeller NY #430/R est:20000-30000

BARETTA, Michele (1916-1987) Italian
£567 $1031 €850 Demolition in Vado (50x40cm-20x16in) s.d.78 masonite. 12-Jul-4 Il Ponte, Milan #419
£574 $1011 €850 Demolition in Valdo (50x40cm-20x16in) s.d.78 masonite. 19-May-4 Il Ponte, Milan #1148
£1067 $1963 €1600 Cetara (50x40cm-20x16in) s.i. masonite. 14-Jun-4 Sant Agostino, Torino #343/R est:1500-2000
£1267 $2331 €1900 Knife grinder (40x30cm-16x12in) s. s.verso masonite prov.exhib.lit. 14-Jun-4 Sant Agostino, Torino #342/R est:1500-2000
£1408 $2338 €2000 Malcensie sul Garda (40x50cm-16x20in) s.i.verso masonite. 14-Jun-3 Meeting Art, Vercelli #649/R est:2000
£1429 $2557 €2100 Thoughtful girl (50x40cm-20x16in) s.d.1955 masonite. 22-Mar-4 Sant Agostino, Torino #379/R est:1800
£1633 $2922 €2400 Quarry (50x60cm-20x24in) s.d.1973 masonite. 22-Mar-4 Sant Agostino, Torino #541/R est:2500
£1769 $3166 €2600 Self-portrait (70x50cm-28x20in) s.d.1958 masonite. 22-Mar-4 Sant Agostino, Torino #506/R est:2500
£2013 $3725 €3000 Red parasol (60x50cm-24x20in) s.d.1967 board lit. 13-Mar-4 Meeting Art, Vercelli #269 est:3000

£2238 $3737 €3200 Horses (100x70cm-39x28in) s. board. 26-Jun-3 Sant Agostino, Torino #266/R est:2000-2500

£2448 $4087 €3500 Macugnaga (70x50cm-28x20in) s. board painted 1962 lit. 26-Jun-3 Sant Agostino, Torino #268/R est:1700-2200

£2622 $4379 €3750 Nude with guitar (70x50cm-28x20in) s.d.1971 board. 26-Jun-3 Sant Agostino, Torino #267/R est:1500-2000

Works on paper

£270 $476 €400 Portrait of woman (50x35cm-20x14in) s. mixed media. 19-May-4 Il Ponte, Milan #1143

£426 $711 €600 Girls and cat (65x46cm-26x18in) s. mixed media card. 20-Oct-3 Sant Agostino, Torino #138/R

£473 $832 €700 In the changing room (69x49cm-27x19in) s.d. mixed media. 19-May-4 Il Ponte, Milan #1139

£473 $832 €700 Portrait of woman (69x49cm-27x19in) s. mixed media. 19-May-4 Il Ponte, Milan #1136

£490 $817 €700 Elsa (66x49cm-26x19in) s.i.d.1984 W/C card. 26-Jun-3 Sant Agostino, Torino #184/R

£559 $934 €800 Crucifixion (50x73cm-20x29in) s. mixed media. 26-Jun-3 Sant Agostino, Torino #313/R

BARETTI, Andrea (19th C) Italian?

£1380 $2250 €2015 Tavern flirtation (91x71cm-36x28in) s.i. 24-Sep-3 Doyle, New York #7/R est:4000-6000

BARFUSS, Ina (1949-) German

£742 $1366 €1083 Last escort (125x150cm-49x59in) s.d.1984 resin prov. 8-Jun-4 Germann, Zurich #74/R (S.FR 1700)

Works on paper

£452 $756 €660 Cheese head (105x76cm-41x30in) s.d.1982 gouache board lit. 24-Jun-3 Germann, Zurich #908/R (S.FR 1000)

BARGHEER, Eduard (1901-1979) German

£2000 $3580 €3000 Composition in blue (31x47cm-12x19in) s.d.53 prov. 15-May-4 Van Ham, Cologne #421/R est:1200

£2013 $3705 €3000 Portrait of Heinrich Kinau (55x40cm-22x16in) s. i. stretcher prov. 26-Mar-4 Ketterer, Hamburg #298/R est:3500-4000

£3000 $5010 €4380 Das rosa haus (46x61cm-18x24in) s.d.26 s.i.verso. 21-Oct-3 Bonhams, Knightsbridge #48/R est:1500-2000

£4184 $7573 €6109 Finkenwerder (50x80cm-20x31in) s. double-sided painted c.1930-1942 prov. 1-Apr-4 Heffel, Vancouver #2/R est:12000-16000 (C.D 10000)

£5944 $10224 €8500 Porcession - Easter procession (62x43cm-24x17in) s.d.1957 i.d. verso. 2-Dec-3 Hauswedell & Nolte, Hamburg #5/R est:6000

£8000 $14720 €12000 Southern city (51x74cm-20x29in) s.d.1950. 10-Jun-4 Hauswedell & Nolte, Hamburg #1/R est:12000

Works on paper

£433 $776 €650 Nude 6 (52x31cm-20x12in) s.i.d.63 col pen. 15-May-4 Van Ham, Cologne #323/R

£455 $782 €650 Street (31x41cm-12x16in) pen. 2-Dec-3 Hauswedell & Nolte, Hamburg #9/R

£567 $1014 €850 Camels in the desert (21x31cm-8x12in) s.d.60 W/C. 15-May-4 Van Ham, Cologne #423/R

£699 $1189 €1000 Winter on the Mediterranean (22x28cm-9x11in) s.d.48 i. verso W/C prov.exhib. 26-Nov-3 Dorotheum, Vienna #180/R

£734 $1248 €1050 Houses by the sea (22x28cm-9x11in) s.d.51 i. verso W/C prov.exhib. 26-Nov-3 Dorotheum, Vienna #181/R

£811 $1451 €1200 Cacti (29x42cm-11x17in) s.d.70 W/C lit. 8-May-4 Schloss Ahlden, Ahlden #851/R

£828 $1382 €1200 At the harbour. Flowering landscape (48x62cm-19x24in) s.indis.d. W/C double-sided. 13-Nov-3 Neumeister, Munich #246/R

£839 $1443 €1200 Southern town (21x31cm-8x12in) s.d.1960 W/C. 4-Dec-3 Van Ham, Cologne #16

£867 $1569 €1300 Landscape (22x31cm-9x12in) s.d. W/C. 2-Apr-4 Winterberg, Heidelberg #693/R

£903 $1426 €1300 Southern landscape (21x28cm-8x11in) s.d.73 W/C. 25-Apr-3 Altus, Berlin #639/R

£933 $1717 €1400 Southern landscape (47x66cm-19x26in) s.d.48 W/C pencil. 11-Jun-4 Villa Grisebach, Berlin #1601/R est:2000-3000

£972 $1536 €1400 Town on Ischia (31x43cm-12x17in) s.d.72 W/C lit. 19-Sep-3 Schloss Ahlden, Ahlden #1671/R

£1007 $1852 €1500 Boats on beach (21x28cm-8x11in) s.d. W/C. 26-Mar-4 Ketterer, Hamburg #299/R est:1800-2400

£1007 $1852 €1500 Southern garden (41x55cm-16x22in) s.d. i.d. verso w/C. 26-Mar-4 Ketterer, Hamburg #301/R est:1800-2000

£1042 $1646 €1500 Southern vegetation (31x44cm-12x17in) s.d.62 W/C lit. 19-Sep-3 Schloss Ahlden, Ahlden #1670/R est:1600

£1067 $1963 €1600 Southern city (31x43cm-12x17in) s.d.1968 i. verso W/C. 10-Jun-4 Hauswedell & Nolte, Hamburg #6/R est:2000

£1067 $1952 €1600 Vegetation (32x44cm-13x17in) s.d.70 W/C. 5-Jun-4 Lempertz, Koln #579/R est:1800

£1119 $1902 €1600 Desert (31x44cm-12x17in) s.i.d.66 W/C double-sided. 29-Nov-3 Villa Grisebach, Berlin #710/R est:1600-1800

£1200 $2148 €1800 Wasserburg am Inn (30x41cm-12x16in) s.d. W/C on pencil. 15-May-4 Dr Sturies, Dusseldorf #8/R

£1200 $2196 €1800 Dunes in summer (32x44cm-13x17in) s.d.68 W/C. 5-Jun-4 Lempertz, Koln #578/R est:2000

£1268 $2028 €1800 Rain (30x42cm-12x17in) s.d.72 W/C. 19-Sep-3 Sigalas, Stuttgart #275/R est:1800

£1433 $2566 €2150 Southern landscape with red sun (21x28cm-8x11in) s.d. W/C on pencil. 15-May-4 Bassenge, Berlin #6713/R est:800

£1517 $2534 €2200 Houses in Ischia (48x65cm-19x26in) s.d.47 W/C over pencil. 13-Nov-3 Neumeister, Munich #243/R est:2000-2500

£1958 $3329 €2800 Spring (21x31cm-8x12in) s.i.d.64 W/C. 26-Nov-3 Lempertz, Koln #564/R est:1800

£2000 $3580 €3000 Sculpture. Painting. Literature. Music (31x23cm-12x9in) W/C Indian in pencil gouache four. 15-May-4 Van Ham, Cologne #422/R est:800

£2028 $3448 €2900 On Ischia (22x28cm-9x11in) s.d.55 W/C. 26-Nov-3 Lempertz, Koln #562/R est:2000

£2098 $3608 €3000 Hilly landscape - mountain and sun (22x28cm-9x11in) s.d.1952 i. verso W/C. 2-Dec-3 Hauswedell & Nolte, Hamburg #6/R est:1500

£2400 $4416 €3600 Houses by sea (22x28cm-9x11in) s.d.1957 W/C. 10-Jun-4 Hauswedell & Nolte, Hamburg #5/R est:1500

£2517 $4330 €3600 Wild garden (23x33cm-9x13in) s.d.1958 i.d. verso W/C. 2-Dec-3 Hauswedell & Nolte, Hamburg #7/R est:2000

£2533 $4661 €3800 Perugia (47x63cm-19x25in) s.d.1936 i. verso W/C on pencil. 10-Jun-4 Hauswedell & Nolte, Hamburg #2/R est:2500

£2667 $4880 €4000 City in Scirocco (43x61cm-17x24in) s.d.53 i. verso W/C on pencil prov. 5-Jun-4 Lempertz, Koln #576/R est:3500-4000

£3310 $5528 €4800 Landscape with palm trees (48x63cm-19x25in) s.d. W/C ink over pencil. 13-Nov-3 Neumeister, Munich #242/R est:4700-4900

£4930 $8528 €7000 Spring (66x81cm-26x32in) s.d.64 i. stretcher gouache lit.exhib. 13-Dec-3 Lempertz, Koln #114/R est:4000

BARGIGGIA, Franco (1889-1966) Italian

Sculpture

£915 $1584 €1300 Mother and child (43cm-17in) bronze. 9-Dec-3 Finarte Semenzato, Milan #25

£2676 $4630 €3800 Maternity (45cm-18in) s. bronze sold with base. 10-Dec-3 Sotheby's, Milan #147/R est:1500-2500

BARIBEAU, Robert (1949-) American

£1618 $2750 €2362 Untitled (145x122cm-57x48in) init.d.77 oil pastel prov. 9-Nov-3 Bonhams & Butterfields, Los Angeles #4093/R est:4000-6000

BARIE, E (?) British?

£705 $1198 €1029 Figures in tavern (55x68cm-22x27in) s. 5-Nov-3 Dobiaschofsky, Bern #326/R (S.FR 1600)

BARIL, Tom (1952-) American

Photographs

£1916 $3200 €2797 Chrysler Building no.460 (59x46cm-23x18in) with sig.d.1995 silver print. 21-Oct-3 Swann Galleries, New York #348/R est:2000-3000

BARILARI, Enrique (1931-) Argentinian

£363 $650 €530 Five figures (99x130cm-39x51in) s.verso acrylic. 7-May-4 Sloans & Kenyon, Bethesda #1137/R

£391 $700 €571 Seven women (99x130cm-39x51in) s. prov. 7-May-4 Sloans & Kenyon, Bethesda #1138/R

£412 $750 €602 Five figures (39x51cm-15x20in) s.verso acrylic prov. 7-Feb-4 Sloans & Kenyon, Bethesda #869/R

BARILLI, Aristide (20th C) Italian?

£503 $931 €750 Spanish landscape (35x43cm-14x17in) s.i.d.1963 masonite. 13-Mar-4 Meeting Art, Vercelli #490

BARILLI, Latino (1883-1961) Italian

£3688 $6159 €5200 Tipping rubbish in the river (45x35cm-18x14in) s. 20-Oct-3 Sant Agostino, Torino #305/R est:3000-4000

BARILLOT, Léon (1844-1929) French

£1648 $3000 €2406 Cows in a pasture by a canal (51x65cm-20x26in) prov. 4-Feb-4 Christie's, Rockefeller NY #40/R est:2000-3000

£3623 $5942 €5000 Le troupeau de vaches (55x65cm-22x26in) s. exhib. 11-May-3 Osenat, Fontainebleau #55/R est:6000-7000

£3706 $6375 €5300 Vaches au paturage en Normandie (50x65cm-20x26in) s. 7-Dec-3 Osenat, Fontainebleau #42 est:5500-6000

BARING, William (1881-?) German

£350 $601 €500 View of River Elbe from Bruhlschen terrace in Dresden (37x49cm-15x19in) s.d.08 board. 5-Dec-3 Bolland & Marotz, Bremen #689/R

BARISON, Giuseppe (1853-1930) Italian

£397 $723 €600 Face of woman (21x15cm-8x6in) s. board. 21-Jun-4 Pandolfini, Florence #89

£699 $1203 €1000 Portrait of lady (39x33cm-15x13in) s. 3-Dec-3 Stadion, Trieste #1033/R

£800 $1432 €1200 Wood (36x26cm-14x10in) i.verso board prov.lit. 12-May-4 Stadion, Trieste #834/R

£4545 $7818 €6500 Out of the Sacchetta (18x29cm-7x11in) s. board. 3-Dec-3 Stadion, Trieste #1164/R est:3000-4000

£4792 $7810 €6900 Fishing boats in harbour (50x55cm-20x22in) s. board. 24-Sep-3 Neumeister, Munich #390/R est:1000

£5594 $9622 €8000 Fishing in the lagoon (46x70cm-18x28in) s. 3-Dec-3 Stadion, Trieste #1179/R est:5000-6000

£6294 $10825 €9000 Chatting in the inn (30x40cm-12x16in) s. board. 3-Dec-3 Stadion, Trieste #1127/R est:7000-8000

£8392 $14434 €12000 Back (30x50cm-12x20in) s. s.i.verso board. 3-Dec-3 Stadion, Trieste #1003/R est:6000-7000

£10839 $18643 €15500 Fishermen coming back (48x67cm-19x26in) s. 3-Dec-3 Stadion, Trieste #978/R est:7000-9000

£54930 $91183 €78000 Dopo una rissa (83x115cm-33x45in) s. lit. 11-Jun-3 Christie's, Rome #260/R est:40000-60000

BARITEAU, Alcide (20th C) French

£6122 $10959 €9000 Campement berbere (73x99cm-29x39in) s. 21-Mar-4 St-Germain-en-Laye Encheres #38/R est:10000-12000

BARJOLA, Juan (1919-) Spanish

Prints

£2013 $3685 €3000 Bull scene (58x80cm-23x31in) s. lithograph. 12-Jul-4 Durán, Madrid #154/R est:3000

£2041 $3653 €3000 Bull scene (59x80cm-23x31in) s. lithograph. 22-Mar-4 Durán, Madrid #123/R est:3000

£2174 $3565 €3000 Tauromaquia (106x75cm-42x30in) s. num.32/99 engraving. 27-May-3 Durán, Madrid #154/R est:3000

£2174 $3565 €3000 Tauromaquia (75x106cm-30x42in) s. num.22/99 engraving. 27-May-3 Durán, Madrid #155/R est:3000

£2303 $4237 €3500 Bull scene (52x81cm-20x32in) s. lithograph. 22-Jun-4 Durán, Madrid #129/R est:3000

Works on paper
£867 $1569 €1300 Untitled (38x31cm-15x12in) s. gouache exec.c.1950. 30-Mar-4 Segre, Madrid #373/R

BARKER OF BATH, Benjamin (1776-1838) British
£400 $640 €584 View of Hampton Cliffs near Bath (55x41cm-22x16in) s. 16-Sep-3 Rosebery Fine Art, London #570
£420 $672 €613 The Vale (38x49cm-15x19in) s.d.1809 prov. 16-Sep-3 Rosebery Fine Art, London #569
£550 $875 €798 Wooded landscape with a cowherd watering his livestock (46x56cm-18x22in) s. 9-Sep-3 Bonhams, Knightsbridge #79/R
£900 $1674 €1314 Drover with cattle watering (4x55cm-2x22in) s. indis d. prov. 4-Mar-4 Christie's, Kensington #411/R

BARKER OF BATH, John Joseph (fl.1835-1866) British
£1300 $2379 €1898 Two ladies and a gentleman in a cottage garden (61x51cm-24x20in) s. 7-Apr-4 Gardiner & Houlgate, Bath #278/R est:1500-2000
£1500 $2775 €2190 Near Harrogate (59x90cm-23x35in) s. 14-Jan-4 Lawrence, Crewkerne #1405 est:1500-2000

BARKER OF BATH, Joseph (19th C) British
£520 $957 €759 Woman sketching on a woodland path (90x70cm-35x28in) s. 29-Mar-4 Bonhams, Bath #70/R

BARKER OF BATH, Thomas (1769-1847) British
£1316 $2118 €1921 Woodsman (95x126cm-37x50in) prov. 13-Oct-3 Joel, Victoria #371 est:4000-6000 (A.D 3250)
£2156 $4011 €3148 Heavy loaded horse and cart in winter landscape (76x126cm-30x50in) s. 2-Mar-4 Rasmussen, Copenhagen #1639/R est:25000 (D.KR 24000)
£2600 $4836 €3796 Three girls resting in a landscape (65x109cm-26x43in) prov. 4-Mar-4 Christie's, Kensington #647/R est:3000-5000
£6000 $10200 €8760 Wood gatherer and his family loading a donkey in a landscape (99x125cm-39x49in) prov. 27-Nov-3 Sotheby's, London #175/R est:4000-6000

BARKER OF BATH, Thomas (attrib) (1769-1847) British
£389 $700 €568 Figures in a landscape (76x64cm-30x25in) bears sig.d.1801. 23-Jan-4 Freeman, Philadelphia #170/R
£420 $739 €613 River landscape with two figures drawing a net (12x15cm-5x6in) panel. 18-May-4 Woolley & Wallis, Salisbury #104/R
£750 $1223 €1095 Figures at the water's edge within an extensive landscape (47x74cm-19x29in) 24-Sep-3 Dreweatt Neate, Newbury #116/R
£1000 $1590 €1460 Ploughman in an extensive landscape (76x127cm-30x50in) 9-Sep-3 Gorringes, Lewes #2046 est:600-800
£1341 $2400 €2251 Landscape with thatched roof house, figures and dog (76x64cm-30x25in) 20-Mar-4 Pook & Pook, Downington #367/R est:1500-2500

BARKER, Clive (1940-) British
Sculpture
£1300 $2210 €1898 Gold Coke (27cm-11in) gold albritin on bronze exec 1992. 18-Nov-3 Bonhams, Knightsbridge #12/R est:1200-1800
£1500 $2550 €2190 Girl and her pussy (22cm-9in) st.d.1995-96 num.4/4 metal sculpture. 18-Nov-3 Bonhams, Knightsbridge #13/R est:1500-1800
£3400 $6290 €4964 Emperor and Empress. s. st.i. num.3/9 bronze aluminium. 13-Jul-4 Bonhams, Knightsbridge #18/R est:3000-4000
Works on paper
£300 $477 €438 Cadillac (32x49cm-13x19in) s. pencil biro W/C. 10-Sep-3 Sotheby's, Olympia #304/R

BARKER, David (1941-) New Zealander
£507 $817 €740 Bank (49x66cm-19x26in) s.d.1983 acrylic board. 12-Aug-3 Peter Webb, Auckland #140/R (NZ.D 1400)
£725 $1174 €1051 Flax (59x90cm-23x35in) s.d.1974 acrylic board. 31-Jul-3 International Art Centre, Auckland #94/R est:2000-3000 (NZ.D 2000)
£797 $1283 €1164 Northland Cove (60x75cm-24x30in) s.d.1984 s.i.d.1984 verso acrylic board. 12-Aug-3 Peter Webb, Auckland #141/R (NZ.D 2200)
£933 $1614 €1362 Pohutukawa shadow (61x91cm-24x36in) s.d.1974 s.i.d.1974 verso board. 9-Dec-3 Peter Webb, Auckland #171/R (NZ.D 2500)
£942 $1517 €1375 Herefords, Northland (69x87cm-27x34in) s.d.1960 board. 20-Aug-3 Peter Webb, Auckland #2002 (NZ.D 2600)
£956 $1788 €1396 Barn in rural landscape (55x74cm-22x29in) s.d.1972 board. 24-Feb-4 Peter Webb, Auckland #48/R (NZ.D 2600)
£1034 $1758 €1510 Rakitu Island from Harataonga (78x90cm-31x35in) s.d.1979 acrylic board. 27-Nov-3 International Art Centre, Auckland #133/R (NZ.D 2750)
Works on paper
£414 $703 €604 On shore wind (40x42cm-16x17in) s.d.76 gouache. 26-Nov-3 Dunbar Sloane, Wellington #512 (NZ.D 1100)

BARKER, Ernest Conyers (20th C) Canadian
£382 $710 €558 Late autumn, Grassmere, near Huntsville (30x41cm-12x16in) s. masonite. 2-Mar-4 Ritchie, Toronto #145/R (C.D 950)

BARKER, George (1882-1965) American
£300 $549 €438 Red grouse in a Highland landscape (49x68cm-19x27in) s. 28-Jan-4 Henry Adams, Chichester #275
£450 $716 €653 Empty beach (61x91cm-24x36in) s. 9-Sep-3 Bonhams, Knightsbridge #63/R
Works on paper
£269 $497 €393 Armadillo (96x64cm-38x25in) s.d.90 i.verso mixed media. 15-Mar-4 Sotheby's, Melbourne #182 (A.D 650)

BARKER, Henry Aston (1774-1856) British
Prints
£15000 $25050 €21900 Panorama of the Constantinople and its Environs, taken from the town of Galata (49x397cm-19x156in) aquatint 8 joined exhib.lit. 14-Oct-3 Sotheby's, London #5/R est:7000-10000

BARKER, John (19th C) British
£1800 $3330 €2628 Sheep in a landscape (76x63cm-30x25in) s. 13-Jan-4 Bonhams, Knightsbridge #94/R est:2500-3500
£4200 $6594 €6090 Sheepdog and flock in the highlands (127x102cm-50x40in) s. 27-Aug-3 Sotheby's, London #1001/R est:2000-3000

BARKER, Kit (1916-1988) British
£299 $500 €437 Dorset upland (91x97cm-36x38in) s.i.verso. 15-Nov-3 Sloans & Kenyon, Bethesda #101/R
£300 $501 €438 Hurst Castle, and Solent (79x116cm-31x46in) s.i.d.68 verso prov. 16-Oct-3 Christie's, Kensington #667

BARKER, Thomas Jones (1815-1882) British
£1700 $3043 €2482 Marriage of Queen Mary (81x61cm-32x24in) s.d.1837. 27-May-4 Christie's, Kensington #316/R est:2000-3000

BARKER, Walter (1921-) American
£949 $1500 €1386 Beneath Assisi (109x145cm-43x57in) s.i.verso. 7-Sep-3 Treadway Gallery, Cincinnati #769/R est:1000-2000

BARKER, William Dean (19th C) British
£660 $1122 €964 In Nant Conway (41x91cm-16x36in) s. s.i.verso. 29-Oct-3 Bonhams, Chester #336

BARKER, Wright (1864-1941) British
£1500 $2775 €2190 Little John (46x61cm-18x24in) s. 10-Feb-4 Bonhams, Knightsbridge #69/R est:1000-1500
£1500 $2805 €2190 Hunting scene with huntsmen on horseback with hounds (91x65cm-36x26in) s. 22-Jul-4 Tennants, Leyburn #868/R est:1500-2000
£2600 $4680 €3796 St Bernard (64x80cm-25x31in) s.d.1889. 21-Jan-4 Sotheby's, Olympia #359/R est:800-1200
£6500 $12025 €9490 Rest from toil (104x146cm-41x57in) s.d.1912. 10-Mar-4 Sotheby's, Olympia #216/R est:5000-7000
£6977 $12000 €10186 Portrait of a boy on a pony (127x102cm-50x40in) s.d.1888. 5-Dec-3 Christie's, Rockefeller NY #50/R est:15000-20000
£9884 $17000 €14431 Mare and her foal at a ford (71x91cm-28x36in) s. 5-Dec-3 Christie's, Rockefeller NY #54/R est:18000-25000

BARKOFF, Alexandre (1870-1942) Finnish
£2200 $3850 €3212 Street in Athens. Church interior (26x29cm-10x11in) s. one d.1936 one d.1934 canvas on hardboard pair. 16-Dec-3 Bonhams, New Bond Street #78/R est:1500-2000
Works on paper
£2000 $3400 €2920 Anafiotika (46x40cm-18x16in) s.i.d.1932 W/C exhib. 18-Nov-3 Sotheby's, London #96/R est:2000-3000
£2000 $3400 €2920 Pireaus (38x46cm-15x18in) s.i.d.1933 W/C exhib. 18-Nov-3 Sotheby's, London #97/R est:2000-3000
£2500 $4375 €3650 Shipyard scenes, Aegina (21x25cm-8x10in) s. one d.1932 W/C pair. 16-Dec-3 Bonhams, New Bond Street #13/R est:1000-1500
£3200 $5440 €4672 Monastiraki (31x49cm-12x19in) s.i.d.1940 W/C exhib. 18-Nov-3 Sotheby's, London #95/R est:2000-3000
£3500 $6125 €5110 Monastiraki, Athens. Mending the nets (41x50cm-16x20in) s.d.1932 W/C pair. 16-Dec-3 Bonhams, New Bond Street #12/R est:1500-2000

BARKSTULB, Elin (19/20th C) Danish?
£322 $516 €470 Seagull with herring by her young (72x101cm-28x40in) s.d.17. 22-Sep-3 Rasmussen, Vejle #115/R (D.KR 3400)

BARLACH, Ernst (1870-1938) German
£1233 $2096 €1800 Sketches (44x33cm-17x13in) s.d.20.6.35 chl. 8-Nov-3 Hans Stahl, Toestorf #53 est:1700
£1233 $2096 €1800 Sketches - figures (33x44cm-13x17in) s.d.28.6 2.7.35 chl. 8-Nov-3 Hans Stahl, Toestorf #54 est:1700
Sculpture
£2797 $4755 €4000 Russian woman begging with dish (29cm-11in) plaster. 29-Nov-3 Villa Grisebach, Berlin #155/R est:4000-6000
£6993 $11888 €10000 Couple kissing I (18cm-7in) s. brown pat.bronze Cast.H.Noack Berlin. 29-Nov-3 Villa Grisebach, Berlin #222/R est:12000-14000
£9333 $17173 €14000 Flute blower (60x38x24cm-24x15x9in) stucco. 10-Jun-4 Hauswedell & Nolte, Hamburg #21/R est:18000
£9790 $16643 €14000 Pregnant girl (42cm-17in) s. dark brown pat.bronze prov. 26-Nov-3 Dorotheum, Vienna #34/R est:14000-18000
£18000 $33120 €26280 Doubter (51cm-20in) i. bronze exec 1941 cast edn of 40 prov.exhib.lit. 22-Jun-4 Sotheby's, London #293/R est:20000-30000
£20979 $35664 €30000 Crucifix II (119cm-47in) plaster shellac prov. 28-Nov-3 Villa Grisebach, Berlin #59/R est:40000-60000
£20979 $36084 €30000 Laughing figure (21x32x13cm-8x13x5in) bronze. 2-Dec-3 Hauswedell & Nolte, Hamburg #17/R est:35000
£27972 $47552 €40000 Book reader - reading man in wind (44cm-17in) s. verso brown pat.bronze prov. 28-Nov-3 Villa Grisebach, Berlin #70/R est:40000-50000
£27972 $47552 €40000 Melon eater (33cm-13in) s. verso brown pat.bronze prov. 29-Nov-3 Villa Grisebach, Berlin #218/R est:35000-45000
£52448 $89161 €75000 Pipe player (58cm-23in) s. verso brown pat.bronze prov. 28-Nov-3 Villa Grisebach, Berlin #68/R est:90000-120000
Works on paper
£3077 $5292 €4400 Man with dog (17x25cm-7x10in) s. chl. 2-Dec-3 Hauswedell & Nolte, Hamburg #18/R est:4000
£3667 $6563 €5500 Seated couple (44x47cm-17x19in) s. chl prov. 14-May-4 Ketterer, Munich #208/R est:4000-5000
£5500 $9185 €8030 Mann mit gewehr (40x50cm-16x20in) s. chl exec 1914 prov.lit. 22-Oct-3 Sotheby's, Olympia #134/R est:800-1200

BARLACH, Ernst (after) (1870-1938) German
Sculpture
£5000 $8000 €7300 Der Racher (53x80cm-21x31in) s.d.1922 bronze one of three. 18-Sep-3 Swann Galleries, New York #36/R est:10000-15000

BARLAG, Philip (1840-1913) Norwegian
£344 $575 €502 Mountain walkers under glazier (27x38cm-11x15in) s. panel. 20-Oct-3 Blomqvist, Lysaker #1020/R (N.KR 4000)
£344 $575 €502 Woman on mountain path (24x36cm-9x14in) s. 20-Oct-3 Blomqvist, Lysaker #1021/R (N.KR 4000)
£370 $677 €540 Punt on calm water (24x36cm-9x14in) s. 2-Feb-4 Blomqvist, Lysaker #1016/R (N.KR 4600)
£484 $803 €702 Woman on path in mountains (32x25cm-13x10in) s. 16-Jun-3 Blomqvist, Lysaker #1006/R (N.KR 5600)
£565 $978 €825 Woman on snow covered road (32x25cm-13x10in) s. 13-Dec-3 Blomqvist, Lysaker #1018/R (N.KR 6500)
£610 $1116 €891 Woman on path (30x36cm-12x14in) s. 7-Jun-4 Blomqvist, Oslo #349/R (N.KR 7500)
£2814 $5149 €4108 Fishing on the ice (48x82cm-19x32in) s. 2-Feb-4 Blomqvist, Lysaker #1017/R est:25000-30000 (N.KR 35000)
£4003 $7166 €5844 Evening landscape in winter (58x81cm-23x32in) s. 22-Mar-4 Blomqvist, Oslo #309/R est:30000-40000 (N.KR 50000)

BARLAND, Adam (fl.1843-1875) British
£380 $608 €555 River landscape with cattle watering and fisherman (36x30cm-14x12in) s.d.69 i.stretcher. 16-Sep-3 Capes Dunn, Manchester #762
£800 $1488 €1168 Returning home (34x46cm-13x18in) indis sig.d.1860. 4-Mar-4 Christie's, Kensington #508/R
£828 $1500 €1209 Two figures on a country lane (20x25cm-8x10in) s. panel pair. 18-Apr-4 Bonhams & Butterfields, Los Angeles #7046/R est:2000-3000

BARLE, Maurice (1903-) French
£250 $443 €365 Shipping scene, baie de bastia (48x60cm-19x24in) s.i.verso. 28-Apr-4 Peter Wilson, Nantwich #110

BARLISON, C (19th C) ?
£900 $1656 €1314 Lady standing by her horse (34x44cm-13x17in) s.d.1856. 10-Jun-4 Christie's, Kensington #79/R

BARLOW, Francis (1626-1704) British
£4200 $7140 €6132 Assembly of birds in a landscape (126x101cm-50x40in) 27-Nov-3 Sotheby's, London #202/R est:4000-6000

BARLOW, Francis (attrib) (1626-1704) British
£4400 $7876 €6424 Peacocks and peahens by a stone balustrade (150x111cm-59x44in) 22-Mar-4 Bonhams & Brooks, Norfolk #296/R est:5000-7000
£4500 $8055 €6570 Spaniel putting up ducks and herons (95x144cm-37x57in) 22-Mar-4 Bonhams & Brooks, Norfolk #300/R est:8000-12000

BARLOW, Gordon Clifford (?) British
£440 $788 €642 Malta boatyard (49x60cm-19x24in) s. 16-Mar-4 Bonhams, Leeds #564

BARLOW, Jeremy (1945-) British
£459 $850 €670 Boats and barges in the harbour at Rotterdam (75x81cm-30x32in) s. board. 10-Feb-4 Christie's, Rockefeller NY #239/R

BARLOW, John Noble (1861-1924) American/British
£350 $637 €511 Evening, Lamorna (30x41cm-12x16in) s. s.i.d.1911 verso. 15-Jun-4 David Lay, Penzance #25
£450 $792 €657 Walk in the woods (25x30cm-10x12in) s. 19-May-4 Christie's, Kensington #537/R
£580 $1073 €847 Early spring Lamorna (41x61cm-16x24in) s. s.i.verso. 10-Feb-4 David Lay, Penzance #381/R
£1059 $1800 €1546 River landscape with birch trees (88x75cm-35x30in) s.d.86. 21-Nov-3 Skinner, Boston #255/R est:2500-3500
£1100 $1870 €1606 Wooded pond with lone figure and silver birch trees (30x38cm-12x15in) s. prov. 5-Nov-3 John Nicholson, Haslemere #594 est:1000
£1475 $2700 €2154 River landscape with trees on either side, and a docked boat (74x86cm-29x34in) 10-Apr-4 Cobbs, Peterborough #119/R

BARLOW, Myron (1873-1937) American
£479 $800 €699 Kettle watch (81x64cm-32x25in) s.d.1904. 16-Nov-3 CRN Auctions, Cambridge #25/R
£4790 $8000 €6993 The letter (102x102cm-40x40in) painted c.1910. 14-Nov-3 Du Mouchelle, Detroit #2007/R est:8000-12000

BARMONT, Honore (1810-?) French
£1807 $3000 €2638 Young lady in a country landscape (55x46cm-22x18in) s.d.1845. 30-Sep-3 Christie's, Rockefeller NY #361/R est:5000-7000

BARNABA DA MODENA (fl.1361-1383) Italian
£281690 $467606 €400000 Noli me tangere (34x22cm-13x9in) tempera gold board lit. 11-Jun-3 Semenzato, Florence #10/R est:500000

BARNABE, Duilio (1914-1961) Italian
£441 $700 €644 Still life with candle and bottle (81x65cm-32x26in) s. 12-Sep-3 Skinner, Boston #326/R
£704 $1218 €1000 Arlequin (33x22cm-13x9in) s. 13-Dec-3 Touati, Paris #22
£909 $1545 €1300 Les religieuses (54x64cm-21x25in) s. 20-Nov-3 Claude Aguttes, Neuilly #49/R
£1391 $2531 €2100 Nature morte (50x100cm-20x39in) s. 15-Jun-4 Blanchet, Paris #272/R est:2200-2500
£1410 $2495 €2100 Femme au bain (45x55cm-18x22in) s. 27-Apr-4 Artcurial Briest, Paris #205/R est:2000-3000
£1410 $2495 €2100 Pecheurs (46x55cm-18x22in) s. 27-Apr-4 Artcurial Briest, Paris #206 est:2000-3000
£1608 $2734 €2300 Architecture (74x93cm-29x37in) s. 20-Nov-3 Claude Aguttes, Neuilly #130 est:3000-4000
£1647 $2800 €2405 Barques sur plage (53x38cm-21x15in) s. prov. 22-Nov-3 Jackson's, Cedar Falls #400/R est:500-750
£2600 $4706 €3796 Dopo il bagno (51x61cm-20x24in) s. 1-Apr-4 Christie's, Kensington #135/R est:2000-3000
£3000 $5520 €4500 Nature morte au broc (73x92cm-29x36in) s. 8-Jun-4 Artcurial Briest, Paris #193 est:3500-4500

BARNARD, Bettie Cilliers (1914-) South African
£314 $562 €458 Still life with a candle (55x45cm-22x18in) s.d.1951. 31-May-4 Stephan Welz, Johannesburg #184 (SA.R 3800)
£388 $648 €566 Ann, head of a woman (25x20cm-10x8in) s.d.1971 board. 20-Oct-3 Stephan Welz, Johannesburg #864 est:800-1200 (SA.R 4500)

BARNARD, Edward Herbert (1855-1909) American
£96591 $170000 €141023 River weeders (102x152cm-40x60in) s. painted c.1893 prov.exhib.lit. 19-May-4 Sotheby's, New York #44/R est:80000-120000

BARNARD, Emily (fl.1884-1911) British
Works on paper
£250 $460 €365 Portrait of a young girl's head (62x49cm-24x19in) s.d.1884 pastel. 8-Jun-4 Bonhams, Ipswich #335

BARNARD, Frederick (1846-1896) British
£650 $1203 €949 Jester and shepherd with flock by a river (125x85cm-49x33in) mono. 9-Mar-4 Bonhams, Knightsbridge #342/R
£700 $1113 €1022 Fisherman by a water mill. Woman carrying water from a well (22x30cm-9x12in) init. two. 10-Sep-3 Cheffins, Cambridge #539
£12500 $20750 €18250 Chaperon (66x71cm-26x28in) mono. 2-Oct-3 Neales, Nottingham #754/R est:3000-5000

BARNARD, George (fl.1883-1891) British
Works on paper
£540 $1021 €788 Sunny brow sunset looking over Surrey Weald (35x49cm-14x19in) s.i. W/C. 23-Feb-4 David Duggleby, Scarborough #681/R

BARNARD, George (1815-1890) British
Works on paper
£280 $501 €420 The Lion Rock, looking towards the Lizard (35x57cm-14x22in) s.i.d.1884 W/C scratching out. 17-Mar-4 John Bellman, Billingshurst #780/R
£750 $1223 €1095 Alpine landscapes, Fallen trees. Travellers. Mountain goats (38x56cm-15x22in) one s.d.1876 two s.d.1875 W/C three. 24-Sep-3 Dreweatt Neate, Newbury #58

BARNARD, J Langton (1853-?) British
£280 $515 €409 Venice (14x28cm-6x11in) init.i. panel. 14-Jun-4 Bonhams, Bath #56

BARNARD, Richard (?) British
Works on paper
£250 $463 €365 Ostler's Dilemma (35x48cm-14x19in) i.verso W/C acrylic collage. 13-Feb-4 Sworder & Son, Bishops Stortford #37/R

BARNAVE, Antoine (attrib) (19th C) French
Sculpture
£2098 $3503 €3000 Buste d'un homme (45cm-18in) terracotta red marble piedouche Carre marble socle. 24-Jun-3 Christie's, Paris #404/R est:2500-3500

BARNES, Archibald George (1887-1934) British
£4200 $7392 €6132 Summer's day (63x88cm-25x35in) s. 19-May-4 Sotheby's, Olympia #135/R est:2000-3000

BARNES, E C (19th C) British
£1500 $2505 €2190 Fish wife (61x46cm-24x18in) 13-Nov-3 Christie's, Kensington #301/R est:1500-2000
£3200 $5952 €4672 Penny a posy (91x71cm-36x28in) s. 4-Mar-4 Christie's, Kensington #607/R est:3000-5000
£3800 $6042 €5510 Helping hand (71x91cm-28x36in) s. 9-Sep-3 Bonhams, Knightsbridge #103/R est:2000-3000

BARNES, Edward Charles (fl.1856-1882) British
£250 $460 €365 Portrait of a gypsy girl (13x11cm-5x4in) init. 11-Jun-4 Keys, Aylsham #737
£599 $1000 €875 Little beggar (26x18cm-10x7in) s. 7-Oct-3 Sotheby's, New York #100
£943 $1500 €1377 Man courting woman with basket (76x64cm-30x25in) 25-Feb-3 Bunch, West Chester #535/R
£4300 $7998 €6278 Who'll buy my roses (50x61cm-20x24in) s. 4-Mar-4 Christie's, Kensington #649/R est:5000-7000

BARNES, Ernest Harrison (1873-?) American
£348 $550 €508 Bend in the river (64x76cm-25x30in) s. 7-Sep-3 Treadway Gallery, Cincinnati #624/R

BARNES, Frank (19/20th C) ?

£278 $442 €406 TSS Wahine off Pencarrow (27x43cm-11x17in) s.i. 1-May-3 Dunbar Sloane, Wellington #7 (NZ.D 800)
£521 $828 €761 U.S.S Rotomahana off New Zealand coast in heavy weather (53x78cm-21x31in) s.i.d.1905 board. 1-May-3 Dunbar Sloane, Wellington #1/R est:1000-2000 (NZ.D 1500)
£532 $941 €777 SS Waiwera off the Cape, S Africa, with the 2nd New Zealand contingent (51x73cm-20x29in) s. board. 28-Apr-4 Dunbar Sloane, Auckland #70/R (NZ.D 1500)
£564 $959 €823 T.E.V Rangatira off Pencarrow (49x72cm-19x28in) s.i. board. 26-Nov-3 Dunbar Sloane, Wellington #130 est:500-1000 (NZ.D 1500)
£694 $1104 €1013 T.I Awatea passing T.S.S Tamahine off Pencarrow (45x62cm-18x24in) s.i. 1-May-3 Dunbar Sloane, Wellington #45/R est:1800-2500 (NZ.D 2000)
£745 $1318 €1088 SS Corinthic, off Pencarrow, Wellington (32x49cm-13x19in) init. board. 28-Apr-4 Dunbar Sloane, Auckland #71/R (NZ.D 2100)
£940 $1598 €1372 French 5 masted barque, France off The Brothers, Cook Straight (48x73cm-19x29in) s.i. board. 26-Nov-3 Dunbar Sloane, Wellington #129/R est:1000-2000 (NZ.D 2500)

BARNES, Gertrude Jameson (1865-?) American

£452 $800 €660 Still life with strawberries, grapes and other fruit (16x24cm-6x9in) s. sold with a still life by another hand. 2-May-4 Bonhams & Butterfields, San Francisco #1151/R

BARNES, James (19/20th C) British

£419 $700 €612 Landscape with mountains (25x41cm-10x16in) s. 19-Oct-3 Susanin's, Chicago #6015/R
Works on paper
£450 $792 €657 Wet path across the moors (48x36cm-19x14in) bears i.verso. 19-May-4 Dreweatt Neate, Newbury #39
£620 $1147 €905 Her only aid (50x34cm-20x13in) s. W/C. 14-Jul-4 Bonhams, Chester #340

BARNES, Marian L (fl.1890-1913) British

Works on paper
£390 $714 €569 White chrysanthemums in a glass vase (79x46cm-31x18in) s. W/C. 28-Jul-4 Mallams, Oxford #203

BARNES, Robert M (1947-) American

£1215 $1955 €1774 Winter vegetables (61x51cm-24x20in) s.d.Jan 2002 i.verso. 25-Aug-3 Sotheby's, Paddington #241 est:3000-5000 (A.D 3000)

BARNES, Samuel John (1847-1901) British

£300 $471 €435 Deer at the foot of Lochnagar (46x91cm-18x36in) s.i.d.92. 28-Aug-3 Christie's, Kensington #128/R
£300 $471 €435 Lochnagar from behind Balmoral Castle (61x91cm-24x36in) s.i.d.93. 28-Aug-3 Christie's, Kensington #131/R
£580 $1067 €847 Highland landscape with deer by a track, near Lochnagar (46x91cm-18x36in) s.d.92. 24-Mar-4 Hamptons Fine Art, Godalming #273/R

BARNES, Wilfred M (1892-1955) Canadian

£323 $594 €472 Golden light in a forest glade (24x33cm-9x13in) s. i.d.1931 verso panel prov. 9-Jun-4 Walker's, Ottawa #82/R (C.D 800)
£1040 $1903 €1518 Blue Hills at dawn, near Stanstead, Quebec (75x90cm-30x35in) s.d.17. 1-Jun-4 Joyner Waddington, Toronto #330/R est:2000-3000 (C.D 2600)

BARNET, Will (1911-) American

£320 $550 €467 Blue still life (30x41cm-12x16in) s. 7-Dec-3 Freeman, Philadelphia #218
£1000 $1600 €1460 Jamaican woman (97x66cm-38x26in) s. prov. 19-Sep-3 Freeman, Philadelphia #67 est:1000-1500

BARNETT, Herbert (1910-1978) American

£437 $800 €638 Hat bath (74x58cm-29x23in) s. s.i.d.1952 verso board. 10-Apr-4 Cobbs, Peterborough #161a/R

BARNETT, Thomas P (1870-1929) American

£1105 $1900 €1613 Fishing fleet, Concarneau (51x56cm-20x22in) s. 6-Dec-3 Neal Auction Company, New Orleans #625/R est:2000-3000

BARNEY, Frank A (1862-?) American

£994 $1600 €1451 Brook fishing (30x41cm-12x16in) s. 20-Aug-3 James Julia, Fairfield #1524/R est:1800-2200

BARNEY, James (20th C) American

Works on paper
£2989 $5500 €4364 Forest of Arden, as you like it (43x66cm-17x26in) s.i.d.1950 gouache pencil. 10-Jun-4 Sotheby's, New York #164/R est:800-1200

BARNEY, Joseph (1751-1829) British

£650 $1105 €949 Portrait of the artist's brother, James (28x23cm-11x9in) board oval. 4-Nov-3 Holloways, Banbury #508
£3100 $5270 €4526 Portrait of the artist's father and mother, Mr and Mrs Joseph Barney, (59x49cm-23x19in) pair. 4-Nov-3 Holloways, Banbury #507507 est:2500-3500

BARNEY, Matthew (1967-) American

Photographs
£8380 $15000 €12235 Cremaster 2, the royal cell of baby Fay (71x51cm-28x20in) s.d.98 verso laminated col print edition 4 of 40 prov. 12-May-4 Christie's, Rockefeller NY #355/R est:10000-15000
£11173 $20000 €16313 Cremaster 3, plumbline (71x61cm-28x24in) s.d.01 verso col coupler print edition 45 of 50 prov. 12-May-4 Christie's, Rockefeller NY #356/R est:8000-12000
£20958 $35000 €30599 CR4, ascending manual (48x43cm-19x17in) s.num.1/3 verso gelatin silver print two parts prov.exhib. 13-Nov-3 Sotheby's, New York #424/R est:40000-60000
£53892 $90000 €78682 Cremaster 3 - Hiram Abiff (137x122cm-54x48in) s.d.02 verso cibachrome print exec 2002 prov.exhib. 12-Nov-3 Christie's, Rockefeller NY #537/R est:100000-150000
£53892 $90000 €78682 Cremaster 4 (49x38cm-19x15in) s.d.1984 verso c-print self lubricating acrylic frame triptych. 13-Nov-3 Phillips, New York #2/R est:60000-80000
£95808 $160000 €139880 Cremaster 2 0 Genealogy (181x60cm-71x24in) s.d.99 cibachrome prints triptych prov.exhib. 11-Nov-3 Christie's, Rockefeller NY #2/R est:120000-180000
£137725 $230000 €201079 Cremaster 5, elvalas (105x88cm-41x35in) s.d.verso gelatin silver print two c-prints triptych. 13-Nov-3 Phillips, New York #10/R est:200000-300000
Sculpture
£41916 $70000 €61197 Unit bolus (68x49x25cm-27x19x10in) stainless steel cast petroleum jelly freezing device 1 of 5 prov. 13-Nov-3 Sotheby's, New York #470/R est:80000-120000

BARNEY, Tina (1945-) American?

Photographs
£1522 $2800 €2222 Real estate office (124x156cm-49x61in) s.d.1992 num.10 verso c-print. 10-Jun-4 Phillips, New York #529/R est:4000-6000
£1630 $3000 €2380 Yellow room (124x156cm-49x61in) s.d.1996 num.10 verso c-print prov. 10-Jun-4 Phillips, New York #530/R est:4000-6000
£4620 $8500 €6745 Father and sons (122x152cm-48x60in) s.d.1996 num.10 verso c-print. 10-Jun-4 Phillips, New York #527/R est:4000-6000

BARNI, Roberto (1939-) Italian

£340 $609 €500 Figures (30x25cm-12x10in) s.d.1989 verso. 22-Mar-4 Sant Agostino, Torino #377/R
£596 $1085 €900 Waves (50x70cm-20x28in) s. cardboard. 21-Jun-4 Pandolfini, Florence #396/R
£1067 $1931 €1600 Parade (80x60cm-31x24in) s.i.d.1988 verso. 2-Apr-4 Farsetti, Prato #148/R est:1300-2200
£5944 $10105 €8500 Pegasus (180x120cm-71x47in) s.i.d.1986-89 verso. 28-Nov-3 Farsetti, Prato #306/R est:3200-4200
Works on paper
£507 $892 €750 Babele (60x70cm-24x28in) s.i.d.1968 verso mixed media on canvas. 22-May-4 Galleria Pananti, Florence #421/R

BARNOIN, Henri Alphonse (1882-1935) French

£260 $434 €380 Britanny church (39x31cm-15x12in) s. board. 22-Oct-3 Cheffins, Cambridge #544/R
£1389 $2292 €2000 Depart de lapeche (45x37cm-18x15in) s. 5-Jul-3 Neret-Minet, Paris #152/R
£1489 $2487 €2100 Thonniers au soleil, Concarneau. Marins au port (38x46cm-15x18in) s.i.verso panel double-sided. 19-Oct-3 Anaf, Lyon #41 est:1200-1500
£1667 $2983 €2500 Thoniers au soleil, Concarneau (38x46cm-15x18in) s.i.verso panel. 16-May-4 Thierry & Lannon, Brest #102 est:2500-3000
£1678 $2887 €2400 Voiliers en bord de mer (50x61cm-20x24in) s. 3-Dec-3 Tajan, Paris #322 est:1200-1500
£2465 $4313 €3500 Le marche de Quimper (22x27cm-9x11in) s. 19-Dec-3 Delvaux, Paris #26/R est:3500-4500
£2483 $4146 €3600 Le marche de dole (22x27cm-9x11in) s. panel. 17-Nov-3 Tajan, Paris #170/R est:1200-1500
£2654 $4750 €3875 Brittany harbour (33x41cm-13x16in) s. 16-May-4 CRN Auctions, Cambridge #5/R
£3020 $5406 €4500 Barques a quai (46x55cm-18x22in) s.d.1938. 30-May-4 Eric Pillon, Calais #4/R
£3841 $7183 €5800 Jour de marche aux etoffes a Quimper, place St Corentin (50x61cm-20x24in) s. 24-Jul-4 Thierry & Lannon, Brest #342/R est:5000-6000
£4037 $6500 €5894 Marche Breton (81x100cm-32x39in) s. 14-Jan-4 Christie's, Rockefeller NY #29/R est:8000-12000
£4336 $7371 €6200 Soleil couchant a Concarneau (50x63cm-20x25in) s. 20-Nov-3 Gioffredo, Nice #7/R
£5629 $10526 €8500 Pardon en Bretagne (45x54cm-18x21in) s. 24-Jul-4 Thierry & Lannon, Brest #117/R est:8000-10000
£6690 $11708 €9500 Marche a Quimper, place de la Cathedrale (60x73cm-24x29in) s. 21-Dec-3 Thierry & Lannon, Brest #125/R est:8000-12000
£7042 $12324 €10000 Jour de fete a Quimperle (53x65cm-21x26in) s. 21-Dec-3 Thierry & Lannon, Brest #127/R est:10000-12000
£10563 $18486 €15000 Jour de pardon a St Geunole (46x58cm-18x23in) s. 21-Dec-3 Thierry & Lannon, Brest #126/R est:8000-9000
Works on paper
£795 $1486 €1200 Le port de Concarneau (27x49cm-11x19in) s.d.1925 chl. 24-Jul-4 Thierry & Lannon, Brest #26

BARNS, G (?) ?

£1049 $1804 €1500 Children fishing in pond (45x35cm-18x14in) s.d.81. 5-Dec-3 Michael Zeller, Lindau #568/R est:1500

BARNS-GRAHAM, Wilhelmina (1912-2004) British

Works on paper
£1000 $1670 €1460 Abstract study of fish (36x41cm-14x16in) s. gouache. 17-Oct-3 Keys, Aylsham #520/R
£5500 $10010 €8030 Underwater - Easter (16x22cm-6x9in) s.d.1958 gouache brush black ink. 1-Jul-4 Christie's, Kensington #406/R est:1500-2000

BARNSLEY, James MacDonald (1861-1929) Canadian

£444 $816 €648 Autumn, Canada (22x29cm-9x11in) s. s.i.verso canvas on board painted 1910 prov.exhib. 9-Jun-4 Walker's, Ottawa #123/R (C.D 1100)
£536 $921 €783 Autumn, Canada (22x29cm-9x11in) canvas on board prov. 2-Dec-3 Joyner Waddington, Toronto #399 (C.D 1200)
£2516 $4000 €3673 Sailing and steam vessels in Boston harbour (41x53cm-16x21in) s.d.1885 board. 10-Sep-3 Alderfer's, Hatfield #267 est:800-1200

Works on paper
£613 $1000 €895 Peaceful stroll (33x48cm-13x19in) s.d.89 W/C gouache. 24-Sep-3 Jackson's, Cedar Falls #758/R

BARNWELL, Alice G C (fl.1931-1940) British
Works on paper
£310 $536 €453 Spray of honeysuckle, with butterflies (30x23cm-12x9in) s. W/C. 11-Dec-3 Neales, Nottingham #523/R

BAROCCI, Federico (1526-1612) Italian
Prints
£1788 $3200 €2610 Annunciation (43x33cm-17x13in) etching engraving executed c.1585. 6-May-4 Swann Galleries, New York #40/R est:5000-8000
Works on paper
£8844 $15830 €13000 Etude de tete d'enfant. Etude de jambe d'enfant. Etude de femme (26x20cm-10x8in) i. graphite pastel pen one sheet double-sided. 17-Mar-4 Maigret, Paris #42/R est:10000-12000

BAROCCI, Federico (attrib) (1526-1612) Italian
Works on paper
£440 $800 €642 Head of a Woman (27x19cm-11x7in) black chk. 4-Feb-4 Christie's, Rockefeller NY #125/R

BAROJA, Ricardo (1871-1953) Spanish
£4138 $6910 €6000 Renaissance figures (50x47cm-20x19in) mono. 17-Nov-3 Durán, Madrid #195/R est:3500
£6338 $11092 €9000 Military attack (20x27cm-8x11in) s.i.d.1937 cardboard. 16-Dec-3 Durán, Madrid #199/R est:9000

BARON, Francis (20th C) American?
Sculpture
£2695 $4500 €3935 Stylised bull (51x71cm-20x28in) s. red brown pat bronze brass stand two piece. 25-Oct-3 David Rago, Lambertville #389 est:600-900

BARON, Henri Charles Antoine (1816-1885) French
£400 $728 €600 Young couple picking apples in summer (16x11cm-6x4in) indis.s. panel. 1-Jul-4 Van Ham, Cologne #1204
£769 $1308 €1100 Diane chasseresse (7x9cm-3x4in) s. panel. 18-Nov-3 Vanderkindere, Brussels #134
£850 $1556 €1241 Children playing on a log (34x26cm-13x10in) s.d.1861 panel. 6-Jul-4 Bearnes, Exeter #488/R
£1225 $2230 €1850 Flore (23x13cm-9x5in) mono. panel. 19-Jun-4 Gerard, Besancon #35
£1259 $2140 €1800 Allegory of summer (25x16cm-10x6in) s. panel. 20-Nov-3 Van Ham, Cologne #1471/R est:1400
£3497 $6014 €5000 Jeune filles musiciennes. Jeune filles dans un parc (29x41cm-11x16in) panel pair. 7-Dec-3 Osenat, Fontainebleau #127
Works on paper
£352 $585 €500 Conversation intime dans le jardin (24x19cm-9x7in) s. W/C htd. 15-Jun-3 Peron, Melun #6
£738 $1373 €1100 Scene de theatre (57x27cm-22x11in) s.d.1881 W/C gouache. 7-Mar-4 Livinec, Gaudcheau & Jezequel, Rennes #42
£1831 $3039 €2600 Marionette (44x29cm-17x11in) s. W/C. 15-Jun-3 Peron, Melun #78

BARON, Henri Charles Antoine (attrib) (1816-1885) French
£1020 $1857 €1500 Serenade dans le parc (43x32cm-17x13in) panel. 8-Feb-4 Anaf, Lyon #79 est:1500-1800

BARON, Stephanie (1830-1921) French
£6383 $10660 €9000 Bohemiens (118x135cm-46x53in) s. 17-Oct-3 Renaud, Paris #51/R est:4000-6000

BARON, Theodor (1840-1899) Belgian
£400 $724 €600 Meules de foin (51x76cm-20x30in) s. 30-Mar-4 Palais de Beaux Arts, Brussels #474/R
£408 $731 €600 Rochers a Lustin (29x22cm-11x9in) s. canvas on panel. 16-Mar-4 Vanderkindere, Brussels #38
£510 $913 €750 Pecheur au bord de la riviere (65x55cm-26x22in) s.d.1881. 16-Mar-4 Vanderkindere, Brussels #48
£559 $934 €800 Landscape painter (26x36cm-10x14in) s. panel. 11-Oct-3 De Vuyst, Lokeren #17
£596 $1085 €900 Le troupeau de moutons (60x40cm-24x16in) s. 16-Jun-4 Hotel des Ventes Mosan, Brussels #159
£927 $1687 €1400 Paysage anime avec pont et troupeau (91x121cm-36x48in) s. 16-Jun-4 Hotel des Ventes Mosan, Brussels #168
£2621 $4848 €3800 Marine (39x59cm-15x23in) s. 19-Jan-4 Horta, Bruxelles #463 est:1200-1500

BARONE, Adolfo C (1861-?) Italian
£3546 $5922 €5000 Turkey keeper (51x72cm-20x28in) s. 14-Oct-3 Finarte Semenzato, Milan #118/R est:7000

BAROOSHIAN, Martin (1929-) American
£815 $1500 €1190 Temptation of Eve (107x107cm-42x42in) 10-Jun-4 Swann Galleries, New York #10a/R est:1500-2500
£1033 $1900 €1508 Portrait of Dante. Study for young bather (51x30cm-20x12in) s.i. one d.1968. 10-Jun-4 Swann Galleries, New York #11/R est:2000-3000

BAROTTE, Léon (1866-1933) French
£245 $450 €358 Autumn landscape (30x48cm-12x19in) s. 26-Jun-4 Sloans & Kenyon, Bethesda #1067/R

BAROVIER, Angelo (20th C) Italian
Works on paper
£276 $500 €403 Geogemma (76x99cm-30x39in) s.d.59 s.i.d.verso mixed media. 2-Apr-4 Freeman, Philadelphia #60
£278 $500 €406 Luci della Citta (99x79cm-39x31in) s.d.1959 mixed media glass board. 23-Jan-4 Freeman, Philadelphia #129/R

BARR, David (1939-) American
Sculpture
£1000 $1700 €1460 Structurist relief no.58 (117x140cm-46x55in) s.i.d.1969 painted wood prov. 9-Nov-3 Wright, Chicago #366 est:2000-3000
£1176 $2000 €1717 Construction no.67 (117x137cm-46x54in) s.i.d.1970 verso painted wood prov. 9-Nov-3 Wright, Chicago #367 est:2000-3000
£1353 $2300 €1975 Construction no.76 (114x147cm-45x58in) s.i.d.1971 painted wood. 9-Nov-3 Wright, Chicago #364 est:2000-3000

BARR, William (1867-1933) American
£1589 $2750 €2320 The Yellow House (30x41cm-12x16in) s. 10-Dec-3 Bonhams & Butterfields, San Francisco #6230/R est:3000-5000
£2116 $4000 €3089 Rocky coastal inlet (30x41cm-12x16in) s. prov. 17-Feb-4 John Moran, Pasadena #175/R est:1000-2000
£3533 $6500 €5158 Mission courtyard in bloom. View of a mission garden (45x61cm-18x24in) s. pair prov. 8-Jun-4 Bonhams & Butterfields, San Francisco #4254/R est:4000-6000

BARRA BARRA, Djambu (c.1936-) Australian
Works on paper
£1220 $1927 €1769 Untitled (122x135cm-48x53in) synthetic polymer paint canvas prov. 28-Jul-3 Sotheby's, Paddington #377/R est:3000-5000 (A.D 3000)
£2148 $4018 €3222 Untitled (176x232cm-69x91in) synthetic polymer paint canvas prov. 26-Jul-4 Sotheby's, Melbourne #283/R est:7000-10000 (A.D 5500)
£2236 $3533 €3242 Untitled (170x130cm-67x51in) synthetic polymer paint canvas prov. 28-Jul-3 Sotheby's, Paddington #376/R est:4000-6000 (A.D 5500)
£4472 $7065 €6484 Ngundungunda (216x178cm-85x70in) synthetic polymer paint canvas prov. 28-Jul-3 Sotheby's, Paddington #375/R est:6000-8000 (A.D 11000)

BARRA, Didier (1590-1650) French
£12000 $21960 €18000 Salomon's judgement (38x49cm-15x19in) 1-Jun-4 Sotheby's, Milan #190/R est:15000-20000

BARRABAND, Jacques (style) (1767-1809) French
£18056 $32500 €26362 Pair of sulphur-crested cockatoos (55x40cm-22x16in) prov. 22-Jan-4 Sotheby's, New York #121/R est:15000-20000
£19444 $35000 €28388 Pair of leadbeaters cockatoos (55x40cm-22x16in) prov. 22-Jan-4 Sotheby's, New York #120/R est:15000-20000

BARRABBINO, Simone (1585-?) Italian
£11111 $20000 €16222 Christ on the road to Calvary with Saint Veronica holding the Sudarium (63x49cm-25x19in) 23-Jan-4 Christie's, Rockefeller NY #49/R est:20000-30000

BARRABBINO, Simone (attrib) (1585-?) Italian
£4832 $8891 €7200 Holy Family with Saint John (71x87cm-28x34in) 29-Mar-4 Pandolfini, Florence #778/R est:7000-9000

BARRABLE, George H (fl.1873-1890) British
£13000 $23920 €18980 Intercepted (81x114cm-32x45in) s. s.i.verso exhib. 11-Jun-4 Christie's, London #187/R est:8000-12000

BARRACHINA, Francisco (1940-) Spanish
£851 $1421 €1200 Girl in profile (23x15cm-9x6in) s.d.85 board. 20-Oct-3 Durán, Madrid #54/R
£1631 $2643 €2300 Young girl with flowers (27x21cm-11x8in) s. panel. 20-May-3 Ansorena, Madrid #117/R est:2000

BARRACLOUGH, James P (?-1942) British
£1000 $1800 €1460 Dales landscape with a farmstead and barns (63x76cm-25x30in) s.d.1924. 21-Apr-4 Tennants, Leyburn #1261 est:400-500

BARRADAS, Rafael (1890-1929) Uruguayan
Works on paper
£761 $1400 €1111 Pilar (21x15cm-8x6in) s.i. pencil dr prov. 22-Jun-4 Galeria y Remates, Montevideo #62/R
£1585 $2600 €2314 Girl (28x21cm-11x8in) chl dr prov. 3-Jun-3 Galeria y Remates, Montevideo #92
£2011 $3800 €2936 Hospital in Llobregat (48x63cm-19x25in) W/C tempera dr cardboard prov. 22-Feb-4 Galeria y Remates, Montevideo #48/R est:4000-5000
£15882 $27000 €23188 Black man walking (31x24cm-12x9in) s.d.1911 pastel. 25-Nov-3 Galeria y Remates, Montevideo #154/R

BARRAGAN, Julio (1928-) Argentinian
£1117 $2000 €1631 1243 (55x76cm-22x30in) board. 11-May-4 Arroyo, Buenos Aires #8
£1319 $2400 €1926 Serrania (50x70cm-20x28in) s. exhib. 29-Jun-4 Arroyo, Buenos Aires #26/R est:2400
£1397 $2500 €2040 Bub (50x70cm-20x28in) s. s.i.verso board. 4-May-4 Arroyo, Buenos Aires #22/R est:1700

BARRAGAN, Luis (20th C) South American

£1868	$3400	€2727	Spatial (60x40cm-24x16in) s. painted 1970. 5-Jul-4 Arroyo, Buenos Aires #77/R est:3400

BARRANCO, Jesus (1960-) Spanish

£403	$753	€600	Landscape (81x122cm-32x48in) s. s.verso board. 24-Feb-4 Durán, Madrid #4/R

BARRANTI, P (19th C) Italian

Sculpture

£1060	$1939	€1600	Peasant boy (65cm-26in) s. white marble. 6-Apr-4 Sotheby's, Amsterdam #333/R est:1000-1500

BARRATT, Goody (c.1930-) Australian

Works on paper

£1804	$3229	€2634	Dingo Dreaming (86x117cm-34x46in) natural earth pigments canvas exec 2002 prov. 25-May-4 Lawson Menzies, Sydney #165/R est:5000-7000 (A.D 4600)

BARRAU, Laureano (1864-1957) Spanish

£3221	$5992	€4800	View of town (65x54cm-26x21in) 2-Mar-4 Ansorena, Madrid #90/R est:4600
£3472	$5660	€5000	Village on the Costa Brava (50x56cm-20x22in) s. 23-Sep-3 Durán, Madrid #124/R est:4800
£10563	$18275	€15000	Washerwomen (40x56cm-16x22in) s. 15-Dec-3 Ansorena, Madrid #36/R est:15000
Works on paper			
£724	$1332	€1100	Eating in the fields (38x53cm-15x21in) s.d.31. 22-Jun-4 Durán, Madrid #608/R

BARRAUD, Aime (1902-1954) Swiss

£431	$772	€629	Cornstooks (46x28cm-18x11in) s. 12-May-4 Dobiaschofsky, Bern #325/R (S.FR 1000)
£905	$1538	€1321	Still life with butterflies (56x48cm-22x19in) s. panel. 1-Dec-3 Koller, Zurich #6549 est:2500-3500 (S.FR 2000)
£1379	$2469	€2013	Still life with white flower in vase (33x24cm-13x9in) s. 14-May-4 Dobiaschofsky, Bern #103/R est:2400 (S.FR 3200)
£1718	$2921	€2508	Still life with colourful Calendula (61x52cm-24x20in) s. 7-Nov-3 Dobiaschofsky, Bern #169/R est:7500 (S.FR 3900)
£1983	$3549	€2895	Still life with onions (55x55cm-22x22in) s.i.d.1935. 14-May-4 Dobiaschofsky, Bern #151/R est:5500 (S.FR 4600)
£2203	$3744	€3216	Still life with onions and knife (61x40cm-24x16in) s. 7-Nov-3 Dobiaschofsky, Bern #164/R est:7500 (S.FR 5000)
£3587	$5848	€5237	Simone (33x24cm-13x9in) s. 29-Sep-3 Christie's, Zurich #87/R est:8000-12000 (S.FR 8000)
£3587	$5991	€5237	Nature morte avec chataignes (73x54cm-29x21in) s. 24-Oct-3 Hans Widmer, St Gallen #65/R est:7500-12000 (S.FR 8000)

BARRAUD, Alfred Thomas (1849-1925) Canadian

£741	$1200	€1082	Landscape, possibly Nauset, Massachusetts. s. 31-Jul-3 Eldred, East Dennis #883/R

BARRAUD, Aurele (1903-1969) Swiss

£345	$617	€504	Still life with peaches (33x46cm-13x18in) s.i.d.27. 12-May-4 Dobiaschofsky, Bern #326 (S.FR 800)
£383	$659	€559	Still life with a tin can (50x38cm-20x15in) s. 8-Dec-3 Philippe Schuler, Zurich #3318 (S.FR 850)
£474	$849	€692	Nature morte a la cruche bleue (46x55cm-18x22in) s.mono. 14-May-4 Dobiaschofsky, Bern #81/R (S.FR 1100)
£2271	$4133	€3316	Theiere d'etain avec pinceau (39x47cm-15x19in) s. 17-Jun-4 Kornfeld, Bern #188/R est:5000 (S.FR 5200)
£2371	$4244	€3462	Girl with doll (59x44cm-23x17in) s. 14-May-4 Dobiaschofsky, Bern #105/R est:4500 (S.FR 5500)

BARRAUD, Charles Decimus (1822-1897) New Zealander/British

Works on paper

£1859	$3197	€2714	Mount Egmont from Urenui (35x52cm-14x20in) s.d.1892 W/C prov. 3-Dec-3 Dunbar Sloane, Auckland #60/R est:8000-10000 (NZ.D 5000)
£2800	$4956	€4088	Lake Wakatipu, New Zealand (32x50cm-13x20in) s.d.1878 W/C. 27-Apr-4 Bonhams, New Bond Street #1/R est:3000-5000
£6000	$11040	€9000	Landscapes with sheep and sailing boat, and with ponies and boat (36x53cm-14x21in) s.d.1870 W/C pair. 25-Jun-4 Bigwood, Stratford on Avon #253/R
£6944	$11042	€10138	Wellington Harbour (24x34cm-9x13in) init.d.1875 W/C. 1-May-3 Dunbar Sloane, Wellington #26/R est:9000-15000 (NZ.D 20000)
£7092	$12553	€10354	White terraces (33x49cm-13x19in) s.d.1888 W/C. 28-Apr-4 Dunbar Sloane, Auckland #35/R est:20000-30000 (NZ.D 20000)
£7500	$13800	€11250	Landscape depicting cottages with wagon train carts and salt flats (46x78cm-18x31in) s.d.1870 W/C sold with a companion. 25-Jun-4 Bigwood, Stratford on Avon #251/R
£8152	$13207	€11820	Artist's camp near Mt. Aspiring (44x74cm-17x29in) s. W/C. 31-Jul-3 International Art Centre, Auckland #37/R est:25000-35000 (NZ.D 22500)

BARRAUD, Francis Philip (1824-1901) British

Works on paper

£340	$578	€496	St. Lo, Normandy (35x53cm-14x21in) s.i. W/C. 4-Nov-3 Bristol Auction Rooms #512/R

BARRAUD, François (1899-1934) Swiss

£837	$1423	€1222	Still life with white roses in blue vase (22x24cm-9x9in) s. prov. 7-Nov-3 Dobiaschofsky, Bern #179/R (S.FR 1900)
£2203	$3744	€3216	Portrait of blonde girl (31x29cm-12x11in) s. board. 7-Nov-3 Dobiaschofsky, Bern #168/R est:6000 (S.FR 5000)
£4741	$8487	€6922	Portrait of Marie Barraud (23x19cm-9x7in) s. panel. 14-May-4 Dobiaschofsky, Bern #82/R est:2200 (S.FR 11000)
£4846	$8238	€7075	Still life with anemones and stone pots (40x36cm-16x14in) s. 7-Nov-3 Dobiaschofsky, Bern #160/R est:8000 (S.FR 11000)
£6787	$11538	€9909	Fleurs de lis (81x65cm-32x26in) s.d.1934 prov. 25-Nov-3 Germann, Zurich #72/R est:6000-8000 (S.FR 15000)

BARRAUD, Gustave François (1883-1968) Swiss

£395	$659	€577	Arbres au bord du lac (60x49cm-24x19in) s.d.1921. 16-Nov-3 Koller, Geneva #1232 (S.FR 900)
£786	$1446	€1148	Le village (50x61cm-20x24in) s.d i. verso. 14-Jun-4 Philippe Schuler, Zurich #4201 (S.FR 1800)
£2193	$3662	€3202	Nu a contre-jour (93x73cm-37x29in) s. 16-Nov-3 Koller, Geneva #1286/R est:3500-5500 (S.FR 5000)
Works on paper			
£688	$1149	€998	Nu de dos (60x37cm-24x15in) s.d. pastel. 21-Jun-3 Galerie du Rhone, Sion #325/R est:1500-2000 (S.FR 1500)
£1131	$1957	€1651	Chrysanthemes (59x49cm-23x19in) s. i. pastel cardboard. 12-Dec-3 Galerie du Rhone, Sion #465/R est:2500-3500 (S.FR 2500)

BARRAUD, Henry (1811-1874) British

£2473	$4500	€3611	Blink Bonny (50x60cm-20x24in) s.i. 29-Jun-4 Sotheby's, New York #174/R est:6000-8000
£2600	$4784	€3796	Mare and foal outside a barn (45x60cm-18x24in) s. 29-Mar-4 Bonhams, Bath #87/R est:2000-3000
£9000	$15300	€13140	Bay hunter in a landscape (60x73cm-24x29in) 27-Nov-3 Sotheby's, London #209/R est:4000-6000
£9302	$16000	€13581	Harrier hounds outside a kennel (46x61cm-18x24in) s.d.1853. 5-Dec-3 Christie's, Rockefeller NY #21/R est:8000-12000
£11173	$20000	€16313	Charles Davis (44x59cm-17x23in) s. prov. 27-May-4 Sotheby's, New York #232/R est:20000-30000

BARRAUD, Henry and William (19th C) British

£8380	$15000	€12235	Gentleman on hunter, hunt beyond (69x91cm-27x36in) s.d.1841. 27-May-4 Sotheby's, New York #267/R est:15000-25000

BARRAUD, Maurice (1889-1954) Swiss

£429	$686	€622	Leda and the swan (19x25cm-7x10in) W/C pencil. 15-May-3 Stuker, Bern #1050/R (S.FR 900)
£476	$852	€695	Dancer (60x42cm-24x17in) W/C over pencil. 22-Mar-4 Philippe Schuler, Zurich #4142/R (S.FR 1100)
£1652	$3023	€2412	Femme a la lorgnette (35x24cm-14x9in) s. board prov. 7-Jun-4 Christie's, Zurich #106/R est:4000-6000 (S.FR 3800)
£2198	$3935	€3209	Femme couchee (27x35cm-11x14in) s. panel. 14-May-4 Dobiaschofsky, Bern #155/R est:4500 (S.FR 5100)
£2609	$4774	€3809	Femme au grand chapeau avec un chale rose (80x65cm-31x26in) s. prov. 7-Jun-4 Christie's, Zurich #107/R est:7000-9000 (S.FR 6000)
£3478	$6365	€5078	L'Americaine (68x57cm-27x22in) s.d.1942 prov. 4-Jun-4 Zofingen, Switzerland #2741/R est:9500 (S.FR 8000)
£3696	$6763	€5396	Portrait of an Oriental girl (62x52cm-24x20in) s. 4-Jun-4 Zofingen, Switzerland #2740/R est:10000 (S.FR 8500)
£5702	$10491	€8325	Gitanes (40x64cm-16x25in) i.verso. 23-Jun-4 Koller, Zurich #3061/R est:8000-12000 (S.FR 13000)
£7175	$11695	€10476	Melancholy (70x59cm-28x23in) s. i. verso canvas on panel. 29-Sep-3 Christie's, Zurich #92/R est:12000-15000 (S.FR 16000)
£11842	$21789	€17289	Flora (81x65cm-32x26in) s. 23-Jun-4 Koller, Zurich #3063/R est:20000-30000 (S.FR 27000)
£13575	$23484	€19820	Ete (56x68cm-22x27in) s.d.1939 prov. 9-Dec-3 Sotheby's, Zurich #48/R est:19000-25000 (S.FR 30000)
£14655	$26233	€21396	Voila les hirondelles (67x75cm-26x30in) s. i. verso canvas on panel. 14-May-4 Dobiaschofsky, Bern #80/R est:40000 (S.FR 34000)
Works on paper			
£226	$385	€330	Figures wearing long clothes (19x21cm-7x8in) s. pencil wash Indian ink. 18-Nov-3 Hans Widmer, St Gallen #1014 (S.FR 500)
£284	$522	€415	Girl leaning on wall (26x19cm-10x7in) s. i. verso Indian ink. 14-Jun-4 Philippe Schuler, Zurich #4106 (S.FR 650)
£302	$540	€441	Mistinguette (13x15cm-5x6in) s. i. verso Indian ink. 13-May-4 Stuker, Bern #534 (S.FR 700)
£317	$538	€463	Woman's portrait (28x21cm-11x8in) pencil. 25-Nov-3 Germann, Zurich #723 (S.FR 700)
£323	$579	€472	Woman with shawl and hat (44x31cm-17x12in) s.d.20 chl. 12-May-4 Dobiaschofsky, Bern #138/R (S.FR 750)
£529	$899	€772	Elegant woman in coach (21x26cm-8x10in) s. Indian ink W/C prov. 5-Nov-3 Dobiaschofsky, Bern #1424/R (S.FR 1200)
£588	$982	€858	Portrait d'une jeune fille (25x19cm-10x7in) s. Indian ink. 24-Jun-3 Germann, Zurich #909 (S.FR 1300)
£631	$1085	€921	Baigneuse et cygne (27x35cm-11x14in) s. ink pen. 8-Dec-3 Philippe Schuler, Zurich #3164 (S.FR 1400)
£636	$1056	€922	Femme dansante/Ballerina (56x38cm-22x15in) pencil. 13-Jun-3 Zofingen, Switzerland #2777/R (S.FR 1400)
£776	$1389	€1133	Portrait of young woman wearing hat (26x29cm-10x11in) s. col chk. 12-May-4 Dobiaschofsky, Bern #327/R est:1500 (S.FR 1800)
£1572	$2814	€2295	Femme a la fontaine. Trois personnages (24x30cm-9x12in) one mono. one ink one ink W/C two. 26-May-4 Sotheby's, Zurich #99/R est:2000-3000 (S.FR 3600)
£2414	$4321	€3524	Au coin de la rue (70x55cm-28x22in) s.d.1913 pastel prov. 14-May-4 Dobiaschofsky, Bern #171/R est:6000 (S.FR 5600)
£4585	$8437	€6694	Mother with child (100x90cm-39x35in) s. gouache board. 14-Jun-4 Philippe Schuler, Zurich #4105/R est:15000-20000 (S.FR 10500)

BARRAUD, William (1810-1850) British

£13953	$24000	€20371	Portrait of a saddle black hunter with a sheep dog in a stable (63x76cm-25x30in) s.d.1837 prov. 5-Dec-3 Christie's, Rockefeller NY #38/R est:25000-35000
Works on paper			
£1300	$2392	€1898	Gentleman with his horse (60x48cm-24x19in) s. pastel. 10-Jun-4 Christie's, Kensington #29/R est:1000-2000

BARRDGADUBA, Curly (1924-1987) Australian

Works on paper

£1172 $2191 €1758 Ngalkunburriyaymi, the female rainbow serpent (153x59cm-60x23in) name.i.verso earth pigment eucalyptus bark exec.c.1978 prov. 26-Jul-4 Sotheby's, Melbourne #396/R est:3000-5000 (A.D 3000)

£1172 $2191 €1758 Rainbow serpent (135x65cm-53x26in) bears name.verso earth pigments eucalyptus bark exec.c.1978 prov. 26-Jul-4 Sotheby's, Melbourne #398/R est:3500-4500 (A.D 3000)

BARRE, Jean Auguste (1811-1896) French

Sculpture

£2000 $3640 €3000 Fanny Elssler dansant (29cm-11in) s.i.d.1837 bronze lit. 30-Jun-4 Piasa, Paris #26 est:3000-3500

£3087 $5681 €4600 Napoleon I (99cm-39in) s. pat bronze. 26-Mar-4 Daguerre, Paris #140/R est:5000-6000

BARRÉ, Martin (1924-1993) French

£2819 $4989 €4200 Peinture au tube (96x88cm-38x35in) s.d.1961 i. verso prov.lit. 28-Apr-4 Artcurial Briest, Paris #270/R est:3000-3500

£5035 $8408 €7200 61-T-4 (114x108cm-45x43in) s. s.i.d.1961 verso prov.lit. 29-Jun-3 Versailles Encheres #119/R

£5333 $9547 €8000 74-75-A-113x105 (113x105cm-44x41in) s.i. verso. 15-May-4 Van Ham, Cologne #429/R est:10000

£5333 $9813 €8000 67-2-21-53 x 49 (53x49cm-21x19in) s.i. verso glycerol acrylic painted 1967 prov.exhib. 8-Jun-4 Artcurial Briest, Paris #281b/R est:15000-20000

£6993 $11678 €10000 67.F.11 (86x80cm-34x31in) s.i.d.1967 verso paint acrylic prov.lit. 29-Jun-3 Versailles Encheres #118/R

£8000 $14720 €12000 Sans titre (73x60cm-29x24in) s.d.1956 prov.lit. 14-Jun-4 Tajan, Paris #196/R est:6000-8000

£8333 $15333 €12500 82-84-88X81 (88x81cm-35x32in) s.i.verso acrylic prov.exhib.lit. 14-Jun-4 Tajan, Paris #197/R est:8000-10000

£8667 $15947 €13000 82-84-84c81 (84x81cm-33x32in) s.i. verso acrylic painted 1982-84 prov.exhib. 8-Jun-4 Artcurial Briest, Paris #282/R est:6000-8000

£8741 $14598 €12500 87-89-54 x 216 A (54x216cm-21x85in) s.i.d.1987-1989 acrylic prov.exhib.lit. 11-Oct-3 Cornette de St.Cyr, Paris #1/R est:10000-15000

£9441 $16238 €13500 60 - T - 4 (96x88cm-38x35in) s.i.d.1960 verso. 2-Dec-3 Calmels Cohen, Paris #78/R est:8000-12000

£13287 $22189 €19000 79-B-62X262 (62x262cm-24x103in) s.i.d.1979-1981 verso acrylic prov.exhib.lit. 11-Oct-3 Cornette de St.Cyr, Paris #3/R est:10000-15000

£14685 $24524 €21000 79-A-131 x 124 (131x124cm-52x49in) acrylic prov.exhib.lit. 11-Oct-3 Cornette de St.Cyr, Paris #2/R est:8000-10000

£15385 $25692 €22000 73-74-B (98x180cm-39x71in) s.i.verso acrylic prov.exhib.lit. 29-Jun-3 Versailles Encheres #117/R

£18531 $30948 €26500 Composition (100x100cm-39x39in) s. s.i.verso prov.exhib.lit. 29-Jun-3 Versailles Encheres #114/R

Works on paper

£1958 $3270 €2800 Composition (59x53cm-23x21in) s.d.1958 gouache prov.exhib.lit. 29-Jun-3 Versailles Encheres #109/R

£2098 $3503 €3000 Composition (62x47cm-24x19in) s.d.1958 gouache prov.exhib.lit. 29-Jun-3 Versailles Encheres #110/R

£2098 $3503 €3000 Composition (85x49cm-33x19in) s.d.1958 gouache prov.exhib.lit. 29-Jun-3 Versailles Encheres #113/R

£2378 $3971 €3400 Composition (49x49cm-19x19in) s.d.1958 gouache prov.exhib.lit. 29-Jun-3 Versailles Encheres #108/R

£2517 $4204 €3600 Composition (70x66cm-28x26in) s.d.1960 gouache prov.exhib.lit. 29-Jun-3 Versailles Encheres #111/R

£3007 $5022 €4300 Composition (59x49cm-23x19in) s.d.1958 gouache prov. 29-Jun-3 Versailles Encheres #112/R

£6127 $10599 €8700 Composition (62x47cm-24x19in) s.d.1958 gouache prov. 14-Dec-3 Versailles Encheres #88/R est:3000-4000

BARRE, Vincent (1948-) French

Works on paper

£1042 $1740 €1500 A giotto (146x155cm-57x61in) s.d.1988 collage on canvas prov. 25-Oct-3 Cornette de St.Cyr, Paris #375 est:300-400

£1493 $2493 €2150 A giotto, magnificat (143x150cm-56x59in) paper on canvas prov. 25-Oct-3 Cornette de St.Cyr, Paris #376/R est:300-400

BARREIRO, Jose Maria (1940-) Spanish

£604 $1130 €900 Cello player (65x50cm-26x20in) s.d.2003 acrylic card. 24-Feb-4 Durán, Madrid #5/R

£1064 $1777 €1500 Gaitero (46x38cm-18x15in) s.d.87. 23-Jun-3 Durán, Madrid #150/R est:1500

£2553 $4264 €3600 Musicians (100x81cm-39x32in) s.d.88 exhib. 20-Oct-3 Durán, Madrid #241/R

BARRERA, Antonio (1948-) Colombian

£4706 $8000 €6871 El amanecer helado en las sabanas de Bogota (110x140cm-43x55in) s.d.80 prov. 18-Nov-3 Christie's, Rockefeller NY #159/R est:10000-15000

BARRERA, Francisco (attrib) (17th C) Spanish

£33333 $60000 €48666 Two vase of white lilies, pears in a porcelain dish and two landscape paintings on a stone ledge (84x104cm-33x41in) 23-Jan-4 Christie's, Rockefeller NY #82/R est:60000-80000

BARRET, George (18/19th C) British

£5168 $9250 €7700 River landscape with figures (70x46cm-28x18in) i.verso. 26-May-4 James Adam, Dublin #12/R est:6000-8000

£6333 $11653 €9500 Hunting party in the Highlands (51x75cm-20x30in) s. 11-Jun-4 Wendl, Rudolstadt #3943/R est:2900

Works on paper

£720 $1332 €1051 Cattle and horses grazing (29x46cm-11x18in) pencil ink W/C pair. 10-Mar-4 Sotheby's, Olympia #33/R

BARRET, George (attrib) (18/19th C) British

£583 $1073 €875 River landscape with building (39x31cm-15x12in) s.d.1827. 14-Jun-4 Lilla Bukowskis, Stockholm #5 (S.KR 8000)

BARRET, George (jnr) (1767-1842) British

Works on paper

£620 $1141 €905 Returning home (21x28cm-8x11in) s.d.1827 W/C. 23-Mar-4 Bonhams, Knightsbridge #60/R

£1800 $3240 €2628 Figures in the moonlight by a classical building (26x22cm-10x9in) s.d.1831 W/C over pencil bodycol. 21-Jan-4 Sotheby's, Olympia #124/R est:1000-1500

BARRET, George (jnr-attrib) (1767-1842) British

£9000 $16740 €13140 English landscape with a figure and hound (71x102cm-28x40in) indis sig. 4-Mar-4 Amersham Auction Rooms, UK #297

BARRET, George (snr) (1728-1784) British

£180000 $322200 €262800 Wooded landscape with figures and horses at a ford and fallow deer (103x127cm-41x50in) prov.lit. 14-May-4 Christie's, London #109/R est:150000-200000

BARRET, George (style) (18/19th C) British

£6200 $10292 €9052 Extensive landscape with distant mountains and goats in foreground (40x52cm-16x20in) 30-Sep-3 Sotheby's, London #259/R est:3000-5000

BARRETO, Pedro (1935-) Venezuelan

Sculpture

£865 $1470 €1263 Untitled (32x28x6cm-13x11x2in) s. wood. 23-Nov-3 Subastas Odalys, Caracas #8/R

BARRETT, Bill (1934-) American

Sculpture

£2273 $4000 €3319 Abstract (36x30cm-14x12in) s.d.1996 bronze. 23-May-4 Treadway Gallery, Cincinnati #750/R est:5000-7000

BARRETT, Jerry (1824-1906) British

£1800 $2862 €2628 Lady with a canary in an interior (51x38cm-20x15in) 9-Sep-3 Bonhams, Knightsbridge #94/R est:1500-2000

Works on paper

£280 $468 €409 View of Dublin harbour by moonlight (15x36cm-6x14in) mono. pencil W/C. 8-Oct-3 Christie's, Kensington #1060

BARRETT, John (19th C) British

£400 $740 €584 Cattle in a Devonshire River (20x24cm-8x9in) s. board. 13-Jan-4 Bearnes, Exeter #558

£1500 $2490 €2190 Reapers (25x46cm-10x18in) s.d.1883 board. 1-Oct-3 Sotheby's, Olympia #82/R est:1000-1500

BARRETT, Joseph (1935 -) American

£190 $350 €277 Water wheel at Peddler's village Lahaska (23x18cm-9x7in) s. board. 9-Jun-4 Alderfer's, Hatfield #455/R

£860 $1600 €1256 Man standing under flag with other figures and carnival booths in background (36x30cm-14x12in) s. i.verso. 3-Mar-4 Alderfer's, Hatfield #384/R est:2000-3000

£1156 $2000 €1688 Summer day near Doylestown (20x25cm-8x10in) s. 10-Dec-3 Alderfer's, Hatfield #443/R est:1500-1800

£1494 $2750 €2181 Old farm orchard (46x41cm-18x16in) s. 9-Jun-4 Alderfer's, Hatfield #454/R est:2500-3500

£1630 $3000 €2380 Upper mountain road (64x56cm-25x22in) s. 9-Jun-4 Alderfer's, Hatfield #453/R est:4000-6000

£2016 $3750 €2943 Winter landscape with roadside buildings (41x30cm-16x12in) s. i.verso. 3-Mar-4 Alderfer's, Hatfield #383/R est:2000-3000

BARRETT, Oliver Glen (1903-1970) American

£297 $550 €434 Rugged Pacific coast (66x91cm-26x36in) s. 15-Jul-4 Doyle, New York #6/R

BARRETTE, Sacha (20th C) Canadian

£588 $982 €858 Ruelle escalier (120x60cm-47x24in) s.i. acrylic. 17-Nov-3 Hodgins, Calgary #420/R est:1500-1800 (C.D 1300)

BARRIAS, Félix (1822-1907) French

£330 $601 €500 Scene antique (32x40cm-13x16in) 3-Dec-3 Oger, Dumont, Paris #101

BARRIAS, Louis Ernest (1841-1905) French

Sculpture

£1014 $1784 €1500 Printemps (46cm-18in) s. pat bronze. 18-May-4 Galerie Moderne, Brussels #1507 est:1300-1800

£1050 $1712 €1533 Female nude balanced on one leg holding thyrsus in one hand (52cm-20in) s. green gold pat bronze rocky base Cast.f.Susse Freres. 28-Sep-3 Wilkinson, Doncaster #30

£1533 $2821 €2300 Buste femme de Bou Saada (19cm-7in) s. pat bronze st.f. Susse lit. 9-Jun-4 Beaussant & Lefèvre, Paris #230/R est:2000-2500

£1712 $2911 €2500 Nature se devoilant devant la science (24cm-9in) s.st.f.Susse pat bronze. 5-Nov-3 Tajan, Paris #17/R

£2100 $3570 €3066 Bust of a young girl (20cm-8in) s. gilt pat. bronze st.f.Susse. 25-Nov-3 Sotheby's, Olympia #67/R est:800-1200

£2600 $4420 €3796 Still life of roses (20x12cm-8x5in) s.st.f.Bingen i. pat bronze wood. 28-Oct-3 Sotheby's, London #76/R

£2875 $4600 €4198 Mozart child (114cm-45in) pat bronze exec.1883. 20-Sep-3 New Orleans Auction, New Orleans #137/R
£4490 $8037 €6600 L'enfant a la mandoline (80cm-31in) s. marble prov. 21-Mar-4 Muizon & Le Coent, Paris #68/R
£5135 $9500 €7703 Nature revealing herself (56cm-22in) s.st.f. Susse bronze ivory slate onyx base. 17-Jul-4 Skinner, Boston #712/R est:8000-12000
£15556 $28000 €22712 Les premieres funerailles (86cm-34in) i. red brown pat. bronze prov.exhib.lit. 23-Apr-4 Sotheby's, New York #40/R est:20000-30000
£53360 $95514 €77906 Nature revealing herself to Science (99cm-39in) s. st.f.Susse Freres white marble gilt bronze prov.lit. 15-May-4 Christie's, Sydney #19/R est:80000-110000 (A.D 135000)

BARRIBAL, William (fl.1919-1938) British
Works on paper
£500 $900 €730 Portrait of a lady (39x29cm-15x11in) s. pastel htd bodycol. 21-Apr-4 Lyon & Turnbull, Edinburgh #240/R
£750 $1388 €1095 At the easel (52x42cm-20x17in) s. chl W/C bodycol. 11-Mar-4 Christie's, Kensington #231

BARRIE, Mardi (1931-) British
£270 $451 €394 Waiting room (111x86cm-44x34in) i. 19-Jun-3 Bonhams, Edinburgh #342
£550 $985 €803 Evening mist (68x89cm-27x35in) s. oil paper exhib. 14-May-4 Christie's, Kensington #598/R
£600 $1092 €876 Cloud sky on Autumn Valley (43x55cm-17x22in) board. 1-Jul-4 Christie's, Kensington #312/R
£900 $1674 €1314 City window, dusk (71x90cm-28x35in) s. prov. 4-Mar-4 Christie's, Kensington #230/R
£1300 $2418 €1898 Evening interlude (76x102cm-30x40in) s. exhib. 4-Mar-4 Christie's, Kensington #231/R est:400-600

BARRIER, Gustave (1885-?) French
£894 $1600 €1305 Vase of flowers (41x33cm-16x13in) s. board. 8-Jan-4 Doyle, New York #4/R est:800-1200
£1078 $1929 €1574 Still life (22x27cm-9x11in) s. board on panel. 13-May-4 Stuker, Bern #25/R est:2500-3000 (S.FR 2500)

BARRINGER, Gwendoline (1883-1960) Australian
Works on paper
£414 $646 €600 Coastal haystacks (38x37cm-15x15in) s. W/C. 1-Aug-2 Joel, Victoria #241 est:2000-3000 (A.D 1200)

BARRINGTON BROWNE (1908-1985) British
£480 $816 €701 Summer landscape with cattle watering in the foreground (61x91cm-24x36in) s. 19-Nov-3 Tennants, Leyburn #1126

BARRINGTON BROWNE, William Ellis (1908-1985) British
£280 $507 €409 Hopeful cast (46x61cm-18x24in) s. 31-Mar-4 Bonhams, Knightsbridge #31
£300 $561 €438 Seascape with distant view of the islands of Eigg and Rhum, Scotland (14x19cm-6x7in) s. board. 25-Feb-4 Mallams, Oxford #147
£550 $1012 €803 Priory pool, the River Wye (35x46cm-14x18in) s. 10-Jun-4 Christie's, Kensington #234/R
Works on paper
£2500 $4600 €3650 Beast coming home, Loch Tayside. November evening, Ben Hue, Perthshire (22x30cm-9x12in) s. W/C bodycol two. 10-Jun-4 Christie's, Kensington #230/R est:400-600

BARRIOS, Armando (1920-) Venezuelan
£2035 $3500 €2971 Portrait of Vicente Emilio Sojo (32x24cm-13x9in) s. 7-Dec-3 Subastas Odalys, Caracas #104/R est:3000
£7941 $13500 €11594 Indian woman (65x50cm-26x20in) s. painted 1955. 23-Nov-3 Subastas Odalys, Caracas #18/R est:12500
£18488 $30875 €26992 Dialogues 2 (41x61cm-16x24in) s. painted 1972. 13-Jul-3 Subastas Odalys, Caracas #86/R est:14000
£18830 $34270 €28245 Composition (82x61cm-32x24in) s. 21-Jun-4 Subastas Odalys, Caracas #51/R est:35000
Works on paper
£457 $750 €667 Study (12x15cm-5x6in) s. W/C card. 1-Jun-3 Subastas Odalys, Caracas #11
£497 $845 €726 Because of melancholy (15x11cm-6x4in) pencil exec.1997. 23-Nov-3 Subastas Odalys, Caracas #55
£497 $845 €726 Souvenir of Venice (13x10cm-5x4in) pencil exec.1990. 23-Nov-3 Subastas Odalys, Caracas #68
£694 $1180 €1013 Untitled (19x13cm-7x5in) pencil exec.1980. 23-Nov-3 Subastas Odalys, Caracas #108/R
£791 $1250 €1155 Figure (29x19cm-11x7in) s. pastel. 1-Dec-2 Subastas Odalys, Caracas #98/R
£794 $1350 €1159 Untitled (13x14cm-5x6in) gouache exec.1975. 23-Nov-3 Subastas Odalys, Caracas #38
£1402 $2300 €2047 Boy's face (28x21cm-11x8in) s. pastel cardboard. 1-Jun-3 Subastas Odalys, Caracas #83
£1538 $2615 €2245 Untitled (13x14cm-5x6in) s. pencil exec.1975. 23-Nov-3 Subastas Odalys, Caracas #140/R est:1600
£1985 $3375 €2898 Evocation (10x14cm-4x6in) s. pencil exec.1987. 23-Nov-3 Subastas Odalys, Caracas #85/R est:1100
£2433 $4185 €3552 Untitled (45x50cm-18x20in) s. gouache card. 7-Dec-3 Subastas Odalys, Caracas #93/R est:5000

BARRIOS, Rafael (1947-) Venezuelan
Sculpture
£3906 $6250 €5703 Screens in profile (150x34x8cm-59x13x3in) s. iron. 16-Mar-3 Subastas Odalys, Caracas #11

BARRIVIERA, Lino Bianchi (1906-1985) Italian
£667 $1193 €1000 Still life of flowers (72x49cm-28x19in) s.d.1967 s.i.d.verso board. 13-May-4 Babuino, Rome #484/R
Works on paper
£267 $477 €400 Venezia Lido (10x33cm-4x13in) s.i. Chinese ink. 13-May-4 Babuino, Rome #454
£267 $477 €400 Venezia LIdo (7x33cm-3x13in) s.i.d.1942 Chinese ink W/C. 13-May-4 Babuino, Rome #453/R

BARRKADUBBU, Curly (1927-1987) Australian
Works on paper
£894 $1413 €1296 Pair of saratoga fish (76x50cm-30x20in) earth pigments eucalyptus bark exec.c.1972 prov.exhib.lit. 28-Jul-3 Sotheby's, Paddington #258 est:800-1200 (A.D 2200)
£1707 $2698 €2475 Hunter and ngamarrd, rock kangaroo (97x65cm-38x26in) i.verso earth pigments eucalyptus bark exec.c.1972 prov. 28-Jul-3 Sotheby's, Paddington #262/R est:2000-3000 (A.D 4200)
£1829 $2890 €2652 Legendary crocodile (135x66cm-53x26in) earth pigments eucalyptus bark exec.c.1972 prov.exhib.lit. 28-Jul-3 Sotheby's, Paddington #261/R est:4000-6000 (A.D 4500)

BARRON Y CARRILLO, Manuel (1814-1884) Spanish
£2069 $3724 €3000 Rider by the sea (33x41cm-13x16in) s. 26-Jan-4 Ansorena, Madrid #234/R est:3000

BARRON, Howard (1900-1991) British
£414 $646 €600 Storm over the Liverpools, N.S.W (48x64cm-19x25in) s. 1-Aug-2 Joel, Victoria #219 est:1500-2000 (A.D 1200)
£552 $861 €800 Valley view, McPherson Ranges (41x59cm-16x23in) s.d.32 board. 1-Aug-2 Joel, Victoria #152 est:1500-2500 (A.D 1600)
£552 $861 €800 In the shade of the old rivergum (49x65cm-19x26in) s.d.38. 1-Aug-2 Joel, Victoria #238 est:1000-2000 (A.D 1600)
£1500 $2355 €2190 Murrumbridgee country. An old gum, Port Stephens, New South Wales (63x76cm-25x30in) s. i.verso two. 28-Aug-3 Christie's, Kensington #247/R est:1500-2000

BARRON, Manuel (19th C) ?
£1111 $1811 €1600 Pastoral scene (30x55cm-12x22in) s. 23-Sep-3 Durán, Madrid #150/R

BARRON, William (20th C) American
£273 $500 €410 Ya can't see the city from here (114x178cm-45x70in) 10-Jul-4 Hindman, Chicago #27/R

BARROW, Edith Isabel (?-1930) British
Works on paper
£500 $915 €730 Still life with roses in a glass vase (41x28cm-16x11in) s.d.1888. 7-Apr-4 Andrew Hartley, Ilkley #1048

BARRUOL, Isabelle (20th C) French
Works on paper
£455 $773 €650 Untitled (80x80cm-31x31in) s. mixed media canvas. 29-Nov-3 Neret-Minet, Paris #71/R

BARRY (?) ?
Sculpture
£2168 $3685 €3100 Cerf au brame (51x57cm-20x22in) s. bronze. 20-Nov-3 Millon & Associes, Paris #489

BARRY, Anne Meredith (1932-) Canadian
£323 $594 €472 The weaver (50x40cm-20x16in) s. i.d.1972 verso board. 9-Jun-4 Walker's, Ottawa #154/R (C.D 800)
£498 $831 €727 Winter picnic no.16, two yellow tea cups (75x104cm-30x41in) s.d.1995 oil on paper prov. 17-Nov-3 Hodgins, Calgary #328/R est:2000-3000 (C.D 1100)
Works on paper
£543 $907 €793 Berg, Growler and Jacko's Island (38x48cm-15x19in) s.d. mixed media prov. 17-Nov-3 Hodgins, Calgary #273/R est:1000-1250 (C.D 1200)
£560 $1025 €818 On the Hope Dale run (75x110cm-30x43in) s.d.2002 mixed media. 1-Jun-4 Joyner Waddington, Toronto #350/R (C.D 1400)

BARRY, Claude-Francis (1883-1970) British
£894 $1601 €1305 Cornish Fishing Village (39x50cm-15x20in) s. 10-May-4 Joel, Victoria #269 est:2000-2500 (A.D 2200)

BARRY, François Pierre Bernard (1813-1905) French
£500 $900 €750 North African market with figures (20x34cm-8x13in) s. panel. 26-Apr-4 Rieber, Stuttgart #973/R
£62411 $104227 €88000 L'entree du port de Smyrne (100x150cm-39x59in) s.d.1852 prov. 19-Jun-3 Millon & Associes, Paris #109/R est:3000-40000

BARRY, James (1741-1806) British
Works on paper
£3060 $5600 €4468 Sacrifice (37x48cm-15x19in) pen ink wash sold with a study by Benjamin West. 29-Jan-4 Swann Galleries, New York #348/R est:1000-1500

BARRY, John (fl.1784-1827) British
Miniatures
£1351 $2500 €1972 Portrait of a gentleman (5x3cm-2x1in) exec.c.1790 oval. 12-Mar-4 Du Mouchelle, Detroit #2033/R est:1000-2000
Works on paper
£700 $1190 €1022 Portrait of a lady (23x18cm-9x7in) s.d.1796 W/C over pencil htd bodycol oval. 27-Nov-3 Sotheby's, London #218/R

BARRY, Jonathan (20th C) British
£950 $1739 €1425 I'm late (46x34cm-18x13in) s. 8-Jul-4 Sotheby's, London #307/R
£950 $1739 €1425 Ahab and the great White Whale, from Moby Dick (50x40cm-20x16in) s. 8-Jul-4 Sotheby's, London #116/R
£1100 $2013 €1650 Pig and pepper (49x39cm-19x15in) s. 8-Jul-4 Sotheby's, London #308/R est:1000-1500

BARRY, Moyra A (1886-1960) Irish
£420 $713 €600 Still life of flowers (49x40cm-19x16in) s. 25-Nov-3 De Veres Art Auctions, Dublin #175/R
£592 $1089 €900 Summer flowers (51x61cm-20x24in) s. 22-Jun-4 De Veres Art Auctions, Dublin #197/R
£2148 $3801 €3200 Spring flowers (61x51cm-24x20in) s. i.verso exhib. 27-Apr-4 Whyte's, Dublin #44/R est:2000-3000
Works on paper
£503 $901 €750 Sweet pea (39x57cm-15x22in) s.d.42 W/C. 26-May-4 James Adam, Dublin #150/R

BARRY, Robert (1936-) American
£3333 $6100 €5000 This also - quietly - listen - afraid (76x76cm-30x30in) mono.d.8 8 acrylic. 4-Jun-4 Lempertz, Koln #23/R est:5000
Works on paper
£282 $487 €400 Untitled (26x35cm-10x14in) s. ink pencil exec.c.1995. 9-Dec-3 Artcurial Briest, Paris #22

BARRY, William (19th C) British
£270 $483 €394 Barry sands, early morning (49x59cm-19x23in) s.d.1902 s.i.d.verso. 22-Mar-4 Bearnes, Exeter #194
£800 $1472 €1168 Neidpath Castle (77x127cm-30x50in) s. s.i.verso. 25-Mar-4 Bonhams, Edinburgh #376/R

BARSCH, Wulf Erich (1943-) American
£223 $400 €326 Mirror image. s. 13-May-4 Dallas Auction Gallery, Dallas #246/R

BARSONY, Piotr (?) ?
£979 $1664 €1400 I love America (56x40cm-22x16in) s.d.1994 oil gouache newspaper canvas. 27-Nov-3 Calmels Cohen, Paris #66/R

BARSTOW, Sarah (19th C) American
£1123 $2100 €1640 Kasterskill creek (30x25cm-12x10in) indis.sig. 29-Feb-4 Grogan, Boston #61/R

BARSUMIAN, Lisa (20th C) American
£400 $732 €584 The other side of the River Avon (70x65cm-28x26in) s.i. 1-Jun-4 Hodgins, Calgary #135/R (C.D 1000)
£600 $1098 €876 Rajastan, lily pond (90x75cm-35x30in) s.i. painted 1999. 1-Jun-4 Hodgins, Calgary #155/R (C.D 1500)

BARTA, Montserrat (1907-) Spanish
£987 $1786 €1500 Dancers (73x60cm-29x24in) s. 14-Apr-4 Ansorena, Madrid #111/R est:1500

BARTAR, John (?) British?
Works on paper
£250 $430 €365 Figures beneath a porch (82x57cm-32x22in) s. W/C. 2-Dec-3 Sworder & Son, Bishops Stortford #503/R

BARTAVAR, Emil M Bartuska (20th C) ?
£400 $720 €600 Murtal in the Steiermark (28x35cm-11x14in) s.d.1923 canvas on board. 22-Apr-4 Dorotheum, Graz #7/R
£433 $780 €650 Early spring - view from Petersbergen of Graz (40x44cm-16x17in) s.d.1921 canvas on board. 22-Apr-4 Dorotheum, Graz #6/R
£537 $961 €800 Murlauf in summer (56x72cm-22x28in) s.d.1923. 27-May-4 Dorotheum, Graz #8/R

BARTELS, Carl Olaf (1869-1945) Danish?
£354 $574 €513 Moonlit landscape with man and woman in rowing boat on river (89x149cm-35x59in) s.i.d.1890. 4-Aug-3 Rasmussen, Vejle #331/R (D.KR 3700)

BARTELS, Hans von (1856-1913) German
£378 $650 €540 Houses in Katwijk (23x32cm-9x13in) s. 2-Dec-3 Hauswedell & Nolte, Hamburg #24/R
£789 $1453 €1200 View of the surf at Cape Arcona, the Island of Rugen (24x34cm-9x13in) s.i.d.86 sold with two other works by same artist three. 28-Jun-4 Sotheby's, Amsterdam #92/R est:1000-1500
£909 $1545 €1300 Dutch woman wearing traditional costume (41x35cm-16x14in) s. i.verso paper on cardboard. 28-Nov-3 Wendl, Rudolstadt #3914/R
£1347 $2250 €1967 Afternoon outing (62x88cm-24x35in) s. 7-Oct-3 Sotheby's, New York #109 est:3000-5000
£1400 $2548 €2100 In the sand dunes on the Dutch coast (45x60cm-18x24in) s. 1-Jul-4 Van Ham, Cologne #1205/R est:1400
£1447 $2663 €2200 Dutch fisherwoman with child on the beach (53x41cm-21x16in) s. paper on canvas. 28-Jun-4 Sotheby's, Amsterdam #86/R est:2500-3500
£1842 $3389 €2800 Dutch fisherwoman carrying buckets (56x44cm-22x17in) s.d.1909. 28-Jun-4 Sotheby's, Amsterdam #87/R est:3000-5000
£1974 $3632 €3000 Dutch fishergirl (46x32cm-18x13in) s.d.1903. 28-Jun-4 Sotheby's, Amsterdam #83/R est:2000-3000
£2632 $4842 €4000 Dutch fisherwoman holding a basket on a crowded beach (102x79cm-40x31in) s.i. 28-Jun-4 Sotheby's, Amsterdam #85/R est:1800-2200
£2685 $4805 €4000 On the Italian coast (48x37cm-19x15in) s.d.82. 27-May-4 Dorotheum, Vienna #76/R est:3800-4200
£3158 $5811 €4800 Volendam sailing vessels at the Zuiderzee (34x48cm-13x19in) s.i.d.VD 93. 28-Jun-4 Sotheby's, Amsterdam #80/R est:2500-3500
£6579 $12105 €10000 Volendam vessels sailing at dusk (99x84cm-39x33in) s.i.d.1900. 28-Jun-4 Sotheby's, Amsterdam #89/R est:3500-5500
Works on paper
£987 $1816 €1500 Return of the fishing boats at the beach (53x67cm-21x26in) s. gouache. 28-Jun-4 Sotheby's, Amsterdam #82/R est:1500-2000
£1250 $2300 €1900 Hollandische Kuche (32x46cm-13x18in) s.d.90 gouache exhib. 28-Jun-4 Sotheby's, Amsterdam #90/R est:1200-1800
£1842 $3389 €2800 Dutch mother and child in a fire lit interior (46x33cm-18x13in) s.d.1904 gouache. 28-Jun-4 Sotheby's, Amsterdam #88/R est:1000-1500
£2105 $3874 €3200 Lavoir in Bretagne (34x45cm-13x18in) s.d.1910 i.d.verso gouache. 28-Jun-4 Sotheby's, Amsterdam #81/R est:2500-3500
£2431 $3962 €3500 French fish market (33x46cm-13x18in) s.i.d.1905 gouache. 24-Sep-3 Neumeister, Munich #257/R est:3500

BARTELS, Hermann (1928-) German
Works on paper
£1220 $2000 €1781 Confinium no133 (30x22cm-12x9in) s. s.i.d.1961 verso synthetic polymer canvas prov.exhib. 28-May-3 Sotheby's, Amsterdam #56/R est:2000-3000

BARTELS, Rudolf (1872-1946) German
£805 $1482 €1200 Landscape (31x42cm-12x17in) s. board. 26-Mar-4 Altus, Berlin #609/R

BARTER, Joseph (19th C) British
£1800 $3222 €2628 St. Nicholas Church, Ghent (73x60cm-29x24in) indis sig.d.1835 prov. 26-May-4 Sotheby's, Olympia #263/R est:2000-3000

BARTEZAGO, Enrico (19th C) Swiss
£1351 $2378 €2000 Farm with horses (17x12cm-7x5in) s. cardboard. 19-May-4 Il Ponte, Milan #708 est:400-450

BARTH, Amade (1899-1926) Swiss
£1208 $2054 €1764 Nature morte aux pommes (24x33cm-9x13in) with sig.verso exhib. 4-Nov-3 Bukowskis, Stockholm #128/R est:15000-18000 (S.KR 16000)

BARTH, Carl (1896-1976) German
£833 $1392 €1200 Mythos (80x100cm-31x39in) s.d. i. verso sack cloth. 24-Oct-3 Ketterer, Hamburg #270/R

BARTH, Carl Wilhelm (1847-1919) Norwegian
£273 $500 €399 St Margerits Bay near Dover (20x25cm-8x10in) s. 2-Feb-4 Blomqvist, Lysaker #1018/R (N.KR 3400)
£338 $618 €493 Ulabrand's last voyage (30x46cm-12x18in) s. panel. 2-Feb-4 Blomqvist, Lysaker #1019/R (N.KR 4200)
£385 $700 €562 Seascape at night (14x18cm-6x7in) init. panel. 7-Feb-4 Rasmussen, Havnen #2100 (D.KR 4200)
£402 $736 €587 Storm (36x46cm-14x18in) s. panel. 2-Feb-4 Blomqvist, Lysaker #1020/R (N.KR 5000)
£696 $1203 €1016 The vessel Strand near Faerder (34x66cm-13x26in) s. 13-Dec-3 Blomqvist, Lysaker #1019/R (N.KR 8000)

BARTH, Johann Wilhelm Gottfried (1779-1852) German
Works on paper
£13889 $25000 €20278 Vue de la forteresse de St. Petersbourg prise du balcon de la maison comte Lieven (62x87cm-24x34in) s.i.d.1811 gouache on board. 23-Apr-4 Sotheby's, New York #1/R est:20000-30000
£16667 $30000 €24334 Vue du pont de Kammenoi Ostrov a St. Petersbourg (64x87cm-25x34in) s.i.d.1811 gouache. 23-Apr-4 Sotheby's, New York #2/R est:20000-30000
£17708 $27979 €25500 Views of St Petersburg (55x78cm-22x31in) s.i.d.1813 gouache pair. 19-Sep-3 Schloss Ahlden, Ahlden #1449/R est:18500

BARTH, Karl (1787-1853) German
Works on paper
£600 $1074 €900 My dear lady (26x20cm-10x8in) i. pencil. 13-May-4 Bassenge, Berlin #5515/R
£2467 $4440 €3700 Sorrento (43x36cm-17x14in) s.i. gouache card. 21-Apr-4 Finarte Semenzato, Milan #567/R est:3800

BARTH, Otto (1876-1916) Austrian
£839 $1443 €1200 Winter landscape with farmhouse (69x89cm-27x35in) s.d.10 fibreboard. 4-Dec-3 Dorotheum, Graz #2/R
Works on paper
£1655 $2748 €2400 Winter's day (40x39cm-16x15in) i. verso pastel. 30-Sep-3 Dorotheum, Vienna #358/R est:1800-2000

BARTH, Paul Basilius (1881-1955) Swiss
£226 $385 €330 Bodensee landscape (37x45cm-15x18in) s.d.51 board. 18-Nov-3 Hans Widmer, St Gallen #1015 (S.FR 500)

£352 $599 €514 Nature morte de pommes (14x19cm-6x7in) s. i. verso board. 5-Nov-3 Dobiaschofsky, Bern #333 (S.FR 800)
£529 $899 €772 Interieur Paris - Rue Vaugirard (36x42cm-14x17in) s.d.1908. 5-Nov-3 Dobiaschofsky, Bern #335/R (S.FR 1200)
£543 $923 €793 In the studio (37x45cm-15x18in) s.d.36 prov. 18-Nov-3 Hans Widmer, St Gallen #1016 (S.FR 1200)
£617 $1048 €901 Self portrait (71x56cm-28x22in) s.d.07. 5-Nov-3 Dobiaschofsky, Bern #334/R (S.FR 1400)
£661 $1123 €965 Still life (22x27cm-9x11in) s. bears i. 5-Nov-3 Dobiaschofsky, Bern #332/R (S.FR 1500)
£826 $1379 €1198 Figure in the dunes (34x27cm-13x11in) s.d.11 board exhib. 19-Jun-3 Kornfeld, Bern #198 (S.FR 1800)
£991 $1705 €1447 Rain clouds over Lake Constance (38x46cm-15x18in) s.d.1951 board exhib. 8-Dec-3 Philippe Schuler, Zurich #3320 (S.FR 2200)
£1043 $1910 €1523 Still life with blue jug (32x40cm-13x16in) s.d.06 canvas on board prov.exhib. 7-Jun-4 Christie's, Zurich #42/R est:3000-4000 (S.FR 2400)
£1357 $2308 €1981 Woman's back (77x46cm-30x18in) s.d.1929. 25-Nov-3 Germann, Zurich #95/R est:5000-7000 (S.FR 3000)
£1522 $2785 €2222 Portrait of a boy (80x59cm-31x23in) s.d.17 prov.exhib. 7-Jun-4 Christie's, Zurich #44/R est:4000-6000 (S.FR 3500)
£1659 $2970 €2422 Studio (46x38cm-18x15in) s.d.1936 prov. 26-May-4 Sotheby's, Zurich #67/R est:2000-3000 (S.FR 3800)
£3696 $6763 €5396 Citadel of Porquerolles, Provence (92x73cm-36x29in) s. prov. 7-Jun-4 Christie's, Zurich #45/R est:6000-8000 (S.FR 8500)

BARTH, Uta (1958-) American
£10983 $19000 €16035 Field number 23 (229x335cm-90x132in) acrylic lacquer one of 3. 10-Dec-3 Phillips, New York #682/R est:15000-25000
Photographs
£5587 $10000 €8157 Untitled, from nowhere near NW 3 (89x228cm-35x90in) col coupler print diptych edition 1 of 4 prov.exhib. 12-May-4 Christie's, Rockefeller NY #448/R est:10000-15000
£6287 $10500 €9179 Ground no.65 (70x79cm-28x31in) s.d.1996 num.8 c-print on wooden panel prov. 14-Nov-3 Phillips, New York #232/R est:5000-7000
£12291 $22000 €17945 Untitled, from nowhere near (89x447cm-35x176in) col coupler print triptych edition 2 of 4 prov. 12-May-4 Christie's, Rockefeller NY #447/R est:15000-20000

BARTH, Wolf (1926-) Swiss
£655 $1205 €956 Arjomari II (100x69cm-39x27in) s.d.1985 verso paper. 8-Jun-4 Germann, Zurich #51/R (S.FR 1500)

BARTHALOT, Marius (1861-?) French
£633 $1159 €950 Village on the Mediterranean Sea (41x53cm-16x21in) s. 7-Jun-4 Glerum, Amsterdam #83/R
£694 $1097 €1000 Couple sur la Corniche. s. 25-Apr-3 Etude de Provence, Marseille #111
£733 $1342 €1100 Mediterranean sea coast (41x53cm-16x21in) s. 7-Jun-4 Glerum, Amsterdam #82/R

BARTHEL, Paul (1862-?) German
£300 $540 €450 Barock interior with oven (101x121cm-40x48in) s. 26-Apr-4 Rieber, Stuttgart #955/R
£538 $1000 €785 At the china cabinet (88x119cm-35x47in) s. panel. 5-Mar-4 Skinner, Boston #388/R
£4667 $8447 €7000 Scene in railway carriage (115x135cm-45x53in) s.d.1912 panel. 1-Apr-4 Van Ham, Cologne #1280/R est:8000
£7432 $13304 €11000 Woodland dance (80x135cm-31x53in) s. lit. 8-May-4 Schloss Ahlden, Ahlden #776/R est:9500
Works on paper
£594 $993 €850 Young woman by tree (70x51cm-28x20in) s.d.96 W/C. 27-Jun-3 Altus, Berlin #676/R

BARTHELEMY, Camille (1890-1961) Belgian
£430 $783 €650 Sur la Semois (23x32cm-9x13in) s.d.1920 board. 15-Jun-4 Galerie Moderne, Brussels #236/R
£1042 $1656 €1500 La cabane (27x45cm-11x18in) s.d.1916 s.d.7/6/17 verso. 15-Sep-3 Horta, Bruxelles #135/R est:1800-2200
£3401 $6088 €5000 Ruelle animee (60x50cm-24x20in) s. panel. 16-Mar-4 Vanderkindere, Brussels #25 est:5000-7000
£7042 $12183 €10000 Vue du village de Our-sur-Our (50x50cm-20x20in) s.d.1952 panel. 9-Dec-3 Vanderkindere, Brussels #150/R est:10000-15000
£8219 $13973 €12000 Eglise de Fontenaille (65x80cm-26x31in) s.d.43. 10-Nov-3 Horta, Bruxelles #72/R
£8392 $14434 €12000 Figures dans un village wallon (50x60cm-20x24in) s. 2-Dec-3 Campo & Campo, Antwerp #17 est:350-450
£10000 $18400 €15000 Vue de village de Bavigne (80x100cm-31x39in) s. 14-Jun-4 Horta, Bruxelles #118/R est:15000-20000
Works on paper
£833 $1325 €1200 Matin (28x46cm-11x18in) s.i.d.1912 W/C. 15-Sep-3 Horta, Bruxelles #136
£1000 $1840 €1500 L'arrivee a l'eglise (20x20cm-8x8in) s. W/C. 14-Jun-4 Horta, Bruxelles #119 est:1500-1800
£2535 $4386 €3600 Village sous la neige (18x24cm-7x9in) s.indis.d. cardboard. 10-Dec-3 Hotel des Ventes Mosan, Brussels #183 est:1400-1800

BARTHELEMY, Emilien Victor (1885-?) French
£650 $1203 €949 Amusing passage (46x38cm-18x15in) s. 14-Jul-4 Christie's, Kensington #871/R

BARTHELEMY, Gerard (1927-2003) French
£267 $477 €400 Paysage de Provence (46x56cm-18x22in) 16-May-4 Osenat, Fontainebleau #61
£397 $743 €600 Paysage de neige (46x65cm-18x26in) s. 25-Jul-4 Feletin, Province #60
£567 $948 €800 Horizons lointains (82x116cm-32x46in) s. i.verso. 19-Oct-3 Charbonneaux, Paris #152
£739 $1279 €1050 Paris, Pont des Arts (50x65cm-20x26in) s. 14-Dec-3 Eric Pillon, Calais #214/R
£811 $1500 €1184 Untitled (114x162cm-45x64in) s. painted c.1990 prov. 12-Feb-4 Sotheby's, New York #335/R est:2000-3000
£1250 $2088 €1800 Helene et le singe (70x70cm-28x28in) s.d.82 prov.exhib. 21-Oct-3 Christie's, Paris #172/R est:600-800
£1319 $2203 €1900 Nu au chat (73x92cm-29x36in) s.d.81 board on panel. 21-Oct-3 Christie's, Paris #171/R est:800-1200
Works on paper
£347 $580 €500 Paysage (57x76cm-22x30in) s.d.1981 pencil. 21-Oct-3 Christie's, Paris #82/R
£347 $580 €500 Les vaches a Saint Agnan, Dordogne (56x75cm-22x30in) s.i.d.August 1984 ink ink wash pencil. 21-Oct-3 Christie's, Paris #81/R
£625 $1044 €900 Commode avec pommes de terre (37x39cm-15x15in) chl prov.exhib. 21-Oct-3 Christie's, Paris #119/R
£903 $1508 €1300 Le repos (51x67cm-20x26in) s.d.1975 chl prov. 21-Oct-3 Christie's, Paris #96/R

BARTHES, Roland (1915-1980) French
Works on paper
£1467 $2699 €2200 Composition abstraite (36x43cm-14x17in) s. gouache. 9-Jun-4 Piasa, Paris #11 est:600-800

BARTHOLD, Manuel (1874-1947) French
£483 $850 €705 Bather (62x50cm-24x20in) s.i.verso. 5-Jan-4 Galeria y Remates, Montevideo #97/R
£516 $950 €753 Young woman in interior (55x45cm-22x18in) s. 22-Jun-4 Galeria y Remates, Montevideo #35/R
£543 $1000 €793 Basque landscape (35x47cm-14x19in) 22-Jun-4 Galeria y Remates, Montevideo #33/R
£652 $1200 €952 Young Dutch woman in interior (60x48cm-24x19in) s.d.1904. 22-Jun-4 Galeria y Remates, Montevideo #34/R
£2282 $4199 €3400 Horse concoves, peasant girl by butter churn tasting butter milk (102x81cm-40x32in) s. 23-Mar-4 Mealy's, Castlecomer #968/R est:1500-2500

BARTHOLDI, Frederic Auguste (1834-1904) French
Sculpture
£18000 $32400 €26280 Switzerland shielding the citizens of Strasbourg (86cm-34in) s.st.f.Jaboeuf and Bezout brown pat bronze lit. 21-Apr-4 Sotheby's, London #107/R est:20000-30000
Works on paper
£993 $1658 €1400 Le lion de Belfort (26x37cm-10x15in) s. pen black ink. 23-Jun-3 Ribeyre & Baron, Paris #21/R

BARTHOLOME, Albert (1848-1928) French
Sculpture
£5000 $9000 €7300 The pain (36x36cm-14x14in) num.E161 brown pat bronze sandstone st.f.Siot lit. 21-Apr-4 Sotheby's, London #150/R est:5000-7000
£9396 $16631 €14000 Source (90x50x50cm-35x20x20in) s. marble prov. 30-Apr-4 Tajan, Paris #52/R est:14000-15000

BARTHOLOMEW, James H (1962-) British
£1639 $3000 €2393 Candida, Shamrock, Astra and Valsheda racing off Cowes (62x92cm-24x36in) s. 29-Jul-4 Christie's, Rockefeller NY #294/R est:10000-15000

BARTHOLOMEW, Ralph (jnr) (20th C) American
Photographs
£3468 $6000 €5063 Empire State Building at night (42x34cm-17x13in) s.d.1946 gelatin silver print prov. 12-Dec-3 Sotheby's, New York #359/R est:3000-5000

BARTHOLOMEW, William Newton (1822-1898) American
£457 $850 €667 Forest interior (25x35cm-10x14in) s.d.87. 5-Mar-4 Skinner, Boston #281/R

BARTLETT, Charles William (1860-?) British
£950 $1701 €1387 View of Venice (41x61cm-16x24in) s.d.92. 11-May-4 Bonhams, Knightsbridge #246/R
£1250 $2300 €1900 Louis XVII au temple (128x102cm-50x40in) s.d.1891. 24-Jun-4 Credit Municipal, Paris #36/R est:1200-1500

BARTLETT, Dana (1878-1957) American
£934 $1700 €1364 Rocky coastal scene (15x20cm-6x8in) s.d.49 board. 15-Jun-4 John Moran, Pasadena #9 est:1200-1800
£1359 $2500 €1984 Upper Basin, Versailles (40x50cm-16x20in) i.verso board prov. 8-Jun-4 Bonhams & Butterfields, San Francisco #4334/R est:2000-4000
£1786 $3250 €2608 Nocturne landscape (51x51cm-20x20in) s. i.verso board prov. 15-Jun-4 John Moran, Pasadena #130 est:4000-6000
£2446 $4500 €3571 Autumn by the river (50x61cm-20x24in) s. i. stretcher prov. 8-Jun-4 Bonhams & Butterfields, San Francisco #4333/R est:5000-7000
£3804 $7000 €5554 In the distance, Rue de Rivoli, Paris (36x43cm-14x17in) s. prov. 8-Jun-4 Bonhams & Butterfields, San Francisco #4336/R est:3000-5000
£5163 $9500 €7538 In the Luxembourg Gardens, Paris (36x43cm-14x17in) s.d.53 prov. 8-Jun-4 Bonhams & Butterfields, San Francisco #4335/R est:3000-5000
£5220 $9500 €7621 California hills (191x76cm-75x30in) s. i.verso board prov. 15-Jun-4 John Moran, Pasadena #129 est:8000-10000
Works on paper
£2116 $4000 €3089 Autumn in the hills (51x61cm-20x24in) s. i. verso W/C. 17-Feb-4 John Moran, Pasadena #139/R est:2000-3000

BARTLETT, Gray (1885-1951) American
£838 $1500 €1223 Indian on horse in desert (25x28cm-10x11in) s. canvasboard. 16-Mar-4 Matthew's, Oregon #72/R est:1200-1800
£1852 $3500 €2704 The lone rider (41x51cm-16x20in) i. stretcher prov. 17-Feb-4 John Moran, Pasadena #125/R est:2500-3500
£2353 $4000 €3435 Saddling a fresh mount (41x51cm-16x20in) s.d.40 canvas on board prov. 1-Nov-3 Santa Fe Art, Santa Fe #249/R est:3000-4000

£2647 $4500 €3865 Arizona range (61x76cm-24x30in) s. prov. 1-Nov-3 Santa Fe Art, Santa Fe #248/R est:4000-6000
£7065 $13000 €10315 Red Mountain, near Sedona (78x101cm-31x40in) s. 8-Jun-4 Bonhams & Butterfields, San Francisco #4148/R est:10000-15000

BARTLETT, Jennifer (1941-) American
Prints
£3352 $6000 €4894 Four shapes for Marian (61x61cm-24x24in) i.verso silkscreen baked enamel steel plate. 16-May-4 Wright, Chicago #332/R est:8000-10000
Works on paper
£978 $1800 €1428 Untitled (23x23cm-9x9in) s.d.2000 gouache prov. 10-Jun-4 Phillips, New York #492/R est:2500-3500
£1796 $3000 €2622 Four o'clock (152x107cm-60x42in) chl gouache ink silkscreen prov. 7-Oct-3 Sotheby's, New York #397 est:3000-5000
£2096 $3500 €3060 In the garden no 2 (50x65cm-20x26in) col pencil over pencil prov. 7-Oct-3 Sotheby's, New York #364 est:2000-3000
£2096 $3500 €3060 In the garden no 4 (50x65cm-20x26in) ink over pencil prov. 7-Oct-3 Sotheby's, New York #365 est:2000-3000
£2428 $4200 €3545 Untitled (23x23cm-9x9in) s.d.2000 gouache prov. 10-Dec-3 Phillips, New York #652/R est:2500-3500

BARTLETT, K (19th C) British?
£600 $948 €876 Flowers in the Dutch manner (77x63cm-30x25in) s. 3-Sep-3 Bonhams, Bury St Edmunds #438

BARTLETT, William H (1858-1932) British
£650 $1216 €975 Arranmore, Burton Point, County Donegal (17x23cm-7x9in) s.d.10 i.verso board prov. 22-Jul-4 Tennants, Leyburn #813
£850 $1590 €1275 Irish coastal scene with land leading to cottages (18x25cm-7x10in) s.d.10 board prov. 22-Jul-4 Tennants, Leyburn #812/R
£1351 $2297 €1972 Landscape in Western Ireland (58x73cm-23x29in) s. 27-Nov-3 Heffel, Vancouver #1/R est:3500-4000 (C.D 3000)
£8500 $15810 €12410 Spring harvest near Burton Port (23x35cm-9x14in) s.d.07 board. 3-Mar-4 John Ross, Belfast #64 est:8000-10000
£24000 $42960 €35040 Fishing off the coast of Ireland (58x93cm-23x37in) s.d.1881 prov. 14-May-4 Christie's, London #141/R est:20000-30000

BARTLETT, William Henry (1809-1854) British
Works on paper
£299 $550 €449 Landscape with country manor (15x25cm-6x10in) s. W/C. 26-Jun-4 Selkirks, St. Louis #408/R
£300 $516 €438 Knight Street, Rhodes (15x22cm-6x9in) pencil W/C. 3-Dec-3 Christie's, Kensington #31/R
£340 $622 €496 View towards Hotwells House, Clifton, Bristol (10x20cm-4x8in) ink wash. 7-Apr-4 Gardiner & Houlgate, Bath #157/R
£3490 $6247 €5200 Glengariff Inn. Castle Howard, Vale of Avoca. Head of the Devil's Glen (13x19cm-5x7in) monochrome W/C set of three. 26-May-4 James Adam, Dublin #198 est:2500-3500

BARTLIEU, J (fl.1860-1900) ?
£1078 $1800 €1563 Chickens in a barn interior (18x36cm-7x14in) indis sig. 29-Jun-3 Butterfields, Los Angeles #7034/R est:600-800

BARTOLENA, Giovanni (1866-1942) Italian
£1611 $2883 €2400 Horses at pasture in Maremma (21x44cm-8x17in) s. board. 25-May-4 Finarte Semenzato, Milan #47/R est:2500-3000
£2400 $4416 €3600 Field labour (9x19cm-4x7in) s. cardboard. 10-Jun-4 Christie's, Rome #170/R est:1000-1500
£3448 $6172 €5034 Still life with summer flowers in stone jug (45x30cm-18x12in) s. panel. 12-May-4 Dobiaschofsky, Bern #329/R est:12000 (S.FR 8000)
£8276 $13821 €12000 Still life (22x59cm-9x23in) s. board. 14-Nov-3 Farsetti, Prato #543/R est:12000-14000
£11745 $21023 €17500 Horses resting in Tuscan landscape (51x77cm-20x30in) s. board prov. 25-May-4 Finarte Semenzato, Milan #220/R est:16000-18000
£15278 $25972 €22000 Still life with green pot and flowers (45x53cm-18x21in) s. board. 1-Nov-3 Meeting Art, Vercelli #108/R est:15000
Works on paper
£433 $784 €650 Little horse (15x23cm-6x9in) pencil dr. 2-Apr-4 Farsetti, Prato #532

BARTOLI, Amerigo (1890-1971) Italian
Works on paper
£1119 $1902 €1600 Little street (75x61cm-30x24in) s. painted c.1957 prov. 24-Nov-3 Christie's, Milan #103 est:1200-1800

BARTOLI, Jacques (1920-1997) French
£282 $487 €400 Lecture (55x46cm-22x18in) s. s.i.verso. 13-Dec-3 Touati, Paris #23/R
£645 $1187 €942 Le corsage Jaune (55x46cm-22x18in) s. s.i.verso prov. 14-Jun-4 Waddingtons, Toronto #269/R est:1000-1500 (C.D 1600)
£778 $1300 €1136 Le lever (64x54cm-25x21in) s. s.i.verso. 7-Oct-3 Sotheby's, New York #311

BARTOLINI (after) (?) Italian
Sculpture
£7747 $13557 €11000 Alexandre I (58cm-23in) marble sold with base. 17-Dec-3 Tajan, Paris #112/R est:3000-4500

BARTOLINI, Frederico (19/20th C) Italian
£3529 $6000 €5152 Orientalist market (74x51cm-29x20in) s. 19-Nov-3 Bonhams & Butterfields, San Francisco #48/R

BARTOLINI, Lorenzo (attrib) (1777-1850) Italian
Sculpture
£8392 $14434 €12000 Infant Hunter (202cm-80in) carved marble incl stone base. 2-Dec-3 Christie's, Paris #22/R est:15000-25000
£16783 $28867 €24000 Buste de Napoleon (70cm-28in) white marble grey marble piedouche. 2-Dec-3 Sotheby's, Paris #82/R est:20000-30000

BARTOLINI, Lorenzo (studio) (1777-1850) Italian
Sculpture
£6993 $12028 €10000 Buste de Napoleon en Empereur Romain (181cm-71in) s. white marble red marble pedestal. 2-Dec-3 Sotheby's, Paris #103/R est:8000-12000

BARTOLINI, Luciano (1948-1994) Italian
Works on paper
£1067 $1963 €1600 Untitled (52x76cm-20x30in) s.d.1986 mixed media collage cardboard. 12-Jun-4 Meeting Art, Vercelli #712/R est:1500

BARTOLINI, Luigi (1892-1963) Italian
£839 $1427 €1200 Peasant women (26x35cm-10x14in) s. cardboard on board. 24-Nov-3 Christie's, Milan #90
£1067 $1920 €1600 Maddalena (40x30cm-16x12in) s. cardboard. 22-Apr-4 Finarte Semenzato, Rome #183 est:1600-1800
Prints
£1724 $2879 €2500 Lonely window (20x16cm-8x6in) s.i. eau forte exhib.lit. 13-Nov-3 Finarte Semenzato, Rome #84/R est:2000-2500

BARTOLINI, Massimo (1962-) Italian
Photographs
£5500 $9185 €8030 Untitled (120x180cm-47x71in) cibachrome print on aluminium exec.1995 num.2/3 prov.exhib. 20-Oct-3 Sotheby's, London #53/R est:4000-6000

BARTOLINI, Philippo (1861-1908) Italian
Works on paper
£2400 $4416 €3504 Figures conversing on a street in Cairo (52x35cm-20x14in) s. pencil W/C. 25-Mar-4 Christie's, Kensington #62/R est:2000-3000

BARTOLINI, Ubaldo (1944-) Italian
£769 $1308 €1100 Tale (24x30cm-9x12in) s.d.1982 s.i.d.verso. 28-Nov-3 Farsetti, Prato #31

BARTOLINI, Ugo Vittore (1906-) Italian
£1087 $1783 €1500 In the study (35x45cm-14x18in) s.d.945 board. 27-May-3 Il Ponte, Milan #884 est:1500

BARTOLOMEO DI GIOVANNI (15th C) Italian
£12000 $21960 €17520 Saint John the Baptist (140x40cm-55x16in) tempera panel exhib.lit. 8-Jul-4 Sotheby's, London #196/R est:15000-20000

BARTOLOZZI, Francesco (1727-1815) Italian
Works on paper
£552 $921 €800 Young woman (23x18cm-9x7in) s. col chk prov. 15-Nov-3 Lempertz, Koln #1254/R
£800 $1440 €1168 Woman seated in profile (24x17cm-9x7in) black red chk prov. 20-Apr-4 Sotheby's, Olympia #156/R
£900 $1647 €1314 Studies of a Roman soldier (17x46cm-7x18in) pen ink wash prov. 7-Jul-4 George Kidner, Lymington #138/R
£1000 $1730 €1460 Mercury carrying his caduceus (44x25cm-17x10in) s.d.1776 col chk brown wash sold with a dr after Paulus Potter. 12-Dec-3 Christie's, Kensington #404/R est:800-1200

BARTOLOZZI, Francesco (attrib) (1727-1815) Italian
Works on paper
£251 $450 €366 Madonna and Child (25x33cm-10x13in) s. pen ink. 7-May-4 Sloans & Kenyon, Bethesda #1127/R

BARTOLOZZI, Rafael Lozano (1943-) Spanish
£1162 $1859 €1650 Tobacco woman (100x82cm-39x32in) s.d.1977 s.i.d.verso lit. 16-Sep-3 Segre, Madrid #151/R est:1350
£1361 $2476 €2000 Kiko (81x100cm-32x39in) s. s.i.d.1969 verso lit. 3-Feb-4 Segre, Madrid #310/R est:1500

BARTON, Donald Blagge (1903-1990) American
£269 $500 €393 Long's Peak, Este's Park, Colorado (40x50cm-16x20in) s. prov. 5-Mar-4 Skinner, Boston #348/R
£538 $850 €785 Snowy landscape (51x69cm-20x27in) s. 7-Sep-3 Treadway Gallery, Cincinnati #631/R

BARTON, Macena Alberta (1901-1986) American
£351 $650 €527 Spring blossoms (66x76cm-26x30in) s.d.1943. 17-Jul-4 Susanin's, Chicago #5181/R
£378 $700 €567 Two o'clock Sunday (61x81cm-24x32in) s.d.1976. 17-Jul-4 Susanin's, Chicago #5184/R
£973 $1800 €1460 Still life with flowers (104x74cm-41x29in) s. 17-Jul-4 Susanin's, Chicago #5202/R est:200-400

BARTON, Mary (1861-1949) British
£420 $773 €613 Pomeranian (35x46cm-14x18in) s.d.1911. 10-Jun-4 Christie's, Kensington #436/R

BARTON, Rose Maynard (1856-1929) British
Works on paper
£1500 $2460 €2190 Henry VII Chapel (50x30cm-20x12in) s. W/C. 4-Jun-3 John Ross, Belfast #158
£1958 $3329 €2800 Henry VII Chapel, Westminster Abbey (50x32cm-20x13in) s. W/C prov. 18-Nov-3 Whyte's, Dublin #120/R est:3000-4000
£6000 $10020 €8760 Street scene (18x11cm-7x4in) s. W/C. 12-Nov-3 Sotheby's, Olympia #138/R est:1000-1500
£11000 $19690 €16060 On the Yarmouth Sands (16x25cm-6x10in) s.d.1893 W/C. 13-May-4 Sotheby's, London #10/R est:6000-8000

BARTON, Sir Ezekiel (1781-1855) British
Works on paper
£400 $708 €584 Tomb of the Emperor Akbar, Agra (28x46cm-11x18in) i. pencil brown wash laid paper. 29-Apr-4 Christie's, Kensington #100
£7000 $11410 €10220 Brindavan near Mathura (43x58cm-17x23in) i. pencil pen grey ink W/C prov. 24-Sep-3 Christie's, London #43/R est:2500-3500

BARTON, William (?-1814) British
£7500 $14175 €10950 Stoney Smith in two positions off a boatbuilding yard (58x76cm-23x30in) init.d.1808 pair prov.lit. 17-Feb-4 Bonhams, New Bond Street #80/R est:5000-8000

BARTSCH, Carl-Frederick (1829-1908) Danish
£269 $491 €393 From Dalsborg near Skotterup with chickens (26x33cm-10x13in) s. 9-Jun-4 Rasmussen, Copenhagen #1660 (D.KR 3000)
£311 $566 €467 Summer's day at North Sjaelland (43x61cm-17x24in) s. 19-Jun-4 Rasmussen, Havnen #2077/R (D.KR 3500)
£373 $679 €560 Landscape with deer in Dyrehaven (43x56cm-17x22in) s. 19-Jun-4 Rasmussen, Havnen #2076/R (D.KR 4200)
£448 $806 €654 Wooded landscape with deer, autumn (30x37cm-12x15in) s. 24-Apr-4 Rasmussen, Havnen #2101/R (D.KR 5000)
£520 $899 €759 Deer by waterhole in the wood (43x59cm-17x23in) s. 9-Dec-3 Rasmussen, Copenhagen #1541/R (D.KR 5500)

BARTSCH, Reinhard (1925-1990) German
£333 $603 €500 Lively street in Montmartre (60x80cm-24x31in) s. s.i. verso lit. 1-Apr-4 Frank Peege, Freiburg #1194/R

BARTSCH, Reinhold (20th C) German
£1486 $2661 €2200 Unter den Linden, Berlin (47x63cm-19x25in) s.i. i. stretcher. 8-May-4 Schloss Ahlden, Ahlden #817/R est:2000

BARTSCH, Wilhelm (1871-1953) German
£490 $842 €700 Early spring at the Wumme near Falkenberg (42x63cm-17x25in) s. i.verso board. 5-Dec-3 Bolland & Marotz, Bremen #338/R
£1329 $2259 €1900 Fish market on Katwijk beach (38x51cm-15x20in) s. 20-Nov-3 Van Ham, Cologne #1472/R est:1300

BARTSCHT, Dietrich (1951-) German
£604 $1081 €900 Untitled (52x44cm-20x17in) s.i.d.81/1988 verso. 25-May-4 Karl & Faber, Munich #430/R

BARTSIUS, Willem (attrib) (1612-?) Dutch
£2000 $3400 €2920 Elegant company playing music and merrymaking in an interior (41x63cm-16x25in) init. panel. 31-Oct-3 Christie's, Kensington #20/R est:2000-3000

BARUCCI, Pietro (1845-1917) Italian
£1471 $2750 €2148 Cattle with calf beside a stream (71x130cm-28x51in) s.i. 24-Feb-4 Peter Webb, Auckland #169/R est:4000-5000 (NZ.D 4000)
£4336 $7241 €6200 Sheperd in the Roman countryside (62x110cm-24x43in) s. 24-Jun-3 Finarte Semenzato, Rome #162/R
£4525 $7240 €6607 Buffalo standing in water (82x148cm-32x58in) s. 19-Sep-3 Koller, Zurich #3108/R est:10000-15000 (S.FR 10000)
£7000 $12530 €10500 View of Palazzo Donn'Anna (60x106cm-24x42in) s. 17-May-4 Finarte Semenzato, Rome #82/R est:12000-14000
£9333 $16707 €14000 Figures on a boat (60x110cm-24x43in) s. 17-May-4 Finarte Semenzato, Rome #81/R est:12000-14000

BARUCHELLO, Gianfranco (1924-) Italian
£726 $1300 €1060 Mechanism for the telecontrol of heart liquefication (28x36cm-11x14in) s.i.d.1964 plexiglas prov. 16-May-4 Wright, Chicago #376/R
Works on paper
£839 $1552 €1250 If you spoke Spanish you would understand (50x70cm-20x28in) s.d.1972 mixed media cardboard. 13-Mar-4 Meeting Art, Vercelli #42
£1449 $2377 €2000 Eveil silencieux 2 (40x40cm-16x16in) s.d.73 s.i.d.verso mixed media on aluminium prov. 27-May-3 Sotheby's, Milan #16 est:3000
£7432 $13081 €11000 Manifesto against mixing (200x200cm-79x79in) s.i.d.1962 verso mixed media on canvas. 24-May-4 Christie's, Milan #49 est:4000-6000

BARWE, Prabhakar (1936-1996) Indian
£3804 $7000 €5554 Fertility goddess (120x153cm-47x60in) i.verso. 24-Mar-4 Sotheby's, New York #196/R est:6000-8000
£4891 $9000 €7141 Blown hourglass (91x107cm-36x42in) s.i.d.1980 verso enamel. 25-Mar-4 Christie's, Rockefeller NY #234/R est:6000-8000

BARWELL, Frederick Bacon (attrib) (?-1897) British
£2111 $3652 €3082 Untitled (76x64cm-30x25in) d.1860 exhib. 9-Dec-3 Pinneys, Montreal #52 est:4000-5000 (C.D 4750)
£3548 $6529 €5180 Nursing mother (76x63cm-30x25in) init.d.1860 exhib. 14-Jun-4 Waddingtons, Toronto #155/R est:5000-6000 (C.D 8800)

BARWOLF, Georges (1872-1935) Belgian
£1300 $2379 €1898 Au jardin a Paris (47x56cm-19x22in) s. indis d. 8-Apr-4 Christie's, Kensington #185/R est:400-600

BARYE (?) French
Sculpture
£2098 $3608 €3000 Tigre (21x44cm-8x17in) s. green pat bronze Cast Barbedienne. 8-Dec-3 Rossini, Paris #240/R est:3000-3800

BARYE, A (19th C) French
Sculpture
£8451 $14789 €12000 Vermout (50x57x20cm-20x22x8in) bears sig pat bronze lit. 19-Dec-3 Piasa, Paris #41/R est:10000-12000

BARYE, Ada (19th C) French?
£600 $1080 €876 Begging pug (22x16cm-9x6in) s.d.1891 verso panel. 21-Apr-4 Christie's, Kensington #376/R

BARYE, Alfred (1839-1882) French
Sculpture
£950 $1729 €1387 Giraffe (17cm-7in) s. green pat bronze. 15-Jun-4 Sotheby's, Olympia #121/R est:1000-1500
£1176 $2000 €1717 Elephant deracinant un arbre (16cm-6in) mono. pat bronze. 28-Oct-3 Christie's, Rockefeller NY #206/R
£1333 $2413 €2000 Faisan (28x23cm-11x9in) s. brown pat. bronze. 31-Mar-4 Sotheby's, Paris #285/R est:1200-1800
£1412 $2400 €2062 Lion devorant sanglier (13cm-5in) s. pat bronze. 28-Oct-3 Christie's, Rockefeller NY #222/R
£1667 $2783 €2350 La charette Flamande (35cm-14in) s.i. brown pat bronze. 12-Oct-3 St-Germain-en-Laye Encheres #24/R est:2200-2500
£1867 $3379 €2800 Chien (35x25cm-14x10in) s. brown green pat bronze. 31-Mar-4 Sotheby's, Paris #279/R est:2400-3000
£1947 $3445 €2900 Walter Scott, cheval de selle de l'empereur (36cm-14in) s. pat bronze. 30-Apr-4 Tajan, Paris #34 est:600-800
£4800 $8160 €7008 Running elephant (21x22cm-8x9in) s. pat bronze. 28-Oct-3 Sotheby's, London #137/R

BARYE, Antoine-Louis (1796-1875) French
Sculpture
£861 $1575 €1300 Seated cat (9cm-4in) s. dark brown pat. bronze. 6-Apr-4 Sotheby's, Olympia #111/R est:800-1200
£882 $1500 €1288 Hercule et le sanglier (12cm-5in) s. pat bronze sold with base. 28-Oct-3 Christie's, Rockefeller NY #214/R
£922 $1494 €1300 Lapin oreilles couchees (5x7cm-2x3in) s.num.45 brown green pat bronze st.f.Barbedienne lit. 23-May-3 Sotheby's, Paris #282/R est:1500-2000
£968 $1800 €1413 Great blue heron (13cm-5in) s. bronze. 3-Mar-4 Alderfer's, Hatfield #243/R est:500-700
£1000 $1600 €1460 Recumbent lioness (10x20cm-4x8in) s. brown pat. bronze st.f.Barbedienne. 20-Sep-3 Sloans & Kenyon, Bethesda #648/R est:800-1000
£1020 $1622 €1500 Levrette attapant un lievre (20x31cm-8x12in) s. pat bronze. 23-Mar-3 Salle des ventes Pillet, Lyon la Foret #149
£1024 $1700 €1495 Walking lion (23x41cm-9x16in) bronze Cast F. Barbedienne lit. 4-Oct-3 South Bay, Long Island #54
£1034 $1914 €1500 Tortue (5cm-2in) s. green pat bronze. 16-Feb-4 Horta, Bruxelles #188/R est:1000-1500
£1049 $1783 €1500 Aigle terrassant un bouquetin (22x22x19cm-9x9x7in) s.i. brown pat bronze. 27-Nov-3 Millon & Associes, Paris #96/R est:1500-2000
£1064 $1723 €1500 Lapin oreilles dressees (6x7cm-2x3in) s.num.14 and 45 brown green pat bronze st.f.F.Barbedienne lit. 23-May-3 Sotheby's, Paris #281/R est:1500-2000
£1099 $1781 €1550 Lion assis (19cm-7in) s. pat bronze. 21-May-3 Daguerre, Paris #377 est:1800-2000
£1117 $2000 €1631 Walking elephant (38cm-15in) s. green brown pat bronze marble plinth. 20-Mar-4 Freeman, Philadelphia #851/R est:2500-3500
£1119 $1869 €1600 Eagle (24cm-9in) s. pat bronze. 7-Oct-3 Sotheby's, Amsterdam #197/R est:1800-2600
£1173 $1958 €1700 Levriere couche (6x9x26cm-2x4x10in) s. green brown pat bronze. 17-Nov-3 Tajan, Paris #37/R est:800-1200
£1208 $2138 €1800 Lion et serpent (20x26x14cm-8x10x6in) s.st.f.Unis pat bronze lit. 30-Apr-4 Tajan, Paris #20/R est:1800-2400
£1294 $2200 €1889 Faisan (12cm-5in) s. pat bronze prov.lit. 28-Oct-3 Christie's, Rockefeller NY #237/R
£1300 $2327 €1950 Lion ecrasant un serpent (16cm-6in) pat bronze. 15-May-4 other European Auctioneer #183/R
£1325 $2424 €2000 Tigre marchant (21x38x9cm-8x15x4in) s. bronze. 9-Apr-4 Claude Aguttes, Neuilly #67a est:3000-5000
£1342 $2483 €2000 Lion au serpent patte levee (14x17x11cm-6x7x4in) s. pat bronze. 14-Mar-4 St-Germain-en-Laye Encheres #74/R est:2000-2500
£1382 $2542 €2100 Elephant marchant (24x14cm-9x6in) s.st.f.Colin pat bronze. 22-Jun-4 Adjug'art, Brest #170/R est:1000-1500
£1391 $2545 €2100 Lionne devorant un gavial (23x9x9cm-9x4x4in) st.f.F. Barbedienne green pat bronze. 9-Apr-4 Claude Aguttes, Neuilly #69/R est:1500-1800
£1400 $2380 €2044 Epagneul en arret (7x11cm-3x4in) pat bronze lit. 28-Oct-3 Sotheby's, London #147/R
£1412 $2400 €2062 Lion marchant (28cm-11in) s. pat bronze. 28-Oct-3 Christie's, Rockefeller NY #229/R
£1412 $2400 €2062 Panthere 2 (8cm-3in) s. pat bronze sold with base lit. 28-Oct-3 Christie's, Rockefeller NY #219/R
£1412 $2400 €2062 Panthere de l'Inde 2 (10cm-4in) s. pat bronze lit. 28-Oct-3 Christie's, Rockefeller NY #218/R
£1420 $2500 €2073 Standing lioness (20cm-8in) s. bronze base. 21-May-4 North East Auctions, Portsmouth #245/R
£1500 $2700 €2190 Wolf (23x36cm-9x14in) incised sig. bronze. 24-Apr-4 Skinner, Boston #104/R est:1000-1500
£1532 $2604 €2237 Bull (20x29x13cm-8x11x5in) s.i.base bronze Cast Barbedienne. 26-Nov-3 Deutscher-Menzies, Melbourne #292/R est:4000-6000 (A.D 3600)

£1589	$2909	€2400	Hibou - owl (9cm-4in) s. brown pat. bronze i.f.F Barbedienne. 6-Apr-4 Sotheby's, Olympia #65/R est:1500-2000
£1600	$2832	€2336	Tiger walking pose (41cm-16in) s.i. bronze i.f.F Barbedienne. 27-Apr-4 Bonhams, Knowle #233/R est:1000-1500
£1613	$3000	€2355	Panthere de l'Inde No 1 (13cm-5in) s. bronze prov.lit. 3-Mar-4 Christie's, Rockefeller NY #424/R est:1000-2000
£1647	$2800	€2405	Lion au serpent 2 (13cm-5in) s. pat bronze lit. 28-Oct-3 Christie's, Rockefeller NY #217/R
£1701	$2704	€2500	Lion et sa proie (41x48cm-16x19in) s. pat bronze. 23-Mar-3 Salle des ventes Pillet, Lyon la Foret #152
£1705	$3000	€2489	Standing tiger (41cm-16in) s.i. bronze base. 21-May-4 North East Auctions, Portsmouth #246/R
£1765	$3000	€2577	Loup pris au piege (11cm-4in) s. pat bronze sold with base. 28-Oct-3 Christie's, Rockefeller NY #215/R
£1765	$3000	€2577	Chat assis (9cm-4in) s. pat bronze prov.lit. 28-Oct-3 Christie's, Rockefeller NY #234/R
£1818	$3200	€2654	Standing lioness (25cm-10in) s.st.f.Barbedienne bronze base. 21-May-4 North East Auctions, Portsmouth #247/R
£1831	$3168	€2600	Tete de chimpanze. s. brown pat bronze exec.c.1877 Cast F.Barbedienne prov.lit. 13-Dec-3 Martinot & Savignat, Pontoise #56/R est:1200-1500
£1854	$3375	€2800	Lion au serpent (35x26x47cm-14x10x19in) s. pat bronze. 19-Jun-4 St-Germain-en-Laye Encheres #42/R est:3000
£1882	$3200	€2748	Hercule et le sanglier (13cm-5in) s. pat bronze lit. 28-Oct-3 Christie's, Rockefeller NY #213/R
£1987	$3616	€3000	Panthere de Tunis I (12x25cm-5x10in) s. bronze Cast Barbedienne. 18-Jun-4 Piasa, Paris #54/R est:3000-3500
£2000	$3620	€3000	Elephant en marche (22x36cm-9x14in) s. bronze. 5-Apr-4 Deburaux, Boulogne #53b/R est:1800-2000
£2000	$3640	€2920	Walking tiger (21cm-8in) s. brown pat. bronze. 29-Jun-4 Bonhams, Knightsbridge #288/R est:2000-2500
£2011	$3600	€2936	Seated lion with paw holding down an open mouth serpent (20cm-8in) i.dark brown green pat. bronze prov. 20-Mar-4 Selkirks, St. Louis #568/R est:3000-4000
£2013	$3725	€3000	Elephant du Senegal (20cm-8in) s. pat bronze. 14-Mar-4 St-Germain-en-Laye Encheres #78/R est:4000-4500
£2053	$3757	€3100	Lionne marchant (22x7x10cm-9x3x4in) num.3018 bronze Cast F.Barbedienne. 9-Apr-4 Claude Aguttes, Neuilly #68/R est:2000-2500
£2059	$3500	€3006	Tigre devorant gazelle (14cm-6in) s. pat bronze. 28-Oct-3 Christie's, Rockefeller NY #197/R
£2059	$3500	€3006	Lion devorant sanglier (19cm-7in) s. pat bronze lit. 28-Oct-3 Christie's, Rockefeller NY #221/R
£2059	$3500	€3006	Epagneul 1 (10cm-4in) s. pat bronze prov.lit. 28-Oct-3 Christie's, Rockefeller NY #240/R
£2098	$3503	€3000	Cerf au jaguar (34x49x25cm-13x19x10in) s. pat bronze Cast Susse. 12-Oct-3 Salle des ventes Pillet, Lyon la Foret #64/R
£2200	$3872	€3212	Rearing bull (21x25cm-8x10in) i. st.f.Barbedienne. 18-May-4 Woolley & Wallis, Salisbury #375/R est:800-1200
£2353	$4000	€3435	Ours assis (13cm-5in) s. pat bronze lit. 28-Oct-3 Christie's, Rockefeller NY #225/R
£2353	$4000	€3435	Cheval demi-sang (12cm-5in) s. pat bronze prov.lit. 28-Oct-3 Christie's, Rockefeller NY #233/R
£2374	$4250	€3466	Tiger (21x42cm-8x17in) s. brown pat. bronze. 6-May-4 Doyle, New York #35/R est:3000-4000
£2471	$4200	€3608	Tigre qui marche (31cm-12in) s. pat bronze prov.lit. 28-Oct-3 Christie's, Rockefeller NY #199/R
£2471	$4200	€3608	Lion qui marche - a walking lion (23x38cm-9x15in) s. brown pat. bronze i.f.F.Barbedienne. 22-Nov-3 Jackson's, Cedar Falls #189/R est:2000-3000
£2483	$4146	€3600	Cerf du Gange (15x17cm-6x7in) pat bronze. 11-Nov-3 Lesieur & Le Bars, Le Havre #120
£2484	$4000	€3627	Standing bull (19cm-7in) i. bronze st.f.F Barbedienne. 14-Jan-4 Christie's, Rockefeller NY #304/R est:2500-3500
£2500	$4550	€3650	Tiger and antelope (33x50cm-13x20in) s. green brown pat bronze. 15-Jun-4 Sotheby's, Olympia #75/R est:2500-3500
£2603	$4425	€3800	Lio marchant (22x40cm-9x16in) s.st.f.Barbedienne bronze. 5-Nov-3 Beaussant & Lefèvre, Paris #164/R
£2621	$4377	€3800	Cerf de Java (14x15cm-6x6in) st.sig. pat bronze. 11-Nov-3 Lesieur & Le Bars, Le Havre #119
£2647	$4500	€3865	Lion assis 4 (18cm-7in) s. pat bronze. 28-Oct-3 Christie's, Rockefeller NY #194/R
£2647	$4500	€3865	Tigre devoart gavial (11cm-4in) s.pat bronze prov.lit. 28-Oct-3 Christie's, Rockefeller NY #196/R
£2647	$4500	€3865	Buffle d'eau (15cm-6in) s. pat bronze lit. 28-Oct-3 Christie's, Rockefeller NY #210/R
£2647	$4500	€3865	Jaguar devorant agouti (7cm-3in) s. pat bronze prov.lit. 28-Oct-3 Christie's, Rockefeller NY #236/R
£2667	$4827	€4000	Panther attacking deer (35x56cm-14x22in) s.i. bronze Cast.F.Barbedienne. 1-Apr-4 Frank Peege, Freiburg #76/R est:4000
£2676	$4630	€3800	Lion marchant (14x25cm-6x10in) s. pat bronze Cast Barbedienne. 12-Dec-3 Piasa, Paris #85/R est:3500-4000
£2676	$4308	€3800	Lion tenant un guib (11x27x11cm-4x11x4in) s. num.4/4 pat bronze Cast Barbedienne lit. 22-Aug-3 Deauville, France #44/R est:5000-6000
£2740	$4301	€4000	Lion marchant (22x39cm-9x15in) s. pat bronze Cast Barbedienne lit. 20-Apr-3 Deauville, France #83/R est:3800-4200
£2752	$4430	€4100	La lionne d'Algerie (28cm-11in) s. green pat bronze Cast Barbedienne. 23-Feb-3 St-Germain-en-Laye Encheres #92/R est:2800-3000
£2752	$5091	€4100	Elephant du Senegal (14x20cm-6x8in) s. pat bronze Cast Barbedienne. 14-Mar-4 Eric Pillon, Calais #12/R
£2752	$5063	€4100	Lion au serpent (15x18x12cm-6x7x5in) s. col pat bronze. 26-Mar-4 Neret-Minet, Paris #47/R est:3000-3500
£2781	$5062	€4200	Lion couche (14x31cm-6x12in) s.d.1837 pat bronze. 16-Jun-4 Hotel des Ventes Mosan, Brussels #193 est:1500-1700
£2800	$4760	€4088	Taureau cabre (23cm-9in) s.st.f.Barbedienne pat bronze. 28-Oct-3 Sotheby's, London #145/R
£2800	$4760	€4088	Vulture (13cm-5in) s. pat bronze onyx base lit. 28-Oct-3 Sotheby's, London #146/R
£2800	$5152	€4200	Flambeaux bout de table avec faisan endormi (21cm-8in) s. green pat bronze pair lit. 10-Jun-4 Camard, Paris #10 est:2000-2500
£2800	$5124	€4088	Rhinoceros attaquant un tigre (10x18cm-4x7in) Terracotta lit. 9-Jul-4 Sotheby's, London #120/R est:3000-5000
£2800	$5124	€4088	Taureau attaque par tigre (22x23cm-9x9in) s.st.f.Barbedienne pat bronze. 9-Jul-4 Sotheby's, London #123/R est:3000-5000
£2824	$4800	€4123	Lion marchant (22cm-9in) s.st.f.Barbedienne pat bronze lit. 28-Oct-3 Christie's, Rockefeller NY #230/R
£2838	$5166	€4143	Elephant du Senegal courant (18cm-7in) i. pat bronze Cast Barbedienne. 16-Jun-4 Fischer, Luzern #1573/R est:3500-4000 (S.FR 6500)
£2933	$5339	€4400	Lion qui marche (23x40cm-9x16in) s. pat bronze Cast Barbedienne. 4-Jul-4 Eric Pillon, Calais #11/R
£2941	$5000	€4294	Cheval (20cm-8in) s. pat bronze lit. 28-Oct-3 Christie's, Rockefeller NY #208/R
£2941	$5000	€4294	Dromadaire (19cm-7in) s. pat bronze lit. 28-Oct-3 Christie's, Rockefeller NY #207/R
£2941	$5000	€4294	Daim (15cm-6in) s. pat bronze prov.lit. 28-Oct-3 Christie's, Rockefeller NY #239/R
£2941	$5000	€4294	Basset debout (16cm-6in) s. pat bronze prov.lit. 28-Oct-3 Christie's, Rockefeller NY #241/R
£2993	$4759	€4400	Tigre marchant (22x42cm-9x17in) s. green pat bronze. 23-Mar-3 Salle des ventes Pillet, Lyon la Foret #148
£3020	$5346	€4500	Tigre marchant (22x37x10cm-9x15x4in) pat bronze lit. 30-Apr-4 Tajan, Paris #18/R est:2000-2500
£3147	$5350	€4500	Chouette attaquee par un ours (19x15x11cm-7x6x4in) s. brown green pat bronze. 27-Nov-3 Millon & Associes, Paris #97/R est:3500-4000
£3200	$5760	€4672	Panther of India (14x24cm-6x9in) s. dark brown pat bronze prov. 21-Apr-4 Sotheby's, London #76/R est:3000-5000
£3333	$6033	€5000	Le lion au serpent (26cm-10in) s. green brown pat bronze lit. 30-Mar-4 Rossini, Paris #239/R est:3000-5000
£3404	$5685	€4800	Lion qui marche (40cm-16in) s. brown green pat bronze Cast Barbedienne. 12-Oct-3 St-Germain-en-Laye Encheres #78/R est:4500-4800
£3448	$6379	€5000	Les Graces (20cm-8in) s. pat bronze sold with socle lit. 13-Feb-4 Rossini, Paris #20/R est:6000-8000
£3529	$6000	€5152	Elephant du Senegal (7cm-3in) s.st.f.Barbedienne pat bronze prov.lit. 28-Oct-3 Christie's, Rockefeller NY #238/R
£3592	$6213	€5100	Tigre devorant une gazelle (12x31cm-5x12in) s. pat bronze trace brown incl. base. 12-Dec-3 Piasa, Paris #86/R est:4000-5000
£3592	$6213	€5100	Crocodile (19cm-7in) brown green pat bronze st.f.Barbedienne. 14-Dec-3 St-Germain-en-Laye Encheres #98/R est:5000
£3624	$6705	€5400	Faon de cerf couche (4x15x6cm-2x6x2in) s.d.46 pat bronze. 14-Mar-4 St-Germain-en-Laye Encheres #75/R est:5500-6000
£3667	$6637	€5500	Tigre devorant un oryx (37x53x20cm-15x21x8in) s. green brown pat bronze. 1-Apr-4 Credit Municipal, Paris #94b est:3000-4000
£3691	$6792	€5500	Taureau debout (19x28x10cm-7x11x4in) st.f. Barbedienne brown pat bronze lit. 26-Mar-4 Pierre Berge, Paris #218/R est:2500-3000
£3824	$6500	€5583	Tigre qui marche (21cm-8in) s. pat bronze prov.lit. 28-Oct-3 Christie's, Rockefeller NY #231/R
£3900	$6630	€5694	Walking lion and walking tiger (25cm-10in) s.num. st.f.F.Barbedienne pair. 5-Nov-3 John Nicholson, Haslemere #1024 est:2500-3500
£3901	$6514	€5500	Aigle ailes etendues (24cm-9in) num.D21 pat bronze exec.c.1860. 17-Jun-3 Christie's, Paris #23/R est:6000-9000
£4000	$6800	€5840	Lion marchant (27x36cm-11x14in) s. pat bronze lit. 28-Oct-3 Sotheby's, London #154/R
£4118	$7000	€6012	Cheval demi-sang (14cm-6in) s. pat bronze prov.lit. 28-Oct-3 Christie's, Rockefeller NY #232/R
£4196	$7133	€6000	Guerrier tartare arretant son cheval (32cm-13in) s.st.f.Barbedienne pat bronze lit. 28-Nov-3 Doutrebente, Paris #45/R est:4000
£4225	$7014	€6000	Thesee et le centaure bienor (35cm-14in) s. black green pat bronze. 11-Jun-3 Delorme & Bocage, Paris #53/R est:3200-3800
£4255	$7106	€6000	Basset assis poils longs (26cm-10in) s. brown pat bronze. 12-Oct-3 St-Germain-en-Laye Encheres #79/R est:4000
£4412	$7500	€6442	Tom, levrier d'Algerie (19cm-7in) s. pat bronze lit. 28-Oct-3 Christie's, Rockefeller NY #226/R
£4648	$8041	€6600	Charles VII le victorieux (30x26x11cm-12x10x4in) s. brown pat bronze htd gold. 14-Dec-3 St-Germain-en-Laye Encheres #99/R est:7000
£4706	$8000	€6871	Jaguar dormant (8cm-3in) s. pat bronze prov.lit. 28-Oct-3 Christie's, Rockefeller NY #198/R
£4706	$8000	€6871	Cheval surpris par lion (40cm-16in) s. pat bronze prov.lit. 28-Oct-3 Christie's, Rockefeller NY #200/R
£4706	$8000	€6871	Lion devorant biche (14cm-6in) s. pat bronze lit. 28-Oct-3 Christie's, Rockefeller NY #220/R
£4706	$8000	€6871	Panthere saisissant cerf (37cm-15in) s. pat bronze lit. 28-Oct-3 Christie's, Rockefeller NY #250/R
£4918	$9000	€7180	Elephant du Senegal (7cm-3in) s.i. green pat. bronze st.f.F Barbedienne. 3-Jun-4 Christie's, Rockefeller NY #744/R est:2000-3000
£5000	$8650	€7300	Horse attacked by a tiger (40x28cm-16x11in) s. green black pat bronze. 12-Dec-3 Sotheby's, London #238/R est:5000-8000
£5000	$9000	€7300	Walking lion (22x39cm-9x15in) s.num.44 brown pat bronze st.f.F.Barbedienne. 21-Apr-4 Sotheby's, London #84/R est:5000-7000
£5294	$9000	€7729	Thesee combattant Bienor (34cm-13in) s. pat bronze lit. 28-Oct-3 Christie's, Rockefeller NY #216/R
£5369	$9504	€8000	Perroquet sur branchage (22x25cm-9x10in) s. pat bronze lit. 30-Apr-4 Tajan, Paris #37/R est:1800-2400
£5588	$9500	€8158	Gaston de Foix (39cm-15in) s. pat bronze lit. 28-Oct-3 Christie's, Rockefeller NY #253/R
£5674	$9475	€8000	Braque en arret sur un faisan (21cm-8in) s.num.8 brown pat bronze. 12-Oct-3 St-Germain-en-Laye Encheres #82/R est:8000-9000
£5957	$9651	€8400	Tortue (3x10x7cm-1x4x3in) s. red green pat bronze exec.c.1860 lit. 24-May-3 Martinot & Savignat, Pontoise #79/R est:8500-9000
£6000	$10200	€8760	Ours assis (13x20cm-5x8in) s.st.f.Barbedienne pat bronze. 28-Oct-3 Sotheby's, London #150/R
£6471	$11000	€9448	Elephant de Cochinchine (15cm-6in) s. pat bronze prov.lit. 28-Oct-3 Christie's, Rockefeller NY #204/R
£6471	$11000	€9448	Cheval surpris par lion (40cm-16in) s. pat bronze lit. 28-Oct-3 Christie's, Rockefeller NY #252/R
£6719	$12028	€9810	Lion qui marche (40cm-16in) s. bronze f.Barbedienne prov.lit. 15-May-4 Christie's, Sydney #419/R est:6000-9000 (A.D 17000)
£7000	$11410	€10220	Walking tiger (21cm-8in) s.i. brown pat bronze Cast.f.Barbedienne. 28-Sep-3 Wilkinson, Doncaster #10/R
£7059	$12000	€10306	Lion au serpent 3 (13cm-5in) s. pat bronze prov.lit. 28-Oct-3 Christie's, Rockefeller NY #235/R
£7103	$11863	€10300	Elan surpris par un lynx (22x31cm-9x12in) s.num.5 brown pat bronze Cast Barye. 16-Nov-3 Muizon & Le Coent, Paris #78/R
£7383	$13068	€11000	Lionne surprenant une antilope (35x57x53cm-14x22x21in) s. pat bronze Cast Brame prov.lit. 30-Apr-4 Tajan, Paris #25/R est:12000-15000
£7647	$13000	€11165	Elephant du Senegal (14cm-6in) s.st.f.Barbedienne pat bronze wooden base lit. 28-Oct-3 Christie's, Rockefeller NY #205/R
£8390	$14850	€12500	Perroquet sur branchage (22x25cm-9x10in) s. pat bronze pair lit. 30-Apr-4 Tajan, Paris #36/R est:1800-2400
£8511	$14213	€12000	Le cavalier tartare (37x36cm-15x14in) s.num.44 green pat bronze Cast Barbedienne. 12-Oct-3 St-Germain-en-Laye Encheres #84/R est:12000-15000
£9000	$15300	€13140	Cheval pur-sang (29x24cm-11x9in) s. pat bronze lit. 28-Oct-3 Sotheby's, London #142/R
£9000	$16470	€13140	Lion marchant (23x39cm-9x15in) s. pat bronze lit. 9-Jul-4 Sotheby's, London #118/R est:10000-15000
£9375	$14719	€13500	Cheval (11x13cm-4x5in) s. pat bronze. 29-Aug-3 Deauville, France #200/R est:10000-12000
£10588	$18000	€15458	Theseus fighting the Centaur (29cm-11in) s. dark green pat bronze st.f.Barbidienne. 28-Oct-3 Sotheby's, New York #106/R est:15000-20000
£12000	$20400	€17520	Lion qui marche (23x39cm-9x15in) s. pat bronze. 28-Oct-3 Sotheby's, London #112/R
£12941	$22000	€18894	Thesee combattant le Minotaure (45cm-18in) s.st.f.Barbedienne pat bronze lit. 28-Oct-3 Christie's, Rockefeller NY #212/R
£14765	$26135	€22000	Thesee combattant le minotaure (60cm-24in) s.st.f.Barbedienne pat bronze prov.lit. 30-Apr-4 Tajan, Paris #51/R est:25000-35000

£15000 $25500 €21900 Thesee combattant le minotaure (45x29cm-18x11in) s.st.f.Barbedienne pat bronze. 28-Oct-3 Sotheby's, London #126/R
£15845 $27729 €22500 Aigles et crocodile (36x104cm-14x41in) s. pat bronze lit. 19-Dec-3 Piasa, Paris #40/R est:12000-15000
£18824 $32000 €27483 Lion assis 1 (35cm-14in) s. pat bronze prov.lit. 28-Oct-3 Christie's, Rockefeller NY #201/R
£24706 $42000 €36071 Guerrier tartare (36cm-14in) s. pat bronze lit. 28-Oct-3 Christie's, Rockefeller NY #254/R
£29412 $50000 €42942 Panthere devorant lievre (41x103cm-16x41in) s. pat bronze lit. 28-Oct-3 Christie's, Rockefeller NY #224/R
£30000 $51900 €43800 Theseus and the minotaur (45cm-18in) s. green brown pat bronze base. 12-Dec-3 Sotheby's, London #232/R est:10000-15000
£30070 $50217 €43000 Lion marchant (24x40x10cm-9x16x4in) num.1 brown red pat bronze exec.1841 lit. 29-Jun-3 St-Germain-en-Laye Encheres #16/R est:20000
£37000 $66600 €54020 Cheval Turc (30x31cm-12x12in) s.i.num.703 43 green pat bronze st.f.F. Barbedienne. 21-Apr-4 Sotheby's, London #86/R est:25000-35000
£48000 $87840 €70080 Cheval turc 2 (30x31cm-12x12in) s.i. pat bronze prov. 9-Jul-4 Sotheby's, London #121/R est:25000-30000
£60000 $103800 €87600 Three seated goddesses, Venus, Minerva and Juno (32cm-13in) s. green brown pat bronze lit. 12-Dec-3 Sotheby's, London #234/R est:30000-50000

BARYE, Antoine-Louis (after) (1796-1875) French
Sculpture
£5705 $10097 €8500 Cheval turc (30cm-12in) bears sig pat bronze. 30-Apr-4 Tajan, Paris #15/R est:2000-2500

BARZAGHI, Francesco (1839-1892) Italian
Sculpture
£20814 $33303 €30388 Young Egyptian girl carrying Moses in basket (175cm-69in) s. marble prov.lit. 19-Sep-3 Koller, Zurich #1244/R est:45000-65000 (S.FR 46000)

BARZAGHI-CATTANEO, Antonio (1837-1922) Swiss
£692 $1100 €1010 Girl with red scarf (48x38cm-19x15in) mono. 12-Sep-3 Skinner, Boston #222/R
£5603 $10030 €8180 Young woman at piano (48x33cm-19x13in) s. panel. 17-May-4 Beurret, Zurich #21/R est:5000-7000 (S.FR 13000)

BARZAGLI, Massimo (1960-) Italian
£333 $613 €500 Impression (60x50cm-24x20in) s.i.d.1992 verso oil collage. 12-Jun-4 Meeting Art, Vercelli #21/R
£500 $920 €750 Bay leaf impressions (100x60cm-39x24in) s.i.d.1992 verso. 12-Jun-4 Meeting Art, Vercelli #781/R
£1033 $1901 €1550 Fish watching (90x120cm-35x47in) s.i.d.1995 verso acrylic. 12-Jun-4 Meeting Art, Vercelli #422/R est:750
£3020 $5406 €4500 Fishwatching (100x100cm-39x39in) s. enamel on lino painted 2001. 28-May-4 Farsetti, Prato #321/R est:4500-5500

BARZANTI, Licinio (1857-1944) Italian
£531 $950 €775 Arrangement of roses (45x30cm-18x12in) s. 14-May-4 Skinner, Boston #346/R
£1056 $1849 €1500 Harvesters (50x75cm-20x30in) s. 17-Dec-3 Il Ponte, Milan #610 est:1500-1800
£1093 $2000 €1596 Still life of chrysanthemum (46x64cm-18x25in) s. 5-Jun-4 Neal Auction Company, New Orleans #229/R est:2500-3500
£1913 $3500 €2793 Still life of roses (46x64cm-18x25in) s. 5-Jun-4 Neal Auction Company, New Orleans #230/R est:2500-3500

BAS, Adrien (20th C) French
Works on paper
£680 $1238 €1000 Caluire sous la neige (29x35cm-11x14in) s. pastel. 8-Feb-4 Anaf, Lyon #82
£1067 $1941 €1600 Place a Lyon (29x36cm-11x14in) s. pastel. 29-Jun-4 Chenu & Scrive, Lyon #14/R est:600-800
£1156 $2105 €1700 Quais de Rhone (29x35cm-11x14in) s. pastel. 8-Feb-4 Anaf, Lyon #80/R est:1500-1600

BAS, Edward le (1904-1966) British
£1500 $2385 €2190 Majorcan farm (41x61cm-16x24in) s. s.i.overlap prov. 10-Sep-3 Sotheby's, Olympia #169/R est:1500-2500
£1600 $2816 €2336 La Place (38x45cm-15x18in) s. board prov. 19-May-4 Dreweatt Neate, Newbury #86/R est:1000-1500
£2000 $3400 €2920 Portrait of a soldier (54x37cm-21x15in) s. board sold with ink dr. by Adrian Daintrey. 21-Nov-3 Christie's, London #60/R est:700-1000
£2200 $3740 €3212 Palace pier, Brighton (18x25cm-7x10in) s. panel. 21-Nov-3 Christie's, London #61/R est:800-1200
£3500 $5950 €5110 Raymond Mortimer, writing at a table in his study (25x35cm-10x14in) panel prov. 21-Nov-3 Christie's, London #54/R est:800-1200
£9500 $15105 €13870 Early morning, Waterloo Bridge (58x107cm-23x42in) s.d.36 board prov. 10-Sep-3 Sotheby's, Olympia #179/R est:10000-15000

BAS, Edward le (attrib) (1904-1966) British
£500 $850 €730 Still life with lemons (38x36cm-15x14in) board. 26-Nov-3 Sotheby's, Olympia #66/R

BASALDUA, Hector (1895-1976) Argentinian
£5604 $10200 €8182 Street (60x79cm-24x31in) s.s.verso. 5-Jul-4 Arroyo, Buenos Aires #96/R est:8500
£7182 $13000 €10486 Tulips (82x66cm-32x26in) 30-Mar-4 Arroyo, Buenos Aires #66
Works on paper
£1302 $2240 €1901 Hello (72x100cm-28x39in) mixed media. 3-Dec-3 Naón & Cia, Buenos Aires #86/R est:3000-4000

BASCH, Andor (1885-?) Hungarian
£923 $1532 €1348 Woman making up (50x40cm-20x16in) s.d.1922 panel. 4-Oct-3 Kieselbach, Budapest #97/R (H.F 340000)
£1212 $2194 €1770 In the studio (80x100cm-31x39in) s. 16-Apr-4 Mu Terem Galeria, Budapest #131/R (H.F 460000)
£1336 $2365 €1951 Mediterranean Park (39x48cm-15x19in) s.d.923. 28-Apr-4 Kieselbach, Budapest #56/R (H.F 500000)
£1629 $2704 €2378 Still life on the window-sill of the studio (73x60cm-29x24in) s.d.30. 4-Oct-3 Kieselbach, Budapest #51/R (H.F 600000)
£2138 $3784 €3121 Provencal landscape with a painter (56x47cm-22x19in) s.d.31. 28-Apr-4 Kieselbach, Budapest #53/R (H.F 800000)

BASCH, Edith (1895-?) Hungarian
£1253 $2167 €1829 Nude in a green armchair (61x50cm-24x20in) s.d.1929. 12-Dec-3 Kieselbach, Budapest #21/R (H.F 480000)

BASCHENIS, Evaristo (attrib) (1617-1677) Italian
£1986 $3316 €2800 Fleurs (57x70cm-22x28in) 17-Jun-3 Galerie Moderne, Brussels #336/R est:500-700

BASCHET, Marcel-Andre (1862-1941) French
Works on paper
£745 $1206 €1050 Jeune femme au collier de perles (112x98cm-44x39in) pastel prov. 21-May-3 Daguerre, Paris #73

BASCOULES, Jean Desire (1886-1976) French
£278 $464 €400 Nature morte au bougeoir (46x55cm-18x22in) s. 21-Oct-3 Artcurial Briest, Paris #214a
£594 $993 €850 Le port d'Alger (52x65cm-20x26in) s. 25-Jun-3 Maigret, Paris #51/R
£1007 $1862 €1500 Personnages dans la casbah, Sud Algerien (46x38cm-18x15in) s.d.34. 15-Mar-4 Gros & Delettrez, Paris #151/R est:1500-2300
£2282 $4221 €3400 Place a Alger (27x35cm-11x14in) s. panel. 15-Mar-4 Gros & Delettrez, Paris #150/R est:2500-3000
£3356 $6208 €5000 Bateaux dans le port d'Alger (52x65cm-20x26in) s. exhib. 15-Mar-4 Gros & Delettrez, Paris #210/R est:5000-7000

BASELEER, Richard (1867-1951) Belgian
£428 $787 €650 Sailing vessels at sea (140x150cm-55x59in) s. 28-Jun-4 Sotheby's, Amsterdam #178/R
£470 $832 €700 Bateaux en mer (46x56cm-18x22in) s. 27-Apr-4 Campo & Campo, Antwerp #4/R

BASELITZ, Georg (1938-) German
£2000 $3580 €3000 Rebel (32x24cm-13x9in) s.i. drypoint etching aquatint. 15-May-4 Dr Sturies, Dusseldorf #12/R
£106667 $197333 €160000 Man (250x200cm-98x79in) init.d.84 s.i.d.verso prov.exhib. 18-Jul-4 Sotheby's, Paris #224/R est:100000-150000
£130000 $217100 €189800 Kopfbild, dogge 1 (162x130cm-64x51in) s.d.69 s.i.d.69 verso prov.exhib. 22-Oct-3 Christie's, London #91/R est:100000-150000
£184358 $330000 €269163 Gelbe Sangerin (250x200cm-98x79in) s.i.d.3.IV.82 verso prov.exhib. 12-May-4 Sotheby's, New York #37/R est:250000-350000
£210000 $382200 €306600 Fingermalerei - Akt (250x180cm-98x71in) init.d.73 s.i.d.Mai-Juli 73 verso prov. 5-Feb-4 Sotheby's, London #55/R est:140000-180000
£290000 $527800 €423400 Jieve in ihrer Hohle (162x129cm-64x51in) init.d.71/2 s.i.d.71/72 stretcher prov. 5-Feb-4 Sotheby's, London #19/R est:200000-300000
Prints
£2113 $3507 €3000 Head in profile (65x50cm-26x20in) s.i.d.11.III.82 woodcut. 13-Jun-3 Hauswedell & Nolte, Hamburg #549/R est:2500
£2933 $5251 €4400 Oberon (30x24cm-12x9in) s.i.d. etching. 15-May-4 Dr Sturies, Dusseldorf #11/R
£5650 $10000 €8249 LR (42x32cm-17x13in) s.d.1966 verso col woodcut. 28-Apr-4 Christie's, Rockefeller NY #258/R est:12000-18000
£8000 $14560 €11680 LR (42x33cm-17x13in) woodcut black green ochre on velin. 30-Jun-4 Christie's, London #170/R est:8000-12000
£8500 $15470 €12410 Partisan (42x35cm-17x14in) s.i.d.1966 woodcut orchre brown black. 30-Jun-4 Christie's, London #171/R est:8000-12000
£10333 $18497 €15500 Untitled (38x31cm-15x12in) s.i.d. col woodcut. 15-May-4 Dr Sturies, Dusseldorf #10/R
£23000 $41860 €33580 Ohne titel (36x30cm-14x12in) s.i.d.1967 woodcut. 30-Jun-4 Christie's, London #172/R est:8000-12000
Works on paper
£664 $1143 €950 Kopf (23x22cm-9x9in) s. felt tip pen paper on card executed 1993 prov. 2-Dec-3 Sotheby's, Amsterdam #341/R est:1000-1500
£688 $1129 €950 Head (22x19cm-9x7in) s.d.93 ink card. 27-May-3 Sotheby's, Amsterdam #568/R
£4667 $8587 €7000 Figure (61x43cm-24x17in) s.d.3/VI/83 W/C. 13-Jun-4 Lombrail & Teucquam, Paris #129/R
£6667 $11933 €10000 Eagle (75x53cm-30x21in) s.d.30.XII.85 col pastel. 15-May-4 Dr Sturies, Dusseldorf #9/R
£8000 $14720 €11680 Mann mit ball (61x43cm-24x17in) s.d.81 i. verso W/C chl. 24-Jun-4 Sotheby's, London #278/R est:8000-12000
£8042 $13671 €11500 Eagle (61x43cm-24x17in) s.d.3.XI.81 chl. 27-Nov-3 Lempertz, Koln #20/R est:6000
£8383 $14000 €12239 Untitled (66x49cm-26x19in) s.d.27.XI.95 ink W/C prov. 12-Nov-3 Christie's, Rockefeller NY #414/R est:10000-15000
£106145 $190000 €154972 Untitled (98x74cm-39x29in) init.d.66 ink gouache wax crayon prov.exhib. 12-May-4 Christie's, Rockefeller NY #144/R est:150000-200000

BASILE, Matteo (1974-) Italian
Prints
£1379 $2303 €2000 Conserving (120x120cm-47x47in) s.i.d.2003 verso digital print on aluminium on board exhib. 13-Nov-3 Finarte Semenzato, Rome #474/R est:2500-2800

BASILICO, Gabriele (1944-) Italian
Photographs
£6500 $10855 €9490 Beirut 1991, rue Dakar (100x120cm-39x47in) s.d.1991 num.4/15 verso gelatin silver print prov.exhib.lit. 21-Oct-3 Christie's, London #76/R est:2500-3500

BASILIDES, Barna (1903-1967) Hungarian
£962 $1703 €1405 Early spring (68x55cm-27x22in) s.d.1931. 28-Apr-4 Kieselbach, Budapest #175/R (H.F 360000)
£1336 $2365 €1951 In the courtyard (72x83cm-28x33in) s. 28-Apr-4 Kieselbach, Budapest #176/R (H.F 500000)

BASKER, Edward (20th C) American
Works on paper
£398 $700 €581 Boats at harbour (36x53cm-14x21in) s. W/C exec.c.1950. 23-May-4 Treadway Gallery, Cincinnati #562/R

BASKIN, Leonard (1922-2000) American
Sculpture
£1657 $3000 €2419 Death (51cm-20in) mono. brown pat bronze prov.exhib. 31-Mar-4 Sotheby's, New York #164/R est:1500-2500
£2162 $4000 €3157 Bird man (42cm-17in) s.num.4/8 brown pat bronze. 11-Mar-4 Christie's, Rockefeller NY #83/R est:4000-6000
£5525 $10000 €8067 Owl (51cm-20in) col pat bronze prov.exhib. 31-Mar-4 Sotheby's, New York #162/R est:4000-6000
£7059 $12000 €10306 Spellbound (91x43cm-36x17in) carved oak prov. 9-Nov-3 Wright, Chicago #360 est:15000-20000
Works on paper
£541 $1000 €790 Head of a man (38x58cm-15x23in) s.d.1961 pen ink wash paper on board. 15-Jul-4 Doyle, New York #7/R est:800-1200
£588 $1000 €858 Blake anguished (58x79cm-23x31in) s.d.1962 ink. 9-Nov-3 Wright, Chicago #356 est:1500-2000
£1000 $1840 €1460 Portrait of Edvard Munch (34x33cm-13x13in) s. W/C sold with two portraits by the same hand. 23-Mar-4 Rosebery Fine Art, London #736 est:700-900
£1176 $2000 €1717 Medea (76x53cm-30x21in) s.d. W/C. 9-Nov-3 Wright, Chicago #355 est:2500-3000

BASKINE, Maurice (20th C) French
Works on paper
£408 $731 €600 Untitled (31x23cm-12x9in) s. gouache exec c.1950 prov. 21-Mar-4 Calmels Cohen, Paris #72/R

BASOLI, Antonio (1774-1848) Italian
Works on paper
£1528 $2597 €2200 Egyptian chimneys (38x48cm-15x19in) sepia ink dr lit. 29-Oct-3 Il Ponte, Milan #448
£3056 $5194 €4400 Egyptian temple (38x48cm-15x19in) sepia ink dr. 29-Oct-3 Il Ponte, Milan #560
£3889 $6611 €5600 View of town (38x48cm-15x19in) sepia ink dr. 29-Oct-3 Il Ponte, Milan #574
£4583 $7792 €6600 Egyptian temple (38x48cm-15x19in) sepia ink dr. 29-Oct-3 Il Ponte, Milan #5709/R

BASORINI, Pierangelo (1905-) Italian
£345 $576 €500 Still life (24x30cm-9x12in) s.d.1932. 13-Nov-3 Galleria Pace, Milan #5/R

BASQUIAT, Jean Michel (1960-1988) American
£8589 $14000 €12540 Untitled (61x46cm-24x18in) s.d.81 verso oilstick prov.exhib. 23-Sep-3 Christie's, Rockefeller NY #163/R est:10000-15000
£9581 $16000 €13988 Untitled - Hans Meyer Jan, Feb Dusseldorf (37x38cm-15x15in) acrylic oil stick on paper painted c.1987 prov. 14-Nov-3 Phillips, New York #134/R est:15000-20000
£11000 $18370 €16060 Anatomy six (76x56cm-30x22in) i.verso oilstick paper prov.exhib. 22-Oct-3 Christie's, London #63/R est:10000-15000
£13408 $24000 €19576 Pigeon anatomy (56x76cm-22x30in) oil col crayon paper prov. 12-May-4 Christie's, Rockefeller NY #400/R est:25000-35000
£14970 $25000 €21856 Untitled, bridge and jail (77x107cm-30x42in) s.d.84 oilstick pencil paper collage on paper prov.exhib. 13-Nov-3 Sotheby's, New York #606/R est:25000-35000
£30000 $50100 €43800 Currency (73x58cm-29x23in) s.i.d.1984 verso oil pastel W/C paper prov. 22-Oct-3 Christie's, London #73/R est:30000-40000
£34000 $62560 €49640 Untitled (57x76cm-22x30in) s.d.85 verso oilstick W/C pencil zerox collage paper prov.exhib. 24-Jun-4 Sotheby's, London #135/R est:30000-40000
£34731 $58000 €50707 Untitled (74x53cm-29x21in) s.d.1982 col oilsticks prov. 12-Nov-3 Christie's, Rockefeller NY #500/R est:30000-40000
£95808 $160000 €139880 Untitled (96x64cm-38x25in) oil stick prov. 13-Nov-3 Sotheby's, New York #440/R est:100000-150000
£104167 $171875 €150000 Sans titre, hotel no 58 (94x94cm-37x37in) acrylic collage photocopy exhib.lit. 2-Jul-3 Cornette de St.Cyr, Paris #92/R est:150000-180000
£122905 $220000 €179441 Brown eggs (61x46cm-24x18in) i. s.verso oilsticks paper prov. 12-May-4 Christie's, Rockefeller NY #395/R est:90000-120000
£149701 $250000 €218563 White man (153x137cm-60x54in) s.i.d.1984 verso acrylic prov.lit. 13-Nov-3 Sotheby's, New York #479/R est:250000-350000
£150350 $258601 €215000 Magic black snakes (168x152cm-66x60in) s.d.1984 verso oil collage photocopies. 4-Dec-3 Piasa, Paris #64/R est:250000-300000
£150838 $270000 €220223 Bird as Buddha (160x152cm-63x60in) s.i.d.1984 verso acrylic oil prov.exhib.lit. 12-May-4 Christie's, Rockefeller NY #391/R est:220000-280000
£167665 $280000 €244791 Flexicon (198x91cm-78x36in) oil wood exhib. 13-Nov-3 Sotheby's, New York #489/R est:280000-350000
£167665 $280000 €244791 Ellington (180x80cm-71x31in) s.i.d.1985 verso acrylic oil stick wood collage xerox collage on. 13-Nov-3 Phillips, New York #22/R est:300000-400000
£184358 $330000 €269163 Untitled - Devil's head (122x102cm-48x40in) init.d.87 overlap acrylic prov. 13-May-4 Phillips, New York #22/R est:250000-350000
£195531 $350000 €285475 Krong thip (168x152cm-66x60in) s.i.d.Nov 1983 verso acrylic oilstick prov.exhib. 13-May-4 Sotheby's, New York #448/R est:250000-350000
£230000 $384100 €335800 Desmond (218x172cm-86x68in) s.i.d.84 verso acrylic prov.lit. 21-Oct-3 Sotheby's, London #421/R est:180000-250000
£262570 $470000 €383352 Spike (155x165cm-61x65in) s.i.d.1984 verso acrylic oilstick prov.exhib.lit. 13-May-4 Sotheby's, New York #371/R est:450000-550000
£279330 $500000 €407822 Untitled (152x102cm-60x40in) oilstick paper painted 1982 prov.exhib. 12-May-4 Sotheby's, New York #7/R est:350000-450000
£323944 $560423 €460000 Brown face (167x152cm-66x60in) acrylic oil painted 1984 prov. 11-Dec-3 Binoche, Paris #6/R est:280000-350000
£329341 $550000 €480838 Masque (142x125cm-56x49in) s.verso painted 1982 prov.exhib.lit. 13-Nov-3 Phillips, New York #20/R est:350000-450000
£335196 $600000 €489386 Pay for soup. Universal. The whole livery line (126x100cm-50x39in) s.i.d.87 verso acrylic oil oilstick three prov.exhib.lit. 12-May-4 Christie's, Rockefeller NY #389/R est:400000-600000
£347305 $580000 €507065 Self portrait (89x150cm-35x59in) s.d.1985 acrylic oil stick crown cork bottle caps on wood prov. 13-Nov-3 Phillips, New York #36/R est:400000-600000
£380000 $691600 €554800 2 half hours of Chinese food (200x150cm-79x59in) s.i.d.Sept 1984 acrylic oilstick xerox collage paper collage. 4-Feb-4 Christie's, London #36/R est:350000-500000
£400000 $736000 €584000 Untitled (178x122cm-70x48in) s.i.d.82 verso acrylic oil prov. 24-Jun-4 Christie's, London #6/R est:250000-350000
£418994 $750000 €611731 Peel quickly (109x132cm-43x52in) s.d.1984 verso acrylic oil sticks prov.exhib.lit. 11-May-4 Christie's, Rockefeller NY #49/R est:500000-700000
£580000 $1067200 €846800 Pyrex jaw (170x160cm-67x63in) s.i.d.1983 verso acrylic crayon on canvas prov. 24-Jun-4 Christie's, London #42/R est:400000-600000
£698324 $1250000 €1019553 Napoleonic Stereotype (168x152cm-66x60in) s.i.d.1983 verso acrylic oil crayon prov.exhib.lit. 11-May-4 Christie's, Rockefeller NY #9/R est:900000-1200000
£1005587 $1800000 €1468157 Blue heads (183x297cm-72x117in) s. i.d.1983 verso acrylic oilstick prov.exhib.lit. 13-May-4 Phillips, New York #26/R est:1800000-2500000
£1061453 $1900000 €1549721 Low pressure zone (151x122cm-59x48in) s.i.d.Sept 1982 verso acrylic oilstick collage canvas prov.exhib. 12-May-4 Sotheby's, New York #11/R est:1200000-1800000
£2200000 $4048000 €3212000 Untitled (239x500cm-94x197in) s.d.82 verso acrylic on canvas prov.exhib.lit. 23-Jun-4 Sotheby's, London #32/R est:1800000-2500000
£2455090 $4100000 €3584431 Untitled - two heads on gold (203x317cm-80x125in) init.d.82 acrylic oilstick prov.exhib.lit. 12-Nov-3 Sotheby's, New York #26/R est:2500000-3500000
Prints
£2027 $3568 €3000 Rinse (101x101cm-40x40in) i.verso num.77/85 col serigraph. 18-May-4 Segre, Madrid #174/R est:3000
£2778 $4583 €4000 Anatomy (76x57cm-30x22in) s. screenprint one of 18 prov.lit. 2-Jul-3 Cornette de St.Cyr, Paris #96a/R est:3000-5000
£2778 $4722 €4000 Head (101x101cm-40x40in) i.verso num.77/85 col serigraph card. 28-Oct-3 Segre, Madrid #222/R est:4000
£2778 $4722 €4000 Per capita (101x101cm-40x40in) i.verso num.77/85 col serigraph card. 28-Oct-3 Segre, Madrid #227/R est:4000
£8042 $13430 €11500 Venus (17x13cm-7x5in) s.verso xerox on canvas prov. 11-Oct-3 Cornette de St.Cyr, Paris #117/R est:12000-15000
£59880 $100000 €87425 Anatomy (76x57cm-30x22in) s. lithograph from edition of 18 eighteen parts prov.exhib.lit. 13-Nov-3 Sotheby's, New York #588/R est:60000-80000
Sculpture
£100559 $180000 €146816 Untitled (56x41x8cm-22x16x3in) acrylic marker wood exec 1981 prov.exhib.lit. 12-May-4 Sotheby's, New York #36/R est:250000-350000
£146707 $245000 €214192 Ass (203x76x13cm-80x30x5in) s.i.d.1984 oil acrylic on wooden door prov.exhib.lit. 14-Nov-3 Phillips, New York #158/R est:300000-400000
£317365 $530000 €463353 All Beef (185x89x54cm-73x35x21in) s.i.d.1983 oil acrylic oilstick nail canvas structure prov.exhib. 12-Nov-3 Christie's, Rockefeller NY #619/R est:350000-450000
Works on paper
£5634 $9859 €8000 Gun dog (60x45cm-24x18in) felt pen. 18-Dec-3 Cornette de St.Cyr, Paris #135/R est:8000-12000
£7042 $12324 €10000 Tan tires (60x45cm-24x18in) wax pastel. 18-Dec-3 Cornette de St.Cyr, Paris #134/R est:10000-15000
£10056 $18000 €14682 Ribbon release (76x57cm-30x22in) s.d.84 verso col crayon graphite prov. 12-May-4 Christie's, Rockefeller NY #403/R est:25000-35000
£10056 $18000 €14682 Flats fix (56x76cm-22x30in) s.verso ink prov. 12-May-4 Christie's, Rockefeller NY #401/R est:18000-22000
£10490 $17517 €15000 Wooden airplane, no 20 (61x46cm-24x18in) wax pastel ink prov. 11-Oct-3 Cornette de St.Cyr, Paris #116/R est:15000-25000
£11333 $20853 €17000 Untitled (30x22cm-12x9in) s.i.d.1985 ink pen pencil prov.exhib. 12-Jun-4 Villa Grisebach, Berlin #441/R est:8000-10000
£16434 $27444 €23500 Ajoco (27x21cm-11x8in) wax pastel prov. 11-Oct-3 Cornette de St.Cyr, Paris #122/R est:25000-35000
£16760 $30000 €24470 Aspuria (60x45cm-24x18in) s.d.81 verso chl oilstick prov. 12-May-4 Christie's, Rockefeller NY #402/R est:40000-60000
£18000 $33120 €27000 Tesla vs Edison (32x43cm-13x17in) col crayon prov.lit. 8-Jun-4 Artcurial Briest, Paris #251/R est:30000-40000
£21229 $38000 €30994 Ape (78x57cm-31x22in) s.d.84 verso col crayon col pencil prov.exhib. 12-May-4 Christie's, Rockefeller NY #399/R est:30000-40000
£27778 $45833 €40000 Liberty, liberty (47x40cm-19x16in) s. wax pastel. 2-Jul-3 Cornette de St.Cyr, Paris #90/R est:35000-40000
£27778 $45833 €40000 Sans titre (61x48cm-24x19in) wax pastel. 2-Jul-3 Cornette de St.Cyr, Paris #91/R est:35000-45000
£27933 $50000 €40782 Ghost (106x75cm-42x30in) s.d.86 verso col pencil graphite prov. 12-May-4 Christie's, Rockefeller NY #396/R est:50000-70000
£46853 $78245 €67000 Sans titre (56x76cm-22x30in) wax pastel prov. 11-Oct-3 Cornette de St.Cyr, Paris #115/R est:70000-80000
£47486 $85000 €69330 Untitled, dog (61x43cm-24x17in) wax crayon W/C graphite prov. 14-May-4 Phillips, New York #215/R est:70000-90000
£108939 $195000 €159051 Untitled (76x56cm-30x22in) ink oilsticks prov.exhib.lit. 12-May-4 Christie's, Rockefeller NY #387/R est:100000-150000

BASQUIAT, Jean Michel and WARHOL, Andy (20th C) American
£22455 $37500 €32784 Crab (41x51cm-16x20in) estate st. acrylic silkscreen ink prov. 13-Nov-3 Sotheby's, New York #607/R est:25000-35000
£110000 $200200 €160600 Origin of Cottony - painted with Francesco Clemente (128x180cm-50x71in) s.i.d.1984 oil acrylic silkscreen ink prov.exhib. 5-Feb-4 Sotheby's, London #54/R est:60000-80000
£195531 $350000 €285475 Untitled (290x447cm-114x176in) s. both artists overlap painted 1984-85 prov.exhib.lit. 12-May-4 Sotheby's, New York #8/R est:400000-500000

BASS, Vaughan Alden (c.1900-?) American?
£1342 $2403 €2000 Rocking chair (81x61cm-32x24in) s. i.verso. 27-May-4 Sotheby's, Paris #99/R est:1000-1500

BASSANO (attrib) (16/17th C) Italian
£5468 $8967 €7600 Vierge a l'enfant. panel. 6-Jun-3 Chochon-Barre & Allardi, Paris #10a
Works on paper
£578 $1035 €850 Le doge Giani avec l'empereur Frederic Barberousse, a mi-corps (37x20cm-15x8in) black white chk prov. 18-Mar-4 Christie's, Paris #4/R

BASSANO, Francesco (studio) (15/16th C) Italian
£6000 $10200 €8760 Birth of the Virgin (45x35cm-18x14in) panel. 30-Oct-3 Sotheby's, Olympia #24/R est:4000-6000

BASSANO, Francesco (younger) (1549-1592) Italian
£6333 $11653 €9500 Winter (127x177cm-50x70in) lit. 8-Jun-4 Della Rocca, Turin #119/R est:7000-9000
£13889 $25000 €20278 Agony in the garden (37x27cm-15x11in) copper. 22-Jan-4 Sotheby's, New York #205/R est:15000-20000
£24581 $44000 €35888 Allegory of Summer (78x111cm-31x44in) prov. 27-May-4 Sotheby's, New York #81/R est:30000-40000
£40000 $73200 €60000 Adoration of the Magi (121x148cm-48x58in) 1-Jun-4 Sotheby's, Milan #132/R est:60000-80000

BASSANO, Gerolamo (style) (1566-1621) Italian
£6944 $11319 €10000 The supper at Emmaus with kitchen scene. Lazarus at feast of Dives. pair. 25-Sep-3 Dr Fritz Nagel, Stuttgart #1216/R est:15000

BASSANO, Jacobo (attrib) (1515-1592) Italian
£12329 $20959 €18000 Jesus at Martha and Maria's (80x100cm-31x39in) 4-Nov-3 Ansorena, Madrid #100/R est:18000

BASSANO, Jacobo (school) (1515-1592) Italian
£5396 $8849 €7500 Calvary (76x96cm-30x38in) prov. 4-Jun-3 Sotheby's, Milan #72/R est:8000-12000

BASSANO, Jacobo (studio) (1515-1592) Italian
£25000 $45000 €36500 Madonna and Child with infant Saint John the Baptist (85x67cm-33x26in) 21-Apr-4 Christie's, London #84/R est:7000-10000
£32000 $57600 €46720 Adoration of the shepherds (149x197cm-59x78in) prov. 21-Apr-4 Christie's, London #94/R est:15000-25000

BASSANO, Jacobo (style) (1515-1592) Italian
£11511 $18878 €16000 Transfixion (92x130cm-36x51in) 4-Jun-3 Sotheby's, Milan #21/R est:3000-4000

BASSANO, Leandro (1557-1622) Italian
£3819 $6378 €5500 Young player of flute (56x45cm-22x18in) 22-Oct-3 Finarte Semenzato, Milan #21/R
£5862 $9731 €8500 Flagellation of Christ (54x44cm-21x17in) copper. 1-Oct-3 Dorotheum, Vienna #295/R est:10000-15000
£14085 $24648 €20000 Market scene (130x181cm-51x71in) 17-Dec-3 Piasa, Paris #53/R est:20000-30000
£43972 $71234 €62000 Ecce Homo (109x90cm-43x35in) 21-May-3 Babuino, Rome #30/R

BASSANO, Leandro (attrib) (1557-1622) Italian
£8130 $14553 €11870 The Deposition (60x75cm-24x30in) 25-May-4 Bukowskis, Stockholm #432/R est:60000-80000 (S.KR 110000)

BASSE, Willem (attrib) (c.1613-1672) Dutch
£699 $1168 €1000 Inn scene (27x19cm-11x7in) init. board. 7-Oct-3 Pandolfini, Florence #503/R

BASSECOUR CAAN, Jeanette de la (1824-1877) Dutch
Works on paper
£878 $1546 €1300 Interior of a room in Huisypenburg (30x42cm-12x17in) i.d.13 okt 1857 verso W/C black chk lit. 19-May-4 Sotheby's, Amsterdam #365/R
£2365 $4162 €3500 Dahlia (34x23cm-13x9in) s.d.1845 W/C gouache black chk. 19-May-4 Sotheby's, Amsterdam #293/R est:2000-3000

BASSEN, Bartholomeus van (1590-1652) Dutch
£9000 $16470 €13140 Church interior with Christ and the woman taken in adultery (37x53cm-15x21in) s.d.1636 panel. 7-Jul-4 Bonhams, New Bond Street #42/R est:4000-6000
£19000 $32870 €27740 Figures in a church interior (112x147cm-44x58in) with sig.d.1637. 10-Dec-3 Bonhams, New Bond Street #24/R est:20000-30000

BASSEN, Bartholomeus van (attrib) (1590-1652) Dutch
£2465 $4264 €3500 Church interior (15x20cm-6x8in) canvas on board. 13-Dec-3 Lempertz, Koln #5/R est:2000

BASSEN, Bartholomeus van (style) (1590-1652) Dutch
£4698 $8644 €7000 Interior of Gothic church with figures (92x130cm-36x51in) i. prov. 24-Mar-4 Dorotheum, Vienna #107/R est:5000-8000
£12000 $20760 €17520 Palace interior with the meeting of Solomon and the Queen of Sheba (53x98cm-21x39in) panel prov. 9-Dec-3 Sotheby's, Olympia #335/R est:6000-8000

BASSETT, Reveau Mott (1897-1981) American
£326 $600 €476 Texas landscape (20x25cm-8x10in) s. canvas on board. 23-Jun-4 Doyle, New York #5007/R
£399 $650 €583 Autumn trees (20x25cm-8x10in) s. canvasboard. 28-Sep-3 Simpson's, Houston #135a/R
£898 $1500 €1311 Fall scene (30x41cm-12x16in) canvasboard. 18-Oct-3 David Dike, Dallas #117/R est:600-1200
£958 $1600 €1399 Fall colour (23x30cm-9x12in) board. 18-Oct-3 David Dike, Dallas #310/R est:1000-2000
£1198 $2000 €1749 Western illustration (64x41cm-25x16in) canvas on masonite. 18-Oct-3 David Dike, Dallas #112/R est:2500-5000
£1198 $2000 €1749 Burned out no 2 (30x38cm-12x15in) canvasboard. 18-Oct-3 David Dike, Dallas #317/R est:900-1800
£1317 $2200 €1923 Mesquite tree (30x41cm-12x16in) canvasboard. 18-Oct-3 David Dike, Dallas #294/R est:1000-2000
£1946 $3250 €2841 Storm clouds (30x41cm-12x16in) canvasboard. 18-Oct-3 David Dike, Dallas #285/R est:1500-3000
£5988 $10000 €8742 Turtle creek (61x76cm-24x30in) 18-Oct-3 David Dike, Dallas #210/R est:8000-12000
£6704 $12000 €9788 Mallards on a marsh (76x91cm-30x36in) 15-May-4 Altermann Galleries, Santa Fe #166/R
£12575 $21000 €18360 Lemon lake (61x76cm-24x30in) 18-Oct-3 David Dike, Dallas #209/R est:20000-30000

BASSETTI, Marcantonio (1588-1630) Italian
Works on paper
£1224 $2192 €1800 Un couple surpris par un enfant (15x11cm-6x4in) black chk pen brown ink wash oval. 18-Mar-4 Christie's, Paris #55/R est:2000-3000
£6338 $11092 €9000 La predication de Saint Jean Baptiste (20x13cm-8x5in) black chk pen brown ink wash prov. 17-Dec-3 Christie's, Paris #10/R est:10000-15000

BASSFORD, Wallace (1900-) American
£363 $650 €530 Portrait of a woman (71x66cm-28x26in) s. 14-May-4 Skinner, Boston #352/R
£552 $950 €806 Docked sailboats (71x84cm-28x33in) s. 6-Dec-3 Selkirks, St. Louis #212
£1398 $2600 €2041 Concarneau, France (71x84cm-28x33in) s. painted c.1930. 7-Mar-4 Treadway Gallery, Cincinnati #573/R est:2500-4500

BASSI, A (?) ?
£873 $1590 €1275 Haymakers in an alpine meadow, the Denti della Vecchia in the distance (42x66cm-17x26in) s. 16-Jun-4 Fischer, Luzern #1353/R (S.FR 2000)
£1397 $2543 €2040 White and blue grapes with apples and pears (67x88cm-26x35in) s. 16-Jun-4 Fischer, Luzern #1351/R est:5000-7000 (S.FR 3200)
£1528 $2782 €2231 Blue grapes (50x85cm-20x33in) s. panel. 16-Jun-4 Fischer, Luzern #1350/R est:5000-7000 (S.FR 3500)
£2183 $3974 €3187 The breadoven in Davesco (75x60cm-30x24in) painted c.1910. 16-Jun-4 Fischer, Luzern #1359/R est:6000-8000 (S.FR 5000)
£2620 $4769 €3825 Shepherd and sheep returning home in the evening sunlight (44x70cm-17x28in) s. 16-Jun-4 Fischer, Luzern #1352/R est:6000-8000 (S.FR 6000)

BASSI, Sofia (1930-1985) Mexican
£595 $1095 €869 Atlantide (37x84cm-15x33in) s.d.1969 panel. 25-Mar-4 Louis Morton, Mexico #45/R (M.P 12000)
£621 $1075 €907 Fortune teller (43x30cm-17x12in) s.d.1972 card. 9-Dec-3 Louis Morton, Mexico #130/R est:20000 (M.P 12000)
£744 $1369 €1086 Landscape (63x43cm-25x17in) s.d.1968 panel. 25-Mar-4 Louis Morton, Mexico #75/R est:14000-16000 (M.P 15000)
£1190 $2190 €1737 Figures (74x41cm-29x16in) s.d.1969 panel. 25-Mar-4 Louis Morton, Mexico #76/R est:14000-16000 (M.P 24000)

BASSINGTHWAITE, Lewin (1928-1983) British
Works on paper
£420 $701 €613 Rose (23x18cm-9x7in) pencil oil board prov. 16-Oct-3 Christie's, Kensington #586/R

BASSINGTHWAITE, Paul (1963-) British
£260 $434 €380 Hot evening (39x49cm-15x19in) s.verso. 16-Oct-3 Christie's, Kensington #658/R
£280 $476 €409 Shade (40x51cm-16x20in) s.verso. 26-Nov-3 Sotheby's, Olympia #135/R
£320 $509 €467 Homeward (40x51cm-16x20in) s.verso. 10-Sep-3 Sotheby's, Olympia #247/R
£400 $740 €584 Beach at night (61x76cm-24x30in) s. 11-Mar-4 Christie's, Kensington #335/R
£480 $874 €701 Repose (61x76cm-24x30in) s. verso. 1-Jul-4 Christie's, Kensington #270/R
£700 $1295 €1022 Clapping hands (76x101cm-30x40in) s.verso. 11-Feb-4 Sotheby's, Olympia #207/R

BASSMAN, Lillian (1947-) American?
Photographs
£3667 $6747 €5500 Harpers Bazar (26x32cm-10x13in) s.i. verso silver gelatin. 10-Jun-4 Villa Grisebach, Berlin #1006/R est:4000-5000
£4196 $7133 €6000 Untitled (34x25cm-13x10in) s.i. verso silver gelatin prov. 27-Nov-3 Villa Grisebach, Berlin #1106/R est:4500-5000

BAST, Dominique de (1781-1842) Belgian
£1538 $2615 €2200 Fishing boats at harbour exit (21x27cm-8x11in) s.d.1825 panel. 22-Nov-3 Arnold, Frankfurt #455/R est:800

BAST, Ornulf (1907-1974) Norwegian
£397 $730 €580 Reclining female nude (47x58cm-19x23in) i.verso. 29-Mar-4 Blomqvist, Lysaker #1015 (N.KR 5000)
Sculpture
£1435 $2440 €2095 Foal (33cm-13in) s. pat.bronze. 5-Nov-3 AB Stockholms Auktionsverk #1145/R est:8000-10000 (S.KR 19000)

BASTERRA, Manuel (20th C) Spanish
£479 $815 €700 Basabe path (19x25cm-7x10in) s. board. 4-Nov-3 Ansorena, Madrid #334/R
£4795 $8151 €7000 Around Bilbao (19x25cm-7x10in) s. 4-Nov-3 Ansorena, Madrid #372/R est:700

BASTERRECHEA ARZADUN, Nestor (1924-) Spanish
Sculpture
£1027 $1747 €1500 Untitled (14x9x9cm-6x4x4in) s. num.22/70 bronze. 4-Nov-3 Ansorena, Madrid #795/R est:1500

BASTERT, Nicolaas (1854-1939) Dutch
£278 $439 €400 Barns in autumn (32x44cm-13x17in) s. 2-Sep-3 Christie's, Amsterdam #257
£1316 $2421 €2000 A polder landscape (40x60cm-16x24in) s. prov. 22-Jun-4 Christie's, Amsterdam #100/R est:1500-2000
£1905 $3467 €2800 View on the river Vecht (37x57cm-15x22in) s. 3-Feb-4 Christie's, Amsterdam #351/R est:3000-5000
£4333 $7800 €6500 View of the river Vecht (32x48cm-13x19in) s. 20-Apr-4 Sotheby's, Amsterdam #157/R est:4000-6000
Works on paper
£528 $950 €771 Herder with flock (30x43cm-12x17in) s. W/C. 23-Jan-4 Freeman, Philadelphia #69/R

BASTET, Jean-Celestin (1858-1942) French
£333 $603 €500 Bouquet d'iris (55x43cm-22x17in) s.i.d.1915. 1-Apr-4 Credit Municipal, Paris #85
£3521 $6092 €5000 Nature morte aux armes orientales (145x106cm-57x42in) s.d.1890. 12-Dec-3 Piasa, Paris #216 est:1200-1500
£3901 $6514 €5500 Le Gange a Benares (55x67cm-22x26in) s.i.d.1904. 16-Jun-3 Gros & Delettrez, Paris #102/R est:4000-6000

BASTIANINI (?) Italian
Sculpture
£3125 $5500 €4563 Bust of a Doge (60cm-24in) terracotta. 18-May-4 Sotheby's, New York #172/R est:2500-3500

BASTIANUTTO, Riccardo (?) Italian
£280 $481 €400 Stall (73x53cm-29x21in) indis.sig.verso. 3-Dec-3 Stadion, Trieste #955/R

BASTIEN LEPAGE, Jules (1848-1884) French
£2292 $3735 €3300 Portraits of young men (60x43cm-24x17in) s. two. 24-Sep-3 Neumeister, Munich #392/R est:3000

BASTIEN, Alfred (1873-1955) Belgian
£272 $487 €400 L'artiste dans son atelier (65x60cm-26x24in) s. cardboard. 16-Mar-4 Vanderkindere, Brussels #280
£278 $442 €400 Riviere en Ardennes (37x46cm-15x18in) s. panel. 9-Sep-3 Vanderkindere, Brussels #65
£313 $497 €450 Carriere (38x55cm-15x22in) s. panel. 9-Sep-3 Vanderkindere, Brussels #45
£315 $535 €450 Vase garni de fleurs (36x26cm-14x10in) s. panel. 18-Nov-3 Galerie Moderne, Brussels #688/R
£317 $548 €450 Sous-bois au Rouge-Cloitre (38x55cm-15x22in) s. 9-Dec-3 Vanderkindere, Brussels #72
£331 $603 €500 Le porteur d'eau et ses anes (50x60cm-20x24in) s. panel. 15-Jun-4 Vanderkindere, Brussels #137
£347 $552 €500 Barques echouees (29x40cm-11x16in) s. panel. 9-Sep-3 Vanderkindere, Brussels #7
£428 $774 €650 Sous-bois ensoleille (38x55cm-15x22in) s. panel. 19-Apr-4 Horta, Bruxelles #256
£428 $787 €650 Saules le long d'une riviere (55x45cm-22x18in) s. 22-Jun-4 Palais de Beaux Arts, Brussels #197
£442 $791 €650 Nature morte au homard (27x30cm-11x12in) s. panel. 16-Mar-4 Vanderkindere, Brussels #23
£500 $905 €750 Vue forestiere (80x100cm-31x39in) s. 30-Mar-4 Palais de Beaux Arts, Brussels #477
£500 $920 €750 Coucher de soleil sur l'etang (47x56cm-19x22in) s. 14-Jun-4 Horta, Bruxelles #26
£514 $873 €750 Paysage cotier meridional (44x55cm-17x22in) s. panel. 4-Nov-3 Servarts Themis, Bruxelles #522
£552 $1021 €800 Ruelle de Montmartre (50x60cm-20x24in) s. i.d.1893 verso. 13-Jan-4 Vanderkindere, Brussels #479
£600 $1104 €900 Maison sous les arbres (48x70cm-19x28in) s. 14-Jun-4 Horta, Bruxelles #25
£655 $1212 €950 Le bois du Rouge-Cloitre (95x120cm-37x47in) s. 13-Jan-4 Vanderkindere, Brussels #81
£664 $1129 €950 Paysage anime en Algerie. s. panel. 18-Nov-3 Vanderkindere, Brussels #202/R
£676 $1189 €1000 Foret des soignes (80x100cm-31x39in) s. 18-May-4 Galerie Moderne, Brussels #225
£699 $1168 €1000 Chariot attele dans un paysage crepusculaire (25x33cm-10x13in) s. panel. 13-Oct-3 Horta, Bruxelles #361
£699 $1203 €1000 Trois-mats au coucher du soleil (21x30cm-8x12in) s. panel. 8-Dec-3 Horta, Bruxelles #500
£728 $1326 €1100 La maison du peintre (65x90cm-26x35in) s. 15-Jun-4 Galerie Moderne, Brussels #142/R
£800 $1448 €1200 Marche sous la brume (38x55cm-15x22in) s. 30-Mar-4 Palais de Beaux Arts, Brussels #478
£811 $1427 €1200 Nature morte aux fruits (90x60cm-35x24in) s. 18-May-4 Galerie Moderne, Brussels #177/R
£828 $1531 €1200 Vue de casbah (37x55cm-15x22in) s. panel. 16-Feb-4 Horta, Bruxelles #50
£1007 $1782 €1500 Etang avec sous-bois (90x70cm-35x28in) s. 27-Apr-4 Campo & Campo, Antwerp #5/R est:2000-3000
£1119 $1902 €1600 Alger (60x40cm-24x16in) s.d.1906. 18-Nov-3 Galerie Moderne, Brussels #693/R est:1200-1800
£1172 $2169 €1700 La ferme de Rouge-Cloitre sous la neige (71x78cm-28x31in) s.d.1913 panel exhib. 13-Jan-4 Vanderkindere, Brussels #481 est:1000-1500
£1216 $2141 €1800 Self-portrait in the studio (90x60cm-35x24in) s. 18-May-4 Galerie Moderne, Brussels #175/R est:500-700
Works on paper
£191 $352 €279 Forest stream (30x40cm-12x16in) s.i.d.January 8/45 gouache prov. 9-Jun-4 Walker's, Ottawa #314/R (C.D 475)
£397 $723 €600 Niewport (40x55cm-16x22in) s. W/C. 15-Jun-4 Galerie Moderne, Brussels #220/R
£420 $722 €600 Paysage a Nieuport (50x65cm-20x26in) s.d.1915 W/C. 2-Dec-3 Campo & Campo, Antwerp #18

BASTIEN, Alfred (attrib) (1873-1955) Belgian
£490 $817 €700 Les eveques (55x38cm-22x15in) bears mono. 7-Oct-3 Palais de Beaux Arts, Brussels #529

BASTIEN-LEPAGE, Émile (1854-1938) French
£671 $1100 €980 Harvest field (46x56cm-18x22in) s.d.1900 fiberboard on board prov. 31-May-3 Brunk, Ashville #479/R

BASTIN, Henri (1896-1979) Australian
£625 $1169 €938 Fireworks (59x90cm-23x35in) s.d.1969 masonite prov. 21-Jul-4 Shapiro, Sydney #146/R (A.D 1600)
£813 $1276 €1179 Tres (71x83cm-28x33in) s.d.1973 enamel board prov. 26-Aug-3 Christie's, Sydney #351 est:2000-3000 (A.D 2000)
Works on paper
£345 $538 €500 Native ware (35x47cm-14x19in) s.d.1964 mixed media. 1-Aug-2 Joel, Victoria #269 est:1000-1500 (A.D 1000)
£1626 $2553 €2358 Forest (50x63cm-20x25in) s.d.1960 W/C gouache paper on board. 27-Aug-3 Christie's, Sydney #554/R est:1800-2500 (A.D 4000)

BASZKOWSKI, Jacek (1935-) Polish
£245 $406 €358 Graceful waves (115x125cm-45x49in) painted 1997. 2-Oct-3 Agra, Warsaw #58/R (P.Z 1600)
£586 $979 €850 Trees (72x52cm-28x20in) s. s.i.d.1996 verso tempera board. 16-Nov-3 Agra, Warsaw #68/R

BATAILLE, Willem (1867-1933) Belgian
£759 $1403 €1100 Au soleil (75x100cm-30x39in) s. 16-Feb-4 Horta, Bruxelles #31/R
£986 $1706 €1400 View of Bruges (70x80cm-28x31in) s. d.d.1927 verso. 13-Dec-3 De Vuyst, Lokeren #15/R
£2324 $4020 €3300 La kermesse au village (60x70cm-24x28in) s. 13-Dec-3 De Vuyst, Lokeren #16/R est:2000-3000

BATALLA, Daniel (20th C) South American?
£442 $720 €645 Untitled (130x97cm-51x38in) s. painted 2000. 20-Jul-3 Subastas Odalys, Caracas #68

BATALLA, Pedro (1893-?) Spanish
£1748 $2920 €2500 Hare, birds and grapes (65x80cm-26x31in) s. 30-Jun-3 Ansorena, Madrid #374/R est:2100

BATCHELDER, Stephen (1849-1932) British
£580 $1038 €847 High Tor, Matlock, Derbyshire (49x36cm-19x14in) s. 18-Mar-4 Neales, Nottingham #736
£600 $966 €870 Malsters Inn, Ranworth (20x28cm-8x11in) mono. 15-Aug-3 Keys, Aylsham #604
£950 $1587 €1387 Norfolk riverscapes (13x25cm-5x10in) 21-Oct-3 Gorringes, Lewes #2031
£1000 $1810 €1460 High Tor, Matlock (46x36cm-18x14in) s. 16-Apr-4 Keys, Aylsham #681/R est:1000-1500
Works on paper
£250 $418 €365 After rain and wind (15x25cm-6x10in) s. W/C. 17-Oct-3 Keys, Aylsham #634
£300 $501 €438 Wherry (23x33cm-9x13in) s. W/C. 17-Oct-3 Keys, Aylsham #635/R
£300 $552 €438 Moored boats in an estuary at sunset (6x9cm-2x4in) s. W/C. 11-Jun-4 Keys, Aylsham #546/R
£320 $573 €467 Thorpe, Norwich (14x10cm-6x4in) s.i.d.1924 W/C. 18-Mar-4 Neales, Nottingham #680
£340 $609 €496 St. Benets, River Bure (14x10cm-6x4in) s.i.d.1928 W/C. 18-Mar-4 Neales, Nottingham #681
£340 $609 €496 Stalham Dyke (18x13cm-7x5in) mono.i.d.1927 W/C. 18-Mar-4 Neales, Nottingham #683
£360 $652 €526 12 miles from Norwich towards Yarmouth (10x15cm-4x6in) mono. i.verso W/C. 16-Apr-4 Keys, Aylsham #624/R
£400 $716 €584 Stiff breeze, near Horning, River Bure (14x10cm-6x4in) s.i.d.1921 W/C. 18-Mar-4 Neales, Nottingham #682
£480 $859 €701 Barton, Broad (14x10cm-6x4in) s.i.d.1926 W/C. 18-Mar-4 Neales, Nottingham #658
£500 $895 €730 Near Barton Broad (18x13cm-7x5in) s.i.d.1923 W/C. 18-Mar-4 Neales, Nottingham #687
£520 $931 €759 Salhouse Broads (18x13cm-7x5in) s.i.d.1925 W/C. 18-Mar-4 Neales, Nottingham #685
£575 $1035 €840 Early morning, Acle Bridge (28x48cm-11x19in) W/C. 20-Apr-4 Rowley Fine Art, Newmarket #418/R
£600 $1002 €876 White hulled yachts (20x48cm-8x19in) s. W/C. 17-Oct-3 Keys, Aylsham #633
£620 $1141 €905 Wherry passing a mill on the Norfolk Broads (9x12cm-4x5in) s. W/C. 11-Jun-4 Keys, Aylsham #543/R
£640 $1146 €934 Companions, Lowestoft (18x13cm-7x5in) s.i.d.1922 W/C. 18-Mar-4 Neales, Nottingham #684/R
£650 $1196 €949 Wherries passing a mill on the Norfolk Broads (12x21cm-5x8in) s. W/C. 11-Jun-4 Keys, Aylsham #542/R
£650 $1196 €949 White hulled yacht and a wherry on the Norfolk Broads (6x4cm-2x2in) mono. W/C pair. 11-Jun-4 Keys, Aylsham #545/R
£650 $1164 €949 Quiet evening, Stalham Dyke (14x10cm-6x4in) s. W/C. 18-Mar-4 Neales, Nottingham #693
£750 $1343 €1095 Stiff breeze, Barton Broad (24x17cm-9x7in) s. W/C. 18-Mar-4 Neales, Nottingham #691
£750 $1343 €1095 Near Norwich (14x10cm-6x4in) s. W/C. 18-Mar-4 Neales, Nottingham #694
£780 $1435 €1139 Wherries approaching cottages and bridge on the Norfolk Broads (13x18cm-5x7in) s. W/C. 11-Jun-4 Keys, Aylsham #547/R
£850 $1522 €1241 View of Cromer (35x54cm-14x21in) s. W/C htd white. 18-Mar-4 Neales, Nottingham #697
£1000 $1610 €1450 Summer shower, near Stracey Arms (33x58cm-13x23in) s. W/C. 15-Aug-3 Keys, Aylsham #599/R est:1000-1200
£1200 $2064 €1752 Yachts on the Norfolk broads (13x23cm-5x9in) s. W/C pair. 5-Dec-3 Keys, Aylsham #521/R est:1200-1400
£1250 $2238 €1825 Early evening (23x33cm-9x13in) s.d.1908 W/C. 18-Mar-4 Neales, Nottingham #696/R est:400-600

£1700	$3094	€2482	Wherries on the Norfolk Broads (18x33cm-7x13in) s. pencil W/C pair. 5-Feb-4 Mellors & Kirk, Nottingham #486 est:200-300
£1900	$3401	€2774	Evening glow (43x30cm-17x12in) s. W/C. 18-Mar-4 Neales, Nottingham #695/R est:600-800
£2300	$4117	€3358	Horning ferry, River Bure (23x33cm-9x13in) s. W/C. 18-Mar-4 Neales, Nottingham #690/R est:1200-1500
£3000	$5370	€4380	Wooded summer broadland scene (43x30cm-17x12in) s. W/C htd white. 18-Mar-4 Neales, Nottingham #698/R est:400-700

BATCHELLER, Frederick S (1837-1889) American

£2174	$4000	€3174	Pause in the day (51x41cm-20x16in) s. 27-Jun-4 Freeman, Philadelphia #73/R est:5000-8000
£8939	$16000	€13051	Still life with fruit and compote (30x25cm-12x10in) s. prov. 6-May-4 Shannon's, Milford #132/R est:15000-25000

BATCHELOR, Roland (1889-1990) British

Works on paper

£850	$1420	€1241	Never mind the weather (21x16cm-8x6in) s. W/C exhib. 16-Oct-3 Christie's, Kensington #245

BATE, William (attrib) (?-c.1845) British

Miniatures

£2600	$4654	€3796	James Butler, 1st Duke of Ormonde, wearing armour (70cm-28in) s.i.d.1831 enamel copper oval gilt-metal mount red leather case. 16-Mar-4 Christie's, Kensington #62 est:300-500

BATEMAN, Arthur (1883-1970) British

£280	$476	€409	Rocky cove with figures on a beach (41x50cm-16x20in) s.d.47. 19-Nov-3 Tennants, Leyburn #1044

BATEMAN, Henry Mayo (1887-1970) British

Works on paper

£250	$463	€365	Jewish gentleman (36x23cm-14x9in) s.d.1903 W/C. 10-Feb-4 David Lay, Penzance #329
£250	$463	€365	Our parson on Christmas Day (20x8cm-8x3in) s.i. W/C. 10-Feb-4 David Lay, Penzance #333
£320	$592	€467	Conductor's view (43x53cm-17x21in) s.d.1904 W/C. 10-Feb-4 David Lay, Penzance #337
£350	$648	€511	A tramp (36x23cm-14x9in) s.d.1903 W/C. 10-Feb-4 David Lay, Penzance #327/R
£500	$910	€730	The London Sketch Club (28x33cm-11x13in) s.i.d.1912 pencil black ink lit. 1-Jul-4 Christie's, Kensington #483/R
£1500	$2730	€2190	Four golfers (28x23cm-11x9in) init.d.1903 W/C. 15-Jun-4 David Lay, Penzance #6 est:500-700
£1500	$2730	€2190	The country squire (35x23cm-14x9in) s.d.1903 pencil black ink W/C two. 1-Jul-4 Christie's, Kensington #486/R est:600-800
£1800	$3060	€2628	Art of hornpiping as practised in the British Navy (46x32cm-18x13in) s.d.1916 pen ink. 4-Nov-3 Bonhams, New Bond Street #154/R est:2000-3000
£2600	$4784	€3796	Contented painters (35x24cm-14x9in) s. pen ink W/C. 8-Jun-4 Bonhams, New Bond Street #143/R est:1500-2000

BATEMAN, James (1893-1959) British

£1243	$2250	€1815	Sale ring (25x20cm-10x8in) s. board. 16-Apr-4 James Julia, Fairfield #748/R est:2250-2750

BATEMAN, Mary Angela (20th C) British

£400	$716	€584	Sampans lying in a harbour (37x40cm-15x16in) s. panel. 18-Mar-4 Christie's, Kensington #645

BATEMAN, Piers (1947-) Australian

£276	$430	€400	Panton hills (62x76cm-24x30in) s.d.68 board. 1-Aug-2 Joel, Victoria #305 (A.D 800)
£732	$1310	€1069	Past Cottlesbridge (122x153cm-48x60in) s.d.80. 10-May-4 Joel, Victoria #229 est:1200-1800 (A.D 1800)

BATEMAN, Robert (1930-) Canadian

£2642	$4730	€3857	Interchange (56x36cm-22x14in) s. egg tempera on masonite prov. 31-May-4 Sotheby's, Toronto #60/R est:4000-6000 (C.D 6500)
£5180	$8806	€7563	Curled up swift fox (30x25cm-12x10in) s.d.1989 acrylic board prov. 23-Nov-3 Levis, Calgary #5/R est:12000-15000 (C.D 11500)
£10976	$18000	€16025	Black-tail in the Olympics (61x91cm-24x36in) i.d.1930 acrylic masonite prov. 31-May-3 Brunk, Ashville #648/R est:15000-25000

Works on paper

£829	$1500	€1210	Elephant head (33x41cm-13x16in) ink board. 16-Apr-4 American Auctioneer #19/R est:1500-2000

BATES, Daniel (?) British

£280	$518	€409	Cattle at the edge of a sunlit loch (47x76cm-19x30in) s.d. 14-Jul-4 Christie's, Kensington #873/R

Works on paper

£950	$1758	€1387	The mill stream (25x36cm-10x14in) 13-Jan-4 British Auctioneer #282

BATES, David (1840-1921) British

£480	$758	€701	Rural landscape with children fishing on the banks of a rocky river (38x53cm-15x21in) s.d.1885. 4-Apr-3 Biddle & Webb, Birmingham #131
£500	$785	€720	Angler by Worcestershire pond (35x60cm-14x24in) s. 30-Aug-3 Hans Stahl, Toestorf #41/R
£600	$1116	€876	Anglers by a castle ruin (20x25cm-8x10in) s.d.1890 canvas on board. 4-Mar-4 Christie's, Kensington #451/R
£800	$1432	€1168	Source of the river (40x61cm-16x24in) s.d.1875. 26-May-4 Sotheby's, Olympia #130/R
£840	$1554	€1226	Fallen giant (34x45cm-13x18in) s.d.1882 s.i.d.verso. 10-Mar-4 Sotheby's, Olympia #202/R est:900-1300
£850	$1488	€1241	Landscape, a woman carrying sticks, dog running behind beside a stream (38x58cm-15x23in) s. 18-Dec-3 John Nicholson, Haslemere #1127
£900	$1665	€1314	Figures and St Bernards in a Swiss valley (61x91cm-24x36in) s.d.1885. 9-Mar-4 Gorringes, Lewes #2030
£960	$1795	€1402	Flock leaving the village (30x46cm-12x18in) s.d.1898 i.verso. 24-Feb-4 Bonhams, Knowle #49
£1267	$2116	€1850	Peasant women and children on a country road (45x35cm-18x14in) s. prov. 17-Nov-3 Waddingtons, Toronto #99/R est:1500-2500 (C.D 2800)
£1400	$2478	€2044	Fern gatherers, Valley of the Llwgwy (45x61cm-18x24in) s.d. i.stretcher. 27-Apr-4 Bonhams, Knowle #116 est:1500-2500
£1400	$2506	€2044	Desert west to the Pyramids of Gizeh (76x116cm-30x46in) s.d.1892 s.i.d.verso. 27-May-4 Christie's, Kensington #247/R est:800-1200
£1613	$2968	€2355	An island in the Llugwy near Capel Craig (76x127cm-30x50in) s.d.1881 s.i.d.verso. 14-Jun-4 Waddingtons, Toronto #150/R est:5000-6000 (C.D 4000)
£1800	$2916	€2610	Watering place (39x61cm-15x24in) s.d.1873. 30-Jul-3 Hamptons Fine Art, Godalming #263/R est:2000-3000
£1800	$2988	€2628	Desert near the Pyramids, Gizeh (51x76cm-20x30in) s.d.1892 s.i.d.verso. 1-Oct-3 Sotheby's, Olympia #140/R est:2000-3000
£1800	$3060	€2628	In the Teme Valley (51x76cm-20x30in) s.d.1904 s.i.d.verso. 25-Nov-3 Bonhams, Knowle #200/R est:2000-3000
£1800	$3330	€2628	Mill on the Kennet (51x76cm-20x30in) s. s.i.verso. 10-Feb-4 David Lay, Penzance #355/R est:1800-2600
£1800	$3330	€2628	Shepherds (51x76cm-20x30in) s. s.i.verso. 10-Feb-4 David Lay, Penzance #356/R est:1800-2600
£1887	$3000	€2755	Path through the wood (26x36cm-10x14in) s.d.1907 i.verso board. 12-Sep-3 Skinner, Boston #249/R
£2200	$3938	€3212	Children on a wayside (46x36cm-18x14in) s.d.1887 prov. 27-May-4 Christie's, Kensington #310/R est:2000-3000
£2200	$4114	€3300	Summer landscape with figures beside a loch gate, church amongst trees (30x46cm-12x18in) s. 22-Jul-4 Tennants, Leyburn #850/R est:1500-2000
£3300	$5973	€4818	Malvern (50x75cm-20x30in) s.d.1882. 30-Mar-4 Sworder & Son, Bishops Stortford #526/R est:1500-2500
£3400	$5440	€4964	Oaks and bracken (61x46cm-24x18in) s.d.1889 s.i.d.verso. 16-Sep-3 Bonhams, Knowle #108/R est:2500-3500
£4000	$7280	€5840	Iffley Mill, Oxford (61x91cm-24x36in) s.d.1872. 16-Jun-4 Bonhams, New Bond Street #48/R est:4000-6000
£5174	$9261	€7554	The farmyard, Brons Norton. Setting down for the night (61x45cm-24x18in) s.i. verso pair. 26-May-4 AB Stockholms Auktionsverk #2424/R est:25000-30000 (S.KR 70000)

Works on paper

£265	$464	€387	Upland river in torrent (25x33cm-10x13in) s. W/C. 16-Dec-3 Capes Dunn, Manchester #731
£270	$491	€394	Landscape with cattle (25x36cm-10x14in) s. indis d. W/C. 30-Jun-4 Neal & Fletcher, Woodbridge #286
£425	$782	€621	Country lane near Banbury (25x36cm-10x14in) s. W/C. 28-Jun-4 British Auctioneer #378
£440	$823	€642	Moorland pasture (10x13cm-4x5in) s. W/C. 24-Feb-4 Canterbury Auctions, UK #200/R
£580	$986	€847	Crossing the moor (36x52cm-14x20in) s.d.1910 W/C. 18-Nov-3 Bonhams, Leeds #20
£580	$916	€847	View near Castle Morton, with shepherd and flock on moorland path (25x36cm-10x14in) s. W/C. 7-Sep-3 Desmond Judd, Cranbrook #664
£600	$948	€876	Welsh landscape with figures (36x51cm-14x20in) s. W/C. 4-Sep-3 Biddle & Webb, Birmingham #908
£950	$1501	€1387	By the Harrocks, Eckington, Derbyshire (36x52cm-14x20in) s. W/C. 23-Jul-3 Hampton & Littlewood, Exeter #421/R
£1050	$1743	€1533	Sheep in a landscape (25x34cm-10x13in) s.d.1900 W/C. 1-Oct-3 Woolley & Wallis, Salisbury #119/R est:400-600
£1300	$2457	€1898	Harvest time (34x51cm-13x20in) s. W/C. 19-Feb-4 Lyon & Turnbull, Edinburgh #12/R est:300-500
£1600	$2720	€2336	Edge of the moor, Bolton Woods, Wharfedale (35x52cm-14x20in) s.d.1904 W/C. 19-Nov-3 Tennants, Leyburn #973/R est:800-1200

BATES, David (attrib) (1840-1921) British

£600	$1002	€900	Countryside study with figures and cattle (33x46cm-13x18in) panel. 26-Oct-3 Tayler & Fletcher, Cheltenham #2

BATES, David (1952-) American

£16763	$29000	€24474	Rodeo (183x152cm-72x60in) prov. 10-Dec-3 Phillips, New York #673/R est:5000-7000

BATES, George William (1930-) Canadian

£240	$439	€350	Off the north coast, Seiner (61x91cm-24x36in) s. i.verso prov. 3-Jun-4 Heffel, Vancouver #5/R (C.D 600)
£351	$639	€512	Summer, Steveston (24x20cm-9x8in) s. i.verso prov. 5-Feb-4 Heffel, Vancouver #3/R (C.D 850)

BATES, H Francis (?) British?

£400	$668	€584	Chapel and church (27x19cm-11x7in) s. canvasboard. 14-Oct-3 Rosebery Fine Art, London #548/R

BATES, Kenneth (1895-1973) American

£438	$700	€639	Laurentian motif (76x91cm-30x36in) exhib. 19-Sep-3 Freeman, Philadelphia #165/R
£4335	$7500	€6329	Winter landscape with sleigh (64x76cm-25x30in) 10-Dec-3 Alderfer's, Hatfield #357/R est:2000-3000

BATES, Maxwell (1906-1980) Canadian

£778	$1276	€1136	Anthem (91x61cm-36x24in) s. prov. board. 28-May-3 Maynards, Vancouver #84 (C.D 1750)
£826	$1496	€1206	Untitled - West of Calagry (30x41cm-12x16in) s.d.1975 canvasboard. 18-Apr-4 Levis, Calgary #2/R est:2500-3000 (C.D 2000)
£1004	$1708	€1466	City view, Victoria (30x41cm-12x16in) s. i.verso prov. 6-Nov-3 Heffel, Vancouver #6/R est:2500-3500 (C.D 2250)
£1222	$2004	€1784	Teacher and students at blackboard (51x61cm-20x24in) s.d.1978. 28-May-3 Maynards, Vancouver #16/R est:3000-4000 (C.D 2750)
£1680	$3074	€2453	Summer landscape (60x75cm-24x30in) s. board. 1-Jun-4 Joyner Waddington, Toronto #16/R est:3000-5000 (C.D 4200)
£3862	$6913	€5639	Still life (61x76cm-24x30in) s.d.1965 i.verso prov.exhib. 27-May-4 Heffel, Vancouver #204/R est:6000-8000 (C.D 9500)

Works on paper

£714	$1229	€1042	Flowers (48x34cm-19x13in) s.d.1974 W/C ink. 2-Dec-3 Joyner Waddington, Toronto #10/R (C.D 1600)
£1033	$1870	€1508	Boy and girl (49x28cm-19x11in) s.d.1948 W/C. 18-Apr-4 Levis, Calgary #2a/R est:1500-2000 (C.D 2500)
£1157	$2094	€1689	Untitled - friends (56x44cm-22x17in) s.d.1948 W/C. 18-Apr-4 Levis, Calgary #3/R est:1500-2000 (C.D 2800)
£1267	$2116	€1850	Owl (46x40cm-18x16in) s.d.1964 ink W/C. 17-Nov-3 Hodgins, Calgary #82/R est:2000-2500 (C.D 2800)
£1577	$2680	€2302	Fortune teller (52x37cm-20x15in) s.d.1977 W/C prov.lit. 18-Nov-3 Sotheby's, Toronto #168/R est:2500-3000 (C.D 3500)

BATES, Robert (1943-) British

Works on paper

£251	$450	€366	Couple walking under a full moon (10x13cm-4x5in) s. pencil. 13-May-4 Dallas Auction Gallery, Dallas #232/R
£265	$475	€387	Me Ebon and Indian poet (20x30cm-8x12in) i. W/C. 13-May-4 Dallas Auction Gallery, Dallas #343/R
£279	$500	€407	Bats over road (10x18cm-4x7in) i. W/C. 13-May-4 Dallas Auction Gallery, Dallas #336/R
£465	$800	€679	In England. In Ireland (28x38cm-11x15in) s.d.1986 W/C two. 3-Dec-3 Doyle, New York #24/R
£988	$1700	€1442	As for men. Herald of new ages. Night train passing through Eden. Mellington Hall, friends waiting (28x24cm-11x9in) s.d.1990/91 W/C four various sizes prov. 3-Dec-3 Doyle, New York #33 est:1200-1600
£1117	$2000	€1631	As for man. On Earth. Trees dying on a hilltop (8x2cm-3x1in) two s.d.1987 one 1981 W/C various sizes set of three. 6-May-4 Doyle, New York #79/R est:1000-1500
£1308	$2250	€1910	Interior landscape. Pointing at the moon. Often in darkness. Evening in the garden (9x17cm-4x7in) s.d.1983 W/C four various sizes. 3-Dec-3 Doyle, New York #25/R est:1200-1600
£1397	$2500	€2040	Garden at the edge of a battlefield. Succession of day's (22x20cm-9x8in) s.d.1984-85 W/C various sizes two. 6-May-4 Doyle, New York #78/R est:1000-1500

BATHA, Gerard (1937-) South African

£1880	$3197	€2745	Kalk Bay (98x148cm-39x58in) s. i.d.85 verso acrylic prov. 4-Nov-3 Stephan Welz, Johannesburg #612/R est:12000-18000 (SA.R 22000)

BATHIEU, Jules (20th C) French

£1061	$1900	€1549	Barnyard scene with chickens (46x38cm-18x15in) 15-May-4 Jeffery Burchard, Florida #104

BATHIOU, R (19/20th C) French

£1659	$3020	€2422	Female nude standing in an exterior setting (166x85cm-65x33in) s. 16-Jun-4 Fischer, Luzern #1154/R est:4000-5000 (S.FR 3800)

BATLEY, Walter Daniel (1850-?) British

£250	$433	€365	Goats in a mountainous lake landscape (63x76cm-25x30in) s.d.1882. 10-Dec-3 Bonhams, Bury St Edmunds #553
£550	$952	€803	Chalk pits at Claydon (87x128cm-34x50in) s.d.1889. 10-Dec-3 Bonhams, Bury St Edmunds #542

BATLLE PLANAS, Juan (1911-1966) Argentinian

£9945	$18000	€14520	Composition (38x18cm-15x7in) canvas on board. 30-Mar-4 Arroyo, Buenos Aires #87
£13736	$25000	€20055	Playing with fire (32x24cm-13x9in) s. tempera paper exhib.lit. 29-Jun-4 Arroyo, Buenos Aires #69/R est:20000
£25683	$47000	€37497	Surrealist composition (31x19cm-12x7in) tempera cardboard. 1-Jun-4 Arroyo, Buenos Aires #85

Works on paper

£279	$500	€407	Figure (9x6cm-4x2in) ink. 11-May-4 Arroyo, Buenos Aires #9
£1319	$2400	€1926	Figure (35x24cm-14x9in) s.d.60 mixed media. 5-Jul-4 Arroyo, Buenos Aires #93/R est:2400
£2912	$5300	€4252	Couple (30x23cm-12x9in) s.d.56 mixed media. 29-Jun-4 Arroyo, Buenos Aires #98/R est:4000

BATLLORI, Cristina (1952-) Spanish

£2267	$4103	€3400	Sand dreams (65x184cm-26x72in) s. s.i.d.2003 verso oil sand. 30-Mar-4 Segre, Madrid #175/R est:1900

BATONI, Pompeo (1708-1787) Italian

£220000	$402600	€321200	Portrait of John Crewe, 1st Baron of Crewe (137x99cm-54x39in) s.i.d.1760 prov.lit. 7-Jul-4 Christie's, London #103/R est:250000-350000

BATONI, Pompeo (after) (1708-1787) Italian

£7237	$13316	€11000	Eneas leaving Dido (86x94cm-34x37in) 24-Jun-4 Christie's, Paris #75/R est:3000-5000

BATT, Arthur (1846-1911) British

£500	$925	€730	Study of a kitten (11x10cm-4x4in) s. board. 10-Feb-4 Bonhams, Knightsbridge #170/R
£540	$853	€788	Head of a donkey (36x30cm-14x12in) s.d.1877. 24-Jul-3 Mallams, Cheltenham #309/R
£600	$966	€870	Portrait of a kitten (10x8cm-4x3in) s. board. 13-Aug-3 Andrew Hartley, Ilkley #829
£1400	$2506	€2044	Sprite, study of a dog watching a parrot (23x33cm-9x13in) s.d.1889 i.verso. 22-Mar-4 Bonhams & Brooks, Norfolk #232/R

BATT, Terry (1949-) Australian

£894	$1404	€1305	Unscheduled stops, mechanical repairs (93x107cm-37x42in) s.i.d.91 verso. 27-Aug-3 Christie's, Sydney #562 est:2000-3000 (A.D 2200)

BATTAGLIA, Alessandro (1870-1940) Italian

£2297	$3584	€3400	Path with man (123x129cm-48x51in) 30-Mar-3 Adma, Formigine #393 est:2000-2500

Works on paper

£1338	$2221	€1900	In campagna (35x55cm-14x22in) s.d.1906 W/C cardboard. 11-Jun-3 Christie's, Rome #45 est:1700-1900

BATTAGLIA, Domenico (1846-?) Italian

£387	$643	€550	Nella stalla (51x71cm-20x28in) s. 11-Jun-3 Christie's, Rome #32

BATTAGLIA, G Pompiani (19th C) Italian

Works on paper

£460	$731	€672	Woman carrying water and corn along a rocky path (53x36cm-21x14in) s. W/C. 10-Sep-3 Edgar Horn, Eastbourne #335/R

BATTAGLIA, Xante (1943-) Italian

£333	$613	€500	Fantastic ancient world (40x50cm-16x20in) s. painted 2003. 12-Jun-4 Meeting Art, Vercelli #292/R
£336	$621	€500	Ancient face (40x50cm-16x20in) s. painted 2003. 13-Mar-4 Meeting Art, Vercelli #161
£352	$585	€500	Futuro-Arcaico (60x70cm-24x28in) s.i.verso oil collage. 14-Jun-3 Meeting Art, Vercelli #397
£369	$683	€550	Faces (40x60cm-16x24in) s. s.verso. 13-Mar-4 Meeting Art, Vercelli #436
£423	$739	€600	Old faces (40x50cm-16x20in) s. i.verso. 17-Dec-3 Il Ponte, Milan #811
£433	$797	€650	Ancient faces (60x50cm-24x20in) s. 12-Jun-4 Meeting Art, Vercelli #686/R

BATTAGLIOLI, Francesco (18th C) Italian

£27632	$50013	€42000	Landscape with tower (66x91cm-26x36in) s.d.1764. 14-Apr-4 Ansorena, Madrid #143/R est:42000

BATTAILLE, Irene (1913-) Belgian

£400	$720	€600	Abstract harbour view (36x66cm-14x26in) s. 26-Apr-4 Bernaerts, Antwerp #578/R
£664	$1143	€950	Caucale-Bretagne (38x46cm-15x18in) s.d.1957. 2-Dec-3 Campo & Campo, Antwerp #19
£738	$1351	€1100	La barriere (85x100cm-33x39in) s. 8-Jul-4 Campo, Vlaamse Kaai #30
£800	$1440	€1200	Still life with fruit bowl (78x88cm-31x35in) s. s.i.d.1970 verso. 26-Apr-4 Bernaerts, Antwerp #582/R
£1333	$2413	€2000	Paysage (80x100cm-31x39in) s.d.1964. 30-Mar-4 Campo, Vlaamse Kaai #5 est:1400-1600
£2133	$3840	€3200	Reclining nude (88x99cm-35x39in) s. 26-Apr-4 Bernaerts, Antwerp #583/R est:1000-1250

BATTAILLE, Jan (1808-1957) Belgian

£2013	$3604	€3000	L'incendie au village (124x148cm-49x58in) s.d.1836. 25-May-4 Palais de Beaux Arts, Brussels #556/R est:3000-4000

BATTAINI, Rino Gaspare (1892-) Italian

£441	$749	€644	Still life with plums, melon and jug (46x45cm-18x18in) s.d.1931 panel. 5-Nov-3 Dobiaschofsky, Bern #336 (S.FR 1000)

BATTARBEE, Rex E (1893-1969) Australian

Works on paper

£382	$695	€558	Sand dune, Central Australia (39x51cm-15x20in) s.d.1947 W/C. 16-Jun-4 Deutscher-Menzies, Melbourne #383/R est:800-1200 (A.D 1000)
£625	$1169	€938	Central Australian landscape (51x34cm-20x13in) s.d.1934 W/C. 21-Jul-4 Shapiro, Sydney #132/R (A.D 1600)
£661	$1170	€965	Baobab tree, Coolibah Station, Northern Territory (37x49cm-15x19in) s.d.1948 W/C. 3-May-4 Christie's, Melbourne #307 (A.D 1600)

BATTEM, Gerard van (1636-1684) Dutch

£4500	$7650	€6570	Mountainous river landscape with figures loading barges (49x37cm-19x15in) s. panel prov. 29-Oct-3 Bonhams, New Bond Street #58/R est:3000-4000
£16447	$30263	€25000	Skaters and figures in frozen river landscape (38x59cm-15x23in) mono. panel. 25-Jun-4 Piasa, Paris #24/R est:25000-35000

Works on paper

£16216	$28541	€24000	Adoration of the shepherds (20x23cm-8x9in) s. gouache en grisaille prov.exhib.lit. 19-May-4 Sotheby's, Amsterdam #111/R est:10000-15000

BATTERSBY, Martin (1914-1982) British

£3593	$6000	€5246	Untitled (162x91cm-64x36in) s.d.1961 exhib. 20-Oct-3 Sotheby's, New York #212/R est:3000-5000

Works on paper

£359	$600	€524	Untitled (10x13cm-4x5in) gouache prov. 20-Oct-3 Sotheby's, New York #213/R
£800	$1480	€1168	Monsieur (27x32cm-11x13in) gouache prov. 11-Mar-4 Christie's, Kensington #164/R

BATTHYANY, Gyula (1887-1959) Hungarian

£2088	$3612	€3048	Ships, sirens (59x754cm-23x297in) 12-Dec-3 Kieselbach, Budapest #79/R (H.F 800000)
£3207	$5676	€4682	Young beauty (80x60cm-31x24in) s. 28-Apr-4 Kieselbach, Budapest #154/R (H.F 1200000)
£5587	$10000	€8157	Floral still life (89x61cm-35x24in) s. board. 21-Mar-4 Jeffery Burchard, Florida #30/R
£21078	$38151	€30774	Diva and her adorers (78x98cm-31x39in) s. 16-Apr-4 Mu Terem Galeria, Budapest #191/R (H.F 8000000)

£21718 $36053 €31708 Lady with an umbrella, autumn (130x80cm-51x31in) s. 4-Oct-3 Kieselbach, Budapest #48/R (H.F 8000000)
£34739 $61488 €50719 Countess in green dress, Count Maria Sztaray (119x79cm-47x31in) s. 28-Apr-4 Kieselbach, Budapest #15/R (H.F 13000000)
£42756 $75677 €62424 Jockey club (110x150cm-43x59in) s. 28-Apr-4 Kieselbach, Budapest #130/R (H.F 16000000)
Works on paper
£923 $1532 €1348 Nude (31x14cm-12x6in) col pencil. 4-Oct-3 Kieselbach, Budapest #103/R (H.F 340000)
£923 $1532 €1348 Nude with raised arms (31x14cm-12x6in) col pencil. 4-Oct-3 Kieselbach, Budapest #104/R (H.F 340000)
£3393 $5870 €4954 Historical scenes (23x33cm-9x13in) pencil six drawings. 12-Dec-3 Kieselbach, Budapest #66/R (H.F 1300000)

BATTIGLIA, E (19th C) Italian
Sculpture
£12941 $22000 €18894 Dancing Nymph (263cm-104in) s.i. marble incl green marble base. 28-Oct-3 Sotheby's, New York #107/R est:15000-20000

BATTIGLIO, Eugenio (19/20th C) Italian
Sculpture
£1060 $1928 €1600 Naiade (86cm-34in) s.i. white marble. 16-Jun-4 Hotel des Ventes Mosan, Brussels #185 est:700-800

BATTISS, Walter (1906-1982) South African
£517 $864 €755 Mountains landscape with clouds (20x34cm-8x13in) s.d.1941 board. 20-Oct-3 Stephan Welz, Johannesburg #567 est:4000-6000 (SA.R 6000)
£1197 $2034 €1748 Water carriers (15x30cm-6x12in) s. s.d.June 1959 verso. 4-Nov-3 Stephan Welz, Johannesburg #692/R est:8000-12000 (SA.R 14000)
£1466 $2447 €2140 Extensive landscape with a river (44x54cm-17x21in) s.d.1942. 20-Oct-3 Stephan Welz, Johannesburg #330/R est:15000-20000 (SA.R 17000)
£1538 $2615 €2245 Road through an extensive landscape (39x48cm-15x19in) s.d.1941 canvas on board. 4-Nov-3 Stephan Welz, Johannesburg #627/R est:15000-20000 (SA.R 18000)
£1569 $2808 €2291 Abstract composition (29x49cm-11x19in) s. 31-May-4 Stephan Welz, Johannesburg #612/R est:10000-15000 (SA.R 19000)
£1880 $3197 €2745 Two washerwomen (19x24cm-7x9in) s. 4-Nov-3 Stephan Welz, Johannesburg #641/R est:10000-15000 (SA.R 22000)
£1940 $3239 €2832 Four figures in a landscape (39x50cm-15x20in) s. 20-Oct-3 Stephan Welz, Johannesburg #302/R est:25000-35000 (SA.R 22500)
£2155 $3599 €3146 Three figures with a blue sky (29x24cm-11x9in) s. 20-Oct-3 Stephan Welz, Johannesburg #324/R est:20000-24000 (SA.R 25000)
£2241 $3743 €3272 Arab town (30x40cm-12x16in) s. 20-Oct-3 Stephan Welz, Johannesburg #327/R est:12000-16000 (SA.R 26000)
£2241 $3743 €3272 Nights spirits, Tahiti (44x49cm-17x19in) s.i. 20-Oct-3 Stephan Welz, Johannesburg #398/R est:20000-30000 (SA.R 26000)
£2586 $4319 €3776 Arab in a landscape (54x42cm-21x17in) s. board. 20-Oct-3 Stephan Welz, Johannesburg #353/R est:10000-15000 (SA.R 30000)
£2689 $4867 €3926 Grazing buck (35x75cm-14x30in) s. 30-Mar-4 Stephan Welz, Johannesburg #498/R est:22000-26000 (SA.R 32000)
£3103 $5183 €4530 Green landscape with figures (34x43cm-13x17in) s. 20-Oct-3 Stephan Welz, Johannesburg #304/R est:25000-35000 (SA.R 36000)
£3193 $5780 €4662 Horses and riders (24x29cm-9x11in) s. board. 30-Mar-4 Stephan Welz, Johannesburg #499/R est:18000-24000 (SA.R 38000)
£3448 $5759 €5034 Karoo images (40x59cm-16x23in) s. 20-Oct-3 Stephan Welz, Johannesburg #303/R est:25000-35000 (SA.R 40000)
£3621 $6047 €5287 Five women in a kraal (50x60cm-20x24in) s. 20-Oct-3 Stephan Welz, Johannesburg #395/R est:40000-60000 (SA.R 42000)
£4310 $7198 €6293 Coloured girl from George (55x45cm-22x18in) s. prov.exhib. 20-Oct-3 Stephan Welz, Johannesburg #289/R est:18000-24000 (SA.R 50000)
£5367 $9608 €7836 Opulence of youth (45x38cm-18x15in) s. i. verso board. 31-May-4 Stephan Welz, Johannesburg #594/R est:30000-40000 (SA.R 65000)
Works on paper
£299 $509 €437 Summer landscape (17x23cm-7x9in) s. W/C. 4-Nov-3 Stephan Welz, Johannesburg #313 est:1200-1500 (SA.R 3500)
£479 $857 €699 Figures outside huts in a landscape (21x30cm-8x12in) s. W/C. 31-May-4 Stephan Welz, Johannesburg #284 (SA.R 5800)
£537 $961 €784 Figures in a landscape (18x30cm-7x12in) s. W/C. 31-May-4 Stephan Welz, Johannesburg #371 (SA.R 6500)
£684 $1162 €999 Birds at a river mouth (31x46cm-12x18in) s. W/C. 4-Nov-3 Stephan Welz, Johannesburg #661 est:5000-8000 (SA.R 8000)
£743 $1330 €1085 Zwartkrans (34x43cm-13x17in) i.d.9.7.52 W/C prov. 31-May-4 Stephan Welz, Johannesburg #113 (SA.R 9000)

BATTISTA, Eric (1933-) ?
£423 $739 €600 Jour de marche a Paimpol (46x55cm-18x22in) s. 16-Dec-3 Adjug'art, Brest #382/R

BATTISTA, Giovanni (1858-1925) Italian
£313 $500 €457 Grandfather's gift (28x20cm-11x8in) s. panel. 21-Sep-3 William Jenack, New York #280
Works on paper
£250 $400 €365 Fishermen, Bay of Naples (36x23cm-14x9in) s. W/C. 21-Sep-3 William Jenack, New York #56/R
£275 $500 €402 View of Amalfi coast (14x8cm-6x3in) s. W/C. 7-Feb-4 Sloans & Kenyon, Bethesda #849/R
£420 $769 €613 Fishing boat in the Bay of Naples, Mount Vesuvius in the distance (25x36cm-10x14in) s. gouache. 6-Apr-4 Bonhams, Chester #894
£700 $1274 €1022 On the Amalfi coast (33x51cm-13x20in) s. bodycol pair. 1-Jul-4 Christie's, Kensington #378/R
£1235 $2000 €1791 Naples (34x52cm-13x20in) s. W/C. 8-Aug-3 Barridorf, Portland #167/R est:2000-3000
£5482 $9484 €8004 Italian views (12x17cm-5x7in) s. gouache 13. 9-Dec-3 Rasmussen, Copenhagen #1505/R est:50000 (D.KR 58000)

BATTKE, Heinz (1900-1966) German
£467 $859 €700 Flower bowl (34x42cm-13x17in) s.d.32 s.i.d.verso oil-tempera oil panel. 12-Jun-4 Villa Grisebach, Berlin #504/R
£800 $1472 €1200 Still life with jug and plant (40x50cm-16x20in) s.d.32 i.d.verso panel. 12-Jun-4 Villa Grisebach, Berlin #503/R
£1333 $2453 €2000 Still life (78x58cm-31x23in) s.d.30 s.i.verso stretcher prov.exhib. 12-Jun-4 Villa Grisebach, Berlin #240/R est:2500-3500

BATZ, Eugen (1905-) German
Works on paper
£839 $1443 €1200 Untitled (39x26cm-15x10in) s.d.71 W/C. 4-Dec-3 Van Ham, Cologne #23/R
£972 $1624 €1400 Yellow accent (58x37cm-23x15in) s.d. s.i.d. verso mixed media panel. 25-Oct-3 Dr Lehr, Berlin #59/R

BAUBE, Claude le (20th C) French
Works on paper
£333 $617 €500 Caravelles (48x79cm-19x31in) s. W/C. 14-Jul-4 Livinec, Gaudcheau & Jezequel, Rennes #74

BAUCH, Jan (1898-1995) Czechoslovakian
£1266 $2227 €1899 Villon's motive (45x41cm-18x16in) s.d.1970. 22-May-4 Dorotheum, Prague #176/R est:60000-90000 (C.KR 60000)
£3089 $5745 €4510 Reclining nude (41x51cm-16x20in) s.i.d.1933 verso. 6-Mar-4 Dorotheum, Prague #126/R est:90000-200000 (C.KR 150000)

BAUCHANT, Andre (1873-1958) French
£300 $540 €450 Les fleurs (9x18cm-4x7in) s.d.1924 panel. 26-Apr-4 Tajan, Paris #272/R
£811 $1500 €1184 Floral still llife (41x51cm-16x20in) board painted c.1920. 12-Mar-4 Du Mouchelle, Detroit #2141/R est:1500-2300
£986 $1706 €1400 Fleurs (13x17cm-5x7in) s.d.1951 s.i.verso panel lit. 9-Dec-3 Artcurial Briest, Paris #268 est:1000-1500
£1259 $2165 €1800 Bouquet de fleurs (42x29cm-17x11in) s. 3-Dec-3 Tajan, Paris #153/R est:2000-2500
£1448 $2607 €2100 L'arrivee du notaire (24x35cm-9x14in) s.d.1941 panel. 26-Jan-4 Gros & Delettrez, Paris #27 est:600-900
£2000 $3340 €2920 Flowers (31x50cm-12x20in) s.d.1941 board prov. 22-Oct-3 Sotheby's, Olympia #164/R est:2000-3000
£2098 $3608 €3000 La rencontre (46x55cm-18x22in) s.d.1943. 3-Dec-3 Tajan, Paris #238/R est:5000-6000
£2937 $4905 €4200 Promenade dans les ruines (39x46cm-15x18in) s. 29-Jun-3 Eric Pillon, Calais #254/R
£2937 $4905 €4200 Vase de fleurs dans un paysage (41x33cm-16x13in) s.d.1949 panel. 29-Jun-3 Eric Pillon, Calais #251/R
£2937 $4993 €4200 Paysanne au bonnet de dentelle (63x48cm-25x19in) s.d.1929 i.verso. 1-Dec-3 Rieunier, Paris #28/R est:4000-5000
£3073 $5500 €4487 Vase aux tulipes (42x56cm-17x22in) s.d.1926 panel prov. 6-May-4 Doyle, New York #80/R est:3000-5000
£3125 $5219 €4500 Fleurs au crepuscule (38x46cm-15x18in) s.d.1944. 21-Oct-3 Artcurial Briest, Paris #210/R est:4500-5500
£3198 $5500 €4669 Antre de trophonos, Grece (73x92cm-29x36in) s.d.1941 prov. 3-Dec-3 Doyle, New York #28/R est:5000-7000
£3289 $6150 €4900 La fuite (44x64cm-17x25in) s.d.1926 prov. 29-Feb-4 Versailles Encheres #106/R est:3000-4000
£6000 $10380 €8760 Bouquet de fleurs dans un paysage (77x59cm-30x23in) s.d.1927. 11-Dec-3 Christie's, Kensington #106/R est:7000-10000
£8500 $15640 €12410 Personnages regardant des fleurs (60x71cm-24x28in) s.d.1938 prov. 24-Mar-4 Sotheby's, Olympia #79/R est:6000-8000

BAUCHKAUPT, Maurice (19th C) French
£368 $600 €537 Village landscape (30x38cm-12x15in) s. 28-Sep-3 Simpson's, Houston #149/R

BAUD, Henri (20th C) Belgian
Works on paper
£248 $400 €362 Polo player (36x46cm-14x18in) s. W/C. 20-Aug-3 James Julia, Fairfield #1051/R
£300 $555 €438 Portrait of a race horse, Ecurie (25x42cm-10x17in) s.i. pastel. 9-Mar-4 Bonhams, Knightsbridge #12/R

BAUDE, François-Charles (1880-1953) French
£352 $599 €514 Landscape with two cows (54x65cm-21x26in) s.d.1914. 5-Nov-3 Dobiaschofsky, Bern #337/R (S.FR 800)

BAUDE-COUILLAUD, Germaine (1885-1980) French
£455 $782 €650 Portrait d'homme en pied (180x100cm-71x39in) s. 5-Dec-3 Gros & Delettrez, Paris #90

BAUDERON, Louis (1809-?) French
£2632 $4842 €4000 Emploi de la dime (108x154cm-43x61in) exhib.lit. 23-Jun-4 Rieunier, Paris #36/R est:4500-6000

BAUDESSON, Nicolas (attrib) (1611-1680) French
£4317 $7079 €6000 Bouquet de fleurs dans un panier (50x65cm-20x26in) 6-Jun-3 Maigret, Paris #100/R est:6000-8000

BAUDIN, Eugène (1843-1907) French
£267 $485 €400 Paysage aux grands arbres (35x27cm-14x11in) s. 29-Jun-4 Chenu & Scrive, Lyon #16/R

BAUDIN, F (19/20th C) French?
£6040 $11174 €9000 Danseuse au harem (163x105cm-64x41in) s. s.i.verso. 15-Mar-4 Gros & Delettrez, Paris #180/R est:10000-15000

BAUDIT, Amedee (1825-1890) French
£419 $711 €612 Still life (31x50cm-12x20in) s.d.1858 board on panel. 5-Nov-3 Dobiaschofsky, Bern #338/R (S.FR 950)
£1100 $2035 €1606 Hunter's return (37x64cm-15x25in) s.d.1866. 10-Mar-4 Sotheby's, Olympia #227/R est:1200-1800
£1173 $1958 €1700 Coucher de soleil sur le lac (35x23cm-14x9in) s.d.1885. 17-Nov-3 Tajan, Paris #154/R est:1000-1500
£1689 $2973 €2500 Landscape in southern France (22x44cm-9x17in) s. panel. 22-May-4 Lempertz, Koln #1477/R est:1500

BAUDRY, Paul (1828-1886) French
£573 $974 €837 Cupid and Psyche (40x32cm-16x13in) s. 5-Nov-3 Dobiaschofsky, Bern #339/R (S.FR 1300)
£775 $1286 €1100 Mise au tombeau d'un saint (54x47cm-21x19in) bears studio st. 16-Jun-3 E & Eve, Paris #70
£927 $1687 €1400 Premier projet pour le plafond de l'Opera Tragedie (22x15cm-9x6in) s.i. oil pen black ink. 16-Jun-4 Piasa, Paris #197
Works on paper
£331 $603 €500 Heliodre d'apres Raphael (21x27cm-8x11in) s.i. W/C black crayon. 16-Jun-4 Piasa, Paris #196
£633 $1146 €950 Rose wreath (9x19cm-4x7in) W/C bodycol two. 2-Apr-4 Winterberg, Heidelberg #385
£1014 $1693 €1450 Rose garland (31x41cm-12x16in) htd white gouache W/C over pencil. 10-Oct-3 Winterberg, Heidelberg #532 est:450
£3448 $5724 €5000 Dieux de l'Olympe (60x50cm-24x20in) s.d.1852 W/C chl. 2-Oct-3 Sotheby's, Paris #31/R

BAUDRY, Paul (attrib) (1828-1886) French
Works on paper
£1200 $2172 €1800 Scythe aiguisant un couteau (35x29cm-14x11in) graphite htd gouache. 5-Apr-4 Deburaux, Boulogne #64 est:200-250

BAUDRY, Roger (?) ?
£738 $1366 €1100 Danseurs Watutsi (100x97cm-39x38in) s. canvas panel. 15-Mar-4 Horta, Bruxelles #295

BAUDUIN, Raphael (1870-1943) Belgian
£331 $603 €500 Paysage de riviere (44x92cm-17x36in) s. 16-Jun-4 Hotel des Ventes Mosan, Brussels #227

BAUER (?) ?
Sculpture
£2586 $4034 €3750 Standing nude females with perched parrot and a monkey (8cm-3in) bears sig. bronze pair. 1-Aug-2 Joel, Victoria #495 est:3000-4000 (A.D 7500)

BAUER, Carl Franz (1879-1954) Austrian
£496 $898 €724 Untitled - jumping the hurdle (20x25cm-8x10in) s. 18-Apr-4 Levis, Calgary #202/R est:400-500 (C.D 1200)
£521 $849 €750 Horse racing (22x33cm-9x13in) s. board. 23-Sep-3 Wiener Kunst Auktionen, Vienna #69/R
£532 $888 €750 Kaiser riding out (33x44cm-13x17in) s. board. 14-Oct-3 Dorotheum, Vienna #52/R
£661 $1197 €965 Untitled - trying to break away (20x25cm-8x10in) s. 18-Apr-4 Levis, Calgary #201/R est:400-500 (C.D 1600)
£694 $1104 €1000 Steeplechase (37x46cm-15x18in) s. panel. 13-Sep-3 Quittenbaum, Hamburg #82/R
£702 $1271 €1025 Untitled - finish line in sight (20x25cm-8x10in) s. 18-Apr-4 Levis, Calgary #203/R est:400-500 (C.D 1700)
£972 $1585 €1400 Tenebroso (33x28cm-13x11in) s.i. panel. 23-Sep-3 Wiener Kunst Auktionen, Vienna #70/R
£1129 $2077 €1648 Race, well away. Race, close finish (25x20cm-10x8in) s. pair. 14-Jun-4 Waddingtons, Toronto #27/R est:1000-1500 (C.D 2800)
£1400 $2380 €2044 Szerenes, a dark brown racehorse in a stable (42x49cm-17x19in) s.i. board. 27-Nov-3 Christie's, Kensington #71/R est:800-1200
£8725 $15443 €13000 Kaiser Franz Joseph I with troops (170x125cm-67x49in) s. 29-Apr-4 Dorotheum, Vienna #100/R est:7000-10000

BAUER, Constantin (1852-?) German
£556 $906 €800 Tyrolean peasant village (29x46cm-11x18in) s.d.1870. 25-Sep-3 Dr Fritz Nagel, Stuttgart #1328/R

BAUER, Gerard (1947-) French
£265 $482 €400 Portrait de Dali a l'etoile de mer (81x65cm-32x26in) s.d.2004 acrylic. 18-Jun-4 Charbonneaux, Paris #125
£268 $475 €400 2004 anne Dali (81x65cm-32x26in) s. s.i.d.verso acrylic. 28-Apr-4 Charbonneaux, Paris #107/R
£278 $453 €400 La medaille (81x65cm-32x26in) s. acrylic. 18-Jul-3 Charbonneaux, Paris #140

BAUER, Gustav (1874-1933) Austrian
Works on paper
£833 $1358 €1200 St Magdalena- southern Tyrol (43x59cm-17x23in) s.i. WC. 25-Sep-3 Neumeister, Munich #258/R

BAUER, Hans (1883-?) German
£533 $981 €800 Early spring landscape with fields and church spire in distance (50x69cm-20x27in) s. board. 11-Jun-4 Wendl, Rudolstadt #3945/R

BAUER, J (18/19th C) ?
£2000 $3640 €2920 Rest between chores (93x72cm-37x28in) s.i.d.1874. 16-Jun-4 Christie's, Kensington #245/R est:2000-3000

BAUER, Johann Balthazar (1811-1883) German
Works on paper
£30769 $52923 €44923 When she woke up, she was lying on the moss in the forest (33x36cm-13x14in) s.d.1913 W/C prov.lit. 7-Dec-3 Uppsala Auktionskammare, Uppsala #152/R est:100000-125000 (S.KR 400000)

BAUER, John (1882-1918) Swedish
Works on paper
£344 $554 €502 The old man and the boy (24x14cm-9x6in) Indian ink exhib. 25-Aug-3 Lilla Bukowskis, Stockholm #155 (S.KR 4500)
£437 $805 €656 Gnome behind tree (20x20cm-8x8in) Indian ink W/C. 14-Jun-4 Lilla Bukowskis, Stockholm #81/R (S.KR 6000)
£3462 $5954 €5055 Troll on forest hill (27x24cm-11x9in) W/C illustration prov.exhib.lit. 7-Dec-3 Uppsala Auktionskammare, Uppsala #154/R est:18000-20000 (S.KR 45000)
£7761 $13891 €11331 Mountain troll with eagles (25x25cm-10x10in) W/C lit. painted 1918. 25-May-4 Bukowskis, Stockholm #22/R est:40000-50000 (S.KR 105000)
£22173 $39690 €32373 The Princess in the forest (26x28cm-10x11in) s.d.1915 W/C lit. 25-May-4 Bukowskis, Stockholm #26/R est:175000-200000 (S.KR 300000)

BAUER, Karl (1905-1993) Austrian
£1206 $2013 €1700 Evening conversation (43x28cm-17x11in) s.d.76 paper. 16-Oct-3 Dorotheum, Salzburg #679/R est:600-800
£4895 $8322 €7000 The vow (81x65cm-32x26in) s.d.1976 canvas on panel. 19-Nov-3 Dorotheum, Klagenfurt #1 est:3600

BAUER, Marius Alexander Jacques (1867-1932) Dutch
£709 $1184 €1000 Eastern city, possibly Cairo (15x20cm-6x8in) indis.s. panel. 20-Oct-3 Glerum, Amsterdam #177/R
£2447 $4087 €3500 Horse riders in the desert (30x50cm-12x20in) s. board prov. 30-Jun-3 Sotheby's, Amsterdam #175
£6028 $10067 €8500 Elephant caravan (31x45cm-12x18in) s. panel. 20-Oct-3 Glerum, Amsterdam #179/R est:2000-3000
£6400 $10112 €9344 Town gate in Morocco (60x75cm-24x30in) s. 6-Sep-3 Shapes, Edinburgh #346/R est:4000-6000
£8333 $14167 €12000 Early morning at the Nile (58x75cm-23x30in) s. prov.exhib. 28-Oct-3 Christie's, Amsterdam #171/R est:10000-15000
Works on paper
£721 $1240 €1053 Pilgrimage to Mecca (40x67cm-16x26in) mono.i. W/C. 8-Dec-3 Philippe Schuler, Zurich #4196 (S.FR 1600)
£1351 $2378 €2000 Jewish family (16x15cm-6x6in) bears i. black chk exhib.lit. 19-May-4 Sotheby's, Amsterdam #355/R est:400-500
£1497 $2724 €2200 At the bazaar (65x51cm-26x20in) s. W/C red black chk pastel prov. 3-Feb-4 Christie's, Amsterdam #170/R est:2500-3500
£5556 $9444 €8000 Benares, on the banks of the river Ganges (59x45cm-23x18in) s. W/C htd white. 28-Oct-3 Christie's, Amsterdam #170/R est:3000-5000

BAUER, Rudolf (1889-1967) Polish
£8054 $14416 €12000 Untitled (50x64cm-20x25in) s. i. verso board exhib.prov. 25-May-4 Dorotheum, Vienna #147/R est:10000-15000
£20000 $35800 €30000 Rounds and triangles (130x130cm-51x51in) s. s. verso oil col oil chk prov. 14-May-4 Ketterer, Munich #350/R est:15000-20000

BAUER, William C (1888-?) American
Works on paper
£532 $850 €777 Coastal seascape (25x74cm-10x29in) s. W/C. 20-Sep-3 New Orleans Auction, New Orleans #482/R

BAUER-PEZELLEN, Tina (1897-1979) German?
Works on paper
£590 $986 €850 Orphans (36x27cm-14x11in) s. W/C over pencil. 25-Oct-3 Dr Lehr, Berlin #60/R

BAUER-STUMPF, Johanna (1873-1964) Dutch
£1208 $2235 €1800 Still life with daisies in a vase (26x37cm-10x15in) s. board. 15-Mar-4 Sotheby's, Amsterdam #195/R est:800-1200

BAUERMEISTER, Mary (1934-) German
Sculpture
£1536 $2750 €2243 Palette (32x32x11cm-13x13x4in) s.i.d.1966 num.1959 verso pen ink gass wood construction in box. 6-May-4 Doyle, New York #85/R est:1200-1600

BAUERNFEIND, Gustav (1848-1904) Austrian
Works on paper
£27000 $45090 €39420 Warden of the mosque, Damascus (50x38cm-20x15in) s. W/C. 14-Oct-3 Sotheby's, London #49/R est:30000-40000

BAUFFE, Victor (1849-1921) Dutch
£700 $1120 €1022 Dutch landscape with canal, cattle and distant windmill (99x76cm-39x30in) s. 16-Sep-3 Holloways, Banbury #328/R
£1141 $2111 €1700 Polder landscape with a peasant in a barge (60x86cm-24x34in) s. 15-Mar-4 Sotheby's, Amsterdam #97/R est:1500-2000
£1600 $2880 €2400 Grazing cows in a polder landscape (100x76cm-39x30in) s. 20-Apr-4 Sotheby's, Amsterdam #121/R est:2000-3000
£2553 $4264 €3600 Two net fishermen on the Kortenhoefse lake (78x119cm-31x47in) s. 20-Oct-3 Glerum, Amsterdam #73/R est:4000-6000
Works on paper
£1049 $1804 €1500 River view (45x61cm-18x24in) s. W/C. 8-Dec-3 Glerum, Amsterdam #26/R est:1800-2200

BAUGH, Dorothy Geraldine (1891-1983) American
£216 $400 €315 California late summer landscape (51x61cm-20x24in) s. 19-Jan-4 O'Gallerie, Oregon #55/R

BAUGIN, Lubin (attrib) (1610-1663) French
£18792 $34577 €28000 Still life with knife, plate, bread and raffia wine bottle (49x42cm-19x17in) mono. lit. 25-Mar-4 Dr Fritz Nagel, Stuttgart #629/R

BAUGNIES, René de (1869-1962) Belgian
£340 $629 €496 Sailing boats in an open sea (17x22cm-7x9in) s. board. 16-Feb-4 Bonhams, Bath #79
£461 $770 €650 Vaches au pres (60x44cm-24x17in) s.1898. 19-Oct-3 Daniel Herry, Beaune #10
£490 $817 €700 Boats (32x45cm-13x18in) s. 10-Oct-3 Stadion, Trieste #886/R

BAUGNIET, Charles (1814-1886) Flemish
£23529 $40000 €34352 Visite de la Nourrice (72x90cm-28x35in) s. panel. 28-Oct-3 Sotheby's, New York #165/R est:35000-45000

BAUGNIET, Charles (circle) (1814-1886) Flemish
£8500 $16065 €12410 Getting ready for the ball (58x44cm-23x17in) 19-Feb-4 Christie's, Kensington #86/R est:4000-6000

BAUGNIET, Marcel Louis (1896-1995) Belgian
£1049 $1752 €1500 Portrait de vieil homme (35x26cm-14x10in) board exhib. 11-Oct-3 De Vuyst, Lokeren #20 est:1500-1700
£1259 $2102 €1800 Portrait d'homme (30x19cm-12x7in) s. paper exhib. 11-Oct-3 De Vuyst, Lokeren #18/R est:1900-2200
£2667 $4880 €4000 Quatuor d'automne (36x27cm-14x11in) s.d.1929 paper on cardboard exhib. 7-Jun-4 Palais de Beaux Arts, Brussels #152/R est:3500-4500
£26471 $45000 €38648 After the ball (66x53cm-26x21in) s.indis.d. panel. 29-Oct-3 Christie's, Rockefeller NY #176/R est:60000-80000
Works on paper
£503 $931 €750 Vierge (23x31cm-9x12in) s. W/C. 13-Mar-4 De Vuyst, Lokeren #18
£634 $1096 €900 Hommage a Ben Nicholson (40x40cm-16x16in) s.d.1967 diluted blue ink mixed media board on canvas. 9-Dec-3 Vanderkindere, Brussels #191
£704 $1218 €1000 Portrait of Salvador Dali (43x33cm-17x13in) s.d.71 collage oil. 13-Dec-3 De Vuyst, Lokeren #17/R
£724 $1310 €1100 Troisieme temps de l'angoisse des machines (25x34cm-10x13in) s. W/C. 19-Apr-4 Horta, Bruxelles #197
£979 $1635 €1400 Bad luck bird (38x28cm-15x11in) s.i.d.1990 gouache pastel exhib. 11-Oct-3 De Vuyst, Lokeren #19/R
£1000 $1790 €1500 Salvador Dali (34x26cm-13x10in) s.d.70 collage oil. 15-May-4 De Vuyst, Lokeren #21/R est:1500-1800
£1958 $3368 €2800 Motard 32 (26x33cm-10x13in) s.d.1929 W/C. 8-Dec-3 Horta, Bruxelles #203/R est:2500-3000
£2000 $3660 €3000 Nature morte aux deux bouteilles (27x35cm-11x14in) s.d.1923 W/C. 7-Jun-4 Palais de Beaux Arts, Brussels #151/R est:2500-3500

BAUKEMA, Sieger (1852-1936) German
£578 $1052 €850 Autumn sky (81x100cm-32x39in) s. 3-Feb-4 Christie's, Amsterdam #186

BAUKHAGE, Gerd (1911-) German
£400 $716 €600 Garden in bloom (60x70cm-24x28in) mono.d.54 s.i. stretcher sackcloth. 15-May-4 Van Ham, Cologne #435/R

BAUKNECHT, Philipp (1884-1933) German
£1171 $2014 €1710 Landscape, Davos (24x32cm-9x13in) oil chk. 2-Dec-3 Koller, Zurich #3086 est:2500-3500 (S.FR 2600)
£1351 $2324 €1972 Chickens in garden (21x21cm-8x8in) oil chk pen. 2-Dec-3 Koller, Zurich #3088 est:3000-4000 (S.FR 3000)
£85973 $146154 €190000 Horse in the field (120x130cm-47x51in) s. i.verso painted 1917 prov. 25-Nov-3 Pierre Berge, Paris #13/R est:80000
Works on paper
£450 $775 €657 Mountain landscape, Davos (12x16cm-5x6in) mono. pastel. 2-Dec-3 Koller, Zurich #3091 (S.FR 1000)
£901 $1550 €1315 Davos mountains (28x25cm-11x10in) pastel. 2-Dec-3 Koller, Zurich #3084a est:2000-3000 (S.FR 2000)
£901 $1550 €1315 Ox cart (31x23cm-12x9in) pastel. 2-Dec-3 Koller, Zurich #3085/R est:2000-3000 (S.FR 2000)
£1171 $2014 €1710 Figure (35x25cm-14x10in) pastel. 2-Dec-3 Koller, Zurich #3092 est:2500-3500 (S.FR 2600)
£1447 $2663 €2200 Landscape of Davos (30x44cm-12x17in) 28-Jun-4 Sotheby's, Amsterdam #203/R est:1200-1500
£1974 $3632 €2882 Davoser landscape with three spruce trees (29x44cm-11x17in) W/C. 23-Jun-4 Koller, Zurich #3035/R est:4500-5500 (S.FR 4500)
£2072 $3564 €3025 Davos landscape (29x45cm-11x18in) s. W/C col pen. 2-Dec-3 Koller, Zurich #3089/R est:4500-5500 (S.FR 4600)
£2658 $4571 €3881 Davos (24x25cm-9x10in) pastel. 2-Dec-3 Koller, Zurich #3090/R est:3500-4500 (S.FR 5900)
£2867 $5246 €4300 Davos mountains (28x26cm-11x10in) pastel chk. 5-Jun-4 Lempertz, Koln #583/R est:3800

BAUM, Bert (20th C) American?
£549 $900 €802 Road to Steinsburg, winter landscape (41x51cm-16x20in) s.d.1963 canvasboard. 4-Jun-3 Alderfer's, Hatfield #352

BAUM, Carl (1812-1877) American
£4595 $8500 €6709 Still life with fruit, champagne flute and bird's nest on a marble ledge (91x74cm-36x29in) s. 11-Mar-4 Christie's, Rockefeller NY #12/R est:6000-8000

BAUM, Carl (1892-1966) German
£299 $550 €437 Team of draft horses plowing a field (23x36cm-9x14in) s. panel. 11-Jun-4 David Rago, Lambertville #362/R
£302 $556 €450 St Hubert from Maastrich and Luttich (34x52cm-13x20in) mono.d.1927 panel. 25-Mar-4 Karlheinz Kaupp, Staufen #2343/R

BAUM, Otto (1900-1977) German
Sculpture
£4167 $6792 €6000 Free form snail (52x28x24cm-20x11x9in) mono.d.1956/57 macassar wood prov. 27-Sep-3 Dr Fritz Nagel, Stuttgart #9464/R est:2500

BAUM, Paul (1859-1932) German
£4196 $7217 €6000 Haystacks (45x60cm-18x24in) s. painted 1891. 2-Dec-3 Sotheby's, Amsterdam #13/R est:5000-7000
£8333 $14917 €12500 Ploughed cornfield (45x60cm-18x24in) s. bears i. verso prov. 14-May-4 Ketterer, Munich #114/R est:12000-16000
£17483 $30070 €25000 St. Anna ter Muiden (50x62cm-20x24in) s. painted 1907. 2-Dec-3 Sotheby's, Amsterdam #12/R est:15000-25000
£34266 $58937 €49000 Taormina in late autumn sun with coastal trees in front of a bay (68x85cm-27x33in) s. prov. 5-Dec-3 Ketterer, Munich #38/R est:28000-35000
Works on paper
£526 $968 €800 Mediterranean Coast (18x30cm-7x12in) s. pencil W/C. 28-Jun-4 Sotheby's, Amsterdam #179/R

BAUM, Robert Emerson (20th C) American
Works on paper
£231 $425 €337 Winter Bucks county landscape (18x23cm-7x9in) s. pastel. 9-Jun-4 Alderfer's, Hatfield #458/R

BAUM, Walter Emerson (1884-1956) American
£503 $900 €734 Landscape with rock wall (30x41cm-12x16in) s. canvasboard. 29-May-4 Brunk, Ashville #335/R
£755 $1200 €1102 Meadows at Sellersville (15x23cm-6x9in) s. board. 10-Sep-3 Alderfer's, Hatfield #381/R
£813 $1300 €1187 Landscape with trees and stream (23x33cm-9x13in) s.d.1944 panel. 20-Sep-3 Pook & Pook, Downington #178 est:800-1000
£815 $1500 €1190 Edge of Old Dam (20x25cm-8x10in) s. board. 9-Jun-4 Alderfer's, Hatfield #521 est:800-1200
£924 $1700 €1349 Girl in black dress (30x23cm-12x9in) s. 9-Jun-4 Alderfer's, Hatfield #523 est:500-700
£932 $1500 €1361 House by the river (25x30cm-10x12in) s. s.i. verso board. 20-Aug-3 James Julia, Fairfield #1342/R est:2000-3000
£943 $1500 €1377 Reflections (25x30cm-10x12in) s. board. 10-Sep-3 Alderfer's, Hatfield #382/R est:1500-2500
£1056 $1700 €1542 Winter landscape (33x23cm-13x9in) board. 20-Aug-3 James Julia, Fairfield #1343/R est:800-1200
£1087 $2000 €1587 Flowered dress (41x30cm-16x12in) s. canvasboard. 9-Jun-4 Alderfer's, Hatfield #538/R est:1000-1500
£1125 $1800 €1643 Street scene of corner grocery, Allentown (38x48cm-15x19in) s. tempera. 20-Sep-3 Pook & Pook, Downington #358/R est:3000-4000
£1209 $2250 €1765 Autumn by sea (30x41cm-12x16in) s. board. 3-Mar-4 Alderfer's, Hatfield #392 est:1000-1500
£1337 $2300 €1952 Winter townscape with factories (30x41cm-12x16in) s. board. 7-Dec-3 Freeman, Philadelphia #228 est:2000-3000
£1359 $2500 €1984 Bouquet (46x38cm-18x15in) s. 11-Jun-4 David Rago, Lambertville #252/R est:2000-4000
£1494 $2750 €2181 Spring landscape with roadside building in the distance (15x20cm-6x8in) s. board. 9-Jun-4 Alderfer's, Hatfield #507/R est:1500-2000
£1572 $2500 €2295 Neshaminy Mill (28x36cm-11x14in) s. board. 10-Sep-3 Alderfer's, Hatfield #383/R est:2500-3500
£1734 $3000 €2532 Easton Bridge (20x25cm-8x10in) s. i.verso board. 10-Dec-3 Alderfer's, Hatfield #479/R est:3000-3500
£1734 $3000 €2532 Pennsylvania in Spring (30x39cm-12x15in) s.indis.d. masonite painted c.1930 prov. 10-Dec-3 Bonhams & Butterfields, San Francisco #6039/R est:3000-5000
£1747 $3250 €2551 Houses on the hill (66x102cm-26x40in) s. masonite. 3-Mar-4 Alderfer's, Hatfield #382/R est:3000-4000
£1747 $3250 €2551 River near Easton (64x76cm-25x30in) s. masonite. 3-Mar-4 Alderfer's, Hatfield #385/R est:3000-4000
£1747 $3250 €2551 Urban landscape (53x91cm-21x36in) s.d.1952 masonite. 3-Mar-4 Alderfer's, Hatfield #386/R est:2000-3000
£1766 $3250 €2578 Urban landscape (51x76cm-20x30in) s. 9-Jun-4 Alderfer's, Hatfield #488/R est:2000-3000
£1882 $3500 €2748 My old studio, impressionist winter landscape (28x30cm-11x12in) s. d.1919 verso. 3-Mar-4 Alderfer's, Hatfield #388 est:1500-2000
£1955 $3500 €2854 Untitled. s. 31-May-4 William A Smith, Plainfield #44/R
£1981 $3250 €2872 Autumn landscape with covered bridge (41x51cm-16x20in) s. 4-Jun-3 Alderfer's, Hatfield #405/R est:2000-2500
£2016 $3750 €2943 Winter landscape with stream (20x23cm-8x9in) s. s.d.1912 verso canvasboard. 3-Mar-4 Alderfer's, Hatfield #389/R est:1200-1800
£2023 $3500 €2954 New England boats Gloucester Harbour scene (41x51cm-16x20in) s. board. 10-Dec-3 Alderfer's, Hatfield #480/R est:2000-3000
£2038 $3750 €2975 Wenholdashtadt (20x25cm-8x10in) s.i.verso board. 9-Jun-4 Alderfer's, Hatfield #522/R est:700-900
£2038 $3750 €2975 Winter landscape with a brook in foreground (20x25cm-8x10in) s. board. 9-Jun-4 Alderfer's, Hatfield #550/R est:1500-2000
£2395 $4000 €3497 Spring house (30x36cm-12x14in) s. board. 9-Oct-3 Christie's, Rockefeller NY #68/R est:4000-6000
£2446 $4500 €3571 Leaves are gone (41x51cm-16x20in) s.d.1922 verso. 9-Jun-4 Alderfer's, Hatfield #469 est:5000-7000
£2446 $4500 €3571 Autumn mood and motion (30x41cm-12x16in) s. canvasboard. 9-Jun-4 Alderfer's, Hatfield #551 est:1500-2000
£2554 $4750 €3729 Late autumn landscape with road and houses (30x36cm-12x14in) s. board. 3-Mar-4 Alderfer's, Hatfield #380 est:7000-9000
£2616 $4500 €3819 Houses by a road (41x51cm-16x20in) s.i.d.1938 verso canvasboard. 7-Dec-3 Freeman, Philadelphia #178 est:4000-6000
£2673 $4250 €3903 Spring Valley (33x41cm-13x16in) board. 10-Sep-3 Alderfer's, Hatfield #384/R est:2000-3000
£2717 $5000 €3967 Winter landscape with river and distance buildings (30x41cm-12x16in) s. board. 9-Jun-4 Alderfer's, Hatfield #478/R est:3000-4000
£2957 $5500 €4317 City hotel, urban landscape (61x76cm-24x30in) s.d.49 board. 3-Mar-4 Alderfer's, Hatfield #381 est:7000-9000
£2989 $5500 €4364 Boulders (51x61cm-20x24in) s. board. 9-Jun-4 Alderfer's, Hatfield #477/R est:4000-6000

£2989	$5500	€4364	Gloucester (40x51cm-16x20in) s.i.d.1937 canvasboard. 27-Jun-4 Freeman, Philadelphia #181/R est:3000-5000
£3049	$5000	€4421	St Michael's, autumn (51x61cm-20x24in) s. 4-Jun-3 Alderfer's, Hatfield #399/R est:2000-3000
£3049	$5000	€4421	Winter brook (36x43cm-14x17in) s.d.1910 board. 4-Jun-3 Alderfer's, Hatfield #401/R est:2000-3000
£3261	$6000	€4761	Autumn (64x76cm-25x30in) s. 9-Jun-4 Alderfer's, Hatfield #451/R est:8000-12000
£3261	$6000	€4761	Carversville (41x50cm-16x20in) s.i.d.1937 verso canvasboard. 27-Jun-4 Freeman, Philadelphia #165/R est:4000-6000
£3261	$6000	€4761	Harvest Web (41x51cm-16x20in) s. i. verso canvasboard. 27-Jun-4 Freeman, Philadelphia #196/R est:3000-5000
£3261	$6000	€4761	Winter landscape (40x50cm-16x20in) s. canvasboard. 27-Jun-4 Freeman, Philadelphia #202/R est:6000-8000
£3659	$6000	€5306	Allentown backyards, church in the city (61x76cm-24x30in) s. masonite. 4-Jun-3 Alderfer's, Hatfield #397/R est:3000-4000
£3693	$6500	€5392	Brook, Sellersvile. Landscape (30x36cm-12x14in) s. double-sided. 21-May-4 Pook & Pook, Downington #374/R est:2000-3000
£3804	$7000	€5554	Hagersville (40x51cm-16x20in) s. s.i.d.12/30/36 verso canvasboard. 27-Jun-4 Freeman, Philadelphia #182/R est:4000-6000
£3804	$7000	€5554	Brook near Boyertown (40x51cm-16x20in) s.i.d.1936 canvasboard. 27-Jun-4 Freeman, Philadelphia #207/R est:4000-6000
£3911	$7000	€5710	Pennsylvania village (41x51cm-16x20in) s. prov. 6-May-4 Shannon's, Milford #4/R est:4000-6000
£4070	$7000	€5942	Allentown (64x71cm-25x28in) s.d.1954. 7-Dec-3 Freeman, Philadelphia #188 est:5000-8000
£4335	$7500	€6329	Pinter of abstraction (58x74cm-23x29in) s.d.1955 casein on board. 10-Dec-3 Alderfer's, Hatfield #477/R est:5000-6000
£4375	$7000	€6388	Interior scene of flowers in a studio (58x74cm-23x29in) s.id.1954 masonite sold with pencil study. 20-Sep-3 Pook & Pook, Downington #357/R est:3500-4500
£4375	$7000	€6388	Winter landscape (38x48cm-15x19in) s. i.verso board prov. 20-Sep-3 Pook & Pook, Downington #454/R est:3000-4000
£4403	$7000	€6428	Bucks County Village (41x51cm-16x20in) s. masonite. 10-Sep-3 Alderfer's, Hatfield #378/R est:5000-7000
£4651	$8000	€6790	Landscape (30x36cm-12x14in) s. board painted c.1922. 7-Dec-3 Freeman, Philadelphia #177 est:5000-8000
£4717	$7500	€6887	Mill and covered Bridge (76x64cm-30x25in) s.d.39 canvas on board. 10-Sep-3 Alderfer's, Hatfield #379/R est:6000-8000
£4913	$8500	€7173	Melting snow (81x102cm-32x40in) s. 10-Dec-3 Alderfer's, Hatfield #474/R est:10000-12000
£4913	$8500	€7173	Autumn landscape with stream and barn (51x61cm-20x24in) s. board. 10-Dec-3 Alderfer's, Hatfield #476/R est:5000-6000
£5163	$9500	€7538	Winter glow (36x48cm-14x19in) s. board. 9-Jun-4 Alderfer's, Hatfield #487/R est:5000-7000
£5163	$9500	€7538	Brook in the woods (60x50cm-24x20in) s. s.i.d.1935 verso canvasboard. 27-Jun-4 Freeman, Philadelphia #198/R est:5000-8000
£5202	$9000	€7595	Downtown (89x114cm-35x45in) s.d.51 masonite. 10-Dec-3 Alderfer's, Hatfield #475 est:5000-7000
£5294	$9000	€7729	Cartersville Church, in winter street scene (33x48cm-13x19in) s. i.verso board prov. 18-Nov-3 John Moran, Pasadena #30 est:2500-4000
£6098	$10000	€8842	Brook, winter landscape (64x76cm-25x30in) s. i.verso painted c.1920. 4-Jun-3 Alderfer's, Hatfield #379/R est:18000-20000
£7317	$12000	€10610	Bucks County autumn (51x61cm-20x24in) s. s.i.verso. 4-Jun-3 Alderfer's, Hatfield #384/R est:10000-12000
£9249	$16000	€13504	Winter landscape with stream in foreground (64x76cm-25x30in) s. 10-Dec-3 Alderfer's, Hatfield #473/R est:15000-20000
£9497	$17000	€13866	Winter, Perkiomen valley (51x61cm-20x24in) s. i.verso. 26-May-4 Doyle, New York #81/R est:6000-8000
£10326	$19000	€15076	Creek, spring, Sellersville (81x102cm-32x40in) s.i.d.April 1925. 11-Jun-4 David Rago, Lambertville #260/R est:30000-40000
£10983	$19000	€16035	Carversville winter (81x102cm-32x40in) s. painted c.1926. 10-Dec-3 Alderfer's, Hatfield #471/R est:18000-22000
£11413	$21000	€16663	Pennsylvania winter landscape with horse and sleigh (51x76cm-20x30in) s. prov. 27-Jun-4 Freeman, Philadelphia #163/R est:12000-18000
£12228	$22500	€17853	Winter sunlight (81x102cm-32x40in) s. 9-Jun-4 Alderfer's, Hatfield #457 est:12000-18000
£13587	$25000	€19837	Quakertown Street (64x76cm-25x30in) s. i.d.1949 verso. 9-Jun-4 Alderfer's, Hatfield #456 est:12000-15000
£20380	$37500	€29755	Winter sunlight and shadow (91x76cm-36x30in) s. 11-Jun-4 David Rago, Lambertville #347/R est:45000-55000
£24566	$42500	€35866	Winter village (61x76cm-24x30in) s. 10-Dec-3 Alderfer's, Hatfield #472/R est:15000-20000
£27174	$50000	€39674	Pennsylvania Hills, Winter (76x91cm-30x36in) s. i. verso. 27-Jun-4 Freeman, Philadelphia #185/R est:10000-15000

Works on paper

£259	$425	€376	Reclining nude (15x15cm-6x6in) s. W/C. 4-Jun-3 Alderfer's, Hatfield #408
£484	$900	€707	Study of nude female (41x28cm-16x11in) s. W/C. 3-Mar-4 Alderfer's, Hatfield #393 est:400-600
£488	$800	€708	Filmore street (23x46cm-9x18in) s.d.2-18-49. 4-Jun-3 Alderfer's, Hatfield #409
£610	$1000	€885	Valley landscape in autumn (25x38cm-10x15in) s. W/C. 4-Jun-3 Alderfer's, Hatfield #406/R
£1033	$1900	€1508	Woods and brook in winter (38x48cm-15x19in) s. W/C gouache. 9-Jun-4 Alderfer's, Hatfield #531/R est:1200-1800
£1494	$2750	€2181	Winter in Mauch Chunk (56x79cm-22x31in) s.d.38 W/C. 9-Jun-4 Alderfer's, Hatfield #508/R est:1500-2500
£2358	$3750	€3443	Upper Bucks County Hills (53x76cm-21x30in) s. gouache board. 10-Sep-3 Alderfer's, Hatfield #380/R est:3500-4500
£2717	$5000	€3967	North 5th Street, Allentown (56x74cm-22x29in) s.d.1955 W/C gouache. 9-Jun-4 Alderfer's, Hatfield #499/R est:2000-3000
£2989	$5500	€4364	O'Brien Farm, Perkasie (23x30cm-9x12in) s.d.1938 verso pastel. 9-Jun-4 Alderfer's, Hatfield #532 est:1000-1500

BAUM, Walter Emerson (attrib) (1884-1956) American

£1879	$3250	€2743	Landscape depicting Bethlehem farm (41x51cm-16x20in) masonite. 10-Dec-3 Alderfer's, Hatfield #478/R est:3500-4500

BAUMANN, Ernst (1909-1992) Swiss

£603	$1080	€880	Blue coat (140x90cm-55x35in) s.d.58 exhib. 12-May-4 Dobiaschofsky, Bern #332/R (S.FR 1400)

BAUMANN, Gustave (1881-1971) American

Prints

£1863	$3000	€2701	Ranchos de Taos church (23x28cm-9x11in) woodblock. 22-Aug-3 Altermann Galleries, Santa Fe #92
£2400	$4392	€3504	Pine and aspen (32x32cm-13x13in) s.i.num.93/120 col woodcut. 3-Jun-4 Christie's, Kensington #5/R est:1500-2000
£3315	$6000	€4840	Indiana red gum trees (24x29cm-9x11in) s.i.num.16/120 col woodcut. 19-Apr-4 Bonhams & Butterfields, San Francisco #7/R est:4000-6000
£3315	$6000	€4840	Road of a morning (27x25cm-11x10in) s.i.num.62/100 col woodcut. 19-Apr-4 Bonhams & Butterfields, San Francisco #10/R est:4000-6000
£4118	$7000	€6012	Ranchos de Taos church (25x28cm-10x11in) woodblock print. 1-Nov-3 Altermann Galleries, Santa Fe #57
£4143	$7500	€6049	Pine and aspen (33x33cm-13x13in) s.i.d.1946 num. III 77/125 col woodcut. 19-Apr-4 Bonhams & Butterfields, San Francisco #8/R est:4000-6000
£4268	$7000	€6189	Silver sky (36x41cm-14x16in) st.sig.i.num.59/125 col woodblock. 2-Jun-3 Grogan, Boston #680/R
£4491	$7500	€6557	Bright angel trail (24x29cm-9x11in) s.i.num.II 33/125 col woodcut. 21-Oct-3 Bonhams & Butterfields, San Francisco #1007/R
£4520	$8000	€6599	Morning sun (31x28cm-12x11in) s.i. col woodcut executed c.1931. 30-Apr-4 Sotheby's, New York #2/R est:7000-10000
£4545	$8000	€6636	April (33x33cm-13x13in) s.d. col woodblock. 23-May-4 Treadway Gallery, Cincinnati #3/R est:6000-8000
£4865	$9000	€7103	Lilac year (31x34cm-12x13in) s.i. col woodcut. 12-Feb-4 Christie's, Rockefeller NY #258/R est:3000-4000
£5248	$9500	€7662	Grand Canon (32x33cm-13x13in) s.i.num. I 22/125 col woodcut. 19-Apr-4 Bonhams & Butterfields, San Francisco #9/R est:4000-6000
£5682	$10000	€8296	My garden (20x15cm-8x6in) s.d. col woodblock. 23-May-4 Treadway Gallery, Cincinnati #2/R est:3000-4000
£5882	$10000	€8588	Lilac year (31x34cm-12x13in) s.i. col woodcut. 31-Oct-3 Sotheby's, New York #182/R
£6471	$11000	€9448	Valle Grande (33x33cm-13x13in) s.i.num.12/125 woodblock exec.c.1922 prov.lit. 1-Nov-3 Santa Fe Art, Santa Fe #58/R est:6000-8000
£9412	$16000	€13742	Day of the deer dance (48x53cm-19x21in) s.num.15/100 woodblock prov.lit. 1-Nov-3 Santa Fe Art, Santa Fe #60/R est:10000-12000
£11364	$20000	€16591	Hopi Katzinas (30x33cm-12x13in) s.d. col woodblock. 23-May-4 Treadway Gallery, Cincinnati #1/R est:4000-6000

Works on paper

£8824	$15000	€12883	Spring in Santa Fe (23x25cm-9x10in) s. gouache prov.lit. 1-Nov-3 Santa Fe Art, Santa Fe #59/R est:20000-30000

BAUMANN, Hans Otto (1862-?) Swiss

£1189	$2021	€1700	Les joueurs de cartes dans la cave a vin (51x41cm-20x16in) s.d.98. 18-Nov-3 Vanderkindere, Brussels #5 est:500-750

BAUMANN, Karl Herman (1911-1984) American

£291	$500	€425	Untitled, KB-4-600-52. board. 6-Dec-3 Harvey Clar, Oakland #1187
£302	$550	€441	Untitled (38x48cm-15x19in) init.d.1969 board. 7-Feb-4 Harvey Clar, Oakland #1338
£302	$550	€441	Abstract (41x51cm-16x20in) s. board. 7-Feb-4 Harvey Clar, Oakland #1345
£385	$700	€562	Untitled (38x48cm-15x19in) s.d.1959 board. 7-Feb-4 Harvey Clar, Oakland #1337
£419	$750	€612	Untitled (38x48cm-15x19in) s.d.1968 board. 10-Jan-4 Harvey Clar, Oakland #1189
£447	$800	€653	Untitled (38x48cm-15x19in) s.d.1968 board. 10-Jan-4 Harvey Clar, Oakland #1194
£467	$850	€682	Untitled. s.d.1967 board. 7-Feb-4 Harvey Clar, Oakland #1339
£479	$800	€699	Untitled abstraction. init.d.1965 board. 18-Oct-3 Harvey Clar, Oakland #1259
£484	$900	€707	Abstract (51x38cm-20x15in) s.d.1968 board. 6-Mar-4 Harvey Clar, Oakland #1261
£503	$900	€734	Space concept (38x48cm-15x19in) s.d.1949 board. 10-Jan-4 Harvey Clar, Oakland #1190
£559	$1000	€816	To Sibelius, Symphony 2, Opus (46x61cm-18x24in) init.verso board. 10-Jan-4 Harvey Clar, Oakland #1191
£663	$1200	€968	Untitled - still life with coffee pots and coctail (41x51cm-16x20in) s.d.1951 canvasboard. 3-Apr-4 Harvey Clar, Oakland #1227
£719	$1200	€1050	Untitled - study of light. s.d.1967 board. 15-Nov-3 Harvey Clar, Oakland #122
£950	$1700	€1387	Buildings on the Bay (38x48cm-15x19in) s.d.1957 board. 10-Jan-4 Harvey Clar, Oakland #1580
£1018	$1700	€1486	Ultra-ultra, war painting. init.d.1952 panel. 15-Nov-3 Harvey Clar, Oakland #1203
£1176	$2000	€1717	Spring - factory interior (61x76cm-24x30in) s.d.53 init.d.verso oil on paperboard prov.exhib. 9-Nov-3 Bonhams & Butterfields, Los Angeles #4028/R
£1453	$2500	€2121	Sierras. s.d.1950. 6-Dec-3 Harvey Clar, Oakland #1174
£1647	$2750	€2405	Untitled - future fantasy. s.d.1952. 18-Oct-3 Harvey Clar, Oakland #1483

Works on paper

£233	$400	€340	End of Stanyon St. s.d.1938 W/C. 6-Dec-3 Harvey Clar, Oakland #1191
£254	$425	€371	Untitled - harbour scene. init.d.1939 W/C. 18-Oct-3 Harvey Clar, Oakland #1257
£254	$425	€371	Pastoral abstraction. init.d.1939 W/C. 18-Oct-3 Harvey Clar, Oakland #1258
£262	$450	€383	Mixed floral. W/C. 6-Dec-3 Harvey Clar, Oakland #1190
£265	$475	€387	The beach (43x28cm-17x11in) s.d.1938 W/C. 10-Jan-4 Harvey Clar, Oakland #1188
£376	$700	€549	Landscape with palm trees (30x46cm-12x18in) estate st. W/C. 6-Mar-4 Harvey Clar, Oakland #1258
£385	$700	€562	Cityscape (30x46cm-12x18in) W/C. 7-Feb-4 Harvey Clar, Oakland #1241
£387	$700	€565	Green oaks (30x46cm-12x18in) s.d.1940 W/C. 3-Apr-4 Harvey Clar, Oakland #1224
£389	$650	€568	Redwoods. s.d.1939 W/C. 18-Oct-3 Harvey Clar, Oakland #1252
£403	$750	€588	Boats (23x36cm-9x14in) s.d.1941 W/C. 6-Mar-4 Harvey Clar, Oakland #1259
£419	$750	€612	Floral still life. init.d.1958 W/C. 10-Jan-4 Harvey Clar, Oakland #1193
£440	$800	€642	Wide River (46x30cm-18x12in) s.d.1939 W/C. 7-Feb-4 Harvey Clar, Oakland #1240
£442	$800	€645	Untitled - grove of trees (30x46cm-12x18in) s.d.1939 W/C. 3-Apr-4 Harvey Clar, Oakland #1223

£467 $850 €682 Boats on the bay (30x46cm-12x18in) init.d.1940 W/C. 7-Feb-4 Harvey Clar, Oakland #1343/R
£470 $850 €686 Untitled - hills and trees (25x38cm-10x15in) s.d.1941 W/C. 3-Apr-4 Harvey Clar, Oakland #1225
£472 $850 €689 Industrial landscape (53x71cm-21x28in) s.d.39 W/C gouache. 25-Apr-4 Bonhams & Butterfields, San Francisco #5555/R
£479 $800 €699 Abstract in blue. s.d.1941 W/C. 15-Nov-3 Harvey Clar, Oakland #1198
£958 $1600 €1399 Studio still life. s.d.1950 gouache. 15-Nov-3 Harvey Clar, Oakland #1201
£1078 $1800 €1574 Redwoods. s.d.1939 W/C double-sided. 15-Nov-3 Harvey Clar, Oakland #1453a

BAUMANN-HUDSON, Edith (20th C) American
£395 $700 €577 Untitled (152x152cm-60x60in) s.d.1988 verso acrylic. 2-May-4 Bonhams & Butterfields, Los Angeles #3037/R

BAUMEISTER, Herman (1867-?) German
£1589 $2909 €2400 Red blossoms on Arabian arch (80x60cm-31x24in) s. panel. 8-Apr-4 Dorotheum, Vienna #174/R est:2400-3200

BAUMEISTER, Samuel (attrib) (17th C) Swedish
Miniatures
£2400 $4296 €3504 Frederick the Great, King of Prussia in uniform. Prince Henry (4cm-2in) g metal frames pair. 25-May-4 Christie's, London #77/R est:600-800

BAUMEISTER, Willi (1889-1955) German
£10917 $19869 €15939 Self portrait, in the studio (55x45cm-22x18in) cardboard painted 1911 prov.exhib.lit. 18-Jun-4 Kornfeld, Bern #7/R est:25000 (S.FR 25000)
£18182 $30909 €26000 Monturi (25x35cm-10x14in) s.d.54 oil pencil board prov.lit. 26-Nov-3 Dorotheum, Vienna #58/R est:25000-28000
£20000 $36800 €29200 Figuren auf blau (36x46cm-14x18in) s. s.i.d.1950 stretcher tempera on board prov.lit. 25-Jun-4 Christie's, London #118/R est:20000-30000
£22333 $40870 €33500 Figur (35x18cm-14x7in) s.i.d.nov 924 tempera crayon prov.lit. 6-Jun-4 Anaf, Lyon #317/R est:30000-35000
£22378 $38042 €32000 Dancer II (41x33cm-16x13in) mono.i.d.1934 verso oil sand board prov.exhib.lit. 26-Nov-3 Lempertz, Koln #576/R est:35000-40000
£33333 $61333 €50000 White butterfly (30x40cm-12x16in) s.d.1954 i.d.verso oil resin putty cardboard prov.exhib.lit. 11-Jun-4 Villa Grisebach, Berlin #69/R est:50000-70000
£48951 $83217 €70000 Landscape with figures - lively walled landscape (45x34cm-18x13in) s.d.46 synthetic resin spackle board prov. 28-Nov-3 Villa Grisebach, Berlin #77/R est:70000-90000
£56667 $102000 €85000 Summer festival (53x64cm-21x25in) s.i.d. verso oil resin spray panel. 24-Apr-4 Dr Lehr, Berlin #45/R est:90000
£120000 $220800 €180000 Black rock on grey (65x81cm-26x32in) s.d.51-55 s.i.verso oil resin putty masonite prov. 11-Jun-4 Villa Grisebach, Berlin #70/R est:180000-240000
Prints
£2867 $5131 €4300 Nocturnal (35x44cm-14x17in) s.i. col silkcut board. 15-May-4 Van Ham, Cologne #437/R est:2500
Works on paper
£5500 $10120 €8030 Relieffiguren (30x47cm-12x19in) s.d.7 49 pastel prov. 24-Jun-4 Sotheby's, London #220/R est:6000-8000
£12667 $22673 €19000 Montaru with gondola (24x16cm-9x6in) s.d.7.54 collage pastel pencil. 15-May-4 Dr Sturies, Dusseldorf #16/R

BAUMER, Eduard (1892-1977) German
£3846 $6538 €5500 Vase of flowers (79x60cm-31x24in) board. 28-Nov-3 Wiener Kunst Auktionen, Vienna #487/R est:5500-12000
£8054 $14255 €12000 Autumn landscape by Neusiedlersee (66x91cm-26x36in) s.d. 28-Apr-4 Wiener Kunst Auktionen, Vienna #233/R est:12000-18000
£10738 $19221 €16000 Blossoming meadow (75x91cm-30x36in) lit. 27-May-4 Hassfurther, Vienna #32/R est:18000-22000
£11111 $18889 €16000 House in the fields (95x70cm-37x28in) mono. 28-Oct-3 Wiener Kunst Auktionen, Vienna #219/R est:13000-20000

BAUMER, Johan Ernst (1870-1919) Dutch
£1389 $2194 €2000 Onweerswolk, Blaricum - leading the flock over the heath (70x90cm-28x35in) s. s.i.verso. 2-Sep-3 Christie's, Amsterdam #200/R est:2000-3000

BAUMER, Wilhelm (1829-1895) German
Works on paper
£6667 $12067 €10000 Deux vues du Chateau de Rohan, l'une cote ville, l'autre cote parc (59x101cm-23x40in) s.d.1856 W/C pen gouache pair. 31-Mar-4 Sotheby's, Paris #84/R est:10000-15000

BAUMGARTEN, Georg (1894-1945) German
£8667 $15860 €13000 Wood (96x81cm-38x32in) s. i. stretcher prov.exhib. 5-Jun-4 Lempertz, Koln #589/R est:13000-15000

BAUMGARTEN, Lothar (1944-) ?
Photographs
£4000 $6680 €5840 Pupeille. Verlorene fruchter (65x82cm-26x32in) c-prints num.5 and 4 of 10 exec.1968 and 1969 pair prov. 22-Oct-3 Christie's, London #152/R est:4000-6000

BAUMGARTEN, Theodor (1902-1968) Austrian
£284 $474 €400 Self portrait with palette (50x50cm-20x20in) s.d.12.8.45 panel. 16-Oct-3 Dorotheum, Salzburg #682/R

BAUMGARTNER, H (1868-1927) German
£2198 $4000 €3209 Travelers resting in an alpine landscape (52x71cm-20x28in) s. 29-Jun-4 Sotheby's, New York #127/R est:4000-6000

BAUMGARTNER, J Jay (1865-1946) American
£1879 $3250 €2743 Annunciation (61x51cm-24x20in) s.d.1942 canvasboard prov.exhib. 10-Dec-3 Bonhams & Butterfields, San Francisco #6284/R est:3000-5000

BAUMGARTNER, Johann Wolfgang (1712-1761) German
Works on paper
£933 $1689 €1400 Philip and Jacob the Younger (13x9cm-5x4in) wash brush over pencil. 2-Apr-4 Winterberg, Heidelberg #271/R
£1567 $2836 €2350 In the Temple (10x8cm-4x3in) Indian ink brush pen. 2-Apr-4 Winterberg, Heidelberg #269/R est:1750

BAUMGARTNER, Peter (1834-1911) German
£2699 $4750 €3941 Blue umbrella (61x46cm-24x18in) s. 21-May-4 North East Auctions, Portsmouth #1518/R
£6291 $11450 €9500 Pickled herring breakfast to get rid of a hangover (74x91cm-29x36in) s.d.1891. 16-Jun-4 Hugo Ruef, Munich #929/R est:9500

BAUMGARTNER, Thomas (1892-1962) German
£1027 $1747 €1500 Greyhound on slope (72x46cm-28x18in) s. 5-Nov-3 Hugo Ruef, Munich #934/R est:300
£1027 $1747 €1500 Small cat on slope (72x46cm-28x18in) s. 5-Nov-3 Hugo Ruef, Munich #933
£2431 $3962 €3500 Portrait of a peasant (52x39cm-20x15in) s.d.1924 panel. 24-Sep-3 Neumeister, Munich #393/R est:1600

BAUMHAUER, Sebald (attrib) (fl.1500-1533) German
Works on paper
£4098 $7500 €5983 Village scene with a lake and distant mountains (19x22cm-7x9in) pen black ink htd gold vellum. 29-Jan-4 Swann Galleries, New York #278/R est:10000-15000

BAUMHOFER, Walter M (1904-1986) American
£331 $600 €483 Men on horseback riding through woods (64x66cm-25x26in) board. 16-Apr-4 American Auctioneer #20/R
£405 $700 €591 Blacksmith at work, boys and dog playing in background (97x74cm-38x29in) s. 10-Dec-3 Alderfer's, Hatfield #354/R
£434 $750 €634 Canal boat days in early Pennsylvania (91x69cm-36x27in) s. board. 10-Dec-3 Alderfer's, Hatfield #355/R
£1453 $2600 €2121 Hunter and pack of dogs under attack by jaguar. tigre dos! (56x84cm-22x33in) s. board. 15-May-4 Illustration House, New York #9/R est:1500-3000
£3293 $5500 €4808 Death message (79x53cm-31x21in) s. 15-Nov-3 Illustration House, New York #13/R est:6000-9000
£4469 $8000 €6525 Doc Savage forces a boat to capsize, red snow (76x51cm-30x20in) s. masonite. 15-May-4 Illustration House, New York #17/R est:9000-12000

BAUMHOFER, Walter M (attrib) (1904-1986) American
£347 $600 €507 Portrait of Davy Crocket (81x61cm-32x24in) 10-Dec-3 Alderfer's, Hatfield #356/R

BAUR, Albert (jnr) (1868-1959) German
£567 $1026 €850 On the Reeser Schanz (45x65cm-18x26in) s. 1-Apr-4 Van Ham, Cologne #1283/R

BAUR, Johann Wilhelm (1607-c.1640) Austrian
Works on paper
£17000 $31110 €24820 Moored shipped with figures on the shoreline. Harbour capriccio with shipmakers (6x13cm-2x5in) gouache vellum on panel pair. 7-Jul-4 Bonhams, New Bond Street #134/R est:5000-8000

BAUR, Theodore (1835-1898) American
Sculpture
£1381 $2500 €2016 Tribute to William Merritt Chase, a bell (19cm-7in) s.d.Nov. 1 1849 brown pat bronze st.f.Henry-Bonnard. 31-Mar-4 Sotheby's, New York #117/R est:4000-6000

BAURIEDL, Otto (1879-1956) German
£1361 $2435 €2000 Winter mountain landscape (74x99cm-29x39in) s. 17-Mar-4 Neumeister, Munich #399/R est:1500

BAURSCHEIT, Jan Pieter van (elder-attrib) (1669-1728) Flemish
Sculpture
£283688 $473759 €400000 Francois Henri de Montmorency (115cm-45in) white marble sold with base. 15-Oct-3 Sotheby's, Paris #78/R est:300000-450000

BAUSCH, A (19th C) German
£563 $901 €800 Southern bay with harbour (32x46cm-13x18in) s. panel. 18-Sep-3 Rieber, Stuttgart #1063/R

BAUST, Fritz (1912-) German
£420 $701 €600 Konigsberg harbour (50x60cm-20x24in) s.i.d.1940 verso. 28-Jun-3 Bolland & Marotz, Bremen #759/R

BAUW, Karel de (1909-) Belgian?
£417 $654 €600 Le porche (34x30cm-13x12in) s. 26-Aug-3 Galerie Moderne, Brussels #348
£599 $1000 €875 Haywagon (81x119cm-32x47in) s.d.1969. 20-Jun-3 Freeman, Philadelphia #259/R

BAUZER, Francisco (1887-1945) South American

Works on paper

£483 $850 €705 Pocitos Hotel (29x45cm-11x18in) s. W/C. 5-Jan-4 Galeria y Remates, Montevideo #98/R

BAVIERA, Vincenzo (1945-) Swiss

Sculpture

£1389 $2319 €2000 Architecture (33x35x15cm-13x14x6in) mono. painted steel. 24-Oct-3 Ketterer, Hamburg #273/R est:2000-3000

BAWA, Manjit (1941-) Indian

£10669 $19203 €15577 Acrobat (77x59cm-30x23in) s.d.27.8.88. 25-Apr-4 Christie's, Hong Kong #611/R est:65000-75000 (HK.D 150000)

BAWDEN, Edward (1903-1989) British

£6000 $11040 €8760 Gold diggings quarry, Minions, Liskeard (44x56cm-17x22in) s. W/C prov. 23-Jun-4 Cheffins, Cambridge #477/R est:2500-3500

Prints

£2200 $3982 €3212 Ives Farm (41x62cm-16x24in) s.num.6/35 linocut. 1-Apr-4 Olivers, Sudbury #80 est:600-800

Works on paper

£300 $546 €438 Figures at a racecourse, some in an enclosure (19x24cm-7x9in) init. pen ink over pencil. 16-Jun-4 Rupert Toovey, Partridge Green #47

£320 $582 €467 View of figures at a horticultural show within a marquee (21x30cm-8x12in) pen ink over pencil. 16-Jun-4 Rupert Toovey, Partridge Green #46

£460 $837 €672 View of a regatta on the Thames with figures on a balcony (20x25cm-8x10in) init. pen ink over pencil. 16-Jun-4 Rupert Toovey, Partridge Green #48

£480 $845 €701 Sixpence that rolled away (27x32cm-11x13in) pen ink prov. 18-May-4 Bonhams, Knightsbridge #70/R

£680 $1190 €993 View of a grand building beside the Algemene Bank, Nederland (53x74cm-21x29in) s. W/C. 19-Dec-3 Mallams, Oxford #94/R

£900 $1629 €1314 Tree trunk (57x45cm-22x18in) s.d.1954 pen W/C. 1-Apr-4 Olivers, Sudbury #81

£1400 $2534 €2044 Heligan jungle (52x62cm-20x24in) s. W/C. 1-Apr-4 Olivers, Sudbury #83/R est:1500-2000

£1600 $2528 €2320 Church in the trees (45x56cm-18x22in) s.d.1958 W/C. 3-Sep-3 Bonhams, Bury St Edmunds #389 est:1000-1500

£1900 $3458 €2774 Sketch book of Ayrshire views (27x18cm-11x7in) pencil. 1-Jul-4 Christie's, Kensington #327/R est:800-1200

£2000 $3400 €2920 Above Gougan Barra (48x58cm-19x23in) s.d.1963 W/C bodycol. 30-Oct-3 Duke & Son, Dorchester #93/R est:600-1200

£2800 $5180 €4088 Cothelstone Church, Somerset (56x74cm-22x29in) s. W/C. 11-Mar-4 Christie's, Kensington #280/R est:2000-3000

£3000 $4770 €4380 Mexphalt, lower rate brotherhood (29x21cm-11x8in) init. pen ink collage sold with 6 similar by the same hand. 10-Sep-3 Sotheby's, Olympia #93/R est:800-1200

£3100 $5611 €4526 Frozen river (44x56cm-17x22in) s.d.1954 pen W/C gouache. 1-Apr-4 Olivers, Sudbury #82/R est:1200-1600

£10500 $19005 €15330 House at Ironbridge (45x56cm-18x22in) s.d.1956 pen W/C. 1-Apr-4 Olivers, Sudbury #84/R est:3000-4000

BAWDEN, Richard (1936-) British

Works on paper

£300 $537 €438 Luccini (35x51cm-14x20in) s.d.1986 W/C. 25-May-4 Sworder & Son, Bishops Stortford #344/R

£3700 $6179 €5402 Patchwork cloth (50x39cm-20x15in) s. W/C prov. 21-Oct-3 Sworder & Son, Bishops Stortford #280/R est:1000-1500

BAWDEN, William A (19th C) British

Works on paper

£400 $708 €584 Fishermen on a river (54x76cm-21x30in) s.i.d.1883 pencil W/C bodycol. 29-Apr-4 Christie's, Kensington #270

BAXON, A (19th C) ?

Miniatures

£1667 $3017 €2500 Eugenie von Montijou - Queen of France (18x15cm-7x6in) s. mixed media ivory. 3-Apr-4 Badum, Bamberg #80/R est:2000

BAXTER, Albert Ernest (1878-1936) New Zealander

Works on paper

£602 $1023 €879 Market place, Tarragona (48x34cm-19x13in) s. W/C exhib. 27-Nov-3 International Art Centre, Auckland #160/R (NZ.D 1600)

BAXTER, Charles (1809-1879) British

£1200 $2196 €1752 Mother and children beside the sea (30x25cm-12x10in) 6-Jul-4 Bonhams, Knightsbridge #209/R est:1200-1800

Works on paper

£260 $447 €380 Portrait of a girl. s. oval. 2-Dec-3 Andrew Smith, Winchester #146

BAXTER, Charles (attrib) (1809-1879) British

£4000 $6680 €5840 At the opera (91x71cm-36x28in) 13-Nov-3 Christie's, Kensington #260/R est:4000-6000

BAXTER, Evelyn (1925-) Australian

£621 $968 €900 Mixed roses (54x65cm-21x26in) s. 1-Aug-2 Joel, Victoria #213 est:2000-3000 (A.D 1800)

£729 $1173 €1064 Still life with white camellias (45x55cm-18x22in) s. 13-Oct-3 Joel, Victoria #382 est:1200-1500 (A.D 1800)

£1034 $1614 €1499 Magnolias (62x64cm-24x25in) s. 1-Aug-2 Joel, Victoria #169 est:1500-2500 (A.D 3000)

£1457 $2347 €2127 Still life with roses (60x65cm-24x26in) s. 13-Oct-3 Joel, Victoria #419 est:2000-3000 (A.D 3600)

BAXTER, Iain (1935-) Canadian

Works on paper

£3153 $5360 €4603 Mount Rundle, Banff, a summer landscape (81x95cm-32x37in) s.d.65 col vacuum formed plastic. 18-Nov-3 Sotheby's, Toronto #81/R est:7000-9000 (C.D 7000)

BAYALIS, John (20th C) American

Works on paper

£246 $450 €369 Chinese tea (76x102cm-30x40in) W/C. 10-Jul-4 Hindman, Chicago #30/R

BAYARD, Émile Antoine (1837-1891) French

£27778 $50000 €40556 Fete champetre (106x79cm-42x31in) s.d.1878 pair. 22-Apr-4 Christie's, Rockefeller NY #155/R est:60000-80000

BAYARD, Hippolyte (1801-1887) French

Photographs

£2400 $4224 €3504 Blanquart-Evrard (19x26cm-7x10in) num.526 process print prov.lit. 19-May-4 Christie's, London #17/R est:2000-3000

BAYARD, Jules (20th C) French

£961 $1720 €1403 Still life of cherries and jug (32x40cm-13x16in) s. 26-May-4 AB Stockholms Auktionsverk #2408/R (S.KR 13000)

BAYARD, Pierre (20th C) ?

£500 $915 €750 La ronde de nuit (133x120cm-52x47in) s.d.92. 7-Jun-4 Palais de Beaux Arts, Brussels #153

£1600 $2928 €2400 Guerre et paix (130x195cm-51x77in) s.d.92. 7-Jun-4 Palais de Beaux Arts, Brussels #154/R est:500-700

BAYAUX, Pierre (1884-1946) Belgian

£638 $1180 €950 Fishing harbour (60x82cm-24x32in) s. 13-Mar-4 De Vuyst, Lokeren #20

BAYEFSKY, Aba (1923-) Canadian

£1124 $2092 €1641 Kensington Market (129x97cm-51x38in) s.d.57 prov.exhib. 2-Mar-4 Ritchie, Toronto #159/R est:1500-2000 (C.D 2800)

BAYER, Herbert (1900-1985) German

£667 $1200 €974 Sweet peas and owls (48x51cm-19x20in) s.d.48 i.verso masonite. 26-Jan-4 Schrager Galleries, Milwaukee #1428

£2817 $4873 €4000 Untitled (76x61cm-30x24in) s.d.57/5 i. stretcher. 13-Dec-3 Lempertz, Koln #115/R est:4500

£4362 $7809 €6500 Untitled (33x99cm-13x39in) s.d.50. 25-May-4 Dorotheum, Vienna #53/R est:6000-8000

£7650 $14000 €11169 Untitled, formation (58x81cm-23x32in) s.d.1949. 6-Jun-4 Wright, Chicago #574/R est:20000-30000

Works on paper

£894 $1600 €1305 Untitled (25x36cm-10x14in) s.d.1949 W/C ink. 16-May-4 Wright, Chicago #250/R est:2000-3000

£1154 $2100 €1685 Tracks of time no.1 (23x31cm-9x12in) s.i.d.54 crayon chk. 29-Jun-4 Sotheby's, New York #435/R est:1000-1500

£4333 $7757 €6500 Berlin items (28x38cm-11x15in) s.d. collage pencil board prov. 14-May-4 Ketterer, Munich #358/R est:6000-8000

BAYER, J (19th C) German

£2600 $4602 €3796 May day celebrations (41x71cm-16x28in) s. prov. 27-Apr-4 Bonhams, Knowle #89/R est:1500-2000

BAYERLEIN, Fritz (1872-1955) German

£524 $902 €750 By the Main (59x69cm-23x27in) s. i. verso board. 4-Dec-3 Neumeister, Munich #2698/R

£2098 $3608 €3000 Haymaking in the Nymphenburger Park (87x110cm-34x43in) s. i. stretcher. 3-Dec-3 Neumeister, Munich #529/R est:2000

£4000 $7280 €6000 Winter morning in the grounds of Seehof Castle (116x140cm-46x55in) s. i.verso lit. 3-Jul-4 Badum, Bamberg #53/R est:6000

BAYES, A W (1832-1909) British

£2400 $4008 €3504 Refuge, children up fruit tree (57x39cm-22x15in) s. 21-Oct-3 Bruton Knowles, Cheltenham #437/R est:800-1200

BAYES, Alfred Walter (1832-1909) British

£480 $802 €701 Mother and children outside a wooded cottage (51x69cm-20x27in) s. 7-Oct-3 Bonhams, Knightsbridge #150/R

£800 $1472 €1168 Comforting words (51x41cm-20x16in) s. 25-Mar-4 Bonhams, Edinburgh #356/R

£900 $1611 €1314 Mother before cottage watching her daughter, father beyond (51x69cm-20x27in) s. 11-Jan-4 Desmond Judd, Cranbrook #742

£8000 $13600 €11680 Double wedding (70x92cm-28x36in) s. 19-Nov-3 Bonhams, New Bond Street #74/R est:8000-10000

BAYES, Gilbert (1872-1953) British

Sculpture

£2800 $5152 €4088 Agriculture (23cm-9in) s.d.1913 brown pat. green marble plinth prov. 11-Jun-4 Christie's, London #83/R est:3000-5000

£3000 $5520 €4380 Seated female nude (18cm-7in) s.d.1909 brown pat. board verde marble plinth. 11-Jun-4 Christie's, London #73/R est:2000-3000

BAYES, Walter (1869-1956) British
£280 $448 €409 Cattle droving on a country lane (29x37cm-11x15in) mono. canvas on board. 16-Sep-3 Rosebery Fine Art, London #601
£700 $1232 €1022 Port (93x103cm-37x41in) mono. 19-May-4 Sotheby's, Olympia #141/R
Works on paper
£480 $898 €701 Expert angler (38x54cm-15x21in) s. W/C. 24-Feb-4 Bonhams, Knowle #21
£620 $1054 €905 Expert angler (38x54cm-15x21in) s. W/C. 25-Nov-3 Bonhams, Knowle #173

BAYEU Y SUBIAS, Francisco (1734-1795) Spanish
£102649 $186821 €155000 Projet pour la fresque ornant la proi de l'autel de la chapelle royale d'Aranjuez (80x111cm-31x44in) 16-Jun-4 Beaussant & Lefèvre, Paris #29/R est:12000-15000

BAYLE, Bertrand Georges de (1788-1851) French
£500 $835 €730 Still life of flowers (22x16cm-9x6in) s. panel. 12-Nov-3 Sotheby's, Olympia #144/R

BAYLIES, William (jnr) (1859-1934) American
£457 $850 €667 Sunset landscape (15x26cm-6x10in) s. panel. 5-Mar-4 Skinner, Boston #452/R

BAYLINSON, Abraham S (1882-1950) American
£1816 $3250 €2651 Reclining nude black woman with bowl of fruit (51x61cm-20x24in) s.d.1937. 7-May-4 Sloans & Kenyon, Bethesda #1635/R est:2000-3000

BAYLISS, Sir Wyke (1835-1906) British
Works on paper
£280 $476 €409 Interior of Treves Cathedral, with figure (26x36cm-10x14in) W/C. 30-Oct-3 Locke & England, Leamington Spa #230/R

BAYNARD, Edward (1941-) American
Works on paper
£423 $800 €618 Irises (104x75cm-41x30in) s. W/C. 22-Feb-4 Bonhams & Butterfields, Los Angeles #7050

BAYNES, Keith (1887-1977) British
£300 $555 €438 Crystal Palace interior (41x32cm-16x13in) s.d.29 prov.exhib. 11-Mar-4 Christie's, Kensington #256

BAYNES, Pauline Diana (1922-) British
Works on paper
£1700 $2941 €2482 The jinnee dropped gently down to the top of a high mountain (24x15cm-9x6in) ink W/C gouache. 11-Dec-3 Sotheby's, London #178/R est:1500-2000

BAYON SALADO, Juan (1903-1995) Spanish
£397 $723 €600 Place de la Concorde animee (38x46cm-15x18in) s. 15-Jun-4 Vanderkindere, Brussels #89
£397 $723 €600 La Place Blanche a Paris (27x35cm-11x14in) s. 15-Jun-4 Vanderkindere, Brussels #83

BAYON, Fernando (1932-) Spanish
£340 $619 €500 River scene in Bilbao (27x42cm-11x17in) s. board. 3-Feb-4 Segre, Madrid #336/R

BAYRLE, Thomas (1937-) German
Works on paper
£423 $701 €600 Rotary (55x63cm-22x25in) s.i.d.1974 Indian ink. 13-Jun-3 Hauswedell & Nolte, Hamburg #552/R
£423 $701 €600 City (23x21cm-9x8in) s.d.1976 i. verso pencil. 13-Jun-3 Hauswedell & Nolte, Hamburg #553/R
£563 $935 €800 Portrait of Herr Wohrl (67x56cm-26x22in) s.i.d.1972 Indian ink. 13-Jun-3 Hauswedell & Nolte, Hamburg #551/R

BAYROS, Franz von (1866-1924) Austrian
Works on paper
£638 $1066 €900 Ch'io erri anzi ad aprir, ch'a tenerla serrata, IX, 127 (39x33cm-15x13in) s. mixed media gold htd white board. 14-Oct-3 Dorotheum, Vienna #2/R

BAZAINE, Jean (1904-1995) French
£789 $1429 €1200 Chataigniers (18x13cm-7x5in) s.d.52 panel exhib. 19-Apr-4 Boscher, Cherbourg #724/R
£5175 $8642 €7400 Printemps noir (27x22cm-11x9in) s.d.1962 exhib. 29-Jun-3 Versailles Encheres #67/R
Works on paper
£282 $487 €400 Composition (29x21cm-11x8in) mono.d.1987 Indian ink prov. 14-Dec-3 Versailles Encheres #7
£296 $512 €420 Arbre (29x20cm-11x8in) mono.d.1987 Indian ink prov. 14-Dec-3 Versailles Encheres #6
£313 $516 €450 Pour Olga (13x20cm-5x8in) s.i.d.91 Indian ink dr. 3-Jul-3 Piasa, Paris #95
£755 $1284 €1102 Untitled (10x13cm-4x5in) s.d.50 mixed media. 4-Nov-3 Bukowskis, Stockholm #275 (S.KR 10000)
£900 $1638 €1314 Untitled (7x22cm-3x9in) s.d.59 pencil ink W/C. 4-Feb-4 Sotheby's, Olympia #183/R
£1208 $2139 €1800 Composition (30x44cm-12x17in) s.d.69 W/C. 28-Apr-4 Artcurial Briest, Paris #262/R est:2000-3000
£1597 $2668 €2300 Dunes (11x17cm-4x7in) s.i.d.63 India ink col crayons gouache page of notebook. 21-Oct-3 Artcurial Briest, Paris #382 est:1500-1800
£2098 $3503 €3000 Paysage (12x40cm-5x16in) s.d.1974 W/C prov. 29-Jun-3 Versailles Encheres #78/R

BAZILE, Alberoi (20th C) Haitian
£223 $400 €326 Chickens (61x51cm-24x20in) s. masonite. 14-May-4 Skinner, Boston #406/R
£546 $1000 €797 Two women with eggplant and red fruit (61x51cm-24x20in) s. panel. 3-Jun-4 Christie's, Rockefeller NY #1117/R est:600-800

BAZILLE, Jean-Frederic (1841-1870) French
£2653631 $4750000 €3874301 Pots de fleurs (100x81cm-39x32in) s.d.66 prov.exhib.lit. 5-May-4 Sotheby's, New York #17/R est:4000000-6000000

BAZIOTES, William (1912-1963) American
Works on paper
£17964 $30000 €26227 Figures against sun. Figures in smoke no 2 (30x46cm-12x18in) s. one s.i.d.1947 verso one i.verso W/C pen ink pencil 2 prov. 13-Nov-3 Sotheby's, New York #102/R est:12000-16000

BAZIRAY (18th C) French?
£5319 $8883 €7500 Portrait de jeune garcon a la veste bleue brodee (81x65cm-32x26in) s.d.1737 verso. 17-Oct-3 Tajan, Paris #97/R est:6000-8000

BAZIRE, Pierre (?) French
£350 $602 €500 Le retour de la chasse (38x46cm-15x18in) s. s.i.verso panel. 3-Dec-3 Tajan, Paris #265/R

BAZOVSKY, Milos Alexander (1899-1968) Czechoslovakian
£633 $1114 €950 Mountain cottage (29x30cm-11x12in) s. cardboard. 22-May-4 Dorotheum, Prague #135/R est:30000-45000 (C.KR 30000)

BAZZANI, Giuseppe (1690-1769) Italian
£30872 $57732 €46000 Christ on the road to Emmaus (119x125cm-47x49in) 25-Feb-4 Porro, Milan #22/R est:42000

BAZZANI, Giuseppe (attrib) (1690-1769) Italian
£3958 $6610 €5700 Madonna and Child (15x12cm-6x5in) oval. 22-Oct-3 Finarte Semenzato, Milan #7/R

BAZZANI, Luigi (1836-1927) Italian
Works on paper
£428 $787 €650 Rome (24x28cm-9x11in) s.d.1920 W/C. 23-Jun-4 Finarte Semenzato, Rome #30/R
£600 $1074 €900 Street in Pompei (36x23cm-14x9in) s. W/C. 17-May-4 Finarte Semenzato, Rome #9/R

BAZZANTI, Pietro (19/20th C) Italian
Sculpture
£2133 $3861 €3200 Buste de femme vetue d'un chemisier en soie damassee (61cm-24in) studio st. white marble exec. c.1890-1900. 31-Mar-4 Sotheby's, Paris #203/R est:800-1200

BAZZARO, Ernesto (1859-1937) Italian
Sculpture
£1056 $1827 €1500 Maternity (55x45cm-22x18in) s. bronze. 9-Dec-3 Pandolfini, Florence #295/R est:1400-1600
£1056 $1827 €1500 Camel with figures (50x53cm-20x21in) s. bronze. 10-Dec-3 Finarte Semenzato, Rome #200/R est:1500-2000
£1267 $2027 €1850 Mother with child (49cm-19in) s. green brown pat.bronze. 16-Sep-3 Philippe Schuler, Zurich #3069/R est:2000-3000 (S.FR 2800)
£1761 $3046 €2500 Maternity (55x45cm-22x18in) s. bronze. 10-Dec-3 Sotheby's, Milan #146/R est:2000-4000

BAZZARO, Leonardo (1853-1937) Italian
£2667 $4907 €4000 Peasant woman with basket (50x35cm-20x14in) s. board. 8-Jun-4 Sotheby's, Milan #129/R est:2000-4000
£2752 $5146 €4100 Scene in Chioggia (59x40cm-23x16in) s. cardboard. 28-Feb-4 Finarte, Venice #189/R est:4000-5000
£2817 $4676 €4000 Portrait of a young man (45x35cm-18x14in) s. board exhib. 11-Jun-3 Christie's, Rome #182/R est:2000-3000
£3873 $6430 €5500 Scorcio di Chioggia (50x35cm-20x14in) s. wood. 11-Jun-3 Christie's, Rome #259/R est:6000-9000
£4317 $7079 €6000 Peasant woman at door (50x33cm-20x13in) board. 10-Jun-3 Pandolfini, Florence #116/R est:5000-6000
£4577 $7599 €6500 Chioggia (69x80cm-27x31in) s. 13-Jun-3 Farsetti, Prato #534/R
£5168 $9250 €7700 Canal in Chioggia (40x57cm-16x22in) s. board. 25-May-4 Finarte Semenzato, Milan #231/R est:8000-9000
£5493 $9503 €7800 Canal in Chioggia (40x60cm-16x24in) s. 11-Dec-3 Christie's, Rome #189/R est:6000-9000
£6944 $11806 €10000 Serenity (40x60cm-16x24in) s. board. 1-Nov-3 Meeting Art, Vercelli #446/R est:10000
£7333 $13493 €11000 Cuddles (90x60cm-35x24in) s. 8-Jun-4 Sotheby's, Milan #108/R est:15000-20000
£10811 $19027 €16000 Confidences (61x81cm-24x32in) s. 19-May-4 Il Ponte, Milan #639 est:12000-15000

BAZZI, Giovanni Antonio (1477-1549) Italian
£30000 $54900 €43800 Pieta' (111x86cm-44x34in) s.i. panel prov.lit. 8-Jul-4 Sotheby's, London #151/R est:30000-40000

BAZZICALUVA, Ercole (17th C) Italian
Works on paper
£950 $1710 €1387 Study of a tree with figures and distant village (18x24cm-7x9in) bears i. pen brown ink prov. 20-Apr-4 Sotheby's, Olympia #25/R

BAZZURRO, Domingo L (1886-1962) Uruguayan
£7059 $12000 €10306 Fishing village (64x54cm-25x21in) s. lit. 25-Nov-3 Galeria y Remates, Montevideo #45/R

BEACH, Edward Dwight (1867-?) American
£318 $550 €464 Wave (56x61cm-22x24in) s.d.1927. 13-Dec-3 Charlton Hall, Columbia #278/R

BEACH, Ernest G (1865-c.1934) British
Works on paper
£260 $434 €380 Break from ploughing (33x49cm-13x19in) s. W/C. 14-Oct-3 Bonhams, Knightsbridge #180/R
£340 $626 €496 Shepherd and his flock (24x33cm-9x13in) s. W/C. 23-Mar-4 Bonhams, Knightsbridge #78/R

BEACH, Thomas (1738-1806) British
£3333 $6000 €4866 Portrait of Miss Maria Margaret Craven (76x63cm-30x25in) s.d.1776 prov. 21-Jan-4 Sotheby's, New York #136/R est:6000-8000

BEACH, Thomas (attrib) (1738-1806) British
£214 $400 €321 Portrait of a boy, holding a sprig of cherries (76x63cm-30x25in) bears sig.i.indis.d.17. 25-Jul-4 Bonhams & Butterfields, San Francisco #6012/R
£1176 $2000 €1717 Portrait of an officer (75x63cm-30x25in) prov. 21-Nov-3 Skinner, Boston #225/R est:2000-3000

BEADLE, Paul John (1917-1993) New Zealander/British
Sculpture
£1923 $3500 €2808 Porgy and Bess (20x15x11cm-8x6x4in) cast bronze. 29-Jun-4 Peter Webb, Auckland #18/R est:6000-8000 (NZ.D 5500)
£3731 $6455 €5447 Way of man (40x22x22cm-16x9x9in) mono. bronze. 9-Dec-3 Peter Webb, Auckland #29/R est:8000-12000 (NZ.D 10000)

BEADLE, Peter (20th C) New Zealander
£277 $496 €404 Skipper's Canyon (60x44cm-24x17in) s. board. 12-May-4 Dunbar Sloane, Wellington #493 (NZ.D 800)
£277 $496 €404 Autumn Kawarua near Queenstown 1972 (44x74cm-17x29in) s. board. 12-May-4 Dunbar Sloane, Wellington #518 (NZ.D 800)
£316 $543 €461 Moses Nugget, Paterson's inlet, Stewart Island (44x89cm-17x35in) s.d.1977 board. 7-Dec-3 International Art Centre, Auckland #335 (NZ.D 850)
£532 $984 €777 Mt. Cook, Mt. Sefton and Tasman River (37x75cm-15x30in) s. 13-Jul-4 Watson's, Christchurch #16/R (NZ.D 1500)
£625 $1131 €913 Evening light, Mt Cook (39x19cm-15x7in) s. board. 4-Apr-4 International Art Centre, Auckland #237/R (NZ.D 1750)
£1159 $1867 €1692 The dart players (74x66cm-29x26in) s. board. 20-Aug-3 Peter Webb, Auckland #2003 est:800-1200 (NZ.D 3200)
£1812 $2935 €2627 Musterers, fairlight, Kingston, Wakatipu (60x90cm-24x35in) s.i.d.1998 verso. 31-Jul-3 International Art Centre, Auckland #62/R est:4500-6500 (NZ.D 5000)

BEAL, Gifford (1879-1956) American
£447 $800 €653 Coastal view (20x25cm-8x10in) canvasboard prov. 14-May-4 Skinner, Boston #282/R
£559 $1000 €816 Snowy peaks (20x25cm-8x10in) board prov. 14-May-4 Skinner, Boston #244/R
£1676 $3000 €2447 Central Park hack (23x30cm-9x12in) indis.sig. masonite painted c.1940 prov. 26-May-4 Doyle, New York #138/R est:4000-6000
£7568 $14000 €11049 Waiting for the show (45x39cm-18x15in) s. panel prov. 11-Mar-4 Christie's, Rockefeller NY #63/R est:6000-8000
£7735 $14000 €11293 Picnic party (42x51cm-17x20in) s. s.i.verso masonite exec.c.1946 prov. 31-Mar-4 Sotheby's, New York #7/R est:12000-18000
£31977 $55000 €46686 Summer day, Rockport (61x76cm-24x30in) s. masonite prov. 3-Dec-3 Sotheby's, New York #7/R est:30000-40000
£40698 $70000 €59419 Woman talking (91x123cm-36x48in) s.d.14 prov. 3-Dec-3 Sotheby's, New York #8/R est:60000-80000
Works on paper
£2095 $3750 €3059 Musicale (20x28cm-8x11in) s. gouache prov. 6-May-4 Shannon's, Milford #238/R est:1500-2500
£4054 $7500 €5919 Chinese restaurant (30x23cm-12x9in) s. s.i.verso W/C gouache pencil prov. 11-Mar-4 Christie's, Rockefeller NY #61/R est:4000-6000
£4324 $8000 €6313 Central Park Lake (23x30cm-9x12in) s. W/C gouache pencil prov.exhib. 11-Mar-4 Christie's, Rockefeller NY #48/R est:4000-6000

BEAL, Jack (1931-) American
Works on paper
£543 $1000 €793 Vegetables (48x69cm-19x27in) s. pastel. 26-Jun-4 Susanin's, Chicago #6099/R est:1500-2000

BEAL, Reynolds (1867-1951) American
£603 $958 €880 Landscape with river (40x30cm-16x12in) s. 29-Apr-3 Louis Morton, Mexico #103/R (M.P 10000)
£2374 $4250 €3466 River Canche, Etaples, France (56x46cm-22x18in) s. prov. 6-May-4 Shannon's, Milford #166/R est:4000-6000
£9143 $16000 €13349 Village by the Hudson River (61x76cm-24x30in) s.d.1915 oil gouache chl board prov. 19-Dec-3 Sotheby's, New York #1124/R est:10000-15000
£14857 $26000 €21691 The lobsterman (76x122cm-30x48in) s.d.1918. 19-Dec-3 Sotheby's, New York #1056/R est:10000-12000
Works on paper
£356 $575 €520 Colourful landscape (25x33cm-10x13in) s. pencil crayon. 20-Aug-3 James Julia, Fairfield #1416/R
£1366 $2200 €1994 Day at the circus (33x41cm-13x16in) s. pencil crayon. 20-Aug-3 James Julia, Fairfield #1415/R est:2000-3000

BEALE, Charles (1660-1714) British
£1800 $3222 €2628 Portrait of lady, identified as Lady Darnell (76x63cm-30x25in) s.d.1689. 27-May-4 Christie's, Kensington #34/R est:2000-3000
Works on paper
£28000 $51240 €40880 Portrait studies of children, bust length (17x13cm-7x5in) red chk oval pair prov. 3-Jun-4 Christie's, London #45/R est:18000-25000

BEALE, Edward (1950-) British
£500 $925 €730 Ship passing dome (30x39cm-12x15in) board exhib. 11-Feb-4 Sotheby's, Olympia #233/R
£750 $1388 €1095 Ship moored at Trinity Bouy wharf (40x61cm-16x24in) board exhib. 11-Feb-4 Sotheby's, Olympia #234/R

BEALE, James (1798-1879) Irish
£5315 $9035 €7600 Procession through Cork (86x114cm-34x45in) 25-Nov-3 De Veres Art Auctions, Dublin #154/R est:8000-12000

BEALE, Mary (1632-1697) British
£2400 $4464 €3504 Portrait of Justice John Shelden in black robes (76x63cm-30x25in) feigned cartouche prov. 4-Mar-4 Christie's, Kensington #300/R est:1500-2000
£3500 $6440 €5110 Portrait of a gentleman holding a scroll (73x63cm-29x25in) s. 26-Mar-4 Sotheby's, London #4/R est:4000-6000

BEALE, Mary (attrib) (1632-1697) British
£3800 $6802 €5548 Portrait of Sir Ralph Asheton within a painted sculpted oval (76x63cm-30x25in) 22-Mar-4 Bonhams & Brooks, Norfolk #199/R est:3000-5000
£4500 $8055 €6570 Portrait of a young boy, believed to be Richard Gulston (76x63cm-30x25in) painted oval. 22-Mar-4 Bonhams & Brooks, Norfolk #334/R est:2000-3000

BEAMAN, Jim (20th C) American
£543 $950 €793 Luncheon on the Grass (41x51cm-16x20in) s. masonite painted 1970. 17-Dec-3 Christie's, Rockefeller NY #144/R
£914 $1600 €1334 Whistler's mother (56x61cm-22x24in) s. masonite painted 1964. 17-Dec-3 Christie's, Rockefeller NY #145/R est:1000-1500
£1600 $2800 €2336 American gothic (59x49cm-23x19in) s. panel painted 1964. 17-Dec-3 Christie's, Rockefeller NY #143/R est:1000-1500

BEAMAN, Waldo Gamaliel (1852-1937) American
£309 $500 €451 June pinks (10x17cm-4x7in) s. i. stretcher. 31-Jul-3 Eldred, East Dennis #1211/R
£370 $600 €540 Impressionistic landscape with path and pink flowers (18x23cm-7x9in) s. 31-Jul-3 Eldred, East Dennis #805
£432 $700 €631 Impressionist landscape with stream and snow (20x36cm-8x14in) s. board. 31-Jul-3 Eldred, East Dennis #803/R
£543 $1000 €793 Haystacks (41x61cm-16x24in) s.d.82. 25-Jun-4 Freeman, Philadelphia #284/R

BEAMENT, Thomas Harold (1898-1984) Canadian
£201 $373 €293 Lac Quimet (25x34cm-10x13in) s. i.verso board. 2-Mar-4 Ritchie, Toronto #129/R (C.D 500)
£270 $459 €394 Brook in spring (18x25cm-7x10in) s. s.i.verso board prov. 27-Nov-3 Heffel, Vancouver #25 (C.D 600)
£289 $524 €422 Untitled - reflection light (25x36cm-10x14in) s. hardboard. 18-Apr-4 Levis, Calgary #4/R (C.D 700)
£293 $498 €428 River bank in spring (18x25cm-7x10in) s. s.i.verso board prov. 27-Nov-3 Heffel, Vancouver #26 (C.D 650)
£320 $586 €467 Crossing the bay (30x40cm-12x16in) s. panel prov. 1-Jun-4 Hodgins, Calgary #29/R (C.D 800)
£325 $582 €475 Laurentian winter (27x39cm-11x15in) s.d.1928 i. verso panel prov. 6-May-4 Heffel, Vancouver #23/R (C.D 800)
£378 $654 €552 Ox Cart (23x28cm-9x11in) s. s.i.d.1929 verso board. 9-Dec-3 Pinneys, Montreal #184 (C.D 850)
£407 $728 €594 Silver birches, autumn (30x40cm-12x16in) s. i.verso board painted c.1936 prov.exhib. 27-May-4 Heffel, Vancouver #97/R (C.D 1000)
£960 $1757 €1402 Labrador Rhythm (60x75cm-24x30in) s. 1-Jun-4 Joyner Waddington, Toronto #12/R est:2000-3000 (C.D 2400)
£1016 $1819 €1483 Winter lay up, Quebec (45x61cm-18x24in) s. i.verso prov. 27-May-4 Heffel, Vancouver #13 est:1800-2200 (C.D 2500)
£1563 $2688 €2282 Winter sunshine, Laurentians (46x51cm-18x20in) s. 2-Dec-3 Joyner Waddington, Toronto #204/R est:3000-4000 (C.D 3500)

BEAN, Caroline van Hook (1879-1980) American
£595 $1100 €869 Fisherman in woodland brook (30x46cm-12x18in) s. 15-Jul-4 Doyle, New York #8/R est:1000-1500

BEANLAND, Frank (1936-) British
£750 $1320 €1095 Turquoise, yellow and orange (121x59cm-48x23in) s.i. i.d.July 1969 verso. 19-May-4 Sotheby's, Olympia #307/R

BEAR, George Telfer (1874-1973) British
£1500 $2355 €2175 Queens Dock, Glasgow (71x92cm-28x36in) s.d.1902. 27-Aug-3 Sotheby's, London #1103/R est:1500-2000

BEARD, Adelia Belle (?-1920) American
£1056 $1700 €1542 New England landscape (20x33cm-8x13in) s. board. 20-Aug-3 James Julia, Fairfield #1637/R est:1800-2200

BEARD, Alice (1867-1949) American
£2793 $5000 €4078 Spring in Central Park (56x53cm-22x21in) s. i.verso exhib. 26-May-4 Doyle, New York #132/R est:2000-3000

BEARD, James Henry (1812-1893) American
£469 $750 €685 Arrangement of fruit on marble table top (28x38cm-11x15in) s.d.1886. 21-Sep-3 William Jenack, New York #48

BEARD, Peter (1938-) ?
Photographs
£2319 $3803 €3200 The end of the game (36x53cm-14x21in) s.i.d. vintage silver gelatin lit. 30-May-3 Villa Grisebach, Berlin #1107/R est:3500-4500
£2395 $4000 €3497 Self-portrait (22x65cm-9x26in) i.d.1962 gelatin silver print board diptych prov.lit. 17-Oct-3 Phillips, New York #231/R est:4000-6000
£2994 $5000 €4371 Large tusker (79x113cm-31x44in) bears sig.i.d.1965 oversized silver print. 21-Oct-3 Swann Galleries, New York #296/R est:9000-12000
£4667 $8587 €7000 Elephants at Buffalo Springs, Uaso Nyiro, Kenya (25x57cm-10x22in) s.i.d. silver gelatin mixed media lit.exhib. 10-Jun-4 Villa Grisebach, Berlin #1012/R est:3000-4000
£5667 $10427 €8500 Giraffes on the Tarn Desert Kenya (16x24cm-6x9in) s.i.d. silver gelatin lit.exhib. 10-Jun-4 Villa Grisebach, Berlin #1013/R est:2500-3000
£8200 $13940 €11972 Black rhino in Tsavo from the end of the game (76x102cm-30x40in) s. photo collage of 9 gelatin silver print. 18-Nov-3 Christie's, Kensington #223/R est:7000-9000

BEARD, William Holbrook (1824-1900) American
£2174 $4000 €3174 The fishwife at work (38x30cm-15x12in) s.d.1885 prov. 8-Jun-4 Bonhams & Butterfields, San Francisco #4008/R est:7000-10000
£4012 $6500 €5858 The missing link (41x30cm-16x12in) 1-Aug-3 North East Auctions, Portsmouth #948/R est:3000-5000

BEARD, William Holbrook (attrib) (1824-1900) American
£1087 $2000 €1587 Doubtful connoisseurs (30x41cm-12x16in) panel. 23-Mar-4 Arthur James, Florida #185/R est:2500-3500

BEARDEN, Ed (1919-1980) American
£598 $1100 €873 Desert landscape (41x51cm-16x20in) s. canvasboard. 23-Jun-4 Doyle, New York #5008/R est:2000-3000
£719 $1200 €1050 Mesas near Marfa (25x56cm-10x22in) masonite. 18-Oct-3 David Dike, Dallas #91/R
Works on paper
£749 $1250 €1094 North of Dallas (48x71cm-19x28in) W/C. 18-Oct-3 David Dike, Dallas #241/R
£2395 $4000 €3497 Skyline, late afternoon (61x86cm-24x34in) W/C. 18-Oct-3 David Dike, Dallas #242/R est:2000-4000

BEARDEN, Romare (1914-1988) American
£9783 $18000 €14283 Alone (30x23cm-12x9in) s. acrylic collage paper on masonite painted 1973. 10-Jun-4 Swann Galleries, New York #14/R est:7000-10000
Prints
£1519 $2750 €2218 Odysseus leaves (46x61cm-18x24in) s.num.55/125 col silkscreen. 19-Apr-4 Bonhams & Butterfields, San Francisco #234/R est:2000-3000
£1657 $3000 €2419 Cattle of the Sun God (46x57cm-18x22in) s.num.55/125 col silkscreen. 19-Apr-4 Bonhams & Butterfields, San Francisco #235/R est:1500-2500
£1676 $3000 €2447 Girl in the garden (56x41cm-22x16in) s.num.30/150 color lithograph. 6-May-4 Swann Galleries, New York #388a/R est:3000-5000
£1828 $3400 €2669 Mother and child (60x46cm-24x18in) s.num.60/150 col screenprint. 2-Mar-4 Swann Galleries, New York #36/R est:2500-3500
£1828 $3400 €2669 Odysseus leaves (46x60cm-18x24in) s.num.9/125 col screenprint. 2-Mar-4 Swann Galleries, New York #37/R est:2000-3000
£1840 $3000 €2686 Walking Bass (85x61cm-33x24in) s. num.41/75 col lithograph wove paper exec 1979. 24-Sep-3 Christie's, Rockefeller NY #211/R est:2000-3000
£2000 $3200 €2920 Conjunction (48x38cm-19x15in) s.num.211/300 col lithograph. 18-Sep-3 Swann Galleries, New York #48/R est:1800-2200
£2000 $3200 €2920 Odysseus leaves (46x61cm-18x24in) s.i. col screenprint. 18-Sep-3 Swann Galleries, New York #49/R est:1000-1500
£2059 $3500 €3006 Troy (46x60cm-18x24in) s.i. col screenprint. 21-Nov-3 Swann Galleries, New York #17/R est:2000-3000
£2125 $3400 €3103 Troy (46x61cm-18x24in) s.i. col screenprint. 18-Sep-3 Swann Galleries, New York #50/R est:1000-1500
£2366 $4400 €3454 Memories (37x44cm-15x17in) s.i. sugarlift etching executed c.1965-70. 2-Mar-4 Swann Galleries, New York #34/R est:1000-1500
£2366 $4400 €3454 Tidings (42x41cm-17x16in) s.i.num.6/68 col screenprint. 2-Mar-4 Swann Galleries, New York #42/R est:1200-1800
£2688 $5000 €3924 Carlina menory (40x60cm-16x24in) s.i. col screenprint. 2-Mar-4 Swann Galleries, New York #35/R est:1500-2500
£2688 $5000 €3924 Girl in the garden (56x41cm-22x16in) s.num.29/150 col lithograph. 2-Mar-4 Swann Galleries, New York #40/R est:2500-3500
£5588 $9500 €8158 Open door. s. col lithograph set of 3. 4-Nov-3 Christie's, Rockefeller NY #219/R est:5000-7000
Works on paper
£5828 $9500 €8509 Untitled (49x65cm-19x26in) s. ink W/C prov. 23-Sep-3 Christie's, Rockefeller NY #12/R est:10000-15000
£7527 $14000 €10989 Summer landscape (66x51cm-26x20in) s. W/C. 2-Mar-4 Swann Galleries, New York #43/R est:5000-8000
£9605 $17000 €14023 Untitled, three figures standing near a doorway (66x51cm-26x20in) s. W/C. 2-May-4 Bonhams & Butterfields, Los Angeles #3064/R est:3000-5000

BEARDSLEY, Aubrey (1872-1898) British
Works on paper
£3977 $7000 €5806 Flosshilde (6x9cm-2x4in) i.verso pen ink lit. 18-May-4 Sotheby's, New York #85/R est:1500-2000
£6818 $12000 €9954 Le morte d Athur (13x9cm-5x4in) pen ink lit. 18-May-4 Sotheby's, New York #88/R est:3500-4000
£7386 $13000 €10784 Vignette in bon-mots of Smith and Sheridan (9x8cm-4x3in) pen ink lit. 18-May-4 Sotheby's, New York #86/R est:5000-7000
£7386 $13000 €10784 Le morte d Arthur (16x9cm-6x4in) pen ink. 18-May-4 Sotheby's, New York #90/R est:2000-3000
£76705 $135000 €111989 Design for the front wrapper of the Savoyno.4 (24x18cm-9x7in) s. pen ink lit. 18-May-4 Sotheby's, New York #87/R est:6000-8000

BEARNE, Edward H (19th C) British
Works on paper
£300 $486 €435 Bargello and Badia, Florence (31x23cm-12x9in) s.d.1887 W/C. 30-Jul-3 Hamptons Fine Art, Godalming #59

BEASLEY, Bruce (1939-) American
Sculpture
£1229 $2200 €1794 Mesa (41cm-16in) polychromed bronze. 7-May-4 Sloans & Kenyon, Bethesda #1750/R est:2500-3500
£1250 $2250 €1825 Zepherus (54cm-21in) s.d.62 num.1/4 bronze incl. base. 25-Apr-4 Bonhams & Butterfields, San Francisco #5641/R est:700-900

BEATON, Penelope (1886-1963) British
£270 $478 €394 Still life by a window (73x102cm-29x40in) s. board. 27-Apr-4 Bonhams, Knowle #134
£480 $850 €701 Yew tree (51x61cm-20x24in) s. 29-Apr-4 Gorringes, Lewes #2543
£1900 $3477 €2774 Flowers on decorative fabrics (64x76cm-25x30in) s. 8-Apr-4 Bonhams, Edinburgh #170 est:1500-2000
£1900 $3477 €2774 Tabletop still life (76x63cm-30x25in) s. 8-Apr-4 Bonhams, Edinburgh #172 est:1500-2500
£3100 $5673 €4526 Holiday (74x102cm-29x40in) s. board. 28-Jan-4 Dreweatt Neate, Newbury #108/R est:800-1200
Works on paper
£300 $501 €438 Autumn (28x35cm-11x14in) s. pen ink W/C. 16-Oct-3 Lyon & Turnbull, Edinburgh #69
£720 $1238 €1051 Harbour, Queensferry (46x57cm-18x22in) s. ink W/C gouache. 4-Dec-3 Bonhams, Edinburgh #6
£1800 $2898 €2610 Storm, Iona (45x51cm-18x20in) s. pen ink W/C. 21-Aug-3 Bonhams, Edinburgh #1096/R est:1000-1500

BEATON, Sir Cecil (1904-1980) British
£894 $1600 €1305 Young damsel standing in front of theatrical backdrop (33x23cm-13x9in) init. oil ink hardboard. 15-May-4 Illustration House, New York #82/R est:3000-5000
Photographs
£3804 $7000 €5554 Katharine Hepburn (23x20cm-9x8in) s. silver print. 10-Jun-4 Sotheby's, New York #438/R est:500-700
£8696 $16000 €12696 Portraits of Katherine Hepburn (23x18cm-9x7in) s. gelatin silver print two. 10-Jun-4 Sotheby's, New York #92/R est:400-600
Works on paper
£260 $447 €380 Costume design (36x25cm-14x10in) studio st. pencil gouache. 2-Dec-3 Gorringes, Lewes #2263
£694 $1159 €1000 Projet de costume XVIII siecle (64x45cm-25x18in) collage. 21-Oct-3 Arcurial Briest, Paris #85
£900 $1665 €1314 Seamstress (32x25cm-13x10in) s. W/C pen ink board col chk. 11-Mar-4 Christie's, Kensington #1/R
£1000 $1830 €1460 Vanessa in Act II (48x27cm-19x11in) s.i. pencil blk ink W/C bodycol prov. 3-Jun-4 Christie's, London #203/R est:800-1200
£1100 $1749 €1606 Theatre design (34x52cm-13x20in) s. ink W/C collage. 10-Sep-3 Sotheby's, Olympia #123/R est:700-900
£1900 $3477 €2774 Countess at home (51x36cm-20x14in) s.i. pencil blk ink W/C bodycol htd white prov. 3-Jun-4 Christie's, London #202/R est:1200-1800
£2000 $3660 €2920 Figures in a park (35x50cm-14x20in) s. blk ink W/C bodycol htd white prov. 3-Jun-4 Christie's, London #199/R est:2500-3500
£2200 $3938 €3212 Portrait of Coco chanel (45x37cm-18x15in) studio st.i. pencil pen black ink. 14-May-4 Christie's, Kensington #499/R est:1500-2000
£2300 $4209 €3358 Eliza (56x38cm-22x15in) s. W/C gouache board prov. 3-Jun-4 Christie's, London #201/R est:1200-1800
£3600 $6660 €5256 Elsie de Wolfe (25x20cm-10x8in) s. pencil pen ink W/C exhib.lit. 11-Feb-4 Sotheby's, Olympia #100/R est:600-800
£8152 $15000 €11902 Portrait of Katharine Hepburn in a pink and green shawl (61x51cm-24x20in) W/C pencil ink paper on board sketch. 10-Jun-4 Sotheby's, New York #130/R est:1500-2000
£21739 $40000 €31739 Portrait of Katharine Hepburn in a pink and green shawl (61x51cm-24x20in) s. W/C ink on board. 10-Jun-4 Sotheby's, New York #131/R est:2000-3000

BEATSON, Charles (19/20th C) British
£726 $1335 €1060 Challenge. Assassin (61x30cm-24x12in) s. i.verso pair. 14-Jun-4 Waddingtons, Toronto #102/R est:1200-1600 (C.D 1800)

BEATTIE, Basil (1935-) British
£2000 $3580 €2920 Ins and outs (213x198cm-84x78in) i.d.1966 stretcher oil wax cotton duck prov. 16-Mar-4 Bonhams, New Bond Street #102/R est:1800-2500

BEATTIE, Robert (19/20th C) Irish?
£795 $1446 €1200 Before the start (50x60cm-20x24in) s. s.i.verso. 15-Jun-4 James Adam, Dublin #79/R
£927 $1687 €1400 Sackville Street (50x60cm-20x24in) s. s.i.verso. 15-Jun-4 James Adam, Dublin #80/R

BEATTY, David (20th C) British
£248 $400 €362 European harbour scene (23x28cm-9x11in) s. panel. 20-Aug-3 James Julia, Fairfield #1022/R

BEATTY, John William (1869-1941) Canadian
£625 $1063 €913 Forest path (37x25cm-15x10in) s. board. 6-Nov-3 Heffel, Vancouver #8/R est:2000-3000 (C.D 1400)
£759 $1305 €1108 Stone building with trees to the fore (15x20cm-6x8in) s. board. 2-Dec-3 Joyner Waddington, Toronto #386 (C.D 1700)

£893 $1536 €1304 Farm buildings (22x32cm-9x13in) s. canvas on board. 2-Dec-3 Joyner Waddington, Toronto #257/R est:2000-3000 (C.D 2000)
£1071 $1843 €1564 European rural scene at dusk (35x40cm-14x16in) s.d.07 canvas on panel. 2-Dec-3 Joyner Waddington, Toronto #506 est:3000-4000 (C.D 2400)
£2236 $4002 €3265 March near Toronto (21x26cm-8x10in) s. i.verso board prov. 6-May-4 Heffel, Vancouver #25/R est:3500-4500 (C.D 5500)
£2455 $4223 €3584 Farm - Autumn (22x29cm-9x11in) s. canvasboard. 2-Dec-3 Joyner Waddington, Toronto #228/R est:4000-5000 (C.D 5500)
£2679 $4607 €3911 Woods in autumn (21x26cm-8x10in) s.d.29 panel. 2-Dec-3 Joyner Waddington, Toronto #138/R est:3000-5000 (C.D 6000)
£2703 $4595 €3946 Untitled, Ontario landscape (24x30cm-9x12in) s. board painted c.1930. 27-Nov-3 Heffel, Vancouver #88/R est:3000-4000 (C.D 6000)
£3153 $5360 €4603 Near Elmsdale, North Ontario (27x35cm-11x14in) s. i.verso panel prov. 18-Nov-3 Sotheby's, Toronto #103/R est:5000-7000 (C.D 7000)
£3153 $5360 €4603 Near Burks Falls, Rocky Country (26x35cm-10x14in) s. panel prov. 18-Nov-3 Sotheby's, Toronto #105/R est:4000-6000 (C.D 7000)
£4279 $7275 €6247 Bridge over the Don Valley River (76x91cm-30x36in) s.d.1934 prov. 27-Nov-3 Heffel, Vancouver #128/R est:8000-10000 (C.D 9500)
£4400 $8052 €6424 Kearney in winter (26x34cm-10x13in) s. panel painted c.1927. 1-Jun-4 Joyner Waddington, Toronto #21/R est:6000-8000 (C.D 11000)
£7207 $12252 €10522 Shoreline, Algonquin Park (20x25cm-8x10in) panel prov. 27-Nov-3 Heffel, Vancouver #184/R est:3000-4000 (C.D 16000)
Works on paper
£313 $531 €457 Dutch port (20x28cm-8x11in) s. W/C prov. 6-Nov-3 Heffel, Vancouver #7/R (C.D 700)

BEAU, Alcide le (1872-1943) French
£560 $1003 €818 Summer landscape near Sanary (38x46cm-15x18in) s. 12-May-4 Dobiaschofsky, Bern #729/R (S.FR 1300)
£3000 $5520 €4500 Femme nue de dos se coiffant (50x35cm-20x14in) cardboard prov. 11-Jun-4 Pierre Berge, Paris #213/R est:4500-6000

BEAUBRUN, Charles and Henri (17th C) French
£2576 $4688 €3890 Portrait de jeune femme au collier de perles (60x50cm-24x20in) 21-Jun-4 Tajan, Paris #82/R est:6000-8000
£15789 $29053 €24000 Portrait presume d'Henriette Marie, Reine d'Angleterre (226x148cm-89x58in) prov.lit. 24-Jun-4 Christie's, Paris #118/R est:10000-15000

BEAUCHAMP, Robert (1923-1995) American
£610 $1000 €891 Untitled (102x102cm-40x40in) s. painted c.1967 prov. 2-Jun-3 Grogan, Boston #672/R

BEAUCLAIR, René (19/20th C) French
£1344 $2500 €1962 Diana the huntress (97x145cm-38x57in) s. painted c.1925. 7-Mar-4 Treadway Gallery, Cincinnati #681/R est:2500-4500

BEAUCORPS, Gustave de (19th C) French
Photographs
£3147 $5255 €4500 Mosquee d'Alger (39x29cm-15x11in) num.67 photograph exec.c.1857 prov. 10-Oct-3 Tajan, Paris #135/R est:5000-6000

BEAUDIN, Andre (1895-1979) French
£1812 $3207 €2700 Balcon fleuri (73x60cm-29x24in) s.d.1949. 27-Apr-4 Artcurial Briest, Paris #208/R est:3000-4000
£2200 $4048 €3212 Les couteaux (27x19cm-11x7in) s.d.1946 i.stretcher prov. 24-Mar-4 Sotheby's, Olympia #132/R est:1500-2000
Sculpture
£1127 $1949 €1600 L'etreinte (32cm-13in) s.num.1/6 brown pat bronze prov. 14-Dec-3 Versailles Encheres #209/R est:1200-1500
Works on paper
£350 $594 €500 La chute d'Icare (48x63cm-19x25in) s.d.1938 chl prov. 23-Nov-3 Cornette de St.Cyr, Paris #5
£594 $1010 €850 Sans titre (32x24cm-13x9in) s.i.d.1924-1925 graphite prov. 23-Nov-3 Cornette de St.Cyr, Paris #4
£664 $1129 €950 Composition (46x32cm-18x13in) s.d.1957 W/C ink graphite. 23-Nov-3 Cornette de St.Cyr, Paris #7
£822 $1397 €1200 Visage de profil (55x42cm-22x17in) s.d.1928 pastel. 9-Nov-3 Eric Pillon, Calais #167/R
£824 $1400 €1203 Curtain (33x53cm-13x21in) s.d.1948 ink W/C prov.exhib. 9-Nov-3 Wright, Chicago #250 est:1500-2000
£1325 $2424 €2000 Paysage aux trois ponts (57x71cm-22x28in) s.d.1949 Indian ink drawing prov. 7-Apr-4 Piasa, Paris #190/R est:2000-3000

BEAUDUIN, Jean (1851-1916) Belgian
£377 $640 €550 Retour de la cueillette (33x24cm-13x9in) s. panel. 10-Nov-3 Horta, Bruxelles #399
£651 $1106 €950 Elegante (33x24cm-13x9in) s.d.1890 panel. 10-Nov-3 Horta, Bruxelles #398
£1600 $2944 €2336 Portrait of a young woman in a winter park (71x54cm-28x21in) s.d.1896. 25-Mar-4 Christie's, Kensington #32/R est:2000-3000

BEAUFORT, Reverend William Louis (1771-1849) Irish
Works on paper
£1200 $2148 €1752 View of Mallow (17x21cm-7x8in) init.i.d.Aug 11th s.verso pencil black ink grey wash. 14-May-4 Christie's, London #85/R est:400-600

BEAUFRERE, Adolphe (1876-1960) French
£458 $801 €650 Personnage pres du pont (10x10cm-4x4in) s. 21-Dec-3 Thierry & Lannon, Brest #274
£986 $1725 €1400 Calvaire en Bretagne, pieta (27x22cm-11x9in) s. studio st. paper on canvas. 21-Dec-3 Thierry & Lannon, Brest #278
£1000 $1790 €1500 Paysage au phare et a la jetee (12x16cm-5x6in) i. oil paper. 16-May-4 Thierry & Lannon, Brest #284/R est:1500-2000
£1000 $1840 €1500 Bord de mer, environs d'Alger (17x19cm-7x7in) s. oil paper on canvas. 14-Jun-4 Gros & Delettrez, Paris #362/R est:1500-2000
£1056 $1849 €1500 Grands arbres, l'entree du parc (27x25cm-11x10in) studio st. paper on canvas. 21-Dec-3 Thierry & Lannon, Brest #277 est:1000-1200
£1126 $2105 €1700 Voilier sur la Laita (23x18cm-9x7in) s. paper. 24-Jul-4 Thierry & Lannon, Brest #120/R est:1500-2000
£1197 $2095 €1700 Bretonne a la voile mauve (10x15cm-4x6in) studio st. paper on canvas. 21-Dec-3 Thierry & Lannon, Brest #141/R est:2000-2500
£1208 $2235 €1800 Personnages en burnous sous les palmiers (13x15cm-5x6in) s. 15-Mar-4 Gros & Delettrez, Paris #137/R est:2000-3000
£1208 $2235 €1800 Jeune fille Algerienne en costume de fete (18x12cm-7x5in) s. oil paper on canvas. 15-Mar-4 Gros & Delettrez, Paris #139/R est:1800-2500
£1268 $2218 €1800 Repos sous l'arbre en Algerie (15x18cm-6x7in) studio st. paper on canvas. 21-Dec-3 Thierry & Lannon, Brest #143 est:1500-1800
£1325 $2477 €2000 Notre Dame de Vie, les grands arbres (21x23cm-8x9in) s. paper. 24-Jul-4 Thierry & Lannon, Brest #119/R est:1500-2000
£1733 $3103 €2600 Bretonne sur le chemin rose (15x22cm-6x9in) s. paper. 16-May-4 Thierry & Lannon, Brest #104/R est:2000-2500
£1733 $3103 €2600 Bretonne gardant sa vache en bord de mer, paysage du Pouldu (13x14cm-5x6in) paper painted c.1903. 16-May-4 Thierry & Lannon, Brest #107/R est:2000-2500
£1745 $3228 €2600 Le petit marchand d'oranges sur la cote pres d'Alger (16x11cm-6x4in) s. oil paper on canvas. 15-Mar-4 Gros & Delettrez, Paris #140/R est:2000-3000
£1767 $3162 €2650 Les bains des chevaux sur la plage des roches noires au Pouldu (19x23cm-7x9in) s. paper painted c.1905. 16-May-4 Thierry & Lannon, Brest #109/R est:2500-3000
£1800 $3222 €2700 Bretonnes aux champs, les sarcleuses de pommes de terre (15x16cm-6x6in) cardboard. 16-May-4 Thierry & Lannon, Brest #105/R est:2000-2500
£1901 $3327 €2700 Chaumiere en bordure de mer (16x26cm-6x10in) studio st. panel on canvas. 21-Dec-3 Thierry & Lannon, Brest #134/R est:3000-3500
£1933 $3461 €2900 La plage de Kerrou au Pouldu, paysage aux deux vaches (13x11cm-5x4in) s. paper painted c.1903. 16-May-4 Thierry & Lannon, Brest #108/R est:2000-2500
£2133 $3819 €3200 Jeune fille au bain (15x13cm-6x5in) s. paper. 16-May-4 Thierry & Lannon, Brest #106/R est:2000-2500
£2133 $3925 €3200 Vue de la Baie d'Alger depuis la Terrasse de la Villa Abd-El-tif (27x35cm-11x14in) s. 14-Jun-4 Gros & Delettrez, Paris #363/R est:2000-3000
£2252 $4211 €3400 Le gardien de vache au Pouldu (19x16cm-7x6in) s. paper. 24-Jul-4 Thierry & Lannon, Brest #118/R est:2000-3000
£2384 $4458 €3600 Paris, vapeur sur la Seine (50x65cm-20x26in) s.verso. 24-Jul-4 Thierry & Lannon, Brest #121/R est:3000-4000
£2394 $4190 €3400 Petite maison rose (16x14cm-6x6in) studio st. paper on canvas. 21-Dec-3 Thierry & Lannon, Brest #140/R est:2000-2500
£2465 $4313 €3500 Animation pres du parasol sur la place de l'eglise (34x33cm-13x13in) studio st. paper on canvas. 21-Dec-3 Thierry & Lannon, Brest #136/R est:3500-4500
£2583 $4830 €3900 Le lavoir et le gardien de vaches (28x21cm-11x8in) 24-Jul-4 Thierry & Lannon, Brest #122/R est:3000-3500
£2676 $4683 €3800 Phare et les mats rouges a Monaco (24x22cm-9x9in) s.d.30 paper on canvas. 21-Dec-3 Thierry & Lannon, Brest #138/R est:4000-4500
£3041 $5443 €4500 Eve tentee par le serpent (46x38cm-18x15in) i.verso isorel. 7-May-4 Millon & Associes, Paris #78/R est:5000-6000
£3662 $6408 €5200 Moulin sur L'Aven (31x29cm-12x11in) studio st. paper on canvas. 21-Dec-3 Thierry & Lannon, Brest #a2
£3826 $7077 €5700 La Baie d'Alger vue des hauteurs de la Villa Abd-el-Tif (25x33cm-10x13in) s. 15-Mar-4 Gros & Delettrez, Paris #138/R est:3000-5000
£3867 $7115 €5800 La conversation (32x29cm-13x11in) s. oil paper on canvas. 14-Jun-4 Gros & Delettrez, Paris #364/R est:3000-4000
£4730 $8466 €7000 La chapelle Notre Dame de la pitie en Guidel (30x26cm-12x10in) mono. painted c.1895 prov.lit. 7-May-4 Millon & Associes, Paris #80/R est:8000-12000
£9718 $17007 €13800 Gardien de vaches en bord de mer houleuse (32x31cm-13x12in) s. paper. 21-Dec-3 Thierry & Lannon, Brest #276/R est:9000-10000
Prints
£2334 $4224 €3500 Femmes au tub (33x21cm-13x8in) col woodcut. 31-Mar-4 Tajan, Paris #82/R est:2000-2500
Works on paper
£282 $493 €400 A l'ombre du grand arbre (18x12cm-7x5in) s. wash gouache. 16-Dec-3 Adjug'art, Brest #356
£296 $518 €420 Sur le petit pont (21x18cm-8x7in) studio st. wax crayon. 21-Dec-3 Thierry & Lannon, Brest #426
£298 $557 €450 Le pignon (12x15cm-5x6in) chl col crayon. 24-Jul-4 Thierry & Lannon, Brest #93
£352 $616 €500 Paysage aux chaumieres (15x15cm-6x6in) studio st. col crayons. 21-Dec-3 Thierry & Lannon, Brest #429
£458 $801 €650 Pouldu - Le Pardon de La Pitie (26x19cm-10x7in) studio st. pen. 21-Dec-3 Thierry & Lannon, Brest #425
£1620 $2835 €2300 Paysage anime aux grands arbres (22x21cm-9x8in) studio st. mixed media. 21-Dec-3 Thierry & Lannon, Brest #142 est:2300-2500
£4366 $7641 €6200 Cavalier sur le chemin (34x28cm-13x11in) s.d.48 mixed media. 21-Dec-3 Thierry & Lannon, Brest #139/R est:5000-6000

BEAUGUREAU, Francis Henry (1920-1991) American
Works on paper
£341 $600 €498 Stream running through a pasture with a farm in the background (43x66cm-17x26in) s. W/C. 3-Jan-4 Cobbs, Peterborough #94/R

BEAUJOUR, Claude (1934-) French
£4345 $7212 €6300 Ballet pantomime (146x114cm-57x45in) s.d. acrylic. 1-Oct-3 Millon & Associes, Paris #272 est:150-200

BEAULIEU, Henri de (1819-1884) French
£1783 $2978 €2550 Oriental figures by garden pond in front of palace wall (80x124cm-31x49in) s.d.1865. 28-Jun-3 Dannenberg, Berlin #652/R est:2500

BEAULIEU, Paul Vanier (1910-1995) Canadian
£444 $769 €648 Portrait de femme (25x20cm-10x8in) s.d.47 canvas on board. 15-Dec-3 Iegor de Saint Hippolyte, Montreal #3b (C.D 1000)
£880 $1610 €1285 Cottage. Abstract (22x26cm-9x10in) s. two. 1-Jun-4 Joyner Waddington, Toronto #506 est:800-1200 (C.D 2200)
£1126 $1914 €1644 The dance (19x24cm-7x9in) s. board prov. 27-Nov-3 Heffel, Vancouver #176 est:3000-3500 (C.D 2500)
£1321 $2365 €1929 Three nudes in a landscape (30x35cm-12x14in) s.d.45 prov. 31-May-4 Sotheby's, Toronto #89/R est:3000-5000 (C.D 3250)
£1840 $3367 €2686 L'Egyptienne (55x45cm-22x18in) s. painted 1944 prov. 1-Jun-4 Joyner Waddington, Toronto #170/R est:3500-4500 (C.D 4600)
£2846 $5093 €4155 Nature morte avec chat (35x30cm-14x12in) s.d.47 prov. 31-May-4 Sotheby's, Toronto #87/R est:3000-4000 (C.D 7000)

£3252	$5821	€4748	Still life with black vase (61x51cm-24x20in) s.d.45 prov. 31-May-4 Sotheby's, Toronto #34/R est:7000-9000 (C.D 8000)
£4878	$8732	€7122	Nude (61x51cm-24x20in) s.d.43 prov. 31-May-4 Sotheby's, Toronto #9/R est:8000-10000 (C.D 12000)
Works on paper			
£536	$921	€783	Landscape in red and orange (44x55cm-17x22in) s.d.71 gouache. 2-Dec-3 Joyner Waddington, Toronto #214/R (C.D 1200)
£580	$998	€847	Landscape with purple sky (44x55cm-17x22in) s.d.71 gouache. 2-Dec-3 Joyner Waddington, Toronto #163/R (C.D 1300)
£640	$1171	€934	Bouquet roussatre (30x46cm-12x18in) s.d.57 W/C prov. 1-Jun-4 Joyner Waddington, Toronto #322/R (C.D 1600)
£640	$1171	€934	Marguerites (30x46cm-12x18in) s.d.57 W/C prov. 1-Jun-4 Joyner Waddington, Toronto #323/R (C.D 1600)
£1022	$1768	€1492	Poire et pomme (32x50cm-13x20in) s.d.70 ink pastel. 15-Dec-3 Iegor de Saint Hippolyte, Montreal #3 (C.D 2300)
£1667	$3050	€2434	Fantaisie (56x76cm-22x30in) s.d.46 gouache. 27-Jan-4 Iegor de Saint Hippolyte, Montreal #2 (C.D 4000)

BEAUMONT, Arthur Edwaine (1890-1978) American

Works on paper			
£2646	$5000	€3863	Rancher with rifle/truck (25x43cm-10x17in) s.d.1939 W/C prov. 17-Feb-4 John Moran, Pasadena #85/R est:2500-3500
£4396	$8000	€6418	Shipyard 3A Richmond, Cal (38x48cm-15x19in) s.i.d.1942 W/C prov. 15-Jun-4 John Moran, Pasadena #131 est:1500-2500

BEAUMONT, Arthur J (1877-1956) American

£260	$450	€380	Nether Bridge, Kendal (13x20cm-5x8in) init. 11-Dec-3 Neales, Nottingham #614/R
£700	$1295	€1022	St. Ives harbour (25x28cm-10x11in) s. board. 10-Feb-4 David Lay, Penzance #406/R
£1300	$2171	€1898	St. Ives Bay (61x107cm-24x42in) s. 14-Oct-3 David Lay, Penzance #590/R est:1000-2000
Works on paper			
£1630	$3000	€2445	US Saint Paul on the Yangtze, China (37x47cm-15x19in) s. W/C pencil. 8-Jun-4 Auctions by the Bay, Alameda #1067/R

BEAUMONT, Charles Edouard de (1812-1888) French

£2797	$4811	€4000	Young boy eating cherries in a tree (61x40cm-24x16in) s. painted oval. 2-Dec-3 Christie's, Paris #357/R est:4000-6000
£6575	$11178	€9600	Marchand d'esclaves (45x60cm-18x24in) s. 6-Nov-3 Sotheby's, Paris #130/R est:2000-3000
£7877	$13390	€11500	Femmes au harem (45x60cm-18x24in) s.d.1860. 6-Nov-3 Sotheby's, Paris #139/R est:3000-5000
£14085	$24366	€20000	Conseil au harem (46x60cm-18x24in) s.d.1860 prov. 15-Dec-3 Gros & Delettrez, Paris #464/R est:22000-30000
Works on paper			
£680	$1218	€1000	La guerre. La paix (12x18cm-5x7in) mono.i. crayon W/C gouache pair. 17-Mar-4 Maigret, Paris #116/R

BEAUMONT, Chris (20th C) Australian

£447	$702	€648	Still life with cabbage and shorthand (101x83cm-40x33in) s.i.d.1990 verso. 27-Aug-3 Christie's, Sydney #604 (A.D 1100)

BEAUMONT, Claudio Francesco (circle) (1694-1766) Italian

£11000	$19800	€16060	Venus and Adonis (103x128cm-41x50in) 23-Apr-4 Christie's, Kensington #266/R est:4000-6000

BEAUQUESNE, Wilfrid Constant (attrib) (1847-1913) French

£778	$1300	€1136	Battle scene (25x30cm-10x12in) 20-Jun-3 Freeman, Philadelphia #252/R

BEAUVAIS, Arnold (1886-?) British

£1150	$2151	€1679	Port Isaac (56x68cm-22x27in) s.d.1964. 20-Jul-4 Sworder & Son, Bishops Stortford #675/R est:850-950

BEAUVAIS, Lubin de (19/20th C) French

Works on paper			
£1020	$1622	€1500	Elegantes a la Belle Epoque (26x21cm-10x8in) s. W/C. 21-Mar-3 Bailly Pommery, Paris #88 est:1500-1800

BEAUVAIS, Walter (1942-) British

£250	$465	€365	Riverside (31x50cm-12x20in) s. board. 7-Mar-4 Lots Road Auctions, London #364
£260	$481	€380	At the party (29x23cm-11x9in) s. canvas on board. 15-Jan-4 Christie's, Kensington #998
£260	$481	€380	Performance at the theatre (62x44cm-24x17in) mono. 15-Jan-4 Christie's, Kensington #1007
£260	$478	€380	Regatta (61x117cm-24x46in) s. 23-Mar-4 Rosebery Fine Art, London #984
£280	$501	€409	River scene (17x34cm-7x13in) mono. panel. 11-Jan-4 Lots Road Auctions, London #372
£280	$493	€409	Boating lake (51x76cm-20x30in) s. 18-May-4 Bonhams, Knightsbridge #9/R
£300	$555	€438	At the boat race (40x50cm-16x20in) s. 15-Jan-4 Christie's, Kensington #1002
£300	$540	€438	Figures in a crowded park (39x54cm-15x21in) s. board. 20-Jan-4 Bonhams, Knightsbridge #54
£300	$555	€438	Beach scene (15x27cm-6x11in) mono. board. 18-Jan-4 Lots Road Auctions, London #336
£300	$555	€438	Beach scene (39x49cm-15x19in) s. board. 15-Feb-4 Lots Road Auctions, London #336/R
£300	$561	€450	Boating on the Somme (25x30cm-10x12in) s. wood panel. 22-Jul-4 Gorringes, Lewes #1959
£320	$576	€467	Deauville (20x25cm-8x10in) mono. board. 20-Jan-4 Bonhams, Knightsbridge #85
£320	$592	€467	Park scene, Paris (15x23cm-6x9in) s. board. 18-Jan-4 Lots Road Auctions, London #337/R
£320	$563	€467	Summer on the beach (41x51cm-16x20in) s. prov. 19-May-4 Christie's, Kensington #756/R
£325	$582	€475	Beach promenade (46x61cm-18x24in) s. plywood on panel. 4-May-4 Ritchie, Toronto #49/R (C.D 800)
£340	$632	€496	Street scene (25x18cm-10x7in) mono. board. 7-Mar-4 Lots Road Auctions, London #366
£350	$648	€511	A day at the beach (51x61cm-20x24in) s. 15-Jan-4 Christie's, Kensington #1000/R
£360	$648	€526	Looking out to sea (21x36cm-8x14in) mono. board. 20-Jan-4 Bonhams, Knightsbridge #29
£360	$666	€526	Harbour scene (18x24cm-7x9in) s. board. 18-Jan-4 Lots Road Auctions, London #338/R
£360	$634	€526	Family on the beach (50x64cm-20x25in) s. canvasboard. 18-May-4 Bonhams, Knightsbridge #178/R
£370	$688	€540	Coastal scene (28x35cm-11x14in) mono. board. 7-Mar-4 Lots Road Auctions, London #365
£380	$692	€555	Sailing boats (29x39cm-11x15in) mono. board. 8-Feb-4 Lots Road Auctions, London #348
£380	$718	€555	Watching the Sailboats (35x46cm-14x18in) mono. board. 22-Feb-4 Lots Road Auctions, London #336
£400	$720	€584	Busy day on the beach (53x72cm-21x28in) s. 20-Jan-4 Bonhams, Knightsbridge #24/R
£400	$720	€584	Figures on a beach with a red awning (44x54cm-17x21in) board. 20-Jan-4 Bonhams, Knightsbridge #55
£400	$704	€584	Figures in the park (30x50cm-12x20in) mono. canvasboard. 18-May-4 Bonhams, Knightsbridge #153
£400	$704	€584	Three children on a beach (51x41cm-20x16in) s. 18-May-4 Bonhams, Knightsbridge #154
£407	$728	€594	Figures strolling the beach at low tide (57x82cm-22x32in) s. board. 4-May-4 Ritchie, Toronto #50/R est:1200-1600 (C.D 1000)
£420	$743	€613	Beach with French flag (20x31cm-8x12in) s. board. 27-Apr-4 Bonhams, Knightsbridge #65
£500	$915	€730	Beach scene (51x75cm-20x30in) s. 1-Feb-4 Lots Road Auctions, London #344
£520	$931	€759	Beach scene (16x35cm-6x14in) s. panel. 11-Jan-4 Lots Road Auctions, London #371
£650	$1144	€949	Two children playing in the sea (68x95cm-27x37in) s. 18-May-4 Bonhams, Knightsbridge #181/R
£1250	$2288	€1825	Boat race (49x74cm-19x29in) s. 1-Feb-4 Lots Road Auctions, London #343

BEAUVALLET, Pierre Nicolas (1750-1818) French

Sculpture			
£21127	$36549	€30000	Narcisse (150cm-59in) plaster exhib.lit. 15-Dec-3 Sotheby's, Paris #128/R est:40000-60000

BEAUVERIE, Charles Joseph (1839-1924) French

£1429	$2600	€2100	Les barques au bord de la riviere (40x32cm-16x13in) s.indis.d. panel. 8-Feb-4 Anaf, Lyon #100 est:2500-3000
£4615	$7938	€6600	Bords de l'Oise pres d'Auvers-sur-Oise (38x63cm-15x25in) s. painted c.1872-1875. 7-Dec-3 Osenat, Fontainebleau #96 est:5000-5500
£8741	$15035	€12500	La vallee d'Optevox l'apres-midi. Paysage du Lignon (37x61cm-15x24in) s. pair. 7-Dec-3 Osenat, Fontainebleau #113

BEAUVILLIERS, Paul Hippolyte de (1684-1776) French?

Works on paper			
£775	$1356	€1100	Un paysage fluvial, avec une maison en ruine (7x11cm-3x4in) i. pen black ink prov. 17-Dec-3 Christie's, Paris #63/R

BEAUX, Cecilia (1855-1942) American

£70588	$120000	€103058	Portrait of Helena Dorothea McGrew (62x46cm-24x18in) s. prov. 21-Nov-3 Skinner, Boston #355/R est:25000-35000
Works on paper			
£1882	$3200	€2748	Emily and Will Biddle at the seashore (14x22cm-6x9in) pen ink prov.exhib. 21-Nov-3 Skinner, Boston #356/R est:1200-1800
£2647	$4500	€3865	Portrait of Rodman Gilder (49x35cm-19x14in) init. graphite. 21-Nov-3 Skinner, Boston #358/R est:3500-5500

BEAVIS, Richard (1824-1896) British

£320	$586	€467	Mountain goats at a tributary of the Rhone (25x36cm-10x14in) s.d.1872 i.verso. 8-Apr-4 Christie's, Kensington #187/R
£550	$952	€803	Clearing timber, Brittany (30x51cm-12x20in) s. s.i.verso. 9-Dec-3 Rosebery Fine Art, London #560/R
£700	$1302	€1022	On the hills (20x30cm-8x12in) s.i. prov. 4-Mar-4 Christie's, Kensington #474/R
£4037	$6500	€5894	Rounding up! (86x61cm-34x24in) s. 14-Jan-4 Christie's, Rockefeller NY #58/R est:4000-6000
£7500	$13725	€10950	Two clippers under full sail with a school of dolphins in the foreground (38x53cm-15x21in) s.d.1890 two. 8-Jul-4 Duke & Son, Dorchester #188/R est:7000-10000
£12000	$18840	€17520	Dunnottar Castle (109x159cm-43x63in) s.i.d.1863. 27-Aug-3 Sotheby's, London #904/R est:12000-18000

BECCAFUMI, Domenico (1486-1551) Italian

£206667	$376133	€310000	Madonna and Child with Saints (70x48cm-28x19in) board lit. 4-Jul-4 Finarte, Venice #51/R est:180000-250000
Prints			
£5294	$9000	€7729	Two male nudes in landscape (27x17cm-11x7in) engraving. 31-Oct-3 Sotheby's, New York #129/R

BECCAFUMI, Domenico (style) (1486-1551) Italian

£5594	$9343	€8000	Madonna and Child with Saint John and a holy woman (40x30cm-16x12in) board. 7-Oct-3 Pandolfini, Florence #527/R est:6000-8000

BECCARIA, Angelo (1820-1897) Italian

£733	$1349	€1100	Landscape (8x16cm-3x6in) s. board. 14-Jun-4 Sant Agostino, Torino #229/R

£6383 $10340 €9000 Diana and Acteon (60x78cm-24x31in) 21-May-3 Babuino, Rome #190/R

BECCHI, Andrea (1849-1926) Italian

£791 $1298 €1100 Woman (88x110cm-35x43in) 5-Jun-3 Adma, Formigine #630
£1370 $2329 €2000 View of town (61x43cm-24x17in) s.d.1878. 7-Nov-3 Tuttarte, Modena #651 est:2500-3000
£1588 $2477 €2350 Out from church (55x45cm-22x18in) 30-Mar-3 Adma, Formigine #1073 est:2000-2200

BECDELIEVRE, François Gabriel (1778-1855) French

Works on paper
£343 $583 €500 Portrait du general Theodore de Lameth (16x12cm-6x5in) i.indis.d.wash brush gouache prov. 6-Nov-3 Tajan, Paris #206

BECH, Almar (19/20th C) Scandinavian

£1729 $2732 €2507 Interior scene with figure seated seen from behind (71x93cm-28x37in) i.verso panel. 3-Sep-3 Museumsbygningen, Copenhagen #160/R est:12000 (D.KR 18500)

BECH, Poul Anker (1942-) Danish

£379 $701 €553 Winter evening behind the monastery wall (27x35cm-11x14in) s. 15-Mar-4 Rasmussen, Vejle #629/R (D.KR 4200)
£722 $1329 €1054 House with barbecue on terrace (39x59cm-15x23in) s. masonite. 29-Mar-4 Rasmussen, Copenhagen #421/R (D.KR 8000)
£1895 $3487 €2767 Morning coffee (105x80cm-41x31in) s. s.d.1990 verso prov. 29-Mar-4 Rasmussen, Copenhagen #339 est:12000 (D.KR 21000)
£2527 $4650 €3689 Transformator - September afternoon (108x98cm-43x39in) s.d.1985 verso prov. 29-Mar-4 Rasmussen, Copenhagen #315/R est:15000 (D.KR 28000)
£2527 $4726 €3689 Summer episode (105x135cm-41x53in) s. 25-Feb-4 Kunsthallen, Copenhagen #53/R est:25000 (D.KR 28000)
£2843 $5316 €4151 The view (98x135cm-39x53in) s. 25-Feb-4 Kunsthallen, Copenhagen #42/R est:25000 (D.KR 31500)

BECHARD, Emile (19th C) French

Photographs
£20000 $35200 €29200 Voyage dans la Haute Egypte et Nubie (27x37cm-11x15in) albumen prints albumen prov.lit. 19-May-4 Christie's, London #109/R est:20000-30000

BECHER, Arthur Ernst (1877-1960) American

£598 $1100 €873 Illustration for the vanishing men (74x51cm-29x20in) s. 25-Mar-4 Doyle, New York #6 est:600-800
Works on paper
£376 $700 €549 In pursuit (17x22cm-7x9in) s. W/C gouache paper on board. 5-Mar-4 Skinner, Boston #485a/R

BECHER, Bernd and Hilla (20th C) German

Photographs
£1630 $3000 €2380 Cooling tower, Stahwerk, Hagen-Haste (74x60cm-29x24in) s.num.60 triplex print prov. 10-Jun-4 Phillips, New York #508/R est:3000-5000
£2639 $4486 €3800 Timbered houses in Siegen industrial area (22x17cm-9x7in) i. verso gelatin silver lit. 30-Oct-3 Van Ham, Cologne #12/R est:400
£2994 $5000 €4371 Montabaur Westerfeld, Germany (61x51cm-24x20in) s.num.1/5 verso gelatin silver print exec 1989 prov. 12-Nov-3 Christie's, Rockefeller NY #585/R est:5000-7000
£3611 $6500 €5272 Cooling tower, Hagen-Haspe, Germany (41x33cm-16x13in) s.num.55 prov.lit. 23-Apr-4 Phillips, New York #110/R est:5000-7000
£3667 $6747 €5500 Youngstown Works blast furnace 5 (40x331cm-16x130in) s.i.d. silver gelatin board. 10-Jun-4 Villa Grisebach, Berlin #1015/R est:6000-8000
£3800 $6992 €5700 Factory in Freudenberg, Siegen (16x21cm-6x8in) silver gelatin two lit.exhib. 10-Jun-4 Villa Grisebach, Berlin #1014/R est:3000-4000
£4000 $6680 €5840 Winding tower, Wales (30x40cm-12x16in) gelatin silver print exec 1967 prov. 21-Oct-3 Sotheby's, London #316/R est:4000-6000
£4444 $8000 €6488 Schotterwerk, kirchberg bei crailsheim (64x51cm-25x20in) i.d.1989 s.verso gelatin silver print. 23-Apr-4 Phillips, New York #11/R est:10000-15000
£7186 $12000 €10492 Zeche Constantin I Bochum, Ruhr Textile Factory Mettman W G (51x41cm-20x16in) s.i.num. d. gelatin silver print on board exec 1988 prov. 12-Nov-3 Christie's, Rockefeller NY #578/R est:10000-15000
£7200 $13248 €10512 Wasserturme in Honfleur (30x40cm-12x16in) s.d.1970 i.verso gelatin silver print prov. 24-Jun-4 Sotheby's, Olympia #437/R est:4000-6000
£9500 $17480 €13870 Transformator (30x40cm-12x16in) s.d.69 gelatin silver print prov. 24-Jun-4 Sotheby's, London #275/R est:8000-10000
£10778 $18000 €15736 Water towers (158x122cm-62x48in) s.verso gelatin silver print pair lit. 16-Oct-3 Phillips, New York #39/R est:20000-30000
£11976 $20000 €17485 Industriebauten (19x15cm-7x6in) gelatin silver print ten box lit. 20-Oct-3 Christie's, Rockefeller NY #240/R est:18000-20000
£17964 $30000 €26227 Winding towers, Germany, France, Britain, perspective views (41x32cm-16x13in) s.i.num.1-6 verso black white photo six prov. 13-Nov-3 Sotheby's, New York #507/R est:30000-40000
£20958 $35000 €30599 Blast Furnaces (41x30cm-16x12in) gelatin silver prints on board on panel exec 1979-86 six prov. 12-Nov-3 Christie's, Rockefeller NY #577/R est:30000-40000
£21229 $38000 €30994 Blast furnaces (50x40cm-20x16in) one s.verso num.1-8 verso gelatin silver print board eight prov. 12-May-4 Christie's, Rockefeller NY #426/R est:40000-60000
£22599 $40000 €32995 Water tower (40x31cm-16x12in) s.num.1-6 gelatin silver print six sequence lit. 27-Apr-4 Christie's, Rockefeller NY #357/R est:25000-30000
£26816 $48000 €39151 Wasserturme-kugeln (45x55cm-18x22in) num.I-IV verso gelatin silver print six prov.exhib. 12-May-4 Christie's, Rockefeller NY #427/R est:35000-45000
£27841 $49000 €40648 Industrial facades (30x40cm-12x16in) with sig. 12 silver print. 20-May-4 Swann Galleries, New York #515/R est:20000-30000
£30168 $54000 €44045 Typologie - Cooling towers (40x30cm-16x12in) gelatin silver print on board 9 parts exec 1989 exhib.lit. 13-May-4 Sotheby's, New York #384/R est:40000-60000
£32934 $55000 €48084 Blast Furnace landscapes (30x40cm-12x16in) each init.num. gelatin silver print twelve exec 1985 prov. 12-Nov-3 Christie's, Rockefeller NY #575/R est:60000-80000
£35000 $64400 €51100 3 Kuhlturme - 3 cooling towers (40x30cm-16x12in) s.d.63-65-67 gelatin silver print three parts prov.lit. 23-Jun-4 Sotheby's, London #18/R est:30000-40000
£45000 $81900 €65700 Blast furnaces typologie (174x192cm-69x76in) gelatin silver prints on cardboard twelve exec 1989 exhib.lit. 5-Feb-4 Sotheby's, London #44/R est:40000-60000
£83799 $150000 €122347 Hochofen - blast furnaces (55x45cm-22x18in) 22 gelatin silver print executed 1997 prov.exhib.lit. 13-May-4 Phillips, New York #33/R est:60000-80000

BECHER, Ulrich (1910-1990) German

Works on paper
£515 $912 €752 Street scene (28x21cm-11x8in) mono. W/C pencil exec. c.1928. 12-Jun-4 Falk & Falk, Zurich #802 (S.FR 1200)
£644 $1139 €940 Place Blanche, Paris (26x26cm-10x10in) s.i. W/C htd silver board exec. 1927. 12-Jun-4 Falk & Falk, Zurich #804 est:900 (S.FR 1500)

BECHI, Luigi (1830-1919) Italian

£728 $1326 €1100 Peasant woman (27x20cm-11x8in) s. 21-Jun-4 Pandolfini, Florence #121
£9333 $17173 €14000 Les conti acquisto (90x65cm-35x26in) s.i.d.1863 verso. 11-Jun-4 Claude Aguttes, Neuilly #5b/R est:12000-15000
£9412 $16000 €13742 Moment of contemplation (30x42cm-12x17in) s. panel. 19-Nov-3 Bonhams & Butterfields, San Francisco #50/R
£16500 $28380 €24090 La raccolta delle olive (96x63cm-38x25in) s. prov. 3-Dec-3 Christie's, London #42/R est:8000-12000
£18000 $32400 €26280 Father's pipe (57x69cm-22x27in) s. 21-Jan-4 Sotheby's, Olympia #456/R est:18000-25000
£49699 $82500 €72561 Cat Nap (132x94cm-52x37in) s. 4-Oct-3 Neal Auction Company, New Orleans #199/R est:50000-80000

BECHLY, Adolf Friedrich (1918-) German

£828 $1531 €1200 Seated woman with fan (92x63cm-36x25in) mono.d.55 board. 14-Feb-4 Hans Stahl, Hamburg #123/R

BECHT, Eduard August (1868-1931) Dutch

£411 $699 €600 Sheep pen in the snow (19x26cm-7x10in) s. marouflе. 5-Nov-3 Vendue Huis, Gravenhage #240/R

BECHTEJEFF, Wladimir Georgiewitsch (1878-1971) Russian

£29371 $49930 €42000 Landscape near Murnau (52x70cm-20x28in) mono. prov. 26-Nov-3 Lempertz, Koln #582/R est:35000-40000

BECHTOLD, Erwin (1925-) German

£299 $500 €437 NO.4 gray (41x33cm-16x13in) s.d.59 s.verso. 15-Nov-3 Sloans & Kenyon, Bethesda #93/R
£423 $739 €600 Painting 81-19 (22x12cm-9x5in) s.i.d.1981 acrylic pencil. 16-Dec-3 Segre, Madrid #221/R
£986 $1577 €1400 Painting 78-22 (40x35cm-16x14in) s.i.d.1978 verso prov.exhib. 16-Sep-3 Segre, Madrid #138/R
£1049 $1752 €1500 Untitled no. 13 (55x55cm-22x22in) s.d.1967 prov. 24-Jun-3 Segre, Madrid #115/R est:1200

BECK, Billy de (1890-1942) American

Works on paper
£898 $1500 €1311 Barney, Spark Plug and Pony Boy wind up as a window display (10x43cm-4x17in) s.d.1931 pen ink. 15-Nov-3 Illustration House, New York #60/R est:1800-2600
£1078 $1800 €1574 Snuffy and Barney arrive at the cabin in time for a surprise party (36x43cm-14x17in) s. pen ink. 15-Nov-3 Illustration House, New York #61/R est:1500-2500

BECK, Christian Frederik (1876-1954) Danish

£609 $1016 €889 Farmhouse at sunset (171x63cm-67x25in) init.d.1900. 25-Oct-3 Rasmussen, Havnen #2021/R (D.KR 6500)

BECK, David (attrib) (1621-1656) Dutch

£10769 $18523 €15723 Portrait of King Karl X Gustaf (120x91cm-47x36in) prov.lit. 2-Dec-3 Bukowskis, Stockholm #297/R est:60000-80000 (S.KR 140000)

BECK, Jacob Samuel (attrib) (1715-1778) German

£1944 $3169 €2800 Polecat with hens (69x103cm-27x41in) 24-Sep-3 Neumeister, Munich #333/R est:2800
Works on paper
£2533 $4535 €3800 Hen with chicks (49x86cm-19x34in) pastel canvas oval lit. 14-May-4 Schloss Ahlden, Ahlden #2767/R est:1800

BECK, Jacob Samuel (circle) (1715-1778) German

£5000 $9150 €7300 Still life with duck, partridges, pigeons and other birds, basket of vegetables (97x131cm-38x52in) 6-Jul-4 Sotheby's, Olympia #560/R est:6000-8000

BECK, Julia (1853-1935) Swedish

£2829 $4554 €4130 Lake with water lilies (50x134cm-20x53in) s. 25-Aug-3 Lilla Bukowskis, Stockholm #8 est:10000-15000 (S.KR 37000)
£6923 $11908 €10108 Spring landscape at dusk, France (110x52cm-43x20in) s. 3-Dec-3 AB Stockholms Auktionsverk #2532/R est:80000-100000 (S.KR 90000)

BECK, Leonard (1480-1542) German

£3500 $6300 €5110 Portrait of a lady, standing by a table (57x44cm-22x17in) prov.lit. 23-Apr-4 Christie's, Kensington #8/R est:4000-6000

BECKER, Adolf von (1831-1909) Finnish

£2517 $4280 €3600 Still life of pears (27x35cm-11x14in) s.d.1901. 29-Nov-3 Bukowskis, Helsinki #25b/R est:2500-4000
£5594 $9510 €8000 Man fishing from rock (27x35cm-11x14in) s.i. board. 29-Nov-3 Bukowskis, Helsinki #77/R est:8000-10000
£6081 $10885 €9000 Wearing national costume (68x48cm-27x19in) s.d.70. 8-May-4 Bukowskis, Helsinki #84/R est:6000-9000

£12727 $21636 €18200 The story book - Interior scene with children (35x27cm-14x11in) s. exhib. 29-Nov-3 Bukowskis, Helsinki #31/R est:15000-17000

BECKER, Albert (1830-1896) German
£2098 $3566 €3000 After a night of drinking (77x62cm-30x24in) s. i.verso lit. 28-Nov-3 Schloss Ahlden, Ahlden #1418/R est:3500
£2098 $3566 €3000 Wife sewing hem on her husband's coat as he is about to go out (77x62cm-30x24in) s. i.verso lit. 28-Nov-3 Schloss Ahlden, Ahlden #1419/R est:3500

BECKER, August (1822-1887) German
£355 $592 €500 Fisherwoman with net by sea (31x24cm-12x9in) s.d.1859. 17-Oct-3 Berlinghof, Heidelberg #1004/R
£1007 $1872 €1500 Romantic night-time landscape with a stream inn full moonlight (63x106cm-25x42in) s. 5-Mar-4 Wendl, Rudolstadt #3578/R est:1700
£26667 $48533 €40000 North wall of the Eiger (173x147cm-68x58in) s.d.86. 30-Jun-4 Neumeister, Munich #500/R est:4000

BECKER, Carl (1862-?) German
£490 $817 €700 Fishing boat off Helgoland (18x24cm-7x9in) board. 11-Oct-3 Hans Stahl, Hamburg #133/R
£537 $988 €800 Ship on the high seas (100x125cm-39x49in) i. 29-Mar-4 Dr Fritz Nagel, Stuttgart #7045/R
£1007 $1852 €1500 Fishing boats returning to harbour, Cuxhaven (35x66cm-14x26in) s. 26-Mar-4 Ketterer, Hamburg #3/R est:1800-2000

BECKER, Carl Ludwig Friedrich (1820-1900) German
£6667 $12000 €9734 Triumphal return (92x150cm-36x59in) s.d.1879. 23-Apr-4 Sotheby's, New York #193/R est:25000-35000

BECKER, Claus (1903-1983) German
£637 $981 €1000 Elbe beach (50x57cm-20x22in) s. i. verso panel. 4-Sep-2 Schopman, Hamburg #242/R
£764 $1177 €1200 Boats (50x62cm-20x24in) mono.d.16.4.80. 4-Sep-2 Schopman, Hamburg #240/R
£828 $1275 €1300 Fishing cutter on slipway (50x59cm-20x23in) s. panel. 4-Sep-2 Schopman, Hamburg #241/R
£909 $1564 €1300 Thatched house in Blankenese (58x75cm-23x30in) s.d.1952 board. 4-Dec-3 Schopman, Hamburg #717/R
£1049 $1804 €1500 Hamburg harbour (50x60cm-20x24in) s.d.1970 panel. 4-Dec-3 Schopman, Hamburg #762/R est:1500

BECKER, Curt Georg (1904-1972) German
£979 $1664 €1400 Bathers (52x63cm-20x25in) canvas on panel. 29-Nov-3 Bassenge, Berlin #6623/R
£2055 $3493 €3000 Bathing beach (56x76cm-22x30in) s. 8-Nov-3 Geble, Radolfzell #763/R est:3000

BECKER, Fides (1962-) German
£559 $951 €800 Figures dressed up (182x166cm-72x65in) s.d.1983 verso acrylic cotton. 29-Nov-3 Arnold, Frankfurt #38/R

BECKER, Franz Helmut (1894-1952) German
Works on paper
£400 $720 €600 Italian coast (37x48cm-15x19in) s.i.d. gouache. 24-Apr-4 Dr Lehr, Berlin #47/R

BECKER, Frederick W (1888-1974) American
£405 $700 €591 View of the valley (23x30cm-9x12in) s. board. 13-Dec-3 Charlton Hall, Columbia #576/R
£2312 $4000 €3376 Ranch in the foothills, New Mexico (36x43cm-14x17in) s. paper laid down prov. 10-Dec-3 Bonhams & Butterfields, San Francisco #6108/R est:3000-5000

BECKER, Gerard (1945-) Belgian
£305 $550 €445 Reclining nude (88x115cm-35x45in) s. 25-Apr-4 Bonhams & Butterfields, San Francisco #5616/R

BECKER, Harry (1865-1928) British
£1900 $3553 €2774 Two trees (16x13cm-6x5in) board prov. 24-Feb-4 Canterbury Auctions, UK #162/R est:400-600
£2700 $5049 €3942 Stormy sky (20x24cm-8x9in) prov. 24-Feb-4 Canterbury Auctions, UK #163/R est:800-1200
£3000 $5370 €4380 February day (101x128cm-40x50in) 22-Mar-4 Bonhams & Brooks, Norfolk #255/R est:2000-3000
Works on paper
£400 $716 €584 Sheep (5x20cm-2x8in) with sig. pencil sketch. 17-Mar-4 Neal & Fletcher, Woodbridge #485
£480 $898 €701 Blyth valley (10x14cm-4x6in) W/C prov. 24-Feb-4 Canterbury Auctions, UK #180
£480 $874 €701 Cat lapping milk (13x15cm-5x6in) pencil. 30-Jun-4 Neal & Fletcher, Woodbridge #264
£680 $1272 €993 Summer sky (11x5cm-4x2in) W/C prov. 24-Feb-4 Canterbury Auctions, UK #179

BECKER, Jakob (1810-1872) German
£13889 $22639 €20000 Child in poultry yard (46x28cm-18x11in) s.d.1845. 25-Sep-3 Dr Fritz Nagel, Stuttgart #1332/R est:14000

BECKER, Jakob (attrib) (1810-1872) German
£2937 $5052 €4200 Homecoming soldier (45x37cm-18x15in) s.d.1844. 5-Dec-3 Bolland & Marotz, Bremen #505/R est:600

BECKER, Johann Gottlieb (attrib) (1720-1782) German
£2568 $4596 €3800 Portrait of Sophie Albertine von Werther (82x67cm-32x26in) i.d.1769 verso lit. 8-May-4 Schloss Ahlden, Ahlden #685/R est:2200

BECKER, Joseph Carl J (1841-1910) American
£203 $350 €296 Forest landscape (41x69cm-16x27in) s. 7-Dec-3 Hindman, Chicago #786/R
£233 $400 €340 On point (28x56cm-11x22in) s. 7-Dec-3 Hindman, Chicago #784/R
£320 $550 €467 Palm tree (51x33cm-20x13in) 7-Dec-3 Hindman, Chicago #785/R

BECKER, Josiane (20th C) French
£533 $955 €800 L'ete des tournesols (27x22cm-11x9in) s. 16-May-4 Thierry & Lannon, Brest #201

BECKER, Peter (1828-1904) German
Works on paper
£1067 $1920 €1600 Landscape with shepherd and flock (27x40cm-11x16in) s.d. W/C temper on pencil paper on board. 24-Apr-4 Reiss & Sohn, Konigstein #5466/R est:1500
£3333 $6000 €5000 Frankfurt Cathedral (107x156cm-42x61in) mono.d. wash htd bodycol pencil. 24-Apr-4 Reiss & Sohn, Konigstein #5465/R est:8000

BECKER, Peter (attrib) (1828-1904) German
£1259 $2140 €1800 Village path with figures (42x54cm-17x21in) i. verso board. 22-Nov-3 Arnold, Frankfurt #459/R est:1600

BECKERS, Hans (1898-?) German
£280 $476 €400 Maar in the Eifel (20x30cm-8x12in) s.mono. canvas on board. 20-Nov-3 Van Ham, Cologne #1477

BECKERT, Fritz (1877-?) German
£1088 $1948 €1600 Palais in the Grossen Garten in Dresden (45x60cm-18x24in) s.d.1939 panel lit. 20-Mar-4 Bergmann, Erlangen #1120 est:1600
Works on paper
£350 $601 €500 View of the Castle in Dresden (31x44cm-12x17in) s.i.d.1931 col chk. 3-Dec-3 Neumeister, Munich #370

BECKET, Mike (1946-) British
£360 $612 €526 Small blue pool (25x44cm-10x17in) init.i.verso acrylic on perspex. 18-Nov-3 Bonhams, Knightsbridge #15/R
£360 $612 €526 White pool (31x31cm-12x12in) i.verso acrylic on perspex. 18-Nov-3 Bonhams, Knightsbridge #17/R
£450 $765 €657 Blue pool with figure (38x38cm-15x15in) acrylic on perspex. 18-Nov-3 Bonhams, Knightsbridge #16/R

BECKETT, Clarice (1887-1935) Australian
£3688 $5828 €5384 Beaumaris cliffs (25x30cm-10x12in) canvas board prov. 2-Sep-3 Deutscher-Menzies, Melbourne #108/R est:10000-15000 (A.D 9000)
£5285 $8297 €7663 Beach scene (15x22cm-6x9in) s. board. 27-Aug-3 Christie's, Sydney #536/R est:7000-10000 (A.D 13000)
£5372 $9132 €7843 Beaumaris seascape (19x23cm-7x9in) s. board painted c.1931 exhib. 29-Oct-3 Lawson Menzies, Sydney #136/R est:14000-18000 (A.D 13000)
£6383 $10851 €9319 Collins Street, Melbourne (17x22cm-7x9in) s. s.i.verso compressed card prov. 25-Nov-3 Christie's, Melbourne #101/R est:10000-15000 (A.D 15000)

BECKLES, Evelyn Lina (1888-?) British
£260 $478 €380 Cattle in a field with estuary beyond (23x31cm-9x12in) s. board. 14-Jun-4 Bonhams, Bath #102

BECKMAN, Ford (1952-) American
£867 $1500 €1266 Black wall painting (122x244cm-48x96in) acrylic industrial varnish canvas on plywood prov. 10-Dec-3 Phillips, New York #514/R est:4000-6000
Works on paper
£1267 $2267 €1900 Spook clown/clown face big time (90x72cm-35x28in) s.i.d. verso collage mixed media paper on board. 15-May-4 Van Ham, Cologne #441/R est:1500
£1271 $2250 €1856 Pop painting, red meat (223x178cm-88x70in) s.i.d.1992 mixed media board sold with clown props. 2-May-4 Bonhams & Butterfields, Los Angeles #3077/R est:3000-5000

BECKMANN, Max (1884-1950) German
£140000 $254800 €204400 Bildnis S H (61x35cm-24x14in) s.d.28 prov.exhib.lit. 3-Feb-4 Christie's, London #210/R est:140000-180000
£250000 $457500 €365000 Beached boats (50x71cm-20x28in) s. painted 1937 prov.exhib.lit. 2-Feb-4 Christie's, London #31/R est:250000-350000
£300000 $546000 €438000 Italian woman (55x22cm-22x9in) s.d.47 i.on stretcher prov.exhib.lit. 3-Feb-4 Sotheby's, London #18/R est:200000-300000
£700000 $1281000 €1022000 Breakfast - blue (40x100cm-16x39in) s.d.34 prov.exhib.lit. 2-Feb-4 Christie's, London #32/R est:180000-250000
£1229050 $2200000 €1794413 Reclining nude sharply foreshortened (73x53cm-29x21in) s.d.48 prov.exhib.lit. 6-May-4 Sotheby's, New York #145/R est:1800000-2500000
£1350000 $2470500 €1971000 Woman with flowers (80x61cm-31x24in) s.d.40. 2-Feb-4 Christie's, London #27/R est:600000-800000
Prints
£1765 $3000 €2577 Society (35x47cm-14x19in) s. drypoint exec.1915 prov. 4-Nov-3 Christie's, Rockefeller NY #31/R est:2000-3000
£1882 $3200 €2748 Vor dem auftritt, akrobaten (57x36cm-22x14in) s.num.24/60 lithograph. 6-Nov-3 Swann Galleries, New York #490/R est:4000-6000
£1882 $3200 €2748 Dressing room (44x30cm-17x12in) s. drypoint exec.1925. 4-Nov-3 Christie's, Rockefeller NY #46/R est:3000-5000
£2000 $3580 €3000 Nigger dance (26x25cm-10x10in) s. drypoint prov. 14-May-4 Ketterer, Munich #186/R est:3000-4000
£2200 $3784 €3212 Tanzendes (18x11cm-7x4in) s.num.12/30 woodcut. 2-Dec-3 Christie's, London #87/R est:2000-3000

£2200 $4048 €3300 Taking Jesus down from the cross (30x25cm-12x10in) s. drypoint exec. 1918 one of 60. 12-Jun-4 Villa Grisebach, Berlin #236/R est:3500-4000
£2238 $3849 €3200 Behind the scenes (21x31cm-8x12in) s. drypoint etching. 2-Dec-3 Hauswedell & Nolte, Hamburg #37/R est:5000
£2308 $3969 €3300 Snake lady (29x25cm-11x10in) s. drypoint one of 75 prov. 5-Dec-3 Ketterer, Munich #66/R est:3000-5000
£2353 $4000 €3435 Behind the scenes (21x31cm-8x12in) s. drypoint. 31-Oct-3 Sotheby's, New York #211/R
£2378 $4042 €3400 Uprising (24x34cm-9x13in) s.i.d. etching drypoint. 26-Nov-3 Lempertz, Koln #589/R est:3500
£2378 $4042 €3400 Lovers I (46x61cm-18x24in) s.i.d.16 drypoint etching. 29-Nov-3 Bassenge, Berlin #6628/R est:3500
£2500 $4000 €3650 Liebespaar I (24x30cm-9x12in) s. drypoint edition of 60. 18-Sep-3 Swann Galleries, New York #53/R est:3500-5000
£2500 $4550 €3650 Cafemusik (31x22cm-12x9in) s.i. drypoint. 30-Jun-4 Christie's, London #173/R est:2500-3500
£2533 $4610 €3698 Children playing. s.i. drypoint. 17-Jun-4 Kornfeld, Bern #201/R est:6000 (S.FR 5800)
£2667 $4907 €4000 Minette (25x20cm-10x8in) s. drypoint etching one of 50 exec. 1922. 12-Jun-4 Villa Grisebach, Berlin #230/R est:4500-5500
£2793 $5000 €4078 Das Karussell (29x26cm-11x10in) s. drypoint. 6-May-4 Swann Galleries, New York #394/R est:5000-8000
£2797 $4671 €4000 Boy at window (32x23cm-13x9in) s. drypoint etching. 10-Oct-3 Winterberg, Heidelberg #955/R est:5200
£2797 $4811 €4000 Madhouse (26x30cm-10x12in) s. drypoint etching. 2-Dec-3 Hauswedell & Nolte, Hamburg #35/R est:5000
£2867 $5131 €4300 Spring (30x20cm-12x8in) s.i.d. drypoint etching. 15-May-4 Bassenge, Berlin #6730/R est:6000
£2941 $5000 €4294 Adam and Eve (44x35cm-17x14in) s.d.17 drypoint. 4-Nov-3 Christie's, Rockefeller NY #34/R est:5000-7000
£3147 $5413 €4500 Behind the scenes (21x31cm-8x12in) s. drypoint exec. 1921. 6-Dec-3 Quittenbaum, Hamburg #75/R est:5000
£3231 $5881 €4717 Dream. s.i. drypoint. 17-Jun-4 Kornfeld, Bern #202/R est:6000 (S.FR 7400)
£3235 $5500 €4723 Reclining female nude (48x35cm-19x14in) s. drypoint exec.1922 prov. 4-Nov-3 Christie's, Rockefeller NY #48/R est:5000-7000
£3319 $6040 €4846 Madhouse. s. drypoint. 17-Jun-4 Kornfeld, Bern #196 est:6000 (S.FR 7600)
£3333 $6133 €5000 Lovers (22x25cm-9x10in) s. drypoint exec. 1918 one of 60. 11-Jun-4 Villa Grisebach, Berlin #1558/R est:2000-3000
£3357 $5706 €4800 Beach (21x33cm-8x13in) s. drypoint etching. 29-Nov-3 Bassenge, Berlin #6630/R est:4500
£3497 $6014 €5000 Town crier - self portrait (34x26cm-13x10in) s. drypoint etching. 2-Dec-3 Hauswedell & Nolte, Hamburg #36/R est:6000
£3497 $6014 €5000 Beggar (56x33cm-22x13in) s. lithograph. 2-Dec-3 Hauswedell & Nolte, Hamburg #42/R est:3500
£3497 $5944 €5000 Negro (29x25cm-11x10in) s. drypoint. 29-Nov-3 Villa Grisebach, Berlin #200/R est:3000-4000
£3800 $6916 €5548 Barker (34x26cm-13x10in) s. drypoint. 30-Jun-4 Christie's, London #174/R est:3000-5000
£3911 $7000 €5710 Familienszene - familie Beckmann (31x26cm-12x10in) s.i. drypoint. 6-May-4 Swann Galleries, New York #393/R est:8000-12000
£4000 $7360 €6000 New Year Greetings (24x29cm-9x11in) s.i.d.1917 drypoint etching. 10-Jun-4 Hauswedell & Nolte, Hamburg #38/R est:8000
£4545 $7727 €6500 Woman with candle (30x15cm-12x6in) s. woodcut prov. 28-Nov-3 Villa Grisebach, Berlin #52/R est:5000-7000
£4667 $8587 €7000 Celebrating New Year (23x29cm-9x11in) s.i. drypoint exec. 1917 one of 40. 11-Jun-4 Villa Grisebach, Berlin #1557/R est:3000-4000
£4706 $8000 €6871 Dinner party (35x23cm-14x9in) s. woodcut exec.c.1919 prov. 4-Nov-3 Christie's, Rockefeller NY #37/R est:10000-15000
£4755 $8179 €6800 Minette (25x20cm-10x8in) s.i.d.1922 drypoint etching. 2-Dec-3 Hauswedell & Nolte, Hamburg #39/R est:5000
£5705 $10211 €8500 Self portrait (19x14cm-7x6in) s. drypoint etching. 25-May-4 Karl & Faber, Munich #205/R est:10000-12000
£5882 $10000 €8588 Konigin bar II (51x35cm-20x14in) s. drypoint exec.1923 prov. 4-Nov-3 Christie's, Rockefeller NY #50/R est:7000-10000
£5944 $10224 €8500 New Year toast (24x29cm-9x11in) s. drypoint etching. 2-Dec-3 Hauswedell & Nolte, Hamburg #33/R est:8000
£6294 $10825 €9000 Self portrait (22x15cm-9x6in) s. woodcut. 2-Dec-3 Hauswedell & Nolte, Hamburg #47/R est:10000
£6471 $11000 €9448 Dream I (64x48cm-25x19in) s. drypoint exec.1924 prov. 4-Nov-3 Christie's, Rockefeller NY #52/R est:7000-10000
£7059 $12000 €10306 Sp. (40x30cm-16x12in) s. lithograph exec.1946. 4-Nov-3 Christie's, Rockefeller NY #53/R est:6000-8000
£8000 $14320 €12000 Theatre (30x31cm-12x12in) s.i.d.16 drypoint etching. 15-May-4 Bassenge, Berlin #6726/R est:7500
£8235 $14000 €12023 Woman with candle (46x28cm-18x11in) s. woodcut exec.1920 prov. 4-Nov-3 Christie's, Rockefeller NY #42/R est:18000-20000
£8383 $14000 €12239 Selebstbildnis von vorn, im hintergrund hausgiebel (30x25cm-12x10in) s. drypoint. 11-Nov-3 Doyle, New York #202/R est:10000-15000
£9790 $16839 €14000 Artist in hotel (45x32cm-18x13in) s. num.96/100 lithograph prov. 5-Dec-3 Ketterer, Munich #67/R est:10000-14000
£10588 $18000 €15458 Grenade (64x48cm-25x19in) s.d.1915 drypoint prov. 4-Nov-3 Christie's, Rockefeller NY #29/R est:7000-10000
£12000 $20640 €17520 Day and dream (40x30cm-16x12in) lithograph portfolio of 15. 2-Dec-3 Christie's, London #88/R est:12000-18000
£12000 $22080 €18000 Toilette - in front of the mirror (28x21cm-11x8in) s.i. drypoint etching. 10-Jun-4 Hauswedell & Nolte, Hamburg #42/R est:15000
£13287 $22587 €19000 Self portrait (37x27cm-15x11in) s.i. lithograph prov. 26-Nov-3 Lempertz, Koln #590/R est:18000-20000
£13974 $25432 €20402 Kasbek (49x21cm-19x8in) s. drypoint exec. 1923. 18-Jun-4 Kornfeld, Bern #9/R est:35000 (S.FR 32000)
£14118 $24000 €20612 Dancers (41x32cm-16x13in) s. drypoint exec.1920 prov. 4-Nov-3 Christie's, Rockefeller NY #38/R est:18000-22000
£14118 $24000 €20612 Frontal self-portrait (56x45cm-22x18in) s. drypoint exec.1918. 4-Nov-3 Christie's, Rockefeller NY #36/R est:20000-30000
£17333 $31893 €26000 Self portrait (30x24cm-12x9in) s.i.d.1917 drypoint etching prov. 10-Jun-4 Hauswedell & Nolte, Hamburg #37/R est:25000
£17647 $30000 €25765 Sp. (48x37cm-19x15in) s. drypoint exec.1914 prov. 4-Nov-3 Christie's, Rockefeller NY #28/R est:16000-20000
£18824 $32000 €27483 Annual fair (53x38cm-21x15in) s. drypoint set of 10 prov. 4-Nov-3 Christie's, Rockefeller NY #45/R est:40000-60000
£25328 $46096 €36979 Two women doing their toilette (60x44cm-24x17in) s.i. num.55 woodcut exec. 1923. 18-Jun-4 Kornfeld, Bern #8/R est:40000 (S.FR 58000)
£48000 $87360 €70080 Gesichter. drypoints nineteen portfolio. 1-Jul-4 Sotheby's, London #109/R est:40000-50000
£70588 $120000 €103058 Group portrait (70x56cm-28x22in) s. woodcut exec.1923 prov. 4-Nov-3 Christie's, Rockefeller NY #51/R est:150000-250000

Works on paper
£1958 $3329 €2800 Tegel lido (14x19cm-6x7in) s.i.d.10 pencil board. 26-Nov-3 Lempertz, Koln #584/R est:3000
£2215 $4075 €3300 Woman sitting on man (19x11cm-7x4in) s.i. pencil. 27-Mar-4 Geble, Radolfzell #778/R est:3000
£2657 $4571 €3800 Profile of man smoking and face from front with hat (9x15cm-4x6in) mono.d.1922 pencil prov.exhib. 5-Dec-3 Ketterer, Munich #65/R est:2500-3500
£2778 $4639 €4000 Lazareth (21x29cm-8x11in) s.d.Sept 1914 wash Indian ink exhib.lit. 24-Oct-3 Ketterer, Hamburg #274/R est:4500-5500
£2797 $4755 €4000 Young woman (28x22cm-11x9in) s.d.1901 Indian ink. 26-Nov-3 Lempertz, Koln #583/R est:4000
£2797 $4755 €4000 Self portrait with hat and holding two bottles (26x18cm-10x7in) s.d.22.6.25 pen. 29-Nov-3 Bassenge, Berlin #6026/R est:6000
£3750 $6000 €5475 Zwei Kopfe (29x22cm-11x9in) s.i. pencil exec.c.1915. 18-Sep-3 Swann Galleries, New York #54/R est:7000-10000
£4000 $7160 €6000 Dutch fishermen on beach (18x24cm-7x9in) i. pen prov. 14-May-4 Ketterer, Munich #185/R est:6000-8000
£58000 $106720 €87000 Self portrait (15x12cm-6x5in) s.i.d.15 ink. 10-Jun-4 Hauswedell & Nolte, Hamburg #36/R est:40000

BECKMANN, Wilhelm Robert August (1852-1942) German
£397 $723 €600 Interior scene (66x72cm-26x28in) s. canvas on board. 19-Jun-4 Quittenbaum, Hamburg #2/R
£940 $1729 €1400 Interior (73x59cm-29x23in) s. board. 26-Mar-4 Ketterer, Hamburg #173/R

BECKWITH, Arthur (1860-1930) American
£353 $650 €515 Crashing waves (43x56cm-17x22in) s. 28-Mar-4 Bonhams & Butterfields, San Francisco #2733

BECKWITH, James Carroll (1852-1917) American
£1852 $3000 €2685 Portrait of a lady (26x21cm-10x8in) s.d.1896. 8-Aug-3 Barridorf, Portland #103/R est:4000-6000
£2484 $4000 €3627 Diana (61x46cm-24x18in) s. 20-Aug-3 James Julia, Fairfield #1234/R est:8000-12000
£2841 $5000 €4262 Portrait of Miss Nellie O Pevear (152x114cm-60x45in) i.verso. 21-May-4 North East Auctions, Portsmouth #1462/R
£3514 $6500 €5130 Portrait of Lida Rose McCabe (41x32cm-16x13in) s. gessoed panel. 11-Mar-4 Christie's, Rockefeller NY #26/R est:7000-9000

BECQUEREL, Andre-Vincent (19/20th C) French
Sculpture
£1438 $2445 €2100 Singe acrobate (32cm-13in) s.st.f.Susse pat bronze. 5-Nov-3 Tajan, Paris #18/R
£1987 $3636 €3000 Two racing jockeys (20x57cm-8x22in) s. brown pat. bronze marble wood base. 6-Apr-4 Sotheby's, Olympia #171/R est:3000-5000
£2199 $3672 €3100 Couple de pantheres (67cm-26in) s. terracotta. 12-Oct-3 St-Germain-en-Laye Encheres #92/R est:1500-2000
£10490 $17517 €15000 Caresse (37x63cm-15x25in) s. pat bronze. 29-Jun-3 Eric Pillon, Calais #173/R
£11594 $19014 €16000 Veneciana (38cm-15in) s. ivory pat bronze. 27-May-3 Durán, Madrid #310/R est:6000

BEDA, Francesco (1840-1900) Italian
£15436 $28403 €23000 Scene in the 17th Century (60x99cm-24x39in) s.d.1874. 24-Mar-4 Finarte Semenzato, Rome #13/R est:24000-28000
£30000 $54600 €43800 Game of chess (81x117cm-32x46in) s. 16-Jun-4 Bonhams, New Bond Street #83/R est:30000-40000

BEDA, Giulio (1879-1954) Italian
£559 $934 €800 Evening landscape with deer (21x27cm-8x11in) s. board. 9-Oct-3 Michael Zeller, Lindau #518/R
£694 $1132 €1000 Landscape (45x59cm-18x23in) s. 25-Sep-3 Neumeister, Munich #2738/R

BEDARD, Gilles (1949-) Canadian
£452 $756 €660 Encors une belle hiver, Charlevoix (40x30cm-16x12in) s.i. 17-Nov-3 Hodgins, Calgary #256/R est:700-900 (C.D 1000)

BEDARD, Pierre (1960-) Canadian
£543 $907 €793 La nappe jaune (50x60cm-20x24in) s.i. board. 17-Nov-3 Hodgins, Calgary #28/R est:1000-1300 (C.D 1200)

BEDAT, Celine (20th C) French
Works on paper
£287 $487 €410 Rouge turquoise (60x60cm-24x24in) s. mixed media. 29-Nov-3 Neret-Minet, Paris #182/R
£350 $594 €500 Spiritus Aka (60x60cm-24x24in) s. mixed media canvas. 29-Nov-3 Neret-Minet, Paris #86/R

BEDER, Jack (1909-) Canadian
£446 $768 €651 Douglas painting on the rocks, N S (26x34cm-10x13in) s. panel painted 1947. 2-Dec-3 Joyner Waddington, Toronto #530 (C.D 1000)
£1280 $2342 €1869 Boats at Wharf - Hunt's Point, N S (55x65cm-22x26in) s. painted 1950. 1-Jun-4 Joyner Waddington, Toronto #265/R est:2000-3000 (C.D 3200)
Works on paper
£380 $695 €555 City Hall Avenue - At Lionais, winter 1980 (21x37cm-8x15in) s. W/C exec 1980. 1-Jun-4 Joyner Waddington, Toronto #487 (C.D 950)
£720 $1318 €1051 City street - Henri Julien (74x57cm-29x22in) s. pastel prov. 1-Jun-4 Joyner Waddington, Toronto #253/R est:3000-5000 (C.D 1800)
£1280 $2342 €1869 Tavern (50x60cm-20x24in) s. mixed media. 1-Jun-4 Joyner Waddington, Toronto #130/R est:1500-2000 (C.D 3200)

BEDFORD, Paddy (c.1922-) Australian
Works on paper
£2157 $3861 €3149 Emu dreaming (80x128cm-31x50in) s. verso natural pigments canvas exec 2001. 25-May-4 Lawson Menzies, Sydney #153/R est:6000-8000 (A.D 5500)
£4878 $7707 €7073 Fish hole (122x135cm-48x53in) i.verso earth pigments binder linen prov.exhib. 28-Jul-3 Sotheby's, Paddington #205/R est:8000-12000 (A.D 12000)
£5078 $9496 €7617 Old Bedford Downs station (122x125cm-48x49in) init.i.verso pigment linen exec. 1998 prov.exhib. 21-Jul-4 Shapiro, Sydney #22/R est:7000-9000 (A.D 13000)
£5490 $9827 €8015 Lungun - Women Devil spirits (125x127cm-49x50in) s. verso natural earth pigments canvas exec 2001. 25-May-4 Lawson Menzies, Sydney #21/R est:10000-15000 (A.D 14000)

BEDIA, Jose (1959-) Cuban
£7692 $14000 €11230 Si se quiere se puede (176x244cm-69x96in) s.d.93 acrylic prov. 29-Jun-4 Sotheby's, New York #683/R est:18000-22000
£17647 $30000 €25765 Isla Madre, Yaya, Yayita, Kinfuto (251cm-99in circular) s.i. acrylic collage painted 1992 prov. 18-Nov-3 Christie's, Rockefeller NY #14/R est:30000-35000

BEDIL, Dewa Putu (1921-1999) Indonesian
£3268 $5915 €4771 Harvest time (100x140cm-39x55in) s. 3-Apr-4 Glerum, Singapore #30/R est:6000-7000 (S.D 10000)

BEDINI, Paolo (1844-1924) Italian
£2013 $3564 €3000 Inn (16x22cm-6x9in) s. board lit. 1-May-4 Meeting Art, Vercelli #227 est:1500

BEECHEY, Anne Phyllis (attrib) (1764-1833) British
Miniatures
£3800 $6840 €5548 Princess Amelia (8cm-3in) gold frame oval exhib.lit. 22-Apr-4 Bonhams, New Bond Street #124/R est:1000-1500

BEECHEY, R (19th C) British?
£17500 $29225 €25550 Glengariff Harbour, Bantry Bay, coast of Ireland (89x58cm-35x23in) s.d.1883. 22-Oct-3 Ibbett Mosely, Sevenoaks #1/R

BEECHEY, Sir William (1753-1839) British
£621 $1000 €900 Portrait of the Duke of Kent (76x64cm-30x25in) indis.sig. 17-Aug-3 Jeffery Burchard, Florida #98
£2600 $4342 €3796 Portrait of Richard Cox wearing a brown coat (76x63cm-30x25in) prov. 11-Nov-3 Bonhams, Knightsbridge #97/R est:1000-1500
£13966 $25000 €20390 Portrait of young man said to be Sir Harry Neal (127x101cm-50x40in) prov. 27-May-4 Sotheby's, New York #249/R est:30000-50000

BEECHEY, Sir William (attrib) (1753-1839) British
£297 $550 €434 Portrait of Earl of Bradford (76x64cm-30x25in) 15-Jul-4 Doyle, New York #9/R
£420 $773 €613 Portrait of a gentleman, wearing a white cravat (76x63cm-30x25in) 23-Jun-4 Cheffins, Cambridge #508/R
£1705 $3000 €2489 Portrait of a barrister holding his brief (127x102cm-50x40in) 18-May-4 Bonhams & Butterfields, San Francisco #148/R est:4000-6000
£3200 $5920 €4672 Portrait of a gentleman (127x100cm-50x39in) prov. 10-Mar-4 Sotheby's, Olympia #11/R est:2000-3000
£4545 $7727 €6500 Portrait of Janet, wife of John Barnes of Finchley (90x69cm-35x27in) 25-Nov-3 Hamilton Osborne King, Dublin #204/R
£8000 $14560 €11680 Portrait of Robert Myddelton Biddulph in a brown coat, Chirk Castle beyond (76x63cm-30x25in) lit. 21-Jun-4 Christie's, London #107/R est:4000-6000

BEECHEY, Sir William (style) (1753-1839) British
£6000 $11160 €8760 Equestrian portrait of king George III, wearing military uniform (143x112cm-56x44in) 4-Mar-4 Christie's, Kensington #338/R est:3000-5000

BEECHING, Graham (?) British?
£900 $1494 €1314 View from a balcony (122x152cm-48x60in) prov. 1-Oct-3 John Ross, Belfast #24

BEECROFT, Vanesa (1969-) American
£5442 $9741 €8000 Portrait of woman (90x85cm-35x33in) init.d.96 verso. 16-Mar-4 Finarte Semenzato, Milan #364/R est:10500
Photographs
£2793 $5000 €4078 Jesse, performance nouveau Musee de Lyon, France (140x110cm-55x43in) vibracol print edition of 3 prov. 14-May-4 Phillips, New York #166/R est:7000-9000
£3000 $5520 €4500 VB 16.009 - Deitch Projects, New York (100x70cm-39x28in) vibracolour print end of 3 exec 1996 exhib. 9-Jun-4 Artcurial Briest, Paris #572/R est:3000-4000
£3243 $6000 €4735 VB 26 (101x129cm-40x51in) vibracolour photograph exec 1997. 12-Feb-4 Sotheby's, New York #366/R est:5000-7000
£3593 $6000 €5246 VB 35 Show, Performance Solomon R. Guggenheim, New York. laser disk, dvd VHS tape prov. 12-Nov-3 Christie's, Rockefeller NY #545/R est:18000-22000
£3593 $6000 €5246 VB.059.VB (102x152cm-40x60in) colour coupler print mounted on aluminum executed 1998 prov.lit. 14-Nov-3 Phillips, New York #256/R est:8000-10000
£4027 $7208 €6000 Performance VB 48 (63x75cm-25x30in) num.3/6 digital print exec.2001 prov. 25-May-4 Sotheby's, Milan #223/R est:4000-6000
£4491 $7500 €6557 VB40 Museum of Contemporary art, Sydney, Australia (51x76cm-20x30in) digital c-print executed 2000 prov. 14-Nov-3 Phillips, New York #254/R est:5000-7000
£5587 $10000 €8157 Royal opening (102x152cm-40x60in) vibracolor print edition 3 of 3 prov. 12-May-4 Christie's, Rockefeller NY #458/R est:12000-18000
£6159 $10101 €8500 VB48 (63x76cm-25x30in) num.3/6 cibachrome. 30-May-3 Farsetti, Prato #481/R est:9500
£6338 $11092 €9000 Performance VB (63x89cm-25x35in) digital C-print exec.1997. 16-Dec-3 Finarte Semenzato, Milan #290/R est:7000-7500
£7143 $12786 €10500 VB34 (63x80cm-25x31in) photograph exec.1998 lit. 16-Mar-4 Finarte Semenzato, Milan #365/R est:9000
£11173 $20000 €16313 VB 42 The Silent Service - Intrepid - New York (127x246cm-50x97in) cibachrome print exec 2000 1 edn 6 prov. 13-May-4 Sotheby's, New York #357/R est:20000-30000
£11377 $19000 €16610 VB 35 Show, Performance, Guggenheim Museum, New York (127x162cm-50x64in) Fujiflex print exec 1998 prov. 12-Nov-3 Christie's, Rockefeller NY #546/R est:10000-15000
£16760 $30000 €24470 VB48, Palazzo Ducale, Genoe, Italy (102x315cm-40x124in) digital c-print edition of six prov. 14-May-4 Phillips, New York #164/R est:8000-12000
£17964 $30000 €26227 VB 42, the silent service, Intrepid, New York, NY (102x218cm-40x86in) num.AP 2/2 c-print prov.exhib. 13-Nov-3 Sotheby's, New York #521/R est:20000-30000
£20958 $35000 €30599 VB 39 US Navy Seals, Museum of Contemporary Art, San Diego (102x152cm-40x60in) num.A.P.2. c-print prov. 13-Nov-3 Sotheby's, New York #520/R est:30000-40000
Sculpture
£12291 $22000 €17945 VB48 02-28-2002, Palazzo Ducale, Genoe, Italy. DVD edition of six prov. 14-May-4 Phillips, New York #167/R est:8000-12000

BEEK, Andre van (?) ?
£872 $1623 €1300 Hortillonnages d'Amieres (27x35cm-11x14in) s. 7-Mar-4 Lesieur & Le Bars, Le Havre #137

BEEK, Bernardus Antonie van (1875-1941) Dutch
£347 $565 €500 Old vicarage of Kortenhoef (26x36cm-10x14in) s. 29-Sep-3 Sotheby's, Amsterdam #155/R

BEEK, Jurrien (1879-1965) Dutch
£461 $847 €700 The Kolkje, Amsterdam (40x30cm-16x12in) s. 22-Jun-4 Christie's, Amsterdam #492/R
£2585 $4705 €3800 Bomschuiten on the beach (61x100cm-24x39in) s. 3-Feb-4 Christie's, Amsterdam #251 est:1500-2000

BEEK, Samuel van (1878-1957) Dutch
£367 $671 €550 Canal scene (46x43cm-18x17in) s.d.1929. 7-Jun-4 Glerum, Amsterdam #60/R

BEEK, Theodor von der (1838-1918) German
£1075 $2000 €1570 Young woman in landscape standing before two lit candles (55x43cm-22x17in) s.d.85. 5-Mar-4 Skinner, Boston #227/R est:4000-6000
£3819 $6302 €5500 Boy and girl with man shining girl's shoe (93x65cm-37x26in) s. 3-Jul-3 Dr Fritz Nagel, Stuttgart #475/R est:8000
£6000 $10320 €8760 Perfect shine (4x65cm-2x26in) s. 4-Dec-3 Christie's, Kensington #147/R est:4000-5000

BEEKMAN, Andries (fl.1651-1657) Dutch
£17308 $29769 €25270 Still life of fruit and white parrot (71x60cm-28x24in) s. panel. 2-Dec-3 Bukowskis, Stockholm #396/R est:100000-120000 (S.KR 225000)

BEEKMAN, Christiaan (1887-1964) Dutch
£7333 $13493 €11000 Naar de demonstartie (45x50cm-18x20in) s. painted c.1934 prov. 9-Jun-4 Christie's, Amsterdam #67/R est:3000-5000

BEELDEMAKER, Adriaen Cornelisz (c.1625-1709) Dutch
£1319 $2085 €1900 Pastoral river landscape with hounds chasing a bull (56x76cm-22x30in) s.d.1670. 2-Sep-3 Christie's, Amsterdam #84/R est:1500-2000
£1855 $3413 €2708 Hounds chasing a bull in a landscape (56x76cm-22x30in) s.d.1670. 14-Jun-4 Waddingtons, Toronto #236/R est:4000-6000 (C.D 4600)
£4577 $8011 €6500 Deux chiens d'arret dans la campagne Anglaise (42x58cm-17x23in) s.d.1695. 18-Dec-3 Tajan, Paris #102/R est:4000-5000

BEELER, Joe Neil (1931-) American
£7647 $13000 €11165 With rain comes the wind (51x76cm-20x30in) 1-Nov-3 Altermann Galleries, Santa Fe #79
£8235 $14000 €12023 Almost home (58x89cm-23x35in) s. panel prov.lit. 1-Nov-3 Santa Fe Art, Santa Fe #35/R est:12000-15000
£28492 $51000 €41598 Land of Alchsey (76x102cm-30x40in) 15-May-4 Altermann Galleries, Santa Fe #54/R
Sculpture
£924 $1700 €1349 Bust of an old Indian man (33cm-13in) s.i. num.2/15 bronze. 8-Jun-4 Bonhams & Butterfields, San Francisco #4143/R est:2000-3000
£1033 $1900 €1508 For no reason, bucking horse (49cm-19in) s. num.14/30 bronze. 8-Jun-4 Bonhams & Butterfields, San Francisco #4142/R est:3000-5000
£1059 $1800 €1546 Charlie (38x13x10cm-15x5x4in) s.num.72/100 bronze prov. 1-Nov-3 Santa Fe Art, Santa Fe #88/R est:2500-3500
£1647 $2800 €2405 Storytellers (18cm-7in) bronze. 1-Nov-3 Altermann Galleries, Santa Fe #80
Works on paper
£435 $700 €635 Untitled (18x13cm-7x5in) pencil pair. 22-Aug-3 Altermann Galleries, Santa Fe #12
£588 $1000 €858 Cowboy (25x20cm-10x8in) s. gouache ink paperboard prov. 1-Nov-3 Santa Fe Art, Santa Fe #179/R
£1163 $2000 €1698 Steer roper on horseback (36x46cm-14x18in) s. W/C. 6-Dec-3 Selkirks, St. Louis #190/R est:1800-2200

BEELT, Cornelis (fl.1660-1702) Dutch
£22000 $39600 €32120 View of the beach of Scheveningen (106x147cm-42x58in) 22-Apr-4 Sotheby's, London #89/R est:15000-20000

BEELT, Cornelis (attrib) (fl.1660-1702) Dutch
£5000 $8600 €7300 Charles II of England leaving Holland for London 1660 (82x111cm-32x44in) lit. 3-Dec-3 AB Stockholms Auktionsverk #2675/R est:50000-60000 (S.KR 65000)

BEER, Andrew (1862-1954) British
£250 $465 €365 Guiding star (29x40cm-11x16in) s.i. 2-Mar-4 Bearnes, Exeter #407

£310 $580 €465 Racing pigeon (29x39cm-11x15in) s.i. 22-Jul-4 Dominic Winter, Swindon #122/R
£400 $632 €580 Racing pigeon, Reliance (30x40cm-12x16in) s.i. 24-Jul-3 Dominic Winter, Swindon #122/R
£500 $835 €730 Mr Oliver Dix's Young Spencer. Mr Oliver Dix's Floss (29x39cm-11x15in) s.d.1916 pair. 22-Oct-3 Cheffins, Cambridge #541/R
£560 $1042 €818 Mr Oliver Dix's. Mr Oliver Dix's Young Spencer (30x41cm-12x16in) s.i.d.1916 pair. 4-Mar-4 Christie's, Kensington #544/R
£840 $1571 €1226 Racing pigeons (30x41cm-12x16in) s. one i. pair. 24-Feb-4 Wotton Auction Rooms, Wotton #747

BEER, Dick (1893-1938) Swedish
£508 $914 €742 Townscape (62x47cm-24x19in) s.indis.d. panel. 26-Apr-4 Bukowskis, Stockholm #55/R (S.KR 7000)
£870 $1566 €1270 French landscape (65x54cm-26x21in) s.d.1914 exhib. 26-Apr-4 Bukowskis, Stockholm #8/R (S.KR 12000)
Works on paper
£306 $563 €459 View from Tunisia (45x30cm-18x12in) s.d.1914 W/C. 14-Jun-4 Lilla Bukowskis, Stockholm #47 (S.KR 4200)

BEER, John (fl.1895-1915) British
£550 $1007 €803 Diamond Jubilee (33x43cm-13x17in) s.i. 28-Jan-4 Dreweatt Neate, Newbury #125/R
£900 $1530 €1314 Exciting dead-heat for the Eclipse Stakes. 19-Nov-3 Sotheby's, Olympia #57/R
Works on paper
£338 $595 €500 Race (27x38cm-11x15in) s. W/C. 18-May-4 Galerie Moderne, Brussels #249
£420 $676 €609 Last fence, Grand National, 1910 (23x33cm-9x13in) s.i. W/C. 15-Aug-3 Keys, Aylsham #347/R
£450 $828 €657 Grand National, 1905, the last fence (34x52cm-13x20in) s.i.d.1905 W/C htd white. 10-Jun-4 Christie's, Kensington #144/R
£500 $850 €730 Baldur wins! the Ascot Stakes 1900 (25x36cm-10x14in) s.i.d.1900 pencil W/C htd white. 27-Nov-3 Christie's, Kensington #171/R
£550 $946 €803 My first appearance in public at Kemptown Park (25x36cm-10x14in) s. W/C. 2-Dec-3 Gorringes, Lewes #2309
£720 $1224 €1051 Finish for the St Leger (22x34cm-9x13in) s.i.d.1908 W/C. 19-Nov-3 Sotheby's, Olympia #56/R
£900 $1656 €1314 Grand National, 1915, at the 5th fence. At the last jump (24x35cm-9x14in) s.i.d.1915 W/C bodycol pair. 10-Jun-4 Christie's, Kensington #150/R
£900 $1638 €1314 The Cambridgeshire Stakes, 1900 (20x29cm-8x11in) s.i.d.1900 pencil W/C bodycol three. 1-Jul-4 Christie's, Kensington #243/R
£1900 $3496 €2774 Grand National, 1904 Beecher's Brook, Valentine's Brook. Two fences before the water. Water jump (24x35cm-9x14in) s.i.d.1904 W/C htd white set of four. 10-Jun-4 Christie's, Kensington #148/R est:2500-3500
£3300 $6072 €4818 Pretty Polly wins the Jockey Club Cup, Newmarket, 1905 (35x55cm-14x22in) s.i.d.1905 W/C htd white. 10-Jun-4 Christie's, Kensington #154/R est:1500-2000

BEER, Wilhelm Amandus (1837-1907) German
£1788 $3254 €2700 Russian couple in an interior (25x19cm-10x7in) s.d.1897 board. 18-Jun-4 Bolland & Marotz, Bremen #581/R est:3200
Works on paper
£699 $1168 €1000 The broken wheel (14x21cm-6x8in) W/C pencil sketch. 10-Oct-3 Winterberg, Heidelberg #534/R
£933 $1708 €1400 Blondie Fedka (9x7cm-4x3in) s.d.1894 W/C. 5-Jun-4 Arnold, Frankfurt #530/R

BEERBOHM, Sir Max (1872-1956) British
Works on paper
£450 $752 €657 Insecurity (34x25cm-13x10in) pencil. 21-Oct-3 Bonhams, Knightsbridge #68/R
£550 $875 €803 Mr W Churchill (45x35cm-18x14in) s.i.d.1944 pen black ink W/C pencil. 10-Sep-3 Sotheby's, Olympia #125/R
£700 $1113 €1022 Prime Ministers (21x27cm-8x11in) s.i. one d.1935 one d.1944 pencil 2 in 1 frame and another prov. 10-Sep-3 Sotheby's, Olympia #126/R
£750 $1193 €1095 Self portrait (16x11cm-6x4in) s.d.1944 pencil sold with 2 photos of artist and his wife. 10-Sep-3 Sotheby's, Olympia #124/R
£1600 $2912 €2336 General election (30x35cm-12x14in) s.i.d.1919 pencil monochrome wash unfinished dr prov. 15-Jun-4 Bonhams, New Bond Street #39/R est:800-1200
£2000 $3140 €2900 Gordon Craig asking them for A Sacrifice worthy of their calling and their ideals (38x26cm-15x10in) s.i.d.1920 pencil W/C lit. 28-Aug-3 Christie's, Kensington #498/R est:2000-3000
£2095 $3750 €3059 Group of ladies listening to Percy Grainger. s. dr. 13-May-4 Dallas Auction Gallery, Dallas #314/R est:2000-4000
£3400 $6086 €4964 Sir Alfred Mond (32x21cm-13x8in) s.i. pencil W/C. 16-Mar-4 Bonhams, New Bond Street #9/R est:1500-2000

BEERE, Gerald Butler (20th C) New Zealander
Works on paper
£400 $628 €580 Totaratiatia, Wanganui river (25x36cm-10x14in) s.i.verso W/C. 27-Aug-3 Dunbar Sloane, Wellington #146 (NZ.D 1100)

BEERNAERT, Euphrosine (1831-1901) Flemish
£759 $1267 €1100 Paysage en campine anime d'une bergere (50x100cm-20x39in) s. 17-Nov-3 Bernaerts, Antwerp #12
£1141 $2111 €1700 La conduite du troupeau (75x61cm-30x24in) s. 15-Mar-4 Horta, Bruxelles #65 est:1800-2200
£1241 $2297 €1800 Paysage de Campine (79x65cm-31x26in) mono. 19-Jan-4 Horta, Bruxelles #183 est:2500-3000
£1477 $2613 €2200 Berger et son troupeau dans le bois (70x115cm-28x45in) s. 27-Apr-4 Campo, Vlaamse Kaai #307 est:1000-1500
£2517 $4204 €3600 Field path by forest edge (70x120cm-28x47in) s. exhib. 11-Oct-3 De Vuyst, Lokeren #511/R est:3500-4500
£2778 $4417 €4000 Bruyere en campine (85x135cm-33x53in) s. 9-Sep-3 Palais de Beaux Arts, Brussels #204/R est:4000-6000

BEERNAERT, Jean Guy (1928-) Belgian
£436 $772 €650 Maisonette dans une ruelle (66x25cm-26x10in) s. panel. 27-Apr-4 Campo & Campo, Antwerp #408

BEERS, Jan van (1852-1927) Belgian
£700 $1295 €1022 Esmeralda (25cm-10in circular) s.i.d.1882 vellum. 13-Jan-4 Bonhams, Knightsbridge #330/R
£1200 $2160 €1800 Portrait of a young girl (33x25cm-13x10in) s. panel. 26-Apr-4 Bernaerts, Antwerp #52/R est:1250-1500
£1528 $2429 €2200 Portrait of a young man in medieval costume (32x24cm-13x9in) s.i.d.1879. 15-Sep-3 Bernaerts, Antwerp #213 est:3000-3500
£1724 $2879 €2500 Mon cher (32x41cm-13x16in) s. panel. 17-Nov-3 Bernaerts, Antwerp #35 est:2500-3000
£1892 $3386 €2800 Portrait de dame (45x36cm-18x14in) panel. 10-May-4 Amberes, Antwerp #330
£2759 $5103 €4000 Elegante sur fond de paysage peint (35x27cm-14x11in) s.i.d.1881 panel oil htd photo. 19-Jan-4 Horta, Bruxelles #204/R est:4000-6000
£7586 $14034 €11000 Les amoureux (92x74cm-36x29in) s. 16-Feb-4 Horta, Bruxelles #155/R est:10000-12000

BEERS, Julie Hart (1835-1913) American
£443 $700 €647 Summer afternoon at the lake (28x43cm-11x17in) s. 6-Apr-3 William Jenack, New York #429

BEERS, Robin (1943-) American
£1829 $3200 €2670 Eat your heart out (53x107cm-21x42in) painted 1973. 17-Dec-3 Christie's, Rockefeller NY #237/R est:2000-3000

BEERSTRATEN, Abraham (17th C) Dutch
£40000 $72000 €58400 Heiligewegspoort, Amsterdam in winter, with skaters on the frozen canal (75x106cm-30x42in) s. panel. 21-Apr-4 Christie's, London #31/R est:25000-35000

BEERSTRATEN, Anthonie (circle) (17th C) Dutch
£11000 $19800 €16060 Winter river landscape with travelers on a path before a castle (115x177cm-45x70in) 21-Apr-4 Bonhams, New Bond Street #65/R est:4000-6000

BEERSTRATEN, Jan Abrahamsz (1622-1666) Dutch
£1067 $1931 €1600 Storm gathering over winter coast (75x110cm-30x43in) 1-Apr-4 Van Ham, Cologne #1163 est:1600

BEERSTRATEN, Jan Abrahamsz (attrib) (1622-1666) Dutch
£6704 $12000 €9788 Animated harbour scene (60x69cm-24x27in) s. prov. 14-May-4 Skinner, Boston #18/R est:8000-12000

BEERT, Osias I (c.1570-1624) Flemish
£140000 $242200 €204400 Still life of wine glasses, orange, sweetmeats, hazelnuts, and moth in stone niche (23x18cm-9x7in) bears i.verso copper prov. 11-Dec-3 Sotheby's, London #53/R est:20000-30000
£203947 $375263 €310000 Still life with grapes and wine glasses (55x76cm-22x30in) panel. 25-Jun-4 Piasa, Paris #14/R est:250000-300000

BEEST, Albertus van (1820-1860) Dutch
£3061 $5571 €4500 Fishermen at dawn (33x51cm-13x20in) s. panel. 3-Feb-4 Christie's, Amsterdam #107/R est:4000-6000

BEEST, Albertus van (attrib) (1820-1860) Dutch
£706 $1200 €1031 Fishing boats by shore (20x25cm-8x10in) 21-Nov-3 Eldred, East Dennis #577/R est:1000-2000

BEEST, Sybrand van (attrib) (1610-1674) Dutch
£1879 $3457 €2800 Une cuisiniere dans un interieur avec un chien savant (41x38cm-16x15in) panel. 24-Mar-4 Tajan, Paris #62 est:2500-3000

BEETHOLME, George Law (19th C) British
£638 $1066 €900 English hill landscape with river (51x41cm-20x16in) s. 17-Oct-3 Behringer, Furth #1530/R

BEEVER, Emanuel Samson van (1876-1912) Dutch
£405 $714 €600 Building (19x13cm-7x5in) s. panel. 24-May-4 Bernaerts, Antwerp #578/R
£732 $1310 €1069 Grinding coffee (29x24cm-11x9in) s. panel prov. 4-May-4 Ritchie, Toronto #67a/R est:2000-3000 (C.D 1800)

BEFANI, Achille Formis (1832-1906) Italian
£13514 $23784 €20000 Washerwomen (76x51cm-30x20in) s. 19-May-4 Il Ponte, Milan #647/R est:25000-30000

BEFANI, Achille Formis (attrib) (1832-1906) Italian
£1351 $2378 €2000 Stream (25x57cm-10x22in) s. board. 19-May-4 Il Ponte, Milan #593 est:2200-2400

BEGA, Cornelis Pietersz (1620-1664) Dutch
£875 $1400 €1278 Sleeping gentleman (30x25cm-12x10in) board. 21-Sep-3 Grogan, Boston #1/R
£1486 $2616 €2200 Two peasants drinking in an inn (27x21cm-11x8in) oil paper on panel prov. 18-May-4 Sotheby's, Amsterdam #68/R est:3000-5000
£3297 $6000 €4814 Peasants in a tavern (37x30cm-15x12in) panel. 17-Jun-4 Christie's, Rockefeller NY #61/R est:8000-12000
£5000 $9150 €7300 Peasant man seated at a table holding a pipe (12cm-5in circular) panel. 7-Jul-4 Bonhams, New Bond Street #66/R est:3000-4000

£17123 $29110 €25000 Tavern interior with peasants making music and children playing (51x74cm-20x29in) panel prov.exhib.lit. 4-Nov-3 Sotheby's, Amsterdam #14/R est:15000-20000
Prints
£2667 $4773 €4000 The three drinkers (9x7cm-4x3in) etching. 13-May-4 Bassenge, Berlin #5019 est:1800
Works on paper
£2055 $3493 €3000 Study of a seated woman, seen from the side (26x17cm-10x7in) black white chk. 4-Nov-3 Sotheby's, Amsterdam #75/R est:3000-5000
£5000 $9150 €7300 Study of a seated man. Unfinished study of a seated man (26x19cm-10x7in) blk chk touches white chk blue paper double-sided. 8-Jul-4 Sotheby's, London #85/R est:6000-8000

BEGA, Cornelis Pietersz (attrib) (1620-1664) Dutch
£1056 $1827 €1500 Scene de taverne (17x15cm-7x6in) panel. 12-Dec-3 Renaud, Paris #132/R est:1500-2000
£1467 $2655 €2200 Peasants drinking in tavern (16x22cm-6x9in) 1-Apr-4 Van Ham, Cologne #1164/R est:2400

BEGAILEI, Kleofas (?) ?
£1064 $1777 €1500 At leisure (21x15cm-8x6in) s. panel. 14-Oct-3 Dorotheum, Vienna #172/R est:1900-2600

BEGARAT, Pierre (19/20th C) French
£298 $497 €420 Bord de mer, Finistere (23x30cm-9x12in) s. cardboard. 20-Jun-3 Drouot Estimations, Paris #90
£482 $805 €680 Bretonnes dans le pre (22x27cm-9x11in) s. cardboard. 20-Jun-3 Drouot Estimations, Paris #91

BEGAS, Karl-Joseph (1794-1854) German
£2098 $3566 €3000 Portrait of female artist at easel. Portrait of young woman with needlework (43x37cm-17x15in) two. 20-Nov-3 Van Ham, Cologne #1480/R est:3800

BEGAS, Karl-Joseph (attrib) (1794-1854) German
£467 $845 €700 Portrait of young man in dark suit (35x29cm-14x11in) mono.d. verso. 1-Apr-4 Van Ham, Cologne #1285

BEGAS, Oskar (attrib) (1828-1883) German
£3167 $5385 €4624 Two sisters (165x109cm-65x43in) 1-Dec-3 Koller, Zurich #6503 est:500-7000 (S.FR 7000)

BEGAS, Reinhold (1831-1911) German
Sculpture
£2000 $3640 €2920 Bust of Otto von Bismarck (44cm-17in) s.i.d.1886 brown pat electrotype. 15-Jun-4 Sotheby's, Olympia #111/R est:2500-3500

BEGAS-PARMENTIER, Louise (1850-?) Austrian
£347 $590 €500 Wooden bridge (24x20cm-9x8in) s. board. 28-Oct-3 Dorotheum, Vienna #256/R

BEGAUD, Pierre Albert (20th C) French
£451 $730 €640 Pecheur a la ligne au port (24x35cm-9x14in) s. panel. 11-Aug-3 Boscher, Cherbourg #883/R

BEGAY, Harrison (1917-) American
Works on paper
£914 $1700 €1334 Mother and daughter on horseback, Haskay yenah yah (41x41cm-16x16in) s. W/C pair. 7-Mar-4 Treadway Gallery, Cincinnati #574/R est:800-1200

BEGEN, J (19th C) ?
£1007 $1862 €1500 Pecheurs dans une barque (48x79cm-19x31in) d.d.78. 15-Mar-4 Horta, Bruxelles #74 est:1800-2200

BEGEYN, Abraham (1637-1697) Dutch
£2217 $3969 €3237 Two rams in an Italian garden (39x48cm-15x19in) init. prov. 26-May-4 AB Stockholms Auktionsverk #2522/R est:35000-40000 (S.KR 30000)
£4000 $6800 €5840 Wooded landscape with piping shepherds and their flocks (59x71cm-23x28in) s. 30-Oct-3 Sotheby's, Olympia #84/R est:4000-6000
£4934 $9079 €7500 Lizard and butterflies by tree (35x47cm-14x19in) prov. 24-Jun-4 Christie's, Paris #18/R est:3000-5000
£5743 $10280 €8500 Evening scene (57x49cm-22x19in) s. lit. 8-May-4 Schloss Ahlden, Ahlden #676/R est:9000

BEGGROF, Alexandre (1841-1914) Russian
£17568 $31446 €26000 The guests (15x23cm-6x9in) s.d.1891 board. 8-May-4 Bukowskis, Helsinki #422/R est:4500-5000

BEGGS, Guy (20th C) British
£450 $833 €657 Sunday on the River II (153x122cm-60x48in) s.i.d.1976-8 verso. 13-Feb-4 Sworder & Son, Bishops Stortford #55/R
£520 $962 €759 Sunday on the River I (153x122cm-60x48in) s.i.d.1976-8 verso. 13-Feb-4 Sworder & Son, Bishops Stortford #54/R

BEGUINE, Michel Leonard (1855-1929) French
Sculpture
£2200 $4114 €3212 Charmeuse (40cm-16in) s. bronze st.f.Soit-Decauville. 21-Jul-4 Lyon & Turnbull, Edinburgh #276/R est:1000-1500

BEHAN, John (1932-) Irish
Sculpture
£1757 $3320 €2600 Famine boat (23cm-9in) bronze. 17-Feb-4 Whyte's, Dublin #217/R est:2500-3500
£1958 $3329 €2800 Bird (46cm-18in) bronze. 25-Nov-3 De Veres Art Auctions, Dublin #114/R est:2000-3000
£2027 $3831 €3000 Titanic (51cm-20in) s.d.2000 bronze marble base. 17-Feb-4 Whyte's, Dublin #216/R est:3000-4000
£2378 $4042 €3400 Two birds in flight (53cm-21in) s.d.2001 bronze stone base. 18-Nov-3 Whyte's, Dublin #86/R est:1500-2000
£2568 $4853 €3800 Children of Lir (43cm-17in) green pat bronze exhib. 17-Feb-4 Whyte's, Dublin #213/R est:2000-3000
£2778 $4528 €4000 Old Ship, Gallilee (51cm-20in) mixed metal prov. 24-Sep-3 James Adam, Dublin #51/R est:3000-4000
£2778 $4528 €4000 Flight of birds (54cm-21in) bronze. 24-Sep-3 James Adam, Dublin #52/R est:2500-3500
Works on paper
£352 $616 €500 Study of four figures (27x40cm-11x16in) s.d.1971 chl W/C. 16-Dec-3 James Adam, Dublin #8/R
£408 $751 €620 Nude (55x37cm-22x15in) s.d.Jan 29th 1986 collage. 22-Jun-4 De Veres Art Auctions, Dublin #238

BEHLER, Will (20th C) American
£1734 $3000 €2532 Loer Saucon Road, late autumn landscape (61x91cm-24x36in) s. masonite. 10-Dec-3 Alderfer's, Hatfield #453/R est:800-1200
£3073 $5500 €4487 Bethlehem Steel (56x74cm-22x29in) s.d.1938 board. 16-May-4 Wright, Chicago #163/R est:2500-3500

BEHM, Vilhelm (1859-1934) Swedish
£1538 $2615 €2200 Archipelago at sunset (71x111cm-28x44in) s.d.1887. 29-Nov-3 Bukowskis, Helsinki #367/R est:1500-1800

BEHMER, Marcus (1879-1958) German
Works on paper
£600 $1074 €900 We wish you a Happy New Year (9x13cm-4x5in) mono.i.d.29.XII.1905 W/C Indian ink. 15-May-4 Bassenge, Berlin #6736/R

BEHNES, William (1794-1864) British
Sculpture
£2800 $5012 €4088 Bust of Benjamin Travers (82cm-32in) i. marble. 16-Mar-4 Woolley & Wallis, Salisbury #100/R est:1500-2000

BEHR, Carel Jacobus (1812-1895) Dutch
£1644 $2795 €2400 View of a country house in The Hague (24x35cm-9x14in) s. panel. 5-Nov-3 Vendue Huis, Gravenhage #54/R est:1000-1200

BEHRENS, Frank (1883-1945) Swiss
£625 $1019 €900 Bacchantin (91x80cm-36x31in) s. 24-Sep-3 Neumeister, Munich #396/R

BEHRENS, Howard (20th C) American
£2235 $4000 €3263 Girls on steps under umbrellas (112x112cm-44x44in) s. 7-May-4 Sloans & Kenyon, Bethesda #1743/R est:3000-5000
£8125 $13000 €11863 Girl on beach (112x168cm-44x66in) s. 20-Sep-3 Sloans & Kenyon, Bethesda #1183a/R est:9000-12000

BEHRENS, Johan (1904-1967) Danish
£549 $1000 €802 View of Helsingor (158x200cm-62x79in) s.d.1932. 7-Feb-4 Rasmussen, Havnen #4034 (D.KR 6000)

BEHRENS-HANGELER, Herbert (1898-1981) German
£420 $713 €600 Untitled (70x48cm-28x19in) mono.i. tempera col chk. 29-Nov-3 Villa Grisebach, Berlin #510/R
£7667 $14107 €11500 Harlequin playing a guitar (119x90cm-47x35in) mono. 12-Jun-4 Villa Grisebach, Berlin #288/R est:7000-9000
Works on paper
£315 $535 €450 Figure seated on balcony (33x25cm-13x10in) mono. Indian ink brush pen board. 29-Nov-3 Villa Grisebach, Berlin #509/R
£350 $594 €500 Female nude with still life (63x50cm-25x20in) Indian ink brush pen. 29-Nov-3 Villa Grisebach, Berlin #507/R

BEICH, Joachim Franz (attrib) (1665-1748) German
£523 $900 €764 Landscape with stream and people (33x23cm-13x9in) board. 7-Dec-3 Grogan, Boston #23/R
£1127 $1803 €1600 Royal procession (50x60cm-20x24in) 18-Sep-3 Rieber, Stuttgart #1311/R est:1980
£1477 $2717 €2200 Idyllic landscape with shepherds (59x78cm-23x31in) 25-Mar-4 Dr Fritz Nagel, Stuttgart #675/R est:800
£2318 $4219 €3500 Rocky landscape with mountains in the distance (90x130cm-35x51in) 16-Jun-4 Hugo Ruef, Munich #875 est:4000
£3020 $5557 €4500 Rocky landscape with trees (90x130cm-35x51in) 24-Mar-4 Hugo Ruef, Munich #876/R est:4500

BEICH, Mary (20th C) French
£1384 $2200 €2021 On the beach (91x122cm-36x48in) s. 14-Sep-3 Susanin's, Chicago #6172/R est:1600-2000

BEIGNEUX, Arlane (20th C) American
£308 $550 €450 Downpour (36x46cm-14x18in) 8-Jan-4 James Julia, Fairfield #1566/R

BEINASCHI, G B (1636-1688) Italian

£4444	$8000	€6488	God the father in glory (50x65cm-20x26in) 23-Jan-4 Christie's, Rockefeller NY #168/R est:10000-15000

BEINKE, Fritz (1842-1907) German

£1678	$2853	€2400	Toy seller (36x26cm-14x10in) s. 24-Nov-3 Dorotheum, Vienna #50/R est:2600-3400
£2533	$4661	€3800	Man selling toys to children in the streets (32x23cm-13x9in) s. panel. 11-Jun-4 Wendl, Rudolstadt #3949/R est:3800
£4054	$7257	€6000	School class on spring outing (45x66cm-18x26in) s. 6-May-4 Michael Zeller, Lindau #587/R est:6000

BEISANJIN, Okada (1744-1820) Japanese

Works on paper

£272	$500	€397	Landscape (20x12cm-8x5in) s. ink hanging scroll. 23-Mar-4 Christie's, Rockefeller NY #103/R

BEISCHLAGER, Emil (1897-1978) Austrian

£674	$1125	€950	Still life with jug and peppers (42x52cm-17x20in) jute. 14-Oct-3 Dorotheum, Vienna #145/R
£867	$1560	€1300	New building - Vienna XI (50x63cm-20x25in) s.d.1948. 21-Apr-4 Dorotheum, Vienna #127/R est:1500-2200

BEJEMARK, K G (1922-) Swedish

Sculpture

£1624	$2761	€2371	Nils Ferlin (9x14cm-4x6in) init. dark pat.bronze. 4-Nov-3 Bukowskis, Stockholm #79/R est:8000-10000 (S.KR 21500)
£2030	$3655	€2964	Nils Ferlin (14cm-6in) init.num.EA dark pat.bronze. 26-Apr-4 Bukowskis, Stockholm #267/R est:15000-18000 (S.KR 28000)

BEK-GRAN, Hermann (1869-?) German

£533	$971	€800	The horn of Nuremperg (99x180cm-39x71in) s. 1-Jul-4 Weidler, Nurnberg #7007

BEKAERT, Maurice (19th C) Belgian

£414	$766	€600	Premiers rayons printaniers (37x69cm-15x27in) s.d.1891. 19-Jan-4 Horta, Bruxelles #298

BEKAERT, Piet (1939-2000) Belgian

£1438	$2445	€2100	Garden (150x150cm-59x59in) s. 10-Nov-3 Horta, Bruxelles #169
£1467	$2625	€2200	In the garden (80x100cm-31x39in) s.d.1989. 15-May-4 De Vuyst, Lokeren #26/R est:1900-2400
£2308	$3854	€3300	Terrace (100x120cm-39x47in) s.d.82 s.d.1982 verso. 11-Oct-3 De Vuyst, Lokeren #23/R est:3300-4000
£3973	$6753	€5800	Vue de jardin (150x150cm-59x59in) s. 10-Nov-3 Horta, Bruxelles #170/R

BEKEL, Josef (1806-1865) Czechoslovakian

Works on paper

£438	$727	€639	Portrait of Count General Thun - Hohenstein (27x22cm-11x9in) s.i.d.851 pencil W/C. 4-Oct-3 Dorotheum, Prague #376/R est:12000-20000 (C.KR 20000)

BEKMAN, Hubertus Cornelis Gerardus (1896-1974) Dutch

£325	$553	€475	House on the canal (54x63cm-21x25in) s. 5-Nov-3 Vendue Huis, Gravenhage #409a

BEKSINSKI, Zdzislaw (1929-) Polish

£2684	$4857	€3919	Untitled (131x96cm-52x38in) s. 4-Apr-4 Agra, Warsaw #33/R (P.Z 19000)

BELANGER, Louis (1736-1816) French

Works on paper

£1231	$2117	€1797	Landscape with bridge across waterfall (46x33cm-18x13in) s.d.1804 gouache. 2-Dec-3 Bukowskis, Stockholm #447/R est:10000-12000 (S.KR 16000)
£1538	$2646	€2245	Park landscape with family out walking (31x24cm-12x9in) s.d.1807 gouache. 2-Dec-3 Bukowskis, Stockholm #446/R est:25000-30000 (S.KR 20000)
£1626	$2911	€2374	Park landscape with young lady reading (27x33cm-11x13in) s.d.1807 W/C gouache. 25-May-4 Bukowskis, Stockholm #541/R est:15000-20000 (S.KR 22000)
£5278	$9500	€7706	Watermill by a stream with figures. Cottage by a stream with boy fishing (50x37cm-20x15in) s.d.1791 bodycol pair. 22-Jan-4 Christie's, Rockefeller NY #205/R est:7000-10000
£6000	$10200	€8760	Windsor Castle, seen from the Eton side of the Thames (74x108cm-29x43in) s. gouache. 27-Nov-3 Sotheby's, London #247/R est:6000-8000
£15035	$25860	€21500	Vue de l'Hotel du Prince Louis Bonaparte, prise du cote des jardins (28x40cm-11x16in) gouache. 2-Dec-3 Sotheby's, Paris #36/R est:5000-7000

BELANGER, Louis (attrib) (1736-1816) French

Works on paper

£759	$1267	€1100	Promenade galante en barque (15x26cm-6x10in) W/C gouache. 14-Nov-3 Drouot Estimations, Paris #12

BELANGER, Louis Joseph Octave (1886-1972) Canadian

£938	$1566	€1360	In Chaleur Bay (56x71cm-22x28in) s.i.verso. 17-Jun-3 Pinneys, Montreal #18 est:1800-2400 (C.D 2100)

BELAY, Pierre de (1890-1947) French

£667	$1193	€1000	Personnage. s.d.24 cardboard. 15-May-4 other European Auctioneer #74
£1245	$2204	€1818	The lawyers (65x80cm-26x31in) s.d.38. 27-Apr-4 AB Stockholms Auktionsverk #1168/R est:25000-30000 (S.KR 17000)
£1447	$2663	€2200	Cabinet particulier (19x24cm-7x9in) s. cardboard prov. 25-Jun-4 Millon & Associes, Paris #167 est:1500-1800
£2113	$3697	€3000	Jeune Bretonne en costume de Pont-Aven. Portrait d'homme (38x30cm-15x12in) s.d.1926 double-sided. 21-Dec-3 Thierry & Lannon, Brest #131/R est:2600-2800
£2533	$4535	€3800	Roulottes (50x61cm-20x24in) cardboard. 15-May-4 other European Auctioneer #76
£2585	$4627	€3800	Audierne, le marche (47x55cm-19x22in) painted 1931. 19-Mar-4 Ribeyre & Baron, Paris #87 est:2000-3500
£2639	$4407	€3800	Les avocats (81x101cm-32x40in) s.d.33 s.i.d.verso exhib. 21-Oct-3 Artcurial Briest, Paris #194/R est:4000-5000
£3000	$5520	€4500	Concarneau (50x61cm-20x24in) s. 8-Jun-4 Livinec, Gaudcheau & Jezequel, Rennes #90/R
£3356	$6007	€5000	Paris, Pont-Neuf (22x34cm-9x13in) s. panel painted c.1945. 30-May-4 Eric Pillon, Calais #6/R
£4333	$7757	€6500	Marins a Lesconil (50x31cm-20x12in) s.d.1944. 16-May-4 Thierry & Lannon, Brest #110/R est:7000-8000
£4400	$7876	€6600	Rue Lepic a Paris (50x60cm-20x24in) s.d.1924 cardboard. 15-May-4 other European Auctioneer #78
£4476	$7474	€6400	Charrette de pommes (50x61cm-20x24in) s. 29-Jun-3 Eric Pillon, Calais #149/R
£4577	$7919	€6500	Marche en Bretagne (50x61cm-20x24in) s. panel. 14-Dec-3 Eric Pillon, Calais #92/R
£4695	$7840	€6855	Fishermen at Le Port d'Audierne (60x73cm-24x29in) s.d.39. 7-Oct-3 Rasmussen, Copenhagen #154/R est:40000 (D.KR 50000)
£5263	$9684	€8000	Bretonnes au pique-nique (61x50cm-24x20in) cardboard. 22-Jun-4 Chassaing Rivet, Toulouse #246
£5862	$9731	€8500	Au bord du lac (100x81cm-39x32in) s. 1-Oct-3 Millon & Associes, Paris #108/R
£6000	$10740	€9000	Le ramassage des pommes (50x61cm-20x24in) s. 16-May-4 Thierry & Lannon, Brest #114/R est:8000-10000
£7303	$13437	€11100	Village de Vitre (50x61cm-20x24in) s.i.d.1918 verso. 24-Jun-4 Credit Municipal, Paris #65/R est:10000-12000
£8054	$14416	€12000	Petit marche sur la place (50x60cm-20x24in) s. panel. 30-May-4 Eric Pillon, Calais #10/R
£8451	$14620	€12000	Amoureux au bord de la riviere (100x81cm-39x32in) s. 14-Dec-3 Eric Pillon, Calais #68/R
£9669	$18081	€14600	Le retour des thoniers (80x52cm-31x20in) s. 24-Jul-4 Thierry & Lannon, Brest #141/R est:10000-12000
£9933	$17781	€14900	Deux marins en discussion sur le quai (60x73cm-24x29in) s.d.39. 16-May-4 Thierry & Lannon, Brest #112/R est:15000-18000
£11258	$20603	€17000	Scene de plage (50x61cm-20x24in) s. 7-Apr-4 Piasa, Paris #118/R est:8000-10000
£12431	$20759	€17900	Willerville, la plage (50x73cm-20x29in) s.d.26. 23-Oct-3 Credit Municipal, Paris #91/R est:5000-6000
£16733	$29953	€25100	Plage (81x100cm-32x39in) s.d.26. 15-May-4 other European Auctioneer #80
£33803	$59155	€48000	Depart pour le peche (200x300cm-79x118in) s. 21-Dec-3 Thierry & Lannon, Brest #132/R est:60000-80000

Works on paper

£265	$495	€400	Marin a Concarneau (32x23cm-13x9in) s.d.1926 chl. 24-Jul-4 Thierry & Lannon, Brest #34
£278	$520	€420	Cheval a Concarneau (24x35cm-9x14in) s.d.1926 chl. 24-Jul-4 Thierry & Lannon, Brest #36
£317	$555	€450	Cheval a Audierne (29x24cm-11x9in) s.d.1927 chl. 21-Dec-3 Thierry & Lannon, Brest #422
£331	$619	€500	Etude de marins a Concarneau (32x24cm-13x9in) s.d.1926 chl. 24-Jul-4 Thierry & Lannon, Brest #33
£367	$656	€550	L'enlevement (42x29cm-17x11in) s.d.1928 W/C gouache. 16-May-4 Thierry & Lannon, Brest #236
£423	$739	€600	Elegante au collier a la Coupole (30x22cm-12x9in) s.d.1932 chl. 21-Dec-3 Thierry & Lannon, Brest #104
£477	$892	€720	Femme de Pont-Aven (32x24cm-13x9in) s.d.1926 chl. 24-Jul-4 Thierry & Lannon, Brest #35
£493	$863	€700	Au cafe a Concarneau (30x23cm-12x9in) s.i.d.1925 chl. 21-Dec-3 Thierry & Lannon, Brest #106
£493	$863	€700	Marins a Concarneau (23x30cm-9x12in) s.i.d.1926 chl. 21-Dec-3 Thierry & Lannon, Brest #107
£528	$924	€750	Femme de l'Ile de Sein (29x24cm-11x9in) s.i.d.1939 chl. 21-Dec-3 Thierry & Lannon, Brest #421
£567	$1014	€850	Marin de dos a Audierne (34x24cm-13x9in) s.d.1940 chl. 16-May-4 Thierry & Lannon, Brest #24
£567	$1014	€850	Etude de marins a Concarneau (32x24cm-13x9in) s.d.1926 chl. 16-May-4 Thierry & Lannon, Brest #25
£634	$1109	€900	Marche a Honfleur (23x33cm-9x13in) s.i.d.1926 chl. 21-Dec-3 Thierry & Lannon, Brest #108
£662	$1238	€1000	Marin en barque pres du port (20x26cm-8x10in) s.d.40 W/C gouache. 24-Jul-4 Thierry & Lannon, Brest #54
£704	$1232	€1000	Marin de dos a Audierne (31x21cm-12x8in) s.i.d.1927 chl. 21-Dec-3 Thierry & Lannon, Brest #105
£733	$1313	€1100	Marin a Audierne (31x22cm-12x9in) s.d.1932 chl. 16-May-4 Thierry & Lannon, Brest #27
£733	$1313	€1100	Marin de dos au panier (32x24cm-13x9in) s.d.1926 chl. 16-May-4 Thierry & Lannon, Brest #28
£845	$1512	€1250	Kiki de Montparnasse. s. W/C gouache. 7-May-4 Millon & Associes, Paris #118/R
£861	$1610	€1300	Portrait de Max Jacob (26x21cm-10x8in) s. pen sketch. 24-Jul-4 Thierry & Lannon, Brest #38/R
£1267	$2318	€1900	Deux femmes et deus hommes au cafe (33x41cm-13x16in) s.d.25 stump dr prov. 6-Jun-4 Rouillac, Vendome #36
£1479	$2588	€2100	Portrait de Paul Verlaine (31x22cm-12x9in) s. gouache wash. 21-Dec-3 Thierry & Lannon, Brest #249 est:1500-1800
£1533	$2745	€2300	Nu au cahpeau sur la plage (37x45cm-15x18in) s.i.d.1946 W/C htd gouache. 16-May-4 Thierry & Lannon, Brest #42/R est:2000-2500
£1809	$3020	€2550	Conversation au tribunal (35x44cm-14x17in) s.d.38 wash gouache. 19-Jun-3 Millon & Associes, Paris #61/R est:2500-3000
£2183	$3777	€3100	Plage animee (24x32cm-9x13in) s. W/C gouache. 14-Dec-3 Eric Pillon, Calais #112/R
£3521	$6162	€5000	Marine a Lesconil (23x40cm-9x16in) s.i.d.45 gouache. 21-Dec-3 Thierry & Lannon, Brest #248/R est:2800-3000
£3667	$6600	€5500	Au cafe (44x53cm-17x21in) s.d.1929 gouache. 26-Apr-4 Tajan, Paris #84/R est:6000
£4085	$7148	€5800	Jeune femme a la lecture et au bouquet (48x63cm-19x25in) s.d.46 gouache. 21-Dec-3 Thierry & Lannon, Brest #82b/R est:6000-7000
£4636	$8669	€7000	Quimper, le Cap Horn (44x53cm-17x21in) s.d.1940 gouache. 24-Jul-4 Thierry & Lannon, Brest #95/R est:7000-8000

£5070 $8873 €7200 Corbeille, la Bourse (54x49cm-21x19in) s.d.1935 gouache. 21-Dec-3 Thierry & Lannon, Brest #82/R est:7000-8000

BELCHER, Hilda (1881-1963) American
Works on paper
£346 $550 €505 Old sinner (30x25cm-12x10in) s. W/C over pencil. 12-Sep-3 Weschler, Washington #129/R

BELCHER, Martha Wood (1844-?) American/British
£391 $700 €571 Country landscape with cows by a stream (23x30cm-9x12in) s. 7-May-4 Sloans & Kenyon, Bethesda #1678/R

BELGRANO, Jose Denis (1844-1917) Spanish
£2604 $4245 €3750 Still life of fruit (54x41cm-21x16in) s.d.1860. 23-Sep-3 Durán, Madrid #207/R

BELI-VOROS, Brno (1882-1922) Hungarian
£474 $858 €692 In the boudoir (71x71cm-28x28in) s. 16-Apr-4 Mu Terem Galeria, Budapest #184/R (H.F 180000)

BELIMBAU, Adolfo (1845-1938) Italian
£400 $716 €600 Landscape (17x24cm-7x9in) s. board. 12-May-4 Stadion, Trieste #758/R
£2270 $4200 €3314 Seated woman with bird nest and birds (89x58cm-35x23in) s. 17-Jul-4 Fallon, Copake #53/R

BELITSKI, Ludwig (1830-1902) German
Photographs
£7222 $13000 €10544 Glassware. Glassware II. Stoneware drinking mugs (17x22cm-7x9in) salt prints set of three prov. 22-Apr-4 Phillips, New York #120/R est:15000-20000

BELJANIN (19/20th C) Russian
£1078 $2005 €1574 Winter on the tundra (40x60cm-16x24in) indis.sig.N or I Beljanin. 2-Mar-4 Rasmussen, Copenhagen #1371/R est:10000 (D.KR 12000)

BELKIN, Arnold (1930-1992) Mexican/Canada
£509 $850 €743 Pavan of the grasshoppers (56x69cm-22x27in) s. i.stretcher. 25-Oct-3 David Rago, Lambertville #390

BELKNAP, Zedekiah (1781-1858) American
£2973 $5500 €4341 Portrait of a young blond boy in a buttoned navy blue jacket (61x45cm-24x18in) panel painted c.1825. 15-Jan-4 Sotheby's, New York #300/R est:8000-10000

BELKNAP, Zedekiah (attrib) (1781-1858) American
£4118 $7000 €6012 Portraits of a man and a woman seated in red table back chairs (66x53cm-26x21in) panel pair. 31-Oct-3 North East Auctions, Portsmouth #1458 est:3500-5500
£6105 $10500 €8913 Half length portraits of young husband and wife (71x58cm-28x23in) pair prov. 6-Dec-3 Pook & Pook, Downington #374/R est:12000-14000

BELKOVSKY, Igor (20th C) Russian
£400 $740 €584 Portrait of a young girl, bust length wearing a hat (59x51cm-23x20in) s. 14-Jul-4 Christie's, Kensington #1161/R

BELL, A D (20th C) British
Works on paper
£260 $434 €380 Running down Channel (25x36cm-10x14in) s.d.1950 W/C. 20-Jun-3 Chrystals Auctions, Isle of Man #212

BELL, Arthur George (1849-1916) British
£550 $1007 €803 Quayside, Honfleur. Study of a harbour (13x22cm-5x9in) s.i. board double-sided. 8-Apr-4 Christie's, Kensington #181/R
£760 $1383 €1110 Potato gatherers (25x35cm-10x14in) s. board. 29-Jun-4 Bonhams, Knowle #105
Works on paper
£300 $552 €438 In Lowestoft harbour (36x53cm-14x21in) s. W/C. 10-Jun-4 Lyon & Turnbull, Edinburgh #82

BELL, Caroline M (?-1940) American
£723 $1200 €1056 Winding river in snow (41x127cm-16x50in) s. canvasboard. 4-Oct-3 South Bay, Long Island #63
£814 $1400 €1188 Harbour scene (46x51cm-18x20in) s. artist board. 6-Dec-3 South Bay, Long Island #136a/R
£1628 $2800 €2377 Hay boat at anchor (46x56cm-18x22in) s. 6-Dec-3 South Bay, Long Island #136/R

BELL, Cecil (1906-1970) American
£1397 $2500 €2040 Figures around the stove (76x61cm-30x24in) s. painted c.1930's. 11-Jan-4 William Jenack, New York #290 est:3000-4000

BELL, Charles (1935-1995) American
£41899 $75000 €61173 Marbles XIII (102x152cm-40x60in) s.d.84 prov.lit. 13-May-4 Sotheby's, New York #229/R est:60000-80000
£72626 $130000 €106034 Gin (152x183cm-60x72in) s.i.d.77 verso prov.exhib.lit. 12-May-4 Christie's, Rockefeller NY #167/R est:150000-200000
£140940 $252282 €210000 Double bonus (152x213cm-60x84in) painted 1987 prov.lit. 27-May-4 Sotheby's, Paris #260/R est:180000-250000
£179641 $300000 €262276 Miami Beach (152x213cm-60x84in) s.d.89 prov.exhib.lit. 12-Nov-3 Christie's, Rockefeller NY #374/R est:250000-350000
Works on paper
£17450 $31235 €26000 Study for Troupe (151x101cm-59x40in) s. gouache pastel exec. 1983 prov.lit. 27-May-4 Sotheby's, Paris #251/R est:15000-20000

BELL, Edward August (1862-1953) American
£2395 $4000 €3497 Blue and brown (51x36cm-20x14in) s. panel prov. 7-Oct-3 Sotheby's, New York #173 est:6000-8000

BELL, George Henry Frederick (1878-1966) Australian
£766 $1302 €1118 Portrait of the Artist's Wife (40x33cm-16x13in) s. board prov. 26-Nov-3 Deutscher-Menzies, Melbourne #239/R (A.D 1800)
£779 $1230 €1137 Gypsy caravan (32x41cm-13x16in) s. i. verso panel. 2-Sep-3 Deutscher-Menzies, Melbourne #366/R est:1000-1500 (A.D 1900)

BELL, Henry Jobson (fl.1887-1916) British
£350 $560 €511 Bend in the river (45x60cm-18x24in) s.d.1904. 18-Sep-3 Bonhams, Edinburgh #311a

BELL, James Torrington (1898-1970) British
£360 $572 €526 Autumn landscape (46x61cm-18x24in) s. 10-Sep-3 Sotheby's, Olympia #195/R

BELL, John D (?) British
Works on paper
£280 $476 €409 Racing on an estuary, perhaps the Clyde (50x90cm-20x35in) init. W/C. 10-Nov-3 Thomson Roddick & Medcalf, Edinburgh #234/R

BELL, John Zephaniah (1794-1885) British
Works on paper
£528 $850 €771 Portrait of mother and child (25x20cm-10x8in) pencil ink. 20-Aug-3 James Julia, Fairfield #1135/R

BELL, Larry (1939-) American
£659 $1100 €962 From the Elipse series (137x90cm-54x35in) s.d.81 vaporized metallic paint. 19-Oct-3 Bonhams & Butterfields, Los Angeles #7070
Works on paper
£405 $750 €591 Vapor drawing (114x91cm-45x36in) s.d.79 spray paint sold with a book. 13-Mar-4 Susanin's, Chicago #6046/R
£694 $1160 €1000 Sans titre (38x28cm-15x11in) s.d.1987 mixed media cardboard prov. 25-Oct-3 Cornette de St.Cyr, Paris #377/R

BELL, Leland (1922-1991) American
£6250 $11000 €9125 Self portrait (132x94cm-52x37in) s. verso prov. 23-May-4 Hindman, Chicago #1012/R est:4000-6000

BELL, Peter (20th C) American
£436 $750 €637 View through the portico (152x122cm-60x48in) s. 6-Dec-3 Neal Auction Company, New Orleans #624

BELL, R (19th C) British
£2647 $4500 €3865 Portrait of the American ship Hampton off Dover (61x76cm-24x30in) s.d.1840. 31-Oct-3 North East Auctions, Portsmouth #1730

BELL, Richard (1953-) Australian
Works on paper
£1362 $2356 €1989 Honest John (90x90cm-35x35in) synthetic polymer paint prov. 10-Dec-3 Shapiro, Sydney #132/R est:2500-4000 (A.D 3200)

BELL, Robert Anning (1863-1933) British
Works on paper
£750 $1350 €1095 Study of children eating and drinking (11x21cm-4x8in) init. pen ink. 21-Jan-4 Sotheby's, Olympia #191/R
£2200 $3740 €3212 See where my love a-maying goes - with sweet Dame Flora playing (38x27cm-15x11in) s.i. blk chk W/C htd white pasteboard prov. 20-Nov-3 Christie's, London #144/R est:1500-2000

BELL, Sandra (20th C) Irish?
Sculpture
£1678 $2853 €2400 Incense burner (61cm-24in) bronze. 25-Nov-3 De Veres Art Auctions, Dublin #100j est:2000-3000

BELL, Stuart H (1823-1896) British
£500 $945 €730 Beached at low tide off South Pier Lighthouse, Sunderland (51x61cm-20x24in) s.i.d.1884 s.i.d.verso. 19-Feb-4 Christie's, Kensington #109/R

BELL, Thomas Currie (fl.1892-1925) British
Works on paper
£1800 $3006 €2628 Elegant portrait of Lady Maud Charrington -Jones (156x110cm-61x43in) s.d.1928 pastel. 16-Oct-3 Lawrence, Crewkerne #664/R est:800-1200

BELL, Trevor (1930-) British
£320 $592 €467 Spring, purple and yellow (25x25cm-10x10in) s.i.d.1962 verso panel. 11-Mar-4 Christie's, Kensington #386

£350 $644 €511 Abstract composition in black and green (71x92cm-28x36in) s. oil stick chl. 23-Mar-4 Rosebery Fine Art, London #916/R
£600 $1080 €876 Little girl (51x36cm-20x14in) s.d.53 i.verso exhib. 21-Apr-4 Tennants, Leyburn #1237
£750 $1193 €1095 Blue and yellows (30x122cm-12x48in) s.i.d.1961 verso canvas on board prov. 10-Sep-3 Sotheby's, Olympia #300/R
£820 $1533 €1197 Snow streams (63x63cm-25x25in) s.i.d.1998 verso. 26-Feb-4 Lane, Penzance #88
£2000 $3700 €2920 Light resisting dark (91x123cm-36x48in) s.i.d.1962 verso. 11-Mar-4 Christie's, Kensington #387/R est:2000-3000

BELL, Vanessa (1879-1961) British
£5500 $9680 €8030 Still life with a cyclamen (40x30cm-16x12in) s. prov. 19-May-4 Dreweatt Neate, Newbury #92/R est:6000-8000
£12000 $20400 €17520 Red hot poker and fuchsia in a vase (43x33cm-17x13in) studio st. painted c.1940 prov. 21-Nov-3 Christie's, London #142/R est:10000-15000
£18000 $28620 €26280 Tuscan house (75x62cm-30x24in) s.d.1935. 10-Sep-3 Sotheby's, Olympia #172/R est:10000-15000
£18000 $30600 €26280 Walled garden, Charleston (81x46cm-32x18in) init.i.verso painted c.1933 prov.exhib. 21-Nov-3 Christie's, London #68/R est:15000-20000
£24000 $42240 €35040 The madonna lily (63x38cm-25x15in) prov. 19-May-4 Dreweatt Neate, Newbury #93/R est:8000-10000
Works on paper
£1400 $2590 €2044 Design for an embroided frame for a looking glass (34x22cm-13x9in) W/C executed c.1928. 11-Mar-4 Christie's, Kensington #132/R est:800-1200

BELL, William Charles (1830-1904) British
Miniatures
£2400 $4080 €3504 Queen Victoria (3cm-1in) i.d.1854 verso oval. 18-Nov-3 Bonhams, New Bond Street #151/R est:800-1200

BELL-SMITH, Frederick Marlett (1846-1923) Canadian/British
£1040 $1903 €1518 Portrait of Queen Victoria (25x20cm-10x8in) s.i.d.1895 card lit. 1-Jun-4 Joyner Waddington, Toronto #404 est:1200-1500 (C.D 2600)
£1182 $1926 €1726 Surf (55x91cm-22x36in) s.d.83. 23-Sep-3 Ritchie, Toronto #73/R est:3000-4000 (C.D 2600)
£1250 $2150 €1825 Early morning, Rijsoord, Holland (35x52cm-14x20in) s. 2-Dec-3 Joyner Waddington, Toronto #317/R est:3000-3500 (C.D 2800)
£1802 $3063 €2631 Tugboat nearing the harbour (37x63cm-15x25in) s. paperboard. 23-Nov-3 Levis, Calgary #8/R est:5000-6000 (C.D 4000)
£1840 $3367 €2686 Canyon (27x18cm-11x7in) s. board. 1-Jun-4 Joyner Waddington, Toronto #162/R est:2500-3000 (C.D 4600)
£2033 $3638 €2968 Lake Louise, Victoria Glacier (22x35cm-9x14in) s. board prov. 27-May-4 Heffel, Vancouver #42/R est:3500-4500 (C.D 5000)
£3348 $5759 €4888 Rapids in the Rockies (37x49cm-15x19in) s. 2-Dec-3 Joyner Waddington, Toronto #249/R est:3500-4000 (C.D 7500)
£14228 $25467 €20773 Coming storm in the Rockies (76x61cm-30x24in) s.d.1914 prov.exhib. 31-May-4 Sotheby's, Toronto #110/R est:15000-20000 (C.D 35000)
Works on paper
£222 $364 €324 Eagle Lake (33x51cm-13x20in) s. W/C. 28-May-3 Maynards, Vancouver #127 (C.D 500)
£282 $519 €412 Sailboats off a rocky shore (25x40cm-10x16in) s. W/C. 9-Jun-4 Walker's, Ottawa #112/R (C.D 700)
£480 $878 €701 Fall out after parade (12x14cm-5x6in) W/C prov. 1-Jun-4 Hodgins, Calgary #27/R (C.D 1200)
£480 $878 €701 Near Land's End, Cornwall (18x25cm-7x10in) s.i. W/C. 1-Jun-4 Hodgins, Calgary #316/R (C.D 1200)
£541 $919 €790 Market morning, Bury St Edmunds (17x25cm-7x10in) s.i. W/C executed c.1897. 27-Nov-3 Heffel, Vancouver #31/R (C.D 1200)
£600 $1098 €876 Wave washed rock (28x43cm-11x17in) s.i.d.1884 W/C. 1-Jun-4 Hodgins, Calgary #413/R (C.D 1500)
£661 $1197 €965 Untitled - breaking waves (32x50cm-13x20in) s. W/C. 18-Apr-4 Levis, Calgary #5/R est:2000-2500 (C.D 1600)
£667 $1153 €974 Ludgate Hill (48x33cm-19x13in) s.d.1912 W/C. 9-Dec-3 Maynards, Vancouver #205a est:3000-4000 (C.D 1500)
£676 $1149 €987 Marble Arch, Hyde Park (19x25cm-7x10in) s. i.verso W/C. 21-Nov-3 Walker's, Ottawa #24/R (C.D 1500)
£766 $1302 €1118 Siwash Indian canoes (25x42cm-10x17in) indis.s. i.d.1889 verso W/C prov. 23-Nov-3 Levis, Calgary #9/R (C.D 1700)
£813 $1455 €1187 London scene with Big Ben (26x17cm-10x7in) s. W/C prov. 6-May-4 Heffel, Vancouver #26/R est:2500-3500 (C.D 2000)
£893 $1536 €1304 Diamond Jubilee, Sir Pratah Singh and Officers of the Indian escort (17x25cm-7x10in) s. W/C lit. 2-Dec-3 Joyner Waddington, Toronto #58/R est:2000-3000 (C.D 2000)
£893 $1536 €1304 Evening - Emerald Lake, B C (22x32cm-9x13in) s. W/C prov. 2-Dec-3 Joyner Waddington, Toronto #401 est:2000-2500 (C.D 2000)
£1016 $1819 €1483 Rainy day near Trafalgar Square (25x18cm-10x7in) s. i.verso W/C. 27-May-4 Heffel, Vancouver #15/R est:2500-3500 (C.D 2500)
£1071 $1843 €1564 Kensington Gardens (17x26cm-7x10in) s.i.d.1922 W/C. 2-Dec-3 Joyner Waddington, Toronto #135/R est:2500-3500 (C.D 2400)
£1120 $2050 €1635 Looking towards Waterloo Bridge form the Strand, before sunset (19x16cm-7x6in) s. W/C prov. 1-Jun-4 Joyner Waddington, Toronto #501 est:1500-2000 (C.D 2800)
£1222 $2029 €1784 Street in Coventry (27x17cm-11x7in) s.d.1908 i.verso W/C prov. 5-Oct-3 Levis, Calgary #4/R est:4000-4500 (C.D 2750)
£1260 $2256 €1840 Daybreak, St Pauls (35x50cm-14x20in) s. W/C. 27-May-4 Heffel, Vancouver #10/R est:2000-3000 (C.D 3100)
£1321 $2365 €1929 Charles I statue, Trafalgar Square, London (26x17cm-10x7in) s. s.i.verso W/C. 27-May-4 Heffel, Vancouver #11/R est:2500-3500 (C.D 3250)
£1360 $2489 €1986 The toboggan run (25x18cm-10x7in) s. W/C. 1-Jun-4 Hodgins, Calgary #28/R est:1750-2250 (C.D 3400)
£1429 $2457 €2086 Fleet Street (34x22cm-13x9in) s.i.d.04 W/C. 2-Dec-3 Joyner Waddington, Toronto #165/R est:2500-3500 (C.D 3200)
£1464 $2489 €2137 Mt Cheops, glacier, B C (38x28cm-15x11in) s.i. W/C prov. 18-Nov-3 Sotheby's, Toronto #117/R est:1800-2200 (C.D 3250)
£1518 $2611 €2216 London street scene (21x31cm-8x12in) s. W/C. 2-Dec-3 Joyner Waddington, Toronto #123/R est:3000-3500 (C.D 3400)
£1577 $2680 €2302 Mount Aberdeen (23x17cm-9x7in) s. i.verso W/C paper on cardboard prov. 18-Nov-3 Sotheby's, Toronto #118/R est:3000-4000 (C.D 3500)
£1577 $2680 €2302 Lower Canadian snowshoe costume. Tobogganing party (18x11cm-7x4in) d.1881 one s.i. one s. W/C four. 23-Nov-3 Levis, Calgary #10/R est:3000-3500 (C.D 3500)
£1931 $3456 €2819 Crest of the Rockies (30x45cm-12x18in) s. W/C prov.exhib. 27-May-4 Heffel, Vancouver #89/R est:3500-4500 (C.D 4750)
£2236 $4002 €3265 Evening, Summit Lake (30x48cm-12x19in) s.i. W/C prov. 27-May-4 Heffel, Vancouver #92/R est:3500-4500 (C.D 5500)
£3604 $6126 €5262 In the Rockies (61x40cm-24x16in) s. W/C executed c.1889. 27-Nov-3 Heffel, Vancouver #23/R est:2500-3500 (C.D 8000)

BELLA, Stefano Della (1610-1664) Italian
Prints
£2105 $3874 €3200 Death during the battle (22x30cm-9x12in) eau forte. 22-Jun-4 Sotheby's, Milan #224 est:1600-2000
Works on paper
£232 $425 €339 Recumbent lion (5x7cm-2x3in) pen brown ink pencil card stock. 29-Jan-4 Swann Galleries, New York #53/R
£360 $576 €500 Popular scene (13x20cm-5x8in) pencil pen ink prov. 14-May-3 Finarte Semenzato, Milan #492
£396 $633 €550 Harbour scene (13x18cm-5x7in) pen ink prov. 14-May-3 Finarte Semenzato, Milan #493
£504 $806 €700 Port worker (15x13cm-6x5in) pen ink. 14-May-3 Finarte Semenzato, Milan #491
£700 $1260 €1022 Putti at play. Caricature of a man (19x17cm-7x7in) pen brown ink double-sided. 20-Apr-4 Sotheby's, Olympia #30/R
£1093 $2000 €1596 Ornamental design (24x11cm-9x4in) pen brown ink wash. 29-Jan-4 Swann Galleries, New York #55/R est:3000-5000
£4200 $7266 €6132 Halberdiers. Two seated men seen from behind (7x3cm-3x1in) pen brown ink three prov. 12-Dec-3 Christie's, Kensington #336/R est:1000-1500
£4218 $7550 €6200 Feuille d'etudes de cavaliers Polonais (19x30cm-7x12in) pen brown ink. 19-Mar-4 Piasa, Paris #20/R est:6000
£6250 $11500 €9500 Madonna and Child (18x4cm-7x2in) pen ink double-sided. 22-Jun-4 Sotheby's, Milan #5/R est:4000-6000

BELLA, Vincenzo la (1872-1954) Italian
£423 $701 €600 Interior scene with figure in costume (25x35cm-10x14in) s. 11-Jun-3 Christie's, Rome #222
£599 $1048 €850 Street with women and soldiers (64x85cm-25x33in) s. 17-Dec-3 Il Ponte, Milan #805
£704 $1218 €1000 Masks (31x24cm-12x9in) s. 10-Dec-3 Finarte Semenzato, Rome #242/R

BELLANDI, Giorgio (1930-) Italian
£599 $994 €850 Composition (72x108cm-28x43in) s.d.59 acrylic. 11-Jun-3 Finarte Semenzato, Milan #552/R

BELLANGE, Henri (19th C) French
Works on paper
£218 $375 €318 Soldier (36x25cm-14x10in) s.i.d.1854 W/C. 7-Dec-3 Hindman, Chicago #753/R

BELLANGE, Hippolyte (1800-1866) French
£20979 $36084 €30000 Le repos du soldat (54x65cm-21x26in) s.d.1838. 2-Dec-3 Sotheby's, Paris #30/R est:10000-15000
£54545 $93818 €78000 Les Vainqueurs, episode de Marengo (73x59cm-29x23in) s.d.1852 prov.exhib. 2-Dec-3 Sotheby's, Paris #52/R est:25000-35000

BELLANGE, Jacques (c.1575-1616) Italian
Prints
£2098 $3566 €3000 Awakening of Lazarus (46x31cm-18x12in) etching. 28-Nov-3 Bassenge, Berlin #5736a/R est:2500
£11000 $20020 €16060 Martydom of Saint Lucy (46x35cm-18x14in) etching engraving. 30-Jun-4 Christie's, London #4/R est:10000-15000
£48035 $87424 €70131 Three Marys at Christ's grave. etching. 17-Jun-4 Kornfeld, Bern #6/R est:100000 (S.FR 110000)

BELLANGER, René-Charles (1895-1964) French
£423 $731 €600 14 juillet en Alsace, Rosheim (38x55cm-15x22in) st.sig. peinture cardboard on canvas exhib. 10-Dec-3 Rossini, Paris #48/R

BELLANGER-ADHEMAR, Paul (1868-1925) French
£1800 $2880 €2628 L'aperitif (46x61cm-18x24in) s. 18-Sep-3 Christie's, Kensington #179/R est:2000-3000

BELLANY, John (1942-) British
£600 $1062 €876 Harbour view with church beyond (60x75cm-24x30in) s. 27-Apr-4 Bonhams, Knightsbridge #19/R
£720 $1260 €1051 Highland scene (91x91cm-36x36in) s. 19-Dec-3 Mallams, Oxford #255/R
£800 $1384 €1168 Coastal seascape (61x76cm-24x30in) s. i.d.94 on stretcher. 9-Dec-3 Rosebery Fine Art, London #634/R
£800 $1408 €1168 Seascape with orange sun (50x50cm-20x20in) init. 18-May-4 Bonhams, Knightsbridge #8/R
£850 $1564 €1241 Off a southern coast (51x61cm-20x24in) init. 24-Mar-4 Hamptons Fine Art, Godalming #288/R
£950 $1539 €1378 Sun seeker (61x51cm-24x20in) s. 30-Jul-3 Hamptons Fine Art, Godalming #236
£1000 $1670 €1460 Ship (30x40cm-12x16in) s.verso. 21-Oct-3 Bonhams, Knightsbridge #173/R est:400-600
£1000 $1840 €1460 Two trawlers near an estuary (51x75cm-20x30in) s. 24-Mar-4 Hamptons Fine Art, Godalming #285/R
£1100 $2046 €1606 Island off the coast (61x76cm-24x30in) s. 4-Mar-4 Christie's, Kensington #260/R est:1000-1500
£1200 $2208 €1752 Trawler at a quay side (58x76cm-23x30in) s. 24-Mar-4 Hamptons Fine Art, Godalming #286/R
£1400 $2226 €2044 Landscape of mystery (91x91cm-36x36in) s.i.overlap. 10-Sep-3 Sotheby's, Olympia #339/R est:1500-2000
£1400 $2422 €2044 Mystic (60x51cm-24x20in) s. i.d.94 on stretcher. 9-Dec-3 Rosebery Fine Art, London #633 est:400-600

£1400	$2590	€2044	Snowy landscape (76x102cm-30x40in) s. 11-Feb-4 Sotheby's, Olympia #269/R est:1500-2000
£1450	$2538	€2117	Still life of a vase of flowers (74x58cm-29x23in) s. 19-Dec-3 Mallams, Oxford #254/R est:800-1200
£1600	$2816	€2336	Harbour scene (51x61cm-20x24in) s. 19-May-4 Sotheby's, Olympia #291/R est:800-1200
£1700	$2890	€2482	At a quayside, Eyemouth harbour (91x122cm-36x48in) s. 26-Nov-3 Hamptons Fine Art, Godalming #248/R est:1500-2000
£1700	$3128	€2482	Portseton (91x122cm-36x48in) s.i.stretcher. 23-Mar-4 Rosebery Fine Art, London #756/R est:1500-2000
£1700	$3094	€2482	Still life with vase of flowers (122x91cm-48x36in) s. 1-Jul-4 Christie's, Kensington #356/R est:1500-2000
£1800	$3060	€2628	Fish and Chips (76x61cm-30x24in) s. 30-Oct-3 Christie's, London #236/R est:2000-3000
£1800	$3060	€2628	Still life with lobster (91x122cm-36x48in) s. 26-Nov-3 Hamptons Fine Art, Godalming #243/R est:2000-3000
£1800	$3330	€2628	Bass rock (91x122cm-36x48in) s. i.overlap. 11-Feb-4 Sotheby's, Olympia #288/R est:2000-3000
£1800	$3186	€2628	Boat and sun (50x50cm-20x20in) s. 27-Apr-4 Bonhams, Knightsbridge #22/R est:500-700
£1900	$3173	€2774	Hilltop town, Tuscany (91x122cm-36x48in) s. 16-Oct-3 Christie's, Kensington #670/R est:1500-2500
£1900	$3344	€2774	Off Dunbar (60x75cm-24x30in) s. i.d.94 verso. 19-May-4 Dreweatt Neate, Newbury #69/R est:800-1200
£2000	$3240	€2900	Eyemouth Harbour (91x121cm-36x48in) s. 30-Jul-3 Hamptons Fine Art, Godalming #250/R est:3000-4000
£2000	$3240	€2900	Trawler at Eyemouth (76x102cm-30x40in) s. 30-Jul-3 Hamptons Fine Art, Godalming #251/R est:2000-3000
£2000	$3440	€2920	Flanders dish (91x91cm-36x36in) s. 3-Dec-3 Christie's, Kensington #674/R est:2000-3000
£2000	$3680	€2920	After the Tempest (121x91cm-48x36in) s.i.stretcher. 23-Mar-4 Rosebery Fine Art, London #757/R est:1500-2000
£2100	$3318	€3045	Two figures in a boat (49x60cm-19x24in) s. 2-Sep-3 Bonhams, Oxford #84 est:600-800
£2100	$3402	€3045	Card player (61x51cm-24x20in) s. 30-Jul-3 Hamptons Fine Art, Godalming #162 est:1200-1800
£2200	$3740	€3212	Fish people (91x91cm-36x36in) s. i.verso. 26-Nov-3 Sotheby's, Olympia #185/R est:2000-3000
£2200	$3872	€3212	North Berwick Harbour (91x122cm-36x48in) s. 19-May-4 Sotheby's, Olympia #313/R est:2500-3500
£2400	$3816	€3504	Still life with boat (91x91cm-36x36in) s. i.overlap. 10-Sep-3 Sotheby's, Olympia #340/R est:1200-1800
£2400	$4440	€3504	Eyemouth harbour (91x122cm-36x48in) s. i.overlap. 11-Feb-4 Sotheby's, Olympia #290/R est:2500-3500
£2400	$4368	€3504	Fishing boat on a dry dock (91x122cm-36x48in) s. 1-Jul-4 Christie's, Kensington #309/R est:1500-2000
£2600	$4732	€3796	Portrait of a lady in the hills (101x76cm-40x30in) s. 1-Jul-4 Christie's, Kensington #201/R est:2000-3000
£2800	$4536	€4060	Still life of a jug of flowers (91x91cm-36x36in) 30-Jul-3 Hamptons Fine Art, Godalming #186/R est:1500-2000
£2800	$5208	€4088	Lobster pots on the quay (91x122cm-36x48in) s. 4-Mar-4 Christie's, Kensington #257/R est:2000-3000
£2800	$5180	€4088	Accordian player (121x91cm-48x36in) s. 11-Mar-4 Christie's, Kensington #211/R est:2000-3000
£2800	$4928	€4088	Port Seton plants (91x91cm-36x36in) s.i. 19-May-4 Sotheby's, Olympia #314/R est:1500-2000
£3000	$4770	€4380	Harbour at Crail (122x122cm-48x48in) s. i.verso. 10-Sep-3 Sotheby's, Olympia #331/R est:3000-5000
£3000	$4770	€4380	Three girls and a horse (152x152cm-60x60in) s. 10-Sep-3 Sotheby's, Olympia #332/R est:3000-5000
£3000	$4740	€4380	Woman standing before the Bass Rock (92x91cm-36x36in) s. 6-Sep-3 Shapes, Edinburgh #319 est:3000-5000
£3000	$5580	€4380	Fish wife (76x61cm-30x24in) s. 4-Mar-4 Christie's, Kensington #258/R est:1500-2000
£3200	$5344	€4672	Fish wives (91x91cm-36x36in) s. 16-Oct-3 Christie's, Kensington #572/R est:2000-3000
£3200	$5440	€4672	Golspie harbour (91x91cm-36x36in) s.i. 26-Nov-3 Sotheby's, Olympia #153/R est:3600-5000
£3200	$5920	€4672	Harbour wall (76x103cm-30x41in) s. 11-Feb-4 Sotheby's, Olympia #297/R est:2500-3500
£3200	$5728	€4672	Trawler entering port (91x91cm-36x36in) s. 14-May-4 Christie's, Kensington #597/R est:1000-1500
£3500	$6475	€5110	Still life with exotic flowers (91x91cm-36x36in) s. 11-Feb-4 Sotheby's, Olympia #285/R est:2000-3000
£3500	$6160	€5110	Still life with flowers and boat in a window (122x91cm-48x36in) s. 19-May-4 Sotheby's, Olympia #211/R est:3000-5000
£3600	$6120	€5256	Portrait of lady with fish (61x77cm-24x30in) s. 26-Nov-3 Sotheby's, Olympia #169/R est:1500-2000
£3600	$6228	€5256	Fisherwoman with a cockerel (101x76cm-40x30in) s. s.d.95 on stretcher. 9-Dec-3 Rosebery Fine Art, London #632/R est:1000-1500
£3600	$6624	€5256	Still life of poppies in a blue vase (122x91cm-48x36in) s. 24-Mar-4 Hamptons Fine Art, Godalming #289/R
£3600	$6552	€5256	Female portrait head with fish (76x60cm-30x24in) s. 3-Jul-4 Shapes, Edinburgh #486/R est:3000-4000
£3800	$6346	€5548	Two trawlers at port (91x122cm-36x48in) s. 16-Oct-3 Christie's, Kensington #673/R est:3000-5000
£3800	$6460	€5548	Three fish wives (122x91cm-48x36in) s. 26-Nov-3 Hamptons Fine Art, Godalming #119/R est:2000-3000
£3800	$6954	€5548	Mayflower in harbour (91x121cm-36x48in) s. 8-Apr-4 Bonhams, Edinburgh #32/R est:3000-5000
£3800	$6802	€5548	Ladies of the harbour (91x91cm-36x36in) s. i.verso. 14-May-4 Christie's, Kensington #568/R est:2500-3500
£4000	$7440	€5840	Still life with lobster (91x121cm-36x48in) s. 4-Mar-4 Christie's, Kensington #256/R est:2500-3500
£4000	$7320	€5840	Still life of irises and canvases (122x91cm-48x36in) s. 8-Apr-4 Bonhams, Edinburgh #29/R est:4000-6000
£4000	$7040	€5840	Celtic dreamer (102x76cm-40x30in) s. i.overlap. 19-May-4 Sotheby's, Olympia #305/R est:3000-5000
£4200	$7518	€6132	Still life with jug of lilies (91x91cm-36x36in) s. 14-May-4 Christie's, Kensington #586/R est:1000-1500
£4200	$7392	€6132	Boats in harbour (91x122cm-36x48in) s. 19-May-4 Sotheby's, Olympia #304/R est:3000-5000
£4300	$7826	€6278	Kirkcaldy Harbour with fishing boat Stella Marie (91x91cm-36x36in) s. 3-Jul-4 Shapes, Edinburgh #485/R est:3000-5000
£5100	$9027	€7446	Harbour scene with The Resplendant decked with ensigns (91x91cm-36x36in) 1-May-4 Shapes, Edinburgh #439/R est:3500-5500
£5500	$8855	€7975	Two figures and a bird (122x122cm-48x48in) s. 21-Aug-3 Bonhams, Edinburgh #1099/R est:5000-7000
£5500	$9185	€8030	Vesperland (190x148cm-75x58in) s.verso. 16-Oct-3 Bonhams, Edinburgh #10/R est:6000-8000
£5500	$10010	€8030	Canal lock (92x122cm-36x48in) s. 3-Jul-4 Shapes, Edinburgh #484/R est:4000-6000
£5600	$9856	€8176	Eyemouth (91x122cm-36x48in) s. i.stretcher. 19-May-4 Sotheby's, Olympia #210/R est:3000-5000
£6000	$9540	€8760	Dieppe harbour (91x122cm-36x48in) s. 10-Sep-3 Sotheby's, Olympia #341/R est:4000-6000
£6200	$11346	€9052	Eyemouth harbour (91x122cm-36x48in) s. 5-Jun-4 Shapes, Edinburgh #484/R est:5000-7000
£8200	$13202	€11890	Rebecca in port (122x122cm-48x48in) s. 21-Aug-3 Bonhams, Edinburgh #1098/R est:5000-7000

Works on paper

£300	$555	€438	Arm of the giant crane bird and the sea at Monte Carlo from Hotel Paris (40x29cm-16x11in) s.i.d.17th and 16th Oct 1984 pencil pastel. 11-Feb-4 Sotheby's, Olympia #289/R
£420	$680	€609	At a dock side (38x56cm-15x22in) s. W/C. 30-Jul-3 Hamptons Fine Art, Godalming #75
£500	$850	€730	Highland landscape (41x56cm-16x22in) s. W/C. 26-Nov-3 Hamptons Fine Art, Godalming #65
£620	$1035	€905	Lighthouse (38x28cm-15x11in) s. W/C. 13-Nov-3 Bonhams, Edinburgh #354
£650	$1105	€949	Scottish hills (38x56cm-15x22in) s. W/C. 26-Nov-3 Sotheby's, Olympia #159/R
£698	$1200	€1019	Voyagers (55x75cm-22x30in) s. W/C pencil prov. 3-Dec-3 Doyle, New York #22/R est:1000-1500
£700	$1134	€1015	Fisherman's wife (57x37cm-22x15in) s. pencil W/C. 30-Jul-3 Hamptons Fine Art, Godalming #123
£700	$1134	€1015	English teacher (57x37cm-22x15in) s. pencil W/C. 30-Jul-3 Hamptons Fine Art, Godalming #143
£850	$1581	€1241	Starella in the harbour (56x75cm-22x30in) s. W/C. 4-Mar-4 Christie's, Kensington #261/R
£900	$1647	€1314	Sea figure (57x37cm-22x15in) s. W/C. 8-Apr-4 Bonhams, Edinburgh #12/R
£950	$1587	€1387	Fishing boats along the quay (56x74cm-22x29in) s. pencil W/C. 16-Oct-3 Christie's, Kensington #672/R
£1000	$1700	€1460	Artist holds the bird of Paradise (76x56cm-30x22in) s. pencil W/C exhib. 30-Oct-3 Christie's, London #235/R est:1500-2500
£1050	$1754	€1533	Self portrait in cap (38x28cm-15x11in) s. W/C. 16-Oct-3 Bonhams, Edinburgh #47 est:1200-1500
£1050	$1754	€1533	Artist holds the birds of paradise (75x56cm-30x22in) s. pencil W/C. 16-Oct-3 Bonhams, Edinburgh #54 est:1000-1500
£1100	$1837	€1606	Radiant Star in harbour (56x75cm-22x30in) s. W/C. 16-Oct-3 Bonhams, Edinburgh #3/R est:1500-2500
£1100	$1870	€1606	Golden valley (52x71cm-20x28in) s. W/C. 26-Nov-3 Sotheby's, Olympia #152/R est:1000-1500
£1100	$2002	€1606	Voyagers (56x75cm-22x30in) pencil W/C prov. 1-Jul-4 Christie's, Kensington #205/R est:1000-1500
£1200	$2196	€1752	Stonehaven fishing boat in harbour (56x76cm-22x30in) s. W/C en grisaille. 8-Apr-4 Bonhams, Edinburgh #54 est:1200-1800
£1300	$2249	€1898	Portrait of Helen (68x49cm-27x19in) s. W/C. 11-Dec-3 Lyon & Turnbull, Edinburgh #102 est:1500-2000
£1500	$2505	€2190	Cat lady (57x38cm-22x15in) s. W/C. 16-Oct-3 Bonhams, Edinburgh #67 est:1500-2000
£1500	$2790	€2190	Trawler in the harbour (56x74cm-22x29in) s. pencil W/C. 4-Mar-4 Christie's, Kensington #259/R est:800-1200
£5200	$8372	€7540	Woman and starfish (76x57cm-30x22in) s. W/C. 21-Aug-3 Bonhams, Edinburgh #1100/R est:1500-2000

BELLASIS, John Brownrigg (1806-1890) British

Works on paper

£500	$850	€730	Lalla butler, India (18x18cm-7x7in) init.i. W/C. 4-Nov-3 Bonhams, New Bond Street #51/R

BELLE, Alexis Simon (1674-1734) French

£4934	$9079	€7500	Portrait de femme a la robe bleue (72x58cm-28x23in) oval. 25-Jun-4 Piasa, Paris #97/R est:3000-4000

BELLE, Alexis Simon (attrib) (1674-1734) French

£3546	$5922	€5000	Portrait d'homme a la veste rouge (81x65cm-32x26in) painted oval. 17-Oct-3 Tajan, Paris #94/R est:4000-6000

BELLE, Charles Ernest de (1873-1939) Canadian/Hungarian

£201	$345	€293	Misty landscape (20x25cm-8x10in) s. 2-Dec-3 Joyner Waddington, Toronto #418 (C.D 450)
£220	$402	€321	Pastoral (25x20cm-10x8in) mono. 1-Jun-4 Joyner Waddington, Toronto #475 (C.D 550)
£600	$1098	€876	Girl holding a puppy (41x35cm-16x14in) mono. 1-Jun-4 Joyner Waddington, Toronto #46/R est:2000-3000 (C.D 1500)
£759	$1267	€1101	Paysage d'ete. Paysage d'automne (20x25cm-8x10in) pair prov. 17-Jun-3 Pinneys, Montreal #181 est:600-800 (C.D 1700)

Works on paper

£290	$485	€421	Young girls in the meadow (23x19cm-9x7in) mono. pastel. 17-Jun-3 Pinneys, Montreal #167 (C.D 650)
£320	$586	€467	Two children (24x19cm-9x7in) mono. pastel. 1-Jun-4 Joyner Waddington, Toronto #527 (C.D 800)
£491	$820	€712	Young girl wearing a bonnet (19x24cm-7x9in) mono. pastel. 17-Jun-3 Pinneys, Montreal #187 est:300-500 (C.D 1100)
£560	$1025	€818	Horse-drawn sleigh on a winter road (34x49cm-13x19in) mono. pastel. 1-Jun-4 Joyner Waddington, Toronto #279/R (C.D 1400)
£640	$1171	€934	Young girl wearing a bonnet (24x19cm-9x7in) mono. pastel. 1-Jun-4 Joyner Waddington, Toronto #297/R (C.D 1600)
£960	$1757	€1402	Young girls at play (34x44cm-13x17in) mono. pastel. 1-Jun-4 Joyner Waddington, Toronto #151/R est:3000-3500 (C.D 2400)
£1518	$2611	€2216	Three figures (40x45cm-16x18in) mono. pastel. 2-Dec-3 Joyner Waddington, Toronto #119/R est:3000-3500 (C.D 3400)

BELLE, Karel van (1884-1959) Belgian

£367	$675	€550	Elegante dans un coup de vente (75x58cm-30x23in) s. 14-Jun-4 Horta, Bruxelles #234
£461	$770	€650	Devant la cathedrale (140x115cm-55x45in) s. 17-Jun-3 Galerie Moderne, Brussels #206/R

£533 $960 €800 Woman sleeping on a setee (84x150cm-33x59in) s.d.1942 panel. 26-Apr-4 Bernaerts, Antwerp #440/R

BELLEFLEUR, Léon (1910-) Canadian
£905 $1421 €1321 Marine imprevue (38x46cm-15x18in) s. s.i.d.97 verso. 26-Aug-3 Iegor de Saint Hippolyte, Montreal #55 (C.D 2000)
£982 $1689 €1434 Base de fleuve en Janvier (37x45cm-15x18in) s.d.82. 2-Dec-3 Joyner Waddington, Toronto #334/R est:2500-3000 (C.D 2200)
£1167 $2135 €1704 Rhodes (35x45cm-14x18in) s.d.83. 27-Jan-4 Iegor de Saint Hippolyte, Montreal #3 (C.D 2800)
£1942 $3341 €2835 Table d'initiation (87x115cm-34x45in) s.d.77. 2-Dec-3 Joyner Waddington, Toronto #216/R est:6000-8000 (C.D 4350)
£2642 $4730 €3857 Souper sur l'herbe (66x81cm-26x32in) s.d.75 s.i.d.verso prov. 31-May-4 Sotheby's, Toronto #114/R est:7000-9000 (C.D 6500)
£7143 $12286 €10429 Remous (144x112cm-57x44in) s.d.84 prov. 2-Dec-3 Joyner Waddington, Toronto #93/R est:10000-15000 (C.D 16000)
Works on paper
£208 $381 €304 Le deuxieme arbre (56x38cm-22x15in) s.i.d.81 ink. 27-Jan-4 Iegor de Saint Hippolyte, Montreal #7 (C.D 500)
£667 $1153 €974 Entre quatre couleurs (50x36cm-20x14in) s. gouache. 15-Dec-3 Iegor de Saint Hippolyte, Montreal #3c (C.D 1500)
£683 $1270 €997 Un ange passe (54x36cm-21x14in) s.i.d.1981 gouache prov. 4-Mar-4 Heffel, Vancouver #4/R (C.D 1700)
£884 $1643 €1291 L'ephemere (57x38cm-22x15in) s.i.d.80 gouache prov. 2-Mar-4 Ritchie, Toronto #169/R est:2500-3500 (C.D 2200)

BELLEFROID, Guillaume (1893-1971) Dutch
£1049 $1804 €1500 Kruisafname (90x60cm-35x24in) s.d.41. 4-Dec-3 Vendue Huis, Gravenhage #903
£1049 $1804 €1500 Taking Christ down from the cross (90x60cm-35x24in) s.d.41. 3-Dec-3 Auction Maastricht #903/R est:1500-2000
£1399 $2406 €2000 Five heads (30x80cm-12x31in) s.d.42. 4-Dec-3 Vendue Huis, Gravenhage #902
£1399 $2406 €2000 The five heads (60x80cm-24x31in) s.d.42. 3-Dec-3 Auction Maastricht #902/R est:2000-2500
Works on paper
£350 $601 €500 Borinage (50x65cm-20x26in) s.d.37 crayon. 3-Dec-3 Auction Maastricht #1004/R
£350 $601 €500 Jemeppe sur Meuse (48x62cm-19x24in) s.d.37 crayon. 3-Dec-3 Auction Maastricht #1008/R
£455 $782 €650 Chateau Neercanne (48x65cm-19x26in) s. crayon. 3-Dec-3 Auction Maastricht #1006/R

BELLEFROID, Guillaume (attrib) (1893-1971) Dutch
£699 $1168 €1000 Harvest (24x30cm-9x12in) s. board. 10-Oct-3 Vendue Huis, Gravenhage #800
Works on paper
£350 $601 €500 Borinage (50x65cm-20x26in) s.d.37 crayon. 4-Dec-3 Vendue Huis, Gravenhage #1004
£350 $601 €500 Jemeppe sur Meuse (48x62cm-19x24in) s.d.37 crayon. 4-Dec-3 Vendue Huis, Gravenhage #1008
£455 $782 €650 Chateau Neercanne (48x65cm-19x26in) s.d.37 crayon. 4-Dec-3 Vendue Huis, Gravenhage #1006

BELLEGAMBE, Jean (attrib) (1470-1534) French
£8553 $15737 €13000 Sainte Barbe (89x29cm-35x11in) panel prov.exhib.lit. 24-Jun-4 Christie's, Paris #8/R est:2000-4000

BELLEGARDE, Claude (1927-) French
£278 $464 €400 Composition (46x38cm-18x15in) s. s.d.62 verso. 21-Oct-3 Artcurial Briest, Paris #643
£280 $476 €400 Le musicien (61x50cm-24x20in) s.i.d.1974 verso prov. 23-Nov-3 Cornette de St.Cyr, Paris #9
£403 $749 €600 Femmes en mouvement (80x54cm-31x21in) s. s.i.verso. 3-Mar-4 Artcurial Briest, Paris #305
£417 $696 €600 Rythmes nocturnes (92x73cm-36x29in) s. s.i.d.1963 verso. 21-Oct-3 Artcurial Briest, Paris #642
£420 $713 €600 Portrait de femme epanouie (61x50cm-24x20in) s.i.d.1969 verso isorel prov. 23-Nov-3 Cornette de St.Cyr, Paris #10
£709 $1184 €1000 Sans titre (21x15cm-8x6in) s. oil raffia blind. 19-Oct-3 Charbonneaux, Paris #139/R
£780 $1303 €1100 Icare (40x57cm-16x22in) s. s.i.d.1966 verso aluminium paint decoupe. 19-Oct-3 Charbonneaux, Paris #137
£800 $1440 €1200 Atlantide (146x114cm-57x45in) s. s.i.d.1961 verso. 24-Apr-4 Cornette de St.Cyr, Paris #434/R

BELLEGHEM, Roger van (1922-) Belgian
£324 $600 €473 Quo vadis (79x99cm-31x39in) s. panel. 12-Mar-4 Jackson's, Cedar Falls #1041/R

BELLEI, Gaetano (1857-1922) Italian
£1370 $2329 €2000 Portrait of lady (33x42cm-13x17in) s.d.1895. 7-Nov-3 Tuttarte, Modena #645 est:3500-4000
£11500 $19550 €16790 Game of cards (39x60cm-15x24in) s. 26-Nov-3 Hamptons Fine Art, Godalming #172/R est:3000-5000
£16500 $30030 €24090 Masquerader (65x49cm-26x19in) s.i. 16-Jun-4 Bonhams, New Bond Street #76/R est:8000-12000
£17738 $31752 €25897 Three generations (49x64cm-19x25in) s.d.1882. 25-May-4 Bukowskis, Stockholm #348/R est:80000-100000 (S.KR 240000)
£30201 $56477 €45000 Welcome (77x103cm-30x41in) s. exhib.lit. 25-Feb-4 Porro, Milan #41/R est:40000

BELLEMARE, Noel (attrib) (?-1546) French
£83916 $140140 €120000 Christ en croix entre Saint-Etienne, la Vierge Marie, Saint-Jean et Saint-Francois (86x103cm-34x41in) panel prov.exhib.lit. 30-Jun-3 Bailly Pommery, Paris #34/R est:70000-90000

BELLEMONT, Léon (1866-1961) French
£430 $805 €650 Maree basse a Audierne (19x24cm-7x9in) s. board. 24-Jul-4 Thierry & Lannon, Brest #123
£2185 $3999 €3300 La lecon de piano (61x50cm-24x20in) s. 9-Apr-4 Claude Aguttes, Neuilly #47/R est:2000-3000

BELLENGE, Michel Bruno (attrib) (1726-1793) French
£4161 $7656 €6200 Nature morte au bouquet de fleurs sur un entablement (33x25cm-13x10in) pair. 26-Mar-4 Piasa, Paris #52/R est:3000-4000

BELLENGER, Georges (1847-1918) French
£1000 $1850 €1460 Still life with roses (46x38cm-18x15in) s. 10-Mar-4 Sotheby's, Olympia #292/R est:2000-3000

BELLEROCHE, Albert de (1864-1944) French
Works on paper
£400 $740 €584 Platter of bread and cheese upon a chair (57x71cm-22x28in) s. mixed media paper on board. 14-Jan-4 Lawrence, Crewkerne #1358

BELLET, Pierre (19/20th C) French
£5674 $9475 €8000 Odalisque au tambourin (38x60cm-15x24in) s.d.1882. 16-Jun-3 Gros & Delettrez, Paris #114/R est:7500-9000

BELLEUD, Gisele (1921-) French
£300 $510 €438 Anna-Marias (55x46cm-22x18in) s. prov.exhib. 19-Nov-3 Tennants, Leyburn #1269

BELLEVAL, Eric de (20th C) French
£315 $535 €450 Untitled (81x100cm-32x39in) s. 29-Nov-3 Neret-Minet, Paris #78/R
£380 $688 €570 Sans titre (59x72cm-23x28in) s. 3-Apr-4 Neret-Minet, Paris #205/R

BELLEVOIS, Jacob Adriaensz (1621-1675) Dutch
£9000 $15570 €13140 Dutch Herring fleet with a merchantman in a light swell (58x83cm-23x33in) s. prov. 11-Dec-3 Sotheby's, London #143/R est:10000-15000
£32877 $55890 €48000 Large flute, a boeier and other shipping under sail and at anchor on the Merwede (91x153cm-36x60in) indis sig.d. panel prov.exhib. 5-Nov-3 Christie's, Amsterdam #21/R est:20000-30000
£111732 $200000 €163129 Dutch attack on the medway (91x157cm-36x62in) s.d.1670. 27-May-4 Sotheby's, New York #70/R est:150000-250000

BELLI, Enrico (fl.1880-1884) British/Italian
£475 $750 €694 Dispute at cards (64x76cm-25x30in) s. 6-Apr-3 William Jenack, New York #98

BELLIAS, Richard (1921-1974) French
£302 $565 €450 Bouquet (65x46cm-26x18in) s. 29-Feb-4 Versailles Encheres #107
£302 $541 €450 Bouquet devant la fenetre (60x73cm-24x29in) s. 27-May-4 Christie's, Paris #120/R
£619 $990 €898 Le bar (82x60cm-32x24in) s. s.i.d.1954 verso. 15-May-3 Stuker, Bern #1060 (S.FR 1300)
£699 $1168 €1000 Paysage (96x130cm-38x51in) s. 25-Jun-3 Blanchet, Paris #78/R

BELLIDO, Angel (1945-) Spanish
£327 $594 €480 Still life of fruit (50x60cm-20x24in) s. prov. 3-Feb-4 Segre, Madrid #332/R

BELLING, Rudolf (20th C) ?
Sculpture
£2394 $4142 €3400 Statuette of pilot (42cm-17in) s.i. iron prov. 13-Dec-3 Lempertz, Koln #283/R est:4000
£4577 $7919 €6500 Dance (69cm-27in) s.i. brown pat.bronze. 13-Dec-3 Lempertz, Koln #284/R est:5000

BELLINGHAM-SMITH, Elinor (1906-) British
£900 $1638 €1314 Winter sun (41x51cm-16x20in) init. exhib. 1-Jul-4 Christie's, Kensington #103/R
Works on paper
£250 $430 €365 Figures in an interior (35x24cm-14x9in) W/C brush black ink. 3-Dec-3 Christie's, Kensington #447
£250 $430 €365 Portrait of a lady (46x30cm-18x12in) W/C brush black ink. 3-Dec-3 Christie's, Kensington #448

BELLINI, Emmanuel (1904-1989) French
£734 $1226 €1050 Cannes, caleches (38x55cm-15x22in) s. 29-Jun-3 Eric Pillon, Calais #238/R
£1000 $1820 €1500 Caleches a Cannes (65x81cm-26x32in) s. 4-Jul-4 Eric Pillon, Calais #260/R
£1040 $1924 €1550 Vase of flowers (41x33cm-16x13in) s.d.1952 panel. 14-Mar-4 Eric Pillon, Calais #277/R

BELLINI, Gentile (attrib) (1429-1507) Italian
£240000 $439200 €350400 Portrait of a young man (42x29cm-17x11in) s. panel prov.lit. 7-Jul-4 Christie's, London #7/R est:20000-30000

BELLINI, Gentile (style) (1429-1507) Italian
£6579 $12105 €10000 Portrait of bearded man (41x31cm-16x12in) panel lit. 24-Jun-4 Christie's, Paris #67/R est:3000-5000

BELLINI, Giovanni (1430-1516) Italian
£633333 $1152667 €950000 Madonna and Child (79x60cm-31x24in) board prov.lit. 4-Jul-4 Finarte, Venice #74/R

BELLINI, Giovanni (style) (1430-1516) Italian
£6711 $12349 €10000 Deposition (108x85cm-43x33in) 29-Mar-4 Pandolfini, Florence #630/R est:10000-11000
£9500 $16150 €13870 Holy Family (45x54cm-18x21in) panel. 30-Oct-3 Sotheby's, Olympia #18/R est:2000-3000

BELLIS, Hubert (1831-1902) Belgian
£364 $663 €550 Nature morte aux huitres (26x22cm-10x9in) s. panel. 15-Jun-4 Vanderkindere, Brussels #119
£384 $652 €560 Verre fleuri de pensees (20x14cm-8x6in) s. panel. 10-Nov-3 Horta, Bruxelles #2
£397 $723 €600 Nature morte aux legumes (48x60cm-19x24in) s. 15-Jun-4 Vanderkindere, Brussels #141
£479 $815 €700 Moules au citron (31x44cm-12x17in) s. panel. 4-Nov-3 Servarts Themis, Bruxelles #526
£492 $900 €718 Floral still life (58x30cm-23x12in) s. 10-Apr-4 Auctions by the Bay, Alameda #1519/R
£503 $841 €720 Nature morte aux huitres et aux moules (16x30cm-6x12in) s. panel. 13-Oct-3 Horta, Bruxelles #359
£699 $1189 €1000 Nature morte aux fromages et aux noix (36x46cm-14x18in) s. 18-Nov-3 Vanderkindere, Brussels #13
£1049 $1752 €1500 Nature morte aux raisins, peches et melon (34x50cm-13x20in) s. 13-Oct-3 Horta, Bruxelles #358 est:1500-2000
£1064 $1777 €1500 Tea roses (30x40cm-12x16in) s. panel. 20-Oct-3 Glerum, Amsterdam #210/R est:1700-1900
£2667 $4853 €4000 Poppies in vase (125x83cm-49x33in) s. 30-Jun-4 Neumeister, Munich #503/R est:6000
£3333 $6067 €5000 Chrysanthemums in blue vase (125x83cm-49x33in) s. 30-Jun-4 Neumeister, Munich #502/R est:6000

BELLIS, Hubert (attrib) (1831-1902) Belgian
£403 $749 €600 Still life with fruit and flowers (38x77cm-15x30in) bears sig. 8-Mar-4 Bernaerts, Antwerp #7

BELLMER, Hans (1902-1975) French/Polish
£4362 $7809 €6500 Composition (25x33cm-10x13in) s. paper on canvas prov.exhib. 26-May-4 Christie's, Paris #46/R est:3000-5000
£27556 $49601 €40232 Composition (100x100cm-39x39in) s. oil Indian ink panel painted c.1959-60 lit. 26-Apr-4 Bukowskis, Stockholm #562/R est:175000-200000 (S.KR 380000)
Photographs
£4306 $7319 €6200 La poupee (14x15cm-6x6in) gelatin silver lit. 31-Oct-3 Lempertz, Koln #66/R est:6000
£60000 $109200 €87600 La poupee (151x100cm-59x39in) s. photograph printed in negative executed 1934 prov.exhib.lit. 3-Feb-4 Sotheby's, London #69/R est:60000-80000
Sculpture
£28000 $51520 €40880 Toupie (52cm-20in) i. num.3/8 bronze conceived 1938 prov.lit. 22-Jun-4 Sotheby's, London #198/R est:18000-25000
£31182 $56128 €45526 La toupie (54cm-21in) s.num.2/8 painted bronze exec.c.1938/1968 on prov.exhib.lit. 26-Apr-4 Bukowskis, Stockholm #561/R est:175000-200000 (S.KR 430000)
Works on paper
£750 $1380 €1095 Composition (21x16cm-8x6in) s. pencil. 24-Mar-4 Sotheby's, Olympia #151/R
£839 $1427 €1200 Composition arachneenne (10x18cm-4x7in) st. crayon prov. 23-Nov-3 Cornette de St.Cyr, Paris #14/R
£917 $1532 €1330 Buste de femme avec grande coiffure (22x16cm-9x6in) s. pencil. 19-Jun-3 Kornfeld, Bern #212 est:2500 (S.FR 2000)
£979 $1664 €1400 Construction onirique (18x10cm-7x4in) st. crayon prov. 23-Nov-3 Cornette de St.Cyr, Paris #12/R
£1101 $1839 €1596 Buste de femme au volant (22x16cm-9x6in) s. pencil. 19-Jun-3 Kornfeld, Bern #213 est:2500 (S.FR 2400)
£1544 $2732 €2300 Composition (26x20cm-10x8in) s. mixed media. 29-Apr-4 Claude Aguttes, Neuilly #109 est:1000-1200
£1608 $2734 €2300 Deux visages (18x10cm-7x4in) st. crayon frottage prov. 23-Nov-3 Cornette de St.Cyr, Paris #11/R est:400-500
£1818 $3127 €2600 Portrait d'Andre Breton (19x11cm-7x4in) st.d.68 crayon prov. 2-Dec-3 Calmels Cohen, Paris #23/R est:1500-2000
£2081 $3828 €3100 Untitled (22x16cm-9x6in) s. lead pencil. 24-Mar-4 Joron-Derem, Paris #101/R est:3000-3500
£2113 $3507 €3000 Untitled (18x24cm-7x9in) s. pencil. 11-Jun-3 Finarte Semenzato, Milan #627/R
£2349 $4322 €3500 Untitled (26x20cm-10x8in) s.d.1961 lead pencil. 24-Mar-4 Joron-Derem, Paris #100/R est:3500-4000
£2349 $4322 €3500 Untitled (23x16cm-9x6in) s. lead pencil. 24-Mar-4 Joron-Derem, Paris #102/R est:3000-3500
£2378 $4042 €3400 Portrait de femme (21x18cm-8x7in) s. graphite htd pastel prov. 23-Nov-3 Cornette de St.Cyr, Paris #13/R est:600-800
£2752 $5063 €4100 Jeunes filles (13x17cm-5x7in) s.d.1942 lead pencil. 24-Mar-4 Joron-Derem, Paris #103 est:3000-3500
£4196 $7133 €6000 Visage - tete de mort (39x32cm-15x13in) s. graphite col pen prov. 26-Nov-3 Lempertz, Koln #593/R est:2500
£7614 $13706 €11116 Untitled (21x16cm-8x6in) s.d.63 pencil gouache lit. 26-Apr-4 Bukowskis, Stockholm #565/R est:20000-25000 (S.KR 105000)
£21000 $38220 €30660 Poupee au bas rayes (28x22cm-11x9in) s. g. executed c.1935-37 prov.exhib.lit. 3-Feb-4 Sotheby's, London #70/R est:12000-16000
£21000 $38220 €30660 Tete de femme (62x50cm-24x20in) s.d.66 pencil pen ink g. p. 3-Feb-4 Sotheby's, London #86/R est:10000-15000
£28000 $51240 €40880 Nora (24x32cm-9x13in) s. gouache wash executed 1948 prov. 2-Feb-4 Christie's, London #96/R est:4000-7000

BELLO PINEIRO, Felipe (1886-1953) Spanish
£748 $1339 €1100 Mountainous landscape (27x35cm-11x14in) s. cardboard. 22-Mar-4 Durán, Madrid #50/R

BELLO, Bruno di (1938-) Italian
Works on paper
£1678 $3003 €2500 SSSS (100x70cm-39x28in) s.d.62 ink paper on canvas prov. 25-May-4 Sotheby's, Milan #151/R est:800

BELLOCQ, Ernest J (1873-1949) American
Photographs
£1928 $3200 €2815 Storyville girl posing out of doors (36x28cm-14x11in) silver gelatin print exec c.1912 prov. 4-Oct-3 Neal Auction Company, New Orleans #631/R est:4000-6000

BELLONI, Giorgio (1861-1944) Italian
£903 $1508 €1300 View of town (50x46cm-20x18in) board. 23-Oct-3 Finarte Semenzato, Milan #324
£3043 $4991 €4200 Summer in the mountains (25x36cm-10x14in) s. board. 27-May-3 Il Ponte, Milan #965
£3472 $5903 €5000 Field in bloom (25x35cm-10x14in) s. board. 29-Oct-3 Il Ponte, Milan #544/R
£3521 $6092 €5000 By the harbour (29x39cm-11x15in) s. cardboard. 10-Dec-3 Sotheby's, Milan #4/R est:5000-7000
£4076 $7500 €5951 Busy port (25x35cm-10x14in) s. panel. 27-Jun-4 Freeman, Philadelphia #52/R est:3000-5000
£4752 $7935 €6700 Brunate (50x88cm-20x35in) s. 14-Oct-3 Finarte Semenzato, Milan #181/R
£8667 $15600 €13000 Marina, dusk on a calm sea (60x72cm-24x28in) s. 21-Apr-4 Christie's, Amsterdam #177/R est:8000-12000

BELLONI, Jose (1882-1965) Uruguayan
Sculpture
£2353 $4000 €3435 Carriage (27cm-11in) bronze Cast Vignali. 25-Nov-3 Galeria y Remates, Montevideo #156/R

BELLONI, Serge (1925-) Italian
£694 $1160 €1000 Sur la Seine (21x27cm-8x11in) s. panel. 22-Oct-3 Ribeyre & Baron, Paris #30/R
£833 $1392 €1200 Le pont et Notre-Dame (21x27cm-8x11in) s. panel. 22-Oct-3 Ribeyre & Baron, Paris #31/R
£833 $1392 €1200 La Seine (27x21cm-11x8in) s. panel. 22-Oct-3 Ribeyre & Baron, Paris #32

BELLOTTI, Pietro (attrib) (1627-1700) Italian
£1293 $2314 €1900 Trying out the opera (58x42cm-23x17in) 22-Mar-4 Durán, Madrid #585/R est:1200
£17450 $32107 €26000 Two women at window (98x71cm-39x28in) prov. 24-Mar-4 Dorotheum, Vienna #10/R est:30000-40000

BELLOTTO, Bernardo (1720-1780) Italian
Prints
£3333 $5967 €5000 Vue de la Grande place du Vieux Marche (54x84cm-21x33in) etching. 13-May-4 Bassenge, Berlin #5353/R est:7500
£4895 $8322 €7000 Dresden (55x85cm-22x33in) etching. 27-Nov-3 Bassenge, Berlin #5397/R est:7500

BELLOTTO, Bernardo (attrib) (1720-1780) Italian
£150000 $270000 €219000 View in Venice from the Punta della Dogana (101x63cm-40x25in) prov.lit. 22-Jan-4 Sotheby's, New York #70/R est:100000-150000

BELLOTTO, Bernardo (circle) (1720-1780) Italian
£5000 $8500 €7300 River landscape with a German fortified town (36x48cm-14x19in) 31-Oct-3 Christie's, Kensington #160/R est:5000-7000
£6623 $12119 €10000 La place Saint Marc animee (59x96cm-23x38in) 7-Apr-4 Libert, Castor, Paris #14/R est:5000-7000
£75540 $123885 €105000 Grand Canal (50x75cm-20x30in) prov. 4-Jun-3 Sotheby's, Milan #83/R est:15000-20000

BELLOTTO, Bernardo (style) (1720-1780) Italian
£12692 $21831 €18530 River landscape with town and ruins (32x43cm-13x17in) 2-Dec-3 Bukowskis, Stockholm #421/R est:20000-25000 (S.KR 165000)
£15000 $27450 €21900 Venice, Rialto Bridge (59x95cm-23x37in) 8-Jul-4 Sotheby's, London #341/R est:15000-20000

BELLOTTO, Pietro (c.1725-1815) Italian
£42000 $72660 €61320 Venice, view of the Molo from the Piazzetta with St Theodore's Column (62x77cm-24x30in) lit. painted c.1760. 11-Dec-3 Sotheby's, London #42/R est:30000-40000

BELLOTTO, Pietro (attrib) (c.1725-1815) Italian
£15000 $27450 €21900 Venice, view of the Lagoon (58x120cm-23x47in) bears sig.d.1763 prov. 8-Jul-4 Sotheby's, London #342/R est:15000-20000

BELLOWS, Albert F (1829-1883) American
£2235 $4000 €3263 Picking berries (33x28cm-13x11in) s. board prov. 6-May-4 Shannon's, Milford #159/R est:4000-6000

BELLOWS, George (1882-1925) American
£23952 $40000 €34970 Sunset, Jersey hills (29x39cm-11x15in) s. s.i.verso canvasboard prov.exhib. 9-Oct-3 Christie's, Rockefeller NY #46/R est:20000-30000
£75581 $130000 €110348 Approach of rain (34x49cm-13x19in) s. s.i.verso panel painted 1913 prov.exhib.lit. 3-Dec-3 Sotheby's, New York #41/R est:80000-120000
£79545 $140000 €116136 Evening swells (28x38cm-11x15in) s. s.i.verso panel painted 1911 prov.exhib.lit. 19-May-4 Sotheby's, New York #106/R est:70000-90000

£119318 $210000 €174204 Upper Broadway (28x38cm-11x15in) s. board on board painted 1907 prov. 19-May-4 Sotheby's, New York #110/R est:18000-22000
£306818 $540000 €447954 Wet night (56x72cm-22x28in) s.i. verso painted 1916 prov.exhib. 18-May-4 Christie's, Rockefeller NY #80/R est:300000-500000

Prints

£2125 $3400 €3103 Barricade, first stone (44x72cm-17x28in) s.i.num.8 lithograph. 18-Sep-3 Swann Galleries, New York #63/R est:2000-3000
£2712 $4800 €3960 Sunday (30x38cm-12x15in) s. lithograph sold with another. 30-Apr-4 Sotheby's, New York #3/R est:3500-5000
£4624 $8000 €6751 Self portrait (27x20cm-11x8in) s. lithograph edition of 28 prov. 13-Dec-3 Weschler, Washington #620 est:3000-5000
£7386 $13000 €10784 Indoor athlete, first stone (18x25cm-7x10in) s. lithograph edition 21. 21-May-4 North East Auctions, Portsmouth #69/R
£8235 $14000 €12023 Counted out (39x29cm-15x11in) s.i. lithograph. 4-Nov-3 Christie's, Rockefeller NY #1/R est:14000-16000
£10227 $18000 €14931 Preliminaries (50x59cm-20x23in) s.i. num.26 lithograph. 18-May-4 Sotheby's, New York #126/R est:7000-10000
£25568 $45000 €37329 Dempsey through the ropes (56x51cm-22x20in) s.i. lithograph. 18-May-4 Sotheby's, New York #127/R est:7000-9000

BELLOWS, Walter (20th C) American

£670 $1200 €978 Three-masted schooner on high seas (51x61cm-20x24in) s. 7-May-4 Sloans & Kenyon, Bethesda #1185/R

BELLUCCI, Antonio (1654-1726) Italian

£32000 $54400 €46720 Triumph of Galatea (283x303cm-111x119in) 29-Oct-3 Christie's, London #96/R est:15000-20000
£34753 $58037 €49000 Venus et cupidon (103x87cm-41x34in) 17-Oct-3 Tajan, Paris #30/R est:15000-20000
£35172 $64366 €51000 Danae recueillant la pluie d'or (91x117cm-36x46in) peinture. 1-Feb-4 Robin & Fattori, Granville #1

BELLUCCI, Antonio (attrib) (1654-1726) Italian

£23448 $38924 €34000 Allegory (98x141cm-39x56in) prov. 1-Oct-3 Dorotheum, Vienna #67/R est:9000-14000

BELLUCCI, Antonio (circle) (1654-1726) Italian

£16552 $27476 €24000 Triumph of Galathea (159x225cm-63x89in) prov. 1-Oct-3 Dorotheum, Vienna #72/R est:26000-30000

BELLUCCI, Antonio (style) (1654-1726) Italian

£8966 $14883 €13000 Mythological scene (117x213cm-46x84in) prov. 1-Oct-3 Dorotheum, Vienna #13/R est:7000-10000

BELLVER, Fernando (1954-) Spanish

£2685 $4805 €4000 Composition (150x250cm-59x98in) s.d.89 verso canvas on board triptych. 25-May-4 Durán, Madrid #212/R est:4000
£2817 $4930 €4000 Composition (150x250cm-59x98in) s.d.89 verso canvas on board triptych. 16-Dec-3 Durán, Madrid #181/R est:4000
£3521 $5634 €5000 American still life (121x121cm-48x48in) s.d.1987 verso board prov.exhib.lit. 16-Sep-3 Segre, Madrid #143/R est:4000

BELLY, Léon Adolphe Auguste (1827-1877) French

£1667 $3017 €2500 Le Gue de Montboulan (70x81cm-28x32in) exhib.lit. 30-Mar-4 Rossini, Paris #289/R est:2500-4000
£2333 $4223 €3500 Ile de Gizeh, Le Caire, femmes de baignant (37x54cm-15x21in) st.verso painted c.1857-1858 exhib.lit. 30-Mar-4 Rossini, Paris #288/R est:3500-5000

BELLY, Léon Adolphe Auguste (attrib) (1827-1877) French

£533 $965 €800 Oriental (36x28cm-14x11in) exhib. 30-Mar-4 Rossini, Paris #897

BELMON, Gaston (1907-1995) French

£426 $711 €600 Portrait de tunisien (46x38cm-18x15in) s. 19-Oct-3 Rabourdin & Choppin de Janvry, Paris #57/R

BELMONDO, Paul (1898-1982) French?

Sculpture

£3356 $6007 €5000 Baigneuse (27cm-11in) s. num.1/12 bronze Cast Valsuani. 30-May-4 Eric Pillon, Calais #29/R
£7986 $13337 €11500 Homme nu (40x11x11cm-16x4x4in) s. brown pat. bronze exec. c.1942 st.f.A.Rudier lit. 21-Oct-3 Christie's, Paris #68/R est:7000-9000

Works on paper

£336 $624 €500 La grille (48x61cm-19x24in) s. W/C. 3-Mar-4 Ferri, Paris #361
£347 $580 €500 Les bateaux (24x31cm-9x12in) s.i.d.6 September 1952 ink ink wash ink prov. 21-Oct-3 Christie's, Paris #74/R
£833 $1392 €1200 Nu assis accoude (36x47cm-14x19in) s.d.1952 chl india ink. 21-Oct-3 Christie's, Paris #69/R est:1400-1800
£915 $1520 €1300 Nu assis de dos (28x29cm-11x11in) s. sanguine. 13-Jun-3 Ferri, Paris #30/R
£1127 $1949 €1600 Nu debout de dos (32x20cm-13x8in) s. sanguine. 14-Dec-3 Eric Pillon, Calais #134/R
£1469 $2452 €2100 Nu debout de dos (42x27cm-17x11in) s. sanguine. 29-Jun-3 Eric Pillon, Calais #178/R
£2083 $3479 €3000 Nu debout de dos (41x30cm-16x12in) s.d.1947 chl. 21-Oct-3 Christie's, Paris #67/R est:1000-1200

BELMONTE, Ayme Odette (1904-) Algerian

Works on paper

£426 $711 €600 Portrait de mauresque (45x52cm-18x20in) s. pastel. 19-Oct-3 Rabourdin & Choppin de Janvry, Paris #139/R

BELOFF, Angelina (1884-1969) Russian

£8000 $14720 €12000 Untitled (55x60cm-22x24in) s. painted c.1920 prov. 10-Jun-4 Christie's, Paris #23/R est:18000-22000

Works on paper

£790 $1344 €1153 Washerwoman (21x19cm-8x7in) s. pen W/C. 30-Oct-3 Louis Morton, Mexico #139 est:14000-18000 (M.P 15000)

BELONI, Andre (1905-) French

£420 $713 €600 A la fontaine (65x45cm-26x18in) s. i.verso. 24-Nov-3 Glerum, Amsterdam #24/R

BELOT, A (?) ?

£1023 $1800 €1494 Portrait of a woman (69x56cm-27x22in) s. painted c.1880. 23-May-4 Treadway Gallery, Cincinnati #508/R est:2000-3000

BELOUSOV, Fedor Vasilevich (1885-1939) Russian

£8000 $14320 €11680 Chechen village scene (84x123cm-33x48in) s. 26-May-4 Sotheby's, London #72/R est:8000-12000

BELOUSOV, Jkov Andreevich (1838-1900) Russian

Works on paper

£559 $951 €800 On the road through the village (9x14cm-4x6in) s. W/C. 29-Nov-3 Bukowskis, Helsinki #414/R

BELOUX, Marie (1860-1897) French

£2800 $5012 €4088 Still life of roses (32x40cm-13x16in) s. 26-May-4 Sotheby's, Olympia #283/R est:2000-3000

BELSKY, Anatoly (1896-1970) Russian

Works on paper

£1317 $2200 €1923 Poster design for the film Chapeav (62x93cm-24x37in) s. pencil gouache W/C cardboard. 21-Oct-3 Christie's, Rockefeller NY #114 est:1500-2500

BELSKY, Vladimir (1949-) Russian

£250 $468 €375 In the bedroom (33x24cm-13x9in) s. 21-Jul-4 John Nicholson, Haslemere #336
£250 $438 €365 Fresh Breeze (27x35cm-11x14in) s. 17-Dec-3 John Nicholson, Haslemere #29
£250 $438 €365 Study of the nude (35x22cm-14x9in) s. 17-Dec-3 John Nicholson, Haslemere #37
£250 $418 €365 White roses in glass vase (41x27cm-16x11in) s. 13-Jul-3 John Nicholson, Haslemere #16
£250 $448 €365 Evening on the sea (27x46cm-11x18in) s. 5-May-4 John Nicholson, Haslemere #134
£250 $468 €375 Before the ballet lesson (27x19cm-11x7in) s. 21-Jul-4 John Nicholson, Haslemere #332/R
£263 $484 €400 In the morning (27x41cm-11x16in) s. 22-Jun-4 Durán, Madrid #697/R
£275 $448 €402 While picking wild flowers (33x22cm-13x9in) s. 28-Sep-3 John Nicholson, Haslemere #48
£275 $514 €413 In the morning (33x19cm-13x7in) s. 21-Jul-4 John Nicholson, Haslemere #333
£275 $514 €413 Ballet dancer with pink bow (33x24cm-13x9in) s. 21-Jul-4 John Nicholson, Haslemere #315
£275 $514 €413 Portrait of little girl (33x24cm-13x9in) s. 21-Jul-4 John Nicholson, Haslemere #424
£300 $489 €438 Still life with sunflowers (50x35cm-20x14in) s. 28-Sep-3 John Nicholson, Haslemere #99/R
£300 $525 €438 Last Beams (38x46cm-15x18in) s. 17-Dec-3 John Nicholson, Haslemere #117
£300 $525 €438 Daybreak (33x55cm-13x22in) s. 17-Dec-3 John Nicholson, Haslemere #195
£300 $501 €438 On the coast in Normandy (27x76cm-11x30in) s. 13-Jul-3 John Nicholson, Haslemere #167
£300 $537 €438 Evening in Venice (27x46cm-11x18in) s. 5-May-4 John Nicholson, Haslemere #174
£317 $555 €450 Dusk (33x46cm-13x18in) s. 16-Dec-3 Durán, Madrid #717/R
£319 $533 €450 Venetian scene (33x50cm-13x20in) s. 20-Oct-3 Durán, Madrid #699/R
£325 $582 €475 Returning of the fishermen (27x41cm-11x16in) s. 5-May-4 John Nicholson, Haslemere #135
£325 $582 €475 Venetian Lagoon (30x60cm-12x24in) s. 5-May-4 John Nicholson, Haslemere #188
£350 $585 €511 Evening fishing (24x35cm-9x14in) s. 13-Jul-3 John Nicholson, Haslemere #46/R
£350 $585 €511 Little fishermen (24x35cm-9x14in) s. 13-Jul-3 John Nicholson, Haslemere #47/R
£350 $585 €511 Bluish morning (33x46cm-13x18in) s. cardboard. 13-Jul-3 John Nicholson, Haslemere #176/R
£369 $653 €550 Saint George's Church, Venice (33x41cm-13x16in) s. 27-Apr-4 Durán, Madrid #711/R
£389 $634 €560 Breakfast by the sea (46x55cm-18x22in) s. 23-Sep-3 Durán, Madrid #661/R
£400 $700 €584 Golden Beams (33x55cm-13x22in) s. 17-Dec-3 John Nicholson, Haslemere #100/R
£400 $668 €584 Sailing (35x50cm-14x20in) s. 13-Jul-3 John Nicholson, Haslemere #186/R
£400 $716 €584 Evening breakers (38x55cm-15x22in) s. 5-May-4 John Nicholson, Haslemere #27/R
£403 $713 €600 Still life with sunflowers (46x44cm-18x17in) s. 27-Apr-4 Durán, Madrid #710/R
£425 $693 €621 Nude from the back (35x22cm-14x9in) s. 28-Sep-3 John Nicholson, Haslemere #9/R
£436 $816 €650 Roses (19x33cm-7x13in) s. 24-Feb-4 Durán, Madrid #716/R
£450 $788 €657 Playing polo (46x33cm-18x13in) s. 17-Dec-3 John Nicholson, Haslemere #5/R

£450 $788 €657 The Duel (46x33cm-18x13in) s. cardboard. 17-Dec-3 John Nicholson, Haslemere #6/R
£450 $806 €657 Still life on the round table (50x61cm-20x24in) s. 5-May-4 John Nicholson, Haslemere #132/R
£450 $842 €675 Study of ballet dancer (41x27cm-16x11in) s. 21-Jul-4 John Nicholson, Haslemere #446
£461 $770 €650 Flowers by the window (46x33cm-18x13in) s. 20-Oct-3 Durán, Madrid #701/R
£550 $1029 €825 Ballerina with fan (50x35cm-20x14in) s. 21-Jul-4 John Nicholson, Haslemere #357
£567 $948 €800 Istanbul harbour (33x46cm-13x18in) s. 20-Oct-3 Durán, Madrid #700/R
£604 $1130 €900 Lilies on the terrace (40x50cm-16x20in) s. 24-Feb-4 Durán, Madrid #717/R

BELTON, Liam (20th C) Irish?
£1389 $2264 €2000 Candlelight still life (46x61cm-18x24in) s.i.d.1979 verso. 23-Sep-3 De Veres Art Auctions, Dublin #163/R est:2000-3000
£3826 $6848 €5700 Soap in a box with vessel and egg (56x45cm-22x18in) s. canvasboard prov. 26-May-4 James Adam, Dublin #172/R est:6000-8000

BELTON, Susan Jane (20th C) American
£229 $425 €334 Reggie's house (46x56cm-18x22in) d.1993 s.verso. 15-Feb-4 Outer Cape Auctions, Provincetown #60/R

BELTRAME, Achille (1871-1945) Italian
£387 $711 €580 Still life with watermelon (69x79cm-27x31in) s.d.1983. 8-Jun-4 Finarte Semenzato, Milan #57/R
£661 $1123 €965 Female nude (22x16cm-9x6in) s. panel. 5-Nov-3 Dobiaschofsky, Bern #343/R (S.FR 1500)
£1489 $2487 €2100 Old houses in Antagnod (34x26cm-13x10in) s.d.1928 board. 20-Oct-3 Sant Agostino, Torino #26/R est:1800

BELTRAN MESSA, Enric (1940-) Spanish
£310 $518 €450 Street (50x61cm-20x24in) s. 17-Nov-3 Durán, Madrid #1225/R

BELTRAN-MASSES, Frederico (1885-1949) Spanish
£1232 $2132 €1750 Meeting (46x55cm-18x22in) s.d.1923. 15-Dec-3 Ansorena, Madrid #57/R est:1750
£1241 $2073 €1800 Woman with head scarf (56x46cm-22x18in) s. canvas on cardboard. 17-Nov-3 Durán, Madrid #31/R est:900
£1342 $2497 €2000 Flamenco dancers (26x21cm-10x8in) s. canvas on cardboard. 2-Mar-4 Ansorena, Madrid #115/R est:1810
£2837 $4738 €4000 Mujer Deco (42x31cm-17x12in) s. board. 23-Jun-3 Durán, Madrid #154/R est:1600
£4027 $7490 €6000 Winged woman with boy (115x93cm-45x37in) s. 2-Mar-4 Ansorena, Madrid #47/R est:7800
£8000 $14720 €12000 L'Espagnole a la mantille (115x196cm-45x77in) s. 9-Jun-4 Beaussant & Lefèvre, Paris #100/R est:3000-4000
£8696 $14261 €12000 La pradera de San Isidro en el dia del Santo (79x97cm-31x38in) s. exhib. 27-May-3 Durán, Madrid #268/R est:10000
£21000 $35700 €30660 Fortune-teller (158x178cm-62x70in) s. 18-Nov-3 Sotheby's, London #268/R

BELVEDERE, Andrea and VACCARO, Nicola (17/18th C) Italian
£36242 $67772 €54000 Nymph and putti arranging flowers (191x145cm-75x57in) prov. 25-Feb-4 Porro, Milan #12/R est:50000

BELYKH, Liubov (1961-) Russian
£1034 $1862 €1500 Still life with vegetables (49x73cm-19x29in) s.d.92 s.d.verso. 26-Jan-4 Ansorena, Madrid #911/R est:1500

BEMEL, G G (?) ?
Works on paper
£400 $668 €584 Continental landscape with travellers (20x25cm-8x10in) indis.sig. gouache. 24-Jun-3 Bonhams, Chester #849

BEMELMANS, Fons (1938-) Dutch?
Sculpture
£4203 $6893 €5800 Marriage (38cm-15in) mono. bronze marble base. 27-May-3 Sotheby's, Amsterdam #383/R est:2500-3500

BEMELMANS, Ludwig (1898-1963) American
£1796 $3000 €2622 Venetian church on a moonlit night (66x51cm-26x20in) s. canvasboard. 7-Oct-3 Sotheby's, New York #279 est:5000-7000
£5233 $9000 €7640 Street corner, Paris (91x58cm-36x23in) s. 3-Dec-3 Doyle, New York #313/R est:12000-18000
Works on paper
£245 $450 €358 Seine with the Hotel du France and Notre Dame (20x28cm-8x11in) ink on vellum. 11-Jun-4 David Rago, Lambertville #186/R
£756 $1300 €1104 Vert gallant (36x28cm-14x11in) s.i.d.57 W/C pencil. 3-Dec-3 Doyle, New York #314/R est:2000-3000
£756 $1300 €1104 Sketch for Marina. Studies of wolf, for Marina (30x38cm-12x15in) one init. pen ink W/C pencil two different sizes. 3-Dec-3 Doyle, New York #315/R est:2500-3500
£973 $1800 €1421 Blond boy (14x9cm-6x4in) s. pencil W/C. 13-Jul-4 Christie's, Rockefeller NY #180/R est:1000-1500
£1374 $2500 €2006 Madeline in London (44x61cm-17x24in) s.i. ink W/C. 29-Jun-4 Sotheby's, New York #268/R est:4000-6000
£1647 $2750 €2405 Portofino (56x76cm-22x30in) s.d.54 W/C gouache pencil. 7-Oct-3 Sotheby's, New York #204 est:4000-6000
£1916 $3200 €2797 Impressions of Brandy (55x76cm-22x30in) s.i. W/C gouache pencil board. 9-Oct-3 Christie's, Rockefeller NY #101/R est:4000-6000
£2054 $3800 €2999 Sly fox from Welcome Home (49x39cm-19x15in) init. W/C. 13-Jul-4 Christie's, Rockefeller NY #181/R est:2000-3000
£2096 $3500 €3060 Madeline with the gypsies (47x33cm-19x13in) s.i. W/C black ink pencil double-sided. 7-Oct-3 Sotheby's, New York #278 est:4000-6000
£2571 $4500 €3754 Summertime, France (65x50cm-26x20in) s. W/C graphite. 19-Dec-3 Sotheby's, New York #1154/R est:3000-5000
£2674 $5000 €3904 Little girl with toy dog (48x56cm-19x22in) s. chl W/C pen ink. 26-Feb-4 Illustration House, New York #15 est:5000-7000
£2762 $5000 €4033 Tack room (74x56cm-29x22in) s. gouache black ink board. 31-Mar-4 Sotheby's, New York #159/R est:2000-4000
£3488 $6000 €5092 Restaurant Cabassud, rue d'Avray, France (69x102cm-27x40in) s. i.verso gouache on board. 3-Dec-3 Doyle, New York #312/R est:8000-12000
£4469 $8000 €6525 Children's orchestra in crowded concert hall (33x30cm-13x12in) s. pen ink gouache. 15-May-4 Illustration House, New York #140/R est:5000-7000

BEMMEL, G von (18th C) German
£1042 $1656 €1500 Idyllic landscape with riders (59x78cm-23x31in) bears sig. 11-Sep-3 Weidler, Nurnberg #317/R

BEMMEL, Georg Christoph Gottlieb von I (1738-1794) German
Works on paper
£742 $1351 €1113 Summer landscape with rider and two farm houses on the edge of the lake (17x23cm-7x9in) gouache prov. 17-Jun-4 Kornfeld, Bern #1/R (S.FR 1700)

BEMMEL, Johann Christoph (?-1778) German
£915 $1584 €1300 Wooded landscape with city in background (66x82cm-26x32in) s. 11-Dec-3 Dr Fritz Nagel, Stuttgart #478/R
£4422 $7915 €6500 Extensive romantic landscape (97x140cm-38x55in) s. lit. 20-Mar-4 Bergmann, Erlangen #1050 est:4800-6500

BEMMEL, Peter von (1685-1754) German
£2384 $4339 €3600 Mountainous winter landscape (21x27cm-8x11in) s.indis.d. 16-Jun-4 Dorotheum, Vienna #407/R est:4000-5000
£6081 $10703 €9000 Two landscapes - sunrise, sunset (19x28cm-7x11in) i. verso panel prov. 22-May-4 Lempertz, Koln #1011/R est:10000-12000

BEMMEL, Wilhelm von (1630-1708) Dutch
Works on paper
£800 $1432 €1200 Landscape with lake, mountains and figures (19x25cm-7x10in) gouache. 13-May-4 Bassenge, Berlin #5028/R

BEMMEL, Wilhelm von (attrib) (1630-1708) Dutch
£724 $1231 €1057 Stormy landscape with two travellers (47x63cm-19x25in) 19-Nov-3 Fischer, Luzern #2016/R (S.FR 1600)
£2282 $4199 €3400 Wooded landscape with anglers near brook (75x101cm-30x40in) 24-Mar-4 Dorotheum, Vienna #395/R est:5000-7000

BEMPORAD, Franco (1926-) Italian
Works on paper
£517 $864 €750 Structure-space (70x100cm-28x39in) s.i.d.1963 verso mixed media. 17-Nov-3 Sant Agostino, Torino #46/R

BEN (1935-) Swiss
£671 $1188 €1000 Je suis triste (28x38cm-11x15in) s.d.80 acrylic collage panel. 28-Apr-4 Artcurial Briest, Paris #413/R
£694 $1160 €1000 You can have (30x40cm-12x16in) s.d.1990 acrylic panel. 25-Oct-3 Cornette de St.Cyr, Paris #586
£903 $1490 €1300 Detail to look at in medium close-up (52x25cm-20x10in) s.d.1990 acrylic magnifying glass panel. 2-Jul-3 Cornette de St.Cyr, Paris #117/R
£972 $1604 €1400 Toile vierge (24x33cm-9x13in) s.d.1990 acrylic. 2-Jul-3 Cornette de St.Cyr, Paris #113/R
£1042 $1719 €1500 L'art c'est les autres (40x31cm-16x12in) s.d.1990 acrylic notebook panel. 2-Jul-3 Cornette de St.Cyr, Paris #120/R est:1500-1800
£1042 $1740 €1500 Portrait de l'artiste (53x40cm-21x16in) s.d.85 acrylic lunette photo panel. 25-Oct-3 Cornette de St.Cyr, Paris #589/R est:1500-2000
£1042 $1740 €1500 L'arbre c'est la vie (125cm-49in) s. acrylic twigs. 25-Oct-3 Cornette de St.Cyr, Paris #591/R est:1500-2000
£1111 $1833 €1600 Nouveau (40x30cm-16x12in) s.d.1991 acrylic picture on board. 2-Jul-3 Cornette de St.Cyr, Paris #119/R est:1500-1800
£1119 $1869 €1600 Cheap art (31x10cm-12x4in) s.d.1990 acrylic panel. 11-Oct-3 Cornette de St.Cyr, Paris #45/R est:1000-1200
£1181 $1948 €1700 Beurk, encore de l'art (33x41cm-13x16in) s. s.d.1989 verso acrylic. 2-Jul-3 Cornette de St.Cyr, Paris #112/R est:1500-2000
£1250 $2063 €1800 Je tiens a poursuivre ma carriere (38x37cm-15x15in) s.d. acrylic photo panel. 2-Jul-3 Cornette de St.Cyr, Paris #116/R est:1800-2000
£1250 $2063 €1800 Vertical (20x23cm-8x9in) s.d.1989 acrylic panel. 2-Jul-3 Cornette de St.Cyr, Paris #118/R est:1500-2000
£1259 $2102 €1800 Cause de l'art je dors mal (38x46cm-15x18in) s. 25-Jun-3 Digard, Paris #117/R est:2000-3000
£1373 $2376 €1950 Grata testa (48x63cm-19x25in) s.d.1984 acrylic collage paint glass black paper prov. 14-Dec-3 Versailles Encheres #191/R est:1800-2000
£1399 $2336 €2000 This is art criticism (50x50cm-20x20in) s.d.1990 acrylic panel. 11-Oct-3 Cornette de St.Cyr, Paris #46/R est:1200-1500
£1678 $2887 €2400 Ecrit en blanc (30x40cm-12x16in) s. s.i.d. veso. 3-Dec-3 Hauswedell & Nolte, Hamburg #1034/R est:2500
£1818 $3036 €2600 May be (44x65cm-17x26in) s.d.1990 acrylic panel. 11-Oct-3 Cornette de St.Cyr, Paris #48/R est:1200-1500
£1958 $3270 €2800 What's the problem (43x64cm-17x25in) s. i.d.90 verso acrylic panel. 11-Oct-3 Cornette de St.Cyr, Paris #47/R est:1200-1500
£1958 $3270 €2800 Open your eyes (30x40cm-12x16in) s.d.1990 acrylic panel. 11-Oct-3 Cornette de St.Cyr, Paris #49/R est:1000-1200
£2222 $3667 €3200 I have an indigestion of apples (41x33cm-16x13in) s.i.d.1992 acrylic plastic apples. 2-Jul-3 Cornette de St.Cyr, Paris #111/R est:1800-2000
£2238 $3849 €3200 Astuce (20x27cm-8x11in) paint wood. 4-Dec-3 Piasa, Paris #5/R est:2000-3000
£3200 $5920 €4800 Nous ne vendons que des oeuvres uniques et signees (50x150cm-20x59in) s. acrylic double-sided painted 1991 prov. 18-Jul-4 Sotheby's, Paris #285/R est:5000-7000
£3472 $5729 €5000 S'il vous plait Monsieur Ben, dessinez moi une maison et un arbre (73x92cm-29x36in) i. acrylic. 2-Jul-3 Cornette de St.Cyr, Paris #114/R est:5500-6000

£3846	$6615	€5500	Look at the floor (46x55cm-18x22in) s.d.71. 4-Dec-3 Piasa, Paris #15/R est:3000-4000
£3846	$6615	€5500	Pour changer l'art (92x72cm-36x28in) s.d.65 verso paint graphite. 4-Dec-3 Piasa, Paris #25/R est:6000-8000
£4348	$7130	€6000	Arte (60x50cm-24x20in) s. s.i.d.1970 verso prov. 27-May-3 Sotheby's, Milan #152/R est:4000-6000
£10738	$19007	€16000	You can have art and no fame (130x195cm-51x77in) i. acrylic. 28-Apr-4 Artcurial Briest, Paris #409/R est:6000-8000
Sculpture			
£1049	$1752	€1500	Un verre d'eau (41x31cm-16x12in) s.d.89 i.verso slate glass acrylic panel. 11-Oct-3 Cornette de St.Cyr, Paris #40/R est:1500-2000
£1119	$1869	€1600	C'est le moment ou jamais de changer de tete (40x30cm-16x12in) s.d.1990 clippers mirror acrylic panel. 11-Oct-3 Cornette de St.Cyr, Paris #43/R est:1500-2000
£1189	$1985	€1700	Marcel, pour ceux qui savent de quoi il s'agit (40x30cm-16x12in) s.d.1990 acrylic collage panel. 11-Oct-3 Cornette de St.Cyr, Paris #41/R est:1200-1500
£1259	$2102	€1800	Monochrome rouge vendu au metre (43x40x10cm-17x16x4in) s.d.1990 Rouleau Venilia acrylic panel. 11-Oct-3 Cornette de St.Cyr, Paris #44/R est:1500-2000
£1259	$2165	€1800	Pot de peinture (16x15cm-6x6in) s.i.d.12.83 paint pot plexiglas. 4-Dec-3 Piasa, Paris #53/R est:500-700
£1538	$2569	€2200	Odeurs de femmes (60x50x20cm-24x20x8in) s.d.1989 bottles acrylic panel. 11-Oct-3 Cornette de St.Cyr, Paris #39/R est:2000-3000
£1748	$2920	€2500	Une corde pour en finir avec l'art (56x32cm-22x13in) s.d.90 cord acrylic panel. 11-Oct-3 Cornette de St.Cyr, Paris #42/R est:1500-2000
£1879	$3477	€2800	Quel est cet oiseau qui me shie sur la tete (80x72cm-31x28in) i. collection of materials. 13-Mar-4 De Vuyst, Lokeren #578/R est:3000-4000
£2448	$4087	€3500	Petit musee de Ben (55x32x80cm-22x13x31in) various objects box. 25-Jun-3 Digard, Paris #119/R est:4000-6000
£2551	$4693	€3800	Un artiste mort est un artiste riche (40x31x20cm-16x12x8in) s.i.d.1998 base various objects acrylic panel. 29-Mar-4 Cornette de St.Cyr, Paris #117/R est:1800-2200
£3867	$7037	€5800	Il y a un rat dans un des cinq tiroirs (106x54x41cm-42x21x16in) paint on chest of drawers. 29-Jun-4 Cornette de St.Cyr, Paris #66/R est:6000-8000
Works on paper			
£244	$400	€356	Ben banana boat (15x21cm-6x8in) s.i. felt-tip pen on card prov. 28-May-3 Sotheby's, Amsterdam #155/R
£366	$656	€534	Lucky year 1947 (53x34cm-21x13in) s. Indian ink newspaper. 12-May-4 Dobiaschofsky, Bern #2146 (S.FR 850)
£403	$713	€600	Effacer ce dessin (62x46cm-24x18in) s.i.d.87 mixed media panel. 28-Apr-4 Artcurial Briest, Paris #414
£738	$1358	€1100	Details qui m'interessent (40x30cm-16x12in) s.d.1990 mixed media collage wood. 24-Mar-4 Joron-Derem, Paris #160
£872	$1605	€1300	Art (38x48cm-15x19in) s. mixed media wood exec 1989 prov. 24-Mar-4 Joron-Derem, Paris #159
£1000	$1840	€1500	Untitled (24x33cm-9x13in) s. writing on canvas prov. 10-Jun-4 Galleria Pace, Milan #71/R est:1500
£1074	$1922	€1600	Poil de sex a Ben (36x36cm-14x14in) i.d.68 felt-tip pen mixed media paper on card. 25-May-4 Sotheby's, Milan #144/R est:1500
£1197	$2095	€1700	Une signature de plus. s. s.i.verso collage panel prov. 18-Dec-3 Cornette de St.Cyr, Paris #105/R est:1800-2000
£1250	$2063	€1800	Declaration des droits de l'homme (45x35cm-18x14in) mixed media panel. 2-Jul-3 Cornette de St.Cyr, Paris #115/R est:1500-2000
£1399	$2378	€2000	Je prends la parole a 18 H 30 (75x56cm-30x22in) s.d.2003 ink cardboard. 27-Nov-3 Calmels Cohen, Paris #61/R est:2500-3000
£1549	$2680	€2200	Ben et la poule piu-piu (55x65cm-22x26in) s. mixed media photograph plexiglass. 9-Dec-3 Artcurial Briest, Paris #534/R est:2000-2500
£1600	$2928	€2400	Untitled (27x15cm-11x6in) collage sweet papers magazine page col print two. 4-Jun-4 Lempertz, Koln #516/R est:1800
£1733	$3172	€2600	Fluxus concert (46x46cm-18x18in) i. cloth wood har bread bandages nuts phot. 4-Jun-4 Lempertz, Koln #517/R est:2500
£4430	$8151	€6600	Moi aussi comme Sol Lewitt (60x50cm-24x20in) s. collage acrylic panel. 29-Mar-4 Cornette de St.Cyr, Paris #70/R est:6000-8000

BEN ALI R'BATI (1861-1939) Moroccan

Works on paper			
£7092	$11844	€10000	La sortie du Sultan pour la priere du vendredi (49x64cm-19x25in) s. gouache. 16-Jun-3 Gros & Delettrez, Paris #49/R est:9000-12000
£12766	$21319	€18000	Fete au village, Maroc (34x48cm-13x19in) s. gouache. 16-Jun-3 Gros & Delettrez, Paris #51/R est:12000-18000
£14184	$23688	€20000	Ceremonie Royale, Maroc (44x60cm-17x24in) s. gouache. 16-Jun-3 Gros & Delettrez, Paris #50/R est:12000-18000

BEN-ZVI, Asaf (1953-) Israeli

£3911	$7000	€5710	Letter (169x158cm-67x62in) s.i.d.1989 exhib. 18-Mar-4 Sotheby's, New York #69/R est:8000-12000

BENAIM, Ricardo (20th C) South American

Works on paper			
£374	$625	€546	Estela (181x21cm-71x8in) mixed media exec.2003. 19-Oct-3 Subastas Odalys, Caracas #144
£420	$713	€600	Les rouleaux (40x30cm-16x12in) s.i.verso collage mixed media. 27-Nov-3 Calmels Cohen, Paris #127/R
£599	$1030	€875	Star (181x21cm-71x8in) s. mixed media painted 2003. 7-Dec-3 Subastas Odalys, Caracas #11
£650	$1060	€949	Estela (181x21cm-71x8in) s.verso mixed media exec.2003. 28-Sep-3 Subastas Odalys, Caracas #32/R

BENARD, Guy (?) French

£302	$565	€450	Pres de l'Aven (54x61cm-21x24in) s. 24-Feb-4 Thierry & Lannon, Brest #300

BENARD, Henri (1860-1927) French

£2318	$4219	€3500	Female nude on the Cote d'Azur (117x81cm-46x32in) s.d.1903. 18-Jun-4 Bolland & Marotz, Bremen #583/R est:1300

BENARD, Jean Baptiste (?-1789) French

£2878	$4719	€4000	Bergeres et moutons (27x35cm-11x14in) pair. 6-Jun-3 Drouot Estimations, Paris #42 est:1800-2000
Works on paper			
£900	$1557	€1314	Elegant company dancing in a landscape (21x40cm-8x16in) black chk pen grey ink wash. 12-Dec-3 Christie's, Kensington #436/R

BENATI, Davide (1949-) Italian

£1594	$2614	€2200	Night scene with lanterns (50x35cm-20x14in) s.i.d.1990 verso oil W/C papier mache. 30-May-3 Farsetti, Prato #80/R
£1745	$3123	€2600	Terraces (30x100cm-12x39in) s.i.d.96 verso oil W/C paper on canvas. 28-May-4 Farsetti, Prato #2/R est:1200-1500
Works on paper			
£1667	$2733	€2300	River (150x120cm-59x47in) s.i.d.1984 verso W/C paper on canvas. 27-May-3 Sotheby's, Milan #17 est:2000-2500
£2113	$3697	€3000	Village (150x174cm-59x69in) i.verso W/C paper on panel. 16-Dec-3 Finarte Semenzato, Milan #211/R est:2300-2700

BENAVIDES ALVAREZ, Rafael (1912-1968) Venezuelan

£2183	$4060	€3187	Village (40x30cm-16x12in) s. 14-Mar-4 Subastas Odalys, Caracas #67

BENAVIDES, Pablo (1918-) Venezuelan

£263	$440	€384	View from Macaracuay (22x36cm-9x14in) s. painted 1978. 19-Oct-3 Subastas Odalys, Caracas #75/R
£290	$450	€423	Florist shop (31x21cm-12x8in) s. painted 1966. 3-Nov-2 Subastas Odalys, Caracas #5/R
£376	$595	€549	Vase of flowers (41x33cm-16x13in) s. 27-Apr-3 Subastas Odalys, Caracas #96
£391	$625	€571	Untitled (44x34cm-17x13in) s. painted 1947. 21-Sep-3 Subastas Odalys, Caracas #67
£433	$805	€632	My garden (30x40cm-12x16in) s. painted 1978. 14-Mar-4 Subastas Odalys, Caracas #20/R
£454	$835	€663	Landscape (37x51cm-15x20in) s. painted 1958. 28-Mar-4 Subastas Odalys, Caracas #14
£456	$720	€666	Landscape (33x47cm-13x19in) s. painted 1972. 1-Dec-2 Subastas Odalys, Caracas #101/R
£485	$810	€708	Santa Clara (26x31cm-10x12in) s. painted 1981. 13-Jul-3 Subastas Odalys, Caracas #78
£516	$800	€753	Still life (33x51cm-13x20in) s. lit. 3-Nov-2 Subastas Odalys, Caracas #23/R
£563	$940	€822	Flowers in the study (50x25cm-20x10in) s. painted 1971. 13-Jul-3 Subastas Odalys, Caracas #2/R
£654	$1125	€955	Mangoes in my garden (46x61cm-18x24in) s. painted 1997. 7-Dec-3 Subastas Odalys, Caracas #91/R
£823	$1375	€1202	View from the lagoon (35x59cm-14x23in) s. painted 1965. 13-Jul-3 Subastas Odalys, Caracas #111/R
£1019	$1875	€1488	Landscape in Los Ruices (65x92cm-26x36in) s. painted 1980. 28-Mar-4 Subastas Odalys, Caracas #48/R
£1103	$2030	€1610	Mariperez (70x90cm-28x35in) s. painted 1958. 28-Mar-4 Subastas Odalys, Caracas #31/R
£1406	$2250	€2053	Cow-girl (62x80cm-24x31in) s. painted 1953. 21-Sep-3 Subastas Odalys, Caracas #112/R
£1800	$3060	€2628	Landscape (70x80cm-28x31in) s. painted 1953. 23-Nov-3 Subastas Odalys, Caracas #84/R

BENAZZI, Raffael (1933-) Swiss

Sculpture			
£823	$1472	€1202	Untitled (20cm-8in) mono.d. dark brown pat.bronze prov. 22-Mar-4 Philippe Schuler, Zurich #4246/R (S.FR 1900)
£2620	$4821	€3825	Work No 1661 (43x62x27cm-17x24x11in) alabaster lit. 8-Jun-4 Germann, Zurich #139/R est:4000-6000 (S.FR 6000)

BENCINI, Antonio (18th C) Austrian

Miniatures			
£1600	$2864	€2336	Maria Theresia of Habsburg (3cm-1in) silver gilt mount blue enamel border seed pearls. 25-May-4 Christie's, London #74/R est:1500-2000

BENCOVICH, Federico (1675-1753) Dalmatian

£10738	$20081	€16000	Monk meditating (42x36cm-17x14in) 25-Feb-4 Porro, Milan #5/R est:16000

BENCZUR, Gyula Julius de (1844-1920) Hungarian

£733	$1312	€1070	Portrait of woman with book (41x34cm-16x13in) 12-May-4 Dobiaschofsky, Bern #335/R est:2400 (S.FR 1700)
£2308	$3831	€3370	Hungarian nobleman (69x55cm-27x22in) s.d.1864. 4-Oct-3 Kieselbach, Budapest #147/R (H.F 850000)
£3258	$5408	€4757	Artist's wife (38x30cm-15x12in) s.d.1884 panel. 4-Oct-3 Kieselbach, Budapest #179/R (H.F 1200000)
£5879	$10406	€8583	Male portrait (128x93cm-50x37in) s. painted 1870's. 28-Apr-4 Kieselbach, Budapest #187/R (H.F 2200000)
£140000	$254800	€204400	Summer picnic (87x115cm-34x45in) s.d.1876 prov. 15-Jun-4 Sotheby's, London #43/R est:60000-80000

BENDA, Wladyslav T (1873-1948) American

Sculpture			
£1564	$2800	€2283	Mask, young woman wearing headpiece (51x58x13cm-20x23x5in) wire paper oil paint tassels. 15-May-4 Illustration House, New York #84/R est:3000-4500
Works on paper			
£963	$1800	€1406	Smiling woman picking daisies (43x36cm-17x14in) s. chl pastel W/C. 26-Feb-4 Illustration House, New York #16 est:2500-3500

BENDALL, Mildred (1891-1977) British/French

£1300	$2067	€1898	Farm buildings, Lot et Garonne (50x60cm-20x24in) board exhib. 10-Sep-3 Sotheby's, Olympia #211/R est:800-1200
£1600	$2544	€2336	Coin de salon Bordelais (46x40cm-18x16in) s. exhib. 10-Sep-3 Sotheby's, Olympia #159/R est:600-800
£1800	$3330	€2628	Still life with flowers (46x38cm-18x15in) s. 11-Feb-4 Sotheby's, Olympia #156/R est:800-1200
£2000	$3180	€2920	Coastal scene (58x73cm-23x29in) s.d.1931 prov. 10-Sep-3 Sotheby's, Olympia #171/R est:1000-1500

£2600 $4134 €3796 Country table (45x54cm-18x21in) prov. 10-Sep-3 Sotheby's, Olympia #162/R est:1000-1500
£5500 $10175 €8030 Flowers before a window (61x50cm-24x20in) s. exhib. 11-Feb-4 Sotheby's, Olympia #155/R est:1500-2000

BENDER, Franz (?-1905) German
£818 $1300 €1194 Alpine scene with figures (48x69cm-19x27in) s. 14-Sep-3 Susanin's, Chicago #6039/R est:1500-2000

BENDER, Sarah E de Wolfe (1852-1935) American
£625 $1100 €913 Floral still life of roses (20x33cm-8x13in) s. 24-May-4 Winter Associates, Plainville #85/R
£1047 $1800 €1529 Still life with yellow flowers (36x76cm-14x30in) s. painted c.1900. 7-Dec-3 Treadway Gallery, Cincinnati #475/R est:1500-2500

BENDINI, Vasco (1922-) Italian
£2667 $4907 €4000 Untitled (150x150cm-59x59in) s.d.1978. 12-Jun-4 Meeting Art, Vercelli #490/R est:4000
£2752 $5091 €4100 Pale gold and natural copper (160x140cm-63x55in) s.i.d.1976 verso lit. 13-Mar-4 Meeting Art, Vercelli #116 est:2500

BENDIX, Hans (1898-1984) Danish
£706 $1199 €1031 Portrait of Bodil Kjaer as Indra's daughter in a dream play (100x62cm-39x24in) init.d.1969. 26-Nov-3 Kunsthallen, Copenhagen #369/R (D.KR 7500)

BENDIXEN, Siegfried Detlev (1786-1864) German
Works on paper
£350 $539 €550 Classical ruins (36x25cm-14x10in) s.d.1834 W/C sepia. 4-Sep-2 Schopman, Hamburg #3/R

BENDRE, Narayan Shridhar (1910-1992) Indian
£8696 $16000 €12696 Mother (76x91cm-30x36in) i.verso. 24-Mar-4 Sotheby's, New York #181/R est:18000-22000
£9957 $17923 €14537 Untitled (91x102cm-36x40in) s.d. 25-Apr-4 Christie's, Hong Kong #603/R est:140000-160000 (HK.D 140000)
£14130 $26000 €20630 Village landscape (114x107cm-45x42in) s. 25-Mar-4 Christie's, Rockefeller NY #224/R est:20000-25000
£16304 $30000 €23804 Gossips (95x79cm-37x31in) s.d. i.verso. 24-Mar-4 Sotheby's, New York #183/R est:20000-30000
£22760 $40967 €33230 Vanjare (92x92cm-36x36in) s.d. 25-Apr-4 Christie's, Hong Kong #602/R est:160000-180000 (HK.D 320000)

BENDTSEN, Folmer (1907-1993) Swedish
£323 $548 €472 The coal terminal, Copenhagen (38x50cm-15x20in) s.d.49. 10-Nov-3 Rasmussen, Vejle #583 (D.KR 3500)
£376 $677 €549 Winter landscape with buildings (33x41cm-13x16in) s.d.23/10 68. 24-Apr-4 Rasmussen, Havnen #4141/R (D.KR 4200)
£398 $637 €577 Factory buildings (80x100cm-31x39in) s.d.42. 17-Sep-3 Kunsthallen, Copenhagen #251 (D.KR 4200)
£407 $729 €594 From the harbour (38x55cm-15x22in) s.d.61. 10-May-4 Rasmussen, Vejle #660/R (D.KR 4500)
£517 $880 €755 Planks (45x55cm-18x22in) s. 26-Nov-3 Kunsthallen, Copenhagen #298 (D.KR 5500)
£553 $940 €807 Park landscape with woman and dog (34x41cm-13x16in) s.i. 10-Nov-3 Rasmussen, Vejle #700/R (D.KR 6000)
£622 $1132 €933 Street scene, Alexandravej (70x100cm-28x39in) s.d.63. 19-Jun-4 Rasmussen, Havnen #4137/R (D.KR 7000)
£641 $1167 €936 Street scene with figure walking (48x40cm-19x16in) s. 7-Feb-4 Rasmussen, Havnen #4099/R (D.KR 7000)
£664 $1062 €969 Harbour scene with ships (60x81cm-24x32in) s.d.65. 22-Sep-3 Rasmussen, Vejle #564/R (D.KR 7000)
£682 $1092 €996 Road through town in winter (75x100cm-30x39in) s.d.51. 22-Sep-3 Rasmussen, Vejle #563/R (D.KR 7200)
£711 $1294 €1067 Town scene from Norrebro (53x58cm-21x23in) s.d.51. 19-Jun-4 Rasmussen, Havnen #4065/R (D.KR 8000)
£812 $1495 €1186 Red ship in Copenhagen Harbour (81x103cm-32x41in) s.d.58. 29-Mar-4 Rasmussen, Copenhagen #452/R (D.KR 9000)
£847 $1439 €1237 Street scene, Alexandravej (67x74cm-26x29in) s.d.59. 29-Nov-3 Rasmussen, Havnen #4133/R (D.KR 9000)
£847 $1439 €1237 Street scene with figure walking (48x40cm-19x16in) s. 29-Nov-3 Rasmussen, Havnen #4202/R (D.KR 9000)
£860 $1539 €1256 Street scene with buildings and figure (73x67cm-29x26in) s.d.69. 10-May-4 Rasmussen, Vejle #659/R (D.KR 9500)
£909 $1473 €1318 Street scene with houses in winter (69x79cm-27x31in) s.d.38. 4-Aug-3 Rasmussen, Vejle #668/R (D.KR 9500)
£995 $1782 €1453 Street scene with figures (60x81cm-24x32in) s.d.69. 10-May-4 Rasmussen, Vejle #658/R (D.KR 11000)
£1518 $2459 €2216 Moonlight and figure (60x81cm-24x32in) s. 9-Aug-3 Hindemae, Ullerslev #1079/R est:15000 (D.KR 16000)
£1895 $3544 €2767 Figures at Alexandravej (73x100cm-29x39in) s. 25-Feb-4 Kunsthallen, Copenhagen #286/R est:20000 (D.KR 21000)

BENDZ, Wilhelm (attrib) (1804-1832) Danish
Works on paper
£280 $443 €406 Young couple seen from behind (29x21cm-11x8in) indis.i.d.Juni 1829 i.verso pencil. 2-Sep-3 Rasmussen, Copenhagen #2025/R (D.KR 3000)

BENE, Geza (1900-1960) Hungarian
£2308 $3831 €3370 Szentendre trees (35x45cm-14x18in) s.d.1956 verso cardboard. 4-Oct-3 Kieselbach, Budapest #173/R (H.F 850000)
Works on paper
£695 $1230 €1015 Girl in red head scarf (61x50cm-24x20in) s.d.933 mixed media. 28-Apr-4 Kieselbach, Budapest #115/R (H.F 260000)
£1001 $1812 €1461 Morning in the city (25x31cm-10x12in) s. W/C. 16-Apr-4 Mu Terem Galeria, Budapest #10/R (H.F 380000)
£1107 $2003 €1616 Woman portrait (48x38cm-19x15in) s. pastel pencil. 16-Apr-4 Mu Terem Galeria, Budapest #157/R (H.F 420000)

BENEDETTI, Alberti de (19th C) Italian
Works on paper
£1986 $3316 €2800 Scenes antiques. s.i. wash Chinese ink gouache pierre noire set of 4. 15-Oct-3 Sotheby's, Paris #179/R est:3500-4500

BENEDETTI, Andries (c.1615-?) Flemish
£30822 $52397 €45000 Still life with lobster, fruit, flute, beaker, pie and hazelnuts on a plate (92x140cm-36x55in) prov.lit. 4-Nov-3 Sotheby's, Amsterdam #27/R est:25000-35000

BENEDETTO, Enzo (1905-1993) Italian
Works on paper
£414 $691 €600 Red game (69x31cm-27x12in) s. mixed media wood sand board. 13-Nov-3 Finarte Semenzato, Rome #329

BENEDIT, Luis F (1937-) Argentinian
Works on paper
£3846 $7000 €5615 Feld grille (100x72cm-39x28in) s.d.88 mixed media. 29-Jun-4 Arroyo, Buenos Aires #62/R est:7000

BENEDITO, Concha (20th C) French
£629 $1070 €900 Fantasia (80x80cm-31x31in) s. acrylic. 29-Nov-3 Neret-Minet, Paris #72/R

BENEDITO-VIVES, Manuel (1875-1963) Spanish
Works on paper
£629 $1051 €900 Landscape with peasant woman (30x27cm-12x11in) s. W/C. 30-Jun-3 Ansorena, Madrid #3/R

BENEDYKTOWICZ, Ludomir von (1844-1926) Polish
£2333 $4223 €3500 Peasants outside farmstead in summer landscape (54x100cm-21x39in) s.d.1879. 1-Apr-4 Van Ham, Cologne #1287/R est:3200

BENEKER, Gerrit Albertus (1882-1934) American
£1471 $2500 €2148 Untitled, house in Truro, Mass (36x30cm-14x12in) s.verso board painted c.1925. 9-Nov-3 Outer Cape Auctions, Provincetown #101/R
£1556 $2800 €2272 Fish still life (30x41cm-12x16in) s.d.14 exhib. 23-Jan-4 Freeman, Philadelphia #279/R est:1000-1500

BENELLI, G (?) Italian
£922 $1540 €1300 Madonna della Seggiola (74x74cm-29x29in) i. verso after Raffael. 21-Jun-3 Klittich Pfankuch, Braunschweig #31

BENELLI, Gino (19/20th C) Italian
£1724 $3086 €2517 Two women in field. Two travelling musicians (82x62cm-32x24in) one s. pair. 12-May-4 Dobiaschofsky, Bern #337/R est:5000 (S.FR 4000)

BENES, Barton Lidice (1942-) American
Works on paper
£272 $462 €397 Untitled (29x19cm-11x7in) s.d.1980 mixed media collage prov. 4-Nov-3 Bukowskis, Stockholm #638/R (S.KR 3600)

BENES, Vincent (1883-1979) Czechoslovakian
Works on paper
£438 $727 €639 Vltava river with legion bridge (33x50cm-13x20in) s. W/C. 4-Oct-3 Dorotheum, Prague #231/R est:20000-30000 (C.KR 20000)

BENESCH, Josef Ferdinand (1875-1954) Austrian
£280 $481 €400 Castle on lake shore (31x25cm-12x10in) s. i.verso board. 4-Dec-3 Dorotheum, Graz #3/R
£280 $481 €400 View of Grimming (23x17cm-9x7in) s. fibreboard. 4-Dec-3 Dorotheum, Graz #4

BENET, Rafael (1889-1979) Spanish
£724 $1310 €1100 Flowers (34x43cm-13x17in) s.i.d.1947. 14-Apr-4 Ansorena, Madrid #84/R
£4000 $7280 €6000 Tossa de Mar, Costa Brava (50x61cm-20x24in) s. s.i.d.1940 verso. 29-Jun-4 Segre, Madrid #101/R est:5000

BENEVIDES, Pablo (20th C) Venezuelan
£514 $935 €771 From my study (40x50cm-16x20in) s. 21-Jun-4 Subastas Odalys, Caracas #146
£714 $1300 €1071 Interior (48x34cm-19x13in) s. painted 1965. 21-Jun-4 Subastas Odalys, Caracas #124

BENEVOLO, Francesco Luigi Maria (1865-1939) ?
Prints
£2533 $4636 €3800 L'armoire des freres Davenport presentee par Benevol (157x118cm-62x46in) col lithograph unique. 5-Jun-4 Gros & Delettrez, Paris #369/R est:1800-2100

BENEZIT, Emanuel Charles Louis (1887-1975) French
£298 $542 €450 Village de Provence (38x46cm-15x18in) s. 15-Jun-4 Blanchet, Paris #194

BENFATTO, Luigi (attrib) (1559-1611) Italian
Works on paper
£7483 $13395 €11000 Le jugement de Salomon. Dieu-le-Pere (24x19cm-9x7in) i. red chk pen brown ink wash double-sided prov. 18-Mar-4 Christie's, Paris #5/R est:3000-5000

BENFIELD, Guy (1964-) Australian
Works on paper
£744 $1376 €1086 Untitled (181x165cm-71x65in) s.i. mixed media on canvas prov.exhib. 15-Mar-4 Sotheby's, Melbourne #150 est:600-800 (A.D 1800)

BENGER, Berenger (1868-1935) British
Works on paper
£380 $635 €555 St Bernard (58x97cm-23x38in) s.d.1890 W/C. 20-Jun-3 Chrystals Auctions, Isle of Man #182/R

BENGLIS, Linda (1941-) American
£706 $1200 €1031 Untitled abstract (23x20cm-9x8in) s.i.d.1963 verso. 22-Nov-3 New Orleans Auction, New Orleans #1350/R est:1500-2500
£706 $1200 €1031 Untitled abstract (25x30cm-10x12in) 22-Nov-3 New Orleans Auction, New Orleans #1352/R est:1500-2500
£1529 $2600 €2232 Abstract (66x102cm-26x40in) oil on paper. 22-Nov-3 New Orleans Auction, New Orleans #1351/R est:1800-2500
Sculpture
£1000 $1800 €1460 Untitled (10x14x14cm-4x6x6in) glass wire paint found objects. 24-Apr-4 David Rago, Lambertville #397/R est:750-1500
£1667 $3000 €2434 1st test work (54x11x9cm-21x4x4in) s.i.d.1978 cast paper iridescent cellophane prov. 24-Apr-4 David Rago, Lambertville #73/R est:2000-4000
£3333 $6000 €4866 Untitled (36x4x3cm-14x2x1in) plaster screen. 24-Apr-4 David Rago, Lambertville #214/R est:1000-2000
£4595 $8500 €6709 Untitled (101x45x35cm-40x18x14in) cotton bunting plaster glitter paint aluminium exec c.1972 prov. 12-Feb-4 Sotheby's, New York #195/R est:3000-4000
£5405 $10000 €7891 Zita (112x38x28cm-44x15x11in) cotton bunting plaster glitter paint aluminium prov.exhib.lit. 12-Feb-4 Sotheby's, New York #199/R est:3000-4000
£6111 $11000 €8922 Untitled (36x4x1cm-14x2x0in) wax wood. 24-Apr-4 David Rago, Lambertville #307/R est:1000-2000
£6748 $11000 €9852 Devaux (122x109x37cm-48x43x15in) bronze wire screen copper nickel chrome prov. 23-Sep-3 Christie's, Rockefeller NY #181/R est:8000-12000
£10556 $19000 €15412 Untitled (66x5x1cm-26x2x0in) wax masonite wood exhib. 24-Apr-4 David Rago, Lambertville #516/R est:1000-2000
£11538 $21000 €16845 India (128cm-50in) aluminum cotton bunting plaster spray zinc executed 1974 prov. 29-Jun-4 Sotheby's, New York #482/R est:7000-9000
Works on paper
£588 $1000 €858 Self portrait (38x30cm-15x12in) graphite executed c.1964. 22-Nov-3 New Orleans Auction, New Orleans #1349/R est:1200-1800

BENGTS, Carl (1876-1934) Finnish
£2148 $3952 €3200 In the sauna (38x33cm-15x13in) s.d.1931 i.verso. 25-Mar-4 Hagelstam, Helsinki #897 est:500

BENGTS, Ole (?) Scandinavian
£333 $613 €500 Winter in the harbour (35x52cm-14x20in) s. 9-Jun-4 Bukowskis, Helsinki #582/R

BENGTS, Oskar (1885-1966) Finnish
£743 $1330 €1100 The cat looking at the harbour (32x41cm-13x16in) s. 8-May-4 Bukowskis, Helsinki #57/R

BENGTSSON, Dick (1936-1989) Swedish
£5589 $9502 €8160 The sick dog (33x41cm-13x16in) panel exhib. 4-Nov-3 Bukowskis, Stockholm #532/R est:30000-40000 (S.KR 74000)

BENHAM, Thomas C S (fl.1878-1922) British
£1600 $2976 €2336 Across the sea to the island beyond (66x114cm-26x45in) s. 4-Mar-4 Christie's, Kensington #133/R est:1000-1500

BENINGTON, R P (19th C) British?
£1796 $3000 €2622 English village scene (25x36cm-10x14in) s. 16-Nov-3 Simpson's, Houston #214/R
£1899 $3000 €2773 English village scene (25x36cm-10x14in) s. 27-Jul-3 Simpson's, Houston #404

BENISCELLI, Alberto (1870-?) Italian
£4225 $7310 €6000 Seascape in Nervi (46x57cm-18x22in) s. 9-Dec-3 Finarte Semenzato, Milan #105/R est:1500-1600

BENITEZ, Nicolas (17th C) Mexican?
£2318 $3941 €3384 Gallant scene (21x15cm-8x6in) s.d.1690 burin copper lit. 29-Oct-3 Louis Morton, Mexico #14/R est:40000-50000 (M.P 44000)

BENITO, Eduard Garcia (1891-1981) Spanish
£1980 $3683 €2950 Man reading (100x80cm-39x31in) s. 2-Mar-4 Ansorena, Madrid #38/R est:2900
Works on paper
£950 $1700 €1387 Cover of Vanity Fair in October of 1927. s. W/C. 13-May-4 Dallas Auction Gallery, Dallas #64/R est:500-800

BENJAMIN, Jason (20th C) Australian
£810 $1304 €1183 Are we free ? (30x30cm-12x12in) s.d.April '02 verso. 25-Aug-3 Sotheby's, Paddington #237 est:2000-3000 (A.D 2000)
£1619 $2607 €2364 Take my hand (127x127cm-50x50in) s. d.June 99 verso. 13-Oct-3 Joel, Victoria #357 est:4000-6000 (A.D 4000)
£5785 $9835 €8446 I don't want to run any more (120x120cm-47x47in) s.i.verso. 29-Oct-3 Lawson Menzies, Sydney #131a/R est:15000-20000 (A.D 14000)
£7287 $11733 €10639 Courage (120x180cm-47x71in) s.d.May 02 i.verso. 25-Aug-3 Sotheby's, Paddington #105/R est:18000-24000 (A.D 18000)
£8936 $15191 €13047 She aches for him (122x122cm-48x48in) s.i.d.03 verso prov. 25-Nov-3 Christie's, Melbourne #5/R est:12000-18000 (A.D 21000)
£8943 $16008 €13057 Something that'd been coming for a long long time (120x120cm-47x47in) s.d.Oct 00 i.verso prov. 4-May-4 Sotheby's, Melbourne #28/R est:15000-20000 (A.D 22000)
£9917 $17554 €14479 Would we ever be so sure (121x121cm-48x48in) s.i.d.Feb 01 verso prov. 3-May-4 Christie's, Melbourne #17/R est:15000-25000 (A.D 24000)
£11992 $21465 €17508 Lost in the night (120x180cm-47x71in) s.d.March 02 i.verso. 4-May-4 Sotheby's, Melbourne #3/R est:18000-28000 (A.D 29500)
£26860 $45661 €39216 Hold on to your friends (244x366cm-96x144in) s. i.d.2000 verso. 29-Oct-3 Lawson Menzies, Sydney #28/R est:50000-70000 (A.D 65000)

BENJAMIN, Karl (1925-) American
£337 $550 €489 Abstract composition (18x43cm-7x17in) s.d.54 masonite. 20-Jul-3 Jeffery Burchard, Florida #30
£1130 $2000 €1650 Untitled (119x58cm-47x23in) s.d.12-52 board. 2-May-4 Bonhams & Butterfields, Los Angeles #3033/R est:2000-3000
£3672 $6500 €5361 Untitled (102x137cm-40x54in) init.d.58. 2-May-4 Bonhams & Butterfields, Los Angeles #3083/R est:3000-5000

BENJAMIN, Pierre (20th C) French
Sculpture
£1544 $2856 €2300 Poisson sur la vague (30x39x12cm-12x15x5in) s. pat bronze Cast Susse. 14-Mar-4 St-Germain-en-Laye Encheres #126/R est:2300-2500

BENJI, Asada (1900-1984) Japanese
Works on paper
£13043 $24000 €19043 Herons (148x142cm-58x56in) ink two panel screens pair exhib. 23-Mar-4 Christie's, Rockefeller NY #90/R est:5000-7000

BENKHART, Agost (1882-1961) Hungarian
£814 $1352 €1188 Susan (80x70cm-31x28in) s.d.1929. 4-Oct-3 Kieselbach, Budapest #85/R (H.F 300000)
£2939 $5203 €4291 Mackerel sky (87x106cm-34x42in) s.d.1918. 28-Apr-4 Kieselbach, Budapest #140/R (H.F 1100000)

BENLLIURE Y GIL, Jose (1855-1937) Spanish
£2465 $4264 €3500 Soldiers smoking (27x21cm-11x8in) s. board. 10-Dec-3 Castellana, Madrid #237/R est:3000
£5556 $10000 €8112 Family in Naples (16x11cm-6x4in) s.i. panel. 23-Apr-4 Sotheby's, New York #202/R est:12000-18000
£10000 $15900 €14600 Sonata, Spanish soldier playing a mandolin (33x23cm-13x9in) s. panel prov. 9-Sep-3 Peter Francis, Wales #28/R est:3000-5000
£24138 $40310 €35000 Pond (53x82cm-21x32in) s. lit. 17-Nov-3 Durán, Madrid #213/R est:32500

BENLLIURE Y GIL, Juan Antonio (19th C) Spanish
£759 $1267 €1100 White shawl (61x49cm-24x19in) s. 17-Nov-3 Durán, Madrid #189/R

BENLLIURE Y GIL, Mariano (1862-1947) Spanish
Works on paper
£604 $1123 €900 Don Alfonso XIII (50x32cm-20x13in) s. ink dr pair. 2-Mar-4 Ansorena, Madrid #329/R
£651 $1106 €950 Gypsy (14x17cm-6x7in) s. ink dr. 4-Nov-3 Ansorena, Madrid #1900/R
£3125 $5094 €4500 Soldiers in action (67x50cm-26x20in) s. W/C. 23-Sep-3 Durán, Madrid #188/R est:3750

BENLLIURE, Blas (1852-1936) Spanish
£759 $1267 €1100 Still life (46x64cm-18x25in) s.d.923. 17-Nov-3 Durán, Madrid #38/R
£2819 $5215 €4200 Vase fleuri de roses blanches, roses et oeillets (90x45cm-35x18in) s.d.1913. 15-Mar-4 Horta, Bruxelles #44 est:1500-1800

BENN (1905-1989) Polish
£456 $808 €680 Vue d'une terrasse (65x81cm-26x32in) s. 28-Apr-4 Charbonneaux, Paris #109
£1342 $2483 €2000 Femme devant la porte (100x73cm-39x29in) s. 15-Mar-4 Claude Boisgirard, Paris #10/R est:1500-1800

BENN, Ben (1884-1983) American
£419 $700 €608 Tied boats (61x74cm-24x29in) s.d.61. 30-Jun-3 Winter Associates, Plainville #69/R
£438 $700 €639 Landscape (36x46cm-14x18in) s. i.d.verso. 17-May-3 Bunte, Elgin #1282
£898 $1500 €1311 Portrait of Velida - artist's wife (203x102cm-80x40in) s.d.1923 prov. 23-Oct-3 Shannon's, Milford #255/R est:2000-3000
£989 $1800 €1444 Autumn flowers (61x51cm-24x20in) s.d.49 s.i.d.verso prov. 29-Jun-4 Sotheby's, New York #393/R est:2500-3500
£1374 $2500 €2006 Still life of flowers and fruit on a table (77x61cm-30x24in) s.d.38 prov. 29-Jun-4 Sotheby's, New York #395/R est:3000-5000
£1648 $3000 €2406 Still life on chair (92x76cm-36x30in) s.d.22 prov. 29-Jun-4 Sotheby's, New York #396/R est:4000-6000
£2188 $3500 €3194 Crap shooters (51x61cm-20x24in) s.d.1950. 17-May-3 Bunte, Elgin #1275 est:800-1200

BENN, Benejou (1905-1989) Polish
£1208 $2235 €1800 Panier de fruits (46x55cm-18x22in) s. panel. 14-Mar-4 Eric Pillon, Calais #119/R

BENNASSAR, Dionis (1905-1967) Spanish?
£704 $1232 €1000 Figure (81x100cm-32x39in) s. exhib. 16-Dec-3 Durán, Madrid #63/R

BENNEDSEN, Jens Christian (1893-1967) Danish
£455 $728 €664 Winter landscape with stream (71x100cm-28x39in) s. 22-Sep-3 Rasmussen, Vejle #369/R (D.KR 4800)

BENNELL, Mary (?) British?
Works on paper
£320 $592 €467 Portrait of St. Cecilia (36x25cm-14x10in) pastel. 13-Feb-4 Keys, Aylsham #370

BENNER, Emmanuel (1836-1896) French
£948 $1697 €1384 Music in wood (55x38cm-22x15in) s.d.1893. 12-May-4 Dobiaschofsky, Bern #338/R est:2700 (S.FR 2200)
£1376 $2298 €1995 Reclining nude (51x65cm-20x26in) s. 23-Jun-3 Philippe Schuler, Zurich #3506/R est:3000-4000 (S.FR 3000)
£3800 $6840 €5548 Le reveil (51x65cm-20x26in) s. 21-Jan-4 Sotheby's, Olympia #391/R est:2000-3000
£30000 $51600 €43800 At the water's edge (157x232cm-62x91in) s.d.1887 exhib. 3-Dec-3 Christie's, London #41/R est:30000-50000

BENNER, Emmanuel Michel (1873-1965) French
£2200 $3784 €3212 Young boy in an interior (79x58cm-31x23in) s. 4-Dec-3 Christie's, Kensington #127/R est:2500-3500

BENNER, Gerrit (1897-1981) Dutch
£420 $701 €600 Man and horse (66x50cm-26x20in) s. 30-Jun-3 Sotheby's, Amsterdam #384/R
£420 $701 €600 Man and bird (66x50cm-26x20in) s. paper. 30-Jun-3 Sotheby's, Amsterdam #385/R
£420 $701 €600 A figure (66x50cm-26x20in) s. paper. 30-Jun-3 Sotheby's, Amsterdam #387/R
£1259 $2102 €1800 Untitled (50x66cm-20x26in) s. paper. 30-Jun-3 Sotheby's, Amsterdam #386/R
£10490 $17832 €15000 White cow (61x61cm-24x24in) board painted c.1964 prov. 25-Nov-3 Christie's, Amsterdam #288/R est:15000-20000
£17483 $30070 €25000 Landschap (80x100cm-31x39in) s. prov.exhib. 2-Dec-3 Sotheby's, Amsterdam #130/R est:25000-35000
£18116 $29710 €25000 Sea (60x75cm-24x30in) s.verso painted c.1979. 27-May-3 Sotheby's, Amsterdam #409/R est:25000-30000
£38667 $71147 €58000 Landscape (80x100cm-31x39in) painted 1973 prov.exhib.lit. 9-Jun-4 Christie's, Amsterdam #332/R est:35000-55000
Works on paper
£252 $421 €360 Roses in a vase (30x21cm-12x8in) s.d.1961 pencil. 30-Jun-3 Sotheby's, Amsterdam #388/R
£329 $605 €500 Dutch coastline (36x52cm-14x20in) s. black ink chl prov. 22-Jun-4 Christie's, Amsterdam #607/R
£385 $643 €550 Roses (33x24cm-13x9in) s. felt-tip pen. 30-Jun-3 Sotheby's, Amsterdam #394/R
£592 $1089 €900 Horses (64x48cm-25x19in) s. gouache W/C exhib. 22-Jun-4 Christie's, Amsterdam #376/R
£646 $1176 €950 Sailing boats at sea (24x34cm-9x13in) s. felt pen. 3-Feb-4 Christie's, Amsterdam #589
£839 $1401 €1200 Flower composition (24x16cm-9x6in) W/C gouache. 30-Jun-3 Sotheby's, Amsterdam #389/R
£1020 $1857 €1500 Sea (48x63cm-19x25in) s. gouache. 3-Feb-4 Christie's, Amsterdam #588 est:1500-2000
£1049 $1751 €1500 Untitled (48x63cm-19x25in) ink. 30-Jun-3 Sotheby's, Amsterdam #393
£1259 $2102 €1800 Flower composition (24x16cm-9x6in) s. gouache. 30-Jun-3 Sotheby's, Amsterdam #390/R
£1259 $2102 €1800 Abstract composition (49x63cm-19x25in) gouache. 30-Jun-3 Sotheby's, Amsterdam #395/R
£1748 $2919 €2500 Seascape (50x66cm-20x26in) s. ink. 30-Jun-3 Sotheby's, Amsterdam #396/R
£1958 $3270 €2800 View of a landscape (29x37cm-11x15in) s. W/C. 30-Jun-3 Sotheby's, Amsterdam #391/R
£2174 $3565 €3000 Two horses (50x65cm-20x26in) gouache prov. 27-May-3 Sotheby's, Amsterdam #535/R est:3000-4000
£2381 $4333 €3500 Woman in interior. Composition (49x65cm-19x26in) s. W/C gouache double-sided. 3-Feb-4 Christie's, Amsterdam #629 est:1500-2000
£3000 $5520 €4500 Flowers (64x49cm-25x19in) s. W/C gouache. 9-Jun-4 Christie's, Amsterdam #116/R est:5000-7000
£3333 $5467 €4600 Children playing (65x49cm-26x19in) s. gouache prov. 27-May-3 Sotheby's, Amsterdam #392/R est:3500-4500
£3478 $5704 €4800 Small horses (61x66cm-24x26in) s. gouache col chk. 27-May-3 Sotheby's, Amsterdam #407/R est:4000-5000
£3846 $6615 €5500 Meer (24x32cm-9x13in) s. W/C gouache. 2-Dec-3 Sotheby's, Amsterdam #150/R est:3000-5000
£5245 $8916 €7500 Landscape with evening sun (37x55cm-15x22in) s. gouache prov. 25-Nov-3 Christie's, Amsterdam #286/R est:5000-7000
£5333 $9813 €8000 Figure (50x37cm-20x15in) s. gouache exec c.1956 prov. 8-Jun-4 Sotheby's, Amsterdam #91/R est:4000-6000
£6000 $11040 €9000 Eenzame ruiter in winterbos - horserider in a winter landscape (70x50cm-28x20in) s. gouache exec. c.1946 prov. 9-Jun-4 Christie's, Amsterdam #117/R est:4000-6000
£6667 $12267 €10000 Ruiterpaar aan zee (50x70cm-20x28in) s. gouache exec 1976 prov. 8-Jun-4 Sotheby's, Amsterdam #85/R est:10000-15000
£6993 $12028 €10000 Ruiterpaar (50x65cm-20x26in) s. gouache executed 1980 prov. 2-Dec-3 Sotheby's, Amsterdam #132/R est:10000-15000

BENNER, Henri (1776-c.1818) French
Miniatures
£9000 $15570 €13140 Tsar Alexander I of Russia in black coat (13cm-5in) s.d.1817 oval. 9-Dec-3 Christie's, London #245/R est:3000-5000

BENNER, Jean (1836-1909) French
£2100 $3885 €3066 Still life of flowers (56x46cm-22x18in) s.i.d.1896. 10-Mar-4 Sotheby's, Olympia #285/R est:1000-1500

BENNERT, Carl (1815-1885) German
£2254 $3899 €3200 Sir Anthony van Dijck painting a portrait of King Charles I of England (90x117cm-35x46in) s.i.d.1849 lit. 10-Dec-3 Christie's, Amsterdam #694/R est:3000-5000

BENNET, Baron Karl Stefan (1800-1878) Swedish
£3077 $5292 €4492 Gripsholm Palace with church in Mariefred (29x37cm-11x15in) s.d.1841 cardboard. 2-Dec-3 Bukowskis, Stockholm #69/R est:20000-25000 (S.KR 40000)
£3077 $5292 €4492 On horseback past the fence during Tsar Nikolaus' visit 1838 (33x45cm-13x18in) 3-Dec-3 AB Stockholms Auktionsverk #2463/R est:35000-40000 (S.KR 40000)

BENNETT, Alfred (1861-1916) British
£330 $600 €482 Collie (51x58cm-20x23in) s.i.d.97. 7-Feb-4 Harvey Clar, Oakland #1305
£541 $1000 €790 North Dramore, Down Ireland, landscape (36x53cm-14x21in) s. i.verso. 24-Jan-4 Jeffery Burchard, Florida #28/R
£900 $1422 €1305 Ferry on the Thames, Wargrave (46x81cm-18x32in) s.i.d.78 i.verso. 4-Sep-3 Christie's, Kensington #120/R
£1000 $1660 €1460 Ferry at Wargrave on Thames (46x82cm-18x32in) s.i.d.78 s.i.verso. 13-Jun-3 Jacobs & Hunt, Petersfield #244/R est:400-600
Works on paper
£340 $551 €496 Figures on a farm track, by a barn (24x36cm-9x14in) s.i.d.90 W/C. 30-Jul-3 Hamptons Fine Art, Godalming #72

BENNETT, Andrew (20th C) Australian
£650 $1164 €949 Britannia and Westward in close quarters in the Channel off Isle of Purbeck (76x122cm-30x48in) s.d.04. 26-May-4 Christie's, Kensington #504/R
£650 $1164 €949 J-class yachts jockeying for position at the start off Cowes (76x122cm-30x48in) s.d.04. 26-May-4 Christie's, Kensington #505/R
£850 $1522 €1241 Edwardian splendour - Big-class yachts racing on the Clyde (76x122cm-30x48in) s.d.03. 26-May-4 Christie's, Kensington #506/R

BENNETT, Brian T N (20th C) British
£360 $666 €526 Wild parsley (66x76cm-26x30in) s. 14-Jul-4 Christie's, Kensington #1096

BENNETT, Edward (19/20th C) British
£688 $1100 €1004 Old village (30x48cm-12x19in) s. i.verso. 21-Sep-3 Grogan, Boston #42/R

BENNETT, F M (1874-1953) British
£223 $400 €326 Woman with a butterfly (48x33cm-19x13in) s. 8-May-4 Susanin's, Chicago #6031/R

BENNETT, Frank (19th C) British
£460 $750 €672 Long horn highland cattle watering in a stream (100x126cm-39x50in) s. 31-Jan-3 Bigwood, Stratford on Avon #263

BENNETT, Frank Moss (1874-1953) British
£300 $525 €438 Portrait of a young soldier (48x38cm-19x15in) s. 19-Dec-3 Mallams, Oxford #251
£300 $552 €438 Great oak in Neadham churchyard (25x35cm-10x14in) s.d.1924 i.verso board. 8-Jun-4 Bonhams, Knightsbridge #84/R
£360 $662 €526 Waterfall in a wooded glade (35x25cm-14x10in) board. 8-Jun-4 Bonhams, Knightsbridge #81a
£360 $666 €526 Doctor Johnson and Boswell at Temple Bar (48x36cm-19x14in) s.d.1933 bears i. verso canvasboard. 14-Jul-4 Bonhams, Chester #436
£400 $736 €584 Front door, Hawkenbury (25x35cm-10x14in) s. i.verso board. 8-Jun-4 Bonhams, Knightsbridge #88/R
£400 $736 €584 Scullery, Hawkenbury (35x25cm-14x10in) mono.i. i.verso board. 8-Jun-4 Bonhams, Knightsbridge #90/R
£550 $1012 €803 William Poyntz and his dog Amber (36x23cm-14x9in) s.d. canvas on board. 8-Jun-4 Bonhams, Knightsbridge #85/R
£600 $1104 €876 Borden, Hawkenbury (25x35cm-10x14in) s.i. i.verso board. 8-Jun-4 Bonhams, Knightsbridge #87/R
£700 $1288 €1022 Portrait of a gentleman in a ruff and doublet (61x51cm-24x20in) i.verso After Velazquez. 8-Jun-4 Bonhams, Knightsbridge #86/R
£750 $1388 €1095 Noblemen playing chess with a Cardinal watching (28x38cm-11x15in) s.d.1936 prov. 11-Feb-4 Cheffins, Cambridge #455/R
£750 $1275 €1095 Merrymaking in a barn (38x53cm-15x21in) s. oil sketch. 30-Oct-3 Duke & Son, Dorchester #153/R
£800 $1472 €1168 Biddenden (25x35cm-10x14in) i.d.1932 verso board. 8-Jun-4 Bonhams, Knightsbridge #82/R
£850 $1360 €1241 Portrait of an Edwardian gentleman (120x80cm-47x31in) s.d.1920. 19-May-3 Bruton Knowles, Cheltenham #207/R
£1000 $1840 €1460 Squire and the keeper (41x31cm-16x12in) s.d.1927 i.verso board. 8-Jun-4 Bonhams, Knightsbridge #91/R est:1000-1500
£1100 $2024 €1606 View of a cottage, Oakridge, Gloucestershire (33x23cm-13x9in) s.d.1920 board. 8-Jun-4 Bonhams, Knightsbridge #268/R est:1000-1500
£1600 $2944 €2336 Weaver cottage, Stroud (24x34cm-9x13in) s.d.1921. 11-Jun-4 Christie's, London #204/R est:700-1000
£1700 $2669 €2465 Fly fishing (33x50cm-13x20in) s.d.1932. 27-Aug-3 Sotheby's, London #931/R est:1500-2000
£1800 $3294 €2628 Roses in a glass vase (38x51cm-15x20in) s.d.July 1951. 6-Apr-4 Bonhams, Knightsbridge #154/R est:1000-1500
£1800 $3312 €2628 Two gentlemen in historical dress on a quayside (25x35cm-10x14in) s.d.1930. 8-Jun-4 Bonhams, Knightsbridge #89/R est:1000-1500
£2200 $4048 €3212 At Bury, Sussex (24x35cm-9x14in) s. canvasboard. 11-Jun-4 Christie's, London #205/R est:600-800

£3200	$5440	€4672	Lute player (52x39cm-20x15in) s.d.1920 prov. 27-Nov-3 Sotheby's, London #433/R est:3000-4000
£3500	$5845	€5110	Midnight skittles (38x51cm-15x20in) s.d.1939. 13-Nov-3 Christie's, Kensington #284/R est:1500-2000
£5587	$10000	€9381	A question of law, four gentlemen around a dining table (33x51cm-13x20in) s.d.1930. 20-Mar-4 Pook & Pook, Downington #318/R est:4000-6000
£5800	$9860	€8468	After dinner smoke (35x49cm-14x19in) s.d.1931 canvasboard. 1-Dec-3 Bonhams, Bath #141/R est:4000-5000
£6800	$12172	€9928	Waiting for a bite (33x48cm-13x19in) s.d.1927 board. 26-May-4 Sotheby's, Olympia #144/R est:3000-5000
£7000	$12880	€10220	Heiress (40x50cm-16x20in) s.d.1947. 11-Jun-4 Christie's, London #207/R est:4000-6000
£8500	$15640	€12410	Dr Johnson of the Cheshire Chesse (37x49cm-15x19in) s.d.1947. 11-Jun-4 Christie's, London #206/R est:3000-4000
£8800	$14608	€12848	Bouquet (36x52cm-14x20in) s.d.1921. 1-Oct-3 Sotheby's, Olympia #116/R est:7000-9000
£8889	$16000	€12978	His best work (32x39cm-13x15in) s.d.1933 prov. 23-Apr-4 Sotheby's, New York #60/R est:20000-30000
£9000	$16560	€13140	Poker players in an interior (49x39cm-19x15in) s.d.1936. 11-Jun-4 Christie's, London #208/R est:4000-6000
£10000	$18400	€14600	Slight lapse. Bishop's move (51x41cm-20x16in) s.d.1935 pair. 26-Mar-4 Sotheby's, London #78/R est:10000-15000
£11667	$21000	€17034	Brothers (36x51cm-14x20in) s.d.1921. 23-Apr-4 Sotheby's, New York #61/R est:20000-30000
£14000	$25760	€20440	Game of chess (36x51cm-14x20in) s.d.1935. 23-Mar-4 Bonhams, New Bond Street #125/R est:12000-18000
£15000	$25500	€21900	Day's catch (63x76cm-25x30in) s.d.1943. 27-Nov-3 Sotheby's, London #432/R est:15000-20000
£15000	$26850	€21900	Fisherman's tale (63x76cm-25x30in) s. prov. 27-May-4 Christie's, Kensington #296/R est:12000-18000
Works on paper			
£400	$736	€584	Market square at Chartres (16x24cm-6x9in) s.d.1903 W/C. 8-Jun-4 Bonhams, Knightsbridge #79/R

BENNETT, Godwin (1888-?) British

£260	$468	€380	View of Corfe Castle (30x40cm-12x16in) s. 20-Jan-4 Bonhams, Knightsbridge #147
£420	$756	€613	Seaside view (46x56cm-18x22in) s. 20-Jan-4 Bonhams, Knightsbridge #190/R
£500	$880	€730	Interior of the Brighton pavilion (41x51cm-16x20in) s. pair. 19-May-4 Christie's, Kensington #617/R
Works on paper			
£280	$507	€409	Oriental fruit market (36x25cm-14x10in) s. W/C gouache. 16-Apr-4 Keys, Aylsham #503/R

BENNETT, Gordon (1955-) Australian

£1423	$2233	€2063	A B C D (61x72cm-24x28in) acrylic. 27-Aug-3 Christie's, Sydney #617/R est:3000-5000 (A.D 3500)
£1702	$2894	€2485	Notes to Basquiat - female pelvis (50x50cm-20x20in) s.i.d.April 1999 acrylic cotton duck exhib.prov. 25-Nov-3 Christie's, Melbourne #90/R est:4000-5000 (A.D 4000)
Works on paper			
£813	$1285	€1179	Interior, shackle (50x50cm-20x20in) s.i.d.1991 verso synthetic polymer paint canvas prov. 28-Jul-3 Sotheby's, Paddington #505/R est:2000-3000 (A.D 2000)
£6107	$11115	€8916	Home decor umbrellas (183x183cm-72x72in) s. i.d.31.3.1997 synthetic polymer prov. 16-Jun-4 Deutscher-Menzies, Melbourne #1/R est:10000-20000 (A.D 16000)
£12602	$19911	€18273	Australian icon (150x150cm-59x59in) synthetic polymer paint canvas prov.exhib.lit. 28-Jul-3 Sotheby's, Paddington #191/R est:15000-25000 (A.D 31000)

BENNETT, Jane (1960-) Australian

£484	$875	€707	Pyrmont Power Station (90x73cm-35x29in) s. oil paper. 31-Mar-4 Goodman, Sydney #465/R (A.D 1175)

BENNETT, Malcolm (1942-) British

£250	$415	€365	Nude and dream chair (50x50cm-20x20in) s. 1-Oct-3 John Ross, Belfast #192
£320	$525	€467	Abstract (61x45cm-24x18in) s. board. 4-Jun-3 John Ross, Belfast #185
£350	$581	€511	Moon shore (91x91cm-36x36in) 1-Oct-3 John Ross, Belfast #214
£400	$664	€584	Window (91x91cm-36x36in) s.verso. 1-Oct-3 John Ross, Belfast #40
£500	$830	€730	Cormorant shore (91x91cm-36x36in) s. 1-Oct-3 John Ross, Belfast #193
£1007	$1802	€1500	Cormorant shore (82x92cm-32x36in) s. i. verso. 31-May-4 Hamilton Osborne King, Dublin #38/R est:1500-2000

BENNETT, Newton (1854-1914) British

Works on paper			
£320	$579	€467	Eton College at sunset (25x37cm-10x15in) W/C prov. 18-Apr-4 Lots Road Auctions, London #336/R

BENNETT, Rainey (1907-) American

Works on paper			
£246	$450	€359	Deep blues (46x66cm-18x26in) W/C. 10-Jul-4 Hindman, Chicago #38/R

BENNETT, Ruth Manerva (1899-1960) American

£1374	$2500	€2006	Fruit trees in bloom (25x36cm-10x14in) s. board prov. 15-Jun-4 John Moran, Pasadena #117 est:1500-2000

BENNETT, William (1811-1871) British

£2500	$4475	€3650	Portrait of Robert Bullough. Portrait of his wife Sarah (76x63cm-30x25in) i. pair. 27-May-4 Christie's, Kensington #38/R est:3000-5000
Works on paper			
£400	$732	€584	On the Conway (43x60cm-17x24in) i.indis d.May 29 W/C. 27-Jan-4 Bonhams, Knightsbridge #61/R
£420	$756	€613	Windsor forest (33x46cm-13x18in) i. pencil W/C. 21-Apr-4 Tennants, Leyburn #914

BENNETT, William James (1787-1844) American

Prints			
£1351	$2500	€1972	Brisk gale, Bay of New York (50x65cm-20x26in) aquatint executed c.1784-1844. 15-Jan-4 Sotheby's, New York #129/R est:2000-3000

BENNETT, William Rubery (1893-1987) Australian

£552	$861	€800	Nolan like landscape (15x20cm-6x8in) s. i.verso board. 1-Aug-2 Joel, Victoria #185 est:1500-2000 (A.D 1600)
£857	$1346	€1251	Ebb tide, Avoca headlands (34x42cm-13x17in) s. 24-Nov-2 Goodman, Sydney #22/R est:3000-5000 (A.D 2400)
£992	$1835	€1448	Camberwarra (34x30cm-13x12in) s.d.41 canvas on board. 10-Mar-4 Deutscher-Menzies, Melbourne #499/R est:2500-3500 (A.D 2400)
£992	$1806	€1448	Lower Burragorang (24x30cm-9x12in) s. canvas on board. 16-Jun-4 Deutscher-Menzies, Melbourne #551/R est:1500-2500 (A.D 2600)
£1053	$1695	€1537	Morning, Mulgoa (14x19cm-6x7in) s. board. 13-Oct-3 Joel, Victoria #308 est:2500-3000 (A.D 2600)
£1074	$1988	€1568	Light gleams (24x30cm-9x12in) s. canvas on board prov. 10-Mar-4 Deutscher-Menzies, Melbourne #500/R est:2500-3500 (A.D 2600)
£1610	$2737	€2351	Figure rowing on a lake (24x29cm-9x11in) s. board prov. 24-Nov-3 Sotheby's, Melbourne #225/R est:3000-5000 (A.D 3800)
£1619	$2607	€2364	Nor'easter, South Coast (37x45cm-15x18in) s. bears i.verso board prov. 25-Aug-3 Sotheby's, Paddington #329/R est:4000-6000 (A.D 4000)
£1949	$3314	€2846	Storm over Robertson (35x43cm-14x17in) s. i.verso prov. 24-Nov-3 Sotheby's, Melbourne #141/R est:5000-7000 (A.D 4600)
£1983	$3511	€2895	Distant landscape (35x43cm-14x17in) s. prov. 3-May-4 Christie's, Melbourne #228/R est:5000-7000 (A.D 4800)
£2049	$3237	€2992	The crossing, Windsor Flats (51x61cm-20x24in) s. i. verso. 2-Sep-3 Deutscher-Menzies, Melbourne #166/R est:5000-7000 (A.D 5000)
£2049	$3237	€2992	Harbour Bridge from north Sydney (15x20cm-6x8in) s. i. verso board. 2-Sep-3 Deutscher-Menzies, Melbourne #168/R est:7000-10000 (A.D 5000)
£2282	$3811	€3423	Country road (56x81cm-22x32in) s. 27-Oct-3 Goodman, Sydney #158/R est:4000-6000 (A.D 5500)
£2321	$3645	€3389	Headwaters Kangaroo River, Kangaroo Valley (35x43cm-14x17in) s. 24-Nov-2 Goodman, Sydney #21/R est:7000-10000 (A.D 6500)
£2331	$3962	€3403	Boiling the Billy (37x35cm-15x14in) s. bears i.verso prov. 24-Nov-3 Sotheby's, Melbourne #193/R est:6000-8000 (A.D 5500)
£2664	$4209	€3889	Land of drought and sudden rains (51x61cm-20x24in) s. i. verso. 2-Sep-3 Deutscher-Menzies, Melbourne #165/R est:7000-9000 (A.D 6500)
£3279	$5180	€4787	Late afternoon, Loves Creek, central Australia (51x61cm-20x24in) s. 2-Sep-3 Deutscher-Menzies, Melbourne #167/R est:7000-9000 (A.D 8000)
£4237	$7203	€6186	Afternoon Currajong (48x58cm-19x23in) s. bears i.verso prov. 24-Nov-3 Sotheby's, Melbourne #202/R est:10000-15000 (A.D 10000)
£4472	$7020	€6484	Kangaroo river crossing, Burragorang Valley (59x75cm-23x30in) s. i.stretcher prov. 27-Aug-3 Christie's, Sydney #550/R est:12000-18000 (A.D 11000)
£4545	$8045	€6636	Mount MacPherson (58x74cm-23x29in) s. board prov. 3-May-4 Christie's, Melbourne #119/R est:12000-16000 (A.D 11000)
Works on paper			
£305	$556	€445	Still life with carafe and mirror (27x19cm-11x7in) s. pastel. 16-Jun-4 Deutscher-Menzies, Melbourne #562/R (A.D 800)

BENNETTE MOORE, C (20th C) American

Photographs			
£1934	$3500	€2824	Stanton Hall, Natchez, Mississippi (102x76cm-40x30in) s. hand col photograph. 3-Apr-4 Neal Auction Company, New Orleans #437/R est:1200-1800

BENNETTER, Henrik (1874-1923) Norwegian

£684	$1163	€999	Seascape with rowing boat and sailing boat (17x27cm-7x11in) s.d.7/5/92 i.verso panel. 19-Nov-3 Grev Wedels Plass, Oslo #27/R (N.KR 8000)
£1198	$2036	€1749	Seascape with vessels (31x41cm-12x16in) s.d.6/5/92 mahogany panel. 19-Nov-3 Grev Wedels Plass, Oslo #26/R est:15000-20000 (N.KR 14000)

BENNETTER, Johan Jacob (1822-1904) Norwegian

£984	$1672	€1437	Harbour view (12x16cm-5x6in) init.d.8/6 90 panel. 19-Nov-3 Grev Wedels Plass, Oslo #28/R (N.KR 11500)
£1240	$2109	€1810	White cliffs of Dover (16x28cm-6x11in) s.d.29/12-88 i.verso panel. 19-Nov-3 Grev Wedels Plass, Oslo #29/R est:12000-15000 (N.KR 14500)
£1631	$2920	€2381	Shipwreck (16x29cm-6x11in) s.d.15/4 1880 mahogany panel. 25-May-4 Grev Wedels Plass, Oslo #7/R est:20000-30000 (N.KR 20000)
£5465	$9127	€7979	Seascape with boats in stormy seas (48x75cm-19x30in) s.d.6/8 1887 panel. 13-Oct-3 Blomqvist, Oslo #258/R est:30000-40000 (N.KR 64000)

BENNO, Benjamin (1901-1980) American

Works on paper			
£326	$600	€476	Still life (15x20cm-6x8in) s.d.1936 black ink col crayon. 25-Jun-4 Freeman, Philadelphia #107/R

BENOIS, Albert Nikolaievitch (1852-1936) Russian

£5000	$8950	€7300	Parisian park in summer (29x43cm-11x17in) s.d.1929 W/C. 26-May-4 Sotheby's, London #188/R est:3000-5000
Works on paper			
£647	$1157	€945	River landscape in evening (30x22cm-12x9in) s. W/C. 13-May-4 Stuker, Bern #29/R est:1500-2000 (S.FR 1500)
£1229	$2200	€1794	Forest stream (51x33cm-20x13in) s. W/C. 7-May-4 Sloans & Kenyon, Bethesda #1640/R est:900-1200
£1300	$2210	€1898	Winter scene in provincial Russia (30x40cm-12x16in) s.d.1919 s. gouache. 19-Nov-3 Sotheby's, London #87/R est:1200-1800
£1745	$3246	€2600	Coastal landscape (32x48cm-13x19in) s.d.1914 W/C. 7-Mar-4 Bukowskis, Helsinki #486/R est:650
£2600	$4420	€3796	Ship sailing in calm seas (26x36cm-10x14in) s.d.1918 gouache. 19-Nov-3 Sotheby's, London #88/R est:1500-2000

£3587	$6600	€5237	Sunset at coast (23x38cm-9x15in) s. W/C. 26-Jun-4 Sloans & Kenyon, Bethesda #1053/R est:800-1200

BENOIS, Alexander (1870-1960) Russian

Works on paper

£350	$627	€511	Costume sketch on a postcard (14x10cm-6x4in) i. ink. 11-May-4 Sotheby's, Olympia #534/R
£661	$1123	€965	Moderato (24x30cm-9x12in) s.d.1924 i.cyrillic W/C. 5-Nov-3 Dobiaschofsky, Bern #1430/R (S.FR 1500)
£800	$1416	€1168	Design for gondola (17x30cm-7x12in) W/C ink. 27-Apr-4 Bonhams, Knightsbridge #30/R
£878	$1546	€1300	Courtisane a la robe verte (30x13cm-12x5in) s. gouache W/C. 19-May-4 Camard, Paris #103
£1000	$1790	€1460	Sketch for a costume design for two peasants from Petroushka (41x27cm-16x11in) s.i. pencil pen W/C exhib. 11-May-4 Sotheby's, Olympia #536/R est:600-800
£1000	$1790	€1460	Costume design for a lady with a falcon (24x16cm-9x6in) s.i. pencil pen black ink exhib. 11-May-4 Sotheby's, Olympia #537/R est:1400-1800
£1300	$2301	€1898	Jugglers of Notre Dame (36x25cm-14x10in) i. pencil W/C. 27-Apr-4 Bonhams, Knightsbridge #33/R est:500-700
£1500	$2685	€2190	Costume design for three peasants women (24x31cm-9x12in) i. pencil pen Indian ink W/C lit. 11-May-4 Sotheby's, Olympia #535/R est:1600-1800
£1500	$2685	€2190	Costume design for a gypsy woman from Petroushka scene IV (24x16cm-9x6in) i. pencil W/C lit. 11-May-4 Sotheby's, Olympia #538/R est:1400-1800
£1500	$2685	€2190	Costume design for the three pageboys from Swan Lake (24x15cm-9x6in) s.i.d.1945 pencil pen ink W/C. 11-May-4 Sotheby's, Olympia #539/R est:1000-1500
£2000	$3580	€2920	Costume design for tradesman from Petroushka (30x21cm-12x8in) s.i.d.1936 pencil ink W/C. 11-May-4 Sotheby's, Olympia #532/R est:2000-3000
£2000	$3580	€2920	Costume design for a drummer (31x23cm-12x9in) i. pencil ink gouache. 11-May-4 Sotheby's, Olympia #541/R est:2500-3000
£2200	$3938	€3212	Costume design for a court lady from Le Bourgeois gentilhomme (30x23cm-12x9in) s.i.d.1932 pencil brush ink W/C gouache lit. 11-May-4 Sotheby's, Olympia #540/R est:800-1200
£2222	$4000	€3244	Falstaff and the wife of the very rich merchant in Petroushka, two costume design (31x24cm-12x9in) s.d.1948 pencil W/C ink pair. 23-Apr-4 Sotheby's, New York #113/R est:4000-6000
£2244	$3500	€	Design for the stage decoration of the Nutcracker. Sketch of a church (18x27cm-7x11in) i.verso W/C ink pencil two. 11-Apr-3 Christie's, Rockefeller NY #50/R est:2000-4000
£2400	$4080	€3504	Costume designs, Rigoletto and Lady in Medieval costume (31x23cm-12x9in) both init.i.d.1937 1957 W/C ink pencil two. 19-Nov-3 Sotheby's, London #170/R est:1800-2500
£2448	$4161	€3500	Paysage (15x22cm-6x9in) s.i.d.1917 W/C. 27-Nov-3 Millon & Associes, Paris #21 est:1500
£2600	$4654	€3796	Coastal landscape (30x47cm-12x19in) i.d.1939 pencil W/C. 26-May-4 Sotheby's, Olympia #431/R est:1000-1500
£2800	$5012	€4088	Costume design for children in the Nutcracker (22x15cm-9x6in) s.i.d.1957 W/C prov. 26-May-4 Sotheby's, Olympia #404/R est:1000-1500
£3000	$5370	€4380	Costume design for a gentleman wearing the Order of St. Andrew from the Queen of Spades (28x20cm-11x8in) i. pencil pen Indian ink W/C. 11-May-4 Sotheby's, Olympia #529/R est:1200-1800
£3000	$5370	€4380	Costume design for an old lady in a ball gown from the queen of spades (28x20cm-11x8in) i. prov. pen Indian ink W/C. 11-May-4 Sotheby's, Olympia #530/R est:1200-1800
£3000	$5370	€4380	Costume design for a dandy from Petroushka (17x23cm-7x9in) s.i.verso pencil W/C prov.exhib. 11-May-4 Sotheby's, Olympia #531/R est:1200-1800
£3243	$5708	€4800	Jardin du Luxembourg (33x47cm-13x19in) s.d.1906 gouache. 19-May-4 Camard, Paris #27 est:3000-4000
£3293	$5500	€4808	Pavlovsk, pavillion of the Three Graces (29x40cm-11x16in) s. pencil W/C. 21-Oct-3 Christie's, Rockefeller NY #84 est:2000-3000
£3500	$6265	€5110	Costume design for a la cigogne from Petroushka (31x24cm-12x9in) s.i. pencil W/C prov. 11-May-4 Sotheby's, Olympia #533/R est:1600-1800
£3611	$6500	€5272	French townscape (29x36cm-11x14in) s.i.d.1925 pencil gouache. 23-Apr-4 Sotheby's, New York #109/R est:6000-8000
£3611	$6500	€5272	Boris Godunov and Swan lake, two costume designs (27x19cm-11x7in) init. pencil W/C pair. 23-Apr-4 Sotheby's, New York #112/R est:4000-6000
£4000	$6800	€5840	Set design for Il Tovatore (27x40cm-11x16in) s.d.18.1X.48 W/C over pencil. 19-Nov-3 Sotheby's, London #168/R est:4000-6000
£5000	$8950	€7300	Set design for the gambling scene from Queen of Spades (28x47cm-11x19in) s.d.1919 i.d.verso W/C gouache. 26-May-4 Sotheby's, London #212/R est:5000-7000
£5500	$9845	€8030	Stage design for the Bal Masque from the Queen of Spades (31x45cm-12x18in) s.d.1921 W/C over pencil. 26-May-4 Sotheby's, London #211/R est:5000-7000
£6000	$10200	€8760	Country House interior (29x41cm-11x16in) s. indis.d. W/C over pencil. 19-Nov-3 Sotheby's, London #187/R est:4000-6000
£6757	$12095	€10000	Costume sketches. s. mixed media four. 8-May-4 Bukowskis, Helsinki #447/R est:10000-13000
£8000	$14320	€11680	View of Peterhof (18x26cm-7x10in) s.i.d.1900 W/C over pencil. 26-May-4 Sotheby's, London #227/R est:3000-4000
£8084	$13500	€11803	Costume design for La Foule des spectateurs, in Petrouchka (26x46cm-10x18in) s. pencil ink W/C paper on cardboard. 21-Oct-3 Christie's, Rockefeller NY #105 est:14000-16000
£10000	$17900	€14600	Character from the theatre (30x41cm-12x16in) s.d.1945 W/C. 26-May-4 Sotheby's, Olympia #403/R est:3000-4000
£15000	$26850	€21900	Villa in Cassis (44x58cm-17x23in) s.i.d.1931 W/C over pencil. 26-May-4 Sotheby's, London #224/R est:4000-6000
£16667	$30000	€24334	Palatial fountain and garden (56x69cm-22x27in) s.d.18.VII gouache. 23-Apr-4 Sotheby's, New York #110/R est:18000-25000
£20000	$35800	€29200	Stage design for Swan lake (32x45cm-13x18in) s.i. pencil W/C. 26-May-4 Sotheby's, Olympia #400/R est:1500-2000
£23000	$41170	€33580	Set design for Giselle act 1 (50x64cm-20x25in) s.i.verso W/C. 26-May-4 Sotheby's, London #218/R est:10000-15000
£40000	$68000	€58400	Marriage of Psyche and Amour, the Arrival of Psyche (65x111cm-26x44in) s.i.d.1928 pencil ink W/C gouache. 19-Nov-3 Sotheby's, London #171/R est:7000-9000

BENOIS, Alexander (attrib) (1870-1960) Russian

Works on paper

£2000	$3400	€2920	Chicken coup (23x31cm-9x12in) d.1953 W/C over pencil. 19-Nov-3 Sotheby's, London #169/R est:1000-1500

BENOIS, Nadia (1896-1975) Russian

£340	$622	€496	Still life of flowers in a vase (56x41cm-22x16in) s. 27-Jan-4 Gorringes, Lewes #1731
£500	$835	€730	Still life (42x34cm-17x13in) s. 16-Oct-3 Christie's, Kensington #352
£520	$920	€759	Peonies and wild roses in a vase (61x47cm-24x19in) s.d.46 prov. 27-Apr-4 Bonhams, Knowle #146
£676	$1189	€1000	Children playing in the river (45x35cm-18x14in) 19-May-4 Camard, Paris #101
£1400	$2464	€2044	Open window (51x63cm-20x25in) s. 19-May-4 Sotheby's, Olympia #189/R est:1200-1800
£1700	$3179	€2550	Paris street scene (56x66cm-22x26in) s.d.1933. 22-Jul-4 Gorringes, Lewes #1864/R est:350-400
£1788	$3200	€2610	Concert (64x90cm-25x35in) s.d.1937. 14-May-4 Skinner, Boston #373/R est:1500-2500
£1800	$3330	€2628	Summer flowers (61x44cm-24x17in) s.d.40 prov. 11-Feb-4 Sotheby's, Olympia #120/R est:1500-2000

Works on paper

£260	$468	€380	Costume design for the Sleeping Princess, Sadlers Wells (38x28cm-15x11in) s. pen wash. 21-Apr-4 Brightwells, Leominster #689

BENOIS, Nicola (1901-1988) Russian

Works on paper

£3000	$5370	€4380	Theatre designs (19x29cm-7x11in) s.i.25-28 pastel pen ink gouache two exhib. 26-May-4 Sotheby's, Olympia #401/R est:1200-1800

BENOIST, Philippe and CICERI, Eugene (19th C) French

Prints

£12000	$18600	€17520	Rio de Janeiro de Castella (61x86cm-24x34in) hand col lithograph two. 26-Sep-2 Christie's, London #114/R est:6000-8000

BENOIT, Camille (1820-1882) French

£461	$770	€650	Entre amis (16x26cm-6x10in) s.i.d.6-2-80 panel. 19-Jun-3 Millon & Associes, Paris #93
£638	$1066	€900	Sans famille (16x21cm-6x8in) s. panel. 19-Jun-3 Millon & Associes, Paris #94/R

BENOIT, Jacqueline (1928-) French?

£385	$662	€550	Bouquet (24x16cm-9x6in) s. 3-Dec-3 Tajan, Paris #151
£755	$1200	€1102	Landscape with colonnade and white lilies (55x38cm-22x15in) s.d.66 prov. 13-Sep-3 Weschler, Washington #685/R
£979	$1684	€1400	Bouquet de fleurs (73x50cm-29x20in) s. 3-Dec-3 Tajan, Paris #150/R est:800-1000
£979	$1684	€1400	Jeune fille a la rose (34x22cm-13x9in) s.d. 3-Dec-3 Tajan, Paris #168/R est:800-1000

BENOIT, Jean (1922-) Canadian

Sculpture

£5782	$10350	€8500	Vivre vit (93cm-37in) init.i.d.1989 wood phallic cane lit. 21-Mar-4 Calmels Cohen, Paris #88/R est:5000-10000

Works on paper

£2381	$4262	€3500	Untitled (48x64cm-19x25in) s.d.1942 pastel. 21-Mar-4 Calmels Cohen, Paris #7/R est:3000-4000

BENOLDI, Walter (20th C) Italian

£492	$900	€718	Homage to women's portraiture (30x15cm-12x6in) s. panel. 31-Jul-4 Sloans & Kenyon, Bethesda #1226/R

BENOUVILLE, Francois Léon (1821-1859) French

£2797	$4755	€4000	La peche et la chasse (105x78cm-41x31in) s.d.1856 lit. 27-Nov-3 Millon & Associes, Paris #117/R est:4000-5000

BENOUVILLE, Jean-Achille (1815-1891) French

£2303	$4237	€3500	Vue de la campagne romaine (25x56cm-10x22in) s.i.d.69 panel. 23-Jun-4 Millon & Associes, Paris #46/R est:3000-4000

Works on paper

£800	$1448	€1200	Vallee et village avec des ruines antiques (29x44cm-11x17in) st. graphite estompe. 30-Mar-4 Rossini, Paris #899
£1667	$3017	€2500	Parc dominant la Seine (27x45cm-11x18in) s.i.d.1872 W/C exhib.lit. 31-Mar-4 Sotheby's, Paris #118/R est:2500-3500
£5634	$9860	€8000	Ruines d'aqueducs antiques dans la campagne Romaine (20x40cm-8x16in) s.d.1858 W/C. 16-Dec-3 Artcurial Briest, Paris #241/R est:8000-10000

BENRATH, Frederic (1930-) French

£280	$467	€400	Composition (73x50cm-29x20in) s.d.1968 verso acrylic gouache paper on cardboard prov. 29-Jun-3 Versailles Encheres #24/R
£400	$720	€600	Embruns (92x72cm-36x28in) s.d.1982 verso. 20-Apr-4 Chenu & Scrive, Lyon #27/R

Works on paper

£276	$461	€400	Composition nuagiste (25x25cm-10x10in) init.d.1987 mixed media. 17-Nov-3 Charbonneaux, Paris #115

BENSA, Alexander von (1820-1902) Austrian

£1737	$3074	€2536	At the market place in Szolnok (22x34cm-9x13in) s. cardboard. 28-Apr-4 Kieselbach, Budapest #23/R (H.F 650000)
£2416	$4518	€3600	Hunting scenes (15x21cm-6x8in) mono.i. two. 24-Feb-4 Dorotheum, Vienna #197/R est:2500-3000
£3800	$6878	€5548	Hunt (45x73cm-18x29in) 31-Mar-4 Bonhams, Knightsbridge #87/R est:4000-6000

BENSA, Francesco (1830-?) Italian
Works on paper
£471 $800 €688 Villa Capponi (29x42cm-11x17in) s.d.1860 gouache. 21-Nov-3 Skinner, Boston #235/R

BENSA, Giuseppe (19th C) European
£1043 $1700 €1512 Pensive peasant woman with water jug (43x30cm-17x12in) s.d.1875 panel. 19-Jul-3 New Orleans Auction, New Orleans #533/R est:1800-2500

BENSA, Joseph (?) ?
£856 $1600 €1250 Woman with parasol (41x30cm-16x12in) s.i. 25-Feb-4 Doyle, New York #43/R est:2500-3500

BENSCO, Charles J (1894-1960) American
£435 $700 €635 Two figures playing instruments (89x84cm-35x33in) s. masonite. 24-Aug-3 Bonhams & Butterfields, Los Angeles #7023

BENSELL, George Frederick (1837-1879) American
£1359 $2500 €1984 Seascape (33x64cm-13x25in) s. 11-Jun-4 David Rago, Lambertville #240/R est:2000-4000
£1734 $3000 €2532 Portrait of a boy with a dog (127x102cm-50x40in) s. 10-Dec-3 Alderfer's, Hatfield #327/R est:1500-2000
£2123 $3800 €3564 Luminescent winter landscape of a sawmill (76x127cm-30x50in) s.d.1873. 20-Mar-4 Pook & Pook, Downington #194/R est:3500-4500
£20000 $35800 €30000 Esther accusant Amann (157x243cm-62x96in) s. 17-May-4 Chayette & Cheval, Paris #169/R est:30000-40000

BENSELL, George Frederick (attrib) (1837-1879) American
£1326 $2400 €1936 Western landscape (76x127cm-30x50in) 3-Apr-4 Neal Auction Company, New Orleans #603/R est:3000-5000

BENSEMANN, Leo (1912-1986) New Zealander
£1264 $2060 €1845 Portrait of Lawrence Baigent (37x30cm-15x12in) i.verso board painted c.1936 prov. 23-Sep-3 Peter Webb, Auckland #47/R est:2000-3000 (NZ.D 3500)
£3971 $6473 €5798 Self portrait with mask (29x20cm-11x8in) canvas on board prov. 23-Sep-3 Peter Webb, Auckland #46/R est:3000-5000 (NZ.D 11000)
£11552 $18830 €16866 Self Portrait (34x31cm-13x12in) s.d.1938 board prov. 23-Sep-3 Peter Webb, Auckland #45/R est:15000-25000 (NZ.D 32000)
Works on paper
£903 $1471 €1318 Tahunanui. Trees. Study of hands. two init. one d.1 May W/C ink pencil three prov. 23-Sep-3 Peter Webb, Auckland #51/R (NZ.D 2500)
£978 $1555 €1428 Mask (32x21cm-13x8in) s. W/C. 9-Sep-3 Watson's, Christchurch #47 (NZ.D 2700)
£1083 $1765 €1581 Portrait of Lawrence Baigent (29x22cm-11x9in) pencil prov. 23-Sep-3 Peter Webb, Auckland #48/R est:1500-2500 (NZ.D 3000)
£1083 $1765 €1581 On the way to Brightwater, railway bridge (27x36cm-11x14in) s. W/C exec. c.1933-1935 prov. 23-Sep-3 Peter Webb, Auckland #50/R est:2000-3000 (NZ.D 3000)
£1444 $2354 €2108 Looking towards Taylor's Mistake and the Heads of Lyttelton Harbour (37x26cm-15x10in) s. W/C exec. c.1933-1935 prov. 23-Sep-3 Peter Webb, Auckland #49/R est:2000-3000 (NZ.D 4000)

BENSO, Giulio (1601-1668) Italian
Works on paper
£1701 $3044 €2500 Sainte Francoise Romaine guerissant un enfant muet (28x19cm-11x7in) black chk pen brown ink wash. 18-Mar-4 Christie's, Paris #60/R est:1500-2000

BENSO, Giulio (attrib) (1601-1668) Italian
Works on paper
£855 $1574 €1300 Eternal (22x28cm-9x11in) pen ink pencil. 22-Jun-4 Sotheby's, Milan #94/R est:1500-2000

BENSON, Ambrosius (?-1550) Flemish
£3472 $5729 €5000 Madonna with Infant Jesus and St Joseph (58x50cm-23x20in) panel. 3-Jul-3 Dr Fritz Nagel, Stuttgart #430/R est:6000
£23684 $42868 €36000 Saint Andrew (46x39cm-18x15in) board. 14-Apr-4 Ansorena, Madrid #132/R est:36000

BENSON, Ambrosius (attrib) (?-1550) Flemish
£17000 $29410 €24820 Sibyl, wearing a fur-trimmed black and gold embroidered dress (62x46cm-24x18in) panel prov. 10-Dec-3 Christie's, London #18/R est:20000-30000

BENSON, Ambrosius (circle) (?-1550) Flemish
£20000 $34600 €29200 Saint Adrian with a male donor. Saint Anne with the virgin and child and a female donor (42x12cm-17x5in) panel prov. two. 11-Dec-3 Sotheby's, London #113/R est:15000-20000

BENSON, Ambrosius (studio) (?-1550) Flemish
£21918 $37260 €32000 Crucifixion (59x97cm-23x38in) board triptych. 4-Nov-3 Ansorena, Madrid #45/R est:30000

BENSON, Frank W (1862-1951) American
£1650 $2607 €2409 Quartich duck studies. Pair of geese. pair. 6-Sep-3 Shapes, Edinburgh #360
£45455 $80000 €66364 Harold D Walker and Katherine M Walker (63x76cm-25x30in) s.d.1895 prov. 18-May-4 Christie's, Rockefeller NY #43/R est:120000-180000
£272727 $480000 €398181 Lower Camp Pool (81x102cm-32x40in) s.d.28 prov. 18-May-4 Christie's, Rockefeller NY #57/R est:300000-500000
Works on paper
£18519 $30000 €26853 Along the shore (36x57cm-14x22in) s.d.30 W/C prov. 8-Aug-3 Barridorf, Portland #349/R est:25000-35000
£21176 $36000 €30917 Eiders in flight (51x69cm-20x27in) s. W/C en grisaille prov. 21-Nov-3 Skinner, Boston #348/R est:30000-50000
£58140 $100000 €84884 At sundown (53x47cm-21x19in) s. W/C pencil executed 1931 prov. 3-Dec-3 Sotheby's, New York #132/R est:40000-60000

BENSON, John Miles (1889-?) British
£500 $880 €730 Multiple portrait of the artist's wife (174x121cm-69x48in) 19-May-4 Sotheby's, Olympia #111/R
£750 $1320 €1095 Artist's wife in the Charlotte Street studio (175x152cm-69x60in) s. 19-May-4 Sotheby's, Olympia #110/R

BENSON, John P (1865-1947) American
£2235 $4000 €3263 Italian port view with ornate galleon (86x152cm-34x60in) s.d.1923 s.i.d.1923 verso. 14-May-4 Skinner, Boston #146/R est:4000-6000
£2374 $4250 €3466 Columbus' ships coming to America (81x226cm-32x89in) s.d.1923. 14-May-4 Skinner, Boston #144/R est:4000-6000

BENT, Ian (1945-) Australian
£1240 $2293 €1810 Figures in the park (59x76cm-23x30in) s. board. 10-Mar-4 Deutscher-Menzies, Melbourne #514/R est:600-900 (A.D 3000)

BENT, Jan van der (1650-1690) Dutch
£1773 $2961 €2500 Halte dans les ruines (59x83cm-23x33in) panel. 14-Oct-3 Vanderkindere, Brussels #128

BENT, Medora Heather (1901-1992) British/Irish
£2300 $4209 €3358 St Ives, panoramic view (91x122cm-36x48in) s. 3-Jun-4 Lane, Penzance #185/R est:2000-3000
Works on paper
£1544 $2732 €2300 The Island, St Ives (41x51cm-16x20in) s.d.1942 W/C gouache. 27-Apr-4 Whyte's, Dublin #70/R est:1500-2000

BENTABOLE, Louis (?-1880) French
£3333 $6100 €5000 Place animee a Dieppe (56x44cm-22x17in) s. panel. 6-Jun-4 Osenat, Fontainebleau #187/R est:6500-7500

BENTELI, Wilhelm Bernhard (1839-1924) Swiss
£776 $1389 €1133 Lake Geneva with dents du Midi (50x73cm-20x29in) s.d.1875. 13-May-4 Stuker, Bern #30/R est:2000-3000 (S.FR 1800)

BENTIVOGLIO, Cesare (1868-1952) Italian
£652 $1070 €900 Trees along the river (44x20cm-17x8in) init. 27-May-3 Finarte Semenzato, Milan #14/R
£690 $1145 €1000 Love declaration (75x43cm-30x17in) s. board. 1-Oct-3 Della Rocca, Turin #216/R
£1042 $1771 €1500 Landscape with herd (50x98cm-20x39in) s. lit. 1-Nov-3 Meeting Art, Vercelli #173 est:1000
£1159 $1901 €1600 Seascape at sunset (31x47cm-12x19in) init. cardboard. 27-May-3 Finarte Semenzato, Milan #16/R
£1769 $3166 €2600 Mountainous landscape in summer (80x140cm-31x55in) s. 22-Mar-4 Sant Agostino, Torino #244/R est:3500

BENTIVOGLIO, Gaetano II (18th C) Italian
Works on paper
£738 $1321 €1100 Prospettiva della Piazza S Marco (44x70cm-17x28in) i. brush graphite. 25-May-4 Karl & Faber, Munich #7/R

BENTLEY, Alfred (1879-1923) British
£700 $1253 €1022 Rhodez, France street scene with figures (39x29cm-15x11in) s.i. s.verso. 16-Mar-4 Bonhams, Oxford #55

BENTLEY, Charles (1806-1854) British
£680 $1258 €993 Figures and horse on the shore (25x38cm-10x15in) W/C. 14-Jul-4 Bonhams, Chester #492
Works on paper
£260 $478 €380 Snowdon (12x19cm-5x7in) s. W/C. 11-Jun-4 Keys, Aylsham #278
£300 $537 €438 Cutter running out to meet the new arrival (33x50cm-13x20in) indis.s.d. pencil W/C htd. bodycol. 26-May-4 Christie's, Kensington #407/R
£550 $1018 €803 Travellers outside a French town (10x15cm-4x6in) init. pencil W/C. 10-Mar-4 Sotheby's, Olympia #135/R
£1100 $1969 €1606 Crowded Channel off Dover (51x74cm-20x29in) s. pencil W/C scratching out gum Arabic. 26-May-4 Christie's, Kensington #405/R est:1000-1500
£1300 $2405 €1898 Shipping off Scarborough (29x41cm-11x16in) W/C pencil bodycol. 14-Jul-4 Sotheby's, Olympia #50/R est:1500-2000

BENTLEY, Claude (1915-1990) American
£824 $1400 €1203 Red core (122x122cm-48x48in) s.verso oil on linen. 9-Nov-3 Wright, Chicago #385 est:500-700

BENTLEY, John W (1880-1951) American
£865 $1600 €1263 House in the forest (51x61cm-20x24in) s. 10-Mar-4 Doyle, New York #6/R est:1500-2000
£1118 $1800 €1632 Late autumn in Woodstock (20x25cm-8x10in) s. board. 20-Aug-3 James Julia, Fairfield #1809/R est:400-600
£1765 $3000 €2577 December afternoon (30x41cm-12x16in) s. i.verso board prov. 18-Nov-3 John Moran, Pasadena #187 est:800-1200
£4491 $7500 €6557 Bearsville Bridge (64x76cm-25x30in) s. i.verso prov. 23-Oct-3 Shannon's, Milford #91/R est:4000-6000

£5689 $9500 €8306 Village road (51x62cm-20x24in) s. i.stretcher. 9-Oct-3 Christie's, Rockefeller NY #48/R est:6000-8000

BENTLEY, Lucy (1968-) British
Works on paper
£500 $880 €730 Celebration (21x27cm-8x11in) s. W/C. 18-May-4 Woolley & Wallis, Salisbury #29/R

BENTON, Fletcher (1931-) American
Sculpture
£2206 $3750 €3221 Synchromatic (196x53cm-77x21in) mixed media sculpture. 9-Nov-3 Bonhams & Butterfields, Los Angeles #4103/R est:3000-5000

BENTON, Thomas Hart (1889-1975) American
£8075 $13000 €11790 The judge (51x38cm-20x15in) s. W/C prov. 20-Aug-3 James Julia, Fairfield #1242/R est:4000-8000
£21591 $38000 €31523 Study for Sorghum Mill (16x22cm-6x9in) s.d.68 tempera board prov. 18-May-4 Christie's, Rockefeller NY #92/R est:20000-30000
£46512 $80000 €67908 Profile of an old man (61x46cm-24x18in) s. tempera canvas on board prov. 3-Dec-3 Sotheby's, New York #75/R est:30000-50000
£116279 $200000 €169767 Flood (40x51cm-16x20in) s.d.38 s.i.d.verso oil tempera on gessoed panel prov. 3-Dec-3 Sotheby's, New York #74/R est:80000-120000
£180233 $310000 €263140 Politics, farming and law in Missouri, mural study for the Jefferson City capitol building (46x72cm-18x28in) s.i.verso tempera oil on board prov.lit. 3-Dec-3 Sotheby's, New York #76/R est:300000-400000
£450581 $775000 €657848 Cotton picker (56x60cm-22x24in) s. tempera on masonite painted c.1943 prov.exhib. 3-Dec-3 Sotheby's, New York #67/R est:500000-700000
Prints
£1676 $3000 €2447 Haystack (26x31cm-10x12in) s. lithograph. 6-May-4 Swann Galleries, New York #399/R est:2500-3500
£1676 $3000 €2447 Boy (24x35cm-9x14in) s. lithograph. 6-May-4 Swann Galleries, New York #403/R est:2000-3000
£1734 $3000 €2532 Ten pound hammer (25x35cm-10x14in) s. lithograph edition of 300 prov. 13-Dec-3 Weschler, Washington #626 est:3000-5000
£1863 $3000 €2720 Wyoming autumn (43x86cm-17x34in) s. lithograph prov. 20-Aug-3 James Julia, Fairfield #1249/R est:1000-2000
£1875 $3000 €2738 Wreck of the old 97 (25x38cm-10x15in) lithograph. 16-Sep-3 Lincoln, Orange #505
£2353 $4000 €3435 Repairing the sloop (35x46cm-14x18in) s. lithograph edition of 250. 6-Nov-3 Swann Galleries, New York #499a/R est:2000-3000
£2473 $4500 €3611 Wreck of the old (38x25cm-15x10in) s. lithograph. 19-Jun-4 Rachel Davis, Shaker Heights #55 est:3000-5000
£2695 $4500 €3935 Departure of the Joads (30x46cm-12x18in) lithograph. 17-Oct-3 Du Mouchelle, Detroit #2027/R est:2000-3500
£3593 $6000 €5246 Huck Finn (55x41cm-22x16in) s. lithograph edition of 100. 21-Oct-3 Bonhams & Butterfields, San Francisco #1016/R
£3824 $6500 €5583 Race (23x34cm-9x13in) s. lithograph. 4-Nov-3 Christie's, Rockefeller NY #2/R est:4000-6000
Works on paper
£369 $650 €539 Rita's house, Chilmark (25x36cm-10x14in) s. ink wash dr prov. 3-Jan-4 Collins, Maine #47/R
£447 $800 €653 Prayer (15x13cm-6x5in) graphite lit. 16-May-4 Wright, Chicago #178/R
£466 $750 €680 Buffalo study (20x28cm-8x11in) s. pencil prov. 20-Aug-3 James Julia, Fairfield #1246/R
£782 $1400 €1142 Landscape with trees and a barn (25x30cm-10x12in) s. pencil. 8-May-4 Susanin's, Chicago #6068/R est:1500-2400
£838 $1500 €1223 Struggle for the wilderness and retribution (18x23cm-7x9in) graphite lit. 16-May-4 Wright, Chicago #177/R est:1500-2000
£870 $1400 €1270 Site of Ft Union drawn from Bodmer's position (20x30cm-8x12in) s.i. pencil prov. 20-Aug-3 James Julia, Fairfield #1247/R est:1500-2500
£1397 $2250 €2040 Mushroom (13x10cm-5x4in) s. W/C prov. 20-Aug-3 James Julia, Fairfield #1244/R est:1000-2000
£1506 $2500 €2199 Swamp (25x48cm-10x19in) init. pencil. 4-Oct-3 Neal Auction Company, New Orleans #467/R est:4000-6000
£2143 $3750 €3129 Mural study for Cultural Progress (15x74cm-6x29in) i. ink pencil prov. 19-Dec-3 Sotheby's, New York #1026/R est:2500-3500
£2143 $3750 €3129 Mural study for Cultural Progress (16x63cm-6x25in) ink pencil prov. 19-Dec-3 Sotheby's, New York #1027/R est:2500-3500
£2174 $4000 €3174 Parrot tulips. Study of two oak trees (24x27cm-9x11in) s. one d.45 chl. 8-Jun-4 Bonhams & Butterfields, San Francisco #4104/R est:3000-5000
£2198 $4000 €3209 Captain Bradford (30x23cm-12x9in) s.i. ink wash prov.lit. 29-Jun-4 Sotheby's, New York #265/R est:5000-7000
£2639 $4250 €3853 Still life of fruit, bowl and knife (15x15cm-6x6in) s. W/C prov. 20-Aug-3 James Julia, Fairfield #1245/R est:1500-2500
£2907 $5000 €4244 House boat (15x18cm-6x7in) s. W/C ink pencil exec.c.1930. 7-Dec-3 Treadway Gallery, Cincinnati #681/R est:5000-7000
£3106 $5000 €4535 Woman at bar (20x18cm-8x7in) s. pencil W/C prov. 20-Aug-3 James Julia, Fairfield #1248/R est:1500-2500
£3198 $5500 €4669 Flooded house (15x18cm-6x7in) s. W/C ink pencil exec.c.1930. 7-Dec-3 Treadway Gallery, Cincinnati #680/R est:5000-7000
£4503 $7250 €6574 The steamboat, Cincinnaati (20x28cm-8x11in) s. W/C ink prov. 20-Aug-3 James Julia, Fairfield #1243/R est:2000-3000
£23256 $40000 €33954 Ozark river (36x43cm-14x17in) s.d.63 ink wash prov. 4-Dec-3 Christie's, Rockefeller NY #102/R est:20000-30000
£51136 $90000 €74659 People of Chilmark - study (33x41cm-13x16in) s. W/C pencil exec c.1922 prov. 19-May-4 Sotheby's, New York #109/R est:40000-60000
£187500 $330000 €273750 Two horses grazing in a desert landscape (43x76cm-17x30in) s.d.52 gouache paper on panel prov. 19-May-4 Sotheby's, New York #122/R est:150000-200000

BENTOS, A (?) Belgian
£621 $1030 €900 Portrait of soldier (140x77cm-55x30in) 6-Oct-3 Amberes, Antwerp #203

BENTZEN, Axel (1893-1952) Danish
£280 $439 €409 Part of a window (100x71cm-39x28in) init. 30-Aug-3 Rasmussen, Havnen #4131/R (D.KR 3000)
£308 $551 €450 Rainbow over village, figure in foreground (127x135cm-50x53in) init. 10-May-4 Rasmussen, Vejle #704 (D.KR 3400)
£329 $560 €480 Coastal landscape with walkers (61x70cm-24x28in) init. prov. 29-Nov-3 Rasmussen, Havnen #4073/R (D.KR 3500)
£341 $613 €498 Summer's day at Svineryggen (60x70cm-24x28in) init. 24-Apr-4 Rasmussen, Havnen #4086 (D.KR 3800)
£361 $667 €527 Reclining female nude (75x100cm-30x39in) init.d.24 exhib. 15-Mar-4 Rasmussen, Vejle #579 (D.KR 4000)
£395 $672 €577 Figures at Bakken (55x63cm-22x25in) s. 29-Nov-3 Rasmussen, Havnen #4356 (D.KR 4200)
£542 $996 €791 Interior scene with hyacinths by open window (100x80cm-39x31in) init. 29-Mar-4 Rasmussen, Copenhagen #558/R (D.KR 6000)
£582 $1048 €850 Interior scene with young woman at window (110x93cm-43x37in) init.i.d.1937 verso. 24-Apr-4 Rasmussen, Havnen #4210 (D.KR 6500)
£611 $1040 €892 From a graveyard (83x71cm-33x28in) init.d.21. 29-Nov-3 Rasmussen, Havnen #4302 (D.KR 6500)

BENVENISTE, Joyce (20th C) ?
£1608 $2734 €2300 Banboo (112x146cm-44x57in) s.verso acrylic. 27-Nov-3 Calmels Cohen, Paris #114/R est:1800-2500

BENVENUTI, Benvenuto (1881-1959) Italian
£4000 $6400 €5800 Willow tree by a goldfish pond (49x30cm-19x12in) s. board. 18-Sep-3 Christie's, Kensington #106/R est:2000-3000
£13333 $24533 €20000 Landscape with hut (40x66cm-16x26in) 11-Jun-4 Farsetti, Prato #554/R est:18000-25000

BENVENUTI, Eugenio (19/20th C) Italian
Works on paper
£318 $550 €464 Venetian canal with gondola and gondolier (38x23cm-15x9in) s. W/C. 10-Dec-3 Alderfer's, Hatfield #306/R
£650 $1021 €943 Canal Grande. Palazzo Ducale (25x38cm-10x15in) s. pencil W/C pair. 28-Aug-3 Christie's, Kensington #408/R

BENVENUTI, Pietro (1769-1844) Italian
£19310 $32248 €28000 Self-portrait in green coat (72x58cm-28x23in) 12-Nov-3 Sotheby's, Milan #125/R est:20000-30000

BENVENUTI, Tito (20th C) Italian
Works on paper
£791 $1298 €1100 Adam and Eve (58x42cm-23x17in) i.d.1949 pencil. 10-Jun-3 Pandolfini, Florence #41

BENWELL, Joseph Austin (fl.1865-1886) British
Works on paper
£2200 $3784 €3212 Arabs with their camels by temple ruins (30x48cm-12x19in) s.d.1873 pencil W/C. 3-Dec-3 Christie's, Kensington #70/R est:2000-3000
£2300 $3910 €3358 Head of the caravan (22x46cm-9x18in) W/C. 4-Nov-3 Bonhams, New Bond Street #94/R est:2000-3000
£2500 $4300 €3650 Watering the camels (49x99cm-19x39in) s.d.1875 W/C. 4-Dec-3 Christie's, Kensington #224/R est:3000-5000
£4000 $7080 €5840 Camel train in the desert (27x47cm-11x19in) s.d. W/C bodycol. 27-Apr-4 Bonhams, New Bond Street #67/R est:4000-6000
£5000 $9100 €7300 Caravan with the Pyramids and Sphinx beyond (49x72cm-19x28in) s.d.1868 W/C htd white. 17-Jun-4 Christie's, London #122/R est:6000-9000
£6690 $11574 €9500 Men praying in the desert (39x51cm-15x20in) s. W/C. 15-Dec-3 Gros & Delettrez, Paris #305/R est:8000-10000

BENZ, J Albert (attrib) (1846-1926) Swiss
£996 $1782 €1454 Still life of fruit (49x65cm-19x26in) s.d. 22-Mar-4 Philippe Schuler, Zurich #4305/R est:1300-1700 (S.FR 2300)

BENZI, Giulio (1907-1955) Italian
£638 $1066 €900 Monferrato Hills (40x50cm-16x20in) s. s.i.verso board. 20-Oct-3 Sant Agostino, Torino #164/R
£733 $1349 €1100 Robilante (49x61cm-19x24in) s.d.1950. 14-Jun-4 Sant Agostino, Torino #210/R

BENZONI, Giovanni Maria (1809-1873) Italian
Sculpture
£18000 $32940 €26280 Bust of Spring (68cm-27in) s.d.1851 marble. 9-Jul-4 Sotheby's, London #105/R est:20000-30000

BEOGNARD, W J (19th C) Dutch
£2428 $4200 €3545 Farm stables (48x69cm-19x27in) s. 13-Dec-3 Charlton Hall, Columbia #359/R est:800-1200

BEOTHY, Étienne (1897-1961) Hungarian
Sculpture
£1667 $2983 €2500 Positive-negative (69x6x43cm-27x2x17in) relief artificial stone. 14-May-4 Ketterer, Munich #181/R est:2500-3500
£4167 $6583 €6000 Suzanne (47cm-19in) s. num.3/6 brown pat bronze Cast Blanchet prov.lit. 27-Apr-3 Versailles Encheres #101
Works on paper
£1736 $2899 €2500 Abstract composition (26x36cm-10x14in) mono. pastel over pencil. 24-Oct-3 Ketterer, Hamburg #276/R est:3000-4000

BEOTHY-STEINER, Anna (1902-1985) Hungarian
£2349 $4064 €3430 Pink composition (53x39cm-21x15in) s. tempera paper. 12-Dec-3 Kieselbach, Budapest #189/R (H.F 900000)
£3393 $5870 €4954 Great red composition (56x44cm-22x17in) s.d.1934 tempera paper. 12-Dec-3 Kieselbach, Budapest #149/R (H.F 1300000)

BERAIN, Jean I (1640-1711) French
Works on paper
£8333 $15000 €12166 Design for a fireplace with a medallion of King Louis XIV (27x18cm-11x7in) i.mount black lead pen black ink grey wash. 22-Jan-4 Christie's, Rockefeller NY #93/R est:15000-20000

BERAIN, Jean I (attrib) (1640-1711) French
Works on paper
£2177 $3897 €3200 La proue de vaisseau Le Volontaire (52x36cm-20x14in) i. graphite pen grey ink wash. 18-Mar-4 Christie's, Paris #118/R est:3000-5000
£2857 $5114 €4200 La poupe du vaisseau Le Volontaire (54x33cm-21x13in) i. graphite pen grey ink wash. 18-Mar-4 Christie's, Paris #117/R est:4000-6000

BERALDO, Franco (1944-) Italian
£352 $585 €500 Tivoli (50x60cm-20x24in) s. d.1986 verso. 14-Jun-3 Meeting Art, Vercelli #152
£352 $585 €500 Landscape (50x40cm-20x16in) s. 14-Jun-3 Meeting Art, Vercelli #428/R
£433 $797 €650 Still life (50x40cm-20x16in) s. s.verso. 12-Jun-4 Meeting Art, Vercelli #543/R
£433 $797 €650 Landscape (35x50cm-14x20in) s. s.verso. 12-Jun-4 Meeting Art, Vercelli #677/R
£467 $859 €700 Landscape (30x40cm-12x16in) s. painted 1992. 12-Jun-4 Meeting Art, Vercelli #160/R
£470 $869 €700 Landscape (35x45cm-14x18in) s. painted 1993. 13-Mar-4 Meeting Art, Vercelli #138
£537 $993 €800 Venice (33x48cm-13x19in) s. board. 13-Mar-4 Meeting Art, Vercelli #426
£599 $994 €850 Paesaggio (40x50cm-16x20in) s. 14-Jun-3 Meeting Art, Vercelli #192/R
£775 $1286 €1100 Still life (50x60cm-20x24in) s. 14-Jun-3 Meeting Art, Vercelli #657/R
£1007 $1862 €1500 Terrace of memories (50x60cm-20x24in) s. 13-Mar-4 Meeting Art, Vercelli #535
£1074 $1987 €1600 Still life (40x50cm-16x20in) s.s.verso fresco. 13-Mar-4 Meeting Art, Vercelli #210 est:1000
Works on paper
£867 $1595 €1300 Big island (40x50cm-16x20in) s. s.verso fresco on canvas. 12-Jun-4 Meeting Art, Vercelli #961/R

BERAN, Aljo (1907-) Czechoslovakian
£329 $613 €480 Summer landscape at the Hana Region (68x98cm-27x39in) s.d.42 board. 6-Mar-4 Dorotheum, Prague #110/R est:12000-18000 (C.KR 16000)

BERANGER, Antoine (1785-1867) French
Works on paper
£455 $773 €650 Deux guerriers au repos (18x24cm-7x9in) s.d.1818 pen brown ink htd white. 1-Dec-3 Coutau Begarie, Paris #153

BERANGER, Charles (attrib) (1816-1853) French
£374 $700 €561 Young girl holding a jug by a stream (33x24cm-13x9in) 25-Jul-4 Bonhams & Butterfields, San Francisco #6063/R

BERANN, Heinrich (1915-) Austrian
£638 $1066 €900 Creation - study for triptych (22x42cm-9x17in) s.i. verso masonite. 16-Oct-3 Dorotheum, Salzburg #694/R

BERARD, Christian (1902-1949) French
£3000 $5370 €4500 Portrait de jeune femme au foulard (54x32cm-21x13in) s. cardboard. 17-May-4 Sotheby's, Paris #8/R est:5000-8000
£3667 $6637 €5500 Portrait de Pierre Andre May (73x54cm-29x21in) s.d.26 s.i.d.verso. 4-Apr-4 St-Germain-en-Laye Encheres #10/R est:4500
£7382 $13067 €11000 Portrait d'un danseur (89x58cm-35x23in) s.d.31 prov. 27-Apr-4 Artcurial Briest, Paris #173/R est:8000-9000
Works on paper
£233 $425 €350 Portrait of a man (10x7cm-4x3in) mono. ink wash gouache. 30-Jun-4 Calmels Cohen, Paris #46/R
£266 $485 €400 Portrait of a man (11x6cm-4x2in) s. ink wash gouache. 30-Jun-4 Calmels Cohen, Paris #47/R
£276 $458 €400 Modele (30x22cm-12x9in) s. ink wash. 6-Oct-3 Blanchet, Paris #197/R
£276 $458 €400 Femme (30x22cm-12x9in) s.i. wash. 6-Oct-3 Blanchet, Paris #200
£300 $546 €450 Sports reunis (13x21cm-5x8in) s. W/C in, wash. 30-Jun-4 Calmels Cohen, Paris #39/R
£333 $606 €500 Hotel (11x15cm-4x6in) s. ink W/C wash. 30-Jun-4 Calmels Cohen, Paris #43/R
£366 $667 €550 Bathers (12x23cm-5x9in) s. ink W/C pastel. 30-Jun-4 Calmels Cohen, Paris #33/R
£372 $702 €550 Elegante au chien (12x26cm-5x10in) s. W/C. 21-Feb-4 Cornette de St.Cyr, Paris #182
£399 $727 €600 Couple dancing (22x10cm-9x4in) s. ink. 30-Jun-4 Calmels Cohen, Paris #49/R
£433 $789 €650 At the door (17x13cm-7x5in) s. ink W/C gouache. 30-Jun-4 Calmels Cohen, Paris #40/R
£433 $789 €650 Bedroom (9x12cm-4x5in) s. ink W/C gouache. 30-Jun-4 Calmels Cohen, Paris #42/R
£448 $744 €650 Loge (35x22cm-14x9in) Chinese ink. 6-Oct-3 Blanchet, Paris #194/R
£448 $744 €650 Maison aux colonnades (24x30cm-9x12in) s. gouache. 6-Oct-3 Blanchet, Paris #198
£466 $849 €700 Conversation (17x24cm-7x9in) s. wash ink gouache. 30-Jun-4 Calmels Cohen, Paris #32/R
£466 $849 €700 Card players (14x13cm-6x5in) s. ink. 30-Jun-4 Calmels Cohen, Paris #48/R
£533 $970 €800 At the window (15x12cm-6x5in) s. W/C gouache. 30-Jun-4 Calmels Cohen, Paris #41/R
£533 $970 €800 Bonne vie (25x23cm-10x9in) s.i. W/C ink pastel. 30-Jun-4 Calmels Cohen, Paris #45/R
£633 $1153 €950 Hotel (22x15cm-9x6in) s. ink W/C wash. 30-Jun-4 Calmels Cohen, Paris #35/R
£733 $1334 €1100 Bathers (23x17cm-9x7in) s. ink W/C pastel. 30-Jun-4 Calmels Cohen, Paris #31/R
£909 $1545 €1300 Personnage (20x26cm-8x10in) s.i.d.45 Indian ink drawing. 1-Dec-3 Camard, Paris #95
£1034 $1717 €1500 Etude de figures (42x26cm-17x10in) s. pen Chinese ink wash. 6-Oct-3 Blanchet, Paris #203
£1300 $2340 €1898 Le bal, robe de soir (32x49cm-13x19in) i. ink W/C bodycol double-sided prov. 21-Apr-4 Lyon & Turnbull, Edinburgh #241/R est:1000-1500
£1974 $3572 €3000 Portraits et paysage (49x34cm-19x13in) pastel W/C. 18-Apr-4 Rouillac, Vendome #103
£3147 $5413 €4500 Les Goudes (47x62cm-19x24in) bears st.sig. W/C gouache exhib. 3-Dec-3 Beaussant & Lefèvre, Paris #18/R est:1500-2000

BERARD, Christian and KLASSEN-SMITH, Margaret (20th C) French
Works on paper
£3357 $5706 €4800 Guerlain (52x60cm-20x24in) i. col leather on leather two parts over wood. 24-Nov-3 Tajan, Paris #88/R est:5000-6000

BERARDO, Ignazio (1888-1978) Italian
£268 $475 €400 Streams (50x40cm-20x16in) s.d.1958 board. 1-May-4 Meeting Art, Vercelli #184

BERAUD, Jean (1849-1936) French
£9412 $16000 €13742 Parisienne au rond-point des Champs Elysees (41x27cm-16x11in) s. panel painted c.1905 lit. 28-Oct-3 Sotheby's, New York #158/R est:12000-18000
£10000 $18000 €14600 Une jeune Parisienne (36x20cm-14x8in) s. panel. 22-Apr-4 Christie's, Rockefeller NY #183/R est:15000-20000
£12778 $23000 €18656 Escrimeuses (41x52cm-16x20in) s. panel lit. 23-Apr-4 Sotheby's, New York #104/R est:25000-35000
£20833 $37500 €30416 Le trottin (38x51cm-15x20in) panel exhib.lit. 23-Apr-4 Sotheby's, New York #105/R est:35000-50000
£58824 $100000 €85883 Cafe Scene (37x45cm-15x18in) s. prov.exhib.lit. 28-Oct-3 Sotheby's, New York #10/R est:120000-180000
£67647 $115000 €98765 Bal a la Presidence (49x91cm-19x36in) s. prov.lit. 29-Oct-3 Christie's, Rockefeller NY #173/R est:40000-60000
£71329 $121259 €102000 Devant la bijouterie (40x32cm-16x13in) s. panel prov.exhib.lit. 24-Nov-3 Boscher, Cherbourg #720/R est:40000-45000
£88235 $150000 €128823 Scene du rue Parisienne (46x32cm-18x13in) s. prov.lit. 29-Oct-3 Christie's, Rockefeller NY #174/R est:200000-300000
£117647 $200000 €171765 La sortie du bourgeos (37x53cm-15x21in) s. panel painted 1889 prov.lit. 29-Oct-3 Christie's, Rockefeller NY #177/R est:220000-260000
£309859 $536056 €440000 Reunion publique a la Salle Graffard (80x120cm-31x47in) s.d.1884. 10-Dec-3 Beaussant & Lefèvre, Paris #65/R est:400000-600000
Works on paper
£5882 $10000 €8588 Devant le Palais de l'Industrie, Paris (41x59cm-16x23in) init. pencil black ink W/C prov. 29-Oct-3 Christie's, Rockefeller NY #171/R est:10000-15000
£5882 $10000 €8588 La promenade (47x34cm-19x13in) s. pencil black ink W/C prov.lit. 29-Oct-3 Christie's, Rockefeller NY #172/R est:10000-15000

BERBER, Mersad (1940-) Yugoslavian
Works on paper
£757 $1400 €1105 Women through the ages (61x51cm-24x20in) mixed media exec.c.1993. 16-Feb-4 Quinn's, Falls Church #528/R
£838 $1500 €1223 Boguhil (63x42cm-25x17in) s. mixed media. 21-Mar-4 Bonhams & Butterfields, Los Angeles #7133/R est:100-150
£1290 $2192 €1883 Little Infantin (41x41cm-16x16in) s. mixed media. 19-Nov-3 Fischer, Luzern #1185/R est:5000-7000 (S.FR 2850)
£3631 $6500 €5301 Infant Margarita (160x118cm-63x46in) s. mixed media two. 21-Mar-4 Bonhams & Butterfields, Los Angeles #7132/R est:300-500

BERBERIAN, Ovanes (20th C) American
£450 $850 €657 In the Arroyo seco (30x41cm-12x16in) s.d.83 i.d. verso masonite prov. 17-Feb-4 John Moran, Pasadena #180a/R
£1005 $1900 €1467 View Pasadena (38x61cm-15x24in) s.d.83 i. verso board prov. 17-Feb-4 John Moran, Pasadena #180/R est:1500-2250

BERBERICH, Fritz (1904-1984) German?
£1141 $2088 €1700 Composition (51x67cm-20x26in) s.d.1964 board. 9-Jul-4 Dawo, Saarbrucken #187/R est:1400

BERCHEM, Nicolaes (1620-1683) Dutch
£333 $607 €500 Shepherd playing the flute (18x15cm-7x6in) panel. 1-Jul-4 Weidler, Nurnberg #363
£948 $1697 €1384 Herdswoman in idealised landscape (50x59cm-20x23in) 13-May-4 Stuker, Bern #32/R est:2000-2500 (S.FR 2200)
£5913 $10584 €8633 Canal landscape in winter with figures (35x41cm-14x16in) s. panel. 25-May-4 Bukowskis, Stockholm #501/R est:80000-100000 (S.KR 80000)
£10000 $18300 €14600 Italianate landscape (50x68cm-20x27in) bears sig panel. 8-Jul-4 Sotheby's, London #286/R est:12000-18000
£30000 $54000 €43800 Italianate river landscape with drovers at a ford at dusk (24x31cm-9x12in) s. panel prov. 21-Apr-4 Christie's, London #33/R est:40000-60000
£60000 $109800 €87600 Italianate landscape with lady riding (53x64cm-21x25in) s. prov.exhib.lit. 8-Jul-4 Sotheby's, London #124/R est:60000-80000
£909091 $1563636 €1300000 Guitar player (84x78cm-33x31in) s. prov.lit. 2-Dec-3 Christie's, Paris #723/R est:100000-150000
Works on paper
£1333 $2387 €2000 Campagna landscape with shepherdess on horse (20x28cm-8x11in) chk wash. 13-May-4 Bassenge, Berlin #5029/R est:1500
£4392 $7730 €6500 River landscape with herdsmen and their cattle (25x40cm-10x16in) black chk prov.lit. 19-May-4 Sotheby's, Amsterdam #94/R est:7000-9000

£40845 $71479 €58000 Vaches traversant un gue avec un couple et un chien (14x18cm-6x7in) s.d.1656 black chk pen brown ink col wash prov. 17-Dec-3 Christie's, Paris #26/R est:15000-20000

BERCHEM, Nicolaes (attrib) (1620-1683) Dutch
£1773 $2961 €2500 Paysans et cavaliers pres d'une riviere (39x53cm-15x21in) panel. 17-Oct-3 Tajan, Paris #49 est:1200-1500
£2956 $5292 €4316 Landscape with herders (47x68cm-19x27in) s. panel prov. 26-May-4 AB Stockholms Auktionsverk #2521/R est:50000-60000 (S.KR 40000)
Works on paper
£380 $657 €555 Wooded hillside landscape scene with figures and animals (31x44cm-12x17in) black chk laid down prov. 9-Dec-3 Bonhams, Knightsbridge #30/R
£881 $1498 €1286 Peasants with cattle (47x41cm-19x16in) i. W/C. 5-Nov-3 Dobiaschofsky, Bern #1098/R (S.FR 2000)

BERCHEM, Nicolaes (circle) (1620-1683) Dutch
£1773 $2961 €2500 Herders watering animals (57x74cm-22x29in) 17-Oct-3 Berlinghof, Heidelberg #1006/R est:3700
Works on paper
£3611 $6500 €5272 Man leaning on a rifle seen from behind (29x16cm-11x6in) black white chk. 21-Jan-4 Sotheby's, New York #64/R est:3000-5000

BERCHEM, Nicolaes (school) (1620-1683) Dutch
£507 $907 €750 Herder landscape (38x52cm-15x20in) canvas on board. 8-May-4 Hans Stahl, Toestorf #96

BERCHEM, Nicolaes (style) (1620-1683) Dutch
£13287 $22189 €19000 Landscape with travellers (94x133cm-37x52in) 7-Oct-3 Pandolfini, Florence #623/R est:20000-23000

BERCHERE, Narcisse (1819-1891) French
£2000 $3680 €3000 Le campement (15x31cm-6x12in) s. panel. 14-Jun-4 Gros & Delettrez, Paris #536/R est:1500-2000
£2809 $5027 €4101 Caravan of camels resting (23x37cm-9x15in) s.d.1857 panel. 28-May-4 Uppsala Auktionskammare, Uppsala #120/R est:30000-40000 (S.KR 38000)
£4225 $7310 €6000 Halte des chameliers (27x38cm-11x15in) s. panel. 15-Dec-3 Gros & Delettrez, Paris #449/R est:5000-6000
£4500 $7515 €6570 Une halte dans le desert (30x40cm-12x16in) s. panel prov. 14-Oct-3 Sotheby's, London #96/R est:5000-7000
Works on paper
£300 $543 €450 Ruines et colonnes a Louxor (13x20cm-5x8in) pierre noire htd white. 30-Mar-4 Rossini, Paris #905
£430 $783 €650 Paysage au soleil couchant (7x32cm-3x13in) i.verso W/C. 16-Jun-4 Piasa, Paris #164
£599 $1036 €850 Nomade dans l'Atlas (17x26cm-7x10in) s. mixed media cardboard. 15-Dec-3 Gros & Delettrez, Paris #236

BERCHERE, Narcisse (attrib) (1819-1891) French
£272 $500 €397 Loading the boats (28x41cm-11x16in) 26-Jun-4 Susanin's, Chicago #6046/R

BERCHMANS, Émile (1867-1947) Belgian
£428 $787 €650 Allegorical scene (36x45cm-14x18in) s. 22-Jun-4 Palais de Beaux Arts, Brussels #198
£2533 $4535 €3800 Lecon de danse (90x50cm-35x20in) s. prov.lit. 15-May-4 De Vuyst, Lokeren #550/R est:4000-5000

BERCHMANS, Henri (19/20th C) ?
£400 $720 €600 La couseuse (46x38cm-18x15in) s. 20-Apr-4 Galerie Moderne, Brussels #265/R
£789 $1429 €1200 Dusk (102x150cm-40x59in) s. 14-Apr-4 Ansorena, Madrid #33/R

BERCHMANS, Jules (1883-1951) Belgian
£839 $1401 €1200 Le petit dejeuner (64x92cm-25x36in) s. 13-Oct-3 Horta, Bruxelles #221

BERCKHEYDE, Gerrit Adriaensz (1638-1698) Dutch
£5500 $10065 €8030 Nieuwemarket, Amsterdam, from the Geldersekade with the tower of the Zuiderkerk (29x41cm-11x16in) bears sig panel prov. 7-Jul-4 Bonhams, New Bond Street #1/R est:6000-8000
£21333 $38187 €32000 View of the north transept of the St Bavo Church (59x46cm-23x18in) s. panel prov.lit. 17-May-4 Christie's, Amsterdam #112/R est:20000-30000

BERCKHEYDE, Gerrit Adriaensz (attrib) (1638-1698) Dutch
£2973 $5232 €4400 Church interior (51x40cm-20x16in) panel. 22-May-4 Lempertz, Koln #1013/R est:4000

BERCKHEYDE, Job Adriaensz (1630-1693) Dutch
£6704 $12000 €9788 Young scholar reading by lamplight in study with ecorche model and plaster head of putto on table (67x58cm-26x23in) indis.sig. prov. 27-May-4 Sotheby's, New York #22/R est:15000-20000

BERCKHEYDE, Job Adriaensz (attrib) (1630-1693) Dutch
£3067 $5489 €4600 Les joueurs de quilles (57x87cm-22x34in) bears sig. 11-May-4 Vanderkindere, Brussels #240/R est:3750-5000
£3429 $5486 €4972 Amsterdam stock exchange (46x58cm-18x23in) 15-May-3 Stuker, Bern #1061/R est:8000-12000 (S.FR 7200)

BERCKHOLTZ, Alexandra von (1821-1899) Russian
£2923 $5028 €4268 Carnations in vase (49x38cm-19x15in) s.d.1846 panel. 3-Dec-3 AB Stockholms Auktionsverk #2565/R est:10000-12000 (S.KR 38000)

BERCZY, William (snr) (1744-1813) Canadian
Miniatures
£1700 $2890 €2482 Lady wearing white veil trimmed with pearls (4cm-2in) oval. 18-Nov-3 Bonhams, New Bond Street #91/R est:250-350

BERDAL, Alex (1945-) French
£559 $1029 €850 Confidence (73x60cm-29x24in) s. i.verso. 25-Jun-4 Millon & Associes, Paris #252/R

BERDANIER, Paul F (1879-1961) American
£543 $1000 €815 Near Valley Park (28x36cm-11x14in) s. board exhib. 26-Jun-4 Selkirks, St. Louis #139

BERDELLE, Johann Baptist (1813-1876) German
£699 $1203 €1000 Bust portrait of a young woman (55x47cm-22x19in) s.d.1840. 5-Dec-3 Bolland & Marotz, Bremen #508/R

BERDIA, Norberto (1900-1983) Uruguayan
£309 $500 €448 Three ranches (54x65cm-21x26in) s. 29-Jul-3 Galeria y Remates, Montevideo #102/R

BERDTSEN, B (?) Danish?
£341 $546 €498 Mountain landscape, Norway in summer (98x110cm-39x43in) s. 22-Sep-3 Rasmussen, Vejle #328/R (D.KR 3600)

BERDYSZAK, Jan (1934-) American?
£240 $435 €350 Abstract (55x55cm-22x22in) s.d.1975 Indian ink mixed media. 4-Apr-4 Agra, Warsaw #25/R (P.Z 1700)
Works on paper
£636 $1150 €929 Composition (70x43cm-28x17in) s.d.1968 gouache Indian ink pen. 4-Apr-4 Agra, Warsaw #55/R (P.Z 4500)

BERENTZ, Christian (1658-1722) German
£16667 $30000 €24334 Peaches and figs on a pewter platter, glass and vessel with Bohemian covered goblets (65x50cm-26x20in) prov. 23-Jan-4 Christie's, Rockefeller NY #36/R est:30000-50000

BERENTZ, Christian (circle) (1658-1722) German
£5500 $10065 €8030 Fruit on draped table (97x73cm-38x29in) 9-Jul-4 Christie's, Kensington #126/R est:4000-6000

BERENTZEN, Paul (?) Scandinavian
£976 $1795 €1464 Drying clothes on a Danish frigate (79x116cm-31x46in) s. 14-Jun-4 Blomqvist, Lysaker #1035/R (N.KR 12000)

BERENY, Robert (1887-1953) Hungarian
£26100 $45153 €38106 Girl on a sofa with cat (77x91cm-30x36in) s. 12-Dec-3 Kieselbach, Budapest #139/R (H.F 10000000)
£41760 $72245 €60970 Houses in Monaco (59x48cm-23x19in) s.d.1905 cardboard. 12-Dec-3 Kieselbach, Budapest #173/R (H.F 16000000)

BERESFORD, Cecilia Melanie (fl.1865-1885) British
Works on paper
£260 $481 €380 Portrait of an Italian girl (17x15cm-7x6in) init.d.1878 W/C oval. 9-Mar-4 Bonhams, Knightsbridge #70/R
£580 $1073 €847 Portrait of an Italian boy on a chair (16x13cm-6x5in) init.d.1878 W/C oval. 9-Mar-4 Bonhams, Knightsbridge #68/R

BERESFORD, Frank Ernest (1881-1967) British
£300 $501 €438 In the garden of Dendy Sadley (25x36cm-10x14in) s.d.1919 panel. 20-Jun-3 Chrystals Auctions, Isle of Man #263/R

BERETTA, Petrus Augustus (1805-1866) Dutch
£1250 $2000 €1825 Church interior (33x23cm-13x9in) board. 19-Sep-3 Du Mouchelle, Detroit #2018/R est:2500-3500

BEREZNICKI, Kiejstut (1935-) Polish
£1977 $3579 €2886 People (110x110cm-43x43in) 4-Apr-4 Agra, Warsaw #17/R (P.Z 14000)

BERG, Adolf Julius (1820-1873) Swedish
£350 $594 €500 Rowing trip (30x30cm-12x12in) s.d.1859. 29-Nov-3 Bukowskis, Helsinki #357/R
£614 $1002 €896 Mountain landscape (71x94cm-28x37in) s.indis.d. 29-Sep-3 Lilla Bukowskis, Stockholm #921 (S.KR 8000)

BERG, Adrian (1929-) British
£450 $716 €657 Gloucester Gate, Regents Park (97x97cm-38x38in) s.d.April 81 prov. 1-May-3 John Nicholson, Haslemere #707/R
Works on paper
£300 $501 €438 Beachy Head, 30 October (30x40cm-12x16in) s. i.d.95 verso pastel prov. 21-Oct-3 Bonhams, Knightsbridge #7/R

BERG, Albert (1832-1916) Swedish
£659 $1232 €962 Coastal cliffs with breakers (112x75cm-44x30in) s.d.78. 29-Feb-4 Uppsala Auktionskammare, Uppsala #280 (S.KR 9000)

BERG, Anna Carolina van den (1873-1942) Dutch
£694 $1097 €1000 Still life of tulips in a vase (37x46cm-15x18in) canvas on plywood. 2-Sep-3 Christie's, Amsterdam #221 est:1000-1500
£2105 $3874 €3200 Flower Still life with roses (58x47cm-23x19in) 28-Jun-4 Sotheby's, Amsterdam #114/R est:800-1200

BERG, Christian (1893-1976) Swedish
Sculpture
£2711 $4798 €3958 Torso - relief (34x15cm-13x6in) s. pat.bronze Cast Rosengren lit. 27-Apr-4 AB Stockholms Auktionsverk #857/R est:20000-25000 (S.KR 37000)
£2930 $5187 €4278 Torso playing (20cm-8in) init.num.3/5 polished bronze incl. marble base prov.exhib.lit. 27-Apr-4 AB Stockholms Auktionsverk #855/R est:25000-30000 (S.KR 40000)
£10989 $19451 €16044 Church sculpture I (56cm-22in) init.num.5/5 silvered bronze incl.stone socle lit. 27-Apr-4 AB Stockholms Auktionsverk #858/R est:175000-200000 (S.KR 150000)

BERG, E (20th C) Dutch
Works on paper
£664 $1129 €950 Farmer sitting with a cow and a goat with an industrial town in background (64x50cm-25x20in) chl. 24-Nov-3 Glerum, Amsterdam #529/R

BERG, Else (1877-1942) Dutch
£455 $773 €650 Sailing ship on the sea (27x35cm-11x14in) tripex. 24-Nov-3 Glerum, Amsterdam #512/R
£839 $1427 €1200 Portrait of a boy (35x27cm-14x11in) triplex. 24-Nov-3 Glerum, Amsterdam #511/R
£1119 $1902 €1600 Mother with child (37x28cm-15x11in) paper. 24-Nov-3 Glerum, Amsterdam #562/R
£1538 $2615 €2200 Nude female sitting (50x42cm-20x17in) s. paper. 24-Nov-3 Glerum, Amsterdam #561/R
£1678 $2853 €2400 Two trees along a path, a tree in the background (35x27cm-14x11in) triplex. 24-Nov-3 Glerum, Amsterdam #509/R
£2238 $3804 €3200 Woman sitting in a garden in front of a house (77x102cm-30x40in) 24-Nov-3 Glerum, Amsterdam #505/R
£4133 $7564 €6200 Madonna with Child (102x90cm-40x35in) 7-Jun-4 Glerum, Amsterdam #131/R est:6000-8000
£4336 $7371 €6200 Portrait of a woman, dressed in a blue sweater (88x77cm-35x30in) s.i. 24-Nov-3 Glerum, Amsterdam #501/R
£9441 $16049 €13500 Portrait of a small boy with a toy rabbit in a box (46x38cm-18x15in) s. 24-Nov-3 Glerum, Amsterdam #503/R
£21333 $39253 €32000 Circus met gitaar (63x72cm-25x28in) s. painted c.1929 prov.exhib.lit. 9-Jun-4 Christie's, Amsterdam #234/R est:18000-22000
Works on paper
£280 $476 €400 Mine construction (64x50cm-25x20in) chl. 24-Nov-3 Glerum, Amsterdam #528/R
£282 $519 €420 Reclining female nude (26x39cm-10x15in) s. pencil. 29-Mar-4 Glerum, Amsterdam #64
£315 $535 €450 Two woman in a Mediterranean city port (30x20cm-12x8in) s.i.d.1931 Indian ink col chk. 24-Nov-3 Glerum, Amsterdam #564/R
£315 $535 €450 Young man nude, standing and viewed from the back (35x27cm-14x11in) s.i. chl. 24-Nov-3 Glerum, Amsterdam #571/R
£336 $571 €480 Mountain village with bridge over a river (47x64cm-19x25in) chl. 24-Nov-3 Glerum, Amsterdam #527/R
£336 $571 €480 Portrait of a woman in between two dolls (65x50cm-26x20in) s. Indian ink. 24-Nov-3 Glerum, Amsterdam #535/R
£336 $571 €480 Portrait of a woman (61x48cm-24x19in) s. pastel. 24-Nov-3 Glerum, Amsterdam #563/R
£385 $654 €550 Industrial town with cow on hill in front (30x38cm-12x15in) chl. 24-Nov-3 Glerum, Amsterdam #530/R
£385 $654 €550 Reclining female nude (47x50cm-19x20in) brown chk. 24-Nov-3 Glerum, Amsterdam #566/R
£420 $713 €600 Hens in a yard with sunflowers, houses and trees (64x49cm-25x19in) s. chl. 24-Nov-3 Glerum, Amsterdam #522/R
£420 $713 €600 Three clowns (51x41cm-20x16in) chl red chk. 24-Nov-3 Glerum, Amsterdam #531/R
£434 $737 €620 Trees in front of a mountain village (63x47cm-25x19in) chl W/C. 24-Nov-3 Glerum, Amsterdam #507/R
£455 $773 €650 Portrait of a man with moustache (52x44cm-20x17in) Indian ink. 24-Nov-3 Glerum, Amsterdam #506/R
£455 $773 €650 Mountain village with a path in the foreground (35x48cm-14x19in) chl red chk. 24-Nov-3 Glerum, Amsterdam #518/R
£455 $773 €650 Two trees in front of house (63x48cm-25x19in) chl. 24-Nov-3 Glerum, Amsterdam #525/R
£455 $773 €650 Man and woman sitting at a table in an interior. Woman sitting (65x50cm-26x20in) chl double-sided. 24-Nov-3 Glerum, Amsterdam #539/R
£490 $832 €700 Portrait of a lady (30x22cm-12x9in) s. pencil black chk. 24-Nov-3 Glerum, Amsterdam #513/R
£545 $927 €780 Portrait of a woman with her children in front of an industrial landscape (65x50cm-26x20in) s. chl. 24-Nov-3 Glerum, Amsterdam #538/R
£559 $951 €800 Young female nude, standing (51x42cm-20x17in) s. brown chk. 24-Nov-3 Glerum, Amsterdam #565/R
£594 $1010 €850 Young farmer (75x50cm-30x20in) Indian ink. 24-Nov-3 Glerum, Amsterdam #514/R
£594 $1010 €850 Activity near a stone factory (28x37cm-11x15in) s. Indian ink. 24-Nov-3 Glerum, Amsterdam #532/R
£594 $1010 €850 Farmer milking with three cows in a farmyard near an industrial town (65x50cm-26x20in) chl. 24-Nov-3 Glerum, Amsterdam #533/R
£664 $1129 €950 Children of the nation, the boy proletariat (65x50cm-26x20in) i.verso chl. 24-Nov-3 Glerum, Amsterdam #537/R
£699 $1189 €1000 Woman on a path in front of an Italian mountain village (26x19cm-10x7in) s. mixed media. 24-Nov-3 Glerum, Amsterdam #517/R
£909 $1545 €1300 Mountain village (18x24cm-7x9in) s. col chk. 24-Nov-3 Glerum, Amsterdam #508/R
£909 $1545 €1300 Portrait of a man and a woman with industrial estate as background (50x65cm-20x26in) s. chl. 24-Nov-3 Glerum, Amsterdam #536/R
£979 $1664 €1400 Mountain village (25x27cm-10x11in) s. chl W/C. 24-Nov-3 Glerum, Amsterdam #510/R
£1049 $1783 €1500 Man sitting with hands folded, in front of an industrial town (65x50cm-26x20in) s. chl. 24-Nov-3 Glerum, Amsterdam #542/R
£1119 $1902 €1600 Man and woman sitting near a stove, heating a kettle (65x50cm-26x20in) s. chl. 24-Nov-3 Glerum, Amsterdam #540/R
£1259 $2140 €1800 Three heads of men (52x44cm-20x17in) s. chl. 24-Nov-3 Glerum, Amsterdam #541/R
£1399 $2378 €2000 Mountain village with bridge in foreground (43x53cm-17x21in) s. chl red chk. 24-Nov-3 Glerum, Amsterdam #516/R

BERG, Freek van den (1918-2000) Dutch
£757 $1392 €1150 Donkey on the beach (39x38cm-15x15in) s. d.66 verso board. 28-Jun-4 Sotheby's, Amsterdam #245/R
£769 $1308 €1100 Landscape with trees (70x90cm-28x35in) s.d.73. 24-Nov-3 Glerum, Amsterdam #23/R
£1224 $2229 €1800 Seated girl with hat (60x50cm-24x20in) s. 3-Feb-4 Christie's, Amsterdam #553 est:2000-3000

BERG, Georg Backer (1900-1980) Norwegian
£285 $524 €416 Smygehaalaa in Stavanger (31x46cm-12x18in) s. i.stretcher. 10-Jun-4 Grev Wedels Plass, Oslo #158/R (N.KR 3500)

BERG, George Louis (1870-1941) American
£469 $750 €685 Landscape Connecticut Woods (30x41cm-12x16in) s.d.1917 panel. 22-Sep-3 O'Gallerie, Oregon #730/R
£475 $850 €694 Landscape with trees, distant hills (30x41cm-12x16in) s. s.verso fiberboard. 29-May-4 Brunk, Ashville #77/R
£1141 $2100 €1666 After the rain (51x61cm-20x24in) s. s.i.d.1927 verso board. 26-Jun-4 Sloans & Kenyon, Bethesda #1094/R est:2000-2500

BERG, Gunnar (1864-1894) Norwegian
£5551 $9270 €8104 The milk boat, possibly Svolvaer (35x57cm-14x22in) s. 13-Oct-3 Blomqvist, Oslo #252/R est:70000-90000 (N.KR 65000)

BERG, Hannes (20th C) German
£352 $599 €514 Herd of cows (70x100cm-28x39in) s.i. 5-Nov-3 Dobiaschofsky, Bern #347/R (S.FR 800)

BERG, Jan van den (1932-) Dutch
£625 $1150 €950 Synthetic garden (60x70cm-24x28in) s.d.83 i. on stretcher tempera oil board. 22-Jun-4 Christie's, Amsterdam #369/R

BERG, Jos van den (1905-1978) Dutch
£685 $1164 €1000 Railway track (39x64cm-15x25in) s. 5-Nov-3 Vendue Huis, Gravenhage #412/R

BERG, Kees van den (1923-) Dutch
£526 $968 €800 View of Enkhuizen (50x60cm-20x24in) s. 28-Jun-4 Sotheby's, Amsterdam #163/R

BERG, Peter (20th C) American?
Works on paper
£889 $1600 €1298 Neo-garfish. Drawing A202 (80x42cm-31x17in) one s.i.d.1983 pastel one s.d.1980 graphite ink two. 24-Apr-4 David Rago, Lambertville #43/R est:300-600

BERG, Siep van den (1913-) Dutch
£1007 $1862 €1500 View of a landscape (38x49cm-15x19in) s.d.50 board prov. 15-Mar-4 Sotheby's, Amsterdam #183/R est:1500-2000
£1342 $2483 €2000 Flower still life (70x50cm-28x20in) s.d.52 prov. 15-Mar-4 Sotheby's, Amsterdam #187/R est:2000-3000
£1745 $3228 €2600 Korenschoven, Zuidlaren (60x81cm-24x32in) s.d.50 prov. 15-Mar-4 Sotheby's, Amsterdam #184/R est:2000-3000
£1812 $2971 €2500 Composition (90x60cm-35x24in) painted c.1960 prov. 27-May-3 Sotheby's, Amsterdam #364/R est:2000-3000
£2013 $3725 €3000 Boats at the beach, South of France (66x80cm-26x31in) s.d.52 prov. 15-Mar-4 Sotheby's, Amsterdam #185/R est:3000-5000
£3478 $5704 €4800 Still life with fruit (60x50cm-24x20in) s.i. on stretcher prov. 27-May-3 Sotheby's, Amsterdam #360/R est:3500-4500

BERG, Simon van den (1812-1891) Dutch
£1053 $1905 €1600 Red spotted cow with her calves in a Dutch landscape (17x23cm-7x9in) s. panel. 19-Apr-4 Glerum, Amsterdam #43/R est:1800-2200
£1974 $3572 €3000 Landscape with shepherd and shepherdess resting with their herd (53x66cm-21x26in) indis.s. 19-Apr-4 Glerum, Amsterdam #55/R est:3000-4000
£3000 $5400 €4500 Watering the cattle in a vast landscape (66x100cm-26x39in) s. panel. 21-Apr-4 Christie's, Amsterdam #11/R est:4000-6000

BERG, Svante (1885-1946) Swedish
£363 $653 €530 Coastal meadow, Kampinge (31x42cm-12x17in) s.d.34 panel. 26-Apr-4 Bukowskis, Stockholm #7/R (S.KR 5000)
£1360 $2311 €1986 Still life of anemones (81x65cm-32x26in) s.d.41. 5-Nov-3 AB Stockholms Auktionsverk #870/R est:20000-25000 (S.KR 18000)

BERG, Werner (1904-1981) Austrian
£17483 $29720 €25000 Winter cherry (38x78cm-15x31in) mono. 25-Nov-3 Hassfurther, Vienna #19/R est:22000-27000
£30405 $53514 €45000 Girl with trees (90x63cm-35x25in) mono. 19-May-4 Dorotheum, Klagenfurt #3/R est:20000
Prints
£2098 $3566 €3000 Waiting between the tracks (22x58cm-9x23in) s.mono.i. woodcut. 19-Nov-3 Dorotheum, Klagenfurt #78/R est:1800

Works on paper
£658 $1211 €1000 Untitled (15x20cm-6x8in) mono.d.1960 pencil. 22-Jun-4 Wiener Kunst Auktionen, Vienna #350/R

BERG, Willem van den (1886-1970) Dutch
£445 $757 €650 Portrait of a fisherman (12x8cm-5x3in) s. panel. 5-Nov-3 Vendue Huis, Gravenhage #371
£467 $854 €700 Portrait of a lady (41x26cm-16x10in) s. panel. 7-Jun-4 Glerum, Amsterdam #345/R
£860 $1462 €1256 Heads of two fishermen (16x12cm-6x5in) s.d.1929 panel. 19-Nov-3 Fischer, Luzern #2017/R (S.FR 1900)
£1250 $2300 €1900 Harvester (42x52cm-17x20in) s. 28-Jun-4 Sotheby's, Amsterdam #228/R est:1500-2000
£1736 $2743 €2500 Hurkende Volendammer - Squatting Volendam people (28x28cm-11x11in) s. i.verso board painted c.1921. 2-Sep-3 Christie's, Amsterdam #364/R est:2000-3000
£2500 $4250 €3650 Old cronies (40x50cm-16x20in) s. board prov. 19-Nov-3 Bonhams & Butterfields, San Francisco #67/R
£5903 $9858 €8500 Two volendam fishermen (71x71cm-28x28in) s. 21-Oct-3 Sotheby's, Amsterdam #162/R est:4000-6000
Works on paper
£490 $842 €700 Fisherman (52x39cm-20x15in) mono.d.43 pastel black chk prov. 8-Dec-3 Glerum, Amsterdam #62/R
£490 $842 €700 Married couple fishing in the harbour (70x50cm-28x20in) mono.d.33 chl pastel prov. 8-Dec-3 Glerum, Amsterdam #82/R

BERGA BOADA, Jose (1872-1923) Spanish
£320 $582 €480 Mountain landscape with house (24x31cm-9x12in) s. 29-Jun-4 Segre, Madrid #33/R

BERGAGNA, Vittorio (1884-1965) Italian
£350 $584 €500 Composition (80x105cm-31x41in) on glass. 10-Oct-3 Stadion, Trieste #496
£467 $835 €700 Village fair (30x37cm-12x15in) board double-sided prov. 12-May-4 Stadion, Trieste #662/R
£638 $1034 €900 Paseggiata a mare (21x30cm-8x12in) s. board. 22-May-3 Stadion, Trieste #189/R est:700-1000
£933 $1671 €1400 In the park (30x20cm-12x8in) s.d.57 cardboard. 12-May-4 Stadion, Trieste #788/R est:800-1200
£1329 $2285 €1900 Piano lesson (28x28cm-11x11in) s. 3-Dec-3 Stadion, Trieste #1129/R est:800-1200
£1600 $2864 €2400 Interior with flowers (50x39cm-20x15in) s.d.1951 cardboard. 12-May-4 Stadion, Trieste #810/R est:2000-3000
£1667 $2983 €2500 Wild flowers and fan (61x81cm-24x32in) s. board. 12-May-4 Stadion, Trieste #716/R est:2200-3200
£1733 $3103 €2600 Still life with vase and painting (51x41cm-20x16in) s. cardboard. 12-May-4 Stadion, Trieste #742/R est:3000

BERGAIGNE, Pierre (18th C) French
£11409 $20993 €17000 Paysans jouant aux des scene de battage du ble (54x67cm-21x26in) pair. 24-Mar-4 Tajan, Paris #107/R est:12000-15000
£38889 $70000 €56778 Carnival parade. Carnival ball (74x91cm-29x36in) pair. 22-Jan-4 Sotheby's, New York #79/R est:80000-120000

BERGAMESE SCHOOL (16th C) Italian
£5594 $9622 €8000 Portrait of gentleman (60x56cm-24x22in) 2-Dec-3 Sotheby's, Milan #63/R est:6000-8000

BERGAMINI, Francesco (1815-1883) Italian
£2174 $4000 €3174 Italian gypsy (46x69cm-18x27in) s. 26-Jun-4 Selkirks, St. Louis #445/R est:8000-10000
£2800 $4480 €4060 Toast (44x63cm-17x25in) s. 18-Sep-3 Christie's, Kensington #71/R est:3000-5000
£4545 $8000 €6636 By the hearth (45x68cm-18x27in) s. 18-May-4 Bonhams & Butterfields, San Francisco #59/R est:8000-12000
£5294 $9000 €7729 Lively discussion (51x82cm-20x32in) s.i. 29-Oct-3 Christie's, Rockefeller NY #234/R est:10000-15000
£8889 $16000 €12978 Nuns at a choir practice (51x83cm-20x33in) s.i. 22-Apr-4 Christie's, Rockefeller NY #229/R est:20000-25000
£11176 $19000 €16317 Watermelon vendor (81x51cm-32x20in) s.d. 29-Oct-3 Christie's, Rockefeller NY #228/R est:20000-30000

BERGE, Auguste Charles de la (1807-1842) French
£1067 $1931 €1600 Le sous-bois (40x31cm-16x12in) oil paper on canvas exhib.lit. 30-Mar-4 Rossini, Paris #226/R est:500-800

BERGE, Edward (1876-1924) American
Sculpture
£12011 $21500 €17536 Wild flower (109cm-43in) s. verdigris pat bronze. 8-Jan-4 James Julia, Fairfield #480/R est:10000-15000

BERGEN, Carl von (1853-1933) German
£5000 $9200 €7300 Girl looking into a goldfish bowl (63x46cm-25x18in) s. 23-Mar-4 Bonhams, New Bond Street #16/R est:2500-3500

BERGEN, Claus (1885-1964) German
£1208 $2223 €1800 Three master at sea beneath heavy skies (90x150cm-35x59in) s. 25-Mar-4 Dr Fritz Nagel, Stuttgart #690/R est:1400
£1293 $2314 €1900 Fishing boat in harbour (70x91cm-28x36in) s. 17-Mar-4 Neumeister, Munich #404/R est:1400
£1622 $3000 €2368 Shafts of sunlight on the Atlantic (35x60cm-14x24in) s. 10-Feb-4 Christie's, Rockefeller NY #243/R est:2000-3000
£1818 $3127 €2600 Naval battle (80x130cm-31x51in) s. 5-Dec-3 Bolland & Marotz, Bremen #691/R est:3500
£1987 $3616 €3000 On the Cornish coast (106x147cm-42x58in) s. 18-Jun-4 Bolland & Marotz, Bremen #804/R est:3300
£3200 $5440 €4672 Fowey fishing fleet (80x110cm-31x43in) s. 19-Nov-3 Christie's, Kensington #610/R
Works on paper
£629 $1000 €918 European harbour scene with docked boats (17x25cm-7x10in) s. W/C. 13-Sep-3 Weschler, Washington #692/R
£1401 $2158 €2200 Seascape (37x60cm-15x24in) s. gouache. 4-Sep-2 Schopman, Hamburg #84a/R est:2200

BERGEN, Dirck van (1645-1690) Dutch
£795 $1446 €1200 Romantic hilly landscape with donkeys and gregarious animals (25x32cm-10x13in) s. 19-Jun-4 Bergmann, Erlangen #770
Works on paper
£1081 $1903 €1600 Two peasant women with their animals (34x44cm-13x17in) s.d.1690 pen col ink brush wash black chk vellum prov.exhib. 19-May-4 Sotheby's, Amsterdam #93/R est:2500-3500

BERGEN, Fritz (1857-?) German
£436 $803 €650 Outside the farmstead (60x83cm-24x33in) i. 29-Mar-4 Dr Fritz Nagel, Stuttgart #6991/R

BERGENSTRAHLE, Marie Louise de Geer (1944-) Swedish
Works on paper
£476 $843 €695 A life-saver (35x49cm-14x19in) s.d.1973 gouache. 27-Apr-4 AB Stockholms Auktionsverk #1064/R (S.KR 6500)
£944 $1605 €1378 This here is a picture (40x30cm-16x12in) s.d.1999 gouache exhib. 5-Nov-3 AB Stockholms Auktionsverk #982/R (S.KR 12500)
£1322 $2247 €1930 A red old man (22x28cm-9x11in) s.d.1976 W/C. 5-Nov-3 AB Stockholms Auktionsverk #978/R est:10000-15000 (S.KR 17500)
£2466 $4438 €3600 Donald Duck painting Olle Baertling portrait monument (39x52cm-15x20in) s.d.1980 gouache. 26-Apr-4 Bukowskis, Stockholm #469/R est:20000-25000 (S.KR 34000)

BERGER, David (20th C) American
£1078 $1800 €1574 Carnival midway scene (48x58cm-19x23in) s. board painted c.1945. 15-Nov-3 Illustration House, New York #95/R est:1500-2400

BERGER, Einar (1893-1960) Norwegian
£254 $467 €371 Cleaning cod. s. panel. 29-Mar-4 Blomqvist, Lysaker #1019 (N.KR 3200)
£284 $474 €415 From Maursund (45x55cm-18x22in) s. 17-Nov-3 Blomqvist, Lysaker #1014/R (N.KR 3400)
£297 $544 €434 Calm day at sea (79x97cm-31x38in) s. panel. 2-Feb-4 Blomqvist, Lysaker #1026/R (N.KR 3700)
£313 $542 €457 Seascape with boat in stormy seas (50x60cm-20x24in) s. panel. 13-Dec-3 Blomqvist, Lysaker #1023/R (N.KR 3600)
£325 $598 €475 Two figures by Norland's boat (38x46cm-15x18in) s. panel. 10-Jun-4 Grev Wedels Plass, Oslo #160/R (N.KR 4000)
£326 $571 €476 Fishing harbour in Lofoten (33x41cm-13x16in) s. panel. 16-Dec-3 Grev Wedels Plass, Oslo #134/R (N.KR 3800)
£448 $720 €654 Farmhouse in winter (54x80cm-21x31in) s. 25-Aug-3 Blomqvist, Lysaker #1020 (N.KR 5200)

BERGER, Emil (1890-?) Swiss
£364 $604 €528 Houses in Sissach in winter (42x48cm-17x19in) s. board. 13-Jun-3 Zofingen, Switzerland #2781 (S.FR 800)

BERGER, Ernst (1857-1919) Austrian
£986 $1765 €1400 Mythological scene with a couple surrounded by flowers in a wood (65x33cm-26x13in) s. lit. 8-Jan-4 Allgauer, Kempten #2344/R

BERGER, Ettore de Maria (1851-1938) Italian
£11957 $22000 €17457 Young fisherman in the shallows (54x103cm-21x41in) s.d.84. 27-Jun-4 Freeman, Philadelphia #48/R est:3000-5000

BERGER, G (?) ?
£1736 $2830 €2500 Mountain goats in winter (85x100cm-33x39in) s. 24-Sep-3 Neumeister, Munich #398/R est:2000

BERGER, Georges (c.1908-1976) French
£336 $628 €500 Le moulin de la galette (55x46cm-22x18in) s.d.1963. 29-Feb-4 Versailles Encheres #109
£336 $628 €500 Montmartre (55x46cm-22x18in) s.d.1963. 29-Feb-4 Versailles Encheres #110
Works on paper
£433 $789 €650 Paris, Montmartre (45x37cm-18x15in) s.d.1956 pastel. 4-Jul-4 Eric Pillon, Calais #237/R

BERGER, Hans (1882-1977) Swiss
£819 $1466 €1196 Rhone et fort de l'ecluse (46x55cm-18x22in) s. i. stretcher. 14-May-4 Dobiaschofsky, Bern #167/R est:2400 (S.FR 1900)
£917 $1532 €1330 Nature morte aux fleurs. Brouette (58x70cm-23x28in) s. d.verso double-sided prov. 21-Jun-3 Galerie du Rhone, Sion #326 est:2000-3000 (S.FR 2000)

BERGER, Jacques (1902-1977) Swiss
£341 $566 €494 Composition (22x26cm-9x10in) s. board. 13-Jun-3 Zofingen, Switzerland #2785 (S.FR 750)
£948 $1697 €1384 Composition (39x31cm-15x12in) s. board exhib. 12-May-4 Dobiaschofsky, Bern #3433/R est:900 (S.FR 2200)
£1478 $2705 €2158 Scene d'interieur (38x46cm-15x18in) s.d.42. 5-Jun-4 Galerie du Rhone, Sion #245/R est:2000-2500 (S.FR 3400)

BERGER, Johan Christian (1803-1871) Swedish
£480 $860 €701 View of Traneryd's cheese farm, Jonkoping (43x59cm-17x23in) s.d.1860. 26-May-4 AB Stockholms Auktionsverk #2311/R (S.KR 6500)
£1077 $1852 €1572 Seascape with boats off rocky coastline (35x55cm-14x22in) s.d.59. 7-Dec-3 Uppsala Auktionskammare, Uppsala #110/R (S.KR 14000)
£2462 $4234 €3595 Goodwin lightship in rough seas with other vessels (77x127cm-30x50in) mono. 3-Dec-3 AB Stockholms Auktionsverk #2391/R est:15000-20000 (S.KR 32000)

BERGER, Johan Christian (attrib) (1803-1871) Swedish
£396 $674 €578 Stormy seascape (42x65cm-17x26in) 5-Nov-3 Dobiaschofsky, Bern #349/R (S.FR 900)
£454 $850 €663 Harbour scene under moonlight (30x41cm-12x16in) indis.i.stretcher. 29-Feb-4 Grogan, Boston #14/R

BERGER, Robert le (1905-1972) French
£400 $728 €600 Paris, quais sous la neige (55x46cm-22x18in) s. 4-Jul-4 Eric Pillon, Calais #221/R
£845 $1462 €1200 Paris, Montmartre (65x54cm-26x21in) s. 14-Dec-3 Eric Pillon, Calais #215/R
Works on paper
£308 $524 €450 Vue de Montmartre (49x41cm-19x16in) s.d.1956 pastel. 9-Nov-3 Eric Pillon, Calais #223/R

BERGER, Sando (?) ?
Works on paper
£230 $375 €336 Spiritual realities (99x46cm-39x18in) s. mixed media on board. 28-Sep-3 Bonhams & Butterfields, Los Angeles #7056
£341 $550 €498 Untitled no.4 (121x90cm-48x35in) s.i. mixed media on canvas. 24-Aug-3 Bonhams & Butterfields, Los Angeles #7050

BERGER, William Merritt (1872-?) American
£265 $450 €387 Girl with a basket (28x15cm-11x6in) s.i.d.Avril 1904 canvas on board. 5-Nov-3 Doyle, New York #11/R

BERGER-BERGNER, Paul (1904-1978) Czechoslovakian
Works on paper
£1620 $2802 €2300 Clown (98x79cm-39x31in) s. mixed media board. 13-Dec-3 Lempertz, Koln #287/R est:2000

BERGERET, Denis Pierre (1846-1910) French
£1259 $2165 €1800 Figures in church cellar (16x32cm-6x13in) s. panel. 5-Dec-3 Michael Zeller, Lindau #571/R est:1500

BERGERON, Christian (1945-) Canadian
£300 $549 €438 Au pieds des Monts (60x75cm-24x30in) s. 1-Jun-4 Joyner Waddington, Toronto #401/R (C.D 750)

BERGEVIN, Albert (20th C) French
Works on paper
£382 $691 €580 Pres-midi sur la plage (22x29cm-9x11in) s. W/C. 17-Apr-4 Deburaux, Boulogne #74

BERGEVIN, Edouard Edmond de (1861-1925) French
£2517 $4204 €3600 Paris, promenade ombragee (61x50cm-24x20in) s.d.1923. 29-Jun-3 Eric Pillon, Calais #6/R

BERGEY, Earle K (1901-1952) American
£1275 $2283 €1900 On ice (71x63cm-28x25in) s. lit. 27-May-4 Sotheby's, Paris #100/R est:800-1200

BERGGREN, B W (19/20th C) Danish?
£448 $819 €654 Returning home from market, afternoon (94x79cm-37x31in) s. 9-Jun-4 Rasmussen, Copenhagen #1745/R (D.KR 5000)

BERGH, Edvard (1828-1880) Swedish
£1846 $3175 €2695 Wooded landscape with torrents, girl and goats, Sweden (88x118cm-35x46in) s.d.1851. 7-Dec-3 Uppsala Auktionskammare, Uppsala #102/R est:25000-30000 (S.KR 24000)
£2000 $3320 €2920 Cows at watering (25x30cm-10x12in) s.d.79. 1-Oct-3 Sotheby's, Olympia #198/R est:2000-3000
£4769 $8203 €6963 Summer landscape with cattle by lake (73x111cm-29x44in) s.d.1875. 2-Dec-3 Bukowskis, Stockholm #168/R est:30000-35000 (S.KR 62000)

BERGH, Hanna (19th C) ?
£1477 $2717 €2200 Model (50x46cm-20x18in) painted c.1887. 25-Mar-4 Hagelstam, Helsinki #858/R est:1500

BERGH, Hans Nielsen (1836-1876) Danish?
£2430 $3839 €3524 Wanderers by waterfall, Norway (81x71cm-32x28in) s.i. 2-Sep-3 Rasmussen, Copenhagen #1673/R est:15000 (D.KR 26000)

BERGH, Joseph van den (1868-1967) Belgian
Works on paper
£336 $617 €500 Herodiade recoit la tete de Jean-Baptiste des mains de sa fille (30x40cm-12x16in) s. W/C. 28-Mar-4 MonsAntic, Maisieres #1348

BERGH, Nicolaas van den (1725-1774) Flemish
£4000 $6920 €5840 Portrait of Maria Sobieska surrounded by Mercury, Minerva and putti (49x38cm-19x15in) s.d.1748 panel prov. 12-Dec-3 Christie's, Kensington #117/R est:5000-8000

BERGH, Rickard (1858-1919) Swedish
£3843 $6880 €5611 Landscape from Grez (19x24cm-7x9in) cardboard exhib. 25-May-4 Bukowskis, Stockholm #103/R est:40000-45000 (S.KR 52000)

BERGHE, Charles Auguste van den (1798-1853) Belgian
£2039 $3753 €3100 Retour de la chasse (116x89cm-46x35in) s. 24-Jun-4 Credit Municipal, Paris #4/R est:5000-6000

BERGHE, Charles Auguste van den (attrib) (1798-1853) Belgian
£2958 $5117 €4200 Paysage de campagne en Italie (18x36cm-7x14in) paper on wood. 10-Dec-3 Piasa, Paris #125/R est:2000-3000
£4225 $7310 €6000 L'ile de San Michele pres de Murano (30x50cm-12x20in) paper on wood. 10-Dec-3 Piasa, Paris #127/R est:6000-8000
£5915 $10234 €8400 Venise vue de la lagune (30x50cm-12x20in) paper on wood. 10-Dec-3 Piasa, Paris #126/R est:6000-8000

BERGHE, Christoffel van den (1617-1642) German
£4362 $7809 €6500 Vue de chateau en hiver avec etang anime de patineurs (14x18cm-6x7in) copper. 25-May-4 Palais de Beaux Arts, Brussels #86/R est:5500-7000
£38000 $68400 €55480 Wooded river landscape with elegant figures on a path (18x23cm-7x9in) copper. 21-Apr-4 Christie's, London #46/R est:40000-60000

BERGHE, Frits van den (1883-1939) Belgian
£2953 $5463 €4400 Young girl with nosegay (31x26cm-12x10in) mono. paper on panel prov.lit. 13-Mar-4 De Vuyst, Lokeren #556/R est:7000-9000
£22535 $38986 €32000 View of the town (63x42cm-25x17in) s. oil paper on panel prov.exhib.lit. 13-Dec-3 De Vuyst, Lokeren #483/R
£97902 $168392 €140000 Fleurs (72x66cm-28x26in) s. painted 1930 prov.lit. 2-Dec-3 Sotheby's, Amsterdam #57/R est:150000-200000
Works on paper
£1049 $1752 €1500 Le voyeur (11x16cm-4x6in) mono. Indian ink. 13-Oct-3 Horta, Bruxelles #332 est:1000-1500

BERGHE, Herman van den (?) Belgian?
£658 $1211 €1000 Pecheurs sur l'Estacade (61x91cm-24x36in) s. 22-Jun-4 Palais de Beaux Arts, Brussels #321/R
£933 $1680 €1400 Beach view with boats and fisherman's wife (56x108cm-22x43in) s. 26-Apr-4 Bernaerts, Antwerp #974/R

BERGIUS, Andreas (1718-1793) Swedish
£1652 $2858 €2412 Portrait of Kirsten Hofgaard (70x54cm-28x21in) s. verso. 13-Dec-3 Blomqvist, Lysaker #1024/R est:20000 (N.KR 19000)

BERGMAN (?) ?
Sculpture
£1149 $2022 €1700 Deer (25x24cm-10x9in) bronze marble socle. 24-May-4 Bernaerts, Antwerp #432 est:1900-2100
£1188 $1900 €1734 Figure of a Blackamoor (23cm-9in) s.num.2879 cold painted Vienna bronze. 21-Sep-3 William Jenack, New York #93 est:1800-2200
£2400 $4008 €3504 Arabesque (39cm-15in) s. pat bronze. 15-Oct-3 Christie's, Kensington #285/R

BERGMAN, Anna-Eva (1909-1987) Swedish/French
£629 $1070 €900 Composition (16x24cm-6x9in) s.d.1971 oil paper. 23-Nov-3 Cornette de St.Cyr, Paris #15a
£979 $1664 €1400 Composition (25x26cm-10x10in) s.d.1977 i.verso panel. 23-Nov-3 Cornette de St.Cyr, Paris #15/R
£1081 $1935 €1600 Untitled (65x50cm-26x20in) mono.d.1958 acrylic silver leaf. 4-May-4 Calmels Cohen, Paris #189/R est:1000-1500
£1711 $3147 €2600 Composition (49x64cm-19x25in) mono. i.verso painted 1969 prov. 27-Jun-4 Versailles Encheres #37/R est:800-1000
Works on paper
£450 $752 €657 Montagne d'argent (57x26cm-22x10in) init.d.1959 gouache silver leaf prov. 21-Oct-3 Bonhams, Knightsbridge #72/R
£1258 $2290 €1900 Untitled (38x46cm-15x18in) init.d.1961 mixed media. 18-Jun-4 Charbonneaux, Paris #75/R est:1800-2000
£1258 $2290 €1900 Untitled (40x52cm-16x20in) init.d.1960 mixed media. 18-Jun-4 Charbonneaux, Paris #76/R est:1800-2000

BERGMAN, Augusta (19th C) Swedish
£1577 $2838 €2302 Landscape with waterfall (65x81cm-26x32in) s.d.1861. 26-Jan-4 Lilla Bukowskis, Stockholm #514 est:20000-25000 (S.KR 21000)

BERGMAN, Charles (20th C) American
£254 $475 €371 Walking through the garden at Mission San Juan Capistrano (76x102cm-30x40in) s. 29-Feb-4 Bonhams & Butterfields, San Francisco #4560
£289 $500 €422 Garden of Mission San Luis Rey (76x101cm-30x40in) s. 10-Dec-3 Bonhams & Butterfields, San Francisco #6311/R
£289 $500 €422 Collecting water at the Santa Barbara Mission (76x102cm-30x40in) s. 10-Dec-3 Bonhams & Butterfields, San Francisco #6316/R

BERGMAN, Franz (19/20th C) Austrian
Sculpture
£1229 $2200 €1794 Two Arabs in a tent (25cm-10in) cold painted bronze exec.c.1900. 20-Mar-4 Freeman, Philadelphia #563/R est:300-500

£1700	$3094	€2482	Arab gentleman seated on horseback (24cm-9in) num.6250 cold pat. bronze. 29-Jun-4 Bonhams, Knightsbridge #325/R est:400-600
£1900	$3458	€2774	Jay with Bergman (19cm-7in) cold pat. bronze. 29-Jun-4 Bonhams, Knightsbridge #309 est:600-800
£2095	$3750	€3059	African orange seller (28cm-11in) st. cold painted bronze exec.c.1900. 20-Mar-4 Freeman, Philadelphia #617/R est:1500-2500

BERGMAN, Karl (1891-1965) Swedish

£668	$1155	€975	Winter landscape in moonlight (28x40cm-11x16in) s.d.1933 panel. 15-Dec-3 Lilla Bukowskis, Stockholm #475/R (S.KR 8500)
£813	$1455	€1187	Sunlit pine trees in the skerries (85x136cm-33x54in) 28-May-4 Uppsala Auktionskammare, Uppsala #219/R (S.KR 11000)

BERGMAN, Oskar (1879-1963) Swedish

£308	$529	€450	Coastal landscape from Klover Island with sailing boats by rocky beach (26x40cm-10x16in) s.d.1942 panel. 7-Dec-3 Uppsala Auktionskammare, Uppsala #226/R (S.KR 4000)
£430	$701	€628	Summer landscape (46x66cm-18x26in) s.i.d.1922. 29-Sep-3 Lilla Bukowskis, Stockholm #628 (S.KR 5600)
£471	$815	€688	Winter landscape, Neglinge (50x70cm-20x28in) s.d.1904. 15-Dec-3 Lilla Bukowskis, Stockholm #29 (S.KR 6000)
£770	$1332	€1124	Winter landscape with trees (22x30cm-9x12in) s.d.1938 panel. 15-Dec-3 Lilla Bukowskis, Stockholm #179 (S.KR 9800)
Works on paper			
£292	$503	€426	Bay with sandy beach and pine trees (26x41cm-10x16in) s.i.d.1948 W/C. 7-Dec-3 Uppsala Auktionskammare, Uppsala #225 (S.KR 3800)
£292	$536	€438	Green tree (20x15cm-8x6in) s.d.1910 W/C. 14-Jun-4 Lilla Bukowskis, Stockholm #824 (S.KR 4000)
£314	$544	€458	View of Visby town wall (10x15cm-4x6in) s.i.d.augusti 1902 W/C. 15-Dec-3 Lilla Bukowskis, Stockholm #579 (S.KR 4000)
£338	$608	€493	Butterfly and flowers (17x12cm-7x5in) s. W/C. 26-Jan-4 Lilla Bukowskis, Stockholm #552 (S.KR 4500)
£355	$635	€518	Town scene from Visby (23x29cm-9x11in) s.i.d.1953 W/C. 28-May-4 Uppsala Auktionskammare, Uppsala #263 (S.KR 4800)
£407	$728	€594	Summer flowers by lake (18x12cm-7x5in) s. W/C. 28-May-4 Uppsala Auktionskammare, Uppsala #264 (S.KR 5500)
£492	$801	€718	Archipelago (17x11cm-7x4in) s. W/C. 29-Sep-3 Lilla Bukowskis, Stockholm #343 (S.KR 6400)
£503	$870	€734	Coastal landscape, Langviksskar (22x30cm-9x12in) s. W/C. 15-Dec-3 Lilla Bukowskis, Stockholm #37 (S.KR 6400)
£517	$926	€755	Woman in flowery landscape (22x29cm-9x11in) s. W/C. 28-May-4 Uppsala Auktionskammare, Uppsala #266/R (S.KR 7000)
£517	$926	€755	Wild flowers (25x17cm-10x7in) s. W/C. 25-May-4 Bukowskis, Stockholm #52/R (S.KR 7000)
£568	$926	€829	Winter games (29x38cm-11x15in) s.d.januari 1938 W/C htd white. 29-Sep-3 Lilla Bukowskis, Stockholm #321 (S.KR 7400)
£568	$926	€829	Thawing (31x49cm-12x19in) s.d.1942 W/C htd white. 29-Sep-3 Lilla Bukowskis, Stockholm #322 (S.KR 7400)
£615	$1058	€898	Spring landscapes (5x4cm-2x2in) s.d.1933 pair W/C. 2-Dec-3 Bukowskis, Stockholm #4/R (S.KR 8000)
£628	$1125	€917	Picnic in the grass by Lund farm (36x51cm-14x20in) s.d.maj 1944 W/C. 28-May-4 Uppsala Auktionskammare, Uppsala #260/R (S.KR 8500)
£665	$1191	€971	Spring landscape with silver birches (32x23cm-13x9in) s. W/C. 25-May-4 Bukowskis, Stockholm #54/R (S.KR 9000)
£776	$1389	€1133	Lamp lights at dusk (25x18cm-10x7in) s. W/C. 25-May-4 Bukowskis, Stockholm #53/R (S.KR 10500)
£846	$1455	€1235	Silver birches in spring (28x18cm-11x7in) s. W/C. 7-Dec-3 Uppsala Auktionskammare, Uppsala #218/R (S.KR 11000)
£887	$1588	€1295	Silver birches and spring flowers (25x17cm-10x7in) s. W/C. 25-May-4 Bukowskis, Stockholm #55/R (S.KR 12000)
£903	$1563	€1318	Birch grove (34x24cm-13x9in) s.d.1939 W/C. 15-Dec-3 Lilla Bukowskis, Stockholm #653 (S.KR 11500)
£923	$1588	€1348	Landscape with rowanberry tree (35x49cm-14x19in) s.i.d.1929 aug. gouache. 7-Dec-3 Uppsala Auktionskammare, Uppsala #220/R (S.KR 12000)
£961	$1720	€1403	Spring flowers in birch grove (18x12cm-7x5in) s.d.1942 W/C. 28-May-4 Uppsala Auktionskammare, Uppsala #257/R (S.KR 13000)
£962	$1654	€1405	Summer verdure, Visby (35x50cm-14x20in) s.i.d.juni 1936 W/C. 2-Dec-3 Bukowskis, Stockholm #3/R (S.KR 12500)
£1183	$2117	€1727	View across field of flowers in hazy sunshine (36x51cm-14x20in) s.i.d.aug.1932 W/C. 28-May-4 Uppsala Auktionskammare, Uppsala #259/R est:8000-10000 (S.KR 16000)
£1231	$2117	€1797	Forest of silver birches (36x41cm-14x16in) s.d.1935 W/C. 2-Dec-3 Bukowskis, Stockholm #2/R est:10000-12000 (S.KR 16000)
£1231	$2117	€1797	View of Vik, Skane (37x55cm-15x22in) s. W/C. 2-Dec-3 Bukowskis, Stockholm #6/R est:20000-25000 (S.KR 16000)
£1848	$3307	€2698	Spring landscape with birches and cottage (35x24cm-14x9in) s.d.1942 W/C. 26-May-4 AB Stockholms Auktionsverk #2345/R est:20000-25000 (S.KR 25000)
£1848	$3307	€2698	Berga farm, Danderyd (38x52cm-15x20in) s.d.april 1943 i. verso W/C prov. 25-May-4 Bukowskis, Stockholm #57/R est:25000-30000 (S.KR 25000)
£2217	$3969	€3237	View from Riddarholmen towards the Old Town (38x56cm-15x22in) s.d.Augusti 1945 W/C prov. 25-May-4 Bukowskis, Stockholm #56/R est:20000-25000 (S.KR 30000)
£2308	$3969	€3370	Spring landscape with birches at dusk (42x30cm-17x12in) s.d.1949 W/C. 3-Dec-3 AB Stockholms Auktionsverk #2449/R est:18000-20000 (S.KR 30000)
£2365	$4234	€3453	Village in winter (36x53cm-14x21in) s.d.1934 W/C. 26-May-4 AB Stockholms Auktionsverk #2100/R est:18000-20000 (S.KR 32000)
£2365	$4234	€3453	Silver birches in autumn sunshine (36x51cm-14x20in) s.d.oktober 1939 W/C. 25-May-4 Bukowskis, Stockholm #58/R est:20000-25000 (S.KR 32000)

BERGMANN, Gerhart (1922-) German

£533	$981	€800	Peaches (135x150cm-53x59in) s.d.78. 12-Jun-4 Villa Grisebach, Berlin #683/R

BERGMANN, Julius Hugo (1861-1940) German

£451	$713	€650	Flight to Egypt (56x81cm-22x32in) s. 5-Sep-3 Wendl, Rudolstadt #3281/R
£533	$976	€800	Lion's head (84x63cm-33x25in) s.d.1884. 5-Jun-4 Arnold, Frankfurt #533/R
£1067	$1952	€1600	Spotted cows on the edge of the Rhein in summer (79x110cm-31x43in) s. 5-Jun-4 Arnold, Frankfurt #534/R est:1200

BERGMANN, Max (1884-1955) German

£669	$1070	€950	Young herder with two cows (45x56cm-18x22in) s. 18-Sep-3 Rieber, Stuttgart #766/R
£804	$1343	€1150	Woman gathering sticks on woodland path (35x26cm-14x10in) s. panel. 10-Oct-3 Winterberg, Heidelberg #968/R
£804	$1343	€1150	Woodland path in winter (35x26cm-14x10in) s. panel. 10-Oct-3 Winterberg, Heidelberg #969
£1946	$3581	€2900	Two ox plough (70x100cm-28x39in) s. 24-Mar-4 Hugo Ruef, Munich #929/R est:2900

BERGMANN, Max (attrib) (1884-1955) German

£497	$904	€750	Hay making (40x60cm-16x24in) s. board. 19-Jun-4 Bergmann, Erlangen #838

BERGMULLER, Johan Georg (1688-1762) German

Works on paper			
£814	$1385	€1188	Ascension of Maria (38x30cm-15x12in) wash Indian ink prov. 19-Nov-3 Fischer, Luzern #2402/R (S.FR 1800)
£2238	$3804	€3200	St Norbert before cross (30x22cm-12x9in) s.d.1721 pen wash. 27-Nov-3 Bassenge, Berlin #5401/R est:2200

BERGNER, Yosl (1920-) Israeli

£625	$1100	€913	Pots in the landscape (27x24cm-11x9in) s. painted c.1975. 1-Jan-4 Ben-Ami, Tel Aviv #4385/R
£994	$1800	€1451	Angels (51x70cm-20x28in) s.d.1961 oil paper on canvas. 1-Apr-4 Ben-Ami, Tel Aviv #4770/R est:2400-3200
£2377	$4350	€3470	Fiddler in red and the green bird (41x33cm-16x13in) s. s.i.verso. 1-Feb-4 Ben-Ami, Tel Aviv #4564/R est:4000-6000
£3369	$6300	€4919	Blind lead the blind (65x97cm-26x38in) s.d.1972 i.verso. 1-Mar-4 Ben-Ami, Tel Aviv #4665/R est:6500-9000
£4863	$8900	€7100	Orchestra with young girl (65x81cm-26x32in) s. s.i.verso painted c.1980. 1-Feb-4 Ben-Ami, Tel Aviv #4640/R est:9000-12000
£12651	$21000	€18470	Artisans (145x224cm-57x88in) s.d.1971 exihb. 2-Oct-3 Christie's, Tel Aviv #66/R est:20000-30000
£21516	$33996	€31413	Tocumwal - loading the train (65x94cm-26x37in) s. i.d.1944 verso prov. 2-Sep-3 Deutscher-Menzies, Melbourne #51/R est:60000-70000 (A.D 52500)
Works on paper			
£894	$1601	€1305	Angel Song (41x56cm-16x22in) s.d.73 pencil W/C. 10-May-4 Joel, Victoria #279 est:2000-3000 (A.D 2200)

BERGNER-MEYER, Lena (1906-1981) German

Works on paper			
£456	$840	€680	Coloured circle (30cm-12in circular) mono.d.26 verso gouache pencil. 26-Mar-4 Bolland & Marotz, Bremen #655/R

BERGOLLI, Aldo (1916-1972) Italian

£2685	$4805	€4000	Composition (70x100cm-28x39in) s.d.55 sold with oil by Giuseppe Allosia prov. 25-May-4 Sotheby's, Milan #80/R est:2000

BERGOUGNAN, Raoul (?) French

Works on paper			
£759	$1267	€1100	Grues en bordure du canal (30x37cm-12x15in) s. gouache. 12-Nov-3 Chassaing Rivet, Toulouse #218

BERGOYS, Claes (fl.c.1651-1668) Dutch

£31000	$55800	€45260	Still life with orange and lemon on a pewter plate, and other objects (73x20cm-29x8in) s.indis.d.166 prov. 22-Apr-4 Sotheby's, London #23/R est:12000-18000

BERGSLIEN, Knud Larsen (1827-1908) Norwegian

£2033	$3720	€2968	The son's farewell (23x21cm-9x8in) paper on panel. 7-Jun-4 Blomqvist, Oslo #327/R est:30000-35000 (N.KR 25000)
£2053	$3490	€2997	Still life of shells and books on wooden block (21x32cm-8x13in) s.d.1846. 19-Nov-3 Grev Wedels Plass, Oslo #54/R est:30000 (N.KR 24000)
£7686	$13758	€11222	Evening landscape with houses in winter (60x95cm-24x37in) s. lit. 22-Mar-4 Blomqvist, Oslo #334/R est:120000-150000 (N.KR 96000)

BERGSLIEN, Nils (1853-1928) Norwegian

£854	$1571	€1281	Gnome being thrown out (29x21cm-11x8in) s. panel. 14-Jun-4 Blomqvist, Lysaker #1037 (N.KR 10500)
£2033	$3740	€3050	Drunken gnomes (45x26cm-18x10in) s. 14-Jun-4 Blomqvist, Lysaker #1038 est:8000-12000 (N.KR 25000)
£3322	$5714	€4850	Girl on steps to outhouse (32x33cm-13x13in) indis.sig. panel. 8-Dec-3 Blomqvist, Oslo #428/R est:40000-45000 (N.KR 39000)
£5988	$10180	€8742	A proposal (67x94cm-26x37in) s. 19-Nov-3 Grev Wedels Plass, Oslo #53/R est:70000-90000 (N.KR 70000)
£48780	$89268	€71219	Wedding at the farm (96x87cm-38x34in) s.d.1899 lit. 7-Jun-4 Blomqvist, Oslo #336/R est:550000-650000 (N.KR 600000)
Works on paper			
£515	$901	€752	Agitator (30x24cm-12x9in) s. W/C. 16-Dec-3 Grev Wedels Plass, Oslo #4 (N.KR 6000)
£674	$1240	€984	Gnome and family of mice (25x21cm-10x8in) s. W/C. 29-Mar-4 Blomqvist, Lysaker #1072/R (N.KR 8500)
£687	$1202	€1003	Gnome (24x17cm-9x7in) s. W/C. 16-Dec-3 Grev Wedels Plass, Oslo #6/R (N.KR 8000)
£858	$1502	€1253	Vicar, prisoner and judge (32x24cm-13x9in) s. W/C. 16-Dec-3 Grev Wedels Plass, Oslo #5 (N.KR 10000)
£864	$1434	€1253	Five cards - last trick (18x21cm-7x8in) W/C. 16-Jun-3 Blomqvist, Lysaker #1008/R (N.KR 10000)
£870	$1504	€1270	Kjepp-jaget (28x20cm-11x8in) s. W/C. 13-Dec-3 Blomqvist, Lysaker #1027 (N.KR 10000)
£1155	$1963	€1686	Leprechauns in wood (30x21cm-12x8in) s. W/C. 19-Nov-3 Grev Wedels Plass, Oslo #52/R est:15000-20000 (N.KR 13500)

BERGSOE, Flemming (20th C) Danish?

£293 $533 €428 Circus (60x80cm-24x31in) s/. 7-Feb-4 Rasmussen, Havnen #4072 (D.KR 3200)

BERGSTROM, Alfred (1869-1930) Swedish

£306 $492 €447 Morning glow (70x92cm-28x36in) s. 25-Aug-3 Lilla Bukowskis, Stockholm #193 (S.KR 4000)

£407 $728 €594 Coastal landscape at dusk (24x32cm-9x13in) s.i.d.95 panel. 28-May-4 Uppsala Auktionskammare, Uppsala #209 (S.KR 5500)

£1020 $1878 €1530 Twilight landscape in winter (101x120cm-40x47in) s.d.1910. 14-Jun-4 Lilla Bukowskis, Stockholm #408 (S.KR 14000)

£2769 $4763 €4043 View of Parliament House, Stockholm (94x124cm-37x49in) s.d.1908. 3-Dec-3 AB Stockholms Auktionsverk #2252/R est:30000-35000 (S.KR 36000)

BERGUE, Tony Francis de (1820-1893) French

£424 $750 €619 Mediterranean coastal landscape (36x58cm-14x23in) s. 2-May-4 Bonhams & Butterfields, San Francisco #1040/R

£816 $1461 €1200 Nature morte (54x65cm-21x26in) s.indis.d.18. 16-Mar-4 Vanderkindere, Brussels #2

£897 $1497 €1300 Mediterranean view of the bay (34x59cm-13x23in) 11-Nov-3 Vendu Notarishuis, Rotterdam #174/R

£2416 $4277 €3600 Scene de naufrage (39x61cm-15x24in) s. panel. 28-Apr-4 Marc Kohn, Paris #145/R est:4500-5000

£2695 $4501 €3800 Vieux port en Normandie (40x70cm-16x28in) s. prov. 19-Oct-3 Anaf, Lyon #42/R est:3000-4000

BERICHAU, Hinrich (?-1716) German

£2667 $4773 €4000 Still life of flowers (51x35cm-20x14in) s. panel. 13-May-4 Bassenge, Berlin #5033/R est:6000

BERISTAYN, Jorge (1894-1964) Argentinian

£4696 $8500 €6856 Beach (53x60cm-21x24in) cardboard. 30-Mar-4 Arroyo, Buenos Aires #108

£4749 $8500 €6934 Plata river (60x67cm-24x26in) s.d.41 cardboard. 4-May-4 Arroyo, Buenos Aires #96/R est:7000

BERJON, Antoine (1754-1843) French

£837 $1423 €1222 Still life of flowers (24x18cm-9x7in) mono. panel. 5-Nov-3 Dobiaschofsky, Bern #350/R (S.FR 1900)

Works on paper

£2381 $4262 €3500 Nature morte de fruits avec un melon (34x51cm-13x20in) s.d.1773 black crayon W/C htd. chk htd white gouache. 17-Mar-4 Tajan, Paris #71/R est:4000-5000

BERJONNEAU, Jehan (1890-1972) French

£2128 $3553 €3000 Ruelle a Tunis (35x27cm-14x11in) s. canvas on cardboard exhib. 16-Jun-3 Gros & Delettrez, Paris #540/R est:2000-2500

BERKE, Ernest (1921-) American

Sculpture

£2235 $4000 €3263 War signal (61cm-24in) bronze edn of 20. 15-May-4 Altermann Galleries, Santa Fe #94/R

BERKE, Hubert (1908-1979) German

£1408 $2437 €2000 Darker at the top (55x31cm-22x12in) s. s.d.54/57 verso i. stretcher. 13-Dec-3 Lempertz, Koln #117/R est:1500

£3846 $6615 €5500 Apellation (90x150cm-35x59in) s. s.i.d. verso. 5-Dec-3 Ketterer, Munich #312/R est:3500-4500

Works on paper

£272 $500 €397 Abstraction in blue, red and yellow (61x46cm-24x18in) s.d.1949 mixed media. 26-Jun-4 Sloans & Kenyon, Bethesda #251/R

£400 $732 €600 By the sea (21x29cm-8x11in) s.i. W/C board. 4-Jun-4 Lempertz, Koln #36/R

£629 $1070 €900 Untitled (62x48cm-24x19in) s.i.d.77 gouache pencil. 27-Nov-3 Lempertz, Koln #26/R

£1800 $3312 €2700 Composition (63x48cm-25x19in) s.d. gouache. 11-Jun-4 Hauswedell & Nolte, Hamburg #1145/R est:2500

BERKES, Antal (1874-1938) Hungarian

£278 $442 €400 Lively street (28x38cm-11x15in) s. 13-Sep-3 Quittenbaum, Hamburg #66/R

£284 $460 €400 Church and houses (25x35cm-10x14in) s. lit. 23-May-3 Karlheinz Kaupp, Staufen #1739

£313 $497 €450 Big city street (37x47cm-15x19in) s. i. verso. 13-Sep-3 Quittenbaum, Hamburg #67/R

£400 $720 €600 Budapest street (55x68cm-22x27in) s. 26-Apr-4 Rieber, Stuttgart #1213/R

£550 $1012 €803 Crowded Europen city street (55x68cm-22x27in) s. 23-Mar-4 Rosebery Fine Art, London #760

£559 $962 €800 Sunny boulevard with figures and coaches on autumn day (49x67cm-19x26in) s. 5-Dec-3 Michael Zeller, Lindau #573/R

£594 $1010 €850 Activity in a Paris street (27x22cm-11x9in) s. board. 24-Nov-3 Glerum, Amsterdam #50/R

£1265 $2289 €1847 Kalvin Square (70x100cm-28x39in) s. oil on card. 16-Apr-4 Mu Terem Galeria, Budapest #114/R (H.F 480000)

£1265 $2289 €1847 Walking in the city (75x100cm-30x39in) s. 16-Apr-4 Mu Terem Galeria, Budapest #130/R (H.F 480000)

£1336 $2365 €1951 Twilight in the town (75x100cm-30x39in) s.d.1913. 28-Apr-4 Kieselbach, Budapest #62/R (H.F 500000)

£1436 $2483 €2097 Banks of the Seine in Paris my lamplight (42x52cm-17x20in) s. 12-Dec-3 Kieselbach, Budapest #30/R (H.F 550000)

£2138 $3784 €3121 Street in the city (75x100cm-30x39in) s. 28-Apr-4 Kieselbach, Budapest #29/R (H.F 800000)

£4000 $7280 €6000 Vue des grands boulevards (95x126cm-37x50in) s. 29-Jun-4 Gioffredo, Nice #42

BERKEY, Ben B (20th C) American

£327 $520 €477 Fair with skydiver ferris wheel (76x104cm-30x41in) s. masonite. 12-Sep-3 Aspire, Cleveland #104

BERKEY, John Conrad (1932-) American

£695 $1300 €1015 Large space station with many smaller craft (61x43cm-24x17in) s. acrylic painted c.2000. 26-Feb-4 Illustration House, New York #18

BERKHOUT, N (19th C) Dutch

£1667 $2750 €2400 Rhine near Boppard (60x84cm-24x33in) s.d.1851. 3-Jul-3 Van Ham, Cologne #1068/R est:2500

BERKOWITZ, Leon (1919-) American

£289 $500 €422 Abstraction (122x97cm-48x38in) s.d.48 verso acrylic. 13-Dec-3 Sloans & Kenyon, Bethesda #516/R

£318 $550 €464 Study no 2 (43x51cm-17x20in) s.i.d.1983 stretcher acrylic. 13-Dec-3 Sloans & Kenyon, Bethesda #514/R

£405 $700 €591 Untitled (43x51cm-17x20in) s.verso acrylic prov.exhib. 13-Dec-3 Sloans & Kenyon, Bethesda #515/R

£1272 $2200 €1857 After the cloud (185x239cm-73x94in) s.verso. 15-Dec-3 Hindman, Chicago #105/R est:3000-4000

BERKOWITZ, Rosalie (1906-1990) American

£2096 $3500 €3060 Family (36x46cm-14x18in) board. 18-Oct-3 David Dike, Dallas #232/R est:3000-5000

BERLAGE, Hendrik Petrus (1856-1934) Dutch

Works on paper

£541 $951 €800 Design for proposed restoration of the Wijnhuistoren, Zutphen (18x10cm-7x4in) s.i.d.April 1921 pencil. 19-May-4 Sotheby's, Amsterdam #356/R

BERLAND, Helen (20th C) American

£506 $800 €739 The hand is quicker than the eye (41x30cm-16x12in) s. masomnite. 7-Sep-3 Treadway Gallery, Cincinnati #732/R

BERLEBORCH, Gerard van (fl.1649-1655) Dutch

£9589 $16301 €14000 Gilt bekerschroef holding a roemer, an overturned tazza, partly peeled lemon on draped table (63x75cm-25x30in) panel prov.lit. 5-Nov-3 Christie's, Amsterdam #12/R est:8000-12000

£28000 $48440 €40880 Still life of fruit and silver, porcelain and glassware on draped tab le (120x155cm-47x61in) 11-Dec-3 Sotheby's, London #164/R est:15000-20000

BERLEWI, Henrik (20th C) Polish

Works on paper

£694 $1160 €1000 Autoportrait (60x46cm-24x18in) s.d. pencil prov. 25-Oct-3 Cornette de St.Cyr, Paris #472

BERLIN SCHOOL (20th C) German

£278 $453 €400 Young woman wearing hat (74x73cm-29x29in) bears s.i.d.1930. 27-Sep-3 Dannenberg, Berlin #522/R

BERLIN, Dis (1959-) Spanish

£1216 $2141 €1800 Fishing boat at sea (53x72cm-21x28in) s. canvas on board painted 1985 exhib. 18-May-4 Segre, Madrid #242/R est:1800

£1761 $3081 €2500 Spanish products (104x63cm-41x25in) s. canvas on board prov. 16-Dec-3 Segre, Madrid #185/R est:2100

BERLIN, Sven Paul (1911-2000) British

£750 $1365 €1095 Forest Sunset (30x41cm-12x16in) s.d.63 board. 1-Jul-4 Christie's, Kensington #336/R

BERLINGERI, Cesare (1948-) Italian

£333 $613 €500 Red and black (25x30cm-10x12in) s.d.1992 verso acrylic kaolin. 12-Jun-4 Meeting Art, Vercelli #14

£467 $859 €700 Untitled (60x60cm-24x24in) s.d.1985. 12-Jun-4 Meeting Art, Vercelli #444/R

£671 $1242 €1000 Untitled (60x60cm-24x24in) s.d.1985 verso. 13-Mar-4 Meeting Art, Vercelli #80

£2081 $3724 €3100 Folding (49x57cm-19x22in) s.i.d.1992. 30-May-4 Meeting Art, Vercelli #29 est:1500

Works on paper

£764 $1207 €1100 Taurianova (100x50cm-39x20in) mixed media pigment on canvas exec.1976. 6-Sep-3 Meeting Art, Vercelli #570

£1408 $2338 €2000 Dipinto Piegato (45x45cm-18x18in) s.i.d.1999 verso mixed media folded canvas. 14-Jun-3 Meeting Art, Vercelli #63/R est:1500

BERLIT, Rudiger (1883-1939) German

Works on paper

£308 $523 €440 Landscape with houses (44x36cm-17x14in) s. 21-Nov-3 Reiss & Sohn, Konigstein #374/R

£559 $1029 €850 Landscape (29x38cm-11x15in) s.d.20 mixed media. 26-Jun-4 C & K, Leipzig #727/R

BERLOT, Jean Baptiste (1775-?) French

£3289 $6053 €5000 Personnages en priere (46x39cm-18x15in) s.d.1821. 24-Jun-4 Christie's, Paris #137/R est:5000-7000

£13028 $22539 €18500 Caprice (71x97cm-28x38in) s.d.1791 prov. 10-Dec-3 Beaussant & Lefèvre, Paris #61/R est:15000-18000

BERLOW, H (?) ?
£310 $517 €453 Calm evening in punt (84x134cm-33x53in) s. 20-Oct-3 Blomqvist, Lysaker #1029 (N.KR 3600)

BERMAN, Eugene (1899-1972) American/Russian
£595 $1100 €869 Paesaggio umbro (36x25cm-14x10in) mono.d.1968 mono.i.d.68 verso. 10-Mar-4 Doyle, New York #70/R
£726 $1300 €1060 Monumental sarcophagus. i. 13-May-4 Dallas Auction Gallery, Dallas #145/R est:3000-5000
£756 $1300 €1104 Winter, Roma (30x41cm-12x16in) s.i.d.1967 board. 7-Dec-3 Treadway Gallery, Cincinnati #647/R
£979 $1664 €1400 Paysage metaphysique (92x65cm-36x26in) s.d.1929 prov.lit. 23-Nov-3 Cornette de St.Cyr, Paris #16/R
£1341 $2400 €1958 Le meduse sommerse - Sunken Medusa. s.i. 13-May-4 Dallas Auction Gallery, Dallas #318/R est:3000-5000
£1397 $2500 €2040 Il Capello della medusa. s.i. 13-May-4 Dallas Auction Gallery, Dallas #146/R est:3000-5000
£1412 $2500 €2062 Souvenir d'Italie (100x81cm-39x32in) s.d.1932 s.i.d.verso prov. 2-May-4 Bonhams & Butterfields, Los Angeles #3010/R est:4000-6000
£1536 $2750 €2243 Ruder, rilievi E obelisco. s.i. 13-May-4 Dallas Auction Gallery, Dallas #264/R est:3000-5000
£2761 $4500 €4031 Crollo di Pilon (75x100cm-30x39in) init.d.1964 init.i.d.April 1964 verso. 25-Sep-3 Christie's, Rockefeller NY #624/R est:6000-8000
£2945 $4800 €4300 Paesaggio con Anfiteatro Ruderi tombe al Tramonito (49x64cm-19x25in) init.d.1950 init.i.d.Dicembre 1958 verso. 25-Sep-3 Christie's, Rockefeller NY #625/R est:6000-8000
£3073 $5500 €4487 Stairs and balconies (77x42cm-30x17in) mono.d.1954 s.i.d.verso canvasboard prov. 6-May-4 Doyle, New York #81/R est:4000-6000
£3073 $5500 €4487 Una via Romana antica con temporalo distante. s.i. 13-May-4 Dallas Auction Gallery, Dallas #317/R est:3000-5000
£4261 $7500 €6221 La salida de puente (114x81cm-45x32in) init. i.d.Oct 1947 verso. 18-May-4 Sotheby's, New York #212/R est:10000-15000
Works on paper
£240 $400 €350 Happy birthday (37x26cm-15x10in) init.d.48 ink. 19-Oct-3 Bonhams & Butterfields, Los Angeles #7002
£671 $1242 €1000 Projet de costume, Count Almaviva (30x22cm-12x9in) mono.d.1953 Indian ink wash pastel. 15-Mar-4 Claude Boisgirard, Paris #12/R
£726 $1300 €1060 Leptis Magnus Medusa un ruins. s.i. W/C. 13-May-4 Dallas Auction Gallery, Dallas #287/R est:3000-5000
£815 $1500 €1190 Night shadows (38x28cm-15x11in) s. i.d.1919 verso brush ink wash W/C pastel. 10-Jun-4 Swann Galleries, New York #18/R est:800-1200
£1593 $2900 €2326 Giselle, stage designs (30x48cm-12x19in) init.d.1946 ink gouache. 29-Jun-4 Sotheby's, New York #361/R est:3000-5000
£2041 $3653 €3000 Saint Cecilia (18x18cm-7x7in) mono.d.1940 gouache W/C lit. 17-Mar-4 Tajan, Paris #5/R est:3000-3200
£2060 $3750 €3008 Study for stage set, ballet imperial (23x30cm-9x12in) init.d.1952 ink W/C cartouche prov. 29-Jun-4 Sotheby's, New York #360/R est:3000-5000

BERMAN, Eugene (attrib) (1899-1972) American/Russian
Works on paper
£311 $500 €454 Honor guard (25x18cm-10x7in) Indian ink W/C. 21-Aug-3 Doyle, New York #64/R

BERMAN, Harry G (1900-1932) American
£318 $550 €464 Spring landscape (41x51cm-16x20in) s.d.27. 10-Dec-3 Alderfer's, Hatfield #440/R

BERMAN, Wallace (1926-1976) American
Works on paper
£3514 $6500 €5130 Sound series (32x34cm-13x13in) verifax collage acrylic board exec 1967-68 prov.exhib. 12-Feb-4 Sotheby's, New York #114/R est:2000-3000
£3514 $6500 €5130 Sound series no.6 (32x34cm-13x13in) verifax collage acrylic board exec 1967-68 prov. 12-Feb-4 Sotheby's, New York #115/R est:2000-3000

BERMOND, Romain (20th C) French
Works on paper
£1033 $1870 €1550 La marche (37x98cm-15x39in) s. mixed media wood. 3-Apr-4 Neret-Minet, Paris #111/R est:2550-2850

BERMUDEZ, Cundo (1914-) Cuban
£6571 $11500 €9594 Mujer en balcon (39x24cm-15x9in) s. 19-Dec-3 Sotheby's, New York #1162/R est:10000-12000
£11765 $20000 €17177 Figuras con reloj (54x64cm-21x25in) s.d.87 prov. 19-Nov-3 Sotheby's, New York #168/R est:20000-25000
£12849 $23000 €18760 Two figures (91x61cm-36x24in) s. prov. 26-May-4 Sotheby's, New York #136/R est:18000-22000
Works on paper
£1882 $3200 €2748 Geometrico naranja y verde. Geometrico rojo y verde (24x17cm-9x7in) W/C ink pencil exec. c.1975 two prov. 18-Nov-3 Christie's, Rockefeller NY #109/R est:4000-6000
£2941 $5000 €4294 Pareja en el balcon - Couple on balcony (22x19cm-9x7in) W/C ink exec. c.1940 prov. 18-Nov-3 Christie's, Rockefeller NY #94/R est:6000-8000
£4396 $8000 €6418 Musicians (72x57cm-28x22in) s. ink W/C over pencil. 29-Jun-4 Sotheby's, New York #416/R est:10000-15000
£4706 $8000 €6871 Figura (55x42cm-22x17in) s.d.68 gouache prov. 19-Nov-3 Sotheby's, New York #166/R est:10000-15000
£4706 $8000 €6871 Pareja con guitarra - Couple with a guitar (16x27cm-6x11in) W/C pencil exec. c.1970 prov. 18-Nov-3 Christie's, Rockefeller NY #108/R est:10000-15000
£6593 $12000 €9626 Dona suerte y su Buena Fortuna (88x71cm-35x28in) s.d.1973 gouache prov. 29-Jun-4 Sotheby's, New York #660/R est:7000-8000
£7821 $14000 €11419 Woman in house with many windows (68x46cm-27x18in) s. gouache board exec.c.1948 prov. 26-May-4 Sotheby's, New York #138/R est:18000-22000

BERMUDEZ, Jorge (1883-1926) Argentinian
£738 $1373 €1100 Figure, Andes behind (49x47cm-19x19in) s. 2-Mar-4 Ansorena, Madrid #28/R

BERNADELLI (20th C) ?
£1832 $3242 €2748 Still life (71x77cm-28x30in) s.i. 27-Apr-4 Bolsa de Arte, Rio de Janeiro #32/R (B.R 10000)

BERNADSKY, Guennadi (1956-) Russian
£250 $408 €365 Ballet dancers in the rehearsal room (65x54cm-26x21in) s. 28-Sep-3 John Nicholson, Haslemere #20

BERNADSKY, Valentin Danilovitch (1917-) Russian
£450 $752 €657 Still life on the balcony (70x63cm-28x25in) s. 13-Jul-3 John Nicholson, Haslemere #133/R

BERNAERTS, Nicasius (1620-1678) Flemish
£13380 $23148 €19000 Portrait de Tambon, chien du Duc de Vendome (130x98cm-51x39in) s. 10-Dec-3 Beaussant & Lefèvre, Paris #21/R est:15000-18000

BERNAERTS, Nicasius (attrib) (1620-1678) Flemish
£10565 $18488 €15000 Un faisan et une poule faisane (53x64cm-21x25in) 18-Dec-3 Tajan, Paris #28/R est:15000-20000

BERNAL, Gonzalez (20th C) Spanish?
£426 $750 €622 Surrealistic figures floating over a landscape (99x81cm-39x32in) s.d.1932 verso panel. 22-May-4 Selkirks, St. Louis #770/R

BERNALDO, Allan T (1900-1988) Australian
£2439 $4366 €3561 Still life with peonies (67x84cm-26x33in) s. W/C. 10-May-4 Joel, Victoria #237 est:6000-8000 (A.D 6000)
Works on paper
£284 $509 €415 Officer and Mount, early Victoria era (62x52cm-24x20in) s.d.64 W/C. 10-May-4 Joel, Victoria #400a (A.D 700)
£311 $570 €467 Still life. W/C. 3-Jun-4 Joel, Victoria #188 (A.D 800)
£311 $570 €467 Horses drinking. W/C. 3-Jun-4 Joel, Victoria #243 (A.D 800)
£345 $538 €500 Red roses in a blue vase (45x37cm-18x15in) s. W/C. 1-Aug-2 Joel, Victoria #174 est:800-1200 (A.D 1000)
£379 $591 €550 Azaleas (37x44cm-15x17in) s. W/C. 1-Aug-2 Joel, Victoria #340a est:1500-2500 (A.D 1100)
£447 $702 €648 Rural lane (33x35cm-13x14in) s. W/C. 26-Aug-3 Christie's, Sydney #395 (A.D 1100)
£483 $753 €700 Stage coach, early days (51x72cm-20x28in) s.d.83 W/C. 1-Aug-2 Joel, Victoria #253 est:1500-2500 (A.D 1400)
£496 $878 €724 Hauling wool (55x65cm-22x26in) s. W/C. 3-May-4 Christie's, Melbourne #375 (A.D 1200)
£586 $914 €850 Mixed bunch (59x54cm-23x21in) s. W/C. 1-Aug-2 Joel, Victoria #233 est:1600-2000 (A.D 1700)
£840 $1528 €1226 Checking the horse's shoe (30x40cm-12x16in) s. W/C. 16-Jun-4 Deutscher-Menzies, Melbourne #324/R est:2400-3400 (A.D 2200)
£1179 $1851 €1710 White camelias (50x42cm-20x17in) s. W/C. 26-Aug-3 Christie's, Sydney #392 est:3000-4000 (A.D 2900)
£1221 $2223 €1783 Brining in the stock horses (50x64cm-20x25in) s. i.verso W/C. 16-Jun-4 Deutscher-Menzies, Melbourne #323/R est:3600-4800 (A.D 3200)

BERNARD, Bruce (1928-2000) British
Photographs
£2000 $3400 €2920 Francis Bacon standing in his studio doorway (40x31cm-16x12in) bromide print exec.1984. 19-Nov-3 Sotheby's, Olympia #239/R est:600-1000
£2400 $4080 €3504 Lucien Freud with a portrait of Leigh Bowery (38x50cm-15x20in) s.i.d.num.19/25 verso bromide print exec.1990. 19-Nov-3 Sotheby's, Olympia #240/R est:600-1000
£2600 $4420 €3796 Francis Bacon in his studio (41x30cm-16x12in) cibachrome exec.1984. 19-Nov-3 Sotheby's, Olympia #237/R est:600-1000
£3200 $5440 €4672 Francis Bacon in his studio (30x40cm-12x16in) cibachrome exec.1984. 19-Nov-3 Sotheby's, Olympia #238/R est:600-1000

BERNARD, Émile (1868-1941) French
£563 $986 €800 Paysage Vallonne region d'Auxerre (60x77cm-24x30in) 21-Dec-3 Thierry & Lannon, Brest #272
£1818 $3091 €2600 Homme accoude a un fauteuil (108x90cm-43x35in) 23-Nov-3 Cornette de St.Cyr, Paris #597/R est:3000-4000
£2098 $3566 €3000 Autoportrait (100x76cm-39x30in) prov. 23-Nov-3 Cornette de St.Cyr, Paris #598/R est:3000-4000
£3521 $6092 €5000 Don Quichotte a cheval (44x36cm-17x14in) s. cardboard. 9-Dec-3 Artcurial Briest, Paris #131/R est:2000-3000
£3642 $6666 €5500 Rue animee (50x35cm-20x14in) s. board. 7-Apr-4 Piasa, Paris #62 est:2500-3000
£4027 $7450 €6000 Reverie au bord de la mer (116x81cm-46x32in) studio st.verso. 15-Mar-4 Blanchet, Paris #72 est:5000-7000
£4287 $7673 €6259 La danseuse Persane aux fleurs (77x55cm-30x22in) painted 1913 lit. 25-May-4 Bukowskis, Stockholm #377/R est:35000-40000 (S.KR 58000)
£5034 $8910 €7500 Nu sur canape (81x129cm-32x51in) s.d.1930. 30-Apr-4 Tajan, Paris #178/R est:8000-10000
£5034 $9211 €7500 Chemin dans un sous-bois (100x69cm-39x27in) s.d.20. 7-Jul-4 Artcurial Briest, Paris #75 est:2000-2500
£5298 $9642 €8000 Corbeille de fruits sur table (50x61cm-20x24in) s.d.1931 cardboard. 15-Jun-4 Rossini, Paris #40/R est:4000-6000
£6000 $11040 €8760 Bathers in the lagoon, Venice (178x150cm-70x59in) 25-Mar-4 Christie's, Kensington #113/R est:6000-8000
£6207 $10366 €9000 Nu a la fleche (99x71cm-39x28in) s.d.23 cardboard. 17-Nov-3 Tajan, Paris #130/R est:8000-10000
£7285 $13331 €11000 Femme et enfants sous les arbres (51x61cm-20x24in) s. 7-Apr-4 Piasa, Paris #61/R est:3000-5000
£10917 $20087 €15939 Salome (88x67cm-35x26in) s.d.1910 prov.exhib. 8-Jun-4 Germann, Zurich #40/R est:25000-35000 (S.FR 25000)

£173333 $317200 €260000 Baigneuses et cygne (45x55cm-18x22in) s.d.1888 prov.lit. 7-Jun-4 Artcurial Briest, Paris #26/R est:150000-200000

Photographs

£5797 $9508 €8000 Paul Cezanne devant les grandes baigneuses (8x11cm-3x4in) i. silver print cardboard. 2-Jun-3 Tajan, Paris #142 est:8000-10000

Prints

£6667 $12267 €10000 La promenade (19x23cm-7x9in) s. print hand col exec. c.1888. 11-Jun-4 Villa Grisebach, Berlin #1515/R est:3000-4000
£13537 $24638 €19764 La lessive (11x39cm-4x15in) s.i.d.1888 print W/C lit. 18-Jun-4 Kornfeld, Bern #10/R est:35000 (S.FR 31000)

Sculpture

£13986 $24056 €20000 Porteuses d'eau sur le bord du Nil (51x74cm-20x29in) s.i. wood. 7-Dec-3 Livinec, Gaudcheau & Jezequel, Rennes #80/R

Works on paper

£268 $497 €400 Interieur d'Eglise (35x28cm-14x11in) s. Indian ink wash. 15-Mar-4 Blanchet, Paris #71
£387 $678 €550 Bretons en costume (24x32cm-9x13in) studio st. chl. 21-Dec-3 Thierry & Lannon, Brest #423
£537 $983 €800 Paysage d'Italie (25x48cm-10x19in) s. brown ink wash. 7-Jul-4 Artcurial Briest, Paris #11
£662 $1212 €1000 Modele (19x25cm-7x10in) s. pen wash. 7-Apr-4 Piasa, Paris #63
£700 $1253 €1050 Tete d'enfant (8x9cm-3x4in) i.verso chl. 16-May-4 Thierry & Lannon, Brest #29
£909 $1545 €1300 Fountain in Tonnerre (36x25cm-14x10in) s.i. sepia W/C Indian ink brush. 21-Nov-3 Reiss & Sohn, Konigstein #375/R est:1200
£1258 $2000 €1837 Landscapes (25x33cm-10x13in) s.d.90 W/C double-sided. 12-Sep-3 Skinner, Boston #469/R
£3521 $6162 €5000 Femme au travail (33x20cm-13x8in) studio st. chl exec c.1886-1888. 21-Dec-3 Thierry & Lannon, Brest #109/R est:4000-6000
£7383 $13732 €11000 Annonciation (104x82cm-41x32in) s.d.30 panel. 3-Mar-4 Tajan, Paris #68/R est:7000-8000

BERNARD, Francisco (fl.1845-1870) American

£591 $1100 €863 Half-length portrait of Lawyer holding book (61x51cm-24x20in) i.verso. 6-Mar-4 North East Auctions, Portsmouth #556/R

BERNARD, Jacques Samuel (attrib) (17th C) French

£7333 $13347 €11000 Tulips and other flowers in vase on ledge and inscents. Flowers in a glass vase on a ledge (39x35cm-15x14in) with sig. pair. 1-Jul-4 Christie's, Amsterdam #713/R est:8000-12000

BERNARD, Joseph (1864-1933) French

Sculpture

£1517 $2519 €2200 Tete de Salome (30cm-12in) s. plaster lit. 2-Oct-3 Sotheby's, Paris #157/R
£7483 $13619 €11000 Faune dansant (34cm-13in) s.num.5 black pat bronze marble base st.f.C.Valsuani. 8-Feb-4 Anaf, Lyon #48/R est:10000-12000
£10000 $17300 €14600 Dancing faun (71cm-28in) s.num.6 brown pat bronze st.f.C.Valsuani. 12-Dec-3 Sotheby's, London #264/R est:12000-18000
£14667 $26987 €22000 La jeunesse charme par l'amour (32cm-13in) s. num.9 brown pat. bronze cire perdue lit. 10-Jun-4 Camard, Paris #65/R est:15000-18000
£17832 $30315 €25500 Jeune fille a sa toilette (64cm-25in) s.verso num.10 brown green pat bronze Cast Valsuani lit. 1-Dec-3 Camard, Paris #25/R est:30000-35000
£23333 $42933 €35000 Tete de la jeune fille a la cruche (32cm-13in) s. num.148 brown gold pat bronze cire perdue prov.lit. 10-Jun-4 Camard, Paris #66/R est:35000-45000
£40000 $66400 €58000 Etreinte (40x45cm-16x18in) s. marble lit. 2-Oct-3 Sotheby's, Paris #40/R est:45000
£63381 $110918 €90000 Jeune fille a la cruche (184x42x54cm-72x17x21in) st.f.Valsuani pat bronze exhib.lit. 18-Dec-3 Tajan, Paris #21/R est:90000-100000

BERNARD, Leon (?) French?

£387 $643 €550 Vue de la Villa Abdel Tif (24x37cm-9x15in) s. cardboard. 16-Jun-3 E & Eve, Paris #176

BERNARD, Louis Michel (1885-1962) French

£3404 $5685 €4800 Paysage d'Algerie (195x230cm-77x91in) s. 16-Jun-3 Gros & Delettrez, Paris #254/R est:4000-6000

BERNARD, M (19th C) German

Works on paper

£550 $935 €803 Poole harbour (29x43cm-11x17in) s.d.June 2 '88. 26-Nov-3 Hamptons Fine Art, Godalming #102/R

BERNARD, Margaret (fl.1883-1924) British

Works on paper

£380 $608 €551 Jetty, Havre (33x33cm-13x13in) s. W/C. 12-Jan-3 Desmond Judd, Cranbrook #765

BERNARD, Mike (?) ?

Works on paper

£500 $880 €730 St Mary's Market, Petersfield (38x58cm-15x23in) s.d.97 mixed media. 18-May-4 Woolley & Wallis, Salisbury #253/R

BERNARD, Regis (?) French?

£567 $1031 €850 Botte d'asperges (27x35cm-11x14in) s. i.d.95 verso. 29-Jun-4 Chenu & Scrive, Lyon #19/R

BERNARD, Renee (20th C) French

£4133 $7605 €6200 Marche a Bamako (73x92cm-29x36in) s. i.verso exhib. 14-Jun-4 Gros & Delettrez, Paris #293/R est:6000-8000

Works on paper

£805 $1490 €1200 Portrait de femme Berbere (40x30cm-16x12in) s. gouache. 15-Mar-4 Gros & Delettrez, Paris #242/R
£851 $1421 €1200 Portrait d'homme Berbere (39x25cm-15x10in) s. gouache. 16-Jun-3 Gros & Delettrez, Paris #531/R

BERNARD, Valere (c.1860-1936) French

£3919 $7015 €5800 Printemps. Ete (175x125cm-69x49in) s. panel pair. 5-May-4 Claude Boisgirard, Paris #26/R est:3000-4000
£4236 $7074 €6100 Ete. Printemps. Automne (120x170cm-47x67in) s. set of 3. 25-Oct-3 Dianous, Marseille #391

BERNARDI, Domenico de (1892-1963) Italian

£851 $1421 €1200 On the kitchen table (20x29cm-8x11in) s. i.verso board. 14-Oct-3 Finarte Semenzato, Milan #10
£961 $1748 €1403 Landscape (25x36cm-10x14in) s.d.1944 panel. 16-Jun-4 Fischer, Luzern #2027/R (S.FR 2200)
£1921 $3497 €2805 Summer landscape with houses on a hill (35x43cm-14x17in) s.d.47 panel. 16-Jun-4 Fischer, Luzern #2028/R est:1800-2500 (S.FR 4400)
£4577 $8011 €6500 Red roofs in Malines (80x100cm-31x39in) s. board. 17-Dec-3 Finarte Semenzato, Milan #77/R est:3000-4000
£6000 $11040 €9000 Old mill in Besozzo (60x80cm-24x31in) s.d.1941 s.d.verso board. 8-Jun-4 Sotheby's, Milan #71/R est:5000-7000

BERNARDI, Joseph (1826-1907) German

£1528 $2414 €2200 Mountain ravine in Berner Oberland (105x88cm-41x35in) s. 5-Sep-3 Wendl, Rudolstadt #3282/R est:1400

BERNARDI, Ridolfo (1889-1968) Italian

£244 $401 €340 Along the Seine (40x50cm-16x20in) s. 10-Jun-3 Pandolfini, Florence #227

BERNARDIN (19/20th C) ?

Sculpture

£3400 $6256 €5100 Bust d'Africain (44x37x16cm-17x15x6in) s. brown pat bronze. 14-Jun-4 Gros & Delettrez, Paris #287/R est:2000-3000

BERNASCONI, Ugo (1874-1960) Argentinian

£2414 $4031 €3500 Still life (38x46cm-15x18in) init. prov.exhib. 17-Nov-3 Sant Agostino, Torino #225/R est:3000-4000
£4698 $8409 €7000 Little sisters (99x69cm-39x27in) init. cardboard exhib.lit. 29-May-4 Farsetti, Prato #443/R est:6000-8000

BERNAT, Martin (15/16th C) Spanish

£4932 $8384 €7200 Holy man praying (46x35cm-18x14in) tempera panel. 4-Nov-3 Ansorena, Madrid #33/R est:7200

BERNATH, Aurel (1895-1982) Hungarian

£5354 $9959 €7817 Flower girl (70x46cm-28x18in) s. 6-Mar-4 Dorotheum, Prague #50/R est:26000-40000 (C.KR 260000)
£15809 $28614 €23081 Badacsony (80x110cm-31x43in) s. 16-Apr-4 Mu Terem Galeria, Budapest #138/R (H.F 6000000)

BERNATH, Sandor (1892-?) American

Works on paper

£248 $400 €362 Yacht racing (28x36cm-11x14in) s. W/c. 20-Aug-3 James Julia, Fairfield #825/R
£267 $425 €390 Flying seagull above crashing waves (25x36cm-10x14in) s. W/C. 10-Sep-3 Alderfer's, Hatfield #326
£299 $475 €437 Figures in boat with full sails, another boat in the distance (41x51cm-16x20in) s. W/C. 10-Sep-3 Alderfer's, Hatfield #323
£314 $500 €458 Three racing sailing boats, flying birds (25x36cm-10x14in) s. W/C. 10-Sep-3 Alderfer's, Hatfield #324/R
£314 $500 €458 Two-masted sail boat with full sails (36x38cm-14x15in) s. W/C. 10-Sep-3 Alderfer's, Hatfield #328
£335 $600 €489 Yacht (27x37cm-11x15in) s. W/C gouache. 14-May-4 Skinner, Boston #290/R
£351 $650 €512 Sloop under sail (51x41cm-20x16in) s. W/C. 13-Feb-4 David Rago, Lambertville #11/R
£377 $600 €550 Three racing boats, flying birds (25x36cm-10x14in) s. W/C. 10-Sep-3 Alderfer's, Hatfield #325
£381 $700 €556 Topographical landscape (33x41cm-13x16in) s. W/C. 25-Jun-4 Freeman, Philadelphia #32/R
£409 $650 €597 Racing boats in full sail (48x41cm-19x16in) s. W/C. 10-Sep-3 Alderfer's, Hatfield #321/R
£432 $800 €631 Schooner under sail (43x43cm-17x17in) s. W/C. 13-Feb-4 David Rago, Lambertville #12/R
£440 $700 €642 Portrait of racing yacht (56x48cm-22x19in) s. W/C. 10-Sep-3 Alderfer's, Hatfield #319/R
£503 $800 €734 Portrait of two-masted ship under way with full sails (36x48cm-14x19in) s. W/C. 10-Sep-3 Alderfer's, Hatfield #320/R
£514 $950 €750 Spinnakers and sails (48x64cm-19x25in) s. W/C. 13-Feb-4 David Rago, Lambertville #14/R
£535 $850 €781 Lighthouse and buildings (43x41cm-17x16in) s. W/C. 10-Sep-3 Alderfer's, Hatfield #322/R
£601 $1100 €877 Two masted schooner under way with full sails (38x53cm-15x21in) W/C. 31-Jan-4 South Bay, Long Island #121
£726 $1300 €1060 Gertrude Thebaud of Gloucester, Mass (50x43cm-20x17in) s. W/C gouache. 14-May-4 Skinner, Boston #292/R est:500-700

BERNATZ, Johann Martin (1802-1878) German

£662 $1205 €1000 View of Ladenburg Church (51x40cm-20x16in) s.d.1833. 21-Jun-4 Dorotheum, Vienna #150/R

BERNAY-THERIC, Sauveur (20th C) French
£1074 $1976 €1600 Port de Marseille (30x45cm-12x18in) s. 29-Mar-4 Rieunier, Paris #47/R est:1000-1500

BERNDT, Carl (1878-1950) German?
£1216 $2177 €1800 Gladioli in vase (85x105cm-33x41in) s. 6-May-4 Michael Zeller, Lindau #592/R est:800

BERNDT, Siegfried (1880-?) German
£1000 $1790 €1500 Mountain landscape (89x74cm-35x29in) prov. 14-May-4 Ketterer, Munich #2/R est:1500-2500

BERNDTSON, Gunnar Fredrik (1854-1895) Finnish
£9859 $17056 €14000 Portrait of lady (33x24cm-13x9in) s.d.1886 panel. 13-Dec-3 Hagelstam, Helsinki #70/R est:15000

BERNE, Albert (1898-?) French?
£364 $618 €520 Le port d'Honfleur (46x55cm-18x22in) s. 24-Nov-3 Boscher, Cherbourg #702

BERNE-BELLECOUR, Étienne Prosper (1838-1910) French
£329 $605 €500 Portrait de jeune femme en rouge (17x12cm-7x5in) s.d.71 panel. 22-Jun-4 Ribeyre & Baron, Paris #43
£806 $1500 €1177 French sailor (36x25cm-14x10in) s. panel painted c.1880. 7-Mar-4 Treadway Gallery, Cincinnati #499/R est:1500-2000
£1132 $1800 €1653 Cavalry officer (48x35cm-19x14in) s.d.1905. 12-Sep-3 Skinner, Boston #224/R
£1210 $2226 €1767 Dragoon on horseback (37x26cm-15x10in) s.d.1899 panel. 14-Jun-4 Waddingtons, Toronto #289/R est:3000-5000 (C.D 3000)
£1259 $2140 €1800 Soldat constatant les degats au chariot (35x26cm-14x10in) s. panel. 18-Nov-3 Vanderkindere, Brussels #60 est:1700-2500
£1321 $2100 €1929 Mending his uniform (37x26cm-15x10in) s.d.1896. 12-Sep-3 Skinner, Boston #225/R
£1500 $2700 €2190 La halte (10x15cm-4x6in) s. panel. 21-Jan-4 Sotheby's, Olympia #423/R est:600-800

BERNE-BELLECOUR, Felix Georges (1867-1905) French
£1034 $1914 €1500 Le hameau (21x27cm-8x11in) s. panel. 11-Feb-4 Beaussant & Lefèvre, Paris #158/R est:1200-1500

BERNE-BELLECOUR, Jean Jacques (1874-?) French
£294 $491 €429 An officer at a campsite (41x33cm-16x13in) s.d.1910 prov. 17-Nov-3 Waddingtons, Toronto #190/R (C.D 650)
£1351 $2500 €1972 Man wearing black hat and red cape (41x33cm-16x13in) 13-Feb-4 Du Mouchelle, Detroit #2170/R est:2500-3500

BERNEKER, Louis Frederick (1876-1937) American
£441 $750 €644 In the park (41x51cm-16x20in) s. 21-Nov-3 Skinner, Boston #482/R

BERNER, Bernd (1930-) German
£362 $615 €529 Coloured dream (61x50cm-24x20in) acrylic prov. 25-Nov-3 Germann, Zurich #727 (S.FR 800)

BERNER, Marie (18/19th C) Danish
Works on paper
£935 $1477 €1356 Bouquet of flowers in vase (49x37cm-19x15in) bears sig.d.1806 verso pastel oval. 2-Sep-3 Rasmussen, Copenhagen #2042/R (D.KR 10000)

BERNERS, Lord Gerald (1883-1950) British
£300 $537 €438 Tivoli (33x41cm-13x16in) s.d.19 canvasboard prov. 14-May-4 Christie's, Kensington #522/R

BERNESE SCHOOL (17th C) Swiss
£560 $1003 €818 Portrait of bearded man (73x58cm-29x23in) panel. 13-May-4 Stuker, Bern #33/R (S.FR 1300)

BERNHARD, Pieter Gerardus (1813-1880) Dutch
£694 $1132 €1000 Interior scene. s.d.1860 panel. 29-Sep-3 Sotheby's, Amsterdam #111
£4514 $7538 €6500 Elegant lady in an interior (49x41cm-19x16in) s. panel. 21-Oct-3 Sotheby's, Amsterdam #166/R est:1500-2000

BERNHARD, Ruth (1905-) American
Photographs
£1693 $3200 €2472 Luminous body (34x15cm-13x6in) s. s.i.d.1962 verso gelatin silver print. 17-Feb-4 Christie's, Rockefeller NY #98/R est:3000-5000
£2000 $3680 €3000 Silk (16x34cm-6x13in) s. silver gelatin board. 10-Jun-4 Villa Grisebach, Berlin #1022/R est:2000-2500
£2156 $3600 €3148 Nude (24x16cm-9x6in) with sig. silver print. 21-Oct-3 Swann Galleries, New York #272/R est:2500-3500
£2395 $4000 €3497 Outside firm joint caliper (23x18cm-9x7in) s.i.d.1933 gelatin silver print exhib. 20-Oct-3 Christie's, Rockefeller NY #11/R est:5000-7000
£2874 $4800 €4196 Classic torso (25x19cm-10x7in) s. gelatin silver print on board. 16-Oct-3 Phillips, New York #121/R est:3000-5000
£3114 $5200 €4546 Silk (18x35cm-7x14in) with sig. s.i.d.1968 on mount silver print. 21-Oct-3 Swann Galleries, New York #271/R est:3500-4500
£3593 $6000 €5246 Classic torso with hands (34x49cm-13x19in) s. s.i.d.1952 verso photo printed later prov. 17-Oct-3 Sotheby's, New York #119/R est:3000-5000
£4491 $7500 €6557 In the box, horizontal (13x24cm-5x9in) s. s.i.d.1962 photo printed later. 17-Oct-3 Sotheby's, New York #1/R est:6000-8000
£14500 $24650 €21170 In the box, horizontal (19x34cm-7x13in) s. s.i.d.verso silver print exec.1962 printed later. 19-Nov-3 Sotheby's, Olympia #100/R est:4000-6000

BERNHARDT, Franz (1800-1860) Swiss
£1987 $3616 €3000 Portrait of a lady (93x102cm-37x40in) s.d.1847. 21-Jun-4 Dorotheum, Vienna #66/R est:2500-3000

BERNHARDT, Helmut (1905-1944) German
£743 $1330 €1100 Durnstein on the Donau (40x60cm-16x24in) s.d.39 board. 6-May-4 Michael Zeller, Lindau #593/R

BERNHARDT, Sarah (1844-1923) French
£4335 $7500 €6329 Self portrait (46x38cm-18x15in) s.i.d.1890. 11-Dec-3 Sotheby's, New York #172/R est:6000-8000
Sculpture
£2148 $3802 €3200 Buste d'homme (51cm-20in) s.d.1875 pat bronze. 30-Apr-4 Tajan, Paris #66/R est:3500-4000
£3636 $6073 €5200 Portrait de M. Daniela (46x33cm-18x13in) s. Carrare marble. 25-Jun-3 Digard, Paris #206b
£10959 $18630 €16000 Auto-portrait chauve-souris (20x15x11cm-8x6x4in) s. brown pat bronze. 5-Nov-3 Tajan, Paris #28/R

BERNI (20th C) ?
Works on paper
£1933 $3480 €2900 Untitled (41x28cm-16x11in) s. gouache exec.1971 lit. 25-Apr-4 Versailles Encheres #179 est:300-400

BERNI, Antonio (1905-1981) Argentinian
£1678 $2803 €2400 Portrait of woman (51x38cm-20x15in) s. cardboard. 30-Jun-3 Ansorena, Madrid #318/R
£4696 $8500 €6856 Ramona at the Moulin Rouge (102x52cm-40x20in) engraving. 30-Mar-4 Arroyo, Buenos Aires #36
£10656 $19500 €15558 Criollita (40x30cm-16x12in) board. 1-Jun-4 Arroyo, Buenos Aires #60
£10989 $20000 €16044 Village (40x55cm-16x22in) s. 29-Jun-4 Arroyo, Buenos Aires #100/R est:15000
£18994 $34000 €27731 Landscape (33x54cm-13x21in) s. board. 4-May-4 Arroyo, Buenos Aires #82/R est:12000
£27473 $50000 €40111 Girl in pink jumper (118x82cm-46x32in) s. 29-Jun-4 Arroyo, Buenos Aires #78/R est:50000
Prints
£3571 $6500 €5214 Bull scene (86x52cm-34x20in) s.i.d.65 engraving. 5-Jul-4 Arroyo, Buenos Aires #87/R est:6300
£3846 $7000 €5615 Bull scene (84x50cm-33x20in) s.d.68 engraving. 29-Jun-4 Arroyo, Buenos Aires #104/R est:7000
£3846 $7000 €5615 Party (77x52cm-30x20in) s.d.1965 i.verso engraving. 5-Jul-4 Arroyo, Buenos Aires #83/R est:3500
£7912 $14400 €11552 Ramona in the street (152x62cm-60x24in) engraving. 29-Jun-4 Arroyo, Buenos Aires #61/R est:9000
Works on paper
£8033 $14700 €11728 Ramona in the show (93x49cm-37x19in) graphite. 1-Jun-4 Arroyo, Buenos Aires #56

BERNI, Oliviero (1931-) Italian
£467 $859 €700 Still life with Chinese vase (52x70cm-20x28in) s. canvas on board painted 2003. 12-Jun-4 Meeting Art, Vercelli #889/R
£503 $931 €750 Autumn colours (51x61cm-20x24in) s. s.d.2003 verso canvas on board. 13-Mar-4 Meeting Art, Vercelli #420

BERNIER, Camille (1823-1903) French
£1060 $1928 €1600 Returning home with the cowherd (40x60cm-16x24in) s.i. 16-Jun-4 Hugo Ruef, Munich #931/R est:1200
£1469 $2453 €2100 Chemin dans un sous-bois (40x30cm-16x12in) s.d.1858. 26-Jun-3 Artcurial Briest, Paris #533 est:800-1200
£4056 $6976 €5800 Vaches au paturage en foret (95x71cm-37x28in) s. 7-Dec-3 Osenat, Fontainebleau #43 est:4200-4500

BERNIER, Camille (attrib) (1823-1903) French
£618 $1149 €902 Landscape (19x27cm-7x11in) s. board. 6-Mar-4 Dorotheum, Prague #29/R est:20000-45000 (C.KR 30000)

BERNIER, Georges (1862-1918) Belgian
£461 $770 €650 Cow and bull in a meadow landscape (40x56cm-16x22in) s. 20-Oct-3 Glerum, Amsterdam #204/R
£816 $1461 €1200 Vaches au pre (78x98cm-31x39in) 22-Mar-4 Amberes, Antwerp #178
£1793 $3317 €2600 Deux anes pres des bateaux de peche (36x51cm-14x20in) s. 16-Feb-4 Horta, Bruxelles #25 est:1200-1500

BERNINGER, Edmund (1843-?) German
£1469 $2526 €2100 Monch and Jungfrau mountains in evening (122x182cm-48x72in) s. 4-Dec-3 Neumeister, Munich #2706/R est:1000

BERNINGER, John E (20th C) American
£629 $1000 €918 Winter landscape with church (36x51cm-14x20in) s. board. 10-Sep-3 Alderfer's, Hatfield #312/R
£1258 $2000 €1837 Still life with pink and white flowers with blue leaves in brown vase (61x51cm-24x20in) s.d.1931. 10-Sep-3 Alderfer's, Hatfield #340/R est:500-700
£1397 $2500 €2040 White church (71x84cm-28x33in) s. prov. 6-May-4 Shannon's, Milford #5/R est:2500-3500
£1677 $2750 €2432 Farm in winter (41x51cm-16x20in) s. board. 4-Jun-3 Alderfer's, Hatfield #388/R est:2500-3500
£1879 $3250 €2743 Autumn landscape (64x76cm-25x30in) s. 10-Dec-3 Alderfer's, Hatfield #343 est:3000-5000

£2312 $4000 €3376 Autumn landscape (64x76cm-25x30in) s.d.1935. 10-Dec-3 Alderfer's, Hatfield #344 est:3000-5000
£2744 $4500 €3979 Autumn landscape with figures on country road (64x76cm-25x30in) s. 4-Jun-3 Alderfer's, Hatfield #391/R est:3000-5000
£7317 $12000 €10610 Winter landscape with snow covered ground and buildings (64x76cm-25x30in) s. 4-Jun-3 Alderfer's, Hatfield #387/R est:7000-9000

BERNINGHAUS, J Charles (1905-1988) American
£2647 $4500 €3865 Native settlement near Taos (41x51cm-16x20in) s. canvas on board prov. 1-Nov-3 Santa Fe Art, Santa Fe #237/R est:7000-10000
£2984 $5490 €4357 Road to Jalpa (56x71cm-22x28in) s. i.stretcher. 14-Jun-4 Waddingtons, Toronto #20/R est:5000-7000 (C.D 7400)

BERNINGHAUS, O E (1874-1952) American
£10588 $18000 €15458 Indian on horseback (25x20cm-10x8in) s.d.1947 canvas on board prov.lit. 1-Nov-3 Santa Fe Art, Santa Fe #72/R est:30000-40000
Works on paper
£4278 $8000 €6246 John Dunn trading post (38x48cm-15x19in) s. mixed media prov. 24-Jul-4 Coeur d'Alene, Hayden #181/R est:8000-12000

BERNINGHAUS, Oscar E (1874-1952) American
£3529 $6000 €5152 Indian summer. Indian on horseback in sunset landscape (9x8cm-4x3in) one s. board pair prov. 18-Nov-3 John Moran, Pasadena #120c est:5000-7000
£9358 $17500 €13663 Saddled horses in moonlight (23x33cm-9x13in) s. canvasboard prov. 24-Jul-4 Coeur d'Alene, Hayden #170/R est:15000-25000
£29412 $50000 €42942 Horses standing in a winter street scene (16x20cm-6x8in) s. prov. 18-Nov-3 John Moran, Pasadena #116 est:50000-70000
£44118 $75000 €64412 Saturday night dance (16x20cm-6x8in) s.i. prov. 18-Nov-3 John Moran, Pasadena #113 est:50000-70000
Works on paper
£40107 $75000 €58556 Indians following a wagon train (28x43cm-11x17in) s. gouache prov. 24-Jul-4 Coeur d'Alene, Hayden #169/R est:40000-60000

BERNINI, Giovanni Lorenzo (style) (1598-1680) Italian
Sculpture
£10694 $18181 €15400 Putto with sparrow (85cm-33in) white marble. 29-Oct-3 Il Ponte, Milan #770/R est:15000-18000

BERNIS, Genevieve (20th C) French
Works on paper
£486 $812 €700 Simoun (65x50cm-26x20in) s.d.2001 mixed media. 25-Oct-3 Cornette de St.Cyr, Paris #594

BERNS, Pamela (20th C) American
Works on paper
£219 $400 €320 Fortress (76x53cm-30x21in) W/C. 10-Jul-4 Hindman, Chicago #44/R

BERNSTEIN, Moshe (1920-) French?
£280 $467 €400 Nature morte aux fruits (29x39cm-11x15in) s. panel. 25-Jun-3 Rabourdin & Choppin de Janvry, Paris #172

BERNSTEIN, Theresa F (1890-2002) American
£479 $800 €699 Man in garden (51x61cm-20x24in) s. canvasboard. 18-Jun-3 Doyle, New York #8/R
£479 $800 €699 Inner harbour, possibly Gloucester (41x51cm-16x20in) s. board. 18-Jun 3 Doyle, New York #6/R
£749 $1400 €1094 Girl with flute (61x51cm-24x20in) s. 29-Feb-4 Grogan, Boston #93/R
£1236 $2100 €1805 Portrait of the artist's mother (61x51cm-24x20in) s.i.d.Jan 28.20. 21-Nov-3 Skinner, Boston #364/R est:2000-4000
£1923 $3500 €2808 Coastal town (30x40cm-12x16in) s. canvasboard. 29-Jun-4 Sotheby's, New York #289/R est:3000-5000
£2907 $5000 €4244 Shakespeare Garen, Central Park (22x27cm-9x11in) s. i.d.verso board prov. 3-Dec-3 Doyle, New York #281/R est:3000-5000
£4321 $7000 €6265 Street down to the water (72x89cm-28x35in) s. prov. 8-Aug-3 Barridorf, Portland #287/R est:7000-9000
£5978 $11000 €8728 Harbour (41x51cm-16x20in) s.d.18 i. verso board. 27-Jun-4 Freeman, Philadelphia #180/R est:1500-2500
£8140 $14000 €11884 Christmas in New York, Columbus Circle (40x30cm-16x12in) s. prov. 3-Dec-3 Doyle, New York #280/R est:6000-8000
Works on paper
£297 $550 €434 After school games (38x56cm-15x22in) s. W/C paper on board. 10-Mar-4 Doyle, New York #7/R
£462 $800 €675 Still life vase of flowers (56x43cm-22x17in) s. W/C. 10-Dec-3 Alderfer's, Hatfield #385/R
£509 $850 €743 Waiting room (33x41cm-13x16in) s.i. exec.c.1976. 20-Jun-3 Freeman, Philadelphia #30/R
£1415 $2250 €2066 Still life of vase of yellow flowers with cup and saucer in room interior (36x46cm-14x18in) s.d.27 W/C. 10-Sep-3 Alderfer's, Hatfield #295/R est:2500-3000

BERNT, Rudolf (1844-1914) Austrian
Works on paper
£345 $572 €500 Hall church square in the Tyrol (40x23cm-16x9in) s.d.1840 W/C. 30-Sep-3 Dorotheum, Vienna #300/R

BERNT, Sylva (20th C) ?
Sculpture
£2657 $4571 €3800 L'enlevement d'Europe (43x40cm-17x16in) terracotta htd painted nets. 3-Dec-3 Fraysse & Associes, Paris #86 est:1200-1500

BERNUTH, Ernst von (1833-1923) German
£1042 $1698 €1500 Girl in wood (74x59cm-29x23in) s.d.1883 canvas on panel. 26-Sep-3 Bolland & Marotz, Bremen #492 est:1500

BERONNEAU, Andre (1905-) French
£450 $766 €657 Mediterranean fishing boats (46x55cm-18x22in) s. 21-Nov-3 Walker's, Ottawa #220/R (C.D 1000)
£500 $850 €730 Noirmoutiers. Sailing vessels in coastal waters (18x23cm-7x9in) s.i.verso board two. 30-Oct-3 Duke & Son, Dorchester #206
£927 $1734 €1400 Douarnenez, les Plomarc'h (33x46cm-13x18in) s. 24-Jul-4 Thierry & Lannon, Brest #124/R
£950 $1511 €1378 Lac du bourget (33x46cm-13x18in) s. 11-Sep-3 Christie's, Kensington #57/R
£1100 $2035 €1606 Noirmoutiers (20x25cm-8x10in) s. s.i.verso board pair. 11-Feb-4 Sotheby's, Olympia #142/R est:1000-1500
£1900 $3021 €2755 Bord de mer au Cap Ferrat (50x100cm-20x39in) s. 11-Sep-3 Christie's, Kensington #56/R est:1500-2000

BEROUD, Louis (1852-1910) French
£1100 $1969 €1606 Figures in a church interior. s.d.1886. 22-Mar-4 Bonhams & Brooks, Norfolk #314/R
£3421 $6295 €5200 Gardien du Louvre (21x16cm-8x6in) s.d.1912 canvas on cardboard. 24-Jun-4 Christie's, Paris #159/R est:2500-3500
£15000 $25500 €21900 Elegante dans le Square Ste Clotilde (55x46cm-22x18in) s.d.1896. 19-Nov-3 Bonhams, New Bond Street #122/R est:20000-30000

BERRA, William (1952-) American
£279 $500 €407 Back road to Chimayo. s.i. 13-May-4 Dallas Auction Gallery, Dallas #330/R

BERRES, Joseph von (1821-1912) Austrian
£915 $1520 €1300 Hussars riding out (69x126cm-27x50in) s. i. verso. 16-Jun-3 Dorotheum, Vienna #150/R
£993 $1808 €1500 Roman countryside (30x40cm-12x16in) s. panel. 21-Jun-4 Dorotheum, Vienna #17/R est:1600-2000

BERRESFORD, Virginia (1904-) American
£7186 $12000 €10492 Under the Bigtop (61x76cm-24x30in) s. 23-Oct-3 Shannon's, Milford #160/R est:10000-15000
Works on paper
£270 $500 €394 Dancing at the Savoy (53x36cm-21x14in) s. W/C. 15-Feb-4 Outer Cape Auctions, Provincetown #46
£419 $775 €612 Dancing at the Savoy (53x36cm-21x14in) s. W/C. 15-Feb-4 Outer Cape Auctions, Provincetown #28/R

BERROCAL, Miguel (1933-) Spanish
Sculpture
£824 $1500 €1203 Alice II (7cm-3in) brass copper steel 14 assembled elements executed 1982. 29-Jun-4 Sotheby's, New York #536/R est:2000-3000
£879 $1600 €1283 Romeo and Juliet (24x16cm-9x6in) brass 17 assembled elements prov. 29-Jun-4 Sotheby's, New York #521/R est:1500-2000
£900 $1656 €1314 Romeo and Juliet (15x24x13cm-6x9x5in) s.num.1166 brass sixteen parts lit. 24-Jun-4 Sotheby's, Olympia #558/R est:800-1200
£1007 $1782 €1500 Torse (30cm-12in) s. num.1127/2000 bronze. 27-Apr-4 Campo & Campo, Antwerp #8/R est:750-1000
£1049 $1804 €1500 La Totoche (22x22x9cm-9x9x4in) bronze. 3-Dec-3 Hauswedell & Nolte, Hamburg #722/R est:1000
£1088 $1948 €1600 Arcimboldo (22cm-9in) s. num.487/1000 brown pat bronze blk pat bronze base. 19-Mar-4 Millon & Associes, Paris #179 est:600-800
£1208 $2223 €1800 Hoplita (25cm-10in) s. bronze. 24-Mar-4 Hugo Ruef, Munich #1651 est:1800
£1297 $2400 €1894 Paloma Jet. s. brass sold with a book. 17-Jan-4 Susanin's, Chicago #122/R est:1500-2500
£1333 $2440 €2000 Romeo et Juliette (15x21x12cm-6x8x5in) num.553/2000 polished bronze. 7-Jun-4 Palais de Beaux Arts, Brussels #350 est:2000-3000
£1409 $2622 €2100 Romeo et Juliette (12x21x9cm-5x8x4in) s. num. base brass exec 1966-1967. 3-Mar-4 Tajan, Paris #222 est:1800-2000
£1419 $2497 €2100 Richelieu (20cm-8in) s. num.847/2000 60 pieces brass exec 1968-1073. 18-May-4 Tajan, Paris #98/R est:1500-2000
£1429 $2557 €2100 Untitled (25cm-10in) s. num.179/1000 polished bronze moving parts blk pat steel base. 19-Mar-4 Millon & Associes, Paris #180 est:2000-3000
£1500 $2715 €2190 Torero (28cm-11in) s.num.1109/2000 brass bronze baze. 1-Apr-4 Christie's, Kensington #214/R est:1000-1500
£1517 $2534 €2200 Goliath (25cm-10in) i. brass Cast G and S Reischauer. 9-Jul-3 Hugo Ruef, Munich #1831/R est:1300
£1613 $3000 €2355 Omaggio and Arcimboldo (29cm-11in) s. st.898/1000 base gold pat bronze. 3-Mar-4 Christie's, Rockefeller NY #379/R est:1500-2000
£1622 $3000 €2368 Richelieu (20x15x12cm-8x6x5in) s.num.1316/2000 injection moulded brass puzzle designed 1972. 12-Feb-4 Sotheby's, New York #118/R est:1500-2000
£1818 $3091 €2600 Romeo et Juliette (16x21x21cm-6x8x8in) s.num.1312 gilt brass. 25-Nov-3 Tajan, Paris #37/R est:1800-2000
£1989 $3500 €2904 Homage to Giuseppe Arcimboldo (28cm-11in) s.num.542/1000 pat bronze puzzle. 23-May-4 Treadway Gallery, Cincinnati #902/R est:3500-4000
£2027 $3750 €2959 Maria of the O (20x10x8cm-8x4x3in) s. num.69/200 black polished bronze 7 parts prov.lit. 12-Feb-4 Sotheby's, New York #197/R est:1000-1500
£2055 $3493 €3000 Totoche. s. pat bronze. 10-Nov-3 Horta, Bruxelles #201
£2198 $4000 €3209 Goliath (25cm-10in) brass 80 assembled elements executed 1968-72. 29-Jun-4 Sotheby's, New York #533/R est:2500-3500
£2273 $4000 €3319 Torero (28x20cm-11x8in) s.num.1690/2000 brass puzzle. 23-May-4 Treadway Gallery, Cincinnati #901/R est:3000-3500
£2448 $4161 €3500 Siextasis (18cm-7in) st.sig.i. pat.bronze. 27-Nov-3 Lempertz, Koln #41/R est:3600
£2797 $4755 €4000 La Menina II (34cm-13in) st.sig.i. pat.bronze. 27-Nov-3 Lempertz, Koln #30/R est:2400
£3000 $5190 €4380 Il cavallo (38cm-15in) s.num.1615/2000 gold pat bronze base. 11-Dec-3 Christie's, Kensington #121/R est:1000-1500
£3061 $5480 €4500 Torrero (28cm-11in) s. num.1122/2000 gilt bronze. 19-Mar-4 Millon & Associes, Paris #178/R est:1500-2000
£3521 $6092 €5000 Lorelei (28x16cm-11x6in) s. num.190/500 brown pat polished bronze lit. 13-Dec-3 De Vuyst, Lokeren #23/R est:3800-4500

£3521 $6092 €5000 Goliath (24cm-9in) st.sig. i. brass Cast.G and S Reischauer. 13-Dec-3 Lempertz, Koln #288/R est:1200
£3741 $6697 €5500 Goliath (24cm-9in) s. num.547/2000 gilt pat bronze st.f.GS Reischauer. 19-Mar-4 Millon & Associes, Paris #177/R est:1500-2000
£4054 $7500 €5919 Torero (27x19cm-11x7in) s.num.1789/2000 injection moulded brass puzzle. 12-Feb-4 Sotheby's, New York #117/R est:2000-2500
£10811 $20000 €15784 St Agatha (32x21cm-13x8in) brown pat bronze incl welded metal base prov.exhib.lit. 12-Feb-4 Sotheby's, New York #190/R est:3000-5000
£12973 $24000 €18941 Woman in armchair (28x20x19cm-11x8x7in) chromate bronze sandstone base 8 parts exec 1963 prov.lit. 12-Feb-4 Sotheby's, New York #178/R est:3000-5000

BERROETA, Pierre de (1914-) French
£270 $500 €394 Figures walking by a canal (66x91cm-26x36in) s. painted c.1950. 15-Jul-4 Sotheby's, New York #94/R
£497 $909 €750 Personnages (92x73cm-36x29in) s.d.67. 7-Apr-4 Piasa, Paris #212
Works on paper
£685 $1164 €1000 Street in Paris (47x62cm-19x24in) s. gouache. 4-Nov-3 Ansorena, Madrid #287/R

BERRY, Arthur (1925-1994) British
Works on paper
£350 $627 €511 Two garages (76x102cm-30x40in) s. mixed media. 16-Mar-4 Bonhams, Leeds #587
£350 $627 €511 Mother and child (73x53cm-29x21in) s. mixed media. 16-Mar-4 Bonhams, Leeds #588

BERRY, Berry F (fl.1874-1893) British
Works on paper
£460 $782 €672 Kew Bridge, winter (34x53cm-13x21in) s. W/C. 27-Nov-3 Greenslade Hunt, Taunton #958

BERRY, Carroll Thayer (1886-?) American
£690 $1250 €1007 Pigeon cove (23x30cm-9x12in) s.i.d.1939 masonite. 16-Apr-4 James Julia, Fairfield #563/R est:1500-2500
£829 $1500 €1210 Rockport coastline (23x33cm-9x13in) s. i.d.1941 verso masonite. 16-Apr-4 James Julia, Fairfield #562/R est:2000-3000

BERRY, Patrick Vincent (1843-1914) American
£818 $1300 €1194 Cows grazing by a forest's edge (32x42cm-13x17in) s. 13-Sep-3 Weschler, Washington #728/R

BERRY, Philippe (1956-) French
Sculpture
£3497 $5944 €5000 Trois petits ours (59x18x13cm-23x7x5in) s. polished gilt brown pat bronze edition 4/8. 27-Nov-3 Calmels Cohen, Paris #68/R est:2000-2500
£7000 $12950 €10500 Hyppos (26x90x20cm-10x35x8in) s.d.97 num.5/8 bronze prov.lit. 18-Jul-4 Sotheby's, Paris #281/R est:2000-4000
£21333 $39467 €32000 Equilibre d'elephants (182cm-72in) s.d.97 num.5/8 bronze prov.lit. 18-Jul-4 Sotheby's, Paris #279/R est:10000-15000

BERSANI, Stefano (1872-1914) Italian
£500 $925 €730 Travellers crossing a marsh (85x140cm-33x55in) s. 13-Jul-4 Rosebery Fine Art, London #588
£650 $1203 €975 Italian mountain landscapes (65x109cm-26x43in) one s. pair. 13-Jul-4 Rosebery Fine Art, London #587

BERSERIK, Herman (1921-2002) Dutch
£1818 $3036 €2600 Two girl friends (13x19cm-5x7in) s.d.1989. 30-Jun-3 Sotheby's, Amsterdam #445/R
Works on paper
£1342 $2483 €2000 Interior. Summer landscape. Goat (24x36cm-9x14in) s. two d.45 gouache set of three. 15-Mar-4 Sotheby's, Amsterdam #199/R est:2000-3000

BERSIER, Jean Eugene (1895-1978) French
£216 $400 €315 Floral still life (66x81cm-26x32in) s. 17-Jan-4 New Orleans Auction, New Orleans #517
£588 $1000 €858 Harlequin (109x66cm-43x26in) s. 22-Nov-3 New Orleans Auction, New Orleans #682 est:1200-1800

BERTA, Alfredo (1895-1974) ?
£647 $1100 €945 Landscape in Atlantide (54x55cm-21x22in) s. cardboard. 25-Nov-3 Galeria y Remates, Montevideo #16/R

BERTALAN, Albert (1899-?) Hungarian
£345 $572 €500 Nu allonge (55x66cm-22x26in) s. 1-Oct-3 Millon & Associes, Paris #132/R
£470 $813 €686 Autumn street in Paris (54x38cm-21x15in) s. 12-Dec-3 Kieselbach, Budapest #9/R (H.F 180000)

BERTANI, Giovanni-Battista (1516-1576) Italian
Works on paper
£1800 $3294 €2628 Rape of Europa (17x22cm-7x9in) i. pen ink brown wash prov. 6-Jul-4 Christie's, London #7/R est:1500-2000

BERTAUX, Jacques (fl.1776-1802) French
£915 $1520 €1300 Scene d'interieur d'etable (22x28cm-9x11in) s. panel. 13-Jun-3 Ferri, Paris #47/R
£5282 $9244 €7500 La vision de Saint Hubert Parodie de la chasse a courre (20x25cm-8x10in) s.d.1778 canvas on panel oval pair. 18-Dec-3 Tajan, Paris #42/R est:4000-6000

BERTAUX, Léon (1827-?) French
Sculpture
£8500 $15300 €12410 Sara at the bath (72x75cm-28x30in) s.i. brown pat bronze green velvet base. 21-Apr-4 Sotheby's, London #118/R est:10000-15000

BERTEAULT, Jules Louis (19/20th C) Swiss
£1761 $3046 €2500 Cotes rocheuses (54x73cm-21x29in) s.d.1907. 9-Dec-3 Chambelland & Giafferi, Paris #20/R est:2500-3000

BERTEAUX, Hippolyte-Dominique (1843-1928) French
Works on paper
£1361 $2436 €2000 Eros et Venus (76x47cm-30x19in) i.d.1870 pierre noire htd white. 17-Mar-4 Tajan, Paris #141/R est:1500-2000

BERTELLI, Flavio (1865-1941) Italian
£1831 $3039 €2600 Sentiero al mare (50x38cm-20x15in) s.verso wood. 11-Jun-3 Christie's, Rome #118/R est:2500-3000
£1831 $3039 €2600 Sentiero a Bellaria (50x40cm-20x16in) s.i.d.1940 verso wood. 11-Jun-3 Christie's, Rome #119/R est:2500-3000
£3099 $5144 €4400 La vigna a Pennabilli (24x37cm-9x15in) s.i.d.1924 panel. 11-Jun-3 Christie's, Rome #117/R est:3300-3800

BERTELLI, Luigi (1832-1916) Italian
£1403 $2301 €1950 Sunset (22x37cm-9x15in) 5-Jun-3 Adma, Formigine #503 est:1200-1400
£2158 $3540 €3000 View of Monte Donato (46x62cm-18x24in) 5-Jun-3 Adma, Formigine #479 est:3200-3500
£2878 $4719 €4000 Quarry (52x64cm-20x25in) 5-Jun-3 Adma, Formigine #491 est:3700-4000

BERTELLI, Renato Guiseppe (1900-1974) Italian
Sculpture
£6936 $12000 €10127 Continuous profile of Mussolini (48cm-19in) ebonized wood metal lit. 11-Dec-3 Sotheby's, New York #199/R est:10000-15000

BERTELSEN, Aage (1873-1945) Danish
£284 $508 €415 Landscape from Susaaen (38x58cm-15x23in) s. 12-Jan-4 Rasmussen, Vejle #243 (D.KR 3000)
£5819 $10649 €8496 Evening in the mess room (39x60cm-15x24in) s.d.1907-08 i.d.verso. 9-Jun-4 Rasmussen, Copenhagen #1768/R est:30000 (D.KR 65000)

BERTELSEN, Albert (1921-) Danish
£461 $783 €673 Pier with figures (34x50cm-13x20in) init.d.52 i.verso. 10-Nov-3 Rasmussen, Vejle #592/R (D.KR 5000)
£957 $1550 €1388 Mountain composition (50x125cm-20x49in) mono. d.1977 verso. 4-Aug-3 Rasmussen, Vejle #563/R (D.KR 10000)
£1087 $1946 €1587 Cliff fragment (90x60cm-35x24in) s.d.85 prov. 12-Jan-4 Rasmussen, Vejle #474/R (D.KR 11500)
£1244 $2015 €1804 The sewing machine (81x100cm-32x39in) s.d.1974 verso. 4-Aug-3 Rasmussen, Vejle #560 est:15000-20000 (D.KR 13000)
£1323 $2369 €1932 Road across the mountains (61x75cm-24x30in) s. s.d.1975 verso prov. 12-Jan-4 Rasmussen, Vejle #471/R est:10000 (D.KR 14000)
£1374 $2199 €2006 Light mountains (40x70cm-16x28in) s.d.1975. 22-Sep-3 Rasmussen, Vejle #562/R est:6000-8000 (D.KR 14500)
£2107 $3518 €3076 Resting in the mountains (60x80cm-24x31in) s.d.1976. 25-Oct-3 Rasmussen, Havnen #4003/R est:10000-15000 (D.KR 22500)
£2268 $4060 €3311 The white house (45x100cm-18x39in) s. s.i.d.1980 verso prov. 12-Jan-4 Rasmussen, Vejle #472/R est:10000 (D.KR 24000)
£2581 $4387 €3768 Grey light, Norway (81x100cm-32x39in) s.i.d.1985. 10-Nov-3 Rasmussen, Vejle #593/R est:15000-20000 (D.KR 28000)
£2891 $4626 €4221 Clochard at Gare du Nord, Paris (116x104cm-46x41in) s.d.81 exhib. 22-Sep-3 Rasmussen, Vejle #561/R est:25000 (D.KR 30500)
£3069 $5738 €4481 Sunshine through fog, Faroe Islands (90x124cm-35x49in) mono. 25-Feb-4 Kunsthallen, Copenhagen #1/R est:5000 (D.KR 34000)
£3592 $6429 €5244 Figures by the fjord, Norway (81x100cm-32x39in) s. prov. 12-Jan-4 Rasmussen, Vejle #470/R est:30000 (D.KR 38000)
£3710 $6642 €5417 Mountain light - houses at foot of snow covered mountains (80x70cm-31x28in) s. s.i.d.1977 verso. 10-May-4 Rasmussen, Vejle #534/R est:20000 (D.KR 41000)
£4055 $6894 €5920 Mountain walking, Norway (81x100cm-32x39in) s. s.d.1982 verso. 10-Nov-3 Rasmussen, Vejle #591/R est:35000 (D.KR 44000)
£4064 $7275 €5933 The mountain farmer (65x80cm-26x31in) s.d.74 verso. 12-Jan-4 Rasmussen, Vejle #473/R est:25000-30000 (D.KR 43000)

BERTELSMANN, Walter (1877-1963) Dutch
£280 $481 €400 Landscape with Worpswede under high cloud (24x32cm-9x13in) mono. fibreboard. 5-Dec-3 Bolland & Marotz, Bremen #350
£417 $679 €600 On the Weser - near Farge (26x39cm-10x15in) s.d.Juli 1908 board. 26-Sep-3 Bolland & Marotz, Bremen #294/R
£451 $736 €650 Evening on the North Sea (49x68cm-19x27in) s. i. verso board. 26-Sep-3 Bolland & Marotz, Bremen #295/R
£559 $962 €800 Evening at the Weser estuary (48x67cm-19x26in) s. board. 5-Dec-3 Bolland & Marotz, Bremen #346/R
£559 $962 €800 Late evening at Weyerberg (50x69cm-20x27in) s. board double-sided. 5-Dec-3 Bolland & Marotz, Bremen #349/R
£699 $1203 €1000 Swamp (39x56cm-15x22in) s. i.verso board. 5-Dec-3 Bolland & Marotz, Bremen #348/R
£927 $1687 €1400 Winter scene in Worpswede (33x40cm-13x16in) s.d.26. 18-Jun-4 Bolland & Marotz, Bremen #327/R
£1399 $2406 €2000 Weser estuary (70x100cm-28x39in) s. exhib. 5-Dec-3 Bolland & Marotz, Bremen #344/R est:3300
£2098 $3608 €3000 Evening cloud over the Hamme (67x96cm-26x38in) s.d.1923. 5-Dec-3 Bolland & Marotz, Bremen #345/R est:3300

BERTHAULT, Pierre Gabriel (attrib) (1748-1819) Dutch
Works on paper
£2817 $4873 €4000 Supplice de Foullon a la Place de Greve (25x29cm-10x11in) i. W/C Chinese ink after Jean Louis Prieur. 10-Dec-3 Beaussant & Lefèvre, Paris #49/R est:6000-6500

BERTHELEMY, Jean Simon (1743-1811) French
£10556 $19000 €15412 Sleeping nude (40x32cm-16x13in) oval prov.exhib.lit. 23-Jan-4 Christie's, Rockefeller NY #12/R est:10000-15000
£15827 $25957 €22000 Bacchante etendue jouant des cymbales. Jupiter et Leda (21x26cm-8x10in) pair prov.lit. 6-Jun-3 Maigret, Paris #102/R est:15000-20000

BERTHELSEN, Christian (1839-1909) Danish
£377 $600 €550 Woodland (53x69cm-21x27in) mono.d.85. 12-Sep-3 Skinner, Boston #242/R
£470 $800 €686 View from Faeno to Hindsgavl (48x82cm-19x32in) mono. 29-Nov-3 Rasmussen, Havnen #2133/R (D.KR 5000)
£719 $1337 €1050 View of Kolding Fjord (42x80cm-17x31in) mono. 2-Mar-4 Rasmussen, Copenhagen #1350/R (D.KR 8000)
£984 $1604 €1437 Wooded landscape with figures walking (66x90cm-26x35in) s.d.1850. 28-Sep-3 Hindemae, Ullerslev #56/R (D.KR 10500)
£1438 $2674 €2099 Danish summer landscape with avenue in sunshine (97x131cm-38x52in) init.d.03 prov. 2-Mar-4 Rasmussen, Copenhagen #1386/R est:15000 (D.KR 16000)
£1968 $3208 €2873 Prospect view of Svendborg (55x87cm-22x34in) init. 27-Sep-3 Rasmussen, Havnen #2118/R est:15000-20000 (D.KR 21000)

BERTHELSEN, Christian (attrib) (1839-1909) Danish
£378 $677 €552 Landscape from Smidstrup near Borgense (68x95cm-27x37in) s.stretcher. 12-Jan-4 Rasmussen, Vejle #436 (D.KR 4000)

BERTHELSEN, Johann (1883-1969) American
£621 $1000 €907 Floral still life's (25x20cm-10x8in) s. board pair. 20-Aug-3 James Julia, Fairfield #1278/R
£1058 $2000 €1545 Vase of flowers (51x41cm-20x16in) s. canvasboard. 22-Feb-4 Bonhams & Butterfields, Los Angeles #7008 est:700-900
£1453 $2500 €2121 Bethesda fountain, Central Park, New York City (30x22cm-12x9in) s. s.i.verso. 3-Dec-3 Doyle, New York #279/R est:3000-5000
£2096 $3500 €3060 United Nations (46x61cm-18x24in) s. s.i.verso prov. 23-Oct-3 Shannon's, Milford #9/R est:4000-6000
£2326 $4000 €3396 Winter in Central Park, New York City (62x75cm-24x30in) s. prov. 3-Dec-3 Doyle, New York #277/R est:7000-9000
£2844 $4750 €4152 United Nations (41x51cm-16x20in) s. prov. 23-Oct-3 Shannon's, Milford #7/R est:4000-6000
£3198 $5500 €4669 Old Trinity Church (40x30cm-16x12in) s. canvasboard prov. 3-Dec-3 Doyle, New York #278/R est:5000-7000
£3281 $5250 €4790 New York City winter scene, Fifth Avenue (41x30cm-16x12in) s. canvasboard. 20-Sep-3 Jeffery Burchard, Florida #59a/R
£3438 $5500 €5019 Fifth Ave view of Trinity Church NYC in winter (41x30cm-16x12in) s. canvasboard. 20-Sep-3 Jeffery Burchard, Florida #59/R
£3784 $7000 €5525 Washington Square in spring (30x41cm-12x16in) s. canvasboard. 11-Mar-4 Christie's, Rockefeller NY #58/R est:4000-6000
£4000 $7000 €5840 View of New York, probably looking towards Queensborough Bridge (51x41cm-20x16in) s. 19-Dec-3 Sotheby's, New York #1126/R est:4000-6000
£4000 $7000 €5840 Grace Church (30x23cm-12x9in) s. board. 19-Dec-3 Sotheby's, New York #1130/R est:4000-6000
£4324 $8000 €6313 Little church around the corner (41x30cm-16x12in) s. prov. 11-Mar-4 Christie's, Rockefeller NY #40/R est:4000-6000
£4360 $7500 €6366 New York City winter scene (41x30cm-16x12in) s. i.verso canvasboard. 6-Dec-3 Pook & Pook, Downington #295/R est:4000-6000
£4469 $8000 €6525 At the Plaza, New York (30x41cm-12x16in) s. prov. 6-May-4 Shannon's, Milford #148/R est:4000-6000
£5389 $9000 €7868 Flags in winter (41x30cm-16x12in) s. canvasboard. 23-Oct-3 Shannon's, Milford #8/R est:5000-7000
£5405 $10000 €7891 Fifth Avenue looking south (41x30cm-16x12in) s. prov. 11-Mar-4 Christie's, Rockefeller NY #39/R est:4000-6000
£5590 $9000 €8161 Brooklyn Bridge (44x34cm-17x13in) s. s.i.verso canvasboard. 14-Jan-4 Christie's, Rockefeller NY #48/R est:5000-7000
£5689 $9500 €8306 Harbour scene in winter (41x30cm-16x12in) s. canvasboard prov. 23-Oct-3 Shannon's, Milford #54/R est:3000-5000
£9497 $17000 €13866 Fifth Avenue, winter (51x61cm-20x24in) s. 26-May-4 Doyle, New York #140/R est:5000-7000

BERTHILS, Birger (1891-1967) Norwegian
£516 $831 €753 Beached boat (35x51cm-14x20in) s. panel. 25-Aug-3 Blomqvist, Lysaker #1023 (N.KR 6000)

BERTHOIS-RIGAL, Bernard (1927-) French
Works on paper
£816 $1461 €1200 Untitled (146x89cm-57x35in) mono.s. mixed media canvas prov. 21-Mar-4 Calmels Cohen, Paris #111/R

BERTHOLLE, Jean (1909-1996) French
£367 $660 €550 Composition (29x20cm-11x8in) s. 24-Apr-4 Cornette de St.Cyr, Paris #436/R
£694 $1159 €1000 Composition abstraite (285x11cm-112x4in) s.d.65 panel. 21-Oct-3 Artcurial Briest, Paris #644
£733 $1320 €1100 Composition (24x41cm-9x16in) s.d.1960 prov. 25-Apr-4 Versailles Encheres #43
£800 $1440 €1200 Composition (54x66cm-21x26in) s.d.1956. 24-Apr-4 Cornette de St.Cyr, Paris #438/R
Works on paper
£387 $670 €550 La piazetta (14x21cm-6x8in) s.i. W/C. 14-Dec-3 Versailles Encheres #8
£476 $794 €680 Sans titre (26x34cm-10x13in) s.d.1958 collage ink. 25-Jun-3 Maigret, Paris #24
£500 $900 €750 Composition (50x50cm-20x20in) s.d.1961 gouache. 24-Apr-4 Cornette de St.Cyr, Paris #437
£1020 $1827 €1500 Untitled (76x88cm-30x35in) s.d.1979 mixed media prov. 21-Mar-4 Calmels Cohen, Paris #112/R est:1800-2000
£1379 $2303 €2000 Composition (23x36cm-9x14in) s.d.1961 gouache. 17-Nov-3 Charbonneaux, Paris #116 est:500-600

BERTHOLO, René (1935-) Portuguese
£16679 $30022 €24351 Nouvelles du Nord (92x65cm-36x26in) s.d.66 exhib. 26-Apr-4 Bukowskis, Stockholm #572a/R est:6000-8000 (S.KR 230000)

BERTHOME-SAINT-ANDRE (1905-1977) French
£268 $502 €400 Devant la ferme scene de village (27x35cm-11x14in) s. board painted c.1932. 24-Feb-4 Thierry & Lannon, Brest #164/R
£302 $565 €450 Sur la plage (20x19cm-8x7in) s. paper painted c.1959. 24-Feb-4 Thierry & Lannon, Brest #158
£309 $577 €460 Sortie de Theatre (24x19cm-9x7in) s. board painted c.1936. 24-Feb-4 Thierry & Lannon, Brest #162
£356 $665 €530 Jardin public (33x24cm-13x9in) s. board. 24-Feb-4 Thierry & Lannon, Brest #154
£403 $753 €600 Maya (46x27cm-18x11in) s. 24-Feb-4 Thierry & Lannon, Brest #159/R
£517 $859 €750 Nu allonge. cardboard. 5-Oct-3 Lombrail & Teucquam, Paris #400
£828 $1382 €1200 Les deux amies (92x72cm-36x28in) s. panel on canvas. 12-Nov-3 Chassaing Rivet, Toulouse #194
Works on paper
£282 $527 €420 Eventail (31x24cm-12x9in) d.1956 verso wash. 24-Feb-4 Thierry & Lannon, Brest #149
£336 $628 €500 Media au port de Philippeville (30x47cm-12x19in) s.d.1927 W/C gouache. 24-Feb-4 Thierry & Lannon, Brest #150/R

BERTHOME-SAINT-ANDRE, Louis (1905-1977) French
£333 $557 €470 La detente (35x27cm-14x11in) oil paper on panel. 23-Jun-3 Lombrail & Teucquam, Paris #107
£355 $592 €500 Le divan (33x46cm-13x18in) panel. 23-Jun-3 Lombrail & Teucquam, Paris #98
£408 $649 €600 Jeune femme a son secretaire (46x27cm-18x11in) s. 23-Mar-3 St-Germain-en-Laye Encheres #66/R
£426 $711 €600 Nicole (38x61cm-15x24in) 23-Jun-3 Lombrail & Teucquam, Paris #97
£461 $770 €650 Le jupon blanc (38x61cm-15x24in) 23-Jun-3 Lombrail & Teucquam, Paris #96
£532 $888 €750 Le bois de la montee rouge (61x50cm-24x20in) 23-Jun-3 Lombrail & Teucquam, Paris #94
£532 $888 €750 Le peignoir bleu (38x61cm-15x24in) 23-Jun-3 Lombrail & Teucquam, Paris #95
£567 $1014 €850 La caleche (38x61cm-15x24in) s. painted c.1948 exhib. 16-May-4 Thierry & Lannon, Brest #289
£619 $990 €898 Catherine au ruban (61x51cm-24x20in) s. s.i. verso. 15-May-3 Stuker, Bern #1068/R (S.FR 1300)
£633 $1134 €950 Le chenal (50x61cm-20x24in) s. painted c.1962. 16-May-4 Thierry & Lannon, Brest #287/R
£1020 $1622 €1500 Petite anglaise (61x38cm-24x15in) s. i.verso. 23-Mar-3 St-Germain-en-Laye Encheres #71/R
£1067 $1909 €1600 Village maritime (50x61cm-20x24in) s. painted c.1959. 16-May-4 Thierry & Lannon, Brest #286/R est:1500-1800
£1342 $2483 €2000 La danseuse (65x81cm-26x32in) s. 14-Mar-4 Feletin, Province #101
£1644 $3042 €2450 Le jeu de cartes (81x65cm-32x26in) s. 14-Mar-4 Feletin, Province #103
£1644 $3042 €2450 Femme assise (73x60cm-29x24in) s. 14-Mar-4 Feletin, Province #104
£1844 $3079 €2600 L'odalisque au repos (61x50cm-24x20in) 23-Jun-3 Lombrail & Teucquam, Paris #86
£1901 $3327 €2700 Le broc blanc (65x81cm-26x32in) s.d.1939. 21-Dec-3 Thierry & Lannon, Brest #282/R est:2700-3000
£2081 $3828 €3100 Charlotte (73x60cm-29x24in) s.i.d.1939 verso. 29-Mar-4 Lombrail & Teucquam, Paris #112/R
Works on paper
£366 $641 €520 Deux amies (34x46cm-13x18in) studio st. pen. 21-Dec-3 Thierry & Lannon, Brest #419
£390 $651 €550 Les baigneurs (31x47cm-12x19in) W/C. 23-Jun-3 Lombrail & Teucquam, Paris #99
£563 $986 €800 Marins au port (60x73cm-24x29in) s. W/C. 21-Dec-3 Thierry & Lannon, Brest #219/R

BERTHON, George Theodore (1806-1892) Canadian
£2928 $4977 €4275 Portrait of Lena Fulton (70x54cm-28x21in) prov. 18-Nov-3 Sotheby's, Toronto #122/R est:7000-9000 (C.D 6500)

BERTHON, Paul (1872-1909) French
£280 $481 €400 Woman in a field (35x34cm-14x13in) init. triplex. 7-Dec-3 Sotheby's, Amsterdam #764
Prints
£24581 $44000 €35888 Les maitres de l'affiche. lithographs set of 240 by different artist. 6-May-4 Swann Galleries, New York #309/R est:35000-50000

BERTHOT, Jake (1939-) American
Works on paper
£361 $650 €527 October group no 3 (30x22cm-12x9in) s.d.1973 pencil graphite enamel prov. 24-Apr-4 David Rago, Lambertville #120/R
£472 $850 €689 Untitled (20x22cm-8x9in) init.d.1975 mixed media prov. 24-Apr-4 David Rago, Lambertville #492/R

BERTHOUD, Auguste Henri (1829-1887) Swiss
£565 $1034 €825 Paysage (16x30cm-6x12in) i.verso. 4-Jun-4 Zofingen, Switzerland #2324 (S.FR 1300)

BERTHOUD, Léon (1822-1892) Swiss
£308 $524 €450 Italian landscape with monastery (15x22cm-6x9in) s.i.d.1848 panel. 5-Nov-3 Dobiaschofsky, Bern #353/R (S.FR 700)

£733 $1312 €1070 Le pont de Sevres (23x36cm-9x14in) s.i.d.1858 board. 14-May-4 Dobiaschofsky, Bern #6/R est:2400 (S.FR 1700)
£862 $1543 €1259 Cattle transport (26x21cm-10x8in) i. verso paper on panel. 12-May-4 Dobiaschofsky, Bern #3437 (S.FR 2000)

BERTI, Vinicio (1921-1991) Italian
£246 $431 €350 Extensive tale (18x24cm-7x9in) s.d.1967. 17-Dec-3 Il Ponte, Milan #885
£317 $549 €450 Image AH 1 (36x25cm-14x10in) s.d.1980 s.i.verso acrylic. 9-Dec-3 Pandolfini, Florence #393
£352 $609 €500 Ban AH (70x100cm-28x39in) s.d.1980 tempera paper. 9-Dec-3 Pandolfini, Florence #128
£360 $590 €500 Object H 7V (60x80cm-24x31in) s.d.1974 acrylic cardboard. 10-Jun-3 Pandolfini, Florence #372
£388 $671 €550 9H AH Ban (49x69cm-19x27in) s.d.1988 tempera paper. 9-Dec-3 Pandolfini, Florence #129
£528 $914 €750 Composition (40x60cm-16x24in) s.d.1990 acrylic. 9-Dec-3 Pandolfini, Florence #126
£530 $964 €800 Composition (49x70cm-19x28in) s.d.1973-74 s.i.d.verso acrylic. 21-Jun-4 Pandolfini, Florence #325
£559 $951 €800 Image (70x100cm-28x39in) s.d.1988 acrylic. 26-Nov-3 Pandolfini, Florence #158/R
£662 $1205 €1000 Simultaneous tale (60x80cm-24x31in) s.d.1974. 17-Jun-4 Galleria Pananti, Florence #472/R
£1060 $1928 €1600 Symbol AH3 (40x50cm-16x20in) s.d.1964 s.i.d.verso acrylic. 21-Jun-4 Pandolfini, Florence #455 est:1500-1700
£1216 $2141 €1800 Antagonism 3 h (80x60cm-31x24in) s.d.1970-71 s.i.d.verso. 22-May-4 Galleria Pananti, Florence #360/R est:1200-1500
£1486 $2616 €2200 Simultaneously (60x80cm-24x31in) s.d.1972-74 s.i.d.verso. 22-May-4 Galleria Pananti, Florence #426/R est:1100-1200
£1589 $2893 €2400 Double positive antagonist (70x120cm-28x47in) s.d.1975 s.i.d.verso. 17-Jun-4 Galleria Pananti, Florence #540/R est:1600-1700
£1854 $3375 €2800 New object (70x100cm-28x39in) s.d.1970. 17-Jun-4 Galleria Pananti, Florence #492/R est:1400-1500
£1854 $3375 €2800 Clash (80x50cm-31x20in) s.d.1964 s.d.verso acrylic. 21-Jun-4 Pandolfini, Florence #493/R est:700-900
£2013 $3604 €3000 Landscape (27x41cm-11x16in) s. 25-May-4 Sotheby's, Milan #125/R est:4000
£3378 $5946 €5000 Departure zero (100x130cm-39x51in) s.d.1970 s.i.d.verso. 22-May-4 Galleria Pananti, Florence #513/R est:2500-3000
£3378 $5946 €5000 Condition ah 1 (100x120cm-39x47in) s.d.1975 s.i.d.verso. 22-May-4 Galleria Pananti, Florence #514/R est:2500-3000
Works on paper
£367 $675 €550 Positive composition AH (40x30cm-16x12in) s.d.1981 waterpaint. 11-Jun-4 Farsetti, Prato #127
£367 $675 €550 Look high (40x30cm-16x12in) s.d.1990 waterpaint on canvas. 11-Jun-4 Farsetti, Prato #234
£369 $683 €550 9H-1H (70x50cm-28x20in) s.d.1977 mixed media cardboard. 13-Mar-4 Meeting Art, Vercelli #87
£379 $633 €550 Positive meeting (40x49cm-16x19in) s.d.1986 s.i.d.verso hydropaint on canvas. 14-Nov-3 Farsetti, Prato #91
£400 $736 €600 Looking up (70x50cm-28x20in) s.i.d.1987 mixed media. 12-Jun-4 Meeting Art, Vercelli #812/R
£403 $745 €600 Florence (50x70cm-20x28in) s.d.1987 mixed media cardboard on canvas. 13-Mar-4 Meeting Art, Vercelli #41
£430 $783 €650 Portrait (37x36cm-15x14in) s.d.945 sanguine Chinese ink paper on canvas. 21-Jun-4 Pandolfini, Florence #485
£537 $961 €800 Antagonism (35x50cm-14x20in) s.d.1985 s.i.d.verso hydropaint on canvas. 28-May-4 Farsetti, Prato #105
£567 $1043 €850 AH1 BAN AH (50x69cm-20x27in) s.d.1979 waterpaint card on cardboard. 11-Jun-4 Farsetti, Prato #24
£621 $1037 €900 Great antagonist object (70x50cm-28x20in) s. s.i.d.1977-78 verso hydropaint on canvas. 14-Nov-3 Farsetti, Prato #479/R
£1103 $1843 €1600 Ban ah (100x70cm-39x28in) s.d.1986 hydropaint on canvas. 14-Nov-3 Farsetti, Prato #5/R est:1200-1500
£1172 $1958 €1700 Project H (70x100cm-28x39in) s.d.1975 hydropaint on canvas. 14-Nov-3 Farsetti, Prato #491/R est:1200-1600
£1333 $2413 €2000 Tale (70x100cm-28x39in) s.d.1979-80 s.i.d.verso hydropaint on canvas. 2-Apr-4 Farsetti, Prato #286 est:650-850

BERTIER, Charles Alexandre (1860-1924) French
£913 $1671 €1333 Snowy lane (45x37cm-18x15in) s. 4-Jun-4 Zofingen, Switzerland #2420/R (S.FR 2100)
£5035 $8409 €7100 Paysage de montagne (80x118cm-31x46in) s.d.1913. 20-Jun-3 Drouot Estimations, Paris #93 est:4000-6000

BERTIN, Alexandre (19/20th C) French
£811 $1500 €1184 Floral still life with roses (61x61cm-24x24in) s. 17-Jul-4 New Orleans Auction, New Orleans #566/R est:1500-2500

BERTIN, François Edouard (attrib) (1797-1871) French
£467 $845 €700 Le nuage (14x24cm-6x9in) oil paper on canvas. 30-Mar-4 Rossini, Paris #104
£1200 $2172 €1800 Royat, chemin du paradis (39x52cm-15x20in) bears sig. 30-Mar-4 Rossini, Paris #102/R est:2000-3000
£1800 $3258 €2700 Soleil couchant derriere les nuages (18x26cm-7x10in) cardboard. 30-Mar-4 Rossini, Paris #103/R est:800-1200
Works on paper
£733 $1327 €1100 Paysage aux environs de Capri (29x26cm-11x10in) s. pierre noire white chk. 30-Mar-4 Rossini, Paris #106/R

BERTIN, Jean-Victor (1775-1842) French
£1711 $3147 €2600 Berger a l'entree d'une ferme (16x22cm-6x9in) 25-Jun-4 Daguerre, Paris #121/R est:2000-3000
£2533 $4636 €3800 Jeune beuvier gardant son troupeau (16x21cm-6x8in) 3-Jun-4 E & Eve, Paris #39/R est:4000-6000
£3916 $6657 €5600 Vue d'un paysage Italien avec un aqueduc (42x31cm-17x12in) 24-Nov-3 E & Eve, Paris #153/R est:4000-6000
£5667 $10257 €8500 Une des entrees du part de Saint Cloud (24x34cm-9x13in) exhib. 30-Mar-4 Rossini, Paris #100/R est:3000-4000
£9000 $16290 €13500 Promenade en barque sur l'Essonne (38x31cm-15x12in) lit. 30-Mar-4 Rossini, Paris #99/R est:6000-8000
£22000 $37400 €32120 River landscape with classical figures in a boat, hilltop castle beyond (204x143cm-80x56in) s.d.1805. 29-Oct-3 Christie's, London #57/R est:25000-35000

BERTIN, Jean-Victor (attrib) (1775-1842) French
£1700 $3060 €2482 Wooded landscape with a shepherd before a hamlet. Travelers on a track, temple beyond (32x40cm-13x16in) pair. 21-Apr-4 Bonhams, New Bond Street #87/R est:2000-3000
£1733 $3137 €2600 Arcueil, les bords de la Bievres (27x16cm-11x6in) paper on canvas. 30-Mar-4 Rossini, Paris #101 est:1200-1500
£1842 $3389 €2800 Paysage neo-classique traverse par une riviere (24x32cm-9x13in) prov. 25-Jun-4 Rossini, Paris #58/R est:1200-1500
£2610 $4750 €3811 Wooded landscape with two figures beside a stream (97x130cm-38x51in) prov. 29-Jun-4 Sotheby's, New York #60/R est:4000-6000

BERTIN, Nicolas (1668-1736) French
£45455 $78182 €65000 Adam et Eve au Paradis Terrestre (127x190cm-50x75in) prov.lit. 3-Dec-3 Fraysse & Associes, Paris #113/R est:30000-40000

BERTIN, Roger (1915-) French
£464 $844 €700 Rue Norvins a Montmartre (60x73cm-24x29in) s,. 18-Jun-4 Piasa, Paris #235
£530 $964 €800 Rue Norvins a Montmartre (60x73cm-24x29in) s. 18-Jun-4 Piasa, Paris #236
£1007 $1872 €1500 Rue animee a Montmartre (31x47cm-12x19in) s. panel. 7-Mar-4 Lesieur & Le Bars, Le Havre #7/R
Works on paper
£278 $453 €400 Montmartre (42x54cm-17x21in) s. W/C. 29-Sep-3 Charbonneaux, Paris #191
£369 $687 €550 La Seine a Notre Dame (47x62cm-19x24in) s. W/C. 7-Mar-4 Lesieur & Le Bars, Le Havre #8

BERTINI, Dante (1878-?) Italian
£326 $597 €476 Young child playing on a swing (45x54cm-18x21in) s. tempera. 4-Jun-4 Zofingen, Switzerland #2421 (S.FR 750)

BERTINI, Gianni (1922-) Italian
£493 $818 €700 Study for "Dailyreport" (50x35cm-20x14in) s. mixed media tempera masonite. 13-Jun-3 Farsetti, Prato #249/R
£867 $1560 €1300 Femme et moto (77x55cm-30x22in) s. acrylic cardboard. 24-Apr-4 Cornette de St.Cyr, Paris #439
£1200 $2160 €1800 Composition (75x75cm-30x30in) s.d.1954 verso prov. 25-Apr-4 Versailles Encheres #53 est:2000-2500
£1399 $2378 €2000 Corinthiennes face a Johnny (60x80cm-24x31in) s.d.1964 acrylic collage paper on board. 20-Nov-3 Finarte Semenzato, Milan #123 est:1500-2000
£1594 $2614 €2200 Untitled (65x81cm-26x32in) s. i.verso s.i.d.53 on stretcher. 27-May-3 Sotheby's, Milan #18 est:1500
£2819 $4989 €4200 Giorno d'estate (116x89cm-46x35in) s.i.d.1976 verso acrylic prov. 28-Apr-4 Artcurial Briest, Paris #411/R est:1800-2200
Works on paper
£300 $540 €450 Golden calf (42x27cm-17x11in) s.i. mixed media exec.1974. 25-Apr-4 Versailles Encheres #183
£470 $869 €700 Composition (23x29cm-9x11in) s.d.1960 mixed media card. 13-Mar-4 Meeting Art, Vercelli #37
£570 $1050 €850 Composition (60x81cm-24x32in) s. s.d.1955 verso mixed media. 24-Mar-4 Binoche, Paris #102
£625 $987 €900 Cyclope (73x54cm-29x21in) s.d.1984 s.i.d.verso mixed media serigraph. 27-Apr-3 Versailles Encheres #77
£903 $1508 €1300 Themis a premiere impression (92x73cm-36x29in) s.i.d.22-XII-1962 verso mixed media canvas. 25-Oct-3 Cornette de St.Cyr, Paris #596/R
£1034 $1728 €1500 Woman (61x51cm-24x20in) s.d.1966 mec art exec.1966 exhib.lit. 17-Nov-3 Sant Agostino, Torino #52/R est:1000-1400
£1088 $1948 €1600 Bike rider (33x46cm-13x18in) s.d.1976 emulsion on canvas. 16-Mar-4 Finarte Semenzato, Milan #61/R est:1000
£1118 $2058 €1700 Naufrage d'Uranie (79x58cm-31x23in) s.d.1986 s.i.d.verso mixed media on canvas prov. 27-Jun-4 Versailles Encheres #137/R est:1500-1800
£1267 $2267 €1900 Untitled (76x56cm-30x22in) s.d.1960 collage oil wood. 16-May-4 Osenat, Fontainebleau #64/R est:1000-1500
£1379 $2207 €2000 Volcan aile (81x54cm-32x21in) s. mec art exec 1969. 13-Mar-3 Galleria Pace, Milan #61/R est:2400-3600

BERTINI, L (?) Italian
£1448 $2462 €2114 Venice with St Marks (60x80cm-24x31in) s. 28-Nov-3 Zofingen, Switzerland #2550 est:1800 (S.FR 3200)

BERTLE, Hans (1880-1943) German?
£789 $1453 €1200 Cavalry charging through a village (24x33cm-9x13in) s. 25-Jun-4 Michael Zeller, Lindau #540/R
£828 $1514 €1200 Village in winter (75x100cm-30x39in) s.d.1911. 27-Jan-4 Dorotheum, Vienna #13/R
£1448 $2462 €2114 Madonna with child (73x52cm-29x20in) s. panel. 28-Nov-3 Zofingen, Switzerland #2551/R est:800 (S.FR 3200)

BERTO, K (19/20th C) ?
Sculpture
£2747 $5000 €4121 Three figures in a troika drawn by three horses (28x53cm-11x21in) pat bronze oval base. 20-Jun-4 Bonhams & Butterfields, Los Angeles #5291/R est:6000-8000

BERTOCCHI, Nino (1900-1956) Italian
£360 $590 €500 Hill (29x44cm-11x17in) board. 5-Jun-3 Adma, Formigine #528

BERTOIA, Harry (1915-1978) American
Prints
£3593 $6000 €5246 Geometric abstraction with cinched forms in colours (58x97cm-23x38in) monographic rice paper. 25-Oct-3 David Rago, Lambertville #172 est:4000-5000

Sculpture

£1602	$2900	€2339	Study for a dandelion (51x43cm-20x17in) gold plated stainless steel rods mounted wooden block. 3-Apr-4 David Rago, Lambertville #470/R est:900-1200
£1639	$3000	€2393	Untitled, direct formed bronze (10x5x13cm-4x2x5in) bronze exec.c.1960. 6-Jun-4 Wright, Chicago #363/R est:1500-2000
£2038	$3750	€2975	Untitled. bronze prov. 28-Mar-4 Wright, Chicago #586/R est:3000-5000
£2096	$3500	€3060	Untitled (66cm-26in) stainless steel rod spray chrome square base. 25-Oct-3 David Rago, Lambertville #165 est:2000-2500
£2717	$5000	€3967	Untitled. bronze prov. 28-Mar-4 Wright, Chicago #585/R est:4000-6000
£2717	$5000	€3967	Hanging sound sculpture. two long brass rods two short brass rods threaded together. 27-Jun-4 Freeman, Philadelphia #150/R est:8000-12000
£2732	$5000	€3989	Untitled, head (10x10x20cm-4x4x8in) brass coated bronze exec.c.1950. 6-Jun-4 Wright, Chicago #365/R est:3000-4000
£2989	$5500	€4364	Untitled - flower (66x28x33cm-26x11x13in) welded bronze prov. 28-Mar-4 Wright, Chicago #587/R est:5000-7000
£2989	$5500	€4364	Untitled (185x150x97cm-73x59x38in) iron prov. 28-Mar-4 Wright, Chicago #589/R est:5000-7000
£5090	$8500	€7431	Untitled (38cm-15in) bronze brass tips exhib. 7-Oct-3 Sotheby's, New York #381 est:7000-9000
£5135	$9500	€7497	Bush (12x27x20cm-5x11x8in) green pat bronze exec 1962 lit. 12-Feb-4 Sotheby's, New York #163/R est:3000-5000
£5389	$9000	€7868	Wheat (61cm-24in) stainless steel rod square brass base. 25-Oct-3 David Rago, Lambertville #164 est:3000-4000
£5495	$10000	€8023	Bush (23cm-9in) welded copper executed c.1964 exhib. 19-Jun-4 Rachel Davis, Shaker Heights #593 est:6000-9000
£5978	$11000	€8728	Untitled (25x8x18cm-10x3x7in) beryllium copper. 28-Mar-4 Wright, Chicago #583/R est:10000-15000
£7104	$13000	€10372	Untitled, bush form (28x8x20cm-11x3x8in) bronze prov. 6-Jun-4 Wright, Chicago #366/R est:7000-9000
£7650	$14000	€11169	Untitled, early sonambient (18x18x94cm-7x7x37in) beryllium copper exec.c.1960. 6-Jun-4 Wright, Chicago #367/R est:15000-20000
£8140	$14000	€11884	36 Bells (56cm-22in) beryllium copper brass of 36 rods prov. 7-Dec-3 Freeman, Philadelphia #102 est:5000-8000
£8152	$15000	€11902	Untitled (91x20x20cm-36x8x8in) beryllium copper. 28-Mar-4 Wright, Chicago #582/R est:15000-20000
£8378	$15500	€12232	Dandelion (177x78cm-70x31in) painted steel bronze. 12-Feb-4 Sotheby's, New York #103/R est:15000-20000
£9392	$17000	€13712	Sonambient in beryllium (53x20x10cm-21x8x4in) twenty six slender rods. 3-Apr-4 David Rago, Lambertville #479a/R est:15000-18000
£9945	$18000	€14520	Sonambient in beryllium copper (71x20cm-28x8in) five rows rods mounted to rectangular base. 3-Apr-4 David Rago, Lambertville #472/R est:20000-30000
£9945	$18000	€14520	Sonambient in berylliun copper (71x28cm-28x11in) five rows of rods mounted on rectangular base. 3-Apr-4 David Rago, Lambertville #474/R est:20000-30000
£10383	$19000	€15159	Untitled, kinetic form (18x10x74cm-7x4x29in) painted wood enameled bent steel copper exec.c.1948. 6-Jun-4 Wright, Chicago #368/R est:15000-20000
£10465	$18000	€15279	Untitled sound sculpture (56cm-22in) beryllium copper brass of 25 rods prov. 7-Dec-3 Freeman, Philadelphia #103 est:5000-8000
£11050	$20000	€16133	Sonambient in beryllium copper (71x30cm-28x12in) five rows of slender rods. 3-Apr-4 David Rago, Lambertville #474a/R est:20000-30000
£12431	$22500	€18149	Untitled (165x15cm-65x6in) copper panel. 3-Apr-4 David Rago, Lambertville #477/R est:25000-30000
£13812	$25000	€20166	Sonambient in beryllium copper (79x30cm-31x12in) slender rods mounted on rectangular base. 3-Apr-4 David Rago, Lambertville #473/R est:15000-20000
£14724	$24000	€21497	Bush (34x63x27cm-13x25x11in) green pat bronze prov.exhib. 23-Sep-3 Christie's, Rockefeller NY #35/R est:8000-12000
£14754	$27000	€21541	Untitled, sonambient (15x15x56cm-6x6x22in) beryllium copper exec.c.1960 prov. 6-Jun-4 Wright, Chicago #361/R est:15000-20000
£15847	$29000	€23137	Untitled, cloud (196x56x132cm-77x22x52in) brass coated copper exec.c.1960. 6-Jun-4 Wright, Chicago #360/R est:20000-30000
£19162	$32000	€27977	Wheat (74x31x25cm-29x12x10in) stainless steel copper bronze prov.exhib.lit. 13-Nov-3 Sotheby's, New York #247/R est:18000-25000
£21739	$40000	€31739	Untitled (124x23x23cm-49x9x9in) beryllium copper. 28-Mar-4 Wright, Chicago #584/R est:30000-40000
£27174	$50000	€39674	Sound sculpture (190cm-75in) beryllium copper brass twenty five rods prov. 27-Jun-4 Freeman, Philadelphia #151/R est:40000-60000
£31138	$52000	€45461	Sound Study (206x40x40cm-81x16x16in) Inconel exec c.1970-72 prov. 12-Nov-3 Christie's, Rockefeller NY #361/R est:30000-40000
£35519	$65000	€51858	Untitled, sonambient (30x30x170cm-12x12x67in) beryllium copper brass exec.c.1960 prov. 6-Jun-4 Wright, Chicago #362/R est:50000-70000
£60773	$110000	€88729	Willow (20x127cm-8x50in) stainless steel rods. 3-Apr-4 David Rago, Lambertville #478/R est:60000-80000

Works on paper

£326	$600	€476	Study for sculpture (23x13cm-9x5in) s. pen. 28-Mar-4 Wright, Chicago #588/R

BERTOLA, Louis (1891-) French/Italian

Sculpture

£1259	$2165	€1800	L'accueil (51cm-20in) s. green pat bronze exec.c.1930 Cast Barbedienne. 5-Dec-3 Chochon-Barre & Allardi, Paris #18/R est:2000-2500

BERTOLDO, B M (17th C) Italian

£1064	$1777	€1500	Madonna and Child and four Saints (102x77cm-40x30in) s.d.1696. 20-Oct-3 Sant Agostino, Torino #35/R est:1500-2000

BERTOLETTI, Nino (1890-1971) Italian

£1333	$2400	€2000	Lyrical souvenir (61x50cm-24x20in) s.d.1918 exhib. 22-Apr-4 Finarte Semenzato, Rome #259/R est:2500-3000

BERTOLLA, Cesare (1845-1920) Italian

£1867	$3435	€2800	Collecting wood (72x35cm-28x14in) s. 10-Jun-4 Christie's, Rome #90/R est:2200-2500

BERTOLOTTI, Cesare (1855-1932) Italian

£6289	$10000	€9182	Back from the market (114x71cm-45x28in) s.d.88. 12-Sep-3 Skinner, Boston #247/R est:500

BERTON-MAIRE, Marie (19/20th C) French

Works on paper

£1800	$3312	€2700	Maternite (63x45cm-25x18in) s.d.1927 i.verso gouache pastel crayon exhib. 14-Jun-4 Gros & Delettrez, Paris #181/R est:1500-2500

BERTONI, Wander (1925-) Italian

Sculpture

£13889	$23611	€20000	The I from the imaginary alphabet (157cm-62in) polished brass marble socle lit. 28-Oct-3 Wiener Kunst Auktionen, Vienna #228/R est:20000-30000

BERTOS, Francesco (fl.1693-1734) Italian

Sculpture

£310000	$567300	€452600	Vintage. Art of War (112cm-44in) bronze pair prov.lit. 9-Jul-4 Sotheby's, London #80/R est:250000-350000

BERTOZZI, Andrea (19th C) Italian

Sculpture

£10069	$16413	€14500	Dog with puppy (105cm-41in) s.i. marble. 25-Sep-3 Dr Fritz Nagel, Stuttgart #1514/R est:3000

BERTRAM, Abel (1871-1954) French

£296	$536	€450	Paysage (17x27cm-7x11in) s. s.verso panel. 19-Apr-4 Boscher, Cherbourg #773/R
£881	$1498	€1286	Seascape (65x81cm-26x32in) s. 5-Nov-3 Dobiaschofsky, Bern #356/R (S.FR 2000)
£1119	$1924	€1600	Bateaux echoues (20x25cm-8x10in) s. panel. 7-Dec-3 Livinec, Gaudcheau & Jezequel, Rennes #83/R
£3087	$5526	€4600	Bateaux sortant du port (65x81cm-26x32in) s. painted 1926. 30-May-4 Eric Pillon, Calais #9/R
£17000	$31280	€25500	Fillette aux capucines (54x65cm-21x26in) s. prov. 11-Jun-4 Claude Aguttes, Neuilly #186/R est:15000-20000

Works on paper

£265	$482	€400	Baigneuse assise dans l'herbe (44x32cm-17x13in) s. W/C. 18-Jun-4 Piasa, Paris #134
£336	$601	€500	Nu allonge (39x59cm-15x23in) s. Chinese ink wash dr. 30-May-4 Eric Pillon, Calais #257/R
£397	$723	€600	Jeune femme denudee assoupie (24x31cm-9x12in) s. W/C. 18-Jun-4 Piasa, Paris #133

BERTRAM, Helge (1919-1988) Danish

£542	$996	€791	Tippen (65x81cm-26x32in) s.i. verso board exhib. 29-Mar-4 Rasmussen, Copenhagen #416/R (D.KR 6000)
£948	$1744	€1384	Prospect I - BEtW (80x102cm-31x40in) s.i.d.77 verso board. 29-Mar-4 Rasmussen, Copenhagen #414/R (D.KR 10500)

BERTRAM, Paul (fl.1900s) British

Works on paper

£300	$480	€438	In the Vale of Aylesbury, sheep and cottage in landscape (34x49cm-13x19in) s. W/C. 17-Sep-3 Bonhams, Brooks & Langlois, Jersey #98/R
£380	$703	€555	Vale of Aylesbury (33x48cm-13x19in) s. W/C. 10-Feb-4 David Lay, Penzance #207
£500	$895	€730	Cattle by a thatched shed. Shepherd driving sheep over a bridge (36x51cm-14x20in) s. W/C pair. 7-May-4 Chrystals Auctions, Isle of Man #235

BERTRAND, Elise (19th C) French

£540	$950	€788	Cat at the piano (33x23cm-13x9in) s. 22-May-4 New Orleans Auction, New Orleans #573/R est:1000-1500

BERTRAND, Eugène (19/20th C) French

£3497	$5944	€5000	Jeune elegante au bouquet de fleurs (116x68cm-46x27in) s.d.86. 1-Dec-3 Palais de Beaux Arts, Brussels #218/R est:5000-7000

BERTRAND, Gaston (1910-1994) Belgian

£1133	$2085	€1700	Petit interieur a la table (22x30cm-9x12in) s. panel prov. 14-Jun-4 Horta, Bruxelles #77 est:1800-2200
£2297	$4250	€3354	Portrait de dame (81x64cm-32x25in) s.d.47 s.i.d.verso prov.exhib. 10-Mar-4 Doyle, New York #60/R est:1500-2500
£9396	$17383	€14000	Composition number 217 (65x81cm-26x32in) s.d.54 s.i.d.1954 verso prov.exhib.lit. 13-Mar-4 De Vuyst, Lokeren #480/R est:9000-12000

Works on paper

£467	$859	€700	Composition (25x35cm-10x14in) wash. 14-Jun-4 Amberes, Antwerp #45
£470	$832	€700	Avant-projet (38x55cm-15x22in) s. ink. 27-Apr-4 Campo, Vlaamse Kaai #311
£604	$1069	€900	Avant-projet (38x55cm-15x22in) s. ink. 27-Apr-4 Campo, Vlaamse Kaai #312
£2098	$3566	€3000	Composition, vers une quatrieme dimension (46x61cm-18x24in) s.d.52 W/C gouache. 1-Dec-3 Palais de Beaux Arts, Brussels #167/R est:3000-5000

BERTRAND, Huguette Aimee (1922-) French

£302	$561	€450	Padirac II (46x55cm-18x22in) s. acrylic. 3-Mar-4 Tajan, Paris #251
£333	$600	€500	Padirac (46x55cm-18x22in) s. i.verso. 25-Apr-4 Versailles Encheres #12

BERTRAND, Jean Baptiste (1823-1887) French

£1538	$2615	€2200	Le lait du chat (83x43cm-33x17in) s. 27-Nov-3 Millon & Associes, Paris #106/R est:1200-1500

BERTRAND, Jean Claude (1928-) French

£599	$1036	€850	Paysage (128x158cm-50x62in) s. 10-Dec-3 Claude Boisgirard, Paris #17

£775 $1340 €1100 Les arbres d'automne (210x81cm-83x32in) s. 10-Dec-3 Claude Boisgirard, Paris #16

BERTRAND, Louis Aloysius (1807-1941) French
Works on paper
£1333 $2453 €2000 Paysage sombre et menacant avec un lac entre les collines (6x11cm-2x4in) init. wax crayon exhib. 9-Jun-4 Piasa, Paris #15 est:1200-1500

BERTRAND, Paulin Andre (1852-1940) French
£570 $1061 €850 Farmstead with hayricks in evening (33x46cm-13x18in) s. 6-Mar-4 Arnold, Frankfurt #690/R
£1704 $2846 €2488 Summer landscape with river (38x61cm-15x24in) s. 24-Oct-3 Hans Widmer, St Gallen #94/R est:1400-2800 (S.FR 3800)
£7778 $14000 €11356 Promenade under the apple blossoms (52x91cm-20x36in) s. prov. 22-Apr-4 Christie's, Rockefeller NY #116/R est:10000-15000

BERTRAND, Philippe (after) (1663-1724) French
Sculpture
£11500 $19895 €16790 Prometheus chained to a rock with an eagle eating his liver (50cm-20in) bronze prov.lit. 12-Dec-3 Sotheby's, London #202/R est:8000-12000

BERTRAND, Pierre-Philippe (1884-1975) French
£483 $893 €700 Bord de riviere (43x45cm-17x18in) s. panel. 16-Feb-4 Giraudeau, Tours #54

BERTRAULT, L (19/20th C) French?
Works on paper
£3000 $5550 €4500 Les terrasses d'Alger (65x92cm-26x36in) s.d.1908 chl canvas. 14-Jul-4 Sotheby's, Olympia #275/R est:1000-1500

BERTUCH-FRORIEP, Charlotte (1779-1856) German
Works on paper
£759 $1267 €1100 Multi-coloured carnations (27x19cm-11x7in) mono. W/C prov. 15-Nov-3 Lempertz, Koln #1447 est:1200

BERTUCHI NIETO, Mariano (1885-1955) Spanish
£1399 $2336 €2000 View of Tetuan (40x30cm-16x12in) s.i. 30-Jun-3 Ansorena, Madrid #271/R est:1200
£9396 $16819 €14000 Pilotos Tower, Rabat (58x48cm-23x19in) s.i. 25-May-4 Durán, Madrid #204/R est:10000

BERTUZZI, Nicola (1710-1777) Italian
£7333 $13127 €11000 Saint Peter in jail (69x52cm-27x20in) 12-May-4 Finarte Semenzato, Milan #49/R est:5000-7000
£19000 $32870 €27740 Biblical scene with a servant driven away by a King, figures restraining him (173x132cm-68x52in) 11-Dec-3 Sotheby's, London #199/R est:15000-20000

BERUETE, Aureliano de (1845-1911) Spanish
£3901 $6514 €5500 Landscape (24x15cm-9x6in) s.i. panel. 23-Jun-3 Durán, Madrid #153/R est:1800
£15000 $25500 €21900 View of the Manzanares, Madrid (22x27cm-9x11in) s. prov. 18-Nov-3 Sotheby's, London #247/R

BERVOETS, Freddy (1941-) Belgian
£671 $1188 €1000 Hallo Tokyo (75x110cm-30x43in) mono. paper on canvas. 27-Apr-4 Campo, Vlaamse Kaai #313/R
£3125 $5219 €4500 Autoportrait sur un ane (286x203cm-113x80in) exhib. 21-Oct-3 Campo, Vlaamse Kaai #539/R est:4000-5000
£3472 $5799 €5000 Sp. (290x203cm-114x80in) acrylic painted 1989 lit. 21-Oct-3 Campo & Campo, Antwerp #13/R est:6000-7000
£3472 $5799 €5000 School (258x203cm-102x80in) acrylic painted 1989 lit. 21-Oct-3 Campo & Campo, Antwerp #12/R est:6000-7000
£3819 $6378 €5500 Autoportrait a l'arc (150x190cm-59x75in) mono. 21-Oct-3 Campo, Vlaamse Kaai #358/R est:5000-6000
£4027 $7128 €6000 The prophet (283x201cm-111x79in) s. lit. 27-Apr-4 Campo & Campo, Antwerp #19/R est:6000-8000
Works on paper
£355 $592 €500 Penis (15x11cm-6x4in) s. mixed media. 20-Oct-3 Bernaerts, Antwerp #223/R

BERVOETS, Leo (1892-1978) Belgian
Works on paper
£486 $812 €700 Kiss (27x24cm-11x9in) s. mixed media. 21-Oct-3 Campo & Campo, Antwerp #14/R
£503 $891 €750 Accordeonistes en rue (35x26cm-14x10in) s. mixed media. 27-Apr-4 Campo & Campo, Antwerp #24/R

BESANCENOT, Jean (1902-1992) French
Works on paper
£664 $1143 €950 Jeune Marocaine. Berbere ait Mguild (25x32cm-10x13in) one s. other s.i. gouache htd gilding two. 8-Dec-3 Tajan, Paris #234/R

BESCHEY, Balthasar (1708-1776) Flemish
£2361 $3731 €3400 Hermit reading by a vaulted grotto (34x28cm-13x11in) s. indis d. panel. 2-Sep-3 Christie's, Amsterdam #92/R est:1500-2500
£4514 $7132 €6500 Hermit reading by a tree, landscape beyond (34x28cm-13x11in) s. indis d. panel. 2-Sep-3 Christie's, Amsterdam #97/R est:2000-4000
£15232 $27722 €23000 Figures in mountainous landscape. Leaving for the market (11x12cm-4x5in) copper pair. 15-Jun-4 Claude Aguttes, Neuilly #36/R est:20000-30000

BESCHEY, Jacob Andries (1710-1786) Flemish
£1972 $3411 €2800 La montee au calvaire (61x50cm-24x20in) s. 12-Dec-3 Libert, Castor, Paris #35/R est:1500-2000

BESCO, Donald (1941-) Canadian
£378 $627 €552 Cambridge St, Galt, Ont (41x61cm-16x24in) s. i.verso hard board. 5-Oct-3 Levis, Calgary #7/R (C.D 850)
£378 $627 €552 Snow squall, Kensington (41x51cm-16x20in) s. i.verso hard board. 5-Oct-3 Levis, Calgary #8/R (C.D 850)
£455 $823 €664 Evening shadows, Kensington (46x61cm-18x24in) s. i.verso hardboard. 18-Apr-4 Levis, Calgary #6/R est:1400-1800 (C.D 1100)
£600 $1098 €876 Sunrise, Dundas Street (50x60cm-20x24in) s.i. board. 1-Jun-4 Hodgins, Calgary #192/R (C.D 1500)
£901 $1532 €1315 Winter morning, Kensington (61x81cm-24x32in) s. i.verso board. 27-Nov-3 Heffel, Vancouver #34/R est:2250-2750 (C.D 2000)
£905 $1511 €1321 Winter evening, Chinese market, Queen and Broadview, Toronto (58x100cm-23x39in) s.i. board. 17-Nov-3 Hodgins, Calgary #268/R est:2500-3000 (C.D 2000)
£1786 $3071 €2608 Old houses by Kensington Market (60x90cm-24x35in) s. board. 2-Dec-3 Joyner Waddington, Toronto #284/R est:2500-3000 (C.D 4000)

BESENZI, Paolo Emilio (1608-1656) Italian
£23743 $42500 €34665 Allegorical figure of woman (118x72cm-46x28in) 27-May-4 Sotheby's, New York #60/R est:20000-30000

BESJI, G (19th C) Italian
Sculpture
£1230 $2250 €1845 Christ with crown of thorns (48cm-19in) carved marble. 9-Jul-4 Du Mouchelle, Detroit #2043/R est:1500-2500
£1230 $2250 €1845 Bust of Christ (48x43cm-19x17in) marble exec. c.1900. 9-Jul-4 Du Mouchelle, Detroit #2044/R est:1000-1500

BESKOW, Elsa (1874-1953) Swedish
Works on paper
£443 $794 €647 The book of flowers (24x21cm-9x8in) W/C front cover lit. 25-May-4 Bukowskis, Stockholm #66/R (S.KR 6000)
£591 $1058 €863 The book of flowers (23x18cm-9x7in) mixed media front fly-leaf exhib.lit. 25-May-4 Bukowskis, Stockholm #65/R (S.KR 8000)
£1478 $2646 €2158 The book of flowers (28x23cm-11x9in) mixed media front cover exhib.lit. 25-May-4 Bukowskis, Stockholm #64/R est:20000-25000 (S.KR 20000)
£2217 $3969 €3237 Little Prince Winter (23x18cm-9x7in) init. mixed media exhib.lit. 25-May-4 Bukowskis, Stockholm #68/R est:40000-50000 (S.KR 30000)
£2956 $5292 €4316 Mrs Maja's girl (23x18cm-9x7in) s. mixed media exhib.lit. 25-May-4 Bukowskis, Stockholm #67/R est:40000-50000 (S.KR 40000)
£2956 $5292 €4316 The dance of the dandelions (24x19cm-9x7in) init. mixed media exhib.lit. 25-May-4 Bukowskis, Stockholm #71/R est:40000-50000 (S.KR 40000)
£2956 $5292 €4316 The cat-foots song (24x20cm-9x8in) init. mixed media exhib.lit. 25-May-4 Bukowskis, Stockholm #72/R est:40000-50000 (S.KR 40000)
£3538 $6086 €5165 Lasse's meeting with the old blackcurrant man (33x43cm-13x17in) init. W/C prov.exhib.lit. 2-Dec-3 Bukowskis, Stockholm #78/R est:50000-60000 (S.KR 46000)
£4615 $7938 €6738 Lasse's meeting with the gooseberry boys and girls (31x42cm-12x17in) init. W/C prov.exhib.lit. 2-Dec-3 Bukowskis, Stockholm #80/R est:60000-80000 (S.KR 60000)
£5846 $10055 €8535 Mr Grey Pear coming out of his tree (32x41cm-13x16in) init. W/C prov.exhib.lit. 2-Dec-3 Bukowskis, Stockholm #79/R est:60000-80000 (S.KR 76000)
£5923 $10188 €8648 Lasse throwing a ball to Prince September in the sycamore tree (34x43cm-13x17in) init. W/C prov.exhib.lit. 2-Dec-3 Bukowskis, Stockholm #77/R est:50000-60000 (S.KR 77000)
£7692 $13231 €11230 Lasse and Prince September seated with Mrs Astrakan in the apple tree (33x41cm-13x16in) init. W/C prov.exhib.lit. 2-Dec-3 Bukowskis, Stockholm #74/R est:80000-100000 (S.KR 100000)
£9231 $15877 €13477 Prince September serenading the garden's flowers (32x42cm-13x17in) init. W/C prov.exhib.lit. 2-Dec-3 Bukowskis, Stockholm #75/R est:80000-100000 (S.KR 120000)
£19586 $35059 €28596 Have you seen Mr Chanterelle (24x19cm-9x7in) init. mixed media exhib.lit. 25-May-4 Bukowskis, Stockholm #80/R est:80000-100000 (S.KR 265000)

BESLER, Basilius (17th C) German?
Prints
£5464 $10000 €7977 Campanula medium. Lilium martagon (48x39cm-19x15in) hand col copperplate engraving pair prov. 7-Apr-4 Sotheby's, New York #162/R est:5000-7000
£5464 $10000 €7977 Paeonia officinalis. Valerian phu (48x39cm-19x15in) hand col copperplate engraving pair prov. 7-Apr-4 Sotheby's, New York #163/R est:5000-7000
£6011 $11000 €8776 Gladiolus communis. Helianthus x multiflorus (48x39cm-19x15in) hand col copperplate engraving pair prov. 7-Apr-4 Sotheby's, New York #160/R est:5000-7000
£6011 $11000 €8776 Mirabilis jalapa. Agave Americana (48x39cm-19x15in) hand col copperplate engraging pair prov. 7-Apr-4 Sotheby's, New York #161/R est:5000-7000

BESNARD, Albert (1849-1934) French
£3057 $5563 €4463 Grandmother with grandchildren (56x50cm-22x20in) s. 17-Jun-4 Kornfeld, Bern #205/R est:7500 (S.FR 7000)
£6207 $10303 €9000 Portrait de jeune femme au bouquet (200x91cm-79x36in) s. 2-Oct-3 Sotheby's, Paris #2/R est:13000
Works on paper
£1007 $1852 €1500 Muse with lute (78x56cm-31x22in) s.d.1877 W/C. 29-Mar-4 Glerum, Amsterdam #165 est:1500-2000
£2218 $3838 €3150 Femme a la chemise rouge (60x49cm-24x19in) s. pastel prov. 13-Dec-3 Touati, Paris #27/R est:4000-5000
£2695 $4501 €3800 Jeune fille pensive (59x48cm-23x19in) s. pastel paper on canvas. 19-Jun-3 Millon & Associes, Paris #14/R est:5000-6000

BESNARD, Jean (1889-1958) French
Sculpture
£4620 $8500 €6745 Marabout (34cm-13in) st.sig. terracotta prov. 10-Jun-4 Phillips, New York #81/R est:5000-7000

BESNARD, Jean Baptiste (18th C) French
£5775 $10106 €8200 Scene de retour du marche (36x28cm-14x11in) s.d.1754. 17-Dec-3 Piasa, Paris #90/R est:6000-8000

BESNUS, Amedee (1831-1909) French
£580 $951 €800 Riviere pres du vieux pont (22x33cm-9x13in) s. panel. 11-May-3 Osenat, Fontainebleau #218

BESS, Forrest (1911-1977) American
£17964 $30000 €26227 Untitled no.18 (23x30cm-9x12in) s. painted 1952 prov.exhib. 12-Nov-3 Christie's, Rockefeller NY #303/R est:30000-40000

BESSA, Pancrace (1772-1846) French
Works on paper
£29412 $50000 €42942 Botanical studies (27x21cm-11x8in) s. bodycol vellum set of 16. 25-Nov-3 Christie's, Rockefeller NY #486/R est:4000-6000

BESSE, Raymond (1899-1969) French
£223 $400 €326 Montmartre (46x56cm-18x22in) s. 7-May-4 Sloans & Kenyon, Bethesda #1157/R
£231 $425 €337 Montmartre en hiver (53x64cm-21x25in) s. s.indis.i.verso. 9-Jun-4 Doyle, New York #3006
£385 $654 €550 La tourelle, rue Vieille du Temple a Paris (45x37cm-18x15in) s. isorel. 20-Nov-3 Gioffredo, Nice #28/R
£621 $1117 €900 Scene de marche sous la neige (52x63cm-20x25in) s. 26-Jan-4 Gros & Delettrez, Paris #33

BESSEDE, Raoul Henri (?-1890) French
£1000 $1810 €1500 Le bouffon (65x55cm-26x22in) s.d.1886. 4-Apr-4 Salle des ventes Pillet, Lyon la Foret #5/R est:1000-1200

BESSEMER, Ariel (?) American?
£2206 $3750 €3221 Harvest scenes (15x36cm-6x14in) s. board pair. 9-Nov-3 Wright, Chicago #165 est:1500-2000

BESSERVE, René (1883-1959) French
£272 $487 €400 Apres-midi familial (27x35cm-11x14in) s. peinture cardboard. 20-Mar-4 Binoche, Orleans #33

BESSET, Cyrille (1864-1902) French
£582 $1065 €850 Still life of brass pot and fish (60x81cm-24x32in) s.d.1895. 9-Jun-4 Rasmussen, Copenhagen #1876/R (D.KR 6500)

BESSIN, Paul Lucien (20th C) French
Sculpture
£778 $1400 €1136 Bust of a lady (46cm-18in) incised sig. bronze. 24-Apr-4 Skinner, Boston #124/R est:600-800

BESSIRE, Dale Phillip (1892-1974) American
£2390 $3800 €3489 Landscape (56x61cm-22x24in) s. 14-Sep-3 Susanin's, Chicago #6063/R est:3000-5000

BESSO, Amalia (1856-1932) Italian
£563 $975 €800 White flowers (70x85cm-28x33in) s. 11-Dec-3 Christie's, Rome #70
£704 $1218 €1000 Yellow daisies (63x101cm-25x40in) s. panel. 11-Dec-3 Christie's, Rome #69

BESSON, Henri (?) French
£633 $1165 €950 Paysage d'Afrique du Nord (27x73cm-11x29in) s. panel. 8-Jun-4 Livinec, Gaudcheau & Jezequel, Rennes #129/R

BESSONOF, Boris (1862-1934) Russian
£862 $1440 €1250 Landscape (65x80cm-26x31in) s. 17-Nov-3 Durán, Madrid #99/R
£5000 $8950 €7300 Winter landscape (46x54cm-18x21in) s. prov. 26-May-4 Sotheby's, London #105/R est:5000-7000
£11000 $19690 €16060 Last rays (54x66cm-21x26in) s. 26-May-4 Sotheby's, London #104/R est:5000-7000

BEST PONTONES, Fernando (1889-1957) Mexican
£580 $985 €847 Landscape (34x46cm-13x18in) s. masonite. 30-Oct-3 Louis Morton, Mexico #130/R (M.P 11000)
£632 $1075 €923 Interior (49x34cm-19x13in) s. masonite. 30-Oct-3 Louis Morton, Mexico #14/R (M.P 12000)

BEST, Arthur W (1859-1935) American
£1618 $2750 €2362 Enchanted mesa (36x51cm-14x20in) s. i.verso prov. 1-Nov-3 Santa Fe Art, Santa Fe #230/R est:3000-5000

BEST, Hans (1874-1942) German
£408 $731 €600 Peasant wearing hat (17x15cm-7x6in) s. board. 18-Mar-4 Neumeister, Munich #2638/R
£411 $699 €600 Man with beard (61x50cm-24x20in) s. 5-Nov-3 Hugo Ruef, Munich #935/R
£833 $1375 €1200 Two peasants arguing over paper (81x75cm-32x30in) s. 2-Jul-3 Neumeister, Munich #607/R

BEST, Harry Cassie (1863-1936) American
£695 $1300 €1015 View of Yosemite valley (41x51cm-16x20in) s. 29-Feb-4 Bonhams & Butterfields, San Francisco #4538 est:600-800
£765 $1300 €1117 Yosemite valley (36x61cm-14x24in) s. prov. 18-Nov-3 John Moran, Pasadena #101
£924 $1700 €1349 Inspiration Point, Yosemite Valley (46x58cm-18x23in) s. oil gouache card. 10-Jun-4 Swann Galleries, New York #20/R est:2000-3000
£1016 $1900 €1483 Landscape with rocky outcrop and figure in the foreground (76x51cm-30x20in) s. 29-Feb-4 Bonhams & Butterfields, San Francisco #4539 est:2000-3000
£1099 $2000 €1605 Landscape (41x51cm-16x20in) s. masonite. 15-Jun-4 John Moran, Pasadena #68 est:2000-3000

BEST, Kevin (1932-) Australian
£265 $488 €387 Brumbies. board. 26-Mar-4 Lawson Menzies, Sydney #2238 (A.D 650)

BEST, Mary Ellen (1809-1891) British
Works on paper
£800 $1496 €1168 Girl paring apples in an interior scene (21x28cm-8x11in) i.verso pencil W/C. 22-Jul-4 Tennants, Leyburn #644/R

BESTER, Willie (1956-) South African
£641 $1090 €936 Loading the transtate bus (29x24cm-11x9in) s. canvasboard. 4-Nov-3 Stephan Welz, Johannesburg #650 est:5000-8000 (SA.R 7500)
£702 $1256 €1025 Mother and child (38x28cm-15x11in) s.d.01. 31-May-4 Stephan Welz, Johannesburg #603/R (SA.R 8500)
£714 $1293 €1042 Still life with a kettle and a paraffin heater (30x24cm-12x9in) s.d.97 canvas on hessian. 30-Mar-4 Stephan Welz, Johannesburg #522/R est:6000-10000 (SA.R 8500)
£756 $1369 €1104 Woman with Doek (38x28cm-15x11in) s.d.01. 30-Mar-4 Stephan Welz, Johannesburg #490/R est:7000-10000 (SA.R 9000)
£908 $1626 €1326 Yes to peace (49x30cm-19x12in) s.d.02. 31-May-4 Stephan Welz, Johannesburg #621/R (SA.R 11000)
£1111 $1889 €1622 Water carriers filling their buckets (26x37cm-10x15in) s. canvasboard. 4-Nov-3 Stephan Welz, Johannesburg #691/R est:6000-10000 (SA.R 13000)
£1897 $3167 €2770 Still life of a bowl of fruit in a war zone (28x25cm-11x10in) s.d.01. 20-Oct-3 Stephan Welz, Johannesburg #367/R est:8000-12000 (SA.R 22000)
Works on paper
£2155 $3599 €3146 Khayelitsha (55x101cm-22x40in) s.d.91 mixed media on board. 20-Oct-3 Stephan Welz, Johannesburg #393/R est:40000-50000 (SA.R 25000)

BETETA, Ignacio Manuel (1898-1988) Mexican?
Works on paper
£224 $409 €327 Nude (50x33cm-20x13in) s.d.1970 W/C. 27-Jan-4 Louis Morton, Mexico #195a/R (M.P 4500)
£248 $456 €362 Grey suburbs (60x90cm-24x35in) s. W/C. 25-Mar-4 Louis Morton, Mexico #29/R (M.P 5000)
£263 $448 €384 Still life with avocado pear (27x29cm-11x11in) s. W/C. 30-Oct-3 Louis Morton, Mexico #4/R est:9000 (M.P 5000)
£263 $448 €384 Still life with fruit (25x28cm-10x11in) s.d.1975 W/C. 30-Oct-3 Louis Morton, Mexico #148/R (M.P 5000)
£474 $806 €692 Oaxaca (49x32cm-19x13in) s.d.1976 W/C. 30-Oct-3 Louis Morton, Mexico #150 (M.P 9000)

BETHELL, Worden Charles (1899-1951) American
Works on paper
£391 $700 €571 Pueblo, New Mexico (51x58cm-20x23in) s. pastel. 21-Mar-4 Bonhams & Butterfields, Los Angeles #7315/R
£879 $1600 €1283 Summer landscape (38x51cm-15x20in) s. gouache board. 15-Jun-4 John Moran, Pasadena #44 est:1500-2000

BETIGNY, Ernest (1873-1960) Belgian
£500 $920 €750 Le sechage du linge au bord de la riviere (60x45cm-24x18in) s. 14-Jun-4 Horta, Bruxelles #425

BETLEM, John (fl.1914-1941) British
£3600 $6012 €5256 Piccadilly (69x90cm-27x35in) s. 7-Oct-3 Bonhams, Knightsbridge #82/R est:3000-5000

BETREMIEUX, Laurent (1959-) French?
£503 $941 €750 Sans titre (130x89cm-51x35in) s.d.1989 acrylic. 29-Feb-4 Versailles Encheres #204/R

BETSBERG, Ernestine (1909-) American
£483 $850 €705 Against the light (81x71cm-32x28in) init. s.i.d.1967 verso. 22-May-4 Selkirks, St. Louis #517/R

BETTENCOURT, Pierre (1917-) French
Sculpture
£3497 $5839 €5000 Untitled (123x250cm-48x98in) terracotta assemblage collage egg shells paint panel prov. 29-Jun-3 Versailles Encheres #182/R
Works on paper
£2207 $4083 €3200 Pierre tombale pour deux jeunes filles (133x68cm-52x27in) init.d.61 mixed media relief panel. 11-Feb-4 Beaussant & Lefèvre, Paris #153/R est:3000
£5200 $9464 €7800 Roi lepreux (153x122cm-60x48in) mono.d.78 verso mixed media panel prov. 29-Jun-4 Cornette de St.Cyr, Paris #7/R est:8000-10000

BETTERA, Bartolomeo (attrib) (1639-?) Italian
£55172 $91586 €80000 Still life with musical instruments (102x145cm-40x57in) prov. 1-Oct-3 Dorotheum, Vienna #59/R est:10000-15000

BETTERA, Bartolomeo (studio) (1639-?) Italian
£12000 $20760 €17520 Lute, cello, violin and guitar with book and music manuscript on table (71x97cm-28x38in) bears sig. 10-Dec-3 Bonhams, New Bond Street #28/R est:10000-15000

BETTERMANN, Gerhard (1910-1992) German
£833 $1308 €1200 Backyard (84x61cm-33x24in) s.d.62 board. 30-Aug-3 Hans Stahl, Toestorf #63/R
£1528 $2399 €2200 Sieseby (62x69cm-24x27in) s. board. 30-Aug-3 Hans Stahl, Toestorf #65/R est:2200

BETTI, Niccolo (c.1550-1616) Italian
£12000 $21960 €17520 Madonna and Child with Saint John the Baptist (61x45cm-24x18in) panel prov. 8-Jul-4 Sotheby's, London #156/R est:10000-15000

BETTI, Sigismondo (1699-1765) Italian
Works on paper
£728 $1326 €1100 Etudes d'homme debout portant un chapeau (19x20cm-7x8in) i. black crayon white crayon prov. 16-Jun-4 Piasa, Paris #26/R

BETTINELLI, Mario (1880-1953) Italian
£805 $1426 €1200 Self-portrait in uniform (200x100cm-79x39in) s.d.1917. 1-May-4 Meeting Art, Vercelli #417
£933 $1699 €1400 Interior with family (44x60cm-17x24in) s. board. 12-Jul-4 Il Ponte, Milan #997 est:1200-1300
£5333 $9813 €8000 Portrait of lady in garden (100x76cm-39x30in) s. 8-Jun-4 Sotheby's, Milan #109/R est:5000-7000

BETTINGER, Gustave (20th C) French
£390 $651 €550 Madam Bettinger at the piano (65x36cm-26x14in) s.d.1906 paper. 20-Oct-3 Glerum, Amsterdam #192/R
£532 $888 €750 Magician's trick for the Dauphin of Fontainbleau (24x33cm-9x13in) init. board prov. 20-Oct-3 Glerum, Amsterdam #193/R
£922 $1540 €1300 Portrait of the lady SEHA Bettinger, daughter of the artist (27x22cm-11x9in) s.d.1905 i.d.97 verso panel prov. 20-Oct-3 Glerum, Amsterdam #190/R

BETTIO, Francesco (1855-1901) Italian
£2507 $4587 €3660 Young girls in loggia (29x38cm-11x15in) s. 9-Jun-4 Rasmussen, Copenhagen #1606/R est:20000-30000 (D.KR 28000)

BETTS, Ethel Franklin (19/20th C) American
£4491 $7500 €6557 Little Johnts's Chris'mus (43x28cm-17x11in) s. canvasboard. 15-Nov-3 Illustration House, New York #71/R est:8000-12000
£5307 $9500 €7748 Grandmother seated with group of children, Granny (41x28cm-16x11in) s. canvasboard. 15-May-4 Illustration House, New York #72/R est:8000-12000

BETTS, Harold H (1881-?) American
£200 $332 €292 Untitled, trees on a roadside (35x43cm-14x17in) board. 2-Oct-3 Heffel, Vancouver #5 (C.D 450)
£328 $600 €479 Coastal scene (66x79cm-26x31in) s. painted c.1940. 5-Jun-4 Treadway Gallery, Cincinnati #653/R
£1512 $2600 €2208 Untitled, landscape (64x76cm-25x30in) s. 7-Dec-3 Hindman, Chicago #769/R est:2500-3000
£1566 $2600 €2286 Spanish Bayou (94x99cm-37x39in) s. 4-Oct-3 Neal Auction Company, New Orleans #559/R est:2000-3000

BETTS, Louis (1873-1961) American
£4790 $8000 €6993 Elizabeth Betts of Wortham (229x153cm-90x60in) s.d.1923 prov.exhib.lit. 7-Oct-3 Sotheby's, New York #220 est:5000-7000

BETTS, Mac (1932-) British
£905 $1639 €1321 Red quay (121x189cm-48x74in) s.d.88. 31-Mar-4 Goodman, Sydney #333 (A.D 2200)

BETTS, Virginia Battaile (1880-1942) American
£1347 $2250 €1967 Landscape (107x122cm-42x48in) 18-Oct-3 David Dike, Dallas #233/R est:2000-4000

BETZOLD, Heinrich (20th C) German
£345 $638 €500 Still life with view of Nurnberg Castle (60x80cm-24x31in) s. 12-Feb-4 Weidler, Nurnberg #6511/R

BEUCHOLT, L (18th C) Dutch
£1818 $3200 €2654 Woman draped in a blue gown, holding a rose (41x33cm-16x13in) s. panel. 21-May-4 North East Auctions, Portsmouth #1463/R

BEUCKER, Pascal de (1861-1945) ?
£541 $968 €800 Bruyere (41x51cm-16x20in) exhib. 10-May-4 Amberes, Antwerp #253
£667 $1200 €1000 Still life with flowers (47x62cm-19x24in) s. 26-Apr-4 Bernaerts, Antwerp #242/R
£2517 $4280 €3600 Fillette au chapeau assis sur une tablette (127x78cm-50x31in) s.d.1908. 1-Dec-3 Palais de Beaux Arts, Brussels #232/R est:2000-3000
£4295 $7989 €6400 Still life with roses (48x40cm-19x16in) s. 8-Mar-4 Bernaerts, Antwerp #9/R est:1200-1500

BEUCLER, Andre (1898-1985) French
Works on paper
£533 $981 €800 Guele d'amour (29x21cm-11x8in) s. pen col crayon. 9-Jun-4 Piasa, Paris #16/R

BEUGELINCK, Johann (19th C) Austrian
£650 $1190 €975 Children playing on a see saw (48x58cm-19x23in) s.d.1868. 28-Jul-4 Mallams, Oxford #370

BEUGHEM, Charles Ferdinand de (1828-1882) Belgian
£1800 $3276 €2700 Figures outside a house with pond in the foreground (55x71cm-22x28in) s.d.1874. 20-Jun-4 Wilkinson, Doncaster #321 est:2000-3000

BEUL, Frans de (1849-1919) Belgian
£302 $562 €450 Farmstead (57x40cm-22x16in) s. 8-Mar-4 Bernaerts, Antwerp #74/R
£532 $888 €750 Fermiere et son troupeau (88x70cm-35x28in) s. 17-Jun-3 Galerie Moderne, Brussels #353
£600 $1098 €900 Berger et troupeau (40x54cm-16x21in) s. 7-Jun-4 Palais de Beaux Arts, Brussels #44
£709 $1184 €1000 Berger avec troupeau (33x46cm-13x18in) s. 15-Oct-3 Hotel des Ventes Mosan, Brussels #125
£1133 $2040 €1700 Boy and girl gathering flowers near a brook (24x17cm-9x7in) s. panel. 26-Apr-4 Bernaerts, Antwerp #121/R est:1250-1500
£1544 $2856 €2300 Cows watering (64x90cm-25x35in) s. 13-Mar-4 De Vuyst, Lokeren #90/R est:1500-2000
£1631 $2724 €2300 Bourgeois interior with noble lady at a mirror (36x27cm-14x11in) s. panel. 20-Oct-3 Bernaerts, Antwerp #111/R est:1500-2000
£3172 $5869 €4600 Gardien et son troupeau de moutons au bord de la mare (66x82cm-26x32in) s. 16-Feb-4 Horta, Bruxelles #180 est:5000-7000

BEUL, Henri de (1845-1900) Belgian
£344 $550 €502 Young woman (69x51cm-27x20in) s. 20-Sep-3 Nadeau, Windsor #131
£1046 $1893 €1527 Shepherd with his flock (61x81cm-24x32in) s.d.1882 prov. 1-Apr-4 Heffel, Vancouver #18/R est:3500-4500 (C.D 2500)
£1436 $2600 €2097 Sheep resting in a barnyard (44x60cm-17x24in) s.d.1868. 30-Mar-4 Christie's, Rockefeller NY #96/R est:2500-3500
£5208 $8854 €7500 L'arrive d'un troupeau de moutons au plateau de Koekelberg, Aout (107x152cm-42x60in) s.i.d.1888 s.d.verso. 28-Oct-3 Christie's, Amsterdam #91/R est:5000-7000

BEUL, Laurent de (1821-1872) Belgian
£521 $859 €750 Herders with sheep by wood (40x57cm-16x22in) s.d.1862 panel. 3-Jul-3 Van Ham, Cologne #1072

BEUL, Oscar de (1881-?) Belgian
Sculpture
£1074 $1987 €1600 Motherhood (50x41cm-20x16in) s.i. dark brown pat bronze marble base Cast Lembecq lit. 13-Mar-4 De Vuyst, Lokeren #91/R est:1400-1600

BEULAS, José (1921-) Spanish
£1207 $2233 €1750 Untitled (32x45cm-13x18in) s. 14-Jan-4 Castellana, Madrid #171/R est:1750
£1408 $2465 €2000 Landscape (43x55cm-17x22in) s.d.60 cardboard. 16-Dec-3 Durán, Madrid #132/R
£2431 $3962 €3500 River in Alto Aragon (46x33cm-18x13in) s. 23-Sep-3 Durán, Madrid #154/R
£2483 $4469 €3600 Landscape (46x65cm-18x26in) s.d.1962. 26-Jan-4 Ansorena, Madrid #904/R est:3600
£2600 $4706 €3900 Park in Rome (49x37cm-19x15in) s. cardboard on board prov. 30-Mar-4 Segre, Madrid #255/R est:3900
£2632 $4763 €4000 Still life with blue bottle (54x65cm-21x26in) s. 14-Apr-4 Ansorena, Madrid #72/R est:4000
£3080 $5051 €4250 Somontano (46x65cm-18x26in) s. s.i.d.95. 27-May-3 Durán, Madrid #203/R est:3500
£3667 $6637 €5500 View of Toledo (60x81cm-24x32in) s. 30-Mar-4 Segre, Madrid #132/R est:5000
£3793 $6297 €5500 Mountain lake (81x60cm-32x24in) s. 1-Oct-3 Ansorena, Madrid #563/R est:3000
£3793 $6297 €5500 Street with houses (61x50cm-24x20in) s.d.1960 board. 1-Oct-3 Ansorena, Madrid #587/R est:2500
£4027 $7530 €6000 Bather (63x78cm-25x31in) s.d.47. 24-Feb-4 Durán, Madrid #77/R est:6000
£4138 $6910 €6000 Aragon landscape (46x65cm-18x26in) s. 17-Nov-3 Durán, Madrid #240/R est:3000
£4483 $7441 €6500 Landscape with peasant and cart (46x61cm-18x24in) s. 1-Oct-3 Ansorena, Madrid #566/R est:3600
£5903 $9740 €8500 Fields in Cuarte (97x146cm-38x57in) s. s.i.verso. 2-Jul-3 Ansorena, Madrid #874/R
£6040 $11295 €9000 Cathedral (116x89cm-46x35in) s. s.id.1960 verso. 24-Feb-4 Durán, Madrid #65/R est:9000
£6207 $10366 €9000 Huesca Cathedral (92x73cm-36x29in) s. s.d.73 verso. 17-Nov-3 Durán, Madrid #198/R est:9000
£6803 $12381 €10000 Rome (80x99cm-31x39in) s.d.1958. 3-Feb-4 Segre, Madrid #128/R est:10000
£11806 $19479 €17000 White Salamanca (123x172cm-48x68in) s.i. 2-Jul-3 Ansorena, Madrid #855a/R est:16000
£12500 $22625 €19000 Face-eyes (130x193cm-51x76in) s. s.i.d.91 verso. 14-Apr-4 Ansorena, Madrid #274a/R est:18000
£19097 $31128 €27500 Landscape in Huesca (114x146cm-45x57in) s. exhib. 23-Sep-3 Durán, Madrid #232/R est:22500
Works on paper
£336 $624 €500 Landscape (16x26cm-6x10in) s.d.1985 W/C. 2-Mar-4 Ansorena, Madrid #359/R
£414 $766 €600 Field (18x25cm-7x10in) W/C. 14-Jan-4 Castellana, Madrid #95/R
£526 $953 €800 Landscapes (31x44cm-12x17in) s.d.1950 W/C double-sided. 14-Apr-4 Ansorena, Madrid #379/R

£549 $950 €780 Landscape (45x32cm-18x13in) s.d.51 W/C. 15-Dec-3 Ansorena, Madrid #154
£604 $1130 €900 Landscape (30x44cm-12x17in) s.d.90 W/C double-sided. 24-Feb-4 Durán, Madrid #73/R
£604 $1130 €900 Landscape (30x44cm-12x17in) s. W/C double-sided. 24-Feb-4 Durán, Madrid #72/R
£625 $1150 €950 Landscape (45x42cm-18x17in) s. W/C. 22-Jun-4 Durán, Madrid #67/R
£690 $1152 €1000 Landscape with vineyards (31x22cm-12x9in) s. W/C. 17-Nov-3 Durán, Madrid #144/R
£897 $1497 €1300 Segovia (45x32cm-18x13in) s.d.52 W/C. 17-Nov-3 Durán, Madrid #103/R
£1034 $1862 €1500 Landscape (40x61cm-16x24in) s.d.1950 W/C. 26-Jan-4 Ansorena, Madrid #300/R est:1500
£1233 $2096 €1800 Landscape (41x43cm-16x17in) s. W/C. 4-Nov-3 Ansorena, Madrid #946/R est:1800

BEULLENS, Andre (1930-) Belgian
£282 $487 €400 Lignes d'or XIX (60x60cm-24x24in) s.d.1967 verso. 9-Dec-3 Vanderkindere, Brussels #134
£1267 $2318 €1900 Silene Silux II (144x120cm-57x47in) s.d.1967 verso prov. 7-Jun-4 Palais de Beaux Arts, Brussels #125/R est:1500-2000

BEURDEN, Alfons van (jnr) (1878-1962) Belgian
£310 $518 €450 Nature morte aux fleurs (61x71cm-24x28in) s. 17-Nov-3 Bernaerts, Antwerp #344/R
£319 $533 €450 Still life with flowers. s. 20-Oct-3 Bernaerts, Antwerp #180/R
£345 $576 €500 Nature morte a la viande, a la terrine et aux fruits (55x65cm-22x26in) s. 17-Nov-3 Bernaerts, Antwerp #342/R
£709 $1184 €1000 Ships at the quay, possibly Gent or Dordrecht (100x110cm-39x43in) s. exhib. 20-Oct-3 Bernaerts, Antwerp #170/R
£1200 $1896 €1752 Still life with a jug of sunflowers (100x85cm-39x33in) 27-Apr-3 Wilkinson, Doncaster #270/R
£1348 $2250 €1900 Shrimpster (60x80cm-24x31in) s. 20-Oct-3 Bernaerts, Antwerp #190/R est:1200-1600
£2128 $3553 €3000 Dejeuner sur l'herbe (102x130cm-40x51in) s. 20-Oct-3 Bernaerts, Antwerp #51/R est:2000-3000

BEURDEN, Alphonse van (snr) (1854-1938) Belgian
Sculpture
£1611 $2948 €2400 La jalousie (75cm-30in) s. marble. 8-Jul-4 Campo, Vlaamse Kaai #250/R est:5000-7000
£3500 $6300 €5110 Nude with an axe (73cm-29in) s. brown pat bronze lit. 21-Apr-4 Sotheby's, London #146/R est:4000-6000
£9500 $16150 €13870 Putti (76cm-30in) s. marble. 28-Oct-3 Sotheby's, London #83/R
Works on paper
£1200 $2172 €1800 Vaches a l'abreuvoir (60x80cm-24x31in) s. pastel. 30-Mar-4 Campo, Vlaamse Kaai #176 est:200-300

BEURMANN, Emil (1862-1951) Swiss
£1472 $2635 €2149 Clara with doll (68x52cm-27x20in) s.i. 22-Mar-4 Philippe Schuler, Zurich #4306/R est:900-1200 (S.FR 3400)
£2174 $3978 €3174 In the boudoir (80x54cm-31x21in) s. 4-Jun-4 Zofingen, Switzerland #2747/R est:1500 (S.FR 5000)

BEUYS, Joseph (1921-1986) German
£1034 $1728 €1500 Untitled (49x34cm-19x13in) s. collage. 13-Nov-3 Galleria Pace, Milan #150/R
£5944 $10105 €8500 Monochrome (31x20cm-12x8in) s.d.61 tempera board prov. 29-Nov-3 Villa Grisebach, Berlin #356/R est:3000-4000
£7000 $12810 €10500 Painting version 1-90 (76x56cm-30x22in) s.i. i. verso oil butter. 4-Jun-4 Lempertz, Koln #45/R est:8000
£34266 $58252 €49000 O.T. (30x21cm-12x8in) s.i.d.1954 verso stain over pencil double-sided prov. 29-Nov-3 Villa Grisebach, Berlin #354/R est:15000-20000
Photographs
£11351 $21000 €16572 Iphigenia and Titus Andronicus (71x55cm-28x22in) s. num.38/45 photographic negative and positive lit. 12-Feb-4 Sotheby's, New York #265/R est:10000-15000
Prints
£2517 $4280 €3600 Deer (37x27cm-15x11in) s.i. col lithograph. 27-Nov-3 Lempertz, Koln #40/R est:2800-3000
£3600 $6624 €5400 Flags (59x79cm-23x31in) s.i. col lithograph. 11-Jun-4 Hauswedell & Nolte, Hamburg #1163/R est:3200
£4167 $7500 €6084 Demokratie Ist Lustig (29x43cm-11x17in) s.i.num.16/80 screenprint prov. 24-Apr-4 David Rago, Lambertville #414/R est:800-1200
Sculpture
£1099 $1945 €1605 Hemd. s.i. wool shirt. 27-Apr-4 AB Stockholms Auktionsverk #998/R est:10000-12000 (S.KR 15000)
£1399 $2406 €2000 Multiple. s. num.68/100 tin container grease screwdriver exec. 1972. 4-Dec-3 Van Ham, Cologne #35/R est:2500
£1573 $2675 €2250 Storage jar (33cm-13in) glass oil chlorophyl. 27-Nov-3 Lempertz, Koln #38/R est:3000
£4000 $7360 €6000 Music as green (21x60x9cm-8x24x4in) 11-Jun-4 Hauswedell & Nolte, Hamburg #1155/R est:7000
£6145 $11000 €8972 First class grilled fishbones (30x11x6cm-12x4x2in) s.i.d.Oktober 70 num.of 25 vellum glass box fishbones prov.exhib. 14-May-4 Phillips, New York #298/R est:3000-4000
£10056 $18000 €14682 Nabbatterie (10x10x23cm-4x4x9in) glass crystals battery prov.exhib. 14-May-4 Phillips, New York #273/R est:15000-20000
£12291 $22000 €17945 Evervess (27x16x9cm-11x6x4in) s.d.1968 verso soda bottles wood box edition of 40 prov.exhib. 14-May-4 Phillips, New York #296/R est:4000-6000
£13408 $24000 €19576 Wer nicht denken will fliegt raus (18x19x2cm-7x7x1in) s. chalkboard white pencil string prov.exhib. 14-May-4 Phillips, New York #253/R est:30000-40000
£25000 $46000 €36500 Zwei Rehe (57x17cm-22x7in) st.sig. bronze relief executed 1950. 25-Jun-4 Christie's, London #205/R est:25000-35000
£34000 $62560 €49640 Filzanzug (180x74x8cm-71x29x3in) s.d.1970 num.100/36 felt wood metal coat hanger. 25-Jun-4 Christie's, London #207/R est:12000-18000
£35000 $63700 €51100 Pieta (33x24cm-13x9in) cast iron relief exec c.1951 prov. 5-Feb-4 Christie's, London #195/R est:10000-15000
£42000 $77280 €61320 Schlitten (36x91x34cm-14x36x13in) st.sig.i.d.1969 wood metal sled felt belt flashlight rope. 25-Jun-4 Christie's, London #208/R est:20000-30000
Works on paper
£300 $540 €450 Intuition (30x21cm-12x8in) s.d. verso pencil wooden box. 24-Apr-4 Reiss & Sohn, Konigstein #5745
£667 $1227 €1000 Self portrait (51x40cm-20x16in) s.i. ink beer mat board. 11-Jun-4 Hauswedell & Nolte, Hamburg #1147/R est:1200
£1000 $1840 €1460 Hasenblut (40x40cm-16x16in) st.sig. hares blood plastic 79 of 150 sold with a book prov.lit. 24-Jun-4 Sotheby's, Olympia #460/R est:1000-1500
£1119 $1902 €1600 90000 DM (50x70cm-20x28in) s.i. collage lit. 24-Nov-3 Christie's, Milan #10/R
£1135 $2066 €1657 Economic worth (18x25cm-7x10in) school tablet. 17-Jun-4 Kornfeld, Bern #206 est:2000 (S.FR 2600)
£1275 $2359 €1900 Untitled (50x35cm-20x14in) s. collage. 11-Mar-4 Galleria Pace, Milan #58/R est:1700-2100
£1467 $2625 €2200 Collage (36x28cm-14x11in) s. bandages clips plaster foil. 15-May-4 Van Ham, Cologne #449/R est:2500
£3356 $5940 €5000 Untitled (20x29cm-8x11in) s.d. s.d. verso wash Indian ink board. 30-Apr-4 Dr Fritz Nagel, Stuttgart #727/R est:4400
£5000 $9200 €7300 Modonna (15x10cm-6x4in) s.d.1955 pencil prov.exhib. 25-Jun-4 Christie's, London #204/R est:5000-7000
£6000 $10980 €9000 Untitled (21x12cm-8x5in) s.d.1973 pencil. 4-Jun-4 Lempertz, Koln #41/R est:10000
£7343 $12483 €10500 Untitled (50x35cm-20x14in) s.i. verso silver board prov. 29-Nov-3 Villa Grisebach, Berlin #355/R est:4000-6000
£10563 $17535 €15000 Untitled (70x42cm-28x17in) s. cloth soap. 11-Jun-3 Finarte Semenzato, Milan #596/R est:16000
£12000 $20040 €17520 Vogel (11x17cm-4x7in) s.i.d.1957 verso pencil printed ink charring prov. 21-Oct-3 Sotheby's, London #369/R est:12000-15000
£12000 $20040 €17520 Schamane (9x18cm-4x7in) s.i.d.1958 verso pencil prov. 21-Oct-3 Sotheby's, London #371/R est:12000-15000
£14000 $23380 €20440 Tierfrau und Tier (12x20cm-5x8in) i.d.1956 verso pencil prov.exhib. 21-Oct-3 Sotheby's, London #368/R est:12000-15000
£15000 $27450 €22500 Untitled - deer (29x21cm-11x8in) s. pencil prov. 4-Jun-4 Lempertz, Koln #40/R est:10000
£17333 $31720 €26000 Untitled (48x100cm-19x39in) s.d.72 feltpen prov. 4-Jun-4 Lempertz, Koln #39/R est:25000
£25175 $42797 €36000 Female nude (29x20cm-11x8in) s.i.d.59 verso pencil. 29-Nov-3 Villa Grisebach, Berlin #353/R est:5000-7000

BEUYS, Joseph and HAFNER, Jonas (20th C) German
Works on paper
£3600 $6624 €5400 Think Thank (108x61cm-43x24in) s.mono.i.d. W/C pencil diptych. 11-Jun-4 Hauswedell & Nolte, Hamburg #1163a/R est:10000

BEVAN, Irvine (1852-1940) British
Works on paper
£950 $1701 €1387 HMS Marlborough going into action at Jutland (25x47cm-10x19in) s.i. W/C. 26-May-4 Christie's, Kensington #468/R

BEVAN, Robert (1865-1925) British
£1500 $2505 €2190 View of gardens in summer (48x58cm-19x23in) s. 17-Oct-3 Keys, Aylsham #770 est:1600
£1800 $3168 €2628 Well at Mydlow, Poland (27x34cm-11x13in) 18-May-4 Bonhams, Knightsbridge #139/R est:1000-1500
£2200 $3784 €3212 Osiers, Brittany (26x37cm-10x15in) studio st. black crayon. 3-Dec-3 Christie's, Kensington #554/R est:1000-1500
£9000 $16380 €13140 The farm (31x46cm-12x18in) prov. 15-Jun-4 Bonhams, New Bond Street #7/R est:10000-15000
£10000 $18300 €14600 Miller's cart (29x37cm-11x15in) st.sig. W/C chk prov.exhib. 2-Jun-4 Sotheby's, London #60/R est:6000-8000
Prints
£2200 $3740 €3212 Horse market (26x37cm-10x15in) lithograph. 30-Oct-3 Christie's, Kensington #4/R est:1500-2000
£2200 $3784 €3212 Rosemary, Devon (23x29cm-9x11in) s.num.34/40 lithograph. 3-Dec-3 Christie's, Kensington #591/R est:700-900
£2200 $3784 €3212 London church (30x36cm-12x14in) s.num.45/45 lithograph. 3-Dec-3 Christie's, Kensington #304/R est:500-700
£3200 $5504 €4672 Hawkridge (35x41cm-14x16in) s. brown black lithograph 1 of 18. 3-Dec-3 Christie's, Kensington #566/R est:400-600
£6500 $11180 €9490 Horse mart (27x38cm-11x15in) s. lithograph edition of 65. 3-Dec-3 Christie's, Kensington #598/R est:1500-2000
£6500 $11180 €9490 Horse dealers at the Barbican (30x46cm-12x18in) s.i. lithograph edition of seventy. 3-Dec-3 Christie's, Kensington #599/R est:1500-2000
£7000 $12040 €10220 Sale at Ward's Repository (32x37cm-13x15in) s.i. lithograph edition of fifty. 3-Dec-3 Christie's, Kensington #600/R est:1500-2000
£8000 $13760 €11680 Horse dealers (28x38cm-11x15in) s.i. lithograph edition of eighty. 3-Dec-3 Christie's, Kensington #597/R est:1500-2000
£20000 $34400 €29200 Horse dealer scenes (28x38cm-11x15in) st.mono. lithograph four. 3-Dec-3 Christie's, Kensington #601/R est:3000-5000
Works on paper
£600 $1032 €876 Study for a London horse market (25x38cm-10x15in) studio st.verso pencil. 3-Dec-3 Christie's, Kensington #601a
£700 $1204 €1022 Breton peasant. Study of a foal suckling (34x24cm-13x9in) studio st.verso pencil W/C chl double-sided. 3-Dec-3 Christie's, Kensington #556/R
£700 $1204 €1022 Farmyard with peasant and child (23x33cm-9x13in) studio st.verso black crayon. 3-Dec-3 Christie's, Kensington #577/R
£700 $1204 €1022 Colchester horse and carriages (25x38cm-10x15in) studio st.verso chl. 3-Dec-3 Christie's, Kensington #603/R
£800 $1376 €1168 Hunting scenes (34x25cm-13x10in) studio st.verso pencil grey wash three. 3-Dec-3 Christie's, Kensington #569/R
£800 $1376 €1168 Polish village shop. Woman seated in a doorway (17x23cm-7x9in) studio st.verso pencil W/C. 3-Dec-3 Christie's, Kensington #570/R
£850 $1462 €1241 Peasant returning home (37x46cm-15x18in) studio st.verso chl. 3-Dec-3 Christie's, Kensington #576/R
£950 $1634 €1387 Near Bolham (25x34cm-10x13in) mono. studio st.verso black crayon exec.c.1918 exhib. 3-Dec-3 Christie's, Kensington #580/R
£1000 $1720 €1460 Hound studies (3x56cm-1x22in) studio st.verso black crayon chk four. 3-Dec-3 Christie's, Kensington #564/R est:500-700

£1000 $1720 €1460 View of Luppitt, Devon, Country village. Country lane (36x46cm-14x18in) studio st.verso pencil three. 3-Dec-3 Christie's, Kensington #584/R est:1000-1500
£1100 $1892 €1606 Preparatory drawing for WHO-O-P (34x51cm-13x20in) studio st.verso pencil black chk. 3-Dec-3 Christie's, Kensington #567/R est:800-1200
£1100 $1892 €1606 Haycart, Cumberland market (23x36cm-9x14in) studio st.verso black chk. 3-Dec-3 Christie's, Kensington #602/R est:500-700
£1200 $2064 €1752 Ploughing in Brittany (22x32cm-9x13in) studio st.verso black chk W/C exec.c.1893 prov. 3-Dec-3 Christie's, Kensington #563/R est:800-1200
£1300 $2236 €1898 Portrait of a man with a bottle of wine (35x26cm-14x10in) studio st.verso chl. 3-Dec-3 Christie's, Kensington #559 est:500-700
£1500 $2580 €2190 Studies of workhorses (37x46cm-15x18in) studio st.verso black crayon five. 3-Dec-3 Christie's, Kensington #594/R est:700-1000
£1700 $2924 €2482 Farmyard cottages. Windmill. Peasants' cottages, Poland (37x46cm-15x18in) studio st.verso black crayon three. 3-Dec-3 Christie's, Kensington #574/R est:1200-1800
£1800 $3096 €2628 Hoeing, Pont Aven (25x36cm-10x14in) studio st.verso black crayon exec.c.1893. 3-Dec-3 Christie's, Kensington #555/R est:600-800
£2000 $3440 €2920 Preparatory drawing for Forrard on. Forrard on (18x16cm-7x6in) studio st. i.verso pencil black crayon pair. 3-Dec-3 Christie's, Kensington #565/R est:600-800
£2200 $3784 €3212 Stable yard (24x34cm-9x13in) mono. W/C black crayon exhib. 3-Dec-3 Christie's, Kensington #596/R est:1200-1800
£2400 $4128 €3504 Gate to the farmhouse, Pont-Aven. Brittany landscape with peasant (19x29cm-7x11in) studio st.verso pencil chl. 3-Dec-3 Christie's, Kensington #552/R est:1000-1500
£2600 $4472 €3796 Threshing, Brittany. Women threshing (33x44cm-13x17in) studio st.verso chl pair. 3-Dec-3 Christie's, Kensington #562/R est:800-1200
£2800 $4816 €4088 Scenes with peasants (35x47cm-14x19in) studio st.verso chl three. 3-Dec-3 Christie's, Kensington #557/R est:1200-1800
£3000 $5160 €4380 Swirling sun. Open meadow. Trees in landscapes. Studies of trees (29x44cm-11x17in) studio st.verso chl five. 3-Dec-3 Christie's, Kensington #551/R est:1500-2000
£3000 $5160 €4380 Peasant studies (42x27cm-17x11in) studio st.verso W/C chl seven. 3-Dec-3 Christie's, Kensington #558/R est:1000-1500
£3800 $6536 €5548 Poplars by the road, Brittany (33x39cm-13x15in) studio st.verso chl. 3-Dec-3 Christie's, Kensington #553/R est:1000-1500
£6000 $10320 €8760 Shepherd and flock on the Downs (37x48cm-15x19in) mono. studio st.verso pencil W/C black chk. 3-Dec-3 Christie's, Kensington #586/R est:3000-5000

BEVAN, Tony (1951-) British
£7821 $14000 €11419 Red table (132x118cm-52x46in) s.i.d.87 verso acrylic sand prov.exhib. 12-May-4 Christie's, Rockefeller NY #464/R est:18000-22000
£12000 $22080 €17520 Exposed arm (221x156cm-87x61in) s.i.d.1986 verso pigment acrylic prov. 24-Jun-4 Sotheby's, London #298/R est:12000-15000
Works on paper
£13000 $23660 €18980 White room, head, leg and red table (205x248cm-81x98in) s.i.d.89 verso pigment acrylic prov. 6-Feb-4 Sotheby's, London #117/R est:12000-15000
£14000 $25480 €20440 Study 2nd version (88x75cm-35x30in) s.i.d.1990 i.verso pigment acrylic canvas prov. 6-Feb-4 Sotheby's, London #262/R est:10000-15000
£22000 $40040 €32120 Self portrait (202x177cm-80x70in) s.i.d.87 verso pigment acrylic canvas prov. 6-Feb-4 Sotheby's, London #263/R est:15000-20000

BEVAN-FORD, John (20th C) New Zealander
Works on paper
£426 $753 €622 Untitled (56x40cm-22x16in) init. ink. 28-Apr-4 Dunbar Sloane, Auckland #248 (NZ.D 1200)
£660 $1049 €964 Bird and Maori motif (76x56cm-30x22in) s. pen crayon. 1-May-3 Dunbar Sloane, Wellington #2 est:500-1000 (NZ.D 1900)

BEVEREN, Charles van (1809-1850) Belgian
£594 $1022 €850 Jeune fille faisant sa priere (45x36cm-18x14in) mono.d.1832 panel exhib. 2-Dec-3 Campo & Campo, Antwerp #361

BEVERLEY, William Roxby (1811-1889) British
Works on paper
£260 $484 €380 Fishing smacks on edge of storm (17x27cm-7x11in) s.d.1872 W/C over pencil scratching out. 2-Mar-4 Bearnes, Exeter #399
£1250 $2338 €1875 Fishing vessels at a quay, viewed from the beach at low tide (76x133cm-30x52in) s.d.1871 W/C. 26-Jul-4 Bonhams, Bath #12/R est:1500-2000
£1300 $2405 €1898 Breakwater (30x66cm-12x26in) s. W/C. 10-Feb-4 David Lay, Penzance #493 est:500-700
£1650 $2607 €2409 Coastal scene with fisher folk and beached boats (24x34cm-9x13in) s.d.1865 W/C. 23-Jul-3 Hampton & Littlewood, Exeter #409/R est:600-800
£2400 $4080 €3504 Figures crossing the sands (23x33cm-9x13in) W/C over pencil htd bodycol. 27-Nov-3 Sotheby's, London #283/R est:2000-3000
£2600 $4316 €3796 Dogger Bank, mouth of the Maas (90x131cm-35x52in) init.i. W/C. 1-Oct-3 Bonhams, Knightsbridge #61/R est:3000-5000
£2900 $4930 €4234 Fresh breeze - fishing smack making for port (63x83cm-25x33in) s.d.1868 W/C. 18-Nov-3 Bonhams, Leeds #115/R est:1500-2000
£2900 $4930 €4234 Scarborough, Yorkshire Dutch vessel putting out to sea (63x83cm-25x33in) s.d.1865 W/C prov. 18-Nov-3 Bonhams, Leeds #116 est:1500-2000

BEVIN, Alice Conklin (1898-?) American
£403 $742 €588 Self portrait on the ski slopes (63x53cm-25x21in) s.d.1935 exhib. 14-Jun-4 Waddingtons, Toronto #5/R est:1000-1500 (C.D 1000)
£1694 $3116 €2473 Young girl seated among cactus (65x53cm-26x21in) s. 14-Jun-4 Waddingtons, Toronto #6/R est:1000-1500 (C.D 4200)

BEVORT, Jan (?) Dutch?
£789 $1453 €1200 Seagulls in the dunes at Schoorl (81x120cm-32x47in) s.i.d.62. 22-Jun-4 Christie's, Amsterdam #534/R

BEWICK, John (?) British
£500 $930 €730 Portrait of the Hon Reverend Henry Montague Villiers, Bishop of Durham (91x76cm-36x30in) i. 4-Mar-4 Christie's, Kensington #350/R

BEWICK, Pauline (1935-) Irish
Works on paper
£1074 $1901 €1600 Yellow man on his belly with an ant on his hand (20x18cm-8x7in) s.i.d.1995 W/C pen ink. 27-Apr-4 Whyte's, Dublin #11/R est:1500-2000
£1400 $2534 €2100 Sarfina (16x22cm-6x9in) s.i.d.89 W/C pen ink. 31-Mar-4 James Adam, Dublin #52/R est:800-1200
£1458 $2377 €2100 Tuscan cherries (25x20cm-10x8in) s.i.d.1985 gouache prov. 23-Sep-3 De Veres Art Auctions, Dublin #254/R est:1000-1500
£1467 $2655 €2200 Girl playing with cat (55x38cm-22x15in) s.d.59 ink W/C. 31-Mar-4 James Adam, Dublin #54/R est:2000-3000
£2013 $3604 €3000 Figure in a tropical sunset (80x59cm-31x23in) s.d.July/21/80 pen ink W/C. 31-May-4 Hamilton Osborne King, Dublin #193/R est:3000-5000
£2238 $3804 €3200 Liza drying up for me (76x59cm-30x23in) s.i. gouache prov. 25-Nov-3 De Veres Art Auctions, Dublin #100d est:3000-5000
£2937 $4993 €4200 Caragh lake (58x79cm-23x31in) s.d.Oct 78 W/C. 25-Nov-3 De Veres Art Auctions, Dublin #30/R est:4500-6000
£3800 $6878 €5700 Asleep with three cats (79x53cm-31x21in) s. gouache. 30-Mar-4 De Veres Art Auctions, Dublin #106/R est:4000-6000

BEWLEY, Murray Percival (1884-1964) American
£1860 $3200 €2716 Repose (36x41cm-14x16in) s. 7-Dec-3 Hindman, Chicago #807/R est:3000-5000
£1860 $3200 €2716 Siesta (46x51cm-18x20in) s. 7-Dec-3 Hindman, Chicago #808/R est:2500-3500

BEYER, Hans (1878-1963) Swiss
£1267 $2154 €1850 Winter in Ftan (31x47cm-12x19in) s.i.d.1912 tempera paper on board. 19-Nov-3 Fischer, Luzern #2596/R est:1200-1500 (S.FR 2800)
Works on paper
£1267 $2154 €1850 Trees in Engadin landscape in winter (31x43cm-12x17in) s. pastel chk. 18-Nov-3 Hans Widmer, St Gallen #1020 est:300-900 (S.FR 2800)

BEYER, Jan de (1703-1780) Swiss
Works on paper
£946 $1665 €1400 View of Castle Bylant (12x14cm-5x6in) mono.d.1737 i.verso pen grey ink brown wash. 19-May-4 Sotheby's, Amsterdam #256/R
£10135 $17838 €15000 Views of Dutch country houses or castles (17x11cm-7x4in) s.i. pen grey ink wash ten views on five sheets prov. 19-May-4 Sotheby's, Amsterdam #254/R est:8000-12000

BEYER, Max Otto (19th C) German
£1119 $1902 €1600 Still life with fruit (76x60cm-30x24in) s.i.d.94. 28-Nov-3 Schloss Ahlden, Ahlden #1412/R est:1700

BEYER, Otto (1885-1962) German
£2098 $3566 €3000 Village path (50x60cm-20x24in) s.d.19. 29-Nov-3 Villa Grisebach, Berlin #126/R est:3000-4000

BEYEREN, Abraham van (1620-1690) Dutch
£8219 $13973 €12000 Ray, salmon steak, crabs and other fish in a basket on a wooden ledge before a window (82x99cm-32x39in) indis sig. 5-Nov-3 Christie's, Amsterdam #39/R est:5000-8000
£10000 $17900 €15000 Still life of fish (107x156cm-42x61in) s. 15-May-4 Hagelstam, Helsinki #35/R est:18000
£20000 $36000 €29200 Still life of an orange and lemon in a porcelain bowl and other objects (56x51cm-22x20in) bears init. 22-Apr-4 Sotheby's, London #22/R est:10000-15000

BEYEREN, Abraham van (attrib) (1620-1690) Dutch
£1200 $2184 €1800 Still life with fish and crabs (26x39cm-10x15in) panel. 1-Jul-4 Van Ham, Cologne #1071/R est:1200

BEYMA, Julia Mathilda Anna Catharina van (1878-1955) Dutch
£395 $726 €600 Polder landscape (87x110cm-34x43in) s. 28-Jun-4 Sotheby's, Amsterdam #159/R

BEYNON, Claire (20th C) New Zealander
Works on paper
£634 $1027 €919 Sit awhile (60x68cm-24x27in) s.d.1997 pastel. 31-Jul-3 International Art Centre, Auckland #12/R est:2400-2800 (NZ.D 1750)

BEYNON, Eric (1935-) Swiss
£1268 $2193 €1800 Untitled (143x213cm-56x84in) s.i.d.1922 verso acrylic photo. 14-Dec-3 Rabourdin & Choppin de Janvry, Paris #75/R est:2000-3000

BEYNON, Jan (1830-1877) Indonesian
£35242 $59912 €51453 Landscape with natives on Java (62x87cm-24x34in) s.i.d.1876. 5-Nov-3 Dobiaschofsky, Bern #359/R est:45000 (S.FR 80000)
£47101 $73007 €68767 Batavia landscape (98x75cm-39x30in) s.d.1875. 6-Oct-2 Sotheby's, Singapore #62/R est:35000-55000 (S.D 130000)

BEYSCHLAG, Robert (1838-1903) German
£600 $978 €876 Young Tyrolean girl with a posy of wild flowers on a mountain top (36x26cm-14x10in) 28-Sep-3 Wilkinson, Doncaster #298/R
Works on paper
£1184 $2179 €1800 Portrait of elegant woman with fan (96x70cm-38x28in) s. pastel board. 24-Jun-4 Dr Fritz Nagel, Stuttgart #525/R est:1300
£1700 $2890 €2482 Young lady with a fan (89x70cm-35x28in) s. pastel sold with books. 4-Nov-3 Bonhams, New Bond Street #4/R est:2000-3000

BEYSCHLAG, Robert (attrib) (1838-1903) German

£317 $567 €450 Interior scene with a woman playing a harp watched by a dog (20x12cm-8x5in) panel lit. 8-Jan-4 Allgauer, Kempten #2347/R

£430 $788 €650 Woman's portrait (45x40cm-18x16in) panel. 8-Apr-4 Dorotheum, Vienna #192

BEZEM, Naphtali (1924-) Israeli

£1960 $3450 €2862 Jacob's ladder (81x65cm-32x26in) s. painted c.1970. 1-Jan-4 Ben-Ami, Tel Aviv #4379/R est:4000-6000

£2169 $3600 €3167 On a lion (81x60cm-32x24in) s. i.stretcher. 2-Oct-3 Christie's, Tel Aviv #92/R est:5000-7000

£2294 $3900 €3349 Jewish symbols (35x46cm-14x18in) s. painted late 1960's. 1-Dec-3 Ben-Ami, Tel Aviv #4336/R est:4000-6000

£3369 $6300 €4919 Landing (116x89cm-46x35in) s. 1-Mar-4 Ben-Ami, Tel Aviv #4666/R est:7000-9000

BEZOMBES, Roger (1913-1994) French

£462 $850 €675 Street scene (36x25cm-14x10in) s. s.i.verso. 25-Jun-4 Freeman, Philadelphia #259/R

£1056 $1900 €1542 Les soleils (71x58cm-28x23in) s. s.i.verso board. 20-Jan-4 Arthur James, Florida #46

£1074 $1922 €1600 Vase de fleurs (33x39cm-13x15in) s. panel. 30-May-4 Eric Pillon, Calais #125/R

£1222 $2200 €1784 Le bouquet Van Gogh (81x99cm-32x39in) s. s.i.verso board. 20-Jan-4 Arthur James, Florida #45

£3333 $5967 €5000 Reverie (31x41cm-12x16in) s. tempera. 16-May-4 Thierry & Lannon, Brest #121/R est:5000-6000

£3873 $6778 €5500 Jeune Bigoudene (73x33cm-29x13in) s. 21-Dec-3 Thierry & Lannon, Brest #133/R est:5000-6000

£3893 $6968 €5800 Bassin de Radoub (55x71cm-22x28in) s. panel exhib. 30-May-4 Eric Pillon, Calais #124/R

£4430 $8195 €6600 Odalisque (24x33cm-9x13in) s. exhib. 15-Mar-4 Gros & Delettrez, Paris #230/R est:6000-8000

£4930 $8528 €7000 Maternity (73x35cm-29x14in) s.i. painted 1938 prov.exhib. 15-Dec-3 Gros & Delettrez, Paris #113/R est:7000-10000

£19333 $35573 €29000 La Roi du Jour, Porto Novo (116x158cm-46x62in) s.i.d.1947 i.verso panel exhib.lit. 14-Jun-4 Gros & Delettrez, Paris #318/R est:30000-45000

Works on paper

£1133 $2085 €1700 Les Peuls, route de Niamy Dosso (51x30cm-20x12in) st.sig. chl exec.c.1946-47 prov. 14-Jun-4 Gros & Delettrez, Paris #314/R est:2000-3000

£2000 $3680 €3000 Chasseur de Natitingou, Haut Dahomey (64x17cm-25x7in) st.sig. i.verso chl exec.c.1946-47 prov. 14-Jun-4 Gros & Delettrez, Paris #316/R est:3000-4000

£2643 $4493 €3859 Les aveugles de Marrakech (73x99cm-29x39in) s.i. 5-Nov-3 Dobiaschofsky, Bern #360/R est:3500 (S.FR 6000)

£6383 $10660 €9000 Le harem (30x35cm-12x14in) s. mixed media cardboard prov.exhib. 16-Jun-3 Gros & Delettrez, Paris #249/R est:2800-3200

BEZOR, Annette Thea (1950-) Australian

£648 $1043 €946 Ennui and insatiate desires (62x64cm-24x25in) s.d.92 oil cotton thread on canvas. 13-Oct-3 Joel, Victoria #311 est:1500-2500 (A.D 1600)

£813 $1276 €1179 Impossible life wish I (93x90cm-37x35in) s.d.92 s.i.d.1992 verso oil mattress ticking linen diptych prov. 27-Aug-3 Christie's, Sydney #652/R est:2500-5000 (A.D 2000)

£1626 $2911 €2374 Veneer No 2 (82x89cm-32x35in) s.d.25 June 97 verso oil synthetic polymer twelve plywood panels. 4-May-4 Sotheby's, Melbourne #99/R est:4000-6000 (A.D 4000)

£8907 $14340 €13004 Tete BI (165x165cm-65x65in) s.d.August 2000 i.verso prov. 25-Aug-3 Sotheby's, Paddington #238/R est:8000-12000 (A.D 22000)

Photographs

£2227 $3585 €3251 Pandora 3. Pandora 4 (105x110cm-41x43in) both s.i.d.2000 verso C-type photo edn 2/5 edn 1/5 two. 25-Aug-3 Sotheby's, Paddington #364/R est:4000-6000 (A.D 5500)

Works on paper

£826 $1529 €1206 Head above water (75x78cm-30x31in) s.d.1984 pastel. 10-Mar-4 Deutscher-Menzies, Melbourne #245/R est:3000-5000 (A.D 2000)

BEZZI, Bartolomeo (attrib) (1851-1925) Italian

£1200 $2148 €1800 Lagoon (26x40cm-10x16in) 12-May-4 Stadion, Trieste #654/R est:1800-2200

BEZZI, Giovanni Francesco (attrib) (?-1571) Italian

Works on paper

£517 $864 €750 Adoration of the shepherds (27x22cm-11x9in) Indian ink prov. 15-Nov-3 Lempertz, Koln #1258

BEZZUOLI, Giuseppe (1784-1855) Italian

Works on paper

£490 $832 €700 Anakreon with boy (22x30cm-9x12in) s. pencil htd white. 27-Nov-3 Bassenge, Berlin #5538

BEZZUOLI, Giuseppe (attrib) (1784-1855) Italian

£3974 $7232 €6000 Woman praying (154x109cm-61x43in) lit. 21-Jun-4 Pandolfini, Florence #65/R est:6500-7500

BHAVSAR, Natvar (1934-) Indian

£444 $800 €648 Untitled (46x35cm-18x14in) s.d.1971. 24-Apr-4 David Rago, Lambertville #49/R

Works on paper

£889 $1600 €1298 Untitled (46x35cm-18x14in) one s.i.d.1968 verso one dried pigment roplex two prov.exhib. 24-Apr-4 David Rago, Lambertville #52/R est:400-800

BHENGU, Gerard (1910-1990) South African

Works on paper

£462 $837 €675 Portrait of smiling Sangoma (38x35cm-15x14in) s. W/C. 30-Mar-4 Cannon & Cannon, Pietermaritzburg #257/R (SA.R 5500)

£578 $1035 €844 Portrait of a Zulu woman (31x23cm-12x9in) s. W/C. 31-May-4 Stephan Welz, Johannesburg #312 (SA.R 7000)

£690 $1152 €1007 Induna (37x28cm-15x11in) s. W/C. 20-Oct-3 Stephan Welz, Johannesburg #617 est:3000-5000 (SA.R 8000)

£756 $1369 €1104 Portrait of a man wearing a kaross headdress (21x17cm-8x7in) s. W/C. 30-Mar-4 Stephan Welz, Johannesburg #235 est:2500-3500 (SA.R 9000)

£776 $1296 €1133 Young married woman (37x28cm-15x11in) s. W/C. 20-Oct-3 Stephan Welz, Johannesburg #618 est:3000-5000 (SA.R 9000)

£776 $1296 €1133 Smiling man (38x28cm-15x11in) s. W/C. 20-Oct-3 Stephan Welz, Johannesburg #640 est:3000-5000 (SA.R 9000)

£1121 $1872 €1637 Zulu kraal in wooded landscape (19x31cm-7x12in) s. W/C. 20-Oct-3 Stephan Welz, Johannesburg #352/R est:10000-15000 (SA.R 13000)

£1724 $2879 €2517 Zululand landscape with two huts (25x37cm-10x15in) s. W/C. 20-Oct-3 Stephan Welz, Johannesburg #295/R est:7000-10000 (SA.R 20000)

£2057 $3765 €3003 Untitled (28x37cm-11x15in) W/C. 6-Jul-4 Dales, Durban #1 (SA.R 23000)

BIAGIO DI ANTONIO (15th C) Italian

£38889 $70000 €56778 Madonna and Child in landscape (44x38cm-17x15in) panel lit. 22-Jan-4 Sotheby's, New York #11/R est:80000-120000

BIAI FOGLEIN, Istvan (1905-1974) Hungarian

£279 $500 €407 Parisian winter (30x71cm-12x28in) s. 21-Mar-4 Jeffery Burchard, Florida #108/R

Works on paper

£313 $542 €457 Modiano - poster design (44x27cm-17x11in) s. Indian ink. 12-Dec-3 Kieselbach, Budapest #220/R (H.F 120000)

BIALA, Janice (1903-) Russian

£3514 $6500 €5130 Interior with Denise and dog (114x145cm-45x57in) s. prov. 13-Jul-4 Christie's, Rockefeller NY #89/R est:1000-1500

BIALETTI, Ferdinando (1864-1958) Italian

£1972 $3273 €2800 Baite e Betulle (125x85cm-49x33in) s. 11-Jun-3 Christie's, Rome #139/R est:1800-2500

BIALINITSKI-BIROULIA, Vitold (1872-1957) Russian

£3020 $5648 €4500 Winter landscape with river (53x68cm-21x27in) s. 28-Feb-4 Quittenbaum, Hamburg #41/R est:1200

£4305 $7834 €6500 Paysage d'hiver (58x62cm-23x24in) s. panel prov. 16-Jun-4 Claude Boisgirard, Paris #26/R est:8000-10000

£5000 $8500 €7300 Dachas in the snow (44x56cm-17x22in) s. board. 19-Nov-3 Sotheby's, London #82/R est:3000-5000

£12000 $20400 €17520 Church at nightfall (72x88cm-28x35in) s. 19-Nov-3 Sotheby's, London #81/R est:12000-15000

BIALY, Miroslaw (20th C) Polish

£612 $1015 €894 Demonstration, 2 (98x79cm-39x31in) painted 1989-1992. 2-Oct-3 Agra, Warsaw #61/R (P.Z 4000)

BIANCHI, Alberto (1882-1969) Italian

£451 $767 €650 Nude (50x35cm-20x14in) s. masonite. 1-Nov-3 Meeting Art, Vercelli #286

Works on paper

£400 $736 €600 Boy at table (64x49cm-25x19in) s. pastel card. 10-Jun-4 Christie's, Rome #3

£537 $961 €800 Tray with fruit (57x44cm-22x17in) s. pastel. 25-May-4 Finarte Semenzato, Milan #44/R

BIANCHI, Daniele (1963-) Italian

£500 $920 €750 Hands (90x90cm-35x35in) s. 12-Jun-4 Meeting Art, Vercelli #670/R

£671 $1242 €1000 QU (100x100cm-39x39in) s.i.d.2001 verso. 13-Mar-4 Meeting Art, Vercelli #81

BIANCHI, Domenico (1955-) Italian

£4138 $6910 €6000 Untitled (180x60cm-71x24in) s.i.d.97 verso paint cardboard on board. 13-Nov-3 Finarte Semenzato, Rome #486/R est:5000-6000

£6000 $10920 €8760 Roma (214x255cm-84x100in) init.d.85 verso oil wax painted wood burlap. 4-Feb-4 Sotheby's, Olympia #206/R est:1000-1500

£9189 $17000 €13416 Untitled (205x164cm-81x65in) init.d.85 verso oil wax paper on burlap prov. 12-Feb-4 Sotheby's, New York #251/R est:1000-1500

BIANCHI, Federico (17/18th C) Italian

£10000 $18000 €14600 Madonna and Child with the infant Saint John the Baptist and two putti, in a cartouch (90x70cm-35x28in) 21-Apr-4 Christie's, London #87/R est:6000-8000

BIANCHI, Isidoro (1602-1690) Italian

£7554 $12388 €10500 Madonna and Child with Saint Catherine and Lucy (112x88cm-44x35in) 4-Jun-3 Sotheby's, Milan #29/R est:10000-15000

£31250 $52187 €45000 Saint Anthony (97x75cm-38x30in) 22-Oct-3 Finarte Semenzato, Milan #61/R

BIANCHI, Luigi (1828-1914) Italian

£1842 $3389 €2800 Gallant scene (71x56cm-28x22in) s. 23-Jun-4 Finarte Semenzato, Rome #111/R est:3000-3500

BIANCHI, Mose (1840-1904) Italian
£2667 $4907 €4000 Study for fresco (39x32cm-15x13in) init. cardboard. 8-Jun-4 Sotheby's, Milan #118/R est:4000-6000
£6806 $11569 €9800 Chioggia costumes (18x14cm-7x6in) s.i. board prov. 28-Oct-3 Il Ponte, Milan #292/R
£12081 $21383 €18000 Venice (37x26cm-15x10in) painted c.1867 lit. 1-May-4 Meeting Art, Vercelli #421 est:18000
£21127 $36972 €30000 Landscape with shepherdess in Gignese (48x66cm-19x26in) s. i.verso cardboard lit. 17-Dec-3 Finarte Semenzato, Milan #115/R est:18000-24000
£33484 $53575 €48887 Maternita (71x95cm-28x37in) s. mono.i. verso. 16-Sep-3 Philippe Schuler, Zurich #3318/R est:15000-20000 (S.FR 74000)
Works on paper
£1067 $1909 €1600 Portrait of the artist's nephew Alberto Bianchi (46x34cm-18x13in) init. pencil chk prov.lit. 13-May-4 Babuino, Rome #311 est:800-1200

BIANCHINI, Arthur (1869-1955) Swedish
£270 $486 €394 Dusk by the canal (32x38cm-13x15in) s. canvas on cardboard. 26-Jan-4 Lilla Bukowskis, Stockholm #75 (S.KR 3600)
£573 $923 €837 Coastal landscape (60x63cm-24x25in) s. 25-Aug-3 Lilla Bukowskis, Stockholm #178 (S.KR 7500)

BIANCHINI, Charles (1860-1905) French
£1104 $1800 €1612 Peasant girl (46x33cm-18x13in) s.i. possibly copy after Jean Baptsiste Greuze. 19-Jul-3 Skinner, Boston #339 est:600-800

BIANCHINI, V (?) Italian
£1181 $1865 €1700 Joseph and Potiphar's wife (120x140cm-47x55in) s. i.d.verso after Giovanni Bilvert. 2-Sep-3 Christie's, Amsterdam #6/R est:1800-2200
£1500 $2745 €2190 Madonna del Granduca (85x56cm-33x22in) i.verso after Raphael. 6-Jul-4 Sotheby's, Olympia #409/R est:2000-3000
£2153 $3401 €3100 Susanna and the Elders (116x153cm-46x60in) s.i.d.verso after Guido Reni. 2-Sep-3 Christie's, Amsterdam #9/R est:2000-3000

BIANCO, Enrico (1918-) Italian
£1300 $2380 €1950 Nu (51x70cm-20x28in) s.d.1983 masonite. 6-Jul-4 Bolsa de Arte, Rio de Janeiro #132/R (B.R 7100)

BIANCO, Pieretto (1875-1937) Italian
£704 $1169 €1000 Venezia, Battesimo del mare (29x35cm-11x14in) i.verso wood. 11-Jun-3 Christie's, Rome #35
£1275 $2257 €1900 Mountainous landscape (27x40cm-11x16in) init. cardboard painted 1912. 1-May-4 Meeting Art, Vercelli #306 est:1000
£2600 $4810 €3796 Venetian backwater (75x55cm-30x22in) s.d.03. 14-Jul-4 Sotheby's, Olympia #260/R est:2000-3000
£6207 $10303 €9000 Village street (100x73cm-39x29in) s. 1-Oct-3 Della Rocca, Turin #31/R est:9000-9500

BIANCO, Remo (1922-1990) Italian
£1333 $2453 €2000 Printing art (25x25cm-10x10in) cardboard on board painted 1950. 12-Jun-4 Meeting Art, Vercelli #838/R est:2000
£1476 $2746 €2200 Ricomposizione di un drama et particolare (84x53cm-33x21in) acrylic collage cardboard screenprint diptych exhib. 3-Mar-4 Artcurial Briest, Paris #308 est:2000-3000
£5797 $9507 €8000 Tableau dore (220x100cm-87x39in) s.d.67 verso mixed media gold leaf board prov. 27-May-3 Sotheby's, Milan #213/R est:8000-10000
Sculpture
£1133 $2085 €1700 3 D (29x30cm-11x12in) wood. 12-Jun-4 Meeting Art, Vercelli #87/R est:1500
£2067 $3803 €3100 Three D (40x50cm-16x20in) wood glass. 12-Jun-4 Meeting Art, Vercelli #844/R est:2500
Works on paper
£1088 $1948 €1600 Print (30x24cm-12x9in) s.i.d.1965 verso mixed media canvas on masonite. 16-Mar-4 Finarte Semenzato, Milan #63/R est:1000
£1216 $2141 €1800 Appropriation (69x44cm-27x17in) collage board lit. 22-May-4 Galleria Pananti, Florence #392/R est:1800-2000
£2378 $4042 €3400 Untitled (60x50cm-24x20in) s.d.1968 collage mixed media on canvas lit. 20-Nov-3 Finarte Semenzato, Milan #23/R est:3500-4000

BIANCONI, Giovanni Lodovico (attrib) (1717-1781) Italian
Works on paper
£260 $450 €380 Design for a candelabra (49x22cm-19x9in) pen brown ink col wash. 12-Dec-3 Christie's, Kensington #392

BIANQUI SANCHEZ, Octavio (1872-1936) Spanish
£987 $1786 €1500 Landscape with tree (32x32cm-13x13in) s. 14-Apr-4 Ansorena, Madrid #39/R

BIARD, François Auguste (1799-1882) French
£1000 $1550 €1460 Polar bear hunt (33x41cm-13x16in) 25-Sep-2 Christie's, London #287/R est:1000-1500

BIASI DA TEULADA, Giuseppe (1885-1945) Italian
£5592 $10289 €8500 Odalisques (38x49cm-15x19in) s.d.1926 board prov. 22-Jun-4 Babuino, Rome #648/R est:4000-6000

BIASI, Alberto (1937-) Italian
£1275 $2359 €1900 One, two, three, fire (67x67cm-26x26in) s.i.d.1990 acrylic collage board. 13-Mar-4 Meeting Art, Vercelli #383 est:1500
£1933 $3557 €2900 Ambiguous plans (60x60cm-24x24in) s.i.d.1976 verso. 12-Jun-4 Meeting Art, Vercelli #501/R est:1500
£2200 $4048 €3300 Untitled (70x100cm-28x39in) s.d.1995. 12-Jun-4 Meeting Art, Vercelli #863/R est:2500
£6757 $11892 €10000 Him and her in black (100x155cm-39x61in) s.i.verso acrylic painted 2000. 22-May-4 Galleria Pananti, Florence #319/R est:15000-18000

BIASI, G de (19th C) Italian
Works on paper
£3000 $5520 €4500 Wedding banquet (54x39cm-21x15in) W/C card. 10-Jun-4 Christie's, Rome #196/R est:2600-2800

BIASI, Guido (1933-1984) Italian
£495 $900 €723 Histoire de l'insomnie (32x45cm-13x18in) s.d.66 s.i.d.verso. 7-Feb-4 Sloans & Kenyon, Bethesda #862/R
£594 $1010 €850 Palimpsest (60x73cm-24x29in) s.i.d.80 verso. 24-Nov-3 Christie's, Milan #78
£839 $1427 €1200 Perhaps by the same master (73x92cm-29x36in) s.i.d.1977 verso prov. 24-Nov-3 Christie's, Milan #82/R
£867 $1569 €1300 Histoire de la recherche de la pierre (116x73cm-46x29in) s.d.62 s.i.d.on stretcher. 2-Apr-4 Farsetti, Prato #121
£1119 $1902 €1600 Voyage (162x129cm-64x51in) s.d.76 verso exhib. 24-Nov-3 Christie's, Milan #81 est:1200-1800
£1633 $2922 €2400 Mnemotheque (80x99cm-31x39in) s.d.71 s.i.d.verso. 16-Mar-4 Finarte Semenzato, Milan #395/R est:3000

BIAZZI, Mario Natale (1880-1965) Italian
£403 $721 €600 Portrait of gentleman (70x65cm-28x26in) s. 25-May-4 Finarte Semenzato, Milan #26/R

BIBEL, Leon (1913-1995) American
£4706 $8000 €6871 Mother and child, death march (74x89cm-29x35in) 9-Nov-3 Wright, Chicago #198 est:9000-12000
£5000 $8500 €7300 Exiled (76x91cm-30x36in) s. 9-Nov-3 Wright, Chicago #199 est:9000-12000
Works on paper
£941 $1600 €1374 Mother, child, bombers (33x25cm-13x10in) ink. 9-Nov-3 Wright, Chicago #204 est:2000-2500
£1006 $1800 €1469 Lunch 25 cents (20x28cm-8x11in) s.d.1938 W/C. 16-May-4 Wright, Chicago #160/R est:2000-3000

BIBERSTEIN, Michael (1948-) Swiss
Works on paper
£417 $696 €600 Clouds (5x25cm-2x10in) s.d. chk Indian ink brush. 24-Oct-3 Ketterer, Hamburg #635/R

BIBIAI, Istefan Foglein (1905-) Hungarian
£405 $750 €591 Parisian winter (30x71cm-12x28in) s. 24-Jan-4 Jeffery Burchard, Florida #108/R

BIBIENA (studio) (17/18th C) Italian
£14085 $24648 €20000 Caprice architectural (205x304cm-81x120in) 16-Dec-3 Artcurial Briest, Paris #225/R est:20000-25000

BIBIENA, Antonio Galli (1700-1774) Italian
Works on paper
£4121 $7500 €6017 Facade study (16x24cm-6x9in) pen ink wash prov. 29-Jun-4 Sotheby's, New York #8/R est:5000-7000

BIBIENA, Ferdinando Galli (1657-1743) Italian
Works on paper
£1038 $1900 €1515 Study for a grand hall (17x21cm-7x8in) pen ink over pencil. 29-Jan-4 Swann Galleries, New York #86/R est:1000-1500
£2800 $5040 €4088 Fantastical views of arched cloisters (14x10cm-6x4in) pen brown ink grey wash black chk pair prov. 20-Apr-4 Sotheby's, Olympia #48/R est:2500-3000

BIBIENA, Ferdinando Galli (attrib) (1657-1743) Italian
Works on paper
£1007 $1852 €1500 Monuments et fontaine (27x20cm-11x8in) pen Indian ink wash oval. 24-Mar-4 Claude Boisgirard, Paris #26/R est:1500
£2055 $3493 €3000 Jesus introduced to the people (48x33cm-19x13in) i.d.1702 pen wash. 5-Nov-3 Beaussant & Lefèvre, Paris #22/R

BIBIENA, Giovanni Carlo Galli (attrib) (1713-1760) Italian
Works on paper
£1530 $2800 €2234 Elaborate stage design with classical city and a canal (24x36cm-9x14in) pen brown ink gray wash. 29-Jan-4 Swann Galleries, New York #128/R est:1000-1500

BIBIENA, Giuseppe Galli (1696-1756) Italian
Works on paper
£4082 $7306 €6000 Une fantaisie de monuments classiques avec des personnages (31x60cm-12x24in) s.d.1735 black chk pen col ink col wash. 18-Mar-4 Christie's, Paris #227/R est:1500-2500

BIBIENA, Giuseppe Galli (attrib) (1696-1756) Italian
Works on paper
£1027 $1747 €1500 Stairs (20x15cm-8x6in) pen ink wash. 6-Nov-3 Tajan, Paris #52/R
£1667 $3017 €2500 Fantaisie architecturale (24x16cm-9x6in) pen brown ink wash gouache. 30-Mar-4 Rossini, Paris #2/R est:2500-3000

£2192 $3726 €3200 Colonnade (18x23cm-7x9in) pen ink wash. 6-Nov-3 Tajan, Paris #51/R

BIBIKOFF, Maria de (20th C) Russian
£987 $1786 €1500 Portraits of horses (48x58cm-19x23in) s. pair. 19-Apr-4 Glerum, Amsterdam #286/R est:1500-2000

BICAT, Andre (1909-1996) French
£1900 $3230 €2774 Portland Bill (51x61cm-20x24in) painted c.1953 prov.exhib.lit. 26-Nov-3 Sotheby's, Olympia #112/R est:600-800

BICCHI, Ottorino (1878-1949) Italian
Works on paper
£352 $609 €500 View of village (47x32cm-19x13in) s. pastel. 9-Dec-3 Pandolfini, Florence #307/R

BICCI, Neri di (1419-1491) Italian
£10000 $18000 €14600 Tobias and the Angel (66x49cm-26x19in) tempera panel transferred to panel prov.exhib.lit. 23-Jan-4 Christie's, Rockefeller NY #39/R est:50000-70000

BICKERSTAFF, George (1893-1954) American
£279 $500 €407 Azure sea (61x76cm-24x30in) s. 16-Mar-4 Matthew's, Oregon #87/R
£367 $650 €536 Mountains and lakes in the High Sierra (61x76cm-24x30in) s. board. 1-May-4 Harvey Clar, Oakland #1245
£471 $800 €688 Landscape (61x76cm-24x30in) s. prov. 18-Nov-3 John Moran, Pasadena #154
£1648 $3000 €2406 Landscape (61x76cm-24x30in) s. 15-Jun-4 John Moran, Pasadena #104a est:1500-2000
£2206 $3750 €3221 Sierra foothills (61x76cm-24x30in) s. painted c.1943 exhib. 18-Nov-3 John Moran, Pasadena #44a est:4000-6000

BICKERTON, Ashley (1959-) American
Sculpture
£3911 $7000 €5710 Untitled (158x152x10cm-62x60x4in) acrylic ceramic tile Astroturf plywood brass prov.exhib.lit. 14-May-4 Phillips, New York #311/R est:8000-12000

BICKNELL, Albion Harris (1837-1915) American
£813 $1300 €1187 Pastoral landscape with cows (160x193cm-63x76in) s. 18-May-3 Auctions by the Bay, Alameda #1041/R
£1955 $3500 €2854 Still life with peonies in a vase (76x64cm-30x25in) s.d.1907. 16-May-4 CRN Auctions, Cambridge #33/R
£2994 $5000 €4371 Drummer and the fife player (38x53cm-15x21in) s. 23-Oct-3 Shannon's, Milford #173/R est:5000-7000

BICKNELL, Evelyn M (1857-1936) American
£489 $900 €714 Marine with small sailboat, ocean liner approaching (69x112cm-27x44in) s. 9-Jun-4 Alderfer's, Hatfield #391/R est:2000-3000

BICKNELL, Frank Alfred (1866-1943) American
£688 $1300 €1004 Landscape (23x30cm-9x12in) s. board. 22-Feb-4 Bonhams & Butterfields, Los Angeles #7027 est:1500-2000
£3468 $6000 €5063 Quiet Pool (56x66cm-22x26in) s. 10-Dec-3 Bonhams & Butterfields, San Francisco #6048/R est:3000-5000
£3906 $6250 €5703 Landscape (61x81cm-24x32in) s. 20-Sep-3 Nadeau, Windsor #210
Works on paper
£232 $425 €339 Cottage by a stream (18x25cm-7x10in) W/C executed c.1930. 5-Jun-4 Treadway Gallery, Cincinnati #670/R

BICKNELL, Frank Alfred (attrib) (1866-1943) American
£284 $500 €415 Landscape with trees (23x30cm-9x12in) init. board. 23-May-4 Bonhams & Butterfields, Los Angeles #7017/R

BICKNELL, William H W (1860-1947) American
Works on paper
£230 $375 €336 Provincetown (33x46cm-13x18in) s. pencil. 19-Jul-3 Outer Cape Auctions, Provincetown #101/R

BICOLLET (?) French?
£455 $782 €650 Scene de genre (38x55cm-15x22in) s. 7-Dec-3 Feletin, Province #128

BIDA, Alexandre (1823-1895) French
Works on paper
£440 $734 €620 Soldat de l'Empire ottoman (46x29cm-18x11in) s.i.d.1846 chl sanguine gouache prov. 20-Jun-3 Drouot Estimations, Paris #30

BIDAULD, Jean Joseph Xavier (1758-1846) French
£6667 $12000 €9734 Landscape with a view of rooftops and grapevine (32x40cm-13x16in) s. 21-Jan-4 Sotheby's, New York #129/R est:15000-20000
£29371 $50517 €42000 Paysage Italien anime de personnages au bord d'un lac (63x54cm-25x21in) s.d.1793. 3-Dec-3 Oger, Dumont, Paris #102/R est:10000-15000
£42764 $78686 €65000 Vue de Forio sur la cote ouest d'Ischia (55x79cm-22x31in) mono.d.1803. 24-Jun-4 Tajan, Paris #68/R est:40000-45000
£130000 $237900 €189800 Still life with flowers (71x55cm-28x22in) s.d.1810 prov. 8-Jul-4 Sotheby's, London #169/R est:40000-60000

BIDAULD, Jean Joseph Xavier (circle) (1758-1846) French
£4396 $8000 €6418 View of Lake Geneva with the glaciers of Mont Blanc beyond (24x44cm-9x17in) paper on canvas. 17-Jun-4 Christie's, Rockefeller NY #54/R est:8000-12000

BIDAULT, Jean Pierre Xavier (attrib) (1743-1813) French
£14333 $25943 €21500 Paysage d'Italie (18x22cm-7x9in) paper on canvas lit. 30-Mar-4 Rossini, Paris #83/R est:6000-8000

BIDAULT, Louis (?) French
£957 $1599 €1350 Maison pres de la riviere (46x38cm-18x15in) s. 22-Jun-3 Versailles Encheres #27/R

BIDDLE, George (1885-1973) American
£264 $500 €385 Portrait of a woman (43x36cm-17x14in) s. 22-Feb-4 Bonhams & Butterfields, Los Angeles #7012
£563 $900 €822 Israeli baby (25x30cm-10x12in) s.d.1949 i.verso. 17-May-3 Bunte, Elgin #1291 est:300-500
£2206 $3750 €3221 Hooverville by night (41x51cm-16x20in) s.d.1940. 9-Nov-3 Wright, Chicago #166 est:4000-6000
£6286 $11000 €9178 House of Arai, Vahive (76x63cm-30x25in) s.d.1922 s.i.verso. 19-Dec-3 Sotheby's, New York #1043/R est:10000-15000
Works on paper
£1061 $1900 €1549 Chagrin (51x74cm-20x29in) s.d.40 W/C exhib. 8-Jan-4 James Julia, Fairfield #563/R est:2000-4000

BIDDLE, Joy (20th C) American
£430 $800 €628 Salt Marsh II (60x101cm-24x40in) s. acrylic. 5-Mar-4 Skinner, Boston #573/R

BIDDLE, Laurence (1888-?) British
£420 $680 €609 Still life of mixed flowers in a glass vase on a table (49x33cm-19x13in) s. 30-Jul-3 Hamptons Fine Art, Godalming #190/R
£600 $972 €870 Still life study of flowers in a vase (41x30cm-16x12in) s.d.44 board. 7-Aug-3 Amersham Auction Rooms, UK #291/R
£620 $1159 €905 Chinese vase (19x29cm-7x11in) s.d.25 panel. 21-Jul-4 Bonhams, New Bond Street #185/R
£650 $1183 €949 Still life with pansies and other flowers in a Chinese jar (33x44cm-13x17in) s. board. 1-Jul-4 Mellors & Kirk, Nottingham #841
£700 $1134 €1015 Pansies, wallflowers, geraniums and other flowers (36x51cm-14x20in) s.d.55. 30-Jul-3 Hamptons Fine Art, Godalming #287
£750 $1365 €1095 Flower in a Chinese vase with an ivory figure (34x29cm-13x11in) s. board. 1-Jul-4 Mellors & Kirk, Nottingham #842/R
£780 $1303 €1139 Flower study (19x32cm-7x13in) s.d.33 board. 12-Nov-3 Sotheby's, Olympia #133/R
£950 $1729 €1387 Pansy, geranium and primrose (35x54cm-14x21in) s.d.35 board prov. 1-Jul-4 Christie's, Kensington #136/R
£1200 $2064 €1752 Still life with geraniums, pansy, primulas and primroses (35x53cm-14x21in) s.d.68 prov. 3-Dec-3 Christie's, Kensington #532/R est:1200-1800
£1300 $2171 €1898 Still life of pansies in an Imari vase (30x51cm-12x20in) s. board. 14-Oct-3 Bearnes, Exeter #418/R est:600-900
£1300 $2366 €1898 Pansies, primulas, wallflowers, geranium and phlox (35x53cm-14x21in) s.d.54 canvas on board. 1-Jul-4 Christie's, Kensington #134/R est:1200-1800
£1300 $2366 €1898 Pansies, geraniums, marigolds and primulas in a chinese sauceboat (35x53cm-14x21in) s. 1-Jul-4 Christie's, Kensington #137/R est:1200-1800
£1400 $2338 €2044 Still life of pansies in a celadon vase (34x51cm-13x20in) s.d.39 board. 14-Oct-3 Bearnes, Exeter #419/R est:400-600
£1700 $2771 €2482 Still life, flowers in a Delft vase, cherries and flowers in blue vase (28x28cm-11x11in) s. panel pair painted 1923. 23-Sep-3 John Nicholson, Haslemere #264/R est:1000-2000
£1900 $3401 €2774 Flowers in a vase (36x53cm-14x21in) s.d.54 i.verso prov. 14-May-4 Christie's, Kensington #512/R est:1000-1500
£2000 $3580 €2920 Still life of flowers in a vase (31x53cm-12x21in) s. panel. 28-May-4 Lyon & Turnbull, Edinburgh #83/R est:1000-1500

BIDDLE, Richard Julius (1832-1883) British
Works on paper
£720 $1238 €1051 Off the Royal Sovereign shoal, Beachy Head (32x50cm-13x20in) s. W/C. 2-Dec-3 Sotheby's, London #84/R

BIDLO, Mike (1955-) American
Sculpture
£3784 $7000 €5525 Untitled (43cm-17in) s.i.d.85 plaster. 12-Feb-4 Sotheby's, New York #286/R est:3000-4000

BIDON, Daniel (19/20th C) ?
£264 $449 €385 Sunny coastline (29x79cm-11x31in) s. panel. 5-Nov-3 Dobiaschofsky, Bern #3308 (S.FR 600)

BIDWELL, Bridget (1956-) New Zealander
£350 $636 €511 Six vessels (80x120cm-31x47in) s.i.d.1995 s.d.verso board. 29-Jun-4 Peter Webb, Auckland #168/R est:2500-3500 (NZ.D 1000)
£1119 $1937 €1634 Quiescent order (120x100cm-47x39in) s.d.1998 linen. 9-Dec-3 Peter Webb, Auckland #175/R est:1800-2500 (NZ.D 3000)
Works on paper
£335 $575 €489 Terrace II (31x120cm-12x47in) s.d.2001 mixed media. 7-Dec-3 International Art Centre, Auckland #203/R (NZ.D 900)

BIE, Eugène de (1914-1983) Belgian
£483 $893 €700 L'enfant au blouson rouge (80x50cm-31x20in) s.d.43. 16-Feb-4 Horta, Bruxelles #46
£483 $893 €700 Les mains dans les poches (70x50cm-28x20in) s.d.43. 16-Feb-4 Horta, Bruxelles #47
£655 $1212 €950 L'homme a la cape rouge (72x63cm-28x25in) s.d.43. 16-Feb-4 Horta, Bruxelles #45

£946 $1693 €1400 L'arlequin (60x40cm-24x16in) s. 10-May-4 Horta, Bruxelles #351
£1351 $2419 €2000 L'oiseleur (40x20cm-16x8in) s. panel. 10-May-4 Horta, Bruxelles #352 est:600-800
£2797 $4755 €4000 Le theatre fantastique (100x70cm-39x28in) s. sold with a book. 18-Nov-3 Galerie Moderne, Brussels #711/R est:3000-5000

BIEBER, Emil (1878-1963) German
Photographs
£5333 $9813 €8000 The painter Adolph Menzel wearing hat, coat, umbrella and gloves (15x10cm-6x4in) vintage sepia toned gelatin silver. 11-Jun-4 Bassenge, Berlin #4115/R est:400

BIEDERMAN, Charles (1906-) American
£3073 $5500 €4487 New York (36x46cm-14x18in) s.d.1934 prov.lit. 16-May-4 Wright, Chicago #238/R est:5000-7000

BIEDERMANN, Johann Jakob (1763-1830) Swiss
£4957 $8873 €7237 Klus near Balsthal with fortress ruins (19x22cm-7x9in) mono. 17-May-4 Beurret, Zurich #6/R est:7000-10000 (S.FR 11500)
£10811 $18595 €15784 Lauerzersee with Insel Schwanau and Rigi Hochfluh (25x33cm-10x13in) mono. canvas on board prov. 2-Dec-3 Koller, Zurich #3008/R est:15000-25000 (S.FR 24000)
£12227 $21886 €17851 Falcheren waterfall, near Meiringen (48x65cm-19x26in) mono. 26-May-4 Sotheby's, Zurich #4/R est:30000-35000 (S.FR 28000)

BIEDERMANN-ARENDTS, Hermine (1855-?) German
£1284 $2298 €1900 Hunting dog in wood (46x56cm-18x22in) s.d.1879 i. verso. 6-May-4 Michael Zeller, Lindau #595/R est:1500

BIEGAS, Boleslas (1877-1954) Polish
£664 $1129 €950 Portrait et femme (70x49cm-28x19in) s. cardboard. 23-Nov-3 Cornette de St.Cyr, Paris #18
£1946 $3445 €2900 Palais des illusions ou des chimeres (59x80cm-23x31in) s. panel painted 1922 exhib. 27-Apr-4 Artcurial Briest, Paris #182/R est:1500-2000
£10738 $19222 €16000 Souvenir de pensees (92x73cm-36x29in) s. painted 1912 exhib. 27-May-4 Tajan, Paris #8/R est:18000-20000
Sculpture
£1189 $2021 €1700 Pleureuses (35x34x9cm-14x13x4in) s.num.1/8 black pat bronze. 23-Nov-3 Cornette de St.Cyr, Paris #17 est:400-600
£1469 $2497 €2100 Pleureuses (35x34x9cm-14x13x4in) s.num.2/8 brown pat bronze. 23-Nov-3 Cornette de St.Cyr, Paris #19/R est:400-600
£1502 $2689 €2193 Loie Fuller dans ses Voils (26cm-10in) s.i.Alexis Rudier golden brown dark brown pat bronze prov. 15-May-4 Christie's, Sydney #371/R est:2500-3500 (A.D 3800)
£1611 $3012 €2400 Personnage en priere (50x15x21cm-20x6x8in) s.num.1/8 brown pat bronze Cast Landowski. 29-Feb-4 Versailles Encheres #111/R est:3000-4000

BIEGEL, Peter (1913-1988) British
£1800 $2844 €2628 End of the gallop, pulling up (48x58cm-19x23in) s. 23-Jul-3 Grant, Worcester #469/R est:2000-3000
£1800 $2844 €2628 Stalking, shooting and fishing (48x58cm-19x23in) s. 23-Jul-3 Grant, Worcester #470 est:2000-3000
£4600 $8418 €6716 Home - The Devon and Somerset Hounds (40x50cm-16x20in) s.d.69. 28-Jul-4 Bonhams, Knightsbridge #94/R est:5000-7000
£5000 $9000 €7300 The Grand National of 1961, jockeys and horses taking a fence (51x61cm-20x24in) s. prov. 21-Apr-4 Tennants, Leyburn #1180/R est:6000-7000
Works on paper
£280 $482 €409 Fox hounds in pursuit of a fox from the edge of a copse (33x40cm-13x16in) s. W/C. 4-Dec-3 Bonhams, Cornwall #420/R
£450 $765 €657 Head of a hunter (22x20cm-9x8in) s. col chk. 27-Nov-3 Christie's, Kensington #139/R
£3488 $6000 €5092 Foxhounds crossing a road (30x44cm-12x17in) s. pencil black chk W/C bodycol htd white. 5-Dec-3 Christie's, Rockefeller NY #68/R est:3000-5000

BIEHLE, August (1885-?) American
Works on paper
£452 $810 €660 Eve and the Devil. Three figures standing, seated female figure (36x36cm-14x14in) s. ballpoint pen pair. 19-Mar-4 Aspire, Cleveland #77

BIEHLER, Sepp (1907-1973) German
£366 $610 €530 Girl resting (19x26cm-7x10in) s.d.1948 verso board. 13-Nov-3 Neumeister, Munich #260/R

BIEHN, Joshua (fl.1891-1899) Canadian
£625 $1075 €913 Stout ale drinker (30x25cm-12x10in) board. 2-Dec-3 Joyner Waddington, Toronto #379/R (C.D 1400)

BIEL, Joseph (1891-1943) American/Russian
£270 $475 €394 Winter townscape (51x64cm-20x25in) s. 3-Jan-4 Outer Cape Auctions, Provincetown #56a/R

BIELER, André Charles (1896-1989) Canadian
£223 $379 €326 La Moisson, Alpes Maritimes (33x43cm-13x17in) s. s.i.verso tempera board. 6-Nov-3 Heffel, Vancouver #12/R (C.D 500)
£901 $1532 €1315 Les voitures (56x76cm-22x30in) s. s.i.d.1967 acrylic board prov.exhib. 21-Nov-3 Walker's, Ottawa #16/R est:2500-3000 (C.D 2000)
£1280 $2342 €1869 Sugar Bush (30x40cm-12x16in) s. prov. 1-Jun-4 Joyner Waddington, Toronto #277/R est:2000-3000 (C.D 3200)
£1429 $2457 €2086 Classic nude (37x26cm-15x10in) s. paper on board painted 1960. 2-Dec-3 Joyner Waddington, Toronto #250/R est:2500-3500 (C.D 3200)
£1802 $3063 €2631 St Francois village church, Ile d'Orleans (25x33cm-10x13in) s. i.d.1925 verso board. 27-Nov-3 Heffel, Vancouver #47/R est:4500-6500 (C.D 4000)
Works on paper
£223 $384 €326 Chez Charles Emile (26x34cm-10x13in) s. gouache prov. 2-Dec-3 Joyner Waddington, Toronto #503 (C.D 500)
£379 $652 €553 Courtyard, Seville (31x39cm-12x15in) s. gouache prov. 2-Dec-3 Joyner Waddington, Toronto #519 (C.D 850)
£400 $732 €584 Mount Gabriel (19x23cm-7x9in) s. W/C prov. 1-Jun-4 Joyner Waddington, Toronto #305/R (C.D 1000)
£402 $691 €587 Entre femmes (26x36cm-10x14in) s. gouache prov. 2-Dec-3 Joyner Waddington, Toronto #423 (C.D 900)
£720 $1318 €1051 Treaty money (27x35cm-11x14in) s. W/C pencil painted 1940 prov.lit. 1-Jun-4 Joyner Waddington, Toronto #191/R est:2000-2500 (C.D 1800)
£1239 $2106 €1809 Abandoned farm (45x61cm-18x24in) s.d.1947 mixed media board prov. 23-Nov-3 Levis, Calgary #12/R est:3000-4000 (C.D 2750)

BIELER, Ernest (1863-1948) Swiss
£13453 $21928 €19641 Arbre Saviese (160x110cm-63x43in) s. tempera panel prov. 29-Sep-3 Christie's, Zurich #19/R est:30000-40000 (S.FR 30000)
Works on paper
£688 $1149 €998 Saviesanne a la coiffe (31x24cm-12x9in) s. crayon. 21-Jun-3 Galerie du Rhone, Sion #327/R est:2000-3000 (S.FR 1500)
£826 $1512 €1206 La moisson (30x47cm-12x19in) s.d.1905 chl gouache prov. 5-Jun-4 Galerie du Rhone, Sion #251 (S.FR 1900)
£870 $1591 €1270 Les conseillers (30x47cm-12x19in) s.d.1905 chl W/C dr verso prov. 5-Jun-4 Galerie du Rhone, Sion #259/R (S.FR 2000)
£870 $1591 €1270 Les vendanges (30x47cm-12x19in) s.d.1905 chl W/C dr verso prov. 5-Jun-4 Galerie du Rhone, Sion #264 (S.FR 2000)
£1217 $2228 €1777 Girl with snowdrop (25x12cm-10x5in) s. W/C over pencil. 7-Jun-4 Christie's, Zurich #23/R est:1200-1500 (S.FR 2800)
£1310 $2345 €1913 Castel a la Montagne (34x49cm-13x19in) mono. pastel. 26-May-4 Sotheby's, Zurich #134/R est:3000-5000 (S.FR 3000)
£1565 $2864 €2285 Les foins (30x47cm-12x19in) s.d.1905 chl W/C dr verso prov. 5-Jun-4 Galerie du Rhone, Sion #261 est:2000-3000 (S.FR 3600)
£1584 $2740 €2313 Petite voisine (40x32cm-16x13in) s.i. crayon. 12-Dec-3 Galerie du Rhone, Sion #629/R est:4000-6000 (S.FR 3500)
£1652 $3023 €2412 La moisson (30x47cm-12x19in) s.d.1905 chl W/C dr verso prov. 5-Jun-4 Galerie du Rhone, Sion #252/R est:2000-3000 (S.FR 3800)
£2183 $3908 €3187 Canal a Venise (46x73cm-18x29in) st.sig. W/C pastel. 26-May-4 Sotheby's, Zurich #135/R est:5000-7000 (S.FR 5000)
£2262 $3914 €3303 Bateau sur le Lac Leman (23x30cm-9x12in) s.d.1894 W/C. 9-Dec-3 Sotheby's, Zurich #91/R est:2500-3500 (S.FR 5000)
£2715 $4697 €3964 Ferme a Roumaz, Saviese (50x63cm-20x25in) s.i. pastel. 9-Dec-3 Sotheby's, Zurich #90/R est:6000-8000 (S.FR 6000)
£3587 $5848 €5237 Study of woman for 'L'eau mysterieuse' (32x69cm-13x27in) s. W/C on pencil prov. 29-Sep-3 Christie's, Zurich #22/R est:8000-12000 (S.FR 8000)
£3587 $5848 €5237 Vue de Rivaz (33x59cm-13x23in) s. W/C pastel over pencil prov. 29-Sep-3 Christie's, Zurich #23/R est:6000-8000 (S.FR 8000)
£3696 $6763 €5396 Crete de Thyon (35x53cm-14x21in) mono. chl pastel paper on board prov. 7-Jun-4 Christie's, Zurich #25/R est:6000-8000 (S.FR 8500)
£4484 $7309 €6547 Paysage de Saviese en hiver (47x63cm-19x25in) s. pastel paper on board prov. 29-Sep-3 Christie's, Zurich #18/R est:7000-9000 (S.FR 10000)
£5882 $10176 €8588 Automne en Valais (58x78cm-23x31in) st.sig. pastel. 9-Dec-3 Sotheby's, Zurich #89/R est:9000-12000 (S.FR 13000)
£54148 $96926 €79056 Le vieux sonneur de saviese (29x29cm-11x11in) s.i. pencil tempera velin board prov.exhib.lit. 26-May-4 Sotheby's, Zurich #20/R est:80000-120000 (S.FR 124000)

BIELER, Ernest (attrib) (1863-1948) Swiss
£1762 $2996 €2573 Young with flute (45x79cm-18x31in) mono. 5-Nov-3 Dobiaschofsky, Bern #361/R est:5000 (S.FR 4000)

BIELING, Hermann Friedrich (1887-1964) Dutch
£267 $477 €400 Stal van Jilles van der Hoek te Rhoon (49x64cm-19x25in) s. 11-May-4 Vendu Notarishuis, Rotterdam #43
£500 $915 €750 Self portrait (40x32cm-16x13in) s.d.28. 7-Jun-4 Glerum, Amsterdam #98/R
£987 $1816 €1500 Landscape in winter (49x36cm-19x14in) s. 22-Jun-4 Christie's, Amsterdam #480/R est:1200-1600
£1133 $2029 €1700 Old village of Bukkenbuurt (39x53cm-15x21in) s. 11-May-4 Vendu Notarishuis, Rotterdam #144 est:1500-2000
£1497 $2724 €2200 Dutch windmill (58x73cm-23x29in) mono.d.28. 3-Feb-4 Christie's, Amsterdam #481/R est:2200-2600
£1733 $3103 €2600 Clown rollerskating (36x44cm-14x17in) s. 11-May-4 Vendu Notarishuis, Rotterdam #104/R est:2000-2500
£2303 $4237 €3500 Romance (67x58cm-26x23in) s.i.d.31. 22-Jun-4 Christie's, Amsterdam #482/R est:4000-6000
£2657 $4517 €3800 Pollard willows at the water side (67x98cm-26x39in) s. burlap painted 1923. 25-Nov-3 Christie's, Amsterdam #170/R est:3000-5000
£5245 $8916 €7500 Paris revue (53x80cm-21x31in) s. painted c.1918 prov. 25-Nov-3 Christie's, Amsterdam #166/R est:8000-12000
£5245 $8916 €7500 Two Heads (91x74cm-36x29in) s.d.30 prov. 25-Nov-3 Christie's, Amsterdam #169/R est:6000-8000
Sculpture
£1053 $1937 €1600 Parting of the cubism (34cm-13in) s. num.5/6 bronze one of six. 22-Jun-4 Christie's, Amsterdam #484/R est:1500-2000
Works on paper
£333 $597 €500 Juggler (50x42cm-20x17in) s.d.61 W/C. 11-May-4 Vendu Notarishuis, Rotterdam #142/R

BIENAIME, Luigi (1795-1878) Italian
Sculpture
£4000 $6800 €5840 Guardian angel (82cm-32in) marble lit. 28-Oct-3 Sotheby's, London #80/R
£10000 $18300 €14600 Divine love (106cm-42in) s.d.1833 marble prov.lit. 9-Jul-4 Sotheby's, London #111/R est:10000-15000
£13408 $24000 €19576 Woman seated at a crib holding a nude baby (91cm-36in) s. white marble. 20-Mar-4 Selkirks, St. Louis #550/R est:22000-28000

BIENAIME, Walow (?) Haitian
£1133 $2029 €1700 Marchand de fleurs (15x20cm-6x8in) s. 17-May-4 Rogeon, Paris #49/R

BIENNE, Gaston de (?) French?

£503	$936	€750	Moored fishing sloop on river Schelde (60x80cm-24x31in) s. 8-Mar-4 Bernaerts, Antwerp #263/R

BIENNOURY, Victor (1823-1893) French

£2535	$4386	€3600	Portrait de Charlemagne-Emile de Maupas, Ministre de la Police Generale (230x145cm-91x57in) s. 12-Dec-3 Libert, Castor, Paris #65/R est:10000-12000

BIENVETU, Gustav (19/20th C) French

£1600	$2752	€2336	Carnations in a vase, a garden beyond (53x45cm-21x18in) s. 4-Dec-3 Christie's, Kensington #104/R est:1500-2000
£1700	$3043	€2482	Still life with roses in a wicker basket (43x53cm-17x21in) s. 7-May-4 Mallams, Oxford #352/R est:500-700

BIERENBROODSPOT, Gerti (1940-) Dutch

Works on paper			
£567	$1037	€850	Study for dancing figures (27x67cm-11x26in) s.d.1989 mixed media. 7-Jun-4 Glerum, Amsterdam #238/R

BIERGE, Roland (1922-1991) French

£246	$409	€350	Fleurs de la Fontanelle (60x60cm-24x24in) s. s.i.d.1969 verso. 11-Jun-3 Finarte Semenzato, Milan #628/R
£249	$450	€364	Tulips rouges sur fond blanc (64x53cm-25x21in) s. s.i.d.12.4.64 verso prov. 2-Apr-4 Freeman, Philadelphia #134
£282	$487	€400	Poires a la boite de the (38x46cm-15x18in) s. s.i.d.20 nov 64 verso. 13-Dec-3 Touati, Paris #28/R
£282	$487	€400	Theiere aux trois fruits (24x41cm-9x16in) s. s.i.d.10.6.61 verso. 13-Dec-3 Touati, Paris #29/R
£282	$487	€400	Plateau de fruits (38x61cm-15x24in) s. s.i.verso. 13-Dec-3 Touati, Paris #39
£317	$548	€450	L'allee aux oliviers (24x33cm-9x13in) s.i.verso. 13-Dec-3 Touati, Paris #33
£638	$1129	€950	Composition (61x50cm-24x20in) s.d.8 fevrier 1977. 28-Apr-4 Charbonneaux, Paris #111/R

BIERK, David (1944-2001) Canadian

£2262	$3778	€3303	Reflective still life (91x66cm-36x26in) s.i.d.1993 canvas on board. 17-Nov-3 Hodgins, Calgary #301/R est:2500-3500 (C.D 5000)
£2928	$4977	€4275	Earth and sky, study 6 (20x20cm-8x8in) board prov. 18-Nov-3 Sotheby's, Toronto #111/R est:5000-7000 (C.D 6500)
Works on paper			
£924	$1718	€1349	Still life with canteloupe and cabbage (54x72cm-21x28in) s.d.March 28 1966 mixed media photo after Juan Sanchez Cotan. 2-Mar-4 Ritchie, Toronto #173a/R est:1000-1500 (C.D 2300)

BIERLE, Rudolf (1920-) German

£441	$749	€644	Hay harvest (18x24cm-7x9in) s. bears d. 5-Nov-3 Dobiaschofsky, Bern #362/R (S.FR 1000)

BIERMAN, Joseph (20th C) American

Works on paper			
£232	$425	€339	Floral still life (30x46cm-12x18in) s. W/C. 5-Jun-4 Treadway Gallery, Cincinnati #674/R

BIERMAN, Rudi (1921-1972) Dutch

£389	$700	€568	Flower cart (112x91cm-44x36in) s.d.68. 23-Jan-4 Freeman, Philadelphia #271/R

BIERMANN, Aenne (1898-1933) German

Photographs			
£7186	$12000	€10492	Feuerwerk - fireworks (29x39cm-11x15in) s.i. num.671 verso gelatin silver print exec. c.1928 prov. 17-Oct-3 Phillips, New York #5/R est:15000-20000

BIERSTADT, Albert (1830-1902) American/German

£4790	$8000	€6993	Sunrise, San Joaquin Valley (15x20cm-6x8in) board painted c.1890. 14-Nov-3 Du Mouchelle, Detroit #2020/R est:5000-6000
£11976	$20000	€17485	Seal Rocks, California (28x38cm-11x15in) init. oil paper on masonite prov.exhib.lit. 9-Oct-3 Christie's, Rockefeller NY #36/R est:20000-30000
£13235	$22500	€19323	The flight (36x48cm-14x19in) s. oil paper on canvas prov.lit. 1-Nov-3 Santa Fe Art, Santa Fe #124/R est:25000-35000
£17045	$30000	€24886	Landscape with mountains (36x48cm-14x19in) s. paper on canvas prov. 23-May-4 Hindman, Chicago #140/R est:30000-50000
£18895	$32500	€27587	Sunset (15x25cm-6x10in) mono. oil on paper prov. 3-Dec-3 Sotheby's, New York #112/R est:20000-30000
£21802	$37500	€31831	Study of Indians, fort Laramie (32x42cm-13x17in) bears sig i.verso oil pencil on paper. 3-Dec-3 Doyle, New York #250/R est:30000-50000
£27907	$48000	€40744	Mountain landscape (34x48cm-13x19in) s. paper on board prov. 4-Dec-3 Christie's, Rockefeller NY #65/R est:30000-50000
£29412	$55000	€42942	Rocky mountains (20x28cm-8x11in) s. prov. 24-Jul-4 Coeur d'Alene, Hayden #93/R est:25000-35000
£31250	$55000	€45625	Cove with beach and church (36x48cm-14x19in) mono. paper prov.exhib. 19-May-4 Sotheby's, New York #56/R est:30000-50000
£31977	$55000	€46686	Autumn landscape (48x69cm-19x27in) mono. board painted c.1880 prov.exhib. 3-Dec-3 Sotheby's, New York #110/R est:60000-80000
£42614	$75000	€62216	Prairie landscape (33x46cm-13x18in) s. paper prov.exhib.lit. 19-May-4 Sotheby's, New York #197/R est:40000-60000
£52326	$90000	€76396	Tobogganing (35x49cm-14x19in) oil on paper prov. 3-Dec-3 Sotheby's, New York #109/R est:30000-50000
£67073	$110000	€97927	Landscape with salmon boats (36x48cm-14x19in) s. oil paper on canvas prov. 31-May-3 Brunk, Ashville #338/R est:10000-20000
£164773	$290000	€240569	Wetterhorn (150x119cm-59x47in) mono.indis.i.d.1857 prov.exhib. 19-May-4 Sotheby's, New York #79/R est:150000-250000
£965909	$1700000	€1410227	El Capitan, Yosemite (46x61cm-18x24in) s.d.64 prov. 19-May-4 Sotheby's, New York #58/R est:1000000-1250000
£3720930	$6400000	€5432558	Yosemite valley (98x155cm-39x61in) mono.d.66 prov.exhib.lit. 3-Dec-3 Sotheby's, New York #27/R est:4500000-6000000

BIERSTADT, Albert (after) (1830-1902) American/German

Prints			
£5405	$10000	€7891	Last of the buffalo (83x107cm-33x42in) s. photograveur. 15-Jan-4 Sotheby's, New York #132/R est:4000-6000

BIERUMA-OOSTING, Jeanne (1898-1995) Dutch

£612	$1114	€900	Park bij avond (18x26cm-7x10in) init. s.i.verso plywood. 3-Feb-4 Christie's, Amsterdam #478
£921	$1695	€1400	A bouquet of flowers (40x50cm-16x20in) s. cardboard. 22-Jun-4 Christie's, Amsterdam #483/R
£1224	$2229	€1800	Stilleven met apples en druiven (45x54cm-18x21in) s. i.d.1930 verso. 3-Feb-4 Christie's, Amsterdam #432/R est:1800-2000
£2448	$4161	€3500	Stationnetje bij Bellevue - bij Paris (48x44cm-19x17in) s. canvasboard painted c.1935 prov.exhib.lit. 25-Nov-3 Christie's, Amsterdam #13/R est:2500-3500
£3497	$5944	€5000	Interieur - Lauswolt - mijn zitkamer (99x69cm-39x27in) s. board painted 1953 exhib.lit. 25-Nov-3 Christie's, Amsterdam #12/R est:5000-7000

BIESE, Helmi (1867-1933) Finnish

£2238	$3804	€3200	Pine trees (73x54cm-29x21in) s. 29-Nov-3 Bukowskis, Helsinki #61/R est:3000-4000
£2797	$4755	€4000	Sunny summer's day in the skerries (61x50cm-24x20in) s. 29-Nov-3 Bukowskis, Helsinki #25/R est:4000-4500

BIESEBROECK, Jules van (1873-1965) Belgian

£400	$720	€600	Plougher with ox-cart (46x48cm-18x19in) s. panel. 26-Apr-4 Bernaerts, Antwerp #118/R
£603	$1007	€850	Vue de Venise (42x58cm-17x23in) bears sig. 17-Jun-3 Vanderkindere, Brussels #28
£728	$1326	€1100	Plage animee (38x46cm-15x18in) s.d.33. 15-Jun-4 Vanderkindere, Brussels #81
£2000	$3680	€3000	Kabyle somnolant (25x21cm-10x8in) s. oil paper on canvas. 14-Jun-4 Gros & Delettrez, Paris #166/R est:2000-3000
£2533	$4661	€3800	Au retour du puits (36x28cm-14x11in) s. oil paper on canvas. 14-Jun-4 Gros & Delettrez, Paris #164/R est:2500-3500
£3194	$5079	€4600	Confidences, Orientaliste (70x57cm-28x22in) s. sold with document. 15-Sep-3 Horta, Bruxelles #130 est:2000-2500
£7333	$13420	€11000	Scene de marche arabe (80x100cm-31x39in) s. 7-Jun-4 Palais de Beaux Arts, Brussels #311/R est:6000-8000
£13287	$22587	€19000	Le chateau de sable, Ostende, plage (84x100cm-33x39in) s. panel. 1-Dec-3 Palais de Beaux Arts, Brussels #321/R est:20000-30000
£21831	$34930	€31000	Ceremonie marocaine (120x86cm-47x34in) s. panel. 20-Sep-3 Compagnie Marocaine des Objets d'Art, Casablanca #129/R
Works on paper			
£2569	$4599	€3751	Urania (61x46cm-24x18in) mono.i.d.1916 pastel prov. 15-May-4 Christie's, Sydney #348/R est:4000-7000 (A.D 6500)

BIESSY, Marie Gabriel (1854-1935) French

£268	$475	€400	Paris, une rue la nuit (22x16cm-9x6in) s. painted c.1892. 28-Apr-4 Beaussant & Lefèvre, Paris #66
£268	$475	€400	L'Arc de Triomphe du Carrousel (24x35cm-9x14in) s. 28-Apr-4 Beaussant & Lefèvre, Paris #72/R
£302	$535	€450	Paris, la Seine a l'Hotel Lambert (24x35cm-9x14in) s.d.1910 s.verso. 28-Apr-4 Beaussant & Lefèvre, Paris #70
£336	$594	€500	Egypte, Raz-el-Bank (15x21cm-6x8in) s.i.d.1917 verso panel. 28-Apr-4 Beaussant & Lefèvre, Paris #63
£403	$713	€600	Bruges, claire de lune (19x15cm-7x6in) 28-Apr-4 Beaussant & Lefèvre, Paris #65/R
£403	$713	€600	Parus rue Royale, la nuit, effet de lumiere (25x36cm-10x14in) s. cardboard. 28-Apr-4 Beaussant & Lefèvre, Paris #74/R
£537	$950	€800	Frans Biessy, le fils de l'artiste, avec son grand-pere maternel (54x65cm-21x26in) s.d.1893. 28-Apr-4 Beaussant & Lefèvre, Paris #79
£604	$1069	€900	Bonne-mere, Marseille (15x21cm-6x8in) s.i.d.1928 verso panel. 28-Apr-4 Beaussant & Lefèvre, Paris #68/R
£604	$1069	€900	Paris, la Seine au Pont Neuf, la nuit (28x29cm-11x11in) 28-Apr-4 Beaussant & Lefèvre, Paris #73/R
£671	$1188	€1000	Ciel rouge sur Paris (34x56cm-13x22in) 28-Apr-4 Beaussant & Lefèvre, Paris #77/R
£738	$1307	€1100	La Tante Helene, soeur du peintre (56x44cm-22x17in) s. s.i.d.1901 verso exhib. 28-Apr-4 Beaussant & Lefèvre, Paris #78/R
£1374	$2500	€2006	Gauchos (55x81cm-22x32in) s.i.d.85. 29-Jun-4 Sotheby's, New York #103/R est:3000-5000
£2000	$3680	€2920	Woman sewing in an interior (38x46cm-15x18in) s.d.1888 panel. 25-Mar-4 Christie's, Kensington #71/R est:2000-3000
£2013	$3564	€3000	Emma Biessy avec Claude enfant (100x81cm-39x32in) s. 28-Apr-4 Beaussant & Lefèvre, Paris #82/R est:2000

BIGAS, Bolise las (19/20th C) French

Sculpture			
£3867	$7000	€5646	Untitled (58x38cm-23x15in) s.d.1904 bronze. 3-Apr-4 David Rago, Lambertville #240/R est:800-1200

BIGATTI, Alfredo (?) Argentinian

£1117	$2000	€1631	Beach (30x50cm-12x20in) on paper. 11-May-4 Arroyo, Buenos Aires #11
Sculpture			
£8242	$15000	€12033	Pain (38x20cm-15x8in) init. pat bronze exec.1957 exhib.lit. 29-Jun-4 Arroyo, Buenos Aires #42/R est:15000

BIGATTI, Tommaso (18/19th C) Italian
Works on paper
£11111 $20000 €16222 Design for wall decoration one with a copy of the Roman fresco. View of ruined temple (32x53cm-13x21in) gouache on vellum pair. 21-Jan-4 Sotheby's, New York #119/R est:6000-8000

BIGAUD, Wilson (1931-) Haitian
£1067 $1909 €1600 Combite (61x76cm-24x30in) s. 17-May-4 Rogeon, Paris #83/R
£2200 $3674 €3212 Military parade, Haiti (58x120cm-23x47in) s. board. 14-Oct-3 Sotheby's, London #233/R est:2500-3500

BIGELOW, Daniel Folger (1823-1910) American
£2353 $4000 €3435 Vermont landscapes (10x15cm-4x6in) one s. board pair exhib. 1-Nov-3 Skinner, Boston #55/R est:1500-2000

BIGELOW, Larry (20th C) British?
Works on paper
£350 $574 €511 Summer, L'Herault (48x61cm-19x24in) s.d.57 W/C. 4-Jun-3 John Ross, Belfast #30
£450 $738 €657 Bridge reflections (56x68cm-22x27in) W/C. 4-Jun-3 John Ross, Belfast #96

BIGG, William Redmore (1755-1828) British
£26000 $44200 €37960 Sailor robbed. Sailor's purse recovered (102x127cm-40x50in) pair. 25-Nov-3 Christie's, London #42/R est:25000-40000

BIGG, William Redmore (attrib) (1755-1828) British
£455 $850 €664 Helping Mummy (43x36cm-17x14in) board. 25-Feb-4 Dallas Auction Gallery, Dallas #399/R

BIGGI, Fausto (19th C) Italian
Sculpture
£2890 $5000 €4219 Getting dressed (69cm-27in) s.i. marble. 13-Dec-3 Weschler, Washington #512 est:800-1200

BIGGI, Felice Fortunato (17th C) Italian
£8667 $15513 €13000 Garland with Madonna (67x58cm-26x23in) lit. 17-May-4 Finarte Semenzato, Rome #123/R est:14000-15000
£33557 $62752 €50000 Flowers and winged putto (90x161cm-35x63in) s.i. prov.lit. 25-Feb-4 Porro, Milan #8/R est:50000

BIGGI, Felice Fortunato (attrib) (17th C) Italian
£16000 $28800 €23360 Foxgloves, parrot tulips and other flowers in a marble vase on a ledge (75x59cm-30x23in) 21-Apr-4 Christie's, London #83/R est:15000-20000

BIGGI, Gastone (1925-) Italian
£586 $979 €850 Tale 2 (60x90cm-24x35in) s.i.d.1957 verso. 14-Nov-3 Farsetti, Prato #271

BIGGIN, Samuel A (19/20th C) American
£6395 $11000 €9337 Parade and flags II (72x60cm-28x24in) bears sig d. 1919 prov. 3-Dec-3 Doyle, New York #273/R est:10000-15000

BIGGS, Frances (20th C) Irish?
£486 $763 €700 Religious frieze (59x29cm-23x11in) s. board polyptich six panel. 26-Aug-3 James Adam, Dublin #46/R

BIGGS, Robert (1920-1984) American
Works on paper
£382 $650 €558 Going up (74x48cm-29x19in) s.i.d.1967 ink dr. 7-Nov-3 Selkirks, St. Louis #412/R
£559 $950 €816 Apple thieves (48x33cm-19x13in) s.i. ink graphite. 7-Nov-3 Selkirks, St. Louis #414/R

BIGGS, Walter (1886-1968) American
£7784 $13000 €11365 Servant has a mishap with firewood (102x84cm-40x33in) s. exhib.lit. 15-Nov-3 Illustration House, New York #159/R est:7000-10000
£8982 $15000 €13114 Tobacco market (86x97cm-34x38in) 17-Oct-3 Du Mouchelle, Detroit #2036/R est:15000-16000

BIGLAND, Percy (fl.1882-1925) British
£1400 $2338 €2044 Half length portrait of John Bellows (97x71cm-38x28in) 19-Jun-3 Mallams, Cheltenham #218/R est:100-200

BIGOT, Guy (20th C) French
Works on paper
£350 $594 €500 Aux gites de la mineralisation (165x165cm-65x65in) s.d.66 s.i.d.verso mixed media collage canvas. 29-Nov-3 Neret-Minet, Paris #138/R

BIGOT, Raymond (1872-1953) French
Works on paper
£302 $562 €450 Couple de perruches (28x37cm-11x15in) s. gouache. 7-Mar-4 Lesieur & Le Bars, Le Havre #9
£638 $1034 €900 L'epervier. s. W/C exec.c.1910/1920. 24-May-3 Martinot & Savignat, Pontoise #22/R

BIHARI, Sandor (1856-1906) Hungarian
£422 $763 €616 Farm yard in Sag (19x32cm-7x13in) s. oil on card. 16-Apr-4 Mu Terem Galeria, Budapest #100/R (H.F 160000)
£1015 $1797 €1482 In the garden (18x28cm-7x11in) s. panel. 28-Apr-4 Kieselbach, Budapest #142/R (H.F 380000)
£3258 $5408 €4757 Sunlit Venice (60x93cm-24x37in) s. 4-Oct-3 Kieselbach, Budapest #11/R (H.F 1200000)

BILBAO Y MARTINEZ, Gonzalo (1860-1938) Spanish
£1197 $2095 €1700 Choir (37x44cm-15x17in) s. cardboard. 16-Dec-3 Durán, Madrid #93/R est:1500
£1310 $2359 €1900 Coastal village (30x40cm-12x16in) s. cardboard. 26-Jan-4 Durán, Madrid #108/R est:1800
£1552 $2591 €2250 Coastal view (24x40cm-9x16in) s. cardboard. 17-Nov-3 Durán, Madrid #157/R est:2250
£1552 $2591 €2250 Landscape with lake and village (34x41cm-13x16in) s. cardboard. 17-Nov-3 Durán, Madrid #159/R est:2250
£1937 $3389 €2750 Posada del Lucero (25x38cm-10x15in) s. cardboard. 16-Dec-3 Durán, Madrid #128/R
£2069 $3724 €3000 Patio in Seville (24x40cm-9x16in) s. cardboard. 26-Jan-4 Durán, Madrid #109/R est:1800
£2113 $3697 €3000 Carriage (22x40cm-9x16in) s.i.d.97 board. 16-Dec-3 Durán, Madrid #127/R est:1800
£2303 $4237 €3500 Painters (50x65cm-20x26in) s. cardboard. 22-Jun-4 Durán, Madrid #133/R est:3000
£2414 $4345 €3500 Lucero farm (24x40cm-9x16in) s. cardboard. 26-Jan-4 Durán, Madrid #110/R est:1800
£2759 $4607 €4000 Landscape with shepherdess and cows (23x39cm-9x15in) s. cardboard. 17-Nov-3 Durán, Madrid #158/R est:2250
£3901 $6514 €5500 Young woman smoking (46x38cm-18x15in) s. 20-Oct-3 Durán, Madrid #143/R
£4138 $7448 €6000 Coastal view (43x55cm-17x22in) s. board lit. 26-Jan-4 Ansorena, Madrid #193/R est:6000
£8725 $15443 €13000 Boat arriving in Seville (45x63cm-18x25in) s. prov.lit. 27-Apr-4 Durán, Madrid #146/R est:12000
£16783 $28028 €24000 La procesion de las Siete Palabras (54x45cm-21x18in) s.d.1902. 24-Jun-3 Segre, Madrid #89/R est:15000

BILCOQ, Marie Marc Antoine (1755-1838) French
£40816 $73061 €60000 Diseuse de bonne aventure (59x73cm-23x29in) s.d.1789. 19-Mar-4 Beaussant & Lefèvre, Paris #73/R est:35000-40000

BILCOQ, Marie Marc Antoine (attrib) (1755-1838) French
£2119 $3878 €3200 Interieurs paysans, la fileuse et la bouille (14x19cm-6x7in) cardboard sketch oval two. 7-Apr-4 Libert, Castor, Paris #43/R est:1500-2000

BILDERS, Johannes Wernardus (1811-1890) Dutch
£1806 $3015 €2600 Cowherd and an anglers by a stream (27x48cm-11x19in) s. panel. 21-Oct-3 Sotheby's, Amsterdam #147/R est:2500-3500
£2431 $4132 €3500 Shepherd on a mountain path, a valley beyond (52x48cm-20x19in) s. 28-Oct-3 Christie's, Amsterdam #101/R est:3500-4500
£2819 $5215 €4200 Sheperd and his flock in a wooded landscape (52x46cm-20x18in) s. 15-Mar-4 Sotheby's, Amsterdam #72/R est:3000-5000
£2917 $4871 €4200 Washer women in a wooded landscape, Wolfheze (32x45cm-13x18in) s. 21-Oct-3 Sotheby's, Amsterdam #172/R est:1500-2000

BILDSTEIN, Franz (1622-?) Austrian
£548 $932 €800 Mother Anna with Maria (70x56cm-28x22in) s.d.78 lit. 6-Nov-3 Allgauer, Kempten #3385/R

BILEK, Alois (1887-1960) French
£659 $1226 €962 Still life with apples and jar (45x82cm-18x32in) s. 6-Mar-4 Dorotheum, Prague #69/R est:20000-30000 (C.KR 32000)
£927 $1724 €1353 Street in Bormes, France (52x67cm-20x26in) s.d.18 board. 6-Mar-4 Dorotheum, Prague #78/R est:30000-45000 (C.KR 45000)

BILEK, Frantisek (1872-1941) Czechoslovakian
£1700 $3145 €2482 Labourers in the fields (100x81cm-39x32in) s. 10-Mar-4 Sotheby's, Olympia #314/R est:1000-1500
Sculpture
£5253 $8720 €7669 Blinds (38cm-15in) mono. panel. 4-Oct-3 Dorotheum, Prague #407/R est:150000-250000 (C.KR 240000)
Works on paper
£350 $581 €511 Excitement of Sokols (47x32cm-19x13in) s. ink white lead. 4-Oct-3 Dorotheum, Prague #169/R est:10000-15000 (C.KR 16000)
£394 $654 €575 Way to Prague (18x57cm-7x22in) ink white lead. 4-Oct-3 Dorotheum, Prague #171/R est:18000-30000 (C.KR 18000)
£438 $727 €639 Christ with disciples (21x29cm-8x11in) chk. 4-Oct-3 Dorotheum, Prague #153/R est:10000-15000 (C.KR 20000)
£548 $965 €822 Memorial: parent's voice (38x39cm-15x15in) init.d.1921 mixed media blue paper. 22-May-4 Dorotheum, Prague #209/R est:10000-12000 (C.KR 26000)

BILGER, Margaret (1904-1971) Austrian
Works on paper
£1748 $2972 €2500 Roses (30x40cm-12x16in) mono.d.1962 pastel. 28-Nov-3 Wiener Kunst Auktionen, Vienna #601/R est:2000-2800

BILGERI, Flora (?) Austrian?
£2162 $3870 €3200 Still life with apples, eggs and jug (48x51cm-19x20in) canvas on board exhib. 6-May-4 Michael Zeller, Lindau #960/R est:2000

BILIBIN, Ivan (1876-1942) Russian

£10738	$19758	€16000	Illustration for 'Belaja utocka' (36x28cm-14x11in) mono.cyrillic d.01 board. 26-Mar-4 Venator & Hansten, Koln #1679/R est:3000
Works on paper			
£2027	$3568	€3000	Projet de costume (44x33cm-17x13in) mono.d.1931 W/C gouache. 19-May-4 Camard, Paris #84/R est:3000-4000
£2365	$4162	€3500	Projet de costume (44x33cm-17x13in) mono.d.1931 W/C gouache. 19-May-4 Camard, Paris #83/R est:3000-4000
£3846	$6000	€	Saint Gabriel (50x25cm-20x10in) s.d.2 September 1936 cyrillic gouache W/C pencil gold paint. 11-Apr-3 Christie's, Rockefeller NY #51/R est:6000-9000

BILIBIN, Ivan (attrib) (1876-1942) Russian

Works on paper			
£251	$450	€366	Firebird (23x18cm-9x7in) W/C. 11-Jan-4 William Jenack, New York #361

BILIVERTI, Giovanni (1576-1666) Italian

Works on paper			
£2041	$3653	€3000	Une homme agenouille, avec une etude subsidiaire du buste (13x15cm-5x6in) col chk. 18-Mar-4 Christie's, Paris #56/R est:3500-4500

BILIVERTI, Giovanni (attrib) (1576-1666) Italian

£8392	$14266	€12000	Saint Agnes (153x25cm-60x10in) 25-Nov-3 Hamilton Osborne King, Dublin #280/R
£12587	$21399	€18000	Saint John the Baptist in the wilderness (172x129cm-68x51in) prov. 25-Nov-3 Hamilton Osborne King, Dublin #281/R est:20000-40000

BILJAN-BILGER, Maria (1912-1997) Austrian

Sculpture			
£2270	$3790	€3200	Woman by river (31x74cm-12x29in) painted terracotta. 14-Oct-3 Dorotheum, Vienna #196/R est:2200-2800

BILL, Jakob (1942-) Swiss

£366	$648	€534	Number 35 (50x50cm-20x20in) s.d.69 verso exhib. 27-Apr-4 AB Stockholms Auktionsverk #1180/R (S.KR 5000)
£1310	$2410	€1913	No 16 (50x50cm-20x20in) s.i.d. verso prov. 8-Jun-4 Germann, Zurich #67/R est:3000-4000 (S.FR 3000)

BILL, Max (1908-1994) Swiss

£4305	$7319	€6285	Rotes Quadrate (47x47cm-19x19in) s.d.1972-73 diagonal. 5-Nov-3 AB Stockholms Auktionsverk #943/R est:40000-50000 (S.KR 57000)
£5405	$10000	€7891	Dynamische Farbdurchdringung (40x40cm-16x16in) s.d.1967-69 verso acrylic. 12-Feb-4 Sotheby's, New York #108/R est:4000-6000
£5521	$9000	€8061	Four superposed colors (56x56cm-22x22in) s.i.d.1965 verso prov.exhib. 23-Sep-3 Christie's, Rockefeller NY #115/R est:6000-8000
£5986	$10356	€8500	Composition (33x33cm-13x13in) s.i.d.1972 verso. 13-Dec-3 Lempertz, Koln #118/R est:5000
£6000	$10740	€9000	Radiation from green (40x40cm-16x16in) s.i.d.1972-73 stretcher s.d. verso. 15-May-4 Van Ham, Cologne #461/R est:10000
£6667	$11933	€10000	Irradiation from violet (40x40cm-16x16in) s.i.d.1972-73 stretcher s.d. verso. 15-May-4 Van Ham, Cologne #462/R est:10000
£8370	$14229	€12220	Transcoloration from red to blue (56x56cm-22x22in) s.d.1972-74 i. stretcher. 7-Nov-3 Dobiaschofsky, Bern #256/R est:20000 (S.FR 19000)
£10480	$19284	€15301	Light radiation (88x88cm-35x35in) s.d.1972-73 verso s.i.d. stretcher. 8-Jun-4 Germann, Zurich #59/R est:18000-23000 (S.FR 24000)
£15000	$27600	€21900	Gelbe und weisse zone (113x113cm-44x44in) s.d.1974/75 verso s.i.d. stretcher prov. 24-Jun-4 Sotheby's, London #152/R est:15000-20000
£16594	$30533	€24227	Rotation in two quadrants (141x141cm-56x56in) s.d. verso s.i.d.1977 stretcher. 8-Jun-4 Germann, Zurich #58/R est:30000-40000 (S.FR 38000)
£17450	$31235	€26000	Rythm on white (61x61cm-24x24in) s.i.d.1967 on stretcher s.i.d.verso prov.eh. 25-May-4 Sotheby's, Milan #169/R est:8000-10000
£18182	$30909	€26000	Blue and red (62x62cm-24x24in) s.d.1972-74 verso. 28-Nov-3 Farsetti, Prato #359/R est:26000-30000
Prints			
£12454	$22044	€18183	Zwilling aus zwei ahnlichen gruppen (60x120cm-24x47in) s.d.1977 verso. 27-Apr-4 AB Stockholms Auktionsverk #1239/R est:200000-230000 (S.KR 170000)
Sculpture			
£5128	$9077	€7487	Konstruktion aus drei gleichen Prismen (15cm-6in) s. executed 1983 nickel steel on white wooden base prov. 27-Apr-4 AB Stockholms Auktionsverk #1016/R est:40000-45000 (S.KR 70000)
£13100	$23450	€19126	Oval composition (26x21x12cm-10x8x5in) s.d.1977 brass. 26-May-4 Sotheby's, Zurich #160/R est:20000-30000 (S.FR 30000)
£22422	$36547	€32736	Endless surface for three positions (17x31x19cm-7x12x7in) gilded brass. 29-Sep-3 Christie's, Zurich #105/R est:30000-40000 (S.FR 50000)
Works on paper			
£1586	$2696	€2316	Young sage (62x44cm-24x17in) s.d.29 Indian ink W/C. 7-Nov-3 Dobiaschofsky, Bern #223/R est:4500 (S.FR 3600)
£2262	$3846	€3303	Bach (70x50cm-28x20in) s.d.1929 W/C paper on board. 25-Nov-3 Germann, Zurich #150/R est:4000-6000 (S.FR 5000)

BILLAUDET, P (20th C) French?

Works on paper			
£2128	$3553	€3000	Vue de Beyrouth (15x22cm-6x9in) s.i.d.1919 W/C. 19-Oct-3 Rabourdin & Choppin de Janvry, Paris #103/R est:2500-3000

BILLE, Carl (1815-1898) Danish

£267	$485	€401	Coastal landscape with sailing vessel and half-timbered house (22x32cm-9x13in) s.d.59 panel. 19-Jun-4 Rasmussen, Havnen #2300/R (D.KR 3000)
£281	$502	€410	Skareklit near Bulbjerg (19x25cm-7x10in) s. 10-May-4 Rasmussen, Vejle #355/R (D.KR 3100)
£314	$585	€458	Calm day in Sundet (22x29cm-9x11in) with sig. 2-Mar-4 Rasmussen, Copenhagen #1451/R (D.KR 3500)
£318	$532	€464	Lifeboat going out (16x25cm-6x10in) s.d.1878 panel. 25-Oct-3 Rasmussen, Havnen #2618 (D.KR 3400)
£325	$608	€475	Light-house on cliff (25x17cm-10x7in) s. canvas on board. 25-Feb-4 Kunsthallen, Copenhagen #497 (D.KR 3600)
£374	$591	€542	Seascape with wrecked ship in rough seas (23x28cm-9x11in) s. 3-Sep-3 Museumsbygningen, Copenhagen #224 (D.KR 4000)
£404	$752	€590	Seascape with boats (12x19cm-5x7in) s. 2-Mar-4 Rasmussen, Copenhagen #1434/R (D.KR 4500)
£459	$744	€666	Coastal landscape with sailing boats (41x54cm-16x21in) init. s.i.d.1890 verso. 4-Aug-3 Rasmussen, Vejle #45/R (D.KR 4800)
£512	$819	€748	Viceadmiral Niels Holt and Peter Bredal on a burning Swedish ship (35x58cm-14x23in) indis.sig.d.1658. 22-Sep-3 Rasmussen, Vejle #296/R (D.KR 5400)
£512	$819	€748	Sunrise, Kattegat (19x30cm-7x12in) s. 22-Sep-3 Rasmussen, Vejle #297/R (D.KR 5400)
£550	$880	€803	Coastal landscape with light house in moonlight (26x37cm-10x15in) s.d.1879. 22-Sep-3 Rasmussen, Vejle #295/R (D.KR 5800)
£702	$1173	€1025	Seascape with steamer in high seas (36x52cm-14x20in) s. 25-Oct-3 Rasmussen, Havnen #2530/R (D.KR 7500)
£839	$1443	€1200	Sailing ship in rough seas (26x36cm-10x14in) s.d.1875 canvas on canvas. 5-Dec-3 Bolland & Marotz, Bremen #509/R
£851	$1523	€1242	Seascape with sailing ship (67x95cm-26x37in) 12-Jan-4 Rasmussen, Vejle #22/R (D.KR 9000)
£941	$1599	€1374	Seascape with sailing vessel in the Mediterranean (38x47cm-15x19in) s. 29-Nov-3 Rasmussen, Havnen #2298/R (D.KR 10000)
£1072	$1736	€1554	Sailing vessels in moonlight off Kronborg (45x67cm-18x26in) s. 4-Aug-3 Rasmussen, Vejle #22/R (D.KR 11200)
£1074	$1966	€1568	Fishing boats at sea, evening (45x66cm-18x26in) s. 9-Jun-4 Rasmussen, Copenhagen #1803/R est:15000 (D.KR 12000)
£1078	$2005	€1574	Seascape with sailing vessels (48x66cm-19x26in) s. 2-Mar-4 Rasmussen, Copenhagen #1430/R est:10000 (D.KR 12000)
£1083	$2025	€1581	The frigate Jylland (40cm-16in circular) s. 25-Feb-4 Kunsthallen, Copenhagen #521/R est:10000 (D.KR 12000)
£1258	$2340	€1837	Sailing vessels at sea in morning glow (32x47cm-13x19in) s.d.1875. 2-Mar-4 Rasmussen, Copenhagen #1412/R est:15000 (D.KR 14000)
£1343	$2457	€1961	Seascape with moonlight. Seascape with sunset (19x25cm-7x10in) s. pair. 9-Jun-4 Rasmussen, Copenhagen #1806/R est:6000 (D.KR 15000)
£1500	$2580	€2190	Steamer on the open seas (71x110cm-28x43in) s.d.1874. 2-Dec-3 Sotheby's, London #56/R est:1500-2000
£2070	$3518	€3022	Seascape with many vessels off Kronborg (47x66cm-19x26in) s. 29-Nov-3 Rasmussen, Havnen #2173/R est:20000-25000 (D.KR 22000)
£2174	$3761	€3174	Fishermen brining their catch ashore in moonlight (40x37cm-16x15in) s. exhib. 9-Dec-3 Rasmussen, Copenhagen #1482/R est:15000 (D.KR 23000)
£2328	$4260	€3399	Norwegian sailing vessel off Bergen (33x50cm-13x20in) s.d.1871. 9-Jun-4 Rasmussen, Copenhagen #1844/R est:20000-25000 (D.KR 26000)
£5372	$9830	€7843	The English royal yacht off Copenhagen (63x95cm-25x37in) s.d.1863. 9-Jun-4 Rasmussen, Copenhagen #1445/R est:60000-80000 (D.KR 60000)
£5671	$9811	€8280	Skirner in Copenhagen Harbour (64x98cm-25x39in) 9-Dec-3 Rasmussen, Copenhagen #1235/R est:60000-75000 (D.KR 60000)

BILLE, Carl (attrib) (1815-1898) Danish

£378	$677	€552	Seascape with sailing boats (18x28cm-7x11in) bears sig. prov. 12-Jan-4 Rasmussen, Vejle #50 (D.KR 4000)
£1170	$1955	€1708	Frigate with American flag (47x71cm-19x28in) s.d.1857 sold with print. 25-Oct-3 Rasmussen, Havnen #2570/R est:6000-8000 (D.KR 12500)

BILLE, Edmond (1878-1959) Swiss

£283	$517	€413	Chemin a Hermance (23x30cm-9x12in) s.d.46 s.i.verso cardboard. 5-Jun-4 Galerie du Rhone, Sion #269 (S.FR 650)
£734	$1226	€1064	Coin de village, Tourtemagne (19x29cm-7x11in) s.d. init.d.verso tempera cardboard. 21-Jun-3 Galerie du Rhone, Sion #332/R est:1500-2000 (S.FR 1600)
£2172	$3757	€3171	Maison aux peupliers (35x49cm-14x19in) s.d.19 cardboard prov. 12-Dec-3 Galerie du Rhone, Sion #635 est:5000-7000 (S.FR 4800)
£2489	$4305	€3634	Paysage au rateau-fane (38x60cm-15x24in) s.i. canvas on panel prov. 12-Dec-3 Galerie du Rhone, Sion #632/R est:7000-9000 (S.FR 5500)
£2982	$4979	€4324	Les maisons blanches, a Grimentz (45x32cm-18x13in) s.i.d. prov. 21-Jun-3 Galerie du Rhone, Sion #463/R est:8000-10000 (S.FR 6500)
£3275	$6026	€4782	L'eglise de Varone, Valais (32x47cm-13x19in) s.i.d.1921 s.i.d. verso board. 8-Jun-4 Germann, Zurich #764/R est:1500-2000 (S.FR 7500)
Works on paper			
£431	$772	€629	Paddle steamer at jetty in Lake Geneva (24x33cm-9x13in) gouache. 12-May-4 Dobiaschofsky, Bern #343/R (S.FR 1000)
£541	$930	€790	La fontaine et le four a Chandolin (48x33cm-19x13in) s. i.d.1911 verso pastel chk card. 8-Dec-3 Philippe Schuler, Zurich #3167/R (S.FR 1200)
£826	$1379	€1198	Eglise de la Noble-Contree (37x51cm-15x20in) s.d. chl W/C. 21-Jun-3 Galerie du Rhone, Sion #330/R est:2000-3000 (S.FR 1800)
£1207	$2160	€1762	Winery in Wallis (25x34cm-10x13in) s.d.19 W/C over pencil. 14-May-4 Dobiaschofsky, Bern #158/R est:2500 (S.FR 2800)
£1739	$3183	€2539	La fontaine et le four a Chandolin (48x33cm-19x13in) s.d.10 s.i.verso crayon gouache tempera cardboard prov. 5-Jun-4 Galerie du Rhone, Sion #539/R est:3500-4500 (S.FR 4000)
£1835	$3064	€2661	Valaisanne en costume (52x34cm-20x13in) s.d. W/C prov.exhib. 21-Jun-3 Galerie du Rhone, Sion #464/R est:2500-3500 (S.FR 4000)
£2174	$3978	€3174	Le Zac, sous Chandolin (36x50cm-14x20in) s.d.09 gouache cardboard prov. 5-Jun-4 Galerie du Rhone, Sion #538/R est:5000-7000 (S.FR 5000)
£3077	$5323	€4492	Valaisannes couchees (54x88cm-21x35in) s.d.1930 chl W/C. 12-Dec-3 Galerie du Rhone, Sion #634/R est:7000-9000 (S.FR 6800)
£7759	$13888	€11328	Young couple from Valais (49x87cm-19x34in) mono. mixed media prov. 14-May-4 Dobiaschofsky, Bern #156/R est:7500 (S.FR 18000)

BILLE, Ejler (1910-) Danish

£13615	$22737	€19878	Composition in blue and green (59x56cm-23x22in) s.i.d.1981. 7-Oct-3 Rasmussen, Copenhagen #66/R est:100000-125000 (D.KR 145000)
£14085	$23521	€20564	Figure composition (38x60cm-15x24in) painted c.1946 prov. 7-Oct-3 Rasmussen, Copenhagen #85/R est:150000-200000 (D.KR 150000)
£15023	$25089	€21934	Figurative (50x45cm-20x18in) s.i.d.1988 verso. 7-Oct-3 Rasmussen, Copenhagen #41/R est:125000-150000 (D.KR 160000)
Sculpture			
£4892	$8316	€7142	Bird (15cm-6in) plaster. 26-Nov-3 Kunsthallen, Copenhagen #4/R est:25000 (D.KR 52000)

BILLE, Frederick (19th C) ?
£333 $600 €486 Portrait of a military officer (36x28cm-14x11in) s. 23-Jan-4 Freeman, Philadelphia #236/R

BILLE, Sigfride (1877-?) Danish
£333 $597 €500 Sailing ship by moonlight (48x49cm-19x19in) s. lit. 14-May-4 Schloss Ahlden, Ahlden #2889/R

BILLE, Sten (1890-1953) Danish
£278 $442 €400 Marina (65x96cm-26x38in) s. 29-Apr-3 Durán, Madrid #63/R

BILLE, Vilhelm (1864-1908) Danish
£202 $371 €295 Fishing boats off a city harbour (68x96cm-27x38in) init. 14-Jun-4 Waddingtons, Toronto #210/R (C.D 500)
£379 $701 €553 Schooner in rough seas (27x42cm-11x17in) s.d.93. 15-Mar-4 Rasmussen, Vejle #186/R (D.KR 4200)
£421 $664 €610 Evening by the sea (37x47cm-15x19in) s. 2-Sep-3 Rasmussen, Copenhagen #1913 (D.KR 4500)
£430 $760 €640 Trois-mats sur mer forte (62x91cm-24x36in) 3-May-4 Giraudeau, Tours #32
£449 $836 €656 Fishing boats by Kullen (37x56cm-15x22in) s. 2-Mar-4 Rasmussen, Copenhagen #1449/R (D.KR 5000)
£756 $1353 €1104 Seascape with sailing boats (47x68cm-19x27in) s. 12-Jan-4 Rasmussen, Vejle #47/R (D.KR 8000)
£768 $1282 €1121 Seascape with sailing vessels off Kronborg (84x63cm-33x25in) s. 25-Oct-3 Rasmussen, Havnen #2603/R (D.KR 8200)
£1049 $1804 €1500 Pansies on a marble table (10x15cm-4x6in) panel. 6-Dec-3 Hans Stahl, Toestorf #146/R est:1500
£1196 $1938 €1734 Steam and sailing vessels off Kronborg (67x97cm-26x38in) s. 4-Aug-3 Rasmussen, Vejle #20/R est:12000-15000 (D.KR 12500)
£1779 $2971 €2597 French three master in high seas and sailing vessels off coast (90x108cm-35x43in) s. 25-Oct-3 Rasmussen, Havnen #2547/R est:15000 (D.KR 19000)
£1797 $3342 €2624 Frigate and fishing vessels at sea (85x127cm-33x50in) s.d.94. 2-Mar-4 Rasmussen, Copenhagen #1229/R est:30000-50000 (D.KR 20000)
£3791 $7088 €5535 Seascape with vessels in Oresund (122x89cm-48x35in) s. 25-Feb-4 Kunsthallen, Copenhagen #535/R est:50000 (D.KR 42000)

BILLE, Vilhelm (attrib) (1864-1908) Danish
£622 $1132 €933 Coastal landscape from a Danish colony (42x62cm-17x24in) 19-Jun-4 Rasmussen, Havnen #2061/R (D.KR 7000)

BILLE-HOLST, Poul (1894-?) Danish
£559 $878 €816 Boxing match (96x80cm-38x31in) s. cardboard exhib. 30-Aug-3 Rasmussen, Havnen #4187/R (D.KR 6000)

BILLEN, Andre (1921-) Belgian
£304 $575 €450 Structure soleil (73x100cm-29x39in) s. 17-Feb-4 Vanderkindere, Brussels #35

BILLER, Joseph (19th C) French
£863 $1416 €1200 Vase de fleurs sur un entablement (65x54cm-26x21in) s.d.83. 6-Jun-3 Maigret, Paris #101

BILLET, Étienne (1821-?) French
£2778 $5000 €4056 L'aiglon (38x29cm-15x11in) s. panel prov. 21-Jan-4 Sotheby's, New York #201/R est:1500-2000
£3688 $6159 €5200 Sur les bords du Nil (54x65cm-21x26in) s. 23-Jun-3 Ribeyre & Baron, Paris #37/R est:3000-4500

BILLET, Pierre (1837-1922) French
£563 $986 €800 Personnages au pied du chateau, Alger (31x42cm-12x17in) s. painted 1884. 21-Dec-3 Thierry & Lannon, Brest #283
£826 $1486 €1206 Boys playing (56x38cm-22x15in) s.d.27/7/75. 26-Jan-4 Lilla Bukowskis, Stockholm #517 (S.KR 11000)
£5587 $10000 €8157 The faggot gatherers (99x142cm-39x56in) s. 20-Mar-4 Pook & Pook, Downington #133/R est:6000-8000

BILLGREN, Ernst (1957-) Swedish
£2198 $3890 €3209 The red chain (66x120cm-26x47in) mono. panel. 27-Apr-4 AB Stockholms Auktionsverk #1111/R est:30000-35000 (S.KR 30000)
£5861 $10374 €8557 Fantasy (89x110cm-35x43in) s.d.83 verso. 27-Apr-4 AB Stockholms Auktionsverk #956/R est:50000-60000 (S.KR 80000)
£12821 $22692 €18719 The fox trap (52x70cm-20x28in) mono. oil mosaic panel painted 1988. 27-Apr-4 AB Stockholms Auktionsverk #1029/R est:175000-200000 (S.KR 175000)
£18129 $32632 €26468 Small Christmas trees - table decoration (155x275cm-61x108in) mono. panel painted 1999 exhib.lit. 26-Apr-4 Bukowskis, Stockholm #557/R est:200000-250000 (S.KR 250000)
£56647 $96299 €82705 Careful moving in (155x275cm-61x108in) mono. oil panel with gilded bronze prov.exhib.lit. 5-Nov-3 AB Stockholms Auktionsverk #936/R est:400000-500000 (S.KR 750000)

Sculpture
£1209 $2140 €1765 The light holder (70cm-28in) init.num.64/100 gilded pat.bronze incl.oak wood base. 27-Apr-4 AB Stockholms Auktionsverk #1050/R est:12000-15000 (S.KR 16500)
£1511 $2568 €2206 The stag Ovin (19cm-7in) mono.num.2/7 pat.bronze part gilded exhib. 5-Nov-3 AB Stockholms Auktionsverk #1031/R est:20000-25000 (S.KR 20000)
£1612 $2853 €2354 Untitled object (25cm-10in) s.num.12/29 polychrome glass. 27-Apr-4 AB Stockholms Auktionsverk #1120/R est:20000-25000 (S.KR 22000)
£1964 $3338 €2867 Squirrel in flight (17cm-7in) mono. pat.bronze exhib.lit. 5-Nov-3 AB Stockholms Auktionsverk #1032/R est:18000-20000 (S.KR 26000)
£3400 $6086 €4964 Mallard. s.num.3/6 glass. 28-May-4 Uppsala Auktionskammare, Uppsala #409/R est:30000-40000 (S.KR 46000)
£3883 $6873 €5669 Frozen friends (31cm-12in) s.num.1/6 polychrome glass lit. 27-Apr-4 AB Stockholms Auktionsverk #1119/R est:35000-40000 (S.KR 53000)
£4061 $7310 €5929 Watchmen - ducks on the lookout (45cm-18in) s.num.6/6 glass exhib.lit. 26-Apr-4 Bukowskis, Stockholm #496/R est:40000-45000 (S.KR 56000)

Works on paper
£3046 $5482 €4447 Political landscapes. init.i. mixed media shaped two prov. 26-Apr-4 Bukowskis, Stockholm #558/R est:40000-45000 (S.KR 42000)

BILLGREN, Ola (1940-2001) Swedish
£9158 $16209 €13371 The fairy story - Snow-white (73x62cm-29x24in) s.d.87. 27-Apr-4 AB Stockholms Auktionsverk #958/R est:125000-150000 (S.KR 125000)
£11707 $19902 €17092 Augusti - 95 (108x99cm-43x39in) s.d.95 verso prov. 4-Nov-3 Bukowskis, Stockholm #591/R est:150000-200000 (S.KR 155000)
£14652 $25934 €21392 Evening, Osterlen II (95x70cm-37x28in) s.d.95. 27-Apr-4 AB Stockholms Auktionsverk #940/R est:150000-200000 (S.KR 200000)
£16616 $28248 €24259 Interior (95x70cm-37x28in) s.d.1967 lit. 4-Nov-3 Bukowskis, Stockholm #553/R est:250000-300000 (S.KR 220000)
£16994 $28890 €24811 Woman and orange (41x35cm-16x14in) s.d.1966 exhib.lit. 4-Nov-3 Bukowskis, Stockholm #552/R est:250000-300000 (S.KR 225000)
£21148 $35952 €30876 Town in rain II (143x250cm-56x98in) s.d.91 verso prov.exhib.lit. 4-Nov-3 Bukowskis, Stockholm #590/R est:275000-325000 (S.KR 280000)
£21978 $38901 €32088 Ben Webster (35x52cm-14x20in) s.d.74. 27-Apr-4 AB Stockholms Auktionsverk #974/R est:200000-225000 (S.KR 300000)
£30967 $52644 €45212 Pastoral - landscape from Kaseberga, Skaane (98x116cm-39x46in) s.d.96 verso prov. 4-Nov-3 Bukowskis, Stockholm #589/R est:200000-250000 (S.KR 410000)
£32234 $57055 €47062 Woman in white (120x150cm-47x59in) s.d.89 verso. 27-Apr-4 AB Stockholms Auktionsverk #1098/R est:400000-500000 (S.KR 440000)

Works on paper
£346 $563 €505 Composition with horses (33x26cm-13x10in) s.d.60 wash. 29-Sep-3 Lilla Bukowskis, Stockholm #229 (S.KR 4500)
£916 $1621 €1337 Woman in profile (21x22cm-8x9in) s.d.73 W/C. 27-Apr-4 AB Stockholms Auktionsverk #1144/R (S.KR 12500)
£989 $1751 €1444 Tragic drama- theatre performance in London (24x33cm-9x13in) s.d.74 W/C prov. 27-Apr-4 AB Stockholms Auktionsverk #1096/R (S.KR 13500)
£1160 $2088 €1694 Shell (31x32cm-12x13in) s.d.73 W/C. 26-Apr-4 Bukowskis, Stockholm #522/R est:15000-20000 (S.KR 16000)
£2393 $4307 €3494 Interior (14x21cm-6x8in) s.d.71 W/C. 26-Apr-4 Bukowskis, Stockholm #516/R est:40000-45000 (S.KR 33000)
£3776 $6420 €5513 Untitled (26x36cm-10x14in) s.d.68 W/C. 4-Nov-3 Bukowskis, Stockholm #531/R est:30000-40000 (S.KR 50000)

BILLING, Teodor (1817-1892) Swedish
£283 $450 €413 Lake in wooded landscape (30x46cm-12x18in) s.d.81. 9-Sep-3 Arthur James, Florida #319
£350 $644 €525 Coastal view with steam launch (46x66cm-18x26in) s.d.1885. 14-Jun-4 Lilla Bukowskis, Stockholm #660 (S.KR 4800)
£375 $611 €548 Coastal landscape with beached boats (16x26cm-6x10in) init. 27-Sep-3 Rasmussen, Havnen #2019/R (D.KR 4000)
£887 $1588 €1295 Interieure L'une foret situee aupres du Fontainbleau en France (49x65cm-19x26in) s.i.d.1859. 28-May-4 Uppsala Auktionskammare, Uppsala #108/R (S.KR 12000)
£1133 $2029 €1700 Winter landscape with the chapel in Djurgarden, Stockholm (65x98cm-26x39in) s.d.1849. 15-May-4 Hagelstam, Helsinki #48/R est:1800

BILLINGHURST, Alfred John (1880-1963) British
£500 $805 €725 Infant before a fire (46x36cm-18x14in) s. 15-Aug-3 Keys, Aylsham #768
£700 $1239 €1022 Young girl in a barrow (50x62cm-20x24in) s. double-sided prov. 27-Apr-4 Bonhams, Knightsbridge #286/R

BILLINGS, Edwin T (1824-1893) American
£958 $1600 €1399 Boy gazing at hour glass. Portrait of a girl in a bonnet (51x41cm-20x16in) one s. one board pair. 16-Nov-3 CRN Auctions, Cambridge #18/R

BILLINGS, Henry (1901-1987) American
£3315 $6000 €4840 Classical building and garden (92x66cm-36x26in) s.d.1929 prov.exhib. 31-Mar-4 Sotheby's, New York #130/R est:4000-6000

BILLOIN, Charles (1813-1869) Belgian
£524 $892 €750 Portrait d'homme assis au journal et au cigarre (31x35cm-12x14in) s.d.1859. 18-Nov-3 Vanderkindere, Brussels #40

BILLOTTE, René (1846-1915) French
£260 $478 €380 Sand quarry (21x26cm-8x10in) s. panel. 14-Jun-4 Bonhams, Bath #132

BILLWILLER, Johann Jakob Lorenz (1779-1832) Swiss
Works on paper
£480 $884 €701 View of Zurichsee (38x56cm-15x22in) s.i.d. W/C. 14-Jun-4 Philippe Schuler, Zurich #4355 (S.FR 1100)

BILQUIN, Jean (1938-) Belgian
£1399 $2336 €2000 Mythological scene (100x120cm-39x47in) s. 11-Oct-3 De Vuyst, Lokeren #32/R est:2000-2200
£1818 $3036 €2600 Figure (170x120cm-67x47in) s.d.88 lit. 11-Oct-3 De Vuyst, Lokeren #31/R est:2000-2200

BILS, Claude (1884-1968) French
£467 $850 €682 Parisian street scene (25x36cm-10x14in) s. masonite. 19-Jun-4 Jeffery Burchard, Florida #74

BILTIUS, Jacobus (1633-1681) Dutch
£166667 $300000 €243334 Trompe l'oeil of leading staff, partizan and musket (169x344cm-67x135in) s.d.1666 prov.lit. 22-Jan-4 Sotheby's, New York #22/R est:150000-200000

BILU, Asher (1936-) Australian
Works on paper
£405 $652 €591 Untitled (96x91cm-38x36in) s.d.14/7/1969 verso mixed media. 13-Oct-3 Joel, Victoria #264 est:1000-1500 (A.D 1000)
£620 $1097 €905 Graphite light (182x183cm-72x72in) s. s.i.verso synthetic polymer paint resin board prov. 3-May-4 Christie's, Melbourne #219 (A.D 1500)

BILYK, Ziggy (20th C) Australian
£746 $1372 €1089 Untitled (137x198cm-54x78in) acrylic pastel. 29-Mar-4 Goodman, Sydney #87/R est:2000-3000 (A.D 1825)

BIMBI, Bartolomeo (1648-1725) Italian
£23490 $43926 €35000 Big metal vase with flowers on ledge (128x104cm-50x41in) 29-Feb-4 Finarte, Venice #15/R est:39000-45000
£53793 $89834 €78000 Flowers in metal vases (56x46cm-22x18in) pair prov.lit. 15-Nov-3 Porro, Milan #219/R est:78000
£110738 $207081 €165000 Still life with artichokes. Still life with basket of cherries (73x94cm-29x37in) pair. 25-Feb-4 Porro, Milan #87/R est:125000
£230263 $423684 €350000 Still lives of flowers with fruit (72x43cm-28x17in) mono. pair. 25-Jun-4 Piasa, Paris #36/R est:30000-40000

BIMBI, Bartolomeo (attrib) (1648-1725) Italian
£9184 $16439 €13500 Vase of flowers (84x69cm-33x27in) 19-Mar-4 Beaussant & Lefèvre, Paris #60/R est:15000-20000
£32000 $57600 €46720 Crown imperial lily, white iris and other flowers in a blue and white porcelain vase (134x97cm-53x38in) pair. 21-Apr-4 Christie's, London #88/R est:25000-35000

BINA, Peter (1888-?) German
£267 $485 €400 View of Venice (58x78cm-23x31in) s. 1-Jul-4 Weidler, Nurnberg #7008/R

BINAEPFEL, Luc (1893-1972) French
£278 $506 €420 Young woman sitting under a tree in a garden in summer (73x60cm-29x24in) s. 17-Jun-4 Frank Peege, Freiburg #1196/R
£278 $506 €420 Still life with flowers (82x65cm-32x26in) s. 17-Jun-4 Frank Peege, Freiburg #1197/R
£1000 $1810 €1500 Vosges in the evening (53x65cm-21x26in) s. sketch verso. 1-Apr-4 Frank Peege, Freiburg #1161/R est:500

BINARD, Henri (1862-1939) Belgian
£625 $1044 €900 Cygne au crepuscule (40x70cm-16x28in) s. 21-Oct-3 Galerie Moderne, Brussels #329
£1135 $1895 €1600 Couple sur le rocher (101x120cm-40x47in) s. 14-Oct-3 Vanderkindere, Brussels #123

BINAZZI, Lapo (1943-) Italian
Works on paper
£2797 $4755 €4000 Drawing for Sherwood Restaurant (72x84cm-28x33in) pencil pastel exhib. 26-Nov-3 Pandolfini, Florence #471/R est:3000-3200

BINCHY, Mary Rose (20th C) Irish?
Works on paper
£638 $1174 €970 Renewal (92x69cm-36x27in) s.d.1994 i.verso mixed media. 22-Jun-4 De Veres Art Auctions, Dublin #119/R

BINDER, Alois (1857-?) German
£282 $504 €400 Munich child (21x16cm 8x6in) s. panel lit. 8-Jan-4 Allgauer, Kempten #2354
£420 $794 €613 Portrait of a Tyrolean man with a hat (32x24cm-13x9in) s. panel. 19-Feb-4 Christie's, Kensington #47/R
£660 $1221 €964 Good brew (35x28cm-14x11in) s. 15-Jan-4 Christie's, Kensington #737/R
£2000 $3200 €2900 Charming melody (36x27cm-14x11in) s.i.d.88 panel. 18-Sep-3 Christie's, Kensington #141/R est:2000-3000
£2980 $5424 €4500 Two young girls teasing a sleeping young man (77x63cm-30x25in) s. 16-Jun-4 Hugo Ruef, Munich #930/R est:4500

BINDER, Avraham (1906-2001) American?
£919 $1700 €1342 Dizingoff Square (64x81cm-25x32in) s. 12-Feb-4 Sotheby's, New York #82/R est:2000-3000
£1486 $2750 €2170 Carmel Market (84x64cm-33x25in) s. 12-Feb-4 Sotheby's, New York #81/R est:2000-3000
Works on paper
£604 $1100 €882 Carmel market (56x76cm-22x30in) s. W/C gouache. 29-Jun-4 Sotheby's, New York #413/R est:1500-2000
£659 $1100 €962 String quartet (55x75cm-22x30in) s. W/C. 7-Oct-3 Sotheby's, New York #350

BINDER, Carl F (1887-?) American
£894 $1600 €1305 Still life (71x61cm-28x24in) s.d.1928. 16-May-4 Wright, Chicago #168/R est:1000-1500

BINDER, Friedrich Gustav (1897-1990) German
£671 $1188 €1000 Lugano Church (84x60cm-33x24in) s. s. verso. 30-Apr-4 Dr Fritz Nagel, Stuttgart #747/R

BINDER, Joseph (1805-1863) Austrian
£1338 $2315 €1900 The crossing of the 3 Holy Kings (44x65cm-17x26in) board. 10-Dec-3 Dorotheum, Vienna #249/R est:2500-3000
£1867 $3360 €2800 Der chaisentragr an der allerheiligenkirche (56x46cm-22x18in) init. 20-Apr-4 Sotheby's, Amsterdam #61/R est:3000-5000

BINDER, Tony (1868-1944) British
£342 $582 €500 Washerwomen at riverside in summer (14x20cm-6x8in) s. panel lit. 6-Nov-3 Allgauer, Kempten #3386/R
£374 $670 €550 Ox cart in narrow street (52x32cm-20x13in) s.i.d.1921. 18-Mar-4 Neumeister, Munich #2640/R
£733 $1327 €1100 Camel with owner (26x35cm-10x14in) i. 2-Apr-4 Dr Fritz Nagel, Leipzig #3977/R
£800 $1448 €1200 Journey through the desert (31x41cm-12x16in) i. 2-Apr-4 Dr Fritz Nagel, Leipzig #3978/R
£933 $1689 €1400 Bazaar (46x31cm-18x12in) i. 2-Apr-4 Dr Fritz Nagel, Leipzig #3979/R
£1020 $1827 €1500 Biedermeier street (53x33cm-21x13in) s.d.1922. 17-Mar-4 Neumeister, Munich #409/R est:1600

BINDESBOLL, Thorvald (1846-1908) Danish
Works on paper
£361 $664 €527 Sketch for floor pattern (35x34cm-14x13in) s.i. W/C pencil. 29-Mar-4 Rasmussen, Copenhagen #564 (D.KR 4000)

BINDING, Wellesley (20th C) New Zealander
£372 $639 €543 Here comes the volcano (53x131cm-21x52in) s. board. 7-Dec-3 International Art Centre, Auckland #208 (NZ.D 1000)

BINET, Adolphe Gustave (1854-1897) French
Works on paper
£2684 $4751 €4000 Aux courses (66x81cm-26x32in) s. gouache. 30-Apr-4 Tajan, Paris #224/R est:4500-5000

BINET, George (1865-1949) French
£537 $999 €800 Bouquet de fleurs (33x64cm-13x25in) s. 7-Mar-4 Lesieur & Le Bars, Le Havre #13
£838 $1400 €1223 Flower market (25x36cm-10x14in) s. panel. 20-Jun-3 Freeman, Philadelphia #94/R
£1141 $2123 €1700 La route de Honfleur (38x46cm-15x18in) s. prov. 2-Mar-4 Artcurial Briest, Paris #127 est:1200-1800
£1141 $2122 €1700 Vue sur la baie (24x33cm-9x13in) s. panel. 7-Mar-4 Lesieur & Le Bars, Le Havre #12
£1633 $2922 €2400 Viewing platform near Le Havre (46x66cm-18x26in) s. 18-Mar-4 Neumeister, Munich #2641 est:250
£1867 $3435 €2800 Printemps sur les hauteurs de Caudebec (27x35cm-11x14in) s. panel. 9-Jun-4 Beaussant & Lefèvre, Paris #103/R est:3000
£2000 $3620 €3000 Le marche pres de la cathedrale de Rouen (37x54cm-15x21in) s. 5-Apr-4 Deburaux, Boulogne #123/R est:3000-3500
£2000 $3680 €3000 Scene de marche a Caudebec (41x33cm-16x13in) s. 9-Jun-4 Beaussant & Lefèvre, Paris #101/R est:3500
£2000 $3680 €3000 Promenade en bord de Seine (26x35cm-10x14in) s. panel. 9-Jun-4 Beaussant & Lefèvre, Paris #109/R est:3000
£2273 $4000 €3319 Senorita (102x74cm-40x29in) s. painted c.1920. 23-May-4 Treadway Gallery, Cincinnati #589/R est:6000-8000
£3103 $5183 €4500 Jeux d'enfants (36x48cm-14x19in) s. 11-Nov-3 Lesieur & Le Bars, Le Havre #3
£3221 $5992 €4800 Le marche de Caudebec (16x24cm-6x9in) s. panel. 7-Mar-4 Lesieur & Le Bars, Le Havre #10/R
£3467 $6379 €5200 La terrasse a Caudebec (27x35cm-11x14in) s. 9-Jun-4 Beaussant & Lefèvre, Paris #106/R est:3000-3500
£3586 $5989 €5200 Bassin du Commerce (27x34cm-11x13in) s. panel. 11-Nov-3 Lesieur & Le Bars, Le Havre #4

BINFORD, Julien (1908-) American
Works on paper
£206 $375 €301 Floral still life (122x81cm-48x32in) s. mixed media painted 1972. 21-Jun-4 Winter Associates, Plainville #130/R

BING, Ilse (1899-1998) German
Photographs
£1556 $2800 €2272 Sandwich man under elevated, 6th Avenue, Ny (28x22cm-11x9in) s.d.1936 gelatin silver print. 23-Apr-4 Phillips, New York #78/R est:5000-7000
£2515 $4200 €3672 Eiffel Tower silhouette (50x41cm-20x16in) s.d.1952 verso gelatin silver print lit. 20-Oct-3 Christie's, Rockefeller NY #107/R est:4000-6000
£2542 $4500 €3711 Tour Eiffel, vue du Pont Bir-Hakeim, Paris, 1932 (25x34cm-10x13in) s.d. s.i.d.verso gelatin silver print lit. 27-Apr-4 Christie's, Rockefeller NY #114/R est:4000-6000
£2778 $5000 €4056 Three men on steps, Seine (26x33cm-10x13in) s.d.1931 gelatin silver print prov. 23-Apr-4 Phillips, New York #2/R est:5000-7000
£3293 $5500 €4808 Chair with dead leaves, Luxembourg Garden, Paris. Untitled (40x50cm-16x20in) s.d.1952 verso gelatin silver print two lit. 20-Oct-3 Christie's, Rockefeller NY #108/R est:3000-5000
£6780 $12000 €9899 Greta Garbo (22x28cm-9x11in) s.d.1932 gelatin silver print lit. 27-Apr-4 Christie's, Rockefeller NY #116/R est:5000-7000

BINGHAM, James (1917-1971) American
£280 $459 €409 Clown (48x38cm-19x15in) s. board. 4-Jun-3 John Ross, Belfast #193
£280 $504 €420 Clown (46x36cm-18x14in) s. board. 20-Apr-4 James Adam, Dublin #124/R
£280 $512 €409 Girl in landscape (50x76cm-20x30in) s. board. 2-Jun-4 John Ross, Belfast #40
£340 $622 €496 Girl with bouquet (43x35cm-17x14in) s.d.1996 verso board. 2-Jun-4 John Ross, Belfast #227
£400 $732 €584 Boat and cottages, Connemara (28x33cm-11x13in) s.d.79 board. 2-Jun-4 John Ross, Belfast #127
£403 $721 €600 Figures on a roadside (50x75cm-20x30in) s. board. 31-May-4 Hamilton Osborne King, Dublin #23/R

£403	$721	€600	Birthday party (42x52cm-17x20in) s. board. 31-May-4 Hamilton Osborne King, Dublin #68/R
£450	$738	€657	Girl in landscape (50x76cm-20x30in) s. board. 4-Jun-3 John Ross, Belfast #86
£450	$824	€657	Piker neck clown (61x50cm-24x20in) s. board. 2-Jun-4 John Ross, Belfast #99
£520	$967	€759	Fetching water (50x76cm-20x30in) s. board. 3-Mar-4 John Ross, Belfast #90
£537	$961	€800	Serenity (43x53cm-17x21in) s. board. 31-May-4 Hamilton Osborne King, Dublin #69/R
£903	$1417	€1300	Girls in a cornfield (39x49cm-15x19in) s. board. 26-Aug-3 James Adam, Dublin #79/R est:800-1200

Works on paper

£671	$1100	€973	Joe sweats it out (33x48cm-13x19in) s. W/C board exec.c.1945. 7-Jun-3 Treadway Gallery, Cincinnati #1510

BINGLEY, Herbert Harding (fl.1927-1933) British

Works on paper

£390	$675	€569	Atlantic breakers (90x70cm-35x28in) s. W/C. 9-Dec-3 Bristol Auction Rooms #400

BINGLEY, James George (1841-1920) British

Works on paper

£550	$1018	€803	Horses in a snow covered landscape (29x24cm-11x9in) init. W/C bodycol. 9-Mar-4 Bonhams, Knightsbridge #63/R

BINI, Gino de (?) Spanish

£600	$1074	€876	After the review (18x28cm-7x11in) s. panel. 5-May-4 John Nicholson, Haslemere #584

BINJE, Franz (1835-1900) Belgian

£265	$482	€400	Brumes d'automne (80x56cm-31x22in) s. 21-Jun-4 Bernaerts, Antwerp #175
£336	$561	€480	Charrette sortant du village (21x31cm-8x12in) s. panel. 13-Oct-3 Horta, Bruxelles #516
£764	$1215	€1100	Promenade dans les dunes (38x26cm-15x10in) s. canvas on panel. 15-Sep-3 Horta, Bruxelles #462
£880	$1523	€1250	Vaches au bord de la riviere (29x44cm-11x17in) s. 9-Dec-3 Vanderkindere, Brussels #109

BINKS, Reuben Ward (fl.1924-1948) British

£3867	$7000	€5646	Scottish terrier, Crich Captain (25x35cm-10x14in) s.i.d.1916 i.verso canvasboard prov. 30-Mar-4 Bonhams & Butterfields, San Francisco #134/R est:1000-1500
£7500	$13800	€10950	Bulldogs on the beach (61x91cm-24x36in) s.d.1914. 26-Mar-4 Sotheby's, London #80/R est:6000-8000

Works on paper

£700	$1204	€1022	Two Irish wolfhounds (26x39cm-10x15in) s. W/C. 2-Dec-3 Sworder & Son, Bishops Stortford #529/R
£1243	$2250	€1815	Springer spaniel, Shot (26x31cm-10x12in) s.i.d.1929 gouache. 30-Mar-4 Bonhams & Butterfields, San Francisco #87/R est:1500-1800
£1243	$2250	€1815	Wire fox terriers, Ch Cockeye of Notts and Ch Roboro Playboy (21x28cm-8x11in) s.i.d.1924 W/C. 30-Mar-4 Bonhams & Butterfields, San Francisco #93/R est:1500-1800
£3315	$6000	€4840	Wire fox terriers (23x33cm-9x13in) s.i.d.1924 W/C. 30-Mar-4 Bonhams & Butterfields, San Francisco #89/R est:1500-1800

BINNEY, Don (1940-) New Zealander

£1123	$1909	€1640	Lion Rock Piha (34x41cm-13x16in) s.i.d.1981 oil pastel. 4-Nov-3 Peter Webb, Auckland #297/R est:2000-3000 (NZ.D 3100)
£2632	$4474	€3843	Landscape (57x70cm-22x28in) s.d.1984 oil paper on board. 27-Nov-3 International Art Centre, Auckland #15/R est:6500-8500 (NZ.D 7000)
£4693	$7650	€6852	Te Henga landscape (25x37cm-10x15in) s.d.1978 board. 23-Sep-3 Peter Webb, Auckland #14/R est:9000-12000 (NZ.D 13000)
£5357	$9696	€7821	Jewish cemetery (88x57cm-35x22in) s.d.1967 acrylic on paper prov. 30-Mar-4 Peter Webb, Auckland #18/R est:15000-20000 (NZ.D 15000)
£10638	$18830	€15531	King George with bird in a landscape (110x92cm-43x36in) s.d.1983 oil paper prov. 28-Apr-4 Dunbar Sloane, Auckland #34/R est:35000-45000 (NZ.D 30000)
£11913	$19419	€17393	Te Henga (105x86cm-41x34in) s.d.1967. 23-Sep-3 Peter Webb, Auckland #82/R est:35000-45000 (NZ.D 33000)
£25000	$45250	€36500	Dotterell over Te Henga (66x61cm-26x24in) s.i.d.1964 board prov. 30-Mar-4 Peter Webb, Auckland #32/R est:60000-75000 (NZ.D 70000)

Works on paper

£1444	$2354	€2108	Landscape (45x60cm-18x24in) s.d.1978 chl crayon. 23-Sep-3 Peter Webb, Auckland #129/R est:3500-4500 (NZ.D 4000)

BINOIT, Peter (17th C) German

£9050	$14480	€13213	Vanitas still life with German almanac (70x50cm-28x20in) i. lit. 19-Sep-3 Koller, Zurich #3010/R est:25000-35000 (S.FR 20000)
£12000	$20760	€17520	Still life of apples, pears and walnuts in a porcelain bowl with other fruits (40x55cm-16x22in) panel prov. 11-Dec-3 Sotheby's, London #109/R est:15000-20000

BINOIT, Peter (attrib) (17th C) German

£12222	$22000	€17844	Vase of flowers, silver platters with fruit and rolls, with insects (41x53cm-16x21in) panel prov. 23-Jan-4 Christie's, Rockefeller NY #151/R est:15000-20000

BINON, M (?) ?

£1042	$1740	€1500	Vasque entouree de cinq chatons (90x60cm-35x24in) s. 21-Oct-3 Galerie Moderne, Brussels #283 est:400-600

BINYINYUWUY (1928-1982) Australian

Works on paper

£325	$514	€471	Hollow log coffin and catfish rangga (83x51cm-33x20in) earth pigments eucalyptus bark exec.c.1963 prov. 28-Jul-3 Sotheby's, Paddington #470 (A.D 800)
£938	$1753	€1407	Banumbirr, morning star ceremony (101x63cm-40x25in) earth pigments eucalyptus bark exec.c.195 prov. 26-Jul-4 Sotheby's, Melbourne #534/R (A.D 2400)

BINYON, Edward (1830-1876) British

£900	$1611	€1314	Twilight, Capri (22x32cm-9x13in) s.i.d.1871. 18-Mar-4 Christie's, Kensington #619/R

BION, Marie Louise (1858-?) Swiss

£870	$1591	€1270	Young girl with a dog (130x80cm-51x31in) s. 4-Jun-4 Zofingen, Switzerland #2748/R est:1500 (S.FR 2000)

BIONDA, Mario (1913-1985) Italian

£423	$701	€600	Sensation (65x45cm-26x18in) s.d.65 tempera paper on canvas. 11-Jun-3 Finarte Semenzato, Milan #557/R
£1127	$1870	€1600	Interior with figure (100x100cm-39x39in) s. s.i.verso. 11-Jun-3 Finarte Semenzato, Milan #553/R
£1497	$2679	€2200	Grey image (81x100cm-32x39in) s.d.1961 s.i.d.verso. 16-Mar-4 Finarte Semenzato, Milan #66/R est:1800

Works on paper

£379	$607	€550	Composition (46x28cm-18x11in) s.d.1964 mixed media. 13-Mar-3 Galleria Pace, Milan #30/R

BIORN, Emil (19th C) ?

£875	$1400	€1278	Landscape with stream (46x66cm-18x26in) s. painted c.1910. 20-Sep-3 Bunte, Elgin #1433 est:800-1200

BIOULES, Vincent (1938-) French?

£1958	$3270	€2800	Untitled (195x130cm-77x51in) mono.d.74. 29-Jun-3 Versailles Encheres #208/R
£2053	$3736	€3100	Composition abstraite (190x130cm-75x51in) 16-Jun-4 Renaud, Paris #67 est:1200-1500

BIOW, Hermann (1804-1850) German

Photographs

£2639	$4486	€3800	Unknown couple (11x8cm-4x3in) s.d.46 daguerreotype lit. 31-Oct-3 Lempertz, Koln #28/R est:5000

BIRAGHI, Ippolito Umberto (1913-) Italian

£540	$885	€750	View of village on the lake (50x70cm-20x28in) s. 10-Jun-3 Pandolfini, Florence #133

BIRCH, David (20th C) British

£1500	$2655	€2190	South Downs landscape - old fashion harvesting (66x76cm-26x30in) s. 27-Apr-4 Lawrences, Bletchingley #1872/R est:1500-2000

BIRCH, Downard (1827-1897) British

£391	$700	€571	Betwys y Coed (38x30cm-15x12in) i.verso. 20-Mar-4 Sloans & Kenyon, Bethesda #1176/R

BIRCH, Lionel (1858-1930) British

£280	$496	€409	American landscape with a cart and horse and a cowboy in the background (62x75cm-24x30in) s.d.15. 28-Apr-4 Peter Wilson, Nantwich #76
£300	$474	€435	Cattle by the old oak tree (61x51cm-24x20in) s. 3-Sep-3 Bonhams, Bury St Edmunds #466
£350	$637	€511	Interior with two cats and a dog (41x30cm-16x12in) s.i. 15-Jun-4 David Lay, Penzance #86
£500	$895	€730	Man and boy watching the hunt in an open landscape (70x91cm-28x36in) s. 16-Mar-4 Bonhams, Leeds #662

BIRCH, Samuel John Lamorna (1869-1955) British

£800	$1408	€1168	Country house with pond (26x35cm-10x14in) s.d.1952 board. 18-May-4 Bonhams, Knightsbridge #127/R
£1550	$2744	€2263	Old castle landscape - between Edinburgh and Falkirk (32x39cm-13x15in) s.d.1949 s.i.verso. 28-Apr-4 Peter Wilson, Nantwich #5 est:1200-1800
£1800	$3366	€2628	Pedn Vounder Treen near Land's End Cornwall (32x39cm-13x15in) s. panel prov. 26-Feb-4 Lane, Penzance #85/R est:1000-1500
£2800	$5236	€4088	Passing fishing boat seen from the garden at Flagstaff Cottage (25x33cm-10x13in) s.d.1952. 26-Feb-4 Lane, Penzance #299 est:1200-1500
£3500	$6475	€5110	Children approaching a cottage (25x18cm-10x7in) s.d.1902 panel. 10-Feb-4 David Lay, Penzance #523/R est:3500-4000
£4200	$7854	€6132	Through a Perthshire woodland (8x55cm-3x22in) s.d.1949 prov.exhib. 26-Feb-4 Lane, Penzance #10/R est:3000-5000
£4500	$8235	€6570	Down-falling stream Lamorna (51x61cm-20x24in) s.d.1954. 28-Jan-4 Dreweatt Neate, Newbury #78/R est:5000-7000
£4700	$8601	€6862	Bystander and cattle on a country path beside a river, village in distance (61x74cm-24x29in) s. 28-Jul-4 Mallams, Oxford #342/R est:2500-3000
£4800	$8880	€7008	Hoskings barn (51x61cm-20x24in) s. s.i.stretcher. 11-Feb-4 Sotheby's, Olympia #122/R est:3000-5000
£5200	$8268	€7592	River (48x58cm-19x23in) s. 12-Sep-3 Gardiner & Houlgate, Bath #153/R est:2000-3000
£5500	$9460	€8030	Yorkshire Beck, Ramsgill (51x61cm-20x24in) s.d.1949 prov. 2-Dec-3 Bonhams, New Bond Street #5/R est:2000-3000
£6000	$10980	€8760	River landscape (51x76cm-20x30in) s.d.1936. 4-Jun-4 Christie's, London #61/R est:5000-8000
£8400	$14532	€12264	Springtime (50x76cm-20x30in) s. 11-Dec-3 Lane, Penzance #352/R est:6750-7500
£21000	$38430	€30660	Rockgirt pools of Spean (76x102cm-30x40in) s. prov. 2-Jun-4 Sotheby's, London #38/R est:10000-15000

Works on paper

£250	$418	€365	Souvenir of. (12x17cm-5x7in) s.i.d.July 23.28 pencil W/C. 21-Oct-3 Bonhams, Knightsbridge #92/R
£250	$463	€365	Pond before a farmhouse (16x25cm-6x10in) s.i.d.1947 W/C. 11-Mar-4 Christie's, Kensington #108

£260 $486 €380 From my window, Lamorna (14x9cm-6x4in) s.i. W/C hand painted postcard. 26-Feb-4 Lane, Penzance #133
£280 $518 €409 Coast scene (8x13cm-3x5in) s. W/C. 10-Feb-4 David Lay, Penzance #358/R
£280 $524 €420 Village street (16x23cm-6x9in) s. W/C. 22-Jul-4 Dominic Winter, Swindon #6/R
£300 $561 €438 Stream Lamorna (14x9cm-6x4in) s. W/C hand painted postcard. 26-Feb-4 Lane, Penzance #134
£320 $576 €467 River landscape (25x36cm-10x14in) indis sig. W/C prov. 20-Apr-4 Clarke Gammon, Guildford #43
£360 $583 €522 Landscape with trees (18x25cm-7x10in) s. W/C prov. 30-Jul-3 Hamptons Fine Art, Godalming #88
£380 $711 €555 Figures before the Wink, Lamorna (118x23cm-46x9in) s.d.1944. 26-Feb-4 Lane, Penzance #84
£400 $724 €584 Coastal scene. s. W/C. 15-Apr-4 Rendalls, Ashburton #1618
£500 $835 €730 Fishing by the river (25x36cm-10x14in) s.d.1950 pencil W/C bodycol. 16-Oct-3 Christie's, Kensington #292/R
£550 $919 €803 Path through the woods (22x15cm-9x6in) s.d.1897 pencil W/C. 16-Oct-3 Christie's, Kensington #291/R
£580 $1038 €847 Paul Church, Cornwall with two figures on a path (18x23cm-7x9in) s.i.d.1900 W/C. 13-May-4 Scarborough Perry Fine Arts, Hove #585
£680 $1244 €993 Clapper Mill, Trewoofe (36x50cm-14x20in) s. i.verso W/C pencil. 28-Jul-4 Hampton & Littlewood, Exeter #585/R
£700 $1295 €1022 Lamorna cottage (36x25cm-14x10in) s. W/C bodycol. 10-Feb-4 David Lay, Penzance #162
£750 $1343 €1095 Yellow fading woods, year's decline (24x29cm-9x11in) s. mixed media. 22-Mar-4 Bonhams & Brooks, Norfolk #146/R
£750 $1365 €1095 Lamorna Cove. Coastal view (14x22cm-6x9in) s.d.1952 indis.i. W/C two. 1-Jul-4 Christie's, Kensington #79
£900 $1665 €1314 Thames at Bourne End (25x35cm-10x14in) s.i.d.Oct 1947 pencil W/C. 11-Mar-4 Christie's, Kensington #71/R
£920 $1684 €1343 Figures on a path before Paul Church (19x23cm-7x9in) s. W/C. 3-Jun-4 Lane, Penzance #314
£1033 $1900 €1508 Crook O'land Doncaster (46x56cm-18x22in) s. W/C. 26-Jun-4 Sloans & Kenyon, Bethesda #1074/R est:2000-2500
£1100 $1837 €1606 River in winter (23x33cm-9x13in) s.d.1897 pencil W/C. 16-Oct-3 Christie's, Kensington #289/R est:800-1200
£1200 $1992 €1752 From the ridge, towards Caldy (43x56cm-17x22in) s. i.verso W/C. 2-Oct-3 Lane, Penzance #343 est:1000-1250
£1300 $2366 €1898 Spey from Dunkeld (30x43cm-12x17in) s.d.1946 W/C. 4-Feb-4 John Nicholson, Haslemere #36/R est:1000-1500
£2600 $4810 €3796 Island pool, Cornishaugh, Devon (24x34cm-9x13in) s.d.1934 W/C pen sepia ink exhib. 14-Jan-4 Lawrence, Crewkerne #1350/R est:1000-1500
£2800 $4564 €4088 Riverscape with house (46x58cm-18x23in) s. exhib. W/C. 27-Sep-3 Rogers Jones, Clwyd #111/R

BIRCH, Thomas (1779-1851) American
£2957 $5500 €4317 Picnic party on Mt Washington with a view of Mt Jefferson (43x59cm-17x23in) 5-Mar-4 Skinner, Boston #276/R est:8000-12000
£4037 $6500 €5894 Fisherman beside mill in summer (64x91cm-25x36in) 20-Aug-3 James Julia, Fairfield #1287/R est:6000-8000
£6452 $12000 €9420 View of the Hudson River near West Point (43x59cm-17x23in) s. 5-Mar-4 Skinner, Boston #274/R est:8000-12000
£11111 $18000 €16111 Off the coast of Maine (51x76cm-20x30in) s.d.1835 prov. 8-Aug-3 Barridorf, Portland #75/R est:20000-30000
£24709 $42500 €36075 Sleigh ride (51x76cm-20x30in) s.d.1844 prov. 3-Dec-3 Sotheby's, New York #107/R est:40000-60000
£26163 $45000 €38198 View of the Delaware River (51x76cm-20x30in) 3-Dec-3 Sotheby's, New York #97/R est:40000-60000
Works on paper
£756 $1300 €1104 Landscape depicting story of Peter and the wolf (15x10cm-6x4in) s. W/C oval. 6-Dec-3 Pook & Pook, Downington #236/R
£2616 $4500 €3819 Solitude, the home of John Penn (18x23cm-7x9in) s. W/C ink. 6-Dec-3 Pook & Pook, Downington #237/R est:1000-1500

BIRCH, Thomas (attrib) (1779-1851) American
Works on paper
£475 $850 €797 Sedgley, with courting couple in foreground (28x36cm-11x14in) W/C. 20-Mar-4 Pook & Pook, Downington #236/R

BIRCH, William Russell (1755-1834) American/British
Works on paper
£1000 $1600 €1460 Garden scene of a courting couple beside a fountain (8x10cm-3x4in) s. W/C pen pencil. 20-Sep-3 Pook & Pook, Downington #493 est:800-1200
£1625 $2600 €2373 Half-length portrait of a young man (20x20cm-8x8in) s.i. W/C pencil. 20-Sep-3 Pook & Pook, Downington #492 est:1000-1500
£2250 $3600 €3285 Profile portrait of a classical marble bust draped with flowers (13x8cm-5x3in) s. W/C pencil. 20-Sep-3 Pook & Pook, Downington #491 est:800-1200

BIRCHALL, Henry (19th C) British
£950 $1615 €1387 Shipping in Swansea Bay (45x61cm-18x24in) s.d.1845 lit. 18-Nov-3 Sotheby's, Olympia #4/R

BIRCHALL, William Minshall (1884-1941) British
Works on paper
£270 $500 €394 East coast fishers (13x18cm-5x7in) s.i.d.1926 W/C. 15-Jul-4 Richardson & Smith, Whitby #447
£280 $515 €409 Titanic (23x39cm-9x15in) s. W/C. 22-Jun-4 Bonhams, Knightsbridge #153/R
£280 $518 €409 Atlantic weather (13x18cm-5x7in) s.i. W/C. 15-Jul-4 Richardson & Smith, Whitby #419
£320 $595 €467 Manoeuvres! - a torpedo attack' (21x31cm-8x12in) s.i.d.1915 W/C htd white. 2-Mar-4 Bearnes, Exeter #304/R
£325 $517 €475 In the North Sea (13x23cm-5x9in) s.d.1918 W/C. 1-May-3 John Nicholson, Haslemere #644
£350 $613 €511 Steam and sale (13x28cm-5x11in) s.d.1912 W/C. 18-Dec-3 John Nicholson, Haslemere #1063
£400 $680 €584 Leaving France for Blighty (12x21cm-5x8in) s.i.d.1917 W/C htd gouache. 25-Nov-3 Bonhams, Knightsbridge #58/R
£400 $716 €584 The King's Ships (25x41cm-10x16in) s.i. W/C dr. 4-May-4 Gorringes, Bexhill #1407
£500 $895 €730 On route for the Argentine (20x38cm-8x15in) s.i. 6-Jan-4 Gildings, Market Harborough #453/R
£550 $946 €803 In Colonial waters. Under the red Ensign (18x26cm-7x10in) s.i.d.1923 W/C gouache pair. 2-Dec-3 Sotheby's, London #109/R
£550 $946 €803 Seaman's highway, Tramp and trawlers (22x44cm-9x17in) s.i.d.1923 W/C pair. 2-Dec-3 Sotheby's, London #112/R
£580 $963 €847 Modern four master (36x25cm-14x10in) s.i.d.1923 W/C. 3-Oct-3 Mallams, Oxford #129/R
£600 $1050 €876 Highway of Nations (33x51cm-13x20in) s.d.1922 W/C. 19-Dec-3 Mallams, Oxford #82/R
£650 $1138 €949 Storm clouds. Fishing fleet (28x20cm-11x8in) s.i.d.1912 1913 pair W/C. 18-Dec-3 John Nicholson, Haslemere #1048/R
£700 $1190 €1022 Speeding homeward (36x25cm-14x10in) s. pencil W/C htd white pair. 19-Nov-3 Christie's, Kensington #371/R
£1800 $3060 €2628 Passing ships, sail and steam in the Bay of Biscay (36x51cm-14x20in) s.i.d.1930 pencil W/C gouache sold with cuttings and photos. 19-Nov-3 Tennants, Leyburn #873/R est:1000-1500

BIRCHER, Alfred Thompson (?) British?
Works on paper
£2235 $4000 €3263 Rocky coast with sailboats (23x51cm-9x20in) s. W/C. 7-May-4 Sloans & Kenyon, Bethesda #1689/R est:3000-5000

BIRCK, Alphonse (1859-?) French
£466 $854 €700 Souk dans la Kasbah (41x33cm-16x13in) s. canvas on isorel. 3-Jun-4 Tajan, Paris #208
£5674 $9475 €8000 Portrait de jeune Ouled-nail (55x47cm-22x19in) s. panel. 16-Jun-3 Gros & Delettrez, Paris #73/R est:8000-10000
Works on paper
£333 $613 €500 Au bord du Nil (34x48cm-13x19in) s.i. W/C. 9-Jun-4 Oger, Dumont, Paris #83
£1275 $2359 €1900 Les souks dans la casbah (46x56cm-18x22in) s. W/C. 15-Mar-4 Gros & Delettrez, Paris #80 est:1100-1500
£2000 $3680 €3000 Femmes dans l'oued de Bou-Saada. Jeune fille kabyle (37x52cm-15x20in) s. W/C double-sided. 14-Jun-4 Gros & Delettrez, Paris #376/R est:3000-4000

BIRD, Cyril Kenneth (1887-1965) British
Works on paper
£750 $1388 €1095 Check (36x26cm-14x10in) s. pencil pen ink. 11-Feb-4 Sotheby's, Olympia #98/R

BIRD, Edward (1772-1819) British
£1800 $3312 €2628 Lesson. Tending to mother (25x33cm-10x13in) s. panel pair. 29-Mar-4 Bonhams, Bath #100/R est:1000-1500
Works on paper
£320 $573 €467 An unusual visitor (26x38cm-10x15in) s. 17-Mar-4 Bonhams, Chester #345

BIRD, George Frederick (1883-1948) British
£400 $732 €584 Portrait of Kitty Bird, wearing a fur cape (56x43cm-22x17in) 27-Jan-4 Gorringes, Lewes #1686
£2900 $5307 €4234 David playing to Saul (127x102cm-50x40in) 27-Jan-4 Gorringes, Lewes #1685/R est:1000-1500

BIRD, Harrington (1846-1936) British
£1600 $2880 €2336 Study of a racehorse with a jockey up on a racecourse (46x61cm-18x24in) s.d. 21-Apr-4 Tennants, Leyburn #1177/R est:1200-1400
Works on paper
£2400 $4392 €3504 Arab stallion in a desert landscape (52x36cm-20x14in) s. W/C. 27-Jan-4 Holloways, Banbury #345/R est:1200-1800
£5500 $8745 €8030 Arab mare and foal, a Bedouin encampment beyond (38x48cm-15x19in) s W/C. 9-Sep-3 Gorringes, Lewes #1913/R est:5000-7000
£5500 $9735 €8030 Arab mare and foal at an oasis (33x45cm-13x18in) s. W/C bodycol. 27-Apr-4 Bonhams, New Bond Street #68/R est:5000-8000
£11000 $20020 €16060 Arab horses in the desert (46x60cm-18x24in) s.d.1905 pencil W/C board. 17-Jun-4 Christie's, London #139/R est:8000-12000
£11200 $18704 €16352 Chestnut and grey stallions at an oasis (52x37cm-20x15in) s.d.1906 W/C. 17-Nov-3 Trembath Welch, Great Dunmow #508/R est:1200-1800
£14200 $23714 €20732 Chestnut and grey stallions being led to the waters edge in Middle Eastern setting (37x52cm-15x20in) s.d.1906 W/C. 17-Nov-3 Trembath Welch, Great Dunmow #507/R est:1200-1800

BIRD, Mary Holden (fl.1923 1936) British
£1500 $2790 €2190 Coast, Iona (41x51cm-16x20in) s.d.1940. 4-Mar-4 Christie's, Kensington #247 est:800-1200
Works on paper
£550 $1023 €803 St. Onen's Bay, Jersey (23x34cm-9x13in) init. W/C. 4-Mar-4 Christie's, Kensington #208/R
£580 $1067 €847 Green seaweed, Morar (24x35cm-9x14in) mono. W/C. 10-Jun-4 Lyon & Turnbull, Edinburgh #13
£950 $1587 €1387 Point of Sleat (33x52cm-13x20in) mono. W/C. 16-Oct-3 Bonhams, Edinburgh #187/R

BIRD, Samuel C (19th C) British
Works on paper
£260 $447 €380 Weathering the storm (36x53cm-14x21in) s.d.1878 W/C bodycol. 3-Dec-3 Christie's, Kensington #129

BIRDSALL, Amos (attrib) (1865-1938) American

£1321	$2100	€1929	Crashing surf (76x91cm-30x36in) 9-Mar-3 William Jenack, New York #301 est:1000-1500

BIRELINE, George Lee (1923-2002) American

£405	$750	€591	Untitled (62x78cm-24x31in) s.d.1965 stretcher prov. 13-Jul-4 Christie's, Rockefeller NY #44/R

BIRGER, Hugo (1854-1887) Swedish

£3308	$5689	€4830	Back yard, Alhambra (62x75cm-24x30in) s. painted c.1882-1884. 2-Dec-3 Bukowskis, Stockholm #85/R est:40000-50000 (S.KR 43000)
£3843	$6880	€5611	By the coast at Lysekil (35x51cm-14x20in) s. painted c.1885 lit. 25-May-4 Bukowskis, Stockholm #60/R est:40000-45000 (S.KR 52000)
£5692	$9791	€8310	The letter (44x60cm-17x24in) prov.lit. 2-Dec-3 Bukowskis, Stockholm #161/R est:100000-125000 (S.KR 74000)
£9231	$15877	€13477	Ekebacken - garden terrace with figures (50x65cm-20x26in) s.i. lit. 3-Dec-3 AB Stockholms Auktionsverk #2407/R est:50000-60000 (S.KR 120000)
£10769	$18523	€15723	Studio interior (27x19cm-11x7in) s. panel. 3-Dec-3 AB Stockholms Auktionsverk #2353/R est:40000-50000 (S.KR 140000)

BIRGER-ERICSON, Birger (1904-1994) Swedish

£307	$501	€448	Summer establishment (33x41cm-13x16in) s. panel. 29-Sep-3 Lilla Bukowskis, Stockholm #844 (S.KR 4000)
£377	$652	€550	Southern harbour scene (38x46cm-15x18in) s. panel. 15-Dec-3 Lilla Bukowskis, Stockholm #87 (S.KR 4800)
£1141	$2054	€1666	Skansen (122x152cm-48x60in) s. panel. 26-Jan-4 Lilla Bukowskis, Stockholm #371 est:16000-18000 (S.KR 15200)
£1450	$2611	€2117	Henri Matisse (88x112cm-35x44in) s. 26-Apr-4 Bukowskis, Stockholm #212/R est:20000-25000 (S.KR 20000)

BIRKBECK, Geoffrey (1875-1954) British

Works on paper

£340	$609	€496	Still life of roses in a blue vase (27x35cm-11x14in) s. W/C. 22-Mar-4 Bonhams & Brooks, Norfolk #102/R
£1100	$1969	€1606	An elegant room interior (42x52cm-17x20in) s. indis i. W/C exhib. 22-Mar-4 Bonhams & Brooks, Norfolk #104/R est:400-600

BIRKEMOSE, Jens (1943-) Danish

£496	$913	€724	Composition (64x53cm-25x21in) s.d.81. 29-Mar-4 Rasmussen, Copenhagen #317/R (D.KR 5500)
£657	$1098	€959	Composition (92x73cm-36x29in) s. verso. 7-Oct-3 Rasmussen, Copenhagen #258/R (D.KR 7000)
£806	$1289	€1169	Composition (75x65cm-30x26in) s.d.81. 17-Sep-3 Kunsthallen, Copenhagen #118/R (D.KR 8500)
£988	$1679	€1442	Composition (80x40cm-31x16in) init. 26-Nov-3 Kunsthallen, Copenhagen #183/R (D.KR 10500)
£1174	$1960	€1714	Composition (92x73cm-36x29in) init. painted c.1993 exhib. 7-Oct-3 Rasmussen, Copenhagen #259/R est:10000 (D.KR 12500)
£1221	$2038	€1783	Composition (60x50cm-24x20in) s.d.1987-89 verso. 7-Oct-3 Rasmussen, Copenhagen #221/R est:8000-12000 (D.KR 13000)
£1221	$2038	€1783	Composition (60x50cm-24x20in) s.d.1988-89 verso. 7-Oct-3 Rasmussen, Copenhagen #226/R est:8000-12000 (D.KR 13000)
£1599	$2719	€2335	Von Gogh's chair (80x60cm-31x24in) mono. 26-Nov-3 Kunsthallen, Copenhagen #119/R est:20000 (D.KR 17000)
£1805	$3321	€2635	Composition (115x90cm-45x35in) init. init.d.85 verso. 29-Mar-4 Rasmussen, Copenhagen #432/R est:20000-25000 (D.KR 20000)
£1878	$3136	€2742	Composition with painted frame (145x185cm-57x73in) init.d.70, 73 masonite. 7-Oct-3 Rasmussen, Copenhagen #236/R est:30000-40000 (D.KR 20000)
£1882	$3387	€2748	Composition (131x99cm-52x39in) s.i.d.1987-88. 24-Apr-4 Rasmussen, Havnen #4249/R est:15000 (D.KR 21000)
£3602	$5763	€5223	Composition (250x200cm-98x79in) panel. 17-Sep-3 Kunsthallen, Copenhagen #89/R est:40000 (D.KR 38000)
£4225	$7056	€6169	Large composition (220x182cm-87x72in) init. 7-Oct-3 Rasmussen, Copenhagen #99/R est:50000-75000 (D.KR 45000)

Works on paper

£287	$516	€419	Figure composition (90x62cm-35x24in) s. gouache on lithograph. 24-Apr-4 Rasmussen, Havnen #4163 (D.KR 3200)

BIRKHAMMER, Axel (1874-1936) Danish

£898	$1671	€1311	Sunny winter's day in the wood (70x100cm-28x39in) s.i.d.1924. 2-Mar-4 Rasmussen, Copenhagen #1651/R (D.KR 10000)
£2149	$3932	€3138	Landscape from Silkeborg Islands with heather (70x106cm-28x42in) s. 9-Jun-4 Rasmussen, Copenhagen #1718/R est:12000-15000 (D.KR 24000)

BIRKHOLM, Jens (1869-1915) Danish

£344	$558	€502	Study for after the bath - nude girl by large stone (41x50cm-16x20in) init. exhib. 4-Aug-3 Rasmussen, Vejle #73/R (D.KR 3600)
£357	$608	€521	Autumn landscape (46x60cm-18x24in) init.d.03. 29-Nov-3 Rasmussen, Havnen #2119/R (D.KR 3800)
£359	$643	€524	Summer landscape with view of sea, Denmark (60x77cm-24x30in) init.d.11. 12-Jan-4 Rasmussen, Vejle #127/R (D.KR 3800)
£1090	$1744	€1591	Winter landscape with view across fields (75x98cm-30x39in) init.d.12. 22-Sep-3 Rasmussen, Vejle #149/R (D.KR 11500)
£2243	$3544	€3252	Landscape from Svanninge Bakker (89x118cm-35x46in) init.d.04 exhib. 2-Sep-3 Rasmussen, Copenhagen #1614/R est:25000 (D.KR 24000)

BIRKINGER, Franz Xaver (1822-1906) Austrian

£1958	$3270	€2800	Austrian summer landscape with poppies (126x65cm-50x26in) s. 28-Jun-3 Bolland & Marotz, Bremen #611 est:2200
£2685	$4805	€4000	Poppies, thistles and ribwort in front of cornfield (65x125cm-26x49in) s. 27-May-4 Dorotheum, Vienna #84/R est:4000-6000

BIRKLE, Albert (1900-1986) Austrian/German

£6294	$10825	€9000	On the ship builder's jetty (65x85cm-26x33in) s. s.i. on stretcher prov.exhib. 5-Dec-3 Ketterer, Munich #94/R est:9000-12000

Works on paper

£467	$840	€700	Untitled (59x46cm-23x18in) s.d. chl. 24-Apr-4 Dr Lehr, Berlin #54/R
£903	$1508	€1300	Old man wearing sailor's cap (45x32cm-18x13in) mono. chl. 25-Oct-3 Dr Lehr, Berlin #65/R
£2083	$3396	€3000	Portrait of woman wearing hat (70x51cm-28x20in) s.d.1926 pastel board. 27-Sep-3 Dr Fritz Nagel, Stuttgart #9459/R est:1800
£2333	$4177	€3500	Salzburg from Monchsberg - with selfportrait (46x65cm-18x26in) s. chl Indian ink prov.exhib. 14-May-4 Ketterer, Munich #213/R est:4000-4500

BIRKNER, Thomas (1966-) American

£500	$920	€750	Standing around (20x30cm-8x12in) s.i.d.1998 verso. 12-Jun-4 Meeting Art, Vercelli #19

BIRKS, Geoffrey W (1929-1993) British

£320	$576	€467	Industrial northern landscape with buildings and factory chimneys (22x31cm-9x12in) s. oil paper. 21-Apr-4 Tennants, Leyburn #1234
£550	$935	€803	Industrial scene under evening sky with figure and at (46x61cm-18x24in) s.d.76 board. 19-Nov-3 Tennants, Leyburn #1296
£600	$1122	€876	Industrial scene with figures walking beside a canal, factory chimneys beyond (46x63cm-18x25in) s.d.74 i.verso board. 22-Jul-4 Tennants, Leyburn #911
£650	$1105	€949	Ghost worker (61x51cm-24x20in) s.d.76 board. 19-Nov-3 Tennants, Leyburn #1293
£860	$1436	€1256	See you tomorrow then (25x31cm-10x12in) s. i.verso prov. 17-Nov-3 Waddingtons, Toronto #86/R est:1500-2000 (C.D 1900)
£1150	$1955	€1679	Mill worker (61x51cm-24x20in) s.i.d.76 board. 19-Nov-3 Tennants, Leyburn #1292/R est:600-800
£1200	$2040	€1752	Fire a't mill (46x61cm-18x24in) s. i.verso board. 19-Nov-3 Tennants, Leyburn #1295/R est:700-900
£1200	$2040	€1752	Industrial scene with factories and chimneys (61x51cm-24x20in) s. board. 19-Nov-3 Tennants, Leyburn #1291/R est:300-800
£1300	$2210	€1898	Tea break (51x61cm-20x24in) s.d.1977 board. 19-Nov-3 Tennants, Leyburn #1294/R est:700-900

BIRMANN, Peter (1758-1844) Swiss

Works on paper

£348	$637	€508	La roche au Lac de Bienne (31x48cm-12x19in) i. ink wash sepia. 4-Jun-4 Zofingen, Switzerland #2329 (S.FR 800)
£957	$1750	€1397	Environs de Raperschwyl au lac de Zurich (50x71cm-20x28in) s.i. ink wash sepia. 4-Jun-4 Zofingen, Switzerland #2328 est:950 (S.FR 2200)
£1087	$1989	€1587	Environs de Bale, prises sur la Carriere de Muttentz (51x73cm-20x29in) s.i. W/C. 4-Jun-4 Zofingen, Switzerland #2325/R est:3000 (S.FR 2500)
£1087	$1989	€1587	Vue d'une partie de Weesen, contre le Glarnisch (50x70cm-20x28in) s.i.d.1805 pen wash sepia. 4-Jun-4 Zofingen, Switzerland #2327 est:1500 (S.FR 2500)
£1810	$3241	€2643	Le bain de KNuttwyl dans le canton de Lucerne (50x72cm-20x28in) sepia W/C. 13-May-4 Stuker, Bern #9237/R est:3000-4000 (S.FR 4200)
£3261	$5967	€4761	Isola Bella on Lake Lugano. Palanzia on Lake Lugano (51x68cm-20x27in) s.i. one d.1805 one d. 1807 pen wash sepia pair. 4-Jun-4 Zofingen, Switzerland #2326/R est:3000 (S.FR 7500)

BIRMANN, Samuel (1793-1847) Swiss

£2586	$4629	€3776	Gsteig church near Wilderswil (30x38cm-12x15in) s.d.1820 i. verso copper. 13-May-4 Stuker, Bern #41/R est:5000-7000 (S.FR 6000)
£3378	$5811	€4932	Top half of Lake Como with a view of Dongo (57x76cm-22x30in) mono.d.1832. 8-Dec-3 Philippe Schuler, Zurich #3321/R est:10000-14000 (S.FR 7500)

BIRMELIN, Robert (1933-) American

£414	$750	€604	The stadium (183x198cm-72x78in) acrylic. 16-Apr-4 American Auctioneer #27/R
£691	$1250	€1009	Landscape for us (122x183cm-48x72in) acrylic. 16-Apr-4 American Auctioneer #25/R
£829	$1500	€1210	Landscape, the Dalles, Oregon (102x183cm-40x72in) acrylic. 16-Apr-4 American Auctioneer #26/R est:2000-4000
£1503	$2600	€2194	The sighting, Deer Island, Maine (122x117cm-48x46in) i.verso acrylic. 13-Dec-3 Weschler, Washington #612 est:1500-2500

BIRNBAUM, Aaron (20th C) American

£333	$600	€486	Flower (53x46cm-21x18in) board. 24-Apr-4 Slotin Folk Art, Buford #391/R
£1138	$1900	€1661	Kids playing in a tree (38x30cm-15x12in) paperboard prov. 15-Nov-3 Slotin Folk Art, Buford #158/R est:1000-2000
£2216	$3700	€3235	Chalfonte Hotel in Cape May (61x61cm-24x24in) plywood prov. 15-Nov-3 Slotin Folk Art, Buford #157/R est:1000-2000
£2695	$4500	€3935	Winter scene (86x91cm-34x36in) acrylic prov. 15-Nov-3 Slotin Folk Art, Buford #156/R est:1000-3000

BIRNEY, William Verplanck (1858-1909) American

£1321	$2100	€1929	Between meals (46x30cm-18x12in) s.i.d.1883 board. 12-Sep-3 Skinner, Boston #255/R
£1397	$2500	€2040	Pipe smoker (20x18cm-8x7in) s. panel. 20-Mar-4 Selkirks, St. Louis #144/R est:1500-2500
£2395	$4000	€3497	By the hearth (61x91cm-24x36in) s.d.91. 9-Oct-3 Christie's, Rockefeller NY #12/R est:5000-7000

BIRNIE, William (1929-) British

£320	$605	€467	Striped blinds, Palais Royal, Paris (24x20cm-9x8in) s.d.93 board. 19-Feb-4 Lyon & Turnbull, Edinburgh #49
£380	$600	€555	Puy L'eveque (90x120cm-35x47in) s.d.1985 board. 6-Sep-3 Shapes, Edinburgh #316
£1500	$2550	€2190	Aimez-vous Escargots (91x61cm-36x24in) s.d.92 board exhib. 30-Oct-3 Christie's, London #210/R est:1500-2500

BIRNSTENGEL, Richard (1881-1968) German

£590	$986	€850	Corsican landscape (76x91cm-30x36in) s.d. 25-Oct-3 Dr Lehr, Berlin #67/R
£833	$1392	€1200	Untitled - Landscape (55x69cm-22x27in) s.d. 25-Oct-3 Dr Lehr, Berlin #66/R

Works on paper
£333 $613 €500 Village street (30x32cm-12x13in) s. W/C. 11-Jun-4 Wendl, Rudolstadt #3962/R

BIROLLI, Renato (1906-1959) Italian
£667 $1227 €1000 Stream in the mountains (22x33cm-9x13in) s.d.31 tempera paper on canvas. 8-Jun-4 Finarte Semenzato, Milan #60/R est:1000-1200
£3357 $5706 €4800 Interior (60x50cm-24x20in) s. 29-Nov-3 Farsetti, Prato #531/R est:3000
£6757 $11892 €10000 Untitled (42x27cm-17x11in) s.d.1957 s.i.d.verso. 24-May-4 Christie's, Milan #191/R est:7000-10000
£6993 $11888 €10000 Rural houses (40x33cm-16x13in) s. painted 1955. 24-Nov-3 Christie's, Milan #215/R est:10000-15000
£11594 $19014 €16000 Etruscan necropolis (46x38cm-18x15in) s.d.955 s.d.verso prov.lit. 27-May-3 Sotheby's, Milan #203/R est:10000-15000
£23864 $42000 €34841 La laguna e bianca (109x79cm-43x31in) s.d.1954 s.i.d.verso prov. 22-May-4 Selkirks, St. Louis #771/R est:10000-14000
£50000 $83500 €73000 Espansione no 4 (115x65cm-45x26in) prov.exhib.lit. 21-Oct-3 Christie's, London #23/R est:40000-50000
£87413 $148601 €125000 Fire in the Cinque Terre, Liguria (119x108cm-47x43in) s.d.955-56 s.d.verso prov.exhib.lit. 25-Nov-3 Sotheby's, Milan #233/R est:90000-120000
Works on paper
£308 $523 €440 Face of young man (33x23cm-13x9in) s.d.39 ink. 19-Nov-3 Finarte Semenzato, Milan #549/R
£408 $731 €600 Landscape (24x22cm-9x9in) s.d. ink. 22-Mar-4 Sant Agostino, Torino #422/R
£638 $1186 €950 La cage a oiseau (48x66cm-19x26in) s.i.d.11.9.47 graphite col crayon prov. 2-Mar-4 Artcurial Briest, Paris #93
£667 $1227 €1000 Thoughtful boy (32x23cm-13x9in) s.d.1941 Chinese ink card. 12-Jun-4 Meeting Art, Vercelli #846/R
£1449 $2377 €2000 Still life (25x34cm-10x13in) s.d.1932 col pencil W/C paper on masonite. 27-May-3 Sotheby's, Milan #19 est:3000
£1884 $3090 €2600 Nudes (28x26cm-11x10in) s.d.43 Chinese ink two. 27-May-3 Sotheby's, Milan #20 est:2000

BIRON, Clemence (1889-?) Belgian
£267 $477 €400 Nature morte aux fruits (48x64cm-19x25in) s. cardboard. 11-May-4 Vanderkindere, Brussels #206
£1333 $2387 €2000 Jardin en fleurs (107x73cm-42x29in) s. panel. 11-May-4 Vanderkindere, Brussels #229 est:1250-1750

BIROTHEAU, Charles (19th C) French
£1206 $2013 €1700 Portrait de Marie Louise C (117x90cm-46x35in) s.d.1865. 19-Jun-3 Millon & Associes, Paris #97 est:2000-2500

BIRR, Jacques (1920-) French
£4604 $8149 €6860 Au bord de l'Iton (60x120cm-24x47in) s. oil paper. 29-Apr-4 Claude Aguttes, Neuilly #71 est:9000-10700

BIRREN, Joseph P (1864-1933) American
£714 $1193 €1035 His master's best friend (61x41cm-24x16in) s. canvas on board prov. 17-Jun-3 Pinneys, Montreal #63 est:1800-2400 (C.D 1600)

BIRREN, Joseph Pierre (1865-1933) American
£405 $700 €591 Lake Michigan (15x23cm-6x9in) board. 12-Dec-3 Du Mouchelle, Detroit #1239/R
£1879 $3250 €2743 Colourful day (51x61cm-20x24in) masonite. 12-Dec-3 Du Mouchelle, Detroit #1238/R est:300-350

BIRRER, Max (1905-1937) Swiss?
£655 $1192 €956 Portrait of a woman with an open book (92x73cm-36x29in) s.d.31. 16-Jun-4 Fischer, Luzern #2030/R (S.FR 1500)

BIRSTINGER, Leopold (1903-1983) Austrian
£6944 $11806 €10000 Blooming garden in Mauer (53x67cm-21x26in) mono. 28-Oct-3 Wiener Kunst Auktionen, Vienna #112/R est:8000-15000

BIRTLES, Harry (fl.1880-1905) British
Works on paper
£800 $1472 €1168 Cattle watering (20x32cm-8x13in) s. W/C pencil. 23-Mar-4 Bonhams, Knightsbridge #161/R

BIRZER, Eugen (1847-1905) German
£795 $1446 €1200 Extensive landscape with view of a village and figures (63x87cm-25x34in) s.d.1902. 19-Jun-4 Bergmann, Erlangen #824

BISAGNI, Getty (1931-) Italian
£250 $458 €365 Musico in Piassa (50x40cm-20x16in) s. 8-Apr-4 Christie's, Kensington #210/R
£900 $1647 €1314 Misfortune at the mine (69x98cm-27x39in) s. 8-Apr-4 Christie's, Kensington #209/R

BISANZIO, Andrea (1918-1994) Italian
Works on paper
£1133 $2085 €1700 Untitled (63x100cm-25x39in) s.d.54 verso mixed media board prov. 8-Jun-4 Finarte Semenzato, Milan #61/R est:1200-1800

BISCAINO, Bartolomeo (1632-1657) Italian
Works on paper
£7394 $12940 €10500 Une bataille de cavaliers et soldats (20x28cm-8x11in) i. red chk htd white prov. 17-Dec-3 Christie's, Paris #14/R est:6000-8000
£11111 $20000 €16222 Finding of Moses (30x23cm-12x9in) i.verso red chk htd white prov. 22-Jan-4 Christie's, Rockefeller NY #54/R est:15000-20000

BISCARDI, Jose Campos (1944-) Colombian
£442 $720 €645 First view (76x86cm-30x34in) s.verso painted 1974. 28-Sep-3 Subastas Odalys, Caracas #15
Works on paper
£226 $415 €339 Plain (50x40cm-20x16in) s. mixed media on canvas. 27-Jun-4 Subastas Odalys, Caracas #98
£330 $600 €495 Avila (80x53cm-31x21in) s. mixed media panel exec.1995. 21-Jun-4 Subastas Odalys, Caracas #132
£602 $1095 €903 Avila (100x150cm-39x59in) s.verso mixed media exec.1996. 21-Jun-4 Subastas Odalys, Caracas #169
£762 $1250 €1113 Eagle flying high (150x150cm-59x59in) s.verso mixed media on canvas. 1-Jun-3 Subastas Odalys, Caracas #109

BISCARRA, Carlo Felice (1825-1894) Italian
£9507 $16447 €13500 Bird keeper (270x149cm-106x59in) s.d.1880. 9-Dec-3 Pandolfini, Florence #64/R est:7000-8000

BISCHOF, Anton (1877-?) German
£1793 $2994 €2600 Holy Night - villages gathered outside snow covered house (41x38cm-16x15in) s. i. verso lit. panel. 10-Jul-3 Allgauer, Kempten #2433/R est:900
Works on paper
£276 $461 €400 Portrait of a soldier (44x38cm-17x15in) s. gouache lit. 10-Jul-3 Allgauer, Kempten #2294/R

BISCHOF, Werner (1916-1954) Swiss
Photographs
£4444 $8000 €6488 Dancer, Anjali Hora (20x25cm-8x10in) i.verso gelatin silver print. 24-Apr-4 Phillips, New York #23/R est:8000-12000

BISCHOFF, Franz A (1864-1929) American
£483 $850 €705 California seascape, Monteray coastline (48x38cm-19x15in) i. stretcher. 24-May-4 Winter Associates, Plainville #104/R
£1630 $3000 €2380 Still life with grapes (23cm-9in circular) s.d.1905 verso painted ceramic plate. 8-Jun-4 Auctions by the Bay, Alameda #1085/R
£1882 $3200 €2748 Point Magu, California seascapes (13x18cm-5x7in) s. set of four prov. 29-Oct-3 Christie's, Los Angeles #30/R est:2500-3500
£2059 $3500 €3006 Sailing in a harbour seascape (17x25cm-7x10in) s. two prov. 29-Oct-3 Christie's, Los Angeles #52/R est:2000-3000
£2514 $4500 €3670 Pink roses (20x28cm-8x11in) s. i.verso paint porcelain plaque. 26-May-4 Doyle, New York #117/R est:4000-6000
£4118 $7000 €6012 Sierra Medre Mountains (33x48cm-13x19in) s. i.verso board prov. 29-Oct-3 Christie's, Los Angeles #45/R est:3000-5000
£4620 $8500 €6745 Four women in an interior (45x61cm-18x24in) s. oil pencil prov. 8-Jun-4 Bonhams & Butterfields, San Francisco #4284/R est:10000-15000
£5000 $8500 €7300 Still life with roses (33x28cm-13x11in) s. paper on board. 29-Oct-3 Christie's, Los Angeles #13/R est:8000-12000
£5291 $10000 €7725 Landscape (33x48cm-13x19in) s. board prov. 17-Feb-4 John Moran, Pasadena #100/R est:7000-9000
£5882 $10000 €8588 Monterey sunset (33x48cm-13x19in) s. board prov. 18-Nov-3 John Moran, Pasadena #74 est:7000-9000
£14946 $27500 €21821 The docks at San Pedro (76x101cm-30x40in) prov. 8-Jun-4 Bonhams & Butterfields, San Francisco #4269/R est:10000-15000
£47619 $90000 €69524 Evening glory - Santa Barbara mountains, Calif (61x86cm-24x34in) s. s.i. verso prov. 17-Feb-4 John Moran, Pasadena #70a/R est:45000-65000
£108696 $200000 €158696 Monterey Coast, golden hours (76x101cm-30x40in) s. i.verso prov. 8-Jun-4 Bonhams & Butterfields, San Francisco #4268/R est:50000-70000
Works on paper
£1176 $2000 €1717 Sailing ship (20x21cm-8x8in) s. W/C gouache two prov. 29-Oct-3 Christie's, Los Angeles #51/R est:2500-3500
£6522 $12000 €9522 Pink roses in a blue vase (66x50cm-26x20in) pencil W/C prov. 8-Jun-4 Bonhams & Butterfields, San Francisco #4197/R est:6000-8000

BISCHOFF, Jak Christoph (1793-1825) Austrian
£2391 $4376 €3491 Children playing in the park at Villa Borghese (27x37cm-11x15in) i.d.1817 verso paper. 4-Jun-4 Zofingen, Switzerland #2331/R est:3500 (S.FR 5500)
£4130 $7559 €6030 Italian landscape with view of a cloister (27x37cm-11x15in) i.d.1817 verso paper. 4-Jun-4 Zofingen, Switzerland #2330/R est:3500 (S.FR 9500)

BISCHOFF, Wilhelm (1858-?) German
£690 $1234 €1007 Zermatt and the Matterhorn (60x51cm-24x20in) s.d.1907. 14-May-4 Dobiaschofsky, Bern #69/R est:1600 (S.FR 1600)

BISCHOFFSHAUSEN, Hans (1927-1987) Austrian
£667 $1200 €1000 Untitled (30x50cm-12x20in) s.d.1980 disperson board. 21-Apr-4 Dorotheum, Vienna #277/R
£671 $1201 €1000 Untitled (31x17cm-12x7in) s.d.61 dispersion. 27-May-4 Dorotheum, Graz #123/R
£1409 $2636 €2100 Espace se dilatant (63x53cm-25x21in) s. prov. 29-Feb-4 Versailles Encheres #205 est:250-300
Works on paper
£280 $476 €400 Man's head (28x19cm-11x7in) mono.i.d.76 feltpen. 19-Nov-3 Dorotheum, Klagenfurt #91/R
£420 $713 €600 Someone is angry (28x19cm-11x7in) s.mono.d.76 feltpen graphite. 19-Nov-3 Dorotheum, Klagenfurt #90/R
£872 $1562 €1300 Untitled (24x24cm-9x9in) s.d.61 mixed media dispersion pencil. 27-May-4 Dorotheum, Graz #122/R
£1014 $1784 €1500 Untitled (39x28cm-15x11in) s.d.49 pencil W/C. 19-May-4 Dorotheum, Klagenfurt #36/R est:1300
£1259 $2140 €1800 Untitled (40x32cm-16x13in) s. paper relief. 19-Nov-3 Dorotheum, Klagenfurt #92/R est:1100
£1678 $2853 €2400 Untitled (50x65cm-20x26in) s.d.59 VIII pencil silk paper on board. 26-Nov-3 Dorotheum, Vienna #234/R est:2400-3200

BISEO, Cesare (1843-1909) Italian
£400 $740 €584 Portrait of an Arab, in traditional dress (23x15cm-9x6in) s.d.1888 panel. 15-Jan-4 Christie's, Kensington #838/R
£7000 $12740 €10220 Cairo (53x73cm-21x29in) s.i.d.1883 prov. 17-Jun-4 Christie's, London #142/R est:8000-12000
Works on paper
£667 $1213 €1000 Interior with figures (18x23cm-7x9in) s. i.verso W/C. 12-Jul-4 Il Ponte, Milan #447
£764 $1276 €1100 Oriental landscape (48x84cm-19x33in) s.d.1896 gouache. 24-Oct-3 Ketterer, Hamburg #43/R

BISEO, Cesare (attrib) (1843-1909) Italian
£1053 $1937 €1600 Oriental market (16x28cm-6x11in) board exhib.lit. 23-Jun-4 Finarte Semenzato, Rome #58/R est:1000-1100

BISHOP, Alfred (19th C) British
£700 $1190 €1022 Bay hunter in a stable (63x76cm-25x30in) s.d.1890. 27-Nov-3 Christie's, Kensington #81a

BISHOP, Henry (1868-1939) British
£250 $463 €365 Chelsea Reach (40x71cm-16x28in) i.verso. 16-Feb-4 Bonhams, Bath #27
£260 $460 €380 Street scene (46x38cm-18x15in) s. 27-Apr-4 Bonhams, Knightsbridge #164
£400 $652 €584 Bridge at Avignon (33x41cm-13x16in) s. indis.d. board. 24-Sep-3 Dreweatt Neate, Newbury #207
£400 $708 €584 View from the hill (30x35cm-12x14in) s. 27-Apr-4 Bonhams, Knightsbridge #198/R
£500 $885 €730 Continental street scene (63x76cm-25x30in) s. 27-Apr-4 Bonhams, Knightsbridge #183/R
£500 $885 €730 Harbour scene (25x30cm-10x12in) s. 27-Apr-4 Bonhams, Knightsbridge #195/R
£750 $1328 €1095 Workers in a village (30x35cm-12x14in) s. 27-Apr-4 Bonhams, Knightsbridge #172
£800 $1416 €1168 Still life with teapot (41x51cm-16x20in) s. 27-Apr-4 Bonhams, Knightsbridge #189/R
£950 $1682 €1387 Landscape with viaduct (60x73cm-24x29in) s. 27-Apr-4 Bonhams, Knightsbridge #186/R
£1700 $3009 €2482 Rabat (36x33cm-14x13in) s. 27-Apr-4 Bonhams, Knightsbridge #192/R est:800-1000
£4400 $7348 €6424 Bridge before the Salute, Venice (34x34cm-13x13in) s. prov. 16-Oct-3 Christie's, Kensington #439/R est:600-800

BISHOP, Isabel (1902-1988) American
Works on paper
£245 $450 €358 Putting on the coat, European way 2 (18x18cm-7x7in) s. pen ink exec. c.1950. 10-Jun-4 Swann Galleries, New York #23/R
£489 $900 €714 Woman at a soda fountain (28x13cm-11x5in) s. pen ink exec. c.1959. 10-Jun-4 Swann Galleries, New York #22/R
£1413 $2600 €2063 Study for subway rider (58x36cm-23x14in) s. brush ink wash exec. 1950 prov. 10-Jun-4 Swann Galleries, New York #21/R est:1500-2500

BISHOP, Maurice (20th C) British
£300 $501 €438 Two children in a cornfield (51x76cm-20x30in) s.d.1981. 26-Jun-3 Greenslade Hunt, Taunton #562/R

BISHOP, Richard (1887-1975) American
£1875 $3000 €2738 Wildlife landscape (28x38cm-11x15in) s.i. 20-Sep-3 Pook & Pook, Downington #420/R est:2000-3000
£1875 $3000 €2738 Wildlife landscape (28x38cm-11x15in) s.i. 20-Sep-3 Pook & Pook, Downington #421/R est:2000-3000
£5820 $11000 €8497 Geese landing in autumn landscape (76x64cm-30x25in) s.d.1951 s.d. verso prov. 17-Feb-4 John Moran, Pasadena #177/R est:5000-7000

BISHOP, W Follen (1856-1936) British
Works on paper
£320 $534 €467 Lonely track (36x51cm-14x20in) s.i. W/C. 12-Nov-3 Halls, Shrewsbury #255/R
£450 $828 €657 Village in summer with cattle and doves in a lane and whitewashed cottages (52x36cm-20x14in) s. W/C. 23-Mar-4 Anderson & Garland, Newcastle #281/R
£500 $905 €730 Wood pigeons in a snowy landscape (40x60cm-16x24in) s. W/C. 4-Apr-4 Lots Road Auctions, London #345/R
£2458 $4178 €3589 English Landscape (58x89cm-23x35in) s. W/C. 24-Nov-3 Sotheby's, Melbourne #312/R est:2000-3000 (A.D 5800)

BISHOP, William Henry (1942-) British
£10000 $17900 €14600 Battle of Trafalgar 21st October 1805 (76x112cm-30x44in) s.d.04. 26-May-4 Christie's, Kensington #680/R est:10000-15000

BISI, Carlo (1890-?) Italian
£280 $467 €400 Flowers (35x23cm-14x9in) s. board. 26-Jun-3 Sant Agostino, Torino #112/R

BISI, Ietta (?) Italian
£369 $690 €550 House with balconies in bloom (62x73cm-24x29in) board. 26-Feb-4 Cambi, Genoa #564/R

BISIAUX, Pierre (1924-) French
£282 $487 €400 Provence sous la neige (54x65cm-21x26in) s. 13-Dec-3 Touati, Paris #43/R
£539 $900 €787 Nature morte au carafon (24x41cm-9x16in) s. board. 19-Oct-3 Bonhams & Butterfields, Los Angeles #7067

BISKINIS, Dimitrios (1891-1947) Greek
£3200 $5600 €4672 Young artist (40x33cm-16x13in) s. 16-Dec-3 Bonhams, New Bond Street #60/R est:2500-3500

BISMOUTH, Maurice (1885-1965) French
£319 $533 €450 Vieil homme au turban gris (17x13cm-7x5in) s. cardboard. 19-Oct-3 Rabourdin & Choppin de Janvry, Paris #172
£360 $590 €500 La jeune Tunisienne (12x8cm-5x3in) s. cardboard. 6-Jun-3 Chochon-Barre & Allardi, Paris #26/R
£390 $651 €550 Fou de la hara (16x12cm-6x5in) s. masonite. 19-Oct-3 Rabourdin & Choppin de Janvry, Paris #175
£426 $711 €600 Entree du village (12x17cm-5x7in) s. cardboard. 19-Oct-3 Rabourdin & Choppin de Janvry, Paris #174
£567 $948 €800 Portrait de jeune tunisien (28x20cm-11x8in) s. cardboard. 19-Oct-3 Rabourdin & Choppin de Janvry, Paris #173
£922 $1540 €1300 Portrait de rabbin (24x16cm-9x6in) s. cardboard. 19-Oct-3 Rabourdin & Choppin de Janvry, Paris #176/R
£1092 $1888 €1550 Femme de Tunis (41x32cm-16x13in) s.i.d.1937 panel. 10-Dec-3 Rossini, Paris #52/R
£1103 $1986 €1600 Viareggio (63x90cm-25x35in) s.d.1924 panel. 25-Jan-4 Chayette & Cheval, Paris #166 est:1500-2000
£1200 $2196 €1800 Trois portraits de femmes (17x12cm-7x5in) s. two canvas one paper three. 3-Jun-4 Tajan, Paris #207/R est:1200-1500
£2113 $3655 €3000 Rabbin en priere (61x38cm-24x15in) s. 15-Dec-3 Gros & Delettrez, Paris #87/R est:3000-3500

BISON, Giuseppe Bernardino (1762-1844) Italian
£6500 $11245 €9490 Capriccio lake landscape with ruins and figures by a well (42x68cm-17x27in) 10-Dec-3 Bonhams, New Bond Street #77/R est:5000-7000
£7000 $12810 €10500 Inn interior. Peasants and gentleman (10x10cm-4x4in) tempera paper pair. 1-Jun-4 Sotheby's, Milan #186/R est:8000-12000
£7333 $13127 €11000 Shelter (29x43cm-11x17in) tempera paper. 12-May-4 Stadion, Trieste #600/R est:3000-4000
£7534 $12808 €11000 Classical landscape with ruins (41x51cm-16x20in) tempera paper oval. 9-Nov-3 Finarte, Venice #13/R est:12000-15000
£8667 $15513 €13000 Travellers in the wood (38x52cm-15x20in) tempera paper. 12-May-4 Stadion, Trieste #601/R est:3000-4000
£13103 $21883 €19000 Venetian carnival (14x20cm-6x8in) tempera paper pair. 12-Nov-3 Sotheby's, Milan #132/R est:15000-20000
£16107 $30121 €24000 Lady at bath. The Fenice (17x22cm-7x9in) canvas on card prov. two. 25-Feb-4 Porro, Milan #49/R est:24000
£17241 $28793 €25000 Landscape with bridge and merchants (31x44cm-12x17in) prov.exhib. 15-Nov-3 Porro, Milan #225/R est:25000
£213793 $357034 €310000 View of Navona Square (33x45cm-13x18in) s.d.1832 board. 12-Nov-3 Sotheby's, Milan #173/R est:40000-60000
Works on paper
£260 $450 €380 Man in armour speaking to an old man (20x14cm-8x6in) s. black lead pen brown ink. 12-Dec-3 Christie's, Kensington #399
£656 $1200 €958 Standing woman in classical dress. Stencil design (23x16cm-9x6in) pen brown ink double-sided. 29-Jan-4 Swann Galleries, New York #140/R
£765 $1400 €1117 Portrait studies of a courtier and a gentlewoman (19x21cm-7x8in) i.verso red chk. 29-Jan-4 Swann Galleries, New York #139/R
£855 $1574 €1300 Study of three musician angels (19x26cm-7x10in) s. pen ink. 22-Jun-4 Sotheby's, Milan #104/R est:1200-1800
£1000 $1730 €1460 Head studies of a woman, a man, putti, horses and goats. Tobias and angel (36x22cm-14x9in) i. pen brown ink black chk double-sided. 12-Dec-3 Christie's, Kensington #397/R est:1000-1500
£1000 $1730 €1460 Girl and bearded Oriental (17x15cm-7x6in) pen brown ink prov. 12-Dec-3 Christie's, Kensington #398/R est:1000-1500
£1391 $2531 €2100 Three graces (28x21cm-11x8in) s. pen ink W/C. 16-Jun-4 Christie's, Rome #457 est:800-1200
£1800 $3294 €2628 Christ on the Cross (29x19cm-11x7in) mono. pen brown ink wash over blk chk. 8-Jul-4 Sotheby's, London #105/R est:1800-2200
£2778 $5000 €4056 Three female heads, perhaps for the Three Graces (21x2cm-8x1in) red chk stumped prov.exhib.lit. 22-Jan-4 Christie's, Rockefeller NY #75/R est:1500-2000
£3611 $6500 €5272 Family crossing a stream with a cow (21x32cm-8x13in) black chk bodycol. 22-Jan-4 Christie's, Rockefeller NY #234/R est:3000-4000

BISON, Giuseppe Bernardino (attrib) (1762-1844) Italian
£596 $1085 €900 Scene de chasse a courre (18x26cm-7x10in) panel. 21-Jun-4 Tajan, Paris #30
Works on paper
£3000 $5400 €4380 Woman and infant with two other children, an allegory of charity (21x29cm-8x11in) pen brown ink wash. 20-Apr-4 Sotheby's, Olympia #105/R est:1000-1500

BISON, Giuseppe Bernardino (style) (1762-1844) Italian
£6711 $12349 €10000 River landscape with figures (210x170cm-83x67in) 29-Mar-4 Pandolfini, Florence #758 est:15000

BISS, Earl (1947-1998) American
£3552 $6500 €5186 Waiting for the rain (56x76cm-22x30in) s.i. d.verso. 10-Apr-4 Auctions by the Bay, Alameda #1624/R

BISSACCO, Martino (1941-) Italian
Works on paper
£400 $736 €600 Composition (27x34cm-11x13in) s. mixed media collage. 12-Jun-4 Meeting Art, Vercelli #6

BISSCHOP, Abraham (1670-1731) Dutch
£18000 $32400 €26280 Classical wooded landscape with a Muscovy duck, a guinea fowl and a kingfisher (100x110cm-39x43in) s.d.1720. 21-Apr-4 Christie's, London #51/R est:20000-30000

BISSCHOP, Jan de (1628-1671) Dutch

Works on paper

£492	$900	€718	Ascension of the Virgin (15x17cm-6x7in) pen brown ink. 29-Jan-4 Swann Galleries, New York #175/R
£669	$1157	€950	Portrait de femme (18x15cm-7x6in) ink lavis. 10-Dec-3 Maigret, Paris #12
£4444	$8000	€6488	Hilly landscape with a fortified town in the foreground (20x27cm-8x11in) brush brown wash htd white prov.exhib. 21-Jan-4 Sotheby's, New York #65/R est:6000-8000
£4452	$7568	€6500	Landscape with bridge over a canal, entrance to the House of Werve (10x15cm-4x6in) s. i.verso pen brown ink wash prov. 4-Nov-3 Sotheby's, Amsterdam #79/R est:4000-6000
£6507	$11062	€9500	View of trees, near Rijswijk (10x15cm-4x6in) s. i.verso pen brown ink wash prov. 4-Nov-3 Sotheby's, Amsterdam #82/R est:3000-4000
£8219	$13973	€12000	Rider and figures by a fallen tree in the Haagse Bos (10x15cm-4x6in) s. i.verso pen brown ink grey brown wash prov. 4-Nov-3 Sotheby's, Amsterdam #78/R est:6000-8000
£9589	$16301	€14000	Wooded landscape near Rijswijk, with two figures by a tall tree (10x15cm-4x6in) s. i.verso pen brown ink grey brown wash prov. 4-Nov-3 Sotheby's, Amsterdam #81/R est:4000-6000

BISSCHOP-SWIFT, Kate (1834-1928) British

Works on paper

£1806	$3069	€2600	Gentle care (73x55cm-29x22in) s. pencil blk chk W/C htd white. 28-Oct-3 Christie's, Amsterdam #94/R est:3000-5000

BISSCHOPS, Charles (1894-1975) Belgian

£467	$859	€700	Martigues (19x22cm-7x9in) s. panel. 14-Jun-4 Horta, Bruxelles #368
£567	$1043	€850	Andalousie (65x100cm-26x39in) s. two. 14-Jun-4 Horta, Bruxelles #367

BISSCHOPS, Charles (attrib) (1894-1975) Belgian

£867	$1577	€1300	Portrait of woman (66x46cm-26x18in) 3-Jul-4 Finarte, Venice #339/R

BISSCHOPS, Joseph (1901-1978) Belgian

£709	$1184	€1000	Souk au Maroc (45x56cm-18x22in) s.i. isorel. 16-Jun-3 Gros & Delettrez, Paris #212

BISSELL, Edgar Julien (1856-?) American

£599	$1000	€875	Lady at her dressing table (94x74cm-37x29in) s. 20-Jun-3 Freeman, Philadelphia #193/R

BISSELL, George Edwin (1839-1920) American

Sculpture

£2402	$4300	€3507	Abraham Lincoln (43cm-17in) s. bronze prov. 20-Mar-4 Selkirks, St. Louis #188/R est:3500-4000

BISSEN, Rudolf (1846-1911) Danish

£391	$615	€571	Summer's day by the coast (80x119cm-31x47in) s.d.90. 30-Aug-3 Rasmussen, Havnen #2089/R (D.KR 4200)
£895	$1638	€1307	Deer on the outskirts of wood (82x60cm-32x24in) s.i.d.Oct.1898 i.verso. 9-Jun-4 Rasmussen, Copenhagen #1634/R (D.KR 10000)
£1025	$1610	€1497	Landscape from Silkeborg Islands (62x100cm-24x39in) init.d.79. 30-Aug-3 Rasmussen, Havnen #2192 (D.KR 11000)
£1168	$2173	€1705	Hunters with dogs on country road (80x60cm-31x24in) s.d.96. 2-Mar-4 Rasmussen, Copenhagen #1342/R est:15000 (D.KR 13000)

BISSI, Cirno Sergio (1902-1987) Italian

£361	$650	€527	Ballet dressing room (79x61cm-31x24in) s.i. 23-Jan-4 Freeman, Philadelphia #109/R
£563	$935	€800	On the grass (40x60cm-16x24in) s. 13-Jun-3 Farsetti, Prato #426
£634	$1096	€900	Masked figures (26x62cm-10x24in) board. 9-Dec-3 Pandolfini, Florence #408/R
£704	$1218	€1000	Masked figures (51x50cm-20x20in) s.verso masonite pair. 9-Dec-3 Pandolfini, Florence #420/R
£882	$1500	€1288	Ballet dancer (70x49cm-28x19in) s. i.verso. 19-Nov-3 Bonhams & Butterfields, San Francisco #166/R
£2762	$5000	€4033	Masked ball (45x80cm-18x31in) s. 30-Mar-4 Christie's, Rockefeller NY #109/R est:4000-6000

BISSIER, Jules (1893-1965) German

£3500	$6440	€5250	Untitled composition (17x20cm-7x8in) s.i.d.19 Nov 58 tempera linen prov. 24-Jun-4 Sotheby's, Olympia #543/R est:3000-4000
£5220	$9500	€7621	28 August 60 (21x26cm-8x10in) s.i. oil tempera on textile painted 1960 prov. 29-Jun-4 Sotheby's, New York #428/R est:8000-12000
£5245	$9545	€7658	3 September 1957 (19x25cm-7x10in) s.i.d.1957 s.i.d.verso acrylic prov. 29-Jun-4 Peter Webb, Auckland #106/R est:15000-20000 (NZ.D 15000)
£6000	$11040	€9000	Monti 60.82 (20x22cm-8x9in) s.i.d. egg oil tempera. 11-Jun-4 Hauswedell & Nolte, Hamburg #1165/R est:10000
£6335	$10579	€9249	16.III.61 (12x17cm-5x7in) mono.d.16.111.61 tempera prov. 24-Jun-3 Germann, Zurich #92/R est:18000-22000 (S.FR 14000)
£8000	$14480	€11680	A9.6.57 (18x23cm-7x9in) s.i. tempera. 1-Apr-4 Christie's, Kensington #208/R est:8000-12000
£8333	$14917	€12500	6. Aug. 58 (16x21cm-6x8in) s.d.6 Aug 58 egg oil tempera canvas on board prov. 14-May-4 Ketterer, Munich #263/R est:10000-12000
£8741	$15035	€12500	Untitled (15x21cm-6x8in) s.d.1963 egg oil tempera cotton prov. 5-Dec-3 Ketterer, Munich #136/R est:10000-12000
£9000	$16380	€13140	28 JUNI 59 (21x24cm-8x9in) s.i.d.28 Juni 59 tempera linen prov. 6-Feb-4 Sotheby's, London #166/R est:5000-7000
£9333	$17173	€14000	Monti 60.7i (21x26cm-8x10in) s.i.d. egg oil tempera gold leaf. 11-Jun-4 Hauswedell & Nolte, Hamburg #1164/R est:12000
£9500	$17290	€13870	A 23 SEPT 63 (26x27cm-10x11in) s.i.d.23 Sept 63 tempera linen prov. 6-Feb-4 Sotheby's, London #165/R est:6000-8000
£13380	$22211	€19000	Miniature 11.11.60 (20x21cm-8x8in) s.d.1960 egg oil tempera. 13-Jun-3 Hauswedell & Nolte, Hamburg #563/R est:12000
£14000	$25480	€20440	18.5.60 D (45x52cm-18x20in) s.i. tempera linen prov.exhib. 6-Feb-4 Sotheby's, London #181/R est:8000-12000

Works on paper

£1700	$3128	€2550	Untitled composition (39x52cm-15x20in) s.i. ink prov.exhib. 24-Jun-4 Sotheby's, Olympia #542/R est:1000-1500
£3219	$5022	€4700	Abstract composition (74x60cm-29x24in) s.d.1957 Indian ink. 10-Apr-3 Weidler, Nurnberg #4405/R
£4790	$8000	€6993	Untitled (20x24cm-8x9in) s.d.15 Jan 64 W/C ink prov. 13-Nov-3 Sotheby's, New York #186/R est:8000-12000
£4853	$8250	€7085	Untitled (14x24cm-6x9in) s.d.25.6.63 W/C prov. 9-Nov-3 Bonhams & Butterfields, Los Angeles #4033/R
£5333	$9547	€8000	4 Juli 1961 (20x24cm-8x9in) s.i.d.4 Juli 1961 W/C prov. 15-May-4 Van Ham, Cologne #464/R est:8000
£5333	$9760	€8000	9 Jan 65 GA (24x30cm-9x12in) s.d.9 Jan 65 W/C. 5-Jun-4 Lempertz, Koln #600/R est:8000-10000
£6000	$10860	€8760	Locarno (14x23cm-6x9in) s.i.d.19.X.60 W/C. 1-Apr-4 Christie's, Kensington #200/R est:5000-7000
£6787	$11335	€9909	Rondine (16x24cm-6x9in) s.i.d.1962 W/C prov. 24-Jun-3 Germann, Zurich #7/R est:13000-18000 (S.FR 15000)
£8667	$15513	€13000	Mont (15x22cm-6x9in) s.d.23.6.60 W/C prov. 14-May-4 Ketterer, Munich #254/R est:10000-12000

BISSIERE, Roger (1884-1964) French

£3289	$6053	€5000	Nature morte (27x46cm-11x18in) s. 28-Jun-4 Rossini, Paris #73/R est:3000-3500
£16000	$25440	€23200	Vers marminiac (33x41cm-13x16in) s.d.56 acrylic. 11-Sep-3 Christie's, Kensington #167/R est:6000-8000
£18000	$33120	€26280	Composition grise (65x54cm-26x21in) s.d.64 prov.exhib.lit. 25-Jun-4 Christie's, London #104/R est:20000-30000
£21277	$35532	€30000	Les anges sont partis (38x46cm-15x18in) s. 19-Jun-3 Millon & Associes, Paris #267/R est:4000-5000
£22368	$41158	€34000	Prairial (38x46cm-15x18in) s.d.1958 prov.exhib.lit. 27-Jun-4 Versailles Encheres #71/R est:40000-45000

Works on paper

£312	$521	€450	Paysanne au village (24x30cm-9x12in) lead pencil lit. 21-Oct-3 Artcurial Briest, Paris #48
£4000	$7280	€5840	Claire de lune (40x26cm-16x10in) s.d.52 s.i.d.1952 verso gouache graphite masonite prov.exhib. 6-Feb-4 Sotheby's, London #146/R est:4000-6000
£6500	$11830	€9490	Untitled (28x21cm-11x8in) wax oil pencil paper on board exec 1947 prov. 4-Feb-4 Sotheby's, Olympia #175/R est:2000-3000

BISSILL, George (1896-1973) British

£520	$946	€759	Harlequins (38x35cm-15x14in) s. 1-Jul-4 Christie's, Kensington #243
£800	$1272	€1168	Miners (57x66cm-22x26in) 10-Sep-3 Sotheby's, Olympia #216/R

BISSOLO, Pier Francesco (attrib) (c.1470-1554) Italian

£10000	$17000	€14600	Madonna and Child with Saint Peter (98x63cm-39x25in) s. panel prov.lit. 29-Oct-3 Christie's, London #90/R est:10000-20000

BISSON BROTHERS (19th C) French

Photographs

£3148	$5069	€4565	Suisse, vue des alpes (24x39cm-9x15in) bears i. albumen. 6-May-3 Koller, Geneva #28 est:6900-7300 (S.FR 6800)

BISSON, Edouard (1856-?) French

£2128	$3553	€3000	Jeune femme tenant une brassee de roses (70x47cm-28x19in) s.d.1898. 19-Jun-3 Millon & Associes, Paris #96 est:1200-1500

BISTAGNE, Paul (1850-1886) French

£1014	$1664	€1400	Bateaux dans le port (14x22cm-6x9in) s. panel. 11-May-3 Osenat, Fontainebleau #172/R

BISTOLFI, Leonardo (1859-1933) Italian

£1533	$2821	€2300	Landscape (17x24cm-7x9in) init. board. 8-Jun-4 Della Rocca, Turin #219/R est:1600-1800
£1831	$3168	€2600	Countryside (18x28cm-7x11in) s.i. board. 11-Dec-3 Christie's, Rome #103/R est:1500-2000
£2254	$3899	€3200	Landscape with stream (17x27cm-7x11in) init. board. 11-Dec-3 Christie's, Rome #104/R est:1000-1500
£2667	$4907	€4000	Rural landscape (17x27cm-7x11in) s. board. 14-Jun-4 Sant Agostino, Torino #282/R est:3000-3500

Sculpture

£1200	$2148	€1800	Victory (61cm-24in) init. pat bronze. 12-May-4 Stadion, Trieste #112/R est:1800-2200
£1206	$2013	€1700	Crucifixion (46x35cm-18x14in) init. bronze relief. 20-Oct-3 Sant Agostino, Torino #95/R est:2000
£2013	$3564	€3000	Lovers (25x66cm-10x26in) s. gesso relief. 1-May-4 Meeting Art, Vercelli #496 est:3000
£5556	$9444	€8000	Untitled (62x22x25cm-24x9x10in) init. bronze. 1-Nov-3 Meeting Art, Vercelli #65/R est:8000

BISTTRAM, Emil (1895-1976) American

£351	$650	€512	Abstract (61x46cm-24x18in) s.d.67 masonite. 17-Jan-4 Susanin's, Chicago #101/R
£1118	$1900	€1632	Untitled (33x23cm-13x9in) s.d.1939 oil encaustic on paper. 9-Nov-3 Wright, Chicago #242 est:1500-2000
£1543	$2500	€2237	Invertebrate visitors (91x81cm-36x32in) s. prov. 8-Aug-3 Barridorf, Portland #265/R est:2000-3000

£1553 $2500 €2267 Geometric abstract I (20x15cm-8x6in) s. paper. 20-Aug-3 James Julia, Fairfield #1207/R est:3000-5000
£1553 $2500 €2267 Geometric abstract II (20x15cm-8x6in) s. paper. 20-Aug-3 James Julia, Fairfield #1207a/R est:3000-5000
£2500 $4250 €3650 Untitled (25x20cm-10x8in) s.d.1939 oil encaustic on paper. 9-Nov-3 Wright, Chicago #244 est:2000-3000
£10169 $18000 €14847 Ranchos de Taos Church (67x90cm-26x35in) s.d.72. 28-Apr-4 Christie's, Los Angeles #46/R est:20000-30000
Works on paper
£326 $600 €476 Abstract composition (20x18cm-8x7in) s.d.1941 encaustic. 10-Jun-4 Swann Galleries, New York #26/R
£326 $600 €476 Abstract composition (20x18cm-8x7in) s.d.1944 encaustic. 10-Jun-4 Swann Galleries, New York #27/R
£412 $750 €602 Kachina doll (14x9cm-6x4in) s. pencil. 7-Feb-4 Sloans & Kenyon, Bethesda #267/R
£765 $1400 €1117 Abstract composition (20x15cm-8x6in) s.d.1939 W/C. 5-Jun-4 Treadway Gallery, Cincinnati #778/R est:2000-3000
£929 $1700 €1356 Abstract composition (18x23cm-7x9in) s.d.1940 W/C. 5-Jun-4 Treadway Gallery, Cincinnati #776/R est:2000-3000
£1087 $2000 €1587 Seascape (46x61cm-18x24in) s.d.1920 col pastel. 10-Jun-4 Swann Galleries, New York #25/R est:3000-5000
£1183 $2200 €1727 Geometric arrangement (25x20cm-10x8in) s.d.1937 W/C col pencil. 7-Mar-4 Treadway Gallery, Cincinnati #697/R est:2000-3000
£1250 $2200 €1825 Geometric abstraction (23x25cm-9x10in) s.d.1944 gouache. 23-May-4 Treadway Gallery, Cincinnati #732/R est:2000-3000
£3763 $7000 €5494 Untitled (46x30cm-18x12in) s. mixed media executed c.1941. 7-Mar-4 Treadway Gallery, Cincinnati #735/R est:3000-4000
£4630 $7500 €6714 Untitled (70x54cm-28x21in) s.d.39 mixed media. 8-Aug-3 Barridorf, Portland #264/R est:6000-9000

BITKER, Colette (1929-) Belgian
£642 $1213 €950 Femmes (130x88cm-51x35in) s. 17-Feb-4 Vanderkindere, Brussels #41
Works on paper
£338 $639 €500 Visages de femme (46x56cm-18x22in) s.d.73 W/C. 17-Feb-4 Vanderkindere, Brussels #43

BITRAN, Albert (1929-) French
£268 $475 €400 Composition (57x75cm-22x30in) s.d.71 paper on canvas. 29-Apr-4 David Kahn, Paris #205
£304 $544 €450 Roue (12x22cm-5x9in) s.d.69 s.i.d.verso. 4-May-4 Calmels Cohen, Paris #171
£793 $1467 €1150 Composition (63x50cm-25x20in) s. 16-Feb-4 Giraudeau, Tours #55
£909 $1564 €1300 Interieur - exterieur (73x60cm-29x24in) s.d.72 s.i.d.verso prov. 2-Dec-3 Sotheby's, Amsterdam #331/R est:1000-1500
Works on paper
£1544 $2840 €2300 Composition (175x190cm-69x75in) s.d.1971 s.d.verso mixed media paper on canvas. 24-Mar-4 Joron-Derem, Paris #169 est:2500-3000

BITTAR, Antoine (1957-) Canadian
£302 $556 €441 River crossing, Quebec (15x20cm-6x8in) s. s.i.d.2003 verso board prov. 9-Jun-4 Walker's, Ottawa #17/R (C.D 750)
£315 $536 €460 Street in Amsterdam (25x30cm-10x12in) s. i.verso board prov. 21-Nov-3 Walker's, Ottawa #115/R (C.D 700)
£400 $732 €584 Au centre Equestre, Bromont (15x20cm-6x8in) s. board painted 1990. 1-Jun-4 Joyner Waddington, Toronto #274/R (C.D 1000)
£405 $689 €591 Au printemps (25x20cm-10x8in) s. s.i.verso board. 27-Nov-3 Heffel, Vancouver #72/R (C.D 900)
£428 $727 €625 Janitzio, Mexico (41x51cm-16x20in) s. s.i.d.1994 verso prov. 21-Nov-3 Walker's, Ottawa #127/R (C.D 950)
£625 $1075 €913 Wine and Fruit (40x30cm-16x12in) s. panel painted 1998. 2-Dec-3 Joyner Waddington, Toronto #349/R (C.D 1400)
£856 $1455 €1250 Blue fog, Mtl (46x61cm-18x24in) s. s.i.d.1991 verso prov. 23-Nov-3 Levis, Calgary #13/R est:1800-2000 (C.D 1900)
£880 $1610 €1285 Railway crossing, Montreal (15x20cm-6x8in) s. board prov. 1-Jun-4 Joyner Waddington, Toronto #482 est:800-1200 (C.D 2200)
£1200 $2196 €1752 In Westmount (35x45cm-14x18in) s. 1-Jun-4 Joyner Waddington, Toronto #202/R est:1000-1200 (C.D 3000)
£1518 $2611 €2216 Winter mist - Quebec City (45x60cm-18x24in) s. prov. 2-Dec-3 Joyner Waddington, Toronto #182/R est:2500-3000 (C.D 3400)

BITTAR, Pierre (1934-) French
£435 $800 €635 Winter landscape (58x48cm-23x19in) s. 27-Jun-4 Hindman, Chicago #842/R
£652 $1200 €952 Winter landscape (38x48cm-15x19in) s. 27-Jun-4 Hindman, Chicago #843/R est:1200-1800
£722 $1300 €1054 Jardin Mediterranean (56x69cm-22x27in) s. prov. 25-Jan-4 Hindman, Chicago #1077/R est:1200-1600
£2111 $3800 €3082 Paris park scene (53x61cm-21x24in) s. prov. 25-Jan-4 Hindman, Chicago #1078/R est:1400-2000
£3552 $6500 €5328 Indian river fishing scene (41x74cm-16x29in) 9-Jul-4 Du Mouchelle, Detroit #2003/R est:2500-3500

BITTER, Ary (1883-1960) French
Sculpture
£1422 $2375 €2062 Petit faune aux deux biches (24x91cm-9x36in) s. i. verso silver pat.bronze Cast.Susse freres loiteurs Paris. 23-Jun-3 Philippe Schuler, Zurich #3111/R est:4000-6000 (S.FR 3100)
£2200 $4004 €3300 Nude female carrying fawn with doe by her side (42x46cm-17x18in) i. silver pat bronze. 20-Jun-4 Wilkinson, Doncaster #163 est:2000-3000
£2958 $4910 €4200 Combat d'elephants (19x49x12cm-7x19x5in) green pat bronze marble socle. 13-Jun-3 Ferri, Paris #175/R est:2000-2500
£5862 $9731 €8500 Deux biches a la fontaine (24x92cm-9x36in) s.st.f.Susse brown pat bronze. 2-Oct-3 Sotheby's, Paris #7/R est:7500
£6643 $11294 €9500 Elephants. s. pat bronze Cast Susse. 25-Nov-3 Millon & Associes, Paris #12/R est:7000-8000
£7000 $12740 €10500 Elephant (26x20cm-10x8in) s. grey green pat bronze ivory wooden base two Cast Susse. 29-Jun-4 Millon & Associes, Paris #26/R est:8000-10000
£7200 $12960 €10512 Elephants (28x31cm-11x12in) s.st.f.Susse brown pat bronze wood book-ends pair. 21-Apr-4 Sotheby's, London #75/R est:5000-7000
£9000 $16290 €13500 Elephants. s.st.f.Susse pat bronze pair. 1-Apr-4 Millon & Associes, Paris #5/R est:7000-8000

BITTER, Karl Theodore Francis (1867-1915) American/Austrian
Sculpture
£4865 $9000 €7103 Allegorical plaque (55x99cm-22x39in) s.d.1899 weathered pat bronze lit. 11-Mar-4 Christie's, Rockefeller NY #30/R est:7000-10000

BITTER, Theo (1916-1994) Dutch
£336 $577 €480 Still life of fruit (17x30cm-7x12in) s. silk. 8-Dec-3 Glerum, Amsterdam #222/R
£559 $962 €800 Still life (60x45cm-24x18in) s. 8-Dec-3 Glerum, Amsterdam #100/R
£671 $1242 €1000 Still life with apples (40x50cm-16x20in) s. 15-Mar-4 Sotheby's, Amsterdam #215/R est:1000-1500
£1027 $1747 €1500 Spanish man (130x65cm-51x26in) s.d.58. 5-Nov-3 Vendue Huis, Gravenhage #447/R est:1800-2200
£2000 $3680 €3000 Untitled (101x101cm-40x40in) s. s.i.stretcher. 9-Jun-4 Christie's, Amsterdam #132/R est:4000-6000
£2319 $3803 €3200 The interior (190x45cm-75x18in) s. s.d.56 on stretcher i.verso. 27-May-3 Sotheby's, Amsterdam #567/R est:1800-2500
Works on paper
£274 $466 €400 Folklore Festival, Vitesse Station Arnhem (26x20cm-10x8in) s. collage gouache. 5-Nov-3 Vendue Huis, Gravenhage #445/R
£1200 $2196 €1800 Three small tables (90x110cm-35x43in) s.d.91 mixed media. 7-Jun-4 Glerum, Amsterdam #250/R est:2000-3000

BITTNER, Della A (20th C) American
£380 $700 €570 Landscape with barns (41x51cm-16x20in) s. board. 11-Jun-4 David Rago, Lambertville #214/R

BIVA, Henri (1848-1928) French
£2467 $4514 €3700 Bouquet de roses (66x54cm-26x21in) s. 6-Jun-4 Osenat, Fontainebleau #81/R est:3000-3500
£3800 $7030 €5548 Lake scene (60x73cm-24x29in) s. 14-Jul-4 Sotheby's, Olympia #282/R est:2500-3500

BIVA, Paul (1851-1900) French
£1500 $2655 €2190 Still life of roses in a cut glass bowl (54x73cm-21x29in) s. 29-Apr-4 Christie's, Kensington #191/R est:600-800

BIVEL, Fernand Achille Lucien (1888-1950) French
Works on paper
£347 $638 €520 Parc a l'anglaise (20x37cm-8x15in) s. gouache. 9-Jun-4 Beaussant & Lefèvre, Paris #111

BIXBEE, William Johnson (1850-1921) American
£759 $1200 €1108 Coastal scene (30x41cm-12x16in) s. 7-Sep-3 Treadway Gallery, Cincinnati #669/R

BIZANZIO, Andrea (1918-1994) Italian
Works on paper
£1259 $2140 €1800 Composition (70x50cm-28x20in) mixed media paper on canvas exec.1950 prov.exhib. 24-Nov-3 Christie's, Milan #261 est:1000-1500

BIZEMONT-PRUNELE, Andre (1752-1837) French
Works on paper
£1600 $2944 €2400 Constantinople and Hagia Sophia (45x64cm-18x25in) s.d.1797 Indian ink W/C over graphite. 11-Jun-4 Hauswedell & Nolte, Hamburg #928/R est:1000
£3867 $7115 €5800 Hagia Sophia, Constantinople and Bosphorus (44x64cm-17x25in) s.d.1797 Indian ink W/C over graphite. 11-Jun-4 Hauswedell & Nolte, Hamburg #927/R est:1200

BIZER, Emil (1881-1957) German
£1277 $2068 €1800 Field flowers in brown ceramic vase (61x48cm-24x19in) s. s. verso panel lit. 23-May-3 Karlheinz Kaupp, Staufen #1809 est:1800

BJERG, Johannes C (1886-1955) Danish
Sculpture
£2076 $3819 €3031 The bird has flown - female figure (61cm-24in) s.d.43 pat.bronze Cast Rasmussen incl.granite base. 29-Mar-4 Rasmussen, Copenhagen #527/R est:25000-30000 (D.KR 23000)

BJERKE-PETERSEN, Vilhelm (1909-1957) Danish
£332 $564 €485 Coastal landscape (28x36cm-11x14in) mono.d.56. 10-Nov-3 Rasmussen, Vejle #614/R (D.KR 3600)
£595 $1083 €869 The old man in town by the fjord (92x74cm-36x29in) init.d.43/15. 7-Feb-4 Rasmussen, Havnen #4202/R (D.KR 6500)
£642 $1091 €937 The light road (24x33cm-9x13in) init.d.49. 5-Nov-3 AB Stockholms Auktionsverk #1136/R (S.KR 8500)
£680 $1156 €993 Untitled (22x27cm-9x11in) init.d.48 i.verso. 5-Nov-3 AB Stockholms Auktionsverk #1138/R (S.KR 9000)
£733 $1297 €1070 Surrealistic landscape (55x47cm-22x19in) init. 27-Apr-4 AB Stockholms Auktionsverk #1208/R (S.KR 10000)
£798 $1436 €1165 Ether wave (66x81cm-26x32in) s.d.46 panel. 26-Apr-4 Bukowskis, Stockholm #259/R (S.KR 11000)
£806 $1289 €1169 Portrait of the artist Bjarne Rise (80x66cm-31x26in) mono.d.28 exhib. 17-Sep-3 Kunsthallen, Copenhagen #74 (D.KR 8500)
£887 $1588 €1295 Composition with female figures (65x80cm-26x31in) mono.d.45. 28-May-4 Uppsala Auktionskammare, Uppsala #306/R (S.KR 12000)

£945 $1692 €1380 De tout s'avise a qui pain faut (82x65cm-32x26in) s.i.d.37. 12-Jan-4 Rasmussen, Vejle #638 (D.KR 10000)
£1026 $1815 €1498 Surrealistic landscape (46x54cm-18x21in) init.d.45 panel. 27-Apr-4 AB Stockholms Auktionsverk #1171/R (S.KR 14000)
£1038 $1910 €1515 Double movement - Abstract composition (33x41cm-13x16in) init.d.52. 29-Mar-4 Rasmussen, Copenhagen #334/R (D.KR 11500)
£1043 $1668 €1512 Harbour scene (66x73cm-26x29in) mono.d.30. 17-Sep-3 Kunsthallen, Copenhagen #30/R (D.KR 11000)
£1099 $1945 €1605 Flowers against black background (54x65cm-21x26in) s.d.46 panel. 27-Apr-4 AB Stockholms Auktionsverk #1183/R est:12000-15000 (S.KR 15000)
£1245 $2204 €1818 Composition (33x41cm-13x16in) init.d.50. 27-Apr-4 AB Stockholms Auktionsverk #1169/R est:10000-15000 (S.KR 17000)
£1305 $2350 €1905 Woman and birds (46x38cm-18x15in) init.d.45 panel prov. 26-Apr-4 Bukowskis, Stockholm #260/R est:8000-10000 (S.KR 18000)
£1319 $2334 €1926 Three shadows (46x55cm-18x22in) init.d.45 panel. 27-Apr-4 AB Stockholms Auktionsverk #1170/R est:20000-25000 (S.KR 18000)
£1557 $2833 €2273 Composition with butterfly (61x46cm-24x18in) init. 7-Feb-4 Rasmussen, Havnen #4193 est:5000 (D.KR 17000)
£1813 $3263 €2647 Surrealistic composition (50x61cm-20x24in) init.d.48. 26-Apr-4 Bukowskis, Stockholm #257/R est:25000-30000 (S.KR 25000)
£2015 $3667 €2942 Surrealistic composition with figures (54x73cm-21x29in) init.d.39. 7-Feb-4 Rasmussen, Havnen #4204/R est:10000 (D.KR 22000)
£3938 $7167 €5749 Lyrical materialisation (70x60cm-28x24in) init.d.37 lit. 7-Feb-4 Rasmussen, Havnen #4206/R est:5000-7000 (D.KR 43000)

Works on paper
£290 $522 €423 Towards universe and eternity - Einstein (32x25cm-13x10in) s.i.d.2 nov.47 collage. 26-Apr-4 Bukowskis, Stockholm #261/R (S.KR 4000)
£355 $561 €515 Surrealistic composition (29x45cm-11x18in) init.d.23-2-34 Indian ink. 3-Sep-3 Museumsbygningen, Copenhagen #57/R (D.KR 3800)
£561 $886 €813 Abstract surrealistic composition (27x37cm-11x15in) Indian ink gouache pencil two exec.c.1933. 3-Sep-3 Museumsbygningen, Copenhagen #61/R (D.KR 6000)

BJERRE, Niels (1864-1942) Danish
£361 $667 €527 Taakjaers farm, Sonderlyngvig (55x78cm-22x31in) init.d.1925. 15-Mar-4 Rasmussen, Vejle #679/R (D.KR 4000)
£553 $940 €807 Snow between houses and fences (45x65cm-18x26in) init.d.1937. 10-Nov-3 Rasmussen, Vejle #623/R (D.KR 6000)
£825 $1319 €1196 Landscape from Bovbjerg in evening glow (57x75cm-22x30in) init.d.1932 exhib. 17-Sep-3 Kunsthallen, Copenhagen #230/R (D.KR 8700)
£1444 $2657 €2108 Sunset over Bovbjerg houses (73x78cm-29x31in) init.d.1939 prov. 29-Mar-4 Rasmussen, Copenhagen #574/R est:12000-15000 (D.KR 16000)

BJERTNAES, Sverre Koren (1976-) Norwegian
£2904 $4849 €4240 Signe (180x90cm-71x35in) s. 13-Oct-3 Blomqvist, Oslo #343/R est:30000-35000 (N.KR 34000)

BJORCK, Oscar (1860-1929) Swedish
£1077 $1852 €1572 Portrait of the artist Gerda Rydberg (30x22cm-12x9in) s. panel. 3-Dec-3 AB Stockholms Auktionsverk #2309/R (S.KR 14000)
£1154 $1985 €1685 Still life of flowers and Oriental figurine (78x46cm-31x18in) s. 3-Dec-3 AB Stockholms Auktionsverk #2524/R est:15000-20000 (S.KR 15000)
£1444 $2700 €2108 Portrait of the artist Wilhelm Xylander (34x26cm-13x10in) s.i.d.1884 panel prov. 25-Feb-4 Museumsbygningen, Copenhagen #194/R est:15000-18000 (D.KR 16000)
£1848 $3307 €2698 Portrait of Zoia (80x64cm-31x25in) i.verso. 25-May-4 Bukowskis, Stockholm #185/R est:30000-40000 (S.KR 25000)
£13846 $23815 €20215 Skagen fishermen smoking pipes (112x86cm-44x34in) s.d.1889. 2-Dec-3 Bukowskis, Stockholm #118/R est:150000-175000 (S.KR 180000)

BJORK, Jakob (attrib) (1726-1793) Swedish
£4154 $7145 €6065 Portrait of Jean Fredrick Bedoire (69x53cm-27x21in) 7-Dec-3 Uppsala Auktionskammare, Uppsala #43/R est:25000-30000 (S.KR 54000)

BJORK, Kurt (1938-) Finnish
£361 $603 €520 Winter landscape with elks (55x74cm-22x29in) s.d.84. 26-Oct-3 Bukowskis, Helsinki #298/R
£1111 $1856 €1600 The eagle's nest (90x123cm-35x48in) s.d.83-84. 26-Oct-3 Bukowskis, Helsinki #299/R est:700

BJORN, Christian Aleth (1859-1945) Danish
£748 $1362 €1100 View of Antwerp harbour (36x56cm-14x22in) s.d.1890. 3-Feb-4 Christie's, Amsterdam #235/R est:1500-2000

BJORN, Emil (1864-?) American
£295 $470 €431 Landscape with flowing river (33x48cm-13x19in) s. 12-Sep-3 Aspire, Cleveland #72

BJORNSSON, T (20th C) Danish?
Works on paper
£395 $672 €577 Mountain landscape, Iceland (50x64cm-20x25in) s. W/C. 26-Nov-3 Kunsthallen, Copenhagen #330 (D.KR 4200)

BJULF, Soren Christian (1890-1958) Danish
£359 $611 €524 Fisherwomen at Gammel Strand (65x54cm-26x21in) s. 10-Nov-3 Rasmussen, Vejle #433/R (D.KR 3900)
£373 $679 €560 Fisherwomen at Gammel Strand (59x53cm-23x21in) s. 19-Jun-4 Rasmussen, Havnen #2133 (D.KR 4200)
£387 $658 €565 Fisherwomen at Gammel Strand (52x57cm-20x22in) s,. 10-Nov-3 Rasmussen, Vejle #432/R (D.KR 4200)
£412 $750 €602 Fisherwomen at Gammel Strand (65x55cm-26x22in) s. 7-Feb-4 Rasmussen, Havnen #2007/R (D.KR 4500)
£458 $833 €669 Fisherwomen at Gammel Strand (70x90cm-28x35in) s. 7-Feb-4 Rasmussen, Havnen #2143 (D.KR 5000)
£466 $839 €680 Fisherwomen at Gammel Strand (56x65cm-22x26in) s. 24-Apr-4 Rasmussen, Havnen #2058/R (D.KR 5200)
£489 $832 €714 Flower market with figures (55x45cm-22x18in) s. 29-Nov-3 Rasmussen, Havnen #2007/R (D.KR 5200)
£491 $880 €717 Flower sellers in Copenhagen (57x48cm-22x19in) s. 12-Jan-4 Rasmussen, Vejle #340/R (D.KR 5200)
£498 $806 €722 Postman visiting fisherwomen at Gammel Strand (56x47cm-22x19in) s. 4-Aug-3 Rasmussen, Vejle #245/R (D.KR 5200)
£565 $915 €819 Flower market at Johbro Plads (65x56cm-26x22in) s. 4-Aug-3 Rasmussen, Vejle #240/R (D.KR 5900)
£582 $1048 €850 The fisherwomen at Gammel Strand (80x100cm-31x39in) s. 24-Apr-4 Rasmussen, Havnen #2364 (D.KR 6500)
£623 $1133 €910 Fisherwomen at Gammel Strand (70x90cm-28x35in) s. 7-Feb-4 Rasmussen, Havnen #2094 (D.KR 6800)
£631 $1168 €921 Flower market, Nytorv (65x55cm-26x22in) s. 15-Mar-4 Rasmussen, Vejle #490/R (D.KR 7000)
£637 $1063 €930 Fisherwomen at Gammel Strand (68x95cm-27x37in) s. 25-Oct-3 Rasmussen, Havnen #2150/R (D.KR 6800)
£659 $1119 €962 Fisherwomen at Gammel Strand (70x95cm-28x37in) s. 29-Nov-3 Rasmussen, Havnen #2065/R (D.KR 7000)
£662 $1184 €967 From Gammel Strand with fisherwomen and postman (95x68cm-37x27in) s. prov. 12-Jan-4 Rasmussen, Vejle #38/R (D.KR 7000)
£664 $1062 €969 Summer's day with fisherwomen at Gammel Strand (83x101cm-33x40in) s. 22-Sep-3 Rasmussen, Vejle #23/R (D.KR 7000)
£664 $1128 €969 Flower sellers in Copenhagen (55x47cm-22x19in) s. 10-Nov-3 Rasmussen, Vejle #431/R (D.KR 7200)
£670 $1085 €972 Flower sellers at Hojbro Plads by Absalon statue (68x57cm-27x22in) s. 4-Aug-3 Rasmussen, Vejle #243/R (D.KR 7000)
£717 $1290 €1047 From Israel's Square with figures (55x47cm-22x19in) s. 24-Apr-4 Rasmussen, Havnen #2297 (D.KR 8000)
£718 $1163 €1041 Fishing harbour with boats and fishermen (90x90cm-35x35in) s. 4-Aug-3 Rasmussen, Vejle #241/R (D.KR 7500)
£766 $1240 €1111 Fishwives at Gammel Strand (58x67cm-23x26in) s. 4-Aug-3 Rasmussen, Vejle #242/R (D.KR 8000)
£800 $1456 €1200 The flower market at Hojbro Plads with policeman (55x50cm-22x20in) s. 19-Jun-4 Rasmussen, Havnen #2258/R (D.KR 9000)
£806 $1467 €1177 From the vegetable market at Israel's Square (91x70cm-36x28in) s. 7-Feb-4 Rasmussen, Havnen #2008/R (D.KR 8800)
£846 $1455 €1235 Fisherwomen at the old market, Copenhagen (75x90cm-30x35in) s.d.26. 3-Dec-3 AB Stockholms Auktionsverk #2603/R (S.KR 11000)
£846 $1455 €1235 Fisherwomen at the old market, Copenhagen (55x65cm-22x26in) s. 3-Dec-3 AB Stockholms Auktionsverk #2604/R (S.KR 11000)
£846 $1455 €1235 Fish market, Gammel Strand, Copenhagen (69x88cm-27x35in) s. 7-Dec-3 Uppsala Auktionskammare, Uppsala #166/R (S.KR 11000)
£851 $1532 €1242 The fisherwomen at Hojbro Plads (91x71cm-36x28in) s. 24-Apr-4 Rasmussen, Havnen #2356/R (D.KR 9500)
£894 $1519 €1305 The flower market at Israel's Square (57x52cm-22x20in) s. 29-Nov-3 Rasmussen, Havnen #2191/R (D.KR 9500)
£1007 $1833 €1470 Fisherwomen at Gammel Strand (70x98cm-28x39in) s. 7-Feb-4 Rasmussen, Havnen #2085/R (D.KR 11000)
£1075 $1935 €1570 Fisherwomen at Gammel Strand (70x91cm-28x36in) s. 24-Apr-4 Rasmussen, Havnen #2114/R est:8000 (D.KR 12000)
£1137 $1820 €1660 Figures buying flowers at Gronttorvet, Israels Plads (96x71cm-38x28in) s. 22-Sep-3 Rasmussen, Vejle #22/R est:12000 (D.KR 12000)
£1613 $2903 €2355 Figures at Hojbro Square (70x90cm-28x35in) s. 24-Apr-4 Rasmussen, Havnen #2347/R est:5000 (D.KR 18000)

BJULF, Soren Christian (attrib) (1890-1958) Danish
£281 $458 €410 Scene with fisherwomen (33x41cm-13x16in) s. 27-Sep-3 Rasmussen, Havnen #2126 (D.KR 3000)
£281 $469 €410 Young woman at fishmarket (41x44cm-16x17in) init. 25-Oct-3 Rasmussen, Havnen #2038 (D.KR 3000)
£300 $500 €438 Fisherwomen at Gammel Strand (43x50cm-17x20in) s. 25-Oct-3 Rasmussen, Havnen #2194 (D.KR 3200)
£339 $576 €495 Fisherwomen at Gammel Strand (47x39cm-19x15in) s. 29-Nov-3 Rasmussen, Havnen #2157y (D.KR 3600)
£357 $608 €521 Fisherwomen at Gammel Strand (56x47cm-22x19in) s. 29-Nov-3 Rasmussen, Havnen #2267 (D.KR 3800)
£376 $640 €549 Fisherwomen at Gammel Strand (56x65cm-22x26in) s. 29-Nov-3 Rasmussen, Havnen #2018/R (D.KR 4000)
£489 $832 €714 Fisherwomen at Gammel Strand (69x55cm-27x22in) s. 29-Nov-3 Rasmussen, Havnen #2055 (D.KR 5200)
£522 $819 €762 Summer's day at Gammel Strand (59x86cm-23x34in) s.d.21. 30-Aug-3 Rasmussen, Havnen #2205/R (D.KR 5600)
£841 $1329 €1219 Fisherwomen receiving the day's catch, Gammel Strand (84x110cm-33x43in) s.d.22. 2-Sep-3 Rasmussen, Copenhagen #1933/R (D.KR 9000)

BJURSTROM, Tor (1888-1966) Swedish
£711 $1279 €1067 Landscape with house (53x62cm-21x24in) s. i.verso. 25-Apr-4 Goteborg Auktionsverk, Sweden #360/R (S.KR 9800)
£718 $1220 €1048 Still life of tureen and candle holder (49x62cm-19x24in) st.sig. 4-Nov-3 Bukowskis, Stockholm #55/R (S.KR 9500)
£718 $1220 €1048 Still life of red books (57x40cm-22x16in) st.sig. 4-Nov-3 Bukowskis, Stockholm #56/R (S.KR 9500)
£765 $1231 €1117 Interior scene with woman knitting (80x64cm-31x25in) s. panel. 25-Aug-3 Lilla Bukowskis, Stockholm #98 (S.KR 10000)
£798 $1436 €1165 The avenue (61x80cm-24x31in) s. 26-Apr-4 Bukowskis, Stockholm #33/R (S.KR 11000)
£834 $1501 €1251 Still life of flowers (73x60cm-29x24in) s. exhib. 25-Apr-4 Goteborg Auktionsverk, Sweden #311/R (S.KR 11500)
£906 $1541 €1323 Still life of melon (45x65cm-18x26in) s. panel. 5-Nov-3 AB Stockholms Auktionsverk #867/R (S.KR 12000)
£943 $1631 €1377 Wet road (52x68cm-20x27in) s. 15-Dec-3 Lilla Bukowskis, Stockholm #610 (S.KR 12000)
£1088 $1958 €1632 Still life of blue jug (45x43cm-18x17in) s. panel. 25-Apr-4 Goteborg Auktionsverk, Sweden #324/R est:12000 (S.KR 15000)
£1511 $2568 €2206 Harbour scene (55x64cm-22x25in) s. panel. 5-Nov-3 AB Stockholms Auktionsverk #895/R est:15000-20000 (S.KR 20000)
£1700 $3043 €2482 Football players (60x70cm-24x28in) s. panel exhib. 28-May-4 Uppsala Auktionskammare, Uppsala #287/R est:25000-30000 (S.KR 23000)
£1905 $3371 €2781 Verdant landscape at dusk (60x73cm-24x29in) s. d.44 verso panel. 27-Apr-4 AB Stockholms Auktionsverk #894/R est:12000-15000 (S.KR 26000)
£1958 $3524 €2859 Nature morte (67x100cm-26x39in) st.sig. exhib.lit. 26-Apr-4 Bukowskis, Stockholm #148/R est:25000-30000 (S.KR 27000)
£3046 $5482 €4447 Bleket, Tjoern (49x53cm-19x21in) s. panel. 26-Apr-4 Bukowskis, Stockholm #113/R est:25000-30000 (S.KR 42000)
£3927 $6677 €5733 Boats in harbour (65x50cm-26x20in) s. 4-Nov-3 Bukowskis, Stockholm #111/R est:50000-55000 (S.KR 52000)
£4834 $8218 €7058 Fruit on a dish (61x74cm-24x29in) s. 4-Nov-3 Bukowskis, Stockholm #110/R est:40000-45000 (S.KR 64000)

Works on paper

£276	$496	€414	Coastal cliffs (48x63cm-19x25in) init. mixed media. 25-Apr-4 Goteborg Auktionsverk, Sweden #385/R (S.KR 3800)

BLAADEREN, Gerrit Willem van (1873-1935) Dutch

£433	$793	€650	Still life with apples and pears (16x32cm-6x13in) s. panel. 7-Jun-4 Glerum, Amsterdam #32/R
£902	$1471	€1300	View of a landscape, Bergen (21x35cm-8x14in) s.i.d.1904 paper on panel. 29-Sep-3 Sotheby's, Amsterdam #113
£1316	$2421	€2000	Mola (92x76cm-36x30in) s.d.1924 s.i.verso prov. 22-Jun-4 Christie's, Amsterdam #463/R est:2000-3000
£2667	$4907	€4000	Houses with orange trees (79x63cm-31x25in) s.d.1924 prov. 9-Jun-4 Christie's, Amsterdam #6/R est:2000-3000

BLAAS, Carl Theodor von (1886-1960) German

£268	$499	€400	Woman on sofa (45x36cm-18x14in) 5-Mar-4 Dorotheum, Salzburg #90/R
£268	$499	€400	Young man from Oblarn (57x42cm-22x17in) s.i. pastel. 5-Mar-4 Dorotheum, Salzburg #140/R
£369	$687	€550	Head of young woman in profile (49x37cm-19x15in) 5-Mar-4 Dorotheum, Salzburg #89/R
£671	$1248	€1000	Two women reading letter (59x66cm-23x26in) 5-Mar-4 Dorotheum, Salzburg #88/R

Works on paper

£268	$499	€400	Young woman (57x38cm-22x15in) s.i. pastel. 5-Mar-4 Dorotheum, Salzburg #126/R
£268	$499	€400	Brother and sister playing musical instruments (51x41cm-20x16in) pastel. 5-Mar-4 Dorotheum, Salzburg #91/R
£268	$499	€400	Young woman from Salzburg in traditional costume (54x43cm-21x17in) s.d.1946 pastel. 5-Mar-4 Dorotheum, Salzburg #96/R
£336	$624	€500	Venice (35x25cm-14x10in) pastel W/C. 5-Mar-4 Dorotheum, Salzburg #146/R
£336	$624	€500	Canal in Venice (35x25cm-14x10in) W/C. 5-Mar-4 Dorotheum, Salzburg #147/R
£1745	$3246	€2600	Tassilo von Furstenberg dressed as hunter with dead deer (70x50cm-28x20in) s.d.1934 pastel chl. 5-Mar-4 Dorotheum, Salzburg #94/R est:1600-2000
£1879	$3495	€2800	Herzog Ludwig Wilhelm in Bavaria dressed as hunter (53x44cm-21x17in) s.d.49. 5-Mar-4 Dorotheum, Salzburg #95/R est:2000-2600

BLAAS, Eugen von (1843-1932) Austrian

£310	$484	€450	Portrait of a girl (29x21cm-11x8in) s. 1-Aug-2 Joel, Victoria #153 est:2500-4500 (A.D 900)
£3000	$5370	€4380	Portrait of a Venetian lady (20x16cm-8x6in) s. panel double-sided. 26-May-4 Sotheby's, Olympia #256/R est:3000-5000
£3472	$5903	€5000	Venetian beauty (32x23cm-13x9in) s. panel. 28-Oct-3 Wiener Kunst Auktionen, Vienna #35/R est:5000-10000
£3497	$5944	€5000	Italian girl with headscarf (40x25cm-16x10in) s. 28-Nov-3 Wiener Kunst Auktionen, Vienna #434/R est:5000-10000
£3500	$5600	€5075	Portrait of a young girl (26x21cm-10x8in) s. panel. 18-Sep-3 Christie's, Kensington #163/R est:1800-2200
£3624	$6415	€5400	Street boy smoking (46x32cm-18x13in) s.d.1896 panel. 28-Apr-4 Schopman, Hamburg #456/R est:5600
£4698	$8409	€7000	Flower seller and three Venetian ladies (48x25cm-19x10in) s. oil paper. 27-May-4 Dorotheum, Vienna #59/R est:6500-7000
£5705	$10611	€8500	Three Venetian women (34x26cm-13x10in) bears sig. i. verso canvas on panel. 5-Mar-4 Dorotheum, Salzburg #33/R est:7200-9000
£10738	$19973	€16000	Three Venetian woman giggling over young man (33x46cm-13x18in) s.d.1884 panel. 5-Mar-4 Dorotheum, Salzburg #32/R est:20000-30000
£13889	$23611	€20000	Venetian beauty (3x26cm-1x10in) bears sig. panel. 28-Oct-3 Wiener Kunst Auktionen, Vienna #36/R est:7000-14000
£27778	$45278	€40000	Portrait of young Italian girl with roses (54x35cm-21x14in) s.d.1894. 25-Sep-3 Dr Fritz Nagel, Stuttgart #1329/R est:9000
£47059	$80000	€68706	La lavandiere (80x44cm-31x17in) s.d.1912 prov. 29-Oct-3 Christie's, Rockefeller NY #220/R est:50000-70000
£60000	$108000	€90000	Die neugierige Jungfer (80x44cm-31x17in) s.d.1909. 21-Apr-4 Christie's, Amsterdam #172/R est:25000-35000
£160000	$291200	€233600	The water carrier (75x44cm-30x17in) s.d.1908 prov. 15-Jun-4 Sotheby's, London #183/R est:60000-80000
£160000	$291200	€233600	After the quarrel (91x66cm-36x26in) s.d.1890. 17-Jun-4 Christie's, London #70/R est:120000-180000

Works on paper

£872	$1623	€1300	Venetian street (21x25cm-8x10in) s. chl W/C. 5-Mar-4 Dorotheum, Salzburg #34/R
£2333	$4293	€3500	Chatting (20x22cm-8x9in) s. W/C paper on cardboard. 10-Jun-4 Christie's, Rome #214/R est:2500-3500
£2333	$4293	€3500	Concert on the balcony (18x24cm-7x9in) s. W/C paper on cardboard. 10-Jun-4 Christie's, Rome #215/R est:2500-3500

BLAAS, Eugen von (attrib) (1843-1932) Austrian

£1316	$2421	€2000	Young girl with fish basket on beach (47x31cm-19x12in) s.d.1897 board. 24-Jun-4 Dr Fritz Nagel, Stuttgart #688/R est:4000

Works on paper

£336	$624	€500	Old Italian building in summer sun (34x30cm-13x12in) W/C. 5-Mar-4 Dorotheum, Salzburg #35/R

BLAAS, Franz (1955-) German

Works on paper

£367	$675	€550	Horse (30x40cm-12x16in) s. chl mixed media. 9-Jun-4 Dorotheum, Salzburg #824/R

BLAAS, Helene von (1895-1985) Austrian

Works on paper

£336	$624	€500	Two roses (23x18cm-9x7in) W/C. 5-Mar-4 Dorotheum, Salzburg #180/R

BLAAS, Julius von (1845-1922) Austrian

£302	$562	€450	Summer wood (44x32cm-17x13in) 5-Mar-4 Dorotheum, Salzburg #41/R
£336	$624	€500	Meadow plants (44x35cm-17x14in) oil tempera canvas on board. 5-Mar-4 Dorotheum, Salzburg #44/R
£336	$624	€500	Horse study (15x10cm-6x4in) s. oil pencil paper. 5-Mar-4 Dorotheum, Salzburg #66/R
£403	$749	€600	Mountain lake in southern Tyrol (37x51cm-15x20in) 5-Mar-4 Dorotheum, Salzburg #56/R
£436	$811	€650	Landscape (25x44cm-10x17in) s. 5-Mar-4 Dorotheum, Salzburg #54/R
£470	$874	€700	Horses in summer wood (49x40cm-19x16in) 5-Mar-4 Dorotheum, Salzburg #64/R
£503	$936	€750	Saddled brown horse (40x56cm-16x22in) 5-Mar-4 Dorotheum, Salzburg #71/R
£503	$936	€750	Choirboy (21x35cm-8x14in) s. canvas on board. 5-Mar-4 Dorotheum, Salzburg #77/R
£537	$999	€800	Grey horse in forest interior (41x54cm-16x21in) s. 5-Mar-4 Dorotheum, Salzburg #63/R
£604	$1123	€900	Farmstead interior (33x42cm-13x17in) s. 5-Mar-4 Dorotheum, Salzburg #52/R
£604	$1123	€900	Ferry (31x47cm-12x19in) canvas on board. 5-Mar-4 Dorotheum, Salzburg #60/R
£604	$1123	€900	Saddled brown horse in summer landscape (36x46cm-14x18in) 5-Mar-4 Dorotheum, Salzburg #70/R
£671	$1248	€1000	Meeting in the park - two figures on horseback (40x32cm-16x13in) panel. 5-Mar-4 Dorotheum, Salzburg #61/R
£671	$1248	€1000	White horse gallopping in landscape (45x70cm-18x28in) s. 5-Mar-4 Dorotheum, Salzburg #69/R
£671	$1248	€1000	Forest clearing in summer. Summer landscape (25x26cm-10x10in) two. 5-Mar-4 Dorotheum, Salzburg #43/R
£671	$1248	€1000	Portrait of sunlit horse (31x45cm-12x18in) s.d.1890. 5-Mar-4 Dorotheum, Salzburg #67/R
£671	$1248	€1000	Boy with dog (65x26cm-26x10in) 5-Mar-4 Dorotheum, Salzburg #78/R
£671	$1248	€1000	Seated dog - Mops Tommy (43x25cm-17x10in) i.d.06. 5-Mar-4 Dorotheum, Salzburg #79/R
£845	$1462	€1200	Boy from Yokahama, Japan. Girl from Jokohama, Japan (35x25cm-14x10in) s.d.1874 board two. 10-Dec-3 Dorotheum, Vienna #274/R
£872	$1623	€1300	Horse study (41x32cm-16x13in) 5-Mar-4 Dorotheum, Salzburg #68/R
£872	$1623	€1300	Girls and boys in traditional costume (22x42cm-9x17in) 5-Mar-4 Dorotheum, Salzburg #73/R
£940	$1748	€1400	Autumn landscape with castle (39x50cm-15x20in) 5-Mar-4 Dorotheum, Salzburg #48/R est:2400-3000
£986	$1706	€1400	Hotel boy, Grand Hotel. Derma Ranji Hindoo Koolie (35x25cm-14x10in) s.d.1873-4 board two. 10-Dec-3 Dorotheum, Vienna #273/R
£1007	$1872	€1500	Meadow plants (41x63cm-16x25in) s. 5-Mar-4 Dorotheum, Salzburg #45/R est:3000-3600
£1141	$2122	€1700	Saddled brown horse (40x46cm-16x18in) 5-Mar-4 Dorotheum, Salzburg #72/R est:1000-1500
£1342	$2510	€2000	Horse called Rahn (52x63cm-20x25in) s.i.d.1915. 24-Feb-4 Dorotheum, Vienna #226/R est:2200-2600
£1549	$2680	€2200	The Persian Mohammed Khan from Schiras. Lalla Cheba (35x25cm-14x10in) s.d.1873 board two. 10-Dec-3 Dorotheum, Vienna #272/R est:1300-1500
£1611	$2996	€2400	Summer garden (17x28cm-7x11in) board two. 5-Mar-4 Dorotheum, Salzburg #42/R est:2000-3000
£1745	$3246	€2600	Tyrolean horse market (140x85cm-55x33in) 5-Mar-4 Dorotheum, Salzburg #38/R est:5200-6000
£1879	$3495	€2800	Albrecht speaking to his troops after the battle of Custoza (51x98cm-20x39in) 5-Mar-4 Dorotheum, Salzburg #36/R est:4000-5000
£1972	$3411	€2800	Portrait sketch of der Singalese. Luis prenadu Gunowarden (36x25cm-14x10in) s.d.1873 board four. 10-Dec-3 Dorotheum, Vienna #271/R est:2000-2200
£2013	$3765	€3000	Race horse in stable (64x79cm-25x31in) s.d.1903. 24-Feb-4 Dorotheum, Vienna #224/R est:3000-3500
£6040	$10812	€9000	On the Lungau (115x176cm-45x69in) exhib. 27-May-4 Dorotheum, Vienna #202/R est:8000-10000
£14765	$26134	€22000	Kaiser Franz Joseph I on horseback (100x80cm-39x31in) s.d.1890. 29-Apr-4 Dorotheum, Vienna #88/R est:20000-25000

Works on paper

£302	$562	€450	Horse study (34x44cm-13x17in) pencil W/C. 5-Mar-4 Dorotheum, Salzburg #84/R
£317	$548	€450	Doblhoff, sitting, and Julius von Blaas his travelling-companion (46x30cm-18x12in) s.d.1874 chk htd white board. 10-Dec-3 Dorotheum, Vienna #268/R

BLAAS, Karl von (1815-1894) Austrian

£403	$749	€600	Campagna landscape (13x30cm-5x12in) paper on board. 5-Mar-4 Dorotheum, Salzburg #12/R
£503	$936	€750	Albanian mountains (18x29cm-7x11in) paper on board. 5-Mar-4 Dorotheum, Salzburg #9/R
£872	$1623	€1300	Interior courtyard of old Italian building with woman at fountain (27x42cm-11x17in) board. 5-Mar-4 Dorotheum, Salzburg #6/R
£940	$1748	€1400	Interior of Tyrolean farmstead kitchen (21x30cm-8x12in) s. 5-Mar-4 Dorotheum, Salzburg #5/R
£1000	$1670	€1460	Wounded soldier (47x96cm-19x38in) s.d.1860. 8-Oct-3 Christie's, Kensington #834/R est:1200-1800
£1342	$2497	€2000	Ruins in summer wood with walker resting (50x62cm-20x24in) 5-Mar-4 Dorotheum, Salzburg #2/R est:4000-5000
£2013	$3745	€3000	Expulsion of St Elisabeth (36x27cm-14x11in) 5-Mar-4 Dorotheum, Salzburg #4/R est:4000-5000
£4545	$7727	€6500	Drinker (40x32cm-16x13in) s.d.1874 panel. 24-Nov-3 Dorotheum, Vienna #99/R est:5000-5500

Works on paper

£369	$687	€550	Sketch of books and other items (22x28cm-9x11in) W/C. 5-Mar-4 Dorotheum, Salzburg #21/R
£369	$687	€550	Italian woman (20x21cm-8x8in) pencil. 5-Mar-4 Dorotheum, Salzburg #30/R
£470	$874	€700	Back view of seated bishop and priest (24x32cm-9x13in) oil tempera board. 5-Mar-4 Dorotheum, Salzburg #18/R
£503	$936	€750	Landscape near Rome with family returning home (29x42cm-11x17in) pencil W/C. 5-Mar-4 Dorotheum, Salzburg #11/R
£503	$936	€750	Study of man in knickerbockers (38x22cm-15x9in) mixed media. 5-Mar-4 Dorotheum, Salzburg #17/R
£570	$1061	€850	Italian house with figures (22x29cm-9x11in) W/C. 5-Mar-4 Dorotheum, Salzburg #10/R
£570	$1061	€850	Water nymph (22x33cm-9x13in) i. chk. 5-Mar-4 Dorotheum, Salzburg #16/R

£738 $1373 €1100 Street vendor (21x13cm-8x5in) s. W/C. 5-Mar-4 Dorotheum, Salzburg #20/R
£872 $1623 €1300 Landscape near Rome (23x39cm-9x15in) mixed media. 5-Mar-4 Dorotheum, Salzburg #8/R

BLAAS, Peter (1942-) German
Works on paper
£300 $552 €450 Head stone (37x24cm-15x9in) s.i. mixed media board. 9-Jun-4 Dorotheum, Salzburg #725/R

BLACHE, Christian (1838-1920) Danish
£269 $484 €393 From Skagen Strand with lighthouse in background (19x32cm-7x13in) s.i. 24-Apr-4 Rasmussen, Havnen #2257 (D.KR 3000)
£282 $480 €412 Tug boat in Copenhagen Harbour (16x25cm-6x10in) s. 29-Nov-3 Rasmussen, Havnen #2338 (D.KR 3000)
£290 $518 €423 Coastal landscape with children playing (27x43cm-11x17in) s.d.1866. 10-May-4 Rasmussen, Vejle #75 (D.KR 3200)
£295 $501 €431 A shipwreck near the coast, Gammel Skagen (20x35cm-8x14in) s. 10-Nov-3 Rasmussen, Vejle #304/R (D.KR 3200)
£316 $591 €461 Fjord landscape with sailing boat and bridge (27x52cm-11x20in) s. 25-Feb-4 Museumsbygningen, Copenhagen #186 (D.KR 3500)
£331 $592 €483 Seascape with sailing boat (16x25cm-6x10in) s. 12-Jan-4 Rasmussen, Vejle #18/R (D.KR 3500)
£343 $634 €501 Ship at Ommelshoved, Aero (16x24cm-6x9in) s.i.d.07. 15-Mar-4 Rasmussen, Vejle #154/R (D.KR 3800)
£345 $617 €504 Seascape (27x51cm-11x20in) s.d.68. 12-May-4 Dobiaschofsky, Bern #345/R (S.FR 800)
£415 $767 €606 Vessels on calm sea (20x35cm-8x14in) s.d.94. 15-Mar-4 Rasmussen, Vejle #156/R (D.KR 4600)
£435 $778 €635 Coastal landscape with bathing jetty (39x63cm-15x25in) s. 12-Jan-4 Rasmussen, Vejle #28/R (D.KR 4600)
£493 $887 €720 Portrait of a boy (35x19cm-14x7in) s. canvas on cardboard. 24-Apr-4 Rasmussen, Havnen #2305 (D.KR 5500)
£496 $928 €724 Seascape with sailing boats (30x49cm-12x19in) s.d.10/9 1910. 25-Feb-4 Kunsthallen, Copenhagen #527/R (D.KR 5500)
£515 $860 €752 Coastal landscape with breakers (40x61cm-16x24in) s.d.1919. 25-Oct-3 Rasmussen, Havnen #2510 (D.KR 5500)
£587 $1097 €857 Seascape with boats (39x63cm-15x25in) s.d.1911. 25-Feb-4 Kunsthallen, Copenhagen #530/R (D.KR 6500)
£609 $1016 €889 Coastal landscape from Kalundborg Fjord (39x62cm-15x24in) s.i.d.1913. 25-Oct-3 Rasmussen, Havnen #2519/R (D.KR 6500)
£633 $1134 €924 Coastal landscape with fishermen and sailing vessels (39x66cm-15x26in) s.d.1884. 10-May-4 Rasmussen, Vejle #351/R (D.KR 7000)
£672 $1210 €981 Harbour view with sailing vessels (20x32cm-8x13in) s.d.63 panel. 24-Apr-4 Rasmussen, Havnen #2295/R (D.KR 7500)
£719 $1337 €1050 Seascape with luxury yacht in fresh breeze (55x91cm-22x36in) s.d.1911. 2-Mar-4 Rasmussen, Copenhagen #1423/R (D.KR 8000)
£750 $1388 €1095 Shipping outside Snekkersten, Denmark (39x63cm-15x25in) s.i. 10-Feb-4 Bonhams, Knightsbridge #145/R
£895 $1638 €1307 Seascape with steamer and sailing vessels (39x63cm-15x25in) s.d.1909. 9-Jun-4 Rasmussen, Copenhagen #1835/R (D.KR 10000)
£948 $1517 €1384 Coastal landscape with large stones and boys bathing (47x79cm-19x31in) s.i.d.1905. 22-Sep-3 Rasmussen, Vejle #313/R (D.KR 10000)
£1236 $2250 €1805 Coastal landscape with sailing vessels (45x71cm-18x28in) s. 7-Feb-4 Rasmussen, Havnen #2239/R (D.KR 13500)
£1422 $2588 €2133 Seascape with many sailing vessels (61x99cm-24x39in) s.d.1912. 19-Jun-4 Rasmussen, Havnen #2221/R est:10000-15000 (D.KR 16000)
£2268 $3924 €3311 Fishermen landing the catch on the beach on a summer's day (47x79cm-19x31in) s.i.d.1904. 9-Dec-3 Rasmussen, Copenhagen #1484/R est:20000-30000 (D.KR 24000)
£6144 $10629 €8970 Seascape with two frigates (77x130cm-30x51in) s.d.1912 exhib. 9-Dec-3 Rasmussen, Copenhagen #1463/R est:40000-50000 (D.KR 65000)
Works on paper
£297 $550 €434 Harbour scene with lighthouse (30x48cm-12x19in) s.d.85 pastel. 24-Jan-4 Jeffery Burchard, Florida #111a/R

BLACHE, Theodor (1864-1910) German
£1581 $2830 €2308 Forest Scene (55x84cm-22x33in) s. 15-May-4 Christie's, Sydney #218/R est:2000-3000 (A.D 4000)

BLACK, Al (20th C) American
£269 $450 €393 Florida coastal scene with palms and gulls (61x91cm-24x36in) s. board. 19-Oct-3 Jeffery Burchard, Florida #112

BLACK, Andrew (1850-1916) British
£420 $722 €613 Pittenweem harbour (29x44cm-11x17in) s. 6-Dec-3 Shapes, Edinburgh #423
£550 $1029 €803 Painting the boat, St Monans. s. 22-Jul-4 Bonhams, Edinburgh #333
£700 $1302 €1022 Pushing off (61x91cm-24x36in) s.d.1880. 4-Mar-4 Christie's, Kensington #76/R
£3500 $5950 €5110 Waiting for the Ferry, The Broomilaw, Glasgow (76x127cm-30x50in) s.d.1880 prov. 30-Oct-3 Christie's, London #102/R est:4000-6000
Works on paper
£320 $592 €467 Goatfell, Arran, September 27 1910 (23x33cm-9x13in) s. W/C. 13-Feb-4 Keys, Aylsham #356

BLACK, Calvin (1903-1972) American
£556 $1000 €812 Dilley sister (41x51cm-16x20in) acrylic metal dinner tray. 24-Apr-4 Slotin Folk Art, Buford #352/R est:1000-3000

BLACK, Constance (20th C) American
£235 $425 €343 On the flats (36x28cm-14x11in) s. board. 3-Apr-4 Outer Cape Auctions, Provincetown #35/R
£243 $450 €355 Heritage museum (41x53cm-16x21in) s. 15-Feb-4 Outer Cape Auctions, Provincetown #78/R

BLACK, Dorrit (1891-1951) Australian
£1657 $3049 €2419 Queen Victoria markets (34x28cm-13x11in) s. canvasboard. 29-Mar-4 Goodman, Sydney #141/R est:4000-6000 (A.D 4060)
Prints
£3719 $6880 €5430 Black swan 1937 (23x32cm-9x13in) mono.i. num.18/50 colour linocut. 10-Mar-4 Deutscher-Menzies, Melbourne #75/R est:8000-12000 (A.D 9000)
Works on paper
£289 $535 €422 Still life (26x35cm-10x14in) s. i.verso W/C. 10-Mar-4 Deutscher-Menzies, Melbourne #460/R (A.D 700)
£1957 $3386 €2857 Untitled, landscape (27x36cm-11x14in) s. W/C double-sided prov. 10-Dec-3 Shapiro, Sydney #9/R est:2000-3000 (A.D 4600)
£7000 $12950 €10220 Tennis (40x40cm-16x16in) mono. gouache pencil pen ink board. 11-Mar-4 Christie's, Kensington #206/R est:4000-6000

BLACK, Francis (?-1939) British
£1278 $2250 €1866 Harbour scene with fishing boats beached in the foreground (61x93cm-24x37in) s.d.1892. 18-May-4 Bonhams & Butterfields, San Francisco #156/R est:3000-5000

BLACK, John (20th C) British
£8800 $16192 €12848 Eagle swooping for a fox (91x119cm-36x47in) s.d.86 canvas on board. 10-Jun-4 Christie's, Kensington #272/R est:4000-6000

BLACK, Laverne Nelson (1887-1938) American
£17442 $30000 €25465 Cowboy herding cattle (51x62cm-20x24in) s. 3-Dec-3 Sotheby's, New York #149/R est:25000-35000

BLACK, Montague (1889-?) British
Prints
£1758 $3200 €2567 White Star Line Europe to America (100x61cm-39x24in) col lithograph exec c.1928. 16-Jun-4 Christie's, Rockefeller NY #93/R est:3000-5000
£1923 $3500 €2808 French Line, Compagnie Generale Transatlantique (102x63cm-40x25in) company poster col lithograph exec c.1936. 16-Jun-4 Christie's, Rockefeller NY #206/R est:3000-5000

BLACK, Norman I (1883-?) British
£642 $1200 €963 House of cards (33x43cm-13x17in) s. 25-Jul-4 Bonhams & Butterfields, San Francisco #6139/R
£1118 $1900 €1632 Loading zone (41x91cm-16x36in) s. masonite. 9-Nov-3 Wright, Chicago #216 est:1500-2000

BLACK, Olive Parker (1868-1948) American
£1308 $2250 €1910 Blue hills (35x50cm-14x20in) s. 3-Dec-3 Doyle, New York #170/R est:4000-6000
£2235 $4000 €3263 Farm landscape in spring (41x61cm-16x24in) s. prov. 6-May-4 Shannon's, Milford #18/R est:3000-5000
£2245 $3750 €3278 Landscape with stream (25x30cm-10x12in) s. canvas board prov. 23-Oct-3 Shannon's, Milford #39/R est:1500-2500
£2395 $4000 €3497 Stream in a summer landscape (41x61cm-16x24in) s. prov. 23-Oct-3 Shannon's, Milford #268/R est:4000-6000
£2994 $5000 €4371 Cows on a path (41x61cm-16x24in) s. prov. 23-Oct-3 Shannon's, Milford #38/R est:3000-5000
£3198 $5500 €4669 Green fields (40x60cm-16x24in) s. 3-Dec-3 Doyle, New York #171/R est:3000-5000
£3352 $6000 €4894 Cattle grazing in spring pastures (61x76cm-24x30in) s. 14-May-4 Skinner, Boston #92/R est:4000-6000
£4192 $7000 €6120 Summer day (41x61cm-16x24in) s. prov. 23-Oct-3 Shannon's, Milford #27/R est:5000-7000
£5389 $9000 €7868 Cows grazing along the river (64x76cm-25x30in) s. 23-Oct-3 Shannon's, Milford #187/R est:5000-7000

BLACKADDER, Elizabeth (1931-) British
£1700 $2737 €2465 Sleeping black cat (71x96cm-28x38in) s.d.1976 s.i.verso. 21-Aug-3 Bonhams, Edinburgh #1182/R est:800-1200
£3000 $5160 €4380 Tuscan Church - Basilica (71x91cm-28x36in) s. s.i.overlap lit. 4-Dec-3 Bonhams, Edinburgh #29/R est:4000-6000
£4800 $8784 €7008 Dark hillside, Fife (65x74cm-26x29in) s. board prov. 8-Apr-4 Bonhams, Edinburgh #46/R est:2000-3000
£6400 $11264 €9344 Beach scene with figure (81x76cm-32x30in) s.d.1967 oil tempera panel. 18-May-4 Woolley & Wallis, Salisbury #67/R est:2500-3500
Works on paper
£950 $1767 €1387 Hearts and Butterflies (18x19cm-7x7in) s.d.1981 W/C. 6-Mar-4 Shapes, Edinburgh #416/R
£1100 $1870 €1606 Lilies in a vase (22x22cm-9x9in) s.d.1977 W/C. 2-Nov-3 Lots Road Auctions, London #331 est:400-600
£1100 $2013 €1606 Still life with Persian carpet (15x15cm-6x6in) s. W/C exhib. 28-Jul-4 Mallams, Oxford #282/R est:1000-1500
£1200 $1932 €1740 Zell, Mosele (42x52cm-17x20in) s.d.1969 i.verso pastel W/C. 21-Aug-3 Bonhams, Edinburgh #1054/R est:1000-1500
£1250 $2150 €1825 Roman Church (21x30cm-8x12in) s. ink gouache. 4-Dec-3 Bonhams, Edinburgh #94 est:400-600
£1500 $2385 €2190 Tuscan landscape (48x64cm-19x25in) s. W/C. 9-Sep-3 Gorringes, Lewes #1999/R est:1500-2000
£1600 $2720 €2336 Interior, morning (68x103cm-27x41in) s.d.1972 pencil W/C bodycol. exhib. 30-Oct-3 Christie's, London #231/R est:2500-3500
£1600 $2576 €2320 Border landscape (40x49cm-16x19in) s.d.1965 W/C. 21-Aug-3 Bonhams, Edinburgh #1222 est:1000-1500
£2200 $4092 €3212 Still life with stargazer lilies (21x21cm-8x8in) s.d.1977 pencil W/C. 4-Mar-4 Christie's, Kensington #215/R est:1500-2000
£2400 $4368 €3504 Cat on a yellow carpet (26x35cm-10x14in) s. W/C exhib. 1-Jul-4 Christie's, Kensington #305/R est:2000-3000
£3500 $6510 €5110 Dark pond (30x40cm-12x16in) s.d.1990 pencil W/C. 4-Mar-4 Christie's, Kensington #217/R est:1800-2500
£4000 $6800 €5840 Still life with Indian Parrot (63x94cm-25x37in) s.d.1978 pencil W/C prov. 30-Oct-3 Christie's, London #229/R est:4000-6000
£5000 $7850 €7250 Poppies (27x36cm-11x14in) s. W/C pencil. 27-Aug-3 Sotheby's, London #1158/R est:2000-3000
£7500 $12750 €10950 Irises (66x77cm-26x30in) s.d.1982 W/C prov. 30-Oct-3 Christie's, London #230/R est:6000-8000

£9000 $16290 €13140 Vanda orchids and moths. s.d.1998 W/C over pencil prov.exhib. 19-Apr-4 Sotheby's, London #143/R est:5000-7000
£16000 $29760 €23360 Anemones and rununculus (57x76cm-22x30in) s.d.1997 pencil W/C exhib. 4-Mar-4 Christie's, Kensington #218/R est:7000-10000

BLACKADDER, Elizabeth (attrib) (1931-) British
Works on paper
£480 $898 €701 Portrait of a Siamese cat (9x13cm-4x5in) W/C board. 25-Feb-4 Mallams, Oxford #149/R

BLACKBURN, Arthur (19/20th C) British
£750 $1403 €1095 The Strid, Bolton Abbey. The sand pit, Blubberhouses (26x35cm-10x14in) s. i.verso pair. 22-Jul-4 Tennants, Leyburn #847
£850 $1420 €1241 The Strid, Bolton Abbey. The Sand Pit, Blubberhouses (23x33cm-9x13in) s. pair. 8-Oct-3 Andrew Hartley, Ilkley #1164

BLACKBURN, David (1939-) British
Works on paper
£286 $521 €418 Landscape, The Olgas (49x70cm-19x28in) s.d.1972 i.verso W/C pastel. 16-Jun-4 Deutscher-Menzies, Melbourne #645 (A.D 750)

BLACKBURN, Morris (1902-1979) American
£511 $950 €746 Mission near Taos (30x41cm-12x16in) s. board. 3-Mar-4 Alderfer's, Hatfield #324/R est:800-1200
£516 $950 €753 Draggers (30x41cm-12x16in) s.d.1957 canvasboard. 25-Jun-4 Freeman, Philadelphia #123/R
Works on paper
£264 $475 €385 Dock scene (48x64cm-19x25in) s. gouache. 23-Jan-4 Freeman, Philadelphia #58/R
£484 $900 €707 Landscape with pueblo (56x76cm-22x30in) s. W/C. 3-Mar-4 Alderfer's, Hatfield #325 est:500-700
£778 $1300 €1136 Pigeon cove (53x76cm-21x30in) s. W/C exhib. 20-Jun-3 Freeman, Philadelphia #51/R

BLACKBURNE, Ernest R Ireland (1864-1947) British
£550 $968 €825 View of a woodland glade with silver birch on the bank of a pond (101x126cm-40x50in) s. i.verso. 19-May-4 Rupert Toovey, Partridge Green #104

BLACKER, Philip (1949-) British
Sculpture
£2000 $3460 €2920 Out on a hack (33x43cm-13x17in) s. bronze. 14-Dec-3 Desmond Judd, Cranbrook #628

BLACKHAM, Dorothy Isobel (1896-1975) Irish
£556 $906 €800 Snow on the playing fields, Donaghadee (42x32cm-17x13in) board. 23-Sep-3 De Veres Art Auctions, Dublin #189
£6338 $10965 €9000 Spring snow (63x39cm-25x15in) s. board. 10-Dec-3 Bonhams & James Adam, Dublin #81/R est:5000-7000
Works on paper
£413 $748 €620 Cottages in a mountain landscape (29x43cm-11x17in) s. pastel. 30-Mar-4 De Veres Art Auctions, Dublin #212/R

BLACKHAM, Warren (19th C) British
£820 $1533 €1197 The wayfarers (51x76cm-20x30in) s. 24-Feb-4 Bonhams, Knowle #91

BLACKLOCK, Thomas Bromley (1863-1903) British
£300 $501 €438 Thunder clouds (26x36cm-10x14in) s. s.i.verso board. 16-Oct-3 Lyon & Turnbull, Edinburgh #9
£372 $658 €543 View through to a farm (24x35cm-9x14in) oil paper card. 3-May-4 Lawson Menzies, Sydney #405 (A.D 900)
£450 $752 €657 A Kirkcudbright farm (26x36cm-10x14in) s.d.1902 board. 16-Oct-3 Bonhams, Edinburgh #162
£1240 $2194 €1810 Children hiding in a wood (41x56cm-16x22in) 3-May-4 Lawson Menzies, Sydney #407 est:3500-4500 (A.D 3000)
£2900 $5191 €4234 By the mill stream (46x35cm-18x14in) s.d.1900. 28-May-4 Lyon & Turnbull, Edinburgh #36/R est:1500-2000

BLACKLOCK, Thomas Bromley (attrib) (1863-1903) British
£760 $1391 €1140 Shoulder length portrait of a lady wearing a veil and brown coat (48x41cm-19x16in) s.d.93. 28-Jul-4 Mallams, Oxford #375/R

BLACKLOCK, William James (1815-1858) British
£8200 $13366 €11972 Lake District landscape with a mountain beyond, fisherman seated on rock (465x61cm-183x24in) s.d.1854. 24-Sep-3 Dreweatt Neate, Newbury #125/R est:2000-3000
Works on paper
£3300 $6039 €4818 On the waste of Cumberland (32x22cm-13x9in) W/C prov. 7-Jun-4 Cumbria Auction Rooms, Carlisle #224/R est:3000-5000

BLACKLOCK, William Kay (1872-?) British
£280 $510 €409 Sunset from Whitburn beach (16x24cm-6x9in) s. i. verso board. 29-Jun-4 Bonhams, Knowle #81
£380 $699 €555 River scene with two children fishing from a rustic bridge (26x22cm-10x9in) s. board. 23-Mar-4 Anderson & Garland, Newcastle #423
£500 $910 €730 Landscape with figures (13x20cm-5x8in) s. board. 16-Jun-4 Andrew Hartley, Ilkley #1065
£520 $884 €759 Two figures resting beside a lake (23x34cm-9x13in) s. indis d. canvasboard. 18-Nov-3 Bonhams, Leeds #224
£1765 $3000 €2577 Cattle watering in a stream (41x51cm-16x20in) s. 19-Nov-3 Bonhams & Butterfields, San Francisco #131/R
£5556 $10000 €8112 Portrait of Mrs Nellie Williams, the artist's wife (71x51cm-28x20in) s. prov. 22-Apr-4 Christie's, Rockefeller NY #72/R est:10000-15000
Works on paper
£250 $453 €365 Bedfordshire lace maker (24x30cm-9x12in) s. W/C. 4-Apr-4 Lots Road Auctions, London #362/R
£360 $587 €526 Fishing cobles in Whitby harbour (24x15cm-9x6in) s.d.96 W/C. 23-Sep-3 Anderson & Garland, Newcastle #306a
£430 $688 €628 An English castle (27x37cm-11x15in) s.d.1911 W/C. 18-Sep-3 Bonhams, Edinburgh #386
£520 $827 €754 Stooks in the harvest field (25x35cm-10x14in) s. W/C. 9-Sep-3 David Duggleby, Scarborough #14
£750 $1290 €1095 Cattle market, Sandwich (23x33cm-9x13in) pencil W/C. 3-Dec-3 Christie's, Kensington #160/R
£1450 $2509 €2117 Cottage interior with woman washing clothes. Woman feeding caged bird (25x23cm-10x9in) s. W/C pair. 9-Dec-3 Anderson & Garland, Newcastle #345/R est:1500-2500
£1600 $2608 €2336 A sunny corner, the artist's wife knitting (29x22cm-11x9in) s. W/C. 23-Sep-3 Anderson & Garland, Newcastle #306/R est:1000-1800
£1600 $2944 €2336 Morning news (22x29cm-9x11in) s. W/C. 8-Jun-4 Bonhams, New Bond Street #103/R est:1000-1500
£1800 $2952 €2628 Mending the net, cottage interior with fisherman before sunlit window (23x30cm-9x12in) s. W/C htd white. 29-May-3 Neales, Nottingham #722/R est:1500-2000
£3200 $5760 €4672 Interior scene with young lady seated on a sofa sewing (61x46cm-24x18in) s.d.1917 pencil W/C htd white. 21-Apr-4 Tennants, Leyburn #1010/R est:2000-3000

BLACKMAN, Charles (1928-) Australian
£496 $843 €744 Girl with vase (10x12cm-4x5in) s. card painted c.1957. 28-Oct-3 Goodman, Sydney #336/R (A.D 1200)
£697 $1101 €1018 Bouquet and tablecloth (50x40cm-20x16in) s. glass. 2-Sep-3 Deutscher-Menzies, Melbourne #279/R est:2000-4000 (A.D 1700)
£1157 $1967 €1689 Children and ferns (57x42cm-22x17in) s. acrylic canvas on paper. 29-Oct-3 Lawson Menzies, Sydney #110/R est:3000-4000 (A.D 2800)
£1191 $2026 €1739 Vase (48x39cm-19x15in) init.i.d.66 paper. 25-Nov-3 Christie's, Melbourne #188/R (A.D 2800)
£1619 $2607 €2364 Lychees, nature morte (73x96cm-29x38in) s. i.verso paper on board prov. 25-Aug-3 Sotheby's, Paddington #366/R est:4000-6000 (A.D 4000)
£1685 $3101 €2460 Dream (42x59cm-17x23in) s. board. 28-Jun-4 Australian Art Auctions, Sydney #138 (A.D 4500)
£1787 $3038 €2609 Restless seas (23x48cm-9x19in) s. board. 26-Nov-3 Deutscher-Menzies, Melbourne #152/R est:3000-4000 (A.D 4200)
£2479 $4587 €3619 Giant flowers, two figures and Genie (50x75cm-20x30in) i.verso oil synthetic polymer canvas on paper. 10-Mar-4 Deutscher-Menzies, Melbourne #372/R est:5000-7000 (A.D 6000)
£3099 $5733 €4525 Tryst (39x29cm-15x11in) s.d.58 oil paper on board. 10-Mar-4 Deutscher-Menzies, Melbourne #114/R est:8000-12000 (A.D 7500)
£3168 $5766 €4625 Children playing (39x49cm-15x19in) s. oil paper on board prov.exhib. 16-Jun-4 Deutscher-Menzies, Melbourne #29/R est:15000-20000 (A.D 8300)
£3306 $5851 €4827 Butterfly face (69x89cm-27x35in) s. prov. 3-May-4 Christie's, Melbourne #3/R est:8000-12000 (A.D 8000)
£6198 $11467 €9049 Crouching nude (121x102cm-48x40in) s. painted c.1970 prov. 10-Mar-4 Deutscher-Menzies, Melbourne #186/R est:18000-24000 (A.D 15000)
£6489 $11809 €9474 Barbara and flowers (70x54cm-28x21in) s.d.58 oil on glass. 16-Jun-4 Deutscher-Menzies, Melbourne #116/R est:18000-24000 (A.D 17000)
£6504 $10211 €9431 Cat and butterfly in garden (73x149cm-29x59in) s. oil paper on board. 26-Aug-3 Christie's, Sydney #50/R est:12000-15000 (A.D 16000)
£7317 $11488 €10610 Nude bending, reflections in a golden eye (47x72cm-19x28in) s.d.1966 oil papercanvas on board prov. 26-Aug-3 Christie's, Sydney #45/R est:18000-25000 (A.D 18000)
£7787 $12303 €11369 Blue paradise by night (47x72cm-19x28in) s. canvas board prov. 2-Sep-3 Deutscher-Menzies, Melbourne #88/R est:18000-24000 (A.D 19000)
£10121 $16296 €14777 Girls and Hibiscus (48x73cm-19x29in) canvas on board prov. 25-Aug-3 Sotheby's, Paddington #214/R est:25000-35000 (A.D 25000)
£10163 $18191 €14838 Christabel in a chair (100x88cm-39x35in) s. canvas on board painted c.1968prov. 4-May-4 Sotheby's, Melbourne #30/R est:28000-35000 (A.D 25000)
£11475 $18131 €16754 Man and windmill (99x134cm-39x53in) s. paper on board. 2-Sep-3 Deutscher-Menzies, Melbourne #85/R est:35000-45000 (A.D 28000)
£11475 $18131 €16754 Figures in the shadows - cat on roof (72x63cm-28x25in) bears sig. board. 2-Sep-3 Deutscher-Menzies, Melbourne #107/R est:30000-40000 (A.D 28000)
£11570 $21405 €16892 Face (76x61cm-30x24in) s.d.1965. 10-Mar-4 Deutscher-Menzies, Melbourne #72a/R est:15000-25000 (A.D 28000)
£11915 $20255 €17396 Nymphet (73x96cm-29x38in) s. paper on board prov. 26-Nov-3 Deutscher-Menzies, Melbourne #55/R est:24000-28000 (A.D 28000)
£12288 $20890 €17940 Seated girl and tall table (98x133cm-39x52in) s. paper on board prov. 24-Nov-3 Sotheby's, Melbourne #31/R est:30000-40000 (A.D 29000)
£14504 $26397 €21176 Reclining black nude (135x170cm-53x67in) s. prov. 16-Jun-4 Deutscher-Menzies, Melbourne #82/R est:40000-50000 (A.D 38000)
£14893 $25319 €21744 Sleeping Alice (48x73cm-19x29in) s. board prov. 26-Nov-3 Deutscher-Menzies, Melbourne #82/R est:30000-35000 (A.D 35000)
£15702 $29050 €22925 Flower cart (104x137cm-41x54in) s. oil paper on board prov. 10-Mar-4 Deutscher-Menzies, Melbourne #107/R est:42000-50000 (A.D 38000)
£16393 $25902 €23934 Christobel's dream (94x94cm-37x37in) s.d.1966 i. verso canvas on board. 2-Sep-3 Deutscher-Menzies, Melbourne #95/R est:40000-50000 (A.D 40000)
£16529 $29256 €24132 Three figures (136x150cm-54x59in) s. enamel paper on board prov. 3-May-4 Christie's, Melbourne #48/R est:40000-50000 (A.D 40000)
£19512 $30634 €28292 Schoolgirl (96x67cm-38x26in) s.d.1955 enamel board prov. 26-Aug-3 Christie's, Sydney #19/R est:45000-55000 (A.D 48000)
£19592 $36049 €28604 The picnic (62x75cm-24x30in) s.d.1954 board prov. 29-Mar-4 Goodman, Sydney #73/R est:50000-60000 (A.D 48000)
£20426 $34723 €29822 Barbara and Auguste (125x121cm-49x48in) s. oil enamel board exhib. 25-Nov-3 Christie's, Melbourne #73/R est:45000-65000 (A.D 48000)
£22358 $35102 €32419 Kiss (62x75cm-24x30in) s.d.1962 canvas on board prov. 26-Aug-3 Christie's, Sydney #97/R est:40000-60000 (A.D 55000)
£22541 $35614 €32910 Flower barrow, London (185x244cm-73x96in) s. prov. 2-Sep-3 Deutscher-Menzies, Melbourne #89/R est:65000-85000 (A.D 55000)
£32520 $51057 €47154 Going home (85x89cm-33x35in) s. oil enamel board prov. 26-Aug-3 Christie's, Sydney #35/R est:65000-85000 (A.D 80000)
£34043 $57872 €49703 Summer field (152x137cm-60x54in) indis.s. painted c.1965 prov. 26-Nov-3 Deutscher-Menzies, Melbourne #22/R est:65000-85000 (A.D 80000)
£34836 $55041 €50861 Alice (98x72cm-39x28in) s.i.d.1956 bears sig.d. verso card prov.exhib. 2-Sep-3 Deutscher-Menzies, Melbourne #61/R est:90000-120000 (A.D 85000)
£35569 $63669 €51931 Window light (151x130cm-59x51in) s. oil chl paper on composition painted 1965 prov.exhib.lit. 4-May-4 Sotheby's, Melbourne #33/R est:90000-120000 (A.D 87500)

£37076 $63030 €54131 Schoolgirl (75x99cm-30x39in) s. enamel composition board prov. 24-Nov-3 Sotheby's, Melbourne #35/R est:90000-120000 (A.D 87500)
£40984 $64754 €59837 White cat's garden in the afternoon (173x275cm-68x108in) s.d.1969 one two canvases prov.exhib. 2-Sep-3 Deutscher-Menzies, Melbourne #49/R est:12000-150000 (A.D 100000)

Works on paper
£341 $570 €494 School kids (41x30cm-16x12in) s. 30-Jun-3 Australian Art Auctions, Sydney #112 (A.D 850)
£344 $625 €502 Figures in the grove (27x35cm-11x14in) pen. 16-Jun-4 Deutscher-Menzies, Melbourne #369/R (A.D 900)
£386 $691 €564 Swimmer (19x23cm-7x9in) s. chl exec c.1952. 4-May-4 Sotheby's, Melbourne #245 (A.D 950)
£496 $917 €724 Diver (27x19cm-11x7in) s.d.26.10.86 ink. 10-Mar-4 Deutscher-Menzies, Melbourne #510/R est:1000-1500 (A.D 1200)
£630 $1084 €920 Cat. W/C gouache. 7-Dec-3 Joel, Victoria #29/R (A.D 1500)
£653 $1202 €953 Erotic scene, from reflections in a wine glass series (15x20cm-6x8in) s. W/C pen ink. 29-Mar-4 Goodman, Sydney #162/R (A.D 1600)
£683 $1140 €990 Hair (56x39cm-22x15in) s. W/C. 30-Jun-3 Australian Art Auctions, Sydney #76 (A.D 1700)
£766 $1302 €1118 Portrait of a girl (50x37cm-20x15in) s.d.51 ink wash. 26-Nov-3 Deutscher-Menzies, Melbourne #157/R est:2000-3000 (A.D 1800)
£816 $1502 €1191 Erotic scenes, from reflections in a wine glass series (20x15cm-8x6in) init.d.75 W/C pen ink pair. 29-Mar-4 Goodman, Sydney #163/R (A.D 2000)
£913 $1524 €1370 In the forest (59x44cm-23x17in) i. W/C. 27-Oct-3 Goodman, Sydney #150/R (A.D 2200)
£972 $1564 €1419 Rabbit clock (19x16cm-7x6in) s. plaster cardboard prov. 25-Aug-3 Sotheby's, Paddington #274/R est:2000-2500 (A.D 2400)
£1094 $2045 €1641 Butterfly (36x53cm-14x21in) init.d.22.10.85 W/C. 20-Jul-4 Goodman, Sydney #110/R est:2500-3500 (A.D 2800)
£1107 $2015 €1616 Little birds (47x61cm-19x24in) init.d.75 ink. 16-Jun-4 Deutscher-Menzies, Melbourne #344/R est:3500-5500 (A.D 2900)
£1157 $2048 €1689 Bundeena (36x48cm-14x19in) s.i.d.31.12.85 W/C ink prov. 3-May-4 Christie's, Melbourne #340/R est:3000-5000 (A.D 2800)
£1220 $1915 €1769 Message in the bottle (72x52cm-28x20in) s.i.d.2002 ink W/C. 26-Aug-3 Christie's, Sydney #285 est:3000-5000 (A.D 3000)
£1240 $2107 €1860 Nude on a horse (70x50cm-28x20in) s. ink W/C. 28-Oct-3 Goodman, Sydney #402/R est:3000-4000 (A.D 3000)
£1328 $2217 €1992 Self portrait (38x28cm-15x11in) s.i. W/C ink. 27-Oct-3 Goodman, Sydney #151/R est:2000-3000 (A.D 3200)
£1441 $2449 €2104 Untitled erotic study (28x38cm-11x15in) s. ink pastel gouache. 24-Nov-3 Sotheby's, Melbourne #218/R est:3000-5000 (A.D 3400)
£1532 $2604 €2237 Dancing girls (76x102cm-30x40in) chl canvas prov. 26-Nov-3 Deutscher-Menzies, Melbourne #166/R est:4000-6000 (A.D 3600)
£1545 $2425 €2240 Calling to angels (71x51cm-28x20in) s. W/C. 26-Aug-3 Christie's, Sydney #279/R est:3000-5000 (A.D 3800)
£1570 $2669 €2292 Portrait of Barnaby (55x44cm-22x17in) s. chl. 29-Oct-3 Lawson Menzies, Sydney #135/R est:2000-3000 (A.D 3800)
£1653 $2926 €2413 Still life, flowers (73x86cm-29x34in) s. gouache W/C. 3-May-4 Christie's, Melbourne #200/R est:4000-6000 (A.D 4000)
£1822 $2933 €2660 Alice (18x28cm-7x11in) ink gouache. 13-Oct-3 Joel, Victoria #301/R est:2000-3000 (A.D 4500)
£1908 $3473 €2786 Stained glass window (73x51cm-29x20in) s.d.9.8.70 synthetic polymer canvas on board prov. 16-Jun-4 Deutscher-Menzies, Melbourne #30/R est:6000-8000 (A.D 5000)
£2376 $4039 €3469 Japanese interior (40x61cm-16x24in) s. pen wash executed c.1982. 29-Oct-3 Lawson Menzies, Sydney #9/R est:3000-4000 (A.D 5750)
£2479 $4587 €3619 Woman and lake shadows, St Albans (52x75cm-20x30in) s.d.76 chl prov.exhib. 10-Mar-4 Deutscher-Menzies, Melbourne #214/R est:7000-10000 (A.D 6000)
£4255 $7234 €6212 Black Alley Kid (42x33cm-17x13in) s. gouache exec c.1951 prov.exhib. 26-Nov-3 Deutscher-Menzies, Melbourne #81/R est:12000-18000 (A.D 10000)
£6809 $11574 €9941 Alice at a table with flowers (72x96cm-28x38in) s. pastel. 26-Nov-3 Deutscher-Menzies, Melbourne #93/R est:14000-18000 (A.D 16000)
£8264 $15289 €12065 Venus with mirror (120x180cm-47x71in) s. pastel. 10-Mar-4 Deutscher-Menzies, Melbourne #115/R est:22000-28000 (A.D 20000)
£24291 $39109 €35465 Towelled girls (122x183cm-48x72in) s. i.d.1967 label verso synthetic polymer paint canvas diptych. 25-Aug-3 Sotheby's, Paddington #192/R est:60000-80000 (A.D 60000)

BLACKMAN, Walter (1847-1928) American
£269 $500 €393 Young woman in profile (46x38cm-18x15in) s. 5-Mar-4 Skinner, Boston #266/R
£838 $1500 €1223 Capri Girl (18x15cm-7x6in) 9-Jan-4 Du Mouchelle, Detroit #2004/R est:2500-3500

BLACKMORE, Arthur Edwards (1854-1921) British/American
£519 $950 €758 Woodland stream (46x30cm-18x12in) s.d.1891 panel. 5-Jun-4 Treadway Gallery, Cincinnati #641/R

BLACKSHAW, Basil (1932-) British
£1100 $1892 €1606 Seated figure (12x10cm-5x4in) s. board. 3-Dec-3 John Ross, Belfast #132 est:800-1000
£2100 $3444 €3066 County Antrim landscape (15x22cm-6x9in) s. board. 4-Jun-3 John Ross, Belfast #147a
£2222 $3622 €3200 Rostrevor hillside (32x25cm-13x10in) s. board prov. 23-Sep-3 De Veres Art Auctions, Dublin #196 est:3000-4000
£8500 $15555 €12410 Fraser Island I (152x132cm-60x52in) s.verso. 2-Jun-4 John Ross, Belfast #24 est:10000-12000
£12162 $22986 €18000 Seated nude (75x51cm-30x20in) s. canvasboard prov. 17-Feb-4 Whyte's, Dublin #76/R est:15000-20000
£14189 $26818 €21000 Orchard (36x61cm-14x24in) s.d.1956 prov.exhib. 17-Feb-4 Whyte's, Dublin #41/R est:15000-20000
£17606 $28169 €25000 Farm at Boardmills, County Down (41x51cm-16x20in) board prov. 16-Sep-3 Whyte's, Dublin #28/R est:15000-20000
£18792 $33638 €28000 Two standing figures - father and son (39x32cm-15x13in) s. board. 26-May-4 James Adam, Dublin #63/R est:25000-30000
£28000 $48160 €40880 Two horses exercising (50x61cm-20x24in) s. 3-Dec-3 John Ross, Belfast #149 est:18000-19000

Works on paper
£1316 $2421 €2000 Seated figure (11x11cm-4x4in) s. mixed media. 22-Jun-4 De Veres Art Auctions, Dublin #98/R est:2000-3000
£1600 $2752 €2336 Wild fowlers (20x25cm-8x10in) s. mixed media. 3-Dec-3 John Ross, Belfast #141 est:1200-1500
£2500 $4600 €3800 Female nude study (28x26cm-11x10in) s. ink wash prov. 22-Jun-4 De Veres Art Auctions, Dublin #97/R est:4000-5000
£2797 $4755 €4000 Seated girl (23x16cm-9x6in) s. col chk. 25-Nov-3 De Veres Art Auctions, Dublin #173/R est:3000-4000

BLACKSTONE, Harriet (1864-1939) American
£284 $475 €415 Self portrait (71x51cm-28x20in) board. 19-Jun-3 Shelley, Hendersonville #1206

BLACKTON, James Stuart (1875-1941) American
£1445 $2500 €2110 Driving (76x63cm-30x25in) s. i.stretcher prov. 10-Dec-3 Bonhams & Butterfields, San Francisco #6253/R est:3000-5000

BLACKWELL, Tom (1938-) American
£19461 $32500 €28413 Main Street, Keene, NH (243x152cm-96x60in) s.i.d.1973-1974 verso prov. 13-Nov-3 Sotheby's, New York #217/R est:15000-20000
£30872 $55262 €46000 Lexington and 59th (122x183cm-48x72in) s.i.d.1991 verso prov. 27-May-4 Sotheby's, Paris #266/R est:15000-20000

BLACKWOOD, David L (1941-) Canadian
Prints
£893 $1536 €1304 Passage (34x85cm-13x33in) s.i.d.1984 num.49/50 etching aquatint. 2-Dec-3 Joyner Waddington, Toronto #387 est:1500-2000 (C.D 2000)
£1339 $2277 €1955 Red Gate, Templeman, Bonavista Bay, Newfoundland (36x86cm-14x34in) s.i.d.1982 num.36/50 etching prov. 6-Nov-3 Heffel, Vancouver #17/R est:3000-4000 (C.D 3000)
£1626 $2911 €2374 Sick captain leaving (81x50cm-32x20in) s.d.1972 etching aquatint one of 25 lit. 27-May-4 Heffel, Vancouver #32/R est:3500-4500 (C.D 4000)
£1626 $2911 €2374 The burning of William Fiefield's forge (50x81cm-20x32in) s.i.d.1974 etching one of 25 prov.lit. 27-May-4 Heffel, Vancouver #124/R est:2500-3500 (C.D 4000)
£1626 $2911 €2374 Loss of the Flora S Nickerson (81x50cm-32x20in) s.i.d.1993 num.21/75 etching prov.lit. 27-May-4 Heffel, Vancouver #33/R est:3000-4000 (C.D 4000)
£1674 $2879 €2444 Captain Jesse Winsor home from the icefields (52x192cm-20x76in) s.i.d.1979/80 num.9/10 Ed 35 etching aquatint prov. 2-Dec-3 Joyner Waddington, Toronto #173/R est:4000-5000 (C.D 3750)
£1736 $3141 €2535 Brian and Martin Winsor (50x81cm-20x32in) s.i.d.1979 num. colour etching. 18-Apr-4 Levis, Calgary #8/R est:800-1000 (C.D 4200)
£2055 $3247 €3000 Loss of the Flora S. Nickerson (81x50cm-32x20in) s.i.d.1993 num.43/74 etching aquatint. 4-Sep-3 Heffel, Vancouver #4 est:3500-4500 (C.D 4500)
£2411 $4146 €3520 Sick Captain leaving (79x49cm-31x19in) s.i.d.1972 etching col aquatint. 2-Dec-3 Joyner Waddington, Toronto #153/R est:3000-4000 (C.D 5400)
£2679 $4607 €3911 SS Imogene leaving for the icefields (50x79cm-20x31in) s.i.d.1973 etching aquatint lit. 2-Dec-3 Joyner Waddington, Toronto #143/R est:3000-4000 (C.D 6000)
£6504 $11642 €9496 Fire down on the Labrador (81x50cm-32x20in) s.i.d.1980 num.6/10 etching one of 50 prov.lit. 27-May-4 Heffel, Vancouver #30/R est:13000-16000 (C.D 16000)

Works on paper
£357 $614 €521 Men from the studio (29x42cm-11x17in) s.d.1981 W/C prov. 2-Dec-3 Joyner Waddington, Toronto #432 (C.D 800)
£580 $998 €847 Wet Day, Bennetts Island (42x61cm-17x24in) s.d.1981 W/C prov. 2-Dec-3 Joyner Waddington, Toronto #454 (C.D 1300)
£691 $1237 €1009 The Reach, Wesleyville (44x62cm-17x24in) s. i.verso W/C prov. 6-May-4 Heffel, Vancouver #34/R (C.D 1700)

BLAGONAVROV, Fedor P (c.1885-1961) Russian
£503 $931 €750 Troika (38x46cm-15x18in) s. 15-Mar-4 Claude Boisgirard, Paris #15

BLAIKLEY, Alexander (1816-1903) British
Works on paper
£800 $1480 €1168 Portrait of Edith and Marion, daughters of Rev D B Cameron (63x49cm-25x19in) s. pastel prov. 9-Mar-4 Bonhams, New Bond Street #131/R

BLAINE, Mahlon (1894-1969) American
Works on paper
£749 $1400 €1094 Sorcerer turning woman into penguin (43x28cm-17x11in) init. crayon double-sided. 26-Feb-4 Illustration House, New York #21

BLAINE, Nell (1922-1996) American
£3514 $6500 €5130 Summer time, Saratoga (61x91cm-24x36in) s.d.61 i. verso. 13-Jul-4 Christie's, Rockefeller NY #28/R est:2000-3000
Works on paper
£604 $1100 €906 Reflections in Smith Cove (38x56cm-15x22in) s.d.1978 W/C. 16-Jun-4 Wolf's, New York #486581/R

BLAIR, Charles Henry (19th C) British
£800 $1328 €1168 Two kittens looking at a vase of flowers (25x35cm-10x14in) s. 1-Oct-3 Woolley & Wallis, Salisbury #227/R
£4400 $7964 €6424 Stand off. Lucky escape (68x51cm-27x20in) s.d.1901 pair. 31-Mar-4 Bonhams, Knightsbridge #40/R est:2000-3000

BLAIR, Gabriel (20th C) British
Works on paper
£280 $507 €409 Blackberry picking on a woodland path (35x26cm-14x10in) W/C. 2-Apr-4 Bracketts, Tunbridge Wells #418/R

BLAIR, John (1850-1934) British
Works on paper
£350 $550 €508 St. Cuthbert's and Edinburgh Castle (18x29cm-7x11in) s.i. pencil W/C. 28-Aug-3 Christie's, Kensington #416/R
£420 $676 €609 Spittal and Berwick (17x26cm-7x10in) s.i. W/C. 21-Aug-3 Bonhams, Edinburgh #1219
£620 $1141 €905 Interior at Lauder (37x52cm-15x20in) s.i.d.1892 W/C. 22-Jun-4 Bonhams, Knightsbridge #29/R
£650 $1118 €949 Edinburgh from Holyrood Park. From Samson's Ribs (18x26cm-7x10in) s.i. W/C pair. 4-Dec-3 Bonhams, Edinburgh #11
£660 $1214 €964 Horncliffe Mill (23x18cm-9x7in) s. W/C. 28-Jun-4 British Auctioneer #374/R
£1700 $3111 €2550 North Berwick from the west (18x26cm-7x10in) s.i. W/C. 12-Jul-4 Lyon & Turnbull, Edinburgh #422/R est:400-600

BLAIR, Philippa (1945-) New Zealander
£362 $587 €525 Yank (45x61cm-18x24in) s.d.1995. 31-Jul-3 International Art Centre, Auckland #139/R est:800-1200 (NZ.D 1000)
£372 $639 €543 Untitled (123x273cm-48x107in) s.d.1994 triptych. 7-Dec-3 International Art Centre, Auckland #212/R (NZ.D 1000)
£404 $756 €590 Sea movement (91x91cm-36x36in) s.d.1974 i.verso. 24-Feb-4 Peter Webb, Auckland #66/R (NZ.D 1100)
£1384 $2478 €2021 Kick start (195x157cm-77x62in) s.d.94 i.verso. 12-May-4 Dunbar Sloane, Wellington #139/R est:4000-6000 (NZ.D 4000)
Works on paper
£362 $587 €525 Metamorphis (60x84cm-24x33in) s.d.1988 pastel. 31-Jul-3 International Art Centre, Auckland #186/R est:1000-1500 (NZ.D 1000)
£376 $639 €549 Cock-a-doodle-do (83x59cm-33x23in) s. pastel. 27-Nov-3 International Art Centre, Auckland #175/R (NZ.D 1000)

BLAIRAT, Marcel (1849-?) French
Works on paper
£1064 $1777 €1500 Campement au bord de l'oued. La koubba sous le palmier (31x46cm-12x18in) s. W/C pair. 16-Jun-3 Gros & Delettrez, Paris #556 est:1600-2000

BLAIS, Jean Charles (1956-) French
£746 $1372 €1089 Gardeur (38x25cm-15x10in) s.d.82 verso acrylic pencil oil crayon prov. 23-Jun-4 Koller, Zurich #3131/R (S.FR 1700)
£1200 $2208 €1800 Untitled (95x75cm-37x30in) s.d.87 paint pastel collage paper prov. 11-Jun-4 Pierre Berge, Paris #70/R est:2000-3000
£1689 $3193 €2500 Sans titre (35x39cm-14x15in) s.d.1980 verso peinture torn poster prov. 21-Feb-4 Cornette de St.Cyr, Paris #249/R est:2500-3000
£3333 $6067 €5000 Russe en soldat (72x52cm-28x20in) s.i.d.1983 verso paint chk col crayon prov. 2-Jul-4 Binoche, Paris #4/R est:7000-8000
£6419 $11298 €9500 Les amoureux (178x198cm-70x78in) s.d.1993 verso acrylic chk board in three parts prov. 18-May-4 Tajan, Paris #128/R est:10000-12000
£7333 $13347 €11000 Tres decide (63x49cm-25x19in) s.i.d.83 verso paint chk crayon prov. 2-Jul-4 Binoche, Paris #3/R est:7000-8000
Sculpture
£2113 $3697 €3000 Full figure II (180x47x6cm-71x19x2in) s. num.4/8 verso painted aluminium exhib. 18-Dec-3 Cornette de St.Cyr, Paris #59/R est:4000-6000
Works on paper
£526 $968 €800 Untitled (20x14cm-8x6in) s.d.84 crayon dr. 27-Jun-4 Versailles Encheres #185/R
£833 $1533 €1216 Ami, tete (30x35cm-12x14in) s.d.83 verso wax crayon pastel. 23-Jun-4 Koller, Zurich #3132/R (S.FR 1900)
£1053 $1759 €1515 Sans titre (94x63cm-37x25in) s.d.28 3 88 ink collage prov. 21-Oct-3 Artcurial Briest, Paris #535/R est:2000-2500
£1074 $1922 €1600 Personnage dans un paysage (34x26cm-13x10in) s. pastel wash ink. 26-May-4 Christie's, Paris #107/R est:1200-1500
£1127 $1949 €1600 Untitled (87x63cm-34x25in) s. Chinese ink collage exec.1987 prov. 9-Dec-3 Artcurial Briest, Paris #580 est:1500-2000
£1333 $2427 €2000 Untitled (22x17cm-9x7in) d.86 s.verso collage pastel prov. 2-Jul-4 Binoche, Paris #2/R est:2000-3000
£1367 $2242 €1900 A table (41x29cm-16x11in) s.i.d. verso pastel W/C. 4-Jun-3 Ketterer, Hamburg #190/R est:1500-1800
£1810 $3077 €2643 Nature morte (95x95cm-37x37in) gouache collage prov. 25-Nov-3 Germann, Zurich #32/R est:5000-7000 (S.FR 4000)
£2000 $3600 €3000 Vence (90x70cm-35x28in) s.i. gouache W/C. 24-Apr-4 Cornette de St.Cyr, Paris #442 est:3500
£2431 $4059 €3500 Sans titre (59x62cm-23x24in) s.d.10.III.84 collage gouache prov. 25-Oct-3 Cornette de St.Cyr, Paris #597/R est:4000-5000
£2533 $4661 €3850 Untitled (64x83cm-25x33in) s.d.1985 gouache collage. 28-Jun-4 Joron-Derem, Paris #185/R est:4000-5000
£2606 $4560 €3700 Untitled (94x67cm-37x26in) s.d.2.87 collage paint pastel prov. 18-Dec-3 Cornette de St.Cyr, Paris #146/R est:4000-6000
£2917 $4813 €4200 La corde rouge (83x97cm-33x38in) s.d.08.06.86 gouache pastel. 2-Jul-3 Cornette de St.Cyr, Paris #158/R est:4500-5000
£3333 $5267 €4800 Untitled (62x77cm-24x30in) s.d.84 ink gouache pastel. 27-Apr-3 Versailles Encheres #143
£12000 $22200 €18000 Arbre bleu (283x77cm-111x30in) s. mixed media torn posters exec.1987 prov. 18-Jul-4 Sotheby's, Paris #268/R est:12000-15000

BLAISE, Saint Louis (20th C) Haitian
£1433 $2566 €2150 Le General Petion (25x19cm-10x7in) s.d.85 panel. 17-May-4 Rogeon, Paris #75/R

BLAKE, Benjamin (?-1830) British
£600 $1032 €876 Still life of pheasants, ducks, woodcock, eggs and lobster in a larder (26x31cm-10x12in) 3-Dec-3 Bonhams, Knightsbridge #103/R
£700 $1190 €1022 Game larder (25x20cm-10x8in) pair. 27-Nov-3 Christie's, Kensington #208/R
£700 $1260 €1022 Cottage interior with dead game beside a window and maid (43x60cm-17x24in) panel prov. 21-Apr-4 Tennants, Leyburn #1203

BLAKE, Benjamin (attrib) (?-1830) British
£900 $1611 €1314 Game in a larder. Fish and game in larder (20x25cm-8x10in) pair. 27-May-4 Christie's, Kensington #264/R
£1000 $1720 €1460 Still life with rabbit, grouse and partridge on a larder shelf (58x48cm-23x19in) 3-Dec-3 Neal & Fletcher, Woodbridge #334 est:600-800

BLAKE, Frederick Donald (1908-1997) British
£560 $969 €818 Autumn group. The contest (46x33cm-18x13in) s. oil card two. 11-Dec-3 Ewbank, Send #393
£600 $1038 €876 Winter landscape (58x89cm-23x35in) s. 11-Dec-3 Ewbank, Send #403

BLAKE, Leo (1887-1976) American
£523 $900 €764 Gloucester fishermen (25x30cm-10x12in) s. canvasboard painted c.1930. 7-Dec-3 Treadway Gallery, Cincinnati #614/R
£629 $1000 €918 Sunlit valley (26x31cm-10x12in) s. canvas on board. 12-Sep-3 Skinner, Boston #414/R

BLAKE, Peter (1932-) British
£16000 $27520 €23360 Gershwin's, An American in Paris, Rhapsody in Blue (45x51cm-18x20in) exhib. 2-Dec-3 Bonhams, New Bond Street #192/R est:6000-8000
Works on paper
£9800 $17836 €14308 African Queen (48x33cm-19x13in) s. backboard W/C collage mixed media prov. 1-Jul-4 Christie's, Kensington #195/R est:4000-6000
£10000 $18200 €14600 Society Bar (48x33cm-19x13in) W/C collage mixed media prov. 1-Jul-4 Christie's, Kensington #192/R est:4000-6000

BLAKE, Quentin (1932-) British
Works on paper
£750 $1298 €1095 Emily's insect (19x22cm-7x9in) s.d.1974 ink W/C. 11-Dec-3 Sotheby's, London #180
£1200 $2196 €1752 Parrot pen-man (30x38cm-12x15in) s. ink W/C. 8-Jul-4 Sotheby's, London #265/R est:200-300

BLAKE, Thomas C (20th C) British
£250 $400 €365 Mountain lake (61x76cm-24x30in) s. 19-Sep-3 Freeman, Philadelphia #184/R
£301 $475 €436 Landscape, sunset with marsh and mountains, possibly Scottish loch (58x89cm-23x35in) s. 8-Sep-3 Winter Associates, Plainville #172
£353 $650 €515 Landscape (58x89cm-23x35in) s. 27-Jun-4 Hindman, Chicago #819/R
£568 $1000 €829 Mountain landscape at Sunset (58x89cm-23x35in) s. 23-May-4 Hindman, Chicago #166/R est:1200-2400

BLAKE, W S (1748-1822) Australian?
Prints
£4959 $9174 €7240 View of the town of Sydney in the colony of New South Wales (24x41cm-9x16in) i. hand col aquatint. 10-Mar-4 Deutscher-Menzies, Melbourne #163/R est:10000-15000 (A.D 12000)

BLAKE, William (1757-1827) British
Prints
£2043 $3800 €2983 Chaucers Canterbury Pilgrims (35x95cm-14x37in) etching engraving drypoint. 2-Mar-4 Swann Galleries, New York #51/R est:2000-3000
£14000 $24080 €20440 Book of Job (38x27cm-15x11in) engravings album. 2-Dec-3 Christie's, London #6/R est:15000-20000
£30000 $54600 €43800 Man sweeping the interpreter's parlour (8x16cm-3x6in) white line metal cut prov.exhib.lit. 30-Jun-4 Christie's, London #5/R est:30000-50000
£1955307 $3500000 €2854748 The good and evil angels struggling for possession of a child (44x58cm-17x23in) monotype pen ink W/C gouache prov.exhib.lit. 5-May-4 Sotheby's, New York #5/R est:1000000-1500000
Works on paper
£13000 $22100 €18980 Judgement of Solomon (13x17cm-5x7in) pen ink W/C htd bodycol over pencil prov. 27-Nov-3 Sotheby's, London #235/R est:15000-20000

BLAKE, William (attrib) (1757-1827) British
Works on paper
£546 $1000 €797 Blake rising out of the flames (22x15cm-9x6in) pen brown ink. 29-Jan-4 Swann Galleries, New York #354/R
£638 $1034 €900 The birth of Venus (31x25cm-12x10in) mono.i. i. verso W/C lit. 23-May-3 Karlheinz Kaupp, Staufen #1686

BLAKELOCK, Ralph Albert (1847-1919) American
£755 $1200 €1102 Autumn landscape (23x25cm-9x10in) s. panel. 14-Sep-3 Susanin's, Chicago #6001/R
£2065 $3800 €3015 Woman by a river (10x15cm-4x6in) 10-Jun-4 Swann Galleries, New York #29/R est:1500-2500
£2235 $4000 €3353 Indian encampment (20x28cm-8x11in) s. panel. 16-May-4 Abell, Los Angeles #159
£2486 $4500 €3630 Landscape (20x30cm-8x12in) panel prov. 31-Mar-4 Sotheby's, New York #93/R est:3000-5000
£3059 $5200 €4466 Winter landscape (12x17cm-5x7in) prov. 30-Oct-3 Phillips, New York #27/R est:5000-7000
£3261 $6000 €4761 Landscape (41x61cm-16x24in) s. 28-Mar-4 Carlsen Gallery, Greenville #198/R
£3757 $6950 €5636 Summer moonlight (46x33cm-18x13in) s. prov. 14-Jul-4 American Auctioneer #490222/R est:4000-6000
£3867 $7000 €5646 Three figures, campfire, and tents (20x30cm-8x12in) indis.sig. panel prov. 31-Mar-4 Sotheby's, New York #89/R est:7000-10000
£4412 $7500 €6442 Sunshine in the woods (76x38cm-30x15in) s.d.1876 prov. 30-Oct-3 Phillips, New York #16/R est:6000-8000
£4469 $8000 €6525 Stormy sunset (25x30cm-10x12in) s. prov. 26-May-4 Doyle, New York #7/R est:6000-8000
£4749 $8500 €6934 Indian encampment (30x56cm-12x22in) s. panel. 26-May-4 Doyle, New York #6/R est:7000-9000

£4972	$9000	€7259	Dark landscape (25x35cm-10x14in) panel prov. 31-Mar-4 Sotheby's, New York #92/R est:5000-7000
£7735	$14000	€11293	Around the campfire (17x24cm-7x9in) panel prov. 31-Mar-4 Sotheby's, New York #86/R est:8000-12000
£8939	$16000	€13051	Moonlit lake (33x28cm-13x11in) s. panel. 26-May-4 Doyle, New York #29/R est:2000-3000
£12570	$22500	€18352	Indian encampment (56x69cm-22x27in) s. prov. 26-May-4 Doyle, New York #16/R est:15000-25000
£14439	$27000	€21081	Indian encampment (20x30cm-8x12in) s.verso board prov. 24-Jul-4 Coeur d'Alene, Hayden #141/R est:15000-25000
Works on paper			
£348	$550	€505	Mexican coast (5x23cm-2x9in) s.i. pen ink dr. 8-Sep-3 Winter Associates, Plainville #145

BLAKELOCK, Ralph Albert (attrib) (1847-1919) American

£472	$850	€689	Sunset landscape (30x45cm-12x18in) board prov. 25-Apr-4 Bonhams & Butterfields, San Francisco #5500/R
£663	$1200	€968	Indian horseman, rider at dusk (33x56cm-13x22in) masonite. 3-Apr-4 Nadeau, Windsor #90/R est:3000-5000
£838	$1400	€1223	Full moon over the forest (20x25cm-8x10in) s. 20-Jun-3 Freeman, Philadelphia #270/R

BLAMEY, Norman (1914-) British

£250	$463	€365	Abstract figures (71x51cm-28x20in) s.d.1966. 10-Feb-4 David Lay, Penzance #168
£500	$800	€730	Daffodils in a glass vase by a window with winter landscape (50x40cm-20x16in) s. board. 16-Sep-3 Rosebery Fine Art, London #496/R

BLAMEY, Thelma (20th C) British

Works on paper			
£320	$563	€467	Cockerels and hens (44x57cm-17x22in) s. W/C gouache. 18-May-4 Woolley & Wallis, Salisbury #208/R

BLAMPIED, Edmund (1886-1966) British

Works on paper			
£700	$1274	€1022	Farmer pulling a horse and cart (12x20cm-5x8in) s. pencil W/C. 1-Jul-4 Christie's, Kensington #71/R
£850	$1445	€1241	Spanish harbour (20x30cm-8x12in) s. pen ink. 26-Nov-3 Sotheby's, Olympia #7/R
£962	$1550	€1405	French river scene (23x38cm-9x15in) s. W/C. 20-Aug-3 James Julia, Fairfield #1033/R est:1750-2250
£3100	$4960	€4526	Gathering Vraic (15x25cm-6x10in) s. W/C. 17-Sep-3 Bonhams, Brooks & Langlois, Jersey #116/R est:1000-1500

BLANC, Annie (?) French?

£408	$743	€600	Bouquet de roses (46x38cm-18x15in) s. cardboard. 8-Feb-4 Anaf, Lyon #102

BLANC, Benoit (attrib) (1812-1887) French

£1208	$2138	€1800	Portrait de aristocrate et son epouse dans un jardin a Rome (100x75cm-39x30in) mono.i.d.1834. 29-Apr-4 David Kahn, Paris #170/R est:1500-2000

BLANC, Joel (20th C) French?

£313	$491	€450	Vente des Yearlings a Deauville (73x54cm-29x21in) 29-Aug-3 Deauville, France #169
Sculpture			
£1497	$2679	€2200	Joueurs de polo (34x30cm-13x12in) s.st.f.Landowski bronze. 21-Mar-4 Rossini, Paris #406/R est:2200-3000
Works on paper			
£764	$1199	€1100	Rond de presentation a Deauville (65x50cm-26x20in) s.d.2002 W/C. 29-Aug-3 Deauville, France #168

BLANC, Joseph-Paul (1846-1904) French

£722	$1350	€1054	Enlevement du Palladium (73x54cm-29x21in) 25-Feb-4 Museumsbygningen, Copenhagen #145/R (D.KR 8000)

BLANC, Louis-Ammy (1810-1885) German

£5705	$10497	€8500	Portrait of woman with two children (54x46cm-21x18in) s.i. 25-Mar-4 Dr Fritz Nagel, Stuttgart #695/R est:8500
£14493	$23768	€20000	Allegory of Music and Poetry (77x96cm-30x38in) 27-May-3 Finarte Semenzato, Milan #90/R est:20000-25000

BLANCH, Arnold (1896-1968) American

£745	$1200	€1088	Rudbeckia (107x76cm-42x30in) s. painted c.1928. 22-Feb-3 Bunte, Elgin #1184
£1242	$2000	€1813	The hunters (76x107cm-30x42in) s.d.1927. 22-Feb-3 Bunte, Elgin #1185 est:800-1200
£1688	$2700	€2464	Lila (66x56cm-26x22in) s. 20-Sep-3 Bunte, Elgin #1202 est:2000-3000
£3022	$5500	€4412	Portrait of Doris Lee (107x76cm-42x30in) s. 29-Jun-4 Sotheby's, New York #264/R est:4000-6000
£3727	$6000	€5441	Portrait of Doris Lee (107x76cm-42x30in) s. 22-Feb-3 Bunte, Elgin #1186 est:800-1200
£4620	$8500	€6745	Seated girl (108x76cm-43x30in) s. prov. 8-Jun-4 Bonhams & Butterfields, San Francisco #4113/R est:3000-5000

BLANCH, Lucille (1895-1981) American

£233	$375	€340	Spontaneous life (112x102cm-44x40in) s. painted c.1955. 22-Feb-3 Bunte, Elgin #1180a
£297	$475	€434	Rain (165x112cm-65x44in) s. s.i.d.1956 verso. 20-Sep-3 Bunte, Elgin #385k
£311	$500	€454	Miakki Jungle (56x76cm-22x30in) painted 1935. 22-Feb-3 Bunte, Elgin #1179a
£342	$550	€499	The wife (51x41cm-20x16in) s.d.1971. 22-Feb-3 Bunte, Elgin #1179
£373	$600	€545	Head of the Virgin (61x46cm-24x18in) painted c.1952. 22-Feb-3 Bunte, Elgin #1174
£373	$600	€545	Irresistible movement (91x56cm-36x22in) s. painted c.1951. 22-Feb-3 Bunte, Elgin #1180
£373	$600	€545	Sun (170x102cm-67x40in) s. painted c.1956. 22-Feb-3 Bunte, Elgin #1182
£435	$700	€635	Venus (79x112cm-31x44in) s. i.verso painted c.1939. 22-Feb-3 Bunte, Elgin #1178
£466	$750	€680	Fresh coloured margarine (51x41cm-20x16in) painted c.1936. 22-Feb-3 Bunte, Elgin #1173
£466	$750	€680	The old incorrigible (79x61cm-31x24in) s. masonite board painted c.1948. 22-Feb-3 Bunte, Elgin #1177
£590	$950	€861	Venus-Eve (127x102cm-50x40in) s. painted c.1963. 22-Feb-3 Bunte, Elgin #1175
£994	$1600	€1451	Music listener (91x61cm-36x24in) 22-Feb-3 Bunte, Elgin #1171 est:600-800
£1923	$3500	€2808	Morning routine (107x66cm-42x26in) s. 29-Jun-4 Sotheby's, New York #270/R est:5000-7000
£1946	$3250	€2841	Orlando (51x61cm-20x24in) s. prov.exhib. 23-Oct-3 Shannon's, Milford #208/R est:2500-3500
£2329	$3750	€3400	The adding machine (127x91cm-50x36in) s. painted c.1947. 22-Feb-3 Bunte, Elgin #1170 est:2000-3000
£3022	$5500	€4412	Still life with flowers (81x61cm-32x24in) s. 29-Jun-4 Sotheby's, New York #273/R est:3500-4500
£3106	$5000	€4535	The shadow (81x61cm-32x24in) s. 22-Feb-3 Bunte, Elgin #1172 est:400-600
£5313	$8500	€7757	Vacationist (91x127cm-36x50in) s. painted c.1929. 20-Sep-3 Bunte, Elgin #1201 est:5000-7000

BLANCHARD, Antoine (1910-1988) French

£968	$1781	€1413	Hausmann Boulevard, Paris (20x25cm-8x10in) s. masonite prov. 14-Jun-4 Waddingtons, Toronto #268/R est:1000-1500 (C.D 2400)
£1049	$1804	€1500	Les boulevards sous la neige (32x23cm-13x9in) s. panel. 7-Dec-3 Lesieur & Le Bars, Le Havre #204
£1307	$2300	€1908	Place de la Republique (33x46cm-13x18in) s. 21-May-4 North East Auctions, Portsmouth #677/R
£1537	$2750	€2244	Paris street scene (30x41cm-12x16in) s. 8-Jan-4 James Julia, Fairfield #893/R est:1500-2500
£2390	$3800	€3489	Paris street scene (46x53cm-18x21in) s. 14-Sep-3 Susanin's, Chicago #6177/R est:2000-3000
£2582	$4750	€3770	Paris street scene (51x61cm-20x24in) s. 8-Jun-4 Auctions by the Bay, Alameda #1128/R
£2600	$4732	€3796	Paris, le Madeleine, Rue Royale (33x46cm-13x18in) s. s.i.verso. 16-Jun-4 Bonhams, New Bond Street #100/R est:2000-3000
£2727	$4800	€3981	Parisian street scene. s. 23-May-4 Hindman, Chicago #65a est:2000-4000
£2795	$4500	€4081	Parisian street scene (51x61cm-20x24in) s. 22-Feb-3 Bunte, Elgin #1257 est:5000-7000
£2800	$4760	€4088	Autumn evening, Paris (33x46cm-13x18in) s. prov. 19-Nov-3 Bonhams, New Bond Street #133/R est:3000-4000
£2994	$5000	€4371	City scene (33x46cm-13x18in) 17-Oct-3 Du Mouchelle, Detroit #2003/R est:3000-4000
£3106	$5000	€4535	La Bastille, Paris (33x46cm-13x18in) s. s.i.verso. 14-Jan-4 Christie's, Rockefeller NY #46/R est:6000-8000
£3145	$5000	€4560	Porte St Denis, Paris (48x58cm-19x23in) s. 12-Sep-3 Aspire, Cleveland #70 est:5000-10000
£3198	$5500	€4669	Parisian street scene (33x46cm-13x18in) s. 7-Dec-3 Hindman, Chicago #809/R est:4000-6000
£3409	$6000	€4977	View of Notre Dame Cathedral, Paris (33x46cm-13x18in) s.i.verso. 18-May-4 Bonhams & Butterfields, San Francisco #187/R est:4000-6000
£3488	$6000	€5092	Moulin Rouge, Paris (33x46cm-13x18in) s. s.i.verso. 2-Dec-3 Christie's, Rockefeller NY #64/R est:7000-9000
£3488	$6000	€5092	Porte Saint-Denis (33x46cm-13x18in) s. s.i.verso. 2-Dec-3 Christie's, Rockefeller NY #63/R est:7000-9000
£3529	$6000	€5152	View of figures on the Boulevard Hausmann (46x55cm-18x22in) s. i.verso. 19-Nov-3 Bonhams & Butterfields, San Francisco #156/R
£3529	$6000	€5152	Parisian street scene with booksellers and Notre Dame beyond (33x46cm-13x18in) s. indis i.verso. 19-Nov-3 Bonhams & Butterfields, San Francisco #157/R
£3600	$6120	€5256	Rue Royale, Paris (33x46cm-13x18in) s. i.verso prov. 19-Nov-3 Bonhams, New Bond Street #136/R est:3000-5000
£3779	$6500	€5517	Parisian street scene with trolley (46x56cm-18x22in) s. i.verso linen. 7-Dec-3 Hindman, Chicago #811/R est:4000-6000
£3824	$6500	€5583	Comedie Francaise Place Palais Royal, Paris (33x46cm-13x18in) s. 20-Nov-3 Auctions by the Bay, Alameda #1130/R
£3846	$7000	€5615	Champs-Elysees, Paris (46x33cm-18x13in) s. 19-Jun-4 Jackson's, Cedar Falls #41/R est:4000-6000
£4000	$6800	€5840	Place du Chatelet, Paris (33x46cm-13x18in) s. i.verso prov. 19-Nov-3 Bonhams, New Bond Street #134/R est:3000-5000
£4000	$7200	€5840	L'Arc de Triomphe (33x46cm-13x18in) s. 21-Jan-4 Sotheby's, Olympia #518/R est:2000-3000
£4070	$7000	€5942	Boulevard parisien sous la pluie (33x46cm-13x18in) s. s.i.verso. 2-Dec-3 Christie's, Rockefeller NY #65/R est:7000-9000
£4190	$7500	€6117	Parisian street scene (33x46cm-13x18in) s. 6-May-4 Doyle, New York #74/R est:6000-8000
£4261	$7500	€6221	View of figures on the Boulevard Des Capucines, Paris (33x46cm-13x18in) s.i.verso. 18-May-4 Bonhams & Butterfields, San Francisco #189/R est:4000-6000
£4942	$8500	€7215	Champs Elysees (33x46cm-13x18in) s. s.i.verso. 2-Dec-3 Christie's, Rockefeller NY #66/R est:7000-9000
£5333	$9707	€8000	Paris, Grands Boulevards (33x46cm-13x18in) s. 4-Jul-4 Eric Pillon, Calais #77/R
£5397	$9500	€7880	View of the place de la Republique in winter (46x55cm-18x22in) s.i.verso. 18-May-4 Bonhams & Butterfields, San Francisco #188/R est:4000-6000
£5966	$10500	€8710	View of the theatre du Gymnase, Paris (33x46cm-13x18in) s.i.verso. 18-May-4 Bonhams & Butterfields, San Francisco #190/R est:4000-6000
£6250	$11000	€9125	View of the Arc de Triomphe, Paris (46x57cm-18x22in) s.i.verso. 18-May-4 Bonhams & Butterfields, San Francisco #191/R est:4000-6000
£6977	$12000	€10186	Parisian winter street scene (46x56cm-18x22in) s. i.verso linen. 7-Dec-3 Hindman, Chicago #810/R est:4000-6000
£7000	$12880	€10220	Boulevard de la Madeleine, Paris (60x91cm-24x36in) s. 23-Mar-4 Bonhams, New Bond Street #110/R est:7000-10000
£8500	$15555	€12410	Boulevard St Michel, Paris (61x91cm-24x36in) s. s.i.verso prov. 7-Apr-4 Woolley & Wallis, Salisbury #291/R est:7000-9000

BLANCHARD, Antoine (attrib) (1910-1988) French

£426	$750	€622	Paris street scene (20x25cm-8x10in) s. 23-May-4 Bonhams & Butterfields, Los Angeles #7063/R

£2841 $5000 €4148 View of the Bouquinists on the Quai with Notre Dame beyond (33x46cm-13x18in) bears sig. 18-May-4 Bonhams & Butterfields, San Francisco #192/R est:3000-5000

BLANCHARD, Émile Theophile (1795-?) French

£2685 $4805 €4000 Roses et cineraires dans un vase (32x24cm-13x9in) s.d.1859. 25-May-4 Palais de Beaux Arts, Brussels #558/R est:4000-5000

BLANCHARD, Emile Theophile and PRETRE, Jean Gabriel (19th C) French

Works on paper

£2621 $4377 €3800 Various animals. s. W/C gouache black crayon 3 sheets 1 frame. 13-Nov-3 Binoche, Paris #67/R est:2000

BLANCHARD, Georges Emee (1900-1972) French

£496 $829 €700 Nue allongee (55x110cm-22x43in) 19-Oct-3 Peron, Melun #315

£1172 $1958 €1700 Female nude on Atlantic coast (160x107cm-63x42in) s.d.1935. 14-Nov-3 Altus, Berlin #682/R est:1200

BLANCHARD, Jacques (attrib) (1600-1638) French

£5319 $8883 €7500 Mise au tombeau (116x141cm-46x56in) prov. 17-Oct-3 Renaud, Paris #26/R est:3000-4000

BLANCHARD, Jacques (1912-) French

£310 $586 €453 Grapes and peach (21x26cm-8x10in) s. board. 19-Feb-4 Christie's, Kensington #274/R

BLANCHARD, Maria (1881-1932) Spanish

£23944 $41423 €34000 Portrait de jeune fille (58x38cm-23x15in) s. 12-Dec-3 Piasa, Paris #24/R est:15000-20000

£76923 $130769 €110000 Enfant au ballon (100x55cm-39x22in) s. 18-Nov-3 Vanderkindere, Brussels #150/R est:50000-75000

£80420 $134301 €115000 Jeune fille lisant (75x55cm-30x22in) s. 30-Jun-3 Bailly Pommery, Paris #109/R est:22000

£82759 $153103 €120000 Jeune femme se coiffant (92x60cm-36x24in) s. prov. 13-Jan-4 Vanderkindere, Brussels #50/R est:30000-40000

£90909 $154545 €130000 L'enfant sur l'escalier (81x50cm-32x20in) s. 18-Nov-3 Vanderkindere, Brussels #102/R est:40000-60000

Works on paper

£17000 $28390 €24820 Tete de jeune fille (61x50cm-24x20in) s. pastel chl paper on canvas executed c.1930 prov.exhib. 21-Oct-3 Sotheby's, London #148/R est:9000-12000

£50000 $89500 €75000 Femme (97x70cm-38x28in) s. pastel. 11-May-4 Vanderkindere, Brussels #60/R est:60000-80000

£90909 $156364 €130000 Fillette assise dans la salle aux bancs (116x76cm-46x30in) s. pastel paper on canvas prov.lit. 8-Dec-3 Artcurial Briest, Paris #22/R est:50000-70000

BLANCHARD, Maurice (1903-) French

Works on paper

£350 $567 €508 Montmartre (26x32cm-10x13in) s.d.53 pencil W/C. 30-Jul-3 Hamptons Fine Art, Godalming #90

BLANCHARD, Nicole (20th C) French

£307 $500 €448 Champs Elysees, Arc de Triomphe (51x61cm-20x24in) s. s.i.verso. 17-Jul-3 Doyle, New York #9/R

BLANCHARD, Pascal (19/20th C) French

£1325 $2411 €2000 Tzigane assise avec enfant (75x62cm-30x24in) s. 21-Jun-4 Bernaerts, Antwerp #178/R est:2000-3000

BLANCHARD, Remy (1958-1993) French

£574 $1085 €850 Sans titre (65x50cm-26x20in) s.d.1982 acrylic paper. 21-Feb-4 Cornette de St.Cyr, Paris #250

£2685 $4940 €4000 Untitled (149x149cm-59x59in) s. acrylic painted 1984. 29-Mar-4 Cornette de St.Cyr, Paris #86/R est:4000-5000

BLANCHE, Jacques Émile (1861-1942) French

£552 $1000 €806 Le martyre de saint Sebastien (65x81cm-26x32in) init. 30-Mar-4 Christie's, Rockefeller NY #100/R est:2000-3000

£660 $1089 €950 Portrait de femme (55x46cm-22x18in) s.d.1932. 3-Jul-3 Claude Aguttes, Neuilly #17

£1028 $1717 €1450 Fin de journee devant la chateau de Versailles (33x41cm-13x16in) s. 20-Jun-3 Drouot Estimations, Paris #71

£1034 $1717 €1500 Projet pour le Memorial d'Offranville (73x60cm-29x24in) i. 2-Oct-3 Sotheby's, Paris #130/R

£3400 $6290 €4964 Portrait of Desiree Manfred (46x38cm-18x15in) init. 10-Mar-4 Sotheby's, Olympia #307/R est:3000-5000

£3448 $5724 €5000 Mater Dolorosa (163x123cm-64x48in) s. s.i.d.1905 verso exhib. 2-Oct-3 Sotheby's, Paris #95/R est:9000

£3497 $5944 €5000 St Martin aux Chartrains (41x33cm-16x13in) mono. i.verso. 24-Nov-3 E & Eve, Paris #140/R est:5000-5500

£3793 $6297 €5500 Portrait de la Duchesse de Clermont-Tonnerre (127x101cm-50x40in) 2-Oct-3 Sotheby's, Paris #66/R est:6500

£4000 $7400 €5840 Bassin Berigny, Dieppe (55x74cm-22x29in) s. prov. 11-Feb-4 Sotheby's, Olympia #124/R est:2500-3500

£4000 $7160 €5840 Portrait of a girl (131x79cm-52x31in) s.d.90. 28-May-4 Lyon & Turnbull, Edinburgh #43/R est:4000-6000

£5000 $9150 €7300 Seaside scene (23x33cm-9x13in) s. board. 2-Jun-4 Sotheby's, London #11/R est:5000-7000

£5172 $8586 €7500 Portrait de fillette au noeud rose (60x52cm-24x20in) oval. 2-Oct-3 Sotheby's, Paris #87/R est:4500

£5500 $10065 €8030 Beach huts (21x33cm-8x13in) s. board. 2-Jun-4 Sotheby's, London #12/R est:5000-7000

£7200 $12240 €10512 Serpentine (50x61cm-20x24in) s.i. prov.exhib. 26-Nov-3 Sotheby's, Olympia #42/R est:6000-8000

£8392 $14266 €12000 Bouquet de glaieuls (116x8cm-46x3in) s. 27-Nov-3 Millon & Associes, Paris #210/R est:12000-15000

£10588 $18000 €15458 Bouquet aux mille couleurs (100x81cm-39x32in) s.d.25. 6-Nov-3 Sotheby's, New York #343/R est:15000-20000

£10596 $19391 €16000 Bouquet et tasse (61x50cm-24x20in) s. 7-Apr-4 Piasa, Paris #15/R est:6000-8000

£22222 $40000 €32444 Bouquet de fleurs (65x54cm-26x21in) s.d.29 s.verso prov. 22-Apr-4 Christie's, Rockefeller NY #163/R est:50000-70000

BLANCHET, Alexandre (1882-1961) Swiss

£353 $600 €515 Printemps en valais (38x49cm-15x19in) s.d.1923. 28-Nov-3 Zofingen, Switzerland #2910 (S.FR 780)

£864 $1434 €1253 Nature morte - Pot bleu, bol jaune (50x65cm-20x26in) s.d.1910. 13-Jun-3 Zofingen, Switzerland #2791/R est:2500 (S.FR 1900)

£1514 $2528 €2195 Interior with chair and cloth (81x81cm-32x32in) s.d. 23-Jun-3 Philippe Schuler, Zurich #3378/R est:3000-3500 (S.FR 3300)

BLANCHET, Louis Gabriel (attrib) (1705-1772) French

£6000 $9960 €8760 Portrait of a gentleman seated by a table with his arm resting on a book (89x71cm-35x28in) s. 1-Oct-3 Woolley & Wallis, Salisbury #253/R est:6000-8000

BLANCHET, Thomas (1614-1689) French

£6667 $12133 €10000 Mythological scene (72x104cm-28x41in) prov. 30-Jun-4 Pierre Berge, Paris #30/R est:10000-15000

BLANCHI, Pio (1848-1917) Italian

Works on paper

£517 $859 €750 Rown in a gondola (67x42cm-26x17in) s.d.1886 W/C card. 1-Oct-3 Della Rocca, Turin #21/R

£707 $1300 €1032 Plotting a voyage (41x56cm-16x22in) s.i.d.75 W/C. 23-Mar-4 Arthur James, Florida #14/R est:1000-1500

BLANCHOT, Gustave (1883-1968) French

£800 $1288 €1168 Impressionist Continental street scenes with figures (28x36cm-11x14in) s. pair. 15-Aug-3 Keys, Aylsham #757

BLANCO, Antonio (1927-1999) Philippino

£14672 $24502 €21421 Reclining nude (40x50cm-16x20in) s. canvas on board prov. 26-Oct-3 Christie's, Hong Kong #10/R est:140000-180000 (HK.D 190000)

£26144 $47320 €38170 Drummer (123x87cm-48x34in) s. 4-Apr-4 Sotheby's, Singapore #13/R est:60000-80000 (S.D 80000)

£41667 $64583 €60834 Nude (72x62cm-28x24in) s. 6-Oct-2 Sotheby's, Singapore #9/R est:28000-35000 (S.D 115000)

Works on paper

£850 $1538 €1241 Blue bottomed lady (38x29cm-15x11in) s. mixed media. 4-Apr-4 Sotheby's, Singapore #11/R est:2500-3800 (S.D 2600)

£850 $1538 €1241 Rainbow colored tapestry (53x44cm-21x17in) s. mixed media. 4-Apr-4 Sotheby's, Singapore #12/R est:2500-3800 (S.D 2600)

£5797 $8986 €8464 Blue nude (35x46cm-14x18in) s.d.89 pencil W/C. 6-Oct-2 Sotheby's, Singapore #6/R est:10000-12000 (S.D 16000)

£6536 $11830 €9543 Ronji and self portrait (36x34cm-14x13in) s. s.i.verso W/C. 4-Apr-4 Sotheby's, Singapore #10/R est:20000-28000 (S.D 20000)

BLANCO, Antonio Maria (20th C) American

£71895 $130131 €104967 Balinese dancer, Oleg Tamulilngan (69x45cm-27x18in) s. 3-Apr-4 Glerum, Singapore #27/R (S.D 220000)

Works on paper

£3595 $6507 €5249 Girl in nude (62x75cm-24x30in) s.i. W/C. 3-Apr-4 Glerum, Singapore #15/R est:12000-16000 (S.D 11000)

BLANCO, Pedro (20th C) Venezuelan?

£235 $405 €343 Untitled (100x80cm-39x31in) s. painted 1998. 7-Dec-3 Subastas Odalys, Caracas #108

£238 $405 €347 Untitled (100x80cm-39x31in) s. painted 1998. 23-Nov-3 Subastas Odalys, Caracas #12

BLANCO, Virxilio (1896-1948) Spanish

£3231 $5784 €4750 Trees (73x60cm-29x24in) s. 22-Mar-4 Durán, Madrid #143/R est:1200

BLAND, Emily Beatrice (1864-1951) British

£600 $960 €876 Still life with flowers and a glass dome on a table (80x65cm-31x26in) s. board. 16-Sep-3 Rosebery Fine Art, London #607

BLAND, John F (1856-1899) British

Works on paper

£480 $797 €701 Scarborough fishing yawl in choppy seas (29x43cm-11x17in) s.d.1868 W/C. 6-Oct-3 David Duggleby, Scarborough #286

BLAND, John F (attrib) (1856-1899) British

£320 $576 €467 Coastal scene with a figure standing beside wreckage on a beach (71x56cm-28x22in) 21-Apr-4 Tennants, Leyburn #1103

BLANDIN, Étienne (1903-1991) French

£268 $499 €400 Vague se brisant sur un rocher (33x41cm-13x16in) s. 7-Mar-4 Livinec, Gaudcheau & Jezequel, Rennes #80

£311 $587 €460 Cotes de l'Esterel, au loin Cannes (41x33cm-16x13in) s.d.1959 verso canvas on cardboard. 21-Feb-4 Livinec, Gaudcheau & Jezequel, Rennes #29

£378 $715 €560 Trois mats vu de travers dans la baie (46x38cm-18x15in) s. cardboard. 21-Feb-4 Livinec, Gaudcheau & Jezequel, Rennes #24

£473 $894 €700 Officier faisant demande aupres de la Tahitienne (21x26cm-8x10in) s. cardboard. 21-Feb-4 Livinec, Gaudcheau & Jezequel, Rennes #27

£507	$958	€750	Le Bison au mouillage a Lock End en Ecosse (43x33cm-17x13in) s. i.verso canvas on cardboard. 21-Feb-4 Livinec, Gaudcheau & Jezequel, Rennes #25
£533	$987	€800	Le Pourquoi-Pas en rade de Trondihem (33x41cm-13x16in) s.i.d.1943 cardboard. 14-Jul-4 Livinec, Gaudcheau & Jezequel, Rennes #139
£533	$987	€800	Le Phoque (50x65cm-20x26in) s. isorel. 14-Jul-4 Livinec, Gaudcheau & Jezequel, Rennes #161b
£541	$1022	€800	Caravelle vue de travers (61x50cm-24x20in) s. 21-Feb-4 Livinec, Gaudcheau & Jezequel, Rennes #41
£574	$1085	€850	Tahitiennes sur un canoe (33x41cm-13x16in) s.d.septembre 1943 isorel. 21-Feb-4 Livinec, Gaudcheau & Jezequel, Rennes #44
£608	$1149	€900	Tahitienne adossee au cocotier (33x41cm-13x16in) s. cardboard. 21-Feb-4 Livinec, Gaudcheau & Jezequel, Rennes #38
£743	$1405	€1100	Voilier trois quart arriere (37x46cm-15x18in) s. isorel. 21-Feb-4 Livinec, Gaudcheau & Jezequel, Rennes #32
£743	$1405	€1100	Marins Francais discutant avec des Chinoises dans une jonque (46x38cm-18x15in) s. panel on cardboard. 21-Feb-4 Livinec, Gaudcheau & Jezequel, Rennes #35
£743	$1405	€1100	Avenue Henri Martin sous la pluie (38x46cm-15x18in) s. cardboard. 21-Feb-4 Livinec, Gaudcheau & Jezequel, Rennes #36
£1081	$2043	€1600	Le beau voyage (38x46cm-15x18in) s. cardboard. 21-Feb-4 Livinec, Gaudcheau & Jezequel, Rennes #39
£1081	$2043	€1600	Effets de lumiere sur la plage au Fort National, a Saint-Malo (55x38cm-22x15in) s. cardboard on cardboard. 21-Feb-4 Livinec, Gaudcheau & Jezequel, Rennes #40
£1081	$2043	€1600	Jeunes Tahitiennes dans des canoes devant le trois mats (54x73cm-21x29in) s. isorel. 21-Feb-4 Livinec, Gaudcheau & Jezequel, Rennes #43/R
£1149	$2171	€1700	Trois mats vu de travers au coucher de soleil (38x46cm-15x18in) s.d.27/1/45 cardboard. 21-Feb-4 Livinec, Gaudcheau & Jezequel, Rennes #42
£1351	$2554	€2000	Vue du Mont-Saint-Michel (32x41cm-13x16in) s. cardboard. 21-Feb-4 Livinec, Gaudcheau & Jezequel, Rennes #34
£1400	$2590	€2100	Le Pourquoi-Pas sous un gros temps (50x61cm-20x24in) s. 14-Jul-4 Livinec, Gaudcheau & Jezequel, Rennes #130
£1824	$3448	€2700	Marins largant un foc (53x64cm-21x25in) s. canvas on cardboard. 21-Feb-4 Livinec, Gaudcheau & Jezequel, Rennes #45
£2230	$4214	€3300	Hommes a la barre (54x73cm-21x29in) s. isorel. 21-Feb-4 Livinec, Gaudcheau & Jezequel, Rennes #46
£2467	$4563	€3700	Quatre mats en mer passant le Phare du Jardin a Saint Malo (90x117cm-35x46in) s. 14-Jul-4 Livinec, Gaudcheau & Jezequel, Rennes #173
£2500	$4725	€3700	Paysage de Norvege (46x33cm-18x13in) s.i. canvas on cardboard. 21-Feb-4 Livinec, Gaudcheau & Jezequel, Rennes #33
£2703	$5108	€4000	Trois mats vu de trois quart au coucher de soleil (46x55cm-18x22in) s. cardboard. 21-Feb-4 Livinec, Gaudcheau & Jezequel, Rennes #47
£2770	$5236	€4100	Trois mats en forte mer (64x80cm-25x31in) s. 21-Feb-4 Livinec, Gaudcheau & Jezequel, Rennes #48/R
£3378	$6385	€5000	Le pourquoi-pas au Lofoten (38x46cm-15x18in) s. 21-Feb-4 Livinec, Gaudcheau & Jezequel, Rennes #37
Works on paper			
£324	$613	€480	Trois mats en mer (21x26cm-8x10in) s.d.1921 W/C. 21-Feb-4 Livinec, Gaudcheau & Jezequel, Rennes #13
£446	$843	€660	Trois mats vu de travers prenant une vague (24x21cm-9x8in) s. W/C. 21-Feb-4 Livinec, Gaudcheau & Jezequel, Rennes #22
£459	$868	€680	Trois mats vu de travers en mer agitee (17x33cm-7x13in) s. W/C. 21-Feb-4 Livinec, Gaudcheau & Jezequel, Rennes #14
£1284	$2426	€1900	Etudes preparatoires de tableaux decorant la salle de Restaurant (15x21cm-6x8in) W/C four exhib. 21-Feb-4 Livinec, Gaudcheau & Jezequel, Rennes #23/R

BLANES VIALE, Pedro (1879-1926) Uruguayan

£3693	$6500	€5392	Summer noon (46x56cm-18x22in) 5-Jan-4 Galeria y Remates, Montevideo #68/R est:9000-12000
£26136	$46000	€38159	Quinta de Posadas Park (85x100cm-33x39in) s. prov.lit. 5-Jan-4 Galeria y Remates, Montevideo #67/R est:52000-58000
Works on paper			
£3824	$6500	€5583	Lady (101x80cm-40x31in) s. pastel on canvas. 25-Nov-3 Galeria y Remates, Montevideo #155/R

BLANES, Juan Luis (1856-1895) Uruguayan

£17196	$28030	€25106	Peasant man (53x38cm-21x15in) s. prov.lit. 17-Jul-3 Naón & Cia, Buenos Aires #1/R

BLANES, Juan Manuel (1830-1901) Uruguayan

£115988	$199500	€169342	Entertaining cow-boys (71x100cm-28x39in) s. cardboard. 3-Dec-3 Naón & Cia, Buenos Aires #1/R
£182353	$310000	€266235	Between two lights (82x100cm-32x39in) prov. 25-Nov-3 Galeria y Remates, Montevideo #149/R

BLANES, Juan Manuel (attrib) (1830-1901) Uruguayan

£471	$800	€688	Model in uniform (28x16cm-11x6in) cardboard prov. 25-Nov-3 Galeria y Remates, Montevideo #170/R

BLANEY, Dwight (1865-1944) American

£2060	$3750	€3008	Forest cabin in winter (65x90cm-26x35in) s. exhib. 29-Jun-4 Sotheby's, New York #220/R est:4000-6000
£7407	$12000	€10740	Ironbound Island, Maine (87x69cm-34x27in) s. prov. 8-Aug-3 Barridorf, Portland #121/R est:15000-25000

BLANK, Andre (1914-1987) Belgian

Works on paper			
£599	$1036	€850	Impasse a Liege, n 2 (243x122cm-96x48in) mixed media. 10-Dec-3 Hotel des Ventes Mosan, Brussels #264

BLANKERHOFF, Jan Teunisz (1628-1669) Dutch

£7000	$12600	€10220	Small Dutch vessels in a short chop (104x75cm-41x30in) 22-Apr-4 Sotheby's, London #77/R est:8000-12000

BLANT, Julien le (1851-1936) French

£605	$963	€890	Chouan (25x19cm-10x7in) s. 18-Mar-3 Adjug'art, Brest #114

BLANVILLAIN, Paul (1891-1965) French

£559	$951	€800	Nature morte a l'oiseau (15x10cm-6x4in) s. cardboard. 24-Nov-3 Boscher, Cherbourg #794

BLARENBERGHE, Henri Joseph van (1741-1826) French

Works on paper			
£7832	$13315	€11200	Paysage fluvial anime (24x31cm-9x12in) gouache prov. 21-Nov-3 Lombrail & Teucquam, Paris #95/R est:6000-8000

BLARENBERGHE, Henri Joseph van and Louis Nicolas van (18th C) French

Works on paper			
£16760	$30000	€24470	Champs Elysees (26x25cm-10x10in) s.d.1776 gouache prov.exhib.lit. 27-May-4 Sotheby's, New York #34/R est:40000-60000

BLARENBERGHE, Louis Nicolas van (1716-1794) French

£3873	$6779	€5500	Choc de cavalerie (25x34cm-10x13in) 18-Dec-3 Tajan, Paris #127/R est:2000-3000
Miniatures			
£1867	$3398	€2800	Assemblee de personnages (5cm-2in circular) s. 30-Jun-4 Pierre Berge, Paris #105/R est:3000-3500
Works on paper			
£300	$519	€438	Landscape with village in the distance (21x15cm-8x6in) black chk pen brown ink W/C bodycol. 12-Dec-3 Christie's, Kensington #456
£1333	$2400	€1946	Column of mounted artillery, castle beyond. Cavalry crossing a stream (17x23cm-7x9in) bodycol vellum pair. 22-Jan-4 Christie's, Rockefeller NY #274/R est:2000-3000
£1667	$3000	€2434	Village on fire by moonlight. Village on fire at night by a river (17x23cm-7x9in) bodycol vellum pair. 22-Jan-4 Christie's, Rockefeller NY #275/R est:3000-5000
£1667	$3000	€2434	Moonlit landscape with figure and cattle. Moonlit river landscape with town (17x22cm-7x9in) bodycol vellum pair. 22-Jan-4 Christie's, Rockefeller NY #278/R est:2000-3000
£1778	$3200	€2596	Night scenes, family cooking in a cave and a village on fire (17x22cm-7x9in) bodycol vellum pair. 22-Jan-4 Christie's, Rockefeller NY #277/R est:2000-3000
£2111	$3800	€3082	Cavalry battle by a river. Cavalry skirmish (17x23cm-7x9in) bodycol vellum pair. 22-Jan-4 Christie's, Rockefeller NY #272/R est:3000-5000
£2222	$4000	€3244	Cavalry battle by a river, an officer fallen from his horse. An ambush (17x23cm-7x9in) bodycol vellum pair. 22-Jan-4 Christie's, Rockefeller NY #273/R est:3000-5000
£2500	$4500	€3650	Town on fire at night. Village on fire. Officers preparing a gibet (17x23cm-7x9in) bodycol vellum three. 22-Jan-4 Christie's, Rockefeller NY #271/R est:2000-3000
£2500	$4500	€3650	Four seasons (18x23cm-7x9in) black chk bodycol vellum four. 22-Jan-4 Christie's, Rockefeller NY #276/R est:5000-8000
£3056	$5500	€4462	Military scenes (17x23cm-7x9in) bodycol vellum four. 22-Jan-4 Christie's, Rockefeller NY #269/R est:6000-8000
£3333	$6000	€4866	Military scenes (17x23cm-7x9in) bodycol vellum four. 22-Jan-4 Christie's, Rockefeller NY #270/R est:6000-8000
£3611	$6500	€5272	Military scenes (17x23cm-7x9in) bodycol vellum four. 22-Jan-4 Christie's, Rockefeller NY #268/R est:6000-8000

BLARENBERGHE, Louis Nicolas van (attrib) (1716-1794) French

£5282	$9243	€7500	Paris, le Louvre (28x42cm-11x17in) gouache. 17-Dec-3 Piasa, Paris #87/R est:4000-6000
Works on paper			
£4000	$7320	€5840	Diana hunting with her nymphs (27x41cm-11x16in) gouache prov. 8-Jul-4 Sotheby's, London #11/R est:4500-6000
£12000	$21960	€17520	Coastal views (17x23cm-7x9in) gouache set of 8. 9-Jul-4 Christie's, Kensington #99/R est:12000-18000
£13158	$24211	€20000	River landscapes with skaters (16x22cm-6x9in) gouache paper on panel pair. 24-Jun-4 Tajan, Paris #72/R est:20000-30000

BLAS, Olleroy (19th C) Italian

£1200	$2208	€1752	Isola di Capri (14x23cm-6x9in) s.indis.i. panel. 25-Mar-4 Christie's, Kensington #139/R est:1500-2000
£1300	$2210	€1898	Isola di Capri, passengers disembarking from a steam ship (144x23cm-57x9in) s. panel. 27-Nov-3 Morphets, Harrogate #428/R est:200-300

BLASCO FERRER, Eleuterio (1907-) Spanish

£347	$590	€500	Village (60x73cm-24x29in) s. 28-Oct-3 Segre, Madrid #343/R

BLASCO, Ros (20th C) ?

£276	$500	€403	Tresor Cache (114x163cm-45x64in) s.d.87 s.i.verso. 2-Apr-4 Freeman, Philadelphia #64

BLASEOTTO, Ricardo (?) Argentinian

£559	$1000	€816	One morning at the seaside (50x50cm-20x20in) 11-May-4 Arroyo, Buenos Aires #12

BLASHKO, Abe (1920-) American

Prints			
£2125	$3400	€3103	Pillars (49x31cm-19x12in) s.i.d.1939 num.27/35 lithograph. 18-Sep-3 Swann Galleries, New York #74/R est:2500-3500
Works on paper			
£707	$1300	€1032	Market. The pencil vendor (38x56cm-15x22in) s.i.d.1937 pencil two. 10-Jun-4 Swann Galleries, New York #30/R
£1196	$2200	€1746	New Years Eve. Sideshow (38x56cm-15x22in) s.i.d.1937 pencil two. 10-Jun-4 Swann Galleries, New York #31/R est:2000-3000
£1522	$2800	€2222	Farmer's market, Seattle. Market vendors (56x36cm-22x14in) s.i. one d.1937 one d.1940. 10-Jun-4 Swann Galleries, New York #32/R est:2000-3000

BLASS, Charlotte L (1908-) American

£525	$940	€767	Indian family overlooking mountainous landscape (61x97cm-24x38in) s. 8-Jan-4 James Julia, Fairfield #776/R

BLASSET, E (19th C) French?

£829	$1500	€1210	Rococo scene, Aristocracy boarding a boat (84x66cm-33x26in) masonite. 16-Apr-4 Du Mouchelle, Detroit #2141/R est:1800-2500

BLASZKO, Martin (1920-) Argentinian

£20588	$35000	€30058	El gran ritmo (93x43cm-37x17in) s.i.verso board prov.lit. 19-Nov-3 Sotheby's, New York #147/R est:25000-35000

BLAT, Ismael (1901-1987) Spanish

£336	$624	€500	Almond trees (25x33cm-10x13in) s. cardboard. 2-Mar-4 Ansorena, Madrid #214/R
£470	$874	€700	Arcades (46x67cm-18x26in) s. 2-Mar-4 Ansorena, Madrid #151/R
£604	$1123	€900	Urban view (54x83cm-21x33in) s. 2-Mar-4 Ansorena, Madrid #149/R
£1562	$2547	€2250	Young woman with apples (72x60cm-28x24in) s. 23-Sep-3 Durán, Madrid #212/R
£1773	$2961	€2500	Street of Tetuan (72x81cm-28x32in) s. i.verso. 23-Jun-3 Durán, Madrid #148/R est:2500

BLATAS, Arbit (1908-1999) American/Lithuanian

£407	$650	€594	Luba Madison as Sonja in Judgement Day (84x41cm-33x16in) s. 20-Sep-3 Bunte, Elgin #1454
£859	$1400	€1254	Venice (66x99cm-26x39in) s.i. 17-Jul-3 Doyle, New York #10/R
£1006	$1800	€1469	Ballerinas (69x60cm-27x24in) s. cardboard painted c.1950 prov. 18-Mar-4 Sotheby's, New York #104/R est:2500-3500
£1236	$2250	€1805	Portrait of Caroline Newhouse (86x66cm-34x26in) s.d.1960. 29-Jun-4 Sotheby's, New York #377/R est:2000-3000
£1397	$2500	€2040	Campo Bandiera e Moro (67x87cm-26x34in) s. 6-May-4 Doyle, New York #70/R est:2500-3500
£1816	$3250	€2651	Paris street scene (78x60cm-31x24in) s. 18-Mar-4 Sotheby's, New York #106/R est:4000-6000
£2761	$4500	€4031	Interieur avec un chien (115x89cm-45x35in) s. 25-Sep-3 Christie's, Rockefeller NY #545/R est:4000-6000

BLATTER, Bruno (19th C) German

£347	$566	€500	Men round table in Dutch interior (61x81cm-24x32in) s. 25-Sep-3 Neumeister, Munich #2743/R
£448	$749	€654	After the shoot (69x98cm-27x39in) s. canvas on board. 20-Oct-3 Stephan Welz, Johannesburg #464 est:3000-5000 (SA.R 5200)
£521	$870	€750	Priests reading in library (66x122cm-26x48in) s. 24-Oct-3 Ketterer, Hamburg #133/R
£594	$993	€850	Mandolin player entertaining guests (70x100cm-28x39in) s. 27-Jun-3 Michael Zeller, Lindau #495/R

BLAU, Tina (1845-1916) Austrian

£13889	$23611	€20000	Prater (21x27cm-8x11in) mono.i.d.84 panel. 28-Oct-3 Wiener Kunst Auktionen, Vienna #50/R est:5000-20000
£20000	$36800	€30000	Landscape with mountain in distance (100x74cm-39x29in) s. prov. 12-Jun-4 Villa Grisebach, Berlin #148/R est:35000-45000
£23490	$41577	€35000	Dutch landscape (31x62cm-12x24in) s. prov. 28-Apr-4 Wiener Kunst Auktionen, Vienna #46/R est:22000-50000
£26846	$47517	€40000	Prater, Vienna (68x55cm-27x22in) s.i.d.187. 28-Apr-4 Wiener Kunst Auktionen, Vienna #48/R est:35000-70000
£37000	$67340	€54020	Still life with irises, peonies and poppy (93x70cm-37x28in) s. prov. 15-Jun-4 Sotheby's, London #11/R est:20000-30000
Works on paper			
£322	$547	€460	Schwarzenberg garden (27x26cm-11x10in) s. 27-Nov-3 Bassenge, Berlin #5539/R

BLAUVELT, Charles F (1824-1900) American

£389	$700	€568	Kept in (30x23cm-12x9in) s. 23-Jan-4 Freeman, Philadelphia #283/R
£559	$900	€816	Decorating the hat (36x28cm-14x11in) s. 20-Aug-3 James Julia, Fairfield #1122/R

BLAXILL, Susannah (1954-) Australian

Works on paper			
£800	$1456	€1168	Pink rhododendron (25x30cm-10x12in) s. W/C. 1-Jul-4 Christie's, Kensington #271/R

BLAY, Albert (19th C) Belgian?

£290	$521	€420	Landscape with village (38x46cm-15x18in) s. s.verso. 26-Jan-4 Ansorena, Madrid #124/R

BLAYLOCK, Thomas Todd (1876-1929) British

Works on paper			
£300	$561	€438	Threshing time (37x49cm-15x19in) s. pastel. 20-Jul-4 Sworder & Son, Bishops Stortford #755/R

BLAZICEK, Oldrich (1887-1953) Hungarian

£548	$965	€822	Village (48x38cm-19x15in) s.i.d.49 cardboard. 22-May-4 Dorotheum, Prague #104/R est:26000-42000 (C.KR 26000)
£569	$945	€831	Spring (22x15cm-9x6in) s. board. 4-Oct-3 Dorotheum, Prague #95/R est:15000-23000 (C.KR 26000)
£1750	$3256	€2555	Winter landscape (30x41cm-12x16in) s. board. 6-Mar-4 Dorotheum, Prague #109/R est:60000-90000 (C.KR 85000)
£4942	$9193	€7215	Winter in village (69x100cm-27x39in) s.d.37. 6-Mar-4 Dorotheum, Prague #105/R est:150000-250000 (C.KR 240000)
£10297	$19152	€15034	Memory of Radesin (80x100cm-31x39in) s. 6-Mar-4 Dorotheum, Prague #100/R est:180000-280000 (C.KR 500000)

BLECKNER, Ross (1949-) American

£586	$1037	€856	Untitled (10x15cm-4x6in) s.d.4/95 verso painted on card with still life. 27-Apr-4 AB Stockholms Auktionsverk #932/R (S.KR 8000)
£2162	$4000	€3157	Untitled (41x31cm-16x12in) paper exec 1988 prov. 12-Feb-4 Sotheby's, New York #246/R est:2500-3500
£2162	$4000	€3157	Study - Que Sera (100x70cm-39x28in) paper exec 1984 prov. 12-Feb-4 Sotheby's, New York #259/R est:2500-3500
£2222	$4000	€3244	Untitled (20x16cm-8x6in) s.d.1984 verso oil encaustic. 24-Apr-4 David Rago, Lambertville #231/R est:4000-6000
£2297	$4250	€3354	Untitled (41x31cm-16x12in) paper exec 1988 prov. 12-Feb-4 Sotheby's, New York #248/R est:2500-3500
£2361	$4250	€3447	The hand before the face (20x16cm-8x6in) prov. 24-Apr-4 David Rago, Lambertville #425/R est:4000-6000
£2811	$5200	€4104	Study for entrance (66x66cm-26x26in) s.i.d.1986 verso prov. 13-Jul-4 Christie's, Rockefeller NY #82/R est:4000-6000
£3611	$6500	€5272	Untitled (39x28cm-15x11in) oil paper. 24-Apr-4 David Rago, Lambertville #317/R est:2000-3000
£3784	$7000	€5525	Untitled (41x31cm-16x12in) paper exec 1988 prov. 12-Feb-4 Sotheby's, New York #243/R est:3000-4000
£3911	$7000	€5710	Falling bird (33x32cm-13x13in) oil linen wood panel prov. 14-May-4 Phillips, New York #349/R est:5000-7000
£4054	$7500	€5919	Untitled (51x41cm-20x16in) s.d.1984 verso linen on panel prov. 13-Jul-4 Christie's, Rockefeller NY #94/R est:3000-5000
£5978	$11000	€8728	Untitled (66x66cm-26x26in) s.i.d.1986 verso prov. 10-Jun-4 Phillips, New York #412/R est:10000-15000
£6522	$12000	€9522	Untitled (76x76cm-30x30in) s.d.1997 acrylic linen prov. 10-Jun-4 Phillips, New York #413/R est:15000-20000
£8000	$13360	€11680	Study, brother's swords (66x66cm-26x26in) s.i.d.1986 verso prov.exhib. 22-Oct-3 Christie's, London #80/R est:8000-12000
£13587	$25000	€19837	Hands and faces (213x152cm-84x60in) s.d.1994 verso oil linen prov. 10-Jun-4 Phillips, New York #417/R est:25000-35000
£16467	$27500	€24042	Untitled (75x75cm-30x30in) s.d.1997 verso prov. 13-Nov-3 Sotheby's, New York #596/R est:20000-30000
£20958	$35000	€30599	Protective vocabulary (244x253cm-96x100in) s.i.d.1989 verso prov. 13-Nov-3 Sotheby's, New York #592/R est:60000-80000
£22346	$40000	€32625	Smell in the room (122x102cm-48x40in) s.d.1992 verso linen prov. 13-May-4 Sotheby's, New York #455/R est:30000-40000
£22346	$40000	€32625	Untitled (94x69cm-37x27in) s.i.d.12/1996 verso oil linen prov. 14-May-4 Phillips, New York #232/R est:25000-35000
£23952	$40000	€34970	Prayer (244x183cm-96x72in) s.i.d.1993 verso prov. 12-Nov-3 Christie's, Rockefeller NY #634/R est:40000-60000
£26946	$45000	€39341	Hothouse (152x122cm-60x48in) init. oil wax linen prov. 13-Nov-3 Sotheby's, New York #600/R est:45000-55000
£29330	$52500	€42822	Pathway with red spots (152x152cm-60x60in) s.i.d.1999 verso prov. 13-May-4 Sotheby's, New York #457/R est:40000-60000
£30726	$55000	€44860	Discipline (152x152cm-60x60in) s.i.d.1993 verso oil encaustic prov. 12-May-4 Christie's, Rockefeller NY #469/R est:25000-35000
£44693	$80000	€65252	Unknown quantities of light, part V (274x366cm-108x144in) s.verso prov.exhib. 14-May-4 Phillips, New York #224/R est:40000-60000
£47904	$80000	€69940	Us together (107x397cm-42x156in) s.i.d.2002 verso oil on linen prov. 14-Nov-3 Phillips, New York #153/R est:60000-80000
£71856	$120000	€104910	Cage (274x183cm-108x72in) s.i.d.1986 verso prov.exhib.lit. 13-Nov-3 Sotheby's, New York #149/R est:45000-65000
Works on paper			
£733	$1297	€1070	Untitled (25x20cm-10x8in) W/C ink wax. 27-Apr-4 AB Stockholms Auktionsverk #936/R (S.KR 10000)
£1359	$2500	€1984	Untitled (41x31cm-16x12in) s.d.1989 verso W/C prov. 10-Jun-4 Phillips, New York #491/R est:3000-5000
£1586	$2696	€2316	Untitled (41x31cm-16x12in) s.d.1/1989 verso W/C. 4-Nov-3 Bukowskis, Stockholm #555a/R est:20000-30000 (S.KR 21000)
£2027	$3750	€2959	Untitled (41x31cm-16x12in) s.d.1988 verso W/C prov. 12-Feb-4 Sotheby's, New York #282/R est:3000-5000

BLECON, Jean Yves (20th C) French

£629	$1083	€900	Ile de Seine (61x50cm-24x20in) s. s.i.verso. 7-Dec-3 Livinec, Gaudcheau & Jezequel, Rennes #63/R
£1049	$1804	€1500	Provence vers les Baux (73x92cm-29x36in) s.d.98 s.i.verso. 7-Dec-3 Livinec, Gaudcheau & Jezequel, Rennes #62/R

BLEECK, Richard van (1670-1733) Dutch

£13000	$23790	€18980	Portrait of the painter Coenraet Roepel, painting a still life with fruit and flowers (112x89cm-44x35in) indis sig.i. 7-Jul-4 Christie's, London #38/R est:15000-20000

BLEGER, Paul-Léon (1889-?) French

£353	$600	€515	Woman from Wallis on donkey (61x50cm-24x20in) s. 19-Nov-3 Fischer, Luzern #2020/R (S.FR 780)
£1837	$3288	€2700	Maisons rouges a Madagascar (60x45cm-24x18in) s. 21-Mar-4 St-Germain-en-Laye Encheres #114/R est:3000

BLEIBTREU, Georg (1828-1892) German

£2813	$4500	€4107	Princes of Bavaria (36x51cm-14x20in) s. 17-May-3 Bunte, Elgin #1220 est:3000-5000

BLEIJS, Adrianus (1877-1964) Dutch

£417	$679	€600	Interior scene with a man reading (50x40cm-20x16in) s. 29-Sep-3 Sotheby's, Amsterdam #282
£442	$805	€650	Fisherman from Volendam reading the paper (24x18cm-9x7in) s. 3-Feb-4 Christie's, Amsterdam #349/R

BLEILE, Franz (19/20th C) German

£389	$716	€580	Autumn bouquet (115x85cm-45x33in) s. 25-Mar-4 Karlheinz Kaupp, Staufen #2357/R

BLEKEN, Hakon (1929-) Norwegian

£1704	$2930	€2488	The town (101x60cm-40x24in) s.d.63. 8-Dec-3 Blomqvist, Oslo #554/R est:18000-22000 (N.KR 20000)

Works on paper
£482 $883 €704 Composition with figures (48x64cm-19x25in) mixed media. 2-Feb-4 Blomqvist, Lysaker #1027/R (N.KR 6000)
£870 $1504 €1270 Figures around table (36x63cm-14x25in) s. chl exhib. 13-Dec-3 Blomqvist, Lysaker #1033/R (N.KR 10000)

BLEKEN, Hakon and GULLVAG, Hakon (20th C) Norwegian
£944 $1652 €1378 Composition (76x65cm-30x26in) s.d.1998 i.verso exhib. 16-Dec-3 Grev Wedels Plass, Oslo #136/R (N.KR 11000)

BLEKER, Gerrit Claesz (fl.1625-1656) Dutch
£2483 $4569 €3700 King Salomon meeting the Queen of Saba (40x68cm-16x27in) s.d.43 panel. 26-Mar-4 Daguerre, Paris #49 est:4000-6000

BLENDERMAN, Robert A (20th C) Canadian
£317 $529 €463 Pears on a platter (30x25cm-12x10in) s.i. 17-Nov-3 Hodgins, Calgary #361/R (C.D 700)

BLENNER, Carle J (1864-1952) American
£2823 $5250 €4122 Chrysanthemums (79x53cm-31x21in) s. painted c.1920. 7-Mar-4 William Jenack, New York #129 est:5000-8000

BLENNERHASSET, Una (?) Irish?
£759 $1388 €1100 Study of the horse Lomond (89x76cm-35x30in) s. 28-Jan-4 Woodwards, Cork #242

BLES, David Joseph (1821-1899) Dutch
£833 $1358 €1200 Cromwell sa famille intercede pour Charles I (42x33cm-17x13in) s.i. verso copper. 29-Sep-3 Sotheby's, Amsterdam #106
£1200 $2220 €1752 Engagement (44x39cm-17x15in) panel. 10-Feb-4 Bonhams, Knightsbridge #114/R est:800-1200
£3200 $5920 €4672 Portrait of Princess Petrocochino, the artist's daughter (133x86cm-52x34in) s. 10-Feb-4 Bonhams, Knightsbridge #255/R est:2500-3500
Works on paper
£1208 $2223 €1800 Love letter (28x20cm-11x8in) s. W/C. 29-Mar-4 Glerum, Amsterdam #140 est:1000-1500
£1879 $3458 €2800 Sweet little words (19x25cm-7x10in) s. W/C. 29-Mar-4 Glerum, Amsterdam #145 est:1500-2000
£3041 $5351 €4500 Portrait of a young man, in eighteenth century costume (18x15cm-7x6in) s.d.64 i.verso pastel oval exhib.lit. 19-May-4 Sotheby's, Amsterdam #336/R est:1000-1500

BLES, Herri met de (1480-1550) Flemish
£50000 $90000 €73000 Landscape with the way to Calvary (56x82cm-22x32in) s. with owl panel. 22-Apr-4 Sotheby's, London #8/R est:50000-70000
£100000 $183000 €146000 Descent into limbo (21x34cm-8x13in) s. panel prov. 7-Jul-4 Christie's, London #20/R est:120000-180000

BLES, Herri met de (studio) (1480-1550) Flemish
£18000 $32400 €26280 Landscape with the calling of Saint peter (32x43cm-13x17in) panel. 22-Apr-4 Sotheby's, London #2/R est:10000-15000

BLES, Joseph (1825-1875) Dutch
£647 $1157 €945 Dutch landscape in winter (26x31cm-10x12in) s.d.1863 panel. 13-May-4 Stuker, Bern #42/R est:1500-2000 (S.FR 1500)
£658 $1211 €1000 The ferry (20x26cm-8x10in) indis.s. panel. 22-Jun-4 Christie's, Amsterdam #35/R est:1200-1600
£724 $1310 €1100 Man and woman in conversation in front of a house (16x12cm-6x5in) init. panel. 19-Apr-4 Glerum, Amsterdam #72/R
£884 $1610 €1300 Fisherfolk in a village in the dunes (20x26cm-8x10in) s. panel. 3-Feb-4 Christie's, Amsterdam #68/R est:1500-2000
£1200 $2160 €1800 An act of charity (24x18cm-9x7in) s. panel. 20-Apr-4 Sotheby's, Amsterdam #36/R est:2000-3000

BLEULER (school) (19th C) Swiss
Works on paper
£3349 $5592 €4856 Lake Como with Tremezzina (32x48cm-13x19in) gouache. 23-Jun-3 Philippe Schuler, Zurich #3875/R est:2500-3000 (S.FR 7300)

BLEULER, Johann Heinrich (1758-1823) Swiss
Works on paper
£284 $460 €400 Ruttlischwur (45x57cm-18x22in) s. gouache lit. 23-May-3 Karlheinz Kaupp, Staufen #1683
£1667 $2750 €2400 Chamonix valley (44x61cm-17x24in) i. i. verso gouache. 5-Jul-3 Geble, Radolfzell #495/R est:2400

BLEULER, Johann Heinrich (attrib) (1758-1823) Swiss
Works on paper
£524 $954 €765 Tusis (55x69cm-22x27in) i.verso W/C. 16-Jun-4 Fischer, Luzern #2861/R (S.FR 1200)

BLEULER, Johann Heinrich (younger) (1787-1857) Swiss
Works on paper
£1267 $2154 €1850 Tusis (55x69cm-22x27in) i. verso W/C. 19-Nov-3 Fischer, Luzern #2715/R est:1900-2200 (S.FR 2800)

BLEULER, Johann Ludwig (1792-1850) Swiss
Works on paper
£1391 $2546 €2031 Federal Palace in Bern (32x47cm-13x19in) s.i. gouache. 7-Jun-4 Christie's, Zurich #11/R est:3000-5000 (S.FR 3200)
£1629 $2769 €2378 Vue du Mont de Tavor pres du couvent de Pfeffers vers le Braettigau (33x48cm-13x19in) s. gouache. 28-Nov-3 Zofingen, Switzerland #2453/R est:4000 (S.FR 3600)
£1810 $3331 €2643 Reunion de l'Ill et du Rhin (32x47cm-13x19in) s.i. gouache sepia. 26-Mar-4 Koller, Zurich #3333/R est:2500-3500 (S.FR 4200)
£2586 $4629 €3776 Heinrich and Idda on Lake Thun, Canton Bern (47x70cm-19x28in) s. gouache. 14-May-4 Dobiaschofsky, Bern #26/R est:5500 (S.FR 6000)
£3400 $5644 €4964 Vue d'unterseen vers le Lac de Thoune dans le Ct. de Berne (39x58cm-15x23in) s.i. W/C gouache. 1-Oct-3 Sotheby's, Olympia #253/R est:2000-3000
£3620 $6262 €5285 Lac de Canton de Berne (47x69cm-19x27in) gouache. 9-Dec-3 Sotheby's, Zurich #6/R est:6000-8000 (S.FR 8000)
£5882 $10000 €8588 Vue de Bacharach et de la ruine Stahleck. Vue d'Oberwesel (32x48cm-13x19in) s.i. gouache pair. 19-Nov-3 Fischer, Luzern #1141/R est:8000-12000 (S.FR 13000)
£6787 $11742 €9909 Vue du Glacier de Grindelwald (47x69cm-19x27in) i. gouache. 9-Dec-3 Sotheby's, Zurich #8/R est:7000-9000 (S.FR 15000)

BLEULER, Johann Ludwig (attrib) (1792-1850) Swiss
Works on paper
£1897 $3395 €2770 Interlaken (49x70cm-19x28in) gouache. 14-May-4 Dobiaschofsky, Bern #16/R est:4500 (S.FR 4400)

BLEY, Fredo (1929-) German?
£280 $467 €400 Summer wooded landscape (37x41cm-15x16in) mono.d.76 i. verso lit. 27-Jun-3 Auktionhaus Georg Rehm, Augsburg #8022/R
£308 $514 €440 Moonlit night in the Vogt (18x24cm-7x9in) s.d.1998 canvas on board. 27-Jun-3 Auktionhaus Georg Rehm, Augsburg #8021/R
£420 $701 €600 Landscape (30x40cm-12x16in) s.d.84 spray panel. 27-Jun-3 Auktionhaus Georg Rehm, Augsburg #8019/R
£470 $864 €700 Spring in Vogtland (65x80cm-26x31in) s.d.1990 panel. 26-Mar-4 Auktionhaus Georg Rehm, Augsburg #8010/R

BLEYENBERG, Karel (1913-) Dutch
£959 $1630 €1400 Abstract figure (142x116cm-56x46in) mono. s.d.68 verso. 5-Nov-3 Vendue Huis, Gravenhage #444/R
Works on paper
£243 $396 €350 Street scene, Paris (49x37cm-19x15in) s.i.d.55 gouache. 29-Sep-3 Sotheby's, Amsterdam #201/R

BLIECK, Daniel de (attrib) (?-1673) Dutch
£1745 $3123 €2600 Interieur d'eglise (64x72cm-25x28in) panel. 25-May-4 Palais de Beaux Arts, Brussels #67/R est:3000-5000

BLIECK, Maurice (1876-1922) Belgian
£750 $1223 €1095 Docked steamer with bridge behind (40x54cm-16x21in) 28-Sep-3 Wilkinson, Doncaster #293
£1056 $1827 €1500 La proue de voilier (52x68cm-20x27in) s. d.1922 verso. 10-Dec-3 Hotel des Ventes Mosan, Brussels #213 est:2000-3000
£1200 $2244 €1752 Continental harbour scene with shipping (45x57cm-18x22in) s. prov. 22-Jul-4 Tennants, Leyburn #804/R est:1000-1500
£5000 $8950 €7300 London Bridge (61x78cm-24x31in) s. s.i.verso. 26-May-4 Sotheby's, Olympia #345/R est:4000-6000
Works on paper
£1133 $2085 €1700 Paris (62x58cm-24x23in) s. chk gouache brown paper prov. 8-Jun-4 Sotheby's, Amsterdam #198/R est:2000-3000

BLIECK, Paul (1867-1901) Belgian
£333 $597 €500 Les toits rouges (38x69cm-15x27in) s. 11-May-4 Vanderkindere, Brussels #233

BLIGH, Jabez (fl.1880-1891) British
Works on paper
£1100 $2024 €1606 Basket of wild mushrooms and blackberries (25x29cm-10x11in) s. pencil W/C bodycol. 25-Mar-4 Christie's, Kensington #243/R est:600-800

BLIGNY, Albert (1849-1908) French
£979 $1664 €1400 La confection du bouquet de fleurs (46x38cm-18x15in) s.d.1884. 27-Nov-3 Millon & Associes, Paris #120
£1035 $1852 €1511 Soldiers chatting (33x23cm-13x9in) s. panel. 26-May-4 AB Stockholms Auktionsverk #2438/R est:8000-10000 (S.KR 14000)

BLIN, Francis (1827-1866) French
£294 $500 €429 Stormy landscape (22x30cm-9x12in) s. 19-Nov-3 Fischer, Luzern #2021 (S.FR 650)
£5081 $8740 €7418 Port de peche (52x92cm-20x36in) s. pan. 3-Dec-3 Naón & Cia, Buenos Aires #53/R est:3000-4000

BLINKS, Thomas (1860-1912) British
£2400 $3816 €3504 Four hounds drinking at a pool (14x22cm-6x9in) s. panel. 18-Mar-3 Anderson & Garland, Newcastle #497/R est:2000-3000
£3800 $6840 €5548 Serve him right (24x34cm-9x13in) s.d.90 board prov. 22-Apr-4 Lawrence, Crewkerne #933/R est:1500-2500
£8500 $15640 €12410 Over the gate (27x36cm-11x14in) s.d.90 board. 10-Jun-4 Christie's, Kensington #60/R est:6000-8000
£11628 $20000 €16977 Terriers fighting (51x41cm-20x16in) mono.d.96. 5-Dec-3 Christie's, Rockefeller NY #48/R est:25000-35000
£20349 $35000 €29710 English and Irish setter on a moor (36x46cm-14x18in) s.d.00. 5-Dec-3 Christie's, Rockefeller NY #55/R est:30000-50000

BLISS, Douglas Percy (1900-1984) British
£260 $460 €380 Windley Hall (51x76cm-20x30in) indis sig.d. i.verso. 27-Apr-4 Bonhams, Knightsbridge #211/R
£3000 $4710 €4350 Snow at Sheen (51x61cm-20x24in) 27-Aug-3 Sotheby's, London #1170/R est:2000-3000

BLISS, Gloria and DOWLING, Julie (20th C) Australian
Works on paper
£3306 $6116 €4827 Tracking our future (120x100cm-47x39in) s.i.d.July 1999 synthetic polymer red ochre mixed media prov. 10-Mar-4 Deutscher-Menzies, Melbourne #11/R est:9000-12000 (A.D 8000)

BLISS, Robert R (1925-1981) American
£299 $475 €437 Purple mountains (80x121cm-31x48in) s.d.78 masonite. 12-Sep-3 Skinner, Boston #399/R
£608 $1100 €888 Beach afternoon (81x122cm-32x48in) masonite. 2-Apr-4 Douglas, South Deerfield #33
£1946 $3250 €2841 Against the wall (69x89cm-27x35in) s. boardexhib. 25-Oct-3 David Rago, Lambertville #384 est:1000-1500
£2703 $5000 €3946 Untitled, two boys (91x76cm-36x30in) painted c.1960 board. 17-Jul-4 Outer Cape Auctions, Provincetown #74/R

BLOAS, Paul (20th C) French?
Works on paper
£867 $1577 €1300 Tziganes (83x60cm-33x24in) s.i.d.90 mixed media. 2-Jul-4 Binoche, Paris #11/R

BLOCH, Alexandre (1860-1919) French
£360 $601 €526 Street skirmish (34x29cm-13x11in) s.d.93. 11-Nov-3 Bonhams, Knightsbridge #127/R
£704 $1218 €1000 Marche (20x40cm-8x16in) s. canvas on panel. 15-Dec-3 Gros & Delettrez, Paris #237

BLOCH, Andreas (1860-1917) Scandinavian
Works on paper
£472 $826 €689 Battle scene (28x41cm-11x16in) init. pencil wash. 16-Dec-3 Grev Wedels Plass, Oslo #10/R (N.KR 5500)
£648 $1075 €940 Home from Sweden after discussion 1905 - Fr Nansen and other men in boat (36x50cm-14x20in) s. Indian ink. 16-Jun-3 Blomqvist, Lysaker #1303/R (N.KR 7500)
£1618 $2784 €2362 Guardsmen on winter exercise, Vestre Aker 1895 (36x29cm-14x11in) s. gouache. 8-Dec-3 Blomqvist, Oslo #183/R est:10000-12000 (N.KR 19000)

BLOCH, Carl (1834-1890) Danish
£314 $565 €458 Still life of copper pot and candleholder (42x51cm-17x20in) s. cardboard on panel. 24-Apr-4 Rasmussen, Havnen #2057 (D.KR 3500)

BLOCH, Julius Thiengen (1888-1966) American
£250 $400 €365 Portrait of a lady (25x20cm-10x8in) s. 19-Sep-3 Freeman, Philadelphia #123/R
£251 $475 €366 Policeman (25x20cm-10x8in) s. 22-Feb-4 Freeman, Philadelphia #134/R
£265 $500 €387 Study of a woman (28x23cm-11x9in) s.i. chl postage stamps. 22-Feb-4 Freeman, Philadelphia #108/R
£291 $550 €425 Negro couple (41x30cm-16x12in) s. s.i.verso canvasboard. 22-Feb-4 Freeman, Philadelphia #120/R
£299 $500 €437 Tabletop still life (64x48cm-25x19in) s.verso. 20-Jun-3 Freeman, Philadelphia #268/R
£847 $1600 €1237 Strawberry shirt (71x56cm-28x22in) s.i.verso. 22-Feb-4 Freeman, Philadelphia #107/R est:2500-4000
£847 $1600 €1237 Man dozing in a chair (41x30cm-16x12in) s. oil paper on board. 22-Feb-4 Freeman, Philadelphia #129/R est:1000-1500
£978 $1800 €1428 Woman with a pitcher (87x69cm-34x27in) s. board. 27-Jun-4 Freeman, Philadelphia #217/R est:2000-3000
£1005 $1900 €1467 AD 1957 (46x38cm-18x15in) s.i.verso. 22-Feb-4 Freeman, Philadelphia #124/R est:2000-3000
£1058 $2000 €1545 Peaches and pears (20x25cm-8x10in) s. 22-Feb-4 Freeman, Philadelphia #139/R est:500-800
£1164 $2200 €1699 Girl with orange cap (30x25cm-12x10in) s. 22-Feb-4 Freeman, Philadelphia #146/R est:1500-2500
£3968 $7500 €5793 Emigrants (76x51cm-30x20in) s.i.verso. 22-Feb-4 Freeman, Philadelphia #114/R est:2500-4000
£16279 $28000 €23767 Box Party (91x114cm-36x45in) i.d.1951-52 stretcher verso prov. 7-Dec-3 Freeman, Philadelphia #230 est:7000-10000
Works on paper
£225 $425 €329 Restaurant scene (28x20cm-11x8in) s. W/C ink. 22-Feb-4 Freeman, Philadelphia #112/R
£238 $450 €347 Card players (33x25cm-13x10in) s. ink W/C. 22-Feb-4 Freeman, Philadelphia #130/R
£251 $475 €366 In the park (23x30cm-9x12in) s. W/C ink. 22-Feb-4 Freeman, Philadelphia #135/R
£255 $475 €372 Head study no.2, portrait of a man (28x20cm-11x8in) s.d.1941 graphite. 3-Mar-4 Alderfer's, Hatfield #387
£265 $500 €387 Fish and fruit (23x20cm-9x8in) s. W/C ink. 22-Feb-4 Freeman, Philadelphia #110/R
£291 $550 €425 Street scene with figures (28x25cm-11x10in) s. W/C ink. 22-Feb-4 Freeman, Philadelphia #118/R
£370 $700 €540 Coal miners (15x13cm-6x5in) s.i. black ink. 22-Feb-4 Freeman, Philadelphia #143/R
£397 $750 €580 Academy of music Saturday night (23x20cm-9x8in) s.i. black ink. 22-Feb-4 Freeman, Philadelphia #123/R
£397 $750 €580 In the night (46x30cm-18x12in) s. black ink. 22-Feb-4 Freeman, Philadelphia #138/R
£423 $800 €618 Haircut, shave, manicure (23x28cm-9x11in) s. ink W/C. 22-Feb-4 Freeman, Philadelphia #119/R
£529 $1000 €772 Joe's bootblack parlor (18x28cm-7x11in) s. W/C ink. 22-Feb-4 Freeman, Philadelphia #105/R
£529 $1000 €772 Barbershop (30x23cm-12x9in) s. W/C ink. 22-Feb-4 Freeman, Philadelphia #126/R
£529 $1000 €772 Peace maker (30x23cm-12x9in) s. W/C ink. 22-Feb-4 Freeman, Philadelphia #149/R
£1217 $2300 €1777 Lynching (23x18cm-9x7in) s.i.d.1933 W/C. 22-Feb-4 Freeman, Philadelphia #136/R est:500-800

BLOCH, Marjorie (1956-) Irish
£350 $641 €511 Chipperfields Circus (20x25cm-8x10in) s.d.90. 2-Jun-4 John Ross, Belfast #231

BLOCH, Pierrette (1928-) Swiss/French
Works on paper
£1792 $2904 €2616 Sans titre (50x65cm-20x26in) s.d.1987 verso. 24-May-3 Burkhard, Luzern #118/R est:4500-5500 (S.FR 3800)

BLOCHERER, Karl (1889-1964) German
£316 $494 €500 Lock near Olching (50x40cm-20x16in) s.i.d.26.4.20 stretcher. 18-Oct-2 Von Zezschwitz, Munich #42/R

BLOCK, Emiel de (1941-) Belgian
Sculpture
£1842 $3334 €2800 Because I love you (75cm-30in) s. Portugal marble. 19-Apr-4 Horta, Bruxelles #35 est:2500-3500

BLOCK, Eugène Francois de (1812-1893) Belgian
£451 $736 €650 An old man reading (18x15cm-7x6in) s.d.1848 panel. 29-Sep-3 Sotheby's, Amsterdam #44/R
£4333 $7843 €6500 Figures outside old watermill (77x63cm-30x25in) s. panel. 1-Apr-4 Van Ham, Cologne #1292/R est:7000

BLOCK, Herbert (1909-) American
Works on paper
£1796 $3000 €2622 I can't do this to me (38x28cm-15x11in) s.i.d.1954 brush ink chl. 15-Nov-3 Illustration House, New York #41/R est:1500-2500

BLOCKLANDT, Anthonie van (attrib) (1532-1583) Dutch
£9934 $18079 €15000 Wedding at Cana (87x136cm-34x54in) panel. 16-Jun-4 Dorotheum, Vienna #52/R est:15000-22000

BLOCTEUR, Charles (20th C) French?
Works on paper
£872 $1605 €1300 Bateau de peche pres du rivage (71x103cm-28x41in) s. pastel. 29-Mar-4 Rieunier, Paris #57/R

BLODGETT, Stanford Earl (1909-) Canadian
Works on paper
£226 $378 €330 Silver springs, Indian reservation (43x63cm-17x25in) s.i. W/C. 17-Nov-3 Hodgins, Calgary #122/R (C.D 500)

BLOEM, Matheus (17th C) Dutch
£7500 $12975 €10950 Roemer of white wine, bowl of wild strawberries and other fruits on a stone ledge (40x32cm-16x13in) s.d.1663 panel prov. 10-Dec-3 Bonhams, New Bond Street #104/R est:6000-8000

BLOEM, Wolf (1896-1971) German
£338 $605 €500 Santa Maria della Salute and the Grand Canal, Venice (17x22cm-7x9in) s. panel. 6-May-4 Michael Zeller, Lindau #596/R
£541 $968 €800 Still life with sunflowers (60x50cm-24x20in) s. i. verso. 6-May-4 Michael Zeller, Lindau #599/R
£669 $1197 €990 Yacht harbour, Constance (50x75cm-20x30in) s. i.verso board. 6-May-4 Michael Zeller, Lindau #601/R
£676 $1209 €1000 Florence (60x90cm-24x35in) s. i. verso board. 6-May-4 Michael Zeller, Lindau #602/R
£811 $1451 €1200 Florence (60x90cm-24x35in) s.d.63 board. 6-May-4 Michael Zeller, Lindau #605/R
£1149 $2056 €1700 Steamer jetty at Wasserburg, Bodensee (60x90cm-24x35in) i. verso. 6-May-4 Michael Zeller, Lindau #603/R est:1200
£1149 $2056 €1700 Oberengadin (80x120cm-31x47in) s. i. verso. 6-May-4 Michael Zeller, Lindau #606/R est:1400
Works on paper
£338 $605 €500 Alps from Hof Rieden (33x49cm-13x19in) s.d.1938 i. verso W/C. 6-May-4 Michael Zeller, Lindau #597/R

BLOEMAERT, Abraham (1564-1651) Dutch
£873 $1590 €1275 Cain killing Abel (19x14cm-7x6in) i. verso Indian ink on pencil bister bodycol wash. 17-Jun-4 Kornfeld, Bern #8 est:2000 (S.FR 2000)
£8000 $14640 €11680 Last Supper (39x29cm-15x11in) s.d.1635 panel prov.exhib.lit. 8-Jul-4 Sotheby's, London #252/R est:8000-12000
Works on paper
£1700 $3111 €2482 Standing draped male figure. Study for the drapery of a reclining figure (29x18cm-11x7in) red chk htd white double-sided prov. 8-Jul-4 Sotheby's, London #70/R est:2000-3000
£1712 $2911 €2500 Adoration of the shepherds (9x12cm-4x5in) pen brown ink wash over black chk prov. 4-Nov-3 Sotheby's, Amsterdam #24/R est:1800-2200
£5500 $10065 €8030 Peasants approaching a bridge over a stream, wood beyond (16x22cm-6x9in) black chk pen ink htd white framing lines. 6-Jul-4 Christie's, London #165/R est:4000-6000
£8844 $15830 €13000 Paysanne portant un enfant, l'autre tenant un panier. Etude de personnages (15x17cm-6x7in) blk crayon htd white gouache pen brown ink double-sided. 17-Mar-4 Tajan, Paris #23/R est:3000-4000

£10204 $18266 €15000 Deux personnages debout tournes vers la gauche. Etudes de personnages (14x18cm-6x7in) blk crayon htd white chk brown ink double-sided. 17-Mar-4 Tajan, Paris #22/R est:6000-8000

£39189 $68973 €58000 Cabbage and pumpkins by a tree, with figures in the background (15x24cm-6x9in) pen brown ink green wash black chk prov.exhib.lit. 19-May-4 Sotheby's, Amsterdam #43/R est:40000-60000

£39189 $68973 €58000 Plants at a ruined arch, with a shepherd approaching (15x23cm-6x9in) pen brown ink green wash black chk prov.exhib.lit. 19-May-4 Sotheby's, Amsterdam #44/R est:40000-60000

£61111 $110000 €89222 Interior of a stable. Study of a tree (13x19cm-5x7in) pen brown ink col wash black lead double-sided prov.exhib. 22-Jan-4 Christie's, Rockefeller NY #113/R est:30000-50000

BLOEMAERT, Abraham (attrib) (1564-1651) Dutch

Works on paper

£820 $1500 €1197 Study of a child's head (8x11cm-3x4in) pencil card stock. 29-Jan-4 Swann Galleries, New York #154/R est:500-750

BLOEMAERT, Abraham (studio) (1564-1651) Dutch

£8000 $14400 €11680 Annunciation to the shepherds (77x118cm-30x46in) canvas on panel. 22-Apr-4 Sotheby's, London #9/R est:8000-12000

BLOEMAERT, Abraham (style) (1564-1651) Dutch

£93333 $170800 €140000 Golden Age (47x62cm-19x24in) copper. 1-Jun-4 Sotheby's, Milan #77/R est:10000-15000

BLOEMAERT, Abraham and ELLIGER, Ottmar I (16/17th C) Dutch/Swedish

Works on paper

£9444 $17000 €13788 Design for a title page, and four designs for illustration of biblical subjects (22x15cm-9x6in) s. pen ink wash htd white over black chk set of five prov. 21-Jan-4 Sotheby's, New York #66/R est:10000-15000

BLOEMAERT, Adriaen (1610-1666) Dutch

£3087 $5526 €4600 Tobie et l'ange (52x66cm-20x26in) 25-May-4 Palais de Beaux Arts, Brussels #527/R est:5000-7000

BLOEMAERT, Cornelis (attrib) (1603-1680) Dutch

Works on paper

£260 $475 €380 Study of a woman's head and clasped hands (15x19cm-6x7in) brush ink wash gouache. 29-Jan-4 Swann Galleries, New York #164/R

BLOEMAERT, Hendrick (attrib) (1601-1672) Dutch

£41667 $75000 €60834 Lot and his daughters (167x233cm-66x92in) 22-Jan-4 Sotheby's, New York #24/R est:70000-100000

Works on paper

£1233 $2096 €1800 Vertumnus and Pomona. Joseph and Potiphar's wife (16x23cm-6x9in) pen brown ink grey wash col chk double-sided prov.lit. 4-Nov-3 Sotheby's, Amsterdam #85/R est:1200-1800

BLOEMEN, Jan Frans van (1662-1749) Flemish

£4698 $8644 €7000 Southern landscape with figures (33x41cm-13x16in) 24-Mar-4 Dorotheum, Vienna #34/R est:10000-15000
£10345 $17172 €15000 Mountainous landscape with castle and figures (36x58cm-14x23in) 1-Oct-3 Dorotheum, Vienna #27/R est:16000-20000
£13605 $21633 €20000 Shepherds in Italianate landscape (49x65cm-19x26in) 21-Mar-3 Bailly Pommery, Paris #59
£34483 $57241 €50000 Landscape with figures and buildings (134x96cm-53x38in) 30-Sep-3 Ansorena, Madrid #43/R est:50000
£48344 $87987 €73000 Figures in classical costumes, Coliseum beyond. Figures and cattles in landscape (70x50cm-28x20in) pair. 16-Jun-4 Christie's, Rome #391/R est:35000-45000

BLOEMEN, Jan Frans van (attrib) (1662-1749) Flemish

£10667 $19093 €16000 Landscape with ruins and figures (84x103cm-33x41in) 17-May-4 Finarte Semenzato, Rome #104/R est:18000-22000
£30769 $56000 €44923 Pastoral landscape with figures resting. Landscape with figures and ruins (57x94cm-22x37in) pair. 4-Feb-4 Christie's, Rockefeller NY #80/R est:10000-15000

BLOEMEN, Jan Frans van (circle) (1662-1749) Flemish

£8000 $14640 €11680 Wooded landscape with figures (47x77cm-19x30in) 9-Jul-4 Christie's, Kensington #70/R est:5000-8000
£8054 $14819 €12000 Landscape with fighting soldiers (115x90cm-45x35in) oval one of three prov. 24-Mar-4 Dorotheum, Vienna #31/R est:16000-22000
£8725 $16054 €13000 Finding of Moses (115x90cm-45x35in) oval one of three. 24-Mar-4 Dorotheum, Vienna #30/R est:16000-22000
£8725 $16054 €13000 Landscape with pastoral scene (115x90cm-45x35in) oval one of three. 24-Mar-4 Dorotheum, Vienna #32/R est:12000-15000

BLOEMEN, Jan Frans van (studio) (1662-1749) Flemish

£18000 $32400 €26280 Classical landscapes with shepherds by a waterfall and by a river (136x98cm-54x39in) pair. 22-Apr-4 Sotheby's, London #120/R est:20000-30000

BLOEMEN, Jan Frans van (style) (1662-1749) Flemish

£15000 $27450 €21900 Extensive Italianate landscape (50x106cm-20x42in) 9-Jul-4 Christie's, Kensington #54/R est:5000-7000
£25000 $45750 €36500 Italianate landscape with figures beside ruins (108x96cm-43x38in) prov. 6-Jul-4 Sotheby's, Olympia #471/R est:4000-6000

BLOEMEN, Norbert van (1670-1746) Flemish

£2961 $5447 €4500 Italian street with woman selling vegetables (67x86cm-26x34in) mono. 24-Jun-4 Dr Fritz Nagel, Stuttgart #591/R est:4000

BLOEMEN, Pieter van (1657-1720) Flemish

£1879 $3458 €2800 La halte des paysans (21x27cm-8x11in) 26-Mar-4 Pierre Berge, Paris #23/R est:2500-3000
£2585 $4627 €3800 Two herders with horses, cows and sheep (37x41cm-15x16in) mono.d.1704. 17-Mar-4 Neumeister, Munich #329/R est:1200
£2672 $4784 €3901 Italian landscape with herdsman and animals (38x33cm-15x13in) 17-May-4 Beurret, Zurich #3/R est:3000-4000 (S.FR 6200)
£2818 $4931 €4000 Campement de cavaliers (34x37cm-13x15in) 18-Dec-3 Tajan, Paris #103/R est:4000-6000
£3546 $5922 €5000 Cavalli e armenti nella stalla di un maniscalco (48x65cm-19x26in) 18-Jun-3 Christie's, Rome #353/R est:8000-10000
£5333 $9547 €8000 Landscape with animals and shepherd (26x38cm-10x15in) 17-May-4 Finarte Semenzato, Rome #106/R est:8000-9000
£5603 $10310 €8180 Cavalry battle between Turks and Poles outside Vienna in 1683 (26x38cm-10x15in) mono. panel. 26-Mar-4 Koller, Zurich #3047/R est:12000-15000 (S.FR 13000)
£28873 $50528 €41000 Travellers resting by inn (73x97cm-29x38in) prov.lit. 17-Dec-3 Christie's, Rome #490/R est:20000-30000

Works on paper

£2703 $4757 €4000 Sleeping dog (11x15cm-4x6in) black chk grey wash. 19-May-4 Sotheby's, Amsterdam #61/R est:1200-1500

BLOEMEN, Pieter van (attrib) (1657-1720) Flemish

£1000 $1870 €1460 Military encampment (45x55cm-18x22in) canvas on panel. 27-Feb-4 Christie's, Kensington #84/R est:1000-1500
£1224 $2192 €1800 Berger et son troupeau (49x62cm-19x24in) 22-Mar-4 Digard, Paris #50/R est:1200-1500
£1888 $3248 €2700 La halte des cavaliers dans un campement (81x57cm-32x22in) 5-Dec-3 Chochon-Barre & Allardi, Paris #7/R est:2000-2500
£2500 $4325 €3650 River landscape with bathers and horseman. Figures before encampment (24x30cm-9x12in) indis.init. pair. 12-Dec-3 Christie's, Kensington #116/R est:2500-3500
£2617 $4633 €3900 Rentree du troupeau (27x30cm-11x12in) 28-Apr-4 Marc Kohn, Paris #137/R est:4500-5500
£2685 $4940 €4000 Horsemen resting near well (77x112cm-30x44in) bears sig. prov. 24-Mar-4 Dorotheum, Vienna #364/R est:4000-6000
£10490 $17832 €15000 Scene champetre (42x58cm-17x23in) i.verso pair. 18-Nov-3 Vanderkindere, Brussels #80/R est:12500-17500

BLOESCH, Alfred (1890-1967) Swiss

£262 $482 €383 Farmstead in southern landscape (29x37cm-11x15in) s.d. 14-Jun-4 Philippe Schuler, Zurich #5714 (S.FR 600)

BLOHM, Carl (1866-?) German

£417 $654 €600 Spring landscape in northern Germany (72x100cm-28x39in) s. 30-Aug-3 Hans Stahl, Toestorf #67/R

BLOIS, François B de (1829-1913) Canadian

£2202 $3500 €3215 Floral still life with lilies (54x44cm-21x17in) s.d.1866 verso. 12-Sep-3 Skinner, Boston #261/R
£3727 $6000 €5441 D'Hayson, France (66x89cm-26x35in) s. 20-Aug-3 James Julia, Fairfield #622/R est:6500-8500

BLOKLAND, Marianne (1950-) Dutch

Works on paper

£486 $768 €700 Sarah's meal (90x100cm-35x39in) s.d.2000 verso mixed media. 26-Apr-3 Auction Maastricht #28/R

BLOM, Gerhard (1866-1930) Danish

£323 $581 €472 Interior scene with woman (34x39cm-13x15in) s.d.1910. 24-Apr-4 Rasmussen, Havnen #2285 (D.KR 3600)
£369 $627 €539 Italian village street with figures (60x74cm-24x29in) s.d.1913. 10-Nov-3 Rasmussen, Vejle #16/R (D.KR 4000)

BLOM, Willem Adriaan (1927-) South African

£328 $547 €479 Figure above red ground (55x70cm-22x28in) s.d.70 i.d.verso. 20-Oct-3 Stephan Welz, Johannesburg #615 est:4000-6000 (SA.R 3800)

BLOMBERGSSON, Albert (1810-1875) Swedish

£2308 $3969 €3370 View across Hudiksvall (56x73cm-22x29in) painted c.1860. 7-Dec-3 Uppsala Auktionskammare, Uppsala #92/R est:30000-40000 (S.KR 30000)

BLOMFIELD, Charles (1848-1926) New Zealander

£326 $525 €476 Pathway through Kauri Forest (39x26cm-15x10in) s.d.1923 board. 12-Aug-3 Peter Webb, Auckland #190 (NZ.D 900)
£471 $758 €688 Evening at Lake Whakatipu (21x37cm-8x15in) s. s.i.verso board. 12-Aug-3 Peter Webb, Auckland #36 (NZ.D 1300)
£893 $1643 €1304 Drop scene, Wanganui river (40x30cm-16x12in) s.d.1922. 25-Mar-4 International Art Centre, Auckland #112 (NZ.D 2500)
£1107 $2037 €1616 Lake Te Anau (15x31cm-6x12in) s. panel. 25-Mar-4 International Art Centre, Auckland #146/R est:1600-2400 (NZ.D 3100)
£1119 $1937 €1634 Napier coastline, prior to earthquake (29x39cm-11x15in) s.d.1890 board. 9-Dec-3 Peter Webb, Auckland #187/R est:3500-4500 (NZ.D 3000)
£1142 $2044 €1667 Piha Beach with fellow artist seated in the foreground (26x40cm-10x16in) s.i.d.16/1/1900. 11-May-4 Peter Webb, Auckland #117/R est:3000-4000 (NZ.D 3300)
£1246 $2230 €1819 Shepherd leading sheep to river's edge (29x45cm-11x18in) s. board. 11-May-4 Peter Webb, Auckland #122/R est:2500-3500 (NZ.D 3600)
£1250 $2300 €1825 Central Otago homestead (34x43cm-13x17in) s.d.1893. 25-Mar-4 International Art Centre, Auckland #101/R est:3500-5500 (NZ.D 3500)
£1453 $2601 €2121 Evening at Lake Wakatipu (21x37cm-8x15in) s.d. board. 11-May-4 Watson's, Christchurch #71/R est:4500-6000 (NZ.D 4200)
£1541 $2620 €2250 Mount Cook at sunrise from the west coast (24x43cm-9x17in) 26-Nov-3 Dunbar Sloane, Wellington #72/R est:2000-4000 (NZ.D 4100)

£1544 $2888 €2254 Manapouri lake (16x30cm-6x12in) s.i. board prov. 24-Feb-4 Peter Webb, Auckland #98/R est:2500-3500 (NZ.D 4200)
£1607 $2957 €2346 Remarkables, Queenstown (27x15cm-11x6in) s. board. 25-Mar-4 International Art Centre, Auckland #145/R est:2500-3500 (NZ.D 4500)
£2500 $4600 €3650 Lower Otira Gorge Road (29x40cm-11x16in) s. board. 25-Mar-4 International Art Centre, Auckland #105/R est:4500-6500 (NZ.D 7000)
£2974 $5115 €4342 Lake Matheson, near Fox Glacier (42x65cm-17x26in) s.d.1891. 3-Dec-3 Dunbar Sloane, Auckland #69a/R est:10000-12000 (NZ.D 8000)
£4511 $7669 €6586 View of White Terraces with visiting tourists (32x42cm-13x17in) s.d.1925. 27-Nov-3 International Art Centre, Auckland #130/R est:12000-18000 (NZ.D 12000)
£4710 $7630 €6830 Haystacks, lake Hayes, Otago (40x65cm-16x26in) s.d.1895. 31-Jul-3 International Art Centre, Auckland #38/R est:12000-18000 (NZ.D 13000)
£5000 $9050 €7300 Remarkables, Lake Wakatipu near Queenstown, summer evening (51x92cm-20x36in) s.d.1884 i.verso. 30-Mar-4 Peter Webb, Auckland #155/R est:15000-20000 (NZ.D 14000)
£5357 $9857 €7821 White terraces, Rotomahana (45x60cm-18x24in) s.d.1926 prov. 25-Mar-4 International Art Centre, Auckland #81/R est:15000-20000 (NZ.D 15000)
£5451 $9267 €7958 Lake Wanaka, Queenstown (30x42cm-12x17in) s. board. 27-Nov-3 International Art Centre, Auckland #119/R est:12000-18000 (NZ.D 14500)
£66915 $115093 €97696 Scene of Kauri Bush, gumdiggers at work (125x89cm-49x35in) s.d.1892 prov. 3-Dec-3 Dunbar Sloane, Auckland #48/R est:180000-250000 (NZ.D 180000)

BLOMME, Alphons (1845-1923) Belgian
£298 $542 €450 Place du village (65x65cm-26x26in) s. 15-Jun-4 Galerie Moderne, Brussels #197
£464 $844 €700 Le marche de Veurne (70x90cm-28x35in) s. panel. 15-Jun-4 Galerie Moderne, Brussels #195/R
£676 $1277 €1000 Place Saint-Marc a Venise (54x59cm-21x23in) s. 17-Feb-4 Vanderkindere, Brussels #60

BLOMME, Alphonse-Joseph (1889-1979) Belgian
£386 $714 €560 Village (75x65cm-30x26in) s. 16-Feb-4 Horta, Bruxelles #338
£400 $716 €600 Le pont (58x55cm-23x22in) s. exhib. 11-May-4 Vanderkindere, Brussels #175
£426 $711 €600 Vue de Zieriksee (64x64cm-25x25in) s. 17-Jun-3 Galerie Moderne, Brussels #409/R
£455 $759 €650 Vue de village (61x70cm-24x28in) s. panel. 7-Oct-3 Palais de Beaux Arts, Brussels #530
£486 $773 €700 Cathedral (63x71cm-25x28in) s. d.1934 verso. 9-Sep-3 Vanderkindere, Brussels #28
£800 $1464 €1200 Vue de village (71x75cm-28x30in) s. 7-Jun-4 Palais de Beaux Arts, Brussels #229
Works on paper
£355 $592 €500 Small street in Bruges (50x59cm-20x23in) s. mixed media canvas. 20-Oct-3 Bernaerts, Antwerp #265/R

BLOMMER, Nils Jakob Olsson (1816-1853) Swedish
£1538 $2646 €2245 Girl holding cornflowers (31x25cm-12x10in) 3-Dec-3 AB Stockholms Auktionsverk #2405/R est:15000-18000 (S.KR 20000)

BLOMMERS, Bernardus Johannes (1845-1914) Dutch
£1701 $3095 €2500 Peeling the potatoes (23x33cm-9x13in) s. s.on stretcher. 3-Feb-4 Christie's, Amsterdam #150/R est:1000-1500
£2466 $4192 €3600 Farmer's wife with child (18x24cm-7x9in) s. panel. 5-Nov-3 Vendue Huis, Gravenhage #114/R est:3000-4000
£4321 $7000 €6309 An afternoon reading, mother with her two children (41x48cm-16x19in) s. 9-Aug-3 Auctions by the Bay, Alameda #1487/R
£11184 $20243 €17000 Girl knitting at an open door with a kitten nearby (29x21cm-11x8in) s. i.verso panel. 19-Apr-4 Glerum, Amsterdam #123/R est:8000-12000
£12097 $22258 €17662 Eene wandeling (72x92cm-28x36in) s. prov.exhib. 14-Jun-4 Waddingtons, Toronto #256/R est:50000-70000 (C.D 30000)
£43333 $78000 €65000 On the beach (116x167cm-46x66in) s. exhib. 21-Apr-4 Christie's, Amsterdam #112/R est:70000-90000
£76389 $127569 €110000 Sorting the catch (75x126cm-30x50in) s. prov. 21-Oct-3 Sotheby's, Amsterdam #230/R est:100000-150000
Works on paper
£299 $500 €437 Woman with basket (15x5cm-6x2in) s. W/C. 20-Jun-3 Freeman, Philadelphia #68/R
£816 $1486 €1200 Fisherwoman on the beach (8x6cm-3x2in) init. pencil W/C bodycol. 3-Feb-4 Christie's, Amsterdam #146/R est:1500-2000
£1600 $2752 €2336 Breakfast time (30x24cm-12x9in) s. W/C bodycol. 3-Dec-3 Christie's, Kensington #184/R est:700-900
£1733 $3120 €2600 Homeward bound (17x13cm-7x5in) s. W/C prov. 20-Apr-4 Sotheby's, Amsterdam #151/R est:2000-3000

BLOMSTEDT, Vaino (1871-1947) Finnish
£1267 $2267 €1900 Swans in flight (24x34cm-9x13in) s. panel. 15-May-4 Hagelstam, Helsinki #151/R est:2500
£2535 $4386 €3600 River in snowy landscape (72x62cm-28x24in) s.d.1902. 13-Dec-3 Hagelstam, Helsinki #136/R est:1800

BLOND, Jean le (17th C) French
£7902 $13434 €11300 Le sacrifice d'Iphigenie (104x112cm-41x44in) s. 1-Dec-3 Millon & Associes, Paris #35/R est:14000-15000

BLOND, Maurice (1899-1974) French
£268 $494 €400 Still life with lemons and red onions on white platter (16x24cm-6x9in) s. canvas on panel. 25-Mar-4 Karlheinz Kaupp, Staufen #2359/R
£400 $716 €600 Paris, la Seine (38x55cm-15x22in) s. 17-May-4 Chayette & Cheval, Paris #133
£450 $797 €657 Portrait of a young woman (41x33cm-16x13in) s. prov. 27-Apr-4 Bonhams, Knightsbridge #32/R
£495 $900 €723 Still life of flowers in a vase (71x58cm-28x23in) s. 7-Feb-4 Sloans & Kenyon, Bethesda #1263/R
Works on paper
£738 $1374 €1100 Paysage (55x74cm-22x29in) studio st. W/C. 2-Mar-4 Artcurial Briest, Paris #159

BLONDAL, Gunnlaugur (1893-1962) Icelandic
£4693 $8635 €6852 Mountain landscape, Iceland (73x100cm-29x39in) s. 29-Mar-4 Rasmussen, Copenhagen #275a est:30000 (D.KR 52000)
Works on paper
£903 $1688 €1318 Portrait of woman (53x38cm-21x15in) s.i.d.27 pastel. 25-Feb-4 Kunsthallen, Copenhagen #208/R (D.KR 10000)
£1229 $2003 €1794 Icelandic landscape (65x96cm-26x38in) s. gouache. 29-Sep-3 Lilla Bukowskis, Stockholm #847 est:8000-10000 (S.KR 16000)
£1354 $2491 €1977 Young girl holding mirror (58x44cm-23x17in) i.verso pastel chk exec.c.1938. 29-Mar-4 Rasmussen, Copenhagen #230/R est:15000 (D.KR 15000)

BLONDAT, Max (1879-1926) French
Sculpture
£2800 $5152 €4200 Enfants (19x63cm-7x25in) s. golden pat bronze st.f. Siot-Decauville. 9-Jun-4 Beaussant & Lefèvre, Paris #260/R est:2500-3000

BLONDEL, Andre (1909-1949) Polish
£530 $964 €800 Bouquet de fleurs (34x24cm-13x9in) s. cardboard. 16-Jun-4 Claude Boisgirard, Paris #29
£629 $1145 €950 Bateau au port (26x35cm-10x14in) s. cardboard. 16-Jun-4 Claude Boisgirard, Paris #28/R
£1724 $2879 €2500 Village anime (55x46cm-22x18in) s. panel. 17-Nov-3 Claude Boisgirard, Paris #7/R est:2800-3000

BLONDEL, Émile (1893-1970) French
£734 $1320 €1100 Les quais de la Seine (27x22cm-11x9in) s.d.1962. 26-Apr-4 Tajan, Paris #310/R
£769 $1323 €1100 Le creux de Genthod (33x41cm-13x16in) s. s.i.verso. 3-Dec-3 Tajan, Paris #250/R
£769 $1323 €1100 Velvert (38x46cm-15x18in) s.d.1963. 3-Dec-3 Tajan, Paris #249/R
£800 $1440 €1200 Les bohemiens (38x46cm-15x18in) s. 26-Apr-4 Tajan, Paris #359
£839 $1443 €1200 La fenaison (46x55cm-18x22in) s.d.1955. 3-Dec-3 Tajan, Paris #243/R
£1000 $1800 €1500 Place du tertre (47x51cm-19x20in) s. 26-Apr-4 Tajan, Paris #309/R est:1800-2000
£1049 $1804 €1500 Le passage a Niveau (38x45cm-15x18in) s.d.51. 3-Dec-3 Tajan, Paris #248/R est:1600-1800
£1200 $2076 €1752 Le lapin agile (46x54cm-18x21in) s.d.54. 11-Dec-3 Christie's, Kensington #179/R est:800-1200
£1500 $2715 €2190 Montmartre et le Sacre-Coeur (38x46cm-15x18in) s.d.54. 1-Apr-4 Christie's, Kensington #138/R est:800-1200
£1700 $3077 €2482 Le cirque royal (46x55cm-18x22in) s. 1-Apr-4 Christie's, Kensington #140/R est:800-1200
£2200 $3806 €3212 Les bouquinistes (46x55cm-18x22in) s.d.1960. 11-Dec-3 Christie's, Kensington #188/R est:800-1200
£2238 $3849 €3200 Automne en Normandie (46x55cm-18x22in) s. s.i.verso. 3-Dec-3 Tajan, Paris #251/R est:1800-2000

BLONDEL, Jacques François (1705-1774) Dutch
Works on paper
£1879 $3458 €2800 Les prisons de Rome (19x14cm-7x6in) s. W/C. 24-Mar-4 Claude Boisgirard, Paris #27/R est:3000

BLONDEL, Merry Joseph (1781-1853) French
£5495 $10000 €8023 Study for Les Trois Glorieuses (45x37cm-18x15in) 4-Feb-4 Christie's, Rockefeller NY #35/R est:2000-3000

BLOOD, Brian (1962-) American
£1902 $3500 €2777 Morning fog, Garapatta State Park (40x50cm-16x20in) init. i. stretcher painted 2003. 8-Jun-4 Bonhams & Butterfields, San Francisco #4387/R est:3000-4000
£2168 $3750 €3165 Laguna Seca Vista (46x61cm-18x24in) init. i.stretcher. 10-Dec-3 Bonhams & Butterfields, San Francisco #6342/R est:4000-6000

BLOOM, Doris (1954-) South African
£610 $1019 €891 Composition (150x95cm-59x37in) s.d.83 stretcher. 7-Oct-3 Rasmussen, Copenhagen #256/R (D.KR 6500)
£845 $1411 €1234 Meyerton spoor (105x125cm-41x49in) s.d.88 verso. 7-Oct-3 Rasmussen, Copenhagen #119/R (D.KR 9000)

BLOOMFIELD, Harry (1870-?) British
£250 $418 €365 Still life with apples and pears (20x28cm-8x11in) s. i.d.1934 stretcher. 16-Oct-3 Christie's, Kensington #356/R

BLOOMSTER, E L (19/20th C) American
£440 $800 €642 Tall sail ship in opalescent seas (91x91cm-36x36in) s. 15-Jun-4 John Moran, Pasadena #155 est:1000-2000
Works on paper
£1511 $2750 €2206 Cabin and figures in the South (46x61cm-18x24in) s. W/C prov. 15-Jun-4 John Moran, Pasadena #134 est:1500-2000

BLOOS, Richard (1878-1957) German
£2933 $5309 €4400 Steps in Castle Park (88x72cm-35x28in) s.d.1923. 1-Apr-4 Van Ham, Cologne #1293/R est:1800
£10067 $18423 €15000 Allee du Luxembourg (117x82cm-46x32in) s.i.d.1911. 9-Jul-4 Dawo, Saarbrucken #80/R est:8500

BLOOT, Pieter de (1602-1658) Dutch
£5307 $9500 €7748 Monks distributing food at gate of cloister (36x46cm-14x18in) init. copper. 27-May-4 Sotheby's, New York #21/R est:10000-15000

£10274	$17466	€15000	Village landscape with the distribution of bread to the poor (41x67cm-16x26in) panel. 5-Nov-3 Christie's, Amsterdam #46/R est:15000-20000

BLOOT, Pieter de (attrib) (1602-1658) Dutch

£2817	$4873	€4000	Dancing in the tavern (56x69cm-22x27in) 11-Dec-3 Dr Fritz Nagel, Stuttgart #454/R est:5000
£3378	$5946	€5000	Tavern interior with peasants smoking and drinking (36x32cm-14x13in) panel. 18-May-4 Sotheby's, Amsterdam #6/R est:6000-8000

BLOOT, Pieter de (style) (1602-1658) Dutch

£5000	$9000	€7300	Village scene with Boors dancing (79x132cm-31x52in) 20-Apr-4 Sotheby's, Olympia #262/R est:5000-7000

BLOPPOEL, Antoon van (1879-1971) Dutch

£390	$651	€550	View of Gelderse quay in Amsterdam with Nicholas church in the distance (18x24cm-7x9in) s. 20-Oct-3 Glerum, Amsterdam #181

BLOPPOEL, Jan van (1920-1972) Dutch

£308	$529	€440	Flower market in Delft (40x30cm-16x12in) s. 8-Dec-3 Glerum, Amsterdam #146/R

BLOS, Peter W (1903-1986) American

£1016	$1900	€1483	Woman in naval outfit with flags (66x51cm-26x20in) s. painted c.1930. 26-Feb-4 Illustration House, New York #24 est:2000-3000

BLOSER, Florence Parker (1889-1935) American

£1912	$3250	€2792	First adobe in Los Angeles, cityscape (56x71cm-22x28in) s. prov.exhib. 18-Nov-3 John Moran, Pasadena #51 est:2000-3000

BLOSSFELDT, Karl (1865-1932) German

Photographs

£8667	$15947	€13000	Working collage of flower heads (13x18cm-5x7in) i. i. verso silver gelatin contact lit.exhib. 10-Jun-4 Villa Grisebach, Berlin #1027/R est:8000-12000

BLOW, Michael (?) New Zealander?

£313	$497	€457	Ducklings (26x37cm-10x15in) s. 1-May-3 Dunbar Sloane, Wellington #374 (NZ.D 900)
£376	$639	€549	Pansies and wedgwood (24x19cm-9x7in) s. 26-Nov-3 Dunbar Sloane, Wellington #508 (NZ.D 1000)
£451	$718	€658	Garlic and onions (24x39cm-9x15in) s. 1-May-3 Dunbar Sloane, Wellington #673 est:300-600 (NZ.D 1300)
£521	$828	€761	Kiwi fruit and walnuts (23x34cm-9x13in) s. 1-May-3 Dunbar Sloane, Wellington #674 est:300-600 (NZ.D 1500)
£543	$880	€787	Serenade of love (48x38cm-19x15in) s. board. 31-Jul-3 International Art Centre, Auckland #132/R est:2000-3000 (NZ.D 1500)
£786	$1446	€1148	Pansies (24x18cm-9x7in) s.d.1990 verso. 25-Mar-4 International Art Centre, Auckland #150/R (NZ.D 2200)
£804	$1479	€1174	Dahlias (49x39cm-19x15in) s.d.1982 board. 25-Mar-4 International Art Centre, Auckland #147/R (NZ.D 2250)

BLOW, Sandra (1925-) British

£1400	$2590	€2044	Abstract composition (30x25cm-12x10in) s.d.66 verso. 11-Feb-4 Sotheby's, Olympia #294/R est:600-800
£1800	$3330	€2628	Composition (71x61cm-28x24in) s.d.69 oil mixed media. 11-Mar-4 Christie's, Kensington #373/R est:600-800
£2600	$4420	€3796	Triptych (138x414cm-54x163in) three. 18-Nov-3 Bonhams, Knightsbridge #23/R est:3000-5000
£2800	$4676	€4088	Composition (137x122cm-54x48in) s.d.66 stretcher prov. 16-Oct-3 Christie's, Kensington #703/R est:1000-1500
£4000	$7280	€5840	Abstract, black and white (61x86cm-24x34in) s. verso oil collage board. 1-Jul-4 Christie's, Kensington #379/R est:4000-6000

Works on paper

£380	$635	€555	Untitled (19x23cm-7x9in) s. gouache felt tip col chk. 16-Oct-3 Christie's, Kensington #711/R
£500	$925	€730	Untitled (10x10cm-4x4in) s.d.2002 W/C gouache pen ink sold with another by the same hand. 11-Feb-4 Sotheby's, Olympia #258/R
£600	$1032	€876	Untitled (13x16cm-5x6in) s.d.70 sand paper collage pair. 3-Dec-3 Christie's, Kensington #779
£700	$1169	€1022	Red grid (29x30cm-11x12in) s.d.98 pencil acrylic collage. 16-Oct-3 Christie's, Kensington #710/R
£1100	$2002	€1606	Abstract (14x14cm-6x6in) s.d.70 sold with another abstract d.2000 two. 1-Jul-4 Christie's, Kensington #381/R est:600-800

BLUEMNER, Oscar (1867-1938) American

£894	$1600	€1305	Views of Bloomfield, New Jersey. init.d. framed as one prov. 6-May-4 Shannon's, Milford #237/R est:1500-2000
£454545	$800000	€663636	American night-red glare (58x76cm-23x30in) mono. i.verso panel painted 1929 prov.exhib.lit. 19-May-4 Sotheby's, New York #128/R est:500000-700000

Works on paper

£265	$450	€387	Stanhope in green (10x15cm-4x6in) s.i. crayon. 9-Nov-3 Wright, Chicago #126
£435	$800	€635	Bllomfield, New Jersey. View at Carlstadt, New Jersey (10x13cm-4x5in) one mono.i. one d.1907 black ink pencil prov. 25-Jun-4 Freeman, Philadelphia #65/R
£457	$800	€667	Paterson (13x20cm-5x8in) s.i.d.16 pencil two. 19-Dec-3 Sotheby's, New York #1008/R
£706	$1200	€1031	Untitled (38x46cm-15x18in) pencil triptych. 9-Nov-3 Wright, Chicago #124 est:1500-2000
£707	$1300	€1032	Three drawings of New Jersey. mono.i. black crayon. 10-Jun-4 Swann Galleries, New York #34/R
£718	$1300	€1048	Delaware River, Lambertville, New Jersey (13x18cm-5x7in) mono.d.Sept 14 1915 black crayon dr. 3-Apr-4 David Rago, Lambertville #105/R est:500-750
£773	$1400	€1129	View at Lambertville, New Jersey (13x18cm-5x7in) mono.d.Sept 14 1915 black crayon dr. 3-Apr-4 David Rago, Lambertville #106/R est:500-750
£1176	$2000	€1717	Along the Harlem River (10x13cm-4x5in) pen ink pair prov. 9-Nov-3 Wright, Chicago #127 est:3000-4000
£1647	$2800	€2405	Flatlands sunset (10x18cm-4x7in) s. W/C. 9-Nov-3 Wright, Chicago #122 est:3000-5000
£1647	$2800	€2405	Views of Bloomfield, New Jersey (13x15cm-5x6in) s.i.d.1919 crayon set of three prov. 9-Nov-3 Wright, Chicago #125/R est:3000-4000
£2286	$4000	€3338	Landscapes (12x16cm-5x6in) mono. two d.18 one d.20 one d.16 one d.19 chl five in one frame. 19-Dec-3 Sotheby's, New York #1015/R est:5000-7000
£2794	$4750	€4079	Six vignettes (15x10cm-6x4in) gouache pencil. 9-Nov-3 Wright, Chicago #128 est:1200-1800
£4118	$7000	€6012	Farm in New Milford, Connecticut (25x17cm-10x7in) mono.i.d.Aug 1923 W/C pencil prov. 30-Oct-3 Phillips, New York #85/R est:8000-12000
£12973	$24000	€18941	Sunrise (13x18cm-5x7in) init.indis.i.d.1925 W/C. 11-Mar-4 Christie's, Rockefeller NY #90/R est:5000-7000
£31138	$52000	€45461	Lock, Bloomfield (13x16cm-5x6in) mono.d.20 i.d.1920 verso gouache prov. 11-Nov-3 Christie's, Rockefeller NY #101/R est:30000-50000

BLUHM, Norman (1920-) American

£9202	$15000	€13435	Sneden's landing (91x65cm-36x26in) s.i.d.1958 verso prov. 23-Sep-3 Christie's, Rockefeller NY #25/R est:4000-6000
£30726	$55000	€44860	Inca (183x202cm-72x80in) s.i.d.59 verso prov.exhib. 13-May-4 Sotheby's, New York #129/R est:30000-40000

BLUHM, Oscar (19/20th C) German

Works on paper

£833	$1317	€1200	The admirer (40x31cm-16x12in) s. grisaille htd white. 5-Sep-3 Wendl, Rudolstadt #3290/R

BLUHM, Ursula (20th C) ?

Works on paper

£233	$429	€350	Untitled (27x41cm-11x16in) mono.d.1959 India ink prov. 9-Jun-4 Artcurial Briest, Paris #383/R

BLUM, Edith (fl.1920-1940) American

£442	$800	€645	Still life with bowl of apples (51x61cm-20x24in) s. 3-Apr-4 Nadeau, Windsor #65/R

BLUM, Gunter (1949-1997) German

Photographs

£1884	$3090	€2600	Heart torso (31x26cm-12x10in) s.i.d. silver getlatin. 30-May-3 Villa Grisebach, Berlin #1113/R est:1000-1500

BLUM, Hans (1858-?) German

£304	$544	€450	Church in southern Tyrol (42x36cm-17x14in) s.d.1932. 6-May-4 Michael Zeller, Lindau #618
£419	$750	€620	On the steps, southern Tyrol (36x27cm-14x11in) s. i. verso canvas on board. 6-May-4 Michael Zeller, Lindau #611/R
£446	$798	€660	Brixen, southern Tyrol (48x39cm-19x15in) s. i. verso. 6-May-4 Michael Zeller, Lindau #617/R
£473	$847	€700	Tree by Bodensee (40x55cm-16x22in) s. 6-May-4 Michael Zeller, Lindau #615/R
£541	$968	€800	Figure on Swabian bridge (29x39cm-11x15in) s. canvas on board. 6-May-4 Michael Zeller, Lindau #613/R
£878	$1572	€1300	Hilltop Benedictine monastery (66x53cm-26x21in) s. 6-May-4 Michael Zeller, Lindau #622/R

Works on paper

£270	$484	€400	Landscape (28x17cm-11x7in) s. W/C. 6-May-4 Michael Zeller, Lindau #616

BLUM, Jerome S (1884-1956) American

£2554	$4750	€3729	Panoramic landscape, Cuba (71x92cm-28x36in) painted c.1919 exhib. 5-Mar-4 Skinner, Boston #522/R est:7000-9000
£5294	$9000	€7729	Untitled - seascape (74x91cm-29x36in) s.d.1910 exhib. 9-Nov-3 Wright, Chicago #135 est:12000-15000
£5723	$9500	€8356	Figure in a garden (74x61cm-29x24in) s.d.1913. 4-Oct-3 Neal Auction Company, New Orleans #429/R est:5000-7000

BLUM, Karl (1888-?) German

£310	$586	€453	Cat and kittens in stable (49x69cm-19x27in) s. 17-Feb-4 Rosebery Fine Art, London #587
£473	$847	€700	Early spring in Breisgau (60x70cm-24x28in) s. i. verso. 6-May-4 Michael Zeller, Lindau #608/R

BLUM, Leonhard (1857-?) German

£470	$864	€700	Young woman wearing hat at garden table (110x95cm-43x37in) s.d.1908. 24-Mar-4 Hugo Ruef, Munich #933

BLUM, Ludwig (1891-1975) Israeli

£2131	$3900	€3111	Eilat (51x74cm-20x29in) s.i.d.1957. 1-Feb-4 Ben-Ami, Tel Aviv #4577/R est:5000-7000
£2166	$4050	€3162	Riding the camel, from har Hatsofim to the Dead Sea (27x36cm-11x14in) s.d.1940. 1-Mar-4 Ben-Ami, Tel Aviv #4705/R est:4500-6000
£2530	$4200	€3694	Tivon (27x35cm-11x14in) s.i.d.1955. 2-Oct-3 Christie's, Tel Aviv #15/R est:3000-4000
£4800	$8880	€7008	Market in the old city of Jerusalem (71x58cm-28x23in) s.d.1955. 11-Mar-4 Duke & Son, Dorchester #139/R est:2000-4000
£5120	$8500	€7475	Citadel of Jerusalem, David's Tower (46x56cm-18x22in) s.i. 2-Oct-3 Christie's, Tel Aviv #12/R est:9000-12000
£5247	$8500	€7608	Jerusalem, 1948 (39x66cm-15x26in) s.d.1938. 8-Aug-3 Barridorf, Portland #156/R est:9000-12000

Works on paper

£1566	$2600	€2286	Jerusalem (28x52cm-11x20in) s. W/C pencil. 2-Oct-3 Christie's, Tel Aviv #7/R est:2000-3000
£1600	$2720	€2336	Synagogue of Santa Maria la blanca toledo, Spain (22x27cm-9x11in) s.i.d.1922. 4-Nov-3 Bonhams, New Bond Street #83/R est:1000-1500

BLUM, Maurice (1832-1909) French
£353 $650 €515 Legal advice (25x20cm-10x8in) s. panel. 9-Jun-4 Doyle, New York #3007/R
£1207 $2160 €1762 In the studio (35x26cm-14x10in) s.d.84 panel. 12-May-4 Dobiaschofsky, Bern #347/R est:2800 (S.FR 2800)

BLUM, Robert Frederick (1857-1903) American
£5988 $10000 €8742 Spanish dancer (26x30cm-10x12in) studio st. canvas on masonite prov. 7-Oct-3 Sotheby's, New York #188 est:5000-7000
Works on paper
£4324 $8000 €6313 Kabuki dancers (19x25cm-7x10in) bears artist st. W/C pencil. 11-Mar-4 Christie's, Rockefeller NY #36/R est:10000-15000

BLUM, Rudolf (1895-1973) Austrian
£330 $600 €482 Stampede of horses (97x79cm-38x31in) s. 19-Jun-4 Jackson's, Cedar Falls #259/R
£355 $592 €500 Woodland lake (70x100cm-28x39in) s. i. verso. 16-Oct-3 Dorotheum, Salzburg #646/R

BLUMANN, Elise (1897-1990) Australian/German
£4065 $7276 €5935 Sunflowers (46x54cm-18x21in) s.d.1939 board. 4-May-4 Sotheby's, Melbourne #138/R est:4000-6000 (A.D 10000)

BLUMBERG, Max (1948-) ?
Works on paper
£769 $1308 €1100 Olibrius (65x50cm-26x20in) s. mixed media. 27-Nov-3 Calmels Cohen, Paris #82/R

BLUME, Edmund (1844-?) German
£2439 $4000 €3537 Portrait of a woman holding a fan (124x89cm-49x35in) s. prov. 31-May-3 Brunk, Ashville #666/R est:2000-4000

BLUME, Richard (1891-?) German
£280 $481 €400 Blois on the Loire (64x81cm-25x32in) s.i. 6-Dec-3 Quittenbaum, Hamburg #79/R

BLUME-SIEBERT, Ludwig (1853-1929) German
£440 $695 €638 Child showing a chicken to an infant (25x20cm-10x8in) s. 17-Nov-2 Desmond Judd, Cranbrook #823
£440 $695 €638 Bringing grandfather a basket (25x20cm-10x8in) s. 17-Nov-2 Desmond Judd, Cranbrook #824

BLUMENFELD, Erwin (20th C) ?
Photographs
£1778 $3200 €2596 New York newspaper (24x30cm-9x12in) gelatin silver print. 23-Apr-4 Phillips, New York #82/R est:3000-5000
£2464 $4041 €3400 Mont Viso passengers in Casablanca harbour (32x25cm-13x10in) i.d. verso vintage silver gelatin lit. 30-May-3 Villa Grisebach, Berlin #1118/R est:2000-3000
£4348 $7130 €6000 Berlin Art and its specialities (30x24cm-12x9in) s.i.d.1930 verso photo collage vintage silver gelatin lit. 30-May-3 Villa Grisebach, Berlin #1117/R est:8000-12000
£5367 $9500 €7836 Nude under wet silk (34x27cm-13x11in) bears another sig.i.verso photo exec.c.1937 prov.lit. 27-Apr-4 Sotheby's, New York #30/R est:15000-25000
£5797 $9507 €8000 Auction houses (23x17cm-9x7in) silver gelatine collage. 30-May-3 Villa Grisebach, Berlin #1116/R est:8000-12000

BLUMENSCHEIN, Ernest L (1874-1960) American
£29412 $55000 €42942 Tree covered mountains (41x48cm-16x19in) s. prov. 24-Jul-4 Coeur d'Alene, Hayden #12/R est:15000-25000

BLUMENSCHEIN, Helen Greene (1909-1989) American
Works on paper
£196 $350 €286 Mexico, Oaxaca (23x33cm-9x13in) s. pen ink. 10-Jan-4 Susanin's, Chicago #5037/R
£297 $550 €434 Portrait of Matilda Luhan (46x36cm-18x14in) chl conte. 13-Mar-4 Susanin's, Chicago #6065/R

BLUMENTHAL, Hermann (1905-1942) German
Sculpture
£4247 $7219 €6200 Girls singing (28cm-11in) s. pat.bronze Cast. Barth, Mariendorf lit. 5-Nov-3 Hugo Ruef, Munich #2155/R est:1000
£34965 $59441 €50000 Kneeling figure - spider (104cm-41in) mono. brown pat.bronze Cast.H.Noack Berlin prov. 28-Nov-3 Villa Grisebach, Berlin #74/R est:50000-70000

BLUMENTHAL, Mathias (18th C) German
£1240 $2071 €1810 View of rapids and sawmill (55x70cm-22x28in) s.indis.d.174. 12-Oct-3 Uppsala Auktionskammare, Uppsala #312 est:4000-5000 (S.KR 16000)

BLUNT, John S (1798-1835) American
£3704 $6000 €5408 Portrait of young woman in lace collared black dress (84x71cm-33x28in) 1-Aug-3 North East Auctions, Portsmouth #928/R est:8000-12000

BLUNT, John S (attrib) (1798-1835) American
£1093 $2000 €1596 Portraits of a Lady and gentleman (5x2090cm-2x823in) pair. 6-Jun-4 Skinner, Boston #87/R est:500-700
£2038 $3750 €2975 Watermelon on blue oblong platter (42x56cm-17x22in) 22-Jun-4 Sotheby's, New York #196/R est:6000-8000

BLYHOOFT, Jacques Zacharias (17th C) Dutch
Works on paper
£1259 $2253 €1850 Scene de chasse a courre (23x37cm-9x15in) s. pen brown ink wash. 17-Mar-4 Maigret, Paris #34/R est:800-1000

BLYTH, Benjamin (1746-?) American
Works on paper
£1852 $3000 €2704 Portrait of Deacon, Jonathan Simpson Ward (53x41cm-21x16in) pastel. 1-Aug-3 North East Auctions, Portsmouth #950/R est:3000-5000

BLYTH, Robert Henderson (1919-1970) British
£880 $1514 €1285 Gateway (27x22cm-11x9in) s. s.i.verso board. 4-Dec-3 Bonhams, Edinburgh #15/R
£2200 $3806 €3212 Autumn on the Dee (90x102cm-35x40in) s. exhib. 11-Dec-3 Lyon & Turnbull, Edinburgh #80/R est:800-1200
Works on paper
£880 $1417 €1276 Comrie (24x25cm-9x10in) s. ink W/C. 21-Aug-3 Bonhams, Edinburgh #1037/R

BO, Giacinto (1832-1912) Italian
£629 $1051 €900 Field flowers (104x47cm-41x19in) s. paper on cardboard. 26-Jun-3 Sant Agostino, Torino #91/R
£704 $1218 €1000 Sunset in Ventimiglia (22x47cm-9x19in) s. cardboard. 10-Dec-3 Sotheby's, Milan #6
£872 $1544 €1300 Landscape at night (26x41cm-10x16in) s. cardboard. 1-May-4 Meeting Art, Vercelli #16
£1034 $1717 €1500 Seascape. Mountainous landscape (77x27cm-30x11in) s. card pair. 1-Oct-3 Della Rocca, Turin #219/R
£1064 $1777 €1500 Little chapel (20x46cm-8x18in) s. cardboard. 20-Oct-3 Sant Agostino, Torino #258/R est:1400
£1275 $2257 €1900 Seascape (34x44cm-13x17in) s. cardboard. 1-May-4 Meeting Art, Vercelli #351 est:1500
£1277 $2132 €1800 Boats and nets on the beach (53x66cm-21x26in) s. 20-Oct-3 Sant Agostino, Torino #261/R est:1500-2000
£1477 $2613 €2200 Storm (33x43cm-13x17in) s. cardboard. 1-May-4 Meeting Art, Vercelli #84 est:1500
£1678 $2803 €2400 Alpine landscape (71x120cm-28x47in) s. 26-Jun-3 Sant Agostino, Torino #126/R est:2000
£1745 $3089 €2600 Little chapel (21x46cm-8x18in) s. cardboard. 1-May-4 Meeting Art, Vercelli #175 est:2000
£2057 $3435 €2900 Mountainous landscape with figures (50x75cm-20x30in) s. 20-Oct-3 Sant Agostino, Torino #259/R est:2000
£2083 $3542 €3000 After the storm (30x46cm-12x18in) s. cardboard. 1-Nov-3 Meeting Art, Vercelli #216/R est:3000
£2958 $5117 €4200 Pasture (101x142cm-40x56in) init. 10-Dec-3 Sotheby's, Milan #44/R est:3000-5000
£3448 $5724 €5000 Seascape with figures (100x135cm-39x53in) s. 1-Oct-3 Della Rocca, Turin #292/R
£4514 $7674 €6500 Alpine landscape (71x120cm-28x47in) s. lit. 1-Nov-3 Meeting Art, Vercelli #444/R est:5000

BOAK, Robert Creswell (1875-?) Irish
Works on paper
£280 $482 €409 Bangor from Ballymacormick Point (15x40cm-6x16in) s. W/C. 3-Dec-3 John Ross, Belfast #14

BOARD, Ernest (1877-1934) British
Works on paper
£1200 $1992 €1752 Legend of our Lady of Boulogne (47x33cm-19x13in) W/C htd gold. 1-Oct-3 Sotheby's, Olympia #173/R est:1200-1800

BOBADILLA, Geronimo de (?-1680) Spanish
Works on paper
£442 $791 €650 Saint Luc (14x14cm-6x6in) pen brown ink col wash sanguine black crayon. 19-Mar-4 Piasa, Paris #26
£3500 $6405 €5110 Saint Luke writing, seated on a bull. Two hands holding a quill (15x14cm-6x6in) black red chk double-sided exhib. 6-Jul-4 Christie's, London #95/R est:4000-6000

BOBAK, Bruno (1923-) Canadian
£444 $769 €648 From Springhill Road (76x102cm-30x40in) s.i.verso prov. 9-Dec-3 Maynards, Vancouver #228 (C.D 1000)
£488 $873 €712 Penzance, Cornwall (51x63cm-20x25in) s. i.verso prov.exhib. 6-May-4 Heffel, Vancouver #35/R (C.D 1200)
£744 $1346 €1086 Untitled - stormy pasture (41x61cm-16x24in) s. 18-Apr-4 Levis, Calgary #10/R est:1500-2000 (C.D 1800)
£773 $1260 €1129 Soft summer evening (41x61cm-16x24in) s. s.i.verso prov. 23-Sep-3 Ritchie, Toronto #121/R est:1500-2000 (C.D 1700)
£880 $1610 €1285 Mazerol River (75x120cm-30x47in) s. prov. 1-Jun-4 Joyner Waddington, Toronto #14/R est:2500-3500 (C.D 2200)
£1760 $3221 €2570 Nashwaak River (75x100cm-30x39in) s. prov. 1-Jun-4 Joyner Waddington, Toronto #141/R est:2500-3500 (C.D 4400)
Works on paper
£240 $439 €350 Sweet peas and willow pattern (31x40cm-12x16in) s. W/C prov. 3-Jun-4 Heffel, Vancouver #7/R (C.D 600)

BOBAK, Molly Lamb (1922-) Canadian
£620 $1122 €905 Untitled - spring bouquet (20x11cm-8x4in) s. canvasboard. 18-Apr-4 Levis, Calgary #11/R est:1200-1500 (C.D 1500)
£960 $1757 €1402 Three members of a quartet (70x60cm-28x24in) board. 1-Jun-4 Joyner Waddington, Toronto #329/R est:1800-2200 (C.D 2400)
£1118 $2001 €1632 Daisies. Roses (15x30cm-6x12in) s. s.i.verso board two prov. 27-May-4 Heffel, Vancouver #17 est:1800-2200 (C.D 2750)
£2703 $4595 €3946 Interior (102x122cm-40x48in) s. prov.lit. 18-Nov-3 Sotheby's, Toronto #20/R est:6000-8000 (C.D 6000)

£3252 $5821 €4748 Firework (76x122cm-30x48in) s. i.stretcher prov.exhib. 31-May-4 Sotheby's, Toronto #51/R est:8000-10000 (C.D 8000)
£3795 $6527 €5541 Soccer on the green (75x100cm-30x39in) s. prov. 2-Dec-3 Joyner Waddington, Toronto #42/R est:5000-7000 (C.D 8500)
Prints
£909 $1482 €1327 Flowers (76x56cm-30x22in) s. prov. 23-Sep-3 Ritchie, Toronto #165/R est:1500-2000 (C.D 2000)
Works on paper
£602 $1120 €879 Marigolds with checked cloth (62x47cm-24x19in) s.d.61 W/C prov. 2-Mar-4 Ritchie, Toronto #144/R (C.D 1500)

BOBBY G (1948-) American
£595 $1100 €869 Untitled (41x30cm-16x12in) one s. verso two. 13-Jul-4 Christie's, Rockefeller NY #167/R est:400-600

BOBELDIJK, Felicien (1876-1964) Dutch
£590 $962 €850 Excavation in Amsterdam (12x20cm-5x8in) s. 29-Sep-3 Sotheby's, Amsterdam #170/R
£972 $1585 €1400 Stationerende rijtuigen - stationary carriage (12x20cm-5x8in) s. canvas on board. 29-Sep-3 Sotheby's, Amsterdam #168/R
Works on paper
£4965 $8291 €7000 Flat-bottomed boat on the canal, Amsterdam (36x56cm-14x22in) s. W/C prov. 20-Oct-3 Glerum, Amsterdam #128/R est:2000-3000

BOBERG, Jorgen (1940-) Swedish
£1129 $1919 €1648 Rie and child (79x48cm-31x19in) s.i.d.marts 85 masonite exhib. 26-Nov-3 Kunsthallen, Copenhagen #105 est:15000 (D.KR 12000)
£1254 $2258 €1831 The legend of The winners and the loosers (72x92cm-28x36in) s.d.1964 lit. 24-Apr-4 Rasmussen, Havnen #4071/R est:8000-10000 (D.KR 14000)

BOBERG, Oliver (1965-) ?
Sculpture
£1304 $2400 €1904 Untitled, gasse (26x51x9cm-10x20x4in) s.i.d.2003 num.13 verso film still lightbox prov. 10-Jun-4 Phillips, New York #520/R est:3000-5000

BOBERMANN, Voldemar (1897-?) ?
£336 $614 €500 Paris, les quais (19x27cm-7x11in) s. 7-Jul-4 Artcurial Briest, Paris #100

BOBHOLZ, George (fl.1930s) American
£210 $350 €307 Village scene (76x122cm-30x48in) s. 14-Nov-3 Aspire, Cleveland #93

BOCARIC, Spiro (1878-1941) Austrian
£2361 $4014 €3400 Three women (71x43cm-28x17in) s.cyrillic canvas on board. 28-Oct-3 Dorotheum, Vienna #190/R est:2600-3000

BOCCACCI, Marcello (1914-1996) Italian
£388 $671 €550 Still life of fruit with bottles (33x47cm-13x19in) s.d.1933 card. 9-Dec-3 Pandolfini, Florence #415/R
£576 $944 €800 Fishermen in Marina di Pisa (29x69cm-11x27in) s. board. 10-Jun-3 Pandolfini, Florence #388/R
Works on paper
£464 $844 €700 Fiorenza (69x49cm-27x19in) s. s.i.d.1968 verso encaustic board. 17-Jun-4 Galleria Pananti, Florence #59/R

BOCCANERA, Giacinto (1666-1746) Italian
Works on paper
£700 $1281 €1022 Two sainted monks, disputing (21x18cm-8x7in) i. brown ink. 7-Jul-4 Bonhams, Knightsbridge #19/R

BOCCHECIAMPE, Vikentios (1856-1933) Greek
Works on paper
£4800 $8592 €7008 Smiling beauty (53x38cm-21x15in) s. W/C. 11-May-4 Bonhams, New Bond Street #6/R est:2500-3500

BOCCHETTI, Gaetano (1888-1992) Italian
£915 $1520 €1300 L'Assunta (89x68cm-35x27in) s.i. wood. 11-Jun-3 Christie's, Rome #160/R

BOCCHI, Faustino (1659-1742) Italian
£6333 $11337 €9500 Hunchback village (90x125cm-35x49in) prov. 13-May-4 Babuino, Rome #103/R est:7000-9000
£17483 $30070 €25000 Battle between dwarfs and frogs. Defeat of the frogs (47x68cm-19x27in) pair. 2-Dec-3 Sotheby's, Milan #118/R est:25000-35000
£38926 $69678 €58000 Dwarf couple trying to escape from a parrot (42x33cm-17x13in) s. on slate prov.lit. 26-May-4 Porro, Milan #43/R est:60000-80000

BOCCHI, Faustino (attrib) (1659-1742) Italian
Works on paper
£263 $484 €400 Four dwarfs (13x35cm-5x14in) pencil. 22-Jun-4 Sotheby's, Milan #102

BOCCIONI, Umberto (1882-1916) Italian
Prints
£4414 $7371 €6400 Those who stay. Farewell (26x35cm-10x14in) i. xilograph two exec.1912. 13-Nov-3 Finarte Semenzato, Rome #29/R est:800-1200
Works on paper
£2183 $3974 €3187 Due machiete virili (18x23cm-7x9in) mono.i. pencil chl. 17-Jun-4 Kornfeld, Bern #213 est:4000 (S.FR 5000)
£3057 $5563 €4463 Figura in movimento (26x20cm-10x8in) i. i. verso pencil. 17-Jun-4 Kornfeld, Bern #214 est:5000 (S.FR 7000)

BOCH, Anna (1848-1933) Belgian
£1342 $2483 €2000 Still life with fish (24x31cm-9x12in) s. board. 15-Mar-4 Sotheby's, Amsterdam #160/R est:1000-1500
£2400 $4416 €3600 Crepuscule sur la Meuse (25x36cm-10x14in) s. 14-Jun-4 Horta, Bruxelles #81 est:2000-2500
£5986 $10356 €8500 La petite boutique, Veere (44x63cm-17x25in) s. 13-Dec-3 De Vuyst, Lokeren #555/R est:8500-10000
£22667 $40800 €34000 Chaumiere au Domaine Parmentier (112x162cm-44x64in) s. 20-Apr-4 Galerie Moderne, Brussels #384/R est:30000-40000
£26846 $49664 €40000 Au jardin (70x59cm-28x23in) s. 15-Mar-4 Horta, Bruxelles #117/R est:25000-30000

BOCH, Anna (attrib) (1848-1933) Belgian
£1293 $2314 €1900 Jardin fleuri (45x60cm-18x24in) 16-Mar-4 Vanderkindere, Brussels #90 est:200-300

BOCHMANN, Gregor von (elder) (1850-1930) German
£364 $607 €520 Farmstead in Estland (17x26cm-7x10in) s. board. 28-Jun-3 Bolland & Marotz, Bremen #613
£559 $934 €800 Forest clearing (13x18cm-5x7in) s. board. 28-Jun-3 Bolland & Marotz, Bremen #614
£667 $1213 €1000 Peasant on horseback in a summer landscape (13x8cm-5x3in) s. panel. 1-Jul-4 Van Ham, Cologne #1220/R
£1200 $2184 €1800 Village scene with horse-drawn carriages (17x24cm-7x9in) s. panel. 1-Jul-4 Van Ham, Cologne #1221/R est:3500
£1557 $2787 €2273 Gentleman with glass of wine (33x41cm-13x16in) s. 12-May-4 Dunbar Sloane, Wellington #105/R est:5000-8000 (NZ.D 4500)
Works on paper
£374 $670 €550 Hungarian peasants with horses outside farmstead (41x51cm-16x20in) s. W/C. 18-Mar-4 Neumeister, Munich #2486/R
£1259 $2140 €1800 Baltic peasants harvesting (73x99cm-29x39in) s. W/C paper on board on panel. 21-Nov-3 Reiss & Sohn, Konigstein #3/R est:800

BOCHMANN, Gregor von (elder-attrib) (1850-1930) German
£1181 $1924 €1700 Barn interior with cows and goats (51x72cm-20x28in) s. 25-Sep-3 Dr Fritz Nagel, Stuttgart #1325/R est:1800

BOCHNER, Mel (1940-) American
£2083 $3750 €3041 Untitled (29x21cm-11x8in) s.d.1982/1986 acrylic chl paper. 24-Apr-4 David Rago, Lambertville #47/R est:2000-4000
Works on paper
£2060 $3750 €3008 Third black quartet (49x65cm-19x26in) s.d.1987 mixed media prov. 29-Jun-4 Sotheby's, New York #573/R est:3000-4000
£2361 $4250 €3447 Untitled (38x50cm-15x20in) s.d.1973/74 pastel prov. 24-Apr-4 David Rago, Lambertville #528/R est:2000-4000
£2533 $4661 €3800 Counting alternative series, L branch, first reading (57x76cm-22x30in) s.i.d.1971 blk ink pencil col crayon. 9-Jun-4 Christie's, Amsterdam #177/R est:2000-3000

BOCION, François (1828-1890) Swiss
£1293 $2315 €1888 Vue de l'Ile Saint Pierre sur le lac de Bienne (9x25cm-4x10in) cardboard. painted c.1870 prov. 13-May-4 Pierre Berge, Paris #6/R est:3000-4000 (S.FR 3000)
£3017 $5552 €4405 Lake Geneva (25x37cm-10x15in) st.sig. paper on board. 26-Mar-4 Koller, Zurich #3100/R est:6000-9000 (S.FR 7000)
£3879 $6944 €5663 Rochers de Rivaz (43x29cm-17x11in) d.8.5.86 canvas on board. 14-May-4 Dobiaschofsky, Bern #73/R est:9000 (S.FR 9000)
£6579 $12105 €9605 Coast near Chillon (29x43cm-11x17in) d.89 prov.exhib.lit. 23-Jun-4 Koller, Zurich #3002/R est:15000-22000 (S.FR 15000)
£6897 $12345 €10070 Le port de Rapallo (30x50cm-12x20in) s. 14-May-4 Dobiaschofsky, Bern #64/R est:24000 (S.FR 16000)
£7240 $12525 €10570 Ruelle a San Remo (42x27cm-17x11in) i.d.1883. 9-Dec-3 Sotheby's, Zurich #22/R est:6000-8000 (S.FR 16000)
£10811 $18595 €15784 Lake landscape (28x43cm-11x17in) s.i. exhib. 2-Dec-3 Koller, Zurich #3003a/R est:10000-15000 (S.FR 24000)
Works on paper
£340 $609 €500 Un homme a cheval, avec deux etudes subsidiaires de la tete du cheval (33x38cm-13x15in) graphite grattages prov. 18-Mar-4 Christie's, Paris #208
£841 $1404 €1228 Paysage du Lac Leman avec la vue des Dents du Midi (9x17cm-4x7in) col ink. 16-Nov-3 Koller, Geneva #423 (S.FR 1915)

BOCION, François (attrib) (1828-1890) Swiss
£381 $610 €552 Goat (14x18cm-6x7in) paper on board. 15-May-3 Stuker, Bern #1078 (S.FR 800)
£1905 $3048 €2762 Donkey with saddle (17x22cm-7x9in) paper on board. 15-May-3 Stuker, Bern #1077/R est:2000-3000 (S.FR 4000)

BOCK, Adolf (1890-1968) Finnish
£1958 $3329 €2800 The sailing vessel Fennia on stormy seas (50x60cm-20x24in) s. 29-Nov-3 Bukowskis, Helsinki #88/R est:2500-3000
£2414 $4466 €3500 Busy northern harbour (29x46cm-11x18in) s.d.1937. 14-Feb-4 Hans Stahl, Hamburg #125/R est:3500
£3099 $5361 €4400 The imperial pleasure yacht (69x100cm-27x39in) s.d.1913. 13-Dec-3 Hagelstam, Helsinki #66/R est:3500
£4225 $7310 €6000 Ship's portrait Suomen Joutsen (50x80cm-20x31in) s.d.1932 exhib. 13-Dec-3 Hagelstam, Helsinki #65/R est:5000
Works on paper
£1408 $2437 €2000 Vessel with full sails (30x450cm-12x177in) s.d.1950 gouache. 13-Dec-3 Hagelstam, Helsinki #64/R est:2200
£1831 $3168 €2600 Vessels and aeroplanes (40x27cm-16x11in) s.d.1918 gouache. 13-Dec-3 Hagelstam, Helsinki #63/R est:2000

£2113 $3655 €3000 Naval base visit (31x44cm-12x17in) s.d.1926 W/C exhib. 13-Dec-3 Hagelstam, Helsinki #62/R est:2000

BOCK, Adolf Georg Friedrich (1854-1917) German

£559 $934 €800 Royal Yacht Hohenzollern (69x100cm-27x39in) s.d.1913. 28-Jun-3 Bolland & Marotz, Bremen #615/R
£972 $1585 €1400 Pious maiden (70x49cm-28x19in) s.i. panel. 29-Sep-3 Sotheby's, Amsterdam #43/R

BOCK, Alfred (20th C) German

Works on paper
£286 $521 €418 Portrait of a boy (37x25cm-15x10in) s. W/C. 16-Jun-4 Deutscher-Menzies, Melbourne #554/R (A.D 750)

BOCK, Hans (elder) (1550-1623) Swiss

Works on paper
£3147 $5350 €4500 Four men on horseback in alpine landscape with lake (16x43cm-6x17in) s. sepia wash Indian ink brush. 21-Nov-3 Reiss & Sohn, Konigstein #45/R est:3000

BOCK, Hans (younger-attrib) (1573-1626) Swiss

Works on paper
£537 $988 €800 Venus and Mars (26x18cm-10x7in) i. verso pen Indian ink brush. 26-Mar-4 Venator & Hansten, Koln #1326

BOCK, Ludwig (1886-1955) German

Works on paper
£268 $481 €400 Still life with roses and peach. 25-May-4 Karl & Faber, Munich #465
£1333 $2387 €2000 Bordello (49x38cm-19x15in) s. pencil Indian ink W/C gouache double-sided prov. 14-May-4 Ketterer, Munich #4/R est:2000-3000

BOCK, Theophile Emile Achille de (1851-1904) Dutch

£467 $840 €700 View in a forest (21x13cm-8x5in) s. panel. 21-Apr-4 Christie's, Amsterdam #109/R
£543 $1000 €793 Figure in a rural landscape (19x28cm-7x11in) s. 27-Jun-4 Freeman, Philadelphia #12/R
£567 $948 €800 Rider under a drawbridge (33x46cm-13x18in) s. 20-Oct-3 Glerum, Amsterdam #69/R
£699 $1203 €1000 Wooded landscape (24x37cm-9x15in) s. canvas on panel. 7-Dec-3 Sotheby's, Amsterdam #601/R
£769 $1323 €1100 Bridge over a brook (39x59cm-15x23in) 8-Dec-3 Glerum, Amsterdam #23/R
£816 $1461 €1200 Cows in summer landscape with trees (42x30cm-17x12in) s. panel. 20-Mar-4 Bergmann, Erlangen #1166
£884 $1610 €1300 On a country path (24x18cm-9x7in) indis sig. panel. 3-Feb-4 Christie's, Amsterdam #131/R est:1200-1600
£909 $1563 €1300 Cows in a meadow (24x30cm-9x12in) s. 7-Dec-3 Sotheby's, Amsterdam #600/R
£958 $1600 €1399 Lowlands landscape (33x51cm-13x20in) s. 16-Nov-3 William Jenack, New York #368 est:3000-4000
£959 $1630 €1400 Paysanne sur la lande (34x59cm-13x23in) s. 9-Nov-3 Eric Pillon, Calais #41/R
£1250 $2263 €1900 Figures on a sandy path in the dunes, a house in the background (28x40cm-11x16in) s. canvas on panel. 19-Apr-4 Glerum, Amsterdam #102/R est:2000-3000
£1275 $2359 €1900 Draw bridge with windmill de Adriaan, Haarlem (23x36cm-9x14in) s. canvas on panel. 15-Mar-4 Sotheby's, Amsterdam #105/R est:1500-2000
£1678 $2887 €2400 Trees (47x36cm-19x14in) s. 8-Dec-3 Glerum, Amsterdam #32/R
£2000 $3600 €3000 Forest (49x36cm-19x14in) s. canvas on panel prov.exhib. 21-Apr-4 Christie's, Amsterdam #107/R est:1200-1600
£3472 $5799 €5000 Farm in a polder landscape (40x60cm-16x24in) s. prov. 21-Oct-3 Sotheby's, Amsterdam #133/R est:3000-5000
£5208 $8854 €7500 Polder landscape with a farm at dusk (53x75cm-21x30in) s. 28-Oct-3 Christie's, Amsterdam #143/R est:6000-8000
£5333 $9600 €8000 View of Castle Doorwerth from the grounds (65x55cm-26x22in) s. prov.exhib. 21-Apr-4 Christie's, Amsterdam #95/R est:7000-9000
£5667 $10200 €8500 October, birch trees by the dunes in autumn (125x110cm-49x43in) s.d. init.i.d.1900 verso prov.exhib. 21-Apr-4 Christie's, Amsterdam #110/R est:7000-9000
£6944 $11806 €10000 River landscape with vessels, a city beyond (70x115cm-28x45in) s. indis.d. prov.lit. 28-Oct-3 Christie's, Amsterdam #137/R est:12000-16000

BOCK, Theophile Emile Achille de (attrib) (1851-1904) Dutch

£816 $1486 €1200 Sunset on a country road (40x60cm-16x24in) indis sig. canvas on plywood. 3-Feb-4 Christie's, Amsterdam #134 est:400-600

BOCKLIN, Arnold (1827-1901) Swiss

Sculpture
£94000 $162620 €137240 Shield with the head of Medusa (60cm-24in) polychrome gilded plaster prov.exhib. 12-Dec-3 Sotheby's, London #270/R est:25000-35000
Works on paper
£633 $1000 €924 Triton and Naevide (8x15cm-3x6in) init. st.i.verso. 7-Sep-3 Treadway Gallery, Cincinnati #543/R

BOCKSTIEGEL, Peter August (1889-1951) German

£9396 $17289 €14000 Still life (50x55cm-20x22in) s.i.d. masonite. 26-Mar-4 Ketterer, Hamburg #330/R est:11000-14000
Prints
£2098 $3566 €3000 Sonja and Hanna (54x70cm-21x28in) s.i.d.97 col lithograph. 29-Nov-3 Bassenge, Berlin #6641/R est:4000
£2238 $3849 €3200 Peasant speaking (65x51cm-26x20in) s.i. lithograph. 2-Dec-3 Hauswedell & Nolte, Hamburg #54/R est:3000
£2416 $4446 €3600 Peasant children (70x54cm-28x21in) s.mono.i. col lithograph. 26-Mar-4 Ketterer, Hamburg #334/R est:2500-3000
Works on paper
£2200 $3960 €3212 Village street (64x48cm-25x19in) s.d.1939 pastel gouache. 20-Jan-4 Bonhams, Knightsbridge #263/R est:2000-3000

BODA, Bela (20th C) American

£331 $600 €483 Southwestern landscape at sunset (61x91cm-24x36in) s. board. 3-Apr-4 Charlton Hall, Columbia #650/R

BODARD, Pierre (1881-1937) French

£594 $1010 €850 Rue en Afrique du Nord (23x33cm-9x13in) s. panel. 28-Nov-3 Doutrebente, Paris #25
£1973 $3531 €2900 Arbre du voyageur (61x50cm-24x20in) s. 21-Mar-4 St-Germain-en-Laye Encheres #109/R est:2000

BODDINGTON, Edwin H (1836-1905) British

£300 $549 €438 River landscape with figure fishing (19x34cm-7x13in) s. 6-Apr-4 Bonhams, Knightsbridge #156/R
£556 $928 €800 Near Shiplake (29x48cm-11x19in) s.d. 24-Oct-3 Ketterer, Hamburg #44/R
£593 $961 €860 Landscape with figures fishing at sunset (30x61cm-12x24in) mono.d.72. 4-Aug-3 Rasmussen, Vejle #430/R (D.KR 6200)
£1400 $2562 €2044 Landscape with men fishing (46x81cm-18x32in) s. 7-Apr-4 Gardiner & Houlgate, Bath #336/R est:1600-2400

BODDINGTON, Edwin H (attrib) (1836-1905) British

£360 $648 €526 Peaceful river landscape in summer, with cattle and fishermen (21x45cm-8x18in) 22-Apr-4 Lawrence, Crewkerne #904/R

BODDINGTON, Henry John (1811-1865) British

£1100 $1870 €1606 Welsh glen (112x86cm-44x34in) 18-Nov-3 Sotheby's, Olympia #188/R est:1200-1800
£4000 $6360 €5840 Extensive landscape with children beside a stream (48x81cm-19x32in) s.d.1847. 9-Sep-3 Gorringes, Lewes #1850/R est:1800-2000
£4200 $6972 €6132 Evening on the Greta (75x126cm-30x50in) s.d.1860. 1-Oct-3 Woolley & Wallis, Salisbury #309/R est:4000-6000
£6704 $12000 €9788 Figures fishing by stream. Children resting on stream banks (76x63cm-30x25in) one s. pair. 27-May-4 Sotheby's, New York #279/R est:15000-20000
£8500 $14110 €12410 Scottish loch (73x120cm-29x47in) 1-Oct-3 Woolley & Wallis, Salisbury #308/R est:3000-5000
£10000 $17000 €14600 Sunday morning (61x51cm-24x20in) s.d.1848. 19-Nov-3 Bonhams, New Bond Street #27/R est:4000-6000
£45000 $76500 €65700 On the hills, North Wales (101x153cm-40x60in) s.d.1860 exhib.lit. 27-Nov-3 Sotheby's, London #361/R est:10000-15000
Works on paper
£260 $473 €380 Sheep and cattle grazing by castle ruins (30x50cm-12x20in) init. W/C htd white. 29-Jun-4 Bonhams, Knowle #32

BODDINGTON, Henry John (attrib) (1811-1865) British

£3000 $5580 €4380 Drovers resting in an extensive landscape, windmill beyond (51x81cm-20x32in) panel. 4-Mar-4 Christie's, Kensington #496/R est:2000-3000

BODDY, William James (c.1831-1911) British

Works on paper
£380 $646 €555 Micklegate, York (28x20cm-11x8in) s.d.1890. 21-Nov-3 Dee Atkinson & Harrison, Driffield #763
£760 $1360 €1110 York (24x35cm-9x14in) s.d.1900 W/C. 17-May-4 David Duggleby, Scarborough #606/R

BODE, Adolf (1904-1970) German

£270 $484 €400 Wild boar in winter wood (61x91cm-24x36in) s. 8-May-4 Dawo, Saarbrucken #44/R

BODECKER, Johann Friedrich (1658-1727) Dutch

£699 $1189 €1000 Portrait of a woman (77x60cm-30x24in) s.d.1691. 20-Nov-3 Van Ham, Cologne #1288

BODELSON, Dan (1949-) American

£621 $1000 €900 1579 Canyon Road (36x46cm-14x18in) board. 22-Aug-3 Altermann Galleries, Santa Fe #179

BODEMAN, Willem (1806-1880) Dutch

£556 $1000 €812 Extensive landscape at dusk (36x43cm-14x17in) s. 25-Jan-4 Bonhams & Butterfields, San Francisco #3561/R
£6711 $11879 €10000 Paysage italien anime de figures (90x125cm-35x49in) s.d.1843. 27-Apr-4 Campo, Vlaamse Kaai #316/R est:15000-18000
£8725 $15443 €13000 Paysage italien anime de figures (90x125cm-35x49in) s.d.1844. 27-Apr-4 Campo, Vlaamse Kaai #315/R est:15000-18000

BODEN, Samuel Standige (1826-1896) British

Works on paper
£290 $476 €423 Figures in a country lane with timbered cottage close by (13x23cm-5x9in) mono. W/C. 28-May-3 Brightwells, Leominster #1066
£500 $895 €730 Old cottage near the sea at Margate (13x21cm-5x8in) mono.d.1862 W/C. 22-Mar-4 Bonhams & Brooks, Norfolk #109/R

BODENMULLER, Friedrich (1845-1913) German

£1021 $1767 €1491 Portrait of lady (24x19cm-9x7in) s.i. panel. 15-Dec-3 Lilla Bukowskis, Stockholm #532 (S.KR 13000)

BODIFEE, Paul (1866-1938) Dutch

£306	$557	€450	Stream in a polder landscape (37x26cm-15x10in) s. panel. 3-Feb-4 Christie's, Amsterdam #288
£428	$774	€650	Building yard at back of houses (40x57cm-16x22in) s. 19-Apr-4 Glerum, Amsterdam #233/R
£851	$1421	€1200	Old town (34x49cm-13x19in) s. panel. 20-Oct-3 Glerum, Amsterdam #151/R
£855	$1574	€1300	Landschap met Berken (80x60cm-31x24in) s. 28-Jun-4 Sotheby's, Amsterdam #101/R
£987	$1786	€1500	Birch trees by the water (54x47cm-21x19in) s. panel. 19-Apr-4 Glerum, Amsterdam #218/R est:800-1200

BODIN, Oscar (1868-?) German

Sculpture

£2297	$4112	€3400	Diana (83cm-33in) s. dark brown pat.bronze marble socle lit. 8-May-4 Schloss Ahlden, Ahlden #1044/R est:2800

BODINGBAUER, Karl (1903-1946) Austrian

£385	$654	€550	Mountain landscape, probably Barenkopf (98x67cm-39x26in) mono.d.25 board. 27-Nov-3 Dorotheum, Linz #477/R

BODINI, Floriano (1933-) Italian

Sculpture

£1399	$2378	€2000	Monument to Virgilio (25cm-10in) num.2/3 bronze. 20-Nov-3 Finarte Semenzato, Milan #100/R est:2000-2500

BODKIN, Frederick E (fl.1872-1930) British

Works on paper

£270	$505	€394	Village street with cattle and ducks (25x38cm-10x15in) s.d.1929 W/C. 26-Feb-4 Mallams, Cheltenham #202

BODLEY, Josselin (1893-1974) British

£850	$1420	€1241	Water mill (46x38cm-18x15in) 21-Oct-3 Gorringes, Lewes #1970/R

BODMER, Walter (1903-1973) Swiss

£952	$1524	€1380	Park landscape (41x33cm-16x13in) 15-May-3 Stuker, Bern #1081/R (S.FR 2000)
£2262	$3846	€3303	Tramontane (99x119cm-39x47in) s.d.1966. 25-Nov-3 Germann, Zurich #121/R est:8000-12000 (S.FR 5000)

BODOM, Erik (1829-1879) Norwegian

£961	$1720	€1403	Fjord landscape with fishing billage (30x40cm-12x16in) s.d.79 panel. 26-May-4 AB Stockholms Auktionsverk #2407/R (S.KR 13000)

BODOY, Ernest Alexandre (19th C) French

£2324	$4067	€3300	Riders (40x33cm-16x13in) s. pair. 19-Dec-3 Pierre Berge, Paris #81/R est:2000-3000

BOE, Frants Didrik (1820-1891) Norwegian

£2002	$3583	€2923	Still life of rose (25x32cm-10x13in) s.d.1877. 22-Mar-4 Blomqvist, Oslo #352/R est:25000-30000 (N.KR 25000)
£2039	$3650	€2977	Birch by lake with water-lilies (35x53cm-14x21in) s.d.1878. 25-May-4 Grev Wedels Plass, Oslo #54/R est:30000 (N.KR 25000)
£3042	$5446	€4441	Winter night in Lofoten (47x70cm-19x28in) s.i.d.1877 i.stretcher exhib.lit. 22-Mar-4 Blomqvist, Oslo #333/R est:50000-70000 (N.KR 38000)
£3138	$5680	€4581	Midnight sun (64x99cm-25x39in) s.i.d.1876 canvas on board prov. 1-Apr-4 Heffel, Vancouver #6/R est:8000-12000 (C.D 7500)
£7000	$12950	€10220	Still life with conch shell and jewels (52x44cm-20x17in) s.i.d.1870. 10-Mar-4 Sotheby's, Olympia #287/R est:3000-5000
£14812	$26513	€21626	Still life of dead birds (80x70cm-31x28in) s.i. after Jan Weenix exhib.lit. 22-Mar-4 Blomqvist, Oslo #350/R est:200000-250000 (N.KR 185000)

BOECK, Felix de (1898-1995) Belgian

£268	$475	€400	Portrait (26x20cm-10x8in) s.d.1979 verso cardboard. 27-Apr-4 Campo, Vlaamse Kaai #370
£278	$464	€400	Point de lumiere (7x8cm-3x3in) s. panel. 21-Oct-3 Campo, Vlaamse Kaai #396
£280	$512	€420	Composition (7x13cm-3x5in) s.d.1963 verso cardboard. 7-Jun-4 Palais de Beaux Arts, Brussels #169/R
£284	$474	€400	Composition (13x11cm-5x4in) s.d.1959 verso panel. 20-Oct-3 Bernaerts, Antwerp #230/R
£313	$522	€450	Autoportrait (20x15cm-8x6in) s.d.1969 verso panel. 21-Oct-3 Campo, Vlaamse Kaai #395
£319	$533	€450	Sunset. s.d.1960 verso panel. 20-Oct-3 Bernaerts, Antwerp #233/R
£400	$732	€600	Composition (14x19cm-6x7in) s.d.1959 panel. 7-Jun-4 Palais de Beaux Arts, Brussels #168/R
£468	$782	€660	Child's head (15x10cm-6x4in) panel. 20-Oct-3 Bernaerts, Antwerp #220/R
£599	$1036	€850	Portrait of a man (77x61cm-30x24in) s.d.1949. 9-Dec-3 Vanderkindere, Brussels #28
£667	$1193	€1000	Portrait of Jean Amery (55x39cm-22x15in) s.d.1950 panel. 15-May-4 De Vuyst, Lokeren #78/R
£714	$1279	€1050	Autoportrait (28x26cm-11x10in) s.d.1946 panel. 16-Mar-4 Vanderkindere, Brussels #513
£800	$1464	€1200	Composition avec oiseau (31x15cm-12x6in) s.d.1958 panel. 7-Jun-4 Palais de Beaux Arts, Brussels #166
£833	$1392	€1200	Crucifix (60x18cm-24x7in) s. panel. 21-Oct-3 Campo, Vlaamse Kaai #392/R
£867	$1586	€1300	Autoportrait (22x11cm-9x4in) s. cardboard on panel. 7-Jun-4 Palais de Beaux Arts, Brussels #167/R
£915	$1584	€1300	Mother sheep (28x18cm-11x7in) s. s.i.d.1980 panel. 13-Dec-3 De Vuyst, Lokeren #85/R
£972	$1624	€1400	Embryo (44x15cm-17x6in) panel. 21-Oct-3 Campo, Vlaamse Kaai #391
£972	$1624	€1400	Maternite (24x19cm-9x7in) panel. 21-Oct-3 Campo, Vlaamse Kaai #393/R
£993	$1658	€1400	Self portrait (64x44cm-25x17in) s.d.1954. 20-Oct-3 Bernaerts, Antwerp #221/R
£1074	$1901	€1600	Composition (50x57cm-20x22in) s.d.1980 verso panel. 27-Apr-4 Campo, Vlaamse Kaai #369 est:1800-2000
£1133	$2074	€1700	Composition avec voiture (25x18cm-10x7in) s.d.1950 panel. 7-Jun-4 Palais de Beaux Arts, Brussels #165 est:600-800
£1154	$1927	€1650	Motherhood (37x30cm-15x12in) s.d.1990 verso panel. 11-Oct-3 De Vuyst, Lokeren #86 est:1200-1400
£1224	$2192	€1800	Autoportrait (87x33cm-34x13in) panel. 22-Mar-4 Amberes, Antwerp #187
£1250	$2088	€1800	Autoportrait (39x14cm-15x6in) s. panel. 21-Oct-3 Campo, Vlaamse Kaai #394/R est:1000-1200
£1379	$2552	€2000	Portrait of Joseph Marvel (58x50cm-23x20in) s.d.1954 panel. 19-Jan-4 Horta, Bruxelles #69 est:2000-3000
£1477	$2732	€2200	Vincent van Gogh (24x17cm-9x7in) s.d.1950 panel. 13-Mar-4 De Vuyst, Lokeren #92a/R est:2000-2500
£1867	$3341	€2800	Self portrait (28x22cm-11x9in) s.d.1974 verso unalit. 15-May-4 De Vuyst, Lokeren #77/R est:1600-2000
£2041	$3653	€3000	La visite (48x22cm-19x9in) panel. 22-Mar-4 Amberes, Antwerp #186
£2324	$4020	€3300	Self portrait (85x70cm-33x28in) s.d.1935 s.d.1938 verso panel. 13-Dec-3 De Vuyst, Lokeren #84/R est:3800-5000
£2333	$4177	€3500	Motherhood (62x40cm-24x16in) s.d.1972 panel. 15-May-4 De Vuyst, Lokeren #500/R est:3800-4500
£3034	$5614	€4400	Les Mains (80x60cm-31x24in) s. d.1983 verso panel. 19-Jan-4 Horta, Bruxelles #68/R est:3500-5500
£3108	$5564	€4600	Don de soi (80x60cm-31x24in) s.i. s.d.1979 verso panel. 10-May-4 Horta, Bruxelles #51/R est:2500-3500
£3221	$5960	€4800	The dance (4x29cm-2x11in) s.d.1946 panel. 13-Mar-4 De Vuyst, Lokeren #92/R est:2500-3500
£4667	$8400	€7000	Zelfgave (80x60cm-31x24in) s.i.d.verso panel. 26-Apr-4 Bernaerts, Antwerp #551/R est:6500-7500

Prints

£5705	$10554	€8500	Red zone (46x58cm-18x23in) s.d.1923s.i.d.1923 unalit. 13-Mar-4 De Vuyst, Lokeren #479a/R est:8750-10000

BOECKEL, Louis van (1857-1944) Belgian

Sculpture

£3546	$5922	€5000	Eagle with prey (136x175cm-54x69in) wrought iron. 20-Oct-3 Bernaerts, Antwerp #206 est:6000-8000

BOECKHORST, Jan (1605-1668) German

£12222	$22000	€17844	Saint Barbara (160x107cm-63x42in) prov. 23-Jan-4 Christie's, Rockefeller NY #5/R est:12000-18000
£80537	$149799	€120000	Scipio (158x203cm-62x80in) prov.lit. 2-Mar-4 Ansorena, Madrid #278/R est:120000

BOECKL, Herbert (1894-1966) Austrian

Works on paper

£1538	$2615	€2200	Friends (45x30cm-18x12in) s.d.1929 ink pen. 25-Nov-3 Hassfurther, Vienna #24 est:2500-3500
£2797	$4755	€4000	Self portrait (50x43cm-20x17in) s.d.32 chl. 28-Nov-3 Wiener Kunst Auktionen, Vienna #530/R est:4000-7000
£3125	$5313	€4500	Erzberg (36x48cm-14x19in) chl. 28-Oct-3 Wiener Kunst Auktionen, Vienna #78/R est:3000-5000
£4698	$8315	€7000	Nude (34x46cm-13x18in) chl. 28-Apr-4 Wiener Kunst Auktionen, Vienna #97/R est:7000-12000
£4895	$8322	€7000	Metamorphosis (33x40cm-13x16in) s.d.45 W/C. 28-Nov-3 Wiener Kunst Auktionen, Vienna #529/R est:6000-12000
£6711	$11879	€10000	Nude (29x39cm-11x15in) s.d. chl. 28-Apr-4 Wiener Kunst Auktionen, Vienna #98/R est:7000-14000
£6944	$11806	€10000	Donawitz (38x52cm-15x20in) i. W/C. 28-Oct-3 Wiener Kunst Auktionen, Vienna #79/R est:10000-18000
£10067	$18020	€15000	Summer evening at Lake Klopeiner (35x50cm-14x20in) W/C double-sided prov. lit. 27-May-4 Hassfurther, Vienna #34/R est:10000-15000

BOEHM, Adolph (1861-1927) Austrian

£2159	$3800	€3239	Street scene of three girls under an umbrella (41x30cm-16x12in) s. panel. 21-May-4 North East Auctions, Portsmouth #832/R

BOEHM, Eduard (1830-1890) German/Austrian

£323	$581	€472	Mountain landscape with woman and cattle, Southern Germany (41x68cm-16x27in) s. 24-Apr-4 Rasmussen, Havnen #2212/R (D.KR 3600)
£430	$688	€628	Landscape with trees, stream and angler (69x105cm-27x41in) s. 16-Sep-3 Philippe Schuler, Zurich #3319/R (S.FR 950)
£474	$849	€692	Landscape with travellers on river bank (53x42cm-21x17in) s. 12-May-4 Dobiaschofsky, Bern #348/R (S.FR 1100)
£474	$849	€692	In the Tyrol (53x42cm-21x17in) s. 12-May-4 Dobiaschofsky, Bern #349/R (S.FR 1100)
£500	$835	€730	Figure on Alpine path (48x64cm-19x25in) s. 17-Oct-3 Keys, Aylsham #787
£580	$1096	€847	Moonlit river scene with figure in the foreground (50x40cm-20x16in) s. 18-Feb-4 Peter Wilson, Nantwich #22
£650	$1216	€949	Austrian woodland scene with figures on a path, mountains beyond (68x105cm-27x41in) s. 22-Jul-4 Tennants, Leyburn #842
£789	$1429	€1200	Woodcutters in a mountain landscape. Panoramic mountain landscape (47x68cm-19x27in) s. pair. 19-Apr-4 Glerum, Amsterdam #62/R
£843	$1375	€1231	Mountain landscape with woman walking, Southern Germany (69x106cm-27x42in) s. 27-Sep-3 Rasmussen, Havnen #2179/R (D.KR 9000)
£993	$1808	€1500	Deer in front of a mountain landscape (38x29cm-15x11in) s.indis.d. board oval. 21-Jun-4 Dorotheum, Vienna #302/R est:1500-1700
£993	$1808	€1500	Twig collector on forest path (38x29cm-15x11in) s.d.870 board oval. 21-Jun-4 Dorotheum, Vienna #304/R est:1500-1700
£1020	$1827	€1500	Mountain landscape (63x79cm-25x31in) s. 17-Mar-4 Neumeister, Munich #411/R est:1500
£1060	$1939	€1600	Mountain landscape with figures (68x105cm-27x41in) s. 8-Apr-4 Dorotheum, Vienna #191/R est:2000-2500
£1216	$2141	€1800	Mountain landscape (32x40cm-13x16in) s. 22-May-4 Lempertz, Koln #1482/R est:2000

BOEHM, Emil (1873-?) German
£753 $1281 €1100 Food (78x135cm-31x53in) s.d.1921. 5-Nov-3 Hugo Ruef, Munich #940

BOEHM, N (?) ?
£628 $1087 €917 Landscape with cattle by watercourse (78x118cm-31x46in) s. 15-Dec-3 Lilla Bukowskis, Stockholm #75/R (S.KR 8000)

BOEHM, Sir Joseph Edgar (1834-1890) British
Sculpture
£1000 $1700 €1460 Captain Anstruther Thomson (55x43cm-22x17in) s.i. plaster lit. 28-Oct-3 Sotheby's, London #108/R
£15500 $28365 €22630 Eurydice (78cm-31in) s. marble prov.lit. 9-Jul-4 Sotheby's, London #112/R est:6000-8000
£46000 $78200 €67160 Cremorne, winner of the Derby (60x67cm-24x26in) s. silver ebonised plinth wooden carrying case. 19-Nov-3 Sotheby's, Olympia #164/R est:25000-35000

BOEHM, Tuomas von (1916-2000) Finnish
£493 $789 €700 Still life (33x40cm-13x16in) s. 18-Sep-3 Hagelstam, Helsinki #844/R
£704 $1127 €1000 Still life (27x33cm-11x13in) s. 21-Sep-3 Bukowskis, Helsinki #318/R
£1056 $1827 €1500 Still life of flowers (65x50cm-26x20in) s. 13-Dec-3 Hagelstam, Helsinki #179/R est:1000
£1189 $2021 €1700 Still life (23x29cm-9x11in) s. board. 29-Nov-3 Bukowskis, Helsinki #265/R est:1000-1300
£1216 $2177 €1800 Still life (24x36cm-9x14in) s.d.57 board. 8-May-4 Bukowskis, Helsinki #242/R est:1500-1800

BOEHME, Karl Theodor (1866-1939) German
£1042 $1656 €1500 Sailing ships and steamer on the high seas (50x80cm-20x31in) s.d.1893 panel. 11-Sep-3 Weidler, Nurnberg #327

BOEL, J H (19/20th C) British?
£350 $560 €508 English rural landscape with farm beyond (25x46cm-10x18in) s. 12-Jan-3 Desmond Judd, Cranbrook #686

BOEL, John Henry (19/20th C) British
£287 $465 €416 Fjord landscape with man in rowing boat (51x77cm-20x30in) s.d.1917. 4-Aug-3 Rasmussen, Vejle #420/R (D.KR 3000)
£500 $835 €730 Highland landscape at sunset (51x76cm-20x30in) s.d.1909. 13-Nov-3 Christie's, Kensington #208/R
£500 $895 €730 In Galloway, near Wigton (51x76cm-20x30in) s.d.1906 i.verso. 27-May-4 Christie's, Kensington #157/R
£550 $919 €803 Quiet stretch of the river (61x107cm-24x42in) s.d.1905. 8-Oct-3 Christie's, Kensington #870
£550 $985 €803 Unloading lobster pots at dusk (41x61cm-16x24in) s.d.1903. 18-Mar-4 Christie's, Kensington #543/R
£1154 $2100 €1685 Angling amongst the lily pads (76x51cm-30x20in) s.d.1892. 19-Jun-4 Jackson's, Cedar Falls #50/R est:1000-1500
£1600 $2976 €2336 Highland cascade (51x76cm-20x30in) s.d.1906. 4-Mar-4 Christie's, Kensington #69/R est:500-700

BOEL, Pieter (style) (1622-1674) Flemish
£11644 $19795 €17000 Still life with armour, silver cup, copper jug, silver bowl and pink cloth (167x117cm-66x46in) 4-Nov-3 Sotheby's, Amsterdam #29/R est:7000-9000

BOELEE, Rudolf (20th C) New Zealander
£471 $763 €683 New Zealand railway cup and saucer (30x40cm-12x16in) board. 31-Jul-3 International Art Centre, Auckland #140/R est:800-1200 (NZ.D 1300)

BOELS, Frans (?-1594) Dutch
Works on paper
£23611 $42500 €34472 Extensive wooded valley with Judah and Tamar (13x20cm-5x8in) s. gouache vellum. 22-Jan-4 Sotheby's, New York #3/R est:10000-15000

BOELTZIG, Reinhold (1863-?) German
Sculpture
£1316 $2421 €2000 Ceres (17cm-7in) s. gilded bronze ivory Cast.Gladenback.Berlin. 24-Jun-4 Dr Fritz Nagel, Stuttgart #937/R est:2000

BOENDERMAKER, Kees (1904-) Dutch
£658 $1211 €1000 Tulips in a vase (100x80cm-39x31in) s.d.28. 22-Jun-4 Christie's, Amsterdam #561/R

BOER, Hessel de (1921-2003) Dutch
£658 $1191 €1000 Girl reclining on a sofa (58x80cm-23x31in) s. canvas on panel. 19-Apr-4 Glerum, Amsterdam #255/R
£2667 $4880 €4000 Trying on clothes in front of the mirror (64x40cm-25x16in) s. 7-Jun-4 Glerum, Amsterdam #34/R est:1000-1500

BOEREWAART, Josephus (19/20th C) German?
£467 $845 €700 Summer's day (40x55cm-16x22in) s.d. 1 Apr-4 Van Ham, Cologne #1296/R

BOERI, Francois Jacque (1929-) French
£213 $375 €311 Boy clown (41x33cm-16x13in) s.d.55. 23-May-4 Hindman, Chicago #976/R

BOERMEESTER, Louis (1908-1992) Dutch
£526 $968 €800 De Posthoorn (110x74cm-43x29in) s.d.41 i. verso board sold with sketch two. 28-Jun-4 Sotheby's, Amsterdam #134a/R
£1184 $2179 €1800 Flower still life (120x90cm-47x35in) s. board. 28-Jun-4 Sotheby's, Amsterdam #135/R est:800-1200

BOERS, Sebastian Theodorus Voorn (1828-1893) Dutch
£950 $1720 €1387 Untitled - floral still life (45x36cm-18x14in) s. 18-Apr-4 Levis, Calgary #218/R est:3000-4000 (C.D 2300)
£2586 $4759 €3776 Still life of fruit (25x32cm-10x13in) s. panel. 26-Mar-4 Koller, Zurich #511/R est:3000-4000 (S.FR 6000)
£4167 $6958 €6000 Still life with fruit, flowers and a pitcher on a ledge (63x52cm-25x20in) s. 21-Oct-3 Sotheby's, Amsterdam #17/R est:6000-8000

BOERS, Willy (1905-1978) Dutch
£1867 $3435 €2800 Untitled (60x52cm-24x20in) s.d.1952 oil gouache. 8-Jun-4 Sotheby's, Amsterdam #270/R est:3500-4500
Works on paper
£1200 $2208 €1800 Untitled (31x48cm-12x19in) s.d.55 gouache lit. 9-Jun-4 Christie's, Amsterdam #131/R est:1800-2200
£1667 $3067 €2500 Landschap met bootjes - landscape with boats (49x40cm-19x16in) s.d.1944 gouache cardboard exhib.lit. 9-Jun-4 Christie's, Amsterdam #122/R est:1800-2200
£2133 $3925 €3200 Collage II (60x42cm-24x17in) s.d.1974 paper cardboard collage lit. 9-Jun-4 Christie's, Amsterdam #121/R est:1200-1600

BOESE, Henry (fl.1847-1863) American
£1078 $1800 €1574 Mountain landscape with cottage (56x91cm-22x36in) s. 20-Jun-3 Freeman, Philadelphia #111/R est:2000-3000
Works on paper
£366 $670 €549 Untitled (18x20cm-7x8in) s. pastel. 6-Jul-4 Bolsa de Arte, Rio de Janeiro #99/R (B.R 2000)

BOESEN, A V (1812-1857) Danish
£313 $500 €457 The coast by Amalphi (23x33cm-9x13in) s.i. 22-Sep-3 Rasmussen, Vejle #488 (D.KR 3300)
£313 $573 €457 Landscape from Vierwaldslatter lake (32x44cm-13x17in) s.d.1850 verso. 9-Jun-4 Rasmussen, Copenhagen #1566/R (D.KR 3500)
£313 $573 €457 Palace ruins by river in moonlight (21x26cm-8x10in) mono. 9-Jun-4 Rasmussen, Copenhagen #1851 (D.KR 3500)
£629 $1170 €918 Alpine landscape at sunset (35x81cm-14x32in) s. 2-Mar-4 Rasmussen, Copenhagen #1613/R (D.KR 7000)
£645 $1097 €942 Mountain landscape with wanderer resting (23x32cm-9x13in) init. panel. 10-Nov-3 Rasmussen, Vejle #360/R (D.KR 7000)

BOESEN, Johannes (1847-1916) Danish
£440 $800 €642 Coastal landscape from Silkeborg Islands (39x64cm-15x25in) s. 7-Feb-4 Rasmussen, Havnen #2016 (D.KR 4800)
£567 $981 €828 Landscape from Ringholmen near Julso, windy day (24x37cm-9x15in) mono.d.93 exhib. 9-Dec-3 Rasmussen, Copenhagen #1498 (D.KR 6000)
£569 $910 €831 Woodland in spring with river (65x96cm-26x38in) mono. 22-Sep-3 Rasmussen, Vejle #355/R (D.KR 6000)
£3364 $5316 €4878 Spring day in the woods (88x121cm-35x48in) init.d.1892 exhib. 2-Sep-3 Rasmussen, Copenhagen #1620/R est:20000 (D.KR 36000)

BOETHIUS, Lars (1903-1968) Swedish
£476 $843 €695 Plants in the greenhouse (35x24cm-14x9in) s.d.27 exhib.prov. 27-Apr-4 AB Stockholms Auktionsverk #840/R (S.KR 6500)

BOETTCHER, Manfred (1933-2001) German
£306 $510 €440 Still life with chanterelle mushrooms (30x40cm-12x16in) s. s. stretcher. 25-Oct-3 Dr Lehr, Berlin #75/R
£400 $720 €600 Still life with mask (38x80cm-15x31in) s. panel. 24-Apr-4 Dr Lehr, Berlin #62/R
£417 $696 €600 Dish and skull (28x58cm-11x23in) s.i.d. verso panel. 25-Oct-3 Dr Lehr, Berlin #77/R
£533 $960 €800 Winter landscape (50x70cm-20x28in) s. prov. 24-Apr-4 Dr Lehr, Berlin #60/R
£567 $1020 €850 Seated nude (31x24cm-12x9in) s.d.1964 panel. 24-Apr-4 Dr Lehr, Berlin #59/R
£633 $1140 €950 Moscow roofs (80x120cm-31x47in) s.i.d. verso panel. 24-Apr-4 Dr Lehr, Berlin #61/R

BOETTI, Alighiero e (1940-1994) Italian
£1333 $2453 €2000 Sagittarius for a miracle (29x21cm-11x8in) s. pencil tempera. 12-Jun-4 Meeting Art, Vercelli #487/R est:2000
£11173 $20000 €16313 Ononimo (70x100cm-28x39in) s.verso ballpoint pen paerboard on canvas prov. 14-May-4 Phillips, New York #218/R est:25000-35000
£11806 $18653 €17000 Mimesis (70x100cm-28x39in) pen cardboard on canvas exec.1974. 6-Sep-3 Meeting Art, Vercelli #368 est:15000
£30000 $50100 €43800 Night provides light for the night (110x259cm-43x102in) ball-point pen paper on canvas exec.1974 prov.exhib. 20-Oct-3 Sotheby's, London #32/R est:40000
Prints
£6884 $11290 €9500 Colourful faces (81x69cm-32x27in) offset print mixed media prov. 27-May-3 Sotheby's, Milan #27/R est:3000-4000
Works on paper
£884 $1583 €1300 Alighieroboetti (15x10cm-6x4in) card exec.1975. 16-Mar-4 Finarte Semenzato, Milan #68
£884 $1583 €1300 They sweat (15x10cm-6x4in) card exec.1975. 16-Mar-4 Finarte Semenzato, Milan #69
£1408 $2338 €2000 Composition (34x37cm-13x15in) s. pencil brush. 13-Jun-3 Hauswedell & Nolte, Hamburg #572/R est:2400
£2162 $3805 €3200 Corriere della SEra (49x36cm-19x14in) s. collage pencil card exec.1976 prov. 24-May-4 Christie's, Milan #232/R est:4000-6000
£2483 $4445 €3700 Seers (100x76cm-39x30in) s.i. mixed media collage paper on canvas. 28-May-4 Farsetti, Prato #66/R est:3100-3400
£2657 $4517 €3800 Untitled (72x51cm-28x20in) s. spray paint card. 25-Nov-3 Sotheby's, Milan #108/R est:1500-2000

£2826	$5200	€4126	Contatore (79x60cm-31x24in) s.verso graphite letraset prov. 10-Jun-4 Phillips, New York #619/R est:5000-7000
£3034	$5068	€4400	Untitled (30x21cm-12x8in) mixed media. 17-Nov-3 Sant Agostino, Torino #308/R est:2000-2500
£3623	$5942	€5000	Untitled (101x71cm-40x28in) spray paint collage card. 27-May-3 Sotheby's, Milan #22 est:2500-3000
£3846	$6538	€5500	Untitled (72x102cm-28x40in) s. spray paint exec.1980. 25-Nov-3 Sotheby's, Milan #112/R est:2000-3000
£4189	$7373	€6200	Untitled (100x70cm-39x28in) s.i.d.80 collage ink pencil card prov. 24-May-4 Christie's, Milan #237/R est:4500-6000
£4196	$7133	€6000	Untitled (72x102cm-28x40in) s. spray paint. 25-Nov-3 Sotheby's, Milan #113/R est:2000-3000
£5034	$9010	€7500	Eleven (70x100cm-28x39in) s.i.d.1974 ink prov. 25-May-4 Sotheby's, Milan #294/R est:6000-8000
£5333	$9813	€8000	Untitled (50x70cm-20x28in) s. mixed media collage pencil exec.1989. 8-Jun-4 Finarte Semenzato, Milan #442/R est:6000-8000
£5423	$9001	€7700	Punto di pensiero (22x21cm-9x8in) embroidery canvas. 14-Jun-3 Meeting Art, Vercelli #101/R est:2500
£5782	$10350	€8500	Untitled (100x70cm-39x28in) mixed media collage. 16-Mar-4 Finarte Semenzato, Milan #403/R est:9000
£5986	$9937	€8500	Ordine e Disordine (55x45cm-22x18in) s. spray paint cardboard. 14-Jun-3 Meeting Art, Vercelli #327/R est:5000
£6000	$11040	€8760	I vedenti (75x100cm-30x39in) s.i. W/C pencil paper collage card on canvas exec c.1987 prov. 24-Jun-4 Sotheby's, London #235/R est:6000-8000
£6040	$10812	€9000	Endless chances to exist (34x36cm-13x14in) s. tapestry exec.1985 prov. 25-May-4 Sotheby's, Milan #310/R est:7000
£7042	$12324	€10000	Untitled (87x67cm-34x26in) pen collage prov. 16-Dec-3 Finarte Semenzato, Milan #264/R est:9000
£7975	$13000	€11644	Untitled (23x49cm-9x19in) s.d.1983 verso ink paper on canvas prov.exhib. 23-Sep-3 Christie's, Rockefeller NY #68/R est:15000-20000
£8108	$14270	€12000	Killing the time (97x69cm-38x27in) s.d.78 collage tempera pastel pencil card. 24-May-4 Christie's, Milan #154/R est:7000-10000
£8784	$15459	€13000	Seers (100x70cm-39x28in) collage felt-tip pen pencil card prov. 24-May-4 Christie's, Milan #246/R est:8000-12000
£9790	$16643	€14000	Planes (70x101cm-28x40in) s.i. spray paint exec.1979 prov. 25-Nov-3 Sotheby's, Milan #248/R est:12000-15000
£10067	$18020	€15000	Endless chances to exist (35x35cm-14x14in) s. tapestry exec.1988 prov.exhib. 25-May-4 Sotheby's, Milan #309/R est:8000-12000
£10135	$17838	€15000	Dumb blind deaf cripple (40x33cm-16x13in) s.d.77 verso pencil ink in 4 parts prov. 24-May-4 Christie's, Milan #152/R est:15000-20000
£10135	$17838	€15000	From 415 to 545 (100x70cm-39x28in) s.i.d.1968 ink pencil paper on card prov. 24-May-4 Christie's, Milan #245/R est:15000-20000
£10145	$16638	€14000	Eleven of December 1991 (100x70cm-39x28in) s. collage mixed media paper on canvas exec.1991. 27-May-3 Sotheby's, Milan #209/R est:6000-8000
£10738	$19221	€16000	Ononimo (70x100cm-28x39in) s.d.1973 verso pen prov. 25-May-4 Sotheby's, Milan #306/R est:12000-15000
£13174	$22000	€19234	Una parola al vento - one word to the wind (88x27cm-35x11in) s. embroidered tapestry executed 1982 prov. 14-Nov-3 Phillips, New York #160/R est:15000-20000
£13408	$24000	€19576	One word to the wind (76x26cm-30x10in) i. s.overlap embroidery exec c.1982 prov. 13-May-4 Sotheby's, New York #463/R est:15000-20000
£13423	$24027	€20000	Planes (22x48cm-9x19in) s. pencil paper on canvas exec.1980 prov. 25-May-4 Sotheby's, Milan #312/R est:12000-15000
£13986	$23776	€20000	Signs (70x100cm-28x39in) s. pen card on canvas. 24-Nov-3 Christie's, Milan #235/R est:22000-26000
£14085	$23380	€20000	Punti di pensiero - Thought topics (71x100cm-28x39in) s. ballpoint pen. 11-Jun-3 Finarte Semenzato, Milan #608/R est:20000
£15385	$26154	€22000	From one to one hundred and viceversa (150x100cm-59x39in) collage ink paper on canvas prov. 24-Nov-3 Christie's, Milan #234/R est:22000-26000
£18000	$33120	€26280	Per nuovi desideri. Ammazzare il tempo (19x19cm-7x7in) init.i. W/C pencil set of nine sheets. 25-Jun-4 Christie's, London #156/R est:15000-20000
£18792	$33638	€28000	Disturbing (100x140cm-39x55in) s. i.d.1979 verso prov. 25-May-4 Sotheby's, Milan #318/R est:20000-30000
£19580	$33287	€28000	Inclined surface (143x102cm-56x40in) s.verso pen. 25-Nov-3 Sotheby's, Milan #242/R est:25000-30000
£21000	$38220	€30660	Ordine e disordine (69x70cm-27x28in) s.d.1980 spray-paint wax crayon ink stamp collage prov. 5-Feb-4 Christie's, London #139/R est:10000-15000
£21622	$38054	€32000	Untitled (18x40cm-7x16in) ink felt-tip pen in 28 parts prov. 24-May-4 Christie's, Milan #243/R est:35000-45000
£22000	$36740	€32120	Senza titolo (70x100cm-28x39in) s.d.69 pencil pastel prov.exhib. 21-Oct-3 Christie's, London #62/R est:22000-28000
£22973	$40432	€34000	Self-portrait (29x21cm-11x8in) s.i.d.1971 pencil in 12 parts prov. 24-May-4 Christie's, Milan #244/R est:30000-40000
£28000	$46760	€40880	Alfabeto (107x109cm-42x43in) s.overlap embroidery prov. 22-Oct-3 Christie's, London #39/R est:20000-30000
£28000	$51520	€40880	Udire tra le parole (95x70cm-37x28in) s.i. ballpoint pen card on canvas four elements prov. 25-Jun-4 Christie's, London #153/R est:25000-35000
£32934	$55000	€48084	Undici giorno (110x107cm-43x42in) s.overlap tapestry. 13-Nov-3 Sotheby's, New York #524a/R est:40000-60000
£33520	$60000	€48939	Centri di pensiero (102x215cm-40x85in) s.d.1982 verso ink triptych prov. 12-May-4 Christie's, Rockefeller NY #406/R est:60000-80000
£35000	$58450	€51100	Planes (64x135cm-25x53in) s.i.d.1985-86 ball-point pen on canvas prov. 20-Oct-3 Sotheby's, London #39/R est:35000
£35211	$61620	€50000	World colours (108x112cm-43x44in) tapestry exec.1988 prov. 16-Dec-3 Porro, Milan #46/R est:40000-45000
£47486	$85000	€69330	Oggi il ventottesimo giorno dodicesimo mese anno millenove 100 ottantotto (110x114cm-43x45in) d.28.12.988 overlap embroidered tapestry prov. 12-May-4 Christie's, Rockefeller NY #407/R est:50000-70000
£83799	$150000	€122347	Tutto (81x133cm-32x52in) embroidered tapestry prov. 12-May-4 Christie's, Rockefeller NY #405/R est:180000-220000
£130000	$217100	€189800	Mappa, per nuovi desideri (114x170cm-45x67in) s.d.1984 embroidery prov. 21-Oct-3 Christie's, London #59/R est:150000-200000
£150000	$276000	€219000	Mappa - immaginando tutto (116x179cm-46x70in) s.i.d.1982-83 embroidery prov. 24-Jun-4 Christie's, London #38/R est:150000-200000
£227545	$380000	€332216	Tutto (231x212cm-91x83in) s.d.1988-89 embroidered tapestry prov.exhib. 12-Nov-3 Christie's, Rockefeller NY #604/R est:350000-450000
£270000	$450900	€394200	Everything (212x194cm-83x76in) s.i.d.1987-88 tapestry prov. 20-Oct-3 Sotheby's, London #34/R est:250000

BOETTINGER, Hugo (1880-1934) Czechoslovakian

£2677	$4979	€3908	The three Graces (66x36cm-26x14in) s. 6-Mar-4 Dorotheum, Prague #41/R est:80000-120000 (C.KR 130000)
£5484	$9652	€8226	Bathing (105x147cm-41x58in) s.d.1913. 22-May-4 Dorotheum, Prague #105/R est:180000-360000 (C.KR 260000)

BOETTINGER, Hugo (attrib) (1880-1934) Czechoslovakian

£293	$528	€440	Young boy reading with sleeping dachshund (105x78cm-41x31in) s.d.1924. 26-Apr-4 Rieber, Stuttgart #983/R

BOETTO, Giulio (1894-1967) Italian

£671	$1188	€1000	Farm along the river (42x48cm-17x19in) s.d.1959 masonite. 1-May-4 Meeting Art, Vercelli #30
£780	$1303	€1100	Countryside around Saluzzo (16x22cm-6x9in) s.d.1940 card. 20-Oct-3 Sant Agostino, Torino #157/R
£1300	$2392	€1950	Landscape covered in snow (26x35cm-10x14in) s.d.34 board. 8-Jun-4 Della Rocca, Turin #361/R est:2000-2400
£1333	$2453	€2000	Street in Saluzzo (24x19cm-9x7in) s.d.1938 board. 8-Jun-4 Della Rocca, Turin #248/R est:1800-2200
£1333	$2453	€2000	Saluzzo (24x19cm-9x7in) s.d.938 board. 8-Jun-4 Della Rocca, Turin #247/R est:1800-2200
£1333	$2453	€2000	Landscape covered in snow (26x35cm-10x14in) s.d.34 board. 8-Jun-4 Della Rocca, Turin #275/R est:1800-2400
£1333	$2453	€2000	Castle (19x24cm-7x9in) s.d.38 board. 8-Jun-4 Della Rocca, Turin #357/R est:1500-2200
£1733	$3189	€2600	Peasants with cart (19x24cm-7x9in) s. board. 8-Jun-4 Della Rocca, Turin #269/R est:1500-2000
£1867	$3435	€2800	Church facade (40x30cm-16x12in) s.d.49 cardboard. 8-Jun-4 Della Rocca, Turin #308/R est:1800-2200
£1931	$3206	€2800	Venice (25x35cm-10x14in) s.d.48 board. 1-Oct-3 Della Rocca, Turin #217/R
£3467	$6379	€5200	Cattle market in Crissolo (34x44cm-13x17in) s.d.1953 cardboard. 8-Jun-4 Della Rocca, Turin #268/R est:3500-4500
£4000	$7360	€6000	Sheep market (42x60cm-17x24in) s.d.1940 board. 8-Jun-4 Della Rocca, Turin #276/R est:4500-5500
£4000	$7360	€6000	Critics (35x49cm-14x19in) s.d.1955 masonite. 8-Jun-4 Della Rocca, Turin #375/R est:3000-4000
£4167	$7083	€6000	Venus bathing (74x117cm-29x46in) s. board lit. 1-Nov-3 Meeting Art, Vercelli #210/R est:6000
£5000	$9200	€7500	Chestnut trees (49x68cm-19x27in) s.d.1944 cardboard exhib. 14-Jun-4 Sant Agostino, Torino #328/R est:7000-9000
£5594	$9343	€8000	Alpine village under snow (54x64cm-21x25in) s. board. 26-Jun-3 Sant Agostino, Torino #302/R est:8000-10000
£7447	$12436	€10500	Bodoni Square in Saluzzo (42x60cm-17x24in) s.d.1943 board. 20-Oct-3 Sant Agostino, Torino #313/R est:7000-9000
£7931	$13166	€11500	Circus (51x62cm-20x24in) s. lit. 1-Oct-3 Della Rocca, Turin #316a/R est:15000
£9934	$18079	€15000	Market in Revello (57x73cm-22x29in) board prov. 21-Jun-4 Pandolfini, Florence #207/R est:1600-1800

BOEUFF, Pierre le (19/20th C) French

£323	$594	€472	Belfry, Ghent (41x61cm-16x24in) s. 14-Jun-4 Waddingtons, Toronto #270/R (C.D 800)
£355	$650	€518	Caridevec, Normandy (28x38cm-11x15in) s. 10-Apr-4 Auctions by the Bay, Alameda #1529/R
£500	$900	€730	Belfry Ghent (25x35cm-10x14in) s. i.verso. 22-Apr-4 Mellors & Kirk, Nottingham #1081/R
Works on paper			
£310	$567	€453	Abbeville, street scene with figures and stalls (52x37cm-20x15in) s.i. W/C. 28-Jan-4 Hampton & Littlewood, Exeter #380/R
£380	$646	€555	Rome, figures and boat before bridges and buildings (27x37cm-11x15in) s.i. W/C. 29-Oct-3 Hampton & Littlewood, Exeter #522/R

BOEVER, Jean François de (1872-1949) Belgian

£541	$1022	€800	Le songe (11x15cm-4x6in) s. panel. 17-Feb-4 Vanderkindere, Brussels #7

BOEYERMANS, Theodore (1620-1678) Flemish

£8844	$15830	€13000	La chasse de Diane (94x173cm-37x68in) bears i.d.1641. 20-Mar-4 Binoche, Orleans #60 est:12000-15000

BOEZIEK, B J (1877-1954) ?

£470	$874	€700	Canals in Amsterdam, with the view of the Saint Nicolaas Church (52x70cm-20x28in) s.d.42 s.i.verso. 4-Mar-4 Auction Maastricht #1153

BOFFA TARLATTA, Luigi (1889-1965) Italian

£267	$491	€400	Portrait of lady (48x40cm-19x16in) s. st.sig.verso cardboard on board. 14-Jun-4 Sant Agostino, Torino #119/R
£382	$649	€550	Dawn in Varazze (34x42cm-13x17in) s. s.i.verso board. 1-Nov-3 Meeting Art, Vercelli #2
£533	$981	€800	Portrait of lady with rose (60x54cm-24x21in) s.d.1936 board. 14-Jun-4 Sant Agostino, Torino #160/R
£828	$1374	€1200	Old man (46x39cm-18x15in) s.d.194. 1-Oct-3 Della Rocca, Turin #254/R

BOFILL BOSCH, Fidel (1934-) Spanish

£448	$749	€650	True Greece (46x55cm-18x22in) s. s.i.verso. 17-Nov-3 Durán, Madrid #81/R

BOFILL, Beltran (?) Spanish?

£635	$1200	€927	Picking flowers (85x63cm-33x25in) s. 22-Feb-4 Bonhams & Butterfields, Los Angeles #7013/R est:2000-3000

BOGAERT, Andre (1920-1986) Belgian

£403	$713	€600	Jardin a la riviere (50x60cm-20x24in) s. 27-Apr-4 Campo & Campo, Antwerp #27
£1733	$3103	€2600	Trees (120x180cm-47x71in) s. 15-May-4 De Vuyst, Lokeren #34/R est:1500-2000

BOGAERT, Bram (1921-) Dutch

£552	$993	€800	Composition (70x100cm-28x39in) s.d.1970 paper. 25-Jan-4 Chayette & Cheval, Paris #226
£733	$1313	€1100	Composition 8 (32x27cm-13x11in) s.d.92 s.i.d.Sept 1992 verso paper. 15-May-4 Van Ham, Cologne #466/R
£940	$1719	€1400	Composition (62x48cm-24x19in) s.d.91 acrylic paper. 7-Jul-4 Artcurial Briest, Paris #212 est:1500-2000

£1879 $3326 €2800 Blue (40x55cm-16x22in) s.d.1985. 27-Apr-4 Campo, Vlaamse Kaai #319 est:3000-4000
£2174 $3565 €3000 Yellow blue (62x68cm-24x27in) s. s.i.d.1968 verso oil sand panel. 27-May-3 Sotheby's, Amsterdam #458/R est:3000-5000
£2448 $4161 €3500 Composition hieroglyphique (40x50cm-16x20in) s. prov. 23-Nov-3 Cornette de St.Cyr, Paris #21 est:120-150
£2535 $4386 €3600 Croix (97x97cm-38x38in) s. 13-Dec-3 De Vuyst, Lokeren #32/R est:3000-4000
£2667 $4907 €4000 Poupee et fantome (55x78cm-22x31in) s. s.i.d.55 verso oil sand canvas on board. 8-Jun-4 Sotheby's, Amsterdam #272/R est:4000-6000
£2800 $5152 €4200 Jets du lumiere (33x93cm-13x37in) s.d.58 s.i.d. verso oil sand burlap. 8-Jun-4 Sotheby's, Amsterdam #261/R est:3000-4000
£2867 $4874 €4100 Sans titre (60x73cm-24x29in) s. prov. 23-Nov-3 Cornette de St.Cyr, Paris #22 est:150-200
£2899 $4754 €4000 White border (85x93cm-33x37in) s.i.d.1969 verso oil sand panel. 27-May-3 Sotheby's, Amsterdam #457/R est:3500-4500
£4545 $7727 €6500 Ocre et marron (50x90cm-20x35in) s. s.i.d.Juli 53 verso tempera hessian prov. 27-Nov-3 Lempertz, Koln #51/R est:8000

Sculpture

£1200 $2208 €1800 Geboken wit (37x45cm-15x18in) s.d.75 i.verso plaster paint. 9-Jun-4 Christie's, Amsterdam #188/R est:2000-3000
£1611 $2964 €2400 Untitled (50x50cm-20x20in) s.d.1998 num.14F ceramic round. 24-Mar-4 Joron-Derem, Paris #116/R est:2500-3000
£2402 $4419 €3507 Blue (74x73x13cm-29x29x5in) s.i.d.1973 verso painted plaster on wood prov. 8-Jun-4 Germann, Zurich #33/R est:6000-8000 (S.FR 5500)
£3490 $6456 €5200 Blanc x 4 (50x61cm-20x24in) s.d.76 s.i.d.1976 verso polymer. 13-Mar-4 De Vuyst, Lokeren #571/R est:3500-4000

Works on paper

£513 $908 €749 Composition (53x66cm-21x26in) s.d.1964 gouache prov. 27-Apr-4 AB Stockholms Auktionsverk #1188/R (S.KR 7000)
£659 $1167 €962 Composition (58x69cm-23x27in) s.d.64 verso gouache prov. 27-Apr-4 AB Stockholms Auktionsverk #1189/R (S.KR 9000)
£805 $1498 €1200 T.A.V (62x48cm-24x19in) s.i.d.91 gouache. 4-Mar-4 Auction Maastricht #1039 est:1400-1600
£833 $1392 €1200 Bleu (40x48cm-16x19in) s.d.1985 verso polymer. 21-Oct-3 Campo, Vlaamse Kaai #360a/R
£940 $1748 €1400 T.A.V (62x48cm-24x19in) s.i.d.91 gouache. 4-Mar-4 Auction Maastricht #1040/R est:1400-1600
£2039 $3467 €2977 Rouge (57x63cm-22x25in) s.d.April 1974 mixed media. 4-Nov-3 Bukowskis, Stockholm #558/R est:10000-15000 (S.KR 27000)
£2083 $3479 €3000 Black and white composition (126x143cm-50x56in) s. ink. 21-Oct-3 Campo & Campo, Antwerp #19/R est:3000-3250
£4895 $8175 €7000 Les brun (75x63cm-30x25in) s.d.56 s.i.d.56 verso polyner canvas on panel. 11-Oct-3 De Vuyst, Lokeren #552/R est:7500-8500
£5333 $9547 €8000 Composition in red (95x100cm-37x39in) s. s.i.d.5.Ock 1993 verso mixed media oil sand panel. 15-May-4 Van Ham, Cologne #468/R est:10000
£10738 $19007 €16000 Les couleurs (100x110cm-39x43in) s. d.1990 verso W/C. 27-Apr-4 Campo & Campo, Antwerp #28/R est:7000-10000

BOGAERT, Gaston (1918-) Belgian

£533 $976 €800 Tempete (46x55cm-18x22in) s. panel. 7-Jun-4 Palais de Beaux Arts, Brussels #30
£559 $934 €800 Le pavillon blanc (45x30cm-18x12in) s. panel. 13-Oct-3 Horta, Bruxelles #304
£574 $1085 €850 Tempete (46x55cm-18x22in) s. panel. 17-Feb-4 Vanderkindere, Brussels #136
£658 $1211 €1000 Hot night (80x60cm-31x24in) s.d.61 verso panel. 22-Jun-4 Palais de Beaux Arts, Brussels #199
£811 $1427 €1200 Arbres rouges (65x81cm-26x32in) s. panel. 18-May-4 Galerie Moderne, Brussels #109/R
£979 $1664 €1400 Le noeud gordien (70x60cm-28x24in) s. panel. 1-Dec-3 Palais de Beaux Arts, Brussels #26/R
£993 $1658 €1400 Interdits (93x72cm-37x28in) s. panel. 14-Oct-3 Vanderkindere, Brussels #490
£1000 $1820 €1500 La tempete (60x50cm-24x20in) s. panel. 4-Jul-4 MonsAntic, Maisieres #389 est:1600-2000
£1027 $1747 €1500 Empire sous-marin (64x79cm-25x31in) s. panel. 10-Nov-3 Horta, Bruxelles #64
£1200 $2196 €1800 Les interdits (72x95cm-28x37in) s. panel. 7-Jun-4 Palais de Beaux Arts, Brussels #31/R est:1000-1400
£1538 $2615 €2200 Les arrivants (54x65cm-21x26in) s. panel. 1-Dec-3 Palais de Beaux Arts, Brussels #25/R est:1500-2000
£1806 $2871 €2600 L'Ephebe d'Agde (100x80cm-39x31in) s. 15-Sep-3 Horta, Bruxelles #95 est:2200-2500
£4196 $7133 €6000 La fin du voyage (100x120cm-39x47in) s. 1-Dec-3 Palais de Beaux Arts, Brussels #27/R est:2000-3000

BOGAERTS, Jan (1878-1962) Dutch

£1184 $2179 €1800 Red poppies in a vase (60x50cm-24x20in) s.d.1905. 22-Jun-4 Christie's, Amsterdam #273/R est:1800-2200
£5592 $10122 €8500 Flower still life with zinnias in a glazed pot (40x45cm-16x18in) s.d.1937. 19-Apr-4 Glerum, Amsterdam #278/R est:3500-4000

BOGAILEI, Kleophas (20th C) Austrian

£604 $1117 €900 Waiting for the frog prince (24x21cm-9x8in) s. panel. 9-Mar-4 Dorotheum, Vienna #121/R
£604 $1117 €900 Red sunshade (24x20cm-9x8in) s. panel. 9-Mar-4 Dorotheum, Vienna #122/R
£897 $1497 €1300 La collation pendant les moissons (31x31cm-12x12in) s.verso wood. 16-Nov-3 Muizon & Le Coent, Paris #47
£1862 $3110 €2700 Scene d'arrestation en hiver (98x98cm-39x39in) s.d.1937 canvas on panel prov. 16-Nov-3 Muizon & Le Coent, Paris #46/R

BOGATIREV, M G (1924-) Russian

£246 $440 €359 Pereslavl, on the banks of the Trubezh (35x49cm-14x19in) cardboard painted 1960. 29-May-4 Shishkin Gallery, Moscow #69/R
£335 $600 €489 Summer (50x45cm-20x18in) cardboard painted 1968. 29-May-4 Shishkin Gallery, Moscow #70/R
£531 $950 €775 On the porch (40x31cm-16x12in) cardboard painted 1960. 29-May-4 Shishkin Gallery, Moscow #71/R

BOGAYEVSKY, Konstantin Fedorovich (1872-1943) Russian

Works on paper

£5500 $9900 €8030 Rainbow over a landscape (46x64cm-18x25in) s. W/C. 20-Jan-4 Bonhams, Knightsbridge #83 est:300-500
£10500 $18900 €15330 Mountainous landscape. W/C. 20-Jan-4 Bonhams, Knightsbridge #84 est:400-600

BOGAYEVSKY, Konstantin Fedorovich (attrib) (1872-1943) Russian

Works on paper

£4934 $9079 €7500 Coastline in summer (45x67cm-18x26in) s.d.42 W/C on pencil. 24-Jun-4 Dr Fritz Nagel, Stuttgart #516/R est:600

BOGDANI, Jakob (1660-1724) Hungarian

£10000 $17000 €14600 Roses, a parrot tulip, carnations and other flowers in an urn on a stone ledge (62x48cm-24x19in) s. 29-Oct-3 Christie's, London #41/R est:10000-15000
£24000 $43200 €35040 Crown imperial lily, tulips, peonies and other flower in an sculpted urn on plinth in a garden (96x95cm-38x37in) 21-Apr-4 Christie's, London #50/R est:25000-35000
£65000 $110500 €94900 Wooded landscape with peacocks and other birds in the foreground (129x151cm-51x59in) 25-Nov-3 Christie's, London #54/R est:40000-60000

BOGDANI, Jakob (attrib) (1660-1724) Hungarian

£2800 $4760 €4088 Grapes on the vine and peaches with two finches on a ledge (26x33cm-10x13in) init. 31-Oct-3 Christie's, Kensington #83/R est:2000-3000

BOGDANI, Jakob (circle) (1660-1724) Hungarian

£11111 $20000 €16222 Still life of grapes, halved peach resting on a table and a parrot. Still life of grapes and figs (75x63cm-30x25in) pair. 22-Jan-4 Sotheby's, New York #272/R est:25000-35000

BOGDANI, Jakob (style) (1660-1724) Hungarian

£870 $1557 €1270 Allegorical scene with peacocks and cherubs (80x126cm-31x50in) prov. 15-May-4 Christie's, Sydney #493/R est:2000-3000 (A.D 2200)

BOGDANOFF, Pierre (19/20th C) Russian

£430 $805 €650 Barques sous voiles (40x80cm-16x31in) s. 24-Jul-4 Thierry & Lannon, Brest #346

BOGDANOFF-BJELSKI, Nikolai (1868-1945) Russian

£1163 $2000 €1698 Landscape of Russian countryside (41x61cm-16x24in) s.d.1910. 7-Dec-3 Grogan, Boston #30/R
£13084 $20673 €18972 Two boys resting in woodland, one playing mouth organ (79x70cm-31x28in) s. 2-Sep-3 Rasmussen, Copenhagen #1557/R est:75000-100000 (D.KR 140000)
£13084 $20673 €18972 By the fire - four boys around open fire in a wood (70x88cm-28x35in) s. exhib.prov. 2-Sep-3 Rasmussen, Copenhagen #1558/R est:100000-125000 (D.KR 140000)
£13889 $25000 €20278 By the campfire (71x89cm-28x35in) s.d.1935. 23-Apr-4 Sotheby's, New York #19/R est:25000-35000
£18800 $34405 €27448 Two boys on a bench, one playing a balalaika (57x45cm-22x18in) s. 9-Jun-4 Rasmussen, Copenhagen #1622/R est:50000-75000 (D.KR 210000)
£20000 $35800 €29200 Zither player (80x100cm-31x39in) s.d.1903. 26-May-4 Sotheby's, London #90/R est:18000-25000
£20038 $35267 €30057 Breakfast (88x70cm-35x28in) s. exhib. 22-May-4 Dorotheum, Prague #103/R est:280000-550000 (C.KR 950000)
£41667 $75000 €60834 In the park, evening (81x97cm-32x38in) s. 23-Apr-4 Sotheby's, New York #58/R est:25000-35000

Works on paper

£8507 $14716 €12420 At the teacher's - children and women at table in garden (43x57cm-17x22in) s. pastel. 9-Dec-3 Rasmussen, Copenhagen #1286/R est:20000-30000 (D.KR 90000)

BOGDANOFF-BJELSKI, Nikolai (attrib) (1868-1945) Russian

£553 $940 €807 Lenin standing by a car with children (26x38cm-10x15in) i.verso cardboard. 10-Nov-3 Rasmussen, Vejle #517/R (D.KR 6000)
£738 $1373 €1100 Portrait of a Russian peasant girl (57x40cm-22x16in) i.verso. 5-Mar-4 Wendl, Rudolstadt #3591/R
£1018 $1700 €1486 Landscape with birches (25x33cm-10x13in) canvasboard. 16-Nov-3 William Jenack, New York #347 est:1000-1500
£3474 $6218 €5072 Portrait of a Russian farmer (81x43cm-32x17in) s.d.1941. 26-May-4 AB Stockholms Auktionsverk #2445/R est:20000-25000 (S.KR 47000)
£15000 $25050 €21900 Children. 21-Oct-3 Gorringes, Lewes #2101/R est:2500-3000

BOGDANOVE, Abraham J (1888-1946) American

£2229 $3700 €3254 Seascape with crashing surf (51x61cm-20x24in) s.d.1935 board. 4-Oct-3 South Bay, Long Island #156
£2346 $3800 €3402 Sitting on the beach, Monhegan Harbor (30x41cm-12x16in) s. panel prov. 8-Aug-3 Barridorf, Portland #275/R est:4000-6000

BOGERT, George H (1864-1944) American

£801 $1450 €1169 Sunset landscape (30x41cm-12x16in) s. 16-Apr-4 James Julia, Fairfield #877/R
£1351 $2500 €1972 Night landscape (51x76cm-20x30in) 13-Feb-4 Du Mouchelle, Detroit #2172/R est:2500-2800
£4696 $8500 €6856 Venice (71x122cm-28x48in) s.d.1930. 31-Mar-4 Sotheby's, New York #102/R est:2500-3500
£5249 $9500 €7664 Country landscape (71x122cm-28x48in) s.d.1930. 31-Mar-4 Sotheby's, New York #101/R est:2500-3500

BOGGIANI, Guido (1861-1902) Italian

£722 $1300 €1054 View of the world (33x43cm-13x17in) s. panel. 23-Jan-4 Freeman, Philadelphia #166/R

BOGGILD, Mogens (1901-1987) Danish
Sculpture
£2708 $4982 €3954 Eagle with open wings (58x61x70cm-23x24x28in) init.num.I/VI pat.bronze. 29-Mar-4 Rasmussen, Copenhagen #218/R est:40000 (D.KR 30000)
£4152 $7639 €6062 Eagle (45x47x30cm-18x19x12in) pat.bronze. 29-Mar-4 Rasmussen, Copenhagen #219/R est:40000 (D.KR 46000)

BOGGIO, Emilio (1857-1920) French/Venezuelan
£2703 $5000 €3946 Mer et rochers par temps gris (27x35cm-11x14in) s.i.d.verso panel. 12-Feb-4 Sotheby's, New York #24/R est:5000-7000
£3546 $5745 €5000 Arbres en fleurs (24x33cm-9x13in) s. s.i.d.1919 verso. 24-May-3 Martinot & Savignat, Pontoise #149
£4808 $8750 €7212 Study of dusk (24x33cm-9x13in) s. painted 1883. 21-Jun-4 Subastas Odalys, Caracas #78/R est:15000
£7097 $11000 €10362 Pier (65x50cm-26x20in) s. painted 1910. 3-Nov-2 Subastas Odalys, Caracas #81/R est:12000
Works on paper
£293 $545 €428 Landscape (23x32cm-9x13in) s.verso W/C. 14-Mar-4 Subastas Odalys, Caracas #50
£305 $510 €445 Soldier (11x18cm-4x7in) s. graphite. 13-Jul-3 Subastas Odalys, Caracas #84
£313 $500 €457 Landscape (21x27cm-8x11in) W/C. 21-Sep-3 Subastas Odalys, Caracas #89
£353 $590 €515 The Seine at Herblay (16x23cm-6x9in) s. chl exec.c.1883. 19-Oct-3 Subastas Odalys, Caracas #53/R
£428 $685 €625 Landscape (24x32cm-9x13in) W/C. 21-Sep-3 Subastas Odalys, Caracas #94/R
£992 $1825 €1488 Landscape (20x14cm-8x6in) chl exec.1881. 27-Jun-4 Subastas Odalys, Caracas #19/R

BOGGIONE, Enrico (1889-1985) Italian
£253 $466 €380 Morning in San Mauro (51x58cm-20x23in) s. cardboard. 8-Jun-4 Della Rocca, Turin #346/R
£268 $475 €400 London (24x30cm-9x12in) s. cardboard. 1-May-4 Meeting Art, Vercelli #139
£336 $594 €500 Cornwall (34x42cm-13x17in) s. i.verso cardboard. 1-May-4 Meeting Art, Vercelli #212

BOGGS, Frank Myers (1855-1926) French/American
£1553 $2500 €2267 Le manege (41x33cm-16x13in) s. 20-Aug-3 James Julia, Fairfield #1725/R est:2500-3500
£2482 $4145 €3500 Vue d'un port de Normandie (80x65cm-31x26in) s. 15-Oct-3 Rabourdin & Choppin de Janvry, Paris #24/R est:3500-4000
£4070 $7000 €5942 Untitled, harbour scene (51x61cm-20x24in) s. 7-Dec-3 Hindman, Chicago #801/R est:7000-9000
£4305 $7877 €6500 Paris la Seine a Notre-Dame (54x65cm-21x26in) s. 7-Apr-4 Doutrebente, Paris #36/R est:3000-4000
£4667 $8587 €7000 Le marche (92x73cm-36x29in) s. 11-Jun-4 Claude Aguttes, Neuilly #23/R est:6000-8000
£5442 $9741 €8000 Canal pres de Delft (54x65cm-21x26in) s. 19-Mar-4 Ribeyre & Baron, Paris #79 est:8000-10000
£5634 $9747 €8000 Quais, Hollande (38x61cm-15x24in) s.d.86 lit. 9-Dec-3 Artcurial Briest, Paris #93/R est:4500-6000
£6486 $12000 €9470 La Seine et Notre Dame (33x41cm-13x16in) s.d.1899 board prov. 11-Mar-4 Christie's, Rockefeller NY #28/R est:10000-15000
£6667 $12000 €10000 Paris, la Seine, Notre-Dame (60x73cm-24x29in) 26-Apr-4 Tajan, Paris #101/R est:6000-8000
£7042 $12183 €10000 Eglise Saint-Medard, Paris (72x96cm-28x38in) s. lit. 9-Dec-3 Artcurial Briest, Paris #105/R est:12000-15000
£9396 $17570 €14000 Paris, Notre Dame (70x90cm-28x35in) s. prov. 29-Feb-4 Versailles Encheres #112/R est:15000-18000
£11972 $20711 €17000 Quai Henri IV a Paris (60x81cm-24x32in) s. lit. 9-Dec-3 Artcurial Briest, Paris #97/R est:18000-20000
Works on paper
£272 $487 €400 Les martigues (12x20cm-5x8in) s.i.d.18 Mars 1922 chl prov. 22-Mar-4 Digard, Paris #99/R
£280 $501 €420 Chateau de Montreuil Bellay (53x32cm-21x13in) s.i.d.1912 W/C. 17-May-4 Chayette & Cheval, Paris #176
£336 $621 €500 Rue a Orange (23x15cm-9x6in) s.i.d.1913 W/C. 14-Mar-4 Eric Pillon, Calais #140/R
£336 $594 €500 Rouen, Place du marche et Cathedrale (40x26cm-16x10in) s.i. W/C traces chl. 27-Apr-4 Artcurial Briest, Paris #23
£436 $807 €650 Rue de village (15x21cm-6x8in) s. W/C. 14-Mar-4 Eric Pillon, Calais #50/R
£455 $850 €664 La Porte St Denis, Paris. s.i. W/C chl. 25-Feb-4 Dallas Auction Gallery, Dallas #53/R
£493 $853 €700 Dreux (25x36cm-10x14in) s.i.d. W/C. 12-Dec-3 Piasa, Paris #132
£533 $981 €800 La cathedrale de Caen (41x27cm-16x11in) s.i. W/C. 14-Jun-4 Tajan, Paris #46
£621 $1037 €900 Clamecy (45x32cm-18x13in) s. chl W/C. 11-Nov-3 Lesieur & Le Bars, Le Havre #6
£658 $1211 €1000 Marine (24x18cm-9x7in) s.d.1901 chl htd W/C. 24-Jun-4 Claude Boisgirard, Paris #13/R
£694 $1160 €1000 Bateaux de peche en mer (17x24cm-7x9in) s.i. W/C. 25-Oct-3 Binoche, Orleans #39
£699 $1203 €1000 Untitled. W/C. 2-Dec-3 Claude Aguttes, Neuilly #39
£1268 $2193 €1800 Notre-Dame de Paris (31x34cm-12x13in) s.i.d.1904 W/C chl. 9-Dec-3 Artcurial Briest, Paris #99/R est:2000-3000
£1678 $3121 €2500 Trouville, la plage animee (26x40cm-10x16in) s.i. W/C. 3-Mar-4 Fraysse & Associes, Paris #16/R est:900-1000
£1736 $2899 €2500 Street scene (37x24cm-15x9in) s.i. W/C chl. 24-Oct-3 Ketterer, Hamburg #286/R est:2700-2900
£2759 $4966 €4000 Paris, une rue a Montmartre en ete (32x40cm-13x16in) s. W/C. 26-Jan-4 Gros & Delettrez, Paris #26/R est:1000-1500

BOGH, Carl Henrik (1827-1893) Danish
£405 $688 €591 Deer and kid in forest (30x42cm-12x17in) s.d.1857. 29-Nov-3 Rasmussen, Havnen #2114/R (D.KR 4300)
£489 $890 €734 Landscape with horse (38x59cm-15x23in) s. 19-Jun-4 Rasmussen, Havnen #2012/R (D.KR 5500)
£614 $1063 €896 In the birch forest, Smaaland (40x58cm-16x23in) s. exhib. 9-Dec-3 Rasmussen, Copenhagen #1560/R (D.KR 6500)
£2617 $4894 €3821 Horses and cattle grazing (69x92cm-27x36in) s. 25-Feb-4 Museumsbygningen, Copenhagen #136/R est:15000-20000 (D.KR 29000)
£2930 $5333 €4278 Road with rider and children (86x110cm-34x43in) s.d.1848. 7-Feb-4 Rasmussen, Havnen #2209/R est:20000 (D.KR 32000)
£4673 $7383 €6776 Flock of elks resting by river in wooded autumn landscape, Sweden (104x140cm-41x55in) s.d.1882 exhib. 2-Sep-3 Rasmussen, Copenhagen #1552/R est:50000-75000 (D.KR 50000)
£6500 $11960 €9490 Animal farm (72x92cm-28x36in) s.d.1869. 25-Mar-4 Christie's, Kensington #184/R est:3000-5000

BOGHOSIAN, Varujan (1926-) American
Sculpture
£1564 $2800 €2283 Story of Orpheus (11x27cm-4x11in) s.i.d.1965 mixed media. 14-May-4 Skinner, Boston #412/R est:300-500

BOGIN, Greg (1965-) American?
£2890 $5000 €4219 Le painting, dk blu (119cm-47in) i. on stretcher acrylic enamel canvas on panel prov. 10-Dec-3 Phillips, New York #653/R est:6000-8000

BOGLE, John (c.1746-1803) British
Miniatures
£4000 $7200 €5840 General Robert Prescott, in staff uniform (3cm-1in) init.d.1780 i.verso gold bracelet clasp frame oval exhib.lit. 22-Apr-4 Bonhams, New Bond Street #30/R est:1200-1800

BOGLIONE, Marcello (1891-1957) Italian
£336 $594 €500 Landscape in Piedmonte (26x37cm-10x15in) s. board. 1-May-4 Meeting Art, Vercelli #200

BOGMAN, Hermanus Adrianus Charles (jnr) (1890-1965) Dutch
Works on paper
£2105 $3874 €3200 Pink flowers in a glass vase (75x59cm-30x23in) s. W/C htd white. 22-Jun-4 Christie's, Amsterdam #178/R est:800-1200

BOGMAN, Hermanus Charles Christiaan (1861-1921) Dutch
£2448 $4210 €3500 View of Grand Church in The Hague (60x80cm-24x31in) s. 8-Dec-3 Glerum, Amsterdam #122/R est:4000-6000

BOGNARD, Auguste Lucien (20th C) French
Works on paper
£302 $559 €450 Gamins de Paris (51x36cm-20x14in) s. pastel chl. 14-Mar-4 Eric Pillon, Calais #72/R

BOGO, Christian (1882-1945) Danish
£280 $482 €409 Light breeze (67x98cm-26x39in) s. 2-Dec-3 Sotheby's, London #62/R
£328 $547 €479 Seascape with sailing vessel (100cm-39in) s. 25-Oct-3 Rasmussen, Havnen #2524 (D.KR 3500)
£362 $587 €525 City canal (71x100cm-28x39in) s. board. 31-Jul-3 International Art Centre, Auckland #178/R est:800-1300 (NZ.D 1000)
£486 $812 €700 Three masted bark off Helsingborg (64x88cm-25x35in) s. 24-Oct-3 Ketterer, Hamburg #3/R
£1600 $2912 €2400 The Battle in Koge Bay (115x181cm-45x71in) s.d.1933. 19-Jun-4 Rasmussen, Havnen #2218/R est:10000 (D.KR 18000)

BOGOLIUBOV, Alexei Petrovich (1824-1896) Russian
£15000 $25500 €21900 Italian pastoral scene (20x27cm-8x11in) s.i.d.1856 verso. 19-Nov-3 Sotheby's, London #8/R est:6000-8000
£85000 $144500 €124100 Russian yacht, possibly the Standart, in difficulties off the Black Sea coast (74x120cm-29x47in) s. 19-Nov-3 Bonhams, New Bond Street #39/R est:8000-12000
Works on paper
£530 $964 €800 Nogent-sur-Marne (13x22cm-5x9in) s.i. ink wash. 16-Jun-4 Claude Boisgirard, Paris #30
£7000 $12530 €10220 Crimean coastal scene (10x16cm-4x6in) s. W/C. 26-May-4 Sotheby's, Olympia #387/R est:800-1200

BOGOLIUBOV, Alexei Petrovich (attrib) (1824-1896) Russian
£2657 $4571 €3800 Fishermen resting by the coast at moonlight (50x87cm-20x34in) mono.d.81. 5-Dec-3 Bolland & Marotz, Bremen #510/R est:3000
£14583 $23771 €21000 Moonlit Bosphorus (55x76cm-22x30in) s.cyrillic. 26-Sep-3 Bolland & Marotz, Bremen #497/R est:12000
£42614 $75000 €62216 Figures in a dinghy whaking in rough seas with other shipping (80x122cm-31x48in) bears sig.d.1854. 18-May-4 Bonhams & Butterfields, San Francisco #84/R est:4000-6000

BOGOMAZOV, Alexander (1880-1930) Russian
£26667 $48800 €40000 Abstract composition (41x42cm-16x17in) mono. prov. 5-Jun-4 Lempertz, Koln #606/R est:35000-40000
£120000 $214800 €175200 Flowers (49x54cm-19x21in) canvas on board prov. 26-May-4 Sotheby's, London #249/R est:80000-100000

BOGOMOLOV, Lev (1933-) Russian
£1844 $2987 €2600 Composition (120x98cm-47x39in) s.d.91 i. verso acrylic gold. 23-May-3 Altus, Berlin #510/R est:650

BOGONI, Adriano (1891-1970) Italian
£839 $1502 €1250 Chair with vase of flowers (78x60cm-31x24in) s. board. 25-May-4 Finarte Semenzato, Milan #92/R

BOGUET, Didier (1755-1839) French
£10000 $18000 €14600 Italianate landscape with shepherd and fishermen by a stream beyond (70x93cm-28x37in) prov. 22-Apr-4 Sotheby's, London #118/R est:10000-15000
£12069 $22207 €17621 Classical landscape (100x160cm-39x63in) s. prov. 26-Mar-4 Koller, Zurich #3065/R est:15000-25000 (S.FR 28000)

BOGUET, Didier (attrib) (1755-1839) French
£10738 $19758 €16000 Capriccio of the Golf of Pozzuoli (98x142cm-39x56in) i.d.18.1. 24-Mar-4 Dorotheum, Vienna #219/R est:8000-12000

BOGUSZ, Marian (1920-1980) Polish
£1835 $3046 €2679 Coloured abstract (155x115cm-61x45in) acrylic painted 1974. 2-Oct-3 Agra, Warsaw #37/R est:3000 (P.Z 12000)
Works on paper
£681 $1178 €994 Composition (98x69cm-39x27in) s.d.69 ink pen. 10-Dec-3 Agra, Warsaw #5/R (P.Z 4500)

BOHATSCH, Erwin (1951-) Austrian
£420 $722 €600 Untitled (70x50cm-28x20in) s.d.1987 verso. 4-Dec-3 Van Ham, Cologne #48
£738 $1358 €1100 The dream (54x79cm-21x31in) s.d. acrylic chk board. 26-Mar-4 Ketterer, Hamburg #336/R
Works on paper
£345 $631 €500 36 km (76x60cm-30x24in) s. mixed media prov. 27-Jan-4 Dorotheum, Vienna #191/R

BOHEMEN, Kees van (1928-1986) Dutch
£385 $662 €550 Untitled (21x27cm-8x11in) s.d.58 oil W/C paper. 4-Dec-3 Van Ham, Cologne #50
£6000 $11040 €9000 Demarrage (160x80cm-63x31in) s.d.68 s.i.d. verso. 8-Jun-4 Sotheby's, Amsterdam #130/R est:9000-12000
£10667 $19627 €16000 Panters (130x130cm-51x51in) s.d.72 prov. 8-Jun-4 Sotheby's, Amsterdam #94/R est:16000-18000
£12667 $23180 €19000 Porsche, Le Mans (130x130cm-51x51in) s.d.72. 7-Jun-4 Glerum, Amsterdam #218/R est:20000-30000
£13043 $21391 €18000 Untitled (150x150cm-59x59in) s.d.83. 27-May-3 Sotheby's, Amsterdam #422/R est:20000-30000
£13986 $24056 €20000 Composition (150x150cm-59x59in) s.d.72 s.d.stretcher prov. 2-Dec-3 Sotheby's, Amsterdam #162/R est:20000-30000
Works on paper
£733 $1342 €1100 Abstract composition with red (32x49cm-13x19in) s.d.55 gouache. 7-Jun-4 Glerum, Amsterdam #311/R
£1329 $2259 €1900 Three figures (50x65cm-20x26in) s.d.72 mixed media. 24-Nov-3 Glerum, Amsterdam #204/R est:1200-1600

BOHLER, Hans (1884-1961) Austrian
£8054 $14416 €12000 Capri (65x90cm-26x35in) mono. i. verso prov. 25-May-4 Dorotheum, Vienna #180/R est:14000-18000

BOHLER, Karl (20th C) German
£1342 $2470 €2000 Sunny winter's day in the Black Forest (64x94cm-25x37in) s.d.1925. 25-Mar-4 Karlheinz Kaupp, Staufen #2361/R est:1500

BOHM, C Curry (1894-1972) American
£2329 $3750 €3400 Impressionistic spring landscape (61x76cm-24x30in) s. canvas on masonite. 20-Aug-3 James Julia, Fairfield #1576/R est:6000-8000
£2616 $4500 €3819 Long shadows (64x69cm-25x27in) s.i. painted c.1930. 7-Dec-3 Treadway Gallery, Cincinnati #627/R est:4000-6000

BOHM, Max (1868-1923) American
£1000 $1700 €1460 Stagecoach (56x76cm-22x30in) s. 21-Nov-3 Skinner, Boston #505/R est:700-900
£3429 $6000 €5006 Two boys with a snail (114x180cm-45x71in) s.i.d.1889. 19-Dec-3 Sotheby's, New York #1098/R est:7000-10000

BOHM, Pal (1839-1905) Hungarian
£1477 $2746 €2200 Gypsy with rose twig in park (54x82cm-21x32in) s. 8-Mar-4 Bernaerts, Antwerp #109/R est:2000-3000
£1737 $3074 €2536 Gathering hay (23x31cm-9x12in) s. panel painted c.1865-1867. 28-Apr-4 Kieselbach, Budapest #31/R (H.F 650000)
£1900 $3040 €2755 Time for a rest (20x26cm-8x10in) s. panel. 18-Sep-3 Christie's, Kensington #50/R est:2000-3000
£2172 $3605 €3171 By the fire (21x27cm-8x11in) s. panel. 4-Oct-3 Kieselbach, Budapest #82/R (H.F 800000)
£2535 $4208 €3600 Still life of apple, pumpkin and plums (34x53cm-13x21in) s. 16-Jun-3 Dorotheum, Vienna #154/R est:3800-4200
£7482 $13244 €10924 Riverside scene (38x76cm-15x30in) s.d.1894 panel. 28-Apr-4 Kieselbach, Budapest #83/R (H.F 2800000)
£10316 $17125 €15061 Evening mood (50x100cm-20x39in) s. 4-Oct-3 Kieselbach, Budapest #41/R (H.F 3800000)

BOHME, Gerd (1899-1978) German
Works on paper
£1200 $2148 €1800 Woman wearing blue dress (55x42cm-22x17in) s. W/C chk study verso prov. 14-May-4 Ketterer, Munich #6/R est:800-1000
£3000 $5370 €4500 Parents (47x55cm-19x22in) i. verso W/C chk prov. 14-May-4 Ketterer, Munich #5/R est:1000-1500

BOHME, Lothar (1938-) German
£800 $1440 €1200 Still life with fruit and pots (26x36cm-10x14in) s. panel. 24-Apr-4 Dr Lehr, Berlin #56/R
£979 $1664 €1400 Seated nude (58x42cm-23x17in) s. 29-Nov-3 Villa Grisebach, Berlin #727/R est:1800-2400

BOHMER, Heinrich (1852-1930) German
£278 $453 €400 Hunting fox (41x50cm-16x20in) s. 26-Sep-3 Bolland & Marotz, Bremen #496
£280 $467 €400 Countryside (81x56cm-32x22in) s. lit. 27-Jun-3 Karrenbauer, Konstanz #1708
£280 $512 €420 Forest glade in the autumn with stream and wild deer (52x70cm-20x28in) s. 5-Jun-4 Arnold, Frankfurt #542/R
£467 $854 €700 Running stream in the Eifel (100x80cm-39x31in) s. 5-Jun-4 Arnold, Frankfurt #541/R
£839 $1427 €1200 Woodland (80x120cm-31x47in) s. 22-Nov-3 Arnold, Frankfurt #470/R est:1600
£1745 $3263 €2600 Autumnal lake shore in the Eifel (80x120cm-31x47in) s. 24-Feb-4 Dorotheum, Vienna #14/R est:2800-3200
£1757 $3092 €2600 Wooded landscape with deer (80x100cm-31x39in) s. 22-May-4 Lempertz, Koln #1483 est:2000

BOHMER-FEST, Ferdinand (20th C) German
£600 $954 €876 Snowy river landscape (79x121cm-31x48in) s. 9-Sep-3 Bonhams, Knightsbridge #272/R

BOHNARD, Mary B (attrib) (?) American?
£344 $550 €502 Still life of geraniums in pots. s. 20-Sep-3 Nadeau, Windsor #232a

BOHRDT, Hans (1857-1945) German
£385 $654 €550 North Sea breakers (71x101cm-28x40in) s. 20-Nov-3 Van Ham, Cologne #1493
Works on paper
£699 $1168 €1000 The ship, Potost in stormy seas (54x45cm-21x18in) s. gouache. 28-Jun-3 Bolland & Marotz, Bremen #618/R
£1467 $2655 €2200 Fishing boats off Lofoten (43x61cm-17x24in) s.i. gouache. 3-Apr-4 Hans Stahl, Hamburg #142/R est:2200

BOHRENS, Josefina (19th C) Cuban
£493 $789 €700 Regla harbour, Cuba (61x82cm-24x32in) s. 16-Sep-3 Segre, Madrid #83/R

BOHRMANN, Karl (1928-) German
Works on paper
£347 $621 €520 Untitled (21x17cm-8x7in) s.d. W/C on graphite col pen. 15-May-4 Dr Sturies, Dusseldorf #28/R
£600 $1098 €900 Untitled (28x38cm-11x15in) s.d.3.77 pencil chk W/C. 4-Jun-4 Lempertz, Koln #58/R
£600 $1098 €900 Mirror (29x21cm-11x8in) s.d.79 pencil. 4-Jun-4 Lempertz, Koln #59/R
£667 $1193 €1000 Red figure at window (18x13cm-7x5in) s.d. chk W/C bodycol. 15-May-4 Bassenge, Berlin #6747/R
£1000 $1830 €1500 Untitled (41x29cm-16x11in) s.d.90 paper collage oil chk. 4-Jun-4 Lempertz, Koln #60/R est:1200

BOHROD, Aaron (1907-1992) American
£306 $550 €447 New Orleans graveyard (27x34cm-11x13in) s. paper on board. 24-Apr-4 Weschler, Washington #646/R
£306 $550 €447 Porch, New Orleans (27x33cm-11x13in) s. paper on board. 24-Apr-4 Weschler, Washington #647/R
£353 $650 €515 Bust of a nude beside a bookcase (30x23cm-12x9in) s.i. masonite. 10-Jun-4 Swann Galleries, New York #36/R
£795 $1400 €1161 Nude female riding horse (30x30cm-12x12in) s. enamel metal painted c.1940. 23-May-4 Treadway Gallery, Cincinnati #679/R est:800-1200
£909 $1600 €1327 Nude female riding bull (30x30cm-12x12in) s. enamel metal painted c.1940. 23-May-4 Treadway Gallery, Cincinnati #678/R est:800-1200
£1183 $2200 €1727 Back view of houses (36x51cm-14x20in) with sig. board. 7-Mar-4 Treadway Gallery, Cincinnati #720/R est:3000-5000
£1452 $2700 €2120 Portrait of a boy (41x36cm-16x14in) s. painted c.1940. 7-Mar-4 Treadway Gallery, Cincinnati #693/R est:3000-5000
£2532 $4000 €3697 Sofa (30x41cm-12x16in) s.i. board. 7-Sep-3 Treadway Gallery, Cincinnati #682/R est:4000-6000
£3005 $5500 €4387 Girl with towel (51x41cm-20x16in) s.i.d.1932. 5-Jun-4 Treadway Gallery, Cincinnati #735/R est:7500-9500
£3125 $5500 €4563 Tete-a-tete (41x30cm-16x12in) s. board painted c.1940. 23-May-4 Treadway Gallery, Cincinnati #641/R est:4000-6000
£3235 $5500 €4723 Parkerville, USA (28x43cm-11x17in) s. board. 9-Nov-3 Wright, Chicago #169 est:5000-7000
£3892 $6500 €5682 Tiger (46x61cm-18x24in) s. s.i.verso gesso panel. 27-Oct-3 Schrager Galleries, Milwaukee #1286/R
£8383 $14000 €12239 Louisiana town at night (51x76cm-20x30in) s.d.38 masonite prov.exhib. 7-Oct-3 Sotheby's, New York #244 est:5000-7000
£10615 $19000 €15498 North Clark Street (58x79cm-23x31in) s. s.i.verso board prov. 16-May-4 Wright, Chicago #145/R est:12000-15000
Works on paper
£249 $450 €364 Woman undressing (28x20cm-11x8in) pastel. 16-Apr-4 American Auctioneer #32/R
£250 $448 €365 Pig in a meadow outside a farmhouse (33x46cm-13x18in) s. gouache. 16-Mar-4 Bonhams, Oxford #13
£276 $500 €403 Farm with silo and two figures (36x43cm-14x17in) pastel. 16-Apr-4 American Auctioneer #31/R
£1747 $3250 €2551 Portrait of a woman (38x28cm-15x11in) s.d.1931 gouache. 7-Mar-4 Treadway Gallery, Cincinnati #690/R est:3000-5000
£3488 $6000 €5092 Chicago Chinatown (43x36cm-17x14in) s. gouache prov.exhib. 7-Dec-3 Freeman, Philadelphia #138 est:6000-8000
£4261 $7500 €6221 Mural study (30x81cm-12x32in) s.d.1933 gouache board. 23-May-4 Treadway Gallery, Cincinnati #666/R est:7500-9500

BOHUS, Irene de (20th C) American
£1413 $2600 €2063 Reclining nude (76x99cm-30x39in) s.d.1941. 26-Jun-4 Sloans & Kenyon, Bethesda #1083/R est:1500-2000

BOHUSZEWICZ, Jan (1878-1935) Polish
£625 $1044 €913 Three children on the beach (20x29cm-8x11in) cardboard. 19-Oct-3 Agra, Warsaw #65/R (P.Z 4000)
£830 $1535 €1212 House in the mountain (24x32cm-9x13in) 14-Mar-4 Agra, Warsaw #18/R (P.Z 6000)

BOICEAU, Ernest (20th C) Swiss
£694 $1159 €1000 Lac Leman (48x48cm-19x19in) s. s.i.verso. 21-Oct-3 Artcurial Briest, Paris #228

BOICHARD, Henri Joseph (1783-1850) French
£300 $528 €438 Portrait of an old lady in a lace bonnet and green dress (65x54cm-26x21in) 19-May-4 Christie's, Kensington #599/R

BOICHOT, Guillaume (1735-1814) French
Sculpture
£1748 $2972 €2500 Vase au decor funeraire (69x37x37cm-27x15x15in) terracotta exec.c.1780 lit. 21-Nov-3 Piasa, Paris #6 est:2500-3000
Works on paper
£12925 $23136 €19000 Historic drawings. black chk pen brown ink wash thirty-four album. 18-Mar-4 Christie's, Paris #173/R est:20000-30000

BOILAUGES, Fernand (1891-?) French
£769 $1323 €1100 Pique-nique dans la foret (33x55cm-13x22in) s. cardboard. 3-Dec-3 Tajan, Paris #266/R
£875 $1400 €1278 La Plage (30x53cm-12x21in) board. 19-Sep-3 Du Mouchelle, Detroit #2014/R

BOILEAU, Philip (1864-1917) American
Works on paper
£326 $600 €476 Portrait of a young woman (51x30cm-20x12in) s. pastel. 27-Jun-4 Hindman, Chicago #914/R

BOILLY, Eugène (19/20th C) French
£4589 $7205 €6700 Interior scene (73x59cm-29x23in) s.d.1864. 20-Apr-3 Deauville, France #47/R est:5000-6000

BOILLY, Jules (1796-1874) French
£2897 $4837 €4200 Collectionneur. Bibliophile (27x21cm-11x8in) s. paper on cardboard pair. 14-Nov-3 Drouot Estimations, Paris #47/R est:1500-2500

BOILLY, Jules (attrib) (1796-1874) French
£267 $483 €400 Portrait du nain Francisco Lezcano (27x20cm-11x8in) cardboard. 30-Mar-4 Rossini, Paris #82
£667 $1207 €1000 Portrait d'homme a la cravate blanche (41x33cm-16x13in) i.verso. 30-Mar-4 Rossini, Paris #79/R
£2667 $4827 €4000 Portrait presume de Boissy d'Anglas (19x15cm-7x6in) paper on cardboard prov. 30-Mar-4 Rossini, Paris #80/R est:600-800

BOILLY, Louis Léopold (1761-1845) French
£2361 $3849 €3400 Portrait d'homme a la cravate blanche (21x17cm-8x7in) cardboard. 26-Sep-3 Millon & Associes, Paris #63
£2500 $4175 €3600 Portrait de monsieur Auber (21x16cm-8x6in) 23-Oct-3 Credit Municipal, Paris #34 est:3000-4000
£2632 $4842 €4000 Portrait de Guillaume Thou (21x16cm-8x6in) 25-Jun-4 Piasa, Paris #132/R est:4000-6000
£3147 $5413 €4500 Portrait de femme en robe rouge (22x16cm-9x6in) 2-Dec-3 Sotheby's, Paris #73/R est:3000-4000
£3586 $5989 €5200 Portrait de Monsieur Nitot. Portrait de Madame Nitot (22x16cm-9x6in) pair. 17-Nov-3 Delorme & Bocage, Paris #83/R est:4000-6000
£3750 $6262 €5400 Portrait de femme (22x16cm-9x6in) 23-Oct-3 Credit Municipal, Paris #33/R est:3000-4000
£4167 $7500 €6084 Peasant family with cattle (38x46cm-15x18in) 21-Jan-4 Sotheby's, New York #107/R est:10000-15000
£4444 $8000 €6488 Portrait of a Hussar (22x16cm-9x6in) prov. 23-Jan-4 Christie's, Rockefeller NY #75/R est:10000-15000
£5034 $9262 €7500 Portrait de H de Montmorency (21x16cm-8x6in) 24-Mar-4 Tajan, Paris #145/R est:7000-9000
£5263 $9684 €8000 Portrait de militaire (22x16cm-9x6in) 24-Jun-4 Christie's, Paris #100/R est:5000-7000
£6711 $12349 €10000 Portrait de jeune homme a la redingote noire (21x16cm-8x6in) 24-Mar-4 Tajan, Paris #141/R est:10000-12000
£8333 $15000 €12166 Putti playing with a goat (77x102cm-30x40in) s. en grisaille. 23-Jan-4 Christie's, Rockefeller NY #174/R est:10000-15000
£9712 $15928 €13500 Portrait d'un jeune femme. Portrait d'homme (21x17cm-8x7in) pair. 6-Jun-3 Maigret, Paris #111/R est:6000-9000
£223464 $400000 €326257 Still life of flowers in glass vase, two birds and a branch of blossoms (32x27cm-13x11in) s. panel prov.exhib.lit. 27-May-4 Sotheby's, New York #38/R est:300000-400000
Works on paper
£8392 $14266 €12000 La serinette (37x26cm-15x10in) s. pierre noire Indian ink wash prov.lit. 1-Dec-3 Millon & Associes, Paris #56/R est:12000-15000
£13605 $24354 €20000 Les politiques (14x22cm-6x9in) s. W/C pen. 22-Mar-4 Digard, Paris #47/R est:20000-30000
£14789 $25585 €21000 L'ebahi (23x18cm-9x7in) blk crayon stumping out htd white. 10-Dec-3 Piasa, Paris #73/R est:3000
£18182 $30364 €26000 Portrait de madame houdon (31x23cm-12x9in) pierre noire. 27-Jun-3 Millon & Associes, Paris #49/R est:6000-9000
£23810 $42619 €35000 Le prefere ou la grande soeur (35x29cm-14x11in) s. chl htd white prov.exhib.lit. 22-Mar-4 Digard, Paris #48/R est:25000-35000
£30668 $55816 €46000 Couple de femmes (69cm-27in circular) chl htd white. 30-Jun-4 Pierre Berge, Paris #54/R est:8000-10000
£36364 $60727 €52000 Portrait de Sabine et Anne-Ange Houdon (31x23cm-12x9in) pierre noire. 27-Jun-3 Millon & Associes, Paris #48/R est:9000-12000
£44218 $79150 €65000 Un cabaret a Paris (63x83cm-25x33in) graphite pen brown ink W/C exec.c.1815 prov.exhib.lit. 18-Mar-4 Christie's, Paris #174/R est:70000-120000
£172414 $286207 €250000 Depart des conscrits (52x93cm-20x37in) s.i.d.1807 chk pen wash htd gouache prov.exhib.lit. 30-Sep-3 Christie's, Paris #3/R est:25000-350000

BOILLY, Louis Leopold (attrib) (1761-1845) French
£1192 $2170 €1800 Biedermeier portrait (21x17cm-8x7in) canvas on canvas. 19-Jun-4 Bergmann, Erlangen #791

BOILLY, Louis Leopold (circle) (1761-1845) French
£5278 $9500 €7706 Trompe-l'oeil with a man's head through a canvas, possibly self portrait (61x47cm-24x19in) 23-Jan-4 Christie's, Rockefeller NY #61/R est:15000-25000

BOISROND, François (1959-) French
£839 $1443 €1200 Sans titre (214x114cm-84x45in) s.d.1982 verso acrylic prov. 3-Dec-3 Tajan, Paris #495/R
£940 $1682 €1400 Untitled (123x211cm-48x83in) s.d.83 verso acrylic prov.exhib. 26-May-4 Christie's, Paris #105/R
£1208 $2139 €1800 Untitled (211x181cm-83x71in) acrylic collage paper on canvas diptych prov. 28-Apr-4 Artcurial Briest, Paris #410 est:2000-3000
£3716 $6540 €5500 Amis de l'Abbaye (195x130cm-77x51in) mono.d.1989 s.i.d.verso acrylic prov. 18-May-4 Tajan, Paris #141/R est:5000-6000
£4000 $7280 €6000 Aire de repos (161x127cm-63x50in) s.d.1989 acrylic prov. 29-Jun-4 Cornette de St.Cyr, Paris #108/R est:6000-8000
Sculpture
£2000 $3700 €3000 Chez Hans (78x100cm-31x39in) s.d.1995 metal painted lava. 18-Jul-4 Sotheby's, Paris #216/R est:3000-5000
£2400 $4440 €3600 Vacances (45x101x101cm-18x40x40in) s.d.1996 metal painted ceramic prov. 18-Jul-4 Sotheby's, Paris #197/R est:2500-3500
£4000 $7400 €6000 Atelier de l'artiste (76x101x101cm-30x40x40in) init.d.95 metal painted ceramic prov. 18-Jul-4 Sotheby's, Paris #202/R est:3000-4000
£6333 $11717 €9500 Fables de la Fontaine (74x201x102cm-29x79x40in) s.d.95 metal painted ceramic prov. 18-Jul-4 Sotheby's, Paris #190/R est:6000-8000

BOISSEAU, Catherine (?) French
Sculpture
£1159 $1901 €1600 Girafe s'abreuvant (15x29cm-6x11in) num 3/8 brn pat bronze Cast Paumelle. 28-May-3 Coutau Begarie, Paris #283/R est:800-900

BOISSEAU, Émile Andre (1842-1923) French
Sculpture
£1210 $2094 €1767 La defense du foyer (42cm-17in) s. exec. 1884 lit. 14-Dec-3 Agra, Warsaw #23/R est:8000 (P.Z 8000)
£2432 $4281 €3600 Oysel le troubadour (80cm-31in) s.mono.i. brown pat.bronze. 24-May-4 Bernaerts, Antwerp #444/R est:2500-3000
£2800 $4760 €4088 Oysel (80cm-31in) s.i. pat bronze. 28-Oct-3 Sotheby's, London #173/R
£20000 $36000 €29200 Twilight (69x56cm-27x22in) s.st.f.Thiebaut brown pat bronze lit. 21-Apr-4 Sotheby's, London #106/R est:12000-18000

BOISSELIER, Antoine (1790-1857) French
£380 $680 €555 Allegorial figures before a waterfall in a wooded glade (45x37cm-18x15in) s.d.1820. 11-May-4 Bonhams, Knightsbridge #61/R

BOISSEVAIN, William (1927-) Australian
£826 $1405 €1206 Gathering firewood (89x120cm-35x47in) s.d.1989 verso board prov. 29-Oct-3 Lawson Menzies, Sydney #182/R est:3000-4000 (A.D 2000)
£950 $1710 €1387 Still life of dog roses (86x90cm-34x35in) s. acrylic board prov. 20-Jan-4 Bonhams, Knightsbridge #302/R
£1452 $2425 €2178 Desert landscape (81x72cm-32x28in) s.d.79 board. 27-Oct-3 Goodman, Sydney #103/R est:3500-4500 (A.D 3500)
£2979 $5064 €4349 Dog roses (91x120cm-36x47in) s.d.90 board prov. 25-Nov-3 Christie's, Melbourne #121/R est:6000-8000 (A.D 7000)

BOISSIEU, Claude Victor de (1784-1869) French
Works on paper
£390 $651 €566 Le lac de Geneve, vu du port du Molard, a Geneve. La ville de Geneve (21x30cm-8x12in) i. crayon wash pair prov. 21-Jun-3 Galerie du Rhone, Sion #445 (S.FR 850)
£459 $766 €666 Vallee de Loech et le Mont Guemmi (16x21cm-6x8in) i.verso crayon wash prov. 21-Jun-3 Galerie du Rhone, Sion #450 (S.FR 1000)
£642 $1072 €931 La vallee et las glaciers de Chamonix (20x26cm-8x10in) i. pencil wash gouache prov. 21-Jun-3 Galerie du Rhone, Sion #500 est:1500-2000 (S.FR 1400)
£688 $1149 €998 Le port et l'ile de Rousseau a Geneve, vue du Bastion (16x28cm-6x11in) init. crayon sepia wash prov. 21-Jun-3 Galerie du Rhone, Sion #446/R est:1500-2000 (S.FR 1500)
£780 $1302 €1131 Source de l'Arveyron (18x25cm-7x10in) i. crayon wash W/C prov. 21-Jun-3 Galerie du Rhone, Sion #501 est:2000-3000 (S.FR 1700)
£826 $1379 €1198 Vue de l'Hospice du Grand St Bernard (20x27cm-8x11in) i.verso crayon wash gouache prov. 21-Jun-3 Galerie du Rhone, Sion #451 est:2000-3000 (S.FR 1800)
£917 $1532 €1330 Vallee de Chamonix (21x46cm-8x18in) i. crayon wash gouache prov. 21-Jun-3 Galerie du Rhone, Sion #502/R est:2500-3500 (S.FR 2000)

BOISSIEU, Jean Jacques de (1736-1810) French
Works on paper
£820 $1500 €1197 Landscape with farmhouse (19x25cm-7x10in) brush black ink wash. 29-Jan-4 Swann Galleries, New York #234/R est:2000-3000

£1267 $2293 €1900 Standing cow (15x19cm-6x7in) mono. wash pen brush over pencil. 2-Apr-4 Winterberg, Heidelberg #274/R est:980
£2600 $4680 €3796 Group of peasants playing cards in a rustic interior (21x32cm-8x13in) mono.d.1768 pen brown ink wash black chk prov. 20-Apr-4 Sotheby's, Olympia #67/R est:1500-2000
£4930 $8627 €7000 Un paysage de montagne avec un troupeau pres d'un riviere (20x30cm-8x12in) s. pen grey ink W/C prov. 17-Dec-3 Christie's, Paris #59/R est:3000-5000

BOISSONNAS, Fred (1858-1946) French
Photographs
£2658 $4438 €3800 Parthenon apres l'orage (28x39cm-11x15in) s. carbon print on cardboard exec.c.1910 exhib. 10-Oct-3 Tajan, Paris #196/R est:1800-2200

BOIT, Charles (1662-1727) Swedish
Miniatures
£4200 $7140 €6132 Thomas Ewer (5cm-2in) s. enamel oval prov. 18-Nov-3 Bonhams, New Bond Street #37/R est:1500-2000

BOITARD, François (c.1670-c.1715) French
Works on paper
£676 $1189 €1000 Wedding of Cupid and Psyche (16x50cm-6x20in) pen col ink col wash exhib. 19-May-4 Sotheby's, Amsterdam #137/R

BOITARD, François (attrib) (c.1670-c.1715) French
Works on paper
£387 $670 €550 Allegorie de l'architecture (41x54cm-16x21in) s. i.verso pen brown ink. 12-Dec-3 Renaud, Paris #23
£496 $829 €700 Scena di sacrificio con baccanti in un paesaggio con rovine (21x34cm-8x13in) i. verso pencil pen grey ink grey W/C prov. 18-Jun-3 Christie's, Rome #398/R

BOITIER, Thierry (20th C) French?
Works on paper
£287 $487 €410 Espace secret (30x30cm-12x12in) s. mixed media canvas. 29-Nov-3 Neret-Minet, Paris #240
£333 $603 €500 Prince d'ocre rouge (35x35cm-14x14in) s. mixed media canvas. 3-Apr-4 Neret-Minet, Paris #213/R
£524 $892 €750 Trilogie au carre vert (80x80cm-31x31in) s. mixed media canvas. 29-Nov-3 Neret-Minet, Paris #111/R
£800 $1448 €1200 Un langage toujours pur (100x100cm-39x39in) s. mixed media canvas. 3-Apr-4 Neret-Minet, Paris #135/R

BOIVIN, Émile (1846-1920) French
£524 $876 €750 L'arrivee de la caravane (14x20cm-6x8in) s. cardboard. 13-Oct-3 Horta, Bruxelles #31
£934 $1708 €1400 Scene de rue (35x21cm-14x8in) s. 3-Jun-4 Tajan, Paris #205/R est:1300-1500
£1134 $2074 €1700 Campement au pied des montagnes (21x32cm-8x13in) s. 3-Jun-4 Tajan, Paris #204/R est:1300-1500
£1560 $2606 €2200 Halte de caravane (24x35cm-9x14in) s. 19-Oct-3 Rabourdin & Choppin de Janvry, Paris #34/R est:1800-2200
£1986 $3316 €2800 Koubba (46x56cm-18x22in) s. 16-Jun-3 Gros & Delettrez, Paris #506/R est:2000-3000
£2837 $4738 €4000 Caravane au bord de l'oued (38x27cm-15x11in) s. canvas on cardboard. 16-Jun-3 Gros & Delettrez, Paris #132/R est:3800-5000

BOIX-VIVES, Anselme (1899-1969) French
£6338 $10965 €9000 Esprits inconnus (109x81cm-43x32in) s.i. wax crayon gouache paper on canvas exhib.lit. 9-Dec-3 Artcurial Briest, Paris #479/R est:4000-5000
Works on paper
£775 $1341 €1100 Feuillage d'automne (66x51cm-26x20in) s. gouache. 9-Dec-3 Artcurial Briest, Paris #479a est:1200-1500
£905 $1566 €1321 Femme moderne (64x46cm-25x18in) s. gouache cardboard. 12-Dec-3 Galerie du Rhone, Sion #144 est:2000-3000 (S.FR 2000)
£1310 $2175 €1900 Fleurs de montagne et son faisan (65x49cm-26x19in) s. i.verso. 30-Sep-3 Blanchet, Paris #226/R est:1500-1800
£1678 $3003 €2500 Portrait imaginaire avec petit singe (80x53cm-31x21in) s.d.11/10/68 gouache paper on canvas. 25-May-4 Chambelland & Giafferi, Paris #87/R est:2000-2500
£3154 $5646 €4700 Portrait imaginaire (67x59cm-26x23in) s. gouache paper on canvas. 25-May-4 Chambelland & Giafferi, Paris #88/R est:2000-2500

BOIZOT, Simon Louis (1743-1809) French
Sculpture
£2028 $3448 €2900 Venus et l'amour (27cm-11in) plaster. 21-Nov-3 Piasa, Paris #7 est:2500-3000

BOJESEN, Claus (1948-) Danish
£306 $496 €444 Section of a not earlier shown interior with view to landscape (123x105cm-48x41in) s.d.1973 i.verso. 4-Aug-3 Rasmussen, Vejle #684/R (D.KR 3200)
£538 $968 €785 Masked Venus in landscape (116x73cm-46x29in) s.d.1980. 24-Apr-4 Rasmussen, Havnen #4229/R (D.KR 6000)
£903 $1688 €1318 Blue-Ba-Kota (130x97cm-51x38in) s.d.1994. 25-Feb-4 Kunsthallen, Copenhagen #183/R (D.KR 10000)

BOK, Hannes Vajn (1914-1964) American
Works on paper
£909 $1700 €1327 Head of green skinned woman with pink hair (18x13cm-7x5in) s. col pencil W/C. 26-Feb-4 Illustration House, New York #25/R est:1000-1500

BOKELMANN, Christian Ludwig (1844-1894) German
£6294 $10510 €9000 Children playing near Worpswede (111x91cm-44x36in) s. 28-Jun-3 Bolland & Marotz, Bremen #619/R est:13000

BOKER, Carl (1836-1905) German
£350 $539 €550 Two friends (16x12cm-6x5in) s. i.d.14.1.80 verso panel. 4-Sep-2 Schopman, Hamburg #5/R
£3472 $5799 €5000 Vagrant children (27x36cm-11x14in) s.d.1871 lit. 24-Oct-3 Ketterer, Hamburg #46/R est:6000-6500

BOKKENHEUSER, Borge (1910-1976) Danish
£766 $1418 €1118 Girl standing wearing a chemise (116x81cm-46x32in) s. 15-Mar-4 Rasmussen, Vejle #624/R (D.KR 8500)

BOKLUND, Johan-Kristofer (1817-1880) Swedish
£2692 $4631 €3930 Bartering (135x97cm-53x38in) s.d.1855 prov.exhib.lit. 3-Dec-3 AB Stockholms Auktionsverk #2362/R est:30000-40000 (S.KR 35000)
£4582 $8203 €6690 Sovoyard boy making his instrument (92x72cm-36x28in) s.i.d.1855 lit. 25-May-4 Bukowskis, Stockholm #186/R est:60000-70000 (S.KR 62000)

BOKS, Evert Jan (1838-1914) Dutch
£17500 $30100 €25550 La demande en mariage (80x112cm-31x44in) s.i.d.1882 panel prov. 3-Dec-3 Christie's, London #8/R est:20000-30000

BOKUSHO (15th C) Japanese
Works on paper
£1100 $1837 €1595 Cat (25x33cm-10x13in) ink hanging scroll. 18-Jun-3 Christie's, London #259/R est:800-1200

BOL, Ferdinand (1616-1680) Dutch
£850 $1556 €1241 Portrait of a gentleman (36x30cm-14x12in) s. 27-Jan-4 Gorringes, Lewes #1684
£22222 $40000 €32444 Portrait of a lady in a white satin dress (109x90cm-43x35in) prov. 23-Jan-4 Christie's, Rockefeller NY #180/R est:15000-20000

BOL, Ferdinand (attrib) (1616-1680) Dutch
£568 $1000 €829 Portrait of a bearded man (30x23cm-12x9in) panel. 19-May-4 Doyle, New York #6039

BOL, Hans (1534-1593) Dutch
Works on paper
£8054 $14738 €12000 Vue de village (16x23cm-6x9in) s.d.1587 ink. 8-Jul-4 Campo, Vlaamse Kaai #39/R est:4400-4800

BOLAND, Charles H D (1850-?) Belgian
£662 $1205 €1000 Chien sur un rocher (80x58cm-31x23in) s.d.April 1889. 21-Jun-4 Bernaerts, Antwerp #167
£2400 $4416 €3504 Cowards die may times before their death (41x61cm-16x24in) s. 10-Jun-4 Christie's, Kensington #374/R est:1000-1500
£2416 $4421 €3600 Chat et chien dans un interieur (75x107cm-30x42in) s.d.1896. 8-Jul-4 Campo, Vlaamse Kaai #40/R est:5000-7000
£3333 $6033 €5000 Flirtation (57x77cm-22x30in) s.d.1887. 30-Mar-4 Campo, Vlaamse Kaai #11/R est:3000-3500
£4392 $7861 €6500 L'odorat (97x50cm-38x20in) s.d.1984 s.i.d.1894 verso. 10-May-4 Horta, Bruxelles #131/R est:7000-9000

BOLANDER, Lars (?-1795) Swedish
£10769 $18523 €15723 Autumn - allegorical harvesting scene with vegetables and fruit (295x155cm-116x61in) s.d.1783 prov.lit. 3-Dec-3 AB Stockholms Auktionsverk #2460/R est:80000-100000 (S.KR 140000)

BOLAY, Veronica (20th C) Irish?
Works on paper
£903 $1472 €1300 Near the sea (51x53cm-20x21in) s. pastel. 23-Sep-3 De Veres Art Auctions, Dublin #275/R

BOLDERHEY, Rie (1890-?) Dutch
£280 $476 €400 Bouquet in a vase (80x100cm-31x39in) s. 24-Nov-3 Glerum, Amsterdam #46/R
£294 $499 €420 Bouquet of wild flowers in a vase (100x80cm-39x31in) s. 24-Nov-3 Glerum, Amsterdam #62/R

BOLDING, Cornelis (1897-?) Dutch
£1408 $2338 €2000 Fisher women (58x84cm-23x33in) s. 12-Jun-3 Auction Maastricht #801/R
£3061 $5571 €4500 Leidsestraat, Amsterdam (90x120cm-35x47in) s.d.21. 3-Feb-4 Christie's, Amsterdam #325/R est:800-1200

BOLDINI, Giovanni (1842-1931) Italian
£9396 $16631 €14000 Deux militaires au restaurant (27x18cm-11x7in) panel prov. 30-Apr-4 Tajan, Paris #163/R est:10000-12000
£9420 $15449 €13000 The pigs' keeper (19x44cm-7x17in) s. board lit. 27-May-3 Finarte Semenzato, Milan #131/R est:10000-12000
£10067 $18020 €15000 Red hair net (20x15cm-8x6in) s. i.verso board lit. 25-May-4 Finarte Semenzato, Milan #195/R est:18000-20000
£10563 $18275 €15000 Riders in Medieval costumes (42x25cm-17x10in) board prov. 10-Dec-3 Finarte Semenzato, Rome #287/R est:15000-18000
£24000 $41280 €35040 Testa di signora con capellino giallo, il cappello giallo (24x17cm-9x7in) s. prov.lit. 3-Dec-3 Christie's, London #37/R est:20000-30000
£28235 $48000 €41223 John Singer Sargent (36x28cm-14x11in) panel painted 1890 prov.lit. 29-Oct-3 Christie's, Rockefeller NY #217/R est:60000-80000

£47887 $82845 €68000 Woman (35x27cm-14x11in) board on board prov. 10-Dec-3 Sotheby's, Milan #123/R est:65000-75000
£138889 $250000 €202778 Portrait of a lady with lilacs (56x39cm-22x15in) s. panel. 23-Apr-4 Sotheby's, New York #115/R est:200000-300000
£377778 $680000 €551556 Portrait of Luis and Pedro Subercaseaux (134x125cm-53x49in) s.d.1887pel. 23-Apr-4 Sotheby's, New York #103/R est:300000-400000
Works on paper
£1987 $3616 €3000 Portrait de femme vue de profil (27x24cm-11x9in) black crayon. 16-Jun-4 Piasa, Paris #195/R est:3000-4000
£2042 $3533 €2900 Portrait of a woman (34x22cm-13x9in) s. i.verso blk crayon. 10-Dec-3 Piasa, Paris #15/R est:3000
£6165 $10480 €9000 Lady (24x16cm-9x6in) s.i. pen ink wash over crayon prov. 6-Nov-3 Tajan, Paris #223/R
£20000 $36400 €29200 Elegante au chien (66x52cm-26x20in) s.i. pastel chl prov. 5-Feb-4 Christie's, London #306/R est:20000-30000
£28000 $51520 €42000 Red velvet hat (76x52cm-30x20in) pastel lit. 8-Jun-4 Sotheby's, Milan #144/R est:40000-60000
£138889 $231944 €200000 Countess of Rasty (45x116cm-18x46in) pastel on silk exec.c.1880 exhib.lit. 21-Oct-3 Sotheby's, Milan #394/R est:70000-100000

BOLDISZAR, Istvan (1897-1984) Hungarian
£2240 $4054 €3270 At the bridge in Nagybanya (72x111cm-28x44in) s. 16-Apr-4 Mu Terem Galeria, Budapest #144/R (H.F 850000)
£3258 $5408 €4757 Reclining nude (100x144cm-39x57in) s. 4-Oct-3 Kieselbach, Budapest #165/R (H.F 1200000)

BOLDRINI, Gustavo (1925-1988) Italian
£268 $497 €400 View of Venice (80x100cm-31x39in) s. painted 1970. 13-Mar-4 Meeting Art, Vercelli #373

BOLDUC, Blanche (1906-) Canadian
£724 $1137 €1057 Dans la cuisine (40x51cm-16x20in) s. s.i.verso. 26-Aug-3 Iegor de Saint Hippolyte, Montreal #56 (C.D 1600)

BOLDUC, David (1945-) Canadian
£1071 $1843 €1564 Untitled (117x232cm-46x91in) s.d.1979 indis.i. acrylic paper. 2-Dec-3 Joyner Waddington, Toronto #324/R est:3000-5000 (C.D 2400)
£4505 $7658 €6577 Late late spring (153x264cm-60x104in) s.d.89 verso acrylic prov. 18-Nov-3 Sotheby's, Toronto #114/R est:7000-10000 (C.D 10000)

BOLDUC, Yvonne (1905-) Canadian
Works on paper
£268 $447 €389 Le halage du bois (41x91cm-16x36in) s. mixed media on board. 17-Jun-3 Pinneys, Montreal #92 (C.D 600)

BOLE, Jeanne (fl.1870-1883) French
£9930 $17080 €14200 La bonne aventure (100x73cm-39x29in) s. 7-Dec-3 Osenat, Fontainebleau #159 est:12000-15000

BOLENS, Ernest (1881-1959) Swiss
£655 $1192 €956 Landscape with the Rhine (65x92cm-26x36in) s. prov.exhib. 17-Jun-4 Kornfeld, Bern #215/R est:2500 (S.FR 1500)

BOLERADSKY, Beno (1885-?) Hungarian
£486 $768 €700 Three white Persian cats (60x80cm-24x31in) s. 5-Sep-3 Wendl, Rudolstadt #3296/R

BOLGIE, Giuseppe (18th C) Italian
Works on paper
£2394 $4190 €3400 Trompe l'oeil for the wedding of Giuseppe Tron to Teresa Boyer (59x42cm-23x17in) W/C paper on cardboard. 17-Dec-3 Finarte Semenzato, Milan #230/R est:2000-3000

BOLIN, Gustave (1920-) Swedish
£671 $1248 €1000 Errances, fond citron (72x104cm-28x41in) s.d.72 d.1972 verso vinylique paper on canvas. 3-Mar-4 Artcurial Briest, Paris #313
£671 $1248 €1000 Labyrinthe, orange et bleu (79x114cm-31x45in) s. d.1971 verso vinylique paper on canvas. 3-Mar-4 Artcurial Briest, Paris #317
£738 $1374 €1100 Composition pour une tapisserie no 2 (100x100cm-39x39in) s.d.70 s.i.d.1970 verso. 3-Mar-4 Artcurial Briest, Paris #310
£738 $1374 €1100 Enigme (67x101cm-26x40in) s. vinylique paper on canvas. 3-Mar-4 Artcurial Briest, Paris #315
£764 $1276 €1100 Composition jaune (150x150cm-59x59in) s. 21-Oct-3 Artcurial Briest, Paris #648 est:1200-1500
£789 $1453 €1200 Bateaux enmer (60x60cm-24x24in) s. prov. 28-Jun-4 Joron-Derem, Paris #229
£921 $1695 €1400 Contrejour au Rond Blanc (89x116cm-35x46in) s.i.d.1980. 28-Jun-4 Joron-Derem, Paris #231
£987 $1816 €1500 Nu etoffe bleue (100x100cm-39x39in) s.i.d.1989. 28-Jun-4 Joron-Derem, Paris #232/R est:1500-1800
£987 $1816 €1500 Arbres jaunes (93x100cm-37x39in) s.i.d.1992. 28-Jun-4 Joron-Derem, Paris #233 est:1500-1800
£1067 $1920 €1600 Composition (130x130cm-51x51in) s.d.71. 20-Apr-4 Chenu & Scrive, Lyon #29/R est:1200-1500
£1149 $2056 €1700 Nature morte au bouquet de fleurs (65x81cm-26x32in) s.d.48. 4-May-4 Calmels Cohen, Paris #169/R est:1500-2000
£1579 $2905 €2400 New York (89x116cm-35x46in) s. i. verso. 28-Jun-4 Joron-Derem, Paris #228/R est:1800-2000
£1597 $2668 €2300 Composition abstraite (182x180cm-72x71in) s. 21-Oct-3 Artcurial Briest, Paris #647/R est:1200-1500
Works on paper
£263 $484 €400 Nude (40x45cm-16x18in) s. mixed media. 27-Jun-4 Versailles Encheres #16/R
£461 $847 €700 Arbres noires (50x65cm-20x26in) s. mixed media canvas. 28-Jun-4 Joron-Derem, Paris #230
£671 $1235 €1000 Composition (79x114cm-31x45in) s.d.1974 gouache paper on canvas. 24-Mar-4 Joron-Derem, Paris #184
£1119 $1924 €1600 Bleu et lignes noires (77x104cm-30x41in) s.d.72 gouache paper on canvas. 2-Dec-3 Calmels Cohen, Paris #90/R est:1200-1500

BOLINGER, Truman (1944-) American
Sculpture
£1471 $2750 €2148 Bringin them in (56x71x23cm-22x28x9in) bronze prov. 24-Jul-4 Coeur d'Alene, Hayden #108/R est:3000-5000

BOLISSIAN, Amie (20th C) British
£1800 $3348 €2628 Turning towards the sea (183x92cm-72x36in) 8-Mar-4 Christie's, London #7
Works on paper
£2600 $4836 €3796 She laughs in her turn (110x76cm-43x30in) ink acrylic. 8-Mar-4 Christie's, London #6

BOLL, Reinholdt Fredrik (1825-1897) Norwegian
£684 $1163 €999 Pilot boat by lighthouse (31x46cm-12x18in) s. 19-Nov-3 Grev Wedels Plass, Oslo #7/R (N.KR 8000)

BOLLARD, William Allen (1869-1941) New Zealander?
£381 $681 €556 Habour with city view (32x53cm-13x21in) s. board. 11-May-4 Peter Webb, Auckland #118/R est:1000-2000 (NZ.D 1100)
£950 $1758 €1387 River landscape with figures in rowing boat (74x124cm-29x49in) s.d.1906. 14-Jan-4 Brightwells, Leominster #912/R

BOLLE, Martin (1912-1968) Belgian
£267 $477 €400 La seance d'habillage (50x40cm-20x16in) s.d.41. 11-May-4 Vanderkindere, Brussels #599
£1418 $2369 €2000 Gouter de la femme en bleu (60x50cm-24x20in) s. 14-Oct-3 Vanderkindere, Brussels #85
£1489 $2487 €2100 Portrait de fillette (50x40cm-20x16in) s.d.43. 14-Oct-3 Vanderkindere, Brussels #572

BOLLER, Louis Jakob (1862-1896) German
£1946 $3581 €2900 Thatched farmstead with figures and animals by stream (140x113cm-55x44in) s. lit. 25-Mar-4 Karlheinz Kaupp, Staufen #2362/R est:2900

BOLLES, Enoch (1883-1976) American
£3020 $5406 €4500 Snake woman (86x66cm-34x26in) mono. lit. 27-May-4 Sotheby's, Paris #102/R est:5000-7000

BOLLES, John (19th C) American
£269 $450 €393 Fisherman in a landscape (25x36cm-10x14in) s. 20-Jun-3 Freeman, Philadelphia #191/R

BOLLES, Reginald (20th C) American
£226 $400 €330 Song of the bird (30x24cm-12x9in) s. sold with magazine cover. 2-May-4 Bonhams & Butterfields, San Francisco #1174/R
£226 $400 €330 Wishbone (28x28cm-11x11in) s. 2-May-4 Bonhams & Butterfields, San Francisco #1179/R
£282 $500 €412 Country fair (29x26cm-11x10in) s. 2-May-4 Bonhams & Butterfields, San Francisco #1169/R
£311 $550 €454 Unhooking the fish (27x26cm-11x10in) s.d.23. 2-May-4 Bonhams & Butterfields, San Francisco #1172/R
£621 $1100 €907 Naughty read (28x24cm-11x9in) s. 2-May-4 Bonhams & Butterfields, San Francisco #1176/R
£734 $1300 €1072 Painting the decoy (38x30cm-15x12in) s. 2-May-4 Bonhams & Butterfields, San Francisco #1173/R est:750-1000
£838 $1400 €1223 Woman admiring birdsnest (76x66cm-30x26in) s. painted c.1920. 15-Nov-3 Illustration House, New York #103/R

BOLLHAGEN, Franz (1881-1971) Swiss
£345 $576 €500 Street in Garmisch Partenkirchen in the spring with figures (61x80cm-24x31in) s. 10-Jul-3 Allgauer, Kempten #2445/R

BOLLIGER, Rodolphe (19th C) Swiss
£543 $923 €793 Still life with apples (24x32cm-9x13in) s. board. 1-Dec-3 Koller, Zurich #6537/R (S.FR 1200)

BOLLING, Svein (1948-) Norwegian
Works on paper
£348 $602 €508 Seated woman in yellow (48x30cm-19x12in) s. gouache. 13-Dec-3 Blomqvist, Lysaker #1039/R (N.KR 4000)
£650 $1190 €949 Woman with cigarette (38x29cm-15x11in) s. pastel. 7-Jun-4 Blomqvist, Oslo #445/R (N.KR 8000)
£2306 $3851 €3367 Quietly listening (66x48cm-26x19in) s. i.verso pastel. 13-Oct-3 Blomqvist, Oslo #379/R est:25000-30000 (N.KR 27000)

BOLMER, M de Forest (1854-1910) American
£435 $800 €653 Coastal landscape (28x38cm-11x15in) s. 13-Jun-4 William Jenack, New York #304

BOLOGNA, Domenico (1845-1885) Italian
£2979 $4974 €4200 Meeting at the gate (40x30cm-16x12in) s.d.1877 i.verso. 14-Oct-3 Finarte Semenzato, Milan #104

BOLOGNESE SCHOOL (16th C) Italian

£5629	$10301	€8500	Vierge a l'enfant avec Saint Jean et Marie-Madeleine (52x62cm-20x24in) panel. 7-Apr-4 Libert, Castor, Paris #5/R est:3000-5000
£7042	$11690	€10000	Christ appearing to Magdalene (77x62cm-30x24in) 11-Jul-3 Finarte, Venice #546/R est:10000-12000
£8108	$14270	€12000	St. Francis receiving the Stigmata (55x37cm-22x15in) panel. 18-May-4 Sotheby's, Amsterdam #46/R est:4000-6000
£13000	$23790	€18980	Old man (66x56cm-26x22in) panel prov.exhib.lit. 8-Jul-4 Sotheby's, London #189/R est:6000-8000
£36667	$67100	€55000	Madonna and Child and bishop (48x39cm-19x15in) board. 1-Jun-4 Sotheby's, Milan #121/R est:5000-7000

BOLOGNESE SCHOOL (17th C) Italian

£5705	$10497	€8500	Madonna and Child with St Anne and Infant Baptist (93x129cm-37x51in) 24-Mar-4 Dorotheum, Vienna #71/R est:2000-3000
£6579	$12105	€10000	Vierge et Enfant benissant un Saint Dominique. panel. 25-Jun-4 Doutrebente, Paris #4/R est:1000-1200
£7000	$12810	€10220	Christ and the Virgin appearing in glory (35x46cm-14x18in) copper hexagonal exhib.lit. 8-Jul-4 Sotheby's, London #203/R est:10000-15000
£10526	$19368	€16000	Rebecca and Elizier (96x130cm-38x51in) 24-Jun-4 Dr Fritz Nagel, Stuttgart #640/R est:11000
£11086	$19845	€16186	Saint Appolonia (89x74cm-35x29in) prov. 25-May-4 Bukowskis, Stockholm #430/R est:200000-250000 (S.KR 150000)
£12057	$20135	€17000	Allegoria della abbondanza (134x189cm-53x74in) 17-Jun-3 Finarte Semenzato, Milan #631/R est:18000-22000
£34667	$62053	€52000	Pieta' (94x293cm-37x115in) 17-May-4 Finarte Semenzato, Rome #120/R est:50000-60000
Works on paper			
£5000	$9000	€7300	River landscape with a tower and a bridge with arches (13x25cm-5x10in) pen ink prov. 21-Jan-4 Sotheby's, New York #121/R est:6000-8000

BOLOGNESE SCHOOL (18th C) Italian

£4934	$9079	€7500	Magdalene (95x77cm-37x30in) 22-Jun-4 Finarte Semenzato, Rome #294/R est:4500-5500
£5000	$8650	€7300	Saint Peter (47x37cm-19x15in) 10-Dec-3 Bonhams, New Bond Street #116/R est:5000-8000
£7383	$13584	€11000	Veronica (95x71cm-37x28in) oval. 24-Mar-4 Dorotheum, Vienna #74/R est:12000-16000
£9667	$17303	€14500	Saint Peter (70x59cm-28x23in) 12-May-4 Finarte Semenzato, Milan #54/R est:15000-20000
£24000	$40800	€35040	Judith holding the head of Holofernes (124x104cm-49x41in) 30-Oct-3 Sotheby's, Olympia #107/R est:5000-7000
Works on paper			
£3333	$6000	€4866	Design for a ceiling fresco (25x20cm-10x8in) pen ink wash htd white. 21-Jan-4 Sotheby's, New York #41/R est:1800-2200

BOLONACHI, Constantin (1837-1907) Greek

£70000	$125300	€102200	By the well (42x81cm-17x32in) s. prov. 10-May-4 Sotheby's, Olympia #16/R est:40000-60000
£100000	$179000	€146000	Promenade by the harbour (55x100cm-22x39in) s. 11-May-4 Bonhams, New Bond Street #34/R est:100000-150000
£140000	$238000	€204400	Disembarkation (74x54cm-29x21in) s. prov. 18-Nov-3 Sotheby's, London #27/R est:100000-150000
£180000	$306000	€262800	Bringing in the catch (61x86cm-24x34in) s. prov. 18-Nov-3 Sotheby's, London #16/R est:100000-150000
£230000	$391000	€335800	Admiring the ships (46x69cm-18x27in) s. prov. 18-Nov-3 Sotheby's, London #10/R est:100000-150000

BOLOTOWSKY, Ilya (1907-1981) American/Russian

£1765	$3000	€2577	Rising tondo (45cm-18in circular) s.d.81 s.i.d.verso acrylic on wood prov. 9-Nov-3 Bonhams & Butterfields, Los Angeles #4079/R est:2500-3500
£2096	$3500	€3060	Miniature yellow tondo II (21cm-8in circular) s.d.71 s.i.d.verso acrylic panel prov. 11-Nov-3 Christie's, Rockefeller NY #102/R est:3000-5000
£2138	$3400	€3121	Yellow tondo with pale blue (99cm-39in circular) s. acrylic. 14-Sep-3 Susanin's, Chicago #6009/R est:800-1200
£3352	$6000	€4894	Tondo. s.d.1973. 16-May-4 Wright, Chicago #302/R est:7000-9000
£4595	$8500	€6709	Tondo in red and yellow (98x98cm-39x39in) s.d.74 acrylic round prov. 13-Jul-4 Christie's, Rockefeller NY #43/R est:6000-8000
£4706	$8000	€6871	Red ellipse (74x64cm-29x25in) s.d.1981 i.d.verso oil on linen prov. 9-Nov-3 Wright, Chicago #378 est:7000-9000
£4706	$8000	€6871	Blue tondo (cm-in circular) s.d.1972 s.i.dv. 9-Nov-3 Wright, Chicago #379 est:7000-9000
£8537	$14000	€12379	Composition (102x30cm-40x12in) s. prov. 31-May-3 Brunk, Ashville #448/R est:2000-4000
£12805	$21000	€18567	Composition (69x38cm-27x15in) s. s.i.verso egg emulsion gesso wood painted c.1949 prov. 31-May-3 Brunk, Ashville #444/R est:3000-5000
£24390	$40000	€35366	Abstract composition (56x91cm-22x36in) s. prov. 31-May-3 Brunk, Ashville #450/R est:3000-6000
Works on paper			
£471	$800	€688	Untitled (41x53cm-16x21in) ink pencil pair prov. 9-Nov-3 Wright, Chicago #266
£838	$1500	€1223	Untitled (23x30cm-9x12in) gouache prov. 16-May-4 Wright, Chicago #236/R est:2000-3000
£1235	$2100	€1803	Abstraction No.1 (33x25cm-13x10in) s. paper collage. 9-Nov-3 Wright, Chicago #239 est:2000-3000
£1235	$2100	€1803	Untitled (30x46cm-12x18in) ink pair prov. 9-Nov-3 Wright, Chicago #265 est:1000-1500

BOLOTOWSKY, Ilya (attrib) (1907-1981) American/Russian

£2439	$4000	€3537	Composition (102x41cm-40x16in) prov. 31-May-3 Brunk, Ashville #449/R est:1500-2500

BOLT, N P (1886-1965) Danish

£1254	$2258	€1831	Interior scene with flowers by mirror (110x91cm-43x36in) s. 24-Apr-4 Rasmussen, Havnen #2040 est:2000-3000 (D.KR 14000)
Works on paper			
£287	$516	€419	Interior scene with young woman (82x79cm-32x31in) s.d.1922 pastel. 24-Apr-4 Rasmussen, Havnen #2038 (D.KR 3200)
£358	$655	€523	Portrait of Rigmor Gabriel Jensen (112x91cm-44x36in) s.d.29 pastel. 7-Jun-4 Museumsbygningen, Copenhagen #64 (D.KR 4000)

BOLT, Ronald William (1938-) Canadian

£680	$1244	€993	Silver day (74x89cm-29x35in) s.d.70 acrylic. 1-Jun-4 Joyner Waddington, Toronto #127/R (C.D 1700)
£714	$1229	€1042	March melt (82x112cm-32x44in) s.d.85 acrylic prov. 2-Dec-3 Joyner Waddington, Toronto #507 est:1200-1500 (C.D 1600)
£1786	$3071	€2608	Northern river series no. 1 - Coppermine at Bloody Falls N W T (125x119cm-49x47in) s.d.82 acrylic. 2-Dec-3 Joyner Waddington, Toronto #481 est:1500-2000 (C.D 4000)

BOLTANSKI, Christian (1944-) French

Photographs			
£2817	$4873	€4000	Composition (100x100cm-39x39in) col photograph prov.exhib.lit. 9-Dec-3 Artcurial Briest, Paris #443/R est:3000-4000
£9333	$17173	€14000	Composition musicale (162x99cm-64x39in) col photograph triptych exec 1982 prov.exhib. 8-Jun-4 Artcurial Briest, Paris #285/R est:15000-20000
Sculpture			
£1793	$3228	€2600	Untitled (15x26x5cm-6x10x2in) s.d.1970 verso wood box typing paper iron thread tape glass. 25-Jan-4 Cornette de St.Cyr, Paris #97 est:2500-3000
£2276	$4097	€3300	Untitled (16x26x5cm-6x10x2in) s.d.1970 verso wooden box clay typing paper iron thread tape glass. 25-Jan-4 Cornette de St.Cyr, Paris #98 est:2500-3000
£12291	$22000	€17945	Le lycee chases (120x60x23cm-47x24x9in) gelatin silver print electric lamp tin boxes prov.exhib. 12-May-4 Christie's, Rockefeller NY #477/R est:15000-20000
£15000	$25050	€21900	Monument (162x61cm-64x24in) col black white photo metal light bulbs wire exec.c.1987 prov. 22-Oct-3 Christie's, London #137/R est:15000-20000
Works on paper			
£1842	$3389	€2800	Grand-pere et petit Christian (28x20cm-11x8in) s.i. mixed media collage cardboard prov. 27-Jun-4 Versailles Encheres #175/R est:3000-3500

BOLTON, Flo (?) British

£310	$518	€453	Lady wearing a white dress (75x62cm-30x24in) 21-Oct-3 Bruton Knowles, Cheltenham #441
£480	$802	€701	Nell Gwyn (114x101cm-45x40in) after Sir Peter Lely. 21-Oct-3 Bruton Knowles, Cheltenham #447
£720	$1202	€1051	Student (68x56cm-27x22in) after G B Moroni. 21-Oct-3 Bruton Knowles, Cheltenham #445

BOLTON, Hale William (1885-1920) American

Works on paper			
£599	$1000	€875	Texas hill country (13x18cm-5x7in) s. pastel. 16-Nov-3 Simpson's, Houston #167/R
£613	$1000	€895	Texas hill country (13x18cm-5x7in) s. pastel. 28-Sep-3 Simpson's, Houston #120/R
£633	$1000	€924	Texas Hill country (13x18cm-5x7in) s. pastel. 27-Jul-3 Simpson's, Houston #410

BOLTON, James (c.1740-1799) British

Works on paper			
£1000	$1850	€1460	Christmas or winter rose (51x35cm-20x14in) s.d.1785 pencil W/C. 15-Jul-4 Bonhams, New Bond Street #4/R est:1000-1500
£1500	$2775	€2190	Snowdrop, fritillary and anemone coronaria tied with a ribbon (51x35cm-20x14in) s.i. pencil W/C. 15-Jul-4 Bonhams, New Bond Street #8/R est:1500-2000
£1500	$2775	€2190	Promrose peerless (51x35cm-20x14in) s.i.d.1785 pencil W/C. 15-Jul-4 Bonhams, New Bond Street #9/R est:1500-2000
£3000	$5550	€4380	Peony (51x35cm-20x14in) s. pencil W/C. 15-Jul-4 Bonhams, New Bond Street #7/R est:3000-5000
£4000	$7400	€5840	Jacobean or St James's lily (51x35cm-20x14in) s.i.d.1785 pencil W/C. 15-Jul-4 Bonhams, New Bond Street #6/R est:4000-6000

BOM, A (19/20th C) ?

Works on paper			
£3200	$5728	€4672	Landscape with Russian church (35x76cm-14x30in) s.d.1924 ink W/C. 26-May-4 Sotheby's, Olympia #377/R est:2000-3000

BOMAN, Lars Henning (c.1730-1799) Swedish

£1769	$3043	€2583	Portrait of a young noble lady (72x58cm-28x23in) s.i.verso. 3-Dec-3 AB Stockholms Auktionsverk #2493/R est:8000-10000 (S.KR 23000)

BOMAN, Lars Henning (attrib) (1730-1799) Swedish

£1923	$3308	€2808	Still life of clay pot (38x31cm-15x12in) 2-Dec-3 Bukowskis, Stockholm #316/R est:30000-35000 (S.KR 25000)

BOMBELLI, Sebastiano (1635-1719) Italian

£10769	$18523	€15723	Senator Michele Foscarini (89x72cm-35x28in) i.verso oval prov. 2-Dec-3 Bukowskis, Stockholm #367/R est:60000-80000 (S.KR 140000)

BOMBELLI, Sebastiano (attrib) (1635-1719) Italian

£3000	$5490	€4380	Portrait of a young man in pink fur trimmed coat (76x65cm-30x26in) 7-Jul-4 Bonhams, New Bond Street #34/R est:3000-5000

BOMBERG, David (1890-1957) British

£3800	$6042	€5548	On the Thames (63x75cm-25x30in) i.d.1922 verso oil paper. 10-Sep-3 Sotheby's, Olympia #141/R est:4000-6000
£6600	$11220	€9636	Players, circus (30x41cm-12x16in) s. oil on paper painted 1920-22 prov.exhib. 21-Nov-3 Christie's, London #120/R est:2000-3000
£9500	$16150	€13870	Bargee women (75x53cm-30x21in) oil on paper. 21-Nov-3 Christie's, London #119/R est:10000-15000

£15000	$26850	€21900	Flowers and laurels (76x58cm-30x23in) s.d.43 prov. 5-May-4 John Nicholson, Haslemere #448/R est:15000-20000
£18000	$30600	€26280	David, self portrait (61x51cm-24x20in) painted 1937 prov.exhib. 21-Nov-3 Christie's, London #118/R est:15000-25000
£30000	$54900	€43800	Self portrait (66x56cm-26x22in) s.d.31 board prov. 4-Jun-4 Christie's, London #93/R est:15000-20000
£65000	$118950	€94900	Jerusalem, looking to Mount Scopos (32x24cm-13x9in) s.d.25 prov. 2-Jun-4 Sotheby's, London #49/R est:25000-35000
£80000	$137600	€116800	St Ives (63x76cm-25x30in) painted 1947 prov.exhib. 3-Dec-3 Sotheby's, London #47/R est:30000-40000
£80000	$146400	€116800	Church of the Holy Sepulchre, Jerusalem (32x24cm-13x9in) s.d.25 prov.lit. 2-Jun-4 Sotheby's, London #48/R est:30000-40000
£82000	$150060	€119720	Ghetto theatre (76x56cm-30x22in) s.d.1920 prov. 4-Jun-4 Christie's, London #92/R est:30000-50000
£95000	$173850	€138700	Farm by the sea (66x76cm-26x30in) s. prov. 2-Jun-4 Sotheby's, London #75/R est:30000-40000
Works on paper			
£750	$1275	€1095	Figure on staircase (25x20cm-10x8in) pen ink W/C. 26-Nov-3 Sotheby's, Olympia #11/R
£2600	$4732	€3796	Round Church, Middle Temple (46x61cm-18x24in) chl exec 1947 prov. 1-Jul-4 Christie's, Kensington #331/R est:2000-3000
£3000	$5460	€4380	Study for Dark street, Ronda (60x64cm-24x25in) blk chk W/C. 1-Jul-4 Christie's, Kensington #329/R est:3000-5000
£5000	$9100	€7300	The barge (47x35cm-19x14in) W/C pencil exec. 1920 double-sided. 15-Jun-4 Bonhams, New Bond Street #23/R est:5000-7000
£6500	$11895	€9490	Bridge and gorge of the Tajo, Ronda, Spain (42x32cm-17x13in) s.d.35 chl prov.exhib. 4-Jun-4 Christie's, London #94/R est:4000-6000
£10000	$18300	€14600	Studies for London group (33x69cm-13x27in) s.i. chl brown chk double-sided prov. 4-Jun-4 Christie's, London #91/R est:4000-6000

BOMBLED, Louis Charles (1862-1927) French

£700	$1295	€1022	Portraits of horses, Dick Turpin and Shakespeare (15x20cm-6x8in) s. panel pair. 9-Mar-4 Gorringes, Lewes #2048
£700	$1295	€1022	Portraits of horses, Maori Chief and Garos (15x20cm-6x8in) s. panel pair. 9-Mar-4 Gorringes, Lewes #2050
£750	$1388	€1095	Portraits of horses, Sly Fox and Deadle (15x20cm-6x8in) s. 9-Mar-4 Gorringes, Lewes #2051
£800	$1480	€1168	Portraits of horses, Avenay and Sultan (15x20cm-6x8in) s. panel pair. 9-Mar-4 Gorringes, Lewes #2049

BOMBOIS, Camille (1883-1970) French

£2027	$3750	€2959	Paysage de Tuziers (14x22cm-6x9in) s. 12-Feb-4 Sotheby's, New York #22/R est:3500-4500
£3243	$6000	€4735	Nature morte aux fleurs et fruits (22x27cm-9x11in) s. 11-Feb-4 Sotheby's, New York #70/R est:7000-9000
£3733	$6234	€5450	Figures in a parkland (15x21cm-6x8in) s. 17-Nov-3 Waddingtons, Toronto #212/R est:1500-2500 (C.D 8250)
£4278	$8000	€6246	Marchande de frites (46x65cm-18x26in) s. prov.exhib. 25-Feb-4 Christie's, Rockefeller NY #1/R est:9000-12000
£6417	$12000	€9369	Fleurs dans un vase de verre (56x38cm-22x15in) s. 25-Feb-4 Christie's, Rockefeller NY #10/R est:14000-18000
£6486	$12000	€9470	Parc es Buttes, Chaumont (50x65cm-20x26in) s. prov. 11-Feb-4 Sotheby's, New York #60/R est:15000-20000
£6704	$12000	€9788	Vase of flowers (24x20cm-9x8in) s. prov. 6-May-4 Sotheby's, New York #464/R est:8000-12000
£7500	$13800	€10950	Debut de l'automne (79x63cm-31x25in) s. painted c.1926 prov. 22-Jun-4 Sotheby's, London #319/R est:8000-12000
£8589	$14000	€12540	Portrait de Damia, Marie-Louise Damien (47x39cm-19x15in) s. prov. 25-Sep-3 Christie's, Rockefeller NY #586/R est:18000-22000
£9091	$17000	€13273	Rentree du soir (33x41cm-13x16in) s. painted c.1935 prov. 25-Feb-4 Christie's, Rockefeller NY #55/R est:12000-16000
£10056	$18000	€14682	Rue dans la campagne (24x35cm-9x14in) s. 6-May-4 Sotheby's, New York #458/R est:10000-15000
£11972	$19873	€17000	La dentelliere (35x27cm-14x11in) s. exhib. 11-Jun-3 Delorme & Bocage, Paris #23/R est:18000-22000
£19334	$34800	€29000	Les soeurs foraines (81x64cm-32x25in) s. 26-Apr-4 Tajan, Paris #281/R est:30000-32000

BOMCHES, Friedrich von (1916-) Rumanian

Works on paper			
£302	$541	€450	Mother with child (42x29cm-17x11in) s.d.76 Indian ink pen brush. 25-May-4 Karl & Faber, Munich #215
£369	$661	€550	Lake with sailing boat (51x37cm-20x15in) s.d.79 chl. 25-May-4 Karl & Faber, Munich #217
£537	$961	€800	Country scene with peasant woman and cart (44x62cm-17x24in) s.d.74 Indian ink brush pen. 25-May-4 Karl & Faber, Munich #214/R
£617	$1105	€920	Houses by canal (43x30cm-17x12in) s.d.60 mixed media. 25-May-4 Karl & Faber, Munich #212
£617	$1105	€920	Don Quixote (59x41cm-23x16in) s.d. gouache col chk. 25-May-4 Karl & Faber, Munich #213/R
£738	$1321	€1100	Coastline (48x67cm-19x26in) s.d.91 pastel. 25-May-4 Karl & Faber, Munich #216

BOMMEL, Elias Pieter van (1819-1890) Dutch

£1049	$1783	€1500	Amsterdam (39x35cm-15x14in) s. 28-Nov-3 Wiener Kunst Auktionen, Vienna #451/R est:1500-3000
£1119	$1902	€1600	Winter landscape with children playing and windmill (25x36cm-10x14in) mono. lit. 28-Nov-3 Schloss Ahlden, Ahlden #1532/R est:2400
£3497	$5944	€5000	Moonlit harbour entrance (63x92cm-25x36in) bears sig. 24-Nov-3 Dorotheum, Vienna #79/R est:5000-6000
£6711	$12013	€10000	Dutch harbour (53x95cm-21x37in) s.d.1881. 27-May-4 Dorotheum, Vienna #14/R est:10000-12000
£8054	$14416	€12000	Ferry-boat arriving (39x49cm-15x19in) s. 27-May-4 Dorotheum, Vienna #15/R est:12000-16000
£11111	$18889	€16000	Moored sailing vessels at Dordrecht harbour (28x48cm-11x19in) s. panel. 28-Oct-3 Christie's, Amsterdam #73/R est:10000-15000
£14667	$26400	€22000	Figures at the entrance of the St. Stevens Church, Nijmegen (51x42cm-20x17in) s.d.1855 panel. 20-Apr-4 Sotheby's, Amsterdam #10/R est:12000-18000
£22378	$38042	€32000	Skaters on Dutch canal (71x106cm-28x42in) s. 24-Nov-3 Dorotheum, Vienna #76/R est:5000-6000

BOMMELS, Peter (1951-) German

Works on paper			
£2817	$4873	€4000	The last step (129x110cm-51x43in) mono.d.86 i. verso mixed media jute. 13-Dec-3 Lempertz, Koln #119/R est:2500

BOMPARD, Luigi (1879-1953) Italian

Works on paper			
£284	$460	€400	Italian cinema (25x36cm-10x14in) s. Chinese ink pencil. 22-May-3 Finarte Semenzato, Rome #96
£284	$460	€400	Sport news (22x32cm-9x13in) i. Chinese ink pencil. 22-May-3 Finarte Semenzato, Rome #97
£496	$804	€700	Traitor (33x25cm-13x10in) s. mixed media card. 22-May-3 Finarte Semenzato, Rome #99

BOMPARD, Maurice (1857-1936) French

£293	$524	€430	Bouquet de fleurs sur une console (35x27cm-14x11in) s. 19-Mar-4 Millon & Associes, Paris #59
£633	$1153	€950	View of Venice (16x21cm-6x8in) s. panel. 4-Jul-4 Eric Pillon, Calais #155/R
£636	$1056	€922	Femme elegante (17x13cm-7x5in) board. 13-Jun-3 Zofingen, Switzerland #2419/R (S.FR 1400)
£1049	$1804	€1500	Jeune orientale aux bijoux (18x14cm-7x6in) s. panel. 8-Dec-3 Tajan, Paris #235/R est:2000-3000
£1086	$1846	€1586	Venice (60x73cm-24x29in) s. 28-Nov-3 Zofingen, Switzerland #2552/R est:3000 (S.FR 2400)
£1189	$1985	€1700	Jeune pecheur (47x33cm-19x13in) s. 29-Jun-3 Eric Pillon, Calais #58/R
£1278	$2250	€1866	Fishing boat on the Venetian Lagoon (65x49cm-26x19in) s. 18-May-4 Bonhams & Butterfields, San Francisco #133/R est:3000-5000
£1667	$3067	€2500	Venetian canal (73x60cm-29x24in) s. 9-Jun-4 Bukowskis, Helsinki #583/R est:800
£2907	$5000	€4244	Grand Canal (70x100cm-28x39in) s. canvas on masonite. 3-Dec-3 Doyle, New York #99/R est:4000-6000
£6623	$12119	€10000	L'entree du village (60x85cm-24x33in) s. 9-Apr-4 Claude Aguttes, Neuilly #122/R est:8000-10000
£7042	$12183	€10000	Maternite (60x49cm-24x19in) s. panel. 15-Dec-3 Gros & Delettrez, Paris #195/R est:10000-12000
£9000	$16380	€13140	L'attente, odalisques dans le harem (53x21cm-21x8in) indis.s. panel prov.lit. 15-Jun-4 Sotheby's, London #130/R est:8000-12000

BOMPIANI, Augusto (1851-1930) Italian

£329	$605	€500	Village street (67x56cm-26x22in) s.d.1925. 23-Jun-4 Finarte Semenzato, Rome #29
Works on paper			
£352	$599	€514	Landscape with washerwoman in narrow pass (51x73cm-20x29in) s. W/C. 5-Nov-3 Dobiaschofsky, Bern #367/R (S.FR 800)
£1734	$3000	€2532	Tyrolean couple (53x36cm-21x14in) W/C. 12-Dec-3 Du Mouchelle, Detroit #2005/R est:3000-4000

BOMPIANI, Roberto (1821-1908) Italian

£1413	$2401	€2020	Roman woman with basket of flowers (46x28cm-18x11in) 1-Dec-3 Babuino, Rome #393/R est:400-600
£2188	$3500	€3194	Portrait of a young gentleman. Portrait of a young lady (66x79cm-26x31in) s.d.1879 pair. 19-Sep-3 Freeman, Philadelphia #83/R est:2000-3000
£26389	$47500	€38528	Two Pompeian ladies (63x100cm-25x39in) s. 23-Apr-4 Sotheby's, New York #176/R est:18000-25000

BOMPIANI-BATTAGLIA, Clelia (1847-1927) Italian

Works on paper			
£333	$603	€500	Scene galante (44x33cm-17x13in) s. W/C. 4-Apr-4 Salle des ventes Pillet, Lyon la Foret #6/R
£633	$1000	€924	Fisherwomen on the beach (56x38cm-22x15in) s. W/C on card. 6-Sep-3 Brunk, Ashville #864

BON, Angelo Del (1898-1952) Italian

£1000	$1820	€1500	Still life (45x50cm-18x20in) s. 12-Jul-4 Il Ponte, Milan #980 est:1800-2000
£1429	$2557	€2100	Flowers (55x46cm-22x18in) s. painted 1951 prov.lit. 16-Mar-4 Finarte Semenzato, Milan #115/R est:1700
£2754	$4516	€3800	Still life with pears (46x55cm-18x22in) s. prov.exhib. 27-May-3 Sotheby's, Milan #55/R est:3000
£3667	$6747	€5500	Watermelons and grapes (50x61cm-20x24in) s. painted 1945 lit. 12-Jun-4 Meeting Art, Vercelli #377/R est:5000
Works on paper			
£676	$1189	€1000	Bacchanal scene (35x39cm-14x15in) W/C painted 1930. 19-May-4 Il Ponte, Milan #1089

BONACCORSI, Antonio (1826-?) Italian

£922	$1567	€1346	Portrait of Italian man and young woman (23x18cm-9x7in) one mono. pair. 10-Nov-3 Rasmussen, Vejle #17/R (D.KR 10000)

BONADEI, Aldo (1906-1974) Brazilian

£3114	$5511	€4671	Interior scene (21x25cm-8x10in) s.d.1928 canvas on masonite. 27-Apr-4 Bolsa de Arte, Rio de Janeiro #56/R (B.R 17000)
Works on paper			
£3297	$5835	€4946	Still life (25x34cm-10x13in) s.d.1972 gouache board on masonite. 27-Apr-4 Bolsa de Arte, Rio de Janeiro #57/R (B.R 18000)

BONALUMI, Agostino (1935-) Italian

£2029	$3328	€2800	Extroflexion (46x75cm-18x30in) s.d.2002 paper on canvas. 29-May-3 Galleria Pace, Milan #137/R est:4000
£2797	$4755	€4000	Untitled (27x27cm-11x11in) s.d.66 verso. 27-Nov-3 Lempertz, Koln #52/R est:3000
£3241	$5413	€4700	Yellow (18x24cm-7x9in) s.i.verso painted 1978. 14-Nov-3 Farsetti, Prato #221/R est:2900-3300

£3356 $6208 €5000 Untitled (35x50cm-14x20in) s.d.2002. 11-Mar-4 Galleria Pace, Milan #49/R est:4500-5500
£5282 $8768 €7500 Untitled (60x60cm-24x24in) s.d.1983 verso folded canvas. 14-Jun-3 Meeting Art, Vercelli #116/R est:6000
£5634 $9352 €8000 Rosso (73x60cm-29x24in) s.d.1993. 14-Jun-3 Meeting Art, Vercelli #368 est:5000
£6884 $11290 €9500 Yellow (70x70cm-28x28in) s.d.80 verso prov. 27-May-3 Sotheby's, Milan #29/R est:3000-4000
£8054 $14899 €12000 White extroflexion (100x80cm-39x31in) s.d.1983 verso. 13-Mar-4 Meeting Art, Vercelli #129 est:10000
£9028 $14264 €13000 Red (100x100cm-39x39in) enamel. 6-Sep-3 Meeting Art, Vercelli #352 est:10000
£9790 $16643 €14000 Untitled (146x96cm-57x38in) s.d.71 verso acrylic. 24-Nov-3 Christie's, Milan #287/R est:14000-18000
£11409 $20423 €17000 Red (100x100cm-39x39in) s.i.d.1979 verso enamel. 30-May-4 Meeting Art, Vercelli #49 est:10000
£12500 $19750 €18000 Black object (90x100cm-35x39in) 6-Sep-3 Meeting Art, Vercelli #607 est:16000
£13768 $22580 €19000 Red (110x82cm-43x32in) s.d.78 verso. 27-May-3 Sotheby's, Milan #298/R est:14000-18000
£16552 $26483 €24000 White (70x60cm-28x24in) s.verso painted 1976. 13-Mar-3 Galleria Pace, Milan #99/R est:29000-38000
£17450 $31235 €26000 Red (100x100cm-39x39in) s.d.71 verso tempera vinyl prov. 25-May-4 Sotheby's, Milan #307/R est:16000-22000
£21014 $34464 €29000 Black (100x70cm-39x28in) s.d.1963. 30-May-3 Farsetti, Prato #520/R
£27000 $45090 €39420 Blue (187x150cm-74x59in) s.d.67 verso tempera prov.exhib.lit. 20-Oct-3 Sotheby's, London #15/R est:30000

Sculpture
£1524 $2500 €2225 Nero (27x27x4cm-11x11x2in) s.i.d.66 verso acrylic prov. 28-May-3 Sotheby's, Amsterdam #4/R est:1000-1500
£10140 $17238 €14500 Blue 294 (70x60cm-28x24in) s.i.d.66 verso tempera vinyl prov. 25-Nov-3 Sotheby's, Milan #237/R est:10000-15000
£12587 $21399 €18000 Untitled (150x75cm-59x30in) s.d.68 verso plastic fabric. 25-Nov-3 Sotheby's, Milan #236/R est:18000-22000

Works on paper
£367 $675 €550 Untitled (50x35cm-20x14in) s. mixed media exec.2001. 12-Jun-4 Meeting Art, Vercelli #395
£1497 $2724 €2200 Untitled (27x31cm-11x12in) s. paper on canvas prov. 6-Feb-4 Galleria Rosenberg, Milan #109/R est:2000
£2013 $3725 €3000 Untitled (50x70cm-20x28in) s. W/C lit. 13-Mar-4 Meeting Art, Vercelli #72 est:3000
£3333 $5267 €4800 Plan (50x73cm-20x29in) mixed media collage on canvas exec.1971. 6-Sep-3 Meeting Art, Vercelli #315 est:4000
£3846 $6154 €5615 Blu (70x60cm-28x24in) s.d.stretcher prov. 16-Sep-3 Philippe Schuler, Zurich #3006/R est:12000-15000 (S.FR 8500)
£5634 $9352 €8000 Untitled (100x80cm-39x31in) s.d.1979 verso. 11-Jun-3 Finarte Semenzato, Milan #600/R est:10000

BONAMI, Giovanni (19th C) Italian?
£1920 $3322 €2803 Triumphant cockerel crowing over his victory. Chicken and a pea-hen in a landscape (23x19cm-9x7in) s. panel pair after Melchior D'Hondecoeter. 9-Dec-3 Sotheby's, Olympia #340/R est:1200-1800

BONAMICI, L (?) ?
£1216 $2250 €1824 Eventide (52x71cm-20x28in) indis.sig. 18-Jul-4 Bonhams & Butterfields, Los Angeles #7021/R est:2000-3000
£1250 $2125 €1825 Seascape with rocks in foreground beneath a cloudy sky (47x48cm-19x19in) s. 31-Oct-3 Moore Allen & Innocent, Cirencester #684/R est:1500-2000

BONAMICI, Louis (1878-1966) Italian
£775 $1340 €1100 Gondolas in Venice (46x62cm-18x24in) s. panel. 13-Dec-3 De Vuyst, Lokeren #34/R
£1300 $2067 €1885 La mer houleuse (38x46cm-15x18in) s. 11-Sep-3 Christie's, Kensington #59/R est:600-800
£1600 $2544 €2320 Un etang au soleil (61x50cm-24x20in) 11-Sep-3 Christie's, Kensington #58/R est:600-800
£1700 $2941 €2482 Voiliers au port (38x55cm-15x22in) s. panel. 11-Dec-3 Christie's, Kensington #64/R est:1000-1500
£1901 $3042 €2700 View of Venice (60x93cm-24x37in) s. 19-Sep-3 Finarte, Venice #233/R
£2600 $4134 €3770 Arbres en fleurs (50x61cm-20x24in) s. 11-Sep-3 Christie's, Kensington #61/R est:1200-1800
£2800 $4452 €4060 Bateaux de pecheurs a Saint Tropez (41x32cm-16x13in) s. panel. 11-Sep-3 Christie's, Kensington #60/R est:1000-1500
£3500 $6055 €5110 Soleil couchant sur le port (74x91cm-29x36in) s. 11-Dec-3 Christie's, Kensington #66/R est:1500-2000

BONAPARTE, Charles Louis Napoleon (1808-1873) French
Works on paper
£1189 $2021 €1700 Une scene de combat naval du XVIIIeme (20x26cm-8x10in) s.d.16 octobre 1865 black ink prov. 1-Dec-3 Coutau Begarie, Paris #311/R est:1700-2200

BONATTI, Vittorio (1890-?) Italian
£268 $475 €400 Landscape covered in snow (27x37cm-11x15in) s. board. 1-May-4 Meeting Art, Vercelli #71

BONAVIA, Carlo (fl.1740-1756) Italian
£31000 $56730 €45260 River landscape with herders and travellers (77x103cm-30x41in) s. prov. 8-Jul-4 Sotheby's, London #177/R est:20000-30000

BONAVIA, Carlo (style) (18th C) Italian
£8197 $15000 €11968 Mediterranean coastline with fishermen (75x123cm-30x48in) shaped canvas pair. 3-Jun-4 Christie's, Rockefeller NY #1136/R est:2000-3000

BONAVITA, Alfonso (1962-) Italian
Works on paper
£1056 $1754 €1500 Dittico I (96x115cm-38x45in) s.d.2000 s.i.verso mixed media panel. 14-Jun-3 Meeting Art, Vercelli #675/R est:1500

BONAZZA, Antonio (circle) (18th C) Italian
Sculpture
£17606 $29225 €25000 Juno (210cm-83in) stone. 11-Jul-3 Finarte, Venice #223/R est:20000-30000
£17606 $29225 €25000 Mercury (195cm-77in) stone. 11-Jul-3 Finarte, Venice #224/R est:20000-30000

BONCOMPAIN, Pierre (1938-) French
£534 $960 €800 Assiette de fruits sur un gueridon (50x50cm-20x20in) s. isorel. 26-Apr-4 Tajan, Paris #194
£1888 $3153 €2700 Still life (49x49cm-19x19in) s. prov. 29-Jun-3 Versailles Encheres #18 est:3000
£2378 $3971 €3400 Fleurs (73x60cm-29x24in) s. prov. 29-Jun-3 Versailles Encheres #19/R est:3000-3500

BOND, Charles V (c.1825-?) American
£438 $700 €639 Mary Williams Smart (91x74cm-36x29in) painted 1855. 19-Sep-3 Du Mouchelle, Detroit #2268/R

BOND, Florence Cynthia (1891-1981) British
£580 $1003 €847 Sussex plough team. s. 14-Dec-3 Desmond Judd, Cranbrook #1103

BOND, Henry (1966-) British?
Photographs
£2800 $5096 €4088 Untitled (121x160cm-48x63in) s.d.1996 verso C-type print on aluminium lit. 4-Feb-4 Sotheby's, Olympia #56/R est:3000-4000
£3378 $5946 €5000 Dog race (25x20cm-10x8in) s.i.d.1991 photograph prov.exhib. 24-May-4 Christie's, Milan #179/R est:5000-7000

BOND, R S (1808-1886) British
£250 $418 €365 Fairy glen (120x155cm-47x61in) s.verso. 11-Nov-3 Bonhams, Ipswich #232

BOND, Richard Sebastian (1808-1886) British
£550 $990 €803 Craggy landscape with lake, drovers on horseback with sheep (48x74cm-19x29in) s.indis.d.1888. 24-Apr-4 Rogers Jones, Clwyd #174

BOND, Terence James (1946-) British
Works on paper
£460 $736 €672 Ducks (50x40cm-20x16in) s. gouache. 20-Sep-3 Lacy Scott, Bury St.Edmunds #436/R
£500 $895 €730 Green finch upon a branch (32x22cm-13x9in) s. W/C bodycol. 20-Mar-4 Lacy Scott, Bury St.Edmunds #450/R
£550 $985 €803 Wren upon a branch (32x22cm-13x9in) s. W/C bodycol. 20-Mar-4 Lacy Scott, Bury St.Edmunds #451

BOND, William Joseph J C (1833-1926) British
£260 $481 €380 Anglers on a river bank with cottages beyond (23x38cm-9x15in) s.d.88 panel. 14-Jul-4 Bonhams, Chester #342
£341 $550 €498 Fishing Swansea Bay (20x25cm-8x10in) bears sig. 20-Aug-3 James Julia, Fairfield #1083/R
£380 $673 €555 Turreted Cheshire house (29x45cm-11x18in) board. 28-Apr-4 Peter Wilson, Nantwich #66
£580 $1073 €847 Fishing vessel at sea (40x32cm-16x13in) s. 14-Jul-4 Christie's, Kensington #977/R
£588 $1065 €858 Fresh breeze (29x23cm-11x9in) s. board. 30-Mar-4 Stephan Welz, Johannesburg #405 est:5000-8000 (SA.R 7000)
£680 $1136 €993 Old stone bridge Clwt-y-bont (28x46cm-11x18in) s.i.d.80 board. 12-Nov-3 Halls, Shrewsbury #296/R
£750 $1245 €1095 Sailing out to sea (30x25cm-12x10in) s.d.1903 panel. 1-Oct-3 Sotheby's, Olympia #127/R
£2100 $3822 €3066 River landscape with a barge by a cottage. Estuary scene with beached boats (19x18cm-7x7in) both s. board pair. 3-Feb-4 Sworder & Son, Bishops Stortford #287/R est:600-800
£4000 $7160 €5840 Farmyard (39x32cm-15x13in) board prov. 27-May-4 Christie's, Kensington #152/R est:700-1000
£6100 $11407 €8906 Unloading the catch (45x37cm-18x15in) s. panel. 24-Feb-4 Bonhams, Knowle #55 est:4000-6000

Works on paper
£260 $442 €380 Sailing boat approaching a harbour wall (24x16cm-9x6in) s. W/C. 29-Oct-3 Bonhams, Chester #332
£480 $878 €701 Beached fishing vessel at low tide (23x32cm-9x13in) s.d.90 W/C. 27-Jan-4 Bonhams, Knightsbridge #7/R
£600 $978 €876 Coastal scene with beached boats and figures (18x38cm-7x15in) s. W/C. 27-Sep-3 Rogers Jones, Clwyd #29/R

BONDE, Peter (1958-) Danish
£329 $549 €480 Dark grey composition (55x46cm-22x18in) s.d.1995 verso. 7-Oct-3 Rasmussen, Copenhagen #224 (D.KR 3500)
£563 $941 €822 Orange composition (63x58cm-25x23in) s.d.1995 verso. 7-Oct-3 Rasmussen, Copenhagen #292/R (D.KR 6000)
£701 $1107 €1016 Abstract composition in grey, green and white (100x81cm-39x32in) s. 3-Sep-3 Museumsbygningen, Copenhagen #158/R (D.KR 7500)

Works on paper
£948 $1744 €1384 Lime (120x100cm-47x39in) s.d.1998 verso mixed media lit. 29-Mar-4 Rasmussen, Copenhagen #404/R (D.KR 10500)

BONE, Henry (1755-1834) British

£9000	$15300	€13140	George IV as Prince Regent (19cm-7in) s.i.d.1826 verso prov. 20-Nov-3 Sotheby's, London #69/R est:4000-6000
£10000	$17000	€14600	Shipwreck of Aeneas (23cm-9in) s.d.1817 enamel. 18-Nov-3 Bonhams, New Bond Street #148/R est:10000-15000
£24000	$40800	€35040	Frederick Duke of York (26cm-10in) s.i.d.1821 verso prov.exhib.lit. 20-Nov-3 Sotheby's, London #71/R est:5000-7000
£30000	$51000	€43800	Captain Sir William Hoste (26cm-10in) s.d.1830 exhib. 20-Nov-3 Sotheby's, London #70/R est:5000-7000
£42000	$71400	€61320	Queen Charlotte (26cm-10in) s.i.d.1821 verso prov.exhib.lit. 20-Nov-3 Sotheby's, London #72/R est:6000-8000
Miniatures			
£1000	$1660	€1460	Prince Regent (8cm-3in) s.d.1819 leather case prov. 2-Oct-3 Sotheby's, Olympia #14/R est:700-900
£1100	$2024	€1606	Gentleman, one of the doctors to George III (7cm-3in) s. s.i.verso enamel gold frame. 24-Jun-4 Bonhams, New Bond Street #19/R est:600-800
£1400	$2506	€2044	Mr Wilson, in a blue coat with gold buttons, red curtain backdrop (7cm-3in) s.d.1801 enamel on copper prov.lit. 25-May-4 Christie's, London #32/R est:800-1200
£1400	$2576	€2044	Caesar Borgia (9cm-4in circular) s. i.verso gilt metal frame circular. 24-Jun-4 Bonhams, New Bond Street #26/R est:800-1200
£2300	$4232	€3358	Mark Anthony, wearing fur-trimmed black double over a white chemise (9cm-4in circular) s.i. metal frame circular. 24-Jun-4 Bonhams, New Bond Street #25/R est:1000-1500
£26000	$43160	€37960	Thomas Howard, 3rd Duke of Norfolk (21cm-8in) s.i.d.1818 enamel gilt wood mount and frame. 30-Sep-3 Sotheby's, London #66/R est:5000-8000
£36000	$64440	€52560	Duchess of Kent with Princess Victoria (25cm-10in) i.d.1824-25 s.verso enamel rect exhib. 27-May-4 Sotheby's, London #61/R est:15000-20000

BONE, Henry Pierce (1779-1855) British

Miniatures			
£2700	$4590	€3942	Lady Audley (6cm-2in circular) i. enamel gilt frame. 18-Nov-3 Bonhams, New Bond Street #36/R est:600-800
£3000	$5520	€4380	Edward VI (11cm-4in) i. enamel gilt metal frame oval. 24-Jun-4 Bonhams, New Bond Street #14/R est:3000-5000
£4000	$7360	€5840	Dorothy Sydney, Countess of Sunderland (17cm-7in) s.i.d.1833 enamel rec. gilt mounted wood frame. 24-Jun-4 Bonhams, New Bond Street #28/R est:4000-6000
£4200	$7140	€6132	Sp. (9cm-4in) enamel prov. 18-Nov-3 Bonhams, New Bond Street #35/R est:800-1200

BONE, Robert Trewick (attrib) (1790-1840) British

£306	$556	€447	La belle assemblee (11x16cm-4x6in) i.verso paper on panel. 16-Jun-4 Fischer, Luzern #2033/R (S.FR 700)

BONE, Sir Muirhead (1876-1953) British

£340	$568	€496	Blackfriars from Southwark Bridge (14x18cm-6x7in) s.d.March 1925 prov. 21-Oct-3 Bonhams, Knightsbridge #188
Prints			
£2825	$5000	€4125	Great Gantry, Charing Cross Station. Rainy day in Rome (30x23cm-12x9in) s. drypoint two. 30-Apr-4 Sotheby's, New York #40 est:2000-3000
£3593	$6000	€5246	Manhattan excavation (33x25cm-13x10in) s. drypoint. 11-Nov-3 Doyle, New York #210/R est:3000-4000
Works on paper			
£250	$430	€365	Baltic, Sweden (21x34cm-8x13in) s.i. W/C chl. 3-Dec-3 Christie's, Kensington #462
£250	$463	€365	Study of baby (14x20cm-6x8in) s.i.d.1905 pencil. 11-Mar-4 Christie's, Kensington #14
£260	$476	€380	Monte Carlo (10x20cm-4x8in) s. pencil col wash. 28-Jul-4 Mallams, Oxford #99/R
£280	$468	€409	Farm near Bilbao (10x14cm-4x6in) s.i. crayon W/C prov. 16-Oct-3 Christie's, Kensington #238
£300	$561	€438	Distant St. Peter's Rome (20x29cm-8x11in) s. pencil wash. 21-Jul-4 Bonhams, New Bond Street #155/R
£315	$535	€450	Street scene with horse drawn cart in London (11x18cm-4x7in) s. pencil. 29-Nov-3 Bassenge, Berlin #6643
£350	$564	€508	Piedrahita. s.i. pencil W/C. 21-Aug-3 Bonhams, Edinburgh #1035
£350	$602	€511	Coast of Portugal (15x30cm-6x12in) s.i.d.1926 pencil W/C. 3-Dec-3 Christie's, Kensington #465
£360	$659	€526	Near the villa Adriana, Rome (13x20cm-5x8in) s. pencil W/C. 8-Apr-4 Bonhams, Edinburgh #140
£420	$685	€609	View at Falmouth (24x14cm-9x6in) s.d.1910 pencil. 23-Sep-3 Bonhams, Knightsbridge #10/R
£450	$774	€657	St Giles Fair (30x21cm-12x8in) s. pencil ink W/C wash buff paper. 4-Dec-3 Bonhams, Edinburgh #76
£451	$712	€658	City ruins (28x50cm-11x20in) s. chl conte ink wash. 2-Sep-3 Deutscher-Menzies, Melbourne #458/R (A.D 1100)
£640	$1069	€934	Evening at Scapa (36x53cm-14x21in) s.i. pencil W/C. 16-Oct-3 Bonhams, Edinburgh #209
£1250	$2338	€1825	Extensive river landscape at Oxford during Eights Week. s.i. pastel. 24-Feb-4 Wotton Auction Rooms, Wotton #731 est:500-600
£2300	$3979	€3358	Flag of the city and the giants Corpus Christi procession, Barcelona (35x26cm-14x10in) s.i.d.8 June 1928 pencil pen ink W/C. 11-Dec-3 Lyon & Turnbull, Edinburgh #10/R est:1000-1500

BONE, Stephen (1904-1958) British

£260	$424	€377	Street scene with figures (29x38cm-11x15in) s. board. 23-Sep-3 Bonhams, Leeds #120/R
£320	$550	€467	Shalloch on Minnoch, Dumfriesshire (27x34cm-11x13in) s. board lit. 3-Dec-3 Christie's, Kensington #548
£351	$650	€512	Wells Cathedral (25x36cm-10x14in) s.d.1946 panel prov. 15-Jul-4 Sotheby's, New York #66
£400	$704	€584	Autumn by the River Leam (27x35cm-11x14in) s.d.1943 board exhib. 18-May-4 Bonhams, Knightsbridge #80/R
Works on paper			
£420	$701	€613	Rock pool (70x100cm-28x39in) s. gouache. 16-Oct-3 Lyon & Turnbull, Edinburgh #72

BONE, William Drummond (1907-1979) British

£450	$851	€657	Still life of flowers in a blue jug (76x61cm-30x24in) s. board. 19-Feb-4 Lyon & Turnbull, Edinburgh #123

BONECHI, Matteo (attrib) (17th C) Italian

£2000	$3400	€2920	Presentation in the temple (50x34cm-20x13in) bears sig.d.1661. 29-Oct-3 Bonhams, New Bond Street #87/R est:2000-3000

BONEH, Schmuel (1930-) Israeli

£546	$1000	€797	Jacob and the Angel (73x54cm-29x21in) s. 1-Jun-4 Ben-Ami, Tel Aviv #4844/R est:1300-1600
£565	$1000	€825	Rabbi blowing the shofar (62x50cm-24x20in) s.d.1968. 1-May-4 Ben-Ami, Tel Aviv #4836/R est:1500-2000

BONELLO, Carmello (20th C) Maltese

Works on paper			
£850	$1335	€1233	Harbour at Valetta (15x57cm-6x22in) s. pencil bodycol. 28-Aug-3 Christie's, Kensington #394/R

BONELLO, Joseph (19/20th C) Maltese

Works on paper			
£320	$589	€467	Grand Harbour, Valetta (13x25cm-5x10in) init. bodycol oval. 25-Mar-4 Christie's, Kensington #94/R

BONET, Francisco (1941-) Spanish

£276	$497	€400	One, two, three, four and five (60x73cm-24x29in) s. 26-Jan-4 Durán, Madrid #36/R
£285	$511	€425	Foc (54x65cm-21x26in) s. 25-May-4 Durán, Madrid #88/R

BONET, Jacques Louis (1822-1894) Belgian

£833	$1325	€1200	Jeune femme dans les bles (80x56cm-31x22in) s.d.1880 canvas on panel. 9-Sep-3 Vanderkindere, Brussels #48

BONEVARDI, Marcelo (1929-1994) Argentinian

Works on paper			
£1117	$2000	€1631	Wall (450x56cm-177x22in) s. i.d.1966 verso mixed media construction canvas on panel. 6-May-4 Doyle, New York #130/R est:2000-3000
£6145	$11000	€8972	Preacher II (138x99cm-54x39in) s.i.d.66 mixed media construction oil wood canvas prov. 6-May-4 Doyle, New York #90/R est:10000-15000

BONFANTI, Arturo (1905-1978) Italian

£4362	$7809	€6500	Abstraction 146 (30x35cm-12x14in) s.i.d.1963 verso prov. 25-May-4 Sotheby's, Milan #171/R est:3000

BONFIELD, George R (1802-1898) American

£2673	$4250	€3903	Delaware River scene (41x61cm-16x24in) 25-Feb-3 Bunch, West Chester #430/R

BONFIELD, William van de Velde (19th C) American

£1333	$2400	€1946	Entering the harbour (38x61cm-15x24in) s.i. indis.d.verso. 23-Jan-4 Freeman, Philadelphia #165/R est:1000-1500
£1757	$3250	€2565	Ride in the snow (51x76cm-20x30in) s. 15-Jul-4 Sotheby's, New York #60/R est:2000-3000

BONFILS, Louise (1856-1933) Danish

£491	$880	€717	Coastal landscape with washerwomen (51x81cm-20x32in) s.d.1891. 12-Jan-4 Rasmussen, Vejle #6/R (D.KR 5200)

BONGART, Sergei R (1918-1985) American/Russian

£963	$1550	€1406	Abstract (79x99cm-31x39in) 15-Aug-3 Douglas, South Deerfield #2

BONHEUR, Auguste (1824-1884) French

£1400	$2534	€2100	Vue d'Auvergne, le Sancy au Loin (17x30cm-7x12in) st.sig. oil paper on canvas prov. 30-Mar-4 Rossini, Paris #286 est:1500-2500
£3631	$6500	€5301	Cattle watering (60x85cm-24x33in) s. i.stretcher. 6-May-4 Doyle, New York #43/R est:8000-12000

BONHEUR, Ferdinand (19th C) French

£1200	$2196	€1800	Ramassage du Varech (40x65cm-16x26in) s. 6-Jun-4 Osenat, Fontainebleau #192 est:2000-2500
£2041	$3245	€3000	Cites lacustres (21x41cm-8x16in) s. panel pair. 23-Mar-3 St-Germain-en-Laye Encheres #45
£6377	$10458	€8800	Voilier en fete dans la lagune, Venise. L'entree de la lagune a Venise (21x40cm-8x16in) s. panel pair. 11-May-3 Osenat, Fontainebleau #161/R est:7000-7500

BONHEUR, Isidore (1827-1901) French

Sculpture			
£1000	$1580	€1450	Tareau chargeant (51cm-20in) i. bronze. 27-Apr-3 Desmond Judd, Cranbrook #584
£1198	$2000	€1749	Mule and rider (33x33cm-13x13in) s. bronze. 19-Oct-3 Susanin's, Chicago #6008/R est:2000-3000
£1500	$2550	€2190	Farmer feeding pig (23x18cm-9x7in) s. pat bronze. 28-Oct-3 Sotheby's, London #139/R
£1712	$2911	€2500	Mouton (29x24cm-11x9in) s. pat bronze. 5-Nov-3 Beaussant & Lefèvre, Paris #176/R
£1882	$3200	€2748	Merino ram and ewe (14cm-6in) s. pat bronze. 28-Oct-3 Christie's, Rockefeller NY #248/R

£1913 $3500 €2793 Possibly Don Quixote on his mule (36x33cm-14x13in) s.st.f.Peyrol bronze. 10-Apr-4 Cobbs, Peterborough #60b/R
£2000 $3400 €2920 Milkmaid with cow and calf (21x29cm-8x11in) s. pat bronze. 28-Oct-3 Sotheby's, London #138/R
£2267 $4103 €3400 Cochons au baquet (12x25cm-5x10in) brown pat. bronze st.f.Peyrol. 31-Mar-4 Sotheby's, Paris #287/R est:2700-3000
£2419 $4452 €3532 Mounted jockey (73cm-29in) s. green brown pat. bronze wood base. 14-Jun-4 Waddingtons, Toronto #294/R est:10000-15000 (C.D 6000)
£2500 $4500 €3650 Bull (40x34cm-16x13in) s.st.f.Peyrol dark brown pat bronze varnished wood base. 21-Apr-4 Sotheby's, London #71/R est:3000-4000
£3020 $4862 €4500 Le taureau (40cm-16in) s.st.f. brown pat bronze. 23-Feb-3 St-Germain-en-Laye Encheres #42/R est:3000-3500
£3352 $6000 €4894 Racehorse with jockey up (58cm-23in) s.num.28/100 brown pat bronze marble base. 20-Mar-4 Freeman, Philadelphia #765/R est:2000-3000
£3472 $5451 €5000 Cheval marchant (19x30x7cm-7x12x3in) s. pat bronze. 29-Aug-3 Deauville, France #208/R est:4000-4200
£4800 $8736 €7008 Saddled race horse (30cm-12in) s. brown pat. bronze. 29-Jun-4 Bonhams, Knightsbridge #287/R est:3000-4000
£5000 $8500 €7300 Standing bull (38x53cm-15x21in) s. pat bronze. 28-Oct-3 Sotheby's, London #125/R
£11500 $20240 €16790 Grand Jockey (93x44x33cm-37x17x13in) bears i. dark brown pat bronze after Isidore. 21-May-4 Christie's, London #37/R est:4000-6000
£17778 $32000 €25956 Thoroughbred horse with jockey up (74x64cm-29x25in) s.st.f.Peyrol bronze rec. base. 23-Apr-4 Christie's, Rockefeller NY #150/R est:20000-30000
£45882 $78000 €66988 Cavalier (100cm-39in) s. pat bronze lit. 28-Oct-3 Christie's, Rockefeller NY #257/R
£87209 $150000 €127325 Steeplechase (88cm-35in) s. dark brown pat. bronze wood plinth lit. 5-Dec-3 Christie's, Rockefeller NY #33/R est:70000-90000

BONHEUR, Isidore (after) (1827-1901) French
Sculpture
£5000 $8800 €7300 Bull and cow group (51cm-20in) i. 18-May-4 Woolley & Wallis, Salisbury #343/R est:2000-3000
£7500 $13200 €10950 Charging bull (57cm-22in) i. 18-May-4 Woolley & Wallis, Salisbury #340/R est:4000-6000

BONHEUR, Juliette Peyrol (1830-1891) French
£894 $1600 €1305 Hen. Study of a figure in red (28x35cm-11x14in) s. board double-sided. 6-May-4 Doyle, New York #4/R est:3000-5000
£1000 $1790 €1460 Chickens in a landscape (46x61cm-18x24in) s. 18-Mar-4 Christie's, Kensington #487/R est:1000-1500

BONHEUR, Raymond (?-1849) French
£2600 $4758 €3900 Denicheurs (45x36cm-18x14in) s. 6-Jun-4 Osenat, Fontainebleau #238/R est:4000-4500

BONHEUR, Rosa (1822-1899) French
£1049 $1783 €1500 Two horses outside door (11x19cm-4x7in) s. panel. 22-Nov-3 Arnold, Frankfurt #472/R est:1200
£1183 $2117 €1727 Pastoral landscape (22x41cm-9x16in) s. 26-May-4 AB Stockholms Auktionsverk #2461/R est:12000-15000 (S.KR 16000)
£1304 $2139 €1800 Les moutons noirs (20x33cm-8x13in) st.sig. 11-May-3 Osenat, Fontainebleau #54 est:1500-1800
£1552 $2778 €2266 Hunting still life with deer (34x26cm-13x10in) s. 26-May-4 AB Stockholms Auktionsverk #2427/R est:15000-20000 (S.KR 21000)
£1986 $3217 €2800 Taureau et vache au pre (40x64cm-16x25in) mono. prov. 23-May-3 Sotheby's, Paris #37/R est:3000-5000
£2412 $4029 €3522 Chevaux (31x36cm-12x14in) s. panel. 16-Nov-3 Koller, Geneva #1251/R est:4000-6000 (S.FR 5500)
£3000 $5550 €4380 Tete de veau (44x53cm-17x21in) s.d.1878. 14-Jul-4 Sotheby's, Olympia #155/R est:1000-1500
£3779 $6500 €5517 Lion in a landscape (33x38cm-13x15in) s. 7-Dec-3 Hindman, Chicago #729/R est:4000-6000
£4000 $6800 €5840 Maltese (33x41cm-13x16in) s. 27-Nov-3 Christie's, Kensington #400/R est:4000-6000
£4500 $7740 €6570 Loading seaweed on the beach (51x76cm-20x30in) s.1877. 4-Dec-3 Christie's, Kensington #26/R est:4000-6000
£4706 $8000 €6871 Tetes de moutons et beliers (30x37cm-12x15in) st. sig. studio st. verso prov. 29-Oct-3 Christie's, Rockefeller NY #110/R est:10000-15000
£8553 $15737 €13000 Le cheval (31x46cm-12x18in) mono. paper on canvas. 25-Jun-4 Daguerre, Paris #138/R est:9000-10000
£12264 $19500 €17905 On guard (61x99cm-24x39in) 25-Feb-3 Bunch, West Chester #482a/R
Sculpture
£1208 $2259 €1800 Taureau (19x33cm-7x13in) brown pat bronze. 1-Mar-4 Coutau Begarie, Paris #231/R est:1800-2000
£1647 $2800 €2405 Merino ewe (14cm-6in) s. pat bronze. 28-Oct-3 Christie's, Rockefeller NY #247/R
£1745 $2809 €2600 Mouton broutant (21cm-8in) s. brown pat bronze. 23-Feb-3 St-Germain-en-Laye Encheres #29/R est:2000-2500
Works on paper
£299 $550 €437 Studies of lions (18x25cm-7x10in) bears sig.verso pencil prov. 9-Jun-4 Doyle, New York #3008/R
£317 $567 €450 Le marche de chevaux (20x30cm-8x12in) s.d.1861 graphite. 11-Jan-4 Rouillac, Vendome #3
£559 $900 €816 Portrait of young girl (20x13cm-8x5in) i. pencil two in one frame. 20-Aug-3 James Julia, Fairfield #99d/R
£800 $1472 €1168 Curassier Espagnol (27x21cm-11x8in) s.i. pen ink prov. 8-Jun-4 Bonhams, New Bond Street #10/R
£1149 $2022 €1700 Donkey (19x22cm-7x9in) s. black red chk exhib.lit. 19-May-4 Sotheby's, Amsterdam #360/R est:800-1200
£2200 $4070 €3212 Ploughing (20x29cm-8x11in) s. black chk htd white. 14-Jul-4 Sotheby's, Olympia #193/R est:1500-2000
£4600 $7820 €6716 Stag and does in a woodland clearing (25x36cm-10x14in) s.d.1875 W/C bodycol. 30-Oct-3 Duke & Son, Dorchester #98/R est:1000-2000

BONHEUR, Rosa (attrib) (1822-1899) French
£2200 $3520 €3190 Forlorn donkey (36x25cm-14x10in) s. paper on canvas. 18-Sep-3 Christie's, Kensington #49/R est:1500-2500
£3524 $5991 €5145 Horse market (52x102cm-20x40in) i. 5-Nov-3 Dobiaschofsky, Bern #368/R est:8000 (S.FR 8000)
£9000 $16380 €13140 Racehorse (90x117cm-35x46in) s.d.1882. 16-Jun-4 Christie's, Kensington #8/R est:7000-10000

BONHOMME, Léon (1870-1924) French
Works on paper
£268 $497 €400 Portrait de femme (23x20cm-9x8in) W/C. 14-Mar-4 Eric Pillon, Calais #121/R
£795 $1454 €1200 Couple au bar (19x21cm-7x8in) s. gouache W/C. 9-Apr-4 Claude Aguttes, Neuilly #57/R
£861 $1575 €1300 Femme assise a la table (20x17cm-8x7in) s.d.1920 gouache W/C. 9-Apr-4 Claude Aguttes, Neuilly #58/R

BONI, Jeanne Louise (1919-) French
£1972 $3451 €2800 Vues de la Croisette a Nice (30x45cm-12x18in) s. pair. 16-Dec-3 Claude Aguttes, Neuilly #121 est:2000-3000

BONICHI, Claudio (1943-) Italian
£909 $1545 €1300 Three pears (40x50cm-16x20in) painted 1987. 19-Nov-3 Cambi, Genoa #472/R

BONIFACIO, Alfonso Gomez (1934-) Spanish
£1342 $2456 €2000 Composition (33x24cm-13x9in) s.d.1980. 12-Jul-4 Durán, Madrid #150 est:2000
£1633 $2971 €2400 Portrait (68x45cm-27x18in) s.d.1974 s.i.d.verso. 3-Feb-4 Segre, Madrid #217/R est:2000
£1678 $2970 €2500 Figure (68x48cm-27x19in) s.d.69 card. 27-Apr-4 Durán, Madrid #685/R est:2000
£2013 $3564 €3000 Man (68x48cm-27x19in) s.d.69 card. 27-Apr-4 Durán, Madrid #686/R est:2000
Works on paper
£420 $701 €600 Untitled (29x21cm-11x8in) s.d.1980 Indian ink gouache prov. 24-Jun-3 Segre, Madrid #186/R
£655 $1088 €950 Untitled (40x30cm-16x12in) s.d.1973 mixed media. 1-Oct-3 Ansorena, Madrid #552/R

BONIFAZI, Adriano (19th C) Italian
£783 $1300 €1143 Peasant boy and girl (20x18cm-8x7in) s. one d.75 panel pair. 4-Oct-3 Neal Auction Company, New Orleans #143/R
£13000 $23660 €18980 Vanity (143x83cm-56x33in) s.i.d.1875. 16-Jun-4 Christie's, Kensington #116/R est:5000-7000

BONIFAZIO, Francesco (attrib) (1637-?) Italian
£5765 $10319 €8417 Jesus aged 12 in the Temple (114x164cm-45x65in) prov. 25-May-4 Bukowskis, Stockholm #466/R est:80000-100000 (S.KR 78000)

BONINGTON, R P (1802-1828) British
Works on paper
£390 $710 €569 Mountain pass (21x15cm-8x6in) sepia. 3-Jul-4 Shapes, Edinburgh #425

BONINGTON, Richard Parkes (1802-1828) British
£380 $700 €555 Portrait of Scottish guardsman (41x28cm-16x11in) s. board. 9-Jun-4 Alderfer's, Hatfield #325
£586 $1050 €856 Shoreline at sunset with ragged cliffs (20x38cm-8x15in) s. 19-Mar-4 Aspire, Cleveland #4 est:1000-2000
Works on paper
£400 $744 €584 Coastal scene with vessels and figures with donkey on a beach (23x33cm-9x13in) init. W/C. 4-Mar-4 Clevedon Sale Rooms #186
£650 $1086 €949 River landscape with a bridge (12x15cm-5x6in) indis.i. pencil prov. 16-Oct-3 Christie's, Kensington #22/R
£1000 $1830 €1460 Park scene, Regents Park (15x15cm-6x6in) i.d.Nov 1942 W/C. 9-Jul-4 Dreweatt Neate, Newbury #393/R est:1000-1500
£1690 $2924 €2400 Voilier sur une riviere (6x14cm-2x6in) s. W/C pen. 9-Dec-3 Chambelland & Giafferi, Paris #9/R est:2000-2500

BONINGTON, Richard Parkes (attrib) (1802-1828) British
£1100 $1969 €1606 Fisherfolk on the beach before buildings, boats high and dry (36x43cm-14x17in) s. 5-May-4 John Nicholson, Haslemere #607/R est:1200-1500

BONIROTE, Pierre (1811-1891) French
£6500 $11960 €9490 Classical pose (92x122cm-36x48in) s.i.d.1860. 25-Mar-4 Christie's, Kensington #52/R est:6000-8000

BONITO, Giuseppe (attrib) (1705-1789) Italian
£4138 $6910 €6000 Card game (76x102cm-30x40in) 11-Jul-3 Rabourdin & Choppin de Janvry, Paris #56/R
£6787 $11335 €9909 Self portrait of the artist drawing perspectives (102x77cm-40x30in) oval. 17-Nov-3 Waddingtons, Toronto #274/R est:3000-4000 (C.D 15000)

BONITO, Giuseppe (circle) (1705-1789) Italian
£6000 $10980 €8760 Peasants drinking and smoking in interior (93x142cm-37x56in) 9-Jul-4 Christie's, Kensington #186a/R est:4000-6000

BONIVENTO, Eugenio (1880-1956) Italian
£350 $601 €500 Piazza with Hercules fountain in small Italian city (60x40cm-24x16in) s. 4-Dec-3 Neumeister, Munich #2711/R
Works on paper
£379 $630 €550 Lagoon (16x31cm-6x12in) s. W/C. 1-Oct-3 Della Rocca, Turin #286/R

ONNAR, James King (1885-1961) American

£794 $1350 €1159 Fishing harbour (38x48cm-15x19in) s. board. 28-Nov-3 Thomaston Place, Thomaston #47
£1013 $1600 €1479 Early spring, Smugglers' Notch (51x61cm-20x24in) s.i. canvasboard. 27-Jul-3 William Jenack, New York #264 est:800-1200
£1543 $2500 €2237 North shore Harbour view (51x61cm-20x24in) s. 8-Aug-3 Barridorf, Portland #237/R est:3000-5000
£1613 $3000 €2355 At the docks (61x51cm-24x20in) s. 5-Mar-4 Skinner, Boston #548/R est:2000-4000
£2695 $4500 €3935 At the Docks (51x61cm-20x24in) s. prov. 23-Oct-3 Shannon's, Milford #85/R est:3000-4500

BONNARD, J (?) ?

£1800 $3276 €2700 Grand Canal, Venice (41x61cm-16x24in) s. 15-Jun-4 Rosebery Fine Art, London #591/R est:250-300

BONNARD, Pierre (1867-1947) French

£12032 $22500 €17567 Peaux rouges (23x28cm-9x11in) s. oil paper on board painted c.1895 prov.exhib.lit. 24-Jul-4 Coeur d'Alene, Hayden #120/R est:5000-10000
£23000 $38410 €33580 Le paquebot (22x27cm-9x11in) s. board painted c.1926 prov.lit. 21-Oct-3 Sotheby's, London #31/R est:25000-35000
£23944 $41902 €34000 Tonnelle (23x19cm-9x7in) indis.sig.d.1890 cardboard prov.exhib.lit. 18-Dec-3 Tajan, Paris #26/R est:35000-40000
£47059 $80000 €68706 Le couchant (27x50cm-11x20in) st.sig. painted c.1939 prov.lit. 5-Nov-3 Christie's, Rockefeller NY #253/R est:70000-90000
£50670 $88671 €71950 Portrait de jeune fille (46x31cm-18x12in) st.sig. prov.lit. 18-Dec-3 Tajan, Paris #27/R est:80000-100000
£55866 $100000 €81564 Faune or La nymphe violee or Pan et la nymphe or L'apres-midi d'un faune (65x71cm-26x28in) s. board on cradled panel painted 1907 prov.exhib.lit. 5-May-4 Christie's, Rockefeller NY #265/R est:120000-160000
£61453 $110000 €89721 Femme s'habillant (71x51cm-28x20in) st.sig. painted c.1906-07 prov.lit. 6-May-4 Sotheby's, New York #235/R est:120000-150000
£67039 $120000 €97877 Solfege (49x40cm-19x16in) s. painted 1917 prov.exhib.lit. 5-May-4 Christie's, Rockefeller NY #249/R est:150000-200000
£85000 $154700 €124100 Paysage a trois personnages et saule (73x69cm-29x27in) st.sig painted 1912 prov.exhib.lit. 3-Feb-4 Christie's, London #188/R est:90000-120000
£100000 $184000 €146000 Femme enfilant ses bas (30x21cm-12x8in) s.d.95 panel prov.lit. 23-Jun-4 Christie's, London #122/R est:80000-120000
£117318 $210000 €171284 Femme au corsage bleu (81x33cm-32x13in) st.sig. prov.exhib.lit. 6-May-4 Sotheby's, New York #253/R est:200000-300000
£130000 $236600 €189800 Tomates (31x42cm-12x17in) st.sig. oil paper on canvas painted c.1924 prov.lit. 3-Feb-4 Christie's, London #184/R est:100000-150000
£145251 $260000 €212066 Nu a l'arrosoir or Toilette a la campagne (46x37cm-18x15in) s. cradled panel painted c.1902 prov.lit. 5-May-4 Christie's, Rockefeller NY #202/R est:150000-200000
£179577 $310669 €255000 Port gris et vapeur ou le port de Cannes (45x64cm-18x25in) s. prov.lit.exhib. 13-Dec-3 Lempertz, Koln #120/R est:180000-220000
£217647 $370000 €317765 Jeune fille dans la rue (32x28cm-13x11in) s. painted c.1898 prov.exhib.lit. 4-Nov-3 Christie's, Rockefeller NY #12/R est:250000-350000
£647059 $1100000 €944706 Nature morte au melon (51x62cm-20x24in) s. painted 1941 prov.exhib.lit. 5-Nov-3 Sotheby's, New York #11/R est:800000-1200000
£782123 $1400000 €1141900 Corbeille de fruits (44x45cm-17x18in) s. painted 1924 prov.exhib.lit. 4-May-4 Christie's, Rockefeller NY #9/R est:1500000-2000000
£823529 $1400000 €1202352 Interieur (54x64cm-21x25in) painted 1913 prov.exhib.lit. 5-Nov-3 Sotheby's, New York #19/R est:1000000-1500000

Prints

£1765 $3000 €2577 Rue vue d'en haut (37x22cm-15x9in) s. col lithograph edition of 100. 6-Nov-3 Swann Galleries, New York #313/R est:3000-5000
£2353 $4000 €3435 Canotage (43x57cm-17x22in) s. col lithograph exec.1897. 4-Nov-3 Christie's, Rockefeller NY #68/R est:5000-8000
£2373 $4200 €3465 La Revue blanche (76x58cm-30x23in) col lithograph. 30-Apr-4 Sotheby's, New York #41/R est:3000-5000
£2400 $4128 €3504 L'Arc de Triomphe (32x47cm-13x19in) col lithograph. 2-Dec-3 Christie's, London #92/R est:2500-3500
£2600 $4472 €3796 Avenue au bois (31x46cm 12x18in) col lithograph. 2-Dec-3 Christie's, London #91/R est:2000-3000
£2600 $4472 €3796 Etude de nu (29x17cm-11x7in) s. lithograph. 2-Dec-3 Christie's, London #94/R est:1800-2200
£2796 $5200 €4082 Rue, le soir, sous la pluie (25x35cm-10x14in) col lithograph. 2-Mar-4 Swann Galleries, New York #59/R est:6000-9000
£2867 $5275 €4300 Arc de Triomphe (31x46cm-12x18in) i. col lithograph. 10-Jun-4 Piasa, Paris #20/R
£3011 $5600 €4396 Coin de vue d'en haut (37x21cm-15x8in) init.i. col lithograph. 2-Mar-4 Swann Galleries, New York #58/R est:5000-8000
£3226 $6000 €4710 Boulevard (17x43cm-7x17in) col lithograph. 2-Mar-4 Swann Galleries, New York #56/R est:6000-9000
£5000 $9200 €7500 Boulevard (17x43cm-7x17in) col lithograph. 10-Jun-4 Hauswedell & Nolte, Hamburg #52/R est:10000
£5500 $9460 €8030 L'enfant a la lampe (34x46cm-13x18in) col lithograph executed c.1897. 2-Dec-3 Christie's, London #90/R est:5000-7000
£6333 $11653 €9500 Coin de rue (27x35cm-11x14in) col lithograph. 10-Jun-4 Piasa, Paris #14/R
£7059 $12000 €10306 Family scene (31x18cm-12x7in) s. col lithograph. 31-Oct-3 Sotheby's, New York #212/R
£8000 $14720 €12000 Coin de rue (37x21cm-15x8in) col lithograph exec.1899. 10-Jun-4 Piasa, Paris #21/R
£10915 $18884 €15500 La promenade des Nourrices, frise de fiacres. mono. col lithograph four folding screen lit. 10-Dec-3 Rossini, Paris #35/R
£11301 $19212 €16500 Petites scenes familieres. lithograph exec.1893. 6-Nov-3 Piasa, Paris #53/R
£12000 $22080 €18000 Enfant a la lampe (32x45cm-13x18in) s. col lithograph. 10-Jun-4 Piasa, Paris #12

Sculpture

£3784 $7000 €5525 Baigneuse (18cm-7in) mono. indis num.12/12 dark brown pat bronze. 12-Feb-4 Sotheby's, New York #11/R est:7000-10000
£9000 $16380 €13140 Femme adossee a un rocher (18cm-7in) mono. bronze conceived in plaster c.1905. 4-Feb-4 Sotheby's, London #220/R est:6000-8000

Works on paper

£625 $1044 €900 Bord de riviere (4x16cm-2x6in) st.mono. st.sig. verso pencil. 24-Oct-3 Ketterer, Hamburg #643/R
£816 $1461 €1200 Vue presumee du port de Cannes. Portrait devant un buffet (13x16cm-5x6in) black pencil estompe double-sided. 19-Mar-4 Piasa, Paris #202/R
£833 $1392 €1200 Voiliers et enfant jouant sur la plage (10x15cm-4x6in) lead pencil exec c.1920-1930. 21-Oct-3 Artcurial Briest, Paris #32
£1042 $1740 €1500 Vue de village (10x16cm-4x6in) st.mono. st.sig.verso pencil. 24-Oct-3 Ketterer, Hamburg #287/R est:1500-1800
£1088 $1948 €1600 Portrait de femme au chapeau (15x11cm-6x4in) black pencil. 19-Mar-4 Piasa, Paris #199/R est:1000
£1224 $2192 €1800 Etude de nu (17x11cm-7x4in) black pencil. 19-Mar-4 Piasa, Paris #200/R est:2000
£1987 $3616 €3000 Deux etudes de nus (14x10cm-6x4in) crayon exec. c.1916. 18-Jun-4 Piasa, Paris #85 est:1500-2000
£2400 $4416 €3504 Scene d'interieur (12x18cm-5x7in) init. chl. 24-Mar-4 Sotheby's, Olympia #24/R est:2000-3000
£2676 $4630 €3800 Deux jeunes femmes (12x12cm-5x5in) graphite. 9-Dec-3 Chambelland & Giafferi, Paris #25 est:1200-1500
£2800 $5124 €4200 Etudes: tete de femme au chapea, visage, nu et souris (24x17cm-9x7in) s. col pen Indian ink htd white prov. 5-Jun-4 Lempertz, Koln #607/R est:3000-3500
£3061 $5480 €4500 Nature morte. Paysage (12x13cm-5x5in) black pencil double-sided. 19-Mar-4 Piasa, Paris #201/R est:4000
£3129 $5601 €4600 Tete de Marthe et tetes de Misia Natanson et Serge Draghilev (32x25cm-13x10in) black pencil. 19-Mar-4 Piasa, Paris #203/R est:3000
£3169 $5482 €4500 Bouquet de fleurs (12x16cm-5x6in) graphite. 9-Dec-3 Chambelland & Giafferi, Paris #23/R est:1200-1500
£3169 $5482 €4500 Coupe de fruits (12x16cm-5x6in) graphite. 9-Dec-3 Chambelland & Giafferi, Paris #24/R est:1200-1500
£3265 $5845 €4800 Une route bordee d'arbres. Un homme sur une route bordee d'arbres (30x24cm-12x9in) chl double-sided. 19-Mar-4 Piasa, Paris #205/R est:4000
£3311 $6026 €5000 Nu au tub de face (17x11cm-7x4in) crayon exec. c.1922-1925. 18-Jun-4 Piasa, Paris #84/R est:3000-4000
£3826 $6848 €5700 Pont sur la Seine a Paris (18x26cm-7x10in) st.init. crayon htd ink. 25-May-4 Chambelland & Giafferi, Paris #55/R est:6000-7000
£4218 $7550 €6200 Nature morte (16x24cm-6x9in) black pencil. 19-Mar-4 Piasa, Paris #204/R est:3000
£5500 $10120 €8030 Nu a la baignoire (31x23cm-12x9in) mono. pencil. 24-Jun-4 Christie's, London #329/R est:8000-12000
£6040 $10812 €9000 Jeune femme tenant un chien dans ses bras (30x21cm-12x8in) s. crayon prov. 26-May-4 Christie's, Paris #40/R est:7000-10000
£6704 $12000 €9788 Kneeling woman (32x25cm-13x10in) st.mono. chl prov. 6-May-4 Sotheby's, New York #219/R est:8000-12000
£8684 $15979 €13200 La Roulotte, vue du parc (32x50cm-13x20in) s. W/C. 28-Jun-4 Rossini, Paris #72/R est:12000-15000
£34899 $62470 €52000 Personnage dans un parc (49x32cm-19x13in) gouache pencil paper on canvas. 25-May-4 Dorotheum, Vienna #4/R est:52000-55000
£50000 $91000 €73000 Le Boulevard (32x49cm-13x19in) gouache W/C ink Japan paper exec c.1890 prov. 5-Feb-4 Christie's, London #322/R est:50000-70000

BONNARDEL, Alexandre François (1867-1942) French

£433 $780 €650 Port de Sanary (22x26cm-9x10in) s.i.verso cardboard. 20-Apr-4 Chenu & Scrive, Lyon #30/R
£667 $1220 €1000 Peches sur un plat blanc et bleu (15x20cm-6x8in) s. panel. 6-Jun-4 Anaf, Lyon #39

BONNAT, Léon (1833-1922) French

£680 $1218 €1000 Palette (40x54cm-16x21in) s.i. 19-Mar-4 Millon & Associes, Paris #11
£3311 $6026 €5000 Presqu'Ile du Sinai (12x25cm-5x10in) s. i.verso canvas on panel. 18-Jun-4 Piasa, Paris #80 est:1500-2000
£4444 $8000 €6488 Italian children (47x34cm-19x13in) s. 21-Jan-4 Sotheby's, New York #187/R est:10000-15000
£6000 $11040 €9000 Le Simoun (89x140cm-35x55in) s. 14-Jun-4 Gros & Delettrez, Paris #463/R est:7600-9500

BONNAUD, Pierre (1865-1930) French

£1722 $3151 €2600 Elegante a Paris (35x24cm-14x9in) s. 9-Apr-4 Claude Aguttes, Neuilly #51/R est:1800-2000

BONNECROY, Sebastien (attrib) (17th C) Dutch

£9589 $16301 €14000 Vanitas still life with skull, watch, candlestick, flute, bottle and bubbles (74x63cm-29x25in) indis.sig.i. 4-Nov-3 Sotheby's, Amsterdam #28/R est:7000-10000

BONNEFOIT, Alain (1939-) French

£800 $1440 €1168 Melanie (50x69cm-20x27in) s.d.97 oil pastel paper on canvas. 20-Jan-4 Bonhams, Knightsbridge #254/R
£800 $1440 €1168 Reflexion (47x61cm-19x24in) s.d. oil gouache paper on canvas. 20-Jan-4 Bonhams, Knightsbridge #257/R
£1267 $2293 €1900 Nu sur fond jaune (79x59cm-31x23in) s.d.69. 1-Apr-4 Credit Municipal, Paris #86 est:1500-1800
£1300 $2353 €1950 Nu au foulard rouge (79x59cm-31x23in) s.d.69. 1-Apr-4 Credit Municipal, Paris #87 est:1500-2000

Works on paper

£283 $517 €413 Femme accroupie (61x47cm-24x19in) s.d.81 ink sepia W/C. 5-Jun-4 Galerie du Rhone, Sion #274 (S.FR 650)

BONNEFOY, Adrien Adolphe (20th C) French

£1400 $2520 €2044 Merchant (27x35cm-11x14in) bears sig.d.1893 panel. 21-Jan-4 Sotheby's, Olympia #441/R est:1000-1500

BONNEFOY, Henri-Arthur (1839-1917) French

£527 $943 €780 Paysans et moutons pres de ruine (49x61cm-19x24in) s. 10-May-4 Giraudeau, Tours #180
£629 $1176 €950 Paysage cotier, femme et enfant devant la mer (45x64cm-18x25in) s. 24-Jul-4 Thierry & Lannon, Brest #128/R
£2098 $3608 €3000 Paysanne dans les champs (49x75cm-19x30in) s. 7-Dec-3 Osenat, Fontainebleau #149 est:2500-3000

BONNEH, Schmuel (20th C) Israeli

£444 $800 €648 King Saul (46x61cm-18x24in) 24-Apr-4 Du Mouchelle, Detroit #3032/R

BONNEN, Folmer (1885-1960) Danish
£319 $519 €466 Children playing in school playground (72x82cm-28x32in) s.d.1939 panel. 28-Sep-3 Hindemae, Ullerslev #224/R (D.KR 3400)
Works on paper
£379 $607 €553 Still life of bird's cage (82x64cm-32x25in) s.d.1915 gouache. 22-Sep-3 Rasmussen, Vejle #613/R (D.KR 4000)
£379 $607 €553 Branch of apples (86x70cm-34x28in) init. exhib. 22-Sep-3 Rasmussen, Vejle #615/R (D.KR 4000)

BONNEN, Peter (1945-) Danish
Sculpture
£2076 $3819 €3031 Untitled (51x45x45cm-20x18x18in) s. pat steel two parts. 29-Mar-4 Rasmussen, Copenhagen #380/R est:25000 (D.KR 23000)
Works on paper
£282 $480 €412 Composition (116x91cm-46x36in) s.d.88 collage. 26-Nov-3 Kunsthallen, Copenhagen #115 (D.KR 3000)

BONNET, Anne (1908-1960) Belgian
£497 $904 €750 Composition (30x25cm-12x10in) s. 15-Jun-4 Galerie Moderne, Brussels #328/R
£931 $1722 €1350 Porte ouverte (61x52cm-24x20in) s.d.44. 19-Jan-4 Horta, Bruxelles #233
£3200 $5856 €4800 Abstraction (46x38cm-18x15in) s.d.54 panel. 7-Jun-4 Palais de Beaux Arts, Brussels #155/R est:2000-3000
Works on paper
£272 $487 €400 Abstraction (26x34cm-10x13in) s. mixed media gouache. 17-Mar-4 Hotel des Ventes Mosan, Brussels #116
£327 $584 €480 Abstraction (29x21cm-11x8in) s. mixed media gouache. 17-Mar-4 Hotel des Ventes Mosan, Brussels #117
£369 $653 €550 Composition (26x20cm-10x8in) gouache. 27-Apr-4 Campo, Vlaamse Kaai #322
£436 $772 €650 Composition (26x20cm-10x8in) gouache. 27-Apr-4 Campo, Vlaamse Kaai #320
£872 $1544 €1300 Composition (34x42cm-13x17in) s. gouache. 27-Apr-4 Campo, Vlaamse Kaai #324
£1208 $2138 €1800 Composition (33x40cm-13x16in) s. gouache. 27-Apr-4 Campo, Vlaamse Kaai #326/R est:500-600
£1342 $2376 €2000 Composition (37x26cm-15x10in) gouache. 27-Apr-4 Campo, Vlaamse Kaai #321 est:500-600
£1342 $2376 €2000 Composition (30x34cm-12x13in) s. mixed media. 27-Apr-4 Campo, Vlaamse Kaai #323/R est:500-600
£3172 $5869 €4600 Sans titre (73x92cm-29x36in) s.d.1959 gouache. 13-Jan-4 Vanderkindere, Brussels #30/R est:1250-1750

BONNET, Felix Alfred (1847-?) French
£20000 $36400 €30000 A la buvette (144x190cm-57x75in) mono.d.96 prov. 1-Jul-4 Van Ham, Cologne #1228/R est:25000

BONNET, Jean (18th C) French
Works on paper
£300 $549 €438 View of the Maison Carree at Nimes (58x88cm-23x35in) i. pen ink black framing lines. 7-Jul-4 Bonhams, Knightsbridge #83/R

BONNET, M (19/20th C) ?
£1049 $1783 €1500 Odalisque a sa toilette (73x54cm-29x21in) s.d.1891. 30-Nov-3 Anaf, Lyon #26 est:1500-1800

BONNET, Rudolf (1895-1978) Dutch
£4979 $8962 €7269 Portrait of a nude boy (61x37cm-24x15in) s.i.d.1949 prov. 25-Apr-4 Christie's, Hong Kong #519/R est:60000-80000 (HK.D 70000)
£332046 $554517 €484787 Temple dienst - temple service (114x124cm-45x49in) s. i.verso tempera. 26-Oct-3 Christie's, Hong Kong #8/R est:550000-650000 (HK.D 4300000)
Works on paper
£417 $696 €609 Boy (24x22cm-9x9in) s.d.47 chl. 12-Oct-3 Sotheby's, Singapore #23/R (S.D 1200)
£680 $1218 €1000 Portrait of an Italian farmer. Standing woman (36x28cm-14x11in) s. chl double-sided. 16-Mar-4 Christie's, Amsterdam #89/R est:1000-1500
£680 $1218 €1000 Seated male nude (54x32cm-21x13in) with sig.d. black chk. 16-Mar-4 Christie's, Amsterdam #103 est:1500-2000
£1087 $1685 €1587 Acteur (53x47cm-21x19in) s.i.d.1969 pastel. 6-Oct-2 Sotheby's, Singapore #34/R est:3000-4000 (S.D 3000)
£1961 $3549 €2863 Man (41x32cm-16x13in) s.i.d.1966 pastel. 4-Apr-4 Sotheby's, Singapore #32/R est:5000-7000 (S.D 6000)
£4086 $6538 €5966 Portrait of a Balinese boy (62x44cm-24x17in) s.d.1949 chl crayon. 18-May-3 Sotheby's, Singapore #52/R est:9000-12000 (S.D 11400)
£9957 $17923 €14537 I. Djenak (55x49cm-22x19in) s.i.d.1932 pastel chl prov.exhib. 25-Apr-4 Christie's, Hong Kong #517/R est:100000-150000 (HK.D 140000)
£10458 $18928 €15269 Portrait of njoming (45x35cm-18x14in) s.i.d.1952 pastel prov. 3-Apr-4 Glerum, Singapore #22/R est:30000-40000 (S.D 32000)
£11438 $20703 €16699 Pentjak (54x54cm-21x21in) s.i.d.1955 pastel. 4-Apr-4 Sotheby's, Singapore #37/R est:25000-35000 (S.D 35000)
£12091 $21764 €17653 Portrait of Mohammed Bensalaben Abdel Kader (109x59cm-43x23in) s.i.d.1928 pastel prov. 25-Apr-4 Christie's, Hong Kong #520/R est:80000-120000 (HK.D 170000)
£12153 $20295 €17743 Kepala Penari, Ardjuna Bertapa (53x58cm-21x23in) s.i.d.1940 pastel. 12-Oct-3 Sotheby's, Singapore #16/R est:30000-50000 (S.D 35000)
£12903 $20645 €18838 Peasant (55x40cm-22x16in) s.d.1941 chl crayon. 18-May-3 Sotheby's, Singapore #8/R est:30000-40000 (S.D 36000)
£15647 $28165 €22845 Portrait of I. Rake from Tebesaya, Bali (57x37cm-22x15in) s.d.1957 chl pastel. 25-Apr-4 Christie's, Hong Kong #518/R est:120000-160000 (HK.D 220000)
£16988 $28371 €24802 Bloemen kinderen - flower children (107x70cm-42x28in) s. chl pastel. 26-Oct-3 Christie's, Hong Kong #21/R est:200000-300000 (HK.D 220000)
£19915 $35846 €29076 Man with headband (30x30cm-12x12in) s.i.d.33 pastel lit. 25-Apr-4 Christie's, Hong Kong #521/R est:150000-200000 (HK.D 280000)
£33977 $56741 €49606 Balinese actor as Arjuna Bertapa (86x49cm-34x19in) s.i.d.1975 chl pastel. 26-Oct-3 Christie's, Hong Kong #9/R est:240000-350000 (HK.D 440000)
£45290 $70199 €66123 Vegetable vendors (50x75cm-20x30in) s.i.d.1953 pastel. 6-Oct-2 Sotheby's, Singapore #36/R est:15000-20000 (S.D 125000)

BONNETON, Louis (19th C) French
£385 $615 €562 View of Rue de Cesar in Mont Dore Les Bains (68x96cm-27x38in) s.d.1895. 16-Sep-3 Philippe Schuler, Zurich #5427 (S.FR 850)

BONNIER, Eva (1857-1909) Swedish
£692 $1191 €1010 Mrs. Therese Hirsch (55x40cm-22x16in) s. exhib.lit. 2-Dec-3 Bukowskis, Stockholm #160/R (S.KR 9000)

BONNIER, Olle (1925-) Swedish
£864 $1495 €1261 Abstract composition (74x34cm-29x13in) s. canvas on panel. 15-Dec-3 Lilla Bukowskis, Stockholm #145 (S.KR 11000)
£2121 $3669 €3097 Plingeling (17x11cm-7x4in) s.d.49 two cardboard. 15-Dec-3 Lilla Bukowskis, Stockholm #121 est:5000-6000 (S.KR 27000)
£4496 $8093 €6564 Untitled (56x46cm-22x18in) s. 26-Apr-4 Bukowskis, Stockholm #225/R est:50000-70000 (S.KR 62000)
£12085 $20544 €17644 Composition (79x48cm-31x19in) init.d.43/47 prov. 4-Nov-3 Bukowskis, Stockholm #240/R est:100000-125000 (S.KR 160000)
£12840 $21828 €18746 Composition (110x110cm-43x43in) s.d.57 oil sand lit. 5-Nov-3 AB Stockholms Auktionsverk #781/R est:80000-100000 (S.KR 170000)
Works on paper
£487 $843 €711 Pling (23x44cm-9x17in) s. W/C. 15-Dec-3 Lilla Bukowskis, Stockholm #53 (S.KR 6200)
£522 $851 €762 Dance of the animals (17x24cm-7x9in) s.d.77 gouache. 29-Sep-3 Lilla Bukowskis, Stockholm #365 (S.KR 6800)
£586 $1037 €856 Composition (46x54cm-18x21in) s.d.72 W/C Indian ink prov. 27-Apr-4 AB Stockholms Auktionsverk #819/R (S.KR 8000)
£644 $1114 €940 Space curve (75x106cm-30x42in) s.d.88 pastel. 15-Dec-3 Lilla Bukowskis, Stockholm #780 (S.KR 8200)
£1245 $2204 €1818 Signs from the north (11x17cm-4x7in) s.d.56 gouache. 27-Apr-4 AB Stockholms Auktionsverk #823/R est:8000-10000 (S.KR 17000)
£1414 $2545 €2064 Street scene with horse, man and dog (21x37cm-8x15in) s. mixed media. 26-Apr-4 Bukowskis, Stockholm #228/R est:12000-15000 (S.KR 19500)
£1888 $3210 €2756 Composition (25x17cm-10x7in) s.d.56 gouache. 5-Nov-3 AB Stockholms Auktionsverk #784/R est:3000-4000 (S.KR 25000)

BONNIN, Maurice (20th C) French?
£867 $1560 €1300 Bretagne, Port de Sainte Marine (46x65cm-18x26in) s. 26-Apr-4 Tajan, Paris #377 est:1200-1500
£979 $1684 €1400 Bord de riviere (38x55cm-15x22in) s. s.i.d.1979 verso. 3-Dec-3 Tajan, Paris #206 est:1500-2000

BONNOR, Rose (fl.1895-1916) British
£3000 $5490 €4380 Portrait of Patti of Gerwn (85x110cm-33x43in) s.d.1911. 6-Apr-4 Bonhams, Knightsbridge #181/R est:300-500

BONNY, John (fl.1870-1892) British
£300 $537 €438 Bacton river landscape scene with swans (24x33cm-9x13in) board. 20-Mar-4 Lacy Scott, Bury St.Edmunds #440
£640 $1146 €934 Mid Suffolk landscape with figures fishing (24x34cm-9x13in) s. board. 20-Mar-4 Lacy Scott, Bury St.Edmunds #438/R

BONOLIS, Giuseppe (1800-1851) Italian
£27027 $47568 €40000 Bather (103x83cm-41x33in) s.d.1840. 18-May-4 Sotheby's, Milan #537/R est:12000-18000

BONOME, Rodrigo (1906-1990) Argentinian
£330 $600 €482 Seashore, Cordoba (25x31cm-10x12in) s.d.59. 5-Jul-4 Arroyo, Buenos Aires #10/R
£638 $1034 €900 Paisaje de Vigo (59x70cm-23x28in) s.d.70 s.i.d.verso. 20-May-3 Ansorena, Madrid #200/R
£769 $1400 €1123 Cortina, Italy (50x35cm-20x14in) s.d.67 s.i.d.verso. 5-Jul-4 Arroyo, Buenos Aires #51/R
£1389 $2264 €2000 Landscape in Vigo (59x69cm-23x27in) s.d.70 s.i.d.verso. 23-Sep-3 Durán, Madrid #128/R est:750

BONOMELLI, Romeo (1871-1943) Italian
£599 $1036 €850 Presolana (25x37cm-10x15in) init. i.d.1922 verso cardboard. 9-Dec-3 Finarte Semenzato, Milan #144/R

BONQUART, Adolphe (1864-1915) French
£2039 $3691 €3100 Cotre pilote du Havre (55x46cm-22x18in) 17-Apr-4 Deburaux, Boulogne #229

BONSI, Giovanni (14th C) Italian
£250000 $450000 €365000 Crucifixion. Annunciation with Archangel Gabriel. Virgin with Saints (91x62cm-36x24in) tempera gold ground panel tabernacle prov.exhib.lit. 23-Jan-4 Christie's, Rockefeller NY #41/R est:200000-300000

BONSIB, Louis W (1892-1979) American
Works on paper
£305 $500 €442 Barnyard scene (12x18cm-5x7in) s. W/C exec.c.1940. 7-Jun-3 Treadway Gallery, Cincinnati #1413

BONSTETTEN, Abraham-Sigmund von (1796-1879) Swiss
£631 $1085 €921 Italian landscape (33x43cm-13x17in) s.d.1828. 8-Dec-3 Philippe Schuler, Zurich #3323/R (S.FR 1400)

BONTA, Marcos (20th C) South American
£280 $520 €409 Portrait of Mercedes Pardo (82x65cm-32x26in) s. painted 1943. 14-Mar-4 Subastas Odalys, Caracas #44/R

BONTECOU, Lee (1931-) American
Prints
£1648 $3000 €2406 Eleventh stone (30x43cm-12x17in) num.16/23 aquatint. 19-Jun-4 Du Mouchelle, Detroit #3032/R est:200-300
£1648 $3000 €2406 Untitled (41x25cm-16x10in) lithograph. 19-Jun-4 Du Mouchelle, Detroit #3028/R est:200-300
£1648 $3000 €2406 Twelfth stone (25x38cm-10x15in) num.10/21 aquatint. 19-Jun-4 Du Mouchelle, Detroit #3033/R est:200-300
£1923 $3500 €2808 Black with white spirals (66x94cm-26x37in) lithograph. 19-Jun-4 Du Mouchelle, Detroit #3027/R est:200-300
£1923 $3500 €2808 Third stone (46x36cm-18x14in) lithograph. 19-Jun-4 Du Mouchelle, Detroit #3029/R est:200-300
£1923 $3500 €2808 Thirteenth stone (38x43cm-15x17in) lithograph. 19-Jun-4 Du Mouchelle, Detroit #3034/R est:200-300
£1923 $3500 €2808 Eighth stone (36x28cm-14x11in) num.25/34 lithograph. 19-Jun-4 Du Mouchelle, Detroit #3030/R est:200-300
£1923 $3500 €2808 Seventh stone (36x25cm-14x10in) lithograph. 19-Jun-4 Du Mouchelle, Detroit #3026/R est:200-300
£2060 $3750 €3008 Ninth stone (28x36cm-11x14in) num.20/43 lithograph. 19-Jun-4 Du Mouchelle, Detroit #3031/R est:200-300
£2198 $4000 €3209 Tenth stone (94x56cm-37x22in) lithograph. 19-Jun-4 Du Mouchelle, Detroit #3018/R est:500-800
£2198 $4000 €3209 Fourteen stone (66x94cm-26x37in) num.14/17 lithograph. 19-Jun-4 Du Mouchelle, Detroit #3024/R est:200-350
£2198 $4000 €3209 Fifth stone (94x69cm-37x27in) num.23/27 lithograph. 19-Jun-4 Du Mouchelle, Detroit #3020/R est:400-600
£2335 $4250 €3409 Sixth stone II (91x71cm-36x28in) lithograph. 19-Jun-4 Du Mouchelle, Detroit #3022/R est:300-500
£2335 $4250 €3409 Sixth stone I (86x71cm-34x28in) lithograph. 19-Jun-4 Du Mouchelle, Detroit #3023/R est:300-500
£2335 $4250 €3409 Untitled (43x30cm-17x12in) aquatint etching. 19-Jun-4 Du Mouchelle, Detroit #3035/R est:150-300
£2335 $4250 €3409 Sixth stone (91x71cm-36x28in) lithograph. 19-Jun-4 Du Mouchelle, Detroit #3021/R est:300-500
£2473 $4500 €3611 Second stone (33x43cm-13x17in) lithograph. 19-Jun-4 Du Mouchelle, Detroit #3025/R est:200-300
£2473 $4500 €3611 First stone (28x38cm-11x15in) lithograph. 19-Jun-4 Du Mouchelle, Detroit #3036/R est:100-200
£5495 $10000 €8023 Fourth stone (94x74cm-37x29in) lithograph. 19-Jun-4 Du Mouchelle, Detroit #3049/R est:400-600
Sculpture
£155689 $260000 €227306 Untitled (58x61x18cm-23x24x7in) s. welded steel canvas copper wire exec 1960 prov.exhib.lit. 11-Nov-3 Christie's, Rockefeller NY #16/R est:50000-70000
£239521 $400000 €349701 Untitled (98x78x25cm-39x31x10in) welded steel canvas fabric copper wire executed 1959-60. 12-Nov-3 Sotheby's, New York #1/R est:50000-70000

BONTEMPI, Renato (1896-?) Italian
£232 $402 €330 Around the Castello Sforzesco, Milan (31x26cm-12x10in) s. s.i.verso cardboard. 10-Dec-3 Finarte Semenzato, Rome #221/R

BONTHOUX, Jean Louis (1828-?) French
£1131 $1923 €1651 Hunting still life with hare and ducks (102x75cm-40x30in) s. 19-Nov-3 Fischer, Luzern #1088/R est:3000-3500 (S.FR 2500)
£17105 $31474 €26000 Jetee de fleurs et panier sur entablement (129x96cm-51x38in) s.d.1864. 23-Jun-4 Sotheby's, Paris #73/R est:20000-30000

BONTJES VAN BEEK, Olga (1896-1995) German
£331 $603 €500 Evening on the banks of the River Wumme (34x44cm-13x17in) mono. board. 18-Jun-4 Bolland & Marotz, Bremen #329/R
£331 $603 €500 Grazing cows, evening (20x30cm-8x12in) mono. i.d.1983 verso board. 18-Jun-4 Bolland & Marotz, Bremen #330
£347 $549 €500 Sunshine over Worpsweder (38x45cm-15x18in) mono. board. 6-Sep-3 Schopman, Hamburg #782/R

BONVIN, François (1817-1887) French
£667 $1207 €1000 Champs de ble devant un village (15x25cm-6x10in) s.d.1873 panel. 30-Mar-4 Rossini, Paris #913/R est:1000-1500
£1333 $2440 €2000 Portrait de jeune femme (18x13cm-7x5in) s. panel oval. 6-Jun-4 Osenat, Fontainebleau #224/R est:2500-3000
£7285 $13258 €11000 Nature morte au chaudron, poissons et ail (25x18cm-10x7in) s.d.1879. 15-Jun-4 Vanderkindere, Brussels #2/R est:3000-4000
Works on paper
£1812 $3352 €2700 Brodeuse (19x12cm-7x5in) s. W/C. 14-Mar-4 Eric Pillon, Calais #29/R
£2042 $3533 €2900 La classe de filles (18x24cm-7x9in) W/C blk crayon beige paper. 10-Dec-3 Piasa, Paris #138/R est:3000
£4392 $7730 €6500 Portrait of a man smoking a pipe (22x17cm-9x7in) s.indis.d.47 black chk exhib.lit. 19-May-4 Sotheby's, Amsterdam #372/R est:1000-1500
£4768 $8678 €7200 Un ouvrier lisant le journal a une table d'auberge (30x24cm-12x9in) s.d.52 W/C. 16-Jun-4 Piasa, Paris #182/R est:3000-4000
£5000 $9150 €7300 Seated woman playing a mandolin (42x31cm-17x12in) s.d.1863 black red chk lit. 6-Jul-4 Christie's, London #200/R est:4000-6000
£12000 $21960 €17520 Apprentice locksmith working at a vice in a workshop (43x31cm-17x12in) s.d.1860 black red white chk prov.lit. 6-Jul-4 Christie's, London #199/R est:7000-10000

BONVIN, François (attrib) (1817-1887) French
£400 $724 €600 Saint-Francois en meditation (35x24cm-14x9in) after Zurbaran. 30-Mar-4 Rossini, Paris #914

BONVOISIN, Joseph (1896-1960) Belgian
£387 $670 €550 Paysage d'automne (21x29cm-8x11in) s. panel. 10-Dec-3 Hotel des Ventes Mosan, Brussels #186

BONZAGNI, Aroldo (1887-1918) Italian
£7042 $12324 €10000 Troubador (96x175cm-38x69in) s.i. tempera paper on canvas. 16-Dec-3 Finarte Semenzato, Milan #322/R est:9000-11000
£8696 $14261 €12000 Hamlet, deny light, if you can (100x175cm-39x69in) s. tempera W/C chl paper on canvas exhib. 27-May-3 Sotheby's, Milan #172/R est:12000-15000
£151724 $253379 €220000 Toselli's serenade (160x110cm-63x43in) s. exhib.lit. 17-Nov-3 Sant Agostino, Torino #245/R est:200000-250000
Works on paper
£966 $1612 €1400 Angel of Peace (37x28cm-15x11in) s.i. Chinese ink. 17-Nov-3 Sant Agostino, Torino #180/R
£2041 $3653 €3000 Other wounds (37x28cm-15x11in) s.i. pencil exhib. 22-Mar-4 Sant Agostino, Torino #428/R est:2200

BOODLE, Walter (19th C) British?
£820 $1361 €1197 Waterfall (40x61cm-16x24in) s. 1-Oct-3 Sotheby's, Olympia #31/R
£900 $1620 €1314 Woodland pond (40x61cm-16x24in) s. 21-Jan-4 Sotheby's, Olympia #347/R est:500-700
£1200 $2004 €1752 Corner of Clapham Common (25x30cm-10x12in) s. board. 12-Nov-3 Sotheby's, Olympia #89/R est:1000-1500

BOOGAARD, Willem Jacobus (1842-1887) Dutch
£1258 $2290 €1900 Ponies in a stall (28x38cm-11x15in) s. 18-Jun-4 Bolland & Marotz, Bremen #590/R est:900
£2500 $4000 €3650 Untitled (20x30cm-8x12in) panel. 19-Sep-3 Du Mouchelle, Detroit #2093/R est:4000-6000
£2700 $4860 €3942 Stable interior with a farmer feeding two shire horses and chickens (25x27cm-10x11in) s.d.1875 panel prov. 21-Apr-4 Tennants, Leyburn #1191/R est:2800-3200
£5000 $8300 €7300 At the end of the day, stable lad and horses (47x62cm-19x24in) s.d.1867 i.verso. 2-Oct-3 Lane, Penzance #290/R est:4500-5500

BOOGAR, William F (jnr) (1893-1958) American
Sculpture
£757 $1400 €1136 Untitled, seagull and wave lamp (53x25x25cm-21x10x10in) s. bronze. 17-Jul-4 Outer Cape Auctions, Provincetown #119/R

BOOK, Max Mikael (1953-) Swedish
£739 $1323 €1079 Town after town (118x119cm-46x47in) s.d.1983 verso panel. 28-May-4 Uppsala Auktionskammare, Uppsala #347/R (S.KR 10000)
£9890 $17505 €14439 Mazlack (100x115cm-39x45in) s.d.1989 verso. 27-Apr-4 AB Stockholms Auktionsverk #1102/R est:30000-35000 (S.KR 135000)
Works on paper
£398 $640 €581 Ste (35x30cm-14x12in) s.d.1986 verso mixed media panel. 25-Aug-3 Lilla Bukowskis, Stockholm #73 (S.KR 5200)
£536 $912 €783 Collage (61x45cm-24x18in) s. mixed media exec.c.1981-1982. 4-Nov-3 Bukowskis, Stockholm #606/R (S.KR 7100)
£642 $1091 €937 Jura (63x60cm-25x24in) s.d.92 verso mixed media panel. 5-Nov-3 AB Stockholms Auktionsverk #1024/R (S.KR 8500)
£755 $1284 €1102 Untitled (42x29cm-17x11in) s. gouache collage. 5-Nov-3 AB Stockholms Auktionsverk #1079/R (S.KR 10000)
£906 $1541 €1323 Loathing (77x88cm-30x35in) s.d.1986 verso mixed media canvas. 5-Nov-3 AB Stockholms Auktionsverk #930/R (S.KR 12000)
£952 $1686 €1390 T-riktare Zink (55x68cm-22x27in) s.d.1979 verso mixed media panel. 27-Apr-4 AB Stockholms Auktionsverk #1031/R (S.KR 13000)
£1020 $1733 €1489 Firebox (24x36cm-9x14in) s.d.1990 verso mixed media panel prov. 5-Nov-3 AB Stockholms Auktionsverk #1023/R est:8000-10000 (S.KR 13500)
£1057 $1798 €1543 Bauk - composition (116x145cm-46x57in) s.d.1983 verso mixed media canvas. 4-Nov-3 Bukowskis, Stockholm #607/R est:18000-20000 (S.KR 14000)
£1172 $2075 €1711 Open door (77x105cm-30x41in) mixed media canvas. 27-Apr-4 AB Stockholms Auktionsverk #1103/R est:20000-25000 (S.KR 16000)
£1208 $2054 €1764 Ductor - composition (24x36cm-9x14in) s.d.1990 verso mixed media panel prov. 5-Nov-3 AB Stockholms Auktionsverk #1025/R est:8000-10000 (S.KR 16000)
£3336 $6004 €4871 Standby (210x150cm-83x59in) s.d.1985/86 verso mixed media canvas. 26-Apr-4 Bukowskis, Stockholm #493a/R est:30000-35000 (S.KR 46000)

BOOKBINDER, Jack (1911-) American
£299 $500 €437 Wear tear and tar pots (51x76cm-20x30in) s.d.52. 20-Jun-3 Freeman, Philadelphia #170/R
£329 $550 €480 Ballerina (51x30cm-20x12in) s.i.verso. 20-Jun-3 Freeman, Philadelphia #159/R
£359 $650 €524 At the beach (25x18cm-10x7in) s. masonite. 2-Apr-4 Freeman, Philadelphia #171

BOOL, Charles A (19/20th C) British
£380 $635 €555 Rocky stream with bridge beyond (30x40cm-12x16in) s. board. 7-Oct-3 Bonhams, Knightsbridge #231/R

BOOM, Charles (1858-1939) Belgian
£1208 $2162 €1800 Un gengilhomme (32x40cm-13x16in) s. panel. 25-May-4 Campo & Campo, Antwerp #18/R est:1500-2500
£1399 $2336 €2000 Family portrait (112x134cm-44x53in) s.d.1984. 11-Oct-3 De Vuyst, Lokeren #37/R est:1500-2000

BOOM, Karel Alexander August Jan (1862-1943) Dutch
£694 $1132 €1000 Teatime (24x19cm-9x7in) s. canvas on panel. 29-Sep-3 Sotheby's, Amsterdam #78/R

BOOMS, Wilhelmine (1856-1943) Dutch
£462 $771 €660 Still life of flowers with roses and poppies (47x69cm-19x27in) s.d.1877. 10-Oct-3 Winterberg, Heidelberg #540

BOON, Constantin (1830-1882) Dutch
£2200 $3674 €3212 Idle words (61x51cm-24x20in) s.d.57 panel. 16-Oct-3 Bonhams, Edinburgh #194/R est:2000-3000

BOON, Constantin and COL, Jan David (19th C) Dutch
£775 $1340 €1100 L'entremetteur (47x61cm-19x24in) s.d.1857 panel. 9-Dec-3 Campo, Vlaamse Kaai #269/R

BOON, Jan (1882-?) Dutch
£1477 $2746 €2200 Vase with white flowers (61x41cm-24x16in) s. 2-Mar-4 Ansorena, Madrid #23/R est:180
£2013 $3564 €3000 Fleurs (40x30cm-16x12in) s. 27-Apr-4 Artcurial Briest, Paris #202/R est:3000-4000

BOONE, Elmer L (1881-1952) American
£2395 $4000 €3497 Vendor (30x41cm-12x16in) canvasboard. 18-Oct-3 David Dike, Dallas #293/R est:2500-3500
£10180 $17000 €14863 West Texas landscape (107x183cm-42x72in) board. 18-Oct-3 David Dike, Dallas #216/R est:8000-12000

BOONSTRA, Klaas (1905-) Dutch
Works on paper
£268 $497 €400 Abstract composition (32x49cm-13x19in) s. mixed media exhib. 15-Mar-4 Sotheby's, Amsterdam #254

BOONYAVANISHKUL, Rearngsak (1961-) Thai
£3268 $5915 €4771 Behind the stage (150x100cm-59x39in) s.d.1999. 3-Apr-4 Glerum, Singapore #46/R est:12000-15000 (S.D 10000)
£11111 $18556 €16222 Peak (150x120cm-59x47in) s.i.d.2003 lit. 12-Oct-3 Sotheby's, Singapore #84/R est:22000-28000 (S.D 32000)
£13725 $24843 €20039 Dancers (150x120cm-59x47in) s.d.2003. 4-Apr-4 Sotheby's, Singapore #115/R est:25000-30000 (S.D 42000)

BOONZAIER, Gregoire (1909-) South African
£1466 $2447 €2140 Headgear, Nourse Mine (29x36cm-11x14in) s.d.1946 canvas on board. 20-Oct-3 Stephan Welz, Johannesburg #319/R est:12000-18000 (SA.R 17000)
£1569 $2808 €2291 Still life of gourds and seed pods (30x40cm-12x16in) s.d.1976. 31-May-4 Stephan Welz, Johannesburg #522/R est:15000-20000 (SA.R 19000)
£1597 $2890 €2332 Fish drying outside a cottage (49x32cm-19x13in) s.d.1990 board. 30-Mar-4 Stephan Welz, Johannesburg #438/R est:12000-16000 (SA.R 19000)
£1897 $3167 €2770 Bridge over a canal buildings in the distance (30x35cm-12x14in) s.d.1926. 20-Oct-3 Stephan Welz, Johannesburg #412/R est:10000-15000 (SA.R 22000)
£2414 $4031 €3524 Street scene, Districr six (24x46cm-9x18in) s.d.1991 canvas on board. 20-Oct-3 Stephan Welz, Johannesburg #332/R est:16000-22000 (SA.R 28000)
£2414 $4031 €3524 Landscape with cloud, lands and windmill (41x58cm-16x23in) s.d.1949. 20-Oct-3 Stephan Welz, Johannesburg #386/R est:25000-35000 (SA.R 28000)
£2521 $4563 €3681 Windswept trees, Cape (40x50cm-16x20in) s.d.1963. 30-Mar-4 Stephan Welz, Johannesburg #474/R est:30000-40000 (SA.R 30000)
£2890 $5173 €4219 Hoses near a large tree (26x19cm-10x7in) s.d.1971 board. 31-May-4 Stephan Welz, Johannesburg #529/R est:12000-16000 (SA.R 35000)
£3248 $5521 €4742 District six (39x50cm-15x20in) s.d.1967. 4-Nov-3 Stephan Welz, Johannesburg #672/R est:30000-40000 (SA.R 38000)
£3276 $5471 €4783 Street scene, Cape Town (25x34cm-10x13in) s.d.1951. 20-Oct-3 Stephan Welz, Johannesburg #333/R est:18000-24000 (SA.R 38000)
£3361 $6084 €4907 Street with Table Mountain (28x43cm-11x17in) s.d.1971 s.i.verso board. 30-Mar-4 Stephan Welz, Johannesburg #507/R est:30000-40000 (SA.R 40000)
£3419 $5812 €4992 Cape houses amongst rolling hills (32x57cm-13x22in) s.d.1941. 4-Nov-3 Stephan Welz, Johannesburg #682/R est:30000-40000 (SA.R 40000)
£4034 $7301 €5890 Two figures outside a Cape cottage (37x42cm-15x17in) s.d.1932. 30-Mar-4 Stephan Welz, Johannesburg #508/R est:25000-30000 (SA.R 48000)
£4310 $7198 €6293 Street, District Six (30x46cm-12x18in) s.d.1966 canvas on board. 20-Oct-3 Stephan Welz, Johannesburg #308/R est:30000-40000 (SA.R 50000)
£4542 $8130 €6631 Stone huts (39x54cm-15x21in) s.d.1953. 31-May-4 Stephan Welz, Johannesburg #562/R est:25000-35000 (SA.R 55000)
£5367 $9608 €7836 Caledon street, District six, Cape Town (26x36cm-10x14in) s.d.1956 s.i.verso. 31-May-4 Stephan Welz, Johannesburg #560/R est:25000-35000 (SA.R 65000)
£5780 $10347 €8439 Huisie met Windlaaier, Naby Struisbaai (40x55cm-16x22in) s.d.1953 i.verso. 31-May-4 Stephan Welz, Johannesburg #556/R est:30000-40000 (SA.R 70000)
Works on paper
£269 $487 €393 Portrait of a seated man (59x47cm-23x19in) s.d.1959 conte. 30-Mar-4 Stephan Welz, Johannesburg #234 est:2000-3000 (SA.R 3200)
£302 $504 €441 Tabak draaiers, Oudstoorn (34x53cm-13x21in) s.i.d.61 W/C. 20-Oct-3 Stephan Welz, Johannesburg #607 est:4000-6000 (SA.R 3500)
£347 $621 €507 Self portrait (36x27cm-14x11in) s.d.1964 chl. 31-May-4 Stephan Welz, Johannesburg #299 (SA.R 4200)
£359 $610 €524 Village with figures (21x28cm-8x11in) s.d.1959 pencil pen ink W/C. 4-Nov-3 Stephan Welz, Johannesburg #371 est:2000-3000 (SA.R 4200)
£454 $813 €663 Tabakdraaiers (23x34cm-9x13in) s.d.1961 pen ink W/C. 31-May-4 Stephan Welz, Johannesburg #357 (SA.R 5500)
£598 $1017 €873 Village street, Hawston, Cape Province (15x37cm-6x15in) s.d.1960 s.i.verso W/C. 4-Nov-3 Stephan Welz, Johannesburg #671 est:4000-6000 (SA.R 7000)
£661 $1182 €965 Canal Venice. Self Portrait (27x31cm-11x12in) s.d.1973 chl pen ink W/C pencil double-sided. 31-May-4 Stephan Welz, Johannesburg #253 (SA.R 8000)
£690 $1152 €1007 House and trees (37x54cm-15x21in) s.d.1983 crayon W/C. 20-Oct-3 Stephan Welz, Johannesburg #356 est:4500-6000 (SA.R 8000)
£690 $1152 €1007 Head of a man (43x29cm-17x11in) s.d.1975 chl. 20-Oct-3 Stephan Welz, Johannesburg #416 est:5000-7000 (SA.R 8000)
£690 $1152 €1007 Fishermens cottages (26x45cm-10x18in) s.d.1960 pen ink W/C. 20-Oct-3 Stephan Welz, Johannesburg #601 est:3500-4500 (SA.R 8000)
£714 $1293 €1042 Hanover Street, District Six, Cape Town (26x37cm-10x15in) s.d.1960 i.verso pencil W/C. 30-Mar-4 Stephan Welz, Johannesburg #462 est:4000-6000 (SA.R 8500)
£743 $1330 €1085 View of a house through a fence (29x48cm-11x19in) s.d.1956 chl W/C. 31-May-4 Stephan Welz, Johannesburg #554 (SA.R 9000)
£756 $1369 €1104 Canal in Venice (26x36cm-10x14in) s.d.1973 s.i.verso W/C. 30-Mar-4 Stephan Welz, Johannesburg #186 est:2500-3500 (SA.R 9000)
£908 $1626 €1326 View of houses through trees (26x42cm-10x17in) s.d.1970 pen ink W/C over conte. 31-May-4 Stephan Welz, Johannesburg #527/R (SA.R 11000)
£948 $1584 €1384 Houses with verandah, District six, Cape Town (26x38cm-10x15in) s.d.1970 s.i.verso W/C. 20-Oct-3 Stephan Welz, Johannesburg #654 est:2000-3000 (SA.R 11000)
£1156 $2069 €1688 Dutch Reformed Church, Wynberg Hill, Wynberg (39x54cm-15x21in) s.i.d.1960 pen ink W/C. 31-May-4 Stephan Welz, Johannesburg #504/R est:7000-10000 (SA.R 14000)
£1239 $2217 €1809 Two Oaks Bovlei, Wellington (46x53cm-18x21in) s.d.1951 i.verso pastel. 31-May-4 Stephan Welz, Johannesburg #528/R est:8000-12000 (SA.R 15000)
£1404 $2513 €2050 Steil straatjue in die Maleise Buurt bo Tafelbaai Tydenis Mistaige Weer (37x55cm-15x22in) s.i.d.1951 chl pen ink W/C. 31-May-4 Stephan Welz, Johannesburg #558/R est:7000-10000 (SA.R 17000)
£1817 $3252 €2653 Crossroads, Cape Town (29x45cm-11x18in) s.d.1991 pastel. 31-May-4 Stephan Welz, Johannesburg #505/R est:7000-10000 (SA.R 22000)

BOOTH, E C (19th C) British
Works on paper
£540 $848 €788 On the sands (13x19cm-5x7in) W/C. 31-Aug-3 Paul Beighton, Rotherham #520/R

BOOTH, Edward C (1821-1883) British
£350 $630 €511 Old Ilkley (35x51cm-14x20in) s.d.1886. 21-Jan-4 Sotheby's, Olympia #346/R
Works on paper
£460 $731 €667 Cullercoats (33x51cm-13x20in) s.d.1891 W/C. 9-Sep-3 David Duggleby, Scarborough #225a
£500 $795 €725 Sandsend (33x51cm-13x20in) s.d.1891 W/C. 9-Sep-3 David Duggleby, Scarborough #225
£620 $1122 €905 Unloading on the beach (34x52cm-13x20in) s.d.1880 W/C. 30-Mar-4 David Duggleby, Scarborough #164/R

BOOTH, Eunice Ellenetta (attrib) (1852-1942) American
£291 $500 €425 Carmel, coastal view (30x41cm-12x16in) s.i. i.stretcher. 6-Dec-3 Skinner, Boston #263/R

BOOTH, Franklin (1874-1948) American
Works on paper
£1006 $1800 €1469 Woman ashore waving to man arriving by boat (5x25cm-2x10in) s. pen ink. 15-May-4 Illustration House, New York #150/R est:1500-2500

BOOTH, George Warren (1917-1996) American
Works on paper
£267 $500 €390 Patron tries too hard to open the Post Office door (18x20cm-7x8in) s. pen ink wash exec.c.1970. 26-Feb-4 Illustration House, New York #27

BOOTH, James W (1867-1953) British
£280 $476 €409 Figure in a field haymaking (41x51cm-16x20in) canvas laid down prov. 19-Nov-3 Tennants, Leyburn #1128
Works on paper
£260 $442 €380 Dallybrack, Ireland No3, river scene with ducks (26x37cm-10x15in) s. i.verso W/C. 18-Nov-3 Bonhams, Leeds #255
£300 $549 €438 Plough team (31x44cm-12x17in) s. crayon W/C. 7-Jul-4 Cheffins, Cambridge #35/R
£320 $544 €467 Still life of roses in a bowl (43x34cm-17x13in) s. pencil W/C prov. 19-Nov-3 Tennants, Leyburn #954
£340 $578 €496 Quai vert, a canal, Bruges (49x61cm-19x24in) s.d.1910 i.verso pencil W/C. 19-Nov-3 Tennants, Leyburn #957
£360 $572 €522 Harvest stooks (27x39cm-11x15in) s. W/C. 9-Sep-3 David Duggleby, Scarborough #41
£380 $646 €555 Two shire horses pulling a farm implement with farmers nearby (24x33cm-9x13in) pencil W/C prov. 19-Nov-3 Tennants, Leyburn #956
£520 $863 €759 Corn stooks with thatched cottage beyond (34x24cm-13x9in) s. W/C. 6-Oct-3 David Duggleby, Scarborough #262/R
£560 $890 €812 Sandsend children playing by boat (33x50cm-13x20in) W/C. 9-Sep-3 David Duggleby, Scarborough #42
£600 $1020 €876 Mother and child at Staithes with chickens in the foreground (36x25cm-14x10in) s. pencil W/C. 19-Nov-3 Tennants, Leyburn #955
£900 $1629 €1314 Village street with stream (40x52cm-16x20in) s. W/C. 30-Mar-4 David Duggleby, Scarborough #59/R

BOOTH, James W (attrib) (1867-1953) British
£900 $1503 €1314 Caedmon's Cross, Whitby (28x38cm-11x15in) board. 10-Oct-3 Richardson & Smith, Whitby #187

BOOTH, Kate E (fl.1850-1870) British
Works on paper
£480 $826 €701 Fishing boats, south coast (33x51cm-13x20in) s.i. W/C. 4-Dec-3 Richardson & Smith, Whitby #417/R
£520 $827 €754 Runswick village (35x36cm-14x14in) s.i.verso W/C. 9-Sep-3 David Duggleby, Scarborough #26/R
£620 $1122 €905 Harbour and old bridge, Whitby (34x50cm-13x20in) s.i. W/C. 30-Mar-4 David Duggleby, Scarborough #86/R

BOOTH, Leonard Hampden (20th C) New Zealander
£1877 $3060 €2740 Reclining nude female figure study in deck chair (27x41cm-11x16in) s.d.1929 board. 23-Sep-3 Peter Webb, Auckland #102/R est:2000-3000 (NZ.D 5200)

BOOTH, Nina Mason (?) American
£282 $525 €412 Tonawanda Creek (30x36cm-12x14in) 6-Mar-4 Page, Batavia #98
£376 $700 €549 Untitled (51x56cm-20x22in) board. 6-Mar-4 Page, Batavia #94

BOOTH, Peter (1940-) Australian
£244 $383 €354 Landscape with death figure (9x25cm-4x10in) acrylic paper prov. 26-Aug-3 Christie's, Sydney #245 (A.D 600)
£1240 $2293 €1810 Drawing - landscape with fly (51x66cm-20x26in) oil chl prov. 10-Mar-4 Deutscher-Menzies, Melbourne #154/R est:2000-3000 (A.D 3000)
£6809 $11574 €9941 Apocalyptic landscape (45x76cm-18x30in) s.i.verso painted c.1980 prov. 26-Nov-3 Deutscher-Menzies, Melbourne #70/R est:20000-30000 (A.D 16000)

£8058	$14907	€11765	Painting 2000 (30x36cm-12x14in) s.d.2000 verso prov. 10-Mar-4 Deutscher-Menzies, Melbourne #155/R est:14000-18000 (A.D 19500)
£8085	$13744	€11804	Apocalyptic Landscape (35x81cm-14x32in) s.d.1999 verso prov. 26-Nov-3 Deutscher-Menzies, Melbourne #51/R est:14000-18000 (A.D 19000)
£11570	$20479	€16892	Untitled, landscape (76x121cm-30x48in) s.d.1995 verso. 3-May-4 Christie's, Melbourne #74/R est:22000-28000 (A.D 28000)
£20661	$36570	€30165	Man (137x168cm-54x66in) s.i.d.1985 verso prov.exhib.lit. 3-May-4 Christie's, Melbourne #78/R est:55000-65000 (A.D 50000)
£27664	$43709	€40389	Painting - figure with hands on ground (92x122cm-36x48in) s.d.1997 verso exhib. 2-Sep-3 Deutscher-Menzies, Melbourne #50/R est:50000-60000 (A.D 67500)

Works on paper

£325	$511	€471	Figure under street light (32x21cm-13x8in) chl prov. 26-Aug-3 Christie's, Sydney #239 (A.D 800)
£363	$660	€530	Red and black face (10x13cm-4x5in) pencil prov. 16-Jun-4 Deutscher-Menzies, Melbourne #398/R (A.D 950)
£425	$723	€621	Apocalyptic scene (25x17cm-10x7in) ball point pen ink wash. 26-Nov-3 Deutscher-Menzies, Melbourne #198/R (A.D 1000)
£492	$777	€718	Small portrait of a man (11x6cm-4x2in) chl gouache prov. 2-Sep-3 Deutscher-Menzies, Melbourne #128/R (A.D 1200)
£492	$777	€718	Drawing - figure, raven and monster in burning street (8x9cm-3x4in) s. verso biro ink prov.exhib. 2-Sep-3 Deutscher-Menzies, Melbourne #134/R (A.D 1200)
£574	$906	€838	Figure walking (11x9cm-4x4in) chl gouache prov. 2-Sep-3 Deutscher-Menzies, Melbourne #123/R est:1400-1800 (A.D 1400)
£575	$977	€840	Apocalyptic scene (17x25cm-7x10in) ball point pen crayon ink wash. 26-Nov-3 Deutscher-Menzies, Melbourne #199/R est:1500-2000 (A.D 1350)
£656	$1036	€958	Winged figure (13x8cm-5x3in) chl gouache pastel prov. 2-Sep-3 Deutscher-Menzies, Melbourne #127/R est:1800-2400 (A.D 1600)
£725	$1320	€1059	Three mythological figures (18x26cm-7x10in) s.d.1981 verso ink pastel. 16-Jun-4 Deutscher-Menzies, Melbourne #397/R est:1800-2400 (A.D 1900)
£779	$1230	€1137	Man reclining on hands (9x15cm-4x6in) chl pastel prov. 2-Sep-3 Deutscher-Menzies, Melbourne #125/R est:2000-2400 (A.D 1900)
£936	$1591	€1367	Man standing in rocky landscape (23x17cm-9x7in) pastel exhib. 26-Nov-3 Deutscher-Menzies, Melbourne #50/R est:1800-2400 (A.D 2200)
£1088	$1980	€1588	Landscape - red sunset (19x28cm-7x11in) s.verso pastel oil exec 1986. 5-Feb-4 Joel, Victoria #98 (A.D 2600)
£1148	$1813	€1676	Man in overcoat (32x17cm-13x7in) chl gouache prov. 2-Sep-3 Deutscher-Menzies, Melbourne #118/R est:2800-3500 (A.D 2800)
£1148	$1813	€1676	Three heads (18x26cm-7x10in) chl pastel prov. 2-Sep-3 Deutscher-Menzies, Melbourne #124/R est:2800-3500 (A.D 2800)
£1298	$2362	€1895	Drawing 1999 (18x29cm-7x11in) s.verso pastel prov. 16-Jun-4 Deutscher-Menzies, Melbourne #399/R est:2500-3500 (A.D 3400)
£1557	$2460	€2273	Man doing handstand (27x17cm-11x7in) chl pastel prov. 2-Sep-3 Deutscher-Menzies, Melbourne #119/R est:2800-3500 (A.D 3800)
£1639	$2590	€2393	Man sitting on figure (25x18cm-10x7in) chl pastel prov. 2-Sep-3 Deutscher-Menzies, Melbourne #120/R est:2800-3500 (A.D 4000)
£1967	$3108	€2872	Acrobats (32x16cm-13x6in) chl gouache prov. 2-Sep-3 Deutscher-Menzies, Melbourne #117/R est:3800-4500 (A.D 4800)
£2273	$4205	€3319	Painting 1979 (75x106cm-30x42in) pastel prov. 15-Mar-4 Sotheby's, Melbourne #17/R est:6000-8000 (A.D 5500)
£2273	$4205	€3319	Apocalyptic landscape (63x101cm-25x40in) W/C gouache ink prov. 10-Mar-4 Deutscher-Menzies, Melbourne #153/R est:4000-6000 (A.D 5500)
£2459	$3885	€3590	Drawing - head and city buildings (59x50cm-23x20in) s.i.d.1978 pastel chl prov.exhib. 2-Sep-3 Deutscher-Menzies, Melbourne #135/R est:8000-10000 (A.D 6000)
£2686	$4969	€3922	Untitled (40x58cm-16x23in) pastel. 15-Mar-4 Sotheby's, Melbourne #16/R est:4000-6000 (A.D 6500)
£3512	$6498	€5128	Untitled (34x64cm-13x25in) pastel executed 1995. 15-Mar-4 Sotheby's, Melbourne #11/R est:4000-6000 (A.D 8500)
£4545	$8409	€6636	Drawing - tree and pink sun (54x72cm-21x28in) s.d.1998 pastel exhib. 10-Mar-4 Deutscher-Menzies, Melbourne #152/R est:6500-8500 (A.D 11000)
£4962	$9031	€7245	Painting (76x54cm-30x21in) synthetic polymer on board prov. 16-Jun-4 Deutscher-Menzies, Melbourne #155/R est:14000-18000 (A.D 13000)

BOOTH, Raymond C (1929-) British

£750	$1373	€1095	Lilium lilies and a Pied Flycatcher (101x52cm-40x20in) board. 28-Jul-4 Bonhams, Knightsbridge #53/R
£850	$1556	€1241	Waterhen (28x33cm-11x13in) s.d.1974 board. 28-Jul-4 Bonhams, Knightsbridge #54/R

BOOTH, Rev John (19th C) American

Works on paper

£278	$450	€406	Indian settlement at Grand Rapids, Michigan (25x33cm-10x13in) s. pen ink. 10-Aug-3 Skinner, Bolton #471/R

BOOTY, Frederick William (1840-1924) British

Works on paper

£260	$465	€380	Scarborough from Cloughton Newlands (33x52cm-13x20in) W/C. 17-May-4 David Duggleby, Scarborough #663/R
£300	$540	€438	Thornwick Bay, Flamborough (36x60cm-14x24in) s.i.d.1916 pencil W/C prov. 21-Apr-4 Tennants, Leyburn #934
£300	$540	€438	Lighthouse Bay, Flamborough (36x60cm-14x24in) s.i.d.1916 pencil W/C. 21-Apr-4 Tennants, Leyburn #935
£520	$952	€759	Near Sandsend, Whitby (38x61cm-15x24in) s.d.1918 W/C. 8-Jul-4 Lawrence, Crewkerne #1542
£600	$1086	€876	Robin Hoods Bay at high tide (25x40cm-10x16in) s.d.1920 W/C. 30-Mar-4 David Duggleby, Scarborough #2/R
£750	$1350	€1095	Figures in fishing boats off Scarborough harbour (85x65cm-33x26in) s.d.1908 pencil W/C scratching out. 21-Apr-4 Tennants, Leyburn #933
£800	$1272	€1160	Church street Staithes (23x35cm-9x14in) s. W/C. 9-Sep-3 David Duggleby, Scarborough #77/R
£875	$1609	€1313	Seabirds on cliff wall (68x106cm-27x42in) s.d.1908 W/C. 14-Jun-4 Lilla Bukowskis, Stockholm #955 (S.KR 12000)
£1100	$2013	€1606	Richmond, Yorkshire (59x95cm-23x37in) s.d.1918 W/C. 8-Jul-4 Lawrence, Crewkerne #1543/R est:300-500
£1450	$2306	€2103	Cottages at runswick Bay (53x43cm-21x17in) s.d.1901 W/C. 9-Sep-3 David Duggleby, Scarborough #76 est:1500-2000
£1600	$2864	€2336	The Keep Scarborough Castle and Marine Drive, with heavy seas (88x67cm-35x26in) s.d.1901 W/C. 17-May-4 David Duggleby, Scarborough #660/R est:1500-2000
£1650	$2954	€2409	Fishing boats outside Scarborough Harbour (49x76cm-19x30in) s.d.1912 W/C. 17-May-4 David Duggleby, Scarborough #651/R est:1500-2000
£3400	$5780	€4964	Fish market, Dover (47x74cm-19x29in) s. pencil W/C. 19-Nov-3 Tennants, Leyburn #865/R est:2000-3000

BOPPO, Carl George (1840-1928) German

£2308	$3969	€3300	Recruiting farm hands (86x111cm-34x44in) s. i.verso. 5-Dec-3 Bolland & Marotz, Bremen #511/R est:3300

BOQUET, Jean (1908-1976) Belgian

£279	$500	€407	Normand, the captain's house (46x53cm-18x21in) s. i.d.1960 verso. 8-Jan-4 Doyle, New York #8/R
£335	$600	€489	Notre Dame from the right bank (53x46cm-21x18in) s. 8-Jan-4 Doyle, New York #10/R
£894	$1600	€1305	Breton inlet. Le Havre in August (38x46cm-15x18in) s. one i.verso. 8-Jan-4 Doyle, New York #9/R est:2000-3000

BOR, Jan (1910-1994) Dutch

£822	$1397	€1200	Still life with jug and pipes (75x63cm-30x25in) s.d.47. 5-Nov-3 Vendue Huis, Gravenhage #379/R

BOR, Pal (1889-1982) Hungarian

£1107	$2003	€1616	Fishers (86x61cm-34x24in) oil on woodrost. 16-Apr-4 Mu Terem Galeria, Budapest #73/R (H.F 420000)

BORA, Piero (1910-1941) Italian

£537	$950	€800	Flowers in landscape (27x37cm-11x15in) s. board. 1-May-4 Meeting Art, Vercelli #79

BORBON, Carlos Maria Isidro de (?) Spanish?

Works on paper

£526	$953	€800	Horse (25x40cm-10x16in) s. pencil dr. 14-Apr-4 Ansorena, Madrid #404/R

BORCH, F (19th C) ?

£341	$628	€512	Sunflower (83x65cm-33x26in) s. 14-Jun-4 Blomqvist, Lysaker #1043 (N.KR 4200)

BORCHGREVINK, Ridley (1898-1981) Norwegian

£301	$503	€439	Arhipelago (73x84cm-29x33in) s. painted c.1952-54. 20-Oct-3 Blomqvist, Lysaker #1035/R (N.KR 3500)

BORCHT, Peter van der II (1545-1608) Flemish

Prints

£2267	$4057	€3400	Peasant festivities (29x47cm-11x19in) etching. 13-May-4 Bassenge, Berlin #5046/R est:1500

BORDA, Osvaldo (20th C) Argentinian

£2067	$3700	€3018	Hidden church (80x80cm-31x31in) s.d.95 s.i.d.verso oil pastel. 4-May-4 Arroyo, Buenos Aires #51/R est:3700

BORDASS, Dorothy (1905-1992) British

£300	$519	€438	Through a hedge (49x60cm-19x24in) init.d.1956 i.verso do. 11-Dec-3 Lane, Penzance #61

BORDEAUX, Pierre Auguste (1904-1995) French

Works on paper

£437	$800	€638	Street in Montmartre, Paris (22x10cm-9x4in) s. ink wash chl. 3-Jun-4 Christie's, Rockefeller NY #1244/R

BORDES, Ernest (1852-1914) French

£1298	$2362	€1895	Slave (41x33cm-16x13in) s. 16-Jun-4 Deutscher-Menzies, Melbourne #432/R est:2000-3000 (A.D 3400)

BORDES, Leonard (1898-1969) French

£738	$1373	€1100	Port Breton (46x55cm-18x22in) s. 7-Mar-4 Lesieur & Le Bars, Le Havre #14

BORDIGNON, Noe (1841-1920) Italian

£16197	$28345	€23000	Interior with family (50x72cm-20x28in) s. 17-Dec-3 Finarte Semenzato, Milan #119/R est:6000-7000

BORDIGNON, Toni (?) Italian

£284	$475	€415	Landscape with pond and stone villa, mountains in the distance (61x122cm-24x48in) s. 27-Oct-3 O'Gallerie, Oregon #813/R
£525	$950	€767	Figure in a landscape (61x122cm-24x48in) s. 16-Apr-4 James Julia, Fairfield #679/R est:1000-2000

BORDONE, Paris (1500-1571) Italian

£23026	$42368	€35000	Le mariage de la vierge (67x88cm-26x35in) 23-Jun-4 Millon & Associes, Paris #1/R est:12000-15000
£496644	$928725	€740000	Resting during the Flight to Egypt (84x99cm-33x39in) s.i. prov.lit. 29-Feb-4 Finarte, Venice #49/R

BORDONE, Paris (attrib) (1500-1571) Italian

£6000	$10800	€8760	Ecce homo (96x103cm-38x41in) prov.lit. 22-Apr-4 Sotheby's, London #59/R est:8000-12000
£27632	$50842	€42000	Berger et nymphe couronnes par Cupidon (100x134cm-39x53in) prov.lit. 24-Jun-4 Christie's, Paris #69/R est:8000-12000
£30201	$55570	€45000	Rest on the Flight into Egypt with the Infant Baptist (72x87cm-28x34in) 24-Mar-4 Dorotheum, Vienna #59/R est:28000-40000

BORDRAEL, Jean (attrib) (20th C) French?
Sculpture
£2312 $4000 €3376 Woman with two swans (66x71cm-26x28in) s.i. marble. 13-Dec-3 Sloans & Kenyon, Bethesda #770/R est:1800-2200

BORDUAS, Paul Emile (1905-1960) Canadian
£18293 $32744 €26708 Vol horizontal (23x33cm-9x13in) s.d.53 prov. 31-May-4 Sotheby's, Toronto #180/R est:25000-35000 (C.D 45000)
£26423 $47297 €38578 Untitled (60x48cm-24x19in) s. prov. 31-May-4 Sotheby's, Toronto #73/R est:70000-90000 (C.D 65000)
£26423 $47297 €38578 Oxydation (41x51cm-16x20in) s.d.53 prov.exhib. 31-May-4 Sotheby's, Toronto #139/R est:40000-60000 (C.D 65000)
£28455 $50935 €41544 Le chaos sympathique (63x72cm-25x28in) s.d.53 prov.exhib. 31-May-4 Sotheby's, Toronto #44/R est:80000-100000 (C.D 70000)
£34553 $61850 €50447 Petit monde (38x45cm-15x18in) s.d.1955 prov.lit. 27-May-4 Heffel, Vancouver #44/R est:80000-100000 (C.D 85000)
£40650 $72764 €59349 Composition (96x119cm-38x47in) s.d.55 prov.exhib. 31-May-4 Sotheby's, Toronto #140/R est:100000-120000 (C.D 100000)

BOREIN, Edward (1872-1945) American
Prints
£1872 $3500 €2733 Ride im cowboy (18x13cm-7x5in) s. etching lit. 24-Jul-4 Coeur d'Alene, Hayden #17/R est:2000-3000
£2273 $4250 €3319 Navajos (23x30cm-9x12in) s. etching lit. 24-Jul-4 Coeur d'Alene, Hayden #244/R est:2000-3000
£2406 $4500 €3513 New bucking horse (20x13cm-8x5in) s. etching lit. 24-Jul-4 Coeur d'Alene, Hayden #18/R est:2000-3000
£6952 $13000 €10150 Ranahan (23x30cm-9x12in) s. monotype exhib.lit. 24-Jul-4 Coeur d'Alene, Hayden #151/R est:15000-25000
Works on paper
£326 $600 €476 Mission San Jose (15x23cm-6x9in) pencil. 13-Jun-4 Bonhams & Butterfields, Los Angeles #7037/R
£1118 $1800 €1621 Stagecoach (8x23cm-3x9in) pen ink. 22-Aug-3 Altermann Galleries, Santa Fe #80
£1471 $2500 €2148 Vaquero on horseback (15x13cm-6x5in) s. W/C prov. 18-Nov-3 John Moran, Pasadena #204 est:800-1200
£1765 $3000 €2577 Weaving a saddle blanket (30x23cm-12x9in) s. Indian ink prov. 1-Nov-3 Santa Fe Art, Santa Fe #11/R est:3000-5000
£2360 $3800 €3422 Stagecoach (18x25cm-7x10in) pen ink. 22-Aug-3 Altermann Galleries, Santa Fe #79
£2941 $5000 €4294 Stagecoach holdup (25x41cm-10x16in) W/C prov.lit. 1-Nov-3 Santa Fe Art, Santa Fe #134/R est:15000-20000
£3235 $5500 €4723 Mexican cattle herders (18x28cm-7x11in) W/C. 31-Oct-3 North East Auctions, Portsmouth #1886
£7955 $14000 €11614 Riding the flank, of a cowboy on his horse (20x23cm-8x9in) s. W/C. 3-Jan-4 Cobbs, Peterborough #74/R
£9626 $18000 €14054 Cowboy on a Palomino horse (18x15cm-7x6in) s. W/C lit. 24-Jul-4 Coeur d'Alene, Hayden #243/R est:8000-12000
£11176 $19000 €16317 Cowboy on horse (15x25cm-6x10in) s. W/C prov.lit. 1-Nov-3 Santa Fe Art, Santa Fe #36/R est:18000-25000
£27941 $47500 €40794 Indian war party (53x69cm-21x27in) s. ink gouache prov.lit. 1-Nov-3 Santa Fe Art, Santa Fe #132/R est:60000-80000
£32086 $60000 €46846 Charros in mission courtyard (36x48cm-14x19in) s. W/C prov. 24-Jul-4 Coeur d'Alene, Hayden #150/R est:30000-50000

BOREL, Paul (1828-1913) French
Works on paper
£2041 $3653 €3000 Le serment d'Henri IV aux protestants apres la bataille de Jarnac (20x27cm-8x11in) s. pen black ink wash print verso sold with engraving and dr by Marillier. 19-Mar-4 Piasa, Paris #167/R est:2500

BORELLI, Mario (?) Venezuelan?
£449 $750 €656 Landscape in a village (56x76cm-22x30in) s. 13-Jul-3 Subastas Odalys, Caracas #99
£563 $940 €822 Landscape in a village (61x92cm-24x36in) s. 13-Jul-3 Subastas Odalys, Caracas #81
£781 $1250 €1140 EStuary (70x100cm-28x39in) s. 21-Sep-3 Subastas Odalys, Caracas #37
£862 $1440 €1259 La Guaira Street (100x80cm-39x31in) s. 13-Jul-3 Subastas Odalys, Caracas #61
£1123 $1875 €1640 La Guaira Street (100x70cm-39x28in) s. 13-Jul-3 Subastas Odalys, Caracas #49/R

BORELLI, Miguel (20th C) Venezuelan?
£387 $600 €565 Eagle (80x137cm-31x54in) s. 3-Nov-2 Subastas Odalys, Caracas #124

BOREN, James (1921-1990) American
£4469 $8000 €6525 Winter morning (61x91cm-24x36in) 15-May-4 Altermann Galleries, Santa Fe #102/R
Works on paper
£531 $950 €775 Rest stop in Canyon de Chelly (23x32cm-9x13in) s. W/C. 14-May-4 Skinner, Boston #203/R
£581 $1000 €848 High country cowboy (36x46cm-14x18in) s.d.1972 W/C. 6-Dec-3 Selkirks, St. Louis #191
£1176 $2000 €1717 Misty morning (36x53cm-14x21in) W/C. 1-Nov-3 Altermann Galleries, Santa Fe #6
£1765 $3000 €2577 Horse by tree (36x53cm-14x21in) W/C. 1-Nov-3 Altermann Galleries, Santa Fe #5
£2358 $3750 €3443 Days' End (53x74cm-21x29in) s.d.1969 W/C htd gouache. 13-Sep-3 Selkirks, St. Louis #46/R est:2500-3500
£2737 $4900 €3996 Two cowboys herding cattle (51x74cm-20x29in) W/C. 15-May-4 Altermann Galleries, Santa Fe #101/R

BOREN, Jodie (1926-) American
£221 $400 €323 Reclining female nude by a fireplace (91x51cm-36x20in) s. 18-Apr-4 Jeffery Burchard, Florida #241/R

BOREN, Nelson (1952-) American
Works on paper
£4469 $8000 €6525 Boot and spur (107x140cm-42x55in) W/C. 15-May-4 Altermann Galleries, Santa Fe #44/R

BORENSTEIN, Samuel (1908-1969) Canadian
£1205 $2013 €1747 Winter street scene (30x40cm-12x16in) s.d.1965 board. 17-Jun-3 Pinneys, Montreal #96 (C.D 2700)
£1696 $2833 €2459 Quebec village street view (41x51cm-16x20in) s.d.1963 s.verso. 17-Jun-3 Pinneys, Montreal #22 est:4000-6000 (C.D 3800)
£1931 $3456 €2819 Booth Bay Harbour (50x40cm-20x16in) s.d.1968 i.d.verso board prov. 6-May-4 Heffel, Vancouver #36/R est:1500-2000 (C.D 4750)
£2000 $3660 €2920 Still life of flowers (60x50cm-24x20in) s. 1-Jun-4 Joyner Waddington, Toronto #48/R est:7000-9000 (C.D 5000)
£3455 $6185 €5044 Street scene (46x102cm-18x40in) s.d.June 22/66 prov. 31-May-4 Sotheby's, Toronto #66/R est:5000-7000 (C.D 8500)

BORES, Francisco (1898-1972) Spanish
£6159 $10101 €8500 Landscape (27x35cm-11x14in) s. board. 27-May-3 Durán, Madrid #280/R est:2500
£6597 $10885 €9500 Houses (24x29cm-9x11in) s.d.31. 2-Jul-3 Ansorena, Madrid #853/R
£7971 $13072 €11000 Vacas en un prado (38x46cm-15x18in) s.d.33 lit. 27-May-3 Durán, Madrid #279/R est:4500
£8451 $14620 €12000 Two figures (46x55cm-18x22in) s.d.1956. 11-Dec-3 Binoche, Paris #12/R est:12000-18000
£8696 $14261 €12000 Ciudad de noche (38x46cm-15x18in) s.d.33 lit. 27-May-3 Durán, Madrid #278/R est:4500
£9063 $15408 €13232 Le pecheur a la ligne (38x47cm-15x19in) s.d.39 prov.lit. 5-Nov-3 AB Stockholms Auktionsverk #1090/R est:35000-40000 (S.KR 120000)
£9220 $14936 €13000 Woman in blue (41x35cm-16x14in) s.d.52 board. 20-May-3 Ansorena, Madrid #324/R est:11500
£11565 $20701 €17000 Jeune fille au vase de fleurs (46x55cm-18x22in) s.d.71. 19-Mar-4 Millon & Associes, Paris #167/R est:4000-6000
£11594 $19014 €16000 Banistas en la sombra (65x54cm-26x21in) s. exhib. 27-May-3 Durán, Madrid #276/R est:16000
£11733 $21588 €17130 Nature morte (46x55cm-18x22in) s.d.47 exhib. 29-Mar-4 Rasmussen, Copenhagen #24/R est:50000-75000 (D.KR 130000)
£12057 $20135 €17000 Paysan (73x50cm-29x20in) s.d.1951. 15-Oct-3 Neret-Minet, Paris #20
£12676 $21930 €18000 Scene de plage (32x40cm-13x16in) s.d.30 prov. 12-Dec-3 Piasa, Paris #187/R est:5000-6000
£12840 $21828 €18746 Voleille sur une table (60x73cm-24x29in) s.d.53 prov.lit. 5-Nov-3 AB Stockholms Auktionsverk #1082/R est:60000-80000 (S.KR 170000)
£13380 $23148 €19000 Beach (38x46cm-15x18in) s.d.37 prov.lit. 9-Dec-3 Artcurial Briest, Paris #274/R est:12000-15000
£14094 $26215 €21000 Plage exotique ou plage a St Jean-de-Luz (46x55cm-18x22in) s.d.1956 prov.exhib.lit. 2-Mar-4 Artcurial Briest, Paris #229/R est:20000-25000
£15363 $27500 €22430 Oranges sur noir et blanc (61x76cm-24x30in) s.d.48 prov.lit. 6-May-4 Doyle, New York #105/R est:3000-5000
£15625 $25469 €22500 Pianist (38x46cm-15x18in) s.d.29 prov. 23-Sep-3 Durán, Madrid #215/R est:18000
£16902 $29240 €24000 Cage (38x46cm-15x18in) s.d.36 prov.exhib.lit. 9-Dec-3 Artcurial Briest, Paris #275/R est:10000-15000
£17075 $30564 €25100 Panier de fruits (54x65cm-21x26in) s.d.71 i.verso. 19-Mar-4 Millon & Associes, Paris #166/R est:5000-7000
£18000 $32580 €27000 Citrouille (38x46cm-15x18in) s.d.1941 exhib.lit. 30-Mar-4 Segre, Madrid #374/R est:27000
£18621 $33517 €27000 Landscape (60x73cm-24x29in) s.d.39. 26-Jan-4 Ansorena, Madrid #891/R est:27000
£19928 $32681 €27500 La Bobine (45x55cm-18x22in) s.d.30 exhib.lit. 27-May-3 Durán, Madrid #277/R est:15000
£20667 $37820 €31000 Fruits et draperie blanche (92x73cm-36x29in) s.d.60 prov. 7-Jun-4 Palais de Beaux Arts, Brussels #156/R est:7000-10000
£21831 $37768 €31000 Winter landscape (65x81cm-26x32in) s.d.40 prov.lit. 9-Dec-3 Artcurial Briest, Paris #273/R est:15000-18000
£22759 $38007 €33000 Portrait au verre (73x60cm-29x24in) s.d.1951. 16-Nov-3 Muizon & Le Coent, Paris #71/R
£38029 $61606 €54000 Nu allonge (67x130cm-26x51in) s.d.1936 prov. 5-Aug-3 Tajan, Paris #37/R est:25000-30000
Works on paper
£667 $1207 €1000 Nu de dos (30x24cm-12x9in) bears st.sig. ink crayon wash. 4-Apr-4 Salle des ventes Pillet, Lyon la Foret #7
£1805 $3321 €2635 Still life of flowers and fruit (27x37cm-11x15in) s.d.47 gouache exhib. 29-Mar-4 Rasmussen, Copenhagen #102/R est:10000-12000 (D.KR 20000)
£2027 $3568 €3000 Boats (19x24cm-7x9in) s.d.1956 W/C exhib.lit. 18-May-4 Segre, Madrid #114/R est:3000
£3000 $5010 €4380 Nude allonge (24x31cm-9x12in) s.d.42 gouache. 22-Oct-3 Sotheby's, Olympia #139/R est:3000-4000
£4200 $7518 €6300 Composition (50x64cm-20x25in) s.d.1964 gouache. 17-May-4 Chayette & Cheval, Paris #210/R est:4500-6000

BORG, Augusta (19th C) Danish
£508 $914 €762 Landscape with figures and cottage by water (65x85cm-26x33in) s.d.1870. 25-Apr-4 Goteborg Auktionsverk, Sweden #198/R (S.KR 7000)

BORG, Axel (1847-1916) Swedish
£1376 $2216 €2009 A short nap (48x65cm-19x26in) s.d.1880. 25-Aug-3 Lilla Bukowskis, Stockholm #657 est:15000-18000 (S.KR 18000)
£3846 $6615 €5615 Winter landscape with elks in evening glow (75x116cm-30x46in) s.d.1906. 3-Dec-3 AB Stockholms Auktionsverk #2527/R est:60000-70000 (S.KR 50000)

BORG, Carl Oscar (1879-1947) American/Swedish
£304 $550 €444 Normandy castle (19x24cm-7x9in) s. 18-Apr-4 Bonhams & Butterfields, Los Angeles #7027
£963 $1800 €1445 Sun drenched hilltop (18x21cm-7x8in) s. canvasboard prov. 25-Jul-4 Bonhams & Butterfields, San Francisco #6092/R est:2000-3000
£1630 $3000 €2380 An oceanside retreat (25x35cm-10x14in) s. prov. 8-Jun-4 Bonhams & Butterfields, San Francisco #4245/R est:3000-5000

£1765	$3000	€2577	Coastal (23x28cm-9x11in) s. canvas on canvas prov. 18-Nov-3 John Moran, Pasadena #186 est:2000-3000
£2198	$4000	€3209	Picnic near the trees (15x20cm-6x8in) s. canvasboard prov. 15-Jun-4 John Moran, Pasadena #3 est:3000-4000
£2941	$5500	€4294	Range rider (25x33cm-10x13in) s. tempera prov.exhib.lit. 24-Jul-4 Coeur d'Alene, Hayden #134/R est:6000-9000
£3326	$5953	€4856	Mountain town (66x47cm-26x19in) s.i. 26-May-4 AB Stockholms Auktionsverk #2348/R est:60000-80000 (S.KR 45000)
£8671	$15000	€12660	Navajo rider (41x37cm-16x15in) s.i. board prov.exhib. 10-Dec-3 Bonhams & Butterfields, San Francisco #6105/R est:15000-20000
£12032	$22500	€17567	Glory of the mountains (41x51cm-16x20in) s. board prov. 24-Jul-4 Coeur d'Alene, Hayden #122/R est:10000-20000
£36932	$65000	€53921	Oraibi, Arizona (64x76cm-25x30in) s. prov.lit. 19-May-4 Sotheby's, New York #207/R est:30000-50000
Works on paper			
£692	$1191	€1010	Head of an Indian - portrait study (18x16cm-7x6in) s. pencil. 3-Dec-3 AB Stockholms Auktionsverk #2439/R (S.KR 9000)
£704	$1218	€1000	Vue de la Salute a Venise (17x12cm-7x5in) s.d.1912 W/C traces blk crayon. 10-Dec-3 Piasa, Paris #158/R
£707	$1300	€1032	View through the trees (12x17cm-5x7in) s. W/C gouache prov.exhib. 8-Jun-4 Bonhams & Butterfields, San Francisco #4135/R est:2000-3000
£707	$1300	€1032	Shade under the trees (11x16cm-4x6in) s. pencil W/C gouache prov.exhib. 8-Jun-4 Bonhams & Butterfields, San Francisco #4136/R est:2000-3000
£714	$1300	€1042	Old barn in a landscape (10x15cm-4x6in) s. gouache board. 15-Jun-4 John Moran, Pasadena #128
£815	$1500	€1190	The stone house (11x16cm-4x6in) s. pencil W/C gouache prov.exhib. 8-Jun-4 Bonhams & Butterfields, San Francisco #4134/R est:2000-3000
£870	$1600	€1270	Three North African men in Burnous (12x17cm-5x7in) s. pencil gouache htd white prov.exhib. 8-Jun-4 Bonhams & Butterfields, San Francisco #4089/R est:2000-3000
£923	$1588	€1348	The fort (12x17cm-5x7in) W/C. 3-Dec-3 AB Stockholms Auktionsverk #2437/R (S.KR 12000)
£941	$1600	€1374	Wagon train in western landscape (16x24cm-6x9in) s. W/C. 18-Nov-3 John Moran, Pasadena #116a est:4000-6000
£978	$1800	€1428	Terme de Caracalla, Rome (38x45cm-15x18in) s. pencil W/C prov.exhib. 8-Jun-4 Bonhams & Butterfields, San Francisco #4082/R est:3000-5000
£978	$1800	€1428	View of St Peter's, Rome (36x54cm-14x21in) s.i. pencil W/C prov.exhib. 8-Jun-4 Bonhams & Butterfields, San Francisco #4084/R est:3000-5000
£978	$1800	€1428	Trappor, Granada (22x29cm-9x11in) s. pencil gouache htd white prov.exhib. 8-Jun-4 Bonhams & Butterfields, San Francisco #4086/R est:3000-5000
£1033	$1900	€1508	Sunrise in the mountains. Cowboy on horseback (17x17cm-7x7in) one s.d.41 one s.d.43 pencil ink pair prov.exhib. 8-Jun-4 Bonhams & Butterfields, San Francisco #4138/R est:2000-3000
£1223	$2250	€1786	Distant pink mountains (12x17cm-5x7in) s. pencil gouache prov.exhib. 8-Jun-4 Bonhams & Butterfields, San Francisco #4139/R est:3000-5000
£1231	$2117	€1797	Landscapes - the American western (12x17cm-5x7in) W/C. 3-Dec-3 AB Stockholms Auktionsverk #2428/R est:6000-8000 (S.KR 16000)
£1231	$2117	€1797	Indian town at dusk (12x17cm-5x7in) W/C. 3-Dec-3 AB Stockholms Auktionsverk #2431/R est:6000-8000 (S.KR 16000)
£1231	$2117	€1797	Desert landscape (12x17cm-5x7in) W/C. 3-Dec-3 AB Stockholms Auktionsverk #2432/R est:6000-8000 (S.KR 16000)
£1231	$2117	€1797	Indian camp (12x17cm-5x7in) s. W/C. 3-Dec-3 AB Stockholms Auktionsverk #2433/R est:6000-8000 (S.KR 16000)
£1231	$2117	€1797	Market square (12x17cm-5x7in) W/C. 3-Dec-3 AB Stockholms Auktionsverk #2438/R est:6000-8000 (S.KR 16000)
£1324	$2250	€1933	Ruins in New Mexico (13x15cm-5x6in) s. W/C prov. 1-Nov-3 Santa Fe Art, Santa Fe #26/R est:2000-3000
£1359	$2500	€1984	Rowing boat near the shore on a cloudy night (12x17cm-5x7in) s. pencil gouache prov.exhib. 8-Jun-4 Bonhams & Butterfields, San Francisco #4090/R est:2000-3000
£1445	$2500	€2110	Storm clouds over a Pueblo (12x17cm-5x7in) s.i.backing pencil W/C prov.exhib. 10-Dec-3 Bonhams & Butterfields, San Francisco #6085/R est:3000-5000
£1471	$2500	€2148	Cairo (14x10cm-6x4in) s.i. i.d.1910 verso W/C prov. 18-Nov-3 John Moran, Pasadena #127b est:2000-3000
£1471	$2750	€2148	Sun shinning through dark clouds. River view (20x25cm-8x10in) s.d.1912 W/C pair prov. 24-Jul-4 Coeur d'Alene, Hayden #111/R est:1500-2500
£1522	$2800	€2222	Bronco buster. Going after a stray (15x10cm 6x4in) one s.d.43 one s.i.d.44 pencil ink W/C gouache pair prov.exhib. 8-Jun-4 Bonhams & Butterfields, San Francisco #4137/R est:2000-3000
£1538	$2646	€2245	Le marchaud de legume (58x43cm-23x17in) s. W/C. 3-Dec-3 AB Stockholms Auktionsverk #2435/R est:25000-30000 (S.KR 20000)
£1538	$2646	€2245	Rome (70x51cm-28x20in) s. W/C. 3-Dec-3 AB Stockholms Auktionsverk #2436/R est:15000-20000 (S.KR 20000)
£1977	$3500	€2886	Summer day, Pacific coast (34x46cm-13x18in) s. i.verso W/C painted c.1913. 28-Apr-4 Christie's, Los Angeles #82/R est:5000-7000
£2385	$4102	€3482	Indians with horses (12x17cm-5x7in) W/C. 3-Dec-3 AB Stockholms Auktionsverk #2427/R est:8000-10000 (S.KR 31000)
£2462	$4234	€3595	Indians on horseback (12x17cm-5x7in) s. gouache. 3-Dec-3 AB Stockholms Auktionsverk #2426/R est:15000-20000 (S.KR 32000)
£2601	$4500	€3797	Indian woman (61x51cm-24x20in) s.i.verso pencil gouache paper board prov.exhib. 10-Dec-3 Bonhams & Butterfields, San Francisco #6103/R est:5000-7000
£2890	$5000	€4219	At the edge of a pueblo (48x58cm-19x23in) s.i.verso pencil W/C prov.exhib. 10-Dec-3 Bonhams & Butterfields, San Francisco #6104/R est:6000-8000
£3154	$5425	€4605	Navajo Race (25x35cm-10x14in) s.i.d.45 W/C. 3-Dec-3 AB Stockholms Auktionsverk #2429/R est:30000-35000 (S.KR 41000)
£3846	$6615	€5615	Cowboy watering his horses (37x40cm-15x16in) s. W/C prov. 3-Dec-3 AB Stockholms Auktionsverk #2430/R est:50000-60000 (S.KR 50000)
£3892	$6500	€5682	Winter day at the Grand Canyon (27x37cm-11x15in) s. gouache board prov. 9-Oct-3 Christie's, Rockefeller NY #76/R est:5000-7000
£7308	$12569	€10670	Women (38x48cm-15x19in) s.i. 3-Dec-3 AB Stockholms Auktionsverk #2434/R est:50000-60000 (S.KR 95000)
£7910	$14000	€11549	Glory of the gorge (50x35cm-20x14in) s. gouache prov.exhib.lit. 28-Apr-4 Christie's, Los Angeles #54/R est:15000-25000

BORG, Olle (1960-) Swedish

£393	$668	€574	Element XX (90x90cm-35x35in) s.d.1988 verso metal prov. 5-Nov-3 AB Stockholms Auktionsverk #945/R (S.KR 5200)
Works on paper			
£604	$1027	€882	Illumination (32x32cm-13x13in) s.d.1998-99 verso laser colours on chk canvas prov. 5-Nov-3 AB Stockholms Auktionsverk #955/R (S.KR 8000)

BORGE, Martha (20th C) Australian

£244	$383	€356	Near Bodega Bay (121x120cm-48x47in) s.i.d.68 acrylic board. 27-Aug-3 Christie's, Sydney #603 (A.D 600)

BORGEAUD, Georges (1913-1997) Swiss

£498	$861	€727	Village breton (27x35cm-11x14in) s.i.d.72. 12-Dec-3 Galerie du Rhone, Sion #468/R (S.FR 1100)
£905	$1620	€1321	Ferme paradisi (30x41cm-12x16in) s.d.69 i. verso. 14-May-4 Dobiaschofsky, Bern #79/R est:3500 (S.FR 2100)
£1233	$2097	€1800	Chapelle Rhodos (65x54cm-26x21in) s. i.d.86 verso. 7-Nov-3 Dobiaschofsky, Bern #94/R est:4000 (S.FR 2800)
£2482	$4145	€3500	Still life with white peonies (33x25cm-13x10in) s. 17-Oct-3 Behringer, Furth #1483/R est:3500

BORGEAUD, Marius (1861-1924) Swiss

£5603	$10030	€8180	Femme au chien (53x44cm-21x17in) board lit. 14-May-4 Dobiaschofsky, Bern #177/R est:12000 (S.FR 13000)
£25217	$46148	€36817	La Bretonne et ses poules (65x81cm-26x32in) s.d.1922 prov.exhib.lit. 7-Jun-4 Christie's, Zurich #65/R est:40000-60000 (S.FR 58000)

BORGELLA, Frederic (19th C) French

£650	$1229	€949	Acquiring a token of affection (34x48cm-13x19in) s. panel. 19-Feb-4 Christie's, Kensington #85/R
£800	$1472	€1200	Les danseuses du Pacha (28x42cm-11x17in) s. 14-Jun-4 Gros & Delettrez, Paris #109/R
£1667	$3067	€2500	Concert dans un clairiere (38x55cm-15x22in) s. 14-Jun-4 Gros & Delettrez, Paris #108/R est:2500-3500
£1800	$3096	€2628	In the harem (65x54cm-26x21in) s. 4-Dec-3 Christie's, Kensington #234/R est:1500-2000
£3191	$5330	€4500	Scene orientale dans un sous-bois (55x46cm-22x18in) s. 16-Jun-3 Gros & Delettrez, Paris #490/R est:2300-3000

BORGES, Jacobo (1931-) Venezuelan

£2769	$4375	€4043	Boy in yellow (64x64cm-25x25in) s. 27-Apr-3 Subastas Odalys, Caracas #45
£2885	$5250	€4328	Tropical wood (40x68cm-16x27in) s. cardboard. 21-Jun-4 Subastas Odalys, Caracas #151
£4245	$7810	€6368	Bridge (67x67cm-26x26in) s. painted 1987. 27-Jun-4 Subastas Odalys, Caracas #34/R
£13621	$24790	€20432	Yare devils (73x100cm-29x39in) s. painted 1953. 21-Jun-4 Subastas Odalys, Caracas #62/R est:26000
Works on paper			
£488	$800	€712	Untitled (23x33cm-9x13in) s. mixed media. 1-Jun-3 Subastas Odalys, Caracas #44
£528	$845	€771	Untitled (25x20cm-10x8in) s. mixed media exec.1970. 21-Sep-3 Subastas Odalys, Caracas #72
£574	$935	€838	Untitled (30x40cm-12x16in) s. mixed media exec.1960. 20-Jul-3 Subastas Odalys, Caracas #139
£652	$1200	€978	Untitled (60x43cm-24x17in) s. gouache exec.1963. 27-Jun-4 Subastas Odalys, Caracas #38
£791	$1345	€1155	Untitled (24x33cm-9x13in) s. mixed media exec.1971. 23-Nov-3 Subastas Odalys, Caracas #40
£1524	$2500	€2225	Repeat, please (68x103cm-27x41in) s. mixed media. 1-Jun-3 Subastas Odalys, Caracas #75

BORGES, Norah (20th C) Argentinian?

£820	$1500	€1197	Pilgrims (45x32cm-18x13in) tempera paper. 1-Jun-4 Arroyo, Buenos Aires #10
Works on paper			
£383	$700	€559	Figures (37x26cm-15x10in) ink. 1-Jun-4 Arroyo, Buenos Aires #42

BORGET, Auguste (1809-1877) French

Works on paper			
£1000	$1670	€1460	Old mosque near Calcutta. Indian street (21x29cm-8x11in) one s.i. one init. pencil pen ink wash htd white. 14-Oct-3 Sotheby's, London #149/R est:1000-1500
£1000	$1670	€1460	Street in China. Chinese interior (12x17cm-5x7in) init. pencil two. 14-Oct-3 Sotheby's, London #162/R est:1000-1500
£2113	$3782	€3000	Habitations de bateaux, cotes de Chine (18x25cm-7x10in) s. W/C. 11-Jan-4 Rouillac, Vendome #4

BORGHESE, Franz (1941-) Italian

£775	$1286	€1100	Passeggiata sui Trampoli (30x20cm-12x8in) s. 14-Jun-3 Meeting Art, Vercelli #425/R
£1049	$1804	€1500	Lovers (35x30cm-14x12in) s. cardboard. 3-Dec-3 Stadion, Trieste #987/R est:1000-1500
£1103	$1766	€1600	Figures (35x20cm-14x8in) s. board. 13-Mar-3 Galleria Pace, Milan #116/R est:2000-2600
£1141	$2111	€1700	And it flies (30x30cm-12x12in) s. s.verso. 13-Mar-4 Meeting Art, Vercelli #244 est:750
£1172	$1958	€1700	Couple (20x45cm-8x18in) s. s.verso. 13-Nov-3 Galleria Pace, Milan #129/R est:2400
£1241	$1986	€1800	Couple (45x20cm-18x8in) s. s.verso. 13-Mar-3 Galleria Pace, Milan #44/R
£1241	$2073	€1800	THree figures (30x40cm-12x16in) s. s.verso. 17-Nov-3 Sant Agostino, Torino #77/R est:2200
£1377	$2258	€1900	Gentleman and boy (40x20cm-16x8in) s. s.verso. 29-May-3 Galleria Pace, Milan #135/R est:2400
£1389	$2194	€2000	Couple with litle dog (30x20cm-12x8in) 6-Sep-3 Meeting Art, Vercelli #660 est:1000
£1655	$2764	€2400	Genlemen wearing hats (40x50cm-16x20in) 13-Nov-3 Galleria Pace, Milan #39/R est:3500
£1667	$3067	€2500	Nine figures (40x60cm-16x24in) s. 12-Jun-4 Meeting Art, Vercelli #232/R est:2500
£1690	$2958	€2400	Winter (40x50cm-16x20in) s. 16-Dec-3 Finarte Semenzato, Milan #339/R est:2300-2700
£1724	$2879	€2500	Meetings (70x50cm-28x20in) s. 13-Nov-3 Finarte Semenzato, Rome #319 est:1800-2000
£1800	$3312	€2700	Violin player (40x50cm-16x20in) s. s.verso. 14-Jun-4 Sant Agostino, Torino #354/R est:2000-2500

£1933 $3557 €2900 Duel (50x70cm-20x28in) s. s.verso. 12-Jun-4 Meeting Art, Vercelli #600/R est:2500
£2000 $3680 €3000 Hand shake (60x80cm-24x31in) s. oil acrylic. 12-Jun-4 Meeting Art, Vercelli #987/R est:3000
£2319 $3803 €3200 Noble art (46x55cm-18x22in) s. s.verso. 27-May-3 Sotheby's, Milan #30 est:3000
£2657 $4517 €3800 General and lady (50x55cm-20x22in) s. s.verso painted 1988. 25-Nov-3 Sotheby's, Milan #84 est:2800-3200
£5000 $9200 €7500 Duel (100x70cm-39x28in) s. 10-Jun-4 Galleria Pace, Milan #158/R est:12000
Works on paper
£382 $603 €550 Bourgeois couple (35x50cm-14x20in) W/C. 6-Sep-3 Meeting Art, Vercelli #399
£423 $701 €600 I tre geometra (50x35cm-20x14in) s. W/C. 14-Jun-3 Meeting Art, Vercelli #380
£537 $993 €800 Stroll (50x35cm-20x14in) s. W/C card. 13-Mar-4 Meeting Art, Vercelli #462
£552 $883 €800 Couple with dog (50x35cm-20x14in) s. W/C. 13-Mar-3 Galleria Pace, Milan #124/R
£600 $1074 €900 Couple (17x13cm-7x5in) s. W/C. 12-May-4 Stadion, Trieste #704/R

BORGHESI, Giovanni Battista (1790-1846) Italian
£3472 $5799 €5000 Allegories (53x88cm-21x35in) oil frescoes pair. 23-Oct-3 Finarte Semenzato, Milan #295/R est:5000-6000

BORGHI, Alfonso (1944-) Italian
£336 $621 €500 Winter (40x50cm-16x20in) s. s.i.d.1999 verso. 13-Mar-4 Meeting Art, Vercelli #64
£336 $621 €500 Autumn (40x50cm-16x20in) s. s.i.d.1999 verso. 13-Mar-4 Meeting Art, Vercelli #63
£336 $621 €500 Summer (40x50cm-16x20in) s. s.i.d.1999 verso. 13-Mar-4 Meeting Art, Vercelli #61
£336 $621 €500 Spring (40x50cm-16x20in) s. s.i.d.1999 verso. 13-Mar-4 Meeting Art, Vercelli #60
£933 $1708 €1400 Untitled (80x60cm-31x24in) painted 2000. 4-Jun-4 Tuttarte, Modena #164
£1409 $2607 €2100 My house beaten by the Ocean (100x80cm-39x31in) s. painted 1999 lit. 13-Mar-4 Meeting Art, Vercelli #66 est:2000
£1678 $3104 €2500 Red arps (120x120cm-47x47in) s. painted 1997. 13-Mar-4 Meeting Art, Vercelli #386 est:2500

BORGHI, Anita (20th C) Italian
£333 $613 €500 Vase of flowers (50x70cm-20x28in) s.d.1930. 14-Jun-4 Sant Agostino, Torino #113/R

BORGHI, Riccardo (1860-1938) Italian
£1333 $2453 €2000 Snowfall in Rivoli (83x57cm-33x22in) s.d.1897. 14-Jun-4 Sant Agostino, Torino #294/R est:700-900

BORGHT, Jacob van der (fl.1685-1699) Flemish
£6849 $11644 €10000 Roses, peonies and other flowers in a bronze vase on a ledge (64x59cm-25x23in) s. prov.exhib.lit. 5-Nov-3 Christie's, Amsterdam #1/R est:5000-8000

BORGHT, Jan Arnold van der (19th C) Belgian
£995 $1592 €1453 Winter landscape with figures, horse and dog by house (46x61cm-18x24in) s.verso. 22-Sep-3 Rasmussen, Vejle #434/R (D.KR 10500)

BORGIANNI, Guido (1915-) American
£388 $671 €550 Street (60x45cm-24x18in) s.d. 9-Dec-3 Pandolfini, Florence #421
£530 $964 €800 Along the Arno (60x80cm-24x31in) s.d.1972. 17-Jun-4 Galleria Pananti, Florence #211/R
£634 $1052 €900 Vase with flowers (70x55cm-28x22in) s.d.1961. 13-Jun-3 Farsetti, Prato #418
£861 $1567 €1300 Cliffs (65x85cm-26x33in) s. 17-Jun-4 Galleria Pananti, Florence #488/R

BORGIOTTI, Mario (1906-1977) Italian
£352 $609 €500 Cow in the stable (35x50cm-14x20in) s. i.verso cardboard. 9-Dec-3 Finarte Semenzato, Milan #19
£387 $670 €550 Oxen in Monza Park (25x35cm-10x14in) s.d.66 i.verso board. 9-Dec-3 Finarte Semenzato, Milan #3

BORGMANN, Resi (1861-?) German
£500 $915 €750 Still life with wine bottle, tin jug and roasted chestnuts (58x53cm-23x21in) s.d.1902. 5-Jun-4 Arnold, Frankfurt #545/R
£567 $1037 €850 Still life with leeks and onions (54x71cm-21x28in) s.d.1902. 5-Jun-4 Arnold, Frankfurt #543/R

BORGNIS, Pietro Maria and ZUCCHI, Antonio (18th C) Italian
£48000 $88320 €70080 Allegorical scenes. canvas on board set of 18 various sizes lit. 26-Mar-4 Sotheby's, London #51/R est:30000-40000

BORGO, Lewis J (1876-?) American
£294 $550 €429 Nocturne (18x23cm-7x9in) s. board. 25-Feb-4 Doyle, New York #24/R
Works on paper
£261 $480 €392 Country village scene (66x66cm-26x26in) s. pastel. 23-Mar-4 American Auctioneer #467348/R

BORGOGNA, Juan de (?-1533) Spanish
£38462 $61538 €56155 St Jacob (96x118cm-38x46in) panel. 19-Sep-3 Koller, Zurich #3016/R est:50000-80000 (S.FR 85000)

BORGOGNA, Juan de (style) (?-1533) Spanish
£8392 $14014 €12000 Saint Roch et Saint Sebastien (88x100cm-35x39in) panel painted c.1500. 26-Jun-3 Artcurial Briest, Paris #456 est:6000-8000

BORGOGNONI, Romeo (1875-1944) Italian
£1007 $1802 €1500 Landscape (30x42cm-12x17in) s. cardboard. 25-May-4 Finarte Semenzato, Milan #37/R est:1500-1700

BORGRAVE, Elie (1916-) Belgian
£486 $812 €700 Composition (65x80cm-26x31in) mono.d.1972. 21-Oct-3 Campo, Vlaamse Kaai #683
£833 $1392 €1200 Composition (100x65cm-39x26in) mono.d.1959 panel. 21-Oct-3 Campo, Vlaamse Kaai #682

BORIANI, Davide (1936-) Italian
Sculpture
£1611 $2883 €2400 Magnetic surface (33x30x12cm-13x12x5in) s. mixed media engine exec.1965. 25-May-4 Sotheby's, Milan #147/R est:1200-1500

BORIE, Adolphe (1877-1934) American
£1508 $2700 €2533 Portrait of a gentleman and his dog (107x89cm-42x35in) s.d.1918. 20-Mar-4 Pook & Pook, Downington #253 est:500-1000

BORIKINE, Ivan (attrib) (1865-1937) Russian
£400 $636 €584 Cossack (100x72cm-39x28in) s. i.verso. 10-Sep-3 Cheffins, Cambridge #546/R

BORING, Wayne (20th C) American
Works on paper
£348 $650 €508 Imposter utilizes dummies of Clark Kent (13x43cm-5x17in) s.i. pen ink craftint. 26-Feb-4 Illustration House, New York #28

BORIONE, Bernard Louis (1865-?) French
£1558 $2790 €2275 Interior with nobleman reading (35x27cm-14x11in) s. panel. 22-Mar-4 Philippe Schuler, Zurich #4386/R est:3000-4000 (S.FR 3600)
£2200 $3938 €3300 La lecture (41x33cm-16x13in) s. 15-May-4 De Vuyst, Lokeren #530/R est:3300-3800
£3416 $5500 €4987 Entertaining the cardinal (65x51cm-26x20in) s.i. 14-Jan-4 Christie's, Rockefeller NY #11/R est:4000-6000
£8500 $15725 €12410 Interlude (74x93cm-29x37in) s.i. 14-Jul-4 Sotheby's, Olympia #194/R est:5000-7000
Works on paper
£250 $455 €365 A letter of affection (26x21cm-10x8in) s.i. pencil W/C htd white. 1-Jul-4 Christie's, Kensington #322
£440 $800 €642 An amusing game of checkers with the Cardinal (51x38cm-20x15in) s.d.1900 W/C. 7-Feb-4 Neal Auction Company, New Orleans #871/R
£600 $1002 €876 Chez le Cardinal (40x29cm-16x11in) s.i.d.1912 pencil W/C. 16-Oct-3 Christie's, Kensington #141/R

BORIS, Rosa (20th C) American
£219 $400 €320 Interior with stove (81x51cm-32x20in) s.verso. 5-Jun-4 Treadway Gallery, Cincinnati #714/R
£455 $800 €664 Still life with lantern and flower (81x51cm-32x20in) s. 23-May-4 Treadway Gallery, Cincinnati #685/R

BORISOV, Aleksandr Alekseevich (1866-1934) Russian
£1500 $2685 €2190 Portrait of Sergei Rachmaninov (41x30cm-16x12in) bears sig. 26-May-4 Sotheby's, Olympia #467/R est:1500-2000
£1552 $2778 €2266 Beached boats by snow covered mountains (20x39cm-8x15in) mono.d.96 panel. 28-May-4 Uppsala Auktionskammare, Uppsala #183 est:3000-4000 (S.KR 21000)
£1950 $3510 €2925 Portrait of Sergei Rachmaninoff. 21-Jan-4 John Bellman, Billingshurst #1824
£2200 $4026 €3212 Hut and boats in a snowy landscape, possibly Novaia Zemlia (32x49cm-13x19in) s. i.d.98 V 91 verso canvas on board prov. 8-Jul-4 Lawrence, Crewkerne #1618/R est:250-400
£2365 $4234 €3453 Ocean covered in ice (31x40cm-12x16in) mono.d.1901. 28-May-4 Uppsala Auktionskammare, Uppsala #182/R est:6000-8000 (S.KR 32000)

BORJA, Mariano (19th C) ?
£321 $600 €469 The Lady (84x58cm-33x23in) s. painted c.1840. 25-Feb-4 Dallas Auction Gallery, Dallas #61/R

BORJE, Gideon (1891-1969) Swedish
£1208 $2054 €1764 On the balcony - girl with pink dress (63x53cm-25x21in) s.d.1920. 4-Nov-3 Bukowskis, Stockholm #7/R est:20000-25000 (S.KR 16000)

BORJESON, Agnes (1827-1900) Swedish
£699 $1189 €1000 Still life of fish (31x66cm-12x26in) s. 29-Nov-3 Bukowskis, Helsinki #394/R

BORJESSON, Ansgarius (1903-1990) Swedish
£290 $522 €435 Landscape from Hanhals (48x64cm-19x25in) s.d.45. 25-Apr-4 Goteborg Auktionsverk, Sweden #1267/R (S.KR 4000)

BORK, Bert van (1928-) American?
Works on paper
£447 $822 €670 Lakeshore Drive - Chicago (75x56cm-30x22in) s. s.i.d. verso W/C chl. 11-Jun-4 Hauswedell & Nolte, Hamburg #1170/R

BORKOWSKI, Wladyslaw (attrib) (1884-1922) Polish
£1145 $1947 €1672 Chateau Chillon Lake Geneva (65x54cm-26x21in) i.d.1915. 5-Nov-3 Dobiaschofsky, Bern #375/R est:1700 (S.FR 2600)

BORLA, Hector (1937-) Argentinian
£4372 $8000 €6383 Thomas More (30x24cm-12x9in) 1-Jun-4 Arroyo, Buenos Aires #77
£4918 $9000 €7180 Still life (60x70cm-24x28in) 1-Jun-4 Arroyo, Buenos Aires #82

BORLASE, Nancy (1914-) New Zealander
£1224 $2253 €1787 Small painting, abstract (52x45cm-20x18in) init. s.i.verso board. 29-Mar-4 Goodman, Sydney #57/R est:2500-3500 (A.D 3000)

BORMAN, Jan (circle) (fl.1490-1500) Flemish
Sculpture
£50000 $91500 €73000 Saint Eligius (56cm-22in) polychrome wood prov.lit. 9-Jul-4 Sotheby's, London #7/R est:50000-70000

BORMAN, Johannes (17th C) Dutch
£20000 $34000 €29200 Vanitas still life with a skull, flowers in a terracotta vase (62x47cm-24x19in) 29-Oct-3 Christie's, London #56/R est:15000-20000

BORNE, E L (?) ?
£993 $1818 €1500 Femme nue et Pegase (80x155cm-31x61in) s. panel. 7-Apr-4 Maigret, Paris #7/R est:1500-1800

BORNEMISZA, Geza (1884-1966) Hungarian
£887 $1535 €1295 House with a sunflower (60x73cm-24x29in) s. 12-Dec-3 Kieselbach, Budapest #56/R (H.F 340000)

BORNFRIEND, Jacob (1904-1976) British
Works on paper
£380 $692 €555 Four Trees (13x18cm-5x7in) s.i.d.1962 verso chl col crayons. 4-Feb-4 Sotheby's, Olympia #140/R

BORNSCHLEGEL, Victor de (1820-1891) French
£327 $584 €480 La lecture (32x24cm-13x9in) s. panel. 17-Mar-4 Hotel des Ventes Mosan, Brussels #90

BORNSTEIN, Eli (20th C) American
Sculpture
£1176 $2000 €1717 Structurist relief no.13 (33x46cm-13x18in) s.i.d.1992 verso enamel on wood. 9-Nov-3 Wright, Chicago #362 est:1000-2000
£3235 $5500 €4723 Structurist relief no.22 (51x51cm-20x20in) s.i.verso enamel wood prov. 9-Nov-3 Wright, Chicago #361 est:2000-3000
£4118 $7000 €6012 Struction relief no.4 (61x86cm-24x34in) s.i.d.1965 painted aluminum prov.exhib. 9-Nov-3 Wright, Chicago #365 est:5000-7000

BORODULIN, Lev (1923-) Russian
Photographs
£2000 $3680 €3000 Gold fish (29x17cm-11x7in) s.i.d. verso silver gelatin. 10-Jun-4 Villa Grisebach, Berlin #1040/R est:1400-1600

BOROFSKY, Jonathan (1942-) American
Prints
£2054 $3800 €2999 Flowers at no 2984194 (122x99cm-48x39in) s. hand col screenprint one of 70. 12-Feb-4 Christie's, Rockefeller NY #33/R est:1500-2500
£4420 $8000 €6453 Hammering man (366x176cm-144x69in) s.d.91 num.16/18 col silkscreen collage. 19-Apr-4 Bonhams & Butterfields, San Francisco #237/R est:10000-12000
Sculpture
£8235 $14000 €12023 Black el salvador painting with chatterman man at 2,845, 327 (193x277cm-76x109in) silkscreen on canvas aluminum wood primer electric motor prov. 9-Nov-3 Bonhams & Butterfields, Los Angeles #4075/R est:12000-16000
Works on paper
£475 $850 €694 Number 2464634 (15x23cm-6x9in) s.i.d.1978 ink pencil paper on paper prov.exhib. 16-May-4 Wright, Chicago #321/R
£514 $950 €750 Untitled (24x14cm-9x6in) init. pencil ink prov. 13-Jul-4 Christie's, Rockefeller NY #145/R
£640 $1100 €934 Untitled (30x23cm-12x9in) i. ink cut collage spiral notebook paper prov. 3-Dec-3 Doyle, New York #80/R est:1200-1600
£667 $1193 €1000 Personnages (28x21cm-11x8in) ink crayon. 12-May-4 Chochon-Barre & Allardi, Paris #136/R

BOROMISZA, Tibor (1880-1960) Hungarian
£706 $1172 €1031 Sunlit winter landscape (50x70cm-20x28in) s. cardboard. 4-Oct-3 Kieselbach, Budapest #18/R (H.F 260000)
Works on paper
£632 $1145 €923 Snowfall at the Duna (24x35cm-9x14in) s. gouache. 16-Apr-4 Mu Terem Galeria, Budapest #129/R (H.F 240000)

BOROS NEPOMUK, Janos (1808-1855) Hungarian
£2672 $4730 €3901 Castle room (41x52cm-16x20in) i.d.1842 panel. 28-Apr-4 Kieselbach, Budapest #157/R (H.F 1000000)
£4276 $7568 €6243 Kastelyszoba (41x52cm-16x20in) s.d.1842 panel. 28-Apr-4 Kieselbach, Budapest #158/R (H.F 1600000)

BOROUGHTON, Chester (20th C) British?
£580 $1079 €847 Nude woman reclining on a chaise longue with lilies (70x91cm-28x36in) s. 2-Mar-4 Bristol Auction Rooms #314/R
£740 $1376 €1080 Female nude against floral wallpaper (91x71cm-36x28in) s. trompe l'oeil. 2-Mar-4 Bristol Auction Rooms #315/R

BOROVSKY, T (19/20th C) Russian
£5000 $8500 €7300 Game, onions, grapes and lobster, basket of fruit on a table top (56x98cm-22x39in) s.d.1898 pair. 6-Nov-3 Christie's, Kensington #935/R est:1000-1500

BOROWER, Djawid (20th C) ?
£972 $1585 €1400 Picture of a face (160x177cm-63x70in) s. 27-Sep-3 Dr Fritz Nagel, Stuttgart #9048/R

BOROWIKOFFSKI, Wladimir Lukitsch (1757-1825) Russian
Miniatures
£4800 $8304 €7008 Prince Aleksandr Andreevich Bezborodko in maroon velvet jacket (15cm-6in) on tin gilt-metal mount oval. 9-Dec-3 Christie's, London #243/R est:1000-1500

BOROWSKI, Waclaw (1885-1954) Polish
Works on paper
£8204 $14438 €11978 Mythological figures (91x69cm-36x27in) pastel cardboard. 23-May-4 Agra, Warsaw #9/R (P.Z 58000)

BORRA, Pompeo (1898-1973) Italian
£800 $1456 €1200 Portrait of woman (80x60cm-31x24in) s. 12-Jul-4 Il Ponte, Milan #974
£811 $1427 €1200 Portrait of woman (80x60cm-31x24in) s. 19-May-4 Il Ponte, Milan #1104
£1000 $1840 €1500 Portrait (80x59cm-31x23in) s. painted 1963 prov. 8-Jun-4 Finarte Semenzato, Milan #63/R est:1500-2000
£1049 $1783 €1500 Rocks (40x50cm-16x20in) s. canvas on card prov.exhib. 24-Nov-3 Christie's, Milan #105 est:1500-2000
£1342 $2483 €2000 Nude (80x60cm-31x24in) s. 13-Mar-4 Meeting Art, Vercelli #209 est:2000
£1528 $2414 €2200 Vitality (80x60cm-31x24in) painted 1969. 6-Sep-3 Meeting Art, Vercelli #478 est:2000
£1678 $3003 €2500 Girl with flowers (70x50cm-28x20in) s. s.verso painted 1969. 30-May-4 Meeting Art, Vercelli #95 est:2500
£1901 $3156 €2700 Ragazza con fiori (70x50cm-28x20in) s. s.i.verso. 14-Jun-3 Meeting Art, Vercelli #224/R est:2500
£2113 $3697 €3000 Untitled (150x110cm-59x43in) s. prov.exhib. 16-Dec-3 Finarte Semenzato, Milan #332/R est:2000-2500
£2333 $4293 €3500 Seascape (40x50cm-16x20in) s. canvas on cardboard. 14-Jun-4 Sant Agostino, Torino #349/R est:3500-4500

BORRACCI, David (19th C) ?
£1000 $1670 €1460 Caricature a Borracci (34x29cm-13x11in) s.d.1859 s.i.d.verso. 14-Oct-3 Bonhams, New Bond Street #236/R est:1000-1500

BORRACK, John Leo (1933-) Australian
£264 $415 €383 Tilba-tilba NSW (36x53cm-14x21in) s.d.75. 26-Aug-3 Lawson Menzies, Sydney #21 (A.D 650)
Works on paper
£264 $414 €383 Approaching rain, Flinders Ranges, SA, near Brachina (53x76cm-21x30in) s.i. s.i.d.96 verso W/C. 27-Aug-3 Christie's, Sydney #537 (A.D 650)
£407 $638 €590 Untitled, Goulburn river (97x148cm-38x58in) s.d.84 W/C prov.exhib.lit. 27-Aug-3 Christie's, Sydney #528 est:3000-5000 (A.D 1000)
£851 $1447 €1242 Evening near Renmark (71x103cm-28x41in) s.d.1985 W/C prov. 26-Nov-3 Deutscher-Menzies, Melbourne #259/R (A.D 2000)

BORRAJO, Moncho (1949-) Spanish
Works on paper
£759 $1366 €1100 Composition with guitar (55x48cm-22x19in) s.d.89 mixed media exhib. 26-Jan-4 Durán, Madrid #10/R

BORRANI, Odoardo (1833-1905) Italian
£23179 $42185 €35000 San Miniato al Monte (38x22cm-15x9in) s. prov.lit. 21-Jun-4 Pandolfini, Florence #96/R est:40000-45000
£46358 $84371 €70000 Old Gate San Gallo (100x70cm-39x28in) s. prov.lit. 21-Jun-4 Pandolfini, Florence #116/R est:80000-100000
£75000 $135000 €109500 Garden walk (43x35cm-17x14in) s. prov.exhib. 23-Apr-4 Sotheby's, New York #68/R est:150000-200000

BORRANI, Odoardo (attrib) (1833-1905) Italian
£4110 $6411 €6000 Portrait of Giuseppina Strepponi (102x74cm-40x29in) s. i.verso. 8-Apr-3 Il Ponte, Milan #591 est:5000

BORRAS CASANOVA, Juan (1909-1987) Spanish
£276 $461 €400 Parasol (105x130cm-41x51in) s. after Goya. 17-Nov-3 Durán, Madrid #574/R

BORRAS Y ABELLA, Vicente (1867-1945) Spanish
£537 $1004 €800 Man in Valencia costume (36x26cm-14x10in) s. board. 24-Feb-4 Durán, Madrid #141/R
£552 $921 €800 Valencian nobleman (36x26cm-14x10in) s. board. 17-Nov-3 Durán, Madrid #151/R
£1206 $2013 €1700 Hacendado valenciano (36x26cm-14x10in) s. panel. 23-Jun-3 Durán, Madrid #142 est:1600

BORRAS, Jorge (1952-) French
Sculpture
£1259 $2140 €1800 Ballerine enfilant son bas (26x30cm-10x12in) s. num.1/8 brown pat bronze cast Candide. 28-Nov-3 Blanchet, Paris #174 est:1500-1800
£1946 $3581 €2900 Atleta au suelo (47x21x20cm-19x8x8in) s.d.2003 num.1/8 brown green pat bronze Cast Candide. 29-Mar-4 Lombrail & Teucquam, Paris #88/R

BORRCHY, A (19th C) French
£1400 $2240 €2044 Returning home after the harvest (34x21cm-13x8in) s.indis.d.80. 18-Sep-3 Christie's, Kensington #10/R est:1500-2000

BORRE, Guillaume Vanden (1896-1984) Belgian
Works on paper
£382 $607 €550 Composition (37x45cm-15x18in) mono.d.1957 mixed media. 9-Sep-3 Palais de Beaux Arts, Brussels #287

BORREGAARD, Eduard (1902-1978) Danish
£271 $506 €396 Still life of autumn flowers (96x96cm-38x38in) 25-Feb-4 Kunsthallen, Copenhagen #253 (D.KR 3000)
£275 $500 €402 Town scene with tram in background (68x94cm-27x37in) s. verso panel. 7-Feb-4 Rasmussen, Havnen #4087 (D.KR 3000)
£373 $679 €560 Still life of flowers in vase on table (97x97cm-38x38in) s. 19-Jun-4 Rasmussen, Havnen #2237 (D.KR 4200)
£521 $823 €750 Zinnia in window (85x58cm-33x23in) s.d.1942. 6-Sep-3 Schopman, Hamburg #783/R

BORREL, Ramon (1876-1963) Spanish
£352 $609 €500 Bowl with oranges (29x37cm-11x15in) s. board. 15-Dec-3 Ansorena, Madrid #8/R

BORRELL, Juli (1877-1957) Spanish
£592 $1072 €900 Leda and the swan (36x54cm-14x21in) s. cardboard. 14-Apr-4 Ansorena, Madrid #181/R
Works on paper
£474 $849 €692 Young Spanish girl (59x46cm-23x18in) s. pastel. 12-May-4 Dobiaschofsky, Bern #350/R (S.FR 1100)
£2098 $3503 €3000 Song (84x75cm-33x30in) s. pastel. 30-Jun-3 Ansorena, Madrid #207/R

BORRIELLO, Vittorio (1896-?) Italian
£380 $700 €555 New York street scene (51x41cm-20x16in) s.d.1943 canvasboard. 25-Mar-4 Doyle, New York #8/R

BORRONI, Paolo (1749-1819) Italian
£31724 $52979 €46000 Spring. Summer (93x72cm-37x28in) pair. 15-Nov-3 Porro, Milan #206/R est:46000
£31724 $52979 €46000 Autumn. Winter (93x72cm-37x28in) pair. 15-Nov-3 Porro, Milan #207/R est:46000

BORSA, Emilio (1857-1931) Italian
£851 $1421 €1200 Path in the wood (24x16cm-9x6in) s. board. 14-Oct-3 Finarte Semenzato, Milan #70
Works on paper
£652 $1070 €900 Hug (59cm-23in circular) s. mixed media card. 27-May-3 Il Ponte, Milan #930

BORSA, Roberto (1880-1965) Italian
£312 $516 €450 Newsagent's in the park (50x40cm-20x16in) s. 1-Jul-3 Il Ponte, Milan #786
£333 $613 €500 Venice (29x40cm-11x16in) s.d.1910 board. 8-Jun-4 Della Rocca, Turin #366/R
£616 $1010 €850 Esino (41x30cm-16x12in) s. i.d.1928 verso board. 27-May-3 Il Ponte, Milan #890
£634 $1096 €900 Girl with blue headscarf (46x31cm-18x12in) s. board. 10-Dec-3 Finarte Semenzato, Rome #212

BORSELEN, Jan Willem van (1825-1892) Dutch
£1848 $3307 €2698 Summer landscape with children (26x21cm-10x8in) s.d.1856 panel. 26-May-4 AB Stockholms Auktionsverk #2412/R est:20000-25000 (S.KR 25000)
£2055 $3493 €3000 Forest edge. Avenue. Polder landscape (10x20cm-4x8in) one s. two maroufle one panel three sold with documents. 5-Nov-3 Vendue Huis, Gravenhage #104a est:700-1000
Works on paper
£600 $1074 €900 Near Wittebrug (19x28cm-7x11in) s. W/C. 13-May-4 Bassenge, Berlin #5525/R

BORSSELER, Pieter (17th C) Dutch
£2000 $3340 €2920 Portrait of a gentleman, in a grey coat (76x63cm-30x25in) 13-Nov-3 Christie's, Kensington #4/R est:2500-3500

BORSSOM, Anthonie van (1630-1677) Dutch
£6000 $10980 €8760 Extensive landscape with cattle (71x91cm-28x36in) lit. 9-Jul-4 Christie's, Kensington #33/R est:3000-5000

BORT, Roberto (1933-) Spanish
£352 $599 €514 Les techniciens (116x89cm-46x35in) s.d.70. 5-Nov-3 Dobiaschofsky, Bern #377/R (S.FR 800)

BORTER, Clara Cecile (1888-1948) Swiss
£1101 $1839 €1596 Peasant woman peeling apples (70x55cm-28x22in) s. d. verso. 23-Jun-3 Philippe Schuler, Zurich #3379/R est:3000-3500 (S.FR 2400)

BORTIGNONI, Giuseppe (19/20th C) Italian
£800 $1416 €1168 Rolling pastry (31x35cm-12x14in) s.d.1886. 27-Apr-4 Bonhams, Knowle #99/R

BORTNYIK, Sandor (1893-1976) Hungarian
£26100 $45153 €38106 Composition (40x30cm-16x12in) s.d.1922 tempera paper. 12-Dec-3 Kieselbach, Budapest #71/R (H.F 10000000)
Works on paper
£1600 $2928 €2400 Colour composition (25x17cm-10x7in) s.i.d.1923 col pen graphite prov. 5-Jun-4 Lempertz, Koln #614/R est:3000
£2004 $3547 €2926 Houses (17x22cm-7x9in) s.d.18 indian ink. 28-Apr-4 Kieselbach, Budapest #192/R (H.F 750000)
£2138 $3784 €3121 Composition with figure (17x23cm-7x9in) s.d.1918 indian ink. 28-Apr-4 Kieselbach, Budapest #188/R (H.F 800000)
£2533 $4636 €3800 Untitled - sheet 1 (28x21cm-11x8in) s.i. gouache prov.exhib. 5-Jun-4 Lempertz, Koln #608/R est:4000-5000
£2533 $4636 €3800 Untitled - sheet 2 (28x21cm-11x8in) s.i. gouache prov.exhib. 5-Jun-4 Lempertz, Koln #609/R est:4000-5000
£2533 $4636 €3800 Untitled - sheet 3 (28x21cm-11x8in) s.i. gouache prov.exhib. 5-Jun-4 Lempertz, Koln #610/R est:4000-5000
£2533 $4636 €3800 Untitled - sheet 5 (28x21cm-11x8in) s.i. gouache prov.exhib. 5-Jun-4 Lempertz, Koln #612/R est:4000-5000
£2533 $4636 €3800 Untitled - sheet 6 (28x21cm-11x8in) s.i. gouache prov.exhib. 5-Jun-4 Lempertz, Koln #613/R est:4000-5000
£2797 $4755 €4000 Composition au cercle blanc (21x16cm-8x6in) init. W/C prov. 23-Nov-3 Cornette de St.Cyr, Paris #25/R est:120-150
£2800 $5124 €4200 Untitled - sheet 4 (28x21cm-11x8in) s.i. gouache prov.exhib. 5-Jun-4 Lempertz, Koln #611/R est:4000-5000
£3287 $5587 €4700 Composition a la boule blanche (28x21cm-11x8in) init.d.1923 gouache prov. 23-Nov-3 Cornette de St.Cyr, Paris #24/R est:120-150

BORTNYIK, Sandor (attrib) (1893-1976) Hungarian
£9333 $17173 €14000 Composition (30x16cm-12x6in) s. cardboard prov. 12-Jun-4 Villa Grisebach, Berlin #279/R est:12000-15000

BORTOLLUZZI, Patrice (1950-) French?
Works on paper
£493 $893 €750 Scene de regate a Carantec (35x53cm-14x21in) s. gouache. 19-Apr-4 Boscher, Cherbourg #867/R

BORTOLUZZI, Camillo (1868-1933) Italian
£2267 $4103 €3400 Venice (37x20cm-15x8in) s. board. 1-Apr-4 Van Ham, Cologne #1299/R est:3000

BORTONE, Antonio (1847-?) Italian
Sculpture
£30000 $54000 €43800 The drinking song (213cm-84in) s. white marble verde antico column lit. 21-Apr-4 Sotheby's, London #116/R est:30000-50000

BOS, Gerard Jan (1860-1943) German
£451 $767 €650 Man in thought smoking pipe (40x32cm-16x13in) s. bears i. i. verso. 28-Oct-3 Dorotheum, Vienna #102/R

BOS, Gerard van den (1825-1898) Dutch
£1842 $3334 €2800 Three children feeding a goat near a farmhouse (30x42cm-12x17in) s. panel. 19-Apr-4 Glerum, Amsterdam #68/R est:1500-2000
£3404 $5685 €4800 Young goat (22x32cm-9x13in) s. panel. 20-Oct-3 Glerum, Amsterdam #9/R est:1500-1800

BOS, Loek (20th C) Dutch
£556 $878 €800 Theft of beauty (40x60cm-16x24in) s.d.2000-2003. 26-Apr-3 Auction Maastricht #29/R

BOS, Willem (1906-1977) Dutch
£382 $603 €550 Tall ship in Rotterdam harbour (80x60cm-31x24in) s. 2-Sep-3 Christie's, Amsterdam #337

BOS, Wim (1941-) Dutch
£283 $516 €425 Fishing boats by the coast (58x98cm-23x39in) s. 30-Jun-4 Vendue Huis, Gravenhage #20
£320 $573 €480 Harbour scene (59x99cm-23x39in) s. 11-May-4 Vendu Notarishuis, Rotterdam #29
£347 $621 €520 Harbour with moored four-master (69x99cm-27x39in) s. 11-May-4 Vendu Notarishuis, Rotterdam #8/R
£367 $656 €550 Harbour activity (58x98cm-23x39in) s. 11-May-4 Vendu Notarishuis, Rotterdam #9
£367 $656 €550 Harbour with grain lifter (57x97cm-22x38in) s. 11-May-4 Vendu Notarishuis, Rotterdam #10/R

BOSA, Louis (1905-1981) American/Italian
£405 $700 €591 Back street (18x23cm-7x9in) s. board. 10-Dec-3 Alderfer's, Hatfield #364
£434 $750 €634 Still life with flowers in a white pitcher (61x36cm-24x14in) s. 10-Dec-3 Alderfer's, Hatfield #363/R

BOSANQUET, John E (fl.1854-1861) Irish
Works on paper
£1310 $2424 €1900 Ballintemple Village, Cork (23x40cm-9x16in) W/C. 11-Feb-4 Woodwards, Cork #8/R est:2000-2500
£1418 $2241 €2000 Blackrock Castle, morning scene. Cattle by Blarney Castle (25x36cm-10x14in) s.d.1867 W/C pair. 23-Jul-3 Woodwards, Cork #8

BOSANQUET, John E (attrib) (fl.1854-1861) Irish
Works on paper
£1056 $1690 €1500 Lismore Castle, sun setting, County Waterford. Banks of the Ayre, Scotland (28x37cm-11x15in) s.i. one d.1869 W/C pair. 16-Sep-3 Whyte's, Dublin #172/R est:1000-1500

BOSBOOM, Johannes (1817-1891) Dutch
£724 $1310 €1100 Church interior (12x9cm-5x4in) s. panel. 19-Apr-4 Glerum, Amsterdam #129/R
£1353 $2502 €1975 Church interior (46x62cm-18x24in) s.i. verso. 15-Mar-4 Rasmussen, Vejle #353/R est:18000-20000 (D.KR 15000)
£2083 $3396 €3000 Service in Brabant Church (21x31cm-8x12in) s. panel. 26-Sep-3 Bolland & Marotz, Bremen #499/R est:3200
£9211 $16947 €14000 Interieur d'eglise (24x18cm-9x7in) s. panel. 23-Jun-4 Maigret, Paris #19/R est:10000-12000
£11806 $19715 €17000 Figures in a church interior (23x33cm-9x13in) s. panel prov.exhib.lit. 21-Oct-3 Sotheby's, Amsterdam #222/R est:7000-10000
£24306 $41319 €35000 Luminous church interior (26x31cm-10x12in) s. panel prov.lit. 28-Oct-3 Christie's, Amsterdam #219/R est:30000-50000
£40000 $72800 €60000 Figures at a church service in the Nieuwe Kerk, Amersterdam (55x43cm-22x17in) s. panel prov.exhib.lit. 1-Jul-4 Christie's, Amsterdam #717/R est:30000-50000
Works on paper
£552 $1000 €806 Figures in a Dutch church interior (35x23cm-14x9in) init. W/C gouache. 30-Mar-4 Christie's, Rockefeller NY #132/R est:2000-3000
£1448 $2317 €2100 Church interior (17x23cm-7x9in) s.d.46 W/C. 12-Mar-3 Auction Maastricht #1149/R
£1608 $2766 €2300 Old poor house of Gravenhage (18x28cm-7x11in) mono.d.1869 W/C. 8-Dec-3 Glerum, Amsterdam #120/R est:2000-3000
£3243 $5708 €4800 Gate of the Nieuwe or Sint Sebastiaansdoelen in Hoorn (37x27cm-15x11in) init.i.d.Sept 83 black chk W/C prov.exhib. 19-May-4 Sotheby's, Amsterdam #349/R est:2400-2800
£3472 $5799 €5000 In het klooster te boxmeer (44x36cm-17x14in) s. W/C prov.lit. 21-Oct-3 Sotheby's, Amsterdam #138/R est:3000-5000

BOSBOOM, Johannes (attrib) (1817-1891) Dutch
£507 $958 €750 Port animе en Hollande (72x90cm-28x35in) s. 17-Feb-4 Vanderkindere, Brussels #120/R

BOSCH, Adriaen (17th C) Dutch
£5034 $9010 €7500 Jeune chasseur et son chien (89x76cm-35x30in) s. 25-May-4 Palais de Beaux Arts, Brussels #530/R est:5600-7200

BOSCH, Edouard van den (1828-1878) Belgian
£1800 $3276 €2628 Herding buffalo (82x102cm-32x40in) s.d.62. 16-Jun-4 Bonhams, New Bond Street #11/R est:2000-3000

BOSCH, Étienne Marie Theodore (1863-1933) Dutch
£671 $1201 €1000 Cygnes (90x100cm-35x39in) s. 25-May-4 Campo & Campo, Antwerp #21/R
£805 $1442 €1200 Vue de Santa Maria della Crocce a Venise (75x100cm-30x39in) s. 25-May-4 Campo & Campo, Antwerp #20/R

BOSCH, Hieronymus (after) (1450-1516) Dutch
Prints
£6471 $11000 €9448 Last judgment (31x21cm-12x8in) engraving executed c.1550-60. 6-Nov-3 Swann Galleries, New York #25/R est:15000-20000

BOSCH, Johannes de (1713-1785) Dutch
Works on paper
£3378 $5946 €5000 Arcadian landscape with figures conversing on a path (16x20cm-6x8in) s.d.1747 verso pen black grey ink brown wash prov.exhib. 19-May-4 Sotheby's, Amsterdam #245/R est:1500-2000

BOSCH, Pieter van den (c.1613-1663) Dutch
£13333 $23867 €20000 Various fruit and grapes in a silver Hercules tazza on stone ledge (66x52cm-26x20in) s.d.1652 prov.exhib.lit. 17-May-4 Christie's, Amsterdam #85/R est:20000-30000

BOSCHETTI, Benedetto (19th C) Italian
Sculpture
£958 $1600 €1399 Standing classical Roman woman (66cm-26in) s. gilt bronze. 16-Nov-3 CRN Auctions, Cambridge #67/R
£1497 $2500 €2186 Sculpture of Hermes, C (119cm-47in) bronze exec.1930. 17-Oct-3 Du Mouchelle, Detroit #2037/R est:3000-5000
£4200 $7266 €6132 Figure of Ariadne (58cm-23in) brown pat. bronze green marble base lit. 11-Dec-3 Christie's, London #137/R est:5000-8000
£4200 $7266 €6132 Figure of the Pan (67cm-26in) brown pat. bronze lit. 11-Dec-3 Christie's, London #138/R est:3000-5000
£6500 $11960 €9490 Bust of Apollo (47cm-19in) s. green brown pat bronze socle. 10-Jun-4 Christie's, London #147/R est:7000-10000

BOSCHI, Dino (1923-) Italian
£300 $552 €450 Factory (39x51cm-15x20in) s.d.1985 tempera paper on canvas. 12-Jun-4 Meeting Art, Vercelli #551

BOSCHI, Fabrizio (1570-1642) Italian
Works on paper
£816 $1461 €1200 Un homme assis tourne vers la gauche (20x14cm-8x6in) red chk. 18-Mar-4 Christie's, Paris #216/R

BOSCHULTE, Richard (20th C) American
£328 $600 €492 Approaching storm (25x51cm-10x20in) masonite. 10-Jul-4 Hindman, Chicago #53/R

BOSCO, Nathalie (20th C) ?
Works on paper
£385 $654 €550 L'echappee (12x47cm-5x19in) s. china ink acrylic pastel. 29-Nov-3 Neret-Minet, Paris #63/R
£453 $821 €680 Gris-Menhir (120x60cm-47x24in) s. mixed media canvas. 3-Apr-4 Neret-Minet, Paris #116/R
£524 $892 €750 Mouvement suspendu (40x50cm-16x20in) s. ink acrylic panel. 29-Nov-3 Neret-Minet, Paris #119

BOSCO, Pierre (1909-) French
£299 $500 €437 Horse race (60x91cm-24x36in) s. lit. 7-Oct-3 Sotheby's, New York #324
£556 $906 €800 Blue horse (56x66cm-22x26in) s. 27-Sep-3 Dr Fritz Nagel, Stuttgart #9049/R

BOSCOVITS, Fritz (younger) (1871-1965) Swiss
£588 $1000 €858 Zollikon - old village houses (41x21cm-16x8in) mono.d.1907 i. verso board. 28-Nov-3 Zofingen, Switzerland #2925 (S.FR 1300)
£750 $1245 €1088 Pensee (24x19cm-9x7in) s.mono.i.d.1908 board. 13-Jun-3 Zofingen, Switzerland #2798/R est:2000 (S.FR 1650)

BOSELLI, Felice (circle) (1650-1732) Italian
£5800 $9860 €8468 Two lobsters, salmon and shells on a forest floor (51x64cm-20x25in) 31-Oct-3 Christie's, Kensington #141/R est:3000-5000

BOSELLI, Felice (style) (1650-1732) Italian
£17731 $28724 €25000 Nature morte au chevreau, chou-fleur, hure de sanglier. Nature morte au dinon, poisson, crustaces et (73x89cm-29x35in) pair. 21-May-3 Artcurial Briest, Paris #245/R est:8000-12000

BOSEVANG, E (?) ?
£450 $733 €657 Copenhagen Harbour with sailing vessels (78x105cm-31x41in) s.d.20. 28-Sep-3 Hindemae, Ullerslev #140/R (D.KR 4800)

BOSHART, Wilhelm (1815-1878) German
£1189 $2045 €1700 Summer landscape with children playing at Chiemsee (42x35cm-17x14in) s. 5-Dec-3 Bolland & Marotz, Bremen #512/R est:1700

BOSHOFF, Adriaan (1935-) South African
£537 $982 €784 Untitled (17x22cm-7x9in) board. 6-Jul-4 Dales, Durban #2 (SA.R 6000)
£862 $1440 €1259 Mother and child on the beach (11x17cm-4x7in) s. canvas on board. 20-Oct-3 Stephan Welz, Johannesburg #247 est:6000-8000 (SA.R 10000)
£862 $1440 €1259 View of a village (26x37cm-10x15in) s. canvas on board. 20-Oct-3 Stephan Welz, Johannesburg #248 est:5000-7000 (SA.R 10000)
£862 $1440 €1259 Children with sun hats on the beach (18x18cm-7x7in) s. canvas on board. 20-Oct-3 Stephan Welz, Johannesburg #800 est:3000-5000 (SA.R 10000)
£905 $1512 €1321 Mother and child on the beach (11x17cm-4x7in) s. canvas on board. 20-Oct-3 Stephan Welz, Johannesburg #246 est:6000-8000 (SA.R 10500)
£1034 $1728 €1510 Children seated on rocks at the beach (16x21cm-6x8in) s. canvas on board. 20-Oct-3 Stephan Welz, Johannesburg #799 est:3000-5000 (SA.R 12000)
£1207 $2016 €1762 Mother and child wading in the surf (18x23cm-7x9in) s. board. 20-Oct-3 Stephan Welz, Johannesburg #250/R est:10000-12000 (SA.R 14000)
£1293 $2159 €1888 Mother and child in a garden (34x24cm-13x9in) s. canvas on board. 20-Oct-3 Stephan Welz, Johannesburg #249 est:5000-7000 (SA.R 15000)
£1345 $2434 €1964 Figures climbing a hillside (24x44cm-9x17in) s. canvasboard. 30-Mar-4 Stephan Welz, Johannesburg #476 est:7000-10000 (SA.R 16000)
£1849 $3346 €2700 Two figures on a mountainous road (49x39cm-19x15in) s. board. 30-Mar-4 Stephan Welz, Johannesburg #478/R est:12000-16000 (SA.R 22000)
£2586 $4319 €3776 Still life of flowers (75x90cm-30x35in) s. canvas on board. 20-Oct-3 Stephan Welz, Johannesburg #245/R est:30000-40000 (SA.R 30000)
£3025 $5476 €4117 On the way home (34x49cm-13x19in) s. canvas on board. 30-Mar-4 Stephan Welz, Johannesburg #477/R est:10000-15000 (SA.R 36000)
£3103 $5183 €4530 Herdsmen with oxen (69x54cm-27x21in) s. canvas on board. 20-Oct-3 Stephan Welz, Johannesburg #251/R est:20000-30000 (SA.R 36000)
£3716 $6652 €5425 Two children in a garden (58x43cm-23x17in) s. canvas on board. 31-May-4 Stephan Welz, Johannesburg #545/R est:25000-35000 (SA.R 45000)

BOSIA, Agostino (1886-1962) Italian
£979 $1635 €1400 Still life with vase of flowers (50x40cm-20x16in) s.d.1945 board. 26-Jun-3 Sant Agostino, Torino #262/R
£1611 $2851 €2400 Still life with flowers and bottle (49x39cm-19x15in) s.d.1946 board lit. 1-May-4 Meeting Art, Vercelli #75 est:2000

BOSIO, François Joseph (1769-1845) French
Sculpture
£38462 $66154 €55000 Buste de Marie-Louise, Archiduchesse d'Autriche (75cm-30in) s. white marble prov.exhib.lit. 2-Dec-3 Sotheby's, Paris #57/R est:55000-70000

BOSKERCK, Robert Ward van (1855-1932) American
£1359 $2500 €1984 Greenport, Long Island (30x46cm-12x18in) s. s.i.verso. 26-Jun-4 Selkirks, St. Louis #112/R est:2000-2500
£1452 $2700 €2120 Lake shores (51x65cm-20x26in) s. 5-Mar-4 Skinner, Boston #297/R est:2000-3000
£2714 $4750 €3962 Cloudy afternoon (50x82cm-20x32in) s. canvas on panel. 19-Dec-3 Sotheby's, New York #1104/R est:2000-4000

BOSMA, Wim (1902-) Dutch
£1088 $1981 €1600 Agion oros (90x120cm-35x47in) s.d.66 s.i.on stretcher. 3-Feb-4 Christie's, Amsterdam #616 est:1200-1600
£1449 $2377 €2000 Composition of harbour in Goteborg (50x61cm-20x24in) s.d.56 s.i.verso board. 27-May-3 Sotheby's, Amsterdam #303/R est:4000-6000

BOSMAN, Richard (1944-) American
£879 $1600 €1283 Shattered (76x61cm-30x24in) prov. 29-Jun-4 Sotheby's, New York #556/R est:2000-3000
£1081 $2000 €1578 Victim (122x183cm-48x72in) s.d.84 verso prov. 12-Feb-4 Sotheby's, New York #278/R est:4000-6000

BOSONI, Pietro (1890-?) Italian
£839 $1401 €1200 Sighs (88x72cm-35x28in) s.d.1922. 26-Jun-3 Sant Agostino, Torino #49/R

BOSQUET, Andree (1900-1980) Belgian
£664 $1129 €950 Bouquet (60x40cm-24x16in) s. board exhib. 24-Nov-3 Glerum, Amsterdam #10/R

BOSS, Eduard (1873-1958) Swiss
£419 $711 €612 Returning home from the fields (49x71cm-19x28in) s. 5-Nov-3 Dobiaschofsky, Bern #379/R (S.FR 950)
£478 $875 €698 Still life with fruit and urns (26x41cm-10x16in) s.d.1910 oval. 4-Jun-4 Zofingen, Switzerland #2757 (S.FR 1100)
£667 $1067 €967 Mountain landscape (99x81cm-39x32in) s.d.02. 15-May-3 Stuker, Bern #1089 (S.FR 1400)

BOSSARD, Jenny (19th C) German
Photographs
£6250 $10625 €9000 Family at coffee table (12x15cm-5x6in) i. verso daguerreotype. 31-Oct-3 Lempertz, Koln #29/R est:8000-10000

BOSSCHAERT, Ambrosius (elder) (1573-1621) Flemish
£1578947 $2905263 €2400000 Still life with bouquet of roses, tulips in roemer (22x17cm-9x7in) copper prov.lit. 25-Jun-4 Piasa, Paris #11/R est:800000-1000000

BOSSCHAERT, Ambrosius (elder-style) (1573-1621) Flemish
£20000 $34600 €29200 Still life of roses, a lily and variegated tulips in a vase with snail nearby (25x18cm-10x7in) copper. 11-Dec-3 Sotheby's, London #107/R est:20000-30000

BOSSCHAERT, Ambrosius (younger-style) (1609-1645) Dutch
£6419 $11297 €9500 Still life with gapes, peaches and other fruit, blue tit on a ledge (67x91cm-26x36in) indis sig.d. 18-May-4 Sotheby's, Amsterdam #89/R est:7000-9000

BOSSCHAERT, Jean Baptiste (1667-1746) Flemish
£4934 $9079 €7500 Nature morte a la guirlande de fleurs (114x72cm-45x28in) s. 25-Jun-4 Piasa, Paris #21/R est:8000-10000
£20280 $33867 €29000 Urne de fleurs sur un entablement (120x99cm-47x39in) s. 13-Oct-3 Pierre Berge, Paris #23/R est:30000-45000

BOSSCHAERT, Jean Baptiste (attrib) (1667-1746) Flemish
£1584 $2692 €2313 Putti hanging flower garlands in park landscape (57x48cm-22x19in) 19-Nov-3 Fischer, Luzern #1046/R est:6000-8000 (S.FR 3500)
£2657 $4438 €3800 Still life with roses, tulips and other flowers in a vase, on a marble ledge (74x71cm-29x28in) 30-Jun-3 Sotheby's, Amsterdam #3/R
£8219 $13973 €12000 Bouquet de fleurs et putti (90x69cm-35x27in) 5-Nov-3 Beaussant & Lefèvre, Paris #20/R

BOSSCHE, Balthasar van den (1681-1715) Flemish
£5517 $9159 €8000 Sculptor's studio. prov. 1-Oct-3 Dorotheum, Vienna #108/R est:8000-14000
£6579 $12105 €10000 Interior of painter's study (68x82cm-27x32in) 24-Jun-4 Tajan, Paris #24/R est:10000-12000

BOSSCHE, Dominique van den (?-1906) Belgian
Sculpture
£1800 $3276 €2628 Bacchante entertaining pan (66cm-26in) brown pat bronze. 15-Jun-4 Sotheby's, Olympia #99/R est:1200-1500

BOSSCKE, Lodew (1900-1980) Belgian
£405 $726 €600 Nu de face (65x93cm-26x37in) s.d.34. 10-May-4 Horta, Bruxelles #328/R
£559 $951 €800 Les elephants du cirque (60x80cm-24x31in) s.d.29. 1-Dec-3 Palais de Beaux Arts, Brussels #216/R

BOSSE, Ernst Gotthilf (1785-1862) Russian
£2361 $3849 €3400 Woman's portrait (71x58cm-28x23in) s.i.d.41. 24-Sep-3 Neumeister, Munich #400/R est:1800

BOSSE, Maria Philippina van (1837-1900) Dutch
Works on paper
£987 $1816 €1500 Cows grazing by willow trees (59x39cm-23x15in) s. W/C bodycol exhib. 22-Jun-4 Christie's, Amsterdam #157/R est:1500-2000

BOSSENROTH, Karl (1869-1935) German
£1000 $1790 €1500 City in the evening (72x67cm-28x26in) s. 13-May-4 Neumeister, Munich #287/R est:700-800

BOSSHARD, Rodolphe-Theophile (1889-1960) Swiss
£1174 $2102 €1750 Portrait de Kenia (55x46cm-22x18in) s. 30-May-4 Eric Pillon, Calais #118/R
£3493 $6253 €5100 Vigne a Cormon-Dreche (46x55cm-18x22in) 26-May-4 Sotheby's, Zurich #137/R est:8000-12000 (S.FR 8000)
£4348 $7957 €6348 Nu allonge sur la plage (22x27cm-9x11in) mono.d.34 panel prov. 5-Jun-4 Galerie du Rhone, Sion #541/R est:9000-12000 (S.FR 10000)
£4405 $7489 €6431 Fruits et feuilles (46x38cm-18x15in) s.d.44 i. verso lit. 7-Nov-3 Dobiaschofsky, Bern #119/R est:8500 (S.FR 10000)
£6550 $11725 €9563 Bust (55x46cm-22x18in) s.d.1949. 26-May-4 Sotheby's, Zurich #103/R est:15000-20000 (S.FR 15000)
£8257 $13789 €11973 Nature morte aux raisins (30x40cm-12x16in) s.d. oil paper on pavatex. 21-Jun-3 Galerie du Rhone, Sion #465/R est:10000-15000 (S.FR 18000)
£10860 $18787 €15856 Paysage des Prealpes (37x61cm-15x24in) s. prov. 12-Dec-3 Galerie du Rhone, Sion #639/R est:20000-30000 (S.FR 24000)
Works on paper
£288 $472 €400 Reclining female nude (26x34cm-10x13in) s. chl. 10-Jun-3 Pandolfini, Florence #235
£381 $610 €552 Female nude (31x21cm-12x8in) W/C. 15-May-3 Stuker, Bern #1090 (S.FR 800)
£435 $796 €635 Nu de dos (28x20cm-11x8in) mono.d.51 chl stump. 5-Jun-4 Galerie du Rhone, Sion #277 (S.FR 1000)
£565 $1034 €825 Couple (29x22cm-11x9in) mono.d.17 sanguine. 5-Jun-4 Galerie du Rhone, Sion #275/R (S.FR 1300)
£671 $1201 €1000 Jeune fille a la couronne de fleurs (43x28cm-17x11in) studio st. gouache. 30-May-4 Eric Pillon, Calais #214/R
£671 $1201 €1000 Jeune fille a la tresse de fleurs (43x28cm-17x11in) studio st. gouache. 30-May-4 Eric Pillon, Calais #213/R
£995 $1722 €1453 Meilleur souvenir (33x24cm-13x9in) s.i. crayon. 12-Dec-3 Galerie du Rhone, Sion #473/R (S.FR 2200)
£1092 $1954 €1594 Nu assis. tete de femme. Fleurs (29x20cm-11x8in) one s.i.d.1940 one s. one i.d.1939 one pencil col pencil three. 26-May-4 Sotheby's, Zurich #100/R est:4000-5000 (S.FR 2500)
£1719 $2975 €2510 Oliviers a Epidaure (20x28cm-8x11in) mono.i.d.33 gouache. 12-Dec-3 Galerie du Rhone, Sion #472/R est:2500-3500 (S.FR 3800)

BOSSHARDT, Caspar (1823-1887) Swiss
£7692 $13308 €11230 Courageous woman in the Swabian war (77x107cm-30x42in) s.d.1883 lit. 9-Dec-3 Sotheby's, Zurich #4/R est:10000-15000 (S.FR 17000)

BOSSHART, A A (19/20th C) American
£1333 $2400 €1946 Pennsylvania winter landscape (51x61cm-20x24in) s.d.18 i.verso. 23-Jan-4 Freeman, Philadelphia #239/R est:1000-1500

BOSSI, Benigno (1729-1793) Italian
Works on paper
£231 $392 €330 Allegory of Charity (15x11cm-6x4in) pen ink. 19-Nov-3 Finarte Semenzato, Milan #499/R

BOSSI, Domenico (1765-1853) Italian
Miniatures
£6500 $11635 €9490 Young gentleman in a blue jacket (6cm-2in circular) s.d.1795 gilt metal frame. 25-May-4 Christie's, London #93/R est:2000-3000
£11500 $20700 €16790 Lady in a blue dress with sash (9cm-4in) s.d.1805 gilt metal mount oval exhib. 22-Apr-4 Bonhams, New Bond Street #82/R est:4000-6000
Works on paper
£872 $1605 €1300 Girl with brown hair (7cm-3in circular) s. W/C ivory. 26-Mar-4 Dorotheum, Vienna #361/R

BOSSI, Giuseppe (19th C) Italian
Works on paper
£432 $691 €600 Allegory of the marriage between Napoleon and Mary Louise of Austria (16x25cm-6x10in) ink. 14-May-3 Finarte Semenzato, Milan #515/R
£935 $1496 €1300 Allegory of Truth (22x15cm-9x6in) pen ink prov. 14-May-3 Finarte Semenzato, Milan #516/R

BOSSO, Francesco (1864-1933) Italian
£367 $675 €550 Borgosesia (14x19cm-6x7in) s. i.d.1916 verso board. 14-Jun-4 Sant Agostino, Torino #128/R
£690 $1145 €1000 Vase of flowers (27x47cm-11x19in) s. board. 1-Oct-3 Della Rocca, Turin #235/R
£922 $1540 €1300 Donkey (30x50cm-12x20in) s. 20-Oct-3 Sant Agostino, Torino #32/R
£2500 $3950 €3625 Still life of flowers in an urn in a garden (71x119cm-28x47in) s.d.921 canvas on board oval. 24-Jul-3 Lawrence, Crewkerne #938/R est:1000-1500
£3472 $5903 €5000 Floral compositions (36x26cm-14x10in) s. board pair. 1-Nov-3 Meeting Art, Vercelli #222/R est:5000

BOSSO, Renato di (1905-1982) French
£4000 $7200 €6000 Portrait of my wife (40x33cm-16x13in) s. board painted 1933 exhib. 22-Apr-4 Finarte Semenzato, Rome #330/R est:6000-7000
£10667 $19200 €16000 Squadron (83x105cm-33x41in) s. board painted 1939. 22-Apr-4 Finarte Semenzato, Rome #332/R est:18000-20000
£18000 $32400 €27000 War machines (101x121cm-40x48in) s. s.i.d.1942 verso exhib. 22-Apr-4 Finarte Semenzato, Rome #333/R est:25000-27000

BOSSOLI, Carlo (1815-1884) Italian
£60000 $102000 €87600 View of the Kremlin (42x68cm-17x27in) s.i.d.1872 prov.lit. 18-Nov-3 Sotheby's, London #311/R
£60000 $102000 €87600 Constantinoples (41x65cm-16x26in) s.i.d.1872 prov.lit. 18-Nov-3 Sotheby's, London #310/R
£104027 $194530 €155000 Constantinople (108x173cm-43x68in) tempera prov.exhib.lit. 25-Feb-4 Porro, Milan #4/R est:150000-170000
Works on paper
£272 $487 €400 Interior of Saint Paul's (16x10cm-6x4in) pencil pastel dr. lit. 22-Mar-4 Sant Agostino, Torino #126/R
£3000 $5550 €4380 View of a continental city (20x28cm-8x11in) s. gouache. 9-Mar-4 Bonhams, New Bond Street #17/R est:1000-1500

BOSSOLI, Carlo (attrib) (1815-1884) Italian
£2113 $3507 €3000 Roma, fuochi d'artificio a Castel S.Angelo (43x60cm-17x24in) s. tempera cardboard. 11-Jun-3 Christie's, Rome #153/R est:3500-4500

BOSSUET, F A (1798-1889) Belgian
£2177 $3897 €3200 Repos devant l'auberge en hiver (60x42cm-24x17in) 22-Mar-4 Amberes, Antwerp #180/R

BOSSUET, François Antoine (1798-1889) Belgian
£10526 $19053 €16000 Grand Canal a Venise (23x40cm-9x16in) s. panel. 19-Apr-4 Horta, Bruxelles #88/R est:15000-20000
£20961 $38148 €30603 View towards Heidelberg with the castle (65x92cm-26x36in) s. i.verso painted c.1855-60 prov. 16-Jun-4 Fischer, Luzern #1192/R est:48000-55000 (S.FR 48000)
Works on paper
£839 $1401 €1200 Venice (21x26cm-8x10in) s.d.1863 W/C. 11-Oct-3 De Vuyst, Lokeren #38/R

BOSSUET, François Antoine (attrib) (1798-1889) Belgian
£2685 $4940 €4000 Church service (52x41cm-20x16in) s. 25-Mar-4 Dr Fritz Nagel, Stuttgart #698/R est:7000

BOSSUIT, Frans van (attrib) (1635-1692) Flemish
Sculpture
£6000 $10980 €8760 Allegory of Spring (12x10cm-5x4in) ivory relief lit. 9-Jul-4 Sotheby's, London #42/R est:6000-8000
£14444 $26000 €21088 Judith with the head of Holofernes (15x11cm-6x4in) ivory relief within painted glazed box lit. 22-Jan-4 Sotheby's, New York #165/R est:12000-18000

BOSTEELS, Prosper (1881-1964) Belgian
£333 $600 €500 Houses near the wood (40x50cm-16x20in) s. 26-Apr-4 Bernaerts, Antwerp #297/R
£915 $1584 €1300 Saint-Gillis mill on mouth of Dender in winter (65x82cm-26x32in) s. 13-Dec-3 De Vuyst, Lokeren #35

BOSTELLE, Tom (1921-) American
Works on paper
£569 $950 €831 Farm landscape (28x46cm-11x18in) s.d.60 W/C. 20-Jun-3 Freeman, Philadelphia #60/R

BOSTIC, Rudy (20th C) American
£236 $425 €345 Jonah and the whale (84x84cm-33x33in) canvasboard. 24-Apr-4 Slotin Folk Art, Buford #782/R

BOSTIER DE BEZ, Jean Joseph (1780-c.1845) French
£1408 $2521 €2000 Le repos pres de la chaumiere (57x82cm-22x32in) s.d.1840. 11-Jan-4 Rouillac, Vendome #101
£1479 $2647 €2100 La rencontre en haut de l'escalier (74x59cm-29x23in) s.d.1836. 11-Jan-4 Rouillac, Vendome #100
£2183 $3908 €3100 Village au moulin a eau (84x57cm-33x22in) s.d.1841. 11-Jan-4 Rouillac, Vendome #102

BOSTON, Joseph H (1860-1954) American
£444 $800 €648 Summer landscape (36x46cm-14x18in) s. 24-Apr-4 Weschler, Washington #596/R
£604 $1100 €882 Walk on the beach (63x76cm-25x30in) s. 29-Jun-4 Sotheby's, New York #275/R est:1500-2000
£1497 $2500 €2186 Moonlight California coast, possibly Avalon-Catalina (76x102cm-30x40in) s. 19-Oct-3 William Jenack, New York #389 est:3000-5000
£2673 $4250 €3903 Moonlight California coast (76x102cm-30x40in) s. 9-Mar-3 William Jenack, New York #201 est:8000-12000

BOSTON, Paul (1952-) Australian
Works on paper
£284 $446 €412 Floating head (49x42cm-19x17in) W/C pastel prov. 27-Aug-3 Christie's, Sydney #521 (A.D 700)
£366 $655 €534 Transistor radios (74x107cm-29x42in) synthetic polymer paint exec c.1983 prov. 4-May-4 Sotheby's, Melbourne #223 (A.D 900)
£723 $1230 €1056 Untitled (108x74cm-43x29in) s. ink wash. 26-Nov-3 Deutscher-Menzies, Melbourne #74a/R est:1500-2500 (A.D 1700)
£894 $1601 €1305 Untitled (76x56cm-30x22in) chl prov. 4-May-4 Sotheby's, Melbourne #224 (A.D 2200)

BOSWELL, James (1906-1971) New Zealander
£500 $885 €730 Figures in the beach (60x76cm-24x30in) s.d.54. 27-Apr-4 Bonhams, Knightsbridge #7/R
£620 $1128 €905 Morning Bathe (76x101cm-30x40in) s.d.56 board. 15-Jun-4 Bonhams, Knightsbridge #182/R

BOSWELL, Jessie (1881-1956) British?
£4762 $8524 €7000 Dear Mis Mai (30x30cm-12x12in) s. s.i.d.1930 onn stretcher. 22-Mar-4 Sant Agostino, Torino #517/R est:5500-6500

BOTELLO, Angel (1913-1986) South American
£4190 $7500 €6117 Head of a young Caribbean girl (33x25cm-13x10in) s. panel. 6-May-4 Doyle, New York #134/R est:6000-8000
£4360 $7500 €6366 Head of a young girl (48x38cm-19x15in) s. masonite prov. 7-Dec-3 Freeman, Philadelphia #72 est:7000-10000
£4469 $8000 €6525 Woman and girl (44x46cm-17x18in) s.i.d.44 burlap on wood. 26-May-4 Sotheby's, New York #152/R est:10000-15000
£4577 $7919 €6500 Young girl (51x41cm-20x16in) s. board. 13-Dec-3 De Vuyst, Lokeren #585/R est:6000-10000
£5587 $10000 €8157 Crouching woman (60x53cm-24x21in) s. masonite. 26-May-4 Sotheby's, New York #151/R est:10000-15000
£6471 $11000 €9448 Haitiana (51x41cm-20x16in) s. masonite painted c.1955. 19-Nov-3 Sotheby's, New York #182/R est:10000-15000
£6471 $11000 €9448 Haitian girl (49x39cm-19x15in) with sig. masonite painted c.1955 prov. 19-Nov-3 Sotheby's, New York #183/R est:10000-15000
£7263 $13000 €10604 Head of a Caribbean girl (33x25cm-13x10in) s. canvas on panel painted c.1940 lit. 6-May-4 Doyle, New York #133/R est:6000-8000
£8380 $15000 €12235 Olga 505 (94x42cm-37x17in) s. canvas on wood prov. 26-May-4 Sotheby's, New York #153/R est:12000-18000
£10000 $17000 €14600 Lavandera - Washerwoman (91x61cm-36x24in) s. board painted c.1965 prov. 18-Nov-3 Christie's, Rockefeller NY #119/R est:20000-25000
£16201 $29000 €23653 Two girls (107x137cm-42x54in) s. panel prov. 26-May-4 Sotheby's, New York #189/R est:25000-35000
£20588 $35000 €30058 Checker players (122x137cm-48x54in) s. panel painted 1986 prov. 19-Nov-3 Sotheby's, New York #184/R est:18000-22000
£22353 $38000 €32635 Figure with bull (61x91cm-24x36in) s. oil panel painted c.1970 prov. 18-Nov-3 Christie's, Rockefeller NY #123/R est:20000-30000
Prints
£2119 $3750 €3094 Mother and child (91x74cm-36x29in) s. serigraph edition 27/100 exec.c.1950. 1-May-4 Thomaston Place, Thomaston #852/R
Sculpture
£44693 $80000 €65252 Woman thinking (115x102x103cm-45x40x41in) st.sig. num.3 pat bronze prov.lit. 26-May-4 Sotheby's, New York #188/R est:35000-45000

BOTERO, Fernando (1932-) Colombian
£26536 $47500 €38743 By the sea (125x107cm-49x42in) s.d.52 exhib.lit. 26-May-4 Sotheby's, New York #95/R est:35000-40000
£40000 $73600 €60000 Jeune fille avec fleur (120x95cm-47x37in) s. oil tempera cardboard painted c.1960. 10-Jun-4 Christie's, Paris #39/R est:65000-95000
£54299 $92308 €120000 Budgie on the terrace (189x156cm-74x61in) s.d.00. 25-Nov-3 Pierre Berge, Paris #28/R est:150000
£55932 $99000 €81661 Girl holding flower (89x86cm-35x34in) s.d.68 prov. 2-May-4 Bonhams & Butterfields, Los Angeles #3108/R est:12000-150000
£60403 $108121 €90000 Portrait (86x84cm-34x33in) s.d.66. 25-May-4 Sotheby's, Milan #260/R est:45000-50000
£70833 $116875 €102000 Hommage a Van Gogh (116x94cm-46x37in) s.d.1970. 2-Jul-3 Cornette de St.Cyr, Paris #11/R est:80000-100000
£83799 $150000 €122347 Fille du Regiment (100x89cm-39x35in) s.i. painted 1996 prov. 26-May-4 Sotheby's, New York #38/R est:150000-200000
£100000 $170000 €146000 CaRDENAL - Nino de Guevara (171x178cm-67x70in) s.d.64 i.d.verso exhib. 19-Nov-3 Sotheby's, New York #36/R est:175000-225000
£141176 $240000 €206117 Santa Lucia (167x100cm-66x39in) s.d.83 prov.lit. 19-Nov-3 Sotheby's, New York #33/R est:250000-300000
£193333 $355733 €290000 Officer (197x122cm-78x48in) s.d.83 prov.exhib.lit. 10-Jun-4 Christie's, Paris #59/R est:285000-365000
Prints
£3442 $5645 €4750 La putica fumadora (45x37cm-18x15in) s. lithograph b/z. 27-May-3 Durán, Madrid #210/R est:3500
£3955 $7000 €5774 La toilette (35x29cm-14x11in) s.num.144/200 col offset lithograph. 28-Apr-4 Christie's, Rockefeller NY #259/R est:3000-4000
Sculpture
£3631 $6500 €5447 Feline (36cm-14in) st.sig. bronze. 16-May-4 Abell, Los Angeles #354
£17333 $31027 €26000 Woman's head (27cm-11in) s. dark brown pat.bronze. 14-May-4 Schloss Ahlden, Ahlden #1986/R est:18000
£90498 $153846 €200000 Cat (32x32x110cm-13x13x43in) s. num.3/6 pat bronze lit. 25-Nov-3 Pierre Berge, Paris #27/R est:80000-120000
£106145 $190000 €154972 Little bird on aperch (140x24x15cm-55x9x6in) st.sig. num.EA2/2 pat bronze steel exec.1988 prov.exhib. 26-May-4 Sotheby's, New York #19/R est:125000-175000
£128492 $230000 €187598 France (45x135x46cm-18x53x18in) st.sig. num.AP1/2 exec.1985 pat bronze lit. 26-May-4 Sotheby's, New York #25/R est:275000-325000
£193333 $355733 €290000 Reclining Venus (152x230x117cm-60x91x46in) pat bronze exec.1989 one of 3 prov.lit. 10-Jun-4 Christie's, Paris #53/R est:325000-500000
Works on paper
£3846 $6538 €5615 Landscape (76x57cm-30x22in) s.d.1980 W/C. 28-Nov-3 Zofingen, Switzerland #2553/R est:9500 (S.FR 8500)
£4857 $8500 €7091 Still life (38x29cm-15x11in) init. pencil ink double-sided prov. 19-Dec-3 Sotheby's, New York #1189/R est:5000-8000
£8721 $15000 €12733 Nina con muneca - girl with doll (40x32cm-16x13in) s. pencil executed c.1985 prov. 3-Dec-3 Doyle, New York #12/R est:10000-15000
£8824 $15000 €12883 Woman with a stole (41x33cm-16x13in) s.d.70 pencil prov. 18-Nov-3 Christie's, Rockefeller NY #133/R est:18000-22000
£8824 $15000 €12883 Horse and rider (41x33cm-16x13in) s.d.70 pencil prov. 18-Nov-3 Christie's, Rockefeller NY #135/R est:18000-22000
£10588 $18000 €15458 Cesta con unvas (36x51cm-14x20in) s.d.76 W/C graphite prov. 19-Nov-3 Sotheby's, New York #129/R est:20000-25000
£12081 $22349 €18000 Nina (41x32cm-16x13in) s.d.71 pencil. 13-Mar-4 De Vuyst, Lokeren #573/R est:7500-10000
£13408 $24000 €19576 Little prostitute (44x35cm-17x14in) s.d.76 graphite paper on board. 26-May-4 Sotheby's, New York #115/R est:30000-40000
£13423 $24832 €20000 Diocelina (41x33cm-16x13in) s.i.d.71 pencil. 13-Mar-4 De Vuyst, Lokeren #494/R est:7500-10000
£14085 $24366 €20000 Homme et cheval (39x31cm-15x12in) s. black crayon prov. 12-Dec-3 Piasa, Paris #45/R est:25000-30000
£18478 $30304 €25500 Woman holding glass (43x35cm-17x14in) s. pencil lead dr prov.exhib. 27-May-3 Il Ponte, Milan #538/R est:12000-15000
£20667 $36993 €31000 Mother with two children and cat (43x34cm-17x13in) s.d.71 pencil. 15-May-4 De Vuyst, Lokeren #504/R est:10000-12000

£27273 $46909 €39000 Couturiere (51x37cm-20x15in) s.d.90 crayon dr prov.exhib. 8-Dec-3 Artcurial Briest, Paris #58/R est:25000-35000
£27941 $47500 €40794 Still life (55x73cm-22x29in) s.d.1977 W/C. 19-Nov-3 Sotheby's, New York #177/R est:35000-45000
£34667 $62053 €52000 Man with cigarette in the street (43x34cm-17x13in) s.d.71 pencil. 15-May-4 De Vuyst, Lokeren #592/R est:10000-12000
£64706 $110000 €94471 Homme au parapluie (190x112cm-75x44in) s.d.80 W/C prov.lit. 19-Nov-3 Sotheby's, New York #50/R est:110000-140000
£123529 $210000 €180352 Girl reading her diary (130x182cm-51x72in) s.d.75 pastel graphite lit. 19-Nov-3 Sotheby's, New York #132/R est:100000-125000

BOTH, Andries (1608-1650) Dutch
£7432 $13304 €11000 Peasants eating and drinking in front of an inn, a village beyond (49x59cm-19x23in) bears sig. panel prov. 5-May-4 Sotheby's, Amsterdam #308/R est:12000-18000

BOTH, Andries (attrib) (1608-1650) Dutch
£1316 $2421 €2000 Moines faisant la charite (28x25cm-11x10in) panel. 25-Jun-4 Piasa, Paris #69 est:2000-2500
Works on paper
£410 $750 €599 Study of a seated gentleman with a hat (32x19cm-13x7in) col chk. 29-Jan-4 Swann Galleries, New York #171/R
£552 $916 €800 Traveller on horseback (20x13cm-8x5in) wash pen htd white over chk. 30-Sep-3 Dorotheum, Vienna #79/R
£1100 $1980 €1606 Schoolroom scene (13x17cm-5x7in) black chk grey wash prov. 20-Apr-4 Sotheby's, Olympia #71/R est:1200-1800

BOTH, Jan (1618-1652) Dutch
£4027 $7409 €6000 Annunciation to the shepherds (92x70cm-36x28in) s.d.Jan 1635 prov. 24-Mar-4 Dorotheum, Vienna #358/R est:6000-9000
£9767 $16800 €14260 Travellers (55x62cm-22x24in) s. 3-Dec-3 Naón & Cia, Buenos Aires #47/R est:10000-15000

BOTH, Jan (after) (1618-1652) Dutch
£6667 $11933 €10000 Italian landscape with mules and riders on a mountain path (106x126cm-42x50in) prov.exhib. 17-May-4 Glerum, Amsterdam #12/R est:3000-5000

BOTH, Jan (attrib) (1618-1652) Dutch
£2095 $3750 €3059 Figures by an aqueduct with a castle in the distance (61x79cm-24x31in) 20-Mar-4 Sloans & Kenyon, Bethesda #1156/R est:3750-4250
£5677 $10332 €8288 Evening landscape with travellers on horseback near a waterfall (58x80cm-23x31in) panel. 16-Jun-4 Fischer, Luzern #1030/R est:10000-12000 (S.FR 13000)

BOTH, Jan (style) (1618-1652) Dutch
£8500 $15300 €12410 Extensive river landscape with travelers on a path (74x109cm-29x43in) bears sig. 20-Apr-4 Sotheby's, Olympia #283/R est:4000-6000

BOTHA, David (1921-) South African
£556 $944 €812 Still life with blossoms in a jar (55x42cm-22x17in) s.d.68. 4-Nov-3 Stephan Welz, Johannesburg #712 est:4000-6000 (SA.R 6500)
£733 $1224 €1070 Fishermens cottages (50x75cm-20x30in) s.d.70 canvas on board. 20-Oct-3 Stephan Welz, Johannesburg #823 est:2000-3000 (SA.R 8500)

BOTHAMS, Walter (c.1850-1914) British
Works on paper
£320 $550 €467 At eventide (13x18cm-5x7in) s. W/C. 2-Dec-3 Gorringes, Lewes #2445
£460 $833 €672 Shepherd's rest (20x30cm-8x12in) s. W/C. 2-Apr-4 Moore Allen & Innocent, Cirencester #754/R

BOTHNER, Einar (1886-1955) Norwegian
£561 $932 €813 Summer's day in the park (72x92cm-28x36in) s. 16-Jun-3 Blomqvist, Lysaker #1010 (N.KR 6500)

BOTHWELL, Dorr (1902-2000) American
Works on paper
£265 $450 €387 From the Ibid series (8x10cm-3x4in) s.i.d. gouache. 9-Nov-3 Wright, Chicago #253
£265 $450 €387 From the Ibid series (8x8cm-3x3in) s.i.d.1948 gouache. 9-Nov-3 Wright, Chicago #254
£279 $500 €407 Untitled (58x46cm-23x18in) airbrush linen. 16-May-4 Wright, Chicago #137/R
£353 $600 €515 From the Ibid series (10x8cm-4x3in) s.i.d.1948 gouache. 9-Nov-3 Wright, Chicago #255

BOTKE, Cornelius (1887-1954) American
£3086 $5000 €4475 From the coast of Southern California (51x61cm-20x24in) s. 8-Aug-3 Barridorf, Portland #260/R est:5000-7000
£3968 $7500 €5793 Eucalyptus southern California coastal (53x61cm-21x24in) s. prov. 17-Feb-4 John Moran, Pasadena #111b/R est:7000-9000

BOTKE, Jessie Arms (1883-1971) American
£751 $1300 €1096 View of the coastal town of Hueneme, California (30x41cm-12x16in) init.i. canvas on masonite prov. 10-Dec-3 Bonhams & Butterfields, San Francisco #6318/R est:2000-3000
£1236 $2250 €1805 Redwing blackbirds (30x41cm-12x16in) s. i.verso canvasboard prov. 15-Jun-4 John Moran, Pasadena #105 est:1000-2000
£2198 $4000 €3209 Mountain landscape (25x20cm-10x8in) s. canvasboard prov. 15-Jun-4 John Moran, Pasadena #7 est:2000-3000
£3704 $7000 €5408 Red parrot on foliage (28x23cm-11x9in) s. gold board prov. 17-Feb-4 John Moran, Pasadena #55a/R est:9000-12000
£8235 $14000 €12023 Cockatoo and hibiscus (46x61cm-18x24in) s. prov. 18-Nov-3 John Moran, Pasadena #106 est:15000-20000
£8523 $15000 €12444 White peacock (61x51cm-24x20in) s. 23-May-4 Treadway Gallery, Cincinnati #547/R est:15000-20000
£10215 $19000 €14914 White peacock (64x69cm-25x27in) s. painted c.1920. 7-Mar-4 Treadway Gallery, Cincinnati #571/R est:15000-20000
£18824 $32000 €27483 Peacock and flowers (76x63cm-30x25in) oil silver leaf on masonite prov. 29-Oct-3 Christie's, Los Angeles #63/R est:30000-50000
Works on paper
£1374 $2500 €2006 Floral still life (30x25cm-12x10in) s. W/C prov. 15-Jun-4 John Moran, Pasadena #132b est:2000-3000
£5556 $9000 €8056 Castle garden (48x38cm-19x15in) s. gouache. 8-Aug-3 Barridorf, Portland #272/R est:10000-15000

BOTKIN, Henry Albert (1896-1983) American
Works on paper
£406 $650 €593 Kano (84x112cm-33x44in) s. s.i.d.1970 verso mixed media. 17-May-3 Bunte, Elgin #1310

BOTMAN, Yegor Ivanovich (?-1891) Russian
£92308 $158769 €134770 Portrait of the Tsar Nikolai I with St Petersburg in background (284x203cm-112x80in) s.i.d.1870 prov.lit. 3-Dec-3 AB Stockholms Auktionsverk #2653/R est:1200000-1500000 (S.KR 1200000)

BOTO, Martha (1925-) Argentinian
£235 $437 €350 Fugues (50x50cm-20x20in) s. s.i.d.1978 verso acrylic. 3-Mar-4 Artcurial Briest, Paris #323

BOTSOGLOU, Chronis (1941-) Greek
£3000 $5250 €4380 Self portrait (45x30cm-18x12in) s.d.1973. 16-Dec-3 Bonhams, New Bond Street #138/R est:1800-2200

BOTT, Francis (1904-1998) German
£900 $1530 €1314 Composition in grey and yellow (37x51cm-15x20in) acrylic oil board. 18-Nov-3 Bonhams, Knightsbridge #31/R
£1100 $1870 €1606 Composition in blue (41x54cm-16x21in) s.d.59 acrylic board. 18-Nov-3 Bonhams, Knightsbridge #29/R est:800-1000
£1100 $1870 €1606 Composition in blue and grey (64x98cm-25x39in) s. acrylic board. 18-Nov-3 Bonhams, Knightsbridge #33/R est:1200-1800
£1100 $1870 €1606 Composition in red and black (41x56cm-16x22in) s.d.59 acrylic board. 18-Nov-3 Bonhams, Knightsbridge #34/R est:1200-1800
£1200 $2040 €1752 Composition in purple (41x54cm-16x21in) s.d.59 acrylic board. 18-Nov-3 Bonhams, Knightsbridge #30/R est:800-1000
£1200 $2040 €1752 Composition in blue and grey (65x97cm-26x38in) s.d.56 acrylic board. 18-Nov-3 Bonhams, Knightsbridge #35/R est:1200-1800
£1310 $2410 €1913 Composition (33x37cm-13x15in) s.d.1962 board. 8-Jun-4 Germann, Zurich #138/R est:2500-3000 (S.FR 3000)
Works on paper
£235 $437 €350 Composition (51x73cm-20x29in) s.d.69 gouache. 3-Mar-4 Artcurial Briest, Paris #324
£302 $553 €450 Composition (21x18cm-8x7in) s.d.58 gouache. 7-Jul-4 Artcurial Briest, Paris #215
£733 $1313 €1100 Composition (22x27cm-9x11in) s.d.57 gouache. 15-May-4 Van Ham, Cologne #477/R
£909 $1564 €1300 Composition (24x21cm-9x8in) s. gouache. 4-Dec-3 Van Ham, Cologne #53
£950 $1615 €1387 Composition in red and yellow (48x63cm-19x25in) s.d.55 gouache. 18-Nov-3 Bonhams, Knightsbridge #32/R
£1141 $2123 €1700 Composition (48x50cm-19x20in) s.d.57 gouache. 3-Mar-4 Artcurial Briest, Paris #326/R est:400-600
£1208 $2223 €1800 Intonation - tone (56x76cm-22x30in) s.d. pastel prov. 26-Mar-4 Ketterer, Hamburg #337/R est:2000-3000
£1930 $3551 €2818 Composition; en temps util (56x76cm-22x30in) s.d.61 pastel prov. 23-Jun-4 Koller, Zurich #3079/R est:4000-5500 (S.FR 4400)

BOTT, Nicholas J (1941-) Canadian
£227 $414 €331 Near Watson Lake (41x30cm-16x12in) s. board prov. 5-Feb-4 Heffel, Vancouver #009/R (C.D 550)
£340 $622 €496 Lake shore in winter (20x25cm-8x10in) s.i. panel. 1-Jun-4 Hodgins, Calgary #5/R (C.D 850)
£362 $605 €529 Keremios (25x30cm-10x12in) s.i. board. 17-Nov-3 Hodgins, Calgary #255/R (C.D 800)
£380 $695 €555 Fall (20x25cm-8x10in) s.i. panel. 1-Jun-4 Hodgins, Calgary #256/R (C.D 950)
£600 $1098 €876 Tree and morning light (40x50cm-16x20in) s. panel prov. 3-Jun-4 Heffel, Vancouver #8/R (C.D 1500)
£670 $1138 €978 Similkameen Valley Ranch (46x61cm-18x24in) s. s.i.d.1991 board. 6-Nov-3 Heffel, Vancouver #19/R est:1800-2000 (C.D 1500)
£893 $1518 €1304 Farm, Burns Lake (46x61cm-18x24in) s. 6-Nov-3 Heffel, Vancouver #18/R est:1800-2000 (C.D 2000)
£1228 $2087 €1793 Winter light Telkwa (61x91cm-24x36in) s. s.i.verso board. 6-Nov-3 Heffel, Vancouver #20/R est:3000-3500 (C.D 2750)

BOTTA, Guido (1921-) Italian
£267 $491 €400 Little wood (40x30cm-16x12in) s.d.1984. 12-Jun-4 Meeting Art, Vercelli #547

BOTTCHER, Hans (1897-1986) German
£417 $696 €600 The bathtub II (80x110cm-31x43in) mono.d. s.i.d. verso. 25-Oct-3 Dr Lehr, Berlin #74/R
£417 $696 €600 Untitled - informal composition (60x100cm-24x39in) mono.d. 25-Oct-3 Dr Lehr, Berlin #73/R
£467 $840 €700 Studio still life (70x60cm-28x24in) mono.d. 24-Apr-4 Dr Lehr, Berlin #58/R

BOTTCHER, Jurgen (1931-) German
£6294 $10699 €9000 What you want (200x170cm-79x67in) s.i.d.1990 acrylic linen on canvas. 29-Nov-3 Villa Grisebach, Berlin #385/R est:10000-15000

Works on paper
£467 $854 €700 Untitled (59x81cm-23x32in) s.d.16.III 1985 s.d. verso Indian ink brush board. 4-Jun-4 Lempertz, Koln #473/R

BOTTERO, Giuseppe (1846-?) Italian
£1135 $1895 €1600 Mori Palace, Venice (60x47cm-24x19in) s. 20-Oct-3 Sant Agostino, Torino #91/R est:800-1000

BOTTET, Nicole (1942-) French
Works on paper
£680 $1217 €1000 Untitled (31x47cm-12x19in) s. W/C prov. 21-Mar-4 Calmels Cohen, Paris #113/R

BOTTEX, Seymour (1923-) Haitian
£300 $537 €450 J J Dessalines a la ferriere (75x60cm-30x24in) s. 17-May-4 Rogeon, Paris #158

BOTTGER, Herbert (1898-1954) German
£1389 $2319 €2000 Madonna with lily (61x51cm-24x20in) mono. prov.lit. 24-Oct-3 Ketterer, Hamburg #289/R est:2000-3000
£1806 $2943 €2600 Still life with flowers (70x65cm-28x26in) mono. 27-Sep-3 Dr Fritz Nagel, Stuttgart #9462/R est:2800
£1818 $3127 €2600 Still life (12x20cm-5x8in) mono.d.1947 cardboard. 4-Dec-3 Van Ham, Cologne #54/R est:2200

BOTTGER, Jacob (1781-1860) German
Works on paper
£1727 $2832 €2400 The brig, Freitag von Hamburg (43x65cm-17x26in) s.i. W/C over Indian ink prov. 4-Jun-3 Ketterer, Hamburg #1/R est:2500-3000

BOTTI, George Italo (1923-2003) American?
£475 $850 €694 Abstract seascape (61x76cm-24x30in) s. 8-May-4 Susanin's, Chicago #6088/R

BOTTI, Italo (1889-1974) Argentinian
£411 $650 €600 Lighthouse (61x91cm-24x36in) s. 6-Sep-3 Susanin's, Chicago #5028/R
£435 $800 €635 Girl in garden (89x89cm-35x35in) s. 26-Jun-4 Susanin's, Chicago #6011/R
£570 $900 €832 Balloons (91x91cm-36x36in) s. 6-Sep-3 Susanin's, Chicago #5029/R est:800-1200
£944 $1700 €1378 Woman arranging flowers (91x91cm-36x36in) s. 24-Jan-4 Susanin's, Chicago #5049/R est:700-900
£1087 $2000 €1587 Boats and children at beach (122x91cm-48x36in) s. 26-Jun-4 Susanin's, Chicago #6010/R est:800-1200
£1694 $3100 €2473 Estuary (24x28cm-9x11in) cardboard. 1-Jun-4 Arroyo, Buenos Aires #24

BOTTICELLI, Sandro (attrib) (1440-1510) Italian
£18534 $34103 €27060 Portrait of Giovanni Picco della Mirandola (44x29cm-17x11in) panel prov.lit. 26-Mar-4 Koller, Zurich #3005/R est:25000-30000 (S.FR 43000)

BOTTICINI, Francesco (attrib) (1446-1497) Italian
£48000 $87840 €70080 Portrait of a young gentleman in a black coat and cap (56x41cm-22x16in) panel prov.lit. 7-Jul-4 Christie's, London #3/R est:15000-25000

BOTTLIK, Jozsef (1876-1941) Hungarian
£1044 $1806 €1524 Woman embroidering - afternoon rest (50x61cm-20x24in) s.d.912. 12-Dec-3 Kieselbach, Budapest #1/R (H.F 400000)

BOTTOM, Robert (1944-) British
£347 $624 €520 On the road to Manorhamilton, Co Leitrim (44x59cm-17x23in) s.d.97 board. 20-Apr-4 James Adam, Dublin #136/R
£420 $689 €613 Old farm, Fanad (50x61cm-20x24in) s.d.1999 verso board. 4-Jun-3 John Ross, Belfast #247

BOTTOMLEY, Albert Ernest (1873-1950) British
£563 $935 €800 Peasants returning home (25x36cm-10x14in) s. 16-Jun-3 Dorotheum, Vienna #231/R
£650 $1203 €949 Horse guards parade, Whitehall, London (33x44cm-13x17in) s.d.1927. 11-Feb-4 Cheffins, Cambridge #443/R
£1000 $1700 €1460 Harvest time (36x46cm-14x18in) s. 26-Nov-3 Hamptons Fine Art, Godalming #217/R est:1000-1500
Works on paper
£260 $442 €380 Rhyl (23x34cm-9x13in) s.i. gouache. 29-Oct-3 Bonhams, Chester #360

BOTTOMLEY, Edwin (1865-1929) British
Works on paper
£235 $400 €343 Jackie and Bob, two terries (34x47cm-13x19in) s.d.1904 W/C. 21-Nov-3 Skinner, Boston #57/R
£2200 $4004 €3212 Farmyard friends (35x53cm-14x21in) s.d.1924 pencil W/C htd white. 1-Jul-4 Christie's, Kensington #217/R est:2000-3000

BOTTOMLEY, Fred (1883-1960) British
£2200 $4070 €3212 The slip way, St Ives (63x76cm-25x30in) s. board exhib. 11-Feb-4 Sotheby's, Olympia #168/R est:1000-1500

BOTTON, Jean Isy de (1898-1978) French
£668 $1115 €975 Family cradle in Tourzine, landscape (64x76cm-25x30in) s. s.i.verso. 19-Oct-3 Jeffery Burchard, Florida #34
£1006 $1600 €1469 Le homard (46x56cm-18x22in) s.d.1952 i.verso prov. 13-Sep-3 Weschler, Washington #684/R est:600-800
£1049 $1752 €1500 Marins en bord de mer (60x73cm-24x29in) s.d.1927. 7-Oct-3 Livinec, Gaudcheau & Jezequel, Rennes #95/R
£1622 $3000 €2368 Parade of circus, Port of Portugal (76x61cm-30x24in) 13-Feb-4 David Rago, Lambertville #28/R est:2500-3500
£1840 $3000 €2686 Rayon de miel (25x35cm-10x14in) s. s.i.d.1953 verso. 25-Sep-3 Christie's, Rockefeller NY #592/R est:3000-5000
£1963 $3200 €2866 Mediterranee (82x102cm-32x40in) s. s.i.d.1962-1970 verso. 25-Sep-3 Christie's, Rockefeller NY #559/R est:4000-6000
£2147 $3500 €3135 Le vieux pont (80x65cm-31x26in) s.d.1927 i.d.1927 stretcher. 25-Sep-3 Christie's, Rockefeller NY #521/R est:4000-6000

BOTTON, Jean Isy de (attrib) (1898-1978) French
£216 $400 €315 Study of Princess Elizabeth (30x18cm-12x7in) s.d.1938 board. 13-Mar-4 Susanin's, Chicago #6194/R

BOTZARIS, Sava (1894-1965) Hungarian
Sculpture
£4000 $7160 €5840 Portrait bust of George Bernard Shaw (52cm-20in) s.i. num.3/8 brown pat bronze sold with wood base prov.lit. 13-May-4 Sotheby's, London #68/R est:4000-6000

BOUBAT, Edouard (1923-) French
Photographs
£1519 $2750 €2218 Lella, Bretagne (34x26cm-13x10in) s.i.d.verso gelatin silver print 1948/printed later. 19-Apr-4 Bonhams & Butterfields, San Francisco #361/R est:2500-3500
£1693 $3200 €2472 Jardin de Luxembourg, Paris (23x35cm-9x14in) s. i.d.1955 verso gelatin silver print. 17-Feb-4 Christie's, Rockefeller NY #17/R est:2000-3000
£1695 $3000 €2475 Lella, Bretagne, France, 1947 (34x27cm-13x11in) s. s.i.d.verso gelatin silver print. 27-Apr-4 Christie's, Rockefeller NY #278/R est:3000-5000
£1799 $3400 €2627 Leila (35x24cm-14x9in) s. i.d. verso silver print. 17-Feb-4 Swann Galleries, New York #106/R est:4000-5000
£2000 $3680 €3000 Lella (37x27cm-15x11in) s. s.i.d. verso silver gelatin lit.exhib. 10-Jun-4 Villa Grisebach, Berlin #1041/R est:1500-2000

BOUCHARD, Edith Marie (1924-) Canadian
Works on paper
£240 $439 €350 Vieille maison aux portes vertes, Baie Street, Paul (42x56cm-17x22in) s. gouache prov. 1-Jun-4 Joyner Waddington, Toronto #449 (C.D 600)

BOUCHARD, Lorne Holland (1913-1978) Canadian
£203 $364 €296 Indian smokehouse, north arm of the Fraser River, Vancouver (30x45cm-12x18in) s. s.i.d.1969 verso board prov. 6-May-4 Heffel, Vancouver #37/R (C.D 500)
£207 $376 €302 Blue Vase (46x30cm-18x12in) s. s.i.d.1977 verso prov. 5-Feb-4 Heffel, Vancouver #10/R (C.D 500)
£269 $489 €393 Oka Farm (23x41cm-9x16in) s. s.i.d.1969 verso prov. 5-Feb-4 Heffel, Vancouver #12/R (C.D 650)
£340 $619 €500 Rue Sanguinard - looking north (30x40cm-12x16in) s.i.d.1965 verso board. 3-Feb-4 Christie's, Amsterdam #459
£491 $820 €712 Houses Quebec (41x51cm-16x20in) s. board. 17-Jun-3 Pinneys, Montreal #120a est:900-1200 (C.D 1100)
£491 $835 €717 Autumn, Lac Beauport, Quebec (20x25cm-8x10in) s.d.1951 i.verso panel. 6-Nov-3 Heffel, Vancouver #21/R est:700-900 (C.D 1100)
£1016 $1819 €1483 Woods in May, St Placide, Quebec (61x91cm-24x36in) s. s.i.d.1963 verso board prov. 6-May-4 Heffel, Vancouver #38/R est:3000-4000 (C.D 2500)
£1607 $2684 €2330 Early spring, Baie St. Paul, P.Q (46x61cm-18x24in) s.i.verso board prov. 17-Jun-3 Pinneys, Montreal #144 est:1500-2500 (C.D 3600)

BOUCHARD, Paul (1853-1937) French
£10000 $16700 €14600 French Moscow street scene. 21-Oct-3 Gorringes, Lewes #2102/R est:10000-15000
£42000 $75180 €61320 Winter morning on the Malaya Dmitrovka in Moscow, by the gates of Strasnoi Monastery (62x73cm-24x29in) s.i.d.1905 stretcher. 26-May-4 Sotheby's, London #91/R est:20000-30000

BOUCHARD, Pierre François (1831-1889) French
£3846 $7000 €5615 Pensive moment (112x69cm-44x27in) s. 7-Feb-4 Neal Auction Company, New Orleans #396/R est:5000-8000

BOUCHARDON, Edme (1698-1762) French
Works on paper
£1293 $2314 €1900 Hercule arme d'une massue s'appretant a passer les Alpes (22cm-9in circular) i.d.1744 red chk. 18-Mar-4 Christie's, Paris #94/R est:1000-1500
£1293 $2314 €1900 Les preliminaires de la paix signes a Vienne (22cm-9in circular) i.d. red chk. 18-Mar-4 Christie's, Paris #107/R est:700-1000
£1361 $2435 €2000 Un char attele, rempli de gerbes qui marche vers un palais (22cm-9in circular) i.d.1741 red chk. 18-Mar-4 Christie's, Paris #92/R est:1000-1500
£1905 $3410 €2800 L'instruction gratuite. Les secours envoyes a l'electeur de Baviere (22cm-9in circular) i.d. red chk pair. 18-Mar-4 Christie's, Paris #96/R est:1500-2000
£1905 $3410 €2800 La peste de Marseilles (22cm-9in circular) i.d. red chk. 18-Mar-4 Christie's, Paris #101/R est:1500-2000
£2381 $4262 €3500 Drawings of medals (22cm-9in circular) i.d. red chk three. 18-Mar-4 Christie's, Paris #97/R est:1000-1500
£2585 $4627 €3800 Drawing of a medal (22cm-9in circular) i.d.1740 red chk. 18-Mar-4 Christie's, Paris #89/R est:1000-1500
£2585 $4627 €3800 Drawings of medals (22cm-9in circular) i.d. red chk pair. 18-Mar-4 Christie's, Paris #98/R est:2000-3000
£2721 $4871 €4000 La campagne d'Italie. Une variation de la meme composition (22cm-9in circular) i.d. red chk pair. 18-Mar-4 Christie's, Paris #99/R est:2000-3000
£2721 $4871 €4000 Drawings of medals (22cm-9in circular) i.d. red chk four. 18-Mar-4 Christie's, Paris #111/R est:1200-1600
£2857 $5114 €4200 La pacification de la Corse. Le bombardement de Tripoli (22cm-9in circular) i.d. red chk pair. 18-Mar-4 Christie's, Paris #93/R est:2000-3000

£3061 $5480 €4500 La ville de Rennes rebatie. Le passage du Rhin (22cm-9in circular) i.d red chk pair. 18-Mar-4 Christie's, Paris #90/R est:3000-5000
£3265 $5845 €4800 Le congres de Soisson (22cm-9in circular) i.d. red chk. 18-Mar-4 Christie's, Paris #104/R est:2000-3000
£3946 $7063 €5800 Drawings of medals (22cm-9in circular) i.d. red chk four. 18-Mar-4 Christie's, Paris #103/R est:3000-5000
£4762 $8524 €7000 Drawings of medals (22cm-9in circular) i.d. red chk six. 18-Mar-4 Christie's, Paris #112/R est:2000-3000
£5782 $10350 €8500 La visite du roi aux academies (22cm-9in circular) i.d. red chk. 18-Mar-4 Christie's, Paris #105/R est:1500-2000
£6122 $10959 €9000 Drawings of medals (22cm-9in circular) i.d. red chk three exhib. 18-Mar-4 Christie's, Paris #91/R est:3000-5000
£6122 $10959 €9000 Drawing of a medal (22cm-9in circular) i.d. red chk. 18-Mar-4 Christie's, Paris #109/R est:2000-3000

BOUCHARDON, Edme (attrib) (1698-1762) French
Works on paper
£800 $1448 €1200 Academie d'homme nu couche (37x55cm-15x22in) sanguine. 30-Mar-4 Rossini, Paris #13
£1224 $2192 €1800 La naissance du Duc de Berry. La naissance du Duc d'Aquataine (22cm-9in circular) i.d. red chk pair. 18-Mar-4 Christie's, Paris #106/R est:800-1200
£2381 $4262 €3500 Drawings of medals (22cm-9in circular) i.d. red chk three. 18-Mar-4 Christie's, Paris #95/R est:800-1200

BOUCHAUD, Jean (1891-1977) French
£1333 $2453 €2000 Nature morte aux agrumes et au bol de Fes (37x52cm-15x20in) s. cardboard. 14-Jun-4 Gros & Delettrez, Paris #224/R est:2000-3000
Works on paper
£1067 $1931 €1600 Vue de Fez (20x13cm-8x5in) s.i.d.1922 W/C lead pencil. 1-Apr-4 Credit Municipal, Paris #38 est:400-600
£1429 $2557 €2100 Femme assise avec poule (31x29cm-12x11in) s.i.d.1933 chl dr graphite dr exhib.lit. 21-Mar-4 St-Germain-en-Laye Encheres #99/R est:1500
£2621 $4796 €3800 Odalisque (24x33cm-9x13in) s. gouache. 31-Jan-4 Gerard, Besancon #1

BOUCHE, Arnulf de (1872-1945) German
£268 $494 €400 Portrait of elegant woman (100x80cm-39x31in) s.d.18. 27-Mar-4 L & B, Essen #72/R
£479 $748 €700 Still life with porcelain figure (80x68cm-31x27in) s.d.41. 10-Apr-3 Weidler, Nurnberg #343
£573 $974 €837 Danae (45x37cm-18x15in) s. board. 5-Nov-3 Dobiaschofsky, Bern #381/R (S.FR 1300)
£667 $1207 €1000 Standing female nude in boudoir (70x60cm-28x24in) s. 3-Apr-4 Hans Stahl, Hamburg #14/R
£669 $1070 €950 Bathers (58x48cm-23x19in) s. board. 18-Sep-3 Rieber, Stuttgart #1378/R
£764 $1276 €1100 Interior with female nude (76x64cm-30x25in) s. 22-Oct-3 Neumeister, Munich #672/R
£814 $1385 €1188 Sin (55x67cm-22x26in) i. 28-Nov-3 Zofingen, Switzerland #2554/R est:1800 (S.FR 1800)
£883 $1465 €1289 Still life with dried flowers in a vase (80x71cm-31x28in) s.d.41. 15-Jun-3 Agra, Warsaw #39/R (P.Z 5500)
£1437 $2486 €2098 Nude female getting out of bed (76x64cm-30x25in) s. painted c.1930. 14-Dec-3 Agra, Warsaw #46/R est:8000 (P.Z 9500)
£1860 $3161 €2716 Erwachen 1913 (51x69cm-20x27in) s. 29-Oct-3 Lawson Menzies, Sydney #250/R est:3500-5000 (A.D 4500)
£2982 $4979 €4324 Favoritin (67x56cm-26x22in) s. s.i.d.13 verso. 23-Jun-3 Philippe Schuler, Zurich #3557/R est:3500-4000 (S.FR 6500)

BOUCHE, François (1924-) French
Works on paper
£317 $538 €463 Les coquilles d'or (66x50cm-26x20in) s.i.d.1980 mixed media exhib. 25-Nov-3 Germann, Zurich #732 (S.FR 700)

BOUCHE, Georges (1874-1941) French
£2384 $4363 €3600 Deux bouquets de fleurs (62x52cm-24x20in) s. 7-Apr-4 Doutrebente, Paris #31/R est:1000-1200

BOUCHE, Louis (1896-1969) American
£430 $800 €628 Copake farm (51x61cm-20x24in) s. 5-Mar-4 Skinner, Boston #474/R
£539 $900 €787 Copake Farm (51x61cm-20x24in) s. 23-Oct-3 Shannon's, Milford #252/R
£1087 $2000 €1587 L'essor (38x43cm-15x17in) s.d.May 1917 prov. 23-Jun-4 Doyle, New York #5087/R est:1200-1600
£2210 $4000 €3227 Myron Watkins, Postmaster (61x76cm-24x30in) 16-Apr-4 American Auctioneer #34/R est:3000-5000
£2762 $5000 €4033 Self portrait in carriage (74x91cm-29x36in) 16-Apr-4 American Auctioneer #35/R est:4000-6000

BOUCHE, Y F (?) ?
£1300 $2171 €1898 Head and shoulder portrait of a young lady (66x53cm-26x21in) s. oval. 22-Oct-3 Wingetts, Wrexham #373/R est:1000-1500

BOUCHEIX, François (1940-) French
£671 $1242 €1000 Coucher de lune (27x35cm-11x14in) s. s.i.verso cardboard. 14-Mar-4 St-Germain-en-Laye Encheres #185/R
£733 $1313 €1100 Paysage imaginaire (36x48cm-14x19in) s. panel. 16-May-4 Renault-Aubry, Pontivy #433/R

BOUCHENE, Dimitri (1893-1993) French
£767 $1388 €1150 Untitled (110x30cm-43x12in) in 4 parts. 4-Apr-4 St-Germain-en-Laye Encheres #13/R
Works on paper
£333 $603 €500 Jeune homme assis (53x41cm-21x16in) s. crayon dr. 4-Apr-4 St-Germain-en-Laye Encheres #12
£532 $888 €750 La tempete, personnage de theatre (73x51cm-29x20in) s. gouache prov. 19-Oct-3 Charbonneaux, Paris #100
£699 $1189 €1000 Ballet a Rome (60x45cm-24x18in) s. pastel. 1-Dec-3 Camard, Paris #81
£699 $1189 €1000 Model (46x62cm-18x24in) s. pastel. 1-Dec-3 Camard, Paris #82
£780 $1303 €1100 Projet de decor de theatre (73x98cm-29x39in) s. gouache prov. 19-Oct-3 Charbonneaux, Paris #99/R
£1800 $3060 €2628 View of Florence (60x48cm-24x19in) s.d.1930 pastel. 19-Nov-3 Sotheby's, London #102/R est:2000-3000
£3500 $6265 €5110 Venice (52x74cm-20x29in) s. gouache. 26-May-4 Sotheby's, Olympia #415/R est:2000-3000

BOUCHER, Alfred (1850-1934) French
£1633 $2596 €2400 Les vaches au pre (62x146cm-24x57in) s. 22-Mar-3 Dubee & Berron, Vernou en Sologne #64
Sculpture
£1563 $2688 €2282 Le terrassier (69cm-27in) s.d.1893 st.f.Barbedienne. 2-Dec-3 Ritchie, Toronto #109/R est:4000-6000 (C.D 3500)
£2222 $3844 €3244 Le terrassier (56cm-22in) bronze st.f F. Barbedienne. 9-Dec-3 Maynards, Vancouver #952 est:6000-8000 (C.D 5000)
£2800 $4760 €4088 Au buti (34cm-13in) s.st.f.Siot-Decauville pat bronze lit. 28-Oct-3 Sotheby's, London #98/R
£3056 $4981 €4400 Elfin (68cm-27in) s. brown green black pat.bronze Cast.Susse Freres. 25-Sep-3 Dr Fritz Nagel, Stuttgart #1575/R est:4400
£3500 $5950 €5110 Terrassier (68cm-27in) s.st.f.Barbedienne pat bronze. 28-Oct-3 Sotheby's, London #175/R
£4336 $7241 €6200 Baigneuse (55cm-22in) s. white marble. 25-Jun-3 Maigret, Paris #201/R est:1800-2000
£7895 $14526 €12000 Repos (90x30x30cm-35x12x12in) s. white marble. 25-Jun-4 Millon & Associes, Paris #77/R est:8000-12000
£10067 $17819 €15000 Volubilis (45cm-18in) marble prov. 30-Apr-4 Tajan, Paris #54/R est:7000-9000
£52778 $95000 €77056 Figure of a femal nude (54x44cm-21x17in) s. white marble exec.c.1900. 23-Apr-4 Christie's, Rockefeller NY #179/R est:40000-60000
£53191 $88830 €75000 Une nymphe endormie (51x39cm-20x15in) s. white marble. 17-Jun-3 Christie's, Paris #129/R est:18000-24000

BOUCHER, Alfred (after) (1850-1934) French
Sculpture
£9341 $17000 €14012 Au but (66cm-26in) i. pat bronze st.f. Siot. 16-Jun-4 Sotheby's, New York #309/R est:10000-15000

BOUCHER, F (18th C) French
£4790 $8000 €6993 Saint Peter (53x43cm-21x17in) bears sig. 7-Oct-3 Sotheby's, New York #24/R est:6000-8000

BOUCHER, François (after) (18th C) French
£5000 $8500 €7300 Diana and Callisto (83x102cm-33x40in) 29-Oct-3 Bonhams, New Bond Street #114/R est:5000-7000

BOUCHER, François (attrib) (18th C) French
£1086 $1846 €1586 Herders (30x23cm-12x9in) ochre prov. 19-Nov-3 Fischer, Luzern #2404/R est:1200-1500 (S.FR 2400)
Works on paper
£822 $1397 €1200 Couple de pecheurs (30x38cm-12x15in) crayon chk. 6-Nov-3 Tajan, Paris #50
£1056 $1690 €1500 Shepherd couple (31x32cm-12x13in) i. chk. 18-Sep-3 Rieber, Stuttgart #4465 est:1650
£2550 $4693 €3800 Nude (20x19cm-8x7in) i. chk htd white ochre prov. 26-Mar-4 Dorotheum, Vienna #59/R est:2500-3500
£4286 $6857 €6215 Two girls (27x21cm-11x8in) chl pastel ochre htd white. 15-May-3 Stuker, Bern #1092/R est:12000-16000 (S.FR 9000)
£5000 $8650 €7300 Boy tickling sleeping girl with straw, infant and cat by her feet (30x22cm-12x9in) i. col chk painted with studio sold with another prov.lit. 12-Dec-3 Christie's, Kensington #434/R est:2000-3000
£5388 $9644 €7866 Girl with flower basket (40x33cm-16x13in) mono.d.1745. 13-May-4 Stuker, Bern #46/R est:20000-25000 (S.FR 12500)

BOUCHER, François (elder) (1703-1770) French
£380000 $695400 €554800 Moulin a eau. Pigeonnier (60x74cm-24x29in) s.d.1750 pair prov.exhib.lit. 7-Jul-4 Sotheby's, London #52/R est:400000-600000
Works on paper
£710 $1300 €1037 Young shepherd and shepherdess (35x27cm-14x11in) i. red chk. 29-Jan-4 Swann Galleries, New York #218/R
£4000 $7320 €5840 Shepherds with flock by ruins (30x23cm-12x9in) i. black lead red white chk after Nicolaes Berchem. 6-Jul-4 Christie's, London #129/R est:3000-5000
£4196 $7217 €6000 Venus etendue sur un dauphin, deux colombes a ses cotes (24x37cm-9x15in) red chk prov. 2-Dec-3 Christie's, Paris #514/R est:2000-3000
£6667 $12000 €9734 Figures on the march (30x41cm-12x16in) s.i. black white chk. 21-Jan-4 Sotheby's, New York #109/R est:15000-20000
£21233 $36097 €31000 Jeune homme chatouillant jeune fille assoupie (30x23cm-12x9in) crayon pastel prov.lit. 6-Nov-3 Tajan, Paris #54/R
£32000 $58560 €46720 Daphnis and Chole, shepherd with a sleeping shepherdess, and his flock (24x28cm-9x11in) s. red chk prov.lit. 6-Jul-4 Christie's, London #128/R est:20000-30000
£34000 $60860 €49640 Young village girl with two cupids all holding roses (33x23cm-13x9in) s. blk white chks touches pastel. 7-May-4 Mallams, Oxford #187/R est:1000-1500

BOUCHER, François (elder-attrib) (1703-1770) French
Works on paper
£1399 $2406 €2000 Amour tenant une pomme (24x18cm-9x7in) crayon. 8-Dec-3 Rossini, Paris #27/R est:2000-2500

BOUCHER, François (school) (18th C) French
£19858 $33163 €28000 Pomona and Vertumnus (115x135cm-45x53in) i. 23-Jun-3 Finarte Semenzato, Rome #165/R

BOUCHER, François (studio) (18th C) French
£5674 $9476 €8000 Jeune berger et bergere endormie (81x100cm-32x39in) 17-Oct-3 Tajan, Paris #108/R est:10000-12000

BOUCHER, François (style) (18th C) French
£19444 $35000 €28388 Abduction of Europa (90x143cm-35x56in) 23-Jan-4 Christie's, Rockefeller NY #173/R est:10000-15000

BOUCHER, Jean (1870-1939) French
Sculpture
£1799 $2950 €2500 La mere (34x40x24cm-13x16x9in) s.i.d.1919 marble. 3-Jun-3 Livinec, Gaudcheau & Jezequel, Rennes #109/R

BOUCHERVILLE, Adrien de (?-1912) French
£2000 $3680 €3000 Misere (163x88cm-64x35in) s.d.1882 lit. 8-Jun-4 Livinec, Gaudcheau & Jezequel, Rennes #156/R

BOUCHERY, Anna (19/20th C) French
£385 $662 €550 Nature morte a la cruche et aux legumes (61x77cm-24x30in) s.d.1906. 2-Dec-3 Campo & Campo, Antwerp #44

BOUCHET, Auguste (?-1937) French
£2013 $3725 €3000 Le depart de la mariee, Algerie (41x27cm-16x11in) s.d.1877. 15-Mar-4 Gros & Delettrez, Paris #60/R est:3000-3500

BOUCHET, Christophe Emmanuel (1959-) French
£552 $1010 €800 Last summer evening on Sylt (150x100cm-59x39in) s. s.i.d.89 verso acrylic. 30-Jan-4 Altus, Berlin #622/R

BOUCHET, Jean (20th C) French
Works on paper
£302 $556 €450 Vue d'une falaise (50x50cm-20x20in) s.d.1982 mixed media canvas. 24-Mar-4 Binoche, Paris #115

BOUCHEZ, Charles (1811-?) French
£1400 $2618 €2044 Coastal scene with fisherman and his family seated beside a basket (40x52cm-16x20in) s. panel. 22-Jul-4 Tennants, Leyburn #807 est:1500-2000

BOUCHOR, Joseph Felix (1853-1937) French
£554 $992 €809 Landscape with women by fire (15x23cm-6x9in) s.d.1890 panel. 26-May-4 AB Stockholms Auktionsverk #2378/R (S.KR 7500)
£1197 $2095 €1700 Gardienne de moutons en bord de mer (46x55cm-18x22in) s. 21-Dec-3 Thierry & Lannon, Brest #144/R est:1500-2000
£2746 $4751 €3900 Bords du Bosphore. s.i.d.1893. 15-Dec-3 Gros & Delettrez, Paris #259/R est:3000-4000
£3873 $6701 €5500 La rue des teinturiers a Marrakech (33x46cm-13x18in) s. 12-Dec-3 Piasa, Paris #81/R est:2000-3000

BOUCLE, Pierre (1610-1673) Flemish
£6000 $10800 €8760 Bantams surprised by a fox (52x63cm-20x25in) init. indis d. 20-Apr-4 Sotheby's, Olympia #301/R est:4000-6000

BOUCLE, Pierre (attrib) (1610-1673) Flemish
£3662 $6409 €5200 Nature morte aux fraises, groseilles et noix (38x52cm-15x20in) 18-Dec-3 Tajan, Paris #97/R est:4000-6000

BOUDET, Pierre (1925-) French
£403 $749 €600 Nature morte au bouquet de roses (27x22cm-11x9in) s. isorel. 7-Mar-4 Lesieur & Le Bars, Le Havre #15
£600 $1092 €900 Place animee (41x33cm-16x13in) s. panel. 4-Jul-4 Eric Pillon, Calais #236/R
£759 $1267 €1100 Honfleur (38x46cm-15x18in) s. 11-Nov-3 Lesieur & Le Bars, Le Havre #8
£940 $1738 €1400 Honfleur, le Quai Saint-Etienne (38x46cm-15x18in) s. s.i.d.1971 verso isorel. 15-Mar-4 Blanchet, Paris #153/R
£5616 $8818 €8200 Honfleur (60x73cm-24x29in) s. 20-Apr-3 Deauville, France #157/R est:5000-6000

BOUDEWYNS, Adriaen Frans (1644-1711) Flemish
£2308 $3969 €3370 Harbour scene (19x22cm-7x9in) 3-Dec-3 AB Stockholms Auktionsverk #2676/R est:18000-20000 (S.KR 30000)
£3311 $6026 €5000 Peasants and cattle outside an abbey (28x45cm-11x18in) 16-Jun-4 Dorotheum, Vienna #106/R est:4000-6000
£3642 $6629 €5500 Mountainous river landscape with castle and shepherd and his flock (18x24cm-7x9in) i. panel prov. 16-Jun-4 Dorotheum, Vienna #103/R est:3000-5000
£8904 $15137 €13000 Italianate harbour with elegant figures (29x42cm-11x17in) mono. 5-Nov-3 Christie's, Amsterdam #7/R est:7000-10000
Works on paper
£524 $902 €750 Paysage italien (36x22cm-14x9in) sanguine. 7-Dec-3 Livinec, Gaudcheau & Jezequel, Rennes #101/R
£1156 $2070 €1700 Une vue de Tivoli avec le temple de Vesta, des figures au premier plan (23x33cm-9x13in) red chk prov. 18-Mar-4 Christie's, Paris #29/R est:1500-2000

BOUDEWYNS, Adriaen Frans and BOUT, Pieter (17/18th C) Flemish
£5674 $9476 €8000 Paysans sur un chemin pres d'une riviere (27x36cm-11x14in) panel. 17-Oct-3 Tajan, Paris #63/R est:8000-12000
£6897 $12690 €10070 Church in the country (30x42cm-12x17in) prov.lit. 26-Mar-4 Koller, Zurich #3045/R est:16000-22000 (S.FR 16000)

BOUDIN (1824-1898) French
Works on paper
£280 $496 €409 Seated nude (19x11cm-7x4in) s. black chk. 27-Apr-4 Henry Adams, Chichester #570

BOUDIN, Eugène (1824-1898) French
£1656 $3030 €2500 Rade de Brest, Baie de Camfrout, quai des Kerhors (30x47cm-12x19in) s. prov.exhib. 7-Apr-4 Piasa, Paris #38/R est:28000-30000
£2282 $4244 €3400 Vaches au pre (11x17cm-4x7in) s. panel. 7-Mar-4 Lesieur & Le Bars, Le Havre #17
£2857 $4571 €4143 Seascape (22x15cm-9x6in) s. panel. 15-May-3 Stuker, Bern #1094/R est:8000-12000 (S.FR 6000)
£4333 $7930 €6500 Vaches en Normandie (27x46cm-11x18in) s. panel. 6-Jun-4 Osenat, Fontainebleau #205/R est:6000-7000
£4846 $8238 €7075 Still life of flowers (32x23cm-13x9in) s. 5-Nov-3 Dobiaschofsky, Bern #383/R est:9000 (S.FR 11000)
£5674 $9475 €8000 Coucher de soleil (12x15cm-5x6in) studio st. oil crayon paper prov. 17-Oct-3 Renaud, Paris #2/R est:3000-4000
£7801 $13028 €11000 Etude de ciel au crepuscule (12x14cm-5x6in) studio st. paper prov. 17-Oct-3 Renaud, Paris #1/R est:3000-4000
£10000 $18400 €14600 Etude de marguerites (32x23cm-13x9in) s. cradled panel painted c.1860-65 prov.lit. 22-Jun-4 Sotheby's, London #218/R est:12000-15000
£10604 $19617 €15800 Vaches en bord de riviere (23x32cm-9x13in) s. panel lit. 14-Mar-4 Eric Pillon, Calais #45/R
£10615 $19000 €15498 Vaches a la paturage (32x46cm-13x18in) s. painted c.1880-85 prov.exhib.lit. 6-May-4 Sotheby's, New York #230/R est:20000-30000
£12000 $21840 €17520 Paysage (21x34cm-8x13in) init. board on panel painted c.1888-98 prov.lit. 4-Feb-4 Sotheby's, London #205/R est:12000-18000
£13966 $25000 €20390 Cour de ferme en Normandie (28x37cm-11x15in) s. panel painted c.1857-1860 prov.lit. 6-May-4 Sotheby's, New York #213/R est:20000-30000
£14110 $23000 €20601 Nature morte aux legumes et aux poissons (70x90cm-28x35in) s. canvas on board prov.exhib.lit. 25-Sep-3 Christie's, Rockefeller NY #528/R est:25000-35000
£14931 $24934 €21500 Cour de ferme en Normandie. s. panel painted c.1857-1860 prov.lit. 23-Oct-3 Credit Municipal, Paris #66/R est:10000-12000
£19022 $35000 €27772 Port de Trouville (38x48cm-15x19in) s.d.1891. 26-Jun-4 Selkirks, St. Louis #427/R est:40000-60000
£19048 $34095 €28000 Trois bateaux de pecheurs (20x28cm-8x11in) st.mono. peinture a l'essence. 19-Mar-4 Piasa, Paris #143/R est:10000
£19580 $33287 €28000 Bateaux a maree basse (23x32cm-9x13in) s.d.72 panel. 30-Nov-3 Anaf, Lyon #27/R est:25000-30000
£21088 $37748 €31000 Barques par temps gris, environ de Trouville (17x22cm-7x9in) s. panel prov.lit. 19-Mar-4 Millon & Associes, Paris #44/R est:20000-22000
£23464 $42000 €34257 Embouchure de l'Elorn aux environs de Brest (55x89cm-22x35in) s.d.72 prov.exhib.lit. 5-May-4 Christie's, Rockefeller NY #230/R est:50000-70000
£24832 $44450 €37000 Bateau de peche a maree basse (26x21cm-10x8in) s. panel prov.lit. 25-May-4 Chambelland & Giafferi, Paris #60/R est:12000-15000
£25000 $45500 €36500 Bassin de Deauville (32x23cm-13x9in) st.sig. panel painted c.1892-1896 prov.exhib. 3-Feb-4 Christie's, London #138/R est:25000-35000
£27465 $44218 €39000 Trouville (24x19cm-9x7in) s. panel prov.exhib.lit. 22-Aug-3 Deauville, France #49/R est:45000-50000
£28000 $50960 €42000 Deauville, le bassin (23x33cm-9x13in) s.d.84 panel prov.lit. 29-Jun-4 Sotheby's, Paris #2/R est:40000-60000
£28562 $44842 €41700 Marche au Faou (18x24cm-7x9in) s. panel lit. 20-Apr-3 Deauville, France #94/R est:40000-50000
£32000 $58240 €46720 La baie et les montagnes de l'Esterel, Golfe-Juan (26x41cm-10x16in) s.d.93 panel painted 1893 prov.exhib.lit. 3-Feb-4 Christie's, London #132/R est:30000-40000
£33000 $60720 €48180 Trouville - Les Jetees - Maree Basse (35x26cm-14x10in) s.d.97 cradled panel prov.lit. 22-Jun-4 Sotheby's, London #117/R est:35000-45000
£33557 $60067 €50000 Coin de bassin a Deauville (32x23cm-13x9in) s.d.95 panel. 26-May-4 Christie's, Paris #17/R est:35000-45000
£35000 $63700 €51100 Environs d'Antibes (20x29cm-8x11in) s.i.d.93 prov.exhib.lit. 3-Feb-4 Christie's, London #109/R est:35000-45000
£35000 $64400 €51100 Madame S et ses enfants dans son jardin a Trouville (34x27cm-13x11in) init.d.11 aout 73 prov.lit. 23-Jun-4 Christie's, London #115/R est:40000-60000
£36014 $61944 €51500 Trouville, le port (27x21cm-11x8in) s.d.97 panel lit. 5-Dec-3 Gros & Delettrez, Paris #84/R est:23000-30000
£36313 $65000 €53017 Portrieux, le Port Maree Basse (23x32cm-9x13in) s.d.73 panel prov.lit. 6-May-4 Sotheby's, New York #214/R est:40000-60000
£38235 $65000 €55823 Laveuses au bord de la Touques (22x33cm-9x13in) s. panel painted c.1885-1890 prov.lit. 5-Nov-3 Christie's, Rockefeller NY #201/R est:70000-90000
£40000 $72800 €58400 Le bassin, Deauville (26x35cm-10x14in) s. panel painted c.1888-1895 prov.exhib.lit. 3-Feb-4 Christie's, London #103/R est:40000-60000
£41612 $73652 €62000 Fecamp, le bassin (26x35cm-10x14in) s. panel prov.lit. 30-Apr-4 Tajan, Paris #150/R est:20000-30000
£41899 $75000 €61173 Bourg de Batz, les rochers (50x74cm-20x29in) st.sig. painted c.1895-1897 prov.lit. 5-May-4 Christie's, Rockefeller NY #212/R est:60000-80000
£43296 $77500 €63212 Quillebeuf - l'Eglise vue du canal (42x55cm-17x22in) s.d.93 prov.exhib.lit. 6-May-4 Sotheby's, New York #224/R est:80000-120000
£44693 $80000 €65252 Trouville, le port (69x51cm-27x20in) s.d.90 prov.exhib.lit. 6-May-4 Sotheby's, New York #206/R est:80000-120000
£45882 $78000 €66988 Etretat, Bateaux depeche et pecheurs sur la plage (40x55cm-16x22in) s.i.d.90 prov.exhib.lit. 5-Nov-3 Christie's, Rockefeller NY #211/R est:50000-70000
£46897 $78319 €68000 Laveuses au bord de la Touques (19x32cm-7x13in) s.d.86 panel prov.exhib.lit. 17-Nov-3 Tajan, Paris #78/R est:55000-65000
£56338 $93521 €80000 Trouville, le port pendant la construction des quais (35x58cm-14x23in) s. painted c.1880-85. 13-Jun-3 Renaud, Paris #43/R est:53000-60000
£58824 $100000 €85883 Anvers, Le port (29x44cm-11x17in) s.i. panel painted c.1871-1874 prov.lit. 5-Nov-3 Christie's, Rockefeller NY #205/R est:70000-90000
£59859 $104754 €85000 Douarnenez (56x90cm-22x35in) s. i.on stretcher prov.lit. 16-Dec-3 Segre, Madrid #95/R est:69000
£70000 $128800 €102200 Berck, arrivee des barques de peche (54x74cm-21x29in) s.d.82 prov.exhib.lit. 22-Jun-4 Christie's, London #15/R est:70000-100000
£70000 $128800 €102200 Laveuses sur un des bras de la Touques (32x46cm-13x18in) s.d.66 prov.lit. 22-Jun-4 Sotheby's, London #118/R est:40000-60000
£70000 $127400 €105000 Le Havre, bassin de la Barre (37x55cm-15x22in) s.i.d.95 panel prov.lit. 29-Jun-4 Sotheby's, Paris #3/R est:100000-150000
£82667 $149627 €124000 Portrieux, bateaux dans le port (36x59cm-14x23in) s.i.d.73 prov.exhib. 5-Apr-4 Deburaux, Boulogne #80/R est:55000-61000
£95000 $174800 €138700 Maree basse, Saint-Vaast-La-Hougue (50x74cm-20x29in) s.d.92 prov.lit. 23-Jun-4 Christie's, London #109/R est:50000-80000
£100000 $170000 €146000 Bateaux de peche (42x56cm-17x22in) s.d.87 prov.exhib.lit. 6-Nov-3 Sotheby's, New York #103/R est:100000-150000
£105882 $180000 €154588 Port de Trouville, Maree Haute (32x41cm-13x16in) s.d.80 cradled panel prov.exhib.lit. 6-Nov-3 Sotheby's, New York #116/R est:180000-250000
£110000 $202400 €160600 Rouen, vue prise du Cours de la Reine (46x65cm-18x26in) s.d.95 prov.exhib.lit. 22-Jun-4 Christie's, London #11/R est:120000-180000
£119205 $216954 €180000 Le Havre, le bassin de l'Eure (55x89cm-22x35in) s.d.72 prov.exhib. 18-Jun-4 Piasa, Paris #11/R est:140000-180000

£122905	$220000	€179441	Le Havre, bassin de l'Eure (54x74cm-21x29in) s. painted 1881 prov.lit. 5-May-4 Christie's, Rockefeller NY #201/R est:150000-200000
£150000	$274500	€219000	Parc Cordier a Trouville (51x62cm-20x24in) s. painted c.1880-85 prov.lit. 2-Feb-4 Christie's, London #6/R est:120000-160000
£170000	$312800	€248200	Trouville scene de plage (22x32cm-9x13in) s.i.d.75 panel prov.lit. 22-Jun-4 Christie's, London #9/R est:200000-300000
£223464	$400000	€326257	Trouville, scene de plage (19x32cm-7x13in) s.i.d.1887 panel prov.exhib.lit. 4-May-4 Christie's, Rockefeller NY #5/R est:400000-600000
£234637	$420000	€342570	Trouville, scene de plage (19x32cm-7x13in) s.i.d.86 panel prov.exhib.lit. 4-May-4 Christie's, Rockefeller NY #1/R est:400000-600000
£235294	$400000	€343529	Trouville scene de plage (20x33cm-8x13in) s.i.d.80 panel prov.exhib.lit. 4-Nov-3 Christie's, Rockefeller NY #2/R est:350000-450000
£280000	$512400	€408800	Scene de plage a Trouville (15x35cm-6x14in) s.d.1875 panel prov.exhib.lit. 2-Feb-4 Christie's, London #2/R est:280000-320000
£470000	$864800	€686200	Venice, Grand Canal (56x91cm-22x36in) s.d.95 prov. 22-Jun-4 Christie's, London #2/R est:200000-300000
£620000	$1128400	€905200	Scene de plage a Trouville (29x48cm-11x19in) s.i. panel prov.lit. 3-Feb-4 Sotheby's, London #31/R est:600000-800000

Prints

£313	$522	€450	Marine (12x16cm-5x6in) etching. 24-Oct-3 Ketterer, Hamburg #136/R

Works on paper

£472	$750	€689	Sailing vessels at sea (11x15cm-4x6in) init. pencil wash. 13-Sep-3 Weschler, Washington #677/R
£563	$975	€800	Etude de vache (12x18cm-5x7in) st.mono. black crayon W/C. 12-Dec-3 Renaud, Paris #59
£1103	$1842	€1600	Etude de pecheurs (10x15cm-4x6in) bears st.init. black crayon estompe two in one frame. 17-Nov-3 Tajan, Paris #75 est:1000-1200
£1745	$3246	€2600	La conversation pres des barques (10x16cm-4x6in) st.init. graphite. 7-Mar-4 Lesieur & Le Bars, Le Havre #16
£1748	$2972	€2500	Les voiliers. wash W/C two in one frame. 28-Nov-3 Blanchet, Paris #43/R est:2500-3000
£1748	$2972	€2500	Sur la plage (7x12cm-3x5in) d.1879 grey crayon W/C. 28-Nov-3 Blanchet, Paris #44 est:2500-3000
£1905	$3410	€2800	Famille de paysans dans un interieur (13x21cm-5x8in) mono.i. black pencil W/C grey wash htd gouache. 19-Mar-4 Piasa, Paris #148/R est:2000
£2000	$3680	€3000	Marche (11x19cm-4x7in) st.init. W/C lead pencil. 9-Jun-4 Le Roux & Morel, Paris #18 est:2500-3000
£2397	$3764	€3500	Vue de Bretagne (12x16cm-5x6in) st.sig. W/C. 20-Apr-3 Deauville, France #95/R est:4200-4800
£3000	$4770	€4350	Les jeunes pecheurs (8x11cm-3x4in) init. pencil set of three in one frame. 11-Sep-3 Christie's, Kensington #3/R est:1500-2000
£3243	$6000	€4735	Personnages sur la plage (13x22cm-5x9in) W/C pencil prov. 11-Feb-4 Sotheby's, New York #6/R est:10000-15000
£3265	$5845	€4800	Etudes de personnages (9x9cm-4x4in) two bear st.mono. black crayon W/C three in one frame. 19-Mar-4 Piasa, Paris #141/R est:4500
£3356	$6007	€5000	Femmes a la plage (13x26cm-5x10in) init. pastel prov. 26-May-4 Christie's, Paris #4/R est:4000-6000
£3946	$7063	€5800	Deux paysannes et leurs enfants dans un interieur (21x26cm-8x10in) st.mono. W/C gouache black pencil. 19-Mar-4 Piasa, Paris #149/R est:4000-5000
£4500	$8145	€6570	Paturage aux moutons, cote Normande (15x22cm-6x9in) s. pastel exec.c.1862-1866. 1-Apr-4 Christie's, Kensington #11/R est:4000-6000
£5173	$8638	€7500	Crinolines sur la plage (11x15cm-4x6in) bears st.mono.d.1869 graphite Indian ink wash W/C prov.exhib. 17-Nov-3 Tajan, Paris #73/R est:8000-10000
£5333	$9813	€8000	Plougastel, le bac (12x20cm-5x8in) st.init. W/C lead pencil. 9-Jun-4 Le Roux & Morel, Paris #19/R est:8000-10000
£5405	$9514	€8000	Fishing boats on the beach at Scheveningen (22x32cm-9x13in) s.i.d.76 W/C black chk prov.exhib.lit. 19-May-4 Sotheby's, Amsterdam #362/R est:4000-6000
£6000	$11040	€8760	Foire a Plougastel (21x26cm-8x10in) s.i. W/C over pencil exhib. 22-Jun-4 Sotheby's, London #409/R est:7000-9000
£7000	$11130	€10150	Paturage en bord de Touques (19x29cm-7x11in) s.d.62 pastel prov. 11-Sep-3 Christie's, Kensington #1/R est:5000-7000
£7362	$12000	€10749	La Greve, environs de Honfleur (27x40cm-11x16in) s. pastel paper on board prov.exhib. 25-Sep-3 Christie's, Rockefeller NY #502/R est:10000-15000
£10000	$18400	€14600	Greve, environs de Honfleur (26x40cm-10x16in) s. pastel buff paper prov.exhib. 24-Jun-4 Christie's, London #309/R est:12000-15000
£13000	$20670	€18850	Etude de ciel (17x22cm-7x9in) init. chk. 11-Sep-3 Christie's, Kensington #4/R est:5000-7000
£14000	$23380	€20440	Lavandieres dans le port de Honfleur (17x22cm-7x9in) s. col pastel executed c.1860-65 prov. 21-Oct-3 Sotheby's, London #15/R est:8000-12000
£17000	$30940	€24820	Femmes assises sur la falaise (11x25cm-4x10in) s. W/C over black red crayon. 4-Feb-4 Sotheby's, London #403/R est:7000-10000
£78231	$140034	€115000	Silhouettes aux ombrelles sur la plage de Trouville par vent fort (24x39cm-9x15in) mono. pastel. 19-Mar-4 Piasa, Paris #140/R est:25000-30000

BOUDIN, Eugène (attrib) (1824-1898) French

£2000	$3620	€3000	Extensive southern landscape with cypresses (25x37cm-10x15in) s. panel. 1-Apr-4 Van Ham, Cologne #1300/R est:3300
£3261	$6000	€4761	Seaside village (25x41cm-10x16in) bears sig.d.73. 26-Jun-4 Selkirks, St. Louis #426/R est:3000-5000

BOUDON, Marcel (20th C) French

£350	$584	€500	Saint-Guenole, Finistere (33x46cm-13x18in) s. cardboard. 30-Jun-3 Ansorena, Madrid #266/R

BOUDON, Patrick (1944-) French

£610	$1091	€891	Composition (65x54cm-26x21in) s. acrylic. 4-May-4 Ritchie, Toronto #87/R est:1000-1500 (C.D 1500)
£1678	$2887	€2400	Faces (65x80cm-26x31in) s. 4-Dec-3 Van Ham, Cologne #55/R est:2500

BOUDOT, Léon (1851-1930) French

£800	$1456	€1200	Fisherman by river (62x110cm-24x43in) s. canvas on panel. 30-Jun-4 Neumeister, Munich #510/R

BOUDRY, Alois (1851-1938) Belgian

£294	$505	€420	Pecheur de Coxyde (21x15cm-8x6in) s. panel. 2-Dec-3 Campo & Campo, Antwerp #45
£541	$951	€800	Portrait of young woman with lace headgear (41x36cm-16x14in) s. 24-May-4 Bernaerts, Antwerp #695/R
£733	$1327	€1100	Pecheurs au ruisseau (51x90cm-20x35in) s. 30-Mar-4 Campo & Campo, Antwerp #18
£1000	$1810	€1500	Jeune homme avec une maquette de bateau (5x36cm-2x14in) s. 30-Mar-4 Campo & Campo, Antwerp #17 est:1000-1250
£1538	$2646	€2200	Interieur aux fleurs et a la jeune fille (44x30cm-17x12in) s. 2-Dec-3 Campo & Campo, Antwerp #46/R est:750-1000

BOUDRY, Pol (1914-1976) Belgian

£556	$883	€800	Fortuna Mazzarella/Anacapri (82x50cm-32x20in) s. 15-Sep-3 Bernaerts, Antwerp #192/R

BOUDRY, Robert (1878-1965) Belgian

£352	$609	€500	Still life with lemons and anemones (58x58cm-23x23in) s. panel. 15-Dec-3 Bernaerts, Antwerp #241

BOUEFF, Pierre le (19th C) French

Works on paper

£260	$442	€380	Chatres, continental street scene with figures, horse and cart (37x54cm-15x21in) s. pencil W/C. 19-Nov-3 Tennants, Leyburn #900a/R

BOUET, Max (20th C) French

Works on paper

£423	$731	€600	Souk el Trouk, Tunis (18x23cm-7x9in) s. W/C. 15-Dec-3 Gros & Delettrez, Paris #100/R
£423	$731	€600	Entree du Cafe du Marabout, Tunis (31x20cm-12x8in) s. W/C. 15-Dec-3 Gros & Delettrez, Paris #98/R

BOUGH, Sam (1822-1878) British

£350	$585	€511	Extensive lake landscape (28x43cm-11x17in) 17-Oct-3 Keys, Aylsham #755
£400	$656	€584	Scottish loch with sailing vessels and figures in the water (32x53cm-13x21in) s. 30-May-3 Bigwood, Stratford on Avon #285/R
£400	$732	€584	Ullswater (24x16cm-9x6in) s. board. 7-Jun-4 Cumbria Auction Rooms, Carlisle #245/R
£520	$853	€759	Vessels moored at low tide with various figures tending to the catch (26x29cm-10x11in) s. panel. 30-May-3 Bigwood, Stratford on Avon #293/R
£600	$1092	€876	Woman and her dog approaching a cottage in the snow (23x32cm-9x13in) s. millboard. 29-Jun-4 Anderson & Garland, Newcastle #487/R
£1000	$1570	€1450	End of the day (28x38cm-11x15in) s.d.1852. 27-Aug-3 Sotheby's, London #938/R est:1500-2000
£1050	$1806	€1533	After the storm (25x30cm-10x12in) s. 4-Dec-3 Bonhams, Edinburgh #35/R est:1500-2000
£1100	$2035	€1606	Sweetheart Abbey (21x31cm-8x12in) s.d.1854 panel. 14-Jul-4 Christie's, Kensington #834/R est:700-1000
£2000	$3460	€2920	Rob Roy crossing the ford at Aberfoyle (32x48cm-13x19in) grisaille sold with an engraving of William Forrest. 11-Dec-3 Lyon & Turnbull, Edinburgh #88/R est:2000-3000
£2027	$3446	€2959	Fishing by the weir (55x80cm-22x31in) s. 21-Nov-3 Walker's, Ottawa #242/R est:5000-7000 (C.D 4500)
£2200	$4048	€3212	Study of a butter burr and a pollarded willow (31x41cm-12x16in) prov. 11-Jun-4 Christie's, London #133/R est:800-1200
£2600	$4758	€3796	Harbour scenes, early morning, Morrison's haven. Sunset (19x11cm-7x4in) s. panel. 7-Jun-4 Cumbria Auction Rooms, Carlisle #253/R est:1200-1800
£2700	$4347	€3915	Culzean Castle, Aryshire, moonlight (24x37cm-9x15in) s.d.65 board. 21-Aug-3 Bonhams, Edinburgh #1075/R est:2000-3000
£3800	$6118	€5510	Landing the catch, Fife Coast (42x30cm-17x12in) s. bears d.1859 prov. 21-Aug-3 Bonhams, Edinburgh #1196/R est:1500-2000
£28000	$43960	€40600	Gaggle of geese (91x152cm-36x60in) s.d.1856. 27-Aug-3 Sotheby's, London #918/R est:25000-35000
£42000	$75180	€61320	Cadzow Forest (101x152cm-40x60in) s.i.d.52. 28-May-4 Lyon & Turnbull, Edinburgh #92/R est:40000-60000

Works on paper

£300	$477	€438	Fishing boat and figures on the sands (25x36cm-10x14in) s. W/C. 12-Sep-3 Gardiner & Houlgate, Bath #35/R
£320	$534	€467	Figures on Scottish coast (18x26cm-7x10in) s.d.1861 W/C. 16-Oct-3 Lawrence, Crewkerne #642
£320	$586	€467	Man and his dog in bracken (22x32cm-9x13in) s. W/C. 29-Jan-4 Bonhams, Edinburgh #330
£600	$1032	€876	Dalmeny (23x34cm-9x13in) s.d.1877 s.i.verso pencil W/C bodycol. 3-Dec-3 Christie's, Kensington #118/R
£700	$1295	€1022	River landscape with cattle (36x51cm-14x20in) s.d.1876 W/C. 14-Jul-4 Sotheby's, Olympia #88/R
£1000	$1610	€1450	Melrose Abbey (29x46cm-11x18in) s.d.1861 W/C. 21-Aug-3 Bonhams, Edinburgh #1082/R est:800-1200
£1000	$1830	€1460	Dunkerque (26x36cm-10x14in) s.i.d.1867 W/C. 8-Apr-4 Bonhams, Edinburgh #89 est:1000-1500
£1000	$1790	€1460	View in Cumberland (27x42cm-11x17in) s.i.d.1861 pencil W/C htd bodycol prov. 26-May-4 Sotheby's, Olympia #209/R est:1000-1500
£1300	$2236	€1898	View of the river Eden, near Carlisle (36x51cm-14x20in) s.i.d.1869 pencil W/C. 3-Dec-3 Christie's, Kensington #116/R est:800-1200
£1400	$2254	€2030	Salmon weir (24x34cm-9x13in) s. W/C htd white. 21-Aug-3 Bonhams, Edinburgh #1023/R est:1000-1500
£2300	$3703	€3335	Clyde at Glasgow (31x50cm-12x20in) s.d.1852 W/C gouache. 21-Aug-3 Bonhams, Edinburgh #1079/R est:1200-1800
£2400	$4128	€3504	Storm at St Monan's Fife (44x60cm-17x24in) s.d.1867 W/C htd white buff paper prov. 4-Dec-3 Bonhams, Edinburgh #20/R est:1000-1500
£2700	$4833	€3942	Extensive view of Edinburgh from Calton Hill (30x41cm-12x16in) W/C prov. 26-May-4 Sotheby's, Olympia #207/R est:2500-3500
£3800	$6878	€5548	Cramond Ferry, near Edinburgh (25x35cm-10x14in) i.verso W/C. 19-Apr-4 Sotheby's, London #18/R est:1500-2000
£4000	$6280	€5800	Madame Sacque, the artist's favourite dog (42x57cm-17x22in) s.d.1864 W/C prov. 27-Aug-3 Sotheby's, London #939/R est:2000-3000
£4800	$8160	€7008	March of the avenging army (28x38cm-11x15in) d.1861 W/C bodycol wash. 24-Nov-3 Tiffin King & Nicholson, Carlisle #203/R est:4000-6000

BOUGH, Sam (attrib) (1822-1878) British

£360	$644	€526	Highland cattle (54x38cm-21x15in) 17-Mar-4 James Thompson, Kirby Lonsdale #60
£375	$638	€548	On the Solway, fishing boats at anchor, figures nearby (21x25cm-8x10in) i. 27-Nov-3 Morphets, Harrogate #415/R

BOUGH, Sam and FRASER, Alexander (jnr) (19th C) British
£1250 $2150 €1825 Crypt, Glasgow Cathedral (45x75cm-18x30in) s. indis.d. 4-Dec-3 Bonhams, Edinburgh #8/R est:1000-1500

BOUGHEY, Arthur (20th C) British
£1000 $1630 €1460 Captain Laurence Edward Grace Oates in the Antarctic (54x30cm-21x12in) s. board. 24-Sep-3 Christie's, London #352/R

BOUGHTON, George Henry (1833-1905) American/British
£1075 $2000 €1570 Woman on skates (26x17cm-10x7in) s. board prov. 3-Mar-4 Christie's, Rockefeller NY #12/R est:3000-5000

BOUGUEREAU, William Adolphe (1825-1905) French
£924 $1700 €1349 Portrait of a girl (33x25cm-13x10in) s.i.d.1900 pencil drawing htd white chk. 26-Jun-4 Sloans & Kenyon, Bethesda #1070/R est:1200-1800
£3971 $6750 €5798 Feminine figure attended by cherubs - Reve D'amour (300x180cm-118x71in) s. or possibly painted by studio. 11-Nov-3 Lincoln, Orange #424
£4444 $8000 €6488 Etude de tete d'Augustine (42x34cm-17x13in) prov. 22-Apr-4 Christie's, Rockefeller NY #132/R est:8000-12000
£6579 $12105 €10000 Etude de tete de femme brune (46x38cm-18x15in) 24-Jun-4 Christie's, Paris #155/R est:7000-10000
£8333 $15000 €12166 Etude pour la fille du pecheur (32x21cm-13x8in) painted c.1882 prov. 22-Apr-4 Christie's, Rockefeller NY #131/R est:8000-12000
£8553 $15737 €13000 Etude de tete de femme brune (46x38cm-18x15in) 24-Jun-4 Christie's, Paris #154/R est:7000-10000
£9412 $16000 €13742 Jeunne femme et enfant (19x16cm-7x6in) paper. 29-Oct-3 Christie's, Rockefeller NY #131/R est:12000-16000
£11842 $21789 €18000 Etude de tete de femme blonde de profil (46x38cm-18x15in) 24-Jun-4 Christie's, Paris #156/R est:7000-10000
£36111 $65000 €52722 Italienne au tambourin (64x54cm-25x21in) s. prov.exhib.lit. 23-Apr-4 Sotheby's, New York #54/R est:80000-120000
£46053 $84737 €70000 Etude de tete de femme blonde (46x38cm-18x15in) 24-Jun-4 Christie's, Paris #157/R est:7000-10000
£91176 $155000 €133117 Bather (64x41cm-25x16in) s.d.1879 prov.exhib.lit. 28-Oct-3 Sotheby's, New York #43/R est:200000-300000
£294118 $500000 €429412 Gue (160x74cm-63x29in) s.d.1895 prov.lit. 28-Oct-3 Sotheby's, New York #36/R est:500000-700000
£300000 $516000 €438000 La vague (117x157cm-46x62in) s.d.1896 prov.exhib.lit. 3-Dec-3 Christie's, London #39/R est:400000-600000
£323529 $550000 €472352 Canephore (244x176cm-96x69in) s. prov.lit. 28-Oct-3 Sotheby's, New York #48/R est:300000-500000
£344444 $620000 €502888 La tricoteuse (91x61cm-36x24in) s.d.1891 prov. 22-Apr-4 Christie's, Rockefeller NY #128/R est:400000-600000
£361111 $650000 €527222 Bohemian (124x150cm-49x59in) s.d.1890 prov.lit. 22-Apr-4 Christie's, Rockefeller NY #133/R est:700000-900000
£370588 $630000 €541058 Baiser (114x86cm-45x34in) s.d.1863 prov.lit. 28-Oct-3 Sotheby's, New York #38/R est:400000-600000
£382353 $650000 €558235 La petite tricoteuse (115x81cm-45x32in) s.d.1875 prov.lit. 29-Oct-3 Christie's, Rockefeller NY #132/R est:650000-950000
£494118 $840000 €721412 Dejeuner du matin (91x56cm-36x22in) s.d.1887 prov.lit. 28-Oct-3 Sotheby's, New York #33/R est:300000-400000
Sculpture
£1667 $2717 €2400 L'amour vaninqueur. s. lit. bronze. 24-Sep-3 Neumeister, Munich #183/R est:500
Works on paper
£10000 $17000 €14600 Apres la bain (35x27cm-14x11in) pencil oil prov. 29-Oct-3 Christie's, Rockefeller NY #126/R est:8000-12000

BOUHOT, Étienne (attrib) (1780-1862) French
£2961 $5447 €4500 Jeu de paume (32x40cm-13x16in) 23-Jun-4 Sotheby's, Paris #55/R est:4000-6000

BOUHUIJS, Jacob (1902-1983) Dutch
£350 $594 €500 Two musical harliquins (50x50cm-20x20in) s.d.48. 24-Nov-3 Glerum, Amsterdam #19/R
£490 $832 €700 Musical harlequins (50x50cm-20x20in) indis.s. 24-Nov-3 Glerum, Amsterdam #20/R

BOUILLETTE, Edgard (1872-1960) French
£352 $630 €500 Fin d'hiver, vallee de Chamonix (37x53cm-15x21in) s.d.1933. 11-Jan-4 Rouillac, Vendome #309

BOUILLON, Georges (1891-1943) Belgian?
£884 $1583 €1300 La Maison Curtius et la Meuse (60x75cm-24x30in) s. 17-Mar-4 Hotel des Ventes Mosan, Brussels #149

BOUILLOT, Maurice (20th C) French
£680 $1218 €1000 Le panier de cerises (59x79cm-23x31in) s.d.42. 22-Mar-4 E & Eve, Paris #56/R

BOULANGE, Louis Jean Baptiste (1812-1878) French
£759 $1259 €1100 Etendage du linge (42x67cm-17x26in) s. 1-Oct-3 Millon & Associes, Paris #134

BOULANGER, François Jean Louis (1819-1873) Belgian
£563 $975 €800 The Graslein in Gent (8x12cm-3x5in) s. cardboard. 15-Dec-3 Bernaerts, Antwerp #86/R
£1933 $3557 €2900 La barque du passer au coucher du soleil (27x33cm-11x13in) s. init.verso panel. 14-Jun-4 Horta, Bruxelles #185/R est:3000-4000
£3497 $6014 €5000 Les preparatifs pour la peche, sur fond de ville (23x17cm-9x7in) s.d.1847 panel. 8-Dec-3 Horta, Bruxelles #204 est:5500-6500
£52632 $96842 €80000 View of the Korenlei (95x121cm-37x48in) s. 22-Jun-4 Palais de Beaux Arts, Brussels #201/R est:60000-80000

BOULANGER, Graciela Rodo (1935-) Bolivian
£2841 $5000 €4148 Premier Jour de Vacances (89x79cm-35x31in) 23-May-4 Hindman, Chicago #998/R est:5000-7000

BOULANGER, Gustave Clarence Rodolphe (1824-1888) French
£559 $951 €800 Vue d'Algerie (16x26cm-6x10in) oil paper on canvas. 26-Nov-3 Daguerre, Paris #54
£6333 $11400 €9500 Flower girl (140x82cm-55x32in) s.d.1888. 20-Apr-4 Sotheby's, Amsterdam #79/R est:4000-6000

BOULANGER, Louis Vercelli (1806-1867) French
£857 $1371 €1243 Hovel (27x39cm-11x15in) s. board. 15-May-3 Stuker, Bern #1095/R (S.FR 1800)

BOULARD, Auguste (1825-1897) French
£1087 $1783 €1500 Le dechargement des poissons (22x17cm-9x7in) mono. panel. 11-May-3 Osenat, Fontainebleau #170 est:2000-2500
£1818 $3036 €2600 Retour de peche (20x29cm-8x11in) cardboard. 12-Oct-3 Salle des ventes Pillet, Lyon la Foret #5/R

BOULCH, Jean Pierre le (1940-2001) French
£280 $476 €400 Personnage (32x24cm-13x9in) s.d.1969 s.verso acrylic. 23-Nov-3 Cornette de St.Cyr, Paris #215

BOULEKOV, Andre (1927-) Russian
£372 $673 €543 Gates of Pianitsky (81x81cm-32x32in) s.d.1992 s.i.d.verso prov. 18-Apr-4 Levis, Calgary #205/R (C.D 900)

BOULENGER, Hippolyte (1837-1874) Belgian
£379 $702 €550 Sous-bois (23x50cm-9x20in) oil paper on panel. 13-Jan-4 Vanderkindere, Brussels #22
£646 $1157 €950 Ruisseau en foret (25x43cm-10x17in) s. panel. 16-Mar-4 Vanderkindere, Brussels #10
£694 $1104 €1000 Basse-cour (43x37cm-17x15in) s. 15-Sep-3 Horta, Bruxelles #303

BOULENGER, Hippolyte (attrib) (1837-1874) Belgian
£303 $557 €460 Bord d'etang (24x33cm-9x13in) studio st. 22-Jun-4 Palais de Beaux Arts, Brussels #202

BOULET, Cyprien-Eugène (1877-1927) French
£1397 $2500 €2040 Portrait of Mildah Polia (117x89cm-46x35in) s.d.1925 exhib. 11-Jan-4 William Jenack, New York #245 est:2500-3500

BOULET, Susan Seddon (20th C) American
£824 $1400 €1203 Jerome and the lion (28x20cm-11x8in) s.d.79 oil pastel paperboard. 8-Nov-3 Auctions by the Bay, Alameda #4444
£864 $1400 €1261 Jerome and the lion (28x20cm-11x8in) s.d.79 oil pastel paperboard. 9-Aug-3 Auctions by the Bay, Alameda #1535/R

BOULEZ, Jules (1889-1960) Belgian
£671 $1188 €1000 Paysage anime (46x65cm-18x26in) s. d.1942 verso. 27-Apr-4 Campo & Campo, Antwerp #29/R
£775 $1340 €1100 Composition (55x65cm-22x26in) s. 13-Dec-3 De Vuyst, Lokeren #37/R

BOULIER, Lucien (1882-1963) French
£251 $450 €366 Roses (23x28cm-9x11in) s. board. 8-Jan-4 Doyle, New York #7/R
£360 $590 €500 Portrait de jeune fille (34x26cm-13x10in) s. 6-Jun-3 Chochon-Barre & Allardi, Paris #28
£491 $800 €717 Les roses jaunes (23x28cm-9x11in) s. 24-Sep-3 Doyle, New York #8
£615 $1100 €898 Anemones (20x25cm-8x10in) s. 8-Jan-4 Doyle, New York #6/R
Works on paper
£331 $603 €500 Ballerine (44x32cm-17x13in) s. graphite htd col crayon. 18-Jun-4 Piasa, Paris #157

BOULINEAU, Aristide (19th C) French
£2254 $3628 €3200 Plage de Dieppe (26x41cm-10x16in) s.i.d.1874. 22-Aug-3 Deauville, France #35/R est:3500-4000

BOULINEAU, N Abel (1839-?) French
£1579 $2858 €2400 Les lavandieres (81x100cm-32x39in) s. 19-Apr-4 Horta, Bruxelles #137 est:3000-5000
£3310 $6124 €4800 Lavandieres (81x100cm-32x39in) s. 19-Jan-4 Horta, Bruxelles #90/R est:5000-7000

BOULIOT, Simon (19/20th C) ?
Sculpture
£2027 $3486 €2959 Allegories of Spring and Autumn (52cm-20in) s.i. gilded bronze pair prov. 3-Dec-3 Koller, Zurich #1280/R est:3000-5000 (S.FR 4500)

BOULLOGNE, Bon de (elder-attrib) (1649-1717) French
£7947 $14464 €12000 Biblical scenes (32x39cm-13x15in) set of 6. 15-Jun-4 Claude Aguttes, Neuilly #46/R est:14000-16000

BOULLOGNE, Louis de (younger) (1654-1733) French
£4452 $7568 €6500 Suzanne et les vieillards (31x24cm-12x9in) s.d.1716. 5-Nov-3 Beaussant & Lefèvre, Paris #16/R

BOULLOGNE, Louis de (younger-attrib) (1654-1733) French
£5906 $10867 €8800 Jupiter et Semele (122x91cm-48x36in) 24-Mar-4 Tajan, Paris #93/R est:9000-12000

BOULOGNE, C (?-1878) Belgian
£1149 $2022 €1700 Landscape with four women in garden (53x65cm-21x26in) s. panel. 22-May-4 Lempertz, Koln #1484/R est:2000

BOULOGNE, Valentin de (style) (1591-1634) French
£14789 $25880 €21000 Erminia amongst the shepherds (128x172cm-50x68in) 17-Dec-3 Christie's, Rome #498/R est:10000-15000
£46667 $85400 €70000 Good fortune (113x115cm-44x45in) 1-Jun-4 Sotheby's, Milan #115/R est:4000-6000

BOULT, Augustus S (fl.1815-1853) British
£2000 $3340 €2920 Portrait of an officer of the Surrey Yeomanry cavalry (52x62cm-20x24in) s. board. 14-Oct-3 Sotheby's, London #468/R est:2000-3000
£6000 $10020 €8760 Portrait of an officer of the 7th Light Dragoon Guards on his charger (49x58cm-19x23in) mono. i.verso. 14-Oct-3 Sotheby's, London #469/R est:4000-6000

BOULTBEE, John (1745-1812) British
£5800 $10614 €8468 Favourite hunter (58x74cm-23x29in) mono.d.1807. 8-Jul-4 Duke & Son, Dorchester #191/R est:3000-6000
£7746 $13401 €11000 Black hunter and dog in a landscape (72x92cm-28x36in) s.d.1801. 10-Dec-3 Christie's, Amsterdam #865/R est:12000-16000
£13260 $24000 €19360 English setter in a landscape (89x104cm-35x41in) 30-Mar-4 Bonhams & Butterfields, San Francisco #38/R est:20000-30000

BOULTON, Frederick William (1904-?) American
Works on paper
£398 $700 €581 Fly fishing (36x43cm-14x17in) s.d.1948 gouache exhib. 23-May-4 Treadway Gallery, Cincinnati #626/R

BOUMAN, Hans (1951-) ?
£300 $531 €438 Flamingos (100x70cm-39x28in) s. 27-Apr-4 Bonhams, Knightsbridge #123/R

BOUMEESTER, Christine (1904-1971) Dutch
£833 $1392 €1200 Composition (50x65cm-20x26in) s.d.62 prov. 21-Oct-3 Artcurial Briest, Paris #383
£872 $1623 €1300 Composition (73x92cm-29x36in) s.d.57 exhib. 3-Mar-4 Artcurial Briest, Paris #327 est:1000-1500
Works on paper
£280 $476 €400 Composition surrealiste (21x16cm-8x6in) s. ink W/C prov. 23-Nov-3 Cornette de St.Cyr, Paris #26
£280 $476 €400 Composition surrealiste (24x15cm-9x6in) s.d.1942 Indian ink prov. 23-Nov-3 Cornette de St.Cyr, Paris #27

BOUMEESTER, Cornelis (attrib) (1652-1733) Dutch
£1300 $2119 €1898 Merchants and other figures eating, drinking and smoking on a beach (24x35cm-9x14in) init. panel. 26-Sep-3 Christie's, Kensington #135/R est:800-1200

BOUQUET, Michel (1807-1890) French
Works on paper
£352 $616 €500 Lavandieres a Kervegen (25x37cm-10x15in) s. wash chl. 21-Dec-3 Thierry & Lannon, Brest #430

BOURAINE (20th C) ?
Sculpture
£2600 $4342 €3796 Diana with fawns (33cm-13in) s.pat bronze. 15-Oct-3 Christie's, Kensington #672/R

BOURAINE, A (20th C) ?
Sculpture
£2000 $3660 €3000 Danseuse au cerceau (20cm-8in) s. ivory metal. 6-Jun-4 Anaf, Lyon #309/R est:2000-2200

BOURAINE, Antoine (20th C) French
Sculpture
£1100 $2002 €1606 Sealion. s. bronze ivory mounted on onyx cube st.f.Cachet Lastele. 1-Jul-4 Mellors & Kirk, Nottingham #973/R est:800-1000

BOURAINE, M (20th C) French
Sculpture
£1319 $2098 €1900 Female nude playing flute (48cm-19in) i. pat.bronze stone socle. 15-Sep-3 Dorotheum, Vienna #198/R est:1300-1600

BOURAINE, Marcel (20th C) French
Sculpture
£1757 $3145 €2600 Satyre charmant biche (44x79x20cm-17x31x8in) s. pat bronze. 5-May-4 Claude Boisgirard, Paris #33/R est:1200-1500
£1867 $3435 €2800 Danseuse de charleston (28cm-11in) s. green pat bronze ivory onyx base. 9-Jun-4 Beaussant & Lefèvre, Paris #268/R est:1800-2000
£2000 $3580 €2920 Nude female dancer with doves (55cm-22in) s. cold pat bronze marble base. 13-May-4 Christie's, Kensington #362/R est:2000-3000
£2095 $3750 €3059 Nude with two antelope (51cm-20in) s. bronze. 21-Mar-4 Jeffery Burchard, Florida #90/R
£2098 $3566 €3000 Penthesilia, la reine des Amazones (27x45cm-11x18in) s. silver bronze Cast Susse Freres lit. 20-Nov-3 Camard, Paris #210/R est:2300-2600
£3500 $5565 €5110 Fan dancer (63cm-25in) i. bronze. 9-Sep-3 Sotheby's, Olympia #379/R est:3000-3500
£5000 $8300 €7300 Diana (70cm-28in) bronze incl stepped base. 30-Sep-3 Sotheby's, London #405/R est:3000-4000
£7333 $13127 €11000 Amazone (46x88cm-18x35in) s.st.f.Susse pat bronze. 17-May-4 Sotheby's, Paris #72/R est:12000-15000

BOURAS, Harry D (1931-) American
Works on paper
£318 $550 €464 Terrain revisited (79x76cm-31x30in) mixed media wood panel prov. 15-Dec-3 Hindman, Chicago #89/R
£455 $800 €664 Untitled (36x28cm-14x11in) s. mixed media. 23-May-4 Treadway Gallery, Cincinnati #751/R

BOURCART, Émile (1827-1900) French
£441 $749 €644 Washerwomen by spring (27x32cm-11x13in) s. 5-Nov-3 Dobiaschofsky, Bern #385/R (S.FR 1000)

BOURCE, Henri Jacques (1826-1899) Belgian
£600 $1110 €876 Journey to school (28x22cm-11x9in) s. panel. 15-Jan-4 Christie's, Kensington #808/R
£2685 $4966 €4000 Fishermen on the beach (118x100cm-46x39in) s.d.1878. 13-Mar-4 De Vuyst, Lokeren #30/R est:3000-4000

BOURDAREL, A (?) French?
Sculpture
£2600 $4784 €3900 Femelle orang-outan et son petit (48cm-19in) s. black pat bronze cire perdue st.f. Valsuani. 9-Jun-4 Beaussant & Lefèvre, Paris #290/R est:2400-2800

BOURDELLE, Émile Antoine (1861-1929) French
Sculpture
£2534 $4308 €3700 Buste de coquelin, cadet, en costume mascarille (47cm-19in) s. terracotta. 6-Nov-3 Rabourdin & Choppin de Janvry, Paris #118/R est:4000-5000
£5348 $10000 €7808 Madame Roussel au chapeau (36cm-14in) s.st.f.Susse pat bronze prov.lit. 25-Feb-4 Christie's, Rockefeller NY #40/R est:12000-16000
£6000 $10800 €8760 Siesta (21x36cm-8x14in) s.i.num. green brown pat bronze st.f.A. Valsuani lit. 21-Apr-4 Sotheby's, London #136/R est:6000-8000
£11905 $21310 €17500 Bacchante (80cm-31in) mono.i. pat plaster prov.lit. 19-Mar-4 Ribeyre & Baron, Paris #96/R est:4000-7000
£12000 $22080 €17520 Study for Herakles the Archer (40cm-16in) mono. num.5 bronze st.f.Susse Fondeur conceived 1909 prov.lit. 22-Jun-4 Sotheby's, London #230/R est:15000-20000
£14724 $24000 €21497 Le fruit (98cm-39in) s.num. green pat bronze conceived 1906-11 st.f.A.Valsuani prov. 25-Sep-3 Christie's, Rockefeller NY #604/R est:25000-35000
£18310 $32042 €26000 Baigneuse accroupie (25cm-10in) s. pat bronze prov.lit. 16-Dec-3 Christie's, Paris #330/R est:7000-9000
£24000 $43680 €36000 Head of Hercules (35cm-14in) s.verso bronze st.f.Hebrard. 30-Jun-4 Calmels Cohen, Paris #54/R est:25000-35000
£26000 $47320 €37960 Cheval sans selle (43cm-17in) i.num.VI bronze exhib. 4-Feb-4 Sotheby's, London #262/R est:18000-25000
£33520 $60000 €48939 Tete de Victoire (76cm-30in) s. num.11 st.f.M Hohwiller bronze prov.lit. 6-May-4 Sotheby's, New York #294/R est:60000-80000
£88235 $150000 €128823 Heracles, archer (56cm-22in) mono.i.num.N.3 green pat bronze Cast Susse, Paris lit. 6-Nov-3 Sotheby's, New York #131/R est:80000-120000
£95000 $172900 €138700 Le fruit, grand modele (226cm-89in) s.i.d.1902-1911 st.f.Susse dark green pat bronze exec. 1969 prov. 3-Feb-4 Christie's, London #145/R est:50000-80000
Works on paper
£1849 $3144 €2700 Portrait de Madame de Marsac (49x35cm-19x14in) s. pastel. 9-Nov-3 Eric Pillon, Calais #32/R

BOURDELLES, Herve le (1928-) French
£302 $559 €450 Rio San Barnaba (54x73cm-21x29in) s. 15-Mar-4 Blanchet, Paris #160

BOURDET, Jules Joseph Guillaume (1799-1869) French
£5988 $10000 €8742 Three Graces (116x89cm-46x35in) s.d.1832 exhib.lit. 7-Oct-3 Sotheby's, New York #74/R est:10000-15000

BOURDICHON, Jean (c.1457-1521) French
Works on paper
£28000 $51240 €40880 Christ on the Cross with Saint Mary Magdelen, Saint Jerome and Saint Francis (40x21cm-16x8in) illumination on vellum tempera liquid gold arch top. 6-Jul-4 Christie's, London #98/R est:30000-50000

BOURDIER, Dieudonne Raphael (1794-1865) French
£5141 $8894 €7300 Still life with fruit and vase (61x51cm-24x20in) s.d.1840. 13-Dec-3 Lempertz, Koln #6/R est:2000

BOURDILLON, Frank (1851-1924) British
£30000 $51000 €43800 Jubilee hat (93x70cm-37x28in) s.d.1887 prov.exhib.lit. 21-Nov-3 Christie's, London #45/R est:30000-50000

BOURDIN, Guy (1928-1991) French?
Photographs
£10000 $18000 €14600 Gilles (28x21cm-11x8in) s.i.d.1956 gelatin silver print prov. 23-Apr-4 Phillips, New York #183/R est:8000-12000

Works on paper

£315	$535	€450	Chat a table (47x59cm-19x23in) s.d.1956 Indian ink sepia gouache tissue on paper. 18-Nov-3 Pierre Berge, Paris #11/R
£629	$1070	€900	Autoportrait au minotaure bleu (43x47cm-17x19in) s.d.1955 Indian ink sepia gouache board. 18-Nov-3 Pierre Berge, Paris #12/R

BOURDIN, Richard (19/20th C) ?

£400	$756	€584	Mother and a small child in forest clearing (38x26cm-15x10in) s. 17-Feb-4 Fellows & Sons, Birmingham #53/R

BOURDON, Sebastien (attrib) (1616-1671) French

£32000	$54400	€46720	Portrait of an artist holding a hammer and chisel before an intaglio oval portrait (83x65cm-33x26in) i.d.1662. 31-Oct-3 Christie's, Kensington #85/R est:8000-10000

BOURDON, Sebastien (circle) (1616-1671) French

£6308	$10849	€9210	At the Art Academy (152x120cm-60x47in) 2-Dec-3 Bukowskis, Stockholm #380/R est:40000-50000 (S.KR 82000)

BOURDON, Sebastien (style) (1616-1671) French

£5000	$9000	€7300	Portrait of the artist, with the muse of the painting (85x63cm-33x25in) 23-Apr-4 Christie's, Kensington #180/R est:2000-3000

BOURDUCE, Antonio (20th C) ?

Works on paper

£278	$500	€406	Black gate (58x46cm-23x18in) s. W/C prov. 25-Jan-4 Hindman, Chicago #1087/R

BOURET, Germaine (1907-1953) French

Works on paper

£275	$504	€410	Tu as une fievre de cheval (35x23cm-14x9in) studio st. chl dr. 9-Jul-4 Coutau Begarie, Paris #45/R
£289	$528	€430	Galerie de portraits (13x38cm-5x15in) studio st. chl dr. 9-Jul-4 Coutau Begarie, Paris #48/R
£322	$590	€480	Vous me prendrez combien pour rempailler mon bibi (31x48cm-12x19in) studio st. chl. 9-Jul-4 Coutau Begarie, Paris #98/R
£336	$614	€500	Je peux bien ramasser les os (26x41cm-10x16in) chl htd gouache. 9-Jul-4 Coutau Begarie, Paris #35/R
£336	$614	€500	Saute-mouton (28x23cm-11x9in) studio st. chl W/C. 9-Jul-4 Coutau Begarie, Paris #106/R
£362	$663	€540	Cycliste (28x23cm-11x9in) studio st. chl W/C. 9-Jul-4 Coutau Begarie, Paris #103/R
£503	$921	€750	Vocation de Michou (27x21cm-11x8in) dr W/C. 9-Jul-4 Coutau Begarie, Paris #119/R
£550	$1007	€820	Le favori est dans les choux (35x46cm-14x18in) studio st. chl W/C. 9-Jul-4 Coutau Begarie, Paris #102/R
£550	$1007	€820	Hollandais (31x20cm-12x8in) studio st. chl W/C. 9-Jul-4 Coutau Begarie, Paris #108/R
£604	$1105	€900	Mangez des gateaux plus souvent (45x31cm-18x12in) studio st. chl dr W/C. 9-Jul-4 Coutau Begarie, Paris #49/R
£638	$1167	€950	Pendant que tu y es, tu colmateras ma poche (47x33cm-19x13in) s. chl dr htd gouache. 9-Jul-4 Coutau Begarie, Paris #110/R
£671	$1228	€1000	Enfant, chien, landau (37x35cm-15x14in) studio st. chl W/C. 9-Jul-4 Coutau Begarie, Paris #97/R
£705	$1290	€1050	Chouette, une sucre (33x44cm-13x17in) s.d.41 chl dr htd gouache. 9-Jul-4 Coutau Begarie, Paris #109/R
£805	$1474	€1200	J'ai attrape une puce (40x30cm-16x12in) s. chl htd white. 9-Jul-4 Coutau Begarie, Paris #99/R
£940	$1719	€1400	Comme tu es pale, Toto ! (39x55cm-15x22in) gouache over chl. 9-Jul-4 Coutau Begarie, Paris #112/R
£1007	$1842	€1500	Modele de tenue de tennis Blanc-Blanc (21x11cm-8x4in) studio st. dr gouache lit. 9-Jul-4 Coutau Begarie, Paris #59/R est:1200-1500

BOURGADE, Augusta de (?-1969) French

£420	$701	€600	Lake amongst mountains (26x35cm-10x14in) i.d.1949 verso board. 30-Jun-3 Ansorena, Madrid #264/R

BOURGEAT, Jean Francois (20th C) French

£353	$600	€515	Bord de Seine a St. Mammes (38x46cm-15x18in) s. 5-Nov-3 Doyle, New York #14/R
£353	$650	€515	Pecheur au bord de la sevre niortais (25x51cm-10x20in) s. i.verso. 23-Jun-4 Doyle, New York #5011/R
£462	$850	€675	Marais poitevin (28x36cm-11x14in) s. s.i.verso. 23-Jun-4 Doyle, New York #5012/R
£882	$1500	€1288	Bord de Seine (61x74cm-24x29in) s.i. 5-Nov-3 Doyle, New York #13/R est:3000-4000

BOURGEOIS du CASTELET, Constant (1767-1841) French

Works on paper

£353	$640	€530	River landscape in the Alps with two anglers (33x46cm-13x18in) s.d. pencil. 2-Apr-4 Winterberg, Heidelberg #390

BOURGEOIS, Charles Guillaume Alexandre (1759-1832) French

Miniatures

£1467	$2669	€2200	Madame Artaud (6x4cm-2x2in) s. oval exec.c.1795 lit. 30-Jun-4 Pierre Berge, Paris #119/R est:800-1200

BOURGEOIS, Eugène (1855-1909) French

£620	$1085	€880	Gardienne de poules (23x32cm-9x13in) s.d.85. 21-Dec-3 Thierry & Lannon, Brest #286

BOURGEOIS, Louis (1873-?) French

£223	$400	€326	A downlands view (53x81cm-21x32in) s.d.08. 8-Jan-4 Doyle, New York #11/R
£280	$482	€409	Fisherman (45x53cm-18x21in) s. 7-Dec-3 Lots Road Auctions, London #356

BOURGEOIS, Louise (1911-) American/French

Sculpture

£5988	$10000	€8742	Give or take, how do you feel this morning (12x25x15cm-5x10x6in) init.d.90 num.2/40 bronze prov. 13-Nov-3 Sotheby's, New York #141/R est:10000-15000
£35928	$60000	€52455	Untitled, house no 5 (12x32x7cm-5x13x3in) init. marble prov. 13-Nov-3 Sotheby's, New York #143/R est:35000-45000
£89820	$150000	€131137	In and out (38x61x82cm-15x24x32in) init. steel lead executed 1997 prov. 13-Nov-3 Phillips, New York #18/R est:200000-300000
£155689	$260000	€227306	Love (190x30x25cm-75x12x10in) stitched i. red fabric exec 2000 prov.lit. 11-Nov-3 Christie's, Rockefeller NY #62/R est:300000-350000
£223464	$400000	€326257	Fillette - Sweeter version (60x27x20cm-24x11x8in) latex over plaster edn 1/3 exec 1968-1999 prov.exhib.lit. 11-May-4 Christie's, Rockefeller NY #57/R est:300000-400000

BOURGEOIS, Sir Peter Francis (1756-1811) British

£10778	$18000	€15736	The chestnut hunter (86x109cm-34x43in) s.d.1781 i.verso exhib. 27-Oct-3 Schrager Galleries, Milwaukee #1285/R

BOURGEOIS-POTAGE, Jean Pierre (20th C) French

£612	$1096	€900	Untitled (62x50cm-24x20in) s. prov. 21-Mar-4 Calmels Cohen, Paris #115/R

BOURGINON, J (17th C) Dutch

£3000	$5100	€4380	Still life with grapes, plums and other fruits on a stone ledge (36x31cm-14x12in) 30-Oct-3 Sotheby's, Olympia #3/R est:3000-4000

BOURGOIN, Marie Desire (1839-1912) French

Works on paper

£2313	$4140	€3400	Interieur de la Galerie Louis XII du Baron A de Rothschild (53x36cm-21x14in) s. W/C traces black crayon. 17-Mar-4 Tajan, Paris #144/R est:2000-2500

BOURGUIGNON, Mady (20th C) French

£382	$607	€550	Printemps, femme au collier vert (98x68cm-39x27in) s.d.1938 sold with document. 15-Sep-3 Horta, Bruxelles #299

BOURKE, Brian (1936-) Irish

£1127	$1949	€1600	Turf cuttings (62x57cm-24x22in) s.d.1981 acrylic board. 10-Dec-3 Bonhams & James Adam, Dublin #151/R est:1000-1500
£1300	$2327	€1898	Knock-a-Lough, Winter (65x51cm-26x20in) s.i.d.77/78 paper on board prov.exhib. 14-May-4 Christie's, London #90/R est:800-1200
£2937	$4993	€4200	Landscape, polling (124x84cm-49x33in) s.i.d.1966 verso exhib. 18-Nov-3 Whyte's, Dublin #60/R est:3000-5000
£4225	$6761	€6000	Landscape, famine series (137x115cm-54x45in) 16-Sep-3 Whyte's, Dublin #44/R est:4000-5000
£5263	$9684	€8000	Scotspine (127x110cm-50x43in) s.i.d.2001 verso. 22-Jun-4 De Veres Art Auctions, Dublin #114/R est:8000-10000

Works on paper

£480	$859	€701	Near Jamestown, autumn (49x40cm-19x16in) s.i.d.85 W/C chl pastel. 14-May-4 Christie's, Kensington #411
£503	$856	€720	Landscape (44x49cm-17x19in) pastel prov. 25-Nov-3 De Veres Art Auctions, Dublin #202/R
£537	$950	€800	Neighbour's child (50x35cm-20x14in) s.i. W/C crayon. 27-Apr-4 Whyte's, Dublin #157/R
£633	$1146	€950	Fran Strutz's cherry tree, Switzerland (49x34cm-19x13in) s.i.d.1924 col chk prov. 30-Mar-4 De Veres Art Auctions, Dublin #70/R
£699	$1189	€1000	Below Albert Lock (52x43cm-20x17in) s.i.d.Autumn 1985 W/C crayon. 18-Nov-3 Whyte's, Dublin #157/R
£789	$1453	€1200	White pines (54x37cm-21x15in) s.i.d.93 col chk. 22-Jun-4 De Veres Art Auctions, Dublin #242/R
£861	$1567	€1300	Lucia (34x24cm-13x9in) s.i.d.94 col crayon. 15-Jun-4 James Adam, Dublin #157/R
£986	$1706	€1400	Ballinskelligis Bay (76x34cm-30x13in) s.i. mixed media. 10-Dec-3 Bonhams & James Adam, Dublin #146/R
£1000	$1810	€1500	Fran Strutz's cherry tree, Switzerland (49x34cm-19x13in) s.i.d.74 col chk prov. 30-Mar-4 De Veres Art Auctions, Dublin #136/R est:1000-2000
£1042	$1698	€1500	Landscape (73x52cm-29x20in) s.i.d.1968 mixed media prov. 24-Sep-3 James Adam, Dublin #148/R est:1000-1500
£1042	$1698	€1500	Portrait of J with basque hat (76x57cm-30x22in) s.d.1982 mixed media prov.exhib. 23-Sep-3 De Veres Art Auctions, Dublin #261/R est:900-1200
£1284	$2426	€1900	Dublin (64x48cm-25x19in) s.i.d.November 1970 mixed media on board prov. 17-Feb-4 Whyte's, Dublin #24/R est:2000-3000
£1351	$2554	€2000	Summer, Ower (67x48cm-26x19in) s.i.d.1989 mixed media prov. 17-Feb-4 Whyte's, Dublin #103/R est:2000-3000
£1867	$3379	€2800	Old ruins, Co Kilkenny (76x55cm-30x22in) s.i.d.75 mixed media. 30-Mar-4 De Veres Art Auctions, Dublin #127a/R est:1000-3000

BOURKE-WHITE, Margaret (1904-1971) American

Photographs

£1693	$3200	€2472	Standard oil of Ohio (24x34cm-9x13in) s.i. gelatin silver print executed c.1930. 17-Feb-4 Christie's, Rockefeller NY #115/R est:4000-6000
£2596	$4750	€3790	Untitled, Zeppelin (43x58cm-17x23in) s. gelatin silver print. 6-Jun-4 Wright, Chicago #154/R est:5000-7000
£2695	$4500	€3935	Rolling sheet aluminum, Aluminum Co of America (30x23cm-12x9in) i. photo. 17-Oct-3 Sotheby's, New York #238/R est:6000-8000
£2890	$5000	€4219	United States airship Akron, 1931 (52x66cm-20x26in) s.i. gelatin silver print. 11-Dec-3 Sotheby's, New York #232/R est:5000-7000
£3175	$6000	€4636	George Washington Bridge (35x25cm-14x10in) s.i. gelatin silver print prov. 17-Feb-4 Christie's, Rockefeller NY #48/R est:7000-9000
£3439	$6500	€5021	U.S.S Akron (44x58cm-17x23in) s. gelatin silver print. 17-Feb-4 Christie's, Rockefeller NY #112/R est:3000-5000

£3593 $6000 €5246 Soviet serenade (33x23cm-13x9in) s. gelatin silver print lit. 20-Oct-3 Christie's, Rockefeller NY #190/R est:5000-7000
£5389 $9000 €7868 Boys studing Talmud, Orthodox Jewish school (25x33cm-10x13in) with sig. silver print. 21-Oct-3 Swann Galleries, New York #131/R est:7000-10000
£5650 $10000 €8249 Pouring the heat, Ford Motor Co., 1929 (34x23cm-13x9in) s. i.verso gelatin silver print lit. 27-Apr-4 Christie's, Rockefeller NY #32/R est:9000-12000
£5689 $9500 €8306 From the Terminal Tower, Cleveland (35x22cm-14x9in) s.i. warm toned photo exec.c.1928. 17-Oct-3 Sotheby's, New York #193/R est:6000-9000
£10000 $18000 €14600 Rolling coiled aluminum sheet (34x24cm-13x9in) s.i.verso toned gelatin silver print prov.exhib.lit. 23-Apr-4 Phillips, New York #243/R est:12000-18000
£11299 $20000 €16497 Terminal Tower, Cleveland (34x25cm-13x10in) s. warm-toned photo board. 28-Apr-4 Sotheby's, New York #115/R est:20000-30000
£15819 $28000 €23096 George Washington Bridge, 1933 (34x23cm-13x9in) i. gelatin silver print lit. 27-Apr-4 Christie's, Rockefeller NY #33/R est:10000-15000

BOURNE, John Cooke (?) ?
Works on paper
£1000 $1790 €1460 Railway at Bristol (45x85cm-18x33in) W/C over pencil bodycol. 26-May-4 Sotheby's, Olympia #49/R est:1000-1500

BOURNE, John Frye (1912-1991) British
£2200 $3674 €3212 Bathing belle (68x90cm-27x35in) s. 16-Oct-3 Christie's, Kensington #304/R est:1000-1500

BOURNE, Joseph (1740-1808) French
£1678 $2853 €2400 Nature morte aux fleurs, aux fruits et aux papillons (50x61cm-20x24in) s. 18-Nov-3 Vanderkindere, Brussels #21 est:1250-1750

BOURRET, Michelle (20th C) French
£361 $667 €527 Wolf (46x55cm-18x22in) mono.d.1956. 15-Mar-4 Rasmussen, Vejle #627/R (D.KR 4000)

BOURRIE, Andre (1936-) French
£285 $450 €413 L'auto-sonte dans le soir (15x28cm-6x11in) s. 27-Jul-3 Simpson's, Houston #231

BOURSIQUOTS, J D (20th C) ?
£346 $579 €505 Jungle scene with figures and animals (120x200cm-47x79in) s. 25-Oct-3 Rasmussen, Havnen #4239 (D.KR 3700)

BOURY, C (20th C) ?
Works on paper
£4333 $7973 €6500 Femmes au marche de Meknes (110x158cm-43x62in) s. pastel prov. 11-Jun-4 Claude Aguttes, Neuilly #125/R est:6000-8000

BOUSSINGAULT, Jean Louis (1883-1943) French
£524 $892 €750 Femme au violon, Ginette Neveu (27x22cm-11x9in) s. 18-Nov-3 Pierre Berge, Paris #73
£1538 $2569 €2200 Apres le bal (45x73cm-18x29in) s.d.25 exhib. 25-Jun-3 Blanchet, Paris #18/R

BOUT, Pieter (1658-1719) Flemish
£4054 $7135 €6000 Landscape with peasants and horse carriage (30x27cm-12x11in) prov. 22-May-4 Lempertz, Koln #1016/R est:6500
£7237 $13316 €11000 Peasants by farm (23x32cm-9x13in) panel. 25-Jun-4 Piasa, Paris #77/R est:12000-15000
£25000 $43250 €36500 Crowded village scene with numerous villagers and animals (37x51cm-15x20in) prov. 11-Dec-3 Sotheby's, London #51/R est:25000-35000

BOUT, Pieter (attrib) (1658-1719) Flemish
£1250 $2250 €1825 View of a market (50x60cm-20x24in) 21-Jan-4 Sotheby's, New York #99/R est:3000-5000
£2349 $4323 €3500 Cavalier et pecheurs dans un paysage de riviere (49x74cm-19x29in) 24-Mar-4 Tajan, Paris #57/R est:4000-5000
£2721 $4871 €4000 Wooded river shore (20x25cm-8x10in) panel. 17-Mar-4 Neumeister, Munich #330/R est:2200

BOUT, Pieter and BOUDEWYNS, Adriaen Frans (17/18th C) Flemish
£12000 $21960 €17520 Landscape with waggoners (15x21cm-6x8in) copper. 8-Jul-4 Sotheby's, London #235/R est:8000-12000

BOUTARD, Clemence Ranche (19th C) Danish
£526 $853 €763 Part of bush with blue petunia and butterflies (40x31cm-16x12in) panel prov. 4-Aug-3 Rasmussen, Vejle #141/R (D.KR 5500)

BOUTELLE, De Witt Clinton (1817-1884) American
£838 $1500 €1223 Moonlight sale (50x76cm-20x30in) s.d.1876. 14-May-4 Skinner, Boston #121/R est:3000-5000
£2326 $4000 €3396 Rural landscape with horseman and haywagon (20x33cm-8x13in) s.d.1863 board. 7-Dec-3 Freeman, Philadelphia #110 est:1000-1500
£4032 $7500 €5887 Sunrise over the Catskills (25x20cm-10x8in) s.d.1871 prov. 3-Mar-4 Christie's, Rockefeller NY #6/R est:4000-6000
£6173 $10000 €8951 View of Troy, New York (66x91cm-26x36in) s.d.1845. 8-Aug-3 Barridorf, Portland #61/R est:15000-20000

BOUTEN, Armand (1893-1965) ?
£3158 $5811 €4800 Landscape with haystacks, a sailing boat in the foreground (35x64cm-14x25in) s. prov. 22-Jun-4 Christie's, Amsterdam #566/R est:1800-2200
£7333 $13200 €11000 Harbour town (98x103cm-39x41in) s. 24-Apr-4 Dr Lehr, Berlin #64/R est:8000
£16333 $30053 €24500 Seated female nude (46x37cm-18x15in) s. painted 1921. 11-Jun-4 Villa Grisebach, Berlin #1560/R est:2000-3000
Works on paper
£2667 $4907 €4000 Untitled (56x73cm-22x29in) s. W/C pastel. 8-Jun-4 Sotheby's, Amsterdam #200/R est:5000-7000

BOUTER, Cornelis (1888-1966) Dutch
£296 $536 €450 At the farrier (30x40cm-12x16in) bears sig. 19-Apr-4 Glerum, Amsterdam #215/R
£340 $569 €480 Shepherd with flock of sheep in the meadow (44x59cm-17x23in) s. 20-Oct-3 Glerum, Amsterdam #143/R
£461 $834 €700 Shepherdess driving her sheep into the pen (29x39cm-11x15in) bears sig. 19-Apr-4 Glerum, Amsterdam #197/R
£517 $864 €750 Milking time (42x57cm-17x22in) s. 11-Nov-3 Vendu Notarishuis, Rotterdam #181/R
£592 $1072 €900 Cows in a polder landscape (29x39cm-11x15in) bears sig. 19-Apr-4 Glerum, Amsterdam #205/R
£603 $1007 €850 Ruminating cows in the meadow (51x70cm-20x28in) s. 20-Oct-3 Glerum, Amsterdam #161/R
£604 $1117 €900 Barn interior (50x70cm-20x28in) s. 15-Mar-4 Sotheby's, Amsterdam #260a/R est:1000-1500
£674 $1125 €950 The unloading of the hay (50x70cm-20x28in) s. 20-Oct-3 Glerum, Amsterdam #145/R
£680 $1238 €1000 First day in the field (50x70cm-20x28in) s. 3-Feb-4 Christie's, Amsterdam #211 est:800-1200
£800 $1432 €1200 Wood gatherers with horse and wagon (59x79cm-23x31in) s. 11-May-4 Vendu Notarishuis, Rotterdam #15/R
£860 $1436 €1256 Gathering wood (40x61cm-16x24in) s. 17-Nov-3 Waddingtons, Toronto #157/R est:1500-2000 (C.D 1900)
£1007 $1862 €1500 Shepherd with his flock (64x77cm-25x30in) s. 15-Mar-4 Sotheby's, Amsterdam #119/R est:1500-2000
£1250 $2263 €1900 In the smithy (60x80cm-24x31in) bears sig. 19-Apr-4 Glerum, Amsterdam #210/R est:1000-1200
£1290 $2374 €1883 Little sister (71x51cm-28x20in) s. prov. 14-Jun-4 Waddingtons, Toronto #247/R est:3000-5000 (C.D 3200)
£1389 $2208 €2000 Mother and child (24x29cm-9x11in) s. 10-Sep-3 James Adam, Dublin #57/R est:2000-3000
£1477 $2732 €2200 Cows near the waterside (65x78cm-26x31in) s. 15-Mar-4 Sotheby's, Amsterdam #120/R est:1500-2000
£1532 $2819 €2237 Playing with dolly (41x51cm-16x20in) s. 14-Jun-4 Waddingtons, Toronto #248/R est:2000-3000 (C.D 3800)
£1935 $3561 €2825 Children playing on the beach (51x71cm-20x28in) s. 14-Jun-4 Waddingtons, Toronto #252/R est:6000-8000 (C.D 4800)
£4028 $6404 €5800 Happy days (54x64cm-21x25in) s. 10-Sep-3 James Adam, Dublin #28/R est:6000-8000
£7500 $12000 €10875 Sewing lesson (51x61cm-20x24in) s. 18-Sep-3 Christie's, Kensington #143/R est:2000-3000

BOUTER, Pieter (1887-1968) Dutch
£266 $425 €388 Shepherd and his flock. s. 20-Sep-3 Harvey Clar, Oakland #1225
£280 $476 €400 Cattle in meadow (50x70cm-20x28in) s. 20-Nov-3 Van Ham, Cologne #1494
£308 $524 €450 Cows watering (39x78cm-15x31in) s. 5-Nov-3 Vendue Huis, Gravenhage #244/R
£369 $679 €550 Shepherd and flock by thatched barn (40x60cm-16x24in) s. lit. 25-Mar-4 Karlheinz Kaupp, Staufen #2363/R
£1150 $2093 €1725 Shepherd releasing his flock from a thatched barn (24x32cm-9x13in) 20-Jun-4 Wilkinson, Doncaster #323 est:1400-1800

BOUTET DE MONVEL, Bernard (1884-1949) French
£3691 $6866 €5500 Jeune fille au bouquet (47x37cm-19x15in) s. 2-Mar-4 Artcurial Briest, Paris #211/R est:5000-6000
£76596 $127915 €108000 Femmes au souk El-Khemis, Marrakech (65x68cm-26x27in) s. painted c.1919. 16-Jun-3 Gros & Delettrez, Paris #350/R est:50000-80000
Works on paper
£4225 $7310 €6000 Architecture Triomphe du temps (38x24cm-15x9in) s.i. W/C drawing. 14-Dec-3 St-Germain-en-Laye Encheres #77/R est:6000-7000

BOUTET, Henri (1851-?) French
Works on paper
£827 $1324 €1150 Femme vue de dos, le corset delace (48x38cm-19x15in) s. pastel. 16-May-3 Tajan, Paris #97

BOUTHEON, Charles (1877-1905) French
£453 $816 €680 Pont et riviere (50x60cm-20x24in) panel. 24-Apr-4 Hotel des Ventes de Vienne, Vienne #181

BOUTHOORN, Willy Leo (1916-) Dutch
£789 $1453 €1200 Abstract composition (74x54cm-29x21in) s.d.89 oil gouache paper prov. 28-Jun-4 Sotheby's, Amsterdam #241/R
£1156 $2105 €1700 Het omtoveren (90x70cm-35x28in) s.d.87 prov. 3-Feb-4 Christie's, Amsterdam #645 est:600-800

BOUTIBONNE, Charles-Edouard (1816-1897) Hungarian
£450 $824 €657 Portrait d'homme (72x59cm-28x23in) s. 8-Apr-4 Christie's, Kensington #43/R
£940 $1757 €1400 Family of Carl and Anthonie von Hornbostel. Portrait of woman (50x39cm-20x15in) s.d.1838 two. 24-Feb-4 Dorotheum, Vienna #149/R
£5026 $8996 €7338 Mythological scene with doves (81x54cm-32x21in) s.d.1883 panel. 25-May-4 Bukowskis, Stockholm #369a/R est:20000-25000 (S.KR 68000)
£5333 $9653 €8000 Allegorie du printemps (195x115cm-77x45in) s. 31-Mar-4 Sotheby's, Paris #154/R est:8000-12000
£55000 $100100 €80300 The young mountaineers (64x49cm-25x19in) s.d.1870 panel prov. 15-Jun-4 Sotheby's, London #189/R est:60000-80000

BOUTIGNY, Xavier (1870-1930) French
£268 $499 €400 Bebe de profil (41x33cm-16x13in) s.d.1894. 7-Mar-4 Livinec, Gaudcheau & Jezequel, Rennes #53

BOUTON, Charles Marie (1781-1853) French

£986	$1725	€1400	Ruines Romanes animees de personnages (18x25cm-7x10in) 18-Dec-3 Tajan, Paris #157 est:1200-1500

BOUTON, Charles Marie (attrib) (1781-1853) French

£800	$1448	€1200	La fontaine de Siloe. La crypte de la Vierge (22x16cm-9x6in) pair exhib. 30-Mar-4 Rossini, Paris #70

BOUTS, Albrecht (1454-1549) Dutch

£43103	$79310	€62930	Ecce homo - Christ wearing crown of thorns (39x27cm-15x11in) panel prov.exhib.lit. 26-Mar-4 Koller, Zurich #3012/R est:100000-150000 (S.FR 100000)

BOUVAL, Maurice (1863-1920) French

Sculpture

£1538	$2646	€2200	The new century (34cm-13in) i. gilded bronze Cast.E Collin and Cie, Paris. 4-Dec-3 Schopman, Hamburg #452/R est:420
£2400	$4008	€3504	Untitled (48cm-19in) s. pat bronze. 15-Oct-3 Christie's, Kensington #283/R
£2400	$4392	€3504	Naked maiden (27x27cm-11x11in) s. bronze. 3-Jun-4 Sotheby's, Olympia #115 est:1500-2000
£2550	$4693	€3800	Femme au pavot (20cm-8in) s. pat bronze. 23-Mar-4 Piasa, Paris #8/R
£5500	$9185	€8030	Untitled (27cm-11in) s. pat bronze. 15-Oct-3 Christie's, Kensington #289/R
£5500	$10065	€8030	Femme fluer (34cm-13in) s.i. bronze. 3-Jun-4 Sotheby's, Olympia #114/R est:3000-5000

BOUVARD (19/20th C) French

£3500	$5845	€5110	Venetian waterway (51x66cm-20x26in) s. 26-Jun-3 Greenslade Hunt, Taunton #557/R est:1500-2000
£3830	$6396	€5400	Gondolier sur un canal a Venise (35x27cm-14x11in) s. pair. 20-Jun-3 Drouot Estimations, Paris #87/R est:5000-6000
£7692	$13077	€11000	Canal in Venice (65x50cm-26x20in) s. 28-Nov-3 Drouot Estimations, Paris #153/R est:7000-9000
£9790	$16643	€14000	View of Venice (64x92cm-25x36in) s. 28-Nov-3 Drouot Estimations, Paris #154/R est:10000-12000

BOUVARD, A (19/20th C) French

£9955	$16624	€14534	Untitled - Venetian canal scene (46x61cm-18x24in) s. prov. 17-Nov-3 Hodgins, Calgary #285/R est:15000-25000 (C.D 22000)

BOUVARD, Antoine (?-1956) French

£2080	$3682	€3100	Venise, canal (27x35cm-11x14in) s. 30-Apr-4 Tajan, Paris #210/R est:2000-3000
£2267	$4103	€3400	Gondola on canal, Venice (73x40cm-29x16in) s. 1-Apr-4 Van Ham, Cologne #1301/R est:3200
£2267	$4103	€3400	Gondola in front of Venetian palace (73x40cm-29x16in) s. 1-Apr-4 Van Ham, Cologne #1302/R est:3200
£3600	$5724	€5220	Figures on the Piazzetta, Venice (50x64cm-20x25in) s. 9-Sep-3 Bonhams, Knightsbridge #168/R est:2000-3000
£3693	$6500	€5392	Venice (33x46cm-13x18in) s. painted c.1920. 23-May-4 Treadway Gallery, Cincinnati #543/R est:6000-8000
£3933	$7198	€5900	Canal a Venise (27x35cm-11x14in) s. 6-Jun-4 Osenat, Fontainebleau #173/R est:5000-6000
£4000	$7200	€5840	Canal a Venise (46x55cm-18x22in) s. 21-Jan-4 Sotheby's, Olympia #520/R est:4000-6000
£4054	$6892	€5919	Venetian Canal with gondolier (24x33cm-9x13in) s. prov. 21-Nov-3 Walker's, Ottawa #225/R est:5000-7000 (C.D 9000)
£4545	$7727	€6500	Venetian square on banks of a canal (73x40cm-29x16in) s. 28-Nov-3 Schloss Ahlden, Ahlden #1428/R est:7800
£4800	$8256	€7008	Venetian canal near the lagoon (24x33cm-9x13in) s. 4-Dec-3 Christie's, Kensington #59/R est:2500-3500
£5000	$9200	€7300	Venetian side canal (27x35cm-11x14in) s. i.verso. 25-Mar-4 Christie's, Kensington #103/R est:4000-6000
£5263	$9526	€8000	Le grand canal, Venise (50x65cm-20x26in) s. 16-Apr-4 Pierre Berge, Paris #6/R est:9000-12000
£5294	$9000	€7729	Canal scene in Venice with Saint Mark's Square (24x33cm-9x13in) s. 19-Nov-3 Bonhams & Butterfields, San Francisco #121/R
£5455	$9382	€7800	Canal a Venise (38x46cm-15x18in) s. 5-Dec-3 Chochon-Barre & Allardi, Paris #20/R est:8000-10000
£5594	$9510	€8000	Venice (54x73cm-21x29in) s. 26-Nov-3 Dorotheum, Vienna #121/R est:6000-8000
£5600	$8904	€8120	Venetian canal scene (28x46cm-11x18in) s. pair. 9-Sep-3 Bonhams, Knightsbridge #275a/R est:5000-7000
£6098	$10915	€8903	Venetian canal with fruitseller's shop (49x65cm-19x26in) s. 4-May-4 Ritchie, Toronto #77/R est:20000-25000 (C.D 15000)
£6294	$10699	€9000	Canal a Venise (50x65cm-20x26in) s. 18-Nov-3 Pierre Berge, Paris #79/R est:10000-12000
£6911	$12370	€10090	Venetian canal with gondolier near villas (46x51cm-18x20in) s. 4-May-4 Ritchie, Toronto #76/R est:18000-22000 (C.D 17000)
£6923	$11562	€9900	Canal a Venise (46x55cm-18x22in) s. 29-Jun-3 Eric Pillon, Calais #11/R
£7000	$12600	€10220	Venetian gondolier (50x65cm-20x26in) s. 21-Jan-4 Sotheby's, Olympia #522/R est:5000-7000
£7000	$12880	€10220	Venetian backwater (53x79cm-21x31in) s. 25-Mar-4 Christie's, Kensington #104/R est:10000-12000
£7600	$12692	€11096	Venetian canal scene (54x81cm-21x32in) s. 12-Nov-3 Sotheby's, Olympia #239/R est:8000-12000
£7931	$14276	€11500	Gondole sur un canal, Venise (50x65cm-20x26in) s. 26-Jan-4 Gros & Delettrez, Paris #38/R est:10000-15000
£8000	$12800	€11680	Venetian canal with gondola and gondolier (50x65cm-20x26in) s. 17-Sep-3 Bonhams, Brooks & Langlois, Jersey #85/R est:8000-12000
£8000	$14560	€11680	Venetian canal (25x33cm-10x13in) s. 16-Jun-4 Christie's, Kensington #94/R est:5000-7000
£8446	$15963	€12500	Canal a Venise (50x65cm-20x26in) s. 17-Feb-4 Galerie Moderne, Brussels #139/R est:10000-15000
£8500	$15640	€12410	On a Venetian canal (56x46cm-22x18in) s. 23-Mar-4 Bonhams, New Bond Street #113/R est:6000-8000
£9000	$16200	€13140	Venetian canal scene (60x81cm-24x32in) s. 21-Jan-4 Sotheby's, Olympia #521/R est:5000-7000
£10000	$16000	€14600	Venetian canal scene with sailing ships and gondolas (48x63cm-19x25in) s. 17-Sep-3 Bonhams, Brooks & Langlois, Jersey #86/R est:10000-12000
£10000	$16000	€14600	Venetian canal scene (52x79cm-20x31in) s. 17-Sep-3 Bonhams, Brooks & Langlois, Jersey #88/R est:10000-15000
£10000	$17000	€14600	Gondola on a Venetian canal (50x65cm-20x26in) s. 19-Nov-3 Bonhams, New Bond Street #135/R est:10000-15000
£10000	$17200	€14600	Venetian canal (50x65cm-20x26in) s. 4-Dec-3 Christie's, Kensington #61a/R est:10000-15000
£10067	$18624	€15000	Coup de soleil (60x92cm-24x36in) s. 14-Mar-4 St-Germain-en-Laye Encheres #73/R est:18000
£10135	$17230	€14797	Venetian Canal with gondolier (51x65cm-20x26in) s. 21-Nov-3 Walker's, Ottawa #222/R est:18000-24000 (C.D 22500)
£11000	$17600	€16060	Grand Canal with St Marks in far left distance (49x63cm-19x25in) s. 17-Sep-3 Bonhams, Brooks & Langlois, Jersey #87/R est:12000-18000
£11000	$18370	€16060	Gondola on Venetian canal (48x63cm-19x25in) s. exhib. 16-Oct-3 Lawrence, Crewkerne #757/R
£11034	$19862	€16000	La Piazzetta et le Palais des Doges (50x65cm-20x26in) s. 26-Jan-4 Gros & Delettrez, Paris #39/R est:10000-15000
£11500	$18400	€16675	Near Campo Santa Marguerita, Venice (51x64cm-20x25in) s. 18-Sep-3 Christie's, Kensington #75/R est:8000-12000
£11500	$19205	€16790	Venetian canal scene (48x63cm-19x25in) s. prov. 16-Oct-3 Lawrence, Crewkerne #756/R
£11765	$20000	€17177	Venetian canal scene (60x81cm-24x32in) s. 29-Oct-3 Christie's, Rockefeller NY #238/R est:10000-15000
£12000	$21840	€17520	Gondolas and sailing boats before the Piazzetta, Venice (50x65cm-20x26in) s. 16-Jun-4 Bonhams, New Bond Street #99/R est:12000-18000
£12000	$22440	€18000	Venetian canal with gondolers (50x65cm-20x26in) s. 26-Jul-4 Bonhams, Bath #86/R est:5000-7000
£13946	$24963	€20500	Venise (65x92cm-26x36in) s. 19-Mar-4 Millon & Associes, Paris #67/R est:5000-8000
£16200	$27054	€23652	Venetian gondolier and canal bridge (51x65cm-20x26in) s. 12-Nov-3 Sotheby's, Olympia #240/R est:10000-15000
£16471	$28000	€24048	View of the Venetian lagoon with St. Mark's Square in the distance (60x118cm-24x46in) s. 19-Nov-3 Bonhams & Butterfields, San Francisco #120/R
£20833	$33958	€30000	Venise, le palais des Doges vu du Grand Canal (50x65cm-20x26in) s. 21-Jul-3 Lesieur & Le Bars, Le Havre #7

Works on paper

£867	$1569	€1300	Venice (65x50cm-26x20in) s.d. pastel. 1-Apr-4 Van Ham, Cologne #1303

BOUVARD, Antoine (attrib) (?-1956) French

£2500	$4150	€3650	Venetian Canal (27x34cm-11x13in) bears sig. 1-Oct-3 Sotheby's, Olympia #298/R est:1500-2000
£15600	$26988	€22776	Figure in a gondola on a Venetian backwater (38x56cm-15x22in) s. 14-Dec-3 Desmond Judd, Cranbrook #1045

BOUVARD, Colette (19th C) French

£700	$1288	€1022	Venice, evening (27x34cm-11x13in) s. 24-Mar-4 Hamptons Fine Art, Godalming #293

BOUVARD, Joseph Antoine (1840-1920) French

£4360	$7500	€6366	Figures on Venetian canal (38x55cm-15x22in) s. 2-Dec-3 Christie's, Rockefeller NY #61/R est:4000-6000
£4545	$7727	€6500	Venetian canal scene (73x40cm-29x16in) s. 28-Nov-3 Schloss Ahlden, Ahlden #1427/R est:7800
£5233	$9000	€7640	Figures by Venetian canal with Saint Mark beyond (38x55cm-15x22in) s. 2-Dec-3 Christie's, Rockefeller NY #62/R est:4000-6000

BOUVARD, Noël (1912-1975) French

£2517	$4505	€3700	Deux gondoles a Venise (19x24cm-7x9in) s. 21-Mar-4 Muizon & Le Coent, Paris #49/R
£3000	$5550	€4380	View towards San Giorgio Maggiore (43x49cm-17x19in) s. 10-Mar-4 Sotheby's, Olympia #313/R est:3000-4000
£4000	$7400	€5840	Venetian canal scene (50x66cm-20x26in) s. 9-Mar-4 Bonhams, Knightsbridge #172a/R est:3000-4000
£4241	$7083	€6149	Docking the gondolas at sunset (51x65cm-20x26in) s. 17-Jun-3 Pinneys, Montreal #45a est:12000-15000 (C.D 9500)
£8500	$14110	€12410	Canal scene (50x65cm-20x26in) s. 1-Oct-3 Sotheby's, Olympia #301/R est:3000-5000
£8844	$15830	€13000	Marchande de fleurs sur un canal a Venise (50x65cm-20x26in) s. 21-Mar-4 Muizon & Le Coent, Paris #50/R

BOUVERIE-HOYTON, Edward (attrib) (?) British?

£700	$1288	€1022	Boys bathing from rocks (76x51cm-30x20in) s. 8-Jun-4 Gorringes, Lewes #2198

BOUVET, Max (19th C) French

£294	$500	€429	Nighttime seascape (54x75cm-21x30in) s. 19-Nov-3 Fischer, Luzern #2024/R (S.FR 650)
£867	$1551	€1300	Maison de paludier, environs du Bourg de Batz (46x55cm-18x22in) s. 16-May-4 Thierry & Lannon, Brest #291
£993	$1808	€1500	Bateaux de peche sortant du port de La Rochelle (43x65cm-17x26in) s. 19-Jun-4 St-Germain-en-Laye Encheres #169/R est:1500

BOUVIE, F A (20th C) Belgian

£1000	$1840	€1500	Vue de la Bourse de Bruxelles (84x97cm-33x38in) s. panel. 14-Jun-4 Horta, Bruxelles #189 est:800-1200
£2416	$4470	€3600	Place Poelaert animee de magistrats (70x90cm-28x35in) s. panel. 15-Mar-4 Horta, Bruxelles #302 est:1000-1200

BOUVIER, Auguste (19th C) French

Works on paper

£280	$512	€409	Minuet (19x27cm-7x11in) s.d.1874 W/C htd white. 27-Jan-4 Bonhams, Knightsbridge #141

BOUVIER, Augustus Jules (c.1827-1881) British

Works on paper

£440	$735	€642	Milkmaid in a alpine landscape (24x36cm-9x14in) s. i.verso W/C htd white. 7-Oct-3 Fellows & Sons, Birmingham #542/R

£800 $1328 €1168 Untitled, lady with owl (65x48cm-26x19in) s.d.1876 W/C. 5-Oct-3 Levis, Calgary #11/R est:2500-3000 (C.D 1800)

BOUVIER, Augustus Jules (attrib) (c.1827-1881) British
£750 $1350 €1095 Girl with water jug (53x40cm-21x16in) 21-Jan-4 Sotheby's, Olympia #272/R
Works on paper
£667 $1227 €1000 Apple pickers (53x34cm-21x13in) s. mixed media. 9-Jun-4 Bukowskis, Helsinki #584/R
£933 $1717 €1400 Picking grapes (53x34cm-21x13in) s. mixed media. 9-Jun-4 Bukowskis, Helsinki #585/R

BOUVIER, Berthe (1868-1936) German
Works on paper
£229 $383 €332 La Place Pury a Neuchatel. s.d. crayon W/C. 21-Jun-3 Galerie du Rhone, Sion #338/R (S.FR 500)

BOUVIER, Gustavus Arthur (fl.1866-1884) British
Works on paper
£260 $416 €380 Rustic hebe (34x18cm-13x7in) s. W/C. 16-Sep-3 Bonhams, Knowle #65
£320 $566 €467 Water carrier (38x28cm-15x11in) s. W/C. 28-Apr-4 Halls, Shrewsbury #442/R

BOUVIER, Jules (1800-1867) British
£550 $919 €803 Orange picker (48x35cm-19x14in) s.i.d.1865. 8-Oct-3 Christie's, Kensington #821
Works on paper
£260 $442 €380 Bridesmaids holding baskets of flowers (28x39cm-11x15in) s. W/C. 25-Nov-3 Bonhams, Knowle #183

BOUVIER, Pierre-Louis (1766-1836) Swiss
Miniatures
£2800 $4844 €4088 Young gentleman (7cm-3in) s.d.1800 oval. 9-Dec-3 Christie's, London #193/R est:1000-1500

BOUVIER, Pietro (1839-1927) Italian
£21127 $36972 €30000 Conversation (36x25cm-14x10in) s. 17-Dec-3 Finarte Semenzato, Milan #114/R est:12000-15000

BOUVIER, Pietro (attrib) (1839-1927) Italian
£315 $542 €460 Portrait of a man's profile (31x22cm-12x9in) s. 8-Dec-3 Philippe Schuler, Zurich #5824 (S.FR 700)

BOUVIOLLE, Maurice (1893-1971) French
£1056 $1827 €1500 Nature morte a la rose des sables (89x116cm-35x46in) s.i.d.1939 lit. 15-Dec-3 Gros & Delettrez, Paris #217/R est:1500-2500
£1986 $3316 €2800 L'ecole coranique (38x46cm-15x18in) s. cardboard on canvas lit. 16-Jun-3 Gros & Delettrez, Paris #486/R est:2500-3000
£2098 $3608 €3000 Musiciens (46x55cm-18x22in) s. 8-Dec-3 Tajan, Paris #237/R est:3000-3500
£5714 $10400 €8400 Marche d'Afrique du Nord (54x65cm-21x26in) s. 8-Feb-4 Anaf, Lyon #106/R est:7500-8000
£9155 $15838 €13000 Marche (60x81cm-24x32in) s. i.verso. 15-Dec-3 Gros & Delettrez, Paris #353/R est:10000-15000
£14184 $23688 €20000 Vue d'Alger de la Villa Abd-el-Tif (73x92cm-29x36in) s. 16-Jun-3 Gros & Delettrez, Paris #527/R est:10000-150000
Works on paper
£493 $853 €700 Guerara (22x31cm-9x12in) s.i.d.1932 Chinese ink W/C. 15-Dec-3 Gros & Delettrez, Paris #93

BOUY, Gaston (1866-?) French
Works on paper
£455 $782 €650 Femme au turban noir (16x11cm-6x4in) s. pastel. 8-Dec-3 Rossini, Paris #77

BOUYS, André (1656-1740) French
£7895 $14526 €12000 Self-portrait (72x60cm-28x24in) 24-Jun-4 Christie's, Paris #121/R est:2000-4000

BOUYSSOU, Jacques (1926-1997) French
£441 $750 €644 Honfleur (23x28cm-9x11in) s. i.d.1964 verso. 5-Nov-3 Doyle, New York #15/R
£759 $1267 €1100 Bouquet de fleurs (35x27cm-14x11in) s. d.63 verso. 11-Nov-3 Lesieur & Le Bars, Le Havre #129
£805 $1498 €1200 Le pont (54x65cm-21x26in) s. 2-Mar-4 Artcurial Briest, Paris #257/R
£845 $1462 €1200 Bord de Seine a Poissy (27x35cm-11x14in) s. 14-Dec-3 Eric Pillon, Calais #197/R
£1007 $1873 €1500 Le pecheur sur la Marne (60x73cm-24x29in) s. i.verso. 2-Mar-4 Artcurial Briest, Paris #256/R est:1500-2000
£1020 $1827 €1500 Honfleur (27x35cm-11x14in) s. painted 1961. 19-Mar-4 Millon & Associes, Paris #110 est:1500-1800
£1074 $1997 €1600 Pais, la peniche (65x81cm-26x32in) s. i.verso. 2-Mar-4 Artcurial Briest, Paris #259 est:1500-2000
£1208 $2247 €1800 Les quais a Paris (54x65cm-21x26in) s. i.verso prov. 2-Mar-4 Artcurial Briest, Paris #258 est:1200-1800
£1233 $2096 €1800 Peniche sur la Marne (54x65cm-21x26in) s. 9-Nov-3 Eric Pillon, Calais #212/R
£1370 $2329 €2000 Ostende, sortie du port (60x73cm-24x29in) s. 9-Nov-3 Eric Pillon, Calais #211/R
£1575 $2678 €2300 Criee sur le port du Croisic (73x92cm-29x36in) s. 9-Nov-3 Eric Pillon, Calais #209/R
£1761 $3046 €2500 La Seine a Paris (65x81cm-26x32in) s.i.d.1964. 10-Dec-3 Rossini, Paris #56/R
£1918 $3260 €2800 Paris, Rue Saint-Germain (73x60cm-29x24in) s. 9-Nov-3 Eric Pillon, Calais #204/R
£2013 $3705 €3000 Port d'Ajaccio (65x54cm-26x21in) s. i.d.Avril 1967 verso. 28-Mar-4 Versailles Encheres #18/R est:1500-2000
£2466 $3871 €3600 Port de Honfleur (46x55cm-18x22in) s. i.d.1965 verso. 20-Apr-3 Deauville, France #114/R est:2800-3200
£2819 $5187 €4200 Canal de la Vilette a Paris (73x92cm-29x36in) s. i.d.1968 verso. 28-Mar-4 Versailles Encheres #17/R est:2800-3000
£3310 $5528 €4800 Honfleur (54x65cm-21x26in) s. d.63 verso. 11-Nov-3 Lesieur & Le Bars, Le Havre #128/R
£3642 $6666 €5500 Port de Dieppe (81x100cm-32x39in) s.i.d.1964. 7-Apr-4 Piasa, Paris #151/R est:2500-3000
Works on paper
£268 $499 €400 Vase de fleurs (50x32cm-20x13in) s. W/C. 7-Mar-4 Lesieur & Le Bars, Le Havre #19
£403 $749 €600 L'estuaire (30x23cm-12x9in) s. chl W/C. 7-Mar-4 Lesieur & Le Bars, Le Havre #18

BOUZIANIS, Georgios (1885-1959) Greek
£50000 $87500 €73000 Seated girl (53x41cm-21x16in) s. prov.exhib.lit. 16-Dec-3 Bonhams, New Bond Street #91/R est:50000-70000
£60000 $102000 €87600 Woman washing clothes (94x45cm-37x18in) s. prov.exhib. 18-Nov-3 Sotheby's, London #62/R est:60000-80000
Works on paper
£10000 $17500 €14600 Portrait of a lady (32x27cm-13x11in) s. W/C prov. 16-Dec-3 Bonhams, New Bond Street #102/R est:10000-15000
£21000 $36750 €30660 Portrait of the artist's wife (44x50cm-17x20in) s.i.d.30 W/C pencil prov.exhib.lit. 16-Dec-3 Bonhams, New Bond Street #98/R est:20000-25000

BOUZO, Manuel (1946-) Spanish
£2000 $3620 €3000 Inn in Prague (195x250cm-77x98in) s.i.d.1997 verso. 30-Mar-4 Segre, Madrid #276/R est:3000

BOVEN, A A (20th C) ?
£1000 $1810 €1500 Reunion (40x50cm-16x20in) s. 30-Mar-4 Campo & Campo, Antwerp #20/R est:1450-1650

BOVIE, Felix (1812-1880) Belgian
£559 $934 €800 Conversation au bord de la cascade sur fond de paysage montagneux (54x80cm-21x31in) s.i.d.1874 verso. 13-Oct-3 Horta, Bruxelles #33
£559 $934 €800 Conversation au bord de l'etang (35x53cm-14x21in) s. 13-Oct-3 Horta, Bruxelles #34

BOVIN, Karl (1907-1985) Danish
£498 $806 €722 Path through Bangsbo woods, winter (37x31cm-15x12in) s. 4-Aug-3 Rasmussen, Vejle #701 (D.KR 5200)
£1254 $2258 €1831 Coastal landscape with dark sky (54x65cm-21x26in) s. 24-Apr-4 Rasmussen, Havnen #4197/R est:6000-8000 (D.KR 14000)

BOWDOIN, Harriette (1880-1947) American
£604 $1100 €882 Floral still life (56x46cm-22x18in) s. canvas on board. 15-Jun-4 John Moran, Pasadena #37a
£1163 $2000 €1698 Footbridge over a stream (22x27cm-9x11in) bears sig prov. 3-Dec-3 Doyle, New York #224/R est:3000-5000
£1308 $2250 €1910 Girl reading (55x67cm-22x26in) bears sig prov. 3-Dec-3 Doyle, New York #234/R est:4000-6000
£1890 $3250 €2759 Woman and children in Central Park (25x20cm-10x8in) s. prov. 3-Dec-3 Doyle, New York #266/R est:2000-3000
£2762 $4750 €4033 Park view (55x67cm-22x26in) s. prov. 3-Dec-3 Doyle, New York #233/R est:8000-12000

BOWEN, Christine (20th C) British?
£550 $1023 €803 Still life (91x81cm-36x32in) s.d.97 acrylic on paper. 3-Mar-4 John Ross, Belfast #24
Works on paper
£250 $465 €365 Roman head (89x61cm-35x24in) s. mixed media. 3-Mar-4 John Ross, Belfast #115
£450 $824 €657 Head (86x61cm-34x24in) s. mixed media. 2-Jun-4 John Ross, Belfast #193
£750 $1373 €1095 Still life (104x68cm-41x27in) s. mixed media. 2-Jun-4 John Ross, Belfast #105
£1100 $1892 €1606 Still life (101x78cm-40x31in) s. mixed media. 3-Dec-3 John Ross, Belfast #115 est:1200-1400

BOWEN, Denis (1921-) British
£650 $1105 €949 Double star A (77x61cm-30x24in) i.d.1989 verso exhib. 26-Nov-3 Hamptons Fine Art, Godalming #115/R

BOWEN, Greta (1880-1981) Irish
£704 $1232 €1000 Village river scene with figures (33x38cm-13x15in) s. board. 16-Dec-3 James Adam, Dublin #87/R
£800 $1312 €1168 Promenade (25x30cm-10x12in) s. board. 4-Jun-3 John Ross, Belfast #82
£800 $1328 €1168 Park (28x40cm-11x16in) s. board. 1-Oct-3 John Ross, Belfast #160a
Works on paper
£500 $860 €730 Town hall, Newry (40x56cm-16x22in) s. mixed media. 3-Dec-3 John Ross, Belfast #220
£500 $930 €730 Street (30x38cm-12x15in) s. mixed media. 3-Mar-4 John Ross, Belfast #152

BOWEN, Howard (20th C) British

£280 $468 €409 Still life with tigerlillies in a green vase (76x63cm-30x25in) s. 11-Nov-3 Bonhams, Ipswich #251
£340 $615 €496 Still life of flowers (76x63cm-30x25in) s. 30-Mar-4 Sworder & Son, Bishops Stortford #528/R

BOWEN, Keith (20th C) British

Works on paper
£325 $530 €475 Study of a Welsh mountain ewe standing (43x64cm-17x25in) s.d.1990 pastel. 27-Sep-3 Rogers Jones, Clwyd #58

BOWEN, Owen (1873-1967) British

£260 $434 €380 Still life study of flowers in a vase (53x38cm-21x15in) s. 10-Oct-3 Richardson & Smith, Whitby #144
£280 $445 €406 Still life vase of flowers with window beyond (15x13cm-6x5in) board. 9-Sep-3 David Duggleby, Scarborough #362
£280 $476 €409 Old Wetherby bridge (50x66cm-20x26in) s. 18-Nov-3 Bonhams, Leeds #262
£280 $510 €409 Dales Street scene with figures (36x25cm-14x10in) s. board. 16-Jun-4 Andrew Hartley, Ilkley #1124
£280 $524 €409 Woodland path with silver birch trees and bracken (46x36cm-18x14in) s.indis.d.97. 22-Jul-4 Tennants, Leyburn #934
£300 $477 €435 Wooded river landscape with path (21x29cm-8x11in) s.d.1921. 11-Sep-3 Morphets, Harrogate #258
£300 $516 €438 Still life with roses (43x33cm-17x13in) s. 3-Dec-3 Andrew Hartley, Ilkley #1230
£300 $510 €438 Autumnal forest landscape (36x25cm-14x10in) s. 26-Nov-3 Hamptons Fine Art, Godalming #238
£300 $546 €438 The flock (24x34cm-9x13in) 15-Jun-4 Bonhams, Leeds #168
£320 $509 €464 Goathland Moor (45x65cm-18x26in) s. 9-Sep-3 David Duggleby, Scarborough #380
£350 $585 €511 Two figures with horses (25x33cm-10x13in) s.d.98. 17-Oct-3 Keys, Aylsham #820
£350 $585 €511 Feeding time (23x28cm-9x11in) s. board. 10-Oct-3 Richardson & Smith, Whitby #92
£350 $585 €511 Riverscene (38x56cm-15x22in) s. board. 8-Oct-3 Andrew Hartley, Ilkley #1151/R
£360 $587 €526 Yorkshire Dales roadside cottage (35x45cm-14x18in) s. canvas on board. 23-Sep-3 Bonhams, Chester #956
£450 $810 €657 Golden light, Fylingdales (25x30cm-10x12in) s. i.verso. 21-Apr-4 Tennants, Leyburn #1259
£480 $888 €701 Chrysanthemums in blue and white jug (76x56cm-30x22in) s. sketch verso. 12-Feb-4 Andrew Hartley, Ilkley #885
£480 $869 €701 Still life study of flowers in a vase (43x33cm-17x13in) s. board. 15-Apr-4 Richardson & Smith, Whitby #114/R
£500 $835 €730 Still life with flowers (43x48cm-17x19in) s. 8-Oct-3 Andrew Hartley, Ilkley #1166
£500 $910 €730 View of Solway Firth Estuary (34x44cm-13x17in) s. prov. 15-Jun-4 Bonhams, Leeds #170
£520 $931 €759 Still life vase of flowers (13x15cm-5x6in) mono. board. 17-May-4 David Duggleby, Scarborough #603/R
£540 $977 €788 The gatherer (25x32cm-10x13in) s. panel. 30-Mar-4 David Duggleby, Scarborough #19/R
£550 $990 €803 Anemones in green vase. Mixed flowers in a vase (18x22cm-7x9in) init. board pair. 22-Apr-4 Mellors & Kirk, Nottingham #1064
£650 $1170 €949 View of Wetherby, Yorkshire (51x66cm-20x26in) s. i.verso. 21-Apr-4 Tennants, Leyburn #1257
£660 $1181 €964 Cottage at Fylingdales, Robin Hoods Bay (29x39cm-11x15in) s. 16-Mar-4 Bonhams, Leeds #656
£700 $1190 €1022 Landscape view with cattle (34x49cm-13x19in) s.d.1919. 18-Nov-3 Bonhams, Leeds #264
£800 $1440 €1168 Still life of anemones in a green bowl (18x22cm-7x9in) board prov. 21-Apr-4 Tennants, Leyburn #1297
£820 $1312 €1197 Cattle by a windmill (30x46cm-12x18in) s. 16-Sep-3 Bonhams, Knowle #83
£850 $1530 €1241 Still life of flowers in a blue vase (34x29cm-13x11in) s.d.1931 board. 21-Apr-4 Tennants, Leyburn #1206
£950 $1710 €1387 Mevagissey (51x66cm-20x26in) s. 21-Apr-4 Tennants, Leyburn #1256
£950 $1710 €1387 Still life of chrysanthemums in a green vase (46x51cm-18x20in) s. 21-Apr-4 Tennants, Leyburn #1208/R
£980 $1558 €1421 Looking towards village and church spire. Figures on a path (11x18cm-4x7in) s. board pair. 9-Sep-3 David Duggleby, Scarborough #281
£1000 $1670 €1460 Dutch river landscape with two figures to the shore (59x44cm-23x17in) s. 7-Oct-3 Fellows & Sons, Birmingham #375/R est:1000-1500
£1300 $2340 €1898 Harbour scene with figures and fishing boats beside stone quayside (46x61cm-18x24in) s. 21-Apr-4 Tennants, Leyburn #1258 est:800-1200
£1550 $2511 €2248 Chrysanthemuns in a glass vase on a table (42x29cm-17x11in) s. panel. 30-Jul-3 Hamptons Fine Art, Godalming #181/R est:500-700
£1650 $2987 €2409 Robin Hoods Bay (24x34cm-9x13in) s.d.98 panel. 30-Mar-4 David Duggleby, Scarborough #1/R est:800-1200
£2100 $3822 €3066 Ploughing the field (28x39cm-11x15in) s.i.indis.d.1921. 15-Jun-4 Bonhams, Leeds #171/R est:1000-1500
£2300 $3910 €3358 Milk maid and cattle in an open landscape (33x49cm-13x19in) s.d.1918. 18-Nov-3 Bonhams, Leeds #261/R est:900-1200
Works on paper
£320 $598 €467 Caernarfon Castle and the Menai Bridge (28x37cm-11x15in) s. pencil W/C htd white. 22-Jul-4 Tennants, Leyburn #777
£620 $1135 €905 Garden scene with a lady in the foreground (25x35cm-10x14in) s.indis.d. W/C. 2-Jun-4 Dickinson, Davy & Markham, Brigg #931
£1900 $3553 €2774 Figures in a summer meadow above the river Wharfe (51x74cm-20x29in) s.d.1917 pencil W/C htd white. 22-Jul-4 Tennants, Leyburn #778/R est:700-900

BOWER, Alexander (1875-1952) American

£867 $1500 €1266 Maine landscape. s.i.on stretcher. 10-Dec-3 Alderfer's, Hatfield #359/R est:1500-2500
£867 $1500 €1266 Monhegan Island (61x91cm-24x36in) s.i.verso. 10-Dec-3 Alderfer's, Hatfield #358/R est:1500-2500
£1006 $1600 €1469 Farm near Boothbay (46x56cm-18x22in) s.verso. 10-Sep-3 Alderfer's, Hatfield #353 est:1500-1800
Works on paper
£432 $700 €626 Green water (34x48cm-13x19in) s.d.1931 W/C prov.exhib. 8-Aug-3 Barridorf, Portland #290/R

BOWER, Edward (attrib) (17th C) British

£7800 $14196 €11388 Portrait of Elizabeth Pickering (75x62cm-30x24in) painted oval. 1-Jul-4 Sotheby's, London #106 est:4000-6000
£14815 $24000 €21630 Portrait of Jane Glanville (109x81cm-43x32in) d.1638 prov.lit. 3-Aug-3 North East Auctions, Portsmouth #1772/R est:7000-10000

BOWERS, Albert Edward (fl.1875-1893) British

Works on paper
£250 $460 €365 Cows before a farm cottage (36x52cm-14x20in) s. pencil W/C htd white. 25-Mar-4 Christie's, Kensington #100
£270 $500 €394 Rural scene with figures, animals and an old cottage (58x74cm-23x29in) s. 10-Feb-4 Dickinson, Davy & Markham, Brigg #814

BOWERS, Henry Robertson (19/20th C) British

Photographs
£4000 $6520 €5840 At the South Pole (32x41cm-13x16in) gelatin silver print card. 25-Sep-3 Christie's, London #419/R est:3000-4000

BOWERS, Stephen J (fl.1874-1891) British

Works on paper
£480 $782 €696 View of Windsor Castle (33x50cm-13x20in) s. W/C. 23-Sep-3 Bonhams, Knightsbridge #47/R

BOWES, David (1957-) American

£873 $1607 €1275 New worlds for all - the mystic lamb (170x140cm-67x55in) s.mono.d.1985 acrylic tempera prov. 8-Jun-4 Germann, Zurich #114/R (S.FR 2000)
£2041 $3653 €3000 Temple (45x48cm-18x19in) init.d.1993. 16-Mar-4 Finarte Semenzato, Milan #367/R est:3200

BOWEY, Olwyn (1936-) British

£350 $648 €511 Country cottage (51x58cm-20x23in) s. board. 11-Mar-4 Christie's, Kensington #269
£600 $1092 €876 At the edge of the fields (91x122cm-36x48in) s. 1-Jul-4 Christie's, Kensington #292/R
£1300 $2288 €1898 Hydrangea (63x53cm-25x21in) s. board. 18-May-4 Woolley & Wallis, Salisbury #123a/R est:400-600
Works on paper
£800 $1456 €1168 Greenhouses, West Dean (55x48cm-22x19in) s.d.1988 W/C bodycol. 1-Jul-4 Christie's, Kensington #293/R

BOWIE, John (1867-1914) British

£270 $432 €394 Off to the goose green (24x35cm-9x14in) init. board. 18-Sep-3 Bonhams, Edinburgh #340

BOWKETT, Jane Maria (1837-1891) British

£726 $1300 €1060 In the parlor (76x51cm-30x20in) init. 14-May-4 Skinner, Boston #56/R est:1500-3000
£2800 $4648 €4088 Just awake (86x126cm-34x50in) init. 1-Oct-3 Sotheby's, Olympia #119/R est:3000-5000
£4000 $6680 €5840 Ophelia (76x30cm-30x12in) mono.d.1881 exhib. 13-Nov-3 Christie's, Kensington #321/R est:5000-8000
£8500 $15300 €12410 Windy day on the beach (61x46cm-24x18in) init. 21-Apr-4 Tennants, Leyburn #1224/R est:4000-6000

BOWLER, Joseph (jnr) (1928-) American

£535 $1000 €781 Beautiful young woman wearing eyeglasses (51x41cm-20x16in) s. painted c.1960. 26-Feb-4 Illustration House, New York #29

BOWLER, Thomas W (1812-1869) British

Works on paper
£650 $1151 €949 Old Peck Inn, Cape. Landscape with a church (18x25cm-7x10in) i.d.Friday 13th Sept 1851 i.verso pencil double-sided prov.lit. 29-Apr-4 Christie's, Kensington #136/R
£1400 $2282 €2044 St Vincent from the sea (22x33cm-9x13in) i.d.1854 W/C prov.lit. 25-Sep-3 Christie's, London #456/R est:1500-2500
£1400 $2478 €2044 Views of Fort and Block House, Simonstown (18x26cm-7x10in) one s.i.d.1866 pencil W/C double-sided one i.W/C pair prov.lit. 29-Apr-4 Christie's, Kensington #137/R est:800-1200
£3361 $6084 €4907 Green Point (24x36cm-9x14in) W/C htd white lit. 30-Mar-4 Stephan Welz, Johannesburg #463/R est:40000-60000 (SA.R 40000)

BOWLES, George (fl.1857-1869) British

Works on paper
£260 $481 €380 Crumlin viaduct, Monmouthshire (49x34cm-19x13in) W/C prov. 14-Jan-4 Lawrence, Crewkerne #1321

BOWLES, Ian (1947-) British

Works on paper
£280 $507 €409 Woodcock resting in the snow (24x34cm-9x13in) s. W/C. 31-Mar-4 Bonhams, Knightsbridge #12/R

BOWLEY, Edward O (attrib) (fl.1843-1870) British

£440 $814 €642 On the Sussex Downs (48x61cm-19x24in) i. stretcher. 14-Jul-4 Christie's, Kensington #817/R

BOWMAN, Albert George (fl.1880-1908) British
£4000 $6800 €5840 On the banks of the Devon, Dollar, N (103x164cm-41x65in) s.d.1904 exhib. 19-Nov-3 Bonhams, New Bond Street #70/R est:4000-6000

BOWMAN, John Shearer (1819-1909) Australian/British
£688 $1108 €1004 Mountain range at sunset (28x41cm-11x16in) s. board prov. 13-Oct-3 Joel, Victoria #260 est:2000-3000 (A.D 1700)
£729 $1173 €1064 Waterhole, Victoria (42x52cm-17x20in) board prov. 13-Oct-3 Joel, Victoria #354 est:2000-3000 (A.D 1800)

BOWRING, Walter Armiger (1874-1931) New Zealander
£344 $585 €502 Paraparaumu landscape (25x34cm-10x13in) s. board. 4-Nov-3 Peter Webb, Auckland #53 (NZ.D 950)

BOWYER, Jason Richard (1957-) British
£700 $1190 €1022 Still life of flowers (51x42cm-20x17in) s. board pair. 26-Nov-3 Sotheby's, Olympia #87/R

BOWYER, William (1926-) British
£720 $1267 €1051 White house, Barnes Pond (46x62cm-18x24in) s. board. 19-May-4 Sotheby's, Olympia #236/R
£760 $1338 €1110 A day out in Walberswick (30x61cm-12x24in) s. board. 18-May-4 Woolley & Wallis, Salisbury #66/R
£920 $1619 €1343 High tide, Chiswick Mall (59x49cm-23x19in) s. board. 18-May-4 Woolley & Wallis, Salisbury #85/R
£1150 $2024 €1679 Morning sun, Richmond (76x101cm-30x40in) prov.exhib. 18-May-4 Woolley & Wallis, Salisbury #76/R est:2000-3000
£1250 $2125 €1825 The Thames near Chiswick (51x61cm-20x24in) s. 26-Nov-3 Sotheby's, Olympia #114/R est:800-1200
£2200 $3872 €3212 Artist's table top with flowers (71x71cm-28x28in) s.d.86. 19-May-4 Sotheby's, Olympia #216/R est:1000-1500
Works on paper
£300 $501 €438 Time for lunch darling (34x29cm-13x11in) s.d.88 i.verso W/C bodycol. 16-Oct-3 Christie's, Kensington #422/R
£350 $585 €511 Rethemoyn (34x51cm-13x20in) s.d.80 W/C pen black ink exhib. 16-Oct-3 Christie's, Kensington #426
£450 $752 €657 Rialto Bridge, Venice (31x38cm-12x15in) s.d.89 W/C bodycol. 16-Oct-3 Christie's, Kensington #438/R
£450 $833 €657 Sunflowers fields, Seville (48x73cm-19x29in) s.d.71 pencil W/C exhib. 11-Mar-4 Christie's, Kensington #267

BOX, Eden (1919-1988) British
£700 $1295 €1022 Before the party (46x51cm-18x20in) s. prov. 11-Feb-4 Sotheby's, Olympia #229/R

BOXALL, Sir William (attrib) (1800-1879) British
£900 $1494 €1314 Portrait of a girl, half length, wearing a white dress (25x20cm-10x8in) 30-Sep-3 Sotheby's, London #361/R

BOXER, Stanley (1926-) American
£2473 $4500 €3611 Softstippledsashes (202x202cm-80x80in) s.d.8/75 verso oil on linen prov. 29-Jun-4 Sotheby's, New York #495/R est:4000-6000

BOY, Gottfried (1701-?) German
£7222 $13000 €10544 Portrait of George II in military uniform (128x97cm-50x38in) s.i.d.1747 prov.lit. 23-Jan-4 Christie's, Rockefeller NY #59/R est:15000-25000

BOY, Peter (c.1648-1727) German
Miniatures
£28000 $50120 €40880 Peter I Alexeievich, The Great Emperor (4cm-2in) i.d.1720 enamel. 27-May-4 Sotheby's, London #63/R est:14000-18000

BOYCE, George Price (1826-1897) British
£23500 $42065 €34310 Abinger Mill Pond, Surrey, a swan in the foreground (30x38cm-12x15in) s. 17-Mar-4 John Nicholson, Haslemere #656/R est:2000-3000
Works on paper
£2000 $3700 €2920 Near Streatley, Berkshire. Dorchester, Oxfordshire (5x23cm-2x9in) one s.d.1868 W/C pair. 9-Mar-4 Bonhams, New Bond Street #73a/R est:1000-1500
£3250 $5818 €4745 Looking eastwards along the Fundamenta Nouva, Venice at sunset (18x25cm-7x10in) mono.d.27.9.54 exhib. 17-Mar-4 John Nicholson, Haslemere #657/R est:1000-1500
£5200 $9464 €7592 Old buildings at Kingswear, South Devon (52x42cm-20x17in) s.d.1874 W/C prov.exhib.lit. 1-Jul-4 Sotheby's, London #264/R est:3000-5000
£6000 $10740 €8760 Portrait of a Turkish girl (36x23cm-14x9in) mono. 17-Mar-4 John Nicholson, Haslemere #655/R est:3000-5000

BOYCE, Norman Septimus (1895-1962) British
Works on paper
£260 $434 €380 Ship at sail with steam vessels beyond (36x51cm-14x20in) s. W/C. 10-Oct-3 Richardson & Smith, Whitby #14

BOYCE, William Thomas Nicholas (1857-1911) British
£360 $572 €526 Sailing vessels off the North East coast with Tynemouth Priory in distance (34x53cm-13x21in) s.d.1911. 18-Mar-3 Anderson & Garland, Newcastle #284
£510 $811 €745 Herring drifters and other vessels off the North East Coast (18x52cm-7x20in) s.d.1903. 18-Mar-3 Anderson & Garland, Newcastle #281
£540 $859 €788 Shipping off the Tyne (36x53cm-14x21in) s.d.1901. 18-Mar-3 Anderson & Garland, Newcastle #282
Works on paper
£280 $524 €409 Fishing boats off a port at sunset (17x51cm-7x20in) s.d.1908 W/C. 20-Jul-4 Dreweatt Neate, Newbury #191/R
£290 $534 €423 North sea with shipping on the horizon and gulls circling (30x66cm-12x26in) s.d.1906 W/C. 23-Mar-4 Anderson & Garland, Newcastle #271/R
£300 $546 €438 Brigantine leaving the Tyne (51x35cm-20x14in) s.d.1900 W/C. 29-Jun-4 Anderson & Garland, Newcastle #211
£340 $554 €496 Shipping off the North East coast (23x49cm-9x19in) s.d.1902 W/C. 23-Sep-3 Anderson & Garland, Newcastle #228
£400 $668 €584 Steamship and other vessels. s. W/C. 10-Oct-3 Richardson & Smith, Whitby #109a
£420 $760 €613 Sailing ship under tow, North Shields trawler in the foreground (25x48cm-10x19in) s.d.1909 W/C. 16-Apr-4 Keys, Aylsham #521/R
£460 $750 €672 Herring drifter at sunrise (49x37cm-19x15in) s.d.1909 W/C. 23-Sep-3 Anderson & Garland, Newcastle #230/R
£500 $915 €750 Ship under sail (51x23cm-20x9in) s.d.1906 W/C. 30-Jul-4 Jim Railton, Durham #357
£520 $848 €759 Fishing boats under a moonlit sky (37x52cm-15x20in) s.d.1908 W/C. 23-Sep-3 Anderson & Garland, Newcastle #229/R

BOYCOTT-BROWN, Hugh (1909-1990) British
£350 $585 €511 Dinghy racing off Aldeburgh (33x39cm-13x15in) s.d.55 board. 8-Oct-3 Christie's, Kensington #869
£350 $585 €511 Bosham harbour (41x51cm-16x20in) s. 16-Oct-3 Christie's, Kensington #388/R
£350 $627 €511 Pin Mill, Suffolk (50x39cm-20x15in) s. board. 11-May-4 Dreweatt Neate, Newbury #483/R
£400 $652 €580 Ostende market (38x48cm-15x19in) s. board. 23-Sep-3 Bonhams, Leeds #159/R
£440 $779 €642 Early evening in port (61x91cm-24x36in) s. 29-Apr-4 Gorringes, Lewes #2529
£500 $895 €730 Ketch soaring, North Wales (58x74cm-23x29in) s.d.1977. 18-Mar-4 Neales, Nottingham #786
£700 $1113 €1022 Fishing vessels (36x51cm-14x20in) s. board. 10-Sep-3 Sotheby's, Olympia #249/R
£700 $1295 €1022 Maldon, rainy day (18x25cm-7x10in) s.i.d.July 18th 1980 verso board. 11-Feb-4 Sotheby's, Olympia #166/R
£950 $1587 €1387 Yachts in an estuary (61x91cm-24x36in) s. 16-Oct-3 Christie's, Kensington #387/R
£1500 $2730 €2190 Fishing boats on Hastings beach (61x91cm-24x36in) s. 1-Jul-4 Christie's, Kensington #88/R est:1500-2500

BOYD, Alexander Stuart (1854-1930) British
£400 $724 €584 Fishing boats at Palma (23x31cm-9x12in) s.d.1916 board. 16-Apr-4 Honiton Galleries, Honiton #631
Works on paper
£950 $1587 €1387 Samples of solicitors (46x36cm-18x14in) init. ink. 14-Oct-3 Bonhams, New Bond Street #242/R

BOYD, Arthur Merric (snr) (1862-1940) Australian
£813 $1455 €1187 Haystacks (28x49cm-11x19in) s. board. 10-May-4 Joel, Victoria #242 est:2000-3000 (A.D 2000)
Works on paper
£1017 $1729 €1485 Shipwright's Point, Tasmania (24x34cm-9x13in) s.d.1930 i.verso W/C. 24-Nov-3 Sotheby's, Melbourne #206/R est:2000-3000 (A.D 2400)

BOYD, Arthur Merric Bloomfield (1920-1999) Australian
£1700 $2738 €2482 Portrait of a young woman (47x38cm-19x15in) s. canvas on board prov. 25-Aug-3 Sotheby's, Paddington #367/R est:4000-6000 (A.D 4200)
£3830 $6510 €5592 Shoalhaven with Swan (22x15cm-9x6in) s. composition board. 26-Nov-3 Deutscher-Menzies, Melbourne #9/R est:10000-15000 (A.D 9000)
£4000 $7080 €5840 Riverside encampment (30x38cm-12x15in) s.d.1994 board. 27-Apr-4 Bonhams, New Bond Street #8/R est:3000-5000
£4472 $7020 €6484 Bundanon (30x22cm-12x9in) s. board. 26-Aug-3 Christie's, Sydney #139/R est:10000-15000 (A.D 11000)
£4483 $6993 €6500 Pink landscape and black swan (29x20cm-11x8in) s. board. 1-Aug-2 Joel, Victoria #155 est:8000-10000 (A.D 13000)
£5263 $8474 €7684 Portrait of Beverley Prowse (122x91cm-48x36in) s. composition board exhib. 25-Aug-3 Sotheby's, Paddington #195/R est:20000-30000 (A.D 13000)
£5725 $10420 €8359 Shoalhaven landscape (23x30cm-9x12in) s. oil synthetic polymer board prov. 16-Jun-4 Deutscher-Menzies, Melbourne #52/R est:14000-18000 (A.D 15000)
£6107 $11115 €8916 I am not coming out (152x22cm-60x9in) s.i. prov.exhib. 16-Jun-4 Deutscher-Menzies, Melbourne #46/R est:25000-35000 (A.D 16000)
£6107 $11115 €8916 Shoalhaven River (38x30cm-15x12in) s. board. 16-Jun-4 Deutscher-Menzies, Melbourne #77/R est:15000-20000 (A.D 16000)
£6557 $10623 €9573 Cockatoos on the Shoalhaven (37x30cm-15x12in) s. board. 30-Jul-3 Goodman, Sydney #18/R est:12000-18000 (A.D 16000)
£6809 $11574 €9941 Shoalhaven landscape (15x22cm-6x9in) s. board painted c.1978 prov. 25-Nov-3 Christie's, Melbourne #99/R est:10000-15000 (A.D 16000)
£6911 $10850 €10021 Nebuchadnezzar and gold lion (27x77cm-11x30in) s. paper on board prov. 26-Aug-3 Christie's, Sydney #66/R est:20000-25000 (A.D 17000)
£8264 $14628 €12065 Shoalhaven River and blackbird (29x21cm-11x8in) s. board prov. 3-May-4 Christie's, Melbourne #46/R est:20000-30000 (A.D 20000)
£9160 $16672 €13374 An hallucinated cow (152x122cm-60x48in) s. prov. 16-Jun-4 Deutscher-Menzies, Melbourne #139/R est:30000-40000 (A.D 24000)
£9836 $15541 €14361 Shoalhaven landscape (15x21cm-6x8in) s.i. board prov.exhib. 2-Sep-3 Deutscher-Menzies, Melbourne #53/R est:18000-24000 (A.D 24000)
£9836 $15541 €14361 Summer morning, Mentone (30x42cm-12x17in) s.d.39 board prov. 2-Sep-3 Deutscher-Menzies, Melbourne #79/R est:28000-35000 (A.D 24000)
£12214 $22229 €17832 Ram in thickets with black cockatoos (63x76cm-25x30in) s. prov.exhib. 16-Jun-4 Deutscher-Menzies, Melbourne #35/R est:25000-35000 (A.D 32000)
£12397 $21942 €18100 Bride by a stream (47x63cm-19x25in) s. board prov. 3-May-4 Christie's, Melbourne #28/R est:30000-40000 (A.D 30000)
£13740 $25008 €20060 Shoalhaven landscape (60x46cm-24x18in) s. oil synthetic polymer on board prov. 16-Jun-4 Deutscher-Menzies, Melbourne #61/R est:30000-40000 (A.D 36000)
£15254 $25932 €22271 Lovers (59x59cm-23x23in) s. perspex. 24-Nov-3 Sotheby's, Melbourne #43/R est:15000-20000 (A.D 36000)
£15254 $25932 €22271 Nudes under a lamp - joined figures II (150x120cm-59x47in) s. composition board painted 1962 prov.exhib. 24-Nov-3 Sotheby's, Melbourne #58/R est:35000-55000 (A.D 36000)
£15267 $27786 €22290 Butterfly hunter (160x182cm-63x72in) s. prov. 16-Jun-4 Deutscher-Menzies, Melbourne #149/R est:45000-65000 (A.D 40000)
£16260 $25528 €23577 Butterfly hunter (160x182cm-63x72in) s. prov.exhib. 26-Aug-3 Christie's, Sydney #33/R est:58000-70000 (A.D 40000)

£20339	$34576	€29695	Lovers (60x60cm-24x24in) s. prov. 24-Nov-3 Sotheby's, Melbourne #22/R est:12000-15000 (A.D 48000)
£20599	$37903	€30075	Fishing on the Shoalhaven (91x122cm-36x48in) s. board. 28-Jun-4 Australian Art Auctions, Sydney #140/R (A.D 55000)
£21694	$40134	€31673	Rock and skull with flowers (122x152cm-48x60in) s. i.verso prov. 10-Mar-4 Deutscher-Menzies, Melbourne #74/R est:42000-50000 (A.D 52500)
£22358	$35102	€32419	Lovers in forest with black birds and nest (17x112cm-7x44in) s. 26-Aug-3 Christie's, Sydney #88/R est:60000-80000 (A.D 55000)
£22358	$35102	€32419	Cockatoo in the gully (89x98cm-35x39in) s. board prov. 26-Aug-3 Christie's, Sydney #123/R est:55000-75000 (A.D 55000)
£22901	$41679	€33435	Rose over Shoalhaven (122x91cm-48x36in) s. prov.exhib. 16-Jun-4 Deutscher-Menzies, Melbourne #16/R est:70000-90000 (A.D 60000)
£24390	$38293	€35366	Potter drawing on the beach (150x120cm-59x47in) s. linen prov.exhib. 26-Aug-3 Christie's, Sydney #120/R est:60000-80000 (A.D 60000)
£25424	$43220	€37119	Nebuchadnezzar (174x183cm-69x72in) s. 24-Nov-3 Sotheby's, Melbourne #46/R est:60000-80000 (A.D 60000)
£29000	$50170	€42340	Douglas Cairns' dam, Victoria (122x152cm-48x60in) s. exhib. 11-Dec-3 Lyon & Turnbull, Edinburgh #24/R est:10000-15000
£30534	$55573	€44580	Charcoal burner (68x91cm-27x36in) s. board prov. 16-Jun-4 Deutscher-Menzies, Melbourne #24/R est:65000-85000 (A.D 80000)
£30992	$57335	€45248	Wimmera landscape (92x122cm-36x48in) s. painted c.1967 prov. 10-Mar-4 Deutscher-Menzies, Melbourne #28/R est:80000-100000 (A.D 75000)
£31780	$54025	€46399	Wimmera landscape (90x121cm-35x48in) s. composition board. 24-Nov-3 Sotheby's, Melbourne #21/R est:70000-90000 (A.D 75000)
£36437	$58664	€53198	Diggers (45x60cm-18x24in) s. painted c.1949 prov.exhib. 25-Aug-3 Sotheby's, Paddington #216/R est:100000-120000 (A.D 90000)
£38168	$69466	€55725	Jinker on a sandbank (153x147cm-60x58in) s. prov. 16-Jun-4 Deutscher-Menzies, Melbourne #55/R est:130000-150000 (A.D 100000)
£38934	$61516	€56844	Landscape with white birds (58x86cm-23x34in) s. prov.exhib. 2-Sep-3 Deutscher-Menzies, Melbourne #52/R est:8000-100000 (A.D 95000)
£40650	$72764	€59349	Nude over a pond (121x152cm-48x60in) s. composition board prov. 4-May-4 Sotheby's, Melbourne #52/R est:180000-280000 (A.D 100000)
£42553	$72340	€62127	Shoalhaven River (120x150cm-47x59in) s. painted c.1982 prov. 26-Nov-3 Deutscher-Menzies, Melbourne #29/R est:120000-150000 (A.D 100000)
£42683	$76402	€62317	Hillside - Shoalhaven (151x120cm-59x47in) s. painted 1976-77 prov. 4-May-4 Sotheby's, Melbourne #20/R est:90000-120000 (A.D 105000)
£48780	$76585	€70731	Nude with beast IV, Diana and Actaeon II (122x152cm-48x60in) s. oil tempera board prov.exhib.lit. 26-Aug-3 Christie's, Sydney #44/R est:120000-180000 (A.D 120000)
£56911	$89350	€82521	Hillside (98x91cm-39x36in) s. painted c.1975 prov.exhib.lit. 27-Aug-3 Christie's, Sydney #584/R est:70000-90000 (A.D 140000)
£60729	$97773	€88664	Shoalhaven Landscape - Australian Scapegoat (242x195cm-95x77in) s. i.verso prov. 25-Aug-3 Sotheby's, Paddington #104/R est:150000-200000 (A.D 150000)
£60729	$97773	€88664	Burning tree stumps (75x90cm-30x35in) s. oil tempera composition board prov.exhib.lit. 25-Aug-3 Sotheby's, Paddington #153/R est:150000-180000 (A.D 150000)

Works on paper

£383	$651	€559	Jonah sitting under Gourd (28x19cm-11x7in) s.i. pen ink executed c.1972-73. 26-Nov-3 Deutscher-Menzies, Melbourne #150/R est:800-1200 (A.D 900)
£574	$906	€838	Jonah with his mother (27x18cm-11x7in) s.i. w/C pen prov. 2-Sep-3 Deutscher-Menzies, Melbourne #322/R est:700-900 (A.D 1400)
£738	$1165	€1077	Reindeer (49x61cm-19x24in) s. pen. 2-Sep-3 Deutscher-Menzies, Melbourne #280/R est:2400-2800 (A.D 1800)
£766	$1325	€1118	Jonah and his mother (17x19cm-7x7in) s. ink wash exhib.lit. 10-Dec-3 Shapiro, Sydney #73 (A.D 1800)
£766	$1325	€1118	Jonah in Joffa (17x18cm-7x7in) s.i. ink W/C exhib.lit. 10-Dec-3 Shapiro, Sydney #74 (A.D 1800)
£936	$1591	€1367	Figure with curly hair (36x26cm-14x10in) i.verso ink W/C prov. 25-Nov-3 Christie's, Melbourne #247/R (A.D 2200)
£992	$1835	€1448	Elektra (62x49cm-24x19in) s.i. synthetic polymer ink. 10-Mar-4 Deutscher-Menzies, Melbourne #373/R est:3000-5000 (A.D 2400)
£1143	$2103	€1669	Untitled (61x49cm-24x19in) s. ink. 29-Mar-4 Goodman, Sydney #218/R est:2000-3000 (A.D 2800)
£1191	$2026	€1739	Joined figures (51x64cm-20x25in) s. W/C ink exec.c.1970 prov. 25-Nov-3 Christie's, Melbourne #256/R (A.D 2800)
£1271	$2161	€1856	Untitled (49x62cm-19x24in) s. W/C. 24-Nov-3 Sotheby's, Melbourne #95/R est:3000-5000 (A.D 3000)
£1695	$2881	€2475	Ram and mystical creatures (52x563cm-20x222in) s. W/C. 24-Nov-3 Sotheby's, Melbourne #236 est:2000-3000 (A.D 4000)
£1780	$3025	€2599	Lovers (49x62cm-19x24in) s. ink exec 1964 prov. 24-Nov-3 Sotheby's, Melbourne #260 est:4000-6000 (A.D 4200)
£2340	$3979	€3416	Joined figures - twelve drawings on one sheet (75x120cm-30x47in) ink exec.c.1970 prov. 25-Nov-3 Christie's, Melbourne #120/R est:6000-8000 (A.D 5500)
£5668	$9126	€8275	Nude and black ram (47x62cm-19x24in) s. pastel exhib. 25-Aug-3 Sotheby's, Paddington #188/R est:15000-20000 (A.D 14000)

BOYD, Byron Bennett (1887-?) American

£232	$425	€339	Coming of the white night (41x51cm-16x20in) s. painted c.1938. 5-Jun-4 Treadway Gallery, Cincinnati #651/R

BOYD, David (1924-) Australian

£405	$652	€591	Bull in landscape (17x16cm-7x6in) s.d.68 bears i.verso board. 25-Aug-3 Sotheby's, Paddington #374 (A.D 1000)
£690	$1076	€1001	Morning sun (24x19cm-9x7in) s.d.2001 board. 1-Aug-2 Joel, Victoria #215 est:2000-3000 (A.D 2000)
£974	$1792	€1422	Child with fruit (21x18cm-8x7in) s. board. 28-Jun-4 Australian Art Auctions, Sydney #125 (A.D 2600)
£1034	$1614	€1499	Trumpet player (44x39cm-17x15in) s.d.1977 board. 1-Aug-2 Joel, Victoria #243 est:3000-4000 (A.D 3000)
£1106	$1881	€1615	Harmony (20x18cm-8x7in) s. oil paper on board prov. 26-Nov-3 Deutscher-Menzies, Melbourne #137/R est:1200-1800 (A.D 2600)
£1191	$2026	€1739	Europa (17x15cm-7x6in) s. board. 26-Nov-3 Deutscher-Menzies, Melbourne #186/R est:2000-3000 (A.D 2800)
£1224	$2253	€1787	Girl with cherries (20x18cm-8x7in) s. board. 29-Mar-4 Goodman, Sydney #216/R est:3000-6000 (A.D 3000)
£1298	$2362	€1895	Young love (19x21cm-7x8in) s. board. 16-Jun-4 Deutscher-Menzies, Melbourne #294/R est:1500-2500 (A.D 3400)
£1322	$2446	€1930	Girl with fruit (15x14cm-6x6in) s. board. 10-Mar-4 Deutscher-Menzies, Melbourne #490/R est:2000-3000 (A.D 3200)
£1322	$2340	€1930	Two for me (18x18cm-7x7in) s. board prov. 3-May-4 Christie's, Melbourne #339 est:2000-3000 (A.D 3200)
£1347	$2479	€1967	Friends (19x17cm-7x7in) s. board. 29-Mar-4 Goodman, Sydney #221/R est:1500-2500 (A.D 3300)
£1527	$2779	€2229	Europa practicing flight (30x25cm-12x10in) s. board prov.exhib. 16-Jun-4 Deutscher-Menzies, Melbourne #44/R est:4000-6000 (A.D 4000)
£1527	$2779	€2229	Europa reaching for a cockatoo from her wattle tree (30x25cm-12x10in) s. board prov.exhib. 16-Jun-4 Deutscher-Menzies, Melbourne #45/R est:4000-6000 (A.D 4000)
£1557	$2460	€2273	The high priest I (46x22cm-18x9in) s. canvas on board. 2-Sep-3 Deutscher-Menzies, Melbourne #267 est:1400-1800 (A.D 3800)
£1606	$2683	€2329	Dancing in the bush (31x38cm-12x15in) s. board. 30-Jun-3 Australian Art Auctions, Sydney #87 (A.D 4000)
£1707	$2850	€2475	Holding hands (31x38cm-12x15in) s. board. 30-Jun-3 Australian Art Auctions, Sydney #136 (A.D 4250)
£1859	$3291	€2714	Children bathing (29x24cm-11x9in) s. board prov. 3-May-4 Christie's, Melbourne #312 est:3000-4000 (A.D 4500)
£1885	$3054	€2752	Playing in the woods (30x38cm-12x15in) s. board. 30-Jul-3 Goodman, Sydney #139/R est:3000-5000 (A.D 4600)
£2049	$3320	€2992	Sorting out the clothes (37x29cm-15x11in) s. board. 30-Jul-3 Goodman, Sydney #145/R est:3000-4000 (A.D 5000)
£2213	$3585	€3231	Children in the glade (29x24cm-11x9in) s. board. 30-Jul-3 Goodman, Sydney #1/R est:3500-5000 (A.D 5400)
£2225	$3782	€3249	Dancing (32x40cm-13x16in) s.d.1968. 24-Nov-3 Sotheby's, Melbourne #81/R est:3000-5000 (A.D 5250)
£2247	$4135	€3281	Sailing in the billabong (31x38cm-12x15in) s. board. 28-Jun-4 Australian Art Auctions, Sydney #89 (A.D 6000)
£2273	$3864	€3319	Children and cockatoos at play (29x24cm-11x9in) s. board. 29-Oct-3 Lawson Menzies, Sydney #22/R est:2500-4000 (A.D 5500)
£2337	$4183	€3412	Frolicking with Cockatoos (37x30cm-15x12in) s. board. 10-May-4 Joel, Victoria #284 est:6000-8000 (A.D 5750)
£2410	$4024	€3495	Swimming in the clearing (8x46cm-3x18in) s. board. 30-Jun-3 Australian Art Auctions, Sydney #120 (A.D 6000)
£2429	$3911	€3546	From the Wanderer, Europe diving on wattle (24x36cm-9x14in) s. board. 13-Oct-3 Joel, Victoria #234 est:4000-6000 (A.D 6000)
£2479	$4215	€3619	Joseph's coat of many colours (43x39cm-17x15in) s.d.67 board. 29-Oct-3 Lawson Menzies, Sydney #112/R est:4000-6000 (A.D 6000)
£2479	$4215	€3619	Bush picnic 1961 (59x49cm-23x19in) s. 29-Oct-3 Lawson Menzies, Sydney #118/R est:5000-7000 (A.D 6000)
£2479	$4388	€3619	Nanny and charges (24x29cm-9x11in) s. board prov. 3-May-4 Christie's, Melbourne #227 est:3000-4000 (A.D 6000)
£2801	$4677	€4202	Children in the bush (35x46cm-14x18in) s. 27-Oct-3 Goodman, Sydney #16/R est:3500-5000 (A.D 6750)
£2905	$4851	€4358	Bather and cockatoos (49x44cm-19x17in) s. i.verso board. 27-Oct-3 Goodman, Sydney #195/R est:3000-5000 (A.D 7000)
£3099	$5269	€4525	Picnic by the lake (28x34cm-11x13in) s. 29-Oct-3 Lawson Menzies, Sydney #186/R est:3000-4000 (A.D 7500)
£3099	$5485	€4525	Europa fallen in the bush (44x40cm-17x16in) s. prov. 3-May-4 Christie's, Melbourne #346 est:6000-8000 (A.D 7500)
£3176	$5145	€4637	Berry pickers by a wattle tree (40x50cm-16x20in) s. s.i.verso. 30-Jul-3 Goodman, Sydney #156/R est:5500-7500 (A.D 7750)
£3178	$5403	€4640	Bather and River Wattle (36x30cm-14x12in) s. board painted c.1973 prov. 24-Nov-3 Sotheby's, Melbourne #163/R est:4000-6000 (A.D 7500)
£3252	$5821	€4748	Picnic series - Children in the bush (33x45cm-13x18in) s.d.1979 composition board prov. 4-May-4 Sotheby's, Melbourne #302/R est:6000-10000 (A.D 8000)
£3435	$6252	€5015	Children playing in water (45x40cm-18x16in) s. board prov.exhib. 16-Jun-4 Deutscher-Menzies, Melbourne #43/R est:6000-9000 (A.D 9000)
£3485	$5821	€5228	Europa mending her wings (49x44cm-19x17in) s. 27-Oct-3 Goodman, Sydney #234/R est:4000-6000 (A.D 8400)
£3527	$5890	€5291	The gold seeker (49x59cm-19x23in) s. 27-Oct-3 Goodman, Sydney #13/R est:5500-6500 (A.D 8500)
£3617	$6149	€5281	Day at the beach (61x50cm-24x20in) s. board. 26-Nov-3 Deutscher-Menzies, Melbourne #135/R est:7500-8500 (A.D 8500)
£3734	$6237	€5601	Cockatoo children (48x41cm-19x16in) s. board. 27-Oct-3 Goodman, Sydney #196/R est:8000-10000 (A.D 9000)
£3817	$6947	€5573	Children playing on a coast (56x50cm-22x20in) s. 16-Jun-4 Deutscher-Menzies, Melbourne #295/R est:8000-12000 (A.D 10000)
£3925	$6948	€5731	Children by a stream (50x44cm-20x17in) s. board. 3-May-4 Christie's, Melbourne #271 est:4000-6000 (A.D 9500)
£3926	$7262	€5732	Picnic (51x45cm-20x18in) s. i.verso board. 10-Mar-4 Deutscher-Menzies, Melbourne #304/R est:4000-6000 (A.D 9500)
£3980	$7322	€5811	Dancing in the orchard (37x45cm-15x18in) s. board. 29-Mar-4 Goodman, Sydney #187/R est:10000-12000 (A.D 9750)
£4082	$7510	€5960	Children playing by the stream (46x50cm-18x20in) s. board. 29-Mar-4 Goodman, Sydney #185/R est:10000-12000 (A.D 10000)
£4082	$7510	€5960	Children waving goodbye (37x45cm-15x18in) s. board. 29-Mar-4 Goodman, Sydney #186/R est:10000-12000 (A.D 10000)
£4198	$7641	€6129	Children in the forest (56x66cm-22x26in) s. 16-Jun-4 Deutscher-Menzies, Melbourne #302/R est:8000-12000 (A.D 11000)
£4357	$7276	€6536	Emerging goddess with judge and ship (45x50cm-18x20in) s. board. 27-Oct-3 Goodman, Sydney #241/R est:8000-10000 (A.D 10500)
£4449	$7564	€6496	Children playing by a stream (60x65cm-24x26in) s. board prov. 24-Nov-3 Sotheby's, Melbourne #240/R est:7000-10000 (A.D 10500)
£4508	$7123	€6582	Angel of the blossom (35x45cm-14x18in) s. 2-Sep-3 Deutscher-Menzies, Melbourne #266/R est:4500-6500 (A.D 11000)
£4545	$8045	€6636	Apple tree (49x75cm-19x30in) s. i.verso board. 3-May-4 Christie's, Melbourne #202/R est:6000-9000 (A.D 11000)
£4675	$7339	€6779	Man in white collar (75x55cm-30x22in) s. oil wax board prov. 26-Aug-3 Christie's, Sydney #411/R est:3000-5000 (A.D 11500)
£4752	$8079	€6938	Race 1984 (50x61cm-20x24in) s. 29-Oct-3 Lawson Menzies, Sydney #23/R est:6000-8000 (A.D 11500)
£4878	$8732	€7122	Study for the Betrayal (44x49cm-17x19in) s. bears i.verso prov. 4-May-4 Sotheby's, Melbourne #308/R est:7000-10000 (A.D 12000)
£4959	$8430	€7240	Picnic in a shady spot (55x45cm-22x18in) s. 29-Oct-3 Lawson Menzies, Sydney #185/R est:5000-7000 (A.D 12000)
£4959	$8430	€7240	In the park (54x65cm-21x26in) s. 29-Oct-3 Lawson Menzies, Sydney #187/R est:8000-12000 (A.D 12000)
£4959	$8777	€7240	Children playing (45x50cm-18x20in) s. board. 3-May-4 Christie's, Melbourne #341/R est:3000-5000 (A.D 12000)
£4979	$8315	€7469	Children in the Dandenongs (24x59cm-9x23in) s.d.72 board. 27-Oct-3 Goodman, Sydney #251/R est:4000-6000 (A.D 12000)
£5187	$8662	€7781	The pool (78x98cm-31x39in) s.d.1970 i.verso. 27-Oct-3 Goodman, Sydney #18/R est:12000-18000 (A.D 12500)
£5243	$9648	€7655	Fantasy of childhood (50x60cm-20x24in) s. 28-Jun-4 Australian Art Auctions, Sydney #134 (A.D 14000)
£5319	$9042	€7766	Angel of the Stream (50x55cm-20x22in) s. 26-Nov-3 Deutscher-Menzies, Melbourne #185/R est:6000-8000 (A.D 12500)
£5372	$9938	€7843	Sacrifice (121x61cm-48x24in) s.d.1967 board prov.exhib. 10-Mar-4 Deutscher-Menzies, Melbourne #302/R est:15000-20000 (A.D 13000)
£5508	$9364	€8042	Aunt with red hair (68x82cm-27x32in) s. bears i.verso prov. 24-Nov-3 Sotheby's, Melbourne #109/R est:7000-10000 (A.D 13000)
£5738	$9295	€8377	Young woman reclining under a jacaranda (64x54cm-25x21in) s. i.verso board. 30-Jul-3 Goodman, Sydney #20/R est:10000-15000 (A.D 14000)
£5785	$10702	€8446	Ocean beach (45x61cm-18x24in) s. i.verso board prov. 10-Mar-4 Deutscher-Menzies, Melbourne #305/R est:7500-8500 (A.D 14000)

£5957 $10128 €8697 Girl in landscape (66x56cm-26x22in) s. 26-Nov-3 Deutscher-Menzies, Melbourne #136/R est:12000-15000 (A.D 14000)
£5992 $10605 €8748 Abandoned judge (70x91cm-28x36in) s. prov. 3-May-4 Christie's, Melbourne #329/R est:4000-7000 (A.D 14500)
£6198 $11467 €9049 Judge and monolith (91x101cm-36x40in) s.d.2001 s.i.d.verso board prov. 10-Mar-4 Deutscher-Menzies, Melbourne #300/R est:17000-20000 (A.D 15000)
£6198 $10971 €9049 Children by a pond (74x99cm-29x39in) s. board. 3-May-4 Christie's, Melbourne #124/R est:8000-12000 (A.D 15000)
£6198 $10971 €9049 Golden butterfly (64x53cm-25x21in) s.d.1973 i.stretcher. 3-May-4 Christie's, Melbourne #294/R est:5000-7000 (A.D 15000)
£6504 $11642 €9496 Watched by an eye of gold a judge is presented with a silver tooth (91x101cm-36x40in) s.d.1985 i.verso prov.exhib. 4-May-4 Sotheby's, Melbourne #227/R est:10000-15000 (A.D 16000)
£6557 $10623 €9573 Abandoned row boat (45x68cm-18x27in) s. board. 30-Jul-3 Goodman, Sydney #142/R est:8000-10000 (A.D 16000)
£6679 $12156 €9751 Judgement at Apollo Bay (54x75cm-21x30in) s.d.68 board prov. 16-Jun-4 Deutscher-Menzies, Melbourne #303/R est:15000-20000 (A.D 17500)
£6809 $11574 €9941 Day of the Picnic (81x91cm-32x36in) s. i.stretcher verso. 26-Nov-3 Deutscher-Menzies, Melbourne #184/R est:10000-14000 (A.D 16000)
£8130 $14553 €11870 Children and an apple tree (95x115cm-37x45in) s. composition board prov. 4-May-4 Sotheby's, Melbourne #281/R est:14000-18000 (A.D 20000)
£9091 $16818 €13273 Girls picking berries (66x71cm-26x28in) s.d.1971 prov. 10-Mar-4 Deutscher-Menzies, Melbourne #301/R est:9000-12000 (A.D 22000)
£9350 $16736 €13651 Chasing the cockatoos (74x90cm-29x35in) s. bears i.verso prov. 4-May-4 Sotheby's, Melbourne #290/R est:6000-10000 (A.D 23000)
£9917 $16860 €14479 Money lenders (90x67cm-35x26in) s.d.1968 board. 29-Oct-3 Lawson Menzies, Sydney #113/R est:18000-22000 (A.D 24000)
£11570 $20479 €16892 Dancing nymphs (117x156cm-46x61in) s. prov. 3-May-4 Christie's, Melbourne #129/R est:20000-30000 (A.D 28000)
£12295 $19918 €17951 Sending up the message (91x100cm-36x39in) s. prov. 30-Jul-3 Goodman, Sydney #19/R est:12000-18000 (A.D 30000)
£12810 $23698 €18703 Fleeing gypsies (109x97cm-43x38in) s. i.verso painted c.1964. 10-Mar-4 Deutscher-Menzies, Melbourne #329/R est:15000-20000 (A.D 31000)
£13278 $22174 €19917 Bush walkers (102x91cm-40x36in) s. 27-Oct-3 Goodman, Sydney #244/R est:14000-18000 (A.D 32000)
£14108 $23560 €21162 Spanish woman with bird (102x91cm-40x36in) s.d.1965 board. 27-Oct-3 Goodman, Sydney #245/R est:12000-18000 (A.D 34000)
£22764 $40748 €33235 Marriage (120x90cm-47x35in) s.d.1965 canvas on board exhib. 4-May-4 Sotheby's, Melbourne #277/R est:5000-7000 (A.D 56000)
£24390 $43659 €35609 Explorer thrown (90x120cm-35x47in) s.d.1957 bears i.verso composition board prov. 4-May-4 Sotheby's, Melbourne #16/R est:30000-40000 (A.D 60000)
Works on paper
£1118 $2001 €1632 Boy with instrument (18x16cm-7x6in) s. mixed media. 10-May-4 Joel, Victoria #334 est:3000-5000 (A.D 2750)
£1230 $1992 €1796 Angel with harmonica (19x16cm-7x6in) s.i.d.1998 mixed media. 30-Jul-3 Goodman, Sydney #144/R est:2000-3000 (A.D 3000)
£2000 $3660 €2920 Figure group (46x61cm-18x24in) pastels prov. 8-Jul-4 Lawrence, Crewkerne #1576/R est:2000-3000
£2344 $4383 €3516 Choristers, sorting the manuscripts (29x39cm-11x15in) s. i.verso mixed media. 20-Jul-4 Goodman, Sydney #111/R est:4000-6000 (A.D 6000)
£2344 $4383 €3516 Flight (76x55cm-30x22in) s.d.66 gouache paper on board. 21-Jul-4 Shapiro, Sydney #157/R est:5000-7000 (A.D 6000)
£7438 $13165 €10859 Judge from behind. Judge and reflection. Judge in a boat. Judge with lamp (49x34cm-19x13in) s.d.63 W/C gouache four. 3-May-4 Christie's, Melbourne #395/R est:2500-3500 (A.D 18000)

BOYD, Diarmuid (20th C) Irish
£535 $840 €770 Bow Street (50x42cm-20x17in) s. board. 26-Aug-3 James Adam, Dublin #101/R

BOYD, Doris J (c.1883-1960) Australian
£511 $868 €746 Still life (40x50cm-16x20in) s. canvas on board. 26-Nov-3 Deutscher-Menzies, Melbourne #274/R (A.D 1200)

BOYD, Emma Minnie (1856-1936) Australian
Works on paper
£732 $1310 €1069 Saplings in the morning light (17x11cm-7x4in) s.d.1909 W/C. 10-May-4 Joel, Victoria #251 est:800-1200 (A.D 1800)
£2158 $3603 €3237 Port Phillip Bay (26x44cm-10x17in) s. W/C. 27-Oct-3 Goodman, Sydney #127 est:4000-6000 (A.D 5200)

BOYD, Guy (1923-1988) Australian
Sculpture
£1498 $2757 €2187 Diver (27x43x10cm-11x17x4in) s. bronze. 28-Jun-4 Australian Art Auctions, Sydney #110a (A.D 4000)
£1570 $2905 €2292 Lovers changing into tree (38cm-15in) s. bronze. 10-Mar-4 Deutscher-Menzies, Melbourne #295/R est:3000-5000 (A.D 3800)
£2246 $3750 €3279 Dancer practicing (89cm-35in) brown pat bronze prov. 7-Oct-3 Sotheby's, New York #342 est:5000-7000
£2340 $3979 €3416 Martin (43cm-17in) s.one of six bronze lit. 25-Nov-3 Christie's, Melbourne #129/R est:5000-7000 (A.D 5500)
£2610 $4750 €3811 Kneeling woman tying her hair (84x56x47cm-33x22x19in) sig.d.1984 num.5/12 brown pat. bronze prov. 29-Jun-4 Sotheby's, New York #569/R est:4000-6000
£2734 $5113 €4101 Three bathers (43x50cm-17x20in) s.num.6/6 bronze relief. 20-Jul-4 Goodman, Sydney #62/R est:8000-12000 (A.D 7000)
£3036 $4889 €4433 Reclining swimmer with hat (90x104x63cm-35x41x25in) polyester resin prov.exhib. 25-Aug-3 Sotheby's, Paddington #292/R est:1500-2000 (A.D 7500)
£3512 $6498 €5128 African dancer (59cm-23in) s.num.2/6 bronze prov. 10-Mar-4 Deutscher-Menzies, Melbourne #54/R est:8000-12000 (A.D 8500)
£3514 $6500 €5130 Swimmer emerging (38cm-15in) s.d.1986 num.3/12 varnished bronze prov. 12-Feb-4 Sotheby's, New York #123/R est:5000-7000
£3832 $6055 €5595 Bather at waterfall (105cm-41in) s.i.d.1986 gold pat.bronze prov. 2-Sep-3 Deutscher-Menzies, Melbourne #149/R est:12000-15000 (A.D 9350)

BOYD, Jamie (1948-) Australian
£386 $606 €560 On the Shoalhaven riverbank (38x57cm-15x22in) s. board. 26-Aug-3 Lawson Menzies, Sydney #41 est:600-800 (A.D 950)
£1012 $1630 €1478 Rocky landscape with eagle in flight (120x90cm-47x35in) s. board. 13-Oct-3 Joel, Victoria #435 est:2500-3500 (A.D 2500)
£1276 $1990 €1850 Shoalhaven theatre (263x178cm-104x70in) s. 1-Aug-2 Joel, Victoria #267 est:2000-2500 (A.D 3700)
£1301 $2328 €1899 Black swan (60x91cm-24x36in) s. board. 10-May-4 Joel, Victoria #199 est:3000-5000 (A.D 3200)

BOYD, John (1937-) British
£800 $1336 €1168 Two labourers (61x61cm-24x24in) s. board. 16-Oct-3 Christie's, Kensington #470/R
£2600 $4420 €3796 Blue umbrella (91x91cm-36x36in) s.verso board. 30-Oct-3 Christie's, London #233/R est:3000-5000

BOYD, John G (1940-) British
£4000 $6280 €5800 Boat house (102x112cm-40x44in) s. 27-Aug-3 Sotheby's, London #1147/R est:4000-6000
Works on paper
£280 $459 €409 Abstract study of candles and glass bottles (57x81cm-22x32in) s. mixed media. 3-Jun-3 Fellows & Sons, Birmingham #261/R
£800 $1472 €1168 Figure studies (53x37cm-21x15in) s.d.77 pastel pair. 23-Mar-4 Anderson & Garland, Newcastle #202/R

BOYD, Lynne (1953-) Australian
£620 $1147 €905 Dusk and sailboat, St. Kilda (152x122cm-60x48in) s.d.1988-89 i.verso prov. 15-Mar-4 Sotheby's, Melbourne #146 est:500-700 (A.D 1500)
£2479 $4587 €3619 You Yangs and Long Gilded hours of the day (152x213cm-60x84in) init. d.91 verso prov. 15-Mar-4 Sotheby's, Melbourne #188 est:600-1000 (A.D 6000)
£3659 $5744 €5342 The You Yangs and the Realms of Gold (121x152cm-48x60in) i.d.1989-90 prov.exhib. 27-Aug-3 Christie's, Sydney #658/R est:3000-6000 (A.D 9000)

BOYD, Theodore Penleigh (1890-1923) Australian
£828 $1291 €1201 Farm (16x24cm-6x9in) s.d.1913 board. 1-Aug-2 Joel, Victoria #160 est:2000-3000 (A.D 2400)
£4255 $7234 €6212 White gum (39x45cm-15x18in) s.d.1921 board. 26-Nov-3 Deutscher-Menzies, Melbourne #170/R est:9000-12000 (A.D 10000)
£6383 $10851 €9319 Landscape with white gum (71x81cm-28x32in) s.d.22. 26-Nov-3 Deutscher-Menzies, Melbourne #63/R est:18000-24000 (A.D 15000)
£7234 $12298 €10562 Across the Plain - Yarra Valley (51x76cm-20x30in) s.i.stretcher verso painted c.1910 prov.exhib. 26-Nov-3 Deutscher-Menzies, Melbourne #66/R est:15000-20000 (A.D 17000)
Works on paper
£729 $1173 €1064 Trees in the mist (25x35cm-10x14in) s. W/C. 13-Oct-3 Joel, Victoria #355 est:1000-1500 (A.D 1800)
£1157 $2048 €1689 Mount Buffalo in summertime (24x32cm-9x13in) s.d.1914 W/C prov. 3-May-4 Christie's, Melbourne #229/R est:3000-5000 (A.D 2800)
£5285 $8297 €7663 Blue haze (42x51cm-17x20in) s.d.19 W/C. 27-Aug-3 Christie's, Sydney #544/R est:7000-10000 (A.D 13000)

BOYDELL, Creswick (fl.1889-1916) British
£440 $700 €642 South Country landscape in summer with sheep in a meadow (30x15cm-12x6in) s. 18-Mar-3 Anderson & Garland, Newcastle #145/R
£2100 $3570 €3066 Birkenhead coast with fishing boats (49x75cm-19x30in) s. 29-Oct-3 Bonhams, Chester #342/R est:2000-3000
Works on paper
£600 $1092 €876 Fading Day awaiting night (51x122cm-20x48in) s.verso. 3-Feb-4 Gorringes, Bexhill #1052

BOYER, Auguste (19th C) French
£1171 $2014 €1710 Coastal landscape with boat builders (35x58cm-14x23in) s. canvas on board. 8-Dec-3 Philippe Schuler, Zurich #3388/R est:2000-2500 (S.FR 2600)

BOYER, Emile (1877-1948) French
£310 $515 €450 Rue a Argences (60x73cm-24x29in) s. 1-Oct-3 Millon & Associes, Paris #61

BOYER, Emile (19/20th C) French
Sculpture
£13989 $26160 €20424 Small musicians (68x97cm-27x38in) s. Carrara marble. 24-Feb-4 Rasmussen, Copenhagen #234/R est:100000-150000 (D.KR 155000)

BOYER, George (1955-) Canadian
£491 $845 €717 Beaches (45x100cm-18x39in) s. board painted 1985 prov. 2-Dec-3 Joyner Waddington, Toronto #457 (C.D 1100)

BOYER, Trevor (1948-) British
£2300 $4232 €3358 Cool spot (63x53cm-25x21in) s. 10-Jun-4 Christie's, Kensington #282/R est:1000-1500

BOYHAN, William Matthew (1916-1996) American
£471 $800 €688 Mule standing on sun dappled grass (56x69cm-22x27in) s. 21-Nov-3 Eldred, East Dennis #874/R

BOYLE FAMILY (20th C) British
Works on paper
£7000 $12040 €10220 Concrete pavement study, London Series 1973 (183x183cm-72x72in) mixed media resin fibreglass exhib. 3-Dec-3 Christie's, Kensington #791 est:4000-6000
£8500 $14620 €12410 Bergheim mine study, World Series 1974 (183x183cm-72x72in) mixed media resin fibreglass exhib. 3-Dec-3 Christie's, Kensington #789/R est:4000-6000

BOYLE, Alicia (1908-1997) Irish
£300 $549 €438 Derry (50x61cm-20x24in) mono. 2-Jun-4 John Ross, Belfast #59

£739 $1183 €1050 Turn with blue (25x15cm-10x6in) s.d.9153 i.verso board exhib. 16-Sep-3 Whyte's, Dublin #22/R

BOYLE, Ferdinand Thomas Lee (1820-1906) American
£1018 $1598 €1486 Enfant au ballon (40x51cm-16x20in) s.d.1876. 26-Aug-3 Iegor de Saint Hippolyte, Montreal #59 (C.D 2250)

BOYLE, George A (fl.1884-1899) British
£380 $711 €570 Anglers beside a stream (46x61cm-18x24in) s. 22-Jul-4 Gorringes, Lewes #2027
£400 $748 €584 Two young girls seated on a wall, one holding a cat, the other a book (41x30cm-16x12in) s. 22-Jul-4 Tennants, Leyburn #905
£699 $1168 €1000 Moor landscape in the morning (24x35cm-9x14in) s. panel. 27-Jun-3 Michael Zeller, Lindau #497/R
£700 $1113 €1015 Figures in a landscape with town in the distance (25x35cm-10x14in) s. panel pair. 9-Sep-3 Bonhams, Knightsbridge #139/R
£750 $1388 €1095 Landscape with figures (18x28cm-7x11in) s. pair. 13-Feb-4 Keys, Aylsham #755

BOYLE, Mark (1934-) British
Sculpture
£8939 $16000 €13051 Corporate yard study, Lorrypark series (183x183cm-72x72in) gravel wood pebbles stones resin oil fiberglass wood. 14-May-4 Phillips, New York #284/R est:10000-15000
Works on paper
£4667 $8540 €7000 Composition (182x182cm-72x72in) earth stones wood leaves fibre glass prov. 4-Jun-4 Lempertz, Koln #66/R est:5000-7000

BOYLEY, Errol (1918-) South African
£431 $720 €629 Figures by a beached boat (21x44cm-8x17in) s. board. 20-Oct-3 Stephan Welz, Johannesburg #919 est:1800-2400 (SA.R 5000)
£578 $1035 €844 Outspanning (30x49cm-12x19in) s. canvas on board. 31-May-4 Stephan Welz, Johannesburg #609 (SA.R 7000)
£733 $1224 €1070 Street scene, Malay quarter, Cape Town (35x45cm-14x18in) s. board. 20-Oct-3 Stephan Welz, Johannesburg #888 est:2500-4000 (SA.R 8500)
£784 $1404 €1145 Street scene with houses and figures (34x44cm-13x17in) s. 31-May-4 Stephan Welz, Johannesburg #279 (SA.R 9500)
£819 $1368 €1196 Alphen (50x75cm-20x30in) s. board. 20-Oct-3 Stephan Welz, Johannesburg #242/R est:5000-7000 (SA.R 9500)
£862 $1440 €1259 Highveld winter landscape (45x60cm-18x24in) s. board. 20-Oct-3 Stephan Welz, Johannesburg #243 est:5000-7000 (SA.R 10000)
£1034 $1728 €1510 Rural landscape (60x90cm-24x35in) s. board. 20-Oct-3 Stephan Welz, Johannesburg #880 est:4000-6000 (SA.R 12000)
£1218 $2205 €1778 Landscape with farm buildings (44x59cm-17x23in) s. canvasboard. 30-Mar-4 Stephan Welz, Johannesburg #473/R est:8000-12000 (SA.R 14500)
£2586 $4319 €3776 Pool in the Knysna Forest (90x120cm-35x47in) s. 20-Oct-3 Stephan Welz, Johannesburg #238 est:12000-16000 (SA.R 30000)

BOYNTON, Raymond Sceptre (1883-1951) American
£652 $1200 €952 The sleeping Endymion (76x91cm-30x36in) s.d.1921 prov. 8-Jun-4 Bonhams & Butterfields, San Francisco #4357/R

BOYS, Thomas Shotter (1803-1874) British
£3000 $5100 €4380 View towards Hampton Court from the Moseley (23x39cm-9x15in) s. panel. 25-Nov-3 Christie's, London #75/R est:3500-4500
Works on paper
£270 $459 €394 On the sands of Wimereux (25x36cm-10x14in) W/C. 24-Nov-3 Tiffin King & Nicholson, Carlisle #211/R
£537 $950 €800 La cathedrale (20x28cm-8x11in) s.d.1830 W/C. 28-Apr-4 Beaussant & Lefèvre, Paris #60
£950 $1587 €1387 Fishing boats at a Continental quayside (18x23cm-7x9in) i. pencil W/C. 16-Oct-3 Christie's, Kensington #69/R
£1300 $2392 €1898 Figures in Van Dyke costume in the grounds of a chateau (15x22cm-6x9in) pencil W/C prov. 25-Mar-4 Christie's, Kensington #17/R est:800-1200
£2400 $3912 €3504 Street scene Rouen (42x30cm-17x12in) s. pencil W/C htd white. 25-Sep-3 Mellors & Kirk, Nottingham #728/R est:1800-2500
£2500 $4550 €3650 St Valery sur Somme (17x26cm-7x10in) W/C over pencil htd bodycol gum arabic. 1-Jul-4 Sotheby's, London #230/R est:3000-4000
£2695 $4501 €3800 Pecheurs sur la plage (13x22cm-5x9in) s.d.1830 W/C. 20-Jun-3 Drouot Estimations, Paris #51/R est:2500-3500
£2800 $5096 €4088 Figures on a street in a Market town Belgium (33x23cm-13x9in) W/C over pencil htd bodycol stopping out gum arabic. 1-Jul-4 Sotheby's, London #213/R est:3000-5000
£3524 $5991 €5145 Hampton Court (21x38cm-8x15in) s.i. W/C over pencil. 5-Nov-3 Dobiaschofsky, Bern #387/R est:2200 (S.FR 8000)
£3800 $6954 €5548 River landscape, possibly near Brussels, Belgium (13x22cm-5x9in) s.d.1830 pencil W/C scratching out prov. 3-Jun-4 Christie's, London #103/R est:4000-6000
£6000 $10980 €8760 View of Rouen Cathedral (70x43cm-28x17in) s.d.1832 pencil W/C gum arabic htd. bodycol scratching out. 3-Jun-4 Christie's, London #156/R est:4000-6000
£9000 $16470 €13140 Landscape with a wagon (12x22cm-5x9in) pencil W/C. 3-Jun-4 Christie's, London #149/R est:10000-15000
£19000 $32300 €27740 Figures on a beach, Northern France (13x22cm-5x9in) s. W/C over pencil stopping out. 27-Nov-3 Sotheby's, London #276/R est:6000-8000

BOZE, Honore (1830-1908) British
£400 $736 €600 Homme a l'entree d'un mosquee (26x12cm-10x5in) s. panel. 9-Jun-4 Oger, Dumont, Paris #85
£433 $797 €650 Mosquee d'un village dans les montagnes (20x13cm-8x5in) s. panel. 9-Jun-4 Oger, Dumont, Paris #84
£1007 $1862 €1500 Ville en Algerie (28x41cm-11x16in) s. panel. 15-Mar-4 Gros & Delettrez, Paris #208/R est:1800-2000
£1064 $1777 €1500 Campement le soir (24x38cm-9x15in) s. canvas on panel. 16-Jun-3 Gros & Delettrez, Paris #267/R est:1200-2000
£1206 $2013 €1700 La halte des chameliers (24x35cm-9x14in) s. canvas on panel. 16-Jun-3 Gros & Delettrez, Paris #264/R est:1700-2500
£1277 $2132 €1800 Chemin cotier, Algerie (28x41cm-11x16in) s. panel. 16-Jun-3 Gros & Delettrez, Paris #265/R est:1700-2500
£10490 $18042 €15000 Cavaliers au pied de la falaise (110x140cm-43x55in) s. 8-Dec-3 Tajan, Paris #240/R est:10000-12000

BOZINO, Attilio (1890-1973) Italian
£333 $613 €500 Roses (49x34cm-19x13in) s.d.1951 cardboard on canvas. 14-Jun-4 Sant Agostino, Torino #159/R

BOZZOLINI, Isabella (18/19th C) Italian
Miniatures
£1655 $2764 €2400 Lady with two boys (7cm-3in circular) exec.c.1810. 12-Nov-3 Sotheby's, Milan #32/R est:1800-2400

BOZZOLINI, Silvano (1911-1998) Italian
£524 $892 €750 Contrastes sensibles (65x50cm-26x20in) s.d.18-7-67 s.i.verso oil paper on canvas prov. 23-Nov-3 Cornette de St.Cyr, Paris #28/R
£2183 $3974 €3187 Le bateau (89x116cm-35x46in) s.d.50. 16-Jun-4 Fischer, Luzern #2034/R est:1000-1200 (S.FR 5000)

BRAAK, Karel van den (1953-) Belgian
Sculpture
£1111 $1856 €1600 Abstract (64cm-25in) s. num.2/3 bronze. 21-Oct-3 Campo & Campo, Antwerp #306/R est:1600-1800

BRAAKMAN, Anthonie (1811-1870) Dutch
£4000 $7280 €5840 Figures on a path beside a cottage, and boy fishing (51x66cm-20x26in) s.d.34 panel prov. 16-Jun-4 John Nicholson, Haslemere #748/R est:4000-5000

BRAAM, J M van (19th C) ?
Works on paper
£950 $1682 €1387 Gibraltar from the sea (28x62cm-11x24in) i. W/C. 27-Apr-4 Bonhams, New Bond Street #74/R

BRAAQ (1951-1997) British
£1100 $1749 €1595 Football match with spectators around the pitch (29x39cm-11x15in) s. boards. board. 11-Sep-3 Morphets, Harrogate #271/R est:1000-1400
£1300 $2405 €1898 Industrial city landscape at sundown with open land and figure (19x29cm-7x11in) s. board. 11-Mar-4 Morphets, Harrogate #313 est:800-1200
£1350 $2201 €1958 Industrial street scene (59x44cm-23x17in) s.i.d.76 board. 23-Sep-3 Bonhams, Leeds #115/R est:1500-2000
£1550 $2527 €2248 John Taylor's Bric-a-Brac Shop (19x24cm-7x9in) s. board. 23-Sep-3 Bonhams, Leeds #114/R est:800-1200
£1600 $2944 €2336 Winter scene with figures (25x35cm-10x14in) s. board. 10-Jun-4 Morphets, Harrogate #516 est:1500-1800
£1750 $3220 €2555 Cricket match with crowds around the field and parkland (29x39cm-11x15in) s. board. 10-Jun-4 Morphets, Harrogate #515/R est:1750-2250
£2200 $3498 €3190 Winter terrace scene with figures and dogs in the snow (29x44cm-11x17in) s. board. 11-Sep-3 Morphets, Harrogate #278/R est:750-1000
£2600 $4810 €3796 Cricket match with spectators and suburban landscape (41x75cm-16x30in) s. 11-Mar-4 Morphets, Harrogate #311 est:1000-1500
£2800 $4452 €4060 Street scene in Liverpool (45x60cm-18x24in) s. 11-Sep-3 Morphets, Harrogate #276/R est:2750-3500
£2800 $4452 €4060 Wavertree Road, Liverpool, winter scene (29x39cm-11x15in) s. board. 11-Sep-3 Morphets, Harrogate #272 est:1500-2000
£3000 $5370 €4380 Industrial landscape (44x59cm-17x23in) s.i.d.76 board. 16-Mar-4 Bonhams, Leeds #573/R est:2000-3000
£7800 $13962 €11388 York races (42x58cm-17x23in) s. board. 16-Mar-4 Bonhams, Leeds #574/R est:2500-3500
Works on paper
£300 $555 €438 Portrait of a ballerina bending to adjust her skirt (17x27cm-7x11in) s. pastel pencil. 11-Mar-4 Morphets, Harrogate #315
£550 $1012 €803 Moonlit winter evening with figures on a pathway to a church (17x14cm-7x6in) s. pastel. 10-Jun-4 Morphets, Harrogate #519
£550 $1012 €803 Moonlint winter evening with figures on a pathway (17x14cm-7x6in) s. pastel. 10-Jun-4 Morphets, Harrogate #520
£600 $1104 €876 Braaq and another boy fighting (15x13cm-6x5in) s. pastel. 10-Jun-4 Morphets, Harrogate #521/R
£600 $1104 €876 Boy crying, his leg cut and bleeding, with his dog beside him (15x13cm-6x5in) s. pastel. 10-Jun-4 Morphets, Harrogate #522/R
£700 $1113 €1015 Portrait of a dark haired girl (19x16cm-7x6in) s. pastel. 11-Sep-3 Morphets, Harrogate #286/R
£800 $1272 €1160 Children playing before a church (21x16cm-8x6in) s. pastel. 11-Sep-3 Morphets, Harrogate #285/R
£800 $1360 €1168 Full portrait of an elderly man in a bowler hat, with a dog (28x21cm-11x8in) s. pastel. 27-Nov-3 Morphets, Harrogate #437/R

BRABANDERE, Mario de (1963-) Belgian
£1533 $2760 €2300 Young girl with basket (200x180cm-79x71in) s. 26-Apr-4 Bernaerts, Antwerp #577/R est:2000-3000

BRABAZON, Hercules Brabazon (1821-1906) British
£250 $418 €365 Figures on the coast among classical ruins, with setting sun (21x27cm-8x11in) init. oil paper. 16-Oct-3 Christie's, Kensington #73
Works on paper
£260 $476 €380 Italian coast scene (23x33cm-9x13in) W/C. 3-Jun-4 Bonhams, Cornwall #232
£280 $445 €409 Sailing boats on the River Cummor (15x28cm-6x11in) W/C. 12-Sep-3 Gardiner & Houlgate, Bath #36/R
£280 $504 €409 Town scene with tower (11x18cm-4x7in) init. W/C pencil. 21-Jan-4 Sotheby's, Olympia #224/R
£280 $504 €409 Beach scene (24x34cm-9x13in) init. W/C. 21-Jan-4 Sotheby's, Olympia #225/R
£320 $550 €467 Sphinx (23x28cm-9x11in) init. W/C. 2-Dec-3 Gorringes, Lewes #2269
£389 $700 €568 Venice (16x17cm-6x7in) init. pencil col chk. 21-Jan-4 Doyle, New York #15

£389 $700 €568 Coastal city (15x20cm-6x8in) init. pencil col chk htd white. 21-Jan-4 Doyle, New York #16
£400 $688 €584 Swiss lake with cattle (19x26cm-7x10in) init. pencil W/C bodycol prov. 3-Dec-3 Christie's, Kensington #38/R
£480 $874 €701 Genoa (16x24cm-6x9in) pencil W/C htd white. 1-Jul-4 Christie's, Kensington #343
£500 $860 €730 Como (14x20cm-6x8in) init.i. pencil col chk prov. 3-Dec-3 Christie's, Kensington #37/R
£580 $1003 €847 English landscape (17x25cm-7x10in) init. W/C bodycol. 10-Dec-3 Bonhams, Bury St Edmunds #532
£600 $1020 €876 Venetian canal scene with gondola (21x26cm-8x10in) init. i.verso W/C. 19-Nov-3 Tennants, Leyburn #897
£600 $1098 €876 River landscape (13x16cm-5x6in) init. W/C. 27-Jan-4 Bonhams, Knightsbridge #326/R
£650 $1086 €949 Felucca on the Nile (20x25cm-8x10in) init. pencil W/C bodycol. 16-Oct-3 Christie's, Kensington #74/R
£700 $1190 €1022 Figures in an interior (21x29cm-8x11in) init. W/C. 4-Nov-3 Bonhams, New Bond Street #146/R
£750 $1380 €1095 Lagoon, Venice (10x15cm-4x6in) init.indis.i. pencil W/C bodycol. 25-Mar-4 Christie's, Kensington #88/R
£820 $1296 €1189 On an Italian lake (15x15cm-6x6in) init. W/C bodycol prov. 3-Sep-3 Bonhams, Bury St Edmunds #358
£900 $1494 €1314 Views of Venice (15x22cm-6x9in) each init. pastel three. 1-Oct-3 Sotheby's, Olympia #13/R
£900 $1548 €1314 Venetian street scene (13x18cm-5x7in) init. W/C. 2-Dec-3 Gorringes, Lewes #2209/R
£950 $1615 €1387 Jodhpur, Rajputana, India (15x22cm-6x9in) init. i.verso W/C. 4-Nov-3 Bonhams, New Bond Street #49/R
£1000 $1720 €1460 On the Sicilian coast (22x28cm-9x11in) indis.sig. bodycol. 3-Dec-3 Christie's, Kensington #42/R est:600-800
£1000 $1790 €1460 Santa Maria Della Salute (14x22cm-6x9in) init. pencil W/C. 28-May-4 Lyon & Turnbull, Edinburgh #87/R est:1000-2000
£1200 $2004 €1752 Italian landscape (23x34cm-9x13in) init. W/C. 14-Oct-3 Bonhams, Knightsbridge #183/R est:600-800
£1200 $2064 €1752 On lake Geneva (16x25cm-6x10in) init.i. pencil col chk sold with two others by the same hand. 3-Dec-3 Christie's, Kensington #39/R est:400-600
£1600 $2928 €2336 Las Meninas (25x30cm-10x12in) pencil W/C htd bodycol after Velasquez prov.exhib. 3-Jun-4 Christie's, London #152/R est:1800-2500
£1800 $3096 €2628 Algiers (33x24cm-13x9in) s.i. pencil W/C bodycol prov. 3-Dec-3 Christie's, Kensington #41/R est:1000-1500
£1800 $3276 €2628 El Souk, Tunis (21x31cm-8x12in) pencil W/C htd white. 1-Jul-4 Christie's, Kensington #330/R est:1200-1500
£2400 $4392 €3504 Possibly Salamanca Cathedral, Valencia, Spain (21x28cm-8x11in) init. pencil W/C htd bodycol prov. 3-Jun-4 Christie's, London #163/R est:2000-3000
£2500 $4250 €3650 Near Swanage, Dorset (13x19cm-5x7in) s. W/C htd bodycol. 27-Nov-3 Sotheby's, London #311/R est:3000-4000
£2600 $4342 €3796 Street market in North Africa (21x24cm-8x9in) s. W/C over pencil bodycol. 14-Oct-3 Sotheby's, London #102/R est:2000-3000
£3500 $6405 €5110 Saragossa, Spain (23x32cm-9x13in) init. pencil W/C htd bodycol prov. 3-Jun-4 Christie's, London #162/R est:3000-5000
£3800 $6346 €5548 Street scene in Cairo (29x23cm-11x9in) init. pencil W/C. 16-Oct-3 Christie's, Kensington #70/R est:1000-1500

BRACCHI, Luigi (1892-?) Italian
Works on paper
£290 $475 €400 Summer (24x34cm-9x13in) s. i.verso mixed media. 27-May-3 Il Ponte, Milan #854

BRACH, Paul (1924-) American
£305 $550 €445 Ghost mesa 13 (102x124cm-40x49in) s.i.d.80-81 verso. 25-Jan-4 Bonhams & Butterfields, San Francisco #3628/R

BRACHO Y MURILLO, Jose Maria (19th C) Spanish
£2113 $3697 €3000 Grapes (43x24cm-17x9in) s. board. 16-Dec-3 Segre, Madrid #93/R est:1700
£5674 $9475 €8000 Vase with flowers (88x71cm-35x28in) s. 23-Jun-3 Durán, Madrid #234/R est:3500

BRACHO, Gabriel (1915-1994) Venezuelan
£258 $400 €377 Study for fresco (56x46cm-22x18in) s. masonite painted 1970. 3-Nov-2 Subastas Odalys, Caracas #9
£395 $660 €577 Untitled (53x44cm-21x17in) s. painted 1972. 13-Jul-3 Subastas Odalys, Caracas #73/R
£449 $750 €656 Lovers (56x77cm-22x30in) s. masonite painted 1975. 19-Oct-3 Subastas Odalys, Caracas #36
£547 $875 €799 Untitled (85x63cm-33x25in) s. 21-Sep-3 Subastas Odalys, Caracas #48
£570 $900 €832 Untitled (73x100cm-29x39in) s. painted 1980. 1-Dec-2 Subastas Odalys, Caracas #121
£867 $1560 €1266 Still life with Saint Benito (118x92cm-46x36in) s. acrylic painted 1989. 25-Apr-4 Subastas Odalys, Caracas #37/R
£968 $1500 €1413 Folklore (80x63cm-31x25in) s. paper on panel painted 1986. 3-Nov-2 Subastas Odalys, Caracas #52/R
£1003 $1825 €1505 Zaragoza (53x44cm-21x17in) s. panel painted 1972. 21-Jun-4 Subastas Odalys, Caracas #63/R
£1288 $2345 €1932 Figure (61x45cm-24x18in) s. panel painted 1970. 21-Jun-4 Subastas Odalys, Caracas #70/R
Works on paper
£226 $415 €339 Killed by a machete (26x36cm-10x14in) s. mixed media cardboard exec.1948. 27-Jun-4 Subastas Odalys, Caracas #130

BRACHT, Eugen (1842-1921) Swiss
£498 $846 €727 View of a castle (41x33cm-16x13in) s.d.1895. 1-Dec-3 Koller, Zurich #6448 (S.FR 1100)
£816 $1461 €1200 Birch wood (25x23cm-10x9in) mono. 18-Mar-4 Neumeister, Munich #2645
£933 $1717 €1400 River landscape (50x60cm-20x24in) s. 11-Jun-4 Wendl, Rudolstadt #3967/R
£1042 $1698 €1500 Lake in evening light (50x61cm-20x24in) s. 24-Sep-3 Neumeister, Munich #401/R est:2500
£1486 $2616 €2200 Don Quichotte and Sancho Pansa (15x20cm-6x8in) s.d.1878 panel. 21-May-4 Mehlis, Plauen #15092/R est:800
£1736 $2743 €2500 Landscape with trees (61x73cm-24x29in) s.d.1916. 5-Sep-3 Wendl, Rudolstadt #3299/R est:250
£1940 $3472 €2832 Barensteinen (54x36cm-21x14in) s. i.d.1907 verso board. 13-May-4 Stuker, Bern #48/R est:1500-2000 (S.FR 4500)
£2308 $3969 €3300 Oberroder Church in wood (42x53cm-17x21in) s.i.d.1894 board. 5-Dec-3 Michael Zeller, Lindau #581/R est:2000
£2781 $5062 €4200 Woodland scene in the autumn sunshine (47x68cm-19x27in) s. board. 18-Jun-4 Bolland & Marotz, Bremen #591/R est:3500
£2797 $4671 €4000 Mediterranean landscape trees and sheep (90x150cm-35x59in) s.i.d.1909. 28-Jun-3 Dannenberg, Berlin #657/R est:4000
£3200 $5824 €4800 River landscape with trees (70x40cm-28x16in) s. board. 1-Jul-4 Van Ham, Cologne #1229/R est:3300
£4196 $7133 €6000 Rocky cliffs in Rauhen Alb (80x85cm-31x33in) s.d.1917. 20-Nov-3 Van Ham, Cologne #1495/R est:4400
£4286 $6857 €6215 Moonlit desert (75x120cm-30x47in) s.d.1884. 15-May-3 Stuker, Bern #1098/R est:6000-8000 (S.FR 9000)
£7000 $12740 €10220 Hannibal's tomb (90x150cm-35x59in) s.d.1909 painted with studio. 15-Jun-4 Sotheby's, London #45/R est:5000-7000
£8054 $14819 €12000 Landscape with broad avenue of trees (75x120cm-30x47in) s. 25-Mar-4 Dr Fritz Nagel, Stuttgart #699/R est:12000

BRACK, Cecil John (1920-1999) Australian
£7287 $11733 €10639 Bowl of fruit (24x30cm-9x12in) s.d.46 canvas on board prov.lit. 25-Aug-3 Sotheby's, Paddington #123/R est:18000-28000 (A.D 18000)
£10163 $18191 €14838 Egyptian maid (44x40cm-17x16in) s.d.1975 wood panel prov.exhib.lit. 4-May-4 Sotheby's, Melbourne #76/R est:18000-28000 (A.D 25000)
£30534 $55573 €44580 Subdivision (56x76cm-22x30in) s.d.54 i.verso exhib. 16-Jun-4 Deutscher-Menzies, Melbourne #58/R est:60000-80000 (A.D 80000)
£49618 $90305 €72442 Nude with frame (122x101cm-48x40in) s.d.1980 i.verso prov.exhib. 16-Jun-4 Deutscher-Menzies, Melbourne #76/R est:140000-180000 (A.D 130000)
£98361 $155410 €143607 Pantomime (91x137cm-36x54in) s.d.1988-94 i. verso prov.exhib. 2-Sep-3 Deutscher-Menzies, Melbourne #48/R est:240000-280000 (A.D 240000)
£127660 $217021 €186384 On Stage (137x122cm-54x48in) s.d.1991 prov.exhib.lit. 26-Nov-3 Deutscher-Menzies, Melbourne #30/R est:300000-350000 (A.D 300000)
£165289 $305785 €241322 Backs and fronts (115x163cm-45x64in) s.d.69 prov.exhib. 10-Mar-4 Deutscher-Menzies, Melbourne #30/R est:450000-550000 (A.D 400000)
Works on paper
£2024 $3259 €2955 Self portrait with self portrait (22x16cm-9x6in) s.i. ink. 25-Aug-3 Sotheby's, Paddington #262/R est:3000-4000 (A.D 5000)
£12766 $21702 €18638 Amateur couple (43x59cm-17x23in) s.d.69 W/C pen ink prov.exhib.lit. 26-Nov-3 Deutscher-Menzies, Melbourne #1/R est:25000-35000 (A.D 30000)
£23404 $39787 €34170 Hairdressing (35x39cm-14x15in) s.d.53 conte prov.exhib.lit. 25-Nov-3 Christie's, Melbourne #20/R est:20000-30000 (A.D 55000)

BRACK, Emil (1860-1905) German
£8667 $15600 €13000 Picture book (34x23cm-13x9in) s.d.1900. 21-Apr-4 Christie's, Amsterdam #18/R est:4000-6000
Works on paper
£500 $910 €750 Woman wearing hat with feathers holding mask (48x35cm-19x14in) s.d.97 W/C htd white. 30-Jun-4 Neumeister, Munich #392/R
£612 $1096 €900 Young couple in bourgeois interior (42x56cm-17x22in) s. W/C. 20-Mar-4 Bergmann, Erlangen #1132

BRACKEN, John (17th C) British
£2000 $3720 €2920 Portrait of lady Chaworth in black dress and lace collar (93x80cm-37x31in) i. lit. 4-Mar-4 Christie's, Kensington #304/R est:2000-3000

BRACKENBURY, Amy (20th C) American
£311 $500 €454 Large mouth bass (91x71cm-36x28in) 22-Aug-3 Altermann Galleries, Santa Fe #223

BRACKETT, Sidney Lawrence (1852-1910) American
£329 $550 €477 Faithful friend (18x23cm-7x9in) s. 13-Jul-3 Butterfields, San Francisco #2021/R
£471 $800 €688 In the study (63x47cm-25x19in) s. board. 21-Nov-3 Skinner, Boston #43/R
£751 $1300 €1096 Four kittens on a table top (56x71cm-22x28in) 10-Dec-3 Alderfer's, Hatfield #326/R est:2000-3000
£1176 $2000 €1717 On velvet cushions (51x41cm-20x16in) s. 21-Nov-3 Skinner, Boston #179/R est:1200-1800
£1912 $3250 €2792 Kittens in a bowl (40x51cm-16x20in) s. 21-Nov-3 Skinner, Boston #1/R est:3000-5000
Works on paper
£471 $800 €688 Chums (18x23cm-7x9in) s.verso pastel. 21-Nov-3 Skinner, Boston #171/R

BRACKETT, Walter M (1823-1919) American
£3824 $6500 €5583 Still life with trout (30x51cm-12x20in) s.d.1877. 21-Nov-3 Skinner, Boston #293/R est:2000-4000

BRACKLE, Jakob (1897-1987) German
£267 $480 €400 Potato harvest near Biberach (12x23cm-5x9in) s.d.1946 board. 26-Apr-4 Rieber, Stuttgart #1185/R
£671 $1188 €1000 Harvest machinery in cornfield (15x17cm-6x7in) s. board. 30-Apr-4 Dr Fritz Nagel, Stuttgart #740/R
£1074 $1901 €1600 Early in the year (26x40cm-10x16in) s.d. d.18. April 1933 verso board. 30-Apr-4 Dr Fritz Nagel, Stuttgart #741/R est:3000
£1197 $1915 €1700 Summer fields (12x11cm-5x4in) s.d.82 panel. 19-Sep-3 Sigalas, Stuttgart #282/R est:1900
£1268 $2028 €1800 Snowy landscape with pine tree (11x13cm-4x5in) s.d.85 panel. 19-Sep-3 Sigalas, Stuttgart #283/R est:2200
£1342 $2376 €2000 Potato harvest (17x13cm-7x5in) s.d. d.18. Okt 1938 verso board. 30-Apr-4 Dr Fritz Nagel, Stuttgart #739/R est:1200
£1620 $2592 €2300 Snowy village (15x16cm-6x6in) s.d.38 board. 19-Sep-3 Sigalas, Stuttgart #285/R est:2500
£1678 $3087 €2500 Winter countryside (19x17cm-7x7in) s.d.48 board. 27-Mar-4 Sigalas, Stuttgart #286/R est:2500
£1690 $2704 €2400 Peasants harvesting in summer (17x18cm-7x7in) s.d.36 panel. 19-Sep-3 Sigalas, Stuttgart #286/R est:2800

£1972 $3155 €2800 Landscape in upper Swabia (14x33cm-6x13in) s.d.1935 board. 18-Sep-3 Rieber, Stuttgart #933/R est:2500
£2086 $3422 €2900 August fields (12x24cm-5x9in) s.d.1973 board. 3-Jun-3 Sigalas, Stuttgart #462/R est:3000
£2215 $3920 €3300 Evening sun (28x28cm-11x11in) s.d. panel. 30-Apr-4 Dr Fritz Nagel, Stuttgart #742/R est:2800
£2431 $3962 €3500 Harvest (22x39cm-9x15in) s.d.1940 board prov. 27-Sep-3 Dr Fritz Nagel, Stuttgart #9463/R est:2800
£4317 $7079 €6000 Colourful fields II (23x32cm-9x13in) s.d.1972 panel. 3-Jun-3 Sigalas, Stuttgart #464/R est:6000

BRACKMAN, David (19th C) British
£8000 $13600 €11680 Astro and Shamrock (76x112cm-30x44in) s.d.03. 19-Nov-3 Christie's, Kensington #418/R
Works on paper
£2186 $4000 €3192 Thermopylae departing from Foochow (51x79cm-20x31in) s.d.02 pencil W/C bodycol. 29-Jul-4 Christie's, Rockefeller NY #299/R est:4000-6000
£3825 $7000 €5585 Two racers, Britannia and Westward neck and neck in Osborne Bay (51x75cm-20x30in) s.d.04 pencil W/C gouache. 29-Jul-4 Christie's, Rockefeller NY #298/R est:6000-8000
£4000 $7160 €5840 HMS Victory breaking through the enemy line at Trafalgar (51x74cm-20x29in) s.d.04 pencil W/C bodycol. 26-May-4 Christie's, Kensington #485/R est:4000-6000

BRACKMAN, Robert (1898-1980) American
£13415 $22000 €19452 Unmasked (152x127cm-60x50in) s. s.i.verso exhib. 31-May-3 Brunk, Ashville #447/R est:15000-25000
Works on paper
£489 $900 €714 Portrait of a young man (46x58cm-18x23in) s. col pastel. 10-Jun-4 Swann Galleries, New York #39/R
£870 $1600 €1270 Two female figures (56x43cm-22x17in) s. col pastel. 10-Jun-4 Swann Galleries, New York #37/R est:2000-3000
£924 $1700 €1349 Female nude (69x43cm-27x17in) s. col pastel. 10-Jun-4 Swann Galleries, New York #38/R est:2000-3000
£930 $1600 €1358 Study of female nude (70x51cm-28x20in) s. pastel. 2-Dec-3 Christie's, Rockefeller NY #90/R est:1000-1500
£1056 $1900 €1542 Two seated nudes (64x84cm-25x33in) s. pastel crayon prov. 20-Jan-4 Arthur James, Florida #79
£1867 $3100 €2726 Nude study (81x66cm-32x26in) s. pastel. 4-Oct-3 Neal Auction Company, New Orleans #609/R est:1500-2500

BRACONY, Guglielmo (attrib) (1828-1921) Italian
Sculpture
£13333 $24000 €19466 Male and female bust of Moors (46cm-18in) s.verso white marble ebonised socle pair or possibly by Leopold. 23-Apr-4 Christie's, Rockefeller NY #33/R est:8000-12000

BRACQUEMOND, Félix (1833-1914) French
£900 $1503 €1314 Rocky coastline (49x42cm-19x17in) s.d.1911 board. 8-Oct-3 Christie's, Kensington #797

BRADBURY, Arthur Royce (1892-1977) British
£300 $486 €435 Mending rigging (25x19cm-10x7in) oil sketch on board. 30-Jul-3 Hamptons Fine Art, Godalming #200
£340 $612 €496 Schooner, M A James off Poole (36x58cm-14x23in) s. 22-Apr-4 Lawrence, Crewkerne #834
£520 $941 €759 Old harbour, St Peter Port, Guernsey (28x37cm-11x15in) s.i.verso. 1-Apr-4 Martel Maides, Guernsey #225
£600 $1110 €876 Female nude (33x43cm-13x17in) s. 15-Jan-4 Christie's, Kensington #753/R
£2400 $4320 €3504 Afternoon on the beach (34x50cm-13x20in) s. 22-Apr-4 Lawrence, Crewkerne #842/R est:1200-1800
Works on paper
£280 $507 €409 Natural Arch, Sark (35x24cm-14x9in) s.d.1931 W/C. 1-Apr-4 Martel Maides, Guernsey #220
£370 $629 €540 Rowing boat and seagulls, Creux Harbour, Sark (40x56cm-16x22in) s. W/C. 25-Nov-3 Martel Maides, Guernsey #186
£520 $941 €759 Cornfields and Sark mill (24x34cm-9x13in) s.d.1931 W/C. 1-Apr-4 Martel Maides, Guernsey #254/R
£580 $986 €847 Fishermen and boats, Creux Harbour, Sark (39x57cm-15x22in) s. W/C. 25-Nov-3 Martel Maides, Guernsey #185/R
£720 $1303 €1051 Ketch Dayspring in Creux harbour, Sark (36x25cm-14x10in) s. W/C. 1-Apr-4 Martel Maides, Guernsey #216/R

BRADBURY, Bennett (1914-1991) American
£1852 $3500 €2704 Seascape (76x102cm-30x40in) s. 17-Feb-4 John Moran, Pasadena #34/R est:1500-2000

BRADBURY, Charles Earl (1888-1967) American
£1076 $1700 €1571 Gloucester Harbour. s.d.1923 board. 7-Sep-3 Treadway Gallery, Cincinnati #613/R est:1500-2000

BRADDOCK, Grahame (?) New Zealander?
£344 $585 €502 Rural landscape (54x79cm-21x31in) s. board. 4-Nov-3 Peter Webb, Auckland #85 (NZ.D 950)

BRADDON, Paul (1864-1938) British
Works on paper
£260 $468 €380 Figures conversing in mediaeval town of Rodez. s. W/C. 25-Jan-4 Desmond Judd, Cranbrook #1108
£260 $468 €380 Figures conversing in mediaeval town of Bruges. s. W/C. 25-Jan-4 Desmond Judd, Cranbrook #1109
£280 $459 €409 Old St. Martins lane (36x53cm-14x21in) mono. W/C. 6-Jun-3 Biddle & Webb, Birmingham #221
£550 $919 €803 Hodnet Hall, Shropshire (36x51cm-14x20in) W/C pair. 12-Nov-3 Halls, Shrewsbury #279
£700 $1190 €1022 Bruges. Rodez (77x50cm-30x20in) s. W/C pair. 29-Oct-3 Edgar Horn, Eastbourne #348

BRADER, Ferdinand A (1833-?) American
Works on paper
£640 $1100 €934 Marriage certificate with floral wreath surrounding joined hands (18x23cm-7x9in) s. graphite. 6-Dec-3 Pook & Pook, Downington #141/R
£6044 $11000 €8824 Property of John and Elizabeth Knapp, Randolph (71x109cm-28x43in) s. graphite. 19-Jun-4 Rachel Davis, Shaker Heights #59/R est:10000-15000
£8380 $15000 €12235 Farm landscape, the Property of Ammon and Susan Winter (79x130cm-31x51in) s.d.1882 graphite prov. 20-Mar-4 Pook & Pook, Downington #130/R est:10000-15000
£13953 $24000 €20371 Residence of Mr and Mrs Henry Snyder Cairo Lacke Tp Stark Co O (79x124cm-31x49in) s. graphite col pencil prov. 6-Dec-3 Pook & Pook, Downington #140/R est:10000-12000
£34375 $55000 €50188 Berks County Pennsylvania farm scene (81x132cm-32x52in) i. graphite prov. sold with deeds. 20-Sep-3 Pook & Pook, Downington #300/R est:25000-30000

BRADFORD, William (1827-1892) American
£29545 $52000 €43136 Coastal sunset (35x53cm-14x21in) s. paper on board prov. 18-May-4 Christie's, Rockefeller NY #38/R est:40000-60000
£34091 $60000 €49773 Arctic intruders (46x76cm-18x30in) s.i.d.1882 canvas on panel exhib.lit. 18-May-4 Christie's, Rockefeller NY #37/R est:60000-80000
£159091 $280000 €232273 Sunset calm in the Bay of Fundy (33x48cm-13x19in) s. board painted c.1860 prov. 18-May-4 Christie's, Rockefeller NY #21/R est:200000-300000

BRADISH, Alvah (1806-1901) American
£1375 $2200 €2008 Portrait of Joseph Campau (107x81cm-42x32in) painted 1856. 19-Sep-3 Du Mouchelle, Detroit #34/R est:2300-2500

BRADLEY, Basil (1842-1904) British
£2300 $4140 €3358 Road in Epping Forest (51x91cm-20x36in) s.i.d.1875. 21-Jan-4 Sotheby's, Olympia #374/R est:2000-3000
£8000 $14560 €11680 Highland incident (92x71cm-36x28in) s.i.d.1888. 16-Jun-4 Bonhams, New Bond Street #50/R est:6000-9000
£10870 $17500 €15870 Young shepherdess (91x142cm-36x56in) s. prov. 20-Aug-3 James Julia, Fairfield #528/R est:20000-40000
Works on paper
£1653 $2992 €2413 Untitled - Gordon setter and pointer (50x35cm-20x14in) s. W/C prov. 18-Apr-4 Levis, Calgary #204/R est:700-900 (C.D 4000)
£2000 $3140 €2900 Their master's shot (38x56cm-15x22in) s. W/C. 27-Aug-3 Sotheby's, London #996/R est:2000-3000
£2000 $3140 €2900 Collies in the highlands. Setters (17x25cm-7x10in) s. W/C pair prov. 27-Aug-3 Sotheby's, London #998/R est:2000-3000
£2100 $3822 €3066 Wild cattle of Chillingham (53x76cm-21x30in) s. 29-Jun-4 Anderson & Garland, Newcastle #155/R est:2000-3000

BRADLEY, Cuthbert (1861-1943) British
Works on paper
£260 $471 €380 Meynell Heedless, portrait of a foxhound (33x25cm-13x10in) s.d.1910 W/C. 2-Apr-4 Bracketts, Tunbridge Wells #422/R
£450 $810 €657 Lord Lonsdale's sergeant (20x22cm-8x9in) s.d.11 W/C gouache htd white. 21-Apr-4 Tennants, Leyburn #986
£850 $1530 €1241 Cottenham Point to point. Cottenham beauty, youth. Biggish place to get over (21x33cm-8x13in) W/C set of three prov. 21-Apr-4 Cheffins, Cambridge #457
£1100 $1980 €1606 Tandem race. Kelsall challenge cup. Fitzgerald hurdle plate. Half mile catch weights (20x35cm-8x14in) s.d.2 June 1886 W/C set of four. 21-Apr-4 Cheffins, Cambridge #463/R est:1000-1500

BRADLEY, Frank (?) British
£320 $566 €467 Homage to Degas (24x14cm-9x6in) s.d.1987 board. 28-Apr-4 Peter Wilson, Nantwich #30
£350 $620 €511 Waiting for the train (39x49cm-15x19in) s.d.1946. 28-Apr-4 Peter Wilson, Nantwich #23
£380 $673 €555 Botany mill (47x57cm-19x22in) s. board. 28-Apr-4 Peter Wilson, Nantwich #32
£650 $1151 €949 Industrial landscape (50x38cm-20x15in) s.d.1945 i.verso. 28-Apr-4 Peter Wilson, Nantwich #31

BRADLEY, Helen (1900-1979) British
£2800 $4816 €4088 Flowers from our hedgerow (23x18cm-9x7in) s.i.d.1966 canvasboard pair. 2-Dec-3 Bonhams, New Bond Street #73/R est:3000-5000
£4000 $7400 €5840 Said naughty Tom Twig to Nelson, I say old chap, they've got birds in their (30x24cm-12x9in) s.with fly canvasboard prov. 11-Feb-4 Sotheby's, Olympia #181/R est:3000-5000
£5000 $9150 €7300 Old roses (30x24cm-12x9in) s. s.i. canvas on panel double-sided. 4-Jun-4 Christie's, London #66/R est:6000-8000
£8000 $14560 €11680 Mother, George and I (17x14cm-7x6in) s.i.d.1970 verso board. 15-Jun-4 Bonhams, New Bond Street #80/R est:8000-12000
£11000 $20350 €16060 Morris dancers (30x17cm-12x7in) s. canvasboard. 11-Feb-4 Sotheby's, Olympia #179/R est:8000-12000
£17000 $30940 €24820 Gathering blackberries (40x50cm-16x20in) s.i. board prov.lit. 15-Jun-4 Bonhams, New Bond Street #83/R est:18000-25000
£18000 $32760 €26280 House for sale (40x43cm-16x17in) s.i. board prov. 15-Jun-4 Bonhams, New Bond Street #82/R est:18000-25000
£20000 $34400 €29200 Alexander park, Oldham (25x35cm-10x14in) mono.i. board prov. 2-Dec-3 Bonhams, New Bond Street #71/R est:20000-25000
£20000 $36600 €29200 Marton Mill (50x61cm-20x24in) s.d.1965 s.i.d.verso board. 4-Jun-4 Christie's, London #65/R est:15000-25000
£30000 $54600 €43800 Our picnic (40x60cm-16x24in) s.i. board lit. 15-Jun-4 Bonhams, New Bond Street #81/R est:30000-40000
£47000 $83190 €68620 Goodbye to L S Lowry (27x36cm-11x14in) s. with fly board prov. 27-Apr-4 Henry Adams, Chichester #771/R

Works on paper
£880 $1575 €1285 Wooded lake landscape (35x52cm-14x20in) s.d.1943 W/C. 17-Mar-4 Bonhams, Chester #259
£1600 $2912 €2336 Sunset over the river (36x52cm-14x20in) mono. d.1968 W/C. 15-Jun-4 Bonhams, Knightsbridge #28/R est:1000-1500
£2000 $3600 €2920 Parkland scene with wooden fence and stream (36x54cm-14x21in) s.i.d.1968 pencil W/C. 21-Apr-4 Tennants, Leyburn #998/R est:2500-3000
£9000 $15300 €13140 Green Woods (27x37cm-11x15in) s. W/C bodycol prov. 20-Nov-3 Christie's, London #188/R est:4000-6000

BRADLEY, James (19th C) British
£1600 $2944 €2336 Ducks and ducklings (37x48cm-15x19in) s.d.1853. 10-Jun-4 Christie's, Kensington #254/R est:800-1200

BRADLEY, Martin (1931-) British
£537 $950 €800 Image d'argent (90x65cm-35x26in) mono.d.55 s.i.verso prov. 28-Apr-4 Artcurial Briest, Paris #523
£832 $1415 €1190 Casa Valles (115x145cm-45x57in) s.d.1962 prov. 18-Nov-3 Babuino, Rome #386/R
£1050 $1848 €1533 Night of the Satyrs (72x123cm-28x48in) init.d.1963 i.overlap. 19-May-4 Sotheby's, Olympia #320/R est:800-1200
£1706 $2730 €2474 The mouse's tale (100x100cm-39x39in) s.d.1989. 17-Sep-3 Kunsthallen, Copenhagen #58/R est:20000 (D.KR 18000)
£2800 $4816 €4088 Kingfisher (100x100cm-39x39in) s.i.d.1988. 3-Dec-3 Christie's, Kensington #774/R est:2000-3000
£3200 $5504 €4672 Columbus comes to Santo Domingo (150x150cm-59x59in) s.i.d.1989. 3-Dec-3 Christie's, Kensington #773/R est:2500-3500
£5000 $9100 €7300 Abstract (128x96cm-50x38in) s. s.i.d.1960 verso prov. 1-Jul-4 Christie's, Kensington #391/R est:1000-1500

BRADLEY, William (19/20th C) British
£1591 $2800 €2323 Letty and Rascal (58x74cm-23x29in) init.d.1833. 20-May-4 American Auctioneer #475003/R
Works on paper
£360 $637 €526 Tranquil river landscape with sheep (66x43cm-26x17in) s.d.1884 W/C. 1-May-4 Hamptons Fine Art, Godalming #51
£620 $1054 €905 Fishing on the Thames (35x62cm-14x24in) s.d.1879 W/C. 1-Dec-3 Bonhams, Bath #80/R
£1350 $2241 €1971 Thames at Marlow (48x89cm-19x35in) s.d.1879 W/C. 1-Oct-3 Sotheby's, Olympia #72/R est:1500-2500

BRADSHAW, Alan (?) British?
£260 $476 €380 Puffins at Hornhead (25x35cm-10x14in) s. board. 2-Jun-4 John Ross, Belfast #195

BRADSHAW, Frank (1884-1969) British
£2100 $3759 €3066 Nude in profile (101x76cm-40x30in) 16-Mar-4 Bonhams, Leeds #576/R est:600-800

BRADSHAW, George Fagan (1887-1960) British
£340 $588 €496 Sunny day on the Cornish Coast (29x39cm-11x15in) board. 9-Dec-3 Bonhams, Oxford #122/R
£360 $569 €522 Choppy sea and cloudy sky (52x72cm-20x28in) s. board. 4-Sep-3 Locke & England, Leamington Spa #128/R
£1200 $2220 €1752 Moonlit sails (25x36cm-10x14in) s. panel. 10-Feb-4 David Lay, Penzance #379/R est:500-600
£1350 $2471 €1971 Rolling home (76x101cm-30x40in) s. 6-Jul-4 Bearnes, Exeter #481/R est:600-900
Works on paper
£460 $741 €667 Coastal view with seagulls and fishing boats by rocks (51x71cm-20x28in) s. gouache. 15-Aug-3 Keys, Aylsham #312
£500 $830 €730 A fishing smack of a rocky coast (58x28cm-23x11in) s. gouache. 2-Oct-3 Lane, Penzance #318

BRADSHAW, Nell Mary (1904-) Canadian
£333 $577 €486 Kwakiutl house pole (86x56cm-34x22in) s. panel. 9-Dec-3 Maynards, Vancouver #235 (C.D 750)

BRADY, Charles (1926-1997) Irish/American
£1888 $3210 €2700 Two trees (57x61cm-22x24in) s.i. s.d.1965 verso. 25-Nov-3 De Veres Art Auctions, Dublin #197 est:3000-4000
£2083 $3396 €3000 Tree in April (71x61cm-28x24in) s.i. s.d.1965 verso. 23-Sep-3 De Veres Art Auctions, Dublin #215/R est:2000-3000
£2600 $4758 €3796 1945 envelope (35x28cm-14x11in) s.d.75 oil on paper. 2-Jun-4 John Ross, Belfast #140 est:3000-4000
£2703 $5108 €4000 Wallet (56x46cm-22x18in) s. prov.exhib. 17-Feb-4 Whyte's, Dublin #81/R est:4000-5000
£3092 $5689 €4700 Pear (24x101cm-9x40in) 22-Jun-4 De Veres Art Auctions, Dublin #136/R est:3500-5000
£3200 $5728 €4672 Still life (30x52cm-12x20in) s. canvasboard. 14-May-4 Christie's, Kensington #403/R est:3000-5000
£3333 $6033 €5000 Artist's tissue (24x28cm-9x11in) s. linen prov. 30-Mar-4 De Veres Art Auctions, Dublin #57/R est:5000-6000
£3500 $6265 €5110 Inner roll (20x33cm-8x13in) s. canvasboard. 14-May-4 Christie's, Kensington #402/R est:2500-3000
£3826 $6771 €5700 Bull ring (46x36cm-18x14in) s.d.1971 oil paper exhib. 27-Apr-4 Whyte's, Dublin #164/R est:5000-7000
£4527 $8556 €6700 Empty match book (56x46cm-22x18in) s. s.i.verso. 17-Feb-4 Whyte's, Dublin #36/R est:4000-5000
£5594 $9510 €8000 Bowl (39x30cm-15x12in) s.d.1974 board. 18-Nov-3 Whyte's, Dublin #88/R est:6000-8000
£6711 $12013 €10000 Caravan (44x42cm-17x17in) s. i.d.1965 verso prov. 31-May-4 Hamilton Osborne King, Dublin #176/R est:8000-12000

BRADY, Emmet (fl.1896-1928) British
Works on paper
£820 $1320 €1189 Unloading the catch at Scarborough harbour (30x41cm-12x16in) s. W/C. 23-Feb-3 Desmond Judd, Cranbrook #1075

BRADY, Mathew (19th C) American
Photographs
£4233 $8000 €6180 Ulysses S Grant, City Point, Virginia (18x12cm-7x5in) bears i. verso albumen. 17-Feb-4 Swann Galleries, New York #7/R est:5000-7000
£7955 $14000 €11614 Civil war. photograph album of 97. 20-May-4 Swann Galleries, New York #222/R est:12000-18000
£35928 $60000 €52455 Portrait of Thomas Cole, Hudson River School painter. daguerreotype exec.c.1845 prov.lit. 20-Oct-3 Christie's, Rockefeller NY #24/R est:15000-20000

BRAEKEL, Joseph Pierre (1831-?) Dutch
£1259 $2140 €1800 A confidential whisper (60x50cm-24x20in) s. 28-Nov-3 Schloss Ahlden, Ahlden #1554/R est:1200

BRAEKELEER, Adrien de (1818-1904) Belgian
£405 $726 €600 Femme et fillette dans un interieur (59x48cm-23x19in) 10-May-4 Amberes, Antwerp #254
£903 $1417 €1300 Interieur anime (45x55cm-18x22in) s. 26-Aug-3 Galerie Moderne, Brussels #232/R

BRAEKELEER, Adrien de (attrib) (1818-1904) Belgian
£532 $888 €750 Curious (35x45cm-14x18in) s. panel. 20-Oct-3 Bernaerts, Antwerp #130
£1042 $1698 €1500 House maid cleaning brass pot watched by young girl (31x23cm-12x9in) s. panel. 25-Sep-3 Dr Fritz Nagel, Stuttgart #1326/R est:2500

BRAEKELEER, Ferdinand de (19th C) Belgian
£709 $1184 €1000 L'adoration du berger (61x54cm-24x21in) s.d.1820. 17-Jun-3 Vanderkindere, Brussels #440
£733 $1327 €1100 Pelerins (36x44cm-14x17in) s. 30-Mar-4 Campo, Vlaamse Kaai #26
£816 $1486 €1200 Couple in an interior (16x15cm-6x6in) s.i. panel. 3-Feb-4 Christie's, Amsterdam #85/R est:1200-1600
£3497 $5944 €5000 Flagrant delit (40x56cm-16x22in) panel. 1-Dec-3 Amberes, Antwerp #287
£16667 $28333 €24000 Letter writer (51x38cm-20x15in) s.i.d.1860 panel. 28-Oct-3 Wiener Kunst Auktionen, Vienna #11/R est:7000-15000
Works on paper
£600 $1098 €876 Figures outside a tavern (24x28cm-9x11in) s.d.1841 pen ink W/C. 7-Apr-4 Woolley & Wallis, Salisbury #178/R
£667 $1200 €1000 Letter (21x26cm-8x10in) s.d.1838 W/C washed ink. 26-Apr-4 Bernaerts, Antwerp #33

BRAEKELEER, Ferdinand de (elder) (1792-1883) Belgian
£8000 $14640 €12000 Le chagrin d'enfant (28x31cm-11x12in) s.d.1873 i.verso panel. 7-Jun-4 Palais de Beaux Arts, Brussels #45/R est:11000-16000

BRAEKELEER, Ferdinand de (younger) (1828-1857) Belgian
£4545 $7818 €6500 Ville de Frascati (49x62cm-19x24in) s. 2-Dec-3 Campo & Campo, Antwerp #92/R est:3000-5000

BRAEKELEER, Henri de (1840-1888) Belgian
£315 $541 €450 Interieur (28x34cm-11x13in) 2-Dec-3 Campo & Campo, Antwerp #93
£400 $736 €600 Interieur (35x26cm-14x10in) 14-Jun-4 Amberes, Antwerp #49
£517 $957 €750 Interieur a la marmite fumante (33x29cm-13x11in) s. 19-Jan-4 Horta, Bruxelles #20
£946 $1693 €1400 Le savetier (16x14cm-6x6in) s. panel. 10-May-4 Horta, Bruxelles #378
£1049 $1783 €1500 Homme se rasant devant un miroir (20x17cm-8x7in) s. panel. 1-Dec-3 Palais de Beaux Arts, Brussels #234/R est:1500-2000

BRAEKELEER, Henri de (attrib) (1840-1888) Belgian
Works on paper
£340 $609 €500 Mere pres du berceau (23x26cm-9x10in) mono. W/C. 22-Mar-4 Amberes, Antwerp #208

BRAEKELEER, Jacques de (1823-1906) Belgian
Sculpture
£60403 $108121 €90000 Jeune femme tenant des fleurs (172cm-68in) s.d.1875 marble. 25-May-4 Palais de Beaux Arts, Brussels #106/R est:62000-86000

BRAGA, Enrico (1841-?) Italian
Sculpture
£1259 $2140 €1800 Buste de jeune femme. s. white Carrare marble. 18-Nov-3 Galerie Moderne, Brussels #1510/R est:1600-2200

BRAGG, Charles (1931-) American
£380 $600 €555 Pierot (30x25cm-12x10in) s. 7-Sep-3 Treadway Gallery, Cincinnati #715/R
£909 $1600 €1327 Untitled (30x51cm-12x20in) s. board. 23-May-4 Hindman, Chicago #1023/R est:1500-2500
Works on paper
£543 $1000 €793 Rossini. Monet (20x15cm-8x6in) s.i. pencil vellum. 10-Jun-4 Swann Galleries, New York #40/R

BRAILOVSKY, Leonid Mikhailovich (1867-1937) Russian
£15000 $25500 €21900 Russian Carnival (63x75cm-25x30in) s. 19-Nov-3 Sotheby's, London #161/R est:15000-20000
£15000 $26850 €21900 Moscow (62x75cm-24x30in) s.d.26. 26-May-4 Sotheby's, London #172/R est:15000-20000
Works on paper
£4829 $8500 €7050 Winter scene, thought to be the Nicholas Gate, Moscow (77x55cm-30x22in) s. pencil W/C htd white. 18-May-4 Bonhams & Butterfields, San Francisco #82/R est:3000-5000

BRAITH, Anton (1836-1905) German
£1250 $2063 €1800 Two calves by fence (15x10cm-6x4in) s.d.1902 W/C over pencil. 3-Jul-3 Dr Fritz Nagel, Stuttgart #477/R est:1800
£1408 $2437 €2000 Back from pasture (74x100cm-29x39in) s.d.1869. 10-Dec-3 Finarte Semenzato, Rome #255/R est:2500-2800
£3125 $5094 €4500 Cows and sheep at lakeside (40x52cm-16x20in) s.i.d.1902. 25-Sep-3 Dr Fritz Nagel, Stuttgart #1327/R est:3000
£10526 $19368 €16000 Young cattle with herds woman by fence (51x97cm-20x38in) s.i.d.1874. 24-Jun-4 Dr Fritz Nagel, Stuttgart #693/R est:8000
£19444 $32083 €28000 Donkeys on beach (50x78cm-20x31in) s.i.d.1898 lit. 2-Jul-3 Neumeister, Munich #609/R est:8000
Works on paper
£302 $556 €450 Sheep by willow (9x12cm-4x5in) mono. chl. 25-Mar-4 Dr Fritz Nagel, Stuttgart #511

BRAITHWAITE, Joanna (1962-) New Zealander?
£2632 $4474 €3843 The vodka drinkers no 3 (152x182cm-60x72in) s.d.1995 verso. 27-Nov-3 International Art Centre, Auckland #20/R est:8000-12000 (NZ.D 7000)
£2909 $4567 €4218 NZ still life no 2 (167x182cm-66x72in) s.i.d.1990 verso. 27-Aug-3 Dunbar Sloane, Wellington #58/R est:10000-15000 (NZ.D 8000)

BRAITOU-SALA, Albert (1885-1972) French
£324 $581 €480 Petite fille a la fenetre (44x38cm-17x15in) s. panel. 5-May-4 Coutau Begarie, Paris #47
£400 $740 €584 Spanish dancer (55x46cm-22x18in) s. 10-Feb-4 Bonhams, Knightsbridge #48/R

BRAKEN, Peter van den (1896-1979) Dutch
£395 $726 €600 View of Rolde (47x75cm-19x30in) s. indis.d. i.verso. 28-Jun-4 Sotheby's, Amsterdam #107/R
£537 $993 €800 Bos te sterksel (70x90cm-28x35in) s.i.verso. 15-Mar-4 Sotheby's, Amsterdam #211/R
£559 $1029 €850 Farmhouse (70x100cm-28x39in) s. 28-Jun-4 Sotheby's, Amsterdam #105/R
£1208 $2235 €1800 Spring landscape with blossom trees (50x70cm-20x28in) s. 15-Mar-4 Sotheby's, Amsterdam #212/R est:1000-1500

BRAKENBURGH, Richard (1650-1702) Dutch
£1357 $2348 €1981 Entremetteuse (35x27cm-14x11in) panel prov. 12-Dec-3 Galerie du Rhone, Sion #160/R est:5000-7000 (S.FR 3000)
£2000 $3580 €3000 Domestic interior with family seated by the hearth (53x63cm-21x25in) indis.sig. 17-May-4 Christie's, Amsterdam #38/R est:3000-5000
£3793 $6334 €5500 High jinks in the tavern (50x57cm-20x22in) s.d.1676 prov. 15-Nov-3 Lempertz, Koln #1013/R est:6000
£4462 $7674 €6515 King Salomon and the Queen of Saba (76x71cm-30x28in) s.d.1675 panel. 7-Dec-3 Uppsala Auktionskammare, Uppsala #8/R est:50000-60000 (S.KR 58000)
Works on paper
£800 $1432 €1200 Mother and daughter (12x9cm-5x4in) W/C. 13-May-4 Bassenge, Berlin #5053/R

BRAKENBURGH, Richard (attrib) (1650-1702) Dutch
£5705 $10211 €8500 Interieur d'auberge avec compagnie attablee (58x73cm-23x29in) indis.sig. 25-May-4 Palais de Beaux Arts, Brussels #63/R est:10000-15000

BRAKENSIEK-DEKKER, Anna Maria (1890-1970) Dutch
£451 $713 €650 Corn sheaves in front of the farm (55x65cm-22x26in) s. 2-Sep-3 Christie's, Amsterdam #432

BRALDS, Braldt (20th C) American/Dutch
£240 $400 €350 Rock Star (48x81cm-19x32in) s.d. 11-Oct-3 Nadeau, Windsor #192/R
£240 $400 €350 Snowshoe (20x20cm-8x8in) s. 11-Oct-3 Nadeau, Windsor #198/R
£269 $450 €393 American shorthair (20x20cm-8x8in) s. 11-Oct-3 Nadeau, Windsor #196/R
£269 $450 €393 Cinnamon tabby maine coon (20x20cm-8x8in) s. 11-Oct-3 Nadeau, Windsor #199/R
£419 $700 €612 Six pack (76x76cm-30x30in) s.d. 11-Oct-3 Nadeau, Windsor #187/R
£778 $1300 €1136 Table manners (76x74cm-30x29in) s. 11-Oct-3 Nadeau, Windsor #189/R
£1198 $2000 €1749 Siamese twins (76x102cm-30x40in) s.d. 11-Oct-3 Nadeau, Windsor #201/R est:7500-10000
£1257 $2100 €1835 Cabinet meeting (66x89cm-26x35in) s. 11-Oct-3 Nadeau, Windsor #200/R est:8000-10000

BRALEY, Clarence (1858-1925) American
Works on paper
£1243 $2200 €1815 Fishing boat in full sail (46x66cm-18x26in) s. pencil W/C sold with another by H H Warren. 2-May-4 Bonhams & Butterfields, San Francisco #1081/R est:400-600

BRAMBATI, Luigi (1925-) Italian
£471 $772 €650 Hills near Varese (40x51cm-16x20in) s. board. 27-May-3 Il Ponte, Milan #856

BRAMBILLA, Carlo Filippo (1684-1752) Italian
£7333 $13493 €11000 Rural landscape with travellers (75x100cm-30x39in) lit. 14-Jun-4 Sant Agostino, Torino #310/R est:4000-5000

BRAMER, Josef (1948-) Austrian
Works on paper
£2411 $4027 €3400 Summer-winter (28x17cm-11x7in) mono.d.87 mixed media. 14-Oct-3 Dorotheum, Vienna #250/R est:3000-3600
£2517 $4280 €3600 Four seasons (27x27cm-11x11in) mono.d.80 mixed media board. 26-Nov-3 Dorotheum, Vienna #276/R est:3000-4000

BRAMER, Leonard (1596-1674) Dutch
£1858 $3326 €2750 Biblical scene (79x65cm-31x26in) s. panel. 6-May-4 Michael Zeller, Lindau #539/R est:2500
£8000 $14320 €12000 Moonlit landscape with travellers leading their mules (20cm-8in circular) slate prov.exhib. 17-May-4 Christie's, Amsterdam #95/R est:10000-15000
£32000 $58560 €46720 Shaphan reading the Book of Law (57x75cm-22x30in) panel. 8-Jul-4 Sotheby's, London #138/R est:15000-20000
£38889 $70000 €56778 Scribe Shaphan (18x28cm-7x11in) s.verso copper prov.exhib.lit. 22-Jan-4 Sotheby's, New York #28/R est:50000-70000
Works on paper
£293 $525 €440 Preacher before Sultan (29x33cm-11x13in) s. W/C pen brush. 14-May-4 Bassenge, Berlin #5748/R
£946 $1665 €1400 God creating Eve from Adam's rib (39x31cm-15x12in) brush black ink grey wash. 19-May-4 Sotheby's, Amsterdam #52/R

BRAMER, Leonard (attrib) (1596-1674) Dutch
£274 $466 €400 Christ beforethe doctors (25x33cm-10x13in) panel. 5-Nov-3 Beaussant & Lefèvre, Paris #3

BRAMER, Leonard (circle) (1596-1674) Dutch
£6114 $11249 €8926 Jewess (60x50cm-24x20in) 14-Jun-4 Philippe Schuler, Zurich #4261 est:3000-5000 (S.FR 14000)

BRAMHAM, Christopher (1952-) British
Works on paper
£320 $573 €467 Trees (40x29cm-16x11in) init.d.87 pastel. 14-May-4 Christie's, Kensington #608
£350 $637 €511 Garden at night (24x32cm-9x13in) s. pastel. 1-Jul-4 Christie's, Kensington #295
£450 $806 €657 Winter morning (28x45cm-11x18in) s.d.88 pastel. 14-May-4 Christie's, Kensington #606

BRAMLEY, Frank (1857-1915) British
£300 $501 €438 Study of an iris (23x18cm-9x7in) 21-Oct-3 Gorringes, Lewes #2184
£4000 $7320 €5840 Vieux marin et sa petite fille (35x21cm-14x8in) init. panel. 2-Jun-4 Sotheby's, London #10/R est:5000-7000

BRAMLEY, William (fl.1900-1932) British
£700 $1274 €1022 Stroll in the garden (46x30cm-18x12in) prov. 1-Jul-4 Christie's, Kensington #140/R

BRAMLEY-MOORE, Mostyn (1952-) Australian
£894 $1546 €1305 Untitled, blue abstract (120x105cm-47x41in) 10-Dec-3 Shapiro, Sydney #42/R (A.D 2100)
£909 $1682 €1327 Kipling's Well (213x182cm-84x72in) painted 1988 prov. 15-Mar-4 Sotheby's, Melbourne #144 est:600-800 (A.D 2200)

BRANCACCIO, Carlo (1861-1920) Italian
£676 $1209 €1000 Street in Naples (41x33cm-16x13in) 10-May-4 Giraudeau, Tours #176
£1189 $1985 €1700 Coastal view (27x28cm-11x11in) s. board. 10-Oct-3 Stadion, Trieste #28/R est:1400-1800
£1656 $3030 €2500 Sailing boat off coast (13x23cm-5x9in) s. panel. 8-Apr-4 Dorotheum, Vienna #56/R est:2500-2800
£1700 $2992 €2482 An Italian villa (65x81cm-26x32in) s. 19-May-4 Dreweatt Neate, Newbury #70/R est:2000-3000
£2183 $4017 €3187 Girl with jug (30x24cm-12x9in) s.i. panel. 14-Jun-4 Philippe Schuler, Zurich #4262/R est:6000-8000 (S.FR 5000)
£8800 $16280 €12848 Napoli Vecchia, busy market scene (41x28cm-16x11in) s.i. 13-Feb-4 Keys, Aylsham #657/R est:2000-3000
£20000 $36800 €30000 Rainy day in Trieste Square, Trento (47x70cm-19x28in) s.i. 8-Jun-4 Sotheby's, Milan #32/R est:15000-20000
£21127 $35070 €30000 Napoli, terrazze a mare e Palazzo Conn'Anna (51x105cm-20x41in) s. 11-Jun-3 Christie's, Rome #209/R est:33000-38000
Works on paper
£4085 $7066 €5800 Garden (51x100cm-20x39in) s. W/C. 10-Dec-3 Finarte Semenzato, Rome #195/R est:6000-6500

BRANCUSI, Constantin (1876-1957) Rumanian
Photographs
£2260 $4000 €3300 Femme se regardant dans un miroir (17x12cm-7x5in) gelatin silver print lit. 27-Apr-4 Christie's, Rockefeller NY #46/R est:4000-6000
£5085 $9000 €7424 Vue de l'Atelier (40x29cm-16x11in) gelatin silver print executed c.1924. 27-Apr-4 Christie's, Rockefeller NY #45/R est:10000-15000
£5389 $9000 €7868 Corner of the artist's studio (12x8cm-5x3in) i.verso gelatin silver print exec.c.1923 prov. 20-Oct-3 Christie's, Rockefeller NY #80/R est:7000-9000
£6000 $10200 €8760 Newborn (17x23cm-7x9in) i.verso gelatin silver print. 18-Nov-3 Christie's, Kensington #145/R est:1500-2000

£8982 $15000 €13114 Leda (17x23cm-7x9in) gelatin silver print exec.1920-21 prov.exhib.lit. 17-Oct-3 Phillips, New York #147/R est:15000-25000
£11000 $18700 €16060 Golden bird (23x16cm-9x6in) i.verso gelatin silver print. 18-Nov-3 Christie's, Kensington #153/R est:2000-3000
Works on paper
£147059 $250000 €214706 Tete de femme (61x48cm-24x19in) s. gouache pencil chl India ink gum tempera paper on board prov. 5-Nov-3 Sotheby's, New York #24/R est:250000-350000

BRAND, Christian Hilfgott (1695-1756) Austrian
£1259 $2165 €1800 Horse riders in a landscape (15x20cm-6x8in) panel. 7-Dec-3 Sotheby's, Amsterdam #621
£2759 $4579 €4000 Wooded landscape with horseman and travellers (62x56cm-24x22in) prov. 1-Oct-3 Dorotheum, Vienna #248/R est:2800-3500

BRAND, Johann Christian (1722-1795) Austrian
Works on paper
£1133 $2029 €1700 River landscape with Vienna suburbs (33x44cm-13x17in) s.d.1790 ochre. 13-May-4 Bassenge, Berlin #5358/R est:1200

BRAND, Johann Christian (attrib) (1722-1795) Austrian
£939 $1700 €1371 Figures by the river (43x49cm-17x19in) indis.s. board. 1-Apr-4 Ben-Ami, Tel Aviv #4756/R est:2500-3500
£1330 $2381 €1942 Landscape with horsemen and figures (12x12cm-5x5in) mono. verso panel pair. 26-May-4 AB Stockholms Auktionsverk #2533/R est:18000-20000 (S.KR 18000)
£3000 $5400 €4380 Wooded river landscapes with shepherds and their flocks (25x30cm-10x12in) pair. 23-Apr-4 Christie's, Kensington #158/R est:4000-6000

BRAND, Johann Christian (circle) (1722-1795) Austrian
£5000 $8500 €7300 Italianate landscape with figures by Roman ruins. Italianate landscape with figures by a fountain (39x51cm-15x20in) pair. 31-Oct-3 Christie's, Kensington #79/R est:5000-7000

BRANDANI, Enrico (1914-) Italian
£1579 $2858 €2400 La dernier valse (60x43cm-24x17in) s. panel. 19-Apr-4 Horta, Bruxelles #181 est:1200-1500

BRANDEGEE, Robert Bolling (1848-1922) American
£262 $475 €383 Portrait of Miss Sarah Porter, Farmington educator. 3-Apr-4 Nadeau, Windsor #49a

BRANDEIS, A (1849-1910) Hungarian
Works on paper
£2200 $4048 €3212 Trajan's Column, Rome (70x31cm-28x12in) s. W/C. 23-Jun-4 Cheffins, Cambridge #470/R est:200-300

BRANDEIS, Antonietta (1849-1910) Hungarian
£1200 $2004 €1752 Figures on a shoreline (35x49cm-14x19in) mono. board. 7-Oct-3 Bonhams, Knightsbridge #144/R est:1000-1500
£1955 $3245 €2835 Amalfi (25x15cm-10x6in) s. board. 13-Jun-3 Zofingen, Switzerland #2422/R est:5500 (S.FR 4300)
£2600 $4420 €3796 Palazzo on the Grand Canal (28x17cm-11x7in) s.d.1884. 19-Nov-3 Bonhams, New Bond Street #91/R est:3000-5000
£2813 $4500 €4107 Gondolier in Venice scene (53x71cm-21x28in) s. 20-Sep-3 Sloans & Kenyon, Bethesda #1165/R est:3500-4500
£3226 $6000 €4710 Amalfi coast (36x23cm-14x9in) s. 5-Mar-4 Skinner, Boston #330/R est:6000-8000
£3800 $6460 €5548 Venetian washday (34x25cm-13x10in) init. panel. 19-Nov-3 Bonhams, New Bond Street #92/R est:3000-5000
£4000 $6800 €5840 Porta Villa Carta, Palazzo Ducale, Venice (21x13cm-8x5in) init. panel. 18-Nov-3 Sotheby's, London #300/R
£4400 $7920 €6424 Albergho dei Cappucini, Amalfi (25x15cm-10x6in) s. i.verso board. 21-Jan-4 Sotheby's, Olympia #427/R est:1500-2000
£4755 $8179 €6800 View of the S Giorgio Maggiore in Venice (16x23cm-6x9in) s. i.verso board. 3-Dec-3 Neumeister, Munich #534/R est:2500
£4755 $8084 €6800 St Mark Square, Venice (13x24cm-5x9in) s. i.verso panel. 28-Nov-3 Wendl, Rudolstadt #3934/R est:1700
£5000 $8500 €7300 Van Axel's Palace, Venice (25x16cm-10x6in) s. board prov. 19-Nov-3 Bonhams, New Bond Street #89/R est:5000-7000
£5285 $9459 €7716 Cavalli Palace. Rio de St. Augustin (23x13cm-9x5in) mono. panel two. 4-May-4 Ritchie, Toronto #103/R est:4000-6000 (C.D 13000)
£5500 $9350 €8030 Desdemona's Palace, Venice (25x16cm-10x6in) s. board prov. 19-Nov-3 Bonhams, New Bond Street #90/R est:5000-7000
£5594 $9622 €8000 Market in front of S Giacomo di Rialto in Venice (24x34cm-9x13in) mono. panel. 3-Dec-3 Neumeister, Munich #533 R est:3000
£5691 $10187 €8309 View of the Doge's Palace and Piazza San Marco (15x26cm-6x10in) mono. panel prov. 4-May-4 Ritchie, Toronto #102/R est:3000-5000 (C.D 14000)
£5734 $9863 €8200 View of Rome (14x24cm-6x9in) s. board. 3-Dec-3 Stadion, Trieste #1009/R est:3500-4500
£6000 $10320 €8760 Piazza San Marco and the Doge's Palace, Venice (16x23cm-6x9in) s. panel. 4-Dec-3 Christie's, Kensington #62/R est:3000-5000
£7200 $13104 €10512 The Sacristy of the Church of Santa Croce, Florence (17x24cm-7x9in) s. panel. 15-Jun-4 Sotheby's, London #185/R est:5000-7000
£8000 $14560 €11680 Grand Canal before Santa Maria della Salute, Venice (12x21cm-5x8in) s. panel. 16-Jun-4 Christie's, Kensington #87/R est:5000-7000
£10000 $18500 €14600 Colliseum, Rome (15x25cm-6x10in) mono. board. 14-Jul-4 Sotheby's, Olympia #228/R est:5000-7000
£11312 $18891 €16516 Grand Canal. Doges Palace, Venice (17x23cm-7x9in) s. board pair prov. 17-Nov-3 Waddingtons, Toronto #27/R est:15000-20000 (C.D 25000)
£13287 $22587 €19000 Vue de Venise animee (16x22cm-6x9in) s. cardboard pair. 18-Nov-3 Vanderkindere, Brussels #110/R est:20000-30000
£13500 $24570 €19710 Piazza san Marco. View from the Ponte Vecchio, Florence (17x23cm-7x9in) s. board two. 3-Feb-4 Sworder & Son, Bishops Stortford #303/R est:4000-6000
£27586 $46069 €40000 The Forum. Trevi fountain (15x25cm-6x10in) s. board pair. 12-Nov-3 Sotheby's, Milan #179/R est:20000-30000

BRANDEL, Alexander Kay (19th C) British?
£7650 $14000 €11169 Flogging on deck (34x50cm-13x20in) s. sold with another by English Primitive School 19th C prov. 7-Apr-4 Sotheby's, New York #90/R est:6000-8000

BRANDEL, Alfred (1889-1973) Hungarian
Sculpture
£1181 $1877 €1700 Girl wearing crinoline (30cm-12in) i. pat.bronze. 15-Sep-3 Dorotheum, Vienna #182/R est:1000-1300

BRANDELIUS, Gustaf (1833-1884) Swedish
£4462 $7674 €6515 The actress Therese Bobergh on horseback (93x73cm-37x29in) s.d.1877. 2-Dec-3 Bukowskis, Stockholm #71/R est:45000-50000 (S.KR 58000)

BRANDEN, A K (?) ?
£1449 $2348 €2101 Coastal scene with ships of different eras (69x108cm-27x43in) s.i.d.1870 canvas on board. 31-Jul-3 International Art Centre, Auckland #144/R est:5000-8000 (NZ.D 4000)

BRANDENBERG, Johann (1661-1729) Swiss
Works on paper
£490 $817 €700 St Meinrad von Einsiedeln (40x25cm-16x10in) s. htd white wash brush. 10-Oct-3 Winterberg, Heidelberg #273

BRANDENBERGER, Hans (1912-2003) Swiss
Sculpture
£3493 $6358 €5100 Bathing woman (183cm-72in) pat bronze exec. c.1963-1965. 16-Jun-4 Fischer, Luzern #37/R est:3000-4000 (S.FR 8000)
£3509 $6456 €5123 Female nude standing (152cm-60in) green black pat bronze sold with base prov. 23-Jun-4 Koller, Zurich #3153/R est:4500-6000 (S.FR 8000)

BRANDENBURG, Paul (1866-?) German
£267 $485 €400 Country landscape (32x44cm-13x17in) s. paper on board. 1-Jul-4 Van Ham, Cologne #1230
£720 $1311 €1051 Village landscape (35x53cm-14x21in) s. paper board. 20-Jun-4 Agra, Warsaw #3/R (P.Z 5000)

BRANDER, Fredrik (1705-1779) Swedish
£739 $1323 €1079 Portrait of boy (37x27cm-15x11in) s. verso. 28-May-4 Uppsala Auktionskammare, Uppsala #77/R (S.KR 10000)
£3843 $6880 €5611 Portrait of Erik Froman and his wife Catharina (82x65cm-32x26in) s.d.1733 pair lit. 26-May-4 AB Stockholms Auktionsverk #2258/R est:30000-35000 (S.KR 52000)

BRANDER, Fredrik (attrib) (1705-1779) Swedish
£599 $1072 €875 Portrait of Brita Johanna Lilliehook (80x67cm-31x26in) 28-May-4 Uppsala Auktionskammare, Uppsala #78/R (S.KR 8100)
£4730 $8467 €6906 Baron Erland Broman and his wife Vilhelmina Magdalena (67x51cm-26x20in) pair. 25-May-4 Bukowskis, Stockholm #407/R est:30000-35000 (S.KR 64000)

BRANDES, Peter (1944-) Danish
£7942 $14614 €11595 Herder (200x115cm-79x45in) s.d.90 s.d.dec.89-jan 90 verso exhib. 29-Mar-4 Rasmussen, Copenhagen #133/R est:30000-40000 (D.KR 88000)

BRANDES, Willy (1876-1956) German
£333 $613 €500 Young boy looking after geese (60x50cm-24x20in) s. 12-Jun-4 Karlheinz Kaupp, Staufen #1034/R

BRANDI, Domenico (1683-1736) Italian
£4887 $8112 €7135 Poultry yard (37x74cm-15x29in) s. 4-Oct-3 Kieselbach, Budapest #45/R (H.F 1800000)

BRANDI, Domenico (attrib) (1683-1736) Italian
£7500 $12750 €10950 Animals gathering to enter the Ark (148x191cm-58x75in) 29-Oct-3 Bonhams, New Bond Street #86/R est:3500-4500

BRANDI, Giacinto (1623-1691) Italian
£4800 $8784 €7008 Heads of two youths (61x91cm-24x36in) lit. 8-Jul-4 Sotheby's, London #205/R est:3000-4000
Works on paper
£3401 $6088 €5000 St Francois agenouille sur un nuage porte par des anges (32x20cm-13x8in) pen brown black ink brown wash prov. 18-Mar-4 Christie's, Paris #19/R est:1500-2000

BRANDI, Giacinto (attrib) (1623-1691) Italian
£2368 $4358 €3600 Saint Paul the hermit (129x97cm-51x38in) lit. 22-Jun-4 Babuino, Rome #16/R est:3000-4000
£3500 $6300 €5110 Penitent Saint Jerome (125x99cm-49x39in) sold with a letter. 23-Apr-4 Christie's, Kensington #239/R est:4000-6000

BRANDIS, August (1862-1947) German
£294 $505 €420 Interior of a Barock salon (82x66cm-32x26in) s. 6-Dec-3 Dannenberg, Berlin #771/R
£320 $502 €464 Interior looking through to the dining room (84x86cm-33x34in) s. 28-Aug-3 Christie's, Kensington #305/R
£600 $1092 €900 Night-time kitchen interior scene (67x50cm-26x20in) s. 1-Jul-4 Van Ham, Cologne #1233/R
£800 $1456 €1200 Landscape with trees (111x82cm-44x32in) s. 1-Jul-4 Van Ham, Cologne #1234/R
£909 $1518 €1300 Castle interior (82x66cm-32x26in) s. 28-Jun-3 Bolland & Marotz, Bremen #622/R

£3333	$5500	€4800	Tea time (112x85cm-44x33in) s. 3-Jul-3 Van Ham, Cologne #1081/R est:2800
£5333	$9707	€8000	In the summer house, a lady playing the mandolin (145x105cm-57x41in) s. 1-Jul-4 Van Ham, Cologne #1235/R est:3200

BRANDISH-HOLTE, Augustus (attrib) (19th C) British

£1300	$2457	€1898	River landscape scenes (28x43cm-11x17in) s.verso pair. 19-Feb-4 Grant, Worcester #425/R est:600-800

BRANDL, Herbert (1959-) Austrian

£2685	$4966	€4000	Untitled (55x55cm-22x22in) s.d.1988 verso oil plaster sand pigment. 9-Mar-4 Dorotheum, Vienna #189/R est:4500-6000
£5594	$9510	€8000	Untitled (120x90cm-47x35in) s.d.92 verso prov. 26-Nov-3 Dorotheum, Vienna #104/R est:8000-10000
£8392	$14266	€12000	Untitled - Green (190x120cm-75x47in) mono.d.85 verso exhib.prov. 26-Nov-3 Dorotheum, Vienna #99/R est:10000-13000

Works on paper

£3147	$5350	€4500	Gato (215x150cm-85x59in) mono.i.d.85 mixed meidal exhib.prov. 26-Nov-3 Dorotheum, Vienna #102/R est:4500-6000
£4167	$7083	€6000	Untitled (326x152cm-128x60in) s.d.88 mixed media exhib.lit. 28-Oct-3 Wiener Kunst Auktionen, Vienna #289/R est:6000-14000
£5034	$8909	€7500	Untitled (330x150cm-130x59in) s. mixed media paper on canvas exhib.lit. 28-Apr-4 Wiener Kunst Auktionen, Vienna #288/R est:6000-9000

BRANDRIFF, George Kennedy (1890-1936) American

£1323	$2500	€1932	Wind blown - Bishop Country 1926 (30x41cm-12x16in) i.d. verso board prov. 17-Feb-4 John Moran, Pasadena #98a/R est:3500-4500
£2038	$3750	€2975	Waves breaking on a rocky coast (40x50cm-16x20in) s. prov. 8-Jun-4 Bonhams & Butterfields, San Francisco #4238/R est:4000-6000
£2198	$4000	€3209	Coastal cityscape (28x36cm-11x14in) i.d.1929 verso canvasboard prov. 15-Jun-4 John Moran, Pasadena #73 est:4000-6000

BRANDS, Eugène (1913-2002) Dutch

£306	$550	€447	Human face (20x20cm-8x8in) s.d.1961 acrylic. 23-Jan-4 Freeman, Philadelphia #90/R
£353	$650	€515	Untitled (28x43cm-11x17in) s.d.4/59 paper prov. 25-Jun-4 Freeman, Philadelphia #102/R
£444	$800	€648	Face in the mirror (23x20cm-9x8in) s.d.61 oil paper. 23-Jan-4 Freeman, Philadelphia #266/R
£462	$850	€675	Abstract (58x46cm-23x18in) paper prov. 25-Jun-4 Freeman, Philadelphia #71/R
£472	$850	€689	Black flower basket (20x28cm-8x11in) s.d.56 oil paper. 23-Jan-4 Freeman, Philadelphia #273/R
£489	$900	€714	Head of Saint John the Baptist (64x48cm-25x19in) s.d.c.11/59 paper prov. 25-Jun-4 Freeman, Philadelphia #67/R
£503	$931	€750	Abstact composition (30x19cm-12x7in) s.d.1966 oil on paper. 15-Mar-4 Sotheby's, Amsterdam #264
£528	$950	€771	Deep sea world (28x28cm-11x11in) s.d.1.58 oil paper. 23-Jan-4 Freeman, Philadelphia #270/R
£543	$1000	€793	Untitled (38x46cm-15x18in) s.d.1960 paper prov. 25-Jun-4 Freeman, Philadelphia #100/R
£652	$1200	€952	Untitled (20x28cm-8x11in) s.d.2/58 paper prov. 25-Jun-4 Freeman, Philadelphia #104/R
£722	$1300	€1054	Motherhood (61x71cm-24x28in) s.d.1960 oil paper. 23-Jan-4 Freeman, Philadelphia #267/R
£722	$1300	€1054	Flowers (46x51cm-18x20in) s.d.60 oil paper. 23-Jan-4 Freeman, Philadelphia #272
£761	$1400	€1111	Sun with flowers (20x23cm-8x9in) s.d.8/1958 s.i.d.verso paper prov. 25-Jun-4 Freeman, Philadelphia #69/R est:500-800
£778	$1400	€1136	Sleeping cat (48x51cm-19x20in) s.d.1960 oil paper. 23-Jan-4 Freeman, Philadelphia #269/R
£814	$1400	€1188	Blue on red abstract (51x56cm-20x22in) s.d.1962 paper on illustration board prov. 7-Dec-3 Freeman, Philadelphia #80 est:1000-1500
£815	$1500	€1190	Cat (20x48cm-8x19in) s.d.3/59 paper on board. 25-Jun-4 Freeman, Philadelphia #75/R est:800-1200
£930	$1600	€1358	Good morning, Mr Frend (20x51cm-8x20in) s.d.6-54 s.i.d.1954 verso prov. 7 Dec 3 Freeman, Philadelphia #78 est:800-1200
£930	$1600	€1358	Child in jungle (23x51cm-9x20in) s.d.4-59 s.i.d.verso paper prov. 7-Dec-3 Freeman, Philadelphia #81 est:800-1200
£1087	$2000	€1587	Apples (33x48cm-13x19in) s.d.10/59 paper prov. 25-Jun-4 Freeman, Philadelphia #99/R est:800-1200
£1087	$2000	€1587	Moon (48x41cm-19x16in) s.d.4/59 paper on board prov. 25-Jun-4 Freeman, Philadelphia #103/R est:700-1000
£1105	$1900	€1613	Demonish nights (33x28cm-13x11in) s.d.65-5i.d.1959-6 verso prov. 7-Dec-3 Freeman, Philadelphia #77 est:500-800
£1163	$2000	€1698	Town at night (28x30cm-11x12in) s.d.4.58 board prov. 7-Dec-3 Freeman, Philadelphia #76 est:500-800
£1315	$2195	€1920	Black flag (24x44cm-9x17in) s. paper prov. 7-Oct-3 Rasmussen, Copenhagen #22/R est:12000-15000 (D.KR 14000)
£1522	$2800	€2222	Still life with fish (33x36cm-13x14in) s.d.1/54 paper on board. 25-Jun-4 Freeman, Philadelphia #76/R est:1500-2500
£1600	$2944	€2400	Vroow in landschap (29x34cm-11x13in) s.i.d.1959-5 paper. 8-Jun-4 Sotheby's, Amsterdam #268/R est:2500-3500
£2238	$3804	€3200	Bright moon (42x34cm-17x13in) s.d.2.57 i.verso paper. 25-Nov-3 Christie's, Amsterdam #257/R est:1800-2200
£2333	$4270	€3500	Dream castle (26x35cm-10x14in) s.d.51. 7-Jun-4 Glerum, Amsterdam #408/R est:1800-2200
£2378	$4090	€3400	Crossed Christ I (28x29cm-11x11in) s.d.3.56 s.i.d.verso oil on paper. 2-Dec-3 Sotheby's, Amsterdam #302/R est:4500-5500
£2448	$4161	€3500	Abstract composition (50x56cm-20x22in) s.d.64 paper. 24-Nov-3 Glerum, Amsterdam #277/R est:2500-3500
£3147	$5413	€4500	Vikingervaart (23x31cm-9x12in) s.d.8.54 i.d.verso oil on paper. 2-Dec-3 Sotheby's, Amsterdam #128/R est:4500-5500
£3497	$6014	€5000	Woman with child (125x120cm-49x47in) s.d.65 prov.lit. 2-Dec-3 Sotheby's, Amsterdam #146/R est:5000-7000
£4333	$7973	€6500	Untitled (50x65cm-20x26in) s.d.12.57 paper on canvas. 8-Jun-4 Sotheby's, Amsterdam #82/R est:6500-8500
£4545	$7727	€6500	Landscape with bird (68x90cm-27x35in) s.d.72 s.verso i.stretcher. 25-Nov-3 Christie's, Amsterdam #125/R est:4000-6000
£4545	$7818	€6500	Het Amsterdams bruidje (28x30cm-11x12in) s.d.5.57 oil paper on card. 2-Dec-3 Sotheby's, Amsterdam #126/R est:4500-5500
£4545	$7818	€6500	Ondergaande zon (24x28cm-9x11in) s.d.8.1958 s.i.d.verso oil on paper prov. 2-Dec-3 Sotheby's, Amsterdam #129/R est:4500-5500
£5000	$9200	€7500	Abstract landscape (90x95cm-35x37in) s. s.i.d.1977 stretcher prov. 8-Jun-4 Sotheby's, Amsterdam #279/R est:4000-6000
£10490	$17832	€15000	Composition (50x68cm-20x27in) s.d.12/49 board prov. 25-Nov-3 Christie's, Amsterdam #248/R est:15000-20000

Works on paper

£280	$467	€400	Abstract composition (11x45cm-4x18in) s.i. gouache. 30-Jun-3 Sotheby's, Amsterdam #526
£379	$607	€550	Panta Rhei - all streams (30x38cm-12x15in) s.d.68 i.d.1968 verso gouache. 17-Sep-3 Kunsthallen, Copenhagen #1/R (D.KR 4000)
£395	$726	€600	Landscape under threatening light (35x40cm-14x16in) s. s.i.d.1971 verso gouache. 22-Jun-4 Christie's, Amsterdam #366/R
£395	$726	€600	Sunset (32x38cm-13x15in) init. s.i.d.1981 verso gouache. 22-Jun-4 Christie's, Amsterdam #385/R
£407	$750	€594	Abstract head (25x20cm-10x8in) s.d.65 gouache prov. 25-Jun-4 Freeman, Philadelphia #66/R
£417	$658	€600	Composition (15x24cm-6x9in) s.d.68 gouache. 2-Sep-3 Christie's, Amsterdam #479
£417	$750	€609	Cosmose camp (38x43cm-15x17in) gouache. 23-Jan-4 Freeman, Philadelphia #88/R
£435	$800	€635	Demon (30x23cm-12x9in) s.d.66 s.i.d.verso gouache prov. 25-Jun-4 Freeman, Philadelphia #70/R
£510	$929	€750	Composition au fond blanc (24x33cm-9x13in) s.d.1992 gouache. 3-Feb-4 Christie's, Amsterdam #607
£516	$950	€753	Abstract (43x53cm-17x21in) gouache prov. 25-Jun-4 Freeman, Philadelphia #68/R
£516	$950	€753	Five black spots (46x64cm-18x25in) s. s.i.d.1979 verso gouache prov. 25-Jun-4 Freeman, Philadelphia #101/R
£528	$950	€771	Large bird picks worm (36x41cm-14x16in) s.d.6.59 W/C. 23-Jan-4 Freeman, Philadelphia #89/R
£543	$1000	€793	Moon rising (43x33cm-17x13in) s.d.66 s.i.d.verso gouache prov. 25-Jun-4 Freeman, Philadelphia #72/R
£543	$1000	€793	Nature morte au fond noir (30x51cm-12x20in) init. s.i.d.1990-94 verso gouache prov. 25-Jun-4 Freeman, Philadelphia #73/R
£598	$1100	€873	Abstract (38x30cm-15x12in) s.d.65 gouache prov. 25-Jun-4 Freeman, Philadelphia #105/R
£658	$1211	€1000	Composition (38x49cm-15x19in) init. gouache on canvasboard. 22-Jun-4 Christie's, Amsterdam #355/R
£658	$1211	€1000	Untitled (45x37cm-18x15in) init. s.i.d.1983 verso gouache. 22-Jun-4 Christie's, Amsterdam #359/R
£667	$1200	€974	Bright moon (28x25cm-11x10in) s. gouache. 23-Jan-4 Freeman, Philadelphia #86/R
£756	$1300	€1104	Abstract (36x25cm-14x10in) s.d.66 s.i.verso gouache prov. 7-Dec-3 Freeman, Philadelphia #79
£769	$1308	€1100	Deep square (50x60cm-20x24in) init. s.i.d.23.VII.1990 verso gouache. 25-Nov-3 Christie's, Amsterdam #61/R
£815	$1500	€1190	Brands paintings (64x48cm-25x19in) s.i.d.65 gouache prov. 25-Jun-4 Freeman, Philadelphia #74/R est:200-300
£839	$1427	€1200	Portret van een Vrow I (44x39cm-17x15in) s.d.65 s.i.d.verso W/C. 25-Nov-3 Christie's, Amsterdam #41/R
£839	$1401	€1200	Abstract composition (22x27cm-9x11in) s. gouache. 30-Jun-3 Sotheby's, Amsterdam #509/R
£889	$1600	€1298	Kosmische kompositie (43x58cm-17x23in) s.i.d.79 verso gouache. 23-Jan-4 Freeman, Philadelphia #87/R est:400-600
£933	$1708	€1400	Untitled (30x30cm-12x12in) init. s.i.d.1983 verso gouache. 7-Jun-4 Glerum, Amsterdam #416/R
£979	$1664	€1400	Black magic (59x49cm-23x19in) i.d.27 VI 1996 verso gouache. 25-Nov-3 Christie's, Amsterdam #49/R
£1000	$1830	€1500	Painting II (30x36cm-12x14in) init. s.i.d.1980 verso gouache. 7-Jun-4 Glerum, Amsterdam #418/R est:1200-1500
£1049	$1783	€1500	My house and the nebula in Sagittarius (33x41cm-13x16in) s.i.d.1990 verso gouache. 25-Nov-3 Christie's, Amsterdam #45/R est:1500-2000
£1049	$1783	€1500	Ancient times (25x26cm-10x10in) s.d.1.58 s.i.d.verso gouache. 25-Nov-3 Christie's, Amsterdam #60/R est:1500-2000
£1049	$1783	€1500	Black Sun (24x28cm-9x11in) s.i.d.1997-2 verso gouache. 25-Nov-3 Christie's, Amsterdam #65/R est:1500-2000
£1049	$1804	€1500	Untitled (38x50cm-15x20in) init. s.d.September 1982 verso gouache. 2-Dec-3 Sotheby's, Amsterdam #314/R est:1500-2000
£1184	$2179	€1800	Untitled (31x55cm-12x22in) init. gouache. 28-Jun-4 Sotheby's, Amsterdam #262/R est:1800-2500
£1189	$2045	€1700	Primaire compositie (24x43cm-9x17in) init. s.i.d.1980 verso gouache. 2-Dec-3 Sotheby's, Amsterdam #308/R est:1200-1500
£1221	$2038	€1783	Figure composition (36x30cm-14x12in) s.d.65 mixed media. 7-Oct-3 Rasmussen, Copenhagen #20/R est:8000-10000 (D.KR 13000)
£1259	$2165	€1800	Holiday (15x20cm-6x8in) s.d.61 s.i.d,v. gouache. 2-Dec-3 Sotheby's, Amsterdam #315/R est:1000-1200
£1259	$2102	€1800	Petit parc (31x27cm-12x11in) s.d.67 s.i.d.67 verso gouache. 30-Jun-3 Sotheby's, Amsterdam #474/R
£1304	$2139	€1800	Composition with sun's spectrum (20x26cm-8x10in) init. gouache card. 27-May-3 Sotheby's, Amsterdam #538/R est:1800-2500
£1449	$2377	€2000	Woman with hat (32x25cm-13x10in) s.d.66 s.i.d.66 verso gouache. 27-May-3 Sotheby's, Amsterdam #545/R est:2000-3000
£1528	$2414	€2200	Walking the dog (30x21cm-12x8in) s.d.3.58 gouache. 2-Sep-3 Christie's, Amsterdam #483/R est:1500-2000
£1538	$2615	€2200	De Maanraket (36x33cm-14x13in) s.d.59 gouache. 24-Nov-3 Glerum, Amsterdam #222/R est:1800-2200
£1538	$2646	€2200	Mystery (56x55cm-22x22in) s. gouache. 2-Dec-3 Sotheby's, Amsterdam #317/R est:2500-3500
£1594	$2614	€2200	Untitled (29x34cm-11x13in) init. gouache. 27-May-3 Sotheby's, Amsterdam #534/R est:1500-2000
£1645	$3026	€2500	Kite head (53x50cm-21x20in) s.d.60 gouache. 22-Jun-4 Christie's, Amsterdam #357/R est:2500-3500
£1667	$3067	€2500	Untitled (55x43cm-22x17in) s.d.68 gouache. 9-Jun-4 Christie's, Amsterdam #133/R est:2500-3000
£1748	$2972	€2500	Embracement (23x25cm-9x10in) s.d.4.56 gouache. 25-Nov-3 Christie's, Amsterdam #274/R est:2500-3500
£1748	$3007	€2500	Love (50x55cm-20x22in) init.i. s.i.d.20 April 1983 verso gouache. 2-Dec-3 Sotheby's, Amsterdam #322/R est:1800-2500
£1958	$3329	€2800	Kompositie tegen zwart fond II (21x49cm-8x19in) init. s.i.d.17 juli 1980-1 verso gouache. 25-Nov-3 Christie's, Amsterdam #114/R est:2000-3000
£2333	$4270	€3500	One blue day (28x32cm-11x13in) s.d.56 i.d.1956 verso gouache. 7-Jun-4 Glerum, Amsterdam #406/R est:2500-3000
£4348	$7130	€6000	Moon over Paris (50x45cm-20x18in) s.d.59 gouache. 27-May-3 Sotheby's, Amsterdam #544/R est:1800-2500

BRANDS, Johannes Lodewyk (1841-1919) Dutch

£592	$1089	€900	By a river at dusk (85x115cm-33x45in) s. 22-Jun-4 Christie's, Amsterdam #87/R

BRANDSTATTER, Ilse (1939-) Austrian

£333	$613	€500	Cloud wings (130x90cm-51x35in) 9-Jun-4 Dorotheum, Salzburg #718/R

BRANDT, Albertus Jonas (1788-1821) Dutch

Works on paper

£541	$951	€800	Yellow rose. Red rose with four rosebuds (13x11cm-5x4in) s.verso W/C black chk pair prov. 19-May-4 Sotheby's, Amsterdam #298/R

BRANDT, Andreas (1935-) German

£491	$835	€717	Gelb-Gelb-Grau (60x90cm-24x35in) s.d.75 verso. 5-Nov-3 AB Stockholms Auktionsverk #1009/R (S.KR 6500)

BRANDT, Bill (1904-1983) German

Photographs

£1587	$3000	€2317	Nude abstraction (23x20cm-9x8in) i. verso silver print. 17-Feb-4 Swann Galleries, New York #90/R est:4000-6000
£1705	$3000	€2489	Derriere abstraction (23x20cm-9x8in) silver print. 20-May-4 Swann Galleries, New York #474/R est:4000-6000
£1796	$3000	€2622	Coal searcher going home to Jarrow (34x29cm-13x11in) with sig. silver print. 21-Oct-3 Swann Galleries, New York #226/R est:3000-5000
£2116	$4000	€3089	London, 1956 (51x40cm-20x16in) s. gelatin silver print. 17-Feb-4 Christie's, Rockefeller NY #230/R est:2500-3500
£2200	$3872	€3212	Wartime pub scene (24x19cm-9x7in) gelatin silver print. 19-May-4 Christie's, London #172/R est:1800-2200
£2200	$4026	€3212	East Sussex coast, perspective of nudes (34x29cm-13x11in) s. silver print 1953 printed later. 8-Jul-4 Sotheby's, London #424/R est:1800-2200
£2600	$4576	€3900	Attic room (23x19cm-9x7in) st.i.verso gelatin silver print exec.c.1935. 21-May-4 Bloomsbury, London #262/R est:300-500
£2778	$5000	€4056	Stonehenge (25x19cm-10x7in) i.verso gelatin silver print prov.lit. 23-Apr-4 Phillips, New York #247/R est:5000-7000
£2825	$5000	€4125	Self portrait, 1966 (23x19cm-9x7in) i.d.1966 verso gelatin silver print lit. 27-Apr-4 Christie's, Rockefeller NY #84/R est:6000-8000
£3000	$5490	€4380	Co Galway, stone cottages near Kilkieran. i. silver print. 8-Jul-4 Sotheby's, London #420/R est:1500-2500
£3600	$6120	€5256	East Sussex Coast (34x29cm-13x11in) s. silver print exec.1958 printed later prov. 19-Nov-3 Sotheby's, Olympia #246/R est:1500-2000
£3955	$7000	€5774	Halifax, 1937 (23x20cm-9x8in) gelatin silver print executed c.1955 lit. 27-Apr-4 Christie's, Rockefeller NY #82/R est:8000-10000
£4000	$7040	€5840	Halifax (47x40cm-19x16in) s. gelatin silver print lit. 19-May-4 Christie's, London #162/R est:5000-7000
£4237	$7500	€6186	Off guard (23x20cm-9x8in) gelatin silver print executed c.1930. 27-Apr-4 Christie's, Rockefeller NY #80/R est:6000-8000
£4722	$8500	€6894	London (23x19cm-9x7in) d.1940 gelatin silver print prov.lit. 23-Apr-4 Phillips, New York #143/R est:8000-12000
£4800	$8448	€7008	Young housewife (25x20cm-10x8in) gelatin silver print prov.lit. 19-May-4 Christie's, London #171/R est:2000-3000
£5000	$9000	€7300	Baie des anges, France (23x20cm-9x8in) i.d.1958 verso gelatin silver print mounted on board prov.lit. 23-Apr-4 Phillips, New York #25/R est:10000-15000
£5367	$9500	€7836	Gull's nest, Isle of Skye (23x20cm-9x8in) i.verso photo. 28-Apr-4 Sotheby's, New York #195/R est:5000-7000
£7345	$13000	€10724	London, nude hip (23x20cm-9x8in) st.sig.verso photo. 28-Apr-4 Sotheby's, New York #194/R est:10000-15000
£8995	$17000	€13133	London, 1952 (34x29cm-13x11in) s. gelatin silver print. 17-Feb-4 Christie's, Rockefeller NY #229/R est:9000-12000
£9500	$16720	€13870	London (51x40cm-20x16in) s. gelatin silver print prov.lit. 19-May-4 Christie's, London #164/R est:12000-18000
£10734	$19000	€15672	London, 1952 (34x29cm-13x11in) s. gelatin silver print lit. 27-Apr-4 Christie's, Rockefeller NY #79/R est:12000-18000

BRANDT, Carl (1852-1930) Swedish

£290	$522	€435	Landscape with farm, Skaane (66x100cm-26x39in) s. 25-Apr-4 Goteborg Auktionsverk, Sweden #317/R (S.KR 4000)
£566	$978	€826	Winter landscape, Jamtland (55x65cm-22x26in) s.d.1914. 15-Dec-3 Lilla Bukowskis, Stockholm #586 (S.KR 7200)
£612	$985	€894	Archipelago (78x112cm-31x44in) s/d/1909. 25-Aug-3 Lilla Bukowskis, Stockholm #985 (S.KR 8000)
£630	$1027	€920	Coastal landscape (54x65cm-21x26in) s.indis.d. 29-Sep-3 Lilla Bukowskis, Stockholm #254 (S.KR 8200)
£645	$1052	€942	Lake landscape (54x65cm-21x26in) s.d.1900. 29-Sep-3 Lilla Bukowskis, Stockholm #249 (S.KR 8400)
£769	$1308	€1100	Lake landscape (90x124cm-35x49in) s. 29-Nov-3 Bukowskis, Helsinki #380/R
£982	$1699	€1434	Winter landscape (59x49cm-23x19in) s. 15-Dec-3 Lilla Bukowskis, Stockholm #20 (S.KR 12500)
£1700	$3043	€2482	Winter landscape in evening sunshine (98x128cm-39x50in) s.d.1921. 28-May-4 Uppsala Auktionskammare, Uppsala #220/R est:12000-15000 (S.KR 23000)

Works on paper

£321	$590	€482	Lake landscape (44x57cm-17x22in) s.d.93 pastel. 14-Jun-4 Lilla Bukowskis, Stockholm #383 (S.KR 4400)

BRANDT, Edgar (1880-1960) French

Sculpture

£2215	$3920	€3300	Pelicans (17x15x7cm-7x6x3in) st.sig. wrought iron pair lit. 27-Apr-4 Claude Aguttes, Neuilly #61/R est:3200
£9333	$17173	€14000	Serpents entrelaces (45cm-18in) s. pat bronze pair lit. 8-Jun-4 Camard, Paris #59/R est:15000-18000
£13006	$22500	€18989	Figural panel (105x35cm-41x14in) st. wrought iron. 11-Dec-3 Sotheby's, New York #12/R est:10000-15000
£20629	$34451	€29500	Cobra (49x16x16cm-19x6x6in) s. gilt bronze glass. 24-Jun-3 Millon & Associes, Paris #57/R est:15000-18000

BRANDT, Elisabeth (1853-1907) Dutch

£933	$1680	€1400	Interior with young girl and cat (32x24cm-13x9in) s. panel. 26-Apr-4 Bernaerts, Antwerp #54/R

BRANDT, Federico (1878-1932) Venezuelan

£6651	$12105	€9977	Flowers with birds (30x49cm-12x19in) s. 21-Jun-4 Subastas Odalys, Caracas #39/R est:12000
£6831	$10930	€9973	Untitled (40x26cm-16x10in) s. cardboard. 21-Sep-3 Subastas Odalys, Caracas #61/R
£7742	$12000	€11303	Patio (54x77cm-21x30in) s. 29-Sep-2 Subastas Odalys, Caracas #61/R
£24818	$42190	€36234	Patio in the artist's house (56x87cm-22x34in) s. painted 1905. 23-Nov-3 Subastas Odalys, Caracas #50/R est:40000

BRANDT, I H (1850-1926) Danish

£302	$541	€441	View of the sea with sailing boat (69x109cm-27x43in) s.d.1894 prov. 12-Jan-4 Rasmussen, Vejle #316 (D.KR 3200)
£357	$608	€521	River landscape with man in rowing boat (50x80cm-20x31in) s. 29-Nov-3 Rasmussen, Havnen #2206 (D.KR 3800)
£360	$576	€526	From Hammershus, Bornholm (28x42cm-11x17in) s.d.1880. 22-Sep-3 Rasmussen, Vejle #330/R (D.KR 3800)
£412	$750	€602	Landscape (46x65cm-18x26in) s.d.1890. 7-Feb-4 Rasmussen, Havnen #2109/R (D.KR 4500)
£470	$800	€686	Landscape from Bornholm near Hammershus. s. 29-Nov-3 Rasmussen, Havnen #2116/R (D.KR 5000)
£567	$981	€828	Coastal landscape from Bornholm (60x85cm-24x33in) s.d.1893. 9-Dec-3 Rasmussen, Copenhagen #1697/R (D.KR 6000)
£578	$1052	€867	Coastal landscape with boats, Bornholm (63x95cm-25x37in) s.d.1881. 19-Jun-4 Rasmussen, Havnen #2344/R (D.KR 6500)

BRANDT, Johann Heinrich (1740-1783) German

£2559	$4095	€3736	Portrait of woman wearing red dress, writing a letter (110x86cm-43x34in) s.d.1775. 22-Sep-3 Rasmussen, Vejle #73/R est:30000 (D.KR 27000)

BRANDT, Johannes Herman (1850-1926) Danish

£1690	$2806	€2400	Open sea (102x150cm-40x59in) s.d.1902 i. verso. 16-Jun-3 Dorotheum, Vienna #184/R est:2000-2200
£1796	$3215	€2622	Breaker with seagulls (75x112cm-30x44in) s.d.1874 prov. 12-Jan-4 Rasmussen, Vejle #30/R est:3000-4000 (D.KR 19000)

BRANDT, Josef von (1841-1915) Polish

£6944	$11319	€10000	Horses dragging cart out of mud (116x149cm-46x59in) s. 24-Sep-3 Neumeister, Munich #402/R est:10000
£31674	$50679	€46244	Horse drawn cart (60x100cm-24x39in) s. prov. 19-Sep-3 Koller, Zurich #3084/R est:30000-50000 (S.FR 70000)
£54299	$86878	€79277	Three washerwomen (80x133cm-31x52in) s.d.1882 prov. 19-Sep-3 Koller, Zurich #3096/R est:120000-150000 (S.FR 120000)
£78125	$130469	€114063	Galloping team (60x100cm-24x39in) s. painted c.1900. 19-Oct-3 Agra, Warsaw #1/R est:390000 (P.Z 500000)

Works on paper

£300	$552	€450	Bearded rider in an evening landscape. Study of three figures (20x24cm-8x9in) mono. s.verso pencil ink htd white double-sided. 12-Jun-4 Karlheinz Kaupp, Staufen #1035/R
£1034	$1717	€1500	Military rider (26x41cm-10x16in) mono. pencil. 30-Sep-3 Dorotheum, Vienna #128

BRANDT, Josef von (attrib) (1841-1915) Polish

£2836	$4905	€4141	Soldiers with flock of horses (78x100cm-31x39in) s.d.1861. 9-Dec-3 Rasmussen, Copenhagen #1533/R est:30000 (D.KR 30000)

BRANDT, Muriel (1909-1981) Irish

Works on paper

£633	$1146	€950	Putney Bridge, Bath (41x30cm-16x12in) s. W/C. 30-Mar-4 De Veres Art Auctions, Dublin #239/R

BRANDT, Rexford Elson (1914-2000) American

Works on paper

£1816	$3250	€2651	Bridge on the Sacramento (33x58cm-13x23in) s.i. W/C pencil. 26-May-4 Doyle, New York #126/R est:3000-5000
£2059	$3500	€3006	Spring sea (15x21cm-6x8in) s.i.d.1961 W/C prov. 18-Nov-3 John Moran, Pasadena #127 est:1000-2000
£3235	$5500	€4723	Mid morning balboa (32x47cm-13x19in) s.i.d.7.3.73 W/C. 29-Oct-3 Christie's, Los Angeles #75/R est:2500-3500
£4624	$8000	€6751	Out the Jetty (30x49cm-12x19in) s.i.d.1961 W/C prov. 10-Dec-3 Bonhams & Butterfields, San Francisco #6297/R est:3000-5000
£5220	$9500	€7621	Winter harbour (30x36cm-12x14in) s. i.verso W/C. 15-Jun-4 John Moran, Pasadena #84a est:3000-4500
£5435	$10000	€7935	Santa Cruz Boardwalk from the Pacific (51x61cm-20x24in) s. W/C. 8-Jun-4 Auctions by the Bay, Alameda #1117/R
£6215	$11000	€9074	Consulting the map (48x43cm-19x17in) s. W/C gouache prov. 28-Apr-4 Christie's, Los Angeles #72/R est:4000-6000

BRANDT, Rolf (1906-) British

£600	$1020	€876	Composition (85x122cm-33x48in) wood. 23-Nov-3 Lots Road Auctions, London #340

BRANDTNER, Fritz (1896-1969) Canadian

£3604	$6126	€5262	Masquerade no 1. Masquerade no. 5 (46x46cm-18x18in) s.i i.verso linoleum on plywood two prov. 18-Nov-3 Sotheby's, Toronto #64/R est:6000-8000 (C.D 8000)
£16964	$29179	€24767	Montreal Harbour (97x122cm-38x48in) s.d.38. 2-Dec-3 Joyner Waddington, Toronto #28/R est:10000-15000 (C.D 38000)
£22321	$38393	€32589	Gay Camp table (66x70cm-26x28in) s. prov. 2-Dec-3 Joyner Waddington, Toronto #18/R est:30000-35000 (C.D 50000)

Works on paper

£200	$366	€292	Summer coastline (21x37cm-8x15in) s. W/C ink. 1-Jun-4 Joyner Waddington, Toronto #472 (C.D 500)
£225	$383	€329	Montreal 34, Fletcher Field (17x24cm-7x9in) s.i.d.1934 W/C mixed media. 23-Nov-3 Levis, Calgary #416/R (C.D 500)
£357	$614	€521	Pink and Black (26x36cm-10x14in) s. W/C ink. 2-Dec-3 Joyner Waddington, Toronto #458 (C.D 800)

£403	$742	€588	Abstract composition (12x16cm-5x6in) s. col ink prov. 9-Jun-4 Walker's, Ottawa #168/R (C.D 1000)
£691	$1237	€1009	Near Lake Louise (31x21cm-12x8in) s. mixed media. 27-May-4 Heffel, Vancouver #141/R (C.D 1700)
£2000	$3660	€2920	Still life (29x32cm-11x13in) s. pastel ink. 1-Jun-4 Joyner Waddington, Toronto #341/R est:2000-3000 (C.D 5000)
£2928	$4977	€4275	Untitled abstract (70x51cm-28x20in) s.d.1950 W/C gouache board prov.exhib. 18-Nov-3 Sotheby's, Toronto #62/R est:5000-7000 (C.D 6500)

BRANEGAN, J F (1843-1909) British/Irish

Works on paper

£540	$1004	€788	Seascape with paddle ship and other vessel, Off the Tyne Mouth. Coastal scene (13x24cm-5x9in) s. pair W/C. 4-Mar-4 Clevedon Sale Rooms #167

BRANEGAN, John F (1843-1909) British/Irish

Works on paper

£300	$501	€438	Near Sunderland (13x20cm-5x8in) s.i. W/C. 10-Oct-3 Richardson & Smith, Whitby #109
£320	$509	€464	Black Nab, Whitby (26x45cm-10x18in) s.i. W/C. 9-Sep-3 David Duggleby, Scarborough #79
£380	$635	€555	Robin Hood's Bay (18x25cm-7x10in) s.i. W/C. 10-Oct-3 Richardson & Smith, Whitby #49
£480	$869	€701	Off Staithes (23x43cm-9x17in) s.i. W/C. 15-Apr-4 Richardson & Smith, Whitby #146
£500	$905	€730	Grimsby (23x33cm-9x13in) s.i. W/C. 15-Apr-4 Richardson & Smith, Whitby #77/R
£580	$969	€847	Schooner ashore, near Whitby (25x46cm-10x18in) s.i. W/C. 10-Oct-3 Richardson & Smith, Whitby #79/R
£580	$1067	€847	Near Sunderland. Yarmouth (25x36cm-10x14in) both s.i. W/C pair. 14-Jun-4 Bonhams, Bath #25
£640	$1018	€928	Near Whitby (40x65cm-16x26in) s. W/C. 9-Sep-3 David Duggleby, Scarborough #35/R
£650	$1144	€949	Runswick (25x43cm-10x17in) s.i. W/C. 20-May-4 Richardson & Smith, Whitby #660
£700	$1267	€1022	Grimsby. Yarmouth (43x28cm-17x11in) s. W/C pair. 30-Mar-4 David Duggleby, Scarborough #129/R
£720	$1267	€1051	Sandsend (23x43cm-9x17in) s.i. W/C. 20-May-4 Richardson & Smith, Whitby #661
£740	$1339	€1080	Moonrise (23x50cm-9x20in) s.i. W/C. 30-Mar-4 David Duggleby, Scarborough #185/R
£840	$1520	€1226	Sandsend, near Whitby (39x62cm-15x24in) s.i. W/C. 30-Mar-4 David Duggleby, Scarborough #20/R
£1250	$2263	€1825	Sunrise off Whitby (38x61cm-15x24in) s.i. W/C. 15-Apr-4 Richardson & Smith, Whitby #101/R est:1000-1500
£1500	$2445	€2190	Whitby sunrise. Deal (35x53cm-14x21in) s.i. W/C pair. 24-Sep-3 Peter Wilson, Nantwich #105

BRANGWYN, Sir Frank (1867-1956) British

£1765	$3000	€2577	Goatherd (49x29cm-19x11in) mono. board prov. 19-Nov-3 Bonhams & Butterfields, San Francisco #151/R
£2300	$4186	€3358	Ships (46x35cm-18x14in) s. 15-Jun-4 Bonhams, New Bond Street #30/R est:2500-3500
£2400	$4296	€3504	Capsized (56x77cm-22x30in) init.d.93 board prov. 16-Mar-4 Bonhams, New Bond Street #8/R est:1500-2500
£3800	$6460	€5548	Ostrich farm (30x43cm-12x17in) init.d.91 panel prov.exhib.lit. 26-Nov-3 Sotheby's, Olympia #27/R est:1000-1500
£3911	$7000	€5867	Fishing boats at sea (53x64cm-21x25in) init. 16-May-4 Abell, Los Angeles #158/R
£5000	$9100	€7300	Flooded field with three labourers (64x75cm-25x30in) init.d.1888. 1-Jul-4 Christie's, Kensington #66/R est:6000-8000
£15000	$26400	€21900	Fisherman's quarters, Venice (63x76cm-25x30in) init. prov. 19-May-4 Sotheby's, Olympia #144/R est:10000-15000
£16000	$27200	€23360	Souk (76x101cm-30x40in) prov. 26-Nov-3 Sotheby's, Olympia #30/R est:6000-8000

Works on paper

£310	$580	€465	View of an Italian hilltop town (12x22cm-5x9in) init. pen ink W/C wash. 22-Jul-4 Dominic Winter, Swindon #10/R
£320	$534	€467	Breton fisherman (24x19cm-9x7in) init. chl. 16-Oct-3 Christie's, Kensington #229/R
£350	$648	€511	Rye Harbour (14x16cm-6x6in) i. blue chk prov. 11-Mar-4 Christie's, Kensington #74
£380	$646	€555	Rustic bridge into a town (38x48cm-15x19in) s. pencil. 30-Oct-3 Bracketts, Tunbridge Wells #1005/R
£440	$735	€642	Sea damage survey (11x24cm-4x9in) i.verso pen ink. 22-Oct-3 Cheffins, Cambridge #482
£450	$774	€657	Figure studies (46x46cm-18x18in) init. pencil chk. 3-Dec-3 Christie's, Kensington #409
£650	$1183	€949	Return from the Raid (34x46cm-13x18in) init. W/C printed base. 1-Jul-4 Christie's, Kensington #51/R
£700	$1204	€1022	Algeciras, Jan (33x46cm-13x18in) s.i. W/C prov. 7-Dec-3 Lots Road Auctions, London #335
£1250	$2238	€1825	Hop pickers (30x48cm-12x19in) mono. chl col chk. 17-Mar-4 John Nicholson, Haslemere #669/R est:250-500
£1300	$2366	€1898	Pirate ship (63x43cm-25x17in) gouache pastel. 15-Jun-4 Bonhams, New Bond Street #19/R est:1500-2500
£1320	$2416	€1927	Unloading the catch (36x25cm-14x10in) mono. W/C. 30-Jan-4 Tring Auctions, Tring #323/R
£1500	$2505	€2190	The Bridge of Empire (38x64cm-15x25in) dr. prov. lit. 18-Jun-3 John Nicholson, Haslemere #654/R est:2000-4000
£1600	$2880	€2336	On the Downs, Ditchling (38x43cm-15x17in) s. W/C prov.exhib. 20-Jan-4 Bonhams, Knightsbridge #12/R est:1000-1500
£3800	$7030	€5548	Puerta de los Passajes, Spain (52x34cm-20x13in) init. pastel executed c.1892-96. 11-Mar-4 Christie's, Kensington #75/R est:4000-6000

BRANNAN, Peter (1926-) British

£300	$546	€438	Street scene - winter (59x49cm-23x19in) s.d.1960 board. 1-Jul-4 Mellors & Kirk, Nottingham #801

BRANSOM, Paul (1885-1979) American

Works on paper

£465	$800	€679	Peaboam (47x32cm-19x13in) s. chl W/C paper on board prov. 2-Dec-3 Christie's, Rockefeller NY #79/R
£1453	$2600	€2121	Pair of lions (58x48cm-23x19in) s. chl gouache W/C. 15-May-4 Illustration House, New York #61/R est:4000-8000

BRANWHITE, Charles (1817-1880) British

£2600	$4654	€3796	Lock (33x61cm-13x24in) indis sig.d.58. 27-May-4 Christie's, Kensington #192/R est:1000-1500

Works on paper

£400	$736	€584	In Leigh Woods (32x50cm-13x20in) s.i.d.May 1869 W/C bodycol over pencil. 29-Mar-4 Bonhams, Bath #11/R
£750	$1380	€1095	Avon Gorge, Bristol (30x52cm-12x20in) init. pencil W/C bodycol. 25-Mar-4 Christie's, Kensington #148/R
£1450	$2639	€2117	Feeding the cattle on winter's evening (40x68cm-16x27in) s.d.70 W/C bodycol. 21-Jun-4 Bonhams, Bath #415 est:600-800

BRANWHITE, Charles Brooke (1851-1929) British

£360	$648	€526	On Bagworthy water, Exmoor with figures (33x51cm-13x20in) s. 21-Apr-4 Brightwells, Leominster #699
£480	$778	€696	Figures conversing before a rural hamlet in a winter landscape (51x76cm-20x30in) s. painted c.1880. 25-May-3 Desmond Judd, Cranbrook #1109

Works on paper

£280	$501	€409	Extensive moorland landscape with figures (28x43cm-11x17in) s. W/C. 16-Mar-4 Bonhams, Leeds #613
£400	$628	€580	Post bridge, Dartmoor (41x68cm-16x27in) s. pencil W/C bodycol. 28-Aug-3 Christie's, Kensington #424/R
£460	$782	€672	St Michaels Mount. s. W/C. 27-Nov-3 Clevedon Sale Rooms #179
£700	$1288	€1022	Shropshire landscape in winter (56x94cm-22x37in) s. W/C bodycol. 29-Mar-4 Bonhams, Bath #26/R
£1200	$2040	€1752	Fisherman's cottage (45x81cm-18x32in) s.d.72 W/C bodycol. 18-Nov-3 Sotheby's, Olympia #28/R est:800-1200

BRAQUAVAL, Louis (1856-1919) French

£2238	$3804	€3200	Autumn market scene (37x46cm-15x18in) s. board. 20-Nov-3 Van Ham, Cologne #1498/R est:3400
£2800	$5180	€4088	French Town views (37x45cm-15x18in) s. panel pair. 10-Mar-4 Sotheby's, Olympia #258/R est:3000-4000
£4138	$7448	€6000	Place de Verdun a Aix-en-Provence (44x60cm-17x24in) s. board painted c.1917. 25-Jan-4 Chayette & Cheval, Paris #240/R est:6000-8000
£4483	$8069	€6500	Place de la Madeleine a Aix-en-Provence (44x60cm-17x24in) s.d.1917 board. 25-Jan-4 Chayette & Cheval, Paris #239/R est:6000-8000

BRAQUE, Georges (1882-1963) French

£3490	$6421	€5200	Oiseau bleu et jaune. s.i. i. verso col lithograph. 26-Mar-4 Karrenbauer, Konstanz #1555/R est:2000
£16000	$26720	€23360	Le bouquet (34x26cm-13x10in) init.i. oil brush ink ash gouache on paper prov. 21-Oct-3 Sotheby's, London #75/R est:12000-15000
£22353	$38000	€32635	Le profil (22x27cm-9x11in) init. plaster exec 1946-1947 prov. 5-Nov-3 Christie's, Rockefeller NY #346/R est:25000-35000
£38000	$69160	€55480	Falaise avec deux barques echouees (18x23cm-7x9in) s. prov. 3-Feb-4 Christie's, London #285/R est:30000-40000
£61453	$110000	€89721	Cabines (23x29cm-9x11in) s. panel painted 1938 prov.exhib.lit. 5-May-4 Sotheby's, New York #28/R est:50000-70000
£64706	$110000	€94471	Verre et citrons (20x37cm-8x15in) s. panel painted 1927 prov.exhib.lit. 5-Nov-3 Christie's, Rockefeller NY #267/R est:120000-180000
£65000	$119600	€94900	Barques bleues (23x33cm-9x13in) s. panel painted 1932 prov.exhib. 22-Jun-4 Sotheby's, London #186/R est:70000-100000
£80000	$147200	€116800	Nature morte au moule (27x41cm-11x16in) s.d.30 prov.lit. 22-Jun-4 Sotheby's, London #183/R est:60000-80000
£123529	$210000	€180352	Still life with fish (50x60cm-20x24in) s. painted c.1936. 5-Nov-3 Christie's, Rockefeller NY #263/R est:70000-100000
£170000	$309400	€248200	Compotier, fruits et couteau (29x73cm-11x29in) s. painted 1935 prov.exhib.lit. 3-Feb-4 Christie's, London #221/R est:150000-200000
£282353	$480000	€412235	Bouteille et fruits (64x54cm-25x21in) s.verso painted 1911 prov.exhib.lit. 5-Nov-3 Sotheby's, New York #43/R est:550000-750000
£949721	$1700000	€1386593	Bouteille et verre (24x35cm-9x14in) s.verso oval painted c.1910-11 prov.exhib.lit. 5-May-4 Sotheby's, New York #26/R est:1200000-1600000
£1061453	$1900000	€1549721	Paysage de l'Estaque (50x61cm-20x24in) s.d.06 prov.exhib. 6-May-4 Sotheby's, New York #129/R est:2500000-3500000
£1061453	$1900000	€1549721	Femme a la guitare (116x89cm-46x35in) s.d.31 prov.exhib.lit. 6-May-4 Sotheby's, New York #136/R est:1500000-2000000

Prints

£1689	$3023	€2500	Helios II (56x38cm-22x15in) s. num.22/22 col lithograph. 4-May-4 Calmels Cohen, Paris #32 est:2500-3000
£1808	$3200	€2640	Astre et oiseau II (44x52cm-17x20in) s.num.73/75 col lithograph. 28-Apr-4 Christie's, Rockefeller NY #3/R est:4000-6000
£1882	$3200	€2748	Envol (51x65cm-20x26in) s. num.36/75 col lithograph exec.1960. 4-Nov-3 Christie's, Rockefeller NY #69/R est:4000-5000
£2000	$3320	€2920	Char noir (43x56cm-17x22in) s.num.7/75 col etching aquatint. 6-Oct-3 Sotheby's, London #70 est:2500-3000
£2027	$3568	€3000	Oiseau bistre (25x20cm-10x8in) s. num.8/75 col lithograph lit. 24-May-4 Christie's, Milan #116/R est:1000-1500
£2069	$3455	€3000	L'iris (26x19cm-10x7in) s. num.49/75 col lithograph. 13-Nov-3 Neumeister, Munich #267/R est:4000-4200
£2083	$3479	€3000	Migration (23x17cm-9x7in) s.mono.i. col etching aquatint. 24-Oct-3 Ketterer, Hamburg #291/R est:3000-4000
£2095	$3750	€3059	Image bird III (13x15cm-5x6in) black white aquatint. 14-May-4 Du Mouchelle, Detroit #2096/R est:4000-6000
£2162	$3871	€3200	Tete verte (50x33cm-20x13in) s. num.2/5 col eau forte. 4-May-4 Calmels Cohen, Paris #31/R est:2500-3000
£2193	$4035	€3202	Cinq poesies en hommage de George Braque (20x56cm-8x22in) s. lithograph. 23-Jun-4 Koller, Zurich #3212/R est:3000-4500 (S.FR 5000)
£2258	$4200	€3297	Cinq poesies en hommage a Georges Braque (20x56cm-8x22in) s.i. col lithograph. 2-Mar-4 Swann Galleries, New York #60/R est:3500-5000
£2276	$3801	€3300	Astre et oiseau II (44x53cm-17x21in) s. num.52/75 col lithograph. 14-Nov-3 Farsetti, Prato #259/R est:1600-2000
£2297	$4112	€3400	Cinq poesies (55x71cm-22x28in) s. num.13/75 col lithograph. 4-May-4 Calmels Cohen, Paris #34 est:2500-3000
£2345	$3916	€3400	Oiseau sur fond carmin, oiseau XIV (33x43cm-13x17in) s. num.21/75 col aquatint. 13-Nov-3 Neumeister, Munich #265/R est:3000-4000
£2400	$4128	€3504	L'oiseau blanc (45x38cm-18x15in) s.i. col lithograph. 4-Dec-3 Sotheby's, London #135/R est:1200-1800

£2400 $4392 €3504 Cinq poesies en hommage a Georges Braque (20x56cm-8x22in) s.i. col lithograph. 3-Jun-4 Christie's, Kensington #10/R est:1500-2500
£2402 $4419 €3507 Oiseau bleu et jaune (54x35cm-21x14in) s. col lithograph lit. 8-Jun-4 Germann, Zurich #276/R est:5000-6000 (S.FR 5500)
£2431 $4132 €3500 Composition (48x37cm-19x15in) s.i. lithograph prov. 28-Oct-3 Il Ponte, Milan #269/R
£2533 $4585 €3800 Oiseaux et etoiles sur fond bleu (53x41cm-21x16in) s.i. col lithograph. 2-Apr-4 Winterberg, Heidelberg #756/R est:4800
£2542 $4500 €3711 Oiseau verni (22x32cm-9x13in) s.i. lithograph. 30-Apr-4 Sotheby's, New York #45/R est:3000-4000
£2657 $4571 €3800 La femme a la mandoline (24x17cm-9x7in) s. s.i.verso num.201/225 col lithograph. 5-Dec-3 Ketterer, Munich #126/R est:3800-4500
£2661 $4443 €3858 Si je mourais la-bas. s.i. col lithograph. 19-Jun-3 Kornfeld, Bern #224 est:5000 (S.FR 5800)
£2703 $4757 €4000 Oiseau bleau et jaune (33x50cm-13x20in) s. num.69/75 col lithograph lit. 24-May-4 Christie's, Milan #113/R est:1500-2000
£2759 $4607 €4000 Profil a la palette (52x71cm-20x28in) s. num.55/75 col lithograph. 13-Nov-3 Neumeister, Munich #264/R est:4000-5000
£2793 $5000 €4078 Athene (27x30cm-11x12in) s.num.29/75 color lithograph. 6-May-4 Swann Galleries, New York #405a/R est:5000-8000
£2825 $5000 €4125 Char noir (24x29cm-9x11in) s.num.46/75 col etching aquatint. 30-Apr-4 Sotheby's, New York #46/R est:3000-4000
£2825 $5000 €4125 L'atelier (43x52cm-17x20in) s.i. col lithograph. 30-Apr-4 Sotheby's, New York #48/R est:6000-8000
£2905 $5200 €4241 Oiseau verni (22x32cm-9x13in) s.num.68/75 lithograph. 6-May-4 Swann Galleries, New York #406/R est:5000-8000
£2953 $5286 €4400 Oiseau sur fond carmin - Oiseau XIV (32x43cm-13x17in) s. col etching. 25-May-4 Karl & Faber, Munich #218/R est:2000
£3000 $5520 €4500 Cinq poesies en homage a George Braque (20x55cm-8x22in) s. col lithograph exec. 1958 one of 25. 12-Jun-4 Villa Grisebach, Berlin #378/R est:3500-4500
£3097 $5264 €4522 Oiseau noir sur fond bleue - Oiseau VIII (14x22cm-6x9in) s.num.5/75 col etching prov.lit. 5-Nov-3 AB Stockholms Auktionsverk #1186/R est:50000-60000 (S.KR 41000)
£3125 $5000 €4563 L'atelier (43x52cm-17x20in) s.num.16/75 col lithograph. 18-Sep-3 Swann Galleries, New York #85/R est:7000-10000
£3200 $5792 €4800 Profile on blue background (43x31cm-17x12in) s. col woodcut. 2-Apr-4 Winterberg, Heidelberg #752/R est:5200
£3231 $5881 €4717 Oiseaux. s.i. col lithograph. 17-Jun-4 Kornfeld, Bern #222 est:6000 (S.FR 7400)
£3288 $5589 €4800 Feuillage. col eau forte aquatint. 6-Nov-3 Piasa, Paris #62/R
£3356 $6007 €5000 Grande tete (64x50cm-25x20in) s. num.25/30 engraving. 25-May-4 Durán, Madrid #699/R est:2500
£3448 $5759 €5000 Aus: L'orde des oiseaux (35x47cm-14x19in) s.i. col aquatint. 13-Nov-3 Neumeister, Munich #266/R est:5000-6000
£3681 $6000 €5374 Oiseau verni (40x49cm-16x19in) s. num.14/75 lithograph varnish Arches paper executed 1954. 24-Sep-3 Christie's, Rockefeller NY #54/R est:3500-4500
£3767 $6404 €5500 Char III. col lithograph. 6-Nov-3 Piasa, Paris #59/R
£3846 $6538 €5500 L'oiseau bleu et gris (32x27cm-13x11in) s. num.47/100 col lithograph. 26-Nov-3 Lempertz, Koln #605/R est:5500
£3986 $6776 €5700 Au couchant (43x61cm-17x24in) s. lithograph. 18-Nov-3 Babuino, Rome #146/R est:4000-4500
£4161 $7365 €6200 Nu allonge. s. eau forte exec.1934. 29-Apr-4 Piasa, Paris #132/R est:2500-3000
£4196 $7007 €6000 Le Char II (49x65cm-19x26in) s. col lithograph. 10-Oct-3 Winterberg, Heidelberg #1001/R est:8600
£4412 $7500 €6442 Oiseaux (48x64cm-19x25in) s. col lithograph. 4-Nov-3 Christie's, Rockefeller NY #70/R est:4000-6000
£5000 $9200 €7500 Urania II (23x32cm-9x13in) s. col lithograph aquatint exec. 1958 one of 75. 12-Jun-4 Villa Grisebach, Berlin #377/R est:5000-7000
£5294 $9000 €7729 Theiere et citrons (50x65cm-20x26in) s.i. col lithograph. 6-Nov-3 Swann Galleries, New York #502/R est:10000-15000
£5367 $9500 €7836 Equinoxe (35x53cm-14x21in) s.num.46/75 col lithograph. 28-Apr-4 Christie's, Rockefeller NY #4/R est:7000-10000
£5500 $10010 €8030 Astre et Oiseau II (44x53cm-17x21in) s.i. col lithograph. 30-Jun-4 Christie's, London #178/R est:3000-5000
£6704 $12000 €9788 L'ordre des oiseaux (35x47cm-14x19in) s.i. color aquatint. 6-May-4 Swann Galleries, New York #409/R est:10000-15000
£7910 $14000 €11549 Les amayllis (54x45cm-21x18in) s.num.17/75 col etching aquatint. 30-Apr-4 Sotheby's, New York #47 est:15000-20000
£9050 $15113 €13213 Fox (55x38cm-22x15in) s.i. drypoint etching. 27-Jun-3 Falk & Falk, Zurich #829 est:25000 (S.FR 20000)
£10588 $18000 €15458 Fox (54x38cm-21x15in) s.num.12 drypoint. 31-Oct-3 Sotheby's, New York #213/R
£12941 $22000 €18894 L'oiseau dans le feuillage (80x105cm-31x41in) s.i. col lithograph card. 6-Nov-3 Swann Galleries, New York #506/R est:10000-15000

Sculpture
£9155 $16021 €13000 Char blanc (21x26cm-8x10in) s. plaster prov. 18-Dec-3 Tajan, Paris #35/R est:12000-15000
£14118 $24000 €20612 Petit Chevial - Gelinotte (19cm-7in) s.i. num.3/6 dk brown pat bronze Cast S Fondeur prov. 5-Nov-3 Christie's, Rockefeller NY #286/R est:30000-40000

Works on paper
£1099 $2000 €1605 Nature morte au poisson (25x33cm-10x13in) pencil. 19-Jun-4 Du Mouchelle, Detroit #3043/R est:3000-5000
£5068 $9071 €7500 La coupe aux pommes (22x33cm-9x13in) s. wash. 10-May-4 Horta, Bruxelles #198/R est:8000-10000
£8500 $15385 €12410 Etude pour Helene (27x21cm-11x8in) s. gouache lit. 1-Apr-4 Christie's, Kensington #49/R est:3000-5000
£11765 $22000 €17177 Trois oiseaux et paysage (32x23cm-13x9in) s. gouache. 25-Feb-4 Christie's, Rockefeller NY #133/R est:12000-16000
£13904 $26000 €20300 Trois oiseaux (25x22cm-10x9in) s. gouache pencil. 25-Feb-4 Christie's, Rockefeller NY #134/R est:10000-15000
£40000 $66800 €58400 Composition (30x24cm-12x9in) init. W/C pen ink crayon over pencil card executed 1920 prov. 21-Oct-3 Sotheby's, London #47/R est:30000-40000
£44693 $80000 €65252 Gueridon (21x16cm-8x6in) s. gouache chl pencil board exec c.1918-1920 prov.exhib. 5-May-4 Christie's, Rockefeller NY #111/R est:70000-90000
£223464 $400000 €326257 Verre et guitare (35x29cm-14x11in) chl pencil chk cardboard on panel exec.1912 prov.exhib.lit. 6-May-4 Sotheby's, New York #115/R est:500000-700000

BRAQUE, Georges (after) (1882-1963) French

Prints
£2400 $4392 €3600 Hommage a J S Bach (44x59cm-17x23in) s. col etching. 5-Jun-4 Lempertz, Koln #618/R est:3000
£2706 $4600 €3951 Hommage a J S Bach (44x59cm-17x23in) s.num.60/300 col aquatint etching. 6-Nov-3 Swann Galleries, New York #507/R est:4000-6000

BRASCASSAT, Jacques Raymond (1804-1867) French

£2282 $4198 €3400 Riviere traversant un paysage de montagne (25x32cm-10x13in) 24-Mar-4 Tajan, Paris #157/R est:3000-4000
£4605 $8474 €7000 Falaises (30x39cm-12x15in) s.d.1848 panel. 25-Jun-4 Piasa, Paris #128/R est:4500-6000
£6289 $10000 €9182 Le paturage (64x81cm-25x32in) s.d.1852 panel. 9-Mar-3 William Jenack, New York #365 est:12000-16000

BRASCASSAT, Jacques Raymond (attrib) (1804-1867) French

£749 $1273 €1094 Summer landscape with goats (46x38cm-18x15in) bears i. 5-Nov-3 Dobiaschofsky, Bern #389/R (S.FR 1700)

BRASCH, Hans (1882-1973) German

£2174 $3565 €3000 Flowers (80x53cm-31x21in) s.d.1922 cardboard. 27-May-3 Sotheby's, Amsterdam #505/R est:2000-3000

BRASCH, Wenzel Ignaz (?-1761) Czechoslovakian

£1216 $2177 €1800 Fox with wild duck, and fox cubs nearby (63x84cm-25x33in) bears sig. lit. 8-May-4 Dawo, Saarbrucken #12/R est:1800
£1397 $2543 €2040 Hunting party in front of castle ruins in a river landscape (32x37cm-13x15in) s. 16-Jun-4 Fischer, Luzern #1175/R est:2400-2800 (S.FR 3200)
£2282 $4199 €3400 Elegant party on horseback returning from hunt (33x39cm-13x15in) s. 24-Mar-4 Dorotheum, Vienna #425/R est:2000-3000
£3356 $6174 €5000 Wooded landscape with stags (41x53cm-16x21in) s. one of pair. 24-Mar-4 Dorotheum, Vienna #417/R est:5000-7000
£3356 $6174 €5000 Wooded landscape with fleeing roe deer (41x53cm-16x21in) s. one of pair. 24-Mar-4 Dorotheum, Vienna #418/R est:5000-7000
£3636 $6255 €5200 Le brame du cerf. Le lancer (41x53cm-16x21in) s. pair. 8-Dec-3 Cornette de St.Cyr, Paris #40/R est:3000-4000
£5333 $9653 €8000 Boar hunt (51x68cm-20x27in) lit. 3-Apr-4 Badum, Bamberg #56/R est:10000

BRASEN, Hans (1849-1930) Danish

£341 $613 €498 Landscape with cattle (23x36cm-9x14in) s.d.1920. 24-Apr-4 Rasmussen, Havnen #2113 (D.KR 3800)
£1078 $2005 €1574 Small girl and red cow in a watering place (41x57cm-16x22in) init. 2-Mar-4 Rasmussen, Copenhagen #1202/R est:10000-15000 (D.KR 12000)
£1134 $1962 €1656 Small girl and her doll in front of farmhouse (28x28cm-11x11in) mono.d.86. 9-Dec-3 Rasmussen, Copenhagen #1396/R est:6000 (D.KR 12000)
£1210 $2177 €1767 Boy with cows in meadow (49x56cm-19x22in) s.d.1915. 24-Apr-4 Rasmussen, Havnen #2283/R est:6000 (D.KR 13500)
£1340 $2170 €1943 Young fisherwoman waiting for the return of her husband (96x122cm-38x48in) s.d.1926 exhib. 4-Aug-3 Rasmussen, Vejle #195/R est:15000 (D.KR 14000)
£1422 $2275 €2076 From the Garden of Eden - Fall of Man (66x152cm-26x60in) s.d.1928 exhib. 22-Sep-3 Rasmussen, Vejle #430/R est:15000-20000 (D.KR 15000)
£1435 $2325 €2081 Landscape with young couple (26x18cm-10x7in) s.d.95. 4-Aug-3 Rasmussen, Vejle #184/R est:15000 (D.KR 15000)
£1805 $3375 €2635 On the beach at sunset (45x60cm-18x24in) mono.d.1898. 25-Feb-4 Kunsthallen, Copenhagen #567/R est:25000 (D.KR 20000)
£3133 $5734 €4574 Passiar by the water pump (80x90cm-31x35in) s.d.1918 exhib.prov. 9-Jun-4 Rasmussen, Copenhagen #1684/R est:35000-40000 (D.KR 35000)

BRASILIER, Andre (1929-) French

£2349 $4369 €3500 Paysage a l'eglise (40x60cm-16x24in) s. 3-Mar-4 Ferri, Paris #309 est:3500-4000
£3500 $6335 €5110 Festival de musique a Menton (63x46cm-25x18in) s. init.i.stretcher. 1-Apr-4 Christie's, Kensington #139/R est:4000-6000
£4595 $8500 €6709 Nature morte devant la fenetre a Loupeigne (116x89cm-46x35in) s. init.i.d.1965-66 verso prov. 12-Feb-4 Sotheby's, New York #46/R est:10000-15000
£5521 $9000 €8061 Village du Tardenois (97x130cm-38x51in) s. prov. 25-Sep-3 Christie's, Rockefeller NY #591/R est:10000-15000
£6040 $11235 €9000 Chantal dans le petit atelier a Loupeigne (91x72cm-36x28in) s.d.62. 3-Mar-4 Tajan, Paris #185/R est:9000-12000
£8108 $15000 €11838 L'ete a Loupeigne (100x73cm-39x29in) s.i. init.d.1979 verso prov. 12-Feb-4 Sotheby's, New York #45/R est:15000-20000
£10564 $18275 €15000 Riviere bleue (65x92cm-26x36in) s. exhib. 9-Dec-3 Artcurial Briest, Paris #325/R est:15000-20000
£13000 $23920 €18980 Chevauchee sauvage (46x55cm-18x22in) s. prov. 22-Jun-4 Sotheby's, London #318/R est:5000-7000
£20000 $36800 €29200 Paddock a la Solle (60x73cm-24x29in) s. i.verso painted 1963. 22-Jun-4 Sotheby's, London #317/R est:7000-9000

Works on paper
£3310 $5726 €4700 New York (48x63cm-19x25in) s. W/C. 14-Dec-3 Eric Pillon, Calais #283/R

BRASS, Hans (1885-1959) German

Works on paper
£420 $713 €600 Head (45x35cm-18x14in) s.d.48 pen col pen pencil. 29-Nov-3 Bassenge, Berlin #6644

BRASS, Italico (1870-1943) Italian

£800 $1432 €1200 Type (75x60cm-30x24in) s. 12-May-4 Stadion, Trieste #820/R
£1419 $2497 €2100 Venice, interior of Saint Mark's church (35x26cm-14x10in) s. s.verso board. 19-May-4 Il Ponte, Milan #614 est:2200-2500
£1467 $2625 €2200 Carnival in Venice (30x42cm-12x17in) s. s.verso. 12-May-4 Stadion, Trieste #818/R est:800-1200
£1533 $2745 €2300 In the countryside. Chatting (15x23cm-6x9in) s. cardboard pair. 12-May-4 Stadion, Trieste #823/R est:1200-1600
£1549 $2572 €2200 Fiori di campo (65x85cm-26x33in) s. lit. 11-Jun-3 Christie's, Rome #189/R est:1200-2000
£1757 $3092 €2600 View in Friuli (16x23cm-6x9in) s. board. 19-May-4 Il Ponte, Milan #559 est:2000
£1757 $3092 €2600 Poor blind woman (50x60cm-20x24in) exhib. 19-May-4 Il Ponte, Milan #621 est:2800-3000
£2000 $3680 €3000 Masks (60x50cm-24x20in) s. 10-Jun-4 Christie's, Rome #206/R est:3500-4000

£2133	$3925	€3200	Field in Venice (15x22cm-6x9in) s. board. 10-Jun-4 Christie's, Rome #204/R est:2300-2800
£2162	$3805	€3200	Piazzetta San Marco, Venice (15x22cm-6x9in) s.d.1920 board. 19-May-4 Il Ponte, Milan #589 est:2000-2200
£5000	$9200	€7500	Venice, Campo della Bragora (26x35cm-10x14in) s. board. 10-Jun-4 Christie's, Rome #205/R est:2800-3200
£6711	$12349	€10000	Canalazzo (46x37cm-18x15in) s. 24-Mar-4 Il Ponte, Milan #565/R est:25000-30000

BRASSAI (1899-1984) Hungarian/French

Photographs

£1657	$3000	€2419	Monastic brothel, Rue Monsieur-le-Prince, Quartier Latin (30x30cm-12x12in) s.verso gelatin silver print 1931/printed later prov. 19-Apr-4 Bonhams & Butterfields, San Francisco #367/R est:1800-2500
£1667	$3000	€2434	Bal tabarin (29x22cm-11x9in) i.d.1932 verso gelatin silver print lit. 23-Apr-4 Phillips, New York #73/R est:7000-10000
£1905	$3600	€2781	Couple fache - quarrel (27x21cm-11x8in) s. verso ferrotype silver print. 17-Feb-4 Swann Galleries, New York #51/R est:3000-4000
£1916	$3200	€2797	Diaghalev dancer (23x15cm-9x6in) ferrotyped silver print. 21-Oct-3 Swann Galleries, New York #137/R est:4000-6000
£2000	$3680	€3000	Staircase in Montmartre (24x30cm-9x12in) s. i. verso board. 11-Jun-4 Bassenge, Berlin #4120/R est:5000
£2000	$3580	€3000	Three Graces (33x24cm-13x9in) s. num.10/30 silver print lit. 13-May-4 Le Mouel, Paris #125 est:3000-4000
£2036	$3400	€2973	A l'academie Julien (23x18cm-9x7in) with sig. silver print. 21-Oct-3 Swann Galleries, New York #138/R est:5000-7500
£2054	$3800	€2999	Prostitute playing Russian billiards, Boulevard Rochechouart, Montmartre (39x28cm-15x11in) s.i.d. gelatin silver print. 13-Jul-4 Christie's, Rockefeller NY #200/R est:3000-5000
£2111	$3800	€3082	Louis Dimier, member of the institute, on the quay (26x21cm-10x8in) s.verso gelatin silver print lit. 23-Apr-4 Phillips, New York #74/R est:5000-7000
£2400	$4224	€3504	Canal de l'Ourcq (23x18cm-9x7in) gelatin silver print. 19-May-4 Christie's, London #134/R est:3000-5000
£2400	$4224	€3504	Canal de l'Ourcq (23x18cm-9x7in) gelatin silver print lit. 19-May-4 Christie's, London #135/R est:3000-5000
£2552	$4339	€3650	Fontaine des Quatre Fleuves, Piazza Navone (38x28cm-15x11in) s.i.verso photo. 21-Nov-3 Piasa, Paris #3/R est:2500-3000
£2727	$4636	€3900	Untitled (22x16cm-9x6in) silver gelatin. 27-Nov-3 Villa Grisebach, Berlin #1127/R est:2500-3000
£3500	$6160	€5110	Involuntary sculpture (17x23cm-7x9in) gelatin silver print. 19-May-4 Christie's, London #130/R est:2000-3000
£3500	$6160	€5110	Involuntary sculpture (18x23cm-7x9in) gelatin silver print. 19-May-4 Christie's, London #131/R est:2000-3000
£3719	$6880	€5430	Couple d'amoureux dans petit cafe (30x23cm-12x9in) s. gelatin silver print. 10-Mar-4 Deutscher-Menzies, Melbourne #249/R est:10000-15000 (A.D 9000)
£3955	$7000	€5774	Le pont des arts, Paris (22x18cm-9x7in) s.i.d. gelatin silver print executed c.1933-34. 27-Apr-4 Christie's, Rockefeller NY #118/R est:7000-9000
£4200	$7392	€6132	Graffiti (23x18cm-9x7in) gelatin silver print lit. 19-May-4 Christie's, London #136/R est:2000-3000
£4520	$8000	€6599	Le premier ballon au parc montsouris, Paris (29x23cm-11x9in) s.i.d. gelatin silver print lit. 27-Apr-4 Christie's, Rockefeller NY #124/R est:7000-9000
£4520	$8000	€6599	Champs Elysees (29x24cm-11x9in) s. gelatin silver print. 27-Apr-4 Christie's, Rockefeller NY #127/R est:15000-25000
£5000	$8800	€7300	La mone bijou, bar de la lune, Montmartre (38x28cm-15x11in) s.i.d.1932 gelatin silver print. 18-May-4 Bonhams, New Bond Street #259/R est:5000-6000
£5334	$9814	€8000	Rue de Rivoli (28x21cm-11x8in) i. silver gelatin print exec.1936. 7-Jun-4 Tajan, Paris #132/R est:1200-1500
£5500	$9680	€8030	Matisse with model (23x29cm-9x11in) gelatin silver print lit. 19-May-4 Christie's, London #138/R est:7000-9000
£6667	$12000	€9734	Self portrait standing in darkroom (23x17cm-9x7in) i. gelatin silver print. 22-Apr-4 Phillips, New York #69/R est:15000-20000
£20339	$36000	€29695	Nu 132 (23x13cm-9x5in) studio st.i. i.verso ferrotyped prov. 27-Apr-4 Sotheby's, New York #31/R est:15000-25000

BRASSAUW, Melchior (1709-1757) Flemish

£3171	$5549	€4500	Le buveur. Le montreur de marmottes (114cm-45in circular) copper pair. 18-Dec-3 Tajan, Paris #113/R est:4000-6000

BRASSEUR, Georges (1880-1950) Belgian

£1284	$2298	€1900	Jeune femme nue se mirant (104x62cm-41x24in) s. 10-May-4 Horta, Bruxelles #132 est:1800-2200

BRASSEUR, Henri (1918-1981) Belgian

£350	$594	€500	Vase garni de fleurs (75x65cm-30x26in) s. 18-Nov-3 Galerie Moderne, Brussels #641

BRASSINGTON, John (19th C) British

£700	$1260	€1022	Portrait of a boy with a favourite dog (75x60cm-30x24in) s.d.1836 i.verso. 22-Apr-4 Mellors & Kirk, Nottingham #1134/R

BRASSINGTON, Pat (1942-) Australian

Photographs

£2119	$3602	€3094	Drink Me (100x80cm-39x31in) C-type photograph. 24-Nov-3 Sotheby's, Melbourne #73/R est:3500-5500 (A.D 5000)

BRATBY, Jean (1927-) British

£450	$833	€657	Ferns (122x122cm-48x48in) s. board. 11-Mar-4 Christie's, Kensington #323
£700	$1309	€1022	Flowers from Cornwall (58x42cm-23x17in) s. board. 24-Feb-4 Bonhams, Knowle #134
£1500	$2775	€2190	On the balcony (127x101cm-50x40in) s. s.i.verso. 11-Mar-4 Christie's, Kensington #328/R est:1500-2000

BRATBY, John (1928-1992) British

£350	$648	€511	Auberon Waugh (41x35cm-16x14in) s. 11-Mar-4 Christie's, Kensington #244
£350	$648	€511	Arthur Lowe (51x41cm-20x16in) s. 11-Mar-4 Christie's, Kensington #325
£360	$569	€522	Portrait of Fred Trueman, cricketer (41x35cm-16x14in) s. 24-Jul-3 Lawrence, Crewkerne #983
£420	$773	€613	Portrait of Captain Alex Rose (61x46cm-24x18in) s.i.stretcher. 23-Mar-4 Rosebery Fine Art, London #910/R
£450	$819	€657	Portrait of Nigel Broackes (40x35cm-16x14in) st.sig. 15-Jun-4 Bonhams, Knightsbridge #11/R
£500	$885	€730	Portrait of Richard Briers (50x40cm-20x16in) s. 27-Apr-4 Bonhams, Knightsbridge #117/R
£580	$1027	€847	White rabbit (40x45cm-16x18in) s. 27-Apr-4 Bonhams, Knightsbridge #92/R
£600	$960	€870	Portrait of Sir Bernard Lovell (45x45cm-18x18in) s.i. 16-Sep-3 Bonhams, Knightsbridge #18/R
£600	$1080	€876	Portrait of Sir Bernard Lovell (45x45cm-18x18in) s.i. 22-Apr-4 Lawrence, Crewkerne #955
£600	$1056	€876	Portrait of a man with pipe (63x50cm-25x20in) s. card. 18-May-4 Bonhams, Knightsbridge #20/R
£600	$1092	€876	Carnival figures on the Rialto (76x61cm-30x24in) s. 1-Jul-4 Christie's, Kensington #307/R
£650	$1040	€943	Portrait of Irene Harris (43x38cm-17x15in) s. 16-Sep-3 Bonhams, Knightsbridge #6/R
£700	$1190	€1022	Still life (91x58cm-36x23in) board. 26-Nov-3 Hamptons Fine Art, Godalming #239/R
£750	$1343	€1095	Patti in Venice (122x91cm-48x36in) s. 14-May-4 Christie's, Kensington #573/R
£750	$1380	€1095	Portrait of Marie Helvin (19x15cm-7x6in) s. 11-Jun-4 Keys, Aylsham #472/R
£800	$1432	€1168	Patti in black plastic mac shown nude (76x51cm-30x20in) s. prov. 14-May-4 Christie's, Kensington #570/R
£850	$1572	€1241	Portrait of John Bratby l (28x19cm-11x7in) s.i.verso board. 11-Feb-4 Sotheby's, Olympia #256/R
£900	$1440	€1314	David with blue coat (51x41cm-20x16in) s.d.1962. 15-May-3 Mitchells, Cockermouth #1077
£940	$1485	€1363	Greenwich Naval College (51x61cm-20x24in) s. 27-Jul-3 Desmond Judd, Cranbrook #1058
£950	$1672	€1387	Thomas Manns journey (122x91cm-48x36in) s.i. 19-May-4 Sotheby's, Olympia #300/R
£1100	$1947	€1606	View of Venice through the window (100x60cm-39x24in) board. 27-Apr-4 Bonhams, Knightsbridge #100/R est:400-600
£1300	$2288	€1898	Single sunflower (76x50cm-30x20in) st.sig. 18-May-4 Bonhams, Knightsbridge #78/R est:1200-1800
£1316	$2421	€2000	Baker and groceries wagon (50x60cm-20x24in) 22-Jun-4 De Veres Art Auctions, Dublin #96/R est:2000-3000
£1400	$2478	€2044	Tzar's bell (122x91cm-48x36in) s.i. 27-Apr-4 Bonhams, Knightsbridge #282/R est:1000-1500
£1500	$2760	€2190	Sun-flower (66x41cm-26x16in) s.d.86. 24-Mar-4 Hamptons Fine Art, Godalming #309/R
£1550	$2434	€2248	Portrait of Jason Bratby, the artist's son, seated in an elbow chair (122x91cm-48x36in) s. i.verso. 15-Dec-2 Desmond Judd, Cranbrook #848
£1750	$2975	€2555	Seated lady in a green jacket and white dress (122x92cm-48x36in) s. 31-Oct-3 Moore Allen & Innocent, Cirencester #883/R est:500-700
£1800	$2934	€2628	Interior, with window, canvasses, heater, clock, broom (56x41cm-22x16in) s. 23-Sep-3 John Nicholson, Haslemere #205/R est:250-500
£1900	$3515	€2774	View through a window, Cornwall (46x40cm-18x16in) s. 11-Feb-4 Sotheby's, Olympia #291/R est:800-1200
£1900	$3344	€2774	Self portrait (91x60cm-36x24in) board. 19-May-4 Sotheby's, Olympia #299/R est:1500-2000
£2200	$3564	€3190	Life and death (126x91cm-50x36in) s.d.76 lit. 30-Jul-3 Hamptons Fine Art, Godalming #177/R est:2000-3000
£2200	$3674	€3212	Triple portrait of Malcolm Muggeridge (157x86cm-62x34in) s.i.d.Feb-Mar 67. 16-Oct-3 Christie's, Kensington #591/R est:2000-3000
£2200	$3938	€3212	Interior scene (122x364cm-48x143in) s. board. 16-Mar-4 Bonhams, New Bond Street #64/R est:2000-3000
£2200	$4070	€3212	Flags (35x51cm-14x20in) s. lit. 11-Mar-4 Christie's, Kensington #330/R est:2000-3000
£2200	$4048	€3212	Cupid and Pysche in a rose garden. Roses and statues (119x89cm-47x35in) one i.stretcher pair. 24-Mar-4 Hamptons Fine Art, Godalming #297/R
£2400	$4128	€3504	Christian snow palaces, Russia (122x91cm-48x36in) s.i. prov. 2-Dec-3 Bonhams, New Bond Street #139/R est:2000-3000
£2400	$4296	€3504	Foscari house and Carnival people (122x91cm-48x36in) s. 14-May-4 Christie's, Kensington #572 est:2500-3500
£2500	$4400	€3650	Lionel Bart (152x101cm-60x40in) s.i. 19-May-4 Sotheby's, Olympia #204/R est:2000-3000
£2517	$4330	€3600	In the garden (55x40cm-22x16in) s. 3-Dec-3 Hauswedell & Nolte, Hamburg #731/R est:2500
£2600	$4134	€3796	Self portrait (61x45cm-24x18in) s. 10-Sep-3 Sotheby's, Olympia #296/R est:1000-1500
£2600	$4732	€3796	Venetian scene (122x76cm-48x30in) s.d.88. 15-Jun-4 Bonhams, New Bond Street #110/R est:3000-5000
£3000	$5280	€4380	Sunflower (76x51cm-30x20in) s. 19-May-4 Sotheby's, Olympia #315/R est:3000-5000
£3000	$5460	€4380	Five Royal red roses in a glass jug (122x88cm-48x35in) s. prov. 1-Jul-4 Christie's, Kensington #358/R est:4000-6000
£3200	$5088	€4672	Portrait of the artist's wife (106x1cm-42x0in) s. 10-Sep-3 Sotheby's, Olympia #297/R est:1200-1800
£3400	$5678	€4964	Regatta boats, Venice (122x91cm-48x36in) s. exhib. 21-Oct-3 Bonhams, Knightsbridge #25/R est:1000-1500
£3500	$6160	€5110	Artist's back garden (76x122cm-30x48in) s. 19-May-4 Sotheby's, Olympia #284/R est:3000-4000
£3800	$7030	€5548	Marina, St Helier (121x91cm-48x36in) s.d.83. 11-Feb-4 Sotheby's, Olympia #274/R est:2500-3500
£3800	$7030	€5548	Pamela (122x91cm-48x36in) s.i. 11-Feb-4 Sotheby's, Olympia #293/R est:2500-3500
£3800	$6688	€5548	Achmea plant (90x58cm-35x23in) board. 19-May-4 Sotheby's, Olympia #249/R est:2500-3500
£4000	$7040	€5840	Portrait of a lady (142x61cm-56x24in) s. 19-May-4 Sotheby's, Olympia #205/R est:3000-5000
£4100	$7052	€5986	Dark blue canal, Venice (122x90cm-48x35in) s. exhib. 3-Dec-3 Cheffins, Cambridge #650/R est:2000-3000
£4200	$7770	€6132	Window to smiling sunflowers (44x34cm-17x13in) s. prov.exhib. 11-Feb-4 Sotheby's, Olympia #257/R est:4000-6000
£4500	$8325	€6570	Sunflowers (122x91cm-48x36in) s.d.79. 11-Mar-4 Christie's, Kensington #326/R est:4000-6000
£5000	$8150	€7300	Sunflowers (111x86cm-44x34in) 24-Sep-3 Dreweatt Neate, Newbury #187 est:600-800
£5500	$9350	€8030	Jean at the fireplace (122x84cm-48x33in) s. board painted 1957 prov. 26-Nov-3 Sotheby's, Olympia #171/R est:5000-7000
£5500	$9845	€8030	Self portrait with yellow pipe (122x91cm-48x36in) s. prov. 14-May-4 Christie's, Kensington #575/R est:4000-6000

£6000 $10020 €8760 Artist's bicycle (121x173cm-48x68in) board. 16-Oct-3 Christie's, Kensington #682/R est:6000-8000
£6000 $10020 €8760 Four sunflowers in blue bucket (116x86cm-46x34in) s. i.verso. 16-Oct-3 Christie's, Kensington #683/R est:4000-6000
£6500 $11180 €9490 Bicycle (91x73cm-36x29in) board. 2-Dec-3 Bonhams, New Bond Street #132/R est:2000-3000
£6800 $11696 €9928 Spirit of Venice (122x91cm-48x36in) s.d.89. 2-Dec-3 Bonhams, New Bond Street #135/R est:6000-8000
£7000 $12040 €10220 Giant bursting sunflower (119x88cm-47x35in) s. i.stretcher prov. 3-Dec-3 Christie's, Kensington #713/R est:4000-6000
£7000 $11900 €10220 Kitchen Table (46x102cm-18x40in) s.d.54 i.stretcher. 29-Oct-3 Hampton & Littlewood, Exeter #554/R est:3000-5000
£7000 $12530 €10220 Hedgerow (122x149cm-48x59in) s. board. 16-Mar-4 Bonhams, New Bond Street #65/R est:3000-5000
£7000 $12950 €10220 Moldering melons (101x51cm-40x20in) s.d.8.61 i.stretcher prov. 11-Mar-4 Christie's, Kensington #324/R est:6000-8000
£7800 $14196 €11388 I really think chaps should dress properly in nice company (247x121cm-97x48in) painted 1963. 15-Jun-4 Bonhams, New Bond Street #111/R est:5000-7000
£8500 $14450 €12410 Venice (122x91cm-48x36in) s.d.88. 26-Nov-3 Sotheby's, Olympia #149/R est:3000-5000
£9500 $16150 €13870 Red arrows voer Hastings (91x122cm-36x48in) s.i.d.88. 26-Nov-3 Sotheby's, Olympia #150/R est:3500-4500
£10500 $16695 €15330 Sunflowers (126x76cm-50x30in) s. 10-Sep-3 Sotheby's, Olympia #298/R est:3000-4000
£11000 $20020 €16060 Burano (121x70cm-48x28in) s.i.d.98. 15-Jun-4 Bonhams, New Bond Street #109/R est:3000-5000
£20000 $37000 €29200 Cantaloup crust and coconut (71x91cm-28x36in) s.d.8'61 s.i.stretcher. 11-Feb-4 Sotheby's, Olympia #255/R est:2000-3000
Works on paper
£260 $468 €380 Leaning gondolier on his gondola beneath the arch at hi tide (34x48cm-13x19in) s.i.d.1992 W/C pencil crayon. 20-Jan-4 Bonhams, Knightsbridge #102
£280 $512 €420 Aphrodite belly dancer (54x36cm-21x14in) s.d.91 W/C pastel. 27-Jul-4 Henry Adams, Chichester #388
£340 $585 €496 Portrait of John Bratby as a young boy (37x27cm-15x11in) s.d.61 pen black ink. 3-Dec-3 Christie's, Kensington #634/R
£360 $648 €526 Combine harvester (36x54cm-14x21in) s.i. W/C pencil. 20-Jan-4 Bonhams, Knightsbridge #101
£420 $777 €613 Self portrait in Missoni cardigan with Patti in red (27x19cm-11x7in) pencil W/C col crayon gouache. 11-Mar-4 Christie's, Kensington #315
£800 $1360 €1168 Rabbit, Mopsy (36x53cm-14x21in) s.i. pastel. 5-Nov-3 John Nicholson, Haslemere #540/R
£800 $1360 €1168 Billie goat (38x56cm-15x22in) s.i. pastel. 5-Nov-3 John Nicholson, Haslemere #541/R
£1100 $1892 €1606 Jason Bratby with his bottle (43x35cm-17x14in) s. gouache. 3-Dec-3 Christie's, Kensington #751/R est:700-1000
£1200 $2040 €1752 Celebration of Pip (51x38cm-20x15in) s.i.d.1990 pencil ink crayon W/C gouache set of 11. 26-Nov-3 Sotheby's, Olympia #186/R est:1000-1500
£2200 $3740 €3212 Lilies (49x40cm-19x16in) s.d.71 W/C ink gouache. 26-Nov-3 Sotheby's, Olympia #151/R est:2000-3000
£4000 $6320 €5800 Father, first-born, and mirrors (55x80cm-22x31in) s.i.d.October 1959 pencil conte crayon exhib. 24-Jul-3 Lawrence, Crewkerne #884/R est:1000-1500

BRATE, Fanny (1861-1940) Swedish
£961 $1720 €1403 Still life of ginger jar and apples (24x32cm-9x13in) s.d.81 prov. 26-May-4 AB Stockholms Auktionsverk #2284/R (S.KR 13000)

BRATLAND, Jacob (1859-1906) Norwegian
£894 $1646 €1305 Farm-yard with seated woman (52x70cm-20x28in) s. 10-Jun-4 Grev Wedels Plass, Oslo #161/R (N.KR 11000)
£2447 $4380 €3573 Interior scene with woman at piano (46x60cm-18x24in) s. 25-May-4 Grev Wedels Plass, Oslo #50/R est:40000 (N.KR 30000)

BRATTELI, Marianne (1951-) Norwegian
£1545 $2827 €2256 Notre Dame (170x154cm-67x61in) mono. d.1946 stretcher exhib. 7-Jun-4 Blomqvist, Oslo #449/R est:15000-18000 (N.KR 19000)

BRAUER, Erich (1929-) Austrian
£4698 $8597 €7000 Zwischen Binsen (37x45cm-15x18in) s. i. verso panel prov. 7-Jul-4 Artcurial Briest, Paris #152 est:3500-4000
£5369 $9611 €8000 On the search for a new building polt (32x24cm-13x9in) s. board on panel. 25-May-4 Dorotheum, Vienna #258/R est:8000-11000
£5667 $10370 €8500 Get out of my path (49x73cm-19x29in) s. s.i. verso paper on panel. 4-Jun-4 Lempertz, Koln #67/R est:10000-12000
£6993 $11888 €10000 Round building (37x41cm-15x16in) s. i. vers panel prov. 26-Nov-3 Dorotheum, Vienna #245/R est:10000-14000
£6993 $11888 €10000 Simson with city gate (30x40cm-12x16in) s. i. verso paper on panel prov. 26-Nov-3 Dorotheum, Vienna #273/R est:10000-13000
£8725 $15443 €13000 Eva (30x50cm-12x20in) s. paper on panel. 28-Apr-4 Wiener Kunst Auktionen, Vienna #234/R est:5000-10000
£13423 $23758 €20000 Last supper (65x51cm-26x20in) s. panel. 28-Apr-4 Wiener Kunst Auktionen, Vienna #216/R est:20000-35000
Sculpture
£1316 $2421 €1921 Cabbage head (30cm-12in) s.verso num.4/6 st.f. Venturi Arts dark light brown pat bronze pr. 23-Jun-4 Koller, Zurich #3213 est:3000-4000 (S.FR 3000)
Works on paper
£355 $592 €500 Boy sleeping in chair (19x25cm-7x10in) s.d.3 Mai 46 pencil. 14-Oct-3 Dorotheum, Vienna #136/R
£930 $1600 €1358 Fiery thoughts (25x18cm-10x7in) s. W/C prov. 3-Dec-3 Doyle, New York #23/R est:1000-1500
£1333 $2400 €2000 Airplane wreck (21x17cm-8x7in) W/C. 24-Apr-4 Cornette de St.Cyr, Paris #454 est:3000
£1645 $3026 €2500 Weather for dogs (18x22cm-7x9in) s. gouache acrylic lit. 22-Jun-4 Wiener Kunst Auktionen, Vienna #311/R est:2000
£1690 $2958 €2400 Thought of in grey, but better in purple (20x14cm-8x6in) s. W/C board exhib. 19-Dec-3 Dorotheum, Vienna #275/R est:2200-2800
£1955 $3500 €2854 Window. s.i. W/C. 13-May-4 Dallas Auction Gallery, Dallas #283/R est:4000-6000
£3333 $6100 €5000 Untitled (68x98cm-27x39in) s. gouache board. 4-Jun-4 Lempertz, Koln #68/R est:5000

BRAUN, Arthur (1906-1977) German?
£400 $724 €600 Young woman holding fruit bowl (50x42cm-20x17in) board lit. 1-Apr-4 Frank Peege, Freiburg #1174/R

BRAUN, Ludwig (1836-1916) German
£272 $487 €400 Peasant and two girls in field (27x38cm-11x15in) s.i. board. 18-Mar-4 Neumeister, Munich #2646/R
£608 $949 €900 Mounted soldiers (20x15cm-8x6in) s.d.1865 paper on board. 28-Mar-3 Behringer, Furth #1116/R
£946 $1476 €1400 Boy and two girls in room (24x15cm-9x6in) s.d.1878 panel. 28-Mar-3 Behringer, Furth #1118/R est:900
£1047 $1634 €1550 Small girl with toy (14x21cm-6x8in) s.i. verso panel. 28-Mar-3 Behringer, Furth #1119/R est:900
£1149 $1792 €1700 Cavalry men and horses in stable (18x13cm-7x5in) s. panel. 28-Mar-3 Behringer, Furth #1117/R est:900
£1284 $2003 €1900 Mounted soldiers on manoeuvres (35x27cm-14x11in) s.d.1906 i. stretcher. 28-Mar-3 Behringer, Furth #1114/R est:1900
£1944 $3169 €2800 A guard horseman from Napoleonic Wars (52x42cm-20x17in) s.d.90. 25-Sep-3 Dr Fritz Nagel, Stuttgart #1330/R est:2500
£2797 $4811 €4000 Stagecoach stopped outside an inn (23x38cm-9x15in) s. panel. 3-Dec-3 Neumeister, Munich #536/R est:5000

BRAUN, Martha (1935-) German
£286 $457 €415 Broye canal at dusk (85x100cm-33x39in) s.d.78. 15-May-3 Stuker, Bern #1099 (S.FR 600)

BRAUN, Maurice (1877-1941) American
£3704 $7000 €5408 Landscape (23x15cm-9x6in) s. board. 17-Feb-4 John Moran, Pasadena #10/R est:4000-6000
£3968 $7500 €5793 Sunlit mountain landscape (20x25cm-8x10in) board prov. 17-Feb-4 John Moran, Pasadena #17a/R est:5500-7500
£4118 $7000 €6012 Spring landscape (41x30cm-16x12in) s. 29-Oct-3 Christie's, Los Angeles #42/R est:8000-12000
£4286 $7500 €6258 Japanese ceremonies (61x51cm-24x20in) s. 19-Dec-3 Sotheby's, New York #1115/R est:4000-6000
£5000 $8500 €7300 Landscape, Mt Palomar meadows (15x23cm-6x9in) s. board. 18-Nov-3 John Moran, Pasadena #60a est:5500-7500
£5435 $10000 €7935 Woman in a red skirt and a colourful shawl with a mortar and pestle (45x35cm-18x14in) s. 8-Jun-4 Bonhams & Butterfields, San Francisco #4287/R est:10000-15000
£6918 $11000 €10100 Foothills (20x30cm-8x12in) s. 13-Sep-3 Selkirks, St. Louis #48/R est:10000-15000
£7407 $14000 €10814 Salton sea (64x76cm-25x30in) s. i. stretcher prov. 17-Feb-4 John Moran, Pasadena #51/R est:15000-22500
£7937 $15000 €11588 Eucalyptus landscape (46cm-18in) s. 17-Feb-4 John Moran, Pasadena #37/R est:14000-18000
£8649 $16000 €12628 Sailing along (51x76cm-20x30in) s. prov. 11-Mar-4 Christie's, Rockefeller NY #55/R est:8000-12000
£8995 $17000 €13133 Boats/harbour - Snow along the river (64x76cm-25x30in) prov. 17-Feb-4 John Moran, Pasadena #76/R est:20000-30000
£10056 $18000 €14682 Evening light, California landscape (40x51cm-16x20in) s. 14-May-4 Skinner, Boston #209/R est:10000-15000
£10405 $18000 €15191 View toward the San Diego Coast (51x61cm-20x24in) s. prov. 10-Dec-3 Bonhams & Butterfields, San Francisco #6247/R est:20000-30000
£10582 $20000 €15450 Sycamores in autumn (51x61cm-20x24in) s. i. stretcher prov. 17-Feb-4 John Moran, Pasadena #95a/R est:20000-30000
£10989 $20000 €16044 Water front a eventide (41x51cm-16x20in) s. i.stretcher. 29-Jun-4 Sotheby's, New York #250/R est:8000-12000
£11176 $19000 €16317 Castle rock (41x51cm-16x20in) s. i.verso exhib. 18-Nov-3 John Moran, Pasadena #44 est:25000-30000
£11561 $20000 €16879 Grey Day in Autumn (51x77cm-20x30in) s. i.stretcher prov. 10-Dec-3 Bonhams & Butterfields, San Francisco #6213/R est:25000-35000
£11561 $20000 €16879 Hills at riverside, California (51x61cm-20x24in) s. i.stretcher prov. 10-Dec-3 Bonhams & Butterfields, San Francisco #6242/R est:20000-30000
£12707 $23000 €18552 Moonrise (61x51cm-24x20in) s. prov. 31-Mar-4 Sotheby's, New York #103/R est:10000-15000
£13587 $25000 €19837 The brook (50x61cm-20x24in) s. i. stretcher prov. 8-Jun-4 Bonhams & Butterfields, San Francisco #4288/R est:30000-50000
£14465 $23000 €21119 Twilight landscape (30x41cm-12x16in) s. 13-Sep-3 Selkirks, St. Louis #47/R est:14000-18000
£19022 $35000 €27772 Valley scene, Southern California (63x76cm-25x30in) s. prov. 8-Jun-4 Bonhams & Butterfields, San Francisco #4317/R est:40000-60000
£20588 $35000 €30058 Rocks and hills (64x76cm-25x30in) s. i.verso prov. 18-Nov-3 John Moran, Pasadena #60 est:40000-60000
£29101 $55000 €42487 Eucalyptus and distant mountains (64x76cm-25x30in) s. prov. 17-Feb-4 John Moran, Pasadena #30a/R est:45000-65000
£41176 $70000 €60117 The dock, figures and boats in harbour (76x91cm-30x36in) i.stretcher. 18-Nov-3 John Moran, Pasadena #72 est:50000-70000
£46703 $85000 €68186 Oaks at Mesa Grande landscape (76x91cm-30x36in) s. i.verso. 15-Jun-4 John Moran, Pasadena #40 est:60000-80000

BRAUN, Reinhold (1821-1884) German
£1119 $1902 €1600 Horses in stable (18x24cm-7x9in) s.i. panel. 20-Nov-3 Dorotheum, Salzburg #147/R est:3200-4000
£9483 $17448 €13845 At village fountain (55x47cm-22x19in) s.d.1861. 26-Mar-4 Koller, Zurich #3121/R est:22000-32000 (S.FR 22000)
Works on paper
£293 $524 €430 Swabian village festival (27x38cm-11x15in) s.d.1859 W/C lit. 20-Mar-4 Bergmann, Erlangen #1098

BRAUN, Vera (1902-1997) Hungarian
£310 $568 €450 Composition. s. 2-Feb-4 Millon & Associes, Paris #336
£310 $568 €450 Composition (60x73cm-24x29in) s. 2-Feb-4 Millon & Associes, Paris #337
£310 $568 €450 Composition (54x65cm-21x26in) 2-Feb-4 Millon & Associes, Paris #338
£416 $778 €620 Soleil sur l'etendu (65x92cm-26x36in) s.i.d.1969 verso acrylic prov. 29-Feb-4 Versailles Encheres #207
£483 $883 €700 Composition (81x65cm-32x26in) s. 2-Feb-4 Millon & Associes, Paris #339
£547 $984 €820 Compositions abstraites (35x27cm-14x11in) s. pair. 26-Apr-4 Millon & Associes, Paris #268/R

£586	$1073	€850	Composition (65x81cm-26x32in) s. 2-Feb-4 Millon & Associes, Paris #340/R

BRAUN, Wilhelm (1873-1937) Austrian

£2000	$3180	€2900	Poppy field (91x126cm-36x50in) s.d.1913. 11-Sep-3 Christie's, Kensington #25/R est:2000-3000

BRAUND, Dorothy Mary (1926-) Australian

£891	$1434	€1301	Figure (42x59cm-17x23in) i. i.verso board. 13-Oct-3 Joel, Victoria #291/R est:2000-3000 (A.D 2200)
£909	$1682	€1327	Ballet (29x40cm-11x16in) s.d.69 board prov. 10-Mar-4 Deutscher-Menzies, Melbourne #269/R est:2000-3000 (A.D 2200)
£972	$1564	€1419	Summer (30x40cm-12x16in) board. 13-Oct-3 Joel, Victoria #242 est:1500-2500 (A.D 2400)
£1518	$2444	€2216	Girl resting (38x48cm-15x19in) i.verso board. 13-Oct-3 Joel, Victoria #268/R est:2000-3000 (A.D 3750)
£1617	$2798	€2361	Boys climbing (95x125cm-37x49in) s. i.verso board. 10-Dec-3 Shapiro, Sydney #3/R est:5000-7000 (A.D 3800)
£2672	$4863	€3901	Beginning (91x122cm-36x48in) s.d.86 i.v board prov.exhib. 16-Jun-4 Deutscher-Menzies, Melbourne #36/R est:6000-8000 (A.D 7000)
£2672	$4863	€3901	After dinner (89x120cm-35x47in) s.d.99 i.verso board. 16-Jun-4 Deutscher-Menzies, Melbourne #223/R est:7500-10000 (A.D 7000)
£3435	$6252	€5015	Heavy heat (89x120cm-35x47in) s.d.01 board. 16-Jun-4 Deutscher-Menzies, Melbourne #314/R est:7500-10000 (A.D 9000)
Works on paper			
£298	$506	€435	Balinese women in market (35x46cm-14x18in) s.d.78 W/C gouache. 25-Nov-3 Christie's, Melbourne #274 (A.D 700)
£690	$1076	€1001	Greek Island (40x53cm-16x21in) W/C. 1-Aug-2 Joel, Victoria #336 est:2000-3000 (A.D 2000)
£766	$1302	€1118	Seated children (37x49cm-15x19in) gouache W/C 1978. 26-Nov-3 Deutscher-Menzies, Melbourne #144/R est:2000-2500 (A.D 1800)
£1362	$2315	€1989	Beach Cafe (39x49cm-15x19in) s.d.79 gouache prov. 26-Nov-3 Deutscher-Menzies, Melbourne #240/R est:2500-3500 (A.D 3200)

BRAUNE, Erwin (1865-?) German

£267	$483	€400	Horse cart on country track (25x30cm-10x12in) s.d.1888 board. 1-Apr-4 Van Ham, Cologne #1306

BRAUNER, Gustav (1880-?) ?

Works on paper			
£268	$494	€400	Washing drying on garden fence (19x27cm-7x11in) s. W/C. 26-Mar-4 Dorotheum, Vienna #351/R

BRAUNER, Victor (1903-1966) French/Rumanian

£5068	$8919	€7500	Portrait (27x21cm-11x8in) s.d.1943 paraffin paper prov.exhib. 18-May-4 Tajan, Paris #4/R est:7500-8500
£6081	$10703	€9000	Tete (65x50cm-26x20in) mono.d.1960 paraffin ink wash prov. 18-May-4 Tajan, Paris #7/R est:7500-8500
£30000	$55200	€43800	Claude Sernet (55x46cm-22x18in) s.d.1930. 22-Jun-4 Sotheby's, London #188/R est:15000-20000
£31334	$57028	€47000	Visages metaphysiques - Portrait de Michael Askenazy (41x49cm-16x19in) painted c.1937 double-sided prov. 30-Jun-4 Calmels Cohen, Paris #67/R est:50000-60000
£35000	$63700	€51100	Mutation de la Natalie (54x65cm-21x26in) s.i.d.1961 prov. 3-Feb-4 Christie's, London #239/R est:30000-40000
£45000	$81900	€65700	Portrait du cote miroir (73x92cm-29x36in) s.d.1959 oil plaster board prov. 3-Feb-4 Christie's, London #242/R est:40000-60000
£45000	$81900	€65700	Portrait aux fleurs (54x65cm-21x26in) init.d.9/XI/1953 exhib. 3-Feb-4 Christie's, London #244/R est:45000-65000
£45139	$74479	€65000	Le promeneur (73x60cm-29x24in) s.d.I.VIII.47 prov. 2-Jul-3 Cornette de St.Cyr, Paris #1/R est:60000-80000
Works on paper			
£1496	$2679	€2200	Projet pour chapeau tandem (26x20cm-10x8in) s.i. crayon exec 1938 prov.exhib. 21-Mar-4 Calmels Cohen, Paris #65/R est:2000-3000
£1800	$3114	€2628	Quatre figures (13x20cm-5x8in) s. pencil. 11-Dec-3 Christie's, Kensington #169/R est:2000-3000
£1905	$3409	€2800	Untitled (18x24cm-7x9in) ink col crayons exec c.1955 prov. 21-Mar-4 Calmels Cohen, Paris #61/R est:3000-4000
£2067	$3720	€3100	Untitled (18x13cm-7x5in) s.i.d.60 ink dr. 25-Apr-4 Versailles Encheres #189 est:500-600
£2162	$3806	€3200	Untitled (25x15cm-10x6in) mono.d.1952 ink W/C prov. 18-May-4 Tajan, Paris #5/R est:2500-3000
£2416	$4325	€3600	Histoire du crime (19x27cm-7x11in) s.d.1933 ink paper on cardboard. 26-May-4 Christie's, Paris #44/R est:3000-5000
£2500	$3975	€3625	Oiseau fantastique (18x14cm-7x6in) s.i.d.1959 pen ink col felt-tipped pens. 11-Sep-3 Christie's, Kensington #168/R est:2000-3000
£2585	$4628	€3800	Untitled (21x15cm-8x6in) i.d.1952 ink W/C. 21-Mar-4 Calmels Cohen, Paris #63/R est:3000-4000
£3041	$5351	€4500	Decision de Pantoganior (25x15cm-10x6in) mono.i.d.1952 ink W/C prov. 18-May-4 Tajan, Paris #6/R est:2800-3500
£3379	$5946	€5000	Untitled (20x67cm-8x26in) s.d.1948 gouache prov. 18-May-4 Tajan, Paris #8/R est:3000-4000
£3402	$6089	€5000	Portrait of Claude Sernet (27x20cm-11x8in) s.d.1927 ink wash. 21-Mar-4 Calmels Cohen, Paris #64/R est:3000-3500
£3816	$7021	€5800	Talisman porte-bonheur (12x6cm-5x2in) s. wax crayon cardboard. 27-Jun-4 Versailles Encheres #112/R est:7000-8000
£4392	$7730	€6500	Tete fantastique, coiffure au chat et au serpent (12x18cm-5x7in) s.d.1944 ink prov. 18-May-4 Tajan, Paris #9/R est:1500-2000
£4730	$8135	€6906	Composition with animals and figures (14x68cm-6x27in) s. Indian ink W/C prov. 2-Dec-3 Koller, Zurich #3063/R est:10000-15000 (S.FR 10500)
£4828	$8062	€7000	Petit oiseau (16x21cm-6x8in) s.d.1957 W/C prov. 13-Nov-3 Finarte Semenzato, Rome #219/R est:5500-6500
£6944	$11806	€10000	Head (50x64cm-20x25in) s.d.1954 mixed media prov. 28-Oct-3 Il Ponte, Milan #256/R
£7000	$11690	€10220	Sans titre (16x24cm-6x9in) s.d.1951 gouache pen ink on card prov. 21-Oct-3 Sotheby's, London #68/R est:5000-7000
£10000	$18401	€15000	Portrait de jeune femme (25x17cm-10x7in) s.d.26/5/1945 wax masonite exhib. 8-Jun-4 Artcurial Briest, Paris #192/R est:10000-15000
£16901	$27211	€24000	Declaration d'amour (50x65cm-20x26in) s.d.1956 W/C ink brush. 22-Aug-3 Deauville, France #118/R est:28000-30000

BRAUNIAS, Mark (20th C) New Zealander?

£692	$1239	€1010	Pam and Megan (63x152cm-25x60in) acrylic collage triptych. 11-May-4 Peter Webb, Auckland #63/R est:1200-1800 (NZ.D 2000)

BRAVO, Claudio (1936-) Chilean

£5000	$8650	€7300	Dama (70x50cm-28x20in) s. oil paper on panel. 11-Dec-3 Christie's, Kensington #213/R est:5000-7000
£22346	$40000	€32625	Helmet (70x80cm-28x31in) s.d.MCMLXXII canvas on wood prov. 26-May-4 Sotheby's, New York #119/R est:50000-70000
£25333	$46613	€38000	Shell (33x23cm-13x9in) s.d.MMI prov. 10-Jun-4 Christie's, Paris #60/R est:48000-65000
£27933	$50000	€40782	Seated man (145x114cm-57x45in) s.d.dMCMLXIX exhib. 26-May-4 Sotheby's, New York #55/R est:100000-150000
£100000	$170000	€146000	Red turban (85x65cm-33x26in) s.d.LXXVII prov.exhib.lit. 19-Nov-3 Sotheby's, New York #25/R est:60000-80000
£111765	$190000	€163177	White package (36x27cm-14x11in) s.d.MCMLXVI prov. 19-Nov-3 Sotheby's, New York #11/R est:90000-120000
£141176	$240000	€206117	Self portrait (200x150cm-79x59in) s.d.MCMLXX prov.exhib.lit. 19-Nov-3 Sotheby's, New York #30/R est:250000-350000
£223529	$380000	€326352	Before the game (199x239cm-78x94in) s.d.LXXIII prov.exhib.lit. 19-Nov-3 Sotheby's, New York #51/R est:450000-550000
£502793	$900000	€734078	White package (100x150cm-39x59in) s.d.MCMLXVII panel prov.exhib. 26-May-4 Sotheby's, New York #13/R est:900000-1100000
Sculpture			
£122905	$220000	€179441	Nudes (95x28x24cm-37x11x9in) st.sig.d.79 pat bronze pair. 26-May-4 Sotheby's, New York #57/R est:40000-60000
Works on paper			
£493	$789	€700	Make up for the Mona Lisa (20x13cm-8x5in) s.i.d.MCMLXV felt-tip pen dr. 16-Sep-3 Segre, Madrid #255/R
£1286	$2250	€1878	Kneeling boy on knees (21x28cm-8x11in) s.d.MCMLXXXIV sanguine. 19-Dec-3 Sotheby's, New York #1200/R est:2500-3500
£1857	$3250	€2711	Enrique (35x27cm-14x11in) s.d.MCMLXX conte crayon. 19-Dec-3 Sotheby's, New York #1203/R est:6000-8000
£2571	$4500	€3754	Study for Before the Game (21x20cm-8x8in) s.d.MCMLXXXIII pencil prov. 19-Dec-3 Sotheby's, New York #1201/R est:3500-4000
£3143	$5500	€4589	Moroccan landscape with building (22x33cm-9x13in) s.d.MCMLXXXII col crayon. 19-Dec-3 Sotheby's, New York #1202/R est:4000-5000
£4000	$7000	€5840	Cupido (44x44cm-17x17in) s.d.MCMLXX pencil red crayon prov. 19-Dec-3 Sotheby's, New York #1204/R est:7000-10000
£5000	$9050	€7300	Portrait of Lucia Pagueguy Metzner (71x56cm-28x22in) s.d.MCMLXI col pencil gouache. 1-Apr-4 Christie's, Kensington #252/R est:5000-7000
£6286	$11000	€9178	Miss piglet (66x51cm-26x20in) s.d.MCMXCI pastel. 19-Dec-3 Sotheby's, New York #1199/R est:6000-8000
£10056	$18000	€14682	Study forsoccer players (105x72cm-41x28in) s.d.MCMLXXXIII chl conte exhib.lit. 26-May-4 Sotheby's, New York #58/R est:35000-45000
£11765	$20000	€17177	Paper bag (65x49cm-26x19in) s.d.MCMLXIX graphite chk prov.exhib.lit. 19-Nov-3 Sotheby's, New York #24/R est:18000-22000
£13235	$22500	€19323	Cushions (28x36cm-11x14in) s.d.MCMXC graphite conte crayon chk prov.lit. 19-Nov-3 Sotheby's, New York #28/R est:10000-15000
£16201	$29000	€23653	Legs and hands (65x50cm-26x20in) s.d.MCMLXXV chl pencil prov.exhib.lit. 26-May-4 Sotheby's, New York #124/R est:18000-22000
£20950	$37500	€30587	Plant in a can (34x24cm-13x9in) s.d.MCMLXXI conte exec.1971 exhib.lit. 26-May-4 Sotheby's, New York #59/R est:10000-15000
£22059	$37500	€32206	David (62x46cm-24x18in) s.d.LXXIX chl graphite chk prov.exhib. 19-Nov-3 Sotheby's, New York #27/R est:25000-30000
£41176	$70000	€60117	Wine jugs (75x110cm-30x43in) s.d.MCMXCII pastel prov.exhib.lit. 19-Nov-3 Sotheby's, New York #29/R est:60000-80000

BRAVO, Gonzalez (1944-) Spanish

£2533	$4535	€3800	Untitled (146x114cm-57x45in) s. s.d.2002 verso. 15-May-4 Van Ham, Cologne #485/R est:4100

BRAWLEY, Robert Julius (1937-) American

£5249	$9500	€7664	The secret (119x89cm-47x35in) 16-Apr-4 American Auctioneer #38/R est:2000-3000

BRAY, Alan (20th C) American

Works on paper			
£3827	$6200	€5549	After the ice (61x81cm-24x32in) s. casein on panel prov. 8-Aug-3 Barridorf, Portland #235/R est:4000-6000
£5864	$9500	€8503	Vernal pond (66x87cm-26x34in) s. casein on panel prov. 8-Aug-3 Barridorf, Portland #233/R est:4000-6000

BRAY, Carl G (1917-) American

£471	$800	€688	Blue mountains (30x41cm-12x16in) s. canvas on board prov. 1-Nov-3 Santa Fe Art, Santa Fe #239/R

BRAY, Dirck de (17th C) Dutch

£31034	$51517	€45000	Still life with flowers and book (38x38cm-15x15in) s.d.1680 exhib.lit.prov. 1-Oct-3 Dorotheum, Vienna #166/R est:38000-50000

BRAY, Jan de (1627-1697) Dutch

£27000	$49410	€39420	Portrait of a young girl (54x44cm-21x17in) panel exhib. 7-Apr-4 Woolley & Wallis, Salisbury #300/R est:6000-8000

BRAY, Salomon de (1597-1664) Dutch

£750000	$1350000	€1095000	Study of young woman in profile (27x20cm-11x8in) s.d.1636 panel oval. 22-Jan-4 Sotheby's, New York #62/R est:750000-950000

BRAYER, Yves (1907-1990) French

£500	$905	€730	Venice canal scene (59x44cm-23x17in) s.i. 30-Mar-4 Bonhams, Oxford #203
£1467	$2625	€2200	Les oiseaux et la barque abandonnee (24x35cm-9x14in) s. 16-May-4 Thierry & Lannon, Brest #122/R est:2000-3000
£1467	$2699	€2200	Longchamp (25x35cm-10x14in) s.i.d.1941. 11-Jun-4 Pierre Berge, Paris #214/R est:2200-2500

£2113	$3655	€3000	Rose blanche et verre bleu (24x19cm-9x7in) s. 10-Dec-3 Ferri, Paris #19 est:1800-2000
£2550	$4565	€3800	Avila (23x34cm-9x13in) s.i. 25-May-4 Chambelland & Giafferi, Paris #74/R est:2000-2500
£3067	$5000	€4478	La Cathedrale de Tucson (38x55cm-15x22in) s.i.d.1979 i.d.1979 verso prov. 25-Sep-3 Christie's, Rockefeller NY #588/R est:6000-8000
£3311	$6026	€5000	Paysage des Baux de Provence (24x35cm-9x14in) s. 18-Jun-4 Piasa, Paris #151/R est:3000-4000
£3356	$5940	€5000	Paysage de Camargue (38x55cm-15x22in) s.i.d.1958 verso prov.lit. 27-Apr-4 Artcurial Briest, Paris #196/R est:4000-6000
£3709	$6935	€5600	Cabanes au petit Rhone (54x65cm-21x26in) s. i.d.1959 verso. 20-Jul-4 Gioffredo, Nice #14/R
£4027	$7409	€6000	Cabanes aux Saintes Maries de la mer (37x45cm-15x18in) s. i.d.1949 verso. 26-Mar-4 Neret-Minet, Paris #13/R est:3000-3500
£4326	$7225	€6100	Paysage des Baux-de-Provence (38x46cm-15x18in) s. 19-Jun-3 Millon & Associes, Paris #238/R est:3000-3500
£4545	$8500	€6636	Paysage d'Arizona (38x55cm-15x22in) s.i.d.1979 s.i.d.verso. 25-Feb-4 Christie's, Rockefeller NY #27/R est:5000-7000
£4966	$7896	€7300	Isbas a Vladimir (65x54cm-26x21in) s. i.d.1974 verso. 23-Mar-3 Mercier & Cie, Lille #286/R est:6800-7500
£5000	$8500	€7300	Paris 1944 (61x81cm-24x32in) s.i.d.1944. 9-Nov-3 Bonhams & Butterfields, Los Angeles #4006/R
£5215	$8500	€7614	Gardians et Arlesiennes (65x54cm-26x21in) s. i.verso prov. 25-Sep-3 Christie's, Rockefeller NY #587/R est:4000-6000
£5369	$9987	€8000	Cuernavaca, au Mexique (73x92cm-29x36in) s. i.verso. 3-Mar-4 Tajan, Paris #166/R est:9000-12000
£6000	$10920	€9000	Printemps a Aureille (50x65cm-20x26in) s. painted 1960. 4-Jul-4 Eric Pillon, Calais #196/R
£6376	$11860	€9500	Pont Saint-martin, Tolede (65x81cm-26x32in) s. i.d.1962 verso. 3-Mar-4 Tajan, Paris #167/R est:8000-10000
£6417	$12000	€9369	Lavandieres a Ramatuelle (49x65cm-19x26in) s. i.d.1972 verso. 25-Feb-4 Christie's, Rockefeller NY #44/R est:5000-7000
£6507	$11062	€9500	Vue des Baux-de-Provence (38x46cm-15x18in) s. 9-Nov-3 Eric Pillon, Calais #131/R
£6596	$11015	€9300	La chapelle Sainte-Sixte a Eygalieres (46x55cm-18x22in) s. 19-Jun-3 Millon & Associes, Paris #241/R est:2500-3000
£7324	$12670	€10400	Mas en Provence dans les Alpilles (38x55cm-15x22in) s. 10-Dec-3 Rossini, Paris #58/R
£7972	$13313	€11400	Paysage de Baux-de-Provence (50x65cm-20x26in) s.d. lit. 29-Jun-3 Eric Pillon, Calais #246/R
£8054	$14899	€12000	Paris, marche aux puces (60x81cm-24x32in) s.d.1944. 14-Mar-4 Eric Pillon, Calais #137/R
£8725	$16228	€13000	Chemin a l'automne aux baux (65x81cm-26x32in) s. i.d.1975 verso. 3-Mar-4 Tajan, Paris #168/R est:8000-10000
£8741	$15035	€12500	Paysage de Provence (73x92cm-29x36in) s. prov. 3-Dec-3 Oger, Dumont, Paris #3/R est:6000-7500
£9732	$18101	€14500	Espagnole a la mantille blanche (100x81cm-39x32in) s. 3-Mar-4 Tajan, Paris #165/R est:15000-18000
£10634	$18396	€15100	Gardians et arlesiennes (65x54cm-26x21in) s. 14-Dec-3 Eric Pillon, Calais #120/R
£13122	$22701	€19158	Oliviers a Mejean (97x130cm-38x51in) s. i.verso prov.exhib. 12-Dec-3 Galerie du Rhone, Sion #187/R est:25000-35000 (S.FR 29000)
Works on paper			
£235	$416	€350	Vanite (14x20cm-6x8in) s. W/C. 27-Apr-4 Artcurial Briest, Paris #45
£280	$501	€420	Cavalier (30x23cm-12x9in) W/C wash. 16-May-4 Osenat, Fontainebleau #8
£307	$558	€460	Passant dans la ville (32x24cm-13x9in) s. Chinese ink wash dr. 4-Jul-4 Eric Pillon, Calais #193/R
£345	$638	€500	Procession aux Saintes Maries de la Mer (41x32cm-16x13in) s. Indian ink. 13-Feb-4 Charbonneaux, Paris #34
£347	$621	€520	Flamenco (26x19cm-10x7in) W/C wash. 16-May-4 Osenat, Fontainebleau #10
£369	$653	€550	Carabinieri (33x24cm-13x9in) s. gouache. 29-Apr-4 David Kahn, Paris #186/R
£467	$849	€700	Aux Saintes-Maries-de-la-Mer (40x31cm-16x12in) s. Chinese ink dr. 4-Jul-4 Eric Pillon, Calais #194/R
£490	$832	€700	Paysage (13x19cm-5x7in) s. gouache W/C. 27-Nov-3 Millon & Associes, Paris #57
£533	$981	€800	Herode (35x22cm-14x9in) s.i. gouache crayon. 11-Jun-4 Pierre Berge, Paris #112/R
£604	$1069	€900	Procession (39x29cm-15x11in) s. W/C. 29-Apr-4 David Kahn, Paris #185/R
£690	$1262	€1000	L'assomption. Procession (21x17cm-8x7in) W/C two. 1-Feb-4 Teitgen, Nancy #18
£804	$1367	€1150	Chevaux de Camargue (14x22cm-6x9in) s. W/C. 21-Nov-3 Coutau Begarie, Paris #48
£940	$1748	€1400	Chevalier de Cape et d'Epee, Vatican, Rome (40x55cm-16x22in) s.i.d.1934 gouache paper on cardboard. 2-Mar-4 Artcurial Briest, Paris #85 est:1500-2000
£1056	$1827	€1500	Cavaliers (16x16cm-6x6in) s. W/C. 14-Dec-3 Eric Pillon, Calais #281/R
£1074	$1987	€1600	Ronde des peintres (29x24cm-11x9in) s. Chinese ink dr. 14-Mar-4 Eric Pillon, Calais #141/R
£1159	$2109	€1750	Toreador (27x19cm-11x7in) s. W/C. 19-Jun-4 St-Germain-en-Laye Encheres #163/R est:1500
£1200	$2148	€1800	Cannes le soir (16x32cm-6x13in) W/C. 16-May-4 other European Auctioneer #45
£1217	$2228	€1777	Gardiens sur la plage, Camargue (46x62cm-18x24in) s. i.verso crayon W/C prov. 5-Jun-4 Galerie du Rhone, Sion #561/R est:2500-3500 (S.FR 2800)
£1343	$2497	€2000	Le pont de Londres (37x51cm-15x20in) s.i.d.1939 W/C gouache paper on cardboard. 2-Mar-4 Artcurial Briest, Paris #87/R est:2000-2500
£1510	$2794	€2250	Cabane du peintre en Camargue (23x31cm-9x12in) s. W/C. 14-Mar-4 Eric Pillon, Calais #142/R
£1544	$2871	€2300	Nu a la barque (52x41cm-20x16in) s. W/C. 3-Mar-4 Ferri, Paris #362 est:2500-3000
£1656	$3013	€2500	Tentes et bateaux sur les dunes (36x49cm-14x19in) s. W/C. 19-Jun-4 St-Germain-en-Laye Encheres #167/R est:2500
£1831	$3168	€2600	La roulette des bohemiens (40x52cm-16x20in) s. W/C. 10-Dec-3 Ferri, Paris #18/R est:2300-2500
£2349	$4370	€3500	Tasco la nuit, Mexique (48x63cm-19x25in) s.i.d.1963 W/C paper on cardboard. 2-Mar-4 Artcurial Briest, Paris #84 est:3000-4000
£2466	$4192	€3600	Cavaliers sur la plage en Camargue (39x53cm-15x21in) s. W/C. 9-Nov-3 Eric Pillon, Calais #155/R
£2684	$4993	€4000	Scene de cirque (38x31cm-15x12in) s. W/C. 3-Mar-4 Tajan, Paris #169/R est:3000-4000
£3020	$5618	€4500	Chevaux de Camargue au printemps (49x64cm-19x25in) s. i.d.1954 verso W/C. 2-Mar-4 Artcurial Briest, Paris #83 est:3000-4000
£3355	$6174	€5100	Les chevaux en Camargue (50x65cm-20x26in) s. W/C. 25-Jun-4 Daguerre, Paris #171/R est:1000-1500
£5369	$9987	€8000	Rome, reception a la villa Medicis (89x109cm-35x43in) s.i.d.1934 gouache paper on canvas. 2-Mar-4 Artcurial Briest, Paris #86 est:3000-5000

BRAZAM, Juan Manuel (1942-) Spanish

£660	$1089	€950	Untitled (71x50cm-28x20in) s.d.69. 2-Jul-3 Ansorena, Madrid #944/R

BREA, Francesco (16th C) French

£40789	$75053	€62000	Saint Sebastien et Saint Roc (120x69cm-47x27in) s.i.indis.d. panel prov.exhib.lit. 24-Jun-4 Christie's, Paris #58/R est:50000-70000

BREACH, Edward R (19th C) British

£2072	$3750	€3025	Setters with the day's bag (52x77cm-20x30in) s.d.85. 30-Mar-4 Bonhams & Butterfields, San Francisco #64/R est:4500-6000

BREAKSPEARE, W A (1856-1914) British

£779	$1395	€1137	Going to church (22x33cm-9x13in) s. 22-Mar-4 Philippe Schuler, Zurich #4388/R (S.FR 1800)

BREAKSPEARE, William A (1856-1914) British

£920	$1619	€1343	Arcadian Idyll - two water nymphs enchanted by a faun playing his pipe (32x21cm-13x8in) s. 18-May-4 Fellows & Sons, Birmingham #107/R
£1600	$2656	€2336	Pianist (34x21cm-13x8in) s. board. 1-Oct-3 Sotheby's, Olympia #183/R est:1000-1500
£2200	$3652	€3212	Portrait of a girl (16x13cm-6x5in) s. panel. 1-Oct-3 Sotheby's, Olympia #184/R est:800-1200
£4500	$7470	€6570	Gardener's daughter (33x15cm-13x6in) s. i.verso panel prov. 1-Oct-3 Sotheby's, Olympia #181/R est:2000-3000
£7778	$14000	€11356	End of the evening (41x102cm-16x40in) s. 22-Apr-4 Christie's, Rockefeller NY #166/R est:12000-18000
Works on paper			
£6000	$10200	€8760	Lover's meeting (90x48cm-35x19in) s. 27-Nov-3 Sotheby's, London #335/R est:3000-5000

BREANSKI, A F de (1877-1957) British

£893	$1491	€1304	Backwater (30x36cm-12x14in) s. 17-Jun-3 Maynards, Vancouver #305 est:2500-3000 (C.D 2000)
£1301	$2030	€1900	Alpine lake with animals (40x60cm-16x24in) s. 10-Apr-3 Weidler, Nurnberg #306/R est:750

BREANSKI, A de (19th C) British

£1034	$1614	€1499	Scottish loch scene (28x48cm-11x19in) mono.d. 1-Aug-2 Joel, Victoria #239 est:4000-6000 (A.D 3000)
£1400	$2562	€2044	Bridge, Polperro, Cornwall (30x20cm-12x8in) s. board. 28-Jan-4 Ibbett Mosely, Sevenoaks #3
£1500	$2745	€2190	Harbour, Polperro, Cornwall (30x20cm-12x8in) s. board. 28-Jan-4 Ibbett Mosely, Sevenoaks #4

BREANSKI, A de (snr) (1852-1928) British

£1395	$2400	€2037	Cader Idris, North Wales (41x61cm-16x24in) s. 6-Dec-3 Neal Auction Company, New Orleans #349/R est:3000-5000
£7000	$13090	€10220	The hills of Skye (61x91cm-24x36in) s. s.i.verso prov. 22-Jul-4 Tennants, Leyburn #827/R est:7000-9000

BREANSKI, Alfred Fontville de (1877-1957) British

£320	$589	€467	Wooded landscape (31x42cm-12x17in) s. 8-Jun-4 Bonhams, Knightsbridge #230/R
£340	$568	€496	On Loch Etive (41x61cm-16x24in) s. 10-Jul-3 Gorringes, Worthing #671
£400	$640	€584	Highland loch scene with trees in the foreground (51x74cm-20x29in) s. 15-May-3 Mitchells, Cockermouth #1054/R
£460	$837	€672	View of Ben Nevis (19x29cm-7x11in) s. board. 15-Jun-4 Bonhams, Oxford #96
£500	$795	€730	The harbour at St Ives with fishing boats (23x30cm-9x12in) s. 1-May-3 John Nicholson, Haslemere #753
£529	$1000	€772	View of a Scottish loch with cattle watering (54x79cm-21x31in) s. 22-Feb-4 Bonhams & Butterfields, Los Angeles #7033/R est:1500-2000
£800	$1360	€1168	Pony-y-Pant, north Wales (61x91cm-24x36in) 19-Nov-3 Tennants, Leyburn #1085
£806	$1484	€1177	In Tavy Cleave, Dartmoor (36x56cm-14x22in) s. s.i.verso. 14-Jun-4 Waddingtons, Toronto #139/R est:3000-4000 (C.D 2000)
£881	$1400	€1286	Mountain landscape with figures (51x76cm-20x30in) s. 9-Mar-3 William Jenack, New York #391
£900	$1620	€1314	Borders of Llyn Gwynant N Wales (43x36cm-17x14in) s.i.verso. 24-Apr-4 Rogers Jones, Clwyd #168/R
£920	$1674	€1343	Polperro - glimpse of the harbour (60x45cm-24x18in) s. s.i.verso. 21-Jun-4 Bonhams, Bath #401/R
£940	$1711	€1372	Ullswater (24x34cm-9x13in) s. i.verso. 15-Jun-4 Bonhams, Leeds #156/R
£1000	$1670	€1460	Borders of Llyn Gwynan, North Wales (46x38cm-18x15in) s. s.i.verso. 16-Oct-3 Bonhams, Edinburgh #117 est:1000-1500
£1100	$1738	€1595	On the Llugwy, north Wales (51x76cm-20x30in) s. canvas on board. 4-Sep-3 Christie's, Kensington #186/R est:1000-1500
£1100	$2024	€1606	Cattle in a river landscape (15x41cm-6x16in) s. 8-Jun-4 Bonhams, Knightsbridge #272/R est:1200-1800
£1300	$2171	€1898	Serpent's Lake, Gap of Dunloe, Killarney, Ireland (20x51cm-8x20in) s. s.i.verso. 13-Nov-3 Christie's, Kensington #182/R est:800-1200
£1450	$2611	€2175	September evening, landscape with shepherd and sheep (77x100cm-30x39in) s. 25-Apr-4 Goteborg Auktionsverk, Sweden #199/R est:15000 (S.KR 20000)
£1676	$3000	€2447	Summer moonlight, Loch Leven (46x61cm-18x24in) s. s.i.verso. 8-May-4 Susanin's, Chicago #6163/R est:3000-5000
£1890	$3250	€2759	Early morning (41x61cm-16x24in) s. i.verso. 6-Dec-3 Selkirks, St. Louis #107/R est:2000-3000
£1950	$3588	€2925	Moonrise at Innisfallen, Killarney (61x91cm-24x36in) s.i.verso. 23-Jun-4 Byrne's, Chester #699/R est:2000-3000
£2000	$3720	€2920	Loch landscape at dusk (61x91cm-24x36in) s. 4-Mar-4 Christie's, Kensington #56/R est:2000-3000
£2200	$3454	€3190	Cattle watering on a loch (40x61cm-16x24in) s. 27-Aug-3 Sotheby's, London #983/R est:2000-3000

£2300 $4255 €3358 Sunrise, Nantile, Lake, North Wales (49x74cm-19x29in) s.i. verso. 14-Jul-4 Bonhams, Chester #459/R est:2500-3500
£2400 $4008 €3504 Tavy Cleave, Dartmoor (51x76cm-20x30in) s. s.i.verso. 13-Nov-3 Christie's, Kensington #185/R est:2000-3000
£2667 $4853 €4000 Swans in evening (51x76cm-20x30in) s. 30-Jun-4 Neumeister, Munich #513/R est:1500
£2800 $4760 €4088 Bolton Abbey, Yorkshire (41x61cm-16x24in) s. i.verso. 25-Nov-3 Christie's, London #108/R est:2500-3500
£2800 $4760 €4088 Tintern Abbey, on the Wye (41x61cm-16x24in) s.d.12 s.i.verso. 25-Nov-3 Christie's, London #110/R est:2500-3500
£2900 $4988 €4234 In the west Highlands (51x76cm-20x30in) s. 6-Dec-3 Shapes, Edinburgh #501/R est:2500-3500
£3000 $5370 €4380 Twickenham ferry. Twickenham from the river Thames (25x36cm-10x14in) s. pair. 25-May-4 Sworder & Son, Bishops Stortford #417/R est:3000-5000
£3243 $6000 €4735 Snowdon from Pen-y-Gwyrd N Wales (61x91cm-24x36in) 13-Feb-4 Du Mouchelle, Detroit #2018/R est:4000-6000
£4200 $7560 €6132 Near Henley-on-Thames (61x87cm-24x34in) s. i.verso. 21-Jan-4 Sotheby's, Olympia #354/R est:1000-2000
£6200 $10292 €9052 Evening in a highland glen. Early morning on a Perthshire river (51x76cm-20x30in) both s.i. init.verso two. 1-Oct-3 Sotheby's, Olympia #88/R est:5000-7000
£6356 $10805 €9280 Silent Pool (61x91cm-24x36in) s. bears i.verso prov. 24-Nov-3 Sotheby's, Melbourne #346/R est:15000-20000 (A.D 15000)
£6500 $11050 €9490 Loch Oich and Ben Tigh, West Highlands (61x91cm-24x36in) s. s.i.verso prov. 30-Oct-3 Christie's, London #83/R est:5000-8000
Works on paper
£360 $601 €526 Outskirts of Marlow Woods (19x34cm-7x13in) s.d.1883 W/C. 14-Oct-3 Bonhams, Knightsbridge #226/R
£1000 $1770 €1460 Figures and ducks by a watermill. On a stone bridge (27x38cm-11x15in) s. W/C over pencil htd white pair. 27-Apr-4 Bonhams, Knowle #52/R est:800-1200

BREANSKI, Alfred de (snr) (1852-1928) British
£350 $637 €511 Summer garden (33x20cm-13x8in) s. board. 15-Jun-4 David Lay, Penzance #508
£750 $1185 €1088 Quarry wood, Marlow (41x56cm-16x22in) with sig. s.i.verso. 4-Sep-3 Christie's, Kensington #118/R
£820 $1468 €1197 Highland lake scene. bears sig. 16-Mar-4 Lawrences, Bletchingley #1708
£898 $1500 €1311 Untitled (51x76cm-20x30in) 14-Nov-3 Du Mouchelle, Detroit #93/R est:1800-2000
£1176 $1965 €1717 An Aberdeenshire valley (40x61cm-16x24in) s.i.verso prov. 17-Nov-3 Waddingtons, Toronto #116/R est:3000-4000 (C.D 2600)
£1650 $3053 €2409 Fringe of the Common, Chislehurst (39x59cm-15x23in) s.d.1883 s.i. stretcher. 14-Jul-4 Bonhams, Chester #456/R est:2000-3000
£2283 $4200 €3333 Bisham Abbey on Thames (41x56cm-16x22in) s. i.verso. 27-Jun-4 Hindman, Chicago #790/R est:2000-3000
£2642 $4729 €3857 Sunrise near the Dolgelly Hills, South Wales. Evening at Llyn Ogwen, Wales (28x49cm-11x19in) s.d.1870 pair. 10-May-4 Joel, Victoria #278 est:5000-7000 (A.D 6500)
£2826 $5200 €4126 North Wales (64x91cm-25x36in) s. i.verso. 27-Jun-4 Hindman, Chicago #791/R est:3000-5000
£2941 $5000 €4294 Spring evening, Burnham Beeches (61x103cm-24x41in) s. s.i.verso. 29-Oct-3 Christie's, Rockefeller NY #80/R est:12000-18000
£3912 $7315 €5712 Dusk in August (39x54cm-15x21in) s. 24-Feb-4 Louis Morton, Mexico #42/R est:8000-10000 (M.P 80000)
£5200 $8840 €7592 At Bettws-y-Coed (60x90cm-24x35in) s. i.verso. 1-Dec-3 Bonhams, Bath #101/R est:2000-3000
£5500 $8635 €7975 Fishing at the loch, evening (30x35cm-12x14in) s. 27-Aug-3 Sotheby's, London #945a/R est:4000-6000
£6538 $11246 €9545 Henley on Thames with church and bridge (61x92cm-24x36in) s. 7-Dec-3 Uppsala Auktionskammare, Uppsala #100/R est:30000-40000 (S.KR 85000)
£7000 $13020 €10220 Dusk, Henley on Thames (41x56cm-16x22in) s. i.verso. 4-Mar-4 Christie's, Kensington #459/R est:5000-7000
£7000 $12880 €10220 Summer's day, Burnham Beeches (61x101cm-24x40in) s. i.verso. 23-Mar-4 Bonhams, New Bond Street #123/R est:5000-7000
£7200 $12240 €10512 Hills of Skye (60x90cm-24x35in) s. s.i.verso prov. 29-Oct-3 Hampton & Littlewood, Exeter #615/R est:8000-12000
£8000 $12960 €11600 Summer evening, near Dunkeld (36x53cm-14x21in) s. i.verso. 30-Jul-3 Hamptons Fine Art, Godalming #281/R est:4500 6000
£8000 $13600 €11680 Lodore (41x56cm-16x22in) s. s.i.verso. 19-Nov-3 Bonhams, New Bond Street #71/R est:3000-5000
£8000 $14800 €11680 View of Windsor from the Thames (61x102cm-24x40in) s. 10-Feb-4 Bonhams, Knightsbridge #191/R est:10000-15000
£9000 $14130 €13050 Rydal water from Ambleside (61x91cm-24x36in) s. 27-Aug-3 Sotheby's, London #962/R est:5000-7000
£9200 $16928 €13432 Llugwy from Pont-Y-Cyfying Capel curing (51x76cm-20x30in) s. i.verso. 24-Mar-4 Hamptons Fine Art, Godalming #302/R
£11200 $20496 €16352 Perthshire valleys (51x76cm-20x30in) s. 8-Apr-4 Bonhams, Edinburgh #165/R est:8000-12000
£11500 $18515 €16675 Perthshire trout stream (39x59cm-15x23in) s. s.i.verso prov. 21-Aug-3 Bonhams, Edinburgh #1135/R est:10000-15000
£14000 $23800 €20440 Setting Sun, Loch Awe (60x90cm-24x35in) s. i.stretcher. 29-Oct-3 Hampton & Littlewood, Exeter #616/R est:12000-15000
£14000 $25340 €20440 Departing day near Blair Atholl (61x91cm-24x36in) s. s.i.verso. 19-Apr-4 Sotheby's, London #24/R est:10000-15000
£14118 $24000 €20612 Cattle watering in a mountainous landscape (61x91cm-24x36in) s. 29-Oct-3 Christie's, Rockefeller NY #81/R est:15000-20000
£15000 $25500 €21900 Falcon Craig, Derwentshire (61x91cm-24x36in) s. s.i.verso. 25-Nov-3 Christie's, London #134/R est:15000-20000
£16471 $28000 €24048 Highland landscape with cattle (76x127cm-30x50in) s. prov. 22-Nov-3 Jackson's, Cedar Falls #5/R est:35000-45000
£50000 $78500 €72500 Rosy morn, near Aberdeen (76x127cm-30x50in) s. 27-Aug-3 Sotheby's, London #985/R est:50000-80000

BREANSKI, Arthur de (20th C) British
£874 $1486 €1250 Gentte springin sunlight dad (92x71cm-36x28in) s. 18-Nov-3 Vanderkindere, Brussels #57

BREANSKI, G de (c.1856-1898) British
£2000 $3640 €2920 Cader idris, North Wales, mountainous landscape with watering cattle (61x107cm-24x42in) s. 4-Feb-4 Goldings, Lincolnshire #500/R

BREANSKI, Gustave de (c.1856-1898) British
£520 $863 €759 Fishing smack and other vessels off a headland (60x90cm-24x35in) s. 1-Oct-3 Woolley & Wallis, Salisbury #190/R
£591 $964 €863 Seascape with stormy seas (61x91cm-24x36in) s. 29-Sep-3 Lilla Bukowskis, Stockholm #494 (S.KR 7700)
£600 $1110 €876 Boats at low tide (30x46cm-12x18in) s. 14-Jul-4 Sotheby's, Olympia #74/R
£800 $1488 €1168 Returning to harbour (41x61cm-16x24in) s. 4-Mar-4 Christie's, Kensington #558/R
£800 $1480 €1168 Hastings (61x92cm-24x36in) s. 9-Mar-4 Bonhams, Knightsbridge #210/R
£900 $1647 €1314 Fishing smack off a headland (61x92cm-24x36in) s. 7-Apr-4 Woolley & Wallis, Salisbury #304/R
£1150 $2105 €1679 The harbour mouth, Gorleston (61x92cm-24x36in) s.i.verso. 7-Apr-4 Woolley & Wallis, Salisbury #303/R est:1000-1500
£1750 $2975 €2555 Hastings beach (74x125cm-29x49in) s. 1-Dec-3 Bonhams, Bath #111/R est:700-1000
£2000 $3680 €2920 Coming into Dover (61x91cm-24x36in) s. 23-Jun-4 Bonhams, Bury St Edmunds #360/R est:1500-2500
£2000 $3680 €2920 Fishing off Dover (61x92cm-24x36in) s. 23-Jun-4 Bonhams, Bury St Edmunds #363/R est:2000-3000
£2469 $4000 €3580 Harbor scene (61x91cm-24x36in) s. 8-Aug-3 Barridorf, Portland #94/R est:4000-6000
Works on paper
£360 $580 €522 Fishing smacks entering harbour on choppy sea (23x36cm-9x14in) s.d.1881-2 W/C. 23-Feb-3 Desmond Judd, Cranbrook #1952

BREARD, Henri Georges (19/20th C) French
£278 $464 €400 Le notaire (55x46cm-22x18in) s. 23-Oct-3 Credit Municipal, Paris #62
£313 $522 €450 Coffret a bijoux et aux lilas (65x54cm-26x21in) s. 23-Oct-3 Credit Municipal, Paris #90
£382 $638 €550 Nature morte a l'eventail, theiere et fleurs (73x60cm-29x24in) s. 23-Oct-3 Credit Municipal, Paris #89
Works on paper
£1053 $1937 €1600 Paysage (17x22cm-7x9in) s. sepia wash. 27-Jun-4 Feletin, Province #91
£1658 $3051 €2520 Etude d'avocat - les bras croises (20x14cm-8x6in) s. sepia wash. 27-Jun-4 Feletin, Province #92

BREBISSON, Louis Alphonse de (19th C) French
Photographs
£1818 $3037 €2600 Etude d'arbres et lavoir se refletant dans l'eau (21x26cm-8x10in) photograph exec.c.1850 prov. 10-Oct-3 Tajan, Paris #134/R est:3500-4000

BRECHER, Bruinette (20th C) South African
£314 $562 €458 Joy forever, snap dragons and Canterbury bells with fruit (69x89cm-27x35in) s.d.2002 i.stretcher. 31-May-4 Stephan Welz, Johannesburg #179 (SA.R 3800)

BRECHER, Samuel (1897-1982) American
£435 $800 €635 Still life atop a table (61x76cm-24x30in) s. 23-Jun-4 Doyle, New York #5013/R

BRECHET, Andre (1921-1993) French
£229 $383 €332 Composition rouge et noire (66x106cm-26x42in) s. 21-Jun-3 Galerie du Rhone, Sion #432 (S.FR 500)
£258 $446 €377 Composition bleue (40x80cm-16x31in) s. 12-Dec-3 Galerie du Rhone, Sion #604 (S.FR 570)
£302 $540 €441 Untitled (44x60cm-17x24in) s. paper. 12-May-4 Dobiaschofsky, Bern #356/R (S.FR 700)

BRECHT, George (1926-) American
Sculpture
£1972 $3273 €2800 Boite en bois (17x30x5cm-7x12x2in) s.i.d.1973 verso metal dice wood. 11-Jun-3 Finarte Semenzato, Milan #594/R

BRECKENRIDGE, Hugh Henry (1870-1937) American
£3315 $6000 €4840 Abstraction no 65 (23x21cm-9x8in) canvas on board painted c.1917-35 prov.exhib. 31-Mar-4 Sotheby's, New York #148/R est:2000-4000
£5280 $8500 €7709 Summer sailing (25x36cm-10x14in) board double-sided. 20-Aug-3 James Julia, Fairfield #1470/R est:4000-6000

BRECKON, Don (?) British?
£320 $573 €467 Train on a coastal track (29x75cm-11x30in) s.d.73. 17-Mar-4 Anthemion, Cardiff #411/R
£350 $627 €511 A G W R train on a woodland track (29x75cm-11x30in) s.d.74. 17-Mar-4 Anthemion, Cardiff #412/R

BREDA, Adolph Fredric von (1785-1832) Swedish
£935 $1477 €1356 Portrait of Hed - Catharin Charlotta Rehbinder as 4 year old (53x47cm-21x19in) s.d.1807 oval. 2-Sep-3 Rasmussen, Copenhagen #1820/R (D.KR 10000)

BREDA, Carl Fredrik von (1759-1818) Swedish
£3385 $5822 €4942 Portrait of an English gentleman (75x62cm-30x24in) s.d.1793. 2-Dec-3 Bukowskis, Stockholm #314/R est:40000-50000 (S.KR 44000)
£3843 $6880 €5611 Baroness Hedvig Charlotta Gyllenhaal (72x61cm-28x24in) s.d.1814 canvas on panel prov.lit. 25-May-4 Bukowskis, Stockholm #410/R est:30000-40000 (S.KR 52000)
£11923 $20508 €17408 Baron Carl Goran Bonde. s.d.1805 exhib. 2-Dec-3 Bukowskis, Stockholm #310/R est:50000-60000 (S.KR 155000)
Works on paper
£559 $951 €800 Study of a male nude (42x53cm-17x21in) s.d.1805 W/C pencil. 26-Nov-3 James Adam, Dublin #59/R

BREDA, Carl Fredrik von (attrib) (1759-1818) Swedish
£1308 $2249 €1910 Baroness Sara Klinckowstrom (45x41cm-18x16in) prov.lit. 2-Dec-3 Bukowskis, Stockholm #311/R est:12000-15000 (S.KR 17000)

BREDA, Lukas von (1676-1752) Swedish
Works on paper
£405 $714 €600 Portrait of a man in profile (20x16cm-8x6in) i.verso oiled black chk htd white. 19-May-4 Sotheby's, Amsterdam #142/R

BREDA, Lukas von (attrib) (1676-1752) Swedish
£923 $1588 €1348 Portrait of chamberlain Carl Fredrik von Saltza (48x41cm-19x16in) 3-Dec-3 AB Stockholms Auktionsverk #2336/R (S.KR 12000)
£3077 $5292 €4492 Portrait of Johan Buccholtz (79x63cm-31x25in) lit. 3-Dec-3 AB Stockholms Auktionsverk #2489/R est:25000-30000 (S.KR 40000)

BREDAEL, Alexandre van (1663-1720) Flemish
£11268 $19719 €16000 Patineurs sur une riviere gelee sous la terrasse d'un palais classique (65x82cm-26x32in) s. 18-Dec-3 Tajan, Paris #26/R est:15000-20000
£29000 $53070 €42340 Ommegang in Antwerp at the meir (103x192cm-41x76in) s.i.d.1689 prov. 7-Jul-4 Bonhams, New Bond Street #136/R est:30000-50000

BREDAEL, Alexandre van (attrib) (1663-1720) Flemish
£2550 $4565 €3800 Paysage fluvial avec personnages et troupeau traversant la riviere (68x83cm-27x33in) s. 25-May-4 Palais de Beaux Arts, Brussels #546/R est:3840-5120
£5220 $9500 €7621 View of a crowded market with village and harbour in a distance (65x84cm-26x33in) 29-Jun-4 Sotheby's, New York #9/R est:6000-8000

BREDAEL, Jan Frans van (elder) (1686-1750) Flemish
£5634 $9860 €8000 Le depart pour la chasse au faucon (37x42cm-15x17in) panel. 16-Dec-3 Artcurial Briest, Paris #210/R est:7000-9000

BREDAEL, Jan Peter van (elder) (1654-1745) Flemish
£30000 $53700 €45000 Winter landscape with villagers skating on a frozen river (30x45cm-12x18in) s. copper prov. 17-May-4 Christie's, Amsterdam #77/R est:8000-12000
£30000 $54900 €43800 River landscape with peasants merrymaking beside a cottage. Village landscape with peasants outside (16x23cm-6x9in) copper pair prov. 7-Jul-4 Christie's, London #26/R est:20000-30000

BREDAEL, Joseph van (1688-1739) Flemish
£10000 $18000 €14600 Riverside town with peasants crossing a river (23x34cm-9x13in) copper. 23-Apr-4 Christie's, Kensington #115/R est:7000-10000
£10345 $18621 €15000 Landscape with river (12x19cm-5x7in) board prov. 26-Jan-4 Ansorena, Madrid #61c/R est:15000
£20000 $36600 €29200 Village landscape with travellers and horse (19x25cm-7x10in) copper prov. 8-Jul-4 Sotheby's, London #101/R est:12000-18000
Works on paper
£3425 $5822 €5000 Landscape with castle near a village and horsemen on a path (20x31cm-8x12in) bears another sig. pen brown ink col wash. 4-Nov-3 Sotheby's, Amsterdam #40/R est:6000-8000

BREDAEL, Joseph van (attrib) (1688-1739) Flemish
£2183 $3777 €3100 REunion dans un parc au milieu des ruines antiques (81x65cm-32x26in) 10-Dec-3 Beaussant & Lefèvre, Paris #26/R est:3000-3500

BREDAEL, Joseph van (circle) (1688-1739) Flemish
£6000 $10800 €8760 Wooded river landscape with fisherman and peasants on a track (29x42cm-11x17in) panel. 23-Apr-4 Christie's, Kensington #116/R est:4000-6000

BREDAEL, Peeter van (1629-1719) Flemish
£8500 $15810 €12410 Courtyard of an elegant mansion with figures departing for the hunt (65x82cm-26x32in) s. 4-Mar-4 Christie's, London #408/R est:7000-10000

BREDAL, Niels-Anders (1841-1888) Danish
£1423 $2306 €2078 From a piazza below Monte Palatino (28x42cm-11x17in) init. 9-Aug-3 Hindemae, Ullerslev #118/R est:15000 (D.KR 15000)

BREDDO, Gastone (1915-1991) Italian
£367 $675 €550 Basket with fruit (70x50cm-28x20in) s. 12-Jun-4 Meeting Art, Vercelli #578/R

BREDIN, R Sloan (1881-1933) American
Works on paper
£1087 $2000 €1587 Nude figure no.1 (28x18cm-11x7in) s.i. pastel. 11-Jun-4 David Rago, Lambertville #346/R est:2000-4000

BREDOW, Albert (1828-1899) Russian
£1500 $2775 €2190 Figures in a winter landscape (98x142cm-39x56in) s. 14-Jul-4 Christie's, Kensington #948/R est:1500-2000

BREDOW, Rudolf (1909-1973) German
Works on paper
£1049 $1783 €1500 Still life with fruit and two wine bottles II (49x60cm-19x24in) s.d.72 W/C brush. 29-Nov-3 Villa Grisebach, Berlin #729/R est:1770-2360

BREDSDORFF, Axel (1883-1947) Danish
£316 $512 €458 Samson and Delilah (109x145cm-43x57in) s.d.1939-1942. 4-Aug-3 Rasmussen, Vejle #641/R (D.KR 3300)
£719 $1337 €1050 Enjoying a small glass in front of the open fire with good friends (84x128cm-33x50in) s.d.1917. 2-Mar-4 Rasmussen, Copenhagen #1658/R (D.KR 8000)

BREDSDORFF, J U (1845-1928) Danish
£561 $886 €813 Landscape with trees on hills near the sea (54x105cm-21x41in) init.d.9. 2-Sep-3 Rasmussen, Copenhagen #1900/R (D.KR 6000)
£562 $938 €821 Landscape from Silkeborg Islands, herder in foreground (58x79cm-23x31in) mono.d.1870. 25-Oct-3 Rasmussen, Havnen #2165 (D.KR 6000)

BREDSDORFF, Majsa (1887-1964) Danish
£979 $1684 €1400 Girl peeling apples (67x51cm-26x20in) mono. 6-Dec-3 Hans Stahl, Toestorf #82/R

BREDT, Ferdinand Max (1860-1921) German
£935 $1477 €1356 Gute Freunde - young woman and her dog (43x55cm-17x22in) s. panel. 2-Sep-3 Rasmussen, Copenhagen #1720/R (D.KR 10000)
£1258 $2340 €1837 Gute Freunde - interior with woman and dog (43x55cm-17x22in) s. panel. 2-Mar-4 Rasmussen, Copenhagen #1571/R est:10000 (D.KR 14000)

BREE, Jos van (17th C) Dutch?
£3000 $4800 €4350 Preparing dinner (65x74cm-26x29in) s. 18-Sep-3 Christie's, Kensington #137/R est:2500-3500

BREE, Mathieu Ignace van (1773-1839) Flemish
£1467 $2655 €2200 Zittende edeldame Dame d'honneur assise (47x37cm-19x15in) s. 30-Mar-4 Campo & Campo, Antwerp #290/R est:2000-4000
Works on paper
£2857 $5114 €4200 Portrait de Lucien Napoleon Charles, troisieme Prince Murat (27x23cm-11x9in) col chk prov. 18-Mar-4 Christie's, Paris #306/R est:2000-3000

BREE, Mathieu Ignace van (attrib) (1773-1839) Flemish
Works on paper
£323 $518 €450 Suzanne et les vieillards (24x16cm-9x6in) crayon. 16-May-3 Tajan, Paris #200

BREE, Philippe Jacques van (1786-1871) Flemish
£2098 $3566 €3000 Evening market in Flemish town (76x65cm-30x26in) s. 20-Nov-3 Van Ham, Cologne #1500/R est:3800
£5248 $8765 €7400 Maternite (89x107cm-35x42in) mono.d.1811. 17-Jun-3 Vanderkindere, Brussels #225 est:2800-3500
£19311 $32249 €28000 Pres de la fontaine (75x88cm-30x35in) s.i.d.1832 panel. 17-Nov-3 Tajan, Paris #15/R est:30000-40000

BREED, Dirk (1920-) Dutch
£263 $484 €400 Veteranen (80x100cm-31x39in) s. i. 28-Jun-4 Sotheby's, Amsterdam #199/R
£685 $1164 €1000 Village street in the evening (79x99cm-31x39in) s. 5-Nov-3 Vendue Huis, Gravenhage #505/R

BREEDON, William (20th C) American
Works on paper
£599 $1000 €875 Sugarbush (36x74cm-14x29in) s. W/C. 11-Oct-3 Nadeau, Windsor #209/R

BREEN, Adam van (circle) (17th C) Dutch
£25000 $45000 €36500 Winter landscape with elegant figures in carnival costume (82x116cm-32x46in) prov. 21-Apr-4 Christie's, London #45/R est:25000-35000

BREEN, Adam van (style) (17th C) Dutch
£21918 $37260 €32000 Winter landscape with elegant figures skating and playing kolf on a frozen river (55x71cm-22x28in) with sig.d.1619 panel prov. 5-Nov-3 Christie's, Amsterdam #22/R est:15000-20000

BREENBERG, Bartholomaus (1599-1659) Dutch
£15500 $27900 €22630 Landscape with Mercury, Argus and Io (44x67cm-17x26in) panel exhib.lit. 21-Apr-4 Christie's, London #38/R est:10000-15000
£30173 $55518 €44053 Christ and the ruler of Kapernaum (37x51cm-15x20in) bears sig. panel prov.exhib.lit. 26-Mar-4 Koller, Zurich #3017/R est:70000-100000 (S.FR 70000)

BREENBERG, Bartholomaus (attrib) (1599-1659) Dutch
Works on paper
£336 $617 €500 Le Temple de Diane a Tivoli (16x20cm-6x8in) pencil wash. 24-Mar-4 Claude Boisgirard, Paris #8

BREENBERG, Bartholomaus (circle) (1599-1659) Dutch
£6207 $10303 €9000 Vast hilly landscape with ruins, town and hill fortress (54x91cm-21x36in) panel. 1-Oct-3 Dorotheum, Vienna #181/R est:9000-15000

BREER, Robert C (1926-) American
Sculpture
£1117 $2000 €1631 Five floats. s.d.1970 five prov. 16-May-4 Wright, Chicago #460/R est:700-900

BREETVELD, Dolf (1892-1975) Dutch

£1053	$1937	€1600	Untitled (120x100cm-47x39in) s. 22-Jun-4 Christie's, Amsterdam #352/R est:1500-2000
£1389	$2194	€2000	Composition (102x130cm-40x51in) s. 2-Sep-3 Christie's, Amsterdam #466 est:1400-1800
£1736	$2743	€2500	Composition (100x100cm-39x39in) s. 2-Sep-3 Christie's, Amsterdam #469/R est:1200-1600
£1818	$3091	€2600	B 57 (100x130cm-39x51in) s. 24-Nov-3 Glerum, Amsterdam #279/R est:1500-2000
£2083	$3292	€3000	Surrealistic landscape with masks (85x106cm-33x42in) s. 2-Sep-3 Christie's, Amsterdam #465/R est:3000-5000
Sculpture			
£1181	$1865	€1700	Composition (71cm-28in) s. hard wood. 2-Sep-3 Christie's, Amsterdam #468 est:700-900
£1528	$2414	€2200	Figure (112cm-44in) s. hard wood on wood base. 2-Sep-3 Christie's, Amsterdam #471/R est:1000-1500
Works on paper			
£280	$476	€400	Composition in grey and white (51x66cm-20x26in) init. gouache. 24-Nov-3 Glerum, Amsterdam #218/R
£280	$476	€400	Composition (50x65cm-20x26in) init. gouache. 24-Nov-3 Glerum, Amsterdam #305/R
£417	$658	€600	Composition (47x56cm-19x22in) init. pen ink. 2-Sep-3 Christie's, Amsterdam #270
£556	$878	€800	Composition (50x64cm-20x25in) s. gouache W/C. 2-Sep-3 Christie's, Amsterdam #467

BREGA, Doug (1948-) American

Works on paper			
£6145	$11000	€8972	Quiet morning (20x37cm-8x15in) s. W/C. 6-May-4 Shannon's, Milford #128/R est:5000-7000

BREGENZER, Gustav (1850-1919) German

£3521	$5634	€5000	Portrait of Prince Leopold of Hohenzollern-Sigmaringen (80x65cm-31x26in) i.d.1882 oval after L. Schafer prov. 22-Sep-3 Sotheby's, Amsterdam #104/R est:1500-2500

BREHM, Worth (1883-1928) American

Works on paper			
£400	$716	€584	Sam's bean (51x39cm-20x15in) s. chl sold with another by George Brehm. 25-May-4 Bonhams, Knightsbridge #180/R

BREIDVIK, Arne (1914-) Norwegian

£285	$524	€416	Composition (55x82cm-22x32in) s. 10-Jun-4 Grev Wedels Plass, Oslo #162/R (N.KR 3500)

BREINLINGER, Hans (1888-1963) Swiss

£317	$538	€463	Portrait of young woman with veil (70x50cm-28x20in) mono. tempera. 18-Nov-3 Hans Widmer, St Gallen #1024 (S.FR 700)
£317	$538	€463	Roman soldier wearing helmt (69x50cm-27x20in) s.mono.d.1933 tempera paper on board. 18-Nov-3 Hans Widmer, St Gallen #1026 (S.FR 700)
£407	$692	€594	Portrait of young woman, seated (66x60cm-26x24in) s.d.1927 verso board. 18-Nov-3 Hans Widmer, St Gallen #1025 (S.FR 900)
£717	$1198	€1047	Peasant women (68x50cm-27x20in) mono. d.1930 verso tempera. 24-Oct-3 Hans Widmer, St Gallen #96/R est:1400-2800 (S.FR 1600)
£837	$1423	€1222	Pastoral scene (91x52cm-36x20in) s.d.1949 panel. 5-Nov-3 Dobiaschofsky, Bern #390/R (S.FR 1900)
£987	$1816	€1500	Resting shepherds (54x70cm-21x28in) s.d.1922. 26-Jun-4 Karrenbauer, Konstanz #170 est:900
£2797	$4755	€4000	Farmstead (76x93cm-30x37in) s.d.26. 29-Nov-3 Villa Grisebach, Berlin #202/R est:6000-8000
Works on paper			
£369	$679	€550	Rider in need (42x55cm-17x22in) mono.d.60 mixed media lit. 26-Mar-4 Karrenbauer, Konstanz #1705
£385	$662	€550	Standing nude (29x21cm-11x8in) s.d.1951 mixed media board. 5-Dec-3 Michael Zeller, Lindau #838/R
£724	$1332	€1100	Mother and child (68x54cm-27x21in) s. mixed media. 26-Jun-4 Karrenbauer, Konstanz #1705

BREITBACH, Carl (1833-1904) German

£400	$728	€600	Young mother with her baby (33x27cm-13x11in) s. canvas on board. 1-Jul-4 Van Ham, Cologne #1236
£1216	$1897	€1800	Children receiving food at church school (94x77cm-37x30in) s.i. 28-Mar-3 Altus, Berlin #535/R est:2400

BREITENBACH, Josef (1896-1984) ?

Photographs			
£3000	$5520	€4500	Dr Riegler and J Greno (25x20cm-10x8in) mono.i.d. verso silver gelatin lit.exhib. 10-Jun-4 Villa Grisebach, Berlin #1042/R est:3500-4000

BREITENSTEIN, Carl August (1864-1921) Dutch

£382	$623	€550	Sailing vessels in the harbour (70x56cm-28x22in) s. 29-Sep-3 Sotheby's, Amsterdam #109
£789	$1453	€1200	Beach with a wooden boat (80x100cm-31x39in) s. s.i. on stretcher prov.exhib. 22-Jun-4 Christie's, Amsterdam #89/R

BREITER, Herbert (1927-) German

£851	$1421	€1200	River landscape with building site (70x96cm-28x38in) mono.d.64. 16-Oct-3 Dorotheum, Salzburg #708/R
Works on paper			
£355	$592	€500	Southern hilly landscape (12x19cm-5x7in) s.d.77 mixed media. 16-Oct-3 Dorotheum, Salzburg #804/R

BREITNER, Georg Hendrik (1857-1923) Dutch

£2222	$3711	€3200	Building site (38x48cm-15x19in) board. 21-Oct-3 Sotheby's, Amsterdam #124/R est:3000-5000
£2639	$4407	€3800	Grondwerkers (33x50cm-13x20in) s. panel prov. 21-Oct-3 Sotheby's, Amsterdam #141/R est:4000-6000
£9929	$16582	€14000	Artilleries on manoeuvre (15x38cm-6x15in) s. panel. 20-Oct-3 Glerum, Amsterdam #103/R est:14000-16000
£17021	$28426	€24000	Artilleries on manoeuvre (15x38cm-6x15in) s. panel prov.exhib. 20-Oct-3 Glerum, Amsterdam #102/R est:14000-16000
£361111	$613889	€520000	Girl in a red kimono (61x49cm-24x19in) s. prov.exhib.lit. 28-Oct-3 Christie's, Amsterdam #178/R est:400000-600000
Works on paper			
£1149	$2022	€1700	Rokin in Amsterdam. Buildings behind trees in winter, Buitenbuurtje (13x23cm-5x9in) one s.i. one s. i.verso chl pair exhib.lit. 19-May-4 Sotheby's, Amsterdam #352/R est:1000-1500
£1667	$3000	€2500	Reclining nude. Seated nude (23x46cm-9x18in) init. black chk double-sided exhib. 21-Apr-4 Christie's, Amsterdam #131/R est:3000-5000
£1944	$3247	€2800	Amsterdamsche dienstmeid (19x14cm-7x6in) init. black chk exhib. 21-Oct-3 Sotheby's, Amsterdam #128/R est:1000-2000
£8333	$14167	€12000	Reclining girl in a kimono. Seated nude and three waspitten (42x55cm-17x22in) init. blk chk double-sided exhib.lit. 28-Oct-3 Christie's, Amsterdam #178a/R est:12000-16000
£9333	$16800	€14000	Waspitten on the Rokin, Amsterdam (42x63cm-17x25in) s. W/C pencil htd white. 21-Apr-4 Christie's, Amsterdam #130/R est:7000-9000
£10417	$17708	€15000	Waspitten on the Rokin, Amsterdam (42x63cm-17x25in) s. W/C pencil htd. white lit. 28-Oct-3 Christie's, Amsterdam #184/R est:15000-20000
£12000	$21600	€18000	Still life with roses (29x41cm-11x16in) W/C black chk htd white prov.exhib. 20-Apr-4 Sotheby's, Amsterdam #103/R est:7000-9000

BREITNER, Georg Hendrik (attrib) (1857-1923) Dutch

£1955	$3500	€2933	Working horse pulling cart (25x33cm-10x13in) s. panel. 16-May-4 Abell, Los Angeles #471/R

BREITZ, Candice (1972-) American

Photographs			
£1413	$2600	€2120	Rainbow series no 7 (152x102cm-60x40in) s.d.1996 num.3 verso c-print Plexiglas prov. 10-Jun-4 Phillips, New York #640/R est:2000-3000
£1413	$2600	€2120	Rainbow series no 1 (152x102cm-60x40in) s.d.1996 num.3 verso c-print Plexiglas prov. 10-Jun-4 Phillips, New York #641/R est:2000-3000

BREKELENKAM, Quiryn Gerritsz van (1620-1668) Dutch

£3600	$6480	€5256	Family scene by the hearthside (55x79cm-22x31in) panel after Leiden prov.lit. 20-Apr-4 Sotheby's, Olympia #263/R est:2000-3000
£4200	$6846	€6132	Angler smoking a pipe in an interior, his catch on a table before him (23x28cm-9x11in) panel. 26-Sep-3 Christie's, Kensington #34/R est:1500-2000
£4525	$7692	€6607	Kitchen maid filletting fish at window (32x29cm-13x11in) mono. panel. 19-Nov-3 Fischer, Luzern #1042/R est:12000-18000 (S.FR 10000)
£5405	$9514	€8000	Maid scaling fish seen through a window (32x29cm-13x11in) mono. panel prov.lit. 18-May-4 Sotheby's, Amsterdam #87/R est:8000-12000
£7000	$12110	€10220	Hermit writing (67x54cm-26x21in) s. indis.d.165. panel prov.lit. 11-Dec-3 Sotheby's, London #137/R est:8000-12000
£16779	$30872	€25000	Kitchen interior with milkman (41x55cm-16x22in) panel prov.lit. 26-Mar-4 Bolland & Marotz, Bremen #437/R est:27000
£21000	$37800	€30660	Woman seated at an inn table holding a roemer (31x24cm-12x9in) panel prov.exhib.lit. 22-Apr-4 Sotheby's, London #34/R est:1000-15000

BREKELENKAM, Quiryn Gerritsz van (attrib) (1620-1668) Dutch

£1399	$2406	€2000	Portrait of a Dutch Rabbi (32x22cm-13x9in) panel. 7-Dec-3 Sotheby's, Amsterdam #555
£1915	$3198	€2700	Smokers in an inn (28x34cm-11x13in) indis.sig. panel. 15-Oct-3 Neret-Minet, Paris #33a est:2000-3000
£6000	$10800	€8760	An alchemist (30x24cm-12x9in) init.i. panel prov.lit. 21-Apr-4 Christie's, London #36/R est:6000-10000
£7263	$13000	€10604	Interior scene with young woman making lace (39x34cm-15x13in) panel. 27-May-4 Sotheby's, New York #7a/R est:10000-15000

BREKER, Arno (1900-1991) German

Sculpture			
£950	$1700	€1387	Stand nude (56cm-22in) bronze. 14-May-4 Du Mouchelle, Detroit #2088/R est:700-1000
£1007	$1782	€1500	Salvador Dali (29cm-11in) s.d. i. verso gold pat.bronze Cast.Venturi Arte. 30-Apr-4 Dr Fritz Nagel, Stuttgart #736/R est:800
£1056	$1690	€1500	Girl in love (28cm-11in) s.i. brown pat.bronze Cast.venturi arte lit. 19-Sep-3 Karlheinz Kaupp, Staufen #1843 est:300
£1127	$1803	€1600	Female figure (37cm-15in) brown pat.bronze marble socle lit. 19-Sep-3 Karlheinz Kaupp, Staufen #1832/R est:300
£2238	$3804	€3200	Romanichel (29cm-11in) s. bronze marble socle Cast.Alexis Rudier Paris lit. 26-Nov-3 Lempertz, Koln #607/R est:3500
£2657	$4571	€3800	Jurgen Hingsen (52x39x27cm-20x15x11in) i.d.83 black green pat bronze st.f.HSD. 4-Dec-3 Van Ham, Cologne #62/R est:3000
£2685	$4752	€4000	Dialogue/conversation (49x73cm-19x29in) s.d. marble relief. 30-Apr-4 Dr Fritz Nagel, Stuttgart #737/R est:4000
Works on paper			
£274	$466	€400	Kneeling female nude (27x35cm-11x14in) s.d.54 pencil. 5-Nov-3 Hugo Ruef, Munich #1237/R
£310	$518	€450	Nude study (32x48cm-13x19in) s. red black wash ink. 13-Nov-3 Neumeister, Munich #268/R

BREKER, Hans (1906-1993) German

Sculpture			
£2200	$3938	€3300	Standing nude (77x30x27cm-30x12x11in) i. brown pat.bronze Cast.Schmake D'd. 15-May-4 Van Ham, Cologne #491/R est:3600

BRELING, Heinrich (1849-1914) German

£258 $451 €377 Prisoners and prison officers in landscape (19x28cm-7x11in) s. mahogany panel. 16-Dec-3 Grev Wedels Plass, Oslo #139/R (N.KR 3000)
£699 $1203 €1000 Lancer riding in winter landscape (27x21cm-11x8in) s. panel prov. 5-Dec-3 Ketterer, Munich #2/R

BREM, Rolf (1926-) Swiss

Sculpture
£1176 $2000 €1717 Bent over figure (20x9x15cm-8x4x6in) s. bronze. 25-Nov-3 Germann, Zurich #66/R est:1000-1500 (S.FR 2600)
£1267 $2154 €1850 Girl with arms raised (40x24x10cm-16x9x4in) s. bronze Cast.Amici, Mendrisio. 25-Nov-3 Germann, Zurich #65/R est:2000-3000 (S.FR 2800)
£1364 $2264 €1978 Lovers (64x10x30cm-25x4x12in) s. bronze relief. 13-Jun-3 Zofingen, Switzerland #2228/R est:3500 (S.FR 3000)
£1454 $2471 €2123 Girl (60cm-24in) s.i. brown pat.bronze. 7-Nov-3 Dobiaschofsky, Bern #132/R est:3000 (S.FR 3300)
£1565 $2864 €2285 The shepherd (20cm-8in) s. num.3/5 bronze. 4-Jun-4 Zofingen, Switzerland #2228/R est:1200 (S.FR 3600)
£1900 $3231 €2774 Standing woman wearing cape (44cm-17in) i. num.20/50 dark pat.bronze. 19-Nov-3 Fischer, Luzern #1468/R est:2800-3800 (S.FR 4200)
£2096 $3689 €3060 Meeting (28x25x480cm-11x10x189in) s.i. pat.bronze Cast.Cera Persa Franco Amici prov. 22-May-4 Galerie Gloggner, Luzern #15/R est:3800-4500 (S.FR 4800)
£3846 $6538 €5615 Standing girl (102x30x21cm-40x12x8in) s. bronze Cast.Amici, Mendrisio. 25-Nov-3 Germann, Zurich #67/R est:4000-6000 (S.FR 8500)
£7240 $12308 €10570 Rosemary (124x49x31cm-49x19x12in) s. bronze Cast.Amici, Mendrisio. 25-Nov-3 Germann, Zurich #64/R est:7000-10000 (S.FR 16000)

BREMAN, Co (1865-1938) Dutch

£3819 $6378 €5500 Haystack in the snow (40x56cm-16x22in) init.d.09 prov. 21-Oct-3 Sotheby's, Amsterdam #140/R est:6000-8000
£11594 $19014 €16000 City meadow (41x70cm-16x28in) s.d.1927 s.i. on stretcher. 27-May-3 Sotheby's, Amsterdam #308/R est:7000-10000
£20000 $36800 €30000 Zomermorgen - summer's day (67x150cm-26x59in) s.d.1922 s.i. stretcher prov.exhib. 9-Jun-4 Christie's, Amsterdam #219/R est:30000-50000

BREME, Ferdinando di (1807-1869) Italian

£15217 $24957 €21000 Birds and flowers (40x49cm-16x19in) s.d.1836 tempera on silk set of 4. 27-May-3 Il Ponte, Milan #1040/R est:5000-6000

BREMER, Anne Millay (1868-1923) American

£5975 $9500 €8724 Untitled - landscape with tress and rocks (76x64cm-30x25in) s. 23-Mar-3 Auctions by the Bay, Alameda #873/R

BREMER, Asger (1891-1963) Danish

£667 $1200 €1000 Boys bathing (60x65cm-24x26in) s.d. 24-Apr-4 Dr Lehr, Berlin #67/R

BREMER, Uwe (1940-) German

£629 $1070 €900 Composition (32x42cm-13x17in) s.d.1969. 29-Nov-3 Bassenge, Berlin #6648/R
Works on paper
£423 $701 €600 Untitled (61x91cm-24x36in) s.d.1972 oil gold panel. 13-Jun-3 Hauswedell & Nolte, Hamburg #573/R

BREN, Jeffrey (1944-) Australian

Works on paper
£410 $664 €599 Fable IV (77x58cm-30x23in) s.d.1996 W/C. 30-Jul-3 Goodman, Sydney #66/R (A.D 1000)
£410 $664 €599 Fable XI (77x58cm-30x23in) s.d.1996 W/C. 30-Jul-3 Goodman, Sydney #67/R (A.D 1000)

BRENAN, James Butler (1825-1889) Irish

£915 $1465 €1300 Portrait of Charles Eyre Coote (36x30cm-14x12in) s.d.1854. 16-Sep-3 Whyte's, Dublin #177/R
£1408 $2254 €2000 Portrait of a clergyman. Portrait of a lady (36x30cm-14x12in) s.d.1871 one indis.i.verso pair. 16-Sep-3 Whyte's, Dublin #176/R est:1800-2200
£1600 $2656 €2336 Portrait of a boy standing wearing tartan (51x40cm-20x16in) s.d.1854. 30-Sep-3 Sotheby's, London #355/R est:800-1200

BRENDA, Pietro (19/20th C) Italian

£352 $599 €514 Fishermen in stormy sea (15x24cm-6x9in) s. canvas on board. 5-Nov-3 Dobiaschofsky, Bern #391/R (S.FR 800)

BRENDEKILDE, Hans Andersen (1857-1942) Danish

£358 $645 €523 The Protestant graveyard in Rome (15x22cm-6x9in) panel. 24-Apr-4 Rasmussen, Havnen #2311/R (D.KR 4000)
£362 $648 €529 Profile portrait of an Egyptian (41x31cm-16x12in) panel prov. 10-May-4 Rasmussen, Vejle #403/R (D.KR 4000)
£420 $722 €600 Conversation in the village street (94x98cm-37x39in) s.d.1938. 5-Dec-3 Bolland & Marotz, Bremen #514
£662 $1145 €967 Byrum church at Laeso (28x35cm-11x14in) init. 9-Dec-3 Rasmussen, Copenhagen #1677/R (D.KR 7000)
£1078 $2005 €1574 Snails in the artist's garden 1930 (46x37cm-18x15in) init. 2-Mar-4 Rasmussen, Copenhagen #1607/R est:15000 (D.KR 12000)
£1137 $1820 €1660 Landscape with white farm (35x47cm-14x19in) s. 22-Sep-3 Rasmussen, Vejle #379/R est:15000-18000 (D.KR 12000)
£1215 $1920 €1762 Autumn in the woods (41x34cm-16x13in) init. 2-Sep-3 Rasmussen, Copenhagen #1752/R est:8000 (D.KR 13000)
£1323 $2369 €1932 Adam and Eve banished from Paradise (166x107cm-65x42in) init. verso. 12-Jan-4 Rasmussen, Vejle #183/R est:8000-12000 (D.KR 14000)
£1438 $2674 €2099 Stocks in a copper pot (74x55cm-29x22in) s.d.1916. 2-Mar-4 Rasmussen, Copenhagen #1520/R est:8000-10000 (D.KR 16000)
£1533 $2836 €2238 Hunter and dog on a clear winter's day (31x38cm-12x15in) init. 15-Mar-4 Rasmussen, Vejle #14/R est:10000 (D.KR 17000)
£1589 $2510 €2304 River through harvest landscape in summer (27x37cm-11x15in) init. 2-Sep-3 Rasmussen, Copenhagen #1610/R est:15000 (D.KR 17000)
£1617 $3008 €2361 From Kedronvalley with Absalom's grave outside Jerusalem (82x72cm-32x28in) s.i.d.17.4.90. 2-Mar-4 Rasmussen, Copenhagen #1307/R est:15000 (D.KR 18000)
£1687 $2750 €2463 Spring landscape with woman picking flowers from rowing boat, Odense river (32cm-13in circular) mono. oil on ceramic tray. 28-Sep-3 Hindemae, Ullerslev #193/R est:20000-25000 (D.KR 18000)
£1781 $3063 €2600 Winter landscape with sunshine and man shovelling snow (29x38cm-11x15in) s. indist.i.d.1901 verso. 3-Dec-3 Museumsbygningen, Copenhagen #206/R est:20000-25000 (D.KR 19000)
£1970 $3604 €2876 Woman by farmhouse with red hollyhocks (32x44cm-13x17in) s. prov. 9-Jun-4 Rasmussen, Copenhagen #1668/R est:30000 (D.KR 22000)
£2174 $3761 €3174 Summer's day in the village (40x50cm-16x20in) s. 9-Dec-3 Rasmussen, Copenhagen #1408/R est:20000-30000 (D.KR 23000)
£2370 $3791 €3460 Winter landscape with house by road (79x61cm-31x24in) s. 22-Sep-3 Rasmussen, Vejle #378/R est:20000 (D.KR 25000)
£2523 $3987 €3658 Early morning across the marshes (39x30cm-15x12in) init. painted c.1890 exhib. 2-Sep-3 Rasmussen, Copenhagen #1678/R est:10000-15000 (D.KR 27000)
£2632 $4263 €3816 Geese by water pump in garden (51x62cm-20x24in) s. 4-Aug-3 Rasmussen, Vejle #114/R est:30000-40000 (D.KR 27500)
£2695 $5013 €3935 Small peasant girl with red coat outside farmhouse (43x30cm-17x12in) init. 2-Mar-4 Rasmussen, Copenhagen #1231/R est:30000-50000 (D.KR 30000)
£2715 $4860 €3964 Towards evening - what are the two old people talking about (51x63cm-20x25in) s. 10-May-4 Rasmussen, Vejle #95/R est:35000-40000 (D.KR 30000)
£3136 $5645 €4579 Village scene with young woman (33x43cm-13x17in) s,. 24-Apr-4 Rasmussen, Havnen #2222/R est:15000-20000 (D.KR 35000)
£3145 $5849 €4592 White farmhouse in sunny winter landscape (41x106cm-16x42in) s. 2-Mar-4 Rasmussen, Copenhagen #1257/R est:30000 (D.KR 35000)
£3402 $6226 €4967 Summer's day in the village street with sunflowers and hollyhocks (42x51cm-17x20in) s. prov. 9-Jun-4 Rasmussen, Copenhagen #1659/R est:35000 (D.KR 38000)
£3571 $6500 €5214 Summer day in the garden with two women (48x62cm-19x24in) s.d.92. 7-Feb-4 Rasmussen, Havnen #2172/R est:30000 (D.KR 39000)
£4297 $7864 €6274 Small girls feeding chickens and fetching water outside farmhouse (25x32cm-10x13in) s. prov. 9-Jun-4 Rasmussen, Copenhagen #1685/R est:50000-60000 (D.KR 48000)
£5385 $9262 €7862 Girls picking flowers (49x63cm-19x25in) s. 3-Dec-3 AB Stockholms Auktionsverk #2589/R est:100000-125000 (S.KR 70000)
£8000 $14560 €11680 A walk in the snow (47x62cm-19x24in) s. prov. 15-Jun-4 Sotheby's, London #343/R est:7000-9000
£9239 $16537 €13489 Would you like a little coffee? (48x68cm-19x27in) s.d.1908. 26-May-4 AB Stockholms Auktionsverk #2371/R est:125000-150000 (S.KR 125000)
£9452 $16352 €13800 Grandfather coming on a visit (64x95cm-25x37in) s. exhib. 9-Dec-3 Rasmussen, Copenhagen #1442/R est:125000 (D.KR 100000)
£13477 $25067 €19676 Young girls picking flowers by Brendekilde church in summer (48x63cm-19x25in) s. 2-Mar-4 Rasmussen, Copenhagen #1270/R est:150000 (D.KR 150000)
£13575 $24299 €19820 The artist's second daughter Maren Meta seated in woods near Odense (67x79cm-26x31in) init.d.01 prov. 10-May-4 Rasmussen, Vejle #1/R est:150000-200000 (D.KR 150000)
£18936 $35032 €27647 Two girls picking flowers in spring wood (71x92cm-28x36in) s.d.03. 15-Mar-4 Rasmussen, Vejle #15/R est:150000-200000 (D.KR 210000)
£21641 $40036 €31596 Cutting of Christmas trees - two men and two children in forest (96x121cm-38x48in) s.d.85. 15-Mar-4 Rasmussen, Vejle #1/R est:200000-250000 (D.KR 240000)
Works on paper
£2381 $4333 €3476 Christmas Eve outside Frue Church (54x45cm-21x18in) mono. pastel. 7-Feb-4 Rasmussen, Havnen #2040/R est:4000-6000 (D.KR 26000)

BRENDEKILDE, Hans Andersen (attrib) (1857-1942) Danish

£326 $583 €476 Portrait of young woman as a saint (34x26cm-13x10in) i.verso panel prov. 10-May-4 Rasmussen, Vejle #404/R (D.KR 3600)

BRENDEKILDE, Jorgen (1920-1993) Danish

£373 $605 €541 View from a village (15x23cm-6x9in) s. 4-Aug-3 Rasmussen, Vejle #333/R (D.KR 3900)

BRENDEL, Albert Heinrich (1827-1895) German

£476 $852 €700 Cows, horses and sheep in field (64x95cm-25x37in) s. 17-Mar-4 Neumeister, Munich #413/R
£1189 $2021 €1700 Horses drinking at the fountain (36x46cm-14x18in) s. 28-Nov-3 Wendl, Rudolstadt #3939/R est:550

BRENDEL, Carl Alexander (1877-1945) German

£532 $840 €750 Five ducks at edge of pond (41x51cm-16x20in) s. 22-Jul-3 Sigalas, Stuttgart #352/R

BRENDER A BRANDIS, Geraldo Abraham (1878-1971) Dutch

Works on paper
£496 $829 €700 Before the hunt (46x64cm-18x25in) s. chl pastel. 20-Oct-3 Glerum, Amsterdam #238/R

BRENDSTRUP, Thorald (1812-1883) Danish

£555 $899 €805 Canal view from Frederiksvaerk (50x67cm-20x26in) init.d.74. 4-Aug-3 Rasmussen, Vejle #265/R (D.KR 5800)
£564 $960 €823 Coastal landscape with houses (16x28cm-6x11in) s.verso. 29-Nov-3 Rasmussen, Havnen #2181 (D.KR 6000)
£900 $1441 €1314 Italian landscape (27x44cm-11x17in) mono. i.verso. 22-Sep-3 Rasmussen, Vejle #166/R (D.KR 9500)
£1254 $2258 €1831 From an Italian loggia with small girl (18x21cm-7x8in) init.d.1850 mahogany panel. 24-Apr-4 Rasmussen, Havnen #2139/R est:6000 (D.KR 14000)
£2238 $4096 €3267 View of Maribo Lake (103x132cm-41x52in) init.d.46 exhib. 9-Jun-4 Rasmussen, Copenhagen #1748/R est:25000 (D.KR 25000)
£7183 $12427 €10487 Italian landscape with tall trees (29x43cm-11x17in) mono. 9-Dec-3 Rasmussen, Copenhagen #1355/R est:20000 (D.KR 76000)

BRENET (?) French
Sculpture
£40789 $75053 €62000 Colonne Vendome (179cm-70in) s.st.f.Douane d.1870 pat bronze lit. 23-Jun-4 Sotheby's, Paris #126/R est:45000-70000

BRENET, Albert (1903-) French
£362 $615 €529 Deer by wood (50x73cm-20x29in) s. 19-Nov-3 Fischer, Luzern #2026/R (S.FR 800)
Works on paper
£1200 $2220 €1752 Scene from the Battle of Trafalgar (64x147cm-25x58in) s. bodycol. 9-Mar-4 Bonhams, Knightsbridge #87/R est:400-600
£1408 $2437 €2000 Aigle (103x72cm-41x28in) s.d.1930 W/C. 14-Dec-3 Eric Pillon, Calais #36/R
£2106 $3874 €3200 Groom devant le Paquebot France a quai (100x66cm-39x26in) s. gouache prov. 25-Jun-4 Tajan, Paris #8/R est:1500-1800
£2817 $4930 €4000 Defile devant l'Arc du Carrousel (70x145cm-28x57in) s. gouache. 21-Dec-3 Thierry & Lannon, Brest #373 est:4000-5000
£2993 $5358 €4400 Homme a la barre et trois mats (72x109cm-28x43in) s. gouache. 21-Mar-4 Claude Boisgirard, Paris #122/R est:4500-5000

BRENNA, Vincenzo (1745-1820) Italian
Works on paper
£8000 $14640 €11680 Design for a ceiling with Jupiter in the centre (48x64cm-19x25in) s. black chk pen ink W/C bodycol htd white prov. 6-Jul-4 Christie's, London #91/R est:2000-3000

BRENNAN, Angela (1960-) Australian
£1157 $2048 €1689 My couch is green and my beams are made of Cedar (61x59cm-24x23in) s.i.d.2000 linen prov.exhib. 3-May-4 Christie's, Melbourne #320/R est:2500-3500 (A.D 2800)
£1721 $2719 €2513 Untitled (122x121cm-48x48in) s.d.1994 verso prov. 2-Sep-3 Deutscher-Menzies, Melbourne #187/R est:5000-8000 (A.D 4200)
£1967 $3108 €2872 My couch is green and my beams are made of cedar (152x122cm-60x48in) prov. 2-Sep-3 Deutscher-Menzies, Melbourne #158/R est:6000-9000 (A.D 4800)
£2231 $3950 €3257 Pro Tanto, Pro Tempo (107x107cm-42x42in) s.d.2000 linen prov.exhib. 3-May-4 Christie's, Melbourne #214/R est:4500-6000 (A.D 5400)
£2893 $5351 €4224 And it seems like (154x115cm-61x45in) s.verso. 15-Mar-4 Sotheby's, Melbourne #2/R est:7000-9000 (A.D 7000)
£4472 $7020 €6484 Untitled (183x152cm-72x60in) s.d.2000 linen prov. 26-Aug-3 Christie's, Sydney #25/R est:12000-15000 (A.D 11000)

BRENNAN, Cecily (1955-) Irish?
Works on paper
£1745 $3089 €2600 Figure (76x140cm-30x55in) chl pastel prov. 27-Apr-4 Whyte's, Dublin #153/R est:3000-4000

BRENNAN, Gerry (1941-) American
£249 $450 €364 Provincetown pier, sunrise (41x51cm-16x20in) s. board. 3-Apr-4 Outer Cape Auctions, Provincetown #47/R

BRENNAN, Ronald (?) British
£300 $537 €438 Over we go. s. board. 7-May-4 Chrystals Auctions, Isle of Man #256

BRENNEIS, Jo (1910-1994) German
£3846 $6615 €5500 Untitled (66x87cm-26x34in) s. cardboard. 4-Dec-3 Van Ham, Cologne #64/R est:3500
Works on paper
£2933 $5309 €4400 Composition 6/52 (43x61cm-17x24in) s.d.52 W/C bodycol. 2-Apr-4 Winterberg, Heidelberg #764/R est:5400

BRENNEISEN, Heinrich (1895-1942) German
£267 $483 €400 Extensive summer landscape (52x50cm-20x20in) s.d.1919 i. verso. 1-Apr-4 Frank Peege, Freiburg #1215/R

BRENNIR, Carl (1850-1920) British
£920 $1674 €1343 Road to Avington, Hampshire, children and a dog with sheep grazing (49x74cm-19x29in) s.d.1907. 15-Jun-4 Bonhams, Oxford #68/R
£1125 $1800 €1643 Landscape (76x64cm-30x25in) 19-Sep-3 Du Mouchelle, Detroit #2004/R est:2000-3000
£1300 $2379 €1898 On the Lledr (35x53cm-14x21in) s.d.86 i.verso pair. 7-Apr-4 Bonhams, Bury St Edmunds #458/R est:1500-2000
£4000 $6680 €5840 Knoles-Hill-on-Trent (60x101cm-24x40in) s.d.1888 s.i.d.verso. 12-Nov-3 Sotheby's, Olympia #33/R est:1500-2500

BRENTANO, A C (?) ?
£1420 $2300 €2073 Gypsy beggar (104x69cm-41x27in) s. 7-Aug-3 Eldred, East Dennis #239/R est:2500-3500

BRENTEL, Friedrich (1580-1651) German
Works on paper
£3000 $5400 €4380 Horatius Cocles defending Rome fromthe Etruscans (12x8cm-5x3in) gouache vellum on panel. 20-Apr-4 Sotheby's, Olympia #75/R est:3000-5000

BRERETON, James Joseph (1954-) British
£460 $731 €667 Wind jammer in full sail (65x91cm-26x36in) s. 9-Sep-3 David Duggleby, Scarborough #296/R
£700 $1190 €1022 High seas race (58x89cm-23x35in) s. 19-Nov-3 Christie's, Kensington #604/R
£900 $1530 €1314 Herald of the Morning (71x91cm-28x36in) s. 19-Nov-3 Christie's, Kensington #601/R
£1048 $1750 €1530 Before the wind the Grace Ross, ship sailing on high seas (41x51cm-16x20in) s. 14-Nov-3 Aspire, Cleveland #102 est:1000-2000

BRERETON, R (fl.1830-1847) British
£3800 $6802 €5548 Family pets before Melton Constable Hall (71x91cm-28x36in) s.d.1846. 22-Mar-4 Bonhams & Brooks, Norfolk #244/R est:2000-3000

BRES, Hendrik (1932-) Canadian
£207 $374 €302 Aspen bushes near Chip Lake (69x105cm-27x41in) s.d.1980 s.i.verso acrylic prov. 18-Apr-4 Levis, Calgary #303/R (C.D 500)

BRESCIAN SCHOOL (16th C) Italian
£27000 $48600 €39420 Portrait of a lady wearing red and gold brocade dress and fur-trimmed overcoat (121x86cm-48x34in) 21-Apr-4 Christie's, London #91/R est:10000-15000

BRESCIANI, Antonio (1902-1998) Italian
£1479 $2455 €2100 Still life with fruit (50x60cm-20x24in) s. canvas on board. 11-Jun-3 Christie's, Rome #214/R est:2000-3000

BRESSAN, Italo (1950-) ?
£732 $1200 €1069 Untitled (50x50cm-20x20in) s.d.1988 verso prov.exhib. 28-May-3 Sotheby's, Amsterdam #178/R
£1220 $2000 €1781 Untitled (120x80cm-47x31in) s.d.1989 verso prov. 28-May-3 Sotheby's, Amsterdam #129/R est:2000-3000

BRESSANIN, Vittorio (1860-1941) Italian
£3580 $6087 €5120 Breakfast in Saint mark's Square (45x98cm-18x39in) 1-Dec-3 Babuino, Rome #432/R est:2000-3000
Works on paper
£280 $504 €420 Bianca Harbit in the garden (33x24cm-13x9in) s.i. chl lead. 21-Apr-4 Finarte Semenzato, Milan #599/R
£333 $600 €500 Portrait of Bianca Harbit (48x31cm-19x12in) s. W/C. 21-Apr-4 Finarte Semenzato, Milan #600/R

BRESSANUTTI, Aldo (1926-) Italian
£909 $1564 €1300 Trieste, fountain (40x60cm-16x24in) s. board. 3-Dec-3 Stadion, Trieste #1143/R
Works on paper
£280 $481 €400 Cittavecchia (60x25cm-24x10in) s. mixed media cardboard. 3-Dec-3 Stadion, Trieste #1093/R

BRESSIN, F (19th C) French
£1497 $2679 €2200 Portrait de cheval sur le champ de course de Chantilly (54x65cm-21x26in) s. 21-Mar-4 Muizon & Le Coent, Paris #36

BRESSLER, Emile (1886-1966) Swiss
£362 $605 €529 Still life with peonies (61x46cm-24x18in) s.d.1931 prov. 24-Jun-3 Germann, Zurich #917 (S.FR 800)
£478 $875 €698 Pecheurs sur la rive (50x60cm-20x24in) s.d.38. 5-Jun-4 Galerie du Rhone, Sion #279 (S.FR 1100)
£482 $806 €704 Village pres de Sarzeau, Morbihan (45x54cm-18x21in) s. 16-Nov-3 Koller, Geneva #1209 (S.FR 1100)
£789 $1318 €1152 Automne aux environs de Paimfol (54x65cm-21x26in) s. 16-Nov-3 Koller, Geneva #1210/R (S.FR 1800)
£872 $1456 €1264 Cavalier au pied du Saleve (50x61cm-20x24in) s.d. prov. 21-Jun-3 Galerie du Rhone, Sion #466/R est:2500-3500 (S.FR 1900)
£6000 $11040 €9000 Le parc (95x128cm-37x50in) s. 11-Jun-4 Claude Aguttes, Neuilly #26/R est:6000-8000

BRESSLER, Emile (attrib) (1886-1966) Swiss
£300 $546 €450 Lebanc (55x46cm-22x18in) s.d.63. 15-Jun-4 Rosebery Fine Art, London #546/R

BRESSLER, Reinhold (1868-?) German
£570 $1010 €850 Interior of marine church in northern Germany (70x58cm-28x23in) s.d.1915. 28-Apr-4 Schopman, Hamburg #600/R

BRESSLERN-ROTH, Norbertine (1891-1978) Austrian
Works on paper
£570 $1021 €850 Woman's portrait (10x8cm-4x3in) s.d.1936 W/C. 27-May-4 Dorotheum, Graz #95/R
£800 $1440 €1200 Alsatian (19x27cm-7x11in) s. W/C. 21-Apr-4 Dorotheum, Vienna #80/R
£909 $1564 €1300 Town by riverbank (27x35cm-11x14in) s.d.1924 W/C. 4-Dec-3 Dorotheum, Graz #69/R
£987 $1816 €1500 Scotch terrier. s.d.1935 mixed media. 22-Jun-4 Wiener Kunst Auktionen, Vienna #137/R est:1500
£1528 $2490 €2200 Animal and plant studies. s.d.1962 chl. 25-Sep-3 Dorotheum, Graz #77 est:500
£1645 $3026 €2500 Draft for an exotic hunting card game. s. i.verso mixed media. 22-Jun-4 Wiener Kunst Auktionen, Vienna #136/R est:2500
£1776 $3268 €2700 Cockatoo (39x24cm-15x9in) s.i. mixed media. 22-Jun-4 Wiener Kunst Auktionen, Vienna #88/R est:1000
£2000 $3600 €3000 Two puppies sleeping (19x27cm-7x11in) s. W/C gouache. 21-Apr-4 Dorotheum, Vienna #79/R est:1500-2000
£2416 $4325 €3600 Dog (23x22cm-9x9in) s.d.1935 W/C. 27-May-4 Dorotheum, Graz #94/R est:1100
£5903 $9326 €8500 Female nude with animals (70x90cm-28x35in) s. gouache lit. 19-Sep-3 Schloss Ahlden, Ahlden #1651/R est:8500

BREST, Germain-Fabius (1823-1900) French
£1678 $3087 €2500 Violas dans un pichet de Delft (61x50cm-24x20in) s.d.1875. 28-Mar-4 Anaf, Lyon #27 est:2000-3000
£2740 $4658 €4000 Views of Venice (33x25cm-13x10in) board pair. 4-Nov-3 Ansorena, Madrid #132b/R est:4000
£11538 $19615 €16500 Vue d'Istanbul (32x24cm-13x9in) s. 27-Nov-3 Millon & Associes, Paris #143/R est:12000-15000
£14474 $26632 €22000 Venise, La Salute (38x55cm-15x22in) s. exhib. 23-Jun-4 Sotheby's, Paris #80/R est:22000-28000
£24828 $41462 €36000 Araba au Bosphore (37x67cm-15x26in) s. 17-Nov-3 Delorme & Bocage, Paris #108/R est:12000-18000
Works on paper
£292 $461 €420 Paysage au pont. dr set of three in one frame. 25-Apr-3 Etude de Provence, Marseille #183

BRET, Paul (1902-1956) French
£280 $468 €409 Santorini, vue generale (65x55cm-26x22in) s. board. 21-Oct-3 Bonhams, Knightsbridge #80/R
£380 $711 €555 Mikonos, evening (45x54cm-18x21in) panel prov. 22-Jul-4 Tennants, Leyburn #835

BRET-CHARBONNIER, Claudia Julia (1863-1951) French
£1400 $2520 €2100 Bouquet de roses (65x54cm-26x21in) s. 20-Apr-4 Chenu & Scrive, Lyon #39/R est:1000-1200

BRETEUIL, Francois Denis (18th C) French
Works on paper
£563 $975 €800 Plan de l'Hopital de Chantilly (29x23cm-11x9in) s.d.1779 verso pen Indian ink W/C. 14-Dec-3 St-Germain-en-Laye Encheres #19/R
£1549 $2680 €2200 Plan de Chantilly (52x67cm-20x26in) pen black ink exec 1779. 14-Dec-3 St-Germain-en-Laye Encheres #20/R est:2000-3000

BRETEUIL, J Nicolas (18th C) French
Works on paper
£1549 $2680 €2200 Carte de la foret de Chantilly (48x65cm-19x26in) col ink wash exec 1748. 14-Dec-3 St-Germain-en-Laye Encheres #16/R est:2000-3000
£1972 $3411 €2800 Foret d'Ermenonville (48x65cm-19x26in) pen col ink wash exec 1747. 14-Dec-3 St-Germain-en-Laye Encheres #18 est:2000-3000
£2183 $3777 €3100 Ancien plan des jardins, chateaux, domaine de Chantilly (62x46cm-24x18in) col ink W/C exec c.1740. 14-Dec-3 St-Germain-en-Laye Encheres #15/R est:3000-4000
£6690 $11574 €9500 Potager de Chantilly (65x100cm-26x39in) col ink wash W/C. 14-Dec-3 St-Germain-en-Laye Encheres #17/R est:3000-4000

BRETLAND, Thomas (1802-1874) British
£760 $1406 €1110 Daniel O'Rourke - a chestnut race horse (32x44cm-13x17in) s.i.d.1852. 14-Jul-4 Bonhams, Chester #498
£900 $1467 €1314 Chestnut and spaniel paused beside a gate within landscape (64x77cm-25x30in) indis.sig. 24-Sep-3 Dreweatt Neate, Newbury #124/R

BRETON (?) French
£269 $500 €393 Harbour scene (30x41cm-12x16in) painted c.1950. 7-Mar-4 Treadway Gallery, Cincinnati #541/R

BRETON, Jules Adolphe (1827-1906) French
£5882 $10000 €8588 Gardeuse de vache (40x27cm-16x11in) s. prov. 29-Oct-3 Christie's, Rockefeller NY #97/R est:10000-15000
£7059 $12000 €10306 Lavandieres bretonnes a Douarnenez (34x39cm-13x15in) s.indis.i. painted c.1875. 29-Oct-3 Christie's, Rockefeller NY #88/R est:15000-20000
£11765 $20000 €17177 La Fontaine - Douarnenez (37x30cm-15x12in) s. prov. 28-Oct-3 Sotheby's, New York #25/R est:25000-35000
£14371 $24000 €20982 Water girl (58x38cm-23x15in) s.d.1872. 19-Oct-3 Susanin's, Chicago #6027/R est:8000-10000
£38889 $70000 €56778 Dans les champs, le soir (74x55cm-29x22in) s. prov. 23-Apr-4 Sotheby's, New York #22/R est:40000-60000
£70588 $120000 €103058 L'Amour (66x91cm-26x36in) s.d.1905 prov.exhib.lit. 28-Oct-3 Sotheby's, New York #29/R est:150000-200000
£76000 $129200 €110960 Jeune fille tricotant (36x30cm-14x12in) s.d.1860 canvas on panel prov. 19-Nov-3 Bonhams, New Bond Street #130/R est:20000-30000
£133333 $240000 €194666 Les mauvaises herbes (99x139cm-39x55in) s.d.1868 prov.exhib.lit. 23-Apr-4 Sotheby's, New York #28/R est:200000-300000
£176471 $300000 €257648 Dans la Plaine (96x137cm-38x54in) s.d.1896 prov.exhib.lit. 28-Oct-3 Sotheby's, New York #24/R est:300000-400000

BRETSCHNEIDER, Eduard (1849-?) German
£503 $936 €750 The love letter (39x33cm-15x13in) s. 5-Mar-4 Wendl, Rudolstadt #3594/R

BRETT, Dorothy (1883-1977) British/American
£1765 $3000 €2577 Blue lake (91x71cm-36x28in) s.d.1971 i.d.verso panel prov. 1-Nov-3 Santa Fe Art, Santa Fe #145/R est:15000-30000
£2121 $3500 €3075 Summer (36x20cm-14x8in) s.d.1963. 7-Jul-3 Schrager Galleries, Milwaukee #1650

BRETT, John (1831-1902) British
£800 $1336 €1168 Saint Agnes point (23x35cm-9x14in) i.d.73 board. 12-Nov-3 Sotheby's, Olympia #90/R
£1258 $2000 €1837 Shrinkle cove (19x36cm-7x14in) i.d.July 2 75 prov. 13-Sep-3 Weschler, Washington #669/R est:3000-5000
£2500 $4650 €3650 St. Agnes, Cornwall (23x35cm-9x14in) i.d.Sep 2.73 board. 4-Mar-4 Christie's, Kensington #552/R est:1500-2000
£2900 $4930 €4234 Oystermouth Castle, Swansea (18x35cm-7x14in) i.d.87 s.i.on stretcher. 18-Nov-3 Sotheby's, Olympia #32/R est:2000-3000
£4743 $8490 €6925 Sunset - low tide (17x35cm-7x14in) d.Oct 21 71 artists board prov. 15-May-4 Christie's, Sydney #424/R est:8000-12000 (A.D 12000)
£5138 $9198 €7501 Windy Day (17x35cm-7x14in) d.Sep 26 71 artists board prov. 15-May-4 Christie's, Sydney #425/R est:8000-12000 (A.D 13000)
£14000 $23800 €20440 Lion, the lizard and the stags (107x214cm-42x84in) s.d.1889 pencil. 25-Nov-3 Christie's, London #165/R est:15000-20000

BRETT, Rosa (1829-1882) Irish
£1035 $1852 €1511 Snipes in landscape (36x59cm-14x23in) s.d.1869. 26-May-4 AB Stockholms Auktionsverk #2610/R (S.KR 14000)

BRETTE, Pierre (1905-1961) French
Works on paper
£369 $583 €520 Chalutier au moteur (14x18cm-6x7in) s. W/C. 24-Jul-3 Adjug'art, Brest #227
£440 $695 €620 Chalutier tirant barque (14x18cm-6x7in) s. W/C. 24-Jul-3 Adjug'art, Brest #226
£645 $1167 €980 Bord de mer a Cosqueville (21x30cm-8x12in) s.i.d.1935 W/C. 19-Apr-4 Boscher, Cherbourg #837/R
£816 $1289 €1150 Bateaux a Carnaret (27x37cm-11x15in) s.i.d.49 W/C. 24-Jul-3 Adjug'art, Brest #228/R
£986 $1597 €1400 Bateau de peche cherbourgeois (35x24cm-14x9in) s. W/C. 11-Aug-3 Boscher, Cherbourg #760/R
£1151 $1888 €1600 Pecheurs pres de leur barque (26x36cm-10x14in) s. W/C. 3-Jun-3 Livinec, Gaudcheau & Jezequel, Rennes #63/R
£1399 $2336 €2000 Port de Saint-Malo (26x34cm-10x13in) s.i. W/C. 7-Oct-3 Livinec, Gaudcheau & Jezequel, Rennes #94
£2400 $4440 €3600 Promeneurs dans la baie du Mont St. Michel (53x75cm-21x30in) s.d.50 W/C. 14-Jul-4 Livinec, Gaudcheau & Jezequel, Rennes #88
£3200 $5920 €4800 Chalutier a Chausey (38x55cm-15x22in) s.i.d.1958 W/C. 14-Jul-4 Livinec, Gaudcheau & Jezequel, Rennes #104/R

BRETTSCHUH, Gerard (1941-) Austrian
Works on paper
£267 $480 €400 Ute painting (62x45cm-24x18in) s.d.29.8.77 Indian ink W/C. 22-Apr-4 Dorotheum, Graz #43/R

BREUER, Clara (1871-1935) Dutch
Works on paper
£839 $1443 €1200 Still life of flowers (50x33cm-20x13in) s. W/C. 8-Dec-3 Glerum, Amsterdam #104/R

BREUER, Henri Joseph (1860-1932) American
£1223 $2250 €1786 An old road (50x61cm-20x24in) s.d.99 i. stretcher prov. 8-Jun-4 Bonhams & Butterfields, San Francisco #4190/R est:3000-5000
£3179 $5500 €4641 Through the woods (96x81cm-38x32in) s. prov. 10-Dec-3 Bonhams & Butterfields, San Francisco #6156/R est:6000-8000

BREUER, Peter (1856-1930) German
Sculpture
£1267 $2305 €1900 Elephants (29cm-11in) i.st.f. Lauchhammer bronze. 1-Jul-4 Van Ham, Cologne #1021/R est:2000
£1497 $2380 €2200 Venus comforting Cupid (42cm-17in) s. dark brown pat.bronze. 28-Feb-3 Altus, Berlin #1648/R est:1500
£1806 $2853 €2600 Venus and Cupid (51cm-20in) i. brown pat.bronze marble socle. 6-Sep-3 Schopman, Hamburg #362/R est:1900

BREUGELMANS, Alphonse (?) Belgian
£1074 $1901 €1600 Village dans un paysage (80x120cm-31x47in) s. 27-Apr-4 Campo & Campo, Antwerp #30/R est:750-1250

BREUGELMANS, Auguste (19/20th C) Belgian
£267 $477 €400 Village scene (54x73cm-21x29in) s. 15-May-4 De Vuyst, Lokeren #39

BREUIL, Georges (1904-1997) French
Works on paper
£352 $567 €500 Composition (54x45cm-21x18in) s.d.1966 mixed media cardboard. 11-May-3 Versailles Encheres #167

BREUILLAUD, Andre (1893-1935) French
£600 $1080 €900 La cueillette des citrons. s. 20-Apr-4 Chenu & Scrive, Lyon #40/R

BREUL, Harold Guenther (1889-?) American
Works on paper
£296 $550 €432 Hunt teams at Jacobs Hill hunt horse show (38x53cm-15x21in) s.i. W/C. 7-Mar-4 William Jenack, New York #242

BREUN, John Ernest (1862-1921) British
Works on paper
£1000 $1830 €1460 Simplicity - Portrait of a young girl with a bunch of spring flowers (73x61cm-29x24in) s.d.1906 pastel. 8-Jul-4 Lawrence, Crewkerne #1545/R est:1000-1500

BREUNING, Olaf (1970-) American
Photographs
£2283 $4200 €3425 Skeletons (122x155cm-48x61in) c-print aluminum edition of 3 prov. 10-Jun-4 Phillips, New York #525/R est:2000-3000

BREUSTEDT, Hans Joachim (1901-) Swiss
Works on paper
£333 $597 €500 Daydream (30x43cm-12x17in) mono.d.57 mixed media. 13-May-4 Dorotheum, Linz #596/R
£500 $895 €750 Shepherd (29x21cm-11x8in) mono. mixed media. 13-May-4 Dorotheum, Linz #598/R

BREUTH, J (19th C) ?
£1156 $2000 €1688 Champion (56x76cm-22x30in) s.d.1831. 13-Dec-3 Charlton Hall, Columbia #358/R est:2000-4000

BREVANNAS, Maurice (20th C) American
£823 $1300 €1202 Red light district (76x51cm-30x20in) s. 7-Sep-3 Treadway Gallery, Cincinnati #726/R

BREVEGLIERI, Cesare (1902-1948) Italian
£2098 $3566 €3000 Landscape cow and shepherd (27x36cm-11x14in) s.d.940. 20-Nov-3 Finarte Semenzato, Milan #202/R est:2500-3000

BREVOORT, James Renwick (1832-1918) American
£348 $550 €508 Chateau, laundry day (33x43cm-13x17in) s. board. 27-Jul-3 William Jenack, New York #310

BREVOORT, James Renwick (attrib) (1832-1918) American
£659 $1200 €962 View of an Italian port (33x51cm-13x20in) 7-Feb-4 Sloans & Kenyon, Bethesda #1310/R

BREWER, Bessie Marsh (1884-1952) American
£234 $375 €342 Provincetown (38x48cm-15x19in) s. painted c.1912. 20-Sep-3 Bunte, Elgin #1248

BREWER, Henry Charles (1866-1950) British
Works on paper
£320 $534 €467 St. Nicholas and keep, Newcastle upon Tyne (33x23cm-13x9in) W/C prov. 12-Nov-3 Halls, Shrewsbury #268
£530 $964 €800 View of Saint Paul's after the bombing (35x54cm-14x21in) s.d.1941 W/C. 21-Jun-4 Pandolfini, Florence #248
£550 $952 €803 View up the High Street, Oxford (31x46cm-12x18in) s. pencil W/C htd white. 9-Dec-3 Bonhams, Oxford #81/R
£1200 $2160 €1752 Durham Cathedral from the river Wear with cottages in foreground (50x65cm-20x26in) s.i. pencil W/C htd white. 21-Apr-4 Tennants, Leyburn #961/R est:800-1200

BREWER, James Alphege (fl.1909-1938) British
Works on paper
£2800 $4760 €4088 Saint Paul's Cathedral and Waterloo Bridge (41x63cm-16x25in) s. pencil W/C htd white. 19-Nov-3 Christie's, Kensington #391/R est:800-1200

BREWER, Nicholas Richard (1857-1949) American
£488 $800 €708 Rocks and mountains (28x38cm-11x15in) s. board painted c.1920. 7-Jun-3 Treadway Gallery, Cincinnati #1383
£556 $1000 €812 Dawn (41x51cm-16x20in) s. 24-Apr-4 Weschler, Washington #623/R
£976 $1600 €1415 Highwood study (23x30cm-9x12in) s. 7-Jun-3 Treadway Gallery, Cincinnati #1389 est:1000-2000
£1067 $1750 €1547 Approaching storm (36x51cm-14x20in) s.d. 7-Jun-3 Treadway Gallery, Cincinnati #1344 est:1500-2500
£2744 $4500 €3979 Edge of corn (61x91cm-24x36in) s. painted c.1900. 7-Jun-3 Treadway Gallery, Cincinnati #1334 est:2500-4500

BREWERTON, George Douglas (1827-1901) American
Works on paper
£314 $500 €458 View along the Hudson river (61x91cm-24x36in) s.d.1870 pastel. 4-May-3 William Jenack, New York #240
£339 $600 €495 Mountainous river valley (71x56cm-28x22in) s. pastel. 2-May-4 Grogan, Boston #93/R

BREWSTER, Anna Richards (1870-1952) American
£220 $350 €321 Autumn in Matunuck (24x33cm-9x13in) 12-Sep-3 Skinner, Boston #447/R
£1250 $2200 €1825 Stream in Surrey England, landscape (33x23cm-13x9in) i. 21-May-4 Pook & Pook, Downington #95/R est:800-1200
£1364 $2400 €1991 Gallantry Bowm, Clovelly England, landscape (23x33cm-9x13in) i. 21-May-4 Pook & Pook, Downington #194/R est:800-1000
£1397 $2500 €2040 Portrait of William Trost Richards (61x46cm-24x18in) prov. 6-May-4 Shannon's, Milford #213/R est:2500-3500
£1571 $2750 €2294 Autumn pasture and sea, Matunuck, Rhode Island (21x30cm-8x12in) 19-Dec-3 Sotheby's, New York #1088/R est:1500-2500

BREWSTER, John (jnr) (1766-1854) American
£9730 $18000 €14206 Portrait of Squire Enoch Perley (77x63cm-30x25in) prov. 17-Jan-4 Sotheby's, New York #1200/R est:30000-50000
£12346 $20000 €17902 Portrait of William Fogg (76x63cm-30x25in) prov. 8-Aug-3 Barridorf, Portland #139/R est:12000-18000
£45946 $85000 €67081 Portraits of General John Perley jr and Sarah Tredwell Perley (77x64cm-30x25in) pair prov. 17-Jan-4 Sotheby's, New York #1199/R est:70000-100000

BREWSTER, John (jnr-attrib) (1766-1854) American
£13529 $23000 €19752 Double portrait of the Bowman children with yellow Windsor chair (36x51cm-14x20in) i.verso prov. 31-Oct-3 North East Auctions, Portsmouth #1516 est:20000-30000

BREWTNALL, Edward Frederick (1846-1902) British
Works on paper
£1100 $1980 €1606 Little chef (39x19cm-15x7in) s. W/C. 21-Jan-4 Sotheby's, Olympia #294/R est:1000-1500
£2500 $4500 €3650 Whist party (35x52cm-14x20in) s. W/C. 21-Jan-4 Sotheby's, Olympia #195/R est:2000-3000
£2800 $5096 €4088 Meditation (31x26cm-12x10in) init.d.1875 pencil W/C htd white. 5-Feb-4 Mellors & Kirk, Nottingham #511/R est:800-1200
£6250 $10750 €9125 Dragon's Cave (41x56cm-16x22in) s. W/C prov.exhib. 2-Dec-3 Ritchie, Toronto #33/R est:12000-18000 (C.D 14000)

BREYDEL, Jan (c.1630-1700) Flemish
£5172 $8638 €7500 River landscapes with figures (19x27cm-7x11in) two s. two s.d.1672 1679 board on panel four. 15-Nov-3 Lempertz, Koln #1020/R est:5000

BREYDEL, Karel (1678-1733) Flemish
£1086 $1879 €1586 Combat de cavalerie contre les Turcs (19x25cm-7x10in) prov. 12-Dec-3 Galerie du Rhone, Sion #162/R est:2000-3000 (S.FR 2400)
£1633 $2596 €2400 Cavalry battle (37x49cm-15x19in) s. 21-Mar-3 Bailly Pommery, Paris #61
£3133 $5703 €4700 Cavalry battle scene in an extensive landscape (28x35cm-11x14in) s. copper. 1-Jul-4 Van Ham, Cologne #1075/R est:2600
£4305 $7834 €6500 Cavalry engagement (23x29cm-9x11in) panel prov. 16-Jun-4 Dorotheum, Vienna #48/R est:4000-4500

BREYDEL, Karel (attrib) (1678-1733) Flemish
£780 $1303 €1100 Charge de cavalerie (40x51cm-16x20in) 17-Oct-3 Tajan, Paris #52
£2262 $3620 €3303 Cavalry battle (21x30cm-8x12in) panel. 19-Sep-3 Koller, Zurich #3049/R est:4500-5500 (S.FR 5000)

BREYER, Benno (1939-) German?
£270 $484 €400 Entrance to Mas, Provence (50x60cm-20x24in) board lit. 8-May-4 Dawo, Saarbrucken #229/R

BREZINA, Vaclav (1862-1928) Czechoslovakian
£1975 $3358 €2884 Summer landscape (24x32cm-9x13in) s.d.95 panel. 29-Nov-3 Dorotheum, Prague #74/R est:40000-80000 (C.KR 90000)

BRIANCHON, Maurice (1899-1979) French
£3087 $5742 €4600 Trois roses blanches (40x24cm-16x9in) s. 3-Mar-4 Ferri, Paris #363 est:3000-3500
£6486 $12000 €9470 Paris metro (81x99cm-32x39in) s. painted 1926 prov. 11-Feb-4 Sotheby's, New York #80/R est:15000-20000
£8609 $15669 €13000 Chevaux dans la prairie (92x64cm-36x25in) s. 18-Jun-4 Piasa, Paris #154/R est:8000-12000
£9884 $17000 €14431 Nature morte pommes et raisins (60x73cm-24x29in) s. prov. 3-Dec-3 Doyle, New York #8/R est:20000-30000
£10067 $18523 €15000 Aux courses, la pelouse (46x55cm-18x22in) s. 28-Mar-4 Anaf, Lyon #28/R est:12000-15000
£13986 $23357 €20000 Pecheurs au bord de la riviere (39x47cm-15x19in) s. panel. 30-Jun-3 Artcurial Briest, Paris #755/R est:8000-12000
£22973 $42500 €33541 Tulips (65x36cm-26x14in) s. prov. 11-Feb-4 Sotheby's, New York #78/R est:20000-30000
£26000 $47840 €37960 Bouquet of flowers in the studio (81x100cm-32x39in) s. prov. 22-Jun-4 Sotheby's, London #252/R est:30000-40000
Works on paper
£268 $499 €400 Chevaux au pre (47x59cm-19x23in) s. pen. 3-Mar-4 Ferri, Paris #325
£352 $609 €500 Douves de Saint-Lye (44x60cm-17x24in) s. pen ink. 10-Dec-3 Ferri, Paris #22
£382 $638 €550 Paysage (46x61cm-18x24in) s. ink white chk exec. c.1950-1960. 21-Oct-3 Christie's, Paris #75/R
£526 $968 €800 Les douves (44x59cm-17x23in) s. W/C prov. 25-Jun-4 Daguerre, Paris #151
£652 $1193 €952 Paysage fluvial (30x37cm-12x15in) s. W/C. 4-Jun-4 Zofingen, Switzerland #2426 (S.FR 1500)
£1549 $2680 €2200 Arlequin (24x32cm-9x13in) s. W/C. 10-Dec-3 Ferri, Paris #21/R est:800-1000
£1818 $3128 €2600 Les regates (49x60cm-19x24in) s. gouache exec.c.1946-1948. 3-Dec-3 Tajan, Paris #46/R est:3000-4000
£6087 $11139 €8887 Jeune femme mediatif (61x43cm-24x17in) s. gouache. 4-Jun-4 Zofingen, Switzerland #2425/R est:10000 (S.FR 14000)
£8681 $14497 €12500 Jeune femme (38x46cm-15x18in) s. W/C gouache wax crayon exhib. 21-Oct-3 Christie's, Paris #86/R est:7000-9000

BRIANSKY, M (19th C) Russian
£8000 $14320 €11680 Survivors (71x111cm-28x44in) i. 26-May-4 Sotheby's, London #55/R est:8000-12000

BRIANTE, Ezelino (1901-1970) Italian
£280 $467 €400 Village street (10x17cm-4x7in) s. cardboard. 24-Jun-3 Finarte Semenzato, Rome #153
£282 $451 €400 Coastal town (21x32cm-8x13in) s. 21-Sep-3 Bukowskis, Helsinki #503/R
£286 $487 €418 Fishermen in harbour (13x18cm-5x7in) s. board. 5-Nov-3 Dobiaschofsky, Bern #395 (S.FR 650)
£302 $540 €441 City (20x25cm-8x10in) s. canvas on board. 12-May-4 Dobiaschofsky, Bern #360 (S.FR 700)
£308 $524 €450 Landscape near Rome (21x34cm-8x13in) s. i. verso board. 5-Nov-3 Dobiaschofsky, Bern #394/R (S.FR 700)
£325 $582 €475 Ischia Harbour (29x39cm-11x15in) s. i.verso canvas on board. 4-May-4 Ritchie, Toronto #93/R (C.D 800)
£336 $601 €500 Harbour (12x19cm-5x7in) s. cardboard. 25-May-4 Finarte Semenzato, Milan #125/R
£339 $577 €495 Genua harbour (20x35cm-8x14in) s. panel. 19-Nov-3 Fischer, Luzern #2027/R (S.FR 750)

£429 $769 €626 Seaside village Capri (50x69cm-20x27in) s. s.i. verso board. 31-May-4 Stephan Welz, Johannesburg #85 (SA.R 5200)
£431 $772 €629 Italian harbour (29x39cm-11x15in) 12-May-4 Dobiaschofsky, Bern #358/R (S.FR 1000)
£493 $818 €700 Mercatino (30x35cm-12x14in) s. board. 11-Jun-3 Christie's, Rome #137
£505 $843 €732 Coastal landscape with sailing ships (40x79cm-16x31in) s. masonite. 23-Jun-3 Philippe Schuler, Zurich #8576 (S.FR 1100)
£528 $850 €766 Sunlit courtyard (58x69cm-23x27in) s. 17-Aug-3 Jeffery Burchard, Florida #75
£633 $1077 €924 Al porto (18x25cm-7x10in) s. board. 28-Nov-3 Zofingen, Switzerland #2557 (S.FR 1400)
£652 $1193 €952 Untitled (16x29cm-6x11in) s. board. 4-Jun-4 Zofingen, Switzerland #2427 (S.FR 1500)
£690 $1234 €1007 Ships in harbour (49x69cm-19x27in) s. 12-May-4 Dobiaschofsky, Bern #359/R est:2300 (S.FR 1600)
£709 $1184 €1000 View of village by the sea (36x25cm-14x10in) s. cardboard. 14-Oct-3 Finarte Semenzato, Milan #74/R
£845 $1403 €1200 Velieri all'ancora (50x35cm-20x14in) s.d.5-1943 i.verso board. 11-Jun-3 Christie's, Rome #109
£855 $1574 €1300 Street in Naples (23x35cm-9x14in) s. cardboard. 23-Jun-4 Finarte Semenzato, Rome #70/R
£872 $1605 €1300 Rocky coast (50x70cm-20x28in) s. lit. 25-Mar-4 Karlheinz Kaupp, Staufen #2370/R
£900 $1656 €1350 Path in Amalfi (50x60cm-20x24in) s. s.i.d.46 verso paper on canvas. 8-Jun-4 Sotheby's, Milan #60/R
£915 $1520 €1300 Barche a Pozzuoli (19x34cm-7x13in) s. faesite. 11-Jun-3 Christie's, Rome #81/R
£1200 $1956 €1752 Italian coastal scene (51x76cm-20x30in) s. board. 23-Sep-3 John Nicholson, Haslemere #246 est:500-1000
£1200 $2208 €1800 Cottages in the mountains (49x70cm-19x28in) s. cardboard painted 1947. 8-Jun-4 Sotheby's, Milan #58/R est:1000-1500
£1342 $2403 €2000 Boat with anglers (40x50cm-16x20in) s. 25-May-4 Finarte Semenzato, Milan #123/R est:1500-2000
£1513 $2784 €2300 Harbour (40x50cm-16x20in) s. 23-Jun-4 Finarte Semenzato, Rome #69/R est:2500-2700
£1549 $2572 €2200 Luci sotto il pergolato (50x50cm-20x20in) s. wood. 11-Jun-3 Christie's, Rome #110/R est:1000-1500
£1600 $2896 €2400 View of the Amalfi coast (50x74cm-20x29in) s. masonite. 30-Mar-4 Babuino, Rome #281/R est:1500
£1629 $2769 €2378 Pergola (70x89cm-28x35in) s. 28-Nov-3 Zofingen, Switzerland #2556/R est:1500 (S.FR 3600)

BRIARD, Lucie (19/20th C) French
£500 $795 €730 Black and white kittens (24x18cm-9x7in) board. 9-Sep-3 Rowley Fine Art, Newmarket #456

BRIASCO RUFETE, Victoriano (1938-) Spanish
£310 $559 €450 Complaints (81x100cm-32x39in) s.d.75. 26-Jan-4 Ansorena, Madrid #869/R
£324 $583 €470 Men chatting at the bar (73x92cm-29x36in) s. s.d.75 verso. 26-Jan-4 Ansorena, Madrid #928/R

BRICARD, G (19/20th C) French
£675 $1100 €986 Paysage (46x54cm-18x21in) s. prov. 25-Sep-3 Christie's, Rockefeller NY #527/R est:1000-1500

BRICE, Edward Kington (1860-1948) British
£360 $580 €522 Still life study of honesty and other foliage in a vase on ledge by a window (48x38cm-19x15in) s. 15-Aug-3 Keys, Aylsham #416
£700 $1106 €1015 Lilies (35x24cm-14x9in) s. panel. 4-Sep-3 Christie's, Kensington #336/R

BRICE, Freddie (20th C) American?
£278 $500 €406 Woman with heart (109x79cm-43x31in) board. 24-Apr-4 Slotin Folk Art, Buford #457/R
£539 $900 €787 Man in helicopter (107x127cm-42x50in) paint board. 15-Nov-3 Slotin Folk Art, Buford #274/R

BRICE, William (1921-) American
£192 $350 €280 Rose Garden (43x56cm-17x22in) s.d.49 acrylic board. 7-Feb-4 Neal Auction Company, New Orleans #806

BRICENO, Pedro (20th C) Venezuelan
Sculpture
£918 $1560 €1340 Maternity (56x32x26cm-22x13x10in) resin exec.c.1960. 23-Nov-3 Subastas Odalys, Caracas #147/R

BRICHER, A T (1837-1908) American
Works on paper
£1075 $2000 €1570 Untitled (15x36cm-6x14in) W/C. 6-Mar-4 Page, Batavia #21

BRICHER, Alfred Thompson (1837-1908) American
£3867 $7000 €5646 Coastal seascape (18x36cm-7x14in) s. panel. 16-Apr-4 James Julia, Fairfield #615/R est:5000-7000
£4969 $8000 €7255 Saco River (38x30cm-15x12in) s. 20-Aug-3 James Julia, Fairfield #1289/R est:8000-12000
£10559 $18900 €15416 Sunset over tranquil beach (36x56cm-14x22in) s. i.stretcher. 8-Jan-4 James Julia, Fairfield #513/R est:8000-10000
£18519 $30000 €26853 Peaceful shore (16x31cm-6x12in) s.d.1871 board prov. 8-Aug-3 Barridorf, Portland #346/R est:12000-18000
£25568 $45000 €37329 Seascape (51x97cm-20x38in) mono.d.82. 18-May-4 Christie's, Rockefeller NY #24/R est:50000-70000
£34091 $60000 €49773 In Gloucester Harbour (56x81cm-22x32in) mono.d.83 i.verso prov.exhib. 19-May-4 Sotheby's, New York #60/R est:70000-90000
£45455 $80000 €66364 Coastal scene (46x76cm-18x30in) s.d.68. 18-May-4 Christie's, Rockefeller NY #39/R est:100000-150000
£46512 $80000 €67908 Sunset coast (43x91cm-17x36in) init. 4-Dec-3 Christie's, Rockefeller NY #8/R
£51136 $90000 €74659 Shore scene (43x91cm-17x36in) mono. prov. 18-May-4 Christie's, Rockefeller NY #40/R est:80000-120000
£55233 $95000 €80640 Seascape with sailboats (38x84cm-15x33in) init.d.1890 prov. 4-Dec-3 Christie's, Rockefeller NY #27/R est:70000-100000
£83833 $140000 €122396 Morning at Narragansett (69x127cm-27x50in) s.i.d.1872 prov.exhib. 23-Oct-3 Shannon's, Milford #73/R est:50000-75000
£84302 $145000 €123081 Seascape with sunset (46x91cm-18x36in) init.d.1875. 4-Dec-3 Christie's, Rockefeller NY #13/R
Works on paper
£1111 $1844 €1622 Sailing ships off a rocky coast (26x54cm-10x21in) W/C. 2-Oct-3 Heffel, Vancouver #7 (C.D 2500)
£1136 $2000 €1659 Shoreline with a prominent peaked rock in centre (48x33cm-19x13in) s. W/C exhib. 24-May-4 Winter Associates, Plainville #86/R est:2250-2750
£1503 $2750 €2194 Entrance to Salem Harbor (23x36cm-9x14in) s. W/C paper on panel prov. 7-Jun-4 O'Gallerie, Oregon #730/R est:3500-4500
£1557 $2600 €2273 Surf and cliffs, Conanicut, Rhode Island (53x38cm-21x15in) init. W/C paper on board. 9-Oct-3 Christie's, Rockefeller NY #20/R est:5000-7000
£2043 $3800 €2983 Coastal inlet with a ship offshore (25x51cm-10x20in) s. pencil W/C. 3-Mar-4 Christie's, Rockefeller NY #27/R est:1000-1500
£2235 $4000 €3263 Coastal view (23x51cm-9x20in) s. W/C. 6-May-4 Shannon's, Milford #152/R est:4000-6000
£3073 $5500 €4610 Lake shore landscape (36x53cm-14x21in) W/C. 16-May-4 Abell, Los Angeles #132
£4190 $7500 €6117 Boathouse (23x38cm-9x15in) s. W/C prov. 6-May-4 Shannon's, Milford #39/R est:5000-7000
£5525 $10000 €8067 Seashore with Rocky Point in background (23x53cm-9x21in) W/C. 16-Apr-4 James Julia, Fairfield #551/R est:12500-17500
£9259 $15000 €13426 Playing on the beach (24x52cm-9x20in) s. W/C. 8-Aug-3 Barridorf, Portland #135/R est:6000-8000
£12291 $22000 €17945 Afternoon gust (20x35cm-8x14in) s. gouache prov. 6-May-4 Shannon's, Milford #114/R est:20000-30000

BRICHERASIO, Sofia (1869-1950) Italian
£1342 $2376 €2000 August afternoon in Holland (24x37cm-9x15in) d.1906 board lit. 1-May-4 Meeting Art, Vercelli #169 est:2000

BRICK, Alphonse (?) French?
£1921 $3515 €2900 Ruelle Algerienne (61x49cm-24x19in) s. 9-Apr-4 Claude Aguttes, Neuilly #139 est:2000-3000

BRICKDALE, Eleanor Fortesque (1871-1945) British
Works on paper
£260 $465 €380 Picnic scene with musician in background (13x18cm-5x7in) init. W/C. 13-May-4 Grant, Worcester #350

BRIDELL, Frederick Lee (1831-1863) British
£865 $1600 €1263 In my atelier (71x89cm-28x35in) s.i.d.1857. 15-Jul-4 Doyle, New York #14/R est:2000-3000
£1400 $2590 €2044 Old Chester - the silhouette of the Castle at sunset (46x56cm-18x22in) indis.s. bears old i. verso. 14-Jul-4 Bonhams, Chester #307/R est:1500-2000

BRIDGEHOUSE, Robert (fl.1844-1846) British
£647 $1100 €945 Coastal landscape (36x25cm-14x10in) s.d.1871. 22-Nov-3 Jackson's, Cedar Falls #9/R est:1500-2500

BRIDGES, Fidelia (1834-1923) American
Works on paper
£642 $1200 €937 Blue birds in a nest (33x23cm-13x9in) i.verso W/C. 29-Feb-4 Grogan, Boston #19/R

BRIDGES, John (19th C) British
£4000 $6320 €5800 Cactus grandiflorus of Linnoeus and cactus speciosissimus (64x77cm-25x30in) 2-Sep-3 Bonhams, Oxford #92/R est:800-1000

BRIDGMAN, Frederick Arthur (1847-1928) American
£500 $920 €730 Bridal Caravan. 8-Jun-4 Lawrences, Bletchingley #1631
£900 $1611 €1350 Pont-Aven (46x33cm-18x13in) s.i.d.1870 paper. 16-May-4 Thierry & Lannon, Brest #292
£1064 $1777 €1500 Conversation au jardin (26x41cm-10x16in) mono.d.1927. 16-Jun-3 Gros & Delettrez, Paris #438/R est:1500-2300
£1445 $2500 €2110 Mother and child on a beach looking out to sea (43x33cm-17x13in) s. 10-Dec-3 Boos Gallery, Michigan #520/R est:5000-7000
£2933 $5251 €4400 Marine a Beaulieu (38x49cm-15x19in) s.d.1918. 16-May-4 Thierry & Lannon, Brest #123/R est:5000-6000
£4000 $7360 €5840 Corner of the bazaar (32x41cm-13x16in) s. board. 25-Mar-4 Christie's, Kensington #217/R est:4000-6000
£4667 $8540 €7000 Enfant et son ane un jour de fete (35x26cm-14x10in) s.d.1880 panel. 3-Jun-4 Tajan, Paris #262/R est:7000-10000
£4967 $9040 €7500 Scene orientaliste (33x41cm-13x16in) s.d.1921. 20-Jun-4 Salle des ventes Pillet, Lyon la Foret #9/R est:7500-8000
£5000 $8350 €7300 Barbary horses at Cairo (48x57cm-19x22in) s. prov. 14-Oct-3 Sotheby's, London #92/R est:5000-7000
£5220 $9500 €7621 Woman in white holding yellow roses (76x66cm-30x26in) s.d.1903 prov. 15-Jun-4 John Moran, Pasadena #70 est:10000-15000
£10227 $18000 €14931 Dilligence (46x71cm-18x28in) s.d.1878 prov.exhib.lit. 19-May-4 Sotheby's, New York #45/R est:12000-18000
£15278 $27500 €22306 Market place in North Africa (79x98cm-31x39in) s. prov. 23-Apr-4 Sotheby's, New York #96/R est:20000-30000
£15294 $26000 €22329 Bathing beauties (58x109cm-23x43in) s.d.1872. 29-Oct-3 Christie's, Rockefeller NY #147/R est:25000-35000
£27778 $50000 €40556 Women drawing water from the Nile (92x132cm-36x52in) s.d. prov.exhib.lit. 23-Apr-4 Sotheby's, New York #100/R est:70000-100000
£43011 $80000 €62796 Halloween (68x114cm-27x45in) s. prov. 5-Mar-4 Skinner, Boston #261/R est:30000-50000
£57746 $101056 €82000 Les femmes d'Alger (75x116cm-30x46in) s.d.1926 exhib. 16-Dec-3 Claude Aguttes, Neuilly #61/R est:30000-40000

£98592 $170563 €140000 Femmes tissant le bournous a Biskra (104x132cm-41x52in) s.d.1880 prov.exhib.lit. 15-Dec-3 Gros & Delettrez, Paris #411/R est:150000-200000
Works on paper
£667 $1227 €1000 Marchand de tissus dans les souks, Alger (27x20cm-11x8in) mono.i. pen Indian ink. 14-Jun-4 Gros & Delettrez, Paris #366/R

BRIDT, Bernaert de (fl.1688-1722) Flemish
£8000 $14320 €12000 Hunting still lifes in landscapes (83x108cm-33x43in) s. pair. 17-May-4 Christie's, Amsterdam #108/R est:12000-16000
£9589 $16301 €14000 Hunting still life with a pheasant and songbirds in a landscape. Hunting still life with a cat (80x66cm-31x26in) s. two. 5-Nov-3 Christie's, Amsterdam #62/R est:12000-16000

BRIE, Anthony de (20th C) British
£850 $1471 €1241 Spring landscape with shepherd and dog herding sheep from a barn (22x30cm-9x12in) s.d.1905. 9-Dec-3 Bonhams, Oxford #120

BRIEDE, Johan (1885-1980) Dutch
£1477 $2732 €2200 Vogelnestjes (35x40cm-14x16in) s.d.1929 prov. 15-Mar-4 Sotheby's, Amsterdam #217/R est:800-1200

BRIELMAN, Jacques-Alfred (?-1892) French
£2464 $4041 €3400 Troupeau traversant le gue (50x73cm-20x29in) s. i.d.1885 verso. 11-May-3 Osenat, Fontainebleau #27/R est:3000-3500
£3357 $5773 €4800 Le passeur (40x68cm-16x27in) s. 7-Dec-3 Osenat, Fontainebleau #153 est:4500-5000
Works on paper
£839 $1443 €1200 Le cafe du coin (35x51cm-14x20in) s.i. W/C. 7-Dec-3 Osenat, Fontainebleau #27/R

BRIERLEY, Argent (fl.1914) British
£500 $800 €730 Evening in Edale (57x68cm-22x27in) s. 16-Sep-3 Rosebery Fine Art, London #461

BRIERLY, Sir Oswald Walter (1817-1894) British
Works on paper
£488 $873 €712 Shipping off Trieste (16x23cm-6x9in) indis.s. W/C. 10-May-4 Joel, Victoria #343 (A.D 1200)
£800 $1432 €1168 Royal Yacht Victoria and Albert II leaving Cherbourg with her escorts (15x40cm-6x16in) s.i.d.1858 pencil W/C htd white. 26-May-4 Christie's, Kensington #399/R
£1600 $2768 €2336 Sebastopol, the British Fleet in action, August 1853 (27x75cm-11x30in) s.d.53 W/C. 9-Dec-3 Anderson & Garland, Newcastle #229/R est:800-1200

BRIET, Arthur (1867-1939) Dutch
£340 $609 €500 Javaansche danseres - dancer from Java (26x31cm-10x12in) s. i.verso. 16-Mar-4 Christie's, Amsterdam #3
£451 $713 €650 Serenity of sewing (30x40cm-12x16in) indis sig. canvas on plywood. 2-Sep-3 Christie's, Amsterdam #243
£676 $1162 €987 Interior of a peasant cottage with open fireplace and hens (31x41cm-12x16in) s. 8-Dec-3 Philippe Schuler, Zurich #3389 (S.FR 1500)

BRIETSCHWERT, Wilhelm von (1828-1875) German
£680 $1218 €1000 Artist's studio (50x61cm-20x24in) s.d.1872. 18-Mar-4 Neumeister, Munich #2647/R

BRIEUX, Jeanne Louise (19/20th C) French
£269 $450 €393 Houses along a river (46x61cm-18x24in) s. 20-Jun-3 Freeman, Philadelphia #164/R
£278 $472 €400 Dusk on the lake (27x10cm-11x4in) s.i.d.1902 board. 28-Oct-3 Segre, Madrid #24/R

BRIGANTI, Nicholas P (1895-1989) American
£408 $750 €596 Amalfi coast scene (58x89cm-23x35in) s. 11-Jun-4 David Rago, Lambertville #230/R
£726 $1300 €1089 Interior scene with family amusing child (74x102cm-29x40in) 29-May-4 Brunk, Ashville #103/R
£795 $1400 €1161 Venice (64x51cm-25x20in) s. painted c.1930. 23-May-4 Treadway Gallery, Cincinnati #528/R
£994 $1800 €1451 View of the Grand Canal, Venice (51x76cm-20x30in) s. 3-Apr-4 Neal Auction Company, New Orleans #314/R est:1000-1500
£1000 $1700 €1460 Venetian lagoon (41x56cm-16x22in) s. 5-Nov-3 Doyle, New York #16/R est:1000-1500
£1136 $2000 €1659 Venetian Canal (61x97cm-24x38in) s. prov. 23-May-4 Hindman, Chicago #167/R est:2000-4000
£1176 $2200 €1717 Venetian scene (46x102cm-18x40in) s. 29-Feb-4 Grogan, Boston #59/R
£5307 $9500 €7961 Ships in the Grand Canal (107x51cm-42x20in) s. 16-May-4 Abell, Los Angeles #34

BRIGDEN, Frederick Henry (1871-1956) Canadian
£240 $439 €350 Don Valley Note (17x25cm-7x10in) s. canvasboard. 1-Jun-4 Joyner Waddington, Toronto #516 (C.D 600)
£995 $1662 €1453 Early spring, Caledon (50x65cm-20x26in) s.i.d. 17-Nov-3 Hodgins, Calgary #364 est:2500-3500 (C.D 2200)
£1280 $2342 €1869 Midsummer day, Don Valley (50x60cm-20x24in) s. board exhib. 1-Jun-4 Joyner Waddington, Toronto #164/R est:2500-3000 (C.D 3200)
Works on paper
£200 $366 €292 Landscape with rolling hills (22x27cm-9x11in) s. W/C. 1-Jun-4 Joyner Waddington, Toronto #418 (C.D 500)
£200 $366 €292 Muskoka River, Bracebridge (24x27cm-9x11in) s. W/C painted 1942. 1-Jun-4 Joyner Waddington, Toronto #473 (C.D 500)
£268 $461 €391 Waterfall - Summer (22x29cm-9x11in) s. W/C. 2-Dec-3 Joyner Waddington, Toronto #409 (C.D 600)
£302 $556 €441 Autumn in Muskoka (20x27cm-8x11in) s. s.i.verso W/C. 9-Jun-4 Walker's, Ottawa #58/R (C.D 750)
£320 $544 €467 Mountain landscape (36x126cm-14x50in) s. W/C. 24-Nov-3 Tiffin King & Nicholson, Carlisle #215/R
£402 $691 €587 Riverscape - Early Spring (30x30cm-12x12in) s. W/C. 2-Dec-3 Joyner Waddington, Toronto #412 (C.D 900)
£413 $748 €603 Untitled - waterfall (22x30cm-9x12in) s. W/C. 18-Apr-4 Levis, Calgary #12/R est:1200-1500 (C.D 1000)
£520 $952 €759 River reflections, summer (25x35cm-10x14in) s. W/C. 1-Jun-4 Hodgins, Calgary #417/R (C.D 1300)
£680 $1244 €993 Waterfalls (22x29cm-9x11in) s. W/C prov. 1-Jun-4 Hodgins, Calgary #129/R (C.D 1700)

BRIGG, Mel (1950-) South African
£372 $665 €543 View of a farm with figures (48x73cm-19x29in) s. canvas on board. 31-May-4 Stephan Welz, Johannesburg #115 (SA.R 4500)

BRIGGS, Austin (1909-1973) American
£227 $425 €331 Sinking aircraft carrier (51x41cm-20x16in) s. board. 26-Feb-4 Illustration House, New York #31
£267 $500 €390 Indian photographs Chevy is woman tourist practices war-whoops (13x33cm-5x13in) masonite. 26-Feb-4 Illustration House, New York #32

BRIGGS, H (19th C) British?
£1333 $2400 €1946 Cows at water (41x51cm-16x20in) s. 25-Apr-4 Hindman, Chicago #1550/R est:2500-5000

BRIGGS, Raymond (1934-) British
Works on paper
£1300 $2249 €1898 Snowman and boy dancing II (15x15cm-6x6in) pencil prov.exhib. 11-Dec-3 Sotheby's, London #181/R est:1000-1500

BRIGHT, Constance M (fl.1905-1937) British
£1250 $2088 €1825 Interrupted sitting (46x38cm-18x15in) s.d.1909. 16-Nov-3 Desmond Judd, Cranbrook #1032

BRIGHT, Harry (fl.1867-1892) British
Works on paper
£250 $468 €365 Bullfinch feeding young (23x18cm-9x7in) s.d.1885 W/C. 23-Jul-4 Tring Auctions, Tring #267/R
£260 $473 €380 Winter landscape with bullfinches (43x20cm-17x8in) s.d.1881 W/C. 30-Jun-4 Neal & Fletcher, Woodbridge #272
£400 $688 €584 Goldfinches with blossom (28x23cm-11x9in) s.d.1887 W/C. 5-Dec-3 Keys, Aylsham #424
£450 $752 €657 Cockatoo (31x23cm-12x9in) s.d.1867 W/C bodycol. 14-Oct-3 Bonhams, Knightsbridge #32/R
£480 $826 €701 Greenfinches on a bramble bush (42x30cm-17x12in) s.d.1876 W/C. 3-Dec-3 Bonhams, Knightsbridge #23/R
£480 $787 €701 Mallard duck fleeing hunters (30x23cm-12x9in) s.d.1887 W/C htd white. 3-Jun-3 Fellows & Sons, Birmingham #156/R
£550 $864 €798 Finches. Robins (48x33cm-19x13in) s.d.1890 pencil W/C htd white pair. 28-Aug-3 Christie's, Kensington #455/R

BRIGHT, Henry (1814-1873) British
Works on paper
£260 $481 €380 Lake scene, Wybroke Park, Devon (15x25cm-6x10in) i. sepia blue wash htd white. 9-Mar-4 Capes Dunn, Manchester #674
£400 $736 €584 Early morning , Calais (10x15cm-4x6in) mono. pastel pencil. 11-Jun-4 Keys, Aylsham #568/R
£520 $957 €759 Mill on the Norfolk Broads (9x13cm-4x5in) s. pencil pastel. 11-Jun-4 Keys, Aylsham #589/R
£800 $1472 €1168 Kingfisher's haunt. Home of the winchat (24x29cm-9x11in) s.i.d.1886 pencil W/C bodycol pair. 25-Mar-4 Christie's, Kensington #103

BRIGHT, Henry and DODD, Charles Tattershall (19th C) British
£2000 $3200 €2920 Old bridge and ancient palace on the Medway at Maidstone (307x41cm-121x16in) 21-Sep-3 Desmond Judd, Cranbrook #1058

BRIGHT, Kate (1964-) British
£1500 $2760 €2250 Warsaw water (100x122cm-39x48in) s.i.d.2000 verso acrylic glitter prov. 24-Jun-4 Sotheby's, Olympia #427/R est:2000-3000

BRIGMAN, Anne (1869-1950) American
Photographs
£1818 $3200 €2654 Lichen (25x20cm-10x8in) s.i.d.1918 silver print. 20-May-4 Swann Galleries, New York #302/R est:3500-4500
£1916 $3200 €2797 Isadora Duncan (24x18cm-9x7in) s.i. silver print. 21-Oct-3 Swann Galleries, New York #96/R est:4000-5000
£2260 $4000 €3300 Dryad (25x20cm-10x8in) mono. s.i.verso photo. 28-Apr-4 Sotheby's, New York #113/R est:5000-7000
£3353 $5600 €4895 Sanctuary (24x20cm-9x8in) s.d.1921 verso silver print. 21-Oct-3 Swann Galleries, New York #95/R est:5000-7000
£5000 $9000 €7300 Heart of the storm (25x20cm-10x8in) s.num.2 gelatin silver print. 22-Apr-4 Phillips, New York #44/R est:10000-15000

BRIGNOLI, Luigi (1881-1952) Italian
£1342 $2403 €2000 Piazza Vecchia, Bergamo (32x43cm-13x17in) s. cardboard on canvas. 25-May-4 Finarte Semenzato, Milan #167/R est:1500-1700

BRIGNONI, Sergio (1903-2002) Swiss
£560 $1003 €818 Abstract composition (31x39cm-12x15in) s.d.94 mixed media. 12-May-4 Dobiaschofsky, Bern #1414 (S.FR 1300)

£881 $1498 €1286 Landscape in the Waadt (25x18cm-10x7in) i.d.1944 stretcher canvas on board. 7-Nov-3 Dobiaschofsky, Bern #232/R (S.FR 2000)
£948 $1697 €1384 Formes en couleur (49x70cm-19x28in) s. 14-May-4 Dobiaschofsky, Bern #247/R est:2400 (S.FR 2200)
£991 $1775 €1447 Figures (32x66cm-13x26in) s. bears d. canvas on board. 14-May-4 Dobiaschofsky, Bern #246/R est:3600 (S.FR 2300)
£991 $1775 €1447 Untitled (50x70cm-20x28in) s.d.79. 14-May-4 Dobiaschofsky, Bern #248/R est:3800 (S.FR 2300)
£1101 $1872 €1607 Walkers on path (57x41cm-22x16in) s.d.1947 i. stretcher. 7-Nov-3 Dobiaschofsky, Bern #261/R est:4500 (S.FR 2500)
£1101 $1872 €1607 Abstract composition (60x44cm-24x17in) s.d.91 board. 7-Nov-3 Dobiaschofsky, Bern #271/R est:3000 (S.FR 2500)
£1207 $2160 €1762 Metamorphosis (37x37cm-15x15in) s.d.91 canvas on board. 13-May-4 Stuker, Bern #51/R est:3000-4000 (S.FR 2800)
£1454 $2471 €2123 Dusk (28x25cm-11x10in) s. i. verso canvas on panel. 7-Nov-3 Dobiaschofsky, Bern #233/R est:4000 (S.FR 3300)
£1552 $2778 €2266 Printemps (34x55cm-13x22in) s.d.72 acrylic sandpaper. 13-May-4 Stuker, Bern #50/R est:4000-5000 (S.FR 3600)
£1586 $2696 €2316 Au bord de la mer (54x80cm-21x31in) s.d.69-73 i. verso panel. 7-Nov-3 Dobiaschofsky, Bern #360/R est:6000 (S.FR 3600)
£1674 $2846 €2444 Formes dans l'espace (69x69cm-27x27in) s.d.78 acrylic prov. 22-Nov-3 Burkhard, Luzern #12/R est:3000-4000 (S.FR 3700)
£1810 $3077 €2643 Composition (45x47cm-18x19in) s. masonite. 28-Nov-3 Zofingen, Switzerland #2932/R est:5500 (S.FR 4000)
£2081 $3538 €3038 Untitled (34x60cm-13x24in) s.d.1988 canvas on board. 22-Nov-3 Burkhard, Luzern #11/R est:2500-3500 (S.FR 4600)
£2203 $3744 €3216 Untitled (80x100cm-31x39in) s.d.1993. 7-Nov-3 Dobiaschofsky, Bern #262/R est:7500 (S.FR 5000)
£2203 $3744 €3216 Abstract composition (80x101cm-31x40in) s.d.91 board. 7-Nov-3 Dobiaschofsky, Bern #264/R est:7000 (S.FR 5000)
£2620 $4821 €3825 Landscape (29x39cm-11x15in) s.d.1950 canvas on pavatex prov. 8-Jun-4 Germann, Zurich #124/R est:5000-6000 (S.FR 6000)
£2620 $4821 €3825 Landscape (30x40cm-12x16in) s.d.1956 canvas on pavatex prov. 8-Jun-4 Germann, Zurich #125/R est:8000-10000 (S.FR 6000)
£3070 $5649 €4482 Fluides (96x84cm-38x33in) acrylic. 23-Jun-4 Koller, Zurich #3123/R est:7000-9000 (S.FR 7000)
£3167 $5385 €4624 Paysage de Collioure (50x73cm-20x29in) s.d.1952 acrylics.i. stretcher prov. 25-Nov-3 Germann, Zurich #61/R est:8000-12000 (S.FR 7000)
£3167 $5385 €4624 L'araignee (66x31cm-26x12in) s.d.1948 panel prov. 25-Nov-3 Germann, Zurich #63/R est:8000-12000 (S.FR 7000)
£3167 $5385 €4624 Composition anthropomorphe (45x24cm-18x9in) s.d.1933 board prov. 25-Nov-3 Germann, Zurich #68/R est:8000-12000 (S.FR 7000)
£3965 $6740 €5789 Wooded landscape with lakeside house (60x70cm-24x28in) s.d.1940 panel. 7-Nov-3 Dobiaschofsky, Bern #229/R est:18000 (S.FR 9000)
£6608 $11233 €9648 Harbour with fishing boats (38x55cm-15x22in) s.d.1950 board. 7-Nov-3 Dobiaschofsky, Bern #234/R est:16000 (S.FR 15000)
£6897 $12345 €10070 Paysage en Espagne (54x76cm-21x30in) s.d.1951 i. verso board. 14-May-4 Dobiaschofsky, Bern #242/R est:22000 (S.FR 16000)
Works on paper
£366 $656 €534 Formes et couleurs (21x27cm-8x11in) s.d.1986 mixed media. 12-May-4 Dobiaschofsky, Bern #1410/R (S.FR 850)
£388 $694 €566 Formes en couleurs (28x35cm-11x14in) s.d.1990 mixed media. 12-May-4 Dobiaschofsky, Bern #1413 (S.FR 900)
£647 $1157 €945 Southern landscape with houses (31x47cm-12x19in) s.i.d.1933 W/C. 14-May-4 Dobiaschofsky, Bern #245/R est:1600 (S.FR 1500)
£661 $1123 €965 Abstract composition (30x45cm-12x18in) s.d.89 mixed media. 7-Nov-3 Dobiaschofsky, Bern #269/R (S.FR 1500)
£749 $1273 €1094 Abstract composition (37x54cm-15x21in) s.d.76 mixed media. 7-Nov-3 Dobiaschofsky, Bern #268/R (S.FR 1700)
£819 $1466 €1196 Southern fields with small house (31x47cm-12x19in) s.i.d.1933 W/C. 14-May-4 Dobiaschofsky, Bern #243/R est:2000 (S.FR 1900)
£819 $1466 €1196 Papillons en couleur (15x19cm-6x7in) s. mixed media. 14-May-4 Dobiaschofsky, Bern #244/R est:2400 (S.FR 1900)
£881 $1498 €1286 Abstract composition (39x54cm-15x21in) s.d.66 mixed media. 7-Nov-3 Dobiaschofsky, Bern #266/R (S.FR 2000)
£969 $1648 €1415 Trinite (55x75cm-22x30in) s.d.1960 mixed media. 7-Nov-3 Dobiaschofsky, Bern #257/R (S.FR 2200)
£1131 $1923 €1651 Composition (34x27cm-13x11in) s.d.1947 gouache. 28-Nov-3 Zofingen, Switzerland #2930/R est:2500 (S.FR 2500)
£1304 $2387 €1904 Figure (38x54cm-15x21in) s.d.1976 mixed media canvas. 4-Jun-4 Zofingen, Switzerland #2760/R est:4000 (S.FR 3000)
£1322 $2247 €1930 Abstract composition (43x60cm-17x24in) s.d.85 mixed media. 7-Nov-3 Dobiaschofsky, Bern #259/R est:4000 (S.FR 3000)

BRIGNONI-ARANIS, Graziella (1906-) Chilean
£308 $524 €450 Summer vegetable garden (42x77cm-17x30in) s. 5-Nov-3 Dobiaschofsky, Bern #396/R (S.FR 700)
£441 $749 €644 Untitled abstract composition (81x112cm-32x44in) s.d.67 panel. 5-Nov-3 Dobiaschofsky, Bern #397/R (S.FR 1000)

BRIGUIBOUL, Jean Pierre Marcel Numa (attrib) (1837-1892) French
£1000 $1850 €1460 Standing female nude (70x48cm-28x19in) 10-Feb-4 Bonhams, Knightsbridge #171/R est:700-900

BRIL, Paul (1554-1626) Flemish
Works on paper
£8108 $14270 €12000 Tree on a rocky outcrop, buildings behind (23x17cm-9x7in) i.verso pen brown ink wash black chk prov.lit. 19-May-4 Sotheby's, Amsterdam #10/R est:2000-3000

BRIL, Paul (attrib) (1554-1626) Flemish
£1800 $2916 €2628 St. Jerome amongst rocks by a river, capriccio townscape beyond (25x36cm-10x14in) copper. 30-Jul-3 Hamptons Fine Art, Godalming #244/R est:2000-3000
£3221 $5992 €4800 The temptation of Saint Antonius (54x71cm-21x28in) s. panel. 5-Mar-4 Wendl, Rudolstadt #3597/R est:6500
Works on paper
£1311 $2400 €1914 Landscape with a town on a river (17x28cm-7x11in) pen brown ink. 29-Jan-4 Swann Galleries, New York #152/R est:1000-1500

BRIL, Paul (circle) (1554-1626) Flemish
£6711 $12013 €10000 Paysage fluvial avec le Christ guerissant le possede de Gerasa (26x35cm-10x14in) copper. 25-May-4 Palais de Beaux Arts, Brussels #64/R est:12500-17500

BRIL, Paul (studio) (1554-1626) Flemish
£12000 $20400 €17520 Classical river landscape with herdsmen and goats resting amongst ruins (50x66cm-20x26in) 29-Oct-3 Christie's, London #13/R est:7000-10000

BRIL, Paul (style) (1554-1626) Flemish
£6960 $12041 €10162 Mars and Venus in an extensive river landscape with putti playing and dancing (57x80cm-22x31in) copper. 9-Dec-3 Sotheby's, Olympia #313/R est:6000-8000

BRILL, Reginald C (1902-1974) British
Works on paper
£300 $561 €438 Artist (28x27cm-11x11in) chl htd white. 26-Feb-4 Bruton Knowles, Cheltenham #54
£6176 $10500 €9017 Rest (87x112cm-34x44in) s.i.verso mixed media paper on board. 19-Nov-3 Bonhams & Butterfields, San Francisco #152/R

BRIN, Émile-Quentin (1863-?) French
£1867 $3379 €2800 Femmes au bord du lac (94x141cm-37x56in) s. 4-Apr-4 Salle des ventes Pillet, Lyon la Foret #19 est:3000-4000

BRINCKMANN, Enrique (1938-) Spanish
Works on paper
£338 $592 €480 Figure (33x23cm-13x9in) s.d.1972 ink wash. 16-Dec-3 Segre, Madrid #194/R

BRINCKMANN, Philip Hieronymus (1709-1761) German
£873 $1590 €1275 Coastal landscape with shrine (19x23cm-7x9in) mono. panel. 16-Jun-4 Fischer, Luzern #1237/R (S.FR 2000)

BRINCKMANN, Philip Hieronymus (attrib) (1709-1761) German
£1702 $2757 €2400 River landscape with three men in boat (50x70cm-20x28in) i. verso lit. 23-May-3 Karlheinz Kaupp, Staufen #1673/R est:800

BRINDEAU DE JARNY, Louis Edouard (1867-1943) French
Works on paper
£355 $592 €500 Portrait d'homme (51x40cm-20x16in) s. pastel. 16-Jun-3 Gros & Delettrez, Paris #257/R

BRINDISI, Remo (1918-1996) Italian
£270 $476 €400 Venice (50x30cm-20x12in) s. tempera paper on canvas. 19-May-4 Il Ponte, Milan #1146
£270 $476 €400 Pastoral scene (40x30cm-16x12in) s. s.verso. 19-May-4 Il Ponte, Milan #1133
£352 $616 €500 View of Venice (40x30cm-16x12in) s. tempera. 17-Dec-3 Il Ponte, Milan #1188
£567 $1043 €850 Venice (25x20cm-10x8in) s. s.verso painted c.1990. 10-Jun-4 Galleria Pace, Milan #74/R
£596 $1085 €900 Maternity (50x40cm-20x16in) s. s.verso. 17-Jun-4 Galleria Pananti, Florence #408/R
£608 $1070 €900 Human condition (72x51cm-28x20in) s. tempera cardboard painted 1967. 24-May-4 Christie's, Milan #37
£612 $1096 €900 Venice (30x20cm-12x8in) s. painted 1970. 16-Mar-4 Finarte Semenzato, Milan #75
£612 $1096 €900 Maternity (70x50cm-28x20in) s. tempera paper on cardboard painted 1970. 22-Mar-4 Sant Agostino, Torino #470/R
£671 $1242 €1000 Landscape (66x48cm-26x19in) s. s.verso tempera. 13-Mar-4 Meeting Art, Vercelli #505
£694 $1097 €1000 Man reading (31x31cm-12x12in) board. 6-Sep-3 Meeting Art, Vercelli #427
£733 $1320 €1100 Venice (40x30cm-16x12in) s. 22-Apr-4 Finarte Semenzato, Rome #164/R
£800 $1448 €1200 Pastoral scene (40x30cm-16x12in) s. 2-Apr-4 Farsetti, Prato #9
£800 $1448 €1200 Venice (30x40cm-12x16in) s. painted 1991. 2-Apr-4 Farsetti, Prato #163/R
£816 $1461 €1200 Venice (20x30cm-8x12in) s. 16-Mar-4 Finarte Semenzato, Milan #72/R
£845 $1479 €1200 View of Venice (40x30cm-16x12in) s. 17-Dec-3 Il Ponte, Milan #1172
£933 $1717 €1400 Pastoral scene (50x40cm-20x16in) s. painted 1994. 12-Jun-4 Meeting Art, Vercelli #258/R
£1014 $1784 €1500 Pastoral scene (40x30cm-16x12in) s. s.verso. 24-May-4 Christie's, Milan #50/R est:1500-2000
£1027 $1747 €1500 Venice (30x40cm-12x16in) s. 7-Nov-3 Galleria Rosenberg, Milan #136/R est:1500
£1034 $1728 €1500 Crucifixion (30x20cm-12x8in) s. s.verso. 13-Nov-3 Galleria Pace, Milan #41/R est:2200
£1049 $1783 €1500 Venice (50x70cm-20x28in) s.i. lit. 29-Nov-3 Farsetti, Prato #520/R
£1056 $1754 €1500 Flowers (40x30cm-16x12in) s. 11-Jun-3 Finarte Semenzato, Milan #713/R
£1074 $1987 €1600 Venice (30x40cm-12x16in) s. 13-Mar-4 Meeting Art, Vercelli #140 est:1000
£1074 $1987 €1600 Lovers (40x30cm-16x12in) s. s.verso. 13-Mar-4 Meeting Art, Vercelli #424 est:1000
£1119 $1869 €1600 Venice (50x40cm-20x16in) s. s.verso. 26-Jun-3 Sant Agostino, Torino #236/R est:2000
£1133 $2085 €1700 Pastoral scene (70x50cm-28x20in) s. tempera paper. 12-Jun-4 Meeting Art, Vercelli #745/R est:1500
£1181 $1865 €1700 Venice (40x30cm-16x12in) 6-Sep-3 Meeting Art, Vercelli #451 est:1000
£1189 $2021 €1700 Maternity (60x50cm-24x20in) s. s.i.verso painted 1971. 25-Nov-3 Sotheby's, Milan #83/R est:800-1000
£1267 $2331 €1900 San Trovaso, Italy (100x80cm-39x31in) s. s.i.verso tempera paper on canvas painted 1986 lit. 12-Jun-4 Meeting Art, Vercelli #622/R est:1500
£1275 $2283 €1900 Venice (70x50cm-28x20in) s. i.d.1971 verso lit. 30-May-4 Meeting Art, Vercelli #94 est:1500

£1333 $2453 €2000 Venice (70x50cm-28x20in) s. s.verso. 12-Jun-4 Meeting Art, Vercelli #369/R est:2000
£1333 $2453 €2000 Venice (70x50cm-28x20in) s. s.verso. 12-Jun-4 Meeting Art, Vercelli #992/R est:2000
£1342 $2483 €2000 Maternity (70x50cm-28x20in) s. s.verso. 13-Mar-4 Meeting Art, Vercelli #511 est:1500
£1379 $2207 €2000 Maternity (40x30cm-16x12in) s. s.verso. 13-Mar-3 Galleria Pace, Milan #107/R est:2500-3000
£1477 $2732 €2200 Venice (50x40cm-20x16in) s. s.i.verso. 11-Mar-4 Galleria Pace, Milan #46/R est:2200-3200
£1497 $2679 €2200 Maternity (80x60cm-31x24in) s. painted 1964. 16-Mar-4 Finarte Semenzato, Milan #74/R est:1100
£1497 $2679 €2200 San Trovaso, Venice (70x50cm-28x20in) s.s.verso. 22-Mar-4 Sant Agostino, Torino #469/R est:2000
£1538 $2615 €2200 Winner and defeated (80x70cm-31x28in) s. s.verso painted 1980. 24-Nov-3 Christie's, Milan #68/R est:2000-3000
£1538 $2615 €2200 Venice (70x50cm-28x20in) s. s.verso. 24-Nov-3 Christie's, Milan #79/R est:1500-2000
£1538 $2615 €2200 Venice (50x70cm-20x28in) s. s.i.verso painted 1971. 25-Nov-3 Sotheby's, Milan #48/R est:800-1000
£1739 $2852 €2400 Venice (40x30cm-16x12in) s. s.verso. 29-May-3 Galleria Pace, Milan #61 est:3800
£1745 $3228 €2600 Pastoral scene (60x50cm-24x20in) s. s.i.verso. 11-Mar-4 Galleria Pace, Milan #116/R
£2013 $3725 €3000 Venice (40x50cm-16x20in) s. painted 1985 lit. 13-Mar-4 Meeting Art, Vercelli #537 est:2000
£2013 $3604 €3000 Venice (70x50cm-28x20in) s..si.verso. 29-May-4 Farsetti, Prato #563/R est:2500-3500
£2069 $3455 €3000 Protesters (60x50cm-24x20in) s.s.verso. 13-Nov-3 Galleria Pace, Milan #113/R est:3000
£2083 $3292 €3000 Figure (60x80cm-24x31in) painted 1960. 6-Sep-3 Meeting Art, Vercelli #710 est:3000
£2200 $4048 €3300 Goat (70x50cm-28x20in) s. s.i.d.1953 verso prov. 8-Jun-4 Finarte Semenzato, Milan #306/R est:2300-2700
£2245 $4018 €3300 Shepherd (100x70cm-39x28in) painted 1967. 16-Mar-4 Finarte Semenzato, Milan #71/R est:1200
£2817 $4676 €4000 Fucilazione (80x70cm-31x28in) s. 14-Jun-3 Meeting Art, Vercelli #222/R est:4000
£2817 $4676 €4000 Gli Amici (100x70cm-39x28in) s. s.i.verso painted 1974. 14-Jun-3 Meeting Art, Vercelli #494/R est:4000
£2953 $5463 €4400 Flute players (60x50cm-24x20in) s. lit. 13-Mar-4 Meeting Art, Vercelli #246 est:2000
£3221 $5766 €4800 Venice. Woman (70x50cm-28x20in) s. two. 25-May-4 Sotheby's, Milan #17a est:2000
£4082 $7306 €6000 Passer-by (80x60cm-31x24in) s. painted 1954 prov. 16-Mar-4 Finarte Semenzato, Milan #314/R est:3300
£5034 $9010 €7500 Stalin's myth destroyed (200x124cm-79x49in) painted 1958 lit. 25-May-4 Sotheby's, Milan #52/R est:7000
£6643 $11294 €9500 Maternity (93x70cm-37x28in) s.d.50 s.i.verso. 25-Nov-3 Sotheby's, Milan #28/R est:5000-6000
Works on paper
£267 $480 €400 Pastoral scene (32x21cm-13x8in) s. graphite exec.1949. 22-Apr-4 Finarte Semenzato, Rome #45
£278 $439 €400 Venice (35x25cm-14x10in) pastel card on canvas. 6-Sep-3 Meeting Art, Vercelli #472
£282 $493 €400 Composition (25x15cm-10x6in) s.d.1984 felt-tip pen on canvas. 17-Dec-3 Il Ponte, Milan #879

BRINDLE, Ewart Melbourne (1906-1995) American
£1257 $2100 €1835 Doctor examining Little Leaguer's throwing arm (66x58cm-26x23in) s. canvasboard painted c.1933-34. 15-Nov-3 Illustration House, New York #153/R est:2500-4000

BRINDLEY, Charles A (fl.1888-1898) British
Works on paper
£280 $493 €409 Winter, Ashbrooke Common, Surrey (35x26cm-14x10in) s.d.1911 W/C. 19-May-4 Dreweatt Neate, Newbury #24/R

BRINKEN, Charlie (1911-?) Australian
Works on paper
£859 $1607 €1289 Ceremony (27x73cm-11x29in) earth pigments eucalyptus bark exec.c.1962 prov. 26-Jul-4 Sotheby's, Melbourne #295/R (A.D 2200)
£1094 $2045 €1641 Untitled (39x29cm-15x11in) earth pigments eucalyptus bark exec.c.1962 prov. 26-Jul-4 Sotheby's, Melbourne #294/R (A.D 2800)
£1172 $2191 €1758 Two crocodiles (24x70cm-9x28in) earth pigments eucalyptus bark exec.c.1960 prov. 26-Jul-4 Sotheby's, Melbourne #521/R est:3000-4000 (A.D 3000)

BRION DE LA TOUR, Louis (18th C) French
Works on paper
£400 $692 €584 Arrest of Charlotte Corday, with Jean Paul Marat's body carried away (20x26cm-8x10in) pen brown ink W/C. 12-Dec-3 Christie's, Kensington #482/R

BRIONES, Fernando (1905-1988) Spanish
£308 $524 €450 Seated female nude (45x38cm-18x15in) s. i. verso panel. 5-Nov-3 Dobiaschofsky, Bern #398/R (S.FR 700)

BRIOSCHI, Antonio (1855-1920) Italian
£604 $1069 €900 Fishermen (26x20cm-10x8in) s. cardboard on canvas. 1-May-4 Meeting Art, Vercelli #77

BRIOSCHI, Athos (20th C) Italian
£336 $594 €500 Lake landscape (30x40cm-12x16in) s. 1-May-4 Meeting Art, Vercelli #13

BRIOSCHI, Othmar (1854-1912) Austrian
£720 $1224 €1051 Forest at sunset (19x35cm-7x14in) s. s.d.1884 verso panel. 19-Nov-3 Bonhams, New Bond Street #31/R

BRISCOE, Arthur (1873-1943) British
Works on paper
£520 $931 €759 Yachts. Yachts and dinghies on a tidal river (26x36cm-10x14in) s.d.36 W/C two. 25-May-4 Sworder & Son, Bishops Stortford #357/R
£750 $1418 €1095 Gulls (38x55cm-15x22in) s.i.d.29 pen ink W/C. 17-Feb-4 Bonhams, New Bond Street #23/R
£1850 $3145 €2701 Calm (51x72cm-20x28in) s.i. W/C prov. 26-Nov-3 Hamptons Fine Art, Godalming #98/R est:1000-1500
£2000 $3640 €2920 Baltic trader, three masted vessel (53x73cm-21x29in) s.d.37 verso W/C. 17-Jun-4 Clevedon Sale Rooms #1056/R est:2000-3000
£2800 $5292 €4088 Fish Market, Brixham (38x55cm-15x22in) s.d.29 pen ink W/C. 17-Feb-4 Bonhams, New Bond Street #24/R est:2000-3000

BRISCOE, Franklin D (1844-1903) American
£495 $900 €723 Along the French coast (35x61cm-14x24in) s.d.1896. 29-Jun-4 Sotheby's, New York #226/R
£1188 $1900 €1734 Winter landscape with central Indian scout on horseback (71x58cm-28x23in) s.d.1870. 20-Sep-3 Pook & Pook, Downington #186/R
£1227 $2000 €1791 Ships in a harbour (43x64cm-17x25in) s. 28-Sep-3 Simpson's, Houston #310/R
£1374 $2500 €2006 Pulling in the nets (72x96cm-28x38in) s. 29-Jun-4 Sotheby's, New York #150/R est:3000-5000
£1375 $2200 €2008 On the seas (36x61cm-14x24in) s.d.1896. 20-Sep-3 Sloans & Kenyon, Bethesda #1190/R est:1500-1750
£1478 $2750 €2158 Portrait of sailing vessel underway (20x30cm-8x12in) s. board. 3-Mar-4 Alderfer's, Hatfield #390/R est:1000-1500
£1529 $2600 €2232 Sunset over an exotic shore with ruins (30x51cm-12x20in) s. indis d. 31-Oct-3 North East Auctions, Portsmouth #1735
£1648 $3000 €2406 Surviving nature's fury at sea (40x71cm-16x28in) s. 29-Jun-4 Sotheby's, New York #189/R est:3000-4000
£1747 $3250 €2551 Portrait of sailing vessel underway under moonlit sky (18x15cm-7x6in) s. panel. 3-Mar-4 Alderfer's, Hatfield #391/R est:1000-1500
£3198 $5500 €4669 Tropical sunset coastal scene with sailboats, crashing waves and figure (74x124cm-29x49in) s. 6-Dec-3 Pook & Pook, Downington #485/R est:3000-5000
£3226 $5935 €4710 Arab caravan in a courtyard (107x71cm-42x28in) s.d.1875. 14-Jun-4 Waddingtons, Toronto #23/R est:10000-15000 (C.D 8000)
£3824 $6500 €5583 Breezy weather on the banks (25x43cm-10x17in) s. s.i.verso. 31-Oct-3 North East Auctions, Portsmouth #1890
£5028 $9000 €7341 Crowded shipping lanes offshore (61x107cm-24x42in) s. 16-Mar-4 Bonhams & Butterfields, San Francisco #6136/R est:3000-5000

BRISCOE, Franklin D (attrib) (1844-1903) American
£269 $450 €393 Forest scene (27x38cm-11x15in) board. 16-Nov-3 Bonhams & Butterfields, Los Angeles #7010/R
Works on paper
£233 $400 €340 Coastal scene (43x69cm-17x27in) gouache. 6-Dec-3 Pook & Pook, Downington #416d

BRISCOE-IRONSIDE, Henry (fl.1908) British
£2419 $4452 €3532 Sala Jupiter, Galleria Pitti (133x107cm-52x42in) s.i. s.i.stretcher. 14-Jun-4 Waddingtons, Toronto #154/R est:6000-8000 (C.D 6000)

BRISGAND, Gustave (?-1950) French
Works on paper
£2800 $4480 €4060 Nude reclining on pink fabric (54x90cm-21x35in) s. pastel. 18-Sep-3 Christie's, Kensington #186/R est:2000-3000

BRISIGHELLA, Carlo (17/18th C) Italian
£5822 $9897 €8500 Stormy river landscape with figure. Stormy mountainous landscape (18x26cm-7x10in) s. copper pair. 4-Nov-3 Sotheby's, Amsterdam #88/R est:6000-8000

BRISPOT, Henri (1846-1928) French
£3691 $6533 €5500 Collation du cardinal (65x54cm-26x21in) s. 30-Apr-4 Tajan, Paris #124/R est:3500-4500

BRISS, Sami (1930-) French
£388 $694 €566 Woman in blue (31x22cm-12x9in) s. tempera. 12-May-4 Dobiaschofsky, Bern #363/R (S.FR 900)
£431 $772 €629 Six poissons dans la nuit (39x80cm-15x31in) s. i. verso panel. 12-May-4 Dobiaschofsky, Bern #362/R (S.FR 1000)

BRISSAUD, Pierre (1885-?) French
Works on paper
£270 $484 €400 Embarras caleches (22x30cm-9x12in) s W/C. 5-May-4 Claude Boisgirard, Paris #12/R
£439 $786 €650 Dans la palmeraie (32x25cm-13x10in) s.d.1922 Chinese ink W/C. 5-May-4 Claude Boisgirard, Paris #13/R

BRISSOT DE WARVILLE, Felix-Saturnin (1818-1892) French
£700 $1169 €1022 Feeding time (27x35cm-11x14in) s. 8-Oct-3 Christie's, Kensington #814/R
£733 $1313 €1100 Oriental market (14x22cm-6x9in) s. panel lit. 14-May-4 Schloss Ahlden, Ahlden #2791/R
£797 $1307 €1100 Moutons au paturage pres de la Vanne (28x56cm-11x22in) s. fan paper. 11-May-3 Osenat, Fontainebleau #69
£828 $1382 €1200 Shepherd with flock in front of barn (40x56cm-16x22in) s. 9-Jul-3 Hugo Ruef, Munich #63/R
£933 $1671 €1400 Moutons. s. panel. 15-May-4 other European Auctioneer #54
£1667 $2717 €2400 Shepherd with his flock (30x40cm-12x16in) s. panel. 29-Sep-3 Sotheby's, Amsterdam #74/R
£1667 $3050 €2500 Berger et moutons (27x35cm-11x14in) s. panel. 6-Jun-4 Osenat, Fontainebleau #97/R est:2500-3000

£1667 $3050 €2500 Berger et moutons (24x19cm-9x7in) s. panel. 6-Jun-4 Osenat, Fontainebleau #95/R est:3500-4000
£1933 $3538 €2900 Paturage des moutons (17x28cm-7x11in) s. panel lit. 6-Jun-4 Osenat, Fontainebleau #93/R est:3000-3500
£3000 $5490 €4500 Berger (54x65cm-21x26in) s. 6-Jun-4 Osenat, Fontainebleau #96/R est:6500-7000
£3261 $5250 €4728 Sheep grazing by the coast (33x41cm-13x16in) s. 17-Aug-3 Jeffery Burchard, Florida #40
£3394 $5769 €4955 Donkey having a drink (43x51cm-17x20in) s. panel. 1-Dec-3 Koller, Zurich #6474/R est:2500-3500 (S.FR 7500)
£5245 $9021 €7500 Cour de ferme animee (41x65cm-16x26in) s. 7-Dec-3 Osenat, Fontainebleau #70 est:7000-7500
£8696 $14261 €12000 La vie a la ferme, jeunes anieres preparant leurs anes (56x45cm-22x18in) s. panel painted c.1861. 11-May-3 Osenat, Fontainebleau #74/R est:12000-14000
Works on paper
£797 $1307 €1100 Berger et ses moutons (30x56cm-12x22in) s. W/C fan mother of pearl. 11-May-3 Osenat, Fontainebleau #70/R

BRISTOL, John Bunyan (1826-1909) American
£1300 $2301 €1898 Extensive landscape at dusk (9x15cm-4x6in) board pair. 27-Apr-4 Bonhams, New Bond Street #114 est:400-600

BRISTOW, Edmund (1787-1876) British
£600 $1110 €876 Farrier (9x9cm-4x4in) s. panel. 14-Jul-4 Christie's, Kensington #931/R
£600 $1122 €876 Figures and dogs in an inn with gentlemen seated smoking and drinking (17x22cm-7x9in) s. panel. 22-Jul-4 Tennants, Leyburn #786
£1700 $2890 €2482 Stable interior with donkey, pig, and figure seated beside vegetables (26x40cm-10x16in) s.indis.d. panel. 19-Nov-3 Tennants, Leyburn #1195/R est:1500-2000
£2200 $4070 €3212 View of Windsor Castle with cattle in the foreground (41x61cm-16x24in) s.d.1860. 11-Mar-4 Duke & Son, Dorchester #221/R est:2000-3000
£3000 $5100 €4380 Grey hunter and stableboy (47x62cm-19x24in) s. indis i. 25-Nov-3 Christie's, London #87/R est:4000-6000
£4000 $7280 €5840 Before the monkey duel and the aftermath (20x28cm-8x11in) one s. pair. 1-Jul-4 Sotheby's, London #156/R est:5000-7000
£4200 $7140 €6132 Bay hunter with a terrier in an extensive landscape (61x75cm-24x30in) 27-Nov-3 Christie's, Kensington #97/R est:2000-3000

BRITISH SCHOOL, 18th C
£5200 $9516 €7592 Portrait of Prince Charles Edward Stewart, in uniform (74x61cm-29x24in) fringed oval. 8-Apr-4 Bonhams, Edinburgh #99/R est:1500-2000
£17500 $29750 €25550 Lady in blue (62x51cm-24x20in) 25-Nov-3 Christie's, London #188/R est:5000-8000

BRITISH SCHOOL, 19th C
£4876 $9020 €7119 Portrait of Rajput Prince or Indian aristocrat in a turban. 14-Mar-4 William A Smith, Plainfield #2/R
£14365 $26000 €20973 Maharaja of Tagore (229x147cm-90x58in) prov. 3-Apr-4 Neal Auction Company, New Orleans #290/R est:8000-12000
Photographs
£34091 $60000 €49773 Grenadier Guards, Crimean war (29x37cm-11x15in) photograph album by several artists. 20-May-4 Swann Galleries, New York #219/R est:40000-50000
Sculpture
£5120 $8500 €7475 Female gardener (173x38x28cm-68x15x11in) carrara marble inc green marble column. 4-Oct-3 Neal Auction Company, New Orleans #396/R est:600-9000
Works on paper
£3533 $6500 €5158 View of Ramsgate (25x38cm-10x15in) W/C pen ink sold with another. 10-Jun-4 Sotheby's, New York #260/R est:500-700
£6500 $11050 €9490 Portrait of General Sir Thomas Saumarex (61x46cm-24x18in) pastel prov. 4-Nov-3 Bonhams, New Bond Street #145/R est:2000-3000

BRITOVA, Nathalia (?) Russian
£272 $495 €400 Fin d'hiver. s. 8-Feb-4 Lesieur & Le Bars, Le Havre #34

BRITTAIN, Miller Gore (1912-1968) Canadian
£40541 $68919 €59190 Second hand store. The second hand shop (56x46cm-22x18in) one init.d.46 s.i.verso one one i. one oil one graphite conte two. 18-Nov-3 Sotheby's, Toronto #147/R est:30000-40000 (C.D 90000)
Works on paper
£880 $1610 €1285 Contemplative head (44x29cm-17x11in) init.i.d.1963 mixed media prov. 1-Jun-4 Hodgins, Calgary #292/R est:1200-1800 (C.D 2200)
£893 $1536 €1304 Woman with a locket (31x19cm-12x7in) init.d.46 mixed media. 2-Dec-3 Joyner Waddington, Toronto #121/R est:1500-2000 (C.D 2000)

BRITTAN, Charles Edward (jnr) (1870-1949) British
Works on paper
£400 $744 €584 Moorland valley (48x72cm-19x28in) s. W/C. 2-Mar-4 Bearnes, Exeter #390
£400 $708 €584 Sheep grazing near Burrator Reservoir (35x26cm-14x10in) s. W/C. 28-Apr-4 Hampton & Littlewood, Exeter #505/R
£400 $732 €584 Near Brodrick, Vale of Aaran (36x53cm-14x21in) s. W/C. 6-Jul-4 Bearnes, Exeter #458/R
£500 $815 €730 Moors at the Currons (27x45cm-11x18in) s. W/C. 23-Sep-3 Bonhams, Knightsbridge #26/R
£560 $1042 €818 Near Lydford, Dartmoor (35x25cm-14x10in) s. W/C prov. 2-Mar-4 Bearnes, Exeter #320/R
£920 $1481 €1334 At Sligachan, Isle of Skye (36x53cm-14x21in) s.i. W/C. 21-Aug-3 Bonhams, Edinburgh #1159
£1150 $2139 €1679 Evening near Cornwood (35x53cm-14x21in) s. W/C. 2-Mar-4 Bearnes, Exeter #321/R est:400-600

BRITTAN, Charles Edward (snr) (1837-1888) British
£300 $549 €438 Terriers in a stable interior (40x56cm-16x22in) s.d.1866 board. 6-Jul-4 Bearnes, Exeter #522/R
Works on paper
£300 $546 €438 The peaks of Arran from the golf course, Springtime (25x35cm-10x14in) s.d.1914 pencil W/C scratching out. 1-Jul-4 Christie's, Kensington #118/R
£380 $654 €555 Exmoor pool (28x46cm-11x18in) s. W/C exhib. 3-Dec-3 Christie's, Kensington #172
£400 $744 €584 Stormy coastal scene (38x58cm-15x23in) s.d.1867 W/C htd white. 2-Mar-4 Bearnes, Exeter #388/R
£440 $779 €642 Cattle on Dartmoor (25x41cm-10x16in) s. 27-Apr-4 Peter Francis, Wales #29/R
£450 $774 €657 A burn (23x34cm-9x13in) s. W/C. 4-Dec-3 Bonhams, Edinburgh #97
£550 $974 €803 Dartmoor ponies in the snow (25x41cm-10x16in) s.d.1908 W/C. 27-Apr-4 Peter Francis, Wales #28/R
£813 $1300 €1187 Owl (74x46cm-29x18in) s. W/C. 19-Sep-3 Freeman, Philadelphia #58/R est:500-800
£938 $1500 €1369 Leopard (46x74cm-18x29in) s. W/C. 19-Sep-3 Freeman, Philadelphia #57 est:500-800
£1250 $2000 €1825 Camel (46x74cm-18x29in) s. W/C. 19-Sep-3 Freeman, Philadelphia #55/R est:500-800
£1375 $2200 €2008 Ostrich (74x46cm-29x18in) s. W/C. 19-Sep-3 Freeman, Philadelphia #56 est:500-800

BRITTAN, Charles Edward (19/20th C) British
Works on paper
£1050 $1943 €1533 Views of Dartmoor (35x51cm-14x20in) s. W/C pair. 10-Mar-4 British Auctioneer #485 est:200-300

BRITTEN, Jack (1925-2002) Australian
£2383 $4123 €3479 Munga Munganoo, Ord river (91x122cm-36x48in) i.verso synthetic polymer paint prov. 10-Dec-3 Shapiro, Sydney #143/R est:6000-8000 (A.D 5600)
Works on paper
£854 $1349 €1238 Red back's camp (91x61cm-36x24in) s.i.d.1997 verso earth pigments binder canvas prov. 28-Jul-3 Sotheby's, Paddington #412/R est:2000-3000 (A.D 2100)
£938 $1753 €1407 Untitled (45x45cm-18x18in) i.verso pigment canvas exec. 2001 prov. 21-Jul-4 Shapiro, Sydney #31/R (A.D 2400)
£976 $1541 €1415 Untitled (40x50cm-16x20in) s.d.1992 verso earth pigments bush gum canvas prov. 28-Jul-3 Sotheby's, Paddington #288/R est:2000-4000 (A.D 2400)
£976 $1541 €1415 Untitled, bungle bungles (92x122cm-36x48in) earth pigments eucalyptus bark binder canvas prov. 28-Jul-3 Sotheby's, Paddington #557 est:3000-5000 (A.D 2400)
£1328 $2484 €1992 Eagle (40x51cm-16x20in) earth pigments bush gum canvas prov. 26-Jul-4 Sotheby's, Melbourne #217/R est:2000-4000 (A.D 3400)
£2051 $3835 €3077 Bungle bungles (53x70cm-21x28in) earth pigments bush gum canvasboard prov. 26-Jul-4 Sotheby's, Melbourne #218/R est:5000-8000 (A.D 5250)
£2734 $5113 €4101 Untitled (98x94cm-39x37in) s.verso earth pigments binder prov. 26-Jul-4 Sotheby's, Melbourne #453/R est:7000-10000 (A.D 7000)
£8203 $15340 €12305 Jarlilnji, plains kangaroo (80x160cm-31x63in) bears name.verso earth pigments bush gum prov.exhib. 26-Jul-4 Sotheby's, Melbourne #130/R est:15000-20000 (A.D 21000)
£9375 $17531 €14063 Eagle and bungle bungles (78x118cm-31x46in) earth pigments bush gum canvas prov. 26-Jul-4 Sotheby's, Melbourne #30/R est:15000-20000 (A.D 24000)
£9766 $18262 €14649 Frog hollow (81x128cm-32x50in) earth pigments bush gum canvas prov. 26-Jul-4 Sotheby's, Melbourne #131/R est:18000-25000 (A.D 25000)
£16406 $30680 €24609 Bungle bungles, Purnululu (100x118cm-39x46in) earth pigments bush gum canvas prov. 26-Jul-4 Sotheby's, Melbourne #31/R est:15000-20000 (A.D 42000)

BRITTEN, William Edward Frank (1848-1916) British
£600 $1116 €876 Maiden seated on a wall (37x23cm-15x9in) mono.d.1878 verso panel. 4-Mar-4 Christie's, Kensington #582/R
£1500 $2685 €2190 Captive audience (46x79cm-18x31in) s.d.1903. 18-Mar-4 Christie's, Kensington #458/R est:1500-2500

BRITTON, Charles (1930-) British
Works on paper
£550 $990 €825 Views on Dartmoor (26x35cm-10x14in) s. W/C pair. 21-Jan-4 John Bellman, Billingshurst #1774

BRITTON, Harry (1878-1958) Canadian
£536 $921 €783 Tidal river, New Brunswick (15x20cm-6x8in) s. canvas on board. 2-Dec-3 Joyner Waddington, Toronto #415 (C.D 1200)
£640 $1171 €934 Tidal river, New Brunswick, winter (30x37cm-12x15in) s. board. 1-Jun-4 Joyner Waddington, Toronto #492 (C.D 1600)
£645 $1187 €942 Landscape with farmstead (24x26cm-9x10in) s. board. 9-Jun-4 Walker's, Ottawa #80/R (C.D 1600)
£667 $1107 €974 Evening clouds, NB (30x30cm-12x12in) s. hard board painted c.1925. 5-Oct-3 Levis, Calgary #13a/R (C.D 1500)
£667 $1107 €974 Early spring, Parrsboro, NS (30x30cm-12x12in) s. hard board painted c.1925. 5-Oct-3 Levis, Calgary #13b/R (C.D 1500)
£1900 $3173 €2774 Canadian homestead (17x22cm-7x9in) s. panel. 14-Oct-3 Sotheby's, London #220/R est:400-600

BRIULLOV, Karl Pavlovich (1799-1852) Russian
Works on paper
£6090 $9500 € Greek lying on a rock. Study of a head. Two Greeks (20x26cm-8x10in) ink pencil three. 11-Apr-3 Christie's, Rockefeller NY #11/R est:10000-12000

BRIULLOV, Karl Pavlovich (circle) (1799-1852) Russian
£7432 $13081 €11000 Southern Italian landscape with girl resting (73x92cm-29x36in) prov. 22-May-4 Lempertz, Koln #1485/R est:3000

BRIZIO, Francesco (attrib) (1574-1623) Italian
Works on paper
£600 $1038 €876 Two figures discovering victims of a massacre (20x27cm-8x11in) i. red chk prov. 12-Dec-3 Christie's, Kensington #335/R

BRIZZI, Ary (1930-) Argentinian
£1955 $3500 €2854 Fraction 1. Foton 35 (80x80cm-31x31in) s.d.82 acrylic pair. 4-May-4 Arroyo, Buenos Aires #43/R est:3500
£3771 $6410 €5506 Division 9 (80x80cm-31x31in) s.verso painted 1973. 23-Nov-3 Subastas Odalys, Caracas #106/R est:6000

BRIZZI, K (19th C) ?
£1049 $1804 €1500 View of Hallstatt and the Hallstatter Lake in Salzkammergut (46x59cm-18x23in) s.d.46 canvas on panel. 3-Dec-3 Neumeister, Munich #538/R est:1500

BROAD, Frank (20th C) British
£400 $628 €580 Padding pool, Regents Park (56x66cm-22x26in) s. 28-Aug-3 Christie's, Kensington #309/R

BROADHEAD, W Smithson (fl.1923-1940) British
£1397 $2500 €2040 Standing man in desert with guide (102x76cm-40x30in) s. 15-May-4 Illustration House, New York #13/R est:3000-4000
£2994 $5000 €4371 Young woman taking photograph (79x53cm-31x21in) s. painted c.1920. 15-Nov-3 Illustration House, New York #160/R est:5000-8000

BROADHURST, Christopher (1953-) Canadian
£447 $800 €653 At the height of summer (182x76cm-72x30in) s.d.1982 verso. 6-May-4 Heffel, Vancouver #39/R (C.D 1100)

BROADLEY, Robert (1908-1988) South African/British
£330 $591 €482 Rose street, Sunday afternoon (35x45cm-14x18in) s. i.verso canvasboard. 31-May-4 Stephan Welz, Johannesburg #280 (SA.R 4000)
£756 $1369 €1104 Dahlias in a jug (48x39cm-19x15in) s.d.44 canvasboard. 30-Mar-4 Stephan Welz, Johannesburg #529 est:3000-5000 (SA.R 9000)
Works on paper
£403 $730 €588 Mosque, Bo-Kaap (25x35cm-10x14in) s.d.July 1970-71 pen ink W/C. 30-Mar-4 Stephan Welz, Johannesburg #200 est:900-1200 (SA.R 4800)

BROCAS, Samuel Frederick (1792-1847) Irish
Works on paper
£669 $1157 €950 Crows Island taken from Ross Island, Killarney (25x39cm-10x15in) s. W/C. 10-Dec-3 Bonhams & James Adam, Dublin #24/R

BROCHART, Constant Joseph (1816-1899) French
Works on paper
£739 $1323 €1079 Jeanne d'Arc (68x43cm-27x17in) s. pastel. 26-May-4 AB Stockholms Auktionsverk #2465/R (S.KR 10000)
£1000 $1570 €1460 Neapolitan beauty, the Bay of Naples beyond (69x59cm-27x23in) s. pastel. 16-Apr-3 Bamfords, Derby #593/R est:800-1200
£3200 $5888 €4800 Elegante a la robe bleue et son chien (123x85cm-48x33in) s. pastel. 9-Jun-4 Le Roux & Morel, Paris #33/R est:1500-2000
£6500 $12025 €9490 Spelling test (67x49cm-26x19in) s. pastel. 10-Mar-4 Sotheby's, Olympia #283/R est:4000-6000

BROCHART, Constant Joseph (attrib) (1816-1899) French
£1105 $2000 €1613 An intimate friend (38x30cm-15x12in) oil on metal. 3-Apr-4 Charlton Hall, Columbia #69/R est:800-1200

BROCK, Charles Edmund (1870-1938) British
Works on paper
£320 $586 €467 Stubborn youngster (25x33cm-10x13in) s. indis.d. W/C. 6-Jul-4 Bearnes, Exeter #453/R
£324 $581 €480 Illustration for The Pickwick Papers (29x22cm-11x9in) s. W/C. 8-May-4 Bukowskis, Helsinki #363/R

BROCK, Gustav (1849-1887) Danish
£1869 $2953 €2710 Scene from the war of 1870 with Napoleon's nephew on horseback (70x102cm-28x40in) s.d.78. 2-Sep-3 Rasmussen, Copenhagen #1695/R est:25000 (D.KR 20000)
£2718 $4675 €3968 Exercising the guards at Faelleden (43x62cm-17x24in) s.d.1881. 2-Dec-3 Kunsthallen, Copenhagen #529/R est:35000 (D.KR 29000)

BROCK, Sir Thomas (1847-1922) British
Sculpture
£2800 $5152 €4088 Frederic, Lorf Leighton (17cm-7in) s.d.1881 brown pat. bronze rouge marble plinth prov.lit. 11-Jun-4 Christie's, London #71/R est:2000-3000

BROCK, William (1874-?) British
£2028 $3387 €2900 Jeune fille tenant son setter dans la campagne (167x242cm-66x95in) s. 12-Oct-3 Salle des ventes Pillet, Lyon la Foret #7/R est:2000-2500

BROCKBANK, Albert Ernest (1862-1958) British
Works on paper
£440 $757 €642 River scene with distant cottages (76x127cm-30x50in) s.d.90. 2-Dec-3 Andrew Smith, Winchester #150
£450 $828 €657 Water meadows, Grez, Seine-et-Marne (24x39cm-9x15in) s. W/C prov.exhib.lit. 23-Jun-4 Cheffins, Cambridge #460/R

BROCKER, Ernst (1893-1963) German
£306 $510 €440 Moor landscape with Deining (61x80cm-24x31in) s.i. i. verso. 22-Oct-3 Neumeister, Munich #674
£406 $650 €593 Besigheim a neckan (51x61cm-20x24in) s.i. i.verso. 19-Sep-3 Freeman, Philadelphia #106/R
£442 $791 €650 Small riverside town (61x80cm-24x31in) s.i. 18-Mar-4 Neumeister, Munich #2649/R
£448 $749 €650 Moor landscape with village (70x100cm-28x39in) s. 9-Jul-3 Hugo Ruef, Munich #64
£467 $849 €700 Farmsteads on river shore (50x60cm-20x24in) s.i. 30-Jun-4 Neumeister, Munich #516/R
£476 $852 €700 Houses by river (50x70cm-20x28in) s.i. 18-Mar-4 Neumeister, Munich #2652
£566 $996 €826 Landscape with pond (30x40cm-12x16in) s. 23-May-4 Agra, Warsaw #48/R (P.Z 4000)
£664 $1109 €950 Farmstead in upper Bavaria (70x80cm-28x31in) s.i. 27-Jun-3 Michael Zeller, Lindau #500/R
£703 $1174 €1026 Rugged landscape with small pond (30x40cm-12x16in) s. painted c.1930. 19-Oct-3 Agra, Warsaw #62/R (P.Z 4500)
£756 $1309 €1104 Autumn landscape with pond (61x80cm-24x31in) s. 14-Dec-3 Agra, Warsaw #55/R (P.Z 5000)
£1061 $1867 €1549 Landscape (60x80cm-24x31in) s. 23-May-4 Agra, Warsaw #30/R (P.Z 7500)
£1061 $1867 €1549 Landscape with church (60x80cm-24x31in) s. 23-May-4 Agra, Warsaw #33/R (P.Z 7500)
£1119 $1924 €1600 Harvest with hay laden ox cart (40x50cm-16x20in) s.i. 5-Dec-3 Michael Zeller, Lindau #583/R est:1000
£1182 $2117 €1750 Hay laden ox cart (40x50cm-16x20in) s.i. 6-May-4 Michael Zeller, Lindau #630/R est:1000

BROCKETT, Violette E (20th C) American
£252 $400 €368 Siesta in Acapulco (102x61cm-40x24in) s. i.verso. 12-Sep-3 Aspire, Cleveland #87

BROCKHOFF, R (19th C) German?
£1351 $2378 €2000 Hunting still life (5x145cm-2x57in) s.d.1846. 22-May-4 Lempertz, Koln #1486 est:2000

BROCKHURST, Gerald Leslie (1890-1978) British
Prints
£6780 $12000 €9899 Adolescence, Kathleen Nancy Woodward (37x26cm-15x10in) s.i. init.i.verso etching. 28-Apr-4 Christie's, Rockefeller NY #6/R est:8000-12000
Works on paper
£1050 $1817 €1533 Portrait head of a girl (26x18cm-10x7in) s. pencil sold with sketch by Dora Carrington. 10-Dec-3 Bonhams, Bury St Edmunds #488/R est:400-450

BROCKHURST, Gerald Leslie (attrib) (1890-1978) British
Works on paper
£276 $500 €403 Portrait of a young woman (30x25cm-12x10in) pastel. 16-Apr-4 American Auctioneer #42/R

BROCKHUSEN, Theo von (1882-1919) German
£4762 $7571 €7000 Flat landscape with trees and cows (65x81cm-26x32in) s. 28-Feb-3 Altus, Berlin #468/R est:3500
£5667 $10427 €8500 Changing cubicles on the beach (64x80cm-25x31in) prov. 12-Jun-4 Villa Grisebach, Berlin #144/R est:9000-12000
£8000 $14720 €12000 Beach in Knokke (64x80cm-25x31in) prov. 12-Jun-4 Villa Grisebach, Berlin #143/R est:10000-15000
£9220 $14936 €13000 High mountain valley near Tolz (95x120cm-37x47in) s.i. lit. 23-May-3 Karlheinz Kaupp, Staufen #1990/R est:10000
£9790 $16643 €14000 Landscape (64x80cm-25x31in) s. exhib. 29-Nov-3 Villa Grisebach, Berlin #123/R est:12000-15000
£11189 $19245 €16000 View from Nieuport (64x80cm-25x31in) painted c.1909. 6-Dec-3 Quittenbaum, Hamburg #81/R est:14000
£19580 $33287 €28000 Havel bridge near Berlin (64x80cm-25x31in) s. prov.exhib. 29-Nov-3 Villa Grisebach, Berlin #124/R est:18000-24000

BROCKLESBURY, Horace (1866-1929) British
Works on paper
£281 $517 €422 The River Thames (27x35cm-11x14in) s.d.1913 W/C. 27-Jun-4 Joel, Victoria #30 (A.D 750)

BROCKTORFF, Charles Frederick de (19th C) German
Works on paper
£3000 $5100 €4380 Greek figures (22x18cm-9x7in) one.s.i. W/C over pencil htd bodycol gum arabic set of 6. 18-Nov-3 Sotheby's, London #124/R est:1500-2000

BROCKY, Karoly (1808-1855) Hungarian
Works on paper
£541 $968 €800 Child playing with doll on chair (14x17cm-6x7in) s. verso W/C board. 6-May-4 Michael Zeller, Lindau #629/R

BROCQUY, Louis le (1916-) Irish
£25503 $45651 €38000 Stephen's Green, July 42 (31x39cm-12x15in) init. s.i.d.1942 verso board. 26-May-4 James Adam, Dublin #122/R est:40000-60000
£36364 $61818 €52000 Garlanded goat (155x130cm-61x51in) s. tapestry. 25-Nov-3 De Veres Art Auctions, Dublin #102/R est:50000-70000
£40000 $71600 €58400 Sunlight in a wood; summer haze (76x61cm-30x24in) s.d.35 s.i.verso prov.lit. 13-May-4 Sotheby's, London #44/R est:20000-30000
£40000 $71600 €58400 Head of a man (91x59cm-36x23in) s.d.68 s.i.d.1968 on stretcher prov.exhib. 13-May-4 Sotheby's, London #106/R est:40000-60000
£50000 $89500 €73000 The Brothers Yeats (55x92cm-22x36in) s. s.i.d.1992 on overlap prov. 13-May-4 Sotheby's, London #72/R est:40000-60000
£52000 $93080 €75920 Reconstructed head and hand (80x80cm-31x31in) s.d.72 verso s.i.d.1972 on stretcher prov.exhib. 13-May-4 Sotheby's, London #108/R est:20000-30000
£200000 $358000 €292000 Lazarus (175x119cm-69x47in) s.d.54 prov.exhib.lit. 13-May-4 Sotheby's, London #70/R est:200000-300000

Prints

£2378	$4042	€3400	Untitled (66x50cm-26x20in) s.d.75 acquaint. 25-Nov-3 De Veres Art Auctions, Dublin #188 est:1000-1500
£2535	$4056	€3600	Head of Strindberg (77x58cm-30x23in) s.num.68/100 chromolithograph. 16-Sep-3 Whyte's, Dublin #196/R est:1500-2000
£2568	$4853	€3800	Head of Strinberg (77x58cm-30x23in) s.num.53/100 chromolithograph. 17-Feb-4 Whyte's, Dublin #28 est:2000-3000
£2917	$4754	€4200	Head of Joyce (53x40cm-21x16in) s.d.1981 edition 21/75 lithograph. 23-Sep-3 De Veres Art Auctions, Dublin #259/R est:1400-1800
£3056	$4981	€4400	Head of Strinberg (77x57cm-30x22in) s. num.55/100 aquatint etching. 24-Sep-3 James Adam, Dublin #117/R est:1200-1800

Sculpture

£2222	$3622	€3200	Child on shoulder (40cm-16in) 5 of 6 bronze raised on Portland stone plinth. 24-Sep-3 James Adam, Dublin #89/R est:2500-3500
£3092	$5689	€4700	The family (27x21x14cm-11x8x6in) s. bronze. 22-Jun-4 De Veres Art Auctions, Dublin #145a/R est:4500-5500

Works on paper

£2282	$4039	€3400	Boy with fish (14x17cm-6x7in) init.d.1954 pencil. 27-Apr-4 Whyte's, Dublin #14/R est:3000-5000
£5385	$9154	€7700	Annamore River, County Wicklow (12x18cm-5x7in) s.d.1947 pen ink wash prov. 18-Nov-3 Whyte's, Dublin #12/R est:6000-8000
£5405	$10216	€8000	James Joyce, study 21 (23x19cm-9x7in) s.i.verso chl prov.exhib. 17-Feb-4 Whyte's, Dublin #78/R est:8000-10000
£5694	$9282	€8200	Head of a young woman (21x19cm-8x7in) init.d.44 s.i.d.verso crayon. 24-Sep-3 James Adam, Dublin #60/R est:3000-5000
£6294	$10699	€9000	Etude pour une image de F G Lorca (23x19cm-9x7in) s.i.d. i.verso W/C prov. 23-Nov-3 Cornette de St.Cyr, Paris #216
£7200	$12888	€10512	Landscape view with distant town, possibly Killarney in Co Kerry (24x31cm-9x12in) s.d.48 pen black ink wax crayons W/C. 13-May-4 Sotheby's, London #99/R est:4000-6000
£8000	$14480	€12000	Iris I (18x25cm-7x10in) s. W/C prov. 30-Mar-4 De Veres Art Auctions, Dublin #72/R est:10000-15000
£8108	$15324	€12000	Apples on a table (14x23cm-6x9in) init.d.1942 W/C gouache. 17-Feb-4 Whyte's, Dublin #77/R est:6000-8000
£8667	$15687	€13000	Study towards an image of Federico Garcia Lorca (23x19cm-9x7in) W/C prov.exhib. 30-Mar-4 De Veres Art Auctions, Dublin #54/R est:9000-12000
£9859	$15775	€14000	Study 21, head of W B Yeats (23x18cm-9x7in) init.d.1975 chl prov.exhib. 16-Sep-3 Whyte's, Dublin #45/R est:3000-4000
£10133	$18341	€15200	Image of Samuel Beckett (40x31cm-16x12in) s.d.88 W/C prov. 30-Mar-4 De Veres Art Auctions, Dublin #20/R est:14000-18000
£18310	$31676	€26000	Image of Seamus Heaney (61x44cm-24x17in) s. W/C prov.exhib. 10-Dec-3 Bonhams & James Adam, Dublin #91/R est:15000-20000
£20000	$35800	€29200	Tinker girl (17x12cm-7x5in) s.d.47 pen black ink gouache W/C wax crayons prov. 13-May-4 Sotheby's, London #102/R est:8000-12000
£21396	$36374	€31238	Tinkers enter the city (33x33cm-13x13in) s.d.1946 W/C prov.exhib. 27-Nov-3 Heffel, Vancouver #3/R est:55000-65000 (C.D 47500)
£21477	$38443	€32000	Image of W B Yates (62x45cm-24x18in) s.d.92 W/C prov. 26-May-4 James Adam, Dublin #144/R est:18000-24000
£23026	$42368	€35000	Eden (108x178cm-43x70in) s.verso tapestry exec. 1952. 22-Jun-4 De Veres Art Auctions, Dublin #76/R est:35000-50000
£32000	$57280	€46720	Images of Sean O'Riada (61x46cm-24x18in) s.d.87 W/C four prov. 13-May-4 Sotheby's, London #73/R est:15000-20000

BROD, Fritzi (1900-1952) American

£329	$550	€480	Woman (20x15cm-8x6in) s. oil on paper. 19-Oct-3 Susanin's, Chicago #6064/R
Works on paper			
£313	$550	€457	Landscape (41x61cm-16x24in) s. W/C exec.c.1955. 23-May-4 Treadway Gallery, Cincinnati #704/R

BRODIE, Gandy (1924-1975) American

£432	$800	€631	Common Pigeons (97x183cm-38x72in) painted c.1961 prov.exhib. 12-Feb-4 Sotheby's, New York #186/R

BRODNAX, Ethel (1904-1963) American

£719	$1200	€1050	Waterfall (61x81cm-24x32in) masonite. 18-Oct-3 David Dike, Dallas #247/R

BRODNEY, Edward (1910-) American

£1117	$2000	€1631	Swan boats, Public Gardens, Boston (61x76cm-24x30in) s. 14-May-4 Skinner, Boston #296/R est:3000-5000

BRODOVITCH, Alexey (1898-1971) American/Russian

Works on paper			
£1105	$2000	€1613	Untitled (53x33cm-21x13in) gouache airbrush pencil on board. 3-Apr-4 David Rago, Lambertville #97/R est:2500-3000

BRODSKY, Vsevolod I and PINKHASOVICH, Boris A (20th C) Russian

£85000	$152150	€124100	Marshall Zhukov receiving the victory parade (297x200cm-117x79in) s. exhib. 26-May-4 Sotheby's, London #311/R est:30000-40000

BRODWOLF, Jurgen (1932-) Swiss

£382	$623	€550	Landscape (58x46cm-23x18in) s.i.d.1959 paper. 27-Sep-3 Dr Fritz Nagel, Stuttgart #9474/R
£1528	$2490	€2200	Zeus with giants (62x40cm-24x16in) s.i.d.1978 tubes tempera canvas. 27-Sep-3 Dr Fritz Nagel, Stuttgart #9482/R est:2400
Sculpture			
£1121	$2006	€1637	Instruments III (46x68cm-18x27in) s.i.d.76 metal plastic glass material paper. 12-May-4 Dobiaschofsky, Bern #2506/R est:2800 (S.FR 2600)
£1981	$3209	€2892	The gardener (36x28x3cm-14x11x1in) s.d.1963 figurine toy shovel prov. 24-May-3 Burkhard, Luzern #57/R est:3500-4500 (S.FR 4200)
£2667	$4907	€4000	Figure (138x83cm-54x33in) s.d.1976 paper mache plaster gauze pencil cotton. 12-Jun-4 Villa Grisebach, Berlin #434/R est:4000-6000
£2778	$4528	€4000	Untitled - stage scene (60x58cm-24x23in) s.d.1968 tube figures metal. 27-Sep-3 Dr Fritz Nagel, Stuttgart #9489/R est:4500
£2953	$5286	€4400	Figuration F (90x140cm-35x55in) s.d.76 plaster oil bandages canvas on board exhib. 25-May-4 Sotheby's, Milan #180/R est:1000-1500
£3125	$5094	€4500	Untitled - con son (64x33x20cm-25x13x8in) s.d.1971 metal wood. 27-Sep-3 Dr Fritz Nagel, Stuttgart #9470/R est:4500
Works on paper			
£467	$859	€700	Tube figure (27x21cm-11x8in) s.d. collage. 11-Jun-4 Hauswedell & Nolte, Hamburg #1178/R
£556	$906	€800	Wounded person (21x29cm-8x11in) s.d.1967 W/C. 27-Sep-3 Dr Fritz Nagel, Stuttgart #9476/R
£903	$1472	€1300	Untitled (66x48cm-26x19in) s.i.d.1972 honeycomb pencil. 27-Sep-3 Dr Fritz Nagel, Stuttgart #9479/R
£4000	$7360	€6000	Composition with figure (182x96cm-72x38in) s.d.1976-77 paper mache gauze cotton earth. 12-Jun-4 Villa Grisebach, Berlin #433/R est:6000-8000

BRODZKY, Horace (1885-1969) Australian

Works on paper			
£260	$450	€380	Study of a female nude (24x42cm-9x17in) s.d.44 pencil. 10-Dec-3 Bonhams, Bury St Edmunds #466
£650	$1034	€949	Jazz merchant (29x18cm-11x7in) s.d.30 pen ink. 10-Sep-3 Sotheby's, Olympia #129/R

BRODZSKY, Sandor (1819-1901) Hungarian

£923	$1532	€1348	Sunny landscape (20x32cm-8x13in) s. oil paper on canvas. 4-Oct-3 Kieselbach, Budapest #56/R (H.F 340000)
£1032	$1713	€1507	Grove (16x19cm-6x7in) cardboard. 4-Oct-3 Kieselbach, Budapest #3/R (H.F 380000)
£1159	$2098	€1692	Detail of the Rakos stream (30x41cm-12x16in) s. oil paper on card. 16-Apr-4 Mu Terem Galeria, Budapest #104/R (H.F 440000)
£2610	$4515	€3811	Riverside (30x42cm-12x17in) cardboard. 12-Dec-3 Kieselbach, Budapest #35/R (H.F 1000000)
£3529	$5859	€5152	Lake Balaton (23x38cm-9x15in) cardboard. 4-Oct-3 Kieselbach, Budapest #120/R (H.F 1300000)
£7482	$13244	€10924	Visegrad (54x79cm-21x31in) s.d.1861. 28-Apr-4 Kieselbach, Budapest #121/R (H.F 2800000)

BROE, Vern (20th C) American

£335	$600	€489	Girls picking flowers (41x51cm-16x20in) s. board. 10-Jan-4 CRN Auctions, Cambridge #16/R
£497	$900	€726	Girls at a beach (41x51cm-16x20in) s. board. 2-Apr-4 Eldred, East Dennis #65/R est:800-1000

BROECK, Clemence van den (1843-1922) Belgian

£833	$1325	€1200	Vase de lilas (44x34cm-17x13in) s. panel. 9-Sep-3 Vanderkindere, Brussels #59
£2345	$3916	€3400	L'heure de the (67x38cm-26x15in) s. panel. 17-Nov-3 Bernaerts, Antwerp #294 est:3750-5000

BROECK, Crispin van den (attrib) (1524-1588) Flemish

£7895	$14526	€12000	The Last Judgement (130x100cm-51x39in) panel. 24-Jun-4 Dr Fritz Nagel, Stuttgart #586/R est:16000
Works on paper			
£800	$1440	€1168	Christ on the Sea of Galilee (14x11cm-6x4in) pen brown ink wash. 20-Apr-4 Sotheby's, Olympia #42/R

BROECK, Dries van den (1927-) Belgian

£300	$543	€450	Moisson (38x47cm-15x19in) s.d.1942. 30-Mar-4 Campo, Vlaamse Kaai #181

BROECK, Elias van den (1650-1708) Dutch

£5556	$10000	€8112	Flowers in a landscape with a lizard (59x51cm-23x20in) indis sig.d.1671. 22-Jan-4 Sotheby's, New York #138/R est:15000-20000
£56000	$96880	€81760	Still life of roses, irises and other flowers in a vase on a stone ledge (51x62cm-20x24in) remains of sig. 11-Dec-3 Sotheby's, London #169/R est:12000-18000

BROECK, Elias van den (circle) (1650-1708) Dutch

£6500	$11050	€9490	Carnations, narcissi and other flowers in a glass vase on a ledge (42x35cm-17x14in) 31-Oct-3 Christie's, Kensington #39/R est:5000-7000

BROECKAERDT, Herman (1878-1930) Belgian

£364	$663	€550	Verger anime en fleurs (53x80cm-21x31in) s. 15-Jun-4 Vanderkindere, Brussels #554

BROEDER, Max (1903-) Belgian

£1267	$2280	€1900	Still life with fruit and flowers (61x75cm-24x30in) s. 26-Apr-4 Bernaerts, Antwerp #257/R est:500-700

BROGE, Alfred (1870-1955) Danish

£364	$589	€528	Autumn landscape with woman and sheep (66x87cm-26x34in) s. i.verso. 4-Aug-3 Rasmussen, Vejle #300/R (D.KR 3800)

BROHEE, C Roland (19/20th C) Belgian

£388	$694	€566	Woman in garden (43x58cm-17x23in) s. 13-May-4 Stuker, Bern #555/R (S.FR 900)

BROISSON, Jean (1941-) Belgian

£690	$1276	€1000	Composition (185x185cm-73x73in) s. 16-Feb-4 Horta, Bruxelles #193

BROKAW, Irvin G (1871-1939) American

Works on paper

£920	$1500	€1343	Near the 7th green. Landscape of trees (41x30cm-16x12in) s.i.d.1928 W/C pastel pair. 27-Sep-3 Charlton Hall, Columbia #673/R est:200-300

BROKER, Ernst (20th C) German

£865	$1573	€1263	Timber lodge by the waterside (60x80cm-24x31in) s. 20-Jun-4 Agra, Warsaw #4/R (P.Z 6000)

BROKER, Wilhelm (1848-1930) German

£300	$501	€438	Sailing boat on a river (13x18cm-5x7in) s.d.1892. 20-Jun-3 Chrystals Auctions, Isle of Man #299
£1133	$2063	€1700	Sailing boats on the lake in summer (14x18cm-6x7in) s.d.1888 panel. 1-Jul-4 Van Ham, Cologne #1238/R est:1100

BROMBO, A (1893-1962) Italian

£1189	$1985	€1700	Fishing boats off Venice (39x50cm-15x20in) i. 11-Oct-3 Dr Fritz Nagel, Leipzig #3931/R est:760

BROMBO, Angelo (1893-1962) Italian

£461	$847	€700	Old houses (40x51cm-16x20in) s. s.i.d.1941 verso. 22-Jun-4 Babuino, Rome #601/R
£650	$1086	€949	On the lagoon, Venice (30x39cm-12x15in) s. 26-Jun-3 Greenslade Hunt, Taunton #556/R
£868	$1372	€1250	Canal with bridge, Venice (51x68cm-20x27in) s. 6-Sep-3 Schopman, Hamburg #789/R
£1173	$2100	€1713	Dockside scene (61x79cm-24x31in) s. 20-Mar-4 Sloans & Kenyon, Bethesda #1171/R est:800-1000
£1216	$2141	€1800	Chioggia (50x62cm-20x24in) s. s.i.verso board. 19-May-4 Il Ponte, Milan #687 est:1200-1300
£1549	$2479	€2200	Venice (30x40cm-12x16in) s. board. 18-Sep-3 Rieber, Stuttgart #1312/R est:2600
£1600	$2512	€2320	Fishermen on the lagoon, Venice (50x70cm-20x28in) s. 28-Aug-3 Christie's, Kensington #238/R est:600-800
£1739	$3183	€2539	Canal scene (50x70cm-20x28in) s. 4-Jun-4 Zofingen, Switzerland #2429/R est:2000 (S.FR 4000)
£2609	$4774	€3809	Venice, San Marco Square (70x100cm-28x39in) s. 4-Jun-4 Zofingen, Switzerland #2428 est:2000 (S.FR 6000)
£2800	$5012	€4200	Little boat (50x70cm-20x28in) s. 12-May-4 Stadion, Trieste #733/R est:900-1200
£4615	$7708	€6600	Market in Venice (70x100cm-28x39in) s. 26-Jun-3 Sant Agostino, Torino #285/R est:4000-5000
£5667	$10143	€8500	Boats and fishermen at the Giudecca, Venice (99x113cm-39x44in) s. 13-May-4 Babuino, Rome #600 est:3000-4000

BROMLEY, David (1960-) Australian

£332	$554	€498	Boy drawing a lighthouse (71x50cm-28x20in) s.i. acrylic screenprint. 27-Oct-3 Goodman, Sydney #29/R (A.D 800)
£373	$624	€560	Two on a log (71x50cm-28x20in) s.i. acrylic screenprint. 27-Oct-3 Goodman, Sydney #26/R (A.D 900)
£394	$658	€591	Sulky boy by lighthouse (71x50cm-28x20in) s.i. acrylic screenprint. 27-Oct-3 Goodman, Sydney #28/R (A.D 950)
£658	$1192	€961	Guide II (18x23cm-7x9in) s. canvasboard. 30-Mar-4 Lawson Menzies, Sydney #71/R est:600-800 (A.D 1600)
£741	$1341	€1082	Boy in blue (78x40cm-31x16in) s. oil paint on rubber. 30-Mar-4 Lawson Menzies, Sydney #5/R est:2000-3000 (A.D 1800)
£810	$1304	€1183	Masked man over house (84x61cm-33x24in) s. paper on board. 25-Aug-3 Sotheby's, Paddington #406/R (A.D 2000)
£992	$1755	€1448	Self portrait series (19x14cm-7x6in) s. one i.verso canvasboard three prov. 3-May-4 Christie's, Melbourne #261/R est:1500-2000 (A.D 2400)
£1240	$2194	€1810	Self portrait series (19x14cm-7x6in) s. canvasboard three prov. 3-May-4 Christie's, Melbourne #258/R est:1500-2000 (A.D 3000)
£1317	$2384	€1923	Untitled - attacked with an axe (200x125cm-79x49in) s.d.89. 30-Mar-4 Lawson Menzies, Sydney #46 est:3000-5000 (A.D 3200)
£1423	$2233	€2063	Nude and lighthouse (60x50cm-24x20in) s. 26-Aug-3 Christie's, Sydney #242/R est:2000-3000 (A.D 3500)
£1527	$2779	€2229	Legs (122x91cm-48x36in) s. synthetic polymer. 16-Jun-4 Deutscher-Menzies, Melbourne #145/R est:4000-6000 (A.D 4000)
£1527	$2779	€2229	Guiding light (61x76cm-24x30in) s. canvasboard. 16-Jun-4 Deutscher-Menzies, Melbourne #271/R est:4000-6000 (A.D 4000)
£1707	$2680	€2475	Boy and boats (60x91cm-24x36in) s. acrylic enamel prov. 26-Aug-3 Christie's, Sydney #226/R est:3000-5000 (A.D 4200)
£2340	$3979	€3416	Getting ready to take on the day II (100x75cm-39x30in) s. i.verso acrylic. 25-Nov-3 Christie's, Melbourne #123/R est:4500-5500 (A.D 5500)
£2642	$4148	€3831	Boxing boy (71x71cm-28x28in) s. acrylic enamel prov. 26-Aug-3 Christie's, Sydney #314/R est:3000-5000 (A.D 6500)
£3049	$4786	€4421	Cassie (152x121cm-60x48in) s. i.d.2002 verso acrylic metal leaf prov. 26-Aug-3 Christie's, Sydney #200/R est:6000-10000 (A.D 7500)
£3909	$7076	€5707	Untitled - the cow, the man and the joker (137x137cm-54x54in) s. 30-Mar-4 Lawson Menzies, Sydney #52/R est:2500-3500 (A.D 9500)

Works on paper

£370	$670	€540	Taking it in (16x13cm-6x5in) s. W/C pen. 30-Mar-4 Lawson Menzies, Sydney #72/R est:400-600 (A.D 900)
£496	$903	€724	Face (40x40cm-16x16in) s. synthetic polymer. 16-Jun-4 Deutscher-Menzies, Melbourne #395/R est:1500-2500 (A.D 1300)
£496	$903	€724	Affinity II (84x111cm-33x44in) s. synthetic polymer prov. 16-Jun-4 Deutscher-Menzies, Melbourne #532/R est:1500-3000 (A.D 1300)
£649	$1181	€948	Pirate tattoo (40x30cm-16x12in) s. synthetic polymer. 16-Jun-4 Deutscher-Menzies, Melbourne #531/R est:1600-2400 (A.D 1700)
£1860	$3440	€2716	Blind leading the blind (101x102cm-40x40in) s. i.verso synthetic polymer. 10-Mar-4 Deutscher-Menzies, Melbourne #365/R est:5000-7000 (A.D 4500)

BROMLEY, John Mallard (1858-1939) British

£460	$768	€672	Children playing in Bosham village (30x41cm-12x16in) s. 16-Nov-3 Desmond Judd, Cranbrook #1042

Works on paper

£1000	$1730	€1460	On the Sid. Devon, ducks before a country house (34x19cm-13x7in) s. W/C. 11-Dec-3 Lane, Penzance #235/R est:1000-1200
£5000	$8350	€7300	Harbour, St. Ives (76x127cm-30x50in) s. W/C. 14-Oct-3 David Lay, Penzance #616/R est:5000-6000

BROMLEY, Valentine Walter (1848-1877) British

£8000	$14320	€12000	Lady Macbeth (102x72cm-40x28in) s.d.1871. 13-May-4 Babuino, Rome #282/R est:5000-7000

BROMLEY, William (19th C) British

£552	$950	€806	Landscape at sunset (38x46cm-15x18in) s. board. 6-Dec-3 South Bay, Long Island #176/R
£1500	$2745	€2190	Penny Whistle (36x45cm-14x18in) s. 28-Jan-4 Dreweatt Neate, Newbury #116/R est:1500-2000

Works on paper

£260	$476	€380	Young girl feeding the farm animals (17x25cm-7x10in) init. W/C htd white. 27-Jan-4 Bonhams, Knightsbridge #8/R
£440	$788	€642	Peaceful fish (39x29cm-15x11in) s.d.83 W/C bodycol. 25-May-4 Bonhams, Knightsbridge #240
£1150	$2070	€1679	Quiet read (20x24cm-8x9in) s.indis.d. W/C. 21-Jan-4 Sotheby's, Olympia #194/R est:1000-1500

BROMLEY, William III (fl.1843-1870) British

£1100	$1870	€1606	Feeding the jackdaw (30x25cm-12x10in) s.indis.d. 18-Nov-3 Sotheby's, Olympia #44/R est:1000-1500

BROMS, Arvid (1910-1968) Finnish

£310	$496	€440	The head (31x42cm-12x17in) 18-Sep-3 Hagelstam, Helsinki #1021
£338	$541	€480	Embrace (65x54cm-26x21in) s.d.52. 21-Sep-3 Bukowskis, Helsinki #320/R

BRONCKHORST, Gerrit van (1637-1673) Dutch

£3400	$6120	€4964	Glaucus and Scylla (34x27cm-13x11in) indis sig.d. panel prov.lit. 20-Apr-4 Sotheby's, Olympia #276/R est:2000-4000

BRONCKHORST, Jan Gerritsz van (1603-1677) Dutch

Works on paper

£1530	$2800	€2234	West African gray parrot (19x15cm-7x6in) s.i. W/C bodycol pen ink framing lines prov. 3-Jun-4 Christie's, Rockefeller NY #1298/R est:2000-3000

BRONCKHORST, Johannes (1648-1727) Dutch

Works on paper

£1000	$1800	€1460	Classical landscape with wildfowl (36x29cm-14x11in) s. bodycol vellum sold with 2 drs one attrib Wybrand Hendriks. 22-Jan-4 Christie's, Rockefeller NY #265/R est:2000-3000
£2162	$3805	€3200	Black grouse and pair of red legged patridge (21x27cm-8x11in) mono. i.verso W/C prov.lit. 19-May-4 Sotheby's, Amsterdam #195/R est:4000-6000
£10811	$19027	€16000	Black curassow (15x20cm-6x8in) init. i.verso W/C gouache black chk prov.exhib.lit. 19-May-4 Sotheby's, Amsterdam #200/R est:6000-8000
£10811	$19027	€16000	Asian elephant, lion and civet cat in a landscape (35x27cm-14x11in) init. pen black ink W/C prov.exhib.lit. 19-May-4 Sotheby's, Amsterdam #203/R est:12000-18000
£12162	$21405	€18000	Exotic waterbirds in a landscape (35x28cm-14x11in) init. i.verso W/C gouache prov.exhib.lit. 19-May-4 Sotheby's, Amsterdam #194/R est:15000-20000
£12162	$21405	€18000	Flamingo and exotic poultry in a landscape (34x27cm-13x11in) init. i.verso W/C gouache prov.exhib.lit. 19-May-4 Sotheby's, Amsterdam #196/R est:12000-18000
£16892	$29730	€25000	Seven exotic beetles (22x32cm-9x13in) init. W/C gouache prov.lit. 19-May-4 Sotheby's, Amsterdam #191/R est:5500-6500
£16892	$29730	€25000	Two ostriches and an ant-eater in a landscape (35x27cm-14x11in) init. W/C gouache prov.exhib.lit. 19-May-4 Sotheby's, Amsterdam #202/R est:14000-18000
£23649	$41622	€35000	Wreath of flowers (32x27cm-13x11in) init. i.verso pen black ink W/C gouache prov.exhib.lit. 19-May-4 Sotheby's, Amsterdam #190/R est:12000-18000

BRONDY, Matteo (1866-1944) French

£634	$1096	€900	Cour de palais a Meknes (38x28cm-15x11in) s.i. 15-Dec-3 Gros & Delettrez, Paris #51/R
£845	$1462	€1200	Environs de Meknes (26x35cm-10x14in) s.i. panel. 15-Dec-3 Gros & Delettrez, Paris #52/R
£4397	$7343	€6200	Cavalier marocain (50x65cm-20x26in) s. 16-Jun-3 Gros & Delettrez, Paris #41/R est:5000-6000

Works on paper

£467	$859	€700	Le Viaduc de Cherchell (27x38cm-11x15in) s.i. W/C. 14-Jun-4 Gros & Delettrez, Paris #246
£734	$1342	€1100	Visite au Mausolee (38x27cm-15x11in) s. W/C gouache. 3-Jun-4 Tajan, Paris #211
£800	$1416	€1168	La halte a dar chorfa, Meknes, Morocco (27x37cm-11x15in) s.i. W/C. 27-Apr-4 Bonhams, New Bond Street #65/R
£805	$1490	€1200	Meknes (46x30cm-18x12in) s.i. W/C. 15-Mar-4 Gros & Delettrez, Paris #206/R
£1408	$2437	€2000	Cheval du Caid (49x62cm-19x24in) s. gouache. 15-Dec-3 Gros & Delettrez, Paris #165/R est:1500-2000
£2746	$4751	€3900	Marocaines dans la mosquee (54x38cm-21x15in) s.i. W/C gouache chk. 15-Dec-3 Gros & Delettrez, Paris #144/R est:2500-3500

BRONKART, Sylvin (1915-1967) Belgian

Works on paper

£278	$464	€400	Composition (61x75cm-24x30in) s. d.1954 verso mixed media. 21-Oct-3 Campo & Campo, Antwerp #20

BRONNIKOFF, Feodor Andrejewitsch (1827-1902) Russian

£8276	$13821	€12000	Marchand de croix et de chapelets (35x26cm-14x10in) s.d.1876 panel. 17-Nov-3 Tajan, Paris #84/R est:5000-6000

BRONSON, Clark (1939-) American
Sculpture
£932 $1500 €1351 It's mine (61x91cm-24x36in) 22-Aug-3 Altermann Galleries, Santa Fe #218
£964 $1600 €1407 Flushing quail (36x38cm-14x15in) s.d.1976 bronze edition 38/50. 4-Oct-3 South Bay, Long Island #22

BRONZINO (1503-1572) Italian
£17045 $30000 €24886 Portrait of Cosimo I (65x55cm-26x22in) panel painted with studio prov.lit. 19-May-4 Doyle, New York #6114/R est:15000-20000

BRONZINO, Angelo (after) (1503-1572) Italian
£8500 $14705 €12410 Portrait of Cosimo de'Medici (82x59cm-32x23in) 12-Dec-3 Christie's, Kensington #192/R est:4000-6000
£12000 $20760 €17520 Portrait of Elenor of Toledo (61x51cm-24x20in) prov. 12-Dec-3 Christie's, Kensington #191/R est:4000-6000

BRONZINO, Angelo (circle) (1503-1572) Italian
£4505 $7748 €6577 Madonna and child (47x33cm-19x13in) panel. 8-Dec-3 Philippe Schuler, Zurich #3390/R est:4000-5000 (S.FR 10000)

BRONZINO, Angelo (studio) (1503-1572) Italian
£12692 $21831 €18530 Cosimo I Medici with the Order of the Golden Skin (66x51cm-26x20in) panel prov. 2-Dec-3 Bukowskis, Stockholm #331/R est:100000-150000 (S.KR 165000)
£14085 $22676 €20000 Ritratto del Granduca Cosimo I de Medici con il toson d'oro (77x60cm-30x24in) panel. 8-May-3 Farsetti, Prato #612/R est:25000-28000

BRONZINO, Angelo (style) (1503-1572) Italian
£8000 $14640 €11680 Portrait of Eleanora of Toledo (76x56cm-30x22in) i. lit. 8-Jul-4 Sotheby's, London #185/R est:4000-6000

BROOD, Herman (1946-2001) Dutch
£490 $832 €700 Flying high (60x50cm-24x20in) s. acrylic. 24-Nov-3 Glerum, Amsterdam #193/R
£680 $1238 €1000 Applaus II (70x100cm-28x39in) spray paint collage on paper two. 3-Feb-4 Christie's, Amsterdam #562 est:800-1200
£867 $1551 €1300 Two heads (100x100cm-39x39in) s. 11-May-4 Vendu Notarishuis, Rotterdam #234
£952 $1733 €1400 Horse rider (100x120cm-39x47in) spray paint. 3-Feb-4 Christie's, Amsterdam #564 est:1500-2000
£1088 $1981 €1600 Glimlach knap jongensgezicht (120x100cm-47x39in) s. spray paint on canvas. 3-Feb-4 Christie's, Amsterdam #561/R est:1200-1600
£1259 $2140 €1800 Papa (118x158cm-46x62in) s.i.d.89 acrylic spray can paint. 25-Nov-3 Christie's, Amsterdam #101/R est:2000-3000
£1259 $2102 €1800 Three faces (100x120cm-39x47in) s.d.90 acrylic. 30-Jun-3 Sotheby's, Amsterdam #410
£1701 $3095 €2500 Herman Brood siert (70x100cm-28x39in) s.i. spray paint. 3-Feb-4 Christie's, Amsterdam #565 est:1000-1500
£1842 $3389 €2800 Football (120x160cm-47x63in) s.d.90 oil spraypaint. 22-Jun-4 Christie's, Amsterdam #381/R est:1500-2000
£1974 $3632 €3000 Two figures (120x160cm-47x63in) s.d.89 oil spraypaint. 22-Jun-4 Christie's, Amsterdam #382/R est:1500-2000
Works on paper
£272 $495 €400 Piss palace (54x63cm-21x25in) s.i.d.89 felt pen collage. 3-Feb-4 Christie's, Amsterdam #603

BROODTHAERS, Marcel (1924-1976) Belgian
£4200 $7728 €6132 Untitled, decor (44x44cm-17x17in) init. ink silkscreen ink exec.c.1975 prov.exhib. 24-Jun-4 Sotheby's, Olympia #463/R est:2000-3000
Photographs
£2162 $4000 €3157 Soupe de daguerre (52x51cm-20x20in) s.i. num.25/60 chromogenic prints mounted together 12. 13-Jul-4 Christie's, Rockefeller NY #202/R est:3000-5000
Prints
£1879 $3439 €2800 Animaux de la ferme (82x61cm-32x24in) mono.d.1974 num.108/120 photo lithograph diptych prov. 7-Jul-4 Artcurial Briest, Paris #194 est:2500-3000
£17000 $28390 €24820 Pot, moule, coeur (60x40cm-24x16in) silkscreen ink canvas prov.exhib. 22-Oct-3 Christie's, London #38/R est:14000-18000
£72626 $130000 €106034 L'art et les mots (79x100cm-31x39in) typographical acrylic on canvas set of nine prov.exhib. 13-May-4 Phillips, New York #40/R est:100000-150000
Sculpture
£2667 $4880 €4000 Pop jam, pot a confiture en verre (10x10cm-4x4in) s.d.65 glass prov. 7-Jun-4 Palais de Beaux Arts, Brussels #157/R est:4000-5000
Works on paper
£3667 $6563 €5500 Le requin (22x14cm-9x6in) feltip collage prov.exhib. 15-May-4 De Vuyst, Lokeren #589/R est:5500-7500
£8392 $14014 €12000 Paquet de lettres (40x47cm-16x19in) collage canvas prov.exhib. 11-Oct-3 De Vuyst, Lokeren #487/R est:10000-12000
£26000 $43420 €37960 Corbeau et le Renard (80x60cm-31x24in) s.d.67 prints cardboard film reel portfolio seven prov. 21-Oct-3 Sotheby's, London #446/R est:12000-15000

BROOK, Alexander (1898-1980) American
£279 $500 €407 Moonlight and sailboats (30x23cm-12x9in) s. board. 7-May-4 Sloans & Kenyon, Bethesda #1692/R
£2941 $5000 €4294 From Wittenberg (51x76cm-20x30in) s.d.1925 i.verso. 30-Oct-3 Phillips, New York #78/R est:6000-8000
£10778 $18000 €15736 Amalia (91x71cm-36x28in) s. prov.exhib.lit. 7-Oct-3 Sotheby's, New York #229 est:3000-5000

BROOK, Edmund (20th C) British
£400 $640 €584 Portrait of a young girl (46x38cm-18x15in) s. 19-May-3 Bruton Knowles, Cheltenham #251

BROOKE, F William (fl.1886-1891) British
Works on paper
£1840 $3000 €2686 Pastoral scene (41x66cm-16x26in) s. 28-Sep-3 Simpson's, Houston #253/R

BROOKE, James Leslie (1903-1973) British
£320 $544 €467 Weeton windmill in a storm (34x45cm-13x18in) s. s.i.verso. 18-Nov-3 Bonhams, Leeds #194

BROOKE, Percy (fl.1894-1916) British
Works on paper
£1600 $2880 €2336 Figures harvesting in a summer landscape (24x34cm-9x13in) s.d.1906 pencil W/C htd white prov. 21-Apr-4 Tennants, Leyburn #1039/R est:400-600

BROOKE, Richard Norris (1847-1920) American
£1564 $2800 €2283 Dutch interior scene with woman spinning yard (69x94cm-27x37in) s. 29-May-4 Brunk, Ashville #165/R

BROOKER, Bertram (1888-1955) Canadian
£1897 $3263 €2770 Double bass (75x60cm-30x24in) s. exhib. 2-Dec-3 Joyner Waddington, Toronto #234/R est:3000-4000 (C.D 4250)
£3482 $5989 €5084 Brooker residence, Toronto (26x21cm-10x8in) s. panel. 2-Dec-3 Joyner Waddington, Toronto #323/R est:2000-3000 (C.D 7800)
£3659 $6549 €5342 Suspension (99x69cm-39x27in) s. s.i.verso prov.exhib. 27-May-4 Heffel, Vancouver #212/R est:3000-5000 (C.D 9000)
£3659 $6549 €5342 First snow. Tree study (37x29cm-15x11in) s.i. double-sided prov. 31-May-4 Sotheby's, Toronto #6/R est:6000-8000 (C.D 9000)
£13514 $22973 €19730 Still life with a bag, 3 (61x76cm-24x30in) s. i.verso painted c.1929 prov.lit. 27-Nov-3 Heffel, Vancouver #28/R est:4000-6000 (C.D 30000)
Works on paper
£843 $1569 €1231 No 4 lilac tree (35x25cm-14x10in) init.d.36 i.d.1936 verso graphite. 2-Mar-4 Ritchie, Toronto #94/R est:600-800 (C.D 2100)
£1364 $2223 €1991 Primula (48x40cm-19x16in) s. i.verso W/C. 23-Sep-3 Ritchie, Toronto #118/R est:1000-1500 (C.D 3000)
£1440 $2635 €2102 Treetop. Study of trees (25x32cm-10x13in) i.d.1931 i.d.1933 verso pencil pair. 1-Jun-4 Joyner Waddington, Toronto #370/R est:1200-1500 (C.D 3600)

BROOKER, Harry (1848-1940) British
£1070 $1937 €1562 Hop garland (44x37cm-17x15in) s.d.1874 s.i.d.verso. 31-Mar-4 Goodman, Sydney #407 est:2000-3000 (A.D 2600)
£20588 $35000 €30058 Training the pigeons (71x91cm-28x36in) s.d.1895 prov. 29-Oct-3 Christie's, Rockefeller NY #77/R est:70000-90000

BROOKER, William (1918-1983) British
£850 $1522 €1241 In the park (23x39cm-9x15in) s.d.80 board prov. 16-Mar-4 Bonhams, New Bond Street #101/R
£3200 $5088 €4672 Blue oil lamp (28x44cm-11x17in) s.d.66 board prov. 10-Sep-3 Sotheby's, Olympia #217/R est:1200-1800
£6200 $11346 €9052 The living room (46x61cm-18x24in) s.d.33 prov. 7-Apr-4 Woolley & Wallis, Salisbury #264/R est:2000-3000
£7200 $12888 €10512 Still life, bowl and pots (63x76cm-25x30in) s.d.69 s.i.d.verso prov. 16-Mar-4 Bonhams, New Bond Street #100/R est:4000-6000
£14500 $26390 €21170 For Guiseppe Abbots (102x127cm-40x50in) i. 3-Feb-4 Gorringes, Bexhill #1045/R est:800-1200

BROOKING, Charles (1723-1759) British
£9500 $17290 €13870 Two views of Blankenburg Castle off the coast of Flanders (34x44cm-13x17in) two prov.exhib. 1-Jul-4 Sotheby's, London #150/R est:10000-15000

BROOKING, Charles (attrib) (1723-1759) British
£14412 $25798 €21042 Harbour view (66x96cm-26x38in) lit. 26-May-4 AB Stockholms Auktionsverk #2554/R est:60000-80000 (S.KR 195000)

BROOKS, Allan (1869-1946) Canadian
Works on paper
£309 $500 €451 American mergansers (18x25cm-7x10in) s. 31-Jul-3 Eldred, East Dennis #558/R

BROOKS, Frances (20th C) American
Works on paper
£815 $1500 €1223 Boats at dock (69x84cm-27x33in) s. mixed media. 8-Jun-4 Bonhams & Butterfields, San Francisco #4322/R est:2500-3500

BROOKS, Frank (1854-1937) British
£950 $1777 €1387 Girl seated on a terrace with doves in foreground and a basket of oranges (41x30cm-16x12in) s. 22-Jul-4 Tennants, Leyburn #903/R

BROOKS, Frank Leonard (1911-1989) Canadian
£362 $605 €529 Spring, Haliburton (45x54cm-18x21in) s.i.d.1932 board. 17-Nov-3 Hodgins, Calgary #172/R (C.D 800)
£496 $898 €724 Delos, Greece (50x65cm-20x26in) s. i.verso hardboard. 18-Apr-4 Levis, Calgary #14/R est:1200-1500 (C.D 1200)
£2080 $3806 €3037 Aegean (74x118cm-29x46in) s.d.68 acrylic collage diptych prov. 1-Jun-4 Joyner Waddington, Toronto #372/R est:2500-3000 (C.D 5200)

BROOKS, James (1906-1992) American
£17877 $32000 €26100 Haley (190x244cm-75x96in) s.i.d.1971 verso acrylic prov.exhib. 12-May-4 Christie's, Rockefeller NY #157/R est:20000-30000
£17964 $30000 €26227 Merrygandering (152x183cm-60x72in) s. s.i.d.1968 verso prov. 12-Nov-3 Christie's, Rockefeller NY #357/R est:15000-20000

Works on paper
£2054 $3800 €2999 Untitled (39x30cm-15x12in) s. gouache exec 1958 prov. 13-Jul-4 Christie's, Rockefeller NY #22/R est:800-1200

BROOKS, Mabel H (?-1927) American
£253 $400 €369 Bluebonnets and cactus (41x51cm-16x20in) s. 27-Jul-3 Bonhams & Butterfields, Los Angeles #7002/R

BROOKS, Maria (1837-1912) British
£3125 $5219 €4531 Weary travelers (127x76cm-50x30in) s.d.83. 17-Jun-3 Pinneys, Montreal #60 est:7000-9000 (C.D 7000)
£3591 $6500 €5243 Reflection (29x22cm-11x9in) s. 30-Mar-4 Christie's, Rockefeller NY #59/R est:6000-8000

BROOKS, Nicholas Alden (fl.1880-1914) American
£2844 $4750 €4152 Ten dollar bill (18x25cm-7x10in) s. board painted c.1893 exhib. 7-Oct-3 Sotheby's, New York #174 est:3000-4000

BROOKS, Nicholas Alden (attrib) (fl.1880-1914) American
£894 $1600 €1305 Boating with his sweetheart, a pond view (36x51cm-14x20in) s.i.d.1886. 14-May-4 Skinner, Boston #91/R est:1500-2500

BROOKS, Robin (?) British
£290 $539 €423 USS President (60x90cm-24x35in) s. i.verso. 2-Mar-4 Bristol Auction Rooms #358/R
£460 $842 €672 HMS Beagle off the Galapagos (49x74cm-19x29in) s. 6-Jul-4 Bearnes, Exeter #479

BROOKS, T (1818-1891) British
£2586 $4034 €3750 Heavenly dreams (92x69cm-36x27in) s.d.1852. 1-Aug-2 Joel, Victoria #287 est:4500-5500 (A.D 7500)

BROOKS, Terri (1958-) Australian
£528 $829 €771 Trail (116x89cm-46x35in) s.i.d.91 verso oil pigment paper on canvas. 27-Aug-3 Christie's, Sydney #637 est:600-1000 (A.D 1300)

BROOKS, William (fl.1780-1801) British
£2800 $5096 €4088 St. Michael's Mount and Mount's Bay (70x90cm-28x35in) s.d.1799. 21-Jun-4 Bonhams, Bath #394/R est:1500-2000

BROOM, Marion L (fl.1925-1939) British
Works on paper
£270 $443 €394 Blue asters in a porcelain jug (51x36cm-20x14in) s. W/C bodycol htd white. 29-May-3 Neales, Nottingham #755/R
£280 $465 €409 Still life of summer flowers in a vase (56x76cm-22x30in) s. W/C. 2-Oct-3 Mitchells, Cockermouth #825/R
£280 $476 €409 Still life of freesias and other flowers in a decorated vase (52x37cm-20x15in) s. W/C. 19-Nov-3 Tennants, Leyburn #921a
£450 $806 €657 Peonies in a glass vase (55x75cm-22x30in) s. W/C. 25-May-4 Bonhams, Knightsbridge #73/R
£480 $883 €701 Tulips and daffodils in a vase (72x56cm-28x22in) s. W/C. 22-Jun-4 Bonhams, Knightsbridge #78/R
£650 $1164 €949 Hydrangeas in a bowl (53x74cm-21x29in) s. W/C. 4-May-4 Gorringes, Bexhill #1353

BROOME, G J (fl.1867-1873) British
£1600 $2928 €2336 Still lives of fruit (36x46cm-14x18in) s. pair. 7-Apr-4 Gardiner & Houlgate, Bath #300/R est:1500-2000

BROOME, William (1838-1892) British
£900 $1530 €1314 Fishing smacks (41x61cm-16x24in) indis.sig.i. 19-Nov-3 Christie's, Kensington #535/R
£1034 $1914 €1500 Going to the wreck. Saved (60x105cm-24x41in) s. pair. 11-Feb-4 Woodwards, Cork #9/R est:1000-1500
£2500 $4250 €3650 Running into harbour (76x127cm-30x50in) indis.sig.indis.d. 19-Nov-3 Christie's, Kensington #537/R

BROOME, William (attrib) (1838-1892) British
£1400 $2338 €2044 Tug towing a ship into a harbour (76x127cm-30x50in) bears sig. 11-Nov-3 Bonhams, Knightsbridge #229/R est:1500-2000

BROPHY, Elizabeth (20th C) Australian/Irish
£1342 $2470 €2000 Quiet moment, children at the edge of a lake (37x44cm-15x17in) s. board. 23-Mar-4 Mealy's, Castlecomer #1125/R est:1500-2200
£1408 $2254 €2000 Picnic day (36x46cm-14x18in) s. i.verso board. 16-Sep-3 Whyte's, Dublin #203/R est:2000-2500
£1408 $2254 €2000 Foreshore (30x41cm-12x16in) s. i.verso board. 16-Sep-3 Whyte's, Dublin #205/R est:1500-1800
£1500 $2460 €2190 Girl in white (40x30cm-16x12in) s. board. 4-Jun-3 John Ross, Belfast #68
£1678 $3003 €2500 Sunny days (35x45cm-14x18in) s. board. 31-May-4 Hamilton Osborne King, Dublin #151/R est:2500-3500
£1800 $2952 €2628 Potting shed (38x45cm-15x18in) s. board. 4-Jun-3 John Ross, Belfast #215
£1800 $3294 €2628 Holidays (40x50cm-16x20in) s. board. 2-Jun-4 John Ross, Belfast #114 est:2000-2500
£1818 $3091 €2600 The flower ladies (41x51cm-16x20in) s. i.verso board prov. 18-Nov-3 Whyte's, Dublin #222/R est:2000-3000
£1974 $3632 €3000 Picnic day (41x51cm-16x20in) s. canvasboard. 22-Jun-4 De Veres Art Auctions, Dublin #163/R est:3000-4000
£2000 $3660 €2920 Flowers in the wood (40x50cm-16x20in) s. board. 2-Jun-4 John Ross, Belfast #206 est:2000-2500
£2162 $4086 €3200 Red shirt (41x51cm-16x20in) s. board. 17-Feb-4 Whyte's, Dublin #239/R est:2000-3000
£2819 $5046 €4200 Carpet of bluebells (40x50cm-16x20in) s. board. 31-May-4 Hamilton Osborne King, Dublin #150/R est:3500-4500
£3077 $5231 €4400 Waiting for lunch (36x46cm-14x18in) s. i.verso board. 18-Nov-3 Whyte's, Dublin #223/R est:2000-3000

BROQUE, Lucien (20th C) French
£1689 $3024 €2500 Lynx (76x100cm-30x39in) s. panel. 5-May-4 Claude Boisgirard, Paris #28/R est:2000-2500

BROSEMER, Carrie (19th C) American
£1429 $2500 €2086 Still life with eggs (38x46cm-15x18in) s.d.92. 19-Dec-3 Sotheby's, New York #1087/R est:2500-3500

BROSEN, Frederick (1954-) American
Works on paper
£1243 $2250 €1865 Riverside at 175th Street (36x51cm-14x20in) W/C. 16-Apr-4 American Auctioneer #44/R est:2000-4000

BROSSA, Joan (1919-1998) Spanish
Sculpture
£1333 $2413 €2000 Through (15x15x7cm-6x6x3in) s. num.1/10 crystal glass nail wooden base exec.1988 prov.lit. 30-Mar-4 Segre, Madrid #325/R est:1800

BROSSARD, A Rosalie (18/19th C) French
£769 $1308 €1100 Portrait d'un juriste (100x82cm-39x32in) s.d.1807. 20-Nov-3 Camard, Paris #2

BROSSARD, Alexandre (19/20th C) French
£1402 $2215 €2033 Thoughtful young girl (73x57cm-29x22in) s. 2-Sep-3 Rasmussen, Copenhagen #1711/R est:15000-20000 (D.KR 15000)

BROSSE, Eugène (1855-?) French
£4000 $6880 €5840 Roses in a glass vase. Summer flowers in an urn (110x89cm-43x35in) s.d.1895 pair. 4-Dec-3 Christie's, Kensington #100/R est:2000-4000

BROSSELARD, Claire (19th C) British?
Works on paper
£1000 $1850 €1500 Camellia japonica. Bourbon rose (26x35cm-10x14in) one s.d.29 Mai 1840 s.d.20 Obre 1841 pencil W/C vellum board pair. 15-Jul-4 Bonhams, New Bond Street #10/R est:1000-1500

BROTAT, Joan (1920-1990) Spanish
£634 $1109 €900 Everyone has his idea (73x92cm-29x36in) s. lit. 16-Dec-3 Durán, Madrid #39/R
£658 $1191 €1000 Apple and pear (46x55cm-18x22in) s. 14-Apr-4 Ansorena, Madrid #254/R
£694 $1132 €1000 Woman in green (27x22cm-11x9in) s. canvas on board. 16-Jul-3 Durán, Madrid #103/R
£822 $1397 €1200 Village street (55x46cm-22x18in) s. 4-Nov-3 Ansorena, Madrid #940/R
£993 $1658 €1400 Woman and dove (81x65cm-32x26in) s. 20-Oct-3 Durán, Madrid #79/R
£1133 $2051 €1700 Man with flute (81x65cm-32x26in) s. lit. 30-Mar-4 Segre, Madrid #313/R est:1600
£1135 $1838 €1600 La mirada (73x92cm-29x36in) s. 20-May-3 Ansorena, Madrid #338/R est:1600
£1135 $1895 €1600 Mujeres y nocturno (73x92cm-29x36in) s. 23-Jun-3 Durán, Madrid #146/R est:1600
£1208 $2138 €1800 Outcast (81x100cm-32x39in) s. 27-Apr-4 Durán, Madrid #98/R est:1800
£1233 $2096 €1800 Figures (74x92cm-29x36in) s. 4-Nov-3 Ansorena, Madrid #896/R est:1800
£1241 $2234 €1800 Titiriteros (73x60cm-29x24in) s. 26-Jan-4 Ansorena, Madrid #881/R est:1200
£1267 $2154 €1850 Couple and doves (100x81cm-39x32in) s. 4-Nov-3 Ansorena, Madrid #945/R est:1850
£1377 $2258 €1900 Para la fiesta (116x89cm-46x35in) s. lit. 27-May-3 Durán, Madrid #102/R est:1900
£1497 $2724 €2200 Turtle seller (81x65cm-32x26in) s. 3-Feb-4 Segre, Madrid #348/R est:1500
£1701 $3044 €2500 Women and jug (116x89cm-46x35in) s. 22-Mar-4 Durán, Madrid #161/R est:2100
£1736 $2865 €2500 Peasants (89x116cm-35x46in) s. 2-Jul-3 Ansorena, Madrid #987/R
Works on paper
£338 $585 €480 Painter (69x48cm-27x19in) s. pastel. 15-Dec-3 Ansorena, Madrid #997/R

BROTO, Jose Manuel (1949-) Spanish
£3169 $5546 €4500 Untitled (103x72cm-41x28in) s.d.1986 prov. 16-Dec-3 Segre, Madrid #180/R est:3500
£5369 $9611 €8000 Reception (195x130cm-77x51in) s.i.d.1991 verso acrylic exhib.lit. 28-May-4 Farsetti, Prato #159/R est:8000-9000
£9507 $16637 €13500 Still life (150x150cm-59x59in) s.i.d.1998 verso acrylic prov.exhib.lit. 16-Dec-3 Segre, Madrid #166/R est:12500
£9524 $17333 €14000 Triptych (120x80cm-47x31in) s.i.d.1997 verso canvas on board. 3-Feb-4 Segre, Madrid #372/R est:9000
£12000 $21840 €17520 Triptico Rojo (162x130cm-64x51in) s.d.1983 verso three panels. 4-Feb-4 Sotheby's, Olympia #201/R est:5000-7000
Works on paper
£4027 $7490 €6000 Untitled (105x73cm-41x29in) s.d.86 mixed media. 2-Mar-4 Ansorena, Madrid #837/R est:6000

BROUARDEL, Laure (20th C) French
£750 $1373 €1095 Le dejeuner campagnard (46x62cm-18x24in) s. 8-Apr-4 Christie's, Kensington #72/R

BROUEL, C (19th C) ?
£1348 $2250 €1900 Marine (54x73cm-21x29in) s. 14-Oct-3 Vanderkindere, Brussels #8 est:1500-2500

BROUET, Auguste (1872-1941) French
Works on paper
£320 $582 €480 Gens du cirque (47x57cm-19x22in) s. pastel paper on canvas. 29-Jun-4 Chenu & Scrive, Lyon #28/R

BROUGH, Catherine (20th C) New Zealander
£470 $799 €686 Untitled (54x72cm-21x28in) s. oil paper. 27-Nov-3 International Art Centre, Auckland #124/R (NZ.D 1250)
£725 $1174 €1051 Porter River I (55x74cm-22x29in) s. oil on paper. 31-Jul-3 International Art Centre, Auckland #115/R est:1800-2600 (NZ.D 2000)

BROUGH, Robert (1872-1905) British
£18000 $32760 €26280 Portrait of Richard Myddelton in hunting dress (122x84cm-48x33in) s.i.d.1901 exhib.lit. 21-Jun-4 Christie's, London #134/R est:8000-12000

BROUGHTON, Sonny (20th C) New Zealander
Works on paper
£725 $1167 €1059 Great gathering - hui-te-ana-nui. init.d.2003 mixed media. 20-Aug-3 Dunbar Sloane, Auckland #12/R est:2000-4000 (NZ.D 2000)

BROUILLARD, Eugène (1870-?) French
£1267 $2280 €1900 Paysage type (57x88cm-22x35in) s. 20-Apr-4 Chenu & Scrive, Lyon #42/R est:1200-1300
Works on paper
£280 $510 €420 Bord d'etang (62x85cm-24x33in) s. gouache. 29-Jun-4 Chenu & Scrive, Lyon #30/R
£933 $1699 €1400 Paysage d'automne (56x44cm-22x17in) s. Chinese ink W/C dr. 29-Jun-4 Chenu & Scrive, Lyon #29
£1293 $2352 €1900 Paysage annime au crepuscule (64x97cm-25x38in) s. pastel. 8-Feb-4 Anaf, Lyon #109 est:1200-1400
£1667 $3000 €2500 Paysage aux grands arbres (57x88cm-22x35in) s. gouache. 20-Apr-4 Chenu & Scrive, Lyon #41/R est:1500-2000

BROUILLET, Pierre Andre (1857-1914) French
£1333 $2453 €2000 Le flutiste (60x32cm-24x13in) s.d.1880. 11-Jun-4 Claude Aguttes, Neuilly #9/R est:1500-2000

BROUILLETTE, Diane (1960-) Canadian
£443 $696 €647 Pommettes sur porcelaine (46x61cm-18x24in) s. i.verso. 26-Aug-3 Iegor de Saint Hippolyte, Montreal #61 (C.D 980)
£679 $1066 €991 Vase (76x76cm-30x30in) s. 26-Aug-3 Iegor de Saint Hippolyte, Montreal #62 (C.D 1500)

BROUTELLES, Theodore (1843-1933) French
£400 $680 €584 Cargo vessel, unloading, Dieppe (36x26cm-14x10in) s. board. 5-Nov-3 Rupert Toovey, Partridge Green #130/R
£1500 $2775 €2190 Storm in Dieppe (145x225cm-57x89in) 13-Jan-4 Bonhams, Knightsbridge #186/R est:1000-1500

BROUTY, Charles (1897-1984) French
Works on paper
£268 $497 €400 Chameliers a Ouargla (13x19cm-5x7in) s. Indian ink W/C. 15-Mar-4 Gros & Delettrez, Paris #91/R
£403 $745 €600 Les deux amis (20x15cm-8x6in) s.d.58 Indian ink W/C. 15-Mar-4 Gros & Delettrez, Paris #93/R
£470 $869 €700 Le retour du troupeau (16x22cm-6x9in) s. Indian ink W/C. 15-Mar-4 Gros & Delettrez, Paris #92/R
£503 $931 €750 La porteuse d'eau (25x19cm-10x7in) Indian ink W/C. 15-Mar-4 Gros & Delettrez, Paris #94/R
£1678 $3104 €2500 Quartier juif a Oran (45x61cm-18x24in) s. gouache. 15-Mar-4 Gros & Delettrez, Paris #217/R est:2500-3000

BROUWER, Adriaen (1606-1638) Flemish
£745 $1378 €1080 Will opening (23x33cm-9x13in) panel. 12-Feb-4 Weidler, Nurnberg #6523/R

BROUWER, Adriaen (attrib) (1606-1638) Flemish
£483 $850 €705 The smoker (28x23cm-11x9in) panel. 19-May-4 Doyle, New York #6035

BROUWER, Adriaen (circle) (1606-1638) Flemish
£15385 $26462 €22000 La potion amere (46x37cm-18x15in) panel exhib. 3-Dec-3 Palais de Beaux Arts, Brussels #1248/R est:5000-7000

BROUWER, Justus (attrib) (17th C) Dutch
Works on paper
£1644 $2795 €2400 Roman ruin (22x25cm-9x10in) s.verso pen brown ink wash. 4-Nov-3 Sotheby's, Amsterdam #97/R est:3000-4000

BROUWERS, Julius (1869-1955) Dutch
£521 $849 €750 View of Zierikzee (50x74cm-20x29in) s. canvas on board. 29-Sep-3 Sotheby's, Amsterdam #82a/R
£625 $1044 €913 Still life with flowers and fruit (50x60cm-20x24in) s. painted c.1900. 19-Oct-3 Agra, Warsaw #66/R (P.Z 4000)
£1544 $2871 €2300 Windmill (18x26cm-7x10in) s. panel. 4-Mar-4 Auction Maastricht #1120/R est:250-400
Works on paper
£526 $968 €800 View of an extensive landscape (63x95cm-25x37in) s. W/C. 28-Jun-4 Sotheby's, Amsterdam #266/R

BROUX, Charles de (19th C) Dutch
£815 $1500 €1190 Figure before a cathedral, early evening (23x33cm-9x13in) s. 25-Jun-4 Freeman, Philadelphia #288/R est:1000-1500

BROWERE, Albertus del Orient (1814-1887) American
£5587 $10000 €8157 Catskill on Hudson (25x30cm-10x12in) s.i.verso masonite prov. 6-May-4 Shannon's, Milford #108/R est:8000-12000

BROWN, Agnes A (1847-1932) American
£1173 $2100 €1713 Kitten sleeping on a cushion (18x25cm-7x10in) s. panel. 14-May-4 Skinner, Boston #97/R est:800-1200

BROWN, Alexander Kellock (1849-1922) British
£543 $907 €793 Haymakers (41x61cm-16x24in) init. 17-Nov-3 Waddingtons, Toronto #145/R (C.D 1200)
£700 $1253 €1022 After rain, Glen Duror (25x34cm-10x13in) init. canvas on board. 26-May-4 Sotheby's, Olympia #227/R
Works on paper
£550 $1023 €803 In Capri (19x29cm-7x11in) init.i.d.77 pencil W/C htd white. 4-Mar-4 Christie's, Kensington #150/R

BROWN, Anna Wood (fl.1890-1920) American
£3593 $6000 €5246 View of the garden (66x53cm-26x21in) s. prov. 23-Oct-3 Shannon's, Milford #33/R est:7000-9000

BROWN, Annora (1899-1987) Canadian
£248 $421 €362 Yellow lady's slipper (25x35cm-10x14in) s. W/C prov. 23-Nov-3 Levis, Calgary #418/R (C.D 550)
Works on paper
£200 $366 €292 Prince of Wales, Waterton (20x27cm-8x11in) s. W/C. 1-Jun-4 Hodgins, Calgary #250/R (C.D 500)
£203 $344 €296 Harebells (22x18cm-9x7in) s. W/C prov. 23-Nov-3 Levis, Calgary #419/R (C.D 450)
£203 $344 €296 Colombine (21x18cm-8x7in) s. W/C prov. 23-Nov-3 Levis, Calgary #420/R (C.D 450)
£262 $475 €383 Untitled - yellow columbines (22x18cm-9x7in) s. W/C. 18-Apr-4 Levis, Calgary #420/R (C.D 635)
£269 $486 €393 Untitled - yellow lady's slipper (22x18cm-9x7in) s. W/C. 18-Apr-4 Levis, Calgary #419/R (C.D 650)
£289 $524 €422 Untitled - gaillardia aristata (22x18cm-9x7in) s. W/C. 18-Apr-4 Levis, Calgary #421/R (C.D 700)

BROWN, Benjamin Chambers (1865-1942) American
£2813 $4500 €4107 Laguna vista (38x51cm-15x20in) s. canvasboard. 18-May-3 Auctions by the Bay, Alameda #1173/R
£3261 $6000 €4761 Sunset, San Pedro Bay (45x30cm-18x12in) s. prov. 8-Jun-4 Bonhams & Butterfields, San Francisco #4297/R est:3000-5000
£3468 $6000 €5063 Evening reflections (41x51cm-16x20in) s. prov. 10-Dec-3 Bonhams & Butterfields, San Francisco #6232/R est:5000-7000
£9341 $17000 €13638 Mount Lowe and lupin landscape (41x51cm-16x20in) s. s.i.verso canvasboard. 15-Jun-4 John Moran, Pasadena #35 est:12000-18000
£14451 $25000 €21098 California Poppy field (69x102cm-27x40in) s.i. prov. 10-Dec-3 Bonhams & Butterfields, San Francisco #6221/R est:15000-20000

BROWN, Bernard Will (1920-) Canadian
£224 $400 €327 Colville Lake (45x61cm-18x24in) s.i.d.1977 canvasboard prov. 6-May-4 Heffel, Vancouver #41/R (C.D 550)
£640 $1171 €934 The Parhelion (60x75cm-24x30in) s.i.d.1989. 1-Jun-4 Hodgins, Calgary #52/R (C.D 1600)

BROWN, Carlyle (1919-1964) American
£297 $550 €434 Jewels and crystals (41x51cm-16x20in) s. s.d.1962 verso prov. 15-Jul-4 Doyle, New York #17/R
£408 $750 €596 Table with glass and napkin (60x70cm-24x28in) s.d.51 i.verso exhib. 27-Jun-4 Bonhams & Butterfields, San Francisco #3848/R

BROWN, Cecily (1969-) American?
£1196 $2200 €1746 Untitled (14x18cm-6x7in) init.d.1997 verso acrylic prov. 10-Jun-4 Phillips, New York #650/R est:800-1200
£40503 $72500 €59134 Untitled - boy trouble (190x190cm-75x75in) s.d.99 verso prov. 13-May-4 Sotheby's, New York #363/R est:50000-70000
Prints
£2370 $4100 €3460 Boudoir (55x69cm-22x27in) s.d.99 lithograph prov. 10-Dec-3 Phillips, New York #634/R est:800-1200
Works on paper
£435 $800 €635 Untitled (13x14cm-5x6in) init.d.1997 verso pastel prov. 10-Jun-4 Phillips, New York #654/R
£2428 $4200 €3545 Study number 15 (31x31cm-12x12in) s.d.99 verso W/C prov. 10-Dec-3 Phillips, New York #635/R est:3000-4000
£4601 $7500 €6717 Four letter heaven. W/C ink col pencil animation cells exec.c.1994 16 prov. 23-Sep-3 Christie's, Rockefeller NY #63/R est:6000-8000
£5389 $9000 €7868 Untitled, study no 18 (61x46cm-24x18in) s.d.99 verso black ink wash prov. 13-Nov-3 Sotheby's, New York #430/R est:7000-9000

BROWN, Charles Porter (1855-1930) American
Works on paper
£335 $600 €489 On rough waters (14x21cm-6x8in) s.d.1876 W/C gouache paperboard. 14-May-4 Skinner, Boston #117/R
£335 $600 €489 Storm tossed ship (14x21cm-6x8in) s.d.1876 W/C gouache paperboard. 14-May-4 Skinner, Boston #130/R

BROWN, Christopher (20th C) American
£2941 $5000 €4294 Bait box (152x183cm-60x72in) s.d.1980 verso. 9-Nov-3 Bonhams & Butterfields, Los Angeles #4052/R

BROWN, D Crosby (20th C) American
£1215 $2200 €1774 Sanderlings at Reid state park (122x180cm-48x71in) acrylic on board. 16-Apr-4 James Julia, Fairfield #520/R est:1000-2000

BROWN, Daniel Price (1939-) Canadian
Works on paper
£893 $1536 €1304 Kitten held in man's hands (29x24cm-11x9in) s. W/C. 2-Dec-3 Joyner Waddington, Toronto #239/R est:2500-3000 (C.D 2000)

BROWN, Deborah (1927-) Irish?
£328 $600 €479 Vincent Beach (124x1041cm-49x410in) 10-Jul-4 Hindman, Chicago #60/R
£1818 $3091 €2600 Man, sea and sky (46x56cm-18x22in) s. board painted c.1951-53 prov. 18-Nov-3 Whyte's, Dublin #63/R est:4000-6000

BROWN, Dexter (1942-) British
£900 $1620 €1314 Ferrari 275P versus Ford GT at ADAC 1000KMS 1964 (43x37cm-17x15in) s. acrylic. 26-Apr-4 Bonhams, New Bond Street #239

BROWN, Don (1962-) British
Sculpture
£1000 $1810 €1460 Don - orange (185x58x48cm-73x23x19in) init.d.97 plaster acrylic on wooden plinth. 1-Apr-4 Christie's, Kensington #342/R est:1500-2000

BROWN, Dorothy Foster (1901-) American
Works on paper
£235 $400 €343 Salome (35x27cm-14x11in) mono. W/C. 21-Nov-3 Skinner, Boston #409/R

BROWN, E (19th C) British
£750 $1358 €1095 Brown horse in landscape (46x61cm-18x24in) s.d.1874. 16-Apr-4 Keys, Aylsham #758
£3200 $5888 €4672 Chestnut hunter in a landscape (51x66cm-20x26in) s. 10-Jun-4 Christie's, Kensington #65/R est:1200-1800
£4865 $9000 €7103 Cow in landscape (51x66cm-20x26in) s.d.1874. 10-Feb-4 Doyle, New York #237/R est:4000-6000

BROWN, Edward (19/20th C) British
£660 $1214 €964 Bay hunter in a stable (43x53cm-17x21in) s.d.1868. 10-Jun-4 Christie's, Kensington #76/R

BROWN, Florence R (20th C) American
£1761 $3100 €2571 Two peacocks (43x38cm-17x15in) s. board. 3-Jan-4 Outer Cape Auctions, Provincetown #117/R
Works on paper
£257 $475 €375 Floral still life (33x51cm-13x20in) s. W/C. 15-Feb-4 Outer Cape Auctions, Provincetown #12a/R
£280 $500 €409 Feeding the geece (37x47cm-15x19in) W/C paperboard. 14-May-4 Skinner, Boston #383/R
£419 $750 €612 Blustery day (61x46cm-24x18in) s. gouache paperboard. 14-May-4 Skinner, Boston #385/R

BROWN, Francis Clark (1908-1992) American
£335 $550 €486 Bean blossom bridge (22x28cm-9x11in) s. i.verso painted c.1950. 7-Jun-3 Treadway Gallery, Cincinnati #1411

BROWN, G (?) ?
£1007 $1802 €1500 Lady seated in the garden (54x35cm-21x14in) s. 25-May-4 Finarte Semenzato, Milan #23/R est:1500-1800

BROWN, G Sterling (20th C) British
£1500 $2760 €2190 Racehorse Cyclonic, with C Elliott up, on Newmarket Heath (68x90cm-27x35in) s.d.1929. 23-Jun-4 Cheffins, Cambridge #521/R est:1500-2000

BROWN, George Loring (1814-1889) American
£647 $1100 €945 Double Head Mt, afternoon, Jackson, NH (28x38cm-11x15in) s. i.d.1877 verso prov. 18-Nov-3 John Moran, Pasadena #29
£860 $1600 €1256 Morning, view at Sorento, including Mt Vesuvius in the distance (30x46cm-12x18in) s.i.d.1883 verso. 5-Mar-4 Skinner, Boston #329/R est:700-900
£4012 $6500 €5817 View of Livermore Falls (28x38cm-11x15in) s.i.d.1868 verso. 8-Aug-3 Barridorf, Portland #70/R est:4000-6000
£4500 $7740 €6570 Traveller in a French pastoral landscape (73x92cm-29x36in) s.i.d.1847. 4-Dec-3 Christie's, Kensington #8/R est:5000-7000
£4500 $7740 €6570 Hudson river (74x92cm-29x36in) 4-Dec-3 Christie's, Kensington #9/R est:5000-7000

BROWN, Harley (1939-) Canadian
Works on paper
£960 $1757 €1402 Indian in full head dress (51x38cm-20x15in) s. pastel. 1-Jun-4 Hodgins, Calgary #171/R est:1500-2000 (C.D 2400)
£1267 $2116 €1850 Old Moccasin (55x43cm-22x17in) s.i. pastel. 17-Nov-3 Hodgins, Calgary #51/R est:1200-1800 (C.D 2800)
£1941 $3300 €2834 Mrs Yellow Sun, Blackfoot (48x41cm-19x16in) s.i. pastel prov. 1-Nov-3 Santa Fe Art, Santa Fe #30/R est:4000-6000
£2793 $5000 €4078 Kanda (30x23cm-12x9in) pastel. 15-May-4 Altermann Galleries, Santa Fe #106/R
£3529 $6000 €5152 Cheyenne chief (43x36cm-17x14in) pastel. 1-Nov-3 Altermann Galleries, Santa Fe #124
£5882 $11000 €8588 Crow dancer (51x33cm-20x13in) s. pastel. 24-Jul-4 Coeur d'Alene, Hayden #13/R est:6000-9000

BROWN, Harold Haven (1869-1932) American
Works on paper
£279 $490 €407 Beached dory (20x30cm-8x12in) s. W/C. 3-Jan-4 Outer Cape Auctions, Provincetown #86/R
£455 $800 €664 Swans on lake (15x23cm-6x9in) s. W/C. 3-Jan-4 Outer Cape Auctions, Provincetown #116/R

BROWN, Harrison B (1831-1915) American
£838 $1500 €1223 Bowdoin College Chapel (36x46cm-14x18in) mono. 14-May-4 Skinner, Boston #75/R est:1000-1500
£1090 $1950 €1591 Coastal landscape (38x30cm-15x12in) s. 8-Jan-4 James Julia, Fairfield #957/R est:750-900
£2077 $3800 €3032 Mill Brook, North Conway, N H (33x43cm-13x17in) 10-Apr-4 Cobbs, Peterborough #84/R
£3704 $6000 €5371 Lighthouse (34x61cm-13x24in) s.d.63. 8-Aug-3 Barridorf, Portland #71/R est:5000-7000

BROWN, Helen (1917-1986) New Zealander
£662 $1238 €967 Angry seagulls (34x46cm-13x18in) s. board. 24-Feb-4 Peter Webb, Auckland #11/R (NZ.D 1800)
£1607 $2957 €2346 Three headlands (67x89cm-26x35in) s.d.1965 board. 25-Mar-4 International Art Centre, Auckland #61/R est:3000-5000 (NZ.D 4500)
£1608 $2927 €2348 Wharf, Opua (37x47cm-15x19in) s.d.1954 board prov. 29-Jun-4 Peter Webb, Auckland #87/R est:3000-5000 (NZ.D 4600)
£1791 $3099 €2615 Kawau bay 2 (40x88cm-16x35in) s.d.1968 i.verso board. 9-Dec-3 Peter Webb, Auckland #165/R est:2500-3500 (NZ.D 4800)
£1964 $3614 €2867 Scotts Landing, Mahurangi (50x75cm-20x30in) s.d.1977. 25-Mar-4 International Art Centre, Auckland #51/R est:3000-5000 (NZ.D 5500)
£2010 $3659 €2935 Bon Accord Harbour (68x91cm-27x36in) s. board prov. 29-Jun-4 Peter Webb, Auckland #86/R est:4000-6000 (NZ.D 5750)

BROWN, Henry Harris (1864-1948) British
£600 $996 €876 Portrait of the artist William Henry Mason of Morton Hall (91x71cm-36x28in) s.i.d.1906. 2-Oct-3 Neales, Nottingham #713

BROWN, Hilton (1938-) American
£412 $700 €602 Sun II (71x71cm-28x28in) s. i.d.1963 verso prov. 9-Nov-3 Wright, Chicago #399
£765 $1300 €1117 Screen series no.14, Virgo St. Louis (180x180cm-71x71in) s.i.d.1967 acrylic polymer. 9-Nov-3 Wright, Chicago #395 est:1000-1500
£2794 $4750 €4079 Screen series no.21, Pisces (178x178cm-70x70in) s.i.d.1968 verso acrylic polymer prov. 9-Nov-3 Wright, Chicago #394 est:1000-1500

BROWN, Horace (1876-1949) American
£299 $550 €437 Live oak, Coral Gables (30x41cm-12x16in) s.i.d.1942 board. 25-Jun-4 Freeman, Philadelphia #117/R

BROWN, Ion (20th C) New Zealander
£347 $552 €507 Rangitikei (19x32cm-7x13in) s. 1-May-3 Dunbar Sloane, Wellington #702 est:200-500 (NZ.D 1000)

BROWN, J G (19th C) British
£3261 $6000 €4761 Portrait of a young woman wearing a straw hat with ostrich plumes (61x41cm-24x16in) s. 9-Jun-4 Alderfer's, Hatfield #369/R est:5000-8000
£5108 $9500 €7458 Man with violin (56x46cm-22x18in) s.d.1877. 3-Mar-4 Alderfer's, Hatfield #438/R est:9000-11000
£10795 $19000 €15761 Young girl carrying a bucket of raspberries (51x36cm-20x14in) s. 1-Jan-4 Nadeau, Windsor #225/R est:6000-9000

BROWN, J Taylor (fl.1893-1940) British
£470 $874 €686 Rowallan Castle. Figures on a track (33x46cm-13x18in) s. two. 4-Mar-4 Christie's, Kensington #139/R

BROWN, James (1951-1991) American
£352 $610 €500 Untitled (65x50cm-26x20in) acrylic peinture W/C pencil collage flax. 9-Dec-3 Artcurial Briest, Paris #53
£915 $1584 €1300 Untitled (73x54cm-29x21in) s. acrylic flax. 9-Dec-3 Artcurial Briest, Paris #54 est:600-700
£1111 $1856 €1600 Sans titre (73x51cm-29x20in) s.d.1994 acrylic tissue. 25-Oct-3 Cornette de St.Cyr, Paris #604/R est:1200-1500
£1622 $3000 €2368 Untitled (127x96cm-50x38in) init.d.1982 oil oil pastel pencil enamel paper. 13-Jul-4 Christie's, Rockefeller NY #146/R est:2000-3000
£2867 $4788 €4100 Untitled (52x38cm-20x15in) s.d.1993 verso prov. 29-Jun-3 Versailles Encheres #212/R est:4500-5500
£3000 $4770 €4380 Cactus flowers, Mexico (33x23cm-13x9in) s.i.d.1996 verso acrylic linen on canvas set of four. 11-Sep-3 Christie's, Kensington #239/R est:3000-4000
£3931 $6800 €5739 Head (151x140cm-59x55in) s.i.d.1982 verso acrylic cardboard prov. 10-Dec-3 Phillips, New York #465/R est:4000-6000
£4000 $6680 €5840 White stabat mater (88x59cm-35x23in) s.d.1989 verso dispersion linen on canvas prov. 22-Oct-3 Christie's, London #83/R est:4000-6000
£4200 $7644 €6132 Stabar Mater IV (243x296cm-96x117in) s.i.d.86-88 verso paper on canvas prov. 4-Feb-4 Sotheby's, Olympia #209/R est:3000-4000

£4800 $8688 €7008 Untitled (102x152cm-40x60in) s.d.1984 oil pencil prov. 1-Apr-4 Christie's, Kensington #270/R est:3000-4000
£9000 $16290 €13140 Anchor composition (122x127cm-48x50in) s.i. i.d.1986 verso oil enamel pencil prov. 1-Apr-4 Christie's, Kensington #271/R est:6000-8000
£14000 $25340 €20440 Untitled (213x122cm-84x48in) s. init.i.d.1983 verso oil enamel on canvas prov. 1-Apr-4 Christie's, Kensington #266/R est:10000-15000
Sculpture
£3007 $5172 €4300 Eleven portraits of Buddha (129x81x58cm-51x32x23in) gold wood bronze bronze plinth on copper base wood base prov. 5-Dec-3 Ketterer, Munich #183/R est:7000-9000
Works on paper
£304 $544 €450 Drawing from the door (21x14cm-8x6in) s.i.d.1986 col crayon prov. 4-May-4 Calmels Cohen, Paris #228
£1333 $2440 €2000 Untitled (42x29cm-17x11in) s.d.95 gouache four. 4-Jun-4 Lempertz, Koln #74/R est:1800
£2081 $3829 €3100 Tetes (66x51cm-26x20in) s.d.1983 lead pencil brown paper prov. 29-Mar-4 Cornette de St.Cyr, Paris #119/R est:3000-3500
£2365 $4163 €3500 Cyclopoid IV (102x61cm-40x24in) s.i.d.1987 gouache canvas prov. 18-May-4 Tajan, Paris #152/R est:2000-2500

BROWN, James Hamilton (fl.1930-1950s) American
Photographs
£2889 $5200 €4218 Multi-toned photogram (28x36cm-11x14in) gelatin silver print prov. 22-Apr-4 Phillips, New York #48/R est:3000-5000

BROWN, Joe (1909-1985) American
Sculpture
£1353 $2300 €1975 Fallen boxer (9cm-4in) s. bronze wooden base. 21-Nov-3 Skinner, Boston #432/R est:700-900

BROWN, John Appleton (1844-1902) American
£699 $1250 €1021 Crashing wave on beach (25x36cm-10x14in) s.d.1860. 8-Jan-4 James Julia, Fairfield #960/R
Works on paper
£5143 $9000 €7509 Spring landscape (46x55cm-18x22in) s. pastel board. 19-Dec-3 Sotheby's, New York #1100/R est:3000-5000

BROWN, John Arnesby (1866-1955) British
£3800 $6346 €5548 Norfolk landscape (20x25cm-8x10in) init. 17-Oct-3 Keys, Aylsham #689 est:3500
£16500 $26565 €24090 Cattle grazing on the marshes, Norfolk (48x58cm-19x23in) s. prov. 15-Aug-3 Keys, Aylsham #690/R est:5000-7000
£35000 $64400 €51100 River afterglow (90x110cm-35x43in) s. prov.exhib.lit. 26-Mar-4 Sotheby's, London #79/R est:40000-60000

BROWN, John George (1831-1913) American
£1676 $3000 €2447 Shoeshine boy (31x23cm-12x9in) s. 14-May-4 Skinner, Boston #105/R est:2000-4000
£3892 $6500 €5682 Milkmaid under cherry tree (61x41cm-24x16in) s.d.1875. 19-Oct-3 Susanin's, Chicago #6048/R est:8000-10000
£5820 $11000 €8497 Boy presenting a bouquet of flowers to girl (61x41cm-24x16in) s. prov. 17-Feb-4 John Moran, Pasadena #102/R est:12000-17000
£6286 $11000 €9178 A bootblack (62x41cm-24x16in) s.d.94 prov. 19-Dec-3 Sotheby's, New York #1068/R est:5000-7000
£20231 $35000 €29537 Daydream (77x51cm-30x20in) s.i.d.1882 prov. 10-Dec-3 Bonhams & Butterfields, San Francisco #6014/R est:40000-60000
£21307 $37500 €31108 By the stream (66x51cm-26x20in) s. prov. 19-May-4 Sotheby's, New York #98/R est:40000-60000
£22727 $40000 €33181 Silver birches (54x34cm-21x13in) s.d.1864 prov.exhib.lit. 18-May-4 Christie's, Rockefeller NY #12/R est:50000-70000
£22727 $40000 €33181 Young Apple Salesman (51x36cm-20x14in) s.d.1878 prov.lit. 18-May-4 Christie's, Rockefeller NY #26/R est:30000-50000
£28409 $50000 €41477 Deep-laid plan (63x51cm-25x20in) s.d.1886 prov.exhib.lit. 18-May-4 Christie's, Rockefeller NY #66/R est:30000-50000
£32353 $55000 €47235 Little servant (77x64cm-30x25in) s. painted 1880. 30-Oct-3 Phillips, New York #45/R est:60000-80000
£34884 $60000 €50931 Stepping stones (76x51cm-30x20in) s. prov. 4-Dec-3 Christie's, Rockefeller NY #16/R
Works on paper
£6630 $12000 €9680 Shoe shine boy (61x41cm-24x16in) W/C prov. 19-Apr-4 Caddigan, Hanover #1/R

BROWN, John Lewis (1829-1890) French
£824 $1500 €1203 Soldiers on horseback (65x54cm-26x21in) s. prov. 4-Feb-4 Christie's, Rockefeller NY #41/R est:6000-8000
£900 $1656 €1314 Figures and horses in a wooded landscape (27x17cm-11x7in) s. panel. 10-Jun-4 Christie's, Kensington #165/R
£1053 $1758 €1537 Tetes de chevaux (92x73cm-36x29in) s.d.1881. 16-Nov-3 Koller, Geneva #1216/R est:2000-3000 (S.FR 2400)
£1126 $2015 €1644 Landscape with horse drawn carriage (24x33cm-9x13in) s. panel. 22-Mar-4 Philippe Schuler, Zurich #4389/R est:2500-3000 (S.FR 2600)
£1600 $2928 €2400 Abois (30x46cm-12x18in) s. 6-Jun-4 Osenat, Fontainebleau #255/R est:3000-3500
£2000 $3620 €3000 Les trois cavaliers (40x32cm-16x13in) s. panel. 5-Apr-4 Deburaux, Boulogne #82 est:3000-3500
£2111 $3800 €3082 Horses in a stable (26x39cm-10x15in) s.d.68 pair prov. 23-Jan-4 Christie's, Rockefeller NY #120/R est:3000-5000
£2649 $4848 €4000 Hussard a cheval (93x73cm-37x29in) s.d.1860. 7-Apr-4 Doutrebente, Paris #29/R est:1200-1500
£2817 $4535 €4000 Scene de chasse (16x21cm-6x8in) s. panel. 22-Aug-3 Deauville, France #37/R
£2897 $5359 €4200 Trois cavaliers sous le regne de Louis XV dans un paysage (24x18cm-9x7in) s. panel. 13-Feb-4 Rossini, Paris #14/R est:700-800
£6133 $11101 €9200 Scene de chasse a courre (29x53cm-11x21in) s. 5-Apr-4 Deburaux, Boulogne #83/R est:4000-4500
£6755 $12294 €10200 Course de steeple-chase (18x36cm-7x14in) s.d.1860. 16-Jun-4 Beaussant & Lefèvre, Paris #3/R est:5000-6000
£7417 $13499 €11200 La halte de chasse a courre (16x41cm-6x16in) s. 16-Jun-4 Renaud, Paris #29/R est:4500-5000
Works on paper
£709 $1184 €1000 Repos au bord de la mer (66x55cm-26x22in) s.d.1878 crayon wash gouache cardboard. 17-Jun-3 Christie's, Paris #126/R

BROWN, John Lewis (attrib) (1829-1890) French
£1477 $2732 €2200 Aux courses (20x37cm-8x15in) i.d.1867 verso panel. 13-Mar-4 De Vuyst, Lokeren #32/R est:2000-2500

BROWN, Jonathan Kumunjara (1960-1997) Australian
£2479 $4587 €3619 Msralinga country (122x183cm-48x72in) natural eath pigments pva linen on canvas executed 1996. 15-Mar-4 Sotheby's, Melbourne #28 est:3000-5000 (A.D 6000)

BROWN, Joseph (?-1923) British
£3800 $5966 €5510 Harbour at Pittenweem (62x92cm-24x36in) s. 27-Aug-3 Sotheby's, London #1107/R est:3000-4000

BROWN, Joseph R (1861-?) American
£559 $1000 €816 Young mariners (34x50cm-13x20in) s.d.1920 i.verso board. 14-May-4 Skinner, Boston #234/R

BROWN, Leonard (1949-) Australian
£413 $764 €603 Woman in the morning sun (84x76cm-33x30in) init.d.91 verso prov.exhib. 15-Mar-4 Sotheby's, Melbourne #88 est:800-1200 (A.D 1000)
£455 $841 €664 Moonlight through the open door (84x76cm-33x30in) init.d.91 prov.exhib. 15-Mar-4 Sotheby's, Melbourne #87 est:800-1200 (A.D 1100)
£1489 $2532 €2174 Brisbane painting (91x83cm-36x33in) init.d.85 linen exhib.prov. 25-Nov-3 Christie's, Melbourne #136/R est:3500-5000 (A.D 3500)

BROWN, Lyndall and GREEN, Charles (20th C) Australian
£2033 $3191 €2968 Dark wood II (152x152cm-60x60in) s.i.d.1992 verso linen prov.exhib. 27-Aug-3 Christie's, Sydney #653/R est:3000-5000 (A.D 5000)

BROWN, Mae Bennett (20th C) American
£396 $650 €574 Still life of flowers in a vase (61x76cm-24x30in) s. 2-Jun-3 Grogan, Boston #640/R

BROWN, Marshall (?) ?
£920 $1564 €1343 Washing the reeds (46x61cm-18x24in) s. 10-Nov-3 Thomson Roddick & Medcalf, Edinburgh #242/R

BROWN, Mary (20th C) British
£400 $680 €584 Summer flowers in a glass vase (45x34cm-18x13in) s. 1-Dec-3 Bonhams, Bath #34

BROWN, Mather (1761-1831) British/American
£400 $632 €584 Portrait of a gentleman (59x46cm-23x18in) 6-Sep-3 Shapes, Edinburgh #364/R
£2000 $3340 €2920 Portrait of a lady, wearing a black dress and bonnet (76x64cm-30x25in) s. 22-Oct-3 Halls, Shrewsbury #104/R est:1500-2000
£90000 $153000 €131400 Portrait of Sir George Augustus Eliott. Baron Heathfield (250x163cm-98x64in) 27-Nov-3 Sotheby's, London #14/R est:100000-150000

BROWN, Mather (attrib) (1761-1831) British/American
£6000 $10020 €8760 Portrait of H R H Frederick, Duke of York and Albany (115x70cm-45x28in) 14-Oct-3 Sotheby's, London #459 est:3000-4000

BROWN, May Marshall (1887-?) British
Works on paper
£270 $440 €394 Blossom. W/C. 17-Jul-3 Bonhams, Edinburgh #311
£300 $489 €438 Brambles. W/C. 17-Jul-3 Bonhams, Edinburgh #312

BROWN, Mike (1938-1997) Australian
£1148 $1813 €1676 Mindscape II (134x131cm-53x52in) s.d.1972 verso prov. 2-Sep-3 Deutscher-Menzies, Melbourne #211/R est:2500-3500 (A.D 2800)
Works on paper
£1311 $2072 €1914 City limits (60x67cm-24x26in) s.i.d.1982-92 verso synthetic polymer canvas on board prov. 2-Sep-3 Deutscher-Menzies, Melbourne #212/R est:2000-3000 (A.D 3200)

BROWN, Nigel (1949-) New Zealander
£551 $1031 €804 Fern Icon (19x13cm-7x5in) s.d.1991 s.i.d.verso board. 24-Feb-4 Peter Webb, Auckland #33/R (NZ.D 1500)
£580 $933 €847 One tree hill (77x57cm-30x22in) init. acrylic. 20-Aug-3 Dunbar Sloane, Auckland #115 est:1700-2500 (NZ.D 1600)
£699 $1306 €1021 Composition after Edvard Munch's The Scream (58x76cm-23x30in) s.d.1981 acrylic paper. 24-Feb-4 Peter Webb, Auckland #116/R (NZ.D 1900)
£804 $1479 €1174 Two journeys (42x36cm-17x14in) s.i.d.1978 acrylic paper. 25-Mar-4 International Art Centre, Auckland #4/R (NZ.D 2250)
£906 $1467 €1314 Let us climb the ridges (35x28cm-14x11in) s.d.1980 oil paper. 31-Jul-3 International Art Centre, Auckland #121/R est:2500-3500 (NZ.D 2500)
£996 $1614 €1444 Crucifixion with aeroplanes 3 (41x30cm-16x12in) s.d.1981 acrylic W/C on board. 31-Jul-3 International Art Centre, Auckland #1/R est:2500-3500 (NZ.D 2750)
£1119 $1937 €1634 Urewera (46x57cm-18x22in) s.d.1987 board. 9-Dec-3 Peter Webb, Auckland #155/R est:3000-5000 (NZ.D 3000)
£1128 $1917 €1647 Laingholm Winter II (60x70cm-24x28in) s.d.1985 board. 27-Nov-3 International Art Centre, Auckland #10/R est:2800-4000 (NZ.D 3000)

£2170 $3451 €3168 Pounamu (70x50cm-28x20in) s. i.d.2001 verso oil on linen. 1-May-3 Dunbar Sloane, Wellington #64/R est:6000-8000 (NZ.D 6250)
£2357 $4337 €3441 Rotokawau/Virginia lake (49x75cm-19x30in) s.d.1993. 25-Mar-4 International Art Centre, Auckland #43/R est:6000-7000 (NZ.D 6600)
£2431 $3865 €3549 Clothesline painting no.12 (117x77cm-46x30in) s.i.d.1981 acrylic on board. 1-May-3 Dunbar Sloane, Wellington #63/R est:7000-10000 (NZ.D 7000)
£2482 $4394 €3624 Man on a pedestal (136x74cm-54x29in) s.d.1997. 28-Apr-4 Dunbar Sloane, Auckland #38/R est:8000-10000 (NZ.D 7000)
£3383 $5752 €4939 Damaged landscape with drinker (110x44cm-43x17in) s.i.d.1990 verso oil on cotton duck. 26-Nov-3 Dunbar Sloane, Wellington #39/R est:6000-8000 (NZ.D 9000)
Works on paper
£362 $616 €529 Reason why (43x30cm-17x12in) s.d.1971 pencil. 4-Nov-3 Peter Webb, Auckland #55/R est:1000-1500 (NZ.D 1000)
£662 $1238 €967 Go fly a kite (40x56cm-16x22in) s.i.d.1982 gouache ink. 24-Feb-4 Peter Webb, Auckland #120/R (NZ.D 1800)
£975 $1726 €1424 Crazy artist (63x49cm-25x19in) s.d.87 mixed media. 28-Apr-4 Dunbar Sloane, Auckland #67/R (NZ.D 2750)

BROWN, Nyuju Stumpy (c.1935-) Australian
Works on paper
£2148 $4018 €3222 Untitled (76x60cm-30x24in) bears name synthetic polymer paint canvas prov. 26-Jul-4 Sotheby's, Melbourne #501/R est:3000-5000 (A.D 5500)

BROWN, Paul D (1893-1958) American
Works on paper
£1078 $1800 €1574 Half way there (33x46cm-13x18in) s.i. chl col pencil prov. 18-Jun-3 Doyle, New York #14/R est:1000-1500
£1397 $2500 €2040 Arthur D B Preece, bridlespur huntsman on Cab Calloway, 1933 (25x19cm-10x7in) s. W/C over pencil htd white. 6-May-4 Doyle, New York #1/R est:600-800

BROWN, Peter (fl.1758-1799) British
Works on paper
£280 $468 €409 Rivers Street, Bath (34x42cm-13x17in) s.d.97 chl. 20-Oct-3 Bonhams, Bath #144
£320 $534 €467 Camden Crescent, Bath (36x50cm-14x20in) s.d.97 chl. 20-Oct-3 Bonhams, Bath #143
£1556 $2800 €2272 Yellow breasted woodpecker on a log (35x24cm-14x9in) s. bodycol sold with another two similar. 22-Jan-4 Christie's, Rockefeller NY #189/R est:3000-5000

BROWN, R G (fl.1844-1859) British
£1000 $1820 €1460 Pony and dog waiting at a gate (53x70cm-21x28in) s.d.1845. 5-Feb-4 Mellors & Kirk, Nottingham #531/R est:1000-1400

BROWN, Ralph (1928-) British
Sculpture
£1387 $2400 €2025 Swimming woman (51x46x56cm-20x18x22in) bronze prov. 15-Dec-3 Hindman, Chicago #79/R est:1500-2500
£4800 $8736 €7008 Relief - bride (102cm-40in) mono.d.6.9 brown pat bronze cast 1975 exhib. 1-Jul-4 Christie's, Kensington #242/R est:3000-5000
Works on paper
£2000 $3200 €2920 Nude studies (50x35cm-20x14in) pencil set of five. 19-May-3 Bruton Knowles, Cheltenham #111 est:400-600

BROWN, Reynold (1917-1991) American
£3529 $6000 €5152 Indian scout for the Seventh Cavalry (56x76cm-22x30in) s.d.74 prov. 1-Nov-3 Santa Fe Art, Santa Fe #100/R est:8000-10000

BROWN, Richard Woodley (attrib) (19th C) British
£320 $506 €464 Figures before an abbey ruin (30x41cm-12x16in) 4-Sep-3 Christie's, Kensington #152/R

BROWN, Robert (18/19th C) British
£260 $458 €380 Mahlar, Winchester (29x21cm-11x8in) s. panel. 18-May-4 Woolley & Wallis, Salisbury #2/R
£580 $1021 €847 Venice flower market (35x30cm-14x12in) s.d.95 board. 18-May-4 Woolley & Wallis, Salisbury #334/R
£720 $1267 €1051 Marrakech market (51x25cm-20x10in) s, panel. 18-May-4 Woolley & Wallis, Salisbury #40/R

BROWN, Robert Woodley (attrib) (19th C) British
£775 $1340 €1100 English landscape (30x40cm-12x16in) canvas on canvas. 10-Dec-3 Hugo Ruef, Munich #2396

BROWN, Roger (1941-1997) American
£1714 $3000 €2502 Four New Poems (36x21cm-14x8in) i. painted 1971 exhib. 17-Dec-3 Christie's, Rockefeller NY #209/R est:3000-4000
£4717 $7500 €6887 Price of admission. Theatre (30x30cm-12x12in) pair. 14-Sep-3 Susanin's, Chicago #6127/R est:4000-6000
£6044 $11000 €8824 Nostalgic history (87x122cm-34x48in) i.d.1971 overlap acrylic prov. 29-Jun-4 Sotheby's, New York #486/R est:4000-6000
£9714 $17000 €14182 Human Fly (91x91cm-36x36in) i. painted 1989 exhib. 17-Dec-3 Christie's, Rockefeller NY #299/R est:8000-12000

BROWN, Roy (1879-1956) American
£235 $400 €343 Valley vista (20x30cm-8x12in) board. 8-Nov-3 Van Blarcom, South Natick #121/R
£235 $400 €343 Upland pasture (20x30cm-8x12in) board. 8-Nov-3 Van Blarcom, South Natick #122/R
£279 $475 €407 Harbour scene with dock side view (23x30cm-9x12in) board. 8-Nov-3 Van Blarcom, South Natick #129/R

BROWN, Samuel John Milton (1873-1965) British
Works on paper
£400 $732 €584 Coastal trader (17x24cm-7x9in) s. W/C. 6-Jul-4 Bearnes, Exeter #407/R
£480 $878 €701 Brigantine in calm seas (17x24cm-7x9in) s. W/C. 6-Jul-4 Bearnes, Exeter #406/R
£550 $946 €803 Morning tide (30x40cm-12x16in) s. W/C. 2-Dec-3 Sotheby's, London #110/R
£600 $1074 €876 Lamport and Holt passenger vessel in the Channel with seagulls hovering (23x37cm-9x15in) s. W/C htd white. 26-May-4 Christie's, Kensington #531/R
£1000 $1720 €1460 Nearing home (43x53cm-17x21in) s. W/C. 2-Dec-3 Sotheby's, London #78/R est:800-1200
£1486 $2661 €2170 Ariel. Cutty Sark. Taeping. Thermopylae (31x38cm-12x15in) all s. pen in, W/C four. 31-May-4 Stephan Welz, Johannesburg #448 est:6000-9000 (SA.R 18000)

BROWN, Samuel John Milton (attrib) (1873-1965) British
£816 $1298 €1200 Ivernia, un paquebot (60x40cm-24x16in) s. cardboard. 21-Mar-3 Neret-Minet, Paris #46

BROWN, Taylor (?) British?
£500 $930 €730 An Ayrshire landscape (63x81cm-25x32in) s. 4-Mar-4 Christie's, Kensington #166/R

BROWN, Thomas Austen (1857-1924) British
£1078 $1800 €1574 Fishing boats of Skegness (53x91cm-21x36in) s.i. painted c.1889. 19-Oct-3 William Jenack, New York #214 est:2000-3000
£1350 $2471 €1971 Homeward (71x67cm-28x26in) s.d.1890. 28-Jan-4 Dreweatt Neate, Newbury #83/R est:700-900
£5500 $9845 €8030 Homeward (72x67cm-28x26in) s.d.1890 prov.lit. 27-May-4 Christie's, Kensington #337/R est:2000-3000
£13000 $23530 €18980 Morning pasture (127x102cm-50x40in) s.d.1894 prov.exhib. 19-Apr-4 Sotheby's, London #45/R est:15000-20000

BROWN, Tom (20th C) British
Works on paper
£240 $439 €350 Manchester Cathedral with river Irwell in the foreground (41x33cm-16x13in) s. 6-Apr-4 Capes Dunn, Manchester #823
£280 $512 €409 Street scene - Castle and Falcon Public House (38x51cm-15x20in) s. pastel. 6-Apr-4 Capes Dunn, Manchester #831/R
£280 $512 €409 Street scene with rag and bone cart (25x38cm-10x15in) s. pastel. 6-Apr-4 Capes Dunn, Manchester #832/R

BROWN, Vincent (1901-2001) Australian
Works on paper
£690 $1076 €1001 Afternoon rest (29x36cm-11x14in) s.d.1928 W/C. 1-Aug-2 Joel, Victoria #167 est:2500-3500 (A.D 2000)

BROWN, W (?) ?
£1100 $1980 €1606 Ruins of Jedburgh Abbey Priory (32x47cm-13x19in) s.d.1856. 21-Apr-4 Tennants, Leyburn #1080 est:600-800

BROWN, William (19th C) British
£307 $550 €448 Mt Shasta, California (33x61cm-13x24in) s. painted c.1910. 16-Mar-4 Matthew's, Oregon #75/R

BROWN, William Beattie (1831-1909) British
£500 $945 €730 Woodland path at sunset (44x65cm-17x26in) s. 19-Feb-4 Lyon & Turnbull, Edinburgh #125
£600 $1002 €876 Highland river landscape with country house-possibly Mar Lodge on Deeside (50x75cm-20x30in) s. 16-Oct-3 Lyon & Turnbull, Edinburgh #98
£740 $1236 €1080 Harvest time. sold with another oil. 19-Jun-3 Bonhams, Edinburgh #383
£950 $1577 €1387 On the River Tay, Perthshire (30x45cm-12x18in) s.i. two. 1-Oct-3 Sotheby's, Olympia #34/R
£1300 $2041 €1885 Highland burn (51x76cm-20x30in) s. prov. 27-Aug-3 Sotheby's, London #955/R est:1500-2000
£1300 $2327 €1898 Fishing above the falls (50x75cm-20x30in) s. 28-May-4 Lyon & Turnbull, Edinburgh #35/R est:1500-2000
£2200 $3652 €3212 Falls of Bruar. On the Findhorn (38x18cm-15x7in) both s. i.verso board pair. 1-Oct-3 Sotheby's, Olympia #68/R est:1200-1800
£2500 $3925 €3625 Sweet auburn loveliest village of the plain (77x137cm-30x54in) s.d.1885 i.verso. 27-Aug-3 Sotheby's, London #926/R est:3000-5000
Works on paper
£650 $1216 €949 October day, Belgium (25x35cm-10x14in) s.d.1883 W/C. 21-Jul-4 Lyon & Turnbull, Edinburgh #116/R
£650 $1216 €949 Gathering firewood (25x35cm-10x14in) s. W/C. 21-Jul-4 Lyon & Turnbull, Edinburgh #117/R
£700 $1309 €1022 Fisherman on the Tummel (16x35cm-6x14in) s. i.verso W/C. 22-Jul-4 Bonhams, Edinburgh #305

BROWN, William Henry (1808-1883) American
Works on paper
£1364 $2400 €1991 Portrait of a fireman (33x28cm-13x11in) W/C gouache. 22-May-4 Pook & Pook, Downington #665/R est:1000-1500

BROWN, William Marshall (1863-1936) British
£750 $1343 €1095 Cockenzie harbour (23x30cm-9x12in) s.d.1897 board. 28-May-4 Lyon & Turnbull, Edinburgh #3
£2600 $4654 €3796 Paddling in the sea (81x101cm-32x40in) init.i. 26-May-4 Sotheby's, Olympia #237/R est:2000-3000
£5385 $9262 €7862 At play (47x51cm-19x20in) s. 3-Dec-3 AB Stockholms Auktionsverk #2651/R est:15000-20000 (S.KR 70000)
£12000 $21960 €17520 Romping (25x36cm-10x14in) s. 27-Jan-4 Gorringes, Lewes #1698/R est:3000-4000

£12000	$21720	€17520	Taking turns (41x51cm-16x20in) s. 19-Apr-4 Sotheby's, London #109/R est:6000-8000
Works on paper			
£2100	$3801	€3066	North country fisher girl (31x36cm-12x14in) s. W/C. 19-Apr-4 Sotheby's, London #110/R est:1500-2000

BROWN, William Marshall (attrib) (1863-1936) British

£450	$828	€675	Bailing out the boat (46x76cm-18x30in) s. canvas on board. 22-Jun-4 Hamptons Fine Art, Godalming #93

BROWN, William Mason (1828-1898) American

£994	$1800	€1451	Autumn landscapes (25x36cm-10x14in) pair. 16-Apr-4 James Julia, Fairfield #613/R est:4000-6000
£15244	$25000	€22104	Mountains with pond, and two Native Americans at shore's edge (61x91cm-24x36in) s. canvas on fiberboard prov. 31-May-3 Brunk, Ashville #109/R est:8000-12000
£15294	$26000	€22329	Twilight on the river (31x46cm-12x18in) init. 30-Oct-3 Phillips, New York #35/R est:30000-50000
£15337	$25000	€22392	Still life with fruit (36x46cm-14x18in) s. 28-Sep-3 Simpson's, Houston #380/R
£15698	$27000	€22919	Still life with peaches (51x41cm-20x16in) s. prov. 4-Dec-3 Christie's, Rockefeller NY #55/R est:20000-30000
£22093	$38000	€32256	Still life with watermelon, grapes, peaches and plums (40x58cm-16x23in) s. painted c.1870. 4-Dec-3 Christie's, Rockefeller NY #21/R

BROWN, William Mason (attrib) (1828-1898) American

£688	$1100	€1004	Camp at river's edge (91x155cm-36x61in) bears sig. 18-May-3 Auctions by the Bay, Alameda #1037/R

BROWN, William Theo (1919-) American

£1017	$1800	€1485	Picnic (30x41cm-12x16in) masonite prov. 2-May-4 Bonhams & Butterfields, Los Angeles #3072/R est:2500-4500
£2174	$4000	€3174	Portrait of girl sitting in a red chair (51x43cm-20x17in) s.d.62 panel. 9-Jun-4 Alderfer's, Hatfield #394/R est:3000-5000
£2907	$5000	€4244	Landscape with figures (39x39cm-15x15in) init.d.68 acrylic on panel prov. 3-Dec-3 Doyle, New York #63/R est:3000-5000
£7647	$13000	€11165	View from the hill (79x96cm-31x38in) init.d.64 s.d.verso prov. 9-Nov-3 Bonhams & Butterfields, Los Angeles #4056/R est:12000-18000
Works on paper			
£941	$1600	€1374	San Francisco view from Pennsylvania at 20th (28x38cm-11x15in) s.d.83 chl prov. 9-Nov-3 Bonhams & Butterfields, Los Angeles #4054/R est:2000-3000
£2119	$3750	€3094	Untitled, football players (108x142cm-43x56in) s.d.56 mixed media. 2-May-4 Bonhams & Butterfields, Los Angeles #3067/R est:3000-5000

BROWNE, Andrew (1960-) Australian

£992	$1835	€1448	Untitled I and II (30x137cm-12x54in) diptych exhib. 15-Mar-4 Sotheby's, Melbourne #177 est:700-900 (A.D 2400)
£1106	$1881	€1615	Untitled (137x167cm-54x66in) s.i.d.1987 verso. 26-Nov-3 Deutscher-Menzies, Melbourne #205/R est:3500-4500 (A.D 2600)

BROWNE, Archibald (1864-1948) Canadian

£320	$586	€467	Path to the lake (61x30cm-24x12in) 1-Jun-4 Hodgins, Calgary #143/R (C.D 800)

BROWNE, Byron (1907-1961) American

£529	$900	€772	Sail, Provincetown (66x51cm-26x20in) s. s.i.d.1952 verso. 5-Nov-3 Doyle, New York #18/R
£598	$1100	€873	Two clowns (48x64cm-19x25in) s.i.d.1947 tempera crayon ink. 10-Jun-4 Swann Galleries, New York #41/R
£994	$1800	€1451	Still life (76x61cm-30x24in) s.d.1954. 18-Apr-4 Bonhams & Butterfields, Los Angeles #7081 est:2000-3000
£1397	$2500	€2040	Girl with guitar (66x51cm-26x20in) s. s.i.d.1959 verso prov. 6-May-4 Shannon's, Milford #65/R est:3000-5000
£1570	$2700	€2292	Jester (66x51cm-26x20in) s.d.1950 s.i.d.verso exhib. 3-Dec-3 Doyle, New York #1/R est:3000-5000
£1944	$3500	€2838	Clown with mask (76x61cm-30x24in) s.d.1948 s.i.d.verso. 23-Jan-4 Freeman, Philadelphia #141/R est:2000-3000
£2147	$3800	€3135	Night owl (50x66cm-20x26in) s.d.1954 tempera crayon ink paper prov. 28-Apr-4 Christie's, Los Angeles #79/R est:3000-5000
£4348	$8000	€6348	Blue lion with dancer (121x91cm-48x36in) s. s.i.d.1946 verso prov. 27-Jun-4 Freeman, Philadelphia #110/R est:4000-6000
Works on paper			
£373	$600	€545	Artist and model (64x48cm-25x19in) s.d.January 22,1958 mixed media. 22-Feb-3 Bunte, Elgin #1213
£543	$1000	€793	Sailboats in a harbour (51x64cm-20x25in) s.d.1955 gouache. 10-Jun-4 Swann Galleries, New York #44/R
£569	$950	€831	Clown juggling (53x33cm-21x13in) s.d.1948 i.verso W/C. 25-Oct-3 David Rago, Lambertville #390a
£652	$1200	€952	Moonlight on a beach (51x66cm-20x26in) s.i.d.1953 brush ink. 10-Jun-4 Swann Galleries, New York #43/R
£667	$1200	€974	Still life with vase of flowers (66x51cm-26x20in) s.d.1956 W/C gouache. 23-Jan-4 Freeman, Philadelphia #51/R
£707	$1300	€1032	Provincetown, Cape Cod (51x66cm-20x26in) s.i.d.1951 verso W/C gouache. 10-Jun-4 Swann Galleries, New York #42/R
£1250	$2000	€1825	Seated figure with an amphora (51x32cm-20x13in) s.d.1945 W/C. 18-Sep-3 Swann Galleries, New York #100/R est:2500-3500
£1744	$3000	€2546	Woman with leaves (34x26cm-13x10in) s.d.1942 pen ink col chk. 3-Dec-3 Doyle, New York #7/R est:1000-1500
£2000	$3200	€2920	Man with ball and lion (51x66cm-20x26in) s.d.1950 gouache W/C. 18-Sep-3 Swann Galleries, New York #101/R est:2500-3500

BROWNE, Charles Francis (1859-1920) American

£335	$550	€489	Pastoral landscape with houses (25x36cm-10x14in) s. masonite. 4-Jun-3 Alderfer's, Hatfield #269
£1582	$2500	€2310	Pastoral landscape (66x102cm-26x40in) s.d.1918. 7-Sep-3 Treadway Gallery, Cincinnati #615/R est:4000-6000
£2762	$4750	€4033	Le Mesnil-Aubry near Ecouen, France (20x30cm-8x12in) s. prov. 3-Dec-3 Doyle, New York #186/R est:2000-3000

BROWNE, George (1918-1958) American

£7111	$11804	€10382	Alpine pasture (62x52cm-24x20in) 2-Oct-3 Heffel, Vancouver #8 (C.D 16000)

BROWNE, George Elmer (1871-1946) American

£272	$500	€397	Portuguese village (25x33cm-10x13in) panel prov. 25-Jun-4 Freeman, Philadelphia #305/R
£598	$1100	€873	Brittany houses (25x33cm-10x13in) panel prov. 25-Jun-4 Freeman, Philadelphia #306/R
£811	$1500	€1184	Returning flock (64x76cm-25x30in) s.d.1902 s.i.d.verso. 15-Jul-4 Doyle, New York #18/R est:2000-3000
£1087	$2000	€1587	Brittany village (54x63cm-21x25in) s.d.1805 prov. 27-Jun-4 Freeman, Philadelphia #100/R est:2500-4000
£2096	$3500	€3060	By the Shore (36x36cm-14x14in) s. masonite prov. 23-Oct-3 Shannon's, Milford #184/R est:3000-5000
£2326	$4000	€3396	New York at evening (50x67cm-20x26in) s. i.d.verso prov. 3-Dec-3 Doyle, New York #276/R est:3000-5000
£4706	$8000	€6871	The slave market (89x91cm-35x36in) s. panel. 22-Nov-3 New Orleans Auction, New Orleans #1169/R est:6000-9000

BROWNE, George Elmer (attrib) (1871-1946) American

£595	$1100	€869	Truro landscape (61x46cm-24x18in) board. 17-Jul-4 Outer Cape Auctions, Provincetown #66a/R

BROWNE, Hablot K (1815-1892) British

Works on paper			
£280	$484	€409	The launch (25x35cm-10x14in) init. pencil W/C. 9-Dec-3 Rosebery Fine Art, London #592/R

BROWNE, Joseph Archibald (1862-1948) Canadian

£200	$366	€292	Evening on the St Lawrence at Lancaster, Ontario (24x32cm-9x13in) s.i. board. 1-Jun-4 Hodgins, Calgary #449/R (C.D 500)
£241	$448	€352	On the banks of the Humber river (25x35cm-10x14in) s. board. 2-Mar-4 Ritchie, Toronto #53/R (C.D 600)
£268	$461	€391	Reflection (16x33cm-6x13in) s.d.1908 verso canvas on board. 2-Dec-3 Joyner Waddington, Toronto #421 (C.D 600)
£300	$549	€438	Spring colours (40x40cm-16x16in) s. prov. 1-Jun-4 Joyner Waddington, Toronto #446 (C.D 750)
£400	$732	€584	Sundown at Tadouwac, Quebec. Rising moon at Tadousac, Quebec (25x35cm-10x14in) s. canvasboard two. 1-Jun-4 Joyner Waddington, Toronto #499 (C.D 1000)
£586	$995	€856	The Amethyst, Adriondacks (51x76cm-20x30in) s.d.1921 s.i.d.1921 verso. 21-Nov-3 Walker's, Ottawa #86/R (C.D 1300)
£640	$1171	€934	Waterview (45x60cm-18x24in) s. 1-Jun-4 Joyner Waddington, Toronto #411 (C.D 1600)
£721	$1225	€1053	Mountainous landscape (41x74cm-16x29in) s. s.verso prov. 21-Nov-3 Walker's, Ottawa #85/R (C.D 1600)
£2846	$5093	€4155	Autumn landscape with rural village (150x170cm-59x67in) s. prov. 31-May-4 Sotheby's, Toronto #153/R est:5000-7000 (C.D 7000)
Works on paper			
£380	$695	€555	Sunset (11x30cm-4x12in) s. pastel prov. 1-Jun-4 Joyner Waddington, Toronto #465 (C.D 950)

BROWNE, Madame Henriette (1829-1901) French

£2384	$4339	€3600	Affectionate scene (55x46cm-22x18in) s. 19-Jun-4 Bergmann, Erlangen #828 est:2500
£2600	$4784	€3796	Pet rabbit (19x14cm-7x6in) s. 8-Jun-4 Bonhams, Knightsbridge #334/R est:700-1000
£3049	$5457	€4452	Portrait of a girl with hat and pierced ears (57x46cm-22x18in) s. prov. 4-May-4 Ritchie, Toronto #81/R est:7000-9000 (C.D 7500)
£5233	$9000	€7640	Frolics (66x86cm-26x34in) s. painted c.1880. 7-Dec-3 Treadway Gallery, Cincinnati #519/R est:15000-20000
Works on paper			
£795	$1446	€1200	Nuns in work room in an abbey (36x34cm-14x13in) s. W/C paper on board. 19-Jun-4 Bergmann, Erlangen #762

BROWNE, Margaret Fitz Hugh (1884-1972) American

£3343	$5750	€4881	Portrait of a lady (76x64cm-30x25in) s. 7-Dec-3 Grogan, Boston #42/R

BROWNE, Matilda (1869-1947) American

£568	$1000	€829	Cow and calf (30x41cm-12x16in) panel. 21-May-4 North East Auctions, Portsmouth #673
£1077	$1950	€1572	Moonlit marsh landscape (76x64cm-30x25in) s. 3-Apr-4 Nadeau, Windsor #102/R est:2500-4500
£1471	$2500	€2148	Lamb in a barn interior (30x41cm-12x16in) s. 21-Nov-3 Eldred, East Dennis #869/R est:1500-2500

BROWNE, Nassau Blair (?-1940) Irish

£3000	$5400	€4380	White horse in stable. Saddled brown horse (50x66cm-20x26in) s.d.97 pair. 21-Jan-4 Sotheby's, Olympia #325/R est:600-800

BROWNE, Piers (1942-) British

£380	$711	€555	Summer afternoon, Wensleydale (26x38cm-10x15in) s.d.81 i.d.verso board. 22-Jul-4 Tennants, Leyburn #927
£400	$720	€584	Wensleydale landscape with sheep (35x54cm-14x21in) s.d.1990 board. 21-Apr-4 Tennants, Leyburn #1232

BROWNE, Warne (19th C) ?

£480	$859	€701	Coverack (17x31cm-7x12in) s.i. panel. 11-May-4 Bonhams, Knightsbridge #145/R

BROWNELL, Franklin (1856-1946) Canadian
£991 $1685 €1447 Portrait of a man (48x44cm-19x17in) init.d.14 prov. 18-Nov-3 Sotheby's, Toronto #121/R est:2000-3000 (C.D 2200)
£1696 $2918 €2476 Logging Scene (22x30cm-9x12in) s. board. 2-Dec-3 Joyner Waddington, Toronto #325/R est:3000-5000 (C.D 3800)
£2722 $5008 €3974 Autumn landscape with sheep (40x50cm-16x20in) s. lit. 9-Jun-4 Walker's, Ottawa #52/R est:6000-8000 (C.D 6750)
Works on paper
£323 $594 €472 Cattle by the Gatineau (22x31cm-9x12in) init. pastel. 9-Jun-4 Walker's, Ottawa #66/R (C.D 800)
£800 $1464 €1168 Combermere (32x49cm-13x19in) s. W/C. 1-Jun-4 Joyner Waddington, Toronto #243/R est:1200-1500 (C.D 2000)

BROWNING, Colleen (1927-) American
£262 $475 €383 An old lady (43x22cm-17x9in) 18-Apr-4 Bonhams & Butterfields, Los Angeles #7082
£1356 $2250 €1980 Grenada Garden (102x132cm-40x52in) s. prov. 4-Oct-3 Neal Auction Company, New Orleans #607/R est:2000-4000

BROWNING, George (fl.1826-1858) British
£480 $878 €701 Turf cutters, Dublin mountains (19x40cm-7x16in) s.d.1878 i. verso. 6-Jul-4 Peter Wilson, Nantwich #25/R

BROWNING, Harriett A E (19th C) British
£1385 $2382 €2022 Charitas (50x60cm-20x24in) s.d.1828. 7-Dec-3 Uppsala Auktionskammare, Uppsala #14/R est:16000-18000 (S.KR 18000)

BROWNLOW, David (1915-) American
£599 $1000 €875 Brahma bull (86x132cm-34x52in) 18-Oct-3 David Dike, Dallas #93/R

BROWNLOW, George Washington (1835-1876) British
£1139 $1800 €1663 The welcome, near Clifden Connemara, Ireland (30x41cm-12x16in) s.d.1861 i. on stretcher. 7-Sep-3 Treadway Gallery, Cincinnati #536/R est:2000-3000
£3000 $5520 €4380 Highland cottage interior with a young mother, two children and a dog (44x60cm-17x24in) s. 23-Mar-4 Anderson & Garland, Newcastle #365/R est:3000-4500

BROWNRIDGE, William Roy (1932-) Canadian
£360 $613 €526 Scoring (41x51cm-16x20in) s. i.verso acrylic prov. 23-Nov-3 Levis, Calgary #16/R (C.D 800)

BROWNSCOMBE, Jennie (1850-1936) American
£235 $400 €343 Portrait of the artist George Henry Hall (28x23cm-11x9in) s.d.1898 prov. 21-Nov-3 Skinner, Boston #300/R
£925 $1600 €1351 Seated elderly man at desk (76x64cm-30x25in) s. 9-Dec-3 Arthur James, Florida #51
£2353 $4000 €3435 Portrait of a young woman in pink and green (32x26cm-13x10in) s.d.Oct 4 1898 prov. 21-Nov-3 Skinner, Boston #297/R est:3500-5500
£3797 $6000 €5544 Walk through the country (69x41cm-27x16in) s.d.1882. 7-Sep-3 Treadway Gallery, Cincinnati #565/R est:6000-8000
£6289 $10000 €9182 American troops in France 1918 (76x99cm-30x39in) s. 12-Sep-3 Skinner, Boston #441/R est:15000
£7735 $14000 €11293 General Washinton's triumphal procession to New York (66x96cm-26x38in) s.d.1911 canvas on board. 31-Mar-4 Sotheby's, New York #135/R est:6000-8000

BROZIK, Wenceslas (1851-1901) Bohemian
£1275 $2385 €1900 Portrait of man wearing cap (46x38cm-18x15in) s. 24-Feb-4 Dorotheum, Vienna #263/R est:1400-1600
£1280 $2100 €1856 Portrait of a woman in a hat (25x25cm-10x10in) s. fiberboard prov. 31-May-3 Brunk, Ashville #52/R est:800-1500
£17647 $30000 €25765 The conversation (65x81cm-26x32in) s. 29-Oct-3 Christie's, Rockefeller NY #30/R est:30000-50000
£19117 $32500 €27911 Falconer's recital (94x141cm-37x56in) s. 19-Nov-3 Bonhams & Butterfields, San Francisco #78/R

BRU, Carlos (1964-) Spanish
£403 $753 €600 Early winter light (33x55cm-13x22in) s.d.2003. 24-Feb-4 Durán, Madrid #7/R

BRUANDET, Lazare (1755-1804) French
£2308 $3969 €3300 La chasse en foret (38x46cm-15x18in) panel. 7-Dec-3 Osenat, Fontainebleau #104
£2416 $4494 €3600 Paysages champetres animes (50x60cm-20x24in) s. pair. 7-Mar-4 Lesieur & Le Bars, Le Havre #22/R
£3147 $5413 €4500 La halte en foret de Fontainebleau (51x61cm-20x24in) s. 7-Dec-3 Osenat, Fontainebleau #105 est:3500-4000
£3333 $6033 €5000 Le passage du Gue (26x35cm-10x14in) panel lit. 30-Mar-4 Rossini, Paris #84/R est:1200-1500
£5132 $9442 €7800 Passage du gue (38x48cm-15x19in) s. panel. 25-Jun-4 Piasa, Paris #109/R est:5000-7000
£6333 $11590 €9500 Promenade en foret (23x31cm-9x12in) s. pair. 6-Jun-4 Osenat, Fontainebleau #46/R est:8000-9000

BRUANDET, Lazare (attrib) (1755-1804) French
£769 $1400 €1123 Landscape with figures, horse and dog (36x48cm-14x19in) s. board. 7-Feb-4 Sloans & Kenyon, Bethesda #1245/R
£2000 $3660 €2920 Stag hunt in wooded landscape (28x36cm-11x14in) panel. 9-Jul-4 Christie's, Kensington #106/R est:2000-3000
£2685 $4940 €4000 Hunters in Ile de France forest (27x36cm-11x14in) panel. 25-Mar-4 Dr Fritz Nagel, Stuttgart #633/R est:1200
Works on paper
£1151 $1888 €1600 Paysage animes (11x18cm-4x7in) gouache vellum pair. 6-Jun-3 Maigret, Paris #52/R est:1800-2000

BRUBAKER, Robert (20th C) American
£264 $425 €385 War party (61x76cm-24x30in) s. 18-Aug-3 O'Gallerie, Oregon #37/R

BRUCCIANI, Domenico (1815-?) British/Italian
Sculpture
£1538 $2615 €2200 Bust of Apollo Belvedere (79cm-31in) s. plaster. 25-Nov-3 Hamilton Osborne King, Dublin #156/R

BRUCE, Heather (20th C) American
£213 $375 €311 Golden Bushes (13x18cm-5x7in) s.verso board. 3-Jan-4 Outer Cape Auctions, Provincetown #54/R

BRUCE, Matt (?) British
£350 $595 €511 First day at Epsom - a horse racing scene (58x51cm-23x20in) s. board. 30-Oct-3 Grant, Worcester #594/R

BRUCE, Patrick Henry (1880-1937) American
£20588 $35000 €30058 Flowers (55x46cm-22x18in) oil over chl on canvas prov.lit. 30-Oct-3 Phillips, New York #92/R est:45000-65000
£23952 $40000 €34970 Wood interior - Summer (43x53cm-17x21in) s. prov.lit. 23-Oct-3 Shannon's, Milford #127/R est:40000-60000

BRUCE, William (19/20th C) American
£2063 $3300 €3012 Landscape near Owasco lake, Cayuga County NY (30x46cm-12x18in) s. board. 21-Sep-3 William Jenack, New York #268 est:1500-2500

BRUCK, Lajos (1846-1910) Hungarian
£2172 $3605 €3171 Little boy in the wood (76x57cm-30x22in) s. 4-Oct-3 Kieselbach, Budapest #139/R (H.F 800000)

BRUCKE, Trude (20th C) ?
£400 $648 €584 Still life (70x100cm-28x39in) s.d.Aug 1935 board. 30-Jul-3 Hamptons Fine Art, Godalming #215

BRUCKE, Wilhelm (19th C) German
£4861 $7924 €7000 Amalfi harbour (26x40cm-10x16in) s.d.1858 paper on board. 25-Sep-3 Dr Fritz Nagel, Stuttgart #1331/R est:14000

BRUCKER, Edmund (1912-) American
£581 $1000 €848 Industrial scene (56x102cm-22x40in) s. board painted c.1950. 7-Dec-3 Treadway Gallery, Cincinnati #685/R

BRUCKMAN, Karel (1903-) Dutch
£280 $501 €420 Varied still life (33x43cm-13x17in) s.d.1967. 11-May-4 Vendu Notarishuis, Rotterdam #611

BRUCKNER, Curt (20th C) German
£1129 $2100 €1648 Architects (61x79cm-24x31in) s. board painted 1950. 7-Mar-4 Treadway Gallery, Cincinnati #491/R est:2000-3000

BRUEGHEL, Abraham (1631-1690) Flemish
£7383 $13732 €11000 Still life with figs, watermelon and cherries (43x30cm-17x12in) mono. 2-Mar-4 Ansorena, Madrid #288/R est:8000
£10274 $17466 €15000 Still life with figs and watermelon (43x30cm-17x12in) 4-Nov-3 Ansorena, Madrid #95/R est:15000
£18182 $31273 €26000 L'adoration des bergers entouree d'une guirlande de fleurs (85x73cm-33x29in) 3-Dec-3 Palais de Beaux Arts, Brussels #651/R est:20000-30000
£24476 $42098 €35000 La Vierge, l'Enfant et St Jean Baptiste dans une guirlande de fleurs (85x73cm-33x29in) 3-Dec-3 Palais de Beaux Arts, Brussels #652/R est:25000-35000
£50336 $94128 €75000 Still life of fruit with woman (102x138cm-40x54in) prov. 25-Feb-4 Porro, Milan #85/R est:75000
£115278 $195972 €166000 Still life of flowers with fruit, little dog and fountain (120x175cm-47x69in) lit. 28-Oct-3 Il Ponte, Milan #351/R est:150000-200000
£115972 $197153 €167000 Still life of flowers with fruit in landscape (120x175cm-47x69in) s. 28-Oct-3 Il Ponte, Milan #352/R est:150000-200000

BRUEGHEL, Abraham (attrib) (1631-1690) Flemish
£4698 $8644 €7000 Still life of fruit (43x51cm-17x20in) 24-Mar-4 Dorotheum, Vienna #342/R est:8000-12000

BRUEGHEL, Abraham (circle) (1631-1690) Flemish
£7432 $13081 €11000 Still life with fruit, hares and monkey (69x124cm-27x49in) 22-May-4 Lempertz, Koln #1023/R est:12000
£8054 $14819 €12000 Bouquet of flowers in vase (27x19cm-11x7in) panel. 24-Mar-4 Dorotheum, Vienna #345/R est:8000-12000
£22173 $39690 €32373 Still life of fruit (99x123cm-39x48in) 25-May-4 Bukowskis, Stockholm #476/R est:100000-150000 (S.KR 300000)

BRUEGHEL, Abraham (studio) (1631-1690) Flemish
£15603 $25277 €22000 Venus and cupid encircled with flowers and fruit (78x56cm-31x22in) 20-May-3 Ansorena, Madrid #94e/R est:20000
£17000 $30940 €25500 Basket with grapes and other fruit (96x146cm-38x57in) 4-Jul-4 Finarte, Venice #30/R est:25000-30000

BRUEGHEL, Abraham (style) (1631-1690) Flemish
£4730 $8324 €7000 Still life with pomegranate, figs and melon in a basket (50x67cm-20x26in) 18-May-4 Sotheby's, Milan #142/R est:7000-10000
£12000 $21960 €17520 Still lives of flowers (57x44cm-22x17in) pair. 9-Jul-4 Christie's, Kensington #26/R est:7000-10000

£153846 $264615 €224615 Still life of silver pot, copper pan, flowers and fruit (80x115cm-31x45in) 2-Dec-3 Bukowskis, Stockholm #397/R est:50000-60000 (S.KR 2000000)

BRUEGHEL, Abraham and COURTOIS, Guillaume (attrib) (17th C) Flemish/French
£24000 $41520 €35040 Young boy arranging flowers in an urn with fruits on a stone step in a garden (152x125cm-60x49in) prov. 11-Dec-3 Sotheby's, London #230/R est:20000-30000

BRUEGHEL, Jan (elder) (1568-1625) Flemish
£197370 $363161 €300000 Saint Margaret and the dragon (26x35cm-10x14in) copper. 24-Jun-4 Tajan, Paris #14/R est:300000-400000
£300000 $549000 €438000 Saint John preaching in the wilderness (25x35cm-10x14in) i.verso copper prov. 7-Jul-4 Sotheby's, London #23/R est:300000-500000
£500000 $915000 €730000 River scene with boats unloading at quay (22x32cm-9x13in) s.d.1606 copper prov. 7-Jul-4 Sotheby's, London #28/R est:600000-800000
Works on paper
£82000 $150060 €119720 Crowded beer-stall with studies of elegant figures drinking. Elegant company drinking (12x18cm-5x7in) i. black chk pen ink double-sided two on one mount. 6-Jul-4 Christie's, London #163/R est:25000-35000

BRUEGHEL, Jan (elder) and BALEN, Hendrik van (16/17th C) Flemish
£155556 $280000 €227112 Diana and Actaeon (27x36cm-11x14in) copper prov.exhib. 22-Jan-4 Sotheby's, New York #29/R est:275000-325000

BRUEGHEL, Jan (elder-after) (1568-1625) Flemish
£6757 $11892 €10000 Wooded landscape with watermill and travellers (26x36cm-10x14in) panel. 22-May-4 Lempertz, Koln #1017/R est:12000

BRUEGHEL, Jan (elder-attrib) (1568-1625) Flemish
Works on paper
£4261 $7500 €6221 View of a city with canal (19x32cm-7x13in) i. W/C. 19-May-4 Doyle, New York #6021/R est:2000-3000
£6000 $10980 €8760 Clump of trees (22x36cm-9x14in) pen brown ink grey blue wash prov. 8-Jul-4 Sotheby's, London #71/R est:7000-9000

BRUEGHEL, Jan (elder-circle) (1568-1625) Flemish
£6579 $12105 €10000 Ships in a storm (23x32cm-9x13in) copper. 24-Jun-4 Christie's, Paris #15/R est:10000-15000
Works on paper
£7778 $14000 €11356 Hilly wooded landscape with windmill, wagon and peasants (14x23cm-6x9in) i.d.1612 pen black ink bodycol prov. 22-Jan-4 Christie's, Rockefeller NY #114/R est:10000-15000

BRUEGHEL, Jan (elder-studio) (1568-1625) Flemish
£16000 $28800 €23360 Basket of tulips and other flowers resting on a stone ledge (52x65cm-20x26in) panel marouflaged. 22-Apr-4 Sotheby's, London #24/R est:12000-18000
£40000 $69200 €58400 Still life of tulips, roses, carnations and other flowers in a glass vase (45x31cm-18x12in) prov. 11-Dec-3 Sotheby's, London #108/R est:25000-35000
£54000 $97200 €78840 Venus in the forge of Vulcan (49x83cm-19x33in) i.d.1612 panel prov. 22-Apr-4 Sotheby's, London #17/R est:30000-50000

BRUEGHEL, Jan (elder-style) (1568-1625) Flemish
£11724 $19462 €17000 Vertumnus and Pomona in palace garden with flowers (62x81cm-24x32in) panel prov. 1-Oct-3 Dorotheum, Vienna #139/R est:17000-25000
£14000 $24220 €20440 Wooded river landscape with elegant figures buying provender (13x20cm-5x8in) bears sig. copper. 11-Dec-3 Sotheby's, London #100/R est:10000-15000
£27000 $48600 €39420 Wooded landscape with hunters and their dogs (41x58cm-16x23in) panel. 20-Apr-4 Sotheby's, Olympia #249/R est:4000-6000

BRUEGHEL, Jan (younger) (1601-1678) Flemish
£5634 $9746 €8000 Scene religieuse entouree d'une guirlande de fleurs (75x71cm-30x28in) copper. 9-Dec-3 Campo, Vlaamse Kaai #265 est:1500-2000
£11000 $18700 €16060 Still life of the Holy Kinship within a stone cartouche adorned by garlands of flowers (75x94cm-30x37in) 30-Oct-3 Sotheby's, Olympia #4/R est:8000-12000
£41379 $69103 €60000 Rest on the Flight to Egypt (58x85cm-23x33in) panel prov. 15-Nov-3 Lempertz, Koln #1017/R est:60000-80000
£52198 $95000 €76209 Roses, peonies, tulips and other flowers in a basket and a gilt tazza, on a table (55x90cm-22x35in) panel prov.exhib. 17-Jun-4 Christie's, Rockefeller NY #23/R est:80000-120000
£79741 $146724 €116422 Flowers in glazed bowl (49x66cm-19x26in) panel prov.lit. 26-Mar-4 Koller, Zurich #3018/R est:150000-200000 (S.FR 185000)
£88000 $158400 €128480 River landscape with ferry and small sailing vessels (38x62cm-15x24in) panel prov.lit. 22-Apr-4 Sotheby's, London #18/R est:60000-80000
£100000 $173000 €146000 Creation (87x112cm-34x44in) s. copper set of three prov. 10-Dec-3 Christie's, London #3/R est:120000-180000
£180556 $325000 €263612 Village street with Holy Family (22x31cm-9x12in) bears sig. copper prov.exhib.lit. 22-Jan-4 Sotheby's, New York #32/R est:300000-400000
£186620 $326585 €265000 Nature morte aupanier de fleurs (53x80cm-21x31in) panel. 17-Dec-3 Piasa, Paris #15/R est:300000-400000
£650000 $1124500 €949000 Still life of roses, tulips and other flowers in a wooden tub (85x70cm-33x28in) oak panel prov.lit. 11-Dec-3 Sotheby's, London #56/R est:400000-600000

BRUEGHEL, Jan (younger) and BALEN, Hendrik van (17th C) Flemish
£20000 $36600 €29200 Landscape with satyrs spying on Diana and her nymphs (27x39cm-11x15in) copper prov. 8-Jul-4 Sotheby's, London #233/R est:20000-30000

BRUEGHEL, Jan (younger) and BALEN, Hendrik van (circle) (17th C) Flemish
£3352 $6000 €4894 Virgin and Child with two angels in landscape (46x51cm-18x20in) panel. 27-May-4 Sotheby's, New York #69/R est:8000-12000

BRUEGHEL, Jan (younger) and BALEN, Hendrik van (studio) (17th C) Flemish
£13000 $23790 €18980 Diana the Huntress and her nymphs with the spoils of the hunt (72x104cm-28x41in) panel. 7-Jul-4 Bonhams, New Bond Street #31/R est:15000-20000

BRUEGHEL, Jan (younger) and FRANCKEN, Frans (younger) (17th C) Flemish
£80000 $146400 €116800 Madonna and Child with Saint John in garland of flowers (60x45cm-24x18in) panel prov.exhib.lit. 7-Jul-4 Sotheby's, London #25/R est:60000-80000

BRUEGHEL, Jan (younger) and FRANCKEN, Frans II (circle) (17th C) Flemish
£6000 $10800 €8760 Allegory of the elements (38x58cm-15x23in) panel. 22-Apr-4 Sotheby's, London #4/R est:6000-8000

BRUEGHEL, Jan (younger) and FRANCKEN, Frans II (studio) (17th C) Flemish
£6081 $10703 €9000 Garland of roses, tulips and other flowers surrounding a medallion of the Virgin and Child (37x31cm-15x12in) copper htd gold. 18-May-4 Sotheby's, Amsterdam #56/R est:8000-12000

BRUEGHEL, Jan (younger) and MOMPER, Joos de (17th C) Flemish
£13333 $24000 €19466 Wooded mountainous river landscape with travelers conversing on a path (53x76cm-21x30in) panel prov.exhib. 23-Jan-4 Christie's, Rockefeller NY #25/R est:40000-60000
£32168 $55329 €46000 Voyageurs, bergers et betails dans un paysage montagneux (45x71cm-18x28in) panel. 3-Dec-3 Palais de Beaux Arts, Brussels #656/R est:35000-50000
£240000 $415200 €350400 Winter landscape with a muleteer and villagers conversing by his train (100x162cm-39x64in) panel prov.lit. 10-Dec-3 Christie's, London #16/R est:180000-220000

BRUEGHEL, Jan (younger) and MOMPER, Joos de (attrib) (17th C) Flemish
£110000 $198000 €160600 Extensive river landscape with peasants gathering the harvest (44x72cm-17x28in) panel prov.lit. 21-Apr-4 Christie's, London #9/R est:15000-25000

BRUEGHEL, Jan (younger) and ROTTENHAMMER, Hans (attrib) (17th C) Flemish
£26316 $48421 €40000 Nativity surrounded by garland of flowers (131x91cm-52x36in) 25-Jun-4 Piasa, Paris #18/R est:30000-40000

BRUEGHEL, Jan (younger-attrib) (1601-1678) Flemish
£2154 $3705 €3145 Landscape with buildings and figures (34x58cm-13x23in) panel prov. 2-Dec-3 Bukowskis, Stockholm #343/R est:30000-35000 (S.KR 28000)
£11409 $20423 €17000 Allegorie de l'eau (46x67cm-18x26in) copper. 25-May-4 Palais de Beaux Arts, Brussels #532/R est:20000-30000
£13423 $24027 €20000 Allegorie de l'air (46x67cm-18x26in) copper. 25-May-4 Palais de Beaux Arts, Brussels #531/R est:20000-30000

BRUEGHEL, Jan (younger-circle) (1601-1678) Flemish
£8163 $14612 €12000 Allegory of air (51x40cm-20x16in) copper. 17-Mar-4 Neumeister, Munich #345/R est:10000
£42000 $75600 €61320 Wooded landscape with peasants and travelers on a path (102x174cm-40x69in) prov. 21-Apr-4 Christie's, London #14/R est:15000-20000

BRUEGHEL, Jan (younger-studio) (1601-1678) Flemish
£4966 $8292 €7200 Allegory of the elements (38x58cm-15x23in) panel prov. 15-Nov-3 Lempertz, Koln #1019/R est:6000
£30000 $54900 €43800 Landscape with the Rest on the Flight into Egypt (54x87cm-21x34in) panel. 8-Jul-4 Sotheby's, London #232/R est:20000-30000
£40000 $69200 €58400 Allegory of the Sense of Taste (72x115cm-28x45in) oak panel. 11-Dec-3 Sotheby's, London #59/R est:40000-60000

BRUEGHEL, Jan (younger-style) (1601-1678) Flemish
£6034 $11103 €8810 Herders by water in front of farmstead. Peasants resting (29x38cm-11x15in) panel pair. 26-Mar-4 Koller, Zurich #3044/R est:14000-20000 (S.FR 14000)
£12000 $20760 €17520 Wooded landscape with villagers by a market (25x36cm-10x14in) panel. 12-Dec-3 Christie's, Kensington #62/R est:8000-12000
£16168 $27000 €23605 Musician's studio (75x116cm-30x46in) 7-Oct-3 Sotheby's, New York #44/R est:10000-15000
£17000 $29410 €24820 Fall of Man (65x85cm-26x33in) copper prov. 11-Dec-3 Sotheby's, London #101/R est:15000-20000
£26027 $44247 €38000 Allegory of the Tulipmania (26x32cm-10x13in) indis.i. panel painted on reverse. 4-Nov-3 Sotheby's, Amsterdam #2/R est:12000-18000

BRUEGHEL, Jan Pieter (attrib) (1628-?) Flemish
£5396 $8849 €7500 Still life of flowers in vase (51x36cm-20x14in) 4-Jun-3 Sotheby's, Milan #86/R est:6000-8000

BRUEGHEL, Pieter (16/17th C) Flemish
Prints
£2000 $3680 €3000 Warship and other ships (22x29cm-9x11in) copperplate. 11-Jun-4 Hauswedell & Nolte, Hamburg #823/R est:4000
£2400 $4416 €3600 Three warships in storm (22x29cm-9x11in) copperplate. 11-Jun-4 Hauswedell & Nolte, Hamburg #822/R est:4000

BRUEGHEL, Pieter (elder-after) (c.1525-1569) Flemish
£20134 $37047 €30000 The Alchemist (46x62cm-18x24in) panel prov. 24-Mar-4 Hugo Ruef, Munich #874/R est:30000
Prints
£2620 $4769 €3825 Alpine landscape. etching copperplate. 17-Jun-4 Kornfeld, Bern #11 est:7500 (S.FR 6000)
£6500 $11830 €9490 Skaters before the gate of St. George at Antwerp (23x29cm-9x11in) engraving. 30-Jun-4 Christie's, London #23/R est:3000-5000
£7667 $13723 €11500 Nemo non querit (23x29cm-9x11in) copperplate. 13-May-4 Bassenge, Berlin #5060/R est:6000

BRUEGHEL, Pieter (elder-school) (c.1525-1569) Flemish
£10588 $18000 €15458 Avocat de village (73x104cm-29x41in) board. 25-Nov-3 Galeria y Remates, Montevideo #183/R

BRUEGHEL, Pieter (younger) (1564-1637) Flemish
£152778 $275000 €223056 Pushed into the pig sty (24cm-9in circular) s.indis.d. panel. 22-Jan-4 Sotheby's, New York #23/R est:100000-150000
£253521 $443662 €360000 Adoration des Mages (34x55cm-13x22in) s.d.1621 panel prov. 17-Dec-3 Piasa, Paris #14/R est:200000-250000
£300000 $543000 €450000 Seven works of compassion (42x56cm-17x22in) s. panel lit.prov. 1-Apr-4 Van Ham, Cologne #1167/R est:260000
£488827 $875000 €713687 Bird trap (41x57cm-16x22in) panel prov.exhib. 27-May-4 Sotheby's, New York #20/R est:400000-500000
£500000 $865000 €730000 Bird trap (37x53cm-15x21in) init. panel prov. 10-Dec-3 Christie's, London #5/R est:250000-350000
£1150000 $2104500 €1679000 Birdtrap (39x55cm-15x22in) s.d.1608 panel prov.lit. 7-Jul-4 Christie's, London #24/R est:600000-800000

BRUEGHEL, Pieter (younger-school) (1564-1637) Flemish
£11565 $20701 €17000 Le paiement de la dime (63x105cm-25x41in) panel. 16-Mar-4 Vanderkindere, Brussels #1/R est:2000-3000

BRUEGHEL, Pieter (younger-studio) (1564-1637) Flemish
£21333 $38187 €32000 Collector of tithes (73x104cm-29x41in) panel on panel. 17-May-4 Christie's, Amsterdam #69/R est:20000-30000
£36667 $65633 €55000 Village fair in Saint Joris (76x106cm-30x42in) panel prov.lit. 17-May-4 Glerum, Amsterdam #30/R est:35000-45000
£90000 $155700 €131400 Return from the Kermesse (36x58cm-14x23in) panel prov.lit. 10-Dec-3 Christie's, London #10/R est:50000-70000

BRUEGHEL, Pieter (younger-style) (1564-1637) Flemish
£7285 $13258 €11000 Building of the Tower of Babel (47x64cm-19x25in) i. panel. 16-Jun-4 Dorotheum, Vienna #481/R est:2000-3000
£8219 $13973 €12000 Village scene with peasants dancing outside an inn (82x181cm-32x71in) bears sig.d.1610 panel prov. 4-Nov-3 Sotheby's, Amsterdam #4/R est:4000-6000
£8453 $14793 €12000 La danse de Noce en plein air (44x57cm-17x22in) panel prov. 18-Dec-3 Tajan, Paris #24/R est:12000-15000
£15753 $26781 €23000 Dance at a wedding (44x59cm-17x23in) board. 9-Nov-3 Finarte, Venice #79/R est:20000-25000
£20000 $34600 €29200 Tax Collectors (100x129cm-39x51in) bears date. 11-Dec-3 Sotheby's, London #120/R est:15000-20000
£58000 $104400 €84680 Bird trap (39x57cm-15x22in) panel. 22-Apr-4 Sotheby's, London #3/R est:20000-30000

BRUEGHEL, Pieter III (1589-1639) Flemish
£60403 $108121 €90000 La danse des Catherinettes (74x97cm-29x38in) s. 25-May-4 Palais de Beaux Arts, Brussels #65/R est:100000-150000

BRUEGHEL, Pieter III (circle) (1589-1639) Flemish
£24000 $43200 €35040 Netherlandish proverbs (92x118cm-36x46in) i. 21-Apr-4 Christie's, London #3/R est:15000-20000

BRUEL, Willem van den (1871-1942) Belgian
£347 $580 €500 La fontaine au parc (65x80cm-26x31in) s. 21-Oct-3 Campo, Vlaamse Kaai #1115
£350 $584 €500 Interieur d'eglise (110x115cm-43x45in) s. 13-Oct-3 Horta, Bruxelles #429
£417 $696 €600 Homme assis (80x60cm-31x24in) s. 21-Oct-3 Campo, Vlaamse Kaai #1116
£448 $829 €650 Enfants sur fond de village ensoleille (60x80cm-24x31in) s. 19-Jan-4 Horta, Bruxelles #446
£490 $817 €700 Le retour a l'ecure (64x80cm-25x31in) s. 13-Oct-3 Horta, Bruxelles #428
£556 $883 €800 Les choux rouges de potager (76x100cm-30x39in) s. 15-Sep-3 Horta, Bruxelles #25
£625 $994 €900 Le lettre (103x80cm-41x31in) s. 15-Sep-3 Horta, Bruxelles #27
£764 $1215 €1100 L'enfant et son cheval pres du moulin a eau (75x90cm-30x35in) s. 15-Sep-3 Horta, Bruxelles #24
£1111 $1767 €1600 Quai vert a Bruges (110x116cm-43x46in) s. 15-Sep-3 Horta, Bruxelles #23 est:1500-2000
£1111 $1767 €1600 Jeune femme a la lecture (66x80cm-26x31in) s. 15-Sep-3 Horta, Bruxelles #28 est:500-750
£1597 $2540 €2300 Vendredi Saint en Flandres (110x115cm-43x45in) s. 15-Sep-3 Horta, Bruxelles #22/R est:1500-2000

BRUEN, Gerald (fl.1939-1979) Irish
£300 $543 €450 Laragh, Co Wicklow (46x59cm-18x23in) canvas on board. 30-Mar-4 De Veres Art Auctions, Dublin #257

BRUENCHENHEIN, Eugene von (1910-1983) American
£3056 $5500 €4462 Red dragon no.550 (66x66cm-26x26in) board prov. 24-Apr-4 Slotin Folk Art, Buford #332/R est:2000-4000
£3889 $7000 €5678 Abstract dragon no.853 (66x66cm-26x26in) board prov. 24-Apr-4 Slotin Folk Art, Buford #333/R est:2000-4000
Works on paper
£278 $500 €406 Abstract line drawing (33x46cm-13x18in) dr. executed c.1966. 24-Apr-4 Slotin Folk Art, Buford #335/R
£329 $550 €480 Abstract (25x41cm-10x16in) ink. 15-Nov-3 Slotin Folk Art, Buford #193/R

BRUESTLE, Bertram G (1902-) American
£1677 $2700 €2448 New England landscape with house (64x76cm-25x30in) s. 20-Aug-3 James Julia, Fairfield #1527/R est:3000-4000

BRUESTLE, George M (1871-1939) American
£934 $1700 €1364 Autumn in Lyme (31x41cm-12x16in) s. s.stretcher. 29-Jun-4 Sotheby's, New York #221/R est:1500-2000
£1271 $2300 €1856 Along the brook, hilly Connecticut landscape (20x25cm-8x10in) 3-Apr-4 Nadeau, Windsor #141/R est:1500-2500
£1374 $2500 €2006 Old New England farm (20x25cm-8x10in) s. s.i.verso board. 29-Jun-4 Sotheby's, New York #222/R est:2000-3000
£1436 $2600 €2097 Wayside, rural Connecticut scene with houses (20x25cm-8x10in) 3-Apr-4 Nadeau, Windsor #140/R est:1500-2500

BRUETON, Frederick (fl.1882-1911) British
Works on paper
£420 $773 €613 Old fisherman (60x36cm-24x14in) s.d.1911 W/C. 23-Mar-4 Rosebery Fine Art, London #943

BRUGAIROLLES, Victor (1869-1936) French
£541 $968 €800 By the pond (38x55cm-15x22in) s. 8-May-4 Bukowskis, Helsinki #390/R
£845 $1403 €1200 Coucher de soleil (26x35cm-10x14in) s. panel. 15-Jun-3 Peron, Melun #212
£1050 $1900 €1533 Day's end (65x91cm-26x36in) s. 30-Mar-4 Christie's, Rockefeller NY #92/R est:1000-2000
£2667 $4773 €4000 Place de la Concorde (38x15cm-15x6in) s. 11-May-4 Christie's, Paris #203/R est:4000-6000
Works on paper
£321 $600 €469 Glow of youth (28x30cm-11x12in) s.d.07 W/C over pencil board. 25-Feb-4 Doyle, New York #951/R

BRUGES SCHOOL (15th C) Belgian
£16447 $30263 €25000 Roi Herode et sa suite (68x52cm-27x20in) panel double-sided. 24-Jun-4 Christie's, Paris #4/R est:6000-8000

BRUGES SCHOOL (16th C) Belgian
£11111 $20000 €16222 Crucifixion with the Virgin and saint John the Evangelist (37x29cm-15x11in) panel prov. 23-Jan-4 Christie's, Rockefeller NY #160/R est:25000-35000
£15278 $27500 €22306 Virgin and child enthroned with singing angles looking on, a river landscape beyond (37x22cm-15x9in) panel arched top prov.exhib. 22-Jan-4 Sotheby's, New York #261/R est:15000-20000
£28384 $51659 €41441 The Holy Family (41x31cm-16x12in) panel. 16-Jun-4 Fischer, Luzern #1003/R est:50000-70000 (S.FR 65000)
£30556 $55000 €44612 Crucifixion (31x21cm-12x8in) panel prov.exhib. 23-Jan-4 Christie's, Rockefeller NY #13/R est:50000-70000

BRUGGEMANN, Hermann (1822-?) German
£894 $1600 €1305 Interior genre scene of fisherman's family and pets (61x51cm-24x20in) s. 16-May-4 CRN Auctions, Cambridge #47/R
£1747 $3179 €2551 On the Pene. Preparing for departure (26x36cm-10x14in) s. pair. 16-Jun-4 Fischer, Luzern #1222/R est:3000-4000 (S.FR 4000)
£2647 $4578 €3865 Hunting on a winter's day in the woods (60x86cm-24x34in) s.d.1845. 9-Dec-3 Rasmussen, Copenhagen #1228/R est:30000-40000 (D.KR 28000)

BRUGGEMANN, J W (fl.1828-1844) German
£15278 $25972 €22000 Calm, French tallships firing a salute in a bay, Italy (97x130cm-38x51in) s.d.1835. 28-Oct-3 Christie's, Amsterdam #111/R est:4000-6000

BRUGGER, Arnold (1888-1975) Swiss
£438 $700 €639 Schooner at dockside (61x76cm-24x30in) s. s.verso. 20-Sep-3 Sloans & Kenyon, Bethesda #1163a/R
£529 $899 €772 Young fruit seller in market (81x60cm-32x24in) s. 7-Nov-3 Dobiaschofsky, Bern #165/R (S.FR 1200)
£2371 $4244 €3462 Country still life (63x70cm-25x28in) s. i. stretcher. 14-May-4 Dobiaschofsky, Bern #150/R est:8000 (S.FR 5500)
£3276 $5864 €4783 Mountain waterfall (90x80cm-35x31in) s. i. stretcher. 14-May-4 Dobiaschofsky, Bern #149/R est:3000 (S.FR 7600)
£6897 $12345 €10070 Milkman (120x160cm-47x63in) s. i. stretcher. 14-May-4 Dobiaschofsky, Bern #140/R est:15000 (S.FR 16000)

BRUGGHEN, Guillaume Anne van der (1811-1891) Dutch
£411 $699 €600 Dog (13x15cm-5x6in) init. panel. 5-Nov-3 Vendue Huis, Gravenhage #58/R

BRUGHETTI, Faustino (1889-1974) Argentinian
£1366 $2500 €1994 Sunrise (50x62cm-20x24in) 1-Jun-4 Arroyo, Buenos Aires #25

BRUGNER, Colestin (1824-1887) German
£1200 $2268 €1752 Figures by a mill on a frozen waterway (30x41cm-12x16in) s. 19-Feb-4 Christie's, Kensington #158/R est:800-1200
£2122 $3734 €3098 Landscape (42x58cm-17x23in) s. 23-May-4 Agra, Warsaw #19/R (P.Z 15000)

BRUGNOLI, Emanuele (1859-1944) Italian
Works on paper
£267 $477 €400 Complicity (47x31cm-19x12in) s. W/C. 12-May-4 Stadion, Trieste #620
£310 $502 €453 Venice, the Grand Canal with Doge's Palace (21x30cm-8x12in) s. W/C. 27-Jan-3 Bristol Auction Rooms #519
£993 $1658 €1400 Rio Rezzonico, Venice (46x28cm-18x11in) s. W/C. 14-Oct-3 Finarte Semenzato, Milan #100
£4667 $8587 €7000 Canal in Venice (51x70cm-20x28in) s. W/C card. 10-Jun-4 Christie's, Rome #105/R est:2000-3000

BRUI, Willy (1946-) French
£2054 $3800 €2999 Untitled (173x150cm-68x59in) s. acrylic prov. 13-Jul-4 Christie's, Rockefeller NY #46/R est:800-1200

BRUIN, Cornelis de (1870-1940) Dutch
£281 $450 €410 Old Amsterdam. s. 20-Sep-3 Harvey Clar, Oakland #1221
£367 $656 €550 Farmer with horse and cart (50x64cm-20x25in) s. 11-May-4 Vendu Notarishuis, Rotterdam #86
£439 $786 €650 Wooded landscape (39x49cm-15x19in) s. lit. 8-May-4 Schloss Ahlden, Ahlden #770/R
£604 $1100 €882 Farmer's wife feeding the chickens on the backyard (41x51cm-16x20in) s. 19-Jun-4 Harvey Clar, Oakland #2179

BRUIN, Pieter de (19th C) Dutch
£1067 $1909 €1600 Windmill (24x32cm-9x13in) s.d.45 panel. 14-May-4 Schloss Ahlden, Ahlden #2845/R est:1800

BRUINE, Adriaan Henricus de (1807-1870) Dutch
£15278 $25514 €22000 Huntsmen in a wooded landscape (35x45cm-14x18in) s. panel. 21-Oct-3 Sotheby's, Amsterdam #61/R est:5000-7000

BRULL (?) ?
Sculpture
£1209 $2250 €1765 Figure of a nude woman dancing (81cm-32in) s. 3-Mar-4 Alderfer's, Hatfield #244/R est:700-900

BRULL Y VINOLAS, Juan (1863-1912) Spanish
£1605 $2600 €2327 Young lady (40x32cm-16x13in) s. 29-Jul-3 Galeria y Remates, Montevideo #38/R est:1500-2000

BRULLER, Jean (20th C) French
Works on paper
£315 $535 €450 Portrait de Joseph Staline (24x18cm-9x7in) s. aerographe. 23-Nov-3 Cornette de St.Cyr, Paris #30
£350 $594 €500 Portrait de Maurice Thorez (24x18cm-9x7in) s. aerographe. 23-Nov-3 Cornette de St.Cyr, Paris #29/R

BRUMATTI, Gianni (1901-1990) Italian
£699 $1168 €1000 Fishermen (37x60cm-15x24in) s. board. 10-Oct-3 Stadion, Trieste #507/R

BRUMBACH, David (1948-1992) American
£1250 $2300 €1825 Red figure (84x81cm-33x32in) oil mixed media board. 25-Jun-4 Freeman, Philadelphia #266/R est:500-800

BRUMENT, Albert (19/20th C) French
£860 $1462 €1256 Still life of oysters (38x55cm-15x22in) s. 19-Nov-3 Fischer, Luzern #2030/R (S.FR 1900)

BRUMIDI, Constantino (1805-1880) American
£9783 $18000 €14283 Portrait of George Washington (94x76cm-37x30in) i. oval prov. 8-Jun-4 Bonhams & Butterfields, San Francisco #4004/R est:5000-7000
£9827 $17000 €14347 Aurora (69x135cm-27x53in) s. sold with a col photo prov.lit. 13-Dec-3 Weschler, Washington #539 est:3000-5000

BRUN, Alexandre (19th C) French
£391 $716 €571 Navires au port (32x41cm-13x16in) s. 5-Jun-4 Galerie du Rhone, Sion #193 (S.FR 900)

BRUN, Edouard (1860-1935) French
Works on paper
£280 $439 €409 Evening sun at Dome du Gouter (54x65cm-21x26in) s. pastel paper on canvas. 30-Aug-3 Rasmussen, Havnen #2168 (D.KR 3000)

BRUN, Georges le (1871-1914) Swiss
Works on paper
£331 $603 €500 Femme au puits (21x44cm-8x17in) mono. pastel. 15-Jun-4 Vanderkindere, Brussels #57

BRUN, Guillaume Charles (1825-1908) French
£2715 $4615 €3964 Le musicien arabe (33x25cm-13x10in) s. 28-Nov-3 Zofingen, Switzerland #2558/R est:4000 (S.FR 6000)
Works on paper
£493 $853 €700 Rue de Constantine (28x21cm-11x8in) s.i. ink wash. 15-Dec-3 Gros & Delettrez, Paris #72/R
£563 $975 €800 Rue de Constantine (28x21cm-11x8in) s.i. ink wash. 15-Dec-3 Gros & Delettrez, Paris #73
£671 $1242 €1000 Le tirailleur Algerien (33x27cm-13x11in) s.i. pen htd W/C. 15-Mar-4 Gros & Delettrez, Paris #87/R
£2000 $3680 €3000 Le petit marchand d'oranges (37x27cm-15x11in) s.i. pastel chl. 14-Jun-4 Gros & Delettrez, Paris #40/R est:2500-3500

BRUN, Louis-Auguste (1758-1815) French
Works on paper
£543 $939 €793 Promeneurs dans le chemin creux (22x18cm-9x7in) W/C wash. 12-Dec-3 Galerie du Rhone, Sion #179/R (S.FR 1200)

BRUN-BUISSON, Gabriel (19/20th C) French
Works on paper
£274 $466 €400 Paris, Notre-Dame et la cite (26x55cm-10x22in) s.d.1934 W/C. 9-Nov-3 Eric Pillon, Calais #114/R

BRUNAIS, Augustin (1730-1796) British
£55000 $89650 €80300 Family of Charaibes in the Island of St Vincent (56x61cm-22x24in) prov. 25-Sep-3 Christie's, London #424/R est:60000-80000
£55000 $89650 €80300 Pacification with the maroon Negroes in the island of Jamaica (56x61cm-22x24in) prov. 25-Sep-3 Christie's, London #425/R est:60000-80000

BRUNAIS, Augustin (attrib) (1730-1796) British
£7500 $13650 €10950 Portrait of a gentleman standing on the shore in the West Indies (64x49cm-25x19in) 1-Jul-4 Sotheby's, London #127/R est:8000-12000

BRUNBERG, Hakan (1905-1978) Finnish
£533 $981 €800 Next year in Jerusalem (40x49cm-16x19in) s. 9-Jun-4 Bukowskis, Helsinki #359/R
£1549 $2680 €2200 The King's party (41x51cm-16x20in) s. 13-Dec-3 Hagelstam, Helsinki #184/R est:2000
£3147 $5350 €4500 The grass widower (55x46cm-22x18in) s.d.75. 29-Nov-3 Bukowskis, Helsinki #271/R est:2200-2500
£4797 $8587 €7100 Owls in the woods (40x50cm-16x20in) s. 8-May-4 Bukowskis, Helsinki #250/R est:4000-5000
£4965 $8441 €7100 The teasing bird - four tigers watching (50x61cm-20x24in) s. 29-Nov-3 Bukowskis, Helsinki #244/R est:3000-4000
£5405 $9676 €8000 Sunday at the zoo (38x46cm-15x18in) s. 8-May-4 Bukowskis, Helsinki #240/R est:2000-2500
Works on paper
£557 $1036 €830 Evening in town (27x35cm-11x14in) s. gouache. 7-Mar-4 Bukowskis, Helsinki #299/R

BRUNDLE, Melbourne (20th C) American
Works on paper
£1111 $1800 €1611 Bentley. s. pencil dr. 1-Aug-3 Bonhams & Butterfields, San Francisco #817/R est:1800-2200

BRUNDRIT, Reginald Grange (1883-1960) British
£400 $748 €584 Port Patrick, South East Scotland (24x35cm-9x14in) s.i. canvasboard. 22-Jul-4 Tennants, Leyburn #949
£450 $842 €657 Extensive Dales landscape with haystacks in the foreground (24x34cm-9x13in) s. canvasboard. 22-Jul-4 Tennants, Leyburn #948
£450 $842 €657 The Silver Valley (25x35cm-10x14in) canvas on panel exhib. 22-Jul-4 Tennants, Leyburn #957
£550 $1029 €803 Pontoon Bridge, built for the landing in Italy by the British (30x40cm-12x16in) s. board. 22-Jul-4 Tennants, Leyburn #950
£600 $1122 €876 Linton Mill (36x46cm-14x18in) s. indis.i.verso stretcher. 22-Jul-4 Tennants, Leyburn #954
£700 $1260 €1022 Dales river landscape (46x61cm-18x24in) s. 21-Apr-4 Tennants, Leyburn #1263
£750 $1403 €1095 Near Grassington, Yorkshire (35x46cm-14x18in) s. 22-Jul-4 Tennants, Leyburn #946
£760 $1292 €1110 Grassington Bridge in winter (25x35cm-10x14in) s.i. board. 18-Nov-3 Bonhams, Leeds #272
£900 $1620 €1314 Broken water, a Dales landscape with cattle beside a river (46x61cm-18x24in) s. i.verso exhib. 21-Apr-4 Tennants, Leyburn #1262/R
£1000 $1870 €1460 Summer meadow with cattle beside a stream (36x46cm-14x18in) s. 22-Jul-4 Tennants, Leyburn #947 est:400-600
£1000 $1870 €1460 River landscape in winter (46x61cm-18x24in) s. 22-Jul-4 Tennants, Leyburn #951 est:500-600
£1000 $1870 €1460 A reach of the Lune (51x61cm-20x24in) s. 22-Jul-4 Tennants, Leyburn #956 est:700-900
£1400 $2618 €2044 The cloudless day, Filey (51x61cm-20x24in) s. i.verso stretcher prov. 22-Jul-4 Tennants, Leyburn #952/R est:1000-1500
£1600 $2992 €2336 The approach of night, stepping stones at Linton, Grassington (76x102cm-30x40in) s. exhib. 22-Jul-4 Tennants, Leyburn #955 est:700-900
£3000 $5490 €4380 Extensive view of Wensleydale (76x102cm-30x40in) s. exhib. 7-Apr-4 Andrew Hartley, Ilkley #1158/R est:3000-4000
£3500 $6545 €5110 Wharfedale in summer with cattle grazing in foreground and farm beyond (76x102cm-30x40in) s. 22-Jul-4 Tennants, Leyburn #960/R est:2500-3000
£3600 $6732 €5256 River landscape with distant hills (46x61cm-18x24in) s. 22-Jul-4 Tennants, Leyburn #953/R est:1000-1500
£4000 $7480 €5840 Linton in Craven, winter river landscape with horse, cart and figure (71x91cm-28x36in) s. exhib. 22-Jul-4 Tennants, Leyburn #959/R est:1500-2000

BRUNDRIT, Reginald Grange (attrib) (1883-1960) British
£550 $1029 €825 Sunlit river valley (25x35cm-10x14in) s. panel. 22-Jul-4 Tennants, Leyburn #958

BRUNE, Heinrich (1869-1945) German
£966 $1612 €1400 Girl in the bath (80x70cm-31x28in) s.d.1910. 13-Nov-3 Neumeister, Munich #270/R

BRUNEAU, Kittie (1929-) Canadian
£489 $812 €714 Perou (62x83cm-24x33in) s. i.d.1980 verso acrylic. 5-Oct-3 Levis, Calgary #14 (C.D 1100)

BRUNEAU, Odette (1891-1984) French
£3592 $6213 €5100 Heure du the (41x54cm-16x21in) s.d.1940 panel. 15-Dec-3 Gros & Delettrez, Paris #111/R est:2300-3000

BRUNEL DE NEUVILLE (19/20th C) French
£931 $1704 €1350 Nature morte aux huitres (31x40cm-12x16in) 1-Feb-4 Teitgen, Nancy #20

BRUNEL DE NEUVILLE, Alfred Arthur (1852-1941) French

£268	$500	€402	Still life with grapes and peaches in a woven basket (38x46cm-15x18in) s. 25-Jul-4 Bonhams & Butterfields, San Francisco #6072/R
£462	$785	€675	Three kittens at play (44x53cm-17x21in) s. canvas on board. 4-Nov-3 Stephan Welz, Johannesburg #579 est:6000-8000 (SA.R 5400)
£723	$1200	€1056	Peaches and currents in a basket on a table (38x46cm-15x18in) s. 30-Sep-3 Christie's, Rockefeller NY #453/R
£750	$1200	€1095	Still life with fruit and brass vessel (48x66cm-19x26in) s. canvas on board. 19-Sep-3 Freeman, Philadelphia #201/R est:400-600
£765	$1400	€1117	Tetee de roses (41x64cm-16x25in) s. 10-Apr-4 Auctions by the Bay, Alameda #1544/R
£900	$1494	€1314	Basket of flowers (54x65cm-21x26in) s. 1-Oct-3 Sotheby's, Olympia #230/R
£1042	$1646	€1500	Roses and lilacs in a vase (54x65cm-21x26in) s. 2-Sep-3 Christie's, Amsterdam #246/R est:2000-3000
£1105	$2000	€1613	Curiosity (28x23cm-11x9in) s. panel. 3-Apr-4 Neal Auction Company, New Orleans #69/R est:2000-4000
£1326	$2400	€1936	Proud mother (25x20cm-10x8in) s. panel. 3-Apr-4 Neal Auction Company, New Orleans #625/R est:2000-4000
£1399	$2378	€2000	Jeunes chats jouant avec une pelote de laine (46x55cm-18x22in) s. 1-Dec-3 Palais de Beaux Arts, Brussels #343/R est:2000-3000
£1400	$2338	€2044	Kittens playing (53x64cm-21x25in) s. 12-Nov-3 Sotheby's, Olympia #225/R
£1400	$2590	€2044	Still life of currents (38x46cm-15x18in) s. 10-Feb-4 Bonhams, Knightsbridge #185/R est:1500-2000
£1606	$2681	€2329	Still life with berries and cherries (33x41cm-13x16in) s. 23-Jun-3 Philippe Schuler, Zurich #3509/R est:2000-3000 (S.FR 3500)
£1667	$3050	€2500	Dahlias (38x56cm-15x22in) s. 6-Jun-4 Osenat, Fontainebleau #82/R est:2500-2800
£1678	$2853	€2400	Chatons jouant sur une table (54x65cm-21x26in) s. 1-Dec-3 Palais de Beaux Arts, Brussels #345/R est:2000-3000
£1705	$3000	€2489	Still life with strawberries and grapes (53x64cm-21x25in) s. 22-May-4 New Orleans Auction, New Orleans #566/R est:4000-7000
£2000	$3580	€2920	Still life of fruit (54x65cm-21x26in) s. 26-May-4 Sotheby's, Olympia #298/R est:2000-3000
£2000	$3700	€2920	Fruit basket (54x65cm-21x26in) s. 14-Jul-4 Sotheby's, Olympia #216/R est:2000-3000
£2013	$3765	€3000	Flower basket (54x65cm-21x26in) s. panel. 24-Feb-4 Dorotheum, Vienna #246/R est:3200-3800
£2069	$3828	€3000	Fruit. Hunting still life with pheasant (54x65cm-21x26in) s. pair. 14-Feb-4 Hans Stahl, Hamburg #10/R est:2000
£2079	$3597	€3035	Cut branches of white and purple lilacs on wooden stool (65x91cm-26x36in) s. 9-Dec-3 Rasmussen, Copenhagen #1580/R est:12000 (D.KR 22000)
£2254	$3899	€3200	Still life with basket, fruit and bottle (54x65cm-21x26in) s. 11-Dec-3 Dr Fritz Nagel, Stuttgart #513/R est:2300
£2477	$4261	€3616	Still life with fruit and jug (65x92cm-26x36in) s. 8-Dec-3 Philippe Schuler, Zurich #3391/R est:3000-3500 (S.FR 5500)
£3067	$5581	€4600	Kittens with inkwell (54x65cm-21x26in) s. 30-Jun-4 Delvaux, Paris #25/R est:5000-6000
£3084	$5242	€4503	Still life with cherries, berries and apricots (65x92cm-26x36in) s. 5-Nov-3 Dobiaschofsky, Bern #401/R est:7500 (S.FR 7000)
£3200	$5920	€4672	Playful kittens (52x64cm-20x25in) s. 14-Jul-4 Sotheby's, Olympia #237/R est:2500-3500
£4225	$7394	€6000	Les chatons (65x92cm-26x36in) s. 16-Dec-3 Galerie Moderne, Brussels #789/R est:4000-6000
£4333	$7800	€6500	Trois chatons se disputant une cotelette (53x65cm-21x26in) s. 20-Apr-4 Galerie Moderne, Brussels #285/R est:5500-6000

BRUNEL DE NEUVILLE, Alfred Arthur (attrib) (1852-1941) French

£509	$850	€743	Fruit on a silver tray (20x25cm-8x10in) oil metal panel. 16-Nov-3 William Jenack, New York #343
£509	$850	€743	Fruit in glass bowl with butterfly on a marble top table (20x25cm-8x10in) oil metal panel. 16-Nov-3 William Jenack, New York #414

BRUNELLESCHI, Umberto (1879-?) Italian

Works on paper

£629	$1070	€900	Untitled (31x48cm-12x19in) s. gouache bodycol over etching. 26-Nov-3 Dorotheum, Vienna #147/R
£833	$1492	€1250	L'absence (28x21cm-11x8in) s. crayon gouache. 11-May-4 Vanderkindere, Brussels #25
£863	$1416	€1200	Lost (32x22cm-13x9in) s. pencil tempera. 10-Jun-3 Pandolfini, Florence #341/R

BRUNERI, Fortunato (?) Italian

£805	$1426	€1200	Odalisk (32x24cm-13x9in) s. board. 1-May-4 Meeting Art, Vercelli #310

BRUNERY, François (1849-1926) Italian

£1389	$2500	€2028	Pinch of sniff (41x32cm-16x13in) s. panel. 21-Jan-4 Sotheby's, New York #198/R est:3000-5000
£3333	$6133	€5000	Promenade en traineau (32x24cm-13x9in) s.d.77 panel. 14-Jun-4 Horta, Bruxelles #168/R est:5000-7000
£15000	$25500	€21900	Love letter (42x33cm-17x13in) s. 19-Nov-3 Bonhams, New Bond Street #84/R est:10000-15000
£25000	$45500	€36500	Amateurs de gravures (101x85cm-40x33in) s. 17-Jun-4 Christie's, London #85/R est:25000-35000
£28000	$48160	€40880	Champagne, bon vintage (48x59cm-19x23in) s. panel. 3-Dec-3 Cheffins, Cambridge #632/R est:20000-30000
£97000	$176540	€141620	Les gourmets (98x130cm-39x51in) s. prov. 15-Jun-4 Sotheby's, London #200/R est:40000-60000

BRUNERY, François (attrib) (1849-1926) Italian

£800	$1472	€1200	Jewel (35x26cm-14x10in) board. 10-Jun-4 Christie's, Rome #131/R
£1344	$2500	€1962	In the garden (46x38cm-18x15in) s. 5-Mar-4 Skinner, Boston #220a/R est:3000-5000
£2013	$3564	€3000	Oratoire de Saint-Michel a Venise (46x37cm-18x15in) indis.sig.i. panel. 30-Apr-4 Tajan, Paris #206/R est:3000-4000

BRUNERY, Marcel (20th C) French

£26389	$47500	€38528	Merry afternoon tea (54x65cm-21x26in) s. 23-Apr-4 Sotheby's, New York #197/R est:15000-20000

BRUNET, Émile Jean Marie (1869-1943) French

£7333	$13493	€11000	L'odalisque, le musicien et la servante dans un palais orientale (202x226cm-80x89in) s. 10-Jun-4 Camard, Paris #50/R est:10000-12000

BRUNET, Fernanda (1964-) American?

£6145	$11000	€8972	SWWWWKKT (169x229cm-67x90in) s.i.d.2003 verso acrylic linen prov. 13-May-4 Sotheby's, New York #352/R est:8000-12000

BRUNET, Jean Marc (20th C) French

£1342	$2376	€2000	Balade solitaire (90x90cm-35x35in) s. 29-Apr-4 Claude Aguttes, Neuilly #163/R est:2000-2200

BRUNET-HOUARD, Pierre Auguste (1829-1922) French

£423	$756	€600	Ours et oursons dans la neige (79x57cm-31x22in) s. 11-Jan-4 Rouillac, Vendome #310
£5333	$9547	€8000	Marshes in Lazio (49x99cm-19x39in) s. 17-May-4 Finarte Semenzato, Rome #79/R est:7000-8000
£5944	$10224	€8500	Le saltimbanque (95x138cm-37x54in) s. 5-Dec-3 Gros & Delettrez, Paris #51/R est:4000-5000

BRUNET-HOUARD, Pierre Auguste (attrib) (1829-1922) French

£1154	$2100	€1685	Embarking on a cruscade (69x160cm-27x63in) s.d.1914. 19-Jun-4 Jackson's, Cedar Falls #68/R est:2000-3000

BRUNETTO, Silvio (1932-) Italian

£347	$590	€500	Market (24x30cm-9x12in) s.i.d.1989 board. 1-Nov-3 Meeting Art, Vercelli #14
£347	$590	€500	Red roofs (40x50cm-16x20in) s. masonite. 1-Nov-3 Meeting Art, Vercelli #163
£537	$950	€800	Vineyards in the Langhe (30x50cm-12x20in) s. s.i.d.1981 verso masonite. 1-May-4 Meeting Art, Vercelli #208
£694	$1181	€1000	Piazza Statuto, Turin (60x50cm-24x20in) s. s.i.verso. 1-Nov-3 Meeting Art, Vercelli #171
£1042	$1771	€1500	Morning in Florence (50x70cm-20x28in) s. s.i.verso masonite. 1-Nov-3 Meeting Art, Vercelli #175/R est:1500

BRUNFAUT, Raymond (20th C) Belgian

£342	$582	€500	Landscape with washerwomen (40x60cm-16x24in) s. lit. 8-Nov-3 Hans Stahl, Toestorf #26/R

BRUNI, Bruno (1935-) Italian

Sculpture

£1053	$1937	€1600	Gymnist (60cm-24in) num.43/250 pat bronze st.f.Venturi. 25-Jun-4 Michael Zeller, Lindau #110/R est:500
£1118	$2058	€1700	Young girl undressing (70cm-28in) i. num.249/450 pat bronze st.f. Venturi. 25-Jun-4 Michael Zeller, Lindau #109/R est:500
£1189	$2021	€1700	The artist (60cm-24in) s.num.62/250 dark brown pat bronze st.f.Venturi. 28-Nov-3 Schloss Ahlden, Ahlden #537/R est:1900
£1267	$2267	€1900	Nude (71x11x15cm-28x4x6in) i. num.171/450brown pat.bronze marble socle. 15-May-4 Van Ham, Cologne #495/R est:1900
£1447	$2663	€2200	Young girl undressing (99cm-39in) num.536/1000 pat bronze st.f.Venturi. 25-Jun-4 Michael Zeller, Lindau #111/R est:1000
£1748	$2920	€2500	La Stradiata (10x22x79cm-4x9x31in) gold pat.bronze. 10-Oct-3 Winterberg, Heidelberg #1033/R est:3200

Works on paper

£738	$1307	€1100	Female nudes (90x60cm-35x24in) s. chl pencil chk. 30-Apr-4 Dr Fritz Nagel, Stuttgart #58/R
£1000	$1790	€1500	Couple from behind (75x58cm-30x23in) s. pencil W/C. 15-May-4 Van Ham, Cologne #493/R est:2000
£1049	$1804	€1500	Standing female nude (100x70cm-39x28in) s. chl cardboard. 4-Dec-3 Van Ham, Cologne #66/R est:1800

BRUNI, Laure-Stella (20th C) French

£390	$651	€566	La mer apres la tempete (95x164cm-37x65in) s. panel. 21-Jun-3 Galerie du Rhone, Sion #340/R (S.FR 850)
£452	$769	€660	Rovia - Tessin summer landscape (90x115cm-35x45in) s.d.1949 i. verso. 28-Nov-3 Zofingen, Switzerland #2560/R (S.FR 1000)

BRUNILLE (?) ?

£2375	$3800	€3468	Mother cat with kittens (66x91cm-26x36in) s. cut canvas on board. 21-Sep-3 William Jenack, New York #403 est:1000-1500

BRUNIN, Charles (1841-1887) Belgian

Sculpture

£1477	$2643	€2200	Homme au pigeon (62cm-24in) s. bronze. 25-May-4 Campo & Campo, Antwerp #25/R est:650-850

BRUNIN, Léon (1861-1949) Belgian

£367	$664	€550	Le pecheur (28x29cm-11x11in) s. panel. 30-Mar-4 Campo & Campo, Antwerp #23/R
£372	$654	€550	Coquelicots (53x37cm-21x15in) s. panel. 24-May-4 Bernaerts, Antwerp #474/R
£537	$961	€800	Fleurs dans un vase (60x50cm-24x20in) s. 25-May-4 Campo & Campo, Antwerp #26/R
£805	$1490	€1200	Vue de la chapelle (56x41cm-22x16in) 15-Mar-4 Horta, Bruxelles #26
£816	$1461	€1200	Le fumeur (58x48cm-23x19in) 22-Mar-4 Amberes, Antwerp #180e
£1000	$1810	€1500	Le garde-barriere (60x50cm-24x20in) s.d.1882. 30-Mar-4 Campo & Campo, Antwerp #24/R est:2000-3000
£1224	$2192	€1800	Le collectionneur (58x48cm-23x19in) 22-Mar-4 Amberes, Antwerp #180d/R

£1600 $2896 €2400 Coq se batant avec un blaireau (83x55cm-33x22in) s. 30-Mar-4 Campo & Campo, Antwerp #21/R est:1500-2000
£3020 $5617 €4500 In the harem (60x90cm-24x35in) s.d.1883. 8-Mar-4 Bernaerts, Antwerp #104/R est:5000-6000
£3667 $6637 €5500 La lettre (80x60cm-31x24in) s. 30-Mar-4 Campo & Campo, Antwerp #22/R est:3000-5000

BRUNIN, Léon (attrib) (1861-1949) Belgian
£724 $1332 €1100 Scholar holding quill pen (27x17cm-11x7in) s. panel. 24-Jun-4 Dr Fritz Nagel, Stuttgart #692/R

BRUNING, Max (1887-1968) German
Works on paper
£383 $704 €570 Portrait of elegant young women (34x31cm-13x12in) s. chk on pencil W/C. 26-Mar-4 Venator & Hansten, Koln #1680/R
£403 $741 €600 Lindau harbour on spring morning (40x45cm-16x18in) s. mixed media. 27-Mar-4 Geble, Radolfzell #710/R

BRUNING, Peter (1929-1970) German
£10000 $18400 €14600 Untitled (96x130cm-38x51in) painted c.1959-60 lit. 24-Jun-4 Sotheby's, London #191/R est:15000-20000
£18000 $32940 €27000 Untitled (80x80cm-31x31in) 4-Jun-4 Lempertz, Koln #75/R est:25000-30000
£20979 $35664 €30000 Untitled (85x120cm-33x47in) prov. 27-Nov-3 Lempertz, Koln #59/R est:40000
£25175 $43301 €36000 Untitled (100x130cm-39x51in) oil chk prov.exhib. 5-Dec-3 Ketterer, Munich #327/R est:25000-30000

BRUNNER, Antonin (1881-?) Czechoslovakian
£2333 $4177 €3500 The five senses (69x99cm-27x39in) s.d.1943 lit. 14-May-4 Schloss Ahlden, Ahlden #2927/R est:3800

BRUNNER, Ferdinand (1870-1945) Austrian
£6944 $11806 €10000 Scharding (20x27cm-8x11in) s.d.1900 board. 28-Oct-3 Wiener Kunst Auktionen, Vienna #54/R est:8000-15000
Works on paper
£365 $653 €540 Interior (31x41cm-12x16in) s.d.92 W/C. 6-May-4 Michael Zeller, Lindau #631/R

BRUNNER, Hans (1813-1888) German
£1724 $3086 €2517 The visit (61x72cm-24x28in) s.i.d.1865. 12-May-4 Dobiaschofsky, Bern #364/R est:2800 (S.FR 4000)

BRUNNER, Hans Alexander (1895-1968) Austrian
Works on paper
£933 $1680 €1400 Mondsee (28x42cm-11x17in) s.d.27 gouache pastel. 21-Apr-4 Dorotheum, Vienna #47/R

BRUNNER, Hattie K (1890-1982) American
Works on paper
£1163 $2000 €1698 Winter landscape with horse drawn sleigh flanked by homesteads and trees (23x33cm-9x13in) s. W/C. 6-Dec-3 Pook & Pook, Downington #160/R est:2500-3500
£2011 $3600 €3377 Winter village scene with horse drawn sleigh (28x33cm-11x13in) s. W/C. 20-Mar-4 Pook & Pook, Downington #49/R est:2500-3500
£2123 $3800 €3564 Winter village scene with red covered bridge (28x38cm-11x15in) s.d.59 W/C. 20-Mar-4 Pook & Pook, Downington #51/R est:3000-3500
£2346 $4200 €3939 Farm auction scene (28x38cm-11x15in) s.d.59 W/C. 20-Mar-4 Pook & Pook, Downington #50/R est:6000-8000

BRUNNER, Joseph (1826-1893) German
£349 $615 €510 Lakeshore with hunter (61x46cm-24x18in) mono. prov. 22-May-4 Galerie Gloggner, Luzern #17/R (S.FR 800)
£497 $904 €750 Vienna landscape (15x20cm-6x8in) s.d.1855 panel. 16-Jun-4 Hugo Ruef, Munich #932/R
Works on paper
£470 $864 €700 Angler by pond (10x14cm-4x6in) s.d.870 W/C. 26-Mar-4 Dorotheum, Vienna #226/R
£470 $864 €700 Landscape with gorge (10x14cm-4x6in) s.d.75 W/C. 26-Mar-4 Dorotheum, Vienna #228/R

BRUNNER, Julienne (?) ?
£903 $1435 €1300 Composition fleurie sur en entablement (91x60cm-36x24in) s. 15-Sep-3 Horta, Bruxelles #180

BRUNNER, Karl (1847-1918) German
£590 $933 €850 Still life with plant and fruit (58x46cm-23x18in) s.d.1869. 5-Sep-3 Wendl, Rudolstadt #3306/R

BRUNNER, Leopold (19th C) Austrian
£412 $672 €602 Village view with old houses (47x38cm-19x15in) s.d.1839 panel prov. 28-Sep-3 Hindemae, Ullerslev #68/R (D.KR 4400)

BRUNNER, Leopold (elder) (1788-1866) Austrian
£2685 $4805 €4000 Still life with goldfinch (25x39cm-10x15in) s.d.1840. 27-May-4 Dorotheum, Vienna #102/R est:3000-3800

BRUNNER, Samuel (1858-?) German?
£2148 $3844 €3200 View of Brunn (26x39cm-10x15in) s.i. 27-May-4 Dorotheum, Vienna #228/R est:3000-3500

BRUNNICH, Morten Thrane (1805-1861) Danish
£567 $981 €828 Portrait of General Major Ferdinand Christian Furchtegott Bauditz (100x85cm-39x33in) s.verso exhib. 9-Dec-3 Rasmussen, Copenhagen #1685/R (D.KR 6000)

BRUNO, Belati (20th C) Italian
£704 $1232 €1000 Kissed by the sun (150x100cm-59x39in) s.d.1951. 17-Dec-3 Il Ponte, Milan #1200

BRUNONI, Serge (1930-) Canadian
£400 $732 €584 Winter camp fire (50x60cm-20x24in) s.i. 1-Jun-4 Hodgins, Calgary #138/R (C.D 1000)
£434 $785 €634 Entre voisins (30x41cm-12x16in) s. s.i.verso. 18-Apr-4 Levis, Calgary #16/R est:800-1200 (C.D 1050)
£480 $878 €701 Flat Iron Building (60x75cm-24x30in) s. 1-Jun-4 Joyner Waddington, Toronto #455 (C.D 1200)
£586 $995 €856 L'ete t'invite (61x76cm-24x30in) s. s.i.verso prov. 23-Nov-3 Levis, Calgary #18/R (C.D 1300)
£600 $1098 €876 Flat Iron Building, Toronto (75x90cm-30x35in) s. prov. 1-Jun-4 Joyner Waddington, Toronto #292/R (C.D 1500)
£676 $1149 €987 Montreal, jeu de ruelle (25x30cm-10x12in) s. s.i.verso acrylic. 27-Nov-3 Heffel, Vancouver #74/R (C.D 1500)
£721 $1225 €1053 La game (61x76cm-24x30in) s. s.i.verso acrylic. 27-Nov-3 Heffel, Vancouver #70/R (C.D 1600)
£744 $1346 €1086 Montreal rue Notre Dame (61x76cm-24x30in) s. s.i.verso. 18-Apr-4 Levis, Calgary #15/R est:2000-2500 (C.D 1800)
£856 $1455 €1250 Montreal, Sherbrooke et Drummond (41x51cm-16x20in) s. s.i.verso prov. 23-Nov-3 Levis, Calgary #19/R est:1200-1500 (C.D 1900)
£880 $1610 €1285 St Paul Street, Montreal (75x100cm-30x39in) s. 1-Jun-4 Joyner Waddington, Toronto #180/R est:1500-2000 (C.D 2200)
£991 $1685 €1447 Le temps des sucre (61x767cm-24x302in) s. s.i.verso. 23-Nov-3 Levis, Calgary #17/R est:1500-2000 (C.D 2200)
£1161 $1996 €1695 Devant le Ritz, Rue Sherbrooke, Montreal (75x100cm-30x39in) s. 2-Dec-3 Joyner Waddington, Toronto #196/R est:2000-2500 (C.D 2600)
£1423 $2547 €2078 Montreal, Rue Sherbrooke (76x91cm-30x36in) s. s.i.verso acrylic. 27-May-4 Heffel, Vancouver #176/R est:2000-3000 (C.D 3500)

BRUNS, Edwin John (1899-?) American
£264 $450 €385 Fall landscape with farm (36x46cm-14x18in) s. board. 22-Nov-3 Jackson's, Cedar Falls #80/R

BRUS, Gunter (1938-) Austrian
£1528 $2551 €2200 House of the supervisor (42x57cm-17x22in) mono.i.d. pencil wash. 25-Oct-3 Dr Lehr, Berlin #80/R est:1200
£2533 $4636 €3800 Frog and spring (30x21cm-12x8in) s.i.d.1974 oil chk col pen. 4-Jun-4 Lempertz, Koln #76/R est:2000
Works on paper
£1111 $1856 €1600 Old Lemberg (30x21cm-12x8in) mono.i.d. col chk graphite. 25-Oct-3 Dr Lehr, Berlin #79/R est:1000
£1342 $2483 €2000 No dream, just experience (41x31cm-16x12in) s.i.d.85 pencil col pen wax chk. 9-Mar-4 Dorotheum, Vienna #194/R est:1800-2600
£3356 $6007 €5000 Europa's balcony (29x37cm-11x15in) s.i.d.72 pencil col pen 3 prov. 25-May-4 Dorotheum, Vienna #82/R est:5000-6000
£3691 $6534 €5500 Screw on shadow (24x38cm-9x15in) s.i.d. col pen. 28-Apr-4 Wiener Kunst Auktionen, Vienna #242/R est:5500-7000
£4027 $7208 €6000 Exile (39x30cm-15x12in) mono.i.d.78 pencil col pen prov. 25-May-4 Dorotheum, Vienna #80/R est:3000-3800
£4362 $7721 €6500 How he seemed to me (35x50cm-14x20in) s.i.d. pencil col pen. 28-Apr-4 Wiener Kunst Auktionen, Vienna #243/R est:4500-6000

BRUSAFERRO, Girolamo (attrib) (1700-1760) Italian
£4196 $7217 €6000 Rebecca at the well (73x97cm-29x38in) 2-Dec-3 Sotheby's, Milan #120/R est:6000-8000
£4500 $8235 €6570 Wife of Darius before Alexander (92x125cm-36x49in) 7-Jul-4 Bonhams, New Bond Street #62/R est:5000-7000

BRUSASORCI, Domenico (1516-1567) Italian
Works on paper
£4200 $7686 €6132 Adoration of the Magi (23x25cm-9x10in) pen ink wash htd white. 6-Jul-4 Christie's, London #27/R est:2000-3000

BRUSASORCI, Felice (1540-1605) Italian
£19000 $32870 €27740 Judgement of Paris (35x42cm-14x17in) i.verso prov.lit. 11-Dec-3 Sotheby's, London #183/R est:10000-15000

BRUSCO, Cornelio (fl.1620-1650) Italian
£5500 $9515 €8030 Wooded river landscape with soldiers resting (95x166cm-37x65in) 10-Dec-3 Bonhams, New Bond Street #106/R est:5000-7000

BRUSELIUS, Frits (1919-1974) Danish
£2230 $3991 €3300 Boys playing on beach (117x120cm-46x47in) i.d.1948 verso lit. 8-May-4 Schloss Ahlden, Ahlden #853/R est:1200

BRUSENBAUCH, Arthur (1881-1957) German
£537 $993 €800 Monkeys (53x42cm-21x17in) board double-sided. 9-Mar-4 Dorotheum, Vienna #65/R
£1974 $3632 €3000 Schrambachscharte and Mandlwand at Hochkonig (68x89cm-27x35in) s.d.1939 s.i.verso. 22-Jun-4 Wiener Kunst Auktionen, Vienna #55/R est:3500
£2533 $4535 €3800 Attersee landscape (70x100cm-28x39in) s.d.1944. 13-May-4 Dorotheum, Linz #496/R est:1500-1800
Works on paper
£1197 $2095 €1700 Female nude, torso (40x27cm-16x11in) s.indis.d. mixed media. 19-Dec-3 Dorotheum, Vienna #16/R est:700-1200

BRUSEWITZ, Gustaf (1812-1899) Swedish
£1256 $2249 €1834 Gathering by the well (46x56cm-18x22in) s. 25-May-4 Bukowskis, Stockholm #126/R est:18000-20000 (S.KR 17000)

BRUSKIN, Grisha (1945-) Russian
£3493 $6428 €5100 Self portrait (59x48cm-23x19in) s. canvas on board. 8-Jun-4 Germann, Zurich #140/R est:10000-15000 (S.FR 8000)
£11173 $20000 €16313 Succoth (101x137cm-40x54in) s.i.verso painted c.1972-73. 18-Mar-4 Sotheby's, New York #120/R est:30000-40000
£27933 $50000 €40782 Message 3 (140x112cm-55x44in) oil linen prov.exhib. 12-May-4 Christie's, Rockefeller NY #482/R est:60000-80000
£41916 $70000 €61197 Alefbet-Lexikon N10 (116x88cm-46x35in) s.i.d.1987-1994 verso linen prov. 12-Nov-3 Christie's, Rockefeller NY #639/R est:50000-70000

BRUSSEL, Hermanus van (1763-1815) Dutch
Works on paper
£616 $1048 €900 Standing peasant with basket, clogs and walking stick (15x24cm-6x9in) bears i.verso black chk. 4-Nov-3 Sotheby's, Amsterdam #140/R
£1149 $2022 €1700 Lime kilns along the Leidse Vaart near Hillegom (26x33cm-10x13in) mono. i.verso W/C black chk exhib. 19-May-4 Sotheby's, Amsterdam #273/R est:2200-2500

BRUSSEL, Paul Theodore van (1754-1791) Dutch
£165517 $274759 €240000 Flowers and fruit. Vase of flowers (87x72cm-34x28in) s.d.1779 pair. 30-Sep-3 Ansorena, Madrid #38/R est:240000

BRUSSELMANS, Jean (1884-1953) Belgian
£1528 $2399 €2200 Paysage d'automne (40x53cm-16x21in) s. 26-Aug-3 Galerie Moderne, Brussels #350/R est:1500-2000
£1879 $3326 €2800 La theiere (42x28cm-17x11in) s.d.1910 lit. 27-Apr-4 Campo & Campo, Antwerp #35/R est:1500-3500
£4196 $7133 €6000 Blue Farm (28x31cm-11x12in) canvas on canvas painted c.1913 lit. 25-Nov-3 Christie's, Amsterdam #201/R est:5000-7000
£4636 $8437 €7000 Les arracheurs de pommes de terre (51x56cm-20x22in) s.d.1925 canvas on panel. 15-Jun-4 Vanderkindere, Brussels #59/R est:7000-10000
£27972 $48112 €40000 Groot interieur (123x113cm-48x44in) s.d.1936 exhib.lit. 2-Dec-3 Sotheby's, Amsterdam #68/R est:25000-35000

BRUSSELMANS, Jean (attrib) (1884-1953) Belgian
Works on paper
£1007 $1782 €1500 Scene au bar I (184x66cm-72x26in) mixed media. 27-Apr-4 Campo & Campo, Antwerp #33/R est:1750-2250
£1007 $1782 €1500 Scene au bar II (184x66cm-72x26in) mixed media. 27-Apr-4 Campo & Campo, Antwerp #34/R est:1750-2250

BRUSSES, B de (19th C) Belgian
£4000 $7280 €5840 Catch. Accident (21x27cm-8x11in) s. panel pair. 16-Jun-4 Christie's, Kensington #151/R est:2000-3000

BRUSSET, Jean Paul (1914-) French
£380 $600 €555 Figure 22 (56x46cm-22x18in) s. board. 7-Sep-3 Treadway Gallery, Cincinnati #762/R

BRUSSOUGH, Eugene (?) American?
£391 $700 €571 Winter scene (56x63cm-22x25in) s. 21-Mar-4 Bonhams & Butterfields, Los Angeles #7128/R

BRUSTOLON, Andrea (attrib) (1662-1732) Italian
Sculpture
£41096 $69863 €60000 Centaurs (32x25x11cm-13x10x4in) wood marble base pair. 8-Nov-3 Finarte, Venice #255/R est:50000-60000

BRUTSCHLIN, Max Franz (1910-) Swiss
£294 $500 €429 View of Rigi (46x81cm-18x32in) s. exhib. 18-Nov-3 Hans Widmer, St Gallen #1031 (S.FR 650)
£480 $884 €701 Harvest (60x73cm-24x29in) 14-Jun-4 Philippe Schuler, Zurich #4203/R (S.FR 1100)
£524 $964 €765 Winter landscape lit by setting sun (38x46cm-15x18in) s. 14-Jun-4 Philippe Schuler, Zurich #4202 (S.FR 1200)

BRUTT, Ferdinand (1849-1936) German
Works on paper
£420 $713 €600 Sunday outing for the family (23x34cm-9x13in) s.d.09 W/C gouache. 20-Nov-3 Van Ham, Cologne #1501

BRUUN, Johan Jacob (1715-1789) Danish
Works on paper
£449 $836 €656 Prospect view of the Royal Palace, Copenhagen (18x25cm-7x10in) wash pencil. 2-Mar-4 Rasmussen, Copenhagen #1674/R (D.KR 5000)

BRUUN, Sven (19/20th C) Danish
£1760 $3291 €2570 Female model seen from behind (98x98cm-39x39in) s.d.1917. 25-Feb-4 Kunsthallen, Copenhagen #298/R est:20000 (D.KR 19500)

BRUUN, Thomas (1742-1800) Danish
£2647 $4578 €3865 Portraits of a noble couple (69x53cm-27x21in) s.d.1776 pair. 9-Dec-3 Rasmussen, Copenhagen #1361/R est:30000 (D.KR 28000)

BRUYCKER, Allda Eugen de (1901-1981) German
£268 $475 €400 Storm gathering over autumnal heathland (60x80cm-24x31in) s. 28-Apr-4 Schopman, Hamburg #601/R

BRUYCKER, Constant de (1823-1896) Belgian
£828 $1382 €1200 Repos pres de la ferme (15x17cm-6x7in) bears sig. panel. 17-Nov-3 Bernaerts, Antwerp #14

BRUYCKER, D de (19th C) Belgian
£1172 $2169 €1700 Le foud du roi (24x20cm-9x8in) s. panel. 19-Jan-4 Horta, Bruxelles #362 est:1800-2200

BRUYCKER, François Antoine de (1816-1882) Belgian
£5333 $9547 €8000 Minette modiste (39x50cm-15x20in) s. panel. 15-May-4 De Vuyst, Lokeren #422/R est:4400-4800
£9500 $17290 €13870 Making a posy. Preparing vegetables (25x20cm-10x8in) s. panel pir. 16-Jun-4 Bonhams, New Bond Street #5/R est:6000-8000

BRUYCKER, Herrmann de (1858-1950) German
£486 $768 €700 Storm over heathland (50x34cm-20x13in) s. i.d.10 verso. 6-Sep-3 Schopman, Hamburg #745/R
£503 $891 €750 Sunny day by heathland stream (66x88cm-26x35in) s. i.d.1943 verso. 28-Apr-4 Schopman, Hamburg #602/R

BRUYCKER, Jules de (1870-1945) Belgian
Works on paper
£307 $561 €460 Homme debout (20x13cm-8x5in) s. crayon. 7-Jun-4 Palais de Beaux Arts, Brussels #241
£2083 $3312 €3000 Balayeur (70x28cm-28x11in) s. W/C. 9-Sep-3 Vanderkindere, Brussels #15
£3333 $5967 €5000 The mender (47x32cm-19x13in) s.i.d.40 pencil chl exhib. 15-May-4 De Vuyst, Lokeren #480/R est:5000-6000
£3497 $6014 €5000 Portrait of Frans Masereel (45x30cm-18x12in) s.d.1909 pencil chk Indian ink. 2-Dec-3 Hauswedell & Nolte, Hamburg #418/R est:400
£5034 $9312 €7500 Street cleaner (69x28cm-27x11in) s.d.1903 W/C chl black chk. 13-Mar-4 De Vuyst, Lokeren #427/R est:6000-8000
£6294 $10510 €9000 The Opera diva (43x51cm-17x20in) s. W/C black chk exhib. 11-Oct-3 De Vuyst, Lokeren #430/R est:9000-11000

BRUYERE, P de (19th C) French
£693 $1240 €1012 Dune landscape (17x23cm-7x9in) s.d.47 paper on canvas. 22-Mar-4 Philippe Schuler, Zurich #6125 (S.FR 1600)

BRUYN, Barthel (elder-attrib) (1493-1555) German
£5034 $9262 €7500 Christ as Salvator mundi (96x63cm-38x25in) panel. 25-Mar-4 Dr Fritz Nagel, Stuttgart #590/R est:1800

BRUYN, Chris de (jnr) (1901-1974) Dutch
£256 $450 €374 Figure by a city gate (41x61cm-16x24in) s. 22-May-4 Harvey Clar, Oakland #2223

BRUYN, Johannes Cornelis de (1800-1844) Dutch
£789 $1453 €1200 Still life with various fruits (43x36cm-17x14in) s. indis.d. 28-Jun-4 Sotheby's, Amsterdam #6/R

BRUYN, Theodore de (attrib) (fl.1760-1804) Flemish
£20000 $36800 €29200 View of Chatsworth House from the south-west, with labourers and livestock (102x127cm-40x50in) prov.exhib. 11-Jun-4 Christie's, London #24/R est:25000-40000

BRUYNE, G C de (?) Belgian
£533 $960 €800 Head (30x28cm-12x11in) panel. 26-Apr-4 Bernaerts, Antwerp #207a
£2133 $3840 €3200 Portrait of Lucy van Dongen's father (99x56cm-39x22in) s.d.1934 panel. 26-Apr-4 Bernaerts, Antwerp #204/R est:3000-4000
£2797 $4755 €4000 Sonya, nu debout vu de dos devant une vue de ville (74x49cm-29x19in) triplex. 1-Dec-3 Amberes, Antwerp #289/R
Works on paper
£1000 $1800 €1500 The threat (80x60cm-31x24in) s.verso mixed media panel. 26-Apr-4 Bernaerts, Antwerp #715/R est:2000-2200
£1333 $2400 €2000 Vrouw in wit (48x59cm-19x23in) s.verso mixed media canvas. 26-Apr-4 Bernaerts, Antwerp #205/R est:2000-3000
£2667 $4800 €4000 Three children (95x55cm-37x22in) s.d.1970 mixed media panel. 26-Apr-4 Bernaerts, Antwerp #206/R est:4000-5000
£2667 $4800 €4000 Standing nude woman (158x57cm 62x22in) s. mixed media panel. 26-Apr-4 Bernaerts, Antwerp #207/R est:4000-5000

BRUYNE, G de (1914-1981) Belgian
£333 $597 €500 Femme assise devant la fenetre (47x38cm-19x15in) s.d.1937. 11-May-4 Vanderkindere, Brussels #114
£2533 $4560 €3800 Boer (50x39cm-20x15in) s.d.1935 cardboard. 26-Apr-4 Bernaerts, Antwerp #198/R est:3000-4000
Works on paper
£433 $780 €650 Standing nudes (50x36cm-20x14in) s. pencil W/C. 26-Apr-4 Bernaerts, Antwerp #717/R

BRUYNE, Gustaaf de (1914-1981) Belgian
£374 $681 €550 Oiseau mort (58x49cm-23x19in) 9-Feb-4 Amberes, Antwerp #250
£3333 $6000 €5000 Portrait of Marcel Mutsaerts (99x68cm-39x27in) s. 26-Apr-4 Bernaerts, Antwerp #203/R est:4500-6000

Works on paper
£278 $464 €400 Femme a l'echarpe (67x42cm-26x17in) s. W/C. 21-Oct-3 Campo, Vlaamse Kaai #400
£2641 $4569 €3750 Ecce Homo (141x90cm-56x35in) s. pastel. 13-Dec-3 De Vuyst, Lokeren #92/R est:4000-5000

BRUZZI, Stefano (1835-1911) Italian
£6250 $10625 €9000 Ritorno dal mercato (44x25cm-17x10in) s. 28-Oct-3 Christie's, Amsterdam #195/R est:10000-15000

BRYANS, Lina (1909-2000) Australian
£909 $1682 €1327 Professor Keith Macartney (59x49cm-23x19in) s. canvas on board prov.exhib. 15-Mar-4 Sotheby's, Melbourne #30 est:2500-3500 (A.D 2200)
£1653 $3058 €2413 Sydney Harbour (43x47cm-17x19in) i.verso canvas on board. 10-Mar-4 Deutscher-Menzies, Melbourne #318/R est:3000-5000 (A.D 4000)

BRYANT, A Moginie (19/20th C) British
£1500 $2760 €2190 Chestnut hunter in a paddock. Dark brown mare by a stable (46x61cm-18x24in) s.d.06 pair. 10-Jun-4 Christie's, Kensington #81/R est:1500-2000

BRYANT, Augusta S (19th C) American
£2186 $4000 €3192 Mississippi river landscape (51x41cm-20x16in) s. 5-Jun-4 Neal Auction Company, New Orleans #410/R est:1500-2500

BRYANT, Bruce (20th C) New Zealander
£1014 $1633 €1480 Mansion House Kawau from jetty (67x80cm-26x31in) s. board. 20-Aug-3 Peter Webb, Auckland #2005 (NZ.D 2800)

BRYANT, Charles (1883-1937) Australian
£1037 $1732 €1556 Boats on the Bay (18x23cm-7x9in) board. 27-Oct-3 Goodman, Sydney #168/R (A.D 2500)
£1638 $2555 €2375 Yacht race, Sydney Harbour (23x56cm-9x22in) s. canvas on board. 1-Aug-2 Joel, Victoria #311 est:4000-6000 (A.D 4750)
£3000 $5490 €4380 Preparing to sail Honfleur fishing boats (62x75cm-24x30in) s. 3-Jun-4 Lane, Penzance #60/R est:3000-5000

BRYANT, Chris (20th C) ?
Sculpture
£1211 $2168 €1768 Tirohia te whenua (160x130cm-63x51in) mixed media caved wood. 12-May-4 Dunbar Sloane, Wellington #72/R est:4000-7000 (NZ.D 3500)

BRYANT, Everett L (1864-1945) American
£280 $500 €409 Floral still life with stemware and vase (76x63cm-30x25in) s. 14-May-4 Skinner, Boston #351/R
£323 $600 €472 Floral still life (53x43cm-21x17in) s. masonite. 6-Mar-4 Dan Ripley, Indianapolis #254
£2374 $4250 €3466 At the ball (64x76cm-25x30in) s. prov. 6-May-4 Shannon's, Milford #149/R est:5000-7000
£3911 $7000 €5710 Costume ball (61x76cm-24x30in) estate st.verso prov. 6-May-4 Shannon's, Milford #147/R est:6000-8000
£4790 $8000 €6993 Waiting for breakfast (76x91cm-30x36in) s. prov. 23-Oct-3 Shannon's, Milford #197/R est:4000-6000

BRYANT, H C (fl.1860-1880) British
£1600 $2976 €2336 Cock with hens and ducks (25x27cm-10x11in) s. board. 4-Mar-4 Christie's, Kensington #598/R est:600-800
£1800 $2844 €2610 Returning from the fields (51x76cm-20x30in) s. 4-Sep-3 Christie's, Kensington #282/R est:2000-3000
£5000 $7900 €7250 Flower and vegetable market (102x61cm-40x24in) s.d.1885. 4-Sep-3 Christie's, Kensington #276/R est:4000-6000

BRYANT, Henry C (fl.1860-1880) British
£600 $1062 €876 Pig and carrot (27x37cm-11x15in) s. 27-Apr-4 Henry Adams, Chichester #696
£700 $1169 €1022 Golden sunset (51x77cm-20x30in) s.d.1909. 21-Oct-3 Sworder & Son, Bishops Stortford #304/R
£700 $1253 €1022 Turkey and a toad (30x35cm-12x14in) s. panel. 11-May-4 Bonhams, Knightsbridge #212/R
£2200 $3652 €3212 Farmyard scene with cattle watering (51x76cm-20x30in) s. 1-Oct-3 Sotheby's, Olympia #39/R est:1000-1500

BRYANT, Henry C (attrib) (fl.1860-1880) British
£500 $850 €730 Young girl feeding chickens, geese, turkeys and ducks, a lamb by her side (35x46cm-14x18in) 19-Nov-3 Tennants, Leyburn #1246

BRYANT, Maude Drein (1880-1946) American
£465 $800 €679 Impressionist landscape, April morning (20x30cm-8x12in) s. board. 6-Dec-3 Pook & Pook, Downington #391a/R
£1887 $3000 €2755 Still life with several pitchers, one with flowers (64x76cm-25x30in) s. 10-Sep-3 Alderfer's, Hatfield #451/R est:4000-6000

BRYCE, Gordon (1943-) British
£350 $651 €511 Roberton by Hawick (29x38cm-11x15in) s.d.90 oil on paper prov. 4-Mar-4 Christie's, Kensington #237/R
£600 $1116 €876 Blue landscape (89x81cm-35x32in) s. s.d.69. 4-Mar-4 Christie's, Kensington #240/R
£750 $1373 €1095 Morning light, North Sea (43x48cm-17x19in) s. s.i.verso canvasboard. 8-Apr-4 Bonhams, Edinburgh #8/R
£1050 $1691 €1523 Fruits and fan (21x29cm-8x11in) s. i.verso board. 21-Aug-3 Bonhams, Edinburgh #1001/R est:1000-1500

BRYDEN, Breten (1961-) American
Works on paper
£261 $425 €381 Heritage Museum (36x25cm-14x10in) s. W/C. 19-Jul-3 Outer Cape Auctions, Provincetown #99/R

BRYDON, Charles (fl.1880-1901) British
Works on paper
£317 $529 €463 Untitled - harbour scene (26x41cm-10x16in) s. W/C. 17-Nov-3 Hodgins, Calgary #41/R (C.D 700)

BRYEN, Camille (1907-1977) French
£1667 $3000 €2500 Composition (27x22cm-11x9in) s.s.d.56 verso. 24-Apr-4 Cornette de St.Cyr, Paris #458 est:3000
£1700 $3060 €2550 Chiffonnette pour Jacqueline (35x27cm-14x11in) s. s.i.d.1976 verso oil collage. 24-Apr-4 Cornette de St.Cyr, Paris #459/R
£2937 $5052 €4200 Composition abstraite (73x60cm-29x24in) s. prov. 4-Dec-3 Piasa, Paris #61/R est:3000-4000
£3333 $6000 €5000 Composition 151 (46x38cm-18x15in) s. exhib. 24-Apr-4 Cornette de St.Cyr, Paris #460 est:6000
£3380 $5848 €4800 Fusee (65x54cm-26x21in) s. s.i.d.1969 verso prov.lit. 14-Dec-3 Versailles Encheres #123/R est:5000-6000
£3867 $6960 €5800 Synego (81x50cm-32x20in) mono.d.1949 panel. 24-Apr-4 Cornette de St.Cyr, Paris #463/R est:4000
£4514 $7132 €6500 Mars (65x54cm-26x21in) s. prov.exhib.lit. 27-Apr-3 Versailles Encheres #36
£4698 $8645 €7000 Existe en ciel (65x54cm-26x21in) s. painted 1962 prov.exhib.lit. 29-Mar-4 Cornette de St.Cyr, Paris #14/R est:7000-8000
£5000 $9000 €7500 Untitled 104 (73x59cm-29x23in) s. painted 1957. 24-Apr-4 Cornette de St.Cyr, Paris #461/R est:8000
£5467 $9840 €8200 Tourbillonaire (92x73cm-36x29in) s.d.1962 s.i.d.verso prov.exhib.lit. 24-Apr-4 Cornette de St.Cyr, Paris #466/R est:10000-12000
Works on paper
£315 $535 €450 Composition (24x20cm-9x8in) studio st. i.verso Indian ink prov. 23-Nov-3 Cornette de St.Cyr, Paris #32/R
£333 $600 €500 Composition (26x19cm-10x7in) s.d.1957 Chinese ink. 24-Apr-4 Cornette de St.Cyr, Paris #465
£372 $702 €550 Composition (40x32cm-16x13in) studio st. ink. 21-Feb-4 Cornette de St.Cyr, Paris #253
£505 $843 €732 Composition (27x21cm-11x8in) s.d.61 bodycol W/C. 19-Jun-3 Kornfeld, Bern #230 (S.FR 1100)
£524 $902 €750 Sans titre (30x24cm-12x9in) s.d.64 W/C gouache canvas. 4-Dec-3 Piasa, Paris #60/R
£550 $919 €798 Composition (32x25cm-13x10in) s. bodycol W/C. 19-Jun-3 Kornfeld, Bern #231 (S.FR 1200)
£704 $1218 €1000 Composition (30x23cm-12x9in) s. s.verso gouache prov. 9-Dec-3 Artcurial Briest, Paris #503
£789 $1453 €1200 Composition (36x26cm-14x10in) s. gouache prov. 27-Jun-4 Versailles Encheres #21/R
£1333 $2400 €2000 Composition (33x26cm-13x10in) s. gouache. 24-Apr-4 Cornette de St.Cyr, Paris #462/R est:1200

BRYER, Cornelis de (17th C) Flemish
£4000 $6800 €5840 Still life with gapes, plums, cherries and a songbirds (31x43cm-12x17in) s. 30-Oct-3 Sotheby's, Olympia #11/R est:4000-6000
£6000 $10200 €8760 Still life with grapes, figs, walnuts on a stone ledge (31x43cm-12x17in) s. 30-Oct-3 Sotheby's, Olympia #10/R est:6000-8000

BRYERS, Duane (1911-) American
£1131 $1889 €1651 His favorite hat (40x50cm-16x20in) s.i. board. 17-Nov-3 Hodgins, Calgary #176/R est:3000-4000 (C.D 2500)
£1955 $3500 €2854 His favourite hat (41x51cm-16x20in) board. 15-May-4 Altermann Galleries, Santa Fe #100/R
£3073 $5500 €4487 Campfire reflections (41x51cm-16x20in) 15-May-4 Altermann Galleries, Santa Fe #99/R

BRYMNER, William (1855-1925) Canadian
£844 $1461 €1232 Lake View through the trees (12x18cm-5x7in) s. board prov. 9-Dec-3 Pinneys, Montreal #20 (C.D 1900)
£1626 $2911 €2374 Country cottage (15x24cm-6x9in) s. board. 27-May-4 Heffel, Vancouver #81/R est:2500-3500 (C.D 4000)
£2140 $3638 €3124 Ross Peak (36x54cm-14x21in) s.i. prov. 27-Nov-3 Heffel, Vancouver #163/R est:3500-4500 (C.D 4750)
£2439 $4366 €3561 River landscape, France (23x32cm-9x13in) s.d.1891 panel prov. 31-May-4 Sotheby's, Toronto #84/R est:2500-3500 (C.D 6000)
£12000 $22680 €17520 Boat on a lake, farmstead beyond (75x102cm-30x40in) s.d.13. 19-Feb-4 Christie's, Kensington #196/R est:1200-1800
Works on paper
£800 $1464 €1168 Wharf (24x36cm-9x14in) s. W/C. 1-Jun-4 Joyner Waddington, Toronto #245/R est:1200-1500 (C.D 2000)
£1411 $2597 €2060 Evening, Ste Famille, Quebec (49x37cm-19x15in) s. i.verso W/C exec. c.1921 prov. 9-Jun-4 Walker's, Ottawa #115/R est:3000-4000 (C.D 3500)
£2009 $3455 €2933 Young man in a metal smith's shop (22x35cm-9x14in) s.d.1895 W/C. 2-Dec-3 Joyner Waddington, Toronto #244/R est:2500-3500 (C.D 4500)

BRYMNER, William (attrib) (1855-1925) Canadian
£360 $613 €526 Drying the laundry (28x43cm-11x17in) panel. 21-Nov-3 Walker's, Ottawa #63/R (C.D 800)

BRYN, Oscar M (20th C) American
£2395 $4000 €3497 Texas (56x41cm-22x16in) board. 18-Oct-3 David Dike, Dallas #204/R est:2000-4000

BRYSON, Hilary (20th C) British?
Works on paper
£250 $410 €365 After the finish (35x55cm-14x22in) s. pastel. 4-Jun-3 John Ross, Belfast #99
£280 $512 €409 Cross country (40x50cm-16x20in) s. pastel. 2-Jun-4 John Ross, Belfast #207

BRYSTORP, O (19/20th C) Norwegian
£1869 $2953 €2710 Norwegian fjord landscapes (74x47cm-29x19in) s. pair. 2-Sep-3 Rasmussen, Copenhagen #1674/R est:25000 (D.KR 20000)

BRZECHWA, Krystyna (1928-) Polish
£706 $1278 €1059 Composition with people (130x114cm-51x45in) s.d.93. 4-Apr-4 Agra, Warsaw #54/R (P.Z 5000)

BRZESKI, Janusz Maria (1907-1957) Polish
Works on paper
£810 $1345 €1183 One, two, three (59x38cm-23x15in) gouache photomontage. 2-Oct-3 Agra, Warsaw #28/R (P.Z 5300)

BRZOZOWSKI, Felix (1836-1892) Polish
£553 $1024 €807 River landscape (12x18cm-5x7in) 14-Mar-4 Agra, Warsaw #19/R (P.Z 4000)

BRZOZOWSKI, Tadeusz (1918-1987) Polish
£1034 $1728 €1500 Untitled (15x11cm-6x4in) s.d.1948-52 panel. 16-Nov-3 Agra, Warsaw #44/R est:1000
£1793 $2994 €2600 Tax collector (21x12cm-8x5in) s.i.d.1986 verso panel. 16-Nov-3 Agra, Warsaw #43/R est:1000
£7440 $12798 €10862 Candlestick (55x46cm-22x18in) s.d.1960 i.verso. 4-Dec-3 Agra, Warsaw #13/R est:19000 (P.Z 50000)
£13793 $23034 €20000 Abstract green figure (163x65cm-64x26in) s.i.d.1981 verso exhib.lit. 16-Nov-3 Agra, Warsaw #14/R est:10000
£18362 $33234 €26809 Composition (68x107cm-27x42in) s.d.1967. 4-Apr-4 Agra, Warsaw #10/R (P.Z 130000)
Works on paper
£297 $532 €434 Seated girl (48x33cm-19x13in) wash exec.1945-1954. 6-May-4 Agra, Warsaw #44/R (P.Z 2100)
£1427 $2582 €2083 Composition (48x69cm-19x27in) s.d.70 Indian ink pen. 4-Apr-4 Agra, Warsaw #68/R (P.Z 10100)
£2401 $4346 €3505 Composition (63x48cm-25x19in) s.d.65 Indian ink pen. 4-Apr-4 Agra, Warsaw #70/R (P.Z 17000)
£3448 $5759 €5000 Mankind made to look like poached eggs (49x39cm-19x15in) s.d.86 s.i.d.verso ink pen. 16-Nov-3 Agra, Warsaw #67/R est:1000

BSTANDIG, Johanna (20th C) Austrian
£411 $699 €600 Farmstead by wood in lower Austria (100x80cm-39x31in) 5-Nov-3 Dorotheum, Vienna #33/R

BUBENICEK, Ota (1871-1962) Czechoslovakian
£245 $450 €358 View over distant hills (33x51cm-13x20in) s. board. 26-Jun-4 Sloans & Kenyon, Bethesda #1056/R
£316 $557 €474 Path to a village (33x49cm-13x19in) s. cardboard. 22-May-4 Dorotheum, Prague #60/R est:15000-23000 (C.KR 15000)
£350 $581 €511 Spring landscape (26x27cm-10x11in) s. board. 4-Oct-3 Dorotheum, Prague #64/R est:12000-18000 (C.KR 16000)
£371 $689 €542 Building under trees (34x49cm-13x19in) s. board. 6-Mar-4 Dorotheum, Prague #89 est:18000-29000 (C.KR 18000)
£372 $618 €543 Autumn late afternoon (21x39cm-8x15in) s. board. 4-Oct-3 Dorotheum, Prague #70/R est:8000-12000 (C.KR 17000)
£380 $668 €570 Landscape with buildings (34x50cm-13x20in) s. cardboard. 22-May-4 Dorotheum, Prague #69/R est:18000-27000 (C.KR 18000)
£489 $900 €714 Above the valley (25x36cm-10x14in) s. board. 26-Jun-4 Sloans & Kenyon, Bethesda #1055/R
£548 $965 €822 Little cottages (33x47cm-13x19in) s.d. cardboard. 22-May-4 Dorotheum, Prague #68/R est:26000-42000 (C.KR 26000)
£591 $1039 €887 Landscape near Kamenicky (37x47cm-15x19in) s.d.18 cardboard. 22-May-4 Dorotheum, Prague #61/R est:18000-28000 (C.KR 28000)

BUBERL, Caspar (1834-1899) American
Sculpture
£2874 $4800 €4196 Newspaper boy (51cm-20in) s.i.d.1888 brown pat bronze. 23-Oct-3 Shannon's, Milford #101/R est:1800-2200

BUBNIC, Maria Clemence (1909-) French
£233 $420 €350 La chasse a courre (45x55cm-18x22in) s. 26-Apr-4 Tajan, Paris #333
£1067 $1941 €1600 Village covered in snow (46x55cm-18x22in) s. 4-Jul-4 Eric Pillon, Calais #256/R

BUCAILLE, Max (1906-1992) French
Works on paper
£909 $1564 €1300 La mesure du temps local d'un abime (13x9cm-5x4in) s.d.1939 collage exhib. 6-Dec-3 Renaud, Paris #37
£1259 $2165 €1800 Toutes les bastilles (14x14cm-6x6in) s.d.1959 collage. 6-Dec-3 Renaud, Paris #38/R

BUCCHI, Danilo (1978-) Italian
Works on paper
£352 $585 €500 Untitled (50x150cm-20x59in) s.i.verso mixed media silicone canvas. 14-Jun-3 Meeting Art, Vercelli #16/R
£352 $585 €500 Stiamo alternando le idee, cambiando i costumi modificando gli stili (106x88cm-42x35in) s.i.d.2002 mixed media silicone panel. 14-Jun-3 Meeting Art, Vercelli #303/R
£671 $1242 €1000 Kiss my soul (80x120cm-31x47in) s.i.d.2003 mixed media collage on canvas in 2 parts. 13-Mar-4 Meeting Art, Vercelli #374
£940 $1738 €1400 Raffaella (50x50cm-20x20in) s.i.d.2003 mixed media collage on canvas in 3 pieces. 13-Mar-4 Meeting Art, Vercelli #65

BUCCHI, Ermocrate (1842-1885) Italian
£1606 $2681 €2329 Still life of flowers (55x39cm-22x15in) s. 23-Jun-3 Philippe Schuler, Zurich #3510/R est:2000-2500 (S.FR 3500)

BUCCI, Anselmo (1887-1955) Italian
£4422 $7915 €6500 Autumn flowers (92x70cm-36x28in) s.d.29 prov.lit. 16-Mar-4 Finarte Semenzato, Milan #454/R est:6000
£4762 $8524 €7000 Lilies and peach flowers (92x73cm-36x29in) s.d.31. 16-Mar-4 Finarte Semenzato, Milan #453/R est:6000
£11409 $20423 €17000 Storm in Milan (77x90cm-30x35in) s.d.1921 s.i.d.verso. 30-May-4 Meeting Art, Vercelli #77 est:15000
Works on paper
£1007 $1802 €1500 Voiture du charbonnier (21x16cm-8x6in) s.i.d.1914 ink. 25-May-4 Sotheby's, Milan #30/R

BUCCI, Mario (1903-1970) Italian
£228 $409 €340 Still life (38x48cm-15x19in) s. s.i.d.1944 verso. 25-May-4 Finarte Semenzato, Milan #73
£318 $579 €480 Vase of flowers (60x50cm-24x20in) s. 17-Jun-4 Galleria Pananti, Florence #519/R

BUCCIARELLI, Daniele (1839-1911) Italian
Works on paper
£500 $925 €730 Fisherfolk on the shore (33x53cm-13x21in) s.i. W/C. 14-Jul-4 Bonhams, Chester #398
£655 $1212 €950 Napolitaine admirant son collier (45x31cm-18x12in) s. W/C. 16-Feb-4 Horta, Bruxelles #505

BUCH, Hugo Arne (20th C) Danish?
£280 $523 €409 Composition (120x66cm-47x26in) s.d.1958 verso exhib. 25-Feb-4 Kunsthallen, Copenhagen #92 (D.KR 3100)
£406 $759 €593 Rod Akcent (90x150cm-35x59in) s.d.1958 verso exhib. 25-Feb-4 Kunsthallen, Copenhagen #172 (D.KR 4500)

BUCH, Karl Hermann (1901-1988) German
Works on paper
£336 $617 €500 Farmstead on shore with sailing boats near Nidden (48x65cm-19x26in) s.d.43 pastel. 26-Mar-4 Venator & Hansten, Koln #1682/R

BUCHAL, Charles (20th C) British
£16000 $24800 €23360 Sir Ernest Henry Shackleton, wearing a blue jacket (61x51cm-24x20in) s.i.d.1921 prov. 25-Sep-2 Christie's, London #384/R est:10000-15000

BUCHANAN, Dean (1952-) New Zealander
£435 $700 €635 Browns Island (100x164cm-39x65in) s.d.2002. 12-Aug-3 Peter Webb, Auckland #236/R (NZ.D 1200)
£478 $894 €698 Karekare (38x54cm-15x21in) s.d.1991. 24-Feb-4 Peter Webb, Auckland #44/R (NZ.D 1300)
£519 $929 €758 Bird bath - night (173x133cm-68x52in) s.d.1988. 11-May-4 Peter Webb, Auckland #194/R est:1500-2000 (NZ.D 1500)
£543 $924 €793 Bird bath, day (147x112cm-58x44in) s.d.d1988. 4-Nov-3 Peter Webb, Auckland #261/R est:1500-2000 (NZ.D 1500)
£558 $959 €815 Waterfall (82x32cm-32x13in) s.d.2001 oil hessian. 7-Dec-3 International Art Centre, Auckland #328/R (NZ.D 1500)
£929 $1709 €1356 Taupo to the mountain (93x154cm-37x61in) s. 25-Mar-4 International Art Centre, Auckland #160/R (NZ.D 2600)

BUCHANAN, E Oughtred (1883-1979) British
£380 $646 €555 Iona (34x42cm-13x17in) s. board. 10-Nov-3 Thomson Roddick & Medcalf, Edinburgh #259
£450 $765 €657 Old reekie (80x95cm-31x37in) s. board. 10-Nov-3 Thomson Roddick & Medcalf, Edinburgh #260

BUCHANAN, George F (fl.1848-1864) British
£1000 $1670 €1460 Loch Riddon, figures in foreground, thatched cottage (61x91cm-24x36in) 18-Jun-3 John Nicholson, Haslemere #741/R est:800-1500
£1600 $2976 €2336 Inverary, Argyll (30x71cm-12x28in) s.d.1845 i.on stretcher. 4-Mar-4 Christie's, Kensington #24/R est:1000-1500

BUCHANAN, Peter Ronald (20th C) British
Works on paper
£340 $568 €496 Mr P Roberts dreams he rides a National winner (35x24cm-14x9in) s.i. W/C. 14-Oct-3 Bonhams, Knightsbridge #33/R

BUCHANAN, Peter S (fl.1860-1911) British
£460 $851 €672 Scottish loch at harvest time (55x90cm-22x35in) s. 16-Feb-4 Bonhams, Bath #168
£720 $1152 €1051 Little duck girl (45x75cm-18x30in) s. 18-Sep-3 Bonhams, Edinburgh #315

BUCHARD, Pablo (20th C) Spanish
£3289 $6053 €5000 Come with me, American love (195x150cm-77x59in) s.d.77 exhib. 22-Jun-4 Durán, Madrid #199/R est:5000

BUCHBERGER, Gottfried (1909-1998) Austrian
Sculpture
£1034 $1893 €1500 Reader (47cm-19in) i. dark light pat.bronze bronze. 27-Jan-4 Dorotheum, Vienna #216/R est:1600-2400

BUCHBINDER, Simeon (1853-1908) Polish
£1250 $2088 €1825 Portrait of a man with a hat (17x13cm-7x5in) s.d.92 cardboard. 19-Oct-3 Agra, Warsaw #43/R est:7000 (P.Z 8000)
£3395 $5975 €4957 Monk reading (18x25cm-7x10in) s. panel. 23-May-4 Agra, Warsaw #16/R (P.Z 24000)

BUCHE, Josef (1848-1917) Austrian
£662 $1212 €1000 Boy's portrait (52x42cm-20x17in) s. 8-Apr-4 Dorotheum, Vienna #268/R
£2333 $4247 €3500 Two peasant girls (151x114cm-59x45in) s. 30-Jun-4 Neumeister, Munich #518/R est:2000
£2685 $4805 €4000 Idyllic rural scene (41x52cm-16x20in) s.d.1875 panel. 27-May-4 Dorotheum, Vienna #186/R est:3000-3500

BUCHEL, Charles A (1872-1950) British
£260 $434 €380 Portrait of a lady (46x35cm-18x14in) s.d.1900. 11-Nov-3 Bonhams, Knightsbridge #114/R
£260 $468 €380 Portrait of Cornelis van der Geest (60x50cm-24x20in) s. s.stretcher. 22-Apr-4 Lawrence, Crewkerne #937
£300 $558 €438 Still life of flowers in copper jug (44x37cm-17x15in) s. board. 2-Mar-4 Bearnes, Exeter #449/R
£560 $1042 €818 Still life of roses and summer flowers (62x70cm-24x28in) s.d.1933 board. 2-Mar-4 Bearnes, Exeter #448/R
£1700 $3162 €2482 Portrait of Miss Barbara Hare (90x70cm-35x28in) s. 2-Mar-4 Bearnes, Exeter #470/R est:600-900

BUCHEL, Jules (1866-1900) Belgian
£1863 $3000 €2720 Au bord de la mer (27x46cm-11x18in) s.d.1885. 14-Jan-4 Christie's, Rockefeller NY #44/R est:2500-3500

BUCHER, Carl (1935-) Swiss
£1810 $3077 €2643 Landing 48 (200x125cm-79x49in) s.i.d.1967 verso panel prov.exhib.lit. 25-Nov-3 Germann, Zurich #5/R est:4500-6500 (S.FR 4000)

BUCHET, Gustave (1888-1963) Swiss
£3448 $6172 €5034 Nu assis (70x98cm-28x39in) s. board. 14-May-4 Dobiaschofsky, Bern #164/R est:14000 (S.FR 8000)
£8734 $15633 €12752 Deux nus. Composition study (25x33cm-10x13in) s.d.1941 board double-sided. 26-May-4 Sotheby's, Zurich #104/R est:20000-30000 (S.FR 20000)
£9955 $17222 €14534 Bord du Lac Leman (54x73cm-21x29in) s.d.1948. 9-Dec-3 Sotheby's, Zurich #93/R est:18000-25000 (S.FR 22000)
£12664 $22668 €18489 Trois femmes (46x38cm-18x15in) s.d.1930. 26-May-4 Sotheby's, Zurich #91/R est:30000-40000 (S.FR 29000)
£50218 $89891 €73318 Composition cubist. Nature morte avec vase, pipes et livre (77x60cm-30x24in) s.d.1926 s.d.1940 verso double-sided. 26-May-4 Sotheby's, Zurich #49/R est:80000-120000 (S.FR 115000)
Works on paper
£1256 $2097 €1834 Street between trees and houses (41x26cm-16x10in) s. wash Indian ink brush. 24-Oct-3 Hans Widmer, St Gallen #21/R est:1800-4500 (S.FR 2800)
£1928 $3220 €2815 Female nude (52x38cm-20x15in) W/C. 24-Oct-3 Hans Widmer, St Gallen #66/R est:2500-6500 (S.FR 4300)

BUCHETTI, Arturo (1911-) Italian
£514 $801 €750 Reclining nude (76x60cm-30x24in) s.d.32 board double-sided. 8-Apr-3 Il Ponte, Milan #641

BUCHHEISTER, Carl (1890-1964) German
£738 $1358 €1100 Composition Fluc (30x31cm-12x12in) s.i.d. verso oil gouache Indian ink prov. 26-Mar-4 Ketterer, Hamburg #341/R
£1399 $2406 €2000 Composition hoko 8 (33x28cm-13x11in) s.i.d. verso masonite prov.exhib. 5-Dec-3 Ketterer, Munich #321/R est:3000-4000
Works on paper
£533 $976 €800 French landscape (22x27cm-9x11in) s.i.d.1918 mono.d.15 col chk board. 5-Jun-4 Lempertz, Koln #621/R
£810 $1344 €1150 Composition WE 5. s.i.d.1953/54 verso gouache Indian ink. 13-Jun-3 Hauswedell & Nolte, Hamburg #579/R
£4196 $7133 €6000 Composition FE 10 (50x65cm-20x26in) s.i.d.10/1954 mixed media board prov.exhib. 29-Nov-3 Villa Grisebach, Berlin #289/R est:6000-8000

BUCHHOLZ, Erich (1891-1972) German
Sculpture
£2491 $4409 €3637 Relief (20x29cm-8x11in) s.d.1972 verso painted wood leaf gold. 27-Apr-4 AB Stockholms Auktionsverk #1001/R est:40000-50000 (S.KR 34000)
£20979 $35664 €30000 Red circle in gold circle - red circle in black (72x52x300cm-28x20x118in) s.mono.i.d.1922 verso wood relief prov.exhib.lit. 26-Nov-3 Lempertz, Koln #611/R est:30000-40000

BUCHHOLZ, Karl (1849-1889) German
£690 $1152 €1000 Wooded landscape near Weimar (20x32cm-8x13in) panel prov. 15-Nov-3 Lempertz, Koln #1586/R est:1300
£3793 $7017 €5500 Woodland in late autumn (32x39cm-13x15in) s.d.73. 14-Feb-4 Hans Stahl, Hamburg #11/R est:1500

BUCHHOLZ, Paul (1868-?) German
£692 $1191 €990 View of the Jenischhaus in Hamburg (65x88cm-26x35in) s. 6-Dec-3 Hans Stahl, Toestorf #100/R

BUCHHOLZ, Wolff (1935-) German
£540 $885 €750 Untitled (120x100cm-47x39in) s.d.1972 verso. 4-Jun-3 Ketterer, Hamburg #210/R

BUCHLER, Edouard (1861-?) Austrian
£661 $1123 €965 Monopteros on rocky coast (101x70cm-40x28in) s. 5-Nov-3 Dobiaschofsky, Bern #403/R (S.FR 1500)

BUCHMANN, Wilfried (1878-1933) Swiss
£839 $1560 €1250 On the way to the fields (100x60cm-39x24in) s.d.33 panel. 5-Mar-4 Wendl, Rudolstadt #3600/R

BUCHNER, Carl (1921-2003) South African
£274 $465 €400 Young man wearing a red headscarf (41x26cm-16x10in) s. 4-Nov-3 Stephan Welz, Johannesburg #652 est:3500-5000 (SA.R 3200)
£776 $1296 €1133 Head of a young woman (49x37cm-19x15in) s. board. 20-Oct-3 Stephan Welz, Johannesburg #648 est:2000-3000 (SA.R 9000)
£991 $1774 €1447 Boats in a harbour (49x70cm-19x28in) s. paper on board. 31-May-4 Stephan Welz, Johannesburg #549/R (SA.R 12000)
£1282 $2179 €1872 Still life of a bowl of fruit in a table (40x60cm-16x24in) s. board. 4-Nov-3 Stephan Welz, Johannesburg #701 est:2500-4000 (SA.R 15000)
£1552 $2591 €2266 Head of a harlequin (51x35cm-20x14in) s. board. 20-Oct-3 Stephan Welz, Johannesburg #346/R est:9000-12000 (SA.R 18000)
£1569 $2808 €2291 Harlequin resting his head in his hand (59x36cm-23x14in) s. card. 31-May-4 Stephan Welz, Johannesburg #570/R est:12000-18000 (SA.R 19000)
£1597 $2890 €2332 Harlequin (61x49cm-24x19in) s. board. 30-Mar-4 Stephan Welz, Johannesburg #491/R est:12000-16000 (SA.R 19000)
£1849 $3346 €2700 Musician with a mandolin (101x77cm-40x30in) s. board. 30-Mar-4 Stephan Welz, Johannesburg #494/R est:14000-18000 (SA.R 22000)
£1897 $3167 €2770 Harlequin with mandolin (90x90cm-35x35in) s. 20-Oct-3 Stephan Welz, Johannesburg #322/R est:18000-24000 (SA.R 22000)
£3468 $6208 €5063 Mandolin player (100x74cm-39x29in) s. board. 31-May-4 Stephan Welz, Johannesburg #605/R est:16000-20000 (SA.R 42000)

BUCHNER, Georg (1858-1914) German
£625 $1019 €900 Portrait of red haired girl (29x23cm-11x9in) s. 26-Sep-3 Bolland & Marotz, Bremen #504/R
£1014 $1744 €1450 Young girl wearing traditional costume (26x22cm-10x9in) s. 3-Dec-3 Neumeister, Munich #540/R

BUCHNER, Gustav Johann (1880-1951) German
£321 $600 €469 Young girl seated in the sunlight (56x38cm-22x15in) s.d.1935. 25-Feb-4 Doyle, New York #38/R

BUCHNER, Hans (1856-1941) German
£420 $701 €600 Carnations (70x85cm-28x33in) s.i. 27-Jun-3 Michael Zeller, Lindau #502/R
£538 $899 €770 Still life of fruit and flowers (67x97cm-26x38in) s. 27-Jun-3 Michael Zeller, Lindau #501/R
£559 $962 €800 Still life of fruit and flowers (67x97cm-26x38in) s. 5-Dec-3 Michael Zeller, Lindau #584/R
£2006 $3710 €2929 Still life with flower in a vase (74x56cm-29x22in) 14-Mar-4 Agra, Warsaw #1/R (P.Z 14500)
£4841 $8375 €7068 Carnations (70x85cm-28x33in) s. painted c.1900. 14-Dec-3 Agra, Warsaw #1/R est:5000 (P.Z 32000)

BUCHNER, Karl Sebastian (?) ?
£423 $739 €600 Still life with bottle. s.d.20. 17-Dec-3 Il Ponte, Milan #485

BUCHNER, Rudolf (1894-1962) Austrian
£690 $1262 €1000 Flowers (74x64cm-29x25in) mono. 27-Jan-4 Dorotheum, Vienna #104/R
£769 $1323 €1100 Colourful bunch of flowers in a vase (72x60cm-28x24in) s. plywood. 4-Dec-3 Dorotheum, Graz #5/R
£3472 $5903 €5000 View of Vienna from Nussberg (62x85cm-24x33in) s.d.1947 i. verso board. 28-Oct-3 Wiener Kunst Auktionen, Vienna #114/R est:5000-12000

BUCHSEL, Elisabeth (1867-1957) German
£461 $747 €650 Farmstead (31x43cm-12x17in) mono.d.1948 board lit. 23-May-3 Karlheinz Kaupp, Staufen #1806/R

BUCHSER, Frank (1828-1890) Swiss
£800 $1480 €1168 Landscape with cathedral beyond (38x55cm-15x22in) 14-Jul-4 Sotheby's, Olympia #145/R
£2703 $4649 €3946 Brown horse in stable (46x62cm-18x24in) i. verso board. 2-Dec-3 Koller, Zurich #3005/R est:6000-9000 (S.FR 6000)
£3378 $5811 €4932 Beach (23x31cm-9x12in) mono. 2-Dec-3 Koller, Zurich #3042/R est:6000-10000 (S.FR 7500)
£4310 $7716 €6293 Girl on beach (23x15cm-9x6in) mono. board. 17-May-4 Beurret, Zurich #34/R est:4000-6000 (S.FR 10000)
£5172 $9259 €7551 North African with drum standing by stone wall (50x24cm-20x9in) mono. exhib. 17-May-4 Beurret, Zurich #33/R est:6000-8000 (S.FR 12000)
£15721 $28611 €22953 Irene, presumed to be Miss Maud Hurst (24x17cm-9x7in) s. cardboard exec. 1875-76 prov.exhib.lit. 18-Jun-4 Kornfeld, Bern #11/R est:40000 (S.FR 36000)
£16143 $26314 €23569 Family in the mountains in evening (82x107cm-32x42in) oval lit. 29-Sep-3 Christie's, Zurich #13/R est:35000-45000 (S.FR 36000)
£51724 $92586 €75517 Girl on beach carrying something on head (76x51cm-30x20in) s. prov.exhib. 17-May-4 Beurret, Zurich #35/R est:30000-40000 (S.FR 120000)

BUCHTA, Anthony (1896-1967) American
£218 $350 €318 Summer clouds (20x25cm-8x10in) s. board painted c.1950. 17-May-3 Bunte, Elgin #1303
£313 $500 €457 Mid summer (20x25cm-8x10in) s. canvasboard. 17-May-3 Bunte, Elgin #1302
£343 $550 €501 Blossom time (20x25cm-8x10in) s. board. 17-May-3 Bunte, Elgin #1301

BUCK, Adam (1759-1833) British
Works on paper
£600 $1074 €876 Portrait of a gentleman, half-length, with black neck tie and brown coat (13x14cm-5x6in) s.d.1832 pencil W/C gum arabic scratching out prov. 14-May-4 Christie's, London #8/R
£1600 $2864 €2336 Portrait of a lady, full-length, in a landscape (29x39cm-11x15in) s.i.d.1803 i.verso pencil W/C htd white prov. 14-May-4 Christie's, London #7/R est:1200-1800
£2400 $4296 €3504 The piano lesson (41x41cm-16x16in) s.d.1800 W/C. 4-May-4 Gorringes, Bexhill #1376/R est:800-1200

BUCK, Adam (attrib) (1759-1833) British
Works on paper
£600 $1074 €876 Portrait of James Hornby Bond. Portrait of Anne Wensley Bond (38x28cm-15x11in) waxed crayon drawings pair. 17-Mar-4 Bonhams, Chester #411

BUCK, Claude (1890-1974) American
£860 $1600 €1256 Shepherd with his flock (30x41cm-12x16in) s. painted c.1919. 7-Mar-4 Treadway Gallery, Cincinnati #556/R est:1000-2000
£1258 $2000 €1837 Symbolist landscape (36x20cm-14x8in) s. panel. 23-Mar-3 Auctions by the Bay, Alameda #860/R
£2235 $4000 €3353 Jewel of the Oceans (51x61cm-20x24in) s. 16-May-4 Abell, Los Angeles #431/R

BUCK, Evariste de (1892-1974) Belgian
£800 $1448 €1200 La ferme (56x74cm-22x29in) s. 30-Mar-4 Campo, Vlaamse Kaai #27
£1667 $2783 €2400 Landscape with river (70x80cm-28x31in) s.d.1927. 21-Oct-3 Campo & Campo, Antwerp #56/R est:2000-3000
£1806 $3015 €2600 Fruit defendu (135x95cm-53x37in) s.d.1924. 21-Oct-3 Campo & Campo, Antwerp #57 est:1500-2000
£2837 $4738 €4000 Bathing nude (152x106cm-60x42in) s. 20-Oct-3 Bernaerts, Antwerp #281/R est:4000-5000
£5263 $9526 €8000 Coucher de soleil sur un paysage enneige avec meules (110x150cm-43x59in) s. 19-Apr-4 Horta, Bruxelles #106/R est:10000-12000

BUCK, Frederick (1771-1840) Irish
Miniatures
£1500 $2550 €2190 Young field officer (6cm-2in) gold frame oval. 18-Nov-3 Bonhams, New Bond Street #101/R est:600-800

BUCK, Frederick (attrib) (1771-1840) Irish
Miniatures
£4324 $8000 €6313 Portrait of a gentleman in uniform (5x5cm-2x2in) oval. 12-Mar-4 Du Mouchelle, Detroit #2037/R est:1500-2000

BUCK, John (1946-) American
£341 $600 €498 Untitled (213x107cm-84x42in) s.i.d.82 acrylic on paper. 23-May-4 Bonhams & Butterfields, Los Angeles #7030/R

BUCK, Rafael de (1902-1986) Belgian
£455 $759 €650 Three woman (70x60cm-28x24in) s. 11-Oct-3 De Vuyst, Lokeren #94
Works on paper
£541 $968 €800 Elegantes (63x53cm-25x21in) s. W/C. 10-May-4 Horta, Bruxelles #492

BUCK, Samucl (attrib) (18th C) British
£1000 $1790 €1460 Prospect of Norman Castle (67x127cm-26x50in) 28-May-4 Lyon & Turnbull, Edinburgh #21/R est:1000-1500

BUCK, William H (1840-1888) American
£9259 $15000 €13426 Bayou farm (15x31cm-6x12in) s. board prov. 8-Aug-3 Barridorf, Portland #225/R est:15000-25000

BUCKLAND, Maurice (20th C) New Zealander
£293 $542 €428 Spring snow, Mt. Talbot, upper Holyford (50x60cm-20x24in) s.d.78 board. 9-Mar-4 Watson's, Christchurch #182 (NZ.D 800)

BUCKLAND-WRIGHT, John (1897-?) New Zealander
Works on paper
£280 $501 €420 Shepherdess and child rest by a river in an extensive landscape (13x18cm-5x7in) i.d.1781 verso W/C pen ink laid paper. 27-May-4 Bloomsbury, London #38/R
£469 $750 €685 Le Zoute, Belgium (26x36cm-10x14in) s.i.d.1926 W/C. 18-Sep-3 Swann Galleries, New York #698/R
£550 $1001 €825 Young Jewish girl (28x23cm-11x9in) st.mono. pen ink wash pencil pair. 2-Jul-4 Bloomsbury, London #84/R
£700 $1275 €1050 Seduction (20x28cm-8x11in) pencil col crayon. 2-Jul-4 Bloomsbury, London #82/R
£800 $1456 €1200 Nudes gathering at a forest pool (23x29cm-9x11in) st.mono.verso pen ink wash pencil. 2-Jul-4 Bloomsbury, London #83/R

BUCKLER, Charles E (1869-?) Canadian/American
£809 $1400 €1181 Horse drawn hay cart with figures in fam setting (51x61cm-20x24in) s. 10-Dec-3 Alderfer's, Hatfield #379 est:700-900
£976 $1600 €1415 Winter landscape with stream (16x20cm-6x8in) s. painted c.1910. 7-Jun-3 Treadway Gallery, Cincinnati #1441 est:1000-2000

BUCKLER, John Chessel (1793-1894) British
Works on paper
£250 $455 €365 The Great West Entrance to Christ Church from the Quadrangle, Oxford (25x16cm-10x6in) s.i.d.1819 pencil brown ink W/C prov. 1-Jul-4 Christie's, Kensington #25/R
£700 $1302 €1022 Part of the Great Quadrangle Christ Church College, Oxford (25x36cm-10x14in) s.d.1816 W/C. 3-Mar-4 Mallams, Oxford #247/R
£1200 $2196 €1752 Transept of the Church of St Cross near Winchester (37x27cm-15x11in) s.d.1829 pencil W/C two. 7-Apr-4 Woolley & Wallis, Salisbury #143/R est:750-1000

BUCKLER, William (fl.1836-1856) British
Works on paper
£486 $900 €710 Young girl with her dog (30x41cm-12x16in) s.d.1848 W/C. 14-Jan-4 Dallas Auction Gallery, Dallas #388/R
£600 $978 €876 Portrait, a group of three young children with a dog (53x41cm-21x16in) s.d.1845 W/C. 23-Sep-3 John Nicholson, Haslemere #84/R

BUCKLEY, Charles F (fl.1841-1869) British
Works on paper
£380 $680 €555 Scene in the Isle of Wight near Shanklin (30x51cm-12x20in) s.d.1866 W/C. 7-May-4 Mallams, Oxford #166/R
£450 $765 €657 River in Spate, with ruins amongst woodland in the distance (26x36cm-10x14in) s.d.1852 pencil W/C. 19-Nov-3 Tennants, Leyburn #975
£3000 $5310 €4380 Travelers resting amid the ruins at Baalbek, Lebanon (15x22cm-6x9in) s. W/C. 27-Apr-4 Bonhams, New Bond Street #53/R est:1000-1500

BUCKLEY, J E (19th C) British
Works on paper
£1000 $1700 €1460 Ladies on a stone terrace in formal garden with other figures nearby (29x47cm-11x19in) s.d.1862 W/C bodycol. 18-Nov-3 Bonhams, Leeds #16 est:1000-1200
£1000 $1700 €1460 Two ladies with a young boy beside a stone gateway (29x48cm-11x19in) s.d.1862 W/C bodycol. 18-Nov-3 Bonhams, Leeds #17/R est:1000-1200

BUCKLEY, John E (1820-1884) British
Works on paper
£300 $555 €438 Mounted cavalier and figures outside thatched cottage (18x28cm-7x11in) s.d.1871. 12-Feb-4 Andrew Hartley, Ilkley #751
£380 $631 €555 Figures before a country house (36x64cm-14x25in) s.d.1860 W/C. 2-Oct-3 Lane, Penzance #310/R
£550 $897 €798 Crossbow contest. Hawking (34x62cm-13x24in) s.d.1873 W/C pair. 23-Sep-3 Bonhams, Knightsbridge #168/R
£700 $1204 €1022 Holland House (33x58cm-13x23in) s.d.1870 pencil W/C. 3-Dec-3 Christie's, Kensington #45/R
£800 $1264 €1168 Elegant figures feeding swans outside a moated country mansion (32x46cm-13x18in) s.d.1858 W/C. 23-Jul-3 Hampton & Littlewood, Exeter #419/R

BUCKLEY, Stephen (1944-) British
£260 $442 €380 Loft (48x106cm-19x42in) s.i.d.1987 verso canvas on wood. 18-Nov-3 Bonhams, Knightsbridge #45
£950 $1701 €1387 Abstract construction (183x295cm-72x116in) acrylic collage. 14-May-4 Christie's, Kensington #630/R
£1400 $2548 €2044 X (183x240cm-72x94in) oil varnish duck tin terylene rope perspex prov.exhib. 4-Feb-4 Sotheby's, Olympia #216/R est:1500-2000
Works on paper
£1000 $1820 €1460 Attendant (203x81cm-80x32in) s.i.d.1983 verso mixed media prov. 4-Feb-4 Sotheby's, Olympia #218/R est:1200-1800

BUCKLOW, Christopher (1957-) American
Photographs
£4790 $8000 €6993 Guest (96x73cm-38x29in) cibachrome photogram exec.1997 prov. 17-Oct-3 Phillips, New York #21/R est:5000-7000

BUCKMAN, Edwin (1841-1930) British
Works on paper
£285 $450 €416 Barnyard scene, Fordwich Kent (25x36cm-10x14in) i.verso W/C on card. 6-Sep-3 Brunk, Ashville #344

BUCKMASTER, Ernest (1897-1968) Australian
£893 $1643 €1304 Manukau harbour (60x80cm-24x31in) s. 25-Mar-4 International Art Centre, Auckland #123/R (NZ.D 2500)
£906 $1458 €1323 The Strand, Tauranga (72x107cm-28x42in) s. board. 20-Aug-3 Peter Webb, Auckland #2023/R (NZ.D 2500)
£1065 $1683 €1555 Mountains (40x38cm-16x15in) s.d.31 canvas on board. 2-Sep-3 Deutscher-Menzies, Melbourne #354/R est:1500-2500 (A.D 2600)
£1124 $2067 €1641 View of Sydney Harbour (54x81cm-21x32in) s. 28-Jun-4 Australian Art Auctions, Sydney #118 (A.D 3000)
£1128 $1917 €1647 Mt. Ruapehu from the Tongariro River (80x115cm-31x45in) s. 26-Nov-3 Dunbar Sloane, Wellington #98/R est:3000-6000 (NZ.D 3000)
£1157 $2140 €1689 Yarra River (34x56cm-13x22in) s. board prov. 10-Mar-4 Deutscher-Menzies, Melbourne #494/R est:2000-3000 (A.D 2800)
£1268 $2042 €1851 Omapere and Hokianga (89x102cm-35x40in) s. 20-Aug-3 Peter Webb, Auckland #2024/R est:3500-5500 (NZ.D 3500)
£1449 $2333 €2116 Ocean haze, Piha (91x128cm-36x50in) s. board. 20-Aug-3 Peter Webb, Auckland #2021/R est:5500-6500 (NZ.D 4000)
£1465 $2286 €2124 Afternoon light (69x92cm-27x36in) s. 1-Aug-2 Joel, Victoria #151 est:3500-4500 (A.D 4250)
£1626 $2911 €2374 Headland (63x82cm-25x32in) s. 10-May-4 Joel, Victoria #341/R est:5000-6000 (A.D 4000)
£1859 $3291 €2714 Whiteroses (37x37cm-15x15in) s. 3-May-4 Christie's, Melbourne #234/R est:3000-4000 (A.D 4500)
£1915 $3255 €2796 Still life of grapes (51x65cm-20x26in) s. painted c.1928 prov. 25-Nov-3 Christie's, Melbourne #157/R est:4500-6500 (A.D 4500)

£1953 $3652 €2930 Gippsland river loch (86x87cm-34x34in) s.d.1932 i.verso. 20-Jul-4 Goodman, Sydney #120/R est:1500-2000 (A.D 5000)
£2083 $3354 €3041 A perfect day, Wakatipu (87x108cm-34x43in) s. 20-Aug-3 Peter Webb, Auckland #2022/R est:3500-5500 (NZ.D 5750)
£2227 $3585 €3251 Still life with roses (50x39cm-20x15in) s.d.1941. 13-Oct-3 Joel, Victoria #238/R est:2500-3500 (A.D 5500)
£2254 $3562 €3291 Peninsular beach scene (89x116cm-35x46in) s. 2-Sep-3 Deutscher-Menzies, Melbourne #151/R est:9000-12000 (A.D 5500)
£2273 $4205 €3319 Riverscape (63x86cm-25x34in) s. 10-Mar-4 Deutscher-Menzies, Melbourne #493/R est:3500-4500 (A.D 5500)
£2290 $4168 €3343 Dandenongs (68x88cm-27x35in) s. 16-Jun-4 Deutscher-Menzies, Melbourne #325/R est:6000-9000 (A.D 6000)
£2341 $3979 €3418 Timber Country (76x91cm-30x36in) s. 26-Nov-3 Deutscher-Menzies, Melbourne #169/R est:3500-5000 (A.D 5500)
£2414 $3766 €3500 Autumn haze, Kallista (67x91cm-26x36in) s.d.1959. 1-Aug-2 Joel, Victoria #170 est:7000-8000 (A.D 7000)
£2429 $3911 €3546 Lancefield, Victoria (78x93cm-31x37in) s. 13-Oct-3 Joel, Victoria #349 est:5000-6000 (A.D 6000)
£2429 $3911 €3546 Grey day, Yarra Glen (54x78cm-21x31in) s.d.1943. 13-Oct-3 Joel, Victoria #393/R est:5000-6000 (A.D 6000)
£2632 $4237 €3843 River in the foothills (62x87cm-24x34in) s. 13-Oct-3 Joel, Victoria #395/R est:5000-6000 (A.D 6500)
£2642 $4729 €3857 Cloud shadows (59x88cm-23x35in) board. 10-May-4 Joel, Victoria #335 est:4000-6000 (A.D 6500)
£2683 $4802 €3917 Summer afternoon (67x85cm-26x33in) s. painted c.1960. 10-May-4 Joel, Victoria #197 est:5000-6000 (A.D 6600)
£2686 $4566 €3922 Tambo River (69x90cm-27x35in) s. 29-Oct-3 Lawson Menzies, Sydney #101/R est:4000-6000 (A.D 6500)
£2733 $4400 €3990 Hollyford Valley, New Zealand on the way Milford Sound (72x93cm-28x37in) s. canvas on board painted 1968. 13-Oct-3 Joel, Victoria #290/R est:5000-6000 (A.D 6750)
£2766 $4702 €4038 From the High Country (72x103cm-28x41in) s. 25-Nov-3 Christie's, Melbourne #208/R est:4000-6000 (A.D 6500)
£2893 $5120 €4224 Flowers in a blue vase (70x55cm-28x22in) s. painted c.1965 prov. 3-May-4 Christie's, Melbourne #282/R est:4000-6000 (A.D 7000)
£3455 $6185 €5044 River reflections, Omeo District (71x92cm-28x36in) s. painted c.1965 prov. 10-May-4 Joel, Victoria #388 est:7000-9000 (A.D 8500)
£3862 $6063 €5600 Sylvan Dam (70x110cm-28x43in) s. 26-Aug-3 Christie's, Sydney #376/R est:6000-8000 (A.D 9500)
£4065 $7276 €5935 River reflections (61x85cm-24x33in) s. 10-May-4 Joel, Victoria #203/R est:5000-6000 (A.D 10000)
Works on paper
£366 $655 €534 Little Hazel Cassidy (52x36cm-20x14in) s.d.26 chl. 10-May-4 Joel, Victoria #320a (A.D 900)

BUCKNALL, Ernest P (1861-?) British
£1400 $2590 €2044 Changing pasture at twilight (49x74cm-19x29in) s. 14-Jan-4 Lawrence, Crewkerne #1421/R est:1500-2000

BUCKNER, Richard (1812-1883) British
£2000 $3640 €3000 Three travelling Musicians resting by a town wall (102x127cm-40x50in) 20-Jun-4 Wilkinson, Doncaster #324 est:3000-4500

BUCKNER, Richard (attrib) (1812-1883) British
£1208 $2223 €1800 Woman's portrait (35x30cm-14x12in) 27-Mar-4 Sigalas, Stuttgart #244/R est:1600

BUCKSTONE, Frederick (fl.1857-1880) British
£900 $1611 €1314 Near the mill, Catford, Kent (76x58cm-30x23in) s.d.1882 i.verso. 27-May-4 Christie's, Kensington #188/R

BUDDENBERG, Wilhelm (1890-?) German
£590 $974 €850 Wild boar in snowy winter wood (60x80cm-24x31in) s. 3-Jul-3 Van Ham, Cologne #1090
£694 $1146 €1000 Looking for food (60x80cm-24x31in) s. 3-Jul-3 Van Ham, Cologne #1089

BUDELL, Emily Hortense (1884-?) American
£484 $900 €707 Landscape with rolling hills and farm buildings (30x41cm-12x16in) s. canvasboard. 3-Mar-4 Alderfer's, Hatfield #395 est:500-700

BUDELOT, Philippe (18/19th C) French
£2098 $3503 €3000 Paysage anime (38x46cm-15x18in) s. panel. 27-Jun-3 Doutrebente, Paris #19/R
£5000 $9000 €7300 Washerwomen in a landscape. Travelers on a path by an estuary (38x45cm-15x18in) s. pair prov. 23-Jan-4 Christie's, Rockefeller NY #101/R est:2000-3000
£5986 $9937 €8500 Chemin dans la foret. La chasse au lievre (24x33cm-9x13in) s. pair. 13-Jun-3 Renaud, Paris #24/R est:6000
£12000 $21480 €17520 Gardens of the Catherine Palace (45x53cm-18x21in) s. panel. 26-May-4 Sotheby's, London #7/R est:10000-15000

BUDICIN, John (20th C) American
£342 $550 €499 Still life with red roses and fruit (23x30cm-9x12in) s. panel. 20-Jan-3 O'Gallerie, Oregon #873/R

BUDIOVSKY, Josef (19th C) Austrian?
£1192 $2170 €1800 Portrait of a General on a horse (50x38cm-20x15in) s.i.d.849. 21-Jun-4 Dorotheum, Vienna #197/R est:2000-2300

BUDTZ-MOLLER, Carl (1882-1953) Danish
£314 $500 €458 Stone building in a landscape with swirling cloud (43x61cm-17x24in) s. 12-Sep-3 Aspire, Cleveland #47
£1308 $2067 €1897 Returning home from Montagnen, Sabine Mountains, Anticoli (105x135cm-41x53in) s. exhib. 2-Sep-3 Rasmussen, Copenhagen #1776/R est:10000-15000 (D.KR 14000)
£2252 $4121 €3400 Evening service (57x79cm-22x31in) s.d.1921. 8-Apr-4 Dorotheum, Vienna #142/R est:3400-3800

BUECKELAER, Joachim (circle) (1530-1573) Flemish
£8108 $14270 €12000 Still life of fruit and vegetables (96x124cm-38x49in) panel prov. 22-May-4 Lempertz, Koln #1014/R est:12000-15000

BUEHR, Karl Albert (1866-1952) American
£615 $1100 €898 Blossoming trees along the coast. Early spring (28x33cm-11x13in) s. one board on board one canvas on board pair. 26-May-4 Doyle, New York #125/R
£2151 $4000 €3140 Country Road (63x76cm-25x30in) s. prov. 3-Mar-4 Christie's, Rockefeller NY #33/R est:3000-5000
£2890 $5000 €4219 Small town beside a river (51x64cm-20x25in) s. prov. 10-Dec-3 Bonhams & Butterfields, San Francisco #6019/R est:6000-8000
£3165 $5000 €4621 Early autumn landscape (64x76cm-25x30in) s. 7-Sep-3 Treadway Gallery, Cincinnati #595/R est:6000-8000
£4651 $8000 €6790 Apple trees, Niles, Michigan (51x61cm-20x24in) s.i.d.1934 verso. 7-Dec-3 Treadway Gallery, Cincinnati #504/R est:2000-3000

BUEL, Hubert (1915-1984) American
Works on paper
£273 $500 €399 Early morning in San Diego (28x36cm-11x14in) s.d.1944 W/C. 10-Apr-4 Auctions by the Bay, Alameda #1572
£284 $475 €415 Waterways. s. W/C. 18-Oct-3 Harvey Clar, Oakland #1251
£299 $500 €437 Houses on the green. s. W/C. 18-Oct-3 Harvey Clar, Oakland #1250
£419 $700 €612 Cabin on the beach. s. W/C. 18-Oct-3 Harvey Clar, Oakland #1248
£882 $1500 €1288 Sierra ranch (53x71cm-21x28in) s. W/C exec.c.1940. 20-Nov-3 Auctions by the Bay, Alameda #1111/R

BUENAVENTURA, Cesar (20th C) Philippino
£1087 $1685 €1587 Market scene (61x91cm-24x36in) s.d.1967. 6-Oct-2 Sotheby's, Singapore #64/R est:3000-4000 (S.D 3000)

BUENAVENTURA, Teodoro (1863-1950) ?
£3922 $7098 €5726 Planting rice (33x39cm-13x15in) s. indis d. canvas on board. 4-Apr-4 Sotheby's, Singapore #97/R est:6000-8000 (S.D 12000)

BUENINCK, Bernardus (1864-1933) Belgian
£1329 $2259 €1900 Still life (37x47cm-15x19in) s. board. 24-Nov-3 Glerum, Amsterdam #90/R est:2000-2500

BUENO DE MESQUITA, David Abraham (1889-1962) Dutch
£294 $499 €420 Portovenere (46x33cm-18x13in) s.i.d.1937. 24-Nov-3 Glerum, Amsterdam #108/R

BUENO, Antonio (1918-1984) Italian
£3245 $5906 €4900 Woman (20x15cm-8x6in) s. i.verso masonite. 21-Jun-4 Pandolfini, Florence #362/R est:4500-5000
£4294 $7000 €6269 Navetto con fiore (30x23cm-12x9in) s. prov. 25-Sep-3 Christie's, Rockefeller NY #629/R est:2000-3000
£4333 $7973 €6500 Portrait of woman (40x30cm-16x12in) s. oil pastel paper on masonite. 8-Jun-4 Finarte Semenzato, Milan #424/R est:6000-7000
£4667 $8400 €7000 Girl (20x15cm-8x6in) s. board. 22-Apr-4 Finarte Semenzato, Rome #169/R est:5000-5500
£5034 $9312 €7500 Girl (40x30cm-16x12in) s. masonite prov. 11-Mar-4 Galleria Pace, Milan #110/R est:8000-10500
£5034 $9010 €7500 Self-portrait (20x15cm-8x6in) s. board painted 1979. 25-May-4 Sotheby's, Milan #45/R est:7000
£5333 $9813 €8000 Colombina (24x18cm-9x7in) s. masonite painted 1975. 12-Jun-4 Meeting Art, Vercelli #607/R est:8000
£6207 $10366 €9000 Zelda (24x18cm-9x7in) s. masonite painted 1973. 14-Nov-3 Farsetti, Prato #445/R est:8500-9500
£6207 $10366 €9000 Monica (30x20cm-12x8in) s. masonite painted 1973. 14-Nov-3 Farsetti, Prato #496/R est:8500-9500
£6623 $12053 €10000 Girl (46x41cm-18x16in) s. s.verso board. 21-Jun-4 Pandolfini, Florence #468/R est:12000-15000
£6643 $11294 €9500 After Campigli (19x14cm-7x6in) s.i. board. 24-Nov-3 Christie's, Milan #270/R est:4000-6000
£6690 $11106 €9500 Spanish lady (30x20cm-12x8in) s. masonite. 11-Jun-3 Finarte Semenzato, Milan #528/R est:8500
£6897 $11517 €10000 Little pupil (25x20cm-10x8in) s. masonite painted 1972. 14-Nov-3 Farsetti, Prato #470/R est:8500-9500
£7047 $13037 €10500 Monica (30x20cm-12x8in) s. masonite. 13-Mar-4 Meeting Art, Vercelli #558 est:9000
£7241 $12093 €10500 Profile with white hat and necklace (35x25cm-14x10in) s. masonite painted 1981 exhib.lit. 14-Nov-3 Farsetti, Prato #561/R est:8000-9000
£7383 $13215 €11000 Girl (50x39cm-20x15in) s. board. 25-May-4 Sotheby's, Milan #39/R est:10000
£7718 $13815 €11500 Little sailor (24x18cm-9x7in) s. board painted 1980. 25-May-4 Sotheby's, Milan #44/R est:7000
£8042 $13671 €11500 Girl in profile (40x29cm-16x11in) s. paper on board painted 1970. 29-Nov-3 Farsetti, Prato #527/R est:10000-12000
£8621 $14397 €12500 Sailor (40x30cm-16x12in) s. board painted 1980. 14-Nov-3 Farsetti, Prato #582/R est:11500-12500
£10490 $17832 €15000 Girl in profile (59x41cm-23x16in) s.d.1970 s.verso masonite prov. 24-Nov-3 Christie's, Milan #272/R est:10000-15000
£10563 $17535 €15000 Le fumatrici (40x50cm-16x20in) s. faesite painted 1981. 14-Jun-3 Meeting Art, Vercelli #716/R est:12000
£10738 $19866 €16000 Zelda (37x25cm-15x10in) s. masonite. 11-Mar-4 Galleria Pace, Milan #138/R est:16000-22000
£12752 $22826 €19000 Little concert (40x50cm-16x20in) s. masonite painted 1976. 30-May-4 Meeting Art, Vercelli #85 est:15000
£16084 $27343 €23000 Seated woman (80x60cm-31x24in) s. 29-Nov-3 Farsetti, Prato #523/R est:20000-25000
Works on paper
£769 $1308 €1100 After Giorgione (22x28cm-9x11in) s. pencil double-sided. 26-Nov-3 Pandolfini, Florence #75/R

£966	$1545	€1400	Figure (41x29cm-16x11in) s. mixed media. 13-Mar-3 Galleria Pace, Milan #51/R est:1450-1700
£1275	$2359	€1900	Faces (24x43cm-9x17in) s. pastel. 11-Mar-4 Galleria Pace, Milan #82/R est:2200-2800
£1800	$3312	€2700	Indian woman (42x32cm-17x13in) i. pastel. 10-Jun-4 Galleria Pace, Milan #98/R est:2600

BUENO, Pedro (1910-1993) Spanish

£414	$691	€600	Portrait of lady (101x90cm-40x35in) s. 11-Nov-3 Castellana, Madrid #73/R
£797	$1307	€1100	Portrait of a young girl (32x27cm-13x11in) s. 27-May-3 Durán, Madrid #70/R
£800	$1448	€1200	Toreador (46x26cm-18x10in) s. i.verso. 30-Mar-4 Segre, Madrid #116/R
£1135	$1895	€1600	Portrait of girl with fan (100x80cm-39x31in) 20-Oct-3 Durán, Madrid #80/R

BUENO, Xavier (1915-1979) Spanish

£5705	$10211	€8500	Girl in profile (20x25cm-8x10in) s. oil mixed media painted 1978. 29-May-4 Farsetti, Prato #558/R est:6000-8000
£5903	$9326	€8500	Girl in blue (24x18cm-9x7in) 6-Sep-3 Meeting Art, Vercelli #498a est:7000
£6040	$9725	€9000	Portrait de Charles Blanc (100x80cm-39x31in) s. s.i.d.1937 verso prov. 23-Feb-3 St-Germain-en-Laye Encheres #124/R est:9000-11000
£6897	$11517	€10000	Girl (24x18cm-9x7in) s. 13-Nov-3 Galleria Pace, Milan #114/R est:13000
£7047	$12614	€10500	Maternity (79x69cm-31x27in) s.d.53. 29-May-4 Farsetti, Prato #474/R est:10000-14000
£7333	$13493	€11000	Girl (30x25cm-12x10in) s. cardboard painted 1964. 12-Jun-4 Meeting Art, Vercelli #279/R est:10000
£7801	$13028	€11000	Carmencita (73x91cm-29x36in) s. painted c.1938 prov. 12-Oct-3 St-Germain-en-Laye Encheres #99/R est:10000-12000
£8451	$14028	€12000	Young boy (40x50cm-16x20in) s. painted 1966. 14-Jun-3 Meeting Art, Vercelli #499/R est:12000
£8966	$14972	€13000	Girl (44x35cm-17x14in) s. painted 1945. 17-Nov-3 Sant Agostino, Torino #283/R est:8000-10000
£9333	$17173	€14000	Girl (55x46cm-22x18in) s. 8-Jun-4 Finarte Semenzato, Milan #425/R est:5000-6000
£10286	$18000	€15018	Young girl (59x49cm-23x19in) s. canvasboard. 19-Dec-3 Sotheby's, New York #1159/R est:10000-15000
£10667	$19627	€16000	Children (50x70cm-20x28in) s. s.verso oil mixed media. 12-Jun-4 Meeting Art, Vercelli #638/R est:15000
£10738	$19221	€16000	Maternity (50x40cm-20x16in) s. s.i.verso oil sand painted 1975. 25-May-4 Sotheby's, Milan #38/R est:7000
£10959	$18630	€16000	Girl (30x40cm-12x16in) s. cardboard on canvas. 7-Nov-3 Galleria Rosenberg, Milan #44/R est:16000
£11034	$18428	€16000	Girl with blue bow (40x30cm-16x12in) s. painted 1976. 14-Nov-3 Farsetti, Prato #497/R est:14000-16000
£12081	$21624	€18000	Boy raising arms (80x60cm-31x24in) s.verso painted 1965-66. 30-May-4 Meeting Art, Vercelli #97 est:15000
£13793	$23034	€20000	Girl in red dress (80x60cm-31x24in) s. painted 1960. 14-Nov-3 Farsetti, Prato #583/R est:15500-17500
£14085	$23380	€20000	Girl with doll (60x50cm-24x20in) s.d.1961 cardboard on canvas lit. 11-Jun-3 Finarte Semenzato, Milan #544/R est:17000

Works on paper

£442	$791	€650	Girl in profile (24x19cm-9x7in) s.i.d.1947 sanguine. 22-Mar-4 Sant Agostino, Torino #405/R
£6623	$12053	€10000	Portrait of girl (30x40cm-12x16in) s. s.verso mixed media on canvas. 21-Jun-4 Pandolfini, Florence #380/R est:8500-9500
£9934	$18079	€15000	Portrait of girl (46x41cm-18x16in) s. mixed media board. 21-Jun-4 Pandolfini, Florence #469/R est:16000-18000

BUERGERNISS, Carl (1877-1956) American

£462	$850	€675	Winter landscape with trees (36x46cm-14x18in) s. 9-Jun-4 Alderfer's, Hatfield #459
£591	$1100	€863	Moonlight landscape with streamside buildings (36x51cm-14x20in) s.d.1912. 3-Mar-4 Alderfer's, Hatfield #396 est:1000-1500

BUES, F (19th C) Dutch

£1100	$2002	€1606	Fun and games before the windmill (77x58cm-30x23in) s. 16-Jun-4 Christie's, Kensington #157/R est:1500-2000

BUETTI, Daniele (1956-) American

Photographs

£1908	$3300	€2786	Louis Vuitton (100x75cm-39x30in) s. c-print one of 4 prov. 10-Dec-3 Phillips, New York #571/R est:1000-1500

BUFANO, Beniamino (1888-1970) American

Sculpture

£1059	$1800	€1546	Owl (17cm-7in) s. bronze. 9-Nov-3 Bonhams & Butterfields, Los Angeles #4106/R est:3000-5000
£3529	$6000	€5152	Madonna (46cm-18in) bronze executed 1941 prov. 9-Nov-3 Bonhams & Butterfields, Los Angeles #4101/R est:6000-8000

BUFF, Conrad (1886-1975) American

£199	$375	€291	Desert forms (17x19cm-7x7in) s. board. 22-Feb-4 Bonhams & Butterfields, Los Angeles #7001
£351	$650	€512	Landscape with rock (5x9cm-2x4in) s. board. 18-Jan-4 Bonhams & Butterfields, Los Angeles #7012/R
£391	$700	€571	Self portrait (25x28cm-10x11in) s. paperboard. 8-May-4 Auctions by the Bay, Alameda #429/R
£568	$1000	€829	Rock formation (25x23cm-10x9in) s. board painted c.1970. 23-May-4 Treadway Gallery, Cincinnati #734/R
£739	$1300	€1079	Desert pool (30x23cm-12x9in) s. board painted c.1970. 23-May-4 Treadway Gallery, Cincinnati #736/R
£1033	$1900	€1508	High Sierras (30x40cm-12x16in) s. board. 8-Jun-4 Bonhams & Butterfields, San Francisco #4373/R est:2000-3000
£1397	$2500	€2040	Monument valley (41x61cm-16x24in) s. plywood. 26-May-4 Doyle, New York #128/R est:2000-3000
£1587	$3000	€2317	Snow capped mountain landscape (30x41cm-12x16in) board. 17-Feb-4 John Moran, Pasadena #129/R est:2000-3000
£1852	$3500	€2704	Atmospheric mountain landscape (30x41cm-12x16in) s. board. 17-Feb-4 John Moran, Pasadena #128/R est:2000-3000
£2038	$3750	€2975	Floral still life (30x40cm-12x16in) board. 8-Jun-4 Bonhams & Butterfields, San Francisco #4372/R est:2000-3000
£2206	$3750	€3221	Lake in a landscape (41x61cm-16x24in) s. board double-sided. 18-Nov-3 John Moran, Pasadena #78a est:2000-3000
£2500	$4250	€3650	Landscape (41x61cm-16x24in) s. board. 18-Nov-3 John Moran, Pasadena #78 est:3000-4000
£3022	$5500	€4412	Sierras Lake (30x41cm-12x16in) s. board. 15-Jun-4 John Moran, Pasadena #127a est:2000-3000
£3175	$6000	€4636	Floral still life (51x41cm-20x16in) s. masonite. 17-Feb-4 John Moran, Pasadena #54/R est:2500-3500
£3571	$6500	€5214	Landscape (41x61cm-16x24in) s. board prov. 15-Jun-4 John Moran, Pasadena #150 est:2000-3000
£41176	$70000	€60117	Landscape, Canyon Land (86x130cm-34x51in) s. masonite prov. 18-Nov-3 John Moran, Pasadena #61 est:7000-9000

BUFFAGNOTTI, Carlo Antonio (1660-1710) Italian

Works on paper

£950	$1710	€1387	Wooded river landscape with cavalry (19x28cm-7x11in) s. pen brown ink sold with two others. 20-Apr-4 Sotheby's, Olympia #24/R

BUFFET, Bernard (1928-1999) French

£6044	$11000	€8824	Saint-cast, Cabines et Tente sur la plage (50x32cm-20x13in) s.i. oil pastel paper on canvas prov. 29-Jun-4 Sotheby's, New York #365/R est:10000-15000
£8000	$12720	€11600	Femme nue (129x88cm-51x35in) s.d.79 prov. 11-Sep-3 Christie's, Kensington #171/R est:8000-12000
£10000	$16700	€14600	Soucis dans un verre (35x27cm-14x11in) s. masonite painted 1985. 21-Oct-3 Sotheby's, London #159/R est:10000-15000
£10429	$17000	€15226	L'hotel du village (50x65cm-20x26in) s.d.70 W/C brush Indian ink over pencil prov. 25-Sep-3 Christie's, Rockefeller NY #590/R est:14000-18000
£10738	$19221	€16000	Interieur provencal (19x26cm-7x10in) s.d.53 prov. 27-May-4 Christie's, Paris #144/R est:5000-7000
£10738	$19221	€16000	Place d'eglise (33x41cm-13x16in) s. isorel panel. 25-May-4 Chambelland & Giafferi, Paris #68/R est:12000-15000
£11176	$19000	€16317	Poisson (81x117cm-32x46in) s.d.55 prov. 6-Nov-3 Sotheby's, New York #375/R est:25000-35000
£12000	$21601	€18000	Nature morte aux verres (50x65cm-20x26in) s.d.1968 prov. 26-Apr-4 Tajan, Paris #206/R est:15000-20000
£12080	$21382	€18000	Orphies et citron (54x65cm-21x26in) s.d.57. 27-Apr-4 Artcurial Briest, Paris #200/R est:18000-20000
£12752	$23591	€19000	Fleurs bleues dans un pot (41x33cm-16x13in) s. panel. 14-Mar-4 Eric Pillon, Calais #218/R
£12752	$22826	€19000	Roses rouges (33x22cm-13x9in) s.d.1953 prov. 27-May-4 Christie's, Paris #143/R est:6000-8000
£12834	$24000	€18738	Nature morte a la cafetiere bleue (35x40cm-14x16in) s. masonite prov. 25-Feb-4 Christie's, Rockefeller NY #118/R est:25000-35000
£12847	$21455	€18500	Nature morte au plat blanc (97x131cm-38x52in) s.d.57 prov.lit. 21-Oct-3 Artcurial Briest, Paris #324/R est:20000-30000
£13235	$22500	€19323	Jacinthes blanches dans un plat (74x55cm-29x22in) s.d.63 prov. 6-Nov-3 Sotheby's, New York #362/R est:20000-30000
£15663	$26000	€22868	Villier, la mare et le grand saule (89x139cm-35x55in) s.d.1974 i.verso. 2-Oct-3 Christie's, Tel Aviv #30/R est:30000-40000
£16107	$28832	€24000	Rascasse (89x130cm-35x51in) s. painted 1957 prov. 26-May-4 Christie's, Paris #52/R est:18000-22000
£16549	$28961	€23500	Bouquet de soucis (73x60cm-29x24in) s.d.1978. 16-Dec-3 Claude Aguttes, Neuilly #23/R est:20000-30000
£16667	$30000	€25000	Les environs de Saint-cast (81x100cm-32x39in) s.d.1968 prov. 26-Apr-4 Tajan, Paris #205/R est:20000-30000
£17000	$31280	€24820	Hareng saurs et moulin a cafe (46x65cm-18x26in) s. painted 1948 prov. 22-Jun-4 Sotheby's, London #308/R est:10000-15000
£17450	$32282	€26000	Jeux de hasard (73x92cm-29x36in) s.d.1979. 14-Mar-4 Eric Pillon, Calais #194/R
£18792	$34389	€28000	La Villa Rose I (97x130cm-38x51in) s.d.1983. 8-Jul-4 Campo, Vlaamse Kaai #43/R est:30000-35000
£20000	$33400	€29200	Pleneuf, le chemin du hameau (130x81cm-51x32in) s.d.1975 i.verso prov. 21-Oct-3 Sotheby's, London #154/R est:20000-30000
£20395	$37526	€31000	Fleurs au vase noir (66x55cm-26x22in) s. 25-Jun-4 Millon & Associes, Paris #184c/R est:25000-30000
£21679	$37287	€31000	Soucis et ombelles (73x54cm-29x21in) s.d.1985 lit. 8-Dec-3 Artcurial Briest, Paris #71/R est:25000-40000
£22000	$40480	€32120	Eglise au village (64x81cm-25x32in) s.d.70 board prov.exhib. 23-Jun-4 Christie's, London #195/R est:15000-20000
£23743	$42500	€34665	Rolls Royce (96x129cm-38x51in) s. i.verso. 6-May-4 Sotheby's, New York #474/R est:30000-40000
£23841	$43629	€36000	Still life of fruit (50x73cm-20x29in) s.d.66. 7-Apr-4 Piasa, Paris #222/R est:23000-25000
£24123	$44386	€35220	Flowers in a vase (91x65cm-36x26in) s.d.55 prov. 23-Jun-4 Koller, Zurich #3036/R est:35000-50000 (S.FR 55000)
£25874	$43210	€37000	Vase d'iris (101x65cm-40x26in) s.d.1961. 29-Jun-3 Eric Pillon, Calais #268/R
£26846	$49664	€40000	Les peniches sur le canal (73x116cm-29x46in) s.d.59 exhib. 15-Mar-4 Blanchet, Paris #131/R est:40000-50000
£27000	$49140	€39420	Flowers on yellow background (65x50cm-26x20in) s.d.61 prov. 21-Jun-4 Bonhams, New Bond Street #70/R est:20000-30000
£28380	$49098	€40300	Le clown fond jaune (66x47cm-26x19in) s.d.66 prov. 13-Dec-3 Touati, Paris #51/R est:30000-35000
£30000	$54900	€45000	Le clown (73x60cm-29x24in) s. painted 1986 lit. 7-Jun-4 Artcurial Briest, Paris #52/R est:30000-40000
£31469	$52552	€45000	Grand duc (130x81cm-51x32in) s.d.1963. 29-Jun-3 Eric Pillon, Calais #267/R
£31469	$54126	€45000	Chateau de cartes sur gueridon (73x100cm-29x39in) s.d.59 prov. 8-Dec-3 Artcurial Briest, Paris #72/R est:50000-70000
£32000	$58880	€46720	Moulin a cafe et l'assiette (46x61cm-18x24in) s. painted 1949 prov. 22-Jun-4 Sotheby's, London #309/R est:12000-18000
£32000	$58880	€46720	Fleurs d'artichaut (92x73cm-36x29in) s. prov. 23-Jun-4 Christie's, London #255/R est:30000-40000
£32353	$55000	€47235	Ombelles jaunes (94x69cm-37x27in) s.d.65 prov. 6-Nov-3 Sotheby's, New York #367/R est:40000-60000
£33099	$57261	€47000	Vue avec viaduc (89x130cm-35x51in) s.d.1973 i.verso. 14-Dec-3 Rabourdin & Choppin de Janvry, Paris #49/R est:50000-60000
£35099	$63881	€53000	Les arums (100x65cm-39x26in) s.d.61. 18-Jun-4 Piasa, Paris #39/R est:38000-40000
£46358	$84371	€70000	Clown au chapeau melon (81x60cm-32x24in) s.d.1977. 18-Jun-4 Piasa, Paris #40/R est:45000-50000

£50704 $87718 €72000 Etretat, barques aux pieds des falaises (89x131cm-35x52in) s.d.1972 i.verso. 14-Dec-3 Rabourdin & Choppin de Janvry, Paris #48/R est:60000-70000
£75000 $136500 €109500 Self portrait (201x96cm-79x38in) s. painted 1948. 4-Feb-4 Sotheby's, London #284/R est:60000-80000
Prints
£1765 $3000 €2577 New York III (48x69cm-19x27in) s. col lithograph. 31-Oct-3 Sotheby's, New York #218/R
£1793 $2995 €2600 La Tour Solidor. s.num.12/120 drypoint vellum. 9-Jul-3 Tajan, Paris #146 est:1000-1200
£2125 $3400 €3103 New York III (48x70cm-19x28in) s.num.105/150 col lithograph. 18-Sep-3 Swann Galleries, New York #107/R est:3000-5000
£3041 $5351 €4500 View of Paris (164x205cm-65x81in) s. num.49/100 serigraph on screen. 24-May-4 Christie's, Milan #119/R est:4000-6000
Works on paper
£262 $482 €383 The open mouth (16x12cm-6x5in) s.i.d.1951 graphite exhib. 9-Jun-4 Walker's, Ottawa #325/R (C.D 650)
£940 $1748 €1400 Projet de costume pour le ballet, Istar (65x50cm-26x20in) s. Indian ink exec.c.1968 prov. 2-Mar-4 Artcurial Briest, Paris #97 est:1500-2000
£1678 $3121 €2500 Etude pour les chants de Maldoror. i. blk crayon drawings seven. 3-Mar-4 Tajan, Paris #191/R est:1200-1500
£1736 $2899 €2500 Passion du Christ, Le pendu (43x18cm-17x7in) s. lead pencil. 21-Oct-3 Artcurial Briest, Paris #131a est:2500-3500
£1931 $3206 €2800 Visage (35x21cm-14x8in) s. crayon exec.1953. 30-Sep-3 Christie's, Paris #23/R est:2000-3000
£2254 $3899 €3200 Annabel (30x22cm-12x9in) s.i. crayon dr. 9-Dec-3 Artcurial Briest, Paris #323/R est:4000-6000
£2349 $4299 €3500 Annabel 1 (30x23cm-12x9in) s.i. lead pencil. 7-Jul-4 Artcurial Briest, Paris #176/R est:4000-6000
£3169 $5134 €4500 Les toits de la ville (31x25cm-12x10in) s. Indian ink dr prov. 5-Aug-3 Tajan, Paris #55/R est:2000-3000
£4028 $6726 €5800 Nature morte a la bouteille et au verre (38x25cm-15x10in) s.d.52 lead pencil. 21-Oct-3 Artcurial Briest, Paris #131/R est:6000-8000
£4861 $8118 €7000 Portrait d'homme (65x48cm-26x19in) s.d. Indian ink. 25-Oct-3 Cornette de St.Cyr, Paris #473/R est:7000-8000
£4895 $8322 €7000 Nature morte a la bouteille (49x63cm-19x25in) s.d.57 pen Chinese ink. 28-Nov-3 Drouot Estimations, Paris #160/R est:4000-4500
£5282 $9137 €7500 Les chrysanthemes (49x64cm-19x25in) s.d.61 mixed media prov. 13-Dec-3 Touati, Paris #50/R est:10000-12000
£5743 $10280 €8500 Hibou (63x48cm-25x19in) s.d.58 chl. 4-May-4 Calmels Cohen, Paris #192/R est:8000-10000
£7324 $12670 €10400 Travesti (71x49cm-28x19in) s.d.1968 mixed media. 14-Dec-3 Eric Pillon, Calais #268/R
£7801 $13028 €11000 Voiliers au port (49x64cm-19x25in) s.d.67 pastel W/C. 20-Jun-3 Drouot Estimations, Paris #188/R est:9000-12000
£8451 $13691 €12000 Travesti (65x50cm-26x20in) W/C varnish paper prov. 5-Aug-3 Tajan, Paris #54/R est:12000-15000
£8500 $15640 €12410 Plage (47x63cm-19x25in) s.d.58 pencil prov. 24-Jun-4 Christie's, London #454/R est:10000-15000
£8589 $14000 €12540 Vase avec bleu fleurs (64x49cm-25x19in) s.d.59 gouache W/C brush Indian ink paper on masonite prov. 25-Sep-3 Christie's, Rockefeller NY #608/R est:7000-9000
£9732 $18101 €14500 Fleurs exotiques (63x46cm-25x18in) s.d.63 mixed media varnished paper prov. 3-Mar-4 Tajan, Paris #190/R est:12000-13000
£10000 $18000 €15000 Table dressee (50x65cm-20x26in) s.d.1950 gouache ink paper on canvas prov. 26-Apr-4 Tajan, Paris #207/R est:8000-12000
£10811 $20000 €15784 Nature morte aux fruits (54x49cm-21x19in) s.d.78 gouache oil prov. 11-Feb-4 Sotheby's, New York #82/R est:18000-22000
£10915 $19102 €15500 Rue de Montmartre (50x65cm-20x26in) s. gouache paper on canvas. 18-Dec-3 Cornette de St.Cyr, Paris #20/R est:12000-15000
£11745 $21023 €17500 Bouquet d'anemones et de liliums (65x48cm-26x19in) s.d.78 mixed media. 25-May-4 Chambelland & Giafferi, Paris #67/R est:9000-12000
£12000 $21840 €17520 Homme nu a genoux (105x77cm-41x30in) s.d.56 W/C pen ink prov. 5-Feb-4 Christie's, London #441/R est:12000-18000
£15000 $27300 €21900 Bouquet de marguerites (65x50cm-26x20in) s.d.1981 gouache. 4-Feb-4 Sotheby's, London #555/R est:10000-15000
£18881 $32476 €27000 St. Tropez (49x65cm-19x26in) s. gouache ink prov. 2-Dec-3 Sotheby's, Amsterdam #107/R est:18000-25000

BUFFET, Bernard (attrib) (1928-1999) French
Works on paper
£282 $451 €400 Portrait of man with red nose (69x49cm-27x19in) s.d.55 chk W/C. 19-Sep-3 Karlheinz Kaupp, Staufen #2187

BUGATTI, Carlo (1856-1940) Italian
£4000 $6640 €5840 L'ebe (128x72cm-50x28in) s. 1-Oct-3 Sotheby's, Olympia #190/R est:4000-6000
Sculpture
£5978 $11000 €8728 Mirror (65x63x2cm-26x25x1in) hammered copper vellum mirrored glass exec.c.1900. 10-Jun-4 Phillips, New York #87/R est:12000-15000
Works on paper
£690 $1152 €1000 Ornamental design (33x31cm-13x12in) pencil canvas. 14-Nov-3 Von Zezschwitz, Munich #652/R
£690 $1152 €1000 Ornamental design (40x40cm-16x16in) st.sig. chl pencil. 14-Nov-3 Von Zezschwitz, Munich #654/R

BUGATTI, Rembrandt (1885-1916) Italian
Sculpture
£13333 $24667 €20000 Faon (31x28cm-12x11in) s.st.f.Hebrard num.A9 bronze exec.1911 exhib.lit. 18-Jul-4 Sotheby's, Paris #289/R est:20000-30000
£18786 $32500 €27428 Pelican a sa toiltte (22x15x9cm-9x6x4in) s. bronze st.f.A A Hebrard prov. 13-Dec-3 Sotheby's, New York #529/R est:30000-50000
£21978 $40000 €32088 Faon (32cm-13in) s. bronze gilt wood plinth cire perdue A. A. Hebrard. 15-Jun-4 Christie's, Rockefeller NY #91/R est:30000-50000
£23179 $42185 €35000 Brebis pleine (20x41cm-8x16in) s. num.2 pat bronze cire perdue one of three prov.lit. 18-Jun-4 Piasa, Paris #2/R est:30000-35000
£30769 $52308 €44000 Chat a l'ecuelle (14x25x13cm-6x10x5in) st.f.Hebrard num.10 pat bronze lit. 28-Nov-3 Drouot Estimations, Paris #21/R est:20000-22000
£45455 $77274 €65000 Femme jabiru (35x17x12cm-14x7x5in) s.st.f.Hebrard num.7 pat bronze prov.lit. 19-Nov-3 Tajan, Paris #86/R est:40000-45000
£50704 $87718 €72000 Elephant blanc (24x14cm-9x6in) s. num.2 brown pat bronze Cast A A Hebrard exhib. 14-Dec-3 St-Germain-en-Laye Encheres #100/R est:45000-50000
£57803 $100000 €84392 Colosse nu assis (205x100x100cm-81x39x39in) s.i.d.1907 stone prov.lit. 11-Dec-3 Sotheby's, New York #167/R est:120000-180000
£57803 $100000 €84392 Petit leopard assis (22x36x11cm-9x14x4in) s. bronze st.f.A A Hebrard cire perue prov. 13-Dec-3 Sotheby's, New York #530/R est:60000-80000
£90909 $154545 €130000 Deux chacals (25x60x18cm-10x24x7in) s.st.f.Hebrard d.1906 num.1 pat bronze prov. 25-Nov-3 Millon & Associes, Paris #11/R est:130000-180000
£98000 $178360 €143080 Lionne devorant (71cm-28in) i.num.7 bronze st.f.A A.Hebrard conceived 1904 prov.lit. 4-Feb-4 Sotheby's, London #222/R est:80000-120000
£100000 $184000 €146000 Panthere devorant (69cm-27in) i. num.2 bronze st.f.Hebrard Cire Perdue prov.lit. 22-Jun-4 Sotheby's, London #208/R est:100000-150000
£109890 $200000 €160439 Puma (28x59cm-11x23in) s. bronze cire perdue A.A. Hebrard. 15-Jun-4 Christie's, Rockefeller NY #90/R est:200000-300000
£120000 $220800 €175200 Chien et deux chiots entre ses pattes (44cm-17in) i.d.1908 bronze st.f.Hebrard Cire Perdue prov.lit. 22-Jun-4 Sotheby's, London #209/R est:70000-90000
£126374 $230000 €184506 Petit leopard marchant (25x48cm-10x19in) s. bronze cire perdude A.A. Hebrard. 15-Jun-4 Christie's, Rockefeller NY #88/R est:100000-150000
£126374 $230000 €184506 Leopard au repos (32x48cm-13x19in) s. bronze cire perdue A.A. Hebrard. 15-Jun-4 Christie's, Rockefeller NY #89/R est:200000-300000
£156069 $270000 €227861 Lionne de nubie (41x69x22cm-16x27x9in) s. bronze st.f.A A Hebrard prov.lit. 13-Dec-3 Sotheby's, New York #531/R est:150000-200000
£190751 $330000 €278496 Lion de nubie (45x67x23cm-18x26x9in) s. bronze st.f. A A Hebrard cire perdue prov.lit. 13-Dec-3 Sotheby's, New York #532/R est:200000-300000

BUGGE, Frida (1874-1964) Danish
£282 $480 €412 Sitting room interior (59x52cm-23x20in) mono. 29-Nov-3 Rasmussen, Havnen #2025 (D.KR 3000)

BUGOEVSKY, Evan (19th C) Russian
£495 $900 €723 Portrait of wealthy woman (58x48cm-23x19in) s. 8-Feb-4 William Jenack, New York #283

BUHAN, Jean Paul le (1946-) French
£284 $474 €400 La cosmogonie du couple (157x22cm-62x9in) s.d.2002 acrylic wood double-sided. 19-Oct-3 Charbonneaux, Paris #171

BUHLER, Franz Xaver (19/20th C) German
£295 $501 €431 Town scene with bridge across river (25x30cm-10x12in) s.i. panel. 10-Nov-3 Rasmussen, Vejle #66 (D.KR 3200)

BUHLER, Robert (1916-1989) British
£480 $802 €701 Playing field (26x31cm-10x12in) s. board. 21-Oct-3 Bonhams, Knightsbridge #144/R
£550 $1018 €803 Trees (51x61cm-20x24in) s. 11-Feb-4 Sotheby's, Olympia #228/R
£1900 $3021 €2774 For high performance - Hawker Hurricane (54x98cm-21x39in) s board exhib. 10-Sep-3 Sotheby's, Olympia #70/R est:1000-1500
£3200 $5728 €4672 Football match (63x76cm-25x30in) s. 14-May-4 Christie's, Kensington #552/R est:1500-2000

BUHLMANN, Johann Rudolf (1802-1890) Swiss
£14084 $24648 €20000 Vue de la campagne Romaine (78x111cm-31x44in) s.i.d.1862. 18-Dec-3 Tajan, Paris #13/R est:20000-25000

BUHOT, Felix (1847-1898) French
Prints
£1695 $3000 €2475 Convoi funebre au boulevard de clichy (32x45cm-13x18in) s.i. aquatint drypoint. 30-Apr-4 Sotheby's, New York #50/R est:3000-5000

BUHRER, Hans (1907-1973) Swiss
£295 $490 €428 Extensive river landscape in summer (45x65cm-18x26in) s.d.1944. 13-Jun-3 Zofingen, Switzerland #2804 (S.FR 650)
£374 $637 €546 Summer landscape (27x38cm-11x15in) s.d.1929 paper on panel. 5-Nov-3 Dobiaschofsky, Bern #404/R (S.FR 850)

BUI XUAN PHAI (1920-1988) Vietnamese
£342 $582 €500 Barques au bord de mer (14x22cm-6x9in) s.d.84 cardboard. 4-Nov-3 Adjug'art, Brest #16/R
£411 $699 €600 Rue d'Hanoi a l'arbre (12x18cm-5x7in) s.d.85 cardboard. 4-Nov-3 Adjug'art, Brest #3/R
£479 $815 €700 Rue d'Hanoi (12x18cm-5x7in) s.d.83 cardboard. 4-Nov-3 Adjug'art, Brest #2/R
£479 $815 €700 Rue d'Hanoi et sa cathedrale (12x18cm-5x7in) s.d.84 cardboard. 4-Nov-3 Adjug'art, Brest #7/R
£548 $932 €800 Rue d'Hanoi (13x19cm-5x7in) s.d.83 cardboard. 4-Nov-3 Adjug'art, Brest #5/R
£582 $990 €850 Bord de mer (17x25cm-7x10in) s.d.87 cardboard. 4-Nov-3 Adjug'art, Brest #17/R
£616 $1048 €900 Bord de mer (14x20cm-6x8in) s.d.85 panel. 4-Nov-3 Adjug'art, Brest #13/R
£719 $1223 €1050 Bord de mer (14x20cm-6x8in) s.d.85 cardboard. 4-Nov-3 Adjug'art, Brest #12/R
£753 $1281 €1100 Rue d'Hanoi (13x19cm-5x7in) s.d.83 cardboard. 4-Nov-3 Adjug'art, Brest #1/R
£753 $1281 €1100 Rue d'Hanoi au poteau electrique (12x18cm-5x7in) s.d.84 cardboard. 4-Nov-3 Adjug'art, Brest #6/R
£753 $1281 €1100 Rue d'Hanoie (14x21cm-6x8in) s.d.83 cardboard. 4-Nov-3 Adjug'art, Brest #10/R
£788 $1339 €1150 Les barques au bord de mer (13x19cm-5x7in) s.d.83 cardboard. 4-Nov-3 Adjug'art, Brest #15/R
£856 $1455 €1250 Rue d'Hanoie (14x22cm-6x9in) s.d.83 cardboard. 4-Nov-3 Adjug'art, Brest #4/R
£890 $1514 €1300 Bateau dans la baie d'Halong (13x19cm-5x7in) s.d.83 cardboard. 4-Nov-3 Adjug'art, Brest #14/R
£890 $1514 €1300 Devant le temple de la litterature (13x19cm-5x7in) s. cardboard. 4-Nov-3 Adjug'art, Brest #20/R
£890 $1514 €1300 La rue des Fer-blantiers a Hanoi (13x19cm-5x7in) s. cardboard. 4-Nov-3 Adjug'art, Brest #21/R
£959 $1630 €1400 Rue d'Hanoie au cyclo (21x27cm-8x11in) s.d.84 cardboard. 4-Nov-3 Adjug'art, Brest #11/R

£993 $1688 €1450 La vieille port d'Hanoie (13x19cm-5x7in) s.d.85 cardboard. 4-Nov-3 Adjug'art, Brest #18/R
£1164 $1979 €1700 Le vieux temple (16x23cm-6x9in) s.d.83 cardboard. 4-Nov-3 Adjug'art, Brest #19/R est:700-900
£1199 $2038 €1750 Rue d'Hanoi (25x33cm-10x13in) s.d.84. 4-Nov-3 Adjug'art, Brest #8/R est:1000-1200
£1422 $2560 €2076 Street scene with cyclist and bull-cart (15x21cm-6x8in) s. cardboard. 25-Apr-4 Christie's, Hong Kong #534/R est:22000-35000 (HK.D 20000)
£1699 $2837 €2481 Temple of Literature in Hanoi (51x40cm-20x16in) s.d.53. 26-Oct-3 Christie's, Hong Kong #41/R est:22000-35000 (HK.D 22000)
£1961 $3549 €2863 Cheo (31x42cm-12x17in) s. board. 4-Apr-4 Sotheby's, Singapore #47/R est:10000-12000 (S.D 6000)
£1991 $3585 €2907 Two Cheo actors with fan (25x35cm-10x14in) cardboard. 25-Apr-4 Christie's, Hong Kong #540/R est:32000-40000 (HK.D 28000)
£2276 $4097 €3323 Two Cheo actors (19x27cm-7x11in) s. cardboard. 25-Apr-4 Christie's, Hong Kong #539/R est:35000-55000 (HK.D 32000)
£2466 $4192 €3600 Rue d'Hanoi (29x39cm-11x15in) s.d.83. 4-Nov-3 Adjug'art, Brest #9/R est:1200-1500
£2581 $4129 €3768 Girl (48x36cm-19x14in) s. board. 18-May-3 Sotheby's, Singapore #99/R est:5500-7500 (S.D 7200)
£3011 $4817 €4396 Village scene (50x65cm-20x26in) s. 18-May-3 Sotheby's, Singapore #123/R est:7500-8500 (S.D 8400)
£3105 $5619 €4533 Hanoi street with trishaw (21x27cm-8x11in) s.d.84 panel prov. 4-Apr-4 Sotheby's, Singapore #89/R est:6000-8000 (S.D 9500)
£3469 $6314 €5100 Le cycliste (59x69cm-23x27in) s. 8-Feb-4 Anaf, Lyon #127/R est:5000-5500
£3922 $7098 €5726 Neighbours (38x48cm-15x19in) s.d.86. 4-Apr-4 Sotheby's, Singapore #82/R est:12000-15000 (S.D 12000)
£3986 $6178 €5820 Landscape, Cat Ba River (45x60cm-18x24in) s. 6-Oct-2 Sotheby's, Singapore #100/R est:8000-10000 (S.D 11000)
£4167 $6958 €6084 Street, Hanoi (25x35cm-10x14in) s.d.78 panel prov. 12-Oct-3 Sotheby's, Singapore #97/R est:10000-12000 (S.D 12000)
£4932 $8384 €7200 Rue d'Hanoi (60x80cm-24x31in) s.d.84. 4-Nov-3 Adjug'art, Brest #22/R est:4500-5500
£19097 $31892 €27882 Cheo Actors (45x60cm-18x24in) s. lacquer panel prov. 12-Oct-3 Sotheby's, Singapore #96/R est:55000-65000 (S.D 55000)
Works on paper
£2489 $4481 €3634 Street scene with people (31x43cm-12x17in) s.d.82 gouache. 25-Apr-4 Christie's, Hong Kong #536/R est:45000-70000 (HK.D 35000)
£2489 $4481 €3634 Street scene with people (30x41cm-12x16in) s.d.82 gouache. 25-Apr-4 Christie's, Hong Kong #537/R est:45000-70000 (HK.D 35000)
£2778 $5028 €4056 Homage to Chagall (25x38cm-10x15in) s.i.d.23.11.75 W/C. 4-Apr-4 Sotheby's, Singapore #90/R est:7000-9000 (S.D 8500)
£5690 $10242 €8307 Cheo actors at back stage (18x27cm-7x11in) s. gouache on cardboard. 25-Apr-4 Christie's, Hong Kong #538/R est:55000-70000 (HK.D 80000)

BUI-LY (20th C) Vietnamese
£1007 $1862 €1500 La mere (100x73cm-39x29in) s.i.d.1960 silk exhib. 15-Mar-4 Blanchet, Paris #161 est:500-600

BUIKEMA, Albert (1949-) Dutch?
£280 $501 €420 Landscape with farms (58x88cm-23x35in) s. 11-May-4 Vendu Notarishuis, Rotterdam #616

BUISSERET, Louis (1888-1956) Belgian
£2533 $4535 €3800 Jeune femme assise avec un panier de fleurs (50x47cm-20x19in) s. cardboard. 16-May-4 MonsAntic, Maisieres #379 est:1800-2200
£7586 $14034 €11000 Imperia (107x87cm-42x34in) s.d.1930. 19-Jan-4 Horta, Bruxelles #225/R est:3500-5000

BUISSON, Georges (attrib) (19/20th C) French
£400 $728 €600 Young woman bathing in a stream (26x20cm-10x8in) s. 1-Jul-4 Van Ham, Cologne #1240/R

BUKKERTI, M (fl.1915) ?
£1200 $2040 €1752 Doves (55x69cm-22x27in) s.d.1915. 27-Nov-3 Christie's, Kensington #241/R est:400-600

BUKOVAC, Vlacho (1855-1923) Yugoslavian
£20000 $36400 €29200 Reclining nude (64x38cm-25x15in) s.d.1897 prov. 15-Jun-4 Sotheby's, London #54/R est:10000-15000
£23000 $38180 €33580 Reclining nude (64x38cm-25x15in) s.i.d.1897. 1-Oct-3 Sotheby's, Olympia #291/R est:3000-5000

BULATOV, Erik (1933-1989) Russian
Works on paper
£3147 $5350 €4500 Mist (27x19cm-11x7in) s. W/C pastel. 27-Nov-3 Calmels Cohen, Paris #84/R est:2500-3000

BULCKE, Guy van den (1931-) Belgian
£347 $580 €500 Red tailed tropic bird (83x109cm-33x43in) s. d.1975 verso. 21-Oct-3 Campo & Campo, Antwerp #308

BULDER, Hans (20th C) British?
£350 $571 €508 Winter landscape with fox under a full moon (15x18cm-6x7in) s. board. 21-Jul-3 Sotheby's, London #89

BULFIELD, Joseph (fl.1894-1912) British
£634 $1096 €900 Etals et roulottes (27x37cm-11x15in) s. cardboard. 10-Dec-3 Rossini, Paris #61
£704 $1218 €1000 Bretonnes au marche. Etude (27x37cm-11x15in) s. cardboard double-sided. 10-Dec-3 Rossini, Paris #60
£1457 $2725 €2200 Scene de marche en Bretagne (19x36cm-7x14in) s. 24-Jul-4 Thierry & Lannon, Brest #129/R est:1000-1500

BULL, Charles Livingston (1874-1932) American
Works on paper
£452 $756 €660 Polar bear on an ice floe (22x17cm-9x7in) s. W/C gouache crayon. 17-Nov-3 Waddingtons, Toronto #15/R (C.D 1000)
£983 $1700 €1435 Two bears on a tree limb (64x48cm-25x19in) s. W/C. 10-Dec-3 Alderfer's, Hatfield #361/R est:1000-1500
£1946 $3250 €2841 When the sun sets over the jungle (48x33cm-19x13in) s. W/C chl pen ink. 15-Nov-3 Illustration House, New York #83/R est:5000-7000

BULL, Simon (?) British
£1000 $1850 €1460 Deep within my heart (119x119cm-47x47in) 15-Jul-4 Mitchells, Cockermouth #620 est:1200-1800

BULL, William H (1861-1940) American
£696 $1100 €1016 Sunrise over Mt. Tamalpias (46x58cm-18x23in) s. 26-Jul-3 Harvey Clar, Oakland #1239/R
£1294 $2200 €1889 Mountain meadow, valley of the Moonshine (46x58cm-18x23in) s. 20-Nov-3 Auctions by the Bay, Alameda #1085/R

BULLEID, George Lawrence (1858-1933) British
Works on paper
£1000 $1850 €1460 Portrait of a pretty young lady picking roses in garden (36x25cm-14x10in) s. w,. 13-Feb-4 Keys, Aylsham #472/R est:900-1200
£2200 $3740 €3212 At the well (26x20cm-10x8in) s.d.MCMXVIII pencil W/C prov. 20-Nov-3 Christie's, London #145/R est:1500-2000

BULLMORE, Edward (1933-1978) New Zealander
£979 $1782 €1429 Park scene, London (52x76cm-20x30in) s.d.1961 s.i.verso board. 29-Jun-4 Peter Webb, Auckland #192/R est:3000-4000 (NZ.D 2800)
Works on paper
£769 $1400 €1123 Hawke No.3 (55x40cm-22x16in) s.d.1977 i.verso ink W/C. 29-Jun-4 Peter Webb, Auckland #193/R est:2000-3000 (NZ.D 2200)
£1115 $1918 €1628 Mamaku Range near Rotorua (37x57cm-15x22in) s.d.1977 W/C. 7-Dec-3 International Art Centre, Auckland #297/R est:3000-5000 (NZ.D 3000)

BULLOCK, Edith (fl.1886-1911) British
£600 $960 €876 In doubt (89x71cm-35x28in) s. 16-Sep-3 Capes Dunn, Manchester #720

BULLOCK, George G (fl.1827-1859) British
£720 $1246 €1051 Young fruit seller (58x48cm-23x19in) s. 11-Dec-3 Neales, Nottingham #632/R

BULLOCK, Wynn (1902-1975) American
Photographs
£2260 $4000 €3300 Nude (25x20cm-10x8in) s.i.d. gelatin silver print executed c.1963. 27-Apr-4 Christie's, Rockefeller NY #8/R est:5000-7000
£2273 $4000 €3319 Untitled (13x24cm-5x9in) with sig.i. silver print. 20-May-4 Swann Galleries, New York #464/R est:2000-3000
£4192 $7000 €6120 Let there be light (19x24cm-7x9in) s. i.d.1954 num.verso photo printed c.1970. 17-Oct-3 Sotheby's, New York #4/R est:5000-7000

BULMAN, Orville (20th C) American
£1667 $3000 €2434 Yacht Particulier (20x25cm-8x10in) s. board. 20-Jan-4 Arthur James, Florida #748
£2310 $4250 €3373 La bargue vendredi (25x20cm-10x8in) s. s.i.d.1975 verso board. 23-Mar-4 Arthur James, Florida #329/R est:3000-4000
£4088 $6500 €5968 Sieste (51x56cm-20x22in) s. s.i.d.1958 verso. 9-Sep-3 Arthur James, Florida #102

BULMER, Lionel (1919-1992) British
£381 $700 €556 The footbridge (102x152cm-40x60in) s. 25-Jun-4 Freeman, Philadelphia #315/R
£900 $1431 €1314 Bathers (91x122cm-36x48in) s. acrylic exhib. 10-Sep-3 Sotheby's, Olympia #232/R
£900 $1431 €1314 Groynes (91x122cm-36x48in) s. acrylic exhib. 10-Sep-3 Sotheby's, Olympia #233/R
£1400 $2548 €2044 On the beach (76x100cm-30x39in) s. 1-Jul-4 Christie's, Kensington #288/R est:1500-2000
£2000 $3640 €2920 Figures on the beach, Suffolk (76x101cm-30x40in) s. 1-Jul-4 Christie's, Kensington #287/R est:2000-3000

BULOW, A (1884-?) German
£504 $917 €736 Seascape with vessels in rough seas (69x106cm-27x42in) s. 7-Feb-4 Rasmussen, Havnen #2153 (D.KR 5500)

BULOW, Agnes von (1884-?) German
£414 $766 €600 St Tropez harbour (50x73cm-20x29in) s.i. 14-Feb-4 Hans Stahl, Hamburg #83/R
£500 $860 €730 Three master barque at sea (53x67cm-21x26in) s,. 3-Dec-3 AB Stockholms Auktionsverk #2582/R (S.KR 6500)

BULZATTI, Aurelio (1954-) Italian
£1818 $3036 €2600 Venus (65x55cm-26x22in) s. s.i.d.2002 verso. 26-Jun-3 Sant Agostino, Torino #252/R est:2200-2600

BUNBURY, Henry William (1750-1811) British
£1850 $3386 €2701 Morning employments - salon interior with figures and dog (47x40cm-19x16in) oval sold with sepia engraving same subject two. 10-Jun-4 Neales, Nottingham #597/R est:2000-3000

BUNBURY, Henry William (attrib) (1750-1811) British
Works on paper
£300 $519 €438 Falstaff's Escape - Merry Wives of Windsor, Act IV, Scene II (32x45cm-13x18in) s. over pen pencil. 10-Dec-3 Bonhams, Bury St Edmunds #462

BUNCEY, Philippe Albin de (20th C) French
£1408 $2338 €2000 Fenaison (27x46cm-11x18in) s. masonite. 15-Jun-3 Peron, Melun #61

BUNCHI, Tani (1812-1850) Japanese
Works on paper
£2055 $3493 €3000 Chojukassengiga (33cm-13in) s. seal Indian ink col handscroll. 8-Nov-3 Dr Fritz Nagel, Stuttgart #1995/R est:3000

BUNCHO, Ippitsusai (fl.c.1766-1770) Japanese
Prints
£2200 $4048 €3212 Actors Segawa Kikunojo II as Toro and Ichikawa Yaozo II as Soga No Juro (31x15cm-12x6in) s. print exec. 1769. 8-Jun-4 Sotheby's, London #134/R est:2200-2500
£2500 $4600 €3650 The actor Onoe Kikugoro I as Sato Tadanobu (31x15cm-12x6in) s. print. 8-Jun-4 Sotheby's, London #133/R est:2500-3500
£3200 $5888 €4672 Segawa Kikunojo II as Tora and Ichikawa Yaozo II as Soga No Juro (29x14cm-11x6in) s. print exec. 1769. 8-Jun-4 Sotheby's, London #132/R est:2500-3500
£14598 $24816 €20875 Ichikawa Komazo dans le role de Karigane Bunshichi (28x20cm-11x8in) s. print exec.1768 exhib.lit. 25-Nov-3 Sotheby's, Paris #1/R est:24000-28000

BUNCHO, Tani (1763-1840) Japanese
Prints
£5200 $9568 €7592 Butterflies and dandelions (20x18cm-8x7in) s. i. print exec. early 1810's. 8-Jun-4 Sotheby's, London #441/R est:900-1200
Works on paper
£408 $750 €596 Flowers and butterflies (18x50cm-7x20in) s. col ink hanging scroll fan. 23-Mar-4 Christie's, Rockefeller NY #116/R

BUNDEL, Willem van den (1577-1655) Dutch
£9000 $15570 €13140 Wooded river landscape with figures on a track (59x88cm-23x35in) panel. 12-Dec-3 Christie's, Kensington #13/R est:7000-10000

BUNDEL, Willem van den (circle) (1577-1655) Dutch
£6849 $11644 €10000 Elegant company eating and drinking in a park landscape (40x64cm-16x25in) panel. 4-Nov-3 Sotheby's, Amsterdam #118/R est:10000-15000

BUNDGAARD, Gunnar (1920-) Danish
£303 $485 €442 Interior scene with elegant figures wearing rococo costumes (64x87cm-25x34in) s.d.46. 22-Sep-3 Rasmussen, Vejle #417/R (D.KR 3200)

BUNDY, Edgar (1862-1922) British
£500 $835 €730 Falconer and ladies on a terrace (33x13cm-13x5in) 21-Oct-3 Gorringes, Lewes #2164
£550 $1018 €803 Bowls umpire (30x46cm-12x18in) s.d.1895 panel. 10-Feb-4 Bonhams, Knightsbridge #301/R
£1000 $1850 €1460 Portrait of a dandy cavalier (36x25cm-14x10in) 14-Jan-4 Brightwells, Leominster #831/R est:500-800
£3600 $6372 €5256 Stradvarius, the violin maker (51x76cm-20x30in) s.d.1913 prov. 27-Apr-4 Bonhams, Knowle #94/R est:2000-3000
£4500 $7515 €6570 Winter waslk (91x71cm-36x28in) s.d.1881-82. 12-Nov-3 Sotheby's, Olympia #95/R est:1500-2000

BUNDY, Horace (1814-1883) American
£755 $1200 €1102 Portrait of a woman with a lace collar (69x61cm-27x24in) s.d.1846 verso. 10-Sep-3 Sotheby's, New York #417/R
£1415 $2250 €2066 Portrait of Chester Hilliard (71x61cm-28x24in) s.i.d.1847 verso. 10-Sep-3 Sotheby's, New York #375/R est:2000-3000

BUNDY, Horace (attrib) (1814-1883) American
£2285 $4250 €3336 Portraits of girl and boy (66x53cm-26x21in) oval pair. 6-Mar-4 North East Auctions, Portsmouth #519/R
£2353 $4000 €3435 Portraits of a boy and a girl (66x53cm-26x21in) prov. pair. 31-Oct-3 North East Auctions, Portsmouth #1520 est:8000-12000

BUNDY, John Elwood (1853-1933) American
£950 $1700 €1387 Autumnal landscape (41x51cm-16x20in) s. 21-Mar-4 Jeffery Burchard, Florida #74/R

BUNGAY, David (1933-) American
£299 $500 €434 Three lakes (157x203cm-62x80in) s. i.d.1986 verso. 29-Jun-3 Butterfields, Los Angeles #7084/R

BUNGKUNI, Micky (?-1978) Australian
Works on paper
£703 $1315 €1055 Brolga and fish (30x23cm-12x9in) earth pigments eucalyptus bark exec.c.1962 prov. 26-Jul-4 Sotheby's, Melbourne #15/R est:2000-4000 (A.D 1800)

BUNGKUNI, Micky (attrib) (?-1978) Australian
Works on paper
£2439 $3854 €3561 Bush turkey (35x22cm-14x9in) earth pigments eucalyptus bark exec.c.1962 prov. 28-Jul-3 Sotheby's, Paddington #73/R est:3000-5000 (A.D 6000)

BUNING, Johan (1893-1963) Dutch
£533 $976 €800 Still life with lilies in a vase, a fan and a book (65x79cm-26x31in) s.d.1918. 7-Jun-4 Glerum, Amsterdam #18/R
£4196 $7217 €6000 Paysage maison blanche (65x82cm-26x32in) s. s.stretcher painted 1961 exhib. 2-Dec-3 Sotheby's, Amsterdam #244/R est:6000-8000

BUNJES, Emil (1902-1974) American
£337 $550 €492 Ft Davis Camp Ground, June (36x36cm-14x14in) s. board. 28-Sep-3 Simpson's, Houston #145a/R

BUNKE, Franz (1857-1939) German
£524 $876 €750 Farmstead in Mecklenburg (28x41cm-11x16in) s. board. 28-Jun-3 Bolland & Marotz, Bremen #624
£556 $906 €800 Autumn landscape on the Beke (27x40cm-11x16in) s. board. 26-Sep-3 Bolland & Marotz, Bremen #505/R
£733 $1349 €1100 View of Brandenburg (35x53cm-14x21in) s. i.verso. 11-Jun-4 Wendl, Rudolstadt #3977/R
£738 $1358 €1100 Boats on shore of Beke (26x36cm-10x14in) s. canvas on board. 26-Mar-4 Bolland & Marotz, Bremen #490/R
£764 $1245 €1100 Evening on the Warnow (40x54cm-16x21in) s. 26-Sep-3 Bolland & Marotz, Bremen #506/R est:500
£828 $1382 €1200 Rostock with St Nikolai Church (12x20cm-5x8in) s. panel. 15-Nov-3 Lempertz, Koln #1587 est:1200
£1831 $3168 €2600 East Frisian landscape (57x44cm-22x17in) s. panel. 10-Dec-3 Dorotheum, Vienna #228/R est:2000-2500

BUNKER, Dennis M (1861-1890) American
£1176 $2000 €1717 Portrait of Maria P Cushing (126x91cm-50x36in) s.d.1886. 21-Nov-3 Skinner, Boston #366/R est:4000-6000

BUNN, George (fl.1885-1898) British
£500 $830 €730 Sailing into Antwerp harbour (52x91cm-20x36in) s.d.91. 1-Oct-3 Bonhams, Knightsbridge #149/R

BUNN, Kenneth (1938-) American
Sculpture
£3235 $5500 €4723 Maasai with thorn (69x20x25cm-27x8x10in) s.num.18/21 bronze prov. 1-Nov-3 Santa Fe Art, Santa Fe #256/R est:7000-10000

BUNNER, Andrew Fisher (1841-1897) American
£2429 $4250 €3546 Venetian fishing boats (30x51cm-12x20in) s. s.i. verso. 19-Dec-3 Sotheby's, New York #1103/R est:3000-5000

BUNNEY, John Wharlton (1828-1882) British
Works on paper
£600 $1074 €900 Saint Mark's interior, Venice (45x38cm-18x15in) s.d.1871 W/C. 13-May-4 Babuino, Rome #207

BUNNY, Rupert Charles Wulsten (1864-1947) Australian
£725 $1320 €1059 Boy at the beach (23x23cm-9x9in) board prov. 16-Jun-4 Deutscher-Menzies, Melbourne #392/R est:1500-2500 (A.D 1900)
£916 $1667 €1337 South of France, landscape (20x24cm-8x9in) s. board. 16-Jun-4 Deutscher-Menzies, Melbourne #389/R est:2500-3500 (A.D 2400)
£1527 $2779 €2229 Mother and child (23x37cm-9x15in) canvasboard prov.exhib. 16-Jun-4 Deutscher-Menzies, Melbourne #47/R est:4000-6000 (A.D 4000)
£1707 $3056 €2492 Farmhouse South of France (18x21cm-7x8in) paper prov. 4-May-4 Sotheby's, Melbourne #125/R est:3000-5000 (A.D 4200)
£3814 $6483 €5568 Goose girl (32x52cm-13x20in) mono. bears d.1898 verso prov. 24-Nov-3 Sotheby's, Melbourne #261/R est:9000-12000 (A.D 9000)
£4132 $7645 €6033 Springtime South of France (50x58cm-20x23in) mono. i.stretcher verso. 10-Mar-4 Deutscher-Menzies, Melbourne #195/R est:12000-16000 (A.D 10000)
£4743 $8490 €6925 In the botanical garden (42x57cm-17x22in) mono. prov.lit. 15-May-4 Christie's, Sydney #498 est:18000-25000 (A.D 12000)
£5106 $8681 €7455 Trees near Tintaldra (50x65cm-20x26in) mono. i.stretcher verso painted c.1926 exhib. 26-Nov-3 Deutscher-Menzies, Melbourne #65/R est:18000-25000 (A.D 12000)
£5285 $9459 €7716 Landscape in Provence (63x48cm-25x19in) mono. prov. 10-May-4 Joel, Victoria #218/R est:12000-15000 (A.D 13000)
£5344 $9725 €7802 Port-Vendres (54x65cm-21x26in) mono. painted c.1926 prov.exhib. 16-Jun-4 Deutscher-Menzies, Melbourne #93/R est:16000-20000 (A.D 14000)
£6324 $11320 €9233 Jean Gabriel Domergue (81x54cm-32x21in) s.i.d.1911 prov. 15-May-4 Christie's, Sydney #34/R est:10000-15000 (A.D 16000)
£8907 $14340 €13004 Harvest time (50x73cm-20x29in) s. painted c.1900 prov. 25-Aug-3 Sotheby's, Paddington #2/R est:28000-38000 (A.D 22000)
£14463 $25599 €21116 Dejeuner sous les arbres (54x45cm-21x18in) s. prov. 3-May-4 Christie's, Melbourne #97/R est:40000-60000 (A.D 35000)
£19433 $31287 €28372 Artist's wife carrying a fur (84x55cm-33x22in) painted c.1914 prov.exhib.lit. 25-Aug-3 Sotheby's, Paddington #12/R est:40000-60000 (A.D 48000)
£24153 $41059 €35263 Spirit of Drink (118x140cm-46x55in) mono. prov.exhib. 24-Nov-3 Sotheby's, Melbourne #60/R est:50000-70000 (A.D 57000)
£39256 $72624 €57314 Cup of chocolate (81x65cm-32x26in) s.d.1911 verso prov.exhib. 10-Mar-4 Deutscher-Menzies, Melbourne #35/R est:110000-140000 (A.D 95000)
£40486 $65182 €59110 The fan, artist's wife on the balcony (81x54cm-32x21in) s. painted c.1909 prov.exhib.lit. 25-Aug-3 Sotheby's, Paddington #7/R est:120000-150000 (A.D 100000)
£44534 $71700 €65020 Sainte Cecile (79x63cm-31x25in) s. painted c.1900 prov.exhib.lit. 25-Aug-3 Sotheby's, Paddington #1/R est:90000-120000 (A.D 110000)
£53644 $86366 €78320 Mrs Bunny, on a green sofa (64x72cm-25x28in) s. prov. 25-Aug-3 Sotheby's, Paddington #9/R est:160000-180000 (A.D 132500)
£82996 $133623 €121174 Les heures (90x130cm-35x51in) s. painted c.1903 prov.exhib.lit. 25-Aug-3 Sotheby's, Paddington #4/R est:250000-300000 (A.D 205000)
£106557 $172623 €155573 In the Luxembourg Gardens (65x81cm-26x32in) s.i. painted c.1909 prov. 30-Jul-3 Goodman, Sydney #81/R est:325000-425000 (A.D 260000)
£158103 $283004 €230830 Jeanne Morel (180x89cm-71x35in) s.i. painted c.1895 prov. 15-May-4 Christie's, Sydney #470/R est:300000-500000 (A.D 400000)

BUNRIN, Maekawa (1837-1917) Japanese
Works on paper
£350 $601 €500 Sparrow on a plum tree branch (132x30cm-52x12in) s.i. ink col hanging scroll. 5-Dec-3 Lempertz, Koln #779/R

BUNRIN, Shiogawa (1808-1877) Japanese
Works on paper
£408 $750 €596 Snowy riverside anchorage (134x50cm-53x20in) s.d.1871 ink hanging scroll. 23-Mar-4 Christie's, Rockefeller NY #114/R

BUNTING, Thomas (1851-1928) British
£480 $802 €701 Altyre near Forres (83x60cm-33x24in) s. i.verso. 16-Oct-3 Lyon & Turnbull, Edinburgh #84

BUNTON, Clair (19th C) British
Works on paper
£440 $788 €642 Portrait of a young woman (97x73cm-38x29in) s. pastel. 18-Mar-4 Neales, Nottingham #723

BUNTZEN, Carl (19th C) Danish
£604 $1003 €876 Pilot meeting vessel near Kronborg Palace (42x65cm-17x26in) s. 16-Jun-3 Blomqvist, Lysaker #1305/R (N.KR 7000)

BUNTZEN, Heinrich (1802-1892) Danish
£412 $742 €602 Landscape with tree (30x27cm-12x11in) i.verso. 24-Apr-4 Rasmussen, Havnen #2047 (D.KR 4600)
£556 $917 €800 Mill by mountain stream (61x48cm-24x19in) s. bears i.d.1840 i.d.1840 verso board. 2-Jul-3 Neumeister, Munich #616/R
£4726 $8176 €6900 Summer landscape with large trees (100x138cm-39x54in) s.d.1869. 9-Dec-3 Rasmussen, Copenhagen #1389/R est:80000-100000 (D.KR 50000)

BUONACCORSI, Pietro (1500-1547) Italian
Works on paper
£5556 $10000 €8112 Allegory of Rhetoric holding a caduceus. Figure (17x13cm-7x5in) i. pen black ink brown wash double-sided. 22-Jan-4 Christie's, Rockefeller NY #5/R est:10000-15000
£9444 $17000 €13788 Standing dragon in profile to the right (16x11cm-6x4in) i. black chk pen brown ink. 22-Jan-4 Christie's, Rockefeller NY #6/R est:10000-15000

BUONACCORSI, Pietro (attrib) (1500-1547) Italian
Works on paper
£662 $1205 €1000 Triumphant procession through the streets (24x17cm-9x7in) i.verso pen prov. 18-Jun-4 Bolland & Marotz, Bremen #470/R

BUONACCORSI, Pietro (circle) (1500-1547) Italian
Works on paper
£6500 $11245 €9490 Roman emperor on horseback with standard bearer and warrior (29x33cm-11x13in) black chk pen brown ink wash two joined sheets prov. 12-Dec-3 Christie's, Kensington #303/R est:2000-3000

BUONGIORNO, Donatus (1865-?) Italian
£966 $1700 €1410 Old musician with cello (38x30cm-15x12in) s. 21-May-4 North East Auctions, Portsmouth #990/R

BUONO, Léon Giuseppe (1888-1975) Italian
£704 $1218 €1000 Shadows (50x40cm-20x16in) s. board. 11-Dec-3 Christie's, Rome #57

BUORA, Vittorio (1910-1966) Italian
£293 $540 €440 Travellers in the desert (50x70cm-20x28in) s.i.verso paperon cardboard. 14-Jun-4 Sant Agostino, Torino #227/R
£367 $675 €550 Neapolitan boy (39x29cm-15x11in) s.d.1937 cardboard. 8-Jun-4 Della Rocca, Turin #322/R
£578 $1035 €850 Little market (50x70cm-20x28in) s. 22-Mar-4 Sant Agostino, Torino #8/R

BURAGLIO, Pierre (1939-) French
Sculpture
£1879 $3326 €2800 Untitled (21x2x0cm-8x1x0in) s.d.85 verso wood iron putty plexiglass. 28-Apr-4 Artcurial Briest, Paris #385/R est:2000-2500
£2333 $4247 €3500 Fenetre (34x34cm-13x13in) s.d.1979 wood glass. 29-Jun-4 Cornette de St.Cyr, Paris #134/R est:3500-4000
Works on paper
£1067 $1941 €1600 Masquage (53x39cm-21x15in) s.d.78 verso collage. 29-Jun-4 Cornette de St.Cyr, Paris #140/R est:1800-2000
£1645 $3026 €2500 Agrafage de Gauloises (30x40cm-12x16in) mono.d.1977 mixed media collage prov.exhib. 27-Jun-4 Versailles Encheres #157/R est:3000-4000
£2000 $3640 €3000 Masquage (70x100cm-28x39in) s.d.78 collage on plexiglas. 29-Jun-4 Cornette de St.Cyr, Paris #138/R est:3000-4000
£2000 $3640 €3000 Masquage (70x100cm-28x39in) s.d.78 collage. 29-Jun-4 Cornette de St.Cyr, Paris #137/R est:3000-4000

BURANDAY (c.1914-1967) Australian
Works on paper
£1020 $1825 €1489 Banumbirr - Morning Star Hollow log Ceremony (71x44cm-28x17in) natural earth pigments stringy bark exec 1960 prov. 25-May-4 Lawson Menzies, Sydney #280/R est:2500-4500 (A.D 2600)

BURATTI, Domenico (1881-1960) Italian
£340 $609 €500 Old Saluzzo (21x25cm-8x10in) board. 22-Mar-4 Sant Agostino, Torino #170/R
£408 $731 €600 Moon (21x26cm-8x10in) cardboard. 22-Mar-4 Sant Agostino, Torino #158/R

BURBANK, Elbridge Ayer (1858-1949) American
£1863 $3000 €2701 Acoma Indian village, Acoma, New Mexico (15x20cm-6x8in) board. 22-Aug-3 Altermann Galleries, Santa Fe #91
£1912 $3250 €2792 Indian weaver and jewelry making (27x41cm-11x16in) s. canvas on paperboard. 20-Nov-3 Auctions by the Bay, Alameda #1089/R
£3757 $6500 €5485 Still life with apples (36x41cm-14x16in) s. prov. 10-Dec-3 Bonhams & Butterfields, San Francisco #6267/R est:4000-6000
£5202 $9000 €7595 Chief Joseph of the Nez Perce Tribe (76x51cm-30x20in) s.i.d.1888 prov. 10-Dec-3 Bonhams & Butterfields, San Francisco #6081/R est:6000-8000
£7692 $14000 €11230 Portrait of Chief Stinking Bear, Sioux (33x23cm-13x9in) s.i.d.1899 board prov. 15-Jun-4 John Moran, Pasadena #139a est:3000-5000
Works on paper
£1648 $3000 €2406 Portrait of Chief Joseph, Nes Perces. Portrait of Chief Sitting Bull, Sioux (33x23cm-13x9in) one s.i.d.1898 one s.i.d.1860 conte two. 15-Jun-4 John Moran, Pasadena #140 est:2500-4000

BURBARINI, Deifebo (1619-1689) Italian
£10000 $17300 €14600 Madonna and Child with Saints and Bernardino of Siena (90x69cm-35x27in) prov. 11-Dec-3 Sotheby's, London #184/R est:6000-8000

BURBURE, Louis de (1837-?) Belgian
£1538 $2569 €2200 Fishing boats and sailingship in storm off Belgian coast (70x100cm-28x39in) s. 28-Jun-3 Bolland & Marotz, Bremen #625/R est:2800

BURCA, Michael de (1913-1985) Irish?
£4500 $8055 €6570 Lough Conn (46x52cm-18x20in) s. s.i.d.1971 verso panel. 14-May-4 Christie's, London #219/R est:4500-6500

BURCH, Dominique Joseph van der (1722-1785) French
Works on paper
£915 $1602 €1300 Nature mortes (7x14cm-3x6in) s. graphite three prov. 17-Dec-3 Christie's, Paris #46/R

BURCH, Henry Jacob (younger) (1763-1834) British
Miniatures
£2800 $4844 €4088 Young lady (7cm-3in) silver-gilt frame oval. 9-Dec-3 Christie's, London #167/R est:1000-1500
£4800 $8640 €7008 Lady wearing a cameo of a gentleman (7cm-3in) s.d.1791 verso gold frame oval exhib.lit. 22-Apr-4 Bonhams, New Bond Street #75/R est:1500-2500

BURCH, Henry van der (19th C) Dutch
£33520 $60000 €48939 Merry company at table with woman and child (55x69cm-22x27in) lit. 27-May-4 Sotheby's, New York #19/R est:30000-40000

BURCH, Lawson (1937-) British
£300 $549 €438 Sea alcove (76x30cm-30x12in) s.d.1985 acrylic on board. 2-Jun-4 John Ross, Belfast #228
Works on paper
£300 $558 €438 Shore (61x45cm-24x18in) s. mixed media. 3-Mar-4 John Ross, Belfast #34

BURCHARTZ, Max (1887-1961) German
£664 $1143 €950 Abstract composition (60x80cm-24x31in) s.d.1958 oil plaster on canvas exhib. 4-Dec-3 Van Ham, Cologne #71
£839 $1443 €1200 Composition IV (100x80cm-39x31in) oil plaster on canvas painted 1954. 4-Dec-3 Van Ham, Cologne #70/R
Works on paper
£267 $477 €400 Untitled (68x53cm-27x21in) s.d.54 W/C Indian ink. 15-May-4 Van Ham, Cologne #499/R

BURCHELL, William F (fl.1909-1937) British
£1150 $1990 €1679 Parish's Department Store, Shields Road, Newcastle upon Tyne in the 1920s (49x68cm-19x27in) s. 9-Dec-3 Anderson & Garland, Newcastle #405/R est:200-400

BURCHFIELD, Charles (1893-1967) American
£2565 $4590 €3745 Tree lined entry way (102x84cm-40x33in) mono.d.1952 board. 8-Jan-4 James Julia, Fairfield #895/R est:2000-3000
Works on paper
£250 $425 €365 Doodle (15x10cm-6x4in) pencil dr. exec. 1836 prov. 7-Nov-3 Selkirks, St. Louis #424
£276 $475 €403 Double-sided doodle (15x10cm-6x4in) pencil exec.c.1940. 7-Dec-3 Treadway Gallery, Cincinnati #648/R
£353 $650 €515 Abstract studies (15x10cm-6x4in) pencil double-sided. 10-Jun-4 Swann Galleries, New York #46/R
£523 $900 €764 Suburban street (30x23cm-12x9in) s.d.48 chl. 2-Dec-3 Christie's, Rockefeller NY #101/R
£539 $900 €787 Study of a tree trunk (26x20cm-10x8in) mono.d.1919 pen ink. 26-Oct-3 Bonhams & Butterfields, San Francisco #6520/R

£1143	$2000	€1669	Study for Thunderclap in Winter (35x28cm-14x11in) studio st. num.22 pencil prov. 19-Dec-3 Sotheby's, New York #1012/R est:1500-2500
£1286	$2250	€1878	Study for two ravines (28x33cm-11x13in) mono.d.1962 conte crayon paper on board prov. 19-Dec-3 Sotheby's, New York #1006/R est:1500-2500
£1688	$2700	€2464	Winter twilight in the village (15x23cm-6x9in) s.d.1918 conte crayon prov. 20-Sep-3 Sloans & Kenyon, Bethesda #1199/R est:3000-5000
£3846	$7000	€5615	Fawcett's thicket, Salem (35x50cm-14x20in) s. W/C pencil on board executed 1916 prov.exhib.lit. 29-Jun-4 Sotheby's, New York #308/R est:7000-9000
£4070	$7000	€5942	Landscape with clouds (30x38cm-12x15in) s.d.1916 d.verso W/C pencil. 3-Dec-3 Doyle, New York #299/R est:3000-4000
£5249	$9500	€7664	Landscape (23x30cm-9x12in) i.d.6-16-1916 verso W/C pencil prov. 31-Mar-4 Sotheby's, New York #22/R est:7000-10000
£5995	$9650	€8753	Landscape with house (30x41cm-12x16in) s.d.1948 W/C. 20-Aug-3 James Julia, Fairfield #1639/R est:1500-2500
£10000	$16000	€14600	Landscape (36x48cm-14x19in) s.d.1916 W/C prov. 20-Sep-3 Pook & Pook, Downington #254/R est:15000-18000
£11050	$20000	€16133	Spring twilight (23x30cm-9x12in) s.d.1916 i.d.May 1916 verso W/C pencil prov.lit. 31-Mar-4 Sotheby's, New York #23/R est:8000-12000
£12088	$22000	€17648	Trees (66x51cm-26x20in) init. W/C paper on board prov.exhib. 29-Jun-4 Sotheby's, New York #309/R est:12000-18000
£15084	$27000	€25325	Landscape with rolling hills (43x53cm-17x21in) mono. W/C. 20-Mar-4 Pook & Pook, Downington #576/R est:6000-9000
£15341	$27000	€22398	Cloud (56x47cm-22x19in) s.d.July 20 1917 i.verso W/C crayon paper on board prov.exhib.lit. 18-May-4 Christie's, Rockefeller NY #90/R est:30000-50000
£18605	$32000	€27163	Autumn twilight (42x56cm-17x22in) s.d.1920 W/C pencil paper on board prov. 4-Dec-3 Christie's, Rockefeller NY #107/R est:30000-50000
£22727	$40000	€33181	Spring landscape (39x48cm-15x19in) mono.d.1953 W/C pencil prov. 18-May-4 Christie's, Rockefeller NY #94/R est:40000-60000
£26946	$45000	€39341	Circus parade (94x141cm-37x56in) bears st. W/C paper on board prov.exhib.lit. 9-Oct-3 Christie's, Rockefeller NY #99/R est:25000-35000
£36932	$65000	€53921	Noonday Heat (59x84cm-23x33in) s.i.d.1921 W/C gouache pencil paper on board prov.exhib.lit. 18-May-4 Christie's, Rockefeller NY #122/R est:40000-60000
£37791	$65000	€55175	Brooding bird (58x75cm-23x30in) s.d.1919 W/C paper on board prov.lit. 4-Dec-3 Christie's, Rockefeller NY #108/R est:80000-120000
£52326	$90000	€76396	View Southeast of Emporium (81x69cm-32x27in) init.d.1941 W/C paper on board prov.exhib.lit. 4-Dec-3 Christie's, Rockefeller NY #101/R est:80000-120000
£56818	$100000	€82954	Country school house (68x81cm-27x32in) mono.d.1948 i.d.verso W/C paper on board prov.exhib. 18-May-4 Christie's, Rockefeller NY #95/R est:70000-100000

BURCHFIELD, Charles (attrib) (1893-1967) American
Works on paper

£640	$1069	€934	Golden Gate Bridge, seen from the roof tops of San Francisco (48x36cm-19x14in) s. W/C paper on board. 8-Oct-3 Andrew Hartley, Ilkley #1057

BURCK, Jacob (1904-1982) American

£2000	$3500	€2920	Hef (122x152cm-48x60in) s. prov. 17-Dec-3 Christie's, Rockefeller NY #52/R est:3000-5000

BURCK, Paul (1878-?) German

£331	$603	€500	Heustadt (87x64cm-34x25in) s.d.43 i.verso. 16-Jun-4 Hugo Ruef, Munich #933

BURCKHARDT, Rudy (1919-) ?

£359	$650	€524	Pond no 1 (61x91cm-24x36in) 16-Apr-4 American Auctioneer #46/R

BURD, Clara Miller (20th C) American
Works on paper

£2695	$4500	€3935	Mother Goose flying by (41x33cm-16x13in) s. gouache. 15-Nov-3 Illustration House, New York #68/R est:2500-4000

BURDEAU, Clemence Louise (1891-1983) French

£1000	$1770	€1460	Peonies (81x58cm-32x23in) init. 29-Apr-4 Christie's, Kensington #194/R est:1000-1500

BURDICK, Horace Robbins (1844-1942) American

£599	$1000	€875	Looking out toward the sea (46x61cm-18x24in) s. 20-Jun-3 Freeman, Philadelphia #226/R
£2500	$4000	€3650	Portrait of boy (69x56cm-27x22in) s.d.1891. 20-Sep-3 New Orleans Auction, New Orleans #379/R

Works on paper

£248	$450	€362	Still life with apples, grapes, Chianti bottle and wineglass (41x51cm-16x20in) s.d.1881 chl. 2-Apr-4 Eldred, East Dennis #952a/R

BURDY (?) French
Works on paper

£1513	$2784	€2300	Fillette au bord de l'eau (101x15cm-40x6in) s. gouache. 28-Jun-4 Joron-Derem, Paris #259 est:1000-1500

BUREAU, Léon (1866-1906) French
Sculpture

£2000	$3640	€3000	Tiger and bird (36cm-14in) s. brown pat. bronze marble plinth. 20-Jun-4 Wilkinson, Doncaster #158 est:3000-4000
£2329	$3656	€3400	Tigre royal du Cambodge (30x47cm-12x19in) s. pat bronze. 20-Apr-3 Deauville, France #82/R est:3500-4000
£2639	$4196	€3800	Chiens de chasse (41cm-16in) s. pat bronze. 9-Sep-3 Vanderkindere, Brussels #177/R
£2917	$4579	€4200	Cheval attache (40x40x11cm-16x16x4in) st.f.E.V pat bronze. 29-Aug-3 Deauville, France #209/R est:3800-4000

BUREN, Daniel (1938-) French

£22000	$40480	€33000	Photo-souvenir (154x141cm-61x56in) white acrylic on striped tissue painted 1973 prov. 8-Jun-4 Artcurial Briest, Paris #281a/R
£28859	$53100	€43000	Peinture acrylique blanche, tissu raye blanc et blue (226x204cm-89x80in) acrylic tissue painted 1969 prov. 29-Mar-4 Cornette de St.Cyr, Paris #36/R

Sculpture

£8092	$14000	€11814	Couleur matiere (200x204cm-79x80in) painted wooden boards prov. 10-Dec-3 Phillips, New York #529/R est:2000-3000

BURFORD, John (attrib) (19th C) American

£3514	$6500	€5130	View of lower Manhattan and South Street from Brooklyn Heights (36x51cm-14x20in) i.d.1836 stretcher. 10-Feb-4 Christie's, Rockefeller NY #198/R est:8000-12000

BURG, Adriaen van der (1693-1733) Dutch

£676	$1054	€1000	Bacchantal scene in antique ruins (24x35cm-9x14in) s.d.1730 ochre. 31-Mar-3 Bloss, Merzhausen #1534/R
£4082	$7306	€6000	Family portrait (85x74cm-33x29in) s.d.1716 copper. 17-Mar-4 Neumeister, Munich #331/R est:5000

BURGARITSKI, J (1836-1890) Austrian

£1888	$3153	€2700	Landscape (155x105cm-61x41in) s. 10-Oct-3 Vendue Huis, Gravenhage #825

BURGARITSKI, Joseph (1836-1890) Austrian

£341	$566	€494	Sunny mountain valley with river (61x85cm-24x33in) s. 13-Jun-3 Zofingen, Switzerland #2351 (S.FR 750)
£420	$722	€600	River landscape with farmhouse (32x47cm-13x19in) s. jute on jute. 4-Dec-3 Dorotheum, Graz #6/R
£1325	$2411	€2000	Landscape with horse riders and figures (106x158cm-42x62in) s. 18-Jun-4 Bolland & Marotz, Bremen #593/R est:2200
£1888	$3153	€2700	Landscape (155x105cm-61x41in) s. 10-Oct-3 Auction Maastricht #825/R
£2098	$3566	€3000	Inn valley from wooded viewpoint (50x82cm-20x32in) s. 20-Nov-3 Van Ham, Cologne #1503/R est:3000

BURGDORFF, Ferdinand (1883-1975) American

£640	$1100	€934	Desert landscape at sunrise (25x33cm-10x13in) s.d.1911. 7-Dec-3 Hindman, Chicago #806/R
£824	$1500	€1203	Desert flowers near Palm Springs, California (36x48cm-14x19in) s. board prov. 15-Jun-4 John Moran, Pasadena #174 est:1500-2000
£1589	$2750	€2320	California poppies on Carmel Point (40x51cm-16x20in) s.d.1949 masonite prov. 10-Dec-3 Bonhams & Butterfields, San Francisco #6194/R est:3000-5000
£5588	$9500	€8158	Covered wagon (102x127cm-40x50in) s.d.1955 canvasboard exhib. 29-Oct-3 Christie's, Los Angeles #40/R est:7000-9000

BURGE, Maude (1865-1957) New Zealander

£692	$1239	€1010	Floral still life on blur table (59x49cm-23x19in) 12-May-4 Dunbar Sloane, Wellington #19/R est:3000-5000 (NZ.D 2000)
£2818	$4425	€4086	Ladies, St Tropez (45x53cm-18x21in) s. 27-Aug-3 Dunbar Sloane, Wellington #57/R est:5000-7000 (NZ.D 7750)

Works on paper

£335	$575	€489	Early evening (25x36cm-10x14in) s. W/C. 7-Dec-3 International Art Centre, Auckland #322/R (NZ.D 900)
£483	$831	€705	Town scene (24x19cm-9x7in) s. W/C. 7-Dec-3 International Art Centre, Auckland #350 (NZ.D 1300)
£1540	$2495	€2233	Flowers in a vase (46x42cm-18x17in) s. W/C. 31-Jul-3 International Art Centre, Auckland #61/R est:3000-5000 (NZ.D 4250)

BURGER, Anton (1824-1905) German

£343	$572	€490	Shepherd with flock (14x29cm-6x11in) i. verso panel. 10-Oct-3 Winterberg, Heidelberg #547
£733	$1320	€1100	Pipe smoking peasant (20x21cm-8x8in) 26-Apr-4 Rieber, Stuttgart #1008/R
£851	$1421	€1200	Village street in winter (11x15cm-4x6in) s.d.1856 panel. 17-Oct-3 Berlinghof, Heidelberg #1011/R

Works on paper

£403	$749	€600	Peasant woman with child outside village (7x5cm-3x2in) W/C. 6-Mar-4 Arnold, Frankfurt #696/R

BURGER, Fritz (1867-1927) German

£268	$494	€400	Young woman with flower basket (65x55cm-26x22in) s.d.1917 panel. 24-Mar-4 Hugo Ruef, Munich #1216

BURGER, Josef (1887-1966) German

£379	$694	€550	Lakeshore with mountains (70x80cm-28x31in) s. 27-Jan-4 Dorotheum, Vienna #74/R
£688	$1149	€998	Still life of flowers (87x77cm-34x30in) s. 23-Jun-3 Philippe Schuler, Zurich #3510a (S.FR 1500)
£705	$1100	€1029	Mountainous landscape with lake (95x110cm-37x43in) s. 30-Mar-3 Agra, Warsaw #50/R (P.Z 4500)
£963	$1599	€1406	View with mountains in the distance (50x60cm-20x24in) s. 15-Jun-3 Agra, Warsaw #36/R est:4000 (P.Z 6000)
£970	$1600	€1407	Floral still life (94x99cm-37x39in) s. 7-Jul-3 Schrager Galleries, Milwaukee #1441
£1176	$1834	€1717	Landscape with river (60x80cm-24x31in) s. 30-Mar-3 Agra, Warsaw #43/R est:4000 (P.Z 7500)

BURGER, Lothar (1866-1943) Austrian

£300	$546	€450	Landscape with country houses (15x40cm-6x16in) s. panel. 1-Jul-4 Van Ham, Cologne #1239/R

BURGER, Willy Friedrich (1882-1964) Swiss

£330	$562	€482	Alpage pres Zinal - Val d'Anniviers (38x46cm-15x18in) s. panel. 5-Nov-3 Dobiaschofsky, Bern #406/R (S.FR 750)
£764	$1406	€1115	Still life of flowers (81x64cm-32x25in) s. masonite. 14-Jun-4 Philippe Schuler, Zurich #4204/R (S.FR 1750)

Works on paper
£500 $830 €725 Still life with flowers, silver box, teapot and cups (46x38cm-18x15in) s. i. verso gouache. 13-Jun-3 Zofingen, Switzerland #2800 (S.FR 1100)

BURGER-WILLING, Willi Hans (1882-1969) German
£433 $789 €650 Elderly peasant couple collecting wood (60x80cm-24x31in) s. 1-Jul-4 Van Ham, Cologne #1242
£490 $832 €700 Fishing boats on Dutch lake (60x80cm-24x31in) s. 20-Nov-3 Van Ham, Cologne #1504
£500 $915 €750 Cargo sailing vessel in the harbour (99x139cm-39x55in) s. 5-Jun-4 Arnold, Frankfurt #550/R
£1538 $2569 €2200 Peasant woman with goat (190x122cm-75x48in) s. panel. 28-Jun-3 Bolland & Marotz, Bremen #763/R est:2000

BURGERHOUT, Johannes Adrianus (1919-1981) Dutch
£461 $847 €700 Girl's school in Charenton (47x56cm-19x22in) s. s.i. on stretcher. 22-Jun-4 Christie's, Amsterdam #478/R

BURGERS, Felix (1870-?) German
£296 $473 €420 Hut in the Dolomites (49x65cm-19x26in) s. 18-Sep-3 Rieber, Stuttgart #1396
£347 $573 €500 Mountain landscape in winter (50x65cm-20x26in) 7-Jul-3 Dr Fritz Nagel, Stuttgart #6982/R
£490 $832 €700 Chapel in snowy alps (67x98cm-26x39in) s. 20-Nov-3 Van Ham, Cologne #1502

BURGERS, Hendricus Jacobus (1834-1899) Dutch
£872 $1614 €1300 Mother and child in a Dutch interior. Teatime (24x20cm-9x8in) s. pair. 15-Mar-4 Sotheby's, Amsterdam #85/R est:1000-1500
£2041 $3653 €3000 Young mother with children (32x46cm-13x18in) s. 17-Mar-4 Neumeister, Munich #416/R est:4000
£3425 $5822 €5000 Woman knitting with child on her lap (64x45cm-25x18in) s. 5-Nov-3 Vendue Huis, Gravenhage #117/R est:5000-6000

BURGESS, Arthur James Wetherall (1879-1957) Australian
£900 $1494 €1314 HMS Orion and Conqueror in Scapa Flow (25x36cm-10x14in) s.i.d.1919 i.verso board. 1-Oct-3 Bonhams, Knightsbridge #120/R
£900 $1647 €1314 Scarborough fishing fleet (29x43cm-11x17in) board. 6-Jul-4 John Taylors, Louth #368
£1100 $1760 €1606 On convoy duty (51x76cm-20x30in) s. 16-Sep-3 Bonhams, New Bond Street #3/R est:1200-1800
£1300 $2327 €1898 HM racing yacht Britannia at Cowes (30x40cm-12x16in) s. paper. 26-May-4 Christie's, Kensington #492/R est:500-700
£1400 $2408 €2044 Holy Loch with shipping and a barrage balloon (47x72cm-19x28in) s. 2-Dec-3 Sotheby's, London #149/R est:1500-2500
£1400 $2408 €2044 Holy Loch (48x74cm-19x29in) s. 2-Dec-3 Sotheby's, London #150/R est:1500-2500
£1400 $2408 €2044 Shipping and tugs, Holy Loch (58x76cm-23x30in) s. 2-Dec-3 Sotheby's, London #153/R est:1500-2500
£1400 $2408 €2044 Holy Loch (48x74cm-19x29in) s. 2-Dec-3 Sotheby's, London #155/R est:1500-2500
£1400 $2408 €2044 Shipping and small craft (42x57cm-17x22in) s. canvasboard. 2-Dec-3 Sotheby's, London #157/R est:1500-2500
£1800 $3096 €2628 Naval ships at anchor with snow capped mountains beyond (49x74cm-19x29in) s. 2-Dec-3 Sotheby's, London #151/R est:2000-3000
£1800 $3096 €2628 Liner at anchor (42x58cm-17x23in) s. canvasboard. 2-Dec-3 Sotheby's, London #152/R est:2000-3000
£2100 $3612 €3066 Shipping and a motor launch (58x76cm-23x30in) s. 2-Dec-3 Sotheby's, London #162/R est:1500-2500
£2300 $3956 €3358 Shipping on Holy Loch (51x76cm-20x30in) s. 2-Dec-3 Sotheby's, London #154/R est:1000-2000
£2400 $4128 €3504 Liner at anchor in Holy Loch with a plane above (52x77cm-20x30in) s. 2-Dec-3 Sotheby's, London #163/R est:1500-2500
£2600 $4472 €3796 Naval vessels and frigates, Holy Loch (47x73cm-19x29in) s. 2-Dec-3 Sotheby's, London #159/R est:1000-2000
Works on paper
£250 $458 €365 Tugs leading in (26x35cm-10x14in) s. W/C. 27-Jan-4 Bonhams, Knightsbridge #337/R
£300 $537 €438 Passenger liner en route to Holland off Gibraltar (15x21cm-6x8in) init.i. W/C bodycol. 26-May-4 Christie's, Kensington #471/R
£600 $1098 €876 Shipping on the Thames (36x52cm-14x20in) s. W/C. 27-Jan-4 Bonhams, Knightsbridge #308/R

BURGESS, Eliza Mary (1873-?) British
Works on paper
£950 $1701 €1387 Portrait of a lady wearing a white and yellow dress (69x50cm-27x20in) s. W/C. 17-Mar-4 John Bellman, Billingshurst #1823/R

BURGESS, Emma R (1882-?) American
£635 $1150 €927 Shoreline view of Watch Hill, Rhode Island (30x38cm-12x15in) s. 3-Apr-4 Nadeau, Windsor #232/R est:1000-1500

BURGESS, James Howard (1817-1890) British
Works on paper
£280 $512 €409 Cotafell Mountains, Isle of Arran (37x51cm-15x20in) W/C htd bodycol scratching out. 6-Jul-4 Peter Wilson, Nantwich #67/R

BURGESS, John (jnr) (1814-1874) British
Works on paper
£300 $531 €450 Figures outside a church at St Etienne, Beauvais, France (55x38cm-22x15in) s.i. W/C. 27-Apr-4 Holloways, Banbury #246/R
£380 $688 €555 Notre Dame, Paris (54x37cm-21x15in) W/C htd white. 2-Apr-4 Moore Allen & Innocent, Cirencester #773/R
£400 $724 €584 Dieppe, street scene (48x36cm-19x14in) W/C. 2-Apr-4 Moore Allen & Innocent, Cirencester #776/R
£500 $885 €750 View in a continental town with figures by a bridge over a canal (55x38cm-22x15in) s. W/C. 27-Apr-4 Holloways, Banbury #245/R

BURGESS, John Bagnold (1830-1897) British
£700 $1106 €1015 Spanish peasant girl (21x16cm-8x6in) panel. 24-Jul-3 Lawrence, Crewkerne #941
£700 $1162 €1022 La Senorita (46x34cm-18x13in) s.d.1888. 1-Oct-3 Sotheby's, Olympia #77/R
£5882 $10000 €8588 Spanish beauty (92x70cm-36x28in) s.d.1872 prov. 29-Oct-3 Christie's, Rockefeller NY #78/R est:12000-18000
£34118 $58000 €49812 Meeting of East and West (112x54cm-44x21in) s. 29-Oct-3 Christie's, Rockefeller NY #86/R est:60000-80000
Works on paper
£280 $501 €409 Lillebonne (34x24cm-13x9in) init.i. pencil W/C. 16-Mar-4 Bonhams, Leeds #609

BURGESS, Rachel (20th C) American
£219 $400 €320 Temptations (97x91cm-38x36in) 10-Jul-4 Hindman, Chicago #66/R

BURGH, Hendrik van der (attrib) (1769-1858) Dutch
£694 $1132 €1000 Three men playing cards in tavern. Woman with men drinking wine (22x18cm-9x7in) canvas copper on board pair. 25-Sep-3 Dr Fritz Nagel, Stuttgart #1333/R

BURGHARDT, Gustav (fl.1935) German
£414 $766 €600 Canal with St Katharine and Nicolai churches (60x50cm-24x20in) 14-Feb-4 Hans Stahl, Hamburg #127
£2252 $4098 €3400 Kehrwiederspitze, Hamburg (135x99cm-53x39in) s. 21-Jun-4 Dorotheum, Vienna #318/R est:3600-4000

BURGHENDE, B (?) ?
£9500 $16150 €13870 Portrait of a girl of the Vivian family in an elaborately embroidered dress (145x102cm-57x40in) s.i. indis d. 1692 prov. 25-Nov-3 Christie's, London #11/R est:10000-15000

BURGMEIER, Max (1881-1947) Swiss
£370 $676 €540 View of Brissago (54x65cm-21x26in) mono.d.1933 lit. 4-Jun-4 Zofingen, Switzerland #2762 (S.FR 850)

BURGOS, Ulloa (20th C) Venezuelan?
£293 $545 €428 Untitled (51x61cm-20x24in) s. 14-Mar-4 Subastas Odalys, Caracas #7

BURGUNDIAN SCHOOL, French
£6294 $10825 €9000 L'adoration des bergers (173x87cm-68x34in) panel. 8-Dec-3 Cornette de St.Cyr, Paris #36/R est:7000-9000

BURI, Max (1868-1915) Swiss
£90498 $156561 €132127 Old man with accordion (110x120cm-43x47in) s.d.1911 exhib.lit. 9-Dec-3 Sotheby's, Zurich #39/R est:200000-250000 (S.FR 200000)

BURI, Samuel (1935-) Swiss
£328 $603 €479 Untitled (54x75cm-21x30in) s. neon col. 8-Jun-4 Germann, Zurich #775 (S.FR 750)
£1810 $3077 €2643 Iris d'eau (116x89cm-46x35in) s.d.1981 s.i.d. stretcher acrylic prov.lit. 25-Nov-3 Germann, Zurich #137/R est:6000-8000 (S.FR 4000)
£2597 $4649 €3792 Iris d'eau (116x89cm-46x35in) s.d. i. stretcher acrylic lit.exhib. 22-Mar-4 Philippe Schuler, Zurich #4307/R est:4000-5300 (S.FR 6000)
£2715 $4615 €3964 Champs Elysees (162x146cm-64x57in) s.d.1983 s.i.d. stretcher acrylic prov.lit. 25-Nov-3 Germann, Zurich #94/R est:8000-12000 (S.FR 6000)
Works on paper
£371 $683 €542 Iris and Oleander (46x31cm-18x12in) s.d. W/C. 8-Jun-4 Germann, Zurich #774 (S.FR 850)
£498 $846 €727 Untitled (31x25cm-12x10in) s. gouache chk exec. 1961 prov. 22-Nov-3 Burkhard, Luzern #229/R (S.FR 1100)
£814 $1360 €1188 La vache sous l'auvent (45x75cm-18x30in) s.i.d.1970 W/C collage. 24-Jun-3 Germann, Zurich #924 est:2000-2500 (S.FR 1800)

BURIAN, Zdenek (1905-1981) Czechoslovakian
Works on paper
£285 $472 €416 Design of Adolf Vesely's book Camp on Sazava (41x30cm-16x12in) mono. mixed media. 4-Oct-3 Dorotheum, Prague #236 est:10000-15000 (C.KR 13000)
£285 $472 €416 Viktorka (38x26cm-15x10in) s. mixed media. 4-Oct-3 Dorotheum, Prague #257/R est:10000-15000 (C.KR 13000)
£4190 $7500 €6117 Brontosauri ans explorers in boat, Plutonia (36x28cm-14x11in) s. W/C. 15-May-4 Illustration House, New York #7/R est:6000-8000

BURKE, Augustus (c.1838-1891) British
£4800 $8016 €7008 Cattle watering (51x76cm-20x30in) s. 12-Nov-3 Sotheby's, Olympia #81/R est:4000-6000

BURKE, Joe (19/20th C) American
£879 $1600 €1283 Chocolates (41x28cm-16x11in) s. painted 1908. 7-Feb-4 Neal Auction Company, New Orleans #801 est:1500-2500

BURKEL, Heinrich (1802-1869) German
£3380 $5848 €4800 Village in winter (17x23cm-7x9in) mono. board lit. 13-Dec-3 Lempertz, Koln #7/R est:2000
£3496 $5838 €5000 The robbery (30x40cm-12x16in) s. 30-Jun-3 Sotheby's, Amsterdam #64/R

£4138 $7655 €6000 Going up to the alpine pastures (28x37cm-11x15in) s. 12-Feb-4 Weidler, Nurnberg #321/R est:10000
£6944 $11319 €10000 Church in snowy mountain landscape (52x65cm-20x26in) s. lit. 25-Sep-3 Dr Fritz Nagel, Stuttgart #1334/R est:18000
£8000 $14560 €11680 The hunting party (27x36cm-11x14in) board painted 1865 prov. 15-Jun-4 Sotheby's, London #12/R est:8000-12000
£9050 $15385 €13213 Little herders making a fire in pasture with cattle (34x46cm-13x18in) s. 19-Nov-3 Fischer, Luzern #1147/R est:15000-18000 (S.FR 20000)
£13333 $24000 €20000 Loading the hay wagon (30x36cm-12x14in) s. 20-Apr-4 Sotheby's, Amsterdam #63/R est:20000-30000
£14444 $26000 €21088 Village cattle market (35x45cm-14x18in) s. panel painted c.1866. 23-Apr-4 Sotheby's, New York #37/R est:30000-40000
£42000 $71400 €61320 Brawl by inn (30x42cm-12x17in) s. prov. 18-Nov-3 Sotheby's, London #322/R
£50000 $86000 €73000 Return from the successful bear hunt (51x75cm-20x30in) s. painted c.1855/57. 3-Dec-3 Christie's, London #65/R est:40000-60000

Works on paper
£671 $1235 €1000 Tavern in Upper Bavaria (25x38cm-10x15in) pencil wash Indian ink. 26-Mar-4 Dorotheum, Vienna #105/R
£2358 $4292 €3443 The Bascilica of Constantin at the Roman Forum (32x46cm-13x18in) W/C prov.exhib. 17-Jun-4 Kornfeld, Bern #3/R est:5000 (S.FR 5400)

BURKEL, Heinrich (attrib) (1802-1869) German
£769 $1323 €1100 Girl with cows and sheep in front of a mountain hut (18x24cm-7x9in) mono. panel. 6-Dec-3 Hans Stahl, Toestorf #4/R
£1319 $2177 €1900 Campagna landscape (39x73cm-15x29in) 3-Jul-3 Dr Fritz Nagel, Stuttgart #478/R est:900

BURKERT, Eugen (19/20th C) ?
£795 $1446 €1200 Mountain village (40x60cm-16x24in) s.d.14 i.verso. 18-Jun-4 Bolland & Marotz, Bremen #595/R

BURKHALTER, Jean (1895-1982) French
£1119 $1924 €1600 Cavaliers antiques (50x65cm-20x26in) s. 5-Dec-3 Gros & Delettrez, Paris #93 est:1500-2500

BURKHARDT, Emerson C (1905-1969) American
£462 $850 €675 Street scene with figures (28x23cm-11x9in) s.i.verso canvasboard. 25-Jun-4 Freeman, Philadelphia #293/R

BURKHARDT, Hans Gustav (1904-1994) American/Swiss
Works on paper
£1130 $2000 €1650 Untitled, two figures (43x56cm-17x22in) s.d.1940 pastel chl. 2-May-4 Bonhams & Butterfields, Los Angeles #3021/R est:3000-5000

BURKHARDT, Jakob (1808-1867) Swiss
Works on paper
£2155 $3858 €3146 Aare glacier with Hotel des Neuchatelois (34x135cm-13x53in) s.i.d.1842 - 1843 gouache. 14-May-4 Dobiaschofsky, Bern #14/R est:3800 (S.FR 5000)

BURKI, Arnold (1850-1917) Swiss
£271 $434 €396 Thun (42x53cm-17x21in) s. 16-Sep-3 Philippe Schuler, Zurich #5610 (S.FR 600)

BURLE-MAX, Roberto (1909-1994) Brazilian
£8791 $15560 €13187 Fish and toy boat (50x73cm-20x29in) s.d.1941. 27-Apr-4 Bolsa de Arte, Rio de Janeiro #49/R (B.R 48000)
£18315 $33516 €27473 Landscape (69x89cm-27x35in) s.d.1937. 6-Jul-4 Bolsa de Arte, Rio de Janeiro #139/R (B.R 100000)

BURLEIGH, Averil (1883-1949) British
£2400 $4224 €3504 Huntresses (60x76cm-24x30in) s. tempera board. 18-May-4 Bonhams, Knightsbridge #133/R est:1500-2000

BURLEIGH, Sidney R (1853-1931) American
£1087 $2000 €1587 Newlyn fishermen (61x46cm-24x18in) s.i. 27-Jun-4 Freeman, Philadelphia #108/R est:2000-3000

BURLIN, Harry Paul (1886-1969) American
£1734 $3000 €2532 Portrait of a seated Indian girl (46x36cm-18x14in) s.i.verso canvasboard painted 1916 prov. 10-Dec-3 Bonhams & Butterfields, San Francisco #6084/R est:3000-5000

BURLING, Gilbert (1843-1875) American
£8000 $14480 €12000 Jeunes femmes dans la campagne (46x76cm-18x30in) s. s.d.1867 verso. 31-Mar-4 Sotheby's, Paris #106/R est:5000-6000

BURLINGAME, Charles Albert (1860-1930) American
£406 $650 €593 Landscape with stream, Rockland County NY (36x36cm-14x14in) s.d.1923. 21-Sep-3 William Jenack, New York #60
£563 $900 €822 On the sideboard (76x117cm-30x46in) s.i.verso. 18-May-3 Auctions by the Bay, Alameda #1059/R
£670 $1200 €978 Field at dawn (41x51cm-16x20in) s.d.1903. 7-May-4 Sloans & Kenyon, Bethesda #1715/R

BURLIUK, David (1882-1967) American/Russian
£933 $1689 €1400 Male profile (33x24cm-13x9in) s. lit. 3-Apr-4 Badum, Bamberg #113/R
£1372 $2250 €1989 Portrait of a woman in Raphael Soyer's garden (36x25cm-14x10in) s.d.1951 board. 4-Jun-3 Alderfer's, Hatfield #281 est:200-400
£1899 $3400 €2773 Landscape with trees (51x61cm-20x24in) s.d.1943. 8-May-4 Susanin's, Chicago #6057/R est:800-1200
£1913 $3500 €2793 Cortez, Florida (30x23cm-12x9in) s.i.d.1949 board. 31-Jul-4 Sloans & Kenyon, Bethesda #1230 est:3500-4500
£1923 $3500 €2808 Russian village (23x29cm-9x11in) s. board. 29-Jun-4 Sotheby's, New York #400/R est:2500-3500
£1946 $3250 €2841 Flowers by water (43x38cm-17x15in) s. 18-Jun-3 Doyle, New York #16/R est:2500-3500
£2032 $3250 €2967 Reclining nude (10x15cm-4x6in) s. canvas on board. 20-Sep-3 Bunte, Elgin #1250 est:300-500
£2133 $3925 €3200 Bird (14x18cm-6x7in) s. panel col. 10-Jun-4 Hauswedell & Nolte, Hamburg #56/R est:2000
£2197 $3800 €3208 Portrait of a peasant girl carrying water pails (25x20cm-10x8in) s. canvasboard prov. 13-Dec-3 Weschler, Washington #574 est:2500-3500
£2297 $4250 €3354 Bridge over a stream (25x20cm-10x8in) s. board. 12-Feb-4 Sotheby's, New York #86/R est:2500-3500
£2373 $3750 €3465 Russian peasants (30x23cm-12x9in) s. 7-Sep-3 Treadway Gallery, Cincinnati #685/R est:2000-3000
£2473 $4500 €3611 Sailboat (25x30cm-10x12in) s. 29-Jun-4 Sotheby's, New York #398/R est:2500-3500
£2543 $4400 €3713 Venetian harbour scene with rowboats (32x46cm-13x18in) s. canvasboard. 13-Dec-3 Weschler, Washington #572 est:1000-2000
£2659 $4600 €3882 Portrait of Barbara and Alice Hastings (20x25cm-8x10in) s.d.1951 i.indis.d.verso canvasboard prov. 13-Dec-3 Weschler, Washington #573 est:2500-3500
£2994 $5000 €4371 Nocturnal carriage ride (22x30cm-9x12in) s.d.1945 canvasboard. 7-Oct-3 Sotheby's, New York #282 est:2500-3500
£3056 $5500 €4462 Still life of flower, along a beach (41x28cm-16x11in) s. 23-Apr-4 Sotheby's, New York #95/R est:5000-7000
£3217 $5469 €4600 On a road in summer (20x29cm-8x11in) s. 29-Nov-3 Bukowskis, Helsinki #425/R est:2500-3000
£3295 $5800 €4811 Marussia leading a white horse (30x36cm-12x14in) s.d.1948 panel prov. 3-Jan-4 Collins, Maine #20/R est:3000-5000
£3495 $6500 €5103 Seaside landscape with jetties and buildings (41x51cm-16x20in) s.d.1930. 3-Mar-4 Alderfer's, Hatfield #326/R est:2000-3000
£3892 $6500 €5682 Still life of flowers in a vase (61x46cm-24x18in) s. d.1942 verso. 7-Oct-3 Sotheby's, New York #275 est:5000-7000
£3911 $7000 €5710 Woman by the sea, Portugal (30x41cm-12x16in) s.i. masonite. 8-Jan-4 Doyle, New York #14/R est:1000-1500
£4000 $6800 €5840 Saint Anthony by the Cove Hotel (30x25cm-12x10in) s.d.1949 canvas on board prov.exhib. 19-Nov-3 Sotheby's, London #220/R est:4000-6000
£4192 $7000 €6120 Peonies in a porcelain pitcher (51x41cm-20x16in) s.d.1928. 7-Oct-3 Sotheby's, New York #281 est:3000-5000
£4301 $8000 €6279 Three horses (29x40cm-11x16in) s.d.1947 board. 5-Mar-4 Skinner, Boston #480/R est:3000-5000
£4491 $7500 €6557 Life on the farm (34x45cm-13x18in) s. 7-Oct-3 Sotheby's, New York #285 est:3000-5000
£4558 $8250 €6655 Miami Beach (36x46cm-14x18in) 3-Apr-4 South Bay, Long Island #119
£4790 $8000 €6993 Street Scene (25x41cm-10x16in) s.i. prov. 23-Oct-3 Shannon's, Milford #246/R est:3000-5000
£4891 $9000 €7141 Sunny hillside (51x61cm-20x24in) s.d.43 prov. 26-Jun-4 Sloans & Kenyon, Bethesda #1072a/R est:8000-12000
£4945 $9000 €7220 Evening in the steppe (22x32cm-9x13in) s. canvasboard prov.lit. 29-Jun-4 Sotheby's, New York #384/R est:6000-8000
£4945 $9000 €7220 Landscape with path to a river (45x63cm-18x25in) s.d.34 prov. 29-Jun-4 Sotheby's, New York #390/R est:8000-12000
£4945 $9000 €7220 Autumn, Long Island, N.Y (41x51cm-16x20in) s.d.1947. 29-Jun-4 Sotheby's, New York #391/R est:5000-7000
£5000 $8950 €7300 Milkmaid (25x20cm-10x8in) s. canvas on board prov. 26-May-4 Sotheby's, Olympia #454/R est:5000-7000
£5389 $9000 €7868 Santa Monica, California (41x30cm-16x12in) s.i.d.18 - 12/1944 i.stretcher. 7-Oct-3 Sotheby's, New York #283 est:3000-5000
£5587 $10000 €8157 Cafe society (71x61cm-28x24in) s. prov. 6-May-4 Shannon's, Milford #212/R est:10000-15000
£5689 $9500 €8306 Italian quarter in Gloucester (36x48cm-14x19in) s.d.1928. 19-Oct-3 Susanin's, Chicago #6042/R est:800-1200
£5689 $9500 €8306 Fishermen in New England (46x61cm-18x24in) s. s.i.stretcher. 7-Oct-3 Sotheby's, New York #284 est:4000-6000
£5882 $11000 €8588 Landscape on LOng Island (36x47cm-14x19in) s. 25-Feb-4 Christie's, Rockefeller NY #28/R est:6000-8000
£5946 $11000 €8681 Vase of flowers (59x36cm-23x14in) s.d.1957. 12-Feb-4 Sotheby's, New York #58/R est:2000-5000
£6000 $10200 €8760 Homage to the artist's wife, Marusya (41x38cm-16x15in) s.d.1945. 19-Nov-3 Sotheby's, London #219/R est:6000-8000
£6000 $10740 €8760 West (36x26cm-14x10in) s. 26-May-4 Sotheby's, London #278/R est:6000-8000
£6044 $11000 €8824 Still life with shells on Long Island (35x46cm-14x18in) s. painted 1928 exhib.lit. 29-Jun-4 Sotheby's, New York #392/R est:4000-6000
£6500 $11635 €9490 Anna Marie Island (25x40cm-10x16in) s.i.d.1946. 26-May-4 Sotheby's, Olympia #417/R est:4000-6000
£6593 $12000 €9626 Winter walk (41x51cm-16x20in) s.d.1959 prov. 29-Jun-4 Sotheby's, New York #388/R est:10000-15000
£7000 $11900 €10220 By the coast (45x60cm-18x24in) s. canvas on board prov. 19-Nov-3 Sotheby's, London #202/R est:4000-6000
£7000 $12530 €10220 Still life with flowers on a beach (40x30cm-16x12in) s. canvasboard. 26-May-4 Sotheby's, Olympia #495/R est:4000-6000
£7778 $14000 €11356 Mount Zion, Isreal (46x65cm-18x26in) s.i.d. 23-Apr-4 Sotheby's, New York #96/R est:6000-8000
£7778 $14000 €11356 Vineyard, Haven, Massachusetts (54x61cm-21x24in) s.i.d.1929. 23-Apr-4 Sotheby's, New York #97/R est:8000-10000
£7955 $14000 €11614 Peasant in a yellow blouse with red horse (20x25cm-8x10in) s. prov. 23-May-4 Hindman, Chicago #175/R est:4000-6000
£8108 $15000 €11838 Crimea (30x40cm-12x16in) s.i.d.1956. 12-Feb-4 Sotheby's, New York #33/R est:4000-6000
£8242 $15000 €12033 Santa Monica sunset (41x51cm-16x20in) s. painted 1944 lit. 29-Jun-4 Sotheby's, New York #382/R est:8000-12000
£8380 $15000 €12235 Circus (33x48cm-13x19in) s. prov. 14-May-4 Skinner, Boston #355/R est:12000-18000
£8696 $16000 €12696 Lighthouse on the coast (50x76cm-20x30in) s.i.d.1958 prov. 8-Jun-4 Bonhams & Butterfields, San Francisco #4116/R est:3000-5000
£9341 $17000 €13638 Peasant couple and their green cow (60x76cm-24x30in) s. canvasboard painted c.1959 prov. 29-Jun-4 Sotheby's, New York #389/R est:15000-20000
£9581 $16000 €13988 Royal Palace (46x53cm-18x21in) s.d.1921 exhib. 21-Oct-3 Christie's, Rockefeller NY #115 est:15000-20000
£10000 $18000 €14600 Berber woman, Morocco (114x76cm-45x30in) s.i.d.1954 prov.lit. 23-Apr-4 Sotheby's, New York #86/R est:25000-35000
£10778 $18000 €15736 Irises (61x76cm-24x30in) s. 7-Oct-3 Sotheby's, New York #273 est:10000-15000
£11538 $21000 €16845 Flowers at the window (61x51cm-24x20in) s.d.1945 lit. 29-Jun-4 Sotheby's, New York #381/R est:10000-15000

£12000	$20400	€17520	Summer meadow (39x63cm-15x25in) s. 19-Nov-3 Sotheby's, London #203/R est:10000-15000
£12000	$21480	€17520	Milkmaid and her cow (81x101cm-32x40in) s. 26-May-4 Sotheby's, London #270/R est:12000-15000
£12000	$21480	€17520	Spring on Long island (46x61cm-18x24in) s. 26-May-4 Sotheby's, London #277/R est:12000-15000
£12162	$22500	€17757	Vase of flowers (76x61cm-30x24in) s.d.1911 burlap. 11-Feb-4 Sotheby's, New York #76/R est:10000-15000
£12500	$22000	€18250	Crimea flowers (58x43cm-23x17in) s. 23-May-4 Hindman, Chicago #174/R est:5000-7000
£13514	$25000	€19730	Flowers and Pipe (42x53cm-17x21in) s.d.1947 prov. 12-Feb-4 Sotheby's, New York #48a/R est:10000-15000
£13889	$25000	€20278	Majorca, Spain (76x51cm-30x20in) s.i. 23-Apr-4 Sotheby's, New York #90/R est:20000-30000
£14000	$23800	€20440	Women down by the farm at night (31x40cm-12x16in) s.d.1947 canvas on board. 19-Nov-3 Sotheby's, London #218/R est:8000-12000
£15278	$27500	€22306	Cliffs, Japan (48x59cm-19x23in) s.d.1921 exhib. 23-Apr-4 Sotheby's, New York #92/R est:20000-30000
£16667	$30000	€24334	Childhood memories (51x122cm-20x48in) s.d.1945. 23-Apr-4 Sotheby's, New York #85/R est:30000-40000
£16667	$30000	€24334	Flowers on the shore no.2 (92x40cm-36x16in) s.d.1950 prov.lit. 23-Apr-4 Sotheby's, New York #89/R est:20000-30000
£16667	$30000	€24334	View of the crimean coast, Koktebel (46x61cm-18x24in) s. 23-Apr-4 Sotheby's, New York #91/R est:12000-18000
£16667	$30000	€24334	University place, Bronx (76x89cm-30x35in) s.i.d.1929. 23-Apr-4 Sotheby's, New York #93/R est:20000-30000
£18333	$33000	€26766	Two sisters, Mildred and Rosalind (93x56cm-37x22in) s.d.1946 lit. 23-Apr-4 Sotheby's, New York #87/R est:20000-30000
£18919	$35000	€27622	Woman by the sea (61x51cm-24x20in) s.d.1949. 12-Feb-4 Sotheby's, New York #38/R est:12000-18000
£18919	$35000	€27622	Allegorical and mythological Scene (51x120cm-20x47in) s.i.d.1944-45. 12-Feb-4 Sotheby's, New York #43/R est:9000-12000
£19000	$34010	€27740	Island of Capri (61x46cm-24x18in) s.i.d.1954. 26-May-4 Sotheby's, London #267/R est:18000-25000
£19753	$32000	€28642	Peasant farm woman (152x152cm-60x60in) s. prov. 8-Aug-3 Barridorf, Portland #159/R est:30000-50000
£22222	$40000	€32444	Flower on the shore (92x40cm-36x16in) s.d.1950 prov.exhib.lit. 23-Apr-4 Sotheby's, New York #88/R est:20000-30000
£27933	$50000	€40782	Egg robbers (104x91cm-41x36in) s. painted c.1938-39 prov.exhib.lit. 6-May-4 Shannon's, Milford #66/R est:10000-15000
£35000	$62650	€51100	Song of youth (78x87cm-31x34in) s. 26-May-4 Sotheby's, London #266/R est:40000-60000
£45000	$76500	€65700	Coastal scene with fishermen and the artist's wife, Long Island (92x132cm-36x52in) s.i.d.1947 1958. 19-Nov-3 Sotheby's, London #221/R est:45000-65000
£48000	$81600	€70080	Sunflowers by the sea (92x66cm-36x26in) s. 19-Nov-3 Sotheby's, London #224/R est:16000-22000
£55000	$93500	€80300	Flowers in the blizzard (126x100cm-50x39in) s.i. 19-Nov-3 Sotheby's, London #222/R est:18000-25000

Works on paper

£285	$450	€416	Head of a woman (25x20cm-10x8in) s.i. W/C. 7-Sep-3 Treadway Gallery, Cincinnati #714/R
£330	$550	€482	Season's greetings (8x15cm-3x6in) s.i. col pencil exec.1951. 25-Oct-3 Rachel Davis, Shaker Heights #93/R
£500	$900	€730	Dancer (38x25cm-15x10in) W/C. 24-Apr-4 Du Mouchelle, Detroit #3049/R
£509	$850	€743	Woman and bull (25x33cm-10x13in) s. W/C. 25-Oct-3 Rachel Davis, Shaker Heights #92/R
£679	$1133	€991	Sailor and his sweetheart on a park bench (26x36cm-10x14in) s. W/C. 17-Nov-3 Waddingtons, Toronto #289/R (C.D 1500)
£824	$1500	€1203	Peasant couple (24x17cm-9x7in) s.i.d.1945 W/C pastel crayon. 29-Jun-4 Sotheby's, New York #402/R est:1500-2500
£1196	$2200	€1746	Seascape (28x38cm-11x15in) s. W/C. 10-Jun-4 Swann Galleries, New York #48/R est:2000-3000
£1216	$2250	€1775	Farm scene, Long Island (28x38cm-11x15in) s.i. W/C gouache. 12-Feb-4 Sotheby's, New York #71/R est:2000-3000
£1421	$2600	€2075	Florida (28x38cm-11x15in) s.i. W/C. 31-Jul-4 Sloans & Kenyon, Bethesda #1232/R est:2500-3500
£1786	$3250	€2608	In honor of Vincent van Gogh (34x26cm-13x10in) s.i.d.1945 W/C lit. 29-Jun-4 Sotheby's, New York #383/R est:3000-5000
£1923	$3500	€2808	Woman on sleigh (28x38cm-11x15in) s.d.1945 W/C ink lit. 29-Jun-4 Sotheby's, New York #385/R est:3000-5000
£3243	$6000	€4735	Peasant couple in a field (28x39cm-11x15in) s.i. W/C exec c.1943. 12-Feb-4 Sotheby's, New York #34/R est:2500-3500
£4000	$7160	€5840	Artist in his garden (54x69cm-21x27in) s. W/C. 26-May-4 Sotheby's, London #272/R est:4000-6000
£16667	$30000	€24334	Russian poet in Siberia (32x23cm-13x9in) s.i.d.1918 mixed media on board. 23-Apr-4 Sotheby's, New York #84/R est:20000-30000

BURLIUK, David (attrib) (1882-1967) American/Russian

£4800	$8592	€7008	Bridge (35x46cm-14x18in) bears sig.d.1917. 26-May-4 Sotheby's, Olympia #429/R est:1500-2000

BURMAN, Peter (?) British

£310	$574	€453	Sand Dune (54x74cm-21x29in) s. board. 13-Feb-4 Sworder & Son, Bishops Stortford #59/R
£340	$629	€496	Estuary view with beached boats (65x90cm-26x35in) s. board. 13-Feb-4 Sworder & Son, Bishops Stortford #58/R

BURMAN, Sakti (1935-) Indian

£915	$1584	€1300	Buste de femme (61x50cm-24x20in) 10-Dec-3 Millon & Associes, Paris #125a
£2961	$5447	€4500	Attirance d'Eros (73x60cm-29x24in) s. 25-Jun-4 Millon & Associes, Paris #251 est:1000-1500
£15647	$28165	€22845	Greenish light (90x71cm-35x28in) s. 25-Apr-4 Christie's, Hong Kong #610/R est:160000-180000 (HK.D 220000)

BURMANN, Fritz (1892-1945) German

£362	$666	€550	Girl on the beach (45x65cm-18x26in) s. board. 22-Jun-4 Christie's, Amsterdam #476/R
£816	$1486	€1200	Madchen mit Feuerlillien - girl with lilies (62x45cm-24x18in) s.d.34 board. 3-Feb-4 Christie's, Amsterdam #457/R est:1500-2500

BURMESTER, Georg (1864-1936) German

£884	$1583	€1300	San Gimignano (54x65cm-21x26in) s. i. stretcher lit. 20-Mar-4 Bergmann, Erlangen #1147
£1007	$1782	€1500	Breaking waves (76x88cm-30x35in) s.d.28 i. stretcher. 28-Apr-4 Schopman, Hamburg #660/R est:1700

BURN, Henry (1807-1884) Australian

£16529	$30579	€24132	Studley Park Bridge over the Yarra, Melbourne (32x44cm-13x17in) board painted c.1868 prov.exhib. 10-Mar-4 Deutscher-Menzies, Melbourne #33/R est:45000-55000 (A.D 40000)

BURNAT-PROVINS, Marguerite (1872-1952) French

£304	$557	€444	Biere (35x23cm-14x9in) s.i.d.mai 95 cardboard prov. 5-Jun-4 Galerie du Rhone, Sion #286 (S.FR 700)
£370	$676	€540	Nature morte a l'assiette fleurie (23x42cm-9x17in) s. s.d.juin 1936 verso canvas on cardboard prov. 5-Jun-4 Galerie du Rhone, Sion #294 (S.FR 850)
£435	$796	€635	Nature morte aux objets maghrebins. Paysage au couchant (32x40cm-13x16in) s. panel double-sided prov. 5-Jun-4 Galerie du Rhone, Sion #283/R (S.FR 1000)
£783	$1432	€1143	Nature morte au pichet bleu (20x29cm-8x11in) s. canvas on cardboard painted c.1900 prov. 5-Jun-4 Galerie du Rhone, Sion #287 (S.FR 1800)
£3043	$5570	€4443	Portrait de ma soeur Marthe Provins (50x41cm-20x16in) s.i.d.1895 verso canvas on cardboard prov. 5-Jun-4 Galerie du Rhone, Sion #543/R est:2000-2500 (S.FR 7000)

Works on paper

£217	$398	€317	Bordure aux olives bleues (48x63cm-19x25in) s. col crayon W/C prov. 5-Jun-4 Galerie du Rhone, Sion #473 (S.FR 500)
£261	$477	€381	Trefles (50x65cm-20x26in) s. crayon W/C prov. 5-Jun-4 Galerie du Rhone, Sion #490 (S.FR 600)
£304	$557	€444	Hortensia rose (39x52cm-15x20in) s.d.26 juin 1947 col crayon gouache white chk prov. 5-Jun-4 Galerie du Rhone, Sion #296 (S.FR 700)
£304	$557	€444	Coeurs bleus et perles d'or (28x24cm-11x9in) s. col crayon W/C prov. 5-Jun-4 Galerie du Rhone, Sion #474/R (S.FR 700)
£304	$557	€444	Croix et arabesques (40x40cm-16x16in) s. col crayon W/C prov. 5-Jun-4 Galerie du Rhone, Sion #476 (S.FR 700)
£304	$557	€444	Feuilles de ginko (37x32cm-15x13in) s. crayon W/C prov. 5-Jun-4 Galerie du Rhone, Sion #48o (S.FR 700)
£348	$637	€508	Maison a Saviese (48x30cm-19x12in) s. chl pastel cardboard prov. 5-Jun-4 Galerie du Rhone, Sion #282 (S.FR 800)
£370	$676	€540	Le Bellerivien (27x20cm-11x8in) s.d.1897 crayon ink wash prov.lit. 5-Jun-4 Galerie du Rhone, Sion #494/R (S.FR 850)
£478	$875	€698	Paysage vaudoise a 'anemone (20x12cm-8x5in) mono.i. chl white chk W/C prov. 5-Jun-4 Galerie du Rhone, Sion #284 (S.FR 1100)
£522	$955	€762	Roses (38x62cm-15x24in) s. pastel col crayon chl prov. 5-Jun-4 Galerie du Rhone, Sion #488 (S.FR 1200)
£565	$1034	€825	La cruche verte (31x24cm-12x9in) s.d.1903 chl W/C prov.lit. 5-Jun-4 Galerie du Rhone, Sion #291/R (S.FR 1300)
£652	$1193	€952	Projet de broderie a motif de physalis (44x62cm-17x24in) s. pastel col crayon W/C chl prov.exhib.lit. 5-Jun-4 Galerie du Rhone, Sion #495/R (S.FR 1500)
£826	$1512	€1206	Le chat endormi (27x36cm-11x14in) s. chl prov. 5-Jun-4 Galerie du Rhone, Sion #281 (S.FR 1900)
£870	$1591	€1270	Feuilles d'automne (43x70cm-17x28in) s. chl pastel W/C prov. 5-Jun-4 Galerie du Rhone, Sion #479/R (S.FR 2000)
£957	$1750	€1397	Saviesan au chapeau (35x30cm-14x12in) mono. graphite exec. c.1900 prov.lit. 5-Jun-4 Galerie du Rhone, Sion #289/R (S.FR 2200)
£957	$1750	€1397	Nature morte au geranium (29x38cm-11x15in) s.i.d.1911 crayon W/C prov. 5-Jun-4 Galerie du Rhone, Sion #292 (S.FR 2200)
£1087	$1989	€1587	Nature morte a la cruche fleurie (50x65cm-20x26in) s. crayon W/C prov. 5-Jun-4 Galerie du Rhone, Sion #542/R est:2500-3500 (S.FR 2500)
£1391	$2546	€2031	Ma ville, la bete appelee Morlante (36x51cm-14x20in) s. s.i.d.1922 verso crayon ink W/C cardboard prov.exhib.lit. 5-Jun-4 Galerie du Rhone, Sion #544/R est:3000-4000 (S.FR 3200)
£1522	$2785	€2222	Ma ville, Scloulouou a son poste (33x46cm-13x18in) s. s.i.d.1929 verso crayon ink W/C cardboard prov.exhib.lit. 5-Jun-4 Galerie du Rhone, Sion #545/R est:3000-4000 (S.FR 3500)
£3261	$5967	€4761	Pot aux fleurs ouatees et fruit rouges (24x17cm-9x7in) s. chl W/C gouache exec. c.1900 prov. 5-Jun-4 Galerie du Rhone, Sion #288/R est:1500-2000 (S.FR 7500)

BURNE-JONES, Sir Edward Coley (1833-1898) British

£4500	$7650	€6570	Study for the Court of Venus (35x52cm-14x20in) i. painted with studio prov. 27-Nov-3 Sotheby's, London #313/R est:5000-8000
£9200	$15640	€13432	Study of a man's head in profile, probably a model for King Cophetua (56x42cm-22x17in) prov. 4-Nov-3 Holloways, Banbury #519/R est:3000-5000
£49133	$85000	€71734	Sacrifice to Hymen (28x37cm-11x15in) prov.exhib.lit. 11-Dec-3 Sotheby's, New York #7/R est:80000-120000
£75000	$127500	€109500	Portrait of Katie Lewis (55x43cm-22x17in) prov. 26-Nov-3 Christie's, London #18/R est:60000-80000

Works on paper

£600	$1092	€876	Study for the Entombment (19x16cm-7x6in) white chk brown paper. 1-Jul-4 Christie's, Kensington #406/R
£1111	$2000	€1622	Study of a male figure (37x22cm-15x9in) init. col chk. 21-Jan-4 Sotheby's, New York #222/R est:3500-4500
£2000	$3640	€2920	Study for the figure of Phyllis. Study for a female slave (21x14cm-8x6in) pencil two. 1-Jul-4 Sotheby's, London #271/R est:2000-3000
£2200	$4004	€3212	Study of a female nude (33x19cm-13x7in) pencil. 1-Jul-4 Christie's, Kensington #407/R est:1800-2500
£2569	$4599	€3751	Distressed and sorrowing Sir Palomydes (23x16cm-9x6in) pencil prov. 15-May-4 Christie's, Sydney #365/R est:6000-9000 (A.D 6500)
£3162	$5660	€4617	Studies for the figure of Merlin - The beguiling of Merlin (33x23cm-13x9in) blk chk. 15-May-4 Christie's, Sydney #366/R est:6000-9000 (A.D 8000)
£4000	$7280	€5840	Study for one of the Gorgons in the finding of Perseus (31x24cm-12x9in) canvas laid down prov. 1-Jul-4 Sotheby's, London #272/R est:4000-6000
£4600	$8418	€6716	Portrait of a lady in profile to the left probably Georgiana Burne-Jones (19x17cm-7x7in) i. pencil prov. 3-Jun-4 Christie's, London #175/R est:5000-8000
£5500	$9350	€8030	Studies of a woman seated and kneeling, possibly Fanny Cornforth (35x51cm-14x20in) pencil. 20-Nov-3 Christie's, London #136/R est:6000-8000
£8500	$14450	€12410	Costume design for Morgan le Fay in J.Comyns Carr's play 'King Arthur' (35x23cm-14x9in) col chks Japanese paper lit. 20-Nov-3 Christie's, London #156/R est:3000-5000
£8874	$15352	€12956	Female figure (115x28cm-45x11in) mixed media. 12-Dec-3 Kieselbach, Budapest #172/R (H.F 3400000)

£10000	$17000	€14600	Two figures on a terrace, a study for 'Arthur in Avalon' (36x26cm-14x10in) pencil W/C htd white. 20-Nov-3 Christie's, London #135/R est:8000-12000
£11561	$20000	€16879	Study of two figures embracing (24x16cm-9x6in) init.d.1896 bodycol htd gold black prov.exhib. 11-Dec-3 Sotheby's, New York #5/R est:20000-30000
£15896	$27500	€23208	Study of a head (19x13cm-7x5in) init.d.1885 pencil prov. 11-Dec-3 Sotheby's, New York #4/R est:10000-15000
£16033	$28379	€23408	Faith, hope, charity (136x120cm-54x47in) mixed media triptych. 28-Apr-4 Kieselbach, Budapest #46/R (H.F 6000000)
£19000	$34960	€27740	Spirit of the Downs (25x20cm-10x8in) pencil W/C htd bodycol prov.exhib.lit. 9-Jun-4 Christie's, London #19/R est:15000-20000
£23715	$42451	€34624	Garland (75x50cm-30x20in) gouache prov.lit. 15-May-4 Christie's, Sydney #118/R est:40000-60000 (A.D 60000)
£26989	$47500	€39404	Study of the head of a young woman (30x20cm-12x8in) init.d.1888 chl. 18-May-4 Sotheby's, New York #93/R est:15000-20000
£34000	$62560	€49640	Portrait of Catherine Ralli. init.d.1892 pencil 2 in one frame prov.exhib.lit. 9-Jun-4 Christie's, London #18/R est:20000-30000
£62640	$108368	€91454	Hope - if hope were not heart should break (211x136cm-83x54in) mixed media. 12-Dec-3 Kieselbach, Budapest #224/R (H.F 24000000)
£141176	$240000	€206117	Sidonia von Bork (29x16cm-11x6in) mono. W/C bodycol panel prov.lit. 28-Oct-3 Sotheby's, New York #4/R est:80000-120000

BURNE-JONES, Sir Edward Coley (attrib) (1833-1898) British

Works on paper

£300	$474	€435	Design for a stained glass window (30x25cm-12x10in) pen ink W/C. 24-Jul-3 Dominic Winter, Swindon #9

BURNET, James M (1788-1816) British

£750	$1275	€1095	Peasants with horses, a hay cart and dog, before a barn and cornfield (47x66cm-19x26in) panel. 29-Oct-3 Hampton & Littlewood, Exeter #608/R

BURNET, James M (attrib) (1788-1816) British

£800	$1496	€1200	Figures and dog beside a cornfield with farmer on horseback (48x66cm-19x26in) panel. 22-Jul-4 Tennants, Leyburn #787

BURNET, John (1784-1868) British

£1600	$2576	€2320	Reading lesson (44x54cm-17x21in) with sig. 21-Aug-3 Bonhams, Edinburgh #1145 est:700-1000

BURNETT, Cecil Ross (1872-1933) British

£600	$1002	€870	Landscape with shepherd boy and dog (39x49cm-15x19in) s/. 26-Jun-3 Ambrose, Loughton #786/R

BURNETT, Fassett (20th C) New Zealander?

£294	$550	€429	Mount Egmont (43x88cm-17x35in) s.d.1981 acrylic board. 24-Feb-4 Peter Webb, Auckland #17/R (NZ.D 800)

BURNETTE, Mabel (1876-1956) American

£952	$1800	€1390	Taxco street scene (25x30cm-10x12in) s. board. 17-Feb-4 John Moran, Pasadena #15/R est:1500-2000

BURNISTON, Martin Ennis (1913-) Canadian

£200	$366	€292	The gold frame (55x38cm-22x15in) s. paper. 3-Jun-4 Heffel, Vancouver #11/R (C.D 500)

BURNITZ, Karl-Peter (1824-1886) German

£280	$481	€400	Winter landscape with a house (10x19cm-4x7in) s. panel. 6-Dec-3 Hans Stahl, Toestorf #5
£467	$854	€700	Landscape with pond in stormy weather (53x82cm-21x32in) s. 5-Jun-4 Arnold, Frankfurt #551/R

Works on paper

£300	$549	€450	View of Segovia (17x27cm-7x11in) s.i.verso W/C. 5-Jun-4 Arnold, Frankfurt #552/R

BURNOIY, G A de (19/20th C) ?

£959	$1630	€1400	Hen and cockerel in a stall. Hens in meadow (12x11cm-5x4in) s. canvas on panel two. 5-Nov-3 Vendue Huis, Gravenhage #297

BURNS, Bill (20th C) Canadian

£207	$374	€302	Near Jasper Icefields Parkway (51x60cm-20x24in) s. i.verso. 18-Apr-4 Levis, Calgary #425/R (C.D 500)
£238	$397	€347	Starting to snow, Bow Lake (25x30cm-10x12in) s.i.d.2002 panel. 17-Nov-3 Hodgins, Calgary #70/R (C.D 525)
£498	$831	€727	Chephren Lake (50x60cm-20x24in) s.i.d.2003. 17-Nov-3 Hodgins, Calgary #189/R est:800-1000 (C.D 1100)

BURNS, Colin W (1944-) British

£1000	$1840	€1460	Hen partridge (18x28cm-7x11in) s. panel prov. 10-Jun-4 Christie's, Kensington #266/R est:1000-1500
£1000	$1840	€1460	Ptarmigan (18x28cm-7x11in) s. panel prov. 10-Jun-4 Christie's, Kensington #267/R est:1000-1500
£1000	$1840	€1460	Red grouse (17x28cm-7x11in) s. panel prov. 10-Jun-4 Christie's, Kensington #270/R est:1000-1500
£1000	$1840	€1460	Capercaille (17x28cm-7x11in) s. panel prov. 10-Jun-4 Christie's, Kensington #271/R est:1000-1500
£1200	$2208	€1752	Blackgame (17x28cm-7x11in) s. panel prov. 10-Jun-4 Christie's, Kensington #269/R est:1000-1500
£1300	$2392	€1898	Woodcock, winter (18x28cm-7x11in) s. panel prov. 10-Jun-4 Christie's, Kensington #268/R est:1000-1500
£1500	$2550	€2190	English partridge (27x16cm-11x6in) s. panel prov. 27-Nov-3 Christie's, Kensington #230/R est:1500-2000
£1500	$2550	€2190	Mallard (17x27cm-7x11in) s. panel prov. 27-Nov-3 Christie's, Kensington #233/R est:1500-2000
£1700	$3145	€2482	Wells Beach, Norfolk (22x35cm-9x14in) s. i. stretcher. 14-Jul-4 Christie's, Kensington #1055/R est:1000-1500
£1850	$3090	€2701	Teal in estuary creek (41x53cm-16x21in) s. 17-Oct-3 Keys, Aylsham #684/R
£1988	$3200	€2902	Venice (24x38cm-9x15in) s. i.on stretcher. 14-Jan-4 Christie's, Rockefeller NY #80/R est:1500-2000
£2000	$3680	€2920	Winter in the Yorkshire Dales (53x76cm-21x30in) s. 10-Jun-4 Christie's, Kensington #265/R est:2500-3500
£2100	$3885	€3066	Woodcock in the moonlight (30x38cm-12x15in) s. 13-Feb-4 Keys, Aylsham #647/R est:1500-2000
£2442	$4200	€3565	Blackgame in autumn, Perthshire (63x76cm-25x30in) s. i.stretcher. 5-Dec-3 Christie's, Rockefeller NY #104/R est:3000-5000
£2500	$4525	€3650	Mallard alighting Fleggburgh (41x56cm-16x22in) s. 16-Apr-4 Keys, Aylsham #675/R est:1800-2500
£2800	$4760	€4088	Evening, River Thurn (41x61cm-16x24in) s. prov. 27-Nov-3 Christie's, Kensington #218/R est:2500-3500
£3000	$5100	€4380	Pheasants in a clearing (41x61cm-16x24in) s. 27-Nov-3 Christie's, Kensington #219/R est:3000-5000
£3100	$5332	€4526	Winter in the Cairngorms (18x64cm-7x25in) s. 5-Dec-3 Keys, Aylsham #578/R est:2000-3000
£3800	$6460	€5548	Woodcock amongst silver birch (47x63cm-19x25in) s. i.stretcher. 30-Oct-3 Christie's, London #58/R est:2500-3500
£3800	$6688	€5548	Widgeon over St Benet's Ludham (49x74cm-19x29in) s. i.stretcher. 21-May-4 Christie's, London #27/R est:2000-3000
£4200	$7392	€6132	Fleggburgh Common (44x61cm-17x24in) s. i.stretcher. 21-May-4 Christie's, London #29/R est:1800-2500
£4348	$7000	€6348	Winter in Swaledale, Yorkshire (39x50cm-15x20in) s. i.on stretcher. 14-Jan-4 Christie's, Rockefeller NY #78/R est:3000-5000
£4500	$7650	€6570	Red deer, luinne Bheinn (81x111cm-32x44in) s. i.stretcher. 30-Oct-3 Christie's, London #55/R est:3000-5000
£5200	$8840	€7592	Red grouse - Knoydart (79x94cm-31x37in) s. i.stretcher. 30-Oct-3 Christie's, London #56/R est:3000-5000
£5523	$9500	€8064	Woodcock (44x55cm-17x22in) s. i.stretcher. 5-Dec-3 Christie's, Rockefeller NY #108/R est:4000-6000
£6977	$12000	€10186	Red grouse, North Yorkshire Moors (71x92cm-28x36in) s. i.stretcher. 5-Dec-3 Christie's, Rockefeller NY #107/R est:5000-7000
£7000	$12320	€10220	Driven game, Norfolk (64x104cm-25x41in) s. i.stretcher. 21-May-4 Christie's, London #25/R est:4000-6000
£7558	$13000	€11035	Red deer, Garbh Bheinn (72x112cm-28x44in) s. i.stretcher. 5-Dec-3 Christie's, Rockefeller NY #105/R est:5000-7000
£9884	$17000	€14431	Mallard alighting, Norfolk (65x101cm-26x40in) s. i.stretcher. 5-Dec-3 Christie's, Rockefeller NY #103/R est:4000-6000
£10000	$17000	€14600	Stags below the cliffs of Lochnager (55x81cm-22x32in) s. i.stretcher. 30-Oct-3 Christie's, London #57/R est:3000-5000
£10500	$18480	€15330	Woodcock at dusk, Hickling (58x71cm-23x28in) s. i.stretcher. 21-May-4 Christie's, London #26/R est:2000-3000
£12000	$21120	€17520	Red grouse, Beinn Fhionnlaidh (55x75cm-22x30in) s. i.stretcher. 21-May-4 Christie's, London #28/R est:2000-3000
£12791	$22000	€18675	Winter in Glen Feshie, Cairngorms (71x91cm-28x36in) s. i.stretcher. 5-Dec-3 Christie's, Rockefeller NY #106/R est:5000-7000

Works on paper

£300	$552	€438	Grouse on a moor (32x38cm-13x15in) s. W/C. 10-Jun-4 Christie's, Kensington #263/R
£500	$805	€725	Winter near Thurne, Norfolk (15x20cm-6x8in) s. W/C. 15-Aug-3 Keys, Aylsham #641
£500	$860	€730	Mill at Halvergate Marshes (36x48cm-14x19in) s. W/C. 5-Dec-3 Keys, Aylsham #572
£550	$886	€798	Sailing on the river Ant (18x23cm-7x9in) s. W/C. 15-Aug-3 Keys, Aylsham #369/R
£550	$886	€798	Winter on Hickling Road, mallard (18x23cm-7x9in) s. W/C. 15-Aug-3 Keys, Aylsham #640/R
£680	$1258	€993	Hall common cottage, Ludham, Norfolk (15x20cm-6x8in) s. W/C. 13-Feb-4 Keys, Aylsham #585/R
£700	$1281	€1022	Norfolk sketches (28x38cm-11x15in) s.i. W/C prov. 7-Apr-4 Woolley & Wallis, Salisbury #86/R
£1000	$1840	€1460	Blackgame, Glen Clova (38x53cm-15x21in) s. W/C. 10-Jun-4 Christie's, Kensington #262/R est:1200-1800
£1200	$2208	€1752	Mallard on the Broad, Martham, Norfolk (12x15cm-5x6in) s. W/C. 11-Jun-4 Keys, Aylsham #580/R est:900-1200
£1300	$2093	€1885	Teal, mallard and coot, Martham (28x38cm-11x15in) s. W/C. 15-Aug-3 Keys, Aylsham #638 est:700-900
£1500	$2580	€2190	Ranworth Church (36x48cm-14x19in) s. W/C. 5-Dec-3 Keys, Aylsham #573/R est:1000-1250
£1550	$2806	€2263	Manor farm, winter (30x41cm-12x16in) s. W/C. 16-Apr-4 Keys, Aylsham #645/R est:900-1200
£1800	$3006	€2628	Grey partridge (36x51cm-14x20in) s. W/C. 17-Oct-3 Keys, Aylsham #544
£2700	$4968	€3942	Horning church (15x20cm-6x8in) s. W/C. 11-Jun-4 Keys, Aylsham #581 est:1200-1600

BURNS, Milton J (1853-1933) American

£3106	$5000	€4535	Boy fishing (15x25cm-6x10in) 20-Aug-3 James Julia, Fairfield #1523/R est:6000-8000
£8982	$15000	€13114	S S Ponce entering New York Harbour (53x94cm-21x37in) s.d.99 prov. 23-Oct-3 Shannon's, Milford #46/R est:8000-12000

BURNS, Milton J (attrib) (1853-1933) American

£8589	$14000	€12540	Ships portrait of pilot boat Caprice, of New York City. 27-Sep-3 Thomaston Place, Thomaston #190

BURNS, Robert (1869-1941) British

£1478	$2646	€2158	Mother and child (91x81cm-36x32in) s.d.98. 26-May-4 AB Stockholms Auktionsverk #2374/R est:25000-30000 (S.KR 20000)
£2074	$3380	€3028	Woman and child in garden (92x81cm-36x32in) s.d.98. 29-Sep-3 Lilla Bukowskis, Stockholm #634 est:20000 (S.KR 27000)
£3000	$4710	€4350	For a special occasion (64x77cm-25x30in) s. 27-Aug-3 Sotheby's, London #1136/R est:3000-5000

Works on paper

£310	$558	€453	Autumn at Humbia Woods. s. W/C. 22-Apr-4 Bonhams, Edinburgh #358

BURNS, William (1921-1972) British

£1000	$1670	€1460	Abstract composition (75x100cm-30x39in) s.backboard board. 16-Oct-3 Lyon & Turnbull, Edinburgh #122
£1000	$1610	€1450	Waterfront (41x50cm-16x20in) s. board prov. 21-Aug-3 Bonhams, Edinburgh #1192 est:1000-1500

Works on paper
£250 $458 €365 Ferrydene (33x44cm-13x17in) s. i.verso W/C pencil. 28-Jan-4 Hampton & Littlewood, Exeter #375/R
£400 $748 €584 Ferryden (13x17cm-5x7in) s. W/C exhib. 25-Feb-4 Mallams, Oxford #156/R

BURNS, William H (1924-) Irish
£350 $651 €511 Glen Head, near Killybegs, Co. Donegal (50x91cm-20x36in) s. 3-Mar-4 John Ross, Belfast #40
£450 $837 €657 Glen Head, near Killybegs, Co. Donegal (50x63cm-20x25in) s. board. 3-Mar-4 John Ross, Belfast #142
£480 $802 €701 Rain clouds, Co. Mayo (48x60cm-19x24in) s. board. 21-Oct-3 Bonhams, Knightsbridge #143/R
£580 $951 €847 Near Renvyle (45x61cm-18x24in) s. 4-Jun-3 John Ross, Belfast #206

BURNS-WILSON, Robert (1851-1916) American
Works on paper
£670 $1200 €978 Kentucky landscape (41x58cm-16x23in) s. W/C gouache. 21-Mar-4 Jeffery Burchard, Florida #68/R
£2919 $4700 €4262 Autumn cornstalks (38x56cm-15x22in) s. W/C. 20-Aug-3 James Julia, Fairfield #1681/R est:1000-1500

BURNSIDE, Richard (1944-) American
£240 $400 €350 African king with lavender shirt (61x61cm-24x24in) paint board. 15-Nov-3 Slotin Folk Art, Buford #510/R
£250 $450 €365 King on purple (61x61cm-24x24in) board. 24-Apr-4 Slotin Folk Art, Buford #561/R
£278 $500 €406 White haired king (61x79cm-24x31in) board painted c.1989. 24-Apr-4 Slotin Folk Art, Buford #559/R
£278 $500 €406 Yellow cat (66x122cm-26x48in) board. 24-Apr-4 Slotin Folk Art, Buford #560/R

BURO DE GARCIA, Carlos (1929-) Spanish
£599 $1048 €850 Surrealist gentleman (100x81cm-39x32in) s.d.98 board. 16-Dec-3 Durán, Madrid #79/R

BURON, Henri Lucien Joseph (1880-1969) French
£1118 $2024 €1700 Bateaux de peche. Marche anime (22x27cm-9x11in) s.d.1942 panel pair. 17-Apr-4 Livinec, Gaudcheau & Jezequel, Rennes #116
£1118 $2024 €1700 Untitled. panel pair. 17-Apr-4 Bretagne Encheres, St Malo #116 est:1000-1200

BURPEE, William P (1846-?) American
£1285 $2300 €1876 Beach view (13x21cm-5x8in) board prov. 14-May-4 Skinner, Boston #272/R est:1800-2200

BURQUART, Rezso (1884-1968) Hungarian
£2088 $3612 €3048 In a Boksz (40x50cm-16x20in) panel. 12-Dec-3 Kieselbach, Budapest #39/R (H.F 800000)

BURR, Alexander Hohenlohe (1837-1899) British
£750 $1388 €1125 By the fireside (39x29cm-15x11in) s. 14-Jul-4 Sotheby's, Olympia #68/R
£4698 $8644 €7000 Two children teasing sleeping grandfather (46x36cm-18x14in) s.d.82. 26-Mar-4 Bolland & Marotz, Bremen #492/R est:9300

BURR, George Elbert (1859-1939) American
Works on paper
£311 $550 €454 Boats in an Italian harbour (25x36cm-10x14in) s. W/C gouache. 1-May-4 Thomaston Place, Thomaston #488/R

BURR, John (1831-1893) British
£700 $1295 €1022 Waking dreams (55x26cm-22x10in) s.d.1869 i.verso. 10-Feb-4 Bonhams, Knightsbridge #251/R
£850 $1607 €1241 By the sea shore (26x36cm-10x14in) s.d.77. 19-Feb-4 Lyon & Turnbull, Edinburgh #156
£1500 $2640 €2190 Children on the shore playing beside fishing boats (41x33cm-16x13in) s.i. 30-Dec-3 British Auctioneer #786 est:1500-1800
£4200 $7518 €6132 First meeting (51x76cm-20x30in) s. 26-May-4 Sotheby's, Olympia #86/R est:2000-3000

BURRA BURRA, Djambo (1946-) Australian
£706 $1264 €1031 Untitled (109x79cm-43x31in) painted 1991 prov. 25-May-4 Lawson Menzies, Sydney #296/R (A.D 1800)

BURRA, Edward (1905-1976) British
Works on paper
£820 $1492 €1197 Female nude (40x23cm-16x9in) st.sig. pen ink sold with two others. 15-Jun-4 Bonhams, New Bond Street #40/R
£5000 $8950 €7300 Fruit seller (21x21cm-8x8in) s. pen ink prov. 16-Mar-4 Bonhams, New Bond Street #37/R est:4000-6000
£11000 $20350 €16060 Les Girls (53x40cm-21x16in) pen ink prov.exhib. 10-Mar-4 Sotheby's, Olympia #117/R est:8000-12000
£48000 $88800 €70080 Composition (54x76cm-21x30in) s. W/C over pencil htd bodycol exec 1933 prov. 10-Mar-4 Sotheby's, Olympia #118/R est:45000-60000
£60000 $109800 €87600 Hop pickers who've lost their mothers (43x39cm-17x15in) s.d.1924 W/C pencil prov. 2-Jun-4 Sotheby's, London #56/R est:40000-60000

BURRAS, James (19th C) ?
£550 $990 €803 Sportsmen on a hillside with their dogs (28x35cm-11x14in) s.d.1868 board. 21-Apr-4 Tennants, Leyburn #1194

BURRELL, A M (fl.1849) American
£12353 $21000 €18035 Portrait of blue eyed girl with red book inscribed Washington cat, in a column landscape (91x74cm-36x29in) s.d.1844. 31-Oct-3 North East Auctions, Portsmouth #1517/R est:5000-8000

BURRELL, Alfred Ray (1877-?) American
£391 $700 €571 California landscape. s. 18-Mar-4 Skinner, Bolton #545/R

BURRI, Alberto (1915-1995) Italian
£5667 $10427 €8500 Piccolo nero (10x7cm-4x3in) s.d.1973 verso tempera cardboard prov. 12-Jun-4 Villa Grisebach, Berlin #399/R est:12000-15000
£12000 $22080 €18000 Untitled (12x18cm-5x7in) s.d.1976 verso tempera cardboard prov. 12-Jun-4 Villa Grisebach, Berlin #398/R est:20000-30000
£30435 $49913 €42000 Burning (17x14cm-7x6in) s.i.d.1968 verso plastic acrylic on cellotex. 29-May-3 Galleria Pace, Milan #84/R est:50000-65000
£41958 $71329 €60000 Tar (53x46cm-21x18in) s. oil tar prov.exhib.lit. 24-Nov-3 Christie's, Milan #332/R est:60000-80000
£55944 $95105 €80000 Tempera (44x55cm-17x22in) s.d.49 prov.lit. 25-Nov-3 Sotheby's, Milan #224/R est:40000-50000
£61333 $112853 €92000 Cretto Bianco (56x77cm-22x30in) s.i.d.1976 verso acrylic vinyl cellotex prov. 11-Jun-4 Villa Grisebach, Berlin #76/R est:80000-100000
£157718 $282315 €235000 White (50x86cm-20x34in) oil fabric stone painted 1952 prov.lit. 25-May-4 Sotheby's, Milan #275/R est:160000-200000
£240000 $400800 €350400 Sack (51x87cm-20x34in) s.d.55 i.verso burlap vinavil oil prov.exhib.lit. 20-Oct-3 Sotheby's, London #11/R est:150000
£300000 $501000 €438000 Sacco combustione (70x100cm-28x39in) s.i.verso oil burlap paper fabric gold leaf prov.lit. 21-Oct-3 Christie's, London #38/R est:300000-500000
£362319 $594203 €500000 White T (79x109cm-31x43in) s.i.d.52 verso fabric oil exhib.lit. 30-May-3 Farsetti, Prato #544/R
Prints
£2098 $3566 €3000 Capodimonte Museum (89x64cm-35x25in) s. num.74/100 eau forte serigraph prov.lit. 24-Nov-3 Christie's, Milan #4/R est:1800-2200
£2238 $3804 €3200 Black A (66x96cm-26x38in) s. num.26/90 eau forte aquatint lit. 24-Nov-3 Christie's, Milan #5/R est:2500-3500
£2759 $4607 €4000 Black (96x66cm-38x26in) s. num.61/90 eau forte aquatint exec.1971 lit. 14-Nov-3 Farsetti, Prato #102/R est:4000-5000
£2800 $5152 €4200 Black (66x95cm-26x37in) s. eau forte aquatint lit. 11-Jun-4 Farsetti, Prato #71/R est:4000-5000
Sculpture
£14000 $25760 €20440 Combustione plastica L.A (26x38cm-10x15in) s.d.67 verso burnt plastic polystyrene glass household paint. 25-Jun-4 Christie's, London #159/R est:4000-6000

BURRI, Johann-Ulrich (1802-?) Swiss
Works on paper
£1216 $2092 €1775 View of the old church of Wollishofen, with Lake Zurich (22x30cm-9x12in) s.d.1841 W/C. 8-Dec-3 Philippe Schuler, Zurich #4014/R est:1200-1500 (S.FR 2700)
£2477 $4261 €3616 View towards Hirzel with Zurich lake in background (23x31cm-9x12in) s.d.1834 W/C. 8-Dec-3 Philippe Schuler, Zurich #4013/R est:1200-1500 (S.FR 5500)

BURRI, Rene (1933-) Swiss
Photographs
£2029 $3328 €2800 Rio de Janeiro, Brazil (36x24cm-14x9in) s.i.d. verso vintage silver gelatin lit. 30-May-3 Villa Grisebach, Berlin #1125/R est:1500-1800
£5556 $10000 €8112 Che Guevara (18x25cm-7x10in) s.d.1963 verso gelatin silver print. 24-Apr-4 Phillips, New York #69/R est:6000-8000

BURRINGTON, Arthur (1856-1924) British
£2900 $4756 €4234 Quiet village, Josselin, Brittany, sunlit scene with figures and poultry (28x38cm-11x15in) s.i.d.1883. 29-May-3 Neales, Nottingham #812/R est:1200-1500
£3300 $5412 €4818 Lazy afternoon, Quimperle, Brittany, figures on a sunlit terrace (28x38cm-11x15in) s.i.d.1883. 29-May-3 Neales, Nottingham #811/R est:1200-1500

BURROUGHS, A Leicester (fl.1881-1916) British
£865 $1600 €1263 Noblemen (102x152cm-40x60in) s. 13-Mar-4 Susanin's, Chicago #6114/R est:1000-2000

BURROUGHS, William (20th C) American
Sculpture
£10490 $17833 €15000 Shrine (40x40x4cm-16x16x2in) s. painted wood prov.lit. 19-Nov-3 Tajan, Paris #144/R est:15000-20000

BURROW, Larry (1926-1971) American
Photographs
£1734 $3000 €2532 Recovery of wounded under fire, near the hill 484, Vietnam (30x46cm-12x18in) dye transfer print. 9-Dec-3 Swann Galleries, New York #423/R est:2500-3500

BURROWS, Harold Longmore (1889-1965) American
Works on paper
£856 $1600 €1250 Let's go home, no boys around (43x36cm-17x14in) s. W/C gouache exec.c.1960. 26-Feb-4 Illustration House, New York #38 est:1800-2400

BURROWS, Robert (1810-1883) British
£1100 $1738 €1595 Cattle watering at a stream (20cm-8in circular) s. board pair. 3-Sep-3 Bonhams, Bury St Edmunds #440/R est:1000-1500
£1100 $1826 €1606 Landscape with donkeys and figure (31x26cm-12x10in) s. 1-Oct-3 Sotheby's, Olympia #124/R est:1000-1500

BURSSENS, Jan (1925-2002) Belgian

£336	$594	€500	Composition aux figures (62x102cm-24x40in) s.d.1968 verso panel. 27-Apr-4 Campo, Vlaamse Kaai #341
£403	$713	€600	Composition (100x69cm-39x27in) s.d.1961 cardboard on panel. 27-Apr-4 Campo, Vlaamse Kaai #337
£417	$663	€600	Composition (70x100cm-28x39in) s. acrylic. 9-Sep-3 Palais de Beaux Arts, Brussels #198
£537	$950	€800	Figure (69x94cm-27x37in) s.d.1961 cardboard on panel. 27-Apr-4 Campo, Vlaamse Kaai #340/R
£604	$1069	€900	Composition (160x38cm-63x15in) s.d.1954 panel. 27-Apr-4 Campo, Vlaamse Kaai #339
£972	$1624	€1400	Echte mama (155x132cm-61x52in) s.d.1966 panel. 21-Oct-3 Campo, Vlaamse Kaai #364/R
£1084	$1810	€1550	Composition (52x41cm-20x16in) s. panel. 11-Oct-3 De Vuyst, Lokeren #44 est:1200-1400
£1154	$1927	€1650	Abstract composition (50x70cm-20x28in) s. 11-Oct-3 De Vuyst, Lokeren #45 est:1100-1300
£1946	$3601	€2900	Self portrait (100x80cm-39x31in) s. s.i.d.1974 verso prov. 13-Mar-4 De Vuyst, Lokeren #570/R est:2000-3000
£3667	$6563	€5500	Self portrait (110x142cm-43x56in) s. exhib. 15-May-4 De Vuyst, Lokeren #518/R est:6000-7000
£5245	$8759	€7500	Self portrait (180x140cm-71x55in) s. s.i.verso exhib. 11-Oct-3 De Vuyst, Lokeren #560/R est:10000-12000
£5594	$9343	€8000	Black pond with light (100x123cm-39x48in) s. s.i.verso exhib. 11-Oct-3 De Vuyst, Lokeren #561/R est:5000-6000
Works on paper			
£933	$1671	€1400	Dog. Self portrait. Soft self portrait (35x26cm-14x10in) s. one d.73 one d.74 one d.1971 ink three. 15-May-4 De Vuyst, Lokeren #45

BURT, Charles Thomas (1823-1902) British

£293	$548	€428	Couple with dog on country road (40x61cm-16x24in) s. 29-Feb-4 Uppsala Auktionskammare, Uppsala #16 (S.KR 4000)
£500	$915	€730	Driving sheep, believed to be across Tennel Lane, Harborne (29x44cm-11x17in) s.indis.d.1861. 6-Apr-4 Bonhams, Knightsbridge #63/R
£535	$850	€781	Drovers in mountainous landscape (41x61cm-16x24in) s.d.1872. 12-Sep-3 Skinner, Boston #240/R
£880	$1470	€1285	Horse and cart on a country lane (40x60cm-16x24in) 20-Oct-3 Bonhams, Bath #28
£1150	$2151	€1679	Train at a level crossing, passengers waiting to board (61x99cm-24x39in) s.d.1900. 24-Feb-4 Bonhams, Knowle #58/R est:1200-1800

BURT, Charles Thomas (attrib) (1823-1902) British

£520	$853	€759	On the Dee Estuary, Cheshire (33x23cm-13x9in) indis.s. i.d.1873. 3-Jun-3 Fellows & Sons, Birmingham #1/R

BURTON, Arthur Gibbes (1883-?) American

£1744	$3000	€2546	Winter landscape (41x51cm-16x20in) s. 7-Dec-3 Freeman, Philadelphia #132 est:1000-1500

BURTON, Arthur P (fl.1894-1914) British

£9500	$17005	€13870	Nymph of the Stream (122x183cm-48x72in) s. exhib. 14-May-4 Christie's, London #138/R est:10000-15000

BURTON, Claire Eva (20th C) British

£280	$445	€409	Defeating the field (30x25cm-12x10in) s. 23-Mar-3 Desmond Judd, Cranbrook #1034
£330	$525	€482	Race (41x30cm-16x12in) s. i.verso. 23-Mar-3 Desmond Judd, Cranbrook #1033
£650	$1105	€949	Steve Cauthen riding Reference Point, winning the Derby (51x56cm-20x22in) s. 19-Nov-3 Sotheby's, Olympia #138/R
£750	$1275	€1095	Charlton, the Harroways and beyond, Goddwood (74x49cm-29x19in) s. panel triptych. 19-Nov-3 Sotheby's, Olympia #141/R

BURTON, F W (?) ?

Works on paper			
£440	$722	€642	Farmstead in winter (25x20cm-10x8in) s. 3-Jun-3 Andrew Smith, Winchester #78/R

BURTON, Jeff (1963-) ?

Photographs			
£1676	$3000	€2447	Untitled, num 105 dreamland (76x102cm-30x40in) c-print edition of three prov.lit. 14-May-4 Phillips, New York #322/R est:3000-4000
£1788	$3200	€2610	Untitled, no 80, terra-cotta (76x102cm-30x40in) c-print edition of three prov. 14-May-4 Phillips, New York #320/R est:3000-4000

BURTON, Mary (20th C) British

£1100	$1947	€1606	Portrait of a terrier (40x51cm-16x20in) 29-Apr-4 Christie's, Kensington #70/R est:300-500

BURTON, Nancy Jane (1891-1972) British

£1500	$2745	€2190	Sleeping Collie (40x65cm-16x26in) s.d.21. 28-Jul-4 Bonhams, Knightsbridge #188/R est:1000-1500
Works on paper			
£260	$478	€380	Donkey study (26x33cm-10x13in) s. W/C. 10-Jun-4 Lyon & Turnbull, Edinburgh #32
£400	$744	€584	Horse and foal (25x34cm-10x13in) init. pencil W/C. 4-Mar-4 Christie's, Kensington #207/R
£541	$1000	€790	Recumbent Jack Russell terrier (25x28cm-10x11in) init. W/C pencil prov. 10-Feb-4 Doyle, New York #268/R
£700	$1253	€1022	Siamese cat (33x45cm-13x18in) s. W/C double-sided. 26-May-4 Sotheby's, Olympia #251/R

BURTON, Ralph W (1905-1984) Canadian

£222	$384	€324	Street Scene, Clayton, Ontario (27x34cm-11x13in) s. s.i.verso board. 9-Dec-3 Pinneys, Montreal #13 (C.D 500)
£222	$408	€324	Tamarac and reflections, Brazil Creek (26x34cm-10x13in) s. s.i.d.1970 verso panel. 9-Jun-4 Walker's, Ottawa #47/R (C.D 550)
£222	$408	€324	Barns at Clayton Lake (26x33cm-10x13in) s. s.i.d.1977 verso panel. 9-Jun-4 Walker's, Ottawa #56/R (C.D 550)
£260	$475	€380	Indian settlement, Yukon (26x34cm-10x13in) s.d.64 panel. 1-Jun-4 Joyner Waddington, Toronto #480 (C.D 650)
£268	$461	€391	Potato - Machine near Burnstown, Ontario (26x34cm-10x13in) s. panel prov. 2-Dec-3 Joyner Waddington, Toronto #527 (C.D 600)
£272	$501	€397	Old barn in autumn, near Ashton (26x34cm-10x13in) s. s.i.verso panel. 9-Jun-4 Walker's, Ottawa #46/R (C.D 675)
£302	$556	€441	Sugar hut (26x34cm-10x13in) s. s.i.d.1977 verso panel. 9-Jun-4 Walker's, Ottawa #4/R (C.D 750)
£302	$556	€441	Ice jam, Jock River (26x34cm-10x13in) s. s.i.d.1975 verso panel. 9-Jun-4 Walker's, Ottawa #10/R (C.D 750)
£302	$556	€441	An Ontario farm (26x33cm-10x13in) s. panel painted c.1950. 9-Jun-4 Walker's, Ottawa #55/R (C.D 750)
£302	$556	€441	Neils Harbour, Cape Breton (26x34cm-10x13in) s. s.i.d.1958 verso panel. 9-Jun-4 Walker's, Ottawa #95/R (C.D 750)
£311	$510	€454	Trout Lake, near Madawaska, Ontario (25x33cm-10x13in) s.i.d.1965 verso panel. 28-May-3 Maynards, Vancouver #4 (C.D 700)
£338	$574	€493	Near Notre Dame de Tours, Que (27x34cm-11x13in) s. s.i.verso board prov. 23-Nov-3 Levis, Calgary #423/R (C.D 750)
£342	$635	€499	On the banks of the Red river, La Conception (27x34cm-11x13in) s. i.d.July 54 verso panel. 2-Mar-4 Ritchie, Toronto #127/R (C.D 850)
£363	$668	€530	Old church, Burritts Rapids (40x50cm-16x20in) s. s.i.d.1977 verso. 9-Jun-4 Walker's, Ottawa #5/R (C.D 900)
£364	$593	€531	Old log house (26x34cm-10x13in) s. s.i.d.Oct 1960 verso panel. 23-Sep-3 Ritchie, Toronto #129/R (C.D 800)
£400	$732	€584	Spring near Ripon, Quebec (26x34cm-10x13in) s. panel painted 1960 prov. 1-Jun-4 Joyner Waddington, Toronto #367/R (C.D 1000)
£403	$742	€588	Spring on the Simon River (50x66cm-20x26in) s. s.i.d.1957 verso. 9-Jun-4 Walker's, Ottawa #20/R (C.D 1000)
£413	$748	€603	Farmer's rapids, Que (27x34cm-11x13in) s. s.d.1962 verso wood board. 18-Apr-4 Levis, Calgary #17/R est:1000-1200 (C.D 1000)
£495	$842	€723	Near Antrim, Ontario (27x34cm-11x13in) s. panel. 21-Nov-3 Walker's, Ottawa #3/R (C.D 1100)
£625	$1075	€913	Early summer near Mt St Patrick Ontario (26x34cm-10x13in) s. panel painted 1963. 2-Dec-3 Joyner Waddington, Toronto #493 (C.D 1400)
£720	$1318	€1051	Earl Bradley's House, Fitzroy Harbour, Ontario (26x34cm-10x13in) s. panel. 1-Jun-4 Joyner Waddington, Toronto #496 est:1000-1200 (C.D 1800)
£804	$1382	€1174	Old farm near Ashton, Ontario (40x50cm-16x20in) s. 2-Dec-3 Joyner Waddington, Toronto #237/R est:1800-2200 (C.D 1800)
£880	$1610	€1285	Indian home, Dieu riviere, Upper Ottawa (35x45cm-14x18in) s. 1-Jun-4 Joyner Waddington, Toronto #325/R est:1200-1500 (C.D 2200)
£1040	$1903	€1518	Fishing Cove N.S (40x50cm-16x20in) s. 1-Jun-4 Joyner Waddington, Toronto #133/R est:2000-3000 (C.D 2600)
£1429	$2457	€2086	Old farm buildings, Fallowfield Rd, Ontario (50x65cm-20x26in) s. painted 1971. 2-Dec-3 Joyner Waddington, Toronto #181/R est:2500-3500 (C.D 3200)

BURTON, Sally (20th C) New Zealander?

£436	$685	€632	Still life (120x292cm-47x115in) s.d.1992 acrylic gold leaf. 27-Aug-3 Dunbar Sloane, Wellington #142 (NZ.D 1200)

BURTON, Samuel Chatwood (1881-c.1955) American

Works on paper			
£269	$500	€393	West Indies coastal trader. Storm in a harbour (46x61cm-18x24in) s. W/C double-sided executed 1925. 7-Mar-4 Treadway Gallery, Cincinnati #513/R

BURTON, Sir Frederick William (1816-1900) British

£520	$936	€759	Hound in a highland landscape (22x30cm-9x12in) s. 20-Apr-4 Rowley Fine Art, Newmarket #413/R
Works on paper			
£85000	$144500	€124100	Sunday morning (30x23cm-12x9in) i. pencil W/C bodycol gum arabic. 26-Nov-3 Christie's, London #14/R est:30000-50000
£180000	$331200	€262800	Child Miranda (47x27cm-19x11in) init.d.1864 pencil W/C htd bodycol prov.exhib.lit. 9-Jun-4 Christie's, London #34/R est:200000-300000

BURTSCHER, Anton (1887-1987) Austrian

Works on paper			
£420	$701	€600	Still life with flowers and mushrooms (33x42cm-13x17in) s. W/C. 9-Oct-3 Michael Zeller, Lindau #532/R
£517	$864	€740	Karnten, Ossiachersee (39x32cm-15x13in) s. i. verso W/C. 9-Oct-3 Michael Zeller, Lindau #533/R est:600

BURWELL, Vernon (1916-1990) American

Sculpture			
£1916	$3200	€2797	Posing nude (69x20x20cm-27x8x8in) concrete sculpture. 15-Nov-3 Slotin Folk Art, Buford #148/R est:2000-4000

BURY BRILLEL, Leonie (19th C) ?

£493	$853	€700	Still life with roses (44x53cm-17x21in) s.d.1890. 9-Dec-3 Pandolfini, Florence #87/R

BURY, Pol (1922-) Belgian

£1844	$3079	€2600	Composition (41x20cm-16x8in) s. fibreboard. 20-Oct-3 Bernaerts, Antwerp #229/R est:500-600
Sculpture			
£4861	$8118	€7000	Sphere sur un cube (50x20x20cm-20x8x8in) s.i.num.7/8 stainless steel electric motor exhib.lit. 21-Oct-3 Artcurial Briest, Paris #503/R est:8000-10000
£5405	$10000	€7891	44 tiges de cuivre marteles sur fond bois noir (67x51x28cm-26x20x11in) hammered copper wood electricity motor wire prov. 13-Jul-4 Christie's, Rockefeller NY #50/R est:3000-4000
£5521	$9000	€8061	Untitled (85x49x16cm-33x19x6in) s.d.63 painted wood aluminum nails electric motor prov. 23-Sep-3 Christie's, Rockefeller NY #107/R est:6000-8000

£9000 $15030 €13140 Untitled (19x75x90cm-7x30x35in) painted metal hanging mobile exec 1955 prov. 21-Oct-3 Sotheby's, London #336/R est:7000-9000
£9146 $15000 €13353 Sur fond noir, 113 points rouges (44x41x24cm-17x16x9in) s.verso oil nylon lines wood electric motor prov.exhib.lit. 28-May-3 Sotheby's, Amsterdam #71/R est:10000-12000
£9441 $16049 €13500 Cones creux (218x43x34cm-86x17x13in) wood nylons s.i.d.1964 verso prov.exhib.lit. 27-Nov-3 Lempertz, Koln #62/R est:13000-15000
Works on paper
£296 $545 €450 Animal surrealiste (36x34cm-14x13in) s.d.1941 Indian ink. 28-Jun-4 Joron-Derem, Paris #147
£347 $580 €500 Manneken piss (17x11cm-7x4in) s. cut postcard exec.c.1965. 25-Oct-3 Cornette de St.Cyr, Paris #608
£369 $679 €550 Eveque au bouquet (27x23cm-11x9in) s.d.1944 gouache. 24-Mar-4 Joron-Derem, Paris #95
£544 $974 €800 Composition (24x32cm-9x13in) s. gouache pair. 19-Mar-4 Millon & Associes, Paris #214
£590 $986 €850 Composition (32x50cm-13x20in) s.d.1952 collage. 25-Oct-3 Cornette de St.Cyr, Paris #609/R
£611 $1021 €880 Composition (35x50cm-14x20in) s.d.1952 collage. 25-Oct-3 Cornette de St.Cyr, Paris #610/R

BURZI, Ettore (1872-1937) Italian
£390 $697 €569 Sotto i platani - Riva Ciani (12x22cm-5x9in) panel. 22-Mar-4 Philippe Schuler, Zurich #4308 (S.FR 900)
£1126 $2015 €1644 Tramonto da Lanzo Intelvi (12x22cm-5x9in) s.d. panel. 22-Mar-4 Philippe Schuler, Zurich #4309 est:900-1200 (S.FR 2600)

BUSATI, Luca Antonio (16th C) Italian
£5000 $8500 €7300 Deposition of Christ (83x66cm-33x26in) panel. 30-Oct-3 Sotheby's, Olympia #17/R est:5000-7000

BUSATO, Mario (1902-1971) Italian
Sculpture
£5918 $10594 €8700 Elephant (32x47x24cm-13x19x9in) mono. pat bronze exec.c.1940. 21-Mar-4 St-Germain-en-Laye Encheres #91/R est:8000

BUSCAGLIONE, Giuseppe (1868-1928) Italian
£533 $981 €800 Moon effect (30x44cm-12x17in) s. board. 14-Jun-4 Sant Agostino, Torino #216/R
£567 $948 €800 Back to the barn (14x20cm-6x8in) s. board lit. 20-Oct-3 Sant Agostino, Torino #260/R
£570 $1010 €850 Back to the barn (14x20cm-6x8in) s. board. 1-May-4 Meeting Art, Vercelli #37
£709 $1184 €1000 Susa Valley (43x30cm-17x12in) s. board. 20-Oct-3 Sant Agostino, Torino #83/R
£733 $1349 €1100 Peasants in the fields (14x20cm-6x8in) s. board. 10-Jun-4 Christie's, Rome #107/R
£805 $1442 €1200 Landscape with figures (32x44cm-13x17in) s. board. 25-May-4 Finarte Semenzato, Milan #104/R
£979 $1635 €1400 Ruins (31x44cm-12x17in) s. i.verso board. 26-Jun-3 Sant Agostino, Torino #68/R
£1007 $1802 €1500 Fishing village (35x47cm-14x19in) s. board. 25-May-4 Finarte Semenzato, Milan #85/R est:1400-1600
£1042 $1771 €1500 Sunset, fishing (31x44cm-12x17in) s. board. 1-Nov-3 Meeting Art, Vercelli #94/R est:1500
£1042 $1771 €1500 Ruins (31x44cm-12x17in) s. s.i.verso board. 1-Nov-3 Meeting Art, Vercelli #231/R
£1049 $1752 €1500 Snow in September (31x44cm-12x17in) s. board. 26-Jun-3 Sant Agostino, Torino #40/R est:1800
£1275 $2283 €1900 In the park (44x31cm-17x12in) s. board. 25-May-4 Finarte Semenzato, Milan #90/R est:1500-1800
£1342 $2376 €2000 Leaves falling (55x41cm-22x16in) s. board. 1-May-4 Meeting Art, Vercelli #128 est:2000
£1342 $2376 €2000 Farms in the Alps (57x42cm-22x17in) s. s.i.verso board. 1-May-4 Meeting Art, Vercelli #426 est:2000
£1389 $2361 €2000 Ruins in Val d'Aosta (43x57cm-17x22in) s. board. 1-Nov-3 Meeting Art, Vercelli #215/R est:2000
£1522 $2496 €2100 Mountain path with figures and chapel (45x64cm-18x25in) s. cardboard on canvas. 27-May-3 Finarte Semenzato, Milan #24/R
£1594 $2614 €2200 Old farms (30x44cm-12x17in) s. board. 27-May-3 Finarte Semenzato, Milan #119/R est:2000
£1611 $2851 €2400 Alpine pastures (41x56cm-16x22in) s. i.verso board. 1-May-4 Meeting Art, Vercelli #320 est:2000
£2083 $3542 €3000 Lake in the woods (31x44cm-12x17in) s. board. 1-Nov-3 Meeting Art, Vercelli #316/R est:3000

BUSCH, Johan Frederik (1825-1883) Danish
£1776 $2806 €2575 Interior scene with figures in a cottage, Northern Sjaelland (55x43cm-22x17in) s.d.1852 exhib.prov. 2-Sep-3 Rasmussen, Copenhagen #1691/R est:15000-20000 (D.KR 19000)

BUSCH, Walter (1898-1980) German
£423 $756 €600 Portrait of an elderly peasant woman (45x30cm-18x12in) s. i.verso. 8-Jan-4 Allgauer, Kempten #2361/R
£685 $1164 €1000 Snow covered farmstead (50x75cm-20x30in) s.i. i. verso lit. 6-Nov-3 Allgauer, Kempten #3398/R

BUSCH, Wilhelm (1832-1908) German
£1879 $3326 €2800 Man in red jacket (13x11cm-5x4in) paper on board. 30-Apr-4 Dr Fritz Nagel, Stuttgart #738/R est:1800
£1974 $3572 €3000 The writer (18x16cm-7x6in) indis.s. paper on board. 19-Apr-4 Glerum, Amsterdam #300/R est:2000-2500
£3618 $6549 €5500 Grazing cows (28x34cm-11x13in) paper on board. 19-Apr-4 Glerum, Amsterdam #298/R est:7000-9000
£3618 $6549 €5500 Farmer with cow (17x34cm-7x13in) paper on board. 19-Apr-4 Glerum, Amsterdam #299/R est:5000-7000
£4667 $8353 €7000 Red peasant with jugs (17x7cm-7x3in) cardboard on panel prov. 14-May-4 Ketterer, Munich #115/R est:7000-9000
£6643 $11294 €9500 Red and green jacket in tavern (18x14cm-7x6in) s. board prov. 29-Nov-3 Villa Grisebach, Berlin #102/R est:10000-15000
£10811 $19351 €16000 Self caricatures (24x42cm-9x17in) panel lit. 8-May-4 Schloss Ahlden, Ahlden #766/R est:16500
Works on paper
£600 $1074 €900 Monk in wood (13x8cm-5x3in) mono. pen brush. 13-May-4 Bassenge, Berlin #5529/R
£600 $1104 €900 Portrait of man in profile (13x12cm-5x5in) pencil. 11-Jun-4 Hauswedell & Nolte, Hamburg #1001/R

BUSCH, Wilhelm (attrib) (1832-1908) German
Works on paper
£3020 $5557 €4500 Officer telling stories at table (18x24cm-7x9in) mono. wash pen chk. 26-Mar-4 Dorotheum, Vienna #120/R est:800-1200

BUSCHELBERGER, Anton (1869-1934) German
Sculpture
£1370 $2329 €2000 Two parrots (79cm-31in) s.d.1927 pat.bronze Cast.Krass, Berlin. 5-Nov-3 Hugo Ruef, Munich #2156/R est:1200

BUSCIOLANO, Vincenzo (1851-?) Italian
£524 $954 €765 Grandfather's pipe (39x51cm-15x20in) s.d.1914. 16-Jun-4 Fischer, Luzern #2041/R (S.FR 1200)
£1719 $2870 €2510 Neapolitanczyk in a scarlet beret (26x21cm-10x8in) s.d.1910. 19-Oct-3 Agra, Warsaw #36/R (P.Z 11000)
£1972 $3411 €2800 Two little boys (37x51cm-15x20in) s. 9-Dec-3 Pandolfini, Florence #245/R est:2000-2200

BUSCIONI, Umberto (1931-) Italian
£1987 $3616 €3000 Study for shirts (70x100cm-28x39in) s.i.verso. 17-Jun-4 Galleria Pananti, Florence #10/R est:5000-6000

BUSH, Harry (1883-1957) British
£300 $528 €438 Favourite chair (51x39cm-20x15in) i. 19-May-4 Christie's, Kensington #698/R

BUSH, Jack (1909-1977) Canadian
£1400 $2562 €2044 Autumn woods (30x40cm-12x16in) s. board prov. 1-Jun-4 Joyner Waddington, Toronto #208/R est:4000-5000 (C.D 3500)
£4878 $8732 €7122 Summer No1 (61x75cm-24x30in) s.i.d.Aug 56 masonite prov.exhib. 31-May-4 Sotheby's, Toronto #28/R est:8000-10000 (C.D 12000)
£6306 $10721 €9207 Pink rain (105x114cm-41x45in) s.i.d.Sept.1968 verso acrylic prov.exhib.lit. 27-Nov-3 Heffel, Vancouver #58/R est:15000-20000 (C.D 14000)
£7200 $13176 €10512 England Green (77x82cm-30x32in) s.d.63 lit. 1-Jun-4 Joyner Waddington, Toronto #86/R est:20000-25000 (C.D 18000)
£9600 $17568 €14016 Big cut off (115x139cm-45x55in) s.d.Nov 1968 verso acrylic prov. 1-Jun-4 Joyner Waddington, Toronto #47/R est:20000-25000 (C.D 24000)
£9821 $16893 €14339 Screen on Green (165x342cm-65x135in) s.i.d.May 1973 acrylic. 2-Dec-3 Joyner Waddington, Toronto #35/R est:25000-30000 (C.D 22000)
£11179 $20010 €16321 Toward blue (203x114cm-80x45in) s.i.d.November 1970 verso acrylic prov.exhib. 31-May-4 Sotheby's, Toronto #143/R est:30000-50000 (C.D 27500)
£16892 $28716 €24662 June mulberry (168x287cm-66x113in) s.i.d.1972 verso acrylic polymer prov.lit. 18-Nov-3 Sotheby's, Toronto #108/R est:40000-60000 (C.D 37500)
£18293 $32744 €26708 Irish rock No2 (166x139cm-65x55in) s.i.d.October 1969 acrylic prov. 31-May-4 Sotheby's, Toronto #30/R est:30000-50000 (C.D 45000)
Works on paper
£2928 $4977 €4275 Top Three and Blue Loop (55x76cm-22x30in) gouache lit. 27-Nov-3 Heffel, Vancouver #202 est:2500-3500 (C.D 6500)
£6098 $10915 €8903 Row sun (57x75cm-22x30in) gouache. 31-May-4 Sotheby's, Toronto #141/R est:4000-6000 (C.D 15000)

BUSH, Norton (1834-1894) American
£2116 $4000 €3089 Volcano, church and figure in semi-tropical South American scene (25x36cm-10x14in) s.d.79. 17-Feb-4 John Moran, Pasadena #150a/R est:1500-2500
£3175 $6000 €4636 Tropical river landscape (51x25cm-20x10in) s.d.1874 prov. 17-Feb-4 John Moran, Pasadena #66/R est:5000-7000

BUSH, Reginald Edgar James (1869-1934) British
Works on paper
£450 $819 €675 The harbour at St Ives, Cornwall (53x74cm-21x29in) indis.init.d.97 pencil W/C. 1-Jul-4 Christie's, Kensington #325/R

BUSH, Stephen (20th C) Australian
£4959 $9174 €7240 Show yourself (106x137cm-42x54in) s.d.22.8.90 i.stretcher prov.exhib. 15-Mar-4 Sotheby's, Melbourne #10/R est:12000-18000 (A.D 12000)
£6147 $9713 €8975 The lure of Paris No 2 (182x182cm-72x72in) s.i.d.September 1992 stretcher prov.exhib. 2-Sep-3 Deutscher-Menzies, Melbourne #1/R est:10000-15000 (A.D 15000)

BUSIERI, Giovanni Battista (1698-1757) Italian
£4861 $8264 €7000 Roamn landscapes with figures (22x33cm-9x13in) tempera paper on canvas pair. 28-Oct-3 Il Ponte, Milan #338/R
£15172 $25338 €22000 The Tiber at Ponte Rotto, Rome (22x34cm-9x13in) tempera paper. 12-Nov-3 Sotheby's, Milan #169/R est:10000-15000
£20690 $34552 €30000 Views of Rome (22x34cm-9x13in) tempera paper on canvas pair. 12-Nov-3 Sotheby's, Milan #171/R est:20000-30000
£26846 $49396 €40000 Landscapes near Rome (56x81cm-22x32in) pair prov. 24-Mar-4 Dorotheum, Vienna #28/R est:40000-50000
£31724 $52979 €46000 Views of Rome (18x25cm-7x10in) tempera paper pair. 12-Nov-3 Sotheby's, Milan #170/R est:20000-30000
Works on paper
£1000 $1730 €1460 Views in Rome (17x23cm-7x9in) black chk pen brown ink four prov. 12-Dec-3 Christie's, Kensington #386/R est:600-800

£4500 $8235 €6570 Landscape with figures resting by a river, a tower to the right (24x30cm-9x12in) gouache. 8-Jul-4 Sotheby's, London #12/R est:2500-3500

BUSLIN, E (?) Belgian?
Sculpture
£1189 $1985 €1700 Jeune fille faisant sa tresse pres d'une vache (31x45cm-12x18in) s.st.f. gilt pat bronze. 13-Oct-3 Horta, Bruxelles #94 est:1800-2200

BUSOM, Simo (1927-) Spanish
£903 $1535 €1300 Rambla Amunt (60x73cm-24x29in) s. s.i.d.1996-99 verso prov. 28-Oct-3 Segre, Madrid #334/R

BUSQUETS SERVERA, Sebastia (1915-) Spanish
Works on paper
£336 $628 €500 Landscape in Majorca (63x88cm-25x35in) s.d.1950 s.i.verso W/C exhib. 24-Feb-4 Durán, Madrid #1154/R

BUSSCHE, Joseph Emanuel van den (1837-1903) Belgian
£331 $612 €480 Troika attaquee par des loups (41x70cm-16x28in) s.d.1883. 19-Jan-4 Horta, Bruxelles #323
£2532 $4000 €3697 Woman, musician, child and older woman with basket of oranges in landscape setting (79x99cm-31x39in) s. 6-Sep-3 Brunk, Ashville #124

BUSSCHERE, Constant de (1876-1951) Belgian
£743 $1330 €1100 Chariot attele dans une rue enneigee (100x75cm-39x30in) s. 10-May-4 Horta, Bruxelles #331
£2000 $3660 €3000 Les chevaux de labour (60x75cm-24x30in) s. 7-Jun-4 Palais de Beaux Arts, Brussels #48/R est:2500-3000

BUSSE, Fritz (1903-) German
Works on paper
£382 $623 €550 Stuttgart Opera (24x35cm-9x14in) s. W/C Indian ink. 27-Sep-3 Dr Fritz Nagel, Stuttgart #9059/R

BUSSE, Georg Heinrich (1810-1868) German
Works on paper
£2009 $3656 €2933 Wooded landscape with gorge, herdsman and view of a church (30x43cm-12x17in) mono. i. pen brush sepia over chk htd white prov.exhib. 17-Jun-4 Kornfeld, Bern #4/R est:5000 (S.FR 4600)

BUSSE, Jacques (1922-) French
£1208 $2223 €1800 Le musicien (33x24cm-13x9in) s.d.1951. 24-Mar-4 Binoche, Paris #73/R est:1500-2000

BUSSEY, Reuben (1818-1893) British
£340 $629 €496 Medieval knight and page in an interior (60x70cm-24x28in) s. 14-Jan-4 Lawrence, Crewkerne #1406

BUSSIERE, Gaston (1862-1929) French
£5500 $10120 €8030 Dance of the veils (92x72cm-36x28in) s.d.1925. 23-Mar-4 Bonhams, New Bond Street #101/R est:5000-8000

BUSSOLINO, Vittorio (1853-1922) Italian
£1293 $2315 €1888 Cowherd with cows (34x56cm-13x22in) s. 12-May-4 Dobiaschofsky, Bern #368/R est:1400 (S.FR 3000)

BUSSON, Charles (1822-1908) French
£625 $1000 €913 Berger et son troupe (86x130cm-34x51in) s. painted c.1870. 18-May-3 Auctions by the Bay, Alameda #1019/R

BUSSON, Charles (attrib) (1822-1908) French
£633 $1134 €950 Vaches au bord du ruisseau (75x102cm-30x40in) s.d.1868. 11-May-4 Vanderkindere, Brussels #134

BUSSON, Georges (1859-1933) French
Works on paper
£600 $1074 €900 Huntsmen on horseback (31x42cm-12x17in) s.d.1886 gouache. 15-May-4 Hagelstam, Helsinki #51/R
£1042 $1698 €1500 Fox (28x36cm-11x14in) W/C. 29-Sep-3 Coutau Begarie, Paris #268/R
£4828 $8931 €7000 Chasse a courre (42x55cm-17x22in) s. W/C. 16-Feb-4 Horta, Bruxelles #108 est:8000-10000

BUSSON, Marcel (1913-) French?
£1312 $2191 €1850 Mosquee a Erfoud (61x38cm-24x15in) s.d.1970 i.verso cardboard on panel. 16-Jun-3 Gros & Delettrez, Paris #347/R est:1600-2300
£1479 $2558 €2100 Casablanca (27x46cm-11x18in) s. i.verso panel. 15-Dec-3 Gros & Delettrez, Paris #43/R est:2000-2200
£1560 $2606 €2200 Casbah dans le Haut Atlas (65x54cm-26x21in) s. i.verso. 16-Jun-3 Gros & Delettrez, Paris #522/R est:2000-3000
£1620 $2802 €2300 Bou Regreg (46x55cm-18x22in) s. cardboard panel. 15-Dec-3 Gros & Delettrez, Paris #42/R est:1800-2300
£2183 $3777 €3100 Fumees du matin (54x65cm-21x26in) s. i.d.1974 verso. 15-Dec-3 Gros & Delettrez, Paris #40/R est:2500-3000
£2254 $3899 €3200 Oliviers, Moulay Idriss (64x54cm-25x21in) s. 15-Dec-3 Gros & Delettrez, Paris #41/R est:3000-3500
£2270 $3790 €3200 Casbah au bord de l'oued (73x54cm-29x21in) s. 16-Jun-3 Gros & Delettrez, Paris #338/R est:1800-2300
£3191 $5330 €4500 Place Djemaa el F'na, Marrakech (60x81cm-24x32in) i.verso cardboard. 16-Jun-3 Gros & Delettrez, Paris #346/R est:3500-4300

BUSSON, Sophie (20th C) French?
£2067 $3699 €3100 La partie d'echecs aux insectes (64x92cm-25x36in) s. 16-May-4 Thierry & Lannon, Brest #203/R est:2000-3000

BUSSY, Jane Simone (20th C) ?
£360 $659 €526 Still life with faience bowl with grapes and tomatoes (33x43cm-13x17in) s. 28-Jul-4 Mallams, Oxford #359/R
£3500 $5950 €5110 Plums and peaches. Roquebrune, South of France (33x41cm-13x16in) s. two prov. 21-Nov-3 Christie's, London #59/R est:1000-1500

BUSSY, Simon (1869-1954) French
£1702 $2945 €2485 Poisson coralien (24x19cm-9x7in) init.d.39 prov. 10-Dec-3 Shapiro, Sydney #59/R est:4000-7000 (A.D 4000)
£2128 $3681 €3107 Red bishop (22x16cm-9x6in) init.d.42 i.verso prov. 10-Dec-3 Shapiro, Sydney #58/R est:5000-7000 (A.D 5000)
Works on paper
£300 $483 €435 Paysage d'Ecosse, Rothiemurchus (40x30cm-16x12in) s. pastel. 21-Aug-3 Bonhams, Edinburgh #1217
£2134 $3840 €3200 Poisson cichlid (29x26cm-11x10in) s. gouache. 26-Apr-4 Tajan, Paris #42/R est:2500-3500
£2334 $4200 €3500 Saint Jeaunet (33x30cm-13x12in) s.d.41 pastel. 26-Apr-4 Tajan, Paris #41/R est:3500-4500
£2600 $4420 €3796 Atrani, Italy. Amalfi (38x33cm-15x13in) s.i. pastel two prov. 21-Nov-3 Christie's, London #57/R est:1200-1800
£3600 $6120 €5256 Coral fish. Brown coral fish (21x15cm-8x6in) s. pastel two prov. 21-Nov-3 Christie's, London #58/R est:1500-2500
£4794 $8151 €7000 Touraco a tete rose (32x24cm-13x9in) s. pastel. 6-Nov-3 Tajan, Paris #224/R
£6122 $10959 €9000 Tigre couche (21x28cm-8x11in) mono. pastel. 17-Mar-4 Maigret, Paris #108/R est:800-1200
£7667 $13800 €11500 La mouette (36x30cm-14x12in) s. pastel prov.exhib. 26-Apr-4 Tajan, Paris #39/R est:4500-5500

BUSTAMANTE ALVARADO, Abelardo (1898-1984) Cuban
£507 $832 €700 Posada de la hermandad (46x32cm-18x13in) s. panel. 27-May-3 Durán, Madrid #1274/R

BUSTAMANTE, Alfredo (1896-?) South American?
£1033 $1900 €1508 Park (101x91cm-40x36in) s.d.1946. 22-Jun-4 Galeria y Remates, Montevideo #66/R est:1700-2200

BUSTAMANTE, Jean Marc (1952-) French
Photographs
£2000 $3680 €3000 Something is missing, I Barcelone - Maisons rouges (86x66cm-34x26in) s.d.1997 num.4/56 verso cibachrome print prov.exhib.lit. 9-Jun-4 Artcurial Briest, Paris #564/R est:2500-3000
£2133 $3926 €3200 Something is missing, IA Barcelone (86x66cm-34x26in) num.4/6 cibachrome print exec 1997 prov.exhib.lit. 9-Jun-4 Artcurial Briest, Paris #563/R est:2500-3000
£2657 $4438 €3800 SIM, sans titre (40x60cm-16x24in) col photo edition of 6 prov. 11-Oct-3 Cornette de St.Cyr, Paris #151/R est:4000-5000
£5988 $10000 €8742 Tableau (103x127cm-41x50in) cibachrome mounted on aluminum executed 1980 prov. 14-Nov-3 Phillips, New York #278/R est:12000-18000
£7000 $11690 €10220 Stationnaire II (62x52cm-24x20in) cibachrome print sold with concrete box lid prov. 22-Oct-3 Christie's, London #115/R est:4000-6000
£8939 $16000 €13051 LPX, L P 10 (180x227cm-71x89in) col coupler print aluminum edition of six prov. 14-May-4 Phillips, New York #199/R est:15000-20000
£36313 $65000 €53017 Cypress (145x116cm-57x46in) s. num.1 2 3 4 cibachrome print 4 parts exec 1991 prov. 13-May-4 Sotheby's, New York #333/R est:60000-80000
Prints
£13174 $22000 €19234 Lumiere (135x185cm-53x73in) silkscreen on plexiglas metal brackets executed 1991 prov. 14-Nov-3 Phillips, New York #206/R est:25000-35000
£16667 $30333 €25000 Panorama (154x244cm-61x96in) serigraph on plexiglas prov. 2-Jul-4 Binoche, Paris #24/R est:20000-30000

BUSTARD, William (1894-1973) Australian
Works on paper
£569 $1019 €831 Rocky Pool, Corrumbin Creek (36x50cm-14x20in) s.d.1960 W/C. 10-May-4 Joel, Victoria #283 est:800-1200 (A.D 1400)

BUTAZZI, Socrates (19/20th C) Italian
£271 $434 €396 Portrait of a man (85x62cm-33x24in) s. after Rembrandt. 16-Sep-3 Philippe Schuler, Zurich #5431 (S.FR 600)

BUTCHART, James (20th C) British
Sculpture
£3500 $6370 €5250 Flight centre table (229cm-90in) sheet tubular aluminium glass lit. 30-Jun-4 Christie's, Kensington #132/R est:2000-3000

BUTCHER, John (fl.1934-1936) British
Works on paper
£250 $440 €365 Spiders web (23x53cm-9x21in) s. W/C. 31-Dec-3 Lambrays, Wadebridge #638

BUTER, Bernhard (1883-1959) German
£289 $531 €430 Cattle grazing in lower Rhine landscape (60x80cm-24x31in) s. panel. 27-Mar-4 L & B, Essen #76/R

BUTHAUD, René (1886-1986) French

£470 $832 €700 Abstract (130x80cm-51x31in) s. masonite lit. 27-Apr-4 Claude Aguttes, Neuilly #11/R
£483 $855 €720 Abstract (130x60cm-51x24in) s. i.d.1942 verso panel lit. 27-Apr-4 Claude Aguttes, Neuilly #12/R
Works on paper
£400 $732 €580 Tete de femme a la capeline (34x24cm-13x9in) mono. pencil. 28-Jan-4 Piasa, Paris #12
£738 $1307 €1100 Femme en buste a la couronne blanche (52x37cm-20x15in) mono. mixed media lit. 27-Apr-4 Claude Aguttes, Neuilly #10/R
£3468 $6000 €5063 Three Graces (116x80cm-46x31in) s. pastel W/C gouache on collaged newspaper mounted on canvas prov. 11-Dec-3 Sotheby's, New York #23/R est:8000-12000

BUTHE, Michael (1944-1994) German

Works on paper
£280 $476 €400 Paysage (51x46cm-20x18in) s. mixed media. 29-Nov-3 Neret-Minet, Paris #170
£385 $642 €562 Untitled (49x30cm-19x12in) gouache collage board paper bag with opening prov. 24-Jun-3 Germann, Zurich #927 (S.FR 850)
£452 $756 €660 Tango (30x40cm-12x16in) s.i.d.1988 mixed media. 24-Jun-3 Germann, Zurich #928 (S.FR 1000)
£543 $923 €793 Untitled (78x88cm-31x35in) s.d.1973 verso mixed media. 25-Nov-3 Germann, Zurich #28/R (S.FR 1200)
£1357 $2267 €1981 Untitled (100x70cm-39x28in) s.d.1973 sparkle black paper. 24-Jun-3 Germann, Zurich #87/R est:2500-3500 (S.FR 3000)
£1357 $2267 €1981 Untitled (79x106cm-31x42in) s.d.1988 mixed media collage. 24-Jun-3 Germann, Zurich #151/R est:3000-4000 (S.FR 3000)
£1448 $2418 €2114 Untitled (100x70cm-39x28in) s.d.1973 chl gold gouache collage. 24-Jun-3 Germann, Zurich #152/R est:2500-3500 (S.FR 3200)

BUTLER, Anton (1819-1874) Swiss

£391 $716 €571 Landscape near Luzern (18x26cm-7x10in) mono.d.66 cardboard. 4-Jun-4 Zofingen, Switzerland #2333 (S.FR 900)

BUTLER, Charles Ernest (1864-c.1918) British

£330 $611 €482 Symonds yat (18x10cm-7x4in) s.d.27. 13-Feb-4 Keys, Aylsham #729
£800 $1272 €1168 Portraits of an officer and a young lady (61x51cm-24x20in) s.d.09 pair. 9-Sep-3 Gorringes, Lewes #2093/R
£900 $1440 €1314 Herm, Jethou and Sark from Guernsey (10x22cm-4x9in) s. artist's board. 17-Sep-3 Bonhams, Brooks & Langlois, Jersey #57/R

BUTLER, David (1898-) American

£361 $650 €527 Santa Claus (71x30cm-28x12in) enamel on tin. 24-Apr-4 Slotin Folk Art, Buford #380/R
£361 $650 €527 Freedoms bus (25x69cm-10x27in) enamel on tin. 24-Apr-4 Slotin Folk Art, Buford #381/R
£361 $650 €527 Flying cow (36x61cm-14x24in) enamel on tin double-sided. 24-Apr-4 Slotin Folk Art, Buford #382/R
£833 $1500 €1216 Cowboy and bucking horse (58x69cm-23x27in) enamel on tin. 24-Apr-4 Slotin Folk Art, Buford #379/R est:1000-2000
Sculpture
£1497 $2500 €2186 Flying elephant (30x69x20cm-12x27x8in) cut painted tin prov. 15-Nov-3 Slotin Folk Art, Buford #196/R est:1000-2000
£1796 $3000 €2622 Noah's ark (56x71cm-22x28in) painted tin cutout. 15-Nov-3 Slotin Folk Art, Buford #194b/R est:1000-3000

BUTLER, Edward Burgess (1853-1928) American

£522 $850 €762 California landscape (64x76cm-25x30in) s. 28-Sep-3 Bonhams & Butterfields, Los Angeles #7027

BUTLER, Elizabeth (1846-1933) British

Works on paper
£280 $512 €409 View of a Spanish monastery (15x22cm-6x9in) init. W/C. 27-Jan-4 Bonhams, Knightsbridge #158/R

BUTLER, George Edmund (1870-1936) New Zealander

£277 $496 €404 Wellington Harbour (17x31cm-7x12in) s.d.1896 board. 11-May-4 Peter Webb, Auckland #61a/R (NZ.D 800)
£301 $511 €439 Landscape (10x15cm-4x6in) s. board. 26-Nov-3 Dunbar Sloane, Wellington #108 (NZ.D 800)

BUTLER, Grace (1887-1962) New Zealander

£376 $639 €549 Rural landscape (35x44cm-14x17in) s. board. 26-Nov-3 Dunbar Sloane, Wellington #159a est:1000-2000 (NZ.D 1000)
£714 $1293 €1042 Landscape (34x44cm-13x17in) s. canvasboard. 30-Mar-4 Peter Webb, Auckland #183/R est:2000-3000 (NZ.D 2000)
£1103 $2063 €1610 Near Arthur's pass (29x34cm-11x13in) s. 24-Feb-4 Peter Webb, Auckland #113/R est:2000-3000 (NZ.D 3000)
£1455 $2284 €2110 Arthur's pass (44x64cm-17x25in) s. 27-Aug-3 Dunbar Sloane, Wellington #64/R est:2500-3500 (NZ.D 4000)

BUTLER, Herbert E (fl.1881-1921) British

£13304 $23814 €19424 Pulling in the nets (101x167cm-40x66in) s. 26-May-4 AB Stockholms Auktionsverk #2384/R est:25000-30000 (S.KR 180000)
Works on paper
£360 $655 €526 Evening, Polperro harbour (16x25cm-6x10in) s. W/C. 21-Jun-4 Bonhams, Bath #444
£500 $825 €730 Woman fetching water from a stream (26x18cm-10x7in) s. W/C. 4-Jul-3 Honiton Galleries, Honiton #63/R
£540 $853 €788 Figures in a cobbled street leading towards the quay (26x35cm-10x14in) s. W/C. 5-Sep-3 Honiton Galleries, Honiton #17
£600 $1110 €876 Boats by the coastline, Polperro (24x36cm-9x14in) s. W/C. 9-Mar-4 Bonhams, New Bond Street #139
£620 $1035 €905 View of the harbour and quay at Polperro, Cornwall (25x36cm-10x14in) s. W/C. 14-Oct-3 Canterbury Auctions, UK #123/R
£750 $1388 €1095 Harbour front, Polperro, Cornwall (35x53cm-14x21in) s. W/C. 9-Mar-4 Bonhams, New Bond Street #138/R
£850 $1547 €1241 Coming into harbour, Polperro (25x35cm-10x14in) s. W/C scratching out. 21-Jun-4 Bonhams, Bath #444a/R
£1000 $1830 €1460 Harbour scenes at dusk (53x74cm-21x29in) s. W/C pastel pair. 7-Jul-4 George Kidner, Lymington #137/R est:1200-1500
£1700 $3145 €2482 Polperro, Cornwall (23x36cm-9x14in) s. W/C bodycol pair. 9-Mar-4 Bonhams, New Bond Street #137/R est:1200-1800
£1800 $3276 €2628 Cornish harbour scene (17x25cm-7x10in) s. W/C pair. 21-Jun-4 Bonhams, Bath #444b est:500-700

BUTLER, Horacio (1897-1983) Argentinian

£3352 $6000 €4894 Conquerors (22x14cm-9x6in) cardboard. 4-May-4 Arroyo, Buenos Aires #52/R est:4000
£16201 $29000 €23653 Grandparents Lainez (50x42cm-20x17in) s. cardboard painted 1953. 4-May-4 Arroyo, Buenos Aires #71/R est:7000
£18579 $34000 €27125 Saint Lawrence battle (50x72cm-20x28in) 1-Jun-4 Arroyo, Buenos Aires #71
£20442 $37000 €29845 Bathers (50x65cm-20x26in) 30-Mar-4 Arroyo, Buenos Aires #81
Works on paper
£5191 $9500 €7579 Dreams (28x40cm-11x16in) mixed media. 1-Jun-4 Arroyo, Buenos Aires #86

BUTLER, Howard Russell (1856-1934) American

£251 $450 €366 Impressionistic river (28x41cm-11x16in) s. 10-Jan-4 CRN Auctions, Cambridge #18
£419 $700 €612 Steamship (38x56cm-15x22in) s. 20-Jun-3 Freeman, Philadelphia #204/R
£2688 $5000 €3924 Glorious day on the Maine coast (63x81cm-25x32in) s. board. 5-Mar-4 Skinner, Boston #534/R est:5000-7000

BUTLER, James H (1925-) American

Works on paper
£656 $1200 €958 Still life with blue light (91x140cm-36x55in) pastel. 10-Jul-4 Hindman, Chicago #70/R est:800-1200
£1421 $2600 €2075 Hanson's hollow (81x97cm-32x38in) pastel. 10-Jul-4 Hindman, Chicago #71/R est:800-1200

BUTLER, Joseph Nikolaus (1822-1885) Swiss

£1325 $2411 €2000 Harbour town by moonlight (55x81cm-22x32in) s. 21-Jun-4 Dorotheum, Vienna #295/R est:2500-3000

BUTLER, Joseph Nikolaus (attrib) (1822-1885) Swiss

£2096 $3815 €3060 Alpine landscapes with peasants (69x55cm-27x22in) mono.d.866 pair. 16-Jun-4 Fischer, Luzern #1297/R est:3000-4000 (S.FR 4800)

BUTLER, Mary (1865-1946) American

£252 $400 €368 Crashing surf (26x31cm-10x12in) canvas on board. 12-Sep-3 Skinner, Boston #486/R
£377 $600 €550 On the coast (25x30cm-10x12in) s. board. 12-Sep-3 Skinner, Boston #496/R
£405 $700 €591 Landscape with trees on rolling hills (20x25cm-8x10in) s. 10-Dec-3 Alderfer's, Hatfield #441
£409 $650 €597 Landscape with wooded hill in foreground, purple hills in distance (28x38cm-11x15in) s. 10-Sep-3 Alderfer's, Hatfield #289
£430 $800 €628 Lehigh county landscape (46x61cm-18x24in) s. painted c.1920. 7-Mar-4 Treadway Gallery, Cincinnati #561/R
£434 $750 €634 Landscape with stone wall and white house in distance (20x25cm-8x10in) s. 10-Dec-3 Alderfer's, Hatfield #442
£870 $1600 €1270 Purple mountain (61x81cm-24x32in) s.verso. 11-Jun-4 David Rago, Lambertville #236/R est:1200-1800
£2395 $4000 €3497 Landscape with blue mountains (61x81cm-24x32in) s. 16-Nov-3 Simpson's, Houston #251a/R
£2454 $4000 €3583 Landscape with blue mountains (61x81cm-24x32in) s. 28-Sep-3 Simpson's, Houston #320/R
£2463 $3965 €3596 Maine coastal view (61x81cm-24x32in) s. 20-Aug-3 James Julia, Fairfield #1381/R est:4000-6000
Works on paper
£809 $1400 €1181 Industrial scene with tugboat (20x30cm-8x12in) s. mixed media. 10-Dec-3 Alderfer's, Hatfield #439/R est:1600-1800

BUTLER, Mary E (fl.1880-1912) British

Works on paper
£900 $1503 €1314 Still life in a blue bowl. Still life of roses (22x28cm-9x11in) s. W/C pair. 14-Oct-3 Bonhams, Knightsbridge #177/R

BUTLER, Mildred Anne (1858-1941) British

Works on paper
£867 $1569 €1300 View Lake Como (10x20cm-4x8in) s. W/C. 30-Mar-4 De Veres Art Auctions, Dublin #112/R
£1080 $1933 €1577 Woodland parkland with distant deer (15x18cm-6x7in) s.d.97 W/C. 6-May-4 Biddle & Webb, Birmingham #963
£1300 $2327 €1898 Lismore, Waterford (25x17cm-10x7in) s. pencil W/C. 14-May-4 Christie's, Kensington #330/R est:1000-1500
£1800 $3222 €2628 Edge of the woods (34x25cm-13x10in) s. W/C. 26-May-4 Sotheby's, Olympia #118/R est:1200-1800
£2800 $5012 €4088 Peacocks (20x27cm-8x11in) s. W/C htd bodycol prov. 14-May-4 Christie's, London #28/R est:3000-5000
£3108 $5874 €4600 Shady corner of the garden (19x27cm-7x11in) W/C prov. 17-Feb-4 Whyte's, Dublin #138/R est:2500-3500
£3243 $6130 €4800 Herbaceous border. Herbaceous border with garden bench (18x13cm-7x5in) W/C pair. 17-Feb-4 Whyte's, Dublin #139/R est:2000-3000

£4225 $7310 €6000 Autumnal river landscape (54x34cm-21x13in) mono. W/C. 10-Dec-3 Bonhams & James Adam, Dublin #36/R est:5000-8000
£4600 $7268 €6670 Side cars (17x25cm-7x10in) s. W/C bodycol over pencil prov. 24-Jul-3 Lawrence, Crewkerne #873/R est:3000-5000
£5000 $8950 €7300 Hollyhocks (24x17cm-9x7in) pencil W/C htd bodycol prov. 14-May-4 Christie's, London #142/R est:3000-5000
£5000 $8950 €7300 In the conservatory (25x17cm-10x7in) pencil W/C htd bodycol board prov. 14-May-4 Christie's, London #144/R est:1500-2000
£5000 $8950 €7300 View in Pembroke Street, Dublin (34x25cm-13x10in) s.i.d.1886 verso W/C exhib. 13-May-4 Sotheby's, London #8/R est:4000-6000
£5068 $9578 €7500 Roses at Kilmurray (36x25cm-14x10in) s. W/C. 17-Feb-4 Whyte's, Dublin #119/R est:4000-5000
£5500 $9845 €8030 Poppies (25x16cm-10x6in) d.04 pencil W/C htd bodycol prov. 14-May-4 Christie's, London #143/R est:3000-5000
£6000 $10740 €8760 Foxgloves (25x16cm-10x6in) pencil W/C htd bodycol prov. 14-May-4 Christie's, London #145/R est:3000-5000
£6000 $10740 €8760 Side-cars (18x26cm-7x10in) s. pencil W/C htd bodycol. 14-May-4 Christie's, London #201/R est:6000-8000
£7432 $14047 €11000 Cattle resting in woodland. Cattle grazing beneath trees (17x24cm-7x9in) s. W/C htd white pair. 17-Feb-4 Whyte's, Dublin #120/R est:4000-5000
£8000 $14320 €11680 The delegates (36x27cm-14x11in) s. s.i.d.1923 verso pencil W/C htd white prov.exhib. 14-May-4 Christie's, London #4/R est:4000-6000
£16500 $29535 €24090 Doves outside the Conservatory, Kilmurry (54x37cm-21x15in) s. pencil W/C htd bodycol prov. 14-May-4 Christie's, London #3/R est:6000-8000

BUTLER, Reg (1913-1981) British

Sculpture
£1600 $2912 €2336 Head (18cm-7in) mono. num.7/8 dark brown pat bronze. 1-Jul-4 Christie's, Kensington #248/R est:1000-1500
£2703 $5000 €3946 Seated nude (19cm-7in) st.init. num.1/8 brown pat bronze incl base st.f.Valsuani. 12-Feb-4 Sotheby's, New York #139/R est:2500-3500
£4500 $8235 €6570 Doll (48cm-19in) mono.num.6/8 gold pat. bronze prov. 4-Jun-4 Christie's, London #148/R est:5000-8000
£5500 $9350 €8030 Study for girl tying her hair I (49cm-19in) mono.num.5/8 black pat. bronze conceived 1959 prov. 21-Nov-3 Christie's, London #158/R est:6000-8000
£5521 $9000 €8061 Ophelia (51cm-20in) init.num.3/8 black pat bronze st.f.Susse. 25-Sep-3 Christie's, Rockefeller NY #594/R est:3000-5000
£5587 $10000 €8157 Study for figure bending (42cm-17in) init. num.6/8 st.f.Susse Fond brown red pat bronze prov.lit. 6-May-4 Sotheby's, New York #293/R est:8000-12000
£7000 $11900 €10220 Girl (54cm-21in) mono.num.6/8 brown pat. bronze conceived 1965-66. 21-Nov-3 Christie's, London #157/R est:4000-6000
£9000 $15480 €13140 Woman on boat (58x71x16cm-23x28x6in) mono.d.3/54 num.2 dark grey pat bronze prov.exhib. 3-Dec-3 Sotheby's, London #77/R est:4000-6000
£13500 $24705 €19710 Summer (55cm-22in) mono.num.7/8 brown pat. bronze prov. 4-Jun-4 Christie's, London #149/R est:10000-15000
£20000 $34400 €29200 Study for girl with vest (93cm-37in) bronze near-blk pat bronze wood base exec 1953-4 prov.exhib. 3-Dec-3 Sotheby's, London #76/R est:4000-6000
Works on paper
£958 $1600 €1399 Nude study (55x75cm-22x30in) s.d.57pencil. 7-Oct-3 Sotheby's, New York #334 est:1500-2500
£1400 $2338 €2044 Girl dressing (51x61cm-20x24in) s.d.60 chl prov. 16-Oct-3 Christie's, Kensington #557/R est:1500-2000
£1900 $3458 €2774 Study for Ophelia (48x62cm-19x24in) s.d.57 chl. 1-Jul-4 Christie's, Kensington #246/R est:1500-2000
£2400 $4368 €3504 Ophelia (70x100cm-28x39in) s.d.72 chl prov. 1-Jul-4 Christie's, Kensington #249/R est:1500-2000

BUTLER, Theodore E (1861-1936) American

£30000 $54000 €45000 Inondation a Giverny (60x73cm-24x29in) s.d.1910 s.i.verso. 24-Apr-4 Cornette de St.Cyr, Paris #339/R est:15000-20000

BUTLERBYS, Edwin (19th C) British

£280 $521 €409 Landscape with figures on the edge of a wood (25x46cm-10x18in) s. 2-Mar-4 Bonhams, Oxford #223

BUTMAN, Frederick A (1820-1871) American

£615 $1100 €898 Distant harbour (13x18cm-5x7in) s. board. 14-May-4 Skinner, Boston #66/R est:1000-1500
£1547 $2800 €2259 In the Androscoggin Bethel Maine, landscape with two cows at water's edge (15x20cm-6x8in) s. i.verso board. 2-Apr-4 Eldred, East Dennis #877/R est:3000-5000
£5085 $9000 €7424 Sierra Sentinels (127x101cm-50x40in) s.d.1867. 28-Apr-4 Christie's, Los Angeles #7/R est:7000-10000

BUTRAGUENO, Felipe (20th C) Spanish

£295 $469 €425 Salamanca (88x98cm-35x39in) s.d.00 s.i.verso panel. 29-Apr-3 Durán, Madrid #39/R
£319 $533 €450 Quarters (46x55cm-18x22in) s. board. 20-Oct-3 Durán, Madrid #1187/R

BUTTERFIELD, Deborah (20th C) American

Sculpture
£20950 $37500 €30587 Horse (87x271x114cm-34x107x45in) welded steel exec 1980 prov. 13-May-4 Sotheby's, New York #138/R est:35000-45000
£41916 $70000 €61197 Untitled (76x104x30cm-30x41x12in) welded steel prov.exhib. 13-Nov-3 Sotheby's, New York #111/R est:25000-35000

BUTTERFIELD, William (1814-1900) British

Works on paper
£820 $1517 €1197 Two women in sanguine and blue (32x42cm-13x17in) s. ink pencil col crayon two exhib. 10-Mar-4 Sotheby's, Olympia #110/R

BUTTERI, Giovanni Maria (attrib) (c.1540-1606) Italian

£25000 $45000 €36500 Birth of the Virgin (27x21cm-11x8in) copper. 21-Apr-4 Christie's, London #70/R est:12000-15000

BUTTERSACK, Bernhard (1858-1925) German

£667 $1200 €1000 Farmstead on the Amper (63x81cm-25x32in) s.d.1909 lit. 22-Apr-4 Allgauer, Kempten #3503/R

BUTTERSWORTH, James E (1817-1894) American

£1863 $3000 €2720 Yacht race off New York harbour (30x41cm-12x16in) init.i. 20-Aug-3 James Julia, Fairfield #681/R est:2500-4000
£5469 $8750 €7985 America's Cup, Colgate family yacht (66x91cm-26x36in) prov. 21-Sep-3 William Jenack, New York #247 est:15000-20000
£15301 $28000 €22339 American ship of the line Pennsylvania (33x25cm-13x10in) s. board prov. 29-Jul-4 Christie's, Rockefeller NY #235/R est:30000-50000
£16770 $27000 €24484 Schooner in stormy seas (20x30cm-8x12in) s.panel. 20-Aug-3 James Julia, Fairfield #680/R est:17500-27500
£24709 $42500 €36075 Comet (30x46cm-12x18in) s. prov. 3-Dec-3 Sotheby's, New York #98/R est:20000-30000
£28409 $50000 €41477 Yachts rounding the Nore light ship (20x30cm-8x12in) s. i.verso board prov. 19-May-4 Sotheby's, New York #63/R est:50000-70000
£41899 $75000 €61173 Shipping in a port (46x61cm-18x24in) s. prov. 26-May-4 Doyle, New York #18/R est:80000-120000
£65882 $112000 €96188 Highflyer (74x91cm-29x36in) s. painted c.1853 prov. 30-Oct-3 Phillips, New York #40/R est:100000-125000
£70588 $120000 €103058 Yacht Columbia (20x30cm-8x12in) s. board. 1-Nov-3 Skinner, Boston #135/R est:10000-15000

BUTTERSWORTH, James E (attrib) (1817-1894) American

£2800 $4760 €4088 Two racing cutters (30x41cm-12x16in) 19-Nov-3 Christie's, Kensington #475/R

BUTTERSWORTH, Thomas (1768-1842) British

£1700 $3043 €2482 British frigate heeling in the breeze (20x25cm-8x10in) 26-May-4 Christie's, Kensington #598/R est:800-1200
£3000 $4800 €4380 Gibraltar Point with English and Spanish cutters engaging. Shipwrecked sailors (18x25cm-7x10in) pair. 16-Sep-3 Bonhams, New Bond Street #12/R est:3000-5000
£3500 $5950 €5110 English cutter yacht in a stiff breeze (40x58cm-16x23in) s. 27-Nov-3 Sotheby's, London #103/R est:2500-4000
£3825 $7000 €5585 First rater in a gale (30x35cm-12x14in) s. 29-Jul-4 Christie's, Rockefeller NY #233/R est:8000-12000
£4200 $6720 €6132 British man-o-war, frigate and local craft off Mediterranean lighthouse (30x41cm-12x16in) 16-Sep-3 Bonhams, New Bond Street #15/R est:3000-5000
£4748 $8500 €6932 His Majesty's Corvette - Rainbow - in a swell (46x61cm-18x24in) s. 16-Mar-4 Bonhams & Butterfields, San Francisco #6122/R est:8000-12000
£5100 $8823 €7446 Orkneys. Off Portsmouth harbour (30x43cm-12x17in) pair. 10-Dec-3 Edgar Horn, Eastbourne #286/R est:3000-5000
£5587 $10000 €8157 74-gun Third Rate HMS Magnificent under reduced sail in heavy weather (46x61cm-18x24in) s. 16-Mar-4 Bonhams & Butterfields, San Francisco #6123/R est:8000-12000
£6800 $11560 €9928 English cutter yacht Venus and a pilot boat off the coast (39x59cm-15x23in) 27-Nov-3 Sotheby's, London #102/R est:5000-7000
£9836 $18000 €14361 HMS Brittania bearing away down the Channel passing the Eddystone lighthouse (46x61cm-18x24in) s. prov. 29-Jul-4 Christie's, Rockefeller NY #229/R est:20000-30000
£10811 $20000 €15784 Armed Naval lugger patrolling off the mouth of the Tagus (42x63cm-17x25in) s. 10-Feb-4 Christie's, Rockefeller NY #187/R est:15000-25000
£13500 $21600 €19710 Two-masted Naval schooner in pursuit off Bass Rock, North Berwick (81x122cm-32x48in) 16-Sep-3 Bonhams, New Bond Street #60/R est:15000-25000
£62000 $99200 €90520 HMS Victory heavily engaged at the battle of Trafalgar (84x142cm-33x56in) s. prov. 16-Sep-3 Bonhams, New Bond Street #88/R est:50000-80000

BUTTERWORTH, J H (19/20th C) British

£1700 $2839 €2482 Castle Rushen. Port St. Mary (38x61cm-15x24in) s. two. 20-Jun-3 Chrystals Auctions, Isle of Man #279 est:600-900
Works on paper
£260 $434 €380 Douglas Harbour (18x13cm-7x5in) s. W/C. 20-Jun-3 Chrystals Auctions, Isle of Man #240f
£380 $635 €555 Wreck of St. George, Fenella Beach, Peel (36x58cm-14x23in) s. chl monochrome. 20-Jun-3 Chrystals Auctions, Isle of Man #244

BUTTERY, Edwin (19th C) British

£380 $635 €555 Extensive river landscape (28x43cm-11x17in) s. 17-Oct-3 Keys, Aylsham #711
£675 $1080 €986 Rural landscape, with figures. s. 18-Sep-3 Goldings, Lincolnshire #874

BUTTGEREIT, Wilhelmine (1851-1900) German

£280 $476 €400 Young woman at village fountain (61x49cm-24x19in) s. 20-Nov-3 Van Ham, Cologne #1507

BUTTI, Argelia (19th C) Italian?

£1111 $1811 €1600 Italian peasant women outside church (64x91cm-25x36in) s.d.1882. 24-Sep-3 Neumeister, Munich #403/R est:1500

BUTTI, C (19th C) American

Works on paper
£936 $1564 €1367 The brig Anna-Margrethe of Dragor (44x65cm-17x26in) pen W/C. 25-Oct-3 Rasmussen, Havnen #2610/R (D.KR 10000)

BUTTI, Lorenzo (1805-1860) Italian

£1149 $2056 €1700 Sailing ships off coast (12x14cm-5x6in) i. lit. 8-May-4 Dawo, Saarbrucken #54/R est:1800

BUTTNER, Bruno (?) German?

£685 $1165 €980 Pier in a Friesian town with figures (70x100cm-28x39in) indis.s. 29-Nov-3 Sigalas, Stuttgart #267/R

BUTTNER, Erich (1889-1936) German
£2533 $4535 €3800 Portrait of Gabriele Esterhardt (78x63cm-31x25in) s.i.d. canvas on panel. 14-May-4 Ketterer, Munich #9/R est:3500-4500

BUTTNER, Georg Hans (1850-?) German
£19000 $34580 €27740 Hunting scenes (42x64cm-17x25in) one s.d.1889 one s.d.1890 panel pair prov.lit. 15-Jun-4 Sotheby's, London #59/R est:15000-20000

BUTTNER, Heinrich (19th C) German
£1056 $1827 €1500 Hunting party (39x48cm-15x19in) s.d.1879. 13-Dec-3 Lempertz, Koln #202/R est:800

BUTTNER, Helena (1861-?) Hungarian
£480 $907 €701 Cart horse in a yard (50x43cm-20x17in) s.i. 19-Feb-4 Christie's, Kensington #327/R

BUTTNER, Werner (1954-) American
£2378 $4042 €3400 Russian Revolution (50x40cm-20x16in) s.d.85 stretcher acrylic cotton. 27-Nov-3 Lempertz, Koln #60/R est:1600
£4196 $7133 €6000 On the search for love in the library of a ghost town (149x119cm-59x47in) s.d.81 i. stretcher acrylic oil cotton exhib. 27-Nov-3 Lempertz, Koln #61/R est:6500

BUTTS, John (attrib) (?-1764) British
£2162 $3805 €3200 Figures by a river in a mountainous landscape (110x150cm-43x59in) 19-May-4 James Adam, Dublin #55 est:3000-5000
£4930 $8528 €7000 Figures in a wooded coastal landscape (61x74cm-24x29in) 10-Dec-3 Bonhams & James Adam, Dublin #15/R est:6000-10000
£52448 $89161 €75000 Extensive Irish river landscape with figures in foreground (119x133cm-47x52in) 18-Nov-3 Mealy's, Castlecomer #1350 est:30000-40000

BUTZ, Rudolf (1948-) Swiss
£693 $1240 €1012 Flower hill (80x120cm-31x47in) s.d. acrylic chk. 22-Mar-4 Philippe Schuler, Zurich #4310 (S.FR 1600)

BUTZKE, Bernhard Johannes Karl (1876-1952) German
Sculpture
£938 $1566 €1369 Fawn (61cm-24in) s. pat bronze exec.c.1920. 19-Oct-3 Agra, Warsaw #54/R est:6000 (P.Z 6000)

BUUREN, Meeuwis van (1902-1992) Dutch
£280 $501 €420 Horse in meadow (39x49cm-15x19in) s. 11-May-4 Vendu Notarishuis, Rotterdam #11

BUURMAN, Kees (1933-1997) Dutch
£1049 $1783 €1500 Untitled (25x99cm-10x39in) s.d.69 board sold with monotype same hand prov. 25-Nov-3 Christie's, Amsterdam #304/R est:800-1200

BUUTVELD, Wim (20th C) Dutch
£274 $466 €400 Kijkduin (39x49cm-15x19in) s.d.91 panel. 5-Nov-3 Vendue Huis, Gravenhage #478/R

BUVELOT, Abram Louis (1814-1888) Swiss
£5785 $10702 €8446 Big tree, Gardiners Creek (41x55cm-16x22in) s. i.verso. 10-Mar-4 Deutscher-Menzies, Melbourne #201/R est:16000-20000 (A.D 14000)
£11336 $18251 €16551 Near Beechworth, One tree Hill, Ovens District (43x63cm-17x25in) s.d.77 s.i.stretcher verso prov.exhib.lit. 25-Aug-3 Sotheby's, Paddington #166/R est:40000-60000 (A.D 28000)
Works on paper
£729 $1173 €1064 Village pump (14x33cm-6x13in) s.d.1861 W/C. 13-Oct-3 Joel, Victoria #441 est:1000-1500 (A.D 1800)
£992 $1806 €1448 Country cottage and horse (18x10cm-7x4in) init.d.79 W/C. 16-Jun-4 Deutscher-Menzies, Melbourne #385/R est:1500-2500 (A.D 2600)
£1134 $1825 €1656 Landscape with gum trees (25x35cm-10x14in) s.d.1878 W/C prov. 25-Aug-3 Sotheby's, Paddington #455/R est:4000-6000 (A.D 2800)

BUXTON, Phyllis and Pricilla (20th C) American
Sculpture
£930 $1600 €1358 Ballerina (94cm-37in) s.d.1974 pat bronze. 7-Dec-3 Grogan, Boston #93/R

BUXTON, William Graham (fl.1885-1893) British
£1050 $1659 €1523 When golden morning light the sky (59x90cm-23x35in) s.d.1890. 2-Sep-3 Bonhams, Oxford #104/R est:800-1200
£1600 $2672 €2336 Dawn of day on the Essex coast (61x91cm-24x36in) s.d.1890 exhib. 13-Nov-3 Christie's, Kensington #175/R est:1800-2200

BUYLE, Robert (1895-1976) Belgian
£642 $1149 €950 La marchande d'oranges (50x65cm-20x26in) s. 10-May-4 Horta, Bruxelles #471

BUYS, Bob (1912-1970) Dutch
Works on paper
£400 $732 €600 Portrait of a young woman doing handwork (13x16cm-5x6in) s. W/C. 7-Jun-4 Glerum, Amsterdam #25/R

BUYS, Cornelis Bernudes (1808-1872) Dutch
£476 $867 €700 Fruits and flowers on a ledge (24x29cm-9x11in) s.d.1857 panel. 3-Feb-4 Christie's, Amsterdam #77

BUYSSE, Georges (1864-1916) Belgian
£2098 $3566 €3000 Paysage boise au coucher du soleil (57x73cm-22x29in) s. 1-Dec-3 Palais de Beaux Arts, Brussels #31/R est:3000-4000

BUZIN, Igor (1957-) Russian
£275 $459 €402 Phloxes (30x35cm-12x14in) s. 13-Jul-3 John Nicholson, Haslemere #25/R
£350 $571 €511 Lilies of the Valley in the glass vase (40x30cm-16x12in) s. 28-Sep-3 John Nicholson, Haslemere #15/R
£550 $963 €803 Cornflowers (45x50cm-18x20in) s. 17-Dec-3 John Nicholson, Haslemere #66/R
£600 $1050 €876 Lilies of the Valley (40x50cm-16x20in) s. 17-Dec-3 John Nicholson, Haslemere #10

BUZIN, Vladimir (1959-) Russian
£260 $460 €380 Town canal (59x69cm-23x27in) 2-May-4 Lots Road Auctions, London #367
£300 $543 €438 Camel (58x68cm-23x27in) s. 4-Apr-4 Lots Road Auctions, London #358/R
£380 $692 €555 Market Day (70x60cm-28x24in) s. 20-Jun-4 Lots Road Auctions, London #349/R

BUZON, Marius de (1879-1958) French
£443 $700 €647 Mariners Basques (66x53cm-26x21in) s.i.d.1934. 7-Sep-3 Treadway Gallery, Cincinnati #598/R
£3000 $5520 €4500 Ruelle de Sidi Bou Said (46x55cm-18x22in) s. panel. 14-Jun-4 Gros & Delettrez, Paris #574/R est:2500-3500
£4366 $7554 €6200 Marche aux chameaux (81x100cm-32x39in) s.i.d.1926. 15-Dec-3 Gros & Delettrez, Paris #95/R est:7600-9200

BUZZATI, Dino (1907-1972) Italian
£4762 $8524 €7000 Dog, bride and groom (40x50cm-16x20in) s.d.1969. 16-Mar-4 Finarte Semenzato, Milan #78/R est:1700
Works on paper
£816 $1461 €1200 Flight (42x31cm-17x12in) s. W/C. 22-Mar-4 Sant Agostino, Torino #311/R
£952 $1705 €1400 Women and cars (42x31cm-17x12in) s. W/C. 22-Mar-4 Sant Agostino, Torino #310/R
£1224 $2192 €1800 Surreal interior (42x31cm-17x12in) s. W/C. 22-Mar-4 Sant Agostino, Torino #312/R est:400
£2721 $4871 €4000 Femme liee (30x39cm-12x15in) s.d.1967 crayon ink. 21-Mar-4 Calmels Cohen, Paris #85/R est:1500-2000

BUZZELL, Taylor (19th C) American
£5398 $9500 €7881 Still life of apples in a silver compote (36x51cm-14x20in) init. verso painted c.1870s exhib. 18-May-4 Christie's, Rockefeller NY #27/R est:12000-18000

BUZZI, Andrea (1964-) Italian
Works on paper
£490 $832 €700 Boundary (50x50cm-20x20in) mixed media on canvas exec.2002 prov.exhib. 24-Nov-3 Christie's, Milan #75/R
£541 $951 €800 Border (50x50cm-20x20in) s.i.d.2002 verso mixed media on canvas prov.exhib. 24-May-4 Christie's, Milan #100/R

BYARS, James Lee (1932-1997) American
Sculpture
£3892 $6500 €5682 Eight cones (15x5x5cm-6x2x2in) Japanese paper different sizes executed 1959-60 prov. 11-Nov-3 Christie's, Rockefeller NY #103/R est:1500-2000
Works on paper
£2275 $3800 €3322 Bird (25x28cm-10x11in) graphite. 11-Nov-3 Christie's, Rockefeller NY #104/R est:500-700
£2374 $4250 €3466 Untitled (30x33cm-12x13in) gold ink on black ink napkin prov. 16-May-4 Wright, Chicago #373/R est:2000-3000
£2533 $4661 €3800 Tantnt - Things are netiehr this nor that (67x49cm-26x19in) gold pen. 11-Jun-4 Hauswedell & Nolte, Hamburg #1190/R est:3800

BYBEL, Janet (20th C) American
£659 $1100 €962 Sunflower glory (76x51cm-30x20in) 18-Oct-3 David Dike, Dallas #268/R

BYCHKOV, Vyacheslav Pavlovich (1877-1954) Russian
£4196 $7133 €6000 Winter landscape (83x114cm-33x45in) s.d.27. 29-Nov-3 Bukowskis, Helsinki #402/R est:2000-2500

BYE, Ranulph de Bayeux (1916-) American
£915 $1500 €1327 Still life with apples (41x61cm-16x24in) s.d.1972. 4-Jun-3 Alderfer's, Hatfield #349/R est:2000-3000
£2286 $3750 €3315 Broadhead creek, winter landscape (41x56cm-16x22in) s. board. 4-Jun-3 Alderfer's, Hatfield #348/R est:2500-3500
Works on paper
£304 $550 €444 Vinalhaven (38x53cm-15x21in) W/C. 16-Apr-4 American Auctioneer #48/R
£314 $500 €458 Reindeer Moss (51x74cm-20x29in) s. W/C. 10-Sep-3 Alderfer's, Hatfield #436
£345 $625 €504 Fishing by the pier (53x74cm-21x29in) W/C. 16-Apr-4 American Auctioneer #50/R
£387 $700 €565 Reading bridge (33x51cm-13x20in) s. W/C executed 1968. 2-Apr-4 Freeman, Philadelphia #101
£414 $750 €604 City building, corner (61x53cm-24x21in) W/C. 16-Apr-4 American Auctioneer #49/R

£489 $900 €714 Cove in Maine (36x53cm-14x21in) s. W/C. 9-Jun-4 Alderfer's, Hatfield #461/R est:1200-1800
£520 $900 €759 West entrance Philadelphia Museum of art (33x51cm-13x20in) s. W/C. 10-Dec-3 Alderfer's, Hatfield #463/R est:600-800
£598 $1100 €873 Bucks county farm (23x33cm-9x13in) s. W/C. 25-Jun-4 Freeman, Philadelphia #25/R
£671 $1100 €973 Industrial view of mill (66x53cm-26x21in) s. W/C. 4-Jun-3 Alderfer's, Hatfield #358
£694 $1200 €1013 Store fronts (48x69cm-19x27in) s. W/C. 13-Dec-3 Weschler, Washington #607
£751 $1300 €1096 Corner of Polk and East 4th, St. Bethlehem, PA (28x38cm-11x15in) s. W/C. 10-Dec-3 Alderfer's, Hatfield #464/R est:600-800
£761 $1400 €1111 Cats and hanging basket (25x36cm-10x14in) s. W/C exec. 1973 prov. 25-Jun-4 Freeman, Philadelphia #1/R est:700-1000
£870 $1600 €1270 Walk in the park (43x56cm-17x22in) s. W/C. 9-Jun-4 Alderfer's, Hatfield #462 est:1200-1800
£915 $1500 €1327 November overcast, farm landscape (33x48cm-13x19in) s.d.1965 W/C. 4-Jun-3 Alderfer's, Hatfield #355/R est:1000-1200
£915 $1500 €1327 Capitol Corner, 11th St, Washington DC (51x71cm-20x28in) s.d.March 25 1986 W/C exhib. 4-Jun-3 Alderfer's, Hatfield #357/R est:800-1000
£1006 $1600 €1469 Wharf with boats (33x53cm-13x21in) s. W/C exec c.1970. 10-Sep-3 Alderfer's, Hatfield #397/R est:800-1200
£1063 $1700 €1552 Lake Galena (36x53cm-14x21in) s. W/C exhib. 19-Sep-3 Freeman, Philadelphia #1/R est:600-1000
£1098 $1800 €1592 Green Lane and Wild Street, Manayunk (36x53cm-14x21in) s.d.Oct 29 1969 W/C. 4-Jun-3 Alderfer's, Hatfield #354/R est:1000-12000
£1098 $1900 €1603 Farm at dusk, Gardenville (33x53cm-13x21in) s. W/C. 10-Dec-3 Alderfer's, Hatfield #462/R est:700-900
£1132 $1800 €1653 Market Scene (53x76cm-21x30in) s. W/C exec c.1976. 10-Sep-3 Alderfer's, Hatfield #396/R est:1000-1500
£1132 $1800 €1653 Bucks County Farmhouse (36x53cm-14x21in) s. W/C. 10-Sep-3 Alderfer's, Hatfield #418/R
£1359 $2500 €1984 Bucks county farm (36x51cm-14x20in) s. W/C. 9-Jun-4 Alderfer's, Hatfield #460/R est:1200-1800

BYLERT, Jan van (1603-1671) Dutch
£30137 $51233 €44000 Woman holding pancakes (38x29cm-15x11in) s. panel. 4-Nov-3 Sotheby's, Amsterdam #130/R est:4000-6000
£42000 $76860 €61320 Young man drinking wine (65x56cm-26x22in) s. prov.exhib.lit. 8-Jul-4 Sotheby's, London #128/R est:25000-35000

BYLERT, Jan van (circle) (1603-1671) Dutch
£6463 $11762 €9500 Man with a tankard (89x70cm-35x28in) panel. 3-Feb-4 Christie's, Amsterdam #44/R est:2000-3000
£8000 $14320 €12000 Young gallant and courtesan playing tric-trac watched by a procuress (92x117cm-36x46in) prov.lit. 17-May-4 Christie's, Amsterdam #93/R est:15000-25000
£20667 $36993 €31000 Three Magi, holding an incense burner, gold pokal and beaker (74x60cm-29x24in) s. panel set of three. 17-May-4 Christie's, Amsterdam #96/R est:15000-25000
£28000 $51240 €42000 Salome holding the Baptist's head (90x109cm-35x43in) 1-Jun-4 Sotheby's, Milan #155/R est:25000-35000

BYNG, Dennis (20th C) American
Sculpture
£870 $1600 €1270 Plexiglass column (46x18x18cm-18x7x7in) s.d. plexiglass prov.exhib. 28-Mar-4 Wright, Chicago #576/R est:1000-1500

BYRNE, Bernard (20th C) Irish
£933 $1689 €1400 Brother and sister (54x46cm-21x18in) s. board prov. 31-Mar-4 James Adam, Dublin #149/R

BYRNE, Gerard (20th C) Irish
£2838 $5364 €4200 Jmes Joyce Tower, Sandycove (76x69cm-30x27in) s. prov.exhib. 17-Feb-4 Whyte's, Dublin #182/R est:3000-4000

BYRNE, Samuel (1883-1978) Australian
£574 $930 €838 Sturt and Quandongs - Native peach (36x61cm-14x24in) s.i. board. 30-Jul-3 Goodman, Sydney #3/R (A.D 1400)
£1356 $2305 €1980 Windlass man power (34x44cm-13x17in) s.i. enamel metallic pyrites board painted 1975. 24-Nov-3 Sotheby's, Melbourne #1238/R est:2000-3000 (A.D 3200)
£1653 $3058 €2413 Camel transport from outback mines (30x40cm-12x16in) s.i. enamel earth minerals on board prov. 10-Mar-4 Deutscher-Menzies, Melbourne #257/R est:4500-6000 (A.D 4000)
£1736 $3072 €2535 Mining, Broken Hill District (44x54cm-17x21in) s.i.d.1883 board prov. 3-May-4 Christie's, Melbourne #260/R est:2000-3000 (A.D 4200)
£1736 $3072 €2535 Mooturngee Rockdale (50x63cm-20x25in) s.i. board. 3-May-4 Christie's, Melbourne #298/R est:4000-6000 (A.D 4200)
£1860 $3440 €2716 Mining by gas lamp light (41x50cm-16x20in) s.i. oil enamel earth minerals on board. 10-Mar-4 Deutscher-Menzies, Melbourne #258/R est:6000-8000 (A.D 4500)
£2254 $3652 €3291 Camel transport, central Australia (59x74cm-23x29in) s. enamel board prov. 30-Jul-3 Goodman, Sydney #34/R est:4000-6000 (A.D 5500)
£2686 $4754 €3922 Thackaringa School (44x60cm-17x24in) s.i.d.1884 board prov. 3-May-4 Christie's, Melbourne #239/R est:2000-4000 (A.D 6500)
£3719 $6880 €5430 Broken hill (61x76cm-24x30in) s.i. board prov. 10-Mar-4 Deutscher-Menzies, Melbourne #259/R est:6000-8000 (A.D 9000)
£3830 $6510 €5592 Camels transport ore, Broken Hill District 1900 (56x76cm-22x30in) s.i. oil enamel composition board painted c.1966 prov.exhib. 26-Nov-3 Deutscher-Menzies, Melbourne #192/R est:9000-12000 (A.D 9000)
£4043 $6872 €5903 Pinnacle Mine (30x61cm-12x24in) s.i.d.1887 oil enamel earth minerals board. 26-Nov-3 Deutscher-Menzies, Melbourne #191/R est:5000-7000 (A.D 9500)
£4357 $7276 €6536 Rabbit plague, Thackaringa (41x59cm-16x23in) s.i.d.1886 board. 27-Oct-3 Goodman, Sydney #79/R est:5000-7000 (A.D 10500)
£4545 $8045 €6636 Railway town, Silver City (49x119cm-19x47in) s.i. board. 3-May-4 Christie's, Melbourne #123/R est:8000-12000 (A.D 11000)
£4878 $7659 €7073 BHP Mine's Smelter and Viaduct, Broken Hill (59x121cm-23x48in) s.i. s.verso oil enamel board prov.exhib.lit. 27-Aug-3 Christie's, Sydney #569/R est:4000-6000 (A.D 12000)

BYRNE, Val (?) ?
£1351 $2554 €2000 West town, Tory Island, County Donegal (46x61cm-18x24in) s. canvasboard. 17-Feb-4 Whyte's, Dublin #91/R est:1500-1800
Works on paper
£400 $688 €584 Portmagee harbour, County Kerry (30x45cm-12x18in) s. W/C. 3-Dec-3 John Ross, Belfast #128
£450 $774 €657 Kinsale, County Cork (35x50cm-14x20in) s. W/C. 3-Dec-3 John Ross, Belfast #58
£550 $913 €803 Kinsale Harbour, West Cork (30x45cm-12x18in) s. W/C. 1-Oct-3 John Ross, Belfast #84

BYRNES, Brian (20th C) ?
£458 $801 €650 Still life with skillet (14x9cm-6x4in) s. 16-Dec-3 James Adam, Dublin #36/R
£467 $840 €700 Still life (75x90cm-30x35in) s.d.03. 20-Apr-4 James Adam, Dublin #100/R

BYRON, Archie (1928-) American
Works on paper
£667 $1200 €974 Country church (58x74cm-23x29in) saw dust glue airbrush. 24-Apr-4 Slotin Folk Art, Buford #424/R est:1000-2000

BYRT, Roger (1959-) Australian
£620 $1147 €905 Hooked (101x136cm-40x54in) s.d.89 s.i.d.verso. 15-Mar-4 Sotheby's, Melbourne #160 est:400-600 (A.D 1500)

BYSS, Johann Rudolf (1660-1738) Swiss
£58190 $107069 €84957 Flowers in stone niche (18x13cm-7x5in) s.d.1693 prov.lit. 26-Mar-4 Koller, Zurich #3021/R est:50000-70000 (S.FR 135000)

BYSTROM, Johan Niklas (1783-1848) Swedish
Sculpture
£3231 $5557 €4717 Reclining nude odalisque (78cm-31in) s.d.1806 plaster prov. 7-Dec-3 Uppsala Auktionskammare, Uppsala #357/R est:8000-10000 (S.KR 42000)

BYTEBIER, Edgar (1875-1940) Belgian
£319 $508 €460 Campagne aux alentours de Dilbeek (59x88cm-23x35in) s. 15-Sep-3 Horta, Bruxelles #512
£367 $664 €550 Bords de riviere (80x120cm-31x47in) s.d.1921. 30-Mar-4 Palais de Beaux Arts, Brussels #485

BYTEL, Jacobus (1893-1983) Dutch
£377 $640 €550 Abstract composition with bottles (58x48cm-23x19in) s. board. 5-Nov-3 Vendue Huis, Gravenhage #515/R

CABAILLOT, Camille Leopold (1839-?) French
£6222 $10329 €9084 Young tutor (30x23cm-12x9in) panel. 2-Oct-3 Heffel, Vancouver #9 (C.D 14000)

CABAILLOT, Louis Simon (1810-?) French
£480 $797 €701 Goose girl (16x11cm-6x4in) s. panel. 1-Oct-3 Sotheby's, Olympia #215/R
£898 $1500 €1311 Wood gatherers in the winter (35x27cm-14x11in) s. panel prov. 7-Oct-3 Sotheby's, New York #105 est:2000-3000
£1250 $2125 €1800 Farmgirls on a path in winter (46x55cm-18x22in) s.d.85. 28-Oct-3 Christie's, Amsterdam #24/R est:2000-3000
£1500 $2730 €2190 Gathering summer blooms. Gathering kindling (16x11cm-6x4in) s. panel pair. 16-Jun-4 Christie's, Kensington #160/R est:1200-1800
£5000 $8000 €7250 On the way to market (46x55cm-18x22in) s. panel prov. 18-Sep-3 Christie's, Kensington #18/R est:5000-8000

CABALLERO, Jose Luis (1916-1991) Spanish
£4276 $7868 €6500 Coffee pots (65x54cm-26x21in) s. s.i.d.1953 verso. 22-Jun-4 Durán, Madrid #125/R est:3000
Works on paper
£414 $691 €600 Landscape (29x41cm-11x16in) s. gouache. 17-Nov-3 Durán, Madrid #96/R
£789 $1453 €1200 Bull scene (61x50cm-24x20in) s. mixed media card. 22-Jun-4 Durán, Madrid #668/R
£1467 $2669 €2200 Surreal composition (30x24cm-12x9in) s. ink drawing. 29-Jun-4 Segre, Madrid #114/R est:1950
£2796 $5145 €4250 Visits in the field (27x37cm-11x15in) s. s.i.d.1935 verso dr. 22-Jun-4 Durán, Madrid #1218/R est:1500
£2796 $5145 €4250 Sangriento Agamenon (93x60cm-37x24in) s. s.i.d.1970 verso mixed media on canvas. 22-Jun-4 Durán, Madrid #121/R est:4250

CABALLERO, Luis (1943-1995) Colombian
£1592 $2500 €2324 Untitled (59x89cm-23x35in) s. 23-Nov-2 Subastas Odalys, Caracas #24/R
£2431 $4060 €3549 Boy's face (53x45cm-21x18in) s. 13-Jul-3 Subastas Odalys, Caracas #109 est:5000
Works on paper
£367 $660 €550 Nude (38x28cm-15x11in) s.d.1977 graphite W/C. 24-Apr-4 Cornette de St.Cyr, Paris #467
£989 $1800 €1444 Figures stretching (25x36cm-10x14in) s, India ink double-sided. 29-Jun-4 Sotheby's, New York #674/R est:2000-3000
£1049 $1752 €1500 Etude de nus (20x29cm-8x11in) graphite drs nine in one frame prov. 25-Jun-3 Digard, Paris #86/R est:1400-1800

CABALLERO, Maximo (1867-1951) Spanish
£6853 $11445 €9800 Reading a letter (46x28cm-18x11in) s.i.d.1919. 30-Jun-3 Ansorena, Madrid #341/R est:9800

£15957 $26649 €22500 Intimate conversation (60x74cm-24x29in) s.d.1902. 23-Jun-3 Durán, Madrid #238/R est:12000

CABALLERO, Salvador (1943-) Spanish
£245 $400 €358 Cazadores en busca de la presa (20x30cm-8x12in) s. board with box and catalogue. 27-Sep-3 Charlton Hall, Columbia #25

CABANE, Edouard (1857-?) French
£811 $1395 €1184 Young mother with her child (65x54cm-26x21in) s. 8-Dec-3 Philippe Schuler, Zurich #5827 (S.FR 1800)
£4000 $7440 €5840 Tete blonde, portrait of a girl with blue ribbon (46x38cm-18x15in) 3-Mar-4 Brightwells, Leominster #916/R est:700-1000

CABANEL, Alexandre (1823-1889) French
£417 $688 €600 Portrait presume de Mme Hippolyte Doyon (80x60cm-31x24in) s. 3-Jul-3 Claude Aguttes, Neuilly #24
£2727 $4555 €3900 Etude de personnage (38x27cm-15x11in) s. prov. 27-Jun-3 Doutrebente, Paris #55/R
£62000 $112840 €90520 Aglae et Boniface (60x65cm-24x26in) s. oval prov. 15-Jun-4 Sotheby's, London #165/R est:50000-70000
£75000 $129000 €109500 Ophelia (75x116cm-30x46in) s.d.1883 prov. 3-Dec-3 Christie's, London #44/R est:80000-120000
Works on paper
£280 $481 €400 Le petit page (29x21cm-11x8in) s.d.1879 W/C. 3-Dec-3 Blanchet, Paris #14
£1259 $2102 €1800 Etude d'anges et d'enfants (34x22cm-13x9in) s. crayon dr prov. 27-Jun-3 Doutrebente, Paris #53/R

CABANES, Louis François (1867-?) French
£3356 $6208 €5000 Le cafetier Constantinois (32x41cm-13x16in) s.i. panel. 15-Mar-4 Gros & Delettrez, Paris #232/R est:5000-6000
£3691 $6829 €5500 Place animee dans une ville du Sud (52x41cm-20x16in) s. panel. 15-Mar-4 Gros & Delettrez, Paris #269/R est:5000-7000

CABANYES, Alejandro de (1877-1972) Spanish
£1846 $3304 €2750 Harbour (50x59cm-20x23in) s.d.1935. 25-May-4 Durán, Madrid #180/R est:800
£7182 $13000 €10486 Elegant lady in a cafe (48x78cm-19x31in) s. indis d. 30-Mar-4 Christie's, Rockefeller NY #107/R est:5000-7000
£8287 $15000 €12099 Cafe de Paris (61x72cm-24x28in) s.d.1900 i.verso. 30-Mar-4 Christie's, Rockefeller NY #108/R est:6000-8000

CABAT, Louis (1812-1893) French
£433 $784 €650 Paysage d'Auvergne (21x32cm-8x13in) st.verso. 30-Mar-4 Rossini, Paris #705
£533 $965 €800 Rome, les Catacombes (32x40cm-13x16in) 30-Mar-4 Rossini, Paris #739/R
£629 $1051 €900 Paysage au soleil couchant (14x24cm-6x9in) st. i.verso paper on cardboard. 27-Jun-3 Calmels Cohen, Paris #14
£1374 $2500 €2006 At the watering hole (39x63cm-15x25in) s. 29-Jun-4 Sotheby's, New York #87/R est:4000-6000
£2133 $3861 €3200 Etude de ciel nuage (11x14cm-4x6in) st. peinture paper. 30-Mar-4 Rossini, Paris #747 est:120-180
£2262 $3846 €3303 Barbizon landscape (52x75cm-20x30in) s. 28-Nov-3 Zofingen, Switzerland #2455/R est:4000 (S.FR 5000)
£2667 $4827 €4000 Les environs de Troyes (20x33cm-8x13in) s.d.1865 oil paper on cardboard exhib.lit. 30-Mar-4 Rossini, Paris #688/R est:1500-2000
£3267 $5978 €4900 Paturage (53x76cm-21x30in) s. 6-Jun-4 Osenat, Fontainebleau #44/R est:5000-5500
£3333 $6033 €5000 Les plaines d'Arques dit Le Buisson (40x59cm-16x23in) s. exhib.lit. 30-Mar-4 Rossini, Paris #232/R est:4500-6000
£3667 $6637 €5500 Hiver en foret de Fontainebleau (65x92cm-26x36in) s. exhib.lit. 30-Mar-4 Rossini, Paris #231/R est:5000-8000
£4348 $7130 €6000 Les pommieres a la ferme Saint-Simeon pres d'Honfleurs (28x38cm-11x15in) s. painted c.1830-35 exhib. 11-May-3 Osenat, Fontainebleau #83/R
£4533 $8205 €6800 Paysage aux environs de Rome (146x113cm-57x44in) lit. 30-Mar-4 Rossini, Paris #230/R est:5000-8000
£4667 $8447 €7000 La passerelle (58x81cm-23x32in) st.sig. lit. 30-Mar-4 Rossini, Paris #234/R est:4000-6000
£5000 $9050 €7500 Etude de ciel au couchant (21x29cm-8x11in) oil paper on canvas lit. 30-Mar-4 Rossini, Paris #755/R est:4000-7000
Works on paper
£267 $483 €400 Femmes a la fontaine pres d'une ville (26x35cm-10x14in) st. pen brown ink wash. 30-Mar-4 Rossini, Paris #686
£267 $483 €400 La lagune a Venise (21x28cm-8x11in) s.d.1837 graphite. 30-Mar-4 Rossini, Paris #687
£267 $483 €400 Paysans et troupeau dans une plaine (45x47cm-18x19in) st. pen brown ink wash two sheets. 30-Mar-4 Rossini, Paris #694
£267 $483 €400 Troupeau et etang dans la foret (55x89cm-22x35in) st. crayon chl htd white. 30-Mar-4 Rossini, Paris #700
£267 $483 €400 Le pont de Narni (46x64cm-18x25in) st.i.d.7 Aout 1838 graphite estompe. 30-Mar-4 Rossini, Paris #709
£267 $483 €400 Etude pour une vue panoramique des environs de Rome (23x41cm-9x16in) graphite several sheets. 30-Mar-4 Rossini, Paris #721
£267 $483 €400 Mortefontaine (23x25cm-9x10in) st.i.d.28 Aout 1846 pen brown ink wash. 30-Mar-4 Rossini, Paris #754
£300 $543 €450 Paysage au bouquet d'arbres, Narni (46x64cm-18x25in) st.i.d.8 Juillet 1838 graphite estompe. 30-Mar-4 Rossini, Paris #710
£300 $543 €450 Premiere pensee pour Soir d'automne, du Musee de Louvre (46x61cm-18x24in) pierre noire htd white chk. 30-Mar-4 Rossini, Paris #716/R
£300 $543 €450 Promeneur sous les arbres, Narni (28x42cm-11x17in) st.i.d.6 Juillet 1838 graphite estompe htd white. 30-Mar-4 Rossini, Paris #724
£300 $543 €450 Rayon de soleil entre les arbres (30x47cm-12x19in) st. pen brown ink wash htd white. 30-Mar-4 Rossini, Paris #727
£300 $543 €450 Etude de ciel, Narni (28x43cm-11x17in) st.i.d.28 juillet 1838 brown ink wash white gouache. 30-Mar-4 Rossini, Paris #752
£300 $543 €450 Arbres penches sur la riviere (24x32cm-9x13in) st. pen brown ink wash. 30-Mar-4 Rossini, Paris #759
£333 $603 €500 Cours d'eau aux rochers, Berry (35x46cm-14x18in) s.i.d.20 Juillet 1853 black crayon pen black ink wash. 30-Mar-4 Rossini, Paris #699
£333 $603 €500 Etude de ciel nuageux (13x23cm-5x9in) st. W/C. 30-Mar-4 Rossini, Paris #704
£333 $603 €500 Abords d'une ville Italienne (47x62cm-19x24in) st. pen brown ink wash graphite. 30-Mar-4 Rossini, Paris #726
£367 $664 €550 La Muraille d'Aurelien, la Vallee des Aqueducs pres de Rome (27x65cm-11x26in) st.i.d.26 juin 1838 chl htd white. 30-Mar-4 Rossini, Paris #683
£367 $664 €550 Paysage du Limousin (26x44cm-10x17in) mono.i.d.1832 pierre noire white chk lit. 30-Mar-4 Rossini, Paris #751
£400 $724 €600 Paysage d'Italie avec deux personnages en conversation (48x65cm-19x26in) st. chl estompe. 30-Mar-4 Rossini, Paris #730
£400 $724 €600 Bergers dans un paysage Italien (31x46cm-12x18in) st. graphite htd white gouache. 30-Mar-4 Rossini, Paris #749
£433 $784 €650 Abreuvoir au pied du Chene en Berry (44x31cm-17x12in) mono.i.d.1832 pierre noire htd white chk. 30-Mar-4 Rossini, Paris #761
£467 $845 €700 Etude de ciel et arbre. Couple de paysans (10x14cm-4x6in) st.i. W/C graphite double-sided. 30-Mar-4 Rossini, Paris #684
£500 $905 €750 Le pont de Narni, Italie (44x62cm-17x24in) st.i.d.10 Aout 1838 graphite lit. 30-Mar-4 Rossini, Paris #697/R
£500 $905 €750 Vue panoramique des environs de Rome (20x65cm-8x26in) st.i.d.22 octobre 1838 graphite. 30-Mar-4 Rossini, Paris #702
£500 $905 €750 Campagne de Rome (20x58cm-8x23in) s.i.d.1836 brown wash graphite estompe. 30-Mar-4 Rossini, Paris #720
£500 $905 €750 La femme de Loth se retournant devant Sodome en Flammes (30x45cm-12x18in) st. pen col ink wash. 30-Mar-4 Rossini, Paris #722
£500 $905 €750 Plaine au cavalier et nuages, Narni (34x62cm-13x24in) s.i.d.8 Juillet 1838 chl htd white chk. 30-Mar-4 Rossini, Paris #733
£533 $965 €800 Bord de riviere au bouquet d'arbres avec un personnage etendu (32x44cm-13x17in) st.sig. pen brown ink graphite. 30-Mar-4 Rossini, Paris #750
£567 $1026 €850 Scene mythologique en sous-bois (47x58cm-19x23in) s. pen brown ink wash exhib.lit. 30-Mar-4 Rossini, Paris #760/R
£600 $1086 €900 Plaine et troupeau en italie (29x54cm-11x21in) st. pierre noire white chk. 30-Mar-4 Rossini, Paris #679
£797 $1307 €1100 Le village de Lariccia (30x56cm-12x22in) s.i.d.4 aout 1839 brown ink W/C wash. 11-May-3 Osenat, Fontainebleau #82
£800 $1448 €1200 Ariccia surplombant la plaine avec un chemin a la porteuse d'eau (43x55cm-17x22in) st.i. pen brown ink wash two sheets. 30-Mar-4 Rossini, Paris #685
£867 $1569 €1300 Berger a la fontaine dans un paysage avec un temple (68x93cm-27x37in) s. pen brown ink graphite. 30-Mar-4 Rossini, Paris #719
£867 $1569 €1300 Etudes de ciel (10x14cm-4x6in) bears st.i. W/C three. 30-Mar-4 Rossini, Paris #762
£1000 $1810 €1500 Chemin en sous-bois, l'Ariccia (42x79cm-17x31in) s.i.d.1839 pen brown ink wash lit. 30-Mar-4 Rossini, Paris #682/R est:500-800
£1067 $1931 €1600 Parc de l'Ariciia (55x46cm-22x18in) s.i.d.1838 pen brown ink W/C graphite two sheets. 30-Mar-4 Rossini, Paris #708/R est:300-500
£1267 $2293 €1900 Fete Champetre (63x76cm-25x30in) st.sig. pen brown ink wash. 30-Mar-4 Rossini, Paris #763 est:250-350
£1467 $2655 €2200 L'Ariccia, la fontaine (43x83cm-17x33in) s.i.d.14 Aout 1839 pen brown ink wash. 30-Mar-4 Rossini, Paris #676/R est:500-800

CABAUD, Paul (19th C) French
£810 $1401 €1150 Portrait of Joseph Dessaix (22x27cm-9x11in) i. board. 14-Dec-3 St-Germain-en-Laye Encheres #30

CABEL, Adrian van der (c.1631-1705) Dutch
£4500 $7650 €6570 Coastal inlet with figures and moored boats. Mediterranean harbour with travelers on a path (60x20cm-24x8in) pair. 29-Oct-3 Bonhams, New Bond Street #85/R est:5000-7000
£5000 $8500 €7200 Harbour with figures (93x128cm-37x50in) init. 29-Oct-3 Il Ponte, Milan #714/R
Works on paper
£2365 $4162 €3500 Italianate landscape (12x16cm-5x6in) mono.d.1656 pen grey ink wash prov.exhib.lit. 19-May-4 Sotheby's, Amsterdam #90/R est:1200-1500

CABEL, Adrian van der (attrib) (c.1631-1705) Dutch
£814 $1385 €1188 Southern harbour (22x29cm-9x11in) 19-Nov-3 Fischer, Luzern #2174/R (S.FR 1800)
£7500 $13500 €10950 Mediterranean harbour scene with figures on a quay beneath a fort (86x117cm-34x46in) prov. 20-Apr-4 Sotheby's, Olympia #291/R est:8000-12000
Works on paper
£507 $892 €750 Italianate coastal scene, with tow figures by a ruin and statue (10x17cm-4x7in) brush black ink grey wash black chk prov.exhib. 19-May-4 Sotheby's, Amsterdam #102/R

CABEL, Adrian van der (circle) (c.1631-1705) Dutch
£5430 $9883 €8200 Scene de port mediterraneen (78x108cm-31x43in) 21-Jun-4 Tajan, Paris #81/R est:4000-6000

CABEZAS, Jorge (20th C) Spanish?
Works on paper
£284 $460 €400 Sardines (60x73cm-24x29in) s.d.1998 mixed media canvas. 20-May-3 Ansorena, Madrid #389/R

CABEZUDO, Fernando (1927-) South American
£353 $600 €515 Abstract (118x97cm-46x38in) s. 25-Nov-3 Galeria y Remates, Montevideo #101

CABIANCA, Vincenzo (1827-1902) Italian
£3200 $5888 €4800 Resting in the mountains (24x30cm-9x12in) s.d.84 cardboard prov. 8-Jun-4 Sotheby's, Milan #49/R est:4000-6000
£3521 $6092 €5000 Landscape in Castiglioncello (19x31cm-7x12in) s. i.verso cardboard prov. 9-Dec-3 Finarte Semenzato, Milan #66/R est:7000
£4823 $8054 €6800 Hilly landscape (17x12cm-7x5in) init. cardboard. 20-Oct-3 Sant Agostino, Torino #286/R est:5000
£5034 $9413 €7500 Roman countryside (21x25cm-8x10in) init.d.1887 card prov.lit. 25-Feb-4 Porro, Milan #2/R est:6000-7000
Works on paper
£5298 $9642 €8000 Back from a walk (32x19cm-13x7in) s. W/C. 17-Jun-4 Finarte Semenzato, Milan #304/R est:9500-10000

CABIE, L (1853-1939) French
£1197 $2071 €1700 Coastal landscape (68x101cm-27x40in) s. 15-Dec-3 Ansorena, Madrid #294/R est:1700

CABIE, Louis Alexandre (1853-1939) French
£280 $518 €409 Haystack (27x33cm-11x13in) s. 10-Mar-4 Sotheby's, Olympia #229/R
£360 $620 €526 Landscape with lake and hunters (35x46cm-14x18in) s.d.1902. 8-Dec-3 Philippe Schuler, Zurich #5828 (S.FR 800)
£440 $704 €642 Autumn wooded landscape (40x32cm-16x13in) s. prov. 16-Sep-3 Rosebery Fine Art, London #598
£450 $765 €657 Landscape (39x31cm-15x12in) s. prov. 2-Nov-3 Lots Road Auctions, London #362
£655 $1094 €950 Cabane en sous-bois (51x72cm-20x28in) s. 11-Nov-3 Lesieur & Le Bars, Le Havre #10
£674 $1125 €950 Les grands chenes a l'automne (37x52cm-15x20in) s.d.88 panel. 20-Jun-3 Drouot Estimations, Paris #86
£940 $1682 €1400 Paysage aux peuplier (26x33cm-10x13in) s.d.1910. 25-May-4 Karl & Faber, Munich #80/R
£1333 $2440 €2000 Chemin le long de la riviere (38x55cm-15x22in) s.d.1903. 6-Jun-4 Osenat, Fontainebleau #48 est:1800-2000
Works on paper
£367 $664 €550 Pecheurs au bord d'une riviere (30x45cm-12x18in) gouache W/C. 30-Mar-4 Gioffredo, Nice #302

CABOI, Jean (1935-) French
£582 $990 €850 Fort d'Antibes (54x81cm-21x32in) s. 9-Nov-3 Eric Pillon, Calais #245/R

CABOT, Edward Clark (1818-1901) American
Works on paper
£202 $375 €295 Bemis stream (34x49cm-13x19in) mono.i.d.Aug 27,87 W/C. 5-Mar-4 Skinner, Boston #282/R
£391 $700 €571 Raven Crag (25x18cm-10x7in) mono.i.d.June W/C. 14-May-4 Skinner, Boston #61/R

CABRAL Y AGUADO, Manuel (1827-c.1890) Spanish
£19366 $33891 €27500 Latest news (59x75cm-23x30in) s.d.1885. 16-Dec-3 Durán, Madrid #189/R est:25000
£41379 $69103 €60000 Party in Torrijos (69x100cm-27x39in) s.d.1883. 17-Nov-3 Durán, Madrid #210/R est:40000

CABRAL Y AGUADO, Manuel (attrib) (1818-1891) Spanish
£35211 $56338 €50000 Arrival of the Earl of Aguila (121x180cm-48x71in) 16-Sep-3 Segre, Madrid #62/R est:15000

CABRAL, Joao (?-1916) Portuguese
£805 $1442 €1200 Landscape with peasant woman by fence (21x15cm-8x6in) s. panel. 31-May-4 Cabral Moncada Leiloes, Lisbon #77/R

CABRE Y MAGRINA, Angel (1863-?) Venezuelan/Spanish
Sculpture
£3076 $5230 €4491 Boy (22x52x34cm-9x20x13in) s. marble. 23-Nov-3 Subastas Odalys, Caracas #19 est:6000

CABRE, Manuel (1890-1983) Venezuelan
£20588 $35000 €30058 Paisaje andino (85x120cm-33x47in) s.d.57. 19-Nov-3 Sotheby's, New York #87/R est:20000-25000

CABRERA MORENO, Servando (1932-1981) Cuban
Works on paper
£2429 $4250 €3546 Desnudo (62x49cm-24x19in) s.d.1960 gouache paper on board. 19-Dec-3 Sotheby's, New York #1173/R est:6000-8000

CABRERA, Ben (1942-) Philippino
£4979 $8962 €7269 Woman in red (75x60cm-30x24in) s.d.94. 25-Apr-4 Christie's, Hong Kong #548/R est:80000-120000 (HK.D 70000)
£15054 $24086 €21979 Women leaving (76x56cm-30x22in) s.d.1978 oil paper. 18-May-3 Sotheby's, Singapore #61/R est:9000-12000 (S.D 42000)
£20077 $33529 €29312 Carrying a banga (122x71cm-48x28in) s.d.98 acrylic exhib.lit. 26-Oct-3 Christie's, Hong Kong #28/R est:120000-180000 (HK.D 260000)
Works on paper
£1720 $2753 €2511 Study of Colombian Indian I (37x27cm-15x11in) s.d.77 mixed media. 18-May-3 Sotheby's, Singapore #71/R est:4000-6000 (S.D 4800)
£7112 $12802 €10384 Urban life (109x74cm-43x29in) s.d.98 ink acrylic collage prov.exhib.lit. 25-Apr-4 Christie's, Hong Kong #555/R est:90000-140000 (HK.D 100000)

CABRERA, Miguel (1695-1768) Mexican
£8939 $16000 €13051 Saint Gertrude (110x88cm-43x35in) s.d.1763. 26-May-4 Sotheby's, New York #69/R est:12000-18000
£12500 $23000 €19000 Virgin of Sorrows (45x33cm-18x13in) s. copper. 24-Jun-4 Christie's, Paris #50/R est:3000-5000
£14118 $24000 €20612 Apostle Santiago worshipping the Virgin and Child on a column (125x105cm-49x41in) s.i. prov. 18-Nov-3 Christie's, Rockefeller NY #77/R est:25000-35000

CABRERA, Rosa (19th C) Spanish
£725 $1188 €1000 Jarron de flores (150x70cm-59x28in) s. 27-May-3 Durán, Madrid #121/R

CABURET, Christian (20th C) French?
£268 $475 €400 Sturm und Dranguerie (81x100cm-32x39in) 29-Apr-4 Claude Aguttes, Neuilly #143

CACCIA, C (19th C) Italian
Sculpture
£15556 $28000 €22712 Male and female busts of Moors - Plinths by Henry Dasson (44cm-17in) s.d.1883 and 1885 bronze white marble ormula granite base 2. 23-Apr-4 Christie's, Rockefeller NY #31/R est:8000-12000

CACCIA, Guglielmo (1568-1625) Italian
£7639 $12757 €11000 Holy Family with Saint John (146x117cm-57x46in) 22-Oct-3 Finarte Semenzato, Milan #67/R
Works on paper
£1389 $2500 €2028 St. Peter and St. Paul (18x23cm-7x9in) pen ink wash over black chk squared in red chk. 21-Jan-4 Sotheby's, New York #20/R est:2500-3500

CACCIA, Guglielmo (circle) (1568-1625) Italian
£6667 $12200 €10000 Nativity (75x54cm-30x21in) board. 1-Jun-4 Sotheby's, Milan #120/R est:5000-7000

CACCIANIGA, Carlo (18th C) Italian
Works on paper
£7000 $12110 €10220 Capriccio with the Castel Sant' Angelo and figures beside a river (57x40cm-22x16in) i.verso gouache on linen. 10-Dec-3 Bonhams, New Bond Street #76/R est:8000-12000

CACCIARELLI, Umberto (19/20th C) Italian
Works on paper
£2600 $4316 €3796 In the harem (50x71cm-20x28in) s.i. W/C. 1-Oct-3 Sotheby's, Olympia #187/R est:1200-1800

CACCIARELLI, Victor (19th C) Italian
Works on paper
£800 $1464 €1168 Important play (37x54cm-15x21in) s. W/C. 6-Jul-4 Bearnes, Exeter #401/R

CACHOUD, François-Charles (1866-1943) French
£544 $865 €800 Bord d'etang au clair de lune (22x27cm-9x11in) s. cardboard on canvas. 18-Mar-3 Adjug'art, Brest #100
£870 $1600 €1270 Landscape by moonlight (51x61cm-20x24in) s. 29-Mar-4 O'Gallerie, Oregon #813/R est:2000-3000
£1111 $1856 €1600 Nuit blonde sur le lac d'Aiguebelette (33x41cm-13x16in) s. 23-Oct-3 Credit Municipal, Paris #70 est:1200-1500
£3293 $5500 €4808 Houses with figures at dusk (71x89cm-28x35in) s. 19-Oct-3 Susanin's, Chicago #6030/R est:4000-6000
£3404 $5685 €4800 Clair de lune sur la riviere (65x51cm-26x20in) s. 19-Oct-3 Anaf, Lyon #49/R est:4500-5000

CADDY, John Herbert (1801-1887) Canadian
Works on paper
£682 $1111 €996 Lake St. Peter. Fall at Fort Frances, Ontario (21x30cm-8x12in) W/C exhib. 23-Sep-3 Ritchie, Toronto #60/R est:600-800 (C.D 1500)

CADEL, Eugène (1862-1942) French
£441 $749 €644 Bedroom with nude on bed (21x26cm-8x10in) one s. one bears sig. board canvas on board pair. 5-Nov-3 Dobiaschofsky, Bern #408/R (S.FR 1000)
£1329 $2285 €1900 Farm in the evening light (49x62cm-19x24in) s. 6-Dec-3 Quittenbaum, Hamburg #6/R est:2400

CADELL, Florence St John (attrib) (fl.1900-1940) British
Works on paper
£479 $800 €699 Coastal scene with rocky shore line and remnants of storm (23x33cm-9x13in) s.d.08 W/C. 27-Oct-3 O'Gallerie, Oregon #754/R

CADELL, Francis Campbell Boileau (1883-1937) British
£17000 $26690 €24650 Ross of Mull from Iona (37x45cm-15x18in) s. board. 27-Aug-3 Sotheby's, London #1221/R est:15000-20000
£24000 $40800 €35040 Iona looking to Mull and Ben More (51x76cm-20x30in) s. 30-Oct-3 Christie's, London #162/R est:25000-35000
£26000 $44980 €37960 Auchnacraig, Isle of Mull (37x48cm-15x19in) s. s.i.verso panel. 11-Dec-3 Lyon & Turnbull, Edinburgh #82/R est:10000-15000
£28000 $43960 €40600 Portrait of a young lady (61x50cm-24x20in) s. prov. 27-Aug-3 Sotheby's, London #1218/R est:30000-40000
£32000 $54400 €46720 Roses (37x44cm-15x17in) s. i.verso panel. 30-Oct-3 Christie's, London #163/R est:35000-50000
£32000 $57920 €46720 Black cockerel (37x45cm-15x18in) s. board prov. 19-Apr-4 Sotheby's, London #68/R est:15000-20000
£35000 $54950 €50750 Adam and Eve (43x38cm-17x15in) s. i.verso panel prov. 27-Aug-3 Sotheby's, London #1220/R est:20000-30000
£40000 $72400 €58400 Iona, looking towards Lunga (37x45cm-15x18in) s.i. s.d.1932 verso board prov. 19-Apr-4 Sotheby's, London #65/R est:25000-35000
£42000 $76020 €61320 Steps to the canal, Venice (38x46cm-15x18in) s.i.d.10 board prov. 19-Apr-4 Sotheby's, London #66/R est:30000-50000
£50000 $85000 €73000 Iona Sound and Ben More (51x76cm-20x30in) s. i.stretcher prov. 30-Oct-3 Christie's, London #161/R est:50000-80000
£100000 $157000 €145000 Famille roses coffee pot (55x46cm-22x18in) s.d.10. 27-Aug-3 Sotheby's, London #1219/R est:100000-150000

Works on paper
£2300 $3703 €3335 Farming County, possibly Galloway (16x20cm-6x8in) s. pen ink pencil. 21-Aug-3 Bonhams, Edinburgh #1027/R est:1000-1500
£3800 $6878 €5548 Continental street (38x26cm-15x10in) s.i.verso W/C. 19-Apr-4 Sotheby's, London #63/R est:2500-3000
£5000 $9050 €7300 Ravenhall Rocks, Galloway (23x33cm-9x13in) s.d.08 i.verso W/C prov. 19-Apr-4 Sotheby's, London #62/R est:4000-6000
£7000 $10990 €10150 Cattle on the dunes, Iona (17x24cm-7x9in) s. W/C. 27-Aug-3 Sotheby's, London #1216/R est:4000-6000
£7800 $13416 €11388 Iona Abbey (17x24cm-7x9in) s. W/C prov. 4-Dec-3 Bonhams, Edinburgh #48/R est:5000-7000
£8383 $14000 €12239 Shuna cottage, Iona, Argyll (18x25cm-7x10in) s.i.verso W/C. 19-Oct-3 Jeffery Burchard, Florida #16
£9500 $16150 €13870 Dunira Castle, Iona (17x25cm-7x10in) s. W/C. 10-Nov-3 Thomson Roddick & Medcalf, Edinburgh #208/R est:2000-3000
£9500 $17195 €13870 Brown and white cow, Iona (18x25cm-7x10in) s. W/C prov. 19-Apr-4 Sotheby's, London #64/R est:5000-7000
£10200 $16422 €14790 Sailor and his girl (33x25cm-13x10in) init.d.16 pen ink W/C. 21-Aug-3 Bonhams, Edinburgh #1026/R est:3000-5000
£10200 $16422 €14790 Two sailors (33x25cm-13x10in) init. pen ink W/C. 21-Aug-3 Bonhams, Edinburgh #1028/R est:3000-5000
£21000 $32970 €30450 Sands of Iona (25x17cm-10x7in) s. i.verso W/C prov.exhib. 27-Aug-3 Sotheby's, London #1217/R est:7000-10000

CADELL, St John (19/20th C) British
£400 $756 €584 Bed time (34x37cm-13x15in) s. board. 19-Feb-4 Lyon & Turnbull, Edinburgh #118

CADENASSO, Giuseppe (1858-1918) American
£4046 $7000 €5907 Pond under the oaks at sunset (61x51cm-24x20in) s. 10-Dec-3 Bonhams & Butterfields, San Francisco #6170/R est:5000-7000
£9239 $17000 €13489 Sunlight, Leona Heights, Oakland (152x101cm-60x40in) s. prov. 8-Jun-4 Bonhams & Butterfields, San Francisco #4233/R est:20000-30000
Works on paper
£1984 $3750 €2897 Landscape (25x36cm-10x14in) s. pastel. 17-Feb-4 John Moran, Pasadena #4/R est:1000-2000
£2457 $4250 €3587 Quiet pool (30x41cm-12x16in) s. pastel prov. 10-Dec-3 Bonhams & Butterfields, San Francisco #6171/R est:3000-5000

CADENHEAD, James (1858-1927) British
Works on paper
£260 $471 €380 Moorland walk (23x33cm-9x13in) s.i. W/C. 15-Apr-4 Richardson & Smith, Whitby #129

CADES, Giuseppe (1750-1799) Italian
Works on paper
£765 $1400 €1117 Naval battle (11x20cm-4x8in) pen brown ink wash. 29-Jan-4 Swann Galleries, New York #135/R
£800 $1440 €1168 Groups of clerical figures (36x24cm-14x9in) s. pen black ink brown wash black chk. 20-Apr-4 Sotheby's, Olympia #113/R
£1038 $1900 €1515 Hercules liberating Hesione (37x29cm-15x11in) black red chk. 29-Jan-4 Swann Galleries, New York #136/R est:3000-5000

CADMUS, Paul (1904-1999) American
Prints
£2905 $5200 €4241 Two boys on a beach, No.1 (13x18cm-5x7in) s.i. etching. 6-May-4 Swann Galleries, New York #414/R est:3000-5000
£3073 $5500 €4487 Two boys on a beach, no 1 (13x18cm-5x7in) s. etching edition of 75. 4-May-4 Doyle, New York #151/R est:3000-4000
£4412 $7500 €6442 Coney Island (23x26cm-9x10in) s. etching exec.1935. 31-Oct-3 Sotheby's, New York #185/R
£4520 $8000 €6599 YMCA locker room (16x32cm-6x13in) s. etching. 30-Apr-4 Sotheby's, New York #6/R est:6000-8000
£4706 $8000 €6871 Y M C A locker room (17x32cm-7x13in) s. etching edition of 50. 6-Nov-3 Swann Galleries, New York #511/R est:5000-8000
£4802 $8500 €7011 Goning south (24x13cm-9x5in) s. etching. 30-Apr-4 Sotheby's, New York #5/R est:4000-6000
£23464 $42000 €34257 Mother and child. Fleet's in. Coney Island (46x36cm-18x14in) s. etching portfolio of 17. 6-May-4 Swann Galleries, New York #416/R est:40000-60000
Works on paper
£1522 $2800 €2222 Study for Le Ruban denoue, hommage a Reynold A Hahn (43x33cm-17x13in) s.i. col crayon pencil. 10-Jun-4 Swann Galleries, New York #49/R est:2000-3000
£4624 $8000 €6751 Reclining nude (33x51cm-13x20in) s.i. col chk prov. 11-Dec-3 Sotheby's, New York #163/R est:8000-12000

CADNESS, Henry (?-1926) British
Works on paper
£300 $510 €438 Cotton, coal, iron and smoke - Sunday scene (29x45cm-11x18in) s.d.1917 W/C. 29-Oct-3 Bonhams, Chester #349

CADOGAN, Lady Augusta Sarah (19th C) British
Works on paper
£320 $579 €467 St James's Church, Guernsey (14x9cm-6x4in) W/C exec.c.1849. 1-Apr-4 Martel Maides, Guernsey #211

CADORIN, Guido (1892-1978) Italian
£367 $656 €550 Winter (50x35cm-20x14in) s.d.1959 tempera paper. 12-May-4 Stadion, Trieste #841
Works on paper
£1159 $1901 €1600 Composition with flowers (43x13cm-17x5in) s. W/C. 27-May-3 Il Ponte, Milan #534/R

CADORIN, Vincenzo (19th C) Italian
Sculpture
£6806 $11569 €9800 Saint Mark's lion (78x49x34cm-31x19x13in) s.i.d.1831 wood. 29-Oct-3 Il Ponte, Milan #659/R est:2500-3000

CADRE, Pierre (19th C) French
£333 $597 €500 Jour de fete au Faouet (18x27cm-7x11in) s. cardboard. 16-May-4 Thierry & Lannon, Brest #294

CADY, Walter Harrison (1877-1970) American
Works on paper
£1514 $2800 €2210 Cady's Store at Gardner Center, Massachusetts (39x132cm-15x52in) i.d.1885 W/C pencil. 11-Mar-4 Christie's, Rockefeller NY #85/R est:4000-6000

CAESAR, Doris (1892-1971) American
Sculpture
£1890 $3250 €2759 Seated woman (40x39x26cm-16x15x10in) s. brown pat. bronze prov. 3-Dec-3 Doyle, New York #6/R est:1500-2500

CAFFE, Nino (1909-1975) Spanish
£753 $1400 €1099 Marchigiano landscape (9x29cm-4x11in) s. i.d.1968 verso tempera panel. 5-Mar-4 Skinner, Boston #610a/R est:1000-1500
£1268 $2218 €1800 Still life with jug and hat (49x38cm-19x15in) s. 17-Dec-3 Il Ponte, Milan #1080 est:2000-2200
£1600 $2880 €2400 Storm (25x35cm-10x14in) s. board. 22-Apr-4 Finarte Semenzato, Rome #171/R est:2400-2700
£1648 $3000 €2406 Educande (15x30cm-6x12in) s. panel. 29-Jun-4 Sotheby's, New York #351/R est:2000-3000
£1648 $3000 €2406 Stanza Rosa (24x34cm-9x13in) s. panel. 29-Jun-4 Sotheby's, New York #352/R est:2000-3000
£1901 $3156 €2700 Cinque pretini (30x40cm-12x16in) s. 14-Jun-3 Meeting Art, Vercelli #465/R est:2500
£2174 $3565 €3000 Bather (30x38cm-12x15in) s. 27-May-3 Il Ponte, Milan #526/R
£2174 $3565 €3000 Still life with chair, coat and hat (69x50cm-27x20in) s. 27-May-3 Il Ponte, Milan #531/R
£2174 $3565 €3000 Still life with grapes, watermelon and bottle (40x50cm-16x20in) s. 27-May-3 Il Ponte, Milan #529/R
£2500 $4250 €3650 Per due innamorati (30x80cm-12x31in) s. board prov. 9-Nov-3 Bonhams & Butterfields, Los Angeles #4029/R
Works on paper
£433 $776 €650 Priests in the park (50x35cm-20x14in) s. W/C. 12-May-4 Stadion, Trieste #703/R

CAFFERATA, J F (19th C) American?
£3261 $6000 €4761 Whitaker's dining room (30x79cm-12x31in) s.d.1868. 10-Jun-4 Sotheby's, New York #637/R est:2000-3000

CAFFI, Ippolito (1809-1866) Italian
£13889 $25000 €20278 Pantheon by moonlight (34x47cm-13x19in) 23-Apr-4 Sotheby's, New York #86/R est:20000-30000
£15278 $27500 €22306 Pantheon, Rome (23x30cm-9x12in) oil paper on canvas. 23-Apr-4 Sotheby's, New York #87/R est:15000-20000
£15333 $27907 €23000 Saint Mark's Square at moonlight (113x94cm-44x37in) s. 4-Jul-4 Finarte, Venice #6/R est:22000-28000
£55172 $92138 €80000 Night view of Castel Sant'Angelo (32x41cm-13x16in) s. tempera paper on canvas. 12-Nov-3 Sotheby's, Milan #180/R est:40000-60000
Works on paper
£7000 $12810 €10220 Piazza del Popolo, Rome (21x30cm-8x12in) pencil W/C. 6-Jul-4 Christie's, London #208/R est:700-1000
£8000 $14720 €11680 Rialto Bridge, Venice. Dogana and Santa Maria della Salute (10x15cm-4x6in) s. one d.1852 boydcol pair. 25-Mar-4 Christie's, Kensington #54a est:4000-6000

CAFFI, Ippolito (attrib) (1809-1866) Italian
£5500 $9515 €8030 View of the choir of the Basilica of Saint Mark, Venice (27x38cm-11x15in) oil paper on canvas. 12-Dec-3 Christie's, Kensington #419/R est:800-1000
Works on paper
£700 $1288 €1022 Piazza St Pietro, Roma (22x28cm-9x11in) i.d.1858 W/C. 8-Jun-4 Bonhams, New Bond Street #17/R

CAFFI, Margherita (c.1650-1710) Italian
£6333 $11337 €9500 Still life (64x80cm-25x31in) 12-May-4 Finarte Semenzato, Milan #45/R est:8000-12000
£8803 $14085 €12500 Still life with flowers in metal vase (118x82cm-46x32in) 19-Sep-3 Finarte, Venice #240/R est:8000-9000
£10345 $17172 €15000 Still life of flowers (105x85cm-41x33in) lit. 1-Oct-3 Dorotheum, Vienna #53/R est:10000-15000
£17333 $31027 €26000 Still life (75x93cm-30x37in) indis.sig. 12-May-4 Finarte Semenzato, Milan #19/R est:30000-40000
£19553 $35000 €28547 Still lives of flowers (74x56cm-29x22in) pair. 27-May-4 Sotheby's, New York #57/R est:30000-40000
£22069 $39724 €32000 Composition with flowers in landscape (142x193cm-56x76in) lit. 26-Jan-4 Ansorena, Madrid #61d/R est:30000

CAFFI, Margherita (attrib) (c.1650-1710) Italian
£8100 $14175 €11500 Nature morte de fleurs (84x111cm-33x44in) oval. 18-Dec-3 Tajan, Paris #61/R est:4000-6000

CAFFI, Margherita (circle) (c.1650-1710) Italian
£8000 $13600 €11680 Still life of flowers in a blue stone urn with a macaw nearby (76x102cm-30x40in) 19-Nov-3 Tennants, Leyburn #1014/R est:8000-12000

£14570 $26517 €22000 Garlands of flowers (83x62cm-33x24in) pair prov. 16-Jun-4 Christie's, Rome #502/R est:7000-10000

CAFFI, Margherita (style) (c.1650-1710) Italian
£12752 $23463 €19000 Still life of flowers (93x107cm-37x42in) prov. 24-Mar-4 Dorotheum, Vienna #38/R est:15000-18000

CAFFIERI, Hector (1847-1932) British
£4800 $8592 €7008 By the river bank (40x60cm-16x24in) s. 26-May-4 Sotheby's, Olympia #195/R est:4000-6000
Works on paper
£260 $468 €380 Still life with flowers in a drinking glass (34x25cm-13x10in) s.d.1874 W/C. 22-Apr-4 Charles Ross, Woburn #247
£444 $816 €648 The Old Port, Chatillon (25x33cm-10x13in) s. W/C. 9-Jun-4 Walker's, Ottawa #358/R (C.D 1100)
£950 $1748 €1387 Fisherwomen with their children on the quayside (34x24cm-13x9in) s. pencil W/C. 25-Mar-4 Christie's, Kensington #256/R
£3000 $5370 €4380 Walk in the woods (51x35cm-20x14in) s. W/C. 26-May-4 Sotheby's, Olympia #124/R est:3000-5000
£4000 $6800 €5840 Fishergirl, le portel, Normandy, France (36x54cm-14x21in) s. i.verso W/C. 4-Nov-3 Bonhams, New Bond Street #100/R est:2000-3000

CAFFIERI, Jean Jacques (attrib) (1725-1792) French
Sculpture
£10211 $16951 €14500 Bust. bears sig. white marble. 11-Jul-3 Finarte, Venice #331/R est:12000-16000

CAFFYN, Walter Wallor (?-1898) British
£588 $1100 €858 Cows wading in a river (20x30cm-8x12in) s.d.1883. 29-Feb-4 Grogan, Boston #23/R
£909 $1700 €1327 Bridge of Sark (25x36cm-10x14in) s. i.verso. 29-Feb-4 Grogan, Boston #24/R
£1000 $1770 €1460 On the Thames near Reading, anglers fishing (18x28cm-7x11in) 27-Apr-4 Lawrences, Bletchingley #1716/R est:800-1200
£3512 $6217 €5128 Chart Lane, Dor Kiny. Quiet spot on the river (59x39cm-23x15in) s. pair. 3-May-4 Lawson Menzies, Sydney #10 est:8000-12000 (A.D 8500)

CAGE, John (1912-1992) American
Works on paper
£1648 $3000 €2406 Where r-ryoanii (25x49cm-10x19in) s.d.12/90 pencil executed 1990. 29-Jun-4 Sotheby's, New York #612/R est:2000-3000

CAGLI, Corrado (1910-1976) Italian
£1342 $2483 €2000 Magician Baku (55x70cm-22x28in) s.d.1968 s.i.verso tempera paper. 13-Mar-4 Meeting Art, Vercelli #365 est:2000
£12414 $20731 €18000 Town foundation (20x80cm-8x31in) s.d.1935 board. 13-Nov-3 Finarte Semenzato, Rome #451/R est:17000-18000
Works on paper
£268 $499 €400 Portrait (20x19cm-8x7in) s.i. ink. 4-Mar-4 Babuino, Rome #53
£403 $749 €600 Bombing in London (27x33cm-11x13in) s.i.d.1943 pencil. 4-Mar-4 Babuino, Rome #82
£704 $1232 €1000 Dunsinane (26x51cm-10x20in) s. frottage paper on canvas. 16-Dec-3 Finarte Semenzato, Milan #149/R
£1007 $1872 €1500 Portrait (43x31cm-17x12in) s.i.d.1970 felt-tip pen. 4-Mar-4 Babuino, Rome #78

CAGLIANI, Luigi (20th C) Italian
Works on paper
£220 $400 €321 Day in the village (51x41cm-20x16in) s. pencil oil masonite. 7-Feb-4 Neal Auction Company, New Orleans #1116

CAGNACCI, Guido (circle) (1601-1681) Italian
£6294 $10699 €9000 Venus et Vulcain (127x106cm-50x42in) painted oval. 1-Dec-3 Millon & Associes, Paris #30/R est:2000-3000

CAGNACCI, Guido (style) (1601-1681) Italian
£7000 $12810 €10220 Rape of Lucretia (76x142cm-30x56in) 9-Jul-4 Christie's, Kensington #167/R est:4000-6000

CAGNACCIO DI SAN PIETRO (1897-1946) Italian
Works on paper
£1633 $2922 €2400 Crucifixion (67x33cm-26x13in) s. pencil. 16-Mar-4 Finarte Semenzato, Milan #80/R est:2000

CAGNIART, Émile (1851-1911) French
Works on paper
£1389 $2264 €2000 Animation sur les boulevards (36x45cm-14x18in) s. pastel. 26-Sep-3 Rabourdin & Choppin de Janvry, Paris #19/R est:2200-2500

CAGNONE, Angelo (1941-) Italian
£313 $494 €450 Still life (90x70cm-35x28in) oil acrylic. 6-Sep-3 Meeting Art, Vercelli #295
£385 $654 €550 Composition (59x49cm-23x19in) s.d.1962 verso oil mixed media prov. 25-Nov-3 Sotheby's, Milan #104
£411 $699 €600 I will bring you a flower (90x70cm-35x28in) s.d.1966 verso. 7-Nov-3 Tuttarte, Modena #702
£816 $1461 €1200 Fragment (100x100cm-39x39in) s.i.d.1971 verso. 16-Mar-4 Finarte Semenzato, Milan #81/R
£1049 $1783 €1500 Red head (145x145cm-57x57in) s.i.d.1968 verso prov. 24-Nov-3 Christie's, Milan #80 est:1500-2000

CAHEN, Oscar (1916-1956) Canadian
Works on paper
£1720 $2735 €2511 Untitled (55x34cm-22x13in) s. mixed media board. 15-Sep-3 Ritchie, Toronto #85/R est:600-800 (C.D 3750)

CAHEN-MICHEL, Lucien (1888-1979) French
£265 $482 €400 Sous-bois (35x27cm-14x11in) s.d.1942 panel. 15-Jun-4 Blanchet, Paris #118
£265 $482 €400 Paysage de campagne (35x27cm-14x11in) s. panel. 15-Jun-4 Blanchet, Paris #119
£1500 $2700 €2190 Rose garden (73x59cm-29x23in) s.d.1922. 21-Jan-4 Sotheby's, Olympia #503/R est:1000-1500

CAHILL, Patrick (?) Irish
£671 $1201 €1000 Rue de Tolibac (30x40cm-12x16in) s. 31-May-4 Hamilton Osborne King, Dublin #79
£733 $1320 €1100 Merchant's arch (51x61cm-20x24in) s. 20-Apr-4 James Adam, Dublin #88/R

CAHILL, William Vincent (1878-1924) American
£156593 $285000 €228626 Dress fitting (77x64cm-30x25in) s.d.1912. 29-Jun-4 Sotheby's, New York #211/R est:2500-3500

CAHN, Marcelle (1895-1981) French
£940 $1663 €1400 Femme (46x38cm-18x15in) s.d.1924. 27-Apr-4 Artcurial Briest, Paris #172/R est:2200-2800
£4363 $8115 €6500 Nue sur fond bleu (55x46cm-22x18in) s. s.i.d.1924 verso exhib.lit. 2-Mar-4 Artcurial Briest, Paris #152/R est:4000-5000
£4564 $8078 €6800 Composition (50x61cm-20x24in) s. s.i.d.1937 verso. 27-Apr-4 Artcurial Briest, Paris #171/R est:5000-6000
Works on paper
£282 $487 €400 Composition (20x26cm-8x10in) s.i.d.1976 mixed media. 9-Dec-3 Artcurial Briest, Paris #247
£336 $571 €480 Composition (33x10cm-13x4in) s. gouache collage prov. 23-Nov-3 Cornette de St.Cyr, Paris #39/R
£350 $594 €500 Nu (28x20cm-11x8in) s. graphite prov. 23-Nov-3 Cornette de St.Cyr, Paris #34/R
£399 $678 €570 Femme nue (34x19cm-13x7in) s.d.1930 graphite prov. 23-Nov-3 Cornette de St.Cyr, Paris #35
£455 $773 €650 Pommes (11x17cm-4x7in) s. graphite prov. 23-Nov-3 Cornette de St.Cyr, Paris #38/R
£664 $1129 €950 Composition abstraite (11x22cm-4x9in) s. gouache collage pastel prov. 23-Nov-3 Cornette de St.Cyr, Paris #37/R
£704 $1218 €1000 Composition (20x13cm-8x5in) s.d.1968 collage graphite prov. 9-Dec-3 Artcurial Briest, Paris #246

CAHN, Miriam (1949-) Swiss
Works on paper
£294 $500 €429 Untitled (47x30cm-19x12in) s. chl oil chk transparent paper. 25-Nov-3 Germann, Zurich #755 (S.FR 650)

CAHOON, Charles D (1861-1951) American
£1852 $3000 €2704 Coastal dune scene (16x22cm-6x9in) s. 31-Jul-3 Eldred, East Dennis #972/R est:3000-4000
£2059 $3500 €3006 At full sail (29x29cm-11x11in) s. board. 21-Nov-3 Skinner, Boston #308/R est:1000-1500
£3704 $6000 €5408 Portrait of man seated by window reading newspaper (11x9cm-4x4in) s. 31-Jul-3 Eldred, East Dennis #990/R est:4000-6000
£3911 $7000 €6566 Marsh scene with hay stacks (30x41cm-12x16in) s. 20-Mar-4 Pook & Pook, Downington #566/R est:6000-9000
£6173 $10000 €9013 Old Mill Point, West Harwich (12x22cm-5x9in) s. 31-Jul-3 Eldred, East Dennis #989/R est:7000-10000
£8025 $13000 €11717 Wychmere Harbour, Harwichport, Massachusets scene (12x16cm-5x6in) s. d.1932 verso board. 31-Jul-3 Eldred, East Dennis #988/R est:9000-11000

CAHOON, Martha (1905-1999) American
£1049 $1700 €1532 Peace (9x12cm-4x5in) s. 31-Jul-3 Eldred, East Dennis #973/R est:1500-2000
£1202 $2200 €1755 Seashells on the shore (25x20cm-10x8in) s. panel. 3-Jun-4 Christie's, Rockefeller NY #810/R est:800-1200
£1529 $2600 €2232 Two piping plovers on the shore with lighthouse and boats in th distance (25x30cm-10x12in) s. masonite. 21-Nov-3 Eldred, East Dennis #811/R est:2000-3000
£7407 $12000 €10814 Waterfront scene (43x58cm-17x23in) s. masonite. 31-Jul-3 Eldred, East Dennis #982a/R est:10000-15000
£11728 $19000 €17123 Sailor's valentine (15cm-6in circular) s. masonite shellwork octagonal. 31-Jul-3 Eldred, East Dennis #982/R est:5000-10000
Works on paper
£802 $1300 €1171 Barnyard scene (9x11cm-4x4in) crayon mirror. 31-Jul-3 Eldred, East Dennis #975/R
£802 $1300 €1171 Boy and girl playing with toy sailing boat on pond (11x14cm-4x6in) s. crayon pen. 31-Jul-3 Eldred, East Dennis #976/R
£802 $1300 €1171 Cat watching boy and girl fishing (9x11cm-4x4in) s. crayon mirror. 31-Jul-3 Eldred, East Dennis #977/R
£1358 $2200 €1983 Ship wrecked sailor (10x14cm-4x6in) crayon ink. 31-Jul-3 Eldred, East Dennis #978/R est:1000-1500

CAHOON, Ralph (1910-1982) American
£4651 $8000 €6790 Sailors and Mermaids (28x38cm-11x15in) s.i. masonite prov. 7-Dec-3 Freeman, Philadelphia #143 est:8000-12000
£4938 $8000 €7209 Partridge shooting. Duck shooting (25x35cm-10x14in) s. masonite two in one frame. 31-Jul-3 Eldred, East Dennis #984/R est:10000-15000
£6790 $11000 €9913 After Tingqua (4x5cm-2x2in) s. i. verso masonite. 31-Jul-3 Eldred, East Dennis #987/R est:5000-7000

£11111	$18000	€16222	Sailor's valentine (15cm-6in circular) s. masonite shellwork octagonal. 31-Jul-3 Eldred, East Dennis #981/R est:5000-10000
£13580	$22000	€19827	Two sailors and mermaid log speed of boat in harbour (14x21cm-6x8in) s. masonite. 31-Jul-3 Eldred, East Dennis #979/R est:10000-15000
£17284	$28000	€25235	Eight sailors bounce three bouquet bearing mermaids on trampoline (24x19cm-9x7in) s. masonite. 31-Jul-3 Eldred, East Dennis #986/R est:15000-20000
£22222	$36000	€32444	Three sailors haul in fishing net containing mermaids (18x24cm-7x9in) s. masonite. 31-Jul-3 Eldred, East Dennis #983/R est:15000-20000
£25157	$40000	€36729	Balloon ride (75x56cm-30x22in) s. board. 12-Sep-3 Skinner, Boston #535/R est:35000
£25926	$42000	€37593	Wharf rats outing (48x61cm-19x24in) s. board prov. 8-Aug-3 Barridorf, Portland #245/R est:20000-30000
£27160	$44000	€39654	Hoopers Landing, Cotuit (22x30cm-9x12in) s. masonite. 31-Jul-3 Eldred, East Dennis #980/R est:30000-35000
Works on paper			
£1118	$1900	€1632	Mermouse naps beneath a pink umbrella at the water's edge. s. pencil gouache. 21-Nov-3 Eldred, East Dennis #812/R est:2000-3000

CAHOURS, Henry Maurice (1889-1974) French

£1013	$1895	€1530	Lumiere impressioniste a Douarnenez (45x63cm-18x25in) s. panel. 24-Jul-4 Thierry & Lannon, Brest #239/R est:800-1000

CAHYA, I Wayan (1965-) Javanese

£8172	$13075	€11931	Leopards (150x90cm-59x35in) s.d.2002. 18-May-3 Sotheby's, Singapore #183/R est:10000-12000 (S.D 22800)

CAI GUO QIANG (1957-) Chinese

Works on paper			
£8494	$14185	€12401	Project for extraterrestrial no.9 (88x64cm-35x25in) s. gunpowder ink. 26-Oct-3 Christie's, Hong Kong #113/R est:120000-160000 (HK.D 110000)
£17070	$30725	€24922	Foetus movement, project for extraterrestrials no 5 (50x65cm-20x26in) s.i.d.October 1990 gunpowder ink. 26-Apr-4 Sotheby's, Hong Kong #521/R est:120000-160000 (HK.D 240000)
£34749	$58031	€50734	Project for the year of Dragon no.2 (200x300cm-79x118in) s.i.d.2000 gunpowder ink. 26-Oct-3 Christie's, Hong Kong #112/R est:280000-360000 (HK.D 450000)
£125000	$227500	€182500	Rebuilding the Berlin wall (200x595cm-79x234in) gunpowder chinese ink executed 1991 prov.exhib.lit. 4-Feb-4 Christie's, London #46/R est:70000-90000

CAICEDO, Joaquin (1915-) Venezuelan

£247	$420	€361	Seascape (34x43cm-13x17in) s. masonite painted 1951. 23-Nov-3 Subastas Odalys, Caracas #61
£253	$470	€369	Seascape (46x60cm-18x24in) s. masonite. 14-Mar-4 Subastas Odalys, Caracas #26/R
£263	$440	€384	Nude (61x51cm-24x20in) s. painted 1969. 13-Jul-3 Subastas Odalys, Caracas #63
£283	$520	€413	Seascape (50x60cm-20x24in) s. 28-Mar-4 Subastas Odalys, Caracas #60/R
£299	$500	€437	La Guaira Street (51x61cm-20x24in) s. painted 1971. 13-Jul-3 Subastas Odalys, Caracas #41

CAILLARD, Christian (1899-1985) French

£388	$694	€566	Summer landscape with vegetable garden (59x72cm-23x28in) s.d.42. 12-May-4 Dobiaschofsky, Bern #369/R (S.FR 900)
£1007	$1862	€1500	Table (92x73cm-36x29in) s. panel painted 1973. 14-Mar-4 Eric Pillon, Calais #145/R
£1034	$1893	€1500	Femme (106x63cm-42x25in) s. panel. 1-Feb-4 Feletin, Province #78
£1056	$1827	€1500	Maisons sur la lande (65x81cm-26x32in) s. 14-Dec-3 Eric Pillon, Calais #156/R
£1549	$2680	€2200	Goulimine (60x92cm-24x36in) s. i.verso panel. 15-Dec-3 Gros & Delettrez, Paris #94/R est:2300-3000

CAILLAUD, Aristide (1902-1990) French

£872	$1544	€1300	Proie (33x24cm-13x9in) s.d.63 i. verso. 27-Apr-4 Artcurial Briest, Paris #220 est:1000-1200
£1074	$1965	€1600	Vesubie (125x55cm-49x22in) s. s.i. verso panel. 7-Jul-4 Artcurial Briest, Paris #151 est:1500-1800
£1842	$3389	€2800	Le phare (61x50cm-24x20in) s. isorel. 25-Jun-4 Daguerre, Paris #165 est:1200-1500
Works on paper			
£336	$594	€500	Paon (22x17cm-9x7in) s.d.72 gouache exhib. 27-Apr-4 Artcurial Briest, Paris #219
£369	$653	€550	Chevauchee des lianes (55x37cm-22x15in) s.d.76 gouache exhib. 27-Apr-4 Artcurial Briest, Paris #225/R
£658	$1211	€1000	Bateaux sur le lac (55x39cm-22x15in) s. mixed media panel. 28-Jun-4 Joron-Derem, Paris #239

CAILLAUX, Rodolphe (1904-1990) French

£243	$450	€355	Vase de fleurs (91x72cm-36x28in) s. paper. 13-Jul-4 Christie's, Rockefeller NY #193/R
£403	$745	€600	Le port do Soccoa (60x81cm-24x32in) s. 15-Mar-4 Blanchet, Paris #108/R
£403	$745	€600	Les danseurs basques (46x38cm-18x15in) s. 15-Mar-4 Blanchet, Paris #109a
£537	$993	€800	Le port de Saint-Jean de Luz (50x100cm-20x39in) s. 15-Mar-4 Blanchet, Paris #109
Works on paper			
£263	$484	€400	Deux pecheurs avec filets (71x51cm-28x20in) s. pastel. 22-Jun-4 Chassaing Rivet, Toulouse #262

CAILLAUX, Roland (20th C) French

Works on paper			
£235	$437	€350	Portrait d'adolescent (46x31cm-18x12in) s.d.1944 graphite. 2-Mar-4 Artcurial Briest, Paris #196
£347	$580	€500	Gentilhomme de la Renaissance (64x48cm-25x19in) s.i.d.1937 W/C. 21-Oct-3 Artcurial Briest, Paris #84

CAILLE, Léon Emile (1836-1907) French

£1224	$2192	€1800	Rencontre (46x38cm-18x15in) s. panel. 19-Mar-4 Millon & Associes, Paris #48/R est:1800-2000
£2000	$3700	€2920	Sound asleep (32x24cm-13x9in) s.d.1883 panel. 10-Mar-4 Sotheby's, Olympia #282/R est:2000-3000
£2795	$4500	€4053	Injured child (30x23cm-12x9in) s. panel. 17-Aug-3 Jeffery Burchard, Florida #30
£2795	$4500	€4081	The family (66x81cm-26x32in) s.d. canvas on masonite. 22-Feb-3 Bunte, Elgin #1255 est:5000-7000
£6000	$9960	€8760	Bedtime story (32x24cm-13x9in) s.d.1873 panel. 1-Oct-3 Sotheby's, Olympia #211/R est:2500-3500

CAILLEBOTTE, Gustave (1848-1894) French

£60000	$109200	€87600	Voiliers sur la Seine a Argenteuil (41x32cm-16x13in) st.sig. painted c.1890-1891 prov.lit. 3-Feb-4 Christie's, London #139/R est:60000-80000
£89385	$160000	€130502	Seine et la pointe de l'Ile Marande (60x73cm-24x29in) s. painted c.1890-1891 prov.exhib.lit. 5-May-4 Christie's, Rockefeller NY #210/R est:180000-220000
£606667	$1116267	€910000	Arbres en fleurs, petit Gennevilliers (54x65cm-21x26in) st.sig. prov.exhib.lit. 9-Jun-4 Tajan, Paris #9/R est:400000-500000
£735294	$1250000	€1073529	Voiliers sur la Seine a Argenteuil (75x43cm-30x17in) bears sig painted 1893 prov.exhib.lit. 4-Nov-3 Christie's, Rockefeller NY #8/R est:700000-900000
£3529412	$6000000	€5152942	Chemin montant (100x125cm-39x49in) s.d.1881 prov.exhib.lit. 4-Nov-3 Christie's, Rockefeller NY #15/R est:6000000-8000000

CAIN, Auguste (1822-1894) French

Sculpture			
£1127	$1949	€1600	Ane d'Afrique (14x16cm-6x6in) s.i. brown pat bronze. 14-Dec-3 St-Germain-en-Laye Encheres #90/R est:1500-1800
£1156	$1839	€1700	Lionne et lionceaux (33x45cm-13x18in) s. pat bronze. 23-Mar-3 Salle des ventes Pillet, Lyon la Foret #153
£1206	$2013	€1700	Canards se disputant une grenouille (12cm-5in) s. brown pat bronze pair. 12-Oct-3 St-Germain-en-Laye Encheres #14/R est:1500
£1974	$3632	€3000	Sphinx et vautour (49cm-19in) s. pat bronze Cast Susse. 25-Jun-4 Millon & Associes, Paris #80/R est:750-1000
£2400	$4080	€3504	Coffret ax murons (20x19cm-8x7in) s. pat bronze. 28-Oct-3 Sotheby's, London #122/R
£2558	$4400	€3735	Nid de faisans - two pheasants and their nest of eggs (64x91cm-25x36in) s. bronze. 6-Dec-3 Selkirks, St. Louis #676/R est:4500-6000
£7250	$11528	€10585	A cock and hen pheasant (61x81cm-24x32in) i. 1-May-3 John Nicholson, Haslemere #293/R est:5000-7500

CAIN, Errol John le (1941-1990) British?

Works on paper			
£1200	$2076	€1752	Peter wanders across the snow covered field, followed by wolves (12x24cm-5x9in) s.d.74 ink W/C gouache. 11-Dec-3 Sotheby's, London #229 est:700-900
£1400	$2422	€2044	Cinderella sharing oranges and lemons with her sisters (19x27cm-7x11in) s. ink wash gouache. 11-Dec-3 Sotheby's, London #228/R est:1500-2000

CAIN, Theron Irving (1893-?) American

£373	$600	€545	View of water garden (36x61cm-14x24in) board. 20-Aug-3 James Julia, Fairfield #1790/R

CAIRATI, Gerolamo (1860-1943) Italian

£1477	$2761	€2200	Autumnal shore (84x112cm-33x44in) s.d.1910. 24-Feb-4 Dorotheum, Vienna #50/R est:2600-3000

CAIRNCROSS, Sam (1913-) New Zealander

£313	$497	€457	Motoiti Island (24x34cm-9x13in) s.d.1963. 1-May-3 Dunbar Sloane, Wellington #261 (NZ.D 900)
£327	$514	€474	Low clouds, view from the desert road (29x56cm-11x22in) s.d.1973 board. 27-Aug-3 Dunbar Sloane, Wellington #103 (NZ.D 900)
£338	$575	€493	Island bay, Wellington (45x75cm-18x30in) s.d.1966 board. 26-Nov-3 Dunbar Sloane, Wellington #83 (NZ.D 900)
£364	$571	€528	Wellington harbour (37x51cm-15x20in) s. board. 27-Aug-3 Dunbar Sloane, Wellington #118 (NZ.D 1000)
£526	$895	€768	Mana Island, Wellington (44x57cm-17x22in) s. i.d.1973 verso board prov. 26-Nov-3 Dunbar Sloane, Wellington #2 est:1000-2000 (NZ.D 1400)
£564	$959	€823	Orange flowers (43x58cm-17x23in) s.d.1950 board. 26-Nov-3 Dunbar Sloane, Wellington #82 est:2000-3000 (NZ.D 1500)
£643	$1183	€939	Self portrait, as Van Gogh (24x20cm-9x8in) s. board. 25-Mar-4 International Art Centre, Auckland #111/R (NZ.D 1800)
£709	$1270	€1035	Willis Street, Wellington (34x42cm-13x17in) s.d.1951 board. 11-May-4 Peter Webb, Auckland #57/R est:2000-3000 (NZ.D 2050)
£752	$1278	€1098	Egmont street, Wellington (40x42cm-16x17in) s.d.1959 board. 26-Nov-3 Dunbar Sloane, Wellington #120/R est:2000-3000 (NZ.D 2000)
£797	$1355	€1164	Queens Wharf (32x27cm-13x11in) s.i.d.1953 s.d.verso board. 4-Nov-3 Peter Webb, Auckland #50/R est:2000-3000 (NZ.D 2200)
£1042	$1656	€1521	Butcher (34x26cm-13x10in) s.d.1954 board. 1-May-3 Dunbar Sloane, Wellington #5/R est:1500-2500 (NZ.D 3000)
£1091	$1713	€1582	Nguruhoe (44x57cm-17x22in) s.d.1972 board exhib. 27-Aug-3 Dunbar Sloane, Wellington #72/R est:3200-4000 (NZ.D 3000)
£1181	$1877	€1724	Boys and boats, regatta day (44x56cm-17x22in) s.d.1973 board. 1-May-3 Dunbar Sloane, Wellington #58/R est:3000-5000 (NZ.D 3400)
£1206	$2134	€1761	Street scene (31x44cm-12x17in) s. board. 28-Apr-4 Dunbar Sloane, Auckland #49/R est:800-1600 (NZ.D 3400)
£1727	$2712	€2504	Bathers (29x29cm-11x11in) s.d.1953 exhib. 27-Aug-3 Dunbar Sloane, Wellington #15/R est:2500-3500 (NZ.D 4750)
£2444	$4154	€3568	Manners St. Wellington (39x46cm-15x18in) s.d.1959 i.verso board. 26-Nov-3 Dunbar Sloane, Wellington #1/R est:2000-4000 (NZ.D 6500)

CAIRNS, R Dickie (19/20th C) British

Works on paper			
£250	$418	€365	Quai Vert, Bruges. init.i.d.1903 W/C. 13-Nov-3 Bonhams, Edinburgh #335

CAIRNS, Robert D (1866-1944) British
£280 $524 €409 Still life of fruit and flowers (35x42cm-14x17in) board. 22-Jul-4 Bonhams, Edinburgh #321

CAIRO, Francesco del (attrib) (1607-1665) Italian
£4828 $8931 €7000 Allegory of Vanity (105x81cm-41x32in) 14-Feb-4 Meeting Art, Vercelli #110/R est:7000
Works on paper
£2585 $4627 €3800 Tete d'homme, les yeux leves vers le ciel (24x23cm-9x9in) i. pierre noire estompe htd white chk. 19-Mar-4 Piasa, Paris #23/R est:2500

CAIRO, Francesco del (circle) (1607-1665) Italian
£12000 $21960 €17520 Rest on the Flight into Egypt (55x43cm-22x17in) 9-Jul-4 Christie's, Kensington #150/R est:4000-6000

CAISERMAN-ROTH, Ghitta (1923-) Canadian
£714 $1229 €1042 Still life with fruit and flowers (17x22cm-7x9in) s. board prov. 2-Dec-3 Joyner Waddington, Toronto #177/R (C.D 1600)

CALA Y MOYA, Jose de (1850-1891) Spanish
£309 $500 €448 Arab encampment (17x25cm-7x10in) s. board. 29-Jul-3 Galeria y Remates, Montevideo #8/R
£604 $1130 €900 Farm scene (51x79cm-20x31in) s. 24-Feb-4 Durán, Madrid #138/R
£1429 $2600 €2100 Rural scene (64x43cm-25x17in) s.i.d.1873. 3-Feb-4 Segre, Madrid #60/R est:2100
£1429 $2600 €2100 Poor job (64x43cm-25x17in) s. s.i.d.1873 verso. 3-Feb-4 Segre, Madrid #59/R est:2100
£10000 $18200 €14600 In the harem (35x27cm-14x11in) s. prov. 15-Jun-4 Sotheby's, London #115/R est:12000-18000

CALABRIA, Ennio (1937-) Italian
£933 $1717 €1400 Untitled (70x50cm-28x20in) s.d.1966 oil paper on canvas. 12-Jun-4 Meeting Art, Vercelli #102/R est:1000
£1724 $2879 €2500 Figure and dog (50x50cm-20x20in) s. s.i.verso. 13-Nov-3 Finarte Semenzato, Rome #242 est:2500-2800
£1745 $3246 €2600 Artist and his muse (75x95cm-30x37in) s. s.i.d.1961 verso. 4-Mar-4 Babuino, Rome #505 est:1800-2200
£2042 $3390 €2900 Studio per Ricordo di Pompei (60x60cm-24x24in) s. s.i.verso painted 1980. 14-Jun-3 Meeting Art, Vercelli #492/R est:2500
£2657 $4517 €3800 Figure (70x50cm-28x20in) s.d.57. 24-Nov-3 Christie's, Milan #93 est:900-1300

CALAME, Alexandre (1810-1864) Swiss
£262 $477 €383 Rocky valley with castle ruins on the hilltop (34x26cm-13x10in) i. cardboard. 16-Jun-4 Fischer, Luzern #2045/R (S.FR 600)
£344 $575 €499 Two ships on stormy sea (33x43cm-13x17in) s. board. 23-Jun-3 Philippe Schuler, Zurich #3382 (S.FR 750)
£476 $852 €695 Roches grantiques au Croisie (34x48cm-13x19in) s. i. verso board exhib. 22-Mar-4 Philippe Schuler, Zurich #4312 (S.FR 1100)
£486 $773 €700 Cascade (54x35cm-21x14in) s. 9-Sep-3 Vanderkindere, Brussels #82
£1299 $2325 €1897 Plant study (24x30cm-9x12in) paper on canvas. 22-Mar-4 Philippe Schuler, Zurich #4311/R est:1300-1700 (S.FR 3000)
£1534 $2900 €2240 Lone pine tree in wooded landscape at dawn (23x18cm-9x7in) s. panel. 21-Feb-4 Brunk, Ashville #49/R est:1000-2000
£2200 $3938 €3212 Alpine river landscape (65x44cm-26x17in) s. 26-May-4 Sotheby's, Olympia #265/R est:1000-1500
£2222 $4000 €3244 Farm house on the side of a mountain (32x51cm-13x20in) oil paper on canvas prov. 22-Jan-4 Sotheby's, New York #241/R est:4000-6000
£2489 $3982 €3634 Savoie landscape (17x49cm-7x19in) canvas on board. 19-Sep-3 Koller, Zurich #3092/R est:2000-3000 (S.FR 5500)
£2632 $4842 €4000 Vue de village en bordure de torrent (34x28cm-13x11in) paper on cardboard. 23-Jun-4 Sotheby's, Paris #59/R est:4000-6000
£3667 $6637 €5500 Mountains (67x57cm-26x22in) s. lit. 3-Apr-4 Badum, Bamberg #270/R est:6000
£4305 $7834 €6500 Landscape with rapid mountain stream (140x199cm-55x78in) i.d.1854. 21-Jun-4 Dorotheum, Vienna #198/R est:6500-7000
£4741 $8487 €6922 Haslital - Handeck (29x41cm-11x16in) paper on canvas. 14-May-4 Dobiaschofsky, Bern #41/R est:9500 (S.FR 11000)
£5172 $9259 €7551 Lac des quatre Cantons (102x86cm-40x34in) mono. painted c.1870 prov. 13-May-4 Pierre Berge, Paris #10/R est:13000-15000 (S.FR 12000)
£5495 $10000 €8023 Paysage au Servas, Switzerland (35x53cm-14x21in) paper on board prov. 17-Jun-4 Christie's, Rockefeller NY #53/R est:10000-15000
£5603 $10030 €8180 Rosenlaui with Wellhorn and Wetterhorn (28x38cm-11x15in) s. board. 14-May-4 Dobiaschofsky, Bern #46/R est:9000 (S.FR 13000)
£5702 $10491 €8325 Brienzersee (36x51cm-14x20in) 23-Jun-4 Koller, Zurich #3005/R est:15000-25000 (S.FR 13000)
£8297 $15100 €12114 Lac des Quatre-Cantons (31x30cm-12x12in) s. painted c.1857-61 exhib.lit. 16-Jun-4 Fischer, Luzern #1275/R est:12000-15000 (S.FR 19000)
£14350 $23390 €20951 Small waterfall in rocky landscape (28x37cm-11x15in) s. 29-Sep-3 Christie's, Zurich #10/R est:15000-20000 (S.FR 32000)
£22624 $36199 €33031 Paysage de montagne, avec sapins et cours d'eau, par temps d'orage (90x111cm-35x44in) s.d.1843 prov.lit. 19-Sep-3 Koller, Zurich #3094/R est:30000-40000 (S.FR 50000)
£28509 $47610 €41623 Foret de pins en Valais (110x152cm-43x60in) s. 16-Nov-3 Koller, Geneva #1240/R est:50000-70000 (S.FR 65000)
£36199 $57919 €52851 Vierwaldstattersee with Urirotstock (121x170cm-48x67in) s.d.1850 prov.lit. 19-Sep-3 Koller, Zurich #3080/R est:80000-120000 (S.FR 80000)
Works on paper
£409 $733 €597 Tree (29x41cm-11x16in) s.d.1834 pencil. 12-May-4 Dobiaschofsky, Bern #1111/R (S.FR 950)
£776 $1389 €1133 Landscape with watch tower ruins (10x13cm-4x5in) s. w/C. 14-May-4 Dobiaschofsky, Bern #43/R est:1800 (S.FR 1800)
£805 $1490 €1200 Pine tree in stormy landscape (25x40cm-10x16in) d.1844 W/C chl lit. 12-Mar-4 Zadick, Uberlingen #4041
£830 $1527 €1212 Orage sur un lac (22x28cm-9x11in) s.d. W/C lit. 14-Jun-4 Philippe Schuler, Zurich #4404/R (S.FR 1900)
£905 $1566 €1321 Tronc d'arbre (28x35cm-11x14in) s. pencil ink. 9-Dec-3 Sotheby's, Zurich #2/R est:2000-3000 (S.FR 2000)
£1250 $2250 €1825 View of a ford with cattle and a herdsman (16x22cm-6x9in) s. pen ink sepia wash. 21-Jan-4 Sotheby's, New York #143/R est:2000-3000
£1357 $2348 €1981 Arbrs au bord d'un lac (15x23cm-6x9in) s.i. pencil ink W/C lit. 9-Dec-3 Sotheby's, Zurich #15/R est:3000-5000 (S.FR 3000)
£1379 $2469 €2013 Etang de montagne (22x34cm-9x13in) W/C. 13-May-4 Pierre Berge, Paris #5/R est:5000-6000 (S.FR 3200)
£2183 $4017 €3187 Paysage avec gros arbres et deux paysans (33x26cm-13x10in) s. sepia brush lit. 14-Jun-4 Philippe Schuler, Zurich #4405/R est:5000-6000 (S.FR 5000)
£2802 $5015 €4091 Lac paisible (59x82cm-23x32in) s. chl crayon htd white lit. 13-May-4 Pierre Berge, Paris #4/R est:7500-9000 (S.FR 6500)
£3043 $5570 €4443 Landscape with mountain stream (15x19cm-6x7in) s.d.1858 W/C. 7-Jun-4 Christie's, Zurich #5/R est:2500-3500 (S.FR 7000)

CALAME, Alexandre (attrib) (1810-1864) Swiss
£724 $1158 €1057 Stream in rocky gorge (5x45cm-2x18in) study paper on canvas. 16-Sep-3 Philippe Schuler, Zurich #3229/R est:1800-2400 (S.FR 1600)
£786 $1431 €1148 Alpine landscape with snow peaks (37x53cm-15x21in) paper on cardboard. 16-Jun-4 Fischer, Luzern #2044/R (S.FR 1800)
£1101 $1872 €1607 Chenes, torrent (140x199cm-55x78in) i. lit. 5-Nov-3 Dobiaschofsky, Bern #409/R est:4000 (S.FR 2500)
£1589 $2893 €2400 Paysage de torrent dans une vallee encaissee (34x26cm-13x10in) 21-Jun-4 Tajan, Paris #131/R est:3000-4000
£1857 $2971 €2693 Oak trees (55x46cm-22x18in) panel. 15-May-3 Stuker, Bern #1107/R est:3000-3500 (S.FR 3900)
Works on paper
£428 $736 €625 Village an the banks of a stream (19x28cm-7x11in) s.d.1848 W/C. 8-Dec-3 Philippe Schuler, Zurich #4197/R (S.FR 950)

CALAME, Arthur (1843-1919) Swiss
£405 $648 €587 Father with children on ship (43x34cm-17x13in) s. board. 15-May-3 Stuker, Bern #1108/R (S.FR 850)
£570 $952 €832 Belle-Isle sur mer en Bretagne (33x47cm-13x19in) s. panel. 16-Nov-3 Koller, Geneva #1207 (S.FR 1300)
£862 $1543 €1259 Fishing boats on beach (20x32cm-8x13in) s. canvas on board. 14-May-4 Dobiaschofsky, Bern #51/R est:2100 (S.FR 2000)
£897 $1497 €1300 Three women on terrace of house on Capri (28x20cm-11x8in) s. i. verso panel. 15-Nov-3 Lempertz, Koln #1590/R est:1000
£2620 $4769 €3825 Un sinistre en mer (21x28cm-8x11in) s. panel. 16-Jun-4 Fischer, Luzern #1292/R est:6000-8000 (S.FR 6000)
£2817 $4873 €4000 Shepherd in the Alps (34x45cm-13x18in) s.d.1893. 13-Dec-3 Hagelstam, Helsinki #34/R est:4000

CALANDRA, Davide (1856-1915) Italian
Sculpture
£1633 $2922 €2400 Spanish woman (31x28x15cm-12x11x6in) s. bronze. 22-Mar-4 Sant Agostino, Torino #228/R est:2000-2500

CALANDRELLI, Alexander (attrib) (1834-1903) German
Works on paper
£1538 $2615 €2200 Sketches for memorial to Friedrich Wilhelm II (13x57cm-5x22in) pencil prov.lit. two. 20-Nov-3 Van Ham, Cologne #1508a/R est:2800

CALANDRI, Mario (1914-1993) Italian
£3034 $5068 €4400 Fish and lemon (34x40cm-13x16in) s. board. 17-Nov-3 Sant Agostino, Torino #224/R est:3500-4500
Works on paper
£680 $1218 €1000 Rugby match (33x48cm-13x19in) s. pencil W/C. 22-Mar-4 Sant Agostino, Torino #427/R
£1103 $1843 €1600 Owl (41x29cm-16x11in) s.d.1976 pencil. 17-Nov-3 Sant Agostino, Torino #4/R est:1400

CALANDRUCCI, Giacinto (1646-1707) Italian
Works on paper
£1020 $1827 €1500 La Vierge a l'Enfant avec Saint Joseph (27x18cm-11x7in) red chk prov. 18-Mar-4 Christie's, Paris #88/R est:1500-2000

CALANDRUCCI, Giacinto (attrib) (1646-1707) Italian
Works on paper
£700 $1211 €1022 Adoration of the shepherds (28x23cm-11x9in) i. red chk pen brown ink sold with a dr after Dufresnoy. 12-Dec-3 Christie's, Kensington #360
£1000 $1800 €1460 Madonna and Child with St Lucy. Madonna and Child and male torso (15x12cm-6x5in) pen brown ink black chk double-sided prov. 20-Apr-4 Sotheby's, Olympia #31/R est:800-1200
£1645 $3026 €2500 Putti (33x23cm-13x9in) sanguine. 22-Jun-4 Sotheby's, Milan #50/R est:2500-3000

CALBET, Antoine (1860-1944) French
Works on paper
£267 $491 €400 Jeunes femmes au bain (52x62cm-20x24in) s. pastel oval. 8-Jun-4 Livinec, Gaudcheau & Jezequel, Rennes #69
£276 $505 €400 Carmencita (33x26cm-13x10in) s. W/C htd white gouache. 31-Jan-4 Gerard, Besancon #2
£379 $702 €550 Nu sur le dos. chl chk dr. 16-Feb-4 Giraudeau, Tours #38
£590 $974 €850 Elegante a la capeline fleurieo (31x23cm-12x9in) crayon W/C gouache. 3-Jul-3 Claude Aguttes, Neuilly #26
£1408 $2437 €2000 Deux femmes dans un parc (32x24cm-13x9in) s. W/C. 13-Dec-3 De Vuyst, Lokeren #44/R est:2000-2500

CALBET, Antoine (attrib) (1860-1944) French
£662 $1145 €967 Model and Cupid (61x51cm-24x20in) 9-Dec-3 Rasmussen, Copenhagen #1587/R (D.KR 7000)

CALBURN, Simon Robert Henry (1938-1992) South African

Works on paper

£248	$443	€362	Cape fly catcher, Batis capensis (43x31cm-17x12in) s.d.1974 i.verso W/C. 31-May-4 Stephan Welz, Johannesburg #167 (SA.R 3000)

CALCAGNADORO, Antonino (1876-1935) Italian

£1197	$1987	€1700	La Signora nera (24x21cm-9x8in) s.d.1920 i.verso panel. 11-Jun-3 Christie's, Rome #23 est:1300-1800

CALCAGNO, Lawrence (1913-1993) American

£529	$900	€772	Morning gold (64x56cm-25x22in) acrylic. 9-Nov-3 Wright, Chicago #444
£782	$1400	€1142	Yellow landscape II (71x102cm-28x40in) s.i.d.1972 acrylic. 16-May-4 Wright, Chicago #317/R
£882	$1500	€1288	Earth legend I (74x104cm-29x41in) s. i.d.1972 verso. 9-Nov-3 Wright, Chicago #440 est:2000-3000
£882	$1500	€1288	Cosmicscape XIV (89x79cm-35x31in) s.i.d.1974-76. 9-Nov-3 Wright, Chicago #445 est:2000-3000
£894	$1600	€1305	Recitation to autumn III (61x81cm-24x32in) s.i.d.1963. 16-May-4 Wright, Chicago #318/R est:1500-2000
£941	$1600	€1374	Taos IV (71x102cm-28x40in) s.i.d.1972 acrylic. 9-Nov-3 Wright, Chicago #441 est:1500-2000
£1006	$1800	€1469	Inscape I (71x97cm-28x38in) s.i.d.1979 acrylic. 16-May-4 Wright, Chicago #308/R est:2000-3000
£1063	$1700	€1552	Landscape without time, XIII (122x132cm-48x52in) s.i.d.1968 verso. 20-Sep-3 Bunte, Elgin #385f
£1176	$2000	€1717	Far horizon V (124x104cm-49x41in) 9-Nov-3 Wright, Chicago #446 est:2500-3500
£1397	$2500	€2040	Red season II (81x91cm-32x36in) s.i.d.1962. 16-May-4 Wright, Chicago #319/R est:3000-4000
£1508	$2700	€2202	Timeless white with grey (71x117cm-28x46in) acrylic. 16-May-4 Wright, Chicago #314/R est:3000-4000
£1508	$2700	€2202	Sunspace 11 (61x117cm-24x46in) s.verso acrylic. 16-May-4 Wright, Chicago #315/R est:3000-4000
£1765	$3000	€2577	Landscape without time VIII (122x132cm-48x52in) s.i.d.1966 verso prov. 9-Nov-3 Wright, Chicago #443 est:2000-3000
£1816	$3250	€2651	Timeless white III (66x183cm-26x72in) acrylic prov. 16-May-4 Wright, Chicago #309/R est:1000-1500
£1912	$3250	€2792	West of East river (97x135cm-38x53in) acrylic. 9-Nov-3 Wright, Chicago #442 est:2500-3500
£2059	$3500	€3006	Cosmicscape XII (104x165cm-41x65in) s.d.i.1976 verso acrylic. 9-Nov-3 Wright, Chicago #439 est:4000-5000
£2235	$4000	€3263	Far horizon (163x127cm-64x50in) s.d.1964 verso prov. 16-May-4 Wright, Chicago #313/R est:5000-7000

Works on paper

£391	$700	€571	Sunbands I (51x76cm-20x30in) s.d.1968 mixed media. 16-May-4 Wright, Chicago #311/R
£447	$800	€653	Low horizon sunbands (51x76cm-20x30in) s.i.d.1968 mixed media. 16-May-4 Wright, Chicago #316/R
£475	$850	€694	Dark sunbands (41x71cm-16x28in) s.i.d.1968 mixed media. 16-May-4 Wright, Chicago #312/R
£531	$950	€775	Sunbands II (51x76cm-20x30in) s.i.d.1969 mixed media. 16-May-4 Wright, Chicago #310/R

CALCAR, Gesina (1850-1936) Dutch

£359	$600	€524	Dutch farmer at work. s. 18-Oct-3 Harvey Clar, Oakland #1183

CALDAS, Waltercio (1946-) Brazilian

Sculpture

£5882	$10000	€8588	Two oranges (91x122x61cm-36x48x24in) 1 of 3 stainless steel enamel exec.1998 prov.lit. 18-Nov-3 Christie's, Rockefeller NY #17/R est:15000-20000

CALDER, Alexander (1898-1976) American

£3733	$6757	€5600	Sillons noirs sur fond rouge (160x230cm-63x91in) s. 1-Apr-4 Credit Municipal, Paris #88 est:2500-3000
£11711	$21196	€17800	Le dejeuner (80x65cm-31x26in) s.d.5 juin 1929. 16-Apr-4 Pierre Berge, Paris #10/R est:5000-6000
£17964	$30000	€26227	Onion (33x28cm-13x11in) s.d.46 prov.exhib. 13-Nov-3 Sotheby's, New York #163/R est:25000-35000
£32934	$55000	€48084	Untitled - Dragon Rouge et Papillon (81x99cm-32x39in) s.i. painted 1950 prov. 12-Nov-3 Christie's, Rockefeller NY #349/R est:60000-80000
£189944	$340000	€277318	Elements (48x9cm-19x4in) painted 1945 prov.exhib. 13-May-4 Sotheby's, New York #103/R est:50000-70000

Prints

£1769	$3166	€2600	Untitled (95x95cm-37x37in) s. num.68/90 aquatint exec.1972. 16-Mar-4 Finarte Semenzato, Milan #84/R est:2000
£1977	$3500	€2886	Study for la grand vitesse (76x112cm-30x44in) s.i. col lithograph prov. 30-Apr-4 Sotheby's, New York #310/R est:3500-4500
£2045	$3600	€2986	Nez et oreilles tres gais (74x109cm-29x43in) s.num.41/75 col lithograph. 22-May-4 Selkirks, St. Louis #715/R est:2750-3250
£2096	$3500	€3060	Composition (74x109cm-29x43in) s.i. col lithograph. 11-Nov-3 Doyle, New York #219/R est:600-900
£5650	$10000	€8249	Construction (77x113cm-30x44in) s. col lithograph. 30-Apr-4 Sotheby's, New York #311/R est:4000-6000

Sculpture

£7000	$12740	€10220	Horse II (11x20x12cm-4x8x5in) init. st.num.36 dark brown pat bronze Cast 1964 prov. 5-Feb-4 Christie's, London #176/R est:8000-10000
£7500	$12975	€10950	N, initial pin (7x8cm-3x3in) silver steel wire exec.c.1948. 11-Dec-3 Christie's, Kensington #134/R est:3000-5000
£25137	$46000	€36700	The sang (81x51x102cm-32x20x40in) s.num.1/6 black pat bronze prov.exhib. 6-Jun-4 Wright, Chicago #342/R est:30000-40000
£26347	$44000	€38467	DM (12x9cm-5x4in) Polished brass executed c.1950 prov.lit. 11-Nov-3 Christie's, Rockefeller NY #106/R est:6000-8000
£31977	$55000	€46686	Wisp of cop (49x38cm-19x15in) init. painted sheet metal wire prov. 3-Dec-3 Doyle, New York #45/R est:80000-120000
£40293	$71319	€58828	Untitled (8x31x18cm-3x12x7in) init. standing mobile painted iron brass prov. 27-Apr-4 AB Stockholms Auktionsverk #1209/R est:500000-700000 (S.KR 550000)
£50898	$85000	€74311	White arrow (32x43x12cm-13x17x5in) painted metal wire prov. 13-Nov-3 Sotheby's, New York #164/R est:60000-80000
£67797	$120000	€98984	Standing mobile (19x15cm-7x6in) sheet metal wire paint prov. 2-May-4 Bonhams & Butterfields, Los Angeles #3029/R est:80000-120000
£70552	$115000	€103006	Untitled (18x16cm-7x6in) painted sheet metal wire mobile exec.c.1950 prov. 23-Sep-3 Christie's, Rockefeller NY #44/R est:50000-70000
£83832	$140000	€122395	Slender Ribs - Maquette (56x57x44cm-22x22x17in) stabile painted sheet metal exec 1962 prov.lit. 12-Nov-3 Christie's, Rockefeller NY #330/R est:70000-90000
£101796	$170000	€148622	Untitled (42x52cm-17x20in) init. standing mobile painted sheet metal wire prov.lit. 12-Nov-3 Christie's, Rockefeller NY #308/R est:120000-180000
£150838	$270000	€220223	Little red dozen (67x91x51cm-26x36x20in) mono. painted hanging mobile wire exec 1963 prov. 13-May-4 Sotheby's, New York #104/R est:150000-200000
£155689	$260000	€227306	White petals and black on red stabile (48x58cm-19x23in) init.base standing mobile painted sheet metal wire prov. 12-Nov-3 Christie's, Rockefeller NY #342/R est:150000-200000
£156425	$280000	€228381	Yellow counterwieght (61x130cm-24x51in) init.d.72 base standing mobile painted sheet metal wire prov. 12-May-4 Christie's, Rockefeller NY #178/R est:250000-350000
£167598	$300000	€244693	National Gallery II - Maquette (36x109x56cm-14x43x22in) mono. standing mobile painted sheet metal wire bolts prov. 12-May-4 Christie's, Rockefeller NY #177/R est:220000-280000
£167598	$300000	€244693	Red Pachyderm (67x127x30cm-26x50x12in) mono.d.70 painted metal rod standing mobile prov.exhib. 13-May-4 Sotheby's, New York #134/R est:300000-400000
£170588	$290000	€249058	Two black discs and six others (81x127cm-32x50in) mono.d.71 black paint steel hanging mobile. 7-Nov-3 Selkirks, St. Louis #426/R est:250000-300000
£178771	$320000	€261006	Esctcheon (112x102x89cm-44x40x35in) painted sheet metal wire exec 1954 prov.exhib.lit. 12-May-4 Christie's, Rockefeller NY #109/R est:200000-300000
£178771	$320000	€261006	Araignee - Maquette (41x61x41cm-16x24x16in) painted metal stabile exec c.1957 prov. 13-May-4 Sotheby's, New York #126/R est:70000-90000
£195531	$350000	€285475	Yellows up, reds down (124x178cm-49x70in) init.d.63 hanging mobile painted sheet metal wire prov.exhib. 12-May-4 Christie's, Rockefeller NY #133/R est:350000-450000
£227545	$380000	€332216	Mother Cow and Calf. brass wire exec 1934-1939 prov. 11-Nov-3 Christie's, Rockefeller NY #8/R est:300000-500000
£270000	$491400	€394200	Plumeau Sioux - Maquette (142x76x56cm-56x30x22in) init.d.69 painted sheet metal standing mobile prov. 5-Feb-4 Sotheby's, London #20/R est:300000-400000
£323353	$540000	€472095	Black Rocker (124cm-49in) mono. standing mobile painted sheet metal exec 1945 prov. 11-Nov-3 Christie's, Rockefeller NY #13/R est:350000-450000
£391061	$700000	€570949	Untitled (105x91x38cm-41x36x15in) painted sheet metal wire exec 1942 prov.exhib. 12-May-4 Sotheby's, New York #18/R est:400000-600000
£395210	$660000	€577007	Red Ghost (43x142cm-17x56in) hanging mobile painted sheet metal wire exec 1949 prov. 11-Nov-3 Christie's, Rockefeller NY #17/R est:500000-700000
£449102	$750000	€655689	Four White at Forty-Five (138x223cm-54x88in) mono.d.68 mobile painted metal wire prov. 11-Nov-3 Christie's, Rockefeller NY #64/R est:700000-900000
£530726	$950000	€774860	Armada (195x70x60cm-77x28x24in) painted metal wire hanging mobile exec 1945 prov.exhib. 11-May-4 Christie's, Rockefeller NY #27/R est:1200000-1800000
£837989	$1500000	€1223464	Yellow W - Orange Y (76x305x152cm-30x120x60in) mono. painted metal hanging mobile exec 1950 prov.exhib. 12-May-4 Sotheby's, New York #24/R est:700000-900000
£1396648	$2500000	€2039106	Small crinkly (360x395x395cm-142x156x156in) init. d.76 base painted metal standing mobile prov.exhib.lit. 12-May-4 Sotheby's, New York #29/R est:2500000-3500000
£3113773	$5200000	€4546109	Untitled (500x600x300cm-197x236x118in) mono.d.68 large stabile painted steel prov. 11-Nov-3 Christie's, Rockefeller NY #58/R est:4000000-5000000

Works on paper

£1135	$2100	€1657	Portrait of a woman - Leslie Aldridge Westoff (27x21cm-11x8in) mono. pencil exec 1950 prov. 12-Feb-4 Sotheby's, New York #126/R est:3000-5000
£1486	$2750	€2170	Portrait of a man - John W Aldridge (28x21cm-11x8in) mono. pencil exec 1950 prov. 12-Feb-4 Sotheby's, New York #127/R est:3000-5000
£2568	$4750	€3749	Untitled (57x77cm-22x30in) s.d.47 ink W/C prov. 12-Feb-4 Sotheby's, New York #112/R est:4000-6000
£3200	$5792	€4672	Untitled (31x24cm-12x9in) s. gouache. 1-Apr-4 Christie's, Kensington #287/R est:3000-5000
£4121	$7500	€6017	McGovern (78x58cm-31x23in) init.d.72 gouache. 29-Jun-4 Sotheby's, New York #499/R est:4000-6000
£4412	$7500	€6442	Black crosses (74x53cm-29x21in) s.d.1961 gouache. 9-Nov-3 Wright, Chicago #376 est:5000-7000
£4412	$7500	€6442	Untitled (79x58cm-31x23in) s.d.1972 gouache prov. 9-Nov-3 Wright, Chicago #427 est:5000-7000
£5000	$8000	€7300	Aquatic forms with red squid (78x58cm-31x23in) init.d.75 gouache. 18-Sep-3 Swann Galleries, New York #126/R est:5000-8000
£5376	$10000	€7849	Untitled - Night with Jupiter (33x27cm-13x11in) s. pen ink double-sided. 2-Mar-4 Swann Galleries, New York #85/R est:8000-12000
£5389	$9000	€7868	Balloon brambles (78x57cm-31x22in) s.d.74 i.verso gouache. 7-Oct-3 Sotheby's, New York #417 est:4000-6000
£5389	$9000	€7868	Composition (53x74cm-21x29in) s.d.70 gouache prov. 7-Oct-3 Sotheby's, New York #418 est:10000-15000
£5665	$9630	€8271	Untitled (58x77cm-23x30in) s.d.73 W/C. 5-Nov-3 AB Stockholms Auktionsverk #1135/R est:50000-60000 (S.KR 75000)
£5828	$9500	€8509	Untitled (109x75cm-43x30in) s.d.70 gouache prov. 23-Sep-3 Christie's, Rockefeller NY #43/R est:7000-9000
£6881	$11491	€9977	Drawing in red and black (74x109cm-29x43in) brush pen Indian ink. 19-Jun-3 Kornfeld, Bern #235/R est:12500 (S.FR 15000)
£7000	$11690	€10220	Dark crosses (75x54cm-30x21in) s.d.64 W/C. 22-Oct-3 Christie's, London #30/R est:5000-7000
£7485	$12500	€10928	1000-A-SIT (50x38cm-20x15in) s.d.74 i.verso gouache prov. 14-Nov-3 Phillips, New York #137/R est:8000-12000
£7639	$12757	€11000	Les pyramides (75x110cm-30x43in) s.d.1975 gouache. 25-Oct-3 Cornette de St.Cyr, Paris #614/R est:10000-12000
£7692	$14000	€11230	Untitled (37x28cm-15x11in) mono.d.69 gouache. 29-Jun-4 Sotheby's, New York #427/R est:5000-7000
£7975	$13000	€11644	Ladies and gentlemen (109x75cm-43x30in) s.d.71 gouache prov.exhib. 23-Sep-3 Christie's, Rockefeller NY #42/R est:10000-15000
£8084	$13500	€11803	Untitled (37x108cm-15x43in) s.d.74 gouache prov. 14-Nov-3 Phillips, New York #139/R est:15000-20000
£8084	$13500	€11803	Pyramids (37x109cm-15x43in) s.d.74 gouache prov. 14-Nov-3 Phillips, New York #140/R est:15000-20000
£8383	$14000	€12239	Symbolic landscape (75x105cm-30x41in) s.d.53 gouache prov. 7-Oct-3 Sotheby's, New York #415 est:10000-15000
£8649	$16000	€12628	Untitled (75x110cm-30x43in) s.d.73 gouache prov.lit. 12-Feb-4 Sotheby's, New York #104/R est:8000-10000
£8649	$16000	€12628	Deux tetes (58x78cm-23x31in) s.d.73 gouache prov. 12-Feb-4 Sotheby's, New York #106/R est:6000-8000

£8649	$16000	€12628	Une fleche rouge et bleu (75x108cm-30x43in) s.d.70 gouache. 12-Feb-4 Sotheby's, New York #113/R est:6000-8000
£8725	$15443	€13000	Untitled (75x55cm-30x22in) s. gouache. 28-Apr-4 Wiener Kunst Auktionen, Vienna #286/R est:13000-16000
£8750	$14000	€12775	Composition with circles and spiral (58x78cm-23x31in) s.d.1966 W/C gouache. 18-Sep-3 Swann Galleries, New York #125/R est:10000-15000
£9091	$15636	€13000	Untitled (74x110cm-29x43in) s.i.d.72 gouache prov. 2-Dec-3 Calmels Cohen, Paris #68/R est:10000-12000
£9202	$15000	€13435	Dense fossil (75x110cm-30x43in) s.d.71 gouache prov. 23-Sep-3 Christie's, Rockefeller NY #47/R est:8000-12000
£9341	$17000	€13638	Study of mobile (35x28cm-14x11in) s. W/C crayon. 29-Jun-4 Sotheby's, New York #491/R est:6000-8000
£9412	$16000	€13742	Untitled (74x104cm-29x41in) s.d.1962 gouache prov. 9-Nov-3 Wright, Chicago #375 est:12000-15000
£9581	$16000	€13988	Yellow boots (75x35cm-30x14in) s.d.76 gouache prov. 14-Nov-3 Phillips, New York #143/R est:18000-25000
£10180	$17000	€14863	Coralies (78x29cm-31x11in) mono.d.71 i.verso gouache prov. 14-Nov-3 Phillips, New York #138/R est:12000-18000
£10599	$18231	€15475	Untitled (50x64cm-20x25in) s.d.53 gouache prov. 2-Dec-3 Koller, Zurich #3096/R est:22000-28000 (S.FR 23530)
£10778	$18000	€15736	Holly day (78x29cm-31x11in) s.d.71 gouache prov. 14-Nov-3 Phillips, New York #136/R est:12000-18000
£10849	$17575	€15840	Untitled (75x109cm-30x43in) s.i.d.69 gouache prov. 24-May-3 Burkhard, Luzern #127/R est:16000-20000 (S.FR 23000)
£11000	$20240	€16500	Papillon et arbre (58x78cm-23x31in) s.d.68 gouache prov. 10-Jun-4 Camard, Paris #143/R est:10000-15000
£11486	$20216	€17000	Lock Ness (75x108cm-30x43in) s.d.1969 gouache prov. 18-May-4 Tajan, Paris #72/R est:15000-18000
£11538	$21000	€16845	Untitled (56x76cm-22x30in) s.d.68 gouache. 29-Jun-4 Sotheby's, New York #481/R est:8000-12000
£11805	$19715	€17000	Composition (73x100cm-29x39in) s.d.71 W/C. 21-Oct-3 Artcurial Briest, Paris #607/R est:12000-18000
£12080	$21382	€18000	Mer noire (75x110cm-30x43in) s.d.76 gouache prov. 28-Apr-4 Artcurial Briest, Paris #268/R est:12000-15000
£12088	$22000	€17648	Untitled (78x58cm-31x23in) s.d.76 gouache. 29-Jun-4 Sotheby's, New York #497/R est:10000-15000
£12162	$20919	€17757	Untitled (75x95cm-30x37in) mono.d.61 gouache prov. 2-Dec-3 Koller, Zurich #3097/R est:18000-25000 (S.FR 27000)
£12270	$20000	€17914	Untitled (74x109cm-29x43in) s.i.d.73 gouache prov. 23-Sep-3 Christie's, Rockefeller NY #41/R est:10000-15000
£13174	$22000	€19234	Suspense (108x74cm-43x29in) s.d.75 gouache prov. 14-Nov-3 Phillips, New York #142/R est:18000-25000
£13473	$22500	€19671	Spirals, pinwheels and loops (74x109cm-29x43in) s.d.74 gouache prov.exhib. 13-Nov-3 Sotheby's, New York #257/R est:12000-18000
£13473	$22500	€19671	Ball game (110x75cm-43x30in) s.d.74 gouache prov. 13-Nov-3 Sotheby's, New York #258/R est:12000-18000
£13514	$23243	€19730	Untitled (65x48cm-26x19in) mono. gouache prov. 2-Dec-3 Koller, Zurich #3099/R est:27000-35000 (S.FR 30000)
£13986	$24056	€20000	Untitled (74x110cm-29x43in) s.i.d.69 gouache prov. 2-Dec-3 Calmels Cohen, Paris #67/R est:10000-12000
£15951	$26000	€23288	Les Passoires (167x223cm-66x88in) i. num.6/6 Aubusson col tapestry. 24-Sep-3 Christie's, Rockefeller NY #59/R est:3000-5000
£16000	$26720	€23360	Untitled (75x110cm-30x43in) s.d.70 gouache prov. 21-Oct-3 Sotheby's, London #342/R est:6000-8000
£16766	$28000	€24478	Seattle (96x131cm-38x52in) s.d.74 gouache prov. 14-Nov-3 Phillips, New York #141/R est:18000-25000
£17000	$30940	€24820	Untitled (58x79cm-23x31in) s.d.49 gouache. 6-Feb-4 Sotheby's, London #141/R est:6000-8000
£17036	$29302	€24873	Campanules (75x110cm-30x43in) s.d.74 gouache prov. 2-Dec-3 Koller, Zurich #3098/R est:37000-45000 (S.FR 37820)
£19162	$32000	€27977	Wage (109x37cm-43x15in) s.d.74 gouache prov. 14-Nov-3 Phillips, New York #144/R est:20000-30000
£22000	$40480	€32120	Coeur Iranien (58x78cm-23x31in) s.d.73 i. verso gouache prov. 24-Jun-4 Sotheby's, London #253/R est:5000-7000
£22346	$40000	€32625	Three discs in space (74x108cm-29x43in) s.i.d.1946 gouache prov.exhib. 12-May-4 Christie's, Rockefeller NY #116/R est:18000-22000
£26946	$45000	€39341	Untitled (57x79cm-22x31in) s.d.44 ink prov. 13-Nov-3 Sotheby's, New York #101/R est:15000-20000

CALDER, Alexander Milne (1846-1923) American

Sculpture

£4420	$8000	€6453	Flamenco dancer (66cm-26in) s.st.f.Bureau Bros brown pat bronze. 31-Mar-4 Sotheby's, New York #116/R est:7000-10000

CALDER, Frank (1890-1968) American

£240	$400	€350	Landscape (20x25cm-8x10in) canvasboard. 18-Oct-3 David Dike, Dallas #174/R

CALDERARA, Antonio (1903-1978) Italian

£1377	$2258	€1900	Bride and groom (14x11cm-6x4in) board painted 1958. 27-May-3 Sotheby's, Milan #31 est:2000
£6159	$10101	€8500	Orta Lake seen from Pella (40x50cm-16x20in) s. prov. 27-May-3 Il Ponte, Milan #541/R est:10000
£10211	$17665	€14500	In spazio nero tensione interrotta (27x24cm-11x9in) s.i.d.1972 verso panel. 13-Dec-3 Lempertz, Koln #292/R est:7000-8000

Works on paper

£933	$1689	€1400	Composition (26x26cm-10x10in) mixed media lit. 1-Apr-4 Frank Peege, Freiburg #1294/R
£995	$1662	€1453	Composition in green (20x19cm-8x7in) mono.d.1967 pencil W/C. 24-Jun-3 Germann, Zurich #930/R est:1200-1500 (S.FR 2200)
£1000	$1840	€1460	Quadrate (16x11cm-6x4in) init.d.69 verso W/C pencil prov. 24-Jun-4 Sotheby's, Milan #524/R est:1000-1500
£1133	$2085	€1700	Untitled (16x15cm-6x6in) init.d.1973 W/C card. 12-Jun-4 Meeting Art, Vercelli #702/R est:1500
£1333	$2453	€2000	Composition (13x13cm-5x5in) mono.d. s.i.d. verso W/C. 11-Jun-4 Hauswedell & Nolte, Hamburg #1191/R est:2500
£1538	$2615	€2200	Untitled (14x18cm-6x7in) mono.d.1960 verso W/C. 27-Nov-3 Lempertz, Koln #71/R est:2000

CALDERINI, Luigi (1880-1973) Italian

£690	$1145	€1000	Boats in Torbole (17x28cm-7x11in) s.d.26 paper. 1-Oct-3 Della Rocca, Turin #88/R
£759	$1259	€1100	Landscape with figures on horseback (17x28cm-7x11in) s. 1-Oct-3 Della Rocca, Turin #319/R
£780	$1303	€1100	Aosta Valley (25x31cm-10x12in) s. board. 20-Oct-3 Sant Agostino, Torino #100/R
£1000	$1840	€1500	Rural path (56x34cm-22x13in) s. cardboard. 8-Jun-4 Della Rocca, Turin #307/R est:1300-1700

Works on paper

£471	$772	€650	Mountainous landscape (35x50cm-14x20in) s. W/C. 27-May-3 Il Ponte, Milan #742

CALDERINI, Marco (1850-c.1941) Italian

£667	$1227	€1000	Mountainous landscape (22x36cm-9x14in) s. cardboard. 8-Jun-4 Della Rocca, Turin #277/R
£1000	$1840	€1500	Autumn (31x15cm-12x6in) i. board. 8-Jun-4 Della Rocca, Turin #217/R est:1300-1700
£3521	$5845	€5000	Coastal landscape (75x100cm-30x39in) s. 11-Jun-3 Christie's, Rome #191/R est:5000-8000
£4255	$7106	€6000	Along the river (29x51cm-11x20in) s.d.1876 cardboard. 20-Oct-3 Sant Agostino, Torino #292/R est:6000
£30000	$54600	€43800	Music in the mountains (70x96cm-28x38in) s.d.94. 17-Jun-4 Christie's, London #80/R est:8000-12000

Works on paper

£306	$548	€450	Albogasio (20x11cm-8x4in) s. W/C. 22-Mar-4 Sant Agostino, Torino #270/R

CALDERON LOPEZ, Pedro (18th C) Mexican

£5263	$9684	€8000	Saint Michael triumphing, surrounded by angels (20x25cm-8x10in) s.i.d.1733 copper. 24-Jun-4 Christie's, Paris #51/R est:5000-7000

CALDERON, Charles-Clement (1870-1906) French

£2600	$4732	€3796	Gondolas before the Doge's Palace, Venice (26x35cm-10x14in) s. panel. 16-Jun-4 Christie's, Kensington #93/R est:2000-3000
£3128	$5380	€4567	Grand Canal, Venice (13x22cm-5x9in) s. board. 3-Dec-3 Naón & Cia, Buenos Aires #17/R est:2000-3000
£3200	$5888	€4672	By the Piazzetta, St Mark's, Venice (46x65cm-18x26in) s. 25-Mar-4 Christie's, Kensington #106/R est:2000-3000
£4363	$7722	€6500	Trois-mats et gondole sur la lagune (46x65cm-18x26in) s. 30-Apr-4 Tajan, Paris #207/R est:8000
£6667	$12267	€10000	Vue de Venise (46x65cm-18x26in) s. 11-Jun-4 Claude Aguttes, Neuilly #31/R est:8000-10000
£11888	$20448	€17000	Voilier et gondole a Venise (54x82cm-21x32in) s. 7-Dec-3 Osenat, Fontainebleau #190 est:9500-10000

CALDERON, Philip Hermogenes (1833-1898) Spanish

£580	$963	€847	Evangeline (25x20cm-10x8in) mono. 1-Oct-3 Sotheby's, Olympia #79/R
£714	$1300	€1042	Battle scene (25x38cm-10x15in) mono. panel. 7-Feb-4 Sloans & Kenyon, Bethesda #1268/R
£28054	$46851	€40959	Hark, hark, the lark (175x125cm-69x49in) s.d.1884 exhib. 17-Nov-3 Waddingtons, Toronto #298/R est:40000-60000 (C.D 62000)

CALDERON, William Frank (1865-1943) British

£350	$620	€511	Boys fishing (37x54cm-15x21in) s. 2-May-4 Lots Road Auctions, London #364
£9028	$15076	€13000	Barzoi sur un divan (77x127cm-30x50in) s.d.1913. 23-Oct-3 Credit Municipal, Paris #71/R est:2000-2500

CALDWELL, Edmund (1852-1930) British

Works on paper

£420	$756	€613	Sleeping beauties (22x30cm-9x12in) indis.s. d.1892. 21-Apr-4 Christie's, Kensington #375/R

CALDWELL, Erskine (1903-1987) French?

Works on paper

£567	$1043	€850	Autoportrait (19x22cm-7x9in) s. green ink exec. 1972 lit. 9-Jun-4 Piasa, Paris #20/R

CALES, Abbe Pierre (1870-1961) French

£1064	$1777	€1500	Les Gresivaudan (45x75cm-18x30in) s.d.20-5-60 cardboard. 19-Oct-3 Anaf, Lyon #67/R est:2000-3000
£1064	$1777	€1500	Les Gresivaudan dans la brume (45x75cm-18x30in) s.d.12/9/56 cardboard. 19-Oct-3 Anaf, Lyon #68/R est:2000-3000
£1533	$2760	€2300	Chemin ensoleille (35x71cm-14x28in) s. cardboard. 20-Apr-4 Chenu & Scrive, Lyon #44/R est:1200-1500
£1915	$3198	€2700	Bord de riviere (32x83cm-13x33in) s.d.18 cardboard. 19-Jun-3 Millon & Associes, Paris #36 est:1800-2300
£2133	$3904	€3200	Village sur les contreforts du Gresivaudan (31x49cm-12x19in) s.d.39 paper. 6-Jun-4 Anaf, Lyon #42 est:3000-3500
£2397	$4075	€3500	Bord de riviere enneige (33x88cm-13x35in) s. panel. 9-Nov-3 Eric Pillon, Calais #110/R
£3675	$6689	€5550	Baie d'Antibes (40x68cm-16x27in) s.d.48 paper. 19-Jun-4 Gerard, Besancon #41

CALFEE, William (1909-) American

Works on paper

£363	$650	€530	Abstraction, landscape with figures (51x66cm-20x26in) s.d.74 gouache exhib. 7-May-4 Sloans & Kenyon, Bethesda #1223/R

CALI, Juan (20th C) Guatemalan?

£291	$500	€425	Champion (61x81cm-24x32in) painted 2000. 5-Dec-3 Arte Maya, Guatemala #7

CALI, Luis (20th C) Guatemalan?

£349	$600	€510	Beauty (81x61cm-32x24in) painted 2002. 5-Dec-3 Arte Maya, Guatemala #10

CALIARI, Benedetto (1538-1598) Italian

£26761	$46831	€38000	L'adoration des Mages (73x56cm-29x22in) prov. 18-Dec-3 Tajan, Paris #6/R est:40000-60000

CALIARI, Benedetto (attrib) (1538-1598) Italian

Works on paper

£1301	$2212	€1900	Crucifixion (30x22cm-12x9in) pen ink wash over crayon prov. 6-Nov-3 Tajan, Paris #2

CALIARI, Carlo (attrib) (1570-1596) Italian

£2267	$4103	€3400	Darius family in fron of Alexander the Great (46x110cm-18x43in) 30-Mar-4 Babuino, Rome #34/R est:3000

CALIERNO, Giosue (1897-1968) Italian

£567	$948	€800	Florence, morning on the Arno (40x49cm-16x19in) s. cardboard. 20-Oct-3 Sant Agostino, Torino #161/R

CALIFANO, Eugene (1893-1974) American

£503	$950	€734	Portrait of a man with a jug (62x46cm-24x18in) s. 22-Feb-4 Bonhams & Butterfields, Los Angeles #7006 est:500-700

CALIFANO, John (1864-1946) American/Italian

£335	$600	€489	Italian village coastline scene (61x91cm-24x36in) 14-May-4 Du Mouchelle, Detroit #2089/R
£538	$850	€785	Alpine landscape with house and figure (33x51cm-13x20in) s. 6-Sep-3 Brunk, Ashville #176
£541	$1000	€790	Landscape with figure (56x69cm-22x27in) 13-Feb-4 Du Mouchelle, Detroit #2193/R
£1347	$2250	€1967	Lion pride (147x249cm-58x98in) s. 7-Oct-3 Sotheby's, New York #168 est:3000-5000
£2483	$4644	€3700	Pasture in the mountains (56x70cm-22x28in) board. 26-Feb-4 Cambi, Genoa #496/R est:2500-3000

CALIGA, Isaac Henry (1857-1940) American

£3889	$7000	€5678	Nude by a curtain (93x57cm-37x22in) s. prov. 21-Jan-4 Sotheby's, New York #258/R est:2000-4000

CALIGIANI, Alberto (1894-1973) Italian

£331	$603	€500	Still life (49x50cm-19x20in) s. 21-Jun-4 Pandolfini, Florence #135

CALIGO, Domenico (19th C) Italian

Works on paper

£6000	$10920	€8760	The Iliad Room, Pitti Palace, Florence (41x57cm-16x22in) s. W/C. 15-Jun-4 Sotheby's, London #184/R est:6000-8000

CALIXTE, G (19th C) ?

£1049	$1804	€1500	Collation (73x92cm-29x36in) s. 7-Dec-3 Livinec, Gaudcheau & Jezequel, Rennes #89

CALIXTO (?) ?

£6227	$11022	€9341	Canoes drawn up on the beach (30x50cm-12x20in) s. 27-Apr-4 Bolsa de Arte, Rio de Janeiro #15/R (B.R 34000)

CALIYANNIS, Manolis (1923-) ?

Works on paper

£267	$480	€400	Montagne en face a Lesbos (35x50cm-14x20in) s.i.d.1955 W/C. 24-Apr-4 Cornette de St.Cyr, Paris #475

CALKIN, Lance (1859-?) British

£450	$824	€657	Chelsea Pensioners in discussion, possibly during the Boer war (42x55cm-17x22in) s. en grisaille. 6-Apr-4 Bonhams, Knightsbridge #132/R

CALLAGHAN, George (?) ?

£1900	$3268	€2774	Newcastle, County Down (50x61cm-20x24in) s. 3-Dec-3 John Ross, Belfast #66 est:2000-2500

Works on paper

£1000	$1800	€1500	Bodhran and accordion player (52x68cm-20x27in) s. mixed media. 20-Apr-4 James Adam, Dublin #76/R est:1200-1500

CALLAHAN, Harry (1912-1999) American

Photographs

£1705	$3000	€2489	Sunbathers (13x20cm-5x8in) with sig. dye transfer print. 20-May-4 Swann Galleries, New York #488/R est:1500-2500
£1795	$3250	€2621	Eleanor, silhouette (216x30cm-85x12in) s. s.i.verso gelatin silver print 1948/printed later lit. 19-Apr-4 Bonhams & Butterfields, San Francisco #379/R est:2000-3000
£1796	$3000	€2622	Cape Cod (24x25cm-9x10in) s. gelatin silver print exec.1973 prov. 17-Oct-3 Phillips, New York #153/R est:4000-6000
£1916	$3200	€2797	Untitled (22x34cm-9x13in) with sig. dye transfer print. 21-Oct-3 Swann Galleries, New York #323/R est:2000-3000
£1916	$3200	€2797	Eleanor, Chicago (23x23cm-9x9in) s. gelatin silver print lit. 16-Oct-3 Phillips, New York #123/R est:3000-5000
£1932	$3400	€2821	Restaurant on 2nd avenue (13x20cm-5x8in) with sig. dye-transfer print. 20-May-4 Swann Galleries, New York #489/R est:1500-2500
£1933	$3500	€2822	Eleanor, Port Huron (18x12cm-7x5in) s. gelatin silver print 1954/printed later. 19-Apr-4 Bonhams & Butterfields, San Francisco #381/R est:3000-4000
£2072	$3750	€3025	Chicago (17x17cm-7x7in) s. gelatin silver print 1948/printed later. 19-Apr-4 Bonhams & Butterfields, San Francisco #380/R est:1000-1500
£2116	$4000	€3089	Chicago, 1951 (26x40cm-10x16in) s. dye transfer print. 17-Feb-4 Christie's, Rockefeller NY #212/R est:3000-5000
£2147	$3800	€3135	Eleanor, Port Huron, 1954 (18x18cm-7x7in) s. gelatin silver print. 27-Apr-4 Christie's, Rockefeller NY #229/R est:3000-5000
£2395	$4000	€3497	Eleanor, Chicago (11x7cm-4x3in) s. i.verso photo exec.1947 printed later prov. 17-Oct-3 Sotheby's, New York #250/R est:4000-6000
£2395	$4000	€3497	Aix-en-Provence (25x18cm-10x7in) s. dye transfer print exec. c.1958 prov.lit. 17-Oct-3 Phillips, New York #279/R est:4000-6000
£2684	$4750	€3919	Eleanor (45x39cm-18x15in) i. photo board printed 1950s or 1960s prov. 28-Apr-4 Sotheby's, New York #212/R est:5000-8000
£2778	$5000	€4056	Eleanor, Chicago, 1949 (19x24cm-7x9in) s.verso gelatin silver print prov. 23-Apr-4 Phillips, New York #49/R est:10000-15000
£2778	$5000	€4056	Chicago (26x40cm-10x16in) s. dye transfer print prov. 23-Apr-4 Phillips, New York #219/R est:3000-5000
£2825	$5000	€4125	Aix-en-Provence (34x27cm-13x11in) i.d.1958 photo printed 1950s or 1960s. 28-Apr-4 Sotheby's, New York #208/R est:5000-7000
£2889	$5200	€4218	New York (22x34cm-9x13in) s. dye transfer print prov. 23-Apr-4 Phillips, New York #185/R est:4000-6000
£2994	$5000	€4371	Eleanor, Chicago (5x5cm-2x2in) gelatin silver print board exec.1949 lit. 17-Oct-3 Phillips, New York #79/R est:7000-10000
£2994	$5000	€4371	Untitled (22x34cm-9x13in) s. dye transfer print exec. c.1959 prov. 17-Oct-3 Phillips, New York #278/R est:4000-6000
£3056	$5500	€4462	New York (28x37cm-11x15in) s. dye transfer print. 23-Apr-4 Phillips, New York #98/R est:3000-5000
£3107	$5500	€4536	Weed against the sky, Michigan (19x18cm-7x7in) s. s.i.d.1948 verso photo printed later prov. 28-Apr-4 Sotheby's, New York #137/R est:4000-6000
£3200	$5440	€4672	Port Huron (18x18cm-7x7in) s. silver print exec.1954 printed later prov. 19-Nov-3 Sotheby's, Olympia #99/R est:1500-2000
£3390	$6000	€4949	Detroit (10x17cm-4x7in) s. photo board printed later prov. 28-Apr-4 Sotheby's, New York #209/R est:4000-6000
£3593	$6000	€5246	Chicago (18x29cm-7x11in) s. i.verso gelatin silver print lit. 16-Oct-3 Phillips, New York #124/R est:3000-5000
£3593	$6000	€5246	Eleanor (11x10cm-4x4in) s. gelatin silver print exec.1947 prov.lit. 17-Oct-3 Phillips, New York #230/R est:6000-8000
£3611	$6500	€5272	New York (17x21cm-7x8in) s. gelatin silver print prov.lit. 23-Apr-4 Phillips, New York #103/R est:5000-7000
£3672	$6500	€5361	Wisconsin (11x24cm-4x9in) s. photo printed later prov. 28-Apr-4 Sotheby's, New York #136/R est:4000-6000
£3693	$6500	€5392	Eleanor, aix-en-Provence (16x13cm-6x5in) with sig.verso silver print. 20-May-4 Swann Galleries, New York #461/R est:5000-7500
£3889	$7000	€5678	Wisconsin (11x24cm-4x9in) s. gelatin silver print prov.lit. 23-Apr-4 Phillips, New York #109/R est:5000-7000
£3892	$6500	€5682	Cape Cod (24x24cm-9x9in) s. gelatin silver print prov.lit. 20-Oct-3 Christie's, Rockefeller NY #178/R est:4000-6000
£4790	$8000	€6993	Eleanor, Chicago (19x24cm-7x9in) s. gelatin silver print exec.1949 printed later. 20-Oct-3 Christie's, Rockefeller NY #117/R est:5000-7000
£4790	$8000	€6993	Eleanor and Barbara, Chicago (19x24cm-7x9in) s. gelatin silver print exec.1953 printed c.1970 prov.lit. 20-Oct-3 Christie's, Rockefeller NY #118/R est:5000-7000
£5000	$9200	€7500	New York - World Trade Centre (24x25cm-9x10in) s. i. verso silver gelatin. 10-Jun-4 Villa Grisebach, Berlin #1046/R est:4000-6000
£5000	$9200	€7500	New York - World Trade Centre (22x22cm-9x9in) s. i. verso silvergalatin. 10-Jun-4 Villa Grisebach, Berlin #1047/R est:4000-6000
£5389	$9000	€7868	Providence (18x62cm-7x24in) s. dye transfer print exec.1978 prov.lit. 17-Oct-3 Phillips, New York #280/R
£5667	$10427	€8500	New York - World Trade Centre (24x23cm-9x9in) s. i. verso silver gelatin lit.exhib. 10-Jun-4 Villa Grisebach, Berlin #1048/R est:4000-6000
£5988	$10000	€8742	Chicago (23x34cm-9x13in) s. gelatin silver print exec.1950 prov.lit. 17-Oct-3 Phillips, New York #44/R est:7000-10000
£6111	$11000	€8922	Eleanor, Chicago, 1953 (16x14cm-6x6in) s.verso gelatin silver print prov.lit. 23-Apr-4 Phillips, New York #48/R est:20000-30000
£6780	$12000	€9899	Eleanor and Barbara in bed, Chicago (17x16cm-7x6in) s.verso printed c.1950 or 1960 photo prov. 28-Apr-4 Sotheby's, New York #134/R est:4000-6000
£7345	$13000	€10724	Aix-en-Provence, nude, back (16x13cm-6x5in) s. photo printed c.1968 prov. 28-Apr-4 Sotheby's, New York #210/R est:6000-8000
£7910	$14000	€11549	Chicago, trees in snow (19x24cm-7x9in) s. photo printed later prov. 28-Apr-4 Sotheby's, New York #138/R est:10000-15000
£8383	$14000	€12239	Chicago, state street (23x34cm-9x13in) s. gelatin silver print board exec.1950. 17-Oct-3 Phillips, New York #68/R est:9000-12000
£8889	$16000	€12978	Chicago, 1950 (19x25cm-7x10in) s. gelatin silver print mounted on board prov.lit. 23-Apr-4 Phillips, New York #66/R est:15000-20000
£9040	$16000	€13198	Asheville, north Carolina (16x24cm-6x9in) s.i.d.1951 verso photo board printed later prov.exhib.lit. 27-Apr-4 Sotheby's, New York #4/R est:10000-15000
£15819	$28000	€23096	Aix-en-Provence, nude front (16x13cm-6x5in) s. photo printed c.1968 prov. 28-Apr-4 Sotheby's, New York #211/R est:6000-8000
£16766	$28000	€24478	Eleanor and Barbara, Chicago (17x17cm-7x7in) s. gelatin silver print board exec.1954 prov. 17-Oct-3 Phillips, New York #82/R est:10000-15000
£17365	$29000	€25353	Chicago, trees in snow (20x24cm-8x9in) s. photo exec.1950 printed later. 17-Oct-3 Sotheby's, New York #253/R est:12000-18000
£18079	$32000	€26395	Grasses (20x24cm-8x9in) s.i.d.12-2-41 gelatin silver print. 27-Apr-4 Christie's, Rockefeller NY #227/R est:10000-15000
£20339	$36000	€29695	Barbara and Eleanor, Chicago (19x24cm-7x9in) s.i.d.1953 verso photo board printed later prov.exhib.lit. 27-Apr-4 Sotheby's, New York #3/R est:20000-30000
£21469	$38000	€31345	New York, building facade (17x20cm-7x8in) s.i.d.1945 verso photo board printed later prov.exhib.lit. 27-Apr-4 Sotheby's, New York #2/R est:15000-25000
£24859	$44000	€36294	Eleanor, double exposure (26x34cm-10x13in) s. s.d.1949 verso photo board prov.lit. 28-Apr-4 Sotheby's, New York #135/R est:25000-35000
£35928	$60000	€52455	Selected images (18x18cm-7x7in) s. dye-transfer print exec.1946-78 printed c.1980 20 prov. 20-Oct-3 Christie's, Rockefeller NY #154/R est:30000-50000
£45198	$80000	€65989	Chicago (19x24cm-7x9in) s.i.d.1950 verso photo board printed later prov.exhib.lit. 27-Apr-4 Sotheby's, New York #1/R est:30000-50000
£50898	$85000	€74311	Eleanor (91x91cm-36x36in) s.num.7 of 8 verso photo aluminum. 17-Oct-3 Sotheby's, New York #249/R est:12000-18000

CALLAHAN, Kenneth L (1906-1986) American

£435	$800	€635	Birth (74x58cm-29x23in) s. tempera W/C masonite painted 1967. 10-Jun-4 Swann Galleries, New York #51/R

Works on paper

£405	$750	€608	Mink (43x48cm-17x19in) s.d.58 ink prov. 14-Jul-4 American Auctioneer #490250/R

CALLANDE DE CHAMPMARTIN, Charles Émile (1797-1883) French

£1831	$3204	€2600	Portrait du Comte Lemercier (99x80cm-39x31in) s. 17-Dec-3 Piasa, Paris #113 est:1000-1500

CALLANDE DE CHAMPMARTIN, Charles Émile (attrib) (1797-1883) French
Works on paper
£414 $757 €600 Personnages moyen-orientaux (23x31cm-9x12in) s. W/C wash. 28-Jan-4 Piasa, Paris #13

CALLCOTT, Sir Augustus Wall (1779-1844) British
£2013 $3765 €3000 Dutch coast (50x78cm-20x31in) s. 28-Feb-4 Quittenbaum, Hamburg #4/R est:3700

CALLCOTT, Sir Augustus Wall (attrib) (1779-1844) British
£703 $1301 €1026 Summer landscape with stone bridge over river (50x77cm-20x30in) mono. 15-Mar-4 Rasmussen, Vejle #342/R (D.KR 7800)

CALLCOTT, William (fl.1856-1865) British
£749 $1250 €1094 Windy shores (41x51cm-16x20in) 16-Nov-3 Simpson's, Houston #207/R

CALLE, Paul (1928-) American
Works on paper
£249 $450 €364 Rowhouses and boy on bike (58x79cm-23x31in) pencil. 16-Apr-4 American Auctioneer #55/R

CALLERY, Simon (1960-) British
£2000 $3680 €2920 Aphide (58x78cm-23x31in) s.i.d. 4 95 verso oil pastel prov. 24-Jun-4 Sotheby's, Olympia #425/R est:1200-1500
£2400 $4080 €3504 4G and Justice (173x242cm-68x95in) s.d.92 stretcher verso oil pastel. 18-Nov-3 Bonhams, Knightsbridge #48/R est:1500-2000
£2601 $4500 €3797 Jsh 2 (147x208cm-58x82in) s.i.d.1991 verso flax prov. 10-Dec-3 Phillips, New York #530/R est:4000-6000

CALLET, A (20th C) French
Works on paper
£1370 $2329 €2000 Portrait de jeune fille aux roses (24x31cm-9x12in) s. W/C. 6-Nov-3 Sotheby's, Paris #9/R est:2000-3000

CALLET, Antoine François (1741-1823) French
£2088 $3800 €3048 Jupiter and Ceres (41x29cm-16x11in) prov.exhib. 17-Jun-4 Christie's, Rockefeller NY #43/R est:5000-7000

CALLI, Ibrahim (1882--1960) Turkish
£1351 $2500 €1972 Lady with oranges (71x56cm-28x22in) canvas on board. 13-Feb-4 Du Mouchelle, Detroit #2148/R est:2500-3500

CALLIYANNIS, Manolis (1926-) Greek
£1000 $1790 €1460 Un coin de Lesbos (49x64cm-19x25in) s. s.i. verso. 11-May-4 Bonhams, New Bond Street #109/R est:1500-2000
£1500 $2550 €2190 Iles chardons a Lesbos (81x100cm-32x39in) s. s.i.d.1960 verso. 18-Nov-3 Sotheby's, London #116/R est:1500-2000

CALLOT, Georges (1857-1903) French
£851 $1523 €1242 Portrait of young woman reading letter (35x26cm-14x10in) s. panel. 12-Jan-4 Rasmussen, Vejle #344/R (D.KR 9000)

CALLOT, Jacques (1592-1635) French
Prints
£1765 $3000 €2577 La grande chasse (19x46cm-7x18in) etching. 6-Nov-3 Swann Galleries, New York #34/R est:3000-5000
£2937 $4993 €4200 La grande chasse (20x47cm-8x19in) etching. 27-Nov-3 Bassenge, Berlin #5054 est:3000
Works on paper
£1900 $3477 €2774 Stooping figure, and a figure seen from behind holding a club (7x7cm-3x3in) red chk prov. 6-Jul-4 Christie's, London #119/R est:1500-2000

CALLOW, George D (fl.1858-1873) British
£1700 $3179 €2550 Fisherfolk and their boats on a beach at low tide. Unloading the catch (30x55cm-12x22in) s.d.1858 pair. 26-Jul-4 Bonhams, Bath #80/R est:1000-1500
Works on paper
£300 $474 €438 Evening on the coast (25x48cm-10x19in) s.i. W/C. 23-Jul-3 Hampton & Littlewood, Exeter #407/R

CALLOW, George William (19th C) British
£941 $1600 €1374 Port views (35x30cm-14x12in) s. i.verso pair. 21-Nov-3 Skinner, Boston #315/R est:1000-1500

CALLOW, John (1822-1878) British
£400 $680 €584 Morning on the coast, low tide (46x81cm-18x32in) s. s.i.d.1873 verso. 19-Nov-3 Tennants, Leyburn #1016
£4000 $7560 €5840 Busy shipping lane (76x127cm-30x50in) 17-Feb-4 Bonhams, New Bond Street #81/R est:4000-6000
Works on paper
£260 $434 €380 Wagon in a forest glade (19x28cm-7x11in) W/C. 14-Oct-3 Bonhams, Knightsbridge #19/R
£320 $586 €467 Dover (23x34cm-9x13in) W/C. 27-Jan-4 Bonhams, Knightsbridge #363/R
£350 $630 €511 Cottage by a lake with hills beyond (18x26cm-7x10in) W/C over pencil. 21-Jan-4 Sotheby's, Olympia #160/R
£600 $1098 €876 Seaton, mouth of the River Axe, Devon (23x49cm-9x19in) s.i.d.Aug 11/69 W/C pencil. 27-Jan-4 Bonhams, Knightsbridge #167/R
£900 $1530 €1314 Venetian scene (18x26cm-7x10in) W/C over pencil. 27-Nov-3 Sotheby's, London #291/R
£1781 $3028 €2600 Fishermen coming back (21x63cm-8x25in) s.d.72 W/C gouache over crayon. 6-Nov-3 Tajan, Paris #248
£1800 $2988 €2628 British frigate making sail out of a Mediterranean port (34x49cm-13x19in) s. W/C. 1-Oct-3 Bonhams, Knightsbridge #76/R est:1000-1500
£1800 $3060 €2628 Shipping off Hastings (18x27cm-7x11in) s. W/C over pencil. 27-Nov-3 Sotheby's, London #281/R est:2000-3000
£1806 $2871 €2600 Boats fishing off Mount Edgemount (63x100cm-25x39in) init. 10-Sep-3 James Adam, Dublin #17 est:2000-4000

CALLOW, John (attrib) (1822-1878) British
£2000 $3400 €2920 Busy anchorage (46x81cm-18x32in) bears sig. 19-Nov-3 Christie's, Kensington #560/R

CALLOW, William (1812-1908) British
Works on paper
£340 $541 €496 Hastings (22x33cm-9x13in) i. W/C. 10-Sep-3 Cheffins, Cambridge #429
£380 $692 €555 North Foreland (15x23cm-6x9in) W/C. 15-Jun-4 David Lay, Penzance #446
£380 $711 €555 East Lyn Valley, Devon (23x33cm-9x13in) s.i.indis.d. pencil W/C. 22-Jul-4 Tennants, Leyburn #638
£400 $668 €584 Fishing boats at the dock (24x34cm-9x13in) init. pencil W/C. 16-Oct-3 Christie's, Kensington #71
£520 $832 €759 Dinan (44x34cm-17x13in) s.indis.d. W/C. 17-Sep-3 Bonhams, Brooks & Langlois, Jersey #93/R
£650 $1203 €949 Windmill in a hilly landscape (25x36cm-10x14in) s. W/C. 10-Mar-4 Sotheby's, Olympia #142/R
£700 $1239 €1022 On the Yare (21x30cm-8x12in) s.d.1851 W/C. 28-Apr-4 George Kidner, Lymington #200/R
£800 $1336 €1168 Carden, on the Moselle (27x47cm-11x19in) s.d.1851 pencil W/C. 16-Oct-3 Christie's, Kensington #66/R
£800 $1480 €1168 Lauterbrunnen, Switzerland (23x33cm-9x13in) s. W/C. 10-Mar-4 Sotheby's, Olympia #139/R
£800 $1480 €1168 Shipping in a storm (18x30cm-7x12in) s.indis.i. W/C pencil bodycol. 14-Jul-4 Sotheby's, Olympia #47/R
£894 $1601 €1305 European city scene with Cathedral possibly Cologne (27x49cm-11x19in) s.d.1851 W/C. 10-May-4 Joel, Victoria #241 est:2000-2500 (A.D 2200)
£935 $1674 €1365 Boatman on the river with Cathedral in the distance possibly Cologne (27x55cm-11x22in) s. W/C. 10-May-4 Joel, Victoria #399 est:1800-2200 (A.D 2300)
£950 $1615 €1387 Glacier du Rhone (56x76cm-22x30in) s.d.1843 WC paper on board. 18-Nov-3 Hans Widmer, St Gallen #1035 est:600-1500 (S.FR 2100)
£980 $1813 €1431 Boathouse at Madeley Manor, Stafford (25x36cm-10x14in) s. W/C. 10-Feb-4 David Lay, Penzance #137/R
£1000 $1630 €1460 Abbey scene with river and boys fishing (46x64cm-18x25in) s.d.1899 W/C. 27-Sep-3 Rogers Jones, Clwyd #110
£1200 $2064 €1752 Ehrenbreitstein on the Rhine (18x36cm-7x14in) s.d.1896 pencil W/C. 3-Dec-3 Christie's, Kensington #159/R est:800-1200
£1200 $2184 €1752 Inverary (24x34cm-9x13in) s.i.d.49 W/C over traces of pencil. 29-Jun-4 Bonhams, Knowle #34 est:600-1000
£1200 $2220 €1752 Twickenham ferry (17x39cm-7x15in) s. W/C. 14-Jul-4 Sotheby's, Olympia #48/R est:1200-1800
£1206 $1953 €1700 Le retour de la peche (17x15cm-7x6in) s. W/C varnish. 21-May-3 Daguerre, Paris #76 est:1000
£2000 $3640 €2920 Fishing boats off the coast at sunset (22x32cm-9x13in) W/C over pencil htd touches bodycol scratching out stopping out. 1-Jul-4 Sotheby's, London #227/R est:2500-3500
£2200 $3960 €3212 Bologna (22x16cm-9x6in) pencil W/C prov. 21-Apr-4 Tennants, Leyburn #924/R est:1400-1800
£2200 $4026 €3212 Seine near Les Andelys, France (15x21cm-6x8in) pencil W/C htd touches bodycol prov. 3-Jun-4 Christie's, London #104/R est:2000-3000
£2500 $4550 €3650 Fishing smack and other shipping on open seas (32x47cm-13x19in) s. W/C over pencil htd touches bodycol scratching out. 1-Jul-4 Sotheby's, London #206/R est:2000-3000
£2800 $4760 €4088 Houses at Trarbach on the Moselle (47x32cm-19x13in) s.d.1895 W/C. 4-Nov-3 Bonhams, New Bond Street #31/R est:3000-5000
£3000 $5520 €4380 Tours on the Loire (13x23cm-5x9in) mono.d.Jn.18.36 W/C over pencil htd white. 26-Mar-4 Sotheby's, London #121/R est:3000-4000
£3000 $5520 €4380 Valence, on the Rhone (11x26cm-4x10in) mono.i. W/C over prov. htd white. 26-Mar-4 Sotheby's, London #122/R est:3000-4000
£3500 $5950 €5110 Figures and horse on the banks of the Rhine at Boppart (24x31cm-9x12in) s. W/C over pencil htd bodycol prov. 27-Nov-3 Sotheby's, London #277/R est:4000-6000
£4000 $6680 €5840 Weighing house, Amsterdam (54x82cm-21x32in) s.d.1882 exhib.lit. 12-Nov-3 Sotheby's, Olympia #32/R est:4000-6000
£5000 $9200 €7300 Castle and town of Cochem on the Moselle (46x64cm-18x25in) s. W/C over pencil htd bodycol exhib. 26-Mar-4 Sotheby's, London #129/R est:4000-6000
£5000 $9100 €7300 Grand Canal, Venice (26x36cm-10x14in) s. W/C over pencil. 1-Jul-4 Sotheby's, London #214/R est:3000-5000
£5000 $9100 €7300 Figure fishing in a mountain stream (57x87cm-22x34in) s.d.1838 W/C over pencil htd bodycol scratching out. 1-Jul-4 Sotheby's, London #231/R est:5000-7000
£6000 $10980 €8760 Rheinfels and village of St Goar, Switzerland (67x102cm-26x40in) s.d.1862 pencil W/C htd white prov.exhib. 3-Jun-4 Christie's, London #139/R est:2000-3000
£7500 $12750 €10950 Riva degli Schiavoni (35x50cm-14x20in) s. pencil W/C htd bodycol prov. 20-Nov-3 Christie's, London #115/R est:5000-8000
£12000 $20400 €17520 Boats moored at a dock (17x15cm-7x6in) s. W/C over pencil htd bodycol prov. 27-Nov-3 Sotheby's, London #274/R est:4000-6000
£12000 $22080 €17520 Grand Canal, Venice, looking towards the Rialto Bridge (26x36cm-10x14in) s. W/C over pencil htd bodycol prov.exhib. 26-Mar-4 Sotheby's, London #87/R est:8000-12000
£16000 $27200 €23360 Palazzo Pisani-Moretta on the Grand Canal Venice (24x32cm-9x13in) s. W/C over pencil htd bodycol. 27-Nov-3 Sotheby's, London #278/R est:4000-6000
£24000 $40800 €35040 Riva degli Shiavonilooking towards the Danieli Hotel (40x57cm-16x22in) s.d.1893 pencil W/C htd white scratching out exhib. 20-Nov-3 Christie's, London #117/R est:7000-10000
£28000 $51520 €40880 Riva Degli Schiavoni, Venice (26x36cm-10x14in) s. W/C over pencil htd bodycol exhib. 26-Mar-4 Sotheby's, London #88/R est:10000-15000

CALLOW, William (circle) (1812-1908) British
£5578 $9985 €8200 Marine avec trois personnages sur la rive (50x65cm-20x26in) 22-Mar-4 Digard, Paris #68 est:8000-13000

CALMELET, Hedwig (1814-?) French
Works on paper
£1034 $1717 €1500 Bucheron aupres de la riviere ombragee (65x96cm-26x38in) s. W/C. 5-Oct-3 Lombrail & Teucquam, Paris #301

CALMEYER, Jacob Mathias (1802-1884) Danish
£1522 $2785 €2222 From a Norwegian cheese farm (27x39cm-11x15in) s.d.1834. 9-Jun-4 Rasmussen, Copenhagen #1699/R est:15000 (D.KR 17000)
£2343 $4030 €3421 Prospect view of manor farm Gravdal outside Bergen (84x116cm-33x46in) prov. 2-Dec-3 Kunsthallen, Copenhagen #500/R est:15000 (D.KR 25000)

CALOGERO, Jean (1922-) Italian
£202 $375 €295 Surrealist still life (73x55cm-29x22in) s. 5-Mar-4 Skinner, Boston #421/R
£247 $450 €361 Surrealist landscape (46x56cm-18x22in) s. 8-Feb-4 William Jenack, New York #199
£447 $800 €653 Surrealistic landscape with masks. s. 13-May-4 Dallas Auction Gallery, Dallas #177/R
£621 $1000 €907 Girl with fish and fruit (53x46cm-21x18in) s. 22-Feb-3 Bunte, Elgin #1238
£671 $1188 €1000 Scene representing the world, with a colourful woman and buildings (26x34cm-10x13in) s.i. 30-Apr-4 Auktionhaus Georg Rehm, Augsburg #7576/R
£800 $1272 €1160 Venezia (45x55cm-18x22in) s. 11-Sep-3 Christie's, Kensington #166/R

CALOSCI, Arturo (1855-1926) Italian
£504 $826 €700 Inn keeper (26x23cm-10x9in) s. 10-Jun-3 Pandolfini, Florence #97/R

CALOUTSIS, Valerios (20th C) ?
£4500 $7650 €6570 Formation II (162x114cm-64x45in) s.d.60 s.i.d.verso oil plaster prov.exhib.lit. 18-Nov-3 Sotheby's, London #117/R est:3000-5000

CALRAET, Abraham van (1642-1722) Dutch
£24161 $45181 €36000 Still life with peaches (41x61cm-16x24in) init. board. 25-Feb-4 Porro, Milan #32/R est:32000

CALRAET, Abraham van (attrib) (1642-1722) Dutch
£1655 $3013 €2500 Nature morte a la coloquinte et peches sur un entablement (30x35cm-12x14in) 21-Jun-4 Tajan, Paris #67 est:2500-3000
£3000 $5490 €4380 Horse and cows in a landscape (28x40cm-11x16in) bears sig panel. 6-Jul-4 Sotheby's, Olympia #475/R est:2000-3000

CALRAET, Barend van (1649-1737) Dutch
£2013 $3725 €3000 Portrait of a lady, standing at a fountain, wearing a purple dress (42x35cm-17x14in) s. prov.exhib. 15-Mar-4 Sotheby's, Amsterdam #27/R est:3000-5000

CALS, Adolphe Felix (1810-1880) French
£533 $965 €800 Vierge entouree de putti (34x24cm-13x9in) s.i.d.1870 after Rubens. 30-Mar-4 Rossini, Paris #303
£671 $1235 €1000 Maisons a Montmartre (22x37cm-9x15in) s. paper on panel. 26-Mar-4 Daguerre, Paris #71/R
£867 $1569 €1300 Sous les arbres (16x26cm-6x10in) st.sig. 30-Mar-4 Rossini, Paris #304
£1101 $1872 €1607 Village in early spring (16x27cm-6x11in) s.d.1867. 5-Nov-3 Dobiaschofsky, Bern #411/R est:5000 (S.FR 2500)
£1200 $2172 €1800 L'enfant endormi, Honfleur (45x53cm-18x21in) s.i.d.4 Oct 1875 oval exhib. 30-Mar-4 Rossini, Paris #302/R est:1800-5000
£1348 $2183 €1900 Portrait de Monsieur Lancosme de Breve (54x65cm-21x26in) s.d.1838. 21-May-3 Daguerre, Paris #60/R est:1500-2200
£7667 $13877 €11500 Saint-Valery en Caux (15x39cm-6x15in) s.i.d.Sept 1864 exhib.lit. 30-Mar-4 Rossini, Paris #301/R est:3000-5000
Works on paper
£816 $1461 €1200 Portrait d'homme (33x26cm-13x10in) s.d.1842 black crayon white chk htd gouache. 22-Mar-4 Digard, Paris #75/R
£873 $1623 €1300 Le chemin (28x25cm-11x10in) s.d.juni 57 paper on canvas on panel. 8-Mar-4 Artcurial Briest, Paris #17 est:500-800

CALS, Adolphe Felix (attrib) (1810-1880) French
£480 $859 €701 Portrait of a woman in a grey dress (41x32cm-16x13in) s.i.d.1876. 18-Mar-4 Christie's, Kensington #443/R

CALSINA, Ramon (1901-1992) Spanish
£1910 $3113 €2750 Angler (60x73cm-24x29in) s. 23-Sep-3 Durán, Madrid #57/R
£3125 $5000 €4563 Artist interior (61x74cm-24x29in) s. 20-Sep-3 Bunte, Elgin #1209 est:2000-3000

CALTHROP, Claude Andrew (1845-1893) British
£988 $1700 €1442 Gentleman in an interior (36x30cm-14x12in) s.d.1871. 7-Dec-3 Grogan, Boston #25/R

CALVAERT, Dionisio (1540-1619) Flemish
£5503 $10126 €8200 La Sainte Famille avec St Jean Baptiste et autres saints (60x46cm-24x18in) copper painted with studio. 29-Mar-4 Rieunier, Paris #14/R est:7000-8000
£22000 $39600 €32120 Christ walking on the water (32x25cm-13x10in) copper prov. 21-Apr-4 Christie's, London #81/R est:25000-35000

CALVAERT, Dionisio (circle) (1540-1619) Flemish
£6623 $12053 €10000 Adoration of the Magi (95x68cm-37x27in) 16-Jun-4 Christie's, Rome #406/R est:10000-15000

CALVELLI, Felix (20th C) French
£1259 $2165 €1800 Vue de la Tour Solidor a Saint-Servan (200x200cm-79x79in) s. 7-Dec-3 Livinec, Gaudcheau & Jezequel, Rennes #64a

CALVERT, Charles (1785-1852) British
£2200 $3520 €3212 Wooded river landscape in the Lake District with figures (64x84cm-25x33in) 16-Sep-3 Capes Dunn, Manchester #780/R

CALVERT, Edward (1799-1883) British
£2973 $5500 €4341 British gunboat firing in port (49x59cm-19x23in) s. 15-Jan-4 Sotheby's, New York #293/R est:3000-5000

CALVERT, Frederick (c.1785-1845) British
£800 $1360 €1168 Fishing fleet (23x33cm-9x13in) s. 19-Nov-3 Christie's, Kensington #480/R
£1600 $2720 €2336 Frigate leaving port (23x27cm-9x11in) prov. 19-Nov-3 Christie's, Kensington #481/R
£6500 $11050 €9490 Crowded lugger (45x60cm-18x24in) init. pair. 19-Nov-3 Christie's, Kensington #479/R

CALVERT, Frederick (attrib) (c.1785-1845) British
£552 $1000 €806 Shipping off the coast (63x76cm-25x30in) 30-Mar-4 Christie's, Rockefeller NY #51/R est:2000-3000

CALVERT, H H (fl.1910-1920s) Australian
Works on paper
£529 $835 €767 Australian eleven. English eleven (28x87cm-11x34in) s.i.d.1918 W/C pair. 22-Jul-3 Lawson Menzies, Sydney #188/R est:1000-1500 (A.D 1300)

CALVERT, Henry (1798-1869) British
£4200 $7140 €6132 Stable interior with a saddled hunters, and a spaniel (61x73cm-24x29in) s.d.1852. 19-Nov-3 Tennants, Leyburn #1194/R est:2000-2200
£4600 $8510 €6716 Bay horse in a landscape (70x92cm-28x36in) s.d.1840. 10-Mar-4 Sotheby's, Olympia #186/R est:1000-1500

CALVERT, Samuel (19th C) British
£350 $594 €500 Seascape (71x92cm-28x36in) s. panel. 20-Nov-3 Van Ham, Cologne #1509/R
£700 $1190 €1022 Sailing boats entering harbour in a stiff breeze (51x74cm-20x29in) s.d.1883. 30-Oct-3 Duke & Son, Dorchester #157/R

CALVES, Léon Georges (1848-1924) French
£1620 $2689 €2300 Cheval de trait (22x27cm-9x11in) s. panel. 15-Jun-3 Peron, Melun #94

CALVES, Léon Georges (attrib) (1848-1924) French
£339 $577 €495 La moisson (38x55cm-15x22in) s. 1-Dec-3 Koller, Zurich #6439 (S.FR 750)

CALVES, Marie (1883-1957) French
£1712 $2911 €2500 Deux chiens dans le ruisseau (16x24cm-6x9in) s. panel. 9-Nov-3 Eric Pillon, Calais #39/R
£1712 $2911 €2500 Trois chien de chasse (16x24cm-6x9in) s. panel. 9-Nov-3 Eric Pillon, Calais #38/R

CALVET, Gerard (1926-) French
£374 $670 €550 Rue Espagnole (60x73cm-24x29in) s. prov. 19-Mar-4 Oger, Dumont, Paris #5
£408 $731 €600 Les toits (65x92cm-26x36in) s. prov. 19-Mar-4 Oger, Dumont, Paris #4

CALVI DI BERGOLO, Gregorio (1904-1994) Italian
£1905 $3410 €2800 Landscape with stream (70x90cm-28x35in) s.d.1958. 22-Mar-4 Sant Agostino, Torino #262/R est:2700-3200

CALVI, Ercole (1824-1900) Italian
£2685 $4940 €4000 Ruins with figures and lake (21x29cm-8x11in) s.d.1864 board. 24-Mar-4 Il Ponte, Milan #586/R est:4000-4500
£2958 $4910 €4200 Country hillside (30x40cm-12x16in) s.d.1858 board. 11-Jun-3 Christie's, Rome #124/R est:4500-5500
£3592 $6285 €5100 View of lake (21x29cm-8x11in) s.d.1864 cardboard. 17-Dec-3 Il Ponte, Milan #666/R est:3000-3500

CALVI, Giuseppe (1895-1983) Italian
£498 $846 €727 Apple blossom in ceramic jug (83x64cm-33x25in) s.d.927 panel. 19-Nov-3 Fischer, Luzern #2033/R (S.FR 1100)
£705 $1247 €1050 House on the river (70x100cm-28x39in) s. 1-May-4 Meeting Art, Vercelli #38

CALVO, Carmen (1950-) Spanish
£4577 $8011 €6500 Composition (85x106cm-33x42in) s.i.d.1978 verso acrylic canvas on board exhib.lit. 16-Dec-3 Segre, Madrid #160/R est:5000
Works on paper
£600 $1092 €900 El Altar de Salomon (36x26cm-14x10in) s.d.2001 s.i.d. verso felt tip pen pencil wax crayon. 29-Jun-4 Segre, Madrid #163/R

CALZA, Antonio (1653-1725) Italian

£5333	$9547	€8000	Christians against Turks (36x47cm-14x19in) 12-May-4 Finarte Semenzato, Milan #20/R est:8000-12000
£10738	$20081	€16000	Cavalry battle (36x68cm-14x27in) 25-Feb-4 Porro, Milan #18/R est:16000
£22819	$42671	€34000	Battle (114x184cm-45x72in) 25-Feb-4 Porro, Milan #37/R est:25000
Works on paper			
£480	$830	€701	Landscape with bridge, a rider in the foreground and village beyond (17x25cm-7x10in) indis.sig. i.verso pen brown ink prov. 12-Dec-3 Christie's, Kensington #387/R
£1400	$2562	€2044	Cavalry scene with a battle in the background (11x26cm-4x10in) pen ink wash. 6-Jul-4 Christie's, London #64/R est:1000-1500

CALZA, Antonio (attrib) (1653-1725) Italian

£1538	$2615	€2200	Course de chevaux (23x34cm-9x13in) d.1683 i.verso. 18-Nov-3 Vanderkindere, Brussels #194 est:1500-2500
£13000	$22100	€18980	Cavalry skirmish (114x166cm-45x65in) prov. 30-Oct-3 Sotheby's, Olympia #130/R est:6000-8000
£18965	$34896	€27689	Cavalry battles (62x97cm-24x38in) pair. 26-Mar-4 Koller, Zurich #3060/R est:20000-30000 (S.FR 44000)

CALZA, Antonio (circle) (1653-1725) Italian

£3000	$5370	€4500	Battle (58x73cm-23x29in) 12-May-4 Finarte Semenzato, Milan #93/R est:2000-3000

CALZA, Antonio (style) (1653-1725) Italian

£9500	$17100	€13870	Battle scene with cavalry skirmishing (73x134cm-29x53in) 22-Apr-4 Sotheby's, London #98/R est:7000-10000

CALZADA, Carl de (19th C) French

£1250	$2125	€1800	Surprised servant (69x55cm-27x22in) s.d.1866 i. verso one of pair. 28-Oct-3 Dorotheum, Vienna #122/R est:1800-2200
£1250	$2125	€1800	The modes maidens (69x55cm-27x22in) s.i.d. i. verso. 28-Oct-3 Dorotheum, Vienna #117/R est:1800-2200

CALZOLARI, Giuseppe (?-1818) Italian

£872	$1632	€1300	Vase de fleurs sur un entablement (68x50cm-27x20in) s. cardboard. 29-Feb-4 Osenat, Fontainebleau #206

CALZOLARI, Pier Paolo (1943-) Italian

Works on paper			
£1200	$2160	€1800	Restored (70x100cm-28x39in) s.d.1973 mixed media prov. 24-Apr-4 Cornette de St.Cyr, Paris #472 est:2000
£1329	$2259	€1900	Untitled (55x74cm-22x29in) s.d.69 sugar collage on W/C pencil prov. 27-Nov-3 Lempertz, Koln #72/R est:2500
£1538	$2615	€2200	Untitled (72x102cm-28x40in) s.d.1978 salt mixed media prov. 25-Nov-3 Sotheby's, Milan #109 est:2000-3000
£2657	$4517	€3800	Untitled (72x102cm-28x40in) s.d.1978 mixed media salt card prov. 25-Nov-3 Sotheby's, Milan #110/R est:2000-3000

CAMACHO, Jorge (1934-) Cuban

£447	$800	€653	Surrealist composition (65x44cm-26x17in) s.d.1965. 14-May-4 Skinner, Boston #410/R
£486	$812	€700	Permeabilite reduite (48x64cm-19x25in) s.d.1978 paper. 21-Oct-3 Campo & Campo, Antwerp #26
£604	$1117	€900	Composition (98x63cm-39x25in) s.d.90 paper. 13-Mar-4 De Vuyst, Lokeren #38
£903	$1507	€1300	Sans titre (73x60cm-29x24in) s.d.60 prov. 21-Oct-3 Artcurial Briest, Paris #639/R est:1500-2000
£1118	$2058	€1700	Untitled (98x63cm-39x25in) s.d.1990 paper. 27-Jun-4 Versailles Encheres #24/R est:1500-1800
£1667	$2783	€2400	Aube-Jet (130x97cm-51x38in) s. d.1970 verso. 21-Oct-3 Campo, Vlaamse Kaai #368/R est:2400-2800
£2041	$3653	€3000	Source, Cible (70x70cm-28x28in) s.i.d.1992 verso contreplaque round prov. 21-Mar-4 Calmels Cohen, Paris #103/R est:3000-4000
£2800	$5012	€4200	La fleur et la Pierre (116x89cm-46x35in) s.i.d.90 verso. 15-May-4 De Vuyst, Lokeren #596/R est:3000-4000
£3356	$6208	€5000	Voyage sur le Nile (97x130cm-38x51in) s.i.d.88 verso. 13-Mar-4 De Vuyst, Lokeren #506/R est:3500-4500
Works on paper			
£268	$491	€400	Untitled (29x19cm-11x7in) s.d.70 lead pencil col crayon. 7-Jul-4 Artcurial Briest, Paris #224
£336	$614	€500	Untitled (33x25cm-13x10in) s.d.70 ink col crayon. 7-Jul-4 Artcurial Briest, Paris #223
£382	$638	€550	Monster (50x65cm-20x26in) s.d.1978 mixed media. 21-Oct-3 Campo & Campo, Antwerp #27/R
£621	$1037	€900	Sans titre (49x63cm-19x25in) s.d.1978 gouache ink crayon. 17-Nov-3 Charbonneaux, Paris #119
£816	$1461	€1200	Untitled (50x65cm-20x26in) s.d.77 col crayons. 21-Mar-4 Calmels Cohen, Paris #102/R
£953	$1705	€1400	Clown I (65x50cm-26x20in) s.d.1992 gouache crayon prov.exhib. 21-Mar-4 Calmels Cohen, Paris #1/R est:1500-2000
£1208	$2247	€1800	Sans titre (74x55cm-29x22in) s.d.88 mixed media. 3-Mar-4 Artcurial Briest, Paris #330/R est:1800-2200
£1486	$2616	€2200	Untitled (100x65cm-39x26in) s.d.1989 mixed media prov. 18-May-4 Tajan, Paris #20/R est:1800-2000
£1611	$2948	€2400	Permeabilite reduite (49x64cm-19x25in) s.d.78 gouache ink. 7-Jul-4 Artcurial Briest, Paris #222/R est:2000-2500

CAMARA FILHO, Joao (1944-) Brazilian

£4853	$8882	€7280	Sunglasses (80x120cm-31x47in) s.d.1975 i.verso masonite. 6-Jul-4 Bolsa de Arte, Rio de Janeiro #152/R (B.R 26500)

CAMARENA, Jorge Gonzalez (1918-) Mexican

Works on paper			
£248	$456	€362	Seed (18x20cm-7x8in) s.d.1945 pencil. 25-Mar-4 Louis Morton, Mexico #88/R (M.P 5000)

CAMARGO, Ibere (1914-1994) Brazilian

£46703	$82665	€70055	Painting II (80x138cm-31x54in) s.d.1966 s.i.d.verso. 27-Apr-4 Bolsa de Arte, Rio de Janeiro #110/R (B.R 255000)

CAMARGO, Sergio de (1930-1990) Brazilian

Sculpture			
£8667	$15947	€13000	Untitled (24x18cm-9x7in) s.d.68 painted wood prov. 10-Jun-4 Christie's, Paris #86/R est:16000-20000
£20588	$35000	€30058	Rayo quadrato (29x27x9cm-11x11x4in) s.d.67 num.132 verso painted wood construction on panel. 19-Nov-3 Sotheby's, New York #145/R est:10000-15000
£105882	$180000	€154588	Relief no.234 (100x99cm-39x39in) s.i.d.69 verso painted wood construction prov.exhib. 19-Nov-3 Sotheby's, New York #14/R est:35000-45000

CAMARLENCH, Ignacio Pinazo (1849-1916) Spanish

£2349	$4158	€3500	Portrait of gentleman (60x50cm-24x20in) s.i.d.1884. 27-Apr-4 Durán, Madrid #81/R est:3000
£25168	$45050	€37500	Choir boy (89x35cm-35x14in) s.d.1894. 25-May-4 Durán, Madrid #149/R est:18000

CAMARO, Alexander (1901-1992) German

£2042	$3533	€2900	Girl at window (114x99cm-45x39in) s. i. stretcher oil plaster. 13-Dec-3 Lempertz, Koln #294/R est:3000
£2448	$4161	€3500	Night (66x86cm-26x34in) s. s.i.d.1956 stretcher. 29-Nov-3 Villa Grisebach, Berlin #274/R est:3000-4000
£3521	$6092	€5000	Composition (72x93cm-28x37in) s. s.d.1958 stretcher exhib. 13-Dec-3 Lempertz, Koln #121/R est:3000

CAMARON TORRA, Vicente (1803-1864) Spanish

£2685	$4805	€4000	Strolling (35x57cm-14x22in) s.d.1850. 25-May-4 Durán, Madrid #164/R est:3000

CAMBELLOTTI, Duilio (1876-1960) Italian

£1200	$2208	€1800	Sailors (23x23cm-9x9in) init. tempera card on cardboard. 10-Jun-4 Christie's, Rome #43 est:800-1200
Works on paper			
£1060	$1928	€1600	Study for figures in costume (24x24cm-9x9in) mixed media double-sided. 21-Jun-4 Pandolfini, Florence #222/R est:1700
£1258	$2290	€1900	Barbarians (56x25cm-22x10in) init. mixed media. 21-Jun-4 Pandolfini, Florence #220/R est:1800-2000
£1589	$2893	€2400	Study for figures in costume (30x70cm-12x28in) init. mixed media. 21-Jun-4 Pandolfini, Florence #221/R est:2300-2400

CAMBI, Andrei (19th C) Italian

Sculpture			
£12941	$22000	€18894	Young girl spinning (105cm-41in) s.i.d.1886 marble. 28-Oct-3 Christie's, Rockefeller NY #156/R est:10000-15000

CAMBI, G (19/20th C) Italian

Sculpture			
£1080	$1900	€1577	Nude female figure with draped scarf resting against a column (81cm-32in) s. white marble alabster luminaire. 22-May-4 Selkirks, St. Louis #773/R est:1500-2000

CAMBIAGGIO, Émile (1857-1930) French

£30000	$51600	€43800	Une charmeuse (141x204cm-56x80in) s. prov.exhib. 3-Dec-3 Christie's, London #90/R est:40000-60000

CAMBIASO, Luca (1527-1585) Italian

£230000	$397900	€335800	Adoration of the Magi (89x117cm-35x46in) panel. 10-Dec-3 Christie's, London #99/R est:70000-100000
Works on paper			
£789	$1453	€1200	Deposition (22x19cm-9x7in) pen ink W/C prov. 22-Jun-4 Sotheby's, Milan #48/R
£1000	$1730	€1460	Resurrection (31x17cm-12x7in) i. pen brown ink wash prov. 12-Dec-3 Christie's, Kensington #315/R est:1500-2000
£1500	$2595	€2190	Nymph and satyr (8x12cm-3x5in) pen brown ink prov. 9-Dec-3 Bonhams, Knightsbridge #57/R est:1500-2000
£1867	$3360	€2800	Nativity (31x19cm-12x7in) pen brush sepia ink. 21-Apr-4 Finarte Semenzato, Milan #538/R est:2000-2500
£2303	$4237	€3500	Circumcision (23x25cm-9x10in) pen ink W/C. 22-Jun-4 Sotheby's, Milan #1/R est:1500-2000
£2632	$4842	€4000	Mercurius taking Psyche to the Olympus (27x20cm-11x8in) init. pen ink W/C over pencil prov. 22-Jun-4 Sotheby's, Milan #38/R est:3000-4000
£3500	$6405	€5110	Man carrying another on his shoulders (39x25cm-15x10in) i. black chk ink wash prov. 6-Jul-4 Christie's, London #35/R est:3000-5000
£5556	$10000	€8112	Darius brought before Alexander (26x34cm-10x13in) pen ink wash over black chk prov. 21-Jan-4 Sotheby's, New York #3/R est:12000-18000
£13889	$25000	€20278	Holy Family seated before a hearth (28x19cm-11x7in) i.verso pen brown ink wash prov.exhib.lit. 21-Jan-4 Sotheby's, New York #6/R est:15000-20000

CAMBIASO, Luca (attrib) (1527-1585) Italian

Works on paper			
£280	$481	€400	Holy family with Holy Elizabeth (29x22cm-11x9in) brown ink brown wash brush. 5-Dec-3 Bolland & Marotz, Bremen #457
£473	$832	€700	Adonis resting in the arms of Venus (31x22cm-12x9in) Indian ink brush wash prov. 22-May-4 Lempertz, Koln #1228/R
£541	$951	€800	Death of Adonis (33x24cm-13x9in) graphite prov. 22-May-4 Lempertz, Koln #1227

CAMBIER, Guy (1923-) French

£324	$531	€450	Maternite (71x53cm-28x21in) s. 6-Jun-3 Chochon-Barre & Allardi, Paris #31
£350	$630	€511	White horse beside a lake with horse and carriage (40x80cm-16x31in) s. 21-Apr-4 Tennants, Leyburn #1229
£590	$939	€850	Neige (50x61cm-20x24in) s. 15-Sep-3 Horta, Bruxelles #437
£932	$1500	€1361	Still life with flowers (66x81cm-26x32in) s. i.verso. 24-Feb-3 O'Gallerie, Oregon #801/R est:1500-2000

CAMBIER, Juliette (1879-1963) Belgian

£658	$1211	€1000	Wild flowers in a green vase (55x46cm-22x18in) s. prov. 22-Jun-4 Christie's, Amsterdam #519/R

CAMBIER, Louis G (1874-1949) Belgian

£596	$1085	€900	Fagotiere en foret de Soignes (60x90cm-24x35in) s.d.98. 15-Jun-4 Vanderkindere, Brussels #58
£3695	$6615	€5395	Interieur de atelier (185x135cm-73x53in) s.d.1891 exhib. 25-May-4 Bukowskis, Stockholm #345/R est:60000-80000 (S.KR 50000)

CAMBIER, Nestor (19/20th C) Belgian

£336	$617	€500	Nu (23x21cm-9x8in) s. wood. 28-Mar-4 MonsAntic, Maisieres #365

CAMBON, Glauco (1875-1930) Italian

£933	$1671	€1400	Bather (24x38cm-9x15in) s. s.verso cardboard lit. 12-May-4 Stadion, Trieste #815/R est:1000-1500
£1678	$2887	€2400	Romance by the bay (92x84cm-36x33in) s.d.1905 board. 3-Dec-3 Stadion, Trieste #1128/R est:3000-4000
£3147	$5413	€4500	Dalmatian islands (49x71cm-19x28in) s.d.14 cardboard. 3-Dec-3 Stadion, Trieste #1180/R est:1800-2400
£4533	$8115	€6800	Banks in the summer (65x90cm-26x35in) s.d.08 lit. 12-May-4 Stadion, Trieste #682/R est:4500-5500

CAMBON, Henri Joseph Armand (1819-1885) French

Works on paper

£345	$576	€500	Portrait d'homme de qualite (42x34cm-17x13in) s.d.1838 pencil chl. 17-Nov-3 Delorme & Bocage, Paris #91/R

CAMBOS, Jean Jules (1828-1917) French

Sculpture

£1038	$1900	€1515	Vainqueur (79cm-31in) s. brown pat. bronze. 7-Jun-4 O'Gallerie, Oregon #729/R est:1200-1800

CAMENISCH, Paul (1893-1970) Swiss

Works on paper

£435	$796	€635	Le clown (49x34cm-19x13in) s.d.34 ink. 5-Jun-4 Galerie du Rhone, Sion #297 (S.FR 1000)
£526	$879	€768	Tellaro landscape (38x50cm-15x20in) i. verso W/C over pencil. 15-Nov-3 Galerie Gloggner, Luzern #9 (S.FR 1200)
£870	$1591	€1270	Roncapiano, Maggiatal (34x51cm-13x20in) s.i.d.27 chl prov. 7-Jun-4 Christie's, Zurich #88/R est:2500-3500 (S.FR 2000)

CAMENZIND, Balz (1907-1989) German

£439	$732	€641	At the water source (110x78cm-43x31in) s.d.67 i. stretcher acrylic prov. 15-Nov-3 Galerie Gloggner, Luzern #10 (S.FR 1000)
£526	$879	€768	Cows grazing (90x110cm-35x43in) s.d.63 prov. 15-Nov-3 Galerie Gloggner, Luzern #12/R (S.FR 1200)
£526	$879	€768	Storm (69x85cm-27x33in) s.d.82 i. stretcher acrylic. 15-Nov-3 Galerie Gloggner, Luzern #16/R (S.FR 1200)
£702	$1172	€1025	Composition (85x77cm-33x30in) s.d.83 i. stretcher. 15-Nov-3 Galerie Gloggner, Luzern #13 (S.FR 1600)
£1140	$1904	€1664	Sweat must pour (100x100cm-39x39in) s.d.61 s.i. stretcher acrylic hessian. 15-Nov-3 Galerie Gloggner, Luzern #11/R est:1800-2500 (S.FR 2600)
£1184	$1978	€1729	Racing horses (79x85cm-31x33in) s. i. stretcher acrylic prov. 15-Nov-3 Galerie Gloggner, Luzern #14/R est:1400-1600 (S.FR 2700)
£1810	$3077	€2643	View out of window of winter landscape (68x69cm-27x27in) s.d.57 panel. 19-Nov-3 Fischer, Luzern #1282/R est:400-4500 (S.FR 4000)

Works on paper

£285	$476	€416	Early spring (67x84cm-26x33in) s. mixed media board prov. 15-Nov-3 Galerie Gloggner, Luzern #17/R (S.FR 650)

CAMERON, Alexander G Beauchamp (?) British

£320	$605	€467	Portrait of the artist Robert Douglas Strachan (90x70cm-35x28in) 19-Feb-4 Lyon & Turnbull, Edinburgh #99

CAMERON, Douglas (19/20th C) British

£249	$450	€364	In the Trossachs (46x56cm-18x22in) s. 18-Apr-4 Jeffery Burchard, Florida #20/R
£500	$935	€730	Glen Nevis, Scottish glen with highland cattle beside a waterfall (61x91cm-24x36in) s. i.verso. 22-Jul-4 Tennants, Leyburn #821
£780	$1427	€1139	Highland cattle before a loch landscape. Highland landscape (49x74cm-19x29in) both s. pair. 2-Feb-4 Bonhams, Chester #949

Works on paper

£231	$400	€337	Highland landscape (51x74cm-20x29in) s. gouache crayon. 13-Dec-3 Weschler, Washington #532

CAMERON, Duncan (1837-1916) British

£250	$425	€365	Coastal scene with a fishing village in the distance (30x50cm-12x20in) s. 19-Nov-3 Tennants, Leyburn #1045
£500	$925	€730	Glimpse of loch (43x28cm-17x11in) s. 12-Feb-4 Andrew Hartley, Ilkley #831
£594	$1010	€850	River landscape with sheep (37x52cm-15x20in) s. 22-Nov-3 Arnold, Frankfurt #478/R
£720	$1303	€1051	Highland loch scene (41x66cm-16x26in) s. indis i.verso. 30-Mar-4 Sworder & Son, Bishops Stortford #553/R
£805	$1442	€1200	On the Lake's Edge (25x40cm-10x16in) s. 25-May-4 Karl & Faber, Munich #81/R
£1350	$2160	€1971	Ben venue with a glimpse of Loch Achray (61x97cm-24x38in) s. 15-May-3 Bonhams, Edinburgh #351 est:700-1000
£9000	$16290	€13140	Harvest at Loch Carron, Ross-shire (61x97cm-24x38in) s. 19-Apr-4 Sotheby's, London #29/R est:6000-8000

CAMERON, Julia Margaret (1815-1879) British

Photographs

£1796	$3000	€2622	Sacred and lovely remains of my little adopted child Adeline Grace Clogstoun (14x20cm-6x8in) albumen print. 21-Oct-3 Swann Galleries, New York #25/R est:4000-6000
£2147	$3800	€3135	Elaine, the lily maid of Astolat (23x28cm-9x11in) s.d.Nov 1874 albumen print prov.lit. 27-Apr-4 Christie's, Rockefeller NY #107/R est:5000-7000
£3390	$6000	€4949	Vestal - Hatty Campbell (28x23cm-11x9in) i. albumen print prov.lit. 27-Apr-4 Christie's, Rockefeller NY #109/R est:3000-5000
£5389	$9000	€7868	Henry Taylor (27x22cm-11x9in) s. albumen print. 21-Oct-3 Swann Galleries, New York #24/R est:5000-7000
£7000	$12320	€10220	Alfred Tennyson's Idylls of the King (33x28cm-13x11in) photograph lit. 19-May-4 Christie's, London #68/R est:6000-9000
£13559	$24000	€19796	Circe - Kate Keown (25x20cm-10x8in) s.i. num.2 albumen print prov.lit. 27-Apr-4 Christie's, Rockefeller NY #106/R est:20000-30000

CAMERON, Katherine (1874-1965) British

Works on paper

£200	$334	€292	Zinnias in sunlight (28x22cm-11x9in) s.d.Sep 1933 W/C. 16-Oct-3 Bonhams, Edinburgh #140
£300	$510	€438	Tropaeolium (19x15cm-7x6in) s. W/C. 10-Nov-3 Thomson Roddick & Medcalf, Edinburgh #245/R

CAMERON, Peter Caledonian (19th C) American

£9091	$16000	€13273	Niagara falls in winter (30x74cm-12x29in) mono.d.1885. 19-May-4 Sotheby's, New York #64/R est:20000-30000
£31250	$55000	€45625	Niagara falls in winter (175x117cm-69x46in) s. i.d.1884. 19-May-4 Sotheby's, New York #65/R est:60000-90000

CAMERON, Sir D Y (1865-1945) British

Works on paper

£500	$915	€730	West Coast scene (29x32cm-11x13in) s. pencil W/C. 29-Jan-4 Bonhams, Edinburgh #357

CAMERON, Sir David Young (1865-1945) British

£333	$577	€486	Castle View. Loch (12x32cm-5x13in) s. pencil two. 9-Dec-3 Pinneys, Montreal #26 (C.D 750)
£1900	$3477	€2774	Snow capped peak (29x39cm-11x15in) s. canvasboard. 8-Apr-4 Bonhams, Edinburgh #178 est:2000-3000
£2100	$3507	€3066	Cantyre. init. s.i.on stretcher. 16-Oct-3 Bonhams, Edinburgh #154/R est:600-800
£2400	$3768	€3480	Benderloch (20x25cm-8x10in) s. panel prov. 27-Aug-3 Sotheby's, London #1075/R est:3000-4000
£2500	$4575	€3650	Loch Linnhe and Kingairloch (28x28cm-11x11in) s. canvas on board. 8-Apr-4 Bonhams, Edinburgh #185/R est:1000-1500
£2600	$4498	€3796	Loch Maree, Morning (22x26cm-9x10in) s. i.verso board. 10-Dec-3 Bonhams, Bury St Edmunds #580/R est:2000-3000
£3400	$5848	€4964	Glen Lyon (32x53cm-13x21in) s. prov. 4-Dec-3 Bonhams, Edinburgh #53/R est:4000-6000
£3800	$5966	€5510	Hills of Mull from Dunollie Castle (25x34cm-10x13in) s. 27-Aug-3 Sotheby's, London #1126/R est:1500-2000
£4000	$6920	€5840	Kerrera Sound, Oban (20x25cm-8x10in) s. panel. 11-Dec-3 Lyon & Turnbull, Edinburgh #60/R est:2000-3000
£4200	$7224	€6132	Morning mists on the Clyde (46x107cm-18x42in) s. prov. 4-Dec-3 Bonhams, Edinburgh #79/R est:8000-10000
£4245	$6750	€6155	Perthshire hills (46x56cm-18x22in) s. exhib. 12-Sep-3 Aspire, Cleveland #40 est:5000-10000
£4500	$8055	€6570	Maison Marcel (28x34cm-11x13in) s. s.d.1922 overlap. 26-May-4 Sotheby's, Olympia #238/R est:1000-1500
£6000	$10860	€8760	Perthshire hills (46x56cm-18x22in) s. s.i.stretcher. 19-Apr-4 Sotheby's, London #100/R est:6000-8000
£8500	$15895	€12410	French riverside town (40x67cm-16x26in) s. 21-Jul-4 Lyon & Turnbull, Edinburgh #128/R est:6000-9000
£9500	$17670	€13870	Sunset, Lona (37x47cm-15x19in) init. 4-Mar-4 Christie's, Kensington #137/R est:5000-6000

Prints

£2100	$3507	€3066	Ben Ledi (37x30cm-15x12in) s. etching drypoint prov. 16-Oct-3 Bonhams, Edinburgh #92 est:600-800

Works on paper

£280	$484	€409	Egyptian Ruins (15x26cm-6x10in) s. W/C. 10-Dec-3 Bonhams, Bury St Edmunds #520
£340	$602	€496	Highland landscape (23x33cm-9x13in) W/C. 29-Apr-4 Gorringes, Lewes #2507
£370	$614	€540	North and south Uist from Harris (18x33cm-7x13in) s.i. ink W/C. 2-Oct-3 Neales, Nottingham #615/R
£440	$735	€642	View of a ruined castle in a landscape (18x23cm-7x9in) init.i. pencil W/C. 26-Jun-3 Greenslade Hunt, Taunton #498/R
£440	$735	€642	Spey at Broomhill (20x19cm-8x7in) init.i. pencil pen ink col wash. 26-Jun-3 Greenslade Hunt, Taunton #499/R
£680	$1095	€986	Upper Clyde (18x26cm-7x10in) init. conte W/C. 21-Aug-3 Bonhams, Edinburgh #1142
£750	$1320	€1095	Hill of Spean (14x29cm-6x11in) s. W/C. 19-May-4 Dreweatt Neate, Newbury #1/R
£780	$1427	€1139	Stirling Castle (27x32cm-11x13in) s.i. pencil W/C. 8-Apr-4 Bonhams, Edinburgh #155
£800	$1288	€1160	Eigg (17x25cm-7x10in) s. indis i. ink W/C. 21-Aug-3 Bonhams, Edinburgh #1137

£850 $1369 €1233 On the Tay (14x18cm-6x7in) s. pen ink W/C. 21-Aug-3 Bonhams, Edinburgh #1046
£850 $1462 €1241 In the Ardennes (25x35cm-10x14in) s. pencil W/C exhib. 3-Dec-3 Christie's, Kensington #549
£1000 $1830 €1460 Sound of Kerrera (14x22cm-6x9in) s. pencil W/C prov. 8-Apr-4 Bonhams, Edinburgh #136 est:300-500
£1150 $1852 €1668 La Tourettes (15x23cm-6x9in) s. pencil W/C. 21-Aug-3 Bonhams, Edinburgh #1022/R est:700-900
£1200 $2196 €1752 Loch Lubnaig (35x51cm-14x20in) s.i. W/C en grisaille exhib. 8-Apr-4 Bonhams, Edinburgh #152 est:600-800
£1500 $2745 €2190 Near Loch Broom (24x35cm-9x14in) s. ink W/C. 8-Apr-4 Bonhams, Edinburgh #145/R est:1200-1800
£1800 $3060 €2628 Loch nan Damph (13x28cm-5x11in) s.i. pencil W/C. 30-Oct-3 Christie's, London #199/R est:1500-2000

CAMERON, William Ross (1893-1971) American
Works on paper
£311 $550 €454 San Francisco, cityscape (41x30cm-16x12in) s. W/C. 1-May-4 Harvey Clar, Oakland #1257

CAMESI, Gianfredo (1940-) Swiss
£2805 $4769 €4095 Space measurement of time (100x200cm-39x79in) s.i.d.1977-1979 verso four parts prov. 22-Nov-3 Burkhard, Luzern #198/R est:6000-8000 (S.FR 6200)
Works on paper
£317 $538 €463 Dimension unique (35x70cm-14x28in) pencil tempera paper on board two parts exec. 1978 prov. 22-Nov-3 Burkhard, Luzern #195/R (S.FR 700)
£439 $807 €641 Dimension unique, transmutation forme de terre (52x42cm-20x17in) s.d.1974 ink pencil W/C. 23-Jun-4 Koller, Zurich #3145/R (S.FR 1000)
£439 $807 €641 Dimension unique, transformation forme de terre (52x42cm-20x17in) s.d.1974 ink pencil W/C. 23-Jun-4 Koller, Zurich #3146/R (S.FR 1000)
£498 $846 €727 Dimension unique (70x70cm-28x28in) pencil tempera paper on board four parts exec. 1978 prov.lit. 22-Nov-3 Burkhard, Luzern #199/R (S.FR 1100)

CAMIN, Joaquin Rubio (1926-) Spanish
£4138 $7448 €6000 Around Gijon (73x92cm-29x36in) s.d.54. 26-Jan-4 Durán, Madrid #155/R est:4250

CAMINATI, Aurelio (20th C) Italian
£544 $974 €800 Study for still life. Still life (70x100cm-28x39in) s.d.1958 s.i.d.verso prov. pair. 16-Mar-4 Finarte Semenzato, Milan #86
£544 $974 €800 Table with objects. Untitled (73x92cm-29x36in) s.d.1960 prov. two. 16-Mar-4 Finarte Semenzato, Milan #85

CAMINETTI, Luis (1930-) Spanish
£247 $420 €361 Rosedal fields (100x100cm-39x39in) s. 20-Nov-3 Galeria y Remates, Montevideo #118/R

CAMM, Robert (1847-?) Australian
£300 $551 €438 Sheep in a landscape (51x76cm-20x30in) s. 28-Jun-4 Australian Art Auctions, Sydney #155 (A.D 800)
£620 $1097 €905 Droving cattle (60x101cm-24x40in) prov. 3-May-4 Christie's, Melbourne #405 est:800-1200 (A.D 1500)
£744 $1317 €1086 Cattle in the creek (60x90cm-24x35in) prov. 3-May-4 Christie's, Melbourne #408 (A.D 1800)

CAMMARANO, Giuseppe (1766-1850) Italian
£6081 $10885 €9000 Scene from Mythology (43x54cm-17x21in) s. 8-May-4 Sebok, Bamberg #1687/R
Works on paper
£5263 $9684 €8000 Virginia's death (42x63cm-17x25in) s. pen ink W/C exhib.lit. 22-Jun-4 Sotheby's, Milan #71/R est:8000-12000
£5921 $10895 €9000 Scare in Pyrrus' camp (41x63cm-16x25in) s. pen ink W/C exhib.lit. 22-Jun-4 Sotheby's, Milan #70/R est:8000-12000

CAMMARANO, Michele (1835-c.1920) Italian
£709 $1184 €1000 Campagna (24x34cm-9x13in) s. cardboard. 21-Jun-3 Stadion, Trieste #265/R
£1295 $2124 €1800 Face of man. 5-Jun-3 Adma, Formigine #809 est:1800-2000
£17606 $29225 €25000 Gregge al pascolo (67x100cm-26x39in) s. lit. 11-Jun-3 Christie's, Rome #210/R est:28000-35000
Works on paper
£1200 $2208 €1800 Maria. Rooftops. Ciociaria (21x14cm-8x6in) one s. pencil chl dr set of 3 prov.exhib. 10-Jun-4 Christie's, Rome #56/R est:700-1000
£1408 $2437 €2000 Soldiers (59x43cm-23x17in) s. chl set of 3. 11-Dec-3 Christie's, Rome #66/R est:2000-3000

CAMMILLIERI, Niccolo S (fl.1820-1855) Maltese
Works on paper
£1522 $2785 €2222 Ship's portrait of an English frigate (43x58cm-17x23in) s. W/C pen. 9-Jun-4 Rasmussen, Copenhagen #2057/R est:10000-12000 (D.KR 17000)
£5208 $8229 €7500 Day and night, S.M de Bier under sail (49x70cm-19x28in) s.i.d.1826 pen ink W/C pair. 2-Sep-3 Christie's, Amsterdam #303/R est:3000-4000

CAMMILLIERI, Niccolo S (attrib) (fl.1820-1855) Maltese
£2206 $3750 €3221 Portrait of the ship Cherub of Boston (41x56cm-16x22in) i. oil paper on linen prov. 1-Nov-3 Skinner, Boston #134/R est:2000-4000

CAMMILLIERI, Nicolas (fl.1804-1835) Italian?
Works on paper
£793 $1348 €1158 Fregatte Angloise de 40. Canons sortant du Mouillage (39x56cm-15x22in) s.d.1806 W/C. 5-Nov-3 Dobiaschofsky, Bern #1103 (S.FR 1800)

CAMOGLI, Stefano (attrib) (fl.1665-1690) Italian
£8333 $15000 €12166 Boy picking grapes in a landscape (106x86cm-42x34in) prov.exhib.lit. 23-Jan-4 Christie's, Rockefeller NY #117/R est:5000-7000

CAMOIN, Charles (1879-1965) French
£1507 $2562 €2200 Moulin a MOntmartre (20x16cm-8x6in) s. panel. 9-Nov-3 Eric Pillon, Calais #69/R
£1589 $2909 €2400 Moulin de la Galette (11x16cm-4x6in) s. paper on canvas exhib. 7-Apr-4 Piasa, Paris #72/R est:2500-3000
£1600 $2960 €2336 Nu dans paysage (22x33cm-9x13in) s. panel. 14-Jan-4 Lawrence, Crewkerne #1403/R est:1500-2500
£1879 $3364 €2800 Portrait d'Yvette (55x46cm-22x18in) s. painted 1931. 26-May-4 Christie's, Paris #57/R est:2000-4000
£2041 $3714 €3000 L'ete, jeune fille sur le chemin (18x24cm-7x9in) s. 8-Feb-4 Anaf, Lyon #131/R est:3000-4000
£2098 $3566 €3000 Reclining nude (24x32cm-9x13in) s. 25-Nov-3 Christie's, Amsterdam #32/R est:3000-5000
£2800 $5096 €4200 Montmartre (11x16cm-4x6in) s. 4-Jul-4 Eric Pillon, Calais #111/R
£3557 $6367 €5300 Vase de fleurs (24x19cm-9x7in) s. 25-May-4 Chambelland & Giafferi, Paris #103/R est:2500-3000
£3867 $7000 €5646 Bouquet de roses au pot de pharmacie (55x38cm-22x15in) s. oil paper on canvas prov.lit. 30-Mar-4 Christie's, Rockefeller NY #101/R est:3000-5000
£4027 $7128 €6000 Village Provencal (50x61cm-20x24in) s. i.verso. 27-Apr-4 Artcurial Briest, Paris #154/R est:5000-6000
£4196 $7133 €6000 Cueillette des olives (32x23cm-13x9in) s. cardboard. 28-Nov-3 Drouot Estimations, Paris #152/R est:6000-7500
£5306 $9498 €7800 Bouquet de fleurs (46x55cm-18x22in) s. 19-Mar-4 Millon & Associes, Paris #87/R est:3000-4000
£6000 $10920 €9000 Vase de fleurs (56x38cm-22x15in) s. 4-Jul-4 Eric Pillon, Calais #96/R
£6711 $12013 €10000 Modele pres d'un poele dans l'atelier (65x54cm-26x21in) s. prov. 26-May-4 Christie's, Paris #25/R est:10000-15000
£7487 $14000 €10931 Bouquet d'anemones (73x60cm-29x24in) s. painted 1939 prov. 25-Feb-4 Christie's, Rockefeller NY #56/R est:15000-20000
£8054 $14899 €12000 Vase de fleurs (61x50cm-24x20in) s. 14-Mar-4 Eric Pillon, Calais #103/R
£8278 $15149 €12500 Village Ramatuelle (27x34cm-11x13in) s. panel. 9-Apr-4 Claude Aguttes, Neuilly #84/R est:8000-10000
£8390 $15605 €12500 Vase de fleurs, livres et tasse jaune (61x46cm-24x18in) s. 2-Mar-4 Artcurial Briest, Paris #213/R est:9000-12000
£8649 $16000 €12628 Paysage mediterraneen (51x61cm-20x24in) s. painted 1950. 11-Feb-4 Sotheby's, New York #22/R est:15000-20000
£9000 $16560 €13140 Passerelle a Sannois-sur-Seine (65x81cm-26x32in) s. painted 1920 prov. 22-Jun-4 Sotheby's, London #235/R est:10000-15000
£9239 $16537 €13489 Interior scene with woman (61x50cm-24x20in) s. prov. 28-May-4 Uppsala Auktionskammare, Uppsala #274/R est:60000-80000 (S.KR 125000)
£9655 $16028 €14000 Portrait de jeune femme (41x33cm-16x13in) s. 1-Oct-3 Millon & Associes, Paris #64/R est:4000
£12000 $21960 €18000 Bouquet de fleurs sur une nappe a carreaux (61x50cm-24x20in) s. sold with letter prov.exhib. 7-Jun-4 Palais de Beaux Arts, Brussels #35/R est:10000-15000
£12162 $22500 €17757 Vase de fleurs sur une table (55x46cm-22x18in) s. painted c.1950. 11-Feb-4 Sotheby's, New York #23/R est:12000-18000
£16000 $29440 €24000 Le port de Saint Tropez (38x46cm-15x18in) s. prov. 11-Jun-4 Pierre Berge, Paris #243/R est:10000-15000
£19553 $35000 €28547 Baie de Collioure (64x81cm-25x32in) s. painted c.1912. 6-May-4 Sotheby's, New York #274/R est:40000-60000
£37000 $68080 €54020 Clocher de Saint Tropez et la Conche (54x73cm-21x29in) s. painted 1905. 22-Jun-4 Sotheby's, London #158/R est:30000-40000
£38411 $69907 €58000 Le port de Saint-Tropez (73x92cm-29x36in) s. 18-Jun-4 Piasa, Paris #19/R est:50000-60000
£38733 $67783 €55000 Port (65x81cm-26x32in) s. prov. 18-Dec-3 Tajan, Paris #15/R est:38000-42000
£39106 $70000 €57095 Fiacres quai Voltaire - Les quais de la Seine a Paris (65x81cm-26x32in) s. painted c.1903-04 prov.exhib.lit. 6-May-4 Sotheby's, New York #277/R est:50000-70000
£44000 $80080 €64240 Fenetre ouverte sur le port de Saint Tropez (60x49cm-24x19in) s. board prov. 4-Feb-4 Sotheby's, London #234/R est:20000-30000
Works on paper
£845 $1462 €1200 Portrait de jeune fille (33x24cm-13x9in) s. pastel. 14-Dec-3 Eric Pillon, Calais #109/R
£986 $1706 €1400 Bain de soleil (16x25cm-6x10in) s. pastel. 14-Dec-3 Eric Pillon, Calais #79/R
£1000 $1820 €1500 Canotage (16x24cm-6x9in) s. W/C. 4-Jul-4 Eric Pillon, Calais #122/R
£1111 $1856 €1600 Woman in cafe (15x10cm-6x4in) s. pastel chk. 24-Oct-3 Ketterer, Hamburg #295/R est:1600-2000
£1189 $1985 €1700 Portrait d'enfant (17x14cm-7x6in) s. W/C. 29-Jun-3 Eric Pillon, Calais #105/R
£4000 $7280 €5840 Femme blonde au chapeau (65x50cm-26x20in) st.sig. pastel chl exec c.1930 prov. 5-Feb-4 Christie's, London #328/R est:4000-6000
£5500 $9185 €8030 Brune au turban a carreaux (46x31cm-18x12in) s. pastel chl exec c.1920. 22-Oct-3 Sotheby's, Olympia #127/R est:3500-4500

CAMOS, Honore (1906-) French
£420 $722 €600 Le bouquet de lilas (63x52cm-25x20in) s. 5-Dec-3 Chochon-Barre & Allardi, Paris #21

CAMP, Camille van (19th C) Belgian
£959 $1630 €1400 Reverie (72x55cm-28x22in) s. 10-Nov-3 Horta, Bruxelles #165
£987 $1816 €1500 Portrait of a lady (130x93cm-51x37in) s.d.1875. 28-Jun-4 Sotheby's, Amsterdam #17/R est:1500-2000

CAMP, Jeffery (1923-) British
£450 $819 €657 Bather and yacht (28x26cm-11x10in) s. board oval. 15-Jun-4 Bonhams, Knightsbridge #71

CAMP, Joseph Rodefer de (1858-1923) American
£25424 $45000 €37119 Pauline Decamp, with pink bow in her hair. s. 1-May-4 Thomaston Place, Thomaston #55/R
£96045 $170000 €140226 Pauline Decamp, age 13. s. 1-May-4 Thomaston Place, Thomaston #50/R

£136364 $240000 €199091 September afternoon (51x69cm-20x27in) s. painted c.1895 prov.exhib.lit. 18-May-4 Christie's, Rockefeller NY #58/R est:250000-350000
£294118 $550000 €429412 Mother and daughters on shore. 28-Feb-4 Thomaston Place, Thomaston #50/R

CAMP, Maxime du (1822-1884) French
Photographs
£1888 $3153 €2700 Nil (13x22cm-5x9in) salt print. 10-Oct-3 Tajan, Paris #57/R
£3000 $5280 €4380 Colosse du Speos (21x17cm-8x7in) process print lit. 19-May-4 Christie's, London #105/R est:2000-3000
£3800 $6688 €5548 Colosse du Speos (22x18cm-9x7in) process print. 19-May-4 Christie's, London #104/R est:2000-3000

CAMPAGNA, Girolamo (circle) (1550-c.1623) Italian
Sculpture
£10915 $18884 €15500 Meleagre (82x19cm-32x7in) bronze marble base. 11-Dec-3 Binoche, Paris #31/R est:8000-10000

CAMPAGNA, Girolamo (studio) (1550-c.1623) Italian
Sculpture
£55000 $95150 €80300 Venus and Marina on dolphins on scroll bearded caryatids (47cm-19in) bronze base pair exec.c.1600. 12-Dec-3 Sotheby's, London #195/R est:12000-18000

CAMPAGNARI, Licinio (1920-1981) Italian
£521 $885 €750 Mount Cervino (70x100cm-28x39in) s. 1-Nov-3 Meeting Art, Vercelli #18/R

CAMPAGNARI, Ottorino (1910-1981) Italian
£400 $736 €600 Ronco Canavese (40x50cm-16x20in) s. s.i.verso board. 14-Jun-4 Sant Agostino, Torino #215/R
£417 $708 €600 Mount Blanc (40x50cm-16x20in) s. board. 1-Nov-3 Meeting Art, Vercelli #54
£533 $981 €800 Around Ulzio (40x50cm-16x20in) s. i.d.1960 verso. 14-Jun-4 Sant Agostino, Torino #144/R
£694 $1181 €1000 Susa Valley (60x50cm-24x20in) s. 1-Nov-3 Meeting Art, Vercelli #418/R
£872 $1544 €1300 Still life with vegetables (40x60cm-16x24in) s. 1-May-4 Meeting Art, Vercelli #338
£972 $1653 €1400 Portofino (60x50cm-24x20in) s. 1-Nov-3 Meeting Art, Vercelli #202/R
£979 $1635 €1400 Cortina d'Ampezzo (40x50cm-16x20in) s. i.on stretcher. 26-Jun-3 Sant Agostino, Torino #128/R
£1277 $2132 €1800 Back from pasture (60x80cm-24x31in) s. 20-Oct-3 Sant Agostino, Torino #98/R est:1600
£1611 $2851 €2400 Back from pasture (60x80cm-24x31in) s. 1-May-4 Meeting Art, Vercelli #232 est:2000

CAMPAGNE, Pierre Étienne Daniel (1851-1914) French
Sculpture
£1300 $2366 €1898 Phyrne (47cm-19in) s. brown pat bronze. 15-Jun-4 Sotheby's, Olympia #98/R est:1200-1800

CAMPAGNOLA, Domenico (1484-1550) Italian
Works on paper
£5278 $9500 €7706 Battle scene (22x24cm-9x9in) pen brown ink wash prov.exhib.lit. 22-Jan-4 Christie's, Rockefeller NY #7/R est:7000-10000

CAMPANA, Ignace Jean Victor (1744-1786) French
Miniatures
£2800 $5040 €4088 Lady with buckled blue bodice, holding a sprig of flowers (8cm-3in circular) gold frame exhib. 22-Apr-4 Bonhams, New Bond Street #78/R est:3000-5000
£3800 $6840 €5548 Lady wearing a white dress with blue bodice (7cm-3in circular) gold frame exhib. 22-Apr-4 Bonhams, New Bond Street #77/R est:3000-5000

CAMPANELLA, Fabrizio (1965-) Italian
£352 $585 €500 Il Becero (60x50cm-24x20in) s. acrylic painted 2002. 14-Jun-3 Meeting Art, Vercelli #507/R
£503 $931 €750 At the stadium (80x70cm-31x28in) s.verso acrylic. 13-Mar-4 Meeting Art, Vercelli #317
£528 $877 €750 L'invastato (70x50cm-28x20in) s.verso acrylic. 14-Jun-3 Meeting Art, Vercelli #281/R
£599 $994 €850 Dissolvenza (70x50cm-28x20in) s.verso acrylic. 14-Jun-3 Meeting Art, Vercelli #292/R

CAMPANELLA, Vito (1932-) Argentinian
£2059 $3500 €3006 Serenade (50x40cm-20x16in) s. 25-Nov-3 Galeria y Remates, Montevideo #181/R
£2824 $4800 €4123 Contemplating (70x60cm-28x24in) s. 25-Nov-3 Galeria y Remates, Montevideo #180/R
£5866 $10500 €8564 Surrealist composition (90x60cm-35x24in) s. s.verso. 4-May-4 Arroyo, Buenos Aires #42/R est:5500
£6044 $11000 €8824 Inverted portrait (90x60cm-35x24in) s.d.73. 29-Jun-4 Arroyo, Buenos Aires #67/R est:7000
£8743 $16000 €12765 Joyful concert in favourable weather (60x70cm-24x28in) 1-Jun-4 Arroyo, Buenos Aires #59

CAMPANO, Miguel Angel (1948-) Spanish
£3873 $6778 €5500 Landscape (41x66cm-16x26in) d.85. 16-Dec-3 Segre, Madrid #173/R est:5000
£7042 $12183 €10000 Musician and model (98x98cm-39x39in) s.i.d.1982-83. 15-Dec-3 Ansorena, Madrid #959/R est:9000
£8099 $14173 €11500 Mohan (170x120cm-67x47in) s.i.d.95 verso oil ash exhib.lit. 16-Dec-3 Segre, Madrid #167/R est:11500
£13380 $23415 €19000 I (118x122cm-46x48in) s.d.1980 s.i.d.1980 prov. 16-Dec-3 Segre, Madrid #164/R est:15000
Works on paper
£473 $832 €700 Untitled (50x32cm-20x13in) s.d.79 collage. 18-May-4 Segre, Madrid #276/R

CAMPBELL, Charles Malcolm (1905-1985) American
£1308 $2250 €1910 Men without women (71x94cm-28x37in) s. prov.exhib. 3-Dec-3 Doyle, New York #302/R est:3000-4000

CAMPBELL, Cressida (1960-) Australian
Works on paper
£1570 $2905 €2292 Bottom of the garden (47x75cm-19x30in) s.d.82 synthetic polymer. 10-Mar-4 Deutscher-Menzies, Melbourne #327/R est:2700-3500 (A.D 3800)
£2429 $3911 €3546 Garden Island (90x147cm-35x58in) s. W/C carved plywood prov. 25-Aug-3 Sotheby's, Paddington #234 est:6000-8000 (A.D 6000)

CAMPBELL, Donald (19/20th C) British
£1070 $2000 €1562 Mountains at sunset looming over a lake with shepherd and flock (69x94cm-27x37in) s. painted c.1890. 28-Feb-4 Thomaston Place, Thomaston #90/R

CAMPBELL, George (1917-1979) British
£1000 $1660 €1460 Beached boats on the Spanish coast (45x56cm-18x22in) s. board. 1-Oct-3 John Ross, Belfast #162 est:800-1000
£1197 $1915 €1700 Landscape with woods and rocks by water (19x25cm-7x10in) W/C col chk painted on verso of printed cartoon prov. 16-Sep-3 Whyte's, Dublin #35/R est:1000-1200
£1579 $2905 €2400 The wreck of the Fanny Crossfield, Strangford Lough (33x38cm-13x15in) s. board. 22-Jun-4 De Veres Art Auctions, Dublin #178/R est:2000-3000
£1711 $3147 €2600 Mountains and houses near Malaga (21x45cm-8x18in) s.i board. 22-Jun-4 De Veres Art Auctions, Dublin #179/R est:3000-4000
£1842 $3389 €2800 Coastal landscape (28x38cm-11x15in) s. board. 22-Jun-4 De Veres Art Auctions, Dublin #149/R est:3000-4000
£2000 $3340 €2920 Mountains near Malaga (22x45cm-9x18in) s. canvasboard. 21-Oct-3 Bonhams, Knightsbridge #176/R est:1000-1500
£2162 $4086 €3200 Mountain stream (39x29cm-15x11in) s. board. 17-Feb-4 Whyte's, Dublin #19/R est:3000-4000
£2533 $4585 €3800 Spanish street procession (36x26cm-14x10in) s. board. 30-Mar-4 De Veres Art Auctions, Dublin #12/R est:2000-3000
£2819 $4989 €4200 Landscape with power station, possibly Ballylumford, Co Antrim (28x42cm-11x17in) s. board. 27-Apr-4 Whyte's, Dublin #30/R est:5000-7000
£3800 $6954 €5548 Near Rosbeg, Donegal (50x76cm-20x30in) s. board. 2-Jun-4 John Ross, Belfast #147 est:4000-5000
£5724 $10532 €8700 Gitana (59x43cm-23x17in) s.i.verso board. 22-Jun-4 De Veres Art Auctions, Dublin #40/R est:9000-12000
£5775 $9990 €8200 Spanish farm (32x42cm-13x17in) s. board. 10-Dec-3 Bonhams & James Adam, Dublin #178/R est:4000-5000
£5874 $9986 €8400 Gwee barra, Donegal (41x46cm-16x18in) s. i.verso board prov. 25-Nov-3 De Veres Art Auctions, Dublin #94/R est:5000-7000
£6081 $11493 €9000 Motorcycles (46x61cm-18x24in) s. i.verso board. 17-Feb-4 Whyte's, Dublin #29/R est:7000-9000
£6500 $11635 €9490 Quiet Sunday (38x30cm-15x12in) s. board. 14-May-4 Christie's, Kensington #466/R est:5000-7000
£7000 $11620 €10220 Clifden, Connemara (61x45cm-24x18in) s.verso board. 1-Oct-3 John Ross, Belfast #146 est:3500-4000
£7047 $12473 €10500 Town, Tenerife (51x41cm-20x16in) s. board prov.exhib. 27-Apr-4 Whyte's, Dublin #67/R est:10000-15000
£8224 $15132 €12500 Connemara highlander (59x46cm-23x18in) s.i. board prov. 22-Jun-4 De Veres Art Auctions, Dublin #11/R est:10000-15000
£9000 $16110 €13140 Guitarist (76x51cm-30x20in) s. board prov. 13-May-4 Sotheby's, London #78/R est:6000-8000
£9155 $14648 €13000 Don Quixote and Sancho Panza (91x76cm-36x30in) s. i.verso board exhib. 16-Sep-3 Whyte's, Dublin #70/R est:20000-25000
£13000 $24180 €18980 Still life with candle (31x41cm-12x16in) s. 3-Mar-4 John Ross, Belfast #127a est:3000-4000
£14765 $26430 €22000 Musicians (50x60cm-20x24in) s. i.verso board prov. 26-May-4 James Adam, Dublin #119/R est:15000-20000
£16216 $30649 €24000 Memory of the Maam Valley (76x102cm-30x40in) s. i.verso board prov. 17-Feb-4 Whyte's, Dublin #25/R est:15000-20000
Works on paper
£408 $751 €620 Study of a young man (19x14cm-7x6in) mixed media prov. 22-Jun-4 De Veres Art Auctions, Dublin #203/R
£563 $1025 €850 Three mermaids (18x30cm-7x12in) gouache card. 15-Jun-4 James Adam, Dublin #88/R
£592 $1089 €900 Bridge over a river (26x35cm-10x14in) s. gouache prov. 22-Jun-4 De Veres Art Auctions, Dublin #3/R
£592 $1089 €900 Bridge over a river (35x26cm-14x10in) gouache prov. 22-Jun-4 De Veres Art Auctions, Dublin #44/R
£733 $1327 €1100 Mechanics (19x27cm-7x11in) s.i.d.74 mixed media. 31-Mar-4 James Adam, Dublin #115/R
£839 $1427 €1200 Model reclining. Pencil study of model seated (25x27cm-10x11in) W/C over pencil double-sided prov. 18-Nov-3 Whyte's, Dublin #18/R
£909 $1545 €1300 Abstract with blue striations (27x20cm-11x8in) s. mixed media. 18-Nov-3 Whyte's, Dublin #67/R
£1056 $1690 €1500 Sand dunes and sea with sailboats on horizon (18x24cm-7x9in) s. gouache wax crayon board prov. 16-Sep-3 Whyte's, Dublin #1/R est:1500-2000
£1056 $1690 €1500 Cityscape (24x18cm-9x7in) s. crayon prov. 16-Sep-3 Whyte's, Dublin #30/R est:1500-1800
£1141 $2042 €1700 My window (44x27cm-17x11in) mixed media collage prov. 26-May-4 James Adam, Dublin #172a/R est:1500-2000
£1197 $1915 €1700 Man and woman in a wooded landscape (41x30cm-16x12in) pastel crayon board prov. 16-Sep-3 Whyte's, Dublin #9/R est:1200-1500
£1500 $2505 €2190 Pedregalejos, night (25x35cm-10x14in) s. pastel pen black ink. 16-Oct-3 Christie's, Kensington #472/R est:1000-1500
£1667 $3017 €2500 Still life with cheese and mushrooms (26x37cm-10x15in) s. mixed media prov. 31-Mar-4 James Adam, Dublin #82/R est:1500-2000
£1831 $2930 €2600 Still life (25x36cm-10x14in) mixed media prov. 16-Sep-3 Whyte's, Dublin #29/R est:2000-2500
£1879 $3326 €2800 Connemara churchyard (48x38cm-19x15in) s. W/C pencil pastel. 27-Apr-4 Whyte's, Dublin #150/R est:4000-5000
£2308 $3923 €3300 Spanish fishermen hauling nets (22x28cm-9x11in) i.verso W/C wax crayon. 18-Nov-3 Whyte's, Dublin #5/R est:2000-3000

£2378 $4042 €3400 Street scene in Spain (18x25cm-7x10in) s. crayon card. 18-Nov-3 Whyte's, Dublin #4/R est:2000-3000
£2533 $4585 €3800 Still life in a window (33x24cm-13x9in) s. mixed media prov. 31-Mar-4 James Adam, Dublin #85/R est:2000-3000
£2535 $4056 €3600 Fishermen at rest, Palo, Spain (22x30cm-9x12in) s.i. W/C chk pen ink. 16-Sep-3 Whyte's, Dublin #7/R est:2000-3000
£2568 $4853 €3800 Still life with radishes (34x52cm-13x20in) s. i.verso chl pastel pen ink exhib. 17-Feb-4 Whyte's, Dublin #90/R est:2500-3500
£3087 $5464 €4600 Fruit seller (64x51cm-25x20in) s.d.1970 collage W/C pencil exhib. 27-Apr-4 Whyte's, Dublin #2/R est:2000-3000
£4027 $7208 €6000 Evening mountain landscape with distant town (38x53cm-15x21in) s.i. gouache. 26-May-4 James Adam, Dublin #75/R est:6000-8000
£4362 $7809 €6500 Fisherman, Palo, Spain (22x30cm-9x12in) s.i. ink W/C. 26-May-4 James Adam, Dublin #135/R est:6000-8000
£4737 $8716 €7200 Flamenco guitarist (59x40cm-23x16in) s. mixed media prov. 22-Jun-4 De Veres Art Auctions, Dublin #20/R est:6000-8000

CAMPBELL, Helen Maria (19th C) British
Works on paper
£2000 $3340 €2920 Sledging and skating scenes (20x30cm-8x12in) one i. W/C over pencil set of six. 14-Oct-3 Sotheby's, London #194/R est:2000-3000
£4000 $6680 €5840 Indian village near Frederiction. Indian settlement by a river (10x14cm-4x6in) W/C over pencil two. 14-Oct-3 Sotheby's, London #196/R est:600-800
£9500 $15865 €13870 Views taken in New Bruswick, Canada (23x29cm-9x11in) s.i. W/C pencil album. 14-Oct-3 Sotheby's, London #193/R est:4000-6000

CAMPBELL, Hugh (20th C) American
£543 $1000 €793 Winter landscape at sunset (64x79cm-25x31in) s. board. 9-Jun-4 Alderfer's, Hatfield #464/R est:800-1200

CAMPBELL, John Henry (1755-1828) Irish
Works on paper
£503 $856 €720 Near Clondalkin (15x22cm-6x9in) s. wash dr. 25-Nov-3 De Veres Art Auctions, Dublin #225/R
£1300 $2327 €1898 View of Ringsend from Merrion Square, Dublin (20x26cm-8x10in) s.i.d.1790 pen grey ink W/C prov. 14-May-4 Christie's, London #2/R est:1500-2000
£1700 $3043 €2482 Dublin Bay from the Martello Tower, Howth (27x36cm-11x14in) init.i. i.verso pencil W/C gum ababic prov. 14-May-4 Christie's, London #1/R est:1500-2000
£2817 $4507 €4000 View of Dublin Bay and harbour from Stillorgan (32x62cm-13x24in) s.d.1812 W/C. 16-Sep-3 Whyte's, Dublin #171/R est:4000-6000

CAMPBELL, John Henry (attrib) (1755-1828) Irish
Works on paper
£320 $592 €467 Dublin from the Liffey (14x23cm-6x9in) i. pencil. 10-Mar-4 Sotheby's, Olympia #42/R
£465 $740 €670 Fishermen by a river (19x27cm-7x11in) W/C. 10-Sep-3 James Adam, Dublin #4/R

CAMPBELL, John Hodgson (1855-1927) British
£2800 $5012 €4088 Blackberry gatherers (76x50cm-30x20in) s. 26-May-4 Sotheby's, Olympia #143/R est:1500-2000
Works on paper
£260 $476 €380 Trees at the stream edge (29x41cm-11x16in) s.d.1906 W/C. 1-Jun-4 Hodgins, Calgary #47/R (C.D 650)

CAMPBELL, Jon (1961-) Australian
Works on paper
£6107 $11115 €8916 View of Double Bay, Sydney (38x64cm-15x25in) s.d.1895 W/C gouache prov. 16-Jun-4 Deutscher-Menzies, Melbourne #119/R est:14000-18000 (A.D 16000)

CAMPBELL, Laura (20th C) Canadian
£537 $972 €784 Chesterfield Ave (30x41cm-12x16in) s. s.i.d.2002 verso. 18-Apr-4 Levis, Calgary #427/R est:900-1200 (C.D 1300)

CAMPBELL, Laurence (1911-1964) British
Sculpture
£1690 $2704 €2400 Head of a girl (46cm-18in) bronze one of six. 16-Sep-3 Whyte's, Dublin #121/R est:2000-3000

CAMPBELL, Laurence A (1940-) American
£1630 $3000 €2380 Church street, Lambertville, winter (41x51cm-16x20in) s. 9-Jun-4 Alderfer's, Hatfield #463/R est:3000-5000
£2793 $5000 €4078 Philadelphia waterfront, winter under the Ben Franklin Bridge (41x51cm-16x20in) s. s.i.verso board. 6-May-4 Shannon's, Milford #244/R est:5000-7000
£2905 $5200 €4241 Winter landscape, the canal at Lambertville (41x51cm-16x20in) s.i. panel. 20-Mar-4 Pook & Pook, Downington #577/R est:3500-4500

CAMPBELL, Leyda (1949-) Canadian
£400 $732 €584 Sunset at sea (60x90cm-24x35in) s. 1-Jun-4 Hodgins, Calgary #78/R (C.D 1000)

CAMPBELL, Raymond (20th C) British?
£360 $634 €526 Still life of glass, pottery and grapes (59x49cm-23x19in) s. 19-May-4 John Bellman, Billingshurst #1762
£2819 $5187 €4200 Still life with blue cheese and grapres in a niche (61x50cm-24x20in) s. 23-Mar-4 Mealy's, Castlecomer #1113/R est:4000-4500
£4605 $8474 €7000 Still life with arrangement of Claret, grapes, bread, fruit and cheese (58x70cm-23x28in) panel. 22-Jun-4 Mealy's, Castlecomer #751/R est:7000-8000

CAMPBELL, Robert (jnr) (1944-1993) Australian
Works on paper
£488 $771 €708 Lane cove (18x27cm-7x11in) s. W/C prov. 22-Jul-3 Lawson Menzies, Sydney #84/R est:1000-2000 (A.D 1200)

CAMPBELL, Robert Richmond (1902-1972) Australian
£287 $523 €419 Horseshoe Bay, Port Elliot, South Australia. 1-Jul-4 Joel, Victoria #419 (A.D 750)
£366 $575 €531 Venice series (15x20cm-6x8in) s. board. 26-Aug-3 Lawson Menzies, Sydney #60 est:1000-1500 (A.D 900)
£1377 $2341 €2010 Louvre (44x54cm-17x21in) s. prov. 24-Nov-3 Sotheby's, Melbourne #94/R est:2800-3800 (A.D 3250)
£2041 $3755 €2980 By the sea (17x11cm-7x4in) init. canvas on cardboard prov. 29-Mar-4 Goodman, Sydney #104/R est:2000-3000 (A.D 5000)

CAMPBELL, Steven (1953-) British
£307 $550 €448 Man with a shy elephant (41x30cm-16x12in) s.d.1985 verso oil on paper. 6-May-4 Doyle, New York #100/R

CAMPBELL, Tom (1865-1943) British
£290 $522 €423 Rainbow (35x45cm-14x18in) s. canvasboard. 22-Apr-4 Bonhams, Edinburgh #361
£700 $1302 €1022 Scottish loch (51x76cm-20x30in) s. 4-Mar-4 Christie's, Kensington #174/R
£709 $1184 €1000 Evening after the rain (62x46cm-24x18in) s.i. 20-Oct-3 Bernaerts, Antwerp #58/R
£780 $1420 €1170 The Dunoon ferry (33x43cm-13x17in) 20-Jun-4 Lawrences, Bletchingley #1426
Works on paper
£260 $473 €380 Sheep grazing by trees (24x34cm-9x13in) s. W/C. 29-Jun-4 Bonhams, Knowle #29
£310 $570 €453 Cattle grazing. s. W/C. 25-Mar-4 Bonhams, Edinburgh #346
£400 $736 €584 On the road to Kirriemuir (25x37cm-10x15in) s. pencil W/C bodycol. 25-Mar-4 Christie's, Kensington #187
£480 $893 €701 Loch ferry (25x37cm-10x15in) s. W/C. 4-Mar-4 Christie's, Kensington #173/R
£550 $1023 €803 Off to market (29x58cm-11x23in) s. pencil W/C. 4-Mar-4 Christie's, Kensington #172/R
£750 $1395 €1095 Artist sketching by a Scottish inlet (33x63cm-13x25in) s. pencil W/C htd white. 4-Mar-4 Christie's, Kensington #175/R

CAMPENDONK, Heinrich (1889-1957) German
£20000 $36800 €29200 Pierrot und Pferde - Pierrot with horses (181x112cm-71x44in) tempera burlap painted c.1924-28. 23-Jun-4 Christie's, London #175/R est:20000-30000
£158371 $269231 €350000 Fisherman (72x92cm-28x36in) mono. painted 1919 lit. 25-Nov-3 Pierre Berge, Paris #16/R est:120000-150000
Prints
£2000 $3680 €3000 New year leaf (21x33cm-8x13in) s.d.1916 woodcut. 12-Jun-4 Villa Grisebach, Berlin #516/R est:2000-3000
£2183 $3974 €3187 Female nude with goat in front of house. s. woodcut. 17-Jun-4 Kornfeld, Bern #233/R est:5000 (S.FR 5000)
£3843 $6994 €5611 Herder with large goat. s.i. col wooduct. 17-Jun-4 Kornfeld, Bern #235/R est:7500 (S.FR 8800)
£11888 $20448 €17000 Herder with goat (32x25cm-13x10in) s. woodcut W/C. 2-Dec-3 Hauswedell & Nolte, Hamburg #63/R est:12000
Works on paper
£667 $1227 €1000 Three female nudes and two cats (21x33cm-8x13in) pencil. 12-Jun-4 Villa Grisebach, Berlin #515/R est:500-700
£1333 $2453 €2000 Two female dancers (40x400cm-16x157in) d.1911 W/C brush pen over pencil. 12-Jun-4 Villa Grisebach, Berlin #513/R est:2000-3000
£1467 $2699 €2200 Three female dancers (40x42cm-16x17in) W/C brush pen over pencil. 12-Jun-4 Villa Grisebach, Berlin #514/R est:2000-3000
£2098 $3608 €3000 Nude girl with sickle (43x36cm-17x14in) mono.d.1918 pencil. 2-Dec-3 Hauswedell & Nolte, Hamburg #62/R est:3000
£5333 $9813 €8000 Wild cat (21x33cm-8x13in) sepia W/C pencil. 12-Jun-4 Villa Grisebach, Berlin #512/R est:1000-1500
£16783 $28531 €24000 Reclining nude with bird (20x25cm-8x10in) mono.d.47 W/C Indian ink over pencil. 26-Nov-3 Lempertz, Koln #614/R est:25000
£27273 $46909 €39000 Hare (9x14cm-4x6in) W/C. 2-Dec-3 Hauswedell & Nolte, Hamburg #61/R est:8000
£100559 $180000 €146816 Composition with two cows (43x54cm-17x21in) gouache W/C exec.c.1913 prov.exhib.lit. 6-May-4 Sotheby's, New York #101/R est:100000-150000

CAMPESINO Y MINGO, Vicente (19th C) Spanish
£464 $844 €700 Historical Spanish scene (31x40cm-12x16in) s.d.93 panel. 19-Jun-4 Bergmann, Erlangen #777
£1993 $3268 €2750 Recordando una buena faena (34x44cm-13x17in) s. panel. 27-May-3 Durán, Madrid #184/R est:2500

CAMPESTRINI, Alcide (1863-1940) Italian
£387 $678 €550 Roofs covered in snow (45x56cm-18x22in) s.d.921 cardboard. 17-Dec-3 Il Ponte, Milan #513
£903 $1535 €1300 Peasant woman (18x26cm-7x10in) s. card. 29-Oct-3 Il Ponte, Milan #590

CAMPESTRINI, Ernesto Alcide (1897-1983) Italian
£474 $849 €692 Bacino di S Marco. Chiesa della Salute (40x49cm-16x19in) s. i. verso panel. 12-May-4 Dobiaschofsky, Bern #373/R (S.FR 1100)

CAMPESTRINI, Gianfranco (1901-) Italian
£582 $908 €850 Spring flowers (50x72cm-20x28in) s. i.verso. 8-Apr-3 Il Ponte, Milan #995

CAMPHAUSEN, Wilhelm (1818-1885) German
£1192 $2170 €1800 Castle interior with a sleeping guard (39x30cm-15x12in) oval. 17-Jun-4 Frank Peege, Freiburg #1123/R est:2200

£1987	$3616	€3000	Portrait of the prince of Anhalt-Dessau (39x31cm-15x12in) mono.d.1858 oval. 17-Jun-4 Frank Peege, Freiburg #1124/R est:2200
£3200	$5344	€4672	Long journey home (51x61cm-20x24in) s. 8-Oct-3 Christie's, Kensington #813/R est:2000-3000
£15278	$27500	€22306	Michael Strogoff, courier to Tsar Alexander II (102x157cm-40x62in) s. prov. 23-Apr-4 Sotheby's, New York #5/R est:15000-20000

CAMPHUYSEN, Joachim Govertsz (1602-1659) Dutch

£8784	$15459	€13000	Wooded landscape with figures conversing near a farm (16x30cm-6x12in) mono. panel. 18-May-4 Sotheby's, Amsterdam #20/R est:6000-8000

CAMPHUYSEN, Raphael Govertsz (1598-1657) Dutch

£5667	$10143	€8500	Moonlit landscape with river (17x24cm-7x9in) init.d. board. 12-May-4 Finarte Semenzato, Milan #95/R est:6000-8000

CAMPI, Antonio (1531-1591) Italian

Works on paper

£13500	$24705	€19710	Feeding of the five thousand. Figure studies (41x34cm-16x13in) blk chk grey wash htd white squared blk chk double-sided lit. 8-Jul-4 Sotheby's, London #33/R est:14000-16000

CAMPI, Felix (attrib) (1764-1817) Italian

£2252	$4098	€3400	Healing of a possessed man (93x70cm-37x28in) indis.sig.i.d.1790 verso. 16-Jun-4 Dorotheum, Vienna #277/R est:1000-1500

CAMPI, Giulio (attrib) (1502-1572) Italian

£600	$1110	€876	Roman figures standing before a portico (23x15cm-9x6in) bears sig. 10-Feb-4 David Lay, Penzance #511/R

CAMPI, Vincenzo (style) (1536-1591) Italian

£8511	$13788	€12000	Boucher a son etale (101x101cm-40x40in) 21-May-3 Artcurial Briest, Paris #230/R est:12000-15000

CAMPIDOGLIO, Michele di (1610-1670) Italian

£1407	$2250	€2054	Still life (51x86cm-20x34in) s. 21-Sep-3 Grogan, Boston #5/R
£53691	$100403	€80000	Still life of fruit with pomgranates and apples (66x91cm-26x36in) prov. 25-Feb-4 Porro, Milan #70/R est:80000

CAMPIDOGLIO, Michele di (attrib) (1610-1670) Italian

£16667	$30000	€24334	Still life of fruit and flowers on a stone ledge with birds and a monkey (19x26cm-7x10in) i. 22-Jan-4 Sotheby's, New York #193/R est:20000-30000

CAMPIDOGLIO, Michele di (circle) (1610-1670) Italian

£4756	$7942	€6800	Nature morte de fruits et de fleurs (65x48cm-26x19in) 26-Jun-3 Artcurial Briest, Paris #483 est:4000-5000

CAMPIGLI, Massimo (1895-1971) Italian

£20290	$33275	€28000	Dancers (33x46cm-13x18in) s.d.65 prov. 27-May-3 Sotheby's, Milan #252/R est:30000-40000
£23529	$40000	€34352	Donna bianchа con le scale (55x48cm-22x19in) s.d.61 prov. 5-Nov-3 Christie's, Rockefeller NY #347/R est:50000-70000
£34965	$59441	€50000	Lady in yellow (34x46cm-13x18in) s.d.55 prov.exhib. 24-Nov-3 Christie's, Milan #251/R est:50000-70000
£36364	$61818	€52000	Labyrinth (40x50cm-16x20in) s.d.57 s.i.d.verso prov. 25-Nov-3 Sotheby's, Milan #201/R est:60000-80000
£44928	$73681	€62000	Seated woman (55x38cm-22x15in) s.d.50. 27-May-3 Sotheby's, Milan #224/R est:50000-70000
£45333	$82960	€68000	Cinque donne (27x37cm-11x15in) s.d.41. 5-Jun-4 Lempertz, Koln #624/R est:50000-60000
£46154	$78462	€66000	Woman with necklace (58x44cm-23x17in) s.d.48 prov. 24-Nov-3 Christie's, Milan #273/R est:60000-80000
£46667	$83533	€70000	Bust (65x50cm-26x20in) s.d. prov.exhib. 14-May-4 Ketterer, Munich #233a/R est:40000-60000
£47826	$78435	€66000	Sisters (40x51cm-16x20in) s.d.66 prov. 27-May-3 Sotheby's, Milan #238/R est:60000-80000
£48276	$77241	€70000	Figure (56x47cm-22x19in) s.d.1962. 13-Mar-3 Galleria Pace, Milan #153/R est:90000-110000
£51049	$86783	€73000	Idole au corsage rouge (100x80cm-39x31in) s.d.62 s.i.d.verso prov. 1-Dec-3 Rieunier, Paris #26/R est:80000-100000
£54054	$95135	€80000	Figure (100x70cm-39x28in) s.d.61 prov. 24-May-4 Christie's, Milan #262/R est:50000-70000
£63758	$114128	€95000	Figure (48x35cm-19x14in) s.d.45. 29-May-4 Farsetti, Prato #499/R est:90000-110000
£66667	$109333	€92000	Painter and model (36x50cm-14x20in) s.d.49 prov. 27-May-3 Sotheby's, Milan #230/R est:65000-80000
£79710	$130725	€110000	Figure (34x27cm-13x11in) s.d.44. 31-May-3 Farsetti, Prato #742/R est:80000-90000
£94406	$160490	€135000	Women (43x63cm-17x25in) s.d.41 prov. 25-Nov-3 Sotheby's, Milan #184/R est:100000-130000
£96070	$174847	€140262	Lady on a balcony (92x73cm-36x29in) s.d.1931 prov.exhib. 18-Jun-4 Kornfeld, Bern #13/R est:50000 (S.FR 220000)
£111888	$190210	€160000	Two little umbrellas (65x91cm-26x36in) s.d.54 exhib.lit. 29-Nov-3 Farsetti, Prato #493/R est:160000-190000
£116197	$203345	€165000	Women strolling (72x91cm-28x36in) s.d.1955 prov.lit. 16-Dec-3 Porro, Milan #11/R
£187919	$336376	€280000	Friends (60x50cm-24x20in) s.d.1928 cardboard on board. 29-May-4 Farsetti, Prato #533/R est:280000-330000
£214765	$384430	€320000	Women at table (116x89cm-46x35in) s.d.53 prov.exhib. 25-May-4 Sotheby's, Milan #249/R est:300000-400000

Prints

£2069	$3455	€3000	Ball game (27x37cm-11x15in) s.d.1944 lithograph lit. 13-Nov-3 Finarte Semenzato, Rome #72/R est:2500-3000
£2313	$4140	€3400	Tour Eiffel (60x74cm-24x29in) s.d.52 num.76/125 col lithograph lit. 16-Mar-4 Finarte Semenzato, Milan #323/R est:3300
£14483	$24186	€21000	Swing (45x31cm-18x12in) s. monotype paper on canvas prov. 13-Nov-3 Finarte Semenzato, Rome #222/R est:14000-16000

Works on paper

£786	$1446	€1148	Donna (20x16cm-8x6in) s.i. chl prov. 8-Jun-4 Germann, Zurich #16/R est:2000-3000 (S.FR 1800)
£2113	$3507	€3000	Two faces (14x20cm-6x8in) s.d.66 Chinese ink. 11-Jun-3 Finarte Semenzato, Milan #504/R est:3600
£2657	$4517	€3800	Composition (17x33cm-7x13in) ink paper on canvas. 20-Nov-3 Finarte Semenzato, Milan #45/R est:4000-4400
£4348	$7130	€6000	Women (32x22cm-13x9in) s.d.43 sanguine prov. 27-May-3 Sotheby's, Milan #32/R est:5000-6000
£5479	$9315	€8000	Untitled (35x29cm-14x11in) s. frottage lit. 7-Nov-3 Galleria Rosenberg, Milan #119/R est:8000
£7383	$13215	€11000	Woman (36x25cm-14x10in) s.d.44 W/C chl tempera col pastel double-sided. 25-May-4 Sotheby's, Milan #130/R est:8000

CAMPION, George Bryant (1796-1870) British

Works on paper

£290	$467	€423	Castle Rocks, Scarborough (33x48cm-13x19in) init.i. W/C htd white. 19-Feb-3 Peter Wilson, Nantwich #75
£380	$692	€555	The novice ice skater (21x29cm-8x11in) s. pencil W/C htd white. 1-Jul-4 Christie's, Kensington #240

CAMPMANY, Ramon de (1899-?) Spanish

£2483	$4469	€3600	Hunter (81x100cm-32x39in) s. s.i.d.1951 verso. 26-Jan-4 Ansorena, Madrid #238/R est:3600

CAMPO, Federico del (19/20th C) Peruvian

£76923	$128462	€110000	Vue de Venise (48x71cm-19x28in) s. 30-Jun-3 Artcurial Briest, Paris #720/R est:25000-30000
£85000	$144500	€124100	Grand Canal, Venice (49x74cm-19x29in) s. 18-Nov-3 Sotheby's, London #306/R

CAMPO, Frederik Willem del (1803-1890) Dutch

£1818	$3127	€2600	Hiver a Breda (40x58cm-16x23in) s.d.1867. 2-Dec-3 Campo & Campo, Antwerp #99/R est:3000-3500

CAMPOLMI, S (19th C) Italian

£5000	$9150	€7300	Brief distraction (57x57cm-22x22in) s. prov. 8-Jul-4 Lawrence, Crewkerne #1617/R est:3000-5000

CAMPOLO, Placido (1693-1743) Italian

Works on paper

£638	$1141	€950	Eminia with the shepherds (20x25cm-8x10in) i. pen wash exhib. 25-May-4 Karl & Faber, Munich #12/R

CAMPOS DIAZ, Pedro (1966-) Spanish

£1418	$2369	€2000	Apples (100x100cm-39x39in) s.d.99 exhib. 20-Oct-3 Durán, Madrid #91/R est:2000

CAMPOS, Florencio Molina (20th C) South American

Works on paper

£1250	$2000	€1825	Man and wife with baby on the river in rowboat (28x38cm-11x15in) s.d.1936 gouache. 20-Sep-3 Sloans & Kenyon, Bethesda #1035/R est:1900-2200
£1250	$2000	€1825	Dancers with guitars (33x46cm-13x18in) s.d.1931 gouache. 20-Sep-3 Sloans & Kenyon, Bethesda #1037/R est:2500-2800
£1250	$2000	€1825	Gaucho by campfire with guitar (28x43cm-11x17in) s.d.1949 gouache. 20-Sep-3 Sloans & Kenyon, Bethesda #1036/R est:2200-2600
£1519	$2750	€2218	Le Santa Fe (33x48cm-13x19in) s.d.939 gouache pencil. 3-Apr-4 Neal Auction Company, New Orleans #674/R est:4000-5000
£1534	$2700	€2240	Gaucho (25x36cm-10x14in) s. gouache. 23-May-4 William Jenack, New York #162 est:2500-3500

CAMPOTOSTO, Henry (?-1910) Belgian

£5285	$9459	€7716	Sleeping babes (37x48cm-15x19in) s.d.78 panel prov. 4-May-4 Ritchie, Toronto #78/R est:8000-10000 (C.D 13000)

CAMPRIANI, Alceste (1848-1933) Italian

£2113	$3507	€3000	Paesaggio con pesco fiorito (45x38cm-18x15in) trace sig. 11-Jun-3 Christie's, Rome #111/R est:3500-4500
£3356	$5940	€5000	In the stable (41x41cm-16x16in) s. i.verso. 1-May-4 Meeting Art, Vercelli #251 est:5000
£9500	$16150	€13870	Fishing on the Amalfi coast (27x44cm-11x17in) s. s.i.stretcher. 19-Nov-3 Bonhams, New Bond Street #85/R est:3000-5000
£12000	$21720	€18000	Fishermen hauling in net in Bay of Naples (26x49cm-10x19in) s.d.75 panel. 1-Apr-4 Van Ham, Cologne #1313/R est:2400

CAMPRIANI, Giovanni (1880-?) Italian

£3873	$6701	€5500	Napoleone Square in Lucca (103x144cm-41x57in) 9-Dec-3 Pandolfini, Florence #254/R est:5800-6200

CAMPRIANI, Tullio (?) Italian

£417	$708	€600	Bird family (20x32cm-8x13in) s. board oval. 1-Nov-3 Meeting Art, Vercelli #334/R

CAMPROBIN, Pedro de (1605-1674) Spanish

£35211	$61620	€50000	Basket of flowers (36x45cm-14x18in) 16-Dec-3 Segre, Madrid #55/R est:50000

CAMPS JUNYENT, Gaspar (1875-1942) Spanish

Works on paper

£517	$941	€760	Young woman at party (48x35cm-19x14in) s. gouache W/C. 3-Feb-4 Segre, Madrid #11/R

CAMPUZANO Y AGUIRRE, Tomas (1857-1934) Spanish

£276	$497	€400	Landscape (9x14cm-4x6in) s. cardboard. 26-Jan-4 Durán, Madrid #557/R

Works on paper

£300	$543	€450	Street in Jijona (21x15cm-8x6in) s.i. W/C. 30-Mar-4 Segre, Madrid #71/R

CAMUCCINI, Vincenzo (1773-1844) Italian

£1974	$3632	€3000	Communion of the Apostles (27x38cm-11x15in) paper on canvas. 22-Jun-4 Sotheby's, Milan #93/R est:3000-4000
£19000	$32300	€27740	Pan and Apollo (53x74cm-21x29in) s.i.verso prov.lit. 30-Oct-3 Sotheby's, Olympia #164/R est:5000-7000

Works on paper

£447	$804	€670	Moderation (24x28cm-9x11in) chl lit. 21-Apr-4 Finarte Semenzato, Milan #552/R
£900	$1557	€1314	Senators and women finding corpses, with soldiers arresting murderers (30x44cm-12x17in) pencil pen brown ink wash. 12-Dec-3 Christie's, Kensington #412/R

CAMUCCINI, Vincenzo (attrib) (1773-1844) Italian

£1986	$3316	€2800	Dieu pan (54x76cm-21x30in) s.verso. 17-Jun-3 Galerie Moderne, Brussels #375/R est:2000-3000

CAMUS, Blanche (19/20th C) French

£873	$1537	€1275	Southern landscape (61x46cm-24x18in) i. prov. 22-May-4 Galerie Gloggner, Luzern #18/R (S.FR 2000)
£1100	$1837	€1606	Pecheurs au matin (18x23cm-7x9in) s. panel prov. 22-Oct-3 Sotheby's, Olympia #35/R est:700-900
£3400	$5678	€4964	Fenetre sur Saint Tropez (73x60cm-29x24in) s. prov. 22-Oct-3 Sotheby's, Olympia #94/R est:3000-5000
£4000	$6360	€5800	Toits rouges a Saint Tropez (60x73cm-24x29in) s. s.verso. 11-Sep-3 Christie's, Kensington #50/R est:4000-6000
£17000	$29410	€24820	Les vendanges en Provence (209x281cm-82x111in) s. prov.exhib.lit. 11-Dec-3 Christie's, Kensington #46/R est:12000-18000

CAMUS, Gustave (1914-1984) Belgian

£470	$832	€700	Jeune fille au collier (122x55cm-48x22in) s. 27-Apr-4 Campo, Vlaamse Kaai #344
£476	$852	€700	La tempete (22x49cm-9x19in) s. panel. 16-Mar-4 Vanderkindere, Brussels #238
£940	$1663	€1400	La rentree au port (49x100cm-19x39in) s. 27-Apr-4 Campo, Vlaamse Kaai #345
£966	$1786	€1400	Bouquet au vase bleu (120x55cm-47x22in) s. i.verso. 19-Jan-4 Horta, Bruxelles #159
£1241	$2297	€1800	Bouquet aux ombrelles (120x55cm-47x22in) s. i.d.1969 verso. 19-Jan-4 Horta, Bruxelles #160 est:2200-2800
£1259	$2102	€1800	Nature morte devant la mer (65x130cm-26x51in) s. 13-Oct-3 Horta, Bruxelles #73 est:2000-3000
£1667	$2783	€2400	Chalutier (39x88cm-15x35in) s. 21-Oct-3 Galerie Moderne, Brussels #361/R
£2083	$3312	€3000	Une action contestataire (89x116cm-35x46in) s.d.1981 panel. 15-Sep-3 Horta, Bruxelles #214/R est:2200-2800
£3014	$5123	€4400	Coron a Peronnes (92x73cm-36x29in) s. d.1952 verso. 10-Nov-3 Horta, Bruxelles #187/R

Works on paper

£272	$487	€400	Port de peche (43x53cm-17x21in) s. W/C. 16-Mar-4 Vanderkindere, Brussels #234
£445	$757	€650	Port de peche (42x51cm-17x20in) s. W/C. 10-Nov-3 Horta, Bruxelles #189

CAMUS, Jacques (1937-) French

£267	$491	€400	Marrakech (19x24cm-7x9in) s. i.d.1993 verso panel. 11-Jun-4 Pierre Berge, Paris #257
£629	$1070	€900	Le Pont-Neuf, la Seine a Paris (24x33cm-9x13in) s.i. i.d.1996 verso canvas on panel. 28-Nov-3 Blanchet, Paris #126/R
£667	$1227	€1000	Marche de la rue Mouffetard (19x24cm-7x9in) s. i.d.1993 verso canvas on panel. 11-Jun-4 Pierre Berge, Paris #224
£1040	$1924	€1550	Notre Dame a Paris en hiver (38x46cm-15x18in) s. i.d.1995-1996 verso canvas on panel. 15-Mar-4 Blanchet, Paris #147/R est:1500-2000

CANA, Louis Emile (1845-1895) French

Sculpture

£3846	$7000	€5615	Combat au coq (61x36cm-24x14in) cast sig. base pat bronze. 7-Feb-4 Neal Auction Company, New Orleans #402/R est:3000-5000

CANAL, Gilbert von (1849-1927) German

£333	$543	€480	Children in the dunes by village (23x36cm-9x14in) s.d.1884 canvas on board. 25-Sep-3 Neumeister, Munich #2748
£533	$976	€800	Water mill on the edge of a village (90x120cm-35x47in) s. 5-Jun-4 Arnold, Frankfurt #553/R
£1208	$2162	€1800	Fishing boats in Dutch harbour (64x86cm-25x34in) s. 27-May-4 Dorotheum, Graz #10/R est:1800

CANALE, Fabio (attrib) (1703-1767) Italian

Works on paper

£1905	$3410	€2800	Un vieillard assis pres d'un cheval, entoure de figures (20x32cm-8x13in) pen brown ink wash. 18-Mar-4 Christie's, Paris #38/R est:800-1200

CANALETTO (1697-1768) Italian

£22000	$38060	€32120	Two scenes of Venice (48x73cm-19x29in) pair prov. 11-Dec-3 Sotheby's, London #237/R est:15000-20000
£26000	$44980	€37960	Venice, a view of the Grand Canal with the Rialto Bridge (60x101cm-24x40in) prov. 11-Dec-3 Sotheby's, London #238/R est:10000-15000
£75000	$129750	€109500	Venice the Cannareggio and the entrance to the Grand Canal (71x98cm-28x39in) prov. 11-Dec-3 Sotheby's, London #239/R est:20000-30000
£111111	$200000	€162222	San Francesco della Vigna, Venice (33x23cm-13x9in) prov.lit. 22-Jan-4 Sotheby's, New York #73/R est:80000-120000
£690000	$1262700	€1007400	Courtyard of the Ducal Palace, Venice (43x31cm-17x12in) prov.exhib.lit. 7-Jul-4 Christie's, London #90/R est:500000-800000

Prints

£1645	$3026	€2500	Bookshop (14x21cm-6x8in) eau forte. 22-Jun-4 Sotheby's, Milan #213/R est:3000-4000
£1765	$3000	€2577	Imaginary view of San Giacomo di Rialto (14x21cm-6x8in) etching. 31-Oct-3 Sotheby's, New York #133/R
£1796	$3000	€2622	View of a town on a river bank (30x43cm-12x17in) etching executed c.1740. 11-Nov-3 Doyle, New York #223/R est:4000-6000
£2358	$4292	€3443	Il portico con la lanterna. etching. 17-Jun-4 Kornfeld, Bern #13 est:4000 (S.FR 5400)
£2358	$4292	€3443	Le procuratie niove e San Ziminian. etching. 17-Jun-4 Kornfeld, Bern #16 est:4000 (S.FR 5400)
£2800	$4816	€4088	Portico with the lantern (30x43cm-12x17in) etching prov. 4-Dec-3 Sotheby's, London #3/R est:1500-2000
£3128	$5600	€4567	Mestre (28x43cm-11x17in) etching executed c.1740. 6-May-4 Swann Galleries, New York #92/R est:3000-5000
£5000	$8500	€7300	Mestre (30x43cm-12x17in) etching exec.1741. 1-Dec-3 Bonhams, New Bond Street #25/R est:1500-2000
£11000	$20240	€16060	La torre di Malghera (31x44cm-12x17in) etching. 28-Jun-4 Bonhams, New Bond Street #27/R est:2000-3000
£14706	$25000	€21471	Imaginary view of Padua (30x43cm-12x17in) etching. 31-Oct-3 Sotheby's, New York #134/R
£29000	$52780	€42340	Vedute altre prese da I luoghi, altre ideate da Antonio Canal. etchings two joined sheets 29. 1-Jul-4 Sotheby's, London #19/R est:15000-20000

Works on paper

£1259	$2102	€1800	Ruins (22x23cm-9x9in) pen brush sketch verso prov. 28-Jun-3 Bolland & Marotz, Bremen #563/R est:2300

CANALETTO (after) (1697-1768) Italian

£8500	$15300	€12410	Venice, a view of the Grand Canal looking south west from Chiesa Degli Scalzi (37x53cm-15x21in) prov. 20-Apr-4 Sotheby's, Olympia #398/R est:6000-8000
£9600	$16608	€14016	Venice, a view of the entrance of the Grand Canal (70x136cm-28x54in) 9-Dec-3 Sotheby's, Olympia #435/R est:7000-10000

CANALETTO (attrib) (1697-1768) Italian

£1200	$2172	€1800	Venice (33x47cm-13x19in) i. 2-Apr-4 Dr Fritz Nagel, Leipzig #3980/R

Works on paper

£795	$1446	€1200	Roman houses on the banks of the Tevere (22x39cm-9x15in) i. ink pen prov. 18-Jun-4 Bolland & Marotz, Bremen #440/R

CANALETTO (circle) (1697-1768) Italian

£80000	$138400	€116800	Entrance to the Grand Canal, Venice, with the church of Santa Maria della Salute (48x101cm-19x40in) prov. 10-Dec-3 Christie's, London #55/R est:70000-100000

CANALETTO (studio) (1697-1768) Italian

£44444	$80000	€64888	Venice, entrance of Grand Canal looking east with Santa Maria della Salute and the Dogana (43x58cm-17x23in) 23-Jan-4 Christie's, Rockefeller NY #89/R est:80000-120000

CANALETTO (style) (1697-1768) Italian

£6500	$11700	€9490	Grand Canal, Venice (41x63cm-16x25in) 21-Apr-4 Christie's, Kensington #99/R est:3000-5000
£7000	$12810	€10220	Molo from the Bacino di San Marco, Venice (59x98cm-23x39in) 7-Jul-4 Bonhams, New Bond Street #114/R est:7000-10000
£7500	$13650	€10950	Before the Doge's Palace, Venice (48x79cm-19x31in) 16-Jun-4 Christie's, Kensington #95/R est:4000-6000
£12324	$21567	€17500	Vue de Venise avec l'Eglise du Redempteur (70x121cm-28x48in) 18-Dec-3 Tajan, Paris #14/R est:25000-30000
£28000	$47600	€40880	Entrance to the Grand Canal Venice (80x132cm-31x52in) exhib. 31-Oct-3 Christie's, Kensington #162/R est:10000-15000
£38000	$68400	€55480	Venice, view of the Rialto Bridge (61x96cm-24x38in) 22-Apr-4 Sotheby's, London #123/R est:15000-20000
£38462	$70000	€56155	Grand Canal, Venice looking north-east from Santa Croce to San Geremia (62x97cm-24x38in) prov. 17-Jun-4 Christie's, Rockefeller NY #57/R est:30000-40000
£50000	$85000	€73000	Riva degli Schiavoni, Venice (88x128cm-35x50in) 31-Oct-3 Christie's, Kensington #163/R est:8000-12000
£120000	$219600	€175200	Venice, the Bucintoro (75x127cm-30x50in) 8-Jul-4 Sotheby's, London #182/R est:30000-40000

CANALS Y LLAMBI, Ricardo (1876-1931) Spanish

Works on paper

£1329	$2259	€1900	Promenade dans le parc (23x31cm-9x12in) s. gouache W/C. 24-Nov-3 E & Eve, Paris #177 est:2000-2300

CANARD, Bertrand (1948-) French

£278	$464	€400	Sans titre (208x156cm-82x61in) acrylic prov. 25-Oct-3 Cornette de St.Cyr, Paris #388/R

CANAS, Carlos (20th C) Argentinian

£442	$800	€645	Untitled (30x60cm-12x24in) 30-Mar-4 Arroyo, Buenos Aires #5

CANCIANI, Jakob (c.1820-1891) Austrian
£2098 $3566 €3000 Faakersee with Mittagskogel (55x69cm-22x27in) 19-Nov-3 Dorotheum, Klagenfurt #5 est:3000
£2797 $4755 €4000 Villach area with Dobratsch (55x68cm-22x27in) s. 19-Nov-3 Dorotheum, Klagenfurt #4 est:4000

CANDEE, George Edward (1837-1907) American
£1453 $2600 €2121 Wyoming Valley at Wilkes Barre Kingston Side, Penn (15x28cm-6x11in) s.i.verso board. 8-Jan-4 James Julia, Fairfield #747/R est:1000-2000

CANDELL, Victor (1903-1977) American
£389 $700 €568 Rooftops, New York City (51x76cm-20x30in) s. 24-Apr-4 Weschler, Washington #637/R

CANDES, Roger Lucien (1907-1972) French
£352 $616 €500 Rue a Montmartre (45x54cm-18x21in) s. 17-Dec-3 Rabourdin & Choppin de Janvry, Paris #62

CANDID, Peter (attrib) (1548-1628) Flemish
Works on paper
£2500 $4500 €3650 Seated woman holding a dish (18x23cm-7x9in) black chk pen ink prov. 21-Jan-4 Sotheby's, New York #2/R est:5000-7000

CANDIO, Roman (1935-) Swiss
Works on paper
£321 $546 €469 Tulips (36x43cm-14x17in) mono. W/C. 28-Nov-3 Zofingen, Switzerland #2937 (S.FR 710)
£498 $846 €727 Fruit trees in bloom (58x78cm-23x31in) mono. W/C. 28-Nov-3 Zofingen, Switzerland #2938 (S.FR 1100)

CANE, Ella du (fl.1893-1910) British
Works on paper
£360 $662 €526 Dutch canal with windmill (30x45cm-12x18in) s. W/C. 29-Mar-4 Bonhams, Bath #28/R

CANE, Louis (1943-) French
£360 $590 €500 Three female nudes (67x56cm-26x22in) s.d. i. verso. 4-Jun-3 Ketterer, Hamburg #234/R
£521 $870 €750 Personnages (76x56cm-30x22in) s.d.1984 oil paper. 25-Oct-3 Cornette de St.Cyr, Paris #619/R
£570 $1050 €850 Paysage (73x60cm-29x24in) s.d.1983 verso. 24-Mar-4 Joron-Derem, Paris #152
£944 $1605 €1350 Femmes assises (73x54cm-29x21in) s. oil paper on canvas. 20-Nov-3 Claude Aguttes, Neuilly #111
£986 $1706 €1400 Untitled (38x50cm-15x20in) s.d.1974 canvas decoupee. 9-Dec-3 Artcurial Briest, Paris #76 est:1200-1400
£1208 $2139 €1800 Nature morte au poisson (73x61cm-29x24in) s.d.1982. 28-Apr-4 Artcurial Briest, Paris #428 est:1500-1800
£1250 $2088 €1800 Causeuses (75x55cm-30x22in) s.d.1992 paper. 21-Oct-3 Artcurial Briest, Paris #622/R est:2000-2500
£2175 $3632 €3130 Trois personnages (162x130cm-64x51in) s.d.85 et 87. 21-Oct-3 Artcurial Briest, Paris #620/R est:2000-2500
£2587 $4321 €3700 Untitled (190x190cm-75x75in) s.i.d.1981 verso prov. 29-Jun-3 Versailles Encheres #214/R
Sculpture
£1042 $1646 €1500 Balancoire femme seule (40x19x13cm-16x7x5in) s. num.2/4 blue pat bronze Cast Oceane lit. 27-Apr-3 Versailles Encheres #125
£1800 $3276 €2628 Femme (93cm-37in) num.7/8 bronze col chks st.f.Barelier. 4-Feb-4 Sotheby's, Olympia #213/R est:1500 2000
£2083 $3292 €3000 Effort (50x40x22cm-20x16x9in) s. num.5/8 blue pat bronze Cast Oceane lit. 27-Apr-3 Versailles Encheres #105
£2400 $4368 €3504 Woman with raised arms (210cm-83in) i. num.1/2 steel iron. 4-Feb-4 Sotheby's, Olympia #214/R est:2000-3000
£3333 $6000 €5000 Untitled (165x38x87cm-65x15x34in) pat bronze glass. 24-Apr-4 Cornette de St.Cyr, Paris #473/R est:7000
£7333 $13493 €11000 Couple allonge (150x78x31cm-59x31x12in) s.num.4/8 green pat bronze lit. 14-Jun-4 Tajan, Paris #236/R est:12000-15000
£10667 $19733 €16000 Moise, Aaron et pharaon (190x77x57cm-75x30x22in) s. num.2/8 bronze exec.1986-87 prov.exhib.lit. 18-Jul-4 Sotheby's, Paris #160/R est:15000-20000
£21333 $39467 €32000 Roi et reine (220x171x180cm-87x67x71in) s. num.1/8 pat bronze exec.1995 prov.exhib.lit. 18-Jul-4 Sotheby's, Paris #162/R est:30000-40000
£26667 $49333 €40000 Trois femmes sur le balancoire (335x240x102cm-132x94x40in) num.18 painted bronze exec.1988 prov.exhib.lit. 18-Jul-4 Sotheby's, Paris #167/R est:25000-35000
Works on paper
£436 $803 €650 Untitled (32x56cm-13x22in) s.d.1985 gouache prov. 24-Mar-4 Joron-Derem, Paris #151
£451 $754 €650 75-HP-26 (75x77cm-30x30in) s.d.1975 verso collage acrylic. 25-Oct-3 Cornette de St.Cyr, Paris #618/R
£888 $1634 €1350 Composition abstraite (58x41cm-23x16in) mixed media. 22-Jun-4 Chassaing Rivet, Toulouse #265
£1333 $2426 €2000 Peinture 14 (268x363cm-106x143in) s.d.1975-6 verso pigments canvas prov.exhib. 30-Jun-4 Calmels Cohen, Paris #79/R est:3000-4000

CANE, Thomas (19th C) ?
Works on paper
£395 $671 €577 Mt Alexander (30x48cm-12x19in) s.d.2003 W/C. 27-Nov-3 International Art Centre, Auckland #108/R (NZ.D 1050)

CANEGALLO, Cesare Sexto (1892-1966) Italian
£1189 $2021 €1700 Blinding sun (40x33cm-16x13in) cardboard. 19-Nov-3 Cambi, Genoa #401 est:1500-2000

CANELLA, Carlo (1800-1879) Italian
£25503 $46926 €38000 San Michele's Fair in Verona (55x80cm-22x31in) s. 24-Mar-4 Finarte Semenzato, Rome #11/R est:25000-28000

CANELLA, G (19th C) Italian
£4895 $8322 €7000 Venice (24x34cm-9x13in) s. paper on canvas. 24-Nov-3 Dorotheum, Vienna #6/R est:3000-4000

CANELLA, Giuseppe (1788-1847) Italian
£4895 $8420 €7000 Vue d'un canal de La Haye (22x30cm-9x12in) s.d.1828 panel. 5-Dec-3 Gros & Delettrez, Paris #54/R est:6000-9000
£4895 $8420 €7000 Un canal a Leyde (22x31cm-9x12in) s. panel. 5-Dec-3 Gros & Delettrez, Paris #55/R est:6000-9000
£6197 $10721 €8800 Shipwreck (30x44cm-12x17in) s.d.1835. 9-Dec-3 Finarte Semenzato, Milan #95/R est:5000-6000
£8108 $13946 €11838 Tellskappelle on the shore of the Urnersee by full moon (51x67cm-20x26in) s.d.1842 prov. 8-Dec-3 Philippe Schuler, Zurich #3393/R est:6000-8000 (S.FR 18000)
£10811 $18595 €15784 Dutch canal scene (90x134cm-35x53in) s.d.1838 prov. 8-Dec-3 Philippe Schuler, Zurich #3392/R est:20000-25000 (S.FR 24000)

CANELLA, Giuseppe (attrib) (1788-1847) Italian
£3474 $6218 €5072 Palazzo Vecchi, Florens (46x62cm-18x24in) 26-May-4 AB Stockholms Auktionsverk #2531/R est:50000-60000 (S.KR 47000)

CANELLA, Giuseppe (younger-attrib) (1837-1913) Italian
£3521 $5845 €5000 Dolci accordi (140x126cm-55x50in) s.d.1867 oval. 11-Jun-3 Christie's, Rome #161/R est:6000-7000

CANESSA, Aurelio (1899-1973) Argentinian
£1538 $2800 €2245 Horses in the field (32x40cm-13x16in) s. s.i.verso. 5-Jul-4 Arroyo, Buenos Aires #86/R est:1500
£2123 $3800 €3100 Saddled horses (36x47cm-14x19in) s. board. 4-May-4 Arroyo, Buenos Aires #1/R est:1700

CANET, Charles Emile (19/20th C) French
£233 $422 €350 Marine (21x41cm-8x16in) s. panel. 31-Mar-4 Sotheby's, Paris #162
£323 $579 €472 Sailing ship with rowing boat on calm sea (32x20cm-13x8in) s. panel. 12-May-4 Dobiaschofsky, Bern #374/R (S.FR 750)

CANET, Marcel (1875-1959) French
£320 $579 €480 Voiliers, effet de brume matinale (45x100cm-18x39in) s. panel. 3-Apr-4 Gerard, Besancon #35
£533 $981 €800 La discussion (31x27cm-12x11in) s. oil on panel. 14-Jun-4 Gros & Delettrez, Paris #102
£629 $1083 €900 Enceinte en bord de mer (28x42cm-11x17in) s. 8-Dec-3 Cornette de St.Cyr, Paris #75
£5000 $9150 €7500 Les maisons blanches du bord de mer. Port de peche anime (46x55cm-18x22in) s. panel pair. 3-Jun-4 Tajan, Paris #212/R est:4500-5000

CANET, Ramon (1950-) Spanish
£6294 $10510 €9000 Ciutat (100x162cm-39x64in) s.i.d.septiembre 1980 diptych prov. 24-Jun-3 Segre, Madrid #152/R est:8000

CANGIULLO, Pascalino (1900-1975) Italian
Works on paper
£3356 $6007 €5000 Sailing boats (51x71cm-20x28in) s.d.1917 W/C prov. 25-May-4 Sotheby's, Milan #12/R est:4000

CANIARIS, Vlassis (1928-) Greek
Works on paper
£1900 $3325 €2774 Composition (59x43cm-23x17in) s.d.58 ink newspaper on canvas. 16-Dec-3 Bonhams, New Bond Street #139/R est:1500-2000

CANINO, Vincenzo (1892-1978) Italian
£450 $729 €653 Figures on a street in winter (25x34cm-10x13in) s. panel. 30-Jul-3 Hamptons Fine Art, Godalming #160
£617 $1048 €901 Gulf of Naples with smoking Vesuvius (41x70cm-16x28in) s. panel. 5-Nov-3 Dobiaschofsky, Bern #413/R (S.FR 1400)
£1197 $2071 €1700 Landscape s (27x36cm-11x14in) s. panel pair sold with another by E d'Angelo. 11-Dec-3 Christie's, Rome #52 est:1000-1500

CANIZALEZ, Alirio (20th C) Venezuelan
Works on paper
£299 $545 €449 Party in the fields (115x143cm-45x56in) s.verso mixed media on canvas. 21-Jun-4 Subastas Odalys, Caracas #72

CANJURA, Noe (20th C) Spanish
£351 $650 €512 Tendresse (64x41cm-25x16in) 12-Mar-4 Du Mouchelle, Detroit #2195/R
£423 $731 €600 Le repas (80x80cm-31x31in) s.i.d.1967 verso. 10-Dec-3 Remi Ader, Paris #63
£423 $731 €600 Le repas (80x80cm-31x31in) s.i.d.1967 verso. 10-Dec-3 Neret-Minet, Paris #63

CANN, Churchill (20th C) Australian
£607 $978 €886 Nine mile (122x143cm-48x56in) s. i.d.verso ochre on board. 13-Oct-3 Joel, Victoria #244 est:1500-2000 (A.D 1500)

Works on paper
£586 $1096 €879 Dingo dreaming (120x122cm-47x48in) earth pigments synthetic binder linen prov.exhib. 26-Jul-4 Sotheby's, Melbourne #454 (A.D 1500)

CANNATA, Antonio (1895-1960) Italian
£336 $617 €500 Landscape with figures (39x59cm-15x23in) s. board. 24-Mar-4 Il Ponte, Milan #495/R
£872 $1605 €1300 Old bell tower (58x69cm-23x27in) s. board. 24-Mar-4 Il Ponte, Milan #515/R
Works on paper
£600 $1074 €900 Rural landscape (57x42cm-22x17in) s. pastel card. 13-May-4 Babuino, Rome #565
£845 $1462 €1200 Rural road (48x58cm-19x23in) s. mixed media board. 10-Dec-3 Finarte Semenzato, Rome #236/R

CANNAVACCIUOLO, Maurizio (1954-) Italian
£1761 $3081 €2500 Happy maths (100x70cm-39x28in) s.i.d.1997 verso acrylic. 16-Dec-3 Finarte Semenzato, Milan #262/R est:2300-2700

CANNEEL, Jean (20th C) Belgian
Sculpture
£5172 $9569 €7500 Femme agenouilee (86cm-34in) s. num.1/12 gilt pat bronze exec c.1925. 19-Jan-4 Horta, Bruxelles #82/R est:8000-10000

CANNEEL, Marcel (1894-1953) Belgian
£616 $1048 €900 Watermael (80x101cm-31x40in) s. 10-Nov-3 Horta, Bruxelles #318

CANNICEI, G (?) ?
£880 $1399 €1285 Portrait of Oliver Cromwell (74x61cm-29x24in) i.verso after Sir peter Lely. 12-Sep-3 Gardiner & Houlgate, Bath #170/R

CANNING, Criss (1941-) Australian
£3484 $5504 €5087 Cornflowers with wicker chair (76x86cm-30x34in) s. prov.exhib. 2-Sep-3 Deutscher-Menzies, Melbourne #153/R est:10000-15000 (A.D 8500)

CANNING, Neil (1960-) British
£1600 $2672 €2336 Force (102x152cm-40x60in) s. prov. 16-Oct-3 Christie's, Kensington #656/R est:600-800

CANNON, Jennie Vennerstrom (1869-1952) American
£1223 $2250 €1786 Southwest mission (41x51cm-16x20in) init. 8-Jun-4 Auctions by the Bay, Alameda #1073/R

CANNON, Walter (19/20th C) British
Works on paper
£236 $368 €342 Hauling in the nets (35x53cm-14x21in) s. W/C. 26-Mar-3 Walker's, Ottawa #61/R (C.D 550)
£650 $1229 €949 Sailing vessels off the coast (23x37cm-9x15in) s.d.1913 W/C. 18-Feb-4 Peter Wilson, Nantwich #88

CANNONE, Angelo (20th C) Italian
£467 $835 €700 Girl writing (60x41cm-24x16in) s.d.1919. 13-May-4 Babuino, Rome #482
£733 $1313 €1100 Cow in Settefrati (34x47cm-13x19in) s.d.1935 board. 13-May-4 Babuino, Rome #602

CANO, Pedro (1944-) Italian
Works on paper
£1133 $2040 €1700 Interior with figure (70x100cm-28x39in) s. pastel card prov. 22-Apr-4 Finarte Semenzato, Rome #102/R est:1600-1800

CANOGAR, Rafael (1934-) Spanish
£2958 $4732 €4200 Head XXVIII (35x27cm-14x11in) s.i.d.1989 board exhib. 16-Sep-3 Segre, Madrid #134/R est:2100
£3401 $6190 €5000 Abstract (67x98cm-26x39in) s.d.2002 oil collage cardboard. 3-Feb-4 Segre, Madrid #375/R est:5000
£4138 $7448 €6000 P-16-76 (73x60cm-29x24in) s.i.d.1976 verso prov. 26-Jan-4 Durán, Madrid #213/R est:6000
£7500 $13650 €10950 P-28-80 (162x130cm-64x51in) s.d.80 s.i.d.verso. 4-Feb-4 Sotheby's, Olympia #200/R est:3000-5000
£9524 $17048 €14000 El Tumulto (103x205cm-41x81in) s.d.69 s.i.d.verso oil wood parts panel. 19-Mar-4 Millon & Associes, Paris #190/R est:6000-8000
£10000 $18401 €15000 Pintura (60x73cm-24x29in) s.d.59 s.i.d. verso prov. 9-Jun-4 Artcurial Briest, Paris #453/R est:15000-20000
£12000 $21840 €17520 Pintura (99x68cm-39x27in) s.d.59 s.i.d.verso prov. 4-Feb-4 Sotheby's, Olympia #203/R est:8000-12000
£25333 $45853 €38000 Apparent life (146x114cm-57x45in) s.d.1963 prov.exhib.lit. 30-Mar-4 Segre, Madrid #375/R est:38000
£45000 $81900 €65700 Pintura no.48 (220x150cm-87x59in) s.d.59 s.i.d.verso prov.exhib.lit. 4-Feb-4 Christie's, London #26/R est:15000-20000
Works on paper
£759 $1366 €1100 Composition (72x48cm-28x19in) s. gouache exec.1979. 26-Jan-4 Durán, Madrid #64/R

CANON, Hans (1829-1885) Austrian
£1400 $2380 €2044 Portrait of lady seated before a window (110x0cm-43x0in) 6-Nov-3 Christie's, Kensington #731/R est:1200-1800
£2517 $4580 €3800 Scene from the Old Testament (82x71cm-32x28in) s.d.1870 prov. 16-Jun-4 Dorotheum, Vienna #452/R est:2000-2500
£3497 $5944 €5000 Young woman wearing straw hat as market trader (163x102cm-64x40in) s.d.1873. 20-Nov-3 Dorotheum, Salzburg #192/R est:6000-9000

CANONE, C (?) ?
£2000 $3660 €2920 Portrait of a bearded gentleman holding a violin (79x63cm-31x25in) s. 6-Apr-4 Bonhams, Knightsbridge #251/R est:500-700

CANONICA, Pietro (1869-?) Italian
Sculpture
£1329 $2338 €1900 Femme pensive, assise sur un rocher (24cm-9in) s.verso silver pat ivory gilt bronze. 4-Jan-4 Rouillac, Vendome #2
£1361 $2435 €2000 Joy in life (27x22x21cm-11x9x8in) s. terracotta. 22-Mar-4 Sant Agostino, Torino #227/R est:2000-2500

CANOVA, Antonio (1757-1822) Italian
Works on paper
£537 $950 €800 King Louis XVI of France (11x8cm-4x3in) s.d.1/81 wax. 29-Apr-4 Dorotheum, Vienna #231/R

CANOVA, Antonio (after) (1757-1822) Italian
Sculpture
£4765 $8434 €7100 Hebe (44cm-17in) i. alabaster. 29-Apr-4 Sotheby's, Paris #89/R est:1500-2500
£5500 $9900 €8030 Two dancing maidens (167cm-66in) white paint wood pair lit. 21-Apr-4 Sotheby's, London #49/R est:6000-8000
£9333 $17080 €14000 Venus and Adonis. marble prov. 6-Jun-4 Rouillac, Vendome #161
£27933 $50000 €41900 Three Graces (175cm-69in) marble. 16-May-4 Abell, Los Angeles #195/R
£36000 $65160 €54000 Buste de Napoleon (67cm-26in) Carrare marble piedouche lit. 30-Mar-4 Rossini, Paris #654/R est:3000-5000

CANOVA, Antonio (studio) (1757-1822) Italian
Sculpture
£65000 $112450 €94900 Three Graces (159cm-63in) marble lit. 11-Dec-3 Christie's, London #136/R est:70000-100000

CANOVA, Antonio (style) (1757-1822) Italian
Sculpture
£21127 $36549 €30000 Flora (114cm-45in) marble. 15-Dec-3 Ansorena, Madrid #1065/R est:30000

CANOVAS DEL CASTILLO Y VALLEJO, Antonio (1828-1897) Spanish
£1224 $2192 €1800 Flowers (101x33cm-40x13in) s.d.1891 pair. 22-Mar-4 Durán, Madrid #190/R est:1800

CANSTEIN-ARNTZENIUS, F B Raab van (?) Dutch
£490 $842 €700 White currant in a ginger pot (30x40cm-12x16in) s. 8-Dec-3 Glerum, Amsterdam #301/R

CANT, James Montgomery (1911-1983) Australian
£687 $1250 €1003 Still life (58x42cm-23x17in) s. paper on board. 16-Jun-4 Deutscher-Menzies, Melbourne #334/R est:2000-3000 (A.D 1800)
£2846 $4467 €4127 Landscape (90x120cm-35x47in) s.d.58 board prov. 27-Aug-3 Christie's, Sydney #589/R est:2000-3000 (A.D 7000)
Works on paper
£372 $688 €543 Dog walking (14x18cm-6x7in) s. pastel pen ink. 10-Mar-4 Deutscher-Menzies, Melbourne #473/R (A.D 900)

CANTA, Johannes Antonius (1816-1888) Dutch
£3073 $5500 €4487 By the duck pond (58x44cm-23x17in) s.d.18 panel. 14-May-4 Skinner, Boston #44/R est:2000-3000

CANTAGALLINA, Remigio (1582-1628) Italian
Works on paper
£2600 $4758 €3796 Building dock by a port, figures in the foreground (15x19cm-6x7in) black chk ink wash prov. 6-Jul-4 Christie's, London #29/R est:2000-3000
£2600 $4758 €3796 Mountainous landscape with a bridge over a river, figures on a road by a farmstead (22x36cm-9x14in) i. black chk ink wash prov. 6-Jul-4 Christie's, London #30/R est:2000-4000
£3041 $5351 €4500 View of Siena (20x28cm-8x11in) i. pen brown ink exhib. 19-May-4 Sotheby's, Amsterdam #25/R est:1500-2000
£5369 $9611 €8000 Paesaggio con contradini ed un asino (26x41cm-10x16in) pen. 25-May-4 Karl & Faber, Munich #13/R est:9000

CANTAGALLINA, Remigio (attrib) (1582-1628) Italian
Works on paper
£669 $1171 €950 Portrait d'une femme en buste de profil (23x16cm-9x6in) pen brown ink prov. 17-Dec-3 Christie's, Paris #11/R

CANTARINI, Simone (1612-1648) Italian
£18456 $32668 €27500 Saint Mary Magdalene (65x52cm-26x20in) 2-May-4 Finarte, Venice #11/R est:20000-25000
£44966 $80490 €67000 Saint John the Baptist (121x215cm-48x85in) lit. 26-May-4 Porro, Milan #28/R est:80000-100000
£53191 $88830 €75000 La Sacra Famiglia come Santissima Trinita (121x103cm-48x41in) prov.exhib.lit. 17-Jun-3 Finarte Semenzato, Milan #647/R est:85000-95000

Works on paper
£2041 $3653 €3000 Le Christ entoure par des anges portant un calice. Un infirme de profil (27x19cm-11x7in) red chk double-sided prov. 18-Mar-4 Christie's, Paris #59/R est:3000-5000
£2800 $5124 €4088 Madonna reading to the Christ Child (16x14cm-6x6in) i. red chk prov. 6-Jul-4 Christie's, London #48/R est:1200-1800

CANTARINI, Simone (attrib) (1612-1648) Italian
£1922 $3440 €2806 Saint Peter being freed by the Angel (42x28cm-17x11in) paper on canvas. 26-May-4 AB Stockholms Auktionsverk #2592/R est:30000-35000 (S.KR 26000)
Works on paper
£510 $913 €750 Deux anges tenant un enfant par la main (17x20cm-7x8in) sanguine. 19-Mar-4 Piasa, Paris #22/R

CANTATORE, Domenico (1906-1998) Italian
£897 $1497 €1300 Crucifixion (45x20cm-18x8in) s.d.1954 verso board. 13-Nov-3 Finarte Semenzato, Rome #266
£1379 $2303 €2000 Flowers in green vase (45x35cm-18x14in) s.d.1951 verso. 13-Nov-3 Finarte Semenzato, Rome #273/R est:3000-3500
£1538 $2615 €2200 Landscape (27x33cm-11x13in) s. s.verso cardboard. 20-Nov-3 Finarte Semenzato, Milan #187/R est:2200-2400
£2000 $3680 €3000 Landscape (30x40cm-12x16in) s. s.verso acrylic. 10-Jun-4 Galleria Pace, Milan #25/R est:4500
£2381 $4262 €3500 Still life (40x50cm-16x20in) s.d.1945. 22-Mar-4 Sant Agostino, Torino #464/R est:4500
£3333 $5567 €4700 Natura morta (45x60cm-18x24in) s. plywood. 21-Jun-3 Stadion, Trieste #192/R est:3000-4000
£4000 $7200 €6000 Mother and daughter (40x35cm-16x14in) s. 22-Apr-4 Finarte Semenzato, Rome #251/R est:3800-4500
£4348 $7130 €6000 Women sowing (40x30cm-16x12in) prov.exhib. 27-May-3 Sotheby's, Milan #33/R est:6000-8000
£4698 $8409 €7000 After Picasso (40x30cm-16x12in) s.i.verso acrylic painted 1979. 29-May-4 Farsetti, Prato #537/R est:6000-8000
£4832 $8650 €7200 After Picasso (40x30cm-16x12in) s.i.verso acrylic painted 1980. 29-May-4 Farsetti, Prato #536/R est:6000-8000
£5333 $9813 €8000 Getting ready (50x35cm-20x14in) s. 12-Jun-4 Meeting Art, Vercelli #278/R est:8000
£5333 $9813 €8000 Landscape (50x60cm-20x24in) s.i.verso painted 1969. 10-Jun-4 Galleria Pace, Milan #119/R est:11000
£5369 $9611 €8000 Woman in interior (80x60cm-31x24in) s. s.i.d.1959 on stretcher prov. 25-May-4 Sotheby's, Milan #132/R est:10000
£5369 $9611 €8000 After Picasso (40x30cm-16x12in) s.i. acrylic painted 1980 lit. 29-May-4 Farsetti, Prato #538/R est:6000-8000
£5517 $8828 €8000 Odalisk (30x40cm-12x16in) s. s.verso. 13-Mar-3 Galleria Pace, Milan #76/R est:9500-12500
£10667 $19627 €16000 Reclining woman (70x100cm-28x39in) s.d.51. 11-Jun-4 Farsetti, Prato #189/R est:14500-16500
Works on paper
£839 $1427 €1200 Landscape (37x48cm-15x19in) s.d.64 W/C prov. 25-Nov-3 Sotheby's, Milan #85/R
£1517 $2428 €2200 Landscape (28x38cm-11x15in) s.d.1972 W/C paper on canvas. 13-Mar-3 Galleria Pace, Milan #12/R est:2800-3200

CANTON CHECA, Miguel (1928-) Spanish
£1370 $2329 €2000 Field (38x46cm-15x18in) s. sid.1989 board. 4-Nov-3 Ansorena, Madrid #436/R est:1700

CANTON, Gustav Jakob (1813-1885) German
£13333 $23867 €20000 Shepherd in Roman countryside (97x181cm-38x71in) s.d.1857. 17-May-4 Finarte Semenzato, Rome #85/R est:32000-35000

CANTON, Shelly (20th C) American
Works on paper
£914 $1600 €1334 Martyrs of Hope - Martin Luther King (56x46cm-22x18in) W/C pencil exec Jan 1969 lit. 17-Dec-3 Christie's, Rockefeller NY #188/R est:1200-1800

CANTONI, Cesare (1906-1970) Italian
£253 $443 €360 Nude (70x55cm-28x22in) s.d.1956. 17-Dec-3 Il Ponte, Milan #817

CANTRE, Jozef (1890-1957) Belgian
Sculpture
£7042 $12183 €10000 Skilful woman (62x40cm-24x16in) s. dark brown pat bronze lit. 13-Dec-3 De Vuyst, Lokeren #481/R est:12000-15000
Works on paper
£278 $464 €400 Tournesols (56x45cm-22x18in) s.d.1918 mixed media. 21-Oct-3 Campo, Vlaamse Kaai #694

CANTRELL, Arthur (20th C) ?
£507 $877 €720 Urban view (57x95cm-22x37in) s.d.79 board. 15-Dec-3 Ansorena, Madrid #933/R

CANTU, Federico (1908-1989) Mexican
£1055 $1900 €1540 Portrait of Maria Felix (47x31cm-19x12in) s.d.32 prov. 25-Apr-4 Bonhams & Butterfields, San Francisco #5598/R est:2000-3000
£3429 $6000 €5006 Maternidad (72x56cm-28x22in) s.d.MCMXXXVI. 19-Dec-3 Sotheby's, New York #1160/R est:6000-8000

CANTZLER, Johan Oscar (1844-1921) Swedish
£311 $567 €454 Summer landscape (34x42cm-13x17in) s. 7-Feb-4 Rasmussen, Havnen #2238/R (D.KR 3400)

CANU, Yvonne (1921-) French
£280 $467 €400 Deux amis (38x46cm-15x18in) s. i.verso. 29-Jun-3 Eric Pillon, Calais #230/R
£420 $701 €600 Conversation pres des peupliers (38x46cm-15x18in) s. 29-Jun-3 Eric Pillon, Calais #229/R
£604 $1081 €900 Le port de Saint-Malo (38x55cm-15x22in) s. 25-May-4 Chambelland & Giafferi, Paris #110/R
£671 $1201 €1000 Petits voiliers a la sortie du port de Saint-Tropez (38x46cm-15x18in) s. 30-May-4 Eric Pillon, Calais #143/R
£805 $1490 €1200 Fleur sous les fleurs (46x55cm-18x22in) s. i.verso. 15-Mar-4 Blanchet, Paris #162
£993 $1808 €1500 Quai de la Tournelle, Paris (46x55cm-18x22in) s. 18-Jun-4 Charbonneaux, Paris #132 est:1500-2000
£1259 $2102 €1800 Paris, la Seine et Notre-Dame (54x73cm-21x29in) s. 29-Jun-3 Eric Pillon, Calais #231/R
£1800 $3006 €2628 Fete de greements a St Tropez (65x93cm-26x37in) s. s.i.verso. 22-Oct-3 Sotheby's, Olympia #193/R est:1500-2000

CANUTI, Domenico Maria (1620-1684) Italian
Works on paper
£1400 $2520 €2044 Head of a young man looking up (27x20cm-11x8in) col chk. 20-Apr-4 Sotheby's, Olympia #57/R est:1200-1800
£1944 $3500 €2838 Foot. Portrait of a woman (22x31cm-9x12in) col chk double-sided prov. 22-Jan-4 Christie's, Rockefeller NY #59/R est:4000-6000

CANUTI, Domenico Maria (attrib) (1620-1684) Italian
Works on paper
£2500 $4500 €3650 Head of a man looking up. Two studies of a bowl (38x25cm-15x10in) red chk double-sided prov. 22-Jan-4 Christie's, Rockefeller NY #56/R est:2000-3000

CANZIANI, Estella Louisa Michaela (1887-1964) British
Works on paper
£270 $484 €400 Guardian angel watching over child as mother sleeps (40x52cm-16x20in) s.d.1919 mixed media. 6-May-4 Michael Zeller, Lindau #637
£508 $950 €762 Dancing sea nymphs (36x51cm-14x20in) mono.i.d.1938 pencil W/C bodycol. 25-Jul-4 Bonhams & Butterfields, San Francisco #6034/R
£650 $1118 €949 Illustration to Costumes and Art Songs of Savoy (20x15cm-8x6in) mono.d.1910 pencil W/C bodycol lit. 3-Dec-3 Christie's, Kensington #258
£800 $1296 €1168 Statue over the cathedral door (34x18cm-13x7in) s.d.1925 W/C. 30-Jul-3 Hamptons Fine Art, Godalming #121

CAO LIWEI (1956-) Chinese
£479 $800 €699 Potala Palace (107x114cm-42x45in) s.d. 11-Oct-3 Nadeau, Windsor #2/R

CAP, Constant (1842-1915) Belgian
£1067 $1963 €1600 Jeune femme dans un interieur (40x29cm-16x11in) panel. 14-Jun-4 Amberes, Antwerp #47
£1333 $2413 €2000 Flirt dans un wagon des-chemins de fer (35x23cm-14x9in) s.d.1892 panel. 30-Mar-4 Campo & Campo, Antwerp #26/R est:2000-4000
£16667 $30000 €25000 Pharmacist (64x78cm-25x31in) s.d.1900. 26-Apr-4 Bernaerts, Antwerp #46/R est:2500-3000

CAPA, Cornell (1918-) American
Photographs
£1444 $2600 €2108 Jack and Miriam Oaar in bed watching Jack's show, 1959 (27x34cm-11x13in) gelatin silver print. 24-Apr-4 Phillips, New York #46/R est:2000-3000

CAPA, Robert (1913-1954) American/Hungarian
Photographs
£2500 $4500 €3650 Italian mothers (17x24cm-7x9in) gelatin silver print. 24-Apr-4 Phillips, New York #6/R est:6000-9000
£3889 $7000 €5678 Falling soldier, Cerro Muriano (25x36cm-10x14in) i.verso gelatin silver print. 24-Apr-4 Phillips, New York #2/R est:8000-12000
£4444 $8000 €6488 Omaha beach, June 6th 1944 (23x36cm-9x14in) gelatin silver print. 24-Apr-4 Phillips, New York #8/R est:10000-15000
£4790 $8000 €6993 D-Day invasion (22x34cm-9x13in) i.verso gelatin silver print exec. June 6, 1944 prov.lit. 17-Oct-3 Phillips, New York #160/R est:7000-10000
£12222 $22000 €17844 World War II (33x24cm-13x9in) album 24 gelatin silver print. 24-Apr-4 Phillips, New York #9/R est:20000-30000

CAPACCI, Bruno (1906-1993) French
£993 $1658 €1400 L'accordeoniste (115x65cm-45x26in) s. 17-Jun-3 Galerie Moderne, Brussels #403/R
£1111 $1767 €1600 Nativita (88x118cm-35x46in) s.i.d.1939 verso panel. 15-Sep-3 Bernaerts, Antwerp #955/R est:500-750
£1408 $2437 €2000 Room screen (122x124cm-48x49in) s. panel triptych prov. 13-Dec-3 De Vuyst, Lokeren #46 est:1200-1500
£2361 $3754 €3400 Italian palazzo with figures, musical instruments and birds (173x119cm-68x47in) s. panel. 15-Sep-3 Bernaerts, Antwerp #957/R est:1000-1250

CAPALDA, A (20th C) Italian
Sculpture
£1589 $2909 €2400 Peasant woman tending to a child surrounded by sheep (17x52cm-7x20in) s. dark brown pat. bronze green marble base. 6-Apr-4 Sotheby's, Olympia #117/R est:2500-3000

CAPARNE, William John (fl.1882-1893) British

Works on paper			
£343	$631	€501	Coastal, Guernsey (46x66cm-18x26in) s. W/C. 14-Jun-4 Waddingtons, Toronto #83/R (C.D 850)
£450	$815	€657	Cliff fire at Icart headland, Guernsey (26x35cm-10x14in) init. s.verso W/C. 1-Apr-4 Martel Maides, Guernsey #224
£480	$898	€701	Coastal scene, Guernsey (24x34cm-9x13in) s. W/C. 22-Jul-4 Martel Maides, Guernsey #200
£520	$972	€759	Early Poeticus (23x15cm-9x6in) i.verso W/C prov. 22-Jul-4 Martel Maides, Guernsey #206/R
£700	$1267	€1022	Dog and Lion Rocks and Jerbourg, Guernsey (26x38cm-10x15in) s. W/C. 1-Apr-4 Martel Maides, Guernsey #223
£780	$1459	€1139	View from Guernsey (28x44cm-11x17in) s. W/C. 22-Jul-4 Martel Maides, Guernsey #201
£820	$1394	€1197	Sandy beach at low tide (28x51cm-11x20in) init. W/C. 25-Nov-3 Martel Maides, Guernsey #194
£820	$1394	€1197	View of Mentone (28x38cm-11x15in) W/C. 25-Nov-3 Martel Maides, Guernsey #223
£820	$1484	€1197	Fauxquets Valley, Guernsey (30x46cm-12x18in) s. pastel. 1-Apr-4 Martel Maides, Guernsey #255
£850	$1539	€1241	Sark coastal scene with Herm and Jethou in the distance (28x38cm-11x15in) s. W/C. 1-Apr-4 Martel Maides, Guernsey #245
£920	$1665	€1343	Path to Bec du Nez, Sark (30x34cm-12x13in) s. W/C. 1-Apr-4 Martel Maides, Guernsey #246
£950	$1777	€1387	Houmet, Cobo (14x28cm-6x11in) s.i. W/C. 22-Jul-4 Martel Maides, Guernsey #184
£1700	$2890	€2482	West coast, Guernsey (25x37cm-10x15in) s. W/C. 25-Nov-3 Martel Maides, Guernsey #223a/R est:1000-1300
£2400	$4344	€3504	Floral terrace in the summertime (28x38cm-11x15in) s. W/C. 1-Apr-4 Martel Maides, Guernsey #248/R est:800-1000

CAPAROLA, Cola da (1957-) German

Works on paper			
£903	$1472	€1300	Traces (120x35cm-47x14in) s. i.d.1998 verso acrylic pigment pastel chk. 27-Sep-3 Dr Fritz Nagel, Stuttgart #9499/R

CAPDEVIELLE, Louis (1850-1905) French

£1844	$3079	€2600	Jeu de billes (41x33cm-16x13in) s.d.1876. 19-Oct-3 Anaf, Lyon #69/R est:3000-4000

CAPDEVILLA PUIG, Genis (1860-1929) Spanish

£360	$652	€526	Connoisseur (46x37cm-18x15in) 30-Mar-4 Sworder & Son, Bishops Stortford #563/R
£1517	$2534	€2200	La frileuse (50x70cm-20x28in) s. 17-Nov-3 Tajan, Paris #129/R est:1200-1500

CAPECCHI, A (19th C) Italian

£1733	$3189	€2600	Composition with roses (78x52cm-31x20in) s.i. 10-Jun-4 Christie's, Rome #188/R est:2700-2900

CAPEINICK, Jean (1838-1890) Belgian

£1957	$3580	€2857	Basket of grapes (54x63cm-21x25in) s. 4-Jun-4 Zofingen, Switzerland #2337/R est:5500 (S.FR 4500)

CAPEINICK, Jean (attrib) (1838-1890) Belgian

£1048	$1907	€1530	Quince in a woodland setting (45x64cm-18x25in) i. panel. 16-Jun-4 Fischer, Luzern #1125/R est:2000-2400 (S.FR 2400)

CAPEK, Josef (1887-1945) Czechoslovakian

Works on paper			
£2634	$4478	€3846	Playing children (38x34cm-15x13in) s.d.1930-35 pastel. 29-Nov-3 Dorotheum, Prague #174/R est:60000-90000 (C.KR 120000)

CAPELAIN, John le (c.1814-1848) British

Works on paper			
£300	$480	€438	Castle near lake (25x35cm-10x14in) s. W/C. 17-Sep-3 Bonhams, Brooks & Langlois, Jersey #103/R

CAPELLA, Cheli (19th C) Italian

£667	$1220	€1000	Flora (80x64cm-31x25in) s.i.verso after Titian. 5-Jun-4 Arnold, Frankfurt #554/R

CAPELLE, Alfred Eugène (1834-1887) French

£455	$773	€650	Boats in a winter landscape (24x32cm-9x13in) s. cardboard lit. 28-Nov-3 Schloss Ahlden, Ahlden #1507/R

CAPELLE, Jan van de (1624-1679) Dutch

£420000	$726600	€613200	Two smalschips and other shipping off a sandbank in a calm (45x51cm-18x20in) s. prov. 10-Dec-3 Christie's, London #29/R est:200000-300000

CAPELLE, Jan van de (attrib) (1624-1679) Dutch

£1552	$2778	€2266	Winter landscape (16x19cm-6x7in) panel. 13-May-4 Stuker, Bern #61/R est:2000-3000 (S.FR 3600)

CAPET, Marie Gabrielle (1761-1818) French

£9539	$17553	€14500	Portrait de jeune officier (22x18cm-9x7in) i.verso. 25-Jun-4 Piasa, Paris #119/R est:4000-5000

CAPOCCHINI, Ugo (1901-1980) Italian

£530	$964	€800	Head of woman (39x29cm-15x11in) s. s.verso. 21-Jun-4 Pandolfini, Florence #386/R
£563	$1025	€850	Girl in profile (36x27cm-14x11in) s.d.1929 board. 17-Jun-4 Galleria Pananti, Florence #491/R
£743	$1308	€1100	Portrait of girl (65x50cm-26x20in) s. cardboard painted 1965. 22-May-4 Galleria Pananti, Florence #440/R
£1854	$3375	€2800	Flowers (65x50cm-26x20in) s. 17-Jun-4 Galleria Pananti, Florence #615/R est:1500-2000
£2517	$4580	€3800	Portrait of Mario del Prete (77x61cm-30x24in) s. i.d.1933 verso. 17-Jun-4 Galleria Pananti, Florence #553/R est:4500-6000

CAPOGROSSI, Giuseppe (1900-1972) Italian

£4392	$7730	€6500	Untitled (24x19cm-9x7in) s. tempera card painted 1961-62 prov. 24-May-4 Christie's, Milan #151/R est:4000-8000
£5442	$9741	€8000	Untitled (33x23cm-13x9in) s.d.1954 tempera paper on canvas. 16-Mar-4 Finarte Semenzato, Milan #350/R est:8500
£5944	$10105	€8500	Composition (45x31cm-18x12in) paper on canvas prov. 24-Nov-3 Christie's, Milan #149/R est:9000-12000
£9375	$14812	€13500	Untitled (50x35cm-20x14in) tempera paper painted 1955. 6-Sep-3 Meeting Art, Vercelli #610 est:5000
£9790	$16643	€14000	Surface 031 (54x38cm-21x15in) s.d.48 s.i.d.verso prov.exhib.lit. 25-Nov-3 Sotheby's, Milan #213/R est:20000-30000
£13287	$22587	€19000	Composition (30x40cm-12x16in) s.d.1956 paper on canvas. 25-Nov-3 Sotheby's, Milan #217/R est:15000-20000
£23077	$39231	€33000	Surface 136 (46x33cm-18x13in) s.d.55 lit. 29-Nov-3 Farsetti, Prato #473/R est:30000-35000
£32000	$57600	€48000	Surface 222 (85x65cm-33x26in) s.d.57 s.i.d.verso prov.exhib.lit. 22-Apr-4 Finarte Semenzato, Rome #287/R est:30000-35000
£38000	$69920	€55480	Porti (74x61cm-29x24in) s.d.52 s.i.d.verso. 25-Jun-4 Christie's, London #149/R est:40000-60000
£42000	$70140	€61320	Surface 443 (81x116cm-32x46in) s.d.51 i.on stretcher prov.exhib.lit. 20-Oct-3 Sotheby's, London #6/R est:60000
£67568	$118919	€100000	Surface 43 (100x70cm-39x28in) s.d.51 prov.exhib.lit. 24-May-4 Christie's, Milan #332/R est:100000-150000
£86957	$142609	€120000	Surface 604 (195x97cm-77x38in) s.d.1967. 29-May-3 Galleria Pace, Milan #133/R est:165000
Works on paper			
£738	$1373	€1100	Seated young man (48x33cm-19x13in) s.d.1938 ink. 4-Mar-4 Babuino, Rome #395
£4196	$7133	€6000	Surface (20x29cm-8x11in) s.i.d.63 gouache paper on board. 25-Nov-3 Sotheby's, Milan #2/R est:4000-6000
£4698	$8409	€7000	Surface CP/442 (39x29cm-15x11in) s.d.1959 felt-tip pen lit. 30-May-4 Meeting Art, Vercelli #35 est:5000

CAPON, Georges Émile (1890-1980) French

£278	$464	€400	Nature morte au bouquet de pivoines (54x65cm-21x26in) s. 21-Oct-3 Artcurial Briest, Paris #179
£312	$521	€450	Nature morte au vase de fleurs (54x65cm-21x26in) s. 21-Oct-3 Artcurial Briest, Paris #180
£353	$632	€530	Tulipes (73x60cm-29x24in) s. s.verso. 17-May-4 Chayette & Cheval, Paris #195
£367	$656	€550	Ecaillere de Toulon (38x46cm-15x18in) s. s.i.verso. 17-May-4 Chayette & Cheval, Paris #196
£667	$1193	€1000	Port de Collioure (32x46cm-13x18in) s. s.i.verso. 17-May-4 Chayette & Cheval, Paris #193/R
£690	$1241	€1000	Femme endormie (72x60cm-28x24in) s. painted c.1960. 25-Jan-4 Chayette & Cheval, Paris #278

CAPONE, Gaetano (1845-1920) Italian

£323	$600	€472	Two fishermen on coastline (36x28cm-14x11in) s. 3-Mar-4 Alderfer's, Hatfield #327
£1338	$2315	€1900	Amalfi street (15x20cm-6x8in) s.i. card. 9-Dec-3 Pandolfini, Florence #237/R
£1386	$2300	€2024	Girl in Kimono (41x30cm-16x12in) s. 4-Oct-3 Neal Auction Company, New Orleans #610/R est:1500-2500
£1848	$3400	€2698	Autumn landscape at sunset (76x102cm-30x40in) s. 27-Mar-4 New Orleans Auction, New Orleans #589/R est:4000-7000
Works on paper			
£314	$500	€458	Monk resting under an arbor in an Italian coastal village (28x45cm-11x18in) s.indis.i. W/C. 13-Sep-3 Weschler, Washington #704/R
£800	$1440	€1200	Kitchen scene with Italian family and hens (50x34cm-20x13in) s.i. lit. 22-Apr-4 Allgauer, Kempten #3380/R
£1840	$3000	€2686	Square with children's parade (28x43cm-11x17in) s. W/C. 28-Sep-3 Simpson's, Houston #122a/R
£1972	$3273	€2800	Corteggiamento a Maiori (33x49cm-13x19in) s. W/C cardboard. 11-Jun-3 Christie's, Rome #61 est:1700-1900

CAPONIGRO, Paul (1932-) American

Photographs			
£1977	$3500	€2886	Running deer, Ireland (17x47cm-7x19in) s.d.1967 gelatin silver print. 27-Apr-4 Christie's, Rockefeller NY #13/R est:4000-6000
£3038	$5500	€4435	Running white deer, Wicklow, Ireland (24x60cm-9x24in) s. gelatin silver print 1967/printed later lit. 19-Apr-4 Bonhams & Butterfields, San Francisco #382/R est:3000-5000

CAPORAEL, Suzanne (1946-) American

£757	$1400	€1105	Study for White snowman (35x30cm-14x12in) s.d.1990 verso wood prov. 12-Feb-4 Sotheby's, New York #312/R est:2000-3000

CAPOZZOLI, Glauco (1929-) Uruguayan

£370	$680	€540	Nude (90x62cm-35x24in) s.d.92. 22-Jun-4 Galeria y Remates, Montevideo #169/R
£1000	$1700	€1460	Nude (60x81cm-24x32in) s. 25-Nov-3 Galeria y Remates, Montevideo #26/R
Works on paper			
£267	$491	€400	Sun's energy (100x70cm-39x28in) s.d.79 mixed media masonite. 9-Jun-4 Dorotheum, Salzburg #642/R

CAPPEL, F (19/20th C) British
£1624 $2761 €2371 Waiting for master. Waiting for supper (39x60cm-15x24in) s. pair. 4-Nov-3 Stephan Welz, Johannesburg #570/R est:6000-10000 (SA.R 19000)

CAPPELLI, Evaristo (1868-1951) Italian
£733 $1335 €1100 Poet (50x65cm-20x26in) s. 29-Jun-4 Pandolfini, Florence #165/R
£2933 $5339 €4400 Portrait of Attilio Giovanni Gionini (98x80cm-39x31in) s.d.1907. 29-Jun-4 Pandolfini, Florence #68/R est:5000-6000

CAPPELLI, Giovanni (1923-1994) Italian
£246 $448 €370 Lake Garda (30x40cm-12x16in) s. 12-Jul-4 Il Ponte, Milan #1034
£1133 $2085 €1700 Still life (61x50cm-24x20in) s.d.1972. 12-Jun-4 Meeting Art, Vercelli #979/R est:1500
£1141 $2111 €1700 Beach on the Adriatic Sea (40x30cm-16x12in) s.s.i.verso. 11-Mar-4 Galleria Pace, Milan #84/R est:2000-2600
£1141 $2111 €1700 Interior (75x60cm-30x24in) s. painted 1972. 13-Mar-4 Meeting Art, Vercelli #236 est:1500
£1156 $2070 €1700 Burning bushes (81x65cm-32x26in) s. s.i.d.1975 verso. 16-Mar-4 Finarte Semenzato, Milan #91/R est:1900
£1361 $2476 €2000 Milan interior (70x70cm-28x28in) s. painted1967. 6-Feb-4 Galleria Rosenberg, Milan #158/R est:2000
£1409 $2607 €2100 Spring on Lake Garda (40x50cm-16x20in) s. s.i.d.1982 verso. 13-Mar-4 Meeting Art, Vercelli #472 est:1500
£1644 $3042 €2450 Landscape with white sky (80x100cm-31x39in) s.d.1969. 13-Mar-4 Meeting Art, Vercelli #274 est:2000
£1879 $3477 €2800 Boats (100x95cm-39x37in) s.d.1979. 13-Mar-4 Meeting Art, Vercelli #522 est:2000
Works on paper
£400 $736 €600 Untitled (50x70cm-20x28in) s.d.1980 mixed media. 12-Jun-4 Meeting Art, Vercelli #930/R

CAPPELLO, Carmelo (1912-1996) Italian
£1467 $2699 €2200 Untitled (70x100cm-28x39in) s.d.1955. 8-Jun-4 Finarte Semenzato, Milan #79/R est:2000-2500
Sculpture
£1620 $2689 €2300 Woman (87cm-34in) polychrome plaster. 11-Jun-3 Finarte Semenzato, Milan #682a/R
Works on paper
£333 $613 €500 Sky eyes (34x48cm-13x19in) s.d.1968 pencil. 8-Jun-4 Finarte Semenzato, Milan #76/R
£340 $609 €500 Models (35x26cm-14x10in) s.d.1945 ink paper on card. 16-Mar-4 Finarte Semenzato, Milan #92/R
£467 $859 €700 Figure (50x70cm-20x28in) s. pen. 10-Jun-4 Galleria Pace, Milan #52/R
£667 $1227 €1000 Study for sculpture (50x70cm-20x28in) s.d.1959 mixed media. 8-Jun-4 Finarte Semenzato, Milan #77/R

CAPPIELLO, Leonetto (1875-1942) French
Works on paper
£1538 $2615 €2200 Untitled (156x115cm-61x45in) s. gouache. 18-Nov-3 Sotheby's, Paris #5/R est:3000-5000
£8392 $14266 €12000 Elegante en robe jaune (130x94cm-51x37in) s. pastel. 18-Nov-3 Sotheby's, Paris #6/R est:4000-6000

CAPRILE, Vincenzo (1856-1936) Italian
£1690 $2924 €2400 Portrait of girl (29x30cm-11x12in) s.i. 10-Dec-3 Sotheby's, Milan #136/R est:2000-4000
£2013 $3765 €3000 Portrait of woman (40x30cm-16x12in) 26-Feb-4 Cambi, Genoa #471/R est:3000-4000
£8054 $15060 €12000 Landscape (19x39cm-7x15in) s. board prov. 25-Feb-4 Porro, Milan #3/R est:16000
£10197 $18763 €15500 Peasant woman in the stable (37cm-15in circular) s.i.d.1886 on vellum prov. 23-Jun-4 Finarte Semenzato, Rome #124/R est:7500-9000
Works on paper
£948 $1697 €1384 Piazzetta in Venice (37x25cm-15x10in) s. w/C. 12-May-4 Dobiaschofsky, Bern #375/R est:3600 (S.FR 2200)
£4085 $6780 €5800 La camicetta rossa (62x39cm-24x15in) s.d.1897 pastel board. 11-Jun-3 Christie's, Rome #173/R est:5000-7000

CAPRILE, Vincenzo (attrib) (1856-1936) Italian
£704 $1169 €1000 Lungo la via (47x33cm-19x13in) s.d.22. 11-Jun-3 Christie's, Rome #100

CAPRINO, Marsiglio (1923-1986) Italian
£302 $535 €450 Market in Santa Giulia Square (23x38cm-9x15in) s.d.1977 board. 1-May-4 Meeting Art, Vercelli #8

CAPROENS, Jacob (17/18th C) Flemish
£6207 $10303 €9000 Bouquet of flowers in gilt vase with fruit (84x67cm-33x26in) 1-Oct-3 Dorotheum, Vienna #160/R est:10000-16000

CAPRON, Jean Pierre (1921-1997) French
£235 $400 €343 Church (53x46cm-21x18in) s.d.57 prov. 22-Nov-3 Jackson's, Cedar Falls #404/R
£493 $853 €700 Bateaux a quai (46x61cm-18x24in) s.d.1954. 14-Dec-3 Eric Pillon, Calais #221/R

CAPUANO, Francesco (1854-?) Italian
£600 $1098 €876 Autumnal river landscape (101x61cm-40x24in) s. canvasboard. 8-Jul-4 Lawrence, Crewkerne #1615
£620 $1135 €905 Cattle by a lake (45x64cm-18x25in) s. 8-Jul-4 Lawrence, Crewkerne #1616
£845 $1462 €1200 River landscape in autumn (51x77cm-20x30in) s. 10-Dec-3 Dorotheum, Vienna #222/R
£1200 $2208 €1800 Capri (37x61cm-15x24in) s. 10-Jun-4 Christie's, Rome #69/R est:2000-2500
£1333 $2387 €2000 Fisherman by the wood (46x35cm-18x14in) s.i. board. 12-May-4 Stadion, Trieste #655/R est:1200-1600
£1958 $3368 €2800 Capri, Punta del Tragaro con i Faraglioni (64x104cm-25x41in) s.i. 5-Dec-3 Bolland & Marotz, Bremen #516/R est:900

CAPULETTI (20th C) Spanish
£1500 $2760 €2190 Surrealist landscape with three figures (26x17cm-10x7in) s,. 11-Jun-4 Keys, Aylsham #240 est:120-160

CAPULETTI, Jose Manuel (1925-1978) Spanish
£2837 $4738 €4000 La lieutenance du Port Honfleur (33x55cm-13x22in) s.i. 23-Jun-3 Durán, Madrid #232/R est:2000
£4965 $8291 €7000 Trompe d'oeil surrealista (65x53cm-26x21in) s. 23-Jun-3 Durán, Madrid #231/R est:2500
£5435 $8913 €7500 No man's land (52x62cm-20x24in) s. exhib. 27-May-3 Durán, Madrid #301/R est:2000
£5592 $10289 €8500 Dream perception of Dali' (80x120cm-31x47in) s. 22-Jun-4 Durán, Madrid #189/R est:6000
£6522 $10696 €9000 Plein soleil (46x64cm-18x25in) s. exhib. 27-May-3 Durán, Madrid #302/R est:2000
£6944 $11319 €10000 Triumph and loneliness (50x60cm-20x24in) s. 23-Sep-3 Durán, Madrid #214/R est:3750
Works on paper
£621 $1117 €900 Surrealist scene (31x24cm-12x9in) s. W/C. 26-Jan-4 Ansorena, Madrid #279/R
£759 $1259 €1100 Flamenco (31x25cm-12x10in) s. W/C. 30-Sep-3 Ansorena, Madrid #1/R
£828 $1374 €1200 Flamenco (29x25cm-11x10in) s. W/C. 30-Sep-3 Ansorena, Madrid #2/R

CAPULINO JAUREGUI, Joaquin (1879-1969) Spanish
£362 $674 €540 Landscape (20x16cm-8x6in) s.d.1907 verso cardboard. 2-Mar-4 Ansorena, Madrid #232/R
£3378 $5946 €5000 View of town (69x100cm-27x39in) s. 18-May-4 Segre, Madrid #90/R est:2700

CAPURRO, Sara (1922-1997) South American?
£256 $420 €374 Composition (41x40cm-16x16in) s. cardboard. 3-Jun-3 Galeria y Remates, Montevideo #44
£317 $520 €463 Urban landscape (36x50cm-14x20in) s. 3-Jun-3 Galeria y Remates, Montevideo #43
£321 $520 €465 Woman (50x45cm-20x18in) s.d.70 board. 29-Jul-3 Galeria y Remates, Montevideo #128/R
£358 $580 €519 Theme park (48x40cm-19x16in) s. board. 29-Jul-3 Galeria y Remates, Montevideo #131
£383 $620 €555 Montevideo (50x47cm-20x19in) s. board. 29-Jul-3 Galeria y Remates, Montevideo #127
£435 $800 €635 Still life with flower (46x58cm-18x23in) s.d.70 cardboard. 22-Jun-4 Galeria y Remates, Montevideo #126/R
£449 $750 €656 Still life with rice (41x59cm-16x23in) s. cardboard. 7-Oct-3 Galeria y Remates, Montevideo #68/R
£899 $1700 €1313 Still life with clock and fruit (55x86cm-22x34in) s.d.70 cardboard exhib. 22-Feb-4 Galeria y Remates, Montevideo #105/R est:2000
£1270 $2400 €1854 Card queen (85x58cm-33x23in) s.d.72 cardboard exhib. 22-Feb-4 Galeria y Remates, Montevideo #104/R est:3000

CAPUTO, Tonino (1933-) Italian
£387 $643 €550 Down Town (50x40cm-20x16in) s. i.d.1996 verso. 14-Jun-3 Meeting Art, Vercelli #382
£403 $745 €600 Village (70x50cm-28x20in) s.d.1967 cardboard on canvas. 13-Mar-4 Meeting Art, Vercelli #423
£458 $760 €650 New York (60x50cm-24x20in) s. s.d.1996 verso. 14-Jun-3 Meeting Art, Vercelli #208/R
£528 $877 €750 Down Town (80x60cm-31x24in) s. 14-Jun-3 Meeting Art, Vercelli #482/R
£533 $981 €800 Other journeys (60x80cm-24x31in) s. s.i.d.1981 verso. 12-Jun-4 Meeting Art, Vercelli #338/R
£533 $981 €800 Still life (60x80cm-24x31in) s. s.verso. 12-Jun-4 Meeting Art, Vercelli #693/R
£634 $1052 €900 Roma Citta Aperta (60x90cm-24x35in) s. 14-Jun-3 Meeting Art, Vercelli #663/R
£993 $1808 €1500 Hope lives until death comes (100x100cm-39x39in) s.i.verso. 17-Jun-4 Galleria Pananti, Florence #264/R est:1000-1100

CAPUTO, Ulisse (1872-1948) Italian
£2133 $3925 €3200 View from the cliffs (24x32cm-9x13in) cardboard prov. 8-Jun-4 Sotheby's, Milan #75/R est:3000-6000
£3000 $5520 €4500 Calvados (24x33cm-9x13in) s.i.d.1908 cardboard. 14-Jun-4 Sant Agostino, Torino #286/R est:2500-3000
£4545 $7591 €6500 Lady in black (73x54cm-29x21in) s. 24-Jun-3 Finarte Semenzato, Rome #178/R
£5245 $8759 €7500 Woman at dressing table (93x74cm-37x29in) s. 24-Jun-3 Finarte Semenzato, Rome #179/R
£7000 $12880 €10220 Portrait of Ninette (100x800cm-39x315in) s. 23-Mar-4 Bonhams, New Bond Street #85/R est:8000-12000

CARA COSTEA, Philippe (1925-) French
£680 $1218 €1000 Nu assis (92x58cm-36x23in) s. peinture isorel. 20-Mar-4 Binoche, Orleans #39
£748 $1339 €1100 Crucifixion (33x46cm-13x18in) s. s.d.71 verso. 20-Mar-4 Binoche, Orleans #40
£952 $1705 €1400 La foule (65x102cm-26x40in) s. peinture isorel. 20-Mar-4 Binoche, Orleans #38

CARABAIN, Emile (19/20th C) Belgian
£372 $654 €550 Vase garni de fleurs (40x53cm-16x21in) s. 18-May-4 Galerie Moderne, Brussels #221

CARABAIN, Jacques (1834-1892) Belgian
£2762 $5000 €4033 View of a town with figures along the banks of a canal (30x41cm-12x16in) s.d.1861 panel. 30-Mar-4 Christie's, Rockefeller NY #84/R est:5000-7000
£4545 $7727 €6500 Une vue d'une vieille port a Bordighera, Italy (60x40cm-24x16in) s.i.d.10 sept 1907 verso. 1-Dec-3 Palais de Beaux Arts, Brussels #227/R est:6000-8000
£4795 $8151 €7000 Manzanti Street in Verona (86x52cm-34x20in) s. 10-Nov-3 Horta, Bruxelles #168/R
£5102 $9133 €7500 Un vieux puits a Westheim (60x47cm-24x19in) 22-Mar-4 Amberes, Antwerp #182/R
£6818 $12000 €9954 View of the Rhine with figures by buildings in the foreground (58x48cm-23x19in) s. 18-May-4 Bonhams & Butterfields, San Francisco #66/R est:12000-18000
£6993 $11678 €10000 Vue a Venise (76x54cm-30x21in) s. 11-Oct-3 De Vuyst, Lokeren #513/R est:10000-12000
£7333 $13127 €11000 Le marche aux poissons a chioggia, Italie (76x56cm-30x22in) s. 15-May-4 De Vuyst, Lokeren #423/R est:10000-12000
£7639 $12757 €11000 Vieille rue a San Remo (46x31cm-18x12in) s. panel. 21-Oct-3 Galerie Moderne, Brussels #359/R
£7667 $13723 €11500 Une noria entre Bordighera et Ventimiglia (43x57cm-17x22in) s. 15-May-4 De Vuyst, Lokeren #532/R est:10000-12000
£7746 $13556 €11000 Vue de la Grand-Place, avec la Fontaine, de Berncastel (40x32cm-16x13in) s. panel. 16-Dec-3 Galerie Moderne, Brussels #810/R est:10000-15000
£7770 $13909 €11500 Vue a Amalfi (69x46cm-27x18in) s. 10-May-4 Horta, Bruxelles #86/R est:12000-15000
£13000 $23920 €18980 Venetian backwater (76x55cm-30x22in) s. 25-Mar-4 Christie's, Kensington #108/R est:8000-12000
£16667 $27833 €24000 Rue a Olevano (77x54cm-30x21in) s. 21-Oct-3 Galerie Moderne, Brussels #344/R
Works on paper
£282 $487 €400 Rue animee, Dinan, Bretagne (54x39cm-21x15in) s. W/C. 10-Dec-3 Hotel des Ventes Mosan, Brussels #168

CARABAIN, Victor (19/20th C) Belgian
£294 $499 €420 Le marche aux oeufs a Bruges (65x50cm-26x20in) s. 1-Dec-3 Palais de Beaux Arts, Brussels #222
£563 $975 €800 Vue a Alkmaar, Pays-Bas (80x60cm-31x24in) s. 9-Dec-3 Campo, Vlaamse Kaai #267
£743 $1330 €1100 Via Di Porretta, Bologna (67x47cm-26x19in) s. 10-May-4 Horta, Bruxelles #87
£805 $1490 €1200 Vue a Nimegue aux Pays-Bas (50x40cm-20x16in) s. 15-Mar-4 Horta, Bruxelles #72
£1119 $1924 €1600 Porte et vieux pont a Moret (65x54cm-26x21in) s. 8-Dec-3 Horta, Bruxelles #22 est:1200-1800

CARABELLI, Casimiro (fl.1807-1808) Italian
Sculpture
£1345 $2232 €1950 Young woman (57cm-22in) s. dark pat bronze. 1-Oct-3 Della Rocca, Turin #70a est:900-1000

CARABIN, Rupert (1862-1932) French
Sculpture
£2886 $5310 €4300 Femme a la coloquinte (14cm-6in) st.mono. stone lit. 23-Mar-4 Piasa, Paris #2/R
£3310 $5528 €4800 Danseuse aux crotales (25cm-10in) s. brown pat bronze exec.c.1905-1906 exhib.lit. 14-Nov-3 Claude Boisgirard, Paris #49/R est:4500-5000

CARACCIOLO, Giovanni Battista (1570-1637) Italian
Works on paper
£2105 $3874 €3200 Putti (26x18cm-10x7in) pen ink over pencil lit. 22-Jun-4 Sotheby's, Milan #30/R est:3000-4000
£7566 $13921 €11500 Jacob's dream (23x18cm-9x7in) pen ink exhib.lit. 22-Jun-4 Sotheby's, Milan #23/R est:10000-15000

CARACCIOLO, Niccolo d'Ardia (1941-1989) Italian
£1538 $2615 €2200 Camden Street (21x18cm-8x7in) board. 25-Nov-3 De Veres Art Auctions, Dublin #7/R est:2000-3000
£2400 $4344 €3600 Aix-en-Provence (35x24cm-14x9in) studio st.verso board prov. 30-Mar-4 De Veres Art Auctions, Dublin #10/R est:2000-3000
£2568 $4853 €3800 Landscape with view over a village (18x32cm-7x13in) s.d.1977 canvas on board. 17-Feb-4 Whyte's, Dublin #63/R est:4000-6000
£3750 $6113 €5400 Roof tops (24x37cm-9x15in) s. board. 24-Sep-3 James Adam, Dublin #57/R est:5000-7000
£5694 $9282 €8200 Place de la Comedeo (25x34cm-10x13in) s.d.1980 board prov. 24-Sep-3 James Adam, Dublin #46/R est:4000-6000
£6133 $11101 €9200 Wearing only a mask (51x40cm-20x16in) studio st.verso board prov. 30-Mar-4 De Veres Art Auctions, Dublin #64/R est:4500-6000
Works on paper
£451 $736 €650 Female study (33x23cm-13x9in) s.d.68 pencil. 23-Sep-3 De Veres Art Auctions, Dublin #159/R
£528 $860 €760 Archway in Sienna (30x23cm-12x9in) W/C prov. 23-Sep-3 De Veres Art Auctions, Dublin #160
£600 $1086 €900 Leaning cypress (31x23cm-12x9in) studio st.verso W/C prov. 30-Mar-4 De Veres Art Auctions, Dublin #129/R
£1007 $1802 €1500 Pizza Navona, Rome (27x38cm-11x15in) s. W/C. 26-May-4 James Adam, Dublin #45/R est:1000-1500

CARACCIOLO, Roberto (20th C) American?
£1189 $2200 €1736 Muro D'Acqua 2 (90x107cm-35x42in) s.i.d.1990 verso prov. 13-Jul-4 Christie's, Rockefeller NY #127/R est:800-1200
£2270 $4200 €3314 Dark Night - maybe - IV Without Mind (208x208cm-82x82in) s.i.d.1992 verso prov. 13-Jul-4 Christie's, Rockefeller NY #128/R est:1500-2000
Works on paper
£2595 $4800 €3789 Untitled (128x119cm-50x47in) init.d.89 chl prov. 13-Jul-4 Christie's, Rockefeller NY #129/R est:800-1200

CARADOSSI, Vittorio (1861-?) Italian
Sculpture
£25000 $45000 €36500 Female nude seated on a cushion (76cm-30in) s. white yellow marble lit. 21-Apr-4 Sotheby's, London #134/R est:25000-30000

CARAGLIO, Giovanni Jacopo (c.1500-1570) Italian
Prints
£2200 $4004 €3212 Fury (25x18cm-10x7in) engraving after Rosso fiorentino. 30-Jun-4 Christie's, London #33 est:1000-1500

CARAS, Christos (1930-) Greek
£3800 $6802 €5548 Apple (50x50cm-20x20in) s. 10-May-4 Sotheby's, Olympia #43/R est:3000-5000

CARASSAN, Marie Gabrielle (20th C) French
£2013 $3564 €3000 Ciel orageux (65x100cm-26x39in) s. 29-Apr-4 Claude Aguttes, Neuilly #258 est:3000-3200

CARASSO, Fred (1899-1969) Dutch
Sculpture
£1594 $2614 €2200 Female nude, sitting (18cm-7in) d.1962 bronze wooden base prov. 27-May-3 Sotheby's, Amsterdam #368/R est:1500-2000

CARAVAGGIO (after) (1573-1610) Italian
£4934 $9079 €7500 Beheading of Saint John the Baptist (220x146cm-87x57in) 22-Jun-4 Babuino, Rome #23/R est:6000-8000
£5674 $9191 €8000 Judith holding Olofernes' head (125x95cm-49x37in) 21-May-3 Babuino, Rome #21/R
£6667 $11933 €10000 Judith (125x95cm-49x37in) 17-May-4 Finarte Semenzato, Rome #95/R est:12000-14000
£8609 $15669 €13000 Bacchus as a child (45x33cm-18x13in) 16-Jun-4 Christie's, Rome #299/R est:9000-12000
£9500 $17385 €13870 Cardsharps (98x137cm-39x54in) 9-Jul-4 Christie's, Kensington #162/R est:5000-7000

CARAVAGGIO (circle) (1573-1610) Italian
£26000 $44980 €37960 Head of Saint John the Baptist (35x45cm-14x18in) 12-Dec-3 Christie's, Kensington #208/R est:3000-5000
£155211 $277827 €226608 King Saul visiting the fortune teller in Endor (105x124cm-41x49in) i.verso. 28-May-4 Uppsala Auktionskammare, Uppsala #31/R est:40000-50000 (S.KR 2100000)

CARAVAGGIO (school) (1573-1610) Italian
£14085 $24366 €20000 Christ in Emmaus (149x114cm-59x45in) 11-Dec-3 Dr Fritz Nagel, Stuttgart #421/R est:40000
£32374 $53094 €45000 Saint Jerome (130x103cm-51x41in) 4-Jun-3 Sotheby's, Milan #49/R est:6000-8000

CARAVANNIEZ, Alfred (1855-?) French
Sculpture
£1818 $3091 €2600 Rene de Monti de Reze (70cm-28in) s. white marble. 26-Nov-3 Daguerre, Paris #172/R est:800-1000

CARAVIA-FLORA, Thalia (1871-1960) Greek
£6000 $10500 €8760 Woman with red hat (35x27cm-14x11in) cardboard. 16-Dec-3 Bonhams, New Bond Street #48/R est:4000-6000
£6200 $10850 €9052 View of the Acropolis (26x33cm-10x13in) s. hardboard. 16-Dec-3 Bonhams, New Bond Street #1/R est:4000-6000

CARBAAT, Jan (1866-1925) ?
£382 $603 €550 Water pump (41x31cm-16x12in) s.d.1910 board. 2-Sep-3 Christie's, Amsterdam #363

CARBILLET, S (19th C) French
£3819 $6226 €5500 Jeune fille vue de face tenant des roses dans la main droite, fond de paysage (65x54cm-26x21in) s.d.1833. 26-Sep-3 Rabourdin & Choppin de Janvry, Paris #95/R est:4500-5000

CARBONE, Roberto (20th C) Italian
Works on paper
£1067 $1920 €1600 Italian tomatoes (106x150cm-42x59in) s.verso mixed media collage board. 22-Apr-4 Finarte Semenzato, Rome #282/R est:1500-1700

CARBONELL, Manuel (1918-) Cuban
£872 $1623 €1300 View of harbour in San Sebastian (60x73cm-24x29in) s. 2-Mar-4 Ansorena, Madrid #178/R est:500

CARBONELL, Miguel (18th C) Spanish
£295 $549 €440 Street (55x46cm-22x18in) s. 2-Mar-4 Ansorena, Madrid #204/R

CARBONERO, Jose Moreno (1860-1942) Spanish
£2721 $4952 €4000 Hunter (27x42cm-11x17in) s.i.d.1898. 3-Feb-4 Segre, Madrid #58/R est:4800

£3356 $6242 €5000 View of seascape in Biarritz (26x34cm-10x13in) s.i.d.1909. 2-Mar-4 Ansorena, Madrid #93/R est:5000
£5313 $8500 €7757 Dama de las palomas - Lady of the doves (89x71cm-35x28in) s.i. 20-Sep-3 Jeffery Burchard, Florida #39/R

CARBONERO, Maria (1956-) Spanish
£1267 $2293 €1900 Black dancers (130x162cm-51x64in) s.i.d.2985 verso prov. 30-Mar-4 Segre, Madrid #233/R est:1800
£1319 $2243 €1900 Woman (110x81cm-43x32in) s.d.1985 verso acrylic. 28-Oct-3 Segre, Madrid #208/R est:1700

CARCANO, Filippo (1840-1910) Italian
£2215 $3964 €3300 Red parasol (27x58cm-11x23in) s. 25-May-4 Finarte Semenzato, Milan #80/R est:2500-3000
Works on paper
£274 $427 €400 Tree of wealth (26x18cm-10x7in) s. W/C. 8-Apr-3 Il Ponte, Milan #649
£563 $975 €800 Lake landscape (25x38cm-10x15in) s. W/C pastel. 9-Dec-3 Finarte Semenzato, Milan #31/R

CARCELLER NUNEZ, Andres (1894-?) Spanish
£268 $475 €400 Vase of flowers (80x64cm-31x25in) s. s.d.1945 verso. 27-Apr-4 Durán, Madrid #10/R
£403 $713 €600 Still life of fruit (64x81cm-25x32in) s. s.i.d.1946 verso. 27-Apr-4 Durán, Madrid #11/R

CARCUPINO, Fernando (1922-) Italian
Works on paper
£352 $616 €500 A thousand miles (72x50cm-28x20in) s. mixed media. 17-Dec-3 Il Ponte, Milan #808

CARD, Stephan J (20th C) American
£280 $482 €409 Merchant Prestige in open seas (60x91cm-24x36in) s.d.95 board. 2-Dec-3 Sotheby's, London #174/R
£360 $619 €526 Rozel off the coast (59x95cm-23x37in) s.d.91. 2-Dec-3 Sotheby's, London #169/R
£360 $619 €526 Merchant Princess (61x91cm-24x36in) s.d.94. 2-Dec-3 Sotheby's, London #171/R
£360 $619 €526 Merchant Promise (61x91cm-24x36in) 2-Dec-3 Sotheby's, London #172/R
£360 $619 €526 Merchant Pioneer in open seas (60x90cm-24x35in) s.d.89. 2-Dec-3 Sotheby's, London #173/R
£360 $619 €526 Merchant Pride off the coast (60x91cm-24x36in) s.d.96. 2-Dec-3 Sotheby's, London #175/R
£360 $619 €526 Merchant Principal (61x91cm-24x36in) s.d.90 board. 2-Dec-3 Sotheby's, London #176/R

CARDENAS, Augustin (1927-2001) Cuban
Sculpture
£3022 $5500 €4412 Sin Titulo (15x26x22cm-6x10x9in) sig.d.X.87 white marble prov. 29-Jun-4 Sotheby's, New York #681/R est:6000-8000
£3497 $5839 €5000 Liberte revee (52x23x11cm-20x9x4in) s. num.EA3/4 pat bronze. 29-Jun-3 Versailles Encheres #198/R
£3533 $6360 €5300 Fleur dynamique (29x31x18cm-11x12x7in) s. num.6/8 pat bronze exec.1979. 25-Apr-4 Versailles Encheres #211/R est:7000-8000
£5594 $9510 €8000 Untitled (44cm-17in) mono.d.57 ebony excl marble base exec 1957 prov. 25-Nov-3 Christie's, Amsterdam #138/R est:10000-15000
£6294 $10699 €9000 Untitled (71cm-28in) mono. ebony incl wooden base exec c.1957 prov. 25-Nov-3 Christie's, Amsterdam #137/R est:12000-16000
£10135 $17838 €15000 Untitled (77x24x36cm-30x9x14in) s. bloke marble incl. wooden base. 18-May-4 Tajan, Paris #18/R est:15000-20000
£12000 $20040 €17520 Untitled (40x35x13cm 16x14x5in) init.d.67 marble prov. 21-Oct-3 Sotheby's, London #373/R est:8000-12000
£13333 $24533 €20000 Shark (53x105cm-21x41in) mono. wood exec. c.1953 unique prov. 9-Jun-4 Christie's, Amsterdam #263/R est:20000-30000
£14000 $25760 €20440 Memoire d'une coquille (51x56x50cm-20x22x20in) s.d.83 white marble prov. 24-Jun-4 Sotheby's, London #153/R est:10000-12000
£14865 $26163 €22000 Untitled (157cm-62in) s.d.1989 wood prov. 18-May-4 Tajan, Paris #1616/R est:20000-25000
£21831 $35367 €31000 Composition aux troix formes (156cm-61in) s.num.3/3 blue pat bronze Cast Christian Mass. 5-Aug-3 Tajan, Paris #40/R est:30000-40000
Works on paper
£1361 $2436 €2000 Untitled (49x65cm-19x26in) s.d.1964 chl embossed paper. 21-Mar-4 Calmels Cohen, Paris #31/R est:2000-3000

CARDENAS, Marta (1944-) Spanish
Works on paper
£590 $1003 €850 Pine trees and foliage in Canencia (51x62cm-20x24in) s.d.86 gouache cardboard prov.exhib.lit. 28-Oct-3 Segre, Madrid #205/R
£1020 $1857 €1500 Untitled (25x33cm-10x13in) s.d.1983 d.verso pastel exhib.lit. 3-Feb-4 Segre, Madrid #313/R est:1200

CARDENAS, Ponciano (?) Argentinian
Works on paper
£559 $1000 €816 Four figures (31x70cm-12x28in) mixed media. 11-May-4 Arroyo, Buenos Aires #13

CARDI, Lodovico (studio) (1559-1613) Italian
£6200 $11160 €9052 Saint Francis receiving the Stigmata (157x116cm-62x46in) mono.d.1602. 20-Apr-4 Sotheby's, Olympia #202/R est:3000-5000

CARDINAL, Émile Valentin (1883-1958) French
£435 $796 €635 Young boy with cats (27x35cm-11x14in) s. panel. 4-Jun-4 Zofingen, Switzerland #2432/R (S.FR 1000)
£800 $1448 €1168 Cat and four kittens playing with a necklace (30x39cm-12x15in) s. 1-Apr-4 Martel Maides, Guernsey #265/R

CARDINAL-SCHUBERT, Joanne (1942-) Canadian
Works on paper
£294 $491 €429 Thunderbird dream (55x20cm-22x8in) s.i. mixed media. 17-Nov-3 Hodgins, Calgary #152/R (C.D 650)
£407 $680 €594 Pleiades (58x19cm-23x7in) s.i. mixed media. 17-Nov-3 Hodgins, Calgary #297/R (C.D 900)
£760 $1391 €1110 Poundmaker (60x74cm-24x29in) s.i. mixed media. 1-Jun-4 Hodgins, Calgary #172/R (C.D 1900)

CARDINAUX, Emile (1877-1936) Swiss
£573 $974 €837 Mountain landscape with small lake (42x50cm-17x20in) s.d.25. 7-Nov-3 Dobiaschofsky, Bern #155/R (S.FR 1300)
£1584 $2740 €2313 Garden in spring (50x55cm-20x22in) s.d.1910 prov. 9-Dec-3 Sotheby's, Zurich #36/R est:2000-4000 (S.FR 3500)
£2423 $4119 €3538 Winter landscape (50x73cm-20x29in) s.d.06 board. 7-Nov-3 Dobiaschofsky, Bern #157/R est:4000 (S.FR 5500)
Prints
£2203 $3744 €3216 Zermatt, Matterhorn (104x72cm-41x28in) s.i. col lithograph. 5-Nov-3 Dobiaschofsky, Bern #2188/R est:1200 (S.FR 5000)

CARDON, Claude (fl.1892-1920) British
£2238 $3804 €3200 Calves and poultry by farm (52x77cm-20x30in) s. 29-Nov-3 Bukowskis, Helsinki #391/R est:3000-4000
£2600 $4160 €3796 Farmyard scene with cattle, chickens and ducks before a barn (48x74cm-19x29in) 16-Sep-3 Gorringes, Bexhill #1540/R est:1500-2500
£2800 $5208 €4088 Feeding time (36x51cm-14x20in) s. 4-Mar-4 Christie's, Kensington #485/R est:1800-2200
£3400 $6222 €4964 Farmyard, with young boy, his dog and a calf (46x66cm-18x26in) s.d.1918. 6-Apr-4 Bonhams, Knightsbridge #188/R est:1500-2000
£4400 $7920 €6424 Calves and ducks in a meadow (34x44cm-13x17in) s.d.98. 22-Apr-4 Mellors & Kirk, Nottingham #1140/R est:2000-2500
£5000 $9000 €7300 Farmer's favourites (34x49cm-13x19in) s.d.98. 22-Apr-4 Mellors & Kirk, Nottingham #1138 est:2000-2500
£5500 $9900 €8030 Inquisitive visitors (34x44cm-13x17in) s.d.98. 22-Apr-4 Mellors & Kirk, Nottingham #1139/R est:2000-2500
£6000 $10740 €8760 Calves and poultry by a farm (51x76cm-20x30in) s. 27-May-4 Christie's, Kensington #194/R est:4000-6000
£6500 $11050 €9490 Farmyard scenes with animals (21x27cm-8x11in) s. panel pair. 19-Nov-3 Tennants, Leyburn #1200 est:4000-5000
Works on paper
£1500 $2685 €2190 Farmyard scenes with calves, ducks and poultry (25x38cm-10x15in) s. W/C pair. 7-May-4 Christopher Matthews, Yorkshire #319/R est:500-800

CARDONA LLADOS, Juan (1877-1934) Spanish
Works on paper
£4196 $7133 €6000 Espagnole a sa coiffure (45x31cm-18x12in) s. pastel. 1-Dec-3 Camard, Paris #47 est:1200-1500

CARDONA MORERA, Juan Jose (1894-?) Spanish
Sculpture
£5081 $8740 €7418 Children playing. bronze. 3-Dec-3 Naón & Cia, Buenos Aires #596/R est:3000-4000

CARDOZO, Eduardo (1965-) Uruguayan
£1087 $2000 €1587 Disappearance order (180x180cm-71x71in) s. oil acrylic. 22-Jun-4 Galeria y Remates, Montevideo #172/R est:2300-2500

CARDUCCI, Adolfo (1901-1984) Italian
£326 $597 €476 Sous la pluie (23x33cm-9x13in) mono. s.verso canvas on cardboard. 5-Jun-4 Galerie du Rhone, Sion #300 (S.FR 750)
£490 $906 €730 Chasse a courre (47x67cm-19x26in) s. 14-Mar-4 Feletin, Province #265

CAREE, Georg (?) ?
£1611 $2883 €2400 View of the Wetterhorn, Canton Bern (36x58cm-14x23in) 27-May-4 Dorotheum, Vienna #47/R est:2600-3000
£1611 $2883 €2400 Fishing houses in Frauenworth, Oberbayern (36x58cm-14x23in) 27-May-4 Dorotheum, Vienna #48/R est:2600-3000

CARELLI, Conrad (1869-?) British
Works on paper
£450 $810 €657 Mediterranean coastal defences (24x17cm-9x7in) s. pencil W/C htd white. 22-Apr-4 Mellors & Kirk, Nottingham #1014

CARELLI, Consalve (1818-1900) Italian
£3846 $6423 €5615 Capri Ponte di Tiberio (38x25cm-15x10in) s. i.verso panel. 17-Nov-3 Waddingtons, Toronto #268/R est:5000-7000 (C.D 8500)
£4895 $8420 €7000 View of Sorrent (24x42cm-9x17in) s.i. panel. 3-Dec-3 Neumeister, Munich #541a/R est:5000
£4930 $8183 €7000 Castel dell'Ovo dal Chiatamone (18x35cm-7x14in) s. panel. 11-Jun-3 Christie's, Rome #195/R est:6500-8000
£6667 $12267 €10000 Peasants in Baia (42x56cm-17x22in) s. 10-Jun-4 Christie's, Rome #152/R est:12000-15000
£7692 $13077 €11000 Fishermen on the Gulf of Sorrent (37x63cm-15x25in) s.i. lit. 28-Nov-3 Schloss Ahlden, Ahlden #1429/R est:2400
£8500 $15725 €12410 Neapolitan view (44x70cm-17x28in) s.i. 10-Mar-4 Sotheby's, Olympia #249/R est:2000-4000
£10563 $17535 €15000 Castellamare (38x64cm-15x25in) s. lit. 11-Jun-3 Christie's, Rome #211/R est:17000-20000

Works on paper

£550	$1001	€803	On the waterfront at Naples. A neo-classical villa on the edge of a lake (33x24cm-13x9in) one s.i. one s. pair pencil W/C. 1-Jul-4 Christie's, Kensington #356/R
£680	$1217	€1000	Vue de Calabre (25x35cm-10x14in) s.i. grey wash traces black crayon. 17-Mar-4 Tajan, Paris #82
£1000	$1840	€1500	View of Paestum (16x26cm-6x10in) s. W/C card. 10-Jun-4 Christie's, Rome #51/R est:1800-2500
£1100	$2035	€1606	Bay of Naples (20x27cm-8x11in) W/C. 9-Mar-4 Bonhams, New Bond Street #8/R est:700-1000
£1974	$3632	€3000	Peasant women and children in wood with the Vesuvius beyond (31x21cm-12x8in) s.d.1850 W/C. 22-Jun-4 Sotheby's, Milan #147 est:1000-1500
£2200	$4026	€3212	Beached vessel (25x39cm-10x15in) s.d.1855 W/C. 7-Apr-4 Dreweatt Neate, Newbury #68 est:180-220

CARELLI, G (19th C) Italian

Works on paper

£1500	$2550	€2190	View of the Bay of Naples with Vesuvius (25x18cm-10x7in) s. W/C. 29-Oct-3 Mallams, Oxford #708/R est:600-800

CARELLI, Gabrielli (1820-1880) Italian

Works on paper

£867	$1569	€1300	Capri harbour (30x48cm-12x19in) s. W/C. 30-Mar-4 Babuino, Rome #431
£915	$1584	€1300	Angler (18x14cm-7x6in) s. pencil W/C. 9-Dec-3 Pandolfini, Florence #188/R est:1300-1400
£1000	$1820	€1460	Castello di Ischia, Corfu. Amalfi from Positano (10x14cm-4x6in) s. pencil W/C pair. 1-Jul-4 Christie's, Kensington #380/R est:1000-1500
£1450	$2465	€2117	Neopolitan villa beside the sea (12x14cm-5x6in) s. gouache sold with 2 companions set of 3 and 2 by the same hand. 1-Dec-3 Bonhams, Bath #83/R est:400-600
£3103	$5183	€4500	Interior of South Lodge (15x26cm-6x10in) s.d.1878 W/C. 12-Nov-3 Sotheby's, Milan #138/R est:2500-3500
£4138	$6910	€6000	Interior of South Lodge (25x37cm-10x15in) s.d.1878 W/C. 12-Nov-3 Sotheby's, Milan #139/R est:3000-5000
£4483	$7486	€6500	Interior of South Lodge (24x37cm-9x15in) s.d. W/C. 12-Nov-3 Sotheby's, Milan #140/R est:4000-6000
£7241	$12093	€10500	Interior of South Lodge (16x27cm-6x11in) s.d.1878 W/C. 12-Nov-3 Sotheby's, Milan #142/R est:2500-3500
£7241	$12093	€10500	Interior of South Lodge (25x37cm-10x15in) s.d.1878 W/C. 12-Nov-3 Sotheby's, Milan #141/R est:3500-4500

CARELLI, Gabrielli (attrib) (1820-1880) Italian

Works on paper

£1197	$2071	€1700	View of Ponte Vecchio, Florence (23x42cm-9x17in) W/C. 9-Dec-3 Pandolfini, Florence #191/R est:1000-1100

CARELLI, Giuseppe (1858-1921) Italian

£893	$1536	€1304	Figures and boats near harbour steps (35x50cm-14x20in) s.i. canvas on panel. 2-Dec-3 Ritchie, Toronto #113/R est:2000-2500 (C.D 2000)
£1067	$1909	€1600	Fishing boats on Gulf of Naples beach (26x45cm-10x18in) s. panel. 13-May-4 Bassenge, Berlin #5530/R est:600
£1198	$2000	€1749	View of the Bay of Naples (36x18cm-14x7in) panel. 19-Oct-3 Jeffery Burchard, Florida #38
£1379	$2303	€2000	Seascape with island (6x7cm-2x3in) s.init. board oval pair. 12-Nov-3 Sotheby's, Milan #153/R est:2000-4000
£1550	$2868	€2263	View of the Bay of Naples (33x18cm-13x7in) s. panel. 9-Mar-4 Bonhams, Knightsbridge #153/R est:500-700
£1727	$2867	€2504	Pescatori davanti a Capri (20x40cm-8x16in) s.i. panel. 13-Jun-3 Zofingen, Switzerland #2427/R est:2000 (S.FR 3800)
£2400	$4008	€3504	Vessels off the Neapolitan coast (24x45cm-9x18in) s. panel. 11-Nov-3 Bonhams, Knightsbridge #100/R est:1500-2500
£2797	$4811	€4000	Fishing boats near Capri (25x47cm-10x19in) s.i. 3-Dec-3 Neumeister, Munich #542/R est:2200
£3472	$5729	€5000	Fishing boats in Gulf of Naples (23x40cm-9x16in) s. panel. 2-Jul-3 Neumeister, Munich #617/R est:2500
£4027	$7409	€6000	Bay of Naples with Vesuvius (39x26cm-15x10in) s. 26-Mar-4 Bolland & Marotz, Bremen #493/R est:6500
£4200	$7770	€6132	Neapolitan steps (51x25cm-20x10in) s.i. panel. 10-Feb-4 David Lay, Penzance #231/R est:3000-3500
£4200	$7644	€6132	Fishing boats at the Bay of Naples (26x48cm-10x19in) s.i. 16-Jun-4 Christie's, Kensington #132/R est:3000-5000
£4333	$7757	€6500	Seascape in Capri (24x45cm-9x18in) s. board. 13-May-4 Babuino, Rome #333/R est:3000-3500

CARELLI, Giuseppe (attrib) (1858-1921) Italian

£993	$1808	€1500	Pecheurs dans la Baie de Naples (32x20cm-13x8in) s.i. panel. 18-Jun-4 Charbonneaux, Paris #133/R est:1800-2000
£2778	$4583	€4000	Fishing boats in early morning light with mountainous island behind (19x36cm-7x14in) s.i. panel one of pair. 3-Jul-3 Dr Fritz Nagel, Stuttgart #479/R est:1400
£2778	$4583	€4000	Coastal landscape near Naples (19x36cm-7x14in) s.i. panel one of pair. 3-Jul-3 Dr Fritz Nagel, Stuttgart #480/R est:1400
£8889	$16000	€12978	Bay of Naples (39x62cm-15x24in) s. 22-Apr-4 Christie's, Rockefeller NY #241/R est:10000-15000

CARELLI, Raffaele (1795-1864) Italian

Works on paper

£987	$1816	€1500	Neapolitan dance (26x20cm-10x8in) s.d.1859 W/C oval. 23-Jun-4 Finarte Semenzato, Rome #19/R est:1500-1700

CARENA, Felice (1879-1966) Italian

£3748	$6372	€5360	Portrait (72x61cm-28x24in) s. prov. 18-Nov-3 Babuino, Rome #277/R est:3000-4000
£8392	$14266	€12000	Self-portrait (144x70cm-57x28in) s. prov.exhib. 25-Nov-3 Sotheby's, Milan #132/R est:12000-15000
£10490	$17832	€15000	Still life (40x50cm-16x20in) s.d.1952. 24-Nov-3 Christie's, Milan #191/R est:10000-15000

Works on paper

£420	$701	€600	Figures on the beach (31x21cm-12x8in) s.i.d.1961 sepia ink. 26-Jun-3 Sant Agostino, Torino #153/R
£476	$852	€700	Pieta' (31x21cm-12x8in) s. ink W/C. 22-Mar-4 Sant Agostino, Torino #423/R
£552	$921	€800	Study of figures (20x320cm-8x126in) s. Chinese ink. 13-Nov-3 Finarte Semenzato, Rome #137
£612	$1096	€900	San Martino (18x22cm-7x9in) s.d.1928 ink W/C. 22-Mar-4 Sant Agostino, Torino #425/R

CARESANA, Domenico (1574-1619) Italian

Works on paper

£4722	$8500	€6894	Angel looking up, holding a scroll (34x22cm-13x9in) i. black chk brush brown wash prov.lit. 22-Jan-4 Christie's, Rockefeller NY #19/R est:7000-10000

CARESME, Jacques Philippe (1734-1796) French

£1135	$1895	€1600	Le char de l'amour (56x21cm-22x8in) 19-Oct-3 Anaf, Lyon #70/R est:1500-2000
£2715	$4615	€3964	Nymps and Satyrs (40x37cm-16x15in) 19-Nov-3 Fischer, Luzern #1057/R est:6000-8000 (S.FR 6000)
£4605	$8474	€7000	Satyre devoilant bacchante endormie (42x54cm-17x21in) paper on canvas. 24-Jun-4 Christie's, Paris #126/R est:5000-7000

Works on paper

£439	$773	€650	River-God seated on a rock (9x10cm-4x4in) s.d. pen brown ink wash black chk exhib.lit. 19-May-4 Sotheby's, Amsterdam #155/R

CAREY, Ida H (1891-1982) New Zealander

£290	$467	€423	Portrait of Maori boy (40x24cm-16x9in) s. board. 20-Aug-3 Dunbar Sloane, Auckland #75 (NZ.D 800)

CAREY, John W (19/20th C) British

Works on paper

£750	$1290	€1095	The harriers (25x35cm-10x14in) s.d.1925 W/C. 3-Dec-3 John Ross, Belfast #187

CAREY, Joseph William (1859-1937) British

Works on paper

£260	$426	€380	Slieve Bingian (17x25cm-7x10in) s.d.1925 W/C. 4-Jun-3 John Ross, Belfast #137
£320	$582	€467	Brickeen, Killarney (15x19cm-6x7in) s.d.1882 pencil W/C scratching out. 1-Jul-4 Christie's, Kensington #459/R
£340	$636	€510	Dun river, Co Antrim (20x38cm-8x15in) s.d.1918 W/C. 22-Jul-4 Gorringes, Lewes #1807
£349	$625	€520	Bogland (25x36cm-10x14in) s.d.1904 W/C prov. 26-May-4 James Adam, Dublin #27/R
£350	$602	€511	Happy valley (31x51cm-12x20in) s.i.d.1923 pencil W/C. 3-Dec-3 Christie's, Kensington #110/R
£380	$631	€555	Lone shieling on the distant island (12x20cm-5x8in) s.d.1907 W/C. 1-Oct-3 John Ross, Belfast #125
£380	$707	€555	Ardlui, Donegal (30x45cm-12x18in) s. W/C. 3-Mar-4 John Ross, Belfast #4
£384	$642	€561	Blue Lake Mourne Mts (25x35cm-10x14in) s.i.d.1932 W/C. 17-Nov-3 Waddingtons, Toronto #137/R (C.D 850)
£400	$740	€584	Glen Gariff (25x36cm-10x14in) s.i.d.1936 W/C. 10-Feb-4 David Lay, Penzance #404
£420	$785	€613	Goatfell, Arran (25x36cm-10x14in) s.i.d.1922 pencil W/C. 22-Jul-4 Tennants, Leyburn #720
£440	$810	€642	Gabbins (18x43cm-7x17in) s.d.1928 W/C. 8-Jun-4 Gorringes, Lewes #2059
£450	$738	€657	Ritchies Dock (20x38cm-8x15in) s. W/C. 4-Jun-3 John Ross, Belfast #126
£500	$830	€730	River Quoile, Downpatrick (25x50cm-10x20in) s.d.91 W/C. 1-Oct-3 John Ross, Belfast #116
£500	$930	€730	Ringhaddy Castle, west side of Strangford Lough (20x28cm-8x11in) s.d.1914 W/C. 3-Mar-4 John Ross, Belfast #78
£550	$946	€803	Scrabo (30x45cm-12x18in) s.d.1929 W/C. 3-Dec-3 John Ross, Belfast #2
£550	$946	€803	Barnsmore Gap, Donegal (22x35cm-9x14in) s.d.1929 W/C. 3-Dec-3 John Ross, Belfast #60
£550	$1012	€803	Muckish, Creeslough, Donegal (32x49cm-13x19in) s.i.d.1928 W/C. 23-Jun-4 Bonhams, Bury St Edmunds #342/R
£600	$1098	€876	Happy valley (30x50cm-12x20in) s.d.1923 W/C. 2-Jun-4 John Ross, Belfast #41
£604	$1081	€900	Fisherman's cottage Kilkeel, Co. Down (25x40cm-10x16in) s.i.d.1919 W/C htd white. 26-May-4 James Adam, Dublin #18/R
£700	$1127	€1015	Peat stacks with cart in wooded bogland, smoke rising in the distance (23x36cm-9x14in) s.d.1913 W/C. 15-Aug-3 Keys, Aylsham #527/R
£700	$1162	€1022	Fairhead, Co. Antrim (25x35cm-10x14in) s.d.1933 W/C. 1-Oct-3 John Ross, Belfast #2
£700	$1162	€1022	Off Blackhead, Belfast Lough (30x25cm-12x10in) s.d.1927 W/C. 1-Oct-3 John Ross, Belfast #260
£720	$1318	€1051	City of Armagh from east (24x43cm-9x17in) s.i.d.1925 W/C pencil htd bodycol. 8-Jul-4 Lawrence, Crewkerne #1544
£750	$1230	€1095	Annalong Valley (35x50cm-14x20in) s.d.1928 W/C. 4-Jun-3 John Ross, Belfast #2
£800	$1312	€1168	Sailing (20x45cm-8x18in) s.d.1920 W/C. 4-Jun-3 John Ross, Belfast #122
£800	$1328	€1168	Octagon house in Arthur Square (25x30cm-10x12in) s. W/C. 1-Oct-3 John Ross, Belfast #14
£800	$1328	€1168	Hercules Street, Belfast, 1860 (22x35cm-9x14in) s.d.1917 W/C. 1-Oct-3 John Ross, Belfast #90
£800	$1456	€1168	Blue Lake, Annalough, Balilore Co Kildare (23x36cm-9x14in) s.i. W/C. 16-Jun-4 John Nicholson, Haslemere #709/R
£850	$1394	€1241	Barnsmore Gap (35x50cm-14x20in) s. W/C. 4-Jun-3 John Ross, Belfast #208
£850	$1411	€1241	Sailing of the Gobbins (23x30cm-9x12in) s.d.1917 W/C. 1-Oct-3 John Ross, Belfast #28
£850	$1462	€1241	Brigantine, Ardrossan (17x28cm-7x11in) s. W/C. 3-Dec-3 John Ross, Belfast #151
£850	$1573	€1241	Happy valley (30x48cm-12x19in) s.d.1923 W/C. 13-Feb-4 Keys, Aylsham #458/R

£900	$1494	€1314	High street, Belfast, 1820 (23x33cm-9x13in) s.d.1917 W/C. 1-Oct-3 John Ross, Belfast #148
£903	$1472	€1300	Killarney (26x38cm-10x15in) s.d.1913 W/C pencil. 24-Sep-3 James Adam, Dublin #17/R est:1000-1500
£940	$1663	€1400	Howth and Ireland's eye (20x37cm-8x15in) s.i.d.1923 W/C. 27-Apr-4 Whyte's, Dublin #48/R
£950	$1558	€1387	Ferry steps (30x22cm-12x9in) s. W/C. 4-Jun-3 John Ross, Belfast #156
£979	$1664	€1400	Killiney (27x37cm-11x15in) s.i.d.1930 W/C board. 18-Nov-3 Whyte's, Dublin #189/R
£979	$1664	€1400	Turf stacks and cart (24x36cm-9x14in) s.d.1913 W/C. 18-Nov-3 Whyte's, Dublin #197/R
£1000	$1790	€1460	Dundrum dunes, Co Down (25x44cm-10x17in) s.i.d.1917 pencil W/C. 14-May-4 Christie's, Kensington #323/R est:1000-1500
£1400	$2534	€2100	Donaghadee (18x50cm-7x20in) s.i.d.1927 W/C. 31-Mar-4 James Adam, Dublin #144/R est:1500-2000
£1600	$2656	€2336	Long bridge, Belfast (20x45cm-8x18in) s. W/C. 1-Oct-3 John Ross, Belfast #33 est:700-800
£1900	$3154	€2774	Ormeau Golf Club (20x43cm-8x17in) s.d.1921 W/C. 1-Oct-3 John Ross, Belfast #141 est:600-800
£2535	$4386	€3600	Girona off the Port na Spaniagh, Co Antrim (36x52cm-14x20in) s.i.d.1922 W/C. 10-Dec-3 Bonhams & James Adam, Dublin #195/R est:1000-2000
£3000	$5370	€4380	Donaghadee and Carrickfergus (25x51cm-10x20in) s.i.d.1921 pencil W/C pair. 14-May-4 Christie's, Kensington #325/R est:800-1200
£7800	$12792	€11388	OffFair Head (50x73cm-20x29in) s.d.1915 W/C. 4-Jun-3 John Ross, Belfast #31 est:3000

CARGALEIRO (20th C) ?

Works on paper			
£2106	$3854	€3159	Untitled (25x17cm-10x7in) s.d.1975 gouache. 6-Jul-4 Bolsa de Arte, Rio de Janeiro #101/R (B.R 11500)

CARGALEIRO, Manuel (1927-) Portuguese

£3289	$6053	€5000	Composition (60x60cm-24x24in) s.i.d.1967 prov. 28-Jun-4 Joron-Derem, Paris #211/R est:5000-6000
£3333	$6133	€5000	Composition au cercle. s. s.d.1966 verso. 9-Jun-4 Beaussant & Lefèvre, Paris #90/R est:5000-6000
£8054	$14255	€12000	Composition (35x27cm-14x11in) s.d.1978. 28-Apr-4 Artcurial Briest, Paris #303/R est:6000-8000
£17832	$30315	€25500	Blue landscape (65x54cm-26x21in) s.i.d.1987. 21-Nov-3 Lombrail & Teucquam, Paris #160/R est:15000-18000
£23490	$43692	€35000	Vesper (100x81cm-39x32in) s.d.1987. 3-Mar-4 Artcurial Briest, Paris #331/R est:20000-25000
Works on paper			
£1711	$3147	€2600	Composition (23x31cm-9x12in) s.d.1962 gouache. 28-Jun-4 Joron-Derem, Paris #210/R est:1000-1500
£2703	$4757	€4000	Untitled (16x16cm-6x6in) s.d.1970 gouache. 18-May-4 Tajan, Paris #66/R est:4000-4500
£2867	$5275	€4300	Composition (31x25cm-12x10in) s.d.1980 gouache. 13-Jun-4 Lombrail & Teucquam, Paris #125/R

CARGNEL, Lucio (?) Italian

£286	$487	€418	Small Italian village by river (39x50cm-15x20in) s. panel. 5-Nov-3 Dobiaschofsky, Bern #3329 (S.FR 650)

CARGNEL, Vittore Antonio (1872-1931) Italian

£1835	$3064	€2661	Casa di pescatori (62x76cm-24x30in) s. s.i.d.1927 verso. 23-Jun-3 Philippe Schuler, Zurich #3558/R est:2500-3500 (S.FR 4000)
£2064	$3447	€2993	Val grande alla Tresana (63x77cm-25x30in) s. s.i.d.1928 verso. 23-Jun-3 Philippe Schuler, Zurich #3559/R est:2500-3500 (S.FR 4500)
£3400	$6256	€4964	Mass beside a hillside chapel (78x196cm-31x77in) s.d.1910. 23-Mar-4 Rosebery Fine Art, London #814 est:2000-3000
Works on paper			
£403	$741	€600	Rainy day (41x28cm-16x11in) s. W/C card. 24-Mar-4 Il Ponte, Milan #662
£455	$782	€650	Town centre (16x20cm-6x8in) s. W/C. 3-Dec-3 Stadion, Trieste #1055/R
£548	$855	€800	Landscape with figures (42x60cm-17x24in) s. mixed media. 8-Apr-3 Il Ponte, Milan #568
£1233	$1923	€1800	Landscapes (50x70cm-20x28in) s. mixed media pair. 8-Apr-3 Il Ponte, Milan #539

CARGO, Ivan (1898-1958) Yugoslavian

£2400	$4296	€3600	Futuristic portrait (46x35cm-18x14in) s.d.20. 12-May-4 Stadion, Trieste #734/R est:2000-3000

CARIGIET, Alois (1902-1985) Swiss

£3587	$5848	€5237	Hen (46x38cm-18x15in) mono.d.48. 29-Sep-3 Christie's, Zurich #99/R est:8000-12000 (S.FR 8000)
£6502	$10859	€9493	Female figure in feather dress with falcon (81x24cm-32x9in) mono.d.48-51. 24-Oct-3 Hans Widmer, St Gallen #26/R est:10000-18000 (S.FR 14500)
£6787	$11538	€9909	Travellers (90x100cm-35x39in) mono. panel. 25-Nov-3 Germann, Zurich #26/R est:10000-15000 (S.FR 15000)
£8597	$14873	€12552	Farmer and horse with cart in the snow (38x55cm-15x22in) s.d.1948. 9-Dec-3 Sotheby's, Zurich #99/R est:16000-20000 (S.FR 19000)
£9865	$16081	€14403	Girl with long hair (80x100cm-31x39in) mono.d.67 exhib. 29-Sep-3 Christie's, Zurich #98/R est:15000-20000 (S.FR 22000)
£13453	$22466	€19641	Acletta (50x65cm-20x26in) mono.d.75. 24-Oct-3 Hans Widmer, St Gallen #28/R est:30000-48000 (S.FR 30000)
£14783	$27052	€21583	Wood carriers (66x92cm-26x36in) s.d.44 prov.exhib.lit. 7-Jun-4 Christie's, Zurich #115/R est:30000-50000 (S.FR 34000)
£17195	$29231	€25105	Sledge (76x98cm-30x39in) mono.d.1979. 25-Nov-3 Germann, Zurich #104/R est:40000-50000 (S.FR 38000)
£29412	$50882	€42942	Winter landscape (74x116cm-29x46in) mono.d.1948. 9-Dec-3 Sotheby's, Zurich #88/R est:40000-60000 (S.FR 65000)
Prints			
£2242	$3744	€3273	Winter's day (76x64cm-30x25in) s.i.d. col lithograph gouache. 24-Oct-3 Hans Widmer, St Gallen #63/R est:5000-9000 (S.FR 5000)
£2915	$4868	€4256	The sledge (64x50cm-25x20in) s.i.d.1962 lithograph. 24-Oct-3 Hans Widmer, St Gallen #25/R est:4500-9000 (S.FR 6500)
Works on paper			
£905	$1538	€1321	Female nude with basket by boat on beach (64x45cm-25x18in) s.d.49 pencil. 18-Nov-3 Hans Widmer, St Gallen #1039 est:2000-4200 (S.FR 2000)
£987	$1648	€1441	Dancer after performance (53x62cm-21x24in) s.d.49 pencil. 24-Oct-3 Hans Widmer, St Gallen #134/R est:3000-5500 (S.FR 2200)
£1131	$1923	€1651	Platenga (50x65cm-20x26in) mono.i.d.23 Juli 43 Indian ink. 18-Nov-3 Hans Widmer, St Gallen #1038 est:1300-2800 (S.FR 2500)
£1267	$2154	€1850	Woman seated by chinese vase I (39x27cm-15x11in) mono.d.73 W/C pencil. 19-Nov-3 Fischer, Luzern #2602/R est:3000-4000 (S.FR 2800)
£1732	$3100	€2529	Village street with lorry and sheep (14x21cm-6x8in) W/C pencil. 22-Mar-4 Philippe Schuler, Zurich #4153/R est:1300-1700 (S.FR 4000)
£1754	$3228	€2561	Farmer with horse and sledge (20x27cm-8x11in) mono. ink W/C. 23-Jun-4 Koller, Zurich #3074/R est:2800-4000 (S.FR 4000)
£2262	$3846	€3303	Girl with pigtails (38x34cm-15x13in) mono.d.50 mixed media. 19-Nov-3 Fischer, Luzern #1291/R est:6000-8000 (S.FR 5000)
£2620	$4769	€3825	Sketch for official Uri standard (65x40cm-26x16in) s.i. gouache. 16-Jun-4 Fischer, Luzern #2733/R est:6000-8000 (S.FR 6000)

CARIGNANI, Roberto (attrib) (1894-1988) Italian

£704	$1218	€1000	Harvest (65x87cm-26x34in) bears sig. panel. 11-Dec-3 Christie's, Rome #11

CARION, Louis (19th C) French?

£1300	$2249	€1898	Sur la plage (72x98cm-28x39in) s. 11-Dec-3 Christie's, Kensington #15/R est:1500-2000

CARION, Marius (1898-1949) Belgian

£567	$1031	€850	Dimanche (30x40cm-12x16in) s. panel. 4-Jul-4 MonsAntic, Maisieres #397
£667	$1213	€1000	Tete de mineur a l'enfant (50x40cm-20x16in) s. panel. 4-Jul-4 MonsAntic, Maisieres #396

CARIOT, Gustave (1872-1950) French

£1842	$3389	€2800	Quais de la Seine a Paris (61x89cm-24x35in) s.d.1936. 25-Jun-4 Millon & Associes, Paris #66 est:500-800

CARL, K A (19th C) American

£1275	$2359	€1900	La lecture de la lettre sous surveillance. s.d.1852 panel. 15-Mar-4 Horta, Bruxelles #48 est:2000-3000

CARLANDI, Onorato (1848-1939) Italian

£1690	$2924	€2400	Landscape in the Roman countryside (22x33cm-9x13in) s. board sold with another by P Barucci. 11-Dec-3 Christie's, Rome #5 est:1300-1800
Works on paper			
£290	$531	€423	Wooded landscape with figures on a bridge (57x39cm-22x15in) s.i. W/C. 28-Jul-4 Hampton & Littlewood, Exeter #596/R
£300	$546	€438	Abruzzo (28x44cm-11x17in) s.i. pencil W/C. 1-Jul-4 Christie's, Kensington #392
£380	$700	€555	Arab warrior peering don rifle barrel (46x30cm-18x12in) s. W/C. 23-Mar-4 Arthur James, Florida #462/R
£400	$740	€584	View of Hyde Park (34x50cm-13x20in) s.i. W/C. 9-Mar-4 Bonhams, New Bond Street #7/R
£450	$774	€657	Trees on the coast at Baveno (38x56cm-15x22in) s.i. W/C. 3-Dec-3 Christie's, Kensington #186/R
£604	$1111	€900	Fiuggi (55x52cm-22x20in) s.i. W/C. 24-Mar-4 Il Ponte, Milan #626/R
£800	$1480	€1168	Roman campagna (51x35cm-20x14in) s.i. W/C. 9-Mar-4 Bonhams, New Bond Street #5/R
£805	$1482	€1200	Rome (53x35cm-21x14in) s.i. W/C. 24-Mar-4 Il Ponte, Milan #645
£1000	$1790	€1500	Marsh in the Roman countryside (35x51cm-14x20in) s.i. W/C card. 13-May-4 Babuino, Rome #315/R est:600-800
£1067	$1931	€1600	Gothic church (53x37cm-21x15in) s.i.d.1894 W/C card. 30-Mar-4 Babuino, Rome #480/R est:500-600
£1100	$1947	€1606	Italian girl on a terrace with basket of fruit. Peasant woman in traditional dress (41x25cm-16x10in) s. W/C two. 28-Apr-4 Halls, Shrewsbury #466/R est:600-800
£1150	$2128	€1679	River landscape (46x64cm-18x25in) s.i. W/C. 9-Mar-4 Gorringes, Lewes #2291 est:500-700
£1173	$2100	€1713	Roma and Tivoli (56x56cm-22x22in) s.i. W/C paperboard pair. 14-May-4 Skinner, Boston #148/R est:300-400
£1197	$1987	€1700	Riflessi (68x68cm-27x27in) s. W/C cardboard. 11-Jun-3 Christie's, Rome #112/R est:1500-2000
£1268	$2193	€1800	Light amongst trees (52x36cm-20x14in) s. W/C card sold with another by E Ferrari. 11-Dec-3 Christie's, Rome #9 est:800-1200
£1400	$2506	€2100	Hyde Park (36x51cm-14x20in) s.i. W/C. 13-May-4 Babuino, Rome #209/R est:800-1000

CARLAW, John (?-1934) British

Works on paper			
£300	$501	€438	Fishing smack at harbour (32x49cm-13x19in) s. W/C. 27-Oct-3 Robin Fenner, Tavistock #1002
£850	$1573	€1241	All on a hunting morn (41x60cm-16x24in) W/C. 9-Mar-4 Bonhams, Knightsbridge #28/R

CARLAW, William (1847-1889) British

Works on paper			
£1400	$2338	€2044	Port St. Mary, Isle of man (32x49cm-13x19in) s. W/C. 27-Oct-3 Robin Fenner, Tavistock #1001/R est:300-400

CARLE, Pontus (1955-) ?

£655	$1212	€950	Sans titre (65x50cm-26x20in) s. 13-Feb-4 Charbonneaux, Paris #87/R

CARLEBUR, François II (1821-1893) Dutch
£351 $629 €520 Fishing boats by shore with figures (37x53cm-15x21in) s. lit. 8-May-4 Dawo, Saarbrucken #57/R
£493 $893 €750 Shipwreck (34x46cm-13x18in) s. panel. 19-Apr-4 Glerum, Amsterdam #9/R

CARLEMAN, Carl Gustaf (1821-1911) Swedish
£933 $1671 €1400 Gathering storm (49x75cm-19x30in) s.d.1865 lit. 14-May-4 Schloss Ahlden, Ahlden #2848/R

CARLES, Arthur B (1882-1952) American
£1899 $3000 €2773 Child reading (61x30cm-24x12in) s. 7-Sep-3 Treadway Gallery, Cincinnati #677/R est:4000-6000
£5946 $11000 €8681 Nude (42x33cm-17x13in) s. panel on panel exhib. 11-Mar-4 Christie's, Rockefeller NY #100/R est:5000-7000
£6395 $11000 €9337 Seascape (18x23cm-7x9in) i.d.1905 verso board prov. 7-Dec-3 Freeman, Philadelphia #221 est:1500-2500
£7065 $13000 €10315 Standing female nude (33x23cm-13x9in) s. panel on masonite prov. 27-Jun-4 Freeman, Philadelphia #161/R est:5000-8000
£8791 $16000 €12835 Italian landscape (33x38cm-13x15in) i.verso panel painted c.1910 prov. 29-Jun-4 Sotheby's, New York #232/R est:12000-18000
£29891 $55000 €43641 Harpist - Edna Phillips Rosenbaum (76x63cm-30x25in) prov. 27-Jun-4 Freeman, Philadelphia #162/R est:12000-18000
£33149 $60000 €48398 Calla lilies (41x33cm-16x13in) s. prov. 31-Mar-4 Sotheby's, New York #30/R est:10000-15000
Works on paper
£359 $600 €524 Sitting nude (30x18cm-12x7in) init. black conte crayon prov. 20-Jun-3 Freeman, Philadelphia #8/R
£1243 $2300 €1815 Portrait of woman. 18-Jan-4 Carlsen Gallery, Greenville #408/R
£1397 $2500 €2040 Harbour scene (13x20cm-5x8in) i.verso W/C prov. 26-May-4 Doyle, New York #92/R est:3000-5000
£1405 $2600 €2051 Portrait of Edward Steicher. chl on canvas. 18-Jan-4 Carlsen Gallery, Greenville #409/R

CARLES, Domingo (1888-1962) Spanish
£537 $999 €800 Vase with roses (61x50cm-24x20in) s. s.d.1943 verso. 2-Mar-4 Ansorena, Madrid #16/R
£1974 $3572 €3000 Flowers and fruit dishes (64x112cm-25x44in) 14-Apr-4 Ansorena, Madrid #73/R est:3000

CARLETTI, Mario (1912-) Italian
£289 $500 €422 Paysage mediterraneen (50x65cm-20x26in) s.d.56. 15-Dec-3 Iegor de Saint Hippolyte, Montreal #60 (C.D 650)

CARLEVARIS, Luca (1665-1731) Italian
£1000000 $1730000 €1460000 Venice, the Rialto Bridge from the north. The Piazza San Marco (96x191cm-38x75in) pair prov.lit. 10-Dec-3 Christie's, London #116/R est:700000-1000000

CARLEVARIS, Luca (after) (1665-1731) Italian
£9396 $17289 €14000 Italian port with tower, boats and figures (53x70cm-21x28in) prov. 24-Mar-4 Dorotheum, Vienna #23/R est:15000-18000

CARLEVARIS, Luca (attrib) (1665-1731) Italian
£46314 $80123 €67618 Elegant men wearing turbans at the harbour in a Mediterranean town (100x179cm-39x70in) 9-Dec-3 Rasmussen, Copenhagen #1236/R est:150000-200000 (D.KR 490000)

CARLIER, Emile François (1827-1879) French
Sculpture
£4828 $7724 €7000 Broken jug (80cm-31in) s. marble. 12-Mar-3 Auction Maastricht #125/R est:9000-12000

CARLIER, Émile Joseph Nestor (1849-1927) French
Sculpture
£879 $1600 €1283 Napoleon in exile (51x43x18cm-20x17x7in) s.st.f. white metal. 20-Jun-4 Charlton Hall, Columbia #601/R est:800-1200

CARLIER, Max (1872-1938) Belgian
£769 $1308 €1100 La bohemienne (49x32cm-19x13in) s.d.1928 panel. 1-Dec-3 Palais de Beaux Arts, Brussels #30/R
£1096 $1863 €1600 Vase de fleurs (52x74cm-20x29in) s. panel. 10-Nov-3 Horta, Bruxelles #51
£1127 $1949 €1600 Still life of fruit (40x60cm-16x24in) s. 15-Dec-3 Bernaerts, Antwerp #12/R est:1500-2000
£1216 $2177 €1800 Vase fleuri de roses (90x60cm-35x24in) s. 10-May-4 Horta, Bruxelles #46 est:2000-3000
£1216 $2177 €1800 Vase fleuri de roses (90x60cm-35x24in) s. 10-May-4 Horta, Bruxelles #47 est:2000-3000
£2098 $3503 €3000 Composition florale aux oeillets et coquelicots (94x96cm-37x38in) s. 13-Oct-3 Horta, Bruxelles #226/R est:2000-3000
£2657 $4517 €3800 Elegante a l'eventail assise sur une terrasse (100x80cm-39x31in) s. 1-Dec-3 Palais de Beaux Arts, Brussels #29/R est:2500-3500
£3217 $5469 €4600 Elegante a sa toilette (100x80cm-39x31in) s. 1-Dec-3 Palais de Beaux Arts, Brussels #28/R est:2500-3500
£3490 $6491 €5200 Still life with dog, lobster, fruit and flowers (110x70cm-43x28in) s. panel. 8-Mar-4 Bernaerts, Antwerp #11/R est:4000-5000
£5102 $9133 €7500 Chien et chats se chamaillant dans un interieur (130x105cm-51x41in) 22-Mar-4 Amberes, Antwerp #183/R
£7383 $13658 €11000 Still life with flowers and fruit (100x150cm-39x59in) s. 13-Mar-4 De Vuyst, Lokeren #519/R est:6500-7500

CARLIERI, Alberto (circle) (1672-1720) Italian
£22000 $37400 €32120 Bacchanals amongst classical ruins (133x97cm-52x38in) pair. 29-Oct-3 Christie's, London #73/R est:15000-20000

CARLIN, James (1909-) American
£698 $1200 €1019 Ice storm (61x76cm-24x30in) s. i.d.1968 verso painted c.1968. 7-Dec-3 Treadway Gallery, Cincinnati #698/R
Works on paper
£220 $350 €321 On the beach (45x67cm-18x26in) s.d.1981 W/C gouache. 12-Sep-3 Skinner, Boston #518/R

CARLIN, John (1813-1891) American
£4054 $7500 €5919 Portrait of a young girl with dog (92x71cm-36x28in) 17-Jan-4 Sotheby's, New York #1053/R est:4000-6000

CARLINE, George (1855-1920) British
£600 $1002 €876 Ragwort (20x29cm-8x11in) s. board. 16-Oct-3 Christie's, Kensington #405
£750 $1253 €1095 Chalets near Diableret, Switzerland (20x29cm-8x11in) s.d.1899 s.i.d.1899 verso panel. 16-Oct-3 Christie's, Kensington #541/R
£1000 $1670 €1460 Hilda playing the harp (91x71cm-36x28in) s.d.1910. 16-Oct-3 Christie's, Kensington #545/R est:1000-1500
Works on paper
£450 $765 €657 Full sail (38x54cm-15x21in) s.d.1930 pencil W/C. 27-Nov-3 Greenslade Hunt, Taunton #987/R

CARLINE, Hilda (1889-1950) British
£250 $418 €365 Cypress trees along the Loing (41x32cm-16x13in) s.d.1939 panel. 16-Oct-3 Christie's, Kensington #497
£260 $434 €380 Trees in spring (42x25cm-17x10in) canvas on board exhib. 16-Oct-3 Christie's, Kensington #504
£350 $585 €511 Deserted street (55x27cm-22x11in) s.d.1946 exhib. 16-Oct-3 Christie's, Kensington #522/R
£480 $802 €701 Standing female nude (60x50cm-24x20in) exhib. 16-Oct-3 Christie's, Kensington #502
£500 $835 €730 Tuscan village on a hill (35x57cm-14x22in) s. 16-Oct-3 Christie's, Kensington #516
£550 $919 €803 Devon coast (30x41cm-12x16in) s.i.verso panel. 16-Oct-3 Christie's, Kensington #526
£600 $1002 €876 Tree by a pond (51x27cm-20x11in) s.d.1921 board. 16-Oct-3 Christie's, Kensington #508/R
£650 $1086 €949 River bank (35x51cm-14x20in) canvasboard. 16-Oct-3 Christie's, Kensington #512
£650 $1086 €949 Boulevard in Paris (39x30cm-15x12in) s.d.1946 exhib. 16-Oct-3 Christie's, Kensington #518/R
£650 $1086 €949 Tree in the wind (56x42cm-22x17in) s.d.1920. 16-Oct-3 Christie's, Kensington #520
£700 $1169 €1022 Lake Orta (41x55cm-16x22in) s.d.1920 exhib. 16-Oct-3 Christie's, Kensington #517/R
£700 $1169 €1022 Count Tossa's children (129x88cm-51x35in) s.d.1920 exhib. 16-Oct-3 Christie's, Kensington #535/R
£750 $1253 €1095 Orange tree in a Spanish patio (41x32cm-16x13in) s.d.1936 panel. 16-Oct-3 Christie's, Kensington #515/R
£850 $1420 €1241 Cliffs at Seaford (41x31cm-16x12in) canvas on board exhib. 16-Oct-3 Christie's, Kensington #525/R
£900 $1503 €1314 Seated nudes (21x15cm-8x6in) pair. 16-Oct-3 Christie's, Kensington #485
£900 $1503 €1314 Luxembourg Gardens, Paris (56x48cm-22x19in) s.d.1946 exhib. 16-Oct-3 Christie's, Kensington #513/R
£900 $1503 €1314 Zeppelin over London (21x21cm-8x8in) i.d.1915.1914 verso exhib. 16-Oct-3 Christie's, Kensington #527/R
£950 $1587 €1387 Fantasy (43x40cm-17x16in) exhib. 16-Oct-3 Christie's, Kensington #530/R
£1000 $1670 €1460 Figures on a beach at Seaford (33x34cm-13x13in) canvas on board exhib. 16-Oct-3 Christie's, Kensington #506/R est:200-300
£1000 $1670 €1460 Fountain in Luxembourg Gardens (54x65cm-21x26in) s.d.1939-46. 16-Oct-3 Christie's, Kensington #511/R est:700-1000
£1000 $1670 €1460 Street scene, Sarajevo (22x34cm-9x13in) canvasboard exhib. 16-Oct-3 Christie's, Kensington #534/R est:300-500
£1900 $3173 €2774 Hilda, Gilbert and friends in the living room (63x76cm-25x30in) 16-Oct-3 Christie's, Kensington #533/R est:400-600
£2400 $4008 €3504 Luxembourg Gardens, Paris (60x73cm-24x29in) exhib. 16-Oct-3 Christie's, Kensington #514/R est:700-1000
£2400 $4008 €3504 Waterfall, Mostar (57x46cm-22x18in) s.d.1922 exhib. 16-Oct-3 Christie's, Kensington #519/R est:800-1200
£2800 $4676 €4088 Cliffs, Seaford (102x62cm-40x24in) exhib. 16-Oct-3 Christie's, Kensington #524/R est:1000-1500
£3000 $5010 €4380 Children with toys in a dell (76x76cm-30x30in) s.d.1933 exhib. 16-Oct-3 Christie's, Kensington #507/R est:3000-5000
£3500 $5845 €5110 Red deckchair (34x25cm-13x10in) s.d.1935 board. 16-Oct-3 Christie's, Kensington #523/R est:500-700
£4800 $8016 €7008 Fireplace (27x35cm-11x14in) canvas on board exhib. 16-Oct-3 Christie's, Kensington #498/R est:2000-3000
£6500 $10855 €9490 Woman in a red hat (61x49cm-24x19in) s.d.1922 exhib. 16-Oct-3 Christie's, Kensington #496/R est:1000-1500
£6500 $10855 €9490 Downshire Hill Garden (56x75cm-22x30in) s.d.1934 exhib. 16-Oct-3 Christie's, Kensington #503/R est:3000-5000
£21000 $35070 €30660 Portrait of Stanley Spencer (61x46cm-24x18in) exhib. 16-Oct-3 Christie's, Kensington #500/R est:7000-10000
Works on paper
£300 $501 €438 Patchwork fields (21x27cm-8x11in) W/C. 16-Oct-3 Christie's, Kensington #509
£350 $585 €511 Miss Silcox (34x23cm-13x9in) i. pencil exhib. 16-Oct-3 Christie's, Kensington #501
£350 $585 €511 Vision of God in Heaven (49x75cm-19x30in) pastel exhib. 16-Oct-3 Christie's, Kensington #529/R
£1100 $1837 €1606 Portrait of Gilbert Spencer (38x28cm-15x11in) i. pencil exec.c.1920. 16-Oct-3 Christie's, Kensington #483/R est:300-500
£1500 $2505 €2190 Reclining nude (21x28cm-8x11in) s. pencil sold with a portfolio of drawings. 16-Oct-3 Christie's, Kensington #484/R est:600-800
£1500 $2505 €2190 Portrait of a woman (25x23cm-10x9in) s.d.1922 pencil sold with figure studies by the same hand. 16-Oct-3 Christie's, Kensington #486/R est:300-1200
£1600 $2672 €2336 Self portrait (26x18cm-10x7in) s.i.d.1922 pencil. 16-Oct-3 Christie's, Kensington #482/R est:400-600

CARLINE, Richard (1896-1980) British
£2200 $3674 €3212 Gilbert and Janet pairing up for tennis (157x96cm-62x38in) 16-Oct-3 Christie's, Kensington #544/R est:1200-1800

CARLINI, Fanny (19th C) Italian?
£629 $1145 €950 Peasants with peasants in background (19x31cm-7x12in) s. board. 18-Jun-4 Stadion, Trieste #182/R

CARLISLE, Fionna (1954-) British
£380 $707 €555 Wick Gala Night (29x24cm-11x9in) s. acrylic paper. 6-Mar-4 Shapes, Edinburgh #446

CARLISLE, John (fl.1866-1893) British
Works on paper
£520 $962 €759 Highland cattle watering in a misty loch landscape (28x51cm-11x20in) s. W/C. 14-Jan-4 Brightwells, Leominster #836

CARLO, Chiostri (19th C) Italian
£659 $1100 €962 Venetian view (36x58cm-14x23in) s. i.verso. 20-Jun-3 Freeman, Philadelphia #227/R

CARLO, Vittorio Maria di (1939-) Italian
£267 $491 €400 From Congo (60x60cm-24x24in) s. oil collage. 12-Jun-4 Meeting Art, Vercelli #655
£275 $509 €410 Sari Sari (80x60cm-31x24in) s. s.verso oil sand. 13-Mar-4 Meeting Art, Vercelli #438
£300 $552 €450 Musical instrument (50x50cm-20x20in) s. oil collage. 12-Jun-4 Meeting Art, Vercelli #450/R
£333 $613 €500 Summer feeling (80x80cm-31x31in) s. 12-Jun-4 Meeting Art, Vercelli #166/R
£340 $619 €500 Figure (60x80cm-24x31in) s. painted 1979. 6-Feb-4 Galleria Rosenberg, Milan #147/R
£340 $619 €500 Maternity (60x80cm-24x31in) s. 6-Feb-4 Galleria Rosenberg, Milan #159/R
£367 $675 €550 Waiting (80x80cm-31x31in) s. oil sand. 12-Jun-4 Meeting Art, Vercelli #538/R
£376 $695 €560 Girls (70x70cm-28x28in) s. s.d.1991 verso. 13-Mar-4 Meeting Art, Vercelli #455
£403 $745 €600 Sari Sari (60x60cm-24x24in) s. s.verso oil collage. 13-Mar-4 Meeting Art, Vercelli #172
£705 $1304 €1050 Sari Sari (60x120cm-24x47in) s. oil collage. 13-Mar-4 Meeting Art, Vercelli #272

CARLONE, Carlo (attrib) (1686-1776) Italian
£1500 $2700 €2190 Assumption of the Virgin (63x49cm-25x19in) 23-Apr-4 Christie's, Kensington #242/R est:1500-2500

CARLONE, Giovan Battista (17th C) Italian
£52000 $95160 €75920 Virgin and Child in glory with Saints (122x97cm-48x38in) prov. 8-Jul-4 Sotheby's, London #161/R est:40000-60000
Sculpture
£13103 $21752 €19000 St John the Baptist (130cm-51in) wood. 30-Sep-3 Dorotheum, Vienna #189/R est:23000-28000

CARLOS, J (20th C) ?
Works on paper
£2015 $3566 €3023 Untitled (45x33cm-18x13in) s. W/C mixed media. 27-Apr-4 Bolsa de Arte, Rio de Janeiro #44/R (B.R 11000)
£2656 $4860 €3984 Untitled (45x33cm-18x13in) s. W/C mixed media. 6-Jul-4 Bolsa de Arte, Rio de Janeiro #62/R (B.R 14500)

CARLOS-LEFEBVRE, Charles (1853-1938) French
Works on paper
£1007 $1873 €1500 Paysage au printemps (70x100cm-28x39in) s.d.1900 pastel cardboard. 2-Mar-4 Artcurial Briest, Paris #106 est:1500-2000

CARLOTTI, Jean Albert (1909-2003) French
£1067 $1941 €1600 Rue de Lyon (68x42cm-27x17in) 29-Jun-4 Chenu & Scrive, Lyon #33/R est:1000-1400

CARLOW, William (?) British?
Works on paper
£290 $499 €423 Chickens feeding near haystacks (23x33cm-9x13in) s. W/C. 4-Dec-3 Richardson & Smith, Whitby #429

CARLSEN, Bjorn (1945-) Norwegian
£425 $710 €621 Woman with wings (55x45cm-22x18in) s. 17-Nov-3 Blomqvist, Lysaker #1021/R (N.KR 5100)
£1281 $2139 €1870 In the development spiral (59x127cm-23x50in) s. panel. 13-Oct-3 Blomqvist, Oslo #326/R est:18000-22000 (N.KR 15000)
£6405 $11465 €9351 Paradise (96x117cm-38x46in) s.d.1996 verso exhib. 22-Mar-4 Blomqvist, Oslo #666/R est:60000-80000 (N.KR 80000)
Works on paper
£329 $560 €480 Composition (84x72cm-33x28in) s.d.1994 W/C. 26-Nov-3 Kunsthallen, Copenhagen #176 (D.KR 3500)

CARLSEN, Carl (1855-1917) Danish
£375 $611 €548 Wooded landscape with path (44x56cm-17x22in) s. 27-Sep-3 Rasmussen, Havnen #2035 (D.KR 4000)
£513 $805 €749 A regular customer (36x31cm-14x12in) s. 30-Aug-3 Rasmussen, Havnen #2125 (D.KR 5500)
£967 $1769 €1412 Coastal landscape towards Kronborg (32x49cm-13x19in) s.d.90. 9-Jun-4 Rasmussen, Copenhagen #1955/R (D.KR 10800)
£1229 $2126 €1794 Landscape with golden cornfield (63x94cm-25x37in) init.d.82. 9-Dec-3 Rasmussen, Copenhagen #1681/R est:6000-8000 (D.KR 13000)
£1253 $2294 €1829 Summer landscape with two children in wood (100x130cm-39x51in) s. 9-Jun-4 Rasmussen, Copenhagen #1712/R est:15000-20000 (D.KR 14000)
£2434 $4066 €3554 Summer's day by river, three girls picking flowers (95x125cm-37x49in) s.d.1900. 25-Oct-3 Rasmussen, Havnen #2051/R est:7000-10000 (D.KR 26000)
£2647 $4578 €3865 Walking on a path north of Kronborg (39x82cm-15x32in) s.d.93. 9-Dec-3 Rasmussen, Copenhagen #1450/R est:30000 (D.KR 28000)
£2991 $4725 €4337 Two girls in a boat (37x47cm-15x19in) s.d.95. 2-Sep-3 Rasmussen, Copenhagen #1608/R est:30000 (D.KR 32000)
£4029 $7372 €5882 River landscape with three girls in summer (94x126cm-37x50in) s.d.1900. 9-Jun-4 Rasmussen, Copenhagen #1441/R est:50000-60000 (D.KR 45000)
£24172 $44235 €35291 Summer outing to the beach (77x117cm-30x46in) s.d.1894. 9-Jun-4 Rasmussen, Copenhagen #1469/R est:60000-80000 (D.KR 270000)

CARLSEN, Dines (1901-1966) American
£299 $550 €437 Boats near coastal rocks (30x38cm-12x15in) masonite. 25-Jun-4 Freeman, Philadelphia #281/R
£682 $1200 €996 Mountain town, mexico (64x81cm-25x32in) s. i.stretcher painted c.1940. 23-May-4 Treadway Gallery, Cincinnati #616/R
£2793 $5000 €4078 Mountain laurel in a vase (97x86cm-38x34in) s. masonite. 6-May-4 Shannon's, Milford #227/R est:5000-7000
£17045 $30000 €24886 Still life with Chinese vase (81x69cm-32x27in) s.d.1918 prov. 19-May-4 Sotheby's, New York #6/R est:15000-25000

CARLSEN, Emil (1853-1932) American/Danish
£950 $1700 €1387 Working men (56x33cm-22x13in) oil onionskin paper exhib. 7-May-4 Sloans & Kenyon, Bethesda #1723/R est:3000-4000
£1341 $2200 €1944 Still life with fruit and goblet (58x74cm-23x29in) s.d.1894 prov. 31-May-3 Brunk, Ashville #669/R est:500-1000
£1436 $2600 €2097 Under sea view with tropical fish (64x76cm-25x30in) s. 3-Apr-4 Nadeau, Windsor #302/R est:2500-4000
£1882 $3500 €2748 Kitchen (66x41cm-26x16in) s. 7-Mar-4 William Jenack, New York #238 est:5000-7000
£2210 $4000 €3227 Signal to the bathers (76x114cm-30x45in) s. 16-Apr-4 James Julia, Fairfield #733/R est:6000-8000
£2346 $3800 €3402 Ogunquit (13x16cm-5x6in) s. s.i.d.1923 verso board. 8-Aug-3 Barridorf, Portland #192/R est:2500-3500
£3073 $5500 €4487 Coastal views (14x16cm-6x6in) s. one s.i.d.1920 verso canvasboard pair prov. 14-May-4 Skinner, Boston #266/R est:2000-4000
£3086 $5000 €4475 Portrait of a young auburn haired lady in a hat full of roses (89x64cm-35x25in) s.d.1897. 26-Jul-3 Thomaston Place, Thomaston #99/R
£3226 $5935 €4710 Still life with bowl of grapes, bottles and stoneware (30x46cm-12x18in) bears sig. 14-Jun-4 Waddingtons, Toronto #17/R est:4000-6000 (C.D 8000)
£4321 $7000 €6265 Bald head cliff, York, Maine (36x41cm-14x16in) s. exhib. 8-Aug-3 Barridorf, Portland #289/R est:4000-6000
£34091 $60000 €49773 Still life with roses and mandolin (64x112cm-25x44in) s.d.84 prov. 19-May-4 Sotheby's, New York #5/R est:30000-40000
£46512 $80000 €67908 Trees in full summer (63x77cm-25x30in) s. painted c.1915 prov. 3-Dec-3 Sotheby's, New York #13/R est:60000-80000

CARLSEN, Peter (1955-) Danish
£422 $725 €616 General Custer realising his defeat (70x100cm-28x39in) init.d.15.2.1983 verso oil collage panel. 3-Dec-3 Museumsbygningen, Copenhagen #54/R (D.KR 4500)
£587 $1079 €857 Warm, wet and Villy (52x46cm-20x18in) s.d.2003 prov. 29-Mar-4 Rasmussen, Copenhagen #420/R (D.KR 6500)

CARLSON, George (1940-) American
Works on paper
£6145 $11000 €8972 Leche con Nescafe (69x48cm-27x19in) pastel. 15-May-4 Altermann Galleries, Santa Fe #6/R

CARLSON, John F (1875-1947) American
£1117 $2000 €1631 Fall thicket (66x94cm-26x37in) i.stretcher. 8-Jan-4 James Julia, Fairfield #745/R est:800-1200
£1285 $2300 €1876 View in Colorado (36x46cm-14x18in) s.d.1933. 11-Jan-4 William Jenack, New York #102 est:2000-3000
£3593 $6000 €5246 Crescendo (46x61cm-18x24in) s.i.stretcher prov. 23-Oct-3 Shannon's, Milford #226/R est:6000-8000
£5028 $9000 €7341 Winter landscape (76x91cm-30x36in) i.verso. 8-Jan-4 James Julia, Fairfield #744/R est:6000-8000
£5780 $10000 €8439 In snowy silence (41x51cm-16x20in) 12-Dec-3 Du Mouchelle, Detroit #2003/R est:2000-3500
£5864 $9500 €8503 Autumn sunlight (50x70cm-20x28in) s. 8-Aug-3 Barridorf, Portland #111/R est:5000-7000
£13966 $25000 €20390 March morning (64x76cm-25x30in) s. i.stretcher prov. 26-May-4 Doyle, New York #72/R est:15000-25000
Works on paper
£267 $425 €390 Landscape with rolling hills with trees and farm fields (15x20cm-6x8in) s. graphite sketch verso. 10-Sep-3 Alderfer's, Hatfield #285/R

CARLSON, Ken (1937-) American
£4278 $8000 €6246 Autumn theater (30x61cm-12x24in) s. board. 24-Jul-4 Coeur d'Alene, Hayden #14/R est:8000-12000
£40107 $75000 €58556 Endless ice (46x91cm-18x36in) s. board. 24-Jul-4 Coeur d'Alene, Hayden #89/R est:20000-30000

CARLSTEDT, Birger (1907-1975) Finnish
£537 $988 €800 Flowers (41x34cm-16x13in) s.d.1945. 25-Mar-4 Hagelstam, Helsinki #1054
£671 $1248 €1000 Waiting (147x114cm-58x45in) s.d.39. 7-Mar-4 Bukowskis, Helsinki #302/R
£1748 $2972 €2500 Flowers in vase (120x80cm-47x31in) s.d.42. 29-Nov-3 Bukowskis, Helsinki #281/R est:2500-2800
£2000 $3580 €3000 Nature morte (103x82cm-41x32in) s.d.1941 exhib. 15-May-4 Hagelstam, Helsinki #205/R est:2500

£2148	$3952	€3200	Aubusson choral I (45x28cm-18x11in) s. painted c.1962. 25-Mar-4 Hagelstam, Helsinki #812/R est:3000
£2394	$4142	€3400	Aubusson, Corrida I (26x40cm-10x16in) s. tempera exhib. 13-Dec-3 Hagelstam, Helsinki #187/R est:3500

CARLSTEDT, Mikko (1892-1964) Finnish

£599	$958	€850	Still life of fruit and flowers (53x64cm-21x25in) s. 18-Sep-3 Hagelstam, Helsinki #781/R
£625	$1044	€900	Flowers (66x55cm-26x22in) s.d.40. 23-Oct-3 Hagelstam, Helsinki #1019
£699	$1189	€1000	The last of the snow (46x62cm-18x24in) s.d.13. 29-Nov-3 Bukowskis, Helsinki #83/R
£705	$1297	€1050	Red peonies in glass vase (61x50cm-24x20in) s.d.1948. 25-Mar-4 Hagelstam, Helsinki #885/R

CARLSTROM, Gustaf (1896-1964) Swedish

£428	$770	€642	Girl picking reeds (82x65cm-32x26in) s. panel. 25-Apr-4 Goteborg Auktionsverk, Sweden #337/R (S.KR 5900)
£480	$865	€701	Summer trousers (81x65cm-32x26in) s. panel. 26-Jan-4 Lilla Bukowskis, Stockholm #160 (S.KR 6400)
£492	$801	€718	Girl by dam (73x81cm-29x32in) s. 29-Sep-3 Lilla Bukowskis, Stockholm #308 (S.KR 6400)
£538	$876	€785	Oh, I've got real pain in my feet (81x65cm-32x26in) s. panel. 29-Sep-3 Lilla Bukowskis, Stockholm #645 (S.KR 7000)
£601	$1081	€877	Look - there is the rainbow (78x65cm-31x26in) s. panel. 26-Jan-4 Lilla Bukowskis, Stockholm #785 (S.KR 8000)
£834	$1501	€1251	Girl seated by water (65x82cm-26x32in) s. 25-Apr-4 Goteborg Auktionsverk, Sweden #346/R (S.KR 11500)
£870	$1566	€1305	Coastal landscape with girl in yellow dress (82x65cm-32x26in) s. panel. 25-Apr-4 Goteborg Auktionsverk, Sweden #393/R (S.KR 12000)
£906	$1632	€1359	Girl seated by water's edge (55x50cm-22x20in) s. 25-Apr-4 Goteborg Auktionsverk, Sweden #373/R (S.KR 12500)
£1293	$2315	€1888	Summer morning (73x81cm-29x32in) s. 26-May-4 AB Stockholms Auktionsverk #2305/R est:20000-25000 (S.KR 17500)
£1308	$2249	€1910	Two boys by the water (73x60cm-29x24in) s. 2-Dec-3 Bukowskis, Stockholm #159/R est:12000-15000 (S.KR 17000)
£1385	$2548	€2078	Girls by water (60x73cm-24x29in) s. 14-Jun-4 Lilla Bukowskis, Stockholm #330 est:15000 (S.KR 19000)

CARLSUND, Otto (1897-1948) Swedish

Works on paper

£302	$514	€441	Geometric diagram (21x21cm-8x8in) init. mixed media prov. 5-Nov-3 AB Stockholms Auktionsverk #711/R (S.KR 4000)
£302	$514	€441	Geometric diagram (21x18cm-8x7in) s. mixed media prov. 5-Nov-3 AB Stockholms Auktionsverk #713/R (S.KR 4000)
£302	$514	€441	Geometric diagram (21x19cm-8x7in) init. mixed media prov. 5-Nov-3 AB Stockholms Auktionsverk #716/R (S.KR 4000)
£317	$539	€463	Tesserakt (16x17cm-6x7in) s. i.verso mixed media prov. 5-Nov-3 AB Stockholms Auktionsverk #714/R (S.KR 4200)
£355	$603	€518	Geometric diagram (20x20cm-8x8in) init. Indian ink prov. 5-Nov-3 AB Stockholms Auktionsverk #712/R (S.KR 4700)
£831	$1412	€1213	Geometric diagram (21x18cm-8x7in) init. mixed media prov. 5-Nov-3 AB Stockholms Auktionsverk #715/R (S.KR 11000)
£1813	$3082	€2647	The town on the mountain (49x32cm-19x13in) s.d.1947 crayon exhib. 5-Nov-3 AB Stockholms Auktionsverk #775/R est:20000-25000 (S.KR 24000)
£10355	$18640	€15118	No.1. Le pompier - fireman (25x12cm-10x5in) s.d.26 i.verso W/C gouache. 26-Apr-4 Bukowskis, Stockholm #70a/R est:40000-50000 (S.KR 142800)
£10355	$18640	€15118	No.2. L'operateur gris - grey machine-man (25x12cm-10x5in) s.d.26 i.verso W/C. 26-Apr-4 Bukowskis, Stockholm #70b/R est:40000-50000 (S.KR 142800)
£10355	$18640	€15118	No.4. Machine rouge - red machine (25x12cm-10x5in) s.d.26 i.verso W/C. 26-Apr-4 Bukowskis, Stockholm #70c/R est:40000-50000 (S.KR 142800)
£10355	$18640	€15118	No.5. Les acteurs - the actors (25x12cm-10x5in) s.d.26 i.verso W/C gouache. 26-Apr-4 Bukowskis, Stockholm #70d/R est:40000-50000 (S.KR 142800)
£10355	$18640	€15118	No.6. Machine verte - green machine (25x12cm-10x5in) s.d.26 i.verso W/C. 26-Apr-4 Bukowskis, Stockholm #70e/R est:40000-50000 (S.KR 142800)
£10355	$18640	€15118	No.8. L'operateur brun - brown machine-man (25x12cm-10x5in) s.d.26 i.verso W/C. 26-Apr-4 Bukowskis, Stockholm #70f/R est:40000-50000 (S.KR 142800)
£10384	$18692	€15161	No.9. L'homme au megaphone - the megaphone man II (25x12cm-10x5in) s.d.26 i.verso W/C. 26-Apr-4 Bukowskis, Stockholm #70g/R est:40000-50000 (S.KR 143200)

CARLTON, Frederick (19th C) British

£226	$378	€330	Thirlemere, Cumberland (30x50cm-12x20in) s. i.verso. 17-Nov-3 Waddingtons, Toronto #94/R (C.D 500)
£320	$598	€480	Highland cattle watering (51x76cm-20x30in) s. 22-Jul-4 Gorringes, Lewes #1796
£1100	$1837	€1606	Rustic conversation (51x74cm-20x29in) s. 13-Nov-3 Christie's, Kensington #150/R
£1200	$2160	€1752	Summer landscape with mother and child beside wooden gate (51x76cm-20x30in) s. 21-Apr-4 Tennants, Leyburn #1143 est:900-1200

CARLU, Anne (1895-1972) French

£2334	$4200	€3500	Paix sur la terre (105x195cm-41x77in) s.d.51 i.verso lit. 26-Apr-4 Tajan, Paris #143/R est:4000-6000
£4667	$8400	€7000	La pluie (199x114cm-78x45in) s.d.1943 lit. 26-Apr-4 Tajan, Paris #141/R est:8000-10000

CARLU, Jean (20th C) French

Works on paper

£493	$853	€700	Collage constructiviste (29x19cm-11x7in) s. collage W/C exec.c.1925. 13-Dec-3 Martinot & Savignat, Pontoise #19
£507	$877	€720	Collage abstrait constructiviste (29x20cm-11x8in) s. collage W/C exec.c.1925 prov. 13-Dec-3 Martinot & Savignat, Pontoise #20

CARLYLE, Florence (1864-1923) Canadian

£2811	$5229	€4104	Kneeling child (18x13cm-7x5in) studio st.verso board. 2-Mar-4 Ritchie, Toronto #54/R est:800-1200 (C.D 7000)
£5285	$9459	€7716	Miss Washington (38x43cm-15x17in) i.verso prov.exhib. 31-May-4 Sotheby's, Toronto #185/R est:5000-7000 (C.D 13000)

CARMAGO, Jesus Pablo (1949-) ?

£400	$716	€600	Sunny landscape (45x37cm-18x15in) s. 11-May-4 Vendu Notarishuis, Rotterdam #124

CARMASSI, Arturo (1925-) Italian

£493	$863	€700	Woman (50x50cm-20x20in) s. s.d.1963 verso. 16-Dec-3 Finarte Semenzato, Milan #341/R
£533	$981	€800	Composition (34x45cm-13x18in) s.d.1960 verso. 8-Jun-4 Finarte Semenzato, Milan #84/R
£1133	$2085	€1700	Composition (122x56cm-48x22in) s.d.1982 canvas on board. 8-Jun-4 Finarte Semenzato, Milan #80/R est:800-1000
£1594	$2614	€2200	Untitled (98x67cm-39x26in) s.d.1955 oil mixed media paper on canvas. 27-May-3 Sotheby's, Milan #34 est:800-1000
£2600	$4784	€3900	L (130x100cm-51x39in) s. s.d.1967 verso. 10-Jun-4 Galleria Pace, Milan #146/R est:6000

Works on paper

£278	$506	€420	Composition (44x64cm-17x25in) s. mixed media exec.1959. 17-Jun-4 Galleria Pananti, Florence #214/R
£467	$845	€700	Untitled (23x20cm-9x8in) s. mixed media card. 2-Apr-4 Farsetti, Prato #276
£800	$1472	€1200	Lucca I (72x91cm-28x36in) s.i.d.1961 verso mixed media on canvas. 8-Jun-4 Finarte Semenzato, Milan #82/R
£800	$1472	€1200	IV (79x79cm-31x31in) s.i.d.1961 verso mixed media on canvas. 8-Jun-4 Finarte Semenzato, Milan #83/R est:800-1000
£933	$1717	€1400	Composition (30x27cm-12x11in) s. mixed media collage exec.1956. 12-Jun-4 Meeting Art, Vercelli #437/R
£7692	$13077	€11000	Farewell VI (73x60cm-29x24in) s.d.58 verso collage mixed media on canvas exhib.lit. 26-Nov-3 Pandolfini, Florence #58/R est:10000-12000

CARMASSI, Enrico (1899-1976) Italian

Sculpture

£1916	$3257	€2740	Greta Garbo (35cm-14in) s. pat bronze marble base exec.1931 prov. 18-Nov-3 Babuino, Rome #380/R est:1000-1200

CARMELO DE ARZADUN (1888-1968) Uruguayan

£556	$900	€806	Cottage scene (35x45cm-14x18in) s. 29-Jul-3 Galeria y Remates, Montevideo #96/R
£571	$1050	€834	Las Flores (33x41cm-13x16in) s. cardboard. 22-Jun-4 Galeria y Remates, Montevideo #65/R
£648	$1050	€940	Sarmiento Avenue and Ramirez beach (36x45cm-14x18in) s. 29-Jul-3 Galeria y Remates, Montevideo #97/R
£909	$1600	€1327	Southern area (40x29cm-16x11in) s. prov. 5-Jan-4 Galeria y Remates, Montevideo #87/R est:1500-2000
£912	$1550	€1332	Baby and doll (60x45cm-24x18in) s. cardboard. 25-Nov-3 Galeria y Remates, Montevideo #31/R
£988	$1600	€1433	Rodo Park (58x69cm-23x27in) s. board. 29-Jul-3 Galeria y Remates, Montevideo #95/R est:2000-3000
£1294	$2200	€1889	Beach and groves (46x61cm-18x24in) s. cardboard. 25-Nov-3 Galeria y Remates, Montevideo #128/R
£1364	$2400	€1991	Fermin's house (56x46cm-22x18in) s. lit. 5-Jan-4 Galeria y Remates, Montevideo #86/R est:3200-3800
£1765	$3000	€2577	Ramirez beach (18x27cm-7x11in) s.d.1916 cardboard. 25-Nov-3 Galeria y Remates, Montevideo #29/R
£1941	$3300	€2834	Peasant eating watermelon (57x42cm-22x17in) s.d.48 cardboard. 25-Nov-3 Galeria y Remates, Montevideo #30/R
£2000	$3400	€2920	Man (65x50cm-26x20in) s.d.1940 cardboard. 25-Nov-3 Galeria y Remates, Montevideo #129/R
£2116	$4000	€3089	Montevideo in abstraction (46x54cm-18x21in) s.d.32 panel. 22-Feb-4 Galeria y Remates, Montevideo #58/R est:4500-5500

CARMI, Eugenio (1920-) Italian

£317	$526	€450	Piccolo equilibrio (20x20cm-8x8in) s.i.d.2002 verso acrylic canvas on panel. 14-Jun-3 Meeting Art, Vercelli #40/R
£336	$621	€500	Silence (25x25cm-10x10in) s.d.2000 verso. 13-Mar-4 Meeting Art, Vercelli #76
£369	$683	€550	Study (20x20cm-8x8in) s.d.1992. 13-Mar-4 Meeting Art, Vercelli #290
£369	$683	€550	Hope (25x25cm-10x10in) s.d.2000. 13-Mar-4 Meeting Art, Vercelli #332
£467	$859	€700	Oxymoron (30x20cm-12x8in) s.i.d.1987. 12-Jun-4 Meeting Art, Vercelli #461/R
£510	$929	€750	Dialogue (30x35cm-12x14in) s.verso painted 1999. 6-Feb-4 Galleria Rosenberg, Milan #36/R
£567	$1043	€850	Fantasy sign (50x40cm-20x16in) s.d.1974. 12-Jun-4 Meeting Art, Vercelli #410/R
£599	$994	€850	Incontro (30x40cm-12x16in) s.d.2001 s.i.d.verso. 14-Jun-3 Meeting Art, Vercelli #555/R
£600	$1104	€900	Triangle on white (80x80cm-31x31in) s.d.1973 verso acrylic. 11-Jun-4 Farsetti, Prato #176/R
£671	$1201	€1000	Strolling in Los Angeles (60x60cm-24x24in) s.d.2001 s.i.d.verso. 30-May-4 Meeting Art, Vercelli #12
£690	$1103	€1000	Revelation (60x80cm-24x31in) s.d.1990 verso. 13-Mar-3 Galleria Pace, Milan #159/R
£800	$1472	€1200	Space (100x80cm-39x31in) s.d.1973 acrylic. 11-Jun-4 Farsetti, Prato #224/R
£1678	$3104	€2500	Stressed look at the world (120x100cm-47x39in) d.2003 s.i.d.verso. 13-Mar-4 Meeting Art, Vercelli #125a est:2500
£1678	$3104	€2500	Situation L (100x100cm-39x39in) s.d.1972. 13-Mar-4 Meeting Art, Vercelli #398 est:2500
£1736	$2743	€2500	Original situation L (100x100cm-39x39in) painted 1972. 6-Sep-3 Meeting Art, Vercelli #596 est:2500
£2183	$3624	€3100	Segnale immaginario (100x100cm-39x39in) s.d.1974 s.i.d.verso. 14-Jun-3 Meeting Art, Vercelli #572/R est:2500

CARMICHAEL, Franklin (1890-1945) Canadian

£40541	$68919	€59190	Grace Lake (24x29cm-9x11in) s.d.1936 panel prov.exhib.lit. 27-Nov-3 Heffel, Vancouver #66/R est:90000-110000 (C.D 90000)
£44643	$76786	€65179	McGregor Bay (25x30cm-10x12in) board prov. 2-Dec-3 Joyner Waddington, Toronto #31/R est:75000-100000 (C.D 100000)

Works on paper

£16000	$29280	€23360	Northern Lake (27x32cm-11x13in) s.d.1927 lit. 1-Jun-4 Joyner Waddington, Toronto #20/R est:40000-50000 (C.D 40000)
£26423	$47297	€38578	Cranberry Lake (26x33cm-10x13in) s.d.1929 i.verso W/C. 27-May-4 Heffel, Vancouver #19/R est:40000-50000 (C.D 65000)
£26786	$46071	€39108	Lake, La Cloche (27x32cm-11x13in) s.d.1934 W/C. 2-Dec-3 Joyner Waddington, Toronto #48/R est:50000-60000 (C.D 60000)

CARMICHAEL, John Wilson (1800-1868) British

£250	$398	€365	Sailing ships at sea (6x10cm-2x4in) i. 18-Mar-3 Anderson & Garland, Newcastle #295/R
£300	$555	€438	Napoleon's troops crossing the Alps into Italy (30x44cm-12x17in) s.d.1859. 16-Feb-4 Bonhams, Bath #34
£340	$541	€496	Cullercoats looking to Tynemouth (9x15cm-4x6in) 18-Mar-3 Anderson & Garland, Newcastle #305
£440	$700	€642	Boats in a harbour (8x10cm-3x4in) 18-Mar-3 Anderson & Garland, Newcastle #293
£800	$1360	€1168	Break in the clouds offshore (30x43cm-12x17in) indis.sig.indis.d. 19-Nov-3 Christie's, Kensington #541/R
£1250	$2088	€1825	Dutch barges riding out a squall off the Low Countries (30x41cm-12x16in) s.d.1851. 7-Oct-3 Bonhams, Knightsbridge #171/R est:1200-1800
£1300	$2340	€1898	Napoleon and his troops crossing a mountain range in Italy (30x42cm-12x17in) s.indis.d. i.verso stretcher. 21-Apr-4 Tennants, Leyburn #1169 est:800-1200
£1374	$2500	€2006	Seascape with vessels and figures in rowing boat (50x61cm-20x24in) s. 7-Feb-4 Rasmussen, Havnen #2019/R est:7000-10000 (D.KR 15000)
£1400	$2506	€2044	Wensleydale, Yorshire (52x76cm-20x30in) s.d.1855. 27-May-4 Christie's, Kensington #163/R est:1000-2000
£1850	$3016	€2701	Sailing smack putting out lobster pots while conveying passengers to a ship (42x59cm-17x23in) s.d.1845 panel. 23-Sep-3 Anderson & Garland, Newcastle #430/R est:600-1000
£1984	$3670	€2897	Seascape with sailing vessel off cliffs in stormy sea (44x62cm-17x24in) s. 15-Mar-4 Rasmussen, Vejle #165/R est:30000-40000 (D.KR 22000)
£2000	$3260	€2920	Georgian country house facing a village square (34x54cm-13x21in) s.d.1863. 23-Sep-3 Anderson & Garland, Newcastle #429/R est:2000-3000
£2500	$4475	€3650	Going to the rescue (28x40cm-11x16in) s.d.1844 panel. 26-May-4 Christie's, Kensington #597/R est:3000-4000
£2800	$5236	€4088	Seaton, coast of Yorkshire with Seaton Carew (20x35cm-8x14in) s.d.1861 board. 22-Jul-4 Tennants, Leyburn #814/R est:1500-2000
£3000	$5160	€4380	Bridport, sailing out in gale (43x71cm-17x28in) s. indis d. i.on stretcher. 2-Dec-3 Sotheby's, London #21/R est:4000-6000
£3000	$5670	€4380	Shipping off a pier by moonlight (36x61cm-14x24in) s. 17-Feb-4 Bonhams, New Bond Street #64/R est:3000-5000
£5000	$9300	€7300	View across the Firth of Forth to Edinburgh, Castle, Holyrood Palace in the distance (66x99cm-26x39in) s.d.1862 prov. 4-Mar-4 Christie's, Kensington #23/R est:7000-10000
£5500	$10395	€8030	Burlington quay (20x36cm-8x14in) s.d.1862. 17-Feb-4 Bonhams, New Bond Street #65/R est:5000-8000
£6000	$9600	€8760	Busy shipping lane in the Channel (25x33cm-10x13in) s.d.1844 panel. 16-Sep-3 Bonhams, New Bond Street #16/R est:3000-5000
£6000	$9780	€8760	An 1840 Planet Locomotive crossing Wetheral Viaduct, River Eden (49x75cm-19x30in) 23-Sep-3 Anderson & Garland, Newcastle #428/R est:3000-5000
£6000	$10320	€8760	Lost oar (41x58cm-16x23in) s.d.1845. 2-Dec-3 Sotheby's, London #20/R est:6000-8000
£8000	$14720	€11680	Bamburgh Castle by moonlight, with figures and boats in the foreground (61x92cm-24x36in) s.d.1840 lit. 11-Jun-4 Christie's, London #65/R est:8000-12000
£8500	$16065	€12410	Shipping off Tynemouth (51x81cm-20x32in) s.d.1851. 17-Feb-4 Bonhams, New Bond Street #53/R est:6000-8000
£18000	$34020	€26280	Fresh Breeze (86x122cm-34x48in) init.d.1838 i.verso. 17-Feb-4 Bonhams, New Bond Street #63/R est:20000-30000

Works on paper

£420	$769	€613	On the Thames approaching Greenwich (14x21cm-6x8in) init. W/C pencil en grisaille. 27-Jan-4 Bonhams, Knightsbridge #277
£550	$985	€803	Funeral cortege waiting at the quayside (23x18cm-9x7in) W/C bodycol. 26-May-4 Christie's, Kensington #408/R
£600	$1020	€876	North Cliff, Flambro. Burlington Quay (25x36cm-10x14in) one s.d. January 1839 W/C htd white. 21-Nov-3 Dee Atkinson & Harrison, Driffield #778
£1200	$2268	€1752	Sketch on the coast at Howick, Northumberland (26x37cm-10x15in) s.d.1841 i.verso pencil W/C htd white prov. 17-Feb-4 Bonhams, New Bond Street #55/R est:600-800
£1200	$2268	€1752	Bass Rock and May Island from County Bay (26x37cm-10x15in) s.i.d.1842 pencil W/C htd white. 17-Feb-4 Bonhams, New Bond Street #56/R est:600-800
£3631	$6500	€5301	View of Berwick on Tweed (33x48cm-13x19in) s.d.1851 pencil W/C. 16-Mar-4 Bonhams & Butterfields, San Francisco #6186/R est:2500-3500
£3911	$7000	€5710	View of Edinburgh from Granton Pier (33x48cm-13x19in) s.d.1852 pencil W/C. 16-Mar-4 Bonhams & Butterfields, San Francisco #6185/R est:3500-5500
£3911	$7000	€5710	View of Chester (33x48cm-13x19in) s.d.1850 pencil W/C. 16-Mar-4 Bonhams & Butterfields, San Francisco #6190/R est:3000-5000
£4190	$7500	€6117	View of Scarborough (30x48cm-12x19in) init.indis.d. pencil W/C. 16-Mar-4 Bonhams & Butterfields, San Francisco #6187/R est:3000-5000
£4190	$7500	€6117	View of Leigh, Scotland (30x48cm-12x19in) s.d.1850 pencil W/C. 16-Mar-4 Bonhams & Butterfields, San Francisco #6191/R est:3000-5000
£6500	$11635	€9490	Trading brig and other vessels off the entrance to Scarborough (32x48cm-13x19in) init.indis.d. pencil W/C. 26-May-4 Christie's, Kensington #402/R est:6000-8000
£11000	$20790	€16060	Crowded Thames off Somerset House (50x73cm-20x29in) s.d.1857 W/C htd white. 17-Feb-4 Bonhams, New Bond Street #57/R est:8000-12000

CARMICHAEL, John Wilson (attrib) (1800-1868) British

£284	$500	€415	Castle on the Hill (38x53cm-15x21in) 23-May-4 Hindman, Chicago #23/R
£500	$935	€730	St Michael's Mount with figures in the bay (44x59cm-17x23in) 20-Jul-4 Dreweatt Neate, Newbury #206/R
£1100	$1969	€1606	Dutch barges unloading on the shore (25x34cm-10x13in) indis sig.d. 16-Mar-4 Bonhams, Leeds #650/R est:800-1200
£1600	$2912	€2336	Royal Navel frigate and small coastal craft in an estuary near a fort (44x60cm-17x24in) with sig.d. 29-Jun-4 Anderson & Garland, Newcastle #476/R est:600-900

CARMICHAEL, Stewart (1867-?) British

Works on paper

£867	$1500	€1266	Portrait of three women (28x41cm-11x16in) init.d.94 prov. 11-Dec-3 Sotheby's, New York #170/R est:2000-3000

CARMIENCKE, Johan-Herman (1810-1867) Danish/American

£2028	$3447	€2961	Landscape with view towards mountain lake (48x67cm-19x26in) 10-Nov-3 Rasmussen, Vejle #361/R est:8000 (D.KR 22000)

Works on paper

£378	$654	€552	Study of an old oak tree (40x28cm-16x11in) s. W/C pencil. 9-Dec-3 Rasmussen, Copenhagen #1725 (D.KR 4000)

CARMIENCKE, Johan-Herman (attrib) (1810-1867) Danish/American

£636	$1100	€929	European lakeside resort (21x16cm-8x6in) init. oil paperboard on board. 13-Dec-3 Weschler, Washington #521

CARMIGNANI, Guido (1838-1909) Italian

£3007	$5022	€4300	Coming storm (28x40cm-11x16in) s.d.1870. 24-Jun-3 Finarte Semenzato, Rome #112/R

CARMONTELLE, Louis Carrogis (1717-1806) French

Works on paper

£5000	$9150	€7300	Bertrand Barthelemi du Chesne de Saint Mars and Jean Baptiste le Moyne de Bellile seated by a window (30x21cm-12x8in) i. black lead red chk W/C. 6-Jul-4 Christie's, London #130/R est:5000-7000
£5587	$10000	€8157	Seated gentleman writing a letter (31x17cm-12x7in) chk W/C prov. 27-May-4 Sotheby's, New York #33/R est:15000-25000
£13605	$24354	€20000	Portrait de la Comtesse de Lenoncourt avec un homme debout derriere elle (34x21cm-13x8in) W/C traces blk crayon htd white gouache. 17-Mar-4 Tajan, Paris #51/R est:12000-15000
£24490	$43837	€36000	Femme assise cousant, accompagnee d'une jeune garcon en habit bleu (33x21cm-13x8in) black red chk W/C htd white prov.exhib. 18-Mar-4 Christie's, Paris #131/R est:30000-50000

CARNACINI, Ceferino (1888-1964) Argentinian

£503	$900	€734	Ambato Gate, Catamarca (24x35cm-9x14in) board. 11-May-4 Arroyo, Buenos Aires #14
£1749	$3200	€2554	Stream in autumn (71x77cm-28x30in) board. 1-Jun-4 Arroyo, Buenos Aires #22
£2486	$4500	€3630	British square (40x50cm-16x20in) board. 30-Mar-4 Arroyo, Buenos Aires #34

CARNEO, Antonio (attrib) (17th C) Italian

£2817	$4676	€4000	Scene de martyre (70x91cm-28x36in) 13-Jun-3 Ferri, Paris #54/R est:4000-6000

CARNERO, Jose Manuel (18th C) Mexican

£3911	$7000	€5710	Martyrdom of Saint Catherine. Martyrdom of Saint Barbara (61x48cm-24x19in) s. copper pair. 26-May-4 Sotheby's, New York #65/R est:10000-15000

CARNEVALI, Nino Giovanni (1849-?) Italian

£9211	$16671	€14000	Portrait of the Marquis of Remisa (42x32cm-17x13in) s. 14-Apr-4 Ansorena, Madrid #158/R est:12000

CARNICERO, Antonio (1748-1814) Spanish

£3409	$6000	€4977	Portrait of a gentleman in front of a lighthouse (62x49cm-24x19in) s.d.1809. 18-May-4 Sotheby's, New York #106/R est:10000-15000
£23944	$41423	€34000	Goyan figure (44x35cm-17x14in) 15-Dec-3 Ansorena, Madrid #320/R est:26000

CARNIEL, Richard (1868-1915) Italian

£369	$616	€520	Piazza della Borsa a Trieste (19x35cm-7x14in) s. 21-Jun-3 Stadion, Trieste #186/R

CARNIELO, Rinaldo (1853-1910) Italian

Sculpture

£3500	$6265	€5250	Winged satyr (83cm-33in) s.d.1883 bronze. 25-May-4 Sotheby's, Billingshurst #383/R est:4000-6000

CARNOVALI, Giovanni (1806-1873) Italian

£4085	$7066	€5800	Face of woman (50x40cm-20x16in) 10-Dec-3 Sotheby's, Milan #116/R est:5800-6800
£6738	$11252	€9500	Aminta's death (16x21cm-6x8in) 14-Oct-3 Finarte Semenzato, Milan #203/R
£8276	$13821	€12000	Allegory (14x43cm-6x17in) paper on canvas. 14-Nov-3 Farsetti, Prato #545/R est:12000-16000

Works on paper

£319	$533	€450	Rest during the Flight to Egypt (19x13cm-7x5in) pencil. 14-Oct-3 Finarte Semenzato, Milan #147/R
£638	$1066	€900	Odalisk playing (12x8cm-5x3in) s. pencil. 14-Oct-3 Finarte Semenzato, Milan #148/R
£1391	$2531	€2100	Self-portrait (15x11cm-6x4in) s.d.1859 sanguine. 17-Jun-4 Finarte Semenzato, Milan #292/R est:1200-1300

CARNOVALI, Giovanni (attrib) (1806-1873) Italian

£528	$914	€750	Nymph (14x11cm-6x4in) board. 9-Dec-3 Finarte Semenzato, Milan #121

CARNWATH, Squeak (1947-) American

£3243	$6000	€4735	Songs hum (92x92cm-36x36in) s.i.d.1990 verso oil alkyd prov.exhib. 12-Feb-4 Sotheby's, New York #231/R est:1800-2200
£3846	$7000	€5615	An inability to remain (178x178cm-70x70in) s.verso i.overlap oil alkyd on linen prov.lit. 29-Jun-4 Sotheby's, New York #613/R est:8000-12000

CARO, Anthony (1924-) British

Sculpture

£3243 $6000 €4735 Cigarette smoker (30x25cm-12x10in) brown pat bronze exec 1957. 12-Feb-4 Sotheby's, New York #140/R est:3000-4000
£5665 $9630 €8271 Little book - hide and seek (20x20x10cm-8x8x4in) brass polished porcelain exec.c.1996-97 exhib. 5-Nov-3 AB Stockholms Auktionsverk #1149/R est:80000-100000 (S.KR 75000)
£7186 $12000 €10492 Table Piece CCLXIII (46x135x76cm-18x53x30in) welded varnished steel exec 1975 prov.lit. 12-Nov-3 Christie's, Rockefeller NY #362/R est:30000-40000
£7500 $12900 €10950 Woman arranging her hair - Spring (79cm-31in) pale green pat bronze exec 1995 prov.exhib.lit. 3-Dec-3 Sotheby's, London #79/R est:9000-12000
£7975 $13000 €11644 Writing piece, this (62x46x41cm-24x18x16in) steel wood prov.lit. 23-Sep-3 Christie's, Rockefeller NY #29/R est:8000-12000
£10000 $18200 €14600 Z-67 (31x140x51cm-12x55x20in) rusted varnished steel exec 1981-82 prov.exhib.lit. 4-Feb-4 Sotheby's, Olympia #81/R est:10000-15000
£10615 $19000 €15498 Writing piece - Through (19x114x41cm-7x45x16in) steel painted blackened sheet steel exec 1978 prov.exhib.lit. 13-May-4 Sotheby's, New York #140/R est:25000-35000
£19553 $35000 €28547 Table Piece CCLXXV (77x86x58cm-30x34x23in) welded varnished rusted steel exec 75-76 prov.exhib.lit. 12-May-4 Christie's, Rockefeller NY #184/R est:22000-30000
£20000 $33400 €29200 Table piece - Catalan double (137x73x30cm-54x29x12in) steel exec 1987-88 prov.lit. 21-Oct-3 Sotheby's, London #418/R est:15000-20000
£22000 $40480 €32120 Piece CCXXNIII (43x135x38cm-17x53x15in) rusted varnished steel exec 1975 prov.lit. 24-Jun-4 Sotheby's, London #240/R est:12000-15000

Works on paper

£1100 $2046 €1606 Waves 1982 (42x34cm-17x13in) pen ink. 8-Mar-4 Christie's, London #8
£1397 $2500 €2040 Oats, paper sculpture number 109 (48x79cm-19x31in) s.i.d.1981 verso chk acrylic paper on Tycore prov. 16-May-4 Wright, Chicago #333/R est:2000-3000

CARO, Baldassare de (1689-c.1755) Italian

£3840 $6643 €5606 Still life with woodcock and other birds in a landscape (52x77cm-20x30in) mono. 9-Dec-3 Sotheby's, Olympia #242/R est:2000-3000

CARO, Baldassare de (attrib) (1689-c.1755) Italian

£2128 $3553 €3000 Tete de Bouledogue (49x59cm-19x23in) 17-Oct-3 Tajan, Paris #9 est:3000
£3104 $5557 €4532 Gundog sitting by dead game (96x134cm-38x53in) 26-May-4 AB Stockholms Auktionsverk #2513/R est:40000-50000 (S.KR 42000)
£4610 $7699 €6500 Still life with various game on stone ledge. Still life with various game on stone ledge (28x39cm-11x15in) two. 18-Jun-3 Christie's, Rome #326/R est:4000-6000

CARO, Giuseppe de (18th C) Italian

£8500 $14705 €12410 Fruit (25cm-10in circular) s. panel set of four. 12-Dec-3 Christie's, Kensington #253/R est:6000-8000

CARO, Pierre (?) French

Works on paper

£532 $840 €750 Jeune femme a l'ombrelle (64x48cm-25x19in) s. pastel. 24-Jul-3 Adjug'art, Brest #230/R

CAROLUS, Jean (1814-1897) Belgian

£839 $1401 €1200 Elegant young woman returning home (52x38cm-20x15in) s. panel. 28-Jun-3 Dannenberg, Berlin #659/R
£1154 $1962 €1650 Elegante songeuse devant la cheminee (32x24cm-13x9in) s. panel. 18-Nov-3 Vanderkindere, Brussels #205 est:1500-2500
£3691 $6829 €5500 La musique (65x47cm-26x19in) s.d.1862. 13-Mar-4 De Vuyst, Lokeren #410/R est:3000-5000
£6643 $11094 €9500 La visit a la jeune mere (82x105cm-32x41in) s.i.d.1868. 11-Oct-3 De Vuyst, Lokeren #508/R est:8000-10000
£7059 $12000 €10306 The letter (81x105cm-32x41in) s. indis.i. d.1866 prov. 28-Oct-3 Sotheby's, New York #146/R est:15000-20000
£7735 $14000 €11293 Letter (79x66cm-31x26in) s.d.1873. 3-Apr-4 Neal Auction Company, New Orleans #294/R est:15000-25000
£9412 $16000 €13742 Eavesdropper (77x96cm-30x38in) s.i.d.1880 prov. 28-Oct-3 Sotheby's, New York #145/R est:15000-20000
£10000 $17200 €14600 Billiards game in the 18th century (74x96cm-29x38in) s. 4-Dec-3 Christie's, Kensington #135/R est:10000-15000

Works on paper

£350 $585 €511 Lady and her maid (42x32cm-17x13in) s. W/C. 14-Oct-3 Bonhams, Knightsbridge #27/R

CAROLUS, Louis Antoine (1814-1865) Belgian

£448 $829 €650 Scene mythologique (77x56cm-30x22in) s. 19-Jan-4 Horta, Bruxelles #341

CAROLUS-DURAN, Émile Auguste (1838-1917) French

£680 $1218 €1000 Palette (40x54cm-16x21in) s.i. 19-Mar-4 Millon & Associes, Paris #13/R
£728 $1333 €1100 Portrait de femme (80x63cm-31x25in) s. 7-Apr-4 Piasa, Paris #9
£800 $1448 €1200 Religieux (26x20cm-10x8in) mono.d.62. 30-Mar-4 Rossini, Paris #768
£989 $1800 €1444 Portrait of General William F Draper (63x51cm-25x20in) s.d.1907 prov. 29-Jun-4 Sotheby's, New York #78/R est:3000-5000
£2649 $4848 €4000 Lamentation (71x101cm-28x40in) 7-Apr-4 Piasa, Paris #10/R est:4000-5000
£6897 $11448 €10000 Portrait de Mounet-Sully (64x53cm-25x21in) s.i.d.1892 prov.lit. 2-Oct-3 Sotheby's, Paris #110/R est:20000
£10345 $17172 €15000 Chien (79x167cm-31x66in) s.d.1861 el. 2-Oct-3 Sotheby's, Paris #68/R est:20000
£13194 $22035 €19000 Le ceuillette des roses au harem (186x109cm-73x43in) s.d.1883 lit. 22-Oct-3 Ribeyre & Baron, Paris #15/R est:20000
£26000 $47580 €39000 Berthe Claire de Rothschild (210x109cm-83x43in) s. prov. 6-Jun-4 Rouillac, Vendome #37
£105882 $180000 €154588 Triumph of Bacchus (360x500cm-142x197in) s.i.d.28 janviere 1889 lit. 28-Oct-3 Sotheby's, New York #49/R est:200000-250000

CARON, Joseph (1866-1944) Belgian

£347 $552 €500 Chemin en foret (67x69cm-26x27in) s. 9-Sep-3 Vanderkindere, Brussels #122
£379 $702 €550 La foret de Soignes sous la neige (81x110cm-32x43in) s. 16-Feb-4 Horta, Bruxelles #297
£426 $711 €600 Fermette (54x73cm-21x29in) s. 14-Oct-3 Vanderkindere, Brussels #34
£455 $782 €650 Meules de foin sur le champ (60x100cm-24x39in) s. 2-Dec-3 Campo & Campo, Antwerp #52
£822 $1397 €1200 Foret de Fontainebleau (85x95cm-33x37in) s.d.1926 i.verso. 10-Nov-3 Horta, Bruxelles #370
£2162 $3805 €3200 Allee des saules (100x150cm-39x59in) s. 18-May-4 Galerie Moderne, Brussels #174/R est:2000-3000

CARON, Louis (19th C) French

£1007 $1883 €1500 Landscape (74x88cm-29x35in) s. 26-Feb-4 Cambi, Genoa #569/R est:1200-1500

CARON, Marcel (1890-1961) Belgian

£352 $609 €500 La ferme (46x53cm-18x21in) s. panel prov. 10-Dec-3 Hotel des Ventes Mosan, Brussels #188
£423 $731 €600 Bord de riviere (23x32cm-9x13in) s. panel. 10-Dec-3 Hotel des Ventes Mosan, Brussels #191
£728 $1326 €1100 Abstraction (46x54cm-18x21in) mono.d.57 panel. 16-Jun-4 Hotel des Ventes Mosan, Brussels #212
£10563 $18275 €15000 L'homme a la cigarette (85x68cm-33x27in) s. i.d.1923 verso prov.lit. 10-Dec-3 Hotel des Ventes Mosan, Brussels #209/R est:12000-15000

Works on paper

£704 $1218 €1000 La foire (28x21cm-11x8in) s.d.juin 27 graphite chl. 10-Dec-3 Hotel des Ventes Mosan, Brussels #230
£1831 $3168 €2600 L'orchestre (21x22cm-8x9in) s. graphite chl exec.c.1925-29. 10-Dec-3 Hotel des Ventes Mosan, Brussels #231/R est:1200-1500

CARON, Paul Archibald (1874-1941) Canadian

£580 $969 €841 Stream in August (17x18cm-7x7in) s. board. 17-Jun-3 Pinneys, Montreal #16 est:1400-1800 (C.D 1300)
£633 $995 €924 Five below zero, Porcupine Rock, Murray River (13x17cm-5x7in) s. s.i.verso board. 26-Aug-3 Iegor de Saint Hippolyte, Montreal #66 (C.D 1400)
£814 $1279 €1188 18th Century houses, rue St Vincent, Montreal (13x17cm-5x7in) board. 26-Aug-3 Iegor de Saint Hippolyte, Montreal #67 (C.D 1800)
£905 $1421 €1321 Early spring, Ste Marguerite, PQ, Canada (24x27cm-9x11in) s. s.i.d.1938 verso. 26-Aug-3 Iegor de Saint Hippolyte, Montreal #65 (C.D 2000)
£1118 $2001 €1632 Village (12x18cm-5x7in) s. s.i.verso board prov. 31-May-4 Sotheby's, Toronto #136/R est:2000-3000 (C.D 2750)
£1220 $2183 €1781 Fir-clad hills in winter (13x17cm-5x7in) s. i.verso panel prov. 27-May-4 Heffel, Vancouver #27/R est:1500-2000 (C.D 3000)

Works on paper

£221 $411 €323 Edifice la sauvegarde (38x33cm-15x13in) s. i.verso graphite. 2-Mar-4 Ritchie, Toronto #83/R (C.D 550)
£804 $1382 €1174 Nude Study. Old Forge, Caughnawage (37x24cm-15x9in) one s. one d.1937 chl pencil ink four. 2-Dec-3 Joyner Waddington, Toronto #490 est:1500-2000 (C.D 1800)
£1760 $3221 €2570 Near La Malfaie, Quebec (26x36cm-10x14in) s. W/C prov. 1-Jun-4 Joyner Waddington, Toronto #19/R est:5000-6000 (C.D 4400)
£2236 $4002 €3265 Early evening Piedmont (28x39cm-11x15in) s. s.d.January 20th 1936 W/C prov. 31-May-4 Sotheby's, Toronto #108/R est:4000-6000 (C.D 5500)
£14640 $24887 €21374 Hauling ice, Old Montreal (38x56cm-15x22in) s. W/C prov. 21-Nov-3 Walker's, Ottawa #7/R est:10000-15000 (C.D 32500)

CAROSELLI, Angelo (1585-1652) Italian

£16667 $30000 €24334 Lady with dog (65x50cm-26x20in) prov. 22-Jan-4 Sotheby's, New York #41/R est:25000-35000

CAROSELLI, Angelo (attrib) (1585-1652) Italian

£19000 $34770 €27740 Portrait of a gentleman in a wide-brimmed red hat holding a mask (67x50cm-26x20in) panel. 7-Jul-4 Bonhams, New Bond Street #15/R est:8000-12000

CAROSI, Alberto (1891-1968) Italian

£567 $1014 €850 Spring landscape (28x33cm-11x13in) s. board. 12-May-4 Stadion, Trieste #741/R
£789 $1453 €1200 Roman countryside (24x34cm-9x13in) s.i. board. 22-Jun-4 Babuino, Rome #493/R
£1056 $1754 €1500 Sulla porta (50x40cm-20x16in) s. wood. 11-Jun-3 Christie's, Rome #22 est:1500-2000
£1733 $3189 €2600 After the rain (30x35cm-12x14in) s. cardboard. 10-Jun-4 Christie's, Rome #95/R est:2600-2800

CAROTO, Giovanni Francesco (circle) (1480-1555) Italian

£3333 $6000 €4866 Saint John the Baptist (32x24cm-13x9in) panel. 22-Jan-4 Sotheby's, New York #263/R est:2000-2500

CAROZZI, Giuseppe (1864-1938) French

£986 $1706 €1400 Study for sunset (50x80cm-20x31in) s. 10-Dec-3 Sotheby's, Milan #8/R

CARPANETTO, Giovanni Battista (1863-1928) Italian

£10145 $16638 €14000 Grand Prix (29x47cm-11x19in) s.d.1887 board exhib.lit. 27-May-3 Finarte Semenzato, Milan #67/R est:10000-12000

CARPANI, Ricardo (?) Argentinian

£2623 $4800 €3830 View (40x100cm-16x39in) 1-Jun-4 Arroyo, Buenos Aires #26
Works on paper
£447 $800 €653 Nude (24x35cm-9x14in) ink. 11-May-4 Arroyo, Buenos Aires #15

CARPEAUX, Jean Baptiste (1827-1875) French

Sculpture
£1313 $2100 €1917 Napoleon assis Sainte-Helene (20cm-8in) s. st.f.Susse Freres bronze. 20-Sep-3 Jeffery Burchard, Florida #21a/R
£1409 $2607 €2100 Rieuse napolitaine (10cm-4in) s. pat bronze. 14-Mar-4 Eric Pillon, Calais #15/R
£1656 $3013 €2500 Bacchante a la couronne de fleurs et laurier (48x27x29cm-19x11x11in) st.f.Susse s.verso pat terracotta. 19-Jun-4 St-Germain-en-Laye Encheres #75/R est:2000
£1678 $3087 €2500 La genie de la danse (35cm-14in) terracotta. 26-Mar-4 Pierre Berge, Paris #227/R est:1500-2000
£2500 $4600 €3800 Printemps 1 (35x33x35cm-14x13x14in) s. terracotta lit. 22-Jun-4 Ribeyre & Baron, Paris #138a/R est:5000-7000
£2966 $5427 €4300 Le petit boudeur (29cm-11in) s.d.1874 white marble. 31-Jan-4 Gerard, Besancon #241
£3020 $5618 €4500 Buste du genie de la danse (38cm-15in) s. brown pat bronze sold with socle. 2-Mar-4 Artcurial Briest, Paris #109/R est:4000-5000
£3265 $5192 €4800 Buste du rieur napolitain (51cm-20in) s. pat terracotta. 23-Mar-3 St-Germain-en-Laye Encheres #82/R
£3593 $6000 €5246 Bust (56cm-22in) s. terracotta prov. 20-Oct-3 Sotheby's, New York #505/R est:6000-8000
£3824 $6500 €5583 Genie de la Danse (103cm-41in) s. pat bronze. 28-Oct-3 Christie's, Rockefeller NY #55/R
£3947 $7262 €6000 Buste du genie de la danse (63cm-25in) brown pat. bronze incl. base. 22-Jun-4 Sotheby's, Amsterdam #184/R est:2200-2500
£4027 $7128 €6000 Genie de la danse (55cm-22in) s.d.1868 brown pat bronze. 27-Apr-4 Artcurial Briest, Paris #133/R est:6000-8000
£4483 $8203 €6500 L'Empereur Napoleon 1er assoupi a Ste Helene. s.st.f.Susse bronze. 31-Jan-4 Osenat, Fontainebleau #588
£4545 $7591 €6500 Genie de la Danse (55cm-22in) brown pat bronze. 29-Jun-3 St-Germain-en-Laye Encheres #14/R
£4610 $7699 €6500 L'amour a la folie, Nouvel Opera (69x60cm-27x24in) s.i.d.1872 pat terracotta. 19-Oct-3 St-Germain-en-Laye Encheres #46/R est:7500-8000
£4667 $8447 €7000 Bacchante aux roses, no 1 (59cm-23in) s.d.1875 pat terracotta lit. 31-Mar-4 Sotheby's, Paris #258/R est:3000-5000
£4762 $8524 €7000 Le Chinois (59x49x31cm-23x19x12in) s. st.verso rose pat terracotta. 18-Mar-4 Peschetau-Badin Godeau & Leroy, Paris #59/R est:7000-8000
£4800 $8640 €7008 Bust of Genie de la Danse (69cm-27in) s. white marble. 21-Apr-4 Sotheby's, London #101/R est:4000-6000
£4828 $8834 €7000 Jeune femme souriant (45cm-18in) s.d.1873 white marble. 31-Jan-4 Gerard, Besancon #242
£5000 $9000 €7300 Child blowing a horn (30cm-12in) s. brown pat bronze. 21-Apr-4 Sotheby's, London #124/R est:5000-7000
£5000 $9150 €7300 Amour a la folie (40x33cm-16x13in) s. marble. 9-Jul-4 Sotheby's, London #108/R est:5000-7000
£5000 $9150 €7300 Bust of Alexandre Dumas son (46cm-18in) s.i.d.1873 pat bronze. 9-Jul-4 Sotheby's, London #156/R est:5000-7000
£5102 $8112 €7500 Pecheuse de vigneaux (73cm-29in) s.i.d.1874 brown pat bronze. 23-Mar-3 St-Germain-en-Laye Encheres #93/R
£5629 $10301 €8500 Le pecheur napolitain (83cm-33in) num.1283 terracotta. 7-Apr-4 Fraysse & Associes, Paris #198 est:500-600
£6200 $10540 €9052 Bruno Cherier (62cm-24in) s.d.1875 terracotta plaster lit. 28-Oct-3 Sotheby's, London #202/R
£6200 $11160 €9052 Bust of a Chinaman (31cm-12in) s.st.num.1972 terracotta. 21-Apr-4 Sotheby's, London #126/R est:3000-4000
£7000 $12600 €10220 Le pecheur a la coquille no 1 (35cm-14in) s.d.1857 brown pat bronze prov. 21-Apr-4 Sotheby's, London #111/R est:3000-5000
£7152 $13017 €10800 Genie de la danse (81cm-32in) s. pat bronze Cast Susse. 19-Jun-4 St-Germain-en-Laye Encheres #94/R est:12000
£10000 $18200 €15000 Genie de la danse (84cm-33in) brown pat bronze st.Carpeaux. 29-Jun-4 Gioffredo, Nice #70/R
£10500 $18900 €15330 Eve after the fall (66cm-26in) pat plaster lit. 21-Apr-4 Sotheby's, London #139/R est:6000-8000
£10667 $19307 €16000 Bacchante aux vignes (57cm-22in) s.d.1875 num.170 pat terracotta lit. 31-Mar-4 Sotheby's, Paris #256/R est:3000-5000
£13333 $24267 €20000 L'amour a la folie (71x63cm-28x25in) s.d.1969 base brown pat bronze. 29-Jun-4 Gioffredo, Nice #74/R
£14965 $24991 €21100 Le genie de la danse (101cm-40in) s. brown pat bronze. 19-Oct-3 Peron, Melun #362
£16667 $30000 €24334 Three Graces (80cm-31in) i. brown pat. bronze prov.lit. 23-Apr-4 Sotheby's, New York #43/R est:30000-40000
£27273 $45545 €39000 Le genie de la danse (101cm-40in) brown pat bronze. 27-Jun-3 Millon & Associes, Paris #118/R est:12000-15000
£31469 $52552 €45000 Le tete de negresse. studio st. terracotta. 27-Jun-3 Calmels Cohen, Paris #40 est:1000-1500
Works on paper
£306 $548 €450 Paysage au clair de lune. Croquis et annotations (14x17cm-6x7in) s. chl white chk double-sided prov. 19-Mar-4 Piasa, Paris #146
£719 $1151 €1000 Couple looking out onto the horizon (16x12cm-6x5in) mono.d.72 chl white chk beige paper. 16-May-3 Tajan, Paris #99
£2128 $3447 €3000 Etudes de personnages. Etude de femme et enfant. black pencil chl one double-sided six in two frames prov. 23-May-3 Sotheby's, Paris #12/R est:3000-4000

CARPEAUX, Jean Baptiste (after) (1827-1875) French

Sculpture
£6164 $10479 €9000 Nuit (67cm-26in) bears sig bronze. 5-Nov-3 Beaussant & Lefèvre, Paris #191/R

CARPEAUX, Jean Baptiste (attrib) (1827-1875) French

£699 $1203 €1000 Charge de cavalerie (20x28cm-8x11in) panel. 3-Dec-3 Beaussant & Lefèvre, Paris #25

CARPENTER, Fred Green (1882-1965) American

£978 $1800 €1428 Indian princess (58x46cm-23x18in) s.d.1942. 26-Jun-4 Selkirks, St. Louis #136/R est:2000-3000
£1163 $2000 €1698 Dancing figures (38x46cm-15x18in) s. board painted c.1930. 7-Dec-3 Treadway Gallery, Cincinnati #625/R est:2000-3000
£1163 $2000 €1698 Woman with a parasol (46x38cm-18x15in) s. painted c.1950. 7-Dec-3 Treadway Gallery, Cincinnati #628/R est:3000-4000
£1193 $2100 €1742 Woman with a parasol (46x38cm-18x15in) s. painted c.1950. 23-May-4 Treadway Gallery, Cincinnati #563/R est:2000-3000

CARPENTER, George (?) American?

£289 $500 €422 Winter landscape with buildings (30x41cm-12x16in) s. canvasboard. 10-Dec-3 Alderfer's, Hatfield #334/R

CARPENTER, Louise M (1867-1963) American

£248 $400 €362 Still life with onions and dead mallard (41x87cm-16x34in) s. 17-Aug-3 Bonhams & Butterfields, San Francisco #5808

CARPENTER, Margaret (1793-1872) British

£600 $954 €876 Portrait of a child (56x43cm-22x17in) oval. 12-Sep-3 Gardiner & Houlgate, Bath #229/R
£745 $1200 €1088 Untitled, portrait of a young man. 15-Aug-3 Du Mouchelle, Detroit #53/R
£3200 $5728 €4672 Portrait of Mrs Simpson as a young woman (110x89cm-43x35in) s.d.1850. 22-Mar-4 Bonhams & Brooks, Norfolk #251/R est:3000-5000
£3800 $6004 €5510 Portrait of a boy in a blue dress and feathered hat (102x81cm-40x32in) 4-Sep-3 Christie's, Kensington #46/R est:4000-6000

CARPENTER, Margaret (attrib) (1793-1872) British

£700 $1260 €1022 Portrait of Emily Harriet Wellesley-Pole, Lady Raglan (29x24cm-11x9in) 21-Jan-4 Sotheby's, Olympia #44/R
£1600 $2880 €2336 Portrait of a lady, possibly Lady Lewin (91x71cm-36x28in) 21-Jan-4 Sotheby's, Olympia #58/R est:1500-2500
£1600 $2976 €2336 Portrait of Jane Elizabeth Coote in a fawn dress, with her dog (62x51cm-24x20in) prov. 4-Mar-4 Christie's, Kensington #361/R est:800-1200

CARPENTER, Mildred Bailey (1894-?) American

£625 $1100 €913 Bridge in Forest Park (46x51cm-18x20in) artist's board. 22-May-4 Selkirks, St. Louis #533/R

CARPENTER, William (1818-1899) British

Works on paper
£360 $612 €526 Sewri Fort from the Parel flagstaff, Bombay, India (9x25cm-4x10in) bears i. W/C. 4-Nov-3 Bonhams, New Bond Street #63

CARPENTERO, F (?) ?

£1622 $2903 €2400 Dejeuner (23x33cm-9x13in) panel. 10-May-4 Amberes, Antwerp #249

CARPENTERO, Henri Joseph Gommarus (1820-1874) Belgian

£710 $1300 €1037 Genre scene outside a tavern (23x30cm-9x12in) s. panel. 5-Jun-4 Neal Auction Company, New Orleans #525 est:1500-2000

CARPENTIER, Adriaen (fl.1739-1778) Dutch

£2632 $4842 €4000 Portrait of a gentleman wearing a brown jacket (75x62cm-30x24in) s.d.1748. 22-Jun-4 Mealy's, Castlecomer #770/R est:2000-3000

CARPENTIER, Evariste (1845-1922) Belgian

£2098 $3566 €3000 Brigands attaquant un village (38x56cm-15x22in) s. 1-Dec-3 Palais de Beaux Arts, Brussels #207 est:3000-4000
£4238 $7714 €6400 La petite ferme (65x84cm-26x33in) 16-Jun-4 Hotel des Ventes Mosan, Brussels #144/R est:8000-10000
£4305 $7834 €6500 La cloture (50x61cm-20x24in) s. 16-Jun-4 Hotel des Ventes Mosan, Brussels #156/R est:8000-12000
£4444 $8000 €6488 Music (55x36cm-22x14in) s.d.1874 panel prov. 23-Apr-4 Sotheby's, New York #191/R est:10000-15000

CARPENTIER, Mahaut (20th C) French?

£839 $1443 €1200 Femme a la fenetre (38x46cm-15x18in) s. 3-Dec-3 Tajan, Paris #166/R

CARPI, Aldo (1886-1973) Italian

£1014 $1784 €1500 Mother Padana (73x54cm-29x21in) s.d.1963. 19-May-4 Il Ponte, Milan #1048 est:1700-1800
£1399 $2378 €2000 Besana roundabout (56x70cm-22x28in) s. s.i.verso board. 20-Nov-3 Finarte Semenzato, Milan #88/R est:2000-2500
£1806 $3069 €2600 Flight to Egypt (25x34cm-10x13in) s.d.1946 cardboard on canvas. 28-Oct-3 Il Ponte, Milan #278/R
£5517 $9214 €8000 Portrait of Cioni (70x55cm-28x22in) s.d.1931. 17-Nov-3 Sant Agostino, Torino #228/R est:8000-10000
Works on paper
£308 $481 €450 Figures (46x32cm-18x13in) s.d. mixed media. 8-Apr-3 Il Ponte, Milan #1008

CARPI, Ugo da (c.1480-c.1520) Italian

Prints
£3356 $6174 €5000 Diogenes - after parmigianino (48x35cm-19x14in) clair obscure woodcut. 25-Mar-4 Dr Fritz Nagel, Stuttgart #517/R est:500

CARPIONI, Giulio (1613-1679) Italian

£14000 $25200 €20440 Allegory of summer (54x44cm-21x17in) 21-Apr-4 Christie's, London #96/R est:6000-8000

CARPIONI, Giulio (attrib) (1613-1679) Italian

£634	$1135	€900	Moise faisant jaillir l'eau du rocher (72x81cm-28x32in) 11-Jan-4 Rouillac, Vendome #103
£1972	$3175	€2800	Festa di Amorini (18x31cm-7x12in) panel. 8-May-3 Farsetti, Prato #603/R est:2800-3200
£3947	$7263	€6000	Little bacchanten playing in arcadian landscape (23x28cm-9x11in) four. 24-Jun-4 Dr Fritz Nagel, Stuttgart #641/R est:1800
£5240	$9537	€7650	The adoration of the shepherds (96x128cm-38x50in) 16-Jun-4 Fischer, Luzern #1019/R est:12000-14000 (S.FR 12000)
£10615	$19000	€15498	Belshazzar's feast (98x123cm-39x48in) prov. 27-May-4 Sotheby's, New York #82a/R est:10000-15000

CARPMAEL, Cecilia (fl.1898-1930) British

£280	$524	€409	River landscape with bridge (24x24cm-9x9in) s.verso. 24-Feb-4 Canterbury Auctions, UK #151/R

CARR, Emily M (1871-1945) Canadian

£16071	$27643	€23464	Cleared land (57x87cm-22x34in) s. paper prov. 2-Dec-3 Joyner Waddington, Toronto #45/R est:30000-40000 (C.D 36000)
£20270	$34459	€29594	Sunlit forest (45x29cm-18x11in) oil paper prov. 27-Nov-3 Heffel, Vancouver #125/R est:35000-45000 (C.D 45000)
£38288	$65090	€55900	Glade (61x91cm-24x36in) paper on board prov. 18-Nov-3 Sotheby's, Toronto #130/R est:50000-70000 (C.D 85000)
£45045	$76577	€65766	Landscape and sky (35x45cm-14x18in) st.sig. painted c.1936 prov. 27-Nov-3 Heffel, Vancouver #29/R est:50000-70000 (C.D 100000)
£52846	$94593	€77155	Light of spring (61x91cm-24x36in) s. indis d. i.verso oil paper on plywood. 31-May-4 Sotheby's, Toronto #149/R est:75000-100000 (C.D 130000)
£101626	$181911	€148374	Haida totem pole (96x31cm-38x12in) s. board painted 1912 prov. 27-May-4 Heffel, Vancouver #143/R est:125000-175000 (C.D 250000)
£101626	$181911	€148374	Summer, Mount Douglas Park (57x86cm-22x34in) s.d.1942 oil paper prov.lit. 27-May-4 Heffel, Vancouver #156/R est:100000-150000 (C.D 250000)
£108108	$183784	€157838	House with slanted roof, Brittany (66x51cm-26x20in) s. board painted 1911 prov. 27-Nov-3 Heffel, Vancouver #49/R est:120000-150000 (C.D 240000)
£396341	$709451	€578658	Quiet (111x68cm-44x27in) s.d.1942 i.verso prov.exhib.lit. 27-May-4 Heffel, Vancouver #137/R est:300000-400000 (C.D 975000)
Works on paper			
£4955	$8423	€7234	Harbour scene (18x22cm-7x9in) s. W/C exec.c.1910 prov. 18-Nov-3 Sotheby's, Toronto #33/R est:10000-15000 (C.D 11000)
£5357	$9214	€7821	Long Point, Vancouver Island, BC (10x16cm-4x6in) W/C prov. 2-Dec-3 Joyner Waddington, Toronto #60/R est:8000-12000 (C.D 12000)
£19309	$34563	€28191	Old growth cedar (62x43cm-24x17in) chl exec. c.1930 prov.lit. 27-May-4 Heffel, Vancouver #144/R est:20000-25000 (C.D 47500)
£34553	$61850	€50447	Indian house with two totems, Koskimo village (38x27cm-15x11in) s. s.i.verso W/C exec. c.1930 prov.lit. 27-May-4 Heffel, Vancouver #147/R est:50000-70000 (C.D 85000)
£45045	$76577	€65766	Gateway in Brittany (39x27cm-15x11in) s. W/C executed 1911 prov.exhib.lit. 27-Nov-3 Heffel, Vancouver #16/R est:60000-80000 (C.D 100000)

CARR, Hamzah (20th C) British

£310	$536	€453	Introduction, from Achievements of an Industry (23x34cm-9x13in) s. i.verso board prov. 9-Dec-3 Rosebery Fine Art, London #719/R

CARR, Lyell (1857-1912) American

Works on paper			
£475	$850	€694	Studies of roosters (36x30cm-14x12in) s.d.1894 W/C pair. 21-Mar-4 Jeffery Burchard, Florida #74a/R

CARR, Samuel S (1837-1908) American

£2989	$5500	€4364	Sheep grazing in a meadow with cottage and stream in background (30x46cm-12x18in) s. 9-Jun-4 Alderfer's, Hatfield #370/R est:4000-6000
£7821	$14000	€11419	Skating in New York (33x25cm-13x10in) s. board prov. 14-May-4 Skinner, Boston #106/R est:7000-9000
£11628	$20000	€16977	Morning after election (61x46cm-24x18in) s.d.84 s.i.d.verso. 4-Dec-3 Christie's, Rockefeller NY #45/R est:25000-35000

CARR, Tom (1912-1977) British

£1000	$1590	€1460	Braes of Derwent Hunt near Sawmill Wood (35x53cm-14x21in) s.i. 18-Mar-3 Anderson & Garland, Newcastle #200/R est:1000-1600
Works on paper			
£280	$515	€409	Tynedale point-to-point - a rider taking a fall (25x34cm-10x13in) i. pencil. 23-Mar-4 Anderson & Garland, Newcastle #183
£520	$957	€759	Tynedale point-to-point 1960 - Well Bob and Jean's Fancy taking a jump (25x34cm-10x13in) s.i. pencil. 23-Mar-4 Anderson & Garland, Newcastle #181
£550	$1029	€825	Hunting scene with huntsman and hounds crossing a river (33x49cm-13x19in) s.d.69 pencil W/C htd white. 22-Jul-4 Tennants, Leyburn #680
£1900	$3496	€2774	Tynedale Hunt point-to-point won my Miss Joan Milburn on Stepping Stone (35x54cm-14x21in) s.i.d.1955 W/C. 23-Mar-4 Anderson & Garland, Newcastle #180/R est:1500-2500
£2100	$3570	€3066	Hunt in full cry (38x56cm-15x22in) s.i.d.1967 W/C bodycol. 30-Oct-3 Duke & Son, Dorchester #40/R

CARR, Tom (1909-1999) British

£1600	$2656	€2336	Still life, wild roses (20x40cm-8x16in) s. board. 1-Oct-3 John Ross, Belfast #64 est:1700-2000
£3500	$5810	€5110	On the beach at Newcastle (30x45cm-12x18in) s. 1-Oct-3 John Ross, Belfast #150 est:4000-5000
£5068	$9578	€7500	Gardener (56x46cm-22x18in) s. board. 17-Feb-4 Whyte's, Dublin #118/R est:8000-10000
£5743	$10855	€8500	Cows in a field (38x51cm-15x20in) s. board prov. 17-Feb-4 Whyte's, Dublin #64/R est:7000-9000
Works on paper			
£550	$946	€803	Out for a trot (10x15cm-4x6in) s. W/C. 3-Dec-3 John Ross, Belfast #21
£600	$996	€876	Figure by a wall (20x12cm-8x5in) s. mixed media. 1-Oct-3 John Ross, Belfast #57
£750	$1230	€1095	Girl reading (17x22cm-7x9in) s. mixed media. 4-Jun-3 John Ross, Belfast #46
£750	$1290	€1095	Sheep in a snowy landscape (12x17cm-5x7in) s. W/C. 3-Dec-3 John Ross, Belfast #77
£750	$1395	€1095	In the farm yard (15x20cm-6x8in) s. W/C. 3-Mar-4 John Ross, Belfast #56
£805	$1426	€1200	Fox and geese (13x15cm-5x6in) s. W/C. 27-Apr-4 Whyte's, Dublin #222/R
£872	$1544	€1300	Shrubs in the meadow (24x27cm-9x11in) s. W/C pen ink. 27-Apr-4 Whyte's, Dublin #151/R
£900	$1548	€1314	Village street (20x17cm-8x7in) s. W/C. 3-Dec-3 John Ross, Belfast #204
£950	$1739	€1387	River Lagan (25x35cm-10x14in) s. W/C. 2-Jun-4 John Ross, Belfast #63
£1000	$1640	€1460	Brambles (28x38cm-11x15in) s.d.1980 verso W/C. 4-Jun-3 John Ross, Belfast #152 est:1200-1400
£1100	$1980	€1606	Ormond Quay, Dublin (27x21cm-11x8in) s. W/C. 20-Jan-4 Bonhams, Knightsbridge #64/R est:600-800
£1100	$2002	€1606	Main Street, Newcastle, Co Down (30x41cm-12x16in) s.i.d.1946 W/C. 16-Jun-4 John Nicholson, Haslemere #707/R est:1000-2000
£1141	$2042	€1700	Ormond Quay Dublin (27x22cm-11x9in) s. W/C. 31-May-4 Hamilton Osborne King, Dublin #146/R est:1800-2200
£1150	$1909	€1679	Patrick's pony (28x22cm-11x9in) s. W/C. 1-Oct-3 John Ross, Belfast #265 est:1000-1200
£1200	$2004	€1752	Farmyard (25x35cm-10x14in) s. W/C. 16-Oct-3 Christie's, Kensington #477/R est:500-700
£1200	$2064	€1752	Out for a walk (28x20cm-11x8in) s. W/C. 3-Dec-3 John Ross, Belfast #23 est:900-1200
£1300	$2379	€1898	Houses, South of France (20x30cm-8x12in) s. W/C. 2-Jun-4 John Ross, Belfast #29 est:1500-1600
£1400	$2562	€2044	Horses exercising (12x17cm-5x7in) s. W/C. 2-Jun-4 John Ross, Belfast #168a est:750-800
£1600	$2976	€2336	Autumn trees (76x56cm-30x22in) s. W/C. 3-Mar-4 John Ross, Belfast #11 est:1800-2000
£1761	$3046	€2500	Lake shore I (57x76cm-22x30in) s. W/C prov. 10-Dec-3 Bonhams & James Adam, Dublin #126/R est:2500-3000
£1800	$3294	€2628	Still evening (53x73cm-21x29in) s. W/C. 2-Jun-4 John Ross, Belfast #138 est:2000-3000
£2000	$3620	€3000	Lough in Co Down (35x53cm-14x21in) s. W/C. 31-Mar-4 James Adam, Dublin #139/R est:3000-5000
£2000	$3720	€2920	Lough Neagh (56x76cm-22x30in) s. W/C. 3-Mar-4 John Ross, Belfast #48 est:1800-2000
£2958	$5117	€4200	Lagan bank (38x57cm-15x22in) s. W/C prov. 10-Dec-3 Bonhams & James Adam, Dublin #71/R est:4000-6000
£3200	$5504	€4672	The robin (76x56cm-30x22in) s. W/C. 3-Dec-3 John Ross, Belfast #144 est:3000-3500
£4400	$7964	€6600	The robin (75x55cm-30x22in) s. W/C prov. 31-Mar-4 James Adam, Dublin #95/R est:7000-10000

CARRA, Carlo (1881-1966) Italian

£4225	$7014	€6000	Latin quarter (35x50cm-14x20in) s.i.d.934 tempera card on canvas. 11-Jun-3 Finarte Semenzato, Milan #692/R
£20979	$35664	€30000	Haystacks (23x33cm-9x13in) s. s.i.d.1909 verso board prov. 29-Nov-3 Farsetti, Prato #536/R est:20000
£25362	$41594	€35000	Still life (50x40cm-20x16in) s.d.956. 27-May-3 Sotheby's, Milan #246/R est:35000-40000
£29371	$49930	€42000	Red house by the stream (60x50cm-24x20in) s.d.957 lit. 20-Nov-3 Finarte Semenzato, Milan #152/R est:45000-60000
£38462	$65385	€55000	Lake in Corenno (40x50cm-16x20in) s.d.944 prov.lit. 25-Nov-3 Sotheby's, Milan #202/R est:60000-80000
£40000	$72000	€60000	Seascape with sailing boat (30x40cm-12x16in) s.d.959 prov.lit. 22-Apr-4 Finarte Semenzato, Rome #310/R est:45000-48000
£40268	$72081	€60000	Quarries in Carrara (50x60cm-20x24in) s.d.958 lit. 29-May-4 Farsetti, Prato #435/R est:60000-75000
£41892	$73730	€62000	Seascape (60x75cm-24x30in) s.d.948. 24-May-4 Christie's, Milan #327/R est:60000-80000
£44595	$78486	€66000	Seascape with boat and sailing boat (40x50cm-16x20in) s.d.950 s.verso prov.lit. 24-May-4 Christie's, Milan #300/R est:45000-65000
£48951	$83217	€70000	Sailing boat (50x40cm-20x16in) s.d.959 prov.lit. 26-Nov-3 Pandolfini, Florence #34/R est:80000-85000
£49275	$80812	€68000	Huts and tree (40x50cm-16x20in) s.d.947 cardboard on canvas prov.lit. 27-May-3 Sotheby's, Milan #231/R est:50000-70000
£52174	$85565	€72000	Naviglio (40x50cm-16x20in) s.d.949 prov.exhib.lit. 27-May-3 Sotheby's, Milan #254/R est:80000-100000
£64189	$112973	€95000	Loggia (35x50cm-14x20in) s.d.1942 s.i.d.verso cardboard on canvas prov.exhib.lit. 24-May-4 Christie's, Milan #302/R est:70000-100000
£73427	$124825	€105000	Pine grove in Forte dei Marmi (56x46cm-22x18in) s.d.938 lit. 29-Nov-3 Farsetti, Prato #513/R est:85000-115000
£121622	$214054	€180000	Vases on window ledge (52x68cm-20x27in) s.d.923 prov.lit. 24-May-4 Christie's, Milan #303/R est:150000-200000
Works on paper			
£1538	$2615	€2200	Seated woman (48x33cm-19x13in) s.i.d.1965 pencil prov. 20-Nov-3 Finarte Semenzato, Milan #148/R est:2500-3000
£2517	$4280	€3600	Leandra in the cave (39x28cm-15x11in) s.d.943 pencil. 20-Nov-3 Finarte Semenzato, Milan #73/R est:3500-4000
£3490	$6247	€5200	Bottle decomposition II (49x34cm-19x13in) s.d.959 chl water exhib.lit. 29-May-4 Farsetti, Prato #417/R est:5000-8000
£3793	$6069	€5500	Seascape (21x30cm-8x12in) s.d.1964 ink. 13-Mar-3 Galleria Pace, Milan #26/R est:6500-8500
£8054	$14416	€12000	Contrasts (17x17cm-7x7in) s.i.d.911 pencil prov.exhib.lit. 25-May-4 Sotheby's, Milan #241/R est:13000-18000
£8392	$14266	€12000	Man running (17x13cm-7x5in) s.d.1913 W/C prov.lit. 20-Nov-3 Finarte Semenzato, Milan #150/R est:12000-14000
£56000	$93520	€81760	Simultaneita, la donna al balcone (42x34cm-17x13in) s.d.912 pencil tracing paper prov.exhib.lit. 21-Oct-3 Christie's, London #1/R est:45000-65000

CARRA, Carmelo (1945-) Italian

£467	$854	€700	L'espoir (81x100cm-32x39in) s.d.74. 7-Jun-4 Palais de Beaux Arts, Brussels #332

CARRACCI, Agostino (1557-1602) Italian

Works on paper			
£10345	$17276	€15000	Figure and head studies (27x21cm-11x8in) pen sepia prov. 15-Nov-3 Lempertz, Koln #1274/R est:15000-18000

CARRACCI, Annibale (1560-1609) Italian
Works on paper
£4500 $8235 €6570 Madonna suckling the infant Christ (17x13cm-7x5in) black chk prov. 6-Jul-4 Christie's, London #39/R est:5000-7000

CARRACCI, Annibale (after) (1560-1609) Italian
£6600 $11418 €9636 Montalto Madonna (36x30cm-14x12in) copper octagonal. 9-Dec-3 Sotheby's, Olympia #385/R est:2000-3000

CARRACCI, Annibale (circle) (1560-1609) Italian
£6643 $11294 €9500 Magdalene (133x97cm-52x38in) 1-Dec-3 Babuino, Rome #120/R est:6000-8000
Works on paper
£7500 $13725 €10950 Seated male nude with raised arm, seen from behind (24x27cm-9x11in) i. red chk. 8-Jul-4 Sotheby's, London #94/R est:5000-7000

CARRACCI, Annibale (style) (1560-1609) Italian
£5846 $10055 €8535 Christ wearing crown of thorns (77x63cm-30x25in) 2-Dec-3 Bukowskis, Stockholm #355/R est:20000-25000 (S.KR 76000)
£7200 $12456 €10512 Portrait of a bearded gentleman (36x30cm-14x12in) panel. 9-Dec-3 Sotheby's, Olympia #326/R est:2000-3000
£7386 $13000 €10784 Boy cutting fruit (63x52cm-25x20in) 19-May-4 Doyle, New York #6119/R est:4000-6000

CARRACCI, Lodovico (1555-1619) Italian
£57931 $96745 €84000 Allegory of Wealth (40x30cm-16x12in) copper prov.lit. 15-Nov-3 Porro, Milan #251/R est:100000
Works on paper
£1399 $2336 €2000 Reclining male figure (19x10cm-7x4in) chk htd white pen. 28-Jun-3 Bolland & Marotz, Bremen #566/R est:2300
£10000 $18000 €14600 Holy Family with St Jerome (13x26cm-5x10in) red chk pen brown ink wash prov. 22-Jan-4 Christie's, Rockefeller NY #34/R est:10000-15000
£32000 $58560 €46720 Ecce Homo (31x19cm-12x7in) red chk prov. 8-Jul-4 Sotheby's, London #57/R est:12000-15000

CARRACCI, Lodovico (studio) (1555-1619) Italian
£11111 $20000 €16222 Saint Jerome in the wilderness (38x28cm-15x11in) 23-Jan-4 Christie's, Rockefeller NY #169/R est:20000-30000

CARRADE, Michel (1923-) French
£700 $1260 €1050 Composition (92x73cm-36x29in) s. prov. 25-Apr-4 Versailles Encheres #15
£789 $1453 €1200 Composition (60x60cm-24x24in) s. s.d.1960 verso prov. 27-Jun-4 Versailles Encheres #34/R
£967 $1740 €1450 Composition 180 (92x73cm-36x29in) s. s.i.d.1960 verso prov. 25-Apr-4 Versailles Encheres #62

CARRAND, Louis (1821-1899) French
£537 $999 €800 Bouquet de fleurs (27x35cm-11x14in) s. panel. 2-Mar-4 Artcurial Briest, Paris #111
£674 $1125 €950 Paysage (32x24cm-13x9in) s. paper on panel. 19-Jun-3 Millon & Associes, Paris #125/R
£800 $1440 €1200 Paysage a la find de l'ete (32x52cm-13x20in) s. 20-Apr-4 Chenu & Scrive, Lyon #49/R
£933 $1680 €1400 Jardin anime (32x23cm-13x9in) s. canvas on panel. 20-Apr-4 Chenu & Scrive, Lyon #45b/R
£1333 $2427 €2000 Rentree du troupeau (31x40cm-12x16in) s. panel. 29-Jun-4 Chenu & Scrive, Lyon #35/R est:2000-2500
£1533 $2791 €2300 Retour des paturages (25x65cm-10x26in) 29-Jun-4 Chenu & Scrive, Lyon #36/R est:2300-2500
£1933 $3480 €2900 Route sur la crete (24x32cm-9x13in) s. 20-Apr-4 Chenu & Scrive, Lyon #47/R est:3000-4500

CARRARD, Louis Samuel (c.1755-1839) Swiss
Works on paper
£423 $731 €600 Vue de Geneve depuis Cologni (19x28cm-7x11in) s.d.1818 W/C traces blk crayon. 10-Dec-3 Piasa, Paris #157/R

CARRARESI, Eugenio (1893-1964) Italian
£342 $582 €500 Autumn landscape (27x39cm-11x15in) s.d.1930 board. 7-Nov-3 Farsetti, Prato #59

CARRE, Ben (1883-1978) American
£203 $375 €296 Quiet pool (32x41cm-13x16in) s. canvasboard. 18-Jan-4 Bonhams & Butterfields, Los Angeles #7015/R

CARRE, E F (19th C) ?
Works on paper
£1500 $2805 €2250 Cathedral Rock, Sark (33x51cm-13x20in) W/C. 22-Jul-4 Martel Maides, Guernsey #181/R est:800-1000

CARRE, Franciscus (1630-1669) Dutch
£4000 $7320 €5840 Boors smoking and drinking in interior (27x23cm-11x9in) s.d.1650 panel. 9-Jul-4 Christie's, Kensington #44/R est:2500-3000

CARRE, Hendrik (elder) (1656-1721) Dutch
£4400 $7920 €6424 Figures smoking and drinking outside an inn (42x36cm-17x14in) bears sig. 20-Apr-4 Sotheby's, Olympia #265/R est:4000-6000

CARRE, Ketty (1882-1964) French
Works on paper
£743 $1330 €1100 Collation sous les arcades du patio (26x34cm-10x13in) s. 5-May-4 Claude Boisgirard, Paris #15

CARRE, Léon (1878-1942) French
£5067 $9323 €7600 Halte en Algerie (50x65cm-20x26in) s.i.d.1916. 9-Jun-4 Oger, Dumont, Paris #86/R est:2500-3000
Works on paper
£470 $869 €700 Orientale et son ane (32x25cm-13x10in) s. gouache. 15-Mar-4 Gros & Delettrez, Paris #79
£496 $829 €700 Legende hindoue (14x11cm-6x4in) s. W/C. 19-Oct-3 Rabourdin & Choppin de Janvry, Paris #14/R

CARRE, Raoul (c.1870-1934) French
£420 $722 €600 La confidence (82x61cm-32x24in) s. cardboard. 3-Dec-3 Blanchet, Paris #24
£3357 $5773 €4800 Elegante dans l'atelier (84x62cm-33x24in) s.d.1907 cardboard. 3-Dec-3 Blanchet, Paris #23 est:300-500

CARREE, Michiel (1657-1747) Dutch
£778 $1400 €1136 Cows and sheep (26x33cm-10x13in) 21-Jan-4 Sotheby's, New York #89/R est:2000-3000
£2740 $4658 €4000 Italianate landscape with shepherds and their cattle near a ruin (64x78cm-25x31in) s.d.1683 prov. 5-Nov-3 Christie's, Amsterdam #52/R est:5000-7000
£2800 $5040 €4088 Circe transforming men into beasts (50x58cm-20x23in) s.d.1689 prov. 23-Apr-4 Christie's, Kensington #118/R est:4000-6000

CARREE, Michiel (attrib) (1657-1747) Dutch
£650 $1164 €949 Drover, cattle and shepherdess in an extensive landscape (37x47cm-15x19in) 18-Mar-4 Christie's, Kensington #423/R

CARRELLI, Juan (20th C) ?
£278 $450 €406 Boats on a sandy beach, viewed through eucalyptus trees (64x79cm-25x31in) i.stretcher painted c.1930. 26-Jul-3 Thomaston Place, Thomaston #609/R

CARRENO, Mario (1913-1999) Cuban
£6207 $11172 €9000 Untitled (57x43cm-22x17in) s.d.53 prov. 26-Jan-4 Ansorena, Madrid #901/R est:9000
£35294 $60000 €51529 Amazonas (61x51cm-24x20in) s.d.45 board prov.exhib. 18-Nov-3 Christie's, Rockefeller NY #43/R est:90000-120000
£36667 $67467 €55000 Sugar factory (122x121cm-48x48in) s.d.1933 cardboard prov.lit. 10-Jun-4 Christie's, Paris #7/R est:55000-75000
Works on paper
£1538 $2569 €2245 El Indio Goldmine, Chile (52x72cm-20x28in) s.d.82 W/C prov. 17-Nov-3 Waddingtons, Toronto #277/R est:3000-5000 (C.D 3400)
£1912 $3250 €2792 Untitled - head (36x25cm-14x10in) s.d.1946 mixed media on board. 9-Nov-3 Wright, Chicago #347 est:3000-5000
£3297 $6000 €4814 Ya Nada importa (39x49cm-15x19in) s.d.65 s.i.d.verso ink wash W/C prov. 29-Jun-4 Sotheby's, New York #655/R est:6000-8000
£14706 $25000 €21471 Chevaux dans un paysage (72x86cm-28x34in) s.d.48 gouache prov. 19-Nov-3 Sotheby's, New York #89/R est:30000-40000
£15882 $27000 €23188 Mujer con guitarra (53x70cm-21x28in) s.d.47 gouache prov. 19-Nov-3 Sotheby's, New York #88/R est:20000-30000

CARRENO, Omar (1927-) Venezuelan
£313 $575 €457 Untitled (50x40cm-20x16in) painted 1989. 28-Mar-4 Subastas Odalys, Caracas #104
£391 $625 €571 Composition 5 (100x100cm-39x39in) acrylic. 16-Mar-3 Subastas Odalys, Caracas #33/R
£581 $900 €848 Enclosed space (100x100cm-39x39in) s. acrylic panel painted 1993. 3-Nov-2 Subastas Odalys, Caracas #87
£645 $1000 €942 Zur C (100x100cm-39x39in) s. acrylic panel. 29-Sep-2 Subastas Odalys, Caracas #65/R

CARRERA PASCUAL, Maria (1937-) Spanish
£280 $467 €400 Landscape (53x73cm-21x29in) s. 30-Jun-3 Ansorena, Madrid #274/R

CARRERA, Augustin (1878-?) French
£1854 $3375 €2800 Partie de campagne (65x81cm-26x32in) s.i.d.1930. 18-Jun-4 Piasa, Paris #160 est:1500-2000
£2000 $3640 €3000 Port de Marseille (54x65cm-21x26in) 4-Jul-4 Eric Pillon, Calais #214/R
£4082 $7306 €6000 Jeune homme appuye a la balustrade (68x48cm-27x19in) 19-Mar-4 Millon & Associes, Paris #81/R est:6000-8000

CARRERAS, Rafael (?) Spanish
£263 $484 €400 Seashore (60x73cm-24x29in) s. s.i.verso. 22-Jun-4 Durán, Madrid #64/R

CARRERE, F Ouillon (20th C) ?
Sculpture
£1250 $2150 €1825 Female on tiptoe between three spears with arms outstretched (36cm-14in) indis.sig. bronze marble base. 2-Dec-3 Gorringes, Lewes #343/R est:600-800

CARRESSE, Pierre (20th C) French
£699 $1189 €1000 La fleur de lune (81x53cm-32x21in) s. isorel panel. 29-Nov-3 Neret-Minet, Paris #99/R

Works on paper			
£267	$483	€400	La petite famille (22x15cm-9x6in) s. gouache. 3-Apr-4 Neret-Minet, Paris #26/R

CARREY, Georges (1902-1953) French

£336	$621	€500	Composition a latabatiere (56x44cm-22x17in) oil paper. 15-Mar-4 Horta, Bruxelles #388
£671	$1188	€1000	Composition (50x65cm-20x26in) s. 27-Apr-4 Campo, Vlaamse Kaai #347

CARRICK, Desmond (1930-) Irish

£1333	$2400	€2000	Landscape (39x29cm-15x11in) s. board. 20-Apr-4 James Adam, Dublin #91/R est:2000-2500
£1477	$2613	€2200	Cattle in an autumnal landscape (41x51cm-16x20in) s. board. 27-Apr-4 Whyte's, Dublin #9/R est:1500-2000
£2013	$3604	€3000	On the jetty, Antibe (45x60cm-18x24in) s. board. 31-May-4 Hamilton Osborne King, Dublin #197/R est:2000-3000

CARRICK, John Mulcaster (1833-?) British

£420	$739	€613	Dover Castle (20x30cm-8x12in) s.d.1880. 19-May-4 Christie's, Kensington #620
£1500	$2790	€2190	Prussia Cove, Cornwall (20x30cm-8x12in) s.d.1880 i.verso board. 4-Mar-4 Christie's, Kensington #520/R est:1500-2500

CARRICK, William (1879-1964) British

£720	$1174	€1051	Tiree (34x58cm-13x23in) s. 17-Jul-3 Bonhams, Edinburgh #351
Works on paper			
£480	$802	€701	North east beach scene (24x38cm-9x15in) s. W/C. 16-Oct-3 Bonhams, Edinburgh #182
£580	$969	€847	Mother and child on the beach (26x37cm-10x15in) s. W/C. 16-Oct-3 Bonhams, Edinburgh #181
£700	$1169	€1022	Hopeman Harbour, Morayshire (25x38cm-10x15in) s. pencil W/C. 16-Oct-3 Bonhams, Edinburgh #179/R
£1800	$2898	€2610	Lossiemouth (31x45cm-12x18in) s. W/C. 21-Aug-3 Bonhams, Edinburgh #1095/R est:800-1200

CARRIER (?) ?

£550	$919	€803	Steamer, Maskelyne, at sea (46x77cm-18x30in) s.d.1891. 8-Oct-3 Christie's, Kensington #753/R

CARRIER, A (19th C) French

Sculpture			
£2300	$3634	€3335	Leder and the swan (59cm-23in) bronze. 24-Jul-3 Lawrence, Crewkerne #1352/R est:1200-1800

CARRIER, Auguste Joseph (1800-1875) French

Works on paper			
£450	$779	€657	Studies of cats (14x21cm-6x8in) s. black chk double-sided. 12-Dec-3 Christie's, Kensington #492/R

CARRIER-BELLEUSE (19/20th C) French

Sculpture			
£1467	$2684	€2200	La fileuse (36cm-14in) s. gold silver pat bronze ivory incl. marble base exec. c.1890. 7-Jun-4 Sotheby's, Amsterdam #5/R est:2200-2800
£2100	$3507	€3066	Bust of females (66cm-26in) pair. 14-Oct-3 Sotheby's, Olympia #59/R est:2500-3500

CARRIER-BELLEUSE, A (1824-1887) French

Sculpture			
£1000	$1810	€1500	Buste de jeune fille fleurie (34cm-13in) s. pat bronze incl. marble base. 30-Mar-4 Palais de Beaux Arts, Brussels #1127/R est:1600-2400
£1391	$2532	€2100	Liseuse (60cm-24in) pat bronze ivory. 15-Jun-4 Artcurial Briest, Paris #420/R est:1800-2000
£2797	$4811	€4000	Melodie, muse assise tenant une lyre (79cm-31in) pat bronze. 3-Dec-3 Palais de Beaux Arts, Brussels #639/R est:5000-7500
£3421	$6295	€5200	Buste de jeune bacchante (63cm-25in) s.d.1885 marble. 22-Jun-4 Ribeyre & Baron, Paris #138/R est:3000-4000
£4000	$6520	€5840	Woman stood reading a book (61cm-24in) i. ivory brown pat bronze round scotia base. 28-Sep-3 Wilkinson, Doncaster #34/R

CARRIER-BELLEUSE, Albert (1824-1887) French

Sculpture			
£932	$1500	€1361	Raphael (56cm-22in) s. bronze. 20-Aug-3 James Julia, Fairfield #1439/R est:1500-2200
£956	$1750	€1434	Figure (51cm-20in) bronze exec. 1855 Cast Deniere. 9-Jul-4 Du Mouchelle, Detroit #2048/R est:1500-2000
£1049	$1783	€1500	Le joueur de mandoline dansant (46cm-18in) s. brown pat bronze base red marble st.f. Colin. 28-Nov-3 Doutrebente, Paris #48 est:1000
£1190	$2131	€1750	Liseuse (37cm-15in) s. silver ivory gilt bronze. 19-Mar-4 Oger, Dumont, Paris #72/R est:1200-1500
£1678	$2853	€2400	Jeune femme assise (68cm-27in) s. terracotta. 18-Nov-3 Sotheby's, Paris #66/R est:2500-3000
£1800	$3276	€2628	Cigale (68cm-27in) s. coppery brown pat bronze. 15-Jun-4 Sotheby's, Olympia #138/R est:1800-2500
£2000	$3460	€2920	Raphael (56cm-22in) s.d.1855 brown pat bronze black marble base. 12-Dec-3 Sotheby's, London #269/R est:2500-3500
£2041	$3653	€3000	La liseuse (60cm-24in) pat. bronze. 21-Mar-4 Muizon & Le Coent, Paris #65/R
£2098	$3504	€3000	Bacchante et ses chevres (52cm-20in) s. terracotta. 26-Jun-3 Artcurial Briest, Paris #711 est:3000-4000
£2267	$4103	€3400	Liseuse (45cm-18in) s. ivory bronze. 31-Mar-4 Segre, Madrid #602/R est:2100
£2303	$4237	€3500	Liseuse (60x18x18cm-24x7x7in) s. ivory pat bronze. 23-Jun-4 Rieunier, Paris #76/R est:2000-3000
£2400	$4296	€3600	Liseuse (72x23cm-28x9in) s. brown pat bronze bronze base lit. 15-May-4 De Vuyst, Lokeren #419/R est:3000-4000
£2400	$4392	€3504	Bust of Rembrandt (51cm-20in) s.st.f.Pinedo pat bronze. 9-Jul-4 Sotheby's, London #154/R est:3000-5000
£2552	$4261	€3700	Le printemps (32x23cm-13x9in) marble exec.c.1854. 16-Nov-3 Muizon & Le Coent, Paris #80/R
£2657	$4517	€3800	Le mousquetaire (90cm-35in) s. brown pat bronze. 18-Nov-3 Galerie Moderne, Brussels #1505/R est:3000-4000
£2667	$4907	€4000	Buste de jeune femme. black wooden base. 9-Jun-4 Le Roux & Morel, Paris #209/R est:4000-6000
£2667	$4773	€4000	La liseuse (40cm-16in) s. ivory gilt bronze. 11-May-4 Vanderkindere, Brussels #795/R est:2000-3000
£2695	$4366	€3800	Denis Papin (65cm-26in) s.i. brown pat bronze. 23-May-3 Sotheby's, Paris #284/R est:4000-6000
£2700	$4995	€3942	Female figure swinging baby aloft (95cm-37in) s. pat bronze pink marble stand. 14-Jul-4 Bonhams, Chester #776/R est:3000-5000
£2956	$5292	€4316	Caresse de l'amour (92cm-36in) s. pat.bronze. 25-May-4 Bukowskis, Stockholm #309/R est:20000-25000 (S.KR 40000)
£3046	$5544	€4600	Melodie (78cm-31in) pat bronze. 15-Jun-4 Rossini, Paris #45/R est:1000-1500
£3077	$5231	€4400	Melodie (80cm-31in) s.i. medaille pat bronze. 30-Nov-3 Anaf, Lyon #235/R est:3000-4000
£3200	$5856	€4672	Confidence (43x62cm-17x24in) s. terracotta. 9-Jul-4 Sotheby's, London #145/R est:3000-5000
£3356	$6208	€5000	La fileuse (36cm-14in) s. ivory gilt bronze marble socle. 15-Mar-4 Horta, Bruxelles #107/R est:5000-6000
£3684	$6668	€5600	Melodie (79cm-31in) s. green pat bronze. 19-Apr-4 Horta, Bruxelles #124 est:2000-2500
£3846	$6423	€5500	Jeune femme a la lecture (61cm-24in) bronze ivory. 26-Jun-3 Artcurial Briest, Paris #709 est:6000-7000
£3916	$6657	€5600	La liseuse (61cm-24in) s. col gilt pat bronze lit. 20-Nov-3 Camard, Paris #211/R est:2500-3000
£4054	$7500	€5919	Orpheus (48x58cm-19x23in) bronze st.f.Berman executed c.1865. 17-Jan-4 New Orleans Auction, New Orleans #924/R est:5000-8000
£4200	$7560	€6132	Bust of John Milton (48cm-19in) s. terracotta wood socle. 21-Apr-4 Sotheby's, London #62/R est:3000-5000
£4276	$7098	€6200	Buste de Flore (57cm-22in) s. pat bronze lit. 2-Oct-3 Sotheby's, Paris #67/R
£5000	$9150	€7300	Secret (59x41cm-23x16in) s. terracotta lit. 9-Jul-4 Sotheby's, London #146/R est:5000-7000
£5000	$9150	€7300	Venus and Cupid (73cm-29in) s. terracotta. 9-Jul-4 Sotheby's, London #148/R est:4000-6000
£5034	$8910	€7500	Nymphe tenant tambourin et entouree par six amours (102cm-40in) s. terracotta. 30-Apr-4 Tajan, Paris #56/R est:8000-10000
£5139	$8736	€7400	Diane victorieuse (67x31x26cm-26x12x10in) brown pat bronze. 28-Oct-3 Rabourdin & Choppin de Janvry, Paris #27/R est:8000-8500
£5500	$10065	€8030	Reveil (58cm-23in) s. terracotta. 9-Jul-4 Sotheby's, London #149/R est:4000-6000
£8000	$14400	€11680	Bust of spring (62cm-24in) s.i. white marble. 21-Apr-4 Sotheby's, London #141/R est:6000-8000
£10345	$17276	€15000	La naissance de Venus (92cm-36in) s. white Carrare marble. 16-Nov-3 Muizon & Le Coent, Paris #81/R
£26950	$45007	€38000	Titan soutenant une jarre, aide par deux nymphes (101cm-40in) s. terracotta rock base wood socle. 17-Jun-3 Christie's, Paris #90/R est:30000-40000
Works on paper			
£306	$548	€450	Femme drapee le bras leve (23x13cm-9x5in) s. black pencil htd gouache. 19-Mar-4 Piasa, Paris #182

CARRIER-BELLEUSE, Andrea (attrib) (?) French

Works on paper			
£1987	$3636	€3000	Baigneuse (200x100cm-79x39in) pastel canvas. 7-Apr-4 Piasa, Paris #13 est:2500-3000

CARRIER-BELLEUSE, Louis (1848-1913) French

£12000	$21840	€17520	Un salon de modes a Paris (90x70cm-35x28in) s.d.1883 prov. 15-Jun-4 Sotheby's, London #187/R est:12000-18000
Sculpture			
£1560	$2606	€2200	Le nid d'hirondelles (41cm-16in) s. sandstone polychrome enamel. 19-Oct-3 St-Germain-en-Laye Encheres #53/R est:2200-2500
£1986	$3316	€2800	La marquise aux roses (70cm-28in) s.i. white marble. 17-Jun-3 Galerie Moderne, Brussels #1531/R est:1200-1600
£3026	$5568	€4600	Nude woman standing with cat (30cm-12in) s. gold bronze ivory marble base. 22-Jun-4 Glerum, Amsterdam #133/R est:800-1200
Works on paper			
£3265	$5845	€4800	Une vue de Paris (58x45cm-23x18in) s. pastel. 19-Mar-4 Piasa, Paris #181/R est:1500-2000

CARRIER-BELLEUSE, Pierre (1851-1932) French

£8000	$14480	€12000	Danseuses et musiciennes sur la plage (146x114cm-57x45in) s.d.1912. 4-Apr-4 St-Germain-en-Laye Encheres #7/R est:10000-12000
£15972	$26674	€23000	La comedienne dans sa loge (51x60cm-20x24in) s. 22-Oct-3 Ribeyre & Baron, Paris #17/R est:6000-9000
£18121	$33523	€27000	Piste du bal (59x40cm-23x16in) st.sig. panel. 14-Mar-4 Eric Pillon, Calais #18/R
Works on paper			
£428	$787	€650	Portrait de jeune fille (98x70cm-39x28in) s.d.1875 pastel. 25-Jun-4 Daguerre, Paris #163
£1000	$1790	€1500	Jeune fille. s.d.1925 pastel. 15-May-4 other European Auctioneer #86
£1422	$2546	€2076	Portrait of young woman with loose hair (52x36cm-20x14in) s.d.1902 pastel. 12-May-4 Dobiaschofsky, Bern #380/R est:4000 (S.FR 3300)
£1786	$3250	€2608	Sunbathing (104x67cm-41x26in) s.d.1901 pastel on canvas. 29-Jun-4 Sotheby's, New York #101/R est:5000-7000
£1974	$3632	€3000	Jeune femme a la bougie (100x65cm-39x26in) s. wax pastel. 28-Jun-4 Joron-Derem, Paris #104/R est:3000-4000
£2797	$4811	€4000	Apres le bain (91x51cm-36x20in) s.d.1899 pastel. 8-Dec-3 Christie's, Paris #55/R est:4000-6000
£9441	$16049	€13500	Ballerines (100x81cm-39x32in) s.d.1909 pastel. 18-Nov-3 Sotheby's, Paris #8/R est:6000-8000

CARRIERA, Rosalba (1675-1757) Italian
Works on paper
£24658 $41918 €36000 Portrait of girl with little bunch of flowers (51x40cm-20x16in) pastel prov.exhib. 9-Nov-3 Finarte, Venice #76/R est:35000-45000
£28188 $52711 €42000 Girl in profile. Head of girl (29x24cm-11x9in) pastel paper on canvas pair prov. 25-Feb-4 Porro, Milan #40/R est:42000

CARRIERA, Rosalba (attrib) (1675-1757) Italian
Works on paper
£1197 $2095 €1700 Portrait of woman (38x30cm-15x12in) pastel. 19-Dec-3 Pierre Berge, Paris #75/R est:800-1200
£11000 $19030 €16060 Head of a girl (30x26cm-12x10in) pastel prov. 12-Dec-3 Christie's, Kensington #394/R est:1500-2500

CARRIERA, Rosalba (circle) (1675-1757) Italian
Works on paper
£13304 $23814 €19424 Girl with white dove symbolising Innocence (53x42cm-21x17in) pastel. 25-May-4 Bukowskis, Stockholm #531/R est:30000-35000 (S.KR 180000)

CARRIERE, Eugène (1849-1906) French
£567 $948 €800 Maternite (40x33cm-16x13in) s. 17-Jun-3 Vanderkindere, Brussels #88
£1007 $1782 €1500 Visage de femme souriante (32x25cm-13x10in) 30-Apr-4 Tajan, Paris #182 est:1200-1500
£1300 $2171 €1898 Portrait of a priest, in traditional hat and robes (56x44cm-22x17in) s. 8-Oct-3 Christie's, Kensington #711/R est:1000-1500
£1778 $3219 €2596 Lucie Carriere (45x38cm-18x15in) s. prov. 1-Apr-4 Heffel, Vancouver #9/R est:4500-6500 (C.D 4250)
£1834 $3338 €2678 Buste de jeune femme (35x27cm-14x11in) s. 17-Jun-4 Kornfeld, Bern #239/R est:3000 (S.FR 4200)
£2098 $3566 €3000 Portrait d'enfant (16x11cm-6x4in) s.d.1886 isorel. 23-Nov-3 Cornette de St.Cyr, Paris #600/R est:800-1000
£2267 $4103 €3400 Sous-bois (39x32cm-15x13in) st.sig. lit. 30-Mar-4 Rossini, Paris #339/R est:1200-1800
£2800 $5152 €4200 Tete (41x33cm-16x13in) s. 9-Jun-4 Beaussant & Lefèvre, Paris #116/R est:3200-3500
£6325 $10500 €9235 Le retour du travail, la famille (27x35cm-11x14in) s. painted c.1897-1900 prov.exhib. 30-Sep-3 Christie's, Rockefeller NY #455/R est:5000-7000
£9639 $16000 €14073 L'exposition mondiale (33x41cm-13x16in) s. prov.exhib. 30-Sep-3 Christie's, Rockefeller NY #456/R est:7000-9000
£12931 $23147 €18879 Maternite (66x82cm-26x32in) s. prov. 13-May-4 Pierre Berge, Paris #27/R est:30000-35000 (S.FR 30000)
Works on paper
£223 $400 €326 Mother and child (33x25cm-13x10in) s. pencil chl. 21-Mar-4 Bonhams & Butterfields, Los Angeles #7331/R
£331 $603 €500 Portrait d'enfant (24x17cm-9x7in) st.sig. chl. 16-Jun-4 Piasa, Paris #173
£431 $719 €620 Maternite (18x14cm-7x6in) st.sig. sanguine. 25-Oct-3 Cornette de St.Cyr, Paris #479
£497 $900 €726 Studies of a woman reading (31x18cm-12x7in) pencil. 30-Mar-4 Christie's, Rockefeller NY #116/R
£1193 $1992 €1730 Maternite (36x30cm-14x12in) s. chk htd white. 19-Jun-3 Kornfeld, Bern #238 est:3000 (S.FR 2600)

CARRIERE, Eugène (attrib) (1849-1906) French
£3357 $5706 €4800 Jeune femme en prier (46x59cm-18x23in) bears sig. 1-Dec-3 Palais de Beaux Arts, Brussels #349/R est:5000-6000

CARRIES, Jean (1855-1894) French
Sculpture
£3846 $6538 €5500 Buste (44x21x25cm-17x8x10in) pat plaster lit. 21-Nov-3 Lombrail & Teucquam, Paris #35/R est:5000
£6434 $10937 €9200 Guerrier (49cm-19in) pat plaster lit. 21-Nov-3 Lombrail & Teucquam, Paris #36/R est:2000-2500
£6993 $11678 €10000 Masque de rive (24cm-9in) sand stone enamel lit. 24-Jun-3 Millon & Associes, Paris #191/R est:10000-12000
£7383 $13068 €11000 Buste de Madame Hals (52x37x37cm-20x15x15in) s. pat bronze Cast Bingen exec.1884 prov.exhib.lit. 30-Apr-4 Tajan, Paris #60/R est:12000-15000
£7902 $13434 €11300 Grenouillard (37x45x43cm-15x18x17in) pat plaster lit. 21-Nov-3 Lombrail & Teucquam, Paris #34/R est:6000-8000
£18000 $33120 €27000 Le grenouillard (31cm-12in) gres enamel exec. c.1892. 11-Jun-4 Claude Aguttes, Neuilly #89/R est:25000-30000
£20000 $36800 €30000 Masque d'horreur (28x20cm-11x8in) gres enamel. 11-Jun-4 Claude Aguttes, Neuilly #88/R est:20000-30000

CARRILLO, Achille (1818-1880) Italian
£985 $1802 €1438 Mountain landscape with church and a procession (16x22cm-6x9in) s.d.1840 paper on cardboard. 7-Jun-4 Museumsbygningen, Copenhagen #130/R (D.KR 11000)
Works on paper
£1478 $2705 €2158 Naples and the surrounding area (27x40cm-11x16in) s. one d.1844 one d.1845 pair. 4-Jun-4 Zofingen, Switzerland #2338/R est:1200 (S.FR 3400)

CARRILLO, Francisco (1954-) Spanish
£1074 $2008 €1600 Apples (100x70cm-39x28in) s. board. 24-Feb-4 Durán, Madrid #8/R est:1000

CARRINGTON, Dora (1893-1932) British
£17000 $28900 €24820 Still life of flowers (56x46cm-22x18in) oil ink silver foil on glass painted c.1928. 21-Nov-3 Christie's, London #73/R est:3000-5000
Works on paper
£550 $919 €803 Portrait of young lady (26x25cm-10x10in) s.indis.i.d.1911 crayon. 21-Oct-3 Gildings, Market Harborough #462

CARRINGTON, Dora (attrib) (1893-1932) British
Works on paper
£800 $1376 €1168 Afternoon in Brindisi (49x29cm-19x11in) red chk prov. 3-Dec-3 Cheffins, Cambridge #585

CARRINGTON, James Yates (1857-1892) British
£3400 $6188 €4964 Strangers yet (40x30cm-16x12in) s.d.91. 16-Jun-4 Bonhams, New Bond Street #53/R est:2000-3000

CARRINGTON, Leonora (1917-) British
£16471 $28000 €24048 Figure in water (26x19cm-10x7in) s.d.1960 indis.i.verso board. 18-Nov-3 Christie's, Rockefeller NY #100/R est:12000-16000
£200000 $364000 €292000 Sacrament at minos (95x45cm-37x18in) s.d.1954 prov.exhib.lit. 3-Feb-4 Sotheby's, London #82/R est:180000-220000
Works on paper
£847 $1500 €1237 Doe (34x46cm-13x18in) s. ink prov. 2-May-4 Bonhams & Butterfields, Los Angeles #3055/R est:3000-4000
£2250 $3600 €3285 Dream (18x27cm-7x11in) s. pen ink. 18-Sep-3 Swann Galleries, New York #128/R est:5000-8000
£24000 $44160 €36000 Scenario for ' the king's death' (50x80cm-20x31in) init. gouache W/C cardboard exec.c.1970 prov.exhib. 10-Jun-4 Christie's, Paris #69/R est:32000-48000

CARRINO, David (1959-) American
Works on paper
£293 $519 €428 George Eliot (120x73cm-47x29in) s.d.1988 verso Indian ink collage cloth prov. 27-Apr-4 AB Stockholms Auktionsverk #1212/R (S.KR 4000)

CARRION, Antonio Lorenzo (1929-) Spanish
£1096 $1863 €1600 Travellers (21x25cm-8x10in) s.d.80 acrylic board. 4-Nov-3 Ansorena, Madrid #942/R est:1500

CARRIZ, Jose Maria (20th C) Spanish
£680 $1218 €1000 The city keys (81x100cm-32x39in) s. 22-Mar-4 Durán, Madrid #46

CARROL, Robert (1934-) American
£733 $1349 €1100 Asp 29 (46x55cm-18x22in) s. s.i.verso. 12-Jun-4 Meeting Art, Vercelli #334/R
£1056 $1754 €1500 Nido di Armadillo (65x54cm-26x21in) s. s.i.verso. 14-Jun-3 Meeting Art, Vercelli #700/R est:1500

CARROLL, John (1892-1959) American
£978 $1800 €1428 Zabelle (41x36cm-16x14in) d.1937. 11-Jun-4 Du Mouchelle, Detroit #1017/R est:1800-2400
£2717 $5000 €3967 Spring bonnet (102x76cm-40x30in) 11-Jun-4 Du Mouchelle, Detroit #1016/R est:2500-3500
£8982 $15000 €13114 White lace (102x76cm-40x30in) s.d.35 prov.exhib.lit. 7-Oct-3 Sotheby's, New York #226 est:2000-4000

CARROLL, Lewis (1832-1898) British
Photographs
£3200 $5856 €4672 Annie and Henry Rogers (14x11cm-6x4in) num.191 albumen print. 8-Jul-4 Sotheby's, London #322/R est:2000-3000
£4192 $7000 €6120 Edith, Lorina and Alice Liddell on a daybed (13x15cm-5x6in) albumen print arch top. 21-Oct-3 Swann Galleries, New York #15/R est:10000-15000
£4200 $7686 €6132 Annie Rogers alseep on a chaise longue (12x16cm-5x6in) i.d.June 1861 verso albumen print card oval. 8-Jul-4 Sotheby's, London #318/R est:700-900
£5500 $10065 €8030 Annie Rogers standing by chair (20x15cm-8x6in) albumen print. 8-Jul-4 Sotheby's, London #323/R est:2500-3500
£7500 $13725 €10950 Annie and Henry Rogers on chaise longue. num.52 albumen print. 8-Jul-4 Sotheby's, London #317/R est:2500-3500
£9000 $15840 €13140 Frederica Harriette Morrell (17x13cm-7x5in) num.2039 albumen print. 19-May-4 Christie's, London #71/R est:3000-5000
£12000 $21960 €17520 Fair Rosamund (23x18cm-9x7in) albumen print. 8-Jul-4 Sotheby's, London #325/R est:3000-5000

CARROLL, Marie (20th C) British?
£250 $465 €365 Sailing, Dublin Bay (23x23cm-9x9in) s. board. 3-Mar-4 John Ross, Belfast #72
£260 $447 €380 The Shelbourne Bar, Dublin (30x20cm-12x8in) s. board. 3-Dec-3 John Ross, Belfast #25
£268 $481 €400 Racing boats off the coast (92x60cm-36x24in) s. board. 31-May-4 Hamilton Osborne King, Dublin #8/R
£280 $482 €409 Sheep grazing, Connemara (25x35cm-10x14in) s. board. 3-Dec-3 John Ross, Belfast #188
£280 $512 €409 Ring-a-ring of roses (30x35cm-12x14in) s. board. 2-Jun-4 John Ross, Belfast #196
£300 $558 €438 Boats near the docks, Dublin (30x40cm-12x16in) s. board. 3-Mar-4 John Ross, Belfast #13
£320 $531 €467 Ryans Bar (23x28cm-9x11in) s. board. 1-Oct-3 John Ross, Belfast #133
£320 $531 €467 Feeding the hens (28x22cm-11x9in) s. board. 1-Oct-3 John Ross, Belfast #207
£320 $550 €467 The Halfpenny Bridge, Dublin (30x25cm-12x10in) s. board. 3-Dec-3 John Ross, Belfast #256
£350 $602 €511 Sailing off Howth (30x40cm-12x16in) s. board. 3-Dec-3 John Ross, Belfast #140
£380 $623 €555 Dublin street scene (45x71cm-18x28in) s. board. 4-Jun-3 John Ross, Belfast #190
£380 $623 €555 Clip to the pin (71x45cm-28x18in) s. board. 4-Jun-3 John Ross, Belfast #230
£380 $654 €555 Hotel interior, Dublin (45x71cm-18x28in) s. board. 3-Dec-3 John Ross, Belfast #206

£400	$688	€584	Rolys Bistro (61x45cm-24x18in) s. board. 3-Dec-3 John Ross, Belfast #11
£400	$688	€584	Across from St Stephen's Green shopping mall, Dublin (48x73cm-19x29in) s. board. 3-Dec-3 John Ross, Belfast #37
£450	$738	€657	Along the Liffey (45x71cm-18x28in) s. board. 4-Jun-3 John Ross, Belfast #109
£450	$774	€657	Busy day, Dublin (96x71cm-38x28in) s. board. 3-Dec-3 John Ross, Belfast #182
£450	$824	€657	Yacht race, Dublin Bay (71x45cm-28x18in) s. board. 2-Jun-4 John Ross, Belfast #202
£480	$787	€701	Night in O'Shea's Bar, Dublin (45x71cm-18x28in) s. board. 4-Jun-3 John Ross, Belfast #238
£480	$797	€701	Full sail (96x66cm-38x26in) s. board. 1-Oct-3 John Ross, Belfast #108
£500	$830	€730	In the Shelbourne Hotel, Dublin (71x48cm-28x19in) s. board. 1-Oct-3 John Ross, Belfast #220
£500	$830	€730	Belfast City Hall. board. 1-Oct-3 John Ross, Belfast #1b
£500	$930	€730	Dublin (81x61cm-32x24in) s. board. 3-Mar-4 John Ross, Belfast #112
£500	$930	€730	Boat race on the Liffey (50x71cm-20x28in) s. board. 3-Mar-4 John Ross, Belfast #243
£500	$915	€730	At the bar in the Shelbourne Hotel (61x68cm-24x27in) s. board. 2-Jun-4 John Ross, Belfast #169
£500	$915	€730	In the Shelbourne Hotel, Dublin (71x48cm-28x19in) s. board. 2-Jun-4 John Ross, Belfast #176
£550	$902	€803	Ball (86x61cm-34x24in) s. board. 4-Jun-3 John Ross, Belfast #174
£550	$1007	€803	Halfpenny Bridge at sunset, Dublin (73x48cm-29x19in) s. board. 2-Jun-4 John Ross, Belfast #112
£580	$1061	€847	Docklands, Dublin (50x76cm-20x30in) s. board. 2-Jun-4 John Ross, Belfast #116
£600	$996	€876	Gresham Hotel, Dublin (71x101cm-28x40in) s. board. 1-Oct-3 John Ross, Belfast #39
£620	$1029	€905	Yacht race (50x76cm-20x30in) s. board. 1-Oct-3 John Ross, Belfast #82
£650	$1066	€949	Bar in Dublin (71x48cm-28x19in) s. board. 4-Jun-3 John Ross, Belfast #202
£650	$1066	€949	Out for a walk (25x30cm-10x12in) s. board. 4-Jun-3 John Ross, Belfast #237a
£650	$1079	€949	Halfpenny Bridge, Dublin (51x71cm-20x28in) s. board. 1-Oct-3 John Ross, Belfast #66
£650	$1079	€949	Boat race on the Liffey, Dublin (45x71cm-18x28in) s. board. 1-Oct-3 John Ross, Belfast #244
£650	$1209	€949	Dublin City centre (122x91cm-48x36in) s. 3-Mar-4 John Ross, Belfast #114
£650	$1190	€949	In the Shelbourne Hotel, Dublin (48x73cm-19x29in) s. board. 2-Jun-4 John Ross, Belfast #39
£650	$1190	€949	Sailing off Dublin Bay (71x45cm-28x18in) s. board. 2-Jun-4 John Ross, Belfast #92
£700	$1162	€1022	In the Shelbourne Hotel, Dublin (71x48cm-28x19in) s. board. 1-Oct-3 John Ross, Belfast #205
£700	$1204	€1022	The ballet class (40x76cm-16x30in) s. board. 3-Dec-3 John Ross, Belfast #127
£800	$1312	€1168	Halfpenny Bridge (45x71cm-18x28in) s. board. 4-Jun-3 John Ross, Belfast #124

CARROLL, Patrick (1949-) Australian

£992	$1686	€1488	The Sydney Harbour Bridge (65x54cm-26x21in) s. acrylic paper. 28-Oct-3 Goodman, Sydney #488 (A.D 2400)

CARROLL, William Joseph (19/20th C) British

£1600	$2880	€2336	Portrait of a young lady wearing a summer dress (61x46cm-24x18in) s.i. 21-Apr-4 Tennants, Leyburn #1211 est:1200-1400
Works on paper			
£400	$728	€584	Hide-and-seek (50x39cm-20x15in) s. W/C bodycol. 1-Jul-4 Christie's, Kensington #183/R

CARRON, William (1930-) Irish?

Works on paper			
£500	$905	€750	Midsummer Purteen Achill Island (28x45cm-11x18in) s.d.01 W/C exhib. 30-Mar-4 De Veres Art Auctions, Dublin #182/R

CARSE, Alexander (c.1770-1843) British

£363	$668	€530	Village tailor (24x32cm-9x13in) oil sketch panel prov. 14-Jun-4 Waddingtons, Toronto #184/R est:700-900 (C.D 900)
£1500	$2445	€2190	Village politicians (40x54cm-16x21in) 17-Jul-3 Bonhams, Edinburgh #303 est:1500-2000

CARSE, J H (1819-1900) Australian/British

£3099	$5733	€4525	Harvest landscape, Fyan's estate, Camperdown (30x45cm-12x18in) exhib. 10-Mar-4 Deutscher-Menzies, Melbourne #204/R est:8000-12000 (A.D 7500)

CARSE, James Howe (1819-1900) Australian/British

£830	$1386	€1245	Wetland scene (30x40cm-12x16in) s.d.1888. 27-Oct-3 Goodman, Sydney #220/R (A.D 2000)
£1897	$3396	€2846	Slab hut and pioneer family (33x45cm-13x18in) s.i. canvas on board. 17-May-4 Sotheby's, Melbourne #568/R est:2000-3000 (A.D 4800)

CARSE, William (19th C) British

£1100	$1727	€1595	Making merry (35x45cm-14x18in) 27-Aug-3 Sotheby's, London #919/R est:1500-2000

CARSMAN, Jon (20th C) American?

Works on paper			
£350	$633	€511	No.6 point breeze (77x58cm-30x23in) s.d.75 i.d.verso W/C. 30-Mar-4 Lawson Menzies, Sydney #263a/R est:300-500 (A.D 850)

CARSON, Frank (1881-c.1962) American

£250	$425	€365	Pemaquid, Maine (46x56cm-18x22in) s.d.77. 21-Nov-3 Skinner, Boston #559/R
£703	$1300	€1026	Harvard yard (64x51cm-25x20in) s.d.1917 board. 17-Jul-4 Outer Cape Auctions, Provincetown #72/R

CARSON, Robert Taylor (1919-) British

£537	$961	€800	Tra-Na-Rossan Bay (30x40cm-12x16in) s. s.i.d.8/4/62 verso. 31-May-4 Hamilton Osborne King, Dublin #141/R
£769	$1308	€1100	Tinker family (30x40cm-12x16in) s. 25-Nov-3 De Veres Art Auctions, Dublin #29/R est:1000-1500
£950	$1739	€1387	Rathmullen, Donegal (50x66cm-20x26in) s. board. 2-Jun-4 John Ross, Belfast #91
£1000	$1590	€1460	Portrait of Maurice C Wilks, with pipe (37x29cm-15x11in) s.d.44 canvasboard. 10-Sep-3 Sotheby's, Olympia #160/R est:1000-1500
£1074	$1922	€1600	Portrait of Maurice Wilks (36x28cm-14x11in) s.d.44 i. verso board. 31-May-4 Hamilton Osborne King, Dublin #173/R est:1000-1500
£1200	$2148	€1752	Winding river (30x41cm-12x16in) s. board. 14-May-4 Christie's, Kensington #377/R est:800-1200
£1208	$2138	€1800	Portrait of a young man, seated (48x39cm-19x15in) s. canvas on board. 27-Apr-4 Whyte's, Dublin #253/R est:1800-2200
£1250	$2275	€1825	Sailing ships beside a quay and a mountainous coast (52x62cm-20x24in) s. board. 3-Feb-4 Sworder & Son, Bishops Stortford #284/R est:500-700
£1250	$2275	€1825	Village street with figures, a car an estuary and mountains beyond (42x62cm-17x24in) s. board. 3-Feb-4 Sworder & Son, Bishops Stortford #283/R est:400-600
£1400	$2408	€2044	Boating at Downings (40x50cm-16x20in) s.d.99 verso board. 3-Dec-3 John Ross, Belfast #148 est:1600-1800
£1400	$2562	€2044	Girl with flowers (61x50cm-24x20in) s. 2-Jun-4 John Ross, Belfast #11 est:800-1000
£1409	$2495	€2100	Winter evening, Downings (30x41cm-12x16in) s. i.verso board. 27-Apr-4 Whyte's, Dublin #233/R est:2000-2500
£1409	$2523	€2100	Road to Kilkeel (40x50cm-16x20in) s. 26-May-4 James Adam, Dublin #100/R est:2000-3000
£1500	$2490	€2190	Magheracloghter, Co. Donegal (50x61cm-20x24in) s. 1-Oct-3 John Ross, Belfast #157 est:1500-2000
£1645	$3026	€2500	Eighteenth hole City of Derry, GC (50x62cm-20x24in) s. s.i.d.58 verso. 22-Jun-4 De Veres Art Auctions, Dublin #202/R est:2500-3500
£1733	$3137	€2600	August flowers (60x50cm-24x20in) s.i.verso. 31-Mar-4 James Adam, Dublin #155/R est:1500-2500
£1800	$2952	€2628	Spanish girl by window (63x76cm-25x30in) s. 4-Jun-3 John Ross, Belfast #140
£1831	$2930	€2600	Children in a Donegal village. Sand castle (32x39cm-13x15in) s. canvas on board double-sided. 16-Sep-3 Whyte's, Dublin #146/R est:2500-3500
£2282	$4039	€3400	Marie (61x51cm-24x20in) s. s.i.verso canvas on board. 27-Apr-4 Whyte's, Dublin #239/R est:3000-4000
£2349	$4158	€3500	Girl in the rain, thought to be Julie Christie (76x44cm-30x17in) s. i.d.1967 verso. 27-Apr-4 Whyte's, Dublin #252/R est:3500-4500
£4400	$7568	€6424	Resting (61x91cm-24x36in) s. 3-Dec-3 John Ross, Belfast #135 est:2000-2500
£4832	$8553	€7200	Mary's kitchen (64x76cm-25x30in) s. i.d.August 1975 verso. 27-Apr-4 Whyte's, Dublin #251/R est:4000-5000
Works on paper			
£350	$602	€511	Autumn tints (45x55cm-18x22in) s. W/C. 3-Dec-3 John Ross, Belfast #103
£400	$664	€584	Still life, apples and chrysanthemums (30x25cm-12x10in) s.d.92 verso pastel. 1-Oct-3 John Ross, Belfast #8
£606	$1060	€860	Agricultural chat (26x37cm-10x15in) s.d.84 verso W/C. 16-Dec-3 James Adam, Dublin #110/R
£1119	$1902	€1600	Taking home the groceries (35x32cm-14x13in) s. W/C. 25-Nov-3 De Veres Art Auctions, Dublin #165/R est:800-1200

CARSTENSEN, Andreas Christian Riis (1844-1906) Danish

£496	$917	€724	Coastal landscape vessels on the horizon (52x79cm-20x31in) s.d.1892. 15-Mar-4 Rasmussen, Vejle #160/R (D.KR 5500)
£687	$1250	€1003	Landscape from Torre Belem in Lisbon (38x35cm-15x14in) mono. 7-Feb-4 Rasmussen, Havnen #2180/R (D.KR 7500)
£1402	$2215	€2033	Seascape with fishing boats (67x102cm-26x40in) s. 2-Sep-3 Rasmussen, Copenhagen #1653/R est:15000 (D.KR 15000)
£5671	$9811	€8280	Princess Dagmar's departure to Russia (52x78cm-20x31in) s.d.Sept.1890. 9-Dec-3 Rasmussen, Copenhagen #1291/R est:40000 (D.KR 60000)

CARSTENSEN, Claus (1957-) Danish

£751	$1254	€1096	Green composition (122x96cm-48x38in) s.d.220600 paper. 7-Oct-3 Rasmussen, Copenhagen #170/R (D.KR 8000)

CARSTENSEN, Ebba (1885-1967) Danish

£284	$518	€426	Field landscape with cattle grazing (65x95cm-26x37in) s. s.d.66 verso. 19-Jun-4 Rasmussen, Havnen #4084 (D.KR 3200)
£402	$651	€583	Landscape with trees (63x80cm-25x31in) s. 4-Aug-3 Rasmussen, Vejle #648 (D.KR 4200)
£1244	$2265	€1866	Autumn landscape with horses (81x91cm-32x36in) s. d.1939 verso. 19-Jun-4 Rasmussen, Havnen #4157 est:1000-2000 (D.KR 14000)
£2256	$4152	€3294	Seated woman (90x64cm-35x25in) s.d.1920 verso prov. 29-Mar-4 Rasmussen, Copenhagen #178/R est:25000 (D.KR 25000)

CARTE, Antoine (1886-1954) Belgian

£382	$623	€550	Fleurs (40x32cm-16x13in) s. cardboard. 23-Sep-3 Galerie Moderne, Brussels #859
£851	$1421	€1200	Fleurs (40x32cm-16x13in) s. double-sided. 17-Jun-3 Galerie Moderne, Brussels #182
£10667	$19627	€16000	Femme a la barre (53x53cm-21x21in) paper. 14-Jun-4 Horta, Bruxelles #139/R est:8000-12000
£73333	$134200	€110000	Le jeune pecheur (100x80cm-39x31in) s. 7-Jun-4 Palais de Beaux Arts, Brussels #232/R est:75000-100000
£125874	$216504	€180000	L'arlequin et les attributs du mariage (105x103cm-41x41in) s. 8-Dec-3 Horta, Bruxelles #118/R est:55000-65000
Works on paper			
£2162	$3870	€3200	Projet de vitrail pour l'eglise Saint Antoine (174x72cm-69x28in) W/C Indian ink. 10-May-4 Horta, Bruxelles #108 est:3000-5000
£4658	$7918	€6800	Chemin de Croix. Crucifixion (25x33cm-10x13in) one s. mixed media pair. 10-Nov-3 Horta, Bruxelles #145

£5667 $10257 €8500 Les cordiers (30x28cm-12x11in) s.d.1917 W/C. 30-Mar-4 Campo, Vlaamse Kaai #16/R est:7000-9000

CARTER, Charles (?) British?
£839 $1427 €1200 Cattle grazing (84x131cm-33x52in) indis.sig. 29-Nov-3 Bukowskis, Helsinki #361/R

CARTER, Clarence Holbrook (1904-2000) American
£462 $800 €675 Landscape of orchard in bloom (48x66cm-19x26in) s.d.54. 10-Dec-3 Alderfer's, Hatfield #396/R
£1138 $1900 €1661 View of Washington Monument (51x72cm-20x28in) s.d.47. 9-Oct-3 Christie's, Rockefeller NY #89/R est:4000-6000
Works on paper
£253 $400 €369 Rolling landscape of a bald with a tree (38x56cm-15x22in) s. s.verso W/C. 6-Sep-3 Brunk, Ashville #137
£301 $475 €439 Abstract (53x53cm-21x21in) s. gouache. 7-Sep-3 Treadway Gallery, Cincinnati #745/R
£435 $800 €635 Portrait of a young woman (33x25cm-13x10in) s.d.1941 W/C brush pen ink. 10-Jun-4 Swann Galleries, New York #54/R
£543 $1000 €793 Tethered bull (36x53cm-14x21in) s.d.1939 W/C. 10-Jun-4 Swann Galleries, New York #53/R
£978 $1800 €1428 Visitors to the sea (56x38cm-22x15in) s.d.1936 col pastel W/C. 10-Jun-4 Swann Galleries, New York #52/R est:1000-1500

CARTER, Frank Thomas (1853-1934) British
£377 $600 €550 Warm day in the mountains (33x47cm-13x19in) s. board. 13-Sep-3 Weschler, Washington #674/R
£400 $688 €584 Great Gate, Barrowdale (29x44cm-11x17in) s. 4-Dec-3 Locke & England, Leamington Spa #164

CARTER, Henry Barlow (1803-1867) British
£360 $634 €526 Robin (30x25cm-12x10in) s. 19-May-4 John Bellman, Billingshurst #1806/R
Works on paper
£260 $432 €380 Beached fishing vessel (13x7cm-5x3in) mono. W/C. 6-Oct-3 David Duggleby, Scarborough #285
£270 $459 €394 Beached fishing boat near the quayside (13x18cm-5x7in) s. W/C. 1-Dec-3 David Duggleby, Scarborough #291
£280 $507 €409 Beached vessels and figures, Whitby (25x36cm-10x14in) s. W/C. 15-Apr-4 Richardson & Smith, Whitby #86/R
£300 $489 €438 Distant view of Scarborough with a shipwreck surrounded by figures (14x20cm-6x8in) W/C. 31-Jan-3 Bigwood, Stratford on Avon #257
£300 $546 €438 Shipwreck (33x45cm-13x18in) pencil W/C scratching out. 1-Jul-4 Mellors & Kirk, Nottingham #744
£480 $816 €701 Staithes (24x34cm-9x13in) W/C. 1-Dec-3 David Duggleby, Scarborough #252/R
£540 $902 €788 Vessels at Sunrise (23x33cm-9x13in) W/C htd white. 10-Oct-3 Richardson & Smith, Whitby #118/R
£560 $952 €818 Stormy seas with wreckage at the cliff foot (29x43cm-11x17in) s.d.44 W/C. 1-Dec-3 David Duggleby, Scarborough #263/R
£600 $966 €870 Off Whitby, wreck in the foreground (23x30cm-9x12in) W/C. 13-Aug-3 Andrew Hartley, Ilkley #781/R
£600 $954 €870 Staithes from the south (22x31cm-9x12in) W/C. 9-Sep-3 David Duggleby, Scarborough #124
£640 $1158 €934 North of Flamborough Head (30x43cm-12x17in) W/C. 30-Mar-4 David Duggleby, Scarborough #196/R
£680 $1081 €986 Waiting on the pier (18x26cm-7x10in) s.d.1830 W/C. 9-Sep-3 David Duggleby, Scarborough #222a
£720 $1145 €1044 Bridlington Harbour (14x22cm-6x9in) s.d.1831 W/C. 9-Sep-3 David Duggleby, Scarborough #195
£720 $1303 €1051 Farne Islands (30x43cm-12x17in) W/C. 30-Mar-4 David Duggleby, Scarborough #195/R
£800 $1336 €1168 Fishing vessel off Whitby (18x29cm-7x11in) s. W/C. 9-Jul-3 Peter Wilson, Nantwich #87
£820 $1304 €1189 Fish pier Scarborough in a storm (17x24cm-7x9in) s. indis d. W/C. 9-Sep-3 David Duggleby, Scarborough #30/R
£900 $1683 €1314 Boat in a squall off a coastal town (31x46cm-12x18in) s.i. W/C bodycol scratching out. 20-Jul-4 Sworder & Son, Bishops Stortford #775/R
£1000 $1700 €1460 View of Scarborough with figures amongst rocks in the foreground (17x23cm-7x9in) W/C scratching out. 18-Nov-3 Bonhams, Leeds #49/R est:1000-1200
£1400 $2618 €2044 View of Whitby Abbey and St Mary's Church from the banks of the River Esk (23x33cm-9x13in) s.d.1848 pencil W/C scratching out. 22-Jul-4 Tennants, Leyburn #646/R est:800-1200

CARTER, Henry Barlow (attrib) (1803-1867) British
Works on paper
£300 $561 €438 Village scene with figures beside a cottage, cattle beside a pool (21x34cm-8x13in) bears sig. i.verso pencil W/C scratching out. 22-Jul-4 Tennants, Leyburn #726
£560 $930 €818 North of Flamborough Head. the wreck. Farne Island (30x43cm-12x17in) i.verso W/C pair. 4-Oct-3 Finan Watkins & Co, Mere #134

CARTER, Henry W (19th C) British
£280 $482 €409 View of Snape Park Well Farm (28x43cm-11x17in) s.d.1889 board. 3-Dec-3 Andrew Hartley, Ilkley #1198
£780 $1342 €1139 Rabbits in landscape (36x30cm-14x12in) s.d.1889 board. 3-Dec-3 Andrew Hartley, Ilkley #1199

CARTER, Hugh (1837-1903) British
Works on paper
£750 $1380 €1095 Haircut day (38x56cm-15x22in) init. pencil W/C. 25-Mar-4 Christie's, Kensington #227

CARTER, Hugh (attrib) (1837-1903) British
£400 $732 €584 Fishermen and boats in a choppy sea (92x120cm-36x47in) init. 28-Jan-4 Hampton & Littlewood, Exeter #403/R

CARTER, Jack (?-1992) British
Works on paper
£270 $500 €405 Still life study of marigolds within a stoneware tankard (36x51cm-14x20in) s.d.55 W/C pastel. 14-Jul-4 Rupert Toovey, Partridge Green #12/R
£320 $592 €480 Still life study of pink roses (35x25cm-14x10in) s.d.1979 W/C. 14-Jul-4 Rupert Toovey, Partridge Green #14/R
£340 $629 €510 Apple blossom (27x38cm-11x15in) s.d.1978 W/C. 14-Jul-4 Rupert Toovey, Partridge Green #13/R

CARTER, James (20th C) American
£915 $1500 €1336 Study for questions of balance (51x41cm-20x16in) s. s.i.verso acrylic fiberboard prov. 31-May-3 Brunk, Ashville #367/R est:800-1500

CARTER, Joseph Newington (1835-1871) British
Works on paper
£260 $442 €380 Ship in distress off rocks, fishing village beyond (23x32cm-9x13in) W/C. 26-Nov-3 Hamptons Fine Art, Godalming #104
£270 $489 €394 Shipping in stormy seas (31x48cm-12x19in) s.d.66 W/C. 30-Mar-4 David Duggleby, Scarborough #192/R
£300 $543 €438 Scarborough Lodge, Torquay (31x48cm-12x19in) s.i.d.1866 W/C. 30-Mar-4 David Duggleby, Scarborough #191/R
£320 $579 €467 Ramsdale mill and house, Scarborough, before Valley Bridge was erected (19x27cm-7x11in) s.d.61 W/C. 30-Mar-4 David Duggleby, Scarborough #76/R
£350 $602 €511 Misty coastal scene (25x33cm-10x13in) s.d.67. 5-Dec-3 Keys, Aylsham #417
£420 $672 €609 Shipping off Scarborough (23x35cm-9x14in) 17-Sep-3 James Thompson, Kirby Lonsdale #59
£480 $782 €701 Moored vessel in the early morning (32x457cm-13x180in) s.d.1865 W/C htd white. 24-Sep-3 Dreweatt Neate, Newbury #7/R
£500 $910 €730 Shipping off the coast ,Scarborough castle beyond. N Yorkshire harbour (11x16cm-4x6in) s.indis.d. W/C pair. 15-Jun-4 Bonhams, Leeds #12/R

CARTER, Norman (1875-1963) Australian
£2024 $3259 €2955 Girl in White (91x75cm-36x30in) s.d.1923 prov.exhib.lit. 25-Aug-3 Sotheby's, Paddington #481/R est:5000-8000 (A.D 5000)

CARTER, Peter J (20th C) British
£650 $1164 €949 Fishing trawlers in close quarters at sea (79x100cm-31x39in) s. canvasboard. 18-Mar-4 Christie's, Kensington #531/R

CARTER, Pruett A (1891-1955) American
£1471 $2500 €2148 It's all in the family (48x51cm-19x20in) s. canvasboard prov. 18-Nov-3 John Moran, Pasadena #90a est:1500-2500

CARTER, Richard Harry (1839-1911) British
Works on paper
£260 $424 €377 Rowing to the village (28x45cm-11x18in) s. W/C bodycol. 23-Sep-3 Bonhams, Knightsbridge #68/R
£470 $870 €686 The armed knight, Lands End, September evening coastal scene with boat (36x53cm-14x21in) s. W/C gouache. 12-Mar-4 Dickins, Middle Claydon #9
£529 $947 €772 Coastal landscape with cliffs (55x95cm-22x37in) s.d.1873 W/C. 12-Jan-4 Rasmussen, Vejle #319 (D.KR 5600)
£800 $1480 €1168 Break of day, coast of Scotland (40x65cm-16x26in) s. W/C. 16-Feb-4 Bonhams, Bath #179
£1000 $1720 €1460 Smoking eels on a Volendam canal (90x60cm-35x24in) s. W/C gouache. 3-Dec-3 AB Stockholms Auktionsverk #2627/R (S.KR 13000)
£1100 $2013 €1606 Fisherwomen waiting for the return of the fleet, Mounts Bay, Cornwall (39x75cm-15x30in) s. W/C. 3-Jun-4 Lane, Penzance #281 est:1000-1200
£2300 $4071 €3358 Fishermen on a beach with their moored boats beyond (46x71cm-18x28in) s. W/C htd. bodycol. 28-Apr-4 Halls, Shrewsbury #475/R est:600-800
£5000 $9250 €7300 Return of the missing boat, St Ives, Cornwall (71x133cm-28x52in) s. W/C. 9-Mar-4 Bonhams, New Bond Street #136/R est:5000-7000

CARTER, Samuel John (1835-1892) British
£2500 $4625 €3650 Huntsman on horseback with dogs at the edge of a wood (48x74cm-19x29in) s. 13-Feb-4 Keys, Aylsham #661/R est:2000-3000
£3385 $5822 €4942 No thoroughfare - Winter landscape with woman and dogs (174x142cm-69x56in) s.d.1868. 7-Dec-3 Uppsala Auktionskammare, Uppsala #83/R est:40000-50000 (S.KR 44000)
£3500 $5530 €5075 Herons feeding their young (146x179cm-57x70in) s.d.1882 prov. 4-Sep-3 Christie's, Kensington #316/R est:4000-6000
£7000 $12740 €10220 Uncle Toby and the widow (70x83cm-28x33in) s.d.1863 exhib. 5-Feb-4 Mellors & Kirk, Nottingham #594/R est:5000-7000

CARTER, Sydney (1874-1945) British
£431 $720 €629 Old de Waal Drive, Cape Town (36x54cm-14x21in) s. canvas on board. 20-Oct-3 Stephan Welz, Johannesburg #511 est:3000-4000 (SA.R 5000)
£454 $813 €663 Mostert's Mill (44x59cm-17x23in) s. canvasboard. 31-May-4 Stephan Welz, Johannesburg #152 (SA.R 5500)
£603 $1008 €880 Farmhouse in the mountains (60x70cm-24x28in) s. 20-Oct-3 Stephan Welz, Johannesburg #784/R est:4000-6000 (SA.R 7000)
Works on paper
£413 $739 €603 Roadway lined with bluegums (31x42cm-12x17in) s. W/C. 31-May-4 Stephan Welz, Johannesburg #190 (SA.R 5000)
£420 $761 €613 Table Mountain from Melkbosstrand (50x62cm-20x24in) s. gouache. 30-Mar-4 Stephan Welz, Johannesburg #188 est:1500-2000 (SA.R 5000)

CARTER, William (fl.1843-1864) British
Works on paper
£280 $468 €409 In the Mawddach Valley N Wales (23x36cm-9x14in) s. 15-Oct-3 Brightwells, Leominster #892

CARTER, William Sylvester (1909-) American
£437 $800 €638 Floral still life (51x41cm-20x16in) s. sold with another. 10-Jul-4 Susanin's, Chicago #5106/R
Works on paper
£301 $475 €439 Floral still life (61x46cm-24x18in) s. W/C. 7-Sep-3 Treadway Gallery, Cincinnati #709/R

CARTIER, Jacques (20th C) French
£7692 $13077 €11000 Panthere noire (74x114cm-29x45in) s. panel gold leaf. 1-Dec-3 Camard, Paris #54/R est:1500-2000

CARTIER, M (19/20th C) French?
£2500 $3900 €3700 Jeune femme sur une meridienne (53x35cm-21x14in) s. 30-Mar-3 Versailles Encheres #10 est:4000-4500

CARTIER, Max (20th C) French?
£600 $1110 €876 Preparing the feast (55x40cm-22x16in) s. 15-Jan-4 Christie's, Kensington #849/R

CARTIER, Thomas (1879-1943) French
Sculpture
£1006 $1800 €1469 Lion (38cm-15in) s. bronze. 8-May-4 Susanin's, Chicago #6011/R est:3000-5000
£1500 $2595 €2190 Snarling panther (64cm-25in) s. dark green pat. bronze on stone base. 9-Dec-3 Clarke Gammon, Guildford #568/R est:1000-1500
£1549 $2572 €2200 Lioness (21x25cm-8x10in) s. rubbed green pat bronze. 11-Jun-3 Sotheby's, Amsterdam #307/R est:1200-1800
£2000 $3780 €2920 Tiger (35x46cm-14x18in) s. brown pat bronze. 17-Feb-4 Sotheby's, Olympia #30/R est:1000-1500

CARTIER-BRESSON, Henri (1908-) French
Photographs
£1695 $3000 €2475 Les Halles (45x29cm-18x11in) gelatin silver print. 27-Apr-4 Christie's, Rockefeller NY #280/R est:3000-5000
£1795 $3250 €2621 Siphnos, Greece (30x45cm-12x18in) s. gelatin silver print 1961/printed later. 19-Apr-4 Bonhams & Butterfields, San Francisco #388/R est:3000-5000
£1796 $3000 €2622 Albert Camus (53x76cm-21x30in) i.verso gelatin silver print. 16-Oct-3 Phillips, New York #25/R est:4000-6000
£1932 $3400 €2821 Coronation ceremony of George VI, Trafalgar Square, London (24x16cm-9x6in) silver print. 20-May-4 Swann Galleries, New York #376/R est:3000-5000
£1977 $3500 €2886 Paris, 1953 (35x24cm-14x9in) s. gelatin silver print. 27-Apr-4 Christie's, Rockefeller NY #279/R est:3000-5000
£1977 $3500 €2886 Queen Charlotte's ball, London, 1959 (35x24cm-14x9in) s. gelatin silver print. 27-Apr-4 Christie's, Rockefeller NY #281/R est:3000-5000
£2011 $3800 €2936 Simiane la Rotonde, France (23x35cm-9x14in) s. gelatin silver print executed c.1970. 17-Feb-4 Christie's, Rockefeller NY #239/R est:2500-3500
£2029 $3328 €2800 Hong Kong (25x17cm-10x7in) i. verso vintage silver gelatin lit. 30-May-3 Villa Grisebach, Berlin #1130/R est:2000-2500
£2254 $3899 €3200 Portrait d'Alberto Giacometti (35x24cm-14x9in) s. silver print lit. 10-Dec-3 Artcurial Briest, Paris #43/R est:3000-4000
£2312 $4000 €3376 Behind the Gare St. Lazare, Paris (45x30cm-18x12in) with sig. silver print. 9-Dec-3 Swann Galleries, New York #429/R est:3500-4500
£2395 $4000 €3497 Brie, France (24x36cm-9x14in) s. photo exec.1968 printed later. 17-Oct-3 Sotheby's, New York #226/R est:3000-5000
£2395 $4000 €3497 Valenica (17x25cm-7x10in) i.verso gelatin silver print exec.1933 prov. 17-Oct-3 Phillips, New York #162/R est:4000-6000
£2400 $4080 €3504 Henri Batisse, Venice (30x44cm-12x17in) s. gelatin silver print prov. 18-Nov-3 Christie's, Kensington #194/R est:1800-2200
£2515 $4200 €3672 Brie (23x36cm-9x14in) with sig. silver print. 21-Oct-3 Swann Galleries, New York #283/R est:2500-3500
£2515 $4200 €3672 Queen Charlotte's Ball (35x24cm-14x9in) s. gelatin silver print exec.1959 printed c.1990. 20-Oct-3 Christie's, Rockefeller NY #92/R est:3000-5000
£2684 $4750 €3919 Rue Mouffetard (36x24cm-14x9in) s. photo printed later. 28-Apr-4 Sotheby's, New York #182/R est:5000-7000
£2695 $4500 €3935 Rue Mouffetard (33x24cm-13x9in) s. gelatin silver print exec.1954 printed later lit. 20-Oct-3 Christie's, Rockefeller NY #174/R est:4000-6000
£2994 $5000 €4371 Rue Mouffetard (36x24cm-14x9in) s. photo exec.1954 printed later. 17-Oct-3 Sotheby's, New York #222/R est:4000-6000
£2994 $5000 €4371 Siphnos, Greece (24x36cm-9x14in) s. gelatin silver print exec.1961 printed c.1970. 20-Oct-3 Christie's, Rockefeller NY #175/R est:3000-5000
£3175 $6000 €4636 Crowd in stadium (20x29cm-8x11in) i. verso silver print. 17-Feb-4 Swann Galleries, New York #91/R est:4000-5000
£3249 $5750 €4744 Behind the Gare St Lazare (36x24cm-14x9in) s. photo printed later prov. 28-Apr-4 Sotheby's, New York #164/R est:4000-6000
£3315 $6000 €4840 Rue Mouffetard (44x30cm-17x12in) s. gelatin silver print 1954/printed later. 19-Apr-4 Bonhams & Butterfields, San Francisco #387/R est:4000-6000
£3333 $6000 €4866 Seville, 1933 (24x38cm-9x15in) s.verso num.13 gelatin silver print. 24-Apr-4 Phillips, New York #1/R est:8000-12000
£3693 $6500 €5392 Behind the gare St. Lazare, Paris (44x30cm-17x12in) with sig. silver print. 20-May-4 Swann Galleries, New York #355/R est:3500-4500
£3693 $6500 €5392 Ireland (24x36cm-9x14in) with sig. silver print. 20-May-4 Swann Galleries, New York #479/R est:2500-3500
£6215 $11000 €9074 Malcolm X (25x17cm-10x7in) i.verso ferrotyped prov. 28-Apr-4 Sotheby's, New York #160/R est:4000-6000
£6667 $12000 €9734 Trafalgar Square on the day of George Vi's coronation, London (37x24cm-15x9in) gelatin silver print prov.lit. 23-Apr-4 Phillips, New York #77/R est:30000-40000
£12029 $19728 €16600 Seville (33x49cm-13x19in) i. verso photo. 27-May-3 Beaussant & Lefèvre, Paris #112/R est:15000-20000

CARTLEDGE, William Ned (1916-) American
Sculpture
£2778 $5000 €4056 Our kind of devil (43x48x3cm-17x19x1in) carved painted wood. 24-Apr-4 Slotin Folk Art, Buford #331/R est:3000-5000

CARTON, Jean (1912-1988) French
Works on paper
£423 $731 €600 Penelope (34x25cm-13x10in) s. W/C. 10-Dec-3 Ferri, Paris #26

CARTON, Norman (1908-1980) Russian
£511 $900 €746 Procession (97x163cm-38x64in) s. prov. 22-May-4 Selkirks, St. Louis #534/R

CARTWRIGHT, Isabel Branson (1885-?) American
£2907 $5000 €4244 Arrangement (61x46cm-24x18in) s. exhib. 7-Dec-3 Freeman, Philadelphia #181 est:2000-3000

CARTWRIGHT, Joseph (1789-1829) British
Works on paper
£950 $1634 €1387 Waterfall at the source of the Cocytus, near Parga (34x53cm-13x21in) init.i.d.Oct 20 1817 pencil W/C. 3-Dec-3 Christie's, Kensington #30/R

CARUELLE D'ALIGNY, Theodore (1798-1871) French
£1400 $2240 €2030 Les Muses (31x23cm-12x9in) mono. paper on canvas prov.exhib. 18-Sep-3 Christie's, Kensington #5/R est:1500-2000
£8451 $14620 €12000 Paysage anime de figures (60x45cm-24x18in) s.d.1845. 10-Dec-3 Beaussant & Lefèvre, Paris #56/R est:12000-15000
Works on paper
£467 $840 €700 Vue d'Italie avec procession (36x31cm-14x12in) s. pen. 20-Apr-4 Chenu & Scrive, Lyon #5/R

CARUELLE D'ALIGNY, Theodore (attrib) (1798-1871) French
£1316 $2421 €2000 Vue de chemin (22x32cm-9x13in) cardboard. 25-Jun-4 Piasa, Paris #112/R
Works on paper
£800 $1448 €1200 Barques de peche a Dieppe (22x28cm-9x11in) i. graphite exhib. 30-Mar-4 Rossini, Paris #920

CARUS, Carl Gustav (1789-1869) German
£13333 $24133 €20000 Tree study near Hosterwitz (18x23cm-7x9in) d.11 Jun 1837 board. 1-Apr-4 Van Ham, Cologne #1314/R est:10000
Works on paper
£21834 $39738 €31878 Water fountain in front of a temple (46x29cm-18x11in) s.i.d.57 black chk htd white blue paper prov.exhib. 17-Jun-4 Kornfeld, Bern #5/R est:10000 (S.FR 50000)

CARUSO, Bruno (1927-) Italian
£733 $1327 €1100 Tutti Frutti and skyline (45x35cm-18x14in) s.d.53 oil board on canvas. 2-Apr-4 Farsetti, Prato #11
Works on paper
£483 $806 €700 Girl on rocking chair (56x69cm-22x27in) s. Chinese ink W/C. 13-Nov-3 Finarte Semenzato, Rome #131

CARUTHERS, Cole (20th C) American
£437 $800 €638 Sunday morning (30x79cm-12x31in) oil glue ground. 10-Jul-4 Hindman, Chicago #78/R

CARVALHO, Flavio Rezende de (1899-1973) Brazilian
Works on paper
£6000 $11040 €9000 Woman (48x34cm-19x13in) s.d.1942 ink prov. 10-Jun-4 Christie's, Paris #31/R est:16000-24000

CARVALLO, Feliciano (1920-) Venezuelan
£271 $420 €396 Wood (40x50cm-16x20in) s. 29-Sep-2 Subastas Odalys, Caracas #125/R
£356 $595 €520 Hounds in the fields (50x40cm-20x16in) s. painted 2002. 19-Oct-3 Subastas Odalys, Caracas #71/R
£362 $595 €529 Untitled (46x55cm-18x22in) s. 1-Jun-3 Subastas Odalys, Caracas #41
£538 $990 €785 Wood (40x30cm-16x12in) s. painted 1980. 28-Mar-4 Subastas Odalys, Caracas #75/R
£1250 $2125 €1825 Wood (80x100cm-31x39in) s. painted 1992. 23-Nov-3 Subastas Odalys, Caracas #69/R
£1416 $2605 €2067 Bird (69x94cm-27x37in) s. painted 1954. 28-Mar-4 Subastas Odalys, Caracas #38

CARVER, Richard (attrib) (fl.1697-1754) Irish
£3500 $6265 €5110 Mountainous wooded landscape with figures and deer (63x95cm-25x37in) prov. 14-May-4 Christie's, London #104/R est:4000-6000

CARVER, Robert (c.1730-1791) Irish
£1800 $3366 €2628 Extensive parkland scene with figures walking in an avenue (24x37cm-9x15in) prov. 25-Feb-4 Mallams, Oxford #105/R est:2000-3000

CARY, Evelyn Rumsey (1855-1924) American
£245 $450 €358 Portrait of Gertrude Albright (81x61cm-32x24in) s.d.1899. 25-Jun-4 Freeman, Philadelphia #286/R

CARY, William de la Montagne (1840-1922) American
£5882 $10000 €8588 Indian boy on pony (23x18cm-9x7in) s.d.1886 prov. 1-Nov-3 Santa Fe Art, Santa Fe #123/R est:30000-40000
£8021 $15000 €11711 Buffalo (20x15cm-8x6in) prov. 24-Jul-4 Coeur d'Alene, Hayden #138/R est:4000-6000
£58824 $110000 €85883 Indians on the plains (23x53cm-9x21in) s. board prov.exhib.lit. 24-Jul-4 Coeur d'Alene, Hayden #113/R est:10000-20000

Works on paper
£14118 $24000 €20612 High toss (38x48cm-15x19in) s. ink wash sold with a book prov.lit. 1-Nov-3 Santa Fe Art, Santa Fe #126/R est:20000-30000

CARYBE (20th C) Latin American
£9524 $16857 €14286 Cosme and Damiao in an African landscape (60x45cm-24x18in) s.d.1980 canvas on board. 27-Apr-4 Bolsa de Arte, Rio de Janeiro #53/R (B.R 52000)

CARZOU, Jean (1907-2000) French
£1208 $2247 €1800 Vue de Menncy (46x55cm-18x22in) s. paper on isorel prov. 3-Mar-4 Tajan, Paris #147 est:2000-3000
£1655 $2979 €2400 La ferme (45x54cm-18x21in) s.d.1947 panel. 25-Jan-4 Chayette & Cheval, Paris #252 est:2000-3000
£1892 $3386 €2800 Quai des Grands Augustins a Paris (37x27cm-15x11in) s.d.82 i.verso. 5-May-4 Coutau Begarie, Paris #48 est:1000-1500
£4636 $8437 €7000 Decor (73x99cm-29x39in) s.d.49. 18-Jun-4 Piasa, Paris #191/R est:7000-10000
Works on paper
£300 $552 €450 Paysage boise (37x45cm-15x18in) s.d.56 pen W/C. 9-Jun-4 Le Roux & Morel, Paris #24
£300 $546 €450 Femme dans la gare (35x27cm-14x11in) s.d.1973 Chinese ink col crayon. 4-Jul-4 Eric Pillon, Calais #277/R
£352 $609 €500 Femme a la fleur (32x49cm-13x19in) s.d. i.verso W/C. 13-Dec-3 Touati, Paris #58/R
£425 $722 €620 Personnage sur le port (25x18cm-10x7in) s.d.1965 ink dr. 9-Nov-3 Eric Pillon, Calais #185/R
£486 $812 €700 Paysage du Vaudoue (66x50cm-26x20in) s.i.d.66 and 1 Fev 1967 ink pen col pencil. 21-Oct-3 Christie's, Paris #97/R
£500 $920 €750 Le port (35x49cm-14x19in) s.d.55 W/C. 9-Jun-4 Beaussant & Lefèvre, Paris #117
£530 $964 €800 Femme devant un paysage (39x31cm-15x12in) s.d.50 pen ink. 18-Jun-4 Piasa, Paris #192
£563 $975 €800 Le vieil arbre (48x63cm-19x25in) s.d.65 ink. 13-Dec-3 Touati, Paris #57/R
£596 $1091 €900 Jeune femme au bouquet (44x36cm-17x14in) i. pen green ink col crayons. 7-Apr-4 Piasa, Paris #218
£599 $1036 €850 Femme a la fontaine (48x63cm-19x25in) s.d.64 ink htd col. 13-Dec-3 Touati, Paris #54/R
£699 $1202 €1000 Montagne enneigee (50x70cm-20x28in) s.d.60 ink W/C gouache. 3-Dec-3 Tajan, Paris #80
£1049 $1804 €1500 Devant le portail (28x25cm-11x10in) s.d.86 W/C ink. 2-Dec-3 Sotheby's, Amsterdam #205/R est:1500-2000
£1141 $2123 €1700 Propriete au bord de la riviere (45x54cm-18x21in) s.d.60 gouache. 3-Mar-4 Tajan, Paris #153 est:600-800
£1268 $2041 €1800 Untitled (49x64cm-19x25in) s.d.1953 W/C gouache. 11-May-3 Versailles Encheres #104

CASA, Nicolo della (attrib) (16th C) Italian
Prints
£3846 $6538 €5500 Portrait of the sculptor Baccio Bandinelli in his workshop (41x31cm-16x12in) etching copperplate. 27-Nov-3 Bassenge, Berlin #5155/R est:6000

CASABONNE, Andre (19/20th C) French
Works on paper
£704 $1218 €1000 Rue el Hadjamine (36x26cm-14x10in) s.i. W/C. 15-Dec-3 Gros & Delettrez, Paris #71/R

CASADEI, Maceo (1899-?) Italian
£355 $574 €500 Assisi (32x40cm-13x16in) s. panel. 22-May-3 Stadion, Trieste #371/R

CASADEMONT POU, Francesc d'Asis (1923-) Spanish
£403 $753 €600 Coast in Minorca (33x40cm-13x16in) s. s.i.d.1981 verso cardboard. 24-Feb-4 Durán, Madrid #1137/R

CASAL, Ricardo (20th C) Spanish?
£2081 $3683 €3100 Belleza (120x60cm-47x24in) s. 29-Apr-4 Claude Aguttes, Neuilly #218/R est:3200-3400

CASALS, Emilio (19th C) Spanish
Works on paper
£616 $1048 €900 Mosquetaire (40x21cm-16x8in) s.d.1875 W/C. 4-Nov-3 Ansorena, Madrid #163/R

CASAMADA, Alberto Rafols (1923-) Spanish
£2183 $3493 €3100 Untitled (46x38cm-18x15in) s.d.1995. 16-Sep-3 Segre, Madrid #133/R est:2900
£3958 $6729 €5700 Urban landscape (37x46cm-15x18in) s.d.1950 cardboard. 28-Oct-3 Segre, Madrid #174/R est:4600
£4054 $7500 €5919 Louche (146x114cm-57x45in) s.d.87 s.i.d. verso. 13-Jul-4 Christie's, Rockefeller NY #63/R est:2000-3000
£4930 $8627 €7000 Souvenir of Milan (46x38cm-18x15in) s. s.i.d.1966 verso. 16-Dec-3 Segre, Madrid #139/R est:4500
£5333 $9707 €8000 Doble Horizo (80x80cm-31x31in) s.d.2002 s.i.d. verso acrylic exhib.lit. 29-Jun-4 Segre, Madrid #140/R est:8000
£6333 $11463 €9500 Side blue (73x60cm-29x24in) s.d.1978 s.i.d.verso prov. 30-Mar-4 Segre, Madrid #176/R est:6500

CASANOVA Y ESTORACH, Antonio (1847-1896) Spanish
£658 $1191 €1000 Bearded man (7x6cm-3x2in) canvas on board. 14-Apr-4 Ansorena, Madrid #115/R
£1007 $1812 €1460 Monk. Cardinal (8x6cm-3x2in) one s.d.1888 board pair. 26-Jan-4 Ansorena, Madrid #78/R
£1133 $2051 €1700 A la sante (9x13cm-4x5in) s. panel. 30-Mar-4 Campo & Campo, Antwerp #28/R est:3000-5000
£2830 $4500 €4132 Instruction of the young prince (25x33cm-10x13in) s.i. panel. 12-Sep-3 Skinner, Boston #212/R
£4828 $8690 €7000 Education of the Prince (23x32cm-9x13in) s.i. board lit. 26-Jan-4 Durán, Madrid #215/R est:6000
£17606 $30810 €25000 Joking butler (47x40cm-19x16in) s.i.d.1892. 16-Dec-3 Durán, Madrid #191/R est:25000
Works on paper
£362 $655 €550 Gentleman (8x6cm-3x2in) s. W/C. 14-Apr-4 Ansorena, Madrid #375/R
£1517 $2731 €2200 Thinker (32x23cm-13x9in) s. W/C. 26-Jan-4 Ansorena, Madrid #297/R est:900
£1793 $3228 €2600 Reading (32x22cm-13x9in) s.d.1884 W/C. 26-Jan-4 Ansorena, Madrid #307/R est:1000

CASANOVA, Carlo (1871-1950) Italian
£1087 $1783 €1500 Ploughs on the Spluga (34x62cm-13x24in) s. 27-May-3 Finarte Semenzato, Milan #3
£3662 $6335 €5200 Shepherdess on Lake Maggiore (120x159cm-47x63in) s. 9-Dec-3 Finarte Semenzato, Milan #83/R est:5000-6000
Works on paper
£352 $609 €500 Tuscan countryside (32x60cm-13x24in) s. W/C card. 9-Dec-3 Finarte Semenzato, Milan #35

CASANOVA, Francesco Giuseppe (1727-1802) Italian
£4333 $7843 €6500 Militaire a cheval. Cantiniere en amazone sur une mule harnachee (32x23cm-13x9in) pair exhib. 2-Apr-4 Rossini, Paris #31/R est:6000-8000
£7000 $12600 €10220 Cavalrymen on a bluff (78x59cm-31x23in) 21-Apr-4 Christie's, London #68/R est:8000-12000
£7383 $13215 €11000 Riders (37cm-15in circular) copper. 26-May-4 Porro, Milan #53/R est:12000-15000
£14085 $24366 €20000 L'equipage du marquis Randon de Pommery (168x228cm-66x90in) prov.lit. 10-Dec-3 Maigret, Paris #48/R est:25000-30000

CASANOVA, Francesco Giuseppe (attrib) (1727-1802) Italian
£493 $789 €700 Attacking Turkish riders (32x22cm-13x9in) 18-Sep-3 Rieber, Stuttgart #1254/R
£887 $1588 €1295 Battle scene (12x19cm-5x7in) panel. 26-May-4 AB Stockholms Auktionsverk #2538/R (S.KR 12000)

CASANOVA, Jose (1933-) Spanish
£5435 $8913 €7500 Young boys on the beach (78x98cm-31x39in) s. 27-May-3 Durán, Madrid #166/R est:7500

CASARES, Alejandro (20th C) ?
£310 $490 €453 Southern lights (60x60cm-24x24in) s. painted 1992 lit. 1-Dec-2 Subastas Odalys, Caracas #4/R

CASARIEGO TERRERO, Francisco (1890-1958) Spanish
£1761 $3081 €2500 Square in mountain village (32x40cm-13x16in) s. cardboard. 16-Dec-3 Segre, Madrid #104/R est:900

CASAS ABARCA, Pedro (1875-1958) Spanish
£470 $841 €700 Woman at toilet (50x60cm-20x24in) s. board. 25-May-4 Durán, Madrid #56/R
£603 $977 €850 Women in interior (63x56cm-25x22in) s.d.78. 20-May-3 Ansorena, Madrid #115/R
£669 $1157 €950 Woman at mae up (60x50cm-24x20in) s. board. 15-Dec-3 Ansorena, Madrid #365/R
Works on paper
£274 $466 €400 Gypsy (51x42cm-20x17in) s. gouache. 4-Nov-3 Ansorena, Madrid #283/R

CASAS, Ramon (1866-1932) Spanish
£150000 $255000 €219000 Female nude (91x60cm-36x24in) s. prov.exhib.lit. 18-Nov-3 Sotheby's, London #229/R est:180000

CASATI, Carlo (?) Italian
£521 $885 €750 Mountainous landscape (70x100cm-28x39in) s. 1-Nov-3 Meeting Art, Vercelli #62/R

CASAUS, Jesus (1926-) Spanish
£604 $1130 €900 Beach in Palafrugell (92x64cm-36x25in) s. 24-Feb-4 Durán, Madrid #147/R
£1250 $2000 €1825 Bermeo - Spanish port scene (71x86cm-28x34in) s. 20-Sep-3 Sloans & Kenyon, Bethesda #1167/R est:1750-2250
£1250 $2000 €1825 Velas rojos - red sails (56x107cm-22x42in) s.i.verso. 20-Sep-3 Sloans & Kenyon, Bethesda #1168/R est:2250-2750

CASAUS, Josep (20th C) Spanish
£403 $749 €600 White village (65x50cm-26x20in) s. 2-Mar-4 Ansorena, Madrid #877

CASAY, Anthony (20th C) American
£569 $950 €825 Sunset behind a cliff (89x119cm-35x47in) s. 13-Jul-3 Butterfields, San Francisco #2015/R

CASCELLA, Andrea (1920-1990) Italian
Sculpture
£1103 $1843 €1600 Untitled (20x23x14cm-8x9x6in) init. num.19/30 marble. 13-Nov-3 Finarte Semenzato, Rome #295/R est:1400-1700

£1236	$2250	€1805	Maquette for Narcissus (11x9cm-4x4in) polished porphyry two pieces executed c.1967 prov. 29-Jun-4 Sotheby's, New York #522/R est:800-1200
£1259	$2140	€1800	Untitled (24x18x25cm-9x7x10in) init. num.32/50 marble. 25-Nov-3 Sotheby's, Milan #124/R est:800-1000
£2148	$3844	€3200	Untitled (15x28x24cm-6x11x9in) marble prov. 25-May-4 Sotheby's, Milan #75/R est:2000
£6593	$12000	€9626	Narcissus (89x71x36cm-35x28x14in) polished Belgian black marble two pieces executed 1967 prov.exhib. 29-Jun-4 Sotheby's, New York #518/R est:6000-8000

Works on paper

£239	$450	€349	Study for sculpture (37x49cm-15x19in) s. ink. 22-Feb-4 Bonhams & Butterfields, Los Angeles #7048

CASCELLA, Michele (1892-1989) Italian

£1958	$3329	€2800	Farm (20x30cm-8x12in) s. i.verso. 26-Nov-3 Pandolfini, Florence #85 est:3000-4000
£2685	$4966	€4000	Farm with orange tree (20x30cm-8x12in) s. 13-Mar-4 Meeting Art, Vercelli #225 est:4000
£2857	$5114	€4200	Landscape (35x50cm-14x20in) s. 16-Mar-4 Finarte Semenzato, Milan #285/R est:4400
£3472	$5486	€5000	Avenue and trees (30x20cm-12x8in) 6-Sep-3 Meeting Art, Vercelli #490 est:5000
£4333	$7757	€6500	San Gioachimo in Milan (48x70cm-19x28in) s.d. board. 13-May-4 Neumeister, Munich #300/R est:5000-6000
£4762	$8524	€7000	Parisian scene (35x50cm-14x20in) s. lit. 16-Mar-4 Finarte Semenzato, Milan #287/R est:7500
£5034	$9010	€7500	Orange tree (35x50cm-14x20in) s. 29-May-4 Farsetti, Prato #554/R est:6500-8000
£5369	$9933	€8000	Still life (40x60cm-16x24in) s. s.verso lit. 13-Mar-4 Meeting Art, Vercelli #549 est:6000
£5397	$9500	€7880	Champs des fleurs (61x79cm-24x31in) s. prov. 18-May-4 Bonhams & Butterfields, San Francisco #194/R est:4000-6000
£5634	$9352	€8000	Portofino (40x60cm-16x24in) s. 14-Jun-3 Meeting Art, Vercelli #235/R est:8000
£5667	$10427	€8500	Vase of flowers (50x35cm-20x14in) s. s.verso. 10-Jun-4 Galleria Pace, Milan #153/R est:12600
£6294	$10699	€9000	San Valentino near Ala (29x45cm-11x18in) s.i.d.1916 masonite lit. 20-Nov-3 Finarte Semenzato, Milan #212/R est:8000-9000
£6522	$10696	€9000	Field in bloom (50x70cm-20x28in) s. i.verso. 27-May-3 Il Ponte, Milan #561/R est:10000
£6711	$12013	€10000	Vase with flowers and fruit (35x50cm-14x20in) painted 1981 prov.lit. 25-May-4 Sotheby's, Milan #57 est:15000
£6757	$11892	€10000	Vase of flowers (69x46cm-27x18in) s. tempera Chinese ink paper prov. 24-May-4 Christie's, Milan #163/R est:10000-15000
£7059	$12000	€10306	Italian farmhouse with cypress trees and yellow flowering shrubs (61x91cm-24x36in) s. prov. 19-Nov-3 Bonhams & Butterfields, San Francisco #164/R
£7383	$13215	€11000	Portofino (50x70cm-20x28in) s. painted 1982. 30-May-4 Meeting Art, Vercelli #87 est:10000
£7947	$14464	€12000	Forte dei Marmi (70x100cm-28x39in) s.d.1929 W/C cardboard. 17-Jun-4 Galleria Pananti, Florence #626/R est:14000-20000
£10490	$17832	€15000	Portofino (50x71cm-20x28in) s.s.verso prov.lit. 24-Nov-3 Christie's, Milan #199/R est:15000-20000
£10667	$19093	€16000	Omaggio a Portofino (112x74cm-44x29in) s.d. board. 13-May-4 Neumeister, Munich #301/R est:6000-8000
£11765	$20000	€17177	Italian landscape with cypress trees and a garden with tress in blossom (152x104cm-60x41in) s. 19-Nov-3 Bonhams & Butterfields, San Francisco #165/R
£12587	$21399	€18000	Vase of flowers (100x70cm-39x28in) s. 20-Nov-3 Finarte Semenzato, Milan #160/R est:12000-15000
£17178	$28000	€25080	Path in Portofino (101x153cm-40x60in) s. prov. 25-Sep-3 Christie's, Rockefeller NY #553/R est:12000-16000
£17568	$30919	€26000	Portofino (76x102cm-30x40in) s. prov. 24-May-4 Christie's, Milan #273/R est:25000-30000
£62319	$102203	€86000	New York obsession (152x102cm-60x40in) s.d.1961 s.i.verso exhib.lit. 27-May-3 Sotheby's, Milan #257/R est:50000-60000

Works on paper

£600	$1104	€900	Bouquinistes (48x66cm-19x26in) s. pencil pen double-sided. 10-Jun-4 Galleria Pace, Milan #99/R
£1184	$2179	€1800	Italian monastery (49x66cm-19x26in) s.i.d. W/C on pen paper board. 24-Jun-4 Dr Fritz Nagel, Stuttgart #517/R est:1800
£1793	$2994	€2600	Tale (22x30cm-9x12in) s. mixed media paper on canvas exec.1958. 13-Nov-3 Galleria Pace, Milan #91/R
£2533	$4661	€3800	Wood (49x58cm-19x23in) s.d.908 pastel. 8-Jun-4 Finarte Semenzato, Milan #85/R est:2000-3000
£4930	$8183	€7000	Pietrasanta (47x65cm-19x26in) s.d.32 gouache. 11-Jun-3 Finarte Semenzato, Milan #700/R
£5646	$10107	€8300	By the river (41x58cm-16x23in) s.d.1912 pastel paper on canvas prov.lit. 16-Mar-4 Finarte Semenzato, Milan #444/R est:9000
£11268	$18704	€16000	Garden in Portofino (75x140cm-30x55in) mixed media paper on board prov.exhib.lit. 11-Jun-3 Finarte Semenzato, Milan #636/R est:18000
£17931	$29945	€26000	Offer to ninety-year-old painter (100x80cm-39x31in) s.d.1983 pastel card. 13-Nov-3 Galleria Pace, Milan #143/R est:35000

CASCELLA, Pietro (1921-) Italian

Sculpture

£1200	$2172	€1800	Bull (64cm-25in) s. bronze marble base. 2-Apr-4 Farsetti, Prato #326/R est:1700-2000
£1379	$2303	€2000	Sphere (25x25x25cm-10x10x10in) init. num.19/30 marble. 13-Nov-3 Finarte Semenzato, Rome #278/R est:1400-1700

CASCELLA, Tommaso (1951-) Italian

£1056	$1754	€1500	Animali da soma (60x60cm-24x24in) s.i.d.1990 oil collage panel. 14-Jun-3 Meeting Art, Vercelli #65/R est:1500

Works on paper

£1310	$2188	€1900	Transparency (71x52cm-28x20in) s.i.verso mixed media card exec.1997. 13-Nov-3 Galleria Pace, Milan #107/R est:3000

CASCELLA, Tommaso (1890-1968) Italian

£759	$1267	€1100	Figures in the wood (30x40cm-12x16in) s. cardboard. 13-Nov-3 Finarte Semenzato, Rome #318
£805	$1442	€1200	Herd (39x50cm-15x20in) s. 25-May-4 Finarte Semenzato, Milan #77/R
£993	$1808	€1500	Evening (50x94cm-20x37in) s.i. 17-Jun-4 Finarte Semenzato, Milan #267/R est:1600-1800

Works on paper

£621	$1037	€900	Fog on the lake (37x48cm-15x19in) s. pastel card. 13-Nov-3 Finarte Semenzato, Rome #142
£671	$1201	€1000	Landscape with herd (50x59cm-20x23in) s. pastel cardboard. 25-May-4 Finarte Semenzato, Milan #78/R

CASCIARO, Giuseppe (1861-1943) Italian

£1467	$2655	€2200	House and olive tree (25x50cm-10x20in) s.d.1918. 2-Apr-4 Farsetti, Prato #565/R est:1400-1800
£1879	$3364	€2800	Winter landscape (51x57cm-20x22in) s.d.915 tempera pastel card. 25-May-4 Finarte Semenzato, Milan #131/R est:2000-2200
£2053	$3736	€3100	Le repos des paysans (50x61cm-20x24in) s. 20-Jun-4 Versailles Encheres #45/R est:1200-1500
£2267	$4171	€3400	Courtyard (43x49cm-17x19in) s.i.d.22 cardboard. 8-Jun-4 Sotheby's, Milan #19/R est:3000-6000

Works on paper

£791	$1298	€1100	View of street with church (33x50cm-13x20in) pastel. 10-Jun-3 Pandolfini, Florence #154/R
£802	$1500	€1171	Capri (41x46cm-16x18in) s.i.d.1926 pastel. 24-Feb-4 Arthur James, Florida #71
£833	$1508	€1250	Patio in Capri (46x52cm-18x20in) s.d.1915 pastel. 30-Mar-4 Babuino, Rome #279/R
£1007	$1652	€1400	Rainbow (20x21cm-8x8in) s.d.37 pastel. 10-Jun-3 Pandolfini, Florence #342/R est:1300-1500
£1056	$1827	€1500	Coastal village (21x40cm-8x16in) s. pastel card. 11-Dec-3 Christie's, Rome #39/R est:1300-1800
£1133	$2029	€1700	People on the beach (31x46cm-12x18in) s.d.907 pastel. 12-May-4 Stadion, Trieste #652/R est:1000-1500
£1293	$2379	€1888	La Seine a Bougenville (24x39cm-9x15in) s.i. pastel. 26-Mar-4 Koller, Zurich #412/R est:3000-4000 (S.FR 3000)
£1342	$2376	€2000	Vietri (44x50cm-17x20in) s.d.1926 pastel card lit. 1-May-4 Meeting Art, Vercelli #359 est:2000
£1467	$2699	€2200	The Po in Turin (18x27cm-7x11in) s. pastel card prov. 10-Jun-4 Christie's, Rome #65/R est:1600-1900
£1489	$2487	€2100	Landscape covered in snow (40x50cm-16x20in) s.d.1920 mixed media cardboard. 20-Oct-3 Sant Agostino, Torino #268/R est:2500
£1600	$2944	€2400	Landscape (24x50cm-9x20in) s.d.25 pastel card on cardboard. 11-Jun-4 Farsetti, Prato #518/R est:2400-2800
£1733	$3189	€2600	The Aniene (44x51cm-17x20in) s.i. pastel card. 10-Jun-4 Christie's, Rome #109/R est:1300-1800
£1761	$3046	€2500	Boats on the beach (29x22cm-11x9in) s. mixed media card. 10-Dec-3 Finarte Semenzato, Rome #211/R est:2200-2700
£1867	$3435	€2800	Naples (18x27cm-7x11in) s. pastel card prov. 10-Jun-4 Christie's, Rome #64/R est:2200-2500
£1972	$3411	€2800	Neapolitan seascape (36x66cm-14x26in) s. pastel tempera. 9-Dec-3 Finarte Semenzato, Milan #49/R est:2000-2300
£2254	$3899	€3200	Seascape in Capri (45x50cm-18x20in) s. pastel exhib. 10-Dec-3 Sotheby's, Milan #19/R est:2000-4000
£2465	$4264	€3500	Coastal landscape (42x62cm-17x24in) s. mixed media card. 10-Dec-3 Finarte Semenzato, Rome #165/R est:4000-5000
£2569	$4368	€3700	Castro harbour (36x41cm-14x16in) s.d.1901 pastel. 1-Nov-3 Meeting Art, Vercelli #66/R est:1500
£2667	$4907	€4000	Impression (20x35cm-8x14in) s. i.d.1896 verso pastel. 8-Jun-4 Sotheby's, Milan #6/R est:4000-6000
£4577	$7919	€6500	Vases and flowers (55x71cm-22x28in) s.d.24 mixed media card. 10-Dec-3 Finarte Semenzato, Rome #166/R est:4000-5000

CASCIARO, Giuseppe (attrib) (1861-1943) Italian

Works on paper

£1000	$1840	€1500	Landscape with figures (32x47cm-13x19in) bears sig. pastel card. 10-Jun-4 Christie's, Rome #66/R est:1200-1500

CASCIARO, Guido (1900-1963) Italian

£369	$653	€550	Shepherdess (30x40cm-12x16in) s. masonite. 1-May-4 Meeting Art, Vercelli #41

CASE, Edmund E (1840-1919) American

£281	$450	€410	Autumn landscape (41x30cm-16x12in) s. canvas on panel. 21-Sep-3 Grogan, Boston #52/R
£1863	$3000	€2720	Massachusetts fall forest interior (64x76cm-25x30in) s. canvas on masonite. 20-Aug-3 James Julia, Fairfield #1505/R est:5000-7000
£3763	$7000	€5494	Plum Island Sound (45x71cm-18x28in) s.d.85. 5-Mar-4 Skinner, Boston #290/R est:4000-6000

CASE, G Russell (1966-) American

£1301	$2250	€1899	November Homestead (45x61cm-18x24in) s. i.d.2002 verso. 10-Dec-3 Bonhams & Butterfields, San Francisco #6132/R est:3000-5000
£1494	$2750	€2181	Into Sand Pass (61x76cm-24x30in) s. i.verso painted 2004. 8-Jun-4 Bonhams & Butterfields, San Francisco #4155/R est:3000-5000
£1589	$2750	€2320	Foothills of the Boulders (51x61cm-20x24in) s. i.verso. 10-Dec-3 Bonhams & Butterfields, San Francisco #6130/R est:3000-5000
£2023	$3500	€2954	Dry Season (46x61cm-18x24in) s.i. i.d.2002 verso. 10-Dec-3 Bonhams & Butterfields, San Francisco #6131/R est:3000-5000

CASEBERE, James (1953-) American?

Photographs

£5587	$10000	€8157	Nine alcoves (122x152cm-48x60in) s.i.d.1995 num. of 5 verso c-print Plexiglas prov.exhib.lit. 14-May-4 Phillips, New York #315/R est:12000-18000
£9581	$16000	€13988	Empty room (122x152cm-48x60in) s.i.d.1994 dye construction print prov. 14-Nov-3 Phillips, New York #241/R est:8000-12000

CASENELLI, Victor (20th C) American

£273	$500	€399	House of Don Toledo (30x23cm-12x9in) s.i. board painted c.1930. 5-Jun-4 Treadway Gallery, Cincinnati #629/R

Works on paper

£323	$600	€472	Arab rider. s. gouache executed c.1900. 7-Mar-4 Treadway Gallery, Cincinnati #516/R

£475 $750 €694 Arab rider. s. gouache. 7-Sep-3 Treadway Gallery, Cincinnati #572/R

CASER, Ettore (20th C) Italian

£1061 $1900 €1549 Moonlit balcony (74x89cm-29x35in) s. 26-May-4 Doyle, New York #73/R est:2500-3500

CASERO SANZ, Antonio (1898-1973) Spanish

£276 $458 €400 Don Tancredo (25x17cm-10x7in) s. 1-Oct-3 Ansorena, Madrid #662/R

Works on paper

£276 $458 €400 Bull fight (24x33cm-9x13in) i. W/C. 1-Oct-3 Ansorena, Madrid #360/R
£296 $518 €420 Bull scene (31x44cm-12x17in) s.d.1953 prov. 16-Dec-3 Segre, Madrid #295/R
£387 $670 €550 Bull scene (24x33cm-9x13in) W/C. 15-Dec-3 Ansorena, Madrid #160/R
£423 $731 €600 Back home (42x50cm-17x20in) W/C lit. 15-Dec-3 Ansorena, Madrid #168/R
£483 $869 €700 Toreador (49x28cm-19x11in) s. gouache. 26-Jan-4 Ansorena, Madrid #406/R
£503 $936 €750 Bull scene (50x63cm-20x25in) s. gouache. 2-Mar-4 Ansorena, Madrid #351/R
£570 $1061 €850 Bull scene (50x63cm-20x25in) s. gouache. 2-Mar-4 Ansorena, Madrid #352/R

CASEY, Daniel (19th C) French

£987 $1816 €1500 Amazon (57x71cm-22x28in) s. 22-Jun-4 Wiener Kunst Auktionen, Vienna #173/R est:1500

CASILE, Alfred (1847-1909) French

£1342 $2470 €2000 Champ fleuri (27x56cm-11x22in) s. panel. 29-Mar-4 Rieunier, Paris #36/R est:1000-1500
£1342 $2470 €2000 Rivage (39x65cm-15x26in) s. 29-Mar-4 Rieunier, Paris #37/R est:2000-3000
£2000 $3580 €2920 Continental landscape with figures in the foreground (45x30cm-18x12in) s.d.1879. 11-May-4 Bonhams, Knightsbridge #93/R est:2000-3000
£2215 $4075 €3300 Voiliers en mer vus du rivage (29x46cm-11x18in) s. 29-Mar-4 Rieunier, Paris #50/R est:2000-3000
£2550 $4693 €3800 Mere et enfant sur un chemin (33x46cm-13x18in) s. 29-Mar-4 Rieunier, Paris #42/R est:2000-3000
£3020 $5557 €4500 Barques et pecheurs pres d'une greve (26x40cm-10x16in) s. cardboard. 29-Mar-4 Rieunier, Paris #44/R est:2000-3000
£3557 $6545 €5300 Deux personnages en bord de mer (33x47cm-13x19in) s. panel. 29-Mar-4 Rieunier, Paris #41/R est:2000-3000
£4000 $7320 €6000 View of a Mediterranean landscape (42x63cm-17x25in) s. exhib. 7-Jun-4 Glerum, Amsterdam #73/R est:3500-4500
£12081 $22228 €18000 Entree du port de Marseille avec le Fort Saint Jean (40x65cm-16x26in) s. canvas laid down. 29-Mar-4 Rieunier, Paris #52/R est:5000-6000

CASILEAR, John W (1811-1893) American

£3827 $6200 €5549 Pastoral landscape (33x25cm-13x10in) s. 8-Aug-3 Barridorf, Portland #130/R est:6000-9000
£14706 $25000 €21471 Moonrise on the coast (31x22cm-12x9in) s.d.63 canvas on masonite. 30-Oct-3 Phillips, New York #10/R est:25000-35000

CASILEAR, John W (circle) (1811-1893) American

£5938 $9500 €8669 Traveller on path in a landscape (51x41cm-20x16in) 20-Sep-3 Sloans & Kenyon, Bethesda #1192/R est:3000-4000

CASIMIR, Laurent (20th C) Haitian

£503 $800 €734 Celebration in a mountainside village (102x76cm-40x30in) s.d.80. 13-Sep-3 Weschler, Washington #720/R

CASINI, Valore (circle) (17th C) Italian

£5594 $9343 €8000 Portrait of Knight of Saint Stephen's (208x129cm-82x51in) i.verso. 7-Oct-3 Pandolfini, Florence #619/R est:2000-4000

CASISSA, Nicola (?-1730) Italian

£9000 $15570 €13140 Peonies, chrysanthemums, tulips and other flowers in a sculpted vase on a ruined column (151x126cm-59x50in) 10-Dec-3 Bonhams, New Bond Street #38/R est:8000-12000
£10738 $19758 €16000 Vase of flowers in garden with birds (54x94cm-21x37in) mono. 24-Mar-4 Finarte Semenzato, Rome #105/R est:16000
£15000 $25950 €21900 Flowers in urns, parrot by a fountain, in an ornamental garden (178x228cm-70x90in) init. 12-Dec-3 Christie's, Kensington #263/R est:15000-20000

CASISSA, Nicola (attrib) (?-1730) Italian

£10667 $19093 €16000 Vase of flowers in garden (130x95cm-51x37in) exhib.lit. 17-May-4 Finarte Semenzato, Rome #101/R est:22000-25000

CASLEY, William (fl.1891-1912) British

Works on paper

£250 $433 €365 Low tide along a rocky beach (33x57cm-13x22in) s. W/C. 9-Dec-3 Bearnes, Exeter #807
£300 $540 €438 Coastal landscape with gulls, possibly Cornwall (33x59cm-13x23in) s. W/C pencil htd white scratching out. 22-Apr-4 Lawrence, Crewkerne #780

CASO, Michel de (20th C) French?

£2416 $4277 €3600 Le temps interrompu (123x70cm-48x28in) s. oil polychrome wood panel double-sided. 29-Apr-4 Claude Aguttes, Neuilly #249 est:3600-3800

CASORATI, Daphne Maugham (1897-1982) Italian

£320 $589 €480 Study for landscape (50x60cm-20x24in) s. 8-Jun-4 Della Rocca, Turin #325/R
£728 $1326 €1100 Landscape (55x44cm-22x17in) s. s.verso. 21-Jun-4 Pandolfini, Florence #154
£733 $1349 €1100 Still life (32x38cm-13x15in) s. cardboard double-sided. 12-Jun-4 Meeting Art, Vercelli #906/R
£1467 $2699 €2200 Garden (60x50cm-24x20in) s. s.i.on stretcher. 14-Jun-4 Sant Agostino, Torino #344/R est:1000-1400

CASORATI, Felice (1883-1963) Italian

£13514 $23784 €20000 Sleeping girl (55x61cm-22x24in) s. tempera card on canvas painted 1962 prov. 24-May-4 Christie's, Milan #305/R est:20000-30000
£14685 $24965 €21000 Rebellious angel (60x55cm-24x22in) s. tempera paper on canvas painted 1962 lit. 29-Nov-3 Farsetti, Prato #537/R est:10000
£15385 $26154 €22000 Bowl with oranges (34x30cm-13x12in) s. tempera paper on canvas prov.lit. 25-Nov-3 Sotheby's, Milan #200/R est:15000-20000
£21127 $35070 €30000 Due Donne (50x70cm-20x28in) s. tempera cardboard on canvas. 14-Jun-3 Meeting Art, Vercelli #247/R est:30000
£24161 $43248 €36000 Still life (55x48cm-22x19in) s. tempera card on canvas painted 1957. 29-May-4 Farsetti, Prato #431/R est:35000-45000
£27586 $46069 €40000 Sleeping nude in landscape (61x48cm-24x19in) s. tempera paper on canvas. 17-Nov-3 Sant Agostino, Torino #255/R est:40000-50000
£31544 $56463 €47000 Livorno harbour (39x45cm-15x18in) s. board prov. 25-May-4 Sotheby's, Milan #253/R est:50000-60000
£57971 $95072 €80000 Landscape with lemons (70x50cm-28x20in) s. prov.lit. 27-May-3 Sotheby's, Milan #243/R est:80000-100000
£73826 $132148 €110000 Still life with jug and lemons (60x50cm-24x20in) s. painted 1947. 29-May-4 Farsetti, Prato #531/R est:100000-150000
£80537 $144161 €120000 Pears and flutes (72x52cm-28x20in) s. board painted 1947 exhib.lit. 29-May-4 Farsetti, Prato #493/R est:120000-140000

Works on paper

£2448 $4161 €3500 Red drawing (33x38cm-13x15in) s. sanguine exec.1961 prov. 25-Nov-3 Sotheby's, Milan #72/R est:4000-5000
£6993 $11888 €10000 Study of nudes (34x48cm-13x19in) s. pencil pen. 20-Nov-3 Finarte Semenzato, Milan #50/R est:10000-12000
£8741 $14598 €12500 Lascaris Palace (35x25cm-14x10in) s. W/C. 26-Jun-3 Sant Agostino, Torino #196/R est:16000
£10000 $18400 €15000 Female nude (44x25cm-17x10in) s. chl prov. 14-Jun-4 Porro, Milan #5/R est:18000-20000

CASORATI, Francesco (1934-) Italian

£690 $1152 €1000 Casle in Aosta Valley (54x48cm-21x19in) s.d.1977 tempera paper. 17-Nov-3 Sant Agostino, Torino #106/R
£2098 $3503 €3000 Fragment theatre (150x110cm-59x43in) s. s.i.d.1967 verso board. 26-Jun-3 Sant Agostino, Torino #270/R est:3000-3500

Works on paper

£272 $487 €400 Riders (32x45cm-13x18in) s. mixed media. 22-Mar-4 Sant Agostino, Torino #426/R

CASPAR, Karl (1879-1956) German

£5333 $9547 €8000 Return of the prodigal son (80x120cm-31x47in) mono. 13-May-4 Neumeister, Munich #302/R est:8000-10000
£5705 $10097 €8500 Easter morning (64x80cm-25x31in) mono. i. verso exhib. 30-Apr-4 Dr Fritz Nagel, Stuttgart #700/R est:1500

CASPAR-FILSER, Maria (1878-1968) German

£3000 $5370 €4500 Still life with fruit (64x80cm-25x31in) s.mono. prov. 14-May-4 Ketterer, Munich #187/R est:6000-8000
£5369 $9503 €8000 Spring storm over Florence (73x99cm-29x39in) mono. i. stretcher exhib. 30-Apr-4 Dr Fritz Nagel, Stuttgart #701/R est:6000
£5369 $9503 €8000 Dark roses, petunias and white lilies in vase (73x50cm-29x20in) mono. exhib. 30-Apr-4 Dr Fritz Nagel, Stuttgart #709/R est:12500
£19792 $32260 €28500 Garden (100x116cm-39x46in) mono. i.stretcher prov. 27-Sep-3 Dr Fritz Nagel, Stuttgart #9501/R est:40000

CASPEL, Johann Georg van (1870-1928) Dutch

£1189 $1985 €1700 Still life (61x91cm-24x36in) s.d.26. 11-Oct-3 De Vuyst, Lokeren #359/R est:1700-2000

CASPER, R (?) ?

£732 $1346 €1098 Still life of grapes and peaches (71x91cm-28x36in) s. panel. 14-Jun-4 Blomqvist, Lysaker #1053/R (N.KR 9000)

CASPERSEN, Hans Christian (1866-1939) Danish

£1156 $2070 €1700 Titbit (62x47cm-24x19in) s.d.97. 17-Mar-4 Neumeister, Munich #417 est:2200

CASS, George Nelson (1831-1882) American

£1657 $3000 €2419 Country landscape with figures at stream side (30x51cm-12x20in) s. 3-Apr-4 Nadeau, Windsor #112/R est:2000-3000

CASSAB, Judy (1920-) Australian/Austrian

£281 $469 €407 Still life (45x35cm-18x14in) s. board. 30-Jun-3 Australian Art Auctions, Sydney #108 (A.D 700)
£325 $511 €471 Rose bay (30x24cm-12x9in) acrylic paper prov. 26-Aug-3 Christie's, Sydney #246 (A.D 800)
£607 $978 €886 Suspended rock (76x103cm-30x41in) s.d.85. 25-Aug-3 Sotheby's, Paddington #431 (A.D 1500)
£744 $1376 €1086 Abstract landscape (27x37cm-11x15in) s.d.69 board. 10-Mar-4 Deutscher-Menzies, Melbourne #387/R est:2000-3000 (A.D 1800)
£992 $1806 €1448 Untitled (76x122cm-30x48in) s.d.1965 board. 16-Jun-4 Deutscher-Menzies, Melbourne #413/R est:3000-5000 (A.D 2600)
£1057 $1659 €1533 Floating rock (98x145cm-39x57in) s.d.78 i.verso prov. 27-Aug-3 Christie's, Sydney #535/R est:3000-5000 (A.D 2600)
£1447 $2503 €2113 Memory of faces (150x104cm-59x41in) i.verso prov. 10-Dec-3 Shapiro, Sydney #75/R est:3000-5000 (A.D 3400)
£1660 $2772 €2490 Still life with sculpture (80x54cm-31x21in) s. board. 27-Oct-3 Goodman, Sydney #183/R est:4000-6000 (A.D 4000)

£2236 $3510 €3242 Girl with breugel 2 (120x100cm-47x39in) s.d.95 i.verso acrylic oil prov.exhib. 27-Aug-3 Christie's, Sydney #581/R est:2000-4000 (A.D 5500)
£2576 $4689 €3761 Self portrait with mirror, model and flowers (99x131cm-39x52in) s.d.1994 s.i.verso prov. 16-Jun-4 Deutscher-Menzies, Melbourne #317/R est:4000-6000 (A.D 6750)
Works on paper
£383 $663 €559 Untitled (56x68cm-22x27in) s. mixed media board. 10-Dec-3 Shapiro, Sydney #76 (A.D 900)

CASSANA, Giovanni Agostino (1658-1720) Italian
£10526 $19369 €16000 Rural scenes (58x76cm-23x30in) pair prov. 24-Jun-4 Tajan, Paris #43/R est:18000-22000

CASSANA, Giovanni Agostino (attrib) (1658-1720) Italian
£2838 $5166 €4143 Two doves (53x61cm-21x24in) 16-Jun-4 Fischer, Luzern #1043/R est:7500-8500 (S.FR 6500)
£14474 $26632 €22000 Still lives with birds in landscape (87x117cm-34x46in) pair. 25-Jun-4 Piasa, Paris #41/R est:25000-30000

CASSANA, Giovanni Agostino (circle) (1658-1720) Italian
£18722 $31828 €27334 Before the Flood (111x121cm-44x48in) 5-Nov-3 Dobiaschofsky, Bern #420/R est:10000 (S.FR 42500)
£18722 $31828 €27334 After the Flood (111x121cm-44x48in) 5-Nov-3 Dobiaschofsky, Bern #421/R est:10000 (S.FR 42500)

CASSANDRE, Adolphe (1901-1968) French
Prints
£6593 $12000 €9626 Normandie (96x58cm-38x23in) col lithograph. 16-Jun-4 Christie's, Rockefeller NY #146/R est:10000-15000
Works on paper
£1333 $2453 €2000 La danseuse etoile (38x27cm-15x11in) s. gouache. 11-Jun-4 Pierre Berge, Paris #113 est:800-1000

CASSARA, Paolo (1968-) Italian
Sculpture
£1000 $1840 €1500 Camilla (70cm-28in) s.d.1995 verso painted terracotta one of 1. 14-Jun-4 Sant Agostino, Torino #368a/R est:1500-2000

CASSAS, Charles Hippolyte (1800-c.1864) French
£2334 $4247 €3500 Jeune romaine au tambourin (51x51cm-20x20in) s.i.d.1848. 30-Jun-4 Pierre Berge, Paris #56/R est:3000-4000

CASSAS, Louis-François (1756-1827) French
Prints
£4084 $7148 €5800 Personnages antiques dans un paysage montagneux pres d'une statue (41x64cm-16x25in) engraving W/C. 16-Dec-3 Artcurial Briest, Paris #234/R est:3500-4500
Works on paper
£201 $375 €293 Landscape with figures fishing (18x25cm-7x10in) s.d.1777 chl. 3-Mar-4 Alderfer's, Hatfield #276
£1020 $1827 €1500 Paysage de riviere anime (17x27cm-7x11in) s. W/C. 19-Mar-4 Piasa, Paris #66/R est:1500
£2128 $3553 €3000 Vue de Constantinople, pris de la mer de Marmara (60x82cm-24x32in) W/C. 16-Jun-3 Gros & Delettrez, Paris #445 est:1500-2300
£2177 $3897 €3200 Sacrifice antique (41x64cm-16x25in) pen Indian ink W/C htd gum arabic. 17-Mar-4 Tajan, Paris #64/R est:4000-6000
£2365 $4162 €3500 Two groups of Oriental men standing and sitting (21x36cm-8x14in) i.verso pen black ink W/C gouache prov.exhib.lit. 19-May-4 Sotheby's, Amsterdam #178/R est:2500-3500
£2819 $5187 €4200 Vue du Temple d'Hercule attenant l'Eglise sans Lorenzo a Milan (28x37cm-11x15in) s.d.1778 bistre pen wash. 24-Mar-4 Claude Boisgirard, Paris #29/R est:4000-5000
£3401 $6088 €5000 Un paysage avec des chutes d'eau, des figures avec un dromadaire (57x78cm-22x31in) pen brown ink W/C. 18-Mar-4 Christie's, Paris #276/R est:5000-8000
£6165 $10480 €9000 Vue idealisee du Forum (61x95cm-24x37in) s. pen ink W/C. 6-Nov-3 Tajan, Paris #91/R
£7778 $14000 €11356 Temple of Agrigento (52x75cm-20x30in) pen ink W/C gouache. 21-Jan-4 Sotheby's, New York #137/R est:8000-12000
£7778 $14000 €11356 Temples of Paestum (52x74cm-20x29in) pen ink W/C gum arabic. 21-Jan-4 Sotheby's, New York #138/R est:8000-12000

CASSATT, Jules (20th C) ?
£680 $1204 €993 Mother and children resting (122x91cm-48x36in) s. 27-Apr-4 Bonhams, Knowle #151

CASSATT, Mary (1844-1926) American
Prints
£1828 $3400 €2669 Manicure (21x15cm-8x6in) drypoint executed 1908. 2-Mar-4 Swann Galleries, New York #105/R est:1500-2500
£2905 $5200 €4241 Looking into the hand mirror (21x14cm-8x6in) drypoint. 6-May-4 Swann Galleries, New York #264/R est:4000-6000
£4800 $8688 €7200 Baby held before oval mirror (48x28cm-19x11in) drypoint. 31-Mar-4 Tajan, Paris #117 est:1200
£7059 $12000 €10306 Nursing (24x18cm-9x7in) sepia drypoint exec.c.1890. 6-Nov-3 Swann Galleries, New York #324/R est:14000-16000
£7345 $13000 €10724 Margot resting her arms on the back of an armchair (22x15cm-9x6in) init. drypoint exec.c.1903. 28-Apr-4 Christie's, Rockefeller NY #9/R est:10000-15000
£9412 $16000 €13742 Lady in black (20x29cm-8x11in) init. etching. 31-Oct-3 Sotheby's, New York #186/R
£10734 $19000 €15672 Sara wearing her bonnet and coat (63x41cm-25x16in) lithograph executed c.1904. 30-Apr-4 Sotheby's, New York #7/R est:10000-15000
£30822 $52397 €45000 Mother's kiss. eau forte one of 25. 6-Nov-3 Piasa, Paris #66/R
£65068 $110616 €95000 Fitting. s. eau forte exec.c.1891. 6-Nov-3 Piasa, Paris #65/R
Works on paper
£610 $1000 €885 Portrait of a cavalier. Study of a girl's head (20x13cm-8x5in) pencil double-sided prov.exhib. 2-Jun-3 Grogan, Boston #612/R
£2994 $5000 €4371 Profile d'une femme (183x218cm-72x86in) red crayon prov. 7-Oct-3 Sotheby's, New York #254 est:5000-10000
£7821 $14000 €11419 Lydia reading (18x10cm-7x4in) init. pencil W/C prov.exhib. 26-May-4 Doyle, New York #83/R est:5000-7000
£18500 $34040 €27010 Deux meres et un enfant dans un bateau (34x49cm-13x19in) W/C exec.1910 prov. 22-Jun-4 Sotheby's, London #422/R est:12000-15000
£28409 $50000 €41477 Head of a baby (36x30cm-14x12in) pastel paper on canvas exec c.1898 prov.lit. 18-May-4 Christie's, Rockefeller NY #59/R est:70000-90000
£152941 $260000 €223294 Tete de femme au grand chapeau (72x60cm-28x24in) s. pastel paper on canvas exec c.1909 prov.exhib.lit. 6-Nov-3 Sotheby's, New York #141/R est:200000-300000

CASSATT, Mary (attrib) (1844-1926) American
Works on paper
£1497 $2500 €2186 Portrait of a young girl (18x25cm-7x10in) mono.d.1890 W/C. 16-Nov-3 Simpson's, Houston #120/R

CASSEL, Axel (1955-) German
Sculpture
£2797 $4755 €4000 Petite figure en forme de feuille (45x14x14cm-18x6x6in) s. wood. 27-Nov-3 Calmels Cohen, Paris #86/R est:2800-3500

CASSEL, Léon Louis (1873-1960) French
£259 $425 €378 Le Moulin de Vyre Cafe Ile pres Bruges-Belgique (71x53cm-28x21in) s. prov. 31-May-3 Brunk, Ashville #646/R
£259 $425 €378 River and boats with distant village (30x46cm-12x18in) s. prov. 31-May-3 Brunk, Ashville #662/R
£301 $475 €439 Arched bridge over tree lined canal, distant cathedral (33x46cm-13x18in) s. 6-Sep-3 Brunk, Ashville #530
£305 $500 €445 River and distant castle (38x48cm-15x19in) s. prov. 31-May-3 Brunk, Ashville #645/R
£366 $600 €534 Young boy with white collar (38x30cm-15x12in) s. i.verso prov. 31-May-3 Brunk, Ashville #641/R
£457 $750 €667 Route de Campagne (15x20cm-6x8in) s.d.1905 artist board prov. 31-May-3 Brunk, Ashville #529/R
£457 $750 €667 Riverscape with distant town (43x58cm-17x23in) s. prov. 31-May-3 Brunk, Ashville #588/R
£457 $750 €667 Still life with vase of lilacs (58x71cm-23x28in) s. prov. 31-May-3 Brunk, Ashville #661/R
£488 $800 €712 Trees and buildings lining a river (33x46cm-13x18in) s. prov. 31-May-3 Brunk, Ashville #658/R
£488 $800 €712 River scene with barge, bridge and cathedral (64x91cm-25x36in) s. prov. 31-May-3 Brunk, Ashville #659/R
£506 $800 €739 Canal with bridge and tree-lined street (140x117cm-55x46in) s. 6-Sep-3 Brunk, Ashville #343
£538 $850 €785 Church courtyard scene (130x97cm-51x38in) s. 6-Sep-3 Brunk, Ashville #790
£671 $1100 €980 Seine with view of Le Palais de Justice and the Pont du Change (43x48cm-17x19in) s.d.1950 prov. 31-May-3 Brunk, Ashville #530/R
£671 $1100 €980 Interior view of cathedral with scattered chairs (64x79cm-25x31in) s. prov. 31-May-3 Brunk, Ashville #657/R
£671 $1100 €980 Venetian canal scene (64x81cm-25x32in) s. prov. 31-May-3 Brunk, Ashville #660/R
£732 $1200 €1069 Le Pont et la Rue du Cheval (51x51cm-20x20in) s. i.verso prov. 31-May-3 Brunk, Ashville #546/R
£732 $1200 €1069 Old ship in port (69x86cm-27x34in) s. i.verso prov. 31-May-3 Brunk, Ashville #640/R
£915 $1500 €1336 Street scene with elderly woman with walking stick and cape (74x66cm-29x26in) s. prov. 31-May-3 Brunk, Ashville #644/R est:600-1200
£976 $1600 €1425 Entree Begur, street scene (51x58cm-20x23in) s. prov. 31-May-3 Brunk, Ashville #475/R est:800-1500
£1098 $1800 €1603 Landscape with field of poppies, distant farm and fields (28x41cm-11x16in) s.d.1909 canvasboard prov. 31-May-3 Brunk, Ashville #27/R est:400-800
£1341 $2200 €1958 La port d'Anvers (66x81cm-26x32in) s. i.verso prov. 31-May-3 Brunk, Ashville #28/R est:2000-4000
£1341 $2200 €1958 Still life of vase of French lilacs (81x64cm-32x25in) s. prov. 31-May-3 Brunk, Ashville #547/R est:1000-2000
£2317 $3800 €3383 Canal scene with swans and buildings (97x145cm-38x57in) s.verso prov. 31-May-3 Brunk, Ashville #531/R est:2000-4000
£4390 $7200 €6409 Interior scene with table set for tea (48x81cm-19x32in) s. prov. 31-May-3 Brunk, Ashville #113/R est:3000-6000

CASSEL, Pol (20th C) ?
Works on paper
£660 $1102 €950 Autumnal wood with woman (35x42cm-14x17in) s.d. W/C board. 25-Oct-3 Dr Lehr, Berlin #89/R
£667 $1200 €1000 Woman (49x33cm-19x13in) s. W/C board double-sided. 24-Apr-4 Dr Lehr, Berlin #69/R

CASSELL, Frank (19th C) British
£310 $567 €465 Wooded landscape with picket fence and stile (50x76cm-20x30in) s.i.verso. 12-Jul-4 Mullucks Wells, Bishop's Stortford #395
£800 $1456 €1168 Terriers ratting in a barn (28x38cm-11x15in) s. pair. 16-Jun-4 Andrew Hartley, Ilkley #1048

CASSELL, Frank and HORLOR, George W (19th C) British
£649 $1200 €948 Spaniels in landscapes (51x76cm-20x30in) s. pair. 10-Feb-4 Sotheby's, New York #251/R

CASSELLI, Henry (1946-) American

Works on paper

£387	$700	€565	Bald black man holding a black hat (56x51cm-22x20in) W/C. 16-Apr-4 American Auctioneer #57/R
£714	$1300	€1042	Mississippi watermelon truck (43x53cm-17x21in) s.d.1970 chl drawing. 7-Feb-4 Neal Auction Company, New Orleans #495 est:1000-1500
£1024	$1700	€1495	Front-Ebony, portrait of Civil War soldier (30x23cm-12x9in) s. i.d.1976 verso drawing. 4-Oct-3 Neal Auction Company, New Orleans #589/R est:1200-1800
£2486	$4500	€3630	Nine minutes to post (36x53cm-14x21in) W/C. 16-Apr-4 American Auctioneer #56/R est:5000-7000

CASSIDY, Ira Diamond Gerald (1879-1934) American

£21390	$40000	€31229	Hillside (41x51cm-16x20in) s. 24-Jul-4 Coeur d'Alene, Hayden #86/R est:20000-30000

CASSIE, James (1819-1879) British

£2400	$4296	€3504	Sword dance. Dancing lesson (40x30cm-16x12in) mono.d.1862 pair. 26-May-4 Sotheby's, Olympia #220/R est:2000-3000
£3200	$5440	€4672	Summer Moonlight, Firth of Forth (36x26cm-14x10in) MONO.D.1876. 30-Oct-3 Christie's, London #108/R est:1500-2000

Works on paper

£425	$774	€621	Scottish castle with distant mountains (18x28cm-7x11in) s.d.1856 prov. 16-Jun-4 John Nicholson, Haslemere #627

CASSIERS, Henry (1858-1944) Belgian

£1233	$2096	€1800	Town by the water (39x59cm-15x23in) s. 5-Nov-3 Vendue Huis, Gravenhage #202 est:1000-1500
£2200	$3938	€3300	Heist beach (40x31cm-16x12in) s.i.d.83 panel prov. 15-May-4 De Vuyst, Lokeren #431/R est:3000-4000
£2308	$3854	€3300	Volendam interior (37x37cm-15x15in) s. gouache W/C. 11-Oct-3 De Vuyst, Lokeren #523/R est:3500-4500
£5352	$9259	€7600	The conversation in a snowy street in Amsterdam (41x54cm-16x21in) s. tempera board. 13-Dec-3 De Vuyst, Lokeren #445/R est:8000-10000

Works on paper

£265	$482	€400	En Flandre (35x41cm-14x16in) s. crayon. 15-Jun-4 Vanderkindere, Brussels #552
£282	$487	€400	Croquis a Overyssche (25x39cm-10x15in) s. W/C. 9-Dec-3 Vanderkindere, Brussels #89
£315	$541	€450	Patinage (25x18cm-10x7in) s. wash htd white gouache. 5-Dec-3 Chochon-Barre & Allardi, Paris #22/R
£350	$584	€500	Rue animee en Hollande (24x18cm-9x7in) s. Chinese ink htd gouache. 29-Jun-3 Eric Pillon, Calais #5/R
£403	$745	€600	Sailing ships at the quay (22x29cm-9x11in) s. W/C. 13-Mar-4 De Vuyst, Lokeren #44
£490	$832	€700	Le quai anime (8x13cm-3x5in) s. W/C. 18-Nov-3 Vanderkindere, Brussels #475
£559	$951	€800	Paysage Hollandais anime. s. W/C gouache. 18-Nov-3 Galerie Moderne, Brussels #574/R
£567	$1031	€850	Dutch landscapes (20x28cm-8x11in) s. W/C htd white two. 30-Jun-4 Neumeister, Munich #394
£574	$1085	€850	Bruges (25x18cm-10x7in) s.d.85 W/C. 17-Feb-4 Galerie Moderne, Brussels #236/R
£604	$1117	€900	Fishing village in the Netherlands (29x38cm-11x15in) s. W/C pastel. 13-Mar-4 De Vuyst, Lokeren #43
£629	$1070	€900	Le port d'Ostende (27x44cm-11x17in) s. W/C. 18-Nov-3 Vanderkindere, Brussels #166
£667	$1213	€1000	Dutch landscapes (25x35cm-10x14in) s. W/C htd white two. 30-Jun-4 Neumeister, Munich #393/R
£690	$1234	€1007	Dutch river landscape (42x46cm-17x18in) s. W/C. 12-May-4 Dobiaschofsky, Bern #381/R est:2400 (S.FR 1600)
£833	$1358	€1200	Vue de village avec moulin a vent. s. W/C. 23-Sep-3 Galerie Moderne, Brussels #622/R
£933	$1717	€1400	Canal a Venise (24x24cm-9x9in) s. gouache. 14-Jun-4 Horta, Bruxelles #309
£1000	$1830	€1500	Jeunes hollandaises. Paysage en Hollande (37x40cm-15x16in) one s. one mono. gouache W/C two. 7-Jun-4 Palais de Beaux Arts, Brussels #36/R est:1500-2000
£1096	$1863	€1600	Coucher de soleil (35x50cm-14x20in) s. W/C. 10-Nov-3 Horta, Bruxelles #375
£2400	$4296	€3600	Place de Bruxelles animee sous la neige (34x46cm-13x18in) s.d.86 W/C. 11-May-4 Vanderkindere, Brussels #75/R est:750-1250

CASSIGNEUL, Jean Pierre (1935-) French

£1411	$2597	€2060	Two women at the beach (45x33cm-18x13in) s.d.65 verso board prov. 9-Jun-4 Walker's, Ottawa #322/R est:2000-3000 (C.D 3500)
£3867	$7115	€5800	Femme allongee (54x65cm-21x26in) s. 11-Jun-4 Pierre Berge, Paris #95
£6486	$12000	€9470	Portrait de femme (92x65cm-36x26in) s. prov. 11-Feb-4 Sotheby's, New York #81/R est:10000-15000
£7042	$12183	€10000	Nature morte a la coupe de fruits (100x65cm-39x26in) s. 15-Dec-3 Marc Kohn, Paris #100/R est:10000-12000
£13497	$22000	€19706	Les coquelicots (92x65cm-36x26in) s. prov. 25-Sep-3 Christie's, Rockefeller NY #598/R est:22000-28000
£23743	$42500	€34665	Femme au bois (116x89cm-46x35in) s. prov. 6-May-4 Sotheby's, New York #440/R est:30000-40000
£167598	$300000	€244693	Au balcon (91x65cm-36x26in) s. prov. 6-May-4 Sotheby's, New York #441/R est:20000-30000

CASSINARI, Bruno (1912-1992) Italian

£1477	$2643	€2200	Head (65x50cm-26x20in) s.d.53 tempera Chinese ink prov. 25-May-4 Sotheby's, Milan #35/R est:2000
£1611	$2883	€2400	Head (72x47cm-28x19in) s.d.53 tempera Chinese ink paper prov. 25-May-4 Sotheby's, Milan #19/R est:2000
£3041	$5351	€4500	Untitled (55x35cm-22x14in) s.d.66. 24-May-4 Christie's, Milan #298 est:3500-5000
£3378	$5946	€5000	Untitled (55x35cm-22x14in) s.d.60. 24-May-4 Christie's, Milan #299/R
£3497	$5944	€5000	Study for still life (40x50cm-16x20in) s.d.67 prov. 24-Nov-3 Christie's, Milan #67/R est:4000-6000
£3846	$6538	€5500	Seascape (50x70cm-20x28in) s. prov. 25-Nov-3 Sotheby's, Milan #26/R est:6000-8000
£3919	$6897	€5800	Still life (56x34cm-22x13in) s.d.60 prov. 24-May-4 Christie's, Milan #205/R est:4000-6000
£5862	$9790	€8500	Study of nude (70x50cm-28x20in) s. s.i.verso exhib.lit. 17-Nov-3 Sant Agostino, Torino #281/R est:8000-10000
£6294	$10510	€9000	Antibes (60x73cm-24x29in) s. s.i.d.1953 verso. 26-Jun-3 Sant Agostino, Torino #258/R est:7000-9000
£6376	$11413	€9500	Still life (70x80cm-28x31in) s.d.61 exhib.lit. 29-May-4 Farsetti, Prato #47/R est:9000-12000
£7383	$13215	€11000	Still life in grey (60x73cm-24x29in) s.d.62 s.i.d.verso lit. 29-May-4 Farsetti, Prato #473/R est:10000-14000
£8000	$14400	€12000	Spanish woman (92x76cm-36x30in) s.d.63 s.d.verso. 22-Apr-4 Finarte Semenzato, Rome #362/R est:15000-18000
£8696	$14261	€12000	Still life in blue (59x100cm-23x39in) s.d.57 s.i.d.verso. 27-May-3 Sotheby's, Milan #196/R est:13000-18000
£8982	$15000	€13114	Paesaggio con maternita (82x100cm-32x39in) s.d.63 s.i.d.verso prov. 7-Oct-3 Sotheby's, New York #325 est:10000-15000
£9396	$16819	€14000	Atelier (60x70cm-24x28in) s.d.1967. 30-May-4 Meeting Art, Vercelli #75 est:10000
£17148	$31552	€25036	Danseuse (166x89cm-65x35in) s.d.50 exhib.prov. 29-Mar-4 Rasmussen, Copenhagen #13/R est:150000-200000 (D.KR 190000)
£17241	$28793	€25000	REd socks (145x85cm-57x33in) s. s.i.d.1983 verso exhib.lit. 17-Nov-3 Sant Agostino, Torino #271/R est:25000-35000

Sculpture

£4648	$8134	€6600	Cock (110cm-43in) bronze stone base exhib. 17-Dec-3 Il Ponte, Milan #1108/R est:7000-8000

Works on paper

£216	$400	€315	Cheval brun (48x69cm-19x27in) s.d.64 ink wash prov. 15-Jul-4 Sotheby's, New York #91
£293	$533	€428	Portrait of woman (59x42cm-23x17in) s. W/C Indian ink. 7-Feb-4 Rasmussen, Havnen #4108/R (D.KR 3200)
£403	$749	€600	Bishop (28x22cm-11x9in) s. ink W/C paper on canvas. 4-Mar-4 Babuino, Rome #32
£459	$850	€670	Arena (53x41cm-21x16in) s. W/C. 17-Jan-4 Susanin's, Chicago #115/R
£511	$900	€746	The arena (74x53cm-29x21in) s. W/C exec.c.1950. 23-May-4 Treadway Gallery, Cincinnati #748/R
£533	$965	€800	Goats (41x55cm-16x22in) s.d.1960 Chinese ink water. 2-Apr-4 Farsetti, Prato #42
£552	$921	€800	Horse (37x55cm-15x22in) s. ink wash dr. 14-Nov-3 Farsetti, Prato #239/R
£667	$1227	€1000	Head of woman (30x20cm-12x8in) s. W/C pen prov. 14-Jun-4 Porro, Milan #18/R
£725	$1188	€1000	Female face (56x42cm-22x17in) s.d.60 gouache Chinese ink. 27-May-3 Sotheby's, Milan #37
£800	$1472	€1200	Nude (49x69cm-19x27in) s. Chinese ink W/C. 8-Jun-4 Finarte Semenzato, Milan #87/R
£1156	$2070	€1700	Vase of flowers (66x48cm-26x19in) s.d.1973 W/C. 16-Mar-4 Finarte Semenzato, Milan #99/R est:1700
£1310	$2188	€1900	Figure (70x50cm-28x20in) s. mixed media. 13-Nov-3 Galleria Pace, Milan #123/R est:2300
£1342	$2483	€2000	Figures (42x57cm-17x22in) s.d.1965 mixed media paper on canvas. 11-Mar-4 Galleria Pace, Milan #131/R est:2500-3300
£1449	$2377	€2000	Cock (73x58cm-29x23in) s.d.1966 mixed media. 29-May-3 Galleria Pace, Milan #57/R est:3300
£1522	$2496	€2100	Figure (70x50cm-28x20in) s. mixed media. 29-May-3 Galleria Pace, Milan #22/R est:2200-3200
£2148	$3844	€3200	Horses (69x50cm-27x20in) s. Chinese ink W/C. 25-May-4 Sotheby's, Milan #34/R est:2000

CASSON, Alfred Joseph (1898-1992) Canadian

£3252	$5821	€4748	Brescia Hall, University of Western Ontario (20x25cm-8x10in) s. panel painted c.1925 prov. 27-May-4 Heffel, Vancouver #206/R est:8000-10000 (C.D 8000)
£4464	$7679	€6517	Fall showers, Pen Lake (30x37cm-12x15in) s. board painted 1979 prov. 2-Dec-3 Joyner Waddington, Toronto #175/R est:10000-15000 (C.D 10000)
£4464	$7679	€6517	Grey October day, l'Original, Ont. (30x37cm-12x15in) s. board. 2-Dec-3 Joyner Waddington, Toronto #207/R est:12000-15000 (C.D 10000)
£4472	$8004	€6529	Autumn storm, Gamtha Lake, Ontario (30x38cm-12x15in) s. s.i.d.1953 verso panel prov. 27-May-4 Heffel, Vancouver #90/R est:7000-9000 (C.D 11000)
£4800	$8784	€7008	October rain (30x38cm-12x15in) s.i.d.1977 panel prov. 1-Jun-4 Hodgins, Calgary #132/R est:12000-15000 (C.D 12000)
£4878	$8732	€7122	Farm on Blythwood Road (24x28cm-9x11in) s. s.i.d.1926 verso panel lit. 27-May-4 Heffel, Vancouver #50/R est:15000-18000 (C.D 12000)
£4911	$8446	€7170	October morning near Dwight (30x37cm-12x15in) s. canvasboard prov. 2-Dec-3 Joyner Waddington, Toronto #141/R est:10000-15000 (C.D 11000)
£5299	$9114	€7737	Autumn morning, Grenville, Que (30x37cm-12x15in) s. board prov. 2-Dec-3 Joyner Waddington, Toronto #9/R est:12000-15000 (C.D 11870)
£5405	$9189	€7891	Near Grenville, Quebec (30x38cm-12x15in) s. s.i.d.1970 verso board prov. 21-Nov-3 Walker's, Ottawa #43/R est:10000-15000 (C.D 12000)
£5580	$9598	€8147	Cumulus clouds, Ostongue Lake (30x37cm-12x15in) s. board painted 1983. 2-Dec-3 Joyner Waddington, Toronto #180/R est:12000-15000 (C.D 12500)
£5600	$10248	€8176	On the Raven's Cliff Road (30x37cm-12x15in) s. board painted 1980. 1-Jun-4 Joyner Waddington, Toronto #193/R est:12000-15000 (C.D 14000)
£5600	$10248	€8176	Oxtongue Lake (30x37cm-12x15in) s. canvasboard painted 1979. 1-Jun-4 Joyner Waddington, Toronto #161/R est:12000-15000 (C.D 14000)
£5804	$9866	€8474	Cloche Hills (30x38cm-12x15in) s. s.i.d.1960 verso board prov. 6-Nov-3 Heffel, Vancouver #26/R est:10000-15000 (C.D 13000)
£5856	$9955	€8550	Quebec near Montabello (30x37cm-12x15in) s. s.i.d.1969 verso board prov. 18-Nov-3 Sotheby's, Toronto #156/R est:10000-12000 (C.D 13000)
£5856	$9955	€8550	Escarpment, Grenville, Quebec (30x38cm-12x15in) s. s.i.d.1968 verso board prov. 27-Nov-3 Heffel, Vancouver #86/R est:8000-10000 (C.D 13000)
£6098	$10915	€8903	Fire haze - Muskoka (23x29cm-9x11in) s. s.i.d.1921 verso board. 31-May-4 Sotheby's, Toronto #7/R est:15000-18000 (C.D 15000)
£6250	$10750	€9125	Farm gate, near Little Current, Manitoulin (30x37cm-12x15in) s. board painted 1958 prov. 2-Dec-3 Joyner Waddington, Toronto #149/R est:12000-15000 (C.D 14000)
£6250	$10750	€9125	Grenville, Quebec, looking across the Ottawa from Hawkesbury (30x37cm-12x15in) s. board prov. 2-Dec-3 Joyner Waddington, Toronto #195/R est:12000-15000 (C.D 14000)
£6306	$10721	€9207	Ontario landscape (24x29cm-9x11in) s. canvasboard prov. 18-Nov-3 Sotheby's, Toronto #44/R est:9000-12000 (C.D 14000)
£6696	$11518	€9776	Grey morning, South Portage (30x37cm-12x15in) board prov. 2-Dec-3 Joyner Waddington, Toronto #219/R est:12000-15000 (C.D 15000)
£7143	$12286	€10429	Old Blacksmith's Shop, Woodbridge (27x21cm-11x8in) indis.s.d.21 board prov. 2-Dec-3 Joyner Waddington, Toronto #17/R est:12000-15000 (C.D 16000)

£7200 $13176 €10512 Old farmhouse, Ottawa River, Grenville, Quebec (30x37cm-12x15in) s. board prov. 1-Jun-4 Joyner Waddington, Toronto #124/R est:12000-15000 (C.D 18000)
£8130 $14553 €11870 Cranberry Lake, autumn (23x28cm-9x11in) s. s.i.verso board painted c.1930 prov. 6-May-4 Heffel, Vancouver #45/R est:13000-16000 (C.D 20000)
£9146 $16372 €13353 Near Parry Sound (23x28cm-9x11in) s. s.i.d.1932 verso panel prov.lit. 27-May-4 Heffel, Vancouver #52/R est:15000-18000 (C.D 22500)
£11261 $19144 €16441 Poverty Lake (24x28cm-9x11in) s. i.d.1945 verso panel prov.lit. 27-Nov-3 Heffel, Vancouver #81/R est:18000-20000 (C.D 25000)
£11261 $19144 €16441 Valley near Glen Williams (23x28cm-9x11in) s. s.i.d.1938 verso panel prov. 27-Nov-3 Heffel, Vancouver #85/R est:10000-15000 (C.D 25000)
£12000 $21960 €17520 Road at Britt (60x75cm-24x30in) s. board. 1-Jun-4 Joyner Waddington, Toronto #37/R est:30000-40000 (C.D 30000)
£20000 $36600 €29200 MacGregor Bay from Dreamer's Rock (50x60cm-20x24in) s. board prov. 1-Jun-4 Joyner Waddington, Toronto #54/R est:30000-40000 (C.D 50000)
£21396 $36374 €31238 October morning (61x76cm-24x30in) s. s.i.d.1975 verso prov. 27-Nov-3 Heffel, Vancouver #79/R est:50000-60000 (C.D 47500)
£22523 $38288 €32884 After cutting, Quebec (76x91cm-30x36in) s. prov. 18-Nov-3 Sotheby's, Toronto #91/R est:50000-60000 (C.D 50000)
£27027 $45946 €39459 Autumn on the Madawaska (76x101cm-30x40in) s. s.i.verso board painted c.1957 prov. 27-Nov-3 Heffel, Vancouver #67/R est:50000-60000 (C.D 60000)
£48000 $87840 €70080 Northern Farm (100x125cm-39x49in) s. painted 1973 prov. 1-Jun-4 Joyner Waddington, Toronto #82/R est:70000-90000 (C.D 120000)
£62500 $107500 €91250 Summer morning (75x90cm-30x35in) s. painted 1948 prov.exhib.lit. 2-Dec-3 Joyner Waddington, Toronto #66/R est:60000-80000 (C.D 140000)

Works on paper

£909 $1482 €1327 Lake Kashawigamog (21x28cm-8x11in) s.i.d.1926 graphite prov. 23-Sep-3 Ritchie, Toronto #153/R est:1500-2000 (C.D 2000)
£1915 $3255 €2796 Irises (28x71cm-11x28in) s. init.d.44 verso gouache paper on board prov. 18-Nov-3 Sotheby's, Toronto #72/R est:4000-6000 (C.D 4250)
£4054 $6892 €5919 Building the campfire (47x58cm-19x23in) s.d.18 gouache prov. 18-Nov-3 Sotheby's, Toronto #6/R est:12000-15000 (C.D 9000)
£6306 $10721 €9207 Decorative landscape (46x57cm-18x22in) s. gouache graphite board prov. 18-Nov-3 Sotheby's, Toronto #87/R est:12000-15000 (C.D 14000)
£6757 $11486 €9865 An old house (24x26cm-9x10in) s. s.i.verso W/C painted c.1929 prov. 27-Nov-3 Heffel, Vancouver #94/R est:16000-18000 (C.D 15000)

CASSON, Sir Hugh (1910-) British

Works on paper

£250 $458 €365 Evening picnic, Loch Fyne (5x15cm-2x6in) init. W/C. 28-Jul-4 Mallams, Oxford #80/R
£260 $486 €380 Mr Toad on the river, scalling on the tideway (11x17cm-4x7in) init. W/C pencil prov. 24-Feb-4 Bonhams, Knowle #121
£260 $478 €380 Torcello (8x18cm-3x7in) init.i. ink W/C. 14-Jun-4 Bonhams, Bath #77
£320 $598 €480 Priests near Teatro Verdi (7x4cm-3x2in) init.i. pen ink W/C. 22-Jul-4 Dominic Winter, Swindon #17/R
£620 $1066 €905 Santa Maria della Salute, Venice (9x15cm-4x6in) init.i. W/C pen black ink. 3-Dec-3 Christie's, Kensington #481/R
£700 $1274 €1022 River Walk, Basel (9x10cm-4x4in) init. i. pencil W/C pen black ink. 1-Jul-4 Christie's, Kensington #316/R
£720 $1267 €1051 Windy day (11x10cm-4x4in) init.i. W/C. 18-May-4 Bonhams, Knightsbridge #186/R

CASTAGNE, Albino dal (1877-1961) Italian

Sculpture

£959 $1496 €1400 Crucified (91cm-36in) wood. 8-Apr-3 Il Ponte, Milan #567

CASTAGNETO, Giovanni (1851-1900) Brazilian

£18498 $32742 €27747 The navy (27x46cm-11x18in) s.d.1892. 27-Apr-4 Bolsa de Arte, Rio de Janeiro #13/R (B.R 101000)

CASTAGNINO, Juan Carlos (1908-1972) Argentinian

£1229 $2200 €1794 Figure (67x49cm-26x19in) chl. 11-May-4 Arroyo, Buenos Aires #16
£2459 $4500 €3590 Tamer (80x50cm-31x20in) 1-Jun-4 Arroyo, Buenos Aires #45
£5866 $10500 €8564 Fishermen (61x46cm-24x18in) s.d.46 s.i.d.verso. 4-May-4 Arroyo, Buenos Aires #53/R est:9000
£6704 $12000 €9788 Figures (100x70cm-39x28in) s.d.66 s.i.d.verso acrylic. 4-May-4 Arroyo, Buenos Aires #17/R est:12000
£8743 $16000 €12765 Untitled (37x57cm-15x22in) 1-Jun-4 Arroyo, Buenos Aires #89
£9341 $17000 €13638 Resting in the mountains (80x60cm-31x24in) s.d.52 s.i.d.verso. 29-Jun-4 Arroyo, Buenos Aires #80/R est:10000
£18033 $33000 €26328 Bagual's birth (100x120cm-39x47in) 1-Jun-4 Arroyo, Buenos Aires #83

Works on paper

£769 $1400 €1123 Posing (64x46cm-25x18in) s. ink. 5-Jul-4 Arroyo, Buenos Aires #14/R
£2198 $4000 €3209 Surreal (41x35cm-16x14in) s.d.70 W/C. 5-Jul-4 Arroyo, Buenos Aires #101/R est:2400
£2473 $4500 €3611 Horse (46x62cm-18x24in) s.d.60 mixed media cardboard. 29-Jun-4 Arroyo, Buenos Aires #68/R est:4500
£2486 $4500 €3630 Tango (64x47cm-25x19in) ink. 30-Mar-4 Arroyo, Buenos Aires #11
£3571 $6500 €5214 Young woman (97x67cm-38x26in) s.d.53 ink wash. 29-Jun-4 Arroyo, Buenos Aires #17/R est:4500
£9497 $17000 €13866 Nude (76x104cm-30x41in) s. pastel. 4-May-4 Arroyo, Buenos Aires #83/R est:7800

CASTAGNOLA, Gabriele (1828-1883) Italian

£1330 $2381 €1942 The rose (23x15cm-9x6in) s.i.d.1873 panel. 25-May-4 Bukowskis, Stockholm #350/R est:12000-15000 (S.KR 18000)
£1946 $3640 €2900 Gallant scene (54x44cm-21x17in) board double-sided. 26-Feb-4 Cambi, Genoa #431/R est:3000-4000

CASTAING, Rene Marie Joseph (1896-1943) French

£800 $1464 €1200 Allegorie de la Lecture (163x74cm-64x29in) s. 3-Jun-4 E & Eve, Paris #66
£933 $1708 €1400 Allegorie de la Peche (200x80cm-79x31in) s.d.1942. 3-Jun-4 E & Eve, Paris #69
£1600 $2928 €2400 Allegorie de la Danse (187x105cm-74x41in) 3-Jun-4 E & Eve, Paris #67 est:1500-2000
£4267 $7808 €6400 Les quatre saisons (190x572cm-75x225in) s.d.1943. 3-Jun-4 E & Eve, Paris #71/R est:5000-6000

CASTAN, Gustave-Eugène (1823-1892) Swiss

£524 $954 €765 Path through the woods (36x54cm-14x21in) s. cardboard. 16-Jun-4 Fischer, Luzern #2047/R (S.FR 1200)
£1101 $1839 €1596 Pre alpine landscape with trees and figures (38x58cm-15x23in) s. paper on board. 23-Jun-3 Philippe Schuler, Zurich #3383/R est:2000-2500 (S.FR 2400)
£1131 $1923 €1651 La chambre du Roi a la Bernerie-Loire Inferieure (37x59cm-15x23in) s. board on panel prov. 19-Nov-3 Fischer, Luzern #2035/R est:1800-2200 (S.FR 2500)
£1147 $1915 €1663 Le Mont Cervin, Zermatt (38x52cm-15x20in) s.i. cardboard on panel prov. 21-Jun-3 Galerie du Rhone, Sion #453/R est:3000-4000 (S.FR 2500)
£1189 $2022 €1736 Country landscape with two children (39x58cm-15x23in) s. paper on canvas. 7-Nov-3 Dobiaschofsky, Bern #6/R est:3000 (S.FR 2700)
£1316 $2197 €1921 Suisse - Mauvoisin / Mont Brule (37x59cm-15x23in) s. board on panel prov. 15-Nov-3 Galerie Gloggner, Luzern #22/R est:2500-2800 (S.FR 3000)
£1454 $2471 €2123 A St Maurice sur Loire pres de Roanne (37x58cm-15x23in) s. i. verso paper on panel. 7-Nov-3 Dobiaschofsky, Bern #41/R est:2500 (S.FR 3300)
£2752 $4596 €3990 Femme a la riviere (39x58cm-15x23in) s. 21-Jun-3 Galerie du Rhone, Sion #455/R est:5000-7000 (S.FR 6000)
£4484 $7309 €6547 Trees (37x58cm-15x23in) s. s.i. verso board on panel. 29-Sep-3 Christie's, Zurich #12/R est:4000-6000 (S.FR 10000)
£5652 $10343 €8252 Two children in a winter landscape (80x130cm-31x51in) s. 7-Jun-4 Christie's, Zurich #14/R est:14000-18000 (S.FR 13000)
£35874 $58475 €52376 Lakeshore in the evening (72x110cm-28x43in) s. 29-Sep-3 Christie's, Zurich #8/R est:18000-22000 (S.FR 80000)

Works on paper

£573 $974 €837 Landscape with rocks (39x59cm-15x23in) s. paper on canvas. 7-Nov-3 Dobiaschofsky, Bern #51/R (S.FR 1300)

CASTAN, Pierre Jean Edmond (1817-?) French

£340 $629 €496 Fly catcher (25cm-10in) s. panel. 13-Jul-4 Rosebery Fine Art, London #534
£3200 $5760 €4672 Bread for the poor (33x23cm-13x9in) s.d.1866 panel. 21-Jan-4 Sotheby's, Olympia #411/R est:3000-5000
£4094 $7328 €6100 Le marchand d'etoffes (60x73cm-24x29in) s.d.1876. 25-May-4 Chambelland & Giafferi, Paris #79/R est:3000-4000
£5500 $9515 €8030 Preparing the meal (26x20cm-10x8in) s.d.1876 panel. 11-Dec-3 Lyon & Turnbull, Edinburgh #98/R est:2000-3000
£6000 $10920 €8760 Toy boat (25x19cm-10x7in) s.d.1862 panel prov. 16-Jun-4 Bonhams, New Bond Street #95/R est:5000-7000
£7500 $12975 €10950 Learning to read (24x18cm-9x7in) s.d.1867 panel. 11-Dec-3 Lyon & Turnbull, Edinburgh #97/R est:2000-3000
£7800 $12948 €11388 Homework time (27x35cm-11x14in) s.d.1869 panel. 1-Oct-3 Sotheby's, Olympia #210/R est:3000-4000

CASTANEDA, Alfredo (1938-) Mexican

£950 $1700 €1387 Our sorcery (19x14cm-7x6in) s.i.verso oil pencil painted 1999. 6-May-4 Doyle, New York #101/R est:2500-3500
£2429 $4250 €3546 Angel (29x44cm-11x17in) s.d.68 oil pencil paper on card prov. 19-Dec-3 Sotheby's, New York #1210/R est:4000-6000

CASTANEDA, Felipe (1933-) Mexican

Sculpture

£1412 $2500 €2062 Seated woman, her hands on crossed legs (20x15cm-8x6in) s.i.d.72 green brown pat bronze. 2-May-4 Bonhams & Butterfields, Los Angeles #3107/R est:3000-5000
£3390 $6000 €4949 Feclining female nude, her hands over her head (18x69cm-7x27in) s.d.1973 white onyx. 2-May-4 Bonhams & Butterfields, Los Angeles #3109/R est:1000-12000
£3571 $6500 €5214 Pensive (33x37x25cm-13x15x10in) incised sig. green black pat. bronze. 29-Jun-4 Sotheby's, New York #672/R est:7000-9000
£4469 $8000 €6525 Solitude (38x26x26cm-15x10x10in) st.sig.d.1981 black marble lit. 26-May-4 Sotheby's, New York #186/R est:10000-15000
£4520 $8000 €6599 Seated female nude, both hands clasped behind her ankle (41x41cm-16x16in) s.d.1973 white onyx. 2-May-4 Bonhams & Butterfields, Los Angeles #3101/R est:10000-12000
£4670 $8500 €6818 Desnudo acostada (19x57x28cm-7x22x11in) s.d.1979 onyx on a wooden base. 29-Jun-4 Sotheby's, New York #659/R est:6000-8000
£10000 $18000 €14600 Amantes (79x81x79cm-31x32x31in) bronze. 24-Apr-4 Du Mouchelle, Detroit #3051/R est:3000-5000
£18156 $32500 €26508 Flower (67x54x27cm-26x21x11in) st.sig.d.1991 num.VII/VII pat bronze lit. 26-May-4 Sotheby's, New York #148/R est:10000-15000

CASTANEDA, Pilar (20th C) Mexican

£202 $371 €295 Descanso (70x110cm-28x43in) s.d.63 exhib. 14-Jun-4 Waddingtons, Toronto #344/R (C.D 500)

CASTBERG, Johan (1911-) Norwegian

£258 $451 €377 Theatre scene (50x70cm-20x28in) s. panel. 16-Dec-3 Grev Wedels Plass, Oslo #143/R (N.KR 3000)

CASTBERG, Oscar (1846-1917) Norwegian

£258 $451 €377 Landscape from Minnesund (27x40cm-11x16in) s.i.d.1897. 16-Dec-3 Grev Wedels Plass, Oslo #144 (N.KR 3000)

CASTEELS, Alexander (attrib) (17th C) Flemish

£9655 $16124 €14000 Deer hunt (115x180cm-45x71in) 15-Nov-3 Lempertz, Koln #1024/R est:10000

CASTEELS, Pauwel (attrib) (17th C) Flemish

£2262 $3846 €3303 Cavalry battle between Turks and Poles (63x98cm-25x39in) bears mono. 19-Nov-3 Fischer, Luzern #1020/R est:7500-8500 (S.FR 5000)

CASTEELS, Peter (fl.1673-1674) Flemish
£3741 $5949 €5500 Chargement d'un bateau a l'aide d'une grue (29x39cm-11x15in) 23-Mar-3 Mercier & Cie, Lille #179/R est:4500-6000

CASTEELS, Peter II (fl.1690-1699) Flemish
£37415 $59490 €55000 View of Pont-Neuf. View of Louvre (30x43cm-12x17in) pair. 21-Mar-3 Bailly Pommery, Paris #60

CASTEELS, Peter II (attrib) (fl.1690-1699) Flemish
£7000 $12110 €10220 Still life of roses, narcissi, bluebells and carnations in a basket (52x103cm-20x41in) prov. 11-Dec-3 Sotheby's, London #221/R est:8000-12000

CASTEELS, Peter III (1684-1749) Flemish
£1400 $2576 €2044 Still life of songbirds on a table before a curtain (38x64cm-15x25in) s. indis d.1718. 8-Jun-4 Bonhams, Knightsbridge #198/R est:1200-1800
£7222 $13000 €10544 Port scene with figures (29x41cm-11x16in) i. pair. 21-Jan-4 Sotheby's, New York #85/R est:6000-8000
£10000 $17900 €15000 Rose garland and dove of peace (62x74cm-24x29in) s.d.1721. 17-May-4 Finarte Semenzato, Rome #112/R est:12000-14000
£24000 $43680 €35040 Ornamental fowl by a pool (89x124cm-35x49in) 21-Jun-4 Christie's, London #90/R est:30000-40000

CASTEELS, Peter III (circle) (1684-1749) Flemish
£8242 $15000 €12033 Mixed flowers in an urn with plums, peaches and a watermelon in a landscape (128x102cm-50x40in) 4-Feb-4 Christie's, Rockefeller NY #76/R est:15000-20000
£16000 $28800 €23360 Cockerel, duck and other birds and chicks in a wooed landscape. Bantam and chicks in landscape (63x76cm-25x30in) pair. 21-Apr-4 Christie's, London #17/R est:8000-12000

CASTEELS, Peter III (studio) (1684-1749) Flemish
£7000 $12810 €10220 Peacocks, white pheasants, doves, hen and cockerel, rabbit in a parkland landscape (150x165cm-59x65in) prov. 6-Jul-4 Sotheby's, Olympia #556/R est:8000-12000

CASTEELS, Peter III (style) (1684-1749) Flemish
£13200 $22836 €19272 Still life with chickens , ducks and a kingfisher, in river landscape (63x75cm-25x30in) prov. 9-Dec-3 Sotheby's, Olympia #341/R est:6000-8000

CASTEL, Moshe (1909-1992) Israeli
£1105 $2000 €1613 Abstract composition (33x49cm-13x19in) s. acrylic painted 1950's. 1-Apr-4 Ben-Ami, Tel Aviv #4759/R est:3000-4000
£1731 $3150 €2597 Abstract (58x43cm-23x17in) s. oil mixed media paper on wood. 1-Jul-4 Ben-Ami, Tel Aviv #4833/R est:4000-5000
£1944 $3500 €2838 Flowers (66x36cm-26x14in) 24-Apr-4 Du Mouchelle, Detroit #3053/R est:3000-5000
£2500 $4500 €3650 Still life of bird (74x53cm-29x21in) 24-Apr-4 Du Mouchelle, Detroit #3052/R est:5000-8000
£7229 $12000 €10554 To the well (46x38cm-18x15in) s. masonite. 2-Oct-3 Christie's, Tel Aviv #59/R est:14000-18000
£7500 $13425 €10950 Scenes from Antiquity (56x71cm-22x28in) s.i. oil brush ink on board prov. 11-May-4 Sotheby's, Olympia #610/R est:2000-2500
Works on paper
£2238 $3737 €3200 Hommage a Miro (43x32cm-17x13in) s. gouache paper on canvas. 25-Jun-3 Rabourdin & Choppin de Janvry, Paris #121/R est:2800-3000
£9036 $15000 €13193 Inscription Basalte I (100x81cm-39x32in) s. s.d.1963 verso i.stretcher lava stone pigement canvas lit. 2-Oct-3 Christie's, Tel Aviv #96/R est:16000-20000

CASTELFRANCHI, Cirano (1912-) Italian
£306 $558 €460 Old Milan (30x42cm-12x17in) s. s.i.verso board. 12-Jul-4 Il Ponte, Milan #1015

CASTELL, Anton (1810-1867) German
£2953 $5434 €4400 Dresden in evening (26x35cm-10x14in) s.d.1861. 26-Mar-4 Bolland & Marotz, Bremen #493b/R est:3800
£8725 $16054 €13000 Fortified town by the Po (54x84cm-21x33in) s.d.1841. 26-Mar-4 Bolland & Marotz, Bremen #493a/R est:10000

CASTELLANI, Enrico (1930-) Italian
£4422 $7915 €6500 Untitled (48x69cm-19x27in) s.d.1974 cardboard. 22-Mar-4 Sant Agostino, Torino #456/R est:8000
£4545 $7727 €6500 White surface (56x77cm-22x30in) s.d.80 paper prov. 24-Nov-3 Christie's, Milan #144/R est:6500-7000
£9091 $15455 €13000 White surface (50x70cm-20x28in) s.i.d.2001 acrylic. 25-Nov-3 Sotheby's, Milan #12/R est:12000-15000
£10000 $18400 €15000 White surface (60x60cm-24x24in) s.i.d.2001 verso tempera. 12-Jun-4 Meeting Art, Vercelli #750/R est:15000
£10067 $18624 €15000 White surface (50x50cm-20x20in) s.i.d.1993 verso. 13-Mar-4 Meeting Art, Vercelli #128 est:15000
£10140 $17238 €14500 Untitled (60x90cm-24x35in) s.d.1966. 20-Nov-3 Finarte Semenzato, Milan #80/R est:14000-16000
£11034 $17655 €16000 Blue surface (50x50cm-20x20in) s.i.d.1993 verso. 13-Mar-3 Galleria Pace, Milan #103/R est:18000-22000
£11034 $17655 €16000 White surface (50x50cm-20x20in) s.i.d.1993 verso. 13-Mar-3 Galleria Pace, Milan #104/R est:18000-22000
£11594 $19014 €16000 White surface (50x50cm-20x20in) s.d.1996 verso. 29-May-3 Galleria Pace, Milan #144/R est:22000
£15000 $27600 €21900 Superficie opaline (80x100cm-31x39in) s.i.d.1973 oil varnish shaped canvas prov. 25-Jun-4 Christie's, London #158/R est:15000-20000
£15172 $25338 €22000 Re surface (80x80cm-31x31in) s.verso painted 1996. 13-Nov-3 Galleria Pace, Milan #130/R est:32000
£20134 $36040 €30000 White surface (100x100cm-39x39in) s.i.d.1989 verso. 30-May-4 Meeting Art, Vercelli #50 est:25000
£28000 $46760 €40880 White surface (70x50cm-28x20in) s.i.d.1977 on stretcher prov.exhib. 20-Oct-3 Sotheby's, London #16/R est:20000
£110000 $183700 €160600 Superficie bianca no 1 (150x120cm-59x47in) s.i.d.1966 stretcher prov. 21-Oct-3 Christie's, London #29/R est:50000-70000
Sculpture
£5235 $9370 €7800 Similarly (69x52cm-27x20in) s.i. relief exec.c.1963 prov. 25-May-4 Sotheby's, Milan #158/R est:2000
Works on paper
£25610 $42000 €37391 Superficie no 20 (22x14cm-9x6in) s.d.59 on stretcher nails canvas prov.exhib. 28-May-3 Sotheby's, Amsterdam #12/R est:20000-30000

CASTELLANOS, Carlos Alberto (1881-1945) Uruguayan
£543 $950 €793 At the Bodega (80x86cm-31x34in) 19-Dec-3 Sotheby's, New York #1174/R
£2045 $3600 €2986 Annunciation (73x91cm-29x36in) prov. 5-Jan-4 Galeria y Remates, Montevideo #83/R est:4700-5500
£2647 $4500 €3865 Petit Trianon (43x60cm-17x24in) s. 25-Nov-3 Galeria y Remates, Montevideo #32/R
£2727 $4800 €3981 Dancer (92x73cm-36x29in) prov.lit. 5-Jan-4 Galeria y Remates, Montevideo #82/R est:4700-5500

CASTELLANOS, Roberto (1871-1942) South American
£435 $800 €635 Horses and carriages (29x37cm-11x15in) s.d.1942 board. 22-Jun-4 Galeria y Remates, Montevideo #85/R
£462 $850 €675 Fishing boats (55x70cm-22x28in) s.d.1934. 22-Jun-4 Galeria y Remates, Montevideo #86/R
£617 $1000 €895 Coast of Piriapolis (41x59cm-16x23in) s. 29-Jul-3 Galeria y Remates, Montevideo #134/R
£671 $1100 €980 Pocitos beach (21x36cm-8x14in) s. cardboard. 3-Jun-3 Galeria y Remates, Montevideo #99
£1294 $2200 €1889 Horse and cart (31x39cm-12x15in) s.d. cardboard. 25-Nov-3 Galeria y Remates, Montevideo #165/R
£1585 $2600 €2314 Sailing boat in Montevideo harbour (80x100cm-31x39in) s.d.1912. 3-Jun-3 Galeria y Remates, Montevideo #98
£2941 $5000 €4294 Gauchos (110x160cm-43x63in) s.d.1937. 25-Nov-3 Galeria y Remates, Montevideo #163/R
£5000 $8500 €7300 Carriage and oxen (100x130cm-39x51in) s.d.1940. 25-Nov-3 Galeria y Remates, Montevideo #164
£7967 $14500 €11632 Sailing vessels (171x232cm-67x91in) s.d.1938 lit. 29-Jun-4 Arroyo, Buenos Aires #49/R est:14000
Works on paper
£261 $480 €381 Lagoon (40x75cm-16x30in) s. W/C. 22-Jun-4 Galeria y Remates, Montevideo #88

CASTELLETTI, Antonio (18th C) Italian
Works on paper
£296 $476 €420 Classic scene (53x44cm-21x17in) ink drawing. 8-May-3 Farsetti, Prato #568

CASTELLI, Alessandro (1809-1902) Italian
£800 $1432 €1168 English landscapes of cattle (23x33cm-9x13in) s. pair after T S Cooper. 5-May-4 John Nicholson, Haslemere #534
£1900 $3515 €2774 Sulla costiera Romana (23x39cm-9x15in) s. indis.d. board. 14-Jul-4 Christie's, Kensington #958/R est:700-900

CASTELLI, Alfio (20th C) Italian
Sculpture
£1664 $2829 €2380 Figure (94cm-37in) s. bronze. 18-Nov-3 Babuino, Rome #36/R est:2500-3000

CASTELLI, Bartolomeo (younger) (1696-1738) Italian
£12081 $22591 €18000 Still life of fruit (23cm-9in circular) copper. 25-Feb-4 Porro, Milan #9/R est:18000
£13423 $23758 €20000 Still life of fruit with pumpkin and figs (59x48cm-23x19in) 27-Apr-4 Porro, Milan #292/R est:20000

CASTELLI, Carlo Lodovico (18th C) Italian
Works on paper
£410 $750 €599 Aurora riding Pegasus and bringing forth the dawn (21x19cm-8x7in) s.d.1711 red chk. 29-Jan-4 Swann Galleries, New York #95/R

CASTELLI, Carmen Dede Bischoff (1936-) Swiss
£317 $538 €463 L'attesa (55x74cm-22x29in) s.d.87 mixed media pavatex. 19-Nov-3 Fischer, Luzern #2050/R (S.FR 700)
Works on paper
£271 $462 €396 Blanche (48x63cm-19x25in) s.i.d.86 mixed media board. 19-Nov-3 Fischer, Luzern #2051 (S.FR 600)

CASTELLI, Clemente (19/20th C) Italian
£440 $800 €642 Stodlden Pont de Kinn (28x46cm-11x18in) s. i.verso. 19-Jun-4 Harvey Clar, Oakland #2176

CASTELLI, Luciano (1951-) Swiss
£350 $602 €500 Portrait (100x70cm-39x28in) acrylic. 3-Dec-3 Tajan, Paris #487
£699 $1202 €1000 Die sonne macht geil (100x80cm-39x31in) s.verso prov. 3-Dec-3 Tajan, Paris #486
£1534 $2760 €2300 Les deux amies (100x80cm-39x31in) s.d.1989 oil wax crayon prov. 26-Apr-4 Tajan, Paris #252/R est:1800-2000
£2667 $4853 €4000 Nu (157x213cm-62x84in) s. acrylic paper on canvas. 29-Jun-4 Cornette de St.Cyr, Paris #110/R est:4000-4500
£3000 $5370 €4500 The sun makes you horny (100x80cm-39x31in) s.d. verso i. stretcher prov. 14-May-4 Ketterer, Munich #266/R est:3500-4500
£6133 $11163 €9200 Portrait de Salome (123x167cm-48x66in) s.d.1982 acrylic paper exhib. 5-Jul-4 Le Mouel, Paris #73/R est:10000-12000

Works on paper
£1810 $3131 €2643 Portrait of a woman (74x55cm-29x22in) s.d.2000 W/C prov. 9-Dec-3 Sotheby's, Zurich #137/R est:5000-6000 (S.FR 4000)
£6000 $10020 €8760 Nackter roken 2 (200x70cm-79x28in) s.d.85 W/C pencil prov. 22-Oct-3 Christie's, London #40/R est:4000-6000
£8392 $14266 €12000 Double portrait (240x200cm-94x79in) s.i.d.79 mixed media cotton. 29-Nov-3 Villa Grisebach, Berlin #379/R est:8000-12000

CASTELLO, Giovanni Battista (1547-1637) Italian
Works on paper
£1944 $3500 €2838 Crucifixion. Saint Lawrence (11x8cm-4x3in) bodycol htd gold oval pair. 22-Jan-4 Christie's, Rockefeller NY #28/R est:4000-6000

CASTELLO, Giovanni Battista (attrib) (1547-1637) Italian
Works on paper
£2200 $4026 €3212 Madonna and Child holding a bird and fruit (14x12cm-6x5in) i. bodycol htd gold on vellum. 6-Jul-4 Christie's, London #34/R est:1500-2000
£2632 $4842 €4000 Christ's birth with allegory of Passion (22x17cm-9x7in) gouache vellum on board. 22-Jun-4 Sotheby's, Milan #84/R est:2500-3500

CASTELLO, Jacopo da (attrib) (1637-1712) Flemish/Italian
£6525 $10571 €9200 Still life with hare (79x65cm-31x26in) 21-May-3 Artcurial Briest, Paris #314/R est:6000-8000

CASTELLO, Valerio (1625-1659) Italian
Works on paper
£6463 $11568 €9500 Une femme marchant, un vase au premier plan (20x14cm-8x6in) i.verso pen brown ink wash htd white. 18-Mar-4 Christie's, Paris #61/R est:1500-2000

CASTELLO, Valerio (attrib) (1625-1659) Italian
Works on paper
£1408 $2437 €2000 Venus et Vulcain (13x19cm-5x7in) i. pen brown ink wash htd gouache. 12-Dec-3 Renaud, Paris #12/R est:2000

CASTELLO, Vianna di (19th C) Italian
£284 $518 €426 Portrait of a Spanish general (71x55cm-28x22in) s.d.1883. 19-Jun-4 Rasmussen, Havnen #2206 (D.KR 3200)

CASTELLON, Federico (1914-1971) American
£236 $425 €345 Reels (26x22cm-10x9in) s. masonite painted 1968. 22-Jan-4 Swann Galleries, New York #125
£16304 $30000 €23804 Untitled. album of 50 paintings and dr. 10-Jun-4 Swann Galleries, New York #57/R est:7000-10000
Works on paper
£598 $1100 €873 Scarecrow (23x36cm-9x14in) s.i. col pastel. 10-Jun-4 Swann Galleries, New York #55/R

CASTELLS CAPURRO, Enrique (1913-1987) Uruguayan
Works on paper
£244 $400 €356 Horses (30x47cm-12x19in) s.d.65 ink. 3-Jun-3 Galeria y Remates, Montevideo #8
£265 $450 €387 Taming (43x60cm-17x24in) s.d.50 ink W/C. 20-Nov-3 Galeria y Remates, Montevideo #150/R
£353 $600 €515 Horses watering (24x30cm-9x12in) s. W/C ink. 25-Nov-3 Galeria y Remates, Montevideo #124
£381 $720 €556 Landscape (30x35cm-12x14in) s. mixed media. 22-Feb-4 Galeria y Remates, Montevideo #12/R
£463 $760 €676 Taming (29x43cm-11x17in) s.d.73 W/C. 3-Jun-3 Galeria y Remates, Montevideo #7
£543 $1000 €793 Back to the ranch (37x54cm-15x21in) s.d.80 ink W/C. 22-Jun-4 Galeria y Remates, Montevideo #154/R
£608 $1150 €888 Field scene (40x52cm-16x20in) s. mixed media. 22-Feb-4 Galeria y Remates, Montevideo #11/R
£1176 $2000 €1717 Maldonado defenders (28x51cm-11x20in) s. W/C ink. 25-Nov-3 Galeria y Remates, Montevideo #123/R

CASTELLUCCI, Kati (1905-1985) Italian
£2585 $4627 €3800 Portrait of girl with headscarf: self-portrait (51x41cm-20x16in) painted c.1940 exhib.lit. 22-Mar-4 Sant Agostino, Torino #505/R est:3800-4200

CASTEX, Simone (20th C) French
£432 $800 €631 Au pierrot gourmand (46x61cm-18x24in) s. canvasboard. 15-Jul-4 Doyle, New York #21/R

CASTIGLIONE, Giovanni Benedetto (1616-1670) Italian
£6338 $10204 €9000 Salome con la testa del Battista (124x95cm-49x37in) 8-May-3 Farsetti, Prato #320 est:11000-13000
£26846 $49396 €40000 Orpheus enchanting animals (126x101cm-50x40in) 24-Mar-4 Dorotheum, Vienna #88/R est:40000-60000
£67873 $115385 €99095 Flock of sheep with shepherds and sheepdog (72x81cm-28x32in) oval. 19-Nov-3 Fischer, Luzern #1026/R est:15000-18000 (S.FR 150000)
Prints
£1899 $3400 €2773 Circe changing Ulysse man into beasts (20x30cm-8x12in) etching executed c.1651. 6-May-4 Swann Galleries, New York #87/R est:2000-3000
£2000 $3580 €3000 Genius of the artist (36x24cm-14x9in) etching. 13-May-4 Bassenge, Berlin #5087 est:900
Works on paper
£24706 $42000 €36071 Classical figures afflicted by the plague (25x41cm-10x16in) pen ink sepia wash prov. 19-Nov-3 Bonhams & Butterfields, San Francisco #1/R

CASTIGLIONE, Giovanni Benedetto (attrib) (1616-1670) Italian
Works on paper
£550 $913 €803 Figures in a brutal struggle (43x56cm-17x22in) brown ink pencil wash. 3-Oct-3 Mallams, Oxford #91/R

CASTIGLIONE, Giovanni Benedetto (circle) (1616-1670) Italian
£6738 $11252 €9500 Il viaggio di Abramo (119x92cm-47x36in) 18-Jun-3 Christie's, Rome #451/R est:8000-12000

CASTIGLIONE, Giuseppe (1829-1908) Italian
£1324 $2250 €1933 View of the place Pigalle under snow (34x60cm-13x24in) s.i.d.Dec 1871 panel. 19-Nov-3 Bonhams & Butterfields, San Francisco #53/R
£1374 $2500 €2061 Young woman seated at a table with a quill pen in her hand (33x23cm-13x9in) board. 16-Jun-4 Wolf's, New York #487180/R est:3500-4500
£9859 $17056 €14000 In the painter's studio (70x106cm-28x42in) s. 9-Dec-3 Finarte Semenzato, Milan #93/R est:15000-16000

CASTIGLIONE, Giuseppe (attrib) (1829-1908) Italian
Works on paper
£92461 $166430 €134993 Still life of nandina berries and blooming wintersweet in vase (24x51cm-9x20in) s.d.1725 ink wash silk. 25-Apr-4 Sotheby's, Hong Kong #86/R est:800000-1200000 (HK.D 1300000)

CASTILLO Y SAAVEDRA, Antonio del (1603-1667) Spanish
Works on paper
£16901 $29239 €24000 Suite de quatorze vignettes a l'effigie des apotres (11x8cm-4x3in) mono. pen brown ink prov. 12-Dec-3 Renaud, Paris #107/R est:15000

CASTILLO, Carlos Alberto (20th C) Venezuelan?
£1139 $1800 €1663 And with other remembrances II (110x135cm-43x53in) s. painted 1987. 1-Dec-2 Subastas Odalys, Caracas #25/R est:2800

CASTILLO, Jorge (1933-) Spanish
£497 $900 €726 Perro degollado (61x91cm-24x36in) s.d.60 s.i.d.verso oil mixed media exhib. 2-Apr-4 Freeman, Philadelphia #55
£634 $1096 €900 Homme seul (60x50cm-24x20in) s.d.74 i. verso. 13-Dec-3 Lempertz, Koln #295/R
£733 $1335 €1100 Cine (63x79cm-25x31in) i. paper. 29-Jun-4 Segre, Madrid #217/R
£922 $1494 €1300 Muchachita (55x40cm-22x16in) s. 20-May-3 Ansorena, Madrid #376/R
£1184 $2179 €1800 Untitled (41x3cm-16x1in) s. 22-Jun-4 Durán, Madrid #98/R est:1800
£1184 $2179 €1800 Untitled (41x33cm-16x13in) s. 22-Jun-4 Durán, Madrid #99/R est:1800
£1560 $2528 €2200 Figures (41x33cm-16x13in) s. 20-May-3 Ansorena, Madrid #337/R est:1500
£1974 $3632 €3000 Acrobat (55x46cm-22x18in) s. 22-Jun-4 Durán, Madrid #145/R est:2500
£2083 $3437 €3000 Table with fruit and birds (64x81cm-25x32in) s. 2-Jul-3 Ansorena, Madrid #847/R
£2349 $4369 €3500 Banana (51x62cm-20x24in) painted 1978. 2-Mar-4 Ansorena, Madrid #833/R est:3500
£2536 $4159 €3500 Figure (63x81cm-25x32in) prov. 27-May-3 Durán, Madrid #295/R est:3500
£4333 $7887 €6500 Still life with fruit (122x75cm-48x30in) s.d.1962 panel. 29-Jun-4 Segre, Madrid #143/R est:6500
£6333 $11590 €9500 Garden in winter (150x150cm-59x59in) s.d.72 oil tempera chl wax prov.lit. 4-Jun-4 Lempertz, Koln #88/R est:9500
Works on paper
£330 $524 €475 Toro en la plaza (46x61cm-18x24in) s.d.60 gouache. 29-Apr-3 Durán, Madrid #720
£405 $714 €600 Scandal (28x38cm-11x15in) s.d.1960 ink pencil. 18-May-4 Segre, Madrid #227/R
£420 $713 €600 Barcelona (70x99cm-28x39in) s.i.d.1966 Indian ink wash board prov. 29-Nov-3 Villa Grisebach, Berlin #739/R
£448 $807 €650 Crucifixion (47x65cm-19x26in) s.d.1962 mixed media. 26-Jan-4 Ansorena, Madrid #875/R
£471 $772 €650 Composition (20x31cm-8x12in) s.d.53 gouache. 27-May-3 Durán, Madrid #26/R
£514 $950 €750 Untitled (52x75cm-20x30in) s.d.75 pencil W/C ink. 13-Jul-4 Christie's, Rockefeller NY #150/R
£629 $1070 €900 Leon, gato, serpente (38x65cm-15x26in) s.d.Dec 1970 i. verso Indian ink wash. 26-Nov-3 Dorotheum, Vienna #268/R
£828 $1374 €1200 Figures (58x76cm-23x30in) s.d.70. 30-Sep-3 Ansorena, Madrid #3/R
£1133 $2051 €1700 Elephant (95x65cm-37x26in) s.d.1963 ink wash. 30-Mar-4 Segre, Madrid #163/R est:1600
£1611 $2851 €2400 Marienza (150x150cm-59x59in) s.d. chl. 30-Apr-4 Dr Fritz Nagel, Stuttgart #762/R est:2400

CASTILLO, Marcos (1897-1966) Venezuelan
£1097 $1700 €1602 Landscape (24x19cm-9x7in) s. 3-Nov-2 Subastas Odalys, Caracas #64/R
£1473 $2710 €2151 Still life (35x45cm-14x18in) s. cardboard. 28-Mar-4 Subastas Odalys, Caracas #32/R
£1497 $2500 €2186 Figure (27x22cm-11x9in) s. painted 1956. 19-Oct-3 Subastas Odalys, Caracas #64/R est:6000
£3935 $6100 €5745 Sunflowers (50x40cm-20x16in) s. exhib. 3-Nov-2 Subastas Odalys, Caracas #31/R
£4430 $7000 €6468 Still life (39x48cm-15x19in) s. el. 1-Dec-2 Subastas Odalys, Caracas #21/R
£4476 $7475 €6535 Roses (37x49cm-15x19in) s. masonite painted 1951. 13-Jul-3 Subastas Odalys, Caracas #114/R est:9000

£5416 $9045 €7907 Still life (33x45cm-13x18in) s. masonite painted 1947. 19-Oct-3 Subastas Odalys, Caracas #54/R est:8000
£5934 $9910 €8664 Untitled (42x49cm-17x19in) s. 13-Jul-3 Subastas Odalys, Caracas #70/R est:12000
£6453 $10970 €9421 Flowers (39x29cm-15x11in) s. canvas on board. 23-Nov-3 Subastas Odalys, Caracas #141/R est:9000
Works on paper
£353 $600 €515 Figures (24x20cm-9x8in) s. chl. 23-Nov-3 Subastas Odalys, Caracas #23/R

CASTLE, Barry (20th C) British
£1757 $3320 €2600 Punch and Judy show (64x39cm-25x15in) s.d.1975 panel exhib. 17-Feb-4 Whyte's, Dublin #242/R est:2000-3000
£2222 $3622 €3200 Elsie and Pal (45x53cm-18x21in) init.d.79 board. 24-Sep-3 James Adam, Dublin #75/R est:3000-5000
Works on paper
£1667 $2717 €2400 Woman with leeks and flowers (76x56cm-30x22in) init.d.91 W/C. 23-Sep-3 De Veres Art Auctions, Dublin #276/R est:2000-3000

CASTLE, G (19th C) British?
£1272 $2200 €1857 Hunter (66x53cm-26x21in) s.d.1865. 13-Dec-3 Charlton Hall, Columbia #356/R est:1000-1500

CASTLEDEN, George Frederick (1869-1945) American/British
£719 $1200 €1050 Broken levee (46x56cm-18x22in) s.d.36 i.verso. 20-Jun-3 Freeman, Philadelphia #176/R

CASTONGUAY, Claudette (1949-) Canadian
£260 $476 €380 Le fiance de Marie-Louise (35x45cm-14x18in) s.i.d.1992 acrylic. 1-Jun-4 Hodgins, Calgary #287/R (C.D 650)
£279 $505 €407 Clara (30x30cm-12x12in) s.d.2003 i.verso acrylic prov. 18-Apr-4 Levis, Calgary #435/R (C.D 675)
£400 $732 €584 Pour la fete (100x75cm-39x30in) s.d.2003 acrylic. 1-Jun-4 Joyner Waddington, Toronto #209/R (C.D 1000)
£400 $732 €584 Le jardin d'Antonio (60x75cm-24x30in) s.i.d.2003. 1-Jun-4 Hodgins, Calgary #311/R (C.D 1000)
£1250 $2150 €1825 Rendez-vous au marche de fleurs (75x100cm-30x39in) s.d.2003. 2-Dec-3 Joyner Waddington, Toronto #211/R est:1500-2000 (C.D 2800)

CASTONGUAY, Gerard (1933-) Canadian
£400 $664 €584 Fleurs d'etageres (51x51cm-20x20in) s. s.i.verso. 5-Oct-3 Levis, Calgary #17/R (C.D 900)

CASTRES, Edouard (1838-1902) Swiss
£431 $772 €629 Two cows with wine barrel on cart (35x57cm-14x22in) s. 12-May-4 Dobiaschofsky, Bern #382/R (S.FR 1000)
£1922 $3440 €2806 In the Japanese Garden (35x27cm-14x11in) s. panel. 25-May-4 Bukowskis, Stockholm #346/R est:30000-40000 (S.KR 26000)

CASTRES, Edouard Gaspard (1881-1964) Swiss
£238 $426 €347 Still life of fish (30x41cm-12x16in) s.d.1943 masonite. 22-Mar-4 Philippe Schuler, Zurich #6006 (S.FR 550)

CASTRO ORTEGA, Pedro (1956-) Spanish
£467 $845 €700 Shades VII (80x99cm-31x39in) s.i.d.1998 verso oil collage. 30-Mar-4 Segre, Madrid #169/R
£733 $1327 €1100 Unlikely river reflections (100x100cm-39x39in) s.i.d.1994 verso oil acrylic paint. 30-Mar-4 Segre, Madrid #174/R

CASTRO, Amilcar de (1920-2002) Brazilian
£3297 $5835 €4946 Untitled (80x120cm-31x47in) acrylic. 27-Apr-4 Bolsa de Arte, Rio de Janeiro #120/R (B.R 18000)
£4212 $7709 €6318 Untitled (60x99cm-24x39in) s.d.1995 verso acrylic. 6-Jul-4 Bolsa de Arte, Rio de Janeiro #163/R (B.R 23000)
£4945 $8753 €7418 Untitled (125x184cm-49x72in) acrylic. 27-Apr-4 Bolsa de Arte, Rio de Janeiro #119/R (B.R 27000)
Sculpture
£5311 $9401 €7967 Untitled (44x42cm-17x17in) s. iron. 27-Apr-4 Bolsa de Arte, Rio de Janeiro #93/R (B.R 29000)

CASTRO, Fabian de (1868-?) Spanish
£1000 $1810 €1500 Portrait de femme (113x98cm-44x39in) s.d.1929. 5-Apr-4 Marie & Robert, Paris #6/R est:1500-2000

CASTRO, Geraldo F (20th C) Brazilian
£481 $900 €702 Fishing boats. Village (48x61cm-19x24in) s. one d.1964 one i.d.1967 pair. 25-Feb-4 Doyle, New York #87/R
£773 $1400 €1129 Boston Harbour (48x58cm-19x23in) s.d.1964. 16-Apr-4 James Julia, Fairfield #624m/R est:1000-1500

CASTRO, Laureys A (attrib) (17th C) French
£13187 $24000 €19253 Port town with ships on the high seas. Fishing boats in rough seas offshore (72x110cm-28x43in) pair. 4-Feb-4 Christie's, Rockefeller NY #68/R est:6000-8000

CASTRO, Leon Pedro (20th C) Venezuelan
£391 $625 €571 Landscape (69x57cm-27x22in) s. 21-Sep-3 Subastas Odalys, Caracas #81/R
£454 $835 €663 Vase of flowers (55x47cm-22x19in) s. 28-Mar-4 Subastas Odalys, Caracas #49/R
£645 $1000 €942 Untitled (60x50cm-24x20in) s. 3-Nov-2 Subastas Odalys, Caracas #24/R

CASTRO, Lorenzo (17th C) Spanish
£45000 $76500 €65700 English fourth rate arriving off Genoa, with another lager English man-o-war already at anchor (100x119cm-39x47in) s. 25-Nov-3 Christie's, London #77/R est:35000-50000

CASTRO, Lorenzo (attrib) (17th C) Spanish
£3200 $5632 €4672 A Barbary gallery and British shipping off a Mediterranean port (61x91cm-24x36in) 18-May-4 Woolley & Wallis, Salisbury #107/R est:3000-5000

CASTRO, Sergio de (1922-) Argentinian
£647 $1157 €945 Bouteille et fruits (46x64cm-18x25in) s. i. verso exhib. 12-May-4 Dobiaschofsky, Bern #383/R est:2000 (S.FR 1500)
£1056 $1827 €1500 Ville arabe (73x73cm-29x29in) s. s.i.verso exhib. 15-Dec-3 Charbonneaux, Paris #187/R est:2500
£1208 $2247 €1800 Terre Crecque (38x61cm-15x24in) s. 3-Mar-4 Artcurial Briest, Paris #335/R est:1000-1200
£1831 $3168 €2600 Nature morte (73x92cm-29x36in) s. s.i.verso exhib. 15-Dec-3 Charbonneaux, Paris #186/R est:4000
Works on paper
£369 $687 €550 Vue de l'atelier (30x21cm-12x8in) s.d.3.3.76 gouache. 3-Mar-4 Artcurial Briest, Paris #334

CASTRO-CID, Enrique (1937-1992) Chilean
£237 $425 €346 Mechanical hips, mechanical heart (41x30cm-16x12in) s.d.1963 oil collage prov. 16-May-4 Wright, Chicago #375/R

CAT, Roland (1943-) French
Works on paper
£658 $1211 €1000 Belle Soiree (25x32cm-10x13in) s.i.d.1993 mixed media board. 28-Jun-4 Joron-Derem, Paris #198/R

CATALAN SCHOOL (15th C) Spanish
£16000 $27680 €23360 Crucifixion (117x104cm-46x41in) panel. 12-Dec-3 Christie's, Kensington #144/R est:15000-25000
£16800 $29064 €24528 Saint Florian (154x89cm-61x35in) tempera gold ground panel. 9-Dec-3 Sotheby's, Olympia #377/R est:5000-7000

CATALAN, Ramos (20th C) South American
£351 $650 €512 South American mountain landscape (74x94cm-29x37in) s. 10-Mar-4 Doyle, New York #14/R
£430 $800 €628 Majestic mountain range (73x95cm-29x37in) s. 5-Mar-4 Skinner, Boston #525/R

CATANI, Giuseppe (1866-?) Italian
Works on paper
£852 $1500 €1244 Celebration of prosperity (36x62cm-14x24in) s.i.d.1887 pencil W/C htd white gold gilt. 18-May-4 Bonhams & Butterfields, San Francisco #63/R est:2000-3000

CATARSINI, Alfredo (1899-1993) Italian
£493 $818 €700 Dopo la pesca (50x70cm-20x28in) s.d.1956 panel. 14-Jun-3 Meeting Art, Vercelli #166

CATEL, Franz Ludwig (1778-1856) German
£17241 $28793 €25000 Gulf of Naples and Vesuvius (24x36cm-9x14in) paper on board prov. 15-Nov-3 Lempertz, Koln #1592/R est:25000
Works on paper
£406 $650 €593 Two figures in interior (20x13cm-8x5in) s. W/C pencil. 20-Sep-3 Sloans & Kenyon, Bethesda #105/R
£699 $1168 €1000 Sailing regatta in Berlin (8x17cm-3x7in) s.i.d.1841 W/C Indian ink. 10-Oct-3 Winterberg, Heidelberg #553/R

CATENE, Gian Gherardo delle (attrib) (16th C) Italian
£19718 $32732 €28000 Saint Jerome praying (16x12cm-6x5in) board. 11-Jul-3 Finarte, Venice #549/R est:30000-35000

CATHCART, Kay (20th C) British
£223 $400 €326 Trawlers at rest, Torbay (36x61cm-14x24in) s. masonite. 20-Mar-4 Sloans & Kenyon, Bethesda #339/R

CATHELIN, Bernard (1919-) French
£3226 $6000 €4710 Vase of flowers (33x38cm-13x15in) s.d.1963 board. 7-Mar-4 Treadway Gallery, Cincinnati #706/R est:3000-5000
£3235 $5500 €4723 Bouquet au paysage d'Hiver (99x74cm-39x29in) s. 11-Nov-3 Lincoln, Orange #484
£3779 $6500 €5517 Les pivoines blanches (92x60cm-36x24in) s. s.i.d.Mai 1968 verso prov. 3-Dec-3 Doyle, New York #9/R est:12000-18000
£10000 $18200 €14600 Bouquet au paysage d'hiver (100x65cm-39x26in) s.d.68 s.d.verso prov. 4-Feb-4 Sotheby's, London #343/R est:8000-12000

CATHERINE, Norman (1949-) South African
£826 $1478 €1206 Last Rites (102cm-40in) s.d.1989 acrylic canvas wood metal. 31-May-4 Stephan Welz, Johannesburg #586/R (SA.R 10000)
£1638 $2735 €2391 Head of a man with cat (61x61cm-24x24in) s.d.2002. 20-Oct-3 Stephan Welz, Johannesburg #375/R est:10000-15000 (SA.R 19000)
£2064 $3695 €3013 Decoy (55x64cm-22x25in) s.d.1999. 31-May-4 Stephan Welz, Johannesburg #618/R est:20000-25000 (SA.R 25000)
£2477 $4434 €3616 Bird man (59x59cm-23x23in) s.d.1991 i. verso. 31-May-4 Stephan Welz, Johannesburg #592/R est:25000-35000 (SA.R 30000)
£4138 $6910 €6041 Secret meeting (80x121cm-31x48in) s.d.93 board prov. 20-Oct-3 Stephan Welz, Johannesburg #396/R est:50000-70000 (SA.R 48000)

Sculpture
£2500 $4175 €3650 Truth. Consequence (40cm-16in) s. wood enamel paint two. 20-Oct-3 Stephan Welz, Johannesburg #400/R est:12000-16000 (SA.R 29000)
Works on paper
£470 $799 €686 Trainer (46x60cm-18x24in) s.i.d.1986 brush ink gouache. 4-Nov-3 Stephan Welz, Johannesburg #660/R est:5000-8000 (SA.R 5500)
£560 $936 €818 Red blood (50x46cm-20x18in) s.i.d.80 airbrush over pencil. 20-Oct-3 Stephan Welz, Johannesburg #374/R est:8000-12000 (SA.R 6500)
£603 $1008 €880 Colourblind (35x28cm-14x11in) s.i.d.76 airbrush. 20-Oct-3 Stephan Welz, Johannesburg #422/R est:5000-7000 (SA.R 7000)
£2155 $3599 €3146 Unidentified (139x120cm-55x47in) s.d.1993 pastel exhib.lit. 20-Oct-3 Stephan Welz, Johannesburg #388/R est:25000-30000 (SA.R 25000)

CATLIN, Christopher Herbert Henry (1902-) British
£750 $1320 €1095 Crowd (29x84cm-11x33in) s. 19-May-4 Sotheby's, Olympia #190/R

CATLIN, Gail (1948-) South African?
Works on paper
£684 $1162 €999 Portrait of a woman (67x57cm-26x22in) mixed media on board. 4-Nov-3 Stephan Welz, Johannesburg #656/R est:10000-15000 (SA.R 8000)

CATLIN, George (1796-1872) American
£22727 $40000 €33181 Ostrich Chase, Buenos Aires (49x68cm-19x27in) s.d.1857 prov. 18-May-4 Christie's, Rockefeller NY #50/R est:40000-60000
£40761 $75000 €59511 Deer hunting by moonlight (48x67cm-19x26in) prov.exhib.lit. 8-Jun-4 Bonhams & Butterfields, San Francisco #4117/R est:80000-120000

CATOIRE, Gustave Albert (19th C) French
£265 $482 €400 Paysanne a l'oree du bois (65x54cm-26x21in) s. 19-Jun-4 Gerard, Besancon #42a

CATS, Jacob (1741-1799) Dutch
£1379 $2552 €2000 Landscape with man on white horse (24x32cm-9x13in) s.d.179. 14-Feb-4 Hans Stahl, Hamburg #175/R est:2000
Works on paper
£1020 $1827 €1500 Le berger et son chien (18x25cm-7x10in) s.d.1799 verso grey wash. 17-Mar-4 Maigret, Paris #30/R est:900-1200
£1712 $2911 €2500 Summer landscape with fisherman and other figures by a farm (10x7cm-4x3in) i. pen black ink W/C over black chk prov.exhib. 4-Nov-3 Sotheby's, Amsterdam #87/R est:2500-3500
£2222 $4000 €3244 Extensive hilly landscape with figures carrying baskets (19x26cm-7x10in) s.d.1777 verso black chk pen black ink grey wash. 22-Jan-4 Christie's, Rockefeller NY #209/R est:4000-6000
£2500 $4500 €3650 Landscape with a traveler resting by a road, farmhouse beyond (14x19cm-6x7in) s.d.1772 verso brush ink wash over black chk prov. 21-Jan-4 Sotheby's, New York #135/R est:4000-6000
£2603 $4425 €3800 Winter landscape with skaters (10x7cm-4x3in) i.verso pen black brown ink W/C over black chk prov.exhib. 4-Nov-3 Sotheby's, Amsterdam #88/R est:2500-3500
£2778 $5000 €4056 Cattle at a pond in a landscape. Woman with cattle crossing a bridge (17x23cm-7x9in) s. one d.1795 verso one d.1780 verso black chk pen ink pair. 22-Jan-4 Christie's, Rockefeller NY #208/R est:4000-6000

CATTANEO, Achille (1872-1931) Italian
£235 $432 €350 Rainy day (22x15cm-9x6in) s. board. 24-Mar-4 Il Ponte, Milan #668
£333 $613 €500 Village street (32x21cm-13x8in) s.d.916 board. 8-Jun-4 Della Rocca, Turin #365/R
£467 $859 €700 Church interior (60x80cm-24x31in) s.d.919. 8-Jun-4 Della Rocca, Turin #368/R
£671 $1188 €1000 Venice (43x57cm-17x22in) s. board. 1-May-4 Meeting Art, Vercelli #197
£1007 $1802 €1500 Venetian arcade with figures (70x90cm-28x35in) s. 25-May-4 Finarte Semenzato, Milan #21/R est:1500-1700
£1087 $1783 €1500 Naviglio at Porta Romana, Milan (60x50cm-24x20in) s. board lit. 27-May-3 Finarte Semenzato, Milan #22/R

CATTANEO, Alvaro (1938-) Italian
£408 $743 €600 Bike shadow (30x40cm-12x16in) s. 6-Feb-4 Galleria Rosenberg, Milan #160/R
£476 $867 €700 Lombard love (30x40cm-12x16in) s. 6-Feb-4 Galleria Rosenberg, Milan #28/R

CATTANEO, Giuseppe (1929-) Italian
£905 $1512 €1321 Lyrical flight (60x79cm-24x31in) s.d.1960 oil gold leaf on paper exhib. 20-Oct-3 Stephan Welz, Johannesburg #414 est:5000-8000 (SA.R 10500)

CATTAPAN, Jon (1956-) Australian
£391 $708 €571 Cat desire (60x45cm-24x18in) s.d.86 s.i.verso. 30-Mar-4 Lawson Menzies, Sydney #47 est:1000-2000 (A.D 950)
£426 $736 €622 Thermometer (45x65cm-18x26in) s.d.85 i.verso. 10-Dec-3 Shapiro, Sydney #96 (A.D 1000)
£1229 $1942 €1794 Cameraman, St Kilda (91x121cm-36x48in) s.d.91. 2-Sep-3 Deutscher-Menzies, Melbourne #189/R est:3500-4500 (A.D 3000)
£4065 $6382 €5894 Rising group (198x168cm-78x66in) s.i.d.2001 verso linen prov. 26-Aug-3 Christie's, Sydney #23/R est:10000-15000 (A.D 10000)

CATTELAN, Maurizo (1960-) Italian
£40000 $66800 €58400 Senza titolo, zorro (70x70cm-28x28in) acrylic prov. 21-Oct-3 Christie's, London #72/R est:40000-60000
Photographs
£8939 $16000 €13051 Untitled, black star (40x60cm-16x24in) black white photo edition of six prov.lit. 14-May-4 Phillips, New York #168/R est:15000-20000
£95808 $160000 €139880 Untitled (183x228cm-72x90in) cibachrome print exec 1999 prov.lit. 12-Nov-3 Christie's, Rockefeller NY #521/R est:60000-80000
Sculpture
£1678 $2853 €2400 Untitled (17x23x17cm-7x9x7in) s.i.d.91 whistle plexiglas card. 24-Nov-3 Christie's, Milan #11/R est:2200-2500
£2000 $3680 €3000 Partner (32x23cm-13x9in) s.i.d.90 T-shirt plastic. 11-Jun-4 Farsetti, Prato #93/R est:2100-2400
£3378 $5946 €5000 Fragment (5x5x2cm-2x2x1in) s. glass exec.1992 lit. 24-May-4 Christie's, Milan #229/R est:5000-7000
£17964 $30000 €26227 Strategies (76x81x21cm-30x32x8in) 15 flash art magazines metal adhesive in eight parts prov. 14-Nov-3 Phillips, New York #123/R est:35000-45000
£122905 $220000 €179441 Untitled - cow (230x140x160cm-91x55x63in) taxidermied cow handlebars from a Vespa motor scooter. 13-May-4 Phillips, New York #52/R est:200000-300000
£131737 $220000 €192336 Untitled (71x38x37cm-28x15x15in) dog skeleton le monde newspaper executed 1997 prov. 13-Nov-3 Phillips, New York #4/R est:200000-300000
£145251 $260000 €212066 Untitled (161x54x16cm-63x21x6in) plexiglas stainless steel neon light executed 1997 prov.exhib.lit. 13-May-4 Phillips, New York #48/R est:120000-180000
£173184 $310000 €252849 Mini-me (37x21x27cm-15x8x11in) resin rubber hair paint executed 1999 prov.exhib.lit. 13-May-4 Phillips, New York #8/R est:200000-250000
£197605 $330000 €288503 Spermini - little sperms (17x8x10cm-7x3x4in) 250 painted latex masks executed 1997 prov.exhib.lit. 13-Nov-3 Phillips, New York #42/R est:300000-400000
£1033520 $1850000 €1508939 Ballad of Trotsky. taxidermied horse leather saddlery rope pulley prov.exhib.lit. 12-May-4 Sotheby's, New York #12/R est:600000-800000
Works on paper
£2994 $5000 €4371 Untitled (24x32cm-9x13in) s.d.94 pen silver on xerox mounted on plexiglas prov. 14-Nov-3 Phillips, New York #122/R est:8000-12000
£7333 $13493 €11000 Ten party story (16x22cm-6x9in) card exec.1998. 14-Jun-4 Porro, Milan #55/R est:12000-15000
£13000 $21710 €18980 Daily grammar (34x25cm-13x10in) s.d.89 verso mixed media cardboard prov.exhib.lit. 20-Oct-3 Sotheby's, London #50/R est:15000

CATTELAN, Maurizo and MANFRIN (20th C) Italian
Works on paper
£2395 $4000 €3497 Comic strip (24x33cm-9x13in) s. s.d.95 verso graphite prov. 14-Nov-3 Phillips, New York #121/R est:7000-9000

CATTERMOLE, Charles (1832-1900) British
£430 $684 €628 Scene in a medieval hall with a jester entertaining a nobleman and court (15x45cm-6x18in) s. 18-Mar-3 Anderson & Garland, Newcastle #216/R
Works on paper
£260 $484 €380 Cavaliers before a tent, one writing a note on a drum (26x37cm-10x15in) s. W/C. 2-Mar-4 Bamfords, Derby #399
£300 $519 €438 Thursday at the Abbey (73x103cm-29x41in) s. W/C. 9-Dec-3 Rosebery Fine Art, London #605
£360 $659 €526 Royal procession (14x44cm-6x17in) s. W/C. 7-Apr-4 Bonhams, Bury St Edmunds #392
£420 $727 €613 Breaking through, a scene from the English Civil War (30x61cm-12x24in) s. W/C bodycol htd white. 11-Dec-3 Neales, Nottingham #532a

CATTERMOLE, Charles (attrib) (1832-1900) British
£500 $875 €730 Sleeping Knight, thieves stealing her armour, cleric listening at the door (51x76cm-20x30in) 18-Dec-3 John Nicholson, Haslemere #1173

CATTERMOLE, George (1800-1868) British
Works on paper
£250 $468 €365 Grandfathers favourite (22x15cm-9x6in) mono. W/C bodycol. 20-Jul-4 Sworder & Son, Bishops Stortford #761/R
£283 $525 €413 The battle, scene with monks, fire, man in armour and young boy (30x41cm-12x16in) mono. W/C. 16-Jan-4 Aspire, Cleveland #122/R
£284 $525 €415 The saucy page (25x38cm-10x15in) W/C. 16-Jan-4 Aspire, Cleveland #123/R
£360 $598 €526 Figures beneath the wall of a castle (48x36cm-19x14in) mono. W/C htd white. 2-Oct-3 Neales, Nottingham #663
£442 $791 €650 The surprise (32x26cm-13x10in) mono. W/C gouache. 17-Mar-4 Maigret, Paris #5/R
£680 $1218 €1000 The Darnley Conspirators (22x54cm-9x21in) W/C gouache. 17-Mar-4 Maigret, Paris #4/R

CATTERMOLE, Leonardo F G (19th C) British
Works on paper
£320 $579 €467 English civil war scene (79x53cm-31x21in) s. W/C bodycol. 17-Apr-4 Dickins, Middle Claydon #15

CATTI, Aurelio (19th C) Italian
£498 $831 €727 Continental street scene (49x90cm-19x35in) s. 17-Nov-3 Waddingtons, Toronto #262/R (C.D 1100)
Works on paper
£267 $461 €390 Windy day (48x33cm-19x13in) s. W/C. 9-Dec-3 Pinneys, Montreal #75 (C.D 600)
£267 $461 €390 After the rain (48x33cm-19x13in) s. W/C. 9-Dec-3 Pinneys, Montreal #42 (C.D 600)
£800 $1472 €1200 Landscape along the alleys (64x50cm-25x20in) s. W/C card. 10-Jun-4 Christie's, Rome #52/R
£845 $1462 €1200 Paris streets with carriages (48x33cm-19x13in) s. W/C. 9-Dec-3 Finarte Semenzato, Milan #70/R
£915 $1584 €1300 Street in Paris with trees (48x33cm-19x13in) s. W/C. 9-Dec-3 Finarte Semenzato, Milan #69/R est:1200-1300

CATTON, Charles (18/19th C) British
£599 $1000 €875 Gathering ice (33x43cm-13x17in) s.d.1797. 16-Nov-3 Simpson's, Houston #182

CATTRANI, Baldassare (18th C) ?
Works on paper
£100000 $185000 €146000 Botanical drawings (66x51cm-26x20in) W/C bodycol vellum exec.c.1800 thirty-five album. 15-Jul-4 Bonhams, New Bond Street #11/R est:100000-150000

CATUSCO, Louis (20th C) American
Works on paper
£882 $1500 €1288 Corridor II (66x84cm-26x33in) s. mixed media. 9-Nov-3 Wright, Chicago #262 est:2000-3000

CATY, H (20th C) Belgian?
£1448 $2679 €2100 Beaute orientale (100x90cm-39x35in) s.d.1942. 19-Jan-4 Horta, Bruxelles #71 est:1200-1500

CAUCHIE, Paul (1875-1952) Belgian
£699 $1168 €1000 Le calvaire (88x88cm-35x35in) s. panel. 13-Oct-3 Horta, Bruxelles #385
Works on paper
£676 $1277 €1000 Berger et moutons (90x70cm-35x28in) s.d.1932 gouache. 17-Feb-4 Galerie Moderne, Brussels #128/R

CAUCHOIS, Eugène-Henri (1850-1911) French
£667 $1227 €1000 Fleurs des champs dans un vase et cerises (40x32cm-16x13in) s. 14-Jun-4 Tajan, Paris #31
£699 $1168 €1000 Vase of flowers (15x12cm-6x5in) s. panel. 29-Jun-3 Eric Pillon, Calais #24/R
£810 $1401 €1150 Vase de fleurs (15x22cm-6x9in) s. panel. 14-Dec-3 Eric Pillon, Calais #7/R
£828 $1531 €1200 Bouquet de fleurs (40x31cm-16x12in) s. 16-Feb-4 Giraudeau, Tours #62
£903 $1417 €1300 Nature morte aux moules et crevettes (40x50cm-16x20in) s. 26-Aug-3 Galerie Moderne, Brussels #228/R
£1418 $2369 €2000 Vase de fleurs et fruits (46x31cm-18x12in) s. panel. 19-Oct-3 Anaf, Lyon #73/R est:1500-2000
£1549 $2572 €2200 Flowers in basket (46x55cm-18x22in) 16-Jun-3 Dorotheum, Vienna #164/R est:2200-2600
£1579 $2858 €2400 Panier de fleurs (12x27cm-5x11in) s. panel. 19-Apr-4 Boscher, Cherbourg #806/R est:2500
£1818 $3091 €2600 Les locomotives (35x50cm-14x20in) s. 27-Nov-3 Millon & Associes, Paris #130/R est:1200-1500
£2041 $3653 €3000 Nature morte a la pie (69x104cm-27x41in) s. 17-Mar-4 Hotel des Ventes Mosan, Brussels #103/R est:3500-4500
£2060 $3750 €3008 Still life with flowers, book and fan (51x76cm-20x30in) s. panel. 29-Jun-4 Sotheby's, New York #89/R est:4000-6000
£2410 $4000 €3519 Bouquet of roses and vase on a draped table (46x55cm-18x22in) s. 30-Sep-3 Christie's, Rockefeller NY #441/R est:5000-7000
£2473 $4500 €3611 Floral still life with porcelain plate (61x48cm-24x19in) s. 7-Feb-4 Neal Auction Company, New Orleans #91/R est:7000-10000
£2533 $4636 €3800 Jetee de roses (30x38cm-12x15in) s. panel. 6-Jun-4 Osenat, Fontainebleau #83/R est:3800-4000
£2797 $4811 €4000 Vase aux fleurs des champs (46x38cm-18x15in) s. 7-Dec-3 Osenat, Fontainebleau #223 est:2800-3000
£3000 $4980 €4380 Private moment (152x151cm-60x59in) s. 1-Oct-3 Sotheby's, Olympia #233/R est:2000-3000
£3000 $5400 €4380 Still life of flowers (54x65cm-21x26in) s. 21-Jan-4 Sotheby's, Olympia #500/R est:3000-4000
£3264 $5451 €4700 Le bouquet de fleurs renverse (54x61cm-21x24in) s. 22-Oct-3 Ribeyre & Baron, Paris #24/R est:3500-4000
£3333 $5567 €4700 Bouquet de pavots (66x81cm-26x32in) s. 15-Oct-3 Claude Aguttes, Neuilly #28/R est:3500-4500
£3400 $6222 €5100 Bouquet tricolore (56x46cm-22x18in) s. 6-Jun-4 Osenat, Fontainebleau #78/R est:5000-5500
£4218 $7550 €6200 Bouquet de fleurs sur en entablement (54x65cm-21x26in) s. 19-Mar-4 Millon & Associes, Paris #35/R est:3000-3500
£5435 $8913 €7500 Le bouquet champetre, le bouquet de violettes (46x55cm-18x22in) s. 11-May-3 Osenat, Fontainebleau #174/R est:7500-8000
£5617 $10055 €8201 The flower basket (81x115cm-32x45in) s. panel prov. 25-May-4 Bukowskis, Stockholm #381/R est:30000-35000 (S.KR 76000)
£6818 $12000 €9954 Floral still life (38x43cm-15x17in) s. painted c.1890. 22-May-4 New Orleans Auction, New Orleans #567/R est:6000-9000
£8333 $15000 €12166 Floral still life with grapes and pomegranates (100x81cm-39x32in) s. prov. 23-Apr-4 Sotheby's, New York #179/R est:20000-30000

CAUER, Emil (19th C) German
Sculpture
£1181 $1924 €1700 Standing female nude (40cm-16in) s.i.d.1918 dark pat.bronze Cast.Lauchhammer. 25-Sep-3 Dr Fritz Nagel, Stuttgart #1577/R est:2000

CAULA, Sigismondo (attrib) (1637-1713) Italian
Works on paper
£464 $850 €677 Grotesques in profile (15x12cm-6x5in) brush red ink wash pair. 29-Jan-4 Swann Galleries, New York #81/R
£3611 $6500 €5272 Madonna and Child with St. John the Baptist and a donor (25x20cm-10x8in) black chk brush wash htd white squared for transfer. 21-Jan-4 Sotheby's, New York #81/R est:4000-6000

CAULAERT, J van (1897-1979) French
£2348 $4250 €3428 Pink hat, pink gloves (86x53cm-34x21in) s.d.38 prov. 30-Mar-4 Sotheby's, New York #361/R est:2000-3000

CAULFIELD, Patrick (1936-) British
£19000 $34770 €27740 Image for the past (49x71cm-19x28in) s.i.verso board. 4-Jun-4 Christie's, London #115/R est:4000-6000
£165000 $301950 €240900 Window at night (204x152cm-80x60in) painted 1969 prov.exhib.lit. 4-Jun-4 Christie's, London #116/R est:25000-35000

CAULLERY, Louis de (16/17th C) French/Flemish
£10345 $17172 €15000 Calvary (40x56cm-16x22in) board. 30-Sep-3 Ansorena, Madrid #49/R est:15000
£11207 $20060 €16362 Garden of love (52x66cm-20x26in) panel. 13-May-4 Stuker, Bern #62/R est:30000-40000 (S.FR 26000)
£12766 $20681 €18000 Camino del Calvario (40x56cm-16x22in) panel. 20-May-3 Ansorena, Madrid #87/R est:18000
£20134 $37450 €30000 Bacchanal (41x56cm-16x22in) board. 2-Mar-4 Ansorena, Madrid #298/R est:19000

CAULLERY, Louis de (attrib) (16/17th C) French/Flemish
£2483 $4146 €3500 L'adoration des bergers (31x40cm-12x16in) i.verso copper. 17-Oct-3 Tajan, Paris #55/R est:4000-6000
£7895 $14526 €12000 Kermesse d'Audenaerde (6x125cm-2x49in) panel. 22-Jun-4 Palais de Beaux Arts, Brussels #160/R est:15000-20000
£13014 $22123 €19000 Elegant company dining and making music in an ornamental garden (50x43cm-20x17in) panel prov. 5-Nov-3 Christie's, Amsterdam #32/R est:12000-18000
£35000 $60550 €51100 Venice, a view of the Piazzetta and the Palazzo Ducale (61x88cm-24x35in) panel prov. 11-Dec-3 Sotheby's, London #122/R est:30000-50000

CAULLERY, Louis de (studio) (16/17th C) French/Flemish
£24000 $43920 €35040 Piazza della Signoria, Florence, with a carriage and figures (51x73cm-20x29in) panel. 7-Jul-4 Bonhams, New Bond Street #32/R est:15000-20000

CAULLET, Albert (1875-1950) Belgian
£563 $975 €800 Near the farm (40x65cm-16x26in) s. 13-Dec-3 De Vuyst, Lokeren #49
£1200 $2148 €1800 Summer landscape (69x100cm-27x39in) s.d.1913. 15-May-4 De Vuyst, Lokeren #52/R est:1600-2000

CAUSSE, Julien (1869-1914) French
Sculpture
£1500 $2505 €2190 Diana (60cm-24in) s. bronze. 13-Nov-3 Christie's, Kensington #240/R

CAUSTON, Mick (?) British?
£310 $493 €453 Grouse in cover (50x76cm-20x30in) s. 30-Apr-3 Peter Wilson, Nantwich #82/R

CAUTERMAN, Cecile (1882-1957) Belgian
Works on paper
£310 $559 €450 Le repos (80x60cm-31x24in) s.d.1938 chl. 20-Jan-4 Galerie Moderne, Brussels #332/R

CAUVIN, Louis Edouard Isidore (1816-1900) French
£1333 $2427 €2000 Ramassage du foin (42x81cm-17x32in) s. 30-Jun-4 Delvaux, Paris #14/R est:3000

CAUVY, Léon (1874-1933) French
£5629 $10245 €8500 Marche arabe (65x92cm-26x36in) s.d.1913. 16-Jun-4 Renaud, Paris #45/R est:10000-12000
£9859 $17056 €14000 Souks, Alger (38x46cm-15x18in) s. 15-Dec-3 Gros & Delettrez, Paris #231/R est:4500-6000
£14000 $25760 €21000 Bateaux au mouillage, Port d'Alger (100x140cm-39x55in) s. lit. 14-Jun-4 Gros & Delettrez, Paris #399/R est:23000-30000
£17254 $29849 €24500 Quais de l'Amiraute (37x46cm-15x18in) s. 15-Dec-3 Gros & Delettrez, Paris #230/R est:3800-4500
Works on paper
£1135 $1895 €1600 Scene de marche (17x12cm-7x5in) s. pen W/C. 16-Jun-3 Gros & Delettrez, Paris #68/R est:1000-2000
£3688 $6159 €5200 Marchands devant Alger (39x47cm-15x19in) s.d.1927 gouache. 16-Jun-3 Gros & Delettrez, Paris #67/R est:4000-5000
£3873 $6701 €5500 Terrasse, Alger (37x46cm-15x18in) s. gouache. 15-Dec-3 Gros & Delettrez, Paris #228/R est:5000-6500
£4859 $8406 €6900 Patio de la villa (46x54cm-18x21in) s. gouache. 15-Dec-3 Gros & Delettrez, Paris #227/R est:6000-7500
£4930 $8528 €7000 Fete de mariage (44x53cm-17x21in) s. mixed media. 15-Dec-3 Gros & Delettrez, Paris #233/R est:4500-6000
£5282 $9137 €7500 Odalisque et servante (37x54cm-15x21in) s. gouache. 15-Dec-3 Gros & Delettrez, Paris #232/R est:6000-7500
£5634 $9746 €8000 Promenade (38x46cm-15x18in) s. gouache prov. 15-Dec-3 Gros & Delettrez, Paris #226/R est:6000-7500

CAUWER, Émile Pierre Joseph de (1828-1873) Belgian
£1342 $2470 €2000 Church interior (60x43cm-24x17in) s.d.1872. 24-Mar-4 Hugo Ruef, Munich #943/R est:3000

CAUWER, Leopold de (19th C) German
£2817 $4873 €4000 Still life with birds (71x58cm-28x23in) s.d.1854 pair. 11-Dec-3 Dr Fritz Nagel, Stuttgart #514/R est:6000

CAVAEL, Rolf (1898-1979) German
£1259 $2165 €1800 Composition (22x30cm-9x12in) mono. 4-Dec-3 Van Ham, Cologne #75/R est:2000
£1389 $2319 €2000 Untitled - informal composition (43x30cm-17x12in) mono. i. verso paper. 25-Oct-3 Dr Lehr, Berlin #90/R est:2000
£1812 $3334 €2700 Composition (23x29cm-9x11in) s.i.d. oil scratching board. 26-Mar-4 Ketterer, Hamburg #789/R est:1000-12080
£2133 $3925 €3200 Compositoin 55/179 (50x72cm-20x28in) mono. i. verso board on canvas. 11-Jun-4 Hauswedell & Nolte, Hamburg #1202/R est:3000
£2797 $4811 €4000 No76/OK7 (37x32cm-15x13in) mono. s.i.verso masonite exec.1976. 4-Dec-3 Van Ham, Cologne #74/R est:3000

£4667	$8540	€7000	No 74/JL 6 (49x38cm-19x15in) mono. s.i. verso panel. 4-Jun-4 Lempertz, Koln #90/R est:6000
£5533	$9905	€8300	58/A 4 (80x60cm-31x24in) mono. s.i. verso prov. 14-May-4 Ketterer, Munich #262/R est:7000-9000
Prints			
£556	$928	€800	Untitled (30x25cm-12x10in) s.mono.i.d.76/186 fibre pen. 24-Oct-3 Ketterer, Hamburg #682/R
Works on paper			
£300	$537	€450	Composition Nr 56 Ag 10 (25x35cm-10x14in) mono. s.i. verso mixed media. 13-May-4 Neumeister, Munich #563/R
£333	$597	€500	Untitled (30x43cm-12x17in) mono. chl. 15-May-4 Van Ham, Cologne #504
£347	$580	€500	Composition (20x16cm-8x6in) s.i.d.74/56 col fibre pen. 24-Oct-3 Ketterer, Hamburg #680/R
£347	$580	€500	Untitled (21x18cm-8x7in) s.i.d.75/70 col feltpen. 24-Oct-3 Ketterer, Hamburg #681/R
£350	$601	€500	78/146 (29x22cm-11x9in) s.d.1978 chk felt tip pen ink. 4-Dec-3 Van Ham, Cologne #81/R
£563	$975	€800	No 69/55 (43x37cm-17x15in) mono.i.d.69 feltpen board prov. 13-Dec-3 Lempertz, Koln #298/R
£594	$1022	€850	No 736 (30x24cm-12x9in) s.i.d.1974 gouache cardboard. 4-Dec-3 Van Ham, Cologne #78/R
£769	$1323	€1100	Untitled (9x9cm-4x4in) mono. W/C ink exec. 1935. 4-Dec-3 Van Ham, Cologne #77/R
£933	$1717	€1400	No 51/173 (25x35cm-10x14in) mono.i. s.i.verso mixed media. 12-Jun-4 Villa Grisebach, Berlin #694/R est:600-800
£979	$1684	€1400	Untitled (21x15cm-8x6in) s.d.1937 ink pen. 4-Dec-3 Van Ham, Cologne #76/R
£1049	$1783	€1500	Untitled (44x57cm-17x22in) mono. col chk. 27-Nov-3 Lempertz, Koln #74/R est:1500-1800
£1467	$2625	€2200	Untitled (22x40cm-9x16in) mono. s.i. verso mixed media board. 13-May-4 Neumeister, Munich #564/R est:400-500
£1600	$2944	€2400	No 51/118 (25x30cm-10x12in) mono. s.i.d.1951 verso mixed media board. 12-Jun-4 Villa Grisebach, Berlin #695/R est:600-800
£2238	$3849	€3200	Composition (32x24cm-13x9in) s.d. mixed media. 3-Dec-3 Hauswedell & Nolte, Hamburg #742/R est:2000

CAVAGLIERI, Mario (1887-1969) Italian

£12319	$20203	€17000	Costume du XVIIIeme siecle (126x91cm-50x36in) s. exhib.lit. 27-May-3 Sotheby's, Milan #226/R est:18000-22000
Works on paper			
£464	$844	€700	Garden (32x26cm-13x10in) s. W/C. 17-Jun-4 Galleria Pananti, Florence #96/R

CAVAILLES, Jules (1901-1977) French

£1478	$2705	€2158	Village gardens in summer (80x60cm-31x24in) s. s.i.verso. 4-Jun-4 Zofingen, Switzerland #2433/R est:3500 (S.FR 3400)
£1711	$3200	€2498	Lande (82x50cm-32x20in) s. s.i.verso. 25-Feb-4 Christie's, Rockefeller NY #77/R est:2000-3000
£2781	$5062	€4200	Vase de fleurs sur un livre (73x59cm-29x23in) s. 18-Jun-4 Piasa, Paris #146/R est:2000-3000
£3000	$5190	€4380	Nu au tapis vert (82x54cm-32x21in) s. s.i.verso prov. 11-Dec-3 Christie's, Kensington #176/R est:4000-6000
£3946	$6273	€5800	Lecture (59x38cm-23x15in) s. s.i.verso. 23-Mar-3 St-Germain-en-Laye Encheres #77/R
£4126	$7014	€5900	La lecture (64x53cm-25x21in) s. painted c.1930. 30-Nov-3 Anaf, Lyon #29/R est:6000-7000
£4422	$7915	€6500	Le bocal a poisson (73x92cm-29x36in) s. i.verso. 19-Mar-4 Ribeyre & Baron, Paris #101/R est:6000-8000
£4762	$8524	€7000	Fleurs et fruits (90x54cm-35x21in) s. i.verso. 19-Mar-4 Ribeyre & Baron, Paris #102/R est:6000-8000
£5034	$9362	€7500	Bouquet de fleurs (81x54cm-32x21in) s. 3-Mar-4 Ferri, Paris #364 est:7000-8000
£9091	$17000	€13273	Saint-Tropez (61x38cm-24x15in) s. s.i.verso. 25-Feb-4 Christie's, Rockefeller NY #79/R est:7000-9000
Works on paper			
£436	$807	€650	Bouquet de fleurs au vase bleu (38x29cm-15x11in) s. W/C gouache. 14-Mar-4 St-Germain-en-Laye Encheres #150/R
£1500	$2595	€2190	Nature morte (37x27cm-15x11in) s. pencil W/C gouache prov. 11-Dec-3 Christie's, Kensington #205/R est:1500-2000
£1800	$3114	€2628	Bouquet de fleurs (71x52cm-28x20in) s.d.46 pencil gouache. 11-Dec-3 Christie's, Kensington #192/R est:2000-3000
£2113	$3655	€3000	La fenetre (65x45cm-26x18in) s. W/C. 10-Dec-3 Ferri, Paris #27 est:2300-2500

CAVALCANTI, Emiliano di (1897-1976) Brazilian

£11538	$20423	€17307	Fishermen (23x35cm-9x14in) s. 27-Apr-4 Bolsa de Arte, Rio de Janeiro #50/R (B.R 63000)
£16471	$28000	€24048	Vaso de flores - Vase of flowers (74x35cm-29x14in) s.d.30 prov. 18-Nov-3 Christie's, Rockefeller NY #103/R est:35000-45000
£23529	$40000	€34352	Testa di Donna (53x46cm-21x18in) oil paper on board painted c.1945 prov. 18-Nov-3 Christie's, Rockefeller NY #38/R est:40000-60000
£25140	$45000	€36704	Still life (60x73cm-24x29in) s. prov. 26-May-4 Sotheby's, New York #102/R est:35000-45000
£41176	$70000	€60117	Porto da bahia (54x65cm-21x26in) s.d.1959 prov. 19-Nov-3 Sotheby's, New York #92/R est:30000-40000
£100733	$178297	€151100	Large composition (114x163cm-45x64in) s. 27-Apr-4 Bolsa de Arte, Rio de Janeiro #64/R (B.R 550000)
£108059	$191264	€162089	Woman in blue (81x65cm-32x26in) s. exhib. 27-Apr-4 Bolsa de Arte, Rio de Janeiro #65/R (B.R 590000)

CAVALERI, Ludovico (1867-1942) Italian

£1611	$2964	€2400	Ponte Seveso (41x44cm-16x17in) s.d.1937 cardboard. 24-Mar-4 Il Ponte, Milan #605/R est:3000-3500

CAVALIERE, Alik (1926-) Italian

Sculpture			
£6122	$10959	€9000	L'arbre (222cm-87in) s. green pat bronze. 19-Mar-4 Millon & Associes, Paris #201/R est:4000-5000

CAVALIERI, Achille (1898-1963) Italian

£709	$1184	€1000	Washing place along the Naviglio, Milan (22x35cm-9x14in) s. board. 14-Oct-3 Finarte Semenzato, Milan #125/R

CAVALIERI, Luigi (19th C) Italian

£10000	$17000	€14600	Inspiration of love (51x90cm-20x35in) s.d. 28-Oct-3 Sotheby's, New York #148/R est:12000-15000

CAVALLA, Mario (1902-1962) Italian

£350	$584	€500	Young officer (59x44cm-23x17in) s.d.1922 card. 26-Jun-3 Sant Agostino, Torino #100/R

CAVALLERI, Ludovico (1861-1942) Italian

£685	$1068	€1000	Wooded landscape (92x71cm-36x28in) s.d.1918 i.verso cardboard. 8-Apr-3 Il Ponte, Milan #610

CAVALLERI, Vittorio (1860-1938) Italian

£347	$590	€500	Storm (20x34cm-8x13in) cardboard. 1-Nov-3 Meeting Art, Vercelli #139
£503	$891	€750	Lake landscape (20x24cm-8x9in) s. i.verso board. 1-May-4 Meeting Art, Vercelli #91
£625	$1063	€900	Communion (19x30cm-7x12in) s. board. 1-Nov-3 Meeting Art, Vercelli #408
£738	$1307	€1100	View of park (34x25cm-13x10in) s. cardboard. 1-May-4 Meeting Art, Vercelli #53
£1042	$1771	€1500	Spring in the mountains (25x37cm-10x15in) s. cardboard. 1-Nov-3 Meeting Art, Vercelli #88/R est:1500
£1342	$2376	€2000	Coming storm (25x34cm-10x13in) s. board. 1-May-4 Meeting Art, Vercelli #225 est:2000
£1342	$2376	€2000	Venice (20x30cm-8x12in) s. cardboard. 1-May-4 Meeting Art, Vercelli #360 est:2000
£1497	$2679	€2200	Sunset on the river (35x45cm-14x18in) s. cardboard. 22-Mar-4 Sant Agostino, Torino #233/R est:2600
£1600	$2944	€2400	Little chapels in the mountains (34x44cm-13x17in) s. board. 14-Jun-4 Sant Agostino, Torino #278/R est:2500-3000
£1678	$2970	€2500	Lights in the wood (35x44cm-14x17in) s. cardboard. 1-May-4 Meeting Art, Vercelli #440 est:2500
£1745	$3089	€2600	Issogne Castle (45x35cm-18x14in) s. cardboard. 1-May-4 Meeting Art, Vercelli #161 est:1000
£2098	$3503	€3000	Snow in Tetti Varro' (35x45cm-14x18in) s. s.i.d.1924 verso. 26-Jun-3 Sant Agostino, Torino #310/R est:3000-3500
£2400	$4416	€3600	Issogne Castle courtyard (26x36cm-10x14in) s.d.1908 board. 14-Jun-4 Sant Agostino, Torino #277/R est:2000-2500
£2857	$5114	€4200	Interior (60x46cm-24x18in) s. board. 22-Mar-4 Sant Agostino, Torino #236/R est:4500
£11268	$19493	€16000	Farm in Calizzano (75x100cm-30x39in) s. 10-Dec-3 Sotheby's, Milan #47/R est:16500-18500

CAVALLI, Emanuele (1904-1981) Italian

£1667	$3000	€2500	Corn fields (17x28cm-7x11in) s. cardboard. 22-Apr-4 Finarte Semenzato, Rome #269/R
£2000	$3600	€3000	Portrait of Mogno (60x50cm-24x20in) s. painted 1932 exhib. 22-Apr-4 Finarte Semenzato, Rome #159/R est:1800-2400
£2817	$4676	€4000	Still life (45x57cm-18x22in) s. s.i.d.verso board. 11-Jun-3 Finarte Semenzato, Milan #514/R
£3580	$6087	€5120	Man riding at sunset (70x61cm-28x24in) s. prov. 18-Nov-3 Babuino, Rome #454/R est:4000-6000

CAVALLI, Luigia (19th C) Italian

£267	$485	€400	Interior with woman (73x54cm-29x21in) s.d.1863. 12-Jul-4 Il Ponte, Milan #148

CAVALLINI, Attilio (1888-1948) Italian

£278	$464	€400	View of Venice (34x19cm-13x7in) board. 23-Oct-3 Finarte Semenzato, Milan #305/R

CAVALLINO, Bernardo (1622-1654) Italian

£56291	$102450	€85000	Bust of elderly man (77x65cm-30x26in) octagonal. 16-Jun-4 Christie's, Rome #514/R est:100000-150000

CAVALLO-PEDUZZI, Émile Gustave (1851-1917) French

£800	$1480	€1200	Chaumieres au champ de choux (43x73cm-17x29in) s. 14-Jul-4 Livinec, Gaudcheau & Jezequel, Rennes #200
Works on paper			
£662	$1212	€1000	Bles coupes (22x29cm-9x11in) s. col crayons exec c.1894 exhib. 7-Apr-4 Piasa, Paris #82
£960	$1757	€1450	Village et meules a Bussy-Saint-Georges (26x45cm-10x18in) s.d.7/6/1890 col crayons exhib. 7-Apr-4 Piasa, Paris #81

CAVALORI, Mirabello (c.1510-1572) Italian

£42254	$70141	€60000	Saint Rocco and the sick (153x155cm-60x61in) board. 11-Jul-3 Finarte, Venice #552/R est:65000-75000

CAVASANTI, Giuseppe (1895-?) Italian

£1701	$3044	€2500	Flowers (70x60cm-28x24in) s. board painted c.1950. 22-Mar-4 Sant Agostino, Torino #476/R est:2500-3500

CAVE, Jules-Cyrille (1859-?) French

£27941	$47500	€40794	Narcissus (99x199cm-39x78in) s.d.1890 prov. 28-Oct-3 Sotheby's, New York #42/R est:50000-70000

CAVE, Matthew (20th C) Irish?
£319 $502 €460 Pub scene number five (59x59cm-23x23in) s.d.2002. 26-Aug-3 James Adam, Dublin #136/R

CAVE, Peter le (fl.1769-1810) British
£1400 $2520 €2044 Peasants and a drover on a country road, a ruined abbey beyond (38x55cm-15x22in) s.i.d.1799 panel. 21-Jan-4 Sotheby's, Olympia #92/R est:1200-1800
Works on paper
£480 $888 €701 Passing mail coach (25x36cm-10x14in) s.d.1804 W/C. 10-Feb-4 David Lay, Penzance #489/R
£500 $860 €730 Drover with animals on the way to market. Drover with cattle in a landscape (19x25cm-7x10in) pencil black ink W/C pair. 3-Dec-3 Christie's, Kensington #8/R
£505 $808 €737 Travellers and cattle by ruins (38x49cm-15x19in) s.d.1798 W/C pen ink over traces pencil. 16-Sep-3 Bonhams, Knowle #54
£750 $1380 €1095 Burning bracken (23x33cm-9x13in) s.d.1800 W/C. 8-Jun-4 Bonhams, New Bond Street #35/R

CAVE, Peter le (attrib) (fl.1769-1810) British
Works on paper
£440 $814 €642 Figures, horse and cart before farm buildings (25x33cm-10x13in) bears sig W/C. 13-Feb-4 Keys, Aylsham #485

CAVEDONE, Giacomo (1577-1660) Italian
£30556 $55000 €44612 Head of a bearded man in a cap, and another head in the corner (36x24cm-14x9in) oiled black chk white chk prov.lit. 22-Jan-4 Christie's, Rockefeller NY #35/R est:20000-30000
Works on paper
£280 $467 €400 John the Baptist (29x21cm-11x8in) i. chk wash. 28-Jun-3 Bolland & Marotz, Bremen #567/R

CAVEDONE, Giacomo (circle) (1577-1660) Italian
£6000 $10980 €9000 Madonna and Child (22x16cm-9x6in) copper. 1-Jun-4 Sotheby's, Milan #1/R est:5000-7000

CAVELLI, Giulio (19th C) Italian
Works on paper
£903 $1472 €1300 Florence - Palazzo Vecchio (16x35cm-6x14in) s.i. W/C. 25-Sep-3 Neumeister, Munich #259/R
£903 $1472 €1300 Florence - Ponte Vecchio (17x35cm-7x14in) s.i. W/C. 25-Sep-3 Neumeister, Munich #260/R

CAVIN, Marylin (20th C) French
Works on paper
£350 $594 €500 Voir le silence (40x40cm-16x16in) s. mixed media canvas. 29-Nov-3 Neret-Minet, Paris #201/R
£559 $951 €800 Miroir d'un moment (60x60cm-24x24in) s. mixed media canvas. 29-Nov-3 Neret-Minet, Paris #75
£667 $1207 €1000 En haut de beaux anges (120x60cm-47x24in) s. mixed media diptych. 3-Apr-4 Neret-Minet, Paris #104/R

CAWEN, Alvar (1886-1935) Finnish
£1197 $2071 €1700 Silver birches (42x26cm-17x10in) s. 13-Dec-3 Hagelstam, Helsinki #152/R est:2000
£1267 $2267 €1900 Girl by window (32x23cm-13x9in) s. later canvas on board. 15-May-4 Hagelstam, Helsinki #150/R est:2500
£2378 $4042 €3400 Model - female nude (55x31cm-22x12in) s. board. 29-Nov-3 Bukowskis, Helsinki #85/R est:2500-3000
£4196 $7133 €6000 Illby - village with many houses (50x61cm-20x24in) s.d.18 exhib. 29-Nov-3 Bukowskis, Helsinki #104/R est:5000-6000
£8333 $14917 €12500 After the hunt (115x80cm-45x31in) s.d.1922 prov.exhib.lit. 15-May-4 Hagelstam, Helsinki #149/R est:10000
£12838 $22980 €19000 Old farm houses (81x65cm-32x26in) s. painted c.1920. 8-May-4 Bukowskis, Helsinki #64/R est:16000-20000
Works on paper
£2517 $4280 €3600 The swing (33x27cm-13x11in) s. mixed media exec.c.1921 lit. 29-Nov-3 Bukowskis, Helsinki #84/R est:2700-3000

CAWSE, John (1779-1862) British
£794 $1255 €1151 Scene in the Opera - Il Fernatico per la Musica composed by Mayer (63x76cm-25x30in) with sig.verso. 2-Sep-3 Rasmussen, Copenhagen #1850/R (D.KR 8500)

CAWTHORNE, Neil (1936-) British
£700 $1288 €1022 After the race, July course, Newmarket (30x46cm-12x18in) s. board. 10-Jun-4 Christie's, Kensington #213/R
£900 $1656 €1314 Winding up gallop, Newmarket (41x61cm-16x24in) s. 10-Jun-4 Christie's, Kensington #212/R
£920 $1674 €1343 Last jump before the finish during the 1948 Grand National (86x121cm-34x48in) s.d.64. 29-Jun-4 Rowley Fine Art, Newmarket #371/R
£1000 $1700 €1460 All to play for (41x79cm-16x31in) s. 27-Nov-3 Christie's, Kensington #174/R est:1200-2000
£1100 $1870 €1606 Homeward bound (46x65cm-18x26in) s. 19-Nov-3 Sotheby's, Olympia #133/R est:1000-1500
£1100 $1870 €1606 End of day (69x46cm-27x18in) s/. 19-Nov-3 Sotheby's, Olympia #137/R est:1000-1500
£1100 $2024 €1606 Away (46x61cm-18x24in) s. 10-Jun-4 Christie's, Kensington #193/R est:1200-1800
£1100 $2024 €1606 Setting the pace (41x61cm-16x24in) s. 10-Jun-4 Christie's, Kensington #211/R est:1000-1500
£1100 $2024 €1606 After the race, Newmarket July course (51x76cm-20x30in) s. 10-Jun-4 Christie's, Kensington #216/R est:1200-1800
£1200 $2040 €1752 First morning out (51x74cm-20x29in) s. 19-Nov-3 Sotheby's, Olympia #136/R est:1200-1800
£1300 $2210 €1898 At the start, Cheltenham (51x73cm-20x29in) s. i.stretcher. 19-Nov-3 Sotheby's, Olympia #129/R est:1200-1800
£1300 $2210 €1898 At the start (46x66cm-18x26in) s. 27-Nov-3 Christie's, Kensington #176/R est:1000-1500
£1400 $2380 €2044 In full cry (41x61cm-16x24in) s. 27-Nov-3 Christie's, Kensington #46/R est:1000-1500
£1400 $2380 €2044 First run of the season (46x66cm-18x26in) s. 27-Nov-3 Christie's, Kensington #48/R est:1000-1500
£1400 $2576 €2044 At the start, Newmarket (51x71cm-20x28in) s. 10-Jun-4 Christie's, Kensington #215/R est:1500-2000
£1500 $2550 €2190 Morning work, Lambourn (51x71cm-20x28in) s.d.86 i.overlap. 19-Nov-3 Sotheby's, Olympia #139/R est:1500-2000
£1700 $2890 €2482 Road home (46x66cm-18x26in) s. 27-Nov-3 Christie's, Kensington #47/R est:1000-1500
£1900 $3230 €2774 Setting the pace, Cheltenham (76x50cm-30x20in) s. 19-Nov-3 Sotheby's, Olympia #128/R est:1200-1800
£1900 $3268 €2774 Over the hedge (61x91cm-24x36in) s. panel. 3-Dec-3 Bonhams, Knightsbridge #169/R est:2000-3000
£2100 $3570 €3066 Eye of the storm, all to play for (40x61cm-16x24in) 19-Nov-3 Sotheby's, Olympia #127/R est:1500-2000
£2400 $4416 €3504 Jockeys get mounted, Epsom (51x71cm-20x28in) s. 10-Jun-4 Christie's, Kensington #214/R est:1500-2000

CAYATTE, Jean (1907-1989) French
£267 $485 €400 Palette rouge et bleue (65x46cm-26x18in) s. 29-Jun-4 Chenu & Scrive, Lyon #44/R
£300 $546 €450 Rouge et vert (55x38cm-22x15in) s. 29-Jun-4 Chenu & Scrive, Lyon #39
£533 $971 €800 Arabesque fond brun (95x58cm-37x23in) s. masonite. 29-Jun-4 Chenu & Scrive, Lyon #45/R
£867 $1577 €1300 Nature morte (60x87cm-24x34in) s. 29-Jun-4 Chenu & Scrive, Lyon #38/R

CAYLA, Jules Joseph (19th C) French
£387 $670 €550 Paysage montagneux a la cascade (60x74cm-24x29in) s.d.1885. 9-Dec-3 Vanderkindere, Brussels #10

CAYLEY, Neville (19/20th C) Australian
Works on paper
£759 $1183 €1101 Gun dog and quarry (33x49cm-13x19in) s. W/C. 1-Aug-2 Joel, Victoria #262 est:1500-2500 (A.D 2200)

CAYLEY, Neville Henry Peniston (1853-1903) Australian
Works on paper
£259 $407 €378 Blue bird with long tail (12x7cm-5x3in) s. W/C. 24-Nov-2 Goodman, Sydney #65/R (A.D 725)
£328 $531 €479 Kookaburra (30x21cm-12x8in) s. pen W/C. 30-Jul-3 Goodman, Sydney #93/R (A.D 800)
£369 $598 €539 Magpie and blue wren (58x46cm-23x18in) s.d.1897 W/C. 30-Jul-3 Goodman, Sydney #92/R (A.D 900)
£435 $778 €635 Magpies (60x32cm-24x13in) s. W/C exec 1900 prov. 15-May-4 Christie's, Sydney #487/R (A.D 1100)
£454 $804 €663 Kingfisher (59x48cm-23x19in) s.d.1897 W/C prov. 3-May-4 Christie's, Melbourne #409 (A.D 1100)
£474 $849 €692 Kookaburras (59x32cm-23x13in) s. W/C exec 1900 prov. 15-May-4 Christie's, Sydney #486 (A.D 1200)
£496 $878 €724 Swallows and dragonfly (19x64cm-7x25in) s. W/C. 3-May-4 Christie's, Melbourne #235 (A.D 1200)
£729 $1173 €1064 Kookaburra feeding chicks (39x34cm-15x13in) s.d.1884 W/C oval. 25-Aug-3 Sotheby's, Paddington #334 est:800-1200 (A.D 1800)
£813 $1455 €1187 Luncheon (61x49cm-24x19in) s.d.1897 W/C. 10-May-4 Joel, Victoria #194 est:1500-2500 (A.D 2000)
£992 $1835 €1448 Robins red breast (66x20cm-26x8in) s.d.1886 W/C. 10-Mar-4 Deutscher-Menzies, Melbourne #532/R est:800-1200 (A.D 2400)
£1728 $3092 €2523 Teal ducks (53x74cm-21x29in) s. W/C. 10-May-4 Joel, Victoria #370 est:2500-3500 (A.D 4250)
£2000 $3140 €2920 Brown ducks 1890 (69x124cm-27x49in) s. W/C. 24-Nov-2 Goodman, Sydney #83/R est:1800-2500 (A.D 5600)

CAYLEY, Neville William (1887-1950) Australian
Works on paper
£687 $1250 €1003 Ducks in flight (72x125cm-28x49in) s.d.1911 W/C paper on canvas. 16-Jun-4 Deutscher-Menzies, Melbourne #388/R est:2000-3000 (A.D 1800)

CAYON, Henri-Felix (1878-?) French
£933 $1699 €1400 Procession a Avila (33x41cm-13x16in) s. panel painted 1910. 4-Jul-4 Eric Pillon, Calais #225/R

CAZABON, Michel J (1813-1888) French
Works on paper
£400 $716 €584 Portrait of a lady (30x21cm-12x8in) s. W/C. 25-May-4 Bonhams, Knightsbridge #199/R

CAZAUBON, Adrien (1872-?) French
£851 $1421 €1200 Marina con barcos (36x28cm-14x11in) s.d.1900 panel. 23-Jun-3 Durán, Madrid #156/R

CAZES, Clovis (?-1922) French
£567 $948 €800 La route de la falaise a Alameda (67x87cm-26x34in) s. 19-Jun-3 Millon & Associes, Paris #228/R
£638 $1066 €900 Le port (46x55cm-18x22in) s. 19-Jun-3 Millon & Associes, Paris #226/R
£674 $1125 €950 Baigneuses (97x82cm-38x32in) s. 19-Jun-3 Millon & Associes, Paris #229/R

CAZES, Pierre-Jacques (1676-1754) French
£1316 $2421 €2000 Diane et Acteon (33x42cm-13x17in) s. 22-Jun-4 Calmels Cohen, Paris #20/R est:2000-3000
£4000 $6800 €5840 Zephyr and Flora (53x65cm-21x26in) 30-Oct-3 Sotheby's, Olympia #146/R est:3000-4000

CAZES, Pierre-Jacques (attrib) (1676-1754) French
£2908 $4711 €4100 Le triomphe de Venus marine (98x106cm-39x42in) 21-May-3 Daguerre, Paris #53/R est:3000-4000
Works on paper
£634 $1096 €900 Anges presentant au Christ les instruments de la Passion (23x17cm-9x7in) pen brown ink grey wash prov. 10-Dec-3 Piasa, Paris #36

CAZIN, Jean Charles (1841-1901) French
£749 $1400 €1124 Landscape by moonlight with a garden in the foreground (37x33cm-15x13in) s. 25-Jul-4 Bonhams & Butterfields, San Francisco #6067/R est:2000-3000
£1176 $2000 €1717 French country lane (33x41cm-13x16in) s. 19-Nov-3 Bonhams & Butterfields, San Francisco #101/R
£1733 $3137 €2600 Clair de lune a la fenetre (55x46cm-22x18in) s. lit. 30-Mar-4 Rossini, Paris #921/R est:1000-1500
£2500 $4625 €3650 Chess game (73x110cm-29x43in) s. 14-Jul-4 Sotheby's, Olympia #192/R est:2500-3500
£3873 $6430 €5500 Lever de lune (66x82cm-26x32in) s. 15-Jun-3 Peron, Melun #198
£3947 $7263 €6000 Tailleurs de pierre (46x55cm-18x22in) s. 25-Jun-4 Millon & Associes, Paris #29/R est:6000-8000

CAZNEAUX, Harold (1878-1953) Australian
Photographs
£4600 $8096 €6900 Spirit of Endurance (18x20cm-7x8in) s. verso vintage gelatin silver print. 18-May-4 Bonhams, New Bond Street #305/R est:4100-5000

CAZZANIGA, Giancarlo (1930-) Italian
£324 $538 €460 Figure (49x34cm-19x13in) s.d.1966 tempera paper. 13-Jun-3 Farsetti, Prato #21/R
£467 $859 €700 Brooms (30x24cm-12x9in) s. s.i.verso. 10-Jun-4 Galleria Pace, Milan #16/R
£700 $1288 €1050 For landscape (24x30cm-9x12in) s. painted 1985. 12-Jun-4 Meeting Art, Vercelli #397/R
£759 $1267 €1100 Jasmine (40x30cm-16x12in) s. s.i.verso painted 2003. 13-Nov-3 Galleria Pace, Milan #19/R
£833 $1317 €1200 Conero (40x50cm-16x20in) 6-Sep-3 Meeting Art, Vercelli #731
£1172 $1876 €1700 Brooms on the Conero (40x50cm-16x20in) s. 13-Mar-3 Galleria Pace, Milan #119/R est:2000-2500
£1479 $2455 €2100 Magnolia leaves (81x100cm-32x39in) sid.1974 verso. 11-Jun-3 Finarte Semenzato, Milan #522/R
Works on paper
£333 $613 €500 Untitled (35x45cm-14x18in) s.d.1965 mixed media card. 12-Jun-4 Meeting Art, Vercelli #672/R
£333 $613 €500 Untitled (35x45cm-14x18in) s.d.1965 mixed media card. 12-Jun-4 Meeting Art, Vercelli #683/R
£559 $951 €800 Trumpet player. Piano player (34x49cm-13x19in) s.d.65 mixed media two. 26-Nov-3 Pandolfini, Florence #74
£600 $1104 €900 Fantasy of flowers (35x50cm-14x20in) s. pastel paper on canvas exec.1978. 10-Jun-4 Galleria Pace, Milan #18/R

CECCARELLI, A (?) Italian
Sculpture
£1049 $1804 €1500 Jeune femme et son enfant. s. Carrare marble. 8-Dec-3 Horta, Bruxelles #84 est:2000-3000

CECCARELLI, Ezio (1865-1927) Italian
Sculpture
£1133 $2029 €1700 Girl and goats (52x25cm-20x10in) s. bronze. 13-May-4 Babuino, Rome #514/R est:1000-1500

CECCARELLI, Simona (1975-) Italian
£541 $951 €800 Suspension (50x50cm-20x20in) s.i.d.2002 verso prov.exhib. 24-May-4 Christie's, Milan #102/R
£629 $1070 €900 Brackets (50x50cm-20x20in) s.i.d.2002 verso prov.exhib. 24-Nov-3 Christie's, Milan #74/R

CECCARINI, Sebastiano (attrib) (1703-1783) Italian
£3691 $6792 €5500 Portrait de jeune femme tenant des fleurs (58x45cm-23x18in) 24-Mar-4 Tajan, Paris #30/R est:6000-8000

CECCHI, Adriano (1850-1936) Italian
£432 $800 €631 Children in a courtyard (20x23cm-8x9in) s. panel. 15-Jul-4 Sotheby's, New York #87/R
£2198 $4000 €3209 Delightful melody (22x27cm-9x11in) s.i. panel. 29-Jun-4 Sotheby's, New York #112/R est:3000-5000
£8000 $14960 €11680 New Sonnet (30x44cm-12x17in) s.i. 21-Jul-4 Lyon & Turnbull, Edinburgh #130/R est:8000-12000

CECCHI, Sergio (1921-1986) Italian
£649 $1162 €948 Canal in Venice (83x57cm-33x22in) s. 22-Mar-4 Philippe Schuler, Zurich #6129 (S.FR 1500)
£965 $1611 €1409 Marche de Coutance (60x81cm-24x32in) 16-Nov-3 Koller, Geneva #1302/R est:1800-2200 (S.FR 2200)

CECCHINI, Loris (1969-) Italian
Photographs
£6522 $10696 €9000 No casting. Camera (60x59cm-24x23in) one s.i.d.2000 verso col photograph one rubber. 30-May-3 Farsetti, Prato #474/R est:10000
Sculpture
£2283 $4200 €3333 Stage evidence, ventilator. urethane rubber edition of five prov. 10-Jun-4 Phillips, New York #620/R est:2000-3000

CECCO di PIETRO (14th C) Italian
£25000 $41500 €35500 Baptism of Christ (23x30cm-9x12in) tempera gold board. 11-Jun-3 Semenzato, Florence #164/R est:40000-45000

CECCO, Guiseppe (18th C) Italian
£1615 $2778 €2358 Portrait of gentleman (94x74cm-37x29in) indis.sig.d.1779. 7-Dec-3 Uppsala Auktionskammare, Uppsala #2/R est:8000-10000 (S.KR 21000)

CECCOBELLI, Bruno (1952-) Italian
£250 $450 €365 UT, triangle (10x11cm-4x4in) board prov. 24-Apr-4 David Rago, Lambertville #74/R
£694 $1097 €1000 Enlightening all greatness (50x40cm-20x16in) oil mixed media card on canvas. 6-Sep-3 Meeting Art, Vercelli #282
£738 $1373 €1100 The Pope (55x55cm-22x22in) s.i.verso mixed media card. 4-Mar-4 Babuino, Rome #417
£1014 $1664 €1400 Double (60x45cm-24x18in) s.i.verso mixed media on canvas. 29-May-3 Galleria Pace, Milan #23/R
£1014 $1784 €1500 Two nights (62x19cm-24x7in) oil fabric key board painted c.1980. 24-May-4 Christie's, Milan #105/R est:1500-2000
£1067 $1963 €1600 No parents for him (60x45cm-24x18in) s.i.verso painted 1999. 10-Jun-4 Galleria Pace, Milan #97/R est:3000
£1189 $2021 €1700 Glued (208x94cm-82x37in) s.i.d.1986 verso oil iron mixed media panel. 25-Nov-3 Sotheby's, Milan #117/R est:4000-5000
Sculpture
£1133 $2085 €1700 Nativo Attivo (37x66cm-15x26in) s.i.d.1987 verso plaster wax panel prov. 9-Jun-4 Christie's, Amsterdam #375/R est:800-1200
Works on paper
£241 $403 €350 L (20x19cm-8x7in) s.i.verso mixed media cardboard. 13-Nov-3 Galleria Pace, Milan #60/R
£276 $461 €400 Quiet (22x26cm-9x10in) mono.i.d.01 verso mixed media on canvas on card. 14-Nov-3 Farsetti, Prato #226
£352 $585 €500 Voglia di Voglia (29x20cm-11x8in) s.i.d.1999 mixed media board. 14-Jun-3 Meeting Art, Vercelli #517
£369 $683 €550 Meeting (40x30cm-16x12in) s.verso mixed media. 11-Mar-4 Galleria Pace, Milan #12/R
£387 $643 €550 Quale dei due e il se (32x24cm-13x9in) s.i.verso mixed media board. 14-Jun-3 Meeting Art, Vercelli #16a
£387 $643 €550 Dottrina arcana (32x24cm-13x9in) s.i.d.1998 mixed media board. 14-Jun-3 Meeting Art, Vercelli #270
£423 $701 €600 Generoso sposo (30x24cm-12x9in) s.i.d.1998 verso mixed media board. 14-Jun-3 Meeting Art, Vercelli #34
£567 $1043 €850 Peace on the ball (48x27cm-19x11in) init.i.d.2000 verso mixed media collage cardboard. 12-Jun-4 Meeting Art, Vercelli #772/R
£570 $1055 €850 Loneliness (35x25cm-14x10in) s.i.d.2000 verso mixed media collage card. 13-Mar-4 Meeting Art, Vercelli #14
£608 $1070 €900 Untitled (47cm-19in circular) mixed media card on board exec.1987. 24-May-4 Christie's, Milan #81/R
£634 $1097 €900 Here and there (72x62cm-28x24in) mixed media collage prov. 9-Dec-3 Artcurial Briest, Paris #556
£652 $1070 €900 Peace (48x26cm-19x10in) s.i.verso mixed media canvas on paper. 29-May-3 Galleria Pace, Milan #49/R
£667 $1200 €1000 Untitled (88x77cm-35x30in) mixed media. 24-Apr-4 Cornette de St.Cyr, Paris #476
£690 $1103 €1000 Open (44x37cm-17x15in) s.i.verso mixed media canvas. 13-Mar-3 Galleria Pace, Milan #45/R
£733 $1349 €1100 Nude (35x25cm-14x10in) init.i. mixed media collage cardboard on canvas. 11-Jun-4 Farsetti, Prato #215/R
£805 $1442 €1200 Twins in air heart (50x40cm-20x16in) s.i.d.1999 verso mixed media cardboard lit. 30-May-4 Meeting Art, Vercelli #41
£872 $1614 €1300 Pansy (60x50cm-24x20in) s.i.verso mixed media. 11-Mar-4 Galleria Pace, Milan #68/R
£1007 $1862 €1500 Double (60x45cm-24x18in) s.i.verso mixed media on canvas exec.1999. 11-Mar-4 Galleria Pace, Milan #81/R est:1700-2200
£1034 $1728 €1500 L (60x45cm-24x18in) s.i.verso mixed media on canvas exec.1999. 13-Nov-3 Galleria Pace, Milan #17/R est:2100
£1141 $2042 €1700 So I heard (80x60cm-31x24in) mixed media collage on canvas. 28-May-4 Farsetti, Prato #35/R est:1700-2000
£1181 $1865 €1700 Eternal consistency (80x60cm-31x24in) mixed media collage on canvas. 6-Sep-3 Meeting Art, Vercelli #314 est:1500
£1216 $2141 €1800 Homines cosmi (60x44cm-24x17in) s.i.verso mixed media collage board. 22-May-4 Galleria Pananti, Florence #403/R est:2000-2500
£2000 $3680 €3000 Piccoli Sentieri (175x104cm-69x41in) s.i.d.1984 verso mixed media collage panel prov. 9-Jun-4 Artcurial Briest, Paris #525/R est:2500-3000

CECCONI, Alberto (1897-1971) Italian
£252 $413 €350 Choppy sea (30x50cm-12x20in) s. 10-Jun-3 Pandolfini, Florence #297
£288 $472 €400 Cortina Church (51x40cm-20x16in) s. 10-Jun-3 Pandolfini, Florence #284/R
£387 $670 €550 Winter landscape (40x50cm-16x20in) s. i.verso. 9-Dec-3 Finarte Semenzato, Milan #6/R
£432 $708 €600 Sunset (40x60cm-16x24in) s. 10-Jun-3 Pandolfini, Florence #286
£724 $1332 €1100 Poppy field (54x65cm-21x26in) 23-Jun-4 Finarte Semenzato, Rome #63/R
£1184 $2179 €1800 Convent by the sea (40x50cm-16x20in) s. board. 23-Jun-4 Finarte Semenzato, Rome #93/R est:2000-2200
£1184 $2179 €1800 San Gimignano, Tuscany (40x50cm-16x20in) s. board. 23-Jun-4 Finarte Semenzato, Rome #92/R est:2000-2200

CECCONI, Eugenio (1842-1903) Italian
£1656 $3013 €2500 Horse (30x38cm-12x15in) i. board. 21-Jun-4 Pandolfini, Florence #107/R est:3500

CECCONI, Lorenzo (1863-1947) Italian
£1127 $1870 €1600 Sulla porta (15x23cm-6x9in) s.i. panel. 11-Jun-3 Christie's, Rome #40 est:1300-1800

CECCONI, N (1835-?) Italian
£1550 $2775 €2263 La Preghiera, a mother, two children and a dog (107x76cm-42x30in) s.d.1866 verso. 6-May-4 Amersham Auction Rooms, UK #307

CECIONI, Adriano (1836-1886) Italian
Sculpture
£1141 $2020 €1700 Enfant boudeur et attelage au coq (53cm-21in) s.i. pat bronze. 30-Apr-4 Tajan, Paris #45 est:1000-1500
£1419 $2540 €2100 Cock (58x23x21cm-23x9x8in) s.i. pat bronze. 5-May-4 Claude Boisgirard, Paris #34/R est:800-1000
£1467 $2625 €2200 Young boy with hen (41x24cm-16x9in) s. st.f.Firenze light brown pat bronze. 15-May-4 De Vuyst, Lokeren #53/R est:1800-2200

CEDERBERG, Karl (1861-1904) Swedish
£1808 $3109 €2640 Summer afternoon (57x74cm-22x29in) s.d.1890. 2-Dec-3 Bukowskis, Stockholm #16/R est:20000-25000 (S.KR 23500)

CEDERCREUTZ, Emil (1879-1949) Finnish?
Sculpture
£1267 $2267 €1900 Motor cyclist (24x32cm-9x13in) s. bronze relief. 15-May-4 Hagelstam, Helsinki #24/R est:1000

CEDERGREN, Per Vilhelm (1823-1896) Swedish
£1692 $2911 €2470 Seascape with the paddle steamer Orebro (60x40cm-24x16in) s.d.1854. 2-Dec-3 Bukowskis, Stockholm #321/R est:25000-30000 (S.KR 22000)

CEDERSTROM, Eva (1909-1995) Finnish
£400 $736 €600 Cubist composition (16x19cm-6x7in) s.d.1971. 9-Jun-4 Bukowskis, Helsinki #365/R
£878 $1572 €1300 Evening (34x42cm-13x17in) s.d.84 board. 8-May-4 Bukowskis, Helsinki #248/R
£1067 $1909 €1600 Coastal view (38x46cm-15x18in) s.d.1976 board. 15-May-4 Hagelstam, Helsinki #199/R est:1500
£1189 $2021 €1700 Woman with baby on her lap (56x46cm-22x18in) s.d.1951. 29-Nov-3 Bukowskis, Helsinki #272/R est:1500-1700
£1400 $2506 €2100 Still life (67x54cm-26x21in) s.d.1961. 15-May-4 Hagelstam, Helsinki #198/R est:2500

CEDERSTROM, Gustaf (1845-1933) Swedish
£1269 $2183 €1853 Trumpeters (49x80cm-19x31in) 2-Dec-3 Bukowskis, Stockholm #125/R est:15000-20000 (S.KR 16500)
£2217 $3969 €3237 Interior scene with woman with distaff (76x100cm-30x39in) s. 25-May-4 Bukowskis, Stockholm #131/R est:40000-45000 (S.KR 30000)
£16154 $27785 €23585 Good quarters - from an inn (103x133cm-41x52in) s.d.1882 lit. 2-Dec-3 Bukowskis, Stockholm #126/R est:125000-150000 (S.KR 210000)

CEDERSTROM, Ture Nikolaus (1843-1924) Swedish
£8235 $14000 €12023 Ballad singer (39x53cm-15x21in) s.i. prov. 29-Oct-3 Christie's, Rockefeller NY #12/R est:12000-18000

CEDIA, Raul (20th C) Italian
£346 $620 €505 Woman with fan (70x60cm-28x24in) s. 22-Mar-4 Philippe Schuler, Zurich #6130 (S.FR 800)

CEJUDO NOGALES, Ricardo (1952-) Spanish
£302 $535 €450 On the beach (33x41cm-13x16in) s. 27-Apr-4 Durán, Madrid #613/R
£355 $592 €500 Landscape (60x81cm-24x32in) s. 23-Jun-3 Durán, Madrid #84/R

CELADA DA VIRGILIO, Ugo (1895-1995) Italian
£490 $832 €700 Portrait (60x50cm-24x20in) s. board. 24-Nov-3 Christie's, Milan #110
£884 $1583 €1300 Landscape with river (34x50cm-13x20in) s. board double-sided. 16-Mar-4 Finarte Semenzato, Milan #101/R
£2649 $4821 €4000 Still life with lemons and glasses. Still life with oranges, apples and glasses (40x48cm-16x19in) s. board pair. 17-Jun-4 Finarte Semenzato, Milan #333/R est:4000-6000
£6250 $10625 €9000 Still life of fruit with plate (38x55cm-15x22in) s.d.1923 board. 29-Oct-3 Il Ponte, Milan #567/R

CELEBRANO, Francesco (1729-1814) Italian
£4362 $8027 €6500 Our Lady of Sorrows (71x62cm-28x24in) 24-Mar-4 Dorotheum, Vienna #328/R est:3000-4500

CELENTANO, Daniel Ralph (1902-1980) American
£9884 $17000 €14431 L' waiting station (70x60cm-28x24in) s. i.verso prov. 3-Dec-3 Doyle, New York #282/R est:10000-15000

CELENTANO, David (20th C) American
Works on paper
£1304 $2400 €1904 125th Street subway station (30x46cm-12x18in) s. pencil exec. c.1940. 10-Jun-4 Swann Galleries, New York #58/R est:1500-2500

CELESTI, Andrea (1637-1706) Italian
£2667 $4773 €4000 Madonna with child and Joseph (47x75cm-19x30in) 13-May-4 Bassenge, Berlin #5091/R est:6000
£20833 $34792 €30000 Paris' judgement (115x153cm-45x60in) 22-Oct-3 Finarte Semenzato, Milan #22/R
Works on paper
£1325 $2411 €2000 Deposition (14x10cm-6x4in) pencil pen ink W/C prov. 16-Jun-4 Christie's, Rome #451/R est:2000-3000

CELESTI, Andrea (circle) (1637-1706) Italian
£4192 $7000 €6120 Finding Moses (91x75cm-36x30in) prov. 7-Oct-3 Sotheby's, New York #20/R est:5000-7000

CELIBERTI, Giorgio (1929-) Italian
£308 $524 €450 White ship off coast (42x62cm-17x24in) s. i. verso panel. 5-Nov-3 Dobiaschofsky, Bern #426/R (S.FR 700)
£629 $1083 €900 Landscape (50x60cm-20x24in) s. oil mixed media. 3-Dec-3 Stadion, Trieste #971
£743 $1308 €1100 Composition (92x67cm-36x26in) s. s.i.d.961 verso paper on canvas. 24-May-4 Christie's, Milan #35
£867 $1595 €1300 Terazin (41x47cm-16x19in) s. s.i.d.1966-67 paper on canvas. 11-Jun-4 Farsetti, Prato #38/R
£1189 $2021 €1700 Composition in silver and black (65x80cm-26x31in) s. s.verso oil collage prov. 26-Nov-3 Pandolfini, Florence #139/R est:1900-2000
£1361 $2435 €2000 Winter in Terezin (67x76cm-26x30in) s. i.d.1996-99 verso fresco canvas on board. 16-Mar-4 Finarte Semenzato, Milan #308 est:2200
£1739 $2852 €2400 L (45x35cm-18x14in) s.i.d.1993 verso. 29-May-3 Galleria Pace, Milan #65/R est:2700
£1745 $3228 €2600 Bird (40x50cm-16x20in) s. fresco painted 1973. 11-Mar-4 Galleria Pace, Milan #27/R est:3000-3900
£2333 $4200 €3500 Hello (81x92cm-32x36in) s. fresco board. 22-Apr-4 Finarte Semenzato, Rome #3175/R est:3500-3800
£2752 $5091 €4100 Passions (122x62cm-48x24in) s.i.d.1995-99 fresco. 13-Mar-4 Meeting Art, Vercelli #381 est:4000
£3056 $5194 €4400 Composition with fruit and glasses (60x96cm-24x38in) s. i.d.1961 verso prov. 28-Oct-3 Il Ponte, Milan #239/R
Works on paper
£537 $999 €800 Composition (48x48cm-19x19in) s. s.i.d.1972 verso mixed media collage. 4-Mar-4 Babuino, Rome #419
£690 $1152 €1000 Composition (50x60cm-20x24in) s. mixed media cardboard on canvas exec.1970. 13-Nov-3 Galleria Pace, Milan #30/R
£699 $1203 €1000 Little theatre (70x50cm-28x20in) s. mixed media. 3-Dec-3 Stadion, Trieste #964/R
£845 $1403 €1200 Untitled (50x40cm-20x16in) s.d.1994 verso mixed media collage panel. 14-Jun-3 Meeting Art, Vercelli #86/R
£867 $1595 €1300 Nest tales (70x60cm-28x24in) s. s.i.d.1969 verso mixed media paper on canvas. 8-Jun-4 Finarte Semenzato, Milan #90/R est:1000-1200
£1241 $2073 €1800 Butterflies (30x40cm-12x16in) polymer pair exec.1973. 13-Nov-3 Finarte Semenzato, Rome #261/R est:1700-2000
£1818 $3091 €2600 Study for tomorrow (89x78cm-35x31in) s.i.d.1989 verso fresco canvas on board. 28-Nov-3 Farsetti, Prato #215/R est:2600-3200

CELIE, Pieter (1942-) Dutch
Works on paper
£503 $891 €750 Homme assis au livre. s.d.1994 verso. 27-Apr-4 Campo, Vlaamse Kaai #349

CELLINI, Giuseppe (1855-?) Italian
£1622 $2903 €2400 Four Graces (66x51cm-26x20in) s. metal lit. 8-May-4 Schloss Ahlden, Ahlden #777/R est:2300

CELLONY, Joseph Andre (1696-1746) French
£6711 $12349 €10000 Portrait of Madame Chateaurenard (30x23cm-12x9in) 24-Mar-4 Dorotheum, Vienna #298/R est:10000-12000

CELMINS, Vija (1939-) American
Prints
£1730 $3200 €2526 Concentric bearings (24x32cm-9x13in) s.num.31/34 aquatint photogravure drypoint. 12-Feb-4 Christie's, Rockefeller NY #40/R est:2800-3500
£2206 $3750 €3221 Saturn (6x6cm-2x2in) s. offset lithograph. 31-Oct-3 Sotheby's, New York #513/R
£2206 $3750 €3221 Untitled (31x41cm-12x16in) s.d.1975 lithograph. 31-Oct-3 Sotheby's, New York #512/R
£2647 $4500 €3865 Untitled (31x41cm-12x16in) s.d.1975 lithograph. 31-Oct-3 Sotheby's, New York #511/R
£3784 $7000 €5525 Untitled, for Parkett (13x13cm-5x5in) s.num.41/60 mezzotint. 12-Feb-4 Christie's, Rockefeller NY #41/R est:4000-6000
£4118 $7000 €6012 Untitled (31x41cm-12x16in) s.d.1975 lithograph. 31-Oct-3 Sotheby's, New York #510/R
£12429 $22000 €18146 Untitled, desert, galaxy, ocean and sky (66x43cm-26x17in) s.d.1975 num.7/75 lithograph four. 28-Apr-4 Christie's, Rockefeller NY #260/R est:18000-25000
Works on paper
£150838 $270000 €220223 Long Ocean 3 (75x110cm-30x43in) s.i.d.1973 verso graphite acrylic ground on paper prov.exhib. 11-May-4 Christie's, Rockefeller NY #39/R est:180000-250000

CELOMMI, Raffaello (19/20th C) Italian
£2550 $4565 €3800 Seascape with fishermen (50x70cm-20x28in) s. 25-May-4 Finarte Semenzato, Milan #150/R est:3300-3500

CELOS, Julien (1884-?) Belgian
£340 $609 €500 Beguinage (79x99cm-31x39in) 22-Mar-4 Amberes, Antwerp #184
£417 $663 €600 Last sacraments in the Vlaaikensgang (141x121cm-56x48in) s. exhib. 15-Sep-3 Bernaerts, Antwerp #193
£451 $718 €650 Jour de marche aux fleurs (28x32cm-11x13in) s. p. 15-Sep-3 Horta, Bruxelles #7

£621	$1148	€900	Carrousel (40x48cm-16x19in) s. panel. 16-Feb-4 Horta, Bruxelles #365
£621	$1148	€900	La ruelle (66x54cm-26x21in) s.i.verso. 16-Feb-4 Horta, Bruxelles #368
£724	$1310	€1100	Ruelle animee (46x54cm-18x21in) s. panel. 19-Apr-4 Horta, Bruxelles #199

CELS, Jean Michel (1819-1894) Belgian

£400	$716	€600	Paysage (14x16cm-6x6in) s.d.1836 oil paper. 16-May-4 MonsAntic, Maisieres #384
£1259	$2102	€1800	Chasseur en foret (38x44cm-15x17in) s.d.1841. 13-Oct-3 Horta, Bruxelles #481 est:500-750

CEMIN, Saint Clair (1951-) American

Sculpture

£1056	$1900	€1542	Untitled (6x8x7cm-2x3x3in) s.d.1989 num.1/5 bronze. 24-Apr-4 David Rago, Lambertville #268/R est:800-1200
£6000	$10020	€8760	Untitled (122x59x94cm-48x23x37in) s.num.III/III aluminium bronze prov. 22-Oct-3 Christie's, London #136/R est:8000-12000

Works on paper

£302	$514	€441	Untitled (23x31cm-9x12in) init.d.89 W/C prov. 4-Nov-3 Bukowskis, Stockholm #555b/R (S.KR 4000)
£472	$850	€689	Double sculpture (18x24cm-7x9in) pencil W/C prov. 24-Apr-4 David Rago, Lambertville #88/R
£778	$1400	€1136	Teakettle (22x37cm-9x15in) graphite prov. 24-Apr-4 David Rago, Lambertville #374/R
£1806	$3250	€2637	Hommage to Darwin (22x30cm-9x12in) graphite prov. 24-Apr-4 David Rago, Lambertville #518/R est:600-1000

CENTENO VALLENILLA, Pedro (1904-1982) Venezuelan

£29779	$50625	€43477	Simon Bolivar (122x88cm-48x35in) s. 23-Nov-3 Subastas Odalys, Caracas #13/R est:40000

Works on paper

£285	$450	€416	Woman (32x21cm-13x8in) s. crayon. 1-Dec-2 Subastas Odalys, Caracas #24/R
£334	$535	€488	Untitled (29x19cm-11x7in) s. graphite. 21-Sep-3 Subastas Odalys, Caracas #28
£336	$625	€491	Study for 'Bride and groom' (32x24cm-13x9in) s. graphite. 14-Mar-4 Subastas Odalys, Caracas #110
£571	$970	€834	Untitled (32x44cm-13x17in) s. pencil. 23-Nov-3 Subastas Odalys, Caracas #114
£606	$1030	€885	Study for fresco (29x18cm-11x7in) s. pencil. 23-Nov-3 Subastas Odalys, Caracas #96/R

CENTER, Addison (1830-1892) American

£1872	$3500	€2733	Sailboats scud along shore under cotton cloud sky (28x43cm-11x17in) s.d.1887. 28-Feb-4 Thomaston Place, Thomaston #97/R

CENTRAL ITALIAN SCHOOL, 15th C

£17606	$30810	€25000	Saint Vito. Saint Sebastian (114x49cm-45x19in) tempera board. 17-Dec-3 Christie's, Rome #395/R est:25000-30000
£27778	$47222	€40000	Saint Peter. Saint Paul (61x13cm-24x5in) board pair prov.lit. 28-Oct-3 Il Ponte, Milan #366/R
£47887	$77099	€68000	Madonna dell'umilta fra quattro angeli et Padre Eterno (85x51cm-33x20in) tempera panel arched. 8-May-3 Farsetti, Prato #687/R est:75000-85000

CENTRAL ITALIAN SCHOOL, 16th C

£26761	$46831	€38000	Madonna and Child (240x175cm-94x69in) 17-Dec-3 Christie's, Rome #474/R est:25000-35000

CENTRAL ITALIAN SCHOOL, 17th C

Sculpture

£15493	$26803	€22000	Angels (113cm-44in) marble pair. 9-Dec-3 Pandolfini, Florence #34/R est:10000-13000

CENTURION, Emilio (20th C) ?

£1497	$2500	€2186	Flower vendor (64x81cm-25x32in) s.d.1948 prov. 23-Oct-3 Shannon's, Milford #232/R est:2500-3500

CEPEDA, Ender (1945-) Venezuelan

£709	$1155	€1035	Untitled (70x65cm-28x26in) s. painted 1978. 20-Jul-3 Subastas Odalys, Caracas #129
£714	$1300	€1071	Don Juan (60x100cm-24x39in) s.verso painted 2001. 21-Jun-4 Subastas Odalys, Caracas #53/R
£1198	$2000	€1749	Reason sleeping produces monsters (124x124cm-49x49in) s. painted 1994. 13-Jul-3 Subastas Odalys, Caracas #83/R

CERACCHI, Giuseppe (1751-1802) Italian

Sculpture

£15385	$26462	€22000	Buste representant Jean Baptiste Jules Bernadotte (80cm-31in) plaster pat bronze lit. 2-Dec-3 Sotheby's, Paris #29/R est:6000-8000

CERACCHI, Giuseppe (studio) (1751-1802) Italian

Sculpture

£15000	$27600	€21900	Bust of George Washington (56cm-22in) marble. 10-Jun-4 Christie's, London #75/R est:15000-25000

CERACCHINI, Gisberto (1899-1982) Italian

£861	$1567	€1300	Madonna (107x68cm-42x27in) s. board. 17-Jun-4 Galleria Pananti, Florence #513/R

CERAGIOLI, Giorgio (1861-1947) Italian

£347	$590	€500	Portrait of old woman (85x68cm-33x27in) s. 1-Nov-3 Meeting Art, Vercelli #135
£800	$1472	€1200	Still life (51x63cm-20x25in) s. board. 14-Jun-4 Sant Agostino, Torino #111/R
£1342	$2376	€2000	Feast of flowers (27x37cm-11x15in) s. board lit. 1-May-4 Meeting Art, Vercelli #483 est:2000

CERAMANO, Charles Ferdinand (1829-1909) Belgian

£875	$1400	€1278	Going to a pasture (43x33cm-17x13in) s. 21-Sep-3 Grogan, Boston #46/R
£1074	$1976	€1600	Bergerie et ses moutons (35x65cm-14x26in) s. 26-Mar-4 Neret-Minet, Paris #11/R est:1200-1500
£1208	$2235	€1800	Bergere et ses moutons (46x55cm-18x22in) s. 14-Mar-4 St-Germain-en-Laye Encheres #43/R est:1800
£1582	$2500	€2294	Nella Foresta Di Fontaine bleu (71x97cm-28x38in) s.d.1880. 27-Jul-3 Simpson's, Houston #416
£2200	$4026	€3300	Bergerie (32x41cm-13x16in) s. 6-Jun-4 Osenat, Fontainebleau #103/R est:3000-3500
£2448	$4210	€3500	Bergere et ses moutons (65x54cm-26x21in) s. 7-Dec-3 Osenat, Fontainebleau #61 est:4500-5000
£2797	$4811	€4000	Moutons en foret (73x60cm-29x24in) s. 7-Dec-3 Osenat, Fontainebleau #60 est:4000-4500
£3300	$5247	€4785	Prize Merino rams (120x162cm-47x64in) s. 9-Sep-3 Bonhams, Knightsbridge #100/R est:800-1200
£3631	$6500	€5301	Grazing sheep in the shade of the forest (65x81cm-26x32in) s. 6-May-4 Doyle, New York #37/R est:8000-12000
£3688	$6159	€5200	Woodview with shepherdess (81x65cm-32x26in) s. 20-Oct-3 Bernaerts, Antwerp #496/R est:6000-8000
£4225	$7014	€6000	Troupeau de moutons (82x101cm-32x40in) s. 15-Jun-3 Peron, Melun #181

CERESA, Carlo (circle) (1609-1679) Italian

£4118	$7000	€6012	Portrait of a lady in black with pearl necklace and earrings (57x44cm-22x17in) prov. 19-Nov-3 Bonhams & Butterfields, San Francisco #9/R
£6000	$10980	€8760	Portrait of Knight of Malta (81x64cm-32x25in) 9-Jul-4 Christie's, Kensington #130/R est:6000-8000

CERETTI, Mino (1930-) Italian

£667	$1227	€1000	Figures (100x81cm-39x32in) s. painted 1962. 12-Jun-4 Meeting Art, Vercelli #121/R
£1200	$2208	€1800	Day images (125x146cm-49x57in) s.i.d.1965 verso. 12-Jun-4 Meeting Art, Vercelli #477/R est:1500

CEREZO, Mateo (attrib) (1635-1685) Spanish

£1127	$1972	€1600	Saint John the Baptist (85x73cm-33x29in) 17-Dec-3 Piasa, Paris #48/R est:1200-1500
£4525	$7240	€6607	Madonna with Child and St Dominikus (131x95cm-52x37in) 19-Sep-3 Koller, Zurich #3057/R est:10000-15000 (S.FR 10000)

CERIA, Edmond (1884-1955) French

£268	$497	€400	Nature morte aux poissons (24x41cm-9x16in) s. 15-Mar-4 Blanchet, Paris #96
£303	$485	€439	Street scene (27x22cm-11x9in) s.i. cardboard. 17-Sep-3 Kunsthallen, Copenhagen #259 (D.KR 3200)
£423	$731	€600	La place du village (33x41cm-13x16in) s. 10-Dec-3 Rossini, Paris #63
£464	$867	€700	Nature morte aux noix (33x41cm-13x16in) s. 24-Jul-4 Thierry & Lannon, Brest #130/R
£467	$835	€700	Port (54x65cm-21x26in) 12-May-4 Brissoneau, France #71
£523	$974	€780	Les Tuileries (27x35cm-11x14in) s. panel. 3-Mar-4 Ferri, Paris #310
£559	$962	€800	Coquillages (46x38cm-18x15in) s. 3-Dec-3 Beaussant & Lefèvre, Paris #23/R
£671	$1248	€1000	La crique (27x35cm-11x14in) s. 3-Mar-4 Ferri, Paris #311
£671	$1248	€1000	Le Pont Marie (26x34cm-10x13in) s. panel. 3-Mar-4 Ferri, Paris #326
£699	$1189	€1000	Vue de Saint Malo (33x41cm-13x16in) s. i.verso wood. 18-Nov-3 Pierre Berge, Paris #92/R
£865	$1548	€1280	Bord de mer anime (27x35cm-11x14in) s. 10-May-4 Giraudeau, Tours #139
£867	$1551	€1300	Port de Bretagne (73x92cm-29x36in) 16-May-4 Osenat, Fontainebleau #69/R
£912	$1633	€1350	Statue dans le parc (27x34cm-11x13in) s. panel. 10-May-4 Giraudeau, Tours #130
£1849	$3144	€2700	Paysage de neige anime (92x60cm-36x24in) s. 9-Nov-3 Eric Pillon, Calais #152/R
£2109	$3353	€3100	Plage de Saint-Guenole (33x41cm-13x16in) s. 21-Mar-3 Bailly Pommery, Paris #122/R

CERIBELLI, Cesar (1841-?) French

Sculpture

£4444	$8000	€6488	Bianca Capella (99cm-39in) i. bronze. 24-Apr-4 Skinner, Boston #54 est:3000-4000

CERIEZ, Theodore (1832-1904) Belgian

£2100	$3843	€3066	Family moving furniture (55x85cm-22x33in) s. 28-Jan-4 Dreweatt Neate, Newbury #60/R est:2500-3500
£8333	$15000	€12166	Flower market (50x80cm-20x31in) s. panel prov.exhib. 22-Apr-4 Christie's, Rockefeller NY #146/R est:20000-30000

CERIO, Laetitia (20th C) Italian?

£323	$579	€472	Snow on Vesuvius (51x63cm-20x25in) s. i. verso. 13-May-4 Stuker, Bern #559 (S.FR 750)

CERIOLI, Francesco (1930-) Italian
£282 $468 €400 Controluce a Rivarossa (50x70cm-20x28in) s. s.i.verso panel. 14-Jun-3 Meeting Art, Vercelli #468

CERMIGNANI, Vincent (20th C) Italian
£336 $628 €500 Le marche aux fleurs place de la Madeleine (67x82cm-26x32in) s. panel. 29-Feb-4 Osenat, Fontainebleau #239

CERNIGOI, Augusto (1898-1985) Italian
Works on paper
£265 $482 €400 Picasso (47x30cm-19x12in) init.d.74 collage. 18-Jun-4 Stadion, Trieste #210/R
£490 $842 €700 Red and green composition (32x25cm-13x10in) init. col pastel. 3-Dec-3 Stadion, Trieste #1141
£559 $962 €800 Picasso (47x30cm-19x12in) init.d.74 collage. 3-Dec-3 Stadion, Trieste #1140
£664 $1143 €950 Thinker (49x35cm-19x14in) init.d.63 mixed media. 3-Dec-3 Stadion, Trieste #946/R

CEROLI, Mario (1938-) Italian
£1000 $1700 €1430 Profiles (50x71cm-20x28in) i. paper painted 1972. 18-Nov-3 Babuino, Rome #27/R
Sculpture
£933 $1717 €1400 Sunny window (80x70x14cm-31x28x6in) s. num.20/180 wood exec.1971. 10-Jun-4 Galleria Pace, Milan #47/R est:1700
£2568 $4519 €3800 Profiles (60x40x11cm-24x16x4in) s. carved wood exec.1985. 24-May-4 Christie's, Milan #87/R est:3000-4000
£2817 $4930 €4000 Portrait of Luca Ronconi (48x50x11cm-19x20x4in) wood exec.1970. 16-Dec-3 Finarte Semenzato, Milan #306/R est:2300-2700
£3448 $5759 €5000 Three Graces (70x80cm-28x31in) wood glass wool lead sand exec.1991 prov. 13-Nov-3 Finarte Semenzato, Rome #352/R est:4500-5500
£3846 $6538 €5500 Little horse (53x54cm-21x21in) s. wooden relief steel. 26-Nov-3 Pandolfini, Florence #169/R est:5600-5900
£11745 $21023 €17500 Seated figure (128x96x30cm-50x38x12in) burnt wood exec.1968. 28-May-4 Farsetti, Prato #359/R est:16500-18500
£11888 $20210 €17000 Positive negative (84x110x15cm-33x43x6in) s.d.1975 wood. 28-Nov-3 Farsetti, Prato #375/R est:15500-17500
£19565 $32087 €27000 M for Keplero (100x100x13cm-39x39x5in) wood exec.1968 prov. 27-May-3 Sotheby's, Milan #209b/R est:18000-25000
Works on paper
£867 $1595 €1300 Homage to Leonardo (70x100cm-28x39in) s.i.d.70 collage wood cardboard. 11-Jun-4 Farsetti, Prato #228/R

CERQUOZZI, Michelangelo (1602-1660) Italian
£6849 $11644 €10000 Soldiers playing dice on a drum in front of a barn (51x41cm-20x16in) 4-Nov-3 Sotheby's, Amsterdam #67/R est:10000-15000
Works on paper
£650 $1125 €949 Peasants pressing grapes and making merry (20x28cm-8x11in) i. black chk. 12-Dec-3 Christie's, Kensington #328

CERQUOZZI, Michelangelo (attrib) (1602-1660) Italian
£8000 $14640 €11680 Roman street scene with figures dancing and drinking outside a tavern (58x69cm-23x27in) 6-Jul-4 Sotheby's, Olympia #541/R est:8000-12000

CERQUOZZI, Michelangelo (circle) (1602-1660) Italian
£14084 $24648 €20000 Nature morte a la pasteque, grappes de raisins et bouquet de roses (97x159cm-38x63in) 18-Dec-3 Tajan, Paris #7/R est:10000-12000

CERRINI, Giandomenico (1609-1681) Italian
£13542 $22615 €19500 Apollus and the Sybill (197x257cm-78x101in) lit. 22-Oct-3 Finarte Semenzato, Milan #48/R
£20112 $36000 €29364 Apollo and the Cumaen sibyl (102x135cm-40x53in) exhib. 27-May-4 Sotheby's, New York #87/R est:15000-20000
£83916 $142657 €120000 Death of Lucretia (157x117cm-62x46in) prov. 25-Nov-3 Hamilton Osborne King, Dublin #282/R est:60000-90000

CERRONE, Eduardo (1928-) Italian
£486 $826 €700 Chick (50x70cm-20x28in) s. board. 1-Nov-3 Meeting Art, Vercelli #208
£521 $885 €750 Young shepherdess (80x60cm-31x24in) s. 1-Nov-3 Meeting Art, Vercelli #380

CERUTI, Giacomo (1698-1767) Italian
£120567 $201348 €170000 Old begger (68x51cm-27x20in) 17-Jun-3 Finarte Semenzato, Milan #674/R est:120000-160000
£158621 $264897 €230000 Meeting at the well (144x115cm-57x45in) prov.exhib.lit. 15-Nov-3 Porro, Milan #233/R est:210000

CERUTI, Giacomo (attrib) (1698-1767) Italian
£3500 $6300 €5110 Laughing boy (64x48cm-25x19in) 23-Apr-4 Christie's, Kensington #246/R est:4000-6000

CERVELLI, Federico (attrib) (1625-1700) Italian
£5667 $10257 €8500 Amour de la vertu (172x113cm-68x44in) 30-Mar-4 Rossini, Paris #48/R est:8000-10000

CERVELLI, Federico (circle) (1625-1700) Italian
£28517 $47624 €41350 Venus (132x182cm-52x72in) 15-Nov-3 Porro, Milan #240/R est:50000

CERVI, Giulio (1854-1893) Italian
£1408 $2437 €2000 Charge (40x30cm-16x12in) i.verso prov. 10-Dec-3 Sotheby's, Milan #95/R est:2000-4000
£3521 $6092 €5000 Cardinal having lunch (59x80cm-23x31in) prov. 10-Dec-3 Sotheby's, Milan #101/R est:5000-7000
£5282 $9137 €7500 Riders (117x80cm-46x31in) s.i. 10-Dec-3 Sotheby's, Milan #94/R est:7000-10000
£7394 $12792 €10500 Hunter at the market (78x57cm-31x22in) s.i.d.1893 prov. 10-Dec-3 Sotheby's, Milan #102/R est:10000-15000

CESAR and FARHI (20th C) French
Works on paper
£1049 $1804 €1500 Mecanique (64x49cm-25x19in) s.d.66 i.verso mixed media. 4-Dec-3 Piasa, Paris #69/R est:800-1200

CESAR and RAYSSE, Martial (20th C) French
Sculpture
£1879 $3514 €2800 Conserve expansion (65x55cm-26x22in) panel jam spread panel. 29-Feb-4 Versailles Encheres #24/R est:2500-3000

CESAR, August (1837-1907) Austrian
£1769 $3219 €2600 Portrait of Countesse Strollberg zu Stollberg (216x137cm-85x54in) s.d.1878 i.verso. 3-Feb-4 Christie's, Amsterdam #102/R est:3000-5000

CESAR, Baldaccini (1921-1998) French
£1250 $2088 €1800 Sein (36x32cm-14x13in) s.i.d.1967 burnt thermoforme plastic. 25-Oct-3 Cornette de St.Cyr, Paris #626/R est:2000-3000
£7718 $14200 €11500 Hommage a Morandi (50x40cm-20x16in) s. enamelled coffee pot pressed on panel exec 1971. 29-Mar-4 Cornette de St.Cyr, Paris #65/R est:7000-8000
Sculpture
£872 $1597 €1300 Cendrier (21x19x5cm-8x7x2in) s. num.4/8 gilt pat bronze st.f.Blanchet exec 1971. 7-Jul-4 Artcurial Briest, Paris #230 est:800-1200
£972 $1624 €1400 Autoportrait (15x11x3cm-6x4x1in) s.d.86 crayon in wood on board. 21-Oct-3 Artcurial Briest, Paris #524/R est:1800-2200
£972 $1624 €1400 Autoportrait Calcine (45x36x5cm-18x14x2in) s.i. burnt plaster on panel prov. 21-Oct-3 Artcurial Briest, Paris #534/R est:2000-2500
£1000 $1840 €1500 Mehari compressee (33x44cm-13x17in) s. num.12/50 mixed media. 10-Jun-4 Camard, Paris #180/R est:2000-3000
£1007 $1873 €1500 Cendrier (22x22cm-9x9in) s. num.70/100 verso gilded bronze. 3-Mar-4 Tajan, Paris #237 est:1500-2000
£1049 $1804 €1500 Cesar par Cesar (20cm-8in) s.d.1972 burnt visiting card. 4-Dec-3 Piasa, Paris #75/R est:500-600
£1111 $1756 €1600 Horse and rider (20cm-8in) s. brown red pat.bronze. 19-Sep-3 Schloss Ahlden, Ahlden #774/R est:1800
£1111 $1855 €1600 Conserve expansion (65x55cm-26x22in) can plexiglas. 21-Oct-3 Artcurial Briest, Paris #499 est:1000-1500
£1111 $1855 €1600 Conserve expansion (65x55cm-26x22in) can plexiglas. 21-Oct-3 Artcurial Briest, Paris #499a est:1000-1500
£1141 $2134 €1700 Papier compresse (45x34cm-18x13in) s.d.1973 num.26/50 compressed paper panel. 29-Feb-4 Versailles Encheres #23/R est:1500-2000
£1329 $2259 €1900 Mehair (33x45cm-13x18in) s.d.1973 num.42/50 compressed plastic car. 20-Nov-3 Gioffredo, Nice #3/R
£1329 $2285 €1900 Index droit, empreinte (22x4x2cm-9x2x1in) s.st.f.Valcamonica gilt pat bronze edition of 600 exec.c.1970. 4-Dec-3 Piasa, Paris #46/R est:800-1000
£1351 $2554 €2000 Expansion (60x23cm-24x9in) s. polyurethane foam prov. 21-Feb-4 Cornette de St.Cyr, Paris #259/R est:1500-2000
£1399 $2378 €2000 Untitled (6x2x2cm-2x1x1in) bottle lids. 20-Nov-3 Finarte Semenzato, Milan #16/R est:1600-2000
£1469 $2526 €2100 Expansion (14x24x41cm-6x9x16in) s.d.1969 glass. 4-Dec-3 Piasa, Paris #45/R est:2000-3000
£1667 $3067 €2500 Compression de passementeries (30x8x8cm-12x3x3in) s. gilt pat bronze Cast Blanchet. 14-Jun-4 Tajan, Paris #200/R est:2000-3000
£1693 $2879 €2472 Motor cycle (33x44cm-13x17in) s.i.d.1971 compression on panel. 26-Nov-3 Kunsthallen, Copenhagen #53/R est:20000 (D.KR 18000)
£1733 $3155 €2600 Compression (6x2x2cm-2x1x1in) s. bottle lids prov. 29-Jun-4 Cornette de St.Cyr, Paris #62/R est:2000-3000
£1800 $3258 €2628 Poulette for a cheval (24cm-9in) s.num.25 gold pat. bronze prov. 1-Apr-4 Christie's, Kensington #215/R est:2000-3000
£1888 $3248 €2700 Schweppes (6x2cm-2x1in) s. compressed Schweppes can. 4-Dec-3 Piasa, Paris #54/R est:800-1200
£2000 $3680 €3000 Pouce (28x14x14cm-11x6x6in) s.num.219/300 verso crystal. 14-Jun-4 Tajan, Paris #199/R est:3000-3500
£2067 $3803 €3100 Poule fer a cheval (23x20cm-9x8in) s. gilt pat bronze Cast Brocquel. 14-Jun-4 Tajan, Paris #204/R est:3000-3500
£2098 $3503 €3000 Compression (6x3x3cm-2x1x1in) s. lids. 29-Jun-3 Versailles Encheres #188/R
£2098 $3566 €3000 Poulette (35x22cm-14x9in) s.num.1/15 black resin multiple. 20-Nov-3 Gioffredo, Nice #6/R
£2113 $3655 €3000 Poule (34x21x17cm-13x8x7in) s.num.90/100 black epoxy resin. 14-Dec-3 Versailles Encheres #178/R est:1500-2000
£2222 $3711 €3200 Compression (4cm-2in) s.num.34/100 18K gold jewel. 25-Oct-3 Cornette de St.Cyr, Paris #622/R est:3200-3500
£2703 $4757 €4000 Compression de limaille de fer (44x33cm-17x13in) s.d.1977 iron filings wax crayon panel under plexiglass prov. 18-May-4 Tajan, Paris #88/R est:3000-3500
£2715 $4534 €3964 Le pouce (40x23x23cm-16x9x9in) lit. white sugar. 24-Jun-3 Germann, Zurich #14/R est:8000-10000 (S.FR 6000)
£2733 $4975 €4100 Self-portrait (50x50cm-20x20in) s.d.1968 polychlorure vinyl. 29-Jun-4 Cornette de St.Cyr, Paris #61/R est:3500-4500
£2800 $5152 €4200 Portrait de compression (60x50cm-24x20in) s. condoms crayon exec 1990 prov.lit. 9-Jun-4 Artcurial Briest, Paris #484/R est:3000-4000
£2867 $4874 €4100 Bleu blanc rouge (31x20x20cm-12x8x8in) s. compressed plastic exec.c.1980. 20-Nov-3 Gioffredo, Nice #1/R
£3020 $5346 €4500 Compression. s.i.d.1975 compressed champagne stoppers prov. 28-Apr-4 Artcurial Briest, Paris #367/R est:5000-6000
£3125 $4938 €4500 Trophee des Cesar (29x7x7cm-11x3x3in) s. bronze Cast Bocquel. 27-Apr-3 Versailles Encheres #96
£3147 $5413 €4500 Cremation (36x24cm-14x9in) s.i.d.1.1.1971 burnt match box matches on paper. 4-Dec-3 Piasa, Paris #6/R est:5000-6000
£3289 $6150 €4900 Oscar (23x18x15cm-9x7x6in) s. brown green pat bronze edition of 40 prov. 29-Feb-4 Versailles Encheres #212/R est:3000-4000
£3322 $5647 €4750 Car (33x42cm-13x17in) compression exec.1971. 20-Nov-3 Finarte Semenzato, Milan #195/R est:5000-5500

£3357	$5706	€4800	Untitled (38x15cm-15x6in) s. chute de poutre de la tour Effel exhib.1980. 20-Nov-3 Gioffredo, Nice #7/R
£3497	$6014	€5000	Petit torse (28cm-11in) s.num.6/8 bronze pat Cast Venturia. 4-Dec-3 Piasa, Paris #3/R est:4000-5000
£3691	$6903	€5500	Compression (5x2x1cm-2x1x0in) s. compressed gold jewellery prov. 29-Feb-4 Versailles Encheres #22/R est:3000-4000
£4196	$7217	€6000	Poulette (16x11cm-6x4in) s.num.1/2 gilt bronze Cast Bocquel. 4-Dec-3 Piasa, Paris #35/R est:5000-6000
£4225	$7310	€6000	Compression (29x14x14cm-11x6x6in) 10-Dec-3 Claude Boisgirard, Paris #40/R est:6000-8000
£4545	$7818	€6500	Moustique (12x12x7cm-5x5x3in) s.num.4/4 pat bronze Cast Barelier. 4-Dec-3 Piasa, Paris #36/R est:5000-6000
£4895	$8322	€7000	Untitled (96x56cm-38x22in) s.d.1977 liquid plastic. 20-Nov-3 Gioffredo, Nice #9/R
£4895	$8420	€7000	Nature morte (68x59cm-27x23in) s.d.73 compressed metal tureen blue enamel panel. 4-Dec-3 Piasa, Paris #20/R est:8000-12000
£4895	$8420	€7000	La mouche (12x21cm-5x8in) s.num.6/8 pat bronze lit. 4-Dec-3 Piasa, Paris #37/R est:5000-6000
£4977	$8462	€7266	Compression Perrier (59x49x2cm-23x19x1in) s. aluminium cans pencil wood base plexibox exec. 1989 prov. 22-Nov-3 Burkhard, Luzern #137/R est:12000-14000 (S.FR 11000)
£5282	$9243	€7500	Daum (13x42x29cm-5x17x11in) s.d.1969 crystal prov. 16-Dec-3 Christie's, Paris #331/R est:8000-12000
£5369	$9503	€8000	Compression de bijoux. s. compressed jewellery prov. 28-Apr-4 Artcurial Briest, Paris #368/R est:2500-3000
£5500	$8745	€7975	Compression (27x15x15cm-11x6x6in) s. white metal prov. 11-Sep-3 Christie's, Kensington #219/R est:6000-8000
£5594	$9510	€8000	Untitled (36x20x20cm-14x8x8in) s. compressed gun cartridges exec.c.1980. 20-Nov-3 Gioffredo, Nice #2/R
£5705	$10097	€8500	Untitled (33x44cm-13x17in) s.d.1971 toy police car compressed on panel prov. 28-Apr-4 Artcurial Briest, Paris #366/R est:8000-10000
£5903	$9326	€8500	Compression (28x28x6cm-11x11x2in) s. chromed steel prov.lit. 27-Apr-3 Versailles Encheres #95
£5944	$10224	€8500	Le bateau ivre (33x50cm-13x20in) s.i. white paint compressed sailing boat wood panel prov. 4-Dec-3 Piasa, Paris #21/R est:6000-8000
£5946	$10465	€8800	Insecte Africain debout (43x24x17cm-17x9x7in) s. num.6/8 bronze exec 1988 f.Bocquel prov. 18-May-4 Tajan, Paris #82/R est:10000-12000
£6000	$9540	€8700	Oscar (29cm-11in) s. gold pat. bronze st.f.Susse prov. 11-Sep-3 Christie's, Kensington #216/R est:3000-4000
£6081	$11493	€9000	La cigale (14x20x9cm-6x8x4in) s.num.3/8 brown pat bronze Cast Bocquel lit. 21-Feb-4 Cornette de St.Cyr, Paris #255/R est:8000-10000
£6294	$10510	€9000	Poulette a patins a roulettes (19x16x9cm-7x6x4in) s. num.6/8 welded bronze. 29-Jun-3 Versailles Encheres #187/R
£6643	$11427	€9500	Autoportrait, le poilu (43cm-17in) s.num.6/8 pat bronze Cast Romain Barelier. 4-Dec-3 Piasa, Paris #72/R est:10000-15000
£6644	$11294	€9500	Sans titre, pseudo expansion (44x40x31cm-17x16x12in) red marble prov. 25-Nov-3 Tajan, Paris #32/R est:15000-18000
£6667	$12267	€10000	Nature morte (85x68cm-33x27in) s. compressed pitcher panel. 14-Jun-4 Tajan, Paris #202/R est:10000-12000
£6667	$12267	€10000	Autoportrait au cadre ovale (48x26x26cm-19x10x10in) s. num.6.8 soldered bronze Cast Venturi exec 1984 prov.exhib.lit. 9-Jun-4 Artcurial Briest, Paris #482/R est:10000-15000
£6944	$11597	€10000	Phenix (35x21x3cm-14x8x1in) s. compressed bottle tops on panel prov. 21-Oct-3 Artcurial Briest, Paris #529/R est:6000-8000
£7317	$12000	€10683	Compression Dirigee (35x13x11cm-14x5x4in) s. compressed paint tubes prov.exhib. 28-May-3 Sotheby's, Amsterdam #48/R est:10000-12000
£7693	$13078	€11000	Animal (40x50x30cm-16x20x12in) s.num.2/8 gilt pat bronze prov.exhib.lit. 25-Nov-3 Tajan, Paris #33/R est:9000-12000
£8000	$12720	€11600	Hommage a Mao (49cm-19in) gold pat. bronze prov. 11-Sep-3 Christie's, Kensington #215/R est:10000-15000
£8333	$13750	€12000	Coca, Kronenbourg (32x15x15cm-13x6x6in) s. compressed cans prov. 2-Jul-3 Cornette de St.Cyr, Paris #76/R est:10000-12000
£8392	$14434	€12000	Autoportrait, le poilu (42cm-17in) s. plaster prov.exhib. 4-Dec-3 Piasa, Paris #71/R est:6000-8000
£8462	$14131	€12100	Compression Kronenbourg (27x11x11cm-11x4x4in) s. compressed cans exec.c.1986 lit. 11-Oct-3 Cornette de St.Cyr, Paris #85/R est:8000-12000
£9000	$14310	€13050	Sculpture plate (63x38x15cm-25x15x6in) s.num.7/8 gold pat. bronze prov. 11-Sep-3 Christie's, Kensington #193/R est:6000-8000
£9441	$16238	€13500	Compression (35x15cm-14x6in) s.d.66 compressed cans. 4-Dec-3 Piasa, Paris #2/R est:6000-8000
£9790	$16839	€14000	Poule en cire (17x16cm-7x6in) s. gilt bronze Cast Valsuani. 4-Dec-3 Piasa, Paris #34/R est:5000-6000
£10000	$18200	€15000	Hommage a Morandi (93x73cm-37x29in) s. compressed coffee pots exec.1989 prov. 29-Jun-4 Cornette de St.Cyr, Paris #70/R est:15000-20000
£10135	$19155	€15000	Autoportrait au cadre ovale (45x24x24cm-18x9x9in) s.num.5/8 brown pat bronze Cast Venturi lit. 21-Feb-4 Cornette de St.Cyr, Paris #258/R est:15000-20000
£10490	$17833	€15000	Compression (66x39x39cm-26x15x15in) compressed cans prov. 25-Nov-3 Tajan, Paris #31/R est:10000-15000
£10839	$18643	€15500	Nadine (39cm-15in) s.num.6/6 gilt bronze Cast Valsuani lit. 4-Dec-3 Piasa, Paris #7/R est:15000-20000
£11000	$18370	€16060	Nu de la belle de mai (40x10x15cm-16x4x6in) s. num.1/2 verso brown pat bronze st.f.Bocquel prov.lit. 22-Oct-3 Christie's, London #28/R est:15000-20000
£11049	$19004	€15800	Montres-bracelets (40x20cm-16x8in) s. compressed metal. 4-Dec-3 Piasa, Paris #50/R est:15000-20000
£11333	$20967	€17000	Compression capsules (38x35x20cm-15x14x8in) bottle lids exec.1968 prov. 18-Jul-4 Sotheby's, Paris #253/R est:10000-15000
£11888	$20448	€17000	Mobylette Peugeot (45x48cm-18x19in) s. compressed mobylette exec.c.1972 prov. 4-Dec-3 Piasa, Paris #33/R est:15000-20000
£12588	$21399	€18000	Chateau magique (95x39x30cm-37x15x12in) s.st.f.Landowski gilt pat bronze prov.lit. 25-Nov-3 Tajan, Paris #34/R est:15000-18000
£14584	$24355	€21000	Plaque tesconi (82x51x65cm-32x20x26in) num.EA base soldered bronze bears st.f.Tesconi prov.exhib.lit. 21-Oct-3 Artcurial Briest, Paris #546/R est:25000-30000
£15734	$27063	€22500	L'homme qui marche (54cm-21in) s.num.1/2 pat bronze Cast Bocquel. 4-Dec-3 Piasa, Paris #58/R est:15000-20000
£16333	$29727	€24500	Compression d'orfevrerie (32x15x15cm-13x6x6in) s. silver plated objects. 29-Jun-4 Cornette de St.Cyr, Paris #59/R est:25000-30000
£16554	$29135	€24500	Lampe (80x55cm-31x22in) s. num.3/8 bronze resin f.Blanchet-Landowski prov. 18-May-4 Tajan, Paris #83/R est:12000-15000
£17333	$31894	€26000	Compression blanche (30x30x30cm-12x12x12in) s.d.69 painted compressed metal prov.exhib. 8-Jun-4 Artcurial Briest, Paris #233/R est:22000-25000
£20667	$38026	€31000	Tete de poisson (17x20x56cm-7x8x22in) soldered iron exec 1956 prov.lit. 8-Jun-4 Artcurial Briest, Paris #204/R est:30000-40000
£20833	$32917	€30000	Poule Julie (37x41x17cm-15x16x7in) s. num.7/8 brown green pat bronze Cast Bocquel prov.lit. 27-Apr-3 Versailles Encheres #91
£21334	$39254	€32000	Compression (32x15x15cm-13x6x6in) s. 15 kg of compressed silver exec 1983 prov. 9-Jun-4 Artcurial Briest, Paris #481/R est:18000-22000
£21678	$37287	€31000	L'homme de draguignan (63x100cm-25x39in) s.num.1/6 pat bronze Cast Valsuani prov.lit. 4-Dec-3 Piasa, Paris #41/R est:35000-40000
£24306	$40591	€35000	Grande Aile (148x180x35cm-58x71x14in) s.num.6/8 bronze st.f.Bocquel prov.exhib. 21-Oct-3 Artcurial Briest, Paris #521/R est:45000-55000
£25000	$41750	€36500	Pouce (42cm-17in) s. marble exec.c.1980 prov. 22-Oct-3 Christie's, London #24/R est:25000-35000
£25175	$43301	€36000	Le tango (44x33cm-17x13in) s.i.num.HC1 gilt pat bronze Cast Valsuani lit. 4-Dec-3 Piasa, Paris #65/R est:20000-30000
£26573	$45706	€38000	Nu de la belle de mai (150cm-59in) s.num.1/8 pat bronze lit. 4-Dec-3 Piasa, Paris #32/R est:40000-60000
£28188	$50456	€42000	Untitled (82x48x20cm-32x19x8in) bronze. 28-May-4 Farsetti, Prato #217/R est:42000-48000
£29371	$50517	€42000	Moteur no 3 (36x57x27cm-14x22x11in) s. soldered iron prov.exhib.lit. 4-Dec-3 Piasa, Paris #38/R est:20000-30000
£30000	$55500	€45000	Expansion fonte de fer (65x272x179cm-26x107x70in) iron exec.1991 prov.exhib.lit. 18-Jul-4 Sotheby's, Paris #151/R est:50000-70000
£30667	$56427	€46000	Poisson (43cm-17in) s. soldered iron lit. 10-Jun-4 Camard, Paris #185/R est:40000-60000
£30667	$55813	€46000	Marianne (32x15x30cm-13x6x12in) s. num.EA1/2 welded bronze Cast Bocquel prov. 29-Jun-4 Cornette de St.Cyr, Paris #75/R est:30000-40000
£35333	$64307	€53000	Parisienne (78x22x14cm-31x9x6in) s. num.8/8 welded bronze lit. 29-Jun-4 Cornette de St.Cyr, Paris #51/R est:30000-40000
£52000	$95680	€78000	Pouce (90x50x40cm-35x20x16in) s.d.66 num.2/6 polished aluminium prov.exhib.lit. 8-Jun-4 Artcurial Briest, Paris #232/R est:80000-100000
£70423	$121831	€100000	L'homme de Villetaneuse (63x205x39cm-25x81x15in) s.num.3/8 brown green pat bronze Cast Bocquel exhib.lit. 14-Dec-3 Versailles Encheres #180/R est:100000-120000
£73427	$122622	€105000	Venus de Villetaneuse (104cm-41in) s.num.5/6 brown pat bronze st.f.Valsuani 1962-1981 lit. 11-Oct-3 Cornette de St.Cyr, Paris #90/R est:100000-120000
£86667	$159467	€130000	Centaure, hommage a Picasso (145x75x120cm-57x30x47in) s. num.HC 2/2 base soldered bronze st.f.Bocquel exhib.lit. 8-Jun-4 Artcurial Briest, Paris #235/R est:180000-220000
£97902	$168392	€140000	Insecte aile (16x31x8cm-6x12x3in) s.d.1958 soldered iron prov.exhib.lit. 4-Dec-3 Piasa, Paris #73/R est:20000-30000
£166667	$308333	€250000	Femme (240x150x59cm-94x59x23in) welded iron exec.1963 prov.exhib.lit. 18-Jul-4 Sotheby's, Paris #248/R est:250000-350000

Works on paper

£300	$552	€450	Cafetiere (20x20cm-8x8in) s.d.1982 ink fingerprints wax crayon catalogue page. 14-Jun-4 Tajan, Paris #243
£451	$754	€650	Autoportrait en Napoleon (23x31cm-9x12in) s.i.d.1984 col crayon felt-tip pen collage prov. 21-Oct-3 Artcurial Briest, Paris #531/R
£524	$902	€750	Visage (25x15cm-10x6in) s.d.8.8.89 ballpoint pen. 4-Dec-3 Piasa, Paris #85/R
£533	$981	€800	Portrait de compression (28x30cm-11x12in) s.d.1976 kraft paper wax crayon page. 14-Jun-4 Tajan, Paris #242
£800	$1472	€1200	Cheque dechire (44x31cm-17x12in) s.d.1987 collage wax crayon isorel. 14-Jun-4 Tajan, Paris #203/R
£921	$1667	€1400	L'oiseau (30x21cm-12x8in) s.d.1981 pastel. 16-Apr-4 Pierre Berge, Paris #4/R
£986	$1706	€1400	Untitled (44x36cm-17x14in) s.d.1972 match box on cardboard prov. 9-Dec-3 Artcurial Briest, Paris #529/R est:1800-2200
£1181	$1972	€1700	Le centaure (33x42cm-13x17in) st.s.i. mixed media. 23-Oct-3 Credit Municipal, Paris #106 est:1000-1200
£1250	$2063	€1800	Arrachage (65x51cm-26x20in) s.d.1970 mixed media. 2-Jul-3 Cornette de St.Cyr, Paris #70/R est:2000-3000
£1268	$2193	€1800	Untitled (44x36cm-17x14in) s.d.1972 match box on cardboard prov. 9-Dec-3 Artcurial Briest, Paris #530 est:1800-2200
£1316	$2421	€2000	Centaure (38x58cm-15x23in) s.d.1985 ink col crayon exhib. 28-Jun-4 Joron-Derem, Paris #186 est:2500-3000
£1419	$2682	€2100	Portrait (31x23cm-12x9in) s.i. ball point pen. 21-Feb-4 Cornette de St.Cyr, Paris #256/- est:1200-1500
£2000	$3680	€3000	Arrachage (68x49cm-27x19in) India ink exec 1962 prov.lit. 9-Jun-4 Artcurial Briest, Paris #475/R est:3000-4000
£2112	$3823	€3084	Composition (45x34cm-18x13in) mixed media steel wool. 31-Mar-4 Zurichsee Auktionen, Erlenbach #198/R est:2200-3000 (S.FR 4900)
£2292	$3735	€3300	Untitled (51x41cm-20x16in) s. mixed media collage masonite plexiglas. 27-Sep-3 Dr Fritz Nagel, Stuttgart #9504/R est:3600
£2467	$4440	€3700	Poule et poulette (24x26cm-9x10in) s.i. mixed media. 24-Apr-4 Cornette de St.Cyr, Paris #477/R est:5000
£2800	$5152	€4088	Bois de cigars (27x22cm-11x9in) s. wood collage graphite canvasboard prov. 24-Jun-4 Sotheby's, Olympia #486/R est:3000-4000
£2800	$5152	€4200	Arrachage (100x72cm-39x28in) s.d.1961 India ink prov.lit. 9-Jun-4 Artcurial Briest, Paris #473/R est:4000-5000
£2917	$4813	€4200	Arrachage (107x76cm-42x30in) s. Indian ink prov.lit. 2-Jul-3 Cornette de St.Cyr, Paris #68/R est:4500-5000
£3636	$6073	€5200	Arrachage (103x75cm-41x30in) s. Indian ink prov.lit. 11-Oct-3 Cornette de St.Cyr, Paris #83/R est:4500-5000
£5245	$9021	€7500	Compressie (83x73cm-33x29in) s. s.verso carton collage black chk ink on board. 2-Dec-3 Sotheby's, Amsterdam #326/R est:2000-3000
£6338	$10965	€9000	Homage to Morandi (76x63cm-30x25in) s. coffeepot on panel exec.1983 prov. 9-Dec-3 Artcurial Briest, Paris #522/R est:10000-15000
£10564	$17113	€15000	Sacs d'emballage de la maison Cartier (180x150cm-71x59in) s. portrait de compression prov. 5-Aug-3 Tajan, Paris #64/R est:15000-20000
£15000	$23850	€21750	Portrait de compression (101x91cm-40x36in) s. pencil crushed metal cans on board prov. 11-Sep-3 Christie's, Kensington #210/R est:5000-7000

CESARE, Ugo de (1950-) Italian

£620	$1035	€905	Mediterranean coast (102x81cm-40x32in) s. 14-Oct-3 David Lay, Penzance #580/R

CESARI, Giuseppe (1568-1640) Italian

£10266	$16631	€14475	Saint Stephen lapidated (71x57cm-28x22in) 21-May-3 Babuino, Rome #14/R
£18056	$32500	€26362	Annunciation (23x15cm-9x6in) copper on panel shaped top. 22-Jan-4 Sotheby's, New York #204/R est:10000-15000
£36667	$67100	€55000	Holy Family and Saint John (24x18cm-9x7in) panel. 3-Jun-4 E & Eve, Paris #32/R est:8000-12000
£59859	$103556	€85000	Venus and Adonis (25x33cm-10x13in) copper. 10-Dec-3 Beaussant & Lefèvre, Paris #7/R est:40000-60000

Works on paper

£36111	$65000	€52722	Adam (25x18cm-10x7in) red chk. 21-Jan-4 Sotheby's, New York #10/R est:25000-30000

CESARI, Giuseppe (attrib) (1568-1640) Italian

£1552	$2855	€2266	Woman with spindle (17x15cm-7x6in) i. i. verso ochr chk prov.lit. 26-Mar-4 Koller, Zurich #3075/R est:3500-4500 (S.FR 3600)

Works on paper

£1447	$2663	€2200	Head of man with hat (13x9cm-5x4in) i. sanguine W/C. 22-Jun-4 Sotheby's, Milan #17/R est:800-1200

CESARI, Roberto (1949-) Italian

£345	$621	€500	View of Venice (46x55cm-18x22in) s. board. 26-Jan-4 Durán, Madrid #586/R
£532	$862	€750	Venetian Canal (61x50cm-24x20in) s. panel. 20-May-3 Ansorena, Madrid #37/R

CESETTI, Giuseppe (1902-1990) Italian

£1127	$1972	€1600	Horses at pasture (23x19cm-9x7in) s. cardboard on canvas. 17-Dec-3 Il Ponte, Milan #1083/R est:1500-2000
£1333	$2413	€2000	Jockeys (30x40cm-12x16in) s. 2-Apr-4 Farsetti, Prato #604/R est:1500-1900
£1633	$2922	€2400	Horses and jockeys (50x64cm-20x25in) s. oil mixed media zinc prov. 16-Mar-4 Finarte Semenzato, Milan #306/R est:2200
£1690	$2958	€2400	Nude with riders (40x30cm-16x12in) s. 17-Dec-3 Il Ponte, Milan #1084/R est:2500-3000
£2000	$3600	€3000	Obstacle (40x50cm-16x20in) s. 22-Apr-4 Finarte Semenzato, Rome #147 est:2800-3500
£2083	$3292	€3000	Jockeys riding (40x50cm-16x20in) 6-Sep-3 Meeting Art, Vercelli #698 est:3000
£2113	$3507	€3000	Horses (60x60cm-24x24in) s. 11-Jun-3 Finarte Semenzato, Milan #539/R
£2113	$3697	€3000	Factory (39x46cm-15x18in) s. 17-Dec-3 Il Ponte, Milan #1082/R est:2500-3000
£2133	$3925	€3200	Horses at pasture (60x80cm-24x31in) s. 11-Jun-4 Farsetti, Prato #505/R est:3000-3500
£2174	$3565	€3000	Camarca 2 (50x65cm-20x26in) s. prov. 27-May-3 Sotheby's, Milan #41 est:3000-4000
£2333	$4293	€3500	Jockeys (30x40cm-12x16in) s. 10-Jun-4 Galleria Pace, Milan #137/R est:4500
£2667	$4907	€4000	Two oxen (50x60cm-20x24in) s. painted 1988. 12-Jun-4 Meeting Art, Vercelli #375/R est:2000
£2838	$4995	€4200	Little horses at pasture (60x80cm-24x31in) s. painted 1964. 24-May-4 Christie's, Milan #55/R est:3000-4000
£3000	$5190	€4380	Tre fantini a cavallo (61x50cm-24x20in) s. prov. 11-Dec-3 Christie's, Kensington #194/R est:2000-3000
£3087	$5526	€4600	Jockeys (50x60cm-20x24in) s. 29-May-4 Farsetti, Prato #557/R est:3500-5000
£3103	$5183	€4500	Horses in Maremma (60x60cm-24x24in) s. 13-Nov-3 Galleria Pace, Milan #63/R est:6500
£3521	$6162	€5000	Derby (50x60cm-20x24in) s. 16-Dec-3 Finarte Semenzato, Milan #343/R est:4500-5500
£3624	$6487	€5400	Interior (38x46cm-15x18in) s. painted 1929. 30-May-4 Meeting Art, Vercelli #67 est:4000

Works on paper

£1000	$1700	€1430	Three horses (50x72cm-20x28in) s. W/C card. 18-Nov-3 Babuino, Rome #262/R
£1049	$1783	€1500	Horses and riders (57x76cm-22x30in) s. chl tempera paper on canvas. 24-Nov-3 Christie's, Milan #46 est:1500-2000
£1275	$2359	€1900	Oxen at pasture (51x60cm-20x24in) s. W/C card. 11-Mar-4 Galleria Pace, Milan #83/R est:2200-2800
£1377	$2258	€1900	Horses (35x45cm-14x18in) s. Chinese ink W/C paper on canvas pair. 27-May-3 Sotheby's, Milan #40 est:800-1000

CESI, Bartolomeo (1556-1629) Italian

Works on paper

£4626	$8280	€6800	Le Christ en croix avec la Vierge et Saint Jean (37x26cm-15x10in) i. black chk pen brown ink. 18-Mar-4 Christie's, Paris #62/R est:3000-5000

CESI, Bartolomeo (attrib) (1556-1629) Italian

Works on paper

£272	$487	€400	Artemise (16x12cm-6x5in) sanguine white chk. 19-Mar-4 Piasa, Paris #2/R

CESTARO, Jacopo (18th C) Italian

£12000	$20760	€17520	Christ and the woman taken in adultery (99x124cm-39x49in) prov.exhib.lit. 11-Dec-3 Sotheby's, London #194/R est:12000-18000
£23448	$39159	€34000	Saint Sebastian martyrdom (204x150cm-80x59in) 15-Nov-3 Porro, Milan #208/R est:30000

CESTE, Piero dalle (1912-1974) Italian

£382	$649	€550	Lute maker (50x69cm-20x27in) s. masonite. 1-Nov-3 Meeting Art, Vercelli #296

CESTERO, Sebastian (1931-1998) Spanish

£1007	$1883	€1500	Concert (73x60cm-29x24in) s. 24-Feb-4 Durán, Madrid #10/R est:850

CEZANNE, Paul (1839-1906) French

£134078	$240000	€195754	La voute (46x43cm-18x17in) painted 1862-1864 prov.exhib.lit. 5-May-4 Christie's, Rockefeller NY #204/R est:300000-400000
£294118	$500000	€429412	Paysage (46x55cm-18x22in) painted c.1881 prov.exhib.lit. 4-Nov-3 Christie's, Rockefeller NY #7/R est:600000-800000
£4000000	$7320000	€5840000	Grand bouquet de fleurs (81x100cm-32x39in) prov.exhib.lit. 2-Feb-4 Christie's, London #13/R
£4588235	$7800000	€6698823	Nature morte, pommes et poires (38x46cm-15x18in) painted c.1889-90 prov.exhib. 5-Nov-3 Sotheby's, New York #10/R est:8000000-12000000

Prints

£4706	$8000	€6871	Bathers (48x63cm-19x25in) lithograph. 4-Nov-3 Christie's, Rockefeller NY #71/R est:8000-10000
£7000	$12110	€10220	Bathers (22x27cm-9x11in) lithograph prov. 11-Dec-3 Lyon & Turnbull, Edinburgh #46/R est:7000-10000
£12227	$22253	€17851	Les baigneurs. col lithograph. 17-Jun-4 Kornfeld, Bern #240/R est:20000 (S.FR 28000)
£14118	$24000	€20612	Bathers (48x59cm-19x23in) st.sig. col lithograph. 4-Nov-3 Christie's, Rockefeller NY #72/R est:15000-20000

Works on paper

£10270	$19000	€14994	Tete et epaules de femme (23x17cm-9x7in) s. chl exec.c.1866-69 prov.lit. 11-Feb-4 Sotheby's, New York #4/R est:8000-10000
£19000	$34960	€27740	Au bord de l'etang (12x15cm-5x6in) W/C pencil exec. 1875-1880 prov.exhib.lit. 24-Jun-4 Christie's, London #306/R est:20000-30000
£23000	$42320	€33580	Tranchee. Trois esquisses (17x24cm-7x9in) pencil pen blk ink double-sided drawn c.1870 prov.lit. 24-Jun-4 Christie's, London #321/R est:8000-12000
£70000	$128800	€102200	Still life (27x42cm-11x17in) pencil drawn c.1881-1884 prov.exhib.lit. 24-Jun-4 Christie's, London #319/R est:80000-120000
£90000	$163800	€131400	Baigneur aux bras ecartes (17x11cm-7x4in) pencil drawn circa 1874-1877 prov.exhib.lit. 5-Feb-4 Christie's, London #312/R est:100000-150000

CHA SHIBIAO (1615-1698) Chinese

Works on paper

£3716	$6541	€5500	Bamboo and rocks (58x29cm-23x11in) seals silk hanging scroll prov. 21-May-4 Dr Fritz Nagel, Stuttgart #763/R est:2500

CHAB, Victor (1930-) Argentinian

£275	$475	€402	Abstract (46x56cm-18x22in) s. masonite. 13-Dec-3 Sloans & Kenyon, Bethesda #761/R
£375	$600	€548	Abstract (36x46cm-14x18in) s.d.1963. 20-Sep-3 Sloans & Kenyon, Bethesda #1031/R
£412	$700	€602	Sfoglen Kuflon (38x46cm-15x18in) s. painted 1997. 23-Nov-3 Subastas Odalys, Caracas #10/R
£625	$1000	€913	Composition in the desert (46x38cm-18x15in) s.verso painted 1991. 21-Sep-3 Subastas Odalys, Caracas #17
£625	$1000	€913	Gesture (52x42cm-20x17in) s.verso painted 1979. 21-Sep-3 Subastas Odalys, Caracas #49
£894	$1600	€1305	Red abstraction (130x97cm-51x38in) s. d.64 verso. 20-Mar-4 Sloans & Kenyon, Bethesda #1161/R est:1800-2200
£1264	$2300	€1845	Dusk (35x42cm-14x17in) s.i.d.1979 verso. 5-Jul-4 Arroyo, Buenos Aires #62/R est:2300
£1264	$2300	€1845	Composition (35x42cm-14x17in) s.i.d.1979. 5-Jul-4 Arroyo, Buenos Aires #61/R est:2300
£1297	$2400	€1894	Bestia no navegable (81x102cm-32x40in) s.d.66 i. verso acrylic prov. 13-Jul-4 Christie's, Rockefeller NY #77/R est:3000-5000
£1657	$3000	€2419	Composition (50x60cm-20x24in) 30-Mar-4 Arroyo, Buenos Aires #13
£2402	$4300	€3507	Composition (46x31cm-18x12in) s.d.58 paper. 4-May-4 Arroyo, Buenos Aires #5/R est:2000

CHABAN, Heran (19/20th C) French?

£1268	$2218	€1800	La plage de la Panne (31x43cm-12x17in) s. s.i.d.1912 verso canvas on panel. 19-Dec-3 Delvaux, Paris #28/R est:1000-1500

CHABANIAN, Arsene (1864-1949) French

£510	$811	€750	Bouquet of hydrangeas (54x46cm-21x18in) s. panel. 23-Mar-3 Mercier & Cie, Lille #282
£839	$1427	€1200	Clair de lune en bord de mer (60x73cm-24x29in) s. 28-Nov-3 Doutrebente, Paris #27/R
£3974	$7272	€6000	Bord de mer (97x130cm-38x51in) s. 9-Apr-4 Claude Aguttes, Neuilly #13/R est:3000-4000

Works on paper

£430	$783	€650	Bateaux a voile (25x35cm-10x14in) s. pastel. 16-Jun-4 Claude Boisgirard, Paris #31
£986	$1725	€1400	Sardiniers au port (51x73cm-20x29in) s. pastel. 21-Dec-3 Thierry & Lannon, Brest #83
£1325	$2411	€2000	Les bateaux au port (44x63cm-17x25in) s. pastel. 16-Jun-4 Claude Boisgirard, Paris #32/R est:2000-2200

CHABANNES, Francois Antoine de (1686-1754) French?

Works on paper

£563	$986	€800	Un Polonais debout vetu d'une longue robe, et autres Polonais (11x17cm-4x7in) pen black ink after Stefano della Bella prov. 17-Dec-3 Christie's, Paris #62/R

CHABANNES, Pim de (?) French

Works on paper

£567	$1020	€850	L'enfant et ses jouets (80x80cm-31x31in) s.d.2002 pastel oil panel. 20-Apr-4 Chenu & Scrive, Lyon #51/R
£1000	$1800	€1500	Cabanes a sucre (80x120cm-31x47in) s.d.2002 pastel oil panel. 20-Apr-4 Chenu & Scrive, Lyon #50/R est:1000-1200

CHABAS, Maurice (1862-1947) French

£336	$624	€500	Bord de mer (33x41cm-13x16in) s. panel. 3-Mar-4 Ferri, Paris #31
£470	$860	€700	Nuees (22x27cm-9x11in) s. prov. 7-Jul-4 Artcurial Briest, Paris #76
£537	$983	€800	Limbes (22x27cm-9x11in) s. prov. 7-Jul-4 Artcurial Briest, Paris #77
£909	$1564	€1300	Bord de mer (55x74cm-22x29in) s. 5-Dec-3 Maigret, Paris #101 est:1200-1500
£1206	$2013	€1700	Reveur adosse a un arbre (54x65cm-21x26in) s. 19-Jun-3 Millon & Associes, Paris #164/R est:1200-1500
£2318	$4334	€3500	Paysage aux ocres rouges (54x72cm-21x28in) s. 24-Jul-4 Thierry & Lannon, Brest #131/R est:3500-4000
£3667	$6563	€5500	Paysage synthetiste sur l'Aven (24x29cm-9x11in) s. cardboard. 16-May-4 Thierry & Lannon, Brest #295/R est:2000-2500
£4267	$7637	€6400	Voilier sur l'Aven (81x100cm-32x39in) s. 16-May-4 Thierry & Lannon, Brest #124/R est:3000-4000
£5068	$9071	€7500	Falaises a Yport (57x41cm-22x16in) s. paper prov. 7-May-4 Millon & Associes, Paris #88/R est:5000-6000

Works on paper
£757 $1392 €1150 Coucher de soleil (37x51cm-15x20in) s. W/C ink pastel. 24-Jun-4 Credit Municipal, Paris #49

CHABAS, Paul (1869-1937) French
£800 $1432 €1200 Voilier et barques dans une crique (60x92cm-24x36in) s. 16-May-4 Lombrail & Teucquam, Paris #157/R
£867 $1595 €1300 Jeune femme rousse accoudee (33x40cm-13x16in) s. peinture a l'essence paper on carboard. 9-Jun-4 Beaussant & Lefèvre, Paris #118/R
£5172 $8586 €7500 Portrait de garconnet (45x38cm-18x15in) s. oval. 2-Oct-3 Sotheby's, Paris #86/R est:5000

CHABAUD, A (1882-1955) French
Works on paper
£1736 $2743 €2500 Buste de femme. s. W/C exec.c.1904. 25-Apr-3 Etude de Provence, Marseille #152 est:800-900

CHABAUD, Auguste (1882-1955) French
£1645 $3026 €2500 Paysage (38x54cm-15x21in) s. 28-Jun-4 Joron-Derem, Paris #172/R est:3000-3500
£1745 $3228 €2600 Nature morte au mimosa (38x46cm-15x18in) s. 15-Mar-4 Claude Boisgirard, Paris #17/R est:1800-2200
£2222 $3711 €3200 Paysage aux oliviers (52x75cm-20x30in) s. 25-Oct-3 Dianous, Marseille #408
£3265 $5845 €4800 Un coin d'atelier (54x73cm-21x29in) s. exhib. 19-Mar-4 Ribeyre & Baron, Paris #97/R est:2000-3000
£4167 $6958 €6000 Conversation au mas (75x52cm-30x20in) s. 25-Oct-3 Dianous, Marseille #417
Works on paper
£629 $1083 €900 Chien mangeant dans sa gamelle (27x43cm-11x17in) black crayon htd col. 3-Dec-3 Tajan, Paris #126
£1146 $1914 €1650 Deux femmes (14x13cm-6x5in) s. Chinese ink wash dr. 25-Oct-3 Dianous, Marseille #380

CHABELLARD, Andre (19/20th C) French
£18500 $33670 €27010 Les lavandieres a pont- sur- Yonne (182x149cm-72x59in) s.d.91. 16-Jun-4 Bonhams, New Bond Street #91/R est:12000-18000

CHABERT DES NOTS-TOLLET, Marie Louise (1892-1979) French
£1333 $2413 €2000 Jeune femme au voile (55x46cm-22x18in) s. 30-Mar-4 Gioffredo, Nice #102/R

CHABERT, Egon (1889-1962) Austrian
£541 $968 €800 Village landscape with figures (50x70cm-20x28in) s.d.1943. 6-May-4 Michael Zeller, Lindau #639/R

CHABOD, Émile Delphes (19th C) French
£3841 $7029 €5800 Vue du Bosphore (95x145cm-37x57in) s.d.1874. 9-Apr-4 Claude Aguttes, Neuilly #139a/R est:4000-6000

CHABOD, Émile Delphes (attrib) (19th C) French
£1765 $3000 €2577 Still life with books and a sherry decanter (37x49cm-15x19in) bears sig.d.1860 oil paper on canvas. 19-Nov-3 Bonhams & Butterfields, San Francisco #112/R

CHABOT, Georges (1883-?) Belgian?
£455 $773 €650 Ferme au crepuscule (75x90cm-30x35in) s. 1-Dec-3 Palais de Beaux Arts, Brussels #224/R

CHABOT, Hendrik (1894-1949) Dutch
£8000 $14720 €12000 Twee mannen (108x124cm-43x49in) s.d.48 prov.exhib. 8-Jun-4 Sotheby's, Amsterdam #4/R est:10000-15000

CHABRIER, Francois (1916-) French
£1381 $2500 €2016 Deux femmes au cafe (79x61cm-31x24in) s. prov. 30-Mar-4 Sotheby's, New York #359/R est:2500-3500
£2348 $4250 €3428 Cafe le select (64x79cm-25x31in) s. prov. 30-Mar-4 Sotheby's, New York #358/R est:3000-5000

CHABRIER, G (?) ?
£1689 $2871 €2466 Parrot seller. Winter sleigh (74x60cm-29x24in) s. prov. pair. 21-Nov-3 Walker's, Ottawa #228/R est:3000-4000 (C.D 3750)

CHABRY, Leonce (1832-1883) French
£1333 $2440 €2000 Chemin a Barbizon. Clairiere a Barbizon (23x33cm-9x13in) s. panel double-sided. 6-Jun-4 Osenat, Fontainebleau #114/R est:3000-3300

CHACATON, Jean Nicolas Henri de (1813-?) French
Works on paper
£559 $962 €800 Rejouissance dans un parc (24x19cm-9x7in) s. W/C. 8-Dec-3 Horta, Bruxelles #443

CHADBOURN, Alfred (1921-1998) Turkish/American
Works on paper
£432 $700 €626 Maine house (42x25cm-17x10in) s.i. W/C. 8-Aug-3 Barridorf, Portland #342/R
£463 $750 €671 Longfellow Square, Portland (32x38cm-13x15in) s.i.d.83 W/C. 8-Aug-3 Barridorf, Portland #341/R
£1358 $2200 €1969 Harbour fish market (36x51cm-14x20in) s.d.83 W/C. 8-Aug-3 Barridorf, Portland #340/R est:900-1200

CHADWICK, Ernest Albert (1876-1955) British
Works on paper
£500 $835 €730 Autumn in Malvern Park (15x25cm-6x10in) s. W/C. 17-Oct-3 Keys, Aylsham #468/R
£500 $835 €730 Autumn farm scene (28x38cm-11x15in) s.d.1921 W/C. 17-Oct-3 Keys, Aylsham #469
£600 $1062 €876 Malvern Park, autumn (17x26cm-7x10in) s. s.i.d.1915 verso W/C prov. 27-Apr-4 Bonhams, Knowle #59
£760 $1376 €1110 Old cottage at Cliffords Mesne, Gloucestershire (28x37cm-11x15in) s. W/C htd bodycol. 2-Apr-4 Moore Allen & Innocent, Cirencester #767/R
£800 $1360 €1168 Henwood Mill, the Ford at Solihull, near Birmingham (17x25cm-7x10in) s. W/C over pencil. 25-Nov-3 Bonhams, Knowle #147
£940 $1720 €1372 Village street, Broadway (26x37cm-10x15in) s.i. verso W/C. 6-Jul-4 Bearnes, Exeter #423/R
£980 $1774 €1431 Norton village, near Gloucester (19x27cm-7x11in) s. W/C htd white bodycol. 2-Apr-4 Moore Allen & Innocent, Cirencester #757/R

CHADWICK, Francis Brook (1850-1943) American
£3800 $6346 €5548 Meditation (57x46cm-22x18in) s. board prov.exhib. 8-Oct-3 Christie's, Kensington #703/R est:2000-3000

CHADWICK, Lynn (1914-2003) British
Sculpture
£1800 $3330 €2628 Miniature figure III (9cm-4in) d.1986 num.6/30 black pat. bronze. 11-Mar-4 Christie's, Kensington #171/R est:1800-2500
£2200 $3784 €3212 Miniature figure III (9cm-4in) d.1986 num.1/30 C41 black pat bronze lit. 3-Dec-3 Christie's, Kensington #702/R est:1800-2500
£2200 $4004 €3212 Miniature figure III (9cm-4in) d.1986 num.7/30 black pat bronze lit. 1-Jul-4 Christie's, Kensington #238/R est:1800-2500
£2703 $5000 €3946 Lion II (21cm-8in) d.1986 num.C49 7/9 pat bronze prov.lit. 11-Feb-4 Sotheby's, New York #52/R est:2500-3500
£4695 $7840 €6855 Winged figures - woman and man (20cm-8in) s.d.74 num.E1,3/8 black pat.bronze in two parts lit.prov. 7-Oct-3 Rasmussen, Copenhagen #84/R est:60000 (D.KR 50000)
£5500 $9460 €8030 Maquette, two winged figures (21cm-8in) mono d.73 num.668M/F black pat bronze lit. 2-Dec-3 Bonhams, New Bond Street #189/R est:5000-7000
£6000 $10320 €8760 Cloaked figure II (23cm-9in) s.d.76 num.C744 1/8 near-blk pat bronze exhib.lit. 3-Dec-3 Sotheby's, London #90/R est:3000-4000
£7000 $12040 €10220 Cloaked figure III (24cm-9in) s.d.76 num.C745 1/8 near-blk pat bronze exhib.lit. 3-Dec-3 Sotheby's, London #93/R est:3000-4000
£7000 $12810 €10220 Maquette V walking woman (19cm-7in) init.num.6/9 black pat. bronze lit. 4-Jun-4 Christie's, London #143/R est:5000-8000
£7500 $13650 €10950 Two lying figures l (12x26x50cm-5x10x20in) st.sig.d.74 num.645 and 1/8 bronze prov.lit. 6-Feb-4 Sotheby's, London #212/R est:6000-8000
£8500 $15470 €12410 Two lying figures on base II (24x46cm-9x18in) st.sig.d.74 num.680 and 1/8 bronze prov.lit. 6-Feb-4 Sotheby's, London #207/R est:8000-12000
£8800 $16192 €12848 Two lying figures on base (24x59x34cm-9x23x13in) st.sig. d.74 num.679 1/8 base bronze prov.lit. 24-Jun-4 Sotheby's, London #239/R est:6000-8000
£8824 $15000 €12883 Cloaked couple VI (20cm-8in) mono. num.3/8 polished bronze blk pat conceived 1977 prov.lit. 6-Nov-3 Sotheby's, New York #259/R est:18000-22000
£9000 $15480 €13140 Cloaked figure VIII (25cm-10in) st.num.755 7/8 near-blk pat bronze conceived 1977 exhib.lit. 3-Dec-3 Sotheby's, London #91/R est:7000-10000
£14525 $26000 €21207 Skyscraper (63x41x20cm-25x16x8in) num.1/9 brown green pat bronze exec 1957 prov.lit. 12-May-4 Christie's, Rockefeller NY #114/R est:30000-40000
£15000 $25500 €21900 Sitting couple (33cm-13in) init.num.79/782 4/8 black pat. bronze conceived 1979 lit. 21-Nov-3 Christie's, London #161/R est:15000-25000
£15000 $27600 €21900 Maquette IV walking woman (44x30x36cm-17x12x14in) st.sig. d.86 num.C16 3/9 underside bronze prov.lit. 24-Jun-4 Sotheby's, London #238/R est:10000-15000
£16860 $29000 €24616 Standing diamond (81cm-32in) sig.d.70 num.597 edn 1/6 brown pat bronze Cast M Singer prov. 7-Dec-3 Freeman, Philadelphia #50 est:10000-15000
£17000 $31110 €24820 Bird III (34x122cm-13x48in) num.3/4 pat bronze prov.exhib.lit. 2-Jun-4 Sotheby's, London #134/R est:20000-25000
£18000 $30960 €26280 Maquette for conjunction II (54cm-21in) iron composition exec 1957 prov.exhib.lit. 3-Dec-3 Sotheby's, London #72/R est:12000-15000
£20000 $36800 €30000 Maquette, two winged figures (51cm-20in) s.d.86 num.5/8 black pat bronze one of eight prov.exhib.lit. 9-Jun-4 Christie's, Amsterdam #274/R est:20000-30000
£20270 $37500 €29594 Maquette V, walking couple (29cm-11in) st.mono.d.76 num.732S/8 bronze prov.lit. 11-Feb-4 Sotheby's, New York #53/R est:20000-30000
£22000 $40040 €32120 Maquette III diamond (33x23x29cm-13x9x11in) mono.num.3/9 and C 14 S bronze pair prov.lit. 6-Feb-4 Sotheby's, London #208/R est:20000-30000
£23952 $40000 €34970 Lion (107x192x63cm-42x76x25in) s.d.60 num. 328 and 1/4 bronze prov.exhib.lit. 13-Nov-3 Sotheby's, New York #110/R est:30000-40000
£24000 $41280 €35040 Maquette VII two winged figures (39cm-15in) mono d.74 num.676 2/8 black pat bronze lit. 2-Dec-3 Bonhams, New Bond Street #191/R est:25000-35000
£24000 $43680 €35040 Stranger (74x51cm-29x20in) bronze edition of 9 lit. 6-Feb-4 Sotheby's, London #204/R est:25000-35000
£25150 $42000 €36719 Orator (55x41x16cm-22x16x6in) mono.num.C 203 3/9 blk beige pat bronze exec 1956 prov.exhib.lit. 12-Nov-3 Christie's, Rockefeller NY #344/R est:25000-35000
£29050 $52000 €42413 Three winged figures (50x109x18cm-20x43x7in) s.num.4/4 base blk green pat bronze exec 1960-61 prov.lit. 12-May-4 Christie's, Rockefeller NY #115/R est:40000-60000
£30000 $55201 €45000 Bird IV (35x74x42cm-14x29x17in) steel concrete prov.exhib.lit. 8-Jun-4 Artcurial Briest, Paris #203/R est:20000-25000
£32000 $58240 €46720 Sitting Couple 797 (48x91x63cm-19x36x25in) st.f.i. num.3/9 bronze conceived 1980 exhib.lit. 4-Feb-4 Sotheby's, Olympia #80/R est:20000-30000
£32934 $55000 €48084 Conjunction XVIII (69x46x47cm-27x18x19in) mono.d.72 num.650S 4/6 gold brown pat bronze prov.lit. 13-Nov-3 Sotheby's, New York #239/R est:30000-40000
£53892 $90000 €78682 Pair of Sitting Figures IV (61x61x48cm-24x24x19in) init.num.657S 1/8 blk pat bronze exec 1973 prov.lit. 12-Nov-3 Christie's, Rockefeller NY #399/R est:40000-60000
£100000 $183000 €146000 Two watchers V third version (176cm-69in) init. s.i.verso grey pat. bronze lit. 4-Jun-4 Christie's, London #140/R est:100000-150000
Works on paper
£550 $1001 €803 Study for standing figure (42x30cm-17x12in) s.d.80 pen blk ink wash. 1-Jul-4 Christie's, Kensington #240/R
£588 $982 €858 Untitled (38x51cm-15x20in) s.d.1957 Indian ink. 24-Jun-3 Germann, Zurich #932 (S.FR 1300)
£656 $1095 €958 Study for a sculpture (62x48cm-24x19in) s.d.62 pen ink wash. 17-Nov-3 Waddingtons, Toronto #79/R (C.D 1450)

£764 $1276 €1100 Study for sculpture. s. ink W/C. 21-Oct-3 Galerie Moderne, Brussels #187/R
£764 $1276 €1100 Twins (60x46cm-24x18in) s. ink dr. 21-Oct-3 Campo & Campo, Antwerp #31
£1100 $2002 €1606 Study for two seated figures (32x49cm-13x19in) s.d.80 pen blk ink wash. 1-Jul-4 Christie's, Kensington #241/R est:800-1200
£1100 $2024 €1650 Standing figure (62x45cm-24x18in) s.d.62 pen ink W/C blue-grey paper. 12-Jun-4 Villa Grisebach, Berlin #696/R est:900-1200
£1300 $2405 €1898 Two standing figure (65x49cm-26x19in) s.d.66 black ink. 11-Mar-4 Christie's, Kensington #168/R est:800-1200
£1564 $2800 €2283 Study for sculpture (48x30cm-19x12in) s.d.1960 ink wash. 16-May-4 Wright, Chicago #276/R est:3000-4000
£1600 $2912 €2336 Drawing for man and woman II (33x25cm-13x10in) s.d.56 pen ink prov. 15-Jun-4 Bonhams, New Bond Street #67/R est:1200-1800

CHADWICK, Robert Lee (1905-1971) Canadian
£249 $416 €364 Winter, Haliburton highlands (30x40cm-12x16in) s.i. board sold with winter scene by William Paeson. 17-Nov-3 Hodgins, Calgary #390/R (C.D 550)

CHADWICK, William (1879-1962) American/British
£11047 $19000 €16129 Stream by the farm. Boats in a harbour (60x75cm-24x30in) s. double-sided prov.exhib. 3-Dec-3 Doyle, New York #220/R est:30000-50000

CHAFFANEL, Eugène (19/20th C) French
£1667 $3067 €2500 Elegante a l'eventail (79x64cm-31x25in) s. 14-Jun-4 Tajan, Paris #21/R est:2500-3000

CHAFFEE, Samuel R (19/20th C) American
£391 $700 €571 Near Wickford, RI. Fall Birches (18x28cm-7x11in) s. pair. 8-Jan-4 James Julia, Fairfield #1032/R
Works on paper
£235 $400 €343 Marshes (29x54cm-11x21in) s. W/C. 21-Nov-3 Skinner, Boston #529/R
£260 $450 €380 Tree lined marsh (28x58cm-11x23in) s. W/C. 10-Dec-3 Alderfer's, Hatfield #402
£472 $750 €689 Crescent moon. Sunrise (23x53cm-9x21in) s. W/C pair. 12-Sep-3 Skinner, Boston #283/R
£588 $1000 €858 Rough seas (38x58cm-15x23in) s. W/C gouache. 21-Nov-3 Skinner, Boston #306/R est:800-1200

CHAGALL, Marc (1887-1985) French/Russian
£14773 $26000 €21569 Story of the Exodus (51x36cm-20x14in) s. col lithograph portfolio of 24. 23-May-4 Hindman, Chicago #121/R est:30000-50000
£42000 $76440 €61320 Les amants au bouquet de fleurs (42x34cm-17x13in) s. oil gouache W/C India ink pencil prov. 5-Feb-4 Christie's, London #341/R est:15000-20000
£48000 $88320 €70080 Enceinte du Mur de Jerusalem (38x31cm-15x12in) st.sig. painted 1931. 22-Jun-4 Sotheby's, London #259/R est:25000-35000
£50000 $85000 €73000 L'artiste sur les toits (24x19cm-9x7in) st.sig. artist's board painted c.1978-1980 prov. 6-Nov-3 Sotheby's, New York #244/R est:60000-80000
£50000 $85000 €73000 Les fiances au-dessus du pont (21x16cm-8x6in) st. canvas mounted card painted c.1978 prov. 6-Nov-3 Sotheby's, New York #333/R est:50000-70000
£50000 $92000 €73000 Le paysan (22x16cm-9x6in) st.sig. canvasboard painted c.1980. 23-Jun-4 Christie's, London #268/R est:20000-30000
£52941 $90000 €77294 Jour et nuit (30x25cm-12x10in) s. canvas on plywood painted c.1965 prov. 6-Nov-3 Sotheby's, New York #300/R est:100000-120000
£52941 $90000 €77294 Autour de Baldaquin (23x32cm-9x13in) st.sig. oil India ink canvas on plywood painted c.1946-50 prov. 6-Nov-3 Sotheby's, New York #349/R est:50000-70000
£69869 $127162 €102009 Les drapeaux rouges (46x37cm-18x15in) st.sig. oil pastel ink canvas on cardboard prov. 18-Jun-4 Kornfeld, Bern #16/R est:200000 (S.FR 160000)
£70000 $128800 €102200 Peintre en bleu (24x19cm-9x7in) s. oil brush ink pastel isorel painted 1975-78 prov. 22-Jun-4 Sotheby's, London #258/R est:25000-35000
£75301 $125000 €109939 Esquisse pour le songe de Jacob (26x21cm-10x8in) board painted 1956-1967. 2-Oct-3 Christie's, Tel Aviv #22/R est:120000-160000
£85000 $156400 €124100 Bella au bouquet (28x23cm-11x9in) s. canvas on panel painted c.1927-1928 prov. 23-Jun-4 Christie's, London #228/R est:60000-80000
£87336 $158952 €127511 Le couple dans le ciel bleu (33x22cm-13x9in) s.verso canvas on cardboard prov. 18-Jun-4 Kornfeld, Bern #17/R est:150000 (S.FR 200000)
£100559 $180000 €146816 Juif a la Thora (33x22cm-13x9in) s. prov. 18-Mar-4 Sotheby's, New York #108/R est:160000-180000
£120000 $220800 €175200 Crucifixion (50x61cm-20x24in) st.sig. painted c.1966-70 prov. 22-Jun-4 Sotheby's, London #274/R est:60000-80000
£126638 $230480 €184891 Couple aux glaieuls (45x37cm-18x15in) st.sig. oil ink canvas on cardboard prov. 18-Jun-4 Kornfeld, Bern #15/R est:250000 (S.FR 290000)
£142000 $261280 €207320 La fenetre bleue (55x46cm-22x18in) st.sig. painted 1968 prov. 23-Jun-4 Christie's, London #223/R est:150000-200000
£150000 $276000 €219000 Mariee au soleil (46x38cm-18x15in) s. tempera board painted 1982 exhib. 22-Jun-4 Sotheby's, London #277/R est:60000-80000
£205882 $350000 €300588 Le pot bleu (55x46cm-22x18in) s. prov. 5-Nov-3 Christie's, Rockefeller NY #292/R est:200000-300000
£209497 $375000 €305866 Peintre et le grand nu (64x54cm-25x21in) st.sig. oil ink painted 1984 prov. 6-May-4 Sotheby's, New York #387/R est:220000-280000
£217877 $390000 €318100 Les amoureux au triangle orange (73x60cm-29x24in) s. oil tempera painted c.1980 prov. 6-May-4 Sotheby's, New York #411/R est:250000-350000
£240000 $436800 €350400 Quai a Paris (65x42cm-26x17in) s. s.verso prov. 21-Jun-4 Sotheby's, London #49/R est:250000-350000
£241176 $410000 €352117 Grand bouquet (73x59cm-29x23in) st.sig. painted 1978 prov. 6-Nov-3 Sotheby's, New York #288/R est:300000-400000
£247059 $420000 €360706 Le mariee (54x65cm-21x26in) s. s.d.1948-52 stretcher prov. 5-Nov-3 Christie's, Rockefeller NY #326/R est:300000-400000
£314411 $572227 €459040 Celebration au village (91x59cm-36x23in) s. painted c.1980 prov. 18-Jun-4 Kornfeld, Bern #18/R est:400000 (S.FR 720000)
£324022 $580000 €473072 Bouquet sur fond jaune et bleu (92x73cm-36x29in) s. painted 1979 prov. 6-May-4 Sotheby's, New York #269a/R est:500000-600000
£375000 $690000 €547500 Grand bouquet de mimosas (100x81cm-39x32in) s. s.i.d.1977 verso prov. 22-Jun-4 Sotheby's, London #166/R est:200000-300000
£380000 $691600 €554800 Au dessus du village (92x73cm-36x29in) s. s.verso painted c.1976 prov. 21-Jun-4 Sotheby's, London #60/R est:300000-400000
£397059 $675000 €579706 Le buisson en fleurs (112x88cm-44x35in) s. s.verso painted c.1959-67 prov.exhib. 5-Nov-3 Sotheby's, New York #33/R est:700000-900000
£441341 $790000 €644358 Couple et bouquet dans le ciel (116x89cm-46x35in) s. painted c.1980 prov. 6-May-4 Sotheby's, New York #291/R est:650000-850000
£580000 $1067200 €846800 Noce et musique (61x38cm-24x15in) s. painted c.1939 prov.exhib. 22-Jun-4 Christie's, London #40/R est:300000-500000
£614525 $1100000 €897207 Le temps n'a point de rives (100x81cm-39x32in) s.d.1930-39 prov.exhib.lit. 4-May-4 Christie's, Rockefeller NY #35/R est:1400000-1800000
£870000 $1592100 €1270200 Musicienne (116x89cm-46x35in) s. painted 1978 prov.exhib.lit. 2-Feb-4 Christie's, London #39/R est:700000-1000000
Prints
£1761 $2800 €2571 Lovers with red sun (48x32cm-19x13in) s.num.13/40 col lithograph. 13-Sep-3 Weschler, Washington #807/R est:4000-6000
£1765 $3000 €2577 Acrobat (40x31cm-16x12in) s. etching drypoint. 31-Oct-3 Sotheby's, New York #219
£1765 $3000 €2577 Hagar in the desert (36x27cm-14x11in) s.num.4/50 col lithograph. 6-Nov-3 Swann Galleries, New York #517/R est:4000-6000
£1765 $3000 €2577 La lune noire (32x25cm-13x10in) s.num.29/40 lithograph. 6-Nov-3 Swann Galleries, New York #520/R est:2000-3000
£1828 $3400 €2669 La lune noire (31x24cm-12x9in) s.num.9/40 lithograph. 2-Mar-4 Swann Galleries, New York #123/R est:2500-3500
£1840 $3000 €2686 Jude mit Thora (47x33cm-19x13in) s. num.11/20 woodcut executed 1922-3. 24-Sep-3 Christie's, Rockefeller NY #61/R est:1500-2000
£1882 $3200 €2748 Moise et l'ange (32x25cm-13x10in) s.num.27/30 lithograph. 6-Nov-3 Swann Galleries, New York #522/R est:2500-3500
£1887 $3000 €2755 Chloe is carried off by the Methymneans (43x64cm-17x25in) lithograph. 14-Sep-3 Susanin's, Chicago #6051/R est:1500-2000
£1892 $3500 €2762 Bouquet sur la ville (64x48cm-25x19in) s. lithograph. 13-Feb-4 David Rago, Lambertville #48/R est:2000-3000
£1935 $3600 €2825 L'ange (32x26cm-13x10in) s.num.9/40 col lithograph. 2-Mar-4 Swann Galleries, New York #119/R est:3000-5000
£1935 $3600 €2825 Le couple a l'arbre (32x25cm-13x10in) s.num.26/40 lithograph. 2-Mar-4 Swann Galleries, New York #124/R est:3000-5000
£1937 $3332 €2828 David and Absalom (31x24cm-12x9in) mono. etching W/C. 2-Dec-3 Koller, Zurich #3315 est:2000-3000 (S.FR 4300)
£1937 $3332 €2828 Moses and Aaron (28x22cm-11x9in) mono. etching W/C. 2-Dec-3 Koller, Zurich #3314 est:2000-3000 (S.FR 4300)
£1958 $3368 €2800 Prophecy over Jerusalem (31x25cm-12x10in) mono. num.61/100 etching W/C exec.c.1931-39. 5-Dec-3 Ketterer, Munich #119/R est:3000-4000
£2000 $3580 €3000 Hymenee (42x64cm-17x25in) col lithograph. 15-May-4 Van Ham, Cologne #510/R est:5000
£2000 $3580 €3000 The red hen (25x37cm-10x15in) s.i. col lithograph. 14-May-4 Ketterer, Munich #232/R est:4000-6000
£2000 $3680 €3000 Le repas de la Paque (29x23cm-11x9in) s.mono. W/C etching. 10-Jun-4 Hauswedell & Nolte, Hamburg #62/R est:3000
£2027 $3750 €2959 White and black (66x48cm-26x19in) s. num.3/30 lithograph. 13-Feb-4 David Rago, Lambertville #54/R est:2000-3000
£2096 $3500 €3060 Musical clown (67x46cm-26x18in) s.num.28/150 col lithograph. 21-Oct-3 Bonhams & Butterfields, San Francisco #1161/R
£2098 $3608 €3000 Le poisson bleu (25x41cm-10x16in) s. col lithograph. 2-Dec-3 Hauswedell & Nolte, Hamburg #78/R est:3000
£2098 $3566 €3000 From: Circus (42x65cm-17x26in) col lithograph. 26-Nov-3 Lempertz, Koln #615/R est:1500
£2118 $3600 €3092 Ange (38x28cm-15x11in) s. col lithograph exec.1956. 4-Nov-3 Christie's, Rockefeller NY #74/R est:2500-3500
£2147 $3800 €3135 Le chemin de croix (34x37cm-13x15in) s.num.18/35 aquatint. 30-Apr-4 Sotheby's, New York #63 est:1500-2000
£2158 $3540 €3000 Daphne and Chloe (42x32cm-17x13in) i. verso col lithograph. 4-Jun-3 Ketterer, Hamburg #247/R est:4000-5000
£2162 $4000 €3157 Painter with hat (64x48cm-25x19in) s. num.36/50 col lithograph. 13-Feb-4 David Rago, Lambertville #51/R est:2000-3000
£2183 $4017 €3187 L'homme a la thora (67x45cm-26x18in) s. col lithograph lit. 8-Jun-4 Germann, Zurich #310/R est:5000-5500 (S.FR 5000)
£2200 $3784 €3212 The bible, Sampson breaking the columns (29x24cm-11x9in) init.num.29/100 hand col etching. 4-Dec-3 Sotheby's, London #137/R est:2000-3000
£2200 $4026 €3212 L'ecuyere (37x53cm-15x21in) s. col lithograph. 3-Jun-4 Christie's, Kensington #33/R est:1500-2000
£2210 $4000 €3227 David et Bath-Scheba (28x25cm-11x10in) init.num.71/100 handcol etching. 19-Apr-4 Bonhams & Butterfields, San Francisco #141/R est:1500-2500
£2254 $3899 €3200 L'arber de Jesse (31x24cm-12x9in) s.i. col lithograph. 13-Dec-3 Lempertz, Koln #123/R est:3000
£2258 $4200 €3297 Le cirque (33x25cm-13x10in) s.num.9/40 col lithograph. 2-Mar-4 Swann Galleries, New York #120/R est:4000-6000
£2294 $3830 €3326 Branche aux joueurs de flute. s.i. lithograph. 19-Jun-3 Kornfeld, Bern #255 est:6000 (S.FR 5000)
£2346 $4200 €3425 Le manteau de noe (30x23cm-12x9in) init.mu.90/100 etching hand coloring W/C. 6-May-4 Swann Galleries, New York #420/R est:3500-5000
£2349 $4158 €3500 Nature morte bleue (28x39cm-11x15in) col lithograph exec.1957. 29-Apr-4 Piasa, Paris #147/R est:1200-1500
£2361 $3731 €3400 L'ecuyere au cheval rouge (31x24cm-12x9in) col lithograph lit. 19-Sep-3 Schloss Ahlden, Ahlden #804/R est:3800
£2366 $4400 €3454 De mauvais sujets (35x27cm-14x11in) s.num.9/9 col aquatint. 2-Mar-4 Swann Galleries, New York #117/R est:3000-5000
£2373 $4200 €3465 Lovers heaven (32x24cm-13x9in) s.num.10/40 col lithograph. 30-Apr-4 Sotheby's, New York #58 est:2000-3000
£2378 $4090 €3400 Le concert (36x56cm-14x22in) s. col lithograph. 2-Dec-3 Hauswedell & Nolte, Hamburg #76/R est:2500
£2378 $4090 €3400 Le joueur de flute (26x44cm-10x17in) s. col lithograph. 2-Dec-3 Hauswedell & Nolte, Hamburg #77/R est:3000
£2381 $4262 €3476 Motherhood and centaur (38x33cm-15x13in) s.i. col lithograph lit.prov. 22-Mar-4 Philippe Schuler, Zurich #4005/R est:3300-4600 (S.FR 5500)
£2390 $3800 €3489 Megacles recognises his daughter. lithograph. 14-Sep-3 Susanin's, Chicago #6050/R est:1500-2000
£2400 $4368 €3504 Le village (34x24cm-13x9in) s.num.16/35 etching. 30-Jun-4 Christie's, London #193 est:1200-1800
£2400 $4368 €3504 Eiffel Tower with donkey (39x28cm-15x11in) s.num.32/75 col lithograph. 1-Jul-4 Sotheby's, London #118/R est:3000-4000
£2402 $4419 €3507 Wedding - from 'My life' (18x21cm-7x8in) s. etching lit. 8-Jun-4 Germann, Zurich #309/R est:5500-6000 (S.FR 5500)
£2412 $4439 €3522 La maison de mon village (43x32cm-17x13in) s. num.29/40 col lithograph. 23-Jun-4 Koller, Zurich #3225/R est:2500-3500 (S.FR 5500)
£2432 $4500 €3551 Artist phoenix (60x41cm-24x16in) s.num.8/50 col lithograph. 12-Feb-4 Christie's, Rockefeller NY #299/R est:3500-4500
£2432 $4500 €3551 L'arbre vert aux amourex (64x48cm-25x19in) s. num.44/50 col lithograph. 13-Feb-4 David Rago, Lambertville #52/R est:3000-4000
£2448 $4161 €3500 Adam and Eve, banishment from paradise (36x27cm-14x11in) s. col lithograph. 29-Nov-3 Villa Grisebach, Berlin #309/R est:3500-4500
£2448 $4161 €3500 Rahad and scouts in Jericho (36x27cm-14x11in) s. col lithograph. 29-Nov-3 Villa Grisebach, Berlin #313/R est:3500-4500
£2467 $4539 €3700 Bella (22x11cm-9x4in) s.i. eau forte drypoint aquatint. 10-Jun-4 Piasa, Paris #27
£2471 $4200 €3608 La jongleuse (31x24cm-12x9in) s.num.22/40 col lithograph. 6-Nov-3 Swann Galleries, New York #519/R est:4000-6000
£2489 $4231 €3634 Joseph Shepherd (34x26cm-13x10in) mono. col etching. 25-Nov-3 Germann, Zurich #297/R est:2500-3000 (S.FR 5500)

£2500	$4250	€3650	Bouquet vert et violet (44x57cm-17x22in) s. col lithograph. 31-Oct-3 Sotheby's, New York #223
£2500	$4300	€3650	L'ateleir de nuit (50x38cm-20x15in) s.num.12/50 col lithograph. 4-Dec-3 Sotheby's, London #140/R est:2500-3000
£2500	$4250	€3650	Red rooster (36x48cm-14x19in) s. num.50/200 col lithograph exec.1952. 1-Dec-3 Bonhams, New Bond Street #139/R est:600-800
£2500	$4550	€3650	Paradise (39x27cm-15x11in) s.num.16/50 col lithograph. 1-Jul-4 Sotheby's, London #124/R est:3000-4000
£2533	$4610	€3698	Jeremie. s.i. col lithograph. 17-Jun-4 Kornfeld, Bern #255 est:5000 (S.FR 5800)
£2538	$4569	€3705	Autoportrait a la veste noire (60x48cm-24x19in) s.num.28/30 lithograph lit. 26-Apr-4 Bukowskis, Stockholm #307/R est:20000-30000 (S.KR 35000)
£2542	$4500	€3711	Moses (60x41cm-24x16in) s.num.46/50 col lithograph. 30-Apr-4 Sotheby's, New York #53/R est:3000-5000
£2552	$4261	€3700	Paysan au bouquet (32x22cm-13x9in) s. num.4/50 col lithograph. 13-Nov-3 Neumeister, Munich #280/R est:3000-3500
£2569	$4290	€3725	Le cheval au parapluie. s. etching. 19-Jun-3 Kornfeld, Bern #246/R est:5000 (S.FR 5600)
£2588	$4400	€3778	Autoportrait au couple (65x50cm-26x20in) s.num.10/30 lithograph. 6-Nov-3 Swann Galleries, New York #521/R est:5000-8000
£2600	$4680	€3900	Revolution (54x47cm-21x19in) s. col lithograph exec.1963 lit. 22-Apr-4 Finarte Semenzato, Rome #25/R est:2500-3000
£2682	$4800	€3916	Vision d'esaie (32x25cm-13x10in) init.num.74/1000 etching hand coloring W/C. 6-May-4 Swann Galleries, New York #419/R est:3000-5000
£2703	$4757	€4000	Lovers in Paris (64x51cm-25x20in) s. lithograph. 18-May-4 Segre, Madrid #339/R est:4000
£2715	$4615	€3964	Flowering tree (50x39cm-20x15in) s. lithograph prov. 22-Nov-3 Burkhard, Luzern #105/R est:5000-6000 (S.FR 6000)
£2756	$4960	€4024	Le peintre devant le village II (38x29cm-15x11in) s.num.25/50 col lithograph lit. 26-Apr-4 Bukowskis, Stockholm #310/R est:35000-40000 (S.KR 38000)
£2793	$5000	€4078	Dessins pour la bible-couverture (40x59cm-16x23in) s.num.48/50 color lithograph. 6-May-4 Swann Galleries, New York #422/R est:6000-9000
£2793	$5000	€4078	Double visage gris (42x31cm-17x12in) s.num.42/50 lithograph. 6-May-4 Swann Galleries, New York #426/R est:3500-5000
£2796	$5200	€4082	La jongleuse (31x24cm-12x9in) s.num.9/40 col lithograph. 2-Mar-4 Swann Galleries, New York #121/R est:4000-6000
£2800	$5152	€4200	Nu a l'eventail (21x28cm-8x11in) s.i. eau forte drypoint. 10-Jun-4 Piasa, Paris #26/R
£2800	$5096	€4088	Blessing of Joshua (32x24cm-13x9in) init.num.90/100 hand col etching. 1-Jul-4 Sotheby's, London #125/R est:3000-4000
£2800	$5096	€4200	Black and blue bouquet (25x17cm-10x7in) s.num.70/90 col lithograph. 2-Jul-4 Bloomsbury, London #293/R est:2000-2500
£2824	$4800	€4123	Le cirque (33x25cm-13x10in) s.num.23/40 col lithograph. 6-Nov-3 Swann Galleries, New York #518/R est:3000-5000
£2900	$5278	€4234	De mauvais sujets (37x27cm-15x11in) init.i. col etching aquatint. 30-Jun-4 Christie's, London #191/R est:1800-2200
£2917	$4871	€4200	Maternite au centaure. s.num.44/90 col lithograph. 23-Oct-3 Credit Municipal, Paris #48 est:2000-2500
£2945	$4800	€4300	Cirque (43x65cm-17x26in) col lithograph on Arches edition of 250 executed 1967. 24-Sep-3 Christie's, Rockefeller NY #65/R est:3000-5000
£2969	$5404	€4335	Le nuage aux amoureux. s.i. col etching. 17-Jun-4 Kornfeld, Bern #251/R est:5000 (S.FR 6800)
£2982	$4979	€4324	Lumiere du cirque. s.i. col lithograph. 19-Jun-3 Kornfeld, Bern #259/R est:6000 (S.FR 6500)
£2994	$5000	€4371	Chloe if carried off by the methymneans (43x64cm-17x25in) col lithograph. 11-Nov-3 Doyle, New York #227/R est:4000-6000
£3000	$5520	€4380	Le petit cheval (34x27cm-13x11in) s. num.32/50 lithograph. 28-Jun-4 Bonhams, New Bond Street #102/R est:3000-5000
£3000	$5460	€4380	De mauvais sujets (37x27cm-15x11in) init.i. col etching. 30-Jun-4 Christie's, London #192/R est:1800-2200
£3000	$5490	€4380	Akt mit Facher (21x28cm-8x11in) s. etching edition of 100. 3-Jun-4 Christie's, Kensington #30/R est:1800-2200
£3017	$5400	€4405	Ruth at the feet of Boaz (36x26cm-14x10in) s. num.47/50 color lithograph. 6-May-4 Swann Galleries, New York #423/R est:5000-8000
£3020	$5346	€4500	Day break (54x42cm-21x17in) s.i. col lithograph. 30-Apr-4 Dr Fritz Nagel, Stuttgart #757/R est:4000
£3103	$5152	€4500	Les coqs sur le toit (34x39cm-13x15in) s.i. col etching. 2-Oct-3 Dorotheum, Salzburg #28/R est:3000
£3107	$5500	€4536	Le Fleuve vert (28x55cm-11x22in) s.num.10/50 col lithograph. 28-Apr-4 Christie's, Rockefeller NY #16/R est:3500-4500
£3111	$5382	€4542	Three green horses (33x25cm-13x10in) s. num.38/50 lithograph. 9-Dec-3 Maynards, Vancouver #181 est:9000-10000 (C.D 7000)
£3119	$5209	€4523	La tribu de Juda. s.i. col lithograph. 19-Jun-3 Kornfeld, Bern #262/R est:4000 (S.FR 6800)
£3125	$4938	€4500	Falling angel (37x27cm-15x11in) s. col lithograph lit. 19-Sep-3 Schloss Ahlden, Ahlden #812/R est:4500
£3144	$5722	€4590	Equilibriste sur cheval. s.i. lithograph. 17-Jun-4 Kornfeld, Bern #256/R est:5000 (S.FR 7200)
£3147	$5413	€4500	Le village grise (68x62cm-27x24in) s. num.17/50 col lithograph. 5-Dec-3 Ketterer, Munich #123/R est:5000-7000
£3200	$5504	€4672	L'arbre vert aux amoureux (50x38cm-20x15in) s.num.44/50 col lithograph. 4-Dec-3 Sotheby's, London #139/R est:2800-3200
£3200	$5504	€4672	Vision of Paris (48x32cm-19x13in) s.num.11/40 col lithograph. 4-Dec-3 Sotheby's, London #142/R est:3000-3500
£3200	$5504	€4672	Circus rider with bouquet (33x25cm-13x10in) s.i.num.40 col lithograph. 2-Dec-3 Christie's, London #110/R est:2800-3200
£3200	$5824	€4672	L'artiste et themes bibliques (38x58cm-15x23in) s.i. col lithograph. 1-Jul-4 Sotheby's, London #154/R est:2500-3000
£3217	$5469	€4600	Aragon poems V (39x29cm-15x11in) s.num.3/25 col etching. 29-Nov-3 Bukowskis, Helsinki #336/R est:3000-5000
£3315	$6000	€4840	Village (29x39cm-11x15in) s.num.45/50 col lithograph. 19-Apr-4 Bonhams & Butterfields, San Francisco #149/R est:4000-6000
£3333	$6133	€5000	Couverture (38x59cm-15x23in) s. col lithograph exec. 1960 one of 50. 12-Jun-4 Villa Grisebach, Berlin #376/R est:5000-7000
£3379	$6048	€5000	Meditation (60x44cm-24x17in) s. num.22/50 col lithograph exec.1979. 4-May-4 Calmels Cohen, Paris #47/R est:3500-4000
£3385	$5822	€4942	Reprenez, muses, reprenez avec moi le chant bucolique (65x50cm-26x20in) s.num.19/75 col lithograph. 7-Dec-3 Uppsala Auktionskammare, Uppsala #335/R est:40000-50000 (S.KR 44000)
£3390	$6000	€4949	On the track (47x24cm-19x9in) s.i. col lithograph. 30-Apr-4 Sotheby's, New York #61/R est:8000-10000
£3399	$5778	€4963	Le coq rouge (37x44cm-15x17in) s.num.35/200 col lithograph. 4-Nov-3 Bukowskis, Stockholm #330/R est:40000-45000 (S.KR 45000)
£3443	$5750	€5027	Megacles recognizes his daughter during the feast (41x64cm-16x25in) col lithograph. 11-Nov-3 Doyle, New York #228/R est:4000-6000
£3467	$6275	€5200	Sirene au pin (74x52cm-29x20in) s. num.XXIII/LXXV col lithograph. 1-Apr-4 Credit Municipal, Paris #19/R est:3000-4000
£3472	$5660	€5000	Sunday (39x28cm-15x11in) s.i. col lithograph. 27-Sep-3 Dr Fritz Nagel, Stuttgart #9506/R est:3000
£3474	$5906	€5072	Le paysan (32x26cm-13x10in) s.num.34/75 col lithograph. 4-Nov-3 Bukowskis, Stockholm #334a/R est:25000-30000 (S.KR 46000)
£3481	$6265	€5082	Trapeziste a l'oiseau (28x22cm-11x9in) s.num.28/75 col lithograph lit. 26-Apr-4 Bukowskis, Stockholm #308/R est:50000-60000 (S.KR 48000)
£3486	$5822	€5055	Musician. s.d.1922 etching drypoint. 19-Jun-3 Kornfeld, Bern #243 est:7500 (S.FR 7600)
£3497	$6014	€5000	L'artiste I (34x27cm-13x11in) s. col lithograph edition of 50. 3-Dec-3 Beaussant & Lefèvre, Paris #2/R est:2500-3000
£3500	$6405	€5110	Saint-Germain-des-Pres (40x28cm-16x11in) s.i. col lithograph. 3-Jun-4 Christie's, Kensington #32/R est:3000-4000
£3500	$6370	€5110	Der gelbe hahn (45x29cm-18x11in) s.num.68/75 col etching aquatint. 1-Jul-4 Sotheby's, London #126/R est:3500-4500
£3500	$6370	€5110	In the Land of the Gods, by the Water of Aulis (64x50cm-25x20in) s.num.XIV/XX col lithograph. 1-Jul-4 Sotheby's, London #136/R est:3000-4000
£3500	$6370	€5110	Fiancailles au cirque (41x31cm-16x12in) s.i. lithograph. 1-Jul-4 Sotheby's, London #155/R est:3000-4000
£3529	$6000	€5152	Rural composition (35x31cm-14x12in) s. col lithograph. 31-Oct-3 Sotheby's, New York #228
£3529	$6000	€5152	Piege (39x29cm-15x11in) s. col lithograph. 31-Oct-3 Sotheby's, New York #225
£3533	$6466	€5300	Poster for the town of Vence (64x50cm-25x20in) s. col lithograph. 5-Jun-4 Lempertz, Koln #629/R est:4000-5000
£3550	$6035	€5183	Pour Berggruen (28x20cm-11x8in) s.num.46/75 col.lithograph lit. 5-Nov-3 AB Stockholms Auktionsverk #1197/R est:35000-40000 (S.KR 47000)
£3593	$6000	€5246	Self portrait with laughing expression (28x23cm-11x9in) s.num.33/100 etching. 11-Nov-3 Doyle, New York #226/R est:7000-9000
£3610	$6643	€5271	L'ecuyere au cheval rouge (52x47cm-20x19in) lithograph in colour lit. 29-Mar-4 Rasmussen, Copenhagen #182/R est:15000 (D.KR 40000)
£3672	$6500	€5361	Munu pour une reception sur le bateau-mouche (24x15cm-9x6in) s.num.69/75 col lithograph. 30-Apr-4 Sotheby's, New York #54/R est:5000-7000
£3672	$6500	€5361	Studio at night (50x38cm-20x15in) s.num.8/50 col lithograph. 30-Apr-4 Sotheby's, New York #71/R est:3000-5000
£3776	$6420	€5513	Le prophete (69x53cm-27x21in) s.num.49/50 col lithograph lit. 4-Nov-3 Bukowskis, Stockholm #343/R est:60000-70000 (S.KR 50000)
£3800	$6536	€5548	St German-des-Pres (38x28cm-15x11in) s.num.26/75 col lithograph. 4-Dec-3 Sotheby's, London #143/R est:3500-4000
£3800	$6916	€5548	Fleur d'Art (61x44cm-24x17in) s. num.3/50 pencil lithograph printed colours prov.lit. 4-Feb-4 Sotheby's, Olympia #110/R est:4000-5000
£3800	$6802	€5548	Blue cow (46x33cm-18x13in) s.i. lithograph. 11-May-4 Sotheby's, Olympia #627/R est:2000-3000
£3800	$6916	€5548	L'artiste a la chevre (32x24cm-13x9in) s.num.29/50 col lithograph. 1-Jul-4 Sotheby's, London #151/R est:3000-4000
£3819	$6035	€5500	Bouquet (75x56cm-30x22in) s. col lithograph lit. 19-Sep-3 Schloss Ahlden, Ahlden #808/R est:5800
£3824	$6500	€5583	Composition (67x51cm-26x20in) s. col lithograph. 31-Oct-3 Sotheby's, New York #226
£3824	$6500	€5583	Abraham and the three angels (38x32cm-15x13in) s. col lithograph. 31-Oct-3 Sotheby's, New York #231/R
£3824	$6500	€5583	Couple in ochre (64x50cm-25x20in) s.num.27/100 col lithograph. 6-Nov-3 Swann Galleries, New York #516/R est:7000-10000
£3824	$6500	€5583	Le petite mariee (28x33cm-11x13in) s.num.46/50 col lithograph. 6-Nov-3 Swann Galleries, New York #524/R est:4000-6000
£3843	$6994	€5611	L'artiste et themes bibliques. s.i. col lithograph. 17-Jun-4 Kornfeld, Bern #257/R est:10000 (S.FR 8800)
£3892	$6500	€5682	Le grand paysan (75x57cm-30x22in) s.num.29/50 col lithograph. 21-Oct-3 Bonhams & Butterfields, San Francisco #1165/R
£3955	$7000	€5774	Flowers of the fields (51x38cm-20x15in) s.num.31/50 col lithograph. 28-Apr-4 Christie's, Rockefeller NY #17/R est:4000-6000
£3955	$7000	€5774	Green and purple bouquet (44x57cm-17x22in) s.num.17/75 col lithograph. 28-Apr-4 Christie's, Rockefeller NY #11/R est:5000-7000
£3955	$7000	€5774	Flowers of the fields (50x38cm-20x15in) s.num.8/50 col lithograph. 30-Apr-4 Sotheby's, New York #70/R est:3000-5000
£4000	$6680	€5800	Bunch of white flowers (60x39cm-24x15in) s. num.5/50 col lithograph. 13-Nov-3 Neumeister, Munich #281/R est:4500-5500
£4000	$7280	€5840	L'artiste II (34x26cm-13x10in) s.num.26/50 col lithograph. 1-Jul-4 Sotheby's, London #144/R est:3000-4000
£4000	$7280	€5840	Les trois nus (36x27cm-14x11in) s.num.17/50 col lithograph. 1-Jul-4 Sotheby's, London #152/R est:3000-4000
£4027	$7128	€6000	Douze maquettes de vitraux pour Jerusalem: La tribu de Gad (74x53cm-29x21in) s.i. col lithograph. 30-Apr-4 Dr Fritz Nagel, Stuttgart #758/R est:2000
£4027	$7208	€6000	Anne au b. s. num.20/50 lithograph. 25-May-4 Durán, Madrid #700/R est:3000
£4061	$7473	€5929	Les amoureux (56x77cm-22x30in) s.num.45/50 lithograph lit. 29-Mar-4 Rasmussen, Copenhagen #81/R est:20000-25000 (D.KR 45000)
£4072	$6923	€5945	Le paradis bleu (91x66cm-36x26in) s. col lithograph lit. 25-Nov-3 Germann, Zurich #302/R est:6000-8000 (S.FR 9000)
£4128	$6894	€5986	Autoportrait au chapeau orne. s. drypoint. 19-Jun-3 Kornfeld, Bern #247/R est:7500 (S.FR 9000)
£4133	$7605	€6200	Le soir d'ete (61x42cm-24x17in) s. num.17/50 col lithograph exec. 1968. 9-Jun-4 Christie's, Amsterdam #249/R est:5000-7000
£4133	$7605	€6200	Les cyclistes (64x49cm-25x19in) s.i. lithograph exec. 1956 one of 30. 11-Jun-4 Villa Grisebach, Berlin #1599/R est:3000-4000
£4143	$7500	€6049	Moise et les Tables de la Loi (66x51cm-26x20in) s.num.45/50 col lithograph. 19-Apr-4 Bonhams & Butterfields, San Francisco #142/R est:5000-7000
£4143	$7500	€6049	Le mariage (63x44cm-25x17in) s.num.25/50 col etching aquatint. 19-Apr-4 Bonhams & Butterfields, San Francisco #145/R est:3000-4000
£4148	$7550	€6056	Sirene au pin (75x53cm-30x21in) s. num.75 col lithograph exec. 1967 lit. 16-Jun-4 Fischer, Luzern #2630/R est:3000-4000 (S.FR 9500)
£4154	$7062	€6065	Soleil Couchant (60x46cm-24x18in) s.num.XLVIII/LXXV col lithograph. 5-Nov-3 AB Stockholms Auktionsverk #1206/R est:50000-70000 (S.KR 55000)
£4167	$6583	€6000	Le paradis blue (91x67cm-36x26in) s. col lithograph lit. 19-Sep-3 Schloss Ahlden, Ahlden #811/R est:6500
£4190	$7500	€6117	Saint Germain de pres (38x28cm-15x11in) s. num.60/75 color lithograph. 6-May-4 Swann Galleries, New York #421/R est:4000-6000
£4190	$7500	€6117	Bonne annee (52x41cm-20x16in) s.i. color lithograph. 6-May-4 Swann Galleries, New York #425/R est:3000-5000
£4200	$7644	€6132	Le rendez-vous (42x32cm-17x13in) s.num.35/50 col lithograph. 1-Jul-4 Sotheby's, London #153/R est:3000-4000
£4237	$7500	€6186	Celebration (30x52cm-12x20in) s.num.22/50 col lithograph. 30-Apr-4 Sotheby's, New York #77/R est:3000-5000
£4305	$7319	€6285	Le joie de vivre (36x56cm-14x22in) s.num.3/50 col lithograph lit. 4-Nov-3 Bukowskis, Stockholm #338/R est:40000-50000 (S.KR 57000)
£4332	$7971	€6325	Vierge aux poissons (76x56cm-30x22in) s.num.20/50 lithograph lit. 29-Mar-4 Rasmussen, Copenhagen #82/R est:20000-25000 (D.KR 48000)
£4332	$7971	€6325	David und Bethsabee (59x43cm-23x17in) s.num.17/50 lithograph in colour lit. 29-Mar-4 Rasmussen, Copenhagen #180/R est:40000 (D.KR 48000)
£4333	$7930	€6500	Blue paradise (76x57cm-30x22in) s. col lithograph. 5-Jun-4 Lempertz, Koln #637/R est:6000-7000
£4412	$7500	€6442	Red rooster (38x56cm-15x22in) s. col lithograph. 31-Oct-3 Sotheby's, New York #221/R

£4420	$8000	€6453	Exhibition poster (77x57cm-30x22in) s.num.140/150 col lithograph. 19-Apr-4 Bonhams & Butterfields, San Francisco #144/R est:8000-10000
£4497	$8409	€6700	Vision de Moise (98x73cm-39x29in) s. col lithograph. 1-Mar-4 Artcurial Briest, Paris #70/R est:6000-7000
£4500	$8190	€6570	Creation (95x60cm-37x24in) s.num.17/50 lithograph. 30-Jun-4 Christie's, London #196/R est:3000-5000
£4500	$8190	€6570	Poetess (44x35cm-17x14in) s.num.32/50 col lithograph. 1-Jul-4 Sotheby's, London #143/R est:2000-3500
£4520	$8000	€6599	Game (47x35cm-19x14in) s.num.12/50 col lithograph. 30-Apr-4 Sotheby's, New York #62/R est:6000-8000
£4520	$8000	€6599	Little red acrobat (31x24cm-12x9in) s.num.8/50 col lithograph. 30-Apr-4 Sotheby's, New York #69/R est:4000-6000
£4520	$8000	€6599	Appearance of King David (39x31cm-15x12in) s.num.8/50 col lithograph. 30-Apr-4 Sotheby's, New York #74/R est:3000-5000
£4532	$7704	€6617	Le petit nu (35x47cm-14x19in) s.num.37/50 col lithograph lit. 4-Nov-3 Bukowskis, Stockholm #339a/R est:60000-80000 (S.KR 60000)
£4545	$7818	€6500	The angel and the music (31x22cm-12x9in) col lithograph. 4-Dec-3 Van Ham, Cologne #84/R est:3500
£4545	$7818	€6500	Couple aux deux bouquets (38x30cm-15x12in) s. col lithograph. 2-Dec-3 Hauswedell & Nolte, Hamburg #81/R est:6000
£4587	$7661	€6651	Le cirque au clown jaune. s.i. col lithograph. 19-Jun-3 Kornfeld, Bern #257/R est:10000 (S.FR 10000)
£4601	$7500	€6717	Rachel Hides her father's Household Gods (50x38cm-20x15in) s. num.24/50 col lithograph exectued 1960. 24-Sep-3 Christie's, Rockefeller NY #64/R est:3000-4000
£4683	$7961	€6837	Le Repos (27x46cm-11x18in) s.i. col lithograph lit. 5-Nov-3 AB Stockholms Auktionsverk #1200/R est:40000-60000 (S.KR 62000)
£4755	$8084	€6800	Maternite (51x67cm-20x26in) s.i. col lithograph. 29-Nov-3 Villa Grisebach, Berlin #310/R est:4000-6000
£4790	$8000	€6993	Mimosas (61x43cm-24x17in) s.num.44/50 col lithograph. 21-Oct-3 Bonhams & Butterfields, San Francisco #1164/R
£4790	$8000	€6993	Three nudes (34x27cm-13x11in) s.num.12/50 col lithograph. 21-Oct-3 Bonhams & Butterfields, San Francisco #1166/R
£4800	$8736	€7008	Les quatres saisons (94x64cm-37x25in) s.i. col lithograph. 1-Jul-4 Sotheby's, London #145/R est:2500-3000
£4800	$8736	€7008	Les quatres saisons (94x64cm-37x25in) s.i. col lithograph. 1-Jul-4 Sotheby's, London #147/R est:2500-3000
£4802	$8500	€7011	David before Bethsheba (33x22cm-13x9in) s.num.8/50 col lithograph. 30-Apr-4 Sotheby's, New York #73/R est:3000-5000
£4802	$8500	€7011	Jacob and the Angels (37x30cm-15x12in) s.num.8/50 col lithograph. 30-Apr-4 Sotheby's, New York #75/R est:5000-7000
£4862	$8120	€7050	Grenade. s.i. col etching. 19-Jun-3 Kornfeld, Bern #249 est:7500 (S.FR 10600)
£4895	$8420	€7000	Paysage au coq (38x56cm-15x22in) s. col lithograph. 2-Dec-3 Hauswedell & Nolte, Hamburg #79/R est:6000
£4895	$8420	€7000	Le bouquet de Paris (65x44cm-26x17in) s.d.1954 col lithograph. 2-Dec-3 Hauswedell & Nolte, Hamburg #82/R est:7500
£4895	$8420	€7000	Les glaieuls (33x25cm-13x10in) s. col lithograph. 2-Dec-3 Hauswedell & Nolte, Hamburg #83/R est:4000
£5000	$8600	€7300	Clown a la chevre jaune (67x52cm-26x20in) s.num.15/50 col lithograph. 4-Dec-3 Sotheby's, London #138/R est:5000-7000
£5000	$8600	€7300	La famille au coq (60x40cm-24x16in) s.i. col lithograph. 2-Dec-3 Christie's, London #111/R est:4000-6000
£5000	$9200	€7500	Paysan au bouquet (31x22cm-12x9in) s. col lithograph. 10-Jun-4 Hauswedell & Nolte, Hamburg #70/R est:5000
£5000	$9100	€7300	Blue sky (68x52cm-27x20in) s.num.58/90 col lithograph. 1-Jul-4 Sotheby's, London #128/R est:4000-6000
£5000	$9100	€7300	La vache bleue (33x25cm-13x10in) s.num.68/75 col lithograph. 1-Jul-4 Sotheby's, London #135/R est:3500-4000
£5000	$9100	€7300	Bouquet rouge et jaune (64x48cm-25x19in) col lithograph. 1-Jul-4 Sotheby's, London #138/R est:5000-6000
£5028	$9000	€7341	Le profil et l'enfant rouge (33x28cm-13x11in) s.num.9/40 color lithograph. 6-May-4 Swann Galleries, New York #424/R est:7000-10000
£5067	$9272	€7600	Bay (40x57cm-16x22in) s. col lithograph. 5-Jun-4 Lempertz, Koln #636/R est:8000
£5221	$9398	€7623	So I came forth of the sea - from Arabian Nights (38x28cm-15x11in) s.num.PI.5 53/90 col lithograph lit. 26-Apr-4 Bukowskis, Stockholm #305/R est:80000-100000 (S.KR 72000)
£5248	$9500	€7662	La famille au coq (60x40cm-24x16in) s.i. col lithograph. 19-Apr-4 Bonhams & Butterfields, San Francisco #146/R est:10000-15000
£5275	$9336	€7702	Le Soir d'Ete (60x42cm-24x17in) s.num.9/50 col lithograph lit. 27-Apr-4 AB Stockholms Auktionsverk #1252/R est:80000-100000 (S.KR 72000)
£5430	$9231	€7928	Le piege (56x42cm-22x17in) s. num.47/75 lithograph exec. 1962 prov. 22-Nov-3 Burkhard, Luzern #106/R est:12000-14000 (S.FR 12000)
£5438	$9245	€7939	Corbeille de fruits et ananas (67x51cm-26x20in) s.num.11/50 col lithograph. 4-Nov-3 Bukowskis, Stockholm #336/R est:80000-100000 (S.KR 72000)
£5442	$8653	€8000	Village bleu (38x31cm-15x12in) col lithograph. 18-Mar-3 Adjug'art, Brest #74/R
£5500	$10010	€8030	Le peintre a la palette (66x50cm-26x20in) s.num.62/70 col lithograph. 30-Jun-4 Christie's, London #183/R est:5000-7000
£5511	$9920	€8046	La fenetre entrouverte (37x27cm-15x11in) s.num.44/50 col.lithograph lit. 26-Apr-4 Bukowskis, Stockholm #311/R est:70000-90000 (S.KR 76000)
£5589	$9502	€8160	Le dauphin mort et les trois cents ecus - Dapnis et Chloe (43x32cm-17x13in) s.num.30/60 col lithograph. 4-Nov-3 Bukowskis, Stockholm #335/R est:70000-90000 (S.KR 74000)
£5650	$10000	€8249	Paris on holiday (39x52cm-15x20in) s.num.32/50 col lithograph. 28-Apr-4 Christie's, Rockefeller NY #18/R est:8000-10000
£5665	$9630	€8271	Le Jour de Mai (63x38cm-25x15in) s.i.num.10/50 col lithograph lit. 5-Nov-3 AB Stockholms Auktionsverk #1202/R est:75000-100000 (S.KR 75000)
£5921	$10895	€8645	Orpheus (28x44cm-11x17in) s. num.21/50 lithograph. 23-Jun-4 Koller, Zurich #3221 est:3500-5000 (S.FR 13500)
£5988	$10000	€8742	From, In the Land of the Gods, what is life, what is pleasure (50x38cm-20x15in) s.i.num.24/25 col lithograph. 21-Oct-3 Bonhams & Butterfields, San Francisco #1163/R
£6000	$10320	€8760	Opera (39x28cm-15x11in) s.num.12/75 col lithograph. 2-Dec-3 Christie's, London #106/R est:4000-6000
£6000	$10320	€8760	La petite Fenetre (33x25cm-13x10in) s.num.8/50 col lithograph. 2-Dec-3 Christie's, London #112/R est:3500-4500
£6114	$11127	€8926	My father's grave, page 20 of the series My Life (11x14cm-4x6in) s. num.110 etching drypoint exec. 1922. 18-Jun-4 Kornfeld, Bern #20/R est:15000 (S.FR 14000)
£6122	$9735	€9000	Nu (54x36cm-21x14in) col lithograph. 18-Mar-3 Adjug'art, Brest #73
£6215	$11000	€9074	Four tales from the Arabian nights (37x28cm-15x11in) col lithograph. 30-Apr-4 Sotheby's, New York #52/R est:4000-6000
£6215	$11000	€9074	Daphnis and Chloe, trampled flowers (42x32cm-17x13in) lithograph. 30-Apr-4 Sotheby's, New York #56/R est:5000-7000
£6294	$10825	€9000	Le fleuve (65x50cm-26x20in) s. col lithograph. 2-Dec-3 Hauswedell & Nolte, Hamburg #80/R est:7500
£6332	$11524	€9245	Le Pierrot. s.i. col etching. 17-Jun-4 Kornfeld, Bern #252/R est:12500 (S.FR 14500)
£6420	$10914	€9373	Les Saltimbanques (57x39cm-22x15in) s.nu.15/50 col lithograph lit. 4-Nov-3 Bukowskis, Stockholm #339/R est:80000-100000 (S.KR 85000)
£6422	$10725	€9312	Wedding. s. W/C over etching drypoint. 19-Jun-3 Kornfeld, Bern #241/R est:12500 (S.FR 14000)
£6471	$11000	€9448	Reading (67x51cm-26x20in) s. col lithograph exec.1973. 4-Nov-3 Christie's, Rockefeller NY #82/R est:8000-10000
£6500	$10790	€9490	Selbstbildnis mit lachendem gesicht (46x37cm-18x15in) s.i. etching drypoint. 6-Oct-3 Sotheby's, London #74/R est:5000-7000
£6587	$11000	€9617	Bouquet with lovers (66x48cm-26x19in) s.num.29/50 col lithograph. 11-Nov-3 Doyle, New York #230/R est:10000-15000
£6597	$11017	€9500	Clown fleuri (43x29cm-17x11in) s. num.13/40 lithograph W/C exec.1962 lit. 21-Oct-3 Sotheby's, Milan #381/R est:4800-6000
£7000	$12880	€10500	L'oiseau bleu (56x43cm-22x17in) s.i. col lithograph. 10-Jun-4 Hauswedell & Nolte, Hamburg #74/R est:8000
£7345	$13000	€10724	Reading (50x40cm-20x16in) s.i. col lithograph. 30-Apr-4 Sotheby's, New York #67/R est:8000-10000
£7386	$13000	€10784	Magic flight (94x58cm-37x23in) s.d.1980 col lithograph edn 34/50. 23-May-4 Hindman, Chicago #122/R est:10000-15000
£7500	$13650	€10950	La fable de syringe (42x32cm-17x13in) s.num.32/60 col lithograph. 30-Jun-4 Christie's, London #185/R est:3000-5000
£7553	$12840	€11027	Arabian Nights - Then the old woman mounted the Ilfrit's back (43x33cm-17x13in) s.num.57/90 col lithograph lit. 5-Nov-3 AB Stockholms Auktionsverk #1194/R est:110000-120000 (S.KR 100000)
£7553	$12840	€11027	L'Age d'Or (57x47cm-22x19in) s.num.25/50 col lithograph prov.lit. 5-Nov-3 AB Stockholms Auktionsverk #1199/R est:80000-100000 (S.KR 100000)
£7647	$13000	€11165	Peasants (77x60cm-30x24in) s. col lithograph one of 50. 4-Nov-3 Christie's, Rockefeller NY #78/R est:9000-11000
£7667	$14107	€11500	Femme au bouquet (62x46cm-24x18in) s.i. col lithograph. 10-Jun-4 Hauswedell & Nolte, Hamburg #73/R est:8000
£7910	$14000	€11549	Daphnis and Chloe, winter (42x33cm-17x13in) s.num.50/60 col lithograph. 30-Apr-4 Sotheby's, New York #55/R est:7000-9000
£7910	$14000	€11549	Angel violinist. Carrousel of the Louvre (49x36cm-19x14in) s.i. col lithograph two. 30-Apr-4 Sotheby's, New York #68/R est:7000-9000
£8000	$14560	€11680	Les amoreux dans le ciel a Saint Paul (44x61cm-17x24in) s.num.9/50 col etching aquatint. 30-Jun-4 Christie's, London #194/R est:7500-8500
£8000	$14640	€12000	David and Bathseba (36x27cm-14x11in) s. col lithograph prov. 5-Jun-4 Lempertz, Koln #631/R est:10000-12000
£8000	$14720	€12000	La nymphe bleue (60x50cm-24x20in) s. col lithograph exec. 1962 one of 50. 11-Jun-4 Villa Grisebach, Berlin #1600/R est:8000-10000
£8000	$14560	€11680	Carrousel of the Louvre (38x28cm-15x11in) s.num.44/75 col lithograph. 1-Jul-4 Sotheby's, London #127/R est:4000-6000
£8235	$14000	€12023	Abdullah discovered before him (42x33cm-17x13in) s.i. col lithograph exec.1948. 4-Nov-3 Christie's, Rockefeller NY #73/R est:12000-16000
£8235	$14000	€12023	We live among the flowers (65x50cm-26x20in) s. col lithograph exec.1967. 4-Nov-3 Christie's, Rockefeller NY #80/R est:12000-15000
£8392	$14266	€12000	From 'Arabian Nights' (37x28cm-15x11in) s. col lithograph. 29-Nov-3 Villa Grisebach, Berlin #314/R est:12000-15000
£8500	$14620	€12410	Les amoureux a l'Isba (60x95cm-24x37in) s.num.17/50 col lithograph. 2-Dec-3 Christie's, London #114/R est:7000-10000
£8500	$14620	€12410	Les deux rives (94x60cm-37x24in) s.num.13/50 col lithograph. 2-Dec-3 Christie's, London #116/R est:10000-15000
£8500	$14620	€12410	La parade (96x61cm-38x24in) s.num.50 col lithograph. 2-Dec-3 Christie's, London #117/R est:10000-15000
£8500	$15470	€12410	Daphnis and chloe, the wolf pit (42x32cm-17x13in) s.num.60/60 col lithograph. 1-Jul-4 Sotheby's, London #132/R est:8000-10000
£8702	$15664	€12705	Now the King loved science and geometry - from Arabian Nights (38x28cm-15x11in) s.num.PI.10 83/90 col lithograph lit. 26-Apr-4 Bukowskis, Stockholm #305a/R est:80000-100000 (S.KR 120000)
£8824	$15000	€12883	Circus girl rider (75x55cm-30x22in) s. col lithograph exec.1964. 4-Nov-3 Christie's, Rockefeller NY #77/R est:12000-15000
£9040	$16000	€13198	Arrival of Dionysophanes (42x32cm-17x13in) s.num.10/60 col lithograph. 28-Apr-4 Christie's, Rockefeller NY #13/R est:14000-18000
£9040	$16000	€13198	Dedication (45x39cm-18x15in) s.num.13/50 col lithograph. 30-Apr-4 Sotheby's, New York #64/R est:15000-20000
£9174	$15321	€13302	Autoportrait au sourire. s.i. etching drypoint. 19-Jun-3 Kornfeld, Bern #245/R est:22500 (S.FR 20000)
£9392	$17000	€13712	Red circle (48x63cm-19x25in) s.i. col lithograph. 19-Apr-4 Bonhams & Butterfields, San Francisco #143/R est:20000-25000
£9500	$17290	€13870	Paysage bleu (49x65cm-19x26in) s.num.60/90 col lithograph. 30-Jun-4 Christie's, London #186/R est:8000-12000
£9500	$17290	€13870	L'ecuyere (63x52cm-25x20in) s.i. col lithograph. 1-Jul-4 Sotheby's, London #131/R est:9000-11000
£9605	$17000	€14023	Island of Poros (43x36cm-17x14in) s.num.8/50 col lithograph. 30-Apr-4 Sotheby's, New York #72/R est:8000-12000
£10000	$18200	€14600	Festin nuptial dans la grotte des nymphes (42x64cm-17x25in) s.num.52/60 col lithograph. 30-Jun-4 Christie's, London #187/R est:10000-15000
£10000	$18200	€14600	Le bouquet bleu (76x56cm-30x22in) s.num.49/50 col lithograph. 1-Jul-4 Sotheby's, London #142/R est:10000-12000
£10044	$18279	€14664	The birth, page 6 of the series My Life (12x17cm-5x7in) s. etching W/C exec. 1922. 18-Jun-4 Kornfeld, Bern #19/R est:25000 (S.FR 23000)
£10067	$18020	€15000	Le peintre a la palette (58x49cm-23x19in) s. col lithograph. 25-May-4 Karl & Faber, Munich #228/R est:18000-20000
£10211	$17665	€14500	Festin nuptial dans la grotte des nymphes (76x54cm-30x21in) s. lithograph exec. 1961 one of 60. 14-Dec-3 Rabourdin & Choppin de Janvry, Paris #3/R est:6000-8000
£10500	$19110	€15330	Bouquet aux amoureux (64x84cm-25x33in) s.i. col lithograph. 1-Jul-4 Sotheby's, London #141/R est:8000-10000
£10563	$18275	€15000	Danseuse refletee dans la glace (33x49cm-13x19in) s. lithograph one of 50 exec. 1927. 14-Dec-3 Rabourdin & Choppin de Janvry, Paris #5/R est:10000-12000
£10588	$18000	€15458	Multicolour bouquet (68x56cm-27x22in) s. col lithograph. 31-Oct-3 Sotheby's, New York #230/R
£10588	$18000	€15458	Golden Age (62x51cm-24x20in) s. col lithograph exec.1968. 4-Nov-3 Christie's, Rockefeller NY #81/R est:15000-20000
£10588	$18000	€15458	Lilac (116x75cm-46x30in) s. num.5/50 col lithograph exec.1980. 4-Nov-3 Christie's, Rockefeller NY #84/R est:18000-22000
£10734	$19000	€15672	Circus with the angel (73x56cm-29x22in) s.i. col lithograph. 30-Apr-4 Sotheby's, New York #65/R est:15000-20000
£10952	$18618	€15990	Le bouquet bleu (67x48cm-26x19in) s.num.49/50 col lithograph lit. 4-Nov-3 Bukowskis, Stockholm #342/R est:120000-140000 (S.KR 145000)
£11173	$20000	€16313	Les amoureux a l'Isba (75x116cm-30x46in) s.num.6/50 color lithograph. 6-May-4 Swann Galleries, New York #427/R est:18000-22000

£11240	$20232	€16410	Then the boy displayed to the Dervish - from Arabian Nights (38x28cm-15x11in) s.num.PI.1 53/90 col lithograph prov.lit. 26-Apr-4 Bukowskis, Stockholm #304/R est:120000-140000 (S.KR 155000)
£12000	$21840	€17520	Paris from my window (83x60cm-33x24in) s.i. col lithograph. 1-Jul-4 Sotheby's, London #129/R est:14000-18000
£12328	$22190	€17999	Le jardin de Pomone (60x43cm-24x17in) s.num.28/50 col lithograph lit. 26-Apr-4 Bukowskis, Stockholm #309/R est:200000-250000 (S.KR 170000)
£12429	$22000	€18146	Paris square (52x38cm-20x15in) s.num.64/75 col lithograph. 30-Apr-4 Sotheby's, New York #66/R est:15000-20000
£12462	$21186	€18195	Mounting the ebony horse - from Arabian Nights (38x29cm-15x11in) s.num.18/90 col lithograph. 4-Nov-3 Bukowskis, Stockholm #329/R est:100000-120000 (S.KR 165000)
£13000	$23660	€18980	Golden age (57x47cm-22x19in) s.num.30/50 col lithograph. 1-Jul-4 Sotheby's, London #130/R est:8000-12000
£13000	$23660	€18980	Paysage bleu (58x75cm-23x30in) s.num.22/90 col lithograph. 1-Jul-4 Sotheby's, London #122/R est:8000-10000
£13287	$22587	€19000	Sorcerer of Paris II (88x68cm-35x27in) s. col lithograph. 29-Nov-3 Villa Grisebach, Berlin #311/R est:18000-24000
£14000	$25480	€20440	Autour du soleil (41x30cm-16x12in) s. monotype. 30-Jun-4 Christie's, London #195/R est:10000-15000
£14000	$25480	€20440	Le femme du peintre (65x51cm-26x20in) s.num.15/50 col lithograph. 30-Jun-4 Christie's, London #188/R est:15000-20000
£14000	$25620	€21000	Bay of Angels (78x58cm-31x23in) s. col lithograph. 5-Jun-4 Lempertz, Koln #635/R est:20000-22000
£14118	$24000	€20612	Hymen (54x76cm-21x30in) s. col lithograph exec.1961. 4-Nov-3 Christie's, Rockefeller NY #76/R est:16000-20000
£14689	$26000	€21446	Le cirque (42x32cm-17x13in) s.num.16/24 col lithograph. 28-Apr-4 Christie's, Rockefeller NY #15/R est:18000-22000
£14689	$26000	€21446	Der geiger (21x16cm-8x6in) s. etching hand coloring. 30-Apr-4 Sotheby's, New York #51/R est:20000-25000
£14706	$25000	€21471	Cirque (42x32cm-17x13in) s. col lithograph. 31-Oct-3 Sotheby's, New York #229/R
£15000	$25800	€21900	Nicolas Gogol (40x30cm-16x12in) etching aquatint set of 96 in a book. 2-Dec-3 Christie's, London #107/R est:15000-20000
£15000	$27300	€21900	Artist's bouquet, behind the looking glass (37x28cm-15x11in) s.i. hand col lithograph. 1-Jul-4 Sotheby's, London #137/R est:12000-18000
£15000	$27300	€21900	Gogol les ames mortes (40x30cm-16x12in) s.num.318 etchings complete set of 96 in two volumes. 1-Jul-4 Sotheby's, London #120/R est:18000-22000
£15819	$28000	€23096	Lilac (92x60cm-36x24in) s.num.7/50 col lithograph. 30-Apr-4 Sotheby's, New York #76/R est:20000-30000
£16000	$29120	€23360	L'arc en ciel (69x69cm-27x27in) s.i. col lithograph. 1-Jul-4 Sotheby's, London #121/R est:12000-14000
£16514	$27578	€23945	L'age d'or. s.i. col lithograph. 19-Jun-3 Kornfeld, Bern #258 est:30000 (S.FR 36000)
£18000	$32760	€26280	La Bastille (51x66cm-20x26in) s.i. col lithograph. 30-Jun-4 Christie's, London #184/R est:15000-25000
£18000	$32760	€26280	Maternite rouge (94x60cm-37x24in) s.num.45/50 col lithograph. 1-Jul-4 Sotheby's, London #149/R est:12000-18000
£19000	$32680	€27740	Petit coq rouge (30x40cm-12x16in) s. col monotype. 2-Dec-3 Christie's, London #108/R est:10000-15000
£19856	$36534	€28990	Figure composition (64x48cm-25x19in) s.d.1949 num.120/400 lithograph in colour hand painted gouache. 29-Mar-4 Rasmussen, Copenhagen #83/R est:60000 (D.KR 220000)
£24891	$45301	€36341	Le nuage aux amoureux (38x34cm-15x13in) etching W/C exec. 1968. 18-Jun-4 Kornfeld, Bern #21/R est:40000 (S.FR 57000)
£33898	$60000	€49491	Tribute to the Eiffel Tower (76x56cm-30x22in) s.i. hand col lithograph. 30-Apr-4 Sotheby's, New York #60/R est:30000-40000
£35294	$60000	€51529	Bible (47x36cm-19x14in) s. etching album. 4-Nov-3 Christie's, Rockefeller NY #75/R est:30000-40000
£38235	$65000	€55823	Matin (50x40cm-20x16in) s. monotype Japan paper exec 1962 prov.lit. 6-Nov-3 Sotheby's, New York #347/R est:70000-90000
£39161	$67357	€56000	The present (25x18cm-10x7in) s. etching gouache W/C. 2-Dec-3 Hauswedell & Nolte, Hamburg #65/R est:65000
£44000	$80080	€64240	L'homme au samovar (41x27cm-16x11in) s.i. hand col lithograph prov. 1-Jul-4 Sotheby's, London #119/R est:40000-60000
£108824	$185000	€158883	Cirque (45x34cm-18x13in) col lithograph album. 4-Nov-3 Christie's, Rockefeller NY #79/R est:120000-160000
£167500	$304850	€244550	Longus Daphnis and Chloe (45x35cm-18x14in) s.num.63 col lithographs forty-two slip case. 1-Jul-4 Sotheby's, London #133/R est:120000-180000
£209040	$370000	€305198	Longus, Daphnis et Chloe, Teriade Editeur, Paris (45x35cm-18x14in) col lithograph 42 slipcase. 28-Apr-4 Christie's, Rockefeller NY #12/R est:320000-350000

Sculpture

£4000	$6680	€5840	Cadeau de mariage (15x15cm-6x6in) s. painted glazed ceramic bowl. 22-Oct-3 Sotheby's, Olympia #89/R est:4000-6000
£22000	$40040	€32120	La traversee de la mer rouge (33x20cm-13x8in) s.verso glazed ceramic executed 1956 prov.exhib.lit. 4-Feb-4 Sotheby's, London #326/R est:18000-25000

Works on paper

£704	$1127	€1000	Page from 'Burning Lights' by Bella Chagall (22x14cm-9x6in) s. col. 19-Sep-3 Sigalas, Stuttgart #292/R
£929	$1700	€1356	Untitled. s. ink envelope stamp. 1-Feb-4 Ben-Ami, Tel Aviv #4648/R est:1600-2400
£1991	$3325	€2907	Homme au bouquet de fleurs (27x21cm-11x8in) s. pastel Indian ink on original letter. 24-Jun-3 Germann, Zurich #170/R est:4500-5500 (S.FR 4400)
£2448	$4087	€3500	Le Jardin d'Eden (25x32cm-10x13in) s. col lithograph. 28-Jun-3 Bolland & Marotz, Bremen #819/R est:4900
£2750	$4400	€4015	Costume designs for Aleko. i. W/C gouache seven. 18-Sep-3 Swann Galleries, New York #150/R est:3000-5000
£3022	$5500	€4412	Artist at an easel (35x53cm-14x21in) s.i.d.1950 ink W/C oilstick. 29-Jun-4 Sotheby's, New York #343/R est:4000-6000
£3500	$5600	€5110	Costume designs for Aleko (56x36cm-22x14in) i. W/C gouache over pencil four. 18-Sep-3 Swann Galleries, New York #147/R est:8000-12000
£3873	$6701	€5500	Pour Pierrette Sorlier (27x20cm-11x8in) s.i.d.1965-6 pastel chk col pen. 13-Dec-3 Lempertz, Koln #122/R est:7500
£4363	$8115	€6500	Le peintre a son chevalet (26x19cm-10x7in) s.i.d.1975 felt Indian ink. 2-Mar-4 Artcurial Briest, Paris #100/R est:6500-7500
£4396	$8000	€6418	Moses with the tablets (30x23cm-12x9in) s.i. ink wash executed c.1950 prov. 29-Jun-4 Sotheby's, New York #341/R est:4000-6000
£5090	$8500	€7431	Profil vert aux deux yeux (33x25cm-13x10in) s.i. col crayon exec.c.1970. 7-Oct-3 Sotheby's, New York #301 est:7000-9000
£5376	$10000	€7849	Peintre avec pallete et cheval (45x28cm-18x11in) s. pen ink pastel painted with unknown artist. 2-Mar-4 Swann Galleries, New York #125/R est:10000-15000
£5389	$9000	€7868	Bouquet pour Silvia Lyons (31x24cm-12x9in) s.i. col crayon exec.c.1972. 7-Oct-3 Sotheby's, New York #302 est:7000-9000
£6044	$11000	€8824	Couple on a horse (31x25cm-12x10in) s.i.d.1950 ink wash prov. 29-Jun-4 Sotheby's, New York #340/R est:3000-5000
£7110	$11874	€10310	Seine et Tour d'Eiffel (15x9cm-6x4in) s. Indian ink over pencil squared. 19-Jun-3 Kornfeld, Bern #239/R est:20000 (S.FR 15500)
£8609	$15669	€13000	Vue de Paris (34x33cm-13x13in) s. wash. 15-Jun-4 Vanderkindere, Brussels #21/R est:4000-6000
£10000	$15900	€14500	La danseuse en couleur (32x26cm-13x10in) st.sig. pencil pen ink fabric collage paper on board. 11-Sep-3 Christie's, Kensington #200/R est:10000-15000
£10490	$18042	€15000	Femme aux fleurs (27x19cm-11x7in) s.i.d.1953 Chinese ink wash prov. 8-Dec-3 Artcurial Briest, Paris #61/R est:18000-25000
£10625	$17000	€15513	Female costume designs for Aleko (56x36cm-22x14in) i. W/C gouache over pencil six. 18-Sep-3 Swann Galleries, New York #149/R est:12000-18000
£13158	$24211	€19211	Autour du nu (39x28cm-15x11in) s. ink. 23-Jun-4 Koller, Zurich #3020/R est:30000-40000 (S.FR 30000)
£17483	$29196	€25000	Jeune fille au bouquet (62x48cm-24x19in) s.i.d.1953 Indian ink lit. 30-Jun-3 Artcurial Briest, Paris #743/R est:25000-30000
£19632	$32000	€28663	Nu au bouquet. Reverie (27x19cm-11x7in) s. pen col ink W/C pencil exec.c.1950 pair. 25-Sep-3 Christie's, Rockefeller NY #615/R est:25000-35000
£19824	$33700	€28943	Untitled (32x24cm-13x9in) s. gouache. 5-Nov-3 Dobiaschofsky, Bern #427/R est:30000 (S.FR 45000)
£20530	$37364	€31000	Espion (15x17cm-6x7in) s.i. ink col crayon exec.1914. 15-Jun-4 Rossini, Paris #72/R est:8000-12000
£20563	$35575	€29200	La noce (19x14cm-7x6in) s. pastel ink exec. c.1945. 14-Dec-3 Rabourdin & Choppin de Janvry, Paris #41/R est:30000-35000
£25140	$45000	€36704	David a la lyre (74x53cm-29x21in) s. W/C pastel brush India ink grey wash exec 1949-50 prov.exhib. 5-May-4 Christie's, Rockefeller NY #145/R est:50000-70000
£26000	$47840	€37960	Dans les nuages (45x32cm-18x13in) s. India ink wash exec 1962 prov. 24-Jun-4 Christie's, London #421/R est:22000-28000
£26000	$47840	€37960	Le ciel bleu (32x22cm-13x9in) s. W/C brush ink exec.c.1964. 22-Jun-4 Sotheby's, London #521/R est:18000-25000
£28249	$50000	€41244	Vase of flowers and fruit (31x23cm-12x9in) st.sig. brush black ink gouache W/C exec.c.1940 prov.exhib. 2-May-4 Bonhams & Butterfields, Los Angeles #3005/R est:60000-80000
£30000	$51600	€43800	Nu sur coq (45x29cm-18x11in) s.d.1957 Indian ink pastel. 7-Dec-3 Uppsala Auktionskammare, Uppsala #217/R est:250000-300000 (S.KR 390000)
£32000	$58240	€46720	L'artiste au chevalet (66x50cm-26x20in) s.d.1958 India ink brush ink wash Japan paper exec 1958 prov. 5-Feb-4 Christie's, London #350/R est:30000-50000
£33099	$57261	€47000	Deux bouquets de fleurs devant le fenetre (36x27cm-14x11in) s.d.936 W/C gouache graphite. 12-Dec-3 Piasa, Paris #21/R est:40000-50000
£33520	$60000	€48939	Saul et David (69x50cm-27x20in) s.d.1966 ink wash W/C gouache paper on canvas prov. 6-May-4 Sotheby's, New York #453/R est:70000-90000
£35000	$64400	€51100	Autoportrait a la mariee (27x19cm-11x7in) st.sig. gouache W/C wax crayon ink pencil exec 1968. 24-Jun-4 Christie's, London #411/R est:25000-35000
£35211	$60915	€50000	Projet pour le livre de Franz Meyer (33x50cm-13x20in) st.sig. gouache ink exec. 1961. 14-Dec-3 Rabourdin & Choppin de Janvry, Paris #42/R est:50000-55000
£35294	$60000	€51529	Hommage a Marc Chagall (31x23cm-12x9in) st. W/C gouache exec 1968 prov. 6-Nov-3 Sotheby's, New York #314/R est:65000-85000
£36313	$65000	€53017	L'auteur Mendel Mann dans son village (28x23cm-11x9in) s. W/C gouache col wax crayons pen India ink prov. 5-May-4 Christie's, Rockefeller NY #117/R est:40000-60000
£36755	$66894	€55500	Fruits et fleurs sur fond vert (29x22cm-11x9in) s. gouache Chinese ink crayon. 15-Jun-4 Rossini, Paris #73/R est:18000-25000
£42254	$73099	€60000	Painter and ladder (53x35cm-21x14in) s. ink gouache W/C dr. 15-Dec-3 Ansorena, Madrid #972/R est:60000
£43709	$79550	€66000	Visite de l'ange a la campagne (19x23cm-7x9in) s. gouache crayon wax crayon. 15-Jun-4 Rossini, Paris #71/R est:20000-28000
£44693	$80000	€65252	Musicien et les maries (37x28cm-15x11in) s.i.d.1975 W/C pen ink wash col pencil prov. 6-May-4 Sotheby's, New York #442/R est:80000-120000
£45000	$81900	€65700	Red Horse (27x48cm-11x19in) s.i.d.1965 gouache W/C pen ink pencil prov.exhib. 5-Feb-4 Christie's, London #398/R est:30000-40000
£47486	$85000	€69330	Bouquet et robe a carreaux (57x38cm-22x15in) s.d.951 pen ink ink wash. 6-May-4 Sotheby's, New York #412/R est:40000-60000
£50000	$92000	€73000	Le vent (38x48cm-15x19in) s. gouache exec 1943 prov.exhib. 24-Jun-4 Christie's, London #422/R est:50000-70000
£50000	$92000	€73000	Priere (62x45cm-24x18in) s.d.1981 pastel col crayon prov. 22-Jun-4 Sotheby's, London #528/R est:50000-70000
£55000	$100100	€80300	L'incendie dans la neige (62x49cm-24x19in) s. gouache pastel pencil exec c.1940-1943 prov.exhib.lit. 5-Feb-4 Christie's, London #399/R est:30000-40000
£59603	$108477	€90000	Esquisse pour les seins rouges (21x23cm-8x9in) s. gouache Chinese ink crayon. 15-Jun-4 Rossini, Paris #70/R est:22000-30000
£64706	$110000	€94471	Les amoureuses (55x40cm-22x16in) s.d.1956-7 W/C gouache wax crayons brush India ink prov. 5-Nov-3 Christie's, Rockefeller NY #158/R est:70000-90000
£66667	$122667	€100000	Soir (107x73cm-42x29in) s.d.1955 ink wash prov. 9-Jun-4 Tajan, Paris #58/R est:50000-70000
£67039	$120000	€97877	Soldat (20x29cm-8x11in) s. gouache exec 1911 prov.exhib. 5-May-4 Christie's, Rockefeller NY #122/R est:120000-160000
£67647	$115000	€98765	L'enlevement (90x61cm-35x24in) s. brush ink ink wash Japan paper prov. 6-Nov-3 Sotheby's, New York #313/R est:60000-80000
£70423	$123239	€100000	Un bouquet mauve (65x47cm-26x19in) pastel blk crayon. 18-Dec-3 Cornette de St.Cyr, Paris #10/R est:100000-120000
£70588	$120000	€103058	Les amants (33x38cm-13x15in) s. W/C brush ink gouache. 6-Nov-3 Sotheby's, New York #200/R est:120000-180000
£72626	$130000	€106034	Coq au petit clown (67x53cm-26x21in) s.d.1958 W/C pastel brush pen India ink Japan paper prov.lit. 5-May-4 Christie's, Rockefeller NY #140/R est:80000-120000
£75000	$136500	€109500	Pretendant (47x36cm-19x14in) s. gouache W/C pen ink wash exec 1972 prov. 5-Feb-4 Christie's, London #381/R est:70000-100000
£75000	$136500	€109500	Le bouquet au-dessus de Vence (66x50cm-26x20in) s.d.1954 W/C gouache prov. 4-Feb-4 Sotheby's, London #450/R est:80000-120000
£75000	$138000	€109500	Paysage a la hache (52x51cm-20x20in) s. gouache W/C pastel Japan paper exec 1978 prov. 24-Jun-4 Christie's, London #355/R est:70000-100000
£76471	$130000	€111648	Couple sous la pluie (46x63cm-18x25in) s.d.26 gouache blk paper exec 1926. 5-Nov-3 Christie's, Rockefeller NY #167/R est:140000-180000
£85000	$156400	€124100	Rabbi holding sefer torah (65x50cm-26x20in) s. gouache W/C brush ink exec.c.1959 prov.exhib. 22-Jun-4 Sotheby's, London #529/R est:70000-90000
£102649	$186821	€155000	De ma fenetre (48x32cm-19x13in) s. gouache W/C. 15-Jun-4 Rossini, Paris #69/R est:60000-90000
£105000	$191100	€153300	Marriage (58x46cm-23x18in) st.sig. gouache W/C brush India ink exec c.1975. 5-Feb-4 Christie's, London #400/R est:120000-150000
£108824	$185000	€158883	Esquisse pour 'Femme sur fond rouge' (77x57cm-30x22in) s. gouache W/C pastel pen India ink prov. 5-Nov-3 Christie's, Rockefeller NY #142/R est:140000-180000
£108824	$185000	€158883	Le violoniste (100x65cm-39x26in) s. W/C brush India ink Japan paper on paper on canvas prov.exhib. 5-Nov-3 Christie's, Rockefeller NY #149/R est:150000-200000
£113537	$206638	€165764	Femme a l'eventail (50x63cm-20x25in) s. gouache W/C exec. 1924-27 prov.exhib.lit. 18-Jun-4 Kornfeld, Bern #14/R est:225000 (S.FR 260000)
£117318	$210000	€171284	Bella a Mourillon (51x66cm-20x26in) s. gouache W/C over pencil exec 1926 prov.lit. 5-May-4 Christie's, Rockefeller NY #114/R est:250000-350000

£125000	$227500	€182500	Crepuscule (48x64cm-19x25in) s. gouache pastel exec c.1949-50 prov.exhib.lit. 5-Feb-4 Christie's, London #380/R est:80000-120000
£134078	$240000	€195754	Orphee jouant (56x67cm-22x26in) s. W/C gouache exec 1970 prov. 6-May-4 Sotheby's, New York #413/R est:200000-300000
£135000	$245700	€197100	Amoureux au-dessus de la ville (65x49cm-26x19in) st.sig. d.1959 gouache W/C wax crayon brush ink pencil prov.lit. 5-Feb-4 Christie's, London #433/R est:140000-180000
£160000	$294400	€233600	Ete (69x50cm-27x20in) s. gouache pastel col crayon pen ink exec.1964 prov. 22-Jun-4 Sotheby's, London #468/R est:120000-150000
£164706	$280000	€240471	Couple et deux bouquets (100x62cm-39x24in) s.i. gouache W/C ink wash brown crayon exec 1959 prov. 6-Nov-3 Sotheby's, New York #305/R est:250000-350000
£170000	$312800	€248200	Cavalier amoureux (62x51cm-24x20in) s. gouache W/C pastel exec c.1970 prov.exhib. 24-Jun-4 Christie's, London #426/R est:160000-200000
£189944	$340000	€277318	Violoniste sur le coq (62x49cm-24x19in) s. gouache paper on board exec 1929 prov. 5-May-4 Christie's, Rockefeller NY #146/R est:180000-220000
£235294	$400000	€343529	Le coq fleuri - etude pour une mosaique (101x153cm-40x60in) s. gouache W/C wax crayons paper on canvas prov.exhib. 5-Nov-3 Christie's, Rockefeller NY #135/R est:200000-300000
£260000	$478400	€379600	Cheval a l'ombrelle et les amoureux sur le toit (65x50cm-26x20in) s. gouache pastel oil wax crayon W/C exec c.1927-1928 prov. 24-Jun-4 Christie's, London #340/R est:200000-300000
£294118	$500000	€429412	L'ane rouge (77x75cm-30x30in) s. gouache pastel oil paper on canvas exec 1958-59 prov.lit. 6-Nov-3 Sotheby's, New York #201/R est:400000-600000

CHAGALL, Marc (after) (1887-1985) French/Russian

Prints

£4336	$7371	€6200	Maternite (52x68cm-20x27in) s. col lithograph. 26-Nov-3 Lempertz, Koln #619/R est:3000
£4802	$8500	€7011	Tribe of Simeon (61x46cm-24x18in) s.i.num.7/25 col lithograph. 28-Apr-4 Christie's, Rockefeller NY #20/R est:4000-6000
£5085	$9000	€7424	Tribe of Ruben (62x46cm-24x18in) s.i.num.7/25 col lithograph. 28-Apr-4 Christie's, Rockefeller NY #19/R est:3000-5000
£5367	$9500	€7836	Tribe of Judah (62x46cm-24x18in) s.num.7/25 col lithograph. 28-Apr-4 Christie's, Rockefeller NY #22/R est:3000-5000
£6215	$11000	€9074	Tribe of Levi (61x46cm-24x18in) s.num.XXXV/C col lithograph. 28-Apr-4 Christie's, Rockefeller NY #21/R est:3000-5000
£6215	$11000	€9074	Tribe of Issachar (62x46cm-24x18in) s.i.num.7/25 col lithograph. 28-Apr-4 Christie's, Rockefeller NY #23/R est:3000-5000
£6780	$12000	€9899	Tribe of Naphtali (62x46cm-24x18in) s.i.num.7/25 col lithograph. 28-Apr-4 Christie's, Rockefeller NY #24/R est:3000-5000
£6798	$11556	€9925	Romeo et Juliette (64x100cm-25x39in) s.num.16/200 col lithograph lit. 5-Nov-3 AB Stockholms Auktionsverk #1205/R est:100000-150000 (S.KR 90000)
£7000	$12740	€10220	Avenue de la Victoire a Nice (61x46cm-24x18in) s.num.139/150 col lithograph. 30-Jun-4 Christie's, London #190/R est:3000-5000
£7059	$12000	€10306	Maternite (52x67cm-20x26in) s.num.90/300 col lithograph. 6-Nov-3 Swann Galleries, New York #525/R est:8000-12000
£7059	$12000	€10306	Avenue de la Victoire (74x53cm-29x21in) s. col lithograph. 4-Nov-3 Christie's, Rockefeller NY #85/R est:7000-9000
£7345	$13000	€10724	Couple and fish (62x46cm-24x18in) s.num.LVIII/LXXV col lithograph. 28-Apr-4 Christie's, Rockefeller NY #25/R est:6000-9000
£7647	$13000	€11165	Song of Songs (71x54cm-28x21in) s. col lithograph exec.1975. 4-Nov-3 Christie's, Rockefeller NY #86/R est:11000-13000
£7667	$14030	€11500	Blue bird (56x43cm-22x17in) s. col lithograph. 5-Jun-4 Lempertz, Koln #645/R est:8000
£14000	$24080	€20440	Carmen (102x66cm-40x26in) s. col lithograph. 2-Dec-3 Christie's, London #118/R est:10000-15000
£14000	$25480	€20440	Romeo et Juliette (65x100cm-26x39in) s.num.16/200 col lithograph. 30-Jun-4 Christie's, London #189/R est:8000-12000

CHAGNIOT, Alfred (1905-1991) French

£265	$475	€387	Spring bouquet (46x36cm-18x14in) s. masonite. 8-Jan-4 Doyle, New York #15/R
£372	$665	€543	At rest during harvest time (58x79cm-23x31in) s. 31-May-4 Stephan Welz, Johannesburg #72 (SA.R 4500)
£769	$1308	€1100	Rue Royale (92x73cm-36x29in) s. 27-Nov-3 Millon & Associes, Paris #237/R

CHAGOT, Edmond (1832-?) French

Works on paper

£1812	$3352	€2700	Musiciens au Caire (26x20cm-10x8in) s.i.d.75 W/C gouache. 15-Mar-4 Gros & Delettrez, Paris #248/R est:1800-2500

CHAHINE, Edgar (1874-1947) French

£4000	$7160	€6000	Rue animee (54x73cm-21x29in) s.d.1942 panel. 16-May-4 Thierry & Lannon, Brest #125/R est:6000-7000

Works on paper

£267	$488	€400	Jeune femme a la palette (45x29cm-18x11in) d.1910 gouache. 6-Jun-4 Osenat, Fontainebleau #243

CHAIGNEAU, Jean Ferdinand (1830-1906) French

£600	$1098	€900	Berger et troupeau (5x8cm-2x3in) s. panel. 6-Jun-4 Osenat, Fontainebleau #153
£1118	$1900	€1632	Paysage a Barbizon (14x22cm-6x9in) s. panel. 20-Nov-3 Auctions by the Bay, Alameda #1016/R
£1468	$2700	€2143	Shepherd and his flock, sunset (56x43cm-22x17in) s. 27-Jun-4 Freeman, Philadelphia #23/R est:2500-4000
£1538	$2569	€2200	Landscape near Barbizon (23x33cm-9x13in) canvas on board. 10-Oct-3 Winterberg, Heidelberg #555/R est:1350
£1867	$3416	€2800	Passage du bac (17x22cm-7x9in) s. panel. 6-Jun-4 Osenat, Fontainebleau #152/R est:2500-3000
£1905	$3410	€2781	Landscape with shepherdess and flock (28x46cm-11x18in) s. 22-Mar-4 Philippe Schuler, Zurich #4392/R est:3000-4000 (S.FR 4400)
£2113	$3507	€3000	Bergere et troupeau (19x28cm-7x11in) s. panel. 15-Jun-3 Peron, Melun #149
£2367	$4331	€3550	Berger et troupeau (16x22cm-6x9in) s. panel. 6-Jun-4 Osenat, Fontainebleau #151/R est:3500-4000
£2536	$4159	€3500	Moutons a la mare a Barbizon (32x41cm-13x16in) s. 11-May-3 Osenat, Fontainebleau #47/R est:3000-3200
£3200	$5856	€4800	Rentree du troupeau (28x41cm-11x16in) s. 6-Jun-4 Osenat, Fontainebleau #154/R est:4500-5000
£3623	$5942	€5000	Troupeau de moutons a la mare (23x38cm-9x15in) s. panel. 11-May-3 Osenat, Fontainebleau #49/R est:6000-6500
£15333	$28060	€23000	Pere Chicore (101x81cm-40x32in) s. exhib.lit. 6-Jun-4 Osenat, Fontainebleau #155/R est:25000-30000

Works on paper

£467	$854	€700	Paysanne descendant vers Barbizon (17x25cm-7x10in) s. W/C. 6-Jun-4 Osenat, Fontainebleau #149
£500	$915	€750	Berger et troupeau (16x22cm-6x9in) s. W/C. 6-Jun-4 Osenat, Fontainebleau #150/R

CHAIGNEAU, Paul (20th C) French

£1053	$1937	€1600	Berger et moutons (33x41cm-13x16in) s. 25-Jun-4 Millon & Associes, Paris #104 est:300-400
£1208	$2223	€1800	Berger et moutons (15x22cm-6x9in) s. panel. 26-Mar-4 Daguerre, Paris #75/R est:1800-2000
£1884	$3090	€2600	Berger et son troupeau (22x27cm-9x11in) s. 11-May-3 Osenat, Fontainebleau #46 est:2700-3000
£2606	$4325	€3700	Berger et moutons (46x55cm-18x22in) s. 15-Jun-3 Peron, Melun #133
£3000	$5490	€4500	Troupeau dans la mare (22x27cm-9x11in) s. panel. 6-Jun-4 Osenat, Fontainebleau #157/R est:4500-5000
£3103	$5741	€4500	Le berger (37x46cm-15x18in) s.i. 13-Feb-4 Rossini, Paris #26/R est:2000-2500
£3380	$5611	€4800	Pere chicoree et troupeau (21x27cm-8x11in) s. panel. 15-Jun-3 Peron, Melun #147
£4336	$7457	€6200	Berger et ses moutons. Bergers et moutons a la mare (22x27cm-9x11in) s. panel pair. 7-Dec-3 Osenat, Fontainebleau #67 est:5000-6000

CHAILLOU, Narcisse (1837-?) French

£609	$1139	€920	Les lavandieres (35x54cm-14x21in) s. board. 24-Jul-4 Thierry & Lannon, Brest #132/R

CHAILLOUX, Robert (1913-) French

£400	$748	€600	Figurines lit by a lantern (25x33cm-10x13in) s. board. 22-Jul-4 Gorringes, Lewes #1977
£1900	$3401	€2774	Still life of earthenware vessels, fruit and horse chesnuts on a ledge (44x53cm-17x21in) s. 17-Mar-4 Bonhams, Chester #295/R est:1000-1500
£2300	$3979	€3358	Still life of blue echinops in a vase (36x30cm-14x12in) s. 14-Dec-3 Desmond Judd, Cranbrook #1021
£2700	$4374	€3915	Still life of fruit, vessels and lamps on a ledge (58x71cm-23x28in) s. 25-May-3 Desmond Judd, Cranbrook #1021
£2900	$5017	€4234	Still life of physalis in a jug (36x28cm-14x11in) s. 14-Dec-3 Desmond Judd, Cranbrook #1077
£3500	$5670	€5075	Still life of fruit and jug on a ledge (46x53cm-18x21in) s. 25-May-3 Desmond Judd, Cranbrook #1100

CHAILOT, R (19/20th C) ?

£872	$1623	€1300	De verlovingsring - engagement ring (60x47cm-24x19in) s. 4-Mar-4 Auction Maastricht #1098/R est:800-1000

CHAISSAC, Gaston (1910-1964) French

£1379	$2303	€2000	Untitled (56x49cm-22x19in) s. board. 14-Nov-3 Farsetti, Prato #292/R est:550-750
£4545	$7727	€6500	Composition (50x65cm-20x26in) s.d.61 tempera paper. 24-Nov-3 Christie's, Milan #155/R est:6000-8000
£5175	$8642	€7400	Souvenir (34x34cm-13x13in) s. i.verso cardboard. 29-Jun-3 Versailles Encheres #149/R
£9859	$17056	€14000	Personnage (50x40cm-20x16in) s. canvas on cardboard. 9-Dec-3 Artcurial Briest, Paris #473/R est:12000-15000
£11888	$20448	€17000	Untitled (100x64cm-39x25in) s. oil kraft paper on canvas prov. 2-Dec-3 Calmels Cohen, Paris #65/R est:15000-20000
£24476	$42098	€35000	Untitled (100x72cm-39x28in) s. oil contreplaque painted c.1963 prov. 2-Dec-3 Calmels Cohen, Paris #66/R est:20000-30000
£32895	$60526	€50000	Personnage (95x64cm-37x25in) s. cardboard on canvas. 27-Jun-4 Versailles Encheres #125/R est:50000-60000

Sculpture

£45455	$77273	€65000	La demoiselle (182x22cm-72x9in) s. polychrome wood prov.exhib.lit. 30-Nov-3 Anaf, Lyon #30/R est:60000-70000

Works on paper

£839	$1427	€1200	Composition a un personnage (27x21cm-11x8in) s.i. ballpoint pen exec.c.1961. 27-Nov-3 Millon & Associes, Paris #86/R est:12000-15000
£909	$1545	€1300	Poeme et dessins (27x20cm-11x8in) s.i.d.1955 ink. 23-Nov-3 Cornette de St.Cyr, Paris #43/R
£1748	$2920	€2500	Pseudos-sorciers (26x20cm-10x8in) s.i.d.49 chl. 29-Jun-3 Versailles Encheres #148/R
£2172	$3692	€3171	Vision (21x15cm-8x6in) s.d.1952 ink prov. 25-Nov-3 Germann, Zurich #y/R est:3000-4000 (S.FR 4800)
£2586	$4629	€3776	Untitled (22x17cm-9x7in) s. Indian ink W/C. 12-May-4 Dobiaschofsky, Bern #386/R est:5400 (S.FR 6000)
£2797	$4671	€4000	Visage (22x19cm-9x7in) s.i.d.18-9-59 gouache. 25-Jun-3 Maigret, Paris #43 est:5000-6000
£2800	$5152	€4200	Untitled (25x32cm-10x13in) s.d.1939-40 India ink prov. 9-Jun-4 Artcurial Briest, Paris #339/R est:4000-5000
£3873	$6430	€5500	Untitled (56x62cm-22x24in) s. mixed media paper on canvas. 11-Jun-3 Finarte Semenzato, Milan #593/R
£5594	$9343	€8000	Ensemble de personnages (47x63cm-19x25in) s.i.d.11-9-61 gouache ink. 25-Jun-3 Maigret, Paris #42/R est:9500-10500
£9155	$15838	€13000	Composition (50x64cm-20x25in) s. ink crayon prov.exhib. 14-Dec-3 Versailles Encheres #138/R est:15000-18000
£13423	$24966	€20000	Composition (48x63cm-19x25in) s.d.6.12.61 gouache. 3-Mar-4 Artcurial Briest, Paris #332/R est:25000-35000
£16084	$26860	€23000	Paysage (48x63cm-19x25in) s.d.61 gouache collage. 29-Jun-3 Versailles Encheres #150/R
£16107	$29637	€24000	Composition a un personnage (50x65cm-20x26in) s. collage painted paper gouache exec 1961 lit. 29-Mar-4 Cornette de St.Cyr, Paris #4/R est:15000-20000
£18310	$31676	€26000	On the way to the moon (83x59cm-33x23in) gouache collage Indian ink panel exec.c.1962 prov. 14-Dec-3 Versailles Encheres #155/R est:30000-35000

CHAIX, Yves (1936-) French
£216 $400 €315 Untitled (33x23cm-13x9in) s. 13-Mar-4 Susanin's, Chicago #6024/R
£250 $450 €365 Le debarcadere et la salute (23x36cm-9x14in) s. 20-Jan-4 Arthur James, Florida #131
£294 $550 €429 Le retour des galions (33x41cm-13x16in) s. 24-Feb-4 Arthur James, Florida #155
£306 $550 €447 Place de la Concorde (36x28cm-14x11in) s. 20-Apr-4 Arthur James, Florida #134/R
£306 $550 €447 Vu de L'Atelier du Peintre (28x33cm-11x13in) s. 20-Apr-4 Arthur James, Florida #135/R
£380 $700 €555 Le jardin du Luxembourg (33x41cm-13x16in) s. 23-Mar-4 Arthur James, Florida #423/R
£398 $700 €581 L'ilot aux pecheurs (38x46cm-15x18in) s. 18-May-4 Arthur James, Florida #183
£417 $750 €609 Palge aux parasols bleus (38x46cm-15x18in) s. 20-Jan-4 Arthur James, Florida #130
£462 $850 €675 Galions et goelettes (61x74cm-24x29in) s. 23-Mar-4 Arthur James, Florida #422/R

CHAKI, Yehouda (1938-) Canadian?
£227 $370 €331 Rooms 2001 (152x122cm-60x48in) s.d.75 i.on stretcher verso acrylic. 23-Sep-3 Ritchie, Toronto #192/R (C.D 500)
£227 $370 €331 Oasis (152x102cm-60x40in) s.d.74 s.i.d.stretcher verso acrylic. 23-Sep-3 Ritchie, Toronto #193/R (C.D 500)
£909 $1482 €1327 Landscape 2025 (122x152cm-48x60in) s.i.on stretcher verso. 23-Sep-3 Ritchie, Toronto #169/R est:1500-2000 (C.D 2000)

CHALE, Gertrudis (19/20th C) Latin American
£2210 $4000 €3227 Figures (30x40cm-12x16in) cardboard. 30-Mar-4 Arroyo, Buenos Aires #9
Works on paper
£357 $650 €521 Singers (42x32cm-17x13in) s.d.46 ink. 5-Jul-4 Arroyo, Buenos Aires #97/R

CHALEYE, Jean (1878-1960) French
£280 $496 €409 Coastal view (59x81cm-23x32in) s. board. 27-Apr-4 Bonhams, Knightsbridge #61
£4706 $8000 €6871 Bouquet with peonies (73x116cm-29x46in) s. prov. 28-Oct-3 Sotheby's, New York #164/R est:8000-12000

CHALGALO (1882-1968) French
£385 $662 €550 Cafe noir au croissant (27x35cm-11x14in) s. s.i.verso panel. 3-Dec-3 Tajan, Paris #183

CHALGRIN, Jean François (1739-1811) French
Works on paper
£13158 $24211 €20000 Fete devant l'entree de la Salle de Bal du Petit-Luxembourg (52x70cm-20x28in) i. pen wash Chinese ink W/C gouache prov. 23-Jun-4 Sotheby's, Paris #33/R est:15000-20000

CHALLE, Charles Michelange (attrib) (1718-1778) French
£2837 $4737 €4000 Clytie changee en tournesol (74x134cm-29x53in) 17-Oct-3 Tajan, Paris #109/R est:4000-6000
£7237 $13316 €11000 Allegory of Painting (77x131cm-30x52in) prov. 24-Jun-4 Tajan, Paris #58/R est:8000-12000

CHALLENER, Frederick (1869-1959) Canadian
£763 $1419 €1114 Margaret Ethelreda Wilson (27x21cm-11x8in) i.verso panel sold with another similar exhib. 2-Mar-4 Ritchie, Toronto #77/R est:1000-1500 (C.D 1900)

CHALLENGER, J D (1951-) American
£2469 $4000 €3580 Rides with lightning (114x132cm-45x52in) 23-May-3 Altermann Galleries, Santa Fe #145

CHALLIE, Jean Laurent (1880-1943) French
£1630 $3000 €2380 Sowing (82x66cm-32x26in) s. 22-Jun-4 Galeria y Remates, Montevideo #32/R est:1500-2000
£1800 $3276 €2700 Cote rocheuse (60x73cm-24x29in) s. 4-Jul-4 Eric Pillon, Calais #129/R
£1933 $3519 €2900 Maisons sur la lande (65x100cm-26x39in) s. 4-Jul-4 Eric Pillon, Calais #128/R
£2349 $4370 €3500 Voile Blanche (33x55cm-13x22in) s. 3-Mar-4 Tajan, Paris #36/R est:4000-6000
£2684 $4993 €4000 Frere et soeur (54x65cm-21x26in) s. 3-Mar-4 Tajan, Paris #37/R est:4000-6000

CHALLULAU, Marcel (20th C) French
£294 $500 €429 Village in Languedoc (46x54cm-18x21in) s. 20-Nov-3 Galeria y Remates, Montevideo #151/R

CHALMERS, George Paul (1833-1878) British
£319 $533 €450 Paysage a la tombee du jour (25x35cm-10x14in) s. 17-Jun-3 Galerie Moderne, Brussels #191
£417 $679 €600 Paysage a la tombee du jour (25x35cm-10x14in) s. 23-Sep-3 Galerie Moderne, Brussels #774
£820 $1410 €1197 Possibly a self portrait, bust length (40x30cm-16x12in) s. paper on board. 4-Dec-3 Bonhams, Edinburgh #98
£900 $1611 €1314 Sunset (33x43cm-13x17in) s. exhib. 27-May-4 Christie's, Kensington #168/R
£1399 $2378 €2000 Portrait of a cavalier (3x25cm-1x10in) s. bears d.63 board. 20-Nov-3 Dorotheum, Salzburg #177/R est:3000-3600

CHALMERS, Hector (c.1849-1943) British
£450 $851 €657 Figures on a country road (28x35cm-11x14in) s. board. 19-Feb-4 Lyon & Turnbull, Edinburgh #30
£650 $1086 €949 Figures boating on a beach (30x46cm-12x18in) s. 10-Jul-3 Gorringes, Worthing #705/R
£1411 $2597 €2060 Village fair (25x36cm-10x14in) s. prov. 14-Jun-4 Waddingtons, Toronto #192/R est:1500-1800 (C.D 3500)

CHALMERS, Sir George (?-1791) British
£2246 $3750 €3279 Portrait of Margaret Hamilton of Dalziel. Portrait of William Lawson of Cairnmuir (72x63cm-28x25in) s. pair. 22-Oct-3 Doyle, New York #81/R est:5000-7000

CHALON (?) ?
Sculpture
£3500 $5845 €5110 Figure (41cm-16in) s. pat bronze. 15-Oct-3 Christie's, Kensington #298/R
£7500 $12525 €10950 Figure (63cm-25in) s. pat bronze. 15-Oct-3 Christie's, Kensington #299/R

CHALON, Alfred Edward (1780-1860) British
Miniatures
£1300 $2340 €1898 Lady wearing a wine coloured dress (8cm-3in) mono. ormolu frame rec. exhib.lit. 22-Apr-4 Bonhams, New Bond Street #159/R est:1500-2500
£1800 $3240 €2628 Elizabeth Deborah Bone (8cm-3in) s. ormolu frame rec. exhib.lit. 22-Apr-4 Bonhams, New Bond Street #160/R est:1000-1500
£1900 $3496 €2774 Lady wearing green dress (7cm-3in) init. gold locket frame prov. 24-Jun-4 Bonhams, New Bond Street #141/R est:2000-3000
£3200 $5760 €4672 Jules Amedee Barbey d'Aurevilly (7cm-3in) mono. verso gold frame oval exhib. 22-Apr-4 Bonhams, New Bond Street #163/R est:2000-3000
Works on paper
£750 $1373 €1095 Portrait of a young girl (44x31cm-17x12in) s.d.1836 W/C. 27-Jan-4 Bonhams, Knightsbridge #371/R

CHALON, Alfred Edward (attrib) (1780-1860) British
£1000 $1670 €1460 Portrait of a gentleman, standing (73x60cm-29x24in) panel. 11-Nov-3 Bonhams, Knightsbridge #83/R est:700-900

CHALON, Christina (1748-1808) Dutch
Works on paper
£274 $466 €400 Studies of children (7x21cm-3x8in) pen brown ink prov. 4-Nov-3 Sotheby's, Amsterdam #127/R
£288 $489 €420 Group of five men in hats (10x10cm-4x4in) pen brown ink prov. 4-Nov-3 Sotheby's, Amsterdam #128/R
£479 $815 €700 Interior peasant studies (14x21cm-6x8in) pen brown ink double-sided prov. 4-Nov-3 Sotheby's, Amsterdam #126/R

CHALON, Henry Bernard (1770-1849) British
£340 $619 €496 Portrait of a spaniel (20x22cm-8x9in) s. feigned vignette panel. 15-Jun-4 Rosebery Fine Art, London #667/R
£650 $1027 €949 Spaniel (19x25cm-7x10in) s.d.1828 board. 3-Sep-3 Bonhams, Bury St Edmunds #431/R
£2844 $4750 €4152 Horse in stall (61x81cm-24x32in) 22-Oct-3 Doyle, New York #104/R
£3200 $5888 €4672 Stallion Smolensko with grey mare and other horse by a fence (29x38cm-11x15in) s.d.1831 panel. 10-Jun-4 Christie's, Kensington #23/R est:1500-2500
£8000 $14560 €11680 Grey hunter in a river landscape. Bay hunter with a groom in a loose box (62x75cm-24x30in) pair prov. 1-Jul-4 Sotheby's, London #164/R est:5000-7000

CHALON, Kingsley S (?) ?
£800 $1304 €1168 Stable interior with two horses and fowl (32x40cm-13x16in) s. panel. 25-Sep-3 Clevedon Sale Rooms #190/R

CHALON, Louis (1687-1741) Dutch
Works on paper
£3060 $5600 €4468 Winter landscape with ice skaters on a lake (21x28cm-8x11in) s.d.1740 W/C gouache. 29-Jan-4 Swann Galleries, New York #185/R est:3000-5000

CHALON, Louis (attrib) (1687-1741) Dutch
£2215 $4075 €3300 Scene de marche devant une tour (24x15cm-9x6in) copper. 24-Mar-4 Tajan, Paris #132/R est:2000-3000

CHALON, Louis (1866-1940) French
Sculpture
£1767 $3251 €2650 Walkyrie (85cm-33in) brown pat. bronze s. incl. base lit. 10-Jun-4 Camard, Paris #7/R est:2000-3000
£3771 $6750 €5657 Sir Lancelot and the Lady of the Lake (56x51cm-22x20in) s. pat bronze. 16-May-4 Abell, Los Angeles #62/R
£5138 $9198 €7501 Valkyrie (73cm-29in) s. bronze green marble base prov.lit. 15-May-4 Christie's, Sydney #72/R est:6000-9000 (A.D 13000)
£7510 $13443 €10965 La mer (79cm-31in) s. bronze parcel gilt bronze green marble prov. 15-May-4 Christie's, Sydney #454/R est:20000-30000 (A.D 19000)

CHALON, Louis (after) (1866-1940) French
Sculpture
£3889 $7000 €5678 Figure of a Valkyrie (51cm-20in) painted bronze ivory green onyx. 24-Apr-4 Skinner, Boston #311 est:3000-5000

CHALONS, Simon de (attrib) (16th C) French
£15894 $28927 €24000 Sainte Famille avec ange et Saint Jean-Baptiste (105x86cm-41x34in) panel. 15-Jun-4 Claude Aguttes, Neuilly #7/R est:18000-20000

CHAMBAS, Jean Paul (1947-) French
£1119 $1902 €1600 Pour en finir (130x162cm-51x64in) s.d.1991 verso. 18-Nov-3 Pierre Berge, Paris #13/R est:1500-2000
Works on paper
£333 $607 €500 Entree de Cheops (51x73cm-20x29in) mono.i.d.1979 gouache W/C. 2-Jul-4 Binoche, Paris #6/R

CHAMBAZ, Marius (1905-1988) Swiss
£226 $391 €330 Place du Temple, Carouge (28x38cm-11x15in) s. board. 12-Dec-3 Galerie du Rhone, Sion #477 (S.FR 500)

CHAMBERLAIN, Brenda (1912-1971) British
Works on paper
£700 $1275 €1050 Abstracts (52x63cm-20x25in) s.d.1962 gouache pencil crayon. 2-Jul-4 Bloomsbury, London #93/R

CHAMBERLAIN, Curtis (1852-1925) American
£1236 $2250 €1805 Laguna coastal scene. Crashing waves on rocks (25x36cm-10x14in) s. board two. 15-Jun-4 John Moran, Pasadena #57 est:900-1400
£3571 $6500 €5214 Old coast road (28x46cm-11x18in) s. board. 15-Jun-4 John Moran, Pasadena #56 est:3000-5000

CHAMBERLAIN, John (1927-) American
£14000 $25760 €20440 Untitled collage (30x30cm-12x12in) oil metal card staples on board prov. 25-Jun-4 Christie's, London #176/R est:8000-12000
£45000 $82800 €65700 Orco (30x30cm-12x12in) oil canvas card paper metal staples on board prov. 25-Jun-4 Christie's, London #178/R est:18000-24000
£50000 $91000 €73000 Untitled (30x30cm-12x12in) metal canvas paint paper collage on board exec 1961 prov. 5-Feb-4 Christie's, London #179/R est:50000-70000
Prints
£3497 $5944 €5000 Untitled (210x76cm-83x30in) s.d.1986 col monotype. 27-Nov-3 Lempertz, Koln #77/R est:6000
Sculpture
£973 $1800 €1421 Untitled (10x16x13cm-4x6x5in) urethane foam string Ritt dye exec 1970 prov. 12-Feb-4 Sotheby's, New York #208/R est:1500-2000
£5307 $9500 €7748 Anthony's trollop (13x33x18cm-5x13x7in) paint stainless steel prov. 7-May-4 Sloans & Kenyon, Bethesda #1759/R est:12000-15000
£6200 $11408 €9052 ME (13cm-5in) steel painted glazed sheet metal prov. 24-Jun-4 Sotheby's, Olympia #596/R est:2000-3000
£7263 $13000 €10604 Abbadabba alobar (13x20x13cm-5x8x5in) paint stainless steel prov. 7-May-4 Sloans & Kenyon, Bethesda #1756/R est:12000-15000
£25140 $45000 €36704 Portrait of a nude with a chrome fan (68x38x25cm-27x15x10in) s. i.verso wall relief painted ceramic exec 1979 prov.lit. 12-May-4 Christie's, Rockefeller NY #149/R est:20000-30000
£26471 $45000 €38648 Asarabaca (69x56cm-27x22in) crush aluminum resin lacquer prov.exhib.lit. 9-Nov-3 Wright, Chicago #430 est:15000-20000
£39106 $70000 €57095 Potato telegram (34x109x41cm-13x43x16in) painted chromium plated steel exec 1990 prov. 13-May-4 Sotheby's, New York #242/R est:55000-65000
£111732 $200000 €163129 Rare Meat (213x50x71cm-84x20x28in) wall relief painted chromium plated steel exec 1977 prov.lit. 12-May-4 Christie's, Rockefeller NY #182/R est:200000-300000
£113772 $190000 €166107 Piece pockets (203x81x51cm-80x32x20in) painted chromium plated steel executed 1977 prov.exhib.lit. 12-Nov-3 Sotheby's, New York #52/R est:120000-180000
£131737 $220000 €192336 Andrea florentina luchezzi (188x96x89cm-74x38x35in) enamel chromium plated steel prov.exhib.lit. 13-Nov-3 Sotheby's, New York #249/R est:150000-200000
£135000 $245700 €197100 Stag's only (249x136x88cm-98x54x35in) painted chromium plated steel executed 1988 prov. 4-Feb-4 Christie's, London #38/R est:150000-200000
£167598 $300000 €244693 Mysting Tonatta (221x162x160cm-87x64x63in) painted steel exec 1990 prov. 11-May-4 Christie's, Rockefeller NY #50/R est:300000-400000
£167598 $300000 €244693 Isadorables (270x156x149cm-106x61x59in) painted stainless and chromium plated steel exec 1990 prov. 12-May-4 Sotheby's, New York #32/R est:300000-400000
£180000 $331200 €262800 Azimuth lamella (280x136x112cm-110x54x44in) painted chromium plated steel executed 1988 prov.exhib. 24-Jun-4 Christie's, London #20/R est:180000-220000
£191617 $320000 €279761 Gangster of Love (228x188x127cm-90x74x50in) painted chromium plated steel exec 1985 prov.exhib.lit. 12-Nov-3 Christie's, Rockefeller NY #380/R est:150000-200000
£299401 $500000 €437125 Murmurous Moto, Maestro (186x165x122cm-73x65x48in) painted and chromium plated steel exec 1991. 12-Nov-3 Christie's, Rockefeller NY #410/R est:150000-200000

CHAMBERLAIN, Norman Stiles (1887-1961) American
£588 $1000 €858 Near Laguna beach, California (41x51cm-16x20in) s.d.1914 s.i.d.verso canvas on board prov. 1-Nov-3 Santa Fe Art, Santa Fe #192/R
£882 $1500 €1288 Northern New Mexico (46x56cm-18x22in) s.i.d.1917 verso canvas on board prov. 1-Nov-3 Santa Fe Art, Santa Fe #193/R est:2000-3000

CHAMBERLAIN, Samuel V (1895-1975) American
Works on paper
£361 $600 €523 Vermeuil (33x20cm-13x8in) pencil. 13-Jun-3 Du Mouchelle, Detroit #2280/R

CHAMBERLAIN, Trevor (1933-) British
£270 $489 €394 Damp day - The seafront at Sandgate (18x25cm-7x10in) s.d.76 W/C. 17-Apr-4 Dickins, Middle Claydon #138
£680 $1217 €993 Passing by Greenwich (19x14cm-7x6in) s. board. 16-Mar-4 Bearnes, Exeter #426
£750 $1253 €1095 Stormy weather, Putney (36x51cm-14x20in) s.d.86 i.verso. 7-Oct-3 Bonhams, Knightsbridge #58/R
£820 $1443 €1197 Tate Gallery (25x35cm-10x14in) s.d.89. 18-May-4 Bonhams, Knightsbridge #101/R
Works on paper
£240 $382 €348 Below Greenwich (12x17cm-5x7in) s.d.81 W/C. 9-Sep-3 Sworder & Son, Bishops Stortford #431/R

CHAMBERLIN, Mason (elder) (1727-1787) British
£3000 $5520 €4380 Portrait of Lady, probably Elizabeth Hartley (76x63cm-30x25in) s. 11-Jun-4 Christie's, London #19/R est:3000-5000

CHAMBERLIN, Mason (elder-attrib) (1727-1787) British
£700 $1169 €1022 Portrait of Frances Butcher, wife of Robert (74x62cm-29x24in) painted 1771 prov. 22-Oct-3 Cheffins, Cambridge #523/R
£700 $1295 €1022 Portrait of Lady Turner (91x71cm-36x28in) 14-Jul-4 Sotheby's, Olympia #4/R
£1271 $2161 €1856 Portrait of a Gentleman in grey (75x62cm-30x24in) 24-Nov-3 Sotheby's, Melbourne #303/R est:3000-5000 (A.D 3000)

CHAMBERS, C Bosseron (1882-1964) American
£3297 $6000 €4814 Adoration of the Magi (81x66cm-32x26in) s. 19-Jun-4 Jackson's, Cedar Falls #13/R est:4000-7500

CHAMBERS, Charles Edward (1883-1942) American
£2514 $4500 €3670 Elderly couple's evening activities by lamplight (81x91cm-32x36in) s. 15-May-4 Illustration House, New York #112/R est:5000-7000

CHAMBERS, G (19th C) British
£5556 $9444 €8000 Unloading the catch (50x63cm-20x25in) bears sig. 28-Oct-3 Mealy's, Castlecomer #231

CHAMBERS, George (attrib) (19th C) British
£1800 $3222 €2628 Royal Naval two-decker backing her sails and making ready to enter port (30x40cm-12x16in) 26-May-4 Christie's, Kensington #607/R est:2000-3000

CHAMBERS, George (jnr) (fl.1848-1868) British
£550 $985 €803 Busy day on the Medway (16x24cm-6x9in) s.indis.d. board. 26-May-4 Christie's, Kensington #703/R
£1100 $1969 €1606 Congested coastal waters with a Dutch barge entering a harbour (61x91cm-24x36in) s. 18-Mar-4 Christie's, Kensington #539/R est:1200-1800

CHAMBERS, George (jnr-attrib) (fl.1848-1868) British
£1800 $2988 €2628 Hauling out of Margate against the tide (70x98cm-28x39in) 1-Oct-3 Bonhams, Knightsbridge #162/R est:1000-1500

CHAMBERS, George (snr) (1803-1840) British
£700 $1253 €1022 Naval brig astern of an armed lugger firing a shot (30x41cm-12x16in) s. 18-Mar-4 Christie's, Kensington #533/R
£7800 $12714 €11388 Portrait of an East Indiaman leaving a South coast port (65x98cm-26x39in) s.d.1826. 23-Sep-3 Anderson & Garland, Newcastle #407/R est:8000-12000
£10000 $17000 €14600 Merchantman (66x99cm-26x39in) s.d.1826. 19-Nov-3 Christie's, Kensington #520/R
£14054 $26000 €20519 Congestion at the harbour mouth, Margate (57x137cm-22x54in) s.d.1836 prov.lit. 10-Feb-4 Christie's, Rockefeller NY #226/R est:20000-30000
£14500 $25955 €21170 Trading brigs at anchor and drying their sails as their cargo is unloaded (51x65cm-20x26in) s.indis.d. 26-May-4 Christie's, Kensington #606/R est:7000-10000
Works on paper
£1900 $3268 €2774 Leaving port (19x30cm-7x12in) s.d.1838 W/C. 2-Dec-3 Sotheby's, London #27/R est:400-600
£3000 $5100 €4380 Merchantman entering port in a strong breeze (39x54cm-15x21in) s. W/C over pencil htd bodycol scratching out prov. 27-Nov-3 Sotheby's, London #258/R est:2500-3500

CHAMBERS, John (1852-1928) British
Works on paper
£380 $695 €555 Shipping on the Thames (50x71cm-20x28in) s. W/C. 6-Apr-4 Bonhams, Chester #844
£700 $1211 €1022 Wellesley ablaze in North Shields harbour (35x54cm-14x21in) s. W/C. 9-Dec-3 Anderson & Garland, Newcastle #225/R

CHAMBERS, John Richard (1931-1978) Canadian
£8108 $13784 €11838 Mantel group (114x152cm-45x60in) s.i.d.1966 verso panel prov.lit. 18-Nov-3 Sotheby's, Toronto #113/R est:20000-30000 (C.D 18000)

CHAMBERS, Thomas (attrib) (1808-1866) American
£3352 $6000 €4894 View of West Point on the Hudson river (61x81cm-24x32in) 8-Jan-4 James Julia, Fairfield #541/R est:8000-12000

CHAMBERS, W H (?) ?
£3279 $6000 €4787 Shipping in a moonlit sea (30x41cm-12x16in) s. 29-Jul-4 Christie's, Rockefeller NY #220/R est:4000-6000

CHAMBERT, Eric (1902-1988) Swedish
Works on paper
£1493 $2582 €2180 Composition in yellow, blue and white (73x92cm-29x36in) s. s.d.1955 verso mixed media. 15-Dec-3 Lilla Bukowskis, Stockholm #725 est:25000-30000 (S.KR 19000)

CHAMBEYRON, Yves (?) French
£276 $505 €400 Paysage (73x59cm-29x23in) 1-Feb-4 Teitgen, Nancy #23

CHAMBON, Emile François (1905-1993) Swiss
£3304 $5617 €4824 L'attente, gare de Milano (54x72cm-21x28in) s.d.72 i. verso board. 7-Nov-3 Dobiaschofsky, Bern #221/R est:4600 (S.FR 7500)

CHAMBON, Marius (1876-1962) French
£267 $485 €400 Nu au sofa (53x64cm-21x25in) s. 29-Jun-4 Chenu & Scrive, Lyon #46
£3057 $5563 €4463 Village scene (50x65cm-20x26in) s. prov. 16-Jun-4 Fischer, Luzern #1151/R est:7000-9000 (S.FR 7000)

CHAMBORD, Fernand Maximilien de (1840-1899) French
Works on paper
£845 $1462 €1200 View of Macao (24x39cm-9x15in) s.i. W/C pair. 15-Dec-3 Gros & Delettrez, Paris #497/R

CHAMBRIN, Jack (1919-) French
£511 $853 €720 Les quais d'alger (73x54cm-29x21in) s. d.1959 verso. 21-Jun-3 Peron, Melun #42a

CHAMERLAT, Jules-Marc (1828-1868) French
£476 $852 €700 Petits enfants derriere des bottes de ble (32x24cm-13x9in) s.d.1861. 19-Mar-4 Millon & Associes, Paris #94

CHAMINADE, Albert (1923-) French
£336 $625 €500 Composition (60x47cm-24x19in) s.d.62. 3-Mar-4 Artcurial Briest, Paris #337

CHAMISSO BROTHERS (18/19th C) German
Miniatures
£3200 $5760 €4672 Portrait of a gentleman - possibly artists brother Adalbert (9cm-4in) s. gold frame oval exhib. 22-Apr-4 Bonhams, New Bond Street #150/R est:2000-3000

CHAMPAGNE, Horace (1937-) Canadian
£248 $421 €362 Ferme Jaune (20x25cm-8x10in) s. s.i.d.1979 verso board prov. 23-Nov-3 Levis, Calgary #432/R (C.D 550)
£270 $459 €394 Golden morning, winter at Lake Connelly, Quebec (22x26cm-9x10in) s. s.i.d.1978 verso board prov. 23-Nov-3 Levis, Calgary #431/R (C.D 600)
Works on paper
£300 $549 €438 River reflections (29x38cm-11x15in) s. pastel. 1-Jun-4 Hodgins, Calgary #307/R (C.D 750)
£600 $1098 €876 No. 2021-7th Street, SW, Corner Durham (28x35cm-11x14in) s.i.d.1983 pastel. 1-Jun-4 Hodgins, Calgary #422/R (C.D 1500)
£732 $1310 €1069 The Vatican, Rome, Italy, (45x61cm-18x24in) s. s.i.d.2002 verso pastel. 27-May-4 Heffel, Vancouver #130/R est:2500-3500 (C.D 1800)
£1071 $1843 €1564 Autumn glory and first fresh snow, Les Eboulements, Quebec (42x57cm-17x22in) s. pastel. 2-Dec-3 Joyner Waddington, Toronto #194/R est:3000-4000 (C.D 2400)
£1120 $2050 €1635 Snowy, blowy day, Rue St Louis, Old Quebec (40x50cm-16x20in) s. pastel. 1-Jun-4 Joyner Waddington, Toronto #73/R est:3000-4000 (C.D 2800)
£1240 $2244 €1810 Rejeanne's peonies from our garden (44x60cm-17x24in) s. pastel prov. 18-Apr-4 Levis, Calgary #18/R est:3000-4000 (C.D 3000)
£1312 $2191 €1916 Extraordinary August snow, Lake O'Hara (50x40cm-20x16in) s.i.d.1995 pastel. 17-Nov-3 Hodgins, Calgary #54/R est:2000-2500 (C.D 2900)
£1360 $2489 €1986 Sabastien and Regeanne on Long Beach near Wickaninnish Bay, BC (53x73cm-21x29in) s. pastel exec. 1984. 1-Jun-4 Hodgins, Calgary #80/R est:3000-3500 (C.D 3400)
£1489 $2442 €2174 Lake O'Hara, summer morning (74x53cm-29x21in) s. pastel. 28-May-3 Maynards, Vancouver #34/R est:6000-8000 (C.D 3350)
£2262 $3778 €3303 St. Fidel looking towards Baie St. Paul (90x120cm-35x47in) s.i. pastel. 17-Nov-3 Hodgins, Calgary #72/R est:6000-8000 (C.D 5000)
£2400 $4392 €3504 Sunday morning sunshine, Rue du Tratt Carre Est, Charlesbourg (75x100cm-30x39in) s. pastel prov. 1-Jun-4 Hodgins, Calgary #409/R est:4500-5500 (C.D 6000)
£6757 $11486 €9865 Coming into Canmore, Alberta (71x102cm-28x40in) s. i.verso pastel prov. 21-Nov-3 Walker's, Ottawa #78/R est:3000-4000 (C.D 15000)

CHAMPAIGNE, Jean Baptiste de (attrib) (1631-c.1681) Flemish
Works on paper
£455 $782 €650 Angelot (20x14cm-8x6in) pierre noire. 3-Dec-3 Oger, Dumont, Paris #78

CHAMPAIGNE, Philippe de (1602-1674) Flemish
£248869 $423077 €363349 Annunciation to Maria (71x72cm-28x28in) s. panel lit.prov. 19-Nov-3 Fischer, Luzern #1018/R est:25000-35000 (S.FR 550000)
Works on paper
£50000 $90000 €73000 View of Jerusalem showing the Temple of Solomon (33x60cm-13x24in) red chk two joined sheets prov.exhib.lit. 22-Jan-4 Christie's, Rockefeller NY #85/R est:30000-50000

CHAMPAIGNE, Philippe de (studio) (1602-1674) Flemish
£16630 $29767 €24280 Moses with the Tablet of the Ten Commandments (100x80cm-39x31in) prov.lit. 26-May-4 AB Stockholms Auktionsverk #2614/R est:80000-100000 (S.KR 225000)

CHAMPEAUX, Bertrand de (19/20th C) French
£993 $1808 €1500 Rue de Lisieux (40x31cm-16x12in) s.i.d.1929 panel. 20-Jun-4 Imberdis, Pont Audemer #54

CHAMPIERRE, Elisabeth (20th C) French
£315 $535 €450 Tanger (90x30cm-35x12in) s. 29-Nov-3 Neret-Minet, Paris #30/R
£420 $713 €600 Terre rouge (70x70cm-28x28in) s. 29-Nov-3 Neret-Minet, Paris #93/R

CHAMPILLOU, Jeanne (20th C) French
£278 $464 €400 Denise et Jeanine (71x58cm-28x23in) s.d.1943 peinture. 25-Oct-3 Binoche, Orleans #43

CHAMPIN, Jean Jacques (1796-1860) French
Works on paper
£352 $616 €500 Paysage du Maine et Loire, village de Beaupreau (25x37cm-10x15in) wash crayon. 17-Dec-3 Delorme & Bocage, Paris #24
£352 $616 €500 Paysage du Maine et Loire, village de Saint Martin (25x37cm-10x15in) wash crayon. 17-Dec-3 Delorme & Bocage, Paris #25
£544 $975 €800 Guenievre et Lancelot allant visiter le tombeau de Tristan et Yseult (61x90cm-24x35in) s.d.1821 W/C traces black crayon grey wash htd white gouache. 17-Mar-4 Tajan, Paris #104/R
£1517 $2534 €2200 Rempart d'Angers (25x37cm-10x15in) s. brown wash pencil. 17-Nov-3 Delorme & Bocage, Paris #107/R est:1000-1800
£1793 $2994 €2600 Vue d'Angers (25x37cm-10x15in) s. brown wash pencil. 17-Nov-3 Delorme & Bocage, Paris #104/R est:1000-1800
£1862 $3110 €2700 Chateau Angers (25x37cm-10x15in) s. brown wash pencil. 17-Nov-3 Delorme & Bocage, Paris #103/R est:1000-1800

CHAMPION, Jeanne (20th C) French
Works on paper
£1701 $3044 €2500 Sir Winston Churchill - d'apres Monsieur Ingres, Le Musee Imaginaire (78x68cm-31x27in) s.d.1976 pastel prov. 21-Mar-4 Calmels Cohen, Paris #118/R est:2000-3000

CHAMPION, Theo (1887-1952) German
£533 $960 €800 Farmstead on the Rhone (58x64cm-23x25in) s.i.d.1912. 26-Apr-4 Rieber, Stuttgart #1020/R
£1049 $1804 €1500 Romantic landscape (37x51cm-15x20in) s.d.1927. 2-Dec-3 Hauswedell & Nolte, Hamburg #85/R est:2200
£1200 $2172 €1800 Table and chairs outside country house (45x43cm-18x17in) s.d.1913 verso double-sided. 2-Apr-4 Winterberg, Heidelberg #819/R est:1800
£1241 $2073 €1800 On the bridge (61x40cm-24x16in) s.d.1951 i.verso canvas on fibreboard. 13-Nov-3 Neumeister, Munich #285/R est:1800-2000
£1467 $2684 €2200 Still life of flowers (45x37cm-18x15in) s.d.1924. 5-Jun-4 Lempertz, Koln #648/R est:2400
£1806 $2979 €2600 In the park (45x37cm-18x15in) s.d.1933 panel. 3-Jul-3 Van Ham, Cologne #1094/R est:1500
£1818 $3127 €2600 Decorated entrance (52x33cm-20x13in) s.d.1932 panel prov. 4-Dec-3 Van Ham, Cologne #89/R est:2500
£2448 $4210 €3500 Uprooted tree (50x40cm-20x16in) s.d.1941 panel exhib.lit. 4-Dec-3 Van Ham, Cologne #88/R est:4000
£2667 $4880 €4000 Ruins on lower Rhine - Lulsdorf (86x96cm-34x38in) s.d.1911 prov. 5-Jun-4 Lempertz, Koln #647/R est:3500-4000
£3497 $6014 €5000 On the banks of the Rhein (32x53cm-13x21in) s.d.1952 i.verso canvas on board prov.exhib. 4-Dec-3 Van Ham, Cologne #87/R est:5000
£8667 $15513 €13000 View from artist's studio in Oberkassel (53x60cm-21x24in) s.d.1922 exhib. 15-May-4 Van Ham, Cologne #512/R est:2000

CHAMPNEY, B (1817-1907) American
£2095 $3750 €3059 Mountain and lake scene. s. 31-May-4 William A Smith, Plainfield #169/R

CHAMPNEY, Benjamin (1817-1907) American
£753 $1400 €1099 Forest stream with birches (41x25cm-16x10in) s. board. 6-Mar-4 North East Auctions, Portsmouth #1131/R
£926 $1500 €1343 Victorian river scene with overhanging birches (23x10cm-9x4in) s.d.1860 board. 26-Jul-3 Thomaston Place, Thomaston #36/R
£1290 $2400 €1883 Mountain view across a field (28x20cm-11x8in) board. 6-Mar-4 North East Auctions, Portsmouth #553/R
£2514 $4500 €3670 Skating on the duck pond (31x46cm-12x18in) s. 14-May-4 Skinner, Boston #62/R est:2000-3000
£3213 $5750 €4691 View from a New England forest (61x41cm-24x16in) s. 8-Jan-4 James Julia, Fairfield #666/R est:5000-7000
£3580 $5800 €5191 Walk in the woods (41x61cm-16x24in) s.d.102. 8-Aug-3 Barridorf, Portland #137/R est:6000-9000

CHAMPNEY, Edwin Graves (1842-1899) American
£1129 $2100 €1648 To work (50x76cm-20x30in) s.d.1881. 5-Mar-4 Skinner, Boston #280/R est:400-600

CHAN, Eric (1979-) Malaysian
£1144 $2070 €1670 Untitled (80x80cm-31x31in) s.d.2003 verso. 3-Apr-4 Glerum, Singapore #60/R est:3000-4000 (S.D 3500)

CHANCE, Georges la (1888-1964) American
£538 $1000 €785 Towards the eternal hills (51x61cm-20x24in) s. painted c.1940. 7-Mar-4 Treadway Gallery, Cincinnati #515/R est:1500-2000
£854 $1400 €1238 Toward the eternal hills (20x24cm-8x9in) s. painted c.1940. 7-Jun-3 Treadway Gallery, Cincinnati #1431
£1341 $2200 €1944 Peace and content (20x24cm-8x9in) s. painted c.1940. 7-Jun-3 Treadway Gallery, Cincinnati #1430 est:2000-3000

CHANCHO CABRE, Joaquin (1943-) Spanish
£2585 $4705 €3800 Painting 300 (120x120cm-47x47in) s.i.d.2002 verso prov. 3-Feb-4 Segre, Madrid #375a/R est:3800

CHANCO, Roland (1914-) French
£690 $1276 €1000 La mort du petit chat (92x73cm-36x29in) s. s.d.21.V.1963 verso prov. 11-Feb-4 Beaussant & Lefevre, Paris #152/R

Works on paper
£267 $477 €400 Personnage (64x49cm-25x19in) s. pastel. 16-May-4 Feletin, Province #162

CHANCOURTOIS, René Louis Beguyer de (1757-1817) French
Works on paper
£533 $965 €800 Paysage classique anime (32x39cm-13x15in) s.i. pen black ink brown wash. 30-Mar-4 Rossini, Paris #91
£800 $1384 €1168 Village of Tivoli. Church of SS Giovanni e Paolo, Venice (21x32cm-8x13in) s.i. black chk pen ink col wash sold with 1 by another hand. 12-Dec-3 Christie's, Kensington #463/R

CHANCRIN, René (1920-1981) French
£1000 $1830 €1500 Fleurs de printemps dans un pichet bleu et blanc (55x46cm-22x18in) s.d.35. 6-Jun-4 Anaf, Lyon #337/R est:1500-2000
£1538 $2646 €2200 Nature morte aux raisins (61x46cm-24x18in) s.d.55. 8-Dec-3 Christie's, Paris #75/R est:1000-1200

CHAND, Lal (17th C) Indian
Works on paper
£21000 $35070 €30660 Saint Mian Mir in discussion (14x10cm-6x4in) i. i.verso gouache gold. 15-Oct-3 Sotheby's, London #36/R est:8000-12000
£21000 $35070 €30660 Six wise men (13x11cm-5x4in) i.verso gouache gold prov. 15-Oct-3 Sotheby's, London #37/R est:8000-12000

CHANDLER, Floyd Copeland (1920-) American
£531 $850 €775 Southern California desert (155x193cm-61x76in) s. 18-May-3 Auctions by the Bay, Alameda #1125/R

CHANDLER, Joseph Goodhue (1813-1880) American
£3529 $6000 €5152 Portrait of George Washington (61x51cm-24x20in) s. after Gilbert Stuart. 31-Oct-3 North East Auctions, Portsmouth #1782
£7784 $13000 €11365 Edward P, aged 11 years and Henry M Smith, aged 9 years (74x61cm-29x24in) 14-Nov-3 Douglas, South Deerfield #1

CHANDLER, Joseph Goodhue (attrib) (1813-1880) American
£14754 $27000 €21541 Portrait of the Dibble twins (99x91cm-39x36in) prov.exhib. 6-Jun-4 Skinner, Boston #84/R est:30000-50000

CHANDLER, Sadie (1963-) Australian
£1053 $1695 €1537 Red dress (120x180cm-47x71in) s.d.2002 verso prov. 25-Aug-3 Sotheby's, Paddington #299/R est:1000-1500 (A.D 2600)

CHANDLER, William (1854-1928) American
Works on paper
£495 $900 €723 Lakeside campfire and teepee (122x30cm-48x12in) s. pastel. 19-Jun-4 Jackson's, Cedar Falls #269/R

CHANEY, Lester Joseph (1907-) American
£355 $650 €518 Crashing waves (61x76cm-24x30in) s. painted c.1938. 5-Jun-4 Treadway Gallery, Cincinnati #642/R
£391 $700 €571 Rocky coast (63x76cm-25x30in) s. 21-Mar-4 Bonhams & Butterfields, Los Angeles #7124/R
£1453 $2500 €2121 Lake Michigan scene (71x91cm-28x36in) s. painted c.1920. 7-Dec-3 Treadway Gallery, Cincinnati #623/R est:800-1200

CHANG SHUSEN (1954-) Chinese
Works on paper
£4267 $7681 €6230 Rooster (80x142cm-31x56in) s. ink col scroll silk. 25-Apr-4 Christie's, Hong Kong #27/R est:60000-80000 (HK.D 60000)

CHANG YU SHU (1900-1966) Chinese
£138996 $232124 €202934 Potted chrysanthemums in a mandarin blue background (70x62cm-28x24in) s. masonite painted c.1950 exhib.lit. 26-Oct-3 Christie's, Hong Kong #128/R est:1300000-2000000 (HK.D 1800000)
£285714 $477143 €417142 Leopard (93x116cm-37x46in) s.d.1931 lit. 26-Oct-3 Christie's, Hong Kong #127/R est:2800000-3200000 (HK.D 3700000)
Works on paper
£1700 $3043 €2482 Seated nude (45x27cm-18x11in) s. ink chl. 6-May-4 Sotheby's, London #101/R est:1400-1700

CHANTEREAU, Jerome François (?-1757) French
£1436 $2600 €2097 Figures resting in a landscape (39x33cm-15x13in) panel. 30-Mar-4 Christie's, Rockefeller NY #32/R est:2000-3000
Works on paper
£616 $1048 €900 Scenes de genre (17x28cm-7x11in) crayon set of 4. 6-Nov-3 Tajan, Paris #58

CHANTRON, Alexandre Jacques (1842-1918) French
£667 $1193 €1000 Barque sur l'etang. s. 15-May-4 other European Auctioneer #67
Works on paper
£377 $640 €550 Cocotte en papier (56x45cm-22x18in) s. pastel. 9-Nov-3 Eric Pillon, Calais #34/R
£19014 $32894 €27000 Nude in atelier (195x95cm-77x37in) s. pastel. 9-Dec-3 Finarte Semenzato, Milan #92/R est:28000-30000

CHANU, Luc (20th C) French?
£434 $786 €660 Porteuses de Goemon. s. 17-Apr-4 Livinec, Gaudcheau & Jezequel, Rennes #112

CHAPA, Marta (1946-) Mexican
£744 $1369 €1086 Enigma (50x70cm-20x28in) s. 25-Mar-4 Louis Morton, Mexico #52/R est:18000-20000 (M.P 15000)

CHAPELAIN-MIDY, Roger (1904-1992) French
£493 $853 €700 La plage (27x41cm-11x16in) s. 10-Dec-3 Claude Boisgirard, Paris #33
£903 $1508 €1300 Les remparts de Saint-Martin de Re (27x46cm-11x18in) s. prov. 23-Oct-3 Credit Municipal, Paris #67
£940 $1682 €1400 Nature morte aux fruits (27x22cm-11x9in) s. 30-May-4 Eric Pillon, Calais #55/R
£952 $1705 €1400 La petite danseuse (46x38cm-18x15in) s. i.verso prov. 19-Mar-4 Oger, Dumont, Paris #6/R
£1060 $1928 €1600 Le fiacre a Bruges (61x73cm-24x29in) s. i.verso. 18-Jun-4 Piasa, Paris #190/R est:2000-3000
£1156 $1839 €1700 Nature morte aux fruits et au carton a dessin (74x50cm-29x20in) s. s.i.verso. 23-Mar-3 St-Germain-en-Laye Encheres #72/R
£1342 $2470 €2000 Bateaux de peche sur la greve (54x65cm-21x26in) s. 26-Mar-4 Neret-Minet, Paris #12/R est:2000-2500
£1342 $2403 €2000 Voiliers au port (60x81cm-24x32in) s. 27-May-4 Christie's, Paris #137/R est:2000-3000
£1761 $3046 €2500 Roses et papillons (40x26cm-16x10in) s. 10-Dec-3 Ferri, Paris #29/R est:2300-2500
£2098 $3608 €3000 La plage (65x81cm-26x32in) s. prov. 3-Dec-3 Oger, Dumont, Paris #7/R est:3000-3800
£2684 $4751 €4000 Jardin des tuileries (65x81cm-26x32in) s. 27-Apr-4 Artcurial Briest, Paris #157 est:1000-1500
£5034 $9010 €7500 Nature morte (81x100cm-32x39in) s. 30-May-4 Eric Pillon, Calais #57/R
Works on paper
£278 $464 €400 Nu au deshabille ou etude pour la chemise (55x42cm-22x17in) s. gouache ink wash prov. 21-Oct-3 Artcurial Briest, Paris #18
£537 $961 €800 View of Venice (67x47cm-26x19in) s. W/C gouache. 30-May-4 Eric Pillon, Calais #142/R

CHAPELET, Roger (1902-1995) French
Works on paper
£288 $460 €400 Le rollon (32x24cm-13x9in) i. gouache. 18-May-3 Claude Boisgirard, Paris #157
£897 $1641 €1300 Trois mats avec un remorqueur en premier plan (33x42cm-13x17in) W/C gouache. 31-Jan-4 Neret-Minet, Paris #120/R
£1042 $1740 €1500 Trois-mats (33x42cm-13x17in) s. W/C gouache. 26-Oct-3 Lesieur & Le Bars, Le Havre #188
£1325 $2424 €2000 Trois-mats (40x60cm-16x24in) s. W/C. 9-Apr-4 Bailly Pommery, Paris #90/R est:2000-3000
£2000 $3660 €3000 Femmes marocaines conversant (49x64cm-19x25in) s. gouache. 3-Jun-4 Tajan, Paris #216/R est:3000-3500

CHAPELLIER, Jose (1946-) Belgian
£2098 $3503 €3000 Flowers (72x59cm-28x23in) s. 11-Oct-3 De Vuyst, Lokeren #50 est:2500-3000

CHAPERON, Eugène (1857-?) French
£3401 $5408 €5000 La diligence sur le pont (87x115cm-34x45in) s.d.1933. 22-Mar-3 Dubee & Berron, Vernou en Sologne #71

CHAPERON, Philippe Marie (1823-1907) French
Works on paper
£1020 $1827 €1500 Bateaux naviguant autour du temple d'Isis (31x41cm-12x16in) s.d.1904 Chinese ink gouache. 21-Mar-4 St-Germain-en-Laye Encheres #25/R est:1000-1200
£1056 $1827 €1500 Projet de decor de theatre (28x41cm-11x16in) s.i. W/C gouache Chinese ink. 15-Dec-3 Bailly Pommery, Paris #74/R est:900-1200

CHAPIN, Bryant (1859-1927) American
£270 $500 €394 On Isle of Mann (41x61cm-16x24in) s. oil on linen. 15-Feb-4 Outer Cape Auctions, Provincetown #70a/R
£883 $1500 €1289 Still life with peaches (23x31cm-9x12in) s. 21-Nov-3 Skinner, Boston #298/R est:3000-5000
£1471 $2500 €2148 Still life with seven plums on a table (25x33cm-10x13in) s. 21-Nov-3 Eldred, East Dennis #815/R est:3000-4000
£2353 $4000 €3435 Still life with apples, plums, peach, pear and grapes (28x36cm-11x14in) s.d.1923 i.verso. 21-Nov-3 Eldred, East Dennis #813/R est:4000-5000
£2706 $4600 €3951 Still life with overturned basket of strawberries (33x43cm-13x17in) s.d.1922. 21-Nov-3 Eldred, East Dennis #814/R est:5000-6000
£3571 $5750 €5214 Strawberry still life (30x41cm-12x16in) s. 20-Aug-3 James Julia, Fairfield #1347/R est:6000-7000
£8235 $14000 €12023 Fruit on a polished table (33x44cm-13x17in) s.d.1903 prov. 30-Oct-3 Phillips, New York #22/R est:15000-20000

CHAPIN, Charles H (1830-1889) American
Works on paper
£447 $800 €653 Seascape (25x43cm-10x17in) s. W/C paper on board. 8-Jan-4 Doyle, New York #16/R
£1429 $2600 €2086 Louisiana Bayou scene with egret (33x48cm-13x19in) s. W/C. 7-Feb-4 Neal Auction Company, New Orleans #512/R est:1500-2500

CHAPIN, Francis (1899-1965) American
£299 $550 €437 Female nude by a river (61x61cm-24x24in) s. masonite. 25-Jun-4 Freeman, Philadelphia #232/R

£852 $1500 €1244 Ice skaters (71x102cm-28x40in) s. painted c.1940. 23-May-4 Treadway Gallery, Cincinnati #715/R est:2500-4500
Works on paper
£230 $425 €336 City vista (23x71cm-9x28in) s. W/C. 16-Jan-4 Aspire, Cleveland #154/R

CHAPIN, Maria W (19th C) American
Works on paper
£3457 $5600 €5047 Lake scene with sightseers and fisherman (38x61cm-15x24in) s.d.1838 W/C. 1-Aug-3 North East Auctions, Portsmouth #998/R est:1000-2000

CHAPIRO, Jacques (1887-1972) Russian
£528 $914 €750 Bouquet de fleurs (55x46cm-22x18in) s.d.1920. 10-Dec-3 Millon & Associes, Paris #93/R
£1049 $1783 €1500 Porte Saint-Cloud (92x73cm-36x29in) s.d.1934. 28-Nov-3 Drouot Estimations, Paris #139 est:1500-1800
Works on paper
£414 $691 €600 Florence (65x50cm-26x20in) s.i.d.1952 gouache. 17-Nov-3 Claude Boisgirard, Paris #8/R

CHAPLIN, Charles (1825-1891) French
£800 $1360 €1168 Jeune femme (66x48cm-26x19in) i.verso. 20-Nov-3 Gorringes, Worthing #749/R
£1611 $2964 €2400 Moulins au crepuscule (22x16cm-9x6in) s. 24-Mar-4 Joron-Derem, Paris #231/R est:3000-4000
£2000 $3640 €2920 Coy look (46x38cm-18x15in) s. 16-Jun-4 Christie's, Kensington #80/R est:4000-6000
£2081 $3580 €3038 Portrait de femme au eventail rouge (45x35cm-18x14in) s. 3-Dec-3 Naón & Cia, Buenos Aires #48/R est:3000-4000
£2532 $4000 €3697 Portrait of a young woman (46x38cm-18x15in) s. 7-Sep-3 Treadway Gallery, Cincinnati #616/R est:5000-7000
£2550 $4743 €3800 Jeune femme demi-nue (35x24cm-14x9in) s. 8-Mar-4 Artcurial Briest, Paris #31/R est:2000-3000
£2944 $5269 €4298 Someilleuse (31x51cm-12x20in) s. 22-Mar-4 Philippe Schuler, Zurich #4393/R est:4000-5300 (S.FR 6800)
£3356 $6007 €5000 Jeune fille a la rose (65x54cm-26x21in) s. 25-May-4 Chambelland & Giafferi, Paris #46/R est:10000-12000
£3907 $6720 €5704 Jeune fille endormie (45x32cm-18x13in) s. 3-Dec-3 Naón & Cia, Buenos Aires #49/R est:6000-8000
£5430 $9938 €8200 Jeune fille a la lecture (42x26cm-17x10in) s. 7-Apr-4 Piasa, Paris #6/R est:5000-6000
£6000 $9600 €8700 Portrait d'une jeune fille (73x50cm-29x20in) 18-Sep-3 Christie's, Kensington #156/R est:3000-5000
£6832 $11000 €9975 Reflection (48x29cm-19x11in) s. prov. 14-Jan-4 Christie's, Rockefeller NY #13/R est:7000-9000
£10556 $19000 €15412 Les joueurs de lotto (66x54cm-26x21in) s. prov. 23-Apr-4 Sotheby's, New York #51/R est:30000-40000
£20000 $36400 €29200 Young girl with a dove (75x44cm-30x17in) s. 17-Jun-4 Christie's, London #31/R est:12000-18000
Works on paper
£267 $483 €400 Paysan (27x18cm-11x7in) s. wash. 5-Apr-4 Deburaux, Boulogne #74
£1074 $1997 €1600 Jeune fille (21x16cm-8x6in) s. W/C. 8-Mar-4 Artcurial Briest, Paris #32/R est:1500-2000

CHAPLIN, Charles (attrib) (1825-1891) French
£680 $1082 €1000 Portrait of young girl in profile (46x31cm-18x12in) 23-Mar-3 Mercier & Cie, Lille #275
£875 $1400 €1278 Portrait of a seated young lady wearing white dress with pink ribbons (41x30cm-16x12in) 20-Sep-3 Pook & Pook, Downington #183/R est:1500-2500

CHAPLIN, E (20th C) French
£1773 $2961 €2500 Deux jeunes femmes sous les ombrages (80x55cm-31x22in) s. 20-Jun-3 Drouot Estimations, Paris #82 est:1000-1100

CHAPLIN, Elisabeth (1890-1982) French
£662 $1205 €1000 Still life of flowers and shoe (60x41cm-24x16in) s. paper on board. 21-Jun-4 Pandolfini, Florence #215/R
£1367 $2242 €1900 Letter (74x90cm-29x35in) s. 10-Jun-3 Pandolfini, Florence #294/R est:2000-2100
Works on paper
£379 $630 €550 Nudes (49x34cm-19x13in) s. chk dr. 1-Oct-3 Della Rocca, Turin #228

CHAPMAN, Carlton Theodore (1860-1925) American
£663 $1100 €961 Taking possession of San Diego Old Town (51x61cm-20x24in) 13-Jun-3 Douglas, South Deerfield #6
£5495 $10000 €8023 The USS Cyane taking possession of San Diego town (51x61cm-20x24in) s.i. 15-Jun-4 John Moran, Pasadena #53b est:6000-8000
Works on paper
£231 $425 €337 Regatta (18x25cm-7x10in) W/C pencil exec. c.1890. 10-Jun-4 Swann Galleries, New York #60/R
£480 $850 €701 Fishermen off shore (5x20cm-2x8in) s.d.90 W/C. 2-May-4 Grogan, Boston #31/R
£538 $850 €785 Rockport harbour (41x66cm-16x26in) s.d.Sept 15 1885 W/C. 27-Jul-3 William Jenack, New York #260

CHAPMAN, Charles S (1879-1962) American
Works on paper
£232 $425 €339 Portrait of a boy (38x28cm-15x11in) s.d.1947 pastel. 5-Jun-4 Treadway Gallery, Cincinnati #645/R

CHAPMAN, Conrad Wise (1842-1910) American
£2733 $4947 €4100 Cavaliers mexicains a cheval (16x22cm-6x9in) s. panel. 5-Apr-4 Marie & Robert, Paris #59/R est:2000-3000
£6500 $11505 €9490 Beach at Houlgate, Normandy. Skating in the Bois de Boulogne, Paris (20x18cm-8x7in) s.d.1880 palette shaped board pair. 27-Apr-4 Bonhams, New Bond Street #115/R est:5000-8000
Works on paper
£13529 $23000 €19752 Cholula (22x47cm-9x19in) s.d.1873 verso W/C prov.exhib. 19-Nov-3 Sotheby's, New York #75/R est:12000-18000

CHAPMAN, Dinos and Jake (20th C) British
Sculpture
£9500 $17480 €13870 Disasters of Yoga (61x55x44cm-24x22x17in) fibreglass resin paint shoes exec 1997 prov.exhib. 24-Jun-4 Sotheby's, London #123/R est:8000-12000
£16760 $30000 €24470 CFC725403102 verso (170x30x30cm-67x12x12in) oil bronze metal support wooden base edition of 3 prov. 14-May-4 Phillips, New York #122/R est:20000-30000

CHAPMAN, Dora (1911-1995) Australian
£305 $556 €445 Urban composition (28x21cm-11x8in) s. canvas on board. 16-Jun-4 Deutscher-Menzies, Melbourne #632 (A.D 800)

CHAPMAN, George (1908-1993) British
£2000 $3640 €2920 Coal train (36x36cm-14x14in) s. board. 21-Jun-4 Bonhams, Bath #319/R est:800-1200

CHAPMAN, James (?) British
£514 $920 €771 Portrait of a young girl with a dog (74x61cm-29x24in) canvas on board. 17-May-4 Sotheby's, Melbourne #609 (A.D 1300)

CHAPMAN, John Gadsby (1808-1889) American
£889 $1600 €1298 Pilgrim beside a roadside shrine (25x36cm-10x14in) mono.i.d.1870 i. verso board. 24-Apr-4 Weschler, Washington #588/R est:1000-1500
£2235 $4000 €3263 Bacchanal (69x53cm-27x21in) mono.d.1856. 26-May-4 Doyle, New York #12/R est:5000-7000

CHAPMAN, John Linton (1839-1905) American
£380 $619 €555 Steam locomotive before an engine shed (51x107cm-20x42in) s. board. 23-Sep-3 Bonhams, Chester #921
£538 $1000 €785 View of Lake Nemi, near Rome (25x36cm-10x14in) s. i. verso. 3-Mar-4 Christie's, Rockefeller NY #18/R est:2000-3000
£1176 $2000 €1717 Two young woman gathering grapes (36x25cm-14x10in) s. 21-Nov-3 Eldred, East Dennis #827/R est:3000-5000
£1285 $2300 €1876 Rome (25x34cm-10x13in) s. board. 14-May-4 Skinner, Boston #25/R est:1800-2200
£24832 $45691 €37000 Ancient Appia (179x73cm-70x29in) s.d.1880. 27-Mar-4 Farsetti, Prato #349/R est:18000

CHAPMAN, John Watkins (1832-1903) British
£1500 $2790 €2190 Country lass (22x13cm-9x5in) s. board. 4-Mar-4 Christie's, Kensington #586/R est:500-800

CHAPMAN, Margaret (20th C) British
£480 $864 €701 Boats for hire (55x75cm-22x30in) s.d.73 i.verso board. 21-Apr-4 Tennants, Leyburn #1233
Works on paper
£750 $1373 €1095 Shopping at the Co-op (51x41cm-20x16in) s. W/C drawing. 6-Apr-4 Capes Dunn, Manchester #809/R

CHAPMAN, Minerva Josephine (1858-1947) American
£552 $1000 €806 Landscape (37x60cm-15x24in) indis d. July 2. 18-Apr-4 Bonhams & Butterfields, Los Angeles #7019 est:1500-2000

CHAPMAN, Philip (20th C) British?
£450 $833 €657 Emanuele's Bassin, Vaugines (55x60cm-22x24in) acrylic. 13-Feb-4 Sworder & Son, Bishops Stortford #122/R

CHAPOVAL, Youla (1919-1951) French/Russian
£1200 $2208 €1800 Untitled (21x38cm-8x15in) studio st. d.1950 verso board. 8-Jun-4 Sotheby's, Amsterdam #249/R est:2500-3500
£3691 $6866 €5500 Mui (81x65cm-32x26in) s.d.1951 i.d.aout 1951 verso. 3-Mar-4 Artcurial Briest, Paris #338/R est:4000-5000
£3800 $6992 €5548 Homme au verre (72x60cm-28x24in) s.d.1947 verso prov. 24-Mar-4 Sotheby's, Olympia #122/R est:3000-4000
£4027 $7450 €6000 Les coups (61x50cm-24x20in) s.d.1947. 15-Mar-4 Claude Boisgirard, Paris #21/R est:6000-7000
Works on paper
£235 $437 €350 Composition abstraite (23x32cm-9x13in) s.d.VI 195 W/C. 3-Mar-4 Artcurial Briest, Paris #339
£526 $968 €800 Composition abstraite (24x17cm-9x7in) s. gouache. 25-Jun-4 Daguerre, Paris #172

CHAPPEL, Edouard (1859-1946) Belgian
£260 $419 €380 Cows in the Watermeadows, Barnham Broom, Norfolk (25x31cm-10x12in) s. 12-Aug-3 Bonhams, Ipswich #234
£600 $1116 €876 Peaceful stretch of the river (41x61cm-16x24in) s. 4-Mar-4 Christie's, Kensington #526

CHAPPELL, Reuben (1870-1940) British
£1257 $2250 €1835 Topsail schooner Little Belle of Par off the Needles, Isle of Wight (51x76cm-20x30in) s.i. 16-Mar-4 Bonhams & Butterfields, San Francisco #6154/R est:3000-5000
£2500 $4175 €3650 Ship portrait, Morning Star of Padstow (51x76cm-20x30in) s.i. 14-Oct-3 David Lay, Penzance #628/R est:1000-1200

Works on paper

£281	$469	€410	Ship's portrait of Waft Brixton (33x51cm-13x20in) s. gouache. 25-Oct-3 Rasmussen, Havnen #2599/R (D.KR 3000)
£350	$595	€511	Three-masted trading schooner Christa von Bremen (37x55cm-15x22in) s.i. bodycol. 19-Nov-3 Christie's, Kensington #368/R
£360	$619	€526	Ship portrait, The Danmark of Thur with a steamer (54x36cm-21x14in) W/C gouache. 4-Dec-3 Bonhams, Cornwall #427
£373	$679	€560	Ship's portrait of J Lotz af Thro (38x54cm-15x21in) s. W/C. 19-Jun-4 Rasmussen, Havnen #2037/R (D.KR 4200)
£467	$869	€682	Ship's portrait of Albertha Marstal (34x53cm-13x21in) s. W/C gouache. 2-Mar-4 Rasmussen, Copenhagen #1428/R (D.KR 5200)
£468	$782	€683	Ship's portrait of Jorgensen of Ronne (34x52cm-13x20in) s. W/C. 25-Oct-3 Rasmussen, Havnen #2612/R (D.KR 5000)
£588	$953	€858	Ship's portrait of Flora from Thuro (32x48cm-13x19in) W/C. 9-Aug-3 Hindemae, Ullerslev #238/R (D.KR 6200)

CHAPPELL, Reuben (attrib) (1870-1940) British

£360	$659	€526	Three masted top sail schooner Susan Vittery (43x56cm-17x22in) 28-Jul-4 Hampton & Littlewood, Exeter #622a/R

CHAPPER, Emile (20th C) French

£699	$1189	€1000	La revue de l'Armee imperiale (24x45cm-9x18in) cardboard on panel. 1-Dec-3 Coutau Begarie, Paris #152

CHAPPERT-GAUJAL, Patrick (20th C) French?

£2431	$4059	€3500	Sans titre (100x100cm-39x39in) s.d.2001 verso oil wood cardboard on canvas. 25-Oct-3 Cornette de St.Cyr, Paris #628/R est:3500-4000

CHAPRON, Nicolas (attrib) (1612-c.1656) French

£7692	$13231	€11230	Madonna and Child (92x78cm-36x31in) 3-Dec-3 AB Stockholms Auktionsverk #2700/R est:50000-60000 (S.KR 100000)

Works on paper

£959	$1631	€1400	Bacchanale (20x28cm-8x11in) pen ink wash over crayon. 6-Nov-3 Tajan, Paris #24/R est:1500

CHAPRONT, Genevieve (1909-) French

£407	$692	€594	Gueridon devant la fenetre (33x41cm-13x16in) s. 19-Nov-3 Fischer, Luzern #2036/R (S.FR 900)

CHAPU, Henri Michel Antoine (1833-1891) French

Sculpture

£1111	$1756	€1600	Jeanne d'Arc - enfant (35cm-14in) s. i. verso carara marble. 19-Sep-3 Schloss Ahlden, Ahlden #787/R est:1200
£1115	$1829	€1550	Allegorie (74x22x20cm-29x9x8in) s. medaille pat bronze Cast F. Barbedienne. 6-Jun-3 David Kahn, Paris #270 est:1200-1500
£1284	$2298	€1900	Une jeune femme drapee (72x42cm-28x17in) s.st.f.Thiebaut Freres dark pat bronze marble socle. 10-May-4 Horta, Bruxelles #214 est:1500-1800
£1300	$2366	€1898	Joan of Arc (32cm-13in) s.st.f.F. Barbedienne white marble. 15-Jun-4 Sotheby's, Olympia #131/R est:1500-1800
£1528	$2551	€2200	Jeanne d'Arc (45cm-18in) s.i. col plaster prov. 24-Oct-3 Ketterer, Hamburg #48/R est:2500-3000
£1793	$2994	€2600	La jeunesse (60cm-24in) s.i. dark brown pat.bronze Cast.Ferdinand Barbedienne, Paris. 15-Nov-3 Von Zezschwitz, Munich #15/R est:3300

CHAPU, Henri Michel Antoine (attrib) (1833-1891) French

Sculpture

£1748	$3007	€2500	Jeune fille assise (46cm-18in) marble. 3-Dec-3 Palais de Beaux Arts, Brussels #633/R est:2500-3250

CHAPUIS, Pierre Marie Alfred (1863-1942) French

Works on paper

£524	$902	€750	Le retour de chasse (18x26cm-7x10in) s.d.1903 Indian ink wash bistre. 3-Dec-3 Coutau Begarie, Paris #46/R

CHARAVEL, Paul (1877-1961) French

£1049	$1804	€1500	Les naiades (93x73cm-37x29in) s. 3-Dec-3 Tajan, Paris #309 est:1500-1800
£1079	$1770	€1500	Nu (66x54cm-26x21in) s.d.39 cardboard. 3-Jun-3 Livinec, Gaudcheau & Jezequel, Rennes #56/R
£1284	$2145	€1862	Gulf of Saint Tropez (24x33cm-9x13in) s.d.26. 23-Jun-3 Philippe Schuler, Zurich #3560/R est:1400-1800 (S.FR 2800)

CHARBONNIER, Pierre (1897-1978) French

£491	$850	€717	Promenade (100x81cm-39x32in) s. 13-Dec-3 Weschler, Washington #515
£1000	$1800	€1500	Lyon (65x100cm-26x39in) s. exhib. 20-Apr-4 Chenu & Scrive, Lyon #55/R est:1500-1800

CHARCHOUNE, Serge (1888-1975) Russian

£594	$993	€850	Composition (8x30cm-3x12in) s. prov. 29-Jun-3 Versailles Encheres #8
£694	$1159	€1000	Galapagos (33x55cm-13x22in) s.i. s.i.d.21/11/73 verso. 21-Oct-3 Artcurial Briest, Paris #396
£769	$1308	€1100	Bourrasque (17x22cm-7x9in) s. panel lit. 30-Nov-3 Anaf, Lyon #61
£839	$1427	€1200	Coeur mystique (20x43cm-8x17in) s.d.IX.53 prov. 23-Nov-3 Cornette de St.Cyr, Paris #45/R
£909	$1545	€1300	Composition (16x20cm-6x8in) s. canvas on panel prov. 23-Nov-3 Cornette de St.Cyr, Paris #44/R
£972	$1624	€1400	Composition (27x19cm-11x7in) s.d.mai 63 verso. 25-Oct-3 Cornette de St.Cyr, Paris #630
£1250	$2300	€1900	Alberiz (73x50cm-29x20in) s. s.i.verso prov.lit. 27-Jun-4 Versailles Encheres #22/R est:2000-3000
£1343	$2497	€2000	Sans titre (13x43cm-5x17in) s. 3-Mar-4 Artcurial Briest, Paris #344 est:3000-4000
£1399	$2378	€2000	Remous (15x22cm-6x9in) s.d.30 lit. 30-Nov-3 Anaf, Lyon #60 est:800-1000
£1538	$2615	€2200	Jeux de l'atome (14x19cm-6x7in) s.d.30 lit. 30-Nov-3 Anaf, Lyon #59 est:800-1000
£1538	$2646	€2200	Composition (17x22cm-7x9in) s. 4-Dec-3 Piasa, Paris #101/R est:2500-3000
£1608	$2734	€2300	Paysage de Grenade (25x21cm-10x8in) s. canvas on cardboard prov. 23-Nov-3 Cornette de St.Cyr, Paris #46/R est:300-400
£1678	$3121	€2500	Composition pour 4 cordes de Paganini (15x61cm-6x24in) s.i.d.V.III.1969. 3-Mar-4 Artcurial Briest, Paris #343/R est:3000-4000
£1745	$3211	€2600	Le sacre-coeur (24x19cm-9x7in) s.d.XII 44 lit. 28-Mar-4 Anaf, Lyon #50/R est:1500-2000
£1867	$3435	€2800	Composition (22x27cm-9x11in) s.d.50 panel prov. 8-Jun-4 Artcurial Briest, Paris #84/R est:3000-4000
£1888	$3210	€2700	Coucher de soleil sur une assiette (27x38cm-11x15in) s.i.d.31 exhib.lit. 30-Nov-3 Anaf, Lyon #64/R est:1500-2000
£1944	$3247	€2800	Monteverde (33x55cm-13x22in) s. s.i.verso. 25-Oct-3 Cornette de St.Cyr, Paris #631/R est:3000-4000
£1958	$3329	€2800	Buisson ardeno no 1 (32x40cm-13x16in) s.d.31 panel exhib.lit. 30-Nov-3 Anaf, Lyon #63 est:1000-1200
£1972	$3411	€2800	Galapagos (46x55cm-18x22in) s.d.1973. 9-Dec-3 Artcurial Briest, Paris #511/R est:1500-2000
£2098	$3503	€3000	Songe d'une nuit d'ete (54x73cm-21x29in) s. s.i.verso prov. 29-Jun-3 Versailles Encheres #48/R
£2098	$3566	€3000	Coupe celadon (27x35cm-11x14in) s.d.26 lit. 30-Nov-3 Anaf, Lyon #56 est:800-1000
£2098	$3566	€3000	Clef de l'arabesque (35x24cm-14x9in) s. panel lit. 30-Nov-3 Anaf, Lyon #74/R est:2500-3000
£2134	$3840	€3200	Nature morte (16x22cm-6x9in) s.d.1943. 26-Apr-4 Tajan, Paris #208/R est:4000-5000
£2254	$3899	€3200	Mozart opus 613-clarinette et orchestre, var V (37x54cm-15x21in) s. s.i.d.1959 verso prov. 14-Dec-3 Versailles Encheres #24/R est:3500-4000
£2349	$4370	€3500	Still life with flowers (33x41cm-13x16in) s. 3-Mar-4 Tajan, Paris #203 est:2000-2500
£2446	$4012	€3400	Guitare II (54x73cm-21x29in) s. s.i.verso. 6-Jun-3 David Kahn, Paris #37 est:3500-4000
£2448	$4161	€3500	Un ours blanc a marche dans les nuages (22x41cm-9x16in) s.d.29 exhib.lit. 30-Nov-3 Anaf, Lyon #57 est:1200-1500
£2448	$4161	€3500	Paysage pour un decour (54x73cm-21x29in) s.d.31 lit. 30-Nov-3 Anaf, Lyon #62/R est:2000-3000
£2448	$4161	€3500	Mont Salvt, Gennant, no 2 (40x80cm-16x31in) s.d.55 s.i.d.55 verso. 30-Nov-3 Anaf, Lyon #86/R est:3500-4500
£2568	$4519	€3800	Nature more a la curlier (20x34cm-8x13in) s.d.1943 prov.lit. 18-May-4 Tajan, Paris #22/R est:2000-3000
£2797	$4755	€4000	Calligraphie-paysage (20x70cm-8x28in) s.d.30 lit. 30-Nov-3 Anaf, Lyon #58 est:800-1000
£2797	$4755	€4000	Les joyaux de la couronne (14x22cm-6x9in) s. panel lit. 30-Nov-3 Anaf, Lyon #70/R est:1500-2000
£2797	$4755	€4000	Le gardien (73x92cm-29x36in) s.d.51 lit. 30-Nov-3 Anaf, Lyon #84/R est:3000-4000
£2817	$4704	€4113	Composition (38x55cm-15x22in) s.d.64 s.i.d. verso prov. 7-Oct-3 Rasmussen, Copenhagen #129/R est:20000-25000 (D.KR 30000)
£3077	$5231	€4400	Hommage a Rembrandt (65x92cm-26x36in) s.d.51 exhib.lit. 30-Nov-3 Anaf, Lyon #83/R est:4000-5000
£3169	$5483	€4500	Composition (19x33cm-7x13in) s.d.30. 9-Dec-3 Artcurial Briest, Paris #254 est:2500-3000
£3200	$5856	€4800	Maison dans l'arbre (54x73cm-21x29in) s. lit. 3-Jun-4 E & Eve, Paris #84/R est:4000-4500
£3239	$5604	€4600	Composition (19x33cm-7x13in) s.d.30. 9-Dec-3 Artcurial Briest, Paris #255/R est:2500-3000
£3357	$5706	€4800	Boite a joujoux (16x22cm-6x9in) s.d.44 cardboard lit. 30-Nov-3 Anaf, Lyon #71 est:1000-1500
£3357	$5773	€4800	Composition (13x17cm-5x7in) s. board prov. 2-Dec-3 Sotheby's, Amsterdam #196/R est:800-1200
£3473	$5799	€5000	Composition (19x32cm-7x13in) s.d.42. 21-Oct-3 Artcurial Briest, Paris #236/R est:5000-6000
£3600	$6588	€5400	Flirt (65x50cm-26x20in) s. lit. 3-Jun-4 E & Eve, Paris #85/R est:4000-4500
£3893	$7162	€5800	Ovni (100x81cm-39x32in) s. lit. 28-Mar-4 Anaf, Lyon #51/R est:4000-5000
£4056	$6895	€5800	La ville engloutie (24x35cm-9x14in) s.d.50 panel lit. 30-Nov-3 Anaf, Lyon #80/R est:2500-3000
£4196	$7217	€6000	Composition (28x76cm-11x30in) s.d.30 s.i.d.verso prov. 2-Dec-3 Sotheby's, Amsterdam #197/R est:1500-2000
£4336	$7371	€6200	Violon mystique (65x92cm-26x36in) s. lit. 30-Nov-3 Anaf, Lyon #73/R est:10000-12000
£4408	$8111	€6700	Bach cantate 138 (54x73cm-21x29in) s. s.i.verso prov. 27-Jun-4 Versailles Encheres #64/R est:2500-3000
£4546	$7728	€6500	Concerto mineur (38x61cm-15x24in) s.i.d.1954. 25-Nov-3 Tajan, Paris #4/R est:1200-1500
£4895	$8322	€7000	Buisson ardent no 2 (38x46cm-15x18in) s.d.21 III 31 panel exhib.lit. 30-Nov-3 Anaf, Lyon #65/R est:1500-2000
£5208	$8698	€7500	Franca da Rimini, de Tschaikowski, no. 1 (46x54cm-18x21in) s.d.54 s.i.d.1 54 XI verso prov. 21-Oct-3 Artcurial Briest, Paris #393/R est:8000-10000
£5333	$9813	€8000	Illumination de Saint Georges (81x100cm-32x39in) s. i.verso painted 1953 lit. 9-Jun-4 Beaussant & Lefèvre, Paris #125/R est:10000-12000
£5503	$10126	€8200	Le moulin de Longchamp (60x73cm-24x29in) s.d.31 lit. 28-Mar-4 Anaf, Lyon #48/R est:3000-4000
£5944	$10224	€8500	Comp, insp. p. la musique Japonaise (64x46cm-25x18in) s.d.59 s.i.d.verso. 2-Dec-3 Sotheby's, Amsterdam #122/R est:3000-4000
£6643	$11294	€9500	Le jardin Japonais (33x41cm-13x16in) s.d.25 19 IV 39 lit. 30-Nov-3 Anaf, Lyon #68/R est:4000-5000
£6853	$11650	€9800	Lampe a petrole (46x27cm-18x11in) s.d.44 panel exhib.lit. 30-Nov-3 Anaf, Lyon #69/R est:5000-6000
£6993	$11888	€10000	Sarabande (54x65cm-21x26in) s. lit. 30-Nov-3 Anaf, Lyon #75/R est:6000-8000
£7047	$12966	€10500	La violoniste Lola Bobesco joue la Rapsodie Espagnole de Lalo (27x45cm-11x18in) s. isorel exhib.lit. 28-Mar-4 Anaf, Lyon #49 est:4000-5000
£7285	$13258	€11000	Cantate D S G de Bach Var II-VI (50x100cm-20x39in) s.d.60 s.i.d.verso prov.exhib. 18-Jun-4 Charbonneaux, Paris #137/R est:12000-15000
£7552	$12839	€10800	La grand sauciere (60x92cm-24x36in) s. exhib.lit. 30-Nov-3 Anaf, Lyon #72 est:8000-10000
£7718	$14201	€11500	La ville engloutie (100x73cm-39x29in) s. it. 28-Mar-4 Anaf, Lyon #52/R est:4000-5000
£8026	$14768	€12200	Composition (73x92cm-29x36in) s.d.1960 i.d.verso lit. 27-Jun-4 Versailles Encheres #65/R est:3000-4000
£8112	$13790	€11600	Formes plastiques ou hommage a Hans Arp (41x33cm-16x13in) s. exhib.lit. 30-Nov-3 Anaf, Lyon #66/R est:2500-3000

£8725 $15443 €13000 Fanome fantome (50x60cm-20x24in) s.i.d.IV.54.V. 28-Apr-4 Artcurial Briest, Paris #266/R est:5000-7000
£9091 $15455 €13000 Jeux d'eau (130x89cm-51x35in) s.d.50 lit. 30-Nov-3 Anaf, Lyon #81/R est:12000-15000
£10070 $16816 €14500 Composition inspiree par la musique Portugaise (50x65cm-20x26in) s.d. s.i.d.XI.60 verso. 21-Oct-3 Artcurial Briest, Paris #394/R est:6000-8000
£10403 $19141 €15500 La mer sauvage (50x61cm-20x24in) s. lit. 28-Mar-4 Anaf, Lyon #53/R est:5000-6000
£11189 $19021 €16000 Nature morte au pichet (23x27cm-9x11in) s.d.1927. 25-Nov-3 Tajan, Paris #1/R est:3500-4000
£13333 $24533 €20000 Danse arabesque (60x73cm-24x29in) s. paper on canvas prov.lit. 8-Jun-4 Artcurial Briest, Paris #85/R est:10000-12000
£21678 $36853 €31000 La mer dechainee (73x60cm-29x24in) s. panel lit. 30-Nov-3 Anaf, Lyon #76/R est:12000-15000
£23776 $40420 €34000 La mer eternelle (73x60cm-29x24in) s. panel exhib.lit. 30-Nov-3 Anaf, Lyon #77/R est:12000-15000
£24825 $42203 €35500 La mer douce-heureuse (81x116cm-32x46in) s.d.V 50 exhib.lit. 30-Nov-3 Anaf, Lyon #79/R est:12000-15000
£31469 $54126 €45000 Une douce melodie de ruines (96x146cm-38x57in) s.d.52 s.i.d.verso lit. 3-Dec-3 Beaussant & Lefèvre, Paris #17/R est:10000-12000
Works on paper
£490 $832 €700 Arabesque (9x20cm-4x8in) s.d.1964 Indian ink prov. 23-Nov-3 Cornette de St.Cyr, Paris #47
£662 $1205 €1000 Composition (22x27cm-9x11in) s. gouache exhib. 15-Jun-4 Blanchet, Paris #262/R
£676 $1189 €1000 Composition abstraite (44x36cm-17x14in) s. s.verso gouache W/C. 19-May-4 Camard, Paris #20
£795 $1446 €1200 Composition (21x25cm-8x10in) s. W/C. 15-Jun-4 Blanchet, Paris #260/R
£1040 $1914 €1550 Composition bleue, jaune et grise (46x38cm-18x15in) s. gouache. 24-Mar-4 Joron-Derem, Paris #121 est:900-1000
£1208 $2223 €1800 Composition blanche et rose (35x27cm-14x11in) s. gouache exhib. 24-Mar-4 Joron-Derem, Paris #123 est:900-1000

CHARD, Daniel (20th C) American
£829 $1500 €1244 Deadwood (30x48cm-12x19in) acrylic. 16-Apr-4 American Auctioneer #63/R est:2000-4000
£1105 $2000 €1658 Across Rte 40 (79x33cm-31x13in) acrylic. 16-Apr-4 American Auctioneer #62/R est:1200-1500

CHARDIN, Jean Baptiste Simeon (1699-1779) French
£98684 $181579 €150000 Trompe-l'oeil au bas-relief (57x45cm-22x18in) s.verso oval en grisaille prov. 24-Jun-4 Tajan, Paris #57/R est:200000-300000

CHARDON, Germaine (1900-) Belgian
£438 $700 €639 Dome des Invalides, Paris (102x155cm-40x61in) s. 18-May-3 Auctions by the Bay, Alameda #1004/R

CHARDURIVE, Serge (?) ?
Works on paper
£369 $653 €550 Composition (30x21cm-12x8in) dr. 27-Apr-4 Campo & Campo, Antwerp #443

CHAREAU, Pierre (1883-1950) French
Sculpture
£22973 $40432 €34000 Untitled (71x18cm-28x7in) metal alabaster pair. 18-May-4 Christie's, Paris #36/R est:35000-45000

CHARETTE-DUVAL, François (1807-1895) Belgian
Works on paper
£3691 $6829 €5500 Composition aux roses et objets precieux (100x67cm-39x26in) s. W/C. 15-Mar-4 Horta, Bruxelles #178/R est:6000-8000

CHARIGNY, Andre Auguste (1902-2000) French
£517 $940 €780 Chardons (38x46cm-15x18in) s. 19-Jun-4 Gerard, Besancon #43
£529 $900 €772 Still life with fruits (33x25cm-13x10in) s.verso board prov. 22-Nov-3 Jackson's, Cedar Falls #390/R est:400-600
£562 $955 €820 Village dans la vallee (19x24cm-7x9in) s. cardboard. 8-Nov-3 Gerard, Besancon #39
£638 $1066 €900 Bouquet jaune et rouge de Septembre (61x50cm-24x20in) s. 20-Jun-3 Drouot Estimations, Paris #186
£941 $1600 €1374 Autumn village landscape (61x51cm-24x20in) s. i.verso prov. 22-Nov-3 Jackson's, Cedar Falls #391/R est:400-600
£1241 $2061 €1800 Vaches paissant (30x35cm-12x14in) s. cardboard. 1-Oct-3 Millon & Associes, Paris #52/R

CHARLAY-POMPON, Charles (19th C) French
£650 $1021 €943 By the orange grove (38x55cm-15x22in) s. 28-Aug-3 Christie's, Kensington #107/R

CHARLEMAGNE, Adolf-Jossifowitsch (1826-1901) Russian
Works on paper
£3000 $5100 €4500 Catherine II at court (15x20cm-6x8in) s.d.1862 pen ink wash. 25-Nov-3 Christie's, London #104/R est:3000-5000
£3800 $6460 €5700 View of city (18x13cm-7x5in) s.d.1855 W/C pencil crayon htd white. 25-Nov-3 Christie's, London #103/R est:3000-5000

CHARLEMAGNE, Iosef Iosefovich (1824-1870) Russian
Works on paper
£690 $1234 €1007 Canal in St Petersburg (14x22cm-6x9in) s.d.1861 W/C bodycol. 12-May-4 Dobiaschofsky, Bern #387/R est:2000 (S.FR 1600)
£13000 $23270 €18980 Fountains at Peterhof (20x31cm-8x12in) s.d.1854 pencil gouache. 26-May-4 Sotheby's, London #9/R est:5000-7000

CHARLEMAGNE, Paul (1892-1972) French
£586 $973 €850 Nu etendu (46x61cm-18x24in) s. 1-Oct-3 Millon & Associes, Paris #143/R
Works on paper
£276 $461 €400 Les dames (36x25cm-14x10in) s. chl ink W/C. 16-Nov-3 Muizon & Le Coent, Paris #59
£310 $518 €450 Paysage (46x71cm-18x28in) s. W/C. 16-Nov-3 Muizon & Le Coent, Paris #60

CHARLEMONT, Eduard (1848-1906) Austrian
£6711 $12013 €10000 At the dressing table (97x52cm-38x20in) s. panel exhib. 27-May-4 Dorotheum, Vienna #219/R est:8000-10000

CHARLEMONT, Hugo (1850-1939) Austrian
£993 $1808 €1500 Still life with lute (52x72cm-20x28in) s. 21-Jun-4 Dorotheum, Vienna #243/R est:1500-1700
£1067 $1941 €1600 Poultry (30x37cm-12x15in) s. board. 30-Jun-4 Neumeister, Munich #520a/R
£1678 $2853 €2400 Feeding chickens in country garden (31x23cm-12x9in) s.d.872 panel. 24-Nov-3 Dorotheum, Vienna #49/R est:2800-3200
£2333 $4177 €3500 Crossing (67x104cm-26x41in) s.d.1905. 13-May-4 Dorotheum, Linz #439/R est:7000-7500
£2416 $4446 €3600 At the village well (54x68cm-21x27in) s.i. i. verso panel. 24-Mar-4 Dorotheum, Vienna #222/R est:3600-4500
£2797 $4755 €4000 Still life (62x87cm-24x34in) s. 28-Nov-3 Wiener Kunst Auktionen, Vienna #444/R est:4000-7000
£3020 $5406 €4500 Goat herder with herd at enclosure (56x85cm-22x33in) s. 27-May-4 Dorotheum, Vienna #185/R est:3500-4000
£5034 $9413 €7500 Fantasy picture with birds (62x117cm-24x46in) s.d.1881. 24-Feb-4 Dorotheum, Vienna #290/R est:2000-2300

CHARLEMONT, Hugo (attrib) (1850-1939) Austrian
£1736 $2743 €2500 Still life with flowers and grapes (50x40cm-20x16in) mono.i. 5-Sep-3 Wendl, Rudolstadt #3311/R est:1800

CHARLES, James (1851-1906) British
£600 $954 €870 Mediterranean scene with a woman in an archway (55x41cm-22x16in) mono. 9-Sep-3 Bonhams, Knightsbridge #90/R
£720 $1332 €1051 Farm shed (37x28cm-15x11in) s. exhib. 14-Jan-4 Lawrence, Crewkerne #1439/R
£3000 $5370 €4380 Break from the harvest, Sussex (51x87cm-20x34in) s.d.1883. 26-May-4 Sotheby's, Olympia #152/R est:2000-3000

CHARLES, Michael Ray (1967-) American
£350 $601 €500 Forever free (152x91cm-60x36in) s.d.00 acrylic latex graphite crayon on canvas prov. 8-Dec-3 Christie's, Paris #83
£4190 $7500 €6117 Liberty Brothers permanent circus, alive (152x91cm-60x36in) s.d.96 acrylic latex stain copper penny paper prov.exhib. 14-May-4 Phillips, New York #356/R est:8000-12000
£4469 $8000 €6525 Lifesaball, forever free (152x91cm-60x36in) s.d.95 acrylic latex copper penny paper prov. 14-May-4 Phillips, New York #358/R est:5000-7000

CHARLESWORTH, John Michael (20th C) British
£520 $915 €759 Hope (39x49cm-15x19in) s.d.1997 acrylic. 18-May-4 Woolley & Wallis, Salisbury #18/R
£520 $915 €759 Sunrise (49x75cm-19x30in) s.d.1993 acrylic. 18-May-4 Woolley & Wallis, Salisbury #21/R
£580 $1021 €847 Third morning (30x44cm-12x17in) s.d.1992 acrylic panel. 18-May-4 Woolley & Wallis, Salisbury #20/R
£1200 $2112 €1752 Annunciation (76x101cm-30x40in) acrylic. 18-May-4 Woolley & Wallis, Salisbury #19/R est:1000-1500

CHARLESWORTH, Rod (1955-) Canadian
£179 $304 €261 Frosted trees (41x51cm-16x20in) s.d.1986 s.i.verso board. 6-Nov-3 Heffel, Vancouver #29/R (C.D 400)
£422 $692 €616 Crooked Lake - Stormy sky (36x46cm-14x18in) s. board. 28-May-3 Maynards, Vancouver #5 (C.D 950)
£563 $957 €822 Outcrop, northern sky (38x76cm-15x30in) s. si.verso prov. 23-Nov-3 Levis, Calgary #20/R (C.D 1250)
£633 $1058 €924 Aspens in autumn (50x60cm-20x24in) s.i. board. 17-Nov-3 Hodgins, Calgary #8/R est:1200-1600 (C.D 1400)
£680 $1244 €993 Across the cove, Peggy's Cove (40x60cm-16x24in) s.i. board. 1-Jun-4 Hodgins, Calgary #18/R (C.D 1700)
£800 $1464 €1168 October reflections, Shuswap (55x70cm-22x28in) s.i. 1-Jun-4 Hodgins, Calgary #62/R est:1500-1800 (C.D 2000)
£840 $1537 €1226 Cape St Marys (40x60cm-16x24in) s.i. board. 1-Jun-4 Hodgins, Calgary #264/R est:1300-1600 (C.D 2100)
£860 $1436 €1256 Soft sun December (50x60cm-20x24in) s.i. board. 17-Nov-3 Hodgins, Calgary #71/R est:1300-1600 (C.D 1900)
£950 $1587 €1387 September light, Kennedy Lake (38x75cm-15x30in) s.i. 17-Nov-3 Hodgins, Calgary #10/R est:1300-1600 (C.D 2100)

CHARLESWORTH, Sarah (1947-) American
£533 $955 €800 Masque sur fond vert (107x76cm-42x30in) lacquer. 12-May-4 Chochon-Barre & Allardi, Paris #4/R
£600 $1074 €900 Vase eclate (48x37cm-19x15in) st.sig. lacquer. 12-May-4 Chochon-Barre & Allardi, Paris #6
£733 $1313 €1100 Deux verres (93x73cm-37x29in) st.sig. lacquer oval. 12-May-4 Chochon-Barre & Allardi, Paris #5
£1100 $1969 €1650 Coupelle jaune sur fond bleu (100x74cm-39x29in) lacquer. 12-May-4 Chochon-Barre & Allardi, Paris #3/R est:1000-1500

CHARLET, Émile (1851-?) Belgian
£1084 $1800 €1583 Women in a well appointed interior (61x76cm-24x30in) s. board. 4-Oct-3 South Bay, Long Island #183

£1773 $2961 €2500 Chasse dans le marais (92x72cm-36x28in) s. 17-Jun-3 Christie's, Paris #34/R est:2500-3500

CHARLET, Frans (1862-1928) Belgian
£4000 $7160 €6000 Parrot (73x54cm-29x21in) s. 15-May-4 De Vuyst, Lokeren #55/R est:2000-3000
£17647 $30000 €25765 At the races (73x60cm-29x24in) 29-Oct-3 Christie's, Rockefeller NY #182/R est:40000-60000

CHARLET, Nicolas Toussaint (1792-1845) French
£345 $617 €504 Soldiers making merry (31x24cm-12x9in) s. panel. 12-May-4 Dobiaschofsky, Bern #388/R (S.FR 800)
Works on paper
£306 $548 €450 Le paiement du semestre (18x13cm-7x5in) s. pen brown ink col wash. 19-Mar-4 Piasa, Paris #159
£533 $965 €800 Paysage (27x35cm-11x14in) s. brown wash black crayon. 30-Mar-4 Rossini, Paris #32
£1383 $2240 €1950 Napoleon a cheval surplombant un champs de bataille (19x20cm-7x8in) s. W/C gouache. 21-May-3 Daguerre, Paris #80/R est:1500

CHARLET, Nicolas Toussaint (attrib) (1792-1845) French
£738 $1366 €1100 Napoleon and his troops (43x59cm-17x23in) panel. 13-Mar-4 De Vuyst, Lokeren #48/R

CHARLIER, Guillaume (1854-1925) Belgian
Sculpture
£3846 $6538 €5500 Buste de la Japonaise (61cm-24in) s. marble. 1-Dec-3 Palais de Beaux Arts, Brussels #33/R est:4000-6000

CHARLIER, Jacques (1720-1790) French
Works on paper
£2000 $3660 €2920 Venus and Cupid asleep on a bed (17x22cm-7x9in) i. bodycol. 6-Jul-4 Christie's, London #147/R est:2000-3000
£7483 $13395 €11000 Trois femmes au bord d'un ruisseau tenant une urne (30x38cm-12x15in) W/C gouache. 18-Mar-4 Christie's, Paris #253/R est:3000-5000

CHARLIER, Jacques (attrib) (1720-1790) French
£1667 $3050 €2500 Nymphe endormie (51x70cm-20x28in) oval. 4-Jun-4 Pierre Berge, Paris #224/R est:1500-2000
Miniatures
£1700 $2890 €2482 Lady in the guise of Diana (5cm-2in) W/C octagonal prov. 18-Nov-3 Bonhams, New Bond Street #54/R est:800-1200

CHARLOPEAU, Gabriel (1889-1967) French
£872 $1597 €1300 Seine au Pont Neuf (54x65cm-21x26in) s. 7-Jul-4 Artcurial Briest, Paris #78 est:1000-1200

CHARLOT, Jean (1898-1979) Mexican/French
£2500 $4400 €3650 Two washerwomen (51x41cm-20x16in) s.d.37. 23-May-4 Hindman, Chicago #970/R est:3000-5000
£2500 $4400 €3650 Malinche, Harmonia Roja (102x76cm-40x30in) s.d.54 prov. 23-May-4 Hindman, Chicago #971/R est:3000-5000
£2605 $4585 €3803 Hawaiian swimmer (30x41cm-12x16in) s.d.1963. 23-May-4 Hindman, Chicago #973/R est:1000-2000
Works on paper
£430 $800 €628 Mexican woman (34x23cm-13x9in) s. pencil. 2-Mar-4 Swann Galleries, New York #130/R

CHARLOT, Raymond (20th C) ?
£500 $905 €760 Nu couche (50x80cm-20x31in) s. 19-Apr-4 Horta, Bruxelles #359
£590 $927 €850 Jeune femme a la fleur (36x45cm-14x18in) s. 26-Aug-3 Galerie Moderne, Brussels #268

CHARLTON, Alan (1948-) British
£2500 $4525 €3650 Untitled (151x129cm-59x51in) s.i.d.1981-82 in two parts prov. 1-Apr-4 Christie's, Kensington #320/R est:3000-5000

CHARLTON, Evan (1904-) British
£900 $1530 €1314 Sunrise (61x91cm-24x36in) s.d.72v. board. 18-Nov-3 Sotheby's, Olympia #218/R
£950 $1615 €1387 Bather (61x91cm-24x36in) s.verso board. 18-Nov-3 Sotheby's, Olympia #216/R

CHARLTON, John (1849-1917) British
£966 $1506 €1401 Just in time, fox hunt (33x54cm-13x21in) s.d.1902 i.d.verso. 1-Aug-2 Joel, Victoria #260 est:1500-2500 (A.D 2800)
£4500 $7650 €6570 Contrast, study of a Manchester terrier and German spitz (30x46cm-12x18in) s. panel. 19-Nov-3 Tennants, Leyburn #1207/R est:2500-3000
£42000 $73920 €61320 Death - Recollection of a kill with the Pytchley hounds (200x153cm-79x60in) init. 21-May-4 Christie's, London #35/R est:30000-50000

CHARMAISON, Raymond Louis (1876-1955) French
£700 $1295 €1050 Garden at Versailles (66x54cm-26x21in) s.d.1910. 14-Jul-4 Sotheby's, Olympia #261/R

CHARMATZ, Bill (1925-) American
Works on paper
£286 $500 €418 Good cigar is a smoke (44x44cm-17x17in) s. gouache ink board exec Dec 1967. 17-Dec-3 Christie's, Rockefeller NY #200/R

CHARME, Maud Bonade la (20th C) American
£833 $1500 €1216 Tulips (61x46cm-24x18in) s. exhib. 23-Jan-4 Freeman, Philadelphia #246/R est:1500-2000

CHARMY, Emilie (1877-1974) French
£430 $783 €650 Nature morte aux fruits (24x31cm-9x12in) s. isorel. 15-Jun-4 Blanchet, Paris #120

CHARNAY, Armand (1844-1916) French
£5775 $10106 €8200 Elegantes sur la plage d'Yport, juillet (22x40cm-9x16in) s.i. 16-Dec-3 Claude Aguttes, Neuilly #98/R est:6000-8000

CHARON, Guy (1927-) French
£387 $670 €550 La soupiere (65x50cm-26x20in) s. s.i.verso. 13-Dec-3 Touati, Paris #65/R
£528 $914 €750 Le portail (46x55cm-18x22in) s. 13-Dec-3 Touati, Paris #66/R
£550 $974 €820 Le jardin fleuri (73x60cm-29x24in) s. 29-Apr-4 Claude Aguttes, Neuilly #93
£577 $999 €820 Voile blanche (54x65cm-21x26in) s. 13-Dec-3 Touati, Paris #67/R
£774 $1200 €1130 Untitled (65x81cm-26x32in) s. 3-Nov-2 Subastas Odalys, Caracas #27/R

CHAROUX, Siegfried (1896-1967) Austrian
Works on paper
£300 $546 €438 Two men reading (56x37cm-22x15in) mixed media. 15-Jun-4 Bonhams, Leeds #64

CHAROY, Bernard (1929-) French
£486 $812 €700 Nu assis (73x60cm-29x24in) s. cardboard. 21-Oct-3 Campo & Campo, Antwerp #34
£1477 $2732 €2200 Jeune femme nue au voile (61x50cm-24x20in) s. 15-Mar-4 Blanchet, Paris #140 est:1500-2000
£1477 $2717 €2200 Jeune femme assise dans un paysage (61x50cm-24x20in) s. 29-Mar-4 Lombrail & Teucquam, Paris #147/R

CHARPENTIER, Albert (1878-c.1914) French
£265 $482 €400 Paysage de la Creuse (73x92cm-29x36in) s. 18-Jun-4 Piasa, Paris #67

CHARPENTIER, Alexandre (1856-1909) French
Sculpture
£1419 $2540 €2100 Danseuse nue au voile (36x25cm-14x10in) s. pat bronze. 5-May-4 Claude Boisgirard, Paris #35/R est:1000-1200
£1531 $2434 €2250 Femme allongee (20cm-8in) s. pat bronze. 23-Mar-3 Salle des ventes Pillet, Lyon la Foret #155

CHARPENTIER, Auguste (1813-1880) French
£2759 $4579 €4000 Jeune fille a la croix (69x54cm-27x21in) s. 2-Oct-3 Sotheby's, Paris #112/R

CHARPENTIER, Constance-Marie (attrib) (1767-1849) French
£5000 $9150 €7500 Portrait de Madame Templier et de sa fille devant un paysage (81x64cm-32x25in) 3-Jun-4 E & Eve, Paris #33/R est:8000-12000

CHARPENTIER, Felix (1858-1924) French
Sculpture
£3077 $5292 €4492 Floating woman (53x70cm-21x28in) s. gold pat.bronze on marble socle. 2-Dec-3 Bukowskis, Stockholm #253a/R est:15000-20000 (S.KR 40000)
£7000 $12600 €10220 Standing nue allegorical awakening (107cm-42in) s.i. white marble. 21-Apr-4 Sotheby's, London #148/R est:7000-12000

CHARPENTIER, Jan (fl.1880) French
£1257 $2250 €1835 Defending the palace (60x92cm-24x36in) s. prov. 6-May-4 Doyle, New York #59/R est:4000-6000

CHARPENTIER, Jean Baptiste (attrib) (18/19th C) French
£1348 $2250 €1900 Jeune mere nourrissant son enfant (100x77cm-39x30in) 19-Oct-3 St Germain en Laye Encheres #16/R est:2000-3000

CHARPENTIER, Jean Baptiste (elder) (1728-1806) French
£7746 $13401 €11000 Portrait de couple et des enfants (64x81cm-25x32in) s. prov. 10-Dec-3 Beaussant & Lefèvre, Paris #32/R est:10000-12000

CHARPENTIER, Philippe (1949-) French
£436 $811 €650 Untitled (100x100cm-39x39in) s.d.1989 acrylic prov. 3-Mar-4 Tajan, Paris #255
Works on paper
£436 $811 €650 Untitled (110x110cm-43x43in) s.d.1988 mixed media. 3-Mar-4 Tajan, Paris #254

CHARPENTIER, R (19/20th C) French
£2517 $4280 €3600 Young woman making music on bench in park (90x125cm-35x49in) s. 20-Nov-3 Van Ham, Cologne #1513/R est:2500

CHARPENTIER-MIO, Maurice (1881-1976) French
Sculpture
£1133 $2029 €1700 Danseurs (29cm-11in) st.sig. stone lit. 17-May-4 Sotheby's, Paris #65/R est:2000-3000
£1150 $2105 €1679 Carnivale (11x29cm-4x11in) mono. i.verso bronze relief. 3-Jun-4 Sotheby's, Olympia #256/R est:500-800

CHARPIDES, Christo (1909-1992) Greek
£563 $913 €800 Port Breton. Port de mer provencal (61x50cm-24x20in) s. two. 11-Aug-3 Boscher, Cherbourg #853

CHARPIN, Albert (1842-1924) French
£685 $1164 €1000 Bergere et ses moutons (73x105cm-29x41in) s. 9-Nov-3 Eric Pillon, Calais #36/R

CHARRETON, Victor (1864-1937) French
£2727 $4555 €3900 Maison au bord de chemin (26x34cm-10x13in) s.d.1911 panel. 29-Jun-3 Eric Pillon, Calais #93/R
£3357 $5774 €4800 Amandiers en fleurs (38x46cm-15x18in) s. cardboard. 3-Dec-3 Tajan, Paris #360/R est:4000-6000
£3600 $6480 €5400 Sous-bois en automne avec moutons (38x46cm-15x18in) cardboard. 20-Apr-4 Chenu & Scrive, Lyon #57/R est:4500-5000
£3611 $6030 €5200 Automne, le petit ruisseau (39x46cm-15x18in) s. board. 21-Oct-3 Artcurial Briest, Paris #167/R est:5000-6000
£4800 $8640 €7200 Sous-bois en automne anime (38x46cm-15x18in) s. cardboard. 20-Apr-4 Chenu & Scrive, Lyon #56/R est:5000-5500
£4832 $8940 €7200 Amandiers en fleurs pres de la maison (37x45cm-15x18in) s. panel. 14-Mar-4 Eric Pillon, Calais #116/R
£5592 $10289 €8500 Arbres en fleurs (50x61cm-20x24in) s. 28-Jun-4 Joron-Derem, Paris #111/R est:10000-12000
£5634 $9747 €8000 Jardin public (50x61cm-20x24in) s. lit. 9-Dec-3 Artcurial Briest, Paris #262/R est:6000-8000
£7000 $12810 €10500 Paysage de neige en montagne, Auvergne (43x59cm-17x23in) s. cardboard lit. 6-Jun-4 Anaf, Lyon #338/R est:10000-12000
£8500 $15640 €12410 Le chateau en ete (60x73cm-24x29in) s. prov. 24-Mar-4 Sotheby's, Olympia #94/R est:7000-9000
£8511 $14213 €12000 Village sous la neige (57x70cm-22x28in) s. cardboard lit. 19-Oct-3 Anaf, Lyon #77/R est:10000-12000
£8865 $14805 €12500 La Tour Fond, Saint Amand (94x65cm-37x26in) s. 19-Oct-3 Anaf, Lyon #76/R est:12000-15000
£8904 $15137 €13000 Petite source dans la prairie (60x73cm-24x29in) s. lit. 9-Nov-3 Eric Pillon, Calais #76/R
£10140 $17441 €14500 Vue de la Tour Fondue (59x71cm-23x28in) s. lit. 5-Dec-3 Gros & Delettrez, Paris #86/R est:6000-8000
£11620 $20102 €16500 Paysage a la Creuse (60x74cm-24x29in) s. 14-Dec-3 Rabourdin & Choppin de Janvry, Paris #29/R est:15000-17000
£12195 $20000 €17683 Printemps en Murol (53x64cm-21x25in) s.i. 31-May-3 Brunk, Ashville #548/R est:8000-15000
£16500 $27555 €24090 Pommiers, La Sauvetat (60x73cm-24x29in) s. painted c.1920s. 22-Oct-3 Sotheby's, Olympia #31/R est:8000-10000

CHARRIN, Fanny (?-1854) French
Miniatures
£1544 $2840 €2300 Portrait presume de Monsieur de Lavoisier (6cm-2in circular) s. Sevres porcelain exec. c.1808 lit. 26-Mar-4 Pierre Berge, Paris #91/R est:800-1000

CHARRON, Amedee (19th C) French
Sculpture
£3500 $6405 €5110 Genie des sciences - Young nymph (41cm-16in) s. bronze marble pedestal. 3-Jun-4 Sotheby's, Olympia #122/R est:1500-2000

CHARTIER, Henri-Georges-Jacques (1859-1924) French
£333 $613 €500 Hussard a cheval (46x38cm-18x15in) s.d.1899 panel. 14-Jun-4 Cornette de St.Cyr, Paris #57

CHARTRAN, Theobald (1849-1907) French
£268 $475 €400 Au salon (33x28cm-13x11in) s. panel. 30-Apr-4 Tajan, Paris #186
£1333 $2413 €2000 La pose dans l'atelier du peintre (17x12cm-7x5in) s. 3-Apr-4 Gerard, Besancon #37

CHARTRAND, Esteban (1824-1884) Cuban
£3955 $7000 €5774 Tropical landscape at dusk (46x30cm-18x12in) s.d.1882. 2-May-4 Bonhams & Butterfields, San Francisco #1062/R est:4000-6000
£14706 $25000 €21471 Paysage en Amerique du sud (41x71cm-16x28in) s.d.1881. 19-Nov-3 Sotheby's, New York #81/R est:18000-22000
£55882 $95000 €81588 Runaways (54x91cm-21x36in) s.d.1880 i.on stretcher verso prov. 19-Nov-3 Sotheby's, New York #44/R est:35000-40000

CHARTRES, Antoine (1903-1968) French
£1020 $1857 €1500 Nu alonge (73x92cm-29x36in) s. 8-Feb-4 Anaf, Lyon #134/R est:1500-2000

CHARVOT, Eugène (1847-?) French
£2624 $4382 €3700 Jetee a Sidi Bou Said (47x71cm-19x28in) s.d.1888. 19-Oct-3 Rabourdin & Choppin de Janvry, Paris #105/R est:4000-4500

CHASE, Clarence Melville (1871-?) American
£252 $400 €368 Savin Hill, Boston (41x51cm-16x20in) s. canvas on board. 12-Sep-3 Skinner, Boston #433/R

CHASE, Emmie (fl.1907-1932) British
£480 $816 €701 Two children (54x44cm-21x17in) s. 29-Oct-3 Bonhams, Chester #508

CHASE, Frank M (fl.1880-1898) British
£1000 $1810 €1500 Two girls picking flowers near woodland (57x103cm-22x41in) s. 1-Apr-4 Van Ham, Cologne #1317/R est:1800

CHASE, Frank Swift (1886-1958) American
£535 $1000 €781 Mountain landscape (30x41cm-12x16in) s. board. 29-Feb-4 Grogan, Boston #69/R
£1374 $2500 €2006 Yellow house in spring landscape (30x41cm-12x16in) s. canvasboard prov. 15-Jun-4 John Moran, Pasadena #190 est:1000-1500
£1788 $3200 €2610 Winter landscape (20x25cm-8x10in) s. board. 16-May-4 CRN Auctions, Cambridge #37/R
£3632 $6500 €5303 Massachusetts street scene (30x41cm-12x16in) s. canvasboard prov. 6-May-4 Shannon's, Milford #3/R est:3000-5000

CHASE, Harry (1853-1889) American
£726 $1300 €1060 Gloucester (30x46cm-12x18in) i. s.verso. 20-Mar-4 Selkirks, St. Louis #148/R est:1200-1800
£867 $1500 €1266 Fine Vintage (35x27cm-14x11in) s.i.d.1878 prov. 10-Dec-3 Bonhams & Butterfields, San Francisco #6001/R est:3000-5000
£2326 $4000 €3396 Making port during a squall (46x91cm-18x36in) s.d.1876 canvas on canvas. 6-Dec-3 Selkirks, St. Louis #176/R est:5000-7000
£2429 $4250 €3546 Dieppe, Normandy (33x56cm-13x22in) s.d.78. 19-Dec-3 Sotheby's, New York #1105/R est:3000-5000
£2457 $4250 €3587 Old Pier (30x51cm-12x20in) s.d.1880 i.verso prov. 10-Dec-3 Bonhams & Butterfields, San Francisco #6000/R est:5000-7000
£2973 $5500 €4341 Fisherfolk on the beach at Scheveningen (39x63cm-15x25in) s. 10-Feb-4 Christie's, Rockefeller NY #231/R est:6000-8000
£3022 $5500 €4412 Ships heading into harbour (46x66cm-18x26in) s. canvas on board. 29-Jun-4 Sotheby's, New York #193/R est:3000-5000

CHASE, John (1810-1879) British
£320 $573 €467 Figures before South Creake Church (40x59cm-16x23in) s.d.1871. 22-Mar-4 Bonhams & Brooks, Norfolk #274/R
Works on paper
£300 $516 €438 Moonlit archway with figure and a boat beyond (31x23cm-12x9in) s. W/C. 2-Dec-3 Sworder & Son, Bishops Stortford #501a/R
£725 $1174 €1051 Ludlow Castle (47x67cm-19x26in) s. W/C. 31-Jul-3 International Art Centre, Auckland #155/R est:2000-3000 (NZ.D 2000)

CHASE, Joseph Cummings (1878-1965) American
£299 $550 €437 Portrait of Ruth Draper (71x53cm-28x21in) s.d.1922 board. 26-Jun-4 Sloans & Kenyon, Bethesda #273/R

CHASE, Louisa (1951-) American
£405 $750 €591 Hug (56x76cm-22x30in) s.i.d.1979 paper prov. 13-Jul-4 Christie's, Rockefeller NY #134/R
£1648 $3000 €2406 Undertow (213x244cm-84x96in) s.i.d.1984 verso prov.exhib. 29-Jun-4 Sotheby's, New York #555/R est:5000-7000

CHASE, Marian (1844-1905) British
Works on paper
£500 $920 €730 Geese in a farmyard (23x29cm-9x11in) s. W/C bodycol. 23-Mar-4 Bonhams, Knightsbridge #28/R

CHASE, Richard A (1892-1985) American
£355 $650 €518 Mountain landscape (43x53cm-17x21in) s. canvas on board. 10-Apr-4 Auctions by the Bay, Alameda #1640/R
£601 $950 €877 Poppies (51x51cm-20x20in) s. canvas on board. 7-Sep-3 Treadway Gallery, Cincinnati #636/R

CHASE, Susan Miller (20th C) American
£216 $400 €315 Playing in the garden (20x25cm-8x10in) s. board. 13-Mar-4 Susanin's, Chicago #6104/R
£294 $550 €429 Game of checkers (20x25cm-8x10in) s. board. 24-Feb-4 Arthur James, Florida #306
£886 $1400 €1294 Afternoon tea (20x25cm-8x10in) s. board. 7-Sep-3 Treadway Gallery, Cincinnati #599/R

CHASE, William Merritt (1849-1916) American
£4609 $8250 €6729 Crashing waves (8x18cm-3x7in) s. hardboard. 8-Jan-4 James Julia, Fairfield #683/R est:8000-10000
£5525 $10000 €8067 Still life with apples and brass ewer (51x76cm-20x30in) exhib. 16-Apr-4 James Julia, Fairfield #641/R est:10000-15000
£7692 $14000 €11230 Portrait of a lady (69x56cm-27x22in) prov. 29-Jun-4 Sotheby's, New York #205/R est:15000-25000
£11976 $20000 €17485 Long Island fisherman, old Mr Woodburn (61x51cm-24x20in) prov.exhib.lit. 9-Oct-3 Christie's, Rockefeller NY #24/R est:6000-8000
£13081 $22500 €19098 Helen Velasquez Chase, daughter of the artist (30x22cm-12x9in) s. i.verso panel prov. 3-Dec-3 Doyle, New York #204/R est:10000-15000
£13587 $25000 €19837 Portrait of Frederick Augustus Guild (68x55cm-27x22in) s. painted c.1909 prov. 8-Jun-4 Bonhams & Butterfields, San Francisco #4002/R est:20000-30000
£14205 $25000 €20739 Portrait of a young boy - Son of Karl Theodor von Piloty (81x51cm-32x20in) s.d.1877 prov.exhib.lit. 19-May-4 Sotheby's, New York #24/R est:25000-35000
£53977 $95000 €78806 Veteran (61x48cm-24x19in) s.d.1878 prov.lit. 19-May-4 Sotheby's, New York #25/R est:30000-50000
£68182 $120000 €99546 self-portrait (61x51cm-24x20in) s. painted c.1912 prov.exhib.lit. 19-May-4 Sotheby's, New York #10/R est:80000-120000
£348837 $600000 €509302 Shinnecock landscape (41x51cm-16x20in) s. painted c.1890 prov.exhib. 3-Dec-3 Sotheby's, New York #23/R est:600000-800000
Works on paper
£85227 $150000 €124431 Grain field, Shinnecock Hills (38x64cm-15x25in) indis.s.i.stretcher pastel exec 1891 prov.exhib. 19-May-4 Sotheby's, New York #11/R est:100000-150000

CHASHNIK, Ilya Grigorevich (1902-1929) Russian
Works on paper
£5333 $9760 €8000 Suprematist composition (12x15cm-5x6in) W/C over pencil prov. 5-Jun-4 Lempertz, Koln #1016/R est:10000-12000
£8667 $15860 €13000 Suprematist composition (15x25cm-6x10in) gouache on pencil prov. 5-Jun-4 Lempertz, Koln #1015/R est:12000-15000

CHASHNIKOV, I D (1888-1971) Russian
Works on paper
£279 $500 €407 Sketch (27x37cm-11x15in) gouache exec. 1920's. 29-May-4 Shishkin Gallery, Moscow #3/R

CHASSARD, Marcel (1907-1991) French
£271 $462 €396 Portrait of a youth (40x29cm-16x11in) s.d.50. 19-Nov-3 Fischer, Luzern #2037/R (S.FR 600)

CHASSERIAU, Theodore (1819-1856) French
£300000 $546000 €438000 Interieur oriental (46x37cm-18x15in) s. panel painted c. 1851-52 prov.exhib.lit. 15-Jun-4 Sotheby's, London #108/R est:250000-350000
Works on paper
£2200 $4048 €3212 Female nude (38x29cm-15x11in) st.sig. pencil red chk. 25-Mar-4 Christie's, Kensington #3/R est:1500-2000

CHASTEL, Roger (1897-1981) French
£3133 $5609 €4700 Petite fille dans un fauteuil (100x73cm-39x29in) exhib.lit. 17-May-4 Chayette & Cheval, Paris #189/R est:6000-7000

CHATAUD, Marc Alfred (1833-1908) French
£3289 $5954 €5000 La caravane dans le desert (33x54cm-13x21in) s. panel. 19-Apr-4 Horta, Bruxelles #130 est:3000-5000
Works on paper
£667 $1227 €1000 Jeune femme allongee (28x40cm-11x16in) mono. pierre noir col chk. 14-Jun-4 Gros & Delettrez, Paris #440
£867 $1595 €1300 Le marchand de volailles (30x23cm-12x9in) mono. W/C chl. 14-Jun-4 Gros & Delettrez, Paris #368/R

CHATEIGNON, Ernest (1851-?) French
£625 $1150 €950 Les moissons (33x46cm-13x18in) s. 25-Jun-4 Daguerre, Paris #120
£1812 $2971 €2500 Francomtoises pres du feu (32x41cm-13x16in) s. 11-May-3 Osenat, Fontainebleau #186 est:3000-3200
£2797 $4811 €4000 Moissons dans le Morvan (60x81cm-24x32in) s. 8-Dec-3 Rossini, Paris #95/R est:4000-5000
£4200 $7728 €6132 Rentree des bles, Auvergne (45x61cm-18x24in) s. 25-Mar-4 Christie's, Kensington #13/R est:3500-4500

CHATELET, Claude Louis (1753-1794) French
£10526 $19369 €16000 Paysage panoramique (70x112cm-28x44in) 24-Jun-4 Tajan, Paris #70/R est:15000-20000
Works on paper
£544 $975 €800 Personnages avec des enfants s'amusant dans un parc (14x21cm-6x8in) black crayon brown wash. 17-Mar-4 Tajan, Paris #83
£1944 $3500 €2838 Alpine waterfall (21x27cm-8x11in) i. black chk pen grey ink wash. 22-Jan-4 Christie's, Rockefeller NY #211/R est:2000-3000
£2667 $4800 €3894 Lac d'Altdorf, Switzerland. Cascade between cliffs. Mountain path (19x25cm-7x10in) black chk pen grey ink wash three. 22-Jan-4 Christie's, Rockefeller NY #212/R est:6000-8000
£3265 $5845 €4800 Un bassin d'une villa Romaine avec des lavandieres (25x31cm-10x12in) i.d.1794 pen black ink grey wash W/C prov. 18-Mar-4 Christie's, Paris #265/R est:1000-1500

CHATELET, Claude Louis (attrib) (1753-1794) French
£16901 $29577 €24000 Pecheurs (49x61cm-19x24in) pair. 17-Dec-3 Piasa, Paris #89/R est:30000-40000
Works on paper
£467 $849 €700 Pecheurs sur le pont (18x20cm-7x8in) W/C pen ink. 30-Jun-4 Delvaux, Paris #100
£3800 $6954 €5548 Via Sacra with the columns of the temple of Castor and Pollux on the left (34x51cm-13x20in) pencil pen ink W/C. 6-Jul-4 Christie's, London #145/R est:2000-3000

CHATER, Paul Chater (1878-1949) British
Works on paper
£260 $408 €380 Study of a soldier (37x19cm-15x7in) init W/C. 16-Apr-3 Bamfords, Derby #624
£300 $471 €438 Soldier, 18th Lancer, Watson's horse (37x19cm-15x7in) init.i. W/C. 16-Apr-3 Bamfords, Derby #618/R

CHATIGNY, Joanny (1834-1886) French
£8511 $14213 €12000 Peasant woman (180x114cm-71x45in) s.d.1876. 23-Jun-3 Finarte Semenzato, Rome #196/R est:15000-20000

CHATILLON, Charles de (18th C) French
£1500 $2400 €2175 Napoleon (74x60cm-29x24in) mono. i.verso. 18-Sep-3 Christie's, Kensington #193/R est:1500-2000

CHATILLON, Louis de (attrib) (1639-1734) French
Miniatures
£4500 $8055 €6570 Gentleman in gold embroidered brown coat (5cm-2in) enamel on gold octagonal prov. 25-May-4 Christie's, London #18/R est:1500-2500

CHATILLON, Pierre (1885-1974) Swiss
Works on paper
£280 $502 €409 View over the Aare (67x55cm-26x22in) s. W/C. 13-May-4 Stuker, Bern #67 (S.FR 650)
£388 $694 €566 Still life with pots and apples (47x62cm-19x24in) s. W/C. 12-May-4 Dobiaschofsky, Bern #389 (S.FR 900)

CHATTEN, Geoffrey (?) British
£260 $471 €380 Kate, nude lady seated in a interior (74x48cm-29x19in) s. 16-Apr-4 Keys, Aylsham #613
£500 $860 €730 Gorleston Beach (48x58cm-19x23in) s. 5-Dec-3 Keys, Aylsham #511/R

CHATTERTON, Clarence K (1880-1973) American
£670 $1200 €978 Glenham (30x41cm-12x16in) s. board. 11-Jan-4 William Jenack, New York #244 est:600-1000
£1571 $2750 €2294 Street in Kennebunkport, Maine (23x26cm-9x10in) s.i.d.1946 board prov. 19-Dec-3 Sotheby's, New York #1117/R est:2500-3500
£1613 $3000 €2355 Street scene (38x57cm-15x22in) s. prov. 3-Mar-4 Christie's, Rockefeller NY #30/R est:3000-5000
£3488 $6000 €5092 Fisherman's cove (62x100cm-24x39in) s. i.overlap prov. 3-Dec-3 Doyle, New York #213/R est:5000-7000
£4261 $7500 €6221 Yellow house (61x76cm-24x30in) s. exhib. 3-Jan-4 Collins, Maine #14/R est:8000-10000
£4261 $7500 €6221 Village street, Ogunquit (61x91cm-24x36in) s. exhib. 3-Jan-4 Collins, Maine #16/R est:8000-10000
£4545 $8000 €6636 Artist's wife (51x61cm-20x24in) st.sig. prov. 3-Jan-4 Collins, Maine #15/R est:8000-10000
£4830 $8500 €7052 House and willow (61x76cm-24x30in) s. exhib. 3-Jan-4 Collins, Maine #13/R est:8000-10000
£13529 $23000 €19752 At the beach, Ogunquit, ME (61x77cm-24x30in) s. prov.exhib. 30-Oct-3 Phillips, New York #76/R est:25000-30000

CHATZIS, Vasilios (1870-1915) Greek
£2400 $4080 €3504 Battleship at sea (14x18cm-6x7in) s. board. 18-Nov-3 Sotheby's, London #121/R

CHAUDE, C (19th C) ?
Works on paper
£991 $1705 €1447 Still life with vegetables and fruit (65x81cm-26x32in) s.d.1865 pastel paper on canvas. 8-Dec-3 Philippe Schuler, Zurich #6149 (S.FR 2200)

CHAUDET (after) (?) French
Sculpture
£5655 $10349 €8200 Napoleon (50cm-20in) white marble. 31-Jan-4 Osenat, Fontainebleau #591

CHAUDET, Antoine Denis (1763-1810) French
Sculpture
£17787 $31838 €25969 Bust of Napoleon (58cm-23in) i. marble prov.lit. 15-May-4 Christie's, Sydney #237/R est:40000-60000 (A.D 45000)
Works on paper
£578 $1035 €850 Femme baisant les pieds de l'Amour. Femme tenant une corbeille (24x17cm-9x7in) s. one d.1807 pen brown ink pair. 19-Mar-4 Piasa, Paris #119

CHAUDET, Antoine Denis (after) (1763-1810) French
Sculpture
£5000 $8300 €7300 L'Amour - cupid feeding a butterfly (32x24cm-13x9in) green brown pat gilt bronze incl veined red marble base. 30-Sep-3 Sotheby's, London #316/R est:1200-1800

CHAUDET, Antoine Denis (attrib) (1763-1810) French
Sculpture
£2282 $4244 €3400 Figure, kneeling angel with gilded butterfly and roses (50x26cm-20x10in) s. bronze pink marble base. 4-Mar-4 Auction Maastricht #150/R est:3000-3500

CHAUDET, Antoine Denis (studio) (1763-1810) French
Sculpture
£12587 $21650 €18000 Buste de Napoleon en Empereur Romain (67cm-26in) white marble piedouche lit. 2-Dec-3 Sotheby's, Paris #79/R est:15000-20000

CHAUDET, Jeanne Elisabeth (attrib) (1767-1832) French
£1800 $3294 €2628 Portrait of a lady wearing a black silk dress (65x53cm-26x21in) 6-Jul-4 Sotheby's, Olympia #584/R est:2000-3000

CHAULEUR, Jane Agnes Ozeel (20th C) French
£625 $987 €900 Harbour in Brittany (26x35cm-10x14in) s. panel. 2-Sep-3 Christie's, Amsterdam #329/R

CHAURAY, Jean Claude (1934-) French
£270 $500 €394 Trois pommes a la feuille (23x33cm-9x13in) s. 17-Jan-4 Susanin's, Chicago #112/R
£1538 $2646 €2200 Composition aux citrons (38x46cm-15x18in) s. 8-Dec-3 Horta, Bruxelles #442 est:600-800

CHAUVEL, Thierry (?) French
Works on paper
£1189 $1985 €1700 Ocre et fushia (50x65cm-20x26in) s. mixed media canvas. 29-Jun-3 Feletin, Province #84/R

CHAUVIER DE LEON, Ernest (1835-1907) French
£816 $1461 €1200 L'etang au canard (60x85cm-24x33in) s. 21-Mar-4 Muizon & Le Coent, Paris #28

CHAUVIN, Jean (1889-1976) French
Works on paper
£369 $597 €520 Composition abstraitie, recherche pour une sculpture (49x30cm-19x12in) s. chl estompe. 24-May-3 Martinot & Savignat, Pontoise #21
£461 $747 €650 Composition abstraite, recherche pour une sculpture (49x30cm-19x12in) s. chl estompe. 24-May-3 Martinot & Savignat, Pontoise #20/R
£476 $852 €700 Untitled (48x32cm-19x13in) s. chl prov. 21-Mar-4 Calmels Cohen, Paris #119/R

CHAVANNES, Alfred (1836-1894) Swiss
£1143 $1829 €1657 Dents du Midi from Rhone valley (33x40cm-13x16in) s. 15-May-3 Stuker, Bern #1115/R est:3000-4000 (S.FR 2400)
£5714 $9143 €8285 Rhone with Dents du Midi (43x36cm-17x14in) s.d.78. 15-May-3 Stuker, Bern #1114/R est:4000-6000 (S.FR 12000)

CHAVANNES, Alfred (attrib) (1836-1894) Swiss
£1714 $2743 €2485 Lake Geneva (47x84cm-19x33in) 15-May-3 Stuker, Bern #1116/R est:2500-3000 (S.FR 3600)

CHAVANNES, Étienne (20th C) Haitian
£267 $425 €390 Marche moule (39x60cm-15x24in) s. masonite prov. 13-Sep-3 Weschler, Washington #719/R

CHAVAZ, Albert (1907-1990) Swiss
£303 $542 €442 Still life with violet (38x17cm-15x7in) s. board. 22-Mar-4 Philippe Schuler, Zurich #4317 (S.FR 700)
£368 $659 €537 Horses in the ring (23x29cm-9x11in) s. board. 22-Mar-4 Philippe Schuler, Zurich #4316 (S.FR 850)
£870 $1591 €1270 Joseph de la Crettaz (39x27cm-15x11in) s. cardboard painted 1948 prov.lit. 5-Jun-4 Galerie du Rhone, Sion #304/R (S.FR 2000)
£905 $1566 €1321 Boucle d'or (40x27cm-16x11in) s. i.verso cardboard. 12-Dec-3 Galerie du Rhone, Sion #478/R (S.FR 2000)
£1126 $2015 €1644 Still life with fruit and ceramic dish (46x55cm-18x22in) s. 22-Mar-4 Philippe Schuler, Zurich #4315/R est:1700-2300 (S.FR 2600)
£1385 $2480 €2022 Prunes sur un tabouret (27x39cm-11x15in) s. board. 22-Mar-4 Philippe Schuler, Zurich #4314/R est:1700-2000 (S.FR 3200)
£1810 $3131 €2643 Peintre Decarli dessinant (36x39cm-14x15in) s. mono.verso exhib.lit. 12-Dec-3 Galerie du Rhone, Sion #644/R est:4000-6000 (S.FR 4000)
£1826 $3342 €2666 Camelias (42x27cm-17x11in) s. cardboard prov. 5-Jun-4 Galerie du Rhone, Sion #563/R est:5000-7000 (S.FR 4200)
£2081 $3601 €3038 Village sous la neige (33x46cm-13x18in) s. prov. 12-Dec-3 Galerie du Rhone, Sion #640 est:5000-7000 (S.FR 4600)
£2294 $3830 €3326 Paysage valaisan (46x55cm-18x22in) s.d. init.verso canvas on cardboard prov. 21-Jun-3 Galerie du Rhone, Sion #468 est:5000-7000 (S.FR 5000)
£3043 $5570 €4443 Granois (55x45cm-22x18in) s. i.verso stretcher painted c.1942 prov. 5-Jun-4 Galerie du Rhone, Sion #565/R est:7000-9000 (S.FR 7000)
£3620 $6262 €5285 Coude du Rhone (55x70cm-22x28in) s. prov. 12-Dec-3 Galerie du Rhone, Sion #643/R est:9000-12000 (S.FR 8000)
£9502 $16439 €13873 Hameau valais (46x65cm-18x26in) s.d.75 verso prov. 12-Dec-3 Galerie du Rhone, Sion #642/R est:20000-25000 (S.FR 21000)
£15596 $26046 €22614 Le bouquet au litre (73x111cm-29x44in) s. lit. 21-Jun-3 Galerie du Rhone, Sion #469/R est:25000-35000 (S.FR 34000)
Works on paper
£409 $733 €597 Evening on the terrace (14x20cm-6x8in) s.i. W/C on biro. 12-May-4 Dobiaschofsky, Bern #391/R (S.FR 950)
£588 $1018 €858 Saviesanne (35x26cm-14x10in) s.i.d.77 crayon. 12-Dec-3 Galerie du Rhone, Sion #481/R est:1500-2000 (S.FR 1300)
£1629 $2818 €2378 Hockeyeurs (24x30cm-9x12in) s. gouache lit. 12-Dec-3 Galerie du Rhone, Sion #482/R est:2500-3500 (S.FR 3600)

CHAVDA, Shiavax (1914-) Indian
£900 $1503 €1314 Light and delight (81x68cm-32x27in) s.d.1968. 17-Oct-3 Christie's, Kensington #520/R

CHAVES LOPEZ, Xaquin Fernando (1959-) Spanish
£390 $632 €550 Untitled (65x54cm-26x21in) s.d.89. 20-May-3 Ansorena, Madrid #380/R

CHAVET, Victor Joseph (1822-1906) French
£881 $1498 €1286 Young woman in park (21x27cm-8x11in) s. 5-Nov-3 Dobiaschofsky, Bern #431/R est:2000 (S.FR 2000)
£900 $1656 €1314 Letter (39x31cm-15x12in) s.d.1872. 8-Jun-4 Bonhams, Knightsbridge #173/R
£3889 $7000 €5678 La jeune aquarelliste (51x73cm-20x29in) s. exhib. 23-Apr-4 Sotheby's, New York #164/R est:8000-12000

CHAVEZ LOPEZ, Gerardo (1937-) Peruvian
Works on paper
£2667 $4906 €4000 Repos des gladiateurs (80x100cm-31x39in) s. s.i.d.1977 pastel canvas. 9-Jun-4 Artcurial Briest, Paris #440/R est:5000-7000
£5000 $9200 €7500 Canon II (130x97cm-51x38in) s. s.i.d.76 verso pastel canvas. 9-Jun-4 Artcurial Briest, Paris #438/R est:8000-10000

CHAVEZ Y ARTIZ, Jose (1839-1903) Spanish
Works on paper
£285 $511 €425 Horses and donkey (14x21cm-6x8in) s. wash. 25-May-4 Durán, Madrid #3/R
£308 $505 €425 Mayoral y garrochista con caballo (15x18cm-6x7in) s. gouache. 27-May-3 Durán, Madrid #217/R
£308 $505 €425 Mayoral con dos burros (16x21cm-6x8in) s. gouache. 27-May-3 Durán, Madrid #218/R
£319 $571 €475 Bulls (20x26cm-8x10in) s. wash. 25-May-4 Durán, Madrid #10/R
£319 $571 €475 Ox (21x14cm-8x6in) s. wash. 25-May-4 Durán, Madrid #9/R
£336 $601 €500 Rider (15x15cm-6x6in) s. wash. 25-May-4 Durán, Madrid #4/R
£344 $564 €475 Garrochita a caballo con cuatro toros (16x21cm-6x8in) s. gouache. 27-May-3 Durán, Madrid #219/R
£369 $661 €550 Three horses (17x23cm-7x9in) s. wash. 25-May-4 Durán, Madrid #5/R
£369 $661 €550 Goats (14x21cm-6x8in) s. wash. 25-May-4 Durán, Madrid #11/R
£399 $654 €550 Pareja de mulos (15x17cm-6x7in) s. gouache. 27-May-3 Durán, Madrid #220/R
£403 $721 €600 Man resting (21x14cm-8x6in) s. wash. 25-May-4 Durán, Madrid #7/R
£403 $721 €600 Rider (30x20cm-12x8in) s. wash. 25-May-4 Durán, Madrid #6/R
£403 $721 €600 Donkeys (10x17cm-4x7in) s. wash. 25-May-4 Durán, Madrid #8/R
£435 $713 €600 Garrochista a caballo (16x21cm-6x8in) s. gouache. 27-May-3 Durán, Madrid #221/R
£435 $713 €600 Grupo de tres toros (12x21cm-5x8in) s. gouache. 27-May-3 Durán, Madrid #222/R
£470 $841 €700 Bull scene (24x15cm-9x6in) s. dr. 25-May-4 Durán, Madrid #2/R
£471 $772 €650 Carro de bueyes (17x22cm-7x9in) s. gouache. 27-May-3 Durán, Madrid #223/R
£507 $832 €700 Ternero mamando (15x16cm-6x6in) s. gouache. 27-May-3 Durán, Madrid #224/R
£604 $1081 €900 Toast (26x17cm-10x7in) s. dr. 25-May-4 Durán, Madrid #1/R
£616 $1010 €850 Toros (15x21cm-6x8in) s. gouache. 27-May-3 Durán, Madrid #225/R

CHAVIGNAUD, Georges (1865-1944) Canadian
Works on paper
£244 $405 €356 Untitled, birch trees in foothills (43x33cm-17x13in) s.d.1920 W/C gouache. 5-Oct-3 Levis, Calgary #225/R (C.D 550)

CHAZAL, Antoine (1793-1854) French
Works on paper
£2345 $3916 €3400 Various animals, one bu Travies, one by Meunier. s.d.1834/1835/1837 W/C gouache crayon 3 sheets 1 mount. 13-Nov-3 Binoche, Paris #29/R est:3000

CHAZAL, Antoine and TRAVIES, Edouard (19th C) French
Works on paper
£2207 $3686 €3200 Various animals. s. two d.1834 one d.1833 W/C gouache crayon 3 sheets 1 mount. 13-Nov-3 Binoche, Paris #28/R

CHAZAL, Antoine and VAUTHIER, Antoine Charles (19th C) French
Works on paper
£1724 $2879 €2500 Various animals. two s. one d.1834 W/C gouache black crayon 3 sheets 1 mount. 13-Nov-3 Binoche, Paris #38/R est:2000

CHAZAL, Malcolm de (1902-1981) French
Works on paper
£268 $475 €400 Papillon aux ailes polychromes (77x52cm-30x20in) s. gouache. 28-Apr-4 Charbonneaux, Paris #127
£276 $461 €400 Fleur jaune sur fond orange (57x78cm-22x31in) s. gouache. 17-Nov-3 Charbonneaux, Paris #162/R
£276 $461 €400 Cases arbre rose (52x77cm-20x30in) s. gouache. 17-Nov-3 Charbonneaux, Paris #169
£276 $461 €400 Deux fleurs (52x77cm-20x30in) s. gouache. 17-Nov-3 Charbonneaux, Paris #175
£276 $461 €400 Voiliers palmier fleurs et case bleue (50x76cm-20x30in) s. gouache. 17-Nov-3 Charbonneaux, Paris #180
£276 $461 €400 La coupole jaune. Fleur jaune (56x77cm-22x30in) s. gouache double-sided. 17-Nov-3 Charbonneaux, Paris #184
£280 $481 €400 Le coq (48x58cm-19x23in) s. gouache. 3-Dec-3 Tajan, Paris #180/R
£300 $543 €450 Carte postale au poisson (22x33cm-9x13in) s. gouache felt tip pen. 31-Mar-4 Sotheby's, Paris #161/R
£302 $535 €450 Fleurs aux petales rouge et blanc (56x77cm-22x30in) s. gouache. 28-Apr-4 Charbonneaux, Paris #121
£310 $518 €450 Fleur fuchsia sur fond bleu (57x78cm-22x31in) s. gouache. 17-Nov-3 Charbonneaux, Paris #163/R
£310 $518 €450 Trois fleurs jaune violette rouge (52x77cm-20x30in) s. gouache. 17-Nov-3 Charbonneaux, Paris #182
£336 $594 €500 Escargot sur fond vert (57x79cm-22x31in) s. gouache. 28-Apr-4 Charbonneaux, Paris #120
£336 $594 €500 Fleurs aux petales bleu et jaune (57x78cm-22x31in) s. gouache. 28-Apr-4 Charbonneaux, Paris #128
£345 $576 €500 Cases fleurs et voilier (55x76cm-22x30in) s. gouache. 17-Nov-3 Charbonneaux, Paris #167
£345 $576 €500 Cases palmier jaune fleurettes rouges. Deux fleurs (57x79cm-22x31in) s. gouache double-sided. 17-Nov-3 Charbonneaux, Paris #172
£345 $576 €500 Fleur et feuillage sur fond rouge (57x79cm-22x31in) s. gouache. 17-Nov-3 Charbonneaux, Paris #183
£369 $653 €550 Fleur sur fond bleu et rayures blanche (52x77cm-20x30in) s. gouache. 28-Apr-4 Charbonneaux, Paris #122

£369	$653	€550	Papillon aux ailes polychromes (52x77cm-20x30in) s. gouache. 28-Apr-4 Charbonneaux, Paris #126
£379	$633	€550	Case palmiers fleurs (50x76cm-20x30in) s. gouache. 17-Nov-3 Charbonneaux, Paris #170
£379	$633	€550	Voilier poisson sur flots rouges (52x77cm-20x30in) gouache. 17-Nov-3 Charbonneaux, Paris #176
£403	$713	€600	Fleur aux petales roses sur fond bleu (58x78cm-23x31in) s. gouache. 28-Apr-4 Charbonneaux, Paris #132/R
£414	$691	€600	Le voilier rouge (52x77cm-20x30in) s. gouache. 17-Nov-3 Charbonneaux, Paris #161/R
£414	$691	€600	Voilier et fleur bleue (50x65cm-20x26in) s. gouache. 17-Nov-3 Charbonneaux, Paris #164/R
£414	$691	€600	Case violette et pirogue (52x77cm-20x30in) s. gouache. 17-Nov-3 Charbonneaux, Paris #171
£436	$772	€650	Fleurs aux petales blanc et jaune (52x77cm-20x30in) s. gouache. 28-Apr-4 Charbonneaux, Paris #124
£448	$749	€650	Voiliers palmiers (52x77cm-20x30in) s. gouache. 17-Nov-3 Charbonneaux, Paris #177
£470	$832	€700	Fleur aux petales jaune et bleu fonce (57x79cm-22x31in) s. gouache double-sided. 28-Apr-4 Charbonneaux, Paris #130
£517	$864	€750	Deux cases et un palmier (52x77cm-20x30in) s. gouache. 17-Nov-3 Charbonneaux, Paris #166/R
£517	$864	€750	Coupe rouge et feuilles vertes (55x76cm-22x30in) s. gouache. 17-Nov-3 Charbonneaux, Paris #190
£537	$950	€800	Paysage aux voiliers (52x63cm-20x25in) s. gouache double-sided. 28-Apr-4 Charbonneaux, Paris #139
£552	$921	€800	Poissons (52x77cm-20x30in) s. gouache. 17-Nov-3 Charbonneaux, Paris #189
£570	$1010	€850	Bateau et bord de mer (52x77cm-20x30in) s. gouache. 28-Apr-4 Charbonneaux, Paris #123/R
£570	$1010	€850	Fleur aux petales bleu turquoise sur fond mouchete blanc (52x77cm-20x30in) s. gouache. 28-Apr-4 Charbonneaux, Paris #135
£604	$1069	€900	Fleur sur fond rouge mouchete (58x78cm-23x31in) s. gouache. 28-Apr-4 Charbonneaux, Paris #129
£638	$1192	€950	Paysage (56x77cm-22x30in) s. gouache prov. 29-Feb-4 Versailles Encheres #117/R
£671	$1188	€1000	Paysage au cactus, a la montagne et au bateau (52x77cm-20x30in) s. gouache. 28-Apr-4 Charbonneaux, Paris #133
£738	$1307	€1100	Bateaux et poissons (53x64cm-21x25in) s. gouache. 28-Apr-4 Charbonneaux, Paris #131
£805	$1426	€1200	Paysage aux maisons (52x63cm-20x25in) mono. gouache double-sided. 28-Apr-4 Charbonneaux, Paris #136
£872	$1544	€1300	Les bateaux devant la maison (52x77cm-20x30in) s. gouache. 28-Apr-4 Charbonneaux, Paris #137
£1074	$1901	€1600	Les bateaux (52x77cm-20x30in) s. gouache. 28-Apr-4 Charbonneaux, Paris #125 est:300
£1141	$2019	€1700	Figure centrale et bateaux (52x77cm-20x30in) s. gouache. 28-Apr-4 Charbonneaux, Paris #134 est:300
£1141	$2019	€1700	Paysage sur fond jaune (50x76cm-20x30in) s. gouache. 28-Apr-4 Charbonneaux, Paris #138 est:300
£1678	$3138	€2500	Table (54x75cm-21x30in) s. gouache prov. 29-Feb-4 Versailles Encheres #118/R est:150-200

CHEADLE, Henry (1852-1910) British

£300	$567	€438	Landscape with gypsy encampment (34x24cm-13x9in) s.i.verso. 17-Feb-4 Fellows & Sons, Birmingham #2/R
£520	$920	€759	Cattle grazing near a chapel (40x65cm-16x26in) s. 27-Apr-4 Bonhams, Knowle #93
£700	$1288	€1022	Welsh landscape with church spire to the centre sheep in foreground (22x35cm-9x14in) s.d.1889. 9-Jun-4 Wingetts, Wrexham #295
£800	$1336	€1168	Highland landscape, with farmhouse and cattle grazing (35x25cm-14x10in) s. 7-Oct-3 Fellows & Sons, Birmingham #351/R

CHECA Y SANZ, Ulpiano (1860-1916) Spanish

£599	$1000	€875	Shoreline seascape (48x74cm-19x29in) s. 16-Nov-3 CRN Auctions, Cambridge #37/R
£2477	$4260	€3616	Kidnap (46x66cm-18x26in) s. 3-Dec-3 Naón & Cia, Buenos Aires #45/R est:1000-1500
£2819	$5243	€4200	Portrait of man (76x59cm-30x23in) s. oval. 2-Mar-4 Ansorena, Madrid #44/R est:4200
£2819	$5243	€4200	Portrait of woman (76x59cm-30x23in) s. 2-Mar-4 Ansorena, Madrid #45/R est:4200
£3304	$5617	€4824	Horses drinking (55x85cm-22x33in) s. 5-Nov-3 Dobiaschofsky, Bern #432/R est:5500 (S.FR 7500)
£3472	$5660	€5000	Lady (66x50cm-26x20in) s.d.1899. 23-Sep-3 Durán, Madrid #45/R
£5172	$8586	€7500	Landscape with horses at stream (40x73cm-16x29in) s. 30-Sep-3 Ansorena, Madrid #79/R est:7500
£8802	$16460	€12851	Arabian riders attacking (79x99cm-31x39in) s. 24-Feb-4 Louis Morton, Mexico #28/R est:240000-300000 (M.P 180000)
£11111	$20000	€16222	Card players (46x61cm-18x24in) s. 22-Apr-4 Christie's, Rockefeller NY #168/R est:20000-30000

Works on paper

£292	$496	€420	Conversion (11x16cm-4x6in) s. gouache. 28-Oct-3 Segre, Madrid #48/R
£1342	$2497	€2000	Canal in Venice (37x22cm-15x9in) s. W/C. 2-Mar-4 Ansorena, Madrid #102/R est:1900
£4610	$7699	€6500	Cavalry battle (34x50cm-13x20in) s. ink dr. 20-Oct-3 Durán, Madrid #130/R est:2000

CHECA, Felipe (1844-1907) Spanish

£295	$481	€425	Landscape (25x34cm-10x13in) s. board. 16-Jul-3 Durán, Madrid #69/R
£590	$962	€850	Landscape (39x75cm-15x30in) s. 23-Sep-3 Durán, Madrid #652/R
£922	$1540	€1300	Flowers (70x50cm-28x20in) s. 20-Oct-3 Durán, Madrid #151/R
£1181	$1877	€1700	Landscape (99x49cm-39x19in) s. 29-Apr-3 Durán, Madrid #95/R est:1000
£1181	$1877	€1700	Landscape (99x49cm-39x19in) s. 29-Apr-3 Durán, Madrid #97/R est:1000
£1275	$2372	€1900	Vase of flowers (121x51cm-48x20in) 2-Mar-4 Ansorena, Madrid #9/R est:1400
£1275	$2372	€1900	Vase of flowers (121x51cm-48x20in) s. 2-Mar-4 Ansorena, Madrid #8/R est:1400
£1449	$2377	€2000	Flowers (60x100cm-24x39in) s. 27-May-3 Durán, Madrid #82/R est:1000
£1449	$2377	€2000	Flowers (60x100cm-24x39in) s. 27-May-3 Durán, Madrid #83/R est:1000
£2345	$3892	€3400	Still life with dead game (48x65cm-19x26in) s.d.1885. 1-Oct-3 Ansorena, Madrid #673/R est:1500
£2621	$4350	€3800	Still life with fish (48x65cm-19x26in) s.d.1886. 1-Oct-3 Ansorena, Madrid #672/R est:1500

CHECA, Jose Luis (1950-) Spanish

£268	$491	€400	Valencia harbour (33x55cm-13x22in) s. 12-Jul-4 Durán, Madrid #33/R
£272	$487	€400	Seascape (11x18cm-4x7in) s. board. 22-Mar-4 Durán, Madrid #2/R
£285	$533	€425	Beach (20x25cm-8x10in) s. board. 24-Feb-4 Durán, Madrid #116/R
£289	$518	€425	Seascape (11x18cm-4x7in) s. board. 22-Mar-4 Durán, Madrid #1/R
£345	$576	€500	On the beach (20x25cm-8x10in) s. board. 17-Nov-3 Durán, Madrid #5/R
£387	$678	€550	Xiqueta, Valencia (19x24cm-7x9in) s. s.i.verso board. 16-Dec-3 Segre, Madrid #286/R
£403	$721	€600	Looking at the sea (20x25cm-8x10in) s. board. 25-May-4 Durán, Madrid #39/R
£442	$791	€650	Fishing in the JUcar (27x41cm-11x16in) s. 22-Mar-4 Durán, Madrid #4/R
£537	$1004	€800	Venice (20x25cm-8x10in) s. board. 24-Feb-4 Durán, Madrid #117/R
£537	$950	€800	Waiting for the fishing boats (38x56cm-15x22in) s. s.i.verso. 27-Apr-4 Durán, Madrid #12/R
£612	$1096	€900	Fishing in the Jucar (27x41cm-11x16in) s. 22-Mar-4 Durán, Madrid #3/R
£671	$1255	€1000	River Jucar (61x50cm-24x20in) s. i.verso. 24-Feb-4 Durán, Madrid #167/R
£671	$1228	€1000	Ereaga beach, Bilbao (27x41cm-11x16in) s. 12-Jul-4 Durán, Madrid #60/R
£704	$1232	€1000	Valencia beach (27x41cm-11x16in) s. i.verso. 16-Dec-3 Durán, Madrid #28/R
£704	$1232	€1000	Valencia beach (27x41cm-11x16in) s. i.verso. 16-Dec-3 Durán, Madrid #26/R
£1014	$1664	€1400	Restaurante La Rana Verde, Aranjuez (54x81cm-21x32in) s. s.i.verso. 27-May-3 Durán, Madrid #88/R
£1074	$2008	€1600	Angler (37x54cm-15x21in) s. i.verso. 24-Feb-4 Durán, Madrid #15/R est:600
£1701	$3044	€2500	Valencia beach (50x100cm-20x39in) s. 22-Mar-4 Durán, Madrid #213/R est:1900
£2778	$4528	€4000	Beach in Valencia (50x100cm-20x39in) s. 23-Sep-3 Durán, Madrid #208/R est:1900

CHECCHI, Arturo (attrib) (1886-1972) Italian

£360	$590	€500	Portrait of young man with pipe (33x29cm-13x11in) 10-Jun-3 Pandolfini, Florence #221

CHEEK, Carl (20th C) British

£340	$636	€496	Fish market, Karlshamn, Sweden (89x122cm-35x48in) s.i.d.1950. 26-Feb-4 Mallams, Cheltenham #213/R

CHEERE, Henry (1703-1781) British

Sculpture

£250000	$432500	€365000	Monument to Sir George Cooke (320x122x107cm-126x48x42in) marble prov. 12-Dec-3 Sotheby's, London #223/R est:250000-350000
£450000	$832500	€657000	Vulcan. Venus (55cm-22in) s. prov. pair. 11-Feb-4 Cheffins, Cambridge #474/R est:5000-8000

CHEESEMAN, Margaret (1949-) American

£1618	$2750	€2362	Caracas (152x152cm-60x60in) s. s.i.d.1982 verso prov. 1-Nov-3 Santa Fe Art, Santa Fe #47/R est:2000-4000

CHEESWRIGHT, Ethel S. (1874-?) British

Works on paper

£250	$453	€365	Still life, pink campion in a glass jar (35x25cm-14x10in) s. W/C. 1-Apr-4 Martel Maides, Guernsey #204
£250	$468	€365	Coastal scene, Sark (49x36cm-19x14in) s. W/C. 22-Jul-4 Martel Maides, Guernsey #176
£270	$505	€394	Coastal scene, Guernsey (29x46cm-11x18in) s. W/C. 22-Jul-4 Martel Maides, Guernsey #177
£300	$543	€438	Still life, heather in a pottery vase (26x19cm-10x7in) s. W/C. 1-Apr-4 Martel Maides, Guernsey #205
£380	$688	€555	Still life, cornflowers in a floral decorated vase (35x25cm-14x10in) s. W/C. 1-Apr-4 Martel Maides, Guernsey #201/R
£420	$714	€613	From the cliffs looking towards Gouliot Passage, Sark (28x45cm-11x18in) s. W/C. 25-Nov-3 Martel Maides, Guernsey #199
£500	$905	€730	Grande Greve looking towards little Sark (32x46cm-13x18in) s. W/C. 1-Apr-4 Martel Maides, Guernsey #242
£520	$894	€759	Coastal scene, probably Jersey (28x46cm-11x18in) s. W/C. 2-Dec-3 Sworder & Son, Bishops Stortford #501/R
£520	$884	€759	Venus Pool, Sark (35x25cm-14x10in) s. W/C. 25-Nov-3 Martel Maides, Guernsey #190
£580	$986	€847	Bluebells on the Sark cliffs (34x46cm-13x18in) s. W/C. 25-Nov-3 Martel Maides, Guernsey #197
£800	$1496	€1168	Peastacks, Guernsey (34x51cm-13x20in) s. W/C. 22-Jul-4 Martel Maides, Guernsey #174/R
£850	$1539	€1241	Sark valley (33x90cm-13x35in) s. W/C. 1-Apr-4 Martel Maides, Guernsey #232
£900	$1530	€1314	Seagulls and gannets on a stormy coastline (29x39cm-11x15in) s. W/C. 25-Nov-3 Martel Maides, Guernsey #191
£900	$1629	€1314	Coastal scene, Sark (28x46cm-11x18in) s. W/C. 1-Apr-4 Martel Maides, Guernsey #217
£950	$1777	€1387	Autelets, Sark (27x43cm-11x17in) s. W/C. 22-Jul-4 Martel Maides, Guernsey #186
£1000	$1870	€1460	Peastacks, Guernsey (43x52cm-17x20in) s. W/C. 22-Jul-4 Martel Maides, Guernsey #202/R est:900-1200

£1100 $1991 €1606 Coastal scene, Sark (34x52cm-13x20in) s. W/C. 1-Apr-4 Martel Maides, Guernsey #218 est:800-1000
£1250 $2125 €1825 Sark coastal scene (35x52cm-14x20in) s. W/C. 25-Nov-3 Martel Maides, Guernsey #180 est:500-700
£1300 $2210 €1898 Coastal scene, Sark (38x53cm-15x21in) s. W/C. 25-Nov-3 Martel Maides, Guernsey #179 est:600-800
£2400 $4488 €3504 Careening Hard, Guernsey (44x27cm-17x11in) s. W/C. 22-Jul-4 Martel Maides, Guernsey #198/R est:1000-1200

CHEFFER, Henry (1860-1957) French?
Works on paper
£265 $495 €400 La buvette a Ouessant (20x20cm-8x8in) mono. W/C chl. 24-Jul-4 Thierry & Lannon, Brest #52/R
£517 $966 €780 Thoniers a sec a Douarnenez (20x26cm-8x10in) s. W/C chl. 24-Jul-4 Thierry & Lannon, Brest #51
£1623 $3034 €2450 Le ramassage des foins (29x38cm-11x15in) mono. gouache chl. 24-Jul-4 Thierry & Lannon, Brest #94/R est:800-1000

CHELIUS, Adolf (1856-1923) German
£403 $749 €600 Hunter returning home along garden fence (27x17cm-11x7in) s.i.d.1911 panel. 6-Mar-4 Arnold, Frankfurt #698/R

CHELL, Edward (1958-) British
£500 $920 €730 Untitled (46x51cm-18x20in) s.d.1994 overlap prov. 24-Jun-4 Sotheby's, Olympia #426/R

CHELLI, Patrick (20th C) ?
Works on paper
£559 $951 €800 Girona quartier Juif (30x40cm-12x16in) s. mixed media wood. 27-Nov-3 Calmels Cohen, Paris #74/R

CHELMINSKI, Jan van (1851-1925) Polish
£1900 $3496 €2774 Cart and horses on a lane (30x43cm-12x17in) s. panel. 8-Jun-4 Gorringes, Lewes #2067/R est:1500-2000
£3500 $6265 €5110 Soldiers reading a roadside notice (25x35cm-10x14in) s.d.1875 panel. 28-May-4 Lyon & Turnbull, Edinburgh #45/R est:2000-3000
£3691 $6792 €5500 Three hunters in blue uniform on horseback with dog pack (25x40cm-10x16in) s.d.1881 lit. 25-Mar-4 Karlheinz Kaupp, Staufen #2381/R est:2500
£3691 $6792 €5500 Elegant couple on horseback riding along woodland path (25x40cm-10x16in) s.d.1881 lit. 25-Mar-4 Karlheinz Kaupp, Staufen #2382/R est:2500
£6383 $10340 €9000 Polish soldiers (38x53cm-15x21in) s.d.1893 panel lit. 23-May-3 Karlheinz Kaupp, Staufen #1764/R est:4000
£7263 $13000 €10604 Generals of World War I (65x55cm-26x22in) s.i.d.1919 set of four. 6-May-4 Doyle, New York #63/R est:15000-25000
£7333 $13273 €11000 Prussian rider on deer hunt (42x61cm-17x24in) s.i.d. 2-Apr-4 Winterberg, Heidelberg #392/R est:1800
£14107 $22006 €20596 Interrogation on the road (30x40cm-12x16in) s.d.1879. 30-Mar-3 Agra, Warsaw #4/R est:80000 (P.Z 90000)

CHELMONSKI, Josef (1850-1914) Polish
£39604 $69703 €57822 Rural scene with horses (60x92cm-24x36in) painted 1882. 23-May-4 Agra, Warsaw #1/R (P.Z 280000)
Works on paper
£1100 $1870 €1650 Russian officer (15x27cm-6x11in) s. pen ink htd white. 25-Nov-3 Christie's, London #102/R est:800-1800

CHEMIAKIN, Mikhail (1943-) Russian
£2800 $4452 €4088 Carnaval de Saint-Petersbourg (117x117cm-46x46in) s.d.1982-89 s.i.d.verso. 11-Sep-3 Christie's, Kensington #226/R est:2500-3500
£3322 $5647 €4850 Personnage (114x89cm-45x35in) s.d.1990. 9-Nov-3 Eric Pillon, Calais #250/R
£3425 $5822 €5000 Carnaval (114x89cm-45x35in) s.d.1991. 9-Nov-3 Eric Pillon, Calais #251/R
£4000 $6360 €5840 Carnaval de Saint-Petersbourg (107x107cm-42x42in) s.d.1997 s.i.d.verso. 11-Sep-3 Christie's, Kensington #233/R est:4000-6000
£4000 $6360 €5840 Carnaval de Saint-Perersbourg (115x89cm-45x35in) s.i.d.1992 s.i.d.verso. 11-Sep-3 Christie's, Kensington #235/R est:4000-6000
£5034 $9312 €7500 Nature morte au pain et a la carafe (200x300cm-79x118in) s. 14-Mar-4 Eric Pillon, Calais #230/R
£8383 $14000 €12239 Grotesques in landscapes (112x112cm-44x44in) s.d.1983. 16-Nov-3 William Jenack, New York #371 est:16000-20000
Sculpture
£1507 $2562 €2200 Nature morte aux bouteilles et au crabe (75x74cm-30x29in) pat bronze one of 8. 9-Nov-3 Eric Pillon, Calais #272/R
£1611 $2980 €2400 Nature morte (100x100cm-39x39in) pat bronze exhib.lit. 14-Mar-4 Eric Pillon, Calais #235/R
£1678 $3104 €2500 Nature morte a la soupiere (103x103cm-41x41in) pat. copper exec.1987 exhib.lit. 14-Mar-4 Eric Pillon, Calais #234/R
Works on paper
£280 $467 €400 Untitled (23x15cm-9x6in) s.d.1974 ink dr prov. 29-Jun-3 Versailles Encheres #3
£559 $934 €800 Composition (57x77cm-22x30in) s.d.1970 W/C ink. 30-Jun-3 Bailly Pommery, Paris #104
£900 $1611 €1314 Surrealist composition with figures and beasts (25x32cm-10x13in) s.d.1976 W/C ink. 26-May-4 Sotheby's, Olympia #496/R est:1000-1500
£1200 $1908 €1752 Personnages (23x23cm-9x9in) s.d.95 pen ink brush col inks. 11-Sep-3 Christie's, Kensington #228/R est:1200-1800
£1200 $1908 €1752 Personnages (23x23cm-9x9in) s.d.95 pen ink brush col inks. 11-Sep-3 Christie's, Kensington #234/R est:1200-1800
£1400 $2226 €2044 Personnages (23x23cm-9x9in) s.d.95 pen ink brush col inks. 11-Sep-3 Christie's, Kensington #232/R est:1200-1800
£1467 $2640 €2200 Masks (30x35cm-12x14in) s. mixed media. 21-Apr-4 Dorotheum, Vienna #264/R est:2200-2400
£1645 $3026 €2500 Arlequin metaphysique - Carnival De Saint Petersbourg (112x76cm-44x30in) s.d.1986 pastel prov. 28-Jun-4 Joron-Derem, Paris #197 est:3000-5000
£1678 $2970 €2500 Carnaval de Saint-Petersbourg (33x33cm-13x13in) s.d.1977-1980 W/C gouache Indian ink. 27-Apr-4 Artcurial Briest, Paris #249b est:3000-4000
£1800 $3222 €2628 Ukrainian Cossacks (29x29cm-11x11in) s.d.1981 ink W/C. 26-May-4 Sotheby's, Olympia #444/R est:2000-3000
£2550 $4565 €3800 Methaphysical figures (112x76cm-44x30in) s.d.1987 pastel. 30-May-4 Eric Pillon, Calais #278/R
£2685 $4805 €4000 Carnaval (112x76cm-44x30in) s.d.1987 pastel. 30-May-4 Eric Pillon, Calais #277/R
£4762 $8524 €7000 Untitled (190x139cm-75x55in) s.d.1976-1987 pastel. 21-Mar-4 Calmels Cohen, Paris #75/R est:8000-10000

CHEMIN, Joseph Victor (1825-1901) French
Sculpture
£1400 $2338 €2044 Tethered dog (25x11cm-10x4in) s. mid brown pat. bronze. 14-Oct-3 Sotheby's, Olympia #49/R est:1500-2000
£19886 $35000 €29034 Figure of a dog and hare (110x132cm-43x52in) s.d.1882 green pat. bronze. 18-May-4 Sotheby's, New York #175/R est:10000-15000

CHEN BANDING (1877-1970) Chinese
Works on paper
£2134 $3841 €3116 Landscape (98x32cm-39x13in) s. ink col hanging scroll. 25-Apr-4 Christie's, Hong Kong #2/R est:12000-15000 (HK.D 30000)

CHEN BI (17th C) Chinese
Works on paper
£2489 $4481 €3634 Eagles on a tree branch (157x50cm-62x20in) i.d.1833 ink col hanging scroll silk. 25-Apr-4 Christie's, Hong Kong #362/R est:30000-40000 (HK.D 35000)

CHEN CHI (1912-) Chinese/American
Works on paper
£824 $1400 €1203 Fifth Avenue (58x46cm-23x18in) s. W/C over pencil. 5-Nov-3 Doyle, New York #19/R est:800-1200

CHEN CHI-KWAN (20th C) Chinese
Works on paper
£1453 $2600 €2121 Floating noise (23x119cm-9x47in) s.d.55 mixed media W/C paperboard two sheets prov. 14-May-4 Skinner, Boston #411/R est:300-500

CHEN DEHONG and LI FENGBAI (20th C) Chinese
Works on paper
£700 $1253 €1022 River landscape. Nu de dos (38x46cm-15x18in) s. col ink two prov. 6-May-4 Sotheby's, London #112/R

CHEN HENGKE (1876-1923) Chinese
Works on paper
£4623 $8321 €6750 Portrait of a monk (109x42cm-43x17in) s.i. ink col hanging scroll. 26-Apr-4 Sotheby's, Hong Kong #555/R est:45000-65000 (HK.D 65000)
£16988 $28371 €24802 Ink lotus (104x37cm-41x15in) s.i.d.1916 ink hanging scroll. 27-Oct-3 Sotheby's, Hong Kong #215/R est:65000-80000 (HK.D 220000)

CHEN MEI (17/18th C) Chinese
Works on paper
£2987 $5377 €4361 Lotus root (92x41cm-36x16in) s.d.1742 ink col hanging scroll. 25-Apr-4 Christie's, Hong Kong #429/R est:30000-40000 (HK.D 42000)

CHEN PEIQIAN (20th C) Chinese
Works on paper
£3861 $6448 €5637 Thousand Island lake (89x50cm-35x20in) s.i.d.1984 ink col hanging scroll. 26-Oct-3 Christie's, Hong Kong #290/R est:30000-40000 (HK.D 50000)

CHEN PEIQIU (1922-) Chinese
Works on paper
£1892 $3330 €2800 Duck under banana leaves (78x46cm-31x18in) s. seal Indian ink col hanging scroll. 21-May-4 Dr Fritz Nagel, Stuttgart #1131/R est:450
£3243 $5416 €4735 Blue and green landscape (18x51cm-7x20in) s.i. i.verso ink col folding fan. 27-Oct-3 Sotheby's, Hong Kong #296/R est:15000-20000 (HK.D 42000)
£3912 $7041 €5712 Green landscape (18x51cm-7x20in) s.i. ink col fan. 26-Apr-4 Sotheby's, Hong Kong #671/R est:20000-25000 (HK.D 55000)
£7824 $14083 €11423 Various subjects (25x25cm-10x10in) s. two d.1986 album eight leaves ink col lit. 26-Apr-4 Sotheby's, Hong Kong #645/R est:40000-60000 (HK.D 110000)

CHEN QIKUAN (1921-) Chinese
Works on paper
£3243 $5416 €4735 Plateau (45x45cm-18x18in) s. ink col hanging scroll. 27-Oct-3 Sotheby's, Hong Kong #382/R est:30000-50000 (HK.D 42000)
£4267 $7681 €6230 Crabs (32x34cm-13x13in) s. ink hanging scroll. 26-Apr-4 Sotheby's, Hong Kong #531/R est:25000-35000 (HK.D 60000)
£8494 $14185 €12401 Morning haze (23x92cm-9x36in) i. ink col hanging scroll. 27-Oct-3 Sotheby's, Hong Kong #381/R est:60000-80000 (HK.D 110000)
£9957 $17923 €14537 Room with a view (91x26cm-36x10in) s. ink col hanging scroll. 26-Apr-4 Sotheby's, Hong Kong #533/R est:45000-60000 (HK.D 140000)

CHEN QIUCAO (1906-1988) Chinese
Works on paper
£270 $476 €400 Fish (52x44cm-20x17in) s. seals Indian ink col hanging scroll. 21-May-4 Dr Fritz Nagel, Stuttgart #1129/R

CHEN SHAN (18th C) Chinese
Works on paper
£50193 $83822 €73282 Untitled (32x29cm-13x11in) s. ink col on silk set of 12 painted with other artists. 26-Oct-3 Christie's, Hong Kong #492/R (HK.D 650000)

CHEN SHAOMEI (1909-1954) Chinese
Works on paper
£2162 $3611 €3157 Nymph of the Luo river (18x51cm-7x20in) s.d.1940 ink col fan. 26-Oct-3 Christie's, Hong Kong #217/R est:25000-35000 (HK.D 28000)
£2471 $4127 €3608 Lady (18x50cm-7x20in) s.i.d.1942 ink col folding fan. 26-Oct-3 Christie's, Hong Kong #216/R est:25000-35000 (HK.D 32000)
£3400 $6086 €4964 Scholar beneath banana trees (117x34cm-46x13in) s. col ink hanging scroll. 6-May-4 Sotheby's, London #103/R est:800-1200
£4623 $8321 €6750 Construction site (34x49cm-13x19in) ink prov.lit. 26-Apr-4 Sotheby's, Hong Kong #567/R est:25000-35000 (HK.D 65000)
£4979 $8962 €7269 Moving home (22x75cm-9x30in) s.i.d.1939 ink col hanging scroll. 25-Apr-4 Christie's, Hong Kong #4/R est:22000-26000 (HK.D 70000)
£5405 $9027 €7891 Pavilion by the willow (133x33cm-52x13in) s.i.d.1936 ink col hanging scroll. 27-Oct-3 Sotheby's, Hong Kong #216/R est:70000-90000 (HK.D 70000)
£5792 $9672 €8456 Lady in a garden (20x51cm-8x20in) s.i.d.1941 ink col folding fan. 27-Oct-3 Sotheby's, Hong Kong #314/R est:25000-35000 (HK.D 75000)
£8494 $14185 €12401 Agriculture co-op (58x79cm-23x31in) artist seal ink hanging scroll prov. 27-Oct-3 Sotheby's, Hong Kong #344/R est:60000-80000 (HK.D 110000)
£10039 $16764 €14657 Contemplating by the river (71x34cm-28x13in) s. ink col hanging scroll. 27-Oct-3 Sotheby's, Hong Kong #271/R est:50000-70000 (HK.D 130000)
£12802 $23044 €18691 Meditation (18x49cm-7x19in) s. ink col hanging scroll lit. 26-Apr-4 Sotheby's, Hong Kong #592/R est:60000-80000 (HK.D 180000)
£18492 $33286 €26998 Melodies of nature (78x33cm-31x13in) s.i.d.1947 ink col hanging scroll lit. 26-Apr-4 Sotheby's, Hong Kong #622/R est:60000-80000 (HK.D 260000)
£18533 $30950 €27058 Buddhist figure (69x34cm-27x13in) s.i.d.1943 ink col hanging scroll. 27-Oct-3 Sotheby's, Hong Kong #282/R est:60000-80000 (HK.D 240000)
£21337 $38407 €31152 Crossing the bridge (107x33cm-42x13in) s.i.d.1950 ink col scroll. 25-Apr-4 Christie's, Hong Kong #49/R est:40000-50000 (HK.D 300000)
£21337 $38407 €31152 Lady in a bamboo grove (69x33cm-27x13in) s.i. ink col. 26-Apr-4 Sotheby's, Hong Kong #552/R est:50000-70000 (HK.D 300000)
£113798 $204836 €166145 Sailing in the river (134x56cm-53x22in) s.d.1950 ink col scroll. 25-Apr-4 Christie's, Hong Kong #122/R est:40000-50000 (HK.D 1600000)
£113798 $204836 €166145 Studio in the grove (135x48cm-53x19in) s.i.d.1950 ink col scroll. 25-Apr-4 Christie's, Hong Kong #123/R est:40000-50000 (HK.D 1600000)

CHEN SHUN (1483-1544) Chinese
Works on paper
£7112 $12802 €10384 Chrysanthemum and rock (127x33cm-50x13in) s.i. ink hanging scroll sink prov. 25-Apr-4 Christie's, Hong Kong #316/R est:80000-100000 (HK.D 100000)

CHEN SHUREN (1883-1948) Chinese
Works on paper
£2845 $5121 €4154 Plum blossom and willow (95x42cm-37x17in) s.i.d.1935 ink col. 26-Apr-4 Sotheby's, Hong Kong #558/R est:20000-30000 (HK.D 40000)

CHEN WENXI (1906-1991) Chinese
£18056 $30153 €26362 Singapore Street (61x76cm-24x30in) s. board. 12-Oct-3 Sotheby's, Singapore #62/R est:40000-60000 (S.D 52000)
Works on paper
£2536 $3931 €3703 Gibbon (134x35cm-53x14in) s. ink W/C. 6-Oct-2 Sotheby's, Singapore #68/R est:8000-10000 (S.D 7000)
£5882 $10647 €8588 Gibbon (70x39cm-28x15in) s, Chinese ink W/C. 4-Apr-4 Sotheby's, Singapore #92/R est:12000-18000 (S.D 18000)
£16340 $29575 €23856 Gibbons (120x57cm-47x22in) st.seal i. ink. 3-Apr-4 Glerum, Singapore #78/R est:40000-50000 (S.D 50000)

CHEN XIONGLI (20th C) Chinese
Works on paper
£3201 $5761 €4673 Dream of the nymph (137x67cm-54x26in) s.i. ink col scroll lit. 25-Apr-4 Christie's, Hong Kong #100/R est:50000-70000 (HK.D 45000)
£4267 $7681 €6230 Deer drinking water (68x101cm-27x40in) s.i.d.2003 ink col scroll. 25-Apr-4 Christie's, Hong Kong #102/R est:60000-80000 (HK.D 60000)

CHEN YANNING (1945-) Chinese
£16760 $30000 €24470 On the other side of river (122x183cm-48x72in) s. prov. 10-May-4 Bonhams & Butterfields, San Francisco #4410/R est:20000-30000
£17877 $32000 €26100 Night a the mid autumn festival (122x152cm-48x60in) s.d.1996 prov. 10-May-4 Bonhams & Butterfields, San Francisco #4412/R est:20000-30000

CHEN YIFEI (1946-) Chinese
£15444 $25792 €22548 Scenery of Jiangnan (127x106cm-50x42in) s.d.83. 26-Oct-3 Christie's, Hong Kong #106/R est:250000-300000 (HK.D 200000)
£29344 $49004 €42842 Canal in Venice (76x112cm-30x44in) s. painted 1988 lit. 26-Oct-3 Christie's, Hong Kong #105/R est:280000-360000 (HK.D 380000)
£34139 $61451 €49843 Relatives (66x66cm-26x26in) s. prov.lit. 25-Apr-4 Christie's, Hong Kong #741/R est:250000-350000 (HK.D 480000)
£106145 $190000 €154972 Poppy (127x147cm-50x58in) s.d.1991 prov.exhib. 10-May-4 Bonhams & Butterfields, San Francisco #4413/R est:225000-300000

CHEN YIMING (1951-) Chinese
£1145 $1900 €1672 Fishing Village (91x127cm-36x50in) s.d.1987 prov. 30-Sep-3 Bonhams & Butterfields, San Francisco #4245/R

CHEN YINPI (1913-1995) Chinese
£5019 $8382 €7328 Nude (61x71cm-24x28in) s. painted c.1940 exhib. 26-Oct-3 Christie's, Hong Kong #137/R est:80000-140000 (HK.D 65000)
£7722 $12896 €11274 Calligraphy I (62x51cm-24x20in) s. oil collage on canvas painted c.1950 exhib.lit. 26-Oct-3 Christie's, Hong Kong #138/R est:75000-110000 (HK.D 100000)
Works on paper
£19915 $35846 €29076 Stone tablet variation (75x63cm-30x25in) s. mixed media canvas exec.c.1950. 25-Apr-4 Christie's, Hong Kong #719/R est:100000-150000 (HK.D 280000)

CHEN YONGMO (1961-) Chinese
Works on paper
£2780 $4642 €4059 Arhats (39x129cm-15x51in) s.i.d.2003 ink col. 27-Oct-3 Sotheby's, Hong Kong #375/R est:28000-35000 (HK.D 36000)

CHEN ZHEN (1955-) Chinese
Sculpture
£5333 $9813 €8000 Citizen LC-510 (69x40x15cm-27x16x6in) num.9/33 iron plexiglas various objects prov. 9-Jun-4 Artcurial Briest, Paris #561/R est:8000-10000
£34013 $60883 €50000 Musicl instrument (146x128x46cm-57x50x18in) wood metal pots exec.1999-2000 lit. 16-Mar-4 Finarte Semenzato, Milan #426/R est:50000-55000

CHEN ZHONGMEI (14th C) Chinese
Works on paper
£46332 $77375 €67645 Scholars' retreat (51x61cm-20x24in) i. ink col hanging scroll prov. 27-Oct-3 Sotheby's, Hong Kong #325/R est:600000-800000 (HK.D 600000)

CHEN ZHUO (17th C) Chinese
Works on paper
£6564 $10961 €9583 Travelling in the mountains (161x71cm-63x28in) s.d.1644 ink col gold on silk. 26-Oct-3 Christie's, Hong Kong #469/R est:40000-50000 (HK.D 85000)

CHEN ZIZHUANG (1913-1976) Chinese
Works on paper
£3861 $6448 €5637 Flower and bird (28x31cm-11x12in) s. ink col eight leaves. 27-Oct-3 Sotheby's, Hong Kong #251/R est:50000-70000 (HK.D 50000)

CHEN, Hilo (1942-) American
£1163 $2000 €1698 Soccer players in Central Park (92x107cm-36x42in) s.d.73 verso. 3-Dec-3 Doyle, New York #68/R est:1200-1600
£3356 $6007 €5000 Bathroom 6 (91x101cm-36x40in) s.i.d.76 verso prov.lit. 27-May-4 Sotheby's, Paris #274/R est:6000-8000
£5828 $9500 €8509 Beach no 15 (101x127cm-40x50in) s.i.d.8902 verso prov.exhib. 23-Sep-3 Christie's, Rockefeller NY #139/R est:10000-15000
Works on paper
£2762 $5000 €4033 Bathroom - 11 (66x97cm-26x38in) W/C. 16-Apr-4 American Auctioneer #64/R est:3000-4000

CHENARD-HUCHE, Georges (1864-1937) French
£537 $988 €800 Usine pres du fleuve (32x40cm-13x16in) s. panel. 29-Mar-4 Rieunier, Paris #38/R
£805 $1482 €1200 Nature morte aux pommes (56x90cm-22x35in) s. 29-Mar-4 Rieunier, Paris #33/R

CHENEY, Anne Wells (20th C) American
£525 $825 €767 Untitled (23x23cm-9x9in) s. board. 20-Apr-3 Outer Cape Auctions, Provincetown #51/R

CHENEY, Harold W (1889-1946) American
£436 $750 €637 Low tide Gloucester (51x61cm-20x24in) s. i.verso masonite. 7-Dec-3 Grogan, Boston #48/R

CHENEY, Nan Lawson (1897-1985) Canadian
£220 $402 €321 Portrait (45x40cm-18x16in) s.d.1936 prov.lit. 3-Jun-4 Heffel, Vancouver #20/R (C.D 550)
£315 $536 €460 Calla lilies (61x51cm-24x20in) s. i.verso. 21-Nov-3 Walker's, Ottawa #48/R (C.D 700)

CHENEY, Russell (1881-1945) American
£377 $600 €550 Beneath the trees (24x33cm-9x13in) s. panel. 12-Sep-3 Skinner, Boston #415/R
£508 $950 €762 Stairway of a chateau, St Aignan, France (44x37cm-17x15in) s. i.verso canvasboard. 25-Jul-4 Bonhams & Butterfields, San Francisco #6096/R

CHENG JIASUI (1565-1643) Chinese
Works on paper
£2703 $4514 €3946 Landscapes (27x18cm-11x7in) s.i. ink set of 8. 26-Oct-3 Christie's, Hong Kong #464/R (HK.D 35000)

CHENG SHIFA (1921-) Chinese
Works on paper
£2400 $4416 €3504 Fish (94x30cm-37x12in) s. ink hanging scroll. 8-Jun-4 Bonhams, New Bond Street #56/R est:1500-2500
£2934 $4900 €4284 Story of the white snake (18x48cm-7x19in) s.i.d.1963 i.verso ink col folding fan. 27-Oct-3 Sotheby's, Hong Kong #315/R est:25000-35000 (HK.D 38000)
£12091 $21764 €17653 Girls feeding deer (69x136cm-27x54in) s.i.d.1973 ink col hanging scroll. 25-Apr-4 Christie's, Hong Kong #95/R est:80000-100000 (HK.D 170000)

CHENG YAJIE (1958-) Chinese
£8170 $14788 €11928 Blooming rose (80x60cm-31x24in) s.d.2002. 4-Apr-4 Sotheby's, Singapore #195/R est:10000-15000 (S.D 25000)

£11438 $20703 €16699 Blossoms (137x173cm-54x68in) lit. 3-Apr-4 Glerum, Singapore #88/R est:17000-22000 (S.D 35000)

CHENOU, Camille (fl.1811-1844) French
£1748 $3007 €2500 Three girls throwing flowers from balcony (24x18cm-9x7in) s. oval. 5-Dec-3 Michael Zeller, Lindau #589/R est:2500

CHENOWETH, Joseph G (fl.1920) American
£967 $1750 €1412 Fall, wooded mountain scene with river (58x76cm-23x30in) 16-Apr-4 Du Mouchelle, Detroit #2135/R est:1800-2300

CHENU, Peter Francis (18/19th C) British
Sculpture
£8000 $13840 €11680 Seated Hercules (69x44x33cm-27x17x13in) s.d.1819 brown pat bronze lit. 12-Dec-3 Sotheby's, London #203/R est:8000-12000

CHEONG SOO PIENG (1917-1983) Chinese
£2778 $4639 €4056 Untitled (84x52cm-33x20in) s.d.59. 12-Oct-3 Sotheby's, Singapore #69/R est:8000-12000 (S.D 8000)
£4167 $6958 €6084 Harbour scene (59x68cm-23x27in) s.d.61 canvas on board. 12-Oct-3 Sotheby's, Singapore #68/R est:12000-18000 (S.D 12000)

CHEPIK, M F (1920-1972) Russian
£278 $500 €406 Sentries at the Mausoleum Guard (31x53cm-12x21in) oil on cardboard sketch. 24-Apr-4 Shishkin Gallery, Moscow #97/R
£289 $520 €422 Skiing walk (32x51cm-13x20in) oil on cardboard. 24-Apr-4 Shishkin Gallery, Moscow #99/R
£306 $550 €447 Sketch for the painting on the swings (39x33cm-15x13in) oil on cardboard. 24-Apr-4 Shishkin Gallery, Moscow #96/R
£380 $700 €555 Dangerous moment, Dinamo training (54x80cm-21x31in) cardboard painted 1960's. 27-Mar-4 Shishkin Gallery, Moscow #38/R
£761 $1400 €1111 Studying at friends (37x30cm-15x12in) painted 1950's. 27-Mar-4 Shishkin Gallery, Moscow #34/R
£815 $1500 €1190 Sketch for the painting of hockey match (37x70cm-15x28in) cardboard painted 1960's. 27-Mar-4 Shishkin Gallery, Moscow #36/R est:2000-3000

CHEPIK, Serguei (1953-) Russian
£850 $1556 €1241 White Christmas (50x50cm-20x20in) s.d.80 prov. 28-Jan-4 Dreweatt Neate, Newbury #109/R
£3800 $6992 €5548 Market (80x80cm-31x31in) s.i.verso prov. 28-Mar-4 Lots Road Auctions, London #343

CHERCHI, Sandro (1911-1998) Italian
£273 $503 €410 Figures (45x35cm-18x14in) s. s.d.1973 verso. 12-Jun-4 Meeting Art, Vercelli #53

CHEREBAEV, Vladimir (20th C) Russian
£347 $650 €507 Summer landscape with figures (41x51cm-16x20in) s. 29-Feb-4 Grogan, Boston #9/R

CHEREDNICHENKO, Anna (1917-) Russian
Works on paper
£280 $510 €409 Chicken yard (49x68cm-19x27in) s. W/C exec 1965. 20-Jun-4 Lots Road Auctions, London #383/R

CHEREL, Janangoo Butcher (c.1920-) Australian
Works on paper
£1563 $2922 €2345 Untitled (76x50cm-30x20in) synthetic polymer paint canvasboard exec.c.1995 prov. 26-Jul-4 Sotheby's, Melbourne #256/R est:5000-7000 (A.D 4000)
£1563 $2922 €2345 Untitled (76x122cm-30x48in) s.verso synthetic polymer paint canvas prov. 26-Jul-4 Sotheby's, Melbourne #461/R est:4000-6000 (A.D 4000)
£1758 $3287 €2637 Warda (137x51cm-54x20in) bears name synthetic polymer paint canvas prov. 26-Jul-4 Sotheby's, Melbourne #258/R est:4000-6000 (A.D 4500)
£2656 $4967 €3984 Gurnti, blackberry (92x61cm-36x24in) bears name.verso synthetic polymer paint canvas prov. 26-Jul-4 Sotheby's, Melbourne #460/R est:7000-10000 (A.D 6800)

CHEREMETEFF, Vassily (1830-?) Russian
£46667 $85867 €70000 La danse des Cosaques (89x140cm-35x55in) s. 11-Jun-4 Claude Aguttes, Neuilly #56/R est:70000-80000

CHEREMETEH, Elisabeth (19th C) ?
Works on paper
£809 $1504 €1181 Women on terrace with view of an Italian town (45x58cm-18x23in) s.d.1841 W/C gouache. 2-Mar-4 Rasmussen, Copenhagen #1667/R (D.KR 9000)

CHERET, Joseph (19th C) French
Sculpture
£3356 $5705 €4900 Putti holding veil (50cm-20in) pat bronze marble base. 5-Nov-3 Beaussant & Lefèvre, Paris #197/R est:2000-2800

CHERET, Jules (1836-1933) French
£312 $550 €456 Letter (36x25cm-14x10in) s.i.d.25/6/97 sepia htd white chk. 23-May-4 Hindman, Chicago #48/R
£3104 $5557 €4532 Girl with tambourine (43x23cm-17x9in) s. 25-May-4 Bukowskis, Stockholm #371/R est:35000-40000 (S.KR 42000)
£3841 $6991 €5800 Jeune femme en bleu (43x23cm-17x9in) s.i.d.22/5/9. 18-Jun-4 Piasa, Paris #69/R est:4000-5000
£4631 $8567 €6900 Jeune fille a la robe jaune (33x24cm-13x9in) s. panel. 14-Mar-4 Eric Pillon, Calais #55/R
£5500 $9515 €8030 Dans le jardin (46x61cm-18x24in) s. 11-Dec-3 Christie's, Kensington #42/R est:2000-3000
Prints
£1730 $3200 €2526 Folies Bergere, Fleur de Lotus (122x84cm-48x33in) s.d.93 col lithograph. 9-Mar-4 Christie's, Rockefeller NY #239/R est:3500-4500
£1730 $3200 €2526 Theatre de l'Opera, Carnaval (122x86cm-48x34in) s. col lithograph exec.c.1894. 9-Mar-4 Christie's, Rockefeller NY #240/R est:3500-4500
Works on paper
£312 $550 €456 Young woman (36x25cm-14x10in) s. crayon chk. 23-May-4 Hindman, Chicago #47/R
£338 $605 €500 Elegante (42x28cm-17x11in) s. pierre noire blue crayon. 7-May-4 Millon & Associes, Paris #63
£563 $975 €800 Jeune femme au masque et lutins (30x23cm-12x9in) sanguine htd white pastel. 12-Dec-3 Piasa, Paris #76
£594 $1022 €850 Saxoleine (121x84cm-48x33in) poster. 5-Dec-3 Maigret, Paris #22/R
£915 $1602 €1300 La danseuse et les clowns (64x49cm-25x19in) pastel. 17-Dec-3 Delorme & Bocage, Paris #28
£1370 $2329 €2000 Lecon de musique (46x37cm-18x15in) s. gouache. 6-Nov-3 Sotheby's, Paris #86/R est:2000-3000
£1848 $3307 €2698 Masquerade (40x32cm-16x13in) s. mixed media oval. 25-May-4 Bukowskis, Stockholm #372/R est:20000-25000 (S.KR 25000)
£1958 $3270 €2800 Danseuses (126x88cm-50x35in) poster pair. 25-Jun-3 Maigret, Paris #35/R est:2000-3000
£2471 $4250 €3608 Young girl with a straw bowler (48x38cm-19x15in) s. pastel brown paper prov. 7-Dec-3 Freeman, Philadelphia #29/R est:4000-6000
£4000 $7240 €6000 La joueuse de mandoline (24x49cm-9x19in) s. pastel. 31-Mar-4 Sotheby's, Paris #155/R est:4000-6000
£4196 $7133 €6000 Carnaval (33x60cm-13x24in) s. pastel. 21-Nov-3 Lombrail & Teucquam, Paris #120/R est:6000-6500
£4435 $7938 €6475 Girl with tambourine (43x23cm-17x9in) s. pastel. 25-May-4 Bukowskis, Stockholm #370/R est:50000-70000 (S.KR 60000)
£4658 $7918 €6800 Portrait de femme a la robe jaune (75x50cm-30x20in) s.d.1906 pastel on canvas. 6-Nov-3 Sotheby's, Paris #79/R est:5000-7000

CHERIANE (1900-?) French
£870 $1591 €1270 Paysage aux deux oliviers (74x54cm-29x21in) s. s.i.d.1927 verso prov. 5-Jun-4 Galerie du Rhone, Sion #305 (S.FR 2000)

CHERMAYEFF, Serge (20th C) ?
Works on paper
£1104 $1800 €1612 Homage to Eugene McCarthy (46x41cm-18x16in) collage executed c.1962-64. 19-Jul-3 Outer Cape Auctions, Provincetown #66/R

CHERNETSOV, Nikanor Grigorevich (1805-1879) Russian
£380000 $646000 €570000 Extensive view of Rome (95x144cm-37x57in) s.d.1850 s.i.d.verso prov. 25-Nov-3 Christie's, London #109/R est:180000-240000

CHERNIKOV, Iakov (1889-1951) Russian
£1538 $2615 €2200 Drawing of cylinders, cones and cubes (31x25cm-12x10in) dispersion Indian ink on pencil prov.lit. 26-Nov-3 Lempertz, Koln #1004/R est:2500

CHERRIER, Fernande (1920-2002) ?
Sculpture
£4667 $8587 €7000 Tendresse (75cm-30in) s. st.f.Delval verso pat bronze. 9-Jun-4 Tajan, Paris #16/R est:7500-11000

CHERRY, Emma Richardson (1859-1954) American
£563 $900 €822 Lady in interior (91x66cm-36x26in) s. 19-Sep-3 Freeman, Philadelphia #68/R
£4790 $8000 €6993 Near Hampton, Virginia (64x76cm-25x30in) 18-Oct-3 David Dike, Dallas #255/R est:8000-12000

CHERRY, Kathryn (1871-1931) American
£1136 $2000 €1659 House nestled in the trees (20x25cm-8x10in) s. board. 22-May-4 Selkirks, St. Louis #538 est:800-1200
£1647 $2800 €2405 Sunlit forest (33x25cm-13x10in) s. board. 7-Nov-3 Selkirks, St. Louis #428/R est:2000-2500
£2717 $5000 €3967 Still life with Asian figurine and vase of flowers (61x51cm-24x20in) s. 26-Jun-4 Selkirks, St. Louis #151/R est:2000-4000

CHERRY, Kathryn (attrib) (1871-1931) American
£489 $900 €734 Harbour scene (43x38cm-17x15in) canvasboard. 26-Jun-4 Selkirks, St. Louis #150/R

CHERRY-GARRARD, Apsley George Benet (1886-1959) British
Works on paper
£1600 $2480 €2336 Untitled (16x21cm-6x8in) W/C htd white. 25-Sep-2 Christie's, London #354/R est:800-1200

CHERSICLA, Bruno (1937-) Italian
£1667 $2983 €2500 Trieste (160x211cm-63x83in) s.d.59 paint on screen. 12-May-4 Stadion, Trieste #806 est:1000-1500

CHERUBINI, Andrea (19th C) Italian
£769 $1308 €1100 Off the coast of Capri (13x27cm-5x11in) s. panel. 20-Nov-3 Van Ham, Cologne #1515/R est:1000
£1272 $2200 €1857 Goat herder and goats in an Italian landscape with ruins (61x76cm-24x30in) s.i.d.1865. 12-Dec-3 Eldred, East Dennis #871/R est:1000-2000

CHERUBINI, Carlo (1890-1978) Italian
£231 $425 €337 Woman reading (28x23cm-11x9in) s. 11-Jun-4 David Rago, Lambertville #316/R

£272 $500 €397 Un lido vernis bathers on the beach (23x28cm-9x11in) s. s.i.d.1963 verso. 11-Jun-4 David Rago, Lambertville #315/R
£387 $700 €565 Summer roses (79x38cm-31x15in) s. 2-Apr-4 Freeman, Philadelphia #102
£696 $1273 €1016 Female nude (24x35cm-9x14in) s. 4-Jun-4 Zofingen, Switzerland #2434 (S.FR 1600)

CHERVIN, Catalina (?) Argentinian
Works on paper
£419 $750 €612 Untitled (47x63cm-19x25in) ink. 11-May-4 Arroyo, Buenos Aires #18

CHESS, Tim (20th C) American
Works on paper
£240 $400 €350 Nine eleven (46x61cm-18x24in) pastel. 15-Nov-3 Slotin Folk Art, Buford #603/R
£344 $575 €502 Two guys talking (46x61cm-18x24in) pastel. 15-Nov-3 Slotin Folk Art, Buford #602/R
£375 $675 €548 Portrait (61x46cm-24x18in) pastel. 24-Apr-4 Slotin Folk Art, Buford #636/R
£472 $850 €689 Face with graffiti (61x46cm-24x18in) pastel. 24-Apr-4 Slotin Folk Art, Buford #637/R

CHESSA, Gigi (1895-1935) Italian
£966 $1612 €1400 Landscape (21x27cm-8x11in) d.1918 board. 17-Nov-3 Sant Agostino, Torino #118/R
Works on paper
£350 $584 €500 Landscape in Anticoli (11x16cm-4x6in) d.1918 pencil. 26-Jun-3 Sant Agostino, Torino #175/R

CHESSA, Mauro (1933-) Italian
£280 $467 €400 Still life with cabbage and knife (38x56cm-15x22in) s. s.i.d.1986 verso paper on masonite. 26-Jun-3 Sant Agostino, Torino #240/R
£521 $823 €750 Crossing (70x100cm-28x39in) paper on cardboard. 6-Sep-3 Meeting Art, Vercelli #439
£671 $1242 €1000 Still life with rotten apple (40x50cm-16x20in) s. s.i.d.1992 verso. 13-Mar-4 Meeting Art, Vercelli #491
£1049 $1783 €1500 Still life (60x80cm-24x31in) s. 20-Nov-3 Finarte Semenzato, Milan #94/R est:1500-2000

CHESTER, George (1813-1897) British
£300 $540 €438 Rural landscape with figure and thatched cottage. 25-Jan-4 Desmond Judd, Cranbrook #1106
£640 $1107 €934 Rural lake scene. 9-Dec-3 Lawrences, Bletchingley #1817

CHETRITE, Jean David (?) ?
Works on paper
£1399 $2378 €2000 Reportage (30x30cm-12x12in) s.verso collage mixed media. 27-Nov-3 Calmels Cohen, Paris #70/R est:1200-1500

CHEURET, Albert (19/20th C) French
Sculpture
£10000 $18400 €15000 Oiseaux (41x22x20cm-16x9x8in) s. bronze pair. 8-Jun-4 Camard, Paris #96/R est:15000-18000
£26667 $47733 €40000 Grues couronnees (40cm-16in) s. pat bronze pair. 17-May-4 Sotheby's, Paris #207/R est:12000-15000
£83892 $150168 €125000 Deux herons (102x134x36cm-40x53x14in) s. green pat bronze marble base and table top two. 27-May-4 Tajan, Paris #29/R est:140000-160000

CHEVALIER, Adolf (1831-?) German
£500 $900 €750 Vierwaldstatter See (42x58cm-17x23in) mono. i. verso. 21-Apr-4 Neumeister, Munich #2623/R
£600 $1104 €900 Group of people on the shores of Lake Constance (42x58cm-17x23in) s. 11-Jun-4 Wendl, Rudolstadt #3983/R
£946 $1693 €1400 Village blacksmith's in Sernowitz (44x71cm-17x28in) s. lit. 8-May-4 Schloss Ahlden, Ahlden #731/R
£1357 $2308 €1981 Vierwaldstattersee (43x68cm-17x27in) s. 19-Nov-3 Fischer, Luzern #1234/R est:3000-3500 (S.FR 3000)

CHEVALIER, Etienne (1910-1982) French
£3020 $5587 €4500 Le bassin aux poissons rouges, Saint Eugene (60x73cm-24x29in) s. 15-Mar-4 Gros & Delettrez, Paris #267/R est:4500-5000

CHEVALIER, Jean (1913-2002) French
£800 $1456 €1200 Ecriture et gris (55x65cm-22x26in) s.d.75 i.verso. 29-Jun-4 Chenu & Scrive, Lyon #48/R
Works on paper
£367 $667 €550 Composition abstraite (31x30cm-12x12in) gouache. 29-Jun-4 Chenu & Scrive, Lyon #50/R

CHEVALIER, Louis Auguste (19/20th C) French
£1996 $3572 €2914 Washerwomen at the shore (27x38cm-11x15in) s. 26-May-4 AB Stockholms Auktionsverk #2365/R est:12000-15000 (S.KR 27000)

CHEVALIER, Nicholas (1828-1902) Australian
£3626 $6599 €5294 Werner's chapel, Bacharach, Rhine (31x46cm-12x18in) s.d.1862 i.verso board. 16-Jun-4 Deutscher-Menzies, Melbourne #224/R est:12000-15000 (A.D 9500)
Works on paper
£550 $935 €803 Alpine village, with figures by a river, bridge and mountain (25x41cm-10x16in) s.d.1887. 5-Nov-3 John Nicholson, Haslemere #463
£687 $1250 €1003 Mediterranean terrace with children playing (25x37cm-10x15in) s. W/C. 16-Jun-4 Deutscher-Menzies, Melbourne #207/R est:1500-2500 (A.D 1800)
£1000 $1700 €1460 Lake of Geneva, Castle of Chilland and Dent de Midi. Lake Lucerne (41x25cm-16x10in) s. pair. 5-Nov-3 John Nicholson, Haslemere #464/R est:1000-2000
£2979 $5064 €4349 Figure by creek (23x34cm-9x13in) s.d.1867 W/C. 25-Nov-3 Christie's, Melbourne #156/R est:7000-10000 (A.D 7000)

CHEVALIER, Peter (1953-) German
£625 $1044 €900 Ideale landschaft III (100x100cm-39x39in) s.d.1985 verso. 21-Oct-3 Campo, Vlaamse Kaai #702
£933 $1717 €1400 Ideal landscape IX (81x100cm-32x39in) s.i.d.85 verso. 12-Jun-4 Villa Grisebach, Berlin #698/R est:1500-2000

CHEVALLIER, Henri (1808-1893) French
£933 $1671 €1400 Scene dans un port mediterraneen (32x50cm-13x20in) s. panel. 16-May-4 Lombrail & Teucquam, Paris #147

CHEVILLARD, Pier (1908-1991) French
£347 $638 €520 Marins et bateaux devant Concarneau (48x78cm-19x31in) s. panel. 8-Jun-4 Livinec, Gaudcheau & Jezequel, Rennes #105

CHEVILLIARD, Vincent Jean Baptiste (1841-1904) French
£691 $1237 €1009 What a good boy! (19x15cm-7x6in) s. panel. 4-May-4 Ritchie, Toronto #80/R est:1200-1800 (C.D 1700)
£2695 $4500 €3935 Monks drinking (25x33cm-10x13in) board. 14-Nov-3 Du Mouchelle, Detroit #2021/R est:4000-6000
£8725 $15617 €13000 Children's feeding time (35x30cm-14x12in) s. panel. 27-May-4 Dorotheum, Vienna #23/R est:13000-15000

CHEVIOT, Lilian (fl.1894-1930) British
£300 $474 €435 Broad langsham fowl (66x56cm-26x22in) s. 4-Sep-3 Christie's, Kensington #313/R
£600 $1032 €876 Grey Polo pony (64x56cm-25x22in) s. 3-Dec-3 Andrew Hartley, Ilkley #1164
£2200 $4026 €3212 A Samoyed puppy with a ball (76x63cm-30x25in) s. 7-Apr-4 Woolley & Wallis, Salisbury #289/R est:2000-3000

CHEVOLLEAU, Jean (1924-1996) French
£439 $786 €650 La plage (50x65cm-20x26in) s. i.verso. 5-May-4 Coutau Begarie, Paris #85
£458 $792 €650 Marais vendeen (54x65cm-21x26in) s. s.i.verso. 13-Dec-3 Touati, Paris #75/R
£458 $792 €650 La cote, le soir (46x55cm-18x22in) s.d.61 s.i.d.verso. 13-Dec-3 Touati, Paris #79/R
£507 $907 €750 Vue sur Tolede (50x61cm-20x24in) s. i.verso painted 1992. 5-May-4 Coutau Begarie, Paris #86/R
£574 $1028 €850 Les peupliers sur le village (74x93cm-29x37in) s. i.verso painted 1977. 5-May-4 Coutau Begarie, Paris #84
£634 $1096 €900 Le trio, orchestre (50x65cm-20x26in) s. s.i.d.1975 verso. 13-Dec-3 Touati, Paris #74/R
£739 $1279 €1050 Nature morte a la grappe de raisin (46x65cm-18x26in) s. s.i.d.73 verso. 13-Dec-3 Touati, Paris #76/R
£927 $1687 €1400 Notre-Dame de Fontenay (46x61cm-18x24in) s. s.i.d.verso. 19-Jun-4 St-Germain-en-Laye Encheres #214/R
£1074 $1901 €1600 L'entree du port de la meule a l'Ile d'Yeu (60x81cm-24x32in) s. s.d.1985 verso. 28-Apr-4 Charbonneaux, Paris #140/R est:1500-2000
£1611 $2851 €2400 Chevaux sur bois (73x91cm-29x36in) 29-Apr-4 Claude Aguttes, Neuilly #230/R est:2500-2800
£1678 $2853 €2400 Les peupliers, marais Poitevin (60x92cm-24x36in) s. s.i.verso. 28-Nov-3 Blanchet, Paris #232/R est:2500-3000

CHEVTSOV, Igor (1963-) Russian
£275 $514 €413 Beach in Cabourg (12x50cm-5x20in) s. cardboard. 21-Jul-4 John Nicholson, Haslemere #306
£282 $493 €400 Sailing boat (27x19cm-11x7in) s. 16-Dec-3 Durán, Madrid #713/R
£308 $505 €425 Domingo al bord del mar (24x52cm-9x20in) s. canvas on board. 27-May-3 Durán, Madrid #768/R
£369 $690 €550 Normandy beach (15x46cm-6x18in) s. cardboard. 24-Feb-4 Durán, Madrid #720/R
£408 $731 €600 On the beach (14x46cm-6x18in) s. cardboard. 22-Mar-4 Durán, Madrid #688/R
£442 $791 €650 Normandy beach (14x46cm-6x18in) s. cardboard. 22-Mar-4 Durán, Madrid #690/R
£470 $879 €700 Beach in Deauville (14x46cm-6x18in) s. cardboard. 24-Feb-4 Durán, Madrid #719/R
£567 $948 €800 Boat in harbour (26x17cm-10x7in) s. canvas on cardboard. 20-Oct-3 Durán, Madrid #703/R
£567 $948 €800 Sunday by the sea (12x38cm-5x15in) s. canvas on cardboard. 20-Oct-3 Durán, Madrid #702/R
£669 $1171 €950 Sunday on the beach (12x38cm-5x15in) s. canvas on cardboard. 16-Dec-3 Durán, Madrid #712/R
£780 $1303 €1100 Normandy (12x38cm-5x15in) s. canvas on cardboard. 20-Oct-3 Durán, Madrid #704/R
£845 $1479 €1200 Normandy beach (12x38cm-5x15in) s. cardboard. 16-Dec-3 Durán, Madrid #711/R

CHEYNEY, S Emma (fl.1889-1906) British?
Works on paper
£320 $550 €467 Still life of flowers on a ledge (28x51cm-11x20in) s. W/C. 2-Dec-3 Gorringes, Lewes #2527
£420 $722 €613 Still life of peonies in a white vase (53x38cm-21x15in) s. W/C. 2-Dec-3 Gorringes, Lewes #2526/R

CHIA, Sandro (1946-) Italian
£867 $1560 €1300 Kneeling figure in studio (31x23cm-12x9in) mono.d. tempera on Indian ink chk pencil board. 24-Apr-4 Reiss & Sohn, Konigstein #5757/R

£2667	$4800	€4000	Drawing (27x21cm-11x8in) s. tempera pencil paper painted 1997 exhib. 22-Apr-4 Finarte Semenzato, Rome #116/R est:3800-4500
£4196	$7133	€6000	Head (95x78cm-37x31in) s. acrylic. 25-Nov-3 Sotheby's, Milan #152/R est:8000-10000
£5944	$10105	€8500	Figures (64x42cm-25x17in) s.d.89 tempera paper on board. 20-Nov-3 Finarte Semenzato, Milan #28/R est:8500-9500
£6000	$10020	€8760	Mother and child (111x70cm-44x28in) s.d.92 oil pastel paper prov. 21-Oct-3 Sotheby's, London #439/R est:8000-12000
£9730	$18000	€14206	Heads and Numbers no 1 (76x61cm-30x24in) s.i.stretcher. 12-Feb-4 Sotheby's, New York #254/R est:12000-18000
£13497	$22000	€19706	Untitled, Henry Geldzahler (136x121cm-54x48in) s.i. oil oilstick paper prov. 23-Sep-3 Christie's, Rockefeller NY #151/R est:10000-15000
£16197	$26887	€23000	Night painter (102x76cm-40x30in) s. painted 1993. 13-Jun-3 Farsetti, Prato #380/R
£20958	$35000	€30599	Horse in the metropolis (154x129cm-61x51in) s.d.82 oil pastel chl gouache pencil paper prov.exhib. 13-Nov-3 Sotheby's, New York #145/R est:20000-25000
£25140	$45000	€36704	Figures at nightfall (181x220cm-71x87in) s.d.86 tempera pastel paper on canvas prov.exhib. 13-May-4 Sotheby's, New York #433/R est:40000-60000
£26000	$43420	€37960	Pils (152x134cm-60x53in) s. oil oil pastel paper painted c.1983. 22-Oct-3 Christie's, London #42/R est:18000-22000
£26536	$47500	€38743	From dusk till dawn (216x163cm-85x64in) painted c.1986 prov. 13-May-4 Sotheby's, New York #429/R est:30000-40000
£27933	$50000	€40782	Boy and dog sleeping (198x234cm-78x92in) painted 1983 prov. 13-May-4 Sotheby's, New York #432/R est:60000-80000
£35135	$61838	€52000	Climbers in green interior (230x155cm-91x61in) s.i.d.1990 verso. 22-May-4 Galleria Pananti, Florence #531/R est:45000-50000
£35928	$60000	€52455	Outdoor scene (234x199cm-92x78in) s. oil paint brushes prov.exhib. 13-Nov-3 Sotheby's, New York #542/R est:60000-80000
£41899	$75000	€61173	Leave the artist alone (165x255cm-65x100in) painted 1985 prov.exhib. 13-May-4 Sotheby's, New York #426/R est:70000-90000
£60000	$100200	€87600	Four figures (195x200cm-77x79in) s.d.83 prov.exhib. 20-Oct-3 Sotheby's, London #45/R est:80000
£65868	$110000	€96167	Passione per la filosofia e l'arte (234x274cm-92x108in) s. prov.exhib.lit. 13-Nov-3 Sotheby's, New York #556/R est:60000-80000
£67114	$120134	€100000	Swedish boy (232x203cm-91x80in) s.i.d.1982 verso. 28-May-4 Farsetti, Prato #364/R est:100000-130000
Sculpture			
£1800	$3258	€2628	Bacchus (46x25x20cm-18x10x8in) with sig num.17/50 green red pat. bronze. 1-Apr-4 Christie's, Kensington #236/R est:2000-3000
£2000	$3620	€2920	L'ange (42x32x25cm-17x13x10in) with sig.blue black gold pat. 1-Apr-4 Christie's, Kensington #237/R est:2000-3000
£2113	$3655	€3000	L'ange bleu (36x28cm-14x11in) s. num.IX/X st.f.Bonvicini blue gold pat bronze marble base. 13-Dec-3 De Vuyst, Lokeren #519/R est:3000-4000
£2215	$4075	€3300	Bacchus (43x21x22cm-17x8x9in) s. num.Vii/X green pat bronze. 24-Mar-4 Joron-Derem, Paris #107/R est:5000-6000
£2238	$3804	€3200	Cupid (48x13x11cm-19x5x4in) s. num.31/50 bronze gold. 25-Nov-3 Sotheby's, Milan #9/R est:2500-3000
£2400	$4416	€3504	Blue angel (36cm-14in) s.num.X/X paint col pat bronze gold sold with base st.f.Bonvicini. 24-Jun-4 Sotheby's, Olympia #590/R est:2500-3500
£2734	$4483	€3800	Bacchus (42x16x19cm-17x6x7in) i. green pat.bronze. 4-Jun-3 Ketterer, Hamburg #256/R est:4000-5000
£3478	$5704	€4800	Untitled (63x28x27cm-25x11x11in) s. num.38/50 painted bronze. 27-May-3 Sotheby's, Milan #43 est:300-4000
£3600	$6552	€5256	Blue Angel (35cm-14in) s.i. num.7/10 painted blue blk pat bronze gold. 4-Feb-4 Sotheby's, Olympia #220/R est:2500-3500
£4324	$8000	€6313	Caballo de Lisa (65cm-26in) s. num.2/3 base dark brown pat bronze exhib. 13-Jul-4 Christie's, Rockefeller NY #174/R est:10000-15000
£7568	$14000	€11049	Untitled (57cm-22in) i.d.84 brown pat bronze. 12-Feb-4 Sotheby's, New York #253/R est:15000-20000
£33333	$61667	€50000	Painter-poet (181x78x116cm-71x31x46in) s.d.83 num.1/4 polychrome bronze Cast Tommasi prov.exhib.lit. 18-Jul-4 Sotheby's, Paris #170/R est:50000-70000
Works on paper			
£667	$1227	€1000	Untitled (39x29cm-15x11in) s.d.1974 pastel. 12-Jun-4 Meeting Art, Vercelli #63/R
£1449	$2377	€2000	Far away relatives (17x25cm-7x10in) s.d.1981 pen Chinese ink. 27-May-3 Sotheby's, Milan #42 est:2000-3000
£1467	$2699	€2200	Untitled (37x30cm-15x12in) s. 12-Jun-4 Meeting Art, Vercelli #488/R est:2000
£1533	$2760	€2300	Dessin bureaucratique (21x28cm-8x11in) s.d.1983 ink col crayon. 25-Apr-4 Versailles Encheres #220 est:1000-1200
£1957	$3209	€2700	Composition (24x34cm-9x13in) s.d.1987 mixed media prov. 27-May-3 Il Ponte, Milan #560/R
£2000	$3180	€2900	Leave the artist alone (76x101cm-30x40in) s.d.85 chl pencil paper on card prov. 11-Sep-3 Christie's, Kensington #240/R est:1000-1500
£2013	$3564	€3000	Untitled (51x55cm-20x22in) s.d.89 mixed media. 28-Apr-4 Wiener Kunst Auktionen, Vienna #283/R est:3800-6000
£2023	$3500	€2954	Untitled (18x25cm-7x10in) s. chl graphite gouache prov. 10-Dec-3 Phillips, New York #472/R est:3000-4000
£2324	$3858	€3300	Untitled (65x50cm-26x20in) s. pastel cardboard. 14-Jun-3 Meeting Art, Vercelli #365/R est:3000
£2448	$4161	€3500	Woman (43x31cm-17x12in) s. pastel tempera W/C chl pencil. 25-Nov-3 Sotheby's, Milan #146/R est:2500-3000
£2657	$4517	€3800	Love for fish (26x21cm-10x8in) s.d.84 W/C graphite biro. 27-Nov-3 Lempertz, Koln #78/R est:3500
£2851	$5246	€4162	Untitled (22x24cm-9x9in) s.d.78 W/C col pencil. 23-Jun-4 Koller, Zurich #3122/R est:1200-2000 (S.FR 6500)
£3293	$5500	€4808	Untitled no.27 (32x23cm-13x9in) W/C mixed media executed 1985 prov. 14-Nov-3 Phillips, New York #307/R est:6000-8000
£3357	$5606	€4800	Composition (56x47cm-22x19in) s. gouache. 11-Oct-3 De Vuyst, Lokeren #504/R est:5500-6500
£3758	$6728	€5600	Seated man (44x42cm-17x17in) s. mixed media card. 28-May-4 Farsetti, Prato #157/R est:2600-3000
£3873	$6430	€5500	Untitled (86x75cm-34x30in) s. mixed media. 14-Jun-3 Meeting Art, Vercelli #588/R est:5000
£4196	$7133	€6000	Woman (78x95cm-31x37in) s.i.d.74 pen acrylic. 25-Nov-3 Sotheby's, Milan #151/R est:8000-10000
£4267	$7808	€6400	Romitorio IV (33x27cm-13x11in) s. chl pencil. 4-Jun-4 Lempertz, Koln #91/R est:3800
£8000	$14720	€12000	Personage au revolver (34x32cm-13x13in) s.d.85 W/C prov. 8-Jun-4 Artcurial Briest, Paris #255/R est:8000-12000
£8389	$15017	€12500	Untitled (55x73cm-22x29in) s. mixed media card exec.1994 lit. 28-May-4 Farsetti, Prato #369/R est:11000-13000
£9000	$15030	€13140	Void is insolent (124x101cm-49x40in) gouache chl enamel bronze prov.exhib. 22-Oct-3 Christie's, London #41/R est:8000-12000
£9783	$16043	€13500	Figure (76x55cm-30x22in) s. mixed media. 30-May-3 Farsetti, Prato #264/R
£11000	$20020	€16060	Casa (74x91cm-29x36in) s.d.85 gouache pastel ink graphite exhib. 5-Feb-4 Christie's, London #138/R est:5000-7000
£11972	$20711	€17000	Father and son (96x70cm-38x28in) crayon gouache prov.exhib. 9-Dec-3 Artcurial Briest, Paris #424/R est:6000-8000
£13000	$23660	€18980	Child is the father of the man (130x87cm-51x34in) init.d.87 gouache crayon prov. 21-Jun-4 Bonhams, New Bond Street #101/R est:8000-12000
£16760	$30000	€24470	Revolution, destitution, execution (163x295cm-64x116in) col chk prov. 12-May-4 Christie's, Rockefeller NY #404/R est:25000-35000

CHIACIGH, Giuseppe (1895-1967) Italian

£1208	$2162	€1800	White horse (68x85cm-27x33in) s. board. 25-May-4 Finarte Semenzato, Milan #88/R est:2000-2500
£2238	$3849	€3200	Extensive seascape (70x101cm-28x40in) s. board. 3-Dec-3 Stadion, Trieste #959/R est:1500-2000

CHIALIVA, Luigi (1842-1914) Swiss

£315	$542	€460	Cows out to pasture (14x24cm-6x9in) s. panel. 8-Dec-3 Philippe Schuler, Zurich #5915 (S.FR 700)
£18824	$32000	€27483	Young girl with a flock of turkeys (80x102cm-31x40in) s. 29-Oct-3 Christie's, Rockefeller NY #195/R est:40000-60000
Works on paper			
£3400	$6290	€4964	Young boy tending geese (29x44cm-11x17in) s. W/C bodycol. 9-Mar-4 Bonhams, New Bond Street #19/R est:3000-5000

CHIANESE, Mario (1928-) Italian

£816	$1461	€1200	Field in March around Lerma (20x44cm-8x17in) s.d.1984 s.i.d.verso board. 22-Mar-4 Sant Agostino, Torino #459/R

CHIAPPA, Nando (1934-) Italian

£537	$950	€800	Friends (30x40cm-12x16in) s. s.i.verso. 1-May-4 Meeting Art, Vercelli #171

CHIAPPELLI, Francesco (1890-1947) Italian

£2267	$4171	€3400	Still life (71x57cm-28x22in) s.d.1927 board. 11-Jun-4 Farsetti, Prato #546/R est:3300-3600

CHIARI, Giuseppe (1926-) Italian

£500	$920	€750	Sunset (44x34cm-17x13in) s. cardboard on canvas. 12-Jun-4 Meeting Art, Vercelli #460/R
£596	$1085	€900	Guitar. s. s.verso oil felt-tip pen collage on guitar. 17-Jun-4 Galleria Pananti, Florence #27/R
£667	$1227	€1000	Piano (70x100cm-28x39in) s. acrylic paper painted 1995. 11-Jun-4 Farsetti, Prato #287/R
Works on paper			
£268	$497	€400	Piano (70x100cm-28x39in) s. mixed media paper on canvas. 13-Mar-4 Meeting Art, Vercelli #9
£290	$464	€420	Untitled. s. mixed media. 13-Mar-3 Galleria Pace, Milan #47/R
£331	$603	€500	Untitled (58x78cm-23x31in) s. mixed media cardboard. 17-Jun-4 Galleria Pananti, Florence #217/R
£333	$613	€500	Piano (70x100cm-28x39in) s. mixed media collage card. 12-Jun-4 Meeting Art, Vercelli #656/R
£333	$613	€500	Guitar (100x70cm-39x28in) s. mixed media. 12-Jun-4 Meeting Art, Vercelli #696/R
£382	$603	€550	Homage to Murger (32x28cm-13x11in) mixed media collage card. 6-Sep-3 Meeting Art, Vercelli #285
£403	$745	€600	Music and artist (58x46cm-23x18in) s. mixed media collage board. 13-Mar-4 Meeting Art, Vercelli #319
£436	$807	€650	Quit classic music (49x45cm-19x18in) s. mixed media collage board. 13-Mar-4 Meeting Art, Vercelli #43
£467	$859	€700	Negative (70x100cm-28x39in) s.d.1001 mixed media collage. 12-Jun-4 Meeting Art, Vercelli #309/R
£517	$828	€750	Music and guitar (100x70cm-39x28in) s. mixed media. 13-Mar-3 Galleria Pace, Milan #130/R

CHIARI, Giuseppe Bartolomeo (1654-1727) Italian

£16000	$27680	€23360	Allegory of Fortitude. Allegory of Prudence bozzetti (33x29cm-13x11in) pair. 10-Dec-3 Bonhams, New Bond Street #35/R est:12000-18000
£26000	$47580	€37960	Holy Family with Saint John (100x70cm-39x28in) prov. 8-Jul-4 Sotheby's, London #319/R est:15000-20000

CHIAROTTINI, Francesco (attrib) (1748-1796) Italian

£6000	$10740	€9000	Capriccio (49x66cm-19x26in) 17-May-4 Finarte Semenzato, Rome #68/R est:12000

CHIATTONE, Mario (1891-1957) Swiss

£362	$615	€529	Scruengo (49x60cm-19x24in) s. i. verso panel. 28-Nov-3 Zofingen, Switzerland #2943 (S.FR 800)

CHIBANOFF, Mikhail (after) (18th C) Russian

£15152	$27121	€22122	Portrait of Empress Katarina II of Russia wearing travelling robe (63x50cm-25x20in) 25-May-4 Bukowskis, Stockholm #520/R est:100000-150000 (S.KR 205000)

CHICHARRO Y AGUERA, Eduardo (1873-1949) Spanish

£483	$806	€700	Interior scene (47x36cm-19x14in) s.d.94. 17-Nov-3 Durán, Madrid #641/R
£810	$1296	€1150	Gypsies (70x49cm-28x19in) s. cardboard. 16-Sep-3 Segre, Madrid #106/R
£940	$1682	€1400	Vase of flowers (43x53cm-17x21in) s. 25-May-4 Durán, Madrid #182/R

CHICHARRO Y AGUERA, Eduardo (attrib) (1873-1949) Spanish

£764	$1215	€1100	El tamborilero (60x46cm-24x18in) s.i.verso. 29-Apr-3 Durán, Madrid #24/R

CHICHESTER, Cecil (1891-1963) American
£391 $700 €571 Landscape with birches (76x91cm-30x36in) s. 11-Jan-4 William Jenack, New York #373
£405 $700 €591 Winter landscape with a stream and wood (30x41cm-12x16in) s. canvasboard. 10-Dec-3 Alderfer's, Hatfield #384/R
£480 $816 €701 Chestnut hunter with a groom in a landscape (38x48cm-15x19in) mono.i.d.1890. 30-Oct-3 Duke & Son, Dorchester #229/R
£793 $1300 €1150 Winter landscape with creek (76x91cm-30x36in) s. 4-Jun-3 Alderfer's, Hatfield #283
£882 $1500 €1288 Gloucester harbour scene (64x76cm-25x30in) s. 29-Nov-3 Carlsen Gallery, Greenville #462/R

CHICHESTER, Nugent (19th C) British?
£550 $1007 €803 Glen Isla, N.C (43x53cm-17x21in) s.i. 6-Jul-4 Bonhams, Knightsbridge #150/R

CHICO PRATS, Joseph Manuel (1916-) Spanish
£2400 $4368 €3600 Gaiteros (73x60cm-29x24in) s. 29-Jun-4 Segre, Madrid #94/R est:3600

CHIERICI, Alfonso (1816-1873) Italian
£2310 $4250 €3373 Girl with rose (58x46cm-23x18in) s. oval. 26-Jun-4 Sloans & Kenyon, Bethesda #1064/R est:1500-2000

CHIERICI, Gaetano (1838-1920) Italian
£9000 $16380 €13140 La carozzina (46x59cm-18x23in) s.d.1868 prov. 16-Jun-4 Christie's, Kensington #107/R est:10000-15000

CHIERICI, Gaetano (circle) (1838-1920) Italian
£6338 $10965 €9000 Bath (61x80cm-24x31in) i. 11-Dec-3 Christie's, Rome #120/R est:9000

CHIESA, Pietro (1876-1959) Swiss
£503 $891 €750 Swiss landscape (50x35cm-20x14in) s. 1-May-4 Meeting Art, Vercelli #125
£969 $1648 €1415 Young girl gardening (50x35cm-20x14in) s. board. 7-Nov-3 Dobiaschofsky, Bern #195/R (S.FR 2200)
£1147 $1915 €1663 Slope before house (32x53cm-13x21in) s. panel. 23-Jun-3 Philippe Schuler, Zurich #3384/R est:3000-4000 (S.FR 2500)
£1638 $2932 €2391 Still life with dahlias and books (65x50cm-26x20in) s. 14-May-4 Dobiaschofsky, Bern #193/R est:3600 (S.FR 3800)
£2477 $4261 €3616 Taking a break (79x110cm-31x43in) s.d.1934. 8-Dec-3 Philippe Schuler, Zurich #3324/R est:5000-7000 (S.FR 5500)
Works on paper
£1135 $2089 €1657 Anita with doll (70x49cm-28x19in) s.d. pastel. 14-Jun-4 Philippe Schuler, Zurich #4118/R est:1800-2400 (S.FR 2600)
£2465 $4264 €3500 Boys and flowers (51x66cm-20x26in) s. mixed media card on canvas. 11-Dec-3 Christie's, Rome #59/R est:1500-2000

CHIESA, Renato (1947-) Italian
£382 $603 €550 Quark (17x34cm-7x13in) mixed media on canvas. 6-Sep-3 Meeting Art, Vercelli #519
£493 $818 €700 Untitled (50x50cm-20x20in) s. acrylic. 14-Jun-3 Meeting Art, Vercelli #594
£563 $935 €800 Untitled (50x70cm-20x28in) s. acrylic. 14-Jun-3 Meeting Art, Vercelli #334
Works on paper
£333 $613 €500 Spheres (24x75cm-9x30in) s.i. mixed media on canvas exec.2003. 12-Jun-4 Meeting Art, Vercelli #285/R
£333 $613 €500 Deep blue (50x40cm-20x16in) s. mixed media on canvas exec.2001. 12-Jun-4 Meeting Art, Vercelli #685/R
£367 $675 €550 Spheres recycled (35x50cm-14x20in) s. mixed media on canvas exec.2002. 12-Jun-4 Meeting Art, Vercelli #805/R
£369 $683 €550 Metal budgie (50x50cm-20x20in) s. mixed media on canvas exec.1988. 13-Mar-4 Meeting Art, Vercelli #33
£382 $603 €550 Red drifting (27x33cm-11x13in) mixed media on canvas. 6-Sep-3 Meeting Art, Vercelli #277
£467 $859 €700 Spheres (35x50cm-14x20in) s. painted 2001. 12-Jun-4 Meeting Art, Vercelli #894/R

CHIESI, Giorgio (1941-) Italian
£336 $621 €500 Omelette (70x60cm-28x24in) cardboard on canvas. 11-Mar-4 Galleria Pace, Milan #4/R
£338 $561 €480 Smoker (50x40cm-20x16in) s. acrylic panel. 13-Jun-3 Farsetti, Prato #57
£500 $920 €750 Travelling knight (120x110cm-47x43in) s. mixed media on canvas lit. 12-Jun-4 Meeting Art, Vercelli #958/R
Works on paper
£268 $497 €400 Romantic dinner (60x70cm-24x28in) s. mixed media paper on canvas. 13-Mar-4 Meeting Art, Vercelli #444
£276 $461 €400 Jug (50x60cm-20x24in) s. s.i.verso mixed media collage on canvas. 13-Nov-3 Galleria Pace, Milan #18/R
£400 $736 €600 Warrior (70x60cm-28x24in) s. mixed media on canvas. 12-Jun-4 Meeting Art, Vercelli #567/R
£533 $981 €800 Training for the Olympics (70x80cm-28x31in) s. mixed media. 12-Jun-4 Meeting Art, Vercelli #213/R

CHIGHINE, Alfredo (1914-1974) Italian
£2432 $4281 €3600 Plant (71x60cm-28x24in) s.i.d.1967 verso prov. 24-May-4 Christie's, Milan #96/R est:4000-6000
£4000 $6680 €5800 Composition (40x30cm-16x12in) s.d.1965 verso. 13-Nov-3 Galleria Pace, Milan #96/R est:5700
Works on paper
£738 $1366 €1100 Untitled (22x28cm-9x11in) s.d.1972 mixed media collage card. 13-Mar-4 Meeting Art, Vercelli #353

CHIGOT, Eugène (1860-1927) French
£340 $609 €500 Paysage au moulin (38x55cm-15x22in) s. 19-Mar-4 Oger, Dumont, Paris #7
£872 $1562 €1300 Parc fleuri (90x75cm-35x30in) s. panel medaillon. 25-May-4 Chambelland & Giafferi, Paris #106/R
£1273 $2113 €1846 Spring in the park (44x55cm-17x22in) s. 13-Jun-3 Zofingen, Switzerland #2432/R est:5500 (S.FR 2800)
£2684 $4751 €4000 Tonnelle devant un chateau (73x101cm-29x40in) s.d.1907. 30-Apr-4 Tajan, Paris #161/R est:3500-4500

CHIHULY, Dale (1941-) American
£3311 $6026 €5000 Lismore Castle (153x105cm-60x41in) acrylic paper. 15-Jun-4 James Adam, Dublin #26/R est:5000-8000

CHIHUNG YANG (1947-) Chinese
£1319 $2334 €1926 Death and transfiguration (167x121cm-66x48in) s.d.1985 verso acrylic. 27-Apr-4 AB Stockholms Auktionsverk #1210/R est:10000-12000 (S.KR 18000)

CHIKKEI, Nakabayashi (1816-1867) Japanese
Works on paper
£408 $750 €596 Arashiyama in spring rain (32x51cm-13x20in) s. col ink hanging scroll. 23-Mar-4 Christie's, Rockefeller NY #115/R

CHIKUTO, Nakabayashi (attrib) (1776-1853) Japanese
Works on paper
£647 $1100 €945 Prunus, bamboo, and rocks (338x178cm-133x70in) s.d.1842 ink hanging scroll. 4-Nov-3 Bonhams & Butterfields, San Francisco #3073/R est:2000-3000

CHILCOTT, Gavin (1950-) New Zealander
£297 $512 €434 Family at home (134x131cm-53x52in) s.i.d.1986 verso. 3-Dec-3 Dunbar Sloane, Auckland #104 (NZ.D 800)
£362 $616 €529 Self with ceramics and landscape (50x65cm-20x26in) s.i.d.22.1.90 acrylic on paper. 4-Nov-3 Peter Webb, Auckland #37 est:1200-1800 (NZ.D 1000)
£629 $1145 €918 Rainforest - pots and rain (55x76cm-22x30in) s.i.d.January 1990 acrylic on paper. 29-Jun-4 Peter Webb, Auckland #11/R est:2000-3000 (NZ.D 1800)
£727 $1142 €1054 Untitled, floral abstract (76x56cm-30x22in) s.d.1977 acrylic. 27-Aug-3 Dunbar Sloane, Wellington #5/R (NZ.D 2000)
£1083 $1765 €1581 Deity - full moon and stars (75x56cm-30x22in) s.d.2001 s.i.d.28 November 2001 verso acrylic. 23-Sep-3 Peter Webb, Auckland #33/R est:2500-3500 (NZ.D 3000)
£1083 $1765 €1581 Temple details - flowers, clouds and mountains (39x112cm-15x44in) s.d.2002 s.i.d.verso acrylic paper. 23-Sep-3 Peter Webb, Auckland #134/R est:2500-3500 (NZ.D 3000)
£1264 $2060 €1845 Self portrait with friends, food and silhouettes (113x115cm-44x45in) s.i.d.1991 acrylic chl pastel. 23-Sep-3 Peter Webb, Auckland #16/R est:4000-6000 (NZ.D 3500)
£1805 $2942 €2635 Interior with figure and lily (74x53cm-29x21in) s.i.d.2002 verso acrylic. 23-Sep-3 Peter Webb, Auckland #32/R est:4000-5000 (NZ.D 5000)
£1859 $3197 €2714 Pacific II (55x150cm-22x59in) s.d.1992 acrylic prov. 3-Dec-3 Dunbar Sloane, Auckland #44/R est:3000-4000 (NZ.D 5000)
Works on paper
£290 $493 €423 Early hellenistic bas-relief - judgement of Paris (54x74cm-21x29in) s.i.d.1985 col pencil. 4-Nov-3 Peter Webb, Auckland #9/R (NZ.D 800)
£521 $828 €761 Yellow landscape with hat (54x73cm-21x29in) s.i.d.1987 crayon pencil. 1-May-3 Dunbar Sloane, Wellington #58a/R est:1500-2500 (NZ.D 1500)

CHILCOTT, Gavin and HAMMOND, Bill (20th C) New Zealander
£1630 $2641 €2364 Untitled II (80x82cm-31x32in) s.d.1991 board. 31-Jul-3 International Art Centre, Auckland #18/R est:4500-6500 (NZ.D 4500)

CHILD, Edwin Burrage (1868-1937) American
£1075 $2000 €1570 Landscape with rolling hills (46x61cm-18x24in) s.d.11.8.93. 3-Mar-4 Alderfer's, Hatfield #296 est:1000-1500

CHILDE, James Warren (c.1778-1862) British
Miniatures
£3800 $7030 €5548 Admiral John Jarvis Tucker (6cm-2in) s. oval. 13-Jul-4 Christie's, Kensington #77/R est:800-1200
Works on paper
£500 $925 €730 Portrait of Mr J H Woodward and Mr J S Urquhart (32x24cm-13x9in) s.d.1817 W/C pencil exhib. 14-Jul-4 Sotheby's, Olympia #37/R
£1000 $1670 €1460 Portrait of a little girl wearing a white frock playing with her pet (41x30cm-16x12in) s.d.1839 W/C. 12-Nov-3 Halls, Shrewsbury #259/R est:500-700

CHILLIDA, Eduardo (1924-2002) Spanish
Prints
£2069 $3434 €3000 Untitled (50x64cm-20x25in) s. num.42/50 engraving. 1-Oct-3 Ansorena, Madrid #393/R est:2800
£2162 $4000 €3157 Argi VI, light (94x68cm-37x27in) s.num.34/50 etching aquatint. 12-Feb-4 Christie's, Rockefeller NY #42/R est:800-1000
£2267 $4103 €3400 Atzapar (40x30cm-16x12in) s. aquatint. 2-Apr-4 Winterberg, Heidelberg #820/R est:4800
£2707 $4928 €3952 Gaur. s.i. etching. 17-Jun-4 Kornfeld, Bern #260/R est:2000 (S.FR 6200)
£2727 $4636 €3900 Untitled (34x35cm-13x14in) s. num.15/50 etching. 27-Nov-3 Lempertz, Koln #84/R est:1800
£3000 $5100 €4380 Hutsune (73x99cm-29x39in) s.num.37/50 aquatint. 30-Oct-3 Christie's, Kensington #238/R est:1000-1500
£3200 $5728 €4800 Banatu II (115x142cm-45x56in) s. etching aquatint. 13-May-4 Neumeister, Munich #566/R est:4500-4800

£3200 $5824 €4672 Sendotasun (49x37cm-19x15in) s.num.5/50 aquatint. 1-Jul-4 Sotheby's, London #321/R est:1500-2000
£3400 $5780 €4964 Bi-aizatu (140x96cm-55x38in) s.num.37/50 etching aquatint. 30-Oct-3 Christie's, Kensington #237/R est:1000-1500
Sculpture
£45000 $82800 €65700 Lurra (24x12x10cm-9x5x4in) mono. terracotta exec 1985 prov.exhib. 24-Jun-4 Sotheby's, London #228/R est:35000-45000
£82000 $150880 €119720 Elogio a la Luz-XV (24cm-9in) s.i. alabaster prov.exhib.lit. 25-Jun-4 Christie's, London #167/R est:30000-40000
£90000 $163800 €131400 Yunque de suenos I (63cm-25in) incised mono. num.1/4 bronze wood base prov.lit. 4-Feb-4 Christie's, London #22/R est:60000-80000
£130000 $236600 €189800 Yunque de suenos III (71cm-28in) incised mono.num.1/4 bronze wood base executed 1958 prov.lit. 4-Feb-4 Christie's, London #23/R est:100000-150000
£250000 $460000 €365000 Yunque de suenos VI (73cm-29in) mono. iron wooden base executed 1959 prov.exhib.lit. 24-Jun-4 Christie's, London #30/R est:120000-160000
£320000 $588800 €467200 Mural G-46 (218x218x6cm-86x86x2in) mono. fired clay oxide copper executed 1984 prov.exhib. 24-Jun-4 Christie's, London #31/R est:250000-350000
£340000 $618800 €496400 Elogio del vacio IV (60cm-24in) incised mono. cot-ten steel executed 1983 prov. 4-Feb-4 Christie's, London #21/R est:150000-200000
Works on paper
£1818 $3127 €2600 Untitled (6x6cm-2x2in) s. crayon. 4-Dec-3 Van Ham, Cologne #92 est:1300
£3497 $6014 €5000 Untitled - eye of a bridge (12x14cm-5x6in) mono. ink paper on card executed 1995 prov. 2-Dec-3 Sotheby's, Amsterdam #343/R est:4000-6000
£4200 $7014 €6132 Untitled (11x15cm-4x6in) s.i. ink prov. 22-Oct-3 Christie's, London #10/R est:4000-6000
£5072 $8319 €7000 Untitled (5x10cm-2x4in) s. ink card. 27-May-3 Sotheby's, Amsterdam #573/R est:4000-6000
£8000 $13360 €11680 Untitled (27x21cm-11x8in) s.i.d.58 ink pencil prov. 22-Oct-3 Christie's, London #11/R est:8000-12000
£12324 $21567 €17500 Untitled (16x18cm-6x7in) s. ink cut paper prov. 18-Dec-3 Cornette de St.Cyr, Paris #88/R est:18000-20000
£14094 $25228 €21000 Untitled (32x26cm-13x10in) s. collage exec.1967. 26-May-4 Christie's, Paris #115/R est:6000-8000
£17000 $28390 €24820 Untitled (26x24cm-10x9in) s. ink cut-out paper collage exec 1986 prov.exhib. 21-Oct-3 Sotheby's, London #374/R est:8000-12000
£46000 $84640 €67160 Gravitacion S 14 (107x120cm-42x47in) mono. ink cut-out paper collage suspended string nails prov. 24-Jun-4 Sotheby's, London #229/R est:40000-60000

CHILONE, Vincenzo (1758-1839) Italian
£38000 $68400 €55480 Venice, view of the Piazza di San Marco (40x58cm-16x23in) prov. 22-Apr-4 Sotheby's, London #124/R est:10000-15000
£46479 $81338 €66000 Venice (41x60cm-16x24in) init. 17-Dec-3 Christie's, Rome #412/R est:10000-15000

CHILONE, Vincenzo (style) (1758-1839) Italian
£4800 $8160 €7008 Venice, view of the Piazza di San Marco (50x58cm-20x23in) 30-Oct-3 Sotheby's, Olympia #186/R est:3000-4000

CHIMCHIDIAN, Ovaness (20th C) American
£1101 $1872 €1607 Portrait of arab with pipe (50x40cm-20x16in) s. 5-Nov-3 Dobiaschofsky, Bern #435/R est:1600 (S.FR 2500)

CHIMENTI, Jacopo (1554-1640) Italian
Works on paper
£5556 $10000 €8112 Adoration of the Shepherds (32x26cm-13x10in) black chk pen brown ink grey wash. 22-Jan-4 Christie's, Rockefeller NY #26/R est:6000-8000

CHIMENTI, Jacopo (studio) (1554-1640) Italian
£6600 $11418 €9636 Madonna and Child with infant Saint John the Baptist and Saint Elizabeth (112x86cm-44x34in) 9-Dec-3 Sotheby's, Olympia #389/R est:5000-7000

CHIMONAS, Nicholaos (1866-1929) Greek
£3000 $5250 €4380 Sunset over Constantinople. Winter seascape (23x31cm-9x12in) s. one panel one cardboard pair. 16-Dec-3 Bonhams, New Bond Street #22/R est:3000-5000
£13500 $24165 €19710 View of Delos (33x49cm-13x19in) s. canvas on board. 11-May-4 Bonhams, New Bond Street #33/R est:6000-8000

CHIMOT, Edouard (20th C) French
£302 $556 €450 Jeune femme accoudee a la fenetre (24x29cm-9x11in) s. paper. 24-Mar-4 Joron-Derem, Paris #79
Works on paper
£268 $494 €400 Femme nue allongee (23x30cm-9x12in) s. pastel wax crayon prov. 24-Mar-4 Joron-Derem, Paris #78
£268 $494 €400 Femme adossee (31x20cm-12x8in) s. pastel lead pencil. 24-Mar-4 Joron-Derem, Paris #80
£350 $594 €500 Jeune fille assise (32x24cm-13x9in) s. chl col crayon. 27-Nov-3 Millon & Associes, Paris #69
£4333 $7973 €6500 Opiomanes (20x25cm-8x10in) s. mixed media. 11-Jun-4 Claude Aguttes, Neuilly #111/R est:3000-4000

CHINA TRADE SCHOOL
£5114 $9000 €7466 Harbour scene (43x56cm-17x22in) 22-May-4 Pook & Pook, Downington #678/R est:3000-3500
£7955 $14000 €11614 Harbour scene (43x58cm-17x23in) 22-May-4 Pook & Pook, Downington #679/R est:10000-15000
£10056 $18000 €14682 American ship entering Chinese harbour (41x64cm-16x25in) 16-May-4 CRN Auctions, Cambridge #58/R
£15084 $27000 €22023 View of the Hongs (46x58cm-18x23in) 16-May-4 CRN Auctions, Cambridge #56/R

CHINESE SCHOOL
£25658 $47211 €39000 Portrait of lady (70x51cm-28x20in) paper on canvas. 23-Jun-4 Piasa, Paris #52/R est:12000
£125000 $230000 €182500 Courtiers at Scholarly pursuits in elaborate garden setting of terraced pavilions (292x53cm-115x21in) twelve fold screen. 23-Mar-4 Sotheby's, New York #580/R est:100000-150000
Sculpture
£7800 $13416 €11388 Figure of a mother feeding her child (62cm-24in) bronze. 2-Dec-3 Bonhams, Leeds #18 est:2500-3500

CHINESE SCHOOL, 12th/13th C
Works on paper
£42471 $70927 €62008 Carrying a qin to visit a friend (47x523cm-19x206in) ink. 26-Oct-3 Christie's, Hong Kong #444/R (HK.D 550000)

CHINESE SCHOOL, 13th C
Works on paper
£216216 $361081 €315675 Breezes along mountain stream (47x137cm-19x54in) ink col on silk. 26-Oct-3 Christie's, Hong Kong #496/R (HK.D 2800000)

CHINESE SCHOOL, 13th/14th C
Works on paper
£11583 $19344 €16911 Untitled (28x51cm-11x20in) ink on silk. 26-Oct-3 Christie's, Hong Kong #405/R (HK.D 150000)
£17070 $30725 €24922 Light breeze over the summer mountains (56x491cm-22x193in) s.i. ink col handscroll silk lit. 25-Apr-4 Christie's, Hong Kong #335/R est:250000-300000 (HK.D 240000)
£20077 $33529 €29312 Landscape of Shu (140x68cm-55x27in) ink on silk. 26-Oct-3 Christie's, Hong Kong #419/R (HK.D 260000)
£270270 $451351 €394594 Historical figures (23x21cm-9x8in) ink on silk set of 6 prov. 26-Oct-3 Christie's, Hong Kong #428/R (HK.D 3500000)

CHINESE SCHOOL, 14th/15th C
Works on paper
£15647 $28165 €22845 Street hawker (94x97cm-37x38in) ink col hanging scroll silk. 25-Apr-4 Christie's, Hong Kong #301/R est:80000-100000 (HK.D 220000)

CHINESE SCHOOL, 18th C
Sculpture
£13265 $21092 €19500 Statuette de Cakymuni assis en dhyanasana (66cm-26in) gold lacquered wood. 23-Mar-3 Mercier & Cie, Lille #44/R est:2500-3000
£13974 $25712 €20402 Children playing in garden (78x113x320cm-31x44x126in) relief two. 14-Jun-4 Philippe Schuler, Zurich #2104/R est:2000-3000 (S.FR 32000)
Works on paper
£21622 $38054 €32000 Dog. Horse - in the style of Castiglione (16cm-6in) i. verso Indian ink col fans pair prov. 21-May-4 Dr Fritz Nagel, Stuttgart #821/R est:4500

CHINESE SCHOOL, 18th/19th C
Sculpture
£9659 $17000 €14102 Geese censers (55cm-22in) bronze pair. 18-May-4 Sotheby's, New York #57/R est:2500-3500
Works on paper
£4348 $8000 €6348 Ancestor portrait (126x96cm-50x38in) col ink on silk. 23-Mar-4 Sotheby's, New York #557/R est:6000-8000

CHINESE SCHOOL, 19th C
£3243 $6000 €4735 Alice Tainter of New York, Capt WMS Hutton, passing flushing (56x78cm-22x31in) d.1860 oil on glass. 17-Jan-4 Sotheby's, New York #1260/R est:10000-15000
£5000 $8500 €7300 View of Whampoa anchorage (46x58cm-18x23in) i.verso prov. 1-Nov-3 Skinner, Boston #94/R est:1500-2500
£7944 $12551 €11519 The schooner Mathilde off Hong Kong (45x59cm-18x23in) 2-Sep-3 Rasmussen, Copenhagen #1631/R est:70000 (D.KR 85000)
£9500 $17195 €13870 View of Pearl River with hongs and paddle steamer (43x102cm-17x40in) 5-Apr-4 British Auctioneer #51/R
£10000 $18100 €14600 View of Hong Kong harbour with sailing ship to fore. 5-Apr-4 British Auctioneer #52/R
£12100 $21417 €17666 Extensive view of Hong Kong with numerous boats at anchor (52x67cm-20x26in) 28-Apr-4 Hampton & Littlewood, Exeter #564/R est:3000-4000
Works on paper
£10494 $17000 €15321 Interior of a bamboo furniture shop (28x36cm-11x14in) gouache prov.lit. 3-Aug-3 North East Auctions, Portsmouth #1892a/R est:15000-25000
£11111 $18000 €16222 Interior of a porcelain shop at Canton (28x36cm-11x14in) gouache. 3-Aug-3 North East Auctions, Portsmouth #1892c/R est:15000-25000
£12022 $22000 €18033 The Hongs at Canton showing Dutch, American, British and French flags (48x71cm-19x28in) gouache exec. c.1825. 29-Jul-4 Eldred, East Dennis #295/R est:16000-18000
£12963 $21000 €18926 Interior of a Cantonese shop making furniture for the West (28x36cm-11x14in) gouache prov.lit. 3-Aug-3 North East Auctions, Portsmouth #1892b/R est:15000-25000
£13000 $24050 €18980 Fruit and vegetables (36x46cm-14x18in) W/C bodycol exec.c.1830 eighteen. 15-Jul-4 Bonhams, New Bond Street #12/R est:10000-12000
£30000 $55200 €43800 Shanghai Bund looking across the mouth of Suzhou Creek (36x70cm-14x28in) W/C prov. 9-Jun-4 Sotheby's, London #116/R est:20000-30000
£34568 $56000 €50469 Cantonese shop making furniture in the Western style (28x36cm-11x14in) gouache prov.lit. 3-Aug-3 North East Auctions, Portsmouth #1892/R est:20000-30000

CHINESE SCHOOL, 20th C
Works on paper
£71124 $128023 €103841 Various subjects (29x18cm-11x7in) s.i. ink col various artists album 23 leaves. 26-Apr-4 Sotheby's, Hong Kong #655/R est:120000-150000 (HK.D 1000000)

CHINET, Charles (1891-1978) Swiss

£543	$1000	€793	Golden field with green hills beyond (33x41cm-13x16in) s. 26-Jun-4 Sloans & Kenyon, Bethesda #1062/R
£917	$1532	€1330	Paysage de Provence (18x37cm-7x15in) s. panel prov. 21-Jun-3 Galerie du Rhone, Sion #349/R est:2500-3500 (S.FR 2000)
£2241	$4012	€3272	Le ciel et l'eau (33x46cm-13x18in) s. 13-May-4 Pierre Berge, Paris #40/R est:6000-7000 (S.FR 5200)

CHING, Raymond (1939-) New Zealander

£2536	$4109	€3677	Shag on rock (71x50cm-28x20in) s.d.1967 board. 31-Jul-3 International Art Centre, Auckland #70/R est:8000-12000 (NZ.D 7000)
£2846	$4467	€4127	Young red kangaroo in a great continent (64x94cm-25x37in) s.d.1989 i.stretcher. 27-Aug-3 Christie's, Sydney #556/R est:7000-10000 (A.D 7000)
£4472	$7020	€6484	Kangaroo (64x120cm-25x47in) s.d.1989. 27-Aug-3 Christie's, Sydney #567/R est:7000-10000 (A.D 11000)
£5357	$9857	€7821	Jackass penguins in cold southern seas (21x64cm-8x25in) s.d.1995 board. 25-Mar-4 International Art Centre, Auckland #90/R est:12000-16000 (NZ.D 15000)
£9023	$15338	€13174	Chimpanzee (36x49cm-14x19in) s.d.1980 board. 27-Nov-3 International Art Centre, Auckland #80/R est:20000-28000 (NZ.D 24000)
£11786	$21686	€17208	Stewart Island Brown Kiwi (56x65cm-22x26in) s.d.1989 panel prov.exhib. 25-Mar-4 International Art Centre, Auckland #58/R est:30000-40000 (NZ.D 33000)
£35714	$60714	€52142	Catalina macaw (71x178cm-28x70in) s. panel prov.exhib. 27-Nov-3 International Art Centre, Auckland #72/R est:110000-150000 (NZ.D 95000)

Works on paper

£338	$575	€493	Study for snow petrol (35x40cm-14x16in) s.d.1970 pencil. 27-Nov-3 International Art Centre, Auckland #182 (NZ.D 900)
£415	$743	€606	Female Huia and letter to fill (41x58cm-16x23in) s. pencil ink. 12-May-4 Dunbar Sloane, Wellington #220 est:1000-2000 (NZ.D 1200)
£471	$763	€683	Bush study (45x29cm-18x11in) s. pencil. 31-Jul-3 International Art Centre, Auckland #130/R est:1500-2500 (NZ.D 1300)
£571	$1051	€834	Nude study (33x50cm-13x20in) s.d.1969 pencil. 25-Mar-4 International Art Centre, Auckland #119/R (NZ.D 1600)
£752	$1278	€1098	Fledgling goldfinch found in Kent (12x11cm-5x4in) s.d.23/9/1979 W/C. 27-Nov-3 International Art Centre, Auckland #148/R (NZ.D 2000)
£893	$1643	€1304	Pukeko (54x36cm-21x14in) s. pencil prov. 25-Mar-4 International Art Centre, Auckland #91/R (NZ.D 2500)
£1071	$1971	€1564	Study for morning tide (42x41cm-17x16in) s. pencil. 25-Mar-4 International Art Centre, Auckland #47/R est:3000-5000 (NZ.D 3000)
£1071	$1971	€1564	Spur winged plover (45x36cm-18x14in) s. pencil prov.exhib. 25-Mar-4 International Art Centre, Auckland #92/R est:3000-4000 (NZ.D 3000)
£1696	$3121	€2476	Dreaming (49x37cm-19x15in) s. pencil. 25-Mar-4 International Art Centre, Auckland #96/R est:3500-4500 (NZ.D 4750)
£3080	$4989	€4466	Pan parrot finches (40x34cm-16x13in) s.d.1964 W/C. 31-Jul-3 International Art Centre, Auckland #68/R est:8000-12000 (NZ.D 8500)
£9783	$15848	€14185	Penny - naughty girl (74x51cm-29x20in) s. W/C. 31-Jul-3 International Art Centre, Auckland #35/R est:20000-30000 (NZ.D 27000)
£19565	$31696	€28369	Christmas day - morning tide (74x53cm-29x21in) s. W/C prov.exhib. 31-Jul-3 International Art Centre, Auckland #32/R est:45000-65000 (NZ.D 54000)

CHINI, Galileo (1873-1956) Italian

£1888	$3153	€2700	From my window (34x44cm-13x17in) s. i.verso cardboard. 24-Jun-3 Finarte Semenzato, Rome #174/R
£2100	$3486	€3066	Pineta di viareggio (40x49cm-16x19in) s. board. 1-Oct-3 Sotheby's, Olympia #300/R est:1000-1500
£10596	$19285	€16000	Icarus (90x115cm-35x45in) s. prov.exhib.lit. 17-Jun-4 Finarte Semenzato, Milan #262/R est:8000-10000

CHINNERY, George (1774-1852) British

£3500	$5950	€5110	Portrait of a gentleman wearing a black coat (27x20cm-11x8in) 27-Nov-3 Sotheby's, London #157/R est:4000-6000
£5000	$8150	€7300	Chinese blacksmith (26x21cm-10x8in) 25-Sep-3 Christie's, London #468/R est:6000-8000
£6800	$11356	€9928	Gentleman wearing a white stock (75x57cm-30x22in) 21-Oct-3 Bruton Knowles, Cheltenham #446/R est:7000-8000
£13000	$23920	€18980	Portrait of a gentleman (28x24cm-11x9in) prov. 9-Jun-4 Sotheby's, London #118/R est:4000-6000

Miniatures

£6000	$10800	€8760	Marian Greer (9cm-4in) gilt mount rec. papier mache frame ormolu slip oval prov.exhib. 22-Apr-4 Bonhams, New Bond Street #161/R est:4000-6000

Works on paper

£280	$482	€409	Street in Macau (18x25cm-7x10in) pencil. 2-Dec-3 Gorringes, Lewes #2216/R
£340	$622	€496	Study of a cow (10x8cm-4x3in) i.d.1845 pen sepia ink over pencil. 7-Apr-4 Bonhams, Bury St Edmunds #378/R
£350	$644	€511	Game of marble (8x8cm-3x3in) pencil brown ink prov. 25-Mar-4 Christie's, Kensington #33
£400	$668	€584	Chinese barber at work and a study of a pig (14x10cm-6x4in) indis.i.d.1840 pencil prov. 16-Oct-3 Christie's, Kensington #17/R
£550	$897	€803	Figure washing pots by a river, Southern India (36x52cm-14x20in) indis.i.d.april 6 1810 pencil. 24-Sep-3 Christie's, London #253
£560	$1019	€818	Portrait of Mr H M Shakespeare seated wearing a grey coat (40x33cm-16x13in) i.d.1826 pencil W/C htd white. 29-Jun-4 Bonhams, Knowle #57
£700	$1141	€1015	Rocky hillside landscape (10x8cm-4x3in) W/C. 23-Sep-3 Bonhams, Knightsbridge #23/R
£700	$1169	€1022	Oxen by a cart, India (15x22cm-6x9in) i. pen ink over pencil. 14-Oct-3 Sotheby's, London #150/R
£780	$1295	€1139	Chinese junk (18x25cm-7x10in) d.1834 pencil. 3-Oct-3 Mallams, Oxford #127/R
£800	$1456	€1168	View of a Ghat (15x22cm-6x9in) i.d.1822 pen ink. 1-Jul-4 Mellors & Kirk, Nottingham #757/R
£1100	$1793	€1606	Figures by ruins of a tomb, Bengal (23x30cm-9x12in) i.d.15.24 pencil prov. 24-Sep-3 Christie's, London #41/R est:1200-1800
£1300	$2210	€1898	Four figure studies (11x12cm-4x5in) three i. one one d.1840 pencil four. 20-Nov-3 Christie's, London #31/R est:1500-2000
£1500	$2655	€2190	Bengal hut (13x17cm-5x7in) W/C prov. 27-Apr-4 Bonhams, New Bond Street #34/R est:1200-1800
£1700	$3128	€2482	Figures bathing in a river. Wooded landscape (11x16cm-4x6in) pen ink W/C over pencil pair. 26-Mar-4 Sotheby's, London #119/R est:1800-2400
£2600	$4342	€3796	Oriental figures and animals. pen ink dr set of 6. 17-Oct-3 Keys, Aylsham #519 est:1500-2000
£2600	$4732	€3796	Indian herdsman on a bank, cattle watering in a river below (8x17cm-3x7in) pen brown ink W/C over pencil prov. 1-Jul-4 Sotheby's, London #237/R est:3000-4000
£4800	$7824	€7008	Shaded ruin at the water's edge, Bengal, with sunlit hills beyond (10x15cm-4x6in) pencil W/C prov.exhib. 24-Sep-3 Christie's, London #79/R est:2500-3500
£6500	$10595	€9490	Portrait of the Marquess of Hastings, half-length (18x18cm-7x7in) pencil red white chk prov.exhib. 24-Sep-3 Christie's, London #80/R est:2000-3000
£13500	$22005	€19710	Fishing boats, Macao (18x21cm-7x8in) W/C. 25-Sep-3 Christie's, London #469/R est:4000-6000

CHINNERY, George (attrib) (1774-1852) British

£621	$1000	€907	Portrait of George Washington, half-length with black coat and white cravat (23x20cm-9x8in) i. verso board. 20-Aug-3 James Julia, Fairfield #33/R est:2000-4000

CHINTREUIL, Antoine (1816-1873) French

£700	$1295	€1022	Paysage (22x28cm-9x11in) s. 14-Jul-4 Christie's, Kensington #904a/R
£845	$1462	€1200	Petite cascade (28x37cm-11x15in) paper on canvas. 15-Dec-3 Bailly Pommery, Paris #100/R
£926	$1500	€1352	Wooded river edge (15x20cm-6x8in) s. board. 2-Aug-3 Neal Auction Company, New Orleans #78 est:1500-2500
£927	$1687	€1400	Paysage (24x33cm-9x13in) paper on canvas exhib. 18-Jun-4 Piasa, Paris #62/R
£940	$1663	€1400	Brouillard dans un vallonnement (26x17cm-10x7in) s. paper on canvas prov. 30-Apr-4 Tajan, Paris #108 est:1200
£1275	$2346	€1900	Tree lined path through field (32x53cm-13x21in) s. lit. 25-Mar-4 Karlheinz Kaupp, Staufen #2384/R est:480
£1678	$3003	€2500	Paysage du Lyonnais (22x40cm-9x16in) s. canvas on panel. 27-May-4 Christie's, Paris #110/R est:600-800
£2333	$4223	€3500	Bas-Breau, foret au printemps (24x35cm-9x14in) s. oil paper on panel exhib.lit. 30-Mar-4 Rossini, Paris #272/R est:2000-3000
£2817	$4676	€4000	Bord de mer en Normandie (44x73cm-17x29in) s. 15-Jun-3 Peron, Melun #132/R
£4710	$7725	€6500	Fagoteuse aux environs du Pont-de-Vaux (32x24cm-13x9in) s.i. 11-May-3 Osenat, Fontainebleau #89/R est:5000-5500
£6800	$12444	€10200	Soir d'automne (46x55cm-18x22in) s. exhib. 6-Jun-4 Osenat, Fontainebleau #139/R est:6000-7000
£8667	$15860	€13000	Promenade (61x101cm-24x40in) s. 6-Jun-4 Osenat, Fontainebleau #140/R est:15000-18000

CHINTREUIL, Antoine (attrib) (1816-1873) French

£266	$480	€400	Paysage au ciel ombrageux (27x36cm-11x14in) 26-Apr-4 Tajan, Paris #87

CHIODO, Enrico (?-1932) Swiss

£1208	$2162	€1800	Nice water (56x75cm-22x30in) s.d.1900. 25-May-4 Finarte Semenzato, Milan #100/R est:2000-2500

CHIOSTRI, Enrichetta (attrib) (1860-1942) Italian

£596	$1085	€900	Hydrangeas (69cm-27in circular) 21-Jun-4 Pandolfini, Florence #142/R

CHIPARUS (1888-1950) Rumanian

Sculpture

£2003	$3645	€3005	Untitled (44x36x26cm-17x14x10in) s. bronze. 21-Jun-4 Subastas Odalys, Caracas #82 est:7000

CHIPARUS, D (1888-1950) Rumanian

Sculpture

£1867	$3416	€2800	Little clown (22cm-9in) i. brown gold pat bronze ivory circular onyx base st.f. Etling. 7-Jun-4 Sotheby's, Amsterdam #127/R est:1500-2000
£1867	$3416	€2800	My puppet (24cm-9in) i. brown pat. bronze ivory exec. 1920's lit. 7-Jun-4 Sotheby's, Amsterdam #128/R est:1000-1500
£1888	$3153	€2700	Jeune femme au levrier (34x76x19cm-13x30x7in) s. silver gold pat bronze. 24-Jun-3 Millon & Associes, Paris #18/R est:3000-4000
£2200	$3674	€3212	Little clown (22cm-9in) s. pat bronze ivory. 13-Nov-3 Christie's, Kensington #328/R
£4200	$7014	€6132	Starlight (32cm-13in) s. col painted bronze ivory onyx base. 11-Nov-3 Rosebery Fine Art, London #189 est:2000-3000

CHIPARUS, Demetre (1888-1950) Rumanian

Sculpture

£856	$1455	€1250	Heracles (51cm-20in) s. green pat bronze. 5-Nov-3 Tajan, Paris #22
£1049	$1783	€1500	Danseuse (44x47x15cm-17x19x6in) s. pat bronzemarble base. 28-Nov-3 Drouot Estimations, Paris #29 est:1000-1200
£1189	$2021	€1700	Voyageur (41x20x13cm-16x8x5in) s. pat bronze. 25-Nov-3 Millon & Associes, Paris #5/R est:1500-2000
£1300	$2171	€1898	Bronze Age (75cm-30in) s. pat bronze marble base. 13-Nov-3 Christie's, Kensington #292/R
£1342	$2456	€2000	Pierrot (54x14cm-21x6in) s. ivory pat bronze. 6-Jul-4 Maigret, Paris #82/R est:750-900
£1565	$2801	€2300	Modele nue, allongee (87x30cm-34x12in) s. pat bronze marble base. 17-Mar-4 Tajan, Paris #8 est:1200-1500
£1800	$3222	€2700	Footsteps (41cm-16in) silver pat. bone marble socle. 13-May-4 Neumeister, Munich #215/R est:800-1200
£2098	$3608	€3000	Jeune femme assise au grand voile (34x57x15cm-13x22x6in) green pat bronze black marble base. 3-Dec-3 Palais de Beaux Arts, Brussels #634/R est:3500-5000
£2100	$3423	€3066	Young woman wrapped in lacy edged drape wiping her eye (17cm-7in) s. gilt bronze ivory square bevelled marble plinth. 28-Sep-3 Wilkinson, Doncaster #31a/R
£2446	$4500	€3669	Leaving the opera (23cm-9in) i. carved ivory pat bronze marble prov.lit. 27-Jun-4 Bonhams & Butterfields, Los Angeles #1264/R est:5000-7000
£2473	$4500	€3710	Art Deco dancer with green dress (29cm-11in) s. bronze ivory marble base. 1-Jul-4 Ben-Ami, Tel Aviv #4952/R est:6000-8000
£2600	$4134	€3796	Reclining female nude (36x60cm-14x24in) s. bronze. 9-Sep-3 Sotheby's, Olympia #381/R est:2000-2500
£2717	$5000	€4076	Cleopatra (28x48cm-11x19in) i. bronze marble onyx prov.lit. 27-Jun-4 Bonhams & Butterfields, Los Angeles #1260/R est:5000-7000
£2907	$5000	€4244	Nude seated on a high stool (38cm-15in) s. bronze exec.c.1920. 7-Dec-3 Treadway Gallery, Cincinnati #690/R est:2000-3000
£3020	$5587	€4500	Jeune femme a la balustrade (36cm-14in) s. gilt ivory col pat bronze. 15-Mar-4 Horta, Bruxelles #174/R est:3500-5000

£3221	$5702	€4800	Danseuse (45x20x8cm-18x8x3in) s.i. pat bronze ivory sold with socle lit. 27-Apr-4 Claude Aguttes, Neuilly #107/R est:7000
£3784	$7000	€5525	Ring dancer (47cm-19in) s. col painted bronze exec.c.1925. 9-Mar-4 Christie's, Rockefeller NY #310/R est:5000-7000
£3804	$7000	€5706	Ayouta (28cm-11in) i. carved ivory gilt bronze onyx base lit. 27-Jun-4 Bonhams & Butterfields, Los Angeles #1259/R est:6000-8000
£4076	$7500	€6114	Dourga (34cm-13in) i. carved ivory gilt bronze onyx prov.lit. 27-Jun-4 Bonhams & Butterfields, Los Angeles #1261/R est:8000-12000
£4076	$7500	€6114	Flapper (41cm-16in) i. carved ivory gilt pat bronze onyx prov. 27-Jun-4 Bonhams & Butterfields, Los Angeles #1262/R est:5000-7000
£4196	$7133	€6000	La bourrasque (31cm-12in) gilt bronze ivory stone socle lit. 25-Nov-3 Dorotheum, Vienna #355/R est:7000-9000
£4276	$7825	€6200	Fillette au cartable (20cm-8in) s. ivory gilt col pat bronze Cast.Etling. 28-Jun-4 Piasa, Paris #32/R est:1200-1400
£4783	$8752	€6983	Danseuse au gilet (24cm-9in) s. pat bronze ivory onyx base. 5-Jun-4 Galerie du Rhone, Sion #461/R est:9000-12000 (S.FR 11000)
£5800	$10846	€8468	Innocence (24cm-9in) s. gilt bronze ivory onyx base exec.c.1925. 24-Feb-4 Sotheby's, Olympia #282/R est:3000-4000
£6000	$10860	€9000	Pierrot (40cm-16in) s. ivory bronze prov.lit. 31-Mar-4 Segre, Madrid #865/R est:9000
£6294	$10699	€9000	Danseuse egyptienne (72cm-28in) s. pat bronze lit. 18-Nov-3 Sotheby's, Paris #116/R est:5000-6000
£6345	$10596	€9200	Innocence (24x7cm-9x3in) s. ivory gilt bronze onyx socle. 14-Nov-3 Claude Boisgirard, Paris #31/R est:3500-4000
£6711	$12013	€10000	Oriental dancer (46cm-18in) bronze ivory marble base. 25-May-4 Durán, Madrid #240/R est:10000
£6800	$12172	€9928	Ayouta (27cm-11in) s. ivory pat bronze onyx base exec.c.1925. 13-May-4 Bonhams, New Bond Street #214/R est:7000-10000
£7383	$13215	€11000	Danseuse (58x33x10cm-23x13x4in) s. pat bronze ivory onyx base. 25-May-4 Palais de Beaux Arts, Brussels #105/R est:12500-17500
£7800	$13962	€11388	Dancer of Lebanon (37cm-15in) ivory pat bronze exec.c.1925. 13-May-4 Bonhams, New Bond Street #213/R est:3000-5000
£7823	$14003	€11500	Solo (55cm-22in) pat bronze ivory wooden socle lit. 17-Mar-4 Tajan, Paris #13/R est:12000-15000
£8392	$14014	€12000	Rameses entertainer (73cm-29in) s. col pat bronze marble socle. 13-Oct-3 Horta, Bruxelles #116/R est:8000-12000
£8487	$14172	€12306	Le tango (30cm-12in) s. cold paint ivory pat bronze onyx socle exec.c.1935 prov.lit. 21-Jun-3 Galerie du Rhone, Sion #575/R est:30000-40000 (S.FR 18500)
£8667	$15687	€13000	Russian dancer (41cm-16in) s. ivory bronze onyx base prov.lit. 31-Mar-4 Segre, Madrid #866/R est:13000
£9700	$18139	€14162	Dancer of Kapurthala (55cm-22in) s. bronze green onyx base exec.c.1925 prov.lit. 24-Feb-4 Sotheby's, Olympia #284/R est:10000-15000
£9943	$17500	€14517	Fancy dress (48x28x23cm-19x11x9in) bronze ivory incl. marble base lit. 20-May-4 American Auctioneer #474975/R
£10533	$19171	€15800	Danseuse au tambourin (70x45cm-28x18in) s. silver pat bronze onyx black marble base. 5-Jul-4 Neret-Minet, Paris #105/R est:2000-2500
£10544	$18874	€15500	Danseuse au gilet (34cm-13in) s. ivory pat bronze onyx base. 17-Mar-4 Tajan, Paris #12/R est:7000-9000
£10882	$18500	€15888	Russian dancer (69cm-27in) s. ivory pat bronze marble onyx base. 7-Nov-3 Selkirks, St. Louis #604/R est:12000-16000
£11000	$17490	€16060	Indiscreet (44cm-17in) i. bronze ivory. 9-Sep-3 Sotheby's, Olympia #385/R est:9000-12000
£11009	$18385	€15963	Danseuse hindoue (59cm-23in) s. ivory pat bronze polychromie d'emaux exec.c.1920 prov.lit. 21-Jun-3 Galerie du Rhone, Sion #576/R est:30000-40000 (S.FR 24000)
£11184	$20579	€17000	Grande - Dourga (47cm-19in) s. gilded bronze ivory onyx base. 25-Jun-4 Tajan, Paris #20/R est:18000-20000
£11513	$20839	€17500	Danseuse (37cm-15in) s.num.25 ivory gilt bronze sold with onyx socle. 19-Apr-4 Horta, Bruxelles #127/R est:6500-8500
£11892	$22000	€17362	Vested dancer (55cm-22in) s. cold painted bronze ivory exec.c.1925. 9-Mar-4 Christie's, Rockefeller NY #313/R est:12000-18000
£12973	$24000	€18941	Fancy dress (51cm-20in) s. cold painted bronze ivory exec.c.1925. 9-Mar-4 Christie's, Rockefeller NY #312/R est:20000-30000
£14054	$26000	€20519	Footsteps (46cm-18in) cold painted bronze ivory exec.c.1925. 9-Mar-4 Christie's, Rockefeller NY #316/R est:15000-20000
£14085	$24648	€20000	Danseuse de ballet (35cm-14in) s. ivory gilt gold silver pat bronze onyx socle. 16-Dec-3 Galerie Moderne, Brussels #2029/R est:3000-5000
£15135	$28000	€22097	Tender promises (27x50x11cm-11x20x4in) cold pat. bronze lit. 11-Mar-4 Sotheby's, New York #125/R est:15000-25000
£16216	$30000	€23675	Nimble dancer (58cm-23in) s. cold painted bronze ivory exec.c.1925. 9-Mar-4 Christie's, Rockefeller NY #317/R est:15000-20000
£16304	$30000	€24456	Friends forever (63x65cm-25x26in) i. carved ivory gilt bronze prov.lit. 27-Jun-4 Bonhams & Butterfields, Los Angeles #1263/R est:25000-40000
£16783	$28531	€24000	Tanara (38x65x20cm-15x26x8in) s. pat bronze ivory onyx base lit. 27-Nov-3 Claude Aguttes, Neuilly #108/R est:6500-7000
£18000	$32400	€26280	Art Deco dancer of Kapurthala (55cm-22in) s. ivory bronze onyx base exec.c.1925. 21-Apr-4 Lyon & Turnbull, Edinburgh #233/R est:20000-25000
£24161	$44940	€36000	Hindu dancer (60cm-24in) s. pat bronze ivory marble base. 2-Mar-4 Ansorena, Madrid #752/R est:18000
£24476	$41608	€35000	Danseuse (58x67x11cm-23x26x4in) s. pat bronze ivory onyx base. 28-Nov-3 Drouot Estimations, Paris #27/R est:8000-10000
£38043	$70000	€57065	Antinea (66cm-26in) i. carved ivory bronze marble prov.lit. 27-Jun-4 Bonhams & Butterfields, Los Angeles #1268/R est:70000-90000
£43243	$80000	€63135	Dancer with slit skirt (57cm-22in) s. bronze ivory exec.c.1925. 9-Mar-4 Christie's, Rockefeller NY #314/R est:60000-80000
£48649	$90000	€71028	Russian dancers (63cm-25in) s. cold painted bronze ivory exec.c.1925. 9-Mar-4 Christie's, Rockefeller NY #319/R est:30000-50000

CHIPARUS, Demetre (after) (1888-1950) Rumanian

Sculpture

£5220	$9500	€7830	Vested dancer (33cm-13in) i. pat bronze ivory onyx base exec. c.1925. 16-Jun-4 Sotheby's, New York #259/R est:7000-9000
£12000	$20040	€17520	Creed (41cm-16in) pat bronze ivory marble base lit. 15-Oct-3 Christie's, Kensington #674/R est:16000
£13000	$23400	€18980	Egyptian dancer (74cm-29in) s.i. silvered cold-painted bronze marble base lit. 22-Apr-4 Christie's, Kensington #532/R est:5000-7000
£14000	$24780	€20440	Vedette (80cm-31in) s. gilt pat bronze stepped marble base. 28-Apr-4 Woolley & Wallis, Salisbury #300/R est:7000-9000

CHIRIACKA, Ernest (1920-) American

£226	$400	€330	Landscape with figures (41x51cm-16x20in) s. masonite. 2-May-4 William Jenack, New York #191
£2108	$3500	€3078	In the Moon of the Love Birds (61x91cm-24x36in) s.d.78 masonite prov. 4-Oct-3 Neal Auction Company, New Orleans #606/R est:3000-5000

CHIRIAEFF, Eugène (1887-1945) Russian

£1329	$2285	€1900	Interieur d'atelier (92x65cm-36x26in) s. 5-Dec-3 Maigret, Paris #118 est:800-1000
£2400	$4296	€3504	Flowers in a vase (65x50cm-26x20in) s. 26-May-4 Sotheby's, Olympia #436/R est:2000-3000
£4500	$8055	€6570	Artist's studio (92x65cm-36x26in) s. 26-May-4 Sotheby's, London #167/R est:5000-7000

CHIRICO, Giacomo di (1845-1884) Italian

£28000	$46480	€40880	Story teller (77x60cm-30x24in) s.i.d.1882 prov. 1-Oct-3 Sotheby's, Olympia #191/R est:8000-12000

CHIRICO, Giorgio de (1888-1978) Italian

£15667	$28200	€23500	Reclining female nude with blue cloth (18x24cm-7x9in) s. s.i.verso cardboard painted1948 lit. 22-Apr-4 Finarte Semenzato, Rome #371/R est:22000-24000
£18182	$30909	€26000	Nereidi (40x30cm-16x12in) i.verso. 29-Nov-3 Farsetti, Prato #540/R est:15000
£18881	$32098	€27000	Troubador (36x25cm-14x10in) s.i. tempera pastel W/C prov. 26-Nov-3 Pandolfini, Florence #31/R est:25000-30000
£19580	$33287	€28000	Silent fruit on table (20x30cm-8x12in) s. s.i.verso. 24-Nov-3 Christie's, Milan #324/R est:30000-40000
£20979	$35664	€30000	Horse and rider (20x30cm-8x12in) s. canvas on cardboard. 24-Nov-3 Christie's, Milan #323/R est:30000-40000
£26174	$46852	€39000	Puritans fighting (27x44cm-11x17in) s. tempera paper on cardboard painted c.1960. 29-May-4 Farsetti, Prato #428/R est:35000-45000
£27972	$47552	€40000	Battle (27x45cm-11x18in) s. canvas on cardboard prov.lit. 24-Nov-3 Christie's, Milan #300/R est:40000-60000
£28322	$48147	€40500	Still life with fruit (20x30cm-8x12in) s. 29-Nov-3 Farsetti, Prato #438/R est:35000-45000
£31034	$49655	€45000	Venice, San Giorgio (20x30cm-8x12in) s. cardboard on canvas painted 1952. 13-Mar-3 Galleria Pace, Milan #157/R est:60000-70000
£31081	$54703	€46000	Unquiet horses (30x40cm-12x16in) s. painted c.1955. 24-May-4 Christie's, Milan #268/R est:40000-60000
£32000	$57600	€48000	Summer metaphysics (25x31cm-10x12in) s. cardboard painted 1970. 22-Apr-4 Finarte Semenzato, Rome #243/R est:35000-38000
£32000	$58880	€46720	Frutta (40x50cm-16x20in) s. s.i.verso painted 1964 prov.exhib.lit. 23-Jun-4 Christie's, London #258/R est:30000-40000
£33333	$60000	€50000	Two horses amongst ruins (25x35cm-10x14in) s. tempera card lit. 22-Apr-4 Finarte Semenzato, Rome #339/R est:55000-58000
£33784	$59459	€50000	Silent life (50x60cm-20x24in) s. s.verso cardboard on canvas prov. 24-May-4 Christie's, Milan #340/R est:50000-70000
£34899	$62470	€52000	Still life (30x40cm-12x16in) s. painted c.1952 lit. 29-May-4 Farsetti, Prato #452/R est:40000-50000
£37838	$66595	€56000	Horse by a castle (35x55cm-14x22in) s. canvas on cardboard prov. 24-May-4 Christie's, Milan #267/R est:35000-45000
£39597	$70879	€59000	Gladiators fighting (39x22cm-15x9in) s. cardboard. 29-May-4 Farsetti, Prato #510/R est:40000-50000
£41379	$69103	€60000	Knights fighting (40x50cm-16x20in) s. i.verso. 13-Nov-3 Finarte Semenzato, Rome #400/R est:60000-65000
£44056	$75776	€63000	Les deux chevaux au bord de mer (49x39cm-19x15in) s. 5-Dec-3 Chochon-Barre & Allardi, Paris #25/R est:20000-25000
£45455	$77273	€65000	Venice, Palazzo Ducale (35x55cm-14x22in) s. prov. 24-Nov-3 Christie's, Milan #282/R est:70000-100000
£45455	$77273	€65000	Gods by the sea (24x35cm-9x14in) s. tempera paper on cardboard painted c.1934 prov.lit. 25-Nov-3 Sotheby's, Milan #183/R est:25000-30000
£50336	$90101	€75000	Still life (40x50cm-16x20in) s. prov.lit. 25-May-4 Sotheby's, Milan #250/R est:50000-70000
£53333	$98133	€80000	Andromeda tied to a cliff (60x50cm-24x20in) s. i.verso painted 1940. 8-Jun-4 Finarte Semenzato, Milan #371/R est:75000-80000
£54348	$89130	€75000	Il cavallo solitario (50x40cm-20x16in) s. i.d.1968 verso. 31-May-3 Farsetti, Prato #637/R est:65000-75000
£54348	$89130	€75000	Cavallo con cavaliere in riva al mare (60x50cm-24x20in) s. 31-May-3 Farsetti, Prato #703/R est:75000-90000
£59441	$101049	€85000	Italian square with Arianna (40x50cm-16x20in) s. 24-Nov-3 Christie's, Milan #283/R est:80000-120000
£60000	$100200	€87000	Battle (40x50cm-16x20in) s. painted 1942. 17-Nov-3 Sant Agostino, Torino #259/R est:75000-90000
£61538	$104615	€88000	Perseus and horse (60x50cm-24x20in) s. 24-Nov-3 Christie's, Milan #336/R est:80000-120000
£62069	$103655	€90000	Venice, San Giorgio (50x60cm-20x24in) s. exhib. 17-Nov-3 Sant Agostino, Torino #250/R est:90000-120000
£63758	$114128	€95000	Head of horse (54x40cm-21x16in) s. s.i.verso painted 1960 prov.lit. 25-May-4 Sotheby's, Milan #261/R est:40000-50000
£64865	$114162	€96000	Via Appia (60x80cm-24x31in) s. s.i.verso painted 1953 prov.exhib.lit. 24-May-4 Christie's, Milan #317/R est:85000-110000
£65734	$111748	€94000	Two horses (50x70cm-20x28in) s. s.i.verso. 24-Nov-3 Christie's, Milan #327/R est:85000-110000
£65772	$117732	€98000	Philosopher's afternoon (40x50cm-16x20in) s.d.1934. 29-May-4 Farsetti, Prato #496/R est:90000-110000
£71034	$118628	€103000	Venice (40x50cm-16x20in) s. s.i.verso prov. 13-Nov-3 Finarte Semenzato, Rome #455/R est:80000-100000
£71329	$121259	€102000	Silent life with figs and grapes (40x50cm-16x20in) s. prov.lit. 24-Nov-3 Christie's, Milan #328/R est:65000-85000
£76923	$130769	€110000	Portrait of Raissa (92x73cm-36x29in) s.d.1926 prov.lit. 24-Nov-3 Christie's, Milan #248/R est:110000-150000
£80537	$144161	€120000	Fruit (50x60cm-20x24in) s. painted 1965. 29-May-4 Farsetti, Prato #508/R est:120000-140000
£86957	$142609	€120000	Still life on white cloth with bananas, apples and citrus (53x64cm-21x25in) s. exhib.lit. 27-May-3 Sotheby's, Milan #228/R est:90000-120000
£87333	$157200	€131000	Italian square (25x35cm-10x14in) s. i.verso painted 1958 lit. 22-Apr-4 Finarte Semenzato, Rome #311/R est:120000-130000
£100000	$167000	€145000	Troubador (40x30cm-16x12in) s. s.verso. 13-Nov-3 Finarte Semenzato, Rome #452/R est:60000-70000
£108696	$178261	€150000	Mysterious bathers (73x92cm-29x36in) s.d.1968 lit. 31-May-3 Farsetti, Prato #735/R est:140000-160000
£115000	$209300	€167900	Cavalli in riva al mare (50x65cm-20x26in) s. painted c.1930 prov.exhib.lit. 3-Feb-4 Christie's, London #231/R est:100000-150000
£127517	$228255	€190000	Chevaux au bord de la mer (27x41cm-11x16in) s. painted c.1928. 29-May-4 Farsetti, Prato #512/R est:190000-220000
£135135	$237838	€200000	Archaeologists (35x27cm-14x11in) s. tempera card painted 1930 prov.lit. 24-May-4 Christie's, Milan #344/R est:90000-130000
£140000	$257600	€204400	Due cavalli nel paesaggio (99x72cm-39x28in) s. painted 1957. 23-Jun-4 Christie's, London #262/R est:80000-120000
£188811	$320979	€270000	Metaphysical interior (55x46cm-22x18in) s. painted 1932-33 exhib.lit. 29-Nov-3 Farsetti, Prato #515/R
£220000	$367400	€321200	Piazza d'Italia (70x111cm-28x44in) s. s.i.verso prov.exhib. 21-Oct-3 Christie's, London #11/R est:140000-180000

£266667 $490667 €400000 Gladiators (55x46cm-22x18in) s. exhib.lit. 8-Jun-4 Finarte Semenzato, Milan #372/R est:400000-450000
£320000 $534400 €467200 Two orses on the beach (90x72cm-35x28in) s. prov.lit. 20-Oct-3 Sotheby's, London #4/R est:350000-450000
£320000 $534400 €467200 Le cheval d'Agamemnon (100x80cm-39x31in) s.i.stretcher prov.exhib.lit. 21-Oct-3 Christie's, London #8/R est:330000-450000
£340580 $558551 €470000 Architettura e filosofia (73x59cm-29x23in) s.d.25 tempera board exhib.lit. 31-May-3 Farsetti, Prato #744/R
£3575419 $6400000 €5220112 Great metaphapsic (105x69cm-41x27in) s.d.1917 prov.exhib.lit. 4-May-4 Christie's, Rockefeller NY #20/R est:7000000-10000000
Prints
£1769 $3166 €2600 Interior (61x45cm-24x18in) s.i. col lithograph exec.1969 lit. 16-Mar-4 Finarte Semenzato, Milan #312/R est:1000
£2000 $3680 €3000 Ancient horses (46x34cm-18x13in) s. col lithograph. 8-Jun-4 Finarte Semenzato, Milan #321/R est:2000-2500
£2041 $3653 €3000 Jason's departure (30x45cm-12x18in) s.i.d.1966 col lithograph lit. 16-Mar-4 Finarte Semenzato, Milan #313/R est:1700
£4667 $8400 €7000 Archaeologists (40x30cm-16x12in) s. lithograph exec.1929. 22-Apr-4 Finarte Semenzato, Rome #29/R est:7000-8000
£7606 $13158 €10800 Metamorphoses (30x41cm-12x16in) s.num.83/100 col lithograph vellum. 11-Dec-3 Piasa, Paris #18/R
£11000 $20240 €16500 Mythology (28x23cm-11x9in) s. lithograph set of 10 exec.1934 lit. 8-Jun-4 Finarte Semenzato, Milan #405/R est:11500-13000
Sculpture
£1333 $2453 €2000 Painter (25cm-10in) num.82/100 polished bronze exec.1971. 10-Jun-4 Galleria Pace, Milan #105/R est:3300
£1477 $2643 €2200 Painter (25cm-10in) s. num.LXXXIII/100 polished bronze. 25-May-4 Sotheby's, Milan #53 est:2000
£1667 $3067 €2500 Muse (30x11x8cm-12x4x3in) s.i. bronze exec.1970. 8-Jun-4 Finarte Semenzato, Milan #393/R est:2500-3500
£1724 $2879 €2500 Castore (27cm-11in) s.i. num.17/50 bronze lit. 13-Nov-3 Finarte Semenzato, Rome #442/R est:2000-2500
£1761 $2923 €2500 Musa con colonna spezzata (30cm-12in) s.i st.f.Bonvicini gilt bronze exec 1970. 14-Jun-3 Meeting Art, Vercelli #544/R est:2500
£1933 $3480 €2900 Story teller (30cm-12in) s.i. num.94/250 pat bronze exec.1970. 22-Apr-4 Finarte Semenzato, Rome #41/R est:2500-3000
£2067 $3720 €3100 Story teller (30cm-12in) s.i. num.111/250 pat bronze exec.1970. 22-Apr-4 Finarte Semenzato, Rome #40/R est:2500-3000
£2083 $3292 €3000 Painter (25x14x14cm-10x6x6in) bronze. 6-Sep-3 Meeting Art, Vercelli #79 est:3000
£2448 $4161 €3500 Muse. Troubador (29cm-11in) s.i. num.72/150 bronze two. 25-Nov-3 Sotheby's, Milan #126/R est:1500-2000
£2483 $4146 €3600 Muse with column (30cm-12in) num.LXXX/C silvered bronze Cast Bonvicini. 13-Nov-3 Galleria Pace, Milan #97/R est:5000
£2754 $4516 €3800 Gladiator (31cm-12in) num.92/100 pat bronze exec.1970. 29-May-3 Galleria Pace, Milan #118/R est:5000
£3378 $5946 €5000 Muse (31cm-12in) s. num.38/50 bronze. 22-May-4 Galleria Pananti, Florence #309/R est:5000-6000
£3741 $6697 €5500 Castor. Muse. s.i. num.19/50 20/50 silver one wooden base Cast Cavallari prov. 16-Mar-4 Finarte Semenzato, Milan #311/R est:2500
£5000 $9000 €7500 Little horse (29x30x18cm-11x12x7in) s. pat bronze Cast Cavallari lit. 22-Apr-4 Finarte Semenzato, Rome #263/R est:6000-7000
£5667 $10200 €8500 Horse (29x30x18cm-11x12x7in) s. pat bronze Cast Cavallari lit. 22-Apr-4 Finarte Semenzato, Rome #262/R est:7000-8000
£13103 $21883 €19000 Archealogists (31x27x22cm-12x11x9in) s. terracotta exec.1940. 17-Nov-3 Sant Agostino, Torino #258/R est:14000-18000
Works on paper
£574 $1028 €850 Study of tree (10x13cm-4x5in) s. chl exec.1935. 4-May-4 Calmels Cohen, Paris #122/R
£845 $1403 €1200 Study figures (12x16cm-5x6in) s. chl dr. 13-Jun-3 Farsetti, Prato #342/R
£1800 $3240 €2700 Study of warrior. Mythological figure (10x8cm-4x3in) s. pencil paper on cardboard. 22-Apr-4 Finarte Semenzato, Rome #128/R est:3000
£1867 $3360 €2800 Study of sailing boat and hills. Study of portrait (10x15cm-4x6in) s. pencil paper on cardboard two. 22-Apr-4 Finarte Semenzato, Rome #127/R est:2800-3000
£2000 $3600 €3000 Trees (29x18cm-11x7in) s. pen ink prov. 22-Apr-4 Finarte Semenzato, Rome #124/R
£2083 $3292 €3000 Juno (8x14cm-3x6in) Chinese ink pencil. 6-Sep-3 Meeting Art, Vercelli #652 est:3000
£2267 $4080 €3400 Head of horse. Study of Rialto Bridge (20x14cm-8x6in) s. chl two. 22-Apr-4 Finarte Semenzato, Rome #122/R est:2800-3200
£2371 $4244 €3462 Apocalisse (26x20cm-10x8in) s.d.14 Giugno 1951 Indian ink. 12-May-4 Dobiaschofsky, Bern #1456/R est:9000 (S.FR 5500)
£2536 $4159 €3500 Mythological figure (34x24cm-13x9in) s. pencil paper on canvas. 27-May-3 Sotheby's, Milan #53 est:3000-4000
£2899 $4754 €4000 Study of horse (10x13cm-4x5in) s. pencil paper on card pair. 27-May-3 Sotheby's, Milan #54/R est:4000-5000
£3000 $5400 €4500 Little horse with red cloth (12x18cm-5x7in) s. W/C cardboard exec.c.1970. 22-Apr-4 Finarte Semenzato, Rome #126/R est:3200-3800
£3497 $5944 €5000 Study for bull (17x15cm-7x6in) s. ink after Rubens prov.lit. 24-Nov-3 Christie's, Milan #127/R est:5000-7000
£6294 $10699 €9000 Cavaliere da Durer (29x22cm-11x9in) s. Indian ink prov. 26-Nov-3 Dorotheum, Vienna #57/R est:10000-14000
£6993 $11888 €10000 Horse (19x20cm-7x8in) s. W/C pencil paper on cardboard prov. 20-Nov-3 Finarte Semenzato, Milan #77/R est:10000-12000
£9790 $16643 €14000 Fight in the wood (38x68cm-15x27in) s. chl card. 24-Nov-3 Christie's, Milan #274/R est:14000-18000
£10000 $18400 €15000 Knight leaving the town (23x31cm-9x12in) s. Chinese ink pencil W/C. 8-Jun-4 Finarte Semenzato, Milan #378/R est:8500-9500
£11486 $20216 €17000 Horses watering and rider (30x40cm-12x16in) s. s.i.verso W/C exec.1956 prov.lit. 24-May-4 Christie's, Milan #265/R est:8000-12000
£24476 $41608 €35000 Aedipus and the sphynx (40x50cm-16x20in) s.i. W/C cardboard. 24-Nov-3 Christie's, Milan #275/R est:15000-20000
£41958 $71329 €60000 Self-portrait with Mercurius' head (35x27cm-14x11in) s.d.1923 pencil card. 29-Nov-3 Farsetti, Prato #419/R est:35000-45000
£127517 $228255 €190000 Archaeologists (77x52cm-30x20in) s. chl tempera. 29-May-4 Farsetti, Prato #430/R est:130000-160000

CHIRKOV, Aleksandr Inokentevich (1865-1913) Russian
£1800 $3060 €2628 Hayricks (37x28cm-15x11in) s. card. 19-Nov-3 Sotheby's, London #50/R est:2000-3000

CHISTOVSKY, Lev (1902-1969) Russian
£5000 $8950 €7300 Roses. Orchids (23x19cm-9x7in) s. pair. 26-May-4 Sotheby's, London #120/R est:5000-7000
Works on paper
£4200 $7140 €6300 Reclining female nude (31x39cm-12x15in) s.d.1933 W/C. 25-Nov-3 Christie's, London #229/R est:2000-3000
£9500 $17005 €13870 Reclining nude (35x49cm-14x19in) s.i. pencil chk pastel. 26-May-4 Sotheby's, Olympia #478/R est:1500-2000
£16000 $28640 €23360 Reclining nude (34x45cm-13x18in) s.i. W/C. 26-May-4 Sotheby's, London #119/R est:3000-4000
£17000 $30430 €24820 Coquette (53x94cm-21x37in) s.d.1936 gouache. 26-May-4 Sotheby's, London #118/R est:6000-8000

CHITARIN, Traiano (1864-1935) Italian
£3521 $6092 €5000 Morning on the river (45x37cm-18x15in) s. prov. 11-Dec-3 Christie's, Rome #185/R est:1500-2000

CHITI, Guido (1918-) Italian
£1329 $2259 €1900 Informal portrait (100x80cm-39x31in) painted 1966. 19-Nov-3 Cambi, Genoa #433 est:250-300
£1399 $2378 €2000 Still life (70x100cm-28x39in) painted 1959. 19-Nov-3 Cambi, Genoa #446/R est:300-400

CHITTENDEN, Alice B (1859-1944) American
£1872 $3500 €2733 Palace of Fine Arts, San Francisco (41x30cm-16x12in) s. prov. 29-Feb-4 Bonhams & Butterfields, San Francisco #4535 est:3000-4000

CHITTUSSI, Anton (1847-1891) Czechoslovakian
£3913 $7278 €5713 Landscape with pasture (12x30cm-5x12in) s. 6-Mar-4 Dorotheum, Prague #36/R est:150000-230000 (C.KR 190000)
£6590 $12257 €9621 Winter landscape with town in background (34x64cm-13x25in) s.d.1876. 6-Mar-4 Dorotheum, Prague #27/R est:150000-250000 (C.KR 320000)

CHIU TENG-HIOK (1903-1972) American/Chinese
£3861 $6448 €5637 Country church (32x40cm-13x16in) s.d.1929 lit. 26-Oct-3 Christie's, Hong Kong #148/R est:50000-70000 (HK.D 50000)

CHIU YA-TSAI (1949-) Chinese
£4267 $7681 €6230 Portrait of a young lady (90x65cm-35x26in) s. 25-Apr-4 Christie's, Hong Kong #743/R est:22000-32000 (HK.D 60000)

CHIURAZZI (18th C) Italian?
Sculpture
£1882 $3500 €2748 Nude male and partially draped female embracing (89cm-35in) bronze. 3-Mar-4 Alderfer's, Hatfield #245/R est:2000-3000

CHIVERS, Frederick H (?) British
£326 $600 €476 Roses and forget me nots (41x51cm-16x20in) s. 27-Jun-4 Hindman, Chicago #845/R

CHIZMARICK, Steven (1898-?) American
£378 $700 €552 Blue flower (61x51cm-24x20in) canvasboard. 12-Mar-4 Du Mouchelle, Detroit #2243/R

CHLANDA, Marek (20th C) Polish
Works on paper
£306 $508 €447 Grey circle (135x129cm-53x51in) pencil collage exec. 1997. 2-Oct-3 Agra, Warsaw #64/R (P.Z 2000)

CHLEBOWSKI, Stanislaus von (1835-1884) Polish
£11765 $20000 €17177 Bashi Bazouks in a doorway (65x51cm-26x20in) s. canvas on board. 28-Oct-3 Sotheby's, New York #64/R est:30000-40000
£46259 $84190 €68000 L'heure de la priere (66x50cm-26x20in) s. 8-Feb-4 Anaf, Lyon #136/R est:15000-20000

CHLEBUS, Joseph (1893-1945) Polish
£652 $1166 €952 Portrait of young woman wearing flowery dress (61x46cm-24x18in) s.d.1930. 10-May-4 Rasmussen, Vejle #397/R (D.KR 7200)

CHMAROFF, Paval (1874-1950) Russian
£1192 $2170 €1800 Beach with parasols (12x18cm-5x7in) s. cardboard. 15-Jun-4 Rossini, Paris #59/R est:1000-1500
£1325 $2411 €2000 Bathers (12x18cm-5x7in) s. cardboard. 15-Jun-4 Rossini, Paris #58/R est:1400-1800
£1457 $2652 €2200 Pink tents on the beach (12x19cm-5x7in) s. cardboard. 15-Jun-4 Rossini, Paris #57/R est:1400-1800
£3974 $7232 €6000 Jeune fille au livre (45x26cm-18x10in) s. 16-Jun-4 Claude Boisgirard, Paris #34/R est:6000-7000
£4305 $7834 €6500 Seashore with cliffs (52x79cm-20x31in) s. canvas on cardboard. 15-Jun-4 Rossini, Paris #55/R est:3000-5000
£10596 $19285 €16000 Enfants au bain (50x68cm-20x27in) s. 16-Jun-4 Claude Boisgirard, Paris #35/R est:12000-15000
£11000 $18700 €16060 Bathing in a forest glade (53x80cm-21x31in) s. 19-Nov-3 Sotheby's, London #155/R est:12000-18000
£11589 $21093 €17500 Peasant women with flowers (49x36cm-19x14in) s. cardboard. 15-Jun-4 Rossini, Paris #56/R est:4000-7000
£12416 $22970 €18500 Baigneuses III (50x73cm-20x29in) s. 15-Mar-4 Claude Boisgirard, Paris #22/R est:13000-15000
£12416 $22970 €18500 Baigneuses IV (50x73cm-20x29in) s. 15-Mar-4 Claude Boisgirard, Paris #23/R est:13000-15000
£14570 $26517 €22000 Red dress (73x47cm-29x19in) s. 15-Jun-4 Rossini, Paris #54/R est:7000-12000
£15894 $28927 €24000 Nature morte au melon (60x92cm-24x36in) s. 16-Jun-4 Claude Boisgirard, Paris #36/R est:18000-20000
£21000 $35700 €30660 Bathing beauties (175x120cm-69x47in) s. 19-Nov-3 Sotheby's, London #154/R est:5000-7000

£28000 $50120 €40880 Portrait of a girl with her cat (116x88cm-46x35in) s.i. 26-May-4 Sotheby's, London #192/R est:6000-8000

CHMIEL, Len (1942-) American
£588 $1000 €858 California celebrating spring (71x71cm-28x28in) board. 1-Nov-3 Altermann Galleries, Santa Fe #175
£5348 $10000 €7808 Western slope (71x91cm-28x36in) s.d.1980 board. 24-Jul-4 Coeur d'Alene, Hayden #224/R est:8000-12000

CHMIELINSKI, W T (1911-1979) Polish
£478 $775 €693 Street scene from Warsaw with figures in winter (35x25cm-14x10in) s. 4-Aug-3 Rasmussen, Vejle #415/R (D.KR 5000)
£622 $1132 €933 Winter landscape with sleigh ride (35x60cm-14x24in) s. 19-Jun-4 Rasmussen, Havnen #2100/R (D.KR 7000)
£968 $1645 €1413 Town scene in winter with horse and sleigh (40x51cm-16x20in) s. 10-Nov-3 Rasmussen, Vejle #519/R (D.KR 10500)
Works on paper
£423 $756 €600 Winter street scene in Warsaw (25x18cm-10x7in) s. W/C gouache lit. 8-Jan-4 Allgauer, Kempten #2053/R
£546 $1000 €797 Old Warsaw (66x46cm-26x18in) s. W/C. 10-Apr-4 Cobbs, Peterborough #124b/R

CHMIELINSKI, Wardek Vladislaw (1912-) ?
£1400 $2520 €2100 Street scene in winter Cracow (35x50cm-14x20in) s. lit. 22-Apr-4 Allgauer, Kempten #3505/R est:2100

CHMIELINSKI, Wladyslaw (1911-1979) Polish
£927 $1706 €1353 Peasants on a hay cart. At the water trough (18x25cm-7x10in) s. board pair. 14-Jun-4 Waddingtons, Toronto #349/R est:2500-3500 (C.D 2300)
£1441 $2622 €2104 Place Zamkowy (56x98cm-22x39in) painted 1935. 20-Jun-4 Agra, Warsaw #5/R (P.Z 10000)
£1778 $3200 €2596 Hunting party, sledding dogs (51x76cm-20x30in) s. 25-Apr-4 Hindman, Chicago #1552/R est:3000-5000
£3012 $5000 €4398 Race home (50x70cm-20x28in) s. 30-Sep-3 Christie's, Rockefeller NY #459/R est:5000-7000
£3867 $7000 €5646 Warsaw Square in winter (35x50cm-14x20in) s. 30-Mar-4 Christie's, Rockefeller NY #99/R est:5000-7000
£4217 $7000 €6157 Summer day in Warsaw (35x50cm-14x20in) s. 30-Sep-3 Christie's, Rockefeller NY #458/R est:5000-7000
£7059 $12000 €10306 Square in Warsaw in winter. Carriage ride in the old town, Warsaw (36x51cm-14x20in) s. pair. 29-Oct-3 Christie's, Rockefeller NY #46/R est:10000-15000

CHOCARNE-MOREAU, Paul Charles (1855-1931) French
£2500 $4525 €3800 Enfants de choeur (46x38cm-18x15in) s. 19-Apr-4 Horta, Bruxelles #138/R est:2500-3500
£3467 $6379 €5200 Le petit patissier et le petit ramoneur (36x46cm-14x18in) s. panel. 13-Jun-4 Lombrail & Teucquam, Paris #108/R
£5862 $9790 €8500 Parisian street with baker's boy and chimney street (41x34cm-16x13in) s. 15-Nov-3 Lempertz, Koln #1594/R est:8000
£6000 $10980 €9000 Enfant de choeur et marmiton (51x46cm-20x18in) s. 6-Jun-4 Anaf, Lyon #44/R est:8000-10000
£9507 $15782 €13500 Jeux d'enfants (45x58cm-18x23in) s. 15-Jun-3 Peron, Melun #105

CHOCHON, Andre (1910-) French
£260 $476 €380 Brittany coastal scene with tiled roofs (13x18cm-5x7in) board. 28-Jul-4 Mallams, Oxford #331
£288 $472 €400 Nelly epluchant des pommes (65x54cm-26x21in) s. 3-Jun-3 Livinec, Gaudcheau & Jezequel, Rennes #97
£320 $573 €467 Carantes 1940 (30x38cm-12x15in) 7-May-4 Mallams, Oxford #291
£360 $590 €500 Plougrescant, pors Hir (65x54cm-26x21in) s. 3-Jun-3 Livinec, Gaudcheau & Jezequel, Rennes #96
£480 $859 €701 View of a bridge with village in the distance (36x43cm-14x17in) s. panel. 7-May-4 Mallams, Oxford #290

CHODOWIECKI, Daniel (1726-1801) German
Works on paper
£308 $523 €440 A la charite (17x12cm-7x5in) s. pencil htd white board. 27-Nov-3 Bassenge, Berlin #5410
£333 $600 €500 Woman with anchor (13x10cm-5x4in) i. w/C. 24-Apr-4 Reiss & Sohn, Konigstein #5388/R
£909 $1545 €1300 Riders outside city (11x18cm-4x7in) s. brush. 27-Nov-3 Bassenge, Berlin #5408
£2657 $4517 €3800 Portrait of woman (53x43cm-21x17in) i. verso ochre. 27-Nov-3 Bassenge, Berlin #5409/R est:3500

CHODOWIECKI, Daniel and Wilhelm (18th C) German
Works on paper
£12587 $21399 €18000 King Frederick II on horseback (19x16cm-7x6in) s.d.786 gouache over etching prov. 28-Nov-3 Villa Grisebach, Berlin #1/R est:12000-15000

CHOFFARD, Pierre Phillipe (1730-1809) French
Works on paper
£500 $900 €730 Cartouche with putti and musical instruments (4x18cm-2x7in) pen black ink brown wash prov. 20-Apr-4 Sotheby's, Olympia #122/R

CHOISEUL-GOUFFIER, Comte de (1752-1817) French
Works on paper
£411 $699 €600 Portrait d'homme a mi-corps (16x13cm-6x5in) s.d.1770 i.verso crayon. 6-Nov-3 Tajan, Paris #146

CHOISNARD, J Felix Clement (1846-?) French
£474 $763 €692 Pastoral landscape (46x60cm-18x24in) s. 25-Aug-3 Lilla Bukowskis, Stockholm #149 (S.KR 6200)

CHOKI, Eishosai (fl.c.1785-1805) Japanese
Prints
£5245 $8916 €7500 La courtisane Kisegawa de la maison Matsubaya (37x24cm-15x9in) s. col print exec.c.1797 prov.lit. 25-Nov-3 Sotheby's, Paris #2/R est:6000-7000

CHONE, Georges (1819-?) French
£933 $1689 €1400 Flowers (40x31cm-16x12in) s. 1-Apr-4 Van Ham, Cologne #1318/R
£1800 $3276 €2628 Summer flowers on a ledge (40x19cm-16x7in) s. 16-Jun-4 Christie's, Kensington #55/R est:1800-2200

CHOO KENG KWANG (1931-) Singaporean
£1634 $2615 €2386 Ladies by the stream (61x91cm-24x36in) s.d.65 board. 18-May-3 Sotheby's, Singapore #60/R est:3500-4500 (S.D 4560)
£4301 $6882 €6279 Singapore river (71x96cm-28x38in) s. s.i.d.1974 verso. 18-May-3 Sotheby's, Singapore #64/R est:10000-15000 (S.D 12000)
£6884 $10670 €10051 Smith Street (71x96cm-28x38in) s. s.i.d.Dec 1976 verso. 6-Oct-2 Sotheby's, Singapore #63/R est:12000-15000 (S.D 19000)

CHOPIN, Florent (20th C) French
Works on paper
£300 $543 €450 Le lit des metamorphoses (27x22cm-11x9in) s. mixed media. 3-Apr-4 Neret-Minet, Paris #55
£315 $535 €450 Une fois fixe au mur (27x22cm-11x9in) s. mixed media canvas. 29-Nov-3 Neret-Minet, Paris #39
£400 $724 €600 Hypnose de l'etoile et de la pierre (40x80cm-16x31in) s. mixed media canvas. 3-Apr-4 Neret-Minet, Paris #125
£441 $749 €630 Expression d'un coup de des (40x80cm-16x31in) s. mixed media canvas. 29-Nov-3 Neret-Minet, Paris #115

CHOPRIX, Rene (1888-1972) Belgian
£1449 $2377 €2000 La grande Marquerite (50x61cm-20x24in) s. s.i.verso cardboard. 27-May-3 Sotheby's, Amsterdam #344/R est:3000-4000
£1449 $2377 €2000 Jeune fille au broc (70x60cm-28x24in) s. painted c.1927 lit. 27-May-3 Sotheby's, Amsterdam #345/R est:3000-4000
£1449 $2377 €2000 Premieres lecons (70x60cm-28x24in) s.d.28 lit. 27-May-3 Sotheby's, Amsterdam #346/R est:2000-3000

CHOQUET, René-Maxime (19th C) French
£500 $865 €730 Bullfight. panel. 13-Dec-3 Nigel Ward, Hereford #1417/R

CHOREMBALSKI, Wawrzyniec (1888-1965) Polish
£303 $523 €442 Ruins of a bombed church in Warsaw, 1944 (36x80cm-14x31in) s.i.d.1944 cardboard. 14-Dec-3 Agra, Warsaw #52/R (P.Z 2000)

CHORLEY, Adrian (1906-) British
£750 $1388 €1095 Gant's Mill, Bruton, Somerset (30x40cm-12x16in) s. board. 11-Feb-4 Sotheby's, Olympia #159/R

CHOTIAU, Yves (20th C) ?
£1538 $2646 €2200 Nu dans la foret (150x150cm-59x59in) s. 5-Dec-3 Gros & Delettrez, Paris #96 est:900-1200

CHOTKA, A (20th C) ?
Sculpture
£1060 $1939 €1600 Figure of an Arab reading the Koran (16cm-6in) s. cold painted bronze. 6-Apr-4 Sotheby's, Amsterdam #391/R est:1500-2000

CHOU TEN CHOUN (20th C) Chinese
Works on paper
£570 $1010 €850 Composition (43x50cm-17x20in) s.i.d.1982 wash Indian ink. 29-Apr-4 Claude Aguttes, Neuilly #270

CHOUBRAC, Alfred (1853-1902) French
£4013 $7384 €6100 Seduction (81x66cm-32x26in) s.d.1909. 25-Jun-4 Millon & Associes, Paris #136/R est:6000-8000

CHOUKLIN, Vladimir (1963-) Russian
£897 $1497 €1300 Roses (88x116cm-35x46in) s. 17-Nov-3 Durán, Madrid #663/R

CHOULGA, Valery (?) Russian
£422 $768 €620 Nature morte aux raisins. s. 8-Feb-4 Lesieur & Le Bars, Le Havre #99

CHOULTSE, Ivan Fedorovich (1874-1939) Russian
£2395 $4000 €3497 Formal garden (48x69cm-19x27in) s. 19-Jun-3 Shelley, Hendersonville #1354
£8392 $14266 €12000 Coucher de soleil au bord de la mer (38x46cm-15x18in) s. 27-Nov-3 Millon & Associes, Paris #118/R est:5000-6000
£11667 $21000 €17034 Garden in the afternoon (55x65cm-22x26in) s. 21-Jan-4 Sotheby's, New York #245/R est:10000-15000
£11732 $21000 €17129 Snowy Alpine scene (61x91cm-24x36in) s. 20-Mar-4 Sloans & Kenyon, Bethesda #1189/R est:5000-7000
£12000 $20400 €17520 Sunrise (32x40cm-13x16in) s.d.22 board. 19-Nov-3 Sotheby's, London #90/R est:5000-7000

£14286 $23000 €20858 Soleil sur la neige, Suisse (50x61cm-20x24in) s. i.on stretcher. 14-Jan-4 Christie's, Rockefeller NY #27/R est:6000-8000
£15000 $25500 €21900 Approaching storm (60x73cm-24x29in) s. 19-Nov-3 Sotheby's, London #92/R est:15000-20000
£17663 $32500 €25788 Lever de lune, Montreax, Lac de Geneve (54x64cm-21x25in) s. 8-Jun-4 Auctions by the Bay, Alameda #1018/R
£18000 $32220 €26280 Evening reflection (54x73cm-21x29in) s. prov. 26-May-4 Sotheby's, London #95/R est:6000-8000
£26000 $44200 €39000 Moonlit seashore (66x102cm-26x40in) s. 25-Nov-3 Christie's, London #165/R est:20000-25000

CHOUMANSKY DE COURVILLE, Olga (fl.1929-1938) French
Works on paper
£1806 $3015 €2600 Femme assise (74x52cm-29x20in) s.d.1929 collage. 21-Oct-3 Campo, Vlaamse Kaai #374 est:500-700

CHOUPPE, Jean Henri (1817-1894) French
Works on paper
£400 $740 €584 Figures by a pool in a pastoral landscape (42x54cm-17x21in) s. W/C. 14-Jan-4 Lawrence, Crewkerne #1322

CHOWDHURY, Jogen (1939-) Indian
Works on paper
£2717 $5000 €3967 Untitled (39x38cm-15x15in) s.d.20/3/95 crayon pastel paper on card pair. 25-Mar-4 Christie's, Rockefeller NY #236/R est:3000-5000
£4076 $7500 €5951 Vinayak (56x71cm-22x28in) s.d.1966 pen ink pastel. 24-Mar-4 Sotheby's, New York #202/R est:6000-8000

CHRETIEN, René Louis (1867-1942) French
£493 $799 €700 Vase of flowers (33x41cm-13x16in) s. 11-Aug-3 Boscher, Cherbourg #759
£586 $973 €850 Nature morte aux figues (46x37cm-18x15in) s. 1-Oct-3 Millon & Associes, Paris #56
£704 $1141 €1000 Nature more aux asperges, radis et soupiere (18x24cm-7x9in) s. panel. 11-Aug-3 Boscher, Cherbourg #758/R
£833 $1500 €1216 Still life with oysters, kettle and bottles (46x56cm-18x22in) s. 21-Jan-4 Sotheby's, New York #262/R est:2000-3000
£839 $1427 €1200 Bouteilles, formage et marrons (46x38cm-18x15in) s. 24-Nov-3 Boscher, Cherbourg #790/R
£1119 $1902 €1600 La soupiere et les fruits (12x15cm-5x6in) s.i. cardboard. 24-Nov-3 Boscher, Cherbourg #789/R est:1000-1200
£1648 $2918 €2472 Still life (46x55cm-18x22in) s. 27-Apr-4 Bolsa de Arte, Rio de Janeiro #34/R (B.R 9000)
£1736 $2743 €2500 Nature morte a la chocolatiere. s. 25-Apr-3 Etude de Provence, Marseille #288 est:2000-2500
£1867 $3397 €2800 Nature morte aux cerises et aux deux bouteilles (20x33cm-8x13in) s. panel. 5-Jul-4 Le Mouel, Paris #19 est:1200-1500
£5263 $9684 €8000 Saint-Germain-des-Pres (81x65cm-32x26in) s. 24-Jun-4 Credit Municipal, Paris #41/R est:1500-2000

CHRISP, Richard (20th C) ?
Works on paper
£335 $575 €489 Still life with pumpkin and peppers (47x39cm-19x15in) s. W/C. 7-Dec-3 International Art Centre, Auckland #268/R (NZ.D 900)
£357 $646 €521 Christmas ciliums (76x56cm-30x22in) s. W/C. 4-Apr-4 International Art Centre, Auckland #234/R (NZ.D 1000)

CHRIST, Fritz (1866-1906) German
Sculpture
£2036 $3258 €2973 Dancer (40cm-16in) s. bronze. 19-Sep-3 Koller, Zurich #1289/R est:4000-6000 (S.FR 4500)

CHRIST, Josef (1732-1788) German
Works on paper
£338 $595 €500 From the life of the martyr St Chrysanthus and Daria (14x10cm-6x4in) brush wash bodycol on chk sketch prov. 22-May-4 Lempertz, Koln #1232/R

CHRIST, Martin Alfred (1900-1979) Swiss
£264 $449 €385 Portrait of woman (91x73cm-36x29in) s. 5-Nov-3 Dobiaschofsky, Bern #437 (S.FR 600)
£517 $926 €755 Spanish fields (63x86cm-25x34in) s. 14-May-4 Dobiaschofsky, Bern #184/R (S.FR 1200)
£749 $1273 €1094 Summer landscape (48x71cm-19x28in) s. 5-Nov-3 Dobiaschofsky, Bern #436/R (S.FR 1700)

CHRISTENSEN, Antonore (1849-1926) Danish
£323 $581 €472 Branch of fruit blossom (28x33cm-11x13in) mono. 24-Apr-4 Rasmussen, Havnen #2233 (D.KR 3600)
£332 $564 €485 Pink bindweed and butterfly (27x20cm-11x8in) i.verso. 10-Nov-3 Rasmussen, Vejle #399/R (D.KR 3600)
£388 $717 €566 White poppies (43x35cm-17x14in) init.d.1900. 15-Mar-4 Rasmussen, Vejle #285 (D.KR 4300)
£395 $672 €577 Yellow iris (59x34cm-23x13in) mono.d.1904. 29-Nov-3 Rasmussen, Havnen #2189 (D.KR 4200)
£469 $806 €685 Pink roses and fruit blossom on ledge (26x29cm-10x11in) mono.d.1904 prov. 3-Dec-3 Museumsbygningen, Copenhagen #203 (D.KR 5000)
£567 $981 €828 Two pale yellow roses (36x22cm-14x9in) mono.d.1890. 9-Dec-3 Rasmussen, Copenhagen #1370/R (D.KR 6000)
£627 $1147 €915 Pink wild roses (23x29cm-9x11in) mono.d.1919. 7-Jun-4 Museumsbygningen, Copenhagen #165/R (D.KR 7000)
£646 $1162 €943 Wood anemones (36x47cm-14x19in) s.indis.d. 26-Jan-4 Lilla Bukowskis, Stockholm #372 (S.KR 8600)
£711 $1137 €1038 Roses (37x27cm-15x11in) mono.d.1893. 22-Sep-3 Rasmussen, Vejle #108/R (D.KR 7500)
£711 $1294 €1067 Still life of berries and leaves (24x29cm-9x11in) mono.d.1881. 19-Jun-4 Rasmussen, Havnen #2058/R (D.KR 8000)
£851 $1532 €1242 Still life of roses. Still life of anemones (29x24cm-11x9in) mono. two. 24-Apr-4 Rasmussen, Havnen #2216/R (D.KR 9500)
£6000 $10740 €8760 Holly hocks (79x61cm-31x24in) mono.d.1894. 26-May-4 Sotheby's, Olympia #287/R est:3000-5000

CHRISTENSEN, C F (19th C) Danish
£302 $550 €453 Portrait of young girl wearing red dress (33x25cm-13x10in) s.d.16 mai 1847. 19-Jun-4 Rasmussen, Havnen #2312 (D.KR 3400)

CHRISTENSEN, Christian Ferdinand (1805-1883) Danish
Works on paper
£355 $561 €515 Street scene in Nuremberg (23x29cm-9x11in) s.i.d.1840 W/C. 2-Sep-3 Rasmussen, Copenhagen #1659/R (D.KR 3800)

CHRISTENSEN, Dan (1942-) American
£428 $727 €625 Zulu (168x130cm-66x51in) s.d.verso acrylic prov. 19-Nov-3 Maynards, Vancouver #76 (C.D 950)
£1229 $2200 €1794 Whale House (112x203cm-44x80in) s.i.d.1977 acrylic gesso crayon prov. 16-May-4 Wright, Chicago #301/R est:1500-2000

CHRISTENSEN, Finn (1920-) Norwegian
£412 $759 €602 Winter in the wood (75x60cm-30x24in) s/. 29-Mar-4 Blomqvist, Lysaker #1031/R (N.KR 5200)
£1283 $2181 €1873 Composition (135x100cm-53x39in) s. exhib. 19-Nov-3 Grev Wedels Plass, Oslo #94/R est:15000 (N.KR 15000)

CHRISTENSEN, Godfred (1845-1928) Danish
£267 $485 €401 Coastal landscape from Hornbaek (43x64cm-17x25in) init.d.11. 19-Jun-4 Rasmussen, Havnen #2137/R (D.KR 3000)
£280 $443 €406 Grib wood September 1904 (32x42cm-13x17in) init. 2-Sep-3 Rasmussen, Copenhagen #1907/R (D.KR 3000)
£287 $516 €419 Coastal heather at Hornbaek (34x55cm-13x22in) init.d.14 exhib. 24-Apr-4 Rasmussen, Havnen #2267 (D.KR 3200)
£298 $468 €435 Mountain landscape (41x62cm-16x24in) init.d.1899. 30-Aug-3 Rasmussen, Havnen #2018 (D.KR 3200)
£313 $533 €457 Figures on bathing bridge by lake (23x35cm-9x14in) mono.d.13. 10-Nov-3 Rasmussen, Vejle #328 (D.KR 3400)
£356 $647 €534 Spring in the forest (49x66cm-19x26in) init.d.1916. 19-Jun-4 Rasmussen, Havnen #2105/R (D.KR 4000)
£356 $647 €534 Path in pine forest (67x51cm-26x20in) init.d.22. 19-Jun-4 Rasmussen, Havnen #2143/R (D.KR 4000)
£361 $667 €527 Summer landscape with woodland lake (33x48cm-13x19in) init.d.1883. 15-Mar-4 Rasmussen, Vejle #459/R (D.KR 4000)
£378 $654 €552 Landscape from the coast of North Sjaelland (54x45cm-21x18in) init. 9-Dec-3 Rasmussen, Copenhagen #1704/R (D.KR 4000)
£402 $651 €583 Landscape with cornflowers (41x61cm-16x24in) init.i.d.1900. 4-Aug-3 Rasmussen, Vejle #296/R (D.KR 4200)
£422 $725 €616 Impressionism - study from Nyvaenge Woods (31x36cm-12x14in) prov. 3-Dec-3 Museumsbygningen, Copenhagen #204/R (D.KR 4500)
£433 $801 €632 Mountain landscape with Konigsee, Bavaria (33x49cm-13x19in) init.d.00. 15-Mar-4 Rasmussen, Vejle #458/R (D.KR 4800)
£467 $738 €677 From Vierwaldstadter Lake (33x45cm-13x18in) init.d.1877 exhib.prov. 2-Sep-3 Rasmussen, Copenhagen #1672/R (D.KR 5000)
£520 $931 €759 Landscape from Albano (31x44cm-12x17in) init.i.d.74. 12-Jan-4 Rasmussen, Vejle #75/R (D.KR 5500)
£533 $971 €800 Wooded landscape with lake (42x61cm-17x24in) init.d.1866. 19-Jun-4 Rasmussen, Havnen #2298/R (D.KR 6000)
£588 $1053 €858 Landscape with rowing boat and sailing vessel on lake (47x71cm-19x28in) mono. 10-May-4 Rasmussen, Vejle #46/R (D.KR 6500)
£691 $1175 €1009 Hilly landscape (53x76cm-21x30in) init.d.06. 10-Nov-3 Rasmussen, Vejle #78/R (D.KR 7500)
£780 $1295 €1139 Harvesting at sunset (25x35cm-10x14in) init.d.94 panel. 1-Oct-3 Sotheby's, Olympia #206/R
£898 $1671 €1311 Wooded landscape with bridge (38x40cm-15x16in) bears sig.i.verso painted c.1870. 2-Mar-4 Rasmussen, Copenhagen #1389/R (D.KR 10000)
£935 $1477 €1356 Apple trees in blossom, spring (44x63cm-17x25in) init.d.26. 3-Sep-3 Museumsbygningen, Copenhagen #226/R (D.KR 10000)
£1282 $2333 €1872 Landscape from Hornbaek (30x38cm-12x15in) init.d.12. 7-Feb-4 Rasmussen, Havnen #2198/R (D.KR 14000)
£2905 $4997 €4241 Woodland road at Herlufsholm with herder and cow (98x137cm-39x54in) mono. exhib.prov. 3-Dec-3 Museumsbygningen, Copenhagen #205/R est:10000-15000 (D.KR 31000)

CHRISTENSEN, Helge (1913-1986) Danish
£452 $810 €660 Composition with birds (80x90cm-31x35in) s. 10-May-4 Rasmussen, Vejle #777/R (D.KR 5000)

CHRISTENSEN, John (1896-1940) Danish
£1552 $2639 €2266 Street scene - Kapelvej by entrance to Assisten's Graveyard (51x39cm-20x15in) s.d.1935 cardboard. 26-Nov-3 Kunsthallen, Copenhagen #295/R est:10000 (D.KR 16500)

CHRISTENSEN, Kay (1899-1981) Danish
£267 $485 €401 Still life of fruit (50x60cm-20x24in) s. 19-Jun-4 Rasmussen, Havnen #4050 (D.KR 3000)
£376 $640 €549 Small boy looking away from his toy (54x65cm-21x26in) 29-Nov-3 Rasmussen, Havnen #4056/R (D.KR 4000)
£395 $672 €577 Franziska (50x66cm-20x26in) s. 29-Nov-3 Rasmussen, Havnen #4075/R (D.KR 4200)
£448 $806 €654 Evening landscape with children standing by house (57x69cm-22x27in) 24-Apr-4 Rasmussen, Havnen #4195/R (D.KR 5000)
£498 $891 €727 The girl and the green plants (50x65cm-20x26in) i.verso. 10-May-4 Rasmussen, Vejle #608 (D.KR 5500)
£633 $1134 €924 Portrait of young girl (65x54cm-26x21in) s.d.1958 i.d.28 oktober 1958 verso. 10-May-4 Rasmussen, Vejle #522/R (D.KR 7000)
£853 $1365 €1245 Krass-Clement playing at table (50x62cm-20x24in) s. s.i.d.1959-61 verso. 22-Sep-3 Rasmussen, Vejle #620/R (D.KR 9000)

£896 $1613 €1308 Girl wearing red (50x66cm-20x26in) s.d.1958 i.d.verso. 24-Apr-4 Rasmussen, Havnen #4122/R (D.KR 10000)
£1087 $1946 €1587 Small girl (73x93cm-29x37in) s. i.verso. 12-Jan-4 Rasmussen, Vejle #533/R (D.KR 11500)
£1181 $2115 €1724 Boy playing with red flowers (92x73cm-36x29in) s.d.1958 exhib. 12-Jan-4 Rasmussen, Vejle #534/R est:12000-15000 (D.KR 12500)
£1222 $2187 €1784 Mother Louise and Henrik (73x92cm-29x36in) s.d.1950-51. 10-May-4 Rasmussen, Vejle #521/R est:10000-15000 (D.KR 13500)
£1222 $2187 €1784 Nude woman by window (82x101cm-32x40in) s. s.d.1944-45 verso. 10-May-4 Rasmussen, Vejle #523/R est:10000-15000 (D.KR 13500)
£1818 $2945 €2636 The perpetual children's stocking (117x81cm-46x32in) s.d.1952 i.verso. 4-Aug-3 Rasmussen, Vejle #575/R est:20000 (D.KR 19000)
£2708 $4982 €3954 Herb pot in love (74x92cm-29x36in) i. 29-Mar-4 Rasmussen, Copenhagen #43/R est:10000 (D.KR 30000)
£3801 $6804 €5549 The sunny spot - young woman in green landscape (75x100cm-30x39in) s.d.1933 verso. 10-May-4 Rasmussen, Vejle #524/R est:10000-15000 (D.KR 42000)

CHRISTENSEN, Neil C (1947-) American
£279 $500 €407 Bottles in a row (41x51cm-16x20in) s. masonite. 8-Jan-4 James Julia, Fairfield #1110/R

CHRISTENSEN, Thorvald (20th C) Danish
£369 $627 €539 Summer landscape with female nude by lake (112x74cm-44x29in) s. 10-Nov-3 Rasmussen, Vejle #159/R (D.KR 4000)

CHRISTIAN, Anton (1940-) Austrian
£541 $930 €790 Untitled (99x72cm-39x28in) s.d.1987. 8-Dec-3 Philippe Schuler, Zurich #5830 (S.FR 1200)

CHRISTIAN, Grant Wright (1911-1989) American
£4012 $6500 €5817 Monhegan Island, Maine (76x94cm-30x37in) s. exhib. 8-Aug-3 Barridorf, Portland #178/R est:8000-12000

CHRISTIANSEN, N H (19th C) Danish
£769 $1377 €1123 Winter landscape with lake (69x95cm-27x37in) s.d.74. 10-May-4 Rasmussen, Vejle #195/R (D.KR 8500)

CHRISTIANSEN, Niels (1873-1960) Danish
£282 $480 €412 Danish village street with water in background (41x45cm-16x18in) s.d.1945. 29-Nov-3 Rasmussen, Havnen #2336 (D.KR 3000)

CHRISTIANSEN, Nils H (1850-1922) Danish
£300 $552 €438 Woodland lake scene, with stag in the foreground (50x73cm-20x29in) s. 8-Jun-4 Bonhams, Knightsbridge #209/R
£343 $631 €501 Horses in a pasture (71x100cm-28x39in) init. 14-Jun-4 Waddingtons, Toronto #209/R (C.D 850)
£350 $637 €511 Reindeer in a snowy landscape (22x30cm-9x12in) s. oil on card. 4-Jul-4 Lots Road Auctions, London #337
£400 $668 €584 Fox stalking hare (31x31cm-12x12in) s. board. 18-Oct-3 Windibank, Dorking #731
£520 $962 €759 River landscape with town in the distance (53x43cm-21x17in) s. 13-Jan-4 Bonhams, Knightsbridge #128/R
£600 $1110 €876 Vessels on a fjord by moonlight (51x76cm-20x30in) s. 14-Jul-4 Christie's, Kensington #963/R
£650 $1086 €949 Figures in a winter landscape (52x40cm-20x16in) s. pair. 11-Nov-3 Bonhams, Knightsbridge #161/R
£700 $1253 €1022 Stags in a winter landscape (50x60cm-20x24in) s. pair. 11-May-4 Bonhams, Knightsbridge #149/R
£750 $1193 €1088 Home by sunset. Snow at sunset (15x23cm-6x9in) s. board pair. 9-Sep-3 Bonhams, Knightsbridge #122/R
£900 $1584 €1314 Fjord at sunset. Winter fjord scene (61x91cm-24x36in) s. pair. 19-May-4 Christie's, Kensington #674/R
£1200 $2220 €1752 Stag in a winter landscape (50x76cm-20x30in) s. 14-Jul-4 Christie's, Kensington #945/R est:1000-1500
£1300 $2405 €1898 Rowing on a fjord at dusk. Rowing on a fjord by moonlight (51x76cm-20x30in) s. pair. 15-Jan-4 Christie's, Kensington #816/R est:1200-1800
Works on paper
£2200 $3542 €3190 Winter landscape with figures in a lane between an avenue of trees (56x86cm-22x34in) s. 15-Aug-3 Keys, Aylsham #698/R est:2000-2500

CHRISTIANSEN, Poul S (1855-1933) Danish
£633 $1134 €924 Coastal landscape with boys bathing (97x127cm-38x50in) mono.d.1913 exhib. 10-May-4 Rasmussen, Vejle #540/R (D.KR 7000)
£719 $1337 €1050 Southern summer landscape study (48x58cm-19x23in) mono.d.1931 exhib.prov. 2-Mar-4 Rasmussen, Copenhagen #1372/R (D.KR 8000)

CHRISTIANSEN, Professor Hans (1866-1945) German
£1007 $1883 €1500 Hessen landscape (40x60cm-16x24in) mono. 28-Feb-4 Quittenbaum, Hamburg #43/R est:1300
£1042 $1646 €1500 Claire Christiansen (40x33cm-16x13in) mono.d.17 masonite prov. 19-Sep-3 Schloss Ahlden, Ahlden #1639/R est:1400

CHRISTIANSEN, Rasmus (1863-1940) Danish
£276 $470 €403 Cattle and horses in meadow (47x63cm-19x25in) init.d.1926. 10-Nov-3 Rasmussen, Vejle #119/R (D.KR 3000)
£452 $810 €660 Watering the cattle, farmer with water wagon (46x55cm-18x22in) init. 10-May-4 Rasmussen, Vejle #331/R (D.KR 5000)
£718 $1163 €1041 The guards at Amalienborg Palace Square (43x62cm-17x24in) init. 4-Aug-3 Rasmussen, Vejle #261/R (D.KR 7500)
£1701 $2943 €2483 The Guards parading at Amalienborg Palace, winter (43x62cm-17x24in) init. 9-Dec-3 Rasmussen, Copenhagen #1667/R est:12000 (D.KR 18000)

CHRISTIANSEN, Soren (1858-1937) Danish
£295 $501 €431 Village scene with girls playing on road (33x36cm-13x14in) init. 10-Nov-3 Rasmussen, Vejle #338/R (D.KR 3200)
£347 $580 €500 Mother and child (37x28cm-15x11in) mono. 24-Oct-3 Ketterer, Hamburg #152/R
£376 $640 €549 The family gathered around dining table, men drinking beer (73x83cm-29x33in) s.indit.d.77. 29-Nov-3 Rasmussen, Havnen #2086 (D.KR 4000)
£593 $961 €860 Interior scene with young woman (33x22cm-13x9in) s. 4-Aug-3 Rasmussen, Vejle #86/R (D.KR 6200)

CHRISTIANSEN, Ursula Reuter (1943-) Danish
£640 $1087 €934 Compositions (70x76cm-28x30in) s.d.1969 verso masonite pair. 26-Nov-3 Kunsthallen, Copenhagen #11 (D.KR 6800)

CHRISTIANUS, Iohannes (17th C) Italian?
Works on paper
£724 $1332 €1100 Gods meeting (9x15cm-4x6in) s.d.1618 pen ink W/C over pencil. 22-Jun-4 Sotheby's, Milan #11/R

CHRISTIDIS, Achilleas (1959-) Greek
£1500 $2685 €2190 The path (130x120cm-51x47in) s.d.99. 11-May-4 Bonhams, New Bond Street #128/R est:1500-2000

CHRISTIE, James Elder (1847-1914) British
£500 $835 €730 Seamill (25x14cm-10x6in) s. s.i.verso board. 16-Oct-3 Lyon & Turnbull, Edinburgh #34
£500 $930 €730 Boy leaning on a tree (30x16cm-12x6in) init.d.81. 4-Mar-4 Christie's, Kensington #83/R
£600 $1092 €876 Taking fish (46x33cm-18x13in) s. s.i.verso. 15-Jun-4 Rosebery Fine Art, London #542
£700 $1302 €1022 Straw hat (30x25cm-12x10in) s. panel. 4-Mar-4 Christie's, Kensington #82/R
£750 $1253 €1095 Winding nairn (40x30cm-16x12in) s. s.i.verso. 16-Oct-3 Lyon & Turnbull, Edinburgh #143
£1500 $2595 €2190 Blue bow (34x30cm-13x12in) s. 11-Dec-3 Lyon & Turnbull, Edinburgh #72/R est:1500-2000

CHRISTIE, James Elder (attrib) (1847-1914) British
£860 $1359 €1247 Portrait of an elegant lady in a fur collar (60x50cm-24x20in) 24-Jul-3 Lawrence, Crewkerne #961

CHRISTIE, Lorraine (1967-) British
£620 $1153 €905 Still life, pears (40x50cm-16x20in) s. board. 3-Mar-4 John Ross, Belfast #190
£650 $1209 €949 Summer garden (50x50cm-20x20in) s. 3-Mar-4 John Ross, Belfast #125
£700 $1302 €1022 Still life, roses (61x50cm-24x20in) s. 3-Mar-4 John Ross, Belfast #208
£720 $1238 €1051 Still life (40x50cm-16x20in) s. 3-Dec-3 John Ross, Belfast #99

CHRISTIE, Robert (fl.1887-1926) British
£313 $550 €457 Brown and white short haired pointer in the reeds (38x48cm-15x19in) s.d.1971. 24-May-4 Winter Associates, Plainville #146/R

CHRISTMANN, Gunther (1936-) German
£511 $883 €746 Untitled (81x81cm-32x32in) i.verso. 10-Dec-3 Shapiro, Sydney #94 (A.D 1200)
£988 $1788 €1442 Untitled 1 (200x243cm-79x96in) 30-Mar-4 Lawson Menzies, Sydney #142 est:3000-5000 (A.D 2400)
£1852 $3352 €2704 Tribal II (228x175cm-90x69in) acrylic. 30-Mar-4 Lawson Menzies, Sydney #131 est:2000-3000 (A.D 4500)
£2273 $4205 €3319 Sentinel (167x137cm-66x54in) d.88 s.i.d.1988 verso prov.exhib. 15-Mar-4 Sotheby's, Melbourne #39/R est:5000-8000 (A.D 5500)
£2881 $5214 €4206 Painters dream (170x119cm-67x47in) s.d.80 i.verso. 30-Mar-4 Lawson Menzies, Sydney #153a/R est:3000-5000 (A.D 7000)
Works on paper
£247 $447 €361 Untitled (51x36cm-20x14in) s.d.1975 W/C ink. 30-Mar-4 Lawson Menzies, Sydney #475/R (A.D 600)
£267 $484 €390 Untitled (37x27cm-15x11in) s.d.74 W/C. 30-Mar-4 Lawson Menzies, Sydney #114 (A.D 650)
£2033 $3638 €2968 Easel painting (167x137cm-66x54in) s.d.1986 i.verso synthetic polymer paint canvas prov. 4-May-4 Sotheby's, Melbourne #191/R est:5000-7000 (A.D 5000)
£2675 $4842 €3906 No.12 (197x88cm-78x35in) s.d.73 verso gouache on canvas. 30-Mar-4 Lawson Menzies, Sydney #230/R est:2500-4500 (A.D 6500)
£2675 $4842 €3906 No.13 (197x88cm-78x35in) s.d.73 verso gouache on canvas. 30-Mar-4 Lawson Menzies, Sydney #231/R est:2500-4500 (A.D 6500)
£2881 $5214 €4206 No.15 (197x88cm-78x35in) s.d.73 verso gouache. 30-Mar-4 Lawson Menzies, Sydney #229/R est:2500-4500 (A.D 7000)

CHRISTMAS, Ernest W (1863-1918) Australian
£797 $1355 €1164 Mountain stream with Mt. Cook in the distance (70x105cm-28x41in) s. 4-Nov-3 Peter Webb, Auckland #230/R est:3000-5000 (NZ.D 2200)

CHRISTO (1935-) American/Bulgarian
£30000 $55200 €43800 Surrounded island - project for Biscayne Bay, Greater Miami (71x87cm-28x34in) s.i.d.1982 acrylic collage oil pastel map. 25-Jun-4 Christie's, London #140/R est:25000-35000
Prints
£1977 $3500 €2886 Wrapped road sign (71x56cm-28x22in) s.i.num.96/100 col lithograph collage. 28-Apr-4 Christie's, Rockefeller NY #261/R est:3500-4500
£2417 $4109 €3529 Wrapped armchair project (64x88cm-25x35in) s.num.83/100 col lithograph collage. 4-Nov-3 Bukowskis, Stockholm #358/R est:15000-20000 (S.KR 32000)
£2600 $4732 €3796 Two lower Manhattan wrapped buildings, project for New York (75x55cm-30x22in) s.num.48/99 col lithograh fabric collage map. 30-Jun-4 Christie's, London #199/R est:1500-2000
£2746 $4806 €3900 Wrapped road sign (91x76cm-36x30in) s. lithograph collage string. 16-Dec-3 Segre, Madrid #208/R est:3500

£2800 $5096 €4088 Surrounded islands, project for Biscayne Bay, Greater Miami, Florida (79x60cm-31x24in) s.num.XXIII/XXX col offset print collage. 1-Jul-4 Sotheby's, London #322/R est:2500-3000
£3020 $5346 €4500 Red store front, project (71x55cm-28x22in) s.i. col serigraph collage. 30-Apr-4 Dr Fritz Nagel, Stuttgart #761/R est:3000
£3107 $5500 €4536 Wrapped building, project for 1 Times Square, Allied Chemical Tower, NY (100x64cm-39x25in) s.num.15/125 col lithograph collage board. 28-Apr-4 Christie's, Rockefeller NY #262/R est:5000-7000
£3374 $5500 €4926 Lower Manhattan Wrapped Buildings (101x66cm-40x26in) s.num.77/125 col lithograph collage map exec 1990. 24-Sep-3 Christie's, Rockefeller NY #221/R est:4000-6000
£3701 $6292 €5403 Wrapped trees - Project for Avenue des Champs Elysees, Paris (71x56cm-28x22in) s.num.1/45 col lithograph collage lit. 5-Nov-3 AB Stockholms Auktionsverk #1208/R est:50000-55000 (S.KR 49000)
£4118 $7000 €6012 Wrapped trees (70x75cm-28x30in) col lithograph. 31-Oct-3 Sotheby's, New York #514/R
£4249 $7521 €6204 Wrapped Opera House, project for the Opera House, Sydney (76x62cm-30x24in) s.d.1989-90 num.39/120 col lithograph collage lit. 27-Apr-4 AB Stockholms Auktionsverk #1270/R est:40000-50000 (S.KR 58000)
£4400 $8008 €6424 Wrapped telephone (54x69cm-21x27in) s.d.85 num.19/100 lithograph collage. 4-Feb-4 Sotheby's, Olympia #125/R est:1500-2000
£8130 $12764 €11789 Wrapped Opera House (77x63cm-30x25in) s.d.1969-90 num.118/120 lithograph cloth thread paper photo tape. 26-Aug-3 Christie's, Sydney #103/R est:20000-30000 (A.D 20000)

Sculpture
£1705 $3000 €2489 Wrapped Modern Art Book (38x58x20cm-15x23x8in) s. edn 30/120 on moulded plexiglass shelf. 23-May-4 Hindman, Chicago #1090/R est:2000-4000
£1852 $3352 €2704 Wrapped New York Times, June 13 1985 (14x37x3cm-6x15x1in) s.i.verso newspaper plastic string. 30-Mar-4 Lawson Menzies, Sydney #235/R est:2500-3500 (A.D 4500)
£1944 $3247 €2800 Journal emballe (79x100cm-31x39in) s.num.79/100 verso journal plastic string. 21-Oct-3 Artcurial Briest, Paris #492/R est:2500-3000
£9790 $16643 €14000 Corridor store front - project (71x57cm-28x22in) s.i.d.1968 plexiglas pencil graphite varnish. 29-Nov-3 Villa Grisebach, Berlin #331/R est:8000-10000
£20958 $35000 €30599 Project for packed tree (10x81x7cm-4x32x3in) s.i.d.1968 branches polyurethane twine fabric masonite prov. 13-Nov-3 Sotheby's, New York #113/R est:20000-30000

Works on paper
£475 $850 €694 Wrapped statues (86x69cm-34x27in) s. mixed media. 20-Mar-4 Rachel Davis, Shaker Heights #542/R
£588 $1000 €858 American house wrapped (91x61cm-36x24in) s. applied collage on silkscreen. 9-Nov-3 Wright, Chicago #420 est:1000-1500
£634 $1097 €900 Untitled (64x50cm-25x20in) s.d.59 Chinese ink prov. 9-Dec-3 Artcurial Briest, Paris #518/R
£915 $1584 €1300 Untitled (64x50cm-25x20in) s.d.1959 Chinese ink prov. 9-Dec-3 Artcurial Briest, Paris #519/R
£1259 $2102 €1800 Vue sur la fenetre (69x54cm-27x21in) chl wax crayon graphite collage. 25-Jun-3 Digard, Paris #111/R est:6000-8000
£2896 $4923 €4228 Wrapped telephone (56x38cm-22x15in) s. collage on lithograph plastic string paint cardboard prov. 22-Nov-3 Burkhard, Luzern #136/R est:5000-6000 (S.FR 6400)
£3873 $6701 €5500 Abudhabi mastaba (28x35cm-11x14in) s.i.d.1977 crayon pastel chl. 14-Dec-3 Versailles Encheres #179/R est:6000-7000
£4514 $7448 €6500 Abu Dhabi Mastraba (28x35cm-11x14in) s.i.d.1978 graphite chl pastel. 2-Jul-3 Cornette de St.Cyr, Paris #55/R est:7000-8000
£5350 $9683 €7811 Packed coast, project for Sydney, Australia (71x56cm-28x22in) s.d.1969 pencil string fabric collage photo on card. 30-Mar-4 Lawson Menzies, Sydney #233/R est:15000-20000 (A.D 13000)
£5405 $10000 €7891 Packed girls, project (56x71cm-22x28in) s.d.1967-68 pencil crayon photos tape board prov.exhib. 12-Feb-4 Sotheby's, New York #90/R est:6000-8000
£6443 $11919 €9600 Project for United Arab Emirates (28x34cm-11x13in) s.i.d.1977 pastel pencil. 13-Mar-4 De Vuyst, Lokeren #499/R est:9000-11000
£6584 $11918 €9613 Wrapped bridge, project for Sydney harbour Bridge (73x57cm-29x22in) s.d.1969 i.verso collage exhib. 30-Mar-4 Lawson Menzies, Sydney #232/R est:15000-20000 (A.D 16000)
£7234 $12298 €10562 Packed coast project (55x72cm-22x28in) s.i.d.1969 plastic string acrylic chl. collage prov.lit. 25-Nov-3 Christie's, Melbourne #22/R est:14000-18000 (A.D 17000)
£7895 $14289 €12000 Untitled (64x50cm-25x20in) s.d.59 mixed media. 14-Apr-4 Ansorena, Madrid #268/R est:12000
£9667 $17400 €14500 Running fence, project for Sonoma County and Masein County (54x70cm-21x28in) s.d.1973 mixed media. 26-Apr-4 Bernaerts, Antwerp #565/R est:15000-20000
£10000 $16700 €14600 Umbrellas, joint project from Japan and USA (36x28cm-14x11in) s.i.d.1989 pencil tape oil pastel paint photo board prov. 22-Oct-3 Christie's, London #104/R est:10000-15000
£11000 $20020 €16060 Running Fence (56x72cm-22x28in) s.i.d.1974 pencil fabric paper collage staples card. 5-Feb-4 Christie's, London #169/R est:10000-15000
£11976 $20000 €17485 Packed Coast - Project for Australia Near Sydney (77x62cm-30x24in) s.i.d.1969 graphite oil photo fabric string collage board prov. 12-Nov-3 Christie's, Rockefeller NY #423/R est:20000-30000
£13000 $21710 €18980 Gates, project for Central Park, New York City (22x28cm-9x11in) s.i.d.1997 pencil acrylic oil pastel photo collage board prov. 22-Oct-3 Christie's, London #103/R est:8000-12000
£13000 $23660 €18980 JFK Center wrapped (70x56cm-28x22in) s.i.d.1974 pencil col crayon string photo collage board prov. 6-Feb-4 Sotheby's, London #237/R est:15000-20000
£13408 $24000 €19576 Umbrellas - Joint project for Japan and USA (61x36cm-24x14in) s.i.d.1988 graphite pastel photo enamel paint mixed media prov. 12-May-4 Christie's, Rockefeller NY #201/R est:20000-30000
£13408 $24000 €19576 Umbrellas - Joint project for Japan and USA (56x36cm-22x14in) s.i.d.1988 graphite pastel photo enamel mixed media prov. 12-May-4 Christie's, Rockefeller NY #202/R est:20000-30000
£15000 $27600 €21900 Packed cost, project for Australia, Little Bay (71x56cm-28x22in) s.i.d.1969 pencil chl pastel paper collage card on board prov. 25-Jun-4 Christie's, London #177/R est:15000-20000
£15385 $26462 €22462 The Pont Neuf wrapped - project (72x57cm-28x22in) s.d.1976 chk pencil collage prov. 7-Dec-3 Uppsala Auktionskammare, Uppsala #292/R est:200000-250000 (S.KR 200000)
£19014 $33275 €27000 Plan for Piazza della Scala, Milan (71x56cm-28x22in) s.i.d.1970 mixed media card prov. 16-Dec-3 Porro, Milan #41/R est:25000-28000
£20000 $36800 €29200 Wrapped Reichstag - project for der Deutsche Reichstag Berlin (86x71cm-34x28in) s.i.d.1978 chl pencil crayon paper on board prov. 25-Jun-4 Christie's, London #139/R est:25000-35000
£20000 $36800 €30000 Wrapped Reichstag, project for Berlin (98x78cm-39x31in) one s.i.d.1992 one i. double-sided cloth string chk dyptych prov. 11-Jun-4 Villa Grisebach, Berlin #83/R est:30000-40000
£20015 $34026 €29222 The umbrellas - joint project for Japan and USA (79x101cm-31x40in) s.d.1989 col crayon pastel pencil c. diptych. 4-Nov-3 Bukowskis, Stockholm #627/R est:250000-300000 (S.KR 265000)
£21472 $35000 €31349 Fifteen miles packed coast (56x71cm-22x28in) s.i.d.1968 col pencil plastic string collage chl. 23-Sep-3 Christie's, Rockefeller NY #94/R est:15000-20000
£21528 $34014 €31000 Wrapped Pont-Neuf (56x71cm-22x28in) s.i. graphite chl crayon pastel collage string paper on panel. 27-Apr-3 Versailles Encheres #92
£22000 $40040 €32120 Valley Curtain - Project for Colorado (56x72cm-22x28in) s.i.d.1971 pastel col pencil gouache fabric paper collage staples. 5-Feb-4 Christie's, London #165/R est:15000-20000
£24000 $40080 €35040 Surrounded islands, project for Biscayne Bay, Florida. s.i.d.1982 oil pastel map photo collage pencil prov. 22-Oct-3 Christie's, London #105/R est:18000-22000
£24000 $43680 €35040 Mastaba of Abu Dhabi. s.i.d.1981 chl pastel map collage board plexiglas prov. 6-Feb-4 Sotheby's, London #128/R est:25000-35000
£25140 $45000 €36704 Wrapped trees project (56x71cm-22x28in) s.i.d.1969 graphite chl wax crayons polyethylene board prov.exhib. 12-May-4 Christie's, Rockefeller NY #153/R est:30000-40000
£26846 $48054 €40000 Wrapped floor (70x56cm-28x22in) s.i.d.1969 graphite fabric staples card prov. 25-May-4 Sotheby's, Milan #295/R est:15000-20000
£30000 $50100 €43800 Surrounded islands - Project for Biscayne Bay, Greater Miami, Florida (166x108cm-65x43in) s.i.d.1983 pastel pencil gouache fabric collage two. 21-Oct-3 Sotheby's, London #349/R est:35000-45000
£30000 $54600 €43800 Museum of Contemporary Art (56x72cm-22x28in) s.i.d.1968 fabric string staples plastic film col pencil card pro. 5-Feb-4 Christie's, London #164/R est:15000-20000
£33803 $59155 €48000 380 wrapped trees (71x55cm-28x22in) s.d.1969 mixed media board. 18-Dec-3 Cornette de St.Cyr, Paris #108/R est:45000-50000
£35000 $58450 €51100 Wrapped Reichstag - Project for Berlin (108x245cm-43x96in) s.i.d.1986 chl chk printed map collage pastel two prov. 21-Oct-3 Sotheby's, London #350/R est:40000-60000
£35000 $64400 €51100 Wrapped Reichstag - Project for Berlin (99x78cm-39x31in) s.i.d.1993 pastel wax crayon card in plexiglass 3 parts prov. 24-Jun-4 Sotheby's, London #164/R est:25000-35000

CHRISTOFFEL, Anton (1871-1953) Swiss

Works on paper
£1086 $1846 €1586 At Silsersee (33x48cm-13x19in) s.d.1918 W/C. 1-Dec-3 Koller, Zurich #6552 est:1500-2500 (S.FR 2400)

CHRISTOFFERSEN, Frede (1919-1987) Danish

£425 $761 €621 Night, Skagen, summer (58x68cm-23x27in) init.d.55 exhib. 12-Jan-4 Rasmussen, Vejle #515/R (D.KR 4500)
£489 $890 €734 Houses in Suresnes. init.d.47 exhib. 19-Jun-4 Rasmussen, Havnen #4039 (D.KR 5500)
£1033 $1725 €1508 Evening (57x78cm-22x31in) init.d.64 init.d.dec 64 verso exhib. 7-Oct-3 Rasmussen, Copenhagen #285/R (D.KR 11000)
£1264 $2325 €1845 Evening (43x63cm-17x25in) init.d.52. 29-Mar-4 Rasmussen, Copenhagen #434/R est:10000 (D.KR 14000)

Works on paper
£451 $830 €658 Composition with painted collage (34x42cm-13x17in) init.d.65 verso collage exhib. 29-Mar-4 Rasmussen, Copenhagen #375 (D.KR 5000)
£542 $996 €791 Composition with painted collage on panel (26x33cm-10x13in) init.d.Jan 71 collage. 29-Mar-4 Rasmussen, Copenhagen #365/R (D.KR 6000)

CHRISTOFFERSEN, Uffe (1947-) Danish

£328 $564 €479 Fantasy composition with elephants and cats (58x85cm-23x33in) s.d.1979 verso. 3-Dec-3 Museumsbygningen, Copenhagen #5 (D.KR 3500)
£328 $564 €479 Fantasy composition with elephants and cats (58x85cm-23x33in) s.d.1979-80 verso. 3-Dec-3 Museumsbygningen, Copenhagen #6 (D.KR 3500)

CHRISTOFIS, Alexandros (1882-1957) Greek

£4200 $7518 €6132 Siesta (33x48cm-13x19in) s. board. 10-May-4 Sotheby's, Olympia #111/R est:3000-5000

CHRISTOFOROU, John (1921-) British

£379 $607 €550 Figure composition (65x50cm-26x20in) paper on canvas prov. 17-Sep-3 Kunsthallen, Copenhagen #136/R (D.KR 4000)
£385 $662 €550 Portrait imaginaire de baudelaire (61x50cm-24x20in) s. i.d.1988 verso acrylic. 3-Dec-3 Tajan, Paris #450
£420 $713 €600 Standing figure (65x55cm-26x22in) s. s.i.d.1975 verso prov. 18-Nov-3 Babuino, Rome #387/R
£574 $1085 €850 Portrait noir (81x65cm-32x26in) s. i.d.1984 verso acrylic. 21-Feb-4 Cornette de St.Cyr, Paris #262
£800 $1280 €1160 Abstract portrait (62x28cm-24x11in) s. board. 16-Sep-3 Bonhams, Knightsbridge #192/R
£1049 $1752 €1500 Untitled (195x130cm-77x51in) s. 26-Jun-3 Sant Agostino, Torino #213/R est:2000
£1208 $2247 €1800 Portrait bleu (100x81cm-39x32in) s. i.d.1985 verso acrylic. 3-Mar-4 Artcurial Briest, Paris #347 est:2000-2500

£1300	$2236	€1898	Phoenix (71x51cm-28x20in) board. 3-Dec-3 Christie's, Kensington #667/R est:1000-1500
£1400	$2408	€2044	Portrait of a lady (91x63cm-36x25in) s. board. 3-Dec-3 Christie's, Kensington #666/R est:1000-1500
£1600	$2544	€2336	Woman with earrings (53x36cm-21x14in) s. board exhib. 10-Sep-3 Sotheby's, Olympia #314/R est:800-1200
£1700	$3094	€2482	Musician (122x94cm-48x37in) s. board prov. 1-Jul-4 Christie's, Kensington #209/R est:1000-1500

CHRISTOPHE, Pierre Robert (1880-1971) French

Sculpture

£1748	$2920	€2500	Oie (19cm-7in) s.st.f.Valsuani brown pat bronze. 13-Oct-3 Horta, Bruxelles #117 est:1500-1800

CHRISTOPHER, Ann (1947-) British

Sculpture

£1000	$1720	€1460	Pavilion of floating cups (35cm-14in) init.num.1/VIII brown pat bronze. 3-Dec-3 Christie's, Kensington #767 est:400-600

CHRISTOPHERSON, John (1921-1996) British

£500	$795	€730	Land at Greenwich (15x20cm-6x8in) init. s.i.d.20/8/68 verso board. 10-Sep-3 Sotheby's, Olympia #262/R
£500	$920	€730	Garden window Westgrove Lane (16x10cm-6x4in) init. 11-Jun-4 Keys, Aylsham #455/R
£600	$954	€876	Haunted coach house (36x30cm-14x12in) s. s.i.d.May 1959 verso board. 10-Sep-3 Sotheby's, Olympia #227/R

CHRISTY, Howard Chandler (1872-1952) American

£2994	$5000	€4371	Reflections (76x61cm-30x24in) s. prov. 7-Oct-3 Sotheby's, New York #189 est:5000-7000
£3352	$6000	€4894	Blossoms along the river (76x64cm-30x25in) s.indis.i. exhib. 6-May-4 Shannon's, Milford #8/R est:4000-6000
£5988	$10000	€8742	Dorothy in a red dress (101x81cm-40x32in) s.i.d.1932 prov. 7-Oct-3 Sotheby's, New York #241 est:10000-20000
£6044	$11000	€8824	Princess in a garden (100x76cm-39x30in) s.d.1911 W/C on board prov. 29-Jun-4 Sotheby's, New York #203/R est:10000-15000

Works on paper

£8380	$15000	€12235	Woman standing with knight and page (99x74cm-39x29in) s.d.1911 gouache. 15-May-4 Illustration House, New York #105/R est:15000-20000

CHROSTRI, Enrichette (20th C) Italian

£600	$1110	€876	Poppies, daisies and other summer flowers in a basket on a ledge (58x74cm-23x29in) s.i. 15-Jan-4 Christie's, Kensington #1041/R

CHRYSSA (1933-) American/Greek

Sculpture

£1647	$2800	€2405	Untitled (152x56cm-60x22in) plexiglass 49 neon lights electric motor rubber. 9-Nov-3 Wright, Chicago #476 est:3000-5000
£3784	$7000	€5525	Seagram Building (145x57cm-57x22in) brown pat bronze exec 1967 prov.lit. 12-Feb-4 Sotheby's, New York #171/R est:3000-5000

CHRYSTOPH, Hans (1891-1962) German

£756	$1300	€1104	Bavarian landscape (71x99cm-28x39in) s.d.1918. 7-Dec-3 Treadway Gallery, Cincinnati #483/R

CHU TEH CHUN (1920-) Chinese

£2324	$4021	€3300	Composition (54x33cm-21x13in) s. paper on canvas. 9-Dec-3 Artcurial Briest, Paris #510/R est:1500-2000
£3451	$5970	€4900	Composition (65x54cm-26x21in) s. oil paper on canvas prov. 14-Dec-3 Versailles Encheres #133/R est:5000-6000
£6598	$11018	€9500	Clartes bleues (65x81cm-26x32in) s.d.89 s.i.d.verso. 21-Oct-3 Artcurial Briest, Paris #401/R est:9000-12000
£13816	$25421	€21000	Errant en flamboyant (73x60cm-29x24in) s.d.1990 s.i.d.verso prov. 27-Jun-4 Versailles Encheres #92/R est:15000-18000
£20724	$38132	€31500	Unite profonde (75x92cm-30x36in) s.d.1989 s.i.d.verso prov. 27-Jun-4 Versailles Encheres #93/R est:15000-18000
£32000	$57600	€48000	Paix des hauteurs (81x100cm-32x39in) s.d.1965 s.i.d.verso. 24-Apr-4 Cornette de St.Cyr, Paris #482/R est:10000
£46332	$77375	€67645	Memories (146x114cm-57x45in) s. painted 1991 lit. 26-Oct-3 Christie's, Hong Kong #130/R est:300000-400000 (HK.D 600000)
£71124	$128023	€103841	Number 70 (130x65cm-51x26in) s. lit. 26-Apr-4 Sotheby's, Hong Kong #525/R est:450000-550000 (HK.D 1000000)

Works on paper

£1736	$2899	€2500	Composition verte (54x33cm-21x13in) s. gouache. 23-Oct-3 Credit Municipal, Paris #73 est:2000-2500
£2014	$3363	€2900	Composition brume (54x33cm-21x13in) s. gouache paper on canvas. 23-Oct-3 Credit Municipal, Paris #74/R est:2000-2500

CHUANG CHE (1934-) Chinese

Works on paper

£1216	$2250	€1775	Day to night (102x127cm-40x50in) s. ink oil paper on canvas prov. 10-Mar-4 Doyle, New York #69/R est:1000-1500

CHUBB, Lee (1904-) American

£215	$400	€314	Italian town (46x61cm-18x24in) board painted c.1960. 7-Mar-4 Treadway Gallery, Cincinnati #746/R

CHULOVICH, V N (1922-1994) Russian

£223	$400	€326	Autumn study (35x37cm-14x15in) cardboard painted 1961. 29-May-4 Shishkin Gallery, Moscow #58/R
£245	$450	€358	The harvest of the sugarbeet (31x70cm-12x28in) cardboard painted 1960. 27-Mar-4 Shishkin Gallery, Moscow #40/R
£246	$440	€359	Wind (32x50cm-13x20in) cardboard painted 1961. 29-May-4 Shishkin Gallery, Moscow #60/R
£272	$500	€397	Forest landscape (20x27cm-8x11in) cardboard painted 1949. 27-Mar-4 Shishkin Gallery, Moscow #42/R
£337	$620	€492	Sunny day (25x34cm-10x13in) cardboard painted 1963. 27-Mar-4 Shishkin Gallery, Moscow #44/R
£359	$660	€524	Country stadium (41x70cm-16x28in) cardboard painted 1959. 27-Mar-4 Shishkin Gallery, Moscow #39/R
£363	$650	€530	Messy table, Aleshunino (70x63cm-28x25in) painted 1976. 29-May-4 Shishkin Gallery, Moscow #59/R
£391	$700	€571	First snow, Martus countryside (46x72cm-18x28in) cardboard painted 1971. 29-May-4 Shishkin Gallery, Moscow #61/R
£500	$900	€730	First snow (65x73cm-26x29in) 24-Apr-4 Shishkin Gallery, Moscow #74/R
£667	$1200	€974	Vologda, rainy day (72x79cm-28x31in) 24-Apr-4 Shishkin Gallery, Moscow #73/R est:2000-3000
£722	$1300	€1054	Getting green (21x42cm-8x17in) canvas on cardboard. 24-Apr-4 Shishkin Gallery, Moscow #75/R est:700-800
£1222	$2200	€1784	Early autumn (26x41cm-10x16in) canvas on cardboard. 24-Apr-4 Shishkin Gallery, Moscow #76/R est:800-900

CHURBERG, Fanny Maria (1845-1892) Finnish

£1549	$2680	€2200	Landscape (26x34cm-10x13in) panel. 13-Dec-3 Hagelstam, Helsinki #94/R est:2500
£4930	$8528	€7000	Birches by water (31x54cm-12x21in) s.d.1877 lit. 13-Dec-3 Hagelstam, Helsinki #93/R est:8000

CHURCH, Frederick Stuart (1842-1923) American

£373	$600	€545	Flowers (48x84cm-19x33in) s. 24-Aug-3 William Jenack, New York #158
£2060	$3750	€3008	Woman seated in a landscape with a doe (30x41cm-12x16in) s.d.86 prov. 15-Jun-4 John Moran, Pasadena #698a est:3000-5000
£2326	$4000	€3396	In harmony with nature (65x107cm-26x42in) s.d.1909. 3-Dec-3 Doyle, New York #198/R est:4000-6000

CHURCH, Katharine (1910-1999) British

Works on paper

£500	$880	€730	Landscape (14x21cm-6x8in) s. ink htd white. 18-May-4 Woolley & Wallis, Salisbury #277/R

CHURCHER, Peter (1964-) Australian

£1240	$2107	€1810	Jana I (31x25cm-12x10in) s.d.95. 29-Oct-3 Lawson Menzies, Sydney #131/R est:1500-2500 (A.D 3000)
£5691	$10187	€8309	Unable to watch (122x208cm-48x82in) s.d.2001 prov.exhib. 4-May-4 Sotheby's, Melbourne #68/R est:14000-18000 (A.D 14000)

CHURCHILL, Martin (1954-) British

£420	$722	€613	Edinburgh church (171x133cm-67x52in) s.d.81. 3-Dec-3 Christie's, Kensington #704/R

CHURCHILL, Sir Winston (1874-1965) British

£70000	$120400	€102200	Sea from La Capponcina (63x76cm-25x30in) init. prov. 3-Dec-3 Sotheby's, London #63/R est:30000-40000

CHURCHILL, Sir Winston (attrib) (1874-1965) British

£3427	$6306	€5003	Lago di Como (33x41cm-13x16in) i.stretcher prov. 14-Jun-4 Waddingtons, Toronto #153/R est:5000-7000 (C.D 8500)

CHURCHILL, Wiley (1900-1987) American

Works on paper

£541	$1000	€790	Mississippi river landscape (46x71cm-18x28in) s. W/C. 17-Jan-4 New Orleans Auction, New Orleans #741/R est:1200-1800
£706	$1200	€1031	Moss gatherers on a flatboat in the bayou. s.d.1947 W/C on board. 22-Nov-3 New Orleans Auction, New Orleans #1079/R est:1500-2500
£824	$1400	€1203	Old road on Gulf Coast (46x66cm-18x26in) s. W/C executed c.1940. 22-Nov-3 New Orleans Auction, New Orleans #1080 est:1500-2500
£1882	$3200	€2748	New Orleans Opera House (46x66cm-18x26in) s. W/C. 22-Nov-3 New Orleans Auction, New Orleans #1078/R est:2500-4000

CHURCHILL, William W (1858-1926) American

£8939	$16000	€13051	Lake view with sailboats (66x81cm-26x32in) s.d.07. 14-May-4 Skinner, Boston #273/R est:4000-6000

CHURCHYARD, Anna (?) British?

£350	$560	€511	Soring Lane, Melton (20x18cm-8x7in) board. 20-Sep-3 Lacy Scott, Bury St.Edmunds #437/R

CHURCHYARD, Thomas (1798-1865) British

£300	$516	€438	Landscape, corner of Deben Road, Woodbridge (15x13cm-6x5in) panel. 3-Dec-3 Neal & Fletcher, Woodbridge #372
£450	$716	€653	Glade near Woodbridge (12x17cm-5x7in) board. 9-Sep-3 Bonhams, Knightsbridge #283/R
£563	$1007	€822	River landscape with fishermen and city (20x31cm-8x12in) board. 22-Mar-4 Philippe Schuler, Zurich #4394/R (S.FR 1300)
£600	$948	€870	View of Woodbridge (12x26cm-5x10in) i.verso panel. 24-Jul-3 Lawrence, Crewkerne #916/R
£600	$1032	€876	Goodings Yard, New Street (20x30cm-8x12in) board. 3-Dec-3 Neal & Fletcher, Woodbridge #374
£600	$1032	€876	East Anglian landscape with windmill to background (20x33cm-8x13in) i.verso oil paper on panel. 3-Dec-3 Neal & Fletcher, Woodbridge #375
£640	$1101	€934	Landscape, The Avenue, Woodbridge (15x13cm-6x5in) panel. 3-Dec-3 Neal & Fletcher, Woodbridge #370
£680	$1170	€993	Landscape path with gate, Long Meadow, Hasketon (15x13cm-6x5in) panel. 3-Dec-3 Neal & Fletcher, Woodbridge #371
£720	$1238	€1051	Landscape with figure on a path, Barndiston Meadow (15x13cm-6x5in) 3-Dec-3 Neal & Fletcher, Woodbridge #373

£750	$1185	€1088	Cottage in a wooded river landscape (16x21cm-6x8in) i.verso panel. 4-Sep-3 Christie's, Kensington #109/R
£840	$1529	€1226	Farmhouse and buildings (15x13cm-6x5in) board. 30-Jun-4 Neal & Fletcher, Woodbridge #275
£1000	$1790	€1460	Moonlight over Woodbridge Abbey (26x33cm-10x13in) 22-Mar-4 Bonhams & Brooks, Norfolk #356/R est:400-600
£1200	$1896	€1740	Five bar gate (16x15cm-6x6in) panel. 4-Sep-3 Christie's, Kensington #108/R est:600-800
£2800	$5012	€4088	Stackyard (26x35cm-10x14in) init.i.verso board. 22-Mar-4 Bonhams & Brooks, Norfolk #222/R est:500-700
£2800	$5012	€4088	Edmunds, the last oil lamp lighter, Woodbridge (25x21cm-10x8in) s.i.verso panel. 22-Mar-4 Bonhams & Brooks, Norfolk #224/R est:300-500

Works on paper

£350	$553	€508	Aldeburgh (11x17cm-4x7in) W/C. 3-Sep-3 Bonhams, Bury St Edmunds #316/R
£360	$569	€522	Gate to the wood (9x12cm-4x5in) W/C sold with another by same hand. 3-Sep-3 Bonhams, Bury St Edmunds #317
£380	$692	€555	River landscape with willows and cattle (13x18cm-5x7in) W/C. 30-Jun-4 Neal & Fletcher, Woodbridge #248
£420	$664	€609	Aldeburgh beach with boats and children (15x20cm-6x8in) W/C. 3-Sep-3 Bonhams, Bury St Edmunds #333
£420	$773	€613	Felixstowe Cliffs (7x9cm-3x4in) W/C. 27-Mar-4 Thos Mawer, Lincoln #28/R
£500	$925	€730	Coastal Scene (17x27cm-7x11in) W/C. 10-Mar-4 Sotheby's, Olympia #31/R
£700	$1253	€1022	Cransford hall, Suffolk (12x18cm-5x7in) i.d.September 1852 W/C. 22-Mar-4 Bonhams & Brooks, Norfolk #136/R
£980	$1548	€1421	Suffolk landscape (14x19cm-6x7in) W/C prov. 3-Sep-3 Bonhams, Bury St Edmunds #312/R
£1600	$2864	€2336	Cornfield by the River Deben, Woodbridge (9x11cm-4x4in) W/C pair. 22-Mar-4 Bonhams & Brooks, Norfolk #141/R est:500-700

CHWALA, Adolf (1836-1900) Czechoslovakian

£458	$792	€650	Moonlight on the Danube (21x31cm-8x12in) s. i.verso panel. 10-Dec-3 Dorotheum, Vienna #10/R
£690	$1152	€1000	High mountain landscape with stream (99x66cm-39x26in) s. panel. 12-Jul-3 Bergmann, Erlangen #628/R est:1200
£839	$1401	€1200	Konigssee in Berchtesgaden (37x58cm-15x23in) s. 28-Jun-3 Dannenberg, Berlin #660/R
£839	$1427	€1200	Angler on the banks of a waterfall (91x126cm-36x50in) s. lit. 28-Nov-3 Schloss Ahlden, Ahlden #1489/R
£839	$1443	€1200	Sleigh ride (34x53cm-13x21in) mono.d.94. 4-Dec-3 Schopman, Hamburg #609/R
£1536	$2612	€2243	Mountain lake (64x92cm-25x36in) s. canvas on canvas. 29-Nov-3 Dorotheum, Prague #31/R est:70000-100000 (C.KR 70000)
£1611	$2996	€2400	Panoramic landscape with farmer's wife and approaching summer storm (61x75cm-24x30in) s. 8-Mar-4 Bernaerts, Antwerp #81/R est:1250-1500
£1867	$3379	€2800	Mountain lake lit by afternoon sun (29x52cm-11x20in) s. 3-Apr-4 Hans Stahl, Hamburg #17/R est:2800
£2649	$4821	€4000	Mondsee against the Drachenwand (79x116cm-31x46in) s. 21-Jun-4 Dorotheum, Vienna #137 est:4000-4400

CHWALA, Fritz (1872-1936) Austrian

£300	$552	€438	Logriegoiol, Norway (15x43cm-6x17in) s. i.verso panel. 8-Jun-4 Bonhams, Knightsbridge #134/R
£552	$921	€800	Gosausee (75x100cm-30x39in) s. 9-Jul-3 Hugo Ruef, Munich #68
£1050	$1943	€1533	Rowing hay across the fjord (69x107cm-27x42in) s. 15-Jan-4 Christie's, Kensington #820/R est:1500-2000

CIACELLI, Arturo (1883-1966) Italian

£1141	$2111	€1700	Composition (70x50cm-28x20in) s.d.1956 tempera paper on canvas. 13-Mar-4 Meeting Art, Vercelli #355 est:1000
£2162	$3805	€3200	Spatial conquest (64x91cm-25x36in) s. s.d.1930 verso prov.exhib. 24-May-4 Christie's, Milan #282/R est:3200-3800
£4730	$8324	€7000	Spatial elements (127x95cm-50x37in) s. s.i.verso. 22-May-4 Galleria Pananti, Florence #507/R est:8000-10000

Works on paper

£510	$913	€750	Compositions (22x31cm-9x12in) s.d.1952 mixed media pair. 16-Mar-4 Finarte Semenzato, Milan #104

CIAMBERLANI, Albert (1864-1956) Belgian

£667	$1220	€1000	Nymphes dans un paysage (54x67cm-21x26in) s. 7-Jun-4 Palais de Beaux Arts, Brussels #37/R
£811	$1532	€1200	Les moissons (74x130cm-29x51in) s. 17-Feb-4 Vanderkindere, Brussels #22

CIAMPELLI, Agostini (attrib) (1578-1640) Italian

Works on paper

£2838	$4995	€4200	Design for a chapel (39x25cm-15x10in) pen col ink wash black chk prov.exhib.lit. 19-May-4 Sotheby's, Amsterdam #35/R est:3000-4000

CIAN, Fernand (19/20th C) Italian

Sculpture

£2500	$4575	€3650	Bust of Beethoven (49cm-19in) s.d.1923 terracotta exhib. 9-Jul-4 Sotheby's, London #141/R est:3000-5000

CIANI, Cesare (1854-1925) Italian

£915	$1584	€1300	Embroidering (12x20cm-5x8in) s. card. 9-Dec-3 Pandolfini, Florence #259/R
£1408	$2437	€2000	SHepherdess (40x26cm-16x10in) s.d.1891 card. 9-Dec-3 Pandolfini, Florence #253/R est:2200-2400
£1467	$2655	€2200	Girls (16x22cm-6x9in) s. cardboard. 2-Apr-4 Farsetti, Prato #547/R est:2000-3000

Works on paper

£599	$1036	€850	Shoe repairer (20x14cm-8x6in) s. Chinese ink. 9-Dec-3 Pandolfini, Florence #168 est:800-900

CIANI, Cesare (attrib) (1854-1925) Italian

£1600	$2928	€2400	Coquettish peasant girl (74x54cm-29x21in) s. canvas on canvas. 5-Jun-4 Arnold, Frankfurt #555/R est:300

CIAPPA, Frederico (fl.1830-1840) Italian

£444	$769	€648	The Scribe (101x76cm-40x30in) s.d.1907. 9-Dec-3 Pinneys, Montreal #45 (C.D 1000)

CIAPPA, Giovanni (19th C) Italian

£820	$1394	€1197	Italianate landscape with classical figures before a temple (64x76cm-25x30in) s.i. 29-Oct-3 Bonhams, Chester #430

CIARALLO, Antonio (1957-) Italian

Works on paper

£333	$613	€500	Untitled (40x30cm-16x12in) s.d.2002 mixed media on canvas. 12-Jun-4 Meeting Art, Vercelli #328/R
£667	$1227	€1000	Untitled (120x60cm-47x24in) s.d. mixed media on canvas lit. 12-Jun-4 Meeting Art, Vercelli #472/R

CIARDI, Beppe (1875-1932) Italian

£733	$1349	€1100	Landscape (10x16cm-4x6in) s. card. 10-Jun-4 Galleria Pace, Milan #115/R
£1408	$2437	€2000	Sheep (15x23cm-6x9in) s.verso cardboard. 9-Dec-3 Finarte Semenzato, Milan #50 est:2500-3000
£1972	$3273	€2800	Horses of S. Marco (20x31cm-8x12in) s. panel. 11-Jun-3 Christie's, Rome #257/R est:3000-5000
£2105	$3874	€3200	The Venetian lagoon (27x36cm-11x14in) s. cardboard. 22-Jun-4 Christie's, Amsterdam #214/R est:2000-3000
£2113	$3655	€3000	San pIetro in Volta (21x31cm-8x12in) s. cardboard. 11-Dec-3 Christie's, Rome #153/R est:2800-3500
£2171	$3995	€3300	Lagoon (20x30cm-8x12in) s.d.190 verso cardboard on canvas. 23-Jun-4 Finarte Semenzato, Rome #119/R est:3000-5000
£2333	$4293	€3500	Entrance to Villa Borghese, Rome (31x20cm-12x8in) s. s.d.1926 verso board. 8-Jun-4 Sotheby's, Milan #78/R est:3500-5000
£3133	$5671	€4700	Canal in Venice (24x19cm-9x7in) s.d.1921 board lit. 30-Mar-4 Babuino, Rome #347/R est:3000
£3311	$5827	€4900	Seascape in Venice (20x33cm-8x13in) s. board. 19-May-4 Il Ponte, Milan #608 est:3800-4000
£3333	$6133	€5000	Pasture by pond (21x31cm-8x12in) s. board. 8-Jun-4 Della Rocca, Turin #266/R est:5500-6500
£3667	$6747	€5500	La Salute, Venice (20x29cm-8x11in) s. cardboard. 10-Jun-4 Christie's, Rome #106/R est:3000-5000
£3901	$6514	€5500	Lagoon with hunter and dog (14x22cm-6x9in) s. s.d.1915 verso cardboard. 14-Oct-3 Finarte Semenzato, Milan #18/R
£4306	$7319	€6200	Mazzorbo (26x44cm-10x17in) s. board. 29-Oct-3 Il Ponte, Milan #532/R
£5634	$9746	€8000	Sea (30x39cm-12x15in) s. panel. 11-Dec-3 Christie's, Rome #152/R est:8000-12000
£13380	$22211	€19000	Venezia, vapore e nuvole in Laguna (50x60cm-20x24in) s. wood prov. 11-Jun-3 Christie's, Rome #258/R est:15000-20000
£14000	$25060	€21000	Dusk (68x45cm-27x18in) s. s.i.verso board. 12-May-4 Stadion, Trieste #649/R est:15000-20000
£17450	$31235	€26000	Sappada houses (70x120cm-28x47in) s. i.verso painted 1897. 25-May-4 Finarte Semenzato, Milan #171/R est:20000-22000

CIARDI, Claudio (1962-) Italian

£714	$1300	€1071	View of Portofino (53x74cm-21x29in) s. 19-Jun-4 Charlton Hall, Columbia #98/R

CIARDI, Emma (1879-1933) Italian

£1972	$3273	€2800	May (22x35cm-9x14in) s. i.verso panel. 11-Jun-3 Christie's, Rome #146/R est:3000-5000
£2667	$4827	€4000	Masked ball (25x20cm-10x8in) s.d.1924 canvas on board lit. 30-Mar-4 Babuino, Rome #346/R est:3000
£2899	$4754	€4000	Najadi fountain (32x27cm-13x11in) s. prov. 27-May-3 Finarte Semenzato, Milan #18/R est:4000-5000
£2966	$4923	€4300	Fontana Theatre (17x32cm-7x13in) s. card. 1-Oct-3 Della Rocca, Turin #230/R
£3188	$5229	€4400	Whispering in autumn (28x28cm-11x11in) s. cardboard prov. 27-May-3 Finarte Semenzato, Milan #17/R est:4000-5000
£4362	$7721	€6500	Masks in the park (20x26cm-8x10in) s. board. 1-May-4 Meeting Art, Vercelli #366 est:6000
£5634	$9746	€8000	Venice (28x37cm-11x15in) indis.sig. board. 11-Dec-3 Christie's, Rome #168/R est:7000-10000
£6000	$10740	€9000	Amongst the bushes (38x49cm-15x19in) s. s.i.verso board. 12-May-4 Stadion, Trieste #725/R est:3500-4500
£6500	$10335	€9490	Dogana, Venice (26x37cm-10x15in) s. panel. 10-Sep-3 Edgar Horn, Eastbourne #380/R est:2000-3000
£9000	$14310	€13140	Giglio Veneziano, depicting busy Venetian canal scene (37x49cm-15x19in) s. panel. 10-Sep-3 Edgar Horn, Eastbourne #378/R est:4000-6000
£10638	$17766	€15000	Entrance to Chilham Castle (37x50cm-15x20in) s. i.verso board prov. 14-Oct-3 Finarte Semenzato, Milan #201/R est:16000
£11111	$20000	€16222	Campo San Barnaba (30x40cm-12x16in) board. 23-Apr-4 Sotheby's, New York #69/R est:20000-25000
£23611	$42500	€34472	Campo San Barnaba (60x81cm-24x32in) s.i.d.1903 prov. 23-Apr-4 Sotheby's, New York #70/R est:30000-40000
£45000	$77400	€65700	Grand fete on the Grand Canal (74x99cm-29x39in) s.i.d.1922. 3-Dec-3 Christie's, London #43/R est:20000-30000

CIARDI, Guglielmo (1842-1917) Italian

£7042	$12183	€10000	Canal in Chioggia (23x39cm-9x15in) s. cardboard exhib. 10-Dec-3 Sotheby's, Milan #2/R est:10000-15000
£9060	$16943	€13500	Lagoon (18x37cm-7x15in) s. board. 25-Feb-4 Porro, Milan #16/R est:10000-12000
£33104	$55283	€48000	Canal de Venise (71x125cm-28x49in) s. 17-Nov-3 Tajan, Paris #77/R est:50000-70000
£33803	$58479	€48000	Washerwomen on the Sile (45x75cm-18x30in) s.d.1870 prov. 11-Dec-3 Christie's, Rome #172/R est:40000-50000
£155556	$280000	€227112	Village life outside Venice (79x128cm-31x50in) s.i.d.1882. 23-Apr-4 Sotheby's, New York #71/R est:120000-180000

Works on paper
£347 $590 €500 View of farm (14x22cm-6x9in) s. pencil card. 1-Nov-3 Meeting Art, Vercelli #24
£521 $885 €750 Farmer with axe (20x20cm-8x8in) pencil lead. 1-Nov-3 Meeting Art, Vercelli #307/R
£521 $885 €750 Farmer with axe (21x16cm-8x6in) s. pencil lead. 1-Nov-3 Meeting Art, Vercelli #400/R
£556 $944 €800 Farm with fence (24x34cm-9x13in) s. pencil. 1-Nov-3 Meeting Art, Vercelli #217/R
£734 $1248 €1050 Rural interior (17x12cm-7x5in) s. pencil. 19-Nov-3 Finarte Semenzato, Milan #522/R

CIARDIELLO, Carmine (1871-?) Italian
£915 $1584 €1300 Old fisherman (34x18cm-13x7in) s. board. 11-Dec-3 Christie's, Rome #13
£2483 $4445 €3700 Landscape in Naples (50x70cm-20x28in) s. 25-May-4 Finarte Semenzato, Milan #119/R est:2500-3000
£3380 $5848 €4800 Naples, serenade (47x48cm-19x19in) s. 11-Dec-3 Christie's, Rome #161/R

CIARDIELLO, Michele (1839-?) Italian
£3169 $5482 €4500 Strolling on the Amalfi coast (78x102cm-31x40in) s. 10-Dec-3 Finarte Semenzato, Rome #210/R est:5000-6000

CIARDO, Vincenzo (1894-1970) Italian
£353 $650 €515 Still life with fruit (36x46cm-14x18in) s. panel prov. 13-Jun-4 Bonhams & Butterfields, Los Angeles #7009/R
£1135 $1895 €1600 Paesaggio (40x50cm-16x20in) s. cardboard. 21-Jun-3 Stadion, Trieste #162/R
£1200 $2208 €1800 Hills in Pozzuoli (30x40cm-12x16in) s. painted 1940 exhib. 14-Jun-4 Sant Agostino, Torino #331/R est:1500-2000
£1831 $3039 €2600 Self-portrait in summer (50x40cm-20x16in) s.d.1960 canvas on cardboard. 13-Jun-3 Farsetti, Prato #62/R
£2394 $3975 €3400 Moon and olive trees (49x59cm-19x23in) s. canvas on cardboard. 13-Jun-3 Farsetti, Prato #376/R
£2817 $4676 €4000 Still life (50x40cm-20x16in) s. 13-Jun-3 Farsetti, Prato #300/R

CIARROCCHI, Arnoldo (1916-) Italian
£1724 $2879 €2500 Landscape (40x30cm-16x12in) s. s.d.1973 verso. 13-Nov-3 Finarte Semenzato, Rome #226/R est:2500-2800

CIBOT, Edouard (1799-1877) French
£1600 $2896 €2400 Paysage champetre (70x100cm-28x39in) s. 1-Apr-4 Credit Municipal, Paris #49/R est:2000-2500

CICCARONE, Julia (1967-) Australian
£1653 $3058 €2413 Struggle to define (133x180cm-52x71in) i. i.d.1989 prov. 15-Mar-4 Sotheby's, Melbourne #34 est:2000-4000 (A.D 4000)
£2553 $4340 €3727 The pilgrimage (198x182cm-78x72in) s.d.99 linen prov. 25-Nov-3 Christie's, Melbourne #236/R est:7000-10000 (A.D 6000)
£2642 $4148 €3857 Oh what a lovely painting, waterfall (200x200cm-79x79in) 27-Aug-3 Christie's, Sydney #750/R est:2000-3000 (A.D 6500)

CICCOTELLI, Beniamino (1937-) Italian
£473 $832 €700 Bowl with ochre base (50x50cm-20x20in) s. s.i.verso. 22-May-4 Galleria Pananti, Florence #486/R

CICERI, Eugène (1813-1890) French
£531 $850 €775 Landscape with cottage with woman standing, man fishing (13x20cm-5x8in) s. panel. 22-Sep-3 O'Gallerie, Oregon #785/R
£1400 $2534 €2100 Cavalier sur le chemin de la chaumiere (32x46cm-13x18in) s.d.1841. 5-Apr-4 Deburaux, Boulogne #68 est:2000-3000
£2098 $3566 €3000 Lavandieres et paysans (21x27cm-8x11in) s.d. panel. 21-Nov-3 Lombrail & Teucquam, Paris #105 est:2800-3000
£2238 $3849 €3200 Le moulin au dessus de la riviere (28x22cm-11x9in) panel painted c.1850. 7-Dec-3 Osenat, Fontainebleau #121 est:3500-4000
£2333 $4293 €3500 Afternoon by the river (22x43cm-9x17in) s.d.49 board. 8-Jun-4 Sotheby's, Milan #46/R est:1500-2500
£2464 $4041 €3400 La vie a la ferme (26x43cm-10x17in) s.d.49 panel. 11-May-3 Osenat, Fontainebleau #37/R est:4000-5000
£3200 $5888 €4672 Woman washing clothes (35x55cm-14x22in) s. panel. 25-Mar-4 Christie's, Kensington #7/R est:2000-3000
£4545 $7818 €6500 Lavandieres pres du moulin (28x24cm-11x9in) s.d.50 panel. 7-Dec-3 Osenat, Fontainebleau #120 est:6500-7000
£8000 $14640 €12000 Lavoir (62x83cm-24x33in) s.d.1878. 6-Jun-4 Osenat, Fontainebleau #138/R est:12000-15000
Works on paper
£284 $474 €400 Vue d'un canal a Venise (11x16cm-4x6in) s. W/C. 20-Jun-3 Drouot Estimations, Paris #54
£288 $472 €400 Paysage Italianisant (15x23cm-6x9in) s.d.1842 pen wash W/C. 6-Jun-3 Chochon-Barre & Allardi, Paris #1/R
£423 $731 €600 Paysage Breton (16x27cm-6x11in) s. d.1847 verso W/C black crayon. 12-Dec-3 Renaud, Paris #60
£471 $772 €650 Route vers la carriere (9x13cm-4x5in) s.d.1865 W/C. 11-May-3 Osenat, Fontainebleau #11
£500 $900 €730 Clam diggers on a coast, beneath cliffs (28x44cm-11x17in) s. W/C. 21-Jan-4 Sotheby's, New York #204/R est:800-1200
£599 $1036 €850 Arriere cour d'une ferme (19x30cm-7x12in) s. W/C varnish pen brown ink. 12-Dec-3 Renaud, Paris #61
£612 $1096 €900 Deux hommes dans un marais (22x28cm-9x11in) s.d.70 W/C htd white gouache. 17-Mar-4 Tajan, Paris #139
£1304 $2139 €1800 Reverie pres du chateau (27x45cm-11x18in) s. W/C. 11-May-3 Osenat, Fontainebleau #12 est:1200-1500
£1701 $3044 €2500 Un paysage montagneux, avec une maison au premier plan (34x48cm-13x19in) s.d.47 graphite W/C gouache htd white. 18-Mar-4 Christie's, Paris #298/R est:3000-5000

CICERI, Eugène (attrib) (1813-1890) French
£839 $1401 €1200 Paysage de bord de riviere (21x30cm-8x12in) bears sig.d.76 panel. 27-Jun-3 Calmels Cohen, Paris #9/R

CICERI, Pierre Luc Charles (1782-1868) French
Works on paper
£719 $1180 €1000 Paysage de neige anime (10x14cm-4x6in) s.d.1838 pen W/C gouache. 6-Jun-3 Chochon-Barre & Allardi, Paris #2/R
£915 $1483 €1300 Young children (13x21cm-5x8in) sepia wash prov. 11-Aug-3 Boscher, Cherbourg #764

CICERO, Carmen (1926-) American
Works on paper
£236 $425 €345 V (20x28cm-8x11in) s.d.57 ink collage prov. 23-Jan-4 Freeman, Philadelphia #5/R
£324 $600 €473 Untitled portrait (30x41cm-12x16in) s. W/C. 15-Feb-4 Outer Cape Auctions, Provincetown #54/R

CICVAREK, Miloslav (1927-) Czechoslovakian
£500 $920 €750 Salzburg Schloss Leopoldskron (60x70cm-24x28in) s. 9-Jun-4 Dorotheum, Salzburg #656/R
£800 $1472 €1200 Women's faces (120x115cm-47x45in) s. 9-Jun-4 Dorotheum, Salzburg #657/R
Works on paper
£467 $859 €700 Village in hilly landscape (38x56cm-15x22in) s. W/C mixed media. 9-Jun-4 Dorotheum, Salzburg #658/R

CIDONCHA, Rafael (1952-) Spanish
£486 $900 €710 Boy on Horse (35x27cm-14x11in) s.d.82 lit. 12-Feb-4 Sotheby's, New York #164/R

CIECIERSKI, Tomasz (20th C) Polish
Works on paper
£229 $381 €334 Sketch 29 of figures (44x63cm-17x25in) crayon exec.1990. 2-Oct-3 Agra, Warsaw #2/R (P.Z 1500)

CIECZKIEWICZ, Edmund (1872-1958) Polish
£908 $1570 €1326 Woodland scene with duck flying towards pond (34x51cm-13x20in) s. cardboard painted c.1920. 14-Dec-3 Agra, Warsaw #34/R est:4000 (P.Z 6000)

CIESLEWSKI, Thaddaus (1870-1950) Polish
£1119 $1924 €1600 Peasant women at the potato harvest (50x62cm-20x24in) s.d.1902. 5-Dec-3 Bolland & Marotz, Bremen #520/R est:1900
£1286 $2225 €1878 View of city wall and church (53x88cm-21x35in) s. cardboard painted 1910 lit. 14-Dec-3 Agra, Warsaw #49/R est:4000 (P.Z 8500)
Works on paper
£1016 $1696 €1483 Winter view of Anny (53x88cm-21x35in) s.d.1937 W/C. 19-Oct-3 Agra, Warsaw #50/R est:6000 (P.Z 6500)

CIFRONDI, Antonio (attrib) (17/18th C) Italian
£4213 $7541 €6151 Portrait of young farmer with jug (73x56cm-29x22in) 26-May-4 AB Stockholms Auktionsverk #2509/R est:25000-30000 (S.KR 57000)

CIGNANI, Carlo (1628-1719) Italian
£5396 $8849 €7500 Saint Elizabeth of Hungary (74x61cm-29x24in) 4-Jun-3 Sotheby's, Milan #113/R est:4000-6000

CIGNANI, Carlo (attrib) (1628-1719) Italian
£4667 $8540 €7000 Madonna and Child (45x39cm-18x15in) 1-Jun-4 Sotheby's, Milan #134/R est:4000-5000
Works on paper
£1400 $2520 €2044 Studies of three angels and two putti (41x26cm-16x10in) red chk htd white prov. 20-Apr-4 Sotheby's, Olympia #28/R est:1000-1500
£3056 $5500 €4462 Head of a boy in a cap, looking down (24x19cm-9x7in) i. red chk prov. 22-Jan-4 Christie's, Rockefeller NY #57/R est:2000-4000

CIGNANI, Carlo (style) (1628-1719) Italian
£20695 $37044 €30215 Allegory of power and peace (142x196cm-56x77in) 26-May-4 AB Stockholms Auktionsverk #2501/R est:100000-125000 (S.KR 280000)

CIGNAROLI, Scipione (studio) (1715-1766) Italian
£8333 $15333 €12500 Rural landscape with peasant (90x120cm-35x47in) painted with Pietro Domenico Ollivero lit. 14-Jun-4 Sant Agostino, Torino #309/R est:5000-7000

CIGNAROLI, Vittorio Amedeo (c.1747-1793) Italian
£15385 $26462 €22000 Landscape with travellers (92x122cm-36x48in) 2-Dec-3 Sotheby's, Milan #124/R est:15000-20000
£29577 $51761 €42000 Two riders by river (110x154cm-43x61in) 17-Dec-3 Christie's, Rome #481/R est:45000-60000
£34965 $59441 €50000 River landscape with hunters and dogs (128x138cm-50x54in) 1-Dec-3 Babuino, Rome #134/R est:20000-30000
£40845 $71479 €58000 Couple in rural landscape (111x153cm-44x60in) 17-Dec-3 Christie's, Rome #480/R est:45000-60000

CIKOVSKY, Nicolai (1894-1984) American
£211 $335 €308 Female nude (23x15cm-9x6in) s. cardboard. 29-Apr-3 Louis Morton, Mexico #162 (M.P 3500)

£313 $550 €457 Autumn pond (23x30cm-9x12in) s. painted c.1930. 23-May-4 Treadway Gallery, Cincinnati #602/R
£353 $650 €515 Standing nude (41x30cm-16x12in) s. canvasboard. 10-Jun-4 Swann Galleries, New York #61/R
£438 $700 €639 Landscape (25x36cm-10x14in) s.d.1938. 17-May-3 Bunte, Elgin #1299
£483 $850 €705 Shoreline (30x41cm-12x16in) s. board painted c.1944. 23-May-4 Treadway Gallery, Cincinnati #649/R
£497 $875 €726 Girl with purple scarf (76x66cm-30x26in) s. 22-May-4 Selkirks, St. Louis #540/R
£546 $1000 €797 Expansive landscape (56x71cm-22x28in) s. board painted c.1900. 5-Jun-4 Treadway Gallery, Cincinnati #662/R est:1500-2000
£1118 $1800 €1632 Reflection (30x41cm-12x16in) s. canvas on board. 22-Feb-3 Bunte, Elgin #1252 est:400-600
£1136 $2000 €1659 Long Island landscape with still life (61x76cm-24x30in) s. prov. 3-Jan-4 Collins, Maine #30/R est:3000-5000
£4396 $8000 €6418 David Burliuk painting his wife Marussia at the beach (36x46cm-14x18in) s. board prov. 29-Jun-4 Sotheby's, New York #387/R est:3000-4000

CILA, Otakar (1894-?) Czechoslovakian
£600 $1110 €876 Road to market (49x63cm-19x25in) s. board. 15-Jan-4 Christie's, Kensington #845/R

CILFONE, Gianni (1908-1990) American/Italian
£247 $425 €361 Winter landscape (48x38cm-19x15in) s. masonite. 7-Dec-3 Hindman, Chicago #777/R
£568 $1000 €829 Seated nude (25x20cm-10x8in) s. board painted c.1940. 23-May-4 Treadway Gallery, Cincinnati #637/R

CILLERO DOLZ, Andres (1934-1993) Spanish
£811 $1427 €1200 Apocalyptic white (92x80cm-36x31in) s.d.1970 oil collage canvas on board. 18-May-4 Segre, Madrid #146/R

CIMA, Luigi (1860-1938) Italian
£471 $772 €650 Landscape (12x6cm-5x2in) s. board. 29-May-3 Galleria Pace, Milan #94/R
£10776 $19289 €15733 Summer landscape with young shepherdess (71x126cm-28x50in) s. 12-May-4 Dobiaschofsky, Bern #395/R est:5000 (S.FR 25000)

CIMAROLI, Giovanni Battista (17/18th C) Italian
£13793 $22897 €20000 River landscape with arched stone bridge (67x112cm-26x44in) 1-Oct-3 Dorotheum, Vienna #39/R est:28000-36000
£189944 $340000 €277318 View of the mills at Dolo on the Brenta. View of the Brenta Canal (72x100cm-28x39in) pair. 27-May-4 Sotheby's, New York #116/R est:150000-200000

CIMAROLI, Giovanni Battista (circle) (17/18th C) Italian
£5000 $8500 €7300 Italianate landscape with figures washing in a river (28x27cm-11x11in) 30-Oct-3 Sotheby's, Olympia #157/R est:2000-3000

CIMINAGHI, Virgilio (1911-2001) Italian
Sculpture
£1379 $2207 €2000 Resurrection (24x27cm-9x11in) s. bronze. 13-Mar-3 Galleria Pace, Milan #88/R est:2000-2600

CIMIOTTI, Emil (1927-) German
Sculpture
£1208 $2223 €1800 Untitled (11x22x17cm-4x9x7in) painted bronze prov. 26-Mar-4 Ketterer, Hamburg #356/R est:1800-2200
£1733 $3103 €2600 Tree III (49x33x23cm-19x13x9in) brown pat.bronze prov. 15-May-4 Van Ham, Cologne #519/R est:3000
£2657 $4571 €3800 Group of figures (41x17x18cm-16x7x7in) bronze exec. 1958 prov. 4-Dec-3 Van Ham, Cologne #104/R est:4000
£3357 $5773 €4800 Southern island (23x37cm-9x15in) bronze exec. 1959 prov. 4-Dec-3 Van Ham, Cologne #103/R est:4800
Works on paper
£267 $477 €400 Untitled (60x85cm-24x33in) s.d.58/1 graphite prov. 15-May-4 Van Ham, Cologne #518/R
£400 $716 €600 Composition (45x71cm-18x28in) s. chl pencil prov. 15-May-4 Van Ham, Cologne #517/R
£764 $1276 €1100 Untitled (19x67cm-7x26in) s.d. verso pencil chl. 24-Oct-3 Ketterer, Hamburg #301/R
£833 $1392 €1200 Untitled (33x52cm-13x20in) s.d. s.i.d. verso pencil chl sketch verso. 24-Oct-3 Ketterer, Hamburg #300/R

CIMIOTTI, Gustave (1875-1969) American
£284 $475 €415 Stream with trees (20x25cm-8x10in) s. canvasboard. 20-Jun-3 Freeman, Philadelphia #188/R
£330 $600 €482 Small wave, Maine (41x51cm-16x20in) s. i.verso canvasboard. 7-Feb-4 Neal Auction Company, New Orleans #781
£376 $700 €549 Coastal scene with a lighthouse (41x51cm-16x20in) s. canvasboard painted c.1920. 7-Mar-4 Treadway Gallery, Cincinnati #555/R
£523 $900 €764 El Toro, California (41x51cm-16x20in) s. i.verso canvasboard painted c.1920. 7-Dec-3 Treadway Gallery, Cincinnati #586/R
£694 $1200 €1013 Talpa New Mexico, farm landscape (30x41cm-12x16in) s. 10-Dec-3 Alderfer's, Hatfield #380/R
£778 $1300 €1136 Old Manse at Monterey, Massachusetts (20x28cm-8x11in) s. canvasboard. 20-Jun-3 Freeman, Philadelphia #123/R est:400-600
£1618 $2750 €2362 Entrance to Taos ranch (30x41cm-12x16in) s. s.i.verso canvas on board prov. 1-Nov-3 Santa Fe Art, Santa Fe #214/R est:2000-3000
£1879 $3250 €2743 Mount Mansfield (102x127cm-40x50in) s. 15-Dec-3 Winter Associates, Plainville #50/R est:2000-3000

CINALLI, Ricardo (1948-) Argentinian
£1511 $2568 €2206 Sunday - Dream Series II (66x49cm-26x19in) s.d.1992 tempera cardboard prov. 5-Nov-3 AB Stockholms Auktionsverk #916/R est:25000-30000 (S.KR 20000)

CINGOLANI, Marco (1961-) Italian
£307 $500 €448 Abstract (120x157cm-47x62in) s. 28-Sep-3 Bonhams & Butterfields, Los Angeles #7050
£1014 $1784 €1500 New house (50x70cm-20x28in) s.i.d.1999. 22-May-4 Galleria Pananti, Florence #348/R est:2000-2200
£1092 $1812 €1550 La Dolce Vita (45x50cm-18x20in) s.i.d.2000. 14-Jun-3 Meeting Art, Vercelli #50/R est:1000
Works on paper
£473 $832 €700 Process (32x24cm-13x9in) s.i.d.1993 verso W/C. 22-May-4 Galleria Pananti, Florence #369/R

CINGRIA, Alexandre (1879-1945) Swiss
Works on paper
£259 $463 €378 Noe (41x41cm-16x16in) s.mono. i. verso gouache. 12-May-4 Dobiaschofsky, Bern #3495 (S.FR 600)

CINI, Alfred (1887-1970) Swiss
£1357 $2348 €1981 Sierre (35x50cm-14x20in) s.i.d.1930 exhib. 12-Dec-3 Galerie du Rhone, Sion #483/R est:2500-3500 (S.FR 3000)

CINI, Enzo (20th C) ?
£2797 $4811 €4000 Le famille cathedrale (92x65cm-36x26in) s.i.d.1976 i.verso prov. 2-Dec-3 Sotheby's, Amsterdam #225/R est:3000-4000

CINOT, Franck (?-1890) French
£1056 $1754 €1500 Chasseur et son chien (35x47cm-14x19in) s. 15-Jun-3 Peron, Melun #229

CINTO, Sandra (1968-) Brazilian
Sculpture
£9412 $16000 €13742 Mesa - Table (91x59x80cm-36x23x31in) pen on painted wooden table exec. 1999 prov.exhib.lit. 18-Nov-3 Christie's, Rockefeller NY #4/R est:12000-18000

CINTOLI, Claudio (1935-1978) Italian
£2414 $4031 €3500 Double head (35x50cm-14x20in) s.d.66. 13-Nov-3 Finarte Semenzato, Rome #440/R est:2500-3000
Works on paper
£552 $921 €800 Balance (32x23cm-13x9in) init.d.64 graphite pastel collage paper on card. 13-Nov-3 Finarte Semenzato, Rome #108
£2667 $4800 €4000 Gerry Sam (30x100cm-12x39in) s.d.1964 verso mixed media collage feathers on canvas. 22-Apr-4 Finarte Semenzato, Rome #193/R est:4500-5000

CIOCCHINI, Cleto (1899-1974) Argentinian
£950 $1700 €1387 Fishermen (14x19cm-6x7in) s.i. 4-May-4 Arroyo, Buenos Aires #54/R est:1000
£1099 $2000 €1605 Fishermen (32x40cm-13x16in) s.i. cardboard on canvas. 29-Jun-4 Arroyo, Buenos Aires #92/R
£1913 $3500 €2793 Arrival in Mar del Plata (47x57cm-19x22in) board. 1-Jun-4 Arroyo, Buenos Aires #43

CIOLI, Valerio di Simone (circle) (1529-1599) Italian
Sculpture
£29000 $50170 €42340 Standing naked boy with arms raised by a tree trunk (73cm-29in) white marble. 12-Dec-3 Sotheby's, London #214/R est:40000-60000

CIOMPI DELLE NOTTI, Fausto (1884-1969) Italian
Works on paper
£329 $605 €500 Carezza Lake (32x33cm-13x13in) s. W/C lit. 23-Jun-4 Finarte Semenzato, Rome #34/R

CIOTTA, Carlo (19th C) Italian
£1056 $1754 €1500 Marche aux poissons sur le canal de Grande (16x31cm-6x12in) s. panel pair. 16-Jun-3 E & Eve, Paris #81/R

CIOTTA, F (19th C) Italian
£1800 $2880 €2610 Herding wild horses in the Roman campagna (45x76cm-18x30in) s. 18-Sep-3 Christie's, Kensington #99/R est:2000-4000

CIOTTI, Giuseppe (1889-1991) Italian
£500 $920 €750 Futurist actor (13x21cm-5x8in) s. oil tempera card. 11-Jun-4 Farsetti, Prato #138/R
£733 $1327 €1100 Fri.muo.tsu (47x39cm-19x15in) s.d.1914-15 oil tempera collage card exhib.lit. 2-Apr-4 Farsetti, Prato #332/R
£733 $1327 €1100 FuturOcchio (47x39cm-19x15in) s.d.1915 oil tempera collage card exhib.lit. 2-Apr-4 Farsetti, Prato #331/R
£733 $1349 €1100 Future success (34x24cm-13x9in) s.d.1914 oil tempera card. 11-Jun-4 Farsetti, Prato #137/R
£759 $1267 €1100 Future theatre (39x47cm-15x19in) s.i. oil tempera collage paper exhib.lit. 14-Nov-3 Farsetti, Prato #59/R
£800 $1448 €1200 FuturAttak (47x39cm-19x15in) s. oil tempera collage paper exhib.lit. 2-Apr-4 Farsetti, Prato #333/R
£828 $1382 €1200 Future engineer (34x30cm-13x12in) s. oil tempera paper exhib. 14-Nov-3 Farsetti, Prato #256/R
£1000 $1840 €1500 Future party (39x45cm-15x18in) s. oil tempera collage card. 11-Jun-4 Farsetti, Prato #140/R est:1300
£1056 $1754 €1500 Pacific invasion in Libia (47x39cm-19x15in) s. oil tempera collage card exhib. 13-Jun-3 Farsetti, Prato #268/R
£1056 $1754 €1500 Future tactics and future war (39x47cm-15x19in) s.d.1915 oil tempera collage card. 13-Jun-3 Farsetti, Prato #273/R

£1067 $1963 €1600 Futurism and war (47x39cm-19x15in) s. oil tempera collage paper. 11-Jun-4 Farsetti, Prato #142/R est:1000-1300
£1067 $1963 €1600 Future flight (39x48cm-15x19in) s. oil tempera collage card. 11-Jun-4 Farsetti, Prato #141/R est:1100-1300
£1200 $2208 €1800 Future Christmas (47x77cm-19x30in) s.d.1915 oil tempera collage card. 11-Jun-4 Farsetti, Prato #139/R est:1400-1700
£1600 $2944 €2400 Italian futurist landscape (47x77cm-19x30in) s.i.d.1915 oil tempera card. 11-Jun-4 Farsetti, Prato #136/R est:1400-1700

CIPPER, Giacomo Francesco (c.1670-1738) Italian
£3546 $5922 €5000 Singing lesson (93x73cm-37x29in) 18-Oct-3 Meeting Art, Vercelli #416/R
£25180 $41295 €35000 Fish market (125x159cm-49x63in) 4-Jun-3 Sotheby's, Milan #130/R est:35000-45000
£35971 $58993 €50000 Dead game market (123x159cm-48x63in) s.d.1701. 4-Jun-3 Sotheby's, Milan #129/R est:50000-70000

CIPRIANI, A (19th C) Italian
Sculpture
£950 $1700 €1387 Young peasant child draped in a shawl with basket at her feet (61cm-24in) s. marble. 15-May-4 Jeffery Burchard, Florida #97
£978 $1800 €1428 Bust of a woman wearing a lace hat and flower on her chest (81cm-32in) white marble pedestal. 26-Jun-4 Selkirks, St. Louis #507/R est:1500-2000
£1600 $2912 €2400 Two winged cherubs playing (56cm-22in) marble incl. pedestal. 20-Jun-4 Wilkinson, Doncaster #57 est:2000-3000

CIPRIANI, Giovanni Battista (1727-1785) Italian
Works on paper
£1000 $1730 €1460 Head of a girl crowned with flowers (40x33cm-16x13in) col chk stumped. 12-Dec-3 Christie's, Kensington #396/R est:500-800

CIPRIANI, Giovanni Battista (attrib) (1727-1785) Italian
£1258 $2290 €1900 Diane chasseresse (86x76cm-34x30in) 15-Jun-4 Vanderkindere, Brussels #4 est:1000-1500
£6800 $11764 €9928 Mediterranean landscape with putti firing arrows to a shield (41x61cm-16x24in) 12-Dec-3 Christie's, Kensington #250/R est:4000-6000
Works on paper
£380 $665 €555 Hercules and Imphale (33x28cm-13x11in) indis.i. pen brown ink over pencil. 16-Dec-3 Capes Dunn, Manchester #730

CIPRIANI, Giuseppe (1826-1911) Italian
Sculpture
£2113 $3507 €3000 Bust of a young girl (46cm-18in) s. white marble executed c.1900. 11-Jun-3 Sotheby's, Amsterdam #295/R est:1500-2000

CIPRIANI, Nazzarreno (1843-1925) Italian
Works on paper
£935 $1534 €1300 Customs in Veice (47x89cm-19x35in) W/C Chinese ink. 10-Jun-3 Pandolfini, Florence #37/R
£1056 $1827 €1500 Old Rome (25x50cm-10x20in) s. W/C card. 11-Dec-3 Christie's, Rome #8/R est:1300-1800

CIRAN, Dusan (20th C) American
£227 $400 €331 Springtime in Wisconsin (41x51cm-16x20in) s.i. painted 1992. 23-May-4 Hindman, Chicago #1025/R

CIRCIELLO, Michele (1944-) Italian
Works on paper
£336 $621 €500 Dusk amongst rocks (90x50cm-35x20in) s. mixed media board exec.2002. 13-Mar-4 Meeting Art, Vercelli #55
£369 $683 €550 Dawn in the mountains (90x50cm-35x20in) s. mixed media board exec.2002. 13-Mar-4 Meeting Art, Vercelli #165

CIRIA, Jose Manuel (1960-) British
£423 $739 €600 Composition (34x28cm-13x11in) s. board. 16-Dec-3 Durán, Madrid #652/R

CIRILLI, Sirio (20th C) Italian
£280 $515 €420 Square in Livorno (55x44cm-22x17in) s.d.1935 board. 11-Jun-4 Farsetti, Prato #474

CIRINO, Antonio (1889-1983) American
£950 $1700 €1387 New England autumn (25x30cm-10x12in) s. i.verso canvasboard prov. 14-May-4 Skinner, Boston #186/R est:800-1200
£2793 $5000 €4078 Up for repairs (63x76cm-25x30in) s. i.verso. 14-May-4 Skinner, Boston #284/R est:5000-7000
£4790 $8000 €6993 Israel Arnold House (91x102cm-36x40in) s. i.verso prov. 23-Oct-3 Shannon's, Milford #84/R est:8000-12000

CIRMEUSE, Gaston de (1886-1963) French
£588 $1000 €858 Sleepy eyed beauty (28x36cm-11x14in) s. 22-Nov-3 Jackson's, Cedar Falls #53/R est:1000-1500

CIRO, G (19th C) Italian?
£4722 $8500 €6894 Feeding the birds (102x62cm-40x24in) s.i. prov. 21-Jan-4 Sotheby's, New York #176/R est:1500-2500

CIROU, Paul (19/20th C) French
£300 $537 €450 Vernissage (48x59cm-19x23in) s. panel. 16-May-4 MonsAntic, Maisieres #385
£4056 $6976 €5800 Jour de fete a Nedroma (35x60cm-14x24in) s.i.d.1928 panel. 8-Dec-3 Tajan, Paris #247/R est:4500-5000
£4756 $8180 €6800 Mariee sur la route (34x55cm-13x22in) mono. s.i.verso board exhib. 8-Dec-3 Tajan, Paris #244/R est:7000-8000

CIRY, Michel (1919-) French
£1192 $2170 €1800 Mise au tombeau (106x106cm-42x42in) s.d.67 s.i.verso. 15-Jun-4 Blanchet, Paris #233/R est:1800-2000
£1192 $2229 €1800 Les Alpilles (27x22cm-11x9in) s.d.62. 24-Jul-4 Thierry & Lannon, Brest #251/R est:1000-1200
£1200 $2196 €1800 Saint Francois d'Assise (60x30cm-24x12in) s.d.57 prov. 6-Jun-4 Anaf, Lyon #342 est:1000-1200
Works on paper
£1074 $2008 €1600 Sans titre (72x104cm-28x41in) s.d.1970 W/C gouache. 29-Feb-4 Versailles Encheres #119/R est:500-600
£1931 $3572 €2800 Arbres en hiver (70x103cm-28x41in) s.d.81 ink W/C. 11-Feb-4 Beaussant & Lefèvre, Paris #163/R est:2500-3000

CISERI, Antonio (1821-1891) Italian
£1295 $2124 €1800 Study for martyrdom (39x30cm-15x12in) paper on canvas. 10-Jun-3 Pandolfini, Florence #17/R est:1600-1800

CISERI, Antonio (attrib) (1821-1891) Italian
£791 $1298 €1100 Christ (57x46cm-22x18in) oval. 10-Jun-3 Pandolfini, Florence #54/R

CITROEN, Paul (1896-1983) Dutch
£699 $1203 €1000 Bridge over the forest brook (44x54cm-17x21in) s. 8-Dec-3 Glerum, Amsterdam #261/R
£1449 $2377 €2000 Frivolite (43x24cm-17x9in) s.verso oil collage cardboard prov. 27-May-3 Sotheby's, Amsterdam #356/R est:1500-2000

CITRON, Minna (1896-?) American
£8287 $15000 €12099 Final adjustments (42x45cm-17x18in) s.d.36 tempera W/C masonite prov.exhib. 31-Mar-4 Sotheby's, New York #133/R est:2500-3500

CITTADINI, Pier Francesco (attrib) (1616-1681) Italian
£2734 $4483 €3800 Portrait de jeune femme devant une fenetre decoree de fleurs (121x92cm-48x36in) i. 6-Jun-3 Drouot Estimations, Paris #24 est:4000-5000
£7692 $13231 €11000 Portrait of boy with vase of flowers (57x45cm-22x18in) 2-Dec-3 Sotheby's, Milan #34/R est:6000-8000
£10791 $17698 €15000 Portrait of family (114x94cm-45x37in) prov. 4-Jun-3 Sotheby's, Milan #82/R est:15000-20000

CITTADINI, Pier Francesco (style) (1616-1681) Italian
£8500 $14450 €12410 Christ child surrounded by floral garland (52x42cm-20x17in) 30-Oct-3 Sotheby's, Olympia #115/R est:6000-8000

CITTADINI, Tito (1886-1960) Argentinian
£1552 $2793 €2250 View of town (15x23cm-6x9in) s. cardboard. 26-Jan-4 Durán, Madrid #217/R est:1100
£2897 $5214 €4200 Seascape with mountains in the background (26x34cm-10x13in) s.d.1948 cardboard. 26-Jan-4 Ansorena, Madrid #187/R est:4000
£5263 $9526 €8000 Rainy day (38x46cm-15x18in) s.d.932 board. 14-Apr-4 Ansorena, Madrid #56/R est:5900

CIVET, Andre (1911-) French
£267 $477 €400 La table dressee avec le coq (82x100cm-32x39in) 16-May-4 Osenat, Fontainebleau #70
£378 $700 €552 Nature morte a la flute (89x89cm-35x35in) s. painted 1955 prov.exhib. 15-Jul-4 Sotheby's, New York #93/R

CIVITARESE, Goffredo (1938-) Italian
£333 $613 €500 Figures with seagull (80x80cm-31x31in) s. lit. 12-Jun-4 Meeting Art, Vercelli #314/R
£336 $621 €500 Offer (80x60cm-31x24in) s. s.i.verso. 13-Mar-4 Meeting Art, Vercelli #197
£400 $736 €600 Charming look (70x50cm-28x20in) s. s.i.verso. 12-Jun-4 Meeting Art, Vercelli #198/R
£400 $736 €600 Interior with figure and still life (60x70cm-24x28in) s. painted 2002. 12-Jun-4 Meeting Art, Vercelli #681/R
£400 $736 €600 Jugs (70x50cm-28x20in) s. s.i.verso. 12-Jun-4 Meeting Art, Vercelli #916/R
£467 $859 €700 Friends with Fanta (80x80cm-31x31in) s. 12-Jun-4 Meeting Art, Vercelli #165/R
£500 $920 €750 Blue profiles (70x60cm-28x24in) s. painted 2002. 12-Jun-4 Meeting Art, Vercelli #570/R
£500 $920 €750 Great talisman (90x70cm-35x28in) s. s.verso painted 2002 lit. 12-Jun-4 Meeting Art, Vercelli #596/R
£503 $931 €750 Onyx vase (70x70cm-28x28in) s. painted 2003. 13-Mar-4 Meeting Art, Vercelli #242
£570 $1055 €850 Girl and warrior (70x100cm-28x39in) s. s.i.verso. 13-Mar-4 Meeting Art, Vercelli #264
£671 $1242 €1000 Eastern beauties (110x80cm-43x31in) s. 13-Mar-4 Meeting Art, Vercelli #520
£1000 $1840 €1500 Girls in red and orange (100x80cm-39x31in) s. s.verso painted 2002 lit. 12-Jun-4 Meeting Art, Vercelli #980/R est:1000

CLAASSEN, George (1890-1975) Dutch
£570 $1061 €850 Mending nets in the dunes at Scheveningen (50x60cm-20x24in) s. 4-Mar-4 Auction Maastricht #1130/R

CLACY, Ellen (fl.1870-1916) British
£900 $1584 €1314 Mother and child, Whitby harbourside, towards the Abbey (33x48cm-13x19in) s.d.1883. 20-May-4 Richardson & Smith, Whitby #671

CLAERHOUT, Frans (1919-) South African

£556 $944 €812 Flower picker in a green landscape (44x58cm-17x23in) s. board. 4-Nov-3 Stephan Welz, Johannesburg #640/R est:7000-10000 (SA.R 6500)
£619 $1109 €904 Portrait of a young girl (69x40cm-27x16in) s. board. 31-May-4 Stephan Welz, Johannesburg #567 (SA.R 7500)
£702 $1256 €1025 Two birds and a figure (45x53cm-18x21in) s. board. 31-May-4 Stephan Welz, Johannesburg #578 (SA.R 8500)
£1121 $1872 €1637 Six labourers in a field (50x59cm-20x23in) s. board. 20-Oct-3 Stephan Welz, Johannesburg #340/R est:5000-8000 (SA.R 13000)
£1817 $3252 €2653 Woodcarrier amongst houses (49x59cm-19x23in) s. board. 31-May-4 Stephan Welz, Johannesburg #585/R est:10000-15000 (SA.R 22000)

Works on paper

£248 $443 €362 Figures embracing (60x42cm-24x17in) s. mixed media. 31-May-4 Stephan Welz, Johannesburg #354 (SA.R 3000)
£274 $465 €400 Nude woman (36x26cm-14x10in) chl oil on paper. 4-Nov-3 Stephan Welz, Johannesburg #333 est:2000-3000 (SA.R 3200)
£289 $517 €422 Figure clasping a bird (58x37cm-23x15in) s. mixed media. 31-May-4 Stephan Welz, Johannesburg #355 (SA.R 3500)
£454 $813 €663 Mother and child with a woman praying in an interior (42x59cm-17x23in) s. mixed media. 31-May-4 Stephan Welz, Johannesburg #370 (SA.R 5500)

CLAERHOUT, Jef (?) ?

£486 $812 €700 Homme bardu (41cm-16in) s. copper. 21-Oct-3 Campo, Vlaamse Kaai #376

CLAES, J (?) Belgian?

£1067 $1909 €1600 Bouquet de roses (40x60cm-16x24in) s. possibly pseudonym of Max Carlier. 11-May-4 Vanderkindere, Brussels #20 est:1000-1500

CLAES-THOLOIS, Albert (1883-?) ?

£800 $1472 €1200 Nu a la meridienne (108x80cm-43x31in) s. 14-Jun-4 Horta, Bruxelles #98

CLAESSENS, Karel (1879-1963) Belgian

£300 $543 €450 Fleurs (65x54cm-26x21in) s. 30-Mar-4 Campo & Campo, Antwerp #40

CLAESZ, Anthony (attrib) (16/17th C) Dutch

Works on paper

£2603 $4425 €3800 Red parrot tulip. Blue parrot tulip. Dark blue parrot tulip (25x9cm-10x4in) W/C bodycol set of three. 5-Nov-3 Christie's, Amsterdam #118/R est:2000-3000

CLAESZ, Pieter (1590-1661) Dutch

£6667 $12133 €10000 Still life with ham (59x84cm-23x33in) panel lit. 30-Jun-4 Neumeister, Munich #472/R est:3000
£20950 $37500 €30587 Still life of cab on pewter plate, salt-cellar and oysters (31x41cm-12x16in) panel prov.lit. 27-May-4 Sotheby's, New York #18/R est:40000-60000
£140000 $256200 €204400 Crab on a pewter plate, a roemer, partly-peeled lemon on a partly draped table (59x79cm-23x31in) mono.d.1636 panel. 7-Jul-4 Christie's, London #54/R est:150000-200000

CLAESZ, Pieter (attrib) (1590-1661) Dutch

Works on paper

£1800 $3114 €2628 Parrot tulip (24x9cm-9x4in) W/C htd white. 12-Dec-3 Christie's, Kensington #528/R est:600-800

CLAESZ, Pieter (circle) (1590-1661) Dutch

£9500 $17670 €13870 Vanitas still life (49x65cm-19x26in) panel. 4-Mar-4 Christie's, London #369/R est:6000-8000

CLAEYS, Albert (1889-1967) Belgian

£671 $1242 €1000 Still life with roses (32x40cm-13x16in) s. canvas on panel. 13-Mar-4 De Vuyst, Lokeren #51
£1007 $1862 €1500 Farms along the River Leie (40x58cm-16x23in) s. canvas on panel. 13-Mar-4 De Vuyst, Lokeren #50/R est:1500-1700
£1268 $2193 €1800 River Leie in winter (48x60cm-19x24in) s. panel. 13-Dec-3 De Vuyst, Lokeren #53/R est:2000-2400
£1467 $2684 €2200 Paysage de la Lys (40x58cm-16x23in) s. 7-Jun-4 Palais de Beaux Arts, Brussels #38/R est:1500-2000
£2041 $3714 €3000 Flooded banks of the river Leie, Belgium (60x70cm-24x28in) s. 3-Feb-4 Christie's, Amsterdam #452 est:1500-2000
£2378 $4042 €3400 Paysage de la Lys (48x61cm-19x24in) s. 1-Dec-3 Palais de Beaux Arts, Brussels #225/R est:3250-4000

CLAGHORN, Joseph C (1869-1947) American

£486 $900 €710 Twilight, Gloucester harbor, Massachusetts (38x43cm-15x17in) canvas on board. 15-Jul-4 Doyle, New York #22/R

Works on paper

£335 $600 €489 Arrivals (46x71cm-18x28in) s. W/C htd white. 8-May-4 Auctions by the Bay, Alameda #492/R
£492 $850 €718 Autumn landscape with roadside house and horse drawn wagon (46x71cm-18x28in) s. W/C. 10-Dec-3 Alderfer's, Hatfield #368/R

CLAIN, Fernand (19th C) French?

Sculpture

£1053 $1937 €1600 Buste representant Mozart (51cm-20in) terracotta marble base. 23-Jun-4 Millon & Associes, Paris #151 est:800-1000

CLAIR, Charles (1860-1930) French

£331 $603 €500 Route enneigee (65x55cm-26x22in) s. 17-Jun-4 Marie & Robert, Paris #57
£993 $1658 €1400 Bergerie (33x46cm-13x18in) s. 20-Jun-3 Drouot Estimations, Paris #64
£1042 $1740 €1500 La bergerie (25x38cm-10x15in) s. panel. 23-Oct-3 Credit Municipal, Paris #98 est:600-800
£1549 $2680 €2200 Moissons (46x55cm-18x22in) s. 14-Dec-3 Eric Pillon, Calais #38/R
£1647 $2750 €2405 Rural scene (64x81cm-25x32in) 17-Oct-3 Du Mouchelle, Detroit #2096/R est:2500-3500
£1700 $3060 €2482 Harvesting (50x64cm-20x25in) s. 21-Jan-4 Sotheby's, Olympia #424/R est:600-800
£1748 $3007 €2500 Troupeau de moutons (63x53cm-25x21in) s. 7-Dec-3 Osenat, Fontainebleau #64 est:2500-3000
£2308 $3969 €3300 La moisson (33x41cm-13x16in) s. panel. 7-Dec-3 Osenat, Fontainebleau #148 est:2400-2600
£3287 $5489 €4700 Bergerie (100x81cm-39x32in) s. 29-Jun-3 Eric Pillon, Calais #43/R

CLAIRIN, Georges (1843-1919) French

£503 $890 €750 Porte-etendard (91x50cm-36x20in) s. 30-Apr-4 Tajan, Paris #185
£922 $1540 €1300 Espagnol (46x26cm-18x10in) bears st.sig. 19-Jun-3 Millon & Associes, Paris #181
£1119 $1869 €1600 Still life (66x125cm-26x49in) s. 30-Jun-3 Ansorena, Madrid #394/R
£1233 $2096 €1800 Rameurs a Belle Isle (9x50cm-4x20in) s.i. panel. 6-Nov-3 Sotheby's, Paris #122/R est:2000-3000
£1333 $2387 €2000 Bord de canal (60x72cm-24x28in) s. 16-May-4 Thierry & Lannon, Brest #127/R est:2000-2200
£4894 $8172 €6900 La comtesse de Castiglione (82x60cm-32x24in) s. 19-Jun-3 Millon & Associes, Paris #179/R est:10000-12000
£6000 $10740 €9000 Au coeur de la cite, preparatifs avant le depart du convoi (51x108cm-20x43in) s. 16-May-4 Thierry & Lannon, Brest #126/R est:9000-10000
£10000 $18300 €15100 La danse des fees (100x165cm-39x65in) s. 9-Apr-4 Claude Aguttes, Neuilly #66/R est:15000-18000

Works on paper

£526 $968 €800 Pour le monument a Beethoven (47x33cm-19x13in) s.i.d.1913 pastel graphite. 25-Jun-4 Millon & Associes, Paris #126
£616 $1048 €900 Lagune a Venise (44x55cm-17x22in) s.i.d.1892 W/C. 6-Nov-3 Sotheby's, Paris #123/R
£7692 $13077 €11000 Femmes alanguies (184x84cm-72x33in) s.d.1906 pastel pair. 27-Nov-3 Millon & Associes, Paris #159/R est:10000-12000
£7945 $12474 €11600 Caravane de maries dans le desert (51x68cm-20x27in) s. gouache htd pastel. 20-Apr-3 Deauville, France #39/R est:9000-12000

CLAIRIN, Pierre Eugène (1897-1980) French

£282 $468 €400 Bords de Seine (61x73cm-24x29in) s.d.59. 10-Jun-3 Adjug'art, Brest #102
£1267 $2267 €1900 Ste-Anne-La-Palud (60x81cm-24x32in) s. 16-May-4 Thierry & Lannon, Brest #296/R est:2000-2500

Works on paper

£333 $597 €500 Le semaphore (27x42cm-11x17in) s. W/C. 16-May-4 Thierry & Lannon, Brest #382

CLAIRMONT, Philip (1949-1984) New Zealander

£338 $575 €493 General (118x75cm-46x30in) board sold with a letter. 26-Nov-3 Dunbar Sloane, Wellington #140 (NZ.D 900)
£376 $639 €549 General (118x75cm-46x30in) board sold with a letter prov. 26-Nov-3 Dunbar Sloane, Wellington #141 est:500-1000 (NZ.D 1000)
£2527 $4119 €3689 Study of Paul seated and reading (120x79cm-47x31in) i.d.1960 acrylic ink. W/C pastel crayon. 23-Sep-3 Peter Webb, Auckland #137/R est:4000-6000 (NZ.D 7000)
£4286 $7757 €6258 Self portrait (30x30cm-12x12in) s.i.d.1975 board prov. 30-Mar-4 Peter Webb, Auckland #24/R est:5500-7500 (NZ.D 12000)
£7857 $14457 €11471 Departure of the soul (147x92cm-58x36in) s. jute prov. 25-Mar-4 International Art Centre, Auckland #84/R est:22000-30000 (NZ.D 22000)
£12635 $20596 €18447 Window (147x92cm-58x36in) s.d.1978. 23-Sep-3 Peter Webb, Auckland #84/R est:40000-60000 (NZ.D 35000)

Works on paper

£830 $1487 €1212 Head (34cm-13in circular) init.i.d.Oct 70 mixed media. 12-May-4 Dunbar Sloane, Wellington #186/R est:2000-3000 (NZ.D 2400)
£1450 $2494 €2117 Portrait of an unhappy Masochist (73x119cm-29x47in) s.i.d.77 mixed media prov. 3-Dec-3 Dunbar Sloane, Auckland #61/R est:3000-5000 (NZ.D 3900)
£2052 $3550 €2996 Interior with vase on a table (45x59cm-18x23in) pastel. 9-Dec-3 Peter Webb, Auckland #122/R est:5500-6500 (NZ.D 5500)

CLAISSE, Genevieve (1935-) French

£432 $800 €631 Organisation active. Untitled (99x81cm-39x32in) one s.d.1978-81 verso acrylic one s. ink over pencil two. 10-Mar-4 Doyle, New York #83a/R
£1674 $2846 €2444 Poseidon (60x60cm-24x24in) s.d.1965 verso prov. 22-Nov-3 Burkhard, Luzern #129/R est:3500-4500 (S.FR 3700)

CLAPERA, Pedro (1906-) Spanish

£423 $739 €600 Clowns (58x42cm-23x17in) s. s.i.verso. 16-Dec-3 Durán, Madrid #45/R

CLAPHAM, James T (fl.1862) British

Works on paper

£300 $546 €438 Primroses, fort-me-nots, white blossom and a bird's nest (28x36cm-11x14in) mono. W/C bodycol. 29-Jun-4 Bonhams, Knowle #58

CLAPP, William H (1879-1954) Canadian

£1359 $2500 €1984 Country landscape (38x46cm-15x18in) s.d.1936 board. 26-Jun-4 Sloans & Kenyon, Bethesda #1097/R est:2000-3000
£1511 $2750 €2206 Cabins in summer landscape (30x25cm-12x10in) board prov. 15-Jun-4 John Moran, Pasadena #28 est:3000-5000
£3252 $5821 €4748 Corner of an old village, Spain (25x33cm-10x13in) s. i.verso board painted c.1907 prov. 27-May-4 Heffel, Vancouver #207/R est:2000-3000 (C.D 8000)

£3804	$7000	€5554	Bathers on the beach (38x46cm-15x18in) s.d.45 board. 26-Jun-4 Sloans & Kenyon, Bethesda #1098/R est:3000-5000
£4076	$7500	€5951	Farm through the trees with mountains beyond (38x45cm-15x18in) s.d.39 masonite prov. 8-Jun-4 Bonhams & Butterfields, San Francisco #4306/R est:4000-6000
£4800	$8784	€7008	Autumn Road, St Eustache (41x51cm-16x20in) s.d.1912 prov. 1-Jun-4 Joyner Waddington, Toronto #107/R est:12000-15000 (C.D 12000)
£8671	$15000	€12660	Country road (76x91cm-30x36in) prov. 10-Dec-3 Bonhams & Butterfields, San Francisco #6260/R est:15000-20000
£9009	$15315	€13153	Two figures in a landscape (30x21cm-12x8in) s.i.d.15 i.d.verso panel prov.lit. 18-Nov-3 Sotheby's, Toronto #60/R est:15000-18000 (C.D 20000)
£13600	$24888	€19856	Diffused nude (37x45cm-15x18in) board exhib. 1-Jun-4 Joyner Waddington, Toronto #115/R est:18000-22000 (C.D 34000)
Works on paper			
£824	$1400	€1203	Reclining nude (18x25cm-7x10in) s. graphite prov. 18-Nov-3 John Moran, Pasadena #87c est:1500-2000

CLARA, Enrico (1870-?) Italian

£1497	$2679	€2200	View of Candia Lake (78x105cm-31x41in) s. 22-Mar-4 Sant Agostino, Torino #253/R est:500-700

CLARA, Jose (1878-1958) Spanish

£403	$753	€600	Landscape (21x27cm-8x11in) s. 24-Feb-4 Durán, Madrid #160/R
£436	$816	€650	Landscape (23x34cm-9x13in) s. 24-Feb-4 Durán, Madrid #161/R

CLARA, Juan (1875-1957) Spanish

Sculpture			
£1000	$1820	€1460	Suzette (33cm-13in) s. brown pat bronze. 15-Jun-4 Sotheby's, Olympia #77/R est:1000-1500

CLARA, Luigi (1875-1925) Italian

£872	$1544	€1300	Autumnal landscape (49x69cm-19x27in) s. 1-May-4 Meeting Art, Vercelli #58

CLARAC, Charles-Othon (1777-1829) French

Works on paper			
£33333	$54333	€48000	Foret vierge du Bresil (62x86cm-24x34in) W/C pen sepia over pencil htd white. 26-Sep-3 Venator & Hansten, Koln #789/R est:30000

CLARAC, Charles-Othon (attrib) (1777-1829) French

Works on paper			
£8500	$13174	€12410	Foret vierge du Bresil (59x80cm-23x31in) bodycol. 26-Sep-2 Christie's, London #109/R est:12000-16000

CLARAMUNT, Luis (1951-2000) Spanish

£1200	$2184	€1800	Figura (100x81cm-39x32in) s.d.3-78 prov.exhib. 29-Jun-4 Segre, Madrid #157/R est:1700

CLARE, George (1835-c.1890) British

£480	$754	€696	Pelargoniums on a mossy bank (18x25cm-7x10in) s. board. 28-Aug-3 Christie's, Kensington #276
£720	$1296	€1051	Still life of apples, plums and strawberries in a basket (25x31cm-10x12in) s. 21-Jan-4 Sotheby's, Olympia #339/R
£726	$1300	€1060	Still life with fruit (15x20cm-6x8in) s. 14-May-4 Skinner, Boston #40/R est:1500-2500
£960	$1651	€1402	Still life of black and white grapes, three strawberries and a peach on a mossy bank (25x30cm-10x12in) s. 2-Dec-3 Canterbury Auctions, UK #160/R
£1048	$1929	€1530	Robin's nest and pansies (15x22cm-6x9in) s. prov. 9-Jun-4 Walker's, Ottawa #336/R est:1000-1500 (C.D 2600)
£1242	$2000	€1813	Pink and white pansies and a bird's nest with eggs on mossy bank. Mixed fruit on mossy bank (15x23cm-6x9in) indis sig. pair. 14-Jan-4 Christie's, Rockefeller NY #73/R est:3000-5000
£1500	$2700	€2190	Still life of plums and apples. Still life of primrose, violets and birds nest on mossy bank (15x22cm-6x9in) s. pair. 21-Apr-4 Cheffins, Cambridge #473/R est:800-1200
£1956	$3500	€2856	Still life with flowers and bird's nest (16x21cm-6x8in) s. 14-May-4 Skinner, Boston #38/R est:1500-2500
£2300	$3680	€3358	Basket of primroses, bird with eggs (30x25cm-12x10in) s. 18-Sep-3 Goldings, Lincolnshire #720/R est:2000-2500
£2394	$4142	€3400	Still life of grapes in gilt bowl (36x31cm-14x12in) s. 13-Dec-3 Hagelstam, Helsinki #28/R est:1500
£3200	$5440	€4672	Still life of raspberries and damsons in a basket, and other fruit on a bank (46x61cm-18x24in) s. 19-Nov-3 Tennants, Leyburn #1218/R est:3000-4000

CLARE, Oliver (1853-1927) British

£360	$612	€526	Still life with a pear and raspberries on a mossy bank (10x15cm-4x6in) s. board. 18-Nov-3 Bonhams, Leeds #181
£360	$644	€526	Still life of apple blossom and a bird's nest on a mossy bank (22x29cm-9x11in) s. 16-Mar-4 Bonhams, Leeds #647
£444	$800	€648	Still life with fruit (22x16cm-9x6in) s. pair prov. 21-Jan-4 Doyle, New York #134
£550	$919	€803	Grapes, plums, gooseberries and peach on a mossy bank (25x20cm-10x8in) s. 13-Nov-3 Christie's, Kensington #352
£550	$1012	€803	Still life of flowers and a bird's nest (22x29cm-9x11in) s. 8-Jun-4 Bonhams, Knightsbridge #324/R
£700	$1281	€1022	Still life with peaches grapes gooseberries and raspberries (18x23cm-7x9in) s. board. 28-Jul-4 Mallams, Oxford #347/R
£750	$1343	€1095	Still life of plums, and other fruit on a mossy bank (25x20cm-10x8in) s. 27-May-4 Christie's, Kensington #345/R
£820	$1550	€1197	Still life of fruit and foliage (15x20cm-6x8in) s.d.99. 19-Feb-4 Grant, Worcester #427
£940	$1683	€1372	Still life of grapes, plums a strawberry and an apple on mossy bank (20x28cm-8x11in) s. 6-Jan-4 Gildings, Market Harborough #397
£950	$1748	€1387	Grapes, apples and gooseberries (15x19cm-6x7in) s. board. 29-Mar-4 Bonhams, Bath #104/R
£975	$1745	€1424	Still life study of grapes and strawberry amongst foliage (13x18cm-5x7in) s. 6-May-4 Biddle & Webb, Birmingham #889
£1000	$1700	€1460	Greengages, plums and a strawberry against a mossy bank (18x23cm-7x9in) s.d.99. 25-Nov-3 Bonhams, Knowle #252 est:1000-1500
£1000	$1720	€1460	Still life with grapes and other fruit on a ledge (23x34cm-9x13in) s. 4-Dec-3 Locke & England, Leamington Spa #150/R est:1000-1500
£1000	$1870	€1460	Various fruits on a mossy bank (25x20cm-10x8in) s. 24-Feb-4 Bonhams, Knowle #100/R est:1000-1500
£1000	$1830	€1460	Still life with peaches, grapes, raspberries and gooseberries (36x25cm-14x10in) s. panel. 28-Jul-4 Mallams, Oxford #346/R est:1000-1200
£1044	$1900	€1566	Still life of fruit (15x20cm-6x8in) s.d.94 board. 16-Jun-4 Wolf's, New York #486560/R
£1050	$1932	€1533	Grapes, strawberries and other fruit (14x19cm-6x7in) s. 29-Mar-4 Bonhams, Bath #103/R est:700-900
£1062	$1900	€1551	Still life with mountain laurel a plein air (23x18cm-9x7in) s. board. 14-May-4 Skinner, Boston #36/R est:1000-1500
£1100	$2002	€1606	Still life with plums, gooseberries and other fruits on a mossy bank (24x19cm-9x7in) 1-Jul-4 Mellors & Kirk, Nottingham #787/R est:800-1200
£1111	$2000	€1622	Still life with grapes and gooseberries. Still life with plums and apples (22x30cm-9x12in) s. two. 21-Jan-4 Doyle, New York #132/R est:3000-5000
£1154	$2100	€1731	Still life of fruit (15x20cm-6x8in) s.d.94. 16-Jun-4 Wolf's, New York #486561/R est:3000-5000
£1200	$2148	€1752	Still life of plums and gooseberries on a mossy bank (23x18cm-9x7in) s.d.88. 18-Mar-4 Christie's, Kensington #722/R est:800-1200
£1200	$2184	€1752	Still life with primroses and a nest of eggs (18x23cm-7x9in) s. 16-Jun-4 Brightwells, Leominster #861/R est:1200-1500
£1258	$2100	€1837	Still life with plums, apples and raspberries (30x25cm-12x10in) s. prov. 23-Oct-3 Shannon's, Milford #167/R est:2500-3500
£1300	$2132	€1898	Still life study of pansies and other flowers on a mossy bank (19x14cm-7x6in) s. 3-Jun-3 Fellows & Sons, Birmingham #15/R est:1000-1500
£1325	$2200	€1935	Still life with flowers and bird's nest (18x25cm-7x10in) s. 4-Oct-3 South Bay, Long Island #184
£1374	$2500	€2006	Still life with grapes and raspberries (30x22cm-12x9in) s.d.1921-22 board pair prov. 29-Jun-4 Sotheby's, New York #178/R est:2500-3500
£1400	$2212	€2044	Still life of plums, apples, white currants and gooseberries on a mossy bank (29x24cm-11x9in) s. 23-Jul-3 Hampton & Littlewood, Exeter #449/R est:1500-1700
£1481	$2800	€2162	Still life of fruit (23x18cm-9x7in) s. board pair. 21-Feb-4 Weschler, Washington #257 est:600-800
£1500	$2370	€2190	Still life study of grapes, plums and a strawberry. s. 4-Apr-3 Biddle & Webb, Birmingham #140 est:1500-2500
£1550	$2480	€2263	Green grapes, plums, strawberries and a gooseberry against a mossy bank (16x23cm-6x9in) s. board. 16-Sep-3 Bonhams, Knowle #84 est:1000-1500
£1550	$2480	€2263	Plums, greengages and pear against mossy bank. Grapes and other fruit against mossy bank (15x19cm-6x7in) s. board pair. 16-Sep-3 Bonhams, Knowle #106 est:1000-1500
£1600	$2864	€2336	Still life of grapes, apples (23x30cm-9x12in) s. 27-May-4 Christie's, Kensington #342/R est:600-800
£1677	$2700	€2448	Still life of fruit with grapes, peaches and plum (25x36cm-10x14in) s. 20-Aug-3 James Julia, Fairfield #604/R est:3500-5000
£1765	$3000	€2577	Still lifes with fruit (41x30cm-16x12in) s. panel pair. 19-Nov-3 Bonhams & Butterfields, San Francisco #143/R
£1770	$2850	€2584	Still life of fruit with grapes, apples and peach (25x36cm-10x14in) s. 20-Aug-3 James Julia, Fairfield #603/R est:2500-5000
£1800	$3222	€2628	Still life of apples blossom and bird's nest on mossy bank (20x25cm-8x10in) s. 27-May-4 Christie's, Kensington #343/R est:2000-3000
£1800	$3294	€2628	Primroses and a birds nest on a mossy bank (20x25cm-8x10in) s. 6-Jul-4 Bonhams, Knightsbridge #106/R est:1000-1500
£1950	$3081	€2847	Still life studies depicting assorted fruit amidst mossy backgrounds (13x20cm-5x8in) s. board pair. 4-Sep-3 Biddle & Webb, Birmingham #895
£2000	$3580	€2920	Primrose in a terracotta pot, apple blossom and a nest of birds eggs (23x33cm-9x13in) s. 7-May-4 Mallams, Oxford #338/R est:2000-3000
£2200	$4070	€3212	Still life (30x20cm-12x8in) 13-Jan-4 British Auctioneer #281
£2301	$3750	€3359	Still lives (18x23cm-7x9in) pair prov. 28-Sep-3 Carlsen Gallery, Greenville #103/R
£2400	$4536	€3504	Still life study of fruit (23x28cm-9x11in) s.d.89. 19-Feb-4 Grant, Worcester #428/R est:400-600
£2454	$4000	€3583	Still lives (18x23cm-7x9in) board pair prov. 28-Sep-3 Carlsen Gallery, Greenville #102/R
£2500	$4400	€3650	Still life of grapes, gooseberries and other fruit on a mossy bank (34x44cm-13x17in) s. canvas on board. 18-May-4 Fellows & Sons, Birmingham #105/R est:1400-2000
£2762	$5000	€4033	Still life with flowers and birds nests, raspberries and grapes (15x20cm-6x8in) pair. 3-Apr-4 South Bay, Long Island #137
£2800	$5012	€4088	Apple blossom, primroses and a bird's nest with eggs on a mossy bank (15x20cm-6x8in) s. 27-May-4 Christie's, Kensington #346/R est:3000-4000
£3500	$5600	€5110	Rasberries and a peach on a cabbage leaf against mossy bank. Mixed fruits agains a mossy bank (18x23cm-7x9in) both s. pair. 16-Sep-3 Bonhams, Knowle #88/R est:2800-3500
£4000	$6640	€5840	Apples, black grapes on mossy bank. Peach, plums on a woodland bank (15x23cm-6x9in) s. board pair. 2-Oct-3 Neales, Nottingham #787/R est:1200-1500
£4300	$8041	€6278	Various fruits on a mossy bank. Fruits and cabbage leaf on a mossy bank (19x25cm-7x10in) s. board pair. 24-Feb-4 Bonhams, Knowle #86/R est:2800-3500
£4800	$8016	€7008	Various fruits on mossy banks (15x23cm-6x9in) s. pair. 13-Nov-3 Christie's, Kensington #351/R est:600-1000
£10500	$17850	€15330	Still life of grapes and other fruit. Still life of bird's nest and flowers (41x30cm-16x12in) s.d.89 pair. 19-Nov-3 Bonhams, New Bond Street #107/R est:5000-7000

CLARE, Oliver (attrib) (1853-1927) British

£471	$800	€688	Still life with grapes and other fruit (27x38cm-11x15in) s. 19-Nov-3 Bonhams & Butterfields, San Francisco #142
£1600	$2960	€2336	Still lifes with fruit and bird's nest on mossy banks (16x20cm-6x8in) pair. 9-Mar-4 Bonhams, Knightsbridge #242/R est:800-1200

CLARE, Vincent (1855-1930) British

£300	$567	€438	Still life study of a basket of flowers (26x32cm-10x13in) s. 17-Feb-4 Fellows & Sons, Birmingham #46/R
£435	$700	€631	Still life with peaches, plums and other fruit (20x25cm-8x10in) s. 24-Aug-3 Bonhams & Butterfields, Los Angeles #7016
£720	$1202	€1051	Grapes and plums (23x30cm-9x12in) s. 12-Nov-3 Sotheby's, Olympia #58/R
£733	$1372	€1070	Still life of fruit (13x21cm-5x8in) s. i.verso. 24-Feb-4 Louis Morton, Mexico #53/R est:20000-30000 (M.P 15000)

£733	$1372	€1070	Still life with white flowers (13x21cm-5x8in) s. i.verso. 24-Feb-4 Louis Morton, Mexico #52/R est:20000-30000 (M.P 15000)
£860	$1462	€1256	Goosberries, strawberries and redcurrants on a mossy bank (17x22cm-7x9in) s. 18-Nov-3 Bonhams, Leeds #182/R
£1100	$1837	€1606	Grapes and raspberries. Spring flowers in a wicker basket on a mossy bank (25x19cm-10x7in) s. pair. 13-Nov-3 Christie's, Kensington #353/R est:800-1200
£1350	$2417	€1971	Still life of apples, grapes in a basket and plums on a mossy bank (19x28cm-7x11in) s. 16-Mar-4 Bonhams, Leeds #649/R est:900-1200
£1600	$2992	€2336	Still life with bird's nest and floral sprays (21x29cm-8x11in) s. 22-Jul-4 Martel Maides, Guernsey #219/R est:1500-2000
£1700	$3213	€2482	Still life of a basket of fruit on a mossy bank (29x22cm-11x9in) s. 17-Feb-4 Fellows & Sons, Birmingham #45/R est:1000-1500
£1750	$2923	€2555	Still life of plums, strawberries and other fruit on a mossy bank (25x19cm-10x7in) s. 7-Oct-3 Fellows & Sons, Birmingham #345/R est:1800-2500
£1850	$3441	€2701	Still life of bird's nest and primroses on mossy bank (22x29cm-9x11in) s. 2-Mar-4 Bearnes, Exeter #451/R est:1000-1500
£1912	$3250	€2792	Plums on a mossy bank (23x30cm-9x12in) s. exhib. 19-Nov-3 Bonhams & Butterfields, San Francisco #141/R
£2000	$3660	€2920	Still life with grapes, apples and plums. Still life with primroses and bird's nest (23x30cm-9x12in) first s. pair. 28-Jan-4 Dreweatt Neate, Newbury #89/R est:1800-2000
£2096	$3500	€3060	Still life with fruit and still life with flowers and birds nest (31x25cm-12x10in) s. pair. 7-Oct-3 Sotheby's, New York #98 est:4000-6000
£2400	$4128	€3504	Still life studies of fruit, birds nest and flowers on mossy banks (13x18cm-5x7in) s. pair. 5-Dec-3 Keys, Aylsham #702/R est:2500-3500
£2500	$4650	€3650	Still life of yellow roses, lilies, primroses and violets (21x29cm-8x11in) s. 2-Mar-4 Bearnes, Exeter #453/R est:1200-1800
£2699	$4750	€3941	Still life with primroses in a vase and a birds nest behind (23x30cm-9x12in) s. 18-May-4 Bonhams & Butterfields, San Francisco #168/R est:3000-5000
£2700	$4509	€3942	Various flowers, wicker basket, and eggs in a nest on a mossy bank (23x30cm-9x12in) s. 13-Nov-3 Christie's, Kensington #350/R est:3000-5000
£2794	$4750	€4079	Still life with flowers and a bird's nest on a mossy bank (23x30cm-9x12in) s. prov. 19-Nov-3 Bonhams & Butterfields, San Francisco #144/R
£3056	$5500	€4462	Hawthorn, apple, primrose blossoms and a bird's nest (51x61cm-20x24in) s. 24-Apr-4 Weschler, Washington #548/R est:3000-5000
£3100	$5859	€4526	Basket of flowers on a mossy bank with bird's nest. Basket of raspberries on a mossy bank. s. pair. 17-Feb-4 Fellows & Sons, Birmingham #44/R est:1800-2500
£3834	$6250	€5598	Basket of flowers (51x51cm-20x20in) prov. 28-Sep-3 Carlsen Gallery, Greenville #104/R
Works on paper			
£300	$474	€435	Bird's nest with primroses against a bank (11x17cm-4x7in) s. W/C. 24-Jul-3 Lawrence, Crewkerne #842

CLARE, Vincent (attrib) (1855-1930) British

£400	$740	€584	Still life of primroses with a bird's nest (11x19cm-4x7in) oil on card. 14-Jan-4 Lawrence, Crewkerne #1422

CLARENBACH, Max (1880-1952) German

£284	$500	€415	Trees alongside a stream (84x97cm-33x38in) s. 21-May-4 North East Auctions, Portsmouth #675
£733	$1349	€1100	Paris street in the evening (40x32cm-16x13in) s.i. board. 9-Jun-4 Dorotheum, Salzburg #554/R
£1268	$2104	€1800	Capri (78x60cm-31x24in) s.d.99. 16-Jun-3 Dorotheum, Vienna #246/R est:2000-2800
£1800	$3006	€2628	Winterlandschaft (50x61cm-20x24in) s. s.i.verso. 22-Oct-3 Bonhams, New Bond Street #31/R est:2000-3000
£2013	$3745	€3000	Trees by stream on sunny winter day (35x44cm-14x17in) s. board. 6-Mar-4 Arnold, Frankfurt #701/R est:1600
£2045	$3600	€2986	Winter twilight along a river (84x97cm-33x38in) 21-May-4 North East Auctions, Portsmouth #807/R
£2222	$3711	€3200	Autumn afternoon (29x43cm-11x17in) s. board. 24-Oct-3 Ketterer, Hamburg #302/R est:3300-4000
£2282	$4199	€3400	Winter sun on stream (53x69cm-21x27in) s. 24-Mar-4 Hugo Ruef, Munich #945/R est:2500
£3103	$5183	€4500	Winter evening (54x62cm-21x24in) s. 15-Nov-3 Lempertz, Koln #1595/R est:4000
£3179	$5785	€4800	Winter evening landscape on the banks of the Erft (60x80cm-24x31in) s. 18-Jun-4 Bolland & Marotz, Bremen #865/R est:6500
£3333	$5500	€4800	Melting snows by stream (60x80cm-24x31in) s.i. verso s. panel. 3-Jul-3 Van Ham, Cologne #1095/R est:4500
£4167	$6875	€6000	View over the Rhine to Rees (40x55cm-16x22in) s. 3-Jul-3 Van Ham, Cologne #1096/R est:12000
£4667	$8400	€7000	Snow covered landscape (40x50cm-16x20in) s. 20-Apr-4 Sotheby's, Amsterdam #70/R est:4000-6000
£4895	$8322	€7000	March day - Black Forest valley with Wittlaer (101x120cm-40x47in) s. 26-Nov-3 Lempertz, Koln #620/R est:6000
£5517	$9214	€8000	Lower Rhine in winter (51x61cm-20x24in) s. 15-Nov-3 Lempertz, Koln #1596/R est:6000
£7746	$13401	€11000	Garden (48x65cm-19x26in) s. 13-Dec-3 Lempertz, Koln #203/R est:3000
£8392	$14266	€12000	Summer garden with sunflowers (60x80cm-24x31in) s. 20-Nov-3 Van Ham, Cologne #1516/R est:8500
£9091	$15455	€13000	Lower Rhineland garden in summer (60x70cm-24x28in) s. 20-Nov-3 Van Ham, Cologne #1517/R est:2400
£9091	$15455	€13000	The thaw on the lower Rhine (81x120cm-32x47in) s. 29-Nov-3 Bassenge, Berlin #6654 est:9000
£14667	$26693	€22000	Beach scene changing tents and bathers (60x80cm-24x31in) s. 1-Jul-4 Van Ham, Cologne #1244/R est:5000
Works on paper			
£315	$535	€450	Alpine valley in winter (34x48cm-13x19in) s. W/C over pencil. 21-Nov-3 Reiss & Sohn, Konigstein #384
£594	$1010	€850	Boats at low tide (46x63cm-18x25in) s. pastel board. 20-Nov-3 Van Ham, Cologne #1518

CLARENBACH, Max (attrib) (1880-1952) German

£1049	$1783	€1500	Stream in summer wood and meadow (44x59cm-17x23in) 20-Nov-3 Van Ham, Cologne #1519/R est:1500

CLARK, Albert (19th C) British

£750	$1275	€1095	Spaniels flushing out a pheasant (29x39cm-11x15in) s. 27-Nov-3 Christie's, Kensington #313/R
£750	$1380	€1095	Bay racehorse in a stable (30x41cm-12x16in) s. 10-Jun-4 Christie's, Kensington #179/R
£920	$1656	€1343	Horse Gypsy in a stable (50x60cm-20x24in) s.d.1883 painted with son. 20-Apr-4 Rowley Fine Art, Newmarket #445/R
£920	$1656	€1343	Study of the horse Lady Tensel saddled in a stable (50x60cm-20x24in) s.d.1896 painted with son. 20-Apr-4 Rowley Fine Art, Newmarket #447/R
£1050	$1890	€1533	Horse Miss Higgins in a stable (50x60cm-20x24in) s.d.1894 painted with son. 20-Apr-4 Rowley Fine Art, Newmarket #446/R
£1693	$3200	€2472	Two dogs with ball in grassing clearing (48x61cm-19x24in) s.d.1874. 21-Feb-4 Brunk, Ashville #637/R est:400-800
£3000	$5520	€4380	Carriage horse with a gig (61x51cm-24x20in) s.d.1857. 10-Jun-4 Christie's, Kensington #112/R est:1500-2000

CLARK, Albert (attrib) (19th C) British

£280	$456	€409	Captain, the first draught horse owned by James Wilton (34x41cm-13x16in) i.verso. 25-Sep-3 Mellors & Kirk, Nottingham #734/R

CLARK, Albert James (fl.1892-1909) British

£1000	$1700	€1460	Dark brown horse in a stable (51x61cm-20x24in) s. 27-Nov-3 Christie's, Kensington #119/R est:1000-1500

CLARK, Allan (1896-1950) American

Sculpture			
£1123	$2100	€1640	Bali dancer. s.st.f. Roman Bronze gilt bronze lacquer. 25-Feb-4 Dallas Auction Gallery, Dallas #76/R
£4088	$6500	€5968	Balinese dancer (21cm-8in) s.i.d.1927 bronze. 12-Sep-3 Skinner, Boston #358/R

CLARK, Alson Skinner (1876-1949) American

£2890	$5000	€4219	Cuernavaca Street (18x23cm-7x9in) s. prov. 10-Dec-3 Bonhams & Butterfields, San Francisco #6215/R est:3000-5000
£3468	$6000	€5063	Early Morning, Palm Springs (66x81cm-26x32in) s. exhib. 10-Dec-3 Bonhams & Butterfields, San Francisco #6248/R est:12000-16000
£3591	$6500	€5243	Courtyard in Giverny, France (61x51cm-24x20in) s. 16-Apr-4 James Julia, Fairfield #812/R est:8000-10000
£5220	$9500	€7621	Bailleu, World War I (97x130cm-38x51in) s. prov.exhib. 15-Jun-4 John Moran, Pasadena #74 est:10000-15000
£9040	$16000	€13198	Redhead (61x55cm-24x22in) painted 1931. 28-Apr-4 Christie's, Los Angeles #38/R est:20000-30000

CLARK, C Myron (1876-1925) American

£726	$1300	€1060	Ship portrait, Constitution (46x61cm-18x24in) s. 8-Jan-4 James Julia, Fairfield #720/R
£907	$1460	€1324	US Frigate Constitution (76x64cm-30x25in) s. s.i.d.1921 verso. 20-Aug-3 James Julia, Fairfield #892/R est:1750-2250
£926	$1500	€1343	Ship portrait (38x48cm-15x19in) s. 26-Jul-3 Thomaston Place, Thomaston #153/R
£1257	$2100	€1835	Esperanto, a ship (48x69cm-19x27in) 14-Nov-3 Douglas, South Deerfield #2

CLARK, Christopher (1875-1942) British

Works on paper			
£700	$1253	€1022	Portrait of HM King George V at the Delhi Durbar (41x26cm-16x10in) s.d.15 W/C. 25-May-4 Bonhams, Knightsbridge #86/R

CLARK, Claude C F (19th C) British?

£667	$1227	€1000	Peasant life (31x46cm-12x18in) s. 10-Jun-4 Christie's, Rome #112/R

CLARK, Claude L (19th C) British

£880	$1610	€1285	By the farm gate (38x51cm-15x20in) s.d.87. 7-Apr-4 Bonhams, Bury St Edmunds #424/R

CLARK, Dixon (1849-1944) British

£360	$572	€526	Shepherd with his flock in a meadow (30x41cm-12x16in) s.d.1886. 12-Sep-3 Halls, Shrewsbury #709/R
£380	$657	€555	Bathing huts by a beach (55x65cm-22x26in) board. 12-Dec-3 Bracketts, Tunbridge Wells #880/R
£500	$790	€725	Cattle and chickens (46x61cm-18x24in) s. 3-Sep-3 Bonhams, Bury St Edmunds #411
£1150	$2116	€1679	Shorthorn calves and poultry in the farmyard (46x61cm-18x24in) s. 28-Jun-4 British Auctioneer #385/R
£1500	$2550	€2190	Summer landscape with cattle beside a pool, thatch cottage beyond (46x66cm-18x26in) s. 19-Nov-3 Tennants, Leyburn #1134/R est:800-1200
£2000	$3400	€2920	Cattle watering. Sheep with lambs (26x36cm-10x14in) s. pair. 1-Dec-3 Bonhams, Bath #35/R est:1000-1500

CLARK, Edward (20th C) American

Works on paper			
£611	$1100	€892	Crete and NY (27x39cm-11x15in) s.i.d.1971 pastel. 24-Apr-4 David Rago, Lambertville #82/R

CLARK, Eliot (1883-1980) American

£272	$500	€397	Autumn in Brandywine country (36x46cm-14x18in) s. exhib. 25-Jun-4 Freeman, Philadelphia #236/R
£284	$500	€415	Sunset (30x41cm-12x16in) s. masonite painted c.1940. 23-May-4 Treadway Gallery, Cincinnati #559/R
£359	$600	€524	Figures by the roadside, a haycart approaching (41x53cm-16x21in) s. board. 20-Jun-3 Freeman, Philadelphia #247/R
£411	$650	€600	Landscape near Noank, CT (25x30cm-10x12in) s. masonite. 7-Sep-3 Treadway Gallery, Cincinnati #625/R
£484	$900	€707	Wind river valley (61x91cm-24x36in) s.i. s.d.1930 stretcher verso. 7-Mar-4 Treadway Gallery, Cincinnati #507/R
£543	$1000	€793	Landscape with farm and cows (46x76cm-18x30in) s. 13-Jun-4 William Jenack, New York #284 est:1500-2000
£552	$950	€806	Summer day (46x36cm-18x14in) s. painted c.1920. 7-Dec-3 Treadway Gallery, Cincinnati #544/R

£647 $1100 €945 Winter farmyard (51x69cm-20x27in) s. 22-Nov-3 Jackson's, Cedar Falls #95/R est:800-1200
£860 $1600 €1256 Baja, California (30x46cm-12x18in) s. canvas on board painted c.1935. 7-Mar-4 Treadway Gallery, Cincinnati #626/R est:600-800
£1038 $1900 €1515 Snowy mountains (81x102cm-32x40in) s. painted c.1930. 5-Jun-4 Treadway Gallery, Cincinnati #615/R est:2000-3000
£1142 $2100 €1667 Figures beneath an oak tree (66x99cm-26x39in) 25-Jun-4 Freeman, Philadelphia #172/R est:1000-1500
£5689 $9500 €8306 Two girls in a field of flowers (76x102cm-30x40in) s. prov. 23-Oct-3 Shannon's, Milford #190/R est:6000-8000
£18895 $32500 €27587 Hotel Windsor fire (76x101cm-30x40in) s. s.i.d.1899 verso prov. 3-Dec-3 Sotheby's, New York #43/R est:20000-30000

CLARK, Emery (20th) American
Works on paper
£1892 $3500 €2838 Louisiana landscape (109x305cm-43x120in) s.d.84 pastel mixed media. 17-Jul-4 New Orleans Auction, New Orleans #873/R est:2500-4000

CLARK, Frederick Albert (fl.1888-1909) British
£509 $850 €743 Ruby, in her stall (51x61cm-20x24in) s.d.1901 canvas on masonite. 18-Jun-3 Doyle, New York #18/R
£1500 $2745 €2190 Hunter - Actress in a loose box (50x61cm-20x24in) s.i.d.1902. 28-Jul-4 Bonhams, Knightsbridge #132/R est:1500-2000

CLARK, Gordon Aubourne (19/20th C) British
£800 $1336 €1168 Into the evening (51x77cm-20x30in) s.d.1913. 11-Nov-3 Bonhams, Knightsbridge #155/R

CLARK, Gordon Matta (1945-1978) American
Photographs
£6000 $10020 €8760 Office baroque (102x76cm-40x30in) cibachrome prov. 22-Oct-3 Christie's, London #107/R est:6000-8000
Works on paper
£2797 $4755 €4000 Untitled - architecture (21x30cm-8x12in) ink feltpen squared paper exhib. 26-Nov-3 Dorotheum, Vienna #263/R est:5500-7500
£3147 $5350 €4500 Untitled - architecture (35x25cm-14x10in) ink feltpen exhib. 26-Nov-3 Dorotheum, Vienna #251/R est:6000-7000

CLARK, Henry Ray (1936-) American
Works on paper
£333 $600 €486 Face in a star (20x28cm-8x11in) col pencil. 24-Apr-4 Slotin Folk Art, Buford #418/R

CLARK, Irene (1927-) American
£436 $750 €637 Woman playing mandolin (41x28cm-16x11in) s. board painted c.1955. 7-Dec-3 Treadway Gallery, Cincinnati #671/R
£494 $850 €721 African heads (38x28cm-15x11in) s. board painted c.1951. 7-Dec-3 Treadway Gallery, Cincinnati #674/R
£1006 $1800 €1469 Metamorphosis of the black man (58x84cm-23x33in) s. board. 16-May-4 Wright, Chicago #179/R est:2000-3000

CLARK, J (?) British
£3000 $5490 €4380 Gentleman driving a bay horse to a gig (48x55cm-19x22in) prov. 27-Jan-4 Holloways, Banbury #360/R est:1000-1500

CLARK, James (fl.1858-1909) British
£480 $816 €701 Hunting scene with riderless horse in foreground (49x74cm-19x29in) s. 28-Oct-3 Henry Adams, Chichester #426/R
£1400 $2380 €2044 Chestnut hunter in a stable (51x61cm-20x24in) s. 27-Nov-3 Christie's, Kensington #121/R est:1000-1500
£2500 $4400 €3650 Prize Hereford bull in a landscape (48x59cm-19x23in) s. 18-May-4 Woolley & Wallis, Salisbury #165/R est:1500-2500

CLARK, James (1858-1943) British
£1700 $3145 €2482 Eastern girl fetching water from a stream (75x543cm-30x214in) s. canvas on board. 14-Jul-4 Christie's, Kensington #862/R est:1500-2000

CLARK, James Lippitt (1883-1957) American
Sculpture
£887 $1615 €1295 Classic horse (38cm-15in) bears sig num.2/25 brown pat. bronze. 15-Jun-4 Waddingtons, Toronto #707/R est:2000-2500 (C.D 2200)

CLARK, Joan (20th C) American
£213 $375 €311 Life Guard Chair (23x30cm-9x12in) s. 3-Jan-4 Outer Cape Auctions, Provincetown #24/R

CLARK, John Clem (20th C) American?
£412 $650 €602 Construction no 16, beveled pink boards. 27-Jul-3 Bonhams & Butterfields, Los Angeles #7040/R

CLARK, John Cosmo (1897-1967) British
£300 $501 €438 Lavender field (25x35cm-10x14in) s.d.1960. 16-Oct-3 Lyon & Turnbull, Edinburgh #57

CLARK, John Heaviside (c.1770-1863) British
Works on paper
£320 $534 €467 View of Bristol (35x54cm-14x21in) s.d.1825 W/C pencil. 16-Oct-3 Lawrence, Crewkerne #631
£400 $728 €584 Fountains Abbey, Yorkshire (30x40cm-12x16in) s. pencil W/C. 1-Jul-4 Christie's, Kensington #58/R

CLARK, Joseph (1834-1926) British
£1500 $2505 €2190 Time for bed (46x36cm-18x14in) s. 16-Nov-3 Desmond Judd, Cranbrook #1067

CLARK, Joseph Benwell (1857-?) British
£400 $636 €580 Sunday afternoon by law my delight (55x53cm-22x21in) 9-Sep-3 Bonhams, Knightsbridge #265/R

CLARK, Kate Freeman (1875-1957) American
£21858 $40000 €31913 Nut trees, marsh meadows (51x66cm-20x26in) s.i. prov. 5-Jun-4 Neal Auction Company, New Orleans #397/R est:10000-15000

CLARK, Larry (1943-) American
Photographs
£1778 $3200 €2596 Untitled (20x30cm-8x12in) s. gelatin silver print prov.lit. 23-Apr-4 Phillips, New York #191/R est:2000-3000
£13473 $22500 €19671 Tulsa portfolio (14x22cm-6x9in) s.num.25/50 verso gelatin silver print 10 portfolio box prov.lit. 13-Nov-3 Sotheby's, New York #419/R est:12000-18000
£15569 $26000 €22731 Tulsa (31x21cm-12x8in) s.i.verso gelatin silver print album lit. 16-Oct-3 Phillips, New York #206/R est:10000-15000
£18750 $33000 €27375 Teenage lust (34x28cm-13x11in) with sig.i. silver prints portfolio of 83. 20-May-4 Swann Galleries, New York #518/R est:20000-25000
£27778 $50000 €40556 Teenage lust (20x30cm-8x12in) s.d.1981 gelatin silver print album of 100 prov. 23-Apr-4 Phillips, New York #45/R est:20000-30000

CLARK, Louis E (19th C) British
£370 $592 €540 On the Lledr (51x76cm-20x30in) s. i.stretcher. 16-Sep-3 Bonhams, Knowle #109

CLARK, Lygia (1920-1988) Brazilian
£5055 $8947 €7583 Village scene (46x33cm-18x13in) s.d.1951. 27-Apr-4 Bolsa de Arte, Rio de Janeiro #63/R (B.R 27600)
£31136 $56978 €46704 Composition (65x100cm-26x39in) s.d.1955. 6-Jul-4 Bolsa de Arte, Rio de Janeiro #168/R (B.R 170000)
Sculpture
£32353 $55000 €47235 Bicho - Creature (37x40x40cm-15x16x16in) aluminium exec. c.1960 prov.exhib. 18-Nov-3 Christie's, Rockefeller NY #18/R est:40000-60000

CLARK, Matt (1903-) American
Works on paper
£291 $500 €425 Shoot out at Overland Mail Company (41x71cm-16x28in) s. drybrush exec.c.1946. 7-Dec-3 Treadway Gallery, Cincinnati #600/R
£291 $500 €425 Wagon train (41x66cm-16x26in) s.d.1947 drybrush. 7-Dec-3 Treadway Gallery, Cincinnati #602/R
£291 $500 €425 Hardships of frontier life (36x61cm-14x24in) s. drybrush exec.c.1937. 7-Dec-3 Treadway Gallery, Cincinnati #603/R
£323 $600 €472 Who is making whom? (48x48cm-19x19in) s. drybrush. 7-Mar-4 Treadway Gallery, Cincinnati #576/R

CLARK, O T (1850-1921) British
£1700 $3111 €2482 Cattle watering in an extensive landscape with figures before a cottage (49x74cm-19x29in) one s. pair. 6-Jul-4 Bonhams, Knightsbridge #203/R est:1200-1800

CLARK, Octavius T (1850-1921) British
£250 $463 €365 Cattle grazing by a highland loch (53x71cm-21x28in) s. 15-Jan-4 Christie's, Kensington #901
£340 $626 €496 Farm hand with work horse and cart in rural landscape (19x29cm-7x11in) s. 11-Jun-4 Keys, Aylsham #643/R
£380 $635 €555 Cottage by river (47x72cm-19x28in) 16-Oct-3 Lawrence, Crewkerne #738
£400 $740 €584 Harvesting at dusk (61x91cm-24x36in) s. 15-Jan-4 Christie's, Kensington #871
£450 $833 €657 Summer in Sussex, extensive landscape with cottage by a country lane (51x76cm-20x30in) s. 11-Mar-4 Morphets, Harrogate #288
£480 $763 €696 Country river landscape with timbered cottages (50x75cm-20x30in) s. 9-Sep-3 Bonhams, Knightsbridge #246/R
£480 $859 €701 Cottage. Watermill (51x76cm-20x30in) s.d.86 pair. 18-Mar-4 Christie's, Kensington #595/R
£528 $950 €771 Summer in Sussex (51x76cm-20x30in) s. 24-Jan-4 Skinner, Boston #350/R est:700-900
£750 $1373 €1095 Figures on a country track a farm beyond (49x74cm-19x29in) s. 6-Jul-4 Bearnes, Exeter #492/R
£815 $1500 €1190 Landscape with ducks in the water and an old bridge in the foreground (51x76cm-20x30in) s. 27-Jun-4 Bonhams & Butterfields, San Francisco #3810/R est:2000-3000
£920 $1702 €1343 Wooded river landscape with girl at a cottage gate. Ducks before a cottage (50x75cm-20x30in) both s. pair. 14-Jul-4 Bonhams, Chester #437
£1100 $1870 €1606 Cottages beside an upland river (50x75cm-20x30in) s. sold with a companion. 1-Dec-3 Bonhams, Bath #103/R est:800-1200
£1150 $2059 €1679 Children before a cottage in an extensive landscape (51x76cm-20x30in) s. 27-May-4 Christie's, Kensington #182a est:1200-1800
£1200 $2148 €1752 Shepherd with his flock on a riverside track (51x76cm-20x30in) s. 27-May-4 Christie's, Kensington #187/R est:500-800
£1398 $2250 €2027 Shepherd with his flock on a country lane (55x79cm-22x31in) s. 24-Aug-3 Bonhams & Butterfields, Los Angeles #7026 est:2000-3000

CLARK, Paraskeva (1898-1986) Canadian
£864 $1408 €1261 Hills of Saguenay (25x30cm-10x12in) board prov. 23-Sep-3 Ritchie, Toronto #110 est:2000-3000 (C.D 1900)
Works on paper
£636 $1037 €929 Summer holidays Joe Lake (49x67cm-19x26in) s.d.63 pastel W/C. 23-Sep-3 Ritchie, Toronto #119/R est:1500-2000 (C.D 1400)

£1126 $1914 €1644 Diana hunting in Caladon Hills (52x83cm-20x33in) s.d.1948-1951 i.verso W/C prov. 27-Nov-3 Heffel, Vancouver #170 est:1000-1500 (C.D 2500)
£1689 $2872 €2466 Wartime Tragedy (34x24cm-13x9in) s.d.1945 i.verso W/C chk prov. 27-Nov-3 Heffel, Vancouver #196/R est:1500-2000 (C.D 3750)

CLARK, Roland H (1874-1957) American
£5233 $9000 €7640 Raising mallards (53x71cm-21x28in) s.d.1942. 6-Dec-3 South Bay, Long Island #28/R
Works on paper
£894 $1600 €1305 Mallards in flight (41x51cm-16x20in) s. W/C prov. 6-May-4 Shannon's, Milford #208/R est:2000-3000

CLARK, Russell (1905-1966) New Zealander
Works on paper
£290 $493 €423 Nativity scene (17x21cm-7x8in) s. ink. 4-Nov-3 Peter Webb, Auckland #18/R (NZ.D 800)

CLARK, S J (19/20th C) British
£620 $1122 €905 Cattle drinking beside river and bridge (28x38cm-11x15in) 31-Mar-4 Brightwells, Leominster #864/R

CLARK, S Joseph (19th C) British
£750 $1253 €1095 Noon day rest (44x59cm-17x23in) 14-Oct-3 Bearnes, Exeter #371/R
£1100 $1716 €1595 Cattle watering in rural river landscape (51x76cm-20x30in) s. painted c.1870-1880. 22-Sep-2 Desmond Judd, Cranbrook #811
£1100 $1969 €1606 Farmyard scene (64x81cm-25x32in) s. 11-May-4 Bonhams, Knightsbridge #260/R est:700-900
£1200 $2196 €1752 River landscape with lady and cattle in the foreground (50x76cm-20x30in) s. 6-Apr-4 Bonhams, Knightsbridge #158/R est:500-700

CLARK, Samuel James (19th C) British
£543 $1000 €793 Figures and horses in an English landscape (51x76cm-20x30in) s. 27-Mar-4 New Orleans Auction, New Orleans #590/R est:2000-4000

CLARK, Stanley (1954-) American
£347 $600 €507 English mountain scene (61x91cm-24x36in) 12-Dec-3 Du Mouchelle, Detroit #2030/R

CLARK, Walter (1848-1917) American
£470 $850 €686 Landscape with cottage (36x51cm-14x20in) s. 3-Apr-4 Charlton Hall, Columbia #651/R
£823 $1300 €1202 Autumn landscape (51x61cm-20x24in) i.verso. 7-Sep-3 Treadway Gallery, Cincinnati #650/R

CLARK, William (1803-1883) British
£11392 $18000 €16632 Shipping off the coast, British merchant bark under sail off of the mountainous coast (61x91cm-24x36in) s.d.1838. 25-Jul-3 Eldred, East Dennis #288/R est:22000-24000
£15000 $25500 €21900 Three masted barque Akbar arriving off Port Louis (61x91cm-24x36in) indis.sig. 19-Nov-3 Christie's, Kensington #457/R est:15000-20000

CLARK, William Albert (20th C) British
£444 $816 €648 Breaking loose (51x77cm-20x30in) s.d.1904. 14-Jun-4 Waddingtons, Toronto #123/R est:1500-2500 (C.D 1100)
£450 $716 €653 Grey hunter, standing four square with bridle before a house (40x50cm-16x20in) s.d.1930. 9-Sep-3 Bonhams, Knightsbridge #270/R
£680 $1136 €986 Wedding bells by Hanover Square (50x60cm-20x24in) s.d.1917. 14-Jul-3 Trembath Welch, Great Dunmow #567/R
£980 $1637 €1421 Peace dove by Hanover Square (50x60cm-20x24in) s.d.1916. 14-Jul-3 Trembath Welch, Great Dunmow #568/R
£1200 $2004 €1752 Merton beauty of the village 6249. Merton Segnet, champion Guernsey cows (50x60cm-20x24in) s.i. pair. 22-Oct-3 Cheffins, Cambridge #542/R est:400-600
£2800 $5040 €4088 Three prize shire horses and a prize shire foal (45x81cm-18x32in) s.d.1909. 22-Apr-4 Mellors & Kirk, Nottingham #1068/R est:1000-2000
£2800 $5152 €4088 Histon Drayman 9th, heavy horse (51x61cm-20x24in) s.i.d.1935. 10-Jun-4 Christie's, Kensington #107/R est:800-1200
£3000 $5400 €4380 Three prize shire horses and a prize shire foal (45x81cm-18x32in) s.i.d.1909. 22-Apr-4 Mellors & Kirk, Nottingham #1069 est:1000-2000

CLARKE, Carey (fl.1957-1979) Irish?
£2550 $4565 €3800 Promise of summer (81x93cm-32x37in) s. 26-May-4 James Adam, Dublin #88/R est:4000-6000
Works on paper
£590 $962 €850 Street, Safad, Israel (27x35cm-11x14in) s. W/C prov. 24-Sep-3 James Adam, Dublin #55/R

CLARKE, David (20th C) Irish
Works on paper
£298 $542 €450 Landscape with shepherd (31x43cm-12x17in) s. W/C. 21-Jun-4 Pandolfini, Florence #57/R

CLARKE, Don (1932-) British
£789 $1453 €1200 Blowing bubbles (40x30cm-16x12in) s.d.1978 plywood. 22-Jun-4 Christie's, Amsterdam #368/R

CLARKE, Emery (20th C) American
Works on paper
£190 $350 €277 Night storm approaching (36x23cm-14x9in) s. W/C mixed media. 27-Mar-4 New Orleans Auction, New Orleans #953

CLARKE, Geoffrey (1924-) British
Sculpture
£3000 $5460 €4380 Portrait of a woman (40x66cm-16x26in) iron. 15-Jun-4 Bonhams, New Bond Street #119/R est:3000-5000

CLARKE, Graham (1941-) British
£300 $510 €438 Surreal landscape (50x47cm-20x19in) s.d.1975. 18-Nov-3 Bonhams, Knightsbridge #60a
Works on paper
£280 $510 €409 Lucky Frenchman (55x45cm-22x18in) s.i.d.85 W/C ink. 15-Jun-4 Bonhams, Knightsbridge #48/R

CLARKE, Harry Harvey (1869-?) British
£380 $680 €555 River Usk, Brecon (61x74cm-24x29in) s. 6-Jan-4 Gildings, Market Harborough #392

CLARKE, Margaret (1888-1961) Irish
£6500 $11635 €9490 Reclining nude (84x99cm-33x39in) s. i.verso. 14-May-4 Christie's, London #14/R est:7000-10000

CLARKE, Peter (1935-) Australian
£2890 $5173 €4219 Legend of Claybank (59x44cm-23x17in) s. i.d.1971 verso acrylic board. 31-May-4 Stephan Welz, Johannesburg #616/R est:12000-16000 (SA.R 35000)
Works on paper
£378 $684 €552 Welcoming committee (18x13cm-7x5in) s.d.1955 ink wash. 30-Mar-4 Stephan Welz, Johannesburg #224 est:1500-2000 (SA.R 4500)

CLARKE, Peter Cameron (1927-) Australian
£1829 $2872 €2670 St Anthony at Montjuic (197x243cm-78x96in) s.d.1986 verso acrylic prov.exhib. 27-Aug-3 Christie's, Sydney #593/R est:2000-4000 (A.D 4500)

CLARKE, S J (19/20th C) British?
£600 $1104 €876 Feeding time (17x25cm-7x10in) init. board. 10-Jun-4 Christie's, Kensington #93/R

CLARKE, Sara Ann Freeman (1808-?) American
£14054 $26000 €20519 Egyptian ruins. s.d.1876 two panel triptych prov. 11-Mar-4 Christie's, Rockefeller NY #24/R est:20000-30000

CLARKE, William Hanna (1882-1924) British
£8500 $15215 €12410 Goose girl (61x51cm-24x20in) s.d.1916. 27-May-4 Christie's, Kensington #333/R est:3000-5000
£15000 $25500 €21900 Goose Girl (86x112cm-34x44in) s.d.13. 30-Oct-3 Christie's, London #125/R est:2500-3500

CLARKSON, Ralph Elmer (1861-1943) American
£10180 $17000 €14863 Moment to relax (69x53cm-27x21in) s.i. prov. 23-Oct-3 Shannon's, Milford #130/R est:12000-18000

CLARKSON, Robert (fl.1880-1914) British
£400 $680 €584 Seamer moor near Scarborough (30x60cm-12x24in) s.i.d.1912 verso board. 1-Dec-3 David Duggleby, Scarborough #307/R
£480 $869 €701 Summer country (76x123cm-30x48in) s. 30-Mar-4 Sworder & Son, Bishops Stortford #509/R

CLAROT, R (?) ?
£372 $702 €550 Nature morte aux fleurs (51x73cm-20x29in) s.d.24. 17-Feb-4 Vanderkindere, Brussels #133

CLAROT, René (1882-1972) Belgian
£379 $702 €550 Cale seche a Zeebruges (50x60cm-20x24in) s.d.49. 16-Feb-4 Horta, Bruxelles #362
£390 $651 €550 Vue de Quimper (80x65cm-31x26in) s.d.37. 14-Oct-3 Vanderkindere, Brussels #111

CLARY, James (20th C) American
£649 $1200 €948 Arrrgh - pirate (41x30cm-16x12in) acrylic canvasboard. 13-Feb-4 Du Mouchelle, Detroit #2041/R
£1892 $3500 €2762 Gold cup winners in Detroit (61x91cm-24x36in) acrylic canvasboard. 13-Feb-4 Du Mouchelle, Detroit #2037/R est:5000-6000

CLARY, Jean Eugène (1856-1930) French
£1645 $2977 €2500 Vue de Rouen, brume du matin (45x81cm-18x32in) s. i.verso. 19-Apr-4 Boscher, Cherbourg #904/R est:3000
£4500 $7470 €6570 Vue de Rouen (59x98cm-23x39in) s. 30-Sep-3 Bristol Auction Rooms #568/R est:5000-6000

CLARY-BAROUX (1865-1933) French
£634 $1096 €900 Peniche sur le quai Henri IV (50x61cm-20x24in) s. 10-Dec-3 Millon & Associes, Paris #88

CLARY-BAROUX, Albert Adolphe (1865-1933) French
£1021 $1787 €1450 Port de Saint Goustan (38x61cm-15x24in) 21-Dec-3 Thierry & Lannon, Brest #293
£2148 $3973 €3200 Alger, vue prise du plateau Barberousse (46x54cm-18x21in) s. i.d.nov 1921 verso exhib. 15-Mar-4 Gros & Delettrez, Paris #271/R est:3500-4500

CLARYS, Alexandre (1857-1912) Belgian
£748 $1362 €1100 Cat and her kittens at ease in a basket (57x73cm-22x29in) s. 3-Feb-4 Christie's, Amsterdam #293/R est:1200-1500

CLASEN, Lorenz (1812-1899) German
£573 $974 €837 Love letter (29x24cm-11x9in) s.d.1851. 5-Nov-3 Dobiaschofsky, Bern #439/R (S.FR 1300)

CLATER, Thomas (1789-1867) British
£5705 $10097 €8500 Reading the letter (51x61cm-20x24in) s. prov. 27-Apr-4 Whyte's, Dublin #124/R est:6000-8000

CLATWORTHY, Robert (1928-) British
Sculpture
£2200 $3872 €3212 Charging bull (23x44cm-9x17in) i. 18-May-4 Woolley & Wallis, Salisbury #353/R est:800-1200
£2800 $5096 €4088 Bull (43cm-17in) init. num.C 2/8 dark brown pat bronze. 1-Jul-4 Christie's, Kensington #263/R est:2000-3000

CLAUDE, Eugène (1841-1923) French
£550 $1007 €803 Fishing boats in Honfleur harbour (64x76cm-25x30in) s. 27-Jan-4 Gorringes, Lewes #1619
£600 $1002 €876 Still life of flowers and a seal (60x81cm-24x32in) s.d.22. 7-Oct-3 Bonhams, Knightsbridge #243/R
£806 $1500 €1177 Venice (40x27cm-16x11in) s.i. board. 5-Mar-4 Skinner, Boston #327/R est:800-1200
£1100 $2035 €1606 Still life of game and fruit (60x49cm-24x19in) s. 10-Mar-4 Sotheby's, Olympia #286/R est:800-1200
£1131 $1923 €1651 Flowers in basket (50x65cm-20x26in) s. 19-Nov-3 Fischer, Luzern #1084/R est:2500-3500 (S.FR 2500)
£1380 $2304 €2000 Le plat de prunes (46x55cm-18x22in) s. 17-Nov-3 Tajan, Paris #94/R est:2000-2500
£1940 $3472 €2832 Still life with pansies in straw basket (46x61cm-18x24in) s. 12-May-4 Dobiaschofsky, Bern #398/R est:3000 (S.FR 4500)
£2600 $4654 €3796 Still life with plums (73x92cm-29x36in) s. prov. 26-May-4 Sotheby's, Olympia #297/R est:2000-3000
£3600 $5976 €5256 Still life of lobster and oysters (54x65cm-21x26in) s. 1-Oct-3 Sotheby's, Olympia #232/R est:1800-2500

CLAUDEL, Camille (1864-1943) French
Sculpture
£2480 $4389 €3695 Age mur (21cm-8in) s. st.f.Coubertin verso pat bronze. 30-Apr-4 Tajan, Paris #80/R est:3000-4000
£2800 $5152 €4200 Le chat (13cm-5in) s. num.10 brown pat. bronze exec. c.1893 lit. 10-Jun-4 Camard, Paris #47/R est:4000-6000
£4196 $7217 €6000 Diane (18cm-7in) i.d.1881 num.2/8 brown pat bronze Cast Delval prov.lit. 5-Dec-3 Chochon-Barre & Allardi, Paris #26/R est:7000-8000
£32566 $59921 €49500 L'implorante (28cm-11in) s. num.31 pat bronze Cast Blot prov.lit. 23-Jun-4 Maigret, Paris #40/R est:50000-60000
£75000 $138000 €109500 L'Aurore (33cm-13in) i. num.3 bronze st.f.Luc Blot conceived c.1893 lit. 22-Jun-4 Sotheby's, London #222/R est:60000-90000

CLAUDIUS, Wilhelm (1854-1942) German
£458 $792 €650 Lubeck interior (68x60cm-27x24in) s.d.1922 i. stretcher. 11-Dec-3 Dr Fritz Nagel, Stuttgart #519/R
£909 $1600 €1327 Interior scene, Library (74x56cm-29x22in) s. 18-May-4 Arthur James, Florida #104 est:2000-3000
£1042 $1698 €1500 Man reading paper in courtyard (63x37cm-25x15in) s. 25-Sep-3 Dr Fritz Nagel, Stuttgart #1339/R est:1400

CLAUDOT, Jean-Baptiste-Charles (1733-1805) French
£4363 $8027 €6500 Nature morte au lievre dans un paysage (100x95cm-39x37in) 24-Mar-4 Tajan, Paris #123/R est:7000-8000
£7667 $13953 €11500 Baigneuses pres de cascade (57x78cm-22x31in) 30-Jun-4 Delvaux, Paris #155/R est:12000-15000
£8553 $15737 €13000 Famille de pecheurs devant les ruines d'un temple (71x97cm-28x38in) 24-Jun-4 Christie's, Paris #108/R est:12000-15000
£18792 $34577 €28000 Berger et son troupeau dans un paysage. Reunion de paysans (97x97cm-38x38in) pair. 26-Mar-4 Piasa, Paris #66/R est:12000-15000

CLAUS, Carl Friedrich (1930-1998) Austrian
Works on paper
£2000 $3680 €3000 Page of languages (10x14cm-4x6in) s.i. s.d.April 1990 verso ink pencil card. 12-Jun-4 Villa Grisebach, Berlin #415/R est:3000-5000

CLAUS, Émile (1849-1924) Belgian
£1600 $2896 €2400 Le Mer du Nord (26x38cm-10x15in) s. cardboard. 30-Mar-4 Campo, Vlaamse Kaai #18 est:2500-3500
£1933 $3461 €2900 Paysage (16x23cm-6x9in) s. canvas on panel. 11-May-4 Vanderkindere, Brussels #15 est:3000-4000
£22378 $38490 €32000 Bord de la lys (93x74cm-37x29in) s. init.i.verso. 2-Dec-3 Sotheby's, Amsterdam #44/R est:40000-60000
£25333 $46613 €38000 La barriere, la Lys (60x73cm-24x29in) s. init.verso painted 1913. 9-Jun-4 Christie's, Amsterdam #88/R est:40000-60000
£27536 $45159 €38000 Garden scene (41x32cm-16x13in) s. init.d.1896 verso. 27-May-3 Sotheby's, Amsterdam #329/R est:35000-45000
£56000 $95200 €81760 Waterloo bridge (51x41cm-20x16in) s.d.18. 18-Nov-3 Sotheby's, London #343/R
£80000 $136000 €116800 Soleil d'hiver (98x142cm-39x56in) s.d. prov.exhib. 18-Nov-3 Sotheby's, London #344/R
£104895 $178322 €150000 Matinee brumeuse en novembre (133x150cm-52x59in) s.d.1922 mono.d.November 1922 verso prov. 1-Dec-3 Palais de Beaux Arts, Brussels #228/R est:100000-150000
Works on paper
£278 $464 €400 Vue de ville en Italie (26x18cm-10x7in) mono. dr. 21-Oct-3 Campo, Vlaamse Kaai #378
£1319 $2203 €1900 Garconnet (29x21cm-11x8in) mono.d.1912 dr. 21-Oct-3 Campo, Vlaamse Kaai #379 est:150-200
£3784 $7151 €5600 Paysage industriel (16x23cm-6x9in) s. pastel. 17-Feb-4 Vanderkindere, Brussels #79 est:4000-6000

CLAUS, Hugo (1929-) Belgian
Works on paper
£336 $621 €500 Composition (103x79cm-41x31in) s.d.1956-1978 W/C collage. 13-Mar-4 De Vuyst, Lokeren #53
£433 $776 €650 Behind many disguises (31x41cm-12x16in) s. W/C. 15-May-4 De Vuyst, Lokeren #59
£470 $832 €700 Composition (72x56cm-28x22in) s. gouache. 27-Apr-4 Campo, Vlaamse Kaai #352

CLAUSADES, Pierre de (1910-1976) French
£235 $400 €343 Coastal scene (51x58cm-20x23in) s. 22-Nov-3 Jackson's, Cedar Falls #392/R
£650 $1216 €975 La Loire (46x55cm-18x22in) s. i.verso prov. 22-Jul-4 Tennants, Leyburn #925
£680 $1258 €993 Sur le lac - Autriche (53x98cm-21x39in) s. 14-Jul-4 Bonhams, Chester #396
£700 $1288 €1022 Val de Loire. Loire en automne (37x45cm-15x18in) both s. pair. 14-Jun-4 Bonhams, Bath #12
£1800 $3330 €2628 Neige sur la cite, Paris. San Giorgio Maggiore, Venice (46x55cm-18x22in) s.i. pair. 14-Jul-4 Sotheby's, Olympia #279/R est:1500-2500

CLAUSE, William Lionel (1887-1946) British
Works on paper
£280 $445 €409 Washing day (25x32cm-10x13in) s. W/C. 10-Sep-3 Sotheby's, Olympia #196/R

CLAUSELL, Joaquin (1866-1935) Mexican
£6322 $10748 €9230 Landscape (22x33cm-9x13in) card prov. 30-Oct-3 Louis Morton, Mexico #70/R est:125000-130000 (M.P 120000)

CLAUSEN, Christian (1862-1911) Danish
£323 $548 €472 Interior scene with woman by window (22x16cm-9x6in) 10-Nov-3 Rasmussen, Vejle #249 (D.KR 3500)
£516 $877 €753 Interior scene with female nude seen from behind (28x15cm-11x6in) mono.d.1884. 10-Nov-3 Rasmussen, Vejle #161/R (D.KR 5600)
£1236 $2250 €1854 Two women reading (94x127cm-37x50in) init.d. 30-Jun-4 Daniel Cooney, Brooklyn #487362/R
£1253 $2294 €1829 Evening in Copenhagen with figures (90x98cm-35x39in) mono. 9-Jun-4 Rasmussen, Copenhagen #1990/R est:10000-15000 (D.KR 14000)
£11176 $19000 €16317 Reclining nude in a studio (37x73cm-15x29in) mono.d.1898. 29-Oct-3 Christie's, Rockefeller NY #17/R est:10000-15000
£42972 $78639 €62739 Sitting room in sunshine - interior with lady (62x49cm-24x19in) mono.d.95 exhib.prov. 9-Jun-4 Rasmussen, Copenhagen #1457/R est:400000-600000 (D.KR 480000)

CLAUSEN, Franciska (1899-1986) Danish
£650 $1196 €949 View from Hojtoft across Aabenraa fjord (39x50cm-15x20in) 29-Mar-4 Rasmussen, Copenhagen #473/R (D.KR 7200)
Works on paper
£1015 $1827 €1482 Untitled (15x10cm-6x4in) s. gouache. 26-Apr-4 Bukowskis, Stockholm #254c/R (S.KR 14000)
£1958 $3524 €2859 Untitled (16x13cm-6x5in) s. gouache. 26-Apr-4 Bukowskis, Stockholm #254b/R est:15000-18000 (S.KR 27000)
£2321 $4177 €3389 Untitled (9x11cm-4x4in) s.d.1930 mixed media. 26-Apr-4 Bukowskis, Stockholm #254a/R est:18000-20000 (S.KR 32000)

CLAUSEN, Sir George (1852-1944) British
£1500 $2430 €2175 Two children in a field (23x24cm-9x9in) init. board. 30-Jul-3 Hamptons Fine Art, Godalming #167/R est:1500-1800
£1500 $2550 €2190 Portrait of Mrs Ida Fewster (49x39cm-19x15in) s.d.1907. 26-Nov-3 Sotheby's, Olympia #24/R est:1500-2500
£1518 $2611 €2216 Corner of the garden (61x51cm-24x20in) s. sold with catalogue and correspondence prov.exhib. 2-Dec-3 Ritchie, Toronto #74/R est:3000-5000 (C.D 3400)
£1786 $3071 €2608 At the edge of the farm (78x64cm-31x25in) s. prov. 2-Dec-3 Ritchie, Toronto #75/R est:6000-9000 (C.D 4000)
£4000 $6880 €5840 Landscape with clouds (67x84cm-26x33in) s. prov. 3-Dec-3 Christie's, Kensington #464/R est:3000-5000
£5000 $8350 €7300 Haystacks (30x35cm-12x14in) s. 16-Oct-3 Christie's, Kensington #411/R est:3000-5000
£5183 $8500 €7515 Evening, pastoral scene with cows and stream (38x51cm-15x20in) s.i. canvas on plywood prov. 31-May-3 Brunk, Ashville #642/R est:2000-4000
£6200 $10726 €9052 Baynards Farm, autumn morning (51x61cm-20x24in) s. i.verso prov. 11-Dec-3 Neales, Nottingham #623/R est:3000-4000
£211111 $380000 €308222 Interior (75x62cm-30x24in) indis sig. s.verso prov. 23-Apr-4 Sotheby's, New York #67/R est:300000-400000
Works on paper
£250 $455 €365 Study of trees (25x30cm-10x12in) s. W/C prov. 1-Jul-4 Christie's, Kensington #61/R
£280 $529 €409 Evening landscape (23x35cm-9x14in) s.d.1896 W/C. 19-Feb-4 Lyon & Turnbull, Edinburgh #133
£420 $764 €613 Study of trees (27x21cm-11x8in) s. W/C prov. 1-Jul-4 Christie's, Kensington #63/R
£440 $823 €660 Ploughed landscape with hay barns. init.d.1892 col pastel. 22-Jul-4 Dominic Winter, Swindon #20/R
£440 $823 €660 Cloudscape (24x33cm-9x13in) init. col pastel. 22-Jul-4 Dominic Winter, Swindon #21/R
£520 $946 €759 Hayricks and trees (33x25cm-13x10in) init. pencil W/C prov. 15-Jun-4 Bonhams, Leeds #53/R
£800 $1336 €1168 Evening, haystack (12x19cm-5x7in) s. pen W/C. 21-Oct-3 Bonhams, Knightsbridge #175/R

£800	$1416	€1168	Barn interior (30x22cm-12x9in) s. i.d.1914 verso W/C. 27-Apr-4 Bonhams, Knightsbridge #27/R
£850	$1420	€1241	Farmyard in winter (17x25cm-7x10in) s. pencil W/C. 16-Oct-3 Christie's, Kensington #281/R
£1000	$1850	€1460	Staircase (27x17cm-11x7in) W/C gouache sold with a letter exhib. 11-Feb-4 Sotheby's, Olympia #105/R est:700-900
£1600	$2928	€2336	Copse in an open landscape by a river. Pond at Widdington, Essex (15x24cm-6x9in) s.d.1897 pencil W/C two prov. 3-Jun-4 Christie's, London #33/R est:1200-1800
£13000	$22360	€18980	Threshers (53x35cm-21x14in) s.d.1898 W/C gouache chk. 2-Dec-3 Bonhams, New Bond Street #6/R est:8000-12000

CLAUSEN, Thor P (19/20th C) Scandinavian

Works on paper

£269	$484	€393	Ship's portrait of Nestved af Ronne (51x63cm-20x25in) s.i.d.28 Februar 1880 pen gouache. 24-Apr-4 Rasmussen, Havnen #2369/R (D.KR 3000)

CLAUSMEYER, Klaus (20th C) German

£318	$550	€464	Floral still life (53x43cm-21x17in) masonite. 12-Dec-3 Du Mouchelle, Detroit #2391/R est:600-700
£431	$720	€629	Still life of flowers in a vase (73x55cm-29x22in) s. 20-Oct-3 Stephan Welz, Johannesburg #195/R est:5000-7000 (SA.R 5000)
£533	$955	€800	Still life (50x61cm-20x24in) s. lit. 14-May-4 Schloss Ahlden, Ahlden #2865/R

CLAVA, Giuseppina (1879-?) Italian

Miniatures

£1888	$3153	€2700	Red-haired beauty (16x11cm-6x4in) s.d.1911. 26-Jun-3 Sant Agostino, Torino #50/R est:3500

CLAVE Y ROQUE, Pelegrin (attrib) (1811-1880) Spanish

Works on paper

£632	$1075	€923	Nude of boy (26x37cm-10x15in) mixed media. 29-Oct-3 Louis Morton, Mexico #94/R (M.P 12000)

CLAVE, Antoni (1913-) Spanish

£9459	$16648	€14000	Still life (38x46cm-15x18in) s. s.d.1946-7 verso board prov. 18-May-4 Tajan, Paris #21/R est:12000-15000
£9867	$17957	€14800	Untitled (64x45cm-25x18in) s.d.1990 oil ink paper collage canvas on paper. 29-Jun-4 Segre, Madrid #142/R est:13800
£10197	$18457	€15500	Blue fish (67x54cm-26x21in) s. paper on canvas. 14-Apr-4 Ansorena, Madrid #272/R est:15500
£15333	$27753	€23000	Warrior (79x58cm-31x23in) oil paint collage pigment steel on board painted c.1965. 30-Mar-4 Segre, Madrid #304/R est:23000
£15951	$26000	€23288	Scene de poisson (54x77cm-21x30in) s. oil collage gouache pen black ink paper on masonite prov. 25-Sep-3 Christie's, Rockefeller NY #595/R est:8000-10000
£16776	$30868	€25500	Collerette (76x56cm-30x22in) s. paper on canvas lit. 27-Jun-4 Versailles Encheres #117/R est:20000-25000
£17000	$28390	€24820	Vase de fleurs (55x38cm-22x15in) s. board exec 1952. 21-Oct-3 Sotheby's, London #385/R est:12000-15000
£18027	$32810	€26500	Untitled (77x58cm-30x23in) s.d.1980 oil collage paper on canvas. 3-Feb-4 Segre, Madrid #207/R est:26500
£18944	$30310	€26900	Leaf (56x76cm-22x30in) s.s.i.d.1966 verso paint wax crayon collage paper on board exhib. 16-Sep-3 Segre, Madrid #126/R est:26900
£20000	$36400	€29200	Nature morte au fond rouge (56x76cm-22x30in) s.d.59 oil collage paper on canvas prov. 5-Feb-4 Christie's, London #108/R est:15000-20000
£20567	$33319	€29000	Still life (39x49cm-15x19in) s. panel. 20-May-3 Ansorena, Madrid #321/R est:29000
£20588	$35000	€30058	Nature morte (81x100cm-32x39in) s.d.1962 i.verso prov. 6-Nov-3 Sotheby's, New York #363/R est:20000-30000
£20833	$33958	€30000	Two fish (50x65cm-20x26in) s. cardboard. 23-Sep-3 Durán, Madrid #244/R est:30000
£22000	$40480	€32120	Untitled (33x26cm-13x10in) s. board painted 1946 prov. 24-Jun-4 Sotheby's, London #200/R est:10000-15000
£24000	$40080	€35040	Nature morte au poisson (73x92cm-29x36in) s. prov.exhib. 22-Oct-3 Christie's, London #2/R est:18000-22000
£24000	$43680	€35040	Toujours lui (105x76cm-41x30in) s. oil paper on canvas exec 1964 prov.exhib. 5-Feb-4 Christie's, London #109/R est:15000-20000
£24828	$41214	€36000	Arlequin (27x41cm-11x16in) s. board painted 1953. 1-Oct-3 Ansorena, Madrid #576/R est:30000
£25000	$46000	€36500	Roi cisquet (76x55cm-30x22in) s.d.58 s.i.verso oil paper on canvas prov. 25-Jun-4 Christie's, London #164/R est:30000-40000
£26000	$47840	€37960	Banc de Gaudi (131x146cm-52x57in) s. s.i. verso painted c.1970 prov. 24-Jun-4 Sotheby's, London #192/R est:25000-35000
£26000	$47840	€37960	Rouge et noire (75x105cm-30x41in) s. oil paper collage paper on canvas on board prov.lit. 24-Jun-4 Sotheby's, London #198/R est:12000-18000
£26761	$46831	€38000	Poisson (73x100cm-29x39in) s. isorel prov. 16-Dec-3 Claude Aguttes, Neuilly #37/R est:20000-25000
£30000	$50100	€43800	Enfant a la cage (56x75cm-22x30in) s. oil mixed media collage board painted c.1951 prov. 22-Oct-3 Christie's, London #1/R est:20000-30000
£30201	$56174	€45000	Mandolin and armchair (57x45cm-22x18in) s. board. 2-Mar-4 Ansorena, Madrid #851/R est:45000
£32609	$53478	€45000	Young boy with bird (50x60cm-20x24in) s. 27-May-3 Durán, Madrid #283/R est:45000
£40000	$72800	€58400	Roi rouge et face (76x56cm-30x22in) s. paper on masonite prov. 5-Feb-4 Christie's, London #106/R est:25000-35000
£54538	$94351	€77445	Roi et reine (72x93cm-28x37in) s.d.59 oil collage prov. 9-Dec-3 Artcurial Briest, Paris #397/R est:40000-60000
£55000	$100100	€80300	Untitled (73x60cm-29x24in) s. prov. 6-Feb-4 Sotheby's, London #171/R est:40000-60000
£58000	$105560	€84680	Rey Verde (73x100cm-29x39in) s. painted 1957-58 prov. 5-Feb-4 Christie's, London #107/R est:50000-70000
£58000	$106720	€84680	Woman with cat (74x67cm-29x26in) painted c.1949 prov. 24-Jun-4 Sotheby's, London #193/R est:50000-70000
£110000	$200200	€160600	Femme peintre et mannequin (130x195cm-51x77in) s. painted 1951 prov.exhib.lit. 4-Feb-4 Christie's, London #25/R est:90000-120000
£120000	$218400	€175200	Gargantua, Cavaller du Moyen age (117x67cm-46x26in) s. painted 1953 prov.exhib. 5-Feb-4 Sotheby's, London #38/R est:80000-120000
£155000	$285200	€226300	Harlequin with guitar (81x60cm-32x24in) s. painted c.1949 prov. 24-Jun-4 Sotheby's, London #196/R est:70000-90000

Prints

£2349	$4205	€3500	Gloves (77x64cm-30x25in) s. engraving. 25-May-4 Durán, Madrid #163/R est:1400
£2621	$4717	€3800	Gargantua (81x63cm-32x25in) s. num.10/50 col lithograph. 26-Jan-4 Ansorena, Madrid #950/R est:2800
£2759	$4966	€4000	Two kings (75x106cm-30x42in) s.i, col lithograph lit. 26-Jan-4 Ansorena, Madrid #953/R est:4000
£3125	$5094	€4500	Composition (39x29cm-15x11in) s. s.d.1976 verso monotype collage. 23-Sep-3 Durán, Madrid #242/R est:4500

Sculpture

£1958	$3270	€2800	Hasard d'atelier (41x36cm-16x14in) s. num.1/6 bronze Cast Guyot lit. 29-Jun-3 Versailles Encheres #197/R
£1974	$3632	€3000	Guerrier au bouclier (29x24x7cm-11x9x3in) s. num.5/6 pat bronze Cast Guyot. 27-Jun-4 Versailles Encheres #150/R est:3000-4000
£2039	$3753	€3100	Untitled (20x11x10cm-8x4x4in) s. num.2/6 pat bronze Cast Guyot. 27-Jun-4 Versailles Encheres #151/R est:2500-3000
£2113	$3655	€3000	Guerrier au bouclier (29x24x7cm-11x9x3in) s.num.EA 3/3 gilt pat bronze Cast Guyot. 14-Dec-3 Versailles Encheres #195/R est:3000-4000
£2200	$3960	€3300	Guerrier au bouclier (29x24x7cm-11x9x3in) s. num.3/6 pat bronze. 25-Apr-4 Versailles Encheres #138 est:3000-4000
£2324	$4020	€3300	Projet pour un monument (29x12x15cm-11x5x6in) s. brown green pat bronze Cast Guyot. 14-Dec-3 Versailles Encheres #196/R est:3000-4000
£2324	$4020	€3300	Empreinte no 2 (38x20cm-15x8in) num.EA I/IV brown green pat bronze exhib. 14-Dec-3 Versailles Encheres #197/R est:3000-4000
£3333	$6000	€5000	Guerrier a la lance (47x19x10cm-19x7x4in) s. num.5/6 pat bronze. 25-Apr-4 Versailles Encheres #137 est:5000-6000
£3401	$6190	€5000	Statue (31x12x9cm-12x5x4in) s. bronze lit. 3-Feb-4 Segre, Madrid #262/R
£3467	$6240	€5200	Untitled (47x35x7cm-19x14x3in) s. mixed media aluminium. 25-Apr-4 Versailles Encheres #139 est:5000-6000
£3497	$5839	€5000	Alu froisse V (65x50x10cm-26x20x4in) s. s.i.d.1980 verso aluminium mixed media panel. 29-Jun-3 Versailles Encheres #143/R
£3684	$6779	€5600	Guerrier a la lance (57x24x11cm-22x9x4in) s. num.8/8 pat bronze. 27-Jun-4 Versailles Encheres #152/R est:5000-6000
£3846	$6423	€5500	Untitled (92x60x8cm-36x24x3in) s.d.1980 mixed media plaster string box. 29-Jun-3 Versailles Encheres #142/R
£4097	$6474	€5900	Guerrier a la lance (57x24x11cm-22x9x4in) s. num.6/8 green pat bronze Cast Guyot exhib.lit. 27-Apr-3 Versailles Encheres #103
£5352	$9259	€7600	Julian a deux faces (47x35x45cm-19x14x18in) s.num.EA3/3 polychrome bronze exhib.lit. 14-Dec-3 Versailles Encheres #198/R est:7000-8000
£5594	$9343	€8000	Alu froisse (59x42x8cm-23x17x3in) s.d.1979 aluminium mixed media panel. 29-Jun-3 Versailles Encheres #141/R

Works on paper

£764	$1276	€1100	Composition (73x53cm-29x21in) s.d.86 mixed media lithograph sheet prov. 21-Oct-3 Artcurial Briest, Paris #539
£1200	$2160	€1800	Untitled (19x14cm-7x6in) s.d.1990 mixed media collage. 25-Apr-4 Versailles Encheres #124 est:2000-3000
£1678	$3003	€2500	Metal (77x64cm-30x25in) collage aluminium engraving lit. 25-May-4 Durán, Madrid #162/R est:1400
£1993	$3268	€2750	Composition (24x22cm-9x9in) s. mixed media. 27-May-3 Durán, Madrid #110/R est:2500
£2000	$3600	€3000	Composition (104x72cm-41x28in) s. gouache over lithograph. 25-Apr-4 Versailles Encheres #120 est:3000-3500
£2027	$3568	€3000	Untitled (34x12cm-13x5in) s.d.1987 ink wash collage. 18-May-4 Segre, Madrid #204/R est:3000
£2333	$4177	€3500	Tete d'homme (29x22cm-11x9in) ink wash. 16-May-4 Osenat, Fontainebleau #15/R est:1000-1500
£2333	$4293	€3500	Carmen (30x105cm-12x41in) pastel black paper exec.c.1949. 14-Jun-4 Tajan, Paris #165/R est:3500-4000
£2448	$4087	€3500	Femme regagnant sa caleche (25x20cm-10x8in) s. W/C. 29-Jun-3 Eric Pillon, Calais #209
£2685	$4993	€4000	Untitled (77x55cm-30x22in) s.d.86 mixed media. 2-Mar-4 Ansorena, Madrid #864/R est:4000
£2817	$4507	€4000	Leaves (17x23cm-7x9in) s.d.1961 pastel wash collage. 16-Sep-3 Segre, Madrid #136/R
£3147	$5255	€4500	Maternidad y pescador (64x48cm-25x19in) s.d.1933 W/C. 24-Jun-3 Segre, Madrid #114/R est:3500
£3681	$5815	€5300	Ficelle bleue (48x35cm-19x14in) s. mixed media collage panel. 27-Apr-3 Versailles Encheres #70
£3873	$6778	€5500	Suite Japon (65x45cm-26x18in) s.d.1990 mixed media. 18-Dec-3 Cornette de St.Cyr, Paris #86/R est:5000-7000
£4000	$7360	€5840	White glove (63x47cm-25x19in) s. gouache pencil collage prov. 24-Jun-4 Sotheby's, Olympia #541/R est:4000-6000
£4079	$7505	€6200	Deux punaises rouges (65x50cm-26x20in) s.d.84 mixed media. 24-Jun-4 Credit Municipal, Paris #52/R est:2500-3000
£4225	$7310	€6000	Alu froisse II (60x42cm-24x17in) s.d.1982 s.i.d.verso mixed media creased aluminium box. 14-Dec-3 Versailles Encheres #203/R est:5000-6000
£4306	$6803	€6200	Retour du Japon (78x56cm-31x22in) s.d.1987 mixed media collage. 27-Apr-3 Versailles Encheres #68
£4577	$7919	€6500	Sans titre (44x34cm-17x13in) s.d.1990 mixed media creased aluminium panel box. 14-Dec-3 Versailles Encheres #205/R est:5000-6000
£4861	$7681	€7000	Deux ficellees rouges (65x50cm-26x20in) s.d.980 mixed media collage panel. 27-Apr-3 Versailles Encheres #71
£5000	$7900	€7200	Avec trois cordes (64x81cm-25x32in) s.d.1980 s.i.d.verso mixed media collage aluminium panel. 27-Apr-3 Versailles Encheres #72
£5000	$9100	€7300	Portrait de Moya Dyring (32x25cm-13x10in) indis.sig.i. gouache prov. 6-Feb-4 Sotheby's, London #185/R est:5000-7000
£5556	$9056	€8000	Carmen (23x18cm-9x7in) s.d.43 ink W/C dr. 23-Sep-3 Durán, Madrid #243/R est:5500
£5903	$9858	€8500	Sans titre (76x56cm-30x22in) s.d.80 mixed media collage. 21-Oct-3 Artcurial Briest, Paris #575/R est:6000-7500
£6667	$12000	€10000	Souvenir (76x56cm-30x22in) s.i.d.1986 mixed media collage paper on canvas. 25-Apr-4 Versailles Encheres #136 est:12000-15000
£7383	$13067	€11000	Retour du Japon (65x22cm-26x9in) s.d.87 mixed media collage exhib.lit. 27-Apr-4 Durán, Madrid #92/R est:7000
£7534	$12808	€11000	Untitled (65x50cm-26x20in) s.d.1976 mixed media collage. 4-Nov-3 Ansorena, Madrid #913/R est:8000
£7639	$12758	€11000	Collage E (114x85cm-45x33in) s. s.i.d.1984 verso mixed media collage panel prov. 21-Oct-3 Artcurial Briest, Paris #538/R est:10000-12000
£8389	$15604	€12500	Fruit and fish (32x26cm-13x10in) s.d.53 W/C paper on canvas. 2-Mar-4 Ansorena, Madrid #843/R est:11500
£10333	$19013	€15500	Le roi et le poisson (30x48cm-12x19in) s. gouache prov. 11-Jun-4 Claude Aguttes, Neuilly #203/R est:8000-12000
£11000	$18370	€16060	Jeune fille au coq (54x32cm-21x13in) s. gouache blk ink pencil exec c.1946. 21-Oct-3 Sotheby's, London #384/R est:6000-8000
£11189	$18685	€16000	Collage au fond noir (113x83cm-44x33in) s. mixed media collage canvas on panel. 29-Jun-3 Versailles Encheres #137/R
£12500	$23000	€19000	Untitled (134x89cm-53x35in) s.d.1987 mixed media collage panel on canvas. 27-Jun-4 Versailles Encheres #116/R est:15000-20000

£12676 $22183 €18000 Le roi et le poisson (30x48cm-12x19in) s. gouache prov. 16-Dec-3 Claude Aguttes, Neuilly #36/R est:8000-12000
£13986 $24056 €20000 Arlequin (47x39cm-19x15in) s. mixed media. 3-Dec-3 Tajan, Paris #144/R est:2000-3000
£15333 $28213 €23000 Tache rouge (120x120cm-47x47in) s.i.d.1987 verso mixed media collage canvas prov. 8-Jun-4 Artcurial Briest, Paris #256/R est:25000-30000
£15385 $25692 €22000 Etoiles et signes (103x74cm-41x29in) s.d.1987 mixed media collage paper on canvas. 29-Jun-3 Versailles Encheres #138/R
£19014 $32894 €27000 Sans titre (130x131cm-51x52in) s.d.1972 s.i.d.verso mixed media collage. 14-Dec-3 Versailles Encheres #202/R est:15000-20000
£23944 $38789 €34000 Hommage a Picasso (105x138cm-41x54in) s.i.d.1981 s.d.verso collage canvas prov. 5-Aug-3 Tajan, Paris #61/R est:18000-22000
£26897 $48414 €39000 Face (75x56cm-30x22in) s. mixed media paper on canvas. 26-Jan-4 Ansorena, Madrid #893/R est:39000
£28000 $51520 €40880 Roi (62x50cm-24x20in) s. gouache W/C ink prov. 25-Jun-4 Christie's, London #163/R est:15000-20000
£28859 $53678 €43000 Composition (111x82cm-44x32in) s. mixed media collage paper on canvas. 2-Mar-4 Ansorena, Madrid #852/R est:39000
£40268 $74899 €60000 Untitled (204x98cm-80x39in) s.d.83 mixed media lit. 2-Mar-4 Ansorena, Madrid #854/R est:60000

CLAVER, Fernand (20th C) French
£387 $670 €550 Paris, quai aux fleurs (38x46cm-15x18in) s. 14-Dec-3 Eric Pillon, Calais #217/R

CLAVERIE, Jules Justin (1859-1932) French
£816 $1362 €1150 Riviere entre les arbres (50x65cm-20x26in) s. 19-Jun-3 Millon & Associes, Paris #189/R

CLAVO, Javier (1918-1994) Spanish
£426 $711 €600 Fish (33x41cm-13x16in) s. 23-Jun-3 Durán, Madrid #71/R
£1056 $1827 €1500 Toledo (45x27cm-18x11in) s. 10-Dec-3 Castellana, Madrid #245/R est:1000
£5479 $9315 €8000 Vivaldi (140x140cm-55x55in) s. 4-Nov-3 Ansorena, Madrid #924/R est:10000
£6849 $11644 €10000 Homage to Bach (148x204cm-58x80in) s. 4-Nov-3 Ansorena, Madrid #923/R est:12000
Works on paper
£350 $584 €500 Grove (32x25cm-13x10in) s. W/C. 30-Jun-3 Ansorena, Madrid #9/R
£559 $1029 €850 Peak (52x68cm-20x27in) s.d.73 wash. 22-Jun-4 Durán, Madrid #100/R
£1761 $2817 €2500 Hills (49x64cm-19x25in) s.i.d.1971 W/C. 16-Sep-3 Segre, Madrid #111/R

CLAXTON, Florence Anne (fl.1859-1879) British
Works on paper
£380 $695 €555 Testimonials (33x29cm-13x11in) s. W/C. 6-Jul-4 Bearnes, Exeter #445/R

CLAXTON, Marshall (1812-1881) British
£260 $481 €380 I'm weary, I'm weary (40x30cm-16x12in) s. i.verso. 10-Feb-4 Bonhams, Knightsbridge #8
£976 $1746 €1425 Skein (77x66cm-30x26in) with sig.d.1860 prov. 4-May-4 Ritchie, Toronto #26/R est:3000-4000 (C.D 2400)
£1320 $2086 €1914 Morning prayers. 27-Jul-3 Desmond Judd, Cranbrook #1146
£1500 $2685 €2190 Workers resting beneath a tree (33x51cm-13x20in) s. 5-May-4 John Nicholson, Haslemere #593/R est:1500-2000

CLAXTON, Marshall (attrib) (1812-1881) British
£744 $1264 €1086 Untitled - Portrait of a girl (75x61cm-30x24in) 29-Oct-3 Lawson Menzies, Sydney #273/R est:3000-5000 (A.D 1800)

CLAY, Alfred Barron (1831-1868) British
£383 $705 €559 Portrait of a seated woman (76x63cm-30x25in) s.d.Aug 1858. 9-Jun-4 Walker's, Ottawa #341/R (C.D 950)

CLAY, Elizabeth C Fisher (fl.1927-1938) American/British
£260 $411 €380 Tenby harbour (41x48cm-16x19in) s. board. 22-Jul-3 Peter Francis, Wales #20
£280 $518 €409 Runswick Bay (38x48cm-15x19in) s. board. 12-Feb-4 Andrew Hartley, Ilkley #876
£349 $600 €510 Old house, Dieppe (13x20cm-5x8in) s.i.d.1907 verso panel. 7-Dec-3 Treadway Gallery, Cincinnati #494/R

CLAYDEN, James (1947-) Australian
Works on paper
£351 $650 €512 Opening No.8, red black and white (203x82cm-80x32in) s.d.1990 i.verso mixed media timber panel exhib. 15-Mar-4 Sotheby's, Melbourne #84/R est:1500-2500 (A.D 850)
£393 $726 €574 Opening, No.2, blue, black and white (203x82cm-80x32in) s.d.1990 i.verso mixed media timber panel exhib. 15-Mar-4 Sotheby's, Melbourne #86 est:1500-2500 (A.D 950)

CLAYDEN, Phillippa (1955-) British
£550 $946 €803 Figure in a landscape (157x198cm-62x78in) oil collage. 3-Dec-3 Christie's, Kensington #629/R

CLAYES, Alice des (1890-?) Canadian
£2846 $5093 €4155 Coach at the Crown and thistle (56x76cm-22x30in) s. prov.exhib. 31-May-4 Sotheby's, Toronto #74/R est:8000-12000 (C.D 7000)

CLAYES, Berthe des (1877-1968) Canadian
£938 $1566 €1360 Low tide (28x35cm-11x14in) s. i.verso board. 17-Jun-3 Pinneys, Montreal #25 est:2400-2800 (C.D 2100)
£1129 $2077 €1648 Autumn, Val Morin (50x63cm-20x25in) s. s.i.verso. 9-Jun-4 Walker's, Ottawa #51/R est:3000-3500 (C.D 2800)
£1696 $2918 €2476 Laurentian farm (30x33cm-12x13in) s. panel. 2-Dec-3 Joyner Waddington, Toronto #13/R est:3000-3500 (C.D 3800)
£1786 $3071 €2608 Silver birches by the river (35x45cm-14x18in) s. 2-Dec-3 Joyner Waddington, Toronto #201/R est:3500-4000 (C.D 4000)
£1802 $3063 €2631 Farm near Sweetsburg, PQ (46x61cm-18x24in) s. i.verso. 21-Nov-3 Walker's, Ottawa #26/R est:3000-5000 (C.D 4000)
Works on paper
£360 $613 €526 Taylors barn, Hill Acres (25x29cm-10x11in) studio st. pastel. 21-Nov-3 Walker's, Ottawa #56/R (C.D 800)
£440 $805 €642 Red horse-drawn sleigh (12x17cm-5x7in) s. pastel. 1-Jun-4 Joyner Waddington, Toronto #412 (C.D 1100)

CLAYS, Paul Jean (1819-1900) Belgian
£448 $829 €650 Marine (18x28cm-7x11in) studio st. panel. 19-Jan-4 Horta, Bruxelles #301
£664 $1109 €950 Les pecheurs a Ostende (19x24cm-7x9in) s. panel. 13-Oct-3 Horta, Bruxelles #315
£680 $1102 €986 Hay barges on a continental canal (20x30cm-8x12in) s. painted c.1860-1880. 26-Jan-3 Desmond Judd, Cranbrook #855
£1000 $1810 €1500 Marine (25x35cm-10x14in) s. panel. 30-Mar-4 Campo & Campo, Antwerp #43/R est:1500-2000
£1050 $1932 €1533 Moonlight view of fishing boats (74x51cm-29x20in) s. 8-Jun-4 Bonhams, Knightsbridge #335/R est:1000-1500
£1216 $2177 €1800 Port Mediterraneen (20x26cm-8x10in) s.d.47 panel. 10-May-4 Horta, Bruxelles #91/R est:1500-2000
£2027 $3628 €3000 Depart des pecheurs (28x40cm-11x16in) s.d.46 panel. 10-May-4 Horta, Bruxelles #90/R est:3000-4000
£2500 $4250 €3650 Harbour scene with schooners (41x58cm-16x23in) s.d.1877 panel. 31-Oct-3 North East Auctions, Portsmouth #1889 est:1500-2500
£2550 $4718 €3800 Ships by the harbour mouth (50x40cm-20x16in) s. panel prov. 13-Mar-4 De Vuyst, Lokeren #54/R est:1200-1800
£3333 $6000 €5000 Moored ships in a small harbour (42x62cm-17x24in) s.d.1877 panel. 20-Apr-4 Sotheby's, Amsterdam #85/R est:4000-6000
£3488 $6000 €5092 Shipping in a Dutch harbour (67x51cm-26x20in) s. 3-Dec-3 Doyle, New York #101/R est:5000-7000
£3533 $6500 €5158 On the Zuyder Zee (91x66cm-36x26in) s. prov.exhib. 27-Jun-4 Freeman, Philadelphia #18/R est:8000-12000
£3693 $6500 €5392 Fishing boats off the Dutch coast (60x47cm-24x19in) s. panel. 18-May-4 Bonhams & Butterfields, San Francisco #71/R est:4000-6000
£4000 $7320 €6000 Voiliers hollandais sur la riviere (58x84cm-23x33in) s. prov. 7-Jun-4 Palais de Beaux Arts, Brussels #236/R est:6000-8000
£4076 $7500 €5951 Sailing ships off the Dutch coast (70x55cm-28x22in) s. 27-Jun-4 Freeman, Philadelphia #21/R est:6000-8000
£5208 $8698 €7500 Fishing boat in an estuary (57x47cm-22x19in) s.d.74 panel prov.exhib. 21-Oct-3 Sotheby's, Amsterdam #117/R est:4000-6000
£6000 $10320 €8760 Royal yacht enters harbour in a gale (44x59cm-17x23in) s.d.1859 panel. 2-Dec-3 Sotheby's, London #63/R est:600-800
£9028 $15347 €13000 Shipping on a calm (54x75cm-21x30in) s. panel prov. 28-Oct-3 Christie's, Amsterdam #200/R est:10000-15000
£9767 $16800 €14260 Barques de peche (75x111cm-30x44in) s.d.72. 3-Dec-3 Naón & Cia, Buenos Aires #16/R est:8000-12000
£10000 $18300 €15000 Marine hollandaise avec voiliers (101x80cm-40x31in) s.d.75 panel prov. 7-Jun-4 Palais de Beaux Arts, Brussels #39/R est:15000-20000

CLAYS, Paul Jean (attrib) (1819-1900) Belgian
£1268 $2193 €1800 Fishermen laying out nets on the beach (20x32cm-8x13in) s. panel. 11-Dec-3 Dr Fritz Nagel, Stuttgart #515/R est:2200

CLAYTON, Harold (1896-1979) British
£6000 $10620 €8760 Still life of summer flowers, in an ormolu mounted urn, on a pedestal (60x50cm-24x20in) s. 27-Apr-4 Henry Adams, Chichester #709/R est:8000-12000
£9000 $16470 €13140 Summer flowers in a classical urn on a marble pedestal (61x51cm-24x20in) s. 4-Jun-4 Christie's, London #104/R est:6000-8000
£9500 $15580 €13870 Still life study of roses, forget-me-nots and other flowers in an urn (48x59cm-19x23in) s. 3-Jun-3 Fellows & Sons, Birmingham #78/R est:10000-15000
£12000 $21960 €17520 Flowers in a china bowl on marble pedestal (56x66cm-22x26in) s. 4-Jun-4 Christie's, London #101/R est:10000-15000
£12500 $21250 €18250 Still life of summer flowers in figural jug (50x60cm-20x24in) s. 28-Oct-3 Henry Adams, Chichester #444/R est:8000-12000
£14000 $25620 €20440 Summer flowers in a bronze urn with primroses. Summer flowers in a bronze urn with roses (51x61cm-20x24in) s. pair. 4-Jun-4 Christie's, London #103/R est:8000-12000

CLAYTON, Inge (20th C) Austrian
£250 $455 €365 Miranda (56x23cm-22x9in) s.d.03 acetate. 15-Jun-4 Bonhams, Knightsbridge #141/R
£300 $555 €438 Idle Woman (78x36cm-31x14in) s.d. oil perspex. 13-Jul-4 Bonhams, Knightsbridge #41/R
£400 $728 €584 Three girls at the opera (52x47cm-20x19in) s.d.03. 15-Jun-4 Bonhams, Knightsbridge #88/R

CLAYTON, J Hughes (fl.1891-1929) British
£460 $823 €672 Where breaks the fury of the sea - Port Erin (55x91cm-22x36in) s. board. 17-Mar-4 Bonhams, Chester #254
Works on paper
£226 $378 €330 Inlet with fishing boat on the beach (26x62cm-10x24in) s. W/C. 17-Nov-3 Waddingtons, Toronto #64/R (C.D 500)
£250 $448 €365 Leasowe, a fishing vessel high and dry (23x29cm-9x11in) s.i. W/C. 26-May-4 Outhwaite & Litherland, Liverpool #287
£290 $519 €423 In a Warwickshire lane near Stratford on Avon (22x34cm-9x13in) s.i.verso W/C. 26-May-4 Outhwaite & Litherland, Liverpool #288/R
£320 $525 €467 Rocky coastal landscape with seagulls and sailing boats (65x32cm-26x13in) s. W/C. 3-Jun-3 Fellows & Sons, Birmingham #160/R
£380 $684 €555 Newlyn Cornwall (26x69cm-10x27in) s. pencil W/C htd white exhib. 22-Apr-4 Mellors & Kirk, Nottingham #1050

£400 $668 €584 Woman standing outside a cottage. s. W/C. 20-Jun-3 Chrystals Auctions, Isle of Man #232
£400 $736 €584 Rural idyll (35x51cm-14x20in) s. W/C. 22-Jun-4 Bonhams, Knightsbridge #162e/R
£400 $740 €584 Figures and animals before a thatched cottage with hollyhocks (35x52cm-14x20in) s. W/C. 16-Jul-4 Charterhouse, Sherborne #464/R
£440 $735 €642 Fishing boats. W/C. 19-Jun-3 Bonhams, Edinburgh #321
£450 $779 €657 Sailing in a quiet cove (26x64cm-10x25in) s. W/C. 11-Dec-3 Lane, Penzance #159
£450 $720 €657 Coast scene with sweeping bay, boats, cottages and figure (25x48cm-10x19in) s. 16-Sep-3 Capes Dunn, Manchester #858
£500 $885 €730 Cottage scene with coastline in background (23x50cm-9x20in) W/C. 28-Apr-4 Peter Wilson, Nantwich #167
£575 $937 €840 Cottage at Cemaes Bay, Anglesey, with boat and figures (25x38cm-10x15in) s. W/C. 27-Sep-3 Rogers Jones, Clwyd #31
£600 $960 €876 Coast scene with small boat coming ashore, cottage and beached boat (28x51cm-11x20in) s. 16-Sep-3 Capes Dunn, Manchester #857
£600 $1116 €876 At Newlyn, Cornwall (31x45cm-12x18in) s. W/C. 4-Mar-4 Hobbs Parker, Ashford #776
£679 $1133 €991 Gathering clams on a rocky shore (27x64cm-11x25in) s. W/C. 17-Nov-3 Waddingtons, Toronto #55/R (C.D 1500)
£700 $1281 €1022 Girl feeding ducks outside a coastal overshot mill (24x51cm-9x20in) s. W/C. 28-Jan-4 Hampton & Littlewood, Exeter #385/R
£700 $1274 €1022 Cemmaes Bay (47x79cm-19x31in) s. W/C htd white. 21-Jun-4 Bonhams, Bath #317
£725 $1182 €1059 Rural scene with thatched cottages and girl feeding poultry (30x43cm-12x17in) s. W/C. 27-Sep-3 Rogers Jones, Clwyd #66/R
£750 $1223 €1095 Anglesey coastalscape with distant boats (30x64cm-12x25in) s. W/C. 27-Sep-3 Rogers Jones, Clwyd #32
£750 $1275 €1095 Crail harbour, with fishing boats, figures and nearby inn (47x73cm-19x29in) s. pencil W/C. 19-Nov-3 Tennants, Leyburn #882/R
£750 $1350 €1095 Thatched cottage with figure on a lane (28x46cm-11x18in) W/C. 24-Apr-4 Rogers Jones, Clwyd #137
£800 $1456 €1168 Newlyn, Cornwall (47x79cm-19x31in) s. W/C htd white. 21-Jun-4 Bonhams, Bath #395
£860 $1436 €1256 Artist's home, Caemaes Bay, Wales (27x66cm-11x26in) s. i.verso W/C. 17-Nov-3 Waddingtons, Toronto #56/R est:1000-1500 (C.D 1900)
£1000 $1830 €1460 Figures outside a coastal cottage with sailing boats beyond (26x56cm-10x22in) s. W/C. 28-Jan-4 Hampton & Littlewood, Exeter #384/R est:400-600
£1000 $1850 €1460 Fregala, Anglesey. Cottage near Cemaes Bay, Anglesey (24x41cm-9x16in) s. bears i. W/C pair. 14-Jul-4 Bonhams, Chester #316 est:1000-1500
£1100 $2057 €1606 Anglesey coastal scene with fisherman and a girl beside a cottage (44x79cm-17x31in) s. pencil W/C. 22-Jul-4 Tennants, Leyburn #653
£1200 $1956 €1740 Low tide at Camaes. Figures on a beach (21x49cm-8x19in) s.i. W/C pair. 23-Sep-3 Bonhams, Knightsbridge #45/R est:700-900

CLAYTON, J W (?) British?
Works on paper
£460 $750 €672 Conwy Castle, bridge and town from the Deganwy side (23x38cm-9x15in) s. W/C. 27-Sep-3 Rogers Jones, Clwyd #22

CLAYTON, John (1961-) American
£255 $400 €372 Untitled, street scene (46x61cm-18x24in) s. 20-Apr-3 Outer Cape Auctions, Provincetown #35/R
£266 $490 €388 Still life (41x51cm-16x20in) d.1999 board. 15-Feb-4 Outer Cape Auctions, Provincetown #50/R

CLEALL, Septimus (19/20th C) British
£500 $895 €730 Royal Yacht Victoria and Albert II (30x46cm-12x18in) s. board. 26-May-4 Christie's, Kensington #679/R

CLEARY, Manon (20th C) American
£983 $1700 €1435 Budding fruit (41x61cm-16x24in) s. 13-Dec-3 Sloans & Kenyon, Bethesda #755/R est:800-1200
£1272 $2200 €1857 White rat (122x152cm-48x60in) 13-Dec-3 Sloans & Kenyon, Bethesda #759/R est:1000-1500
£1272 $2200 €1857 Mystery series no 2 (152x122cm-60x48in) prov. 13-Dec-3 Sloans & Kenyon, Bethesda #758/R est:900-1200
Works on paper
£520 $900 €759 White rat no 8 (53x66cm-21x26in) s.d.8/87 pastel sanded paper prov. 13-Dec-3 Sloans & Kenyon, Bethesda #757/R

CLEARY, Pat (?) British
£320 $589 €467 Sheep on a mountain pass (65x106cm-26x42in) s. board. 8-Jun-4 Bonhams, Chester #1022/R

CLEIS, Hugo (1903-1979) Swiss
£591 $981 €857 Window view of Ligornetto church (45x37cm-18x15in) s. 13-Jun-3 Zofingen, Switzerland #2809 (S.FR 1300)

CLELAND, Thomas Maitland (1880-1964) American
Works on paper
£1437 $2400 €2098 Cadillac sport phaeton (53x38cm-21x15in) init. pen ink gouache W/C. 15-Nov-3 Illustration House, New York #90/R est:2000-3000

CLELLAND, Mary Alberta (1876-1919) Canadian
£813 $1455 €1187 Quebec farmhouse (58x66cm-23x26in) s. 27-May-4 Heffel, Vancouver #80/R est:2000-3000 (C.D 2000)
£1240 $2244 €1810 Untitled - Laurentian winter (58x66cm-23x26in) s.d.1930. 18-Apr-4 Levis, Calgary #19/R est:3000-4000 (C.D 3000)

CLEM, Robert Verity (20th C) American
Works on paper
£941 $1600 €1374 Gyrfalcon on monomoy (44x72cm-17x28in) s.d.1973 s.i.verso W/C. 21-Nov-3 Skinner, Boston #339/R est:1500-2500
£1950 $3100 €2847 Looking down Nauset (30x41cm-12x16in) s.d.1975 W/C. 12-Sep-3 Skinner, Boston #530/R est:2000-40000
£2206 $3750 €3221 Shore patrol, Nauset light brach, Eastham (44x71cm-17x28in) s. W/C gouache. 21-Nov-3 Skinner, Boston #552/R est:7000-9000

CLEMENCIN, A (19th C) French
Sculpture
£1352 $2150 €1974 Possibly Diana, Goddess of the hunt, running with a dog (46x43x10cm-18x17x4in) s. green brown pat bronze marble base. 12-Sep-3 Aspire, Cleveland #226 est:1500-2500

CLEMENS, Curt (1911-1947) Swedish
£982 $1669 €1434 Girl with red hair band (31x30cm-12x12in) s.d.1938 panel. 5-Nov-3 AB Stockholms Auktionsverk #803/R (S.KR 13000)

CLEMENS, G A (1870-1918) Danish
£358 $655 €523 Fisherman on beach in evening sunshine (54x75cm-21x30in) init.d.1909. 7-Jun-4 Museumsbygningen, Copenhagen #40 (D.KR 4000)
£2156 $4011 €3148 Sunset at Vesterhavet, young woman looking at the lovely evening light (70x120cm-28x47in) s. exhib. 2-Mar-4 Rasmussen, Copenhagen #1351/R est:15000-20000 (D.KR 24000)

CLEMENS, Paul Lewis (1911-1992) American
£1193 $2100 €1742 Babe Ruth (36x30cm-14x12in) s. board painted c.1930. 23-May-4 Treadway Gallery, Cincinnati #663/R est:1500-2000
£10294 $17500 €15029 Tuesday's child (102x71cm-40x28in) s. prov.exhib. 29-Oct-3 Christie's, Los Angeles #36/R est:6000-8000
Works on paper
£3529 $6000 €5152 After the bath (74x61cm-29x24in) s. pastel on board. 29-Oct-3 Christie's, Los Angeles #35/R est:3000-5000

CLEMENT, Charles (1889-1972) Swiss
£1121 $2006 €1637 Farmstead in sunshine (60x81cm-24x32in) s.d.10.42. 14-May-4 Dobiaschofsky, Bern #88/R est:3000 (S.FR 2600)

CLEMENT, Felix Auguste (1826-1888) French
£890 $1451 €1299 Portrait of an Egyptian woman (27x22cm-11x9in) s.d.1887. 27-Sep-3 Rasmussen, Havnen #2072/R (D.KR 9500)

CLEMENT, G F (1867-1933) Danish
£270 $501 €394 Seated girl (23x16cm-9x6in) i.d.1902 verso panel exhib.prov. 2-Mar-4 Rasmussen, Copenhagen #1544/R (D.KR 3000)
£276 $470 €403 Southern landscape with two women (83x114cm-33x45in) s. 10-Nov-3 Rasmussen, Vejle #7/R (D.KR 3000)
£622 $1132 €933 Summer in the garden (49x38cm-19x15in) s. 19-Jun-4 Rasmussen, Havnen #2052/R (D.KR 7000)

CLEMENT, P (?) ?
£2600 $4654 €3900 Mendiants musiciens (98x130cm-39x51in) s. 15-May-4 other European Auctioneer #55

CLEMENT, Therese (1889-1984) French
£333 $597 €500 Camaret (50x61cm-20x24in) s. 16-May-4 Thierry & Lannon, Brest #297
£537 $988 €800 Port du Nord (60x73cm-24x29in) s. 26-Mar-4 Neret-Minet, Paris #4
£1224 $2192 €1800 Fontaine Nedjardine a Fez (41x32cm-16x13in) s. panel. 21-Mar-4 St-Germain-en-Laye Encheres #29/R est:2000-2200

CLEMENT-CHASSAGNE, Louis Henri Lucien (20th C) French
£267 $488 €400 Neige foret d'Othe (38x46cm-15x18in) i.verso exhib. 5-Jun-4 Arnold, Frankfurt #556/R

CLEMENTE PEREZ, Salvador (1859-1909) Spanish
£569 $950 €831 Spanish village (53x30cm-21x12in) s. 19-Jun-3 Shelley, Hendersonville #1400

CLEMENTE, Francesco (1952-) Italian
£20000 $36800 €29200 Head (39x41cm-15x16in) pigment exec 1990-91 prov.exhib. 24-Jun-4 Sotheby's, London #294/R est:12000-15000
£26946 $45000 €39341 Meditation, trigonometrie (186x196cm-73x77in) s.d.1993-95 overlap enamel silkscreen ink linen prov.exhib. 13-Nov-3 Sotheby's, New York #543/R est:40000-60000
£45000 $81900 €65700 Sulla lingua (130x100cm-51x39in) painted 1982-83 prov. 5-Feb-4 Christie's, London #137/R est:30000-40000
£50000 $83500 €73000 Tools (112x234cm-44x92in) painted 1997 prov.exhib. 20-Oct-3 Sotheby's, London #46/R est:70000
£72626 $130000 €106034 Self-portrait (40x45cm-16x18in) s.d.1980 verso prov.exhib. 13-May-4 Sotheby's, New York #431/R est:60000-80000
Works on paper
£468 $767 €650 Composition with purple (54x55cm-21x22in) s. mixed media W/C bodycol carpenter's pencil collage board. 4-Jun-3 Ketterer, Hamburg #267/R
£10615 $19000 €15498 Darkness touch (67x102cm-26x40in) pastel exec 1989 prov. 13-May-4 Sotheby's, New York #425/R est:20000-30000
£11377 $19000 €16610 Muse (66x51cm-26x20in) s.d.1998 verso col chks prov.exhib. 12-Nov-3 Christie's, Rockefeller NY #636/R est:10000-15000
£12291 $22000 €17945 Ecapni, in freiden (189x150cm-74x59in) graphite chl metallic paint prov.exhib.lit. 14-May-4 Phillips, New York #236/R est:15000-20000
£12291 $22000 €17945 Accobni, im mundi (178x152cm-70x60in) graphite chl metallic paint prov.exhib.lit. 14-May-4 Phillips, New York #237/R est:25000-35000

£13174 $22000 €19234 Beauty is mine (60x51cm-24x20in) s.d.1998 verso col chks prov.exhib. 12-Nov-3 Christie's, Rockefeller NY #635/R est:10000-15000
£13408 $24000 €19576 Omou, mensch (144x150cm-57x59in) graphite chl metallic paint prov.exhib.lit. 14-May-4 Phillips, New York #228/R est:25000-35000
£14371 $24000 €20982 Mother, Lover, Daughter (66x51cm-26x20in) s.d.1998 verso col chks prov.exhib. 12-Nov-3 Christie's, Rockefeller NY #637/R est:10000-15000
£15642 $28000 €22837 Onesni, im schob (192x150cm-76x59in) pastel metallic paint prov.exhib.lit. 14-May-4 Phillips, New York #225/R est:25000-35000
£19553 $35000 €28547 Untitled (112x123cm-44x48in) W/C handmade Indian paper exec 1992 prov. 13-May-4 Sotheby's, New York #441/R est:35000-45000
£20958 $35000 €30599 Simmetria (241x234cm-95x92in) s.i.d.1980 verso chl W/C col pencil gold leaf linen prov. 13-Nov-3 Sotheby's, New York #554/R est:40000-60000
£32000 $58880 €46720 Autoritratto antico (151x153cm-59x60in) s.i.d.1985 verso W/C pastel paper collage on board prov. 25-Jun-4 Christie's, London #161/R est:14000-18000
£38000 $69160 €55480 Heart (81x71cm-32x28in) pigment prov.exhib. 6-Feb-4 Sotheby's, London #245/R est:18000-25000
£67039 $120000 €97877 Untitled (46x58cm-18x23in) W/C eighteen elements prov. 12-May-4 Christie's, Rockefeller NY #390/R est:120000-180000

CLEMENTS, Alling (?) American?
£370 $700 €540 Figures walking along a wooded trail (51x61cm-20x24in) s. panel board. 21-Feb-4 Jeffery Burchard, Florida #99a/R

CLEMENTS, George Henry (1854-1935) American
Works on paper
£376 $700 €549 Cattle resting in a pasture (26x34cm-10x13in) s.d.1885 pencil W/C. 3-Mar-4 Christie's, Rockefeller NY #43/R

CLEMENTS, Grace (1905-1969) American
£2890 $5000 €4219 Yard Sale (91x76cm-36x30in) s.d.35. 10-Dec-3 Bonhams & Butterfields, San Francisco #6263/R est:6000-8000

CLEMENTS, Richard (1951-1999) Australian
£1116 $2064 €1629 Untitled (183x136cm-72x54in) s.d.July 89 verso prov.exhib. 15-Mar-4 Sotheby's, Melbourne #54 est:3000-5000 (A.D 2700)

CLEMENTSCHITSCH, Arnold (1887-1970) Austrian
£1818 $3091 €2600 Man's portrait (54x43cm-21x17in) s.d.1933. 19-Nov-3 Dorotheum, Klagenfurt #6 est:1500
£5921 $10895 €9000 Draubrucke with Mittagskogel (52x70cm-20x28in) s.d.1959. 22-Jun-4 Wiener Kunst Auktionen, Vienna #76/R est:8000
£6579 $12105 €10000 Salzburg (36x53cm-14x21in) s. canvas on board. 22-Jun-4 Wiener Kunst Auktionen, Vienna #75/R est:15000

CLEMINSON, Robert (19th C) British
£260 $419 €380 Stag and his herd in a snow capped Highland landscape (63x76cm-25x30in) s. 12-Aug-3 Bonhams, Ipswich #226
£300 $510 €438 Deer in a highland landscape (90x70cm-35x28in) s. 4-Nov-3 Bonhams, Oxford #181
£450 $716 €653 Hunting dogs with a stag in a highland landscape (51x76cm-20x30in) s. 9-Sep-3 Bonhams, Knightsbridge #206/R
£450 $765 €657 Gun dog with dead game (45x35cm-18x14in) s. 28-Oct-3 Henry Adams, Chichester #424/R
£528 $830 €771 Rewards, victory (61x92cm-24x36in) s. i.d.1888 verso. 1-Sep-3 Shapiro, Sydney #348 (A.D 1300)
£569 $894 €831 Untitled, terrier, fox and duck (61x92cm-24x36in) s. 1-Sep-3 Shapiro, Sydney #349 (A.D 1400)
£600 $1038 €876 Disturbed at the Banquet (76x128cm-30x50in) s.d.1883 s.i.verso sold with companion pair. 10-Dec-3 Bonhams, Bury St Edmunds #587
£600 $1104 €876 Gundogs with the day's bag (25x35cm-10x14in) s. 10-Jun-4 Christie's, Kensington #404/R
£720 $1238 €1051 Moorland pony and three hounds (40x61cm-16x24in) s. 6-Dec-3 Shapes, Edinburgh #412/R
£880 $1399 €1285 Two retrievers on a Scottish moor (29x39cm-11x15in) s. 18-Mar-3 Anderson & Garland, Newcastle #495/R
£980 $1558 €1431 Three spaniels at the shore of a lake (36x49cm-14x19in) init. 18-Mar-3 Anderson & Garland, Newcastle #496/R
£1100 $1826 €1606 Spaniels putting up pheasant (10x14cm-4x6in) s. pair. 1-Oct-3 George Kidner, Lymington #167/R est:500-800
£1154 $1985 €1685 Gundogs out hunting (41x61cm-16x24in) s. 7-Dec-3 Uppsala Auktionskammare, Uppsala #98/R est:6000-8000 (S.KR 15000)
£1250 $2288 €1825 Stag and hinds (76x126cm-30x50in) s. 8-Apr-4 Bonhams, Edinburgh #114 est:1000-1500
£1300 $2171 €1898 Coming off the hill (60x90cm-24x35in) s. 16-Oct-3 Bonhams, Edinburgh #172/R est:1500-2000
£1300 $2210 €1898 Setters with the day's bag (71x91cm-28x36in) s. 27-Nov-3 Christie's, Kensington #431/R est:1500-2000
£1300 $2379 €1898 Waiting for the ferry boat (76x127cm-30x50in) s.d.1886. 8-Apr-4 Bonhams, Edinburgh #184/R est:1200-1800
£1800 $3060 €2628 Gundogs on a grouse moor (51x76cm-20x30in) s. pair. 27-Nov-3 Christie's, Kensington #432/R est:2000-3000
£2600 $4836 €3796 Stag with hinds by a loch (91x71cm-36x28in) s. 4-Mar-4 Christie's, Kensington #29/R est:1500-2000
£4889 $8458 €7138 Highland pastures (27x103cm-11x41in) s.d.1880. 9-Dec-3 Pinneys, Montreal #62 est:12000-18000 (C.D 11000)

CLEMMER, John (1921-) American
Works on paper
£275 $500 €402 Abstraction (30x25cm-12x10in) s.d.56 pen ink. 7-Feb-4 Neal Auction Company, New Orleans #804

CLENDINNING, Max (20th C) British
Sculpture
£1400 $2548 €2100 Maxima lounge chair (71x64x64cm-28x25x25in) flat pack lacquered plywood upholstery. 30-Jun-4 Christie's, Kensington #21/R est:1500-2000

CLENIN, Walter (1897-1988) Swiss
£543 $869 €793 Grapeharvest on Bielersee (64x100cm-25x39in) s. 16-Sep-3 Philippe Schuler, Zurich #3230 (S.FR 1200)
£1454 $2471 €2123 Group of riders (85x113cm-33x44in) s. 7-Nov-3 Dobiaschofsky, Bern #250/R est:2800 (S.FR 3300)

CLEPHANE, Lewis (1869-1948) American
£216 $400 €315 Shenandoah Valley landscape (46x71cm-18x28in) s. painted c.1930. 16-Feb-4 Quinn's, Falls Church #479/R

CLERC, Oscar de (1892-1968) Belgian
Sculpture
£1517 $2807 €2200 Homme debout (68cm-27in) s. pat plaster. 19-Jan-4 Horta, Bruxelles #86 est:2200-2800
£1538 $2615 €2200 Nu assis (95x65cm-37x26in) plaster relief. 1-Dec-3 Palais de Beaux Arts, Brussels #40/R est:2500-3000

CLERC, Philippe le (1755-1826) German
Works on paper
£12752 $23336 €19000 Pony standing in a clearing (60x75cm-24x30in) s. W/C gouache prov. 9-Jul-4 Dawo, Saarbrucken #11/R est:4800

CLERC, Philippe le (attrib) (1755-1826) German
Works on paper
£276 $461 €400 Joseph and Potiphar's wife (21x29cm-8x11in) pen sepia wash prov. 15-Nov-3 Lempertz, Koln #1346

CLERC, Yves (1947-) French
£8982 $15000 €13114 No 197 (130x130cm-51x51in) s.d.2000 acrylic prov. 13-Nov-3 Sotheby's, New York #559/R est:15000-20000

CLERCK, Hendrick de (1570-1629) Flemish
Works on paper
£24324 $42811 €36000 Martydom of St Sebastian (35x40cm-14x16in) bears sig. indis.i.d.1634 verso pen brown ink wash chk prov.exhib. 19-May-4 Sotheby's, Amsterdam #37/R est:22000-28000

CLERCK, Jan de (1881-1962) Belgian
£658 $1211 €1000 View of village. Stream in the woods (38x44cm-15x17in) s. panel pair. 22-Jun-4 Palais de Beaux Arts, Brussels #219
£4333 $7973 €6500 De oude Vismijn (152x122cm-60x48in) s.d.1913 prov.exhib. 8-Jun-4 Sotheby's, Amsterdam #33/R est:7000-10000

CLERCQ, Alphonse de (1868-1945) Belgian
£369 $653 €550 Vue a Knokke (45x60cm-18x24in) s. 27-Apr-4 Campo, Vlaamse Kaai #375
£1111 $1767 €1600 City near the water (70x100cm-28x39in) s.d.99. 15-Sep-3 Bernaerts, Antwerp #74 est:1500-1800

CLERCQ, Louis de (1836-1901) French?
Photographs
£3056 $5500 €4462 Alcasar Seville, two arches of small courtyard of the harem (28x20cm-11x8in) num.24 albumen print. 22-Apr-4 Phillips, New York #171/R est:8000-12000
£4722 $8500 €6894 Heliopolis, interior of the temple of Jupiter, Syria (23x29cm-9x11in) num.verso waxed paper negative. 22-Apr-4 Phillips, New York #168/R est:10000-15000
£5278 $9500 €7706 Heliopolis, view of the ruins, Syria (21x28cm-8x11in) i. albumen print. 22-Apr-4 Phillips, New York #167/R est:12000-16000
£12222 $22000 €17844 Heliopolis, Baalbeck, temple of the sun, Syria (22x29cm-9x11in) waxed paper negative lit. 22-Apr-4 Phillips, New York #32/R est:25000-35000

CLERCQ, Pieter Jan de (1891-1964) Belgian
£278 $464 €400 Vue de l'Escaut (32x43cm-13x17in) s. cardboard. 21-Oct-3 Campo, Vlaamse Kaai #745
£872 $1544 €1300 Concarneau (81x101cm-32x40in) s. 27-Apr-4 Campo & Campo, Antwerp #54/R

CLEREN, Jean Paul (1940-) French
£805 $1426 €1200 Deux personnages (73x54cm-29x21in) s. 27-Apr-4 Campo & Campo, Antwerp #41

CLERGE, Auguste Joseph (1891-1963) French
£1074 $1997 €1600 Paris sous la neige (74x86cm-29x34in) s. 3-Mar-4 Tajan, Paris #110 est:800-1000

CLERGERIE, Yvonne (20th C) French
Sculpture
£1447 $2663 €2200 Jeune femme (33x10x8cm-13x4x3in) s. bronze Cast Chapon. 27-Jun-4 Feletin, Province #85
£2055 $3493 €3000 Lumiere (77cm-30in) s. num.6/8 pat bronze Cast Delval. 9-Nov-3 Eric Pillon, Calais #203/R

CLERICI, Fabrizio (1913-1993) Italian
£1600 $2880 €2400 Three (50x70cm-20x28in) s. board painted c.1969. 22-Apr-4 Finarte Semenzato, Rome #298 est:2800-3500
Works on paper
£298 $542 €450 Piano lessons (23x33cm-9x13in) s. Chinese ink. 17-Jun-4 Galleria Pananti, Florence #419/R

£667 $1200 €1000 Eclypse painters (21x27cm-8x11in) s. pen W/C card. 22-Apr-4 Finarte Semenzato, Rome #92/R
£1333 $2400 €2000 General (41x34cm-16x13in) s. ink W/C. 22-Apr-4 Finarte Semenzato, Rome #123 est:1500
£1600 $2880 €2400 Horus' tree. Presences (38x28cm-15x11in) s. pen card two. 22-Apr-4 Finarte Semenzato, Rome #125/R est:3000
£2292 $3896 €3300 Lions barking (29x45cm-11x18in) s. mixed media prov. 28-Oct-3 Il Ponte, Milan #242/R

CLERICI, L (19th C) Italian?
Sculpture
£1397 $2500 €2040 Bust of Augustus (56cm-22in) s. white marble. 20-Mar-4 Freeman, Philadelphia #642/R est:800-1200

CLERICI, Leone (19th C) Italian
Sculpture
£1300 $2171 €1898 Caesar Augustus (26cm-10in) s. marble waisted socle. 14-Oct-3 Sotheby's, Olympia #27/R est:700-900
£5500 $9515 €8030 Callipygian Venus (88cm-35in) s.d.1882 white marble lit. 12-Dec-3 Sotheby's, London #246/R est:4000-6000

CLERISSEAU, Charles Louis (1721-1820) French
£3125 $5219 €4500 Ruins with figures (37x42cm-15x17in) 22-Oct-3 Finarte Semenzato, Milan #63/R
Works on paper
£4444 $8000 €6488 Arch of the Argentieri, Rome, with figures in the foreground (43x36cm-17x14in) s.d.1789 bodycol oval. 22-Jan-4 Christie's, Rockefeller NY #231/R est:7000-10000
£11000 $20130 €16060 Extensive mountainous landscape with a waterfall by a town (59x47cm-23x19in) bodycol prov. 6-Jul-4 Christie's, London #135/R est:10000-15000

CLERK, Pierre Jean (1928-) Canadian
£610 $1091 €891 Multicolour design (50x60cm-20x24in) s.d.55 prov. 31-May-4 Sotheby's, Toronto #96/R est:2000-4000 (C.D 1500)
Works on paper
£191 $355 €279 Composition (48x67cm-19x26in) s.i.d.1960 gouache. 2-Mar-4 Ritchie, Toronto #207/R (C.D 475)

CLERMONT, Auguste Henri Louis de (19th C) French
£1168 $2173 €1705 Donkey and cattle by waterhole in meadow (60x73cm-24x29in) s. exhib. 2-Mar-4 Rasmussen, Copenhagen #1375/R est:15000 (D.KR 13000)

CLERMONT, Jean François (1717-1807) French
£483 $806 €700 Figures outside farmstead (28x41cm-11x16in) s. Indian ink pen brush prov. sold with another. 15-Nov-3 Lempertz, Koln #1278/R

CLERTE, Jean (1930-) French
Works on paper
£699 $1189 €1000 Sans titre (54x39cm-21x15in) s.d.84 W/C pencil. 27-Nov-3 Calmels Cohen, Paris #113/R

CLESINGER, Jean Baptiste (1814-1883) French
Sculpture
£1391 $2531 €2100 Le joueuse de lyre (43cm-17in) s.i.d.1857 gold pat bronze Cast Barbedienne. 15-Jun-4 Vanderkindere, Brussels #193/R est:1500-2000
£2028 $3448 €2900 Diane au repos (38cm-15in) s.i.d.1860 pat bronze Cast Barbedienne. 28-Nov-3 Doutrebente, Paris #46/R est:3000-4000
£2059 $3500 €3006 Taureau romain (21cm-8in) s.st.f.Barbedienne d.1858 pat bronze. 28-Oct-3 Christie's, Rockefeller NY #211/R
£2372 $4245 €3463 Femme piquee par un Serpent (22x55cm-9x22in) s.i.F Barbedienne bronze prov.lit. 15-May-4 Christie's, Sydney #13/R est:4000-6000 (A.D 6000)
£3000 $5490 €4380 Bacchante (59cm-23in) s.d.1868 marble. 9-Jul-4 Sotheby's, London #107/R est:4000-6000
£3333 $5967 €5000 Jeune femme aux camelias (75cm-30in) s. marble. 16-May-4 other European Auctioneer #180
£4138 $6869 €6000 Buste d'Ariane (79cm-31in) s. terracotta. 2-Oct-3 Sotheby's, Paris #104/R
£4500 $8100 €6570 Woman bitten by a snake (21x51cm-8x20in) s.i. brown pat bronze st.f.F. Barbedienne lit. 21-Apr-4 Sotheby's, London #104/R est:3000-5000
£21277 $35532 €30000 Taureau Romain (113x127x50cm-44x50x20in) s.i.d.1858 brown pat bronze st.f.F.Barbedienne. 17-Jun-3 Christie's, Paris #111/R est:15000-25000

CLESINGER, Jean Baptiste (attrib) (1814-1883) French
Works on paper
£367 $664 €550 Paysage d'Italie (7x24cm-3x9in) gouache. 30-Mar-4 Rossini, Paris #926

CLESSE, Louis (1889-1961) Belgian
£270 $476 €400 Vieille facade Abbaye de la Cambre (52x36cm-20x14in) s. panel. 24-May-4 Bernaerts, Antwerp #572/R
£276 $508 €420 Vase de roses (39x49cm-15x19in) s. panel. 22-Jun-4 Palais de Beaux Arts, Brussels #211
£315 $535 €450 Perdreaux (56x46cm-22x18in) s. 18-Nov-3 Galerie Moderne, Brussels #648
£336 $624 €500 Woodstream (40x50cm-16x20in) s. panel. 8-Mar-4 Bernaerts, Antwerp #866
£382 $607 €550 At the edge of the wood (34x50cm-13x20in) s. panel. 15-Sep-3 Bernaerts, Antwerp #68
£385 $654 €550 Nature morte, lievre et faisan (100x80cm-39x31in) s. 18-Nov-3 Galerie Moderne, Brussels #663/R
£390 $651 €550 Chemin de campagne (40x30cm-16x12in) s. d.17 verso panel. 14-Oct-3 Vanderkindere, Brussels #27
£400 $716 €600 Paysage au Rouge-Cloitre (30x40cm-12x16in) s. panel. 11-May-4 Vanderkindere, Brussels #239
£403 $741 €600 Chaumiere au bord de l'etang (36x45cm-14x18in) s. panel. 23-Mar-4 Galerie Moderne, Brussels #290/R
£604 $1123 €900 La vieille maison (75x60cm-30x24in) s.d.1933 panel. 8-Mar-4 Bernaerts, Antwerp #610/R
£633 $1134 €950 L'etang du rouge-cloitre (60x70cm-24x28in) s.d.1940. 15-May-4 De Vuyst, Lokeren #60
£655 $1212 €950 Riviere au printemps (45x53cm-18x21in) s. 19-Jan-4 Horta, Bruxelles #368
£1007 $1862 €1500 Les pecheurs conversant sur le quai (45x55cm-18x22in) s.d.1926 panel. 15-Mar-4 Horta, Bruxelles #140 est:1700-2000
£1049 $1752 €1500 Barque de peche et voilier a quai (41x50cm-16x20in) s.i.d.1935 panel. 13-Oct-3 Horta, Bruxelles #343 est:1200-1800
£1275 $2359 €1900 Summer landscape (40x50cm-16x20in) s.d.1932 panel. 13-Mar-4 De Vuyst, Lokeren #55/R est:1800-2200
£1408 $2437 €2000 Le long du canal (45x66cm-18x26in) s.d.37 panel. 9-Dec-3 Campo, Vlaamse Kaai #268/R est:1500-1800
£2200 $3938 €3300 Canal en Flandre (46x66cm-18x26in) s.d.36 s.i.verso panel. 15-May-4 De Vuyst, Lokeren #557/R est:3300-4000
£2740 $4658 €4000 Etang (75x100cm-30x39in) s.d.1916. 10-Nov-3 Horta, Bruxelles #63
£5245 $8916 €7500 Hiver en Flandres (100x130cm-39x51in) s. 18-Nov-3 Galerie Moderne, Brussels #635/R est:1500-2000
£5282 $9137 €7500 Paysage au canal (100x130cm-39x51in) s. indis.d. 9-Dec-3 Vanderkindere, Brussels #45 est:3750-6250
£5352 $9259 €7600 Retour a la ferme sous le vent (116x130cm-46x51in) s.d.1936. 9-Dec-3 Vanderkindere, Brussels #25/R est:3750-6250

CLEVE, Cornelis van (studio) (1520-1567) Dutch
£16443 $29104 €24500 Madonna and Child (45x34cm-18x13in) panel. 28-Apr-4 Marc Kohn, Paris #133/R est:15000-18000

CLEVE, Hendrick van III (1525-1589) Flemish
£11348 $18951 €16000 La tour de Babel (74x105cm-29x41in) panel. 17-Oct-3 Tajan, Paris #57/R est:15000-20000
£13000 $23400 €18980 Nimrod amongst the monuments (36x58cm-14x23in) panel. 22-Apr-4 Sotheby's, London #1/R est:10000-15000
£23944 $41901 €34000 Rome, vue de la Place Saint-Pierre (76x106cm-30x42in) panel prov. 18-Dec-3 Tajan, Paris #19/R est:30000-35000

CLEVE, Hendrick van III (attrib) (1525-1589) Flemish
Works on paper
£1192 $2170 €1800 View of the Island of Tevere in Rome. Study of a young woman (21x27cm-8x11in) pen sanguine double-sided prov. 18-Jun-4 Bolland & Marotz, Bremen #443/R est:1900

CLEVE, Hendrick van III (style) (1525-1589) Flemish
£12752 $23463 €19000 La Tour de Babel (96x124cm-38x49in) panel on panel painted c.1600. 26-Mar-4 Neret-Minet, Paris #31/R est:20000

CLEVE, Joos van (after) (1485-1540) Dutch
£8966 $14972 €13000 Maria with child - Madonna with the cherries (6x53cm-2x21in) panel prov. 15-Nov-3 Lempertz, Koln #1026/R est:12000-15000

CLEVE, Joos van (circle) (1485-1540) Dutch
£10943 $18166 €15977 Virgin Mary with child (33x25cm-13x10in) tempera panel. 4-Oct-3 Dorotheum, Prague #1/R est:300000-500000 (C.KR 500000)

CLEVE, Joos van (studio) (1485-1540) Dutch
£24658 $41918 €36000 Deposition (66x45cm-26x18in) i. board triptych. 4-Nov-3 Ansorena, Madrid #43/R est:30000

CLEVE, Joos van (style) (1485-1540) Dutch
£8904 $15137 €13000 St Jerome in his study (49x63cm-19x25in) i. panel. 4-Nov-3 Sotheby's, Amsterdam #122/R est:8000-12000

CLEVE, Marten van (1527-1581) Flemish
£8054 $14416 €12000 Interieur d'auberge (26x37cm-10x15in) panel. 25-May-4 Palais de Beaux Arts, Brussels #551/R est:10000-15000
£60000 $103800 €87600 Village kermesse (94x155cm-37x61in) panel lit. 10-Dec-3 Christie's, London #9/R est:60000-80000

CLEVE, Marten van (attrib) (1527-1581) Flemish
£10067 $18523 €15000 Le cortege de la mariee (42x79cm-17x31in) panel. 24-Mar-4 Claude Boisgirard, Paris #43/R est:15000-20000

CLEVE, Marten van (circle) (1527-1581) Flemish
£5000 $8500 €7300 Weeding feast (27x37cm-11x15in) panel. 31-Oct-3 Christie's, Kensington #6/R est:5000-7000

CLEVE, Marten van (studio) (1527-1581) Flemish
£18000 $32400 €26280 Wedding feast, departure of the newly-wed couple (58x87cm-23x34in) 22-Apr-4 Sotheby's, London #12/R est:15000-20000
£25000 $43250 €36500 King drinks (68x103cm-27x41in) panel prov. 10-Dec-3 Christie's, London #8/R est:25000-35000

CLEVE-JONAND, Agnes (1876-1951) Swedish
£1100 $1903 €1606 Bay at sunset (57x70cm-22x28in) s.d.47 panel. 15-Dec-3 Lilla Bukowskis, Stockholm #178 (S.KR 14000)
£1172 $2075 €1711 Study of female nude (74x56cm-29x22in) s.d.14. 27-Apr-4 AB Stockholms Auktionsverk #851/R est:20000-25000 (S.KR 16000)
£1208 $2054 €1764 St Erik's Bridge (58x44cm-23x17in) s.d.29 panel. 4-Nov-3 Bukowskis, Stockholm #54/R est:15000-20000 (S.KR 16000)

£1284	$2183	€1875	Arild's Chapel (69x49cm-27x19in) s.d.34 tempera. 4-Nov-3 Bukowskis, Stockholm #166/R est:20000-25000 (S.KR 17000)
£2538	$4569	€3705	Girl with plaits (72x58cm-28x23in) s.d.18. 26-Apr-4 Bukowskis, Stockholm #52/R est:40000-50000 (S.KR 35000)
£3336	$6004	€4871	Roof tops (59x73cm-23x29in) s. 26-Apr-4 Bukowskis, Stockholm #53/R est:40000-50000 (S.KR 46000)
£3626	$6526	€5294	Evening in Bohuslan (60x46cm-24x18in) st.sig. painted c.1916. 26-Apr-4 Bukowskis, Stockholm #163/R est:50000-60000 (S.KR 50000)
£3776	$6420	€5513	The embrace (65x53cm-26x21in) s.d.15. 4-Nov-3 Bukowskis, Stockholm #169/R est:35000-40000 (S.KR 50000)
£3843	$6918	€5611	West coast landscape (74x52cm-29x20in) s.d.29 panel. 26-Apr-4 Bukowskis, Stockholm #50/R est:50000-70000 (S.KR 53000)
Works on paper			
£302	$514	€441	Woman (44x24cm-17x9in) st.sig. mixed media. 4-Nov-3 Bukowskis, Stockholm #165/R (S.KR 4000)
£541	$973	€790	Aquarium (53x41cm-21x16in) s.d.30 W/C. 26-Jan-4 Lilla Bukowskis, Stockholm #188 (S.KR 7200)
£831	$1412	€1213	View of Fiskebackskil (35x27cm-14x11in) s.i. chk. 4-Nov-3 Bukowskis, Stockholm #162/R (S.KR 11000)

CLEVELEY, John (snr) (?-1792) British

£517	$926	€755	Seascape (25x36cm-10x14in) s.d.1776 panel. 12-May-4 Dobiaschofsky, Bern #399/R (S.FR 1200)

CLEVELEY, Robert (attrib) (1747-1809) British

Works on paper			
£400	$732	€584	Men of war and numerous figures in boats (18x21cm-7x8in) ink grey wash. 7-Apr-4 Woolley & Wallis, Salisbury #162/R

CLEVENBERGH, Antoine (1755-1810) Flemish

£2416	$4325	€3600	Trophee de chasse dans un paysage (51x62cm-20x24in) bears sig. panel. 25-May-4 Palais de Beaux Arts, Brussels #528/R est:4000-5000
£2550	$4565	€3800	Trophee de chasse dans un parc (67x50cm-26x20in) s. panel. 25-May-4 Palais de Beaux Arts, Brussels #529/R est:4000-5000

CLEVENBERGH, Charles-Antoine (attrib) (c.1791-?) Flemish

£4545	$7727	€6500	Still life of hare and fowl (62x51cm-24x20in) board. 29-Nov-3 Bukowskis, Helsinki #389/R est:7000-8000

CLEVERLEY, Peter (20th C) New Zealander

£827	$1406	€1207	Three chairs (39x58cm-15x23in) s. oil graphite paper. 27-Nov-3 International Art Centre, Auckland #38/R (NZ.D 2200)
Works on paper			
£1349	$2416	€1970	Kakanui youth (76x56cm-30x22in) s.i. mixed media. 11-May-4 Watson's, Christchurch #38/R est:15000-18000 (NZ.D 3900)

CLIFFE, Henry (1919-1983) British

£300	$555	€438	Flower garden (27x37cm-11x15in) s.d.56 board. 14-Jul-4 Bonhams, Chester #395
£1200	$2004	€1752	Blue garden (31x17cm-12x7in) s.d.55 board. 21-Oct-3 Bonhams, Knightsbridge #69/R est:300-500
Works on paper			
£650	$1105	€949	Study for lithograph (51x34cm-20x13in) ink W/C chl gouache prov. 26-Nov-3 Sotheby's, Olympia #181/R

CLIFFORD, Charles (c.1819-1863) American

Photographs			
£2200	$3872	€3212	Alhambra, Granada (41x29cm-16x11in) albumen print lit. 19-May-4 Christie's, London #83/R est:2000-3000
£4722	$8500	€6894	Puerta del sol, Puerta Morisca, Toledo (43x32cm-17x13in) albumen print lit. 22-Apr-4 Phillips, New York #177/R est:8000-12000
£6500	$11440	€9490	Alhambra, Granada (38x29cm-15x11in) albumen print prov.lit. 19-May-4 Christie's, London #86/R est:4000-6000
£10000	$17600	€14600	Alhamba, Granada (22x20cm-9x8in) albumen print prov.lit. 19-May-4 Christie's, London #87/R est:4000-6000
£28889	$52000	€42178	Sevilla, Alcazar real, arch details of the principal patio (42x31cm-17x12in) albumen print lit. 22-Apr-4 Phillips, New York #17/R est:40000-60000

CLIFFORD, Edward (1844-1907) British

Works on paper			
£1000	$1660	€1460	Lady with a psalter (66x47cm-26x19in) s.d.1867 W/C. 1-Oct-3 Sotheby's, Olympia #165/R est:600-800

CLIFFORD, Edward (attrib) (1844-1907) British

Works on paper			
£320	$586	€467	Bacchus and Ariadne (51x30cm-20x12in) W/C after Titian. 6-Jul-4 Hamptons Fine Art, Godalming #105

CLIFFORD, Henry Charles (1861-?) British

£400	$664	€584	Arundel Park (37x44cm-15x17in) s. board. 1-Oct-3 Sotheby's, Olympia #160/R
Works on paper			
£500	$910	€750	Bowing green at Barford. Entrance to Bartford Park. (18x24cm-7x9in) three init. i.d.1899 four in two frames pencil W/C. 1-Jul-4 Christie's, Kensington #87/R
£700	$1274	€1050	Barford House, Somerset. Barford Park (18x24cm-7x9in) one init. i.d.1899 four in two frames. 1-Jul-4 Christie's, Kensington #89/R

CLIFT, William (1944-) American

Photographs			
£1693	$3200	€2472	La mesita from Cerro Seguro, New Mexico (34x48cm-13x19in) s.i.d.1978 gelatin silver print. 17-Feb-4 Christie's, Rockefeller NY #158/R est:1500-2000

CLIFTON, F (19th C) British

£1111	$1767	€1600	Pidgeon (60x75cm-24x30in) s.i.d.78. 10-Sep-3 James Adam, Dublin #84/R

CLIMENT, Elena (1955-) Mexican

£22346	$40000	€32625	Holy Child (101x80cm-40x31in) s.d.93 board prov.exhib. 26-May-4 Sotheby's, New York #167/R est:15000-20000
Works on paper			
£629	$1100	€918	Bird on book. Tepoztlan and Chicago with blue background (18x26cm-7x10in) one s.d.67 one s.d.98 W/C two. 19-Dec-3 Sotheby's, New York #1224/R

CLINCH, Robert (1957-) Australian

£14876	$27521	€21719	Dovetailed 2001 (40x99cm-16x39in) egg tempera on panel. 10-Mar-4 Deutscher-Menzies, Melbourne #37/R est:30000-40000 (A.D 36000)

CLINEDINST, Mary Spear (1887-1960) American

£495	$900	€743	New England fishing boats in port (76x91cm-30x36in) painted c.1920. 16-Jun-4 Wolf's, New York #487200/R

CLINT, Alfred (1807-1883) British

£520	$863	€759	Entrance to Boulogne harbour (43x74cm-17x29in) s. 3-Oct-3 Mallams, Oxford #186/R
£700	$1253	€1022	Barges in a calm on the estuary (40x56cm-16x22in) 26-May-4 Christie's, Kensington #662/R
£800	$1488	€1168	Boulogne Harbour (46x76cm-18x30in) s. 4-Mar-4 Christie's, Kensington #555/R
£1078	$2005	€1574	Fisherman and fishergirl working on beach (42x70cm-17x28in) s. 2-Mar-4 Rasmussen, Copenhagen #1349/R est:5000-7000 (D.KR 12000)
£3700	$6734	€5402	Cornelian Bay, near Scarborough (118x180cm-46x71in) s. exhib. 15-Jun-4 Bonhams, Leeds #113/R est:2000-3000

CLINT, George (1770-1854) British

Works on paper			
£300	$552	€438	Merchant of Venice (30x24cm-12x9in) s. W/C. 8-Jun-4 Bonhams, Knightsbridge #19/R

CLIVE, Henry (1881-1960) American

£1796	$3000	€2622	Wistfully winsome young woman writing love letter (58x48cm-23x19in) s. board. 15-Nov-3 Illustration House, New York #148/R est:3000-4000

CLODION (1738-1814) French

Sculpture			
£1119	$1902	€1600	Sacrifice (20x50cm-8x20in) i. bronze relief. 20-Nov-3 Van Ham, Cologne #1249/R est:900
£1316	$2382	€2000	Faunesse aux raisins (32cm-13in) s. brown pat bronze red marble socle. 19-Apr-4 Horta, Bruxelles #128/R est:2500-3000
£1418	$2369	€2000	Bacchante et satyre (47cm-19in) pat bronze socle. 17-Jun-3 Galerie Moderne, Brussels #1525/R est:2000-2500
£1477	$2643	€2200	Groupe de satyre et nymphe (32x36x28cm-13x14x11in) pat bronze oval socle green marble base. 25-May-4 Palais de Beaux Arts, Brussels #96/R est:2400-3200
£1931	$3572	€2800	Faune et sa muse (57cm-22in) s. green pat bronze. 16-Feb-4 Horta, Bruxelles #123/R est:2500-3500
£4545	$7591	€6500	Faune musicien (58cm-23in) s. brown pat bronze. 13-Oct-3 Horta, Bruxelles #139/R est:3500-5500
£11268	$19493	€16000	Dancers (67cm-26in) s.d.1762 gilt pat bronze. 10-Dec-3 Finarte Semenzato, Rome #460/R est:28000-34000
Works on paper			
£492	$900	€718	Studies of putto holding a drapery (26x22cm-10x9in) i.verso black chk. 29-Jan-4 Swann Galleries, New York #235/R

CLODION (after) (1738-1814) French

Sculpture			
£4200	$7560	€6132	Satyresse avec enfants, l'un sur ses genoux, l'autre etendu a ses pieds (47cm-19in) s. terracotta giltwood base. 21-Apr-4 Sotheby's, London #45/R est:2500-3000

CLODION (attrib) (1738-1814) French

Sculpture			
£16000	$27680	€23360	Figure of a Bacchante (50cm-20in) s. terracotta prov.lit. 11-Dec-3 Christie's, London #81/R est:15000-25000

CLODION (style) (1738-1814) French

Sculpture			
£8840	$16000	€12906	Group of two Bacchantes and Satyr (63cm-25in) s.verso terracotta prov.lit. 16-Apr-4 Sotheby's, New York #29/R est:6000-8000

CLOKE, Rene (20th C) ?

Works on paper			
£600	$1020	€876	Mortals value not (27x18cm-11x7in) s. W/C. 26-Nov-3 Hamptons Fine Art, Godalming #62
£900	$1530	€1314	Jack o'lantern (25x19cm-10x7in) s. W/C. 26-Nov-3 Hamptons Fine Art, Godalming #60

CLOSAY, E Tiger de (19th C) French

£781	$1242	€1140	Nymph and satyr (40x25cm-16x10in) s. 1-May-3 Dunbar Sloane, Wellington #80a/R est:4000-6000 (NZ.D 2250)

CLOSE, Chuck (1940-) American
Photographs
£3333 $6000 €4866 Roy I (118x87cm-46x34in) s.d.1996 num.5/10 digital inkjet print. 23-Apr-4 Phillips, New York #162/R est:6000-8000
£4444 $8000 €6488 Self portrait (118x87cm-46x34in) s.d.1996 digital inkjet print prov. 23-Apr-4 Phillips, New York #163/R est:8000-10000
£4520 $8000 €6599 Phil, 1998 (62x53cm-24x21in) s.i.d.1998 polaroid print. 27-Apr-4 Christie's, Rockefeller NY #353/R est:10000-15000
£23952 $40000 €34970 Self-portrait (135x52cm-53x20in) s.i.d.1987 polaroid polacol photographs diptych. 17-Oct-3 Phillips, New York #95/R est:40000-60000
Prints
£1963 $3200 €2866 Keith/Four Times (76x203cm-30x80in) s.i.d.1975 num.A.P.III col lithographs four on one sheet. 24-Sep-3 Christie's, Rockefeller NY #222/R est:2500-3500
£2095 $3750 €3059 Susan (97x79cm-38x31in) s.d.1988 num.36/50 col print. 7-May-4 Sloans & Kenyon, Bethesda #1753/R est:3000-5000
£2095 $3750 €3059 Self portrait (33x23cm-13x9in) s.d.1988 num.19/50 spit bite etching prov. 7-May-4 Sloans & Kenyon, Bethesda #1755/R est:5000-7000
£2175 $3916 €3176 Keith/four times (76x223cm-30x88in) s.num.43/50 four lithographs on one sheet. 26-Apr-4 Bukowskis, Stockholm #335/R est:30000-40000 (S.KR 30000)
£2647 $4500 €3865 Alex Katz (71x59cm-28x23in) s.d.1991 col woodcut. 4-Nov-3 Christie's, Rockefeller NY #224/R est:5000-7000
£2825 $5000 €4125 Susan (97x79cm-38x31in) s.i. col handmade paper pulp. 30-Apr-4 Sotheby's, New York #314/R est:2500-3500
£3107 $5500 €4536 Robert - manipulated (84x65cm-33x26in) s.i.d.1982 handmade paper pulp tones of grey. 30-Apr-4 Sotheby's, New York #313a/R est:4000-6000
£5085 $9000 €7424 Alex Katz (71x59cm-28x23in) s.d.1991 num.68/75 col woodcut. 30-Apr-4 Sotheby's, New York #313/R est:6000-8000
£22941 $39000 €33494 Phil (171x135cm-67x53in) s.d.1982 paper bulb. 31-Oct-3 Sotheby's, New York #515/R
Works on paper
£30726 $55000 €44860 Bob (48x38cm-19x15in) s.d.1984 silk paper prov. 7-May-4 Sloans & Kenyon, Bethesda #1760/R est:50000-70000
£1396648 $2500000 €2039106 Gwynne (188x148cm-74x58in) s.i.d.1982 W/C paper on canvas prov.exhib.lit. 11-May-4 Christie's, Rockefeller NY #40/R est:2500000-3500000

CLOSTERMAN, Johann Baptist (attrib) (1660-1713) German
£1200 $2148 €1752 Portrait of George Jeffreys, 1st Baron Jeffreys of Wem (37x31cm-15x12in) 27-May-4 Christie's, Kensington #9/R est:1200-1800

CLOUARD, Albert (1866-1952) French
£2238 $3849 €3200 Cote rocheuse (30x44cm-12x17in) st.sig. cardboard. 7-Dec-3 Livinec, Gaudcheau & Jezequel, Rennes #67/R

CLOUET, Felix (?-1882) French
£3217 $5533 €4600 Hunting still life with rabbit and pheasant. Hunting still life with jay (91x74cm-36x29in) s.d.1877 pair. 7-Dec-3 Sotheby's, Amsterdam #528/R

CLOUET, François (circle) (1522-1572) French
£7383 $13584 €11000 Portrait of nobleman (63x50cm-25x20in) d.1563 panel prov. 24-Mar-4 Dorotheum, Vienna #292/R est:15000-20000

CLOUGH, George L (1824-1901) American
£3293 $5500 €4808 Panoramic landscape (48x96cm-19x38in) s. 7-Oct-3 Sotheby's, New York #181 est:8000-12000
£8982 $15000 €13114 Pulling the boat ashore (61x91cm-24x36in) s. 23-Oct-3 Shannon's, Milford #94/R est:15000-20000

CLOUGH, George L and GIFFORD, William Birdsall (19/20th C) American
£1630 $3000 €2445 Log cabin, lakeshore (17x61cm-7x24in) s. 8-Jun-4 Bonhams & Butterfields, San Francisco #4028/R est:3000-5000

CLOUGH, Prunella (1919-2000) British
£4200 $7770 €6132 Untitled (71x76cm-28x30in) s. painted 1966 prov. 11-Mar-4 Christie's, Kensington #371/R est:3000-5000
£4800 $8496 €7008 Deserted gravel pit (38x48cm-15x19in) s. 29-Apr-4 Gorringes, Lewes #2434 est:4000-6000
£5400 $10098 €7884 Painting (66x86cm-26x34in) s. prov. 24-Feb-4 Bonhams, Knowle #127/R est:400-600
Prints
£2600 $4784 €3796 Geological landscape (18x24cm-7x9in) s.num.verso lithograph. 29-Mar-4 Bonhams, New Bond Street #120a est:800-1200
Works on paper
£400 $716 €584 Untitled (39x48cm-15x19in) s. W/C. 16-Mar-4 Bonhams, Knightsbridge #35
£450 $806 €657 Untitled (42x49cm-17x19in) s. W/C. 16-Mar-4 Bonhams, Knightsbridge #37/R

CLOUGH, Tom (1867-1943) British
£2188 $3500 €3194 Woman strolling by a pond (51x61cm-20x24in) s. 21-Sep-3 Grogan, Boston #45
Works on paper
£380 $669 €555 Country lane with cottages and distant cart (37x50cm-15x20in) s. W/C. 19-May-4 James Thompson, Kirby Lonsdale #210
£420 $752 €613 River flowing past a village (42x63cm-17x25in) s. W/C. 17-Mar-4 Bonhams, Chester #219
£1200 $2148 €1752 Dovecote beside a bridge with a figure (75x49cm-30x19in) s.d.95 W/C. 25-May-4 Sworder & Son, Bishops Stortford #412/R est:1100-1500
£1600 $2864 €2336 Village scene with brook, geese and maid fetching water (34x50cm-13x20in) s. W/C. 17-Mar-4 Bonhams, Chester #234 est:700-900

CLOUTIER, Albert Edward (1902-1965) Canadian
£323 $594 €472 Montreal Harbour (40x30cm-16x12in) s. i.d.1961 verso board. 9-Jun-4 Walker's, Ottawa #111/R (C.D 800)
£360 $659 €526 Forest landscape, Indian Brook N B (75x100cm-30x39in) s. 1-Jun-4 Joyner Waddington, Toronto #317/R (C.D 900)
£442 $822 €645 On the Saguenay (27x34cm-11x13in) s. masonite prov. 2-Mar-4 Ritchie, Toronto #137/R (C.D 1100)

CLOVER, Francois (1918-) ?
£550 $935 €803 Street scene in Paris (51x61cm-20x24in) s. 5-Nov-3 John Nicholson, Haslemere #549

CLOVER, Susan (1944-) American
£3390 $6000 €4949 Boy and girl float in a pool (107x183cm-42x72in) s.d.85. 2-May-4 Bonhams & Butterfields, Los Angeles #3046/R est:2000-3000

CLOWES, Daniel (1774-1829) British
£3600 $6516 €5256 Chestnut hunter and two greyhounds by a building, landscape beyond (60x86cm-24x34in) 1-Apr-4 Martel Maides, Guernsey #256/R est:2500-3000
£7000 $12600 €10220 Bay racehorse held by a trainer, with a jockey by his side (58x77cm-23x30in) s. 21-Apr-4 Christie's, Kensington #378/R est:5000-8000

CLOWES, Henry (1799-1871) British
£2500 $4650 €3650 5th Duke of Oxford, a prize bull in a yard (55x76cm-22x30in) s.d.1858 i.verso. 4-Mar-4 Christie's, Kensington #533/R est:3000-5000

CLUSEAU-LANAUVE, Jean (1914-) French
£406 $698 €580 Barques echouees (33x41cm-13x16in) s. s.d.1947 verso. 7-Dec-3 Livinec, Gaudcheau & Jezequel, Rennes #61

CLUSERET, Gustave (1823-1900) French
Works on paper
£1000 $1820 €1460 Arabs outside the Suleyman Mosque, Istanbul (60x42cm-24x17in) s. pastel. 1-Jul-4 Christie's, Kensington #332/R est:800-1200

CLUSMANN, William (1859-1927) American
£706 $1200 €1031 Twilight landscape (38x51cm-15x20in) s. 22-Nov-3 Jackson's, Cedar Falls #98/R est:750-900
£22703 $42000 €33146 In the Loop, Chicago (102x76cm-40x30in) s. prov. 11-Mar-4 Christie's, Rockefeller NY #62/R est:25000-35000

CLUSSERATH, August (1899-1966) German
£347 $566 €500 Klarenthal landscape (50x65cm-20x26in) s. board. 26-Sep-3 Bolland & Marotz, Bremen #724/R
£417 $679 €600 Landscape with woman (58x54cm-23x21in) 26-Sep-3 Bolland & Marotz, Bremen #726/R

CLUTTERBUCK, Violet (19/20th C) British
£480 $859 €701 Corner of the old hall, Aylsham, flowering azalea (56x43cm-22x17in) sold with a W/C by same hand. 22-Mar-4 Bonhams & Brooks, Norfolk #361/R
£1400 $2506 €2044 Japanese figures on a bridge (53x43cm-21x17in) s.d.08. 22-Mar-4 Bonhams & Brooks, Norfolk #360/R est:300-500
Works on paper
£780 $1396 €1139 Lady seated at a writing table in an interior (46x35cm-18x14in) s.d.1914 W/C. 22-Mar-4 Bonhams & Brooks, Norfolk #105/R

CLUTTERBUCK, Violet (attrib) (19/20th C) British
£600 $1098 €876 Portrait of a Moorish cleric reading (74x58cm-29x23in) mono. 7-Apr-4 Andrew Hartley, Ilkley #1090/R

CLUVER, Bernt (1897-1941) Norwegian
£448 $747 €654 Man by field (46x53cm-18x21in) s. panel. 20-Oct-3 Blomqvist, Lysaker #1044/R (N.KR 5200)
£504 $873 €736 Landscape with house (48x58cm-19x23in) 13-Dec-3 Blomqvist, Lysaker #1057 (N.KR 5800)

CLUYSENAAR, Alfred Jean Andre (1837-1902) Belgian
£433 $776 €650 Small boy (31x40cm-12x16in) s. panel. 15-May-4 De Vuyst, Lokeren #61
£733 $1349 €1100 Portrait of a day labourer (63x29cm-25x11in) s.d.1883. 11-Jun-4 Wendl, Rudolstadt #3985/R
£1100 $1892 €1606 Une femme nue (54x24cm-21x9in) s.d.59 canvas on panel. 4-Dec-3 Christie's, Kensington #166/R est:1000-1500
£2378 $4042 €3400 Scene de plage a Blankenberge (33x24cm-13x9in) s. canvas laid down. 18-Nov-3 Galerie Moderne, Brussels #646/R est:300-500

CLYMER, John Ford (1907-1989) American
£568 $1000 €829 Harbour scene (30x41cm-12x16in) s. 23-May-4 Hindman, Chicago #162/R
£625 $1100 €913 Harbor view (89x58cm-35x23in) s. 28-May-4 Aspire, Cleveland #37/R est:1500-2000
£795 $1400 €1161 Harbour entrance (30x41cm-12x16in) s. 23-May-4 Hindman, Chicago #164/R est:1000-1500
£3593 $6000 €5246 Loggers (61x51cm-24x20in) s. board. 9-Oct-3 Christie's, Rockefeller NY #75/R est:4000-6000
£9581 $16000 €13988 Kids riding ponies past valley farm fields (76x69cm-30x27in) s. masonite. 15-Nov-3 Illustration House, New York #111/R est:20000-30000
£10778 $18000 €15736 Hunter watches as elk pass through landscape (64x46cm-25x18in) board painted c.1950. 15-Nov-3 Illustration House, New York #112/R est:18000-24000
£12291 $22000 €17945 Farm children seeing the first robin of spring (76x58cm-30x23in) s. board. 15-May-4 Illustration House, New York #65/R est:25000-35000
£13559 $24000 €19796 The ski run (60x121cm-24x48in) s. 28-Apr-4 Christie's, Los Angeles #45/R est:15000-25000
£13661 $25000 €19945 Down on the farm (81x64cm-32x25in) s. prov. 10-Apr-4 Cobbs, Peterborough #113a/R
£16766 $28000 €24478 Two rams (51x76cm-20x30in) masonite. 14-Nov-3 Du Mouchelle, Detroit #2016/R est:2500-3000

£18824	$32000	€27483	Dall sheep (61x91cm-24x36in) s. i.verso board prov. 29-Oct-3 Christie's, Los Angeles #41/R est:40000-60000
£34950	$59415	€51027	Successful hunt (23x51cm-9x20in) s. panel prov. 1-Nov-3 Santa Fe Art, Santa Fe #172/R est:25000-35000
£69519	$130000	€101498	Game trail (91x91cm-36x36in) s. 24-Jul-4 Coeur d'Alene, Hayden #129/R est:50000-100000

Works on paper

£3279	$6000	€4787	Yachting off San Francisco (100x122cm-39x48in) s.d.1982 gouache board. 29-Jul-4 Christie's, Rockefeller NY #315/R est:2000-3000

COATES, Edmund C (1816-1871) American

£19774	$35000	€28870	View of Meredith, New Hampshire. Lake Winnipesaukee. White mountains (86x122cm-34x48in) s.d.1855 set of four. 2-May-4 Grogan, Boston #48/R

COATES, Tom (1941-) British

£260	$478	€380	Joe - a study (55x37cm-22x15in) mono. 14-Jun-4 Bonhams, Bath #175
£380	$695	€555	At close quarters (183x61cm-72x24in) board. 6-Apr-4 Bonhams, Knightsbridge #11
£400	$740	€584	Lecture at the New England Art Club 3 (15x46cm-6x18in) mono. board prov. 11-Mar-4 Christie's, Kensington #242
£400	$736	€584	Umbrella in Tolo (25x20cm-10x8in) mono. board. 14-Jun-4 Bonhams, Bath #163
£450	$752	€657	Museum and high bridge (26x30cm-10x12in) mono. board prov. 16-Oct-3 Christie's, Kensington #637
£700	$1281	€1022	Stable studies (41x81cm-16x32in) mono. 8-Apr-4 Christie's, Kensington #136/R
£720	$1267	€1051	Sunset on the south coast (24x59cm-9x23in) init. 18-May-4 Woolley & Wallis, Salisbury #91/R
£750	$1365	€1095	Michael Beddow, Frame-maker (51x61cm-20x24in) init. painted 1989. 1-Jul-4 Christie's, Kensington #253/R
£800	$1360	€1168	Dressing table (29x39cm-11x15in) init. canvas on board. 26-Nov-3 Sotheby's, Olympia #139/R
£1050	$1785	€1533	Female nude (61x50cm-24x20in) init. 26-Nov-3 Sotheby's, Olympia #94/R est:1200-1800
£1300	$2405	€1898	Piazza della Signoria (51x41cm-20x16in) mono. 11-Feb-4 Sotheby's, Olympia #222/R est:1000-1500
£1350	$2376	€1971	Walk to the Louvre, Paris (40x51cm-16x20in) s. 18-May-4 Woolley & Wallis, Salisbury #75/R est:800-1200
£1500	$2775	€2190	Louvre, Paris (51x41cm-20x16in) mono. 11-Feb-4 Sotheby's, Olympia #194/R est:1000-1500
£2000	$3520	€2920	Early visit, Rialto Bridge (51x61cm-20x24in) mono. 19-May-4 Sotheby's, Olympia #234/R est:1000-1500
£2000	$3520	€2920	View looking over to the Redentore, Venice (51x61cm-20x24in) mono. 19-May-4 Sotheby's, Olympia #235/R est:1000-1500
£2000	$3520	€2920	Pier, St. Ives (51x61cm-20x24in) mono. i.stretcher. 19-May-4 Sotheby's, Olympia #242/R est:800-1200
£3400	$5984	€4964	Concourse, the Louvre (61x76cm-24x30in) init. 18-May-4 Woolley & Wallis, Salisbury #106/R est:1000-1500

Works on paper

£260	$458	€380	A quiet practice (18x18cm-7x7in) s. W/C pastel. 18-May-4 Woolley & Wallis, Salisbury #294/R

COATS, Randolph (1891-?) American

£914	$1700	€1334	Sailboats (30x30cm-12x12in) s. board. 7-Mar-4 Treadway Gallery, Cincinnati #621/R est:1000-2000

COBB, Charles David (1921-) British

£362	$605	€529	Armed Knight Rock, Land's End (61x76cm-24x30in) s. 17-Nov-3 Waddingtons, Toronto #89/R (C.D 800)
£400	$716	€584	Cahoe II riding out a gale (50x61cm-20x24in) s. 26-May-4 Christie's, Kensington #495/R

Works on paper

£271	$453	€396	Sail past on Thames for Queen's Jubilee (19x30cm-7x12in) s. mixed media masonite. 17-Nov-3 Waddingtons, Toronto #85/R (C.D 600)

COBB, Ruth (1914-) American

Works on paper

£266	$425	€388	School assembly (53x41cm-21x16in) s. W/C ink. 21-Sep-3 Bonhams & Butterfields, San Francisco #2835/R

COBB, Warren (19th C) American

Works on paper

£240	$400	€350	Tugboat Ida M Daley (33x48cm-13x19in) W/C. 16-Nov-3 CRN Auctions, Cambridge #17/R

COBBAERT, Jan (1909-1995) Belgian

£738	$1366	€1100	Composition (35x35cm-14x14in) s. acrylic paper. 13-Mar-4 De Vuyst, Lokeren #57
£1067	$1909	€1600	Personnages (54x54cm-21x21in) s. panel. 11-May-4 Vanderkindere, Brussels #160 est:1250-1750
£1111	$1767	€1600	Poppewinkel (70x50cm-28x20in) s. 9-Sep-3 Vanderkindere, Brussels #46
£1119	$1869	€1600	Switzerland composition (73x55cm-29x22in) s. s.i.verso acrylic paper on canvas. 11-Oct-3 De Vuyst, Lokeren #58/R est:1600-2000
£1399	$2336	€2000	Autumn landscape composition, Oostenrijk (80x73cm-31x29in) s. i.verso acrylic paper on canvas. 11-Oct-3 De Vuyst, Lokeren #57/R est:2000-2400
£1611	$2851	€2400	Composition a la figure (81x101cm-32x40in) s. 27-Apr-4 Campo, Vlaamse Kaai #354/R est:2500-3000
£3478	$5704	€4800	Night (100x125cm-39x49in) s. 27-May-3 Sotheby's, Amsterdam #408/R est:4500-6000
£4027	$7450	€6000	Evening carnival (200x150cm-79x59in) s. s.i. verso. 13-Mar-4 De Vuyst, Lokeren #505/R est:8000-9500
£4225	$7310	€6000	Sails in the mist (100x130cm-39x51in) s. i.verso exhib. 13-Dec-3 De Vuyst, Lokeren #503/R est:4500-5500

Works on paper

£1000	$1830	€1500	In the zoo (36x36cm-14x14in) s. gouache. 7-Jun-4 Palais de Beaux Arts, Brussels #352/R est:900-1200

COBBE, Bernard (19th C) British

£732	$1310	€1069	Fish seller (63x42cm-25x17in) s. 10-May-4 Joel, Victoria #316/R est:1500-2200 (A.D 1800)
£1564	$2800	€2283	Pretty miscreant (66x91cm-26x36in) s. 8-May-4 Susanin's, Chicago #6048/R est:2000-4000
£1705	$3000	€2489	Pretty miscreant (66x91cm-26x36in) s. 28-May-4 Aspire, Cleveland #22/R est:3500-5500
£2100	$3759	€3066	Dangerous intruder (36x49cm-14x19in) s. 25-May-4 Sworder & Son, Bishops Stortford #413/R est:1500-1800

COBBETT, Edward John (1815-1899) British

£1000	$1670	€1450	Landscape, with a young woman and boy wearing provincial costume (77x107cm-30x42in) s. 26-Jun-3 Ambrose, Loughton #760/R est:2000-3000
£6500	$11635	€9490	Incentive to talk (61x51cm-24x20in) s. 27-May-4 Christie's, Kensington #293/R est:7000-10000
£12000	$21840	€17520	Fern gatherers (94x165cm-37x65in) s.d.1859. 3-Feb-4 Gorringes, Bexhill #1088/R est:3000-5000
£20000	$36200	€30000	Rural idyll (97x168cm-38x66in) s.d.1859 prov. 30-Mar-4 De Veres Art Auctions, Dublin #60/R est:30000-50000

COBBETT, Hilary (1885-?) British

£900	$1593	€1314	French fishing boats in a harbour (51x61cm-20x24in) s. 27-Apr-4 Bonhams, Knightsbridge #273/R
£950	$1682	€1387	Fisherman unloading the catch. Still life (51x61cm-20x24in) s. double-sided. 27-Apr-4 Bonhams, Knightsbridge #276/R

COBELLE, Charles (1902-1998) French

£221	$400	€323	Horse race (30x41cm-12x16in) s. acrylic. 2-Apr-4 Freeman, Philadelphia #184
£296	$550	€432	Paris scene (25x20cm-10x8in) s. painted c.1960. 7-Mar-4 Treadway Gallery, Cincinnati #687/R
£359	$650	€524	Home stretch (41x51cm-16x20in) s. acrylic. 2-Apr-4 Freeman, Philadelphia #128
£359	$650	€524	Nantucket (51x61cm-20x24in) s. i.verso acrylic. 2-Apr-4 Freeman, Philadelphia #146
£387	$700	€565	Wedding (74x76cm-29x30in) s. acrylic. 2-Apr-4 Freeman, Philadelphia #49
£414	$750	€604	Off to the races (61x76cm-24x30in) s. acrylic. 2-Apr-4 Freeman, Philadelphia #78
£414	$750	€604	At the finishing post (61x76cm-24x30in) s. acrylic. 2-Apr-4 Freeman, Philadelphia #88
£608	$1100	€888	Les girls Paris street (61x76cm-24x30in) s. acrylic. 2-Apr-4 Freeman, Philadelphia #137 est:300-500
£667	$1200	€974	L'Arc de Triomphe (61x76cm-24x30in) s. acrylic. 23-Jan-4 Freeman, Philadelphia #95/R
£667	$1200	€974	Coronado (61x76cm-24x30in) s. acrylic. 23-Jan-4 Freeman, Philadelphia #98/R
£722	$1300	€1054	Montmartre with angels (61x76cm-24x30in) s. acrylic. 23-Jan-4 Freeman, Philadelphia #151/R
£773	$1400	€1129	Hunt race (61x76cm-24x30in) s. acrylic. 2-Apr-4 Freeman, Philadelphia #100 est:300-500
£773	$1400	€1129	Monaco (61x76cm-24x30in) s. acrylic. 2-Apr-4 Freeman, Philadelphia #116 est:300-500
£829	$1500	€1210	Grand palace (51x61cm-20x24in) s. acrylic. 2-Apr-4 Freeman, Philadelphia #123 est:300-500
£994	$1800	€1451	Paris opera house (61x76cm-24x30in) s. acrylic. 2-Apr-4 Freeman, Philadelphia #153 est:300-500

COBIAN, Carlos (1952-) Spanish

£805	$1506	€1200	Flying kites (46x53cm-18x21in) s.d.02. 24-Feb-4 Durán, Madrid #11/R

COBO, Chema (1952-) Spanish

£1049	$1752	€1500	Breaking the glass (56x76cm-22x30in) s.i.d.1984 acrylic paper exhib. 24-Jun-3 Segre, Madrid #147/R est:1500
£1049	$1752	€1500	Beginning a painting (76x56cm-30x22in) s.i.d.1984 acrylic exhib. 24-Jun-3 Segre, Madrid #148/R est:1500
£1049	$1752	€1500	Artist in the Ash Country (56x76cm-22x30in) s.i.d.1984 acrylic paper exhib. 24-Jun-3 Segre, Madrid #149/R est:1500
£1049	$1752	€1500	Finding Light (76x56cm-30x22in) s.i.d.1984 acrylic paper exhib. 24-Jun-3 Segre, Madrid #150/R est:1500
£9155	$16021	€13000	Aphroditis at bath (120x100cm-47x39in) s.d.1977 s.i.d.verso prov. 16-Dec-3 Segre, Madrid #155/R est:3200

COBURN, Alvin Langdon (1882-1966) American

Photographs

£3955	$7000	€5774	Basket weaver, Madeira (29x19cm-11x7in) i.d.1955 gelatin silver print prov.lit. 27-Apr-4 Christie's, Rockefeller NY #252/R est:7000-9000
£10795	$19000	€15761	Henri Matisse holding a pakette (28x22cm-11x9in) with sig.d.1913 varnished platinum print. 20-May-4 Swann Galleries, New York #295/R est:10000-15000
£39548	$70000	€57740	House of a thousand windows, New York, 1912 (24x19cm-9x7in) gelatin silver print prov.exhib.lit. 27-Apr-4 Christie's, Rockefeller NY #248/R est:70000-90000
£101695	$180000	€148475	Vortograph (28x21cm-11x8in) s.i.d.1917 gelatin silver print prov.lit. 27-Apr-4 Christie's, Rockefeller NY #249/R est:180000-220000
£180791	$320000	€263955	Shadows and reflections, Venice (36x29cm-14x11in) s.i.d.1905 gum platinum print prov.lit. 27-Apr-4 Christie's, Rockefeller NY #246/R est:120000-180000

COBURN, Frank (1866-1931) American

£1176	$2000	€1717	Seated nude (48x36cm-19x14in) s. board. 29-Oct-3 Christie's, Los Angeles #58 est:2000-3000
£4046	$7000	€5907	Still life with fish and lettuce. Still life with fish and a pot (41x51cm-16x20in) s. first board second canvas pair. 10-Dec-3 Bonhams & Butterfields, San Francisco #6270/R est:3000-5000

COBURN, Frederick Simpson (1871-1960) Canadian

£901 $1532 €1315 Laurentian landscape, autumn (30x43cm-12x17in) s.d.16. 21-Nov-3 Walker's, Ottawa #44/R est:2500-3500 (C.D 2000)
£1044 $1942 €1524 Paysage (27x34cm-11x13in) s. board prov. 2-Mar-4 Ritchie, Toronto #74/R est:2500-3000 (C.D 2600)
£3049 $5457 €4452 Dutch scene (59x81cm-23x32in) s. prov.exhib. 31-May-4 Sotheby's, Toronto #79/R est:5000-7000 (C.D 7500)
£3378 $5743 €4932 Portrait of the artist's wife Malvina (35x26cm-14x10in) s.i. board prov.lit. 27-Nov-3 Heffel, Vancouver #139/R est:3500-4500 (C.D 7500)
£4955 $8423 €7234 Mlle Savoie Modele (77x54cm-30x21in) i.verso prov.lit. 27-Nov-3 Heffel, Vancouver #118/R est:6000-8000 (C.D 11000)
£6306 $10721 €9207 Winter sun, Laurentians (47x64cm-19x25in) s.d.1933 prov.lit. 27-Nov-3 Heffel, Vancouver #99/R est:15000-18000 (C.D 14000)
£6306 $10721 €9207 Hauling logs near Mt Roland (27x32cm-11x13in) s.d.27 prov. 21-Nov-3 Walker's, Ottawa #6/R est:12000-16000 (C.D 14000)
£6500 $10855 €9490 Logging team (46x56cm-18x22in) s. prov. 14-Oct-3 Sotheby's, London #203/R est:3000-5000
£6757 $11486 €9865 Laurentian winter (39x46cm-15x18in) s.d.1931 prov.lit. 27-Nov-3 Heffel, Vancouver #48/R est:16000-20000 (C.D 15000)
£6800 $12444 €9928 Horse-drawn sled in winter (46x55cm-18x22in) s.d.32. 1-Jun-4 Joyner Waddington, Toronto #35/R est:15000-20000 (C.D 17000)
£6911 $12370 €10090 Horse-drawn sleigh in winter (40x66cm-16x26in) s.d.1929 prov. 27-May-4 Heffel, Vancouver #28/R est:18000-22000 (C.D 17000)
£8000 $13840 €11680 Portrait of his wife (76x61cm-30x24in) painted c.1900. 9-Dec-3 Maynards, Vancouver #206 est:16000-18000 (C.D 18000)
£8929 $15357 €13036 Homeward bound, winter (44x65cm-17x26in) s.d.21. 2-Dec-3 Joyner Waddington, Toronto #100/R est:20000-25000 (C.D 20000)
£10222 $17684 €14924 Logging team (46x56cm-18x22in) s.d.26. 9-Dec-3 Pinneys, Montreal #155 est:15000-25000 (C.D 23000)
£15766 $26802 €23018 Bonjour Alphonse (58x81cm-23x32in) s.d.1951 prov. 27-Nov-3 Heffel, Vancouver #46/R est:20000-25000 (C.D 35000)
£16071 $27643 €23464 Hauling logs, winter (50x78cm-20x31in) s.d.29 prov. 2-Dec-3 Joyner Waddington, Toronto #59/R est:25000-30000 (C.D 36000)
£16260 $29106 €23740 Hauling logs in winter (76x102cm-30x40in) s.d.30 prov. 31-May-4 Sotheby's, Toronto #15/R est:30000-50000 (C.D 40000)
£17276 $30925 €25223 Logging in winter (63x80cm-25x31in) s.d.1941 prov.lit. 27-May-4 Heffel, Vancouver #20/R est:30000-40000 (C.D 42500)
£18400 $33672 €26864 Reclining nude (50x80cm-20x31in) s.d.38 lit. 1-Jun-4 Joyner Waddington, Toronto #52/R est:30000-35000 (C.D 46000)

Prints

£2027 $3446 €2959 Logging in winter (30x55cm-12x22in) s.d.1919 etching prov.lit. 27-Nov-3 Heffel, Vancouver #37 est:700-900 (C.D 4500)

Works on paper

£227 $414 €331 Two figures (16x22cm-6x9in) s. pastel prov. 5-Feb-4 Heffel, Vancouver #21/R (C.D 550)
£260 $475 €380 Timbers, Eastern Townships (21x26cm-8x10in) col crayons prov. 1-Jun-4 Joyner Waddington, Toronto #439 (C.D 650)
£625 $1075 €913 Near Brompton, Quebec. Reclining Nude. Landscape with trees (14x20cm-6x8in) each s. second d.Jan 17-40 third i. col pencil chk three. 2-Dec-3 Joyner Waddington, Toronto #449 (C.D 1400)

COBURN, Frederick Simpson (style) (1871-1960) Canadian

£2000 $3660 €2920 Top of the hill (62x80cm-24x31in) bears indis.s.d. prov. 1-Jun-4 Joyner Waddington, Toronto #200/R est:3000-5000 (C.D 5000)

COBURN, John (1925-) Australian

£1423 $2233 €2063 Maquette for tapestry discs (52x67cm-20x26in) s.i.d.1971 acrylic paper. 26-Aug-3 Christie's, Sydney #211 est:3000-5000 (A.D 3500)
£1810 $2824 €2625 Picadors (31x48cm-12x19in) s. board. 1-Aug-2 Joel, Victoria #261 est:2000-3000 (A.D 5250)
£2075 $3465 €3113 Celebration (15x22cm-6x9in) s. board. 27-Oct-3 Goodman, Sydney #2/R est:1500-1800 (A.D 5000)
£2686 $4754 €3922 Island Spirit (52x51cm-20x20in) s. i.verso board. 3-May-4 Christie's, Melbourne #362/R est:6000-8000 (A.D 6500)
£3513 $5971 €5129 Flight of the bluebirs II (50x40cm-20x16in) s. acrylic gold leaf on board prov. 29-Oct-3 Lawson Menzies, Sydney #12/R est:3500-5000 (A.D 8500)
£3846 $6192 €5615 Centaur (68x51cm-27x20in) s. card on board prov. 25-Aug-3 Sotheby's, Paddington #250/R est:7000-9000 (A.D 9500)
£3926 $6674 €5732 Flight of the bluebird III (50x40cm-20x16in) s. acrylic gold leaf on board prov. 29-Oct-3 Lawson Menzies, Sydney #13/R est:3500-5000 (A.D 9500)
£4132 $7025 €6033 Icon landscape (50x40cm-20x16in) s. acrylic gold leaf on board prov. 29-Oct-3 Lawson Menzies, Sydney #14/R est:3500-5000 (A.D 10000)
£4472 $7020 €6484 Study for the perfumed garden (39x74cm-15x29in) s.i. acrylic paper lit. 26-Aug-3 Christie's, Sydney #128a/R est:6000-9000 (A.D 11000)
£4580 $8336 €6687 Fire dancer (51x70cm-20x28in) s. oil paper on board. 16-Jun-4 Deutscher-Menzies, Melbourne #183/R est:8000-12000 (A.D 12000)
£4661 $7924 €6805 Sepik (75x75cm-30x30in) s.d.84 bears i.verso. 24-Nov-3 Sotheby's, Melbourne #12/R est:12000-16000 (A.D 11000)
£8163 $15020 €11918 Perfumed night (107x122cm-42x48in) s.d.90 i.verso. 29-Mar-4 Goodman, Sydney #86/R est:20000-25000 (A.D 20000)
£8264 $15289 €12065 Imaginary landscape (51x71cm-20x28in) s. oil paper on board. 10-Mar-4 Deutscher-Menzies, Melbourne #150/R est:11000-15000 (A.D 20000)
£8402 $13611 €12267 Festival at Avignon, Paris (73x100cm-29x39in) s. i.d.1971 verso acrylic prov. 30-Jul-3 Goodman, Sydney #49/R est:12000-18000 (A.D 20500)
£9362 $15915 €13669 Ace (153x153cm-60x60in) s.d.66 s.i.stretcher verso prov.exhib.lit. 26-Nov-3 Deutscher-Menzies, Melbourne #19/R est:25000-35000 (A.D 22000)
£10526 $16947 €15368 Early Bird I (66x86cm-26x34in) s. prov.exhib. 25-Aug-3 Sotheby's, Paddington #412/R est:12000-16000 (A.D 26000)
£14050 $24868 €20513 Pandora's box (119x139cm-47x55in) s. s.i.d.1978 verso acrylic prov. 3-May-4 Christie's, Melbourne #1/R est:18000-28000 (A.D 34000)
£25615 $40471 €37398 Abundant garden (137x183cm-54x72in) s.d.86 s.i.d.1986 verso. 2-Sep-3 Deutscher-Menzies, Melbourne #38/R est:40000-50000 (A.D 62500)
£26971 $45041 €40457 Earth Song. s.i. three panels various sizes. 27-Oct-3 Goodman, Sydney #109/R est:70000-90000 (A.D 65000)

Works on paper

£1441 $2449 €2104 Sun Festival (64x51cm-25x20in) s. gouache prov. 24-Nov-3 Sotheby's, Melbourne #151/R est:4000-6000 (A.D 3400)
£1531 $2816 €2235 Lament (49x56cm-19x22in) s.i. pen ink wash prov. 29-Mar-4 Goodman, Sydney #7/R est:3000-5000 (A.D 3750)
£1878 $3455 €2742 Study for earth rhythm (12x53cm-5x21in) s.i. i.verso gouache. 29-Mar-4 Goodman, Sydney #49/R est:3000-5000 (A.D 4600)
£1908 $3473 €2786 Study for tapestry (35x52cm-14x20in) s.i.d.1968 W/C exhib. 16-Jun-4 Deutscher-Menzies, Melbourne #312/R est:4500-6500 (A.D 5000)
£3435 $6252 €5015 Dry summer (69x51cm-27x20in) s. i.verso gouache paper on board prov. 16-Jun-4 Deutscher-Menzies, Melbourne #161/R est:10000-15000 (A.D 9000)
£14050 $24868 €20513 Tree of life II (182x217cm-72x85in) s. wool tapestry prov.lit. 3-May-4 Christie's, Melbourne #138/R est:20000-30000 (A.D 34000)
£14893 $25319 €21744 Resurrection Tree (202x171cm-80x67in) s. s.i.d.1973 verso synthetic polymer paint canvas lit. 26-Nov-3 Deutscher-Menzies, Melbourne #42/R est:35000-45000 (A.D 35000)

COCAGNE, Paul (1907-1984) Belgian

£1126 $2049 €1700 Jeu nautique en bord de l'Ourthe (109x152cm-43x60in) s. 16-Jun-4 Hotel des Ventes Mosan, Brussels #260 est:1200-1400

COCCHI, Mario (1898-1957) Italian

£397 $723 €600 Landscape (46x53cm-18x21in) s.d.26 board. 21-Jun-4 Pandolfini, Florence #166

COCCO, Francesco di (1900-1989) Italian

£369 $683 €550 Composition (70x50cm-28x20in) s. masonite painted 1969. 13-Mar-4 Meeting Art, Vercelli #45

COCCORANTE, Leonardo (1680-1750) Italian

£11034 $18428 €16000 Landscapes with ruins (20x18cm-8x7in) copper pair. 12-Nov-3 Sotheby's, Milan #147/R est:12000-16000
£12000 $21600 €17520 Capriccio of a Mediterranean port with classical ruins and shipping (43x31cm-17x12in) 23-Apr-4 Christie's, Kensington #261/R est:10000-15000
£12766 $21319 €18000 Night capriccio (98x74cm-39x29in) 15-Oct-3 Finarte Semenzato, Rome #145/R est:20000
£75000 $135000 €109500 Capriccio of classical ruins with figures (183x162cm-72x64in) 22-Jan-4 Sotheby's, New York #65/R est:60000-80000

COCCORANTE, Leonardo (attrib) (1680-1750) Italian

£2759 $4607 €4000 Capriccios with figures (6cm-2in circular) copper pair. 12-Nov-3 Sotheby's, Milan #146/R est:4000-6000

COCCORANTE, Leonardo (circle) (1680-1750) Italian

£8889 $16000 €12978 Capriccio with figures by a port (75x98cm-30x39in) 21-Jan-4 Sotheby's, New York #132/R est:10000-15000

COCCORANTE, Leonardo (style) (1680-1750) Italian

£4412 $7500 €6442 Figures resting by ruins (113x79cm-44x31in) 21-Nov-3 Skinner, Boston #205/R est:3000-5000

COCEANI, Antonio (1894-1983) Italian

£909 $1564 €1300 Vase of flowers (50x39cm-20x15in) s.d.1954 board. 3-Dec-3 Stadion, Trieste #970/R

COCHIN, Charles-Nicolas (18th C) French

Miniatures

£1000 $1800 €1460 J Le Gros, in profile (8cm-3in circular) s.i.d.1783 pencil wash Indian ink card gilded wood frame exhib. 22-Apr-4 Bonhams, New Bond Street #21/R est:1200-1500

Works on paper

£432 $691 €600 Nymphs bathing (10x18cm-4x7in) i. blk crayon. 16-May-3 Tajan, Paris #49
£650 $1125 €949 Three music making angels seated on a cloud (11x20cm-4x8in) i.mount red chk prov. 12-Dec-3 Christie's, Kensington #443/R
£1020 $1827 €1500 Diana aparaissant a telemaque (17x10cm-7x4in) sanguine. 17-Mar-4 Tajan, Paris #45/R est:1500
£1769 $3166 €2600 Portrait presume de Madame de Beaufort, en buste (15x10cm-6x4in) s.d.1782 black chk estompe prov.exhib.lit. 18-Mar-4 Christie's, Paris #122/R est:4000-6000
£2585 $4627 €3800 Scene de l'histoire de Telemaque (17x10cm-7x4in) sanguine. 19-Mar-4 Piasa, Paris #97/R est:1500-2000
£2676 $4683 €3800 Une allegorie de l'amour (12x14cm-5x6in) s. black chk pen grey ink prov. 17-Dec-3 Christie's, Paris #47/R est:1500-2000
£5102 $9133 €7500 Portrait de H J Perignon en buste (8cm-3in circular) i. graphite prov. 18-Mar-4 Christie's, Paris #121/R est:1500-1800
£9524 $17047 €14000 Profile of a man playing cards (18x14cm-7x6in) pierre noire prov. 17-Mar-4 Tajan, Paris #49/R est:12000-15000

COCHIN, Charles-Nicolas (younger) (1715-1790) French

Works on paper

£476 $757 €700 Portrait de femme (8cm-3in circular) crayon. 23-Mar-3 St-Germain-en-Laye Encheres #12
£500 $850 €730 Standing man in profile (18x10cm-7x4in) chk prov. 25-Nov-3 Christie's, Rockefeller NY #509/R
£685 $1164 €1000 Academie d'hommes (33x40cm-13x16in) crayon chk prov. 6-Nov-3 Tajan, Paris #61
£1507 $2561 €2200 Vieillard et trois jeunes hommes (24x19cm-9x7in) crayon prov. 6-Nov-3 Tajan, Paris #59
£2740 $4657 €4000 Ane et maitres (24x19cm-9x7in) crayon prov. 6-Nov-3 Tajan, Paris #67
£12291 $22000 €17945 Portrait of Claude Joseph Vernet (13x10cm-5x4in) s.d.1779 chk stumping htd white prov.exhib. 27-May-4 Sotheby's, New York #36/R est:15000-25000

COCHRAN, Allen Dean (1888-1935) American

£528 $950 €771 Winter landscape (28x41cm-11x16in) s. 23-Jan-4 Freeman, Philadelphia #247/R
£598 $1100 €873 Rainy day. Bather by a stream (20x25cm-8x10in) s. canvas on board double-sided. 25-Mar-4 Doyle, New York #13 est:1500-2500
£659 $1200 €962 Winter scene (18x23cm-7x9in) s. board. 7-Feb-4 Neal Auction Company, New Orleans #115/R est:1200-1800
£1509 $2400 €2203 Winter morning (30x41cm-12x16in) s. board. 13-Sep-3 Weschler, Washington #755/R est:1000-1500
£1744 $3000 €2546 Winter forest (50x40cm-20x16in) s. canvasboard. 3-Dec-3 Doyle, New York #216/R est:4000-6000

£2793 $5000 €4078 New England village in winter (61x76cm-24x30in) s. 8-Jan-4 James Julia, Fairfield #764/R est:6000-8000

COCHRANE, Constance (1888-?) American
£1220 $2000 €1769 Lonesome trail (25x20cm-10x8in) s. board exhib. 4-Jun-3 Alderfer's, Hatfield #334/R est:700-900

COCINCELLI, H (19/20th C) Italian
£2000 $3440 €2920 Bazaar (53x74cm-21x29in) s. 4-Dec-3 Christie's, Kensington #231/R est:2500-3500

COCK, Cesar de (1823-1904) Flemish
£1399 $2378 €2000 Brook in forest (35x48cm-14x19in) s. 29-Nov-3 Bukowskis, Helsinki #362/R est:1200-1500
£1495 $2363 €2168 Country road and trees in open landscape (45x64cm-18x25in) s. 2-Sep-3 Rasmussen, Copenhagen #1895/R est:8000-10000 (D.KR 16000)
£1549 $2680 €2200 Landscape (30x40cm-12x16in) s. 13-Dec-3 Hagelstam, Helsinki #41/R est:1500
£2222 $3622 €3200 Couple de bergers (46x66cm-18x26in) s. 23-Sep-3 Galerie Moderne, Brussels #720/R
£2657 $4517 €3800 Lavandiere pres de la riviere (48x58cm-19x23in) s. 1-Dec-3 Palais de Beaux Arts, Brussels #41/R est:3000-4000
£2800 $5180 €4088 Fishing in the woods (65x54cm-26x21in) s.d.1874. 15-Jan-4 Christie's, Kensington #798/R est:200-300

COCK, Gilbert de (1928-) Belgian
£318 $579 €480 Composition (40x30cm-16x12in) s.d.63 paper. 21-Jun-4 Bernaerts, Antwerp #289
£909 $1518 €1300 Composition (50x50cm-20x20in) s.d.79. 11-Oct-3 De Vuyst, Lokeren #97
£1736 $2899 €2500 Jamal (150x150cm-59x59in) s.d.1972. 21-Oct-3 Campo & Campo, Antwerp #60/R est:2750-3250

COCK, Hieronymus (1507-1570) Flemish
Prints
£2667 $4773 €4000 Landscape with ruins and St Hieronymus (22x34cm-9x13in) etching after Maerten van Heemskerck. 13-May-4 Bassenge, Berlin #5095/R est:1500

COCK, Jan Wellens de (c.1480-c.1526) Flemish
Prints
£6294 $10699 €9000 Temptation of St Jerome (26x38cm-10x15in) woodcut. 27-Nov-3 Bassenge, Berlin #5157/R est:12000

COCK, Louis de (19th C) ?
£898 $1500 €1311 Still life with fruit (46x61cm-18x24in) s. 19-Oct-3 Susanin's, Chicago #6028/R est:1500-2500

COCK, Xavier de (1818-1896) Flemish
£336 $561 €480 Cow (16x20cm-6x8in) s. paper. 11-Oct-3 De Vuyst, Lokeren #100
£420 $701 €600 Study of a goat, cow and sheep (27x36cm-11x14in) s. paper. 11-Oct-3 De Vuyst, Lokeren #99
£26761 $46296 €38000 Shepherd with flock (66x95cm-26x37in) s.d.1881. 13-Dec-3 De Vuyst, Lokeren #429/R est:13000-15000

COCKBURN, Edwin (fl.1837-1868) British
£280 $468 €409 Vessels off the coast of Whitby Sands (25x41cm-10x16in) board. 7-Oct-3 Bonhams, Knightsbridge #312/R

COCKBURN, Major General James Pattison (1778-1847) British
Works on paper
£1300 $2171 €1898 View on the ice pond, Quebec City (15x24cm-6x9in) s.verso W/C over pencil scratching out. 14-Oct-3 Sotheby's, London #200/R est:1000-1500
£2928 $4977 €4275 Montreal from St Gabriel farm (17x24cm-7x9in) i.verso W/C executed c.1830 prov. 27-Nov-3 Heffel, Vancouver #45/R est:1500-2500 (C.D 6500)

COCKBURN, W Laughland (fl.1909-1938) British
£380 $703 €555 Blakeney Shoreline (44x53cm-17x21in) s. board. 11-Feb-4 Cheffins, Cambridge #468/R

COCKERAM, Bertha (fl.1914) British
£250 $408 €365 St Ives, Cornwall from the hilltop overlooking building to the harbour (46x58cm-18x23in) mono. 23-Sep-3 John Nicholson, Haslemere #329

COCKERELL, Christabel A (1863-1951) British
£1600 $2672 €2336 Momentous question (23x30cm-9x12in) s.d.1903 panel prov.exhib. 13-Nov-3 Christie's, Kensington #277/R est:1500-2500

COCKRAM, George (1861-1950) British
£450 $806 €657 Evening glow, Mactog, Anglesey (28x43cm-11x17in) s. 17-Mar-4 John Nicholson, Haslemere #701
Works on paper
£350 $627 €511 Eventide, coastal scene (23x33cm-9x13in) s. 17-Mar-4 John Nicholson, Haslemere #702
£360 $666 €526 Cefn - Du, Snowdonia (33x55cm-13x22in) s. W/C. 14-Jul-4 Bonhams, Chester #331
£400 $652 €584 The evening glow, Maclog, Anglesey (28x43cm-11x17in) s. W/C. 23-Sep-3 John Nicholson, Haslemere #66
£480 $864 €701 Coastal scene near Rhosneigr (25x43cm-10x17in) s. i.verso W/C. 24-Apr-4 Rogers Jones, Clwyd #122/R
£800 $1336 €1168 Eventide Cymmerau Bay, Anglesey (61x43cm-24x17in) s. W/C. 12-Nov-3 Halls, Shrewsbury #263/R

COCKRILL, Maurice (1936-) British
£260 $458 €380 Generation, First Group, Horizon (51x41cm-20x16in) s.i.d.1993 verso. 18-May-4 Rosebery Fine Art, London #719/R
£280 $504 €409 Falling Moon (41x51cm-16x20in) s.i.d.1990 verso. 20-Jan-4 Bonhams, Knightsbridge #212
£300 $501 €438 Generation study (38x46cm-15x18in) s. i.d.1993 verso. 21-Oct-3 Bonhams, Knightsbridge #163/R
£420 $701 €613 Upward (50x46cm-20x18in) s.i.d.1993 verso prov. 21-Oct-3 Bonhams, Knightsbridge #70/R
£420 $756 €613 Fallen Idol (60x92cm-24x36in) s.i.d.1983 verso. 20-Jan-4 Bonhams, Knightsbridge #208
£480 $802 €701 Ancient tools (91x99cm-36x39in) s.i.d.1983 verso. 21-Oct-3 Bonhams, Knightsbridge #135
£600 $1002 €876 Red and blue axes (91x122cm-36x48in) 21-Oct-3 Bonhams, Knightsbridge #165/R
£600 $1080 €876 Generation study (20x25cm-8x10in) s.i.d.1993 verso. 20-Jan-4 Bonhams, Knightsbridge #175/R
£600 $1080 €876 Summerhouse, Wern, North Wales (70x90cm-28x35in) s. s.i.d.1983 verso. 20-Jan-4 Bonhams, Knightsbridge #38
£680 $1217 €993 Tree and lights (41x51cm-16x20in) s.i.d.1990 verso. 16-Mar-4 Bonhams, Knightsbridge #39/R
£750 $1320 €1095 Untitled (33x46cm-13x18in) s.i.d.1993 verso prov. 19-May-4 Sotheby's, Olympia #321/R
£1800 $3006 €2628 Delta (71x91cm-28x36in) s. i.d.1989 verso prov. 21-Oct-3 Bonhams, Knightsbridge #49/R est:2000-3000
£1800 $3330 €2628 Sheep behind a hedge (122x122cm-48x48in) s.d.1973 s.d.verso. 11-Mar-4 Christie's, Kensington #239/R est:800-1200
£2600 $4654 €3796 Landscape with red flower (50x61cm-20x24in) s.i.d.1993 verso. 16-Mar-4 Bonhams, New Bond Street #105/R est:2000-3000

COCKX, Marcel (1930-) Belgian
£400 $720 €600 Girl with doll (110x86cm-43x34in) s. 26-Apr-4 Bernaerts, Antwerp #809
£533 $960 €800 Figures in the village (100x95cm-39x37in) s.d.M.COCKX. 26-Apr-4 Bernaerts, Antwerp #808

COCKX, Philibert (1879-1949) Belgian
£352 $609 €500 L'homme au chapeau (40x50cm-16x20in) s. d.1920 verso panel. 9-Dec-3 Vanderkindere, Brussels #149
£507 $907 €750 Maison dans la neige (62x52cm-24x20in) s.d.1944 s.d.1946 verso. 10-May-4 Horta, Bruxelles #487
£1034 $1914 €1500 Journee d'automne ensoleillee (64x73cm-25x29in) s. 19-Jan-4 Horta, Bruxelles #230 est:1800-2200
£1702 $2843 €2400 Maisons dans la neige (60x50cm-24x20in) s. 17-Jun-3 Galerie Moderne, Brussels #369/R est:2000-3000
£2267 $4057 €3400 Nature morte aux fleurs et aux fruits (38x53cm-15x21in) s.d.1916 canvas on cardboard. 11-May-4 Vanderkindere, Brussels #42/R est:2000-3000
£2838 $5364 €4200 Le peintre dans son atelier vu du jardin (34x54cm-13x21in) s. 17-Feb-4 Vanderkindere, Brussels #5/R est:1250-1750
£3077 $5231 €4400 Paysage de neige a Auderghem (38x55cm-15x22in) s.d.1914 verso panel. 1-Dec-3 Palais de Beaux Arts, Brussels #226/R est:3000-4000
Works on paper
£329 $595 €500 Paysage (34x49cm-13x19in) s.d.1938 mixed media. 19-Apr-4 Horta, Bruxelles #409
£367 $671 €550 Reunion galante (57x54cm-22x21in) s.d.1948 mixed media cardboard. 7-Jun-4 Palais de Beaux Arts, Brussels #237
£372 $702 €550 Femme assise (63x50cm-25x20in) s.d.1917 ink wash W/C. 17-Feb-4 Vanderkindere, Brussels #6
£1027 $1747 €1500 Vase de Bruxelles fleuri (41x49cm-16x19in) s. mixed media cardboard. 10-Nov-3 Horta, Bruxelles #23

COCLERS, Jean George Christian (studio) (1715-1751) Flemish
£5882 $10000 €8588 Still life with flowers in an urn (76x62cm-30x24in) 19-Nov-3 Bonhams & Butterfields, San Francisco #14/R

COCLERS, Louis Bernard (attrib) (1741-1817) Flemish
£590 $939 €850 Sainte en priere (95x72cm-37x28in) 9-Sep-3 Vanderkindere, Brussels #6

COCQUIO, Carlo (1889-?) Italian
£268 $475 €400 Venice, Rio S. Aponal (35x25cm-14x10in) s. cardboard. 1-May-4 Meeting Art, Vercelli #64

COCTEAU, Jean (1889-1963) French
£417 $696 €600 L'ange de la poesie (14x7cm-6x3in) s.d. Indian ink. 24-Oct-3 Ketterer, Hamburg #696/R
£3636 $6182 €5200 Portrait d'homme, le danseur Georges Rech, ami de Jean Marais (41x30cm-16x12in) s.d.1951. 26-Nov-3 Pierre Berge, Paris #47/R est:2000-3000
Photographs
£2667 $4773 €4000 Montage (24x24cm-9x9in) photograph exec.1932 lit. 13-May-4 Le Mouel, Paris #57/R est:2500-3000
Works on paper
£258 $475 €377 Muse (30x23cm-12x9in) s. felt tip pen. 25-Jun-4 Freeman, Philadelphia #108/R
£376 $700 €549 Profil d'homme (21x17cm-8x7in) s.d.1953 col pencils. 2-Mar-4 Swann Galleries, New York #137/R
£407 $750 €594 Fighting centaurs (25x18cm-10x7in) s.d.1961 col pencil. 25-Jun-4 Freeman, Philadelphia #19/R
£419 $750 €612 Boy in profile holding a flower (28x36cm-11x14in) s. ink. 8-May-4 Susanin's, Chicago #6081/R
£423 $731 €600 Projets de Monsieur Lagarde (19x14cm-7x6in) studio st.i. ink graphite dr. 9-Dec-3 Artcurial Briest, Paris #295
£426 $689 €600 Head (13x10cm-5x4in) s.i. Indian ink. 23-May-3 Altus, Berlin #519/R
£448 $749 €650 Portrait of young man with harp (14x9cm-6x4in) s.i. Indian ink. 9-Jul-3 Hugo Ruef, Munich #335/R

£458	$792	€650	Two heads (21x19cm-8x7in) s.i. pen. 12-Dec-3 Altus, Berlin #555/R
£474	$849	€692	Profil d'Orphee a la lyrre (22x14cm-9x6in) s. pencil col pen. 12-May-4 Dobiaschofsky, Bern #1475 (S.FR 1100)
£489	$900	€714	Head (25x18cm-10x7in) s.d.1955 col pencil. 25-Jun-4 Freeman, Philadelphia #33/R
£493	$853	€700	Lancelot du Lac (26x20cm-10x8in) studio st. graphite dr. 9-Dec-3 Artcurial Briest, Paris #282
£528	$913	€750	A Jacques Lartigues (24x19cm-9x7in) s.i.d.1952 ink. 9-Dec-3 Artcurial Briest, Paris #284
£530	$964	€800	Monstre marin (36x30cm-14x12in) s.d.1966 felt tip W/C exhib. 18-Jun-4 Piasa, Paris #215
£556	$928	€800	Visage de Joseph D'Arimathie (51x33cm-20x13in) s.i.d.1959 lead pencil. 21-Oct-3 Artcurial Briest, Paris #76
£564	$975	€800	Edmond Rostand (19x14cm-7x6in) studio st.d.10 graphite dr. 9-Dec-3 Artcurial Briest, Paris #280
£604	$1069	€900	Ah - Mon dieu (21x26cm-8x10in) s. ink. 27-Apr-4 Artcurial Briest, Paris #75
£633	$1134	€950	Souvenir de Jean Cocteau - two heads (29x21cm-11x8in) s.i. pencil biro two. 13-May-4 Neumeister, Munich #310/R
£647	$1100	€945	Sketch (25x18cm-10x7in) s.i.d.1939 graphite. 21-Nov-3 Skinner, Boston #598/R est:300-500
£647	$1158	€970	Lettre a l'autoportrait (19x14cm-7x6in) s. 16-May-4 Feletin, Province #81
£648	$1043	€946	Le sucre (29x23cm-11x9in) s.i. ink gouache. 13-Oct-3 Joel, Victoria #294 est:1500-2000 (A.D 1600)
£670	$1200	€978	Youth dreaming (20x18cm-8x7in) s. ink exhib. 16-May-4 Wright, Chicago #129/R
£699	$1202	€1000	Homme aux cornes de taureau et torero (30x40cm-12x16in) crayon. 3-Dec-3 Tajan, Paris #72
£815	$1500	€1190	Orpheus (64x51cm-25x20in) s.d.1950 felt pen. 26-Jun-4 Susanin's, Chicago #6119/R est:800-1200
£851	$1421	€1200	Visage de profil (27x21cm-11x8in) s.i. col crayon. 14-Oct-3 Millon & Associes, Paris #95/R
£872	$1623	€1300	Profil a l'etoile (45x32cm-18x13in) s. col crayons. 3-Mar-4 Tajan, Paris #127/R est:1500-2000
£925	$1600	€1351	Portraits of Jean Marais (25x19cm-10x7in) s.i. graphite pair. 13-Dec-3 Weschler, Washington #516 est:2000-3000
£944	$1577	€1350	Portrait de Jean Marais. s.d.1947 Chinese ink dr. 30-Jun-3 Bailly Pommery, Paris #23
£958	$1600	€1389	Face surmounted by a lyre (23x30cm-9x12in) s. pastel. 25-Jun-3 Butterfields, San Francisco #3108 est:300-500
£986	$1706	€1400	La mairie laure de Noailles (26x18cm-10x7in) s. i.verso dr. 10-Dec-3 Claude Boisgirard, Paris #8
£986	$1706	€1400	Mon souvenir de rejane (25x16cm-10x6in) s.i. ink crayon. 12-Dec-3 Piasa, Paris #183
£1049	$1783	€1500	Youth (16x12cm-6x5in) mono. feltpen. 29-Nov-3 Bassenge, Berlin #6656/R est:1800
£1056	$1828	€1500	Creon (37x24cm-15x9in) s. graphite dr. 9-Dec-3 Artcurial Briest, Paris #278 est:1500-2000
£1078	$1929	€1574	Visage (21x13cm-8x5in) s.d.1951 col pen. 12-May-4 Dobiaschofsky, Bern #1476 est:2900 (S.FR 2500)
£1189	$2045	€1700	Le fumeur d'opium (20x30cm-8x12in) s. crayon. 3-Dec-3 Tajan, Paris #71 est:1500-2000
£1216	$2250	€1775	Qui est Cegesti (27x22cm-11x9in) s. ink prov. 12-Feb-4 Sotheby's, New York #74/R est:1000-1500
£1233	$2219	€1800	Figure composition - Eric Mandell (26x20cm-10x8in) s.i. Indian ink prov. 26-Apr-4 Bukowskis, Stockholm #245/R est:10000-15000 (S.KR 17000)
£1259	$2140	€1800	Profil d'homme (26x20cm-10x8in) st.init. black felt crayon blue ballpoint pen. 26-Nov-3 Pierre Berge, Paris #54/R est:1800-2000
£1259	$2140	€1800	Profil et patineurs (35x24cm-14x9in) s.d.52 col crayon. 28-Nov-3 Drouot Estimations, Paris #184/R est:2000-2500
£1300	$2249	€1898	Couple amoureux (206x20cm-81x8in) estate st. pencil. 11-Dec-3 Christie's, Kensington #115/R est:1000-1500
£1338	$2315	€1900	Arlequin (34x25cm-13x10in) s.d.1961 felt tip pen. 10-Dec-3 Claude Boisgirard, Paris #9 est:1000-1200
£1343	$2376	€2000	Jeune femme a l'etoffe rouge (40x32cm-16x13in) s.d.1950 col crayon. 27-Apr-4 Artcurial Briest, Paris #72 est:2000-2500
£1357	$2308	€1981	Adam et Eve (27x21cm-11x8in) mono.d.1963 felt tip pen. 22-Nov-3 Burkhard, Luzern #91/R est:800-1200 (S.FR 3000)
£1467	$2625	€2200	Untitled. dr sold with book. 11-May-4 Christie's, Paris #156/R
£1511	$2750	€2206	Nude (27x23cm-11x9in) s.d.1936 pencil. 29-Jun-4 Sotheby's, New York #347/R est:2000-3000
£1552	$2778	€2266	Orphee (27x21cm-11x8in) s. col pen. 12-May-4 Dobiaschofsky, Bern #1473/R est:4400 (S.FR 3600)
£1611	$2980	€2400	Jean Marais (15x11cm-6x4in) mono. col feltpen. 9-Mar-4 Dorotheum, Vienna #80/R est:1800-2000
£1630	$2771	€2380	Youth with bow and arrow (62x46cm-24x18in) s.i. Indian ink. 5-Nov-3 Dobiaschofsky, Bern #1494/R est:400 (S.FR 3700)
£1659	$3020	€2422	Tete de faune (55x46cm-22x18in) s.d.1959 col chk felt pen. 17-Jun-4 Kornfeld, Bern #262 est:4000 (S.FR 3800)
£1678	$2970	€2500	Halbardier (54x37cm-21x15in) s.d.1959 col felt pens. 27-Apr-4 Artcurial Briest, Paris #74 est:1200-1500
£1718	$2921	€2508	Surreal head (26x20cm-10x8in) s.i.d.1938 Indian ink. 5-Nov-3 Dobiaschofsky, Bern #1493/R est:1200 (S.FR 3900)
£1733	$3189	€2600	Orphee (64x49cm-25x19in) s.d.1960 crayon htd col. 14-Jun-4 Tajan, Paris #132/R est:1500-2000
£1736	$2899	€2500	Arlequin en buste (49x32cm-19x13in) s.d.1954 pastel. 21-Oct-3 Artcurial Briest, Paris #73/R est:2500-3000
£1766	$3250	€2578	Male profile (63x49cm-25x19in) s. pastel brown paper. 27-Jun-4 Freeman, Philadelphia #65/R est:2500-4000
£1810	$3241	€2643	Le crime d'Oxford (26x21cm-10x8in) s. pencil. 12-May-4 Dobiaschofsky, Bern #1470/R est:4300 (S.FR 4200)
£1867	$3435	€2800	Licorne couchee, une femme tenant une corne d'abondance derriere elle (71x90cm-28x35in) s.d.1947 pen. 9-Jun-4 Piasa, Paris #31/R est:3000-5000
£1892	$3500	€2762	Machine Infernal (22x15cm-9x6in) init. col pencil. 12-Feb-4 Sotheby's, New York #64/R est:1500-2000
£1944	$3247	€2800	Erotique, deux hommes (22x19cm-9x7in) Indian ink drawing. 21-Oct-3 Artcurial Briest, Paris #71/R est:3000-4000
£1958	$3329	€2800	Man undressing (27x19cm-11x7in) blk ink prov. 25-Nov-3 Christie's, Amsterdam #40/R est:3000-5000
£2042	$3390	€2900	Un signe du coeur, autoportrait presume (25x19cm-10x7in) s.i.d.7 juin 1957 black crayon. 11-Jun-3 Delorme & Bocage, Paris #43 est:500-600
£2045	$3600	€2986	La closerie des lilas (41x28cm-16x11in) s.i.d.1960 mixed media. 22-May-4 Selkirks, St. Louis #776/R est:3000-4000
£2045	$3600	€2986	Male nude (41x33cm-16x13in) s.d.1950 mixed media. 22-May-4 Selkirks, St. Louis #777/R est:3500-4500
£2083	$3479	€3000	Autoportrait (20x13cm-8x5in) studio st. ink exec c.1960-1962 prov. 21-Oct-3 Artcurial Briest, Paris #16/R est:1800-2000
£2098	$3566	€3000	Autportrait. i.d.1960 col crayon. 26-Nov-3 Pierre Berge, Paris #52/R est:3000-4000
£2100	$3633	€3066	Le besoin pressant (35x27cm-14x11in) s. col crayon. 11-Dec-3 Christie's, Kensington #117/R est:1500-2000
£2133	$3925	€3200	Baigneuse en maillot de bain quittant son peignoir (27x21cm-11x8in) pen exec. 1923. 9-Jun-4 Piasa, Paris #29/R est:1000-1500
£2200	$4048	€3300	Profil de jeune homme (34x26cm-13x10in) s.i.d.1962 pastel. 8-Jun-4 Livinec, Gaudcheau & Jezequel, Rennes #73/R
£2324	$3742	€3300	Sphinx (41x31cm-16x12in) col crayon dr. 22-Aug-3 Deauville, France #85/R
£2378	$3971	€3400	Profil de centaure (30x20cm-12x8in) s.d.44 Chinese ink. 25-Jun-3 Blanchet, Paris #35/R
£2483	$4543	€3600	Guitare (50x65cm-20x26in) s.i. chl col pen. 27-Jan-4 Dorotheum, Vienna #113/R est:3500-4000
£2600	$4498	€3796	Profil laure aux etoiles (65x51cm-26x20in) s.d.1959 brown felt tipped pen. 11-Dec-3 Christie's, Kensington #116/R est:1000-1500
£2703	$5000	€3946	Un secret environne ma naissance (27x21cm-11x8in) s.i. ink exec 1937 prov. 12-Feb-4 Sotheby's, New York #75/R est:3000-5000
£2731	$4643	€3987	Chevreuil, le matin (35x25cm-14x10in) s. pencil col pen. 5-Nov-3 Dobiaschofsky, Bern #1492/R est:1400 (S.FR 6200)
£2762	$4750	€4033	Profile portrait (147x117cm-58x46in) s. pastel blk paper. 7-Dec-3 Freeman, Philadelphia #58 est:2000-3000
£2917	$4871	€4200	Autoportrait Santo Sospir (26x20cm-10x8in) s. col crayons exec c.1960. 21-Oct-3 Artcurial Briest, Paris #14 est:1500-2000
£2925	$5236	€4300	Visage de profil (41x25cm-16x10in) s.d.51 col crayons. 19-Mar-4 Millon & Associes, Paris #119b/R est:2000-2500
£2979	$4974	€4200	Faune ecorche (31x21cm-12x8in) s.i.d.38 graphite. 19-Jun-3 Millon & Associes, Paris #44a/R est:4000-5000
£3000	$5520	€4380	L'homme (30x21cm-12x8in) s.d.38 black crayon. 24-Mar-4 Sotheby's, Olympia #180/R est:3000-4000
£3000	$5459	€4500	Profil d'Orphee a la lyre (70x50cm-28x20in) s.i.d.1960 blk marker. 30-Jun-4 Calmels Cohen, Paris #52/R est:4000-5000
£3125	$5219	€4500	Profil de jeune femme (40x28cm-16x11in) s. col crayons prov. 21-Oct-3 Artcurial Briest, Paris #12/R est:1200-1500
£3169	$5483	€4500	Voix humaine (37x24cm-15x9in) s.i.d.1930 ink Chinese ink wash stump. 9-Dec-3 Artcurial Briest, Paris #276/R est:5000-8000
£3468	$6000	€5063	Les amants (42x29cm-17x11in) s. black felt tip pen prov. 11-Dec-3 Sotheby's, New York #160/R est:6000-8000
£3500	$6440	€5110	Maison hantee (35x21cm-14x8in) s.i.d.1938 pen ink. 24-Mar-4 Sotheby's, Olympia #181/R est:4000-6000
£3667	$6747	€5500	Profil d'homme (39x26cm-15x10in) s. crayon stump. 9-Jun-4 Piasa, Paris #30 est:1500-2000
£3873	$6701	€5500	Raymond Radiguet (33x25cm-13x10in) s. pastel ink. 9-Dec-3 Artcurial Briest, Paris #277/R est:6000-7000
£4167	$6959	€6000	Profil de faune (41x31cm-16x12in) s.d.1957 col crayons wax crayon prov. 21-Oct-3 Artcurial Briest, Paris #13/R est:1500-2000
£4362	$7721	€6500	Profil au soleil (49x64cm-19x25in) s.d.1958 pastel Canson paper. 27-Apr-4 Artcurial Briest, Paris #70/R est:4000-5000
£4564	$8078	€6800	Profil de faune devant la mer (49x64cm-19x25in) s.d.1958 pastel Canson paper. 27-Apr-4 Artcurial Briest, Paris #71/R est:4000-5000
£6200	$11408	€9052	Allegorie de L'Espagne (26x23cm-10x9in) s.d.Sept 1936 verso pencil. 24-Mar-4 Sotheby's, Olympia #183/R est:5000-6000
£6250	$10438	€9000	Joueur de flute au soleil (73x54cm-29x21in) s.d.1962 col crayon rov. 21-Oct-3 Artcurial Briest, Paris #11/R est:3000-4000

COCTEAU, Jean (attrib) (1889-1963) French

Works on paper

£1513	$2739	€2300	Portrait (53x40cm-21x16in) s. ink. 18-Apr-4 Rouillac, Vendome #114

COCTEAU, Jean and MORETTI, Lucien Philippe (20th C) French

Works on paper

£1910	$3189	€2750	Profils au poissons (48x62cm-19x24in) s. both artists d.1962 gouache ink col felt-tip pen prov. 21-Oct-3 Artcurial Briest, Paris #15/R est:2000-3000

COCTEAU, Jean and MORETTI, Raymond (20th C) French

Works on paper

£265	$482	€400	Etude pour l'age du verseau (47x62cm-19x24in) s.d.62 W/C ink. 18-Jun-4 Piasa, Paris #213
£278	$506	€420	Etude pour l'age du verseau (74x47cm-29x19in) s.d.1962 W/C. 18-Jun-4 Piasa, Paris #207

CODAZZI, Niccolo (1648-1693) Italian

£6000	$10980	€9000	Capriccio with figures (73x57cm-29x22in) 1-Jun-4 Sotheby's, Milan #191/R est:10000-15000

CODAZZI, Viviano (attrib) (1603-1672) Italian

£6000	$10860	€9000	Personnages sous une voute antique dans la campagne romaine (49x60cm-19x24in) 2-Apr-4 Rossini, Paris #21/R est:4000-4500

CODAZZI, Viviano (circle) (1603-1672) Italian

£7000	$12110	€10220	Architectural capriccio with figures (75x102cm-30x40in) bears sig. 10-Dec-3 Bonhams, New Bond Street #103/R est:7000-10000
£7895	$14289	€12000	Biblical scene in landscape (48x65cm-19x26in) s.d.1740. 14-Apr-4 Ansorena, Madrid #163/R est:6000

CODAZZI, Viviano (studio) (1603-1672) Italian

£7667	$13877	€11500	Columns by harbour (128x77cm-50x30in) 30-Mar-4 Babuino, Rome #56/R est:4000

CODAZZI, Viviano and GARGIULIO, Domenico (17th C) Italian

£102778	$185000	€150056	View of the Villa Poggioreale, Naples (77x101cm-30x40in) 22-Jan-4 Sotheby's, New York #54/R est:30000-40000

CODAZZI, Viviano and GINER, Vicente (17th C) Italian

£46000	$82800	€67160	Architectural capriccio, with huntsman and riders among ruined arches (115x168cm-45x66in) prov.exhib.lit. 22-Apr-4 Sotheby's, London #91/R est:30000-50000

CODDE, Pieter (1599-1678) Dutch
£2041 $3653 €3000 The hearing (41x54cm-16x21in) bears mono. panel. 17-Mar-4 Neumeister, Munich #332/R est:5000
£3297 $6000 €4814 Travelers resting on a path (28x28cm-11x11in) s. panel prov. 29-Jun-4 Sotheby's, New York #37/R est:4000-6000
£65000 $112450 €94900 Interior with a lady seated at virginals, viola da gamba resting beside her (43x32cm-17x13in) oak panel prov. 11-Dec-3 Sotheby's, London #134/R est:20000-30000

CODDE, Pieter (attrib) (1599-1678) Dutch
£6294 $10699 €9000 Soldiers playing cards (38x48cm-15x19in) panel. 21-Nov-3 Coutau Begarie, Paris #109/R est:5000-8000

CODDRON, Oscar (1881-1960) Belgian
£567 $948 €800 Femme nue accoudee (45x35cm-18x14in) s. panel. 17-Jun-3 Vanderkindere, Brussels #22
£728 $1326 €1100 Fenaison (40x50cm-16x20in) s. 16-Jun-4 Hotel des Ventes Mosan, Brussels #198

CODE, Ernva (1900-1989) Canadian
£200 $366 €292 Dories docked by fishing shacks (30x35cm-12x14in) s. board. 1-Jun-4 Hodgins, Calgary #17/R (C.D 500)
£222 $369 €324 Untitled, fishing boats at dock (25x35cm-10x14in) s. wood board double-sided. 5-Oct-3 Levis, Calgary #19/R (C.D 500)
£269 $486 €393 Untitled - low tide rhythms (30x38cm-12x15in) s. hard board. 18-Apr-4 Levis, Calgary #20/R (C.D 650)
£317 $529 €463 Untitled - windy day (30x38cm-12x15in) s. board. 17-Nov-3 Hodgins, Calgary #168/R (C.D 700)

CODESIDO, Julia (1892-1972) Peruvian
£5882 $10000 €8588 Frutera ayacuchana (76x74cm-30x29in) s.d.1933 oil on burlap. 19-Nov-3 Sotheby's, New York #95/R est:10000-15000

CODINA Y LANGLIN, Victoriano (1844-1911) Spanish
£604 $1105 €900 Visit to the vicar (31x23cm-12x9in) s. board. 12-Jul-4 Durán, Madrid #92

CODINO, Francesco (17th C) Italian
£25000 $45750 €36500 Still life with grapes and sparrow (34x53cm-13x21in) panel lit. 8-Jul-4 Sotheby's, London #323/R est:20000-30000
£80537 $144161 €120000 Table with fruit and butterflies. Table with berries and ladybird (44x61cm-17x24in) board pair exhib.lit. 26-May-4 Porro, Milan #16/R est:125000-150000

COEDES, Louis Eugène (1810-1906) French
Works on paper
£933 $1699 €1400 Nu drape (80x64cm-31x25in) s. pastel. 29-Jun-4 Gioffredo, Nice #347

COEN, Margaret (1913-1993) Australian
Works on paper
£277 $435 €404 Spring bouquet with elephant (62x52cm-24x20in) s. W/C. 24-Nov-2 Goodman, Sydney #93/R (A.D 775)
£413 $702 €603 Wildflowers with kangaroo Paw (56x50cm-22x20in) s. W/C executed c.1956. 29-Oct-3 Lawson Menzies, Sydney #106/R est:600-800 (A.D 1000)

COEN, Sigismondo (1835-?) Italian
£9220 $15397 €13000 Reader (200x120cm-79x47in) exhib.lit. 20-Oct-3 Sant Agostino, Torino #299/R est:14000-18000

COENE, Constantinus Fidelio (1780-1841) Flemish
£1769 $3043 €2583 Peasants dancing (28x35cm-11x14in) s. panel. 3-Dec-3 AB Stockholms Auktionsverk #2552/R est:20000-25000 (S.KR 23000)

COENE, Jean Henri de (1798-1866) Flemish
£8099 $14011 €11500 Proposal (67x54cm-26x21in) s. panel. 13-Dec-3 De Vuyst, Lokeren #526/R est:13000-16000
Works on paper
£367 $675 €550 Zeebruges (50x60cm-20x24in) s. W/C. 14-Jun-4 Horta, Bruxelles #426

COENE, Jozef de (1875-1950) Belgian
£567 $1014 €850 Fishing port (90x100cm-35x39in) s. s.i.d.33 verso. 15-May-4 De Vuyst, Lokeren #85/R
£694 $1160 €1000 Paysage sous la neige (80x100cm-31x39in) s. 21-Oct-3 Campo & Campo, Antwerp #61

COENRAETS, Charles (?) Belgian?
Works on paper
£267 $480 €400 Le Moulin. W/C. 20-Apr-4 Galerie Moderne, Brussels #213

COENRAETS, F (19th C) Belgian?
Works on paper
£1049 $1783 €1500 Barques de peche sur un canal a Dordrecht (36x24cm-14x9in) W/C. 1-Dec-3 Amberes, Antwerp #285
£2098 $3566 €3000 Vachere dans un paysage fluvial (42x37cm-17x15in) W/C. 1-Dec-3 Amberes, Antwerp #284/R

COENRAETS, Ferdinand (19th C) Belgian?
Works on paper
£1724 $2862 €2500 View of Sluis (36x54cm-14x21in) W/C. 6-Oct-3 Amberes, Antwerp #210

COESSIN DE LA FOSSE, Charles Alexandre (1829-1910) French
£3500 $6125 €5110 Two young ladies in a rowing boat on lake in a park with sailing boats (53x76cm-21x30in) s. exhib. 18-Dec-3 John Nicholson, Haslemere #1155 est:2500-5000

COETZEE, Albee (20th C) New Zealander
£465 $799 €679 Reminiscence (100x70cm-39x28in) s. 7-Dec-3 International Art Centre, Auckland #201/R (NZ.D 1250)

COETZEE, Christo (1929-2001) South African
£259 $432 €378 Young girl with flowers in her hair (25x17cm-10x7in) s. board. 20-Oct-3 Stephan Welz, Johannesburg #649 est:2000-3000 (SA.R 3000)
£362 $605 €529 Still life of flowers (28x24cm-11x9in) s. board. 20-Oct-3 Stephan Welz, Johannesburg #610 est:4000-6000 (SA.R 4200)
£378 $684 €552 Untitled 1960 (117x90cm-46x35in) s.i.verso prov.lit. 30-Mar-4 Stephan Welz, Johannesburg #513/R est:5000-7000 (SA.R 4500)
£733 $1224 €1070 Face and figure (55x50cm-22x20in) s.d.1948. 20-Oct-3 Stephan Welz, Johannesburg #415/R est:5000-8000 (SA.R 8500)
£812 $1380 €1186 Untitled (116x89cm-46x35in) s.d.9/7/60 i.verso. 4-Nov-3 Stephan Welz, Johannesburg #697/R est:8000-12000 (SA.R 9500)
£1345 $2434 €1964 Portrait of a woman (44x29cm-17x11in) s. board. 30-Mar-4 Stephan Welz, Johannesburg #489/R est:7000-10000 (SA.R 16000)
£3716 $6652 €5425 Flora (121x120cm-48x47in) s.d.98 s.i.d. verso board. 31-May-4 Stephan Welz, Johannesburg #573/R est:12000-18000 (SA.R 45000)
Works on paper
£276 $461 €403 Head (63x49cm-25x19in) s.i.d.90-62 mixed media. 20-Oct-3 Stephan Welz, Johannesburg #623 est:2000-3000 (SA.R 3200)
£385 $654 €562 Still life of flowers in a blue vase (53x37cm-21x15in) s.d.69 pencil W/C gouache. 4-Nov-3 Stephan Welz, Johannesburg #708 est:2500-3500 (SA.R 4500)
£948 $1584 €1384 Untitled (81x130cm-32x51in) s.d.3.6.60 mixed media on canvas. 20-Oct-3 Stephan Welz, Johannesburg #373/R est:12000-18000 (SA.R 11000)
£991 $1774 €1447 Untitled (81x130cm-32x51in) s.d.3/6/60 i.verso prov.lit. 31-May-4 Stephan Welz, Johannesburg #614/R (SA.R 12000)
£991 $1774 €1447 Untitled (162x160cm-64x63in) s.d.1962 i.verso mixed media prov.lit. 31-May-4 Stephan Welz, Johannesburg #615/R (SA.R 12000)
£1121 $1872 €1637 Untitled (81x116cm-32x46in) s.i.d.63 mixed media on hessian prov.lit. 20-Oct-3 Stephan Welz, Johannesburg #403/R est:15000-20000 (SA.R 13000)

COETZEE, Herbert (1921-) South African
£427 $726 €623 Landskap by Winburg (44x56cm-17x22in) s.d.68 i.verso board. 4-Nov-3 Stephan Welz, Johannesburg #673 est:2500-4000 (SA.R 5000)

COETZER, Willem H (1900-1983) South African
£328 $547 €479 Figures by a dam (22x29cm-9x11in) s.d.71 board. 20-Oct-3 Stephan Welz, Johannesburg #797 est:3000-4000 (SA.R 3800)
£337 $620 €492 Hills with huts and figures (46x60cm-18x24in) 8-Jun-4 Dales, Durban #2 (SA.R 4000)
£474 $792 €692 By Bergville, Natal (30x52cm-12x20in) s.i.verso board. 20-Oct-3 Stephan Welz, Johannesburg #252/R est:6000-9000 (SA.R 5500)
£495 $887 €723 Landscape with mountains in the distance (21x29cm-8x11in) s.d.67 board. 31-May-4 Stephan Welz, Johannesburg #204 (SA.R 6000)
£619 $1109 €904 View of a beach (44x36cm-17x14in) s.d.60 canvas on board. 31-May-4 Stephan Welz, Johannesburg #247 (SA.R 7500)
£647 $1080 €945 Drakensberg (39x49cm-15x19in) s. canvasboard. 20-Oct-3 Stephan Welz, Johannesburg #253 est:5000-7000 (SA.R 7500)
£647 $1080 €945 Drakensberg (50x41cm-20x16in) s.d.44 board. 20-Oct-3 Stephan Welz, Johannesburg #780 est:4000-6000 (SA.R 7500)
£702 $1256 €1025 Near Mount Aux Sources (29x39cm-11x15in) s.d.73 i.verso board. 31-May-4 Stephan Welz, Johannesburg #208 (SA.R 8500)
£702 $1256 €1025 Roadway after the rain (38x49cm-15x19in) s.d.61 canvas on board. 31-May-4 Stephan Welz, Johannesburg #491 (SA.R 8500)
£756 $1369 €1104 Wine, women and song (50x40cm-20x16in) s.d.1980 i.verso canvasboard. 30-Mar-4 Stephan Welz, Johannesburg #526/R est:10000-15000 (SA.R 9000)
£798 $1445 €1165 Panoramic view of the Drakensberg (40x50cm-16x20in) s.d.42. 30-Mar-4 Stephan Welz, Johannesburg #444 est:5000-7000 (SA.R 9500)
£908 $1626 €1326 Barberton near Sheba mine (39x49cm-15x19in) s.d.74 s.i.verso board. 31-May-4 Stephan Welz, Johannesburg #490/R (SA.R 11000)
£991 $1774 €1447 Naby Blyde River Canyon (38x49cm-15x19in) s. s.i.verso board. 31-May-4 Stephan Welz, Johannesburg #532 (SA.R 12000)
£1073 $1922 €1567 Mountain roadway with huts (39x49cm-15x19in) s.d.44. 31-May-4 Stephan Welz, Johannesburg #561 (SA.R 13000)
£1207 $2016 €1762 Near Golden Gate (30x40cm-12x16in) s.d.69 canvas on board. 20-Oct-3 Stephan Welz, Johannesburg #782 est:4000-6000 (SA.R 14000)
£2002 $3443 €2923 Back facade of a Cape farmhouse amongst trees (60x70cm-24x28in) s.d.48 board. 3-Dec-3 Stephan Welz, Johannesburg #27/R est:9000-12000 (SA.R 22000)

COFFA, Andrea (19th C) Italian
£1450 $2320 €2117 Women winding wool, Portici (51x30cm-20x12in) s.d.78 panel. 16-Sep-3 Bonhams, Knowle #125 est:300-500
£4974 $9152 €7560 Village with women spinning (50x30cm-20x12in) s.d.1878 board lit. 22-Jun-4 Babuino, Rome #441/R est:2000-2500

COFFEE, Will (20th C) American
£479 $800 €699 Near Harrowgate lane (51x61cm-20x24in) s. 20-Jun-3 Freeman, Philadelphia #131/R

COFFERMANS, Marcellus (16th C) Flemish
£1842 $3389 €2800 Crucifixion (22x15cm-9x6in) panel. 25-Jun-4 Piasa, Paris #68/R est:4000-6000
£32895 $59539 €50000 Deposition (54x38cm-21x15in) board prov.exhib. 14-Apr-4 Ansorena, Madrid #134/R est:48000

COFFEY, Alfred (1869-1950) Australian
£943 $1527 €1377 Fishing boat (40x50cm-16x20in) s. board. 30-Jul-3 Goodman, Sydney #109/R (A.D 2300)

£1230 $1992 €1796 Maria Island (24x39cm-9x15in) s. 30-Jul-3 Goodman, Sydney #103/R est:2500-3500 (A.D 3000)
£3074 $4980 €4488 Fruit seller (32x19cm-13x7in) s.i. board. 30-Jul-3 Goodman, Sydney #90/R est:4000-6000 (A.D 7500)

COFFIERI, H (?) ?
Works on paper
£1600 $2720 €2336 Young boy seated on an anchor (52x35cm-20x14in) s. W/C. 25-Nov-3 Outhwaite & Litherland, Liverpool #444

COFFIN, George Albert (1856-1922) American
£443 $700 €647 Early English arrivals (20x15cm-8x6in) s. 7-Sep-3 Treadway Gallery, Cincinnati #552/R

COFFIN, William A (1855-1925) American
£17647 $30000 €25765 Early morning (76x102cm-30x40in) s. 30-Oct-3 Phillips, New York #58/R est:15000-20000

COFFIN, William H (1837-1898) American
£1271 $2300 €1856 Two schooners with several vessels in distance and lighthouse to the right (36x51cm-14x20in) s.d.90 panel. 2-Apr-4 Eldred, East Dennis #676/R est:700-1000

COFFIN, William Haskell (1878-1941) American
£588 $1000 €858 Seated Jack Russell terrier (46x56cm-18x22in) s.d.96 oil on tin. 21-Nov-3 Skinner, Boston #55/R est:2000-3000
Works on paper
£802 $1500 €1171 Smiling brunette (69x48cm-27x19in) s. pastel. 26-Feb-4 Illustration House, New York #41 est:1500-2400

COFFINIERES DE NORDEK, Leon Gabriel (1844-1898) French
Works on paper
£1667 $3000 €2434 Day of a gentleman artist, design for a fan (27x58cm-11x23in) s.d.1877 pencil W/C bodycol prov.exhib.lit. 22-Jan-4 Christie's, Rockefeller NY #147/R est:3000-5000

COFFRE, Benoit le (attrib) (1671-1722) French
£378 $654 €552 Figure composition - Negro boy reaching for girl with fruit (80x63cm-31x25in) prov. 9-Dec-3 Rasmussen, Copenhagen #1608/R (D.KR 4000)

COGGESHALL, Calvert (1907-1990) American
Works on paper
£1677 $2800 €2448 Greens with reds (102x102cm-40x40in) s.d.1962 Japan pigment rectified petroleum. 11-Nov-3 Christie's, Rockefeller NY #111/R est:800-1200
£1677 $2800 €2448 Untitled - green and red (23x30cm-9x12in) Japan pigment rectified petroleum executed c.1962. 11-Nov-3 Christie's, Rockefeller NY #112/R est:400-600
£2275 $3800 €3322 Untitled - white (73x65cm-29x26in) s.verso Japan pigment rectified petroleum. 11-Nov-3 Christie's, Rockefeller NY #113/R est:500-700

COGGINS, Jack (20th C) American
£267 $425 €390 Drying nets (46x61cm-18x24in) s. 10-Sep-3 Alderfer's, Hatfield #330

COGHILL, K (19th C) Irish
£2550 $4565 €3800 Study of a young woman seated reading a book outside on a summer's day (95x70cm-37x28in) s. 31-May-4 Hamilton Osborne King, Dublin #153/R est:2000-3000

COGHLAN, Elaine E (1897-1989) Australian
£432 $782 €631 Untitled. s. board. 31-Mar-4 Goodman, Sydney #341 (A.D 1050)

COGHUF (1905-1976) Swiss
£1048 $1907 €1530 Dark head (39x28cm-15x11in) s.d.29. 17-Jun-4 Kornfeld, Bern #263 est:3000 (S.FR 2400)
Works on paper
£1310 $2345 €1913 Part of the forest (62x48cm-24x19in) s.i.d.1960 pencil W/C gouache prov. 26-May-4 Sotheby's, Zurich #136/R est:3000-4000 (S.FR 3000)

COGLE, Henry George (1875-1957) British
£280 $476 €409 Still life with fish (30x40cm-12x16in) s. board. 9-Nov-3 Lots Road Auctions, London #365

COGNEE, Philippe (1957-) French
£268 $491 €400 Untitled - animal (60x50cm-24x20in) acrylic Japan paper prov. 7-Jul-4 Artcurial Briest, Paris #231
£1067 $1963 €1600 Untitled (130x102cm-51x40in) s.d.2/85 acrylic Japan paper on canvas prov. 9-Jun-4 Artcurial Briest, Paris #523/R est:1500-2000
£1934 $3480 €2900 Untitled (231x180cm-91x71in) s.d.1986 acrylic paper on canvas prov. 26-Apr-4 Tajan, Paris #253/R est:3000-3500
£2587 $4321 €3700 Paysage en automne I (72x89cm-28x35in) s.d.1992 verso prov. 29-Jun-3 Versailles Encheres #224/R
Works on paper
£242 $443 €360 Untitled - animal (60x50cm-24x20in) s. gouache Japan paper prov. 7-Jul-4 Artcurial Briest, Paris #232
£417 $696 €600 Portrait d'homme (61x50cm-24x20in) s.d.85 verso mixed media canvas. 21-Oct-3 Artcurial Briest, Paris #566b
£1018 $1700 €1486 Untitled (150x109cm-59x43in) 19-Oct-3 Susanin's, Chicago #6084/R est:2000-4000

COGNIET, Léon (1794-1880) French
Works on paper
£909 $1564 €1300 Roland a Roncevaux (25x19cm-10x7in) crayon wash gouache. 5-Dec-3 Gros & Delettrez, Paris #20/R
£1224 $2192 €1800 Etude d'Oriental debout (37x25cm-15x10in) bears mono. chl estompe white chk. 19-Mar-4 Piasa, Paris #127/R est:1500

COGORNO, Santiago (1915-2001) Argentinian
£742 $1350 €1083 Untitled (17x23cm-7x9in) s.d.55 tempera paper pair. 5-Jul-4 Arroyo, Buenos Aires #70/R
£838 $1500 €1223 Blue vase with flowers (38x28cm-15x11in) tempera paper. 11-May-4 Arroyo, Buenos Aires #22
£2210 $4000 €3227 Reclining female nude (29x42cm-11x17in) board. 30-Mar-4 Arroyo, Buenos Aires #109
£4972 $9000 €7259 Vase of flowers (100x80cm-39x31in) 30-Mar-4 Arroyo, Buenos Aires #88
£8470 $15500 €12366 Composition with flowers (90x110cm-35x43in) 1-Jun-4 Arroyo, Buenos Aires #40
Works on paper
£989 $1800 €1444 Nude in grey (58x37cm-23x15in) s. mixed media. 29-Jun-4 Arroyo, Buenos Aires #16/R est:1800
£989 $1800 €1444 Nude (35x50cm-14x20in) s. mixed media. 5-Jul-4 Arroyo, Buenos Aires #4/R est:1800
£1044 $1900 €1524 Nude with fan (58x40cm-23x16in) s. mixed media. 5-Jul-4 Arroyo, Buenos Aires #39/R est:1700
£1209 $2200 €1765 Flowers (60x42cm-24x17in) s. mixed media. 29-Jun-4 Arroyo, Buenos Aires #14/R est:2200
£1639 $3000 €2393 Italian figure (62x50cm-24x20in) mixed media. 1-Jun-4 Arroyo, Buenos Aires #27
£2198 $4000 €3209 Model (40x60cm-16x24in) s.d.68 mixed media. 29-Jun-4 Arroyo, Buenos Aires #91/R est:2800
£2402 $4300 €3507 Figure (60x42cm-24x17in) mixed media. 11-May-4 Arroyo, Buenos Aires #20

COHELEACH, Guy Joseph (1933-) American
£898 $1500 €1311 Tiger (30x46cm-12x18in) s.d.98. 20-Oct-3 Sotheby's, New York #509/R est:500-700
£29412 $55000 €42942 Lion eyes (56x76cm-22x30in) s. exhib.lit. 24-Jul-4 Coeur d'Alene, Hayden #176/R est:30000-50000

COHEN, Alfred (1920-) American
£300 $528 €438 Conservatory (63x76cm-25x30in) s.i.d.1962-63 verso. 18-May-4 Bonhams, Knightsbridge #221/R
£380 $684 €555 Boutiques (38x62cm-15x24in) s.i.d.1959 verso board. 20-Jan-4 Bonhams, Knightsbridge #130/R

COHEN, Arthur (20th C) American
£249 $450 €364 Provincetown (25x30cm-10x12in) s.d.1988 board. 3-Apr-4 Outer Cape Auctions, Provincetown #38/R
£341 $600 €498 Provincetown Harbour (36x46cm-14x18in) s.verso board painted c.1993. 3-Jan-4 Outer Cape Auctions, Provincetown #104/R
£432 $800 €631 View from Sal's Wharf, Provincetown (46x53cm-18x21in) s.d.1967. 17-Jul-4 Outer Cape Auctions, Provincetown #49/R
£483 $850 €705 Provincetown (36x46cm-14x18in) s. board painted c.89-92. 3-Jan-4 Outer Cape Auctions, Provincetown #69/R
£649 $1200 €948 Provincetown harbour (71x122cm-28x48in) s.d.1997. 15-Feb-4 Outer Cape Auctions, Provincetown #78a/R
£973 $1800 €1421 Provincetown and sunset (71x122cm-28x48in) s.d.1997. 17-Jul-4 Outer Cape Auctions, Provincetown #40a/R
£1118 $1900 €1632 Provincetown (76x122cm-30x48in) s. 9-Nov-3 Outer Cape Auctions, Provincetown #63/R
£1350 $2200 €1971 Provincetown (76x102cm-30x40in) s. 19-Jul-3 Outer Cape Auctions, Provincetown #139/R

COHEN, Bernard (1933-) British
£3000 $5490 €4380 Generation (244x244cm-96x96in) oil egg tempera exhib. 2-Jun-4 Sotheby's, London #120/R est:5000-7000
Works on paper
£420 $701 €613 Untitled (74x94cm-29x37in) mixed media. 21-Oct-3 Bonhams, Knightsbridge #33/R

COHEN, George (20th C) American?
£1412 $2400 €2062 Office (97x97cm-38x38in) s.d.1964-65 verso oil canvas mirror prov.exhib. 9-Nov-3 Wright, Chicago #406 est:3000-5000

COHEN, Isabel M (1867-1945) American
£663 $1100 €968 Marigolde (71x61cm-28x24in) s. canvas laid down. 4-Oct-3 Neal Auction Company, New Orleans #1091/R
£2048 $3400 €2990 Still life of chrysanthemums (99x66cm-39x26in) s. 4-Oct-3 Neal Auction Company, New Orleans #584/R est:800-1200

COHEN, Larry (20th C) American
£1412 $2500 €2062 Untitled, cityscape (112x168cm-44x66in) s.verso. 2-May-4 Bonhams & Butterfields, Los Angeles #3079/R est:3000-5000

COHEN, Minnie Agnes (1864-1940) British
£4000 $7160 €5840 Fisherwomen gossiping on the foreshore (46x31cm-18x12in) mono. 27-May-4 Christie's, Kensington #224/R est:1200-1800
£66000 $112200 €96360 At the Capstan bars (113x176cm-44x69in) mono. 4-Nov-3 Bristol Auction Rooms #580/R est:80000-120000

COHEN, Mirit (1945-1990) Israeli
£3352 $6000 €4894 Carvings (70x65cm-28x26in) scored panel two frames. 18-Mar-4 Sotheby's, New York #60/R est:7000-9000

COHEN-GAN, Pinchas (1942-) Israeli

Works on paper

£3073	$5500	€4487	Untitled (32x42cm-13x17in) s.d.76 ink oil folded newsprint four. 18-Mar-4 Sotheby's, New York #63/R est:2000-3000

COHN, Harold (?) ?

£351	$650	€512	Female in mantilla against yellow (102x64cm-40x25in) 13-Feb-4 Du Mouchelle, Detroit #2215/R
£757	$1400	€1105	Still life with pitcher, platter of fish and lemon (41x51cm-16x20in) 13-Feb-4 Du Mouchelle, Detroit #2007/R
£865	$1600	€1263	Red tulips in a vase (91x61cm-36x24in) masonite. 12-Mar-4 Du Mouchelle, Detroit #2247/R est:1250-1500
£867	$1500	€1266	Female nude with flower vase (76x97cm-30x38in) 12-Dec-3 Du Mouchelle, Detroit #2246/R est:1500-2200
£967	$1750	€1412	Mother and child (91x61cm-36x24in) masonite. 16-Apr-4 Du Mouchelle, Detroit #2140/R est:1800-2500
£1012	$1750	€1478	Woman leaning on her chin (43x36cm-17x14in) masonite. 12-Dec-3 Du Mouchelle, Detroit #2121/R est:1800-2300

Works on paper

£301	$550	€439	Nude (30x23cm-12x9in) s. ink executed c.1952. 5-Jun-4 Treadway Gallery, Cincinnati #700/R
£811	$1500	€1184	Portrait of a woman (58x43cm-23x17in) gouache W/C. 13-Feb-4 Du Mouchelle, Detroit #2006/R est:1400-2000

COHN, Max Arthur (1903-) American

£195	$350	€285	Nude study (46x61cm-18x24in) s. 14-May-4 Skinner, Boston #397/R

COIGNARD, James (1925-1997) French

£417	$696	€600	Perturbation a la tache rose (65x49cm-26x19in) s. oil gouache collage. 21-Oct-3 Artcurial Briest, Paris #312
£448	$829	€650	Matiere forte (39x23cm-15x9in) s. acrylic mixed media paper on wood. 13-Feb-4 Charbonneaux, Paris #36
£521	$869	€750	Partie de cartes (55x65cm-22x26in) s. 21-Oct-3 Artcurial Briest, Paris #313
£671	$1188	€1000	Untitled (56x44cm-22x17in) s. s.d.1993 verso oil collage paper on canvas. 28-Apr-4 Artcurial Briest, Paris #481
£726	$1300	€1060	Assemblage dur rouge. s. acrylic. 13-May-4 Dallas Auction Gallery, Dallas #72/R est:1500-2500
£903	$1563	€1318	Landscape with cattle (54x73cm-21x29in) s. 15-Dec-3 Lilla Bukowskis, Stockholm #694 (S.KR 11500)
£2533	$4535	€3800	Porposition dualisee (81x100cm-32x39in) s.d. s.i. verso. 15-May-4 Van Ham, Cologne #523/R est:5700
£4072	$6801	€5945	Structure lineaire (82x198cm-32x78in) s. i.d.1986 verso acrylic mixed media three parts. 24-Jun-3 Germann, Zurich #84/R est:10000-13000 (S.FR 9000)

Works on paper

£262	$483	€393	Composition (24x16cm-9x6in) s. mixed media. 14-Jun-4 Lilla Bukowskis, Stockholm #414 (S.KR 3600)
£268	$499	€400	Composition (25x21cm-10x8in) s. mixed media collage. 3-Mar-4 Artcurial Briest, Paris #348a
£286	$487	€418	Untitled (40x31cm-16x12in) s.i. mixed media. 5-Nov-3 Dobiaschofsky, Bern #1501 (S.FR 650)
£345	$617	€504	Untitled (66x53cm-26x21in) s.i. mixed media. 12-May-4 Dobiaschofsky, Bern #1485/R (S.FR 800)
£347	$624	€520	Composition (36x52cm-14x20in) s. felt-tip pen collage ink. 24-Apr-4 Cornette de St.Cyr, Paris #486
£382	$615	€558	Untitled (51x39cm-20x15in) s. mixed media. 25-Aug-3 Lilla Bukowskis, Stockholm #525 (S.KR 5000)
£566	$978	€826	Pig (60x73cm-24x29in) s. mixed media. 15-Dec-3 Lilla Bukowskis, Stockholm #498 (S.KR 7200)
£814	$1385	€1188	Composition (87x70cm-34x28in) s. mixed media collage on etching board. 25-Nov-3 Germann, Zurich #758 est:2000-2500 (S.FR 1800)

COIGNARD, Louis (1810-1883) French

£1035	$1852	€1511	Cattle in woodland glade (38x55cm-15x22in) s. 25-May-4 Bukowskis, Stockholm #373/R (S.KR 14000)
£1333	$2440	€2000	Vaches au pre (17x29cm-7x11in) s. panel. 6-Jun-4 Osenat, Fontainebleau #201/R est:1800-2000
£1399	$2378	€2000	Ecluse a l'entree du village anime (55x65cm-22x26in) s. 18-Nov-3 Galerie Moderne, Brussels #630/R est:3000-4000
£1477	$2732	€2200	Vaches pres de la mare (54x73cm-21x29in) s.d.1871. 14-Mar-4 Eric Pillon, Calais #11/R
£2067	$3782	€3100	Troupeau de vaches (40x60cm-16x24in) s. 6-Jun-4 Osenat, Fontainebleau #202/R est:3200-3500
£2867	$5246	€4300	Troupeau pres de la mare (54x73cm-21x29in) s.d.1871. 6-Jun-4 Osenat, Fontainebleau #203/R est:4500-5000
£8451	$14620	€12000	Peasants resting beneath tree in the country (28x49cm-11x19in) s. board on panel. 11-Dec-3 Dr Fritz Nagel, Stuttgart #511/R est:1400

COIGNET, Jules Louis Philippe (1798-1860) French

£1678	$3087	€2500	Vue presume de Heidelberg (27x41cm-11x16in) s. 24-Mar-4 Tajan, Paris #159/R est:2000-3000
£2697	$4963	€4100	Paysage anime (46x38cm-18x15in) s.i.d.1837 paper on canvas. 25-Jun-4 Daguerre, Paris #116/R est:4000-6000

Works on paper

£733	$1335	€1100	Sous-bois anime (20x30cm-8x12in) pastel. 29-Jun-4 Chenu & Scrive, Lyon #52/R
£950	$1634	€1387	Travellers on a road (13x20cm-5x8in) s. W/C prov. 5-Dec-3 Keys, Aylsham #453/R

COIGNET, Jules Louis Philippe (attrib) (1798-1860) French

£238	$426	€350	Sous-Bois (31x22cm-12x9in) paper on canvas. 17-Mar-4 Tajan, Paris #119

COINCHON, Jacques Antoine Theodore (1814-1881) French

Sculpture

£993	$1818	€1500	Figure of Andromeda (56cm-22in) s. brown pat. bronze on marble plinth. 6-Apr-4 Sotheby's, Amsterdam #299/R est:1500-2000

COINER, Charles Toucey (1898-1989) American

£224	$375	€325	Goose Bay (76x102cm-30x40in) s. 29-Jun-3 Butterfields, Los Angeles #7072/R
£497	$800	€726	The branch (43x79cm-17x31in) s. board painted c.1953 exhib. 22-Feb-3 Bunte, Elgin #1247
£543	$1000	€793	Modernist landscape (43x56cm-17x22in) s. board. 9-Jun-4 Alderfer's, Hatfield #465/R est:400-600

Works on paper

£407	$650	€594	Spring thaw (81x104cm-32x41in) s.d.1963 mixed media board. 20-Sep-3 Bunte, Elgin #1260

COINS, Raymond (1904-) American

Sculpture

£1000	$1800	€1460	Man riding large animal (25x28cm-10x11in) carved soapstone prov. 24-Apr-4 Slotin Folk Art, Buford #339/R est:1000-3000
£1198	$2000	€1749	Large stone bear (30x71cm-12x28in) river-stone. 15-Nov-3 Slotin Folk Art, Buford #233/R est:2000-4000
£1377	$2300	€2010	Bear (23x53cm-9x21in) soapstone prov. 15-Nov-3 Slotin Folk Art, Buford #235/R est:1000-2000
£1437	$2400	€2098	Crucifixion (43x28cm-17x11in) i. soapstone prov.lit. 15-Nov-3 Slotin Folk Art, Buford #234/R est:2000-4000
£1722	$3100	€2514	Adrem (51x30cm-20x12in) carved stone tablet prov. 24-Apr-4 Slotin Folk Art, Buford #338/R est:3000-5000
£1806	$3250	€2637	Humpback fish (18x46cm-7x18in) carved soapstone prov. 24-Apr-4 Slotin Folk Art, Buford #341/R est:1000-2000
£1946	$3250	€2841	I dream a dream (66x33cm-26x13in) stone prov. 15-Nov-3 Slotin Folk Art, Buford #232/R est:3000-5000

COKER, Peter (1926-) British

£1500	$2730	€2190	Chrossavaig, Skye (91x122cm-36x48in) mono.d.1987 prov.exhib. 4-Feb-4 John Nicholson, Haslemere #74/R est:1500-2000

COL, D (19th C) ?

£3000	$5460	€4500	Farmhand sleeping in a hay trough being tickled by a young woman (53x44cm-21x17in) 20-Jun-4 Wilkinson, Doncaster #315 est:4000-6000

COL, Jan David (1822-1900) Belgian

£664	$1129	€950	Pecheur pres de l'etang (28x22cm-11x9in) s. panel. 1-Dec-3 Palais de Beaux Arts, Brussels #231/R
£1049	$1804	€1500	Nature morte aux truites et a la cruche (42x62cm-17x24in) s.d.1878. 2-Dec-3 Campo & Campo, Antwerp #71/R est:1200-1800
£2667	$4827	€4000	Deux personnages dans un cour interieure (53x44cm-21x17in) s. 30-Mar-4 Campo & Campo, Antwerp #46/R est:8000-12000
£5333	$9653	€8000	Berger se reposant avec ses vaches au bord du bois (85x71cm-33x28in) s. 30-Mar-4 Campo & Campo, Antwerp #47/R est:6000-8000

COL, Jan David (attrib) (1822-1900) Belgian

£814	$1458	€1188	Cellar interior with jugs and barrels by stairs (44x53cm-17x21in) 10-May-4 Rasmussen, Vejle #496/R (D.KR 9000)
£1843	$3134	€2691	Cellar interior with jugs and barrels by stairs (44x53cm-17x21in) 10-Nov-3 Rasmussen, Vejle #364/R est:20000-30000 (D.KR 20000)

COL, Jan David and SCHOUTEN, Henry (19th C) Belgian

£2533	$4585	€3800	Bergerie avec berger et moutons (65x55cm-26x22in) s. 30-Mar-4 Campo & Campo, Antwerp #48/R est:5000-7000
£4545	$7727	€6500	Berger a la pipe dans un etable (62x57cm-24x22in) 1-Dec-3 Amberes, Antwerp #347

COLA, Pietro (attrib) (19th C) Italian

£2400	$4416	€3504	Neapolitan beauty (35x27cm-14x11in) indis.mono. board oval. 25-Mar-4 Christie's, Kensington #135/R est:1500-2000

COLACICCHI, Giovanni (1900-1993) Italian

£800	$1472	€1200	Giudecca, Venice (30x40cm-12x16in) s. s.i.d.1972 verso canvas on cardboard. 11-Jun-4 Farsetti, Prato #419/R
£3401	$6088	€5000	LOt's wife (63x50cm-25x20in) s. i.verso board painted 1933. 22-Mar-4 Sant Agostino, Torino #525/R est:5000-7000
£5282	$9137	€7500	Still life with shells (43x65cm-17x26in) s. board. 9-Dec-3 Pandolfini, Florence #394/R est:7500-8500

COLACICCO, Salvatore (1935-) British/Italian

£650	$1164	€949	British man-o-war and other vessels at the entrance to Portsmouth Harbour (53x76cm-21x30in) s. panel. 26-May-4 Christie's, Kensington #747/R
£680	$1244	€993	Ships at anchor off Malta (51x76cm-20x30in) s. 7-Apr-4 Bonhams, Bury St Edmunds #473

COLAGROSSI, Angelo (1960-) Italian

£667	$1200	€1000	Together - separate (40x50cm-16x20in) s. 22-Apr-4 Finarte Semenzato, Rome #144/R

COLANTONI, Domenico (?) South American

£588	$1000	€858	Portrait of fruit (200x150cm-79x59in) s.d.1985. 25-Nov-3 Galeria y Remates, Montevideo #205/R

COLARES, Raymundo (1944-1986) Brazilian?

Works on paper

£3388	$5997	€5082	Abstract (36x36cm-14x14in) s.d.1971 i.verso collage. 27-Apr-4 Bolsa de Arte, Rio de Janeiro #131/R (B.R 18500)
£4396	$8044	€6594	Abstract (43x43cm-17x17in) s.i.d.1970 collage. 6-Jul-4 Bolsa de Arte, Rio de Janeiro #95/R (B.R 24000)

COLAS, Pierre le (1930-) French
£302 $559 €450 L'arbre aux licornes (25x70cm-10x28in) s. 15-Mar-4 Blanchet, Paris #154

COLBRON, Paul (1902-1952) American
£1059 $1800 €1546 Grand Tetons from Aspen Ranch Jackson Hole, Wyo (25x36cm-10x14in) i.d.1938 verso masonite prov. 18-Nov-3 John Moran, Pasadena #23 est:2000-3000

COLBURN, Francis Peabody (1909-) American
£419 $750 €612 Untitled Vermont landscape (53x84cm-21x33in) s.d.1956. 21-Mar-4 Hindman, Chicago #843/R

COLCHESTER-WEMYSS, Sir Francis (20th C) British
Works on paper
£250 $418 €363 Montego Bay, Jamaica (19x47cm-7x19in) s.d.1936 pencil W/C htd white. 26-Jun-3 Mellors & Kirk, Nottingham #819

COLDSTREAM, Sir William (1908-1987) British
£7500 $13725 €10950 Flowers in a vase (46x35cm-18x14in) s. 4-Jun-4 Christie's, London #16/R est:5000-8000

COLE, Alphaeus P (1876-?) American
£1257 $2250 €1835 Portrait of a woman. Portrait of Eugene Higgins (91x71cm-36x28in) one s.d.1920 one s.d.1954 pair. 26-May-4 Doyle, New York #87/R est:4000-6000

COLE, Chisolm (?-c.1902) British
£320 $544 €467 Autumn evening (36x46cm-14x18in) s. 4-Nov-3 Dreweatt Neate, Newbury #117/R

COLE, Donald (1930-) American
£333 $600 €486 Cock-a-doodle-do (60x43cm-24x17in) s.i.d.1980 verso acrylic. 24-Apr-4 David Rago, Lambertville #89/R

COLE, Edwin (1868-?) British
£231 $400 €337 English cottage in a landscape with roadway (30x41cm-12x16in) s. 10-Dec-3 Boos Gallery, Michigan #524
£231 $400 €337 Landscape with English cottage, roadway and stream (30x41cm-12x16in) s. 10-Dec-3 Boos Gallery, Michigan #525

COLE, Fred (20th C) American
£1198 $2000 €1749 Man fitted for new suit (66x56cm-26x22in) s. lit. 15-Nov-3 Illustration House, New York #91/R est:3000-5000

COLE, George (1810-1883) British
£800 $1440 €1168 Highland landscape with figures amongst rocks near a loch (50x75cm-20x30in) s. 21-Apr-4 Rupert Toovey, Partridge Green #105/R
£1451 $2424 €2118 Landscape with shepherd (62x51cm-24x20in) s. 25-Oct-3 Rasmussen, Havnen #2175 est:2000-3000 (D.KR 15500)
£2600 $4134 €3796 The dying of the day, a windmill on hillside, shepherd in valley (41x61cm-16x24in) s. 1-May-3 John Nicholson, Haslemere #738/R est:3000-4000
£2800 $4844 €4088 Rural scene with figures, a horse, dog, with river and cottage (51x74cm-20x29in) s.d.1856. 11-Dec-3 Mitchells, Cockermouth #960/R est:2000-3000
£3600 $6120 €5256 Fittleworth mill (61x91cm-24x36in) s.d.1881. 19-Nov-3 Bonhams, New Bond Street #46/R est:4000-6000
£8000 $13600 €11680 Returning from the fields (61x91cm-24x36in) s.d.1883. 25-Nov-3 Christie's, London #141/R est:8000-12000

COLE, George (attrib) (1810 1883) British
£600 $1074 €876 Loch Katrine (37x52cm-15x20in) board prov. 27-May-4 Christie's, Kensington #215/R
£1448 $2592 €2114 Sunshine after rain, Cosham, Hants. (61x107cm-24x42in) s. possibly by George Vicat Cole. 10-May-4 Rasmussen, Vejle #479/R est:20000 (D.KR 16000)

COLE, George Vicat (1833-1893) British
£450 $716 €657 Near Bradfield - Walhampton School, Lymington (30x50cm-12x20in) indis sig. 18-Mar-3 Anderson & Garland, Newcastle #542/R
£1600 $2928 €2336 Near Dorking, Surrey. River landscape with figures seated on a bank (29x39cm-11x15in) mono.d.1876 pair. 28-Jul-4 Hampton & Littlewood, Exeter #645 est:1500-2000
£1800 $3006 €2628 On the Arun (51x77cm-20x30in) mono.d.1889. 13-Nov-3 Christie's, Kensington #104/R est:2000-4000
£35000 $64400 €51100 Summer showers (124x183cm-49x72in) mono.d.1877 exhib.lit. 26-Mar-4 Sotheby's, London #60/R est:35000-50000
Works on paper
£300 $510 €438 Thames scenes with swans on river in foreground (30x60cm-12x24in) mono. W/C htd white. 31-Oct-3 Moore Allen & Innocent, Cirencester #520/R
£400 $740 €584 Study of a tree (22x14cm-9x6in) mono. W/C. 9-Mar-4 Bonhams, Knightsbridge #61/R
£400 $744 €584 Cattle in river valley (18x22cm-7x9in) mono. W/C. 2-Mar-4 Bearnes, Exeter #343/R
£580 $1056 €847 River landscape (46x74cm-18x29in) mono.d.88 W/C. 15-Jun-4 David Lay, Penzance #653
£820 $1296 €1189 Young lady with a bun (13x18cm-5x7in) chk wash. 3-Sep-3 Bonhams, Bury St Edmunds #345/R

COLE, George Vicat (attrib) (1833-1893) British
£927 $1706 €1353 Near Haslemere, Surrey (41x61cm-16x24in) bears sig. 14-Jun-4 Waddingtons, Toronto #125/R est:1500-2000 (C.D 2300)

COLE, Jack (1914-1958) American
Works on paper
£2857 $5000 €4171 No thanks, just looking (37x31cm-15x12in) s. artist st.verso ink wash exec July 1954 exhib. 17-Dec-3 Christie's, Rockefeller NY #42/R est:5000-7000
£2857 $5000 €4171 Your Wife, and all the while I though it was TV (48x38cm-19x15in) s. W/C illus board exec Aug 1957 exhib. 17-Dec-3 Christie's, Rockefeller NY #44/R est:5000-7000
£4571 $8000 €6674 Man pulling down woman's dress (43x32cm-17x13in) bears init.verso mat pastel W/C illus board exec 1955 exhib. 17-Dec-3 Christie's, Rockefeller NY #29/R est:5000-7000

COLE, John (1903-1975) British
£2600 $4238 €3770 Sothebys, Bond Street (28x37cm-11x15in) s. board. 23-Sep-3 Bonhams, Leeds #119/R est:2500-3500

COLE, Joseph Foxcroft (1837-1892) American
£2690 $4250 €3927 Farm pond (46x69cm-18x27in) s.d.1873. 7-Sep-3 Treadway Gallery, Cincinnati #535/R est:3000-5000

COLE, Joseph Greenleaf (attrib) (1803-1858) American
£694 $1200 €1013 Portrait of woman wearing black dress with white collar seated in red chair (91x71cm-36x28in) i.verso. 10-Dec-3 Alderfer's, Hatfield #281/R est:700-900

COLE, Peter D (1947-) Australian
Sculpture
£3158 $5084 €4611 Modern dilemma (203cm-80in) s.i. base mixed media construction prov. 25-Aug-3 Sotheby's, Paddington #308/R est:1200-1800 (A.D 7800)
Works on paper
£1074 $1826 €1568 Studio - sound of the anvil (123x80cm-48x31in) s.d.93 pastel prov. 29-Oct-3 Lawson Menzies, Sydney #4/R est:1200-1800 (A.D 2600)

COLE, Philip William (1884-1964) British
£280 $468 €409 View of Hastings, East Sussex (51x61cm-20x24in) s.d.45. 16-Oct-3 Christie's, Kensington #403/R

COLE, R R (19th C) British
£2700 $5022 €3942 Stalking in the highlands (171x42cm-67x17in) s. 2-Mar-4 Bearnes, Exeter #403/R est:600-900

COLE, Rex Vicat (1870-1940) British
£600 $1110 €876 Entrance to St. Mary at Hill, Love Lane, London (28x25cm-11x10in) s. i.verso board. 15-Jan-4 Christie's, Kensington #909/R
£780 $1240 €1139 Blossom trees (49x58cm-19x23in) s.d.1918. 10-Sep-3 Sotheby's, Olympia #174/R
£1300 $2171 €1898 Lambeth Palace from across the Thames (31x41cm-12x16in) s. panel. 7-Oct-3 Bonhams, Knightsbridge #77/R est:800-1200
£1800 $3330 €2628 Young girl in a bluebell wood (70x94cm-28x37in) s.d.1918. 13-Jan-4 Bonhams, Knightsbridge #259b/R est:2000-3000
Works on paper
£1000 $1820 €1460 Cromer from the cliffs (27x43cm-11x17in) W/C htd white. 1-Jul-4 Christie's, Kensington #140/R est:1000-1500

COLE, Thomas (1801-1848) American
£116279 $200000 €169767 Hunters in landscape (72x90cm-28x35in) s. prov. 4-Dec-3 Christie's, Rockefeller NY #23/R
£755814 $1300000 €1103488 Catskillmountain house (38x59cm-15x23in) init. prov.exhib.lit. 4-Dec-3 Christie's, Rockefeller NY #14/R
Works on paper
£1796 $3250 €2622 Roman aquaduct (23x30cm-9x12in) W/C. 16-Apr-4 Du Mouchelle, Detroit #2128/R est:1500-2500

COLE, Thomas C (1888-1976) American
£279 $500 €407 Sailing along coast (38x51cm-15x20in) s. canvas on board. 8-Jan-4 James Julia, Fairfield #1051/R

COLELLA, Franco (1900-?) Italian
£442 $791 €650 Seascape with figures (19x50cm-7x20in) s. board. 22-Mar-4 Sant Agostino, Torino #44/R
£476 $852 €700 Landscape in Puglia (20x49cm-8x19in) s. board. 22-Mar-4 Sant Agostino, Torino #45/R
£544 $974 €800 Seascape in Puglia (40x60cm-16x24in) s. board. 22-Mar-4 Sant Agostino, Torino #46/R
£922 $1540 €1300 Seaside (25x40cm-10x16in) s. board. 20-Oct-3 Sant Agostino, Torino #167/R
£993 $1658 €1400 Still life with figs (40x60cm-16x24in) s. board. 20-Oct-3 Sant Agostino, Torino #156/R
£1418 $2369 €2000 Waiting whilst fishing (24x54cm-9x21in) s. board. 20-Oct-3 Sant Agostino, Torino #168/R est:800-1000

COLEMAN, C (?-1874) British
£1300 $2353 €1898 Cattle in the Roman Capana (38x53cm-15x21in) s.i. painted 1875. 17-Apr-4 Dickins, Middle Claydon #17

COLEMAN, Carlo (20th C) Italian
£8152 $15000 €11902 Late afternoon, herding the buffalo on the Mediterranean coast (99x138cm-39x54in) s. i.verso. 8-Jun-4 Auctions by the Bay, Alameda #1004/R

COLEMAN, Charles Caryl (1840-1928) American
£1553 $2500 €2252 Sailboats in Venice (10x20cm-4x8in) panel. 17-Aug-3 Jeffery Burchard, Florida #20

£2500 $4500 €3650 Summer afternoon (30x25cm-12x10in) mono.d.1861. 24-Apr-4 Weschler, Washington #602/R est:5000-7000
£18605 $32000 €27163 Still life with pineapple and grapes (79x89cm-31x35in) mono. prov. oval. 4-Dec-3 Christie's, Rockefeller NY #5/R
£34884 $60000 €50931 My studio window, Island of Capri (53x80cm-21x31in) mono. prov.exhib. 3-Dec-3 Sotheby's, New York #120/R est:75000-100000

COLEMAN, Eamon (20th C) Irish?
£1200 $2172 €1800 The Gods Light Fireworks, Mount Etna (40x50cm-16x20in) s. 31-Mar-4 James Adam, Dublin #94/R est:1800-2200

COLEMAN, Edward (?-1867) British
£700 $1253 €1022 Catch of freshwater fish (59x69cm-23x27in) s.i.verso. 11-May-4 Bonhams, Knightsbridge #244/R

COLEMAN, Edward Thomas (attrib) (fl.1839-1877) British
£5634 $9746 €8000 Lugano Lake (66x116cm-26x46in) prov. 10-Dec-3 Sotheby's, Milan #30/R est:8000-12000

COLEMAN, Enrico (1846-1911) Italian
£533 $981 €800 River and bridge (17x23cm-7x9in) s. board. 10-Jun-4 Christie's, Rome #110
Works on paper
£769 $1285 €1100 Landscape near Arsoli (17x23cm-7x9in) s.d.1906 pastel. 24-Jun-3 Finarte Semenzato, Rome #65/R
£1972 $3411 €2800 Landscape in Abruzzo (20x30cm-8x12in) s. W/C. 10-Dec-3 Finarte Semenzato, Rome #179/R est:2000-2500
£2400 $4416 €3504 Young bullocks carting the hay (35x55cm-14x22in) s.i. W/C. 8-Jun-4 Bonhams, New Bond Street #16/R est:1400-1800
£6500 $12025 €9490 Wild horses watering at a stream (41x69cm-16x27in) s.i. W/C. 13-Feb-4 Keys, Aylsham #531/R est:5000-8000
£6696 $11183 €9776 Men on horseback (33x51cm-13x20in) s. W/C. 17-Jun-3 Maynards, Vancouver #306 est:3000-4000 (C.D 15000)
£11000 $18700 €16060 Lassoing the wild horses (45x65cm-18x26in) s.i. W/C. 4-Nov-3 Bonhams, New Bond Street #10/R est:5000-8000

COLEMAN, Francesco (1851-1918) Italian
£4469 $8000 €6525 Court scene (64x94cm-25x37in) s. 8-May-4 Susanin's, Chicago #6022/R est:8000-10000
Works on paper
£1200 $2184 €1752 An unwanted intrusion (54x38cm-21x15in) s.i.d.1880 pencil W/C. 1-Jul-4 Christie's, Kensington #423/R est:1200-1800
£1341 $2400 €1958 Wait (53x74cm-21x29in) s.i. W/C. 14-May-4 Skinner, Boston #51/R est:800-1200
£2465 $4092 €3500 Pastore nella campagna Romana (55x40cm-22x16in) s. W/C cardboard. 11-Jun-3 Christie's, Rome #90/R est:3800-4500

COLEMAN, Henry (19/20th C) British
Works on paper
£16000 $27200 €23360 Scenes in the Roman Campagna of landscapes and Roman ruins. W/C album painted with Charles Poignedstre and other artist. 27-Nov-3 Sotheby's, London #352/R est:3000-4000

COLEMAN, Loring W (20th C) American
Works on paper
£276 $500 €403 Working harbour low tide (61x86cm-24x34in) W/C. 16-Apr-4 American Auctioneer #68a/R

COLEMAN, Mary Dartes (1894-?) American
£269 $450 €393 Landscape (30x41cm-12x16in) board. 18-Oct-3 David Dike, Dallas #322/R

COLEMAN, Michael (1946-) American
£276 $500 €403 Old tree (51x41cm-20x16in) masonite. 16-Apr-4 American Auctioneer #69/R
£1445 $2500 €2110 Isis Temple from Mather point, South Rim, Grand Canyon (76x61cm-30x24in) s.i.d.1985 verso prov. 10-Dec-3 Bonhams & Butterfields, San Francisco #6126/R est:3000-5000
£2717 $5000 €3967 Hunter's camp, Wasatch Mountains, Squaw Peak (45x60cm-18x24in) s.i.d.1972 masonite. 8-Jun-4 Bonhams & Butterfields, San Francisco #4152/R est:3000-5000
£6952 $13000 €10150 Back in camp - warming up (58x76cm-23x30in) s. board. 24-Jul-4 Coeur d'Alene, Hayden #16/R est:10000-15000
£10000 $17000 €14600 Rocky mountain goat, Ospika River (51x76cm-20x30in) board. 1-Nov-3 Altermann Galleries, Santa Fe #165
£10695 $20000 €15615 Rocky mountain majesty (61x91cm-24x36in) s. board. 24-Jul-4 Coeur d'Alene, Hayden #177/R est:15000-25000
£17380 $32500 €25375 Grizzlies at rock Creek (61x76cm-24x30in) s. board prov. 24-Jul-4 Coeur d'Alene, Hayden #194/R est:10000-15000
£24064 $45000 €35133 Under eagle's wings (86x122cm-34x48in) s. board prov. 24-Jul-4 Coeur d'Alene, Hayden #167/R est:30000-50000
Works on paper
£3824 $6500 €5583 Geyser basin (23x41cm-9x16in) gouache. 1-Nov-3 Altermann Galleries, Santa Fe #163
£4545 $8500 €6636 Winter hunter (28x38cm-11x15in) s. gouache. 24-Jul-4 Coeur d'Alene, Hayden #15/R est:6000-9000
£10160 $19000 €14834 Yellowstone Park (56x97cm-22x38in) s. gouache prov. 24-Jul-4 Coeur d'Alene, Hayden #33/R est:15000-25000

COLEMAN, Nicholas (1978-) American
£3352 $6000 €4894 Return from the hunt (51x76cm-20x30in) board. 15-May-4 Altermann Galleries, Santa Fe #104/R
£3911 $7000 €5710 Cold night (76x61cm-30x24in) board. 15-May-4 Altermann Galleries, Santa Fe #103/R
£4118 $7000 €6012 Camp at dusk (51x76cm-20x30in) masonite. 1-Nov-3 Altermann Galleries, Santa Fe #126

COLEMAN, Ralph Pallen (1892-1968) American
£419 $700 €612 Rainstorm over Mt Tokuhnivatz, Utah (46x36cm-18x14in) s.i. i.verso board. 20-Jun-3 Freeman, Philadelphia #251/R
£1229 $2200 €1794 English air raid shelter scene (89x76cm-35x30in) s. 15-May-4 Illustration House, New York #115/R est:2500-4000

COLEMAN, Seamus (20th C) Irish?
£403 $721 €600 Ladies day at the Galway Races (35x45cm-14x18in) s. 31-May-4 Hamilton Osborne King, Dublin #115/R

COLEMAN, Trevor (1936-) South African
£248 $443 €362 Figures seated on a bench (120x180cm-47x71in) s.d.84. 31-May-4 Stephan Welz, Johannesburg #341 (SA.R 3000)

COLEMAN, W S (1829-1904) British
Works on paper
£1850 $3330 €2701 Mother and children standing and seated beside logs near a cottage (17x32cm-7x13in) s. W/C. 21-Apr-4 Rupert Toovey, Partridge Green #201/R est:600-1000

COLEMAN, William (1922-1993) Australian
£313 $584 €470 Father and daughter (29x39cm-11x15in) s. canvasboard. 21-Jul-4 Goodman, Sydney #216 (A.D 800)
£414 $646 €600 Landscape with car (32x39cm-13x15in) s. board. 1-Aug-2 Joel, Victoria #298 est:1000-1500 (A.D 1200)
£453 $819 €661 Accordionist. board. 1-Apr-4 Joel, Victoria #74 (A.D 1100)
£486 $890 €729 Express. board. 3-Jun-4 Joel, Victoria #175/R (A.D 1250)
£607 $978 €886 Still life with jug (30x37cm-12x15in) s. card. 25-Aug-3 Sotheby's, Paddington #342 (A.D 1500)
£611 $1111 €892 Seated nude with vase (24x16cm-9x6in) s. canvas on board. 16-Jun-4 Deutscher-Menzies, Melbourne #572/R est:600-900 (A.D 1600)
£676 $1095 €987 Still life with bottles, jugs and fruit (28x31cm-11x12in) s. card. 30-Jul-3 Goodman, Sydney #5/R (A.D 1650)
£700 $1266 €1022 Girl in an armchair. board. 1-Apr-4 Joel, Victoria #17p (A.D 1700)
£700 $1266 €1022 Jazz trumpeter. board. 1-Apr-4 Joel, Victoria #103 (A.D 1700)
£813 $1455 €1187 Bridge (29x39cm-11x15in) s. canvasboard. 10-May-4 Joel, Victoria #195 est:1200-1800 (A.D 2000)
£813 $1455 €1187 Girl in red dress (47x14cm-19x6in) s. board. 10-May-4 Joel, Victoria #424 est:1500-2000 (A.D 2000)
£840 $1528 €1226 Girls (26x30cm-10x12in) s. board. 16-Jun-4 Deutscher-Menzies, Melbourne #403/R est:2000-3000 (A.D 2200)
£840 $1445 €1226 Fortune teller. board. 7-Dec-3 Joel, Victoria #129/R (A.D 2000)
£894 $1601 €1305 Morning gossip (29x39cm-11x15in) s. board. 10-May-4 Joel, Victoria #244 est:1000-1500 (A.D 2200)
£894 $1601 €1305 Seated nude (66x42cm-26x17in) s. board. 10-May-4 Joel, Victoria #338 est:2500-3500 (A.D 2200)
£1012 $1630 €1478 Guitarist (59x44cm-23x17in) s. board. 13-Oct-3 Joel, Victoria #271 est:1200-1500 (A.D 2500)
£1220 $2183 €1781 City (34x42cm-13x17in) s. board. 10-May-4 Joel, Victoria #352 est:2000-3000 (A.D 3000)
£1240 $2293 €1810 Still life with teapot (32x38cm-13x15in) s. oil on card. 10-Mar-4 Deutscher-Menzies, Melbourne #272/R est:3000-5000 (A.D 3000)
£1298 $2362 €1895 Girl reading (40x30cm-16x12in) s. canvas on board. 16-Jun-4 Deutscher-Menzies, Melbourne #315/R est:2500-3500 (A.D 3400)
£1377 $2216 €2010 Lane (60x44cm-24x17in) s. canvasboard. 13-Oct-3 Joel, Victoria #338/R est:2000-3000 (A.D 3400)
£1465 $2286 €2124 Nude on a couch (44x59cm-17x23in) s. board. 1-Aug-2 Joel, Victoria #255 est:2000-3000 (A.D 4250)
£1524 $2729 €2225 Pink nude (50x40cm-20x16in) s. board. 10-May-4 Joel, Victoria #391 est:2000-3000 (A.D 3750)
£1557 $2460 €2273 Street scene (45x61cm-18x24in) s. canvas on board. 2-Sep-3 Deutscher-Menzies, Melbourne #299/R est:1500-2000 (A.D 3800)
£1557 $2460 €2273 At the gallery (56x36cm-22x14in) s. canvas on board. 2-Sep-3 Deutscher-Menzies, Melbourne #300/R est:2500-3500 (A.D 3800)
£1617 $2749 €2361 Seated nude (50x40cm-20x16in) s. board. 26-Nov-3 Deutscher-Menzies, Melbourne #236/R est:3000-4000 (A.D 3800)
£1803 $2849 €2632 Saying goodnight (45x56cm-18x22in) s. canvas on board. 2-Sep-3 Deutscher-Menzies, Melbourne #275/R est:3000-5000 (A.D 4400)
£1822 $2933 €2660 Old church (58x72cm-23x28in) s. board. 13-Oct-3 Joel, Victoria #245/R est:2000-2500 (A.D 4500)
£2099 $3821 €3065 Reclining nude (61x86cm-24x34in) s. canvas on board. 16-Jun-4 Deutscher-Menzies, Melbourne #293/R est:6000-9000 (A.D 5500)
£2642 $4729 €3857 Family (45x60cm-18x24in) s. canvas on board. 10-May-4 Joel, Victoria #359 est:3000-4000 (A.D 6500)
£2642 $4729 €3857 Feeding the birds (90x120cm-35x47in) s.d.89. 10-May-4 Joel, Victoria #366/R est:4000-5000 (A.D 6500)
£2660 $4521 €3884 Fruitstall in Fitzroy (85x59cm-33x23in) s. i.d.68 verso canvas on board. 26-Nov-3 Deutscher-Menzies, Melbourne #132/R est:5000-7000 (A.D 6250)
£6098 $10915 €8903 Fish and Chip shop (89x120cm-35x47in) s. board. 10-May-4 Joel, Victoria #383/R est:6000-8000 (A.D 15000)
Works on paper
£972 $1564 €1419 Port (45x60cm-18x24in) s. pastel. 13-Oct-3 Joel, Victoria #359 est:1000-1500 (A.D 2400)

COLEMAN, William (attrib) (1922-1993) Australian
£276 $430 €400 Two figures (30x40cm-12x16in) board. 1-Aug-2 Joel, Victoria #155a (A.D 800)

COLEMAN, William Stephen (1829-1904) British
£3527 $5890 €5291 Lone figure (88x120cm-35x47in) s.d.72. 27-Oct-3 Goodman, Sydney #162/R est:4000-6000 (A.D 8500)
£6846 $11434 €10269 Seated couple (90x60cm-35x24in) s.d.74 board. 27-Oct-3 Goodman, Sydney #192/R est:5000-7000 (A.D 16500)

£8500 $14450 €12410 Fair musician (73x52cm-29x20in) s. 19-Nov-3 Bonhams, New Bond Street #117/R est:6000-8000

COLEMAN, William Stephen (attrib) (1829-1904) British
Works on paper
£820 $1361 €1197 Picking wild flowers (16x24cm-6x9in) bears mono. W/C. 1-Oct-3 Sotheby's, Olympia #95/R
£2600 $4680 €3796 Riverside landscape with a man and woman pulling a woman and child in boat (17x34cm-7x13in) W/C. 21-Apr-4 Rupert Toovey, Partridge Green #200/R est:400-600

COLEMAN, Yvonne (20th C) New Zealander
£290 $493 €423 Along Devon Street (60x59cm-24x23in) s.i.d.1990 board. 4-Nov-3 Peter Webb, Auckland #44 (NZ.D 800)

COLERIDGE, Frederick G (fl.1866-1914) British
Works on paper
£4200 $7140 €6132 On the Thames, said to be near Henley (24x36cm-9x14in) s. W/C. 26-Nov-3 Hamptons Fine Art, Godalming #79/R est:700-1000

COLESCOTT, Robert (1925-) American
£13174 $22000 €19234 The Triumph of Christianity (228x289cm-90x114in) s.d.93 acrylic prov.exhib. 12-Nov-3 Christie's, Rockefeller NY #641/R est:15000-20000

COLETTI, Basilio (1863-?) Italian
£1192 $2170 €1800 Fishermen's children on the beach (16x26cm-6x10in) s.d.1892. 21-Jun-4 Dorotheum, Vienna #201/R est:1800-2400

COLEY, John (1935-) New Zealander
£489 $778 €714 Street scene (59x74cm-23x29in) s.d.75 acrylic. 9-Sep-3 Watson's, Christchurch #85 (NZ.D 1350)

COLFS, Pieter (1906-1983) Belgian
£1333 $2453 €2000 The athlete (111x83cm-44x33in) s.d.36. 9-Jun-4 Christie's, Amsterdam #90/R est:2000-3000

COLIN, Alexandre Marie (1798-1873) French
£1379 $2303 €2000 Les enfants russes en patineurs (40x32cm-16x13in) s. 14-Nov-3 Drouot Estimations, Paris #39 est:2000-2200
£1379 $2303 €2000 Les enfants dansant en costume espagnol (40x32cm-16x13in) s. 14-Nov-3 Drouot Estimations, Paris #38 est:2000-2200
Works on paper
£320 $592 €480 Village en bord de mer (14x22cm-6x9in) s. W/C. 14-Jul-4 Livinec, Gaudcheau & Jezequel, Rennes #95
£350 $655 €511 Mother and child on a path beside a rocky ravine (27x21cm-11x8in) s.d.1830 pencil W/C prov. 22-Jul-4 Tennants, Leyburn #708
£867 $1569 €1300 Faust et Marguerite (28x22cm-11x9in) st.mono. W/C varnish exhib. 30-Mar-4 Rossini, Paris #249/R
£3800 $7030 €5548 Richard Parkes Bonington asleep (8x13cm-3x5in) bears init.i. W/C pencil prov.lit. 9-Mar-4 Bonhams, New Bond Street #26/R est:800-1200

COLIN, Alexandre Marie (attrib) (1798-1873) French
Works on paper
£5986 $10356 €8500 Portrait of a young man (36x25cm-14x10in) blk crayon stumping. 10-Dec-3 Piasa, Paris #123b est:1000

COLIN, Gustave (1828-1910) French
£733 $1327 €1100 Femme du pays basque (48x38cm-19x15in) s. exhib. 30-Mar-4 Rossini, Paris #929
£909 $1627 €1327 Village street with figures (46x37cm-18x15in) s. 22-Mar-4 Philippe Schuler, Zurich #4395/R (S.FR 2100)
£1333 $2413 €2000 Paysage montagneux (65x54cm-26x21in) s. 30-Mar-4 Rossini, Paris #928 est:1800-2500
£1377 $2258 €1900 Maison dans le pays basque (26x41cm-10x16in) s. panel prov. 11-May-3 Osenat, Fontainebleau #203 est:2200-2500
£1467 $2684 €2200 Pont des Pecheurs (38x55cm-15x22in) s. panel. 6-Jun-4 Osenat, Fontainebleau #64/R est:2000-2200
£1812 $2971 €2500 Deux marins basques (37x46cm-15x18in) s.d.1909 verso panel prov. 11-May-3 Osenat, Fontainebleau #169 est:3000-3200
£6000 $11040 €9000 Entree du port (82x104cm-32x41in) s.i.d.1899 prov. 11-Jun-4 Pierre Berge, Paris #247/R est:4000-6000
£11111 $20000 €16222 Summer afternoon in a French village (75x96cm-30x38in) s.d.76. 21-Jan-4 Sotheby's, New York #196/R est:5000-7000
£21477 $38014 €32000 Corrida (73x92cm-29x36in) s.i. 30-Apr-4 Tajan, Paris #159/R est:5000-8000

COLIN, Jean (1881-1961) Belgian
£347 $566 €500 Nature morte aux pommes. s. 23-Sep-3 Galerie Moderne, Brussels #749/R
£556 $906 €800 Roses (60x50cm-24x20in) s. 23-Sep-3 Galerie Moderne, Brussels #731/R
£559 $951 €800 Still life with flowers (96x70cm-38x28in) s. lit. 28-Nov-3 Schloss Ahlden, Ahlden #722/R
£594 $1022 €850 Vase fleuri de roses (66x81cm-26x32in) s. 8-Dec-3 Horta, Bruxelles #479
£828 $1531 €1200 Composition au homard et aux legumes (75x92cm-30x36in) s. 16-Feb-4 Horta, Bruxelles #72

COLIN, Paul (1892-1985) French
£268 $494 €400 Roses, tulipes et lilas (73x92cm-29x36in) s. panel. 24-Mar-4 Joron-Derem, Paris #83
Prints
£10000 $15900 €14600 Tumulte noir (47x32cm-19x13in) pochoir lit. 9-Sep-3 Sotheby's, Olympia #306/R est:5000-7000
Works on paper
£420 $713 €600 Le cafe (30x21cm-12x8in) s. gouache chl. 27-Nov-3 Millon & Associes, Paris #58
£437 $755 €620 Etude de deux danseuses pour la Revue Negre (41x21cm-16x8in) s.d.1925 chl. 13-Dec-3 Martinot & Savignat, Pontoise #14
£444 $768 €630 Etude de deux danseurs pour la revue Negre (29x21cm-11x8in) s.d.1925 chl sanguine. 13-Dec-3 Martinot & Savignat, Pontoise #13/R
£451 $780 €640 Etude de deux danseurs pour la Revue Negre (41x20cm-16x8in) s. chl. 13-Dec-3 Martinot & Savignat, Pontoise #15
£451 $780 €640 Etude de silhouette de danseur (39x20cm-15x8in) s. 13-Dec-3 Martinot & Savignat, Pontoise #16
£2098 $3566 €3000 Anita Lueza (158x117cm-62x46in) s. gouache chl. 28-Nov-3 Drouot Estimations, Paris #185 est:600-800
£3357 $5773 €4800 Le clown jongleur (35x23cm-14x9in) s. W/C gouache. 5-Dec-3 Chochon-Barre & Allardi, Paris #27/R est:1600-1800

COLIN, Paul Alfred (1838-1916) French
£738 $1358 €1100 Paysage champetre (74x54cm-29x21in) s. 26-Mar-4 Neret-Minet, Paris #10

COLIN-LEFRANQ, Helene (20th C) French
£1250 $2000 €1825 Still life (38x46cm-15x18in) s. 20-Sep-3 Sloans & Kenyon, Bethesda #1163/R est:1500-1750

COLIN-LIBOUR, Uranie (1833-?) French
£1348 $2507 €1968 Girl with her small baby brother (87x72cm-34x28in) s. 2-Mar-4 Rasmussen, Copenhagen #1577/R est:15000 (D.KR 15000)

COLINET, Claire Jeanne Roberte (fl.1913-1945) French
Sculpture
£949 $1500 €1386 L'acte balance (18cm-7in) s. gilt bronze onyx plateau. 6-Apr-3 William Jenack, New York #84 est:1500-2000
£2200 $3740 €3212 Egyptian dancer (28cm-11in) i. gilt bronze onyx pedestal. 25-Nov-3 Sotheby's, Olympia #140/R est:1000-1500
£6434 $10937 €9200 Danseuse (54x61cm-21x24in) s. pat bronze marble base. 21-Nov-3 Lombrail & Teucquam, Paris #77/R est:3000-3500

COLKETT, Samuel David (1806-1863) British
£450 $752 €657 Figures on a wooded track with a church tower beyond (23x18cm-9x7in) panel on panel. 13-Nov-3 Christie's, Kensington #116/R
£1700 $3043 €2482 Figures on a wooded track, cottage beyond (29x38cm-11x15in) panel. 27-May-4 Christie's, Kensington #133/R est:1200-1800

COLKETT, Samuel David (attrib) (1806-1863) British
£1100 $2002 €1606 Country landscape with figures and cattle before a cottage (25x31cm-10x12in) 3-Feb-4 Sworder & Son, Bishops Stortford #274/R est:700-900
£1500 $2700 €2190 Wooded landscape (31x25cm-12x10in) panel. 21-Jan-4 Sotheby's, Olympia #314/R est:2000-3000
£1700 $2822 €2482 Gypsy encampment (61x101cm-24x40in) 1-Oct-3 Woolley & Wallis, Salisbury #200/R est:1500-2500

COLL JULIA, Gabriel (1915-) Spanish
£1049 $1752 €1500 Still life of fruit (51x66cm-20x26in) s. 30-Jun-3 Ansorena, Madrid #400/R

COLL, Joseph Clement (1881-1921) American
Works on paper
£428 $800 €625 Lillian Russell as Rosalinda in As You Like It (28x25cm-11x10in) pen ink exec.c.1910. 26-Feb-4 Illustration House, New York #43

COLLAERT, Adriaen (1560-1618) Flemish
Prints
£2867 $5131 €4300 Youngest court (42x29cm-17x11in) copperplate after Stradanus. 13-May-4 Bassenge, Berlin #5096/R est:400

COLLANTES, Francisco (1599-1656) Spanish
£120000 $219600 €175200 Rocky river landscape with fishermen and shepherds resting with their flock (107x143cm-42x56in) s. 7-Jul-4 Christie's, London #73/R est:60000-80000

COLLARD, Marie Anne Herminie (?-1871) French
£4558 $8159 €6700 Le bief du moulin (110x98cm-43x39in) s. 17-Mar-4 Hotel des Ventes Mosan, Brussels #100/R est:6000-8000

COLLART, Marie (1842-1911) Belgian
£439 $773 €650 Carriole sur le chemin (45x60cm-18x24in) s. 18-May-4 Galerie Moderne, Brussels #117

COLLAS, Louis Antoine (1775-?) French
Miniatures
£2717 $5000 €3967 Young matron (8x8cm-3x3in) s.d.1817 oval. 27-Mar-4 New Orleans Auction, New Orleans #1107/R est:2000-4000
£5500 $9900 €8030 Catharina Paulovna, Grand Duchess of Russia (7cm-3in) gilt metal mount oval exhib.lit. 22-Apr-4 Bonhams, New Bond Street #83/R est:2000-3000

COLLE, A M (19/20th C) French
£1100 $1727 €1595 Panorama de Chambery (60x108cm-24x43in) s.i.d.1911. 28-Aug-3 Christie's, Kensington #229/R est:800-1200

COLLE, Gino de (19/20th C) Italian
Works on paper
£1000 $1850 €1460 Ca' D'Oro. View from Grand Canal. Doorway between Doge's Palace and the Basilica, Venice (39x20cm-15x8in) W/C three. 11-Feb-4 Cheffins, Cambridge #382/R est:200-300

COLLE, Michel-Auguste (1872-1949) French
£2686 $4915 €3922 View towards a garden with iris (105x77cm-41x30in) s.d.1906. 9-Jun-4 Rasmussen, Copenhagen #1982/R est:30000 (D.KR 30000)

COLLEGE, Adrien (20th C) Belgian
£403 $745 €600 La basse-cour (50x75cm-20x30in) s. 15-Mar-4 Horta, Bruxelles #321

COLLEL, Jose (1912-) Spanish
£986 $1577 €1400 Composition (40x32cm-16x13in) s.d.1946 prov. 16-Sep-3 Segre, Madrid #253/R

COLLEN, Henry (1798-1872) British
Miniatures
£2100 $3780 €3066 Ottoman diplomat, in a scarlet cloak (8cm-3in) s.d.1826 gilt metal frame ormolu slip rec. exhib. 22-Apr-4 Bonhams, New Bond Street #162/R est:1500-2500

COLLES, Dorothy (1917-2003) British
£250 $448 €365 Portrait of a pretty young girl (41x30cm-16x12in) s. 5-May-4 John Nicholson, Haslemere #462

COLLEY, Andrew (19th C) British
£980 $1666 €1431 Barn interior with man standing next to a hay trough (76x101cm-30x40in) s. 18-Nov-3 Bonhams, Leeds #155

COLLIER, Alan Caswell (1911-1990) Canadian
£280 $512 €409 Ingonish harbour, Cape Breton (30x40cm-12x16in) s. board. 1-Jun-4 Joyner Waddington, Toronto #438 (C.D 700)
£284 $500 €415 Alberta sky, south of Longview (30x41cm-12x16in) s. board painted c.1970. 23-May-4 Treadway Gallery, Cincinnati #647/R
£313 $550 €457 Cooper Landing, Kenai River, Alaska (30x41cm-12x16in) s. board painted c.1970. 23-May-4 Treadway Gallery, Cincinnati #648/R
£320 $586 €467 Kamloops Lake on Thompson River (30x40cm-12x16in) s. board prov. 1-Jun-4 Joyner Waddington, Toronto #479 (C.D 800)
£360 $659 €526 Grande-Vallee, Gaspe (30x40cm-12x16in) s. s.i.verso board prov. 3-Jun-4 Heffel, Vancouver #21/R (C.D 900)
£361 $672 €527 White breast of the ice sheet (30x61cm-12x24in) s. masonite prov. 2-Mar-4 Ritchie, Toronto #126a/R (C.D 900)
£426 $750 €622 House by the sea, near Grand-Etang, Cape Breton (20x61cm-8x24in) s. i.verso masonite painted c.1970. 23-May-4 Treadway Gallery, Cincinnati #646/R
£537 $972 €784 Flying 5, lac la hache, Caribou, B.C (30x41cm-12x16in) s. s.i.verso oil paper board prov. 18-Apr-4 Levis, Calgary #21/R est:1000-1200 (C.D 1300)
£562 $1046 €821 Over Lake Oesa, above Lake O'Hara (41x51cm-16x20in) s. masonite. 2-Mar-4 Ritchie, Toronto #126/R est:1000-1500 (C.D 1400)
£640 $1171 €934 On Medonte Conc. Road 5, Simcoe Country, Ontario (30x40cm-12x16in) s. board prov. 1-Jun-4 Joyner Waddington, Toronto #421/R (C.D 1600)
£680 $1244 €993 From 25 side road at 1 Concession East, Mulmur TWP (30x40cm-12x16in) s. board prov. 1-Jun-4 Joyner Waddington, Toronto #489 (C.D 1700)
£800 $1464 €1168 Labrador Iceberg (45x60cm-18x24in) s. board prov. 1-Jun-4 Joyner Waddington, Toronto #234/R est:2000-2500 (C.D 2000)
£854 $1528 €1247 Kennedy Lake, Vancouver Island, BC (30x40cm-12x16in) s. s.i.verso board. 27-May-4 Heffel, Vancouver #93/R est:1200-1600 (C.D 2100)
£1200 $2196 €1752 Edge of the sea (75x100cm-30x39in) s. prov.exhib. 1-Jun-4 Joyner Waddington, Toronto #192/R est:3500-4500 (C.D 3000)
£1280 $2342 €1869 Autumn river, Madawaska river near Quadville, Ontario (75x125cm-30x49in) s. prov. 1-Jun-4 Joyner Waddington, Toronto #156/R est:4000-5000 (C.D 3200)
£1357 $2267 €1981 Sun shines hot into the trees (60x75cm-24x30in) s.i. 17-Nov-3 Hodgins, Calgary #404/R est:3500-4500 (C.D 3000)
£1403 $2343 €2048 North of Terrace, BC (50x75cm-20x30in) s.i. 17-Nov-3 Hodgins, Calgary #111/R est:2750-3250 (C.D 3100)
£1451 $2467 €2118 Lower Kananaskis Lake (41x51cm-16x20in) s. i.verso canvasboard prov. 6-Nov-3 Heffel, Vancouver #30/R est:1800-2200 (C.D 3250)

COLLIER, Evert (1640-1706) Dutch
£2550 $4718 €3800 Portrait of a lady standing, wearing a black dress with white collar and cuffs (81x66cm-32x26in) s.d.1669 prov.exhib. 15-Mar-4 Sotheby's, Amsterdam #35/R est:2000-3000
£13889 $25000 €20278 Vanitas still life (47x37cm-19x15in) s.d.1689. 22-Jan-4 Sotheby's, New York #270/R est:20000-30000

COLLIER, Evert (attrib) (1640-1706) Dutch
£3867 $6999 €5800 Vanite (33x32cm-13x13in) i. panel. 30-Mar-4 Millon & Associes, Paris #2/R est:4000-6000

COLLIER, H (?) ?
£1900 $3230 €2774 Charlie Smirke on Tulyar (40x51cm-16x20in) s. prov. 19-Nov-3 Sotheby's, Olympia #68/R est:400-600

COLLIER, John (1708-1786) British
£800 $1480 €1168 Dentist pulling a tooth (65x100cm-26x39in) i. 10-Feb-4 Bonhams, Knightsbridge #300/R
£2500 $4600 €3650 Caricature of an angry woman wielding a wooded spoon (70x48cm-28x19in) s.d.1762 canvas on board. 8-Jun-4 Holloways, Banbury #298/R est:400-600
£2639 $4750 €3853 Life's little moments (65x89cm-26x35in) set of 12. 21-Jan-4 Sotheby's, New York #146/R est:5000-7000

COLLIER, The Hon John (1850-1934) British
£1000 $1860 €1460 Spring wood (60x38cm-24x15in) s. canvas on board. 4-Mar-4 Christie's, Kensington #528/R est:800-1200
£4000 $6680 €5840 Portrait of Alice Crowder (234x140cm-92x55in) s.d.1900. 17-Oct-3 Keys, Aylsham #742/R est:8000
£75000 $127500 €109500 Priestess of Bacchus (147x112cm-58x44in) s. s.i.verso prov. 26-Nov-3 Christie's, London #27/R est:60000-100000

COLLIER, The Hon John (attrib) (1850-1934) British
£700 $1190 €1022 Portrait of Cecil Hugh Junes, MA Cambs (143x91cm-56x36in) 19-Nov-3 Tennants, Leyburn #1169
£1100 $1870 €1606 Portrait of Evan Davies Jones MA Cambs of Pentower Fishguard (142x91cm-56x36in) s.d.1918. 19-Nov-3 Tennants, Leyburn #1168 est:250-350

COLLIER, Thomas (1840-1891) British
Works on paper
£280 $476 €409 Rustic bridge near Bettws y Coed (12x17cm-5x7in) i.verso W/C. 29-Oct-3 Bonhams, Chester #418
£320 $544 €467 Extensive country landscape (23x33cm-9x13in) W/C. 29-Oct-3 Bonhams, Chester #417
£750 $1253 €1095 View of Glen Dochart, Perthshire (16x25cm-6x10in) s. pencil W/C prov. 16-Oct-3 Christie's, Kensington #131/R
£1600 $2960 €2336 Surrey common (58x88cm-23x35in) s. W/C. 9-Mar-4 Bonhams, New Bond Street #81/R est:800-1200

COLLIER, Thomas Frederick (fl.1848-1874) British
Works on paper
£420 $685 €613 Summer, a flower study (28x38cm-11x15in) s.d.1881 W/C. 23-Sep-3 Anderson & Garland, Newcastle #250/R
£460 $791 €672 Still life of pansies (18x28cm-7x11in) s. 2-Dec-3 Gorringes, Lewes #2491
£500 $860 €730 Still life of pansies (18x28cm-7x11in) s. W/C. 2-Dec-3 Gorringes, Lewes #2490/R
£580 $963 €847 Still life of white and pink rhododendrons on a table top (18x25cm-7x10in) s. W/C. 2-Oct-3 Neales, Nottingham #610/R
£850 $1590 €1241 Still life of plums, damsons and strawberries against a mossy bank (27x38cm-11x15in) s. pencil W/C. 22-Jul-4 Tennants, Leyburn #692
£860 $1591 €1256 Still life of apples and grapes. Still life of plums (27x38cm-11x15in) s.d.1875 W/C pair. 10-Mar-4 Sotheby's, Olympia #170/R est:800-1200

COLLIGNON, Georges (1923-2002) Belgian
£2800 $5124 €4200 Composition bleue (100x72cm-39x28in) s.d.66. 7-Jun-4 Palais de Beaux Arts, Brussels #353/R est:3500-4500
£3249 $6076 €4744 Composition (54x81cm-21x32in) s. i.d.Janvier 57 verso prov. 25-Feb-4 Kunsthallen, Copenhagen #100/R est:30000 (D.KR 36000)
£4846 $8238 €7075 Peinture No 9 (190x71cm-75x28in) s.d.1951 i. verso. 5-Nov-3 Dobiaschofsky, Bern #441/R est:15000 (S.FR 11000)
£5944 $10105 €8500 Composition II (80x100cm-31x39in) s. s.i.d.1950 verso. 25-Nov-3 Christie's, Amsterdam #249/R est:4000-6000
Works on paper
£397 $723 €600 Untitled (60x50cm-24x20in) s.d.61 collage. 21-Jun-4 Bernaerts, Antwerp #292
£470 $869 €700 Composition (60x50cm-24x20in) s.d.61 collage. 15-Mar-4 Horta, Bruxelles #297
£524 $892 €750 Au coeur (33x50cm-13x20in) s.d.52 mixed media. 1-Dec-3 Palais de Beaux Arts, Brussels #158/R
£767 $1372 €1150 Composition (65x50cm-26x20in) s.d.65 mixed media paper on canvas. 15-May-4 De Vuyst, Lokeren #65/R
£845 $1462 €1200 Territoire (63x48cm-25x19in) s. i.d.1960 verso mixed media. 10-Dec-3 Hotel des Ventes Mosan, Brussels #291
£1056 $1827 €1500 Abstraction (48x63cm-19x25in) s.d.58 W/C. 10-Dec-3 Hotel des Ventes Mosan, Brussels #261 est:1200-1600
£1667 $2717 €2400 Composition bleue. s. W/C. 23-Sep-3 Galerie Moderne, Brussels #621/R
£2177 $3897 €3200 Untitled (64x49cm-25x19in) s.d.59 gouache prov. 21-Mar-4 Calmels Cohen, Paris #121/R est:2000-3000

COLLIN DE VERMONT, Hyacinthe (1693-1761) French
£2800 $5040 €4088 Oladaya feeding the hundred prophets (32x40cm-13x16in) 20-Apr-4 Sotheby's, Olympia #369/R est:3000-4000

COLLIN DE VERMONT, Hyacinthe (attrib) (1693-1761) French
£1773 $2961 €2500 Moise et le serpent d'Airain (42x53cm-17x21in) 17-Oct-3 Tajan, Paris #90 est:3000-4000

COLLIN, Alberic (1886-1962) Belgian
Sculpture
£1644 $2795 €2400 Quatre ours polaires (14x55cm-6x22in) s. pat bronze. 10-Nov-3 Horta, Bruxelles #18
£3497 $6014 €5000 Elephant et elphanteau (35x40cm-14x16in) s.num.3/8 green pat bronze Cast Rocher. 8-Dec-3 Horta, Bruxelles #131 est:5000-7500
£10490 $17832 €15000 Poema debout. brown pat bronze socle Cast Valsuani. 1-Dec-3 Amberes, Antwerp #567/R

COLLIN, Andre (1862-1930) Belgian
£320 $550 €467 Die Sennezin, cottage interior (20x25cm-8x10in) s. panel. 2-Dec-3 Gorringes, Lewes #2249
£320 $550 €467 Der erste Gebertstag, cottage interior (20x25cm-8x10in) s. panel. 2-Dec-3 Gorringes, Lewes #2250

COLLIN, Marcus (1882-1966) Finnish
£278 $464 €400 Tree. Sketch of street scene with figures (55x40cm-22x16in) s.d.1905 double-sided. 23-Oct-3 Hagelstam, Helsinki #982
£458 $765 €660 Snow thawing (29x40cm-11x16in) i. 26-Oct-3 Bukowskis, Helsinki #312/R

£1399 $2378 €2000 Dawn (58x85cm-23x33in) s.d.20. 29-Nov-3 Bukowskis, Helsinki #94/R est:1700-2200
£1538 $2615 €2200 Sunset (55x81cm-22x32in) s.d.41. 29-Nov-3 Bukowskis, Helsinki #95/R est:1500-1700
£2378 $4042 €3400 Landscape from Grundsund (65x100cm-26x39in) s.d.46 exhib. 29-Nov-3 Bukowskis, Helsinki #180/R est:3500-4000
£2400 $4296 €3600 Shovelling snow (46x56cm-18x22in) s. prov. 15-May-4 Hagelstam, Helsinki #147/R est:2500
£3217 $5469 €4600 The fish market (61x73cm-24x29in) s.d.48. 29-Nov-3 Bukowskis, Helsinki #51/R est:4500-5500
Works on paper
£278 $464 €400 Harbour street (34x41cm-13x16in) s.d.1952 pastel. 23-Oct-3 Hagelstam, Helsinki #918/R
£278 $464 €400 Man with cigar (32x24cm-13x9in) s.d.48 pastel. 26-Oct-3 Bukowskis, Helsinki #311/R
£295 $549 €440 Working in the garden (31x23cm-12x9in) s.d.28 pastel. 7-Mar-4 Bukowskis, Helsinki #305/R
£302 $556 €450 At the market (24x32cm-9x13in) s.d.1950 pastel. 25-Mar-4 Hagelstam, Helsinki #989
£338 $605 €500 The fish market (25x32cm-10x13in) s.d.52 pastel exhib. 8-May-4 Bukowskis, Helsinki #122/R
£387 $620 €550 The yellow apron (24x32cm-9x13in) s. pastel. 18-Sep-3 Hagelstam, Helsinki #851
£417 $696 €600 Market square. s.d.1922 pastel. 23-Oct-3 Hagelstam, Helsinki #844
£470 $864 €700 Old woman and samovar (32x24cm-13x9in) s.d.1943 pastel. 25-Mar-4 Hagelstam, Helsinki #987
£500 $800 €710 Making nets (24x31cm-9x12in) s.d.1933 pastel. 18-Sep-3 Hagelstam, Helsinki #1016/R
£563 $901 €800 Traders (31x23cm-12x9in) s. pastel. 18-Sep-3 Hagelstam, Helsinki #848/R
£739 $1323 €1079 Carelean girl (59x45cm-23x18in) init.d.35 pastel. 26-May-4 AB Stockholms Auktionsverk #2485/R (S.KR 10000)
£1408 $2437 €2000 Figures at cafe (37x55cm-15x22in) s.d.1925 pastel. 13-Dec-3 Hagelstam, Helsinki #156/R est:1200

COLLINA, Giuliano (1938-) Italian
£1087 $1783 €1500 Window (70x70cm-28x28in) s.d.62 verso prov. sold with oil by Dino Lanaro and Bobo Piccoli. 27-May-3 Sotheby's, Milan #44 est:1300-1500

COLLINARI, A (17/18th C) Italian
Works on paper
£1908 $3511 €2900 La crucifixion (25x21cm-10x8in) s.d.1703 gouache. 23-Jun-4 Millon & Associes, Paris #15 est:1600-1800

COLLINET, Henri (c.1860-1906) French
£294 $490 €420 Garden, village and river with busy bridge (38x55cm-15x22in) s.i. 11-Oct-3 Hans Stahl, Hamburg #49/R

COLLINGS, Albert Harry (?-1947) British
Works on paper
£1300 $2340 €1898 Girl with lilac (51x36cm-20x14in) s. W/C. 21-Jan-4 Sotheby's, Olympia #255/R est:500-700

COLLINGS, Charles John (1848-1931) British
£769 $1285 €1123 In the glow, Chudleigh (48x33cm-19x13in) s.d.95 indis.i.verso. 17-Nov-3 Waddingtons, Toronto #90/R (C.D 1700)
Works on paper
£602 $1120 €879 By lake and mountain (17x37cm-7x15in) s. W/C prov. 2-Mar-4 Ritchie, Toronto #36/R est:500-700 (C.D 1500)

COLLINGWOOD, Joseph (20th C) British
£450 $752 €657 New top hat (69x61cm-27x24in) s. 17-Oct-3 Keys, Aylsham #465

COLLINS, Cecil (1908-1989) British
£2400 $4440 €3504 Portrait of the artist's wife (29x26cm-11x10in) s.d.1955 canvas on board. 11-Feb-4 Sotheby's, Olympia #252/R est:1500-2000
Works on paper
£950 $1758 €1387 Classical head (22x13cm-9x5in) s.d.1960 chl sanguine bodycol. 11-Mar-4 Christie's, Kensington #192/R
£1300 $2405 €1898 Mother and child (54x37cm-21x15in) s.d.1955 W/C bodycol. 11-Mar-4 Christie's, Kensington #188/R est:1000-1500
£2200 $4070 €3212 Visionary landscape (45x54cm-18x21in) s.d.1961 pencil W/C pen ink. 11-Mar-4 Christie's, Kensington #190/R est:800-1200

COLLINS, Charles (1851-1921) British
£640 $1190 €934 Low tide, near Brixham, Devon (34x75cm-13x30in) s.d.1899. 2-Mar-4 Bearnes, Exeter #446/R
£1600 $2864 €2336 Coastal scene with estuary and cattle (61x91cm-24x36in) 5-May-4 British Auctioneer #815 est:900-1200
£2300 $4255 €3450 Black mill (51x69cm-20x27in) s. 14-Jul-4 Sotheby's, Olympia #61/R est:1800-2200
£3400 $6222 €4964 Cattle watering (34x49cm-13x19in) s. 7-Apr-4 Woolley & Wallis, Salisbury #266/R est:1200-1800
Works on paper
£333 $600 €486 Cows at rest in a landscape (36x53cm-14x21in) s.d.1896 W/C. 23-Jan-4 Freeman, Philadelphia #71/R
£380 $695 €555 Pleasant pastures (36x54cm-14x21in) s. W/C. 27-Jan-4 Bonhams, Knightsbridge #5/R
£480 $816 €701 Cattle by a windmill, coastal view beyond (25x35cm-10x14in) s. W/C. 25-Nov-3 Bonhams, Knowle #165

COLLINS, Earl (20th C) American
£348 $550 €508 Portrait of the full rigged ship Kailani (61x91cm-24x36in) s. 25-Jul-3 Eldred, East Dennis #317h
£652 $1050 €952 Schooner, Elsie (51x76cm-20x30in) s. prov. 20-Aug-3 James Julia, Fairfield #868/R
£838 $1350 €1223 Sidewheeler, Nantucket (61x91cm-24x36in) s. prov. 20-Aug-3 James Julia, Fairfield #869/R est:500-1000
£1272 $2200 €1857 Seascape at sunset (61x91cm-24x36in) s. 13-Dec-3 Weschler, Washington #563 est:1000-1500

COLLINS, Hugh (fl.1868-1892) British
£900 $1674 €1314 Potato pickers (78x112cm-31x44in) s.d.1879. 4-Mar-4 Christie's, Kensington #645/R
£1319 $2098 €1900 Portrait of J G Paton Esq and his wife (124x100cm-49x39in) s.d.1881 pair. 10-Sep-3 James Adam, Dublin #90/R est:2000-3000
£2000 $3400 €2920 Granny's letter writer (75x90cm-30x35in) s. i.stretcher. 1-Dec-3 Bonhams, Bath #142/R est:2000-3000
£2900 $5191 €4234 Blowing bubbles (36x31cm-14x12in) s.d.1875 i.verso panel. 26-May-4 Sotheby's, Olympia #140/R est:1500-2000

COLLINS, James Edgell (1820-?) British
£300 $501 €438 Pearl of the east (27x22cm-11x9in) board. 20-Oct-3 Bonhams, Bath #194
£538 $850 €785 Three children seated on rooks at a beach, sailboat in the distance (51x76cm-20x30in) 6-Sep-3 Brunk, Ashville #346

COLLINS, Loretta L (20th C) American
£640 $1100 €934 The coast (51x56cm-20x22in) 6-Dec-3 Neal Auction Company, New Orleans #618

COLLINS, Majella (20th C) Irish
£658 $1211 €1000 Pier winter I, Sherkin Island (28x46cm-11x18in) i.d.2003 verso. 22-Jun-4 De Veres Art Auctions, Dublin #211/R
£1049 $1783 €1500 South wind (76x51cm-30x20in) s. 25-Nov-3 De Veres Art Auctions, Dublin #209 est:1400-1800

COLLINS, Mary Susan (1880-?) American
£313 $550 €457 Autumn flowers, landscape (76x64cm-30x25in) i. 21-May-4 Pook & Pook, Downington #192/R

COLLINS, Patrick (1911-1994) British
£4200 $7518 €6132 Bog pool (25x37cm-10x15in) s. board prov. 14-May-4 Christie's, Kensington #453/R est:3000-5000
£4583 $7471 €6600 Still life with flowers in a jug (19x20cm-7x8in) s. panel. 24-Sep-3 James Adam, Dublin #49/R est:3000-5000
£6783 $11531 €9700 Declining sun (41x49cm-16x19in) s.d.84. 25-Nov-3 De Veres Art Auctions, Dublin #95/R est:10000-15000
£13514 $25541 €20000 Bird flying in the wood (30x41cm-12x16in) s. exhib.lit. 17-Feb-4 Whyte's, Dublin #21/R est:18000-22000
£20979 $35664 €30000 Church in a landscape (56x66cm-22x26in) s. board prov. 25-Nov-3 De Veres Art Auctions, Dublin #57/R est:30000-40000
Works on paper
£599 $1036 €850 Penelope sleeping (28x30cm-11x12in) s.i. pencil. 10-Dec-3 Bonhams & James Adam, Dublin #165/R
£839 $1427 €1200 Fish (17x21cm-7x8in) s. pencil. 18-Nov-3 Whyte's, Dublin #90/R
£867 $1560 €1300 Fragment (54x53cm-21x21in) s.d.90 mixed media. 20-Apr-4 James Adam, Dublin #70/R

COLLINS, Richard (1755-1831) British
Miniatures
£1400 $2380 €2044 Mr LF Cork (7cm-3in) s.i.d.1802 verso gold frame oval. 18-Nov-3 Bonhams, New Bond Street #112/R est:1000-1200
£5200 $9360 €7592 Officer, possibly General Henry Chamion (8cm-3in) s.indis.i.verso metal frame oval exhib.lit. 22-Apr-4 Bonhams, New Bond Street #118/R est:1200-1800

COLLINS, Richard (?-1732) British
£3000 $5400 €4380 Portrait of Mrs Battell (126x102cm-50x40in) 21-Jan-4 Sotheby's, Olympia #28/R est:3000-4000

COLLINS, Thomas (fl.1857-1893) British
£360 $659 €526 Still life of roses (39x34cm-15x13in) s. 7-Apr-4 Woolley & Wallis, Salisbury #213/R

COLLINS, William (1788-1847) British
£450 $711 €653 Children on a beach (25x38cm-10x15in) init. 4-Sep-3 Christie's, Kensington #246
£400 $859 €701 Portrait of Lady Hamilton as a Baccante (20x17cm-8x7in) panel after Sir Joshua Reynolds. 17-Mar-4 Bonhams, Chester #405
£486 $773 €710 Coastal scene (28cm-11in circular) 1-May-3 Dunbar Sloane, Wellington #73a est:600-1200 (NZ.D 1400)
£766 $1410 €1118 Highland fisherman (41x30cm-16x12in) s. s.verso. 14-Jun-4 Waddingtons, Toronto #113/R est:1500-2000 (C.D 1900)
£1695 $2881 €2475 Cherry (61x45cm-24x18in) s.d.1846 wood panel. 24-Nov-3 Sotheby's, Melbourne #316/R est:4000-6000 (A.D 4000)
£2000 $3720 €2920 Portrait of James Campbell of Hampton Court House (61x51cm-24x20in) s.d.1812. 4-Mar-4 Christie's, Kensington #378/R est:2000-3000
£2500 $4650 €3650 Young fisherman (67x84cm-26x33in) s.d.1817 prov. 4-Mar-4 Christie's, Kensington #503/R est:3000-6000
£4500 $7650 €6570 Ave Maria scene near Tivoli (63x76cm-25x30in) s.d.1840 exhib. 25-Nov-3 Christie's, London #50/R est:6000-8000

COLLINS, William (attrib) (1788-1847) British
£320 $531 €467 Coastal scene with beached fishing boats and figures (25x45cm-10x18in) panel. 2-Oct-3 Locke & England, Leamington Spa #167/R
£380 $703 €555 Idle gossip on the shore (25x30cm-10x12in) panel. 15-Jan-4 Christie's, Kensington #884

£980 $1637 €1431 Hauling in the boat (56x73cm-22x29in) 12-Nov-3 Sotheby's, Olympia #21/R

COLLINS, William Wiehe (1862-1952) British
Works on paper
£390 $647 €569 The weeks washing (30x20cm-12x8in) s. W/C. 3-Oct-3 Mallams, Oxford #132/R
£400 $744 €584 Market square with figures (13x18cm-5x7in) s.d.1900 W/C. 4-Mar-4 Clevedon Sale Rooms #183
£520 $936 €759 Lucca (17x26cm-7x10in) s.i. W/C prov. 22-Apr-4 Lawrence, Crewkerne #807
£650 $1183 €949 Figures in a courtyard and figures in the street (38x25cm-15x10in) s. pair. 16-Jun-4 John Nicholson, Haslemere #660

COLLINSON, Fergus (20th C) New Zealander
£709 $1255 €1035 Taumaranui express (118x89cm-46x35in) s.d.1980 acrylic. 28-Apr-4 Dunbar Sloane, Auckland #77/R (NZ.D 2000)

COLLINSON, James (1825-1881) British
£3326 $5953 €4856 Sister love (61x51cm-24x20in) s. 26-May-4 AB Stockholms Auktionsverk #2452/R est:25000-30000 (S.KR 45000)

COLLIS, Peter (1929-) Irish
£473 $894 €700 Forest clearing, Glencree (11x17cm-4x7in) s. board. 17-Feb-4 Whyte's, Dublin #75/R
£764 $1245 €1100 Wicklow landscape (19x21cm-7x8in) s. 24-Sep-3 James Adam, Dublin #119/R est:1000-1500
£800 $1448 €1200 Old farm, Connemara (30x31cm-12x12in) s. board. 31-Mar-4 James Adam, Dublin #51/R
£850 $1522 €1241 Road to Lough (38x27cm-15x11in) s. board. 14-May-4 Christie's, Kensington #468/R
£855 $1574 €1300 Wicklow landscape (22x37cm-9x15in) s. board. 22-Jun-4 De Veres Art Auctions, Dublin #1/R
£1014 $1916 €1500 Killiney Hill (20x25cm-8x10in) s. board. 17-Feb-4 Whyte's, Dublin #232 est:1500-2000
£1049 $1783 €1500 Delphi, County Mayo (15x22cm-6x9in) s. prov. 18-Nov-3 Whyte's, Dublin #201/R est:800-1200
£1081 $2043 €1600 Landscape, Country Wicklow (25x24cm-10x9in) s. canvasboard. 17-Feb-4 Whyte's, Dublin #109/R est:1500-2000
£1100 $1892 €1606 Wicklow (35x45cm-14x18in) s. board. 3-Dec-3 John Ross, Belfast #59 est:600-800
£1181 $1924 €1700 Landscape Templemore (20x23cm-8x9in) s. board. 24-Sep-3 James Adam, Dublin #139/R est:1500-2500
£1467 $2655 €2200 House in a Wicklow landscape (42x45cm-17x18in) s. board. 30-Mar-4 De Veres Art Auctions, Dublin #69/R est:2000-3000
£1544 $2763 €2300 Still life with seascape (26x25cm-10x10in) s. canvass on board. 26-May-4 James Adam, Dublin #62/R est:2000-3000
£1597 $2603 €2300 Enniskerry Road (212x29cm-83x11in) board. 24-Sep-3 James Adam, Dublin #64/R est:1000-1500
£1608 $2734 €2300 Landscape at Brittas, County Dublin (22x32cm-9x13in) s. canvas board. 18-Nov-3 Whyte's, Dublin #36/R est:1500-2000
£1611 $2883 €2400 Still life with fruit (45x50cm-18x20in) s. 31-May-4 Hamilton Osborne King, Dublin #39/R est:2000-3000
£1733 $3137 €2600 Near Roundwood, Co Wicklow (23x31cm-9x12in) s. board. 31-Mar-4 James Adam, Dublin #37/R est:1800-2200
£1800 $3258 €2700 Farm at Glenasmole (29x41cm-11x16in) s. 30-Mar-4 De Veres Art Auctions, Dublin #160/R est:2000-3000
£2222 $3622 €3200 Obelisk, Killiney (34x44cm-13x17in) s. board. 24-Sep-3 James Adam, Dublin #42/R est:2000-3000
£2282 $4039 €3400 The sea, Galway Bay (27x38cm-11x15in) s. board prov.exhib. 27-Apr-4 Whyte's, Dublin #84/R est:2500-3500
£2400 $4296 €3504 Snow at Glencar (76x86cm-30x34in) s. 14-May-4 Christie's, Kensington #467/R est:2500-3500
£2416 $4277 €3600 Flowers in a vase (41x36cm-16x14in) s. prov.exhib. 27-Apr-4 Whyte's, Dublin #74/R est:3000-4000
£2431 $3962 €3500 Wicklow landscape (41x48cm-16x19in) s. canvasboard. 23-Sep-3 De Veres Art Auctions, Dublin #202/R est:1200-1800
£2778 $4528 €4000 Snow on Bray Head (19x23cm-7x9in) s. canvas on board prov. 23-Sep-3 De Veres Art Auctions, Dublin #219/R est:4000-5000
£4027 $7128 €6000 Still life with green plate (86x86cm-34x34in) s. prov.exhib. 27-Apr-4 Whyte's, Dublin #35/R est:5000-7000
£4228 $7484 €6300 Still life of fruit (64x76cm-25x30in) s. prov.exhib. 27-Apr-4 Whyte's, Dublin #10/R est:5000-7000
£5500 $9845 €8030 Still life with fruit (61x61cm-24x24in) s. 14-May-4 Christie's, Kensington #400 est:3000-5000

COLLISHAW, Mat (1966-) British
Photographs
£2133 $3926 €3200 Flowers and butterfly (20x30cm-8x12in) cibachrome print prov.exhib. 9-Jun-4 Artcurial Briest, Paris #570/R est:2500-3000
£3200 $5824 €4672 Awakening of Conscience, Emily (200x200cm-79x79in) Nova print wood glass exec 1997 prov.exhib. 5-Feb-4 Christie's, London #213/R est:4000-6000
Sculpture
£2400 $4368 €3504 Self portrait (51x43x7cm-20x17x3in) 3D col transparency lightbox edition of 10 prov. 6-Feb-4 Sotheby's, London #285/R est:2000-3000

COLLISTER, Alfred James (fl.1895-1939) British
Works on paper
£250 $425 €365 Bosham (41x55cm-16x22in) W/C prov. 4-Nov-3 Bonhams, Oxford #188
£300 $537 €438 Peel Castle (25x33cm-10x13in) W/C. 7-May-4 Chrystals Auctions, Isle of Man #346h
£320 $573 €467 Peel Castle (25x33cm-10x13in) init. W/C. 7-May-4 Chrystals Auctions, Isle of Man #346

COLLIVADINO, Pio (1869-1945) Argentinian
£1878 $3400 €2742 Amongst trees (21x27cm-8x11in) cardboard. 30-Mar-4 Arroyo, Buenos Aires #59
£2235 $4000 €3263 Puesta del Sol (26x38cm-10x15in) s. exhib.lit. 4-May-4 Arroyo, Buenos Aires #45/R est:3000
£5307 $9500 €7748 Cangallo Street (38x25cm-15x10in) s. cardboard exhib.lit. 4-May-4 Arroyo, Buenos Aires #44/R est:3500

COLLOCOTT, Martin (1945-) Australian
£1423 $2233 €2063 Burnt reminder (120x150cm-47x59in) s.d.1969 i.verso acrylic prov.exhib. 27-Aug-3 Christie's, Sydney #673/R est:2000-3000 (A.D 3500)

COLLOMB, Paul (1921-) French
£350 $616 €511 Lecture (48x60cm-19x24in) s. s.i.stretcher. 18-May-4 Bonhams, Knightsbridge #128/R

COLLOT, Marie (18th C) French
Sculpture
£6294 $10825 €9000 Bust of a young girl (44cm-17in) s.verso d.1765 terracotta white marble base lit. 2-Dec-3 Christie's, Paris #81/R est:12000-18000

COLLS, Ebenezer (1812-1887) British
£280 $476 €409 Limping into port (30x46cm-12x18in) s. 19-Nov-3 Christie's, Kensington #513
£450 $824 €657 Shipping in choppy seas off the coast (30x47cm-12x19in) s. 6-Apr-4 Bonhams, Knightsbridge #54/R
£580 $1003 €847 Mount Orgueil Castle, Jersey, with a ship driven onto rocks in the foreground (19x29cm-7x11in) s. panel. 9-Dec-3 Anderson & Garland, Newcastle #486
£900 $1611 €1314 Screw two-decker lying at anchor at dusk (18x23cm-7x9in) s. panel. 26-May-4 Christie's, Kensington #649/R
£1300 $2080 €1898 Running down the coast in heavy swell (30x51cm-12x20in) s. 16-Sep-3 Bonhams, New Bond Street #30/R est:1500-2000
£3000 $5370 €4380 Three-decker reducing sail in Spithead arriving in Portsmouth harbour (40x66cm-16x26in) 26-May-4 Christie's, Kensington #648/R est:4000-6000
£4000 $6400 €5840 Hauling in the nets off an east coast light beacon (51x76cm-20x30in) s. arched top. 16-Sep-3 Bonhams, New Bond Street #8/R est:4000-6000

COLLVER, Ethel Blanchard (1875-1955) American
£2554 $4750 €3729 Marblehead street views (40x50cm-16x20in) s.d.45 two. 5-Mar-4 Skinner, Boston #559/R est:2000-3000

COLLYER, Margaret (fl.1897-1910) British
£300 $531 €438 Equestrian portrait (70x90cm-28x35in) s.d.1910. 2-May-4 Lots Road Auctions, London #369
£469 $750 €685 Guarding the baby (37x54cm-15x21in) s.d.1909. 21-Sep-3 Bonhams & Butterfields, San Francisco #2797/R
Works on paper
£330 $551 €482 Head portrait of a Jack Russell (35x27cm-14x11in) indis.s. W/C. 9-Oct-3 Greenslade Hunt, Taunton #479

COLLYER, Nora Frances Elisabeth (1898-1979) Canadian
£489 $812 €714 Untitled, seated woman (36x25cm-14x10in) s. canvasboard. 5-Oct-3 Levis, Calgary #20/R (C.D 1100)

COLMAIRE, Horace (1875-?) French
£4196 $7133 €6000 La lettre (108x84cm-43x33in) s. sold with a photo lit. 27-Nov-3 Millon & Associes, Paris #132/R est:6000-8000

COLMAN OF BRISTOL, Samuel (1780-1845) British
£7059 $12000 €10306 Sketching the ruins of Tintern Abbey (87x117cm-34x46in) s. prov. 29-Oct-3 Christie's, Rockefeller NY #76/R est:15000-25000

COLMAN, Roi Clarkson (1884-1945) American
£815 $1500 €1190 Morning sea from La Jolla coast (30x40cm-12x16in) s. i.verso board. 8-Jun-4 Bonhams & Butterfields, San Francisco #4346/R est:3000-5000
£894 $1600 €1305 Road to painted hills (56x76cm-22x30in) s. i.verso. 15-May-4 Jeffery Burchard, Florida #152
£1044 $1900 €1524 Late afternoon landscape, San Gorgonio (41x51cm-16x20in) s. i. stretcher. 15-Jun-4 John Moran, Pasadena #34a est:2000-3000

COLMAN, Samuel (1832-1920) American
£3073 $5500 €4487 Panoramic landscape (18x28cm-7x11in) s. board. 8-Jan-4 James Julia, Fairfield #664/R est:2500-3500
£6818 $12000 €9954 View of British Columbia (28x46cm-11x18in) s. prov.exhib. 19-May-4 Sotheby's, New York #48/R est:12000-18000
£8380 $15000 €12235 Campagna di Roma (20x36cm-8x14in) s. canvas on board. 7-May-4 Sloans & Kenyon, Bethesda #1731/R est:6000-8000
£11602 $21000 €16939 Along the shore (38x77cm-15x30in) s. 31-Mar-4 Sotheby's, New York #47/R est:15000-25000
£15470 $28000 €22586 Autumn, Mt Chocurua, New Hampshire (41x58cm-16x23in) init. prov. 31-Mar-4 Sotheby's, New York #49/R est:12000-18000
Works on paper
£6145 $11000 €8972 Naples harbour (8x20cm-3x8in) i.d.Feb 1873 W/C double-sided prov. 6-May-4 Shannon's, Milford #97/R est:8000-12000

COLMEIRO, Antonio (1932-) Spanish
£570 $1067 €850 Look (36x25cm-14x10in) s. board. 24-Feb-4 Durán, Madrid #12/R

COLMEIRO, Manuel (1901-1999) Spanish
Works on paper
£411 $699 €600 Tree at spring (26x21cm-10x8in) ink dr lit. 4-Nov-3 Ansorena, Madrid #184/R
£414 $745 €600 Tree (25x20cm-10x8in) ink dr lit. 26-Jan-4 Durán, Madrid #12/R

£586 $1055 €850 Peasant women (21x31cm-8x12in) s.d.1975 ink dr. 26-Jan-4 Ansorena, Madrid #337/R
£604 $1069 €900 Fall of the dictator (32x25cm-13x10in) ink dr lit. 27-Apr-4 Durán, Madrid #647/R
£608 $1070 €900 Fruit market (21x29cm-8x11in) s. ink dr. 18-May-4 Segre, Madrid #315/R
£884 $1610 €1300 Maternity (31x21cm-12x8in) s.d.1970 W/C pencil. 3-Feb-4 Segre, Madrid #168/R
£933 $1699 €1400 Mujer (21x15cm-8x6in) s.d.1946 W/C ink. 29-Jun-4 Segre, Madrid #120/R
£933 $1699 €1400 Mythological scene with Hercules (32x25cm-13x10in) s. ink drawing. 29-Jun-4 Segre, Madrid #280/R
£993 $1658 €1400 Peeling potatoes (31x22cm-12x9in) s. pencil dr. 20-Oct-3 Durán, Madrid #208/R
£1027 $1747 €1500 Maternity (30x21cm-12x8in) s.d.1949 ink dr. 4-Nov-3 Ansorena, Madrid #216/R est:1500
£1757 $3092 €2600 Jelly fish fair (32x23cm-13x9in) s.d.1931 W/C. 18-May-4 Segre, Madrid #112/R est:1200

COLMENAREZ, Asdrubal (1936-) South American
Works on paper
£276 $450 €403 Untitled (72x113cm-28x44in) s. mixed media exec.1986. 28-Sep-3 Subastas Odalys, Caracas #78
£375 $675 €548 Adrenaline (68x84cm-27x33in) s.verso mixed media on canvas exec.1979. 25-Apr-4 Subastas Odalys, Caracas #13/R
£1070 $1840 €1562 Untitled (50x65cm-20x26in) s. mixed media panel. 7-Dec-3 Subastas Odalys, Caracas #60/R est:2000
£1074 $1750 €1568 Multiple II (96x96cm-38x38in) s.verso mixed media on canvas exec.2001. 20-Jul-3 Subastas Odalys, Caracas #86
£1186 $2135 €1732 Rings, Paris (122x17cm-48x7in) s.verso mixed media on canvas exec.1997. 25-Apr-4 Subastas Odalys, Caracas #12/R

COLMO, Giovanni (1867-1947) Italian
£436 $772 €650 Lake landscape (9x13cm-4x5in) s. cardboard. 1-May-4 Meeting Art, Vercelli #35
£436 $772 €650 Murello Church (26x19cm-10x7in) s. cardboard. 1-May-4 Meeting Art, Vercelli #56
£436 $772 €650 Landscape (12x15cm-5x6in) s. cardboard. 1-May-4 Meeting Art, Vercelli #448
£467 $859 €700 Sunset (13x11cm-5x4in) s. card. 8-Jun-4 Della Rocca, Turin #337/R
£500 $920 €750 View of Valtournanche (38x25cm-15x10in) board. 10-Jun-4 Christie's, Rome #5
£503 $891 €750 Landscape in Piedmonte (14x24cm-6x9in) s. cardboard. 1-May-4 Meeting Art, Vercelli #66
£552 $916 €800 Landscape with stream (25x38cm-10x15in) s. card. 1-Oct-3 Della Rocca, Turin #208/R
£600 $1104 €900 River landscape (18x17cm-7x7in) s. card. 8-Jun-4 Della Rocca, Turin #334/R
£690 $1145 €1000 Cottage in the countryside (40x49cm-16x19in) s. card. 1-Oct-3 Della Rocca, Turin #17/R
£733 $1349 €1100 Stream in the mountains (34x24cm-13x9in) s. card. 14-Jun-4 Sant Agostino, Torino #150/R
£800 $1472 €1200 Little church in the mountains (34x24cm-13x9in) s. card. 14-Jun-4 Sant Agostino, Torino #149/R
£870 $1426 €1200 Mountain path with figures (35x27cm-14x11in) s. cardboard. 27-May-3 Finarte Semenzato, Milan #126/R
£940 $1663 €1400 Back from pasture (27x38cm-11x15in) s.d.1938 cardboard lit. 1-May-4 Meeting Art, Vercelli #407
£993 $1658 €1400 Rural scene (34x27cm-13x11in) s. cardboard. 20-Oct-3 Sant Agostino, Torino #84/R
£1103 $1832 €1600 Landscape with church (39x30cm-15x12in) s. card. 1-Oct-3 Della Rocca, Turin #281/R
£1597 $2715 €2300 Mountain cottages in Macugnaga (30x47cm-12x19in) s. canvas on cardboard lit. 1-Nov-3 Meeting Art, Vercelli #196/R est:1500
£1600 $2944 €2400 Winter landscape (40x58cm-16x23in) s. cardboard. 14-Jun-4 Sant Agostino, Torino #276/R est:2000
£1611 $2851 €2400 Courmayeur (35x45cm-14x18in) s.d.1934 cardboard. 1-May-4 Meeting Art, Vercelli #101 est:1500

COLMORE, Nina (1889-1973) British
£420 $668 €613 Reliance, owned and trained by H Blagave (50x30cm-20x12in) s.d.69. 9-Sep-3 Bamfords, Derby #1146/R
£600 $1104 €876 Reliance, bay racehorse (51x61cm-20x24in) s.i.d.69. 10-Jun-4 Christie's, Kensington #182/R
£1081 $2000 €1578 Twopence (33x46cm-13x18in) s.i.d.39. 10-Feb-4 Doyle, New York #267/R est:2000-3000
£1300 $2392 €1898 Melton, black horse with white socks (63x76cm-25x30in) s.i.d.28. 10-Jun-4 Christie's, Kensington #186/R est:1000-1500
£2200 $4048 €3212 Setting off with the Cottesbrook (61x91cm-24x36in) s.d.50. 10-Jun-4 Christie's, Kensington #171/R est:2000-3000

COLNOT, Arnout (1887-1983) Dutch
£544 $990 €800 Farmhouse (39x47cm-15x19in) s. 3-Feb-4 Christie's, Amsterdam #441
£1389 $2264 €2000 Still life with flowers and fruit (66x55cm-26x22in) s. 29-Sep-3 Sotheby's, Amsterdam #209/R
£1733 $3172 €2600 The old garden in Bergen (78x60cm-31x24in) s. 7-Jun-4 Glerum, Amsterdam #127/R est:4000-6000
£2447 $4087 €3500 Moored boat in a polder landscape (70x80cm-28x31in) s. 30-Jun-3 Sotheby's, Amsterdam #424/R
£2937 $5052 €4200 Winter in the Schermer (59x72cm-23x28in) s. 7-Dec-3 Sotheby's, Amsterdam #716/R
£3333 $5433 €4800 View of the path with farm in the distance (58x73cm-23x29in) s. prov. 29-Sep-3 Sotheby's, Amsterdam #195/R
£5208 $8489 €7500 Village in snow (61x47cm-24x19in) s. prov. 29-Sep-3 Sotheby's, Amsterdam #194/R
£5594 $9622 €8000 River landscape in Noord Holland (80x100cm-31x39in) s. painted c.1928. 2-Dec-3 Sotheby's, Amsterdam #243/R est:5000-6000

COLNOT, Karel (1921-) Dutch
£245 $409 €350 Flower still life (60x50cm-24x20in) s. board. 30-Jun-3 Sotheby's, Amsterdam #240

COLOGNESE, Giovanni (1901-) Italian
£240 $374 €350 Landscape with stream and factory (44x60cm-17x24in) s. 8-Apr-3 Il Ponte, Milan #961
£243 $401 €350 Landscape with stream and factory (44x60cm-17x24in) s. 1-Jul-3 Il Ponte, Milan #601

COLOM Y AGUSTI, Juan (1879-1969) Spanish
£2000 $3640 €3000 Cala de Mallorca (61x81cm-24x32in) s.d.1917. 29-Jun-4 Segre, Madrid #92a/R est:3000

COLOM, Joan (?) Spanish?
Works on paper
£442 $805 €650 Study for composition of the Divina Commedia (28x28cm-11x11in) s.i. pencil dr. 3-Feb-4 Segre, Madrid #354/R

COLOMBI, Plinio (1873-1951) Swiss
£386 $641 €560 Silver thistles in vase (50x40cm-20x16in) s.d.1942. 13-Jun-3 Zofingen, Switzerland #2811 (S.FR 850)
£498 $846 €727 Flowers (55x45cm-22x18in) s.d.1936. 28-Nov-3 Zofingen, Switzerland #2949 (S.FR 1100)
£845 $1352 €1200 Early spring (65x100cm-26x39in) s.d.1903. 18-Sep-3 Rieber, Stuttgart #829/R
£1322 $2247 €1930 Lake Thun with Stockhorn (84x100cm-33x39in) s.d.1925. 5-Nov-3 Dobiaschofsky, Bern #442/R est:1600 (S.FR 3000)

COLOMBIER, Amelie (19/20th C) French
Sculpture
£4297 $8035 €6446 Carmencita (53cm-21in) st.f.Goldscheider bronze ivory onyx base exec.c.1930. 25-Jul-4 Lawson Menzies, Sydney #148/R est:12000-15000 (A.D 11000)

COLOMBINI, Maurilio (20th C) Italian
£300 $552 €450 Ferrari (70x100cm-28x39in) s. i.verso masonite. 12-Jun-4 Meeting Art, Vercelli #879

COLOMBO, Ambrogio (1821-?) Italian
Sculpture
£9500 $15770 €13870 Bust of Emperor Napoleon Bonaparte on Campaign (56cm-22in) s.i.d.1885 rich dark brown pat bronze Cast f.Pinedo Bronzier. 30-Sep-3 Sotheby's, London #298/R est:2000-3000

COLOMBO, Gianni (1937-1993) Italian
£4196 $7133 €6000 Elasticated space (20x20cm-8x8in) s.d.1974-76 verso elastic bands acrylic board prov.exhib. 24-Nov-3 Christie's, Milan #140/R est:6000-8000
Sculpture
£10067 $18020 €15000 Fluid structure (44x34x15cm-17x13x6in) s. steel engine plexiglas exec.1960 prov.exhib. 25-May-4 Sotheby's, Milan #149/R est:8000-10000
Works on paper
£3623 $5942 €5000 Untitled (70x90cm-28x35in) s. s.i.d.1968 verso collage card exhib. 27-May-3 Sotheby's, Milan #45/R est:2500-3000
£14000 $23380 €20440 Elastic space (101x101cm-40x40in) s.verso painted wood nails elastic bands acrylic board exec.1974. 20-Oct-3 Sotheby's, London #25/R est:14000-18000

COLOMBO, Paolo (20th C) ?
Works on paper
£417 $750 €609 Ideal landscape (37x73cm-15x29in) init.i.d.1983-4 graphite W/C acrylic rice paper prov. 24-Apr-4 David Rago, Lambertville #31/R

COLOMBO, R (19th C) Italian
Sculpture
£3566 $6063 €5100 Empereur couvert de son chapeau et un aigle (58cm-23in) s.d.1885 col bronze. 1-Dec-3 Coutau Begarie, Paris #280/R est:6000-7000

COLOMBO, Renzo (19th C) Italian
Sculpture
£2270 $3790 €3200 Boheme Orientale (57cm-22in) s.d.1884 pat bronze. 17-Jun-3 Christie's, Paris #163/R est:2500-3000

COLOMBO, Virgilio (19th C) Italian
£780 $1302 €1131 Lago di Presiano (30x60cm-12x24in) s. 23-Jun-3 Philippe Schuler, Zurich #8579 (S.FR 1700)
Works on paper
£420 $668 €613 Suitor playing court to a lady (26x18cm-10x7in) s. W/C prov. 10-Sep-3 Cheffins, Cambridge #462/R

COLOMBOTTO ROSSO, Enrico (1925-) Italian
£367 $675 €550 Head of girl (60x50cm-24x20in) s. board. 8-Jun-4 Della Rocca, Turin #342/R
£559 $934 €800 Doll (68x48cm-27x19in) s. mixed media paper on canvas. 26-Jun-3 Sant Agostino, Torino #180/R
£966 $1612 €1400 Figure (60x50cm-24x20in) s. 17-Nov-3 Sant Agostino, Torino #99/R
£966 $1612 €1400 Figure (60x50cm-24x20in) s. 17-Nov-3 Sant Agostino, Torino #101/R
£1133 $2085 €1700 Play (100x50cm-39x20in) s. s.verso tempera painted 2003 exhib.lit. 12-Jun-4 Meeting Art, Vercelli #981/R est:1500

£1678 $3104 €2500 Giano's scream (100x50cm-39x20in) s. tempera lit. 13-Mar-4 Meeting Art, Vercelli #83 est:1500
Works on paper
£350 $584 €500 Woman (50x35cm-20x14in) s. mixed media. 26-Jun-3 Sant Agostino, Torino #179/R
£442 $791 €650 Blue cat (78x57cm-31x22in) s. W/C. 22-Mar-4 Sant Agostino, Torino #348/R

COLOMBRES, Ignacio (?) Argentinian
£279 $500 €407 Street boy (44x34cm-17x13in) oil acrylic canvas on cardboard. 11-May-4 Arroyo, Buenos Aires #23

COLOMINA, Jorge (20th C) ?
£2000 $3600 €3000 Venus and Joconde (100x73cm-39x29in) s. painted 2003. 24-Apr-4 Cornette de St.Cyr, Paris #489/R est:3000-4000

COLOMO BRAVO, Moises (1932-) Spanish
£470 $874 €700 Valley (73x92cm-29x36in) s. 2-Mar-4 Ansorena, Madrid #150/R
Works on paper
£369 $687 €550 Female nude (60x44cm-24x17in) s. pastel. 2-Mar-4 Ansorena, Madrid #338/R

COLONE, Adam de (fl.1622-1628) British
£46000 $72680 €67160 Portrait of Sir William Stewart of Grandtully (109x71cm-43x28in) d.1613 panel. 6-Sep-3 Shapes, Edinburgh #302/R est:20000-30000

COLONELLI-SCIARRA, Salvatore (18th C) Italian
£35862 $59890 €52000 Navona Square flooded, Rome (20x34cm-8x13in) s.d.1735 tempera paper on board lit. 12-Nov-3 Sotheby's, Milan #172/R est:15000-20000

COLONELLO, Giuseppe (1903-1977) Italian
£336 $594 €500 Chateau des Dames (40x50cm-16x20in) s. s.i.d.1968 verso. 1-May-4 Meeting Art, Vercelli #45
£355 $592 €500 Chateau des Dames (40x50cm-16x20in) s. s.i.d.1968 verso. 20-Oct-3 Sant Agostino, Torino #128/R

COLONIA, Adam de (attrib) (1634-1685) Dutch
£4803 $8454 €7012 Pastorale (84x113cm-33x44in) i. prov. 22-May-4 Galerie Gloggner, Luzern #22 est:3800-4500 (S.FR 11000)

COLOT, Robert (1927-1993) Belgian
£338 $639 €500 Vue de ville (30x40cm-12x16in) s. panel. 17-Feb-4 Galerie Moderne, Brussels #124/R

COLOURIS, Mary Louise (20th C) British
Works on paper
£460 $846 €672 Fireworks I (73x52cm-29x20in) s.d.03 W/C. 29-Mar-4 Thomson Roddick & Medcalf, Edinburgh #255/R

COLQUHOUN, Amalie Sara (?-1974) Australian
£314 $571 €458 Southern Ocean. board. 5-Feb-4 Joel, Victoria #89 (A.D 750)

COLQUHOUN, Archibald Douglas (1894-1983) Australian
£648 $1043 €946 Still life with poppies in an oriental vase (58x48cm-23x19in) s. 13-Oct-3 Joel, Victoria #274/R est:1200-1800 (A.D 1600)
£810 $1304 €1183 Still life with chrysanthemums (49x40cm-19x16in) s. board. 13-Oct-3 Joel, Victoria #368 est:1500-2000 (A.D 2000)

COLQUHOUN, Brett (1958-) Australian
£289 $512 €422 Lure (63x97cm-25x38in) s.i.d.1986 verso board prov. 3-May-4 Christie's, Melbourne #253 (A.D 700)
£496 $917 €724 Moiety (192x126cm-76x50in) s.d.July 1988 i.verso prov. 15-Mar-4 Sotheby's, Melbourne #72 est:1500-2500 (A.D 1200)

COLQUHOUN, Ithell (1906-1988) British
£260 $434 €380 Volcanic eruption (70x109cm-28x43in) mono.d.1966 acrylic paper on board. 7-Oct-3 Fellows & Sons, Birmingham #350/R
£500 $910 €730 Abstract, vegetation in black, green, yellow and red (51x66cm-20x26in) 16-Jun-4 John Nicholson, Haslemere #711/R
£750 $1200 €1095 Self portrait (20x15cm-8x6in) s.d.1931 i.verso. 19-May-3 Bruton Knowles, Cheltenham #209a
Works on paper
£280 $468 €409 Star painting (43x33cm-17x13in) mono.d.1964 i.verso mixed media. 14-Oct-3 David Lay, Penzance #149/R
£280 $518 €409 Ephesian Dreams (62x42cm-24x17in) mono. mixed media. 13-Jul-4 Bonhams, Knightsbridge #42

COLQUHOUN, Robert (1914-1962) British
Works on paper
£350 $585 €511 Nadia (33x24cm-13x9in) i. pen ink. 16-Oct-3 Bonhams, Edinburgh #18
£750 $1253 €1095 Man with a microscope (34x24cm-13x9in) s.d.47 carbon dr. 16-Oct-3 Bonhams, Edinburgh #32
£1450 $2422 €2117 Two men by a table (50x36cm-20x14in) s.d.58 carbon dr. gouache. 16-Oct-3 Bonhams, Edinburgh #30 est:600-800

COLSON, Charles Jean Baptiste (1810-?) French
£7530 $12500 €10994 Portraits of elegant man and woman (201x127cm-79x50in) s.i.d.1859 pair. 4-Oct-3 Neal Auction Company, New Orleans #1077/R est:3000-5000

COLSON, Roger (1958-) British
£3000 $5580 €4380 Morning in Milan (100x127cm-39x50in) 8-Mar-4 Christie's, London #17

COLSOULLE, Gustave (1843-1895) Belgian
£333 $603 €500 Paire de chevaux dans un paysage d'ete (92x70cm-36x28in) s. 30-Mar-4 Campo & Campo, Antwerp #50
£347 $552 €500 Cavalier ramenant cheval (48x53cm-19x21in) s. 9-Sep-3 Vanderkindere, Brussels #13
£979 $1684 €1400 Cavalier en hiver (57x43cm-22x17in) s. panel. 2-Dec-3 Campo & Campo, Antwerp #73
£8511 $14213 €12000 Cavaliers Arabes (80x96cm-31x38in) s. 16-Jun-3 Gros & Delettrez, Paris #400/R est:8000-12000

COLUCCI, Gio (1892-1974) Italian?
£280 $476 €400 Visage (50x30cm-20x12in) s. oil paper on cardboard. 20-Nov-3 Claude Aguttes, Neuilly #148
£2324 $4020 €3300 Village (65x81cm-26x32in) s. panel. 14-Dec-3 Eric Pillon, Calais #128/R

COLUNGA, Alejandro (1948-) Mexican
£1029 $1800 €1502 Vaca sagrada con trompa de ubre (40x33cm-16x13in) init. s.i.d.1995 verso. 19-Dec-3 Sotheby's, New York #1205/R est:3000-4000
£1176 $2000 €1717 El sueno del raton (36x34cm-14x13in) s. prov. 9-Nov-3 Bonhams & Butterfields, Los Angeles #4141/R est:3000-5000
£1176 $2000 €1717 La muertw del raton miguelito (41x36cm-16x14in) s.verso prov. 9-Nov-3 Bonhams & Butterfields, Los Angeles #4142/R est:3000-5000
£2714 $4750 €3962 La luna es cuadrada (100x80cm-39x31in) mono. s.i.d.1994 verso prov. 19-Dec-3 Sotheby's, New York #1182/R est:8000-10000
Sculpture
£1714 $3000 €2502 Personaje con peces (70cm-28in) terracotta. 19-Dec-3 Sotheby's, New York #1194/R est:5000-6000

COLVILLE, Alex (1920-) Canadian
£19643 $33786 €28679 Group of horses (70x95cm-28x37in) s.d.47 prov.lit. 2-Dec-3 Joyner Waddington, Toronto #32/R est:50000-75000 (C.D 44000)
Prints
£1802 $3063 €2631 Morning (55cm-22in circular) s.d.1981 num.21/70 col serigraph prov. 18-Nov-3 Sotheby's, Toronto #47/R est:4000-6000 (C.D 4000)
£1802 $3063 €2631 Sleeper (43x53cm-17x21in) s.d.1975 num.3/70 serigraph lit. 27-Nov-3 Heffel, Vancouver #12/R est:3000-4000 (C.D 4000)
£1802 $3063 €2631 Cat and artist (22x22cm-9x9in) s.d.1979 num.29/70 serigraph lit. circular. 27-Nov-3 Heffel, Vancouver #15/R est:2500-3500 (C.D 4000)
£6250 $10750 €9125 After swimming (62x37cm-24x15in) s.d.1955 col serigraph prov.lit. 2-Dec-3 Joyner Waddington, Toronto #96/R est:4000-6000 (C.D 14000)
Works on paper
£1004 $1708 €1466 Dog gnawing a bone (26x34cm-10x13in) s.d.1956 ink prov. 6-Nov-3 Heffel, Vancouver #31/R est:2500-3500 (C.D 2250)

COLVILLE, George Garden (1887-1970) Australian
Works on paper
£489 $846 €714 Scott Monument, Edinburgh (39x27cm-15x11in) s.i. W/C. 9-Dec-3 Pinneys, Montreal #60/R (C.D 1100)

COLVIN, J M (?) ?
£377 $675 €550 Women harvesting fruit in fields (41x20cm-16x8in) s. board pair. 20-Mar-4 Selkirks, St. Louis #153

COLYN THOMSON, C L (20th C) British
£1257 $2100 €1835 Clock house, Woodbridge, Suffolk (71x91cm-28x36in) s.d.1914. 7-Oct-3 Sotheby's, New York #85/R est:3000-5000

COMAS Y BLANCO, Augusto (1862-1953) Spanish
£323 $578 €475 Cuenca (16x22cm-6x9in) s. cardboard. 22-Mar-4 Durán, Madrid #86/R

COMBA, Pierre (?-1934) French
Works on paper
£400 $720 €600 Le repos des chasseurs a pieds (17x35cm-7x14in) W/C. 25-Apr-4 Daniel Herry, Beaune #80
£550 $1012 €803 Reconnoitre in the Alps. On patrol (34x18cm-13x7in) s. W/C pair. 8-Jun-4 Bonhams, Knightsbridge #1/R

COMBAS, Robert (1957-) French
£403 $737 €600 Portrait (21x16cm-8x6in) s. W/C sequins invitation card exec c.1997. 7-Jul-4 Artcurial Briest, Paris #237
£486 $812 €700 Once upon a star (30x30cm-12x12in) s.d.1994 verso acrylic on vinyl disk. 21-Oct-3 Artcurial Briest, Paris #572
£733 $1320 €1100 Nu (34x24cm-13x9in) s.d.1998 acrylic ink. 24-Apr-4 Cornette de St.Cyr, Paris #496/R
£733 $1320 €1100 Couple (34x24cm-13x9in) s.d.1998 acrylic ink. 24-Apr-4 Cornette de St.Cyr, Paris #497
£764 $1276 €1100 Messieurs (23x18cm-9x7in) s.d.1998 acrylic paillette magazine sheet. 25-Oct-3 Cornette de St.Cyr, Paris #637
£833 $1317 €1200 Untitled (35x24cm-14x9in) s. acrylic paper on canvas prov. 27-Apr-3 Versailles Encheres #139
£833 $1392 €1200 I love (35x25cm-14x10in) s.d.1998 acrylic magazine sheet. 25-Oct-3 Cornette de St.Cyr, Paris #638
£1215 $1920 €1750 Untitled (38x46cm-15x18in) s.d.1998 acrylic collage on canvas exhib. 27-Apr-3 Versailles Encheres #140

£1329 $2285 €1900 Rave techno (45x37cm-18x15in) s. acrylic. 3-Dec-3 Tajan, Paris #496/R est:2000-2500
£1678 $2803 €2400 Untitled (39x29cm-15x11in) s.d.1987 acrylic paper prov. 29-Jun-3 Versailles Encheres #225/R
£1972 $3194 €2800 Totem (65x46cm-26x18in) s. acrylic. 5-Aug-3 Tajan, Paris #74/R est:3000-3500
£2168 $3685 €3100 La garden-party (62x66cm-24x26in) s.d.1986 acrylic. 27-Nov-3 Millon & Associes, Paris #251/R est:3000-4000
£2200 $3960 €3300 Untitled (46x55cm-18x22in) s.verso acrylic mixed media paper on canvas. 25-Apr-4 Versailles Encheres #219 est:3000-4000
£2349 $4299 €3500 General me voila (61x50cm-24x20in) s. acrylic sequins canvas. 7-Jul-4 Artcurial Briest, Paris #238 est:3500-4500
£2416 $4325 €3600 Compagnie Nationale Electrique (65x50cm-26x20in) s. acrylic. 30-May-4 Eric Pillon, Calais #298/R
£2431 $3840 €3500 Portrait d'Henri Maculot (65x50cm-26x20in) s.d.1989 acrylic paper prov. 27-Apr-3 Versailles Encheres #136
£2465 $3968 €3500 Ecstasy (54x46cm-21x18in) s. acrylic. 22-Aug-3 Deauville, France #133/R est:3000-4000
£2533 $4611 €3800 Portrait (61x54cm-24x21in) s.d.1989 acrylic brush prov. 29-Jun-4 Cornette de St.Cyr, Paris #100/R est:4000-5000
£2685 $4940 €4000 Animal en relief (65x81cm-26x32in) s. acrylic canvas wood painted c.2000. 24-Mar-4 Binoche, Paris #94/R est:4000-5000
£2797 $4671 €4000 Nu (65x46cm-26x18in) s. acrylic. 11-Oct-3 Cornette de St.Cyr, Paris #132/R est:4000-5000
£3000 $5520 €4500 Punk (99x72cm-39x28in) s. acrylic canvas on canvas painted 1986 prov. 9-Jun-4 Artcurial Briest, Paris #519/R est:5000-7000
£3125 $5219 €4500 Paysage aquatique (98x85cm-39x33in) s.d.1992 acrylic. 25-Oct-3 Cornette de St.Cyr, Paris #648 est:4500-5000
£3169 $5546 €4500 Plante carnivore (80x63cm-31x25in) s.d.1988 acrylic. 18-Dec-3 Cornette de St.Cyr, Paris #147/R est:4000-5000
£3355 $6174 €5100 Marie Lime (57x77cm-22x30in) acrylic over photograph painted 2000 exhib. 27-Jun-4 Versailles Encheres #181/R est:3000-3500
£3472 $5486 €5000 Untitled (100x74cm-39x29in) s. acrylic prov. 27-Apr-3 Versailles Encheres #135
£3472 $5486 €5000 Untitled (108x75cm-43x30in) s. acrylic paper on canvas prov. 27-Apr-3 Versailles Encheres #137
£3472 $5799 €5000 Sans titre (120x88cm-47x35in) s. acrylic prov. 25-Oct-3 Cornette de St.Cyr, Paris #635 est:5000-7000
£3497 $6014 €5000 La fausse gitane et cartofaille et raquetouffe cartofaille et (114x154cm-45x61in) s.d.1989 prov. 2-Dec-3 Calmels Cohen, Paris #94/R est:6000-8000
£3846 $7000 €5615 Quand elle le regard, Il est toute embrousine (139x112cm-55x44in) init.d.82. 29-Jun-4 Sotheby's, New York #547/R est:5000-7000
£4595 $8225 €6800 Untitled (150x115cm-59x45in) s. 4-May-4 Calmels Cohen, Paris #233/R est:7000-8000
£4698 $8645 €7000 Coca for me (93x73cm-37x29in) s. acrylic painted 1991. 29-Mar-4 Cornette de St.Cyr, Paris #124/R est:8000-10000
£4722 $7886 €6800 Le plongeur (97x135cm-38x53in) s. acrylic. 25-Oct-3 Cornette de St.Cyr, Paris #646/R est:6000-8000
£5034 $9010 €7500 Composition (134x86cm-53x34in) s.d.1986 acrylic. 28-May-4 Farsetti, Prato #140/R est:4200-5200
£5634 $9747 €8000 Untitled (128x106cm-50x42in) s.d.1987 acrylic prov.lit. 9-Dec-3 Artcurial Briest, Paris #384/R est:7000-9000
£7895 $14526 €11527 Mon ami (234x163cm-92x64in) s. acrylic. 23-Jun-4 Koller, Zurich #3087/R est:7000-9000 (S.FR 18000)
£8053 $14818 €12000 Rerock du peintre (116x89cm-46x35in) s.d.1982 acrylic. 29-Mar-4 Cornette de St.Cyr, Paris #123/R est:13000-15000
£8054 $14416 €12000 Pan dans les jambes (154x138cm-61x54in) s.d.83 acrylic. 26-May-4 Christie's, Paris #106/R est:15000-20000
£8108 $14271 €12000 Autoportrait (89x170cm-35x67in) s. acrylic painted c.1985 prov. 18-May-4 Tajan, Paris #140/R est:12000-15000
£8724 $16053 €13000 L'homme Poisson (200x150cm-79x59in) s. acrylic painted 1987. 29-Mar-4 Cornette de St.Cyr, Paris #110/R est:15000-18000
£9139 $17090 €13800 La bastille (184x100cm-72x39in) peinture acrylic. 20-Jul-4 Gioffredo, Nice #3/R
£9333 $17173 €14000 Femme et l'oiseau (194x266cm-76x105in) s.d.87 acrylic prov. 9-Jun-4 Artcurial Briest, Paris #512/R est:15000-20000
£9589 $15055 €14000 Rolls-Royce (130x195cm-51x77in) s. acrylic painted 1988 prov. 20-Apr-3 Deauville, France #151/R est:12000-15000
£9790 $16350 €14000 Personnages (228x138cm-90x54in) s.d.1983 acrylic. 11-Oct-3 Cornette de St.Cyr, Paris #124/R est:15000-18000
£10140 $16934 €14500 I love the beat (220x150cm-87x59in) s.d.1984 acrylic. 11-Oct-3 Cornette de St.Cyr, Paris #126/R est:15000-18000
£10490 $17833 €15000 Sans titre (206x133cm-81x52in) s.d.1984 acrylic prov. 25-Nov-3 Tajan, Paris #68/R est:15000-18000
£10564 $17113 €15000 Couple au vase de fleurs (207x123cm-81x48in) s.d. acrylic prov. 5-Aug-3 Tajan, Paris #69/R est:15000-20000
£11189 $18685 €16000 Fete a Marcel (162x140cm-64x55in) s.d.1983 acrylic prov. 29-Jun-3 Versailles Encheres #217/R
£11333 $20400 €17000 Self-portrait (127x204cm-50x80in) s. acrylic. 24-Apr-4 Cornette de St.Cyr, Paris #494/R est:18000
£11620 $20335 €16500 Jungle (156x137cm-61x54in) s.d.1986 acrylic. 18-Dec-3 Cornette de St.Cyr, Paris #145/R est:15000-20000
£12000 $21600 €18000 Repas frugal de deux con-vifs (97x162cm-38x64in) s. acrylic painted 1997 exhib. 25-Apr-4 Versailles Encheres #218 est:18000-20000
£12000 $21840 €18000 Homme poursuivi par des pirates (208x215cm-82x85in) s.i. acrylic prov.exhib.lit. 29-Jun-4 Cornette de St.Cyr, Paris #107/R est:15000-18000
£12238 $20437 €17500 Les musiciens (235x127cm-93x50in) s.d.1983 acrylic. 11-Oct-3 Cornette de St.Cyr, Paris #127/R est:18000-22000
£12333 $22817 €18500 Tete a l'envers (96x160cm-38x63in) s.d.1987 acrylic prov. 18-Jul-4 Sotheby's, Paris #286/R est:10000-15000
£12937 $21993 €18500 Personnages (152x116cm-60x46in) s.d.1987 acrylic prov. 25-Nov-3 Tajan, Paris #67/R est:10000-12000
£16000 $29600 €24000 Pensees d'amour et de problemes (250x250cm-98x98in) s. acrylic painted 1988 prov.lit. 18-Jul-4 Sotheby's, Paris #283/R est:15000-20000
£17449 $32107 €26000 Bataille (112x267cm-44x105in) s. acrylic printed tissue painted 1996. 29-Mar-4 Cornette de St.Cyr, Paris #120/R est:12000-15000
£18182 $30364 €26000 Il est des notres (150x216cm-59x85in) s. acrylic prov. 29-Jun-3 Versailles Encheres #218/R est:30000
£20134 $37047 €30000 La Fiancee (227x156cm-89x61in) s.d.1984 acrylic. 29-Mar-4 Cornette de St.Cyr, Paris #10/R est:20000-25000

Sculpture

£1275 $2257 €1900 Christ (31x23x0cm-12x9x0in) s. verso mixed media brush tubes of paint exec 1994. 28-Apr-4 Artcurial Briest, Paris #423/R est:1000-1200
£1399 $2336 €2000 Untitled (32cm-13in) mixed media paint on brush prov. 29-Jun-3 Versailles Encheres #223/R
£2778 $4583 €4000 Arc de triomphe (33x45cm-13x18in) s.num.5/8 paint resin. 2-Jul-3 Cornette de St.Cyr, Paris #160/R est:4000-5000
£6000 $11100 €9000 Craignos (90x80x50cm-35x31x20in) s. painted wood exec.1995 prov. 18-Jul-4 Sotheby's, Paris #212/R est:5000-7000
£8667 $16033 €13000 Commode (76x110cm-30x43in) painted wood prov.exhib. 18-Jul-4 Sotheby's, Paris #192/R est:6000-8000

Works on paper

£287 $516 €430 Pour Margot (30x21cm-12x8in) s. felt-tip pen. 24-Apr-4 Cornette de St.Cyr, Paris #493
£300 $540 €450 Extra-terrestre (24x15cm-9x6in) s. felt-tip pen dr. 24-Apr-4 Cornette de St.Cyr, Paris #492
£317 $510 €450 Tuer (32x24cm-13x9in) s. felt-tip pen dr. 11-May-3 Versailles Encheres #171
£347 $580 €500 Le photographe (29x21cm-11x8in) s. felt. 25-Oct-3 Cornette de St.Cyr, Paris #647
£373 $672 €560 Autour de Lautrec (23x19cm-9x7in) s. felt-tip pen. 24-Apr-4 Cornette de St.Cyr, Paris #490
£400 $736 €600 Robert Combas, autoportrait (30x21cm-12x8in) s.d.2000 felt tip. 11-Jun-4 Pierre Berge, Paris #97/R
£405 $766 €600 Bataille (22x22cm-9x9in) s. black felt pen. 21-Feb-4 Cornette de St.Cyr, Paris #265
£440 $792 €660 Photographer (27x19cm-11x7in) s.d.1999 felt-tip pen dr. 24-Apr-4 Cornette de St.Cyr, Paris #491
£507 $958 €750 Femme (21x15cm-8x6in) ball point pen col felt pen. 21-Feb-4 Cornette de St.Cyr, Paris #267/R
£526 $968 €800 Untitled (21x29cm-8x11in) s. felt-tip pen dr exec.1990. 27-Jun-4 Versailles Encheres #195
£556 $928 €800 La femme suceuse de sexe (21x15cm-8x6in) s.i.d.1983 verso ink prov. 25-Oct-3 Cornette de St.Cyr, Paris #639
£559 $934 €800 Untitled (21x16cm-8x6in) s.d.1981 felt-tip pen prov. 29-Jun-3 Versailles Encheres #234
£571 $1061 €850 Personnage (61x47cm-24x19in) s.d.1998 gouache. 3-Mar-4 Artcurial Briest, Paris #349
£600 $1098 €900 Scene de bataille (28x40cm-11x16in) s.d.87 felt tip pen. 7-Jun-4 Palais de Beaux Arts, Brussels #164
£671 $1188 €1000 Composition en noir (50x50cm-20x20in) s. marker acrylic. 28-Apr-4 Artcurial Briest, Paris #422
£694 $1160 €1000 Nation (23x18cm-9x7in) s. felt paillette. 25-Oct-3 Cornette de St.Cyr, Paris #636/R
£743 $1405 €1100 Sans titre (29x21cm-11x8in) s. sanguine double-sided prov. 21-Feb-4 Cornette de St.Cyr, Paris #272/R
£839 $1544 €1250 Buste tatoue (46x31cm-18x12in) s. lead pencil ink. 29-Mar-4 Lombrail & Teucquam, Paris #141/R
£940 $1682 €1400 Jambes poilues (32x40cm-13x16in) s.d.82 felt-tip pen. 26-May-4 Christie's, Paris #104/R
£1423 $2461 €2020 Le roi (110x84cm-43x33in) s. mixed media. 10-Dec-3 Millon & Associes, Paris #116 est:1500-2000
£1944 $3247 €2800 Composition aux mannequins (30x64cm-12x25in) s. mixed media. 23-Oct-3 Credit Municipal, Paris #72 est:1200-1500
£2098 $3503 €3000 Untitled (20x29cm-8x11in) s.d.1984 wax crayon. 29-Jun-3 Versailles Encheres #227/R
£2276 $3641 €3300 Rage de dents (58x21cm-23x8in) s.d. pastel. 13-Mar-3 Galleria Pace, Milan #54/R

COMBAZ, Ghisbert (1869-1941) Belgian

£336 $594 €500 Village ardennais (65x50cm-26x20in) s.d.1913 cardboard. 27-Apr-4 Campo & Campo, Antwerp #44

COMBES, Andre (20th C) French

£463 $750 €676 Still life with roses (61x48cm-24x19in) s. 2-Aug-3 Neal Auction Company, New Orleans #579/R

COMBET-DESCOMBES, Pierre (1885-1966) French

£1034 $1717 €1500 Sunset (33x54cm-13x21in) board. 1-Oct-3 Della Rocca, Turin #244/R est:1000-1200

Works on paper

£400 $720 €600 Village sous la neige (23x30cm-9x12in) s. pastel. 20-Apr-4 Chenu & Scrive, Lyon #84/R
£600 $1080 €900 Nu couche, tete en bas (48x33cm-19x13in) sanguine. 20-Apr-4 Chenu & Scrive, Lyon #64/R
£633 $1140 €950 Nu (28x38cm-11x15in) s. chl htd white chk. 20-Apr-4 Chenu & Scrive, Lyon #65/R
£667 $1227 €1000 Female nude (48x62cm-19x24in) chl sanguine exhib. 8-Jun-4 Della Rocca, Turin #222/R
£733 $1320 €1100 Femme au buste nu (47x30cm-19x12in) s. pastel. 20-Apr-4 Chenu & Scrive, Lyon #61/R
£800 $1440 €1200 Bouquet de fleurs (41x33cm-16x13in) s. pastel. 20-Apr-4 Chenu & Scrive, Lyon #63/R
£1200 $2160 €1800 Nu aux bas roses (47x30cm-19x12in) s.d.29 chl pastel. 20-Apr-4 Chenu & Scrive, Lyon #62/R est:700-800

COMBS, Scott (20th C) British?

£306 $480 €440 Howth Lighthouse (7x10cm-3x4in) s.d.26 oil on card. 26-Aug-3 Thomas Adams, Dublin #2

COMENSOLI, Mario (1922-1993) Swiss/Italian

£969 $1648 €1415 Still life with fishes in dish (55x66cm-22x26in) s. panel. 7-Nov-3 Dobiaschofsky, Bern #219/R (S.FR 2200)
£1223 $2225 €1786 Untitled (70x61cm-28x24in) s. oil tempera. 16-Jun-4 Fischer, Luzern #1338/R est:3000-4000 (S.FR 2800)
£4741 $8487 €6922 Man resting (50x25cm-20x10in) s. verso prov. 17-May-4 Beurret, Zurich #44/R est:2000-4000 (S.FR 11000)
£11312 $19570 €16516 The cat (130x150cm-51x59in) s.d.1966. 9-Dec-3 Sotheby's, Zurich #117/R est:19000-25000 (S.FR 25000)

Works on paper

£524 $964 €765 Untitled (37x34cm-15x13in) s. Indian ink. 14-Jun-4 Philippe Schuler, Zurich #4119/R (S.FR 1200)
£611 $1125 €892 For flute or pistol (49x36cm-19x14in) s. gouache. 8-Jun-4 Germann, Zurich #782 (S.FR 1400)
£679 $1133 €991 Couple with child (45x34cm-18x13in) s. chl gouache. 24-Jun-3 Germann, Zurich #933 (S.FR 1500)
£877 $1614 €1280 Two figures (48x31cm-19x12in) s.d.90 chl gouache. 23-Jun-4 Koller, Zurich #3124/R (S.FR 2000)
£1053 $1937 €1537 Flowerpot with geraniums (103x72cm-41x28in) s. mixed media. 23-Jun-4 Koller, Zurich #3127/R (S.FR 2400)

£1135	$2089	€1657	Film scene (47x36cm-19x14in) s. mixed media. 8-Jun-4 Germann, Zurich #780 est:1500-2000 (S.FR 2600)
£1357	$2267	€1981	Untitled (47x35cm-19x14in) s.d.1990 mixed media. 24-Jun-3 Germann, Zurich #97/R est:2200-2600 (S.FR 3000)
£1629	$2720	€2378	Untitled (68x51cm-27x20in) s.d.1990 mixed media. 24-Jun-3 Germann, Zurich #98/R est:3800-4200 (S.FR 3600)
£2155	$3858	€3146	Young footballer (99x69cm-39x27in) s.d.78 gouache. 14-May-4 Dobiaschofsky, Bern #239/R est:7000 (S.FR 5000)

COMERFORD, John (1770-1832) Irish

Miniatures

£1800	$3060	€2628	Thomas Manners-Sutton (13cm-5in) papier mache frame lit. 18-Nov-3 Bonhams, New Bond Street #131/R est:1000-1500

COMERRE, Léon (1850-1916) French

£493	$853	€700	Porte de palais (29x18cm-11x7in) studio st. studio st.verso panel. 15-Dec-3 Gros & Delettrez, Paris #163/R
£789	$1453	€1200	Portrait de jeune femme (45x34cm-18x13in) s. 25-Jun-4 Millon & Associes, Paris #35/R
£1611	$2980	€2400	Projet pour le Triomphe de Venus. st.sig. lit. 14-Mar-4 St-Germain-en-Laye Encheres #57/R est:2500-3000
£1987	$3636	€3000	Portrait de Madame Comerre (49x36cm-19x14in) s. prov.lit. 9-Apr-4 Bailly Pommery, Paris #70/R est:3000-4000
£2128	$3447	€3000	Depart pour le bal (69x50cm-27x20in) s. 23-May-3 Sotheby's, Paris #44/R est:3000-4000
£3020	$5406	€4500	Elegante a l'eventail (98x89cm-39x35in) s. 25-May-4 Chambelland & Giafferi, Paris #47/R est:5000-6000
£3901	$6319	€5500	Jeune fille au soleil (65x47cm-26x19in) s. lit. 23-May-3 Sotheby's, Paris #42/R est:3000-4000
£8824	$15000	€12883	L'Orientale (106x60cm-42x24in) s. studio st.verso lit. 28-Oct-3 Sotheby's, New York #93/R est:18000-25000
£11268	$18704	€16000	Au soleil (18x131cm-7x52in) s. 13-Jun-3 Renaud, Paris #42/R est:6000
£14706	$25000	€21471	Study for le Manteau Legendaire (74x116cm-29x46in) s. lit. 28-Oct-3 Sotheby's, New York #89/R est:30000-40000
£18972	$33960	€27699	Le Triomphe du Cygne (64x99cm-25x39in) s. prov.lit. 15-May-4 Christie's, Sydney #114/R est:40000-60000 (A.D 48000)
£19763	$35375	€28854	Luna (68x148cm-27x58in) s. prov.exhib. 15-May-4 Christie's, Sydney #111/R est:60000-80000 (A.D 50000)

COMFORT, Charles Fraser (1900-1994) Canadian

£1040	$1903	€1518	Outer Islands, Georgian Bay (30x40cm-12x16in) s.d.50 board. 1-Jun-4 Joyner Waddington, Toronto #1/R est:2500-3000 (C.D 2600)
£1040	$1903	€1518	Roseate Haze, Lake Clear (30x40cm-12x16in) s. panel painted 1979 prov. 1-Jun-4 Joyner Waddington, Toronto #142/R est:3000-4000 (C.D 2600)
£1239	$2106	€1809	Lake Clear (30x41cm-12x16in) s. i.d.1979 verso panel prov. 21-Nov-3 Walker's, Ottawa #75/R est:2000-3000 (C.D 2750)
£2800	$5124	€4088	Ile au Pirate, Georgian Bay (25x30cm-10x12in) s.d.30 board prov. 1-Jun-4 Joyner Waddington, Toronto #97/R est:4000-6000 (C.D 7000)
£2928	$4977	€4275	Shoreline, Starr's Island (51x66cm-20x26in) s. s.i.verso. 18-Nov-3 Sotheby's, Toronto #84/R est:5000-7000 (C.D 6500)
£3125	$5375	€4563	Fisherman's Wharf, Ingonish NS (50x65cm-20x26in) s. 2-Dec-3 Joyner Waddington, Toronto #12/R est:5000-7000 (C.D 7000)
£3348	$5759	€4888	Outer shoreline, Georgian Bay - Split Rock Island (30x40cm-12x16in) s. canvasboard painted 1960 prov. 2-Dec-3 Joyner Waddington, Toronto #62/R est:6000-7000 (C.D 7500)

Works on paper

£541	$919	€790	Break in the clouds (35x49cm-14x19in) s. i.d.1942 verso W/C. 21-Nov-3 Walker's, Ottawa #74/R (C.D 1200)

COMFORT, Tom Tyrone (1909-1939) American

£1044	$1900	€1524	Ferrets in landscape (30x41cm-12x16in) s. board. 15-Jun-4 John Moran, Pasadena #14 est:800-1200

COMINAL, Achille (19th C) French?

Photographs

£5594	$9343	€8000	Vue d'Algerie. s. salt print exec.c.1853. 10-Oct-3 Beaussant & Lefèvre, Paris #63/R est:5000-6000

COMINETTI, Ernesto (1900-1990) Italian

£272	$487	€400	Garden in Scafa (60x45cm-24x18in) s. i.on stretcher. 22-Mar-4 Sant Agostino, Torino #11/R

COMINOTTO, Leonardo (1898-?) Italian

£426	$689	€600	Natura morta con pesci e limoni (30x40cm-12x16in) s. canvas on board. 22-May-3 Stadion, Trieste #327/R
£574	$1085	€850	Bread and nuts (30x40cm-12x16in) s. 20-Feb-4 Stadion, Trieste #180/R

COMINS, Eben F (1875-1949) American

£1267	$2267	€1900	Marine a Concarneau (24x28cm-9x11in) s. 16-May-4 Thierry & Lannon, Brest #129/R est:2000-3000

COMMENT, Jean-François (1919-2002) Swiss

£362	$615	€529	Petit poeme du matin (25x35cm-10x14in) s.d.1978-80. 22-Nov-3 Burkhard, Luzern #21/R (S.FR 800)
£362	$615	€529	Poeme du soir (25x35cm-10x14in) s.d.1978-80. 22-Nov-3 Burkhard, Luzern #24/R (S.FR 800)

Works on paper

£881	$1498	€1286	Jeune fille (28x19cm-11x7in) s.d.46 i. verso W/C bodycol. 5-Nov-3 Dobiaschofsky, Bern #443/R (S.FR 2000)

COMMERE, Jean Yves (1920-1986) French

£870	$1591	€1270	Zuzette et Jaquine (146x114cm-57x45in) s. exhib. 5-Jun-4 Galerie du Rhone, Sion #306/R (S.FR 2000)
£960	$1796	€1450	Apres-midi a Chausey (99x71cm-39x28in) s. 24-Jul-4 Thierry & Lannon, Brest #252/R
£1761	$3046	€2500	Nature morte au coq (97x130cm-38x51in) s. 9-Dec-3 Chambelland & Giafferi, Paris #36/R est:2500-3000
£1840	$3000	€2686	Les bles (89x129cm-35x51in) s. 25-Sep-3 Christie's, Rockefeller NY #537/R est:4000-6000
£2148	$3995	€3200	Barque dans la lumiere (89x130cm-35x51in) s. 3-Mar-4 Tajan, Paris #173/R est:3000-4000
£2817	$4873	€4000	Champ de ble (89x130cm-35x51in) s. 14-Dec-3 Eric Pillon, Calais #267/R

Works on paper

£280	$445	€409	Tourville en Normandie (74x99cm-29x39in) s.d.1963 W/C ink. 9-Sep-3 Gorringes, Lewes #1994

COMMUNAL, Joseph (1876-1962) French

£599	$994	€850	Les sommets enneiges (25x34cm-10x13in) s. panel. 11-Jun-3 Delorme & Bocage, Paris #61
£669	$1157	€950	Paysage de Montagne (50x61cm-20x24in) s. panel exhib. 13-Dec-3 Martinot & Savignat, Pontoise #221
£699	$1168	€1000	Paysage de montagne enneige (33x41cm-13x16in) s. cardboard. 25-Jun-3 Blanchet, Paris #12
£733	$1335	€1100	Cruet en Savoie (49x59cm-19x23in) s. panel. 29-Jun-4 Chenu & Scrive, Lyon #54/R
£1067	$1920	€1600	Neige sur les monts de Chambery. s.i.verso isorel. 20-Apr-4 Chenu & Scrive, Lyon #66/R est:1500-2000
£1986	$3316	€2800	Pointe de Mean Martin, Glaciers des Roches vue prise des evettes (32x40cm-13x16in) s. isorel panel. 19-Oct-3 Anaf, Lyon #78/R est:1000-1500
£2133	$3883	€3200	Barque en bord de riviere (60x90cm-24x35in) s. panel. 4-Jul-4 Eric Pillon, Calais #135/R
£2340	$3909	€3300	Aiguilles de petaret, vue du refuge fornio (40x32cm-16x13in) s. panel. 19-Oct-3 Anaf, Lyon #79 est:1000-1500

Works on paper

£1184	$2179	€1800	Crepuscule (27x35cm-11x14in) s. s.i. verso wax pastel panel prov. 28-Jun-4 Joron-Derem, Paris #100 est:600-800
£1184	$2179	€1800	Impression (27x35cm-11x14in) s. s.i. verso was pastel panel prov. 28-Jun-4 Joron-Derem, Paris #101/R est:600-800

COMOLERA, Melanie de (fl.1816-1854) French

£19553	$35000	€28547	Peonies, roses, carnations,iris and other flowers in terracotta vase (74x59cm-29x23in) s.d.1827. 27-May-4 Sotheby's, New York #94/R est:30000-40000

COMOLERA, Paul (1818-1897) French

Sculpture

£2348	$4250	€3428	Champion Marco (51cm-20in) s.i. pat bronze. 30-Mar-4 Bonhams & Butterfields, San Francisco #18/R est:2000-3000

COMOLLI, Gigi (1893-1976) Italian

£282	$487	€400	Wood (25x23cm-10x9in) s. 9-Dec-3 Finarte Semenzato, Milan #135/R
£336	$601	€500	Bushes (21x34cm-8x13in) s. i.verso board. 25-May-4 Finarte Semenzato, Milan #163/R
£432	$708	€600	River landscape (40x50cm-16x20in) 5-Jun-3 Adma, Formigine #734
£1449	$2377	€2000	On the Ticino (51x39cm-20x15in) s. board. 27-May-3 Il Ponte, Milan #912/R
£1549	$2572	€2200	Boats and fisherman on the river (50x65cm-20x26in) s.d.1964 wood. 11-Jun-3 Christie's, Rome #178/R est:1000-1500
£1678	$3003	€2500	Vase of flowers (50x60cm-20x24in) s. 25-May-4 Finarte Semenzato, Milan #43/R est:2000-2200
£5797	$9507	€8000	Landscape of Rocca of Angera (91x116cm-36x46in) s.d.1921. 27-May-3 Finarte Semenzato, Milan #25/R est:8000-9000

COMOLLI, Gigi (attrib) (1893-1976) Italian

£559	$1029	€850	Woodland pasture near Milan (60x50cm-24x20in) s. panel. 24-Jun-4 Dr Fritz Nagel, Stuttgart #696/R
£987	$1816	€1500	Woodland near Milan (60x69cm-24x27in) s. 24-Jun-4 Dr Fritz Nagel, Stuttgart #695/R est:900

COMPAGNO, Scipione (attrib) (1624-1685) Italian

£3667	$6563	€5500	Saint John the Baptist preaching. Moses and the snakes (37x47cm-15x19in) pair. 12-May-4 Finarte Semenzato, Milan #97/R est:6000-8000
£8000	$14320	€12000	River landscape with soldiers (96x165cm-38x65in) 17-May-4 Finarte Semenzato, Rome #99/R est:16000-18000

COMPARD, Émile (1900-1977) French

£267	$480	€400	Composition (49x118cm-19x46in) s.d.1945 panel. 24-Apr-4 Cornette de St.Cyr, Paris #500
£464	$867	€700	Doelan (41x27cm-16x11in) s. 24-Jul-4 Thierry & Lannon, Brest #241
£497	$929	€750	Doelan (73x60cm-29x24in) s. 24-Jul-4 Thierry & Lannon, Brest #356/R
£733	$1313	€1100	Doelan (65x54cm-26x21in) s. d.1969 verso. 16-May-4 Thierry & Lannon, Brest #298
£739	$1294	€1050	Port de Doelan (73x60cm-29x24in) s. 21-Dec-3 Thierry & Lannon, Brest #295
£775	$1356	€1100	Tahitienne de profil (92x74cm-36x29in) s. 21-Dec-3 Thierry & Lannon, Brest #294
£861	$1610	€1300	Doelan (73x54cm-29x21in) s.d.41. 24-Jul-4 Thierry & Lannon, Brest #240/R est:1200-1500
£1329	$2285	€1900	Doelan, pahre (79x65cm-31x26in) 7-Dec-3 Livinec, Gaudcheau & Jezequel, Rennes #64/R

COMPLOJ, Heinrich (1879-1967) Austrian

£533	$981	€800	Still lfie with sunflowers and clock (57x50cm-22x20in) s.d.1954 masonite. 9-Jun-4 Dorotheum, Salzburg #563/R
£667	$1227	€1000	Still lfie with daisies and grapes (57x50cm-22x20in) s.d.1963 canvas on masonite. 9-Jun-4 Dorotheum, Salzburg #559/R

COMPRIS, Maurice (1885-1939) American

£503	$900	€734	Fall landscape (66x61cm-26x24in) 7-May-4 Douglas, South Deerfield #33
£2235	$4000	€3263	Gloucester winter scene (71x76cm-28x30in) s. 8-Jan-4 James Julia, Fairfield #572/R est:4000-6000
£3580	$5800	€5191	Winter thaw (102x91cm-40x36in) s. 8-Aug-3 Barridorf, Portland #198/R est:5000-7000

COMPTE-CALIX, François Claudius (1813-1880) French

£4400	$7920	€6600	Marchand d'amour (31x38cm-12x15in) s.i.d.1851 panel. 25-Apr-4 Chenu & Scrive, Lyon #61/R est:5000-5500
£5333	$9813	€8000	La lecon de dessin sur la plage (25x43cm-10x17in) s. panel. 11-Jun-4 Claude Aguttes, Neuilly #7/R est:6000-8000
£7895	$14526	€12000	Reve d'amour brise (99x141cm-39x56in) s. 24-Jun-4 Christie's, Paris #140/R est:12000-15000

COMPTON, Edward Harrison (1881-1960) British

£437	$769	€638	Landscape with mountain stream (50x70cm-20x28in) s. prov. 22-May-4 Galerie Gloggner, Luzern #23/R (S.FR 1000)
£634	$1096	€900	Mountains with trees and rocks (71x91cm-28x36in) s. 12-Dec-3 Altus, Berlin #601/R
£739	$1353	€1079	Mountain landscape (69x99cm-27x39in) s. 4-Jun-4 Zofingen, Switzerland #2435/R (S.FR 1700)
£1528	$2521	€2200	Hilly landscape with stream (63x80cm-25x31in) s. 2-Jul-3 Neumeister, Munich #619/R est:2500
£1667	$2717	€2400	Racing mountain stream (80x70cm-31x28in) s. 25-Sep-3 Dr Fritz Nagel, Stuttgart #1340/R est:1700
£1879	$3364	€2800	Piece of forest (70x90cm-28x35in) s. 27-May-4 Dorotheum, Vienna #232/R est:3000-3600
£1931	$3225	€2800	Eiger (60x80cm-24x31in) s. 9-Jul-3 Hugo Ruef, Munich #70/R est:1800
£2467	$4489	€3700	High mountain landscape (75x97cm-30x38in) s. canvas on panel. 30-Jun-4 Neumeister, Munich #523/R est:1800
£2585	$4627	€3800	Ehrwald near the Zugspitze (61x81cm-24x32in) s.d.1920. 17-Mar-4 Neumeister, Munich #421/R est:2500
£3020	$5406	€4500	Mountain landscape (75x105cm-30x41in) s. 27-May-4 Dorotheum, Vienna #30/R est:3400-4000

Works on paper

£308	$529	€440	Mountain landscape with village church, water source and figures (15x21cm-6x8in) s. W/C. 5-Dec-3 Michael Zeller, Lindau #592/R
£308	$529	€440	Rowberrow (26x32cm-10x13in) s.i.d.14 W/C. 5-Dec-3 Michael Zeller, Lindau #594/R
£333	$543	€480	Rothenburg o d T - Hegereiterhaus in Spitalhof (32x25cm-13x10in) s.d.49 W/C over pencil. 24-Sep-3 Neumeister, Munich #263/R
£333	$607	€500	Mountain landscape (24x33cm-9x13in) s. pencil. 1-Jul-4 Weidler, Nurnberg #4502/R
£345	$572	€500	Red stone entrance (23x19cm-9x7in) mono. w/C. 30-Sep-3 Dorotheum, Vienna #261/R
£361	$589	€520	Muhltal near Gauting (14x22cm-6x9in) s.i. brush. 24-Sep-3 Neumeister, Munich #264/R
£361	$667	€527	Southern landscape with mountains and rapids (34x25cm-13x10in) s. W/C. 15-Mar-4 Rasmussen, Vejle #110/R (D.KR 4000)
£371	$637	€530	Sunny woodland path on spring day (33x24cm-13x9in) s.d.1906 W/C. 5-Dec-3 Michael Zeller, Lindau #593/R
£427	$777	€640	Building ins Nurnberg (42x31cm-17x12in) s.d.1911 W/C htd white double-sided. 30-Jun-4 Neumeister, Munich #396/R
£434	$746	€620	High mountain landscape with farmstead (21x31cm-8x12in) s.d.1917 W/C. 5-Dec-3 Michael Zeller, Lindau #596/R
£462	$794	€660	Harbour with sailing ships and Monte Pellegrino (23x30cm-9x12in) s.i.d.24 W/C. 5-Dec-3 Michael Zeller, Lindau #599/R
£517	$859	€750	Mountain lake (23x30cm-9x12in) mono.d.16.7.20 pencil W/C. 30-Sep-3 Dorotheum, Vienna #259/R
£528	$860	€760	Alpine landscape with gathering storm (28x36cm-11x14in) s. W/C gouache. 26-Sep-3 Bolland & Marotz, Bremen #642/R
£533	$971	€800	View of the theatre in Saarbrucken (32x42cm-13x17in) s. W/C. 1-Jul-4 Van Ham, Cologne #1248
£567	$1031	€850	Entrance to Greifenburg Castle (25x33cm-10x13in) s.i.d.11.8.28 W/C on pencil htd white. 30-Jun-4 Neumeister, Munich #397/R
£567	$1031	€850	Castle garden, Vienna (33x26cm-13x10in) s.i.d.25.7.30 W/C on pencil htd white. 30-Jun-4 Neumeister, Munich #398/R
£690	$1234	€1007	Visp (27x18cm-11x7in) s. i.d.26 IX.07 W/C. 13-May-4 Stuker, Bern #9134/R est:2000-3000 (S.FR 1600)
£699	$1203	€1000	High mountain landscape (28x38cm-11x15in) s.d.1944 W/C. 5-Dec-3 Michael Zeller, Lindau #600/R
£738	$1358	€1100	Berchtesgaden, Kehlstein, Goll, Brett (21x34cm-8x13in) s.i.d.1911 verso W/C. 26-Mar-4 Dorotheum, Vienna #198/R
£769	$1285	€1100	Farmstead near Neustift in Stubaital (30x43cm-12x17in) s. i. verso W/C. 11-Oct-3 Hans Stahl, Hamburg #10/R
£769	$1323	€1100	Mountain landscape with stream and walkers (26x34cm-10x13in) s. W/C over pencil htd white. 3-Dec-3 Neumeister, Munich #375/R
£769	$1323	€1100	Mountain stream (36x27cm-14x11in) s.d.1923 W/C over pencil. 3-Dec-3 Neumeister, Munich #376/R
£800	$1456	€1200	Glacier in a mountainous landscape (37x34cm-15x13in) s.d.1934 W/C. 1-Jul-4 Van Ham, Cologne #1249
£872	$1605	€1300	Berchtesgaden, Hochkalter (23x34cm-9x13in) s.i. verso W/C. 26-Mar-4 Dorotheum, Vienna #200
£1007	$1852	€1500	Berchtesgaden, Watzmann, Grunstein, Hochkalter (23x34cm-9x13in) s.i. verso W/C. 26-Mar-4 Dorotheum, Vienna #201 est:1800-2000
£1259	$2165	€1800	The Alster (36x48cm-14x19in) s.d.1958 W/C over pencil. 2-Dec-3 Hauswedell & Nolte, Hamburg #86/R est:1500
£1329	$2285	€1900	Sicilian landscape with church (42x61cm-17x24in) s. 5-Dec-3 Michael Zeller, Lindau #601/R est:1500

COMPTON, Edward Theodore (1849-1921) British

£833	$1358	€1200	Autumn meadow landscape (50x73cm-20x29in) s. canvas on board. 24-Sep-3 Neumeister, Munich #407
£1048	$1907	€1530	Mountain landscape in the Maderaner Valley (27x36cm-11x14in) i.d.18/8/83 cardboard. 16-Jun-4 Fischer, Luzern #1208/R est:2000-3000 (S.FR 2400)
£3493	$6358	€5100	On the Tirol border (49x69cm-19x27in) s. cardboard. 16-Jun-4 Fischer, Luzern #1206/R est:8000-10000 (S.FR 8000)
£4196	$7133	€6000	Alpine flowers (64x45cm-25x18in) s.d.1887. 28-Nov-3 Wiener Kunst Auktionen, Vienna #445/R est:6000-12000
£5240	$9537	€7650	View of a mountain lake, with a village in the distance (56x92cm-22x36in) s.i.d.DCLXXIX 1889. 16-Jun-4 Fischer, Luzern #1207/R est:12000-15000 (S.FR 12000)
£6711	$12349	€10000	Wooden huts round chapel in alpine panorama (35x54cm-14x21in) s. i. verso lit. 25-Mar-4 Karlheinz Kaupp, Staufen #2386/R est:1500
£7692	$12846	€11000	Bernese Oberland on summer's day with Eiger, Monch and Jungfrau (89x118cm-35x46in) s. 27-Jun-3 Michael Zeller, Lindau #507/R est:5000
£9441	$16238	€13500	The Winklerturm from Vashutte (66x46cm-26x18in) s.d.1909 canvas on canvas prov. 5-Dec-3 Ketterer, Munich #18/R est:4000-6000
£10667	$19413	€16000	Morning in the high mountains - Monte Cristallo (70x100cm-28x39in) s.d.1904. 30-Jun-4 Neumeister, Munich #525/R est:7000

Works on paper

£355	$592	€500	Mediterranean coast with small boat (22x27cm-9x11in) s.i. 17-Oct-3 Behringer, Furth #1879/R
£620	$1141	€905	Alpine scene with foreground lake (25x45cm-10x18in) s. W/C htd white. 29-Mar-4 Bonhams, Bath #20/R
£662	$1205	€1000	Les Aiguilles, Montblanc massiv (26x32cm-10x13in) s. W/C. 16-Jun-4 Hugo Ruef, Munich #1152/R
£867	$1551	€1300	Heathland (22x35cm-9x14in) s.d.12.V.1909 W/C board. 13-May-4 Dorotheum, Linz #534/R
£1000	$1840	€1460	Lyn Ogwen and Tryfan, Wales (30x43cm-12x17in) init.d.09 W/C exhib. 8-Jun-4 Bonhams, New Bond Street #12/R est:800-1200
£1300	$2405	€1898	Winter landscape (26x36cm-10x14in) s.d.1878 W/C. 9-Mar-4 Bonhams, New Bond Street #16/R est:700-1000
£1818	$3036	€2600	Southern Tyrolean farmstead (41x31cm-16x12in) s.d.1905 W/C. 10-Oct-3 Winterberg, Heidelberg #557/R est:1850
£2600	$4784	€3900	View of the Monch and Jungfrau from Lauterbrunnental (31x50cm-12x20in) s. i.verso W/C. 11-Jun-4 Wendl, Rudolstadt #3986/R est:950
£2715	$4615	€3964	Alpine landscape with ruined fortress overlooking extensive valley (31x49cm-12x19in) s.d.1878 W/C. 19-Nov-3 Fischer, Luzern #2446 est:4500-5500 (S.FR 6000)
£3000	$5370	€4500	Saas Fee (22x36cm-9x14in) s.i.d.19.VII.07 grisaille W/C board. 13-May-4 Dorotheum, Linz #535/R est:2000-2800
£3020	$5406	€4500	Dolsach in Karnten (25x36cm-10x14in) s.d.4.X.05 pencil W/C. 27-May-4 Dorotheum, Graz #96/R est:1100
£3394	$5769	€4955	Monte Rosa - Head of Val Amizasca (45x68cm-18x27in) s.d.1878 i. verso W/C. 19-Nov-3 Fischer, Luzern #2445/R est:7500-8500 (S.FR 7500)
£3867	$6921	€5800	Latemar towers in front of the Rotlahn (37x25cm-15x10in) s.i. board prov.lit. 14-May-4 Ketterer, Munich #117/R est:3000-4000
£8000	$14320	€12000	Forcla Surloy (27x36cm-11x14in) s.i.d.19.VII.14 W/C board. 13-May-4 Dorotheum, Linz #533/R est:3000-4000

COMPTON, Henry Eugene (fl.1907-1933) British

£900	$1665	€1314	Rural landscape with figures by a mill and cattle watering (13x20cm-5x8in) one s.indis d. pair. 13-Feb-4 Keys, Aylsham #765

COMTOIS, Henry le (?) ?

£1773	$2961	€2500	Les jeunes danseurs sur la terrasse du palais (73x92cm-29x36in) s. 19-Oct-3 St-Germain-en-Laye Encheres #25/R est:1300-1500
£1773	$2961	€2500	Les jeunes musiciens sur la terrasse du palais (73x92cm-29x36in) s. 19-Oct-3 St-Germain-en-Laye Encheres #26/R est:1300-1500

COMTOIS, Louis (1945-1990) Canadian?

Works on paper

£1200	$2196	€1752	Chromatic presence 7 (40x57cm-16x22in) s.d.1987 mixed media. 1-Jun-4 Joyner Waddington, Toronto #210/R est:3000-4000 (C.D 3000)

CONAN, Gilbert (20th C) French

£350	$594	€500	Greve (33x41cm-13x16in) s. 29-Nov-3 Neret-Minet, Paris #35/R

CONANT, Lucy Scarborough (1867-1921) American

Works on paper

£1087	$2000	€1587	View of a snowy peak. Landscapes (34x19cm-13x7in) s. gouache W/C set of four different sizes. 27-Jun-4 Bonhams & Butterfields, San Francisco #3829/R est:2000-3000

CONCA, Juan (?) ?

£4388	$6932	€6406	Our Lady of La Manga (37x28cm-15x11in) board. 24-Jul-3 Louis Morton, Mexico #9/R (M.P 72000)

CONCA, Sebastiano (1676-1764) Italian

£8219	$13973	€12000	Mac with Saint Filippo Neri and Saint Nicholas (64x50cm-25x20in) oval lit. 7-Nov-3 Farsetti, Prato #520/R est:12000-15000
£13000	$23790	€18980	Saint Cecillia (136x100cm-54x39in) 7-Jul-4 Christie's, London #102/R est:15000-20000
£14765	$27168	€22000	La Saint Famille avec le petit Saint Jean Baptiste (48x39cm-19x15in) copper. 24-Mar-4 Tajan, Paris #24/R est:12000-15000
£197183	$345070	€280000	Allegory of Justice. Allegory of Carefulness. Allegory of Temperance. Allegory of Strength (324x195cm-128x77in) set of 4 prov.lit. 17-Dec-3 Christie's, Rome #492/R est:300000-400000

CONCA, Sebastiano (style) (1676-1764) Italian

£10000	$17200	€14600	Madonna and Child (90x70cm-35x28in) prov. 2-Dec-3 Bukowskis, Stockholm #406/R est:40000-50000 (S.KR 130000)

CONCA, Tommaso (attrib) (?-1815) Italian

£5298	$9642	€8000	Dates miracle (31x20cm-12x8in) copper. 16-Jun-4 Christie's, Rome #365/R est:9000-12000
£5500	$10285	€8030	Penitent Magdalen (62x49cm-24x19in) s.i.d.1761 verso. 27-Feb-4 Christie's, Kensington #201/R est:1000-1500
£5822	$9897	€8500	Holy Family with Saint John (111x85cm-44x33in) lit. 7-Nov-3 Farsetti, Prato #495/R est:6500-7500

CONCEPCION PEREZ, Francisco (1930-) Spanish

£328	$590	€475	Fishing boats (60x75cm-24x30in) s.d.58 canvas on board. 26-Jan-4 Durán, Madrid #1159/R

CONCHA, Felix de la (1962-) ?
£4514 $7674 €6500 On the way (119x74cm-47x29in) s. board exhib.lit. 28-Oct-3 Segre, Madrid #143/R est:6500

CONCONI, Luigi (1852-1917) Italian
£4648 $7715 €6600 Giovane donna (44x30cm-17x12in) prov. 11-Jun-3 Christie's, Rome #284/R est:3000-5000
Works on paper
£1348 $2250 €1900 Woman by wall (28x29cm-11x11in) s. W/C cardboard. 14-Oct-3 Finarte Semenzato, Milan #158/R
£2464 $4041 €3400 Woman in profile (43x32cm-17x13in) s.d.1900 W/C. 27-May-3 Finarte Semenzato, Milan #70/R
£3873 $6701 €5500 Fairy tales and legends (27x47cm-11x19in) s. Chinese ink W/C. 9-Dec-3 Finarte Semenzato, Milan #71/R est:5000-6000

CONDAMY, Charles Fernand de (1855-1913) French
£1342 $2510 €2000 Concours de chant (21x27cm-8x11in) panel. 1-Mar-4 Coutau Begarie, Paris #214/R est:1500-1800
£1409 $2636 €2100 Le reveil (27x21cm-11x8in) panel. 1-Mar-4 Coutau Begarie, Paris #215/R est:1500-1800
£2550 $4769 €3800 Valet de limier allumant sa pipe (40x31cm-16x12in) panel. 1-Mar-4 Coutau Begarie, Paris #216/R est:3000-3500
Works on paper
£267 $477 €400 Le coq et le bouledogue (14x21cm-6x8in) W/C three in one frame. 12-May-4 Coutau Begarie, Paris #200/R
£387 $692 €580 Chien poursuivant un rat (11x15cm-4x6in) W/C. 12-May-4 Coutau Begarie, Paris #84/R
£400 $716 €600 Le chien et la ratiere (11x15cm-4x6in) W/C. 12-May-4 Coutau Begarie, Paris #83/R
£403 $753 €600 Chien en pleine course (11x15cm-4x6in) W/C. 1-Mar-4 Coutau Begarie, Paris #184/R
£442 $791 €650 Etude de chien savant (15x11cm-6x4in) s. W/C traces black crayon. 17-Mar-4 Tajan, Paris #148
£470 $879 €700 Chien aboyant sur un animal perche (15x11cm-6x4in) W/C. 1-Mar-4 Coutau Begarie, Paris #182/R
£500 $865 €730 Basset hounds (15x23cm-6x9in) s. W/C. 12-Dec-3 Halls, Shrewsbury #609
£503 $941 €750 Chien assis (15x11cm-6x4in) W/C. 1-Mar-4 Coutau Begarie, Paris #183/R
£514 $950 €750 Racing dachshunds (15x25cm-6x10in) s. W/C over pencil paper on paperboard. 10-Feb-4 Doyle, New York #147/R
£533 $955 €800 Le chien et l'insecte (15x11cm-6x4in) W/C. 12-May-4 Coutau Begarie, Paris #82/R
£537 $1004 €800 Joueurs de polo (32x23cm-13x9in) W/C. 1-Mar-4 Coutau Begarie, Paris #116/R
£537 $1004 €800 Chien courant (11x15cm-4x6in) W/C. 1-Mar-4 Coutau Begarie, Paris #186/R
£570 $1067 €850 Chien fier d'avoir capture un rat (11x15cm-4x6in) W/C. 1-Mar-4 Coutau Begarie, Paris #185/R
£667 $1193 €1000 Joueur de polo (31x23cm-12x9in) W/C. 12-May-4 Coutau Begarie, Paris #207/R
£704 $1169 €1000 Chien courant apres un lievre (15x26cm-6x10in) s. W/C. 15-Jun-3 Peron, Melun #77
£733 $1313 €1100 Joueur de polo (32x24cm-13x9in) W/C. 12-May-4 Coutau Begarie, Paris #167/R
£909 $1564 €1300 Fetiche et Bribri (28x21cm-11x8in) W/C. 3-Dec-3 Coutau Begarie, Paris #45/R
£1232 $2020 €1700 Les chiens dans la charrette (15x24cm-6x9in) ink. 28-May-3 Coutau Begarie, Paris #311/R est:1600-2000
£1338 $2315 €1900 Fox-terrier jouant avec des insectes. Fox-terrier tirant sur une nappe (11x15cm-4x6in) s. pen blk ink W/C pair. 10-Dec-3 Piasa, Paris #139 est:600-800
£1342 $2510 €2000 Joueurs de polo (32x23cm-13x9in) W/C pair. 1-Mar-4 Coutau Begarie, Paris #115/R est:2300-2800
£1533 $2775 €2300 Quatrieme tete, hallali courant (30x48cm-12x19in) s. W/C gouache. 2-Apr-4 Rossini, Paris #57/R est:800-1000
£1818 $3036 €2600 Scene de chasse a courre (28x47cm-11x19in) s. W/C. 25-Jun-3 Maigret, Paris #50/R est:2800-3000
£2188 $3434 €3150 Bulldogs (10x14cm-4x6in) W/C set if 4. 29-Aug-3 Deauville, France #139 est:3500-4000
£2639 $4301 €3800 Rallie Picardie (40x30cm-16x12in) W/C. 29-Sep-3 Coutau Begarie, Paris #133/R

CONDE, Georges Jean (1891-1980) French
£479 $815 €700 Jeune homme fumant une cigarette (54x65cm-21x26in) s.d.1933. 8-Nov-3 Gerard, Besancon #41
£1842 $3389 €2800 Repos (113x161cm-44x63in) d.1926. 27-Jun-4 Teitgen, Nancy #45
Works on paper
£329 $605 €500 Biches (24x31cm-9x12in) d.1951 wax crayon. 27-Jun-4 Teitgen, Nancy #42

CONDE, Miguel (1939-) American
£1067 $1931 €1600 Figure (65x51cm-26x20in) s.d.1981 verso prov. 30-Mar-4 Segre, Madrid #236/R est:2100
£1412 $2500 €2062 Untitled (124x137cm-49x54in) s.d.1973 verso. 2-May-4 Bonhams & Butterfields, Los Angeles #3116/R est:4000-6000
£1937 $3389 €2750 Acrobats (95x106cm-37x42in) s.d.1985-88 verso. 16-Dec-3 Durán, Madrid #133/R est:2500
£3333 $5500 €4800 Figures (95x106cm-37x42in) s.d.1985-88 verso. 2-Jul-3 Ansorena, Madrid #871/R
Works on paper
£600 $1092 €900 Hombre emergente (46x29cm-18x11in) s.d.1979 W/C ink wash. 29-Jun-4 Segre, Madrid #214/R

CONDER, Charles (1868-1909) British
£3239 $5215 €4729 Portrait of a lady (92x71cm-36x28in) prov. 25-Aug-3 Sotheby's, Paddington #337/R est:8000-12000 (A.D 8000)
£12397 $22934 €18100 Verandah (71x91cm-28x36in) prov. 10-Mar-4 Deutscher-Menzies, Melbourne #103/R est:28000-35000 (A.D 30000)
£14000 $25620 €20440 Orchard on the Seine near Vetheuil (73x60cm-29x24in) s.d.1893 prov.exhib.lit. 4-Jun-4 Christie's, London #58/R est:15000-20000
£14170 $22814 €20688 Swing (75x60cm-30x24in) s. 25-Aug-3 Sotheby's, Paddington #157/R est:35000-40000 (A.D 35000)
Works on paper
£480 $782 €696 Allegory of love (13x18cm-5x7in) W/C bodycol silk. 23-Sep-3 Bonhams, Knightsbridge #57/R
£500 $925 €750 Three Graces, coastal landscape with partially naked maidens (71x86cm-28x34in) W/C silk. 14-Jul-4 Rupert Toovey, Partridge Green #59
£600 $1002 €876 Vignette fan (11x40cm-4x16in) W/C silk. 16-Oct-3 Christie's, Kensington #223/R
£700 $1169 €1022 Seated lady (28x21cm-11x8in) col chk. 16-Oct-3 Christie's, Kensington #218/R
£700 $1169 €1022 Nymphs bathing in a river (39x43cm-15x17in) W/C on silk. 14-Oct-3 Sotheby's, London #183/R
£1230 $1992 €1796 The ball (27x26cm-11x10in) s. mixed media. 30-Jul-3 Goodman, Sydney #88/R est:1500-2500 (A.D 3000)
£1653 $2926 €2413 Three ladies (16x13cm-6x5in) s. W/C silk. 3-May-4 Christie's, Melbourne #293a/R est:2500-3500 (A.D 4000)
£3805 $5974 €5555 Untitled, female nudes in garden balcony (62x75cm-24x30in) s. W/C silk oval. 1-Sep-3 Shapiro, Sydney #325/R est:10000-15000 (A.D 9360)
£5000 $9250 €7300 Peacock lady (44x44cm-17x17in) s. W/C silk on canvas. 11-Mar-4 Christie's, Kensington #22/R est:5000-7000
£5372 $9938 €7843 Backview of a nude in classical landscape. Five figures in landscape (54x76cm-21x30in) W/C on silk two diptych prov. 10-Mar-4 Deutscher-Menzies, Melbourne #66/R est:6000-9000 (A.D 13000)

CONDO, George (1957-) American
£1867 $3435 €2800 Exploration of the South (30x24cm-12x9in) s.d.83 verso prov. 9-Jun-4 Artcurial Briest, Paris #552/R est:3000-4000
£1867 $3435 €2800 Lonely American (40x30cm-16x12in) s.d.84 verso prov. 9-Jun-4 Artcurial Briest, Paris #553/R est:3000-4000
£2095 $3750 €3059 Jazz forms (91x91cm-36x36in) acrylic prov. 7-May-4 Sloans & Kenyon, Bethesda #1758/R est:5000-7000
£2335 $4250 €3409 Untitled (61x30cm-24x12in) s. painted 1989 prov. 29-Jun-4 Sotheby's, New York #584/R est:3000-4000
£3000 $5430 €4380 Untitled (30x24cm-12x9in) s.d.84.6 s.d.verso prov. 1-Apr-4 Christie's, Kensington #268/R est:1000-1500
£3804 $7000 €5554 Television improvisation (81x81cm-32x32in) s.d.1998 acrylic prov. 10-Jun-4 Phillips, New York #455/R est:8000-12000
£11043 $18000 €16123 Pink nude in prison (152x122cm-60x48in) s.d.89 oil pastel collage prov. 23-Sep-3 Christie's, Rockefeller NY #150/R est:15000-20000
£11189 $19021 €16000 Bunny rap (100x70cm-39x28in) s.d.85 prov. 25-Nov-3 Christie's, Amsterdam #323/R est:10000-15000
£12000 $21840 €17520 Blue clown (194x130cm-76x51in) s.d.85 s.i.d.85 verso prov. 6-Feb-4 Sotheby's, London #250/R est:8000-10000
£17877 $32000 €26100 Dots (173x152cm-68x60in) s.i.d.2003 verso acrylic prov. 14-May-4 Phillips, New York #230/R est:15000-20000
£18000 $30060 €26280 High on a hill (213x274cm-84x108in) s.d.92 verso oil mixed media collage prov.exhib. 21-Oct-3 Sotheby's, London #304/R est:6000-8000
£19162 $32000 €27977 Widow's Watch (170x170cm-67x67in) painted 1995 prov. 12-Nov-3 Christie's, Rockefeller NY #617/R est:18000-25000
£26000 $43420 €37960 Effervescent Pope (105x96cm-41x38in) s.d.94 prov.exhib. 21-Oct-3 Sotheby's, London #305/R est:4000-6000
£33520 $60000 €48939 Chiclets (229x208cm-90x82in) s.i.d.03 verso acrylic prov. 14-May-4 Phillips, New York #133/R est:20000-30000
Works on paper
£233 $429 €350 Untitled (28x23cm-11x9in) s.d.82 pastel chl. 9-Jun-4 Artcurial Briest, Paris #555
£500 $920 €750 Untitled (51x56cm-20x22in) s.d.82 mixed media. 9-Jun-4 Artcurial Briest, Paris #554
£800 $1472 €1168 Expanding green insect (33x41cm-13x16in) s.i.d.86-9 i.verso oil col pencil prov. 24-Jun-4 Sotheby's, Olympia #434/R
£934 $1700 €1364 Untitled (38x46cm-15x18in) s.d.85 pencil prov. 29-Jun-4 Sotheby's, New York #559/R est:2000-3000
£1500 $2760 €2190 Untitled (36x50cm-14x20in) s.d.93 col crayon pencil prov. 24-Jun-4 Sotheby's, Olympia #433/R est:2000-2500
£1600 $2896 €2336 Untitled (36x26cm-14x10in) s.d.85 prov. 1-Apr-4 Christie's, Kensington #267/R est:1000-1500
£20950 $37500 €30587 Girl with mirror (202x269cm-80x106in) pastel exec 1989 prov. 13-May-4 Sotheby's, New York #449/R est:40000-60000

CONDOY, Honorio Garcia (1900-1953) Spanish
Sculpture
£2800 $4676 €4088 Group of figures (47cm-19in) s. pat bronze. 15-Oct-3 Christie's, Kensington #651/R
£3333 $6133 €5000 Female nude (82cm-32in) i. num.4/4 bronze conceived 1949 prov.lit. 8-Jun-4 Sotheby's, Amsterdam #54/R est:5000-7000

CONDY, Nicholas (1793-1857) British
£1500 $2745 €2190 The fortune teller (38x30cm-15x12in) s.d.1836 panel. 7-Apr-4 Woolley & Wallis, Salisbury #316/R est:1500-2500
£2600 $4654 €3796 Fishermen gossiping as they work, with a large three-decker beyond (30x25cm-12x10in) s.d.1831 panel. 26-May-4 Christie's, Kensington #613/R est:2000-4000
£3800 $6840 €5548 News from the town (41x30cm-16x12in) s.d.1840 panel. 21-Jan-4 Sotheby's, Olympia #265/R est:3000-5000
£5000 $9000 €7300 Fish market at Plymouth (40x30cm-16x12in) board. 21-Jan-4 Sotheby's, Olympia #266/R est:4000-6000
£8400 $15120 €12264 Good tidings (42x53cm-17x21in) s.d.1834 panel. 21-Jan-4 Sotheby's, Olympia #270/R est:4000-6000
Works on paper
£520 $936 €759 Clergymen reading in an interior (15x22cm-6x9in) W/C over pencil bodycol. 21-Jan-4 Sotheby's, Olympia #268/R

CONDY, Nicholas Matthew (1816-1851) British
£2800 $4480 €4088 Paying off the St Vincent, Plymouth (20x25cm-8x10in) 16-Sep-3 Bonhams, New Bond Street #32/R est:2000-3000
£35000 $59500 €51100 Fernande (49x76cm-19x30in) s.i.d.1849 pair prov. 19-Nov-3 Christie's, Kensington #405/R est:35000

CONE, Davis (1950-) American
£21477 $38443 €32000 Cameo (93x115cm-37x45in) i. acrylic painted 1988 prov.lit. 27-May-4 Sotheby's, Paris #254/R est:8000-10000

CONE, Marvin D (1891-1964) American
£11765 $20000 €17177 Plant and apples (46x38cm-18x15in) s. board painted c.1932 prov.exhib.lit. 22-Nov-3 Jackson's, Cedar Falls #67/R est:18000-25000
£12973 $24000 €18941 Express clouds (51x46cm-20x18in) s. i.stretcher painted c.1922 prov.exhib. 12-Mar-4 Jackson's, Cedar Falls #766/R est:25000-30000
£15135 $28000 €22097 On Guard (61x25cm-24x10in) s. s.i.verso canvasboard painted c.1957 prov. 12-Mar-4 Jackson's, Cedar Falls #768/R est:20000-25000
£17297 $32000 €25254 October afternoon (51x46cm-20x18in) s. i.stretcher painted c.1923 prov. 12-Mar-4 Jackson's, Cedar Falls #765/R est:30000-40000
£22727 $40000 €33181 Green door (91x61cm-36x24in) s. i.d.1964 stretcher prov.exhib.lit. 19-May-4 Sotheby's, New York #157/R est:40000-60000
£23243 $43000 €33935 Barns and shed (53x28cm-21x11in) s. s.i.d.1957 verso board prov. 12-Mar-4 Jackson's, Cedar Falls #767/R est:25000-35000
£41765 $71000 €60977 Old stone quarry (46x38cm-18x15in) s. board prov. 22-Nov-3 Jackson's, Cedar Falls #65/R est:30000-35000
£49451 $90000 €72198 Fall landscape (81x97cm-32x38in) s.d.1923 prov. 19-Jun-4 Jackson's, Cedar Falls #1/R est:75000-125000
£85227 $150000 €124431 Cook's Barn No.1 (46x86cm-18x34in) s.i. painted c.1939-40 prov.exhib.lit. 19-May-4 Sotheby's, New York #123/R est:125000-175000

CONEY, Paul (20th C) New Zealander
Works on paper
£372 $639 €543 Rosa (70x100cm-28x39in) s.d.May 1999 W/C acrylic. 7-Dec-3 International Art Centre, Auckland #246/R (NZ.D 1000)

CONFORTINI, Jacopo (attrib) (17th C) Italian
Works on paper
£1370 $2329 €2000 Apostle (39x23cm-15x9in) crayon chk. 6-Nov-3 Tajan, Paris #22/R est:2000
£1600 $2928 €2336 Standing cloaked male figure, his right hand clasping the hit of his sword (25x14cm-10x6in) red chk prov. 7-Jul-4 Bonhams, Knightsbridge #75/R est:800-1200

CONGDON, Anne Ramsdell (1873-1958) American
£3145 $5000 €4592 Wharf scene (20x25cm-8x10in) s.d. board. 23-Mar-3 Auctions by the Bay, Alameda #870/R

CONGDON, Thomas R (1862-1917) American
£559 $1000 €816 Brittany forest (66x51cm-26x20in) s. 16-May-4 CRN Auctions, Cambridge #8/R
Works on paper
£312 $509 €450 Unloading the catch (32x43cm-13x17in) s. W/C. 29-Sep-3 Sotheby's, Amsterdam #108/R

CONGNET, Gillis (attrib) (1538-1599) Dutch
£33113 $60265 €50000 Venus et l'amour entoures d'attributs militaires (112x162cm-44x64in) panel prov.exhib.lit. 15-Jun-4 Artcurial Briest, Paris #206/R est:50000-60000

CONILL ORRIOLS, Jacinto (1914-) Spanish
£2069 $3434 €3000 Landscape (98x195cm-39x77in) s. s.verso. 1-Oct-3 Ansorena, Madrid #669/R est:3000

CONINCK, David de (1636-1699) Flemish
£16000 $28800 €23360 Still life of pigeons, rabbits, cat, chicken and guinea pig in a farmyard (53x70cm-21x28in) i.verso prov. 22-Apr-4 Sotheby's, London #93/R est:12000-18000
£20690 $37241 €30000 Cats attacking dog (76x100cm-30x39in) prov. 26-Jan-4 Ansorena, Madrid #66/R est:30000
£30000 $54000 €43800 Waterfowl assailed by dogs and a buzzard, in a river landscape (117x171cm-46x67in) prov. 22-Apr-4 Sotheby's, London #92/R est:30000-50000

CONINCK, David de (attrib) (1636-1699) Flemish
£10612 $19527 €15494 Hounds and game (75x100cm-30x39in) prov. 29-Mar-4 Goodman, Sydney #139/R est:20000-30000 (A.D 26000)
£10769 $18523 €15723 Still life of flowers (21x31cm-8x12in) pair. 2-Dec-3 Bukowskis, Stockholm #393/R est:50000-60000 (S.KR 140000)

CONINCK, David de (circle) (1636-1699) Flemish
£6512 $11200 €9508 Cocks and turkeys (118x151cm-46x59in) 3-Dec-3 Naón & Cia, Buenos Aires #26/R est:8000-10000

CONINCK, David de (style) (1636-1699) Flemish
£9890 $18000 €14439 Two hens by a basket of fruit in a landscape. Two turkeys by a vase of flowers (80x110cm-31x43in) pair. 4-Feb-4 Christie's, Rockefeller NY #75/R est:10000-15000

CONINCK, Pierre Louis Joseph de (1828-1910) French
£4444 $8000 €6488 Red shawl (71x49cm-28x19in) s. 22-Apr-4 Christie's, Rockefeller NY #143/R est:10000-15000

CONINXLOO, Gillis van (16/17th C) Flemish/Dutch
£10000 $17000 €14600 Huntsmen shooting in a wooded landscape, with distant castle (30x51cm-12x20in) panel. 19-Nov-3 Tennants, Leyburn #1007/R est:10000-15000

CONINXLOO, Gillis van (attrib) (16/17th C) Flemish/Dutch
Works on paper
£6500 $11895 €9490 Wooded autumnal landscape with figures and a distant townscape (25x41cm-10x16in) W/C touches of oil. 8-Jul-4 Sotheby's, London #19/R est:5000-7000

CONINXLOO, Gillis van (circle) (16/17th C) Flemish/Dutch
£8000 $13600 €11680 Figures picnicking in a wooded landscape (58x78cm-23x31in) panel. 19-Nov-3 Tennants, Leyburn #1009/R est:15000-20000
£15000 $27450 €21900 Wooded landscape with Saints (45x63cm-18x25in) copper prov.exhib. 8-Jul-4 Sotheby's, London #237/R est:15000-20000

CONINXLOO, Gillis van III (attrib) (1544-1607) Flemish
Works on paper
£1216 $2141 €1800 Wooded landscape with house (29x24cm-11x9in) pen brown ink col wash. 19-May-4 Sotheby's, Amsterdam #11/R est:2200-2800

CONLON, George (?) American
£419 $700 €612 Moment's rest. s. 18-Oct-3 Harvey Clar, Oakland #1174

CONLON, William (20th C) American
£2198 $4000 €3209 Halley's comet (183x219cm-72x86in) s.d.1979 i.verso acrylic prov.lit. 29-Jun-4 Sotheby's, New York #506/R est:4000-6000

CONNARD, Charlotte E (19th C) American
£540 $950 €788 Hunting dogs. s. painted c.1880. 23-May-4 Treadway Gallery, Cincinnati #506/R

CONNARD, Philip (1875-1958) British
£340 $629 €496 Richmond Bridge, Surrey (30x41cm-12x16in) s. board. 9-Mar-4 Gorringes, Lewes #2154
£1100 $1870 €1606 H.M.S. Caesar at Galata Bridge (30x40cm-12x16in) s. panel. 26-Nov-3 Sotheby's, Olympia #6/R est:1000-1500
£16000 $27520 €23360 Summer (51x61cm-20x24in) mono. prov.exhib. 3-Dec-3 Sotheby's, London #13/R est:6000-8000

CONNAVALE, Robert (20th C) American
£615 $1100 €898 Rockport Street view, winter (63x76cm-25x30in) s. 14-May-4 Skinner, Boston #232/R

CONNAWAY, Jay Hall (1893-1970) American
£837 $1515 €1222 Crashing sea (39x50cm-15x20in) s. i.verso board prov. 1-Apr-4 Heffel, Vancouver #14/R est:1000-1500 (C.D 2000)
£8642 $14000 €12531 Trouble on the coast (61x91cm-24x36in) s. board prov. 8-Aug-3 Barridorf, Portland #179/R est:15000-25000

CONNEL, Fergus (20th C) British?
£250 $465 €365 Study of 16 dogs in a wooded landscape (58x78cm-23x31in) s. 5-Mar-4 Moore Allen & Innocent, Cirencester #325
£380 $669 €555 Pair of hounds, Luke and Pat (53x61cm-21x24in) s. 30-Dec-3 British Auctioneer #790
£500 $920 €730 Hide and seek (66x38cm-26x15in) s.i. canvas on board. 10-Jun-4 Christie's, Kensington #364/R

CONNELL, Anne (?) British
Works on paper
£310 $570 €453 Edinburgh Castle (25x35cm-10x14in) s. pen ink W/C. 10-Jun-4 Lyon & Turnbull, Edinburgh #133

CONNELL, Edwin (1859-?) American
£440 $700 €642 Path through a forest clearing (51x36cm-20x14in) s.d.87. 13-Sep-3 Weschler, Washington #741/R
£924 $1700 €1349 Ram's Head (41x61cm-16x24in) s. 26-Jun-4 Sloans & Kenyon, Bethesda #1081/R est:700-900

CONNELLY, Chuck (20th C) American
£306 $550 €447 Untitled (55x55cm-22x22in) s.d.1982. 24-Apr-4 David Rago, Lambertville #332/R

CONNELLY, Pierre Francis (1841-1902) American
Sculpture
£2412 $4029 €3522 Bust of Princess Eleonora Cenci-Bolognetti di Vicovaro (70cm-28in) s.d.1868 verso carrara marble prov. 15-Nov-3 Galerie Gloggner, Luzern #23/R est:2500-2800 (S.FR 5500)
£3513 $6500 €5129 Bust of a young woman (72cm-28in) s.d.1865 marble socle. 15-Mar-4 Bonhams & Butterfields, San Francisco #1114/R est:3000

CONNER, John Anthony (1892-1971) American
£247 $450 €361 River landscape (23x30cm-9x12in) s. canvasboard. 15-Jun-4 John Moran, Pasadena #4a
£265 $450 €387 Autumn landscape (51x86cm-20x34in) s. 21-Nov-3 Eldred, East Dennis #805/R
£522 $950 €762 Eucalyptus landscape (51x61cm-20x24in) s. board. 15-Jun-4 John Moran, Pasadena #36b est:1000-2000
£604 $1100 €882 Desert flowers (36x53cm-14x21in) s. i.verso. 15-Jun-4 John Moran, Pasadena #160
£607 $1100 €886 Flowering dunes (68x91cm-27x36in) s. 18-Apr-4 Bonhams & Butterfields, Los Angeles #7018 est:1500-2000
£635 $1200 €927 Landscape (61x76cm-24x30in) s. prov. 17-Feb-4 John Moran, Pasadena #197/R
£1720 $3250 €2511 Mission San Juan Capistrano (46x33cm-18x13in) i. verso. 17-Feb-4 John Moran, Pasadena #52/R est:1800-2200

CONNER, John Ramsey (1867-1952) American

£357	$650	€521	Christ before Pilate (64x76cm-25x30in) s. s.i.verso. 7-Feb-4 Sloans & Kenyon, Bethesda #1292/R
Works on paper			
£326	$600	€476	The artist's studio (28x36cm-11x14in) s. pastel. 25-Jun-4 Freeman, Philadelphia #113/R
£435	$800	€635	Woman sewing (53x43cm-21x17in) s.d.1903 pastel. 25-Jun-4 Freeman, Philadelphia #89/R

CONNER, Paul (1881-1968) American

£412	$700	€602	San Juan Capistrano Mission (152x25cm-60x10in) s. i.verso board. 18-Nov-3 John Moran, Pasadena #2
£450	$850	€657	Wilmington Harbour (30x41cm-12x16in) s. 17-Feb-4 John Moran, Pasadena #117/R

CONNOR, Kevin (1932-) Australian

£661	$1223	€965	Neutral Bay landscape (30x45cm-12x18in) s.d.73 s.i.verso board. 10-Mar-4 Deutscher-Menzies, Melbourne #515/R est:2000-3000 (A.D 1600)
£725	$1320	€1059	Metung (76x61cm-30x24in) s.d.64 board prov. 16-Jun-4 Deutscher-Menzies, Melbourne #340/R est:1800-2400 (A.D 1900)
£1826	$3049	€2739	Seated man (45x29cm-18x11in) indis.s.d.65 board. 27-Oct-3 Goodman, Sydney #98/R est:4000-6000 (A.D 4400)
£6073	$9777	€8867	View from above the Art Gallery (121x151cm-48x59in) i.verso linen canvas prov. 25-Aug-3 Sotheby's, Paddington #169/R est:15000-17000 (A.D 15000)
£6870	$12504	€10030	Looking out from the studio and the camphor laurel tree willow (199x549cm-78x216in) s.d.86 oil on linen triptych prov.exhib. 16-Jun-4 Deutscher-Menzies, Melbourne #90/R est:20000-30000 (A.D 18000)
£13008	$20423	€18862	Self portrait, of the gardener in the little sparrow garden, Erskineville (181x197cm-71x78in) s.d.88 i.verso prov. 27-Aug-3 Christie's, Sydney #638/R est:18000-25000 (A.D 32000)
Works on paper			
£490	$901	€715	Prisoner (56x40cm-22x16in) s.d.65 W/C. 29-Mar-4 Goodman, Sydney #188/R (A.D 1200)
£694	$1277	€1013	Hay Market (41x51cm-16x20in) s. W/C prov. 29-Mar-4 Goodman, Sydney #6/R (A.D 1700)

CONNOR, Moses (19th C) American

Works on paper			
£3825	$7000	€5585	Birth record of Mary Hoyt (23x18cm-9x7in) s.verso W/C ink. 6-Jun-4 Skinner, Boston #8/R est:4000-6000

CONOR, William (1881-1968) Irish

£850	$1462	€1241	The edge of the wood, Craigavad (35x25cm-14x10in) s. 3-Dec-3 John Ross, Belfast #263
£10500	$19215	€15330	Steeplechase (40x50cm-16x20in) s. 2-Jun-4 John Ross, Belfast #148 est:12000-14000
£10563	$18275	€15000	Old clothes market (44x34cm-17x13in) s. 10-Dec-3 Bonhams & James Adam, Dublin #106/R est:8000-12000
Works on paper			
£400	$664	€584	Landscape, Co. Down (17x25cm-7x10in) s.d.45 W/C. 1-Oct-3 John Ross, Belfast #38
£680	$1244	€993	Lady in green dress (25x17cm-10x7in) s.d.1938 verso W/C. 2-Jun-4 John Ross, Belfast #80
£750	$1395	€1095	Ballad singer (14x11cm-6x4in) s.d.1908 mixed media. 3-Mar-4 John Ross, Belfast #22
£800	$1488	€1168	Lady in green dress (25x17cm-10x7in) s.d.1938 verso W/C. 3-Mar-4 John Ross, Belfast #23
£850	$1411	€1241	Aw-you! (10x7cm-4x3in) s. W/C. 1-Oct-3 John Ross, Belfast #209
£1000	$1830	€1460	Portrait (43x30cm-17x12in) s. W/C. 2-Jun-4 John Ross, Belfast #218 est:600-800
£1074	$1901	€1600	Firemen (24x28cm-9x11in) s.d.April 1909 pen ink pencil prov. 27-Apr-4 Whyte's, Dublin #143/R est:2000-3000
£1500	$2595	€2190	Young woman carrying a basket (26x19cm-10x7in) s. crayon. 9-Dec-3 Anderson & Garland, Newcastle #269/R est:1500-2500
£1711	$3147	€2600	Mother with her children (29x22cm-11x9in) s.d.1902 pencil col chk. 22-Jun-4 De Veres Art Auctions, Dublin #241/R est:2000-3000
£1812	$3244	€2700	Belfast weaver (20x15cm-8x6in) s.i.d.1906 crayon. 26-May-4 James Adam, Dublin #125/R est:1500-2500
£2416	$4325	€3600	Old woman (21x15cm-8x6in) s. crayon. 26-May-4 James Adam, Dublin #123/R est:1500-2500
£2800	$5012	€4088	Woman holding a baby (33x25cm-13x10in) s. pastel chl prov. 14-May-4 Christie's, London #194/R est:3000-5000
£3356	$6007	€5000	Officers of the Ulster Division (54x70cm-21x28in) s.d.1916 chl red chk. 26-May-4 James Adam, Dublin #124/R est:5000-8000
£3356	$6007	€5000	Vips (46x38cm-18x15in) s. chl crayon. 26-May-4 James Adam, Dublin #126/R est:5000-8000
£4000	$7160	€5840	Churning butter (49x38cm-19x15in) s. wax crayons prov. 13-May-4 Sotheby's, London #86/R est:4000-6000
£4400	$7964	€6600	Mill girl (26x20cm-10x8in) s. wax crayon pen ink prov. 31-Mar-4 James Adam, Dublin #33/R est:2000-3000
£4500	$7740	€6570	Chaffin (26x36cm-10x14in) s. chk. 3-Dec-3 Cheffins, Cambridge #590/R est:2000-3000
£5000	$9150	€7300	Children playing on the see-saw (45x56cm-18x22in) s. wax crayon. 2-Jun-4 John Ross, Belfast #150 est:6000-7000
£7800	$12714	€11388	Carrying home turf (39x30cm-15x12in) s. coloured crayon. 23-Sep-3 Anderson & Garland, Newcastle #133/R est:250-400
£7800	$14274	€11388	Fife and drums (28x38cm-11x15in) s. wax crayon. 2-Jun-4 John Ross, Belfast #32 est:4000-5000
£8000	$14480	€12000	Reflections (35x26cm-14x10in) s. wax crayon pen ink prov. 31-Mar-4 James Adam, Dublin #34/R est:7000-10000
£8000	$14320	€11680	Cellist (66x54cm-26x21in) pencil pastel oil. 14-May-4 Christie's, Kensington #319/R est:6000-8000
£8355	$15374	€12700	Enjoying a joke (29x21cm-11x8in) s. wax crayon prov. 22-Jun-4 De Veres Art Auctions, Dublin #17/R est:8000-10000
£8500	$14960	€12410	Sing song (38x28cm-15x11in) s. crayon. 19-May-4 Sotheby's, Olympia #181/R est:5000-7000
£9500	$16340	€13870	Colloquing (30x28cm-12x11in) s. wax crayon. 3-Dec-3 John Ross, Belfast #54 est:8000-10000
£10563	$18275	€15000	Cellist (68x51cm-27x20in) s. wax crayon. 10-Dec-3 Bonhams & James Adam, Dublin #193/R est:15000-20000
£12000	$19920	€17520	Friendly like (45x33cm-18x13in) s. wax crayon. 1-Oct-3 John Ross, Belfast #63 est:12000-15000
£15000	$25800	€21900	The water carrier (48x38cm-19x15in) s. wax crayon. 3-Dec-3 John Ross, Belfast #154 est:15000-18000
£16500	$30195	€24090	By winding roads (46x35cm-18x14in) s. wax crayon. 2-Jun-4 John Ross, Belfast #55 est:18000-20000

CONOR, William (attrib) (1881-1968) Irish

£1750	$2975	€2555	Ulster village, fir trees in the foreground (61x51cm-24x20in) s. 5-Nov-3 John Nicholson, Haslemere #548/R est:2000-3000

CONRAD, Charles (1912-) Belgian

Sculpture			
£1277	$2068	€1800	Coq debout (21x16cm-8x6in) s.num.2 black pat bronze st.f.CAI. 24-May-3 Martinot & Savignat, Pontoise #121/R est:2000-2200

CONRADI, Moritz (fl.1865-1876) British

Works on paper			
£750	$1253	€1095	Shepherd's daughter (60x46cm-24x18in) s.d.1872 W/C. 21-Oct-3 Sworder & Son, Bishops Stortford #276/R

CONRADSEN, M (?) ?

£2778	$4639	€4000	Furit and flowers in basket (54x64cm-21x25in) s.d.1839 i. stretcher. 24-Oct-3 Ketterer, Hamburg #54/R est:4500-5000

CONROY, George T (19th C) American

£395	$700	€577	Fall landscape (56x71cm-22x28in) s. 2-May-4 William Jenack, New York #216

CONROY, Stephen (1964-) British

£3681	$6000	€5374	Study - staircase IV (81x51cm-32x20in) s.d.1994 verso board prov. 23-Sep-3 Christie's, Rockefeller NY #108/R est:8000-12000
£22000	$37400	€32120	Louise (122x101cm-48x40in) init. s.i.d.1986 on stretcher prov.lit. 21-Nov-3 Christie's, London #152/R est:15000-20000
Works on paper			
£400	$756	€584	Head study (15x12cm-6x5in) ink pencil prov. 19-Feb-4 Lyon & Turnbull, Edinburgh #152
£480	$840	€701	Nude study (42x31cm-17x12in) s. pencil chl. 18-Dec-3 Bonhams, Edinburgh #336

CONSADORI, Silvio (1909-1996) Italian

£704	$1169	€1000	Serrada (45x35cm-18x14in) s. i.verso canvasboard. 14-Jun-3 Meeting Art, Vercelli #178/R
£816	$1486	€1200	Burano (40x30cm-16x12in) s. cardboard on canvas painted 1970. 6-Feb-4 Galleria Rosenberg, Milan #90/R

CONSAGRA, Pietro (1920-) Italian

£874	$1486	€1250	Untitled (47x32cm-19x13in) s.i. lacquer card. 18-Nov-3 Babuino, Rome #417/R
£2621	$4377	€3800	Planets (100x120cm-39x47in) s. 13-Nov-3 Finarte Semenzato, Rome #345/R est:4000-4500
£2657	$4517	€3800	Fronts (62x90cm-24x35in) s. masonite prov. 18-Nov-3 Babuino, Rome #405/R est:3000
Sculpture			
£1333	$2400	€2000	Untitled (34x27x5cm-13x11x2in) s. steel. 22-Apr-4 Finarte Semenzato, Rome #44/R est:2000
£1379	$2303	€2000	Untitled (33cm-13in) s. num.10/30 bronze. 13-Nov-3 Finarte Semenzato, Rome #280/R est:2000-2500
£1620	$2689	€2300	Very thin (23cm-9in) s.i. stainless steel in 2 parts. 11-Jun-3 Finarte Semenzato, Milan #674/R
£1678	$2853	€2400	Double-sided (32x20cm-13x8in) s. num.9/25 wax gold exec.1991. 25-Nov-3 Sotheby's, Milan #8/R est:1500-2000
£2394	$3975	€3400	Very thin (24cm-9in) s.i. stainless steel in 3 parts. 11-Jun-3 Finarte Semenzato, Milan #673/R
£4027	$7208	€6000	Bi-frontal (38x25x8cm-15x10x3in) s. num.3/6 bronze. 30-May-4 Meeting Art, Vercelli #9 est:5000
£5172	$8638	€7500	Conversation with the devil (35x25cm-14x10in) s. num.0/5 bronze exhib. 13-Nov-3 Finarte Semenzato, Rome #338/R est:6000-7000
£7047	$12614	€10500	Untitled (24cm-9in) stone exec.1980 exhib.lit. 29-May-4 Farsetti, Prato #484/R est:10000-12000
£8451	$14789	€12000	Solid (50x47cm-20x19in) s.d.66 num.1/3 bronze. 16-Dec-3 Porro, Milan #23/R est:10000-12000
£9420	$15449	€13000	Clochard (33x36cm-13x14in) s.d.61 bronze prov.lit. 27-May-3 Sotheby's, Milan #199/R est:10000-15000
£15333	$28213	€23000	Roman chat (66x68x5cm-26x27x2in) s. bronze prov.lit. 14-Jun-4 Porro, Milan #30/R est:18000-20000
£25000	$41750	€36500	The devil's tale 4 (84cm-33in) st.sig.d.1962 bronze exhib. 20-Oct-3 Sotheby's, London #5/R est:22000

CONSETTI, Antonio (1686-1766) Italian

£6250	$10625	€9000	Il sogno di San Giuseppe (172x117cm-68x46in) 28-Oct-3 Della Rocca, Turin #130/R est:10000-12000

CONSOLI, Salvatori A (19th C) Italian

£6486	$12000	€9470	Judgement of a page (33x56cm-13x22in) panel. 13-Feb-4 Du Mouchelle, Detroit #2019/R est:5000-7000

CONSTABLE OF ARUNDEL, George (19th C) British

£700	$1253	€1022	Trees in an extensive landscape (15x15cm-6x6in) board sketch. 27-May-4 Christie's, Kensington #116/R

CONSTABLE, John (1776-1837) British
£170000 $311100 €248200 Sketch of East Bergholt, from East Bergholt House (12x19cm-5x7in) i. canvas on panel prov. 7-Jul-4 Bonhams, New Bond Street #130/R est:60000-80000
£500000 $850000 €730000 View of the City London from Sir Richard Steele's cottage, Hampstead (21x28cm-8x11in) prov.lit. 26-Nov-3 Christie's, London #8/R est:400000-600000
Works on paper
£45000 $76500 €65700 Startford Mill, Suffolk (10x14cm-4x6in) pencil corners cut prov.exhib.lit. 20-Nov-3 Christie's, London #43/R est:20000-30000

CONSTABLE, John (attrib) (1776-1837) British
£620 $1035 €905 Hampstead (10x18cm-4x7in) 17-Oct-3 Keys, Aylsham #690
£7143 $13000 €10429 English landscape with rider (87x113cm-34x44in) with sig. 7-Feb-4 Rasmussen, Havnen #2156/R est:5000 (D.KR 78000)
Works on paper
£290 $537 €423 Landscape with trees (8x10cm-3x4in) i. pencil. 13-Feb-4 Keys, Aylsham #316
£370 $585 €537 River landscape with trees (18x30cm-7x12in) pencil prov. 24-Jul-3 Dominic Winter, Swindon #135/R

CONSTABLE, John (school) (1776-1837) British
£484 $890 €707 Dedham Vale (32x44cm-13x17in) panel. 14-Jun-4 Waddingtons, Toronto #130/R est:1500-2000 (C.D 1200)

CONSTABLE, Lionel (1828-1884) British
£2700 $4860 €3942 Extensive landscape with distant view of windmills (15x24cm-6x9in) oil paper. 21-Jan-4 Sotheby's, Olympia #313/R est:2000-3000

CONSTABLE, William (1783-1861) American
Works on paper
£2125 $3400 €3103 View on the Juniatta, two miles west of Bedford (20x30cm-8x12in) s.d.1807 W/C. 20-Sep-3 Pook & Pook, Downington #125/R est:3000-4000

CONSTANCE SCHOOL (15th C) German
£10000 $18300 €14600 Vision of Saint John the Evangelist on Patmos (56x41cm-22x16in) oil gold panel. 8-Jul-4 Sotheby's, London #245/R est:8000-12000

CONSTANT (1920-) Dutch
Works on paper
£5594 $9622 €8000 Untitled (50x50cm-20x20in) s.d.63 ink. 2-Dec-3 Sotheby's, Amsterdam #157/R est:8000-12000
£6993 $12028 €10000 Le couple (52x44cm-20x17in) s.d.1977 W/C gouache pastel prov.lit. 2-Dec-3 Sotheby's, Amsterdam #148/R est:10000-15000
£15217 $24957 €21000 Love in (108x117cm-43x46in) s.i.d.67 gouache pencil prov. 27-May-3 Sotheby's, Amsterdam #397/R est:18000-25000
£16783 $28531 €24000 Chantier (55x76cm-22x30in) s.d.72 blk ink W/C pastel prov.lit. 25-Nov-3 Christie's, Amsterdam #278/R est:15000-20000

CONSTANT, Benjamin (1845-1902) French
£260 $442 €380 Spanish dancers (24x30cm-9x12in) s. board. 6-Nov-3 Christie's, Kensington #748
£748 $1339 €1100 Palette. s.i. 19-Mar-4 Millon & Associes, Paris #12
£1341 $2400 €2251 Portrait of a young woman (56x43cm-22x17in) s. panel. 20-Mar-4 Pook & Pook, Downington #312 est:1000-2000
£2945 $4800 €4270 Portrait of an Orientalist beauty (56x46cm-22x18in) s. 19-Jul-3 New Orleans Auction, New Orleans #535/R est:5000-8000
£5000 $8000 €7250 A l'opera (66x51cm-26x20in) s. 18-Sep-3 Christie's, Kensington #180/R est:8000-12000
£41060 $75139 €62000 Le marchand de tapis (91x64cm-36x25in) s. prov. 9-Apr-4 Claude Aguttes, Neuilly #130/R est:70000-80000
£43750 $69125 €63000 Odalisk (100x210cm-39x83in) s. lit. 19-Sep-3 Schloss Ahlden, Ahlden #1529/R est:65000
£59155 $103521 €84000 Femme Orientale etendue sur un sofa (100x201cm-39x79in) s. lit. 16-Dec-3 Claude Aguttes, Neuilly #54/R est:80000-100000
Prints
£3356 $6208 €5000 Les cherifas (64x92cm-25x36in) s. col etching W/C. 15-Mar-4 Gros & Delettrez, Paris #114/R est:2500-3000
Works on paper
£1831 $3168 €2600 Terrasse, Tanger (64x92cm-25x36in) W/C over print. 15-Dec-3 Gros & Delettrez, Paris #307/R est:2000-3000
£2535 $4386 €3600 Marocaines dans le harem (64x92cm-25x36in) W/C over print. 15-Dec-3 Gros & Delettrez, Paris #308/R est:2000-3000

CONSTANT, Joseph (1892-1969) French
Sculpture
£1536 $2750 €2243 Hen (35cm-14in) wood base prov. 18-Mar-4 Sotheby's, New York #105/R est:3000-5000

CONSTANT, Maurice (19/20th C) French
Sculpture
£1788 $3200 €2610 Knight (43cm-17in) bronze ivory. 8-May-4 Susanin's, Chicago #6009/R est:1500-2400

CONSTANTIN, Jean Antoine (1756-1844) French
£7237 $13316 €11000 Vue de l'interieur du Colisee a Rome (24x30cm-9x12in) paper on cardboard. 24-Jun-4 Christie's, Paris #147/R est:3500-5500
Works on paper
£1701 $3044 €2500 Hermine chez les bergers (55x43cm-22x17in) s. pen wash. 22-Mar-4 Digard, Paris #5/R est:2500-3000

CONSTANTIN, Joseph Sebastien (1793-1864) French
£7042 $12323 €10000 L'atelier du peintre Francois-Marius Granet (32x40cm-13x16in) s. canvas on panel. 18-Dec-3 Tajan, Paris #50/R est:5000-7000

CONSTANTIN, René Auguste (fl.1712-1726) Dutch
£28000 $50120 €42000 Portrait of two sons and four daughters of Don Francisco Lopes Suasso (65x83cm-26x33in) s.d.1730 prov. 17-May-4 Christie's, Amsterdam #109/R est:5000-7000

CONSTANTINE, G Hamilton (1875-1967) British
Works on paper
£250 $430 €365 Street scene with houses and figures (33x49cm-13x19in) s. W/C. 5-Dec-3 ELR Auctions, Sheffield #695/R
£360 $619 €526 Woodland stream (38x62cm-15x24in) s. W/C. 5-Dec-3 ELR Auctions, Sheffield #701
£500 $860 €730 Ecclesall Woods, with figure (25x17cm-10x7in) s. W/C. 5-Dec-3 ELR Auctions, Sheffield #673/R
£500 $860 €730 Rural scene with a cottage and cows in the foreground (23x27cm-9x11in) s. W/C. 5-Dec-3 ELR Auctions, Sheffield #674/R
£580 $969 €847 Scarborough Beach (25x36cm-10x14in) s. W/C. 12-Nov-3 Halls, Shrewsbury #267
£700 $1274 €1022 Ecclesall woods, with children picking bluebells (25x17cm-10x7in) s. W/C. 15-Jun-4 Bonhams, Leeds #23
£720 $1195 €1051 Ducks in a marsh (24x34cm-9x13in) s.d.1914 W/C. 1-Oct-3 Sotheby's, Olympia #113/R
£980 $1558 €1421 September, Greystones, Sheffield (17x25cm-7x10in) s.i. W/C. 12-Sep-3 ELR Auctions, Sheffield #270
£1000 $1590 €1450 Harbour scene, unloading the catch, possibly Grimsby (24x44cm-9x17in) s. W/C. 12-Sep-3 ELR Auctions, Sheffield #274/R est:200-300
£1400 $2380 €2044 Ballochantuay, Cantyre (24x35cm-9x14in) s.i. W/C. 29-Oct-3 Bonhams, Chester #402/R est:1000-1500
£1650 $2805 €2409 Near Inverness (24x34cm-9x13in) s.i. W/C. 18-Nov-3 Bonhams, Leeds #86/R est:1000-1500
£2900 $5133 €4234 Farmyard pond with a woman and child. Harvesting houses and trees beyond (45x50cm-18x20in) one s.d.1914 W/C pair. 28-Apr-4 Peter Wilson, Nantwich #139 est:3000-3500

CONSTANTINE, G Hamilton and OUTRAM, George (20th C) British
Works on paper
£640 $1088 €934 Shady lane, Crowers, Yorkshire (33x26cm-13x10in) s. W/C. 29-Oct-3 Bonhams, Chester #403

CONSTANTINI, G (19th C) Italian
£8700 $15921 €12702 When the cats away. s. board. 28-Jan-4 Ibbett Mosely, Sevenoaks #1

CONTARINI, Giovanni (1549-1605) Italian
£9655 $16028 €14000 Portrait of the Venetian Procurator Marco Molin (113x119cm-44x47in) i. bears d.1.5.7.7. 1-Oct-3 Dorotheum, Vienna #268/R est:18000-25000
Works on paper
£1748 $2920 €2500 Christ healing the lame (16x23cm-6x9in) pen. 28-Jun-3 Bolland & Marotz, Bremen #568/R est:2700

CONTE, Dante Mose (1885-1919) Italian
£1333 $2453 €2000 Sunny street (35x26cm-14x10in) cardboard. 8-Jun-4 Sotheby's, Milan #44/R est:2000-4000
£5705 $10668 €8500 Genoa harbour (32x51cm-13x20in) s. cardboard lit. 25-Feb-4 Porro, Milan #21/R est:12000

CONTE, Guillermo (1956-) Argentinian
£1099 $2000 €1605 Untitled (129x102cm-51x40in) s. s.d.1988 verso. 29-Jun-4 Sotheby's, New York #594/R est:3000-5000

CONTE, Jacopino del (attrib) (1510-1598) Italian
£2819 $5187 €4200 Le Christ portant sa croix (100x71cm-39x28in) panel. 24-Mar-4 Tajan, Paris #14/R est:4000-6000

CONTE, Michelangelo (1913-) Italian
£380 $700 €555 Winter approaching (46x61cm-18x24in) s.i.d.1957 verso. 11-Jun-4 David Rago, Lambertville #139/R

CONTE, Sauveur le (attrib) (1659-1694) French
£1879 $3457 €2800 Louis XIV chassant devant le Chateau de Vincennes (60x86cm-24x34in) 24-Mar-4 Tajan, Paris #110/R est:3000-4000

CONTEL, Jean Charles (1895-1928) French
£1338 $2168 €1900 Vieille rue de Lisieux (61x50cm-24x20in) s. 11-Aug-3 Boscher, Cherbourg #796/R est:230-300

CONTENCIN, Charles Henry (20th C) French
£667 $1200 €1000 Lac de montagne (38x55cm-15x22in) s. isorel. 20-Apr-4 Chenu & Scrive, Lyon #67/R
£1497 $2679 €2200 Paysage alpin (60x80cm-24x31in) s. 19-Mar-4 Ribeyre & Baron, Paris #81 est:1500-2000
£1544 $2871 €2300 Paysage des Alpes (49x64cm-19x25in) s. 3-Mar-4 Ferri, Paris #399 est:1000-1500

CONTENEL, T (19th C) ?
£1500 $2655 €2190 In Rembrandt's studio (76x62cm-30x24in) s. panel. 27-Apr-4 Bonhams, Knowle #73/R est:1200-1800

CONTENT, Daniel (1902-1990) American
£1117 $2000 €1631 Golden to the winds (56x107cm-22x42in) s.d.September 1929. 15-May-4 Illustration House, New York #27/R est:3000-6000

CONTENTE, Jose (1907-1957) Portuguese?
£1678 $3003 €2500 Harbour, Rio Douro (25x34cm-10x13in) s.i. panel. 31-May-4 Cabral Moncada Leiloes, Lisbon #95/R est:2500-3750

CONTI, Aldo (20th C) Italian
£282 $454 €400 Interior (100x100cm-39x39in) s.i.d.1977 verso acrylic prov. 11-May-3 Versailles Encheres #173

CONTI, Primo (1900-1989) Italian
£433 $797 €650 Nude (46x34cm-18x13in) s.d.75 tempera paper on canvas. 11-Jun-4 Farsetti, Prato #498/R
£533 $965 €800 Figure (30x20cm-12x8in) s.d.1969 cardboard lit. 2-Apr-4 Farsetti, Prato #471/R
£690 $1152 €1000 Madonna and Child (31x21cm-12x8in) s.d.1957 paper on board. 14-Nov-3 Farsetti, Prato #405
£1056 $1849 €1500 Nude (39x35cm-15x14in) s.d.1976. 16-Dec-3 Finarte Semenzato, Milan #337/R est:1300-1600
£1788 $3254 €2700 Sunset amongst tree branch (47x34cm-19x13in) s. paper. 17-Jun-4 Galleria Pananti, Florence #475/R est:3000-3500
£29371 $49930 €42000 Inn interior (57x41cm-22x16in) s.d.1917 cardboard. 26-Nov-3 Pandolfini, Florence #30/R est:22000-26000
Works on paper
£1049 $1783 €1500 Glass and fruit. Two men (21x15cm-8x6in) s.d.1914-15 Chinese ink W/C chl two prov. 25-Nov-3 Sotheby's, Milan #75/R est:1500-2000

CONTI, Regina (1890-1960) Swiss
£633 $1077 €924 Al pozzo (55x40cm-22x16in) s.i. 28-Nov-3 Zofingen, Switzerland #2951 (S.FR 1400)

CONTI, Sandra (20th C) Italian?
£470 $864 €700 Still life with samovar and fruit (67x64cm-26x25in) s.d.1927 board. 24-Mar-4 Il Ponte, Milan #477/R

CONTI, Tito (1842-1924) Italian
£986 $1587 €1400 Scene galante in costume siecentesco (31x22cm-12x9in) 8-May-3 Farsetti, Prato #230
£1151 $1888 €1600 Lady with hat (35x23cm-14x9in) s. 10-Jun-3 Pandolfini, Florence #100 est:1000-1200
£2437 $4191 €3558 Portrait of young gentleman wearing hat with roses (36x26cm-14x10in) s. 3-Dec-3 Museumsbygningen, Copenhagen #124/R est:10000-15000 (D.KR 26000)
£7647 $13000 €11165 In the wine cellar (40x50cm-16x20in) s.d.1871. 29-Oct-3 Christie's, Rockefeller NY #233/R est:15000-20000
£10500 $19215 €15330 Musician (34x25cm-13x10in) s.i.verso board. 7-Apr-4 Bonhams, Bury St Edmunds #467/R est:1500-2500
£12000 $20400 €17520 Castanet dancer (62x52cm-24x20in) s. prov. 18-Nov-3 Sotheby's, London #349/R
£15000 $27300 €21900 The love letter (85x62cm-33x24in) s. prov. 15-Jun-4 Sotheby's, London #203/R est:15000-20000

CONTINENTAL SCHOOL
£1117 $2000 €1631 Portrait of a woman (61x76cm-24x30in) board. 8-May-4 Susanin's, Chicago #6074/R est:400-600
£5114 $9000 €7466 Still life of a flower filled urn on gray marble slab laden with fruit (56x76cm-22x30in) 21-May-4 North East Auctions, Portsmouth #1459
£5400 $9936 €7884 Giverny (51x61cm-20x24in) 8-Jun-4 Gorringes, Lewes #2028 est:150-200

CONTINENTAL SCHOOL, 16th/17th C
£3300 $6138 €4818 Madonna and Child (37x25cm-15x10in) gesso on canvas on panel. 5-Mar-4 Moore Allen & Innocent, Cirencester #134/R est:300-500

CONTINENTAL SCHOOL, 17th C
£4630 $7500 €6760 Figures in a humorous tavern scene (64x53cm-25x21in) panel. 3-Aug-3 North East Auctions, Portsmouth #1775/R
£6704 $12000 €9788 Death of a maiden, possibly Dido (89x143cm-35x56in) 14-May-4 Skinner, Boston #11/R est:800-1200
£7000 $11900 €10220 Christ crucified (79x76cm-31x30in) panel. 23-Nov-3 Wilkinson, Doncaster #240/R
£7192 $11219 €10500 View of palace (154x111cm-61x44in) 8-Apr-3 Il Ponte, Milan #135/R
£7192 $11219 €10500 Landscape with classical buildings (153x110cm-60x43in) 8-Apr-3 Il Ponte, Milan #160/R
£7447 $12436 €10500 Market scene (94x124cm-37x49in) 17-Jun-3 Finarte Semenzato, Milan #421/R est:7000
£8904 $13890 €13000 Saint Jerome (96x79cm-38x31in) 8-Apr-3 Il Ponte, Milan #154/R
£88889 $160000 €129778 Still life with chestnuts, fruit, glass of wine and pitcher with flowers, all resting on ledge (48x26cm-19x10in) s. 22-Jan-4 Sotheby's, New York #45a/R est:100000-150000

CONTINENTAL SCHOOL, 17th/18th C
£4480 $7750 €6541 Battle scene, warriors on horseback (71x135cm-28x53in) 13-Dec-3 Sloans & Kenyon, Bethesda #795/R est:1800-2500

CONTINENTAL SCHOOL, 18th C
£5072 $8319 €7000 Tobiolo and the angel (57x80cm-22x31in) 27-May-3 Il Ponte, Milan #1064 est:8000
£6627 $11000 €9675 Siege of Troy (145x193cm-57x76in) 30-Sep-3 Christie's, Rockefeller NY #389/R est:3000-5000
£9868 $18158 €15000 Untitled (229x324cm-90x128in) on leather screen. 23-Jun-4 Sotheby's, Paris #56/R est:15000-20000
£11732 $21000 €17129 Portrait of Samuel Falk, Baal Shem of London (76x63cm-30x25in) prov.lit. 18-Mar-4 Sotheby's, New York #250/R est:30000-40000
£14184 $23688 €20000 Landscape with temple, washerwomen and sheperds (113x135cm-44x53in) 23-Jun-3 Finarte Semenzato, Rome #116/R est:20000
Sculpture
£18792 $34389 €28000 Bacchus (76cm-30in) pat bronze. 6-Jul-4 Marc Kohn, Paris #50/R
£18919 $33865 €28000 Lions (61x120x38cm-24x47x15in) stone pair. 9-May-4 Sotheby's, Amsterdam #181/R est:12000-18000

CONTINENTAL SCHOOL, 18th/19th C
£5204 $9315 €7598 Still life of objects on table with carpet, shells and vases (128x163cm-50x64in) 22-Mar-4 Blomqvist, Oslo #338/R est:40000-60000 (N.KR 65000)

CONTINENTAL SCHOOL, 19th C
£2350 $4371 €3431 Allegorical study of an Angel appearing to a frightened couple (127x101cm-50x40in) 5-Mar-4 Moore Allen & Innocent, Cirencester #326/R est:1000-1500
£3605 $6200 €5263 Harbour of Naples at dawn (69x132cm-27x52in) 6-Dec-3 Neal Auction Company, New Orleans #107/R est:2000-3000
£3765 $6250 €5497 Dancing gypsy girl (157x99cm-62x39in) 4-Oct-3 Neal Auction Company, New Orleans #913/R est:2000-3000
£6500 $10855 €9490 Shipping on the Golden Horn, Constantinople (63x77cm-25x30in) 14-Oct-3 Sotheby's, London #8/R est:5000-7000
£9000 $14580 €13050 Destruction of a city by a volcano (71x93cm-28x37in) 30-Jul-3 Hamptons Fine Art, Godalming #288/R est:6000-10000
£11348 $18950 €16000 Historic scene (92x155cm-36x61in) 17-Jun-3 Finarte Semenzato, Milan #415/R
Sculpture
£9392 $17000 €13712 Achilles in a tragic scene from the Iliad (112x58x43cm-44x23x17in) i. bronze. 3-Apr-4 Neal Auction Company, New Orleans #357/R est:12000-18000
£10500 $17850 €15330 Hercules (92x44x42cm-36x17x17in) bronze. 22-Nov-3 Bonhams, Chester #125/R est:2000-3000
£13408 $24000 €19576 Figure of Prometheus (51cm-20in) carved ivory. 8-May-4 Susanin's, Chicago #2036/R est:6000-8000
£15333 $27600 €23000 Minerve. Apollon (111cm-44in) marble sold with base pair prov. 22-Apr-4 Christie's, Paris #712/R est:15000-20000
£20270 $36284 €30000 Sphynxes (62x88x28cm-24x35x11in) granite pair. 9-May-4 Sotheby's, Amsterdam #808/R est:30000-50000

CONTINENTAL SCHOOL, 19th/20th C
£5988 $10000 €8742 Setter in an extensive landscape (90x71cm-35x28in) s. 7-Oct-3 Sotheby's, New York #146 est:3000-5000

CONTINENTAL SCHOOL, 20th C
Sculpture
£1196 $2200 €1746 Figure group of two lambs (30x64x43cm-12x25x17in) i. bronze wooden base prov. 26-Jun-4 Selkirks, St. Louis #501/R est:2750-3250
£5705 $10097 €8500 Victoire de Samothrace (80cm-31in) pat bronze. 29-Apr-4 Sotheby's, Paris #96/R est:2000-3000

CONTRERAS, Jesus Fructuoso (1867-1902) Mexican
Sculpture
£8000 $14400 €11680 L'eveil (75cm-30in) s.d. white marble lit. 21-Apr-4 Sotheby's, London #133/R est:8000-12000

CONVERSANO, Romano (1920-) Italian
£333 $613 €500 Female nude (25x20cm-10x8in) s. cardboard on canvas. 8-Jun-4 Finarte Semenzato, Milan #95/R

CONVERY, Francis (1956-) British
£450 $837 €657 Head of a diver (41x39cm-16x15in) s. canvas on board. 4-Mar-4 Christie's, Kensington #253/R

CONWAY, Fred (1900-1972) American
£870 $1600 €1270 Putter (20x41cm-8x16in) s. i.verso board. 26-Jun-4 Selkirks, St. Louis #149/R est:1000-1500
Works on paper
£559 $950 €816 Union Station, platform cafeteria (43x58cm-17x23in) s.d.1944 W/C. 7-Nov-3 Selkirks, St. Louis #429/R

CONWAY, Harold Edward (1872-?) British
£550 $935 €803 Still life with spring flowers (35x30cm-14x12in) s.d.1944. 26-Nov-3 Sotheby's, Olympia #38/R

COOGHEN, Leendert van der (1610-1681) Dutch
£1733 $3103 €2600 Stateley landscape with anglers and riders at the bank of a river (19x15cm-7x6in) mono. panel. 17-May-4 Glerum, Amsterdam #6/R est:1200-1600

COOK OF PLYMOUTH, William (fl.1870-1880) British
Works on paper
£250 $395 €363 After the wreck, Lynmouth (45x38cm-18x15in) s.d.1880 W/C. 24-Jul-3 Dominic Winter, Swindon #13/R
£300 $510 €438 Peaceful day at the lock (43x60cm-17x24in) init.d.80 W/C. 25-Nov-3 Bonhams, Knightsbridge #43/R
£360 $601 €526 Shipwreck on a rocky coast (25x46cm-10x18in) mono.d.77 W/C htd white. 14-Oct-3 Bearnes, Exeter #322
£380 $600 €551 Polperro harbour (25x42cm-10x17in) mono.d.82 W/C pencil. 24-Jul-3 Lawrence, Crewkerne #852
£580 $969 €847 Kelp gatherers in a rocky cove (30x50cm-12x20in) mono.d.73 W/C. 14-Oct-3 Bearnes, Exeter #323/R
£1250 $1975 €1813 Figures mending a sail before a harbour and cottages in Devon (44x75cm-17x30in) mono.d.81 W/C. 2-Sep-3 Bonhams, Oxford #34/R est:800-1200

COOK, Allan (20th C) Australian
£268 $488 €391 Seascape. d.55 board. 1-Jul-4 Joel, Victoria #385 (A.D 700)

COOK, Arthur M (1931-) American
Works on paper
£331 $600 €483 Ducks landing (51x71cm-20x28in) s. W/C. 16-Apr-4 James Julia, Fairfield #769/R

COOK, Barrie (1929-) British
£750 $1388 €1095 Black and white optical (78x137cm-31x54in) s.d.69 acrylic paper. 11-Feb-4 Sotheby's, Olympia #299/R

COOK, Beryl (1926-) British
£9000 $16380 €13140 Groovy granny (53x53cm-21x21in) s. board. 15-Jun-4 Bonhams, New Bond Street #112/R est:5000-8000
£10000 $17000 €14600 Out walking the dog (59x45cm-23x18in) board. 4-Nov-3 Bristol Auction Rooms #543/R est:10000-15000
£14000 $25900 €20440 British eight (91x27cm-36x11in) s. board lit. 11-Mar-4 Christie's, Kensington #207/R est:8000-12000
Prints
£3000 $5580 €4380 Girls night out (84x74cm-33x29in) lithograph. 8-Mar-4 Christie's, London #20

COOK, Charles Henry (1830-1906) Irish?
£250 $418 €365 Interior with man smoking (33x23cm-13x9in) s. 17-Oct-3 Keys, Aylsham #298

COOK, Ebenezer Wake (1843-1926) British
£440 $761 €642 Unloading the Catch, St Michael's Mount, Cornwall (41x61cm-16x24in) s. 11-Dec-3 Neales, Nottingham #607/R
Works on paper
£320 $589 €467 Entrance to the St. Gothard Pass from Bellinzona (14x21cm-6x8in) s. W/C htd scratching out. 23-Jun-4 Bonhams, Bury St Edmunds #327/R
£550 $946 €803 At the water fountain (30x17cm-12x7in) s.d.99 pencil W/C. 3-Dec-3 Christie's, Kensington #107/R
£850 $1471 €1241 Ups and downs of Clovelly, with figure and donkeys (33x23cm-13x9in) s. W/C. 11-Dec-3 Neales, Nottingham #549/R
£2300 $3841 €3358 Doge's Palace and the Campanile of St Mark's, Venice (22x47cm-9x19in) mono.d.79 pencil W/C prov. 16-Oct-3 Christie's, Kensington #59/R est:1500-2000

COOK, Francis (20th C) British
£310 $586 €453 Woodland scene. s.d.1943. 19-Feb-4 Rendalls, Ashburton #1503

COOK, Frederick T W (1907-1982) British
£400 $732 €584 The river Dart (450x210cm-177x83in) s. 28-Jan-4 Hampton & Littlewood, Exeter #405/R
Works on paper
£320 $534 €467 View of Polperro (28cm-11in) s. gouache. 16-Oct-3 Mallams, Cheltenham #207/R

COOK, George E (1867-1930) American
£518 $850 €751 Western landscape (41x51cm-16x20in) s. painted c.1920. 7-Jun-3 Treadway Gallery, Cincinnati #1400

COOK, Herbert Moxon (1844-c.1920) British
Works on paper
£330 $594 €482 Rushing river in the Ogwen Valley (33x43cm-13x17in) s.d.1876 W/C. 24-Apr-4 Rogers Jones, Clwyd #83
£600 $1074 €876 Mists lifting, Achill Island, County Mayo (23x34cm-9x13in) s. W/C. 25-May-4 Bonhams, Knightsbridge #64/R

COOK, Howard (1901-1980) American
Prints
£2825 $5000 €4125 Financial district (34x26cm-13x10in) s.d.1931 num.75 lithograph. 28-Apr-4 Christie's, Rockefeller NY #26/R est:4000-6000
Works on paper
£938 $1500 €1369 Coconut tree, Acapulco (122x91cm-48x36in) s.d.1932 W/C. 18-May-3 Auctions by the Bay, Alameda #1065/R

COOK, James (?) ?
£489 $831 €714 Portrait of a friend (44x32cm-17x13in) indis.s. canvasboard. 27-Nov-3 International Art Centre, Auckland #164/R (NZ.D 1300)
£1119 $1937 €1634 Portrait of Rita Angus and Alfred Cook working in studio (28x23cm-11x9in) s. 9-Dec-3 Peter Webb, Auckland #26/R est:3000-5000 (NZ.D 3000)

COOK, John A (1870-1936) American
Works on paper
£205 $375 €308 Fishing boats in Gloucester harbour (25x18cm-10x7in) s. W/C. 29-Jul-4 Eldred, East Dennis #433
£294 $500 €429 Rockport Wharf view (19x28cm-7x11in) s. W/C. 21-Nov-3 Skinner, Boston #575/R

COOK, Joshua (snr) (fl.1838-1848) British
£1400 $2506 €2044 Still life of pineapple and other fruit, displayed on a ledge (49x59cm-19x23in) s. 11-May-4 Bonhams, Knightsbridge #235/R est:1500-2000

COOK, Olive (1916-) British
£380 $703 €555 Flowers and birds (35x63cm-14x25in) s.i. verso board. 13-Feb-4 Sworder & Son, Bishops Stortford #63/R

COOK, Otis (1900-1980) American
£939 $1700 €1371 Vermont hills (61x51cm-24x20in) 2-Apr-4 Douglas, South Deerfield #25
£1062 $1900 €1551 Fishing boat, beached (63x76cm-25x30in) s. prov. 14-May-4 Skinner, Boston #252/R est:800-1200
£1176 $2000 €1717 Boats at the pier (46x51cm-18x20in) s. 21-Nov-3 Skinner, Boston #542/R est:800-1200
£1676 $3000 €2447 Fishing shack (63x76cm-25x30in) s. prov. 14-May-4 Skinner, Boston #242/R est:800-1200
£2374 $4250 €3466 Harbour view, early morning (76x91cm-30x36in) s. prov. 14-May-4 Skinner, Boston #243/R est:1000-1500

COOK, Theodore (19th C) British
£1117 $2000 €1631 Mediterranean port (25x41cm-10x16in) s.d.1858. 8-Jan-4 James Julia, Fairfield #534/R est:2000-4000
£1117 $2000 €1631 Bringing home the catch (25x20cm-10x8in) s. 8-Jan-4 James Julia, Fairfield #535/R est:2000-4000

COOK, Timothy (1958-) Australian
Works on paper
£938 $1753 €1407 Untitled (92x94cm-36x37in) bears name.verso earth pigments bush gum linen prov. 26-Jul-4 Sotheby's, Melbourne #224/R (A.D 2400)

COOK, William (fl.1877-1879) British
Works on paper
£350 $637 €511 St. Michael's Mount (35x55cm-14x22in) mono.d.81 pencil W/C htd white. 1-Jul-4 Mellors & Kirk, Nottingham #723

COOK, William Delafield (jnr) (1936-) Australian
£2846 $4467 €4127 Untitled, two trees and a wall (125x125cm-49x49in) s.d.71 exhib.lit. 27-Aug-3 Christie's, Sydney #557/R est:15000-20000 (A.D 7000)
Works on paper
£2893 $5351 €4224 Untitled - cauliflowers (62x95cm-24x37in) s.i.d.1977 verso chl conte paper on canvas. 10-Mar-4 Deutscher-Menzies, Melbourne #83/R est:8000-12000 (A.D 7000)
£51907 $88242 €75784 Hillside (195x216cm-77x85in) s.d.86 synthetic polymer paint prov.exhib. 24-Nov-3 Sotheby's, Melbourne #10/R est:120000-160000 (A.D 122500)

COOK, William Delafield (snr) (1861-1931) Australian
£407 $728 €594 Winter pastures (45x74cm-18x29in) s. 10-May-4 Joel, Victoria #367 (A.D 1000)
£488 $873 €712 By the river (53x74cm-21x29in) s. canvas on board painted c.1920. 10-May-4 Joel, Victoria #333 (A.D 1200)
£529 $946 €772 Evening light (39x55cm-15x22in) s. board. 10-May-4 Joel, Victoria #394 est:1000-1200 (A.D 1300)
£891 $1434 €1301 By the bay (43x71cm-17x28in) s. canvasboard. 13-Oct-3 Joel, Victoria #340/R est:2500-3500 (A.D 2200)

COOKE, Arthur Claude (attrib) (1867-?) British
£4085 $7067 €5964 The morning toilet (66x58cm-26x23in) s. panel. 15-Dec-3 Lilla Bukowskis, Stockholm #46 est:20000 (S.KR 52000)

COOKE, Barrie (1931-) British
£915 $1584 €1300 Burren landscape (18x24cm-7x9in) s.d.63 oil plaster board. 10-Dec-3 Bonhams & James Adam, Dublin #169/R
£1678 $2853 €2400 Stone's Lake, County Clare (25x36cm-10x14in) s.i.d.1979 board. 18-Nov-3 Whyte's, Dublin #61/R est:2000-3000
£1818 $3091 €2600 Lough arrow Algal growth (42x47cm-17x19in) s. i.d.1997 verso board prov. 25-Nov-3 De Veres Art Auctions, Dublin #145/R est:3000-4000
£1958 $3329 €2800 Lianas (46x46cm-18x18in) s.d.75. 25-Nov-3 De Veres Art Auctions, Dublin #26/R est:3000-4000
£2162 $4086 €3200 Junction (76x76cm-30x30in) s.d.1972 i.on stretcher prov.exhib. 17-Feb-4 Whyte's, Dublin #82/R est:4000-5000
£2297 $4342 €3400 Dark forest III (23x25cm-9x10in) s.i.d.1997 verso masonite on board. 17-Feb-4 Whyte's, Dublin #74/R est:3000-4000
£2958 $4732 €4200 Untitled (140x127cm-55x50in) s.d.August 1970. 16-Sep-3 Whyte's, Dublin #37/R est:4000-6000
£3000 $5430 €4500 Sweeney under fire (71x71cm-28x28in) s.d.84 verso prov. 30-Mar-4 De Veres Art Auctions, Dublin #148/R est:5000-7000
£3133 $5671 €4700 Lough arrow algae IV (56x64cm-22x25in) s. i.d.96 verso prov. 30-Mar-4 De Veres Art Auctions, Dublin #80/R est:5000-7000
£10811 $20432 €16000 Lying (102x102cm-40x40in) s.d.1963 prov.exhib. 17-Feb-4 Whyte's, Dublin #331/R est:10000-12000
Works on paper
£420 $752 €613 Yellow night fishing I (27x33cm-11x13in) s.d.80 W/C prov. 14-May-4 Christie's, London #93/R
£1133 $2051 €1700 Walk (72x39cm-28x15in) s.d.67 gouache pencil prov. 31-Mar-4 James Adam, Dublin #133/R est:1000-1500
£1141 $2019 €1700 Seated nude (76x58cm-30x23in) s.d.1986 black crayon. 27-Apr-4 Whyte's, Dublin #154/R est:1800-2200
£1733 $3137 €2600 Salmon (37x55cm-15x22in) W/C. 31-Mar-4 James Adam, Dublin #86/R est:2000-4000
£1733 $3137 €2600 Knockrae (31x41cm-12x16in) s.i.d.2000 W/C. 30-Mar-4 De Veres Art Auctions, Dublin #104/R est:1800-2200
£2400 $4344 €3600 Aphanizomenon (56x76cm-22x30in) s. i.d.93 verso gouache. 30-Mar-4 De Veres Art Auctions, Dublin #74/R est:3500-4500

COOKE, Edward William (1811-1880) British
£838 $1500 €1223 Docked boat with man and wagon (20x30cm-8x12in) panel. 7-May-4 Sloans & Kenyon, Bethesda #1673/R est:2000-2500

£1150 $1909 €1679 Sunset on the Lagune, Venice, with the Armenian Convent in the distance (8x16cm-3x6in) s. canvas on board. 1-Oct-3 Bonhams, Knightsbridge #170/R est:1200-1800
£1420 $2300 €2059 Roman Campagnia (15x20cm-6x8in) s.verso academy panel. 26-Jul-3 Thomaston Place, Thomaston #331/R
£1900 $3097 €2774 Shipping off Portsmouth harbour (30x41cm-12x16in) s.d.1836. 24-Sep-3 Dreweatt Neate, Newbury #93/R est:1800-2200
£2700 $4428 €3942 Dutch coastal scene with fishing vessel on choppy seas (100x59cm-39x23in) s.d.1870. 3-Jun-3 Fellows & Sons, Birmingham #77/R est:1800-2500
£3000 $5160 €4380 Coming into port in stormy weather (26x31cm-10x12in) s.d.1872 panel. 2-Dec-3 Sotheby's, London #39/R est:3000-5000
£14000 $25760 €20440 Isola della Certosa, in the Venetian Lagoon (32x48cm-13x19in) s.d.1865 oil paper on canvas prov.lit. 11-Jun-4 Christie's, London #149/R est:15000-20000
£19000 $34010 €27740 On the sands at Scheveningen (27x43cm-11x17in) s. panel. 26-May-4 Christie's, Kensington #602/R est:6000-8000
£68000 $121720 €99280 Scheveling - Landing fish, coast of Holland (81x107cm-32x42in) s.d.1869 prov.exhib.lit. 26-May-4 Christie's, Kensington #605/R est:70000-90000
£70000 $128800 €102200 Arrival of Otho, ex-king of Greece, at Venice 29th October, 1862, in H.M Corvette Scylla (49x95cm-19x37in) s.i.d.1862 prov.exhib.lit. 11-Jun-4 Christie's, London #148/R est:30000-50000

Works on paper
£400 $716 €584 Fishing boat moored in an estuary (16x22cm-6x9in) s.d.July 28 1829 pencil. 26-May-4 Christie's, Kensington #409/R
£1500 $2730 €2190 View of St Agnes, Scilly Isles (21x33cm-8x13in) s. W/C over pencil htd bodycol. 1-Jul-4 Sotheby's, London #262/R est:2000-3000

COOKE, Hereward Lester (1916-1973) American
Works on paper
£232 $425 €348 Busy harbour (18x56cm-7x22in) s.d.1964 W/C. 31-Jul-4 Sloans & Kenyon, Bethesda #1202/R

COOKE, Isaac (1846-1922) British
Works on paper
£260 $476 €380 Coastal landscape, thought to be Great Orme (22x52cm-9x20in) s. W/C. 2-Feb-4 Bonhams, Chester #896
£280 $510 €409 Snowden, Welsh mountains landscape (30x51cm-12x20in) s. W/C. 29-Jun-4 Capes Dunn, Manchester #774/R
£1100 $2013 €1606 Mountains solitude, Cwm Einon, with cottages and mountains beyond (49x75cm-19x30in) s. W/C. 6-Jul-4 Peter Wilson, Nantwich #87/R est:700-900

COOKE, Pat (20th C) British
£360 $666 €526 Ulystration - a woman wants to be embraced 20 times a day (42x30cm-17x12in) s.i.d.1969 W/C. 14-Jul-4 Bonhams, Chester #382
Works on paper
£280 $512 €409 Weavers Houses, Pickford street Macclesfield (13x23cm-5x9in) s.i.d.1971 pen blk ink W/C. 6-Apr-4 Capes Dunn, Manchester #796/R
£360 $666 €526 Hot pants in Hacking Hey (18x38cm-7x15in) s.d.1971 pen ink W/C. 14-Jul-4 Bonhams, Chester #381
£380 $695 €555 Rumanian evening (23x28cm-9x11in) s.i.d.1972 pen blk ink W/C. 6-Apr-4 Capes Dunn, Manchester #794/R
£380 $695 €555 I backed a couple of donkeys yesterday (15x10cm-6x4in) s.i.d.1971 pen blk ink W/C. 6-Apr-4 Capes Dunn, Manchester #795/R
£380 $703 €555 Zap (31x17cm-12x7in) s.d.70 pen ink W/C. 14-Jul-4 Bonhams, Chester #385
£400 $740 €584 Old Bond Street shoppers (46x31cm-18x12in) s.d.1970 pen ink W/C. 14-Jul-4 Bonhams, Chester #384
£550 $1007 €803 Ma Boyle's Oyster Bar Liverpool (15x36cm-6x14in) s.i.d.1971 pen blk ink W/C. 6-Apr-4 Capes Dunn, Manchester #798/R

COOKE, Roger (1941-) American
£405 $750 €591 Daughter of the prairie (30x38cm-12x15in) s. panel. 19-Jan-4 O'Gallerie, Oregon #99/R

COOKE, William Edward (fl.1880-1886) British
£1600 $2960 €2336 Haddon Hall (61x91cm-24x36in) s.d.1911. 14-Jul-4 Sotheby's, Olympia #60/R est:2000-3000

COOKMAN, Charles Edwin (1856-1913) American
£595 $1100 €869 Pomeranian on a daybed (51x61cm-20x24in) s. bears i. 10-Feb-4 Doyle, New York #130/R est:2000-3000

COOKSEY, May Louise Greville (1878-1943) British
£2000 $3180 €2920 Beatrice seated on a terrace combing out her hair with a golden comb (44x29cm-17x11in) s.d.1913. 18-Mar-3 Anderson & Garland, Newcastle #219/R est:2000-3000

COOLE, Brian (19th C) British
£782 $1400 €1142 Busy shipping lane (28x33cm-11x13in) s. 8-Jan-4 James Julia, Fairfield #553/R est:1000-1500

COOLEY, Brian (20th C) American?
Sculpture
£1471 $2456 €2148 Parasaurolophus (80cm-31in) s. bronze. 17-Nov-3 Hodgins, Calgary #344/R est:3750-4250 (C.D 3250)

COOLEY, Jack (20th C) American
£330 $600 €482 Art Gallery, French Quarter (76x61cm-30x24in) s.d.72 masonite. 7-Feb-4 Neal Auction Company, New Orleans #777

COOLEY, Lydia (1907-) American
£550 $1007 €803 Girl reading in a orchard (28x35cm-11x14in) s. board. 7-Apr-4 Woolley & Wallis, Salisbury #293/R

COOLEY, Thomas (1795-1872) British
Works on paper
£760 $1383 €1110 Portrait of a Cork Gentleman and a lady (58x43cm-23x17in) init.d.1840 W/C pair. 16-Jun-4 Andrew Hartley, Ilkley #1007/R

COOMANS, Auguste (attrib) (1855-?) Belgian
£816 $1461 €1200 Moutons au pre (23x32cm-9x13in) s. st.init.verso panel. 16-Mar-4 Vanderkindere, Brussels #295

COOMANS, Heva (19th C) Belgian
£3593 $6000 €5246 Puppeteer (44x35cm-17x14in) s. 7-Oct-3 Sotheby's, New York #93 est:8000-12000

COOMANS, J (20th C) Belgian?
£739 $1323 €1079 Sheep grazing (25x35cm-10x14in) s. panel. 26-May-4 AB Stockholms Auktionsverk #2431/R (S.KR 10000)

COOMANS, P J B (1903-1984) Dutch?
£268 $499 €400 House near the water (59x49cm-23x19in) s. 8-Mar-4 Bernaerts, Antwerp #750

COOMANS, Pierre Olivier Joseph (1816-1889) Belgian
£1200 $2172 €1800 Au lit de riviere (25x35cm-10x14in) s.d.1865 panel. 30-Mar-4 Campo & Campo, Antwerp #51/R est:3000-5000
£1706 $2900 €2491 La rieuse (11x32cm-4x13in) s. prov. 21-Nov-3 Skinner, Boston #250/R est:3000-5000
£4722 $8500 €6894 Meditation (82x66cm-32x26in) s.d.1878. 21-Jan-4 Sotheby's, New York #237/R est:3000-4000
£8889 $16000 €12978 An eastern beauty (55x43cm-22x17in) s.d.1878 prov. 23-Apr-4 Sotheby's, New York #175/R est:15000-20000

COOMBS, Delbert Dana (1850-1938) American
£323 $600 €472 Pastoral landscape with hay wagon (51x36cm-20x14in) s.d.1890. 6-Mar-4 North East Auctions, Portsmouth #227
£806 $1500 €1177 Coast of Maine (28x61cm-11x24in) s.d.1892. 6-Mar-4 North East Auctions, Portsmouth #226 est:2500-3500
£852 $1500 €1244 Landscape of woods with a stone bridge over a stream (33x48cm-13x19in) s. 3-Jan-4 Cobbs, Peterborough #140a/R
£2793 $5000 €4078 Portrait of Maine Governor Dingley (127x102cm-50x40in) s.d.1899 prov. 8-Jan-4 James Julia, Fairfield #426/R est:10000-20000
£5247 $8500 €7661 Going to the country fair in Maine (51x91cm-20x36in) s.d.1915. 1-Aug-3 North East Auctions, Portsmouth #945/R est:7000-10000

COOMBS, Delbert Dana (attrib) (1850-1938) American
£279 $500 €407 Cliffs along the shore (38x61cm-15x24in) 16-May-4 CRN Auctions, Cambridge #6/R

COON, Ray (1896-1980) American
£261 $425 €381 Along the marginal way (28x38cm-11x15in) s. board. 27-Sep-3 Thomaston Place, Thomaston #369

COONEY, M B (20th C) Swiss?
£856 $1600 €1250 View of friendship (38x51cm-15x20in) s. d.1929 verso. 28-Feb-4 Thomaston Place, Thomaston #233/R

COONEY, Mary Wheeler (1866-1957) American
£276 $450 €403 Old courtyard (23x18cm-9x7in) s. canvas on board. 28-Sep-3 Simpson's, Houston #105a/R

COOP, Hubert (1872-1953) British
£1700 $3145 €2482 Landscape with windmill (63x76cm-25x30in) s. 9-Mar-4 Bonhams, Knightsbridge #270/R est:1800-2200
Works on paper
£300 $552 €438 Conway Castle (23x42cm-9x17in) init. W/C. 23-Mar-4 Bonhams, Knightsbridge #66/R
£600 $1092 €876 Boats on the foreshore at dusk (28x47cm-11x19in) s.d.1895 pencil W/C bodycol. 1-Jul-4 Christie's, Kensington #311/R
£750 $1350 €1095 Rainbow (61x74cm-24x29in) s. W/C. 21-Jan-4 Sotheby's, Olympia #221/R
£900 $1503 €1314 Steam tug and sailing vessel in an estuary (36x43cm-14x17in) s.i. W/C. 12-Nov-3 Halls, Shrewsbury #245/R
£920 $1693 €1343 On the banks of a river (58x71cm-23x28in) s. W/C. 22-Jun-4 Bonhams, Knightsbridge #81/R
£1000 $1830 €1460 Beached fishing vessel. Coastal scene (34x49cm-13x19in) s. W/C pair. 27-Jan-4 Bonhams, Knightsbridge #210/R est:700-900
£1100 $1727 €1595 Tenby Harbour, Pembrokeshire (34x52cm-13x20in) s. pencil W/C. 28-Aug-3 Christie's, Kensington #457/R est:800-1200
£1600 $2928 €2336 Beached fishing vessel (29x49cm-11x19in) s. W/C. 27-Jan-4 Bonhams, Knightsbridge #67/R est:1000-1500

COOP, Hubert (attrib) (1872-1953) British
£5000 $9300 €7300 Drying the nets (41x63cm-16x25in) 4-Mar-4 Christie's, Kensington #632/R est:800-1200

COOPER, A R (?) British?
£1275 $2346 €1900 Portrait of Thomas 2nd Lord Lyttelton. i. after Richard Cosway. 23-Mar-4 Mealy's, Castlecomer #1094/R est:800-900

COOPER, Abraham (1787-1868) British

£1500 $2760 €2190 Approaching storm (25x34cm-10x13in) s.d.1812 panel. 10-Jun-4 Christie's, Kensington #8 est:600-800
£2000 $3600 €2920 Breaking cover. Gone away (18x22cm-7x9in) i. pair. 21-Apr-4 Christie's, Kensington #379/R est:1500-2500
£2600 $4680 €3796 Two Mamluk soldiers outside a walled town (28x25cm-11x10in) mono.d.1827 panel. 21-Jan-4 Sotheby's, Olympia #99/R est:2500-4000
£7000 $12600 €10220 Portrait of Thomas Oldachre mounted on a chestnut hunter with hounds in a landscape (72x92cm-28x36in) mono.d.1817. 21-Apr-4 Bonhams, New Bond Street #105/R est:8000-12000
£8287 $15000 €12099 Sporting dogs, belonging to Lord Charles Vere Ferrers Townshend (64x76cm-25x30in) 30-Mar-4 Bonhams & Butterfields, San Francisco #37/R est:10000-15000
£17000 $31280 €24820 Richard I at the Battle of Ascalon (76x102cm-30x40in) exhib. 11-Jun-4 Christie's, London #55/R est:12000-18000

COOPER, Abraham (attrib) (1787-1868) British

£1250 $2125 €1825 The shot (14x19cm-6x7in) board. 19-Nov-3 Sotheby's, Olympia #21/R est:800-1200

COOPER, Alexander (c.1605-1660) British

Miniatures
£65000 $117000 €94900 Gaston d'Orleans, wearing an open shirt (5cm-2in) vellum silver frame oval exhib.lit. 22-Apr-4 Bonhams, New Bond Street #5/R est:20000-30000

COOPER, Alfred Egerton (1883-1974) British

£320 $534 €467 View from Malden, Devon (30x46cm-12x18in) init. board. 10-Jul-3 Gorringes, Worthing #763
£420 $777 €613 Portrait Paul Wyeth (61x51cm-24x20in) init. 11-Mar-4 Christie's, Kensington #162/R
£450 $833 €657 Portrait of an officer from the artist's rifles (61x51cm-24x20in) init.d.1917. 11-Mar-4 Christie's, Kensington #35/R

COOPER, Alfred Heaton (1864-1929) British

Works on paper
£390 $671 €569 Early spring, Little Langdale Tarn (23x28cm-9x11in) W/C. 5-Dec-3 Keys, Aylsham #409
£460 $782 €672 Lakeland Bridge and Chapel (16x19cm-6x7in) s. 19-Nov-3 James Thompson, Kirby Lonsdale #172
£500 $805 €725 Figure on a loch side path at sunset (36x25cm-14x10in) s. W/C. 15-Aug-3 Keys, Aylsham #536/R
£550 $974 €803 View of Buttermere in the Lake District (38x27cm-15x11in) s. 28-Apr-4 Peter Wilson, Nantwich #164
£550 $1029 €803 Shades of evening, Hawes Water from above Colly Tarn, Measand (27x36cm-11x14in) s.d.1925 pencil W/C prov. 22-Jul-4 Tennants, Leyburn #731/R
£680 $1251 €993 Courtyard in summer with a young woman carrying a pail and a man sweeping (27x37cm-11x15in) s. W/C. 23-Mar-4 Anderson & Garland, Newcastle #307
£700 $1162 €1022 Bowness Bay (20x33cm-8x13in) s. W/C prov. 2-Oct-3 Mitchells, Cockermouth #839/R
£700 $1141 €1022 Street scene in Morocco (38x28cm-15x11in) s. W/C pair. 24-Sep-3 Peter Wilson, Nantwich #94
£1100 $1903 €1606 Scene in the Lake District (25x36cm-10x14in) s.d.04 W/C htd white. 11-Dec-3 Neales, Nottingham #510/R est:600-700
£1100 $2002 €1606 Dove Cottage, Grasmere, Cumbria (28x37cm-11x15in) s. pencil W/C. 1-Jul-4 Christie's, Kensington #467/R est:300-500
£1400 $2478 €2044 Early spring, Langdale (37x55cm-15x22in) W/C. 28-Apr-4 Peter Wilson, Nantwich #150
£1500 $2775 €2190 Harvest time (38x55cm-15x22in) s. W/C. 14-Jul-4 Bonhams, Chester #314/R est:1500-2000
£1800 $3060 €2628 Sunny bank, near Coniston, Cumbria (31x37cm-12x15in) s. pencil W/C. 19-Nov-3 Tennants, Leyburn #991/R est:500-700
£3200 $5440 €4672 Lake Windermere, Cumbria (54x76cm-21x30in) s.d.1917 W/C. 4-Nov-3 Bonhams, New Bond Street #105/R est:2000-3000

COOPER, Alfred W (19th C) British

£2800 $5012 €4088 Secret passage (51x76cm-20x30in) s.d.1875 exhib. 27-May-4 Christie's, Kensington #318/R est:1500-2000
Works on paper
£350 $641 €511 Milkmaid and cattle at a ford. Farmyard scene with children and goat (18x14cm-7x6in) s.d.1904 W/C over pencil pair. 6-Jul-4 Peter Wilson, Nantwich #93/R

COOPER, Anthony J (1907-1992) American

£229 $425 €334 Chicago scene (61x51cm-24x20in) s.d.1934 verso. 3-Mar-4 Alderfer's, Hatfield #365

COOPER, Astley D M (1856-1924) American

£642 $1200 €937 Tree by a stream (57x39cm-22x15in) s.d.1921. 29-Feb-4 Bonhams & Butterfields, San Francisco #4533
£695 $1300 €1015 Buck by a forest stream (57x41cm-22x16in) s.d.1921. 29-Feb-4 Bonhams & Butterfields, San Francisco #4534 est:600-800
£696 $1100 €1016 Sunset through the clearing (46x28cm-18x11in) s. board. 7-Sep-3 Treadway Gallery, Cincinnati #582/R
£1125 $1800 €1643 Buffalo and Indian on snowy range (76x127cm-30x50in) s.d.1910. 20-Sep-3 Sloans & Kenyon, Bethesda #361/R est:2000-2500
£1188 $1900 €1734 Stream and pasture. s. 20-Sep-3 Harvey Clar, Oakland #1536
£1563 $2500 €2282 Surf breaking on the beach (117x168cm-46x66in) s.d.1914. 18-May-3 Auctions by the Bay, Alameda #1108/R

COOPER, Astley D M (attrib) (1856-1924) American

£305 $500 €445 Wooded landscape with lake (76x46cm-30x18in) 7-Jun-3 Auctions by the Bay, Alameda #583/R

COOPER, Colin Campbell (1856-1937) American

£1087 $2000 €1587 Street scene with figures (32x46cm-13x18in) 8-Jun-4 Bonhams & Butterfields, San Francisco #4339/R est:3000-5000
£1398 $2600 €2041 Astor Library (38x45cm-15x18in) 3-Mar-4 Christie's, Rockefeller NY #28/R est:3000-5000
£1599 $2750 €2335 North African market (25x32cm-10x13in) oil crayon paper on board prov. 3-Dec-3 Doyle, New York #184/R est:4000-6000
£1613 $3000 €2355 Apple blossoms (43x30cm-17x12in) s. lit. 5-Mar-4 Skinner, Boston #456/R est:3000-5000
£1648 $3000 €2406 European river cityscape (18x25cm-7x10in) s. canvasboard prov. 15-Jun-4 John Moran, Pasadena #29 est:2000-3000
£1902 $3500 €2777 View of a European village (26x34cm-10x13in) s. board prov. 8-Jun-4 Bonhams & Butterfields, San Francisco #4042/R est:4000-6000
£2206 $3750 €3221 Cityscape (18x12cm-7x5in) with sig. board. 21-Nov-3 Skinner, Boston #589/R est:4000-6000
£2500 $4250 €3650 Flowered villa (41x25cm-16x10in) s. masonite prov. 18-Nov-3 John Moran, Pasadena #20 est:3000-4000
£6395 $11000 €9337 Woolworth building, New York City (45x35cm-18x14in) i.verso board prov. 3-Dec-3 Doyle, New York #261/R est:20000-30000
£17442 $30000 €25465 Wall Street (74x46cm-29x18in) s. prov.exhib.lit. 4-Dec-3 Christie's, Rockefeller NY #75/R est:30000-50000
Works on paper
£743 $1300 €1085 An afternoon walk (29x23cm-11x9in) s. W/C pencil. 19-Dec-3 Sotheby's, New York #1154b/R est:2000-3000
£773 $1400 €1129 Paris exposition in 1990 (13x19cm-5x7in) s. gouache. 18-Apr-4 Bonhams & Butterfields, Los Angeles #7024 est:1500-2000
£1087 $1750 €1587 Near Naples (25x30cm-10x12in) s. W/C. 20-Aug-3 James Julia, Fairfield #1558/R est:2000-3000
£1902 $3500 €2777 Sun breaking through the clouds (14x22cm-6x9in) s.i.d.1919 W/C gouache silkboard prov. 8-Jun-4 Bonhams & Butterfields, San Francisco #4247/R est:1500-2500
£6977 $12000 €10186 Chatham Square, new York City (37x42cm-15x17in) s.i. chl pencil gouache prov. 3-Dec-3 Doyle, New York #274/R est:10000-15000

COOPER, Colin Campbell (attrib) (1856-1937) American

£389 $650 €568 Impressions of Manhattan (102x84cm-40x33in) painted c.1930. 29-Jun-3 William Jenack, New York #97
£569 $950 €831 Manhattan sentinel no 41 (102x84cm-40x33in) painted c.1930. 29-Jun-3 William Jenack, New York #172

COOPER, Duncan E (c.1813-1904) British

£8197 $12951 €11968 Challicum, Victoria (17x25cm-7x10in) s.d.July 1844 i. verso W/C four prov. 2-Sep-3 Deutscher-Menzies, Melbourne #29/R est:20000-30000 (A.D 20000)

COOPER, Edward L (20th C) American

£279 $500 €407 Boat cabin (61x81cm-24x32in) board. 7-May-4 Sloans & Kenyon, Bethesda #1219/R
£447 $800 €653 Docked white boat (61x81cm-24x32in) s. board. 7-May-4 Sloans & Kenyon, Bethesda #1220/R

COOPER, Edwin (1785-1833) British

£800 $1336 €1168 Grimm, grey hunter by a stable (60x75cm-24x30in) 14-Oct-3 Sotheby's, London #431
£2210 $4000 €3227 Liver and white spaniel in a landscape (43x58cm-17x23in) s.d.1823. 30-Mar-4 Bonhams & Butterfields, San Francisco #40/R est:4000-6000
£2465 $4264 €3500 Bay hunter with dog by a fence (48x61cm-19x24in) s.d.1827. 10-Dec-3 Christie's, Amsterdam #874/R est:2500-3500
£2600 $4784 €3796 Preparing to set off (61x76cm-24x30in) s. indis d. 10-Jun-4 Christie's, Kensington #10/R est:1200-1800
£8000 $13600 €11680 Foxhound and her litter (63x76cm-25x30in) s.d.1828. 27-Nov-3 Christie's, Kensington #368/R est:8000-12000

COOPER, Edwin (attrib) (1785-1833) British

Works on paper
£412 $700 €602 Race horse (18x22cm-7x9in) init.d.1806 pen ink W/C prov. 21-Nov-3 Skinner, Boston #224/R

COOPER, Eileen (1953-) British

£800 $1480 €1168 Family (168x198cm-66x78in) s.d.1985 verso prov. 13-Jul-4 Bonhams, Knightsbridge #44/R
Works on paper
£400 $740 €584 Remembering (66x48cm-26x19in) s.d.1991 conte prov. 13-Jul-4 Bonhams, Knightsbridge #43/R

COOPER, Emma Lampert (1860-1920) American

£828 $1500 €1209 Normandy farm house (31x41cm-12x16in) s. 18-Apr-4 Bonhams & Butterfields, Los Angeles #7025 est:2000-3000

COOPER, George Gordon Byron (?-1933) British

Works on paper
£260 $434 €380 Autumn at the lake's edge (46x61cm-18x24in) s. W/C. 14-Oct-3 Bonhams, Ipswich #318

COOPER, Gerald (1898-1975) British

£1400 $2548 €2044 Still life of glass bottles (52x76cm-20x30in) s. board. 15-Jun-4 Bonhams, Knightsbridge #114/R est:1500-2000
£2600 $4758 €3796 Sunflowers on a stone ledge (13x61cm-5x24in) s. 8-Jul-4 Duke & Son, Dorchester #175
£2800 $5124 €4088 January (51x41cm-20x16in) s.d.1950 board. 4-Jun-4 Christie's, London #105/R est:3000-5000
£3800 $6954 €5548 August (51x40cm-20x16in) s.d.1956 board. 4-Jun-4 Christie's, London #106/R est:3000-5000
£6000 $10800 €8760 Bowl of peonies, flags and other flowers (74x61cm-29x24in) s. board. 20-Apr-4 Clarke Gammon, Guildford #80/R est:5000-7000
£6800 $12240 €9928 Still life study of hollyhocks and other flowers within a glass vase upon a ledge (75x62cm-30x24in) s.d.1945. 21-Apr-4 Rupert Toovey, Partridge Green #25/R est:4000-6000
£7000 $11900 €10220 Flower piece no.1 (74x61cm-29x24in) s.i.verso prov. 30-Oct-3 Duke & Son, Dorchester #267/R

COOPER, Henry (19/20th C) British
£380 $646 €555 Landscape scene with river and thatched cottages (74x48cm-29x19in) s. 30-Oct-3 Grant, Worcester #611/R
£400 $708 €584 River Ford, Sussex (41x61cm-16x24in) s. 29-Apr-4 Gorringes, Lewes #2366
£500 $790 €725 At Abinger near Dorking, Surrey (51x76cm-20x30in) s. 4-Sep-3 Christie's, Kensington #117/R
£500 $895 €730 English landscapes (41x61cm-16x24in) s. pair. 5-May-4 John Nicholson, Haslemere #591
£800 $1416 €1168 Shepherd and flock passing thatched cottage (41x61cm-16x24in) s. pair. 29-Apr-4 Gorringes, Lewes #2294
£1500 $2685 €2190 Serene river landscape, with hills beyond (51x76cm-20x30in) s. 27-May-4 Christie's, Kensington #155/R est:600-800

COOPER, John (20th C) British
£300 $555 €438 Wharfedale farm (43x53cm-17x21in) i. 15-Jan-4 Christie's, Kensington #1012/R
£350 $595 €511 Nyria racing White Heather (48x63cm-19x25in) s. acrylic. 19-Nov-3 Christie's, Kensington #434/R
£450 $765 €657 Vigilant racing Britannia (53x71cm-21x28in) s. acrylic. 19-Nov-3 Christie's, Kensington #432/R
£500 $850 €730 Royal London Yacht Club Regatta (63x83cm-25x33in) s. acrylic. 19-Nov-3 Christie's, Kensington #431/R
£900 $1530 €1314 Antigua Classic Yacht Regatta (66x76cm-26x30in) s. acrylic. 19-Nov-3 Christie's, Kensington #433/R

COOPER, Margaret Miles (1874-1965) American
£1258 $2000 €1837 Fall, Hamburg Cove (61x91cm-24x36in) s. s.i.verso. 12-Sep-3 Skinner, Boston #445/R est:2000-3000

COOPER, Richard (?) British
£727 $1142 €1054 Te Hau - Takiri Wharepapa, a Chieftain of the Ngapuhi Tribe (94x74cm-37x29in) s. after Goldie. 27-Aug-3 Dunbar Sloane, Wellington #121/R (NZ.D 2000)

COOPER, Ronald (20th C) American
Sculpture
£898 $1500 €1311 Devil and the lion's den (69x51cm-27x20in) paint wood tree-stump prov. 15-Nov-3 Slotin Folk Art, Buford #444/R est:500-800

COOPER, Royston (20th C) British
Works on paper
£350 $637 €511 London Docks (37x32cm-15x13in) s. brush blk ink W/C oil. 1-Jul-4 Christie's, Kensington #337

COOPER, Samuel (1609-1672) British
Miniatures
£2800 $5040 €4088 Lady, in a white dress with sapphire and pearl armband (3cm-1in) vellum leaf from table-book silver frame oval ebony case exhib. 22-Apr-4 Bonhams, New Bond Street #12/R est:2500-3500
£4000 $7160 €5840 Young gentleman, in gilt studded armour (3cm-1in) mono. vellum tortoiseshell frame prov. 25-May-4 Christie's, London #61/R est:2500-3500
£26000 $46800 €37960 Sir Richard Fanshawe (6cm-2in) vellum leaf from a table-book silver gilt frame oval exhib. 22-Apr-4 Bonhams, New Bond Street #9/R est:20000-30000
£34000 $57800 €49640 Gentleman (7cm-3in) W/C oval. 18-Nov-3 Bonhams, New Bond Street #18/R est:20000-30000

COOPER, Samuel (after) (1609-1672) British
£5500 $9845 €8030 Portrait of Oliver Cromwell (76x61cm-30x24in) feigned oval. 27-May-4 Christie's, Kensington #16/R est:2500-3500

COOPER, Suzanne (20th C) British
£500 $880 €730 Bloomfield Terrace (61x51cm-24x20in) s. 18-May-4 Bonhams, Knightsbridge #94/R

COOPER, Thomas George (1836-1901) British
Works on paper
£420 $722 €613 Two sheep on a grass knoll with sea to background (23x33cm-9x13in) s.d.1898. 2-Dec-3 Canterbury Auctions, UK #179

COOPER, Thomas Sidney (1803-1902) British
£850 $1581 €1241 Rocky coast (18x32cm-7x13in) s.d.1870 board prov. 4-Mar-4 Christie's, Kensington #498/R
£972 $1624 €1400 Sheep in mountain landscape (35x32cm-14x13in) s. board lit. 25-Oct-3 Bergmann, Erlangen #922/R
£1591 $2800 €2323 Sheep on a moor (30x46cm-12x18in) s.d.82. 21-May-4 North East Auctions, Portsmouth #831/R
£1700 $2839 €2482 Study of a seated bull (26x38cm-10x15in) s.d.1883 panel. 7-Oct-3 Bonhams, Knightsbridge #342/R est:800-1200
£2000 $3260 €2920 Three sheep on a hillock (18x23cm-7x9in) s.d.1872. 27-Sep-3 Rogers Jones, Clwyd #122
£2200 $3872 €3212 Cattle watering (15x21cm-6x8in) s. panel. 18-May-4 Woolley & Wallis, Salisbury #190/R est:600-800
£3600 $5976 €5256 In the Canterbury meadows (28x40cm-11x16in) s.d.1886 board. 1-Oct-3 Sotheby's, Olympia #86/R est:4000-6000
£4000 $6800 €5840 Cattle and sheep on a hillside with distant landscape view (71x91cm-28x36in) s.d.1856. 5-Nov-3 John Nicholson, Haslemere #647/R est:4000-6000
£5000 $8500 €7300 Mountain sheep (75x75cm-30x30in) s.d.1852 panel prov. 29-Oct-3 Christie's, Rockefeller NY #83/R est:10000-15000
£5357 $9214 €7821 In the Canterbury Meadows (81x107cm-32x42in) s.d.1868 prov. 2-Dec-3 Ritchie, Toronto #63/R est:10000-15000 (C.D 12000)
£5500 $9350 €8030 Woman on a donkey herding cattle and sheep (36x48cm-14x19in) panel. 19-Nov-3 Bonhams, New Bond Street #18/R est:2000-3000
£6000 $10200 €8760 Three cows in a river landscape (30x40cm-12x16in) s.d.1893 panel. 19-Nov-3 Bonhams, New Bond Street #41/R est:2000-3000
£6500 $11050 €9490 Summer (51x76cm-20x30in) s.d.1870 exhib. 19-Nov-3 Bonhams, New Bond Street #42/R est:5000-8000
£6500 $11050 €9490 Three sheep in a landscape (36x46cm-14x18in) s.d.1854 panel. 19-Nov-3 Bonhams, New Bond Street #47/R est:5000-7000
£7000 $12880 €10220 Cattle in an extensive landscape (53x43cm-21x17in) s.d.1896 s.d.verso board prov. 11-Jun-4 Christie's, London #126/R est:8000-12000
£7143 $12286 €10429 In the Canterbury meadows (77x123cm-30x48in) s. prov. 2-Dec-3 Ritchie, Toronto #67/R est:10000-15000 (C.D 16000)
£7800 $13260 €11388 Head of a sheep and a ram (72x60cm-28x24in) s.i. board on panel prov. 25-Nov-3 Christie's, London #208/R est:4000-6000
£8000 $13600 €11680 Canterbury meadows (76x112cm-30x44in) s. prov. 25-Nov-3 Christie's, London #205/R est:10000-15000
£10000 $18200 €14600 Cattle and sheep under a tree by a river (58x74cm-23x29in) s.d.1891 prov. 16-Jun-4 John Nicholson, Haslemere #792/R est:6000-10000
£10500 $18795 €15330 Noonday rest, Canterbury (56x40cm-22x16in) s.d.1889 board. 26-May-4 Sotheby's, Olympia #104/R est:8000-12000
£13000 $23920 €18980 From a sketch in Skye (75x51cm-30x20in) s. 11-Jun-4 Christie's, London #173/R est:7000-10000
£14000 $23800 €20440 Highland landscape with a girl and goat (61x91cm-24x36in) s.d.1850 s.i.verso prov.exhib. 25-Nov-3 Christie's, London #206/R est:7000-10000
£15000 $27600 €21900 Before the storm (45x60cm-18x24in) s.d.1883 panel prov. 11-Jun-4 Christie's, London #172/R est:10000-15000
£18792 $33638 €28000 Taureaux au paturage (123x182cm-48x72in) s.d.1872. 25-May-4 Palais de Beaux Arts, Brussels #559/R est:35000-50000
£19000 $32300 €27740 Views of cattle and sheep resting in a landscape (30x46cm-12x18in) s.d.1876 pair. 5-Nov-3 John Nicholson, Haslemere #658/R est:15000-25000
£21000 $38220 €30660 Lowland herd (73x108cm-29x43in) s.d.1872 i.verso. 1-Jul-4 Sotheby's, London #344/R est:20000-30000
£22000 $37400 €32120 On the cliffs, East Sussex (76x107cm-30x42in) s. 27-Nov-3 Sotheby's, London #364/R est:15000-20000
£35000 $64400 €51100 Bull and cows in a landscape (165x132cm-65x52in) s. prov.exhib. 11-Jun-4 Christie's, London #128/R est:25000-35000
£42000 $71400 €61320 Warm October (93x154cm-37x61in) s.d.1889 prov.exhib.lit. 25-Nov-3 Christie's, London #126/R est:35000-45000
£60000 $110400 €87600 Cattle and sheep in an extensive landscape (107x183cm-42x72in) s.d.1857 prov. 11-Jun-4 Christie's, London #174/R est:25000-35000
Works on paper
£272 $487 €400 Cows and sheep (39x54cm-15x21in) s. W/C. 22-Mar-4 Sant Agostino, Torino #177/R
£480 $883 €701 Cows resting on a riverbank (24x20cm-9x8in) s. pencil W/C. 25-Mar-4 Christie's, Kensington #161/R
£720 $1289 €1051 Group of mountain sheep (17x21cm-7x8in) s.d.1860 W/C. 26-May-4 Sotheby's, Olympia #54/R
£720 $1267 €1051 Grazing cow (16x23cm-6x9in) s.d.1842 pencil. 18-May-4 Woolley & Wallis, Salisbury #215/R
£1300 $2236 €1898 Sheep resting in the snow (16x22cm-6x9in) s.d.1862 pencil W/C. 3-Dec-3 Christie's, Kensington #139/R est:1200-1800
£1800 $2988 €2628 Cattle and sheep (21x33cm-8x13in) s.d.1861 W/C. 1-Oct-3 Sotheby's, Olympia #73/R est:2000-3000
£1800 $3330 €2628 Cattle watering (36x51cm-14x20in) s.d.1859 W/C. 10-Mar-4 Sotheby's, Olympia #167/R est:2000-3000
£1800 $3312 €2628 On the meadows, evening (23x30cm-9x12in) s.indis.d.188 W/C. 8-Jun-4 Bonhams, New Bond Street #53/R est:1500-2000
£2400 $4080 €3504 Cattle grazing by a river (22x29cm-9x11in) s.d.1881 W/C. 4-Nov-3 Bonhams, New Bond Street #81/R est:1200-1800
£2600 $4784 €3796 Cattle and sheep resting by a riverbank (22x28cm-9x11in) s. W/C prov. 23-Jun-4 Cheffins, Cambridge #445/R est:2000-3000
£3000 $5010 €4380 Sheep resting in the snow (29x44cm-11x17in) s.d.1863 pencil W/C. 16-Oct-3 Christie's, Kensington #190/R est:1000-1500
£3400 $6120 €4964 Winter, sheep and cattle (27x44cm-11x17in) s.d.1863 W/C over pencil. 21-Jan-4 Sotheby's, Olympia #187/R est:2500-3500
£4018 $6911 €5866 Near Canterbury (44x60cm-17x24in) s.d.1861 W/C paper on board sold with catalogue prov. 2-Dec-3 Ritchie, Toronto #30/R est:2500-4000 (C.D 9000)
£4508 $7303 €6582 Canterbury meadows (44x70cm-17x28in) s.d.1866 W/C prov. 30-Jul-3 Goodman, Sydney #203/R est:12000-15000 (A.D 11000)

COOPER, Thomas Sidney (attrib) (1803-1902) British
£350 $637 €511 Cattle watering (28cm-11in) s. 5-Feb-4 Biddle & Webb, Birmingham #905
£1150 $2105 €1679 Horse and cattle in a landscape (51x61cm-20x24in) s. 7-Apr-4 Gardiner & Houlgate, Bath #356/R est:800-1200
£1181 $1924 €1700 Cows resting under tree with herdsmen (41x57cm-16x22in) s. 25-Sep-3 Dr Fritz Nagel, Stuttgart #1337/R est:2000
Works on paper
£360 $634 €526 Bull and two cows. bears sig. pencil. 18-May-4 Woolley & Wallis, Salisbury #180/R
£420 $756 €613 Cattle crossing a ford (22x30cm-9x12in) s.d.35 W/C. 21-Apr-4 Christie's, Kensington #116/R
£650 $1105 €949 Cows and a sheep in a landscape (20x32cm-8x13in) s.indis.d. W/C. 4-Nov-3 Holloways, Banbury #493/R

COOPER, W Savage (fl.1880-1926) British
£500 $895 €730 Young girl and boy reading under the shade of a tree by a river (53x42cm-21x17in) s. 11-May-4 Bonhams, Knightsbridge #81/R
£1500 $2685 €2190 Committee boat dressed overall at the Regatta (36x25cm-14x10in) s.d.1920 board. 26-May-4 Christie's, Kensington #488/R est:500-800

COOPER, Wayne (1942-) American
£412 $750 €602 Barn (61x122cm-24x48in) s. 7-Feb-4 Neal Auction Company, New Orleans #515/R

COOPER, William Heaton (1903-1995) British
£271 $453 €396 The cart shed (34x50cm-13x20in) s. i.d.1923 stretcher. 17-Nov-3 Waddingtons, Toronto #84/R (C.D 600)
£1300 $2379 €1898 Winterseeds, Grasmere (36x51cm-14x20in) s.i.verso. 7-Apr-4 Gardiner & Houlgate, Bath #76/R est:300-400
Works on paper
£300 $498 €438 Lake District scene with mountain rising in the background (26x35cm-10x14in) s. W/C. 6-Oct-3 David Duggleby, Scarborough #242
£400 $636 €580 Lakeland scene with farmhouse (26x36cm-10x14in) s. W/C. 9-Sep-3 David Duggleby, Scarborough #118

£400	$716	€584	Lakeland scene (26x36cm-10x14in) s. W/C. 17-May-4 David Duggleby, Scarborough #618/R
£470	$874	€686	Boo tarn, Coniston (25x38cm-10x15in) s. W/C sketch. 4-Mar-4 Mitchells, Cockermouth #802/R
£498	$831	€727	Looking south from Wanstell (38x55cm-15x22in) s. i.verso W/C. 17-Nov-3 Waddingtons, Toronto #46/R (C.D 1100)
£600	$1080	€876	Sunrise, Westminster (36x48cm-14x19in) s. W/C. 20-Apr-4 Clarke Gammon, Guildford #74
£780	$1396	€1139	Lakeland scene (52x74cm-20x29in) s. W/C. 17-May-4 David Duggleby, Scarborough #723/R
£800	$1400	€1168	Morning Silver, Crummock Water (38x56cm-15x22in) W/C. 18-Dec-3 Bonhams, Edinburgh #353
£800	$1440	€1168	Lakeland landscape with trees and a stone barn (27x35cm-11x14in) s. pencil W/C. 21-Apr-4 Tennants, Leyburn #1027
£880	$1602	€1285	High fell in the Lake District (27x37cm-11x15in) s. W/C. 29-Jun-4 Anderson & Garland, Newcastle #246/R
£1000	$1760	€1460	Coniston and Coniston Old Hall (39x56cm-15x22in) s. W/C. 19-May-4 James Thompson, Kirby Lonsdale #163
£1000	$1870	€1460	Pike O'Stickle (27x38cm-11x15in) s. i.verso pencil W/C. 22-Jul-4 Tennants, Leyburn #732/R est:1000-1200
£1100	$2013	€1606	November snow above Langdale (27x36cm-11x14in) s. W/C. 7-Apr-4 Woolley & Wallis, Salisbury #142/R est:600-800
£1600	$2992	€2400	Langdale and The Pikes (37x55cm-15x22in) s. W/C. 26-Jul-4 Bonhams, Bath #27/R est:800-1200
£1650	$2805	€2409	Thirlmere (37x48cm-15x19in) s. W/C over pencil lit. 25-Nov-3 Bonhams, Knowle #169 est:800-1200
£1700	$3060	€2482	After sunset, Buttermere (37x56cm-15x22in) s. pencil W/C. 21-Apr-4 Tennants, Leyburn #1029/R est:700-900
£1800	$3240	€2628	Lakeland farm with trees and mountains beyond (36x55cm-14x22in) s. pencil W/C. 21-Apr-4 Tennants, Leyburn #1028/R est:600-800

COOPER, William Henry (1858-?) British

£253	$400	€369	Children playing on frozen mill pond (61x51cm-24x20in) s. 6-Sep-3 Brunk, Ashville #139

COOPER, William Sidney (1854-1927) British

£300	$528	€438	Landscape with cows on a track meandering towards a farmstead (25x34cm-10x13in) s.indis.d. canvasboard. 19-May-4 Rupert Toovey, Partridge Green #78/R
£440	$788	€642	Evening in Summer (41x61cm-16x24in) s. 8-Jan-4 Mallams, Cheltenham #324
£480	$782	€701	Driving sheep (34x52cm-13x20in) s.d.1918. 25-Sep-3 Mellors & Kirk, Nottingham #761
£950	$1549	€1387	Cattle resting in a meadow (29x50cm-11x20in) s.d.06. 25-Sep-3 Mellors & Kirk, Nottingham #762
£1200	$1956	€1752	Morning on the Leith (61x92cm-24x36in) s.d.1900. 24-Sep-3 Dreweatt Neate, Newbury #82 est:1000-1500
£2100	$3780	€3066	Sunny pasture, Herne (40x60cm-16x24in) s. 21-Jan-4 James Thompson, Kirby Lonsdale #200/R
£2200	$3960	€3212	Cattle grazing by the sea (58x112cm-23x44in) s.d.1891. 21-Jan-4 Sotheby's, Olympia #326/R est:2000-3000
£2300	$4232	€3358	Cattle watering in a rural landscape (61x89cm-24x35in) 8-Jun-4 Lawrences, Bletchingley #1708/R est:2500-3000
£3700	$6808	€5402	Marshlands, Kent, drover with sheep along a river (45x90cm-18x35in) s.d.1900. 29-Mar-4 Bonhams, Bath #80/R est:2000-3000
£4800	$8880	€7008	Shepherd driving sheep along side a lake (74x124cm-29x49in) s. 14-Jan-4 Brightwells, Leominster #932/R est:1000-1500

Works on paper

£181	$302	€264	Near Herne Bay (13x19cm-5x7in) s.d.1927 i.verso W/C. 17-Nov-3 Waddingtons, Toronto #51/R (C.D 400)
£400	$664	€584	Springtime, sheep and lambs in a sunlit meadow (15x23cm-6x9in) s.d.1923 W/C. 2-Oct-3 Neales, Nottingham #659/R
£650	$1118	€949	Summer's evening (38x51cm-15x20in) s.d.1907 pencil W/C. 3-Dec-3 Christie's, Kensington #122/R
£900	$1647	€1314	River landscape with cattle, sheep and drover (20x28cm-8x11in) s.d.1911 W/C. 6-Jul-4 Peter Wilson, Nantwich #50/R
£1000	$1670	€1460	Near Herne (25x35cm-10x14in) s.d.1920 W/C pair. 12-Nov-3 Sotheby's, Olympia #50/R est:1000-1500
£1200	$2184	€1752	Southern end of Buttermere looking North (37x54cm-15x21in) s. W/C. 29-Jun-4 Bonhams, Knowle #21 est:800-1200
£1200	$2244	€1752	Summer landscape with cattle standing in a stream (35x52cm-14x20in) s.d.1911 pencil W/C. 22-Jul-4 Tennants, Leyburn #742/R est:800-1200
£2000	$3740	€2920	The rivals, two young bulls in a meadow (49x70cm-19x28in) s.d.1897. 26-Feb-4 Lane, Penzance #250/R est:2000-3000
£2200	$3740	€3212	Springtime. Summertime (33x24cm-13x9in) s.d.1924-25 W/C pair. 4-Nov-3 Bonhams, New Bond Street #155/R est:1200-1800

COOPER, William T (1934-) Australian

Works on paper

£1440	$2607	€2102	Banksian black cockatoo (47x34cm-19x13in) W/C. 30-Mar-4 Christie's, Melbourne #363/R est:800-1200 (A.D 3500)

COOPSE, Pieter (?-1677) Dutch

Works on paper

£6164	$10479	€9000	Winter landscape with men fishing through the ice, a town beyond (11x22cm-4x9in) bears sig. pen brown ink wash over black chk prov.exhib. 4-Nov-3 Sotheby's, Amsterdam #86/R est:4000-6000

COORDE, Charles de (1890-1963) Belgian

£372	$665	€550	Roulottes dans les dunes (70x55cm-28x22in) s. 10-May-4 Horta, Bruxelles #281

COOSEMANS, Alexander (1627-1689) Flemish

£17605	$30809	€25000	Nature morte de raisins, artichauts et citrouilles (80x115cm-31x45in) s. 18-Dec-3 Tajan, Paris #22/R est:25000-30000
£18792	$34577	€28000	Still life with grapes, figs, peaches, strawberries and wicker bottle (51x69cm-20x27in) s. 24-Mar-4 Dorotheum, Vienna #169/R est:25000-35000
£32000	$57600	€46720	Still life with fruit, crabs, bread and other objects, on a wooden table (29x40cm-11x16in) s. panel. 22-Apr-4 Sotheby's, London #25/R est:15000-20000
£34483	$57241	€50000	Still life with grapes, melons and other fruit (59x82cm-23x32in) s. 1-Oct-3 Dorotheum, Vienna #147/R est:5000-70000

COOSEMANS, Alexander (attrib) (1627-1689) Flemish

£2318	$4219	€3500	Still life with fruit and jug (70x80cm-28x31in) 16-Jun-4 Hugo Ruef, Munich #876 est:1200
£5676	$9989	€8400	Still life of fruit with silver salver and stoneware jug (57x74cm-22x29in) prov. 22-May-4 Lempertz, Koln #1030/R est:12000
£7333	$13200	€11000	Still life with oysters and fruit on table (51x38cm-20x15in) 25-Apr-4 Chenu & Scrive, Lyon #51/R est:11000

COOSEMANS, Joseph (1828-1904) Belgian

£993	$1808	€1500	Saint Jean a Thuin (40x60cm-16x24in) s. 15-Jun-4 Galerie Moderne, Brussels #143/R est:1500-2000
£1277	$2132	€1800	Vue de ferme (53x80cm-21x31in) s. 15-Oct-3 Hotel des Ventes Mosan, Brussels #111 est:500-700
£1879	$3364	€2800	Promeneur dans un sous bois (70x50cm-28x20in) s. 25-May-4 Campo & Campo, Antwerp #45/R est:1250-2000
£3311	$6026	€5000	Paysage hivernal a la tombee du jour (60x90cm-24x35in) s.d.1879. 15-Jun-4 Galerie Moderne, Brussels #394/R est:4000-6000

COOVER, Nell Baker (1869-1955) American

£1648	$3000	€2406	At the fountain in Luxembourg Gardens (48x64cm-19x25in) s. prov. 15-Jun-4 John Moran, Pasadena #31 est:2000-3000

COOYAMA, Homer (20th C) American

£248	$400	€360	Warm desert morning (64x76cm-25x30in) s. 23-Aug-3 Harvey Clar, Oakland #1238

COPE, Charles West (1811-1890) British

£3315	$6000	€4840	Setting out of the train bands of London to relieve Gloucester (51x61cm-20x24in) 3-Apr-4 Neal Auction Company, New Orleans #379/R est:3000-5000

Works on paper

£325	$543	€475	Moonlit Bay of Naples (13x18cm-5x7in) W/C. 18-Jun-3 John Nicholson, Haslemere #578

COPE, Elizabeth (1952-) Irish

£480	$845	€701	Abstract floral still life (29x25cm-11x10in) s.i.verso panel. 21-May-4 Bracketts, Tunbridge Wells #267/R
£537	$961	€800	Binoculars (50x40cm-20x16in) s. board. 31-May-4 Hamilton Osborne King, Dublin #172/R
£800	$1448	€1200	View from the ridge, Carlow (69x71cm-27x28in) s. i.verso board prov. 30-Mar-4 De Veres Art Auctions, Dublin #109b/R
£845	$1479	€1200	Winter landscape with cattle and sheep (90x74cm-35x29in) board. 16-Dec-3 James Adam, Dublin #148/R
£987	$1816	€1500	Cat in the landscape (64x31cm-25x12in) s. board. 22-Jun-4 De Veres Art Auctions, Dublin #199 est:1400-1800
£1067	$1931	€1600	Landscape with red path (61x76cm-24x30in) s. s.d.91 verso board. 31-Mar-4 James Adam, Dublin #148/R est:1500-2000
£1208	$2138	€1800	Rocky cove (56x66cm-22x26in) s. board. 27-Apr-4 Whyte's, Dublin #190/R est:1800-2200
£1208	$2162	€1800	Artichokes (55x65cm-22x26in) s.d.97. 31-May-4 Hamilton Osborne King, Dublin #164/R est:1800-2400
£1284	$2426	€1900	Country house and garden (76x61cm-30x24in) s. indis d. masonite board. 17-Feb-4 Whyte's, Dublin #193/R est:2000-3000
£1748	$2972	€2500	Mixed flowers in hand-painted pottery jugs (61x76cm-24x30in) s.d.2000 board. 18-Nov-3 Whyte's, Dublin #207/R est:2000-3000
£2267	$4103	€3400	Red chair with yellow stripes (95x76cm-37x30in) s. panel. 31-Mar-4 James Adam, Dublin #146/R est:3500-4500
£2797	$4755	€4000	Interior, Shankill Castle, Paulstown (102x122cm-40x48in) s. s.i.verso. 18-Nov-3 Whyte's, Dublin #206/R est:4000-5000
£2819	$4989	€4200	Cactus and green secateurs (76x61cm-30x24in) s. s.i.verso board. 27-Apr-4 Whyte's, Dublin #188/R est:2500-3500
£9500	$17005	€13870	Goldfish, lemon and Braun violin with roses at window (100x81cm-39x32in) s.d.97. s.i. on stretcher s.d.verso prov. 13-May-4 Sotheby's, London #117/R est:2000-3000

COPE, Gordon Nicholson (1906-1970) American

Works on paper

£217	$350	€317	View of Golden Gate Bridge from Land's End (50x67cm-20x26in) s.d.1953 W/C gouache board. 17-Aug-3 Bonhams & Butterfields, San Francisco #5813

COPE, Leslie (1913-) American

£2059	$3850	€3006	Sleigh ride (61x91cm-24x36in) 28-Feb-4 William A Smith, Plainfield #102/R

COPE, Sir Arthur Stockdale (1857-1940) British

£350	$627	€511	High up the Tamar (46x61cm-18x24in) i.verso. 27-May-4 Christie's, Kensington #232/R

COPELAND, Alfred Bryant (1840-1909) American

£2515	$4200	€3672	South Malden, Massachusetts (76x127cm-30x50in) prov. 9-Oct-3 Christie's, Rockefeller NY #3/R est:4000-6000

COPELAND, Charles (1858-1945) American

£520	$900	€759	Doe and fawn (46x71cm-18x28in) s. 13-Dec-3 Weschler, Washington #549

COPELAND, Patrick Forbes (1860-1933) Canadian

£223	$373	€323	Pointer approaching the snipe (21x30cm-8x12in) s.d.1914. 17-Jun-3 Pinneys, Montreal #12a (C.D 500)

COPIEUX, Albert (19/20th C) French
£408 $649 €600 Cheval a l'ecurie (54x65cm-21x26in) 23-Mar-3 Salle des ventes Pillet, Lyon la Foret #1
Works on paper
£340 $541 €500 Etudes de lapins (38x70cm-15x28in) s. chl W/C. 23-Mar-3 Salle des ventes Pillet, Lyon la Foret #2
£442 $703 €650 Cheval de trait (70x38cm-28x15in) s. chl W/C. 23-Mar-3 Salle des ventes Pillet, Lyon la Foret #3

COPLANS, John (1920-) British
Photographs
£1648 $3000 €2406 Self portrait - torso front (52x33cm-20x13in) s.d.1984 num.12/12 gelatin silver print. 29-Jun-4 Sotheby's, New York #632/R est:2500-3500
£1977 $3500 €2886 Self portrait, three quarter back hand clasped (121x96cm-48x38in) s.i.d.1986 gelatin silver print. 27-Apr-4 Christie's, Rockefeller NY #174/R est:4000-6000
£2793 $5000 €4078 Self portrait - Front hand II (80x69cm-31x27in) s.i.d.1987 num.2/12 gelatin silver print prov. 13-May-4 Sotheby's, New York #404/R est:3000-4000
£3521 $6092 €5000 Self-portrait (67x72cm-26x28in) s. num.3/12 silver print exhib. 10-Dec-3 Artcurial Briest, Paris #58/R est:4000-5000
£3667 $6747 €5500 Hands holding feet (52x63cm-20x25in) silver print on paper exec 1985 prov.lit. 8-Jun-4 Artcurial Briest, Paris #295/R est:5000-6000
£4000 $7360 €6000 Back with arms above (53x43cm-21x17in) s.d.1985 num.3/12 silver print on paper lit. 8-Jun-4 Artcurial Briest, Paris #296/R est:5000-6000

COPLEY, John Singleton (1738-1815) American
£19444 $35000 €28388 Portrait of Mary Clarke, Mrs Samuel Barrett (15x12cm-6x5in) copper oval prov.exhib.lit. 23-Jan-4 Christie's, Rockefeller NY #77/R est:40000-60000
£20000 $36800 €29200 Portrait of Henry Belasyse, 2nd Earl Fauconberg in uniform (79x66cm-31x26in) prov.exhib.lit. 11-Jun-4 Christie's, London #20/R est:25000-40000

COPLEY, John Singleton (after) (1738-1815) American
£1477 $2600 €2156 Portrait of mother and child (71x58cm-28x23in) i.verso. 22-May-4 Pook & Pook, Downington #771/R est:2000-3000

COPLEY, John Singleton (attrib) (1738-1815) American
£3691 $6792 €5500 Jeune mere et son enfant (74x61cm-29x24in) 26-Mar-4 Piasa, Paris #58/R est:6000-8000

COPLEY, William Nelson (1919-1996) American
£1517 $2534 €2200 Shirt (40x30cm-16x12in) s.d.1984 acrylic collage canvas on board. 13-Nov-3 Neumeister, Munich #520/R est:4000-4500
£2345 $3916 €3400 Backstairs (74x56cm-29x22in) acrylic printed material. 13-Nov-3 Neumeister, Munich #518/R est:3000-3300
£6486 $12000 €9470 Untitled (122x183cm-48x72in) s.d.82. 13-Jul-4 Christie's, Rockefeller NY #92/R est:8000-12000
£6748 $11000 €9852 School ties (127x254cm-50x100in) s.d.86 acrylic window shade pulls linen prov. 23-Sep-3 Christie's, Rockefeller NY #132/R est:8000-10000
£11189 $19245 €16000 Betsy, Ross (165x132cm-65x52in) s.d.75 i. on stretcher acrylic prov. 5-Dec-3 Ketterer, Munich #185/R est:15000-20000

COPMANN, Peter (1794-1850) Danish
Works on paper
£425 $736 €621 Portrait of the composer Frederik Kuhlau (49x40cm-19x16in) mono.d.1832 pastel after Christian Horemann. 9-Dec-3 Rasmussen, Copenhagen #1690/R (D.KR 4500)

COPNALL, Frank T (1870-1949) British
£550 $935 €803 Interior scene with lady and gentleman seated at a table (42x61cm-17x24in) s. panel. 29-Oct-3 Bonhams, Chester #351

COPPARD, C Law (fl.1858-1891) British
£522 $950 €762 Landscape (17x22cm-7x9in) s.d.1864 panel. 7-Feb-4 Sloans & Kenyon, Bethesda #902/R
£600 $1122 €900 Wood gatherers on a lane (71x91cm-28x36in) s.d.1864. 22-Jul-4 Gorringes, Lewes #1848/R

COPPEDE, Carlo (1868-1952) Italian
£1871 $3068 €2600 Garden (61x75cm-24x30in) 10-Jun-3 Pandolfini, Florence #275/R est:1500-1700

COPPEDGE, Arthur (1938-) American
£264 $425 €385 Wines and liquors (74x38cm-29x15in) s. painted c.1974. 22-Feb-3 Bunte, Elgin #250

COPPEDGE, Fern Isabel (1888-1951) American
£2793 $5000 €4078 After the storm (41x51cm-16x20in) s. i.stretcher. 8-Jan-4 James Julia, Fairfield #562/R est:8000-10000
£3757 $6500 €5485 Barnett's Mound, Topeka, Kansas (30x36cm-12x14in) s. 13-Dec-3 Weschler, Washington #551 est:2000-3000
£7065 $13000 €10315 In Old Virginia (30x30cm-12x12in) s. i. stretcher verso. 27-Jun-4 Freeman, Philadelphia #197/R est:10000-15000
£14000 $25480 €20440 Florentine Gold, on the Arno river, near Florence, Italy (46x51cm-18x20in) s. prov. 21-Jun-4 Bonhams, New Bond Street #8/R est:15000-20000
£18895 $32500 €27587 Autumn in Jersey (46x51cm-18x20in) s. prov. 7-Dec-3 Freeman, Philadelphia #213 est:30000-50000
£20231 $35000 €29537 Winter landscape with buildings on roadside (51x61cm-20x24in) s. 10-Dec-3 Alderfer's, Hatfield #500/R est:40000-50000
£21739 $40000 €31739 Marten's Creek (46x51cm-18x20in) s. exhib. 27-Jun-4 Freeman, Philadelphia #192/R est:25000-40000
£24457 $45000 €35707 New Hope - early spring (41x51cm-16x20in) s. prov. 27-Jun-4 Freeman, Philadelphia #187/R est:30000-50000
£28902 $50000 €42197 Paunnacussing Creek at Carversville (30x25cm-12x10in) s. board painted c.1924. 10-Dec-3 Alderfer's, Hatfield #501/R est:30000-35000
£31977 $55000 €46686 House with a red roof by a stone bridge (41x41cm-16x16in) s. prov. 7-Dec-3 Freeman, Philadelphia #193 est:30000-50000
£32609 $60000 €47609 Hills of Pennsylvania near New Hope (46x51cm-18x20in) s. 27-Jun-4 Freeman, Philadelphia #176/R est:30000-50000
£34091 $60000 €49773 Red bud time (41x51cm-16x20in) s. prov. 19-May-4 Sotheby's, New York #191/R est:30000-50000
£34884 $60000 €50931 Near New Hope (61x61cm-24x24in) s. i.verso prov. 7-Dec-3 Freeman, Philadelphia #192 est:40000-60000
£44025 $70000 €64277 Autumn landscape with lake, sailboats and lakeside buildings (64x76cm-25x30in) s. 10-Sep-3 Alderfer's, Hatfield #369/R est:20000-30000
£56757 $105000 €82865 Beside the river, winter scene (51x61cm-20x24in) s. 24-Jan-4 Jeffery Burchard, Florida #30/R est:30000-50000
£63953 $110000 €93371 Houses along a stream, early Autumn (41x41cm-16x16in) s. prov. 7-Dec-3 Freeman, Philadelphia #220 est:30000-50000

COPPEE, Francois (1842-1908) French
Works on paper
£1133 $2085 €1700 Portrait de Barbey d'Aurevilly (20x15cm-8x6in) s. pen exhib. 9-Jun-4 Piasa, Paris #32/R est:1000-1500

COPPENOLLE, Edmon van (1846-1914) Belgian
£800 $1464 €1200 Bouquet (54x40cm-21x16in) s. 3-Jun-4 E & Eve, Paris #76/R
£2133 $3861 €3200 Pommiers en fleurs (58x50cm-23x20in) s. 30-Mar-4 Campo & Campo, Antwerp #291/R est:2500-3000
£3706 $6301 €5300 Pichet de cuivre et jete de roses (73x92cm-29x36in) s. 30-Nov-3 Anaf, Lyon #32/R est:5000-6000
£6028 $10067 €8500 Still life of fruit and vases (73x92cm-29x36in) s. 20-Oct-3 Sant Agostino, Torino #308/R est:5000-7000

COPPENOLLE, Jacques van (1878-1915) French
£385 $642 €550 Femme pres de la mare (32x46cm-13x18in) s. 29-Jun-3 Eric Pillon, Calais #46/R
£867 $1569 €1300 Geese by pond (43x54cm-17x21in) s. 1-Apr-4 Van Ham, Cologne #1326/R
£1316 $2421 €2000 Brassee de lilas dasn un panier. Jete de roses (32x55cm-13x22in) s. pair. 25-Jun-4 Millon & Associes, Paris #61

COPPENS, Frans (1895-1975) Belgian
£329 $605 €500 Snow in Brabant (27x35cm-11x14in) s. panel. 22-Jun-4 Palais de Beaux Arts, Brussels #212
£461 $847 €700 Landscape covered in snow (38x46cm-15x18in) s. 22-Jun-4 Palais de Beaux Arts, Brussels #213
£493 $908 €750 Flemish landscape (60x72cm-24x28in) s. 22-Jun-4 Palais de Beaux Arts, Brussels #214

COPPENS, Omer (1864-1926) Belgian
£403 $745 €600 Rue St Jean au Marais, Bruges (23x32cm-9x13in) s.d.19 i.verso panel. 13-Mar-4 De Vuyst, Lokeren #70
£805 $1490 €1200 L'entree de l'eglise de Nieuport (43x75cm-17x30in) s.i. panel. 15-Mar-4 Horta, Bruxelles #300
£833 $1325 €1200 L'entree de mosquee (35x25cm-14x10in) s. panel. 9-Sep-3 Palais de Beaux Arts, Brussels #202/R
£1119 $1902 €1600 Vue de la gare au crepuscule (36x55cm-14x22in) s.d.94. 1-Dec-3 Palais de Beaux Arts, Brussels #35/R est:1200-1800
Works on paper
£1667 $3050 €2500 Vue nocturne de Bruges (88x83cm-35x33in) s.d.1907 pastel. 7-Jun-4 Palais de Beaux Arts, Brussels #238/R est:2000-3000

COPPIER, Andre Charles (1867-?) French
£1338 $2221 €1900 Jeune fille tenant un nid d'oisillons (58x36cm-23x14in) s. 15-Jun-3 Peron, Melun #145

COPPIETERS, Alberic (19/20th C) Belgian
£897 $1659 €1300 Composition a la porcelaine blanche (57x81cm-22x32in) 16-Feb-4 Horta, Bruxelles #336

COPPINI, Fausto Eliseo (1870-1945) Italian
£335 $600 €489 Ribera del Plata (12x20cm-5x8in) cardboard. 11-May-4 Arroyo, Buenos Aires #25
£782 $1400 €1142 Path with big tree (30x40cm-12x16in) s.d.1942 board. 4-May-4 Arroyo, Buenos Aires #23/R
£820 $1500 €1197 Bridge (21x33cm-8x13in) board. 1-Jun-4 Arroyo, Buenos Aires #12
£838 $1500 €1223 Goats (37x50cm-15x20in) board. 11-May-4 Arroyo, Buenos Aires #24
£1397 $2500 €2040 Landscape (15x21cm-6x8in) s. cardboard. 4-May-4 Arroyo, Buenos Aires #12/R est:700

COPPINI, Pompeo (1870-1957) American
Sculpture
£14689 $26000 €21446 Indian on horseback (40cm-16in) i. brown pat bronze. 28-Apr-4 Christie's, Los Angeles #68/R est:8000-12000

COPPOLA, Antonio (1839-?) Italian
Works on paper
£320 $579 €480 Island off the coast of Amalfi at sunset (16x34cm-6x13in) s. W/C. 1-Apr-4 Van Ham, Cologne #1324/R
£367 $664 €550 Capri (16x34cm-6x13in) s. W/C. 1-Apr-4 Van Ham, Cologne #1325
£550 $974 €803 Fishing boats in the Bay of Naples (43x64cm-17x25in) s. gouache. 29-Apr-4 Gorringes, Lewes #2393
£550 $985 €803 La maison de cornelio rufo (33x62cm-13x24in) s.i. gouache. 26-May-4 Sotheby's, Olympia #301/R

£680	$1204	€993	Fishing boat under moonlight (41x56cm-16x22in) s. gouache. 29-Apr-4 Gorringes, Lewes #2392
£1241	$2061	€1800	Bay of Naples with Vesuvius (36x50cm-14x20in) s. gouache paper on board. 30-Sep-3 Dorotheum, Vienna #256/R est:1500-1700
£2483	$4593	€3600	La baie de Naples (31x59cm-12x23in) one s. gouache pair. 13-Jan-4 Vanderkindere, Brussels #59 est:1000-1500

COPPOLA, Carlo (17th C) Italian

£5396	$8849	€7500	Battle (72x97cm-28x38in) mono. 4-Jun-3 Sotheby's, Milan #107/R est:7000-10000

COPPOLA, Carlo (attrib) (17th C) Italian

£4225	$7394	€6000	Cavalry scene (32x75cm-13x30in) 17-Dec-3 Piasa, Paris #59/R est:3000-4000

COQUES, Gonzales (1614-1684) Flemish

£6040	$11114	€9000	Portrait d'un officier de trois quarts (16x13cm-6x5in) copper prov. 24-Mar-4 Tajan, Paris #70/R est:6000-8000

COQUES, Gonzales (attrib) (1614-1684) Flemish

£3030	$5424	€4424	Portrait of gentleman (13x9cm-5x4in) panel. 26-May-4 AB Stockholms Auktionsverk #2566/R est:25000-30000 (S.KR 41000)

CORBELLA, Tito (1885-1966) Italian

£604	$1123	€900	Lady with putto. Lady in red (42x27cm-17x11in) tempera card. 4-Mar-4 Babuino, Rome #39

CORBELLI, Edgardo (1918-1989) Italian

£282	$468	€400	Giuliana (41x30cm-16x12in) s.d.1980 board. 14-Jun-3 Meeting Art, Vercelli #160

CORBELLINI, Luigi (1901-1968) French

£423	$701	€600	Portrait de jeune femme (24x19cm-9x7in) s. 16-Jun-3 E & Eve, Paris #82
£887	$1632	€1295	Spanish girl (41x28cm-16x11in) s. prov. 14-Jun-4 Waddingtons, Toronto #322/R est:2500-3000 (C.D 2200)
£979	$1635	€1400	Nu allonge (45x81cm-18x32in) s. 29-Jun-3 Eric Pillon, Calais #181/R
£1154	$1962	€1650	Espagnole a la mantille (81x65cm-32x26in) s. 27-Nov-3 Millon & Associes, Paris #184/R est:1200-1500
£1408	$2437	€2000	Portrait de jeune enfant (41x24cm-16x9in) s. 13-Dec-3 Martinot & Savignat, Pontoise #255/R est:600-800
£2098	$3566	€3000	La musicienne (65x81cm-26x32in) s. s.i.verso prov.exhib. 18-Nov-3 Pierre Berge, Paris #74/R est:3000-4000

CORBELLINI, Quintilio (attrib) (19th C) French

Sculpture

£9155	$16021	€13000	Tamar di Giuda (110cm-43in) s. marble. 17-Dec-3 Delorme & Bocage, Paris #42/R est:6000-8000

CORBERO, Xavier (1935-) Spanish

Sculpture

£1467	$2699	€2200	Untitled (46x46x10cm-18x18x4in) black pat bronze conceived c.1958. 9-Jun-4 Christie's, Amsterdam #298/R est:1500-2000
£1622	$3000	€2368	Black Dove (28x43cm-11x17in) s.base black marble stainless steel base two parts exec 1975 lit. 12-Feb-4 Sotheby's, New York #162/R est:1500-2500

CORBET, Edith (fl.1891-1916) British

£780	$1451	€1139	Seat of learning (60x48cm-24x19in) i. verso. 2-Mar-4 Bearnes, Exeter #461/R

CORBET, Matthew Ridley (1850-1902) British

£1100	$1969	€1606	Artist's apprentice (61x46cm-24x18in) mono.d.1871 i.verso. 27-May-4 Christie's, Kensington #308/R est:1200-1800
£25000	$42500	€36500	Classical maidens (61x147cm-24x58in) mono.d.1876-9 i.verso lit. 19-Nov-3 Bonhams, New Bond Street #61/R est:25000-35000

Works on paper

£300	$546	€438	Harvesters in a highland landscape (30x48cm-12x19in) pencil W/C scratching out. 1-Jul-4 Christie's, Kensington #51/R

CORBIN, Peter (20th C) ?

£10160	$19000	€14834	Headed for quiet water (61x102cm-24x40in) s. 24-Jul-4 Coeur d'Alene, Hayden #178/R est:15000-20000

CORBINEAU, Charles August (1835-1901) French

£282	$487	€400	Portrait de Margueritte Taine a l'age de 4 ans (46x33cm-18x13in) s. 9-Dec-3 Chambelland & Giafferi, Paris #35/R
£757	$1400	€1105	Landscape with distant bell tower (25x33cm-10x13in) s.i. panel. 17-Jan-4 New Orleans Auction, New Orleans #526 est:800-1200

CORBINEAU, Charles August (attrib) (1835-1901) French

£326	$554	€476	Woman seated at edge of wood (23x33cm-9x13in) i. panel. 19-Nov-3 Fischer, Luzern #2040/R (S.FR 720)

CORBINO, Jon (1905-1964) American

£315	$500	€460	Untitled (21x25cm-8x10in) s. canvas on board. 12-Sep-3 Skinner, Boston #483/R
£353	$650	€515	Bull (46x61cm-18x24in) s. card. 10-Jun-4 Swann Galleries, New York #65/R
£503	$800	€734	Letter (53x46cm-21x18in) s. board. 12-Sep-3 Skinner, Boston #385/R
£1398	$2600	€2041	Centurion's horse (60x50cm-24x20in) s. i.verso. 5-Mar-4 Skinner, Boston #606/R est:1500-2500
£1946	$3250	€2841	New Hat (71x41cm-28x16in) s. board prov. 23-Oct-3 Shannon's, Milford #202/R est:1000-1500
£13772	$23000	€20107	Stampeding bulls (71x106cm-28x42in) s. prov.exhib.lit. 7-Oct-3 Sotheby's, New York #214 est:10000-20000
£21505	$40000	€31397	Harvest festival (101x162cm-40x64in) s.d.38 exhib.lit. 5-Mar-4 Skinner, Boston #440/R est:15000-25000

CORBOULD, Edward Henry (1815-1905) British

£995	$1662	€1453	Scene from Shakespeare's Henry VI, Countess of Auvergne, porter and John Talbot (91x61cm-36x24in) s.d.1849 panel. 17-Nov-3 Waddingtons, Toronto #111/R est:3000-5000 (C.D 2200)

CORBUSIER, le (1887-1965) French

Prints

£1676	$3000	€2447	Totem (72x80cm-28x31in) s.num.47/75 color lithograph. 6-May-4 Swann Galleries, New York #436/R est:4000-6000
£2123	$3800	€3100	L femme Rose (65x95cm-26x37in) s.num.50/75 colour lithograph. 6-May-4 Swann Galleries, New York #435/R est:4000-6000
£2133	$3925	€3200	Totem (70x79cm-28x31in) s.mono.d.1963 col lithograph. 10-Jun-4 Hauswedell & Nolte, Hamburg #422/R est:2000
£2235	$3800	€3263	Femme rose (65x96cm-26x38in) s.num.56/75 col lithograph. 6-Nov-3 Swann Galleries, New York #528/R est:3000-5000
£2458	$4400	€3589	Bouteilles (65x82cm-26x32in) s.num.45/75 color lithograph. 6-May-4 Swann Galleries, New York #434/R est:5000-8000
£3077	$5292	€4400	La femme rose (65x95cm-26x37in) s.mono.i.d.1932/61 col lithograph. 2-Dec-3 Hauswedell & Nolte, Hamburg #357/R est:3000

Works on paper

£1086	$1846	€1586	Etude (18x26cm-7x10in) pencil prov. 22-Nov-3 Burkhard, Luzern #78/R (S.FR 2400)
£1360	$2311	€1986	La cruche - girl with waterjug (31x21cm-12x8in) init.d.33 chl prov.lit. 5-Nov-3 AB Stockholms Auktionsverk #1095/R est:8000-10000 (S.KR 18000)
£2400	$4008	€3504	Famille cocasse (46x47cm-18x19in) mono.i.d.62 and 1942 casein on rhodoid. 22-Oct-3 Sotheby's, Olympia #144/R est:2000-3000
£2477	$4137	€3592	Self portrait (18x14cm-7x6in) s. Indian ink. 19-Jun-3 Kornfeld, Bern #608/R est:4000 (S.FR 5400)
£2819	$5046	€4200	Personnage (21x34cm-8x13in) pastel gouache chl exec.1953. 30-May-4 Eric Pillon, Calais #260/R
£3169	$5483	€4500	Femme (22x24cm-9x9in) mono.d.52 ink collage prov. 9-Dec-3 Artcurial Briest, Paris #251/R est:4000-5000
£3394	$5871	€4955	Tete de peintre, artiste et modele. Ange (20x18cm-8x7in) ink scratching out double-sided prov. 9-Dec-3 Sotheby's, Zurich #124/R est:4500-6500 (S.FR 7500)
£3493	$6253	€5100	Femme agenouillee (20x30cm-8x12in) pastel prov. 26-May-4 Sotheby's, Zurich #153/R est:8000-12000 (S.FR 8000)
£4072	$7045	€5945	Back view of three girls (20x30cm-8x12in) s.i. ink pastel. 9-Dec-3 Sotheby's, Zurich #120/R est:12000-16000 (S.FR 9000)
£5286	$8987	€7718	Femme avec violon (40x30cm-16x12in) mono.d.62 s.i.d.1962 verso mixed media collage. 7-Nov-3 Dobiaschofsky, Bern #225/R est:16000 (S.FR 12000)
£6042	$10272	€8821	Femme nu (27x21cm-11x8in) init.d.1/9 56 collage. 5-Nov-3 AB Stockholms Auktionsverk #1093/R est:40000-50000 (S.KR 80000)
£6740	$11930	€9840	Femme nu (31x47cm-12x19in) init.d.63 W/C collage. 27-Apr-4 AB Stockholms Auktionsverk #1157/R est:80000-100000 (S.KR 92000)
£7326	$12967	€10696	La femme (41x33cm-16x13in) init.d.59 mixed media collage. 27-Apr-4 AB Stockholms Auktionsverk #1215/R est:30000-35000 (S.KR 100000)
£8072	$13480	€11785	Le reve (37x48cm-15x19in) collage gouache. 24-Oct-3 Hans Widmer, St Gallen #54/R est:18000-25000 (S.FR 18000)
£9633	$16087	€13968	Femme se reposant (30x32cm-12x13in) s.mon.d.46-63 Indian ink brush on paper collage newspaper. 19-Jun-3 Kornfeld, Bern #609/R est:20000 (S.FR 21000)
£13986	$24056	€20000	Couple en bord de mer (21x34cm-8x13in) s.i.d.Aout 1962 Indian ink wash W/C graphite collage cardboard. 4-Dec-3 Piasa, Paris #97/R est:12000-15000
£15678	$26653	€22890	Unesco (360x660cm-142x260in) init.d. woven wool tapestry edn 4/20 exec 1962 prov. 24-Nov-3 Sotheby's, Melbourne #301/R est:30000-50000 (A.D 37000)
£43578	$72775	€63188	Josephine Baker sleeping (41x24cm-16x9in) mono.d.29 Indian ink. 19-Jun-3 Kornfeld, Bern #606/R est:10000 (S.FR 95000)
£44960	$80928	€65642	Femme avec une lettre (83x62cm-33x24in) init.d.59 mixed media collage prov. 26-Apr-4 Bukowskis, Stockholm #238/R est:250000-300000 (S.KR 620000)
£53073	$95000	€77487	Taureau (112x69cm-44x27in) s.i.d.1952-1961 gouache brush India ink newsprint collage prov. 6-May-4 Sotheby's, New York #370/R est:30000-50000

CORBYN, Anton (1955-) Dutch

Photographs

£2828	$5091	€4129	U2, Death Valley 1986 (75x155cm-30x61in) s.num.10/10 verso black/white photo prov. 26-Apr-4 Bukowskis, Stockholm #539/R est:35000-40000 (S.KR 39000)
£3496	$6013	€5000	Johnny Depp (125x185cm-49x73in) col print prov. 3-Dec-3 Sotheby's, Amsterdam #480/R est:5000-7000

CORCHON Y DIAQUE, Federico (19th C) Spanish

£336	$594	€500	Landscape (27x35cm-11x14in) s. cardboard. 27-Apr-4 Durán, Madrid #17/R
£1712	$2911	€2500	In the kitchen (46x38cm-18x15in) s. 4-Nov-3 Ansorena, Madrid #59/R est:2500

CORCOS, Vittorio (1859-1933) Italian

£800	$1472	€1200	Queen Mother (39x31cm-15x12in) s.i. cardboard. 10-Jun-4 Christie's, Rome #130
£5755	$9439	€8000	Portrait of gentleman (224x110cm-88x43in) s.d.1921. 10-Jun-3 Pandolfini, Florence #132/R est:8000-10000
£11765	$20000	€17177	Elegant player (108x66cm-43x26in) s.d.97. 28-Oct-3 Sotheby's, New York #2/R est:30000-40000
£12931	$23147	€18879	Sad clown (198x107cm-78x42in) s.d.89. 13-May-4 Stuker, Bern #73/R est:40000-60000 (S.FR 30000)

CORCOS, Vittorio (attrib) (1859-1933) Italian

£3380	$5848	€4800	Lady (59x36cm-23x14in) prov. 11-Dec-3 Christie's, Rome #113/R est:4000-6000

CORDA, Mauro (1960-) French
Sculpture
£3732 $6532 €5300 Taureau (25x46cm-10x18in) s.num.3/8 brown pat bronze. 19-Dec-3 Delvaux, Paris #70/R est:4200

CORDELLA, Tony (?) ?
£300 $483 €438 Coastal village (30x38cm-12x15in) s. board. 13-Aug-3 Andrew Hartley, Ilkley #828/R

CORDEN, Victor Milton (1860-?) British
£556 $900 €812 River landscapes with figures (20x13cm-8x5in) s. panel. 7-Aug-3 Eldred, East Dennis #359/R

CORDEN, William (19th C) British
£1162 $1859 €1650 Portrait of Prince Leopold of Saxe-Coburg-Gotha (53x43cm-21x17in) i.d.1850 verso after Franz Xavier Winterhalter. 22-Sep-3 Sotheby's, Amsterdam #6/R est:600-800
Works on paper
£268 $461 €391 Portrait of Mrs Wynn Williams with her three children (35x28cm-14x11in) i. graphite W/C card prov. 2-Dec-3 Ritchie, Toronto #16/R (C.D 600)
£550 $1012 €803 Queen Victoria (21x16cm-8x6in) i.d.June 1838 W/C. 29-Mar-4 Bonhams, Bath #5/R

CORDER, Rosa (fl.1879-1884) British
£300 $567 €438 Collie in a landscape (44x61cm-17x24in) s.d.1885. 19-Feb-4 Christie's, Kensington #308

CORDERO, Francisco (19th C) Mexican
£2759 $4607 €4000 Landscape (85x125cm-33x49in) s. 17-Nov-3 Durán, Madrid #181/R est:4000

CORDES, Johann Wilhelm (1824-1869) German
£1269 $2183 €1853 Alcohol smugglers in the mountain pass (127x113cm-50x44in) s.d.1863. 3-Dec-3 AB Stockholms Auktionsverk #2536/R est:20000-25000 (S.KR 16500)

CORDEUX, Thomas F (fl.1901-1902) British
£550 $1007 €803 Mouth of the Conway (60x121cm-24x48in) s. 6-Apr-4 Bonhams, Knightsbridge #157/R

CORDEY, Frederic (attrib) (1854-1911) French
£1133 $2063 €1700 Summer's day (44x62cm-17x24in) indis.s. 1-Jul-4 Van Ham, Cologne #1250 est:1500

CORDIER, Charles Henri Joseph (1827-1905) French
Sculpture
£12000 $21600 €17520 Married couple (50cm-20in) s. brown pat bronze verde antico socle pair lit. 21-Apr-4 Sotheby's, London #128/R est:12000-18000

CORDIER, Jacques (1937-1975) French
£514 $873 €750 Porto Cervo (65x100cm-26x39in) s. i.verso. 9-Nov-3 Eric Pillon, Calais #233/R
£706 $1180 €1010 Lumiere du matin sur le port (65x92cm-26x36in) s. 29-Jun-3 Eric Pillon, Calais #217/R

CORDIER, Marie Louise (?-1927) French
£467 $845 €700 Fillette apprivoisant un oiseau (81x60cm-32x24in) s. 3-Apr-4 Gerard, Besancon #40
£2394 $4142 €3400 Fillette sur la terrasse au bord du Rhone (74x92cm-29x36in) s. oval. 14-Dec-3 Eric Pillon, Calais #63/R

CORDIER, Pierre (1933-) Belgian
Photographs
£3667 $6747 €5500 Chimigramme (36x51cm-14x20in) s.d.61 verso silver print. 10-Jun-4 Artcurial Briest, Paris #254/R est:6000-8000
£3819 $6493 €5500 Chimigramme 22/12/61 IV (24x30cm-9x12in) s.i.d.22/12/61 verso gelatin silver. 31-Oct-3 Lempertz, Koln #117/R est:6000
£4167 $7083 €6000 Chimigramme 30/10/61 (30x40cm-12x16in) s.i.d.30/10/61 gelatin silver. 31-Oct-3 Lempertz, Koln #118/R est:6000

CORDIVIOLA, Luis Adolfo (1892-1967) Argentinian
£1326 $2400 €1936 Against the light (35x43cm-14x17in) cardboard. 30-Mar-4 Arroyo, Buenos Aires #30
£2088 $3800 €3048 Buenos Aires (27x35cm-11x14in) s.d.1927 cardboard. 29-Jun-4 Arroyo, Buenos Aires #101/R est:1300

CORDREY, John (fl.1765-1825) British
£1600 $2944 €2336 Coach and four in a landscape (32x42cm-13x17in) s. panel prov. 10-Jun-4 Christie's, Kensington #114/R est:800-1200
£1768 $3200 €2581 Norwich to London Royal Mail coach (48x76cm-19x30in) i.d.1801. 30-Mar-4 Christie's, Rockefeller NY #39/R est:3000-5000

CORELLI, Conrad H R (1869-?) Italian
Works on paper
£769 $1400 €1123 Fisherman drying his nets by the shore (18x25cm-7x10in) s. W/C. 7-Feb-4 Sloans & Kenyon, Bethesda #1248/R

CORELLI, Filiberto (1886-1969) Italian
Works on paper
£333 $597 €500 In the yard (64x46cm-25x18in) s. W/C. 12-May-4 Stadion, Trieste #642/R

CORELLI, Lorenzo (fl.1855-1920) Italian
Sculpture
£13750 $22000 €20075 Neapolitan fisherboy (211cm-83in) s. Carrara marble sold with base. 20-Sep-3 New Orleans Auction, New Orleans #909/R est:4000-7000

CORENS, R (20th C) ?
£820 $1500 €1230 Ball on shipboard (76x102cm-30x40in) s. after James Tissot. 31-Jul-4 Sloans & Kenyon, Bethesda #291 est:900-1200

CORENZIO, Belisario (1558-1640) Greek
Works on paper
£1200 $2196 €1752 Saint John the Baptist preaching before Herod (10x31cm-4x12in) black chk ink htd white prov. 6-Jul-4 Christie's, London #28/R est:1200-1600
£2500 $4600 €3800 Ecce Homo (14x16cm-6x6in) brush W/C lit. 22-Jun-4 Sotheby's, Milan #29/R est:3500-4000

COREY, Bernard (1914-2000) American
£280 $500 €409 January storm (21x30cm-8x12in) s. board prov. 14-May-4 Skinner, Boston #245/R
£543 $1000 €793 Stream in winter (23x30cm-9x12in) s. 25-Jun-4 Freeman, Philadelphia #159/R
£599 $1000 €875 Rockport Cove (20x33cm-8x13in) s. masonite. 20-Jun-3 Freeman, Philadelphia #112/R
£615 $1100 €898 Boat landing (21x31cm-8x12in) s. i.verso canvasboard prov. 14-May-4 Skinner, Boston #241/R
£659 $1100 €962 Uxbridge, Massachusetts landscape (25x36cm-10x14in) s. canvasboard. 20-Jun-3 Freeman, Philadelphia #216/R
£659 $1100 €962 Massachusetts landscape (23x36cm-9x14in) s. board. 20-Jun-3 Freeman, Philadelphia #250/R
£707 $1300 €1032 Winter's sunlight (25x36cm-10x14in) s. canvasboard. 25-Jun-4 Freeman, Philadelphia #151/R est:1000-1500
£854 $1400 €1238 Old New England barns (23x36cm-9x14in) s.i.verso canvas over masonite. 4-Jun-3 Alderfer's, Hatfield #286/R est:800-1000
£1159 $1900 €1681 Hill farm (25x41cm-10x16in) s. canvas over masonite. 4-Jun-3 Alderfer's, Hatfield #285/R est:1000-1200

CORINTH, Lovis (1858-1925) German
£2797 $4811 €4000 Self portrait (26x20cm-10x8in) oil chk. 2-Dec-3 Hauswedell & Nolte, Hamburg #87/R est:3000
£3243 $5805 €4800 Boy poking fun (30x29cm-12x11in) mono. board lit. 8-May-4 Schloss Ahlden, Ahlden #827/R est:4800
£30667 $54893 €46000 Dalliance (74x111cm-29x44in) s.d. prov.el. 14-May-4 Ketterer, Munich #127/R est:45000-65000
£36000 $65520 €52560 Kahn im Schilf am Muritzsee (47x62cm-19x24in) s.d.1915 board on panel prov.exhib.lit. 3-Feb-4 Christie's, London #180/R est:15000-20000
£43357 $72406 €62000 Flowers (54x71cm-21x28in) s.d.1912. 26-Jun-3 Sant Agostino, Torino #297/R est:30000-40000
£70000 $128800 €102200 Woman in a deckchair by the window (64x43cm-25x17in) s.d.1913 prov.lit. 22-Jun-4 Sotheby's, London #143/R est:70000-100000
£166667 $306667 €250000 Tulips, lilac and calla lilies (62x50cm-24x20in) s.d.1915 prov. 11-Jun-4 Villa Grisebach, Berlin #16/R est:250000-350000
£300000 $546000 €438000 Romische blumen im krug - Roman flowers in a jug (93x77cm-37x30in) s.d.1914 prov.lit. 3-Feb-4 Sotheby's, London #9/R est:200000-300000
£520000 $946400 €759200 Apple tree in blossom (70x90cm-28x35in) s.d.1922 prov.exhib.lit. 21-Jun-4 Sotheby's, London #42/R est:250000-350000
£720000 $1310400 €1051200 Walchensee, morning fog (70x90cm-28x35in) s.d.1924 prov.exhib.lit. 3-Feb-4 Sotheby's, London #7/R est:350000-450000
Prints
£268 $499 €400 Walchensee in winter (14x19cm-6x7in) s. 6-Mar-4 Arnold, Frankfurt #703/R
£2098 $3608 €3000 Zoo (22x30cm-9x12in) s.i.d.Januar 1922 drypoint etching. 2-Dec-3 Hauswedell & Nolte, Hamburg #106/R est:1800
£2378 $4090 €3400 Larch by Walchensee (18x24cm-7x9in) s. drypoint etching. 2-Dec-3 Hauswedell & Nolte, Hamburg #108/R est:2600
£2797 $4755 €4000 Walchensee landscape (30x49cm-12x19in) s. drypoint prov. 29-Nov-3 Villa Grisebach, Berlin #142/R est:4000-5000
Works on paper
£331 $603 €500 Walchenssee (21x29cm-8x11in) s.d.27.Juli 1923 W/C. 19-Jun-4 Dannenberg, Berlin #549/R
£486 $768 €700 Interior study (28x47cm-11x19in) s.d.1886 pencil lit. 19-Sep-3 Schloss Ahlden, Ahlden #1624/R
£724 $1332 €1100 The battle (51x34cm-20x13in) s.i.d.1914 pencil cardboard. 26-Jun-4 C & K, Leipzig #732/R
£833 $1392 €1200 Handing over the child (23x17cm-9x7in) chk bodycol. 25-Oct-3 Dr Lehr, Berlin #105/R
£1000 $1840 €1500 Two men (44x29cm-17x11in) s. pencil prov. 12-Jun-4 Villa Grisebach, Berlin #519/R est:2000-3000
£1250 $2000 €1825 Die Zeichnungsklasse (41x33cm-16x13in) s.i.d.1887 pencil. 18-Sep-3 Swann Galleries, New York #171/R est:2500-3500
£1267 $2331 €1900 Walchensee (10x15cm-4x6in) s. pencil. 10-Jun-4 Hauswedell & Nolte, Hamburg #77/R est:1200
£1467 $2699 €2200 Girl's portrait (13x10cm-5x4in) s.d.1882 Indian ink wash. 10-Jun-4 Hauswedell & Nolte, Hamburg #75/R est:1400
£1733 $3189 €2600 Female nude sitting and boy (51x34cm-20x13in) s. pencil prov. 12-Jun-4 Villa Grisebach, Berlin #520/R est:2000-3000
£2000 $3680 €3000 Waterfall (40x32cm-16x13in) s.i. pencil exhib. 10-Jun-4 Hauswedell & Nolte, Hamburg #76/R est:3500
£5500 $10010 €8030 Prechtal im Schwarzwald - Prechtal in the Black Forest (29x44cm-11x17in) s.d.1885 W/C pencil prov.exhib. 4-Feb-4 Sotheby's, London #478/R est:7000-10000

CORIOLANO, Bartolomeo (c.1599-1676) Italian
Prints

£1899	$3400	€2773	Fall of the Giants (86x61cm-34x24in) chiaroscuro woodcut four joined sheets. 6-May-4 Swann Galleries, New York #88/R est:4000-6000
£2667	$4773	€4000	Giant fall (87x62cm-34x24in) woodcut after Guido Reni. 13-May-4 Bassenge, Berlin #5100 est:3500

CORLETT, Peter (1944-) Australian
Sculpture

£3894	$6152	€5685	Seated figure (130x59x87cm-51x23x34in) fibre glass timber prov. 2-Sep-3 Deutscher-Menzies, Melbourne #129/R est:12000-18000 (A.D 9500)

CORMON, Fernand (1854-1924) French

£795	$1446	€1200	Scene de la prehistoire (35x81cm-14x32in) 18-Jun-4 Piasa, Paris #56
£1611	$2996	€2400	Portrait du peintre Leon-Germaine Pelouse (45x34cm-18x13in) s. 3-Mar-4 Ferri, Paris #380/R est:500-800
£1867	$3360	€2800	Guerriere au repos (40x32cm-16x13in) d.1923. 24-Apr-4 Hotel des Ventes de Vienne, Vienne #182
£5517	$9931	€8000	Ramania's death (60x73cm-24x29in) 26-Jan-4 Ansorena, Madrid #223/R est:8000
£7143	$12786	€10500	Still life (120x79cm-47x31in) s.d.72. 19-Mar-4 Millon & Associes, Paris #52/R est:7000-8000
£28000	$50960	€40880	Le harem (95x121cm-37x48in) s. prov. 15-Jun-4 Sotheby's, London #129/R est:20000-35000

CORNAGLIA, Carlo (19th C) Italian
Works on paper

£1400	$2380	€2044	Interior of Bizantine church (59x73cm-23x29in) s. pen ink W/C htd bodycol. 18-Nov-3 Sotheby's, London #80/R est:1500-2000

CORNEAU, Eugène (1894-1976) French

£345	$576	€500	Still life of flowers (45x51cm-18x20in) s. board. 9-Jul-3 Hugo Ruef, Munich #71
£800	$1448	€1168	Figures reading on a terrace (90x49cm-35x19in) s. 30-Mar-4 Sworder & Son, Bishops Stortford #584/R

CORNEILLE (1922-) Belgian

£302	$535	€450	Femme a l'oiseau (50cm-20in circular) s.d.1998. 27-Apr-4 Campo, Vlaamse Kaai #358
£369	$653	€550	Femme au chat (48cm-19in circular) s.d.1998. 27-Apr-4 Campo, Vlaamse Kaai #357
£567	$1014	€850	Cigalle (18x24cm-7x9in) s.i.d.94 oil chk Indian ink. 15-May-4 Van Ham, Cologne #533/R
£733	$1320	€1100	Nu bleu (20x29cm-8x11in) s.d.2003 crayon gouache. 24-Apr-4 Cornette de St.Cyr, Paris #501/R
£1389	$2264	€2000	Two snakes (70x100cm-28x39in) s.d.73 88 oil mixed media. 26-Sep-3 Bolland & Marotz, Bremen #728/R est:2300
£1486	$2616	€2200	Untitled (27x21cm-11x8in) s.d.68 tempera paper prov. 24-May-4 Christie's, Milan #36/R
£1972	$3293	€2879	Reclining woman and bird (54x74cm-21x29in) s.d.92 acrylic on lithograph. 7-Oct-3 Rasmussen, Copenhagen #61/R est:20000-25000 (D.KR 21000)
£3333	$6000	€5000	Untitled (70x100cm-28x39in) s.i.d.73-88 tempera paper. 22-Apr-4 Finarte Semenzato, Rome #103/R est:3500-4000
£3336	$6172	€4871	Woman and sun (66x51cm-26x20in) s.d.73 acrylic paper on canvas. 15-Mar-4 Rasmussen, Vejle #501/R est:40000 (D.KR 37000)
£5594	$9622	€8000	Composition abstraite (25x25cm-10x10in) s.d.54. 8-Dec-3 Christie's, Paris #78/R est:2500-3000
£7383	$13584	€11000	Genie de la Bastille et la Colombe (146x114cm-57x45in) s.i.d.1989 acrylic lit. 24-Mar-4 Joron-Derem, Paris #126/R est:18000-20000
£7692	$13231	€11230	Couple a L'oiseau (81x99cm-32x39in) s.d.86 acrylic lit. 7-Dec-3 Uppsala Auktionskammare, Uppsala #297/R est:100000 120000 (S.KR 100000)
£9859	$16465	€14394	Temps ouvert (50x65cm-20x26in) s.d.65 exhib. 7-Oct-3 Rasmussen, Copenhagen #15/R est:125000 (D.KR 105000)
£10870	$17826	€15000	L'oiseau survole jardin (100x100cm-39x39in) s.d.67 i.d.67 verso prov. 27-May-3 Sotheby's, Amsterdam #391/R est:20000-30000
£10952	$18618	€15990	Ka mer est une tendre colline (50x50cm-20x20in) s.d.58 s.d.59 verso. 4-Nov-3 Bukowskis, Stockholm #281/R est:20000-25000 (S.KR 145000)
£13333	$24533	€20000	Montagnard au sourire (25x35cm-10x14in) s. i.d.48 verso. 8-Jun-4 Sotheby's, Amsterdam #80/R est:12000-18000
£15333	$28213	€23000	Ete flamboyant (70x100cm-28x39in) s.d.80 s.i.d. verso acrylic. 8-Jun-4 Artcurial Briest, Paris #259/R est:16000-20000
£16000	$26720	€23360	Habitations dans le desert (101x101cm-40x40in) s.d.51 s.indis.i. verso i.d.1951 stretcher prov.exhib.lit. 22-Oct-3 Christie's, London #13/R est:15000-20000
£34000	$62560	€49640	Le jardin des desirs (81x100cm-32x39in) s.d.67 s.i.d.verso prov. 25-Jun-4 Christie's, London #146/R est:22000-28000

Sculpture

£1333	$2453	€2000	L'envol (66x45x28cm-26x18x11in) s. num.X/X wood paint. 11-Jun-4 Pierre Berge, Paris #1/R est:2000-2500
£2447	$4087	€3500	Cat (54cm-21in) s. num.II/II paint wood. 30-Jun-3 Sotheby's, Amsterdam #477/R
£3261	$5348	€4500	Woman and bird (60x60cm-24x24in) s.d.97 num.10/15 painted glazed ceramic plate. 27-May-3 Sotheby's, Amsterdam #547/R est:2000-3000

Works on paper

£400	$736	€600	Etoile (32x26cm-13x10in) s.d.1974 mixed media. 8-Jun-4 Finarte Semenzato, Milan #94/R
£592	$1089	€900	Noire et la retour d'Afrique (50x60cm-20x24in) s.d.92 gouache printed base prov. 28-Jun-4 Sotheby's, Amsterdam #291a
£658	$1211	€1000	Untitled (77x55cm-30x22in) s.d.98 gouache on lithograph on canvas. 28-Jun-4 Sotheby's, Amsterdam #270/R
£805	$1498	€1200	Sans titre (64x35cm-25x14in) s.d.55 gouache W/C. 3-Mar-4 Artcurial Briest, Paris #351
£816	$1486	€1200	Three woman in front of a hut (32x32cm-13x13in) s.d.1973 gouache pencil. 3-Feb-4 Christie's, Amsterdam #581 est:1000-1500
£952	$1733	€1400	African female profile (31x31cm-12x12in) s.d.1973 gouache white crayon. 3-Feb-4 Christie's, Amsterdam #578/R est:1000-1500
£1007	$1862	€1500	Compositions (29x21cm-11x8in) s.d.49 Indian ink three. 13-Mar-4 De Vuyst, Lokeren #72 est:750-1000
£1088	$1981	€1600	Figure in a garden (31x31cm-12x12in) s.d.1973 gouache white crayon. 3-Feb-4 Christie's, Amsterdam #580 est:1000-1500
£1333	$2440	€2000	Woman with bird (33x15cm-13x6in) s.d.82 gouache W/C. 7-Jun-4 Glerum, Amsterdam #357/R est:1800-2200
£1373	$2376	€1950	Composition (14x24cm-6x9in) s.d.1959 W/C ink prov. 14-Dec-3 Versailles Encheres #49/R est:2000-2500
£1400	$2576	€2044	Untitled (14x25cm-6x10in) s.d.59 brush ink prov. 24-Jun-4 Sotheby's, Olympia #526/R est:1500-2000
£1422	$2275	€2062	Pinocchio (70x100cm-28x39in) s.d.73 gouache on lithograph. 17-Sep-3 Kunsthallen, Copenhagen #55/R est:20000 (D.KR 15000)
£1433	$2580	€2150	Composition (19x23cm-7x9in) s.d.1954 W/C ink prov. 25-Apr-4 Versailles Encheres #16 est:1500-2000
£1465	$2681	€2198	Untitled (46x33cm-18x13in) s.d.1967 gouache. 6-Jul-4 Bolsa de Arte, Rio de Janeiro #74/R (B.R 8000)
£1600	$2544	€2320	Composition (41x54cm-16x21in) s.d.58 black felt-tipped pen gouache. 11-Sep-3 Christie's, Kensington #172/R est:2000-3000
£1667	$3067	€2500	Carta del giorno (34x31cm-13x12in) s.i.d.60 gouache blk ink collage. 9-Jun-4 Christie's, Amsterdam #156/R est:2000-3000
£1736	$2899	€2500	Claudia Saskia (56x76cm-22x30in) s.i.d. chl oil chk gouache acrylic. 24-Oct-3 Ketterer, Hamburg #309/R est:2500-2700
£1958	$3329	€2800	Petite famille (18x25cm-7x10in) s.i.d.50 bl ink. 25-Nov-3 Christie's, Amsterdam #68/R est:3000-5000
£2174	$3565	€3000	Woman with tree (31x24cm-12x9in) s.d.81 gouache prov. 27-May-3 Sotheby's, Amsterdam #419/R est:3000-4000
£2200	$4048	€3212	Untitled (22x28cm-9x11in) s.d.61 pencil ink crayon. 24-Jun-4 Sotheby's, Olympia #527/R est:800-1200
£2238	$3804	€3200	Woman and bird (64x51cm-25x20in) s.d.75 pencil W/C gouache. 25-Nov-3 Christie's, Amsterdam #126/R est:3000-5000
£3497	$5944	€5000	Untitled (15x19cm-6x7in) s.i.d.62 wax crayons. 25-Nov-3 Christie's, Amsterdam #75/R est:5000-7000
£4333	$7973	€6500	Untitled (38x49cm-15x19in) s.d.69 gouache. 8-Jun-4 Sotheby's, Amsterdam #266/R est:4500-5500
£4348	$7130	€6000	Untitled (64x49cm-25x19in) s. gouache printed base on paper on canvas. 27-May-3 Sotheby's, Amsterdam #418/R est:6000-8000
£4351	$7832	€6352	Composition (50x38cm-20x15in) s.d.55 W/C. 26-Apr-4 Bukowskis, Stockholm #237/R est:25000-30000 (S.KR 60000)
£6000	$11040	€9000	L'ete incendiaire (49x66cm-19x26in) s.d.63 gouache prov. 9-Jun-4 Christie's, Amsterdam #308/R est:10000-15000
£6962	$12531	€10165	La vie de feuilles (50x68cm-20x27in) s.d.1963 gouache prov. 26-Apr-4 Bukowskis, Stockholm #237a/R est:30000-40000 (S.KR 96000)
£11268	$18817	€16451	Figure composition (50x57cm-20x22in) s.d.64 W/C paper on canvas. 7-Oct-3 Rasmussen, Copenhagen #4/R est:125000-150000 (D.KR 120000)
£14094	$25933	€21000	Cobra - Revue International d'Art Experimental no.7 (48x64cm-19x25in) gouache collage exec 1951 prov.exhib.lit. 24-Mar-4 Joron-Derem, Paris #106/R est:20000-25000

CORNEILLE, Michel (attrib) (17th C) French
Works on paper

£482	$771	€670	Two men (36x25cm-14x10in) blk crayon prov. 16-May-3 Tajan, Paris #9

CORNEILLE, Michel (elder-attrib) (1602-1664) French

£2517	$4581	€3800	Moise et le serpent d'Airain (76x93cm-30x37in) 21-Jun-4 Tajan, Paris #94/R est:6000-8000

CORNEILLE, Michel (younger) (1642-1708) French

£1127	$1949	€1600	Jeunes enfants jouant aux billes (45x62cm-18x24in) 10-Dec-3 Maigret, Paris #57/R est:2000-2500

Works on paper

£260	$450	€380	Fisherman on a beach, Miraculous Draught of Fishes in background (27x40cm-11x16in) black chk pen brown ink. 12-Dec-3 Christie's, Kensington #422
£530	$964	€800	Homme debout vu de trois quarts. Etude d'homme (28x16cm-11x6in) sanguine htd pen ink double-sided prov. 16-Jun-4 Piasa, Paris #74
£1900	$3477	€2774	Studies of heads (30x19cm-12x7in) i. pen brown ink after Raphael. 6-Jul-4 Christie's, London #120/R est:1500-2000
£2817	$4873	€4000	Bacchus (23x19cm-9x7in) pierre noire htd white. 10-Dec-3 Beaussant & Lefèvre, Paris #28/R est:5000-6000
£42177	$75497	€62000	La Sainte Famille avec St Jean Baptiste et des putti (39x50cm-15x20in) black chk pen brown ink wash htd white. 18-Mar-4 Christie's, Paris #116/R est:30000-50000

CORNELIANO, Francesco (attrib) (1740-1815) Italian

£5298	$9642	€8000	Flora (120x125cm-47x49in) 16-Jun-4 Christie's, Rome #251/R est:10000-15000

CORNELIS, William (attrib) (19/20th C) ?
Works on paper

£750	$1253	€1095	Drover with her cattle on a river path (23x34cm-9x13in) init.indis.d. pencil W/C. 8-Oct-3 Christie's, Kensington #1068/R

CORNELISZ, Cornelis van Haarlem (1562-1638) Dutch

£4121	$7500	€6017	Portrait of a man as Apollo, possibly a self portrait (61x46cm-24x18in) mono.d.1620 panel prov.lit. 29-Jun-4 Sotheby's, New York #21/R est:10000-15000
£11111	$20000	€16222	Venus and Adonis with Cupid in landscape (32x42cm-13x17in) mono.d.1600 prov.lit. 22-Jan-4 Sotheby's, New York #38/R est:25000-35000

CORNELISZ, Cornelis van Haarlem (attrib) (1562-1638) Dutch

£1136	$2000	€1659	In the Bath House. panel. 23-May-4 Hindman, Chicago #2/R est:3000-5000

CORNELISZ, Cornelis van Haarlem (circle) (1562-1638) Dutch

£6479	$11338	€9200	Salomon's judgment (125x167cm-49x66in) d.1618. 17-Dec-3 Christie's, Rome #394/R est:6000-9000
£8333	$15000	€12166	Fall of man (66x51cm-26x20in) panel lit. 22-Jan-4 Sotheby's, New York #251a/R est:15000-20000

CORNELIUS, Jean Georges (1880-1963) French
£1233 $2208 €1850 Le reve du marin (54x46cm-21x18in) i. panel. 16-May-4 Thierry & Lannon, Brest #301 est:1500-2000
£1549 $2711 €2200 L'Ange redempteur (90x64cm-35x25in) s. panel. 21-Dec-3 Thierry & Lannon, Brest #148/R est:2000-2500
£1690 $2958 €2400 L'envol de la mouette (68x68cm-27x27in) panel. 21-Dec-3 Thierry & Lannon, Brest #147 est:2000-2500
£1959 $3507 €2900 La barque de Notre-Dame des tempetes (60x92cm-24x36in) s. i.verso cardboard. 7-May-4 Millon & Associes, Paris #89/R est:1500-2000
£2053 $3839 €3100 Les bons buveurs (57x64cm-22x25in) mono. panel painted c.1900. 24-Jul-4 Thierry & Lannon, Brest #137 est:2000-2200
Works on paper
£1081 $1935 €1600 L'alphabet des diables (23x16cm-9x6in) mono. ink gouache set of four. 7-May-4 Millon & Associes, Paris #90/R est:1200-1800

CORNELIUS, Marie Lucie (fl.1885-1893) French
£4161 $7656 €6200 Pivoines dans un panier d'osier (119x150cm-47x59in) s.d.1887. 28-Mar-4 Anaf, Lyon #76/R est:6000-7000

CORNELIUS, Max (?) ?
£229 $375 €334 Countryside villa (61x102cm-24x40in) s. 4-Jun-3 Alderfer's, Hatfield #248/R

CORNELL, Joseph (1903-1972) American
Photographs
£4200 $7602 €6132 Untitled, 1967 (25x20cm-10x8in) s.i. i.verso photograph collage on board prov. 1-Apr-4 Christie's, Kensington #269/R est:5000-7000
Sculpture
£25150 $42000 €36719 Yellow Sand with Spools (22x43x10cm-9x17x4in) wood box paper collage oil spools and other objects prov. 12-Nov-3 Christie's, Rockefeller NY #345/R est:40000-60000
£47904 $80000 €69940 Eclipsing binary, algol with magnitude changes (25x36x9cm-10x14x4in) s.verso box construction steel painted wood ball executed 1960. 12-Nov-3 Sotheby's, New York #28/R est:60000-80000
£47904 $80000 €69940 Untitled, winter night skies (24x30x10cm-9x12x4in) s.verso painted wood box glass cork ball exec.c.1956 prov.exhib. 13-Nov-3 Sotheby's, New York #159/R est:60000-80000
£53892 $90000 €78682 Solar set (23x38x9cm-9x15x4in) s. wood box oil printed paper collage other items prov. 12-Nov-3 Christie's, Rockefeller NY #309/R est:100000-150000
£125749 $210000 €183594 Untitled - Grand Hotel De L'Univers, Orion (48x32x15cm-19x13x6in) s. box construction paper collage executed c.1955 prov.exhib. 12-Nov-3 Sotheby's, New York #19/R est:100000-150000
Works on paper
£3557 $6367 €5300 7 angelic (24x20cm-9x8in) s.i.verso collage on engraving prov.exhib. 26-May-4 Christie's, Paris #90/R est:5000-7000
£10056 $18000 €14682 Quiet autumnal - Jeann Eagels (30x23cm-12x9in) s.i.d.6-21-65 paper collage pencil masonite double-sided prov. 12-May-4 Christie's, Rockefeller NY #151/R est:18000-25000

CORNELL, Pamela (20th C) British
£250 $415 €365 Day at the races (52x73cm-20x29in) s.d.1989. 5-Oct-3 Lots Road Auctions, London #361
£320 $592 €467 Eisteddffod (56x76cm-22x30in) s. s.i.d.1984 verso. 11-Mar-4 Christie's, Kensington #240

CORNER, Thomas C (1865-1938) American
£435 $800 €635 Summer landscape (23x30cm-9x12in) s. 26-Jun-4 Sloans & Kenyon, Bethesda #1088/R

CORNET, Alphonse (1814-1874) French
£4514 $7538 €6500 Pancake day (47x62cm-19x24in) s.d.1843. 21-Oct-3 Sotheby's, Amsterdam #23/R est:5000-7000

CORNET, Marcel Charles (1886-?) French
£437 $800 €638 En bord de la Seine (38x56cm-15x22in) s. 10-Apr-4 Auctions by the Bay, Alameda #1540/R

CORNILLIET, Jules (1830-1886) French
£2844 $4750 €4152 Loving sisters (99x66cm-39x26in) s.d.1880. 16-Nov-3 CRN Auctions, Cambridge #56/R

CORNILLON, Jean Baptiste (1821-?) French
£679 $1086 €991 Still life with flowers (22x16cm-9x6in) s. panel. 16-Sep-3 Philippe Schuler, Zurich #3323/R est:1400-1800 (S.FR 1500)

CORNISH, Hubert (c.1770-1832) British
Works on paper
£500 $835 €730 Cavern at Tunbridge Wells. Pope's house and Summer Hill, Tunbridge Wells (24x33cm-9x13in) i.verso pencil W/C pair. 16-Oct-3 Christie's, Kensington #103

CORNISH, Norman (1919-) British
£1000 $1590 €1460 Back street bustle - view in Spennymoor (22x27cm-9x11in) s. 18-Mar-3 Anderson & Garland, Newcastle #152/R est:700-900
£6000 $10920 €8760 Snow scene, Edward Street, Spennymoor (33x44cm-13x17in) s. board. 29-Jun-4 Anderson & Garland, Newcastle #395/R est:2000-3000
Works on paper
£650 $1203 €949 Children under a street lamp (13x18cm-5x7in) s. W/C. 10-Feb-4 David Lay, Penzance #589
£650 $1196 €949 Durham Miner (20x25cm-8x10in) felt tip pen. 23-Mar-4 Anderson & Garland, Newcastle #241
£900 $1557 €1314 Pigeon Cree III (9x9cm-4x4in) wash over pencil sold with sale catalogue prov. 9-Dec-3 Anderson & Garland, Newcastle #309a
£900 $1656 €1314 Durham Miner (19x23cm-7x9in) felt tip pen prov. 23-Mar-4 Anderson & Garland, Newcastle #240/R
£1100 $1749 €1606 The Gossips (40x28cm-16x11in) s. pastel. 18-Mar-3 Anderson & Garland, Newcastle #154/R est:1000-1800
£1500 $2550 €2190 The Gantry (28x40cm-11x16in) s. pastel. 27-Nov-3 Morphets, Harrogate #443/R est:400-600
£1550 $2465 €2263 Man at the bar (30x17cm-12x7in) s. col chk prov. 18-Mar-3 Anderson & Garland, Newcastle #153/R est:800-1200

CORNOYER, Paul (1864-1923) American
£2688 $5000 €3924 Street in Gloucester (46x61cm-18x24in) s. painted c.1920 prov. 7-Mar-4 Treadway Gallery, Cincinnati #569/R est:5000-7000
£17442 $30000 €25465 Madison Square in New Nork (46x51cm-18x20in) s. 7-Dec-3 Hindman, Chicago #799/R est:8000-10000

CORNU, Pierre (1895-1996) French
£243 $450 €355 Study of a nude (55x46cm-22x18in) s. board. 18-Jan-4 Bonhams & Butterfields, Los Angeles #7028/R
£306 $562 €447 Catherine (47x33cm-19x13in) s. 14-Jun-4 Philippe Schuler, Zurich #5834 (S.FR 700)
£546 $1004 €797 Seated nude (54x37cm-21x15in) s. 14-Jun-4 Philippe Schuler, Zurich #5833 (S.FR 1250)
£572 $950 €830 Le modele en vacances (38x46cm-15x18in) s. 30-Sep-3 Blanchet, Paris #250/R
£661 $1123 €965 Reclining female nude reading (46x33cm-18x13in) s. i. verso. 5-Nov-3 Dobiaschofsky, Bern #446/R (S.FR 1500)
£728 $1326 €1100 Jeune femme assise au corsage rouge (55x46cm-22x18in) s. 15-Jun-4 Blanchet, Paris #240/R
£775 $1356 €1100 Le modele assis sur une bergere (46x38cm-18x15in) s. 19-Dec-3 Delvaux, Paris #56
£1067 $1963 €1600 Nu a la draperie (46x55cm-18x22in) s. i.verso. 8-Jun-4 Livinec, Gaudcheau & Jezequel, Rennes #80/R
£1111 $1856 €1600 Jeune fille a la robe bleue ecrivant (38x46cm-15x18in) s. 25-Oct-3 Dianous, Marseille #423
£1111 $1856 €1600 Jeune fille au peignoir fleuri (55x38cm-22x15in) s. 25-Oct-3 Dianous, Marseille #432
£1208 $2235 €1800 Modele lisant devant la fontaine (73x50cm-29x20in) s. 15-Mar-4 Blanchet, Paris #158/R est:1000-1200
£1678 $3104 €2500 Fauteuil mauve (46x38cm-18x15in) s. 14-Mar-4 St-Germain-en-Laye Encheres #148/R est:2200-2500
£1875 $3131 €2700 Liseuse au pichet bleu. s. 25-Oct-3 Dianous, Marseille #370
£2349 $4369 €3500 Jeune fille a la robe rouge (65x54cm-26x21in) s. 7-Mar-4 Lesieur & Le Bars, Le Havre #26

CORNU, Sebastien (1804-1870) French
£5405 $9514 €8000 Faust and Gretchen (93x73cm-37x29in) s.d.1865. 22-May-4 Lempertz, Koln #1490/R est:4000
£6207 $10303 €9000 Italienne au tambourin (100x74cm-39x29in) mono.d.1853. 2-Oct-3 Sotheby's, Paris #32/R est:9000-12000

CORNU, Vital (1851-?) French
Sculpture
£2000 $3600 €2920 Portrait bust of a painter (55cm-22in) s. brown pat bronze lit. 21-Apr-4 Sotheby's, London #131/R est:3000-5000

CORNUT, Armand (1904-1989) Belgian
£268 $497 €400 Cote Mediterraneenne (50x60cm-20x24in) s. panel. 15-Mar-4 Horta, Bruxelles #343

CORNWELL, Dean (1892-1960) American
£1446 $2400 €2111 Stevedores (76x74cm-30x29in) s.i.d.1920. 4-Oct-3 Neal Auction Company, New Orleans #574/R est:4000-6000
£2674 $5000 €3904 Mountie reclining (56x71cm-22x28in) s.d.1919. 26-Feb-4 Illustration House, New York #46 est:3500-5000
£3757 $6500 €5485 Founding of Los Angeles (99x193cm-39x76in) 10-Dec-3 Bonhams & Butterfields, San Francisco #6285/R est:4000-6000
£3911 $7000 €5710 Audience with the Empress (69x94cm-27x37in) init.d.1938 board. 15-May-4 Illustration House, New York #24/R est:6000-9000
£5389 $9000 €7868 Arrival of the stagecoach at George Prince Inn (74x99cm-29x39in) init.d.1925 canvas on masonite. 15-Nov-3 Illustration House, New York #119/R est:9000-12000
£7186 $12000 €10492 No place for a nice girl (64x89cm-25x35in) i. board. 15-Nov-3 Illustration House, New York #132/R est:15000-20000
£9392 $17000 €13712 He lay face down (86x100cm-34x39in) s.d.36 lit. 31-Mar-4 Sotheby's, New York #145/R est:20000-30000
£9581 $16000 €13988 Couple cooking around night time campfire (71x114cm-28x45in) s. 15-Nov-3 Illustration House, New York #118/R est:18000-24000
£12291 $22000 €17945 Desert healer (46x99cm-18x39in) init.d.1923. 15-May-4 Illustration House, New York #23/R est:7000-10000

COROMALDI, Umberto (1870-1948) Italian
£855 $1574 €1300 Rural house (26x24cm-10x9in) s. cardboard. 23-Jun-4 Finarte Semenzato, Rome #66/R
£1067 $1963 €1600 Head of cow (45x39cm-18x15in) s. canvas on cardboard. 10-Jun-4 Christie's, Rome #85/R est:1000-1200
Works on paper
£563 $975 €800 Avenue. Landscape (34x49cm-13x19in) s. graphite two. 10-Dec-3 Finarte Semenzato, Rome #175/R

COROMINAS, Joaquin (1899-?) Spanish
£1049 $1752 €1500 Vista de Palma de Mallorca (52x42cm-20x17in) s.d.1924 panel. 24-Jun-3 Segre, Madrid #290/R est:900

CORONA, Jose (19th C) Spanish

£2400	$4344	€3600	Portraits of toreadors (79x57cm-31x22in) s.i.d.1868 verso. 30-Mar-4 Segre, Madrid #83/R est:3400

CORONA, Leonardo (attrib) (1561-1605) Italian

Works on paper

£1655	$2764	€2400	Adoration of the Kings (23x25cm-9x10in) Indian ink brush htd white. 15-Nov-3 Lempertz, Koln #1279/R est:3000

CORONA, Poul (1872-1945) Danish

£459	$749	€670	Afternoon sunshine at Skagen with old woman walking (86x127cm-34x50in) s.i.d.sept.1911. 27-Sep-3 Rasmussen, Havnen #2182/R (D.KR 4900)
£898	$1671	€1311	Girls in the woods (64x73cm-25x29in) s.d.Aug.1915. 2-Mar-4 Rasmussen, Copenhagen #1502/R (D.KR 10000)

CORONA, Vittorio (1901-1966) Italian

£6993	$11888	€10000	Spinner (26x35cm-10x14in) s. painted c.1920 prov.lit. 24-Nov-3 Christie's, Milan #311/R est:10000-15000

CORONEL, Pedro (1923-1985) Mexican

£2371	$4031	€3462	Hands (80x60cm-31x24in) s.d.1951 masonite. 30-Oct-3 Louis Morton, Mexico #102/R est:55000-65000 (M.P 45000)
£2762	$4750	€4033	Deshabitados (35x26cm-14x10in) s.i.d.61 oil sand two. 3-Dec-3 Doyle, New York #20/R est:6000-8000
£2907	$5000	€4244	Deshabitados (35x27cm-14x11in) s.i.d.61 verso two. 3-Dec-3 Doyle, New York #19/R est:6000-8000
£61765	$105000	€90177	Femmes papillons - Butterfly women (330x194cm-130x76in) s.i.d.67-68 verso lit. 18-Nov-3 Christie's, Rockefeller NY #60/R est:35000-45000
£106145	$190000	€154972	At JUstino's grave (200x240cm-79x94in) s.i.d.1975 verso mixed media on canvas prov. 26-May-4 Sotheby's, New York #40/R est:120000-150000

CORONEL, Rafael (1932-) Mexican

£2353	$4000	€3435	Estudio (70x60cm-28x24in) s. 9-Nov-3 Bonhams & Butterfields, Los Angeles #4137/R est:4000-6000
£6322	$10748	€9230	Figure (110x80cm-43x31in) s. 30-Oct-3 Louis Morton, Mexico #86/R est:130000-140000 (M.P 120000)
£8475	$15000	€12374	Retrato de la Serie la Cristina (77x129cm-30x51in) s.d.68 prov. 2-May-4 Bonhams & Butterfields, Los Angeles #3113/R est:15000-20000

Works on paper

£243	$450	€355	Fish in ice (64x48cm-25x19in) s.d.58 mixed media. 13-Mar-4 Susanin's, Chicago #6047/R
£1163	$2000	€1698	Nina Sobre fondo azul (59x45cm-23x18in) s. col chk on board prov. 3-Dec-3 Doyle, New York #13/R est:3000-5000

COROT, Jean Baptiste Camille (1796-1875) French

£2335	$3900	€3409	Pastoral landscape with figure and cows (38x56cm-15x22in) s. 16-Nov-3 William Jenack, New York #225 est:5000-8000
£8333	$13583	€12000	Lakeshore in the evening (54x81cm-21x32in) s. 26-Sep-3 Bolland & Marotz, Bremen #508/R est:17000
£8333	$15000	€12166	L'etang aux deux arbres (14x18cm-6x7in) s. painted c.1870-75. 22-Apr-4 Christie's, Rockefeller NY #108/R est:10000-15000
£10526	$19368	€16000	Homme ssis sous un arbre (22x16cm-9x6in) canvas on cardboard. 24-Jun-4 Christie's, Paris #160/R est:8000-12000
£11189	$19245	€16000	Paysage a la tour (21x34cm-8x13in) s. 7-Dec-3 Osenat, Fontainebleau #109
£12676	$21042	€18000	Personnage dans un paysage. s. on ceramic. 15-Jun-3 Peron, Melun #141
£13333	$24000	€19466	Bord du bois (27x21cm-11x8in) s. panel prov. 23-Apr-4 Sotheby's, New York #13/R est:30000-40000
£15942	$26145	€22000	Effet de lune (24x27cm-9x11in) s. prov. 11-May-3 Osenat, Fontainebleau #88/R est:18000-20000
£23490	$42047	€35000	Souvenir de l'Ocean (25x37cm-10x15in) s. panel prov.lit. 27-May-4 Christie's, Paris #114/R est:50000-70000
£29605	$54474	€45000	Paysans dans la foret (23x27cm-9x11in) s. prov. 24-Jun-4 Christie's, Paris #150/R est:30000-40000
£30000	$54600	€43800	Paysage (32x21cm-13x8in) studio st. canvas on board prov.lit. 3-Feb-4 Christie's, London #108/R est:30000-40000
£32353	$55000	€47235	Grez-sur-Loing, Pecheur in Barque, le matin (26x34cm-10x13in) s. prov.lit. 28-Oct-3 Sotheby's, New York #17/R est:60000-80000
£33333	$60000	€48666	Un ruisseau sous bois (58x45cm-23x18in) s. prov.lit. 23-Apr-4 Sotheby's, New York #27/R est:100000-150000
£38889	$70000	€56778	Les bords de la Midouze, Mont-de-Marsan (34x50cm-13x20in) s. prov.exhib.lit. 22-Apr-4 Christie's, Rockefeller NY #87/R est:70000-90000
£38889	$70000	€56778	Le dormoir (47x37cm-19x15in) s. prov.lit. 23-Apr-4 Sotheby's, New York #25/R est:70000-90000
£41176	$70000	€60117	Paysage (27x49cm-11x19in) s. prov. 28-Oct-3 Sotheby's, New York #15/R est:70000-100000
£44118	$75000	€64412	Jeune fille lisant au bord de l'eau (23x34cm-9x13in) s. painted c.1870-1874 lit. 29-Oct-3 Christie's, Rockefeller NY #106/R est:60000-80000
£48000	$88320	€70080	Suresnes (22x35cm-9x14in) s. painted 1855-1870 prov. 23-Jun-4 Christie's, London #101/R est:30000-40000
£50000	$91000	€73000	Le bapteme du Christ (45x24cm-18x9in) s. panel painted c.1844-1845 prov.exhib.lit. 3-Feb-4 Christie's, London #110/R est:50000-70000
£50704	$87718	€72000	Landscape (24x47cm-9x19in) s. panel. 13-Dec-3 Lempertz, Koln #9/R est:15000
£52778	$95000	€77056	Torrent des Abruzzes (37x62cm-15x24in) s. prov.lit. 23-Apr-4 Sotheby's, New York #5/R est:100000-150000
£65789	$121053	€100000	Plage a Trouville (21x38cm-8x15in) paper on canvas prov.lit. 24-Jun-4 Christie's, Paris #152/R est:120000-150000
£88889	$160000	€129778	La gelee blanche a Auvers-sur-Oise (34x46cm-13x18in) s. prov.exhib.lit. 23-Apr-4 Sotheby's, New York #15/R est:150000-200000
£88889	$160000	€129778	Ronde de nymphes (65x86cm-26x34in) s. canvas on panel prov.exhib. 23-Apr-4 Sotheby's, New York #29/R est:200000-250000
£105556	$190000	€154112	Paturage dans les marais, souvenir des environs d'Amiens (40x60cm-16x24in) s. painted c.1865-1870 prov.exhib.lit. 22-Apr-4 Christie's, Rockefeller NY #91/R est:150000-200000
£116667	$210000	€170334	Vue de Venise (25x32cm-10x13in) i. oil paper on canvas. 23-Apr-4 Sotheby's, New York #4/R est:150000-200000
£144444	$260000	€210888	L'Italienne a la fontaine (53x33cm-21x13in) studio st. painted c.1870-75 prov.lit. 22-Apr-4 Christie's, Rockefeller NY #94/R est:70000-90000
£152941	$260000	€223294	Groupe d'arbres au bord d'un etang (44x75cm-17x30in) s. painted 1855-60 prov.exhib.lit. 29-Oct-3 Christie's, Rockefeller NY #100/R est:300000-500000
£333333	$600000	€486666	Nymphes et faunes (98x131cm-39x52in) s. prov.exhib.lit. 22-Apr-4 Christie's, Rockefeller NY #104/R est:600000-800000
£446927	$800000	€652513	Chaumieres et moulins au bord de torrent, Morvan ou Auvergne (52x63cm-20x25in) s.d.1831 prov.exhib.lit. 5-May-4 Sotheby's, New York #4/R est:1000000-1500000

Prints

£3733	$6869	€5600	Grand cavalier sous bois (28x22cm-11x9in) print. 10-Jun-4 Piasa, Paris #39/R
£13408	$24000	€19576	Corot par lui-meme (21x15cm-8x6in) cliche-verre print. 6-May-4 Swann Galleries, New York #269/R est:15000-20000

Works on paper

£556	$906	€800	Barock doorway in Toledo (14x9cm-6x4in) pencil. 26-Sep-3 Bolland & Marotz, Bremen #430/R
£1056	$1827	€1500	Arbres (26x35cm-10x14in) chl. 12-Dec-3 Libert, Castor, Paris #15/R est:1200-1500
£1400	$2576	€2044	Maison Normande (9x15cm-4x6in) pencil lit. 25-Mar-4 Christie's, Kensington #4/R est:1500-2000
£1769	$3166	€2600	Un paysage avec un massif d'arbres (27x21cm-11x8in) black chk estompe oval prov. 18-Mar-4 Christie's, Paris #176/R est:2000-3000
£3200	$5888	€4800	Landscape (17x27cm-7x11in) s. chl paper on board prov. 12-Jun-4 Villa Grisebach, Berlin #525/R est:1500-2000
£3401	$6088	€5000	Campagne Romaine, vue d'Olevano Romano (18x29cm-7x11in) graphite htd white chk. 22-Mar-4 Digard, Paris #45/R est:3000-5000
£4348	$7130	€6000	Le repos du charretier (16x22cm-6x9in) s.d.1832 graphite. 11-May-3 Osenat, Fontainebleau #87/R est:6000-6500
£4422	$7915	€6500	Campagne Romaine, vue de Marino (19x29cm-7x11in) graphite htd white chk. 22-Mar-4 Digard, Paris #46/R est:3000-5000
£5000	$9000	€7300	Italianate landscape with a house in a forest by a pond (23x39cm-9x15in) i.mount black lead prov. 22-Jan-4 Christie's, Rockefeller NY #138/R est:5000-7000
£5556	$10000	€8112	Wooded landscape near St. Germain (22x15cm-9x6in) s.i.d.1823 graphite. 23-Apr-4 Sotheby's, New York #10/R est:10000-15000
£5944	$10105	€8500	Profil (16x11cm-6x4in) s.i.d.1830 crayon gouache. 28-Nov-3 Doutrebente, Paris #17/R est:2000-3000
£8099	$14011	€11500	Vue d'une coupole d'eglise Valmontone (27x21cm-11x8in) i. black crayon. 12-Dec-3 Artus Associes, Paris #68
£9000	$16470	€13140	La fete du dieu terme (24x31cm-9x12in) s. i.verso black chk prov.lit. 6-Jul-4 Christie's, London #192/R est:10000-15000

COROT, Jean Baptiste Camille (attrib) (1796-1875) French

£782	$1400	€1142	Study of trees (23x41cm-9x16in) indis sig. board on panel. 8-May-4 Susanin's, Chicago #6075/R est:1000-1500
£4082	$7306	€6000	Landscape with trees (46x33cm-18x13in) i. 17-Mar-4 Neumeister, Munich #423/R est:4500

Works on paper

£652	$1200	€952	Landscape studies (30x20cm-12x8in) init. black chk pair prov. 28-Mar-4 Bonhams & Butterfields, San Francisco #2721 est:1000-1500

CORPAATO (1950-) Swiss

£419	$711	€612	Coloured composition (80x120cm-31x47in) s.i. i.d.1988 verso. 7-Nov-3 Dobiaschofsky, Bern #272/R (S.FR 950)

CORPORA, Antonio (1909-) Italian

£600	$1104	€900	Untitled (32x42cm-13x17in) s. tempera card. 11-Jun-4 Farsetti, Prato #316/R
£667	$1207	€1000	Femme assise a la terrasse, Saint Germain, banlieue de Tunis (33x41cm-13x16in) s. cardboard. 5-Apr-4 Marie & Robert, Paris #87/R
£1216	$2141	€1800	Golden ubu (40x50cm-16x20in) s.i. mixed media collage on canvas exec.1990. 19-May-4 Il Ponte, Milan #1132 est:1000-1200
£1724	$2879	€2500	Cubist study (45x40cm-18x16in) s.d.1945 tempera paper. 13-Nov-3 Finarte Semenzato, Rome #213/R est:2400-2600
£1818	$3091	€2600	Cleopatra ship (38x45cm-15x18in) s. s.i.d.78 verso prov. 24-Nov-3 Christie's, Milan #176/R est:2000-3000
£2069	$3455	€3000	Morning (65x50cm-26x20in) s.d.71 s.d.verso. 13-Nov-3 Finarte Semenzato, Rome #332 est:2800-3200
£2329	$3959	€3330	Women sorting grapes (73x60cm-29x24in) s.d.1945 prov. 18-Nov-3 Babuino, Rome #401/R est:1500-2000
£2414	$4031	€3500	Light (65x81cm-26x32in) s. s.verso. 13-Nov-3 Finarte Semenzato, Rome #285 est:3500-4000
£2416	$4325	€3600	Vecchia Darsena a Venezia (81x100cm-32x39in) s.i.d.1981 verso. 25-May-4 Karl & Faber, Munich #247/R est:4000-5000
£2621	$4377	€3800	Untitled (35x45cm-14x18in) s. oil sand. 13-Nov-3 Finarte Semenzato, Rome #422/R est:3500-4000
£2667	$4907	€4000	Sunset in the East (60x73cm-24x29in) s. acrylic painted 2001. 12-Jun-4 Meeting Art, Vercelli #493/R est:4000
£3169	$5261	€4500	Vase of flowers (55x46cm-22x18in) s.d.1939. 11-Jun-3 Finarte Semenzato, Milan #703/R
£3172	$5298	€4600	Interior sea (100x81cm-39x32in) s.d.70 s.d.verso. 13-Nov-3 Finarte Semenzato, Rome #437 est:4000-5000
£3329	$5659	€4760	Seated woman (50x40cm-20x16in) s.d.1946 prov. 18-Nov-3 Babuino, Rome #398/R est:2000-2500
£3356	$6007	€5000	Childhood field (81x100cm-32x39in) s. painted 1974. 28-May-4 Farsetti, Prato #32/R est:4500-5500
£3413	$5801	€4880	Little lake (60x73cm-24x29in) s. i.d.2000 verso acrylic. 18-Nov-3 Babuino, Rome #530/R est:1500-2000
£3472	$5486	€5000	Seville (81x65cm-32x26in) acrylic painted 1997. 6-Sep-3 Meeting Art, Vercelli #609 est:5000
£3521	$5845	€5000	La contrada del Silenzio (81x100cm-32x39in) s. s.i.verso mural. 14-Jun-3 Meeting Art, Vercelli #119/R est:5000
£3667	$6600	€5500	Study for Saladino's tent (60x50cm-24x20in) s.d.60 s.i.d.verso. 22-Apr-4 Finarte Semenzato, Rome #238/R est:4000-4500
£3893	$7240	€5800	Notes (60x50cm-24x20in) s.d.1957 s.i.d.verso. 4-Mar-4 Babuino, Rome #9
£4027	$7450	€6000	Window overlooking the sea (70x100cm-28x39in) s. s.i.d.1996 verso acrylic. 13-Mar-4 Meeting Art, Vercelli #403 est:6000
£4027	$7208	€6000	Like the sun (60x73cm-24x29in) s. s.i.d.71 verso. 28-May-4 Farsetti, Prato #269/R est:4200-4700
£4362	$7809	€6500	Towards East (100x81cm-39x32in) s. s.i.d.1989 verso lit. 30-May-4 Meeting Art, Vercelli #46 est:5000
£5667	$10427	€8500	Saladino's banners (100x81cm-39x32in) s. s.i.d.1989 verso acrylic. 12-Jun-4 Meeting Art, Vercelli #869/R est:8000

£6376 $11413 €9500 Wind on the Lagoon (100x81cm-39x32in) s. acrylic painted 1991. 28-May-4 Farsetti, Prato #286/R est:5200-6200
£6897 $11517 €10000 Untitled (69x50cm-27x20in) s. s.verso painted 1945. 13-Nov-3 Finarte Semenzato, Rome #416/R est:9000-12000
£7746 $12859 €11000 The most beautiful morning (130x195cm-51x77in) s. prov. 11-Jun-3 Finarte Semenzato, Milan #569/R
£8333 $13667 €11500 Composition (100x81cm-39x32in) s. painted 1954. 30-May-3 Farsetti, Prato #539/R
£8392 $14266 €12000 Afternoon (100x81cm-39x32in) s.d.57. 28-Nov-3 Farsetti, Prato #85/R est:11000-14000
£10067 $18020 €15000 Tree (195x130cm-77x51in) s.d.66 s.d.verso exhib. 25-May-4 Sotheby's, Milan #140/R est:15000
£10067 $18020 €15000 Ancient poetry (130x162cm-51x64in) s. s.d.66 verso exhib. 25-May-4 Sotheby's, Milan #139/R est:10000
£13423 $24027 €20000 Still life with fish (99x80cm-39x31in) s.d.47 exhib.lit. 29-May-4 Farsetti, Prato #481/R est:20000-25000
Works on paper
£399 $654 €550 Untitled (34x24cm-13x9in) s. W/C. 29-May-3 Galleria Pace, Milan #141/R
£671 $1242 €1000 East (51x36cm-20x14in) s. s.i.verso W/C. 11-Mar-4 Galleria Pace, Milan #23/R
£704 $1169 €1000 Le Dune (36x51cm-14x20in) s. i.verso W/C. 14-Jun-3 Meeting Art, Vercelli #95/R
£704 $1169 €1000 Tramonto in Sicilia (36x51cm-14x20in) s. i.verso W/C. 14-Jun-3 Meeting Art, Vercelli #272/R est:1000
£704 $1169 €1000 Mare e Cielo (51x36cm-20x14in) s. i.verso W/C. 14-Jun-3 Meeting Art, Vercelli #539/R
£729 $1152 €1050 Trip to Persia (51x36cm-20x14in) W/C pastel card. 6-Sep-3 Meeting Art, Vercelli #324 est:750
£764 $1207 €1100 Mars sun (51x36cm-20x14in) W/C exec.1996. 6-Sep-3 Meeting Art, Vercelli #562
£800 $1448 €1200 Trip to Marsala (51x36cm-20x14in) s. s.i.verso W/C. 2-Apr-4 Farsetti, Prato #152/R
£927 $1687 €1400 Untitled (50x65cm-20x26in) s. pastel. 17-Jun-4 Galleria Pananti, Florence #420/R
£1067 $1920 €1600 Wood (76x56cm-30x22in) s. W/C paper on canvas. 22-Apr-4 Finarte Semenzato, Rome #105/R est:1600-2000
£1200 $2208 €1800 Untitled (65x50cm-26x20in) s. s.i.d.1974 versopastel card. 11-Jun-4 Farsetti, Prato #212/R est:1600-1900
£1208 $2235 €1800 Carlo Magno's tent (51x36cm-20x14in) s. i.verso W/C. 13-Mar-4 Meeting Art, Vercelli #110 est:1000
£1216 $2141 €1800 Composition (69x50cm-27x20in) s. mixed media board. 22-May-4 Galleria Pananti, Florence #420/R est:2000-2200
£1241 $2073 €1800 Sunset in the East (51x36cm-20x14in) s. s.i.d.2000 verso W/C. 13-Nov-3 Finarte Semenzato, Rome #180 est:1600-1800
£1259 $2140 €1800 Untitled (64x50cm-25x20in) s. pastel paper on board. 24-Nov-3 Christie's, Milan #32/R est:1800-2200
£1267 $2331 €1900 Valencia (51x36cm-20x14in) s. W/C exec.1996. 12-Jun-4 Meeting Art, Vercelli #81/R est:1000
£1477 $2732 €2200 Sunset on the Nile (36x51cm-14x20in) s. W/C pastel exec.1989 lit. 13-Mar-4 Meeting Art, Vercelli #366 est:1000
£1538 $2615 €2200 Ancient Egypt (76x56cm-30x22in) s.i. W/C. 28-Nov-3 Farsetti, Prato #203/R est:1700-2200
£1667 $3067 €2500 Tuna fishing (76x55cm-30x22in) s.i.d.1992 verso mixed media cardboard. 12-Jun-4 Meeting Art, Vercelli #366/R est:2500
£1667 $3067 €2500 Untitled (56x76cm-22x30in) s. W/C. 12-Jun-4 Meeting Art, Vercelli #808/R est:2500
£1678 $2853 €2400 Composition (46x63cm-18x25in) s. pastel. 20-Nov-3 Finarte Semenzato, Milan #156/R est:2400-2800
£2013 $3604 €3000 Untitled (49x65cm-19x26in) s. pastel card two. 25-May-4 Sotheby's, Milan #142/R est:4000
£2324 $3858 €3300 Composition (46x68cm-18x27in) s.d.1960 mixed media board. 14-Jun-3 Meeting Art, Vercelli #593/R est:3000
£2550 $4565 €3800 Untitled (50x65cm-20x26in) s. pastel card pair. 25-May-4 Sotheby's, Milan #141/R est:4000
£3000 $5460 €4380 Composition (73x53cm-29x21in) s.d.42 gouache. 21-Jun-4 Bonhams, New Bond Street #71/R est:3000-5000

CORPUS, Paul (?) ?
£236 $375 €345 Oursins et Journal (53x64cm-21x25in) s. 10-Sep-3 Alderfer's, Hatfield #298/R

CORRADI, Alfonso (1889-1972) Italian
£268 $475 €400 Landscape (40x50cm-16x20in) s. board. 1-May-4 Meeting Art, Vercelli #130
£709 $1184 €1000 Peak in Emilian landscape (64x99cm-25x39in) s. 14-Oct-3 Finarte Semenzato, Milan #108
£877 $1465 €1280 Il giorno della biancheria (54x71cm-21x28in) s. prov. 15-Nov-3 Galerie Gloggner, Luzern #25/R (S.FR 2000)
£1151 $1888 €1600 Wood (75x39cm-30x15in) 5-Jun-3 Adma, Formigine #241 est:1600-1800

CORRADI, Konrad (1813-1878) Swiss
Works on paper
£338 $581 €493 The waterfall at Reichenbach with hotel and the Blattenstock in background (32x47cm-13x19in) s. gouache. 8-Dec-3 Philippe Schuler, Zurich #4015/R (S.FR 750)
£1267 $2293 €1900 View from Wengeneralp of Eiger, Mionch and Jungfrau (32x47cm-13x19in) s.i. gouache. 3-Apr-4 Hans Stahl, Hamburg #18/R est:2200

CORRAL Y GONZALEZ, Imeldo (1889-1976) Spanish
£2270 $3677 €3200 Landscape (33x49cm-13x19in) s. canvas on board. 20-May-3 Ansorena, Madrid #183/R est:2400
£2778 $4528 €4000 Green landscape (65x81cm-26x32in) s. 23-Sep-3 Durán, Madrid #42/R est:1500

CORREA, Rafael (19/20th C) South American
£545 $900 €790 Untitled, cattle in a landscape (46x64cm-18x25in) s. 7-Jul-3 Schrager Galleries, Milwaukee #1175

CORREGGIO, Joseph (1810-1891) German
£1236 $2250 €1805 Still life with fruit and game (97x86cm-38x34in) s. 29-Jun-4 Sotheby's, New York #118/R est:3000-5000

CORREGGIO, Joseph Kaspar (1870-1920) German
£1512 $2600 €2208 Over the fence (46x52cm-18x20in) s. 5-Dec-3 Christie's, Rockefeller NY #77/R est:3000-5000
Works on paper
£268 $499 €400 Gypsy camp near Silistria, Bulgaria (40x61cm-16x24in) s.d.1917 gouache pastel. 6-Mar-4 Arnold, Frankfurt #705/R

CORREGGIO, Ludwig (1846-1920) German
£333 $603 €500 Autumn landscape (22x31cm-9x12in) s. 2-Apr-4 Winterberg, Heidelberg #394
£342 $582 €500 Hunting lodge in wooded mountain landscape (30x40cm-12x16in) s. lit. 6-Nov-3 Allgauer, Kempten #3400/R
£476 $852 €700 Starnberger See near Leoni (16x29cm-6x11in) s. canvas on panel. 17-Mar-4 Neumeister, Munich #424/R
£563 $901 €800 Mill by mountain stream (29x43cm-11x17in) s. 18-Sep-3 Rieber, Stuttgart #877/R
£633 $987 €1000 Summer landscape (19x28cm-7x11in) s. board. 18-Oct-2 Von Zezschwitz, Munich #11/R

CORREGIO, Max (1854-1908) German
£1958 $3270 €2800 Hunting still life (80x60cm-31x24in) s.d.1887. 9-Oct-3 Michael Zeller, Lindau #539/R est:2800

CORREIA, Charles (1945-1988) French
Sculpture
£1712 $2911 €2500 Joueurs de polo (20x29cm-8x11in) s.st.f.Caprelli brown pat bronze. 9-Nov-3 Eric Pillon, Calais #174/R

CORRELEAU, Ernest Pierre Joseph (20th C) French
£867 $1551 €1300 Les vaches a Lezaven (46x65cm-18x26in) s. 16-May-4 Thierry & Lannon, Brest #131/R

CORRENS, Josef Cornelius (1814-1907) Flemish
£445 $757 €650 Portrait de noir (25x21cm-10x8in) s. panel. 10-Nov-3 Horta, Bruxelles #403
£769 $1284 €1100 Portrait of an elegant young lady (58x44cm-23x17in) s. s.d.1885 verso oval panel. 30-Jun-3 Sotheby's, Amsterdam #108

CORRIERO, Guy (20th C) American
£1765 $3000 €2577 Eyeball to eyeball (61x76cm-24x30in) 1-Nov-3 Altermann Galleries, Santa Fe #12

CORRODI, F (?) ?
£1130 $2069 €1650 View of the old baths at Reichenbach, Canton Bern (46x55cm-18x22in) s. i.verso. 4-Jun-4 Zofingen, Switzerland #138/R est:3000 (S.FR 2600)

CORRODI, Hermann David Salomon (1844-1905) Italian
£1057 $1797 €1543 Evening river landscape (12x22cm-5x9in) s. panel. 5-Nov-3 Dobiaschofsky, Bern #450/R est:3000 (S.FR 2400)
£1458 $2377 €2100 Southern shore in evening (27x16cm-11x6in) s. i. verso panel. 26-Sep-3 Bolland & Marotz, Bremen #510/R est:1600
£2083 $3396 €3000 Egyptian woman at water hole on the Nile (27x16cm-11x6in) s. i. verso panel. 26-Sep-3 Bolland & Marotz, Bremen #509/R est:1600
£2817 $4676 €4000 Preghiera in laguna (20x15cm-8x6in) s. panel. 11-Jun-3 Christie's, Rome #114/R est:2800-3200
£3073 $5500 €4487 Under the red umbrella (72x43cm-28x17in) s.i. 14-May-4 Skinner, Boston #42/R est:4000-6000
£3500 $6020 €5110 On a Venetian balcony (72x37cm-28x15in) s.i. 4-Dec-3 Christie's, Kensington #50/R est:4000-6000
£4514 $7358 €6500 Two girls chatting in window of Venetian house (72x38cm-28x15in) s. 25-Sep-3 Dr Fritz Nagel, Stuttgart #1338/R est:3200
£4706 $8000 €6871 Rustic concert (100x65cm-39x26in) s.i. 29-Oct-3 Christie's, Rockefeller NY #237/R est:10000-15000
£5988 $10479 €8500 Vue du Mont Blanc depuis Nyon (25x20cm-10x8in) mono. cardboard. 18-Dec-3 Tajan, Paris #152/R est:3000-4000
£6643 $11294 €9500 Sunset over Rome (101x76cm-40x30in) s.i. lit. 28-Nov-3 Schloss Ahlden, Ahlden #1415/R est:9500
£13889 $25000 €20278 In the courtyard (100x64cm-39x25in) s.i. 23-Apr-4 Sotheby's, New York #183/R est:25000-35000
£20139 $33229 €29000 Spring morning in the Campagna near Ponte Molle am Tiber (86x162cm-34x64in) s.d.1877 lit. 3-Jul-3 Van Ham, Cologne #1099/R est:45000
£21477 $39517 €32000 Stop (123x65cm-48x26in) s. 24-Mar-4 Il Ponte, Milan #569/R est:20000-25000
£25000 $45500 €36500 View of the Bosphorus, Constantinople (85x45cm-33x18in) s.i. 17-Jun-4 Christie's, London #112/R est:25000-35000
£31915 $53298 €45000 Climbing MountAthos (126x233cm-50x92in) s.i. 23-Jun-3 Finarte Semenzato, Rome #197/R
£40000 $72800 €58400 Morning rituals (102x74cm-40x29in) s.i. 17-Jun-4 Christie's, London #102/R est:40000-60000
£40761 $75000 €59511 Busy street scene Rome (152x77cm-60x30in) s.i. 27-Jun-4 Freeman, Philadelphia #50/R est:30000-50000
£43478 $71304 €60000 Street in Cairo (67x156cm-26x61in) s. 27-May-3 Finarte Semenzato, Milan #85/R est:85000
£55000 $100100 €80300 Carpet merchants (100x91cm-39x36in) s.i. prov. 17-Jun-4 Christie's, London #100/R est:60000-100000
Works on paper
£647 $1062 €900 Praying (23x31cm-9x12in) s.i. W/C. 10-Jun-3 Pandolfini, Florence #165/R

CORRODI, Salomon (1810-1892) Swiss
Works on paper
£1100 $2024 €1606 Rome, seen from Monte Mario (33x50cm-13x20in) s. pencil W/C. 25-Mar-4 Christie's, Kensington #98/R est:1200-1800

£2676 $4442 €3800 View of the coast at Sorrentina (31x48cm-12x19in) s. W/C cardboard. 11-Jun-3 Christie's, Rome #245/R est:3500-5000
£3169 $5261 €4500 Coastal view (39x57cm-15x22in) W/C cardboard. 11-Jun-3 Christie's, Rome #247/R est:4000-6000
£4577 $7919 €6500 View of Nemi Lake (40x61cm-16x24in) s.d.73 W/C card. 11-Dec-3 Christie's, Rome #130/R est:7000-9000
£5583 $8933 €8151 Bergamo (32x50cm-13x20in) s.d.39 W/C. 19-Sep-3 Koller, Zurich #3069/R est:7000-10000 (S.FR 12340)
£6600 $11022 €9570 Entrance to St. Mark's Square, Venice (51x77cm-20x30in) s.d.1847 W/C. 21-Jun-3 Lacy Scott, Bury St.Edmunds #491/R

CORSARO, Prof A (19/20th C) ?
£2750 $4510 €4015 Generous Musician (61x41cm-24x16in) s. 29-May-3 Neales, Nottingham #808/R est:2500-3000

CORSELLIS, Jane (1940-) British
£1200 $2220 €1752 In the sun (90x113cm-35x44in) s. prov.lit. 11-Feb-4 Sotheby's, Olympia #200/R est:800-1200
£1350 $2295 €1971 Evening interior (76x61cm-30x24in) s. exhib. 4-Nov-3 Dreweatt Neate, Newbury #139/R est:300-500
Works on paper
£270 $432 €394 Marie in the studio (82x46cm-32x18in) W/C bodycol. 17-Sep-3 Henry Adams, Chichester #398
£320 $509 €467 Estuary at low tide (28x25cm-11x10in) s. W/C. 12-Sep-3 Gardiner & Houlgate, Bath #85
£320 $509 €467 Figures in an estuary at low tide (28x25cm-11x10in) s. W/C. 12-Sep-3 Gardiner & Houlgate, Bath #86/R

CORSETTI, Attilio (1907-1978) Italian
£500 $920 €750 Venice (47x60cm-19x24in) s. 14-Jun-4 Sant Agostino, Torino #221/R
£748 $1339 €1100 Outside (60x74cm-24x29in) s.d.1947. 22-Mar-4 Sant Agostino, Torino #365/R

CORSI DI BOSNASCO, Giacinto (1829-1909) Italian
£1667 $3067 €2500 Strolling to the woods (45x80cm-18x31in) s. 8-Jun-4 Della Rocca, Turin #311/R est:1600-2200

CORSI, Carlo (1879-1966) Italian
£1533 $2760 €2300 Vortex (45x65cm-18x26in) s. tempera paper on board painted 1951 prov.exhib. 22-Apr-4 Finarte Semenzato, Rome #335 est:1300-1500
Works on paper
£225 $410 €340 Portrait of old woman (47x36cm-19x14in) s.d.1906 Chinese ink. 21-Jun-4 Pandolfini, Florence #49
£239 $434 €360 Portrait of young woman (41x30cm-16x12in) s.d.1906 W/C. 21-Jun-4 Pandolfini, Florence #50
£298 $542 €450 Study of head of girl (45x31cm-18x12in) s.d.1904 chl. 21-Jun-4 Pandolfini, Florence #46
£331 $603 €500 Male nude (131x74cm-52x29in) chl. 21-Jun-4 Pandolfini, Florence #47
£497 $904 €750 Lisetta (48x36cm-19x14in) pastel. 21-Jun-4 Pandolfini, Florence #48
£500 $920 €750 Composition (20x24cm-8x9in) s. W/C canvas on board. 10-Jun-4 Galleria Pace, Milan #11/R
£3000 $5520 €4500 Composition (48x40cm-19x16in) s. mixed media paper on cardboard. 10-Jun-4 Galleria Pace, Milan #130/R est:7000

CORSI, Nicolas de (1882-1956) Italian
£1626 $2911 €2374 Italian coastal landscape (49x70cm-19x28in) s.d.22. 26-May-4 AB Stockholms Auktionsverk #2395/R est:8000-10000 (S.KR 22000)
£1933 $3557 €2900 Back from fishing (41x56cm-16x22in) s. 14-Jun-4 Sant Agostino, Torino #288/R est:2300-2800
£3200 $5888 €4800 Naples (37x50cm-15x20in) s. panel. 10-Jun-4 Christie's, Rome #150/R est:1800-2500
£4333 $7973 €6500 View of town (52x73cm-20x29in) s. cardboard. 10-Jun-4 Christie's, Rome #149/R est:6800-7500

CORSI, Santi (19/20th C) Italian
£9000 $14130 €13050 Iliad room in the Pitti Palace (104x143cm-41x56in) s.i.d.17 i.verso. 28-Aug-3 Christie's, Kensington #239/R est:2000-3000

CORSIA, Gilbert (1915-1985) French
£306 $548 €450 Jeune femme a la fenetre (51x67cm-20x26in) s. oil paper. 16-Mar-4 Chochon-Barre & Allardi, Paris #26
£408 $731 €600 Les comediens (40x40cm-16x16in) s. panel. 16-Mar-4 Chochon-Barre & Allardi, Paris #69/R
£442 $791 €650 Bouquet de fleurs (55x46cm-22x18in) s. panel. 16-Mar-4 Chochon-Barre & Allardi, Paris #56
£476 $852 €700 Paysage de campagne (46x49cm-18x19in) panel. 16-Mar-4 Chochon-Barre & Allardi, Paris #63
£476 $852 €700 Abstraction au voilier (46x55cm-18x22in) s. panel. 16-Mar-4 Chochon-Barre & Allardi, Paris #67
£646 $1157 €950 Modeles a l'atelier (55x46cm-22x18in) s. panel. 16-Mar-4 Chochon-Barre & Allardi, Paris #73/R
£748 $1339 €1100 La maison de Pennedepie (46x55cm-18x22in) s. 16-Mar-4 Chochon-Barre & Allardi, Paris #76/R
£748 $1339 €1100 Portrait (61x50cm-24x20in) s. panel. 16-Mar-4 Chochon-Barre & Allardi, Paris #82/R
£816 $1461 €1200 Les courses (82x97cm-32x38in) s. panel. 16-Mar-4 Chochon-Barre & Allardi, Paris #93
£918 $1644 €1350 Paysage de Normandie (54x65cm-21x26in) s. panel. 16-Mar-4 Chochon-Barre & Allardi, Paris #78/R
£952 $1705 €1400 Nu au miroir (94x73cm-37x29in) s. panel. 16-Mar-4 Chochon-Barre & Allardi, Paris #94/R
£1020 $1827 €1500 Cycle de la barque (38x46cm-15x18in) s. 16-Mar-4 Chochon-Barre & Allardi, Paris #66 est:1300-1400
Works on paper
£286 $511 €420 Le clown (66x53cm-26x21in) s. mixed media collage. 16-Mar-4 Chochon-Barre & Allardi, Paris #29
£306 $548 €450 A l'academie de peinture (59x52cm-23x20in) s. pastel oil. 16-Mar-4 Chochon-Barre & Allardi, Paris #45
£327 $584 €480 Scene de maison close (51x63cm-20x25in) s. mixed media. 16-Mar-4 Chochon-Barre & Allardi, Paris #27

CORSINI, Raffaele (19th C) Italian
Works on paper
£2600 $4654 €3796 American sloop-of-war Lexington off Smyrna (43x57cm-17x22in) i.d.1828 bodycol. 26-May-4 Christie's, Kensington #392/R est:2000-3000

CORSINO DA PRATO, Bettino di (fl.1288-1313) Italian
£190141 $315634 €270000 Madonna and Child with Saints. Crucifixion. Annunciation (39x25cm-15x10in) tempera gold board triptych lit. 11-Jun-3 Semenzato, Florence #18/R est:300000-350000

CORT, Hendrik Frans de (1742-1810) Dutch
£2632 $4842 €4000 Figures by the entrance of a villa (54x77cm-21x30in) s. panel. 24-Jun-4 Credit Municipal, Paris #3/R est:5000-7000
£11000 $19030 €16060 View of a town by a river with peasants and travellers on a path in foreground (54x80cm-21x31in) mono. panel. 11-Dec-3 Sotheby's, London #206/R est:7000-10000

CORTAZAR, Roberto (1962-) Mexican
£1429 $2500 €2086 Blue Composition number 1 (150x100cm-59x39in) s.d.1989 s.i.d.1989 verso oil mixed media. 19-Dec-3 Sotheby's, New York #1187/R est:7000-8000

CORTAZZI, Giacomo (1870-1948) Italian
£320 $589 €480 Houses and stream (46x35cm-18x14in) s. board. 8-Jun-4 Della Rocca, Turin #330/R
£396 $673 €570 Summer bloom (28x38cm-11x15in) s. board. 1-Nov-3 Meeting Art, Vercelli #290
£833 $1417 €1200 Mount Blanc (64x50cm-25x20in) s. board. 1-Nov-3 Meeting Art, Vercelli #75/R

CORTAZZO, Oreste (1836-?) Italian
£839 $1401 €1200 Portrait de jeune femme (35x26cm-14x10in) s.d.1895 panel. 29-Jun-3 Eric Pillon, Calais #20/R
£4167 $7500 €6084 Musical interlude (40x32cm-16x13in) s. 21-Jan-4 Sotheby's, New York #177/R est:10000-15000

CORTEGIANI, Michele (1857-?) Italian
Works on paper
£233 $420 €350 Arab scene (21x15cm-8x6in) s. W/C. 21-Apr-4 Finarte Semenzato, Milan #595/R

CORTELLARI, Jacques (1942-2002) French
£268 $502 €400 Les Arbres (46x61cm-18x24in) s.d.1973. 24-Feb-4 Thierry & Lannon, Brest #44
£282 $493 €400 Nu courbe dans les ruines (89x116cm-35x46in) s. 21-Dec-3 Thierry & Lannon, Brest #377
£282 $527 €420 Maisons de pecheurs a Quiberon (46x61cm-18x24in) s.d.1973. 24-Feb-4 Thierry & Lannon, Brest #43/R
£282 $527 €420 Pont Marie a l'ile St Louis (46x61cm-18x24in) s.d.1973. 24-Feb-4 Thierry & Lannon, Brest #46
£302 $565 €450 Autumn (90x130cm-35x51in) s. 24-Feb-4 Thierry & Lannon, Brest #111
£302 $565 €450 Femme ammonite et mouettes (89x131cm-35x52in) s. 24-Feb-4 Thierry & Lannon, Brest #285
£322 $602 €480 Village Italien au pont (50x150cm-20x59in) s. 24-Feb-4 Thierry & Lannon, Brest #278
£336 $628 €500 Paysage de Provence (50x61cm-20x24in) s. 24-Feb-4 Thierry & Lannon, Brest #42
£336 $628 €500 Nude with flowers (65x50cm-26x20in) s.d.1970. 24-Feb-4 Thierry & Lannon, Brest #283
£336 $628 €500 Sommeil et la ville (130x89cm-51x35in) s. 24-Feb-4 Thierry & Lannon, Brest #286/R
£369 $690 €550 Port du Croisic (50x61cm-20x24in) s.d.1973. 24-Feb-4 Thierry & Lannon, Brest #45/R
£369 $690 €550 Croisic (61x50cm-24x20in) s. 24-Feb-4 Thierry & Lannon, Brest #47/R
£369 $690 €550 Quai de la Seine le Palais de Justice (46x61cm-18x24in) s.d.1973. 24-Feb-4 Thierry & Lannon, Brest #48
£369 $690 €550 Port d'Etel (60x73cm-24x29in) s. 24-Feb-4 Thierry & Lannon, Brest #192/R
£387 $678 €550 Femme Ammonite Arlequin (92x65cm-36x26in) s. board. 21-Dec-3 Thierry & Lannon, Brest #378/R
£470 $879 €700 Bain (147x115cm-58x45in) s.d.70. 24-Feb-4 Thierry & Lannon, Brest #262/R
£483 $904 €720 Summer (89x130cm-35x51in) s. 24-Feb-4 Thierry & Lannon, Brest #100
£638 $1192 €950 Rue (92x65cm-36x26in) s.d.59. 24-Feb-4 Thierry & Lannon, Brest #240

CORTES Y AGUILAR, Andres (1810-1879) Spanish
£933 $1717 €1400 Cattle watering (57x81cm-22x32in) s. 10-Jun-4 Christie's, Rome #16
£2899 $4754 €4000 Country scene (64x83cm-25x33in) s. 27-May-3 Durán, Madrid #252/R est:4000
£2899 $4754 €4000 Idyllic pastoral scene (35x70cm-14x28in) s. 27-May-3 Durán, Madrid #253/R est:4000

CORTES Y CORDERO, Antonio (1826-1908) Spanish
£1101 $1872 €1607 Cattle in meadow landscape (38x46cm-15x18in) s. 5-Nov-3 Dobiaschofsky, Bern #451/R est:3600 (S.FR 2500)

£2465 $4264 €3500 Pasture (60x80cm-24x31in) s. canvas on board prov. 11-Dec-3 Christie's, Rome #29/R est:3700-4200

CORTES, A (?) ?
£1479 $2455 €2100 Vaches dans un paysage (46x38cm-18x15in) s. 15-Jun-3 Peron, Melun #151

CORTES, Andre (1815-1880) Spanish
£1469 $2526 €2100 Troupeau a la mare (19x26cm-7x10in) s. 7-Dec-3 Osenat, Fontainebleau #36/R est:2300-2500

CORTES, Andres (1810-1879) Spanish
£679 $1086 €991 River landscape with figures and animals (35x70cm-14x28in) s.i. 16-Sep-3 Philippe Schuler, Zurich #5433 est:800-1200 (S.FR 1500)

CORTES, Antonio (19th C) Spanish
£1892 $3386 €2800 Landscape with cows (41x65cm-16x26in) s. lit. 8-May-4 Schloss Ahlden, Ahlden #785/R est:2800

CORTES, Edouard (1882-1969) French
£1944 $3500 €2838 Flower market (16x19cm-6x7in) s. panel. 21-Jan-4 Sotheby's, New York #194/R est:4000-6000
£2414 $4031 €3500 Moulin pres d'un cascade (19x27cm-7x11in) bears st.sig. panel lit. 17-Nov-3 Tajan, Paris #169/R est:3500-4000
£2684 $4751 €4000 Ferme en Automne (23x33cm-9x13in) s. board painted c.1913 lit. 27-Apr-4 Artcurial Briest, Paris #137/R est:4500-5000
£3333 $5567 €4800 Pre en ete (16x22cm-6x9in) s. s.d.Juin 1913 verso board. 21-Oct-3 Artcurial Briest, Paris #159 est:5000-6000
£4027 $7128 €6000 Paris, le Moulin Rouge (32x40cm-13x16in) s.verso panel. 27-Apr-4 Artcurial Briest, Paris #136/R est:7000-9000
£5960 $10848 €9000 Paris street scene with figures and cars in the evening (37x51cm-15x20in) s. lit. 19-Jun-4 Bergmann, Erlangen #869 est:9000
£8276 $14897 €12000 Le quai de louvre sous la neige (24x36cm-9x14in) s. 26-Jan-4 Gros & Delettrez, Paris #34/R est:12000-15000
£9184 $16439 €13500 Vase de glaieuls et dahlias (91x72cm-36x28in) s. painted c.1945. 18-Mar-4 Peschetau-Badin Godeau & Leroy, Paris #80/R est:12000-15000
£9444 $17000 €13788 Place de la Republique (24x33cm-9x13in) s. 21-Jan-4 Sotheby's, New York #193/R est:12000-18000
£10556 $19000 €15412 L'Arc de Triomphe (16x22cm-6x9in) s. board. 23-Apr-4 Sotheby's, New York #131/R est:10000-15000
£10839 $18643 €15500 La porte Saint Martin (46x54cm-18x21in) s. 8-Dec-3 Horta, Bruxelles #110/R est:15000-20000
£11176 $19000 €16317 Parisian boulevard in winter (33x45cm-13x18in) s. 29-Oct-3 Christie's, Rockefeller NY #189/R est:15000-20000
£12000 $22080 €18000 Place de Furstenberg a Paris (50x65cm-20x26in) s. 11-Jun-4 Claude Aguttes, Neuilly #21/R est:12000-15000
£12500 $22500 €18250 Place Vendome (33x46cm-13x18in) s. 21-Jan-4 Sotheby's, New York #189/R est:15000-20000
£12500 $22500 €18250 Place de la Republique (33x46cm-13x18in) s. 23-Apr-4 Sotheby's, New York #130/R est:20000-30000
£12575 $21000 €18360 Paris, La Porte St Denis (33x46cm-13x18in) s. prov. 23-Oct-3 Shannon's, Milford #169/R est:20000-30000
£12778 $23000 €18656 Boulevard Bonne Nouvelle (24x33cm-9x13in) s. 21-Jan-4 Sotheby's, New York #190/R est:12000-18000
£12778 $23000 €18656 Place du Chatelet en hiver, Paris (39x46cm-15x18in) s. 22-Apr-4 Christie's, Rockefeller NY #190/R est:20000-30000
£12941 $22000 €18894 St Michel en hiver (46x55cm-18x22in) s. 29-Oct-3 Christie's, Rockefeller NY #193/R est:20000-30000
£13194 $22035 €19000 Parisian street (27x35cm-11x14in) s. lit. 25-Oct-3 Bergmann, Erlangen #971/R est:12000
£13966 $25000 €20390 Paris street scene (51x66cm-20x26in) s. 8-May-4 Susanin's, Chicago #6004/R est:15000-20000
£15294 $26000 €22329 Place de la Republique (33x46cm-13x18in) s. 29-Oct-3 Christie's, Rockefeller NY #192/R est:20000-30000
£15934 $29000 €23264 Rue Royale, Madeleine at dusk (33x46cm-13x18in) s. 19-Jun-4 Jackson's, Cedar Falls #40/R est:25000-35000
£16176 $27500 €23617 View of the place Vendome, Paris (34x46cm-13x18in) s. prov. 19-Nov-3 Bonhams & Butterfields, San Francisco #158/R
£16484 $30000 €24067 Boulevard de la Madeleine (46x54cm-18x21in) s. canvas on board. 29-Jun-4 Sotheby's, New York #92/R est:25000-35000
£16667 $30000 €24334 Theatre de Gymnase, Paris (46x53cm-18x21in) s. prov. 22-Apr-4 Christie's, Rockefeller NY #195/R est:20000-30000
£17647 $30000 €25765 Place de la Republique (33x46cm-13x18in) s. 29-Oct-3 Christie's, Rockefeller NY #190/R est:20000-30000
£17778 $32000 €25956 Les Champs Elysees, le Lido, Paris (46x55cm-18x22in) s. 22-Apr-4 Christie's, Rockefeller NY #188/R est:30000-40000
£17778 $32000 €25956 Rue Royale, Place de la Concorde, Paris (33x45cm-13x18in) s. 22-Apr-4 Christie's, Rockefeller NY #192/R est:20000-30000
£18056 $32500 €26362 Place de Clichy (33x46cm-13x18in) s. prov. 23-Apr-4 Sotheby's, New York #127/R est:25000-35000
£18182 $32000 €26546 View of place, St. Michel, Paris (46x54cm-18x21in) s. i.verso. 18-May-4 Bonhams & Butterfields, San Francisco #185/R est:20000-30000
£18994 $34000 €27731 Flower market, Rue Royale (46x56cm-18x22in) s. 20-Mar-4 Selkirks, St. Louis #535/R est:20000-30000
£19117 $32500 €27911 View of the Pantheon, Paris (33x46cm-13x18in) s. 19-Nov-3 Bonhams & Butterfields, San Francisco #159/R
£19117 $32500 €27911 View of the Arc de Triomphe, Paris (33x46cm-13x18in) s. 19-Nov-3 Bonhams & Butterfields, San Francisco #160/R
£19117 $32500 €27911 Cottage interior with a woman knitting by the hearth (37x46cm-15x18in) s. 19-Nov-3 Bonhams & Butterfields, San Francisco #161/R
£19444 $35000 €28388 Place de la Bastille (33x46cm-13x18in) s. 23-Apr-4 Sotheby's, New York #129/R est:20000-30000
£19767 $34000 €28860 Blvd Bonne Nouvelle Theatre du Gymnase (51x61cm-20x24in) s. painted c.1950. 7-Dec-3 Treadway Gallery, Cincinnati #506/R est:35000-45000
£19886 $35000 €29034 Parisian street scene (34x46cm-13x18in) s. 18-May-4 Bonhams & Butterfields, San Francisco #186/R est:20000-30000
£21176 $36000 €30917 L'Opera, Paris (33x46cm-13x18in) 29-Oct-3 Christie's, Rockefeller NY #188/R est:20000-30000
£21978 $40000 €32088 Theatre du Chatelet (46x55cm-18x22in) s. 29-Jun-4 Sotheby's, New York #90/R est:30000-50000
£22000 $37400 €32120 Boulevard de la Madeleine (25x33cm-10x13in) s. prov.exhib. 18-Nov-3 Sotheby's, London #342/R
£24706 $42000 €36071 Le marche aux fleurs, Paris (33x46cm-13x18in) s. 29-Oct-3 Christie's, Rockefeller NY #187/R est:20000-30000
£24706 $42000 €36071 Pont St Denis (33x46cm-13x18in) s. 29-Oct-3 Christie's, Rockefeller NY #191/R est:20000-30000
£26087 $48000 €38087 Paris street scene (46x53cm-18x21in) s. 26-Jun-4 Susanin's, Chicago #6088/R est:15000-20000
£30769 $56000 €44923 Theatre du Vaudeville, Paris (46x53cm-18x21in) s. 19-Jun-4 Jackson's, Cedar Falls #39/R est:35000-45000
£38000 $65740 €55480 Figures in a Paris street at dusk (33x46cm-13x18in) s. 14-Dec-3 Desmond Judd, Cranbrook #1065
Works on paper
£4348 $8000 €6348 Paris street scene (23x38cm-9x15in) s. gouache. 26-Jun-4 Susanin's, Chicago #6134/R est:4000-6000
£5163 $9500 €7538 Paris street scene (23x33cm-9x13in) s. gouache. 26-Jun-4 Susanin's, Chicago #6089/R est:3000-4000
£18000 $32760 €26280 Porte Saint Martin, neige. Boulevard de la Madelaine (24x55cm-9x22in) s. gouache board pair. 15-Jun-4 Sotheby's, London #215/R est:10000-15000
£23464 $42000 €34257 Cityscape (28x56cm-11x22in) gouache board. 15-May-4 Altermann Galleries, Santa Fe #150/R

CORTESE, Federico (1829-1913) Italian
£5493 $9503 €7800 Duck hunters (41x69cm-16x27in) s. 10-Dec-3 Sotheby's, Milan #76/R est:7800-8200

CORTESE, Federico (attrib) (1829-1913) Italian
£2617 $4135 €3795 Italian landscape with figures on old stone bridge across river (80x110cm-31x43in) bears sig. 2-Sep-3 Rasmussen, Copenhagen #1658/R est:8000-10000 (D.KR 28000)

CORTET, J (20th C) ?
£1408 $2437 €2000 Marocains devant Tanger (32x46cm-13x18in) s. 15-Dec-3 Gros & Delettrez, Paris #518/R est:1500-2000

CORTHALS, Léon (1877-1935) Belgian
£329 $595 €500 Nu sur fond de tableau representant un moulin a eau (117x81cm-46x32in) s. 19-Apr-4 Horta, Bruxelles #466
£345 $638 €500 Elegante de profil (58x46cm-23x18in) s. 19-Jan-4 Horta, Bruxelles #51
£448 $829 €650 Moulin a eau sous le neige (61x80cm-24x31in) s. 19-Jan-4 Horta, Bruxelles #48
£493 $893 €750 Portrait de fillette au chapeau rouge (66x53cm-26x21in) s.d.1914. 19-Apr-4 Horta, Bruxelles #465
£517 $957 €750 Vase fleuri de tulipes (55x45cm-22x18in) s. 19-Jan-4 Horta, Bruxelles #50
£655 $1212 €950 Chemin en sous-bois (129x100cm-51x39in) s. 19-Jan-4 Horta, Bruxelles #46
£690 $1276 €1000 Elegante a la couture devant une fenetre (60x75cm-24x30in) s. 19-Jan-4 Horta, Bruxelles #43
£759 $1403 €1100 Sous-bois avec ruisseau (131x101cm-52x40in) s. 19-Jan-4 Horta, Bruxelles #47
£828 $1531 €1200 Elegante au collier de perles (116x81cm-46x32in) s.d.1927. 19-Jan-4 Horta, Bruxelles #45
£855 $1548 €1300 Elegante a la couture devant une fenetre (60x75cm-24x30in) s. 19-Apr-4 Horta, Bruxelles #467
£966 $1786 €1400 Elegante au chapeau de paille dans un paysage avec riviere (128x99cm-50x39in) s. 19-Jan-4 Horta, Bruxelles #44
£966 $1786 €1400 Quai Vert a Bruges. Paysage ensoleille (60x74cm-24x29in) pair. 19-Jan-4 Horta, Bruxelles #49
£1034 $1914 €1500 Portrait of a young girl wearing a red hat (66x53cm-26x21in) s.d.1914. 19-Jan-4 Horta, Bruxelles #41 est:1800-2200
£1034 $1914 €1500 Nu sur fond de tableau representant un moulin a eau (117x81cm-46x32in) s. 19-Jan-4 Horta, Bruxelles #42 est:2000-3000

CORTIELLO, Mario (1907-1982) Italian
£338 $595 €500 Beach on Lake Ameno (50x60cm-20x24in) s. 19-May-4 Il Ponte, Milan #1047
£352 $585 €500 Pulcinella sulle rive del fiume (50x70cm-20x28in) s.d.1971 mixed oil. 14-Jun-3 Meeting Art, Vercelli #143/R
£769 $1285 €1100 Caracciolo Street at dusk (40x50cm-16x20in) s.d.1951. 26-Jun-3 Sant Agostino, Torino #120/R

CORTIER, Amedee (1921-1976) Belgian
£872 $1614 €1300 Still life (65x55cm-26x22in) s. panel. 13-Mar-4 De Vuyst, Lokeren #78
£1049 $1752 €1500 Black blue (66x54cm-26x21in) s. tempera paper. 11-Oct-3 De Vuyst, Lokeren #67 est:1600-1800
£1329 $2219 €1900 Red black blue 186 (51x39cm-20x15in) s. 11-Oct-3 De Vuyst, Lokeren #66/R est:1600-1800
Works on paper
£940 $1738 €1400 Composition (63x47cm-25x19in) s. casein tempera. 13-Mar-4 De Vuyst, Lokeren #77/R
£1000 $1790 €1500 Composition (89x64cm-35x25in) s. gouache. 15-May-4 De Vuyst, Lokeren #71/R est:1500-1700

CORTIJO, Francisco (1936-) Spanish
£1197 $2071 €1700 Toreador (70x50cm-28x20in) board. 15-Dec-3 Ansorena, Madrid #986/R est:1500
£1507 $2562 €2200 Boy on a chair (90x68cm-35x27in) s.d.74. 4-Nov-3 Ansorena, Madrid #947/R

CORTONA, Pietro da (1596-1669) Italian
£95302 $178215 €142000 Madonna and Child with Saints (135x98cm-53x39in) prov.exhib.lit. 25-Feb-4 Porro, Milan #77/R est:125000
Works on paper
£282 $451 €400 Bearded man on throne with woman collapsed at feet (23x21cm-9x8in) s. wash lit. 19-Sep-3 Karlheinz Kaupp, Staufen #1916/R

CORTONA, Pietro da (attrib) (1596-1669) Italian
Works on paper
£2254 $3944 €3200 Phalaris ordonnant de jeter Perille dans le taureau d'arain (16x14cm-6x6in) pen brown ink col wash after Polidoro da Caravaggio. 17-Dec-3 Christie's, Paris #12/R est:3000-5000

CORTONA, Pietro da (circle) (1596-1669) Italian
£9000 $16470 €13140 Finding of Romulus and Remus (83x98cm-33x39in) 9-Jul-4 Christie's, Kensington #173/R est:7000-10000
£13333 $24400 €20000 Silver Age (173x130cm-68x51in) 1-Jun-4 Sotheby's, Milan #194/R est:20000-30000
£13333 $24400 €20000 Golden Age (173x130cm-68x51in) 1-Jun-4 Sotheby's, Milan #193/R est:20000-30000

CORTONA, Pietro da (studio) (1596-1669) Italian
£5913 $10584 €8633 Agar and the Angel (112x161cm-44x63in) 26-May-4 AB Stockholms Auktionsverk #2590/R est:100000-120000 (S.KR 80000)

CORTONA, Urbano di Pietro (attrib) (1426-1504) Italian
Sculpture
£60000 $109800 €87600 Dead Christ supported by angels (57x59x11cm-22x23x4in) marble relief lit. 9-Jul-4 Sotheby's, London #29/R est:60000-80000

CORTOT, Jean (1925-) French
Works on paper
£245 $421 €350 Louise Labbe Lyonnaise (57x77cm-22x30in) s.d.1988 s.i.d.verso mixed media paper on panel. 3-Dec-3 Tajan, Paris #466

CORTOT, Jean-Pierre (1787-1843) French
Sculpture
£6711 $11879 €10000 Soldat de Marathon annoncant la victoire (52x58cm-20x23in) s.st.f.Barbedienne pat bronze marbe socle lit. 29-Apr-4 Sotheby's, Paris #201/R est:7000-9000

CORWIN, Charles Abel (1857-1938) American
£279 $500 €407 Cows wading in the stream (30x41cm-12x16in) s. board. 10-Jan-4 Susanin's, Chicago #5025/R
£299 $500 €437 American buffalo (38x48cm-15x19in) s. canvasboard. 29-Jun-3 William Jenack, New York #344
£950 $1700 €1387 Dam in Washington, DC (61x41cm-24x16in) s.i.verso. 7-May-4 Sloans & Kenyon, Bethesda #1701/R est:900-1200
£1630 $3000 €2380 Forest interior (66x92cm-26x36in) s. 8-Jun-4 Bonhams & Butterfields, San Francisco #4033/R est:3000-5000
£2373 $3750 €3465 Watering hole (74x99cm-29x39in) s. 7-Sep-3 Treadway Gallery, Cincinnati #660/R est:5000-7000
£4121 $7500 €6017 Pheasants in tropical foliage (152x61cm-60x24in) s.d.1921 panel. 15-Jun-4 John Moran, Pasadena #108 est:4000-6000

CORWIN, Salmon W (1829-1855) American
£860 $1600 €1256 Portraits of Joseph Ketcham and Mary T Ketcham (76x64cm-30x25in) s.d.1854 pair. 6-Mar-4 North East Auctions, Portsmouth #770/R est:1500-2500

CORY, Bernard (20th C) ?
£581 $1000 €848 Low tide (23x33cm-9x13in) s. board. 7-Dec-3 Grogan, Boston #52/R

COSENZA, Giuseppe (1847-1922) Italian
£1600 $2944 €2400 Boys fishing in evening (23x17cm-9x7in) s.i.d. panel. 11-Jun-4 Hauswedell & Nolte, Hamburg #1005/R est:1800
£7095 $12486 €10500 Little market in Naples (47x35cm-19x14in) s. 19-May-4 Il Ponte, Milan #627 est:6000-6500
£23759 $39677 €33500 Naples Bay (40x79cm-16x31in) s.d.82. 14-Oct-3 Finarte Semenzato, Milan #190/R est:20000

COSGROVE, Stanley Morel (1911-2002) Canadian
£1161 $1996 €1695 Trees (25x30cm-10x12in) s. board prov. 2-Dec-3 Joyner Waddington, Toronto #298/R est:2000-3000 (C.D 2600)
£1250 $2150 €1825 Annunciation (40x30cm-16x12in) s.d.51 board prov. 2-Dec-3 Joyner Waddington, Toronto #308/R est:2000-3000 (C.D 2800)
£1351 $2297 €1972 Forest in winter (46x36cm-18x14in) s. 21-Nov-3 Walker's, Ottawa #8/R est:3500-4500 (C.D 3000)
£1444 $2499 €2108 Still life (51x61cm-20x24in) s. 9-Dec-3 Pinneys, Montreal #146 est:3500-4500 (C.D 3250)
£1518 $2611 €2216 Still life with apple and green bowl (30x40cm-12x16in) s. board prov. 2-Dec-3 Joyner Waddington, Toronto #120/R est:2500-3000 (C.D 3400)
£1778 $3076 €2596 Forest and lake (61x51cm-24x20in) s. acrylic. 9-Dec-3 Maynards, Vancouver #216 est:10000-12000 (C.D 4000)
£1802 $3063 €2631 Sous bois (40x50cm-16x20in) s. i.verso canvas on board prov.lit. 27-Nov-3 Heffel, Vancouver #191/R est:3500-4500 (C.D 4000)
£2000 $3660 €2920 Nature morte au pichet (60x80cm-24x31in) s. prov. 1-Jun-4 Joyner Waddington, Toronto #79/R est:5000-6000 (C.D 5000)
£2846 $5093 €4155 Trees in a landscape (63x81cm-25x32in) s.d.74 prov. 31-May-4 Sotheby's, Toronto #37/R est:7000-9000 (C.D 7000)
£3049 $5457 €4452 Still life with blue grapes (41x51cm-16x20in) s.i. prov. 31-May-4 Sotheby's, Toronto #36/R est:5000-7000 (C.D 7500)
£3100 $5673 €4526 Forest interior (50x60cm-20x24in) s. prov. 1-Jun-4 Joyner Waddington, Toronto #177/R est:8000-10000 (C.D 7750)
£3111 $5382 €4542 Forest scene (81x71cm-32x28in) s. acrylic. 9-Dec-3 Maynards, Vancouver #222a est:10000-12000 (C.D 7000)
£3604 $6126 €5262 Still life with blue jug (51x62cm-20x24in) s.d.54 prov.exhib. 18-Nov-3 Sotheby's, Toronto #16/R est:7000-10000 (C.D 8000)
£5405 $9189 €7891 Anne (50x40cm-20x16in) s.d.1953 i.verso board prov. 27-Nov-3 Heffel, Vancouver #123/R est:6000-8000 (C.D 12000)
£11200 $20496 €16352 Still life (60x80cm-24x31in) s.d.49 board. 1-Jun-4 Joyner Waddington, Toronto #24/R est:30000-35000 (C.D 28000)
Works on paper
£407 $728 €594 Nude study. Nude Study (43x30cm-17x12in) s. one chl one conte two prov. 6-May-4 Heffel, Vancouver #48/R (C.D 1000)
£465 $799 €679 Head of a woman (24x19cm-9x7in) s.d.1940 dry brush. 2-Dec-3 Joyner Waddington, Toronto #291/R (C.D 1040)
£536 $921 €783 Standing female nude (45x35cm-18x14in) s. conte crayon. 2-Dec-3 Joyner Waddington, Toronto #390 (C.D 1200)
£670 $1152 €978 Seated female nude (49x36cm-19x14in) s. chl. 2-Dec-3 Joyner Waddington, Toronto #450 (C.D 1500)

COSMADOPOULOS, Georges (1899-?) Greek
£2800 $4760 €4088 Landscape (50x50cm-20x20in) s. 18-Nov-3 Sotheby's, London #146/R est:3000-5000
£9500 $17005 €13870 Seaside Cafe (35x49cm-14x19in) s. board. 10-May-4 Sotheby's, Olympia #25/R est:4000-6000

COSOLA, Demetrio (1851-1895) Italian
£1067 $1963 €1600 Young man (12x18cm-5x7in) s. exhib. 8-Jun-4 Della Rocca, Turin #223/R est:800-1200
£4483 $7441 €6500 Washerwoman at stream (36x58cm-14x23in) s. board lit. 1-Oct-3 Della Rocca, Turin #20/R est:6500-7500
£6000 $11040 €9000 The Po in Turin (72x59cm-28x23in) s. exhib.lit. 14-Jun-4 Sant Agostino, Torino #305/R est:8000-10000
Works on paper
£284 $474 €400 Woman in profile (16x12cm-6x5in) s.pencil. 20-Oct-3 Sant Agostino, Torino #15/R
£320 $589 €480 Study (30x21cm-12x8in) Chinese ink prov.exhib. 14-Jun-4 Sant Agostino, Torino #195/R
£367 $675 €550 Hen plucker (8x5cm-3x2in) s. card exhib. 8-Jun-4 Della Rocca, Turin #286/R
£433 $797 €650 Shepherdess (15x20cm-6x8in) Chinese ink W/C exhib. 8-Jun-4 Della Rocca, Turin #285/R
£600 $1104 €900 Chivasso (9x15cm-4x6in) pencil prov.exhib. 14-Jun-4 Sant Agostino, Torino #184/R

COSOLA, Demetrio (attrib) (1851-1895) Italian
£3034 $5037 €4400 Women sewing (28x39cm-11x15in) 1-Oct-3 Della Rocca, Turin #245/R est:1500-2000

COSOMATI, Ettore (1873-1960) Italian
£391 $716 €571 Flowers (53x46cm-21x18in) s.i. verso. 4-Jun-4 Zofingen, Switzerland #2436 (S.FR 900)
£3020 $5406 €4500 Carrara quarries (60x75cm-24x30in) mono. painted c.1926 exhib.lit. 29-May-4 Farsetti, Prato #550/R est:3200-4200

COSSAAR, Jan (1874-1966) Dutch
£280 $518 €409 Church interior (62x47cm-24x19in) s. 13-Jan-4 Bonhams, Knightsbridge #84/R
£428 $787 €650 Reclining female nude (29x40cm-11x16in) s. plywood. 22-Jun-4 Christie's, Amsterdam #259/R
£658 $1211 €1000 Figures in a church interior (50x40cm-20x16in) s. 22-Jun-4 Christie's, Amsterdam #294/R est:700-900
£986 $1766 €1450 Woman wearing dresses at the market stall (51x77cm-20x30in) 17-Mar-4 De Zwann, Amsterdam #4641b/R est:900-1100
£1041 $1697 €1500 View of Rome (39x72cm-15x28in) s.i. 29-Sep-3 Sotheby's, Amsterdam #143/R
£1447 $2663 €2200 Barges on the river Amstel, Amsterdam (61x51cm-24x20in) s. prov. 22-Jun-4 Christie's, Amsterdam #308/R est:2000-3000
£1645 $3026 €2500 Early morning on the Thames, London (51x77cm-20x30in) s. 22-Jun-4 Christie's, Amsterdam #255/R est:3000-5000
£1842 $3389 €2800 A view of St Paul's Cathedral, London (61x46cm-24x18in) s. prov. 22-Jun-4 Christie's, Amsterdam #266/R est:3000-5000
£1974 $3632 €3000 View from Trafalgar Square towards Whitehall, London (51x76cm-20x30in) s. 22-Jun-4 Christie's, Amsterdam #191/R est:2000-3000

COSSIERS, Jan (attrib) (1600-1671) Flemish
£1800 $3240 €2628 Bravo smoking (64x49cm-25x19in) panel. 23-Apr-4 Christie's, Kensington #47/R est:2000-3000

COSSIERS, Jan (circle) (1600-1671) Flemish
£5000 $9150 €7300 Head of youth (38x31cm-15x12in) 9-Jul-4 Christie's, Kensington #14/R est:1500-2000

COSSIO, Pancho (1898-1970) Spanish
£11842 $21434 €18000 Circus (96x87cm-38x34in) s. 14-Apr-4 Ansorena, Madrid #274/R est:18000
£14000 $23380 €20440 Les matelots (92x73cm-36x29in) s.d.31 prov. 22-Oct-3 Sotheby's, Olympia #178/R est:15000-20000
£15172 $27310 €22000 Figures (93x73cm-37x29in) s.d.1931. 26-Jan-4 Ansorena, Madrid #890/R est:22000

COSSMANN, Hermann Maurice (1821-1890) French
£2215 $4075 €3300 Cavalier (54x45cm-21x18in) s. lit. 25-Mar-4 Karlheinz Kaupp, Staufen #2387/R est:1600

COSSON, Marcel (1878-1956) French
£753 $1281 €1100 Vase de fleurs (54x67cm-21x26in) s. 9-Nov-3 Eric Pillon, Calais #163/R
£1259 $2140 €1800 At the theatre (24x33cm-9x13in) s. plywood prov. 25-Nov-3 Christie's, Amsterdam #33/R est:2000-3000
£1275 $2372 €1900 Le foyer (27x35cm-11x14in) s. panel. 2-Mar-4 Artcurial Briest, Paris #200 est:2000-3000
£1310 $2410 €1913 Reclining nude (46x60cm-18x24in) s. 14-Jun-4 Philippe Schuler, Zurich #4340 est:2000-2500 (S.FR 3000)
£1333 $2427 €2000 Ballerines dans la loge (55x45cm-22x18in) s. panel. 4-Jul-4 Eric Pillon, Calais #178/R

£1525	$2546	€2150	Dans la loge (46x27cm-18x11in) s. 20-Jun-3 Drouot Estimations, Paris #169 est:1800-2000
£1549	$2510	€2200	Le bas vert (15x21cm-6x8in) s. panel. 5-Aug-3 Tajan, Paris #18/R est:2500-3000
£1667	$3000	€2500	Au cirque (33x41cm-13x16in) s. panel. 26-Apr-4 Tajan, Paris #171/R est:2800-3000
£1667	$3033	€2500	Dans la loge (46x38cm-18x15in) s. 4-Jul-4 Eric Pillon, Calais #180/R
£1711	$3147	€2600	Dans la loge (33x41cm-13x16in) s. panel. 28-Jun-4 Joron-Derem, Paris #175 est:2500-3000
£1840	$3000	€2686	Deux danseuses (46x38cm-18x15in) s. paper on masonite. 25-Sep-3 Christie's, Rockefeller NY #534/R est:3000-5000
£1842	$3389	€2800	Foyer de l'opera (38x46cm-15x18in) s. wood. 28-Jun-4 Joron-Derem, Paris #176/R est:2500-3000
£2000	$3340	€2920	Nu entoure de danseuses (46x38cm-18x15in) s. panel prov. 22-Oct-3 Sotheby's, Olympia #43/R est:2000-2500
£2041	$3653	€3000	Loge (33x41cm-13x16in) s. panel. 19-Mar-4 Millon & Associes, Paris #93/R est:2000-3000
£2133	$3926	€3200	Ballerines de l'Opera (39x46cm-15x18in) s. isorel prov. 8-Jun-4 Artcurial Briest, Paris #162/R est:3000-4000
£2303	$4237	€3500	Danseuses au tambourin (50x61cm-20x24in) 24-Jun-4 Claude Boisgirard, Paris #15/R est:3500-4000
£2517	$4204	€3650	Le foyer de l'opera (38x46cm-15x18in) s. panel. 17-Nov-3 Delorme & Bocage, Paris #151 est:3000-3500
£2778	$4639	€4000	Aux courses. s. 25-Oct-3 Dianous, Marseille #411
£2817	$4873	€4000	Ballerines (46x37cm-18x15in) s. panel. 14-Dec-3 Eric Pillon, Calais #149/R
£2817	$4535	€4000	Dans la loge (41x33cm-16x13in) s. panel. 22-Aug-3 Deauville, France #115/R est:4000-5000
£2817	$4535	€4000	Avant le bal (54x46cm-21x18in) s. panel. 22-Aug-3 Deauville, France #116/R est:4000-5000
£2877	$4890	€4200	Dejeuner dans le jardin de l'auberge (27x35cm-11x14in) s. panel. 9-Nov-3 Eric Pillon, Calais #122/R
£2945	$4624	€4300	Foyer de l'Opera (33x46cm-13x18in) s. prov. 20-Apr-3 Deauville, France #133/R est:4300-5000
£2953	$5286	€4400	Le foyer de l'opera (38x46cm-15x18in) s. 25-May-4 Chambelland & Giafferi, Paris #98/R est:2500-3000
£3000	$5460	€4500	Ballerines devant la coiffeuse (73x60cm-29x24in) s. panel. 4-Jul-4 Eric Pillon, Calais #177/R
£3147	$5350	€4500	La loge (83x54cm-33x21in) s. 27-Nov-3 Millon & Associes, Paris #227/R est:4500-6000
£3265	$5845	€4800	Danseuses (54x65cm-21x26in) s. 19-Mar-4 Oger, Dumont, Paris #10 est:3000-4000
£3356	$5940	€5000	Trois danseuses au repos (60x73cm-24x29in) s. 27-Apr-4 Artcurial Briest, Paris #166/R est:6000-8000
£3400	$6256	€4964	Au casino (38x55cm-15x22in) s. prov. 24-Mar-4 Sotheby's, Olympia #53/R est:3000-4000
£3473	$5799	€5000	Foyer apres la repetition (58x73cm-23x29in) s. isorel panel. 21-Oct-3 Artcurial Briest, Paris #207/R est:5000-6000
£3497	$5944	€5000	Foyer de l'Opera (61x73cm-24x29in) s. 28-Nov-3 Drouot Estimations, Paris #164 est:1900-2000
£3521	$6092	€5000	Ballerine a l'opera (35x24cm-14x9in) s. panel. 10-Dec-3 Ferri, Paris #31 est:4500-5000
£3800	$7068	€5548	Carriage ride (46x55cm-18x22in) s. panel. 4-Mar-4 Christie's, London #436/R est:2000-3000
£3800	$6992	€5548	Dans les coulisses (38x55cm-15x22in) s. prov. 24-Mar-4 Sotheby's, Olympia #52/R est:3000-4000
£4000	$6680	€5840	At the races (54x65cm-21x26in) s. 22-Oct-3 Sotheby's, Olympia #97/R est:4000-6000
£4225	$7310	€6000	Le foyer de l'opera (23x32cm-9x13in) s. 10-Dec-3 Ferri, Paris #30/R est:6500-7000
£4832	$8988	€7200	Les voiles blanches (54x73cm-21x29in) s. 2-Mar-4 Artcurial Briest, Paris #199/R est:4000-6000
£6000	$11160	€8760	At the races (46x37cm-18x15in) s. one panel one board pair. 4-Mar-4 Christie's, London #437/R est:3000-5000
Works on paper			
£355	$592	€500	Assemblee orientale (21x30cm-8x12in) s. d.verso prov. 16-Jun-3 Gros & Delettrez, Paris #530/R
£772	$1382	€1150	Venise (26x38cm-10x15in) s. W/C. 25-May-4 Chambelland & Giafferi, Paris #100/R
£1333	$2453	€2000	La ballerine de dos (44x60cm-17x24in) s. pastel prov. 11-Jun-4 Pierre Berge, Paris #196/R est:2000-2500

COSTA BEIRO, Alfonso (1943-) Spanish

£493	$789	€700	Untitled (40x28cm-16x11in) s. board. 16-Sep-3 Segre, Madrid #152/R
£1014	$1784	€1500	Team (80x100cm-31x39in) s.d.1974 s.i.d.verso. 18-May-4 Segre, Madrid #223/R est:1500
£3061	$5571	€4500	Dancer (200x150cm-79x59in) s. s.d.1978 verso lit. 3-Feb-4 Segre, Madrid #193/R est:5600
£3333	$5500	€4800	Two figures (116x90cm-46x35in) s. s.verso. 2-Jul-3 Ansorena, Madrid #873/R

COSTA VILLA, Jose (1953-) Spanish

Works on paper			
£414	$745	€600	View of Girona (45x54cm-18x21in) s. mixed media on canvas. 26-Jan-4 Ansorena, Madrid #874/R

COSTA, Catharina da (fl.1712-1730) British

Works on paper			
£778	$1400	€1136	Woman addressing a seated nude in a classical landscape (24x27cm-9x11in) s.d.1722 bodycol vellum. 22-Jan-4 Christie's, Rockefeller NY #256/R

COSTA, Claudio (1942-) Italian

Sculpture			
£1486	$2616	€2200	Mask (78x34cm-31x13in) s.i.d.1987 verso wood iron. 22-May-4 Galleria Pananti, Florence #363/R est:2000-3000

COSTA, Emanuele (1833-1913) French/Italian

£389	$650	€568	Fishermen, beach at Capri (28x43cm-11x17in) s. 29-Jun-3 William Jenack, New York #169
£486	$900	€710	Still life with chocolate pot and vase. Blue and white pitcher (38x28cm-15x11in) s. two board prov. 15-Jul-4 Doyle, New York #25/R
Works on paper			
£1000	$1820	€1500	Rue animee du vieux Menton (38x22cm-15x9in) s. W/C. 29-Jun-4 Gioffredo, Nice #2/R

COSTA, Giovanni (1833-1903) Italian

£2797	$4755	€4000	Girl with canary (63x50cm-25x20in) s. 24-Nov-3 Dorotheum, Vienna #43/R est:4500-5500
Prints			
£5882	$10000	€8588	Young Italian beauty with a plate of oranges (74x58cm-29x23in) silkscreen. 29-Oct-3 Christie's, Rockefeller NY #224/R est:15000-20000

COSTA, Giovanni (attrib) (1833-1903) Italian

£900	$1638	€1314	Figures with boats moored on a beach, possibly Capri (24x31cm-9x12in) canvas on card prov. 16-Jun-4 Bonhams, New Bond Street #81/R
£1408	$2338	€2000	The red cart (12x21cm-5x8in) sig. panel. 11-Jun-3 Christie's, Rome #156/R
£3333	$6133	€5000	View of the Roman countryside (31x90cm-12x35in) s. canvas on board. 10-Jun-4 Christie's, Rome #148/R est:4500-5500

COSTA, John da (1866-1931) British

£380	$635	€555	Landscape, Clanfield, Oxfordshire (46x56cm-18x22in) 21-Oct-3 Gorringes, Lewes #2005/R
£600	$1002	€876	Landscape, Clanfield, Oxfordshire (48x58cm-19x23in) 21-Oct-3 Gorringes, Lewes #1987/R

COSTA, Lorenzo (1460-1535) Italian

£230263	$423684	€350000	Madonna and Child with robin (39x30cm-15x12in) panel. 25-Jun-4 Piasa, Paris #33/R est:100000-150000

COSTA, Milton da (1915-1988) Brazilian

£1282	$2269	€1923	Landscape near Santo Antonio de Padua (27x35cm-11x14in) s.d.1943 panel. 27-Apr-4 Bolsa de Arte, Rio de Janeiro #19/R (B.R 7000)
£2106	$3728	€3159	Reclining female nude (16x22cm-6x9in) s.d.1968 verso. 27-Apr-4 Bolsa de Arte, Rio de Janeiro #75/R (B.R 11500)
Works on paper			
£4579	$8379	€6869	Head (18x11cm-7x4in) s.d.1954 gouache. 6-Jul-4 Bolsa de Arte, Rio de Janeiro #10/R (B.R 25000)

COSTA, Navarro da (1883-1931) Portuguese

£1074	$1922	€1600	German steam boat in Naples harbour (38x27cm-15x11in) s.i.d.1915 panel. 31-May-4 Cabral Moncada Leiloes, Lisbon #84/R est:800-1200
Works on paper			
£366	$670	€549	Grande Canale, Venice (27x38cm-11x15in) s.i.d.28 Jun 1923 mixed media. 6-Jul-4 Bolsa de Arte, Rio de Janeiro #48/R (B.R 2000)

COSTA, Nino Giovanni (1826-1903) Italian

£12081	$22591	€18000	Mountains near Lucca (16x29cm-6x11in) s. i.verso board exhib.lit. 25-Feb-4 Porro, Milan #7/R est:18000-20000

COSTA, O (?) ?

£2432	$4500	€3551	Untitled (48x64cm-19x25in) s. 13-Mar-4 DeFina, Austinburg #580/R est:2000-4000

COSTA, Olga (1913-1993) Mexican/German

Works on paper			
£8824	$15000	€12883	Banistas (34x25cm-13x10in) s. gouache executed c.1945 prov.exhib. 19-Nov-3 Sotheby's, New York #103/R est:18000-22000

COSTA, Oreste (1851-?) Italian

£2095	$3750	€3059	Still lifes (81x64cm-32x25in) s.i.d.1878 oval pair prov. 6-May-4 Shannon's, Milford #206/R est:4000-6000

COSTA, Peter Paul (1863-1919) Austrian

Sculpture			
£1189	$2021	€1700	Adoration of the shepherds (51x61x4cm-20x24x2in) s.i.d.1918 painted wooden relief. 20-Nov-3 Dorotheum, Salzburg #603/R est:2000-2600

COSTA, Richard (19/20th C) British?

Works on paper			
£500	$865	€730	Portrait of a lady, three-quarter length turned to the left (101x72cm-40x28in) s.i.d.1917 oval. 9-Dec-3 Rosebery Fine Art, London #651

COSTA, Tomas (1882-1940) Portuguese

£1678	$3003	€2500	Algarve, Vau Beach (37x55cm-15x22in) s. 31-May-4 Cabral Moncada Leiloes, Lisbon #78/R est:2500-3750

COSTA, Tur (1926-) Spanish

£851	$1379	€1200	Untitled (130x97cm-51x38in) s.d.1969. 20-May-3 Segre, Madrid #197/R

COSTANTINI, Giovanni (1872-1947) Italian

£1690	$2806	€2400	Le spia (73x120cm-29x47in) s. 11-Jun-3 Christie's, Rome #21 est:1500-2000

COSTANTINO, Massimo (1955-) Italian
£287 $527 €430 Ground zero (80x60cm-31x24in) s. acrylic oil painted 2001. 12-Jun-4 Meeting Art, Vercelli #15
£333 $613 €500 She is asleep (70x70cm-28x28in) s.d.2003 oil acrylic. 12-Jun-4 Meeting Art, Vercelli #443/R

COSTARE, J (19/20th C) German?
£1181 $1924 €1700 Two monks in monastery kitchen (74x100cm-29x39in) s. 24-Sep-3 Neumeister, Munich #408/R est:1000

COSTE, Jean Baptiste (18/19th C) French
Works on paper
£863 $1416 €1200 Vue d'un arsenal (42x53cm-17x21in) s. pen Indian ink grey wash W/C. 6-Jun-3 Maigret, Paris #59/R

COSTE, Waldemar (1887-1948) German
£322 $547 €460 Portrait of artist's wife (75x60cm-30x24in) s.d.1931 panel. 29-Nov-3 Arnold, Frankfurt #110
£694 $1097 €1000 Workers with ship's propeller (60x65cm-24x26in) i. verso panel. 6-Sep-3 Schopman, Hamburg #834/R

COSTELLO, Eileen (1911-1976) Irish
£403 $632 €580 Landscape between showers (38x53cm-15x21in) s. board. 26-Aug-3 James Adam, Dublin #161/R
Works on paper
£605 $1114 €920 Through a window (57x36cm-22x14in) s. gouache prov. 22-Jun-4 De Veres Art Auctions, Dublin #28/R

COSTER, Adam de (circle) (1586-1643) Flemish
£7328 $13483 €10699 Young singer with candle (60x50cm-24x20in) 26-Mar-4 Koller, Zurich #3050/R est:8000-12000 (S.FR 17000)

COSTETTI, Giovanni (1875-1949) Italian
£3311 $6026 €5000 Christ praying (124x77cm-49x30in) s.d.1917. 21-Jun-4 Pandolfini, Florence #168/R est:5500-6500
£3521 $6092 €5000 Portrait of man (50x30cm-20x12in) s.d.1923 card. 9-Dec-3 Pandolfini, Florence #405/R est:5500-6000
£4507 $7797 €6400 Old woman. s.d.1909 on terracotta prov. 9-Dec-3 Pandolfini, Florence #388/R est:6500-7000
£7241 $12093 €10500 Portrait of lady (79x59cm-31x23in) s. board. 14-Nov-3 Farsetti, Prato #581/R est:7600-8600
Works on paper
£423 $731 €600 Profile of man (28x21cm-11x8in) s. pastel pencil. 9-Dec-3 Pandolfini, Florence #317/R
£845 $1462 €1200 Face of man (27x20cm-11x8in) s. pastel. 9-Dec-3 Pandolfini, Florence #315/R est:950-1000

COSTI (1906-) Greek
Sculpture
£46980 $87384 €70000 Comedia del Arte (197cm-78in) plaster rectangular base four prov.lit. 4-Mar-4 Tajan, Paris #115/R est:75000-85000

COSTIGAN, John E (1888-1972) American
£1599 $2750 €2335 Winter along the brook (26x40cm-10x16in) s. s.i.verso canvasboard. 3-Dec-3 Doyle, New York #242/R est:3000-5000
£3198 $5500 €4669 Sun bathers (26x40cm-10x16in) s. i.verso canvas on board. 3-Dec-3 Doyle, New York #246/R est:3000-5000
£4469 $8000 €6525 Figure group (61x89cm-24x35in) s. exhib. 26-May-4 Doyle, New York #102/R est:12000-15000
£5587 $10000 €8157 Sheep and shepherd in trees (43x43cm-17x17in) s. i.d.1919 verso board. 26-May-4 Doyle, New York #103/R est:6000-9000
£5707 $10500 €8332 Carnival (71x88cm-28x35in) s. prov. 8-Jun-4 Bonhams & Butterfields, San Francisco #4115/R est:15000-20000
£5814 $10000 €8488 Bathers (60x75cm-24x30in) s. prov. 3-Dec-3 Doyle, New York #241/R est:6000-8000
£7514 $13000 €10970 Winter watering (91x114cm-36x45in) s.d.1934 prov. 10-Dec-3 Bonhams & Butterfields, San Francisco #6036/R est:5000-7000
Works on paper
£377 $600 €550 Landscape study (51x61cm-20x24in) s. W/C. 4-May-3 William Jenack, New York #217
£838 $1400 €1223 War Dog Batallion (46x58cm-18x23in) s. ink W/C prov. 15-Nov-3 Illustration House, New York #5/R
£1512 $2600 €2208 Young girl and her doll (74x66cm-29x26in) s. gouache. 7-Dec-3 Freeman, Philadelphia #145 est:1500-2500

COSTIGLIOLO, Jose P (1902-1985) Uruguayan
£518 $850 €756 Abstract cup (43x33cm-17x13in) s.d.1949. 3-Jun-3 Galeria y Remates, Montevideo #13
£529 $900 €772 Squares and rectangles (71x71cm-28x28in) s. 25-Nov-3 Galeria y Remates, Montevideo #84
£1059 $1800 €1546 Abstract (60x32cm-24x13in) s. cardboard. 25-Nov-3 Galeria y Remates, Montevideo #83/R
£1080 $1900 €1577 Volumes (49x41cm-19x16in) s.d.46 s.d.verso. 5-Jan-4 Galeria y Remates, Montevideo #14/R est:1800-2500

COSWAY, Richard (1742-1821) British
£2000 $3700 €2920 Portrait of a lady (57x55cm-22x22in) painted oval. 10-Mar-4 Sotheby's, Olympia #10/R est:2000-3000
Miniatures
£800 $1432 €1168 Lady wearing a feathered hat, possibly Lady Jenny Beresford (9x7cm-4x3in) s.d.1785 oval. 7-Jan-4 George Kidner, Lymington #217/R
£1200 $2040 €1752 Lady (4cm-2in circular) gold frame. 18-Nov-3 Bonhams, New Bond Street #63/R est:800-1200
£1486 $2750 €2170 Portrait of a gentleman (8x8cm-3x3in) exec.c.1786 oval. 12-Mar-4 Du Mouchelle, Detroit #2015/R est:700-1200
£1700 $2890 €2482 Charles Ingoldsby Paulet (5cm-2in) oval prov. 18-Nov-3 Bonhams, New Bond Street #103/R est:700-900
£2000 $3460 €2920 Young gentleman (8cm-3in) s.d.1785 verso oval. 9-Dec-3 Christie's, London #155 est:2000-3000
£2400 $4320 €3504 Lieutnenant John Mackintosh (6cm-2in) gold frame oval exhib.lit. 22-Apr-4 Bonhams, New Bond Street #117/R est:3000-5000
£3000 $5400 €4380 Mary, Countess Ducie (8cm-3in) gold frame oval prov.exhib. 22-Apr-4 Bonhams, New Bond Street #95/R est:2500-3500
£3200 $5760 €4672 Anne Sawbridge (4cm-2in) gold plated locket frame oval prov.exhib.lit. 22-Apr-4 Bonhams, New Bond Street #51/R est:2000-3000
£3500 $6055 €5110 Lady Margaret Cameron (7cm-3in) s.d.1790 gold frame oval. 9-Dec-3 Christie's, London #170/R est:3000-5000
£3800 $6840 €5548 Major Gale, in a grey coat (5cm-2in) gold fausse-montre frame oval prov.exhib.lit. 22-Apr-4 Bonhams, New Bond Street #73/R est:4000-6000
£3800 $6992 €5548 Alexander Hume. Anna Hume (3cm-1in) gold locket frame pair. 24-Jun-4 Bonhams, New Bond Street #46/R est:2000-3000
£4054 $7500 €5919 Mrs Dawson Damer (5x5cm-2x2in) exec.c.1790 oval. 12-Mar-4 Du Mouchelle, Detroit #2016/R est:2000-3000
£4500 $8100 €6570 Lady wearing a white dress and pearls (6cm-2in) mono.verso gold fausse-montre frame oval exhib.lit. 22-Apr-4 Bonhams, New Bond Street #71/R est:5000-7000
£5000 $9000 €7300 Nobleman, possibly Douglas, 8th Duke of Hamilton (5cm-2in) i.verso gilt metal frame oval exhib. 22-Apr-4 Bonhams, New Bond Street #74/R est:3000-5000
£5500 $9900 €8030 Mrs Phillipson (7cm-3in) gold frame oval exhib.lit. 22-Apr-4 Bonhams, New Bond Street #112/R est:5000-7000
£6000 $10800 €8760 Gentleman in a blue coat with large brass buttons (8cm-3in) mono.verso gold frame oval exhib. 22-Apr-4 Bonhams, New Bond Street #88/R est:3000-5000
£6500 $11700 €9490 Augustus Duke of Sussex (8cm-3in) gold frame oval exhib.lit. 22-Apr-4 Bonhams, New Bond Street #90/R est:3000-5000
£7500 $13425 €10950 Sir Peter Paker Bt, in blue coat (5cm-2in) gold frame seed pearls blue white enamel border prov. 25-May-4 Christie's, London #108/R est:3000-5000
£8000 $14400 €11680 Mrs Fitzherbert (10cm-4in) i.verso gold frame oval exhib.lit. 22-Apr-4 Bonhams, New Bond Street #100/R est:6000-8000
£9400 $17296 €13724 Dr. Stephen Lushington as a boy (5cm-2in) gilt metal frame easel back prov. 24-Jun-4 Bonhams, New Bond Street #89/R est:3000-5000
£9500 $17480 €13870 Lord Henry Fitzgerald, wearing a blue coat (7cm-3in) s.d.1791 verso gold frame. 24-Jun-4 Bonhams, New Bond Street #105/R est:3000-5000
£18000 $32400 €26280 Infancy, Lady Caroline Lamb (8cm-3in) s.d.1787 verso gold fausse-montre frame oval prov.exhib. 22-Apr-4 Bonhams, New Bond Street #110/R est:20000-30000
£21000 $37800 €30660 Lady Elizabeth Bingham (7cm-3in) i.verso gold frame oval exhib.lit. 22-Apr-4 Bonhams, New Bond Street #111/R est:6000-8000
£25000 $46000 €36500 Mrs Parson wearing straw bonnet trimmed with blue ribbons (7cm-3in) gold frame with silver mounted diamond border prov.exhib.lit. 24-Jun-4 Bonhams, New Bond Street #106/R est:8000-12000
£28000 $50400 €40880 George IV, as Prince of Wales (8cm-3in) s.d.1795 verso pearl gold frame oval prov.exhib. 22-Apr-4 Bonhams, New Bond Street #99/R est:10000-15000
Works on paper
£800 $1480 €1168 Portrait of Mrs Woodforde and her son (29x21cm-11x8in) pencil. 10-Mar-4 Sotheby's, Olympia #13/R
£1300 $2327 €1898 Couple embracing with parrot above (15x10cm-6x4in) W/C over pencil. 22-Mar-4 Bonhams & Brooks, Norfolk #73/R est:600-800
£3600 $6624 €5256 St. George and the Dragon. Madonna and Child (32x26cm-13x10in) pen ink set of three different sizes. 26-Mar-4 Sotheby's, London #95/R est:2000-3000
£12000 $20400 €17520 Sp. (28cm-11in) graphite red chk wash prov. 18-Nov-3 Bonhams, New Bond Street #122/R est:4000-6000

COSWAY, Richard (after) (1742-1821) British
Miniatures
£3200 $5760 €4672 Lady, tradionally called Mrs Mary Robinson, nee Darby, Perdita (2cm-1in) col enamel diamond ruby floral border oval exhib.lit. 22-Apr-4 Bonhams, New Bond Street #31/R est:1000-1500

COSWAY, Richard (attrib) (1742-1821) British
£528 $850 €771 Portrait of john, Eldest son of Philip Egerton (36x26cm-14x10in) i. verso pencil. 17-Aug-3 Bonhams & Butterfields, San Francisco #5780

COSYN, Pieter (1630-1667) Dutch
£2447 $4209 €3500 Wooded river landscape with figures near a village (45x60cm-18x24in) panel prov.lit. 7-Dec-3 Sotheby's, Amsterdam #540/R
£11000 $20130 €16060 View of Leiden, with figures resting in the foreground (47x65cm-19x26in) init. panel. 6-Jul-4 Sotheby's, Olympia #476/R est:6000-8000

COSYNS, Gies (1920-1997) Belgian
£302 $553 €450 Paysage d'hiver (54x80cm-21x31in) s. 8-Jul-4 Campo, Vlaamse Kaai #54
£338 $595 €500 Winter landscape (50x40cm-20x16in) s.d.1962. 24-May-4 Bernaerts, Antwerp #563
£378 $677 €560 Vue de la mer du Nord (50x72cm-20x28in) s. 10-May-4 Horta, Bruxelles #489
£403 $721 €600 Paysage d'automne (45x40cm-18x16in) s. 25-May-4 Campo & Campo, Antwerp #47
£667 $1207 €1000 Paysage des Ardennes Flamandes (60x70cm-24x28in) s. cardboard. 30-Mar-4 Campo & Campo, Antwerp #52
£671 $1248 €1000 Landscape at Kwaremont (50x60cm-20x24in) s. 8-Mar-4 Bernaerts, Antwerp #839/R
£1241 $2061 €1800 Landscape (58x69cm-23x27in) cardboard painted 1953. 6-Oct-3 Amberes, Antwerp #213
£1549 $2680 €2200 Winter landscape (85x122cm-33x48in) s.d.1964. 13-Dec-3 De Vuyst, Lokeren #66/R est:1900-2400

COT, Pierre Auguste (1837-1883) French
£530 $970 €800 Portrait de Madame Michel Heine, vue de profil (53x42cm-21x17in) s.i.d.1878 oval. 7-Apr-4 Libert, Castor, Paris #55/R
£685 $1164 €1000 L'orage (33x24cm-13x9in) s. 8-Nov-3 Gerard, Besancon #42
£2400 $4344 €3600 La balancoire (33x24cm-13x9in) s. 3-Apr-4 Gerard, Besancon #41
£23529 $40000 €34352 Pause for thought (66x40cm-26x16in) s. 28-Oct-3 Sotheby's, New York #51/R est:40000-60000

COTANDA, Vicente Nicolau (1852-1898) Spanish
£1351 $2378 €2000 Lady with hat (39x19cm-15x7in) s. board. 18-May-4 Segre, Madrid #45/R est:1200
£3516 $6400 €5133 Sharing the light (66x41cm-26x16in) s.d.89. 7-Feb-4 Neal Auction Company, New Orleans #398/R est:5000-7000

COTE, Bruno (1940-) Canadian
£267 $461 €390 Sunset Sagauney River, Quebec (76x102cm-30x40in) s. 9-Dec-3 Maynards, Vancouver #236 (C.D 600)
£480 $878 €701 Ste-Rose du Nord (30x35cm-12x14in) s. board. 1-Jun-4 Joyner Waddington, Toronto #236/R (C.D 1200)
£640 $1171 €934 Lumiere sur la montagne (60x76cm-24x30in) s. board prov. 1-Jun-4 Joyner Waddington, Toronto #261/R est:2000-3000 (C.D 1600)
£766 $1302 €1118 Foret en fete (51x61cm-20x24in) s. s.i.verso board prov. 23-Nov-3 Levis, Calgary #23/R (C.D 1700)
£804 $1382 €1174 Pied des monts, St Urbain (40x50cm-16x20in) s.d.81. 2-Dec-3 Joyner Waddington, Toronto #300/R est:800-1200 (C.D 1800)
£888 $1608 €1296 Tadoussac (75x102cm-30x40in) s. s.i.d.1992 stretcher. 18-Apr-4 Levis, Calgary #22/R est:2000-2500 (C.D 2150)
£893 $1536 €1304 Ilets - Caribou (50x60cm-20x24in) s. board prov. 2-Dec-3 Joyner Waddington, Toronto #259/R est:1500-2000 (C.D 2000)
£1009 $1664 €1463 Sunrise, Cap aux Oies (61x76cm-24x30in) s. s.d.1992 verso prov. 3-Jul-3 Heffel, Vancouver #7/R est:2250-2750 (C.D 2250)
£1014 $1723 €1480 Sous bois en rouge (50x61cm-20x24in) s. s.i.verso board. 27-Nov-3 Heffel, Vancouver #180/R est:1500-2000 (C.D 2250)
£1464 $2489 €2137 Indian village, Mingan (61x76cm-24x30in) s. s.i.d.1985 verso board. 27-Nov-3 Heffel, Vancouver #89/R est:2000-3000 (C.D 3250)
£1520 $2782 €2219 Cet Automne (120x150cm-47x59in) s. 1-Jun-4 Joyner Waddington, Toronto #268/R est:3000-4000 (C.D 3800)

COTE, Hippolyte (1816-?) French
£559 $934 €800 Jeune fille (32x23cm-13x9in) s.1854 panel. 11-Oct-3 De Vuyst, Lokeren #69

COTER, Colijn de (1455-1540) Flemish
£80000 $138400 €116800 Christ as the man of sorrows (65x43cm-26x17in) oak panel prov.lit. 11-Dec-3 Sotheby's, London #3/R est:80000-120000

COTES, Francis (1726-1770) British
£1944 $3500 €2838 Portrait of Miss Cunningham (63x49cm-25x19in) prov. 21-Jan-4 Doyle, New York #125/R est:4000-6000
£17000 $31280 €24820 Portrait of Lady Anne Windsor, standing landscape (75x62cm-30x24in) bears i. painted oval prov.lit. 26-Mar-4 Sotheby's, London #26/R est:15000-20000
Works on paper
£6000 $10980 €8760 Portrait of Captain Nugent, half-length wearing Van Dyke costume (59x44cm-23x17in) s.i.d.1748 pastel paper on canvas lit. 3-Jun-4 Christie's, London #49/R est:2500-3500

COTES, Francis (attrib) (1726-1770) British
£216 $400 €315 Portrait of a young man (76x64cm-30x25in) i. stretcher. 24-Jan-4 Jeffery Burchard, Florida #82a/R
£2941 $5000 €4294 Portrait of Mary Dering holding a looking glass (102x77cm-40x30in) i.verso. 19-Nov-3 Bonhams & Butterfields, San Francisco #41/R

COTES, Francis (circle) (1726-1770) British
Works on paper
£5000 $9100 €7300 Portrait of Elizabeth Rushout. later Mrs Myddelton (60x48cm-24x19in) pastel. 21-Jun-4 Christie's, London #81/R est:2000-4000

COTES, Samuel (1734-1818) British
Miniatures
£16000 $27680 €23360 Boy (8cm-3in) init.d.1779 oval. 9-Dec-3 Christie's, London #113/R est:3000-5000

COTMAN, Frederick George (1850-1920) British
£700 $1162 €1022 Boy playing with a model boat on a pond (26x20cm-10x8in) s.d.1877. 1-Oct-3 Woolley & Wallis, Salisbury #241/R
£950 $1720 €1387 Shoreline at dusk (30x48cm-12x19in) s. indis d. 16-Apr-4 Keys, Aylsham #682/R
£950 $1748 €1387 Young boy sailing a toy boat at riverside (10x7cm-4x3in) s.d.1877. 11-Jun-4 Keys, Aylsham #605/R
Works on paper
£320 $589 €467 Houses on the riverbank at Strand on the Green (22x38cm-9x15in) s.d.1910 W/C. 25-Mar-4 Christie's, Kensington #207/R
£2100 $3843 €3066 Sun Inn, Dedham (63x49cm-25x19in) s.d.1884 W/C. 7-Apr-4 Bonhams, Bury St Edmunds #412/R est:400-600

COTMAN, John Joseph (1814-1878) British
Works on paper
£360 $644 €526 Sunset over Whittingham, Near Norwich (25x71cm-10x28in) s.i. 6-Jan-4 Gildings, Market Harborough #433/R
£540 $929 €788 Sunset at Costessey (38x43cm-15x17in) s.d.1874 W/C. 5-Dec-3 Keys, Aylsham #564/R
£1000 $1850 €1460 River Yare (23x69cm-9x27in) s. indis d. W/C. 13-Feb-4 Keys, Aylsham #631/R est:1000-1500
£1550 $2852 €2263 Thorpe watering (17x29cm-7x11in) s.d.1876 W/C. 11-Jun-4 Keys, Aylsham #601/R est:1500-2000
£2600 $4108 €3770 Ransom's timber yard on the Wensum looking towards Foundry Bridge, Norwich (32x49cm-13x19in) s.d.1869 W/C over pencil pair. 3-Sep-3 Bonhams, Bury St Edmunds #321/R est:2000-3000

COTMAN, John Joseph (attrib) (1814-1878) British
Works on paper
£300 $555 €438 Norfolk landscape with Norwich in distance (36x66cm-14x26in) W/C. 13-Feb-4 Keys, Aylsham #632

COTMAN, John Sell (1782-1842) British
£2817 $4873 €4000 River landscape (21x31cm-8x12in) 13-Dec-3 Lempertz, Koln #10/R est:4000
Works on paper
£260 $434 €380 Coastal scene (8x15cm-3x6in) pencil dr. 14-Oct-3 David Lay, Penzance #377
£610 $1153 €891 A cavalier - after Van Dyck (28x22cm-11x9in) pencil chk W/C prov. 17-Feb-4 Rosebery Fine Art, London #565/R
£900 $1656 €1314 Yorkshire manor house (13x30cm-5x12in) pencil W/C exhib. 25-Mar-4 Christie's, Kensington #30/R
£2400 $4080 €3504 Mill on the Norfolk Coast (18x25cm-7x10in) s.i. pencil sketch. 30-Oct-3 Duke & Son, Dorchester #55/R est:500-1000
£3200 $5344 €4672 Gate house, Thornton Abbey, Humberside (32x24cm-13x9in) s. i.verso pencil. 16-Oct-3 Christie's, Kensington #49/R est:1000-2000
£4200 $7140 €6132 Figure on a bridge below cottages, Wales (17x28cm-7x11in) pencil W/C prov. 20-Nov-3 Christie's, London #45/R est:2000-3000
£5300 $9699 €7738 Leigh High woods (32x47cm-13x19in) i. verso W/C. 10-Jun-4 Neales, Nottingham #557/R est:2000-2500
£6200 $10540 €9052 Abbatial House, Abbey of St Ouen, Rouen (41x56cm-16x22in) s.d.1824 pencil W/C htd. bodycol scratching out prov.exhib.lit. 20-Nov-3 Christie's, London #88/R est:8000-12000

COTMAN, John Sell (attrib) (1782-1842) British
Works on paper
£350 $641 €511 Harlech Castle (69x119cm-27x47in) i. pencil htd white. 28-Jul-4 Mallams, Oxford #131/R

COTMAN, Miles Edmund (1810-1858) British
Works on paper
£550 $1012 €803 Extensive landscape with figures and sheep (6x11cm-2x4in) W/C. 11-Jun-4 Keys, Aylsham #579/R
£700 $1295 €1022 Shipping in a breeze (22x34cm-9x13in) W/C. 9-Mar-4 Bonhams, New Bond Street #46/R

COTMAN, Miles Edmund (attrib) (1810-1858) British
£1104 $1800 €1612 Fishing boats under storm clouds (38x51cm-15x20in) indis.i. on stretcher. 24-Sep-3 Doyle, New York #21 est:1000-1500
Works on paper
£300 $552 €438 Figure before a village inn (8x11cm-3x4in) monotone W/C. 11-Jun-4 Keys, Aylsham #574

COTTA, Heinrich (19th C) German
£307 $564 €460 Portrait of Johann Ferdinand Schilling (38x31cm-15x12in) i.d.1839 verso. 11-Jun-4 Wendl, Rudolstadt #3989/R

COTTAAR, Piet (1878-1950) Dutch
£500 $895 €750 Still life of various fruit, Cologne jar and book (58x97cm-23x38in) s. 11-May-4 Vendu Notarishuis, Rotterdam #40
£594 $950 €867 Riches of Holland. s. 20-Sep-3 Harvey Clar, Oakland #1361
£667 $1200 €1000 Pink flowers in glass vase (101x151cm-40x59in) s. lit. 22-Apr-4 Allgauer, Kempten #3506/R

COTTAVOZ, Andre (1922-) French
£302 $561 €450 Genes, no 3 (17x20cm-7x8in) s. 2-Mar-4 Artcurial Briest, Paris #241
£336 $625 €500 Plaine de Cortona (22x32cm-9x13in) s. 2-Mar-4 Artcurial Briest, Paris #243
£436 $811 €650 Bles rouges (19x22cm-7x9in) s.d.61 s.i.d.1961 verso. 2-Mar-4 Artcurial Briest, Paris #239
£537 $999 €800 Rome, no 5 (22x32cm-9x13in) s.d.61 s.i.verso. 2-Mar-4 Artcurial Briest, Paris #242
£629 $1051 €900 Campagne a Vallauris (18x23cm-7x9in) s. 25-Jun-3 Blanchet, Paris #86/R
£800 $1456 €1200 View of Venice (22x33cm-9x13in) s.d.1984. 4-Jul-4 Eric Pillon, Calais #269/R
£933 $1699 €1400 Nature morte (24x33cm-9x13in) s. 4-Jul-4 Eric Pillon, Calais #268/R
£1007 $1873 €1500 Les soucis (33x22cm-13x9in) s.d.60 s.i.d.5-60 verso. 2-Mar-4 Artcurial Briest, Paris #245 est:800-1000
£1408 $2437 €2000 Portail rouge (50x73cm-20x29in) s. 14-Dec-3 Eric Pillon, Calais #273/R
£1958 $3329 €2800 Quais de Saone (33x55cm-13x22in) s.d.60 s.i.d.4-60 verso. 28-Nov-3 Blanchet, Paris #178/R est:1500-2000
£2113 $3782 €3000 Nature morte au pot blanc (37x60cm-15x24in) s. 11-Jan-4 Rouillac, Vendome #318
£2238 $3849 €3200 Nature morte grise (60x92cm-24x36in) s.d.77 s.i.d.verso prov. 2-Dec-3 Sotheby's, Amsterdam #195/R est:2500-3500
£2797 $4755 €4000 Les baux de Provence (54x65cm-21x26in) s. s.i.verso. 28-Nov-3 Blanchet, Paris #183/R est:4000-5000
Works on paper
£455 $800 €664 Jardin (53x74cm-21x29in) s.c.92 W/C textured pressed paper. 23-May-4 Hindman, Chicago #1060/R

COTTET, Charles (1863-1924) French
£300 $537 €450 Cote sauvage aux environs de Quibron (36x53cm-14x21in) s. canvas on cardboard. 12-May-4 Brissoneau, France #97
£429 $686 €622 Beach (49x65cm-19x26in) s. 15-May-3 Stuker, Bern #1130/R (S.FR 900)

£800 $1432 €1200 Bord de mer anime en Bretagne (41x55cm-16x22in) s. cardboard. 16-May-4 Thierry & Lannon, Brest #302
£1119 $1869 €1600 Lever du soleil (32x42cm-13x17in) s.d.1894 panel. 29-Jun-3 Eric Pillon, Calais #142/R
£1127 $1870 €1600 Venise au soleil couchant (34x52cm-13x20in) s. cardboard. 11-Jun-3 Delorme & Bocage, Paris #51/R est:1200-1500
£1330 $2381 €1942 Red sails in the lagoon, Venice (28x36cm-11x14in) s. canvas on cardboard. 25-May-4 Bukowskis, Stockholm #379/R est:12000-15000 (S.KR 18000)
£1457 $2725 €2200 Notre Dame de la Joie (55x83cm-22x33in) s. board. 24-Jul-4 Thierry & Lannon, Brest #138/R est:2000-3000
£1477 $2702 €2200 Quatre Bretonnes dans un paysage (23x29cm-9x11in) s.d.1905 paper. 7-Jul-4 Artcurial Briest, Paris #82 est:1000-1200
£1882 $3200 €2748 Red sailing boats (54x90cm-21x35in) s. cardboard. 25-Nov-3 Galeria y Remates, Montevideo #186/R
£2148 $4016 €3200 Douarnenistes. 24-Feb-4 Thierry & Lannon, Brest #370a
£2535 $4437 €3600 Cote rocheuse en Bretagne (54x74cm-21x29in) s. 21-Dec-3 Thierry & Lannon, Brest #300/R est:3500-4000
£5603 $9357 €7900 Cafe des Nattes, Sidi Bou Said (60x49cm-24x19in) s. 20-Jun-3 Drouot Estimations, Paris #39/R est:1200-1500
£9091 $15636 €13000 Bateaux de peche (74x110cm-29x43in) s.d.1903 cardboard. 7-Dec-3 Livinec, Gaudcheau & Jezequel, Rennes #77a

COTTIER, Maurice (1822-1881) French
£862 $1440 €1250 Jeune fille a la fontaine (46x37cm-18x15in) s. 9-Jul-3 Peschetau-Badin Godeau & Leroy, Paris #13/R
£2069 $3455 €3000 Oriental au bord d'une fontaine (46x38cm-18x15in) s.d.1848. 9-Jul-3 Peschetau-Badin Godeau & Leroy, Paris #14 est:1200-1500

COTTIN, Eugène (1840-1902) French
£1259 $2165 €1800 Le poulailler (20x15cm-8x6in) s. 7-Dec-3 Osenat, Fontainebleau #51 est:2000-2200
£6200 $10292 €9052 Feeding time (136x191cm-54x75in) s. 1-Oct-3 Sotheby's, Olympia #207/R est:3000-5000

COTTINGHAM, Grenville (c.1945-) British
£280 $512 €409 St Ives (59x73cm-23x29in) s. 3-Jun-4 Lane, Penzance #169

COTTINGHAM, Lewis Nockalls (1787-1847) British
Works on paper
£500 $860 €730 Plans, elevations and sections of pineries and pine pits for John Harrison Esqr (29x48cm-11x19in) s.i. pen ink wash. 4-Dec-3 Mellors & Kirk, Nottingham #809
£700 $1204 €1022 Ground plan of proposed additions to Snelston Hall (45x69cm-18x27in) s.d.1826 pen pencil ink wash. 4-Dec-3 Mellors & Kirk, Nottingham #795/R
£1400 $2408 €2044 Design for a sideboard in the gothic style (96x63cm-38x25in) pen ink col wash. 4-Dec-3 Mellors & Kirk, Nottingham #802/R est:400-600
£1800 $3096 €2628 Design for a villa with a wrought iron veranda (61x97cm-24x38in) s.i. pen pencil ink W/C. 4-Dec-3 Mellors & Kirk, Nottingham #788/R est:2000-3000
£1800 $3096 €2628 Design for a gothic armoire for the great drawing room at Snelston Hall (52x73cm-20x29in) s.i. pen ink. 4-Dec-3 Mellors & Kirk, Nottingham #803/R est:800-1200
£2000 $3440 €2920 Design for a villa in the neo classical style (50x74cm-20x29in) s.i. pen ink W/C. 4-Dec-3 Mellors & Kirk, Nottingham #787/R est:2000-3000
£2100 $3612 €3066 Elevation of the south side library of Snelston Hall (46x65cm-18x26in) s.i. pen pencil ink W/C. 4-Dec-3 Mellors & Kirk, Nottingham #800/R est:2000-3000
£2400 $4128 €3504 Entrance front of Snelston Hall (48x69cm-19x27in) s.i.d.July 1827 pen pencil ink W/C. 4-Dec-3 Mellors & Kirk, Nottingham #798/R est:2000-3000
£2600 $4472 €3796 Terrace front of Snelston Hall (47x69cm-19x27in) s. i. pen pencil ink W/C. 4-Dec-3 Mellors & Kirk, Nottingham #799/R est:2000-3000
£3600 $6192 €5256 Design for a gothic elevation for Snelston Hall (48x70cm-19x28in) s.i.d.Feby 21st 1826 pen pencil ink W/C. 4-Dec-3 Mellors & Kirk, Nottingham #797/R est:3000-4000

COTTINGHAM, Robert (1935-) American
£5705 $10211 €8500 Alarm bell (26x26cm-10x10in) s. acrylic crayon paper painted 1972 prov.lit. 27-May-4 Sotheby's, Paris #262/R est:3000-4000
£19632 $32000 €28663 Joseph's liquors (81x81cm-32x32in) s.i.d.1981 verso prov.exhib.lit. 23-Sep-3 Christie's, Rockefeller NY #141/R est:18000-25000

COTTON, Alan (1936-) British
£300 $546 €438 Harvest at golden Valley (45x50cm-18x20in) s. i.verso. 21-Jun-4 Bonhams, Bath #416
£300 $546 €438 Northern Way, Upper Froyle Church and Trelawn School (41x51cm-16x20in) s. 16-Jun-4 John Nicholson, Haslemere #695
£550 $1012 €803 Hartland quay, storm seas (75x100cm-30x39in) s. 29-Mar-4 Bonhams, Bath #43
£550 $1001 €803 Cattle watering (100x90cm-39x35in) s. 21-Jun-4 Bonhams, Bath #417/R
£600 $1122 €876 Gourdes, warm sunshine (50x40cm-20x16in) s.d.1998 prov. 26-Feb-4 Lane, Penzance #104
£1300 $2054 €1898 Looking from Gordes, across the valley, Provence (50x38cm-20x15in) s. i.d.1988 stretcher. 23-Jul-3 Hampton & Littlewood, Exeter #440/R est:600-800

COTTON, John (1844-?) British
£500 $935 €750 Spencer Street, Leamington Spa (30x35cm-12x14in) s. panel. 22-Jul-4 Tennants, Leyburn #826
£934 $1700 €1364 When autumn's golden touch adorns (46x36cm-18x14in) s.d.1900 s.d.1899 stretcher. 7-Feb-4 Sloans & Kenyon, Bethesda #1294/R est:700-900

COTTON, John Wesley (1860-1931) Canadian
Works on paper
£471 $800 €688 California artist painting under a tree (18x13cm-7x5in) s. gouache board. 18-Nov-3 John Moran, Pasadena #15a

COTTON, Lillian (1901-1962) American
£599 $1000 €875 Young lady wearing a white blouse, she gazes at us but dose not smile (74x58cm-29x23in) s. 14-Nov-3 Aspire, Cleveland #74 est:1500-2500

COTTON, Olive Edith (1911-) Australian
Photographs
£3894 $6152 €5685 Tea cup ballet (35x28cm-14x11in) s.i.d. silver gelatin prov.exhib. 2-Sep-3 Deutscher-Menzies, Melbourne #8/R est:10000-15000 (A.D 9500)

COTTON, Shane (1964-) New Zealander
£1179 $1851 €1710 Untitled (20x20cm-8x8in) init.d.1999 prov. 26-Aug-3 Christie's, Sydney #252/R est:1000-1500 (A.D 2900)
£1805 $2942 €2635 Ngi Ti Rangi (20x20cm-8x8in) init.d.1999. 23-Sep-3 Peter Webb, Auckland #15/R est:4500-6500 (NZ.D 5000)
£2000 $3140 €2900 Tu (20x20cm-8x8in) s.i.d.2000. 27-Aug-3 Dunbar Sloane, Wellington #1/R est:2000-4000 (NZ.D 5500)
£2182 $3425 €3164 Cell block and system (126x126cm-50x50in) s.i.d.1989 verso. 27-Aug-3 Dunbar Sloane, Wellington #17/R est:6000-10000 (NZ.D 6000)
£2679 $4848 €3911 Untitled (20x20cm-8x8in) init.d.1994. 30-Mar-4 Peter Webb, Auckland #52/R est:6000-8000 (NZ.D 7500)
£3571 $6571 €5214 St Elliferons, Biblia 31 (36x35cm-14x14in) s.d.2001 verso. 25-Mar-4 International Art Centre, Auckland #59/R est:9000-14000 (NZ.D 10000)
£7942 $12946 €11595 Untitled (61x45cm-24x18in) init.d.1995 s.d.1995 verso acrylic. 23-Sep-3 Peter Webb, Auckland #1/R est:8000-15000 (NZ.D 22000)
£9929 $17574 €14496 Cross (67x83cm-26x33in) s.i.d.1997-98 verso. 28-Apr-4 Dunbar Sloane, Auckland #20/R est:28000-38000 (NZ.D 28000)
£16418 $28403 €23970 Last laugh (141x141cm-56x56in) s.i.d.2002 verso acrylic. 9-Dec-3 Peter Webb, Auckland #71/R est:40000-60000 (NZ.D 44000)
£39711 $64729 €57978 Whenua Rangi (180x160cm-71x63in) s.d.2000 i.verso. 23-Sep-3 Peter Webb, Auckland #61/R est:85000-100000 (NZ.D 110000)
Works on paper
£3717 $6394 €5427 Te Kore - Fact (23x123cm-9x48in) s.d.91 mixed media prov. 3-Dec-3 Dunbar Sloane, Auckland #27/R est:10000-20000 (NZ.D 10000)

COTTON, William (1880-1958) American
Works on paper
£4192 $7000 €6120 Overly enthusiastic shoppers at Valentine's card display (36x25cm-14x10in) s. pastel sold with magazine cover. 15-Nov-3 Illustration House, New York #106/R est:5000-7000

COTTRELL, H S (fl.1840-1860) British
£600 $1104 €876 Saddled grey with terriers in a stable (23x30cm-9x12in) 10-Jun-4 Christie's, Kensington #86/R
£1700 $2890 €2482 Setting off a day's shooting. At the end of the day (15x20cm-6x8in) s. panel pair. 27-Nov-3 Christie's, Kensington #88/R est:1500-2000

COTTRELL, Henry S (fl.1840-1860) British
£1000 $1600 €1460 Horse and groom with dogs in stable. Saddled hunter and two dogs by stable (14x20cm-6x8in) one s. panel pair. 16-Sep-3 Rosebery Fine Art, London #621/R est:500-800
£1100 $2024 €1606 Partridge shooting (16x23cm-6x9in) panel. 10-Jun-4 Christie's, Kensington #235/R est:1200-1800

COTTRELL, Wellesley (fl.1882-1913) British
£410 $697 €599 Farm near Olan, Conway (23x36cm-9x14in) s. i.verso. 6-Nov-3 Biddle & Webb, Birmingham #792/R
£900 $1683 €1314 Waiting for the tide, Swansea Bay (69x18cm-27x7in) s.d.1904. 26-Feb-4 Lane, Penzance #290/R

COUBINE, Othon (1883-1969) Czechoslovakian
£1027 $1747 €1500 Still life with fruit and beans (33x46cm-13x18in) s. 9-Nov-3 Eric Pillon, Calais #165/R
£1476 $2613 €2200 Maison de campagne (22x27cm-9x11in) s. 27-Apr-4 Artcurial Briest, Paris #145a est:1000-1200
£1724 $3103 €2500 Portrait of Madame Osucka (55x46cm-22x18in) s. painted c.1937. 25-Jan-4 Chayette & Cheval, Paris #229 est:2800-3500
£5370 $9827 €8000 Paysage de Provence (54x65cm-21x26in) s. 7-Jul-4 Artcurial Briest, Paris #110/R est:7500-8000

COUCH, Shane (1963-) British
£13580 $22000 €19691 Mohawk and Madeleine, off New York, 1875 (61x91cm-24x36in) s.d.03. 1-Aug-3 Bonhams & Butterfields, San Francisco #685/R est:25000-35000
£27778 $45000 €40278 Ashbury Cup 1870, racing yachts Cambia, Magic, Madeleine, Rhode Island (102x152cm-40x60in) s.d.03. 1-Aug-3 Bonhams & Butterfields, San Francisco #686/R est:50000-70000

COUCHAUX, Marcel (1877-1939) French
£1788 $3272 €2700 Jeune fille (46x50cm-18x20in) s. 9-Apr-4 Claude Aguttes, Neuilly #20/R est:1500-2000

COUCILL, Irma (20th C) Canadian
Works on paper
£556 $1039 €812 Portrait of Wayne Gretzky (20x35cm-8x14in) s. chl pencil board prov. 24-Feb-4 Ritchie, Toronto #2185/R est:2200-2400 (C.D 1400)

COUCILL, Walter Jackson (1915-1982) Canadian
£205 $334 €299 Moor End, Mellor, England (46x60cm-18x24in) s.i.d.75 board. 23-Sep-3 Ritchie, Toronto #125/R (C.D 450)
Works on paper
£240 $439 €350 Freight train, Saskatchewan (39x53cm-15x21in) s.i.d.1975 ink W/C. 1-Jun-4 Hodgins, Calgary #10/R (C.D 600)
£250 $408 €365 Niagara escarpment (52x70cm-20x28in) s. W/C. 23-Sep-3 Ritchie, Toronto #126/R (C.D 550)

COUCKE, Johannes (1783-1853) Belgian
£2740 $4301 €4000 Retour du troupeau (50x67cm-20x26in) s. panel. 20-Apr-3 Deauville, France #50/R est:4500-5000

COUDENHOVE-KALERGI, Michael (1937-) Czechoslovakian
Works on paper
£470 $841 €700 Tower tops (58x37cm-23x15in) mono.d.56 gouache. 27-May-4 Dorotheum, Graz #128/R

COUDER, Alexandre (1808-1879) French
£800 $1480 €1168 Oriental urn and other decorative objects on an oak coffer (25x20cm-10x8in) s.d.1849 arched shaped top. 14-Jul-4 Christie's, Kensington #1196/R
£1831 $3039 €2600 Peches et raisins (33x41cm-13x16in) s.d.1871. 15-Jun-3 Peron, Melun #191

COUDRAY, Francois Gaston (fl.1886-1893) French
Sculpture
£1027 $1747 €1500 Palace guard (40cm-16in) bronze. 5-Nov-3 Hugo Ruef, Munich #2157/R est:1200

COUDRAY, Georges Charles (fl.1883-1903) French
Sculpture
£1160 $2100 €1694 Bust of a maiden (58x41x20cm-23x16x8in) bears sig polychromed terracotta. 3-Apr-4 Neal Auction Company, New Orleans #649/R est:1500-2500

COUDRES, Adolf des (1862-1924) German
£724 $1332 €1100 Autumn water meadows with cloudy skies (29x41cm-11x16in) s.d.91. 24-Jun-4 Dr Fritz Nagel, Stuttgart #698/R

COUGHLAN, Jack (20th C) Irish?
Works on paper
£417 $679 €600 Hippo (21x30cm-8x12in) s. wash prov.exhib. 23-Sep-3 De Veres Art Auctions, Dublin #200
£526 $968 €800 Study of W B Yeats (25x25cm-10x10in) s.i.d.1985 W/C ink oval. 22-Jun-4 De Veres Art Auctions, Dublin #246/R

COUGHTRY, John Graham (1931-) Canadian
£1525 $2729 €2227 Reclining figure (88x114cm-35x45in) s.d.53 canvas on masonite prov. 31-May-4 Sotheby's, Toronto #177/R est:3000-5000 (C.D 3750)
£2439 $4366 €3561 Study II for triptych II (152x152cm-60x60in) s.i.d. 1966 verso prov. 31-May-4 Sotheby's, Toronto #161/R est:7000-9000 (C.D 6000)
Works on paper
£250 $408 €365 Two Figure studies (20x25cm-8x10in) s.i.d.80-81 graphite. 23-Sep-3 Ritchie, Toronto #197/R (C.D 550)
£296 $482 €432 Sonada variation no.8 (28x38cm-11x15in) s.d.80 W/C graphite prov. 23-Sep-3 Ritchie, Toronto #196/R (C.D 650)
£301 $560 €439 Sonada variations 22 (26x22cm-10x9in) s.d.1980 W/C prov.exhib. 4-Mar-4 Heffel, Vancouver #7/R (C.D 750)

COUILLARD, Jean Marie (1926-) French
£310 $550 €453 Paris street scene (51x99cm-20x39in) s. 2-May-4 Grogan, Boston #92/R

COUILLAUD, Christian (1904-1964) French
£324 $581 €480 Marais Poitevin (55x46cm-22x18in) s. 10-May-4 Giraudeau, Tours #133
£946 $1693 €1400 Ramassage du Varech (46x55cm-18x22in) s. 10-May-4 Giraudeau, Tours #132

COULAUD, Martin (?-1906) French
£472 $850 €689 Watering the horses (33x46cm-13x18in) s. 23-Jan-4 Freeman, Philadelphia #243/R

COULDERY, Horatio H (1832-1893) British
£734 $1350 €1072 Study of a kitten drinking from a bowl of milk (14x19cm-6x7in) init. board. 24-Mar-4 Eldred, East Dennis #114
£1049 $1783 €1500 Professional jealousy (43x58cm-17x23in) s. 27-Nov-3 Dorotheum, Linz #429/R est:2000-2800
£1200 $1908 €1740 Cat with kittens (19x30cm-7x12in) s. 9-Sep-3 David Duggleby, Scarborough #345 est:300-400
£2624 $4750 €3831 Puppies playing with a doll (45x61cm-18x24in) init. 30-Mar-4 Bonhams & Butterfields, San Francisco #125/R est:5500-8000
£3700 $6179 €5402 Best of friends (34x42cm-13x17in) 16-Oct-3 Lyon & Turnbull, Edinburgh #125 est:1000-1500
£4696 $8500 €6856 Dandie Dinmont in a landscape (18x27cm-7x11in) init. board. 30-Mar-4 Bonhams & Butterfields, San Francisco #63/R est:4000-6000

COULDERY, Horatio H (attrib) (1832-1893) British
£650 $1216 €949 Study of two kittens looking at a mouse in a cage (30x40cm-12x16in) 22-Jul-4 Tennants, Leyburn #880/R

COULENTIANOS, Costas (20th C) French
Sculpture
£1611 $2980 €2400 Untitled (168x85cm-66x33in) mono.d.86 steel one of one. 13-Mar-4 De Vuyst, Lokeren #79/R est:2500-3500
£7500 $12750 €10950 Mother and child (56cm-22in) pat bronze. 18-Nov-3 Sotheby's, London #111/R est:2000-3000

COULOM, Jean Baptiste (fl.1695-1735) French
£3312 $6027 €5000 Scene de sorcellerie (72x50cm-28x20in) 21-Jun-4 Tajan, Paris #104/R est:6000-8000

COULON, Emile Antoine (1868-1937) Belgian
£268 $497 €400 Retour (39x26cm-15x10in) s.i. panel. 15-Mar-4 Sotheby's, Amsterdam #58/R

COULON, George D (1822-1904) American
£864 $1400 €1261 Portrait of a man from the Derbigny family (61x51cm-24x20in) s. prov. 2-Aug-3 Neal Auction Company, New Orleans #418/R est:1500-2500

COULON, Louis (19th C) ?
£429 $686 €622 Mediterranean coast (38x45cm-15x18in) bears s.i. 15-May-3 Stuker, Bern #1131 (S.FR 900)

COULON, R (20th C) French
£2793 $5000 €4190 Dancer in the harem (56x130cm-22x51in) s. 16-May-4 Abell, Los Angeles #205/R

COULTER, William Alexander (1849-1936) American
£419 $750 €612 Brigantine running before the wind (25x20cm-10x8in) s. canvasboard. 16-Mar-4 Bonhams & Butterfields, San Francisco #6160/R
£909 $1700 €1327 View of a rocky shore (35x57cm-14x22in) s. board prov. 29-Feb-4 Bonhams & Butterfields, San Francisco #4532 est:1000-1500
£2168 $3750 €3165 Ships leaving San Francisco (28x47cm-11x19in) 10-Dec-3 Bonhams & Butterfields, San Francisco #6174/R est:3000-5000
£9444 $17000 €13788 San Francisco Bay Harbour with a view of the Ferry Building (75x62cm-30x24in) s. prov. 24-Apr-4 Weschler, Washington #613/R est:20000-30000
£10494 $17000 €15216 Harbor scenes. (62x91cm-24x36in) 8-Aug-3 Barridorf, Portland #78/R est:12000-18000
Works on paper
£423 $800 €618 Sail ships in harbour (33x28cm-13x11in) s. W/C prov. 17-Feb-4 John Moran, Pasadena #165/R

COULTRE, Andree le (1917-1986) French
£267 $485 €400 Composition (69x54cm-27x21in) s. masonite. 29-Jun-4 Chenu & Scrive, Lyon #120/R

COUNHAYE, Charles (1884-1971) Belgian
£352 $609 €500 Cabanes et barques sur la plage (37x55cm-15x22in) s. 9-Dec-3 Vanderkindere, Brussels #135
£664 $1129 €950 La grande soeur (55x45cm-22x18in) s.d. prov. 1-Dec-3 Palais de Beaux Arts, Brussels #233/R
£993 $1808 €1500 La grande soeur (55x45cm-22x18in) s.d.30 i.verso. 16-Jun-4 Hotel des Ventes Mosan, Brussels #262 est:1700-1900

COUNIHAN, Noel Jack (1913-1986) Australian
£2273 $4022 €3319 Queenscliff (91x120cm-36x47in) s.d.72 i.d.72 verso. 3-May-4 Christie's, Melbourne #342/R est:4000-6000 (A.D 5500)
Works on paper
£289 $535 €422 Nude (56x36cm-22x14in) s.d.60 chl. 10-Mar-4 Deutscher-Menzies, Melbourne #536/R (A.D 700)
£488 $766 €708 Noel (98x67cm-39x26in) s.d.72 chl prov. 26-Aug-3 Christie's, Sydney #358 (A.D 1200)

COUNTESS OF FLANDERS, Marie Louise (?) Belgian
£2465 $3944 €3500 Madonna della Sedia (40x40cm-16x16in) after Raphael prov. 22-Sep-3 Sotheby's, Amsterdam #305/R est:1500-2000

COUPE, Louise (1877-1915) Belgian
£517 $957 €750 Composition aux fleurs (60x50cm-24x20in) s. 19-Jan-4 Horta, Bruxelles #317

COUPER, William (1853-1942) American
Sculpture
£1776 $3250 €2593 Abram Stevens hewitt (64cm-25in) s.i. bronze stf. Hennry Bonnard. 10-Apr-4 Cobbs, Peterborough #60/R

COUR, Janus la (1837-1909) Danish
£269 $491 €393 Large stones by the sea (35x49cm-14x19in) 9-Jun-4 Rasmussen, Copenhagen #1725/R (D.KR 3000)
£300 $489 €438 From Vejle fjord (31x38cm-12x15in) s.d.13 Juli 18. 27-Sep-3 Rasmussen, Havnen #2014 (D.KR 3200)
£332 $538 €485 Coastal landscape (13x27cm-5x11in) init. 9-Aug-3 Hindemae, Ullerslev #97/R (D.KR 3500)
£375 $645 €548 Olive grove (33x31cm-13x12in) init.i. canvas on panel. 2-Dec-3 Kunsthallen, Copenhagen #506 (D.KR 4000)
£379 $709 €553 Castll' Gandolfo near Lake Albano (31x39cm-12x15in) init.d.3 Okt.1869 panel. 25-Feb-4 Kunsthallen, Copenhagen #500 (D.KR 4200)
£406 $689 €593 View of lake and mountains (44x56cm-17x22in) s.d.28 august 1876. 10-Nov-3 Rasmussen, Vejle #281 (D.KR 4400)
£412 $709 €602 Landscape, Jylland (44x63cm-17x25in) d.14/7/87. 2-Dec-3 Kunsthallen, Copenhagen #533/R (D.KR 4400)
£421 $664 €610 From the old Ravelin (24x29cm-9x11in) 2-Sep-3 Rasmussen, Copenhagen #1993/R (D.KR 4500)
£492 $901 €718 Woodland lake, Moesgaard forest (38x44cm-15x17in) s.d.31 oktbr.1891. 9-Jun-4 Rasmussen, Copenhagen #1965/R (D.KR 5500)
£629 $1170 €918 Sailing ship at sea in summer (26x39cm-10x15in) i. verso prov. 2-Mar-4 Rasmussen, Copenhagen #1415 (D.KR 7000)
£670 $1085 €972 Moesgaard river (38x44cm-15x17in) mono. 4-Aug-3 Rasmussen, Vejle #321/R (D.KR 7000)

£748 $1181 €1085 Drying clothes in Helgenaes Woods (34x42cm-13x17in) init.d.28.S.1859. 2-Sep-3 Rasmussen, Copenhagen #1616/R (D.KR 8000)
£957 $1550 €1388 Coastal landscape with large stone (45x66cm-18x26in) s.d.7 juli 1875. 4-Aug-3 Rasmussen, Vejle #283/R (D.KR 10000)
£995 $1782 €1453 Coastal landscape with large stones (32x58cm-13x23in) s.d.juni 1893. 10-May-4 Rasmussen, Vejle #45/R (D.KR 11000)
£1134 $1962 €1656 Landscape from Chateau Chillon (36x55cm-14x22in) s.d.1887. 9-Dec-3 Rasmussen, Copenhagen #1348/R est:7000-10000 (D.KR 12000)
£1323 $2289 €1932 Farmhouse by country road at outskirts of wood (45x70cm-18x28in) s.d.4 Juni 1883. 9-Dec-3 Rasmussen, Copenhagen #1546/R est:10000-15000 (D.KR 14000)
£1418 $2453 €2070 Coastal landscape, Kaboe Bay, afternoon in August (46x78cm-18x31in) s.d.24 aug.1880 study exhib.prov. 9-Dec-3 Rasmussen, Copenhagen #1575/R est:10000-15000 (D.KR 15000)
£2363 $4088 €3450 Fruit trees in blossom (45x73cm-18x29in) s.d.85 prov. 9-Dec-3 Rasmussen, Copenhagen #1356/R est:20000-30000 (D.KR 25000)
£2488 $4031 €3608 Alpine landscape (45x75cm-18x30in) s.d.Juli 1890. 4-Aug-3 Rasmussen, Vejle #280/R est:30000 (D.KR 26000)
£3133 $5734 €4574 By Juel Lake, summer evening in June (46x70cm-18x28in) s.d.1876 exhib.prov. 9-Jun-4 Rasmussen, Copenhagen #1677/R est:40000-50000 (D.KR 35000)
£3414 $6350 €4984 Landscape from Lake of Geneva with Chateau Chillon (95x147cm-37x58in) s.d.1877. 2-Mar-4 Rasmussen, Copenhagen #1365/R est:30000-40000 (D.KR 38000)
£4509 $8341 €6583 Summer's day by Juel Lake (54x79cm-21x31in) s.d.1881. 15-Mar-4 Rasmussen, Vejle #20/R est:20000 (D.KR 50000)
£5957 $11139 €8697 View of Nemisoen with large trees (53x80cm-21x31in) s.d.1877. 25-Feb-4 Museumsbygningen, Copenhagen #184/R est:10000-15000 (D.KR 66000)
£6087 $11139 €8887 Voiles sur le Leman, vue depuis Chillon (95x148cm-37x58in) s.d.1877 prov. 5-Jun-4 Galerie du Rhone, Sion #532/R est:15000-20000 (S.FR 14000)
£7162 $13107 €10457 View towards Monte Rosa, early morning (140x210cm-55x83in) s.d.1898 exhib. 9-Jun-4 Rasmussen, Copenhagen #1512/R est:75000-100000 (D.KR 80000)
£8696 $15043 €12696 Summer's day off the coast, Capri (42x66cm-17x26in) init.i.d.18 Aug 1874. 9-Dec-3 Rasmussen, Copenhagen #1455/R est:12000-15000 (D.KR 92000)
£26858 $49150 €39213 Rainy summer's day by the beach at Kalo Bay, afternoon (124x189cm-49x74in) s.d.1878-83 exhib. 9-Jun-4 Rasmussen, Copenhagen #1701/R est:75000 (D.KR 300000)

COURANT, Maurice (1847-1925) French
£350 $601 €500 La cote sauvage (73x100cm-29x39in) s. 7-Dec-3 Lesieur & Le Bars, Le Havre #209
£669 $1157 €950 La ramassage des coquillages sur la greve (46x65cm-18x26in) s.d.1891. 10-Dec-3 Rossini, Paris #64/R
£1007 $1872 €1500 Retour de peche en baie de Seine (46x55cm-18x22in) s. panel. 7-Mar-4 Lesieur & Le Bars, Le Havre #28
£1379 $2303 €2000 Le Havre harbour (33x55cm-13x22in) s. i. verso. 9-Jul-3 Hugo Ruef, Munich #73/R est:1800
£1831 $3277 €2600 Bateaux a quai (24x40cm-9x16in) s.d.1901. 11-Jan-4 Rouillac, Vendome #319
£3448 $5759 €5000 Bateaux dans le port du Havre (38x55cm-15x22in) s.i.d.1904. 11-Nov-3 Lesieur & Le Bars, Le Havre #14

COURBET (1819-1877) French
£1848 $3307 €2698 Landscape with waterway (81x53cm-32x21in) bears sig. 26-May-4 AB Stockholms Auktionsverk #2411/R est:15000-18000 (S.KR 25000)

COURBET, Gustave (1819-1877) French
£7143 $11429 €10357 Waterfall (61x50cm-24x20in) s. 15-May-3 Stuker, Bern #1132/R est:16000-22000 (S.FR 15000)
£9333 $16987 €14000 Bord de riviere (50x61cm-20x24in) s. 1-Jul-4 Van Ham, Cologne #1251/R est:16000
£10000 $17000 €14600 Marine, le peuplier (50x61cm-20x24in) s. painted 1875-1877. 29-Oct-3 Christie's, Rockefeller NY #107/R est:15000-20000
£12752 $23463 €19000 Le Doubs a la maison de Monsieur (50x61cm-20x24in) i. verso lit. 25-Mar-4 Dr Fritz Nagel, Stuttgart #700/R est:20000
£17333 $31373 €26000 Deer in forest clearing (50x61cm-20x24in) s. prov.exhib.lit. 1-Apr-4 Van Ham, Cologne #1327/R est:16000
£17333 $31027 €26000 Chateau de Fcey-en-Varay (51x60cm-20x24in) s.d.64 16-May-4 Joron-Derem, Paris #46/R est:40000-50000
£19000 $32680 €27740 Woman with donkey in a snowy landscape (32x42cm-13x17in) s. 4-Dec-3 Christie's, Kensington #12/R est:20000-30000
£23529 $40000 €34352 Chute d'eau esquim (23x23cm-9x9in) s. painted c.1875. 28-Oct-3 Sotheby's, New York #19/R est:15000-20000
£25862 $47586 €37759 Seascape (35x53cm-14x21in) bears i. 26-Mar-4 Koller, Zurich #3104/R est:70000-90000 (S.FR 60000)
£30556 $55000 €44612 Etude pour paysage au torrent (61x49cm-24x19in) s. painted c.1877 prov.lit. 23-Apr-4 Sotheby's, New York #14/R est:40000-60000
£117647 $200000 €171765 Mer calme (54x72cm-21x28in) s. painted c.1865-1866 prov.lit. 29-Oct-3 Christie's, Rockefeller NY #104/R est:150000-200000
£127778 $230000 €186556 Bichesdans la neige (38x61cm-15x24in) s. prov.exhib.lit. 23-Apr-4 Sotheby's, New York #23/R est:150000-200000
£138889 $250000 €202778 Fishing boats on the Normandy coast (49x73cm-19x29in) s. prov. 23-Apr-4 Sotheby's, New York #12/R est:300000-400000
£165000 $280500 €240900 Parc de Rochemont (85x109cm-33x43in) s.d.62 prov.exhib.lit. 18-Nov-3 Sotheby's, London #318/R
£194444 $350000 €283888 La vague, aux trois barques (53x65cm-21x26in) s. prov.lit. 22-Apr-4 Christie's, Rockefeller NY #88/R est:250000-350000
Sculpture
£6738 $11252 €9500 Gentleman (96cm-38in) s.d.1855 marble. 15-Oct-3 Finarte Semenzato, Rome #103/R
Works on paper
£3169 $5482 €4500 Vue de port (32x46cm-13x18in) s. graphite. 9-Dec-3 Chambelland & Giafferi, Paris #37/R est:4000-5000

COURBET, Gustave (attrib) (1819-1877) French
£1810 $2895 €2625 Landscape with stream (28x36cm-11x14in) mono. canvas on board. 15-May-3 Stuker, Bern #1133/R est:4000-4500 (S.FR 3800)

COURBET, Gustave and PATA, Cherubino (19th C) French
£2649 $4821 €4000 Cariole et chien dans un paysage (46x55cm-18x22in) s. 15-Jun-4 Rossini, Paris #19/R est:4000-5000
£3873 $6430 €5500 Riviere, paysage du Doubs (32x40cm-13x16in) s. 15-Jun-3 Peron, Melun #71

COURBIER, Marcel Louis Maurice (1898-1976) French
Sculpture
£2667 $4800 €4000 Art Deco kneeling nude with corn and lamb (45x68cm-18x27in) s.st.f.F. Barbedienne green pat bronze. 26-Apr-4 Bernaerts, Antwerp #421/R est:4000-5000
£3333 $5967 €5000 Jeune femme et mouton. pat bronze Cast Barbedienne. 15-May-4 other European Auctioneer #150/R

COURBOIN, Eugène (19th C) French
Works on paper
£420 $722 €600 La diligence, projet d'eventail (31x62cm-12x24in) s. W/C. 3-Dec-3 Blanchet, Paris #4/R

COURDOUAN, Vincent-Joseph-François (1810-1893) French
£10000 $18100 €15000 La vallee du village des Angles, Var (49x91cm-19x36in) s. canvas on panel. 30-Mar-4 Rossini, Paris #224/R est:15000-25000
Works on paper
£1380 $2304 €2000 Village de pecheurs (19x27cm-7x11in) s.d.90 W/C. 17-Nov-3 Tajan, Paris #11/R est:2000-3000
£1477 $2717 €2200 Moulin en bord de mer (21x37cm-8x15in) s.d.1877 chl. 29-Mar-4 Rieunier, Paris #48/R est:1000-1200
£1621 $2966 €2350 Bord de mer (20x32cm-8x13in) pastel. 1-Feb-4 Teitgen, Nancy #28

COURMES, Alfred (1898-1993) French
£2639 $4407 €3800 Sans titre (70x56cm-28x22in) s.d.1929. 25-Oct-3 Cornette de St.Cyr, Paris #488 est:6000-7500
£6294 $10825 €9000 Paysage (35x41cm-14x16in) s.d.48. 6-Dec-3 Renaud, Paris #77/R

COURNAULT, Étienne (1891-1948) French
£4800 $8592 €7200 Place de la Concorde (47x35cm-19x14in) s. 17-May-4 Sotheby's, Paris #7/R est:5000-8000

COURT, John (20th C) American
£782 $1400 €1142 Blue white vase (51x36cm-20x14in) s.d.1974 verso exhib. 7-May-4 Sloans & Kenyon, Bethesda #1720/R

COURT, Joseph-Desire (1797-1865) French
£4669 $7750 €6817 Mr and Mrs DeNeaux (147x99cm-58x39in) both s.d.1864 pair. 4-Oct-3 Neal Auction Company, New Orleans #144/R est:4000-6000
£6577 $12102 €9800 Commission du Musee Napoleon (57x75cm-22x30in) s. prov. 26-Mar-4 Daguerre, Paris #60/R est:6000-8000
£19858 $33163 €28000 Le fil de la vie ou les trois parques (304x360cm-120x142in) s. 19-Jun-3 Millon & Associes, Paris #88/R

COURT, Lee Winslow (1903-) American
£279 $475 €407 Rocky coast with crashing surf, Maine (46x38cm-18x15in) s. canvasboard. 21-Nov-3 Skinner, Boston #535/R

COURT, M L (18th C) ?
£5000 $9000 €7300 Italianate landscape with drovers beside a waterfall (69x88cm-27x35in) s. indis d. 20-Apr-4 Sotheby's, Olympia #384/R est:5000-7000

COURTEILLE, Eugène (19th C) French
£379 $633 €550 Servant standing at the doorway (92x77cm-36x30in) 11-Nov-3 Vendu Notarishuis, Rotterdam #161

COURTENS, Alfred (1889-1967) Belgian
Sculpture
£2113 $3380 €3000 Bust of Princess Marie Christine (51cm-20in) s.d.1956 white marble grey marble console. 22-Sep-3 Sotheby's, Amsterdam #158/R est:1000-1500

COURTENS, Franz (1854-1943) Belgian
£1655 $3062 €2400 Sous-bois (35x50cm-14x20in) s. 16-Feb-4 Horta, Bruxelles #195 est:2500-3500
£1773 $2961 €2500 Les moulins a vent (60x80cm-24x31in) s. 17-Jun-3 Vanderkindere, Brussels #184/R est:2500-3500
£1818 $3036 €2600 In the sheep stall, motherhood (63x45cm-25x18in) s. 11-Oct-3 De Vuyst, Lokeren #70/R est:2400-2800
£2148 $3973 €3200 Brouillard dans la dune a Coxyde (31x40cm-12x16in) s. panel. 15-Mar-4 Horta, Bruxelles #135/R est:2000-3000
£2639 $4407 €3800 Dusk (53x71cm-21x28in) s.d.1885. 21-Oct-3 Campo & Campo, Antwerp #50/R est:4500-5500
£4000 $7160 €6000 Return of the fishermen (71x101cm-28x40in) s. prov.lit. 15-May-4 De Vuyst, Lokeren #433/R est:7500-8500
£4225 $7310 €6000 Vaches au bord d'une riviere. Les raccommodeuse de filets (29x40cm-11x16in) s. one panel one canvas on panel two exhib. 13-Dec-3 De Vuyst, Lokeren #431/R est:4000-5000
£6000 $10740 €9000 Coucher de soleil (76x110cm-30x43in) s. 15-May-4 De Vuyst, Lokeren #541/R est:8000-9000
£12766 $21319 €18000 Le givre (214x180cm-84x71in) s. prov.exhib. 20-Oct-3 Bernaerts, Antwerp #61/R est:25000-30000
£17333 $31200 €26000 Cows by the Zaan, holland (216x179cm-85x70in) s. prov. 21-Apr-4 Christie's, Amsterdam #195/R est:15000-20000
Works on paper
£567 $1014 €850 Morning mist (45x60cm-18x24in) s. chl prov. 15-May-4 De Vuyst, Lokeren #75

COURTENS, Hermann (1884-1956) Belgian
£267 $488 €400 Vases de fleurs (38x46cm-15x18in) s. 7-Jun-4 Palais de Beaux Arts, Brussels #239
£272 $501 €397 Still life of white flowers on a table (58x79cm-23x31in) s. canvas on masonite. 14-Jun-4 Waddingtons, Toronto #38/R (C.D 675)
£625 $994 €900 Femme au faisan (105x81cm-41x32in) s. 9-Sep-3 Palais de Beaux Arts, Brussels #203
£839 $1443 €1200 Composition a la table dressee (46x38cm-18x15in) s. 8-Dec-3 Horta, Bruxelles #27
Works on paper
£352 $609 €500 Flower seller (62x5cm-24x2in) s.i. chl pastel. 13-Dec-3 De Vuyst, Lokeren #67

COURTENS, Hermann (attrib) (1884-1956) Belgian
£1611 $2964 €2400 Interior with old lady (80x60cm-31x24in) s. 25-Mar-4 Dr Fritz Nagel, Stuttgart #696/R est:3800

COURTENS, Jef (20th C) Belgian
£300 $543 €450 Barque de peche au crepuscule (80x60cm-31x24in) s. 30-Mar-4 Campo, Vlaamse Kaai #23

COURTER, Franklin C (1854-1947) American
£289 $500 €422 Landscape with sheep (25x36cm-10x14in) s. 13-Dec-3 Weschler, Washington #544

COURTICE, Rody Kenny (1895-?) Canadian
Works on paper
£402 $691 €587 Quebec Farm, St Blessed, Quebec (19x20cm-7x8in) first s. second init. ink scratch board two. 2-Dec-3 Joyner Waddington, Toronto #355/R (C.D 900)

COURTIN, Jacques François (attrib) (1672-1752) French
£596 $1085 €900 La diseuse de bonne aventure (32x40cm-13x16in) 21-Jun-4 Tajan, Paris #106
£19719 $34508 €28000 La diseuse de bonne aventure (120x165cm-47x65in) 18-Dec-3 Tajan, Paris #38/R est:30000-40000

COURTINES, Alexandre (1857-?) French
£470 $864 €700 Portrait de dame a l'eventail. s.d.1890. 26-Mar-4 Neret-Minet, Paris #37

COURTNEY, Sidney Lee (20th C) American
£2168 $3750 €3165 Trail trouble (117x97cm-46x38in) board. 12-Dec-3 Du Mouchelle, Detroit #2002/R est:1000-1500

COURTOIS, Guillaume (1628-1679) French
£4444 $8000 €6488 Christ on the road to Calvary (74x60cm-29x24in) prov. 22-Jan-4 Sotheby's, New York #279/R est:8000-10000
£15278 $27500 €22306 Portrait of Jacques Courtois (44x34cm-17x13in) oil paper on canvas. 22-Jan-4 Sotheby's, New York #268/R est:15000-20000
Works on paper
£710 $1300 €1037 Study for the head of Filippo Neri (22x16cm-9x6in) col chk. 29-Jan-4 Swann Galleries, New York #207/R

COURTOIS, Jacques (1621-1676) French
£2349 $4205 €3500 Le champ de bataille (50x75cm-20x30in) 25-May-4 Campo & Campo, Antwerp #48/R est:1800-2400
£2763 $5084 €4200 Combat de cavalerie sous les murs d'une ville (75x136cm-30x54in) 25-Jun-4 Rossini, Paris #38/R est:4500-5500
£5442 $9741 €8000 Cavalry battle (197x215cm-78x85in) 17-Mar-4 Neumeister, Munich #333/R est:7000
£5872 $10100 €8573 Combat de cavalerie (90x125cm-35x49in) bears sig. 3-Dec-3 Naón & Cia, Buenos Aires #27/R est:10000-15000
£40268 $75302 €60000 Battle scenes (32x90cm-13x35in) pair. 25-Feb-4 Porro, Milan #57/R est:60000
Works on paper
£548 $932 €800 Horsemen ambushing a wagon train (13x23cm-5x9in) black chk pen ink wash. 5-Nov-3 Christie's, Amsterdam #107/R

COURTOIS, Jacques (attrib) (1621-1676) French
£1467 $2655 €2200 Cavalry battle (46x56cm-18x22in) 1-Apr-4 Van Ham, Cologne #1171 est:800
£2083 $3396 €3000 Wild board hunt (66x105cm-26x41in) panel. 27-Sep-3 Dannenberg, Berlin #528/R est:2000
£3524 $5991 €5145 Battle scene (53x71cm-21x28in) canvas on board. 5-Nov-3 Dobiaschofsky, Bern #454/R est:5500 (S.FR 8000)
£5960 $10848 €9000 Cavalry battle scene (87x76cm-34x30in) 18-Jun-4 Bolland & Marotz, Bremen #488/R est:9600
£5998 $10317 €8757 After the battle (47x67cm-19x26in) 3-Dec-3 Museumsbygningen, Copenhagen #156/R est:50000-75000 (D.KR 64000)
£6154 $10585 €8985 Battle scene (116x150cm-46x59in) 2-Dec-3 Bukowskis, Stockholm #378/R est:100000-125000 (S.KR 80000)
£12000 $20760 €17520 Cavalry skirmish on a bridge (72x92cm-28x36in) 10-Dec-3 Bonhams, New Bond Street #107/R est:7000-10000
£40541 $71351 €60000 Battle scenes (48x74cm-19x29in) pair. 18-May-4 Sotheby's, Milan #473/R est:50000-70000
Works on paper
£676 $1189 €1000 Battle scene (16x24cm-6x9in) i. pen brown ink grey wash black chk lit. 19-May-4 Sotheby's, Amsterdam #149/R

COURTOIS, Jacques (circle) (1621-1676) French
£5000 $9000 €7300 Cavalry skirmish (82x150cm-32x59in) 23-Apr-4 Christie's, Kensington #179/R est:3000-5000
£5634 $9070 €8000 Battle with cavalry (62x88cm-24x35in) 8-May-3 Farsetti, Prato #792/R est:5500-6500
£6000 $10200 €8760 Cavalry battle between Christians and Turks (60x164cm-24x65in) 31-Oct-3 Christie's, Kensington #126/R est:2000-3000
£12000 $21960 €17520 Cavalry battle (75x148cm-30x58in) 9-Jul-4 Christie's, Kensington #172/R est:6000-8000

COURTOIS, Jacques (style) (1621-1676) French
£3977 $7000 €5806 Battle scene with numerous figures (83x100cm-33x39in) 18-May-4 Bonhams & Butterfields, San Francisco #38/R est:3000-5000
£5500 $10065 €8030 Battle scene with cavaliers and infantry fighting before a fortified town (72x135cm-28x53in) 6-Jul-4 Sotheby's, Olympia #479/R est:4000-6000
£10886 $19595 €15894 Battle scenes (51x59cm-20x23in) pair prov. 26-Jan-4 Lilla Bukowskis, Stockholm #94 est:25000-30000 (S.KR 145000)

COUSE, E Irving (1866-1936) American
£9884 $17000 €14431 Indian boy on a hilltop (56x89cm-22x35in) painted c.1916-24 prov.lit. 3-Dec-3 Sotheby's, New York #150/R est:15000-25000
£14706 $27500 €21471 Indian fishing by a stream (20x28cm-8x11in) s. board prov. 24-Jul-4 Coeur d'Alene, Hayden #23/R est:15000-25000
£16043 $30000 €23423 Papoose by moonlight (20x25cm-8x10in) s. board prov.exhib.lit. 24-Jul-4 Coeur d'Alene, Hayden #62/R est:15000-25000
£17683 $29000 €25640 Native American youth with bow and arrows at river's edge (30x41cm-12x16in) s. prov. 31-May-3 Brunk, Ashville #36/R est:10000-20000
£20588 $35000 €30058 Turkey hunting among the Aspens (20x25cm-8x10in) s. i.verso canvas on board prov.lit. 1-Nov-3 Santa Fe Art, Santa Fe #217/R est:50000-60000
£22059 $37500 €32206 Sacred water (30x41cm-12x16in) s. panel prov.lit. 1-Nov-3 Santa Fe Art, Santa Fe #54/R est:40000-50000
£27933 $50000 €40782 Columbia river, near Arlington, Oregon, full moon, Indian camp (41x91cm-16x36in) s. 16-Mar-4 Matthew's, Oregon #70/R est:40000-60000
£31285 $56000 €45676 Arrow maker (30x41cm-12x16in) board. 15-May-4 Altermann Galleries, Santa Fe #61/R
£33520 $60000 €48939 Doll maker (30x41cm-12x16in) board. 15-May-4 Altermann Galleries, Santa Fe #62/R
£85677 $145650 €125088 Moccasin maker (61x74cm-24x29in) 1-Nov-3 Altermann Galleries, Santa Fe #44
Prints
£3235 $5500 €4723 Roasting corn (36x53cm-14x21in) s.i.d.1904 chromolithograph prov.lit. 1-Nov-3 Santa Fe Art, Santa Fe #164/R est:2500-4500
Works on paper
£149733 $280000 €218610 Arrow maker (66x102cm-26x40in) s. gouache chl prov.exhib.lit. 24-Jul-4 Coeur d'Alene, Hayden #60/R est:150000-250000

COUSIN, Charles (19/20th C) French
£426 $711 €600 Portrait de femme (65x55cm-26x22in) s.d.1904. 17-Jun-3 Vanderkindere, Brussels #100
£533 $976 €800 Canal a Venise (22x16cm-9x6in) s. panel. 4-Jun-4 Pierre Berge, Paris #123/R
£940 $1663 €1400 Venise (24x33cm-9x13in) s. 30-Apr-4 Tajan, Paris #208/R
£1357 $2267 €1981 Canal in Venice (46x55cm-18x22in) s. prov. 17-Nov-3 Waddingtons, Toronto #196/R est:1500-2000 (C.D 3000)

COUSIN, Jean II (attrib) (1525-1594) French
Works on paper
£1497 $2679 €2200 Un homme barbu tourne vers la droite, appuye a un pilastre (16x10cm-6x4in) i. pen brown ink. 18-Mar-4 Christie's, Paris #113/R est:2000-3000

COUSINS, Harold B (1916-) American
Sculpture
£2162 $4000 €3157 Sculpture (137cm-54in) welded iron incl bas exec 1958 prov. 13-Jul-4 Christie's, Rockefeller NY #52/R est:3000-3500

COUSINS, Thomas Selby (20th C) New Zealander?
Works on paper
£300 $531 €438 Early morning in Waikouaiti Bay (27x53cm-11x21in) s.d.1880 W/C. 29-Apr-4 Christie's, Kensington #84/R

COUSSENS, Armand (1881-1935) French
£500 $850 €730 Le fort St. Andre, Villeneuve des Avignon. Les Collines Cevenoles (52x76cm-20x30in) s. board pair. 6-Nov-3 Christie's, Kensington #844/R

COUST, Jacob van (?) Dutch?
£420 $701 €613 Still life with flowers on a stone ledge (75x63cm-30x25in) s. 11-Nov-3 Bonhams, Knightsbridge #123/R

COUSTOU, Guillaume I (1677-1746) French
Sculpture
£1250 $1962 €1800 Cheval de Marly (63cm-25in) green pat bronze. 26-Aug-3 Galerie Moderne, Brussels #1017/R est:1200-1800
£4075 $6357 €5950 Rearing horses (59cm-23in) s. pat bronze pair. 30-Mar-3 Agra, Warsaw #13/R est:25000 (P.Z 26000)

COUSTURIER, Lucie (1876-1925) French
£2937 $4993 €4200 Fleurs et fruits sur nappe blanche (45x81cm-18x32in) s.d.1905. 21-Nov-3 Lombrail & Teucquam, Paris #131 est:3800-4500
£6952 $13000 €10150 Dejeuner (50x65cm-20x26in) s.d.2899 prov. 25-Feb-4 Christie's, Rockefeller NY #23/R est:3000-5000
Works on paper
£504 $826 €700 Village de oukomadou (19x14cm-7x6in) s. W/C. 6-Jun-3 Chochon-Barre & Allardi, Paris #35

£733 $1313 €1100 Bateaux au port (37x54cm-15x21in) s. W/C. 16-May-4 Lombrail & Teucquam, Paris #158/R

COUTAN, Jules Felix (1848-1939) French
Sculpture
£6207 $10303 €9000 Cupidon debout (113cm-44in) s.i.d.1875 brown pat bronze. 2-Oct-3 Sotheby's, Paris #17/R est:18000
£8000 $14640 €11680 Jeune femme au tambourin (142cm-56in) s.st.f.Thiebaut pat bronze. 9-Jul-4 Sotheby's, London #139/R est:8000-12000

COUTAUD, Lucien (1904-1977) French
£524 $892 €750 Japon (38x61cm-15x24in) s.d.64 s.i.d.verso. 28-Nov-3 Blanchet, Paris #150/R
£738 $1321 €1100 Orientales a maree basse (55x46cm-22x18in) s. s.i.d.59 verso. 27-May-4 Christie's, Paris #140/R
£1162 $2010 €1650 Interieur a la pendule (60x73cm-24x29in) i.verso. 10-Dec-3 Millon & Associes, Paris #62/R est:1800-2000
£2083 $3479 €3000 Autre Normandie pittoresque (65x100cm-26x39in) s.d.71 s.i.d.13-8-71 verso. 21-Oct-3 Artcurial Briest, Paris #347/R est:2500-3000
Works on paper
£352 $609 €500 Composition surrealiste (15x34cm-6x13in) s.d.2-40 gouache. 10-Dec-3 Millon & Associes, Paris #60/R
£352 $650 €514 Surrealist figures (23x20cm-9x8in) col pencil gouache. 17-Jan-4 New Orleans Auction, New Orleans #525
£395 $726 €600 Personnage surrealiste (44x30cm-17x12in) s.d.1945 gouache. 28-Jun-4 Joron-Derem, Paris #144
£428 $787 €650 Pere de la Porteuse de Pain (40x33cm-16x13in) s.d.47 W/C. 27-Jun-4 Feletin, Province #165
£537 $999 €800 Jetee (15x30cm-6x12in) s.d.64 gouache. 3-Mar-4 Tajan, Paris #135

COUTTS, Alice Gray (1880-1973) American
£875 $1400 €1278 New puppies. board. 20-Sep-3 Harvey Clar, Oakland #1295
£898 $1500 €1311 Playing with the kitty (16x22cm-6x9in) s.i. board. 26-Oct-3 Bonhams & Butterfields, San Francisco #6526/R
£1104 $1800 €1612 Play nice (20x25cm-8x10in) s. 17-Jul-3 Doyle, New York #19/R est:2000-3000
£2116 $4000 €3089 Indian girl crossing stream (28x20cm-11x8in) s. 17-Feb-4 John Moran, Pasadena #60a/R est:2000-3000

COUTTS, Gordon (1868-1937) British/American
£838 $1500 €1223 Desert landscape (56x71cm-22x28in) s. 21-Mar-4 Bonhams & Butterfields, Los Angeles #7328/R est:2000-3000
£1078 $1800 €1574 Last rights (91x114cm-36x45in) s. 19-Oct-3 Bonhams & Butterfields, Los Angeles #7014/R est:3000-5000
£1323 $2500 €1932 Figure - Tangier (36x28cm-14x11in) s. verso. 17-Feb-4 John Moran, Pasadena #16/R est:1500-2000
£1899 $3400 €2773 Untitled landscape (51x76cm-20x30in) s. 21-Mar-4 Hindman, Chicago #845/R est:2000-3000
£2114 $3319 €3086 Sydney harbour (35x56cm-14x22in) s. 26-Aug-3 Christie's, Sydney #355/R est:7000-10000 (A.D 5200)

COUTURE, Thomas (attrib) (1815-1879) French
£3487 $6416 €5300 Un philosophe assis a une table (65x54cm-26x21in) prov. 25-Jun-4 Rossini, Paris #68/R est:1200-1500

COUTURIER, Léon Antoine Lucien (1842-1935) French
£483 $806 €700 A la manoeuvre (44x27cm-17x11in) s. 11-Nov-3 Lesieur & Le Bars, Le Havre #142

COUTURIER, Philibert Léon (1823-1901) French
£797 $1307 €1100 Coq et poule (12x18cm-5x7in) s. panel pair. 11-May-3 Osenat, Fontainebleau #57
£1429 $2286 €2072 Poultry yard (28x46cm-11x18in) s. panel. 15-May-3 Stuker, Bern #1135/R est:1500-2000 (S.FR 3000)
£1724 $2879 €2500 La basse-cour (46x56cm-18x22in) s. 17-Nov-3 Tajan, Paris #53/R est:2500-3000
£2113 $3697 €3000 Le conseil des rats (100x81cm-39x32in) s. exhib. 19-Dec-3 Delvaux, Paris #9/R est:3000-4000

COUTURIER, Robert (1905-) French
Sculpture
£1974 $3632 €3000 Trophee (36cm-14in) s. gilded bronze st.f.Susse freres. 25-Jun-4 Tajan, Paris #22/R est:3000-4000
£2199 $3562 €3100 Femme assise (29x9cm-11x4in) s.num.2/6 brown pat bronze st.f.Susse exec.c.1960 exhib. 24-May-3 Martinot & Savignat, Pontoise #126/R est:3000-3500
£2797 $4755 €4000 Decoupage (27x7x7cm-11x3x3in) s.num.1/3 and 2/3 bronze gold leaf lit. 24-Nov-3 Tajan, Paris #90/R est:1000-1200
£2817 $4563 €4000 Femme modele nue assise (24cm-9in) s. brown pat bronze. 5-Aug-3 Tajan, Paris #59/R est:2000-3000
£2958 $4792 €4200 La danse (34cm-13in) s.num.2/8 brown pat bronze. 5-Aug-3 Tajan, Paris #58/R est:2000-3000
£4225 $6845 €6000 Le bain de pieds (35x14x9cm-14x6x4in) s.st.f.Valsuani brown pat bronze. 5-Aug-3 Tajan, Paris #57/R est:3000-4000
£5634 $9127 €8000 Couple (71cm-28in) s.num.6/6 brown pat bronze. 5-Aug-3 Tajan, Paris #56/R est:5000-7000

COUTY, Jean (1907-1991) French
£646 $1028 €950 Meules (65x81cm-26x32in) s. s.on stretcher. 23-Mar-3 St-Germain-en-Laye Encheres #68
£800 $1432 €1200 Paysage du dauphine (73x60cm-29x24in) s. 16-May-4 Osenat, Fontainebleau #71/R
£1467 $2684 €2200 Le petit dejeuner (60x73cm-24x29in) s. 6-Jun-4 Anaf, Lyon #361/R est:2000-3000
£1544 $2840 €2300 L'Ecolier (116x73cm-46x29in) s.d.1951 exhib. 28-Mar-4 Versailles Encheres #10/R est:1200-1500
£1888 $3210 €2700 Nature morte a la coupiere en Strasbourg (60x73cm-24x29in) s. 30-Nov-3 Anaf, Lyon #35/R est:1800-2000
£2000 $3600 €3000 La Cathedrale de Saint Severin a Toulouse (73x60cm-29x24in) s. s.i.verso. 20-Apr-4 Chenu & Scrive, Lyon #68/R est:2000-3000
£2067 $3782 €3100 Salle a manger de reception (74x60cm-29x24in) s. 6-Jun-4 Anaf, Lyon #360/R est:3000-3500
£2333 $4270 €3500 Nature morte a la cafetiere emaillee blanc (60x73cm-24x29in) s. 6-Jun-4 Anaf, Lyon #359/R est:3500-4000
£3467 $6344 €5200 La Dombes (54x65cm-21x26in) s. 6-Jun-4 Anaf, Lyon #358/R est:3500-4000
£3467 $6309 €5200 Palmeraie au Maroc (61x50cm-24x20in) s. 29-Jun-4 Chenu & Scrive, Lyon #55/R est:1000-1500

COUTY, Jean Frederic (1829-1904) French
£757 $1369 €1150 Jetee de fleurs (38x55cm-15x22in) s. 19-Apr-4 Boscher, Cherbourg #709/R
£2310 $4250 €3373 Waiting for his master (82x65cm-32x26in) s. panel. 27-Jun-4 Freeman, Philadelphia #36/R est:3000-5000

COUVELET, Jean Baptiste (1772-1830) French
Miniatures
£2021 $3274 €2850 Portrait du Colonel Baron Mugnier (8x7cm-3x3in) s. gold frame oval. 21-May-3 Daguerre, Paris #228 est:300-400

COUVER, J van (1836-1909) Dutch
Works on paper
£291 $495 €425 Enkhuyzen, Holland (52x34cm-20x13in) W/C. 5-Nov-3 Vendue Huis, Gravenhage #106

COUVER, Jan van (1836-1909) Dutch
£957 $1550 €1388 Dutch landscape with town and mill by canal (77x52cm-30x20in) s. 4-Aug-3 Rasmussen, Vejle #428/R (D.KR 10000)
£1138 $1900 €1661 View of Sliedrecht Holland. Evening view of Sliedrecht, Holland (20x30cm-8x12in) one s. i.verso one s. panel panel. 11-Oct-3 Auctions by the Bay, Alameda #1616
£1176 $2000 €1717 Dutch harbour at dusk (61x92cm-24x36in) s. 19-Nov-3 Bonhams & Butterfields, San Francisco #64/R
£1536 $2750 €2243 Dutch windmill (61x107cm-24x42in) s. 6-May-4 Doyle, New York #54/R est:5000-7000
£2663 $4180 €3888 Untitled, canal scene with windmills (61x91cm-24x36in) s. i.verso. 1-Sep-3 Shapiro, Sydney #358/R est:8000-12000 (A.D 6550)
£5500 $9900 €8030 View of a Dutch town (56x89cm-22x35in) s. 21-Jan-4 Sotheby's, Olympia #470/R est:2000-3000

COUWENBERG, Abraham Johannes (1806-1844) Dutch
£3472 $5903 €5000 Figures conversing by a crag in a panoramic summer landscape (47x57cm-19x22in) s. 28-Oct-3 Christie's, Amsterdam #34/R est:4000-6000

COVARRUBIAS, Miguel (1904-1957) Mexican
£54054 $90270 €78919 Aves del paraiso - bird of paradise (75x60cm-30x24in) s. lit. 26-Oct-3 Christie's, Hong Kong #18/R est:700000-900000 (HK.D 700000)
£289855 $449275 €423188 Balinesa en el rio (76x61cm-30x24in) s. prov. 6-Oct-2 Sotheby's, Singapore #48/R (S.D 800000)
Works on paper
£306 $550 €447 Girl and long dress (13x20cm-5x8in) ink. 24-Apr-4 Du Mouchelle, Detroit #3068/R
£500 $900 €730 Balinese woman (25x15cm-10x6in) chl. 24-Apr-4 Du Mouchelle, Detroit #3069/R
£591 $1100 €863 Piasaje no.16 (28x19cm-11x7in) s. pen ink. 2-Mar-4 Swann Galleries, New York #143/R est:1000-1500
£722 $1300 €1054 Two dancers, man and woman (25x18cm-10x7in) ink. 24-Apr-4 Du Mouchelle, Detroit #3067/R est:800-1200
£944 $1500 €1378 Woman (22x17cm-9x7in) s. pen ink. 12-Sep-3 Skinner, Boston #374/R
£1200 $2100 €1752 At the cafe (35x25cm-14x10in) ink inkwash. 19-Dec-3 Sotheby's, New York #1177/R est:3000-4000
£1467 $2655 €2200 Scene de personnages mexicains (45x60cm-18x24in) s. crayon htd gouache. 5-Apr-4 Marie & Robert, Paris #61/R est:2000-3000
£5294 $9000 €7729 Mujer Balinesa - Balinese woman (39x26cm-15x10in) s. gouache exec. c.1935 prov. 18-Nov-3 Christie's, Rockefeller NY #89/R est:10000-15000
£17318 $31000 €25284 Mother and child (51x37cm-20x15in) s. W/C pencil prov. 26-May-4 Sotheby's, New York #91/R est:20000-25000

COVENTRY, Gertrude Mary (1886-1964) British
£300 $549 €438 Autumn river landscape (45x60cm-18x24in) s. 29-Jan-4 Bonhams, Edinburgh #320

COVENTRY, Keith (1958-) British
£3500 $5845 €5110 Untitled (35x43cm-14x17in) s.d.1999 verso prov. 22-Oct-3 Christie's, London #131/R est:2000-3000
£6000 $10860 €8760 White abstract - Royal family (110x131cm-43x52in) oil canvas wood gesso glass frame executed 1994 prov.exhib. 1-Apr-4 Christie's, Kensington #319/R est:7000-9000

COVENTRY, Robert McGown (1855-1914) British
£700 $1225 €1022 River in spate (71x91cm-28x36in) s. 18-Dec-3 Bonhams, Edinburgh #338
Works on paper
£580 $1067 €847 Belfry at Bruges (25x19cm-10x7in) s. W/C. 23-Mar-4 Bonhams, Knightsbridge #57/R
£860 $1591 €1256 Burges. Continental harbour scene (24x34cm-9x13in) both s. one i. W/C pair. 14-Jul-4 Bonhams, Chester #440
£950 $1634 €1387 Belgian market scene (25x36cm-10x14in) s. W/C. 2-Dec-3 Gorringes, Lewes #2286/R
£980 $1578 €1421 Amsterdam (27x37cm-11x15in) s.i. W/C. 21-Aug-3 Bonhams, Edinburgh #1148

£2100 $3801 €3066 Sailing vessels in harbour (30x51cm-12x20in) s. W/C. 19-Apr-4 Sotheby's, London #117/R est:1500-2000

COVERLEY-PRICE, A Victor (1901-1988) British
£260 $434 €380 View of Westminster (38x47cm-15x19in) s. 7-Oct-3 Bonhams, Knightsbridge #66/R
£1300 $2405 €1898 Limone, lake Garda (37x46cm-15x18in) s. i.verso board exhib. 11-Feb-4 Sotheby's, Olympia #158/R est:800-1200
£1500 $2385 €2190 San Gimignano, Italy (30x26cm-12x10in) s. board. 10-Sep-3 Sotheby's, Olympia #205/R est:500-800

COVEY, Arthur Sinclair (1877-1960) American
Works on paper
£323 $600 €472 On the lagoon (17x31cm-7x12in) init.i.d.05 gouache paper on board. 5-Mar-4 Skinner, Boston #508/R

COWAN (?) American?
Sculpture
£1402 $2300 €2033 Nymph (33cm-13in) ivory. 7-Jun-3 Treadway Gallery, Cincinnati #179 est:1500-2000

COWAN, Alexander (19/20th C) British
£270 $451 €394 On the Sulby River, Ramsey Isle of Man (22x30cm-9x12in) s.i.d.July 1909 panel. 16-Oct-3 Bonhams, Edinburgh #160
£320 $550 €467 On the Sulby River (23x30cm-9x12in) s.d.1909 i.verso board. 5-Dec-3 Chrystals Auctions, Isle of Man #234

COWAN, Frances (20th C) American
£264 $475 €385 Townscape with telephone poles (41x48cm-16x19in) s. 23-Jan-4 Freeman, Philadelphia #245/R

COWAN, Mabel G (20th C) British
£1100 $1760 €1606 Weather clears, Ballintoy (51x76cm-20x30in) s. 16-Sep-3 Bonhams, Knightsbridge #125/R est:400-600

COWAN, Roy (20th C) New Zealander
£277 $496 €404 Fractured land (90x120cm-35x47in) init.i.verso acrylic on board. 12-May-4 Dunbar Sloane, Wellington #405/R (NZ.D 800)
£329 $588 €480 Sunlight on leaves (119x89cm-47x35in) init.i. verso acrylic on board painted c.1960. 12-May-4 Dunbar Sloane, Wellington #406/R (NZ.D 950)
£519 $929 €758 Volcanic landscape (58x80cm-23x31in) init. acrylic on board. 12-May-4 Dunbar Sloane, Wellington #129/R est:1000-2000 (NZ.D 1500)
£1038 $1858 €1515 Fiordland territory (117x120cm-46x47in) s. acrylic on board prov. 12-May-4 Dunbar Sloane, Wellington #130/R est:2000-4000 (NZ.D 3000)
£1176 $2106 €1717 Alzheimers/ figure in Matagouri (74x120cm-29x47in) i.verso acrylic on board prov. 12-May-4 Dunbar Sloane, Wellington #132/R est:1000-2000 (NZ.D 3400)

COWAN, Wilson (?) British
£1200 $2208 €1752 Portrait of an elegant lady in black (85x73cm-33x29in) s.d.1913. 11-Jun-4 Bonhams, Edinburgh #241/R est:300-500

COWARD, Malcolm (20th C) British
Works on paper
£250 $468 €365 Study of four geese resting amongst vegetation (30x47cm-12x19in) s. W/C. 22-Jul-4 Tennants, Leyburn #685

COWARD, Sir Noel (1899-1973) British
£3800 $6802 €5548 Stubborn donkey (23x32cm-9x13in) s. i.d.1948 verso canvas on board. 14-May-4 Christie's, Kensington #564/R est:3000-5000
£4200 $7392 €6132 Mountain road, Jamaica (51x60cm-20x24in) s. canvas on board. 19-May-4 Sotheby's, Olympia #230/R est:2500-3500
£14946 $27500 €21821 Blue Harbor, Jamaica (41x30cm-16x12in) s. canvasboard. 10-Jun-4 Sotheby's, New York #369/R est:3000-5000
£26000 $47580 €37960 Jamaica bay (61x76cm-24x30in) s. prov. 4-Jun-4 Christie's, London #53/R est:20000-30000
Works on paper
£280 $518 €409 Musical carousel (20x23cm-8x9in) s. W/C bodycol. 11-Mar-4 Duke & Son, Dorchester #126/R

COWARD, Sir Noel (attrib) (1899-1973) British
£700 $1295 €1022 Sunbathers on a Jamaican beach (28x41cm-11x16in) board. 9-Mar-4 Gorringes, Lewes #2135

COWBOY, Dick (1941-) Australian
Works on paper
£938 $1753 €1407 Yatingjarra (119x59cm-47x23in) bears name.verso synthetic polymer paint canvas prov. 26-Jul-4 Sotheby's, Melbourne #423/R (A.D 2400)

COWEN, William (attrib) (1797-1860) British
Works on paper
£1100 $1980 €1606 The Plain of Jarascon and the Castle of Beaucaire (12x30cm-5x12in) i.d.1833 W/C. 21-Apr-4 Rupert Toovey, Partridge Green #94 est:100-150

COWERN, Jenny (?) British
£300 $558 €438 Light and vine (84x91cm-33x36in) s. 4-Mar-4 Mitchells, Cockermouth #849

COWHANDY, H (?) ?
Works on paper
£1200 $2160 €1752 Fairy visit (36x25cm-14x10in) s. pencil W/C bodycol. 21-Apr-4 Lyon & Turnbull, Edinburgh #245/R est:100-200

COWIE, James (1886-1956) British
£540 $853 €788 Cattle and figures in rural hamlet (30x46cm-12x18in) s.d.1881. 7-Sep-3 Desmond Judd, Cranbrook #672
Works on paper
£750 $1208 €1088 Woman's head (30x22cm-12x9in) pencil prov. 21-Aug-3 Bonhams, Edinburgh #1134/R

COWIESON, Agnes M (fl.1882-1940) British
£1381 $2500 €2016 Bulldogs at the show (28x38cm-11x15in) s.d.96. 30-Mar-4 Bonhams & Butterfields, San Francisco #109/R est:1000-1500

COWIN, Jack Lee (1947-) Canadian
Works on paper
£220 $403 €321 Spaniel (50x45cm-20x18in) s.d.1947 pencil. 1-Jun-4 Hodgins, Calgary #74/R (C.D 550)

COWLES, Fleur (20th C) American
£1198 $2000 €1749 Untitled (51x35cm-20x14in) s.d.82 board prov. 20-Oct-3 Sotheby's, New York #177/R est:1000-1500
£1497 $2500 €2186 Untitled (76x30cm-30x12in) s.d.62 panel prov.exhib. 20-Oct-3 Sotheby's, New York #176/R est:1500-2500
Works on paper
£217 $400 €317 Ballet (89x81cm-35x32in) s.d.75 mixed media on board. 13-Jun-4 Bonhams & Butterfields, Los Angeles #7052/R

COWLEY, Charles George (fl.1880-1892) British
£2000 $3660 €2920 Race (53x90cm-21x35in) s. 28-Jul-4 Bonhams, Knightsbridge #117/R est:2000-3000

COWLEY, Reta (1910-) Canadian
Works on paper
£201 $345 €293 Pasture East on Warman (39x55cm-15x22in) s.d. May 30 1985 prov. 2-Dec-3 Joyner Waddington, Toronto #438 (C.D 450)
£268 $461 €391 West of Perdue, East of Bigger, mid afternoon (56x75cm-22x30in) s.d.June 23, 1981 prov. 2-Dec-3 Joyner Waddington, Toronto #253/R (C.D 600)
£400 $732 €584 Morning, fast moving clouds (55x75cm-22x30in) s.i.d.1980 W/C prov. 1-Jun-4 Hodgins, Calgary #99/R (C.D 1000)

COWNIE, Alan (20th C) British
Works on paper
£500 $800 €730 Kneeling female nude figure (36x28cm-14x11in) s. 16-Sep-3 Capes Dunn, Manchester #714

COWPER, Frank Cadogan (1877-1958) British
£64706 $110000 €94471 Fair Rosamund and Eleanor (102x127cm-40x50in) s.d.1920 exhib. 28-Oct-3 Sotheby's, New York #69/R est:80000-120000
Works on paper
£20000 $34000 €29200 Margaret - alone at her spinning wheel (43x33cm-17x13in) s.i.d.1907 pencil W/C htd white prov.exhib. 20-Nov-3 Christie's, London #138/R est:20000-30000
£20000 $36800 €30000 Vanite (53x44cm-21x17in) s.d.1918 pastel exhib. 11-Jun-4 Claude Aguttes, Neuilly #106/R est:3000-5000

COX, Albert Scott (1863-?) American
£1956 $3500 €2856 Central Park (51x102cm-20x40in) s. prov. 14-May-4 Skinner, Boston #294/R est:3500-5500

COX, Alfred Wilson (c.1820-1888) British
Works on paper
£290 $458 €423 Panoramic landscape scene with numerous cows and sheep. s.d. W/C. 6-Sep-3 Hogben, Folkstone #178

COX, Allyn (1896-?) American
£31250 $55000 €45625 Still lifes of floral arrangements and seashells (91x91cm-36x36in) pair. 21-May-4 North East Auctions, Portsmouth #562/R

COX, Arthur (?) British
Works on paper
£580 $1038 €847 Mann Island bridge (17x24cm-7x9in) s. W/C. 17-Mar-4 James Thompson, Kirby Lonsdale #109

COX, Arthur W (19th C) Canadian
£901 $1532 €1315 Broad mountain valley (50x136cm-20x54in) s.indis.d. prov. 23-Nov-3 Levis, Calgary #24/R est:4500-5500 (C.D 2000)

COX, David (jnr) (1809-1885) British
£850 $1420 €1241 Shepherd leading flock (61x91cm-24x36in) s.d.59 prov. 17-Oct-3 Keys, Aylsham #727
£1400 $2282 €2044 Shepherd and sheep on hillside being rounded up by dog (28x36cm-11x14in) s.d.1857. 23-Sep-3 John Nicholson, Haslemere #317/R est:1500-3000

Works on paper

£250	$400	€365	Elegant Party (33x50cm-13x20in) s.d.1857 W/C over traces pencil htd white. 16-Sep-3 Bonhams, Knowle #74
£260	$424	€380	Bridge over a river (30x51cm-12x20in) s.i.d.1850 W/C. 27-Sep-3 Rogers Jones, Clwyd #74
£280	$512	€409	Cattle by a ruined abbey (25x35cm-10x14in) W/C. 7-Apr-4 Woolley & Wallis, Salisbury #107
£300	$480	€438	Saltwood Castleruins in background and figures by water well. s.d.1854 W/C. 17-May-3 Hogben, Folkstone #174
£300	$549	€438	Continental landscape with a monastery on a hill (28x39cm-11x15in) W/C. 7-Apr-4 Woolley & Wallis, Salisbury #103/R
£300	$549	€438	Brough Castle (25x40cm-10x16in) i. W/C. 7-Apr-4 Woolley & Wallis, Salisbury #109/R
£310	$567	€453	Figure in front of a mill (36x46cm-14x18in) s.d.1843 W/C. 27-Jan-4 Bonhams, Knightsbridge #152/R
£350	$571	€511	Llanberis Pass with snow covered peaks and farmer and dog on track (15x36cm-6x14in) W/C. 27-Sep-3 Rogers Jones, Clwyd #19
£360	$662	€526	Figures in conversation in a cornfield (33x49cm-13x19in) s. W/C bodycol. 23-Jun-4 Bonhams, Bury St Edmunds #341
£400	$652	€584	Landscape witj drover and sheep on a track, Moel Siabod (20x30cm-8x12in) s.d.1850 W/C. 27-Sep-3 Rogers Jones, Clwyd #25
£420	$756	€613	Craggy hills with trees (30x48cm-12x19in) s.i.d.1873 W/C. 24-Apr-4 Rogers Jones, Clwyd #127
£500	$815	€730	Above Blaenau Ffestiniog, path and cottage with cattle (23x33cm-9x13in) W/C. 27-Sep-3 Rogers Jones, Clwyd #46
£500	$835	€730	Peat cutters in a mountainous landscape (47x74cm-19x29in) s.d.1871 pencil W/C. 16-Oct-3 Christie's, Kensington #31/R
£500	$850	€730	Figures with a goat in a rural landscape (29x38cm-11x15in) s.d.1860 W/C. 25-Nov-3 Bonhams, Knightsbridge #190/R
£500	$910	€750	Paysage anime (24x33cm-9x13in) s.d.1850 W/C. 29-Jun-4 Chenu & Scrive, Lyon #56/R
£600	$978	€876	Conway valley lead mine scene with figures (20x30cm-8x12in) W/C. 27-Sep-3 Rogers Jones, Clwyd #41
£640	$1043	€934	Castle keep with farmer at gate with cattle (23x36cm-9x14in) W/C. 27-Sep-3 Rogers Jones, Clwyd #63
£800	$1360	€1168	Sunset on the beach, Hastings (24x29cm-9x11in) W/C prov. 4-Nov-3 Bonhams, New Bond Street #50
£1500	$2655	€2190	Cattle on a track in an extensive mountainous landscape (33x51cm-13x20in) W/C. 28-Apr-4 Halls, Shrewsbury #476/R est:1500-2000

COX, David (jnr-attrib) (1809-1885) British

Works on paper

£250	$455	€365	Harvesters loading the hay wagon (15x24cm-6x9in) pencil W/C. 1-Jul-4 Christie's, Kensington #77/R
£280	$448	€409	Shanklin, Isle of Wight (25x43cm-10x17in) i.verso. 16-Sep-3 Capes Dunn, Manchester #870

COX, David (1783-1859) British

£400	$632	€584	On the Sands (14x19cm-6x7in) indis.i. arched board. 24-Jul-3 Dominic Winter, Swindon #90/R
£540	$956	€788	Female figure crossing a timber bridge with windswept tree and distance windmill (28x37cm-11x15in) s. 30-Apr-4 Bigwood, Stratford on Avon #343/R
£1100	$2013	€1606	Rehearsal (46x33cm-18x13in) s. board. 27-Jan-4 Gorringes, Lewes #1567 est:150-200
£1300	$2158	€1898	Stepping stones (27x37cm-11x15in) s. board prov. 1-Oct-3 Sotheby's, Olympia #40/R est:1500-2500
£1600	$2720	€2336	White pony on heathland (16x25cm-6x10in) s.d.1851 i.verso panel. 25-Nov-3 Martel Maides, Guernsey #219a/R est:1000-1500
£2500	$4175	€3650	Figures in an open landscape (28x36cm-11x14in) s.d.1854. 8-Oct-3 Andrew Hartley, Ilkley #1117/R est:2500-3500

Works on paper

£206	$350	€301	Entrance to Woodhall (33x23cm-13x9in) i.d.1832 W/C. 22-Nov-3 New Orleans Auction, New Orleans #318
£320	$589	€467	Near Abergavenny, South Wales (17x25cm-7x10in) s.d.1849 pencil W/C. 25-Mar-4 Christie's, Kensington #24
£350	$606	€511	Rhyl Sands (10x18cm-4x7in) s. W/C. 12-Dec-3 Halls, Shrewsbury #528
£420	$785	€630	Study of an abbey (9x12cm-4x5in) s. W/C. 26-Jul-4 Bonhams, Bath #9/R
£480	$874	€701	Windsor Castle from the Great Park (19x28cm-7x11in) pencil W/C scratching out prov.exhib. 1-Jul-4 Christie's, Kensington #78/R
£480	$898	€701	Overlooking the flock (17x25cm-7x10in) s.d.1847 pencil W/C htd white. 22-Jul-4 Tennants, Leyburn #643
£500	$860	€730	Windsor Castle from the Great Park (19x28cm-7x11in) pencil W/C prov.exhib. 3-Dec-3 Christie's, Kensington #10/R
£500	$900	€730	Bay at Llandudno looking towards the Little Orme with figures and boats (20x33cm-8x13in) s.i. 24-Apr-4 Rogers Jones, Clwyd #128
£520	$848	€759	River valley in summer with small bridge in foreground (23x36cm-9x14in) s.d.1846 W/C. 23-Sep-3 Anderson & Garland, Newcastle #280/R
£550	$1012	€803	Old Calais fortifications, France (21x14cm-8x6in) pencil wash. 22-Jun-4 Bonhams, Knightsbridge #186/R
£640	$1197	€934	View of Haddon Hall (11x15cm-4x6in) bears sig. W/C over pencil. 24-Feb-4 Bonhams, Knowle #25
£1000	$1850	€1460	Moel Siabod, North Wales (22x29cm-9x11in) s. W/C prov.exhib. 9-Mar-4 Bonhams, New Bond Street #65/R est:1200-1800
£1000	$1800	€1460	French market place with awnings (20x26cm-8x10in) pencil W/C htd white prov. 21-Apr-4 Tennants, Leyburn #912 est:1000-1200
£1150	$2128	€1679	Near Kenilworth, Warwickshire (20x26cm-8x10in) blk chk prov.lit. 10-Mar-4 Sotheby's, Olympia #129/R est:600-800
£1200	$2184	€1752	View of Valle Crucis Abbey, Denbighshire (20x28cm-8x11in) s.d.58 W/C. 15-Jun-4 Canterbury Auctions, UK #120/R est:1200-1500
£1300	$2405	€1898	Windermere with Wray Castle beyond (19x30cm-7x12in) s.indis.d. W/C. 9-Mar-4 Bonhams, New Bond Street #67/R est:1000-1500
£1400	$2380	€2044	Changing pasture (20x30cm-8x12in) s.d.1854 W/C. 4-Nov-3 Bonhams, New Bond Street #54/R est:1200-1800
£1500	$2400	€2190	Highland landscape, possibly Snowdonia, with figures. W/C. 16-Sep-3 Lawrences, Bletchingley #1864/R
£1500	$2745	€2190	View in Snowdonia (20x28cm-8x11in) s. pencil W/C prov. 3-Jun-4 Christie's, London #124/R est:600-800
£1650	$2805	€2409	Drovers on hillside with riverside town in background (25x47cm-10x19in) W/C prov. 25-Nov-3 Martel Maides, Guernsey #213/R est:600-800
£1700	$2839	€2482	Cattle on wooded bank (17x24cm-7x9in) s. W/C prov. 12-Nov-3 Sotheby's, Olympia #8/R est:1500-2000
£1900	$3458	€2774	Passing shower, Yorkshire (19x26cm-7x10in) pencil W/C scratching out prov. 1-Jul-4 Christie's, Kensington #69/R est:800-1200
£2200	$4070	€3212	Landscape with a man washing his feet (29x40cm-11x16in) s. W/C exec.c.1820 after Nicholas Poussin. 9-Mar-4 Bonhams, New Bond Street #64/R est:2500-3000
£2200	$4070	€3212	Traveller on horseback (18x28cm-7x11in) s. W/C. 10-Mar-4 Sotheby's, Olympia #132/R est:800-1200
£2200	$4026	€3212	Travellers on a road, North Wales (21x31cm-8x12in) s.d.1851 pencil W/C htd touches bodycol scratching out prov.exhib. 3-Jun-4 Christie's, London #122/R est:2000-3000
£2200	$4026	€3212	Terrace, Haddon Hall, Derbyshire (21x44cm-8x17in) init.d.1845 blk chk W/C two joined sheets prov.exhib. 3-Jun-4 Christie's, London #153/R est:2500-3500
£2700	$4590	€3942	Going to market, possibly Coventry (15x24cm-6x9in) W/C prov. 4-Nov-3 Bonhams, New Bond Street #51/R est:3000-5000
£2700	$4860	€3942	Figures in Elizabethan costume on terrace and steps (23x33cm-9x13in) s.d.1841 W/C prov. 20-Apr-4 Canterbury Auctions, UK #199/R est:1250-2400
£2800	$5152	€4088	Great Orme Head from the mouth of the Conway, North Wales (19x25cm-7x10in) W/C over pencil htd stopping out. 26-Mar-4 Sotheby's, London #116/R est:3000-5000
£3000	$5490	€4380	Going to the Hayfield (20x30cm-8x12in) s. W/C prov.exhib. 7-Apr-4 Woolley & Wallis, Salisbury #102/R est:2000-3000
£3200	$5440	€4672	Shepherd and sheep by a barn on a country road (21x32cm-8x13in) s. W/C over pencil htd bodycol prov. 27-Nov-3 Sotheby's, London #267/R est:2000-3000
£3500	$6405	€5110	Old Border Castle (19x28cm-7x11in) pencil W/C htd touches of bodycol scratching out prov. 3-Jun-4 Christie's, London #121/R est:3000-5000
£3600	$6660	€5256	Brigands lying in wait for a stage coach (33x48cm-13x19in) s. 14-Jan-4 Brightwells, Leominster #848/R est:2000-3000
£3600	$6552	€5256	Fisherfolk on the shore (15x22cm-6x9in) s. W/C over pencil htd bodycol. 1-Jul-4 Sotheby's, London #207/R est:3000-4000
£3700	$6845	€5402	Cattle in stream (10x28cm-4x11in) W/C pencil studies verso double-sided. 10-Mar-4 Sotheby's, Olympia #131/R est:1000-1500
£4000	$7280	€5840	Figures on the terraces at Powis Castle, Montgomeryshire (24x34cm-9x13in) s. W/C over pencil htd bodycol prov. 1-Jul-4 Sotheby's, London #223/R est:4000-6000
£4200	$7686	€6132	Figures in highland dress (16x24cm-6x9in) pencil W/C htd touches bodycol prov. 3-Jun-4 Christie's, London #120/R est:3000-5000
£5000	$9250	€7300	Sandy common (26x39cm-10x15in) s.d.1833 W/C prov. 9-Mar-4 Bonhams, New Bond Street #63/R est:4000-6000
£6000	$10200	€8760	Courtyard, Haddon Hall (15x24cm-6x9in) pen ink W/C over pencil. 27-Nov-3 Sotheby's, London #252/R est:3000-5000
£6000	$10920	€8760	Travellers on a country track (20x31cm-8x12in) s. W/C over pencil htd bodycol. 1-Jul-4 Sotheby's, London #224/R est:2000-3000
£7500	$13725	€10950	Shipping off Gravesend (13x18cm-5x7in) s.d.1829 pencil W/C htd touches bodycol prov. 3-Jun-4 Christie's, London #143/R est:5000-8000
£8500	$14450	€12410	Fish market on the beach at Hastings (13x21cm-5x8in) s. W/C htd white prov. 4-Nov-3 Bonhams, New Bond Street #49/R est:4000-6000
£8500	$15470	€12410	Fishing boats at Dover (14x19cm-6x7in) W/C over pencil htd bodycol scratching out prov.exhib. 1-Jul-4 Sotheby's, London #229/R est:5000-7000
£11000	$18370	€16060	Rain cloud, Carig Cenin, near Llandelio (58x76cm-23x30in) s. W/C prov. 12-Nov-3 Halls, Shrewsbury #286/R est:7000-10000
£14000	$23800	€20440	Porte Saint Denis, Paris (31x22cm-12x9in) i.verso pencil W/C prov. 20-Nov-3 Christie's, London #89/R est:10000-15000
£14000	$23800	€20440	Lancaster Sands (19x26cm-7x10in) s. pencil W/C prov. 20-Nov-3 Christie's, London #48/R est:6000-8000

COX, David (attrib) (1783-1859) British

£420	$773	€613	Horse cart on a country road (38x51cm-15x20in) with sig. board. 23-Mar-4 Anderson & Garland, Newcastle #429
£550	$919	€803	Driving the sheep (25x39cm-10x15in) panel prov. 13-Nov-3 Christie's, Kensington #101/R
£3467	$6275	€5200	Cascatelle au pied d'une montagne (26x44cm-10x17in) paper on panel. 30-Mar-4 Rossini, Paris #85/R est:2000-3000

Works on paper

£260	$468	€380	Ship in choppy seas off harbour (10x13cm-4x5in) W/C oval. 20-Apr-4 Canterbury Auctions, UK #197
£280	$490	€409	Pomoroy Castle (15x20cm-6x8in) W/C. 19-Dec-3 Mallams, Oxford #123
£310	$518	€453	Valley scene near Snowdon, North Wales (33x43cm-13x17in) indis.sig. W/C. 17-Oct-3 Keys, Aylsham #365
£850	$1386	€1241	River landscape with trees and two figures seated on a bank (20x29cm-8x11in) W/C. 24-Sep-3 Dreweatt Neate, Newbury #25/R
£2200	$4026	€3212	Wooded summer landscape with cattle watering (18x28cm-7x11in) bears sig. pencil W/C htd white. 10-Jun-4 Neales, Nottingham #554 est:200-300
£9000	$15030	€13140	Figures with horse and sheep in landscape with distsnt hills. Figures in landscape with distsnt hill (20x32cm-8x13in) one bears sigd.1834 W/C pencil pair. 16-Oct-3 Lawrence, Crewkerne #634/R est:1500-2000

COX, David (attrib) (1914-) British

Works on paper

£544	$975	€800	Trois voyageuses dans un paysage. Un homme indiquant son chemin (19x29cm-7x11in) i. W/C gouache traces black crayon two. 17-Mar-4 Tajan, Paris #174

COX, Garstin (1892-1933) British

£450	$833	€657	Bulmershe Court, Berkshire (46x91cm 18x36in) s. 15 Jun 4 Christie's, Kensington #1008/R
£640	$1107	€934	The pool at the edge of the wood (57x43cm-22x17in) s. board. 11-Dec-3 Lane, Penzance #298
£700	$1295	€1022	Lizard cove (48x61cm-19x24in) s. 10-Feb-4 David Lay, Penzance #592
£750	$1403	€1095	Golden lights, view of the Lizard coastline (71x91cm-28x36in) s.i.verso. 26-Feb-4 Lane, Penzance #306
£900	$1638	€1314	Moonlight over a woodland pool (70x90cm-28x35in) s. 21-Jun-4 Bonhams, Bath #442/R
£1300	$2379	€1898	Sundown, Kynance (101x127cm-40x50in) s. s.i. overlap. 6-Jul-4 Bearnes, Exeter #540/R est:800-1000
£1500	$2745	€2190	Roseworthy hamlet near Camborne (71x90cm-28x35in) s. 3-Jun-4 Lane, Penzance #238 est:1200-1500
£2800	$5180	€4088	Woodland stream and pool (71x91cm-28x36in) s. 10-Feb-4 David Lay, Penzance #556/R est:3500-4500
£2800	$5124	€4088	Old Cornwall, Roseworthy Valley (67x112cm-26x44in) s. i.verso. 3-Jun-4 Lane, Penzance #85/R est:3000-4000

COX, Gerard (snr) (19/20th C) ?
Works on paper
£509 $850 €743 Shepherd and his flock. s.d.1916 pastel. 18-Oct-3 Harvey Clar, Oakland #1186

COX, Jack (?) ?
£250 $418 €365 Harbour Wells-next-the-Sea (48x61cm-19x24in) s. 17-Oct-3 Keys, Aylsham #674
£260 $471 €380 Mallard alighting on water (43x64cm-17x25in) s. 16-Apr-4 Keys, Aylsham #661
£270 $489 €394 Harbour, Well-next-the-sea (33x48cm-13x19in) s. 16-Apr-4 Keys, Aylsham #665
£280 $507 €409 North Norfolk coastal view with bait diggers (48x58cm-19x23in) s. 16-Apr-4 Keys, Aylsham #664
£290 $525 €423 North Norfolk coastal view with bait diggers (48x74cm-19x29in) s. 16-Apr-4 Keys, Aylsham #663
£300 $501 €438 North Norfolk river estaury scene (38x48cm-15x19in) s. 17-Oct-3 Keys, Aylsham #681
£320 $589 €467 Mallard rising from a North Norfolk estuary in winter (19x23cm-7x9in) s. 11-Jun-4 Keys, Aylsham #598
£360 $666 €526 Mallard rising from salt marshes, North Norfolk (38x46cm-15x18in) s. 13-Feb-4 Keys, Aylsham #615a
£380 $703 €555 North Norfolk river estuary view with sailing boats (43x69cm-17x27in) s. 13-Feb-4 Keys, Aylsham #613
£400 $668 €584 Harbour, Wells-next-the-Sea (48x58cm-19x23in) 17-Oct-3 Keys, Aylsham #683
£400 $724 €584 Wells-next-the-sea (43x69cm-17x27in) s. 16-Apr-4 Keys, Aylsham #662
£420 $701 €613 Creek at Wells-next-the-Sea (38x46cm-15x18in) s. 17-Oct-3 Keys, Aylsham #679/R
£440 $814 €642 North Norfolk river estuary scene with sailing boats (43x69cm-17x27in) s. 13-Feb-4 Keys, Aylsham #615
£580 $1067 €847 Geese rising from a north Norfolk estuary in winter (20x30cm-8x12in) s. 11-Jun-4 Keys, Aylsham #599/R
£680 $1231 €993 Unloading whelks, East End, Wells-next-the-sea (48x74cm-19x29in) s. 16-Apr-4 Keys, Aylsham #676/R
£680 $1231 €993 Fishermen at the slipway, Wells-next-the-sea (74x94cm-29x37in) s. 16-Apr-4 Keys, Aylsham #677/R
£750 $1388 €1095 Boats at Burnham Overy, Staithe (43x66cm-17x26in) s. 13-Feb-4 Keys, Aylsham #614/R
Works on paper
£310 $518 €453 Fishermen by boats (38x46cm-15x18in) s. W/C. 17-Oct-3 Keys, Aylsham #680

COX, Jan (1919-1980) Belgian
£909 $1518 €1300 Formes de la terre (29x20cm-11x8in) s.d.56 panel prov. 11-Oct-3 De Vuyst, Lokeren #74/R
£1479 $2558 €2100 Stayr and nymph (49x71cm-19x28in) i. prov. 13-Dec-3 De Vuyst, Lokeren #68/R est:800-1200
£2028 $3387 €2900 Window (86x62cm-34x24in) s.d.46 paper on panel. 11-Oct-3 De Vuyst, Lokeren #72/R est:1500-2000
Works on paper
£1189 $1985 €1700 Self portrait, waking and sleeping (36x74cm-14x29in) s.d.52 gouache pencil prov. 11-Oct-3 De Vuyst, Lokeren #73/R est:1200-1500
£1678 $2803 €2400 Two figures in a boat (21x54cm-8x21in) s.i.d.52 gouache pastel Indian ink prov. 11-Oct-3 De Vuyst, Lokeren #75/R est:800-1200
£2797 $4671 €4000 The movie house (102x67cm-40x26in) s.d.62 pastel chl prov.exhib.lit. 11-Oct-3 De Vuyst, Lokeren #477/R est:4000-5000

COX, Marjorie (1915-2003) British
Works on paper
£250 $460 €365 Two King Charles Spaniels (37x42cm-15x17in) s. pastel. 10-Jun-4 Christie's, Kensington #402/R
£260 $411 €377 Clover, a terrier seated (38x40cm-15x16in) s.d.1968 pastel. 2-Sep-3 Bonhams, Oxford #35
£270 $500 €394 Storm, a retriever (46x38cm-18x15in) s.i.d.1962 pastel. 10-Feb-4 Doyle, New York #167/R
£300 $474 €435 Tarn, a border terrier standing foresquare (43x48cm-17x19in) s.d.1972 pastel. 2-Sep-3 Bonhams, Oxford #55
£469 $850 €685 Brutus and Pucci Cassardi (48x50cm-19x20in) s.i.d.1966 col chk. 30-Mar-4 Bonhams & Butterfields, San Francisco #135/R

COX, Neil (?) British
Works on paper
£220 $374 €321 Woodcock amidst silver birch (46x67cm-18x26in) s. pencil W/C. 27-Nov-3 Christie's, Kensington #220/R
£300 $510 €438 Stags on a moor (15x31cm-6x12in) s. W/C bodycol. 27-Nov-3 Christie's, Kensington #197/R
£300 $567 €438 Red squirrels on a branch (30x44cm-12x17in) s. W/C bodycol. 19-Feb-4 Christie's, Kensington #336
£850 $1445 €1241 Pheasants in a clearing (44x67cm-17x26in) s. W/C htd white. 27-Nov-3 Christie's, Kensington #215/R
£1000 $1700 €1460 Pheasants in the snow (40x71cm-16x28in) s. W/C bodycol. 27-Nov-3 Christie's, Kensington #216/R est:800-1200

COX, P P (20th C) American
£2229 $3700 €3254 Man with a carpet bag (97x53cm-38x21in) s. 4-Oct-3 Neal Auction Company, New Orleans #1068/R est:1500-2500

COX, Patrick Douglass (1953-) Canadian
£452 $756 €660 Ditchrider, Darrell McCoomb, near Gem, AB (29x25cm-11x10in) s.i. egg tempera on board. 17-Nov-3 Hodgins, Calgary #195/R est:2000-2500 (C.D 1000)
Works on paper
£249 $416 €364 School teacher (19x25cm-7x10in) s.d.1997 pencil. 17-Nov-3 Hodgins, Calgary #276/R (C.D 550)

COX, Stephen (1958-) Australian
£851 $1472 €1242 New Aguarian (176x145cm-69x57in) s.i.d.1991 oil enamel chl. 10-Dec-3 Shapiro, Sydney #98/R (A.D 2000)

COX, Stephen (1946-) British
Works on paper
£750 $1365 €1095 Study for Square (66x126cm-26x50in) s.d.87 mixed media. 15-Jun-4 Bonhams, Knightsbridge #223/R

COX, Walter I (1866-1930) American/British
£647 $1100 €945 Oak trees landscape (12x18cm-5x7in) s. board prov. 18-Nov-3 John Moran, Pasadena #111
£1497 $2500 €2186 Willotta Ranch, Suisin, California (56x71cm-22x28in) s. indis.i.d.verso. 26-Oct-3 Bonhams & Butterfields, San Francisco #6493/R

COX, William (?) British?
£1100 $1936 €1606 Shipping before St. Michael's Mount (52x61cm-20x24in) s. 19-May-4 Christie's, Kensington #564/R est:1000-1500

COXCIE, Michiel (circle) (16/17th C) Flemish
£7639 $12069 €11000 Youthful Saint John the Baptist (102x73cm-40x29in) panel prov. 2-Sep-3 Christie's, Amsterdam #15/R est:10000-15000

COXCIE, Michiel I (attrib) (1499-1592) Flemish
£6500 $11245 €9490 Christ carrying the Cross (89x68cm-35x27in) panel prov. 11-Dec-3 Sotheby's, London #176/R est:6000-8000

COXCIE, Michiel III (attrib) (1603-c.1669) Flemish
£1250 $2250 €1825 Circumcision (32x49cm-13x19in) 21-Jan-4 Doyle, New York #74/R est:4000-6000

COY, Anna (1851-1930) American
£270 $500 €394 Landscape with stream (23x30cm-9x12in) s. board. 24-Jan-4 Jeffery Burchard, Florida #64/R

COYLE, John (1928-) British
£521 $849 €750 View of buildings (40x32cm-16x13in) s. board. 23-Sep-3 De Veres Art Auctions, Dublin #174
£1141 $2042 €1700 Still life with pottery jug and bowl (35x46cm-14x18in) s. board. 26-May-4 James Adam, Dublin #103/R est:1000-1500

COYNE, Rod (20th C) Irish?
£333 $523 €480 Howth (40x59cm-16x23in) s. acrylic on paper. 26-Aug-3 James Adam, Dublin #187/R

COYORA (20th C) American?
£1235 $2100 €1803 Untitled (132x102cm-52x40in) s. 29-Nov-3 Carlsen Gallery, Greenville #363/R

COYPEL, Antoine (1661-1722) French
£9500 $16435 €13870 Cupid riding a satyr (22x25cm-9x10in) canvas on panel oval prov.exhib.lit. 11-Dec-3 Sotheby's, London #220/R est:7000-9000
Works on paper
£2192 $3726 €3200 Deux anges (34x28cm-13x11in) crayon. 6-Nov-3 Tajan, Paris #25/R

COYPEL, Charles Antoine (1694-1752) French
Works on paper
£4500 $8235 €6570 Man with his hands clasped over his head (24x41cm-9x16in) black red white chk. 6-Jul-4 Christie's, London #122/R est:3000-5000

COYPEL, Charles Antoine (attrib) (1694-1752) French
£1690 $2958 €2400 Historical scene (59x84cm-23x33in) 17-Dec-3 Christie's, Rome #312/R est:2000-3000
Works on paper
£320 $573 €480 Jeune homme etudiant sous l'autorite de Minerve. i. crayon stump. 15-May-4 other European Auctioneer #124
£2000 $3660 €3000 Magicien a la cour (37x54cm-15x21in) chl white chk prov. 5-Jun-4 Gros & Delettrez, Paris #66/R est:3000-4500

COYPEL, Noel (1628-1707) French
£8667 $15947 €13000 Mars et Venus (82x65cm-32x26in) prov. 11-Jun-4 Maigret, Paris #59/R est:15000-20000

COYPEL, Noel (attrib) (1628-1707) French
£1847 $3250 €2697 Allegorical scene of Adonis and Venus resting on the banks of a river (109x91cm-43x36in) masonite. 3-Jan-4 Cobbs, Peterborough #44

COYSEVOX, Antoine (after) (1640-1720) French
Sculpture
£11667 $21467 €17500 Hamadryade (160cm-63in) bears sig.d.1709 terracotta. 14-Jun-4 Cornette de St.Cyr, Paris #160/R est:15000-20000

COYSEVOX, Antoine (studio) (1640-1720) French
Sculpture
£16901 $29577 €24000 Louis XV enfant (51cm-20in) i. marble prov.lit. 16-Dec-3 Christie's, Paris #337/R est:15000-20000

COZAR, Jose (1944-) Spanish
£369 $690 €550 Autumn landscape (54x65cm-21x26in) s. 24-Feb-4 Durán, Madrid #115/R

COZENS, Alexander (c.1717-1786) British
Works on paper
£1100 $2013 €1606 Castle in a landscape (10x18cm-4x7in) s. grey wash. 3-Jun-4 Christie's, London #61/R est:1200-1800
£2400 $4080 €3504 Italianate view (10x14cm-4x6in) init. brown wash. 20-Nov-3 Christie's, London #11/R est:1000-1500
£4200 $7728 €6132 Classical landscape with a tower by a lake and mountains beyond (10x16cm-4x6in) s. ink wash. 26-Mar-4 Sotheby's, London #102/R est:2000-3000

COZZENS, Frederick Schiller (1846-1928) American
Works on paper
£419 $750 €612 Ships at sea (41x33cm-16x13in) s.d.99 W/C. 7-May-4 Sloans & Kenyon, Bethesda #1221/R
£642 $1200 €937 British warship parading into port (28x43cm-11x17in) s.d.90 W/C gouache. 29-Feb-4 Grogan, Boston #55/R
£677 $1150 €988 Pond landscape (20x33cm-8x13in) s. W/C. 21-Nov-3 Eldred, East Dennis #259g est:600-800

COZZOLINO, Ciro (19th C) Italian
£278 $472 €400 Shepherdess in the stable (44x25cm-17x10in) s. 1-Nov-3 Meeting Art, Vercelli #439
£3500 $5810 €5110 Luxembourg Gardens, paris (46x55cm-18x22in) s. 1-Oct-3 Sotheby's, Olympia #296/R est:2000-3000

CRABEELS, Florent (1829-1896) Flemish
£600 $1086 €900 Berger (25x17cm-10x7in) s. 30-Mar-4 Campo, Vlaamse Kaai #24

CRABETH, Wouter II (attrib) (1593-1644) Dutch
£5405 $9514 €8000 The doubting Thomas (104x143cm-41x56in) 24-May-4 Bernaerts, Antwerp #88/R est:8000-10000

CRACE, John Dibblee (1838-1919) British
£1250 $2250 €1825 Palace of Ramses The Third (46x35cm-18x14in) s.d.1877. 21-Jan-4 Sotheby's, Olympia #375/R est:1500-2000

CRACKING ART (20th C) Italian
Sculpture
£1533 $2760 €2300 S.O.S. World (13x43x30cm-5x17x12in) s. plastic pigment exec.2001 exhib.lit. 22-Apr-4 Finarte Semenzato, Rome #281/R est:1900-2200
£11189 $19021 €16000 S.O.S. World. plastic pigment exec.2001 in many parts exhib.lit. 24-Nov-3 Christie's, Milan #241/R est:10000-12000

CRADOCK, Marmaduke (1660-1717) British
£2800 $5012 €4088 Silver houdon hen with chick. Turkey with peacock (30x35cm-12x14in) pair prov. 26-May-4 Sotheby's, Olympia #29/R est:3000-5000
£12000 $22080 €17520 Peacock, chickens, jay and other birds by a barn. Chicken and ducks by a wall in a river landscape (38x68cm-15x27in) pair prov. 11-Jun-4 Christie's, London #38/R est:15000-20000
£20000 $36800 €29200 Ducks on a river. Peacock, turkey and chickens on a riverbank (35x44cm-14x17in) pair. prov. 11-Jun-4 Christie's, London #46/R est:12000-18000

CRADOCK, Marmaduke (attrib) (1660-1717) British
£20000 $37200 €29200 Ducks on a pond with a pavilion beyond (56x97cm-22x38in) indis sig. 4-Mar-4 Christie's, Kensington #396/R est:4000-6000
£22000 $40480 €32120 Peacock and other birds in an ornamental landscape (135x163cm-53x64in) 11-Jun-4 Christie's, London #45/R est:15000-25000

CRAEN, Laurens (17th C) Dutch
£36913 $67919 €55000 Still life with grapes, peaches, oranges, ham in Ming bowl (49x64cm-19x25in) panel. 24-Mar-4 Dorotheum, Vienna #158/R est:60000-80000

CRAESBEECK, Joos van (attrib) (1606-1654) Flemish
£1818 $3091 €2600 La colere. L'avarice (25x19cm-10x7in) panel pair. 18-Nov-3 Vanderkindere, Brussels #230 est:2000-3000
Works on paper
£690 $1152 €1000 Peasants making merry (40x33cm-16x13in) chk prov. 15-Nov-3 Lempertz, Koln #1282/R

CRAEYVANGER, Gijsbertus (1810-1895) Dutch
Works on paper
£537 $988 €800 Horse and cart (10x17cm-4x7in) s.d.1849 pen W/C. 29-Mar-4 Glerum, Amsterdam #129

CRAFFONARA, Aurelio (1875-1945) Italian
Works on paper
£867 $1551 €1300 Masks in Venice (18x18cm-7x7in) s. W/C. 12-May-4 Stadion, Trieste #664/R est:500-700
£1067 $1909 €1600 Canal in Venice (38x38cm-15x15in) s. W/C. 12-May-4 Stadion, Trieste #663/R est:600-800
£2083 $3542 €3000 Abandoned village (100x70cm-39x28in) s.d.1919 W/C card. 1-Nov-3 Meeting Art, Vercelli #102/R est:3000

CRAFT, Kinuko (20th C) ?
£514 $900 €750 Humanist Little Football Movie (56x76cm-22x30in) painted 1977. 17-Dec-3 Christie's, Rockefeller NY #214/R

CRAFT, Percy R (1856-1934) British
£1100 $1837 €1606 Cambridge days (27x35cm-11x14in) s.i. board. 16-Oct-3 Christie's, Kensington #412/R est:1000-1500
Works on paper
£270 $494 €394 Changing pasture (39x54cm-15x21in) s.i.d.1905 W/C. 8-Jul-4 Lawrence, Crewkerne #1536

CRAFTY, Victor Geruzez (1840-1906) French
Works on paper
£1812 $3389 €2700 Chasse a courre, bat-l'eau (17x27cm-7x11in) W/C gouache. 1-Mar-4 Coutau Begarie, Paris #190/R est:2000-2500
£3154 $5899 €4700 Attelage de chevaux (33x49cm-13x19in) W/C gouache. 1-Mar-4 Coutau Begarie, Paris #170/R est:1500-1800

CRAGG, Tony (1949-) British
Sculpture
£10056 $18000 €14682 Gazelle (137x74x178cm-54x29x70in) found bicycle steel rods glass bottles prov. 12-May-4 Christie's, Rockefeller NY #479/R est:15000-20000
£14970 $25000 €21856 Adontoid pegs (104x104x91cm-41x41x36in) found objects prov.lit. 13-Nov-3 Sotheby's, New York #137/R est:25000-35000
£23952 $40000 €34970 Atmos. brown pat bronze three parts. 13-Nov-3 Sotheby's, New York #488/R est:80000-120000
£23952 $40000 €34970 Tower (183x51x51cm-72x20x20in) found objects prov. 13-Nov-3 Sotheby's, New York #136/R est:25000-35000
£30000 $50100 €43800 Three modern buildings (350cm-138in) clay cement bricks exec 1984 prov.exhib.lit. 21-Oct-3 Sotheby's, London #327/R est:30000-40000
£40000 $71600 €60000 Untitled (105x145x120cm-41x57x47in) s. num.1/5 st.f.Schmake black pat bronze prov. 15-May-4 De Vuyst, Lokeren #525/R
Works on paper
£32000 $58880 €46720 Plastic palette I (192x157cm-76x62in) found plastic elements exec 1985 prov.exhib. 24-Jun-4 Sotheby's, London #115/R est:12000-15000

CRAIG, Charles (1846-1931) American
£802 $1500 €1171 With his dog (33x25cm-13x10in) s.d.1885 board prov. 24-Jul-4 Coeur d'Alene, Hayden #276/R est:1500-2500
£2652 $4800 €3872 Apache brave (51x41cm-20x16in) s. prov. 3-Apr-4 Neal Auction Company, New Orleans #604/R est:1500-2500
Works on paper
£3529 $6000 €5152 Indian Chief (38x25cm-15x10in) s.d.1895 W/C prov.lit. 1-Nov-3 Santa Fe Art, Santa Fe #118/R est:3000-5000

CRAIG, Henry Robertson (1916-1984) British
£805 $1482 €1200 Cloud study (8x15cm-3x6in) s. two in one frame pair. 23-Mar-4 Mealy's, Castlecomer #1126/R est:800-1500
£1600 $2624 €2336 Rose garden (76x63cm-30x25in) s. 4-Jun-3 John Ross, Belfast #118 est:1200
£1600 $2624 €2336 Afternoon in the garden (63x76cm-25x30in) s. 4-Jun-3 John Ross, Belfast #119
£2941 $5000 €4294 St. Mark's, Venice (61x102cm-24x40in) s. 19-Nov-3 Bonhams & Butterfields, San Francisco #168/R

CRAIG, J Humbert (1878-1944) Irish
£1400 $2604 €2044 Beach at Newcastle, Co. Down (25x33cm-10x13in) s. board. 3-Mar-4 John Ross, Belfast #164 est:1000-1200
£2028 $3448 €2900 Lake and mountains landscape (24x36cm-9x14in) s. board. 25-Nov-3 De Veres Art Auctions, Dublin #75/R est:3000-4000
£2800 $5068 €4200 Picnic in the woods (30x40cm-12x16in) s. board. 31-Mar-4 James Adam, Dublin #32/R est:4000-6000
£2800 $5068 €4200 Alton lake, Donegal (29x38cm-11x15in) s. board. 30-Mar-4 De Veres Art Auctions, Dublin #27/R est:3500-5000
£2838 $5364 €4200 Dun River and chapel (25x36cm-10x14in) s.i. canvas on board prov. 17-Feb-4 Whyte's, Dublin #123/R est:4000-5000
£3356 $5940 €5000 Getting to Bangor (25x36cm-10x14in) s. s.i.verso canvasboard prov. 27-Apr-4 Whyte's, Dublin #210/R est:4000-6000
£3662 $6335 €5200 Sunshine and showers, Carraroe, Co Galway (50x60cm-20x24in) s. i.verso board prov. 10-Dec-3 Bonhams & James Adam, Dublin #162/R est:5000-8000
£3732 $6457 €5300 Donegal river landscape (27x37cm-11x15in) s.d.1915 board. 10-Dec-3 Bonhams & James Adam, Dublin #76/R est:4000-5000
£3800 $6042 €5548 After rain, Co Donegal (30x43cm-12x17in) s. board prov.exhib. 10-Sep-3 Sotheby's, Olympia #164/R est:4000-6000
£3800 $6954 €5548 Unloading the catch, Donegal (22x30cm-9x12in) mono. board. 2-Jun-4 John Ross, Belfast #77 est:2000-2500
£3986 $6776 €5700 The Old Layde Road to Cushendun (28x42cm-11x17in) s. s.i.verso board. 18-Nov-3 Whyte's, Dublin #45/R est:6000-8000
£4000 $6560 €5840 Digging turf (30x43cm-12x17in) s. board. 4-Jun-3 John Ross, Belfast #114
£4070 $7000 €5942 Fish house, Port Na Blagh Barbour, Co. Donegal (30x44cm-12x17in) s. i.verso panel. 3-Dec-3 Doyle, New York #126/R est:6000-8000
£4200 $7686 €6132 Waterfoot. Co. Antrim (40x56cm-16x22in) s. board. 2-Jun-4 John Ross, Belfast #151 est:4000-5000
£4336 $7371 €6200 Summers day on the river (21x29cm-8x11in) s. 25-Nov-3 De Veres Art Auctions, Dublin #23/R est:6000-8000
£4800 $8928 €7008 Distant thunder (36x50cm-14x20in) s. board. 3-Mar-4 John Ross, Belfast #154 est:3000-3500
£4800 $8592 €7008 Landscape with peat stacks and turf cutters (30x41cm-12x16in) s. 14-May-4 Christie's, Kensington #371/R est:3000-5000

£4832 $8650 €7200 Figure and horse and cart on a windy beach (34x51cm-13x20in) s. prov. 26-May-4 James Adam, Dublin #46/R est:4000-6000
£4895 $8322 €7000 An Irish village (26x21cm-10x8in) card on board. 25-Nov-3 De Veres Art Auctions, Dublin #68/R est:7000-10000
£5068 $9578 €7500 River landscape with a couple in a boat (38x51cm-15x20in) s. 17-Feb-4 Whyte's, Dublin #60/R est:8000-10000
£5369 $9611 €8000 Lough Anure, Co Donegal (49x59cm-19x23in) s. prov. 26-May-4 James Adam, Dublin #93/R est:6000-10000
£5400 $10044 €7884 Working he field, Donegal (40x50cm-16x20in) s. 3-Mar-4 John Ross, Belfast #63 est:3000-4000
£5405 $10216 €8000 Glashercoo, County Donegal (38x51cm-15x20in) s. i.verso panel prov. 17-Feb-4 Whyte's, Dublin #122/R est:6000-8000
£5500 $9130 €8030 Flower seller (24x20cm-9x8in) s. board. 1-Oct-3 John Ross, Belfast #159 est:2000-2500
£5743 $10855 €8500 Cottages by the sea (38x51cm-15x20in) s. prov. 17-Feb-4 Whyte's, Dublin #61/R est:8000-10000
£6000 $10740 €8760 Cattle returning (29x38cm-11x15in) s. panel. 14-May-4 Christie's, London #215/R est:5000-8000
£6200 $10168 €9052 Fair Head (50x61cm-20x24in) s. 4-Jun-3 John Ross, Belfast #148
£6200 $11346 €9052 On the path home (43x38cm-17x15in) s. 2-Jun-4 John Ross, Belfast #145 est:3000-4000
£7000 $12530 €10220 The Bloody Foreland (51x61cm-20x24in) s. s.i. on overlap prov. 13-May-4 Sotheby's, London #37/R est:6000-8000
£7746 $12394 €11000 Fluke fishing at Killyhoe, County Donegal (36x47cm-14x19in) s. s.i.verso panel prov.lit. 16-Sep-3 Whyte's, Dublin #106/R est:10000-12000
£9091 $15455 €13000 Bathers (38x51cm-15x20in) s. i.verso board. 25-Nov-3 De Veres Art Auctions, Dublin #61/R est:9000-12000
£9155 $14648 €13000 Garron Point from Cushendun (38x51cm-15x20in) s. i.verso panel prov. 16-Sep-3 Whyte's, Dublin #92/R est:10000-12000
£9396 $16819 €14000 After rain in the Rosses (39x49cm-15x19in) s. s.i.verso board. 26-May-4 James Adam, Dublin #51/R est:14000-18000
£12000 $21480 €17520 Bathers at Cushendall (30x40cm-12x16in) s. canvasboard exhib.lit. 13-May-4 Sotheby's, London #90/R est:8000-12000
£17450 $30886 €26000 Woman and children on the Fairy Strand, Donegal (38x51cm-15x20in) s. 27-Apr-4 Whyte's, Dublin #50/R est:15000-20000
£18182 $30909 €26000 Children sailing toy boats on a park pond (38x51cm-15x20in) s. 18-Nov-3 Whyte's, Dublin #50/R est:18000-20000
£22000 $39380 €32120 Galway pig fair (25x36cm-10x14in) s. i.verso panel. 14-May-4 Christie's, London #213/R est:25000-35000
£22973 $43419 €34000 Sunday in Connemara (38x51cm-15x20in) s. panel prov. 17-Feb-4 Whyte's, Dublin #59/R est:15000-20000

Works on paper
£1399 $2378 €2000 Boats at Killyhoey, County Donegal (28x41cm-11x16in) s. i.verso W/C. 18-Nov-3 Whyte's, Dublin #186/R est:1500-2000

CRAIG, J Humbert (attrib) (1878-1944) Irish
£556 $906 €800 At the seaside (25x33cm-10x13in) bears sig. board. 23-Sep-3 De Veres Art Auctions, Dublin #307

CRAIG, James Stevenson (fl.1854-1870) British
£4500 $7650 €6570 Highland romance (77x63cm-30x25in) s.d.1869. 19-Nov-3 Bonhams, New Bond Street #51/R est:2000-3000

CRAIG, John (20th C) American
Works on paper
£457 $800 €667 Great moments in Pinball History (56x52cm-22x20in) ink mylar exec Dec 1972. 17-Dec-3 Christie's, Rockefeller NY #218/R
£1486 $2600 €2170 Just which kind of man are you (30x25cm-12x10in) each s. ink col film four collages exec 1974. 17-Dec-3 Christie's, Rockefeller NY #211/R est:1500-2000

CRAIG, Philip (1951-) Canadian
£2054 $3532 €2999 Country Garden (120x150cm-47x59in) s.d.1990. 2-Dec-3 Joyner Waddington, Toronto #319/R est:2500-3500 (C.D 4600)

CRAIG, Sybil (1901-1989) Australian
£246 $388 €359 HMVS Cerberus, Half Moon Bay, Melbourne (47x51cm-19x20in) s. paper. 2-Sep-3 Deutscher-Menzies, Melbourne #369/R (A.D 600)
£287 $453 €419 Seascape (20x25cm-8x10in) s. board. 2-Sep-3 Deutscher-Menzies, Melbourne #368/R (A.D 700)
£369 $583 €539 Flower piece (51x35cm-20x14in) s. i. verso canvasboard. 2-Sep-3 Deutscher-Menzies, Melbourne #325/R (A.D 900)
£738 $1165 €1077 Boats on the bay (28x21cm-11x8in) s. board. 2-Sep-3 Deutscher-Menzies, Melbourne #309/R est:800-1200 (A.D 1800)

CRAIG, Thomas (19th C) ?
£1563 $2500 €2282 Mid-summer (41x51cm-16x20in) s. i.verso. 20-Sep-3 Nadeau, Windsor #55/R

CRAIG, Thomas Bigelow (1849-1924) American
£511 $950 €746 Catskill Mountains (20x28cm-8x11in) s. board. 3-Mar-4 Alderfer's, Hatfield #297 est:1500-2000
£691 $1250 €1009 In the morning light October (58x84cm-23x33in) s.i.verso. 3-Apr-4 Neal Auction Company, New Orleans #103/R est:1800-2500
£1242 $2000 €1801 Evening hour (64x76cm-25x30in) s. s.i.verso. 17-Aug-3 Jeffery Burchard, Florida #81
£1890 $3250 €2759 Cattle and sheep grazing by water (51x76cm-20x30in) s. 7-Dec-3 Freeman, Philadelphia #162 est:1500-2500
£1934 $3500 €2824 Where the brook runs through the meadow (46x66cm-18x26in) s. s.i.verso. 18-Apr-4 Jeffery Burchard, Florida #96/R

Works on paper
£353 $650 €515 Sheep grazing in field with nearby barn and distant trees (23x38cm-9x15in) s. W/C. 9-Jun-4 Alderfer's, Hatfield #371/R
£407 $750 €594 Pasture scene with grazing cows (23x38cm-9x15in) s. W/C. 9-Jun-4 Alderfer's, Hatfield #372/R

CRAIG, Thomas Theodore (1909-1969) American
Works on paper
£312 $550 €456 Spring time (30x47cm-12x19in) s. W/C. 23-May-4 Bonhams & Butterfields, Los Angeles #7005/R

CRAIG, William Marshall (fl.1788-1828) British
Works on paper
£350 $655 €511 Young lady standing by a pianoforte (32x19cm-13x7in) i. pencil wash. 22-Jul-4 Tennants, Leyburn #633
£520 $884 €759 Scene of Scott's Rokeby on the Tees (16x22cm-6x9in) i. pencil W/C exec.c.1798-1800. 19-Nov-3 Tennants, Leyburn #982

CRAIG, William Marshall (attrib) (fl.1788-1828) British
Miniatures
£4600 $8464 €6716 Officer called George Byron, in the uniform of a Scottish Fencible cavalry regiment (8cm-3in) gold frame plaited hair border. 24-Jun-4 Bonhams, New Bond Street #71/R est:3000-5000

CRAIG-MARTIN, Michael (1941-) Irish
£7200 $13104 €10512 Untitled, sardine (56x56cm-22x22in) s.d.2001 overlap acrylic prov. 6-Feb-4 Sotheby's, London #265/R est:5000-7000
£9000 $16380 €13140 Sandal (56x43cm-22x17in) s.i.d.2000 overlap acrylic prov. 6-Feb-4 Sotheby's, London #264/R est:4000-6000

CRAIGER, Beatrice (1891-1946) American
£235 $400 €343 Floral still life (53x61cm-21x24in) s. 22-Nov-3 Jackson's, Cedar Falls #103/R

CRALI, Tullio (1910-2000) Italian
£966 $1612 €1400 Composition II (20x27cm-8x11in) s. cardboard. 13-Nov-3 Finarte Semenzato, Rome #263 est:800-1200
£1259 $2165 €1800 Science triumph (18x24cm-7x9in) s.d.34 tempera paper. 3-Dec-3 Stadion, Trieste #1046/R est:700-1000
£4196 $7133 €6000 High flight (20x25cm-8x10in) s.d.29 tempera pastel card ehl. 24-Nov-3 Christie's, Milan #307/R est:6000-8000

CRAM, Allen G (1886-1947) American
£193 $350 €282 Clouds (25x36cm-10x14in) board. 16-Apr-4 James Julia, Fairfield #917/R

CRAMER, Anna (1857-1941) Swedish
£443 $794 €647 Girl reading wearing pink dress (26x20cm-10x8in) panel. 26-May-4 AB Stockholms Auktionsverk #2215/R (S.KR 6000)

CRAMER, Helene (1844-1916) German
£621 $1148 €900 Blossom on twig (50x41cm-20x16in) board. 14-Feb-4 Hans Stahl, Hamburg #130/R

CRAMER, Konrad (1888-1963) American
£4706 $8000 €6871 Landscape with brook (41x48cm-16x19in) board. 9-Nov-3 Wright, Chicago #192 est:6000-8000
£13636 $24000 €19909 Doors - window and hall (121x76cm-48x30in) s.d.1930 s.i.d.verso board prov.lit. 18-May-4 Christie's, Rockefeller NY #128/R est:20000-30000

Works on paper
£245 $400 €358 Nude (38x20cm-15x8in) s. graphite. 19-Jul-3 Outer Cape Auctions, Provincetown #168/R
£323 $600 €472 Abstract proflies (48x30cm-19x12in) s. W/C. 7-Mar-4 William Jenack, New York #168
£380 $700 €555 Female nude (48x30cm-19x12in) s.d.1952 pen ink W/C. 10-Jun-4 Swann Galleries, New York #69/R
£435 $800 €635 Seated woman (41x20cm-16x8in) s.d.1929 gouache W/C crayon. 10-Jun-4 Swann Galleries, New York #67/R
£484 $900 €707 Abstract figure (48x30cm-19x12in) s. W/C. 7-Mar-4 William Jenack, New York #144
£1294 $2200 €1889 Study for a lampshade (20x25cm-8x10in) W/C executed c.1916 exhib. 9-Nov-3 Wright, Chicago #119 est:2500-3500

CRAMER, Molly (1862-?) German
£420 $701 €600 Birch trees in spring (47x33cm-19x13in) s. canvas on panel. 28-Jun-3 Bolland & Marotz, Bremen #629/R

CRAMER, Rie (20th C) Dutch
£816 $1486 €1200 Woman and child bowing. Making baskets. Looking at the ceiling (15x13cm-6x5in) s. ink W/C book illustrations. 3-Feb-4 Christie's, Amsterdam #272 est:600-800

CRAMER, S (19th C) American
£1377 $2300 €2010 View of the Hudson River Narrows (61x91cm-24x36in) s. 16-Nov-3 William Jenack, New York #406 est:2000-3000

CRAMPEL, Paule (19/20th C) French
Works on paper
£280 $481 €400 Jument et son poulain (18x23cm-7x9in) s. W/C. 3-Dec-3 Coutau Begarie, Paris #75/R

CRAMPTON, Rollin (20th C) Australian?
£485 $839 €708 Arrow series no 4 (90x126cm-35x50in) s.i.d.1968 acrylic ink prov. 9-Dec-3 Peter Webb, Auckland #103/R (NZ.D 1300)
£485 $839 €708 No 12 (108x53cm-43x21in) s.i.d.1963 prov. 9-Dec-3 Peter Webb, Auckland #104/R (NZ.D 1300)

CRAMPTON, Sean (1918-1999) British
Sculpture
£1500 $2505 €2190 Three running figures (54cm-21in) init.num.3/12 bronze. 21-Oct-3 Bonhams, Knightsbridge #211/R est:1500-1800

CRAMPTON, William James Smith (1855-1935) British
£600 $1020 €876 Scottish glen with cattle and sheep. Highland cattle on a moor (51x76cm-20x30in) s. pair. 19-Nov-3 Tennants, Leyburn #1097
£700 $1190 €1022 River landscape with cattle watering. River landscape with angler (30x61cm-12x24in) s. pair. 19-Nov-3 Tennants, Leyburn #1098

CRANACH, Lucas (15/16th C) German
Prints
£2096 $3500 €3060 Second tournament with the tapestry of Samson and the lion (29x42cm-11x17in) woodcut prov. 21-Oct-3 Bonhams & Butterfields, San Francisco #1113/R

CRANACH, Lucas (circle) (15/16th C) German
£6291 $11450 €9500 Portraits of Martin Luther and his wife Katharina von Bora. i. panel pair prov.lit. 16-Jun-4 Dorotheum, Vienna #160/R est:5000-6000

CRANACH, Lucas (elder) (1472-1553) German
£10667 $19413 €16000 Taking Christ down from the cross (87x37cm-34x15in) panel prov.lit. 30-Jun-4 Neumeister, Munich #441/R est:8000
£38889 $70000 €56778 Virgin and child with the infant Saint John the Baptist (89x50cm-35x20in) panel. 23-Jan-4 Christie's, Rockefeller NY #32/R est:150000-250000
£41958 $71329 €60000 Venus (48x24cm-19x9in) s.d.1532. 20-Nov-3 Weidler, Nurnberg #320/R est:16000
£95000 $173850 €138700 Portrait of the Elector Frederick the Wise in his old age (56x38cm-22x15in) i. panel prov.exhib.lit. 7-Jul-4 Sotheby's, London #33/R est:70000-100000
£140000 $256200 €204400 Portrait of young woman as court beauty (37x25cm-15x10in) s. panel prov. 7-Jul-4 Sotheby's, London #32/R est:80000-120000
£151724 $251862 €220000 Portraits of Duke John II of Anhalt and Duke Joachim of Anhalt (52x36cm-20x14in) bears d.1532 i. verso panel two. 1-Oct-3 Dorotheum, Vienna #266/R est:150000-200000
£600000 $1098000 €876000 Head of Christ crowned with thorns (27x21cm-11x8in) panel prov. 7-Jul-4 Sotheby's, London #31/R est:100000-150000
£870000 $1592100 €1270200 Lot and his daughters (56x39cm-22x15in) s. panel prov.exhib.lit. 7-Jul-4 Christie's, London #65/R est:800000-1200000
Prints
£2000 $3640 €2920 Second tournament with the tapestry of Samson and the lion (29x42cm-11x17in) woodcut. 1-Jul-4 Sotheby's, London #22/R est:2500-3000
£2500 $4150 €3650 Penitence of St Jerome (33x24cm-13x9in) woodcut prov. 6-Oct-3 Sotheby's, London #17/R est:3000-4000
£2600 $4316 €3796 Sermon of St John the Baptist (34x24cm-13x9in) woodcut prov. 6-Oct-3 Sotheby's, London #16/R est:2000-4000
£3240 $5800 €4730 Second tournament with the tapestry of Samson and the lion (28x43cm-11x17in) woodcut. 6-May-4 Swann Galleries, New York #24/R est:7000-10000
£4333 $7973 €6500 Adam and Eve in pardise (33x23cm-13x9in) woodcut. 11-Jun-4 Hauswedell & Nolte, Hamburg #830/R est:6000

CRANACH, Lucas (elder) and Lucas (younger) (16th C) German
£74324 $130811 €110000 Lamentation of Christ (42x78cm-17x31in) panel prov. 22-May-4 Lempertz, Koln #1033/R est:120000-140000

CRANACH, Lucas (elder-attrib) (1472-1553) German
£10563 $18275 €15000 Ill assorted couples (34x24cm-13x9in) board pair. 14-Dec-3 Finarte, Venice #153/R est:12000-15000

CRANACH, Lucas (elder-circle) (1472-1553) German
£12000 $20760 €17520 Mocking of Christ (86x57cm-34x22in) s. panel. 10-Dec-3 Christie's, London #45/R est:15000-20000

CRANACH, Lucas (elder-school) (1472-1553) German
£13000 $22100 €18980 Lady in decorated dress. Annunciation fragment (41x32cm-16x13in) gold ground panel double-sided. 29-Oct-3 Christie's, London #44/R est:7000-10000

CRANACH, Lucas (elder-studio) (1472-1553) German
£5517 $9214 €8000 Madonna with child and Infant St John (38x25cm-15x10in) panel prov. 15-Nov-3 Lempertz, Koln #1030/R est:8500
£7000 $11900 €10220 Portrait of John the Steadfast, elector of Saxony (15x13cm-6x5in) oil paper on panel prov. 29-Oct-3 Christie's, London #45/R est:7000-10000
£16667 $27500 €24000 Adam and Eve beneath tree of knowledge (31x23cm-12x9in) panel. 2-Jul-3 Neumeister, Munich #530/R est:25000

CRANACH, Lucas (younger-after) (1515-1586) German
£6944 $11319 €10000 Portrait of John Frederic the Magnanimous (58x36cm-23x14in) i. 25-Sep-3 Dr Fritz Nagel, Stuttgart #1279/R est:800

CRANACH, Lucas (younger-circle) (1515-1586) German
£13014 $22123 €19000 Betsabea (45x37cm-18x15in) board. 9-Nov-3 Finarte, Venice #94/R est:16000-20000

CRANACH, Lucas (younger-studio) (1515-1586) German
£20000 $36000 €29200 Saint John the Evangelist (77x29cm-30x11in) panel prov.lit. 21-Apr-4 Christie's, London #56/R est:15000-20000

CRANCH OF BATH, John (1751-1821) British
£380 $703 €555 Penitents (13x16cm-5x6in) init. i.d.1813 verso panel. 16-Feb-4 Bonhams, Bath #112

CRANCH, Christopher Pearse (1813-1892) American
£3704 $7000 €5408 Landscape by seas (30x46cm-12x18in) init.d.1879 prov. 17-Feb-4 John Moran, Pasadena #155/R est:3000-5000

CRANE, Bruce (1857-1937) American
£769 $1400 €1123 Golden glow (25x36cm-10x14in) bears sig. 19-Jun-4 Jackson's, Cedar Falls #6/R est:2000-3000
£1509 $2700 €2203 Landscape near Newport (25x32cm-10x13in) s. panel. 14-May-4 Skinner, Boston #151/R est:1800-2200
£1524 $2500 €2210 Autumn landscape (38x41cm-15x16in) s. 2-Jun-3 Grogan, Boston #663/R
£1832 $2950 €2675 Late winter landscape (46x56cm-18x22in) s. canvas on masonite. 20-Aug-3 James Julia, Fairfield #1312/R est:2500-3500
£2000 $3160 €2900 Barn in summer (46x41cm-18x16in) s.d.1898. 4-Sep-3 Christie's, Kensington #161/R est:1000-1500
£2177 $4006 €3178 Meadow near East Hampton (36x51cm-14x20in) s. s.verso. 14-Jun-4 Waddingtons, Toronto #14/R est:3000-5000 (C.D 5400)
£2198 $4000 €3209 Atmospheric sunset landscape (38x51cm-15x20in) s. prov. 15-Jun-4 John Moran, Pasadena #162 est:3000-5000
£2209 $3800 €3225 Golden west (25x33cm-10x13in) s.d.1923 s.i.verso. 2-Dec-3 Christie's, Rockefeller NY #68/R est:2000-3000
£2312 $4000 €3376 Golden Days (36x51cm-14x20in) s.i.d.1925 i.verso prov. 10-Dec-3 Bonhams & Butterfields, San Francisco #6027/R est:5000-7000
£3073 $5500 €4487 Hay field (64x76cm-25x30in) s. prov. 6-May-4 Shannon's, Milford #81/R est:6000-8000
£3468 $6000 €5063 Late Autumn (36x51cm-14x20in) s.i. i.stretcher prov. 10-Dec-3 Bonhams & Butterfields, San Francisco #6026/R est:6000-8000
£3488 $6000 €5092 Autumn landscape (41x51cm-16x20in) s. painted c.1905. 7-Dec-3 Treadway Gallery, Cincinnati #573/R est:6000-8000
£3727 $6000 €5441 Early spring landscape (64x86cm-25x34in) s. 20-Aug-3 James Julia, Fairfield #1311/R est:6000-8000
£3763 $7000 €5494 November sunset (36x51cm-14x20in) s. 3-Mar-4 Alderfer's, Hatfield #330/R est:5000-7000
£3911 $7000 €5710 Afternoon sun (36x51cm-14x20in) s. i.verso prov. 6-May-4 Shannon's, Milford #177/R est:6000-8000
£4233 $8000 €6180 Houses in autumn landscape (30x41cm-12x16in) s. panel prov. 17-Feb-4 John Moran, Pasadena #114b/R est:3500-5500
£4237 $7500 €6186 Fall morning (35x50cm-14x20in) s. 28-Apr-4 Christie's, Los Angeles #11/R est:6000-8000
£4348 $7000 €6348 The river bend (61x91cm-24x36in) s. 20-Aug-3 James Julia, Fairfield #1310/R est:9000-12000
£4469 $8000 €6525 Snowy landscape at dusk (30x41cm-12x16in) s. prov. 6-May-4 Shannon's, Milford #17/R est:5000-7000
£4802 $8500 €7011 Autumn landscape (40x61cm-16x24in) s. 28-Apr-4 Christie's, Los Angeles #23/R est:8000-12000
£5090 $8500 €7431 Spring (46x61cm-18x24in) s. 9-Oct-3 Christie's, Rockefeller NY #70/R est:7000-9000
£7059 $12000 €10306 Approach of darkness (64x76cm-25x30in) s. 29-Nov-3 Carlsen Gallery, Greenville #246/R
£7186 $12000 €10492 Field in late Autumn (51x61cm-20x24in) s. 23-Oct-3 Shannon's, Milford #138/R est:10000-15000
£10056 $18000 €14682 Winter morning (41x61cm-16x24in) s. i.verso prov. 6-May-4 Shannon's, Milford #11/R est:8000-12000
Works on paper
£2095 $3750 €3059 Morning in June (38x28cm-15x11in) s.i.d.1879 W/C gouache. 14-May-4 Skinner, Boston #86/R est:2000-4000

CRANE, H (19/20th C) British
Works on paper
£276 $470 €403 Ship's portrait of Hans Broge, Copenhagen (25x40cm-10x16in) s.i. gouache. 10-Nov-3 Rasmussen, Vejle #274/R (D.KR 3000)

CRANE, Walter (1845-1915) British
£4000 $7200 €5840 The swan maidens (27x20cm-11x8in) mono.d.1894 oil gouache mixed media paper prov.lit. 21-Apr-4 Tennants, Leyburn #1009/R est:2500-3500
Works on paper
£940 $1720 €1372 Here's some supper for you. What babes in the wood they;s make (18x12cm-7x5in) mono ink laid down pair. 8-Jul-4 Sotheby's, London #306/R
£1105 $2000 €1613 Four designs for a silver cup (71x58cm-28x23in) pencil. 16-Apr-4 American Auctioneer #75/R est:3000-5000
£2200 $4026 €3212 Morning, Traeth Mawr, Harlech (13x35cm-5x14in) s.d.1887 i. verso W/C scratching out prov.lit. 3-Jun-4 Christie's, London #31/R est:2000-3000
£13000 $23790 €18980 Pegasus (71x71cm-28x28in) s.d.1889 pencil W/C bodycol gum arabic paper on linen exhib.lit. 3-Jun-4 Christie's, London #177/R est:10000-15000

CRANS, Johannes Marinus Schmidt (1830-1908) Dutch
Works on paper
£559 $1029 €850 Kewrmes te Calmpthout (31x46cm-12x18in) s. W/C. 28-Jun-4 Sotheby's, Amsterdam #33/R

CRANSHAW, L (?) ?
£880 $1426 €1276 Harbour scene with children paddling (35x26cm-14x10in) s,. 4-Aug-3 Rasmussen, Vejle #438/R (D.KR 9200)

CRANSTOUN, James H (1821-1907) British
£800 $1488 €1168 Figures seated by a wooded path, valley town beyond (41x61cm-16x24in) init. 4-Mar-4 Christie's, Kensington #452/R
£3800 $6460 €5548 View of Perth and the Tay (44x67cm-17x26in) init. strengthened sig.d.1852. 30-Oct-3 Christie's, London #19/R est:2500-3500
Works on paper
£300 $501 €438 After the storm (36x48cm-14x19in) init. W/C. 17-Oct-3 Keys, Aylsham #512

CRANTZ, Bengt (1916-) Swedish
£276 $496 €414 Interior from Mallosund (73x64cm-29x25in) s. 25-Apr-4 Goteborg Auktionsverk, Sweden #383/R (S.KR 3800)

CRAPELET, Louis-Amable (1822-1867) French
£1000 $1770 €1460 Le Nil au coucher du soleil (25x32cm-10x13in) s.d.1862 panel. 27-Apr-4 Bonhams, New Bond Street #64/R est:1000-1500

CRARY, Amy (1856-1950) American
£692 $1100 €1010 Kittens playing (41x51cm-16x20in) s.d.1889. 25-Feb-3 Bunch, West Chester #419/R

CRAS, Monique (1910-) French
£408 $731 €600 Enfant au bracelet bleu (40x31cm-16x12in) s. 21-Mar-4 St-Germain-en-Laye Encheres #83/R
£544 $974 €800 Village d'Afrique noire (62x101cm-24x40in) s. panel double-sided. 21-Mar-4 St-Germain-en-Laye Encheres #73/R
£544 $974 €800 Village d'Afrique du Nord (62x101cm-24x40in) s. panel double-sided painted 1910. 21-Mar-4 St-Germain-en-Laye Encheres #76/R
£748 $1339 €1100 Portrait d'homme Mossi (36x26cm-14x10in) s. panel. 21-Mar-4 St-Germain-en-Laye Encheres #80/R
£986 $1766 €1450 Guerrier Lobi en buste (67x60cm-26x24in) s.i. panel double-sided. 21-Mar-4 St-Germain-en-Laye Encheres #71/R
£1054 $1887 €1550 Famille noire (101x60cm-40x24in) s. s.i.verso panel. 21-Mar-4 St-Germain-en-Laye Encheres #74/R est:1000-1200
£1361 $2435 €2000 Femme Bobo (67x60cm-26x24in) s.i. panel double-sided. 21-Mar-4 St-Germain-en-Laye Encheres #75/R est:1000
Works on paper
£259 $463 €380 Femme soudanaise (68x24cm-27x9in) s.i. W/C gouache. 21-Mar-4 St-Germain-en-Laye Encheres #67/R
£272 $487 €400 Femme soudanaise et son enfant (70x30cm-28x12in) s.i. W/C gouache. 21-Mar-4 St-Germain-en-Laye Encheres #66/R
£272 $487 €400 Sorcier (42x24cm-17x9in) s. W/C gouache. 21-Mar-4 St-Germain-en-Laye Encheres #78/R
£306 $548 €450 Couple de Touaregs (42x31cm-17x12in) s.i. W/C. 21-Mar-4 St-Germain-en-Laye Encheres #81/R
£395 $706 €580 Portrait de jeune garcon (31x20cm-12x8in) s. gouache. 21-Mar-4 St-Germain-en-Laye Encheres #84/R
£408 $731 €600 Femme en tunique bleue (42x33cm-17x13in) s. W/C. 21-Mar-4 St-Germain-en-Laye Encheres #82/R
£476 $852 €700 Paysage de Man, Cote d'Ivoire (43x75cm-17x30in) s.i. gouache. 21-Mar-4 St-Germain-en-Laye Encheres #69/R
£537 $993 €800 Fete a Tunis (31x41cm-12x16in) s.i. W/C gouache chl Indian ink. 15-Mar-4 Gros & Delettrez, Paris #117/R
£604 $1117 €900 Colloque a Fes (24x32cm-9x13in) s.i. gouache ink. 15-Mar-4 Gros & Delettrez, Paris #88/R
£680 $1218 €1000 Portrait de jeune guerrier (35x25cm-14x10in) s.i. W/C. 21-Mar-4 St-Germain-en-Laye Encheres #68/R
£714 $1279 €1050 Afrique equatoriale francaise (60x46cm-24x18in) s. gouache. 21-Mar-4 St-Germain-en-Laye Encheres #65/R
£1064 $1777 €1500 Femme du Hoggar (43x37cm-17x15in) s.i. W/C gouache. 16-Jun-3 Gros & Delettrez, Paris #176/R est:1500-2000

CRAVATH, Glenn (20th C) American
£1198 $2000 €1749 Stagecoach robbery scene (64x46cm-25x18in) s. i.verso board. 15-Nov-3 Illustration House, New York #15/R est:2000-3000

CRAVEN, Edgar Malin (1891-?) American
£335 $600 €489 Trees at the Grand Canyon. s. board. 13-May-4 Dallas Auction Gallery, Dallas #49/R
£391 $700 €571 Florida landscape. s.i. board. 13-May-4 Dallas Auction Gallery, Dallas #255/R

CRAVERO, Gian (20th C) Italian
£333 $600 €486 Swimmers (81x129cm-32x51in) s.d.1981 prov. 25-Apr-4 Bonhams & Butterfields, San Francisco #5619/R

CRAWFORD, Cair (20th C) American
£447 $800 €653 Connection (30x244cm-12x96in) i. oil crayon. 13-May-4 Dallas Auction Gallery, Dallas #254/R

CRAWFORD, Edmund Thornton (1806-1885) British
£700 $1127 €1015 Crossing the ford. s.d.1882 panel. 21-Aug-3 Bonhams, Edinburgh #1211
£950 $1587 €1387 Entrance to the port of Rotterdam (21x59cm-8x23in) s. s.d.1837 verso panel. 16-Oct-3 Bonhams, Edinburgh #122/R
£3200 $5024 €4640 Bass Rock, Canty Bay (51x76cm-20x30in) s. prov.exhib. 27-Aug-3 Sotheby's, London #916/R est:2000-3000

CRAWFORD, Edmund Thornton (attrib) (1806-1885) British
£350 $595 €511 Stormy coastal scene with figures in a boat (17x23cm-7x9in) panel. 19-Nov-3 Tennants, Leyburn #1039

CRAWFORD, Hugh Adana (1898-1982) British
£400 $636 €584 Artist's wife with cat (102x91cm-40x36in) s. board. 10-Sep-3 Sotheby's, Olympia #225/R

CRAWFORD, John Gardiner (1941-) British
£520 $868 €759 Summer sea (60x120cm-24x47in) s.i.d.84 acrylic. 16-Oct-3 Bonhams, Edinburgh #14

CRAWFORD, Julia Tilley (1896-1968) Canadian
£217 $393 €317 Morning calm, Rockport Mass (61x52cm-24x20in) s.d.1938. 18-Apr-4 Levis, Calgary #443/R (C.D 525)

CRAWFORD, Leonard Gordon (1920-1996) Australian
£2479 $4587 €3619 Trio No.2 interplay (183x91cm-72x36in) s.i.verso panel oil on three connecting canvas prov.exhib. 15-Mar-4 Sotheby's, Melbourne #98/R est:2000-3000 (A.D 6000)
£4132 $7645 €6033 Moonrise at Sounion (137x122cm-54x48in) s.d.63 i.verso enamel string canvas on board prov.exhib. 15-Mar-4 Sotheby's, Melbourne #97/R est:5000-7000 (A.D 10000)

CRAWFORD, Ralston (1906-1978) American
£4587 $7660 €6697 Anducia to Yorkshire (114x76cm-45x30in) init. s.i.d.Dec.12 1972 verso prov. 23-Oct-3 Shannon's, Milford #47/R est:10000-15000
Works on paper
£870 $1600 €1270 On the dock (15x23cm-6x9in) pencil exec. c.1940. 10-Jun-4 Swann Galleries, New York #70/R est:1200-1800

CRAWHALL, Joseph (1821-1896) British
£480 $778 €701 Three foxhounds in full flight (19x60cm-7x24in) s.d.187. 27-Jan-3 Bristol Auction Rooms #539
Works on paper
£640 $1037 €934 Buff, a coursing greyhound in landscape with quarry (31x41cm-12x16in) s.i.d.1882 W/C. 27-Jan-3 Bristol Auction Rooms #509

CRAWHALL, Joseph (1861-1913) British
Sculpture
£1000 $1790 €1460 Ibex (21x18cm-8x7in) bronze. 28-May-4 Lyon & Turnbull, Edinburgh #64 est:1000-1500
Works on paper
£400 $668 €584 Who-Hoop, gone to ground at Fuller's earth (11x19cm-4x7in) i. pencil W/C. 13-Nov-3 Bonhams, Edinburgh #352a
£1000 $1730 €1460 Your money or your life (16x21cm-6x8in) W/C prov. 11-Dec-3 Lyon & Turnbull, Edinburgh #94/R est:1000-1500
£1000 $1790 €1460 Study of ducks (14x21cm-6x8in) init.i. chk W/C prov. 28-May-4 Lyon & Turnbull, Edinburgh #63 est:1000-1500
£2800 $4844 €4088 Crow and the frog (17x25cm-7x10in) W/C prov. 11-Dec-3 Lyon & Turnbull, Edinburgh #93/R est:2000-3000
£6500 $11245 €9490 Huntsman and hounds (20x26cm-8x10in) W/C prov.lit. 11-Dec-3 Lyon & Turnbull, Edinburgh #91/R est:3000-5000

CRAWHALL, W (fl.1858-1894) British
£1180 $1971 €1723 Beach scene with children playing with a model boat (71x119cm-28x47in) s. i.verso. 19-Jun-3 Mallams, Cheltenham #181/R est:1000-1500

CRAWHALL, William (fl.1858-1894) British
£1200 $1896 €1740 Children playing on a beach (74x122cm-29x48in) s.i.verso. 4-Sep-3 Christie's, Kensington #200/R est:1500-2000

CRAWLEY, Michael (?) British
Works on paper
£260 $411 €377 St. Andrew's Golf Course. s.i. W/C. 5-Sep-3 Moore Allen & Innocent, Cirencester #936
£270 $451 €394 St. Pauls, River Thames (53x37cm-21x15in) s.i.verso W/C. 7-Oct-3 Fellows & Sons, Birmingham #447/R
£320 $525 €467 Early morning, Whitby Bay, with fishing boats (38x51cm-15x20in) s. W/C. 29-May-3 Neales, Nottingham #748/R
£330 $614 €482 Horse fair (22x48cm-9x19in) s. W/C. 2-Mar-4 Bamfords, Derby #425
£950 $1710 €1387 New York in winter (55x51cm-22x20in) s. pencil W/C htd bodycol. 22-Apr-4 Mellors & Kirk, Nottingham #1005

CRAWSHAW, John (1810-1880) ?
£599 $1000 €875 Still life with fruit (38x43cm-15x17in) s.d.1867 panel. 16-Nov-3 Simpson's, Houston #287/R

CRAWSHAW, Lionel Townsend (1864-1949) British
£640 $1197 €934 Notre Dame, possibly. mono. 25-Feb-4 Hales, Bovey Tracey #733
£1900 $3021 €2755 La place de la Concorde (21x26cm-8x10in) mono.i. board. 9-Sep-3 David Duggleby, Scarborough #298 est:2000-3000
£4500 $7155 €6525 Children's play time (36x25cm-14x10in) s. 9-Sep-3 David Duggleby, Scarborough #381 est:2500-3500
Works on paper
£800 $1272 €1160 Genoese fountain Corte, Corsica (22x29cm-9x11in) s. W/C. 9-Sep-3 David Duggleby, Scarborough #123/R

CRAXTON, John (1922-) British
£5000 $7950 €7300 House by the sea (42x60cm-17x24in) s.d.20/8/46 board prov. 10-Sep-3 Sotheby's, Olympia #272/R est:5000-7000
£38000 $65360 €55480 Homage to alones (165x204cm-65x80in) s.d.Feb.March 49 exhib. 3-Dec-3 Sotheby's, London #58/R est:40000-60000
Works on paper
£260 $473 €380 Sailor in a Greek taverna (69x46cm-27x18in) s.i.d.84 col chk. 1-Jul-4 Christie's, Kensington #248
£5000 $9150 €7300 Bathers near the hotel (63x48cm-25x19in) crayon exec.1948 prov. 2-Jun-4 Sotheby's, London #72/R est:5000-7000

CRAYER, Gaspar de (attrib) (1584-1669) Flemish
£3642 $6629 €5500 Sainte conversation (83x57cm-33x22in) oval. 21-Jun-4 Tajan, Paris #36/R est:4000-6000

CRAYER, Gaspar de (circle) (1584-1669) Flemish
£5862 $10845 €8500 Agathe de Catane, vierge et martyre sicilienne (205x138cm-81x54in) 19-Jan-4 Horta, Bruxelles #128/R est:8000-12000

CREAMER, Mary (20th C) American
£270 $500 €394 Blooms of the Orient (51x61cm-20x24in) s. 24-Jan-4 Jeffery Burchard, Florida #64a/R

CREE, Edward Hodges (?-c.1869) British
Works on paper
£400 $744 €584 Mount Hermon - moonlit desert scene (46x68cm-18x27in) s.i. W/C htd white. 2-Mar-4 Bearnes, Exeter #355/R

CREEFT, Jose de (1884-1982) American/Spanish
Sculpture
£2096 $3500 €3060 Standing woman (47cm-19in) i. brown pat bronze sold with marble base. 7-Oct-3 Sotheby's, New York #332 est:2000-4000
Works on paper
£1374 $2500 €2006 Group of figures (158x103cm-62x41in) s. pastel gouache. 29-Jun-4 Sotheby's, New York #311/R est:3000-5000

CREER, Deirdre Henty (?) ?
£350 $557 €511 Children tobogganing in the snow (48x64cm-19x25in) s. 1-May-3 John Nicholson, Haslemere #702/R
£400 $636 €584 Zebra by the river (51x61cm-20x24in) s. prov. 1-May-3 John Nicholson, Haslemere #701/R
£425 $761 €621 Portsmouth from Priddys Head, Gospel (61x91cm-24x36in) s. 5-May-4 John Nicholson, Haslemere #478
£450 $806 €657 Submarines at HMS Dolphin, HMS Otis and companion submarines (61x91cm-24x36in) s. 5-May-4 John Nicholson, Haslemere #476
£450 $806 €657 Destroyers and frigates at Portsmouth (61x91cm-24x36in) s. 5-May-4 John Nicholson, Haslemere #477
£450 $819 €657 Skiing in the Austrian Tyrol (48x58cm-19x23in) s. prov. 16-Jun-4 John Nicholson, Haslemere #722/R
£450 $819 €657 Skiing in the Austrian Tyrol (48x58cm-19x23in) s. prov. 16-Jun-4 John Nicholson, Haslemere #723
£500 $795 €730 Zebra in the game reserve (46x61cm-18x24in) s. prov. 1-May-3 John Nicholson, Haslemere #700/R
£600 $1002 €876 Alpine winter landscapes, figures on the ski slopes (48x58cm-19x23in) s. pair. 18-Jun-3 John Nicholson, Haslemere #625/R

CREGAN, Martin (1788-1870) Irish
£3221 $5766 €4800 Portrait of Emma Inez Archdale (77x64cm-30x25in) s. 26-May-4 James Adam, Dublin #2/R est:4500-5500

CREHAY, Gerard Antoine (1844-1936) Belgian
£500 $900 €750 Woodview with Oriental woman beside a saddled horse (31x23cm-12x9in) s. panel. 26-Apr-4 Bernaerts, Antwerp #48/R
£537 $993 €800 Summer landscape with moorings (29x44cm-11x17in) s.d.1865. 13-Mar-4 De Vuyst, Lokeren #82
£1745 $3246 €2600 Hilly evening landscape with farmer's wife near water (77x100cm-30x39in) s. 8-Mar-4 Bernaerts, Antwerp #854/R est:2000-3000

CREIFELDS, Richard (1853-1939) American
£276 $500 €403 Portrait of Mary Louisa Halsted (74x63cm-29x25in) s. oval. 30-Mar-4 Christie's, Rockefeller NY #118/R

CREIXAMS, Pierre (1893-1965) Spanish
£284 $474 €400 Portrait d'un bebe (24x19cm-9x7in) s. panel. 19-Jun-3 Millon & Associes, Paris #247/R
£379 $630 €550 Female nude (65x63cm-26x25in) 1-Oct-3 Della Rocca, Turin #6/R
£738 $1373 €1100 Vase of flowers (63x46cm-25x18in) s. 2-Mar-4 Ansorena, Madrid #14/R
£839 $1401 €1200 Gitans (38x55cm-15x22in) s. 25-Jun-3 Blanchet, Paris #76/R
£1586 $2649 €2300 Serenade (73x54cm-29x21in) s.d.27. 11-Jul-3 Rabourdin & Choppin de Janvry, Paris #27/R
£2174 $3565 €3000 Flowers (89x72cm-35x28in) s. 27-May-3 Durán, Madrid #273/R est:2500
£3473 $5799 €5000 Saltimbanques (116x90cm-46x35in) s. 21-Oct-3 Artcurial Briest, Paris #206/R est:5000-6000
£3521 $6092 €5000 Antequera Fair (38x55cm-15x22in) s. 15-Dec-3 Ansorena, Madrid #337/R est:5000
Works on paper
£987 $1786 €1500 Saint Malo - Pardon des Terreneuvas (35x51cm-14x20in) s.i. gouache. 17-Apr-4 Deburaux, Boulogne #123

CRELINGER, Marie (19th C) German
£252 $400 €365 Portrait of Hendrickje Stoffels (64x53cm-25x21in) after Rembrandt. 12-Sep-3 Aspire, Cleveland #68

CREMA, Giovanni Battista (1883-1964) Italian
£430 $783 €650 Female nude (24x18cm-9x7in) s. paper. 17-Jun-4 Galleria Pananti, Florence #183/R
£704 $1218 €1000 Woman (30x24cm-12x9in) s. 11-Dec-3 Christie's, Rome #98
£872 $1562 €1300 Landscapes (6x13cm-2x5in) s. cardboard set of 3. 25-May-4 Finarte Semenzato, Milan #59/R est:1000-1500
£933 $1671 €1400 Smile (35x31cm-14x12in) s. 12-May-4 Stadion, Trieste #761/R est:1400-1800
£1259 $2102 €1800 Procession (27x26cm-11x10in) s. board. 24-Jun-3 Finarte Semenzato, Rome #95/R
£3497 $5839 €5000 Nymphs in the wood (79x65cm-31x26in) s. board. 24-Jun-3 Finarte Semenzato, Rome #97/R
£4577 $7919 €6500 Medieval scene (65x85cm-26x33in) s. cardboard. 11-Dec-3 Christie's, Rome #116/R est:6500-8000
Works on paper
£699 $1168 €1000 Mythological sc. (23cm-9in circular) s. W/C. 24-Jun-3 Finarte Semenzato, Rome #94/R
£769 $1285 €1100 Procession at night (18x28cm-7x11in) s. pastel. 24-Jun-3 Finarte Semenzato, Rome #93/R
£1189 $1985 €1700 Ballerina (60x39cm-24x15in) s. pastel. 24-Jun-3 Finarte Semenzato, Rome #96/R
£3916 $6540 €5600 Battle (65x94cm-26x37in) s. pastel. 24-Jun-3 Finarte Semenzato, Rome #98/R

CREMER, Jan (1940-) Dutch
£1200 $2208 €1800 Kop (31x16cm-12x6in) panel painted c.1957. 9-Jun-4 Christie's, Amsterdam #343/R est:1500-2000
£1477 $2732 €2200 Landscape number 3 (134x93cm-53x37in) s.d.87 panel. 13-Mar-4 De Vuyst, Lokeren #83/R est:2000-3000

CREMONA, Italo (1905-1979) Italian
£533 $981 €800 Buildings (37x47cm-15x19in) s. canvas on cardboard. 12-Jun-4 Meeting Art, Vercelli #944/R
£3448 $5759 €5000 Nude with palette (55x42cm-22x17in) s.d.1955 board exhib.lit. 17-Nov-3 Sant Agostino, Torino #212/R est:5000-6000
£3448 $5759 €5000 Houses in Borgo San Salvario (50x40cm-20x16in) init.d.1946 exhib.lit. 17-Nov-3 Sant Agostino, Torino #231/R est:5000-7000

CREMONA, Tranquillo (1837-1878) Italian
£7746 $13401 €11000 Tenderly (58x70cm-23x28in) canvas on board. 10-Dec-3 Sotheby's, Milan #122/R est:7000-10000
Works on paper
£704 $1169 €1000 L'Albanese (19x10cm-7x4in) mono. pencil exhib.lit. 11-Jun-3 Christie's, Rome #171
£1667 $2983 €2500 Vittorio Emanuele III meeting Radetzky (29x20cm-11x8in) s. W/C. 12-May-4 Stadion, Trieste #821/R est:1800-2200
£2113 $3507 €3000 Figura di bimba (40x28cm-16x11in) i.verso prov.exhib.lit. 11-Jun-3 Christie's, Rome #169/R est:3000-5000

CREMONINI, Leonardo (1925-) Italian
£6145 $11000 €8972 Lutte de chats (74x53cm-29x21in) init.d.56. 14-May-4 Skinner, Boston #405/R est:1500-3000
£8392 $14266 €12000 Rocks (38x46cm-15x18in) init.d.60 s.i.d.on stretcher prov.lit. 25-Nov-3 Sotheby's, Milan #142/R est:12000-15000
£11189 $19021 €16000 Intrusive plants (38x46cm-15x18in) init.d.58 s.i.d.verso prov.lit. 25-Nov-3 Sotheby's, Milan #143/R est:12000-15000
£19580 $33287 €28000 Intrusive plants (97x132cm-38x52in) init.d.60-61 s.i.d.verso prov. 25-Nov-3 Sotheby's, Milan #225/R est:28000-32000
£26846 $48054 €40000 Colin maillard (70x100cm-28x39in) init.d.67 s.i.d.verso prov.exhib. 26-May-4 Christie's, Paris #100/R est:1500-2000
£38667 $70373 €58000 Yeux de lunettes (114x116cm-45x46in) s.d.70-71 prov.exhib. 29-Jun-4 Sotheby's, Paris #23/R est:20000-30000

CREPALDI, Luciano (1949-) Italian
£333 $613 €500 Sardinian sea (100x140cm-39x55in) s.d.1996. 12-Jun-4 Meeting Art, Vercelli #230

CREPET, Angelo Maria (1885-?) Italian
£252 $413 €350 Strozzino Church, Bellosguardo (40x29cm-16x11in) s. cardboard. 10-Jun-3 Pandolfini, Florence #167
Works on paper
£468 $767 €650 Battistero (53x38cm-21x15in) s. W/C. 10-Jun-3 Pandolfini, Florence #359/R

CREPIN (?) French
£1479 $2558 €2100 Paysage de foret (28x36cm-11x14in) s.d.1764 panel. 10-Dec-3 Neret-Minet, Paris #73b/R est:3000-4000

CREPIN D'ORLEANS (18th C) French
£680 $1218 €1000 Paysage de cascade anime de pecheurs (25x33cm-10x13in) panel. 20-Mar-4 Binoche, Orleans #57

CREPIN, Joseph (1875-1948) French
£2041 $3653 €3000 No 242 (46x33cm-18x13in) s.i.d.1944. 21-Mar-4 Calmels Cohen, Paris #20/R est:3000-4000
£5102 $9133 €7500 No 351 (38x48cm-15x19in) s.d.1946. 21-Mar-4 Calmels Cohen, Paris #22/R est:8000-10000

CREPIN, Louis Philippe (1772-1851) French
£640 $1100 €934 Winter landscape (20x13cm-8x5in) s. panel. 7-Dec-3 Grogan, Boston #57/R

CRES, Charles (?-1908) French
£12941 $22000 €18894 Mother and child (55x38cm-22x15in) s.d.1888. 28-Oct-3 Sotheby's, New York #161/R est:18000-25000

CRESCENZO, Gennaro de (19th C) Italian
Sculpture
£12500 $21250 €18250 Faun and Bacchus (97cm-38in) s.d.1843 marble. 28-Oct-3 Sotheby's, London #90/R

CRESCIMANNO, Nicola F (19th C) Italian
£2600 $4420 €3796 Gozo boat, dusk. Goze boat in rough seas (22x31cm-9x12in) s.d.1880 board pair. 4-Nov-3 Bonhams, New Bond Street #119/R est:1500-2000

CRESPEL, Hubert (20th C) French
£395 $726 €600 Paysage du nord (46x55cm-18x22in) s. panel. 28-Jun-4 Joron-Derem, Paris #91

CRESPI, Daniele (1590-1630) Italian
£50000 $91500 €73000 Christ as Salvator Mundi (64x48cm-25x19in) i. panel. 8-Jul-4 Sotheby's, London #304/R est:10000-15000

CRESPI, Daniele (style) (1590-1630) Italian
£8553 $15737 €13000 St Magdalena with pot (44x35cm-17x14in) 24-Jun-4 Dr Fritz Nagel, Stuttgart #645/R est:800

CRESPI, Giovanni Battista (attrib) (1557-1633) Italian
£1793 $2977 €2600 St Charles Borromeo (68x54cm-27x21in) prov. 1-Oct-3 Dorotheum, Vienna #297/R est:3000-5000
£3020 $5557 €4500 Penitent Magdalene (100x80cm-39x31in) 24-Mar-4 Dorotheum, Vienna #12/R est:4000-6000

CRESPI, Giuseppe Maria (attrib) (1665-1747) Italian
£4964 $8291 €7000 Paysage avec un jardinier au puits (42x54cm-17x21in) 17-Oct-3 Tajan, Paris #35/R est:3000-4000

CRESPIGNY, Rose de (fl.1891-1929) British
Works on paper
£250 $400 €365 London bridge (33x25cm-13x10in) s. W/C. 18-Sep-3 Mallams, Cheltenham #254
£550 $919 €803 Early morning in the pool of London (45x64cm-18x25in) s. W/C. 7-Oct-3 Bonhams, Knightsbridge #29/R

CRESPIN, Adolphe Louis Charles (1859-1944) Belgian
Works on paper
£270 $511 €400 Interieur d'eglise, Anvers (117x83cm-46x33in) s. W/C. 17-Feb-4 Vanderkindere, Brussels #66
£272 $487 €400 Resistance des Boers (30x27cm-12x11in) W/C gouache. 21-Mar-4 St-Germain-en-Laye Encheres #45/R
£422 $755 €620 Arrivee du roi (40x29cm-16x11in) s. W/C gouache. 21-Mar-4 St-Germain-en-Laye Encheres #44/R
£517 $957 €750 Procession a Sainte Gudule, Bruxelles (112x70cm-44x28in) s. s.i.verso W/C. 16-Feb-4 Horta, Bruxelles #486
£530 $991 €800 Eglise St Turgen Audierne (60x41cm-24x16in) W/C. 24-Jul-4 Thierry & Lannon, Brest #53

CRESS, Fred (1938-) Australian/Indian
Works on paper
£410 $664 €599 Sisters 2 (50x71cm-20x28in) s.i. pastel exec.1990. 30-Jul-3 Goodman, Sydney #7/R (A.D 1000)
£638 $1085 €931 Tales of Hoffman 2 (47x74cm-19x29in) s.i.d.88 chl pastel prov. 25-Nov-3 Christie's, Melbourne #171/R (A.D 1500)

CRESSINI, Carlo (1864-1938) Italian
£21477 $40161 €32000 Poplars (137x103cm-54x41in) s. prov.exhib.lit. 25-Feb-4 Porro, Milan #29/R est:40000

CRESSWELL, Alexander (1957-) British
Works on paper
£260 $460 €380 Azaleas at Enys, Cornwall (36x54cm-14x21in) s. W/C prov. 27-Apr-4 Bonhams, Knightsbridge #230/R
£360 $637 €526 Oxleas (36x56cm-14x22in) s. W/C prov. 27-Apr-4 Bonhams, Knightsbridge #244

CRESSWELL, William Nichol (1822-1888) Canadian
Works on paper
£223 $379 €326 Atlantic breakers (19x36cm-7x14in) s.d.1882 i.verso W/C prov. 6-Nov-3 Heffel, Vancouver #32/R (C.D 500)
£285 $509 €416 On the St Vrain, Colorado (33x48cm-13x19in) s.d.1888 i.verso W/C. 27-May-4 Heffel, Vancouver #105/R (C.D 700)

CRESTI, Domenico (1558-1638) Italian
£9929 $16085 €14000 Player with dog in landscape (116x97cm-46x38in) 21-May-3 Babuino, Rome #8/R

CRESWICK, Mortimer (?) British?
Works on paper
£725 $1305 €1059 Conwy Castle with cottages and figures (38x66cm-15x26in) s. W/C. 24-Apr-4 Rogers Jones, Clwyd #136/R

CRESWICK, Thomas (1811-1869) British
£276 $500 €420 Woman with red cape and holding a child's hand on a woodland path (24x39cm-9x15in) s.d.1863 board. 19-Apr-4 Glerum, Amsterdam #71
£300 $549 €438 Figures, horses and sheep by a cottage (45x81cm-18x32in) s. 7-Apr-4 Woolley & Wallis, Salisbury #258/R
£360 $612 €526 Manor house by moonlight (15x13cm-6x5in) i.verso oval panel. 30-Oct-3 Duke & Son, Dorchester #201
£446 $768 €651 Figures on a farmyard track (61x50cm-24x20in) s.indis.d. 2-Dec-3 Ritchie, Toronto #70/R (C.D 1000)
£500 $835 €730 Cascading woodland stream, with a figure (29x21cm-11x8in) s. panel. 7-Oct-3 Fellows & Sons, Birmingham #354/R
£584 $1068 €876 Tinkers on the patch. 3-Jun-4 Joel, Victoria #349 (A.D 1500)
£633 $1165 €950 Painter in rocky gorge (35x28cm-14x11in) mono. board. 11-Jun-4 Hauswedell & Nolte, Hamburg #1006/R
£950 $1729 €1387 Cattle in stream. Watermill (46x46cm-18x18in) s.d.1842 pair. 16-Jun-4 Brightwells, Leominster #889/R
£1600 $2880 €2336 Summer landscape with girl standing beside a wooden gate (41x61cm-16x24in) s.d.1836. 21-Apr-4 Tennants, Leyburn #164 est:1500-2000
£1696 $2918 €2476 The road through (60x91cm-24x36in) prov. 2-Dec-3 Ritchie, Toronto #69/R est:4000-6000 (C.D 3800)
£1800 $3330 €2628 Untitled (29x24cm-11x9in) init.d.1838 oil paper on canvas. 13-Jan-4 Bonhams, Knightsbridge #334/R est:600-800
£1806 $3250 €2637 Walk through the woods (40x61cm-16x24in) s. prov. 21-Jan-4 Sotheby's, New York #226/R est:4000-6000
£2300 $4117 €3358 An over shot water mill (71x53cm-28x21in) s. 27-May-4 Christie's, Kensington #147/R est:1200-1800
£3000 $5010 €4380 Cattle fording a river (101x126cm-40x50in) 13-Nov-3 Christie's, Kensington #102/R est:3000-4000
£4500 $8055 €6570 View in Surrey (61x89cm-24x35in) s. prov. 18-Mar-4 Neales, Nottingham #735/R est:2500-3500
£6000 $11040 €8760 View in Surrey, with figures and a dog by a barn, church tower beyond (65x92cm-26x36in) with sig. prov. 11-Jun-4 Christie's, London #130/R est:6000-8000
£8333 $15000 €12166 Figures by a river in the woods (73x103cm-29x41in) s. 22-Apr-4 Christie's, Rockefeller NY #51/R est:20000-30000
£32000 $58880 €46720 London Road a hundred years ago (107x152cm-42x60in) init.d.1847 s.i.stretcher. 11-Jun-4 Christie's, London #60/R est:18000-25000

CRETELLE, Georges (20th C) French
Works on paper
£423 $731 €600 Africaine au pagne (49x37cm-19x15in) s. pastel. 15-Dec-3 Gros & Delettrez, Paris #221

CRETEN-GEORGES (1887-1966) Belgian
£405 $766 €600 Nature morte a la statuette (45x50cm-18x20in) s. canvas laid down. 17-Feb-4 Galerie Moderne, Brussels #169/R
£680 $1218 €1000 Jardin en fleurs (43x41cm-17x16in) s. cardboard. 16-Mar-4 Vanderkindere, Brussels #84
£1399 $2378 €2000 Fille sous les neons (93x71cm-37x28in) s.d.56 exhib. 1-Dec-3 Palais de Beaux Arts, Brussels #36/R est:2000-3000
Works on paper
£362 $666 €550 View of Paris (26x35cm-10x14in) s.verso W/C. 22-Jun-4 Palais de Beaux Arts, Brussels #215
£890 $1514 €1300 Jeune femme de profil (62x48cm-24x19in) s.d.1925 chl dr. 10-Nov-3 Horta, Bruxelles #474
£1049 $1783 €1500 Portrait de jeune femme (61x47cm-24x19in) s.d.28 chl. 1-Dec-3 Palais de Beaux Arts, Brussels #37/R est:1500-2000

CRETI, Donato (1671-1749) Italian
£137931 $230345 €200000 Alexander showing a letter to Phillip (62x77cm-24x30in) exhib.lit. 15-Nov-3 Porro, Milan #254/R est:130000
Works on paper
£1400 $2562 €2044 Venus and Cupid (10x18cm-4x7in) pen ink prov. 7-Jul-4 Bonhams, Knightsbridge #32/R est:700-1000
£2000 $3640 €3000 Study of fortress and figures (18x24cm-7x9in) pen ink. 30-Jun-4 Delvaux, Paris #86/R est:2000
£2667 $4853 €4000 Head of woman (22x17cm-9x7in) sanguine paper on card. 4-Jul-4 Finarte, Venice #1/R est:3000-4000

CRETI, Donato (attrib) (1671-1749) Italian
£2222 $4000 €3244 Study of a young boy, seen from behind (19x14cm-7x6in) oil on paper en grisaille. 22-Jan-4 Sotheby's, New York #181/R est:5000-7000
£6755 $12294 €10200 Saint Francois de Paule distribuant l'aumone dans un ovale peint (94x120cm-37x47in) 21-Jun-4 Tajan, Paris #20/R est:12000-15000
Works on paper
£1067 $1941 €1600 Study of figures (23x17cm-9x7in) i. pen ink. 30-Jun-4 Delvaux, Paris #87 est:1500

CRETIUS, Constantin (1814-1901) German
£2200 $3784 €3212 Young boy in a garden (33x28cm-13x11in) s.d.1851 oval. 4-Dec-3 Christie's, Kensington #148/R est:2500-3500

CREUZ, Serge (1924-1996) Belgian
£483 $869 €700 Les barques a Nieuwport (55x66cm-22x26in) s.d.47. 20-Jan-4 Galerie Moderne, Brussels #308/R

CREVATIN, Giovan Battista (1837-1910) Italian
£1067 $1909 €1600 Nosy (46x36cm-18x14in) s. cardboard. 12-May-4 Stadion, Trieste #712/R est:1200-1600
£1277 $2068 €1800 In lettura (28x37cm-11x15in) s.d.1880 board. 22-May-3 Stadion, Trieste #390/R est:1000-1500

CREWDSON, Gregory (1962-) American
Photographs
£1800 $3312 €2628 Untitled (45x59cm-18x23in) s.d.1992 num.9/10 verso cibachrome print lit. 24-Jun-4 Sotheby's, Olympia #450/R est:2000-3000
£3611 $6500 €5272 Untitled (29x36cm-11x14in) s. chromogenic colour print prov. 23-Apr-4 Phillips, New York #237/R est:3000-5000
£3611 $6500 €5272 Untitled (65x75cm-26x30in) s.d.1996 gelatin silver print mounted on board prov.exhib.lit. 23-Apr-4 Phillips, New York #238/R est:3000-5000
£4790 $8000 €6993 Untitled, underwater corpse (102x127cm-40x50in) c-print prov. 13-Nov-3 Sotheby's, New York #456/R est:10000-15000
£8000 $14720 €11680 Untitled pregnant woman (120x151cm-47x59in) s. cibachrome print exec 2001 prov. 24-Jun-4 Sotheby's, London #106/R est:7000-9000
£10000 $18200 €14600 Untitled, family dinner (120x151cm-47x59in) cibachrome print edition 7 of 10 prov. 6-Feb-4 Sotheby's, London #278/R est:7000-10000
£10778 $18000 €15736 Girl on window (122x152cm-48x60in) s. laser direct cibachrome on Cintra exec 1999 prov.exhib.lit. 12-Nov-3 Christie's, Rockefeller NY #534/R est:15000-20000

£11173 $20000 €16313 Untitled, empty house (122x152cm-48x60in) Cibachrome print Cintra edition 3 of 10 prov.exhib.lit. 12-May-4 Christie's, Rockefeller NY #354/R est:15000-20000
£12570 $22500 €18352 Untitled - Twilight series (122x152cm-48x60in) s.d.1998 num.A.P Cibachrome print on foamcore prov.exhib.lit. 13-May-4 Sotheby's, New York #319/R est:15000-20000
£13174 $22000 €19234 Untitled - twilight series (122x152cm-48x60in) c-print prov.exhib.lit. 14-Nov-3 Phillips, New York #240/R est:15000-20000
£13500 $24570 €19710 Untitled, overturned bus (120x151cm-47x59in) cibachrome print edition 10 of 10 prov. 6-Feb-4 Sotheby's, London #102/R est:7000-10000
£14525 $26000 €21207 Untitled, car and spooky garage (122x152cm-48x60in) Cibachrome print aluminum edition 8 of 10 prov.exhib.lit. 12-May-4 Christie's, Rockefeller NY #353/R est:15000-20000
£16766 $28000 €24478 Flower Pile (122x152cm-48x60in) s. colour coupler print on Cintra exec 2001 prov.exhib.lit. 12-Nov-3 Christie's, Rockefeller NY #535/R est:12000-18000
£22222 $40000 €32444 Untitled (122x152cm-48x60in) chromogenic colour print on aluminum prov.exhib.lit. 23-Apr-4 Phillips, New York #69/R est:15000-20000

CREYKE, Mrs Walter (19th C) British?
£650 $1203 €949 Portrait of Everilda Creyke in a red coat (38x23cm-15x9in) init.i.d.1878. 9-Mar-4 Bonhams, Knightsbridge #135/R

CREYTENS, Julien (1897-1972) Belgian
£340 $569 €480 Ships at the quay (60x80cm-24x31in) s.d.59. 20-Oct-3 Bernaerts, Antwerp #174/R
£594 $1022 €850 Nature morte aux cerises et aux fraises (60x80cm-24x31in) s.d.1949. 2-Dec-3 Campo & Campo, Antwerp #81

CRICK, Alfred Egide (1858-1931) Belgian
Sculpture
£1119 $1869 €1600 Le Gavroche (42cm-17in) s.st.f.Petermann a Saint Gilles gilt pat bronze. 13-Oct-3 Horta, Bruxelles #189 est:1500-1800

CRIGHTON, Hugh Ford (fl.1865) British
Works on paper
£360 $662 €526 Portrait of a young girl (61x47cm-24x19in) s.d.1872 pastel. 8-Jun-4 Bonhams, Knightsbridge #26/R

CRILLEY, Joseph (1920-) American
£1195 $1900 €1745 Old Lime Kiln (20x30cm-8x12in) s. board. 10-Sep-3 Alderfer's, Hatfield #399/R est:800-1200

CRIMI, Alfredo di Giorgio (1900-?) American
£233 $375 €340 Cathy (46x36cm-18x14in) s. canvas on board. 22-Feb-3 Bunte, Elgin #1158
£295 $475 €431 Space platform (91x107cm-36x42in) 22-Feb-3 Bunte, Elgin #1159a
£342 $550 €499 Untitled (86x61cm-34x24in) s. 22-Feb-3 Bunte, Elgin #1159
£404 $650 €590 Rising Forms (102x76cm-40x30in) s. canvas on board. 22-Feb-3 Bunte, Elgin #1156
£404 $650 €590 Dead City (51x61cm-20x24in) s. canvas on board. 22-Feb-3 Bunte, Elgin #1157
£466 $750 €680 The journey (51x66cm-20x26in) s. canvas on board. 22-Feb-3 Bunte, Elgin #1154
£497 $800 €726 The three Mary's (102x76cm-40x30in) s. 22-Feb-3 Bunte, Elgin #1152
£625 $1000 €913 Mobile and variable (168x61cm-66x24in) s. 17-May-3 Bunte, Elgin #1202 est:1000-1500
£745 $1200 €1088 Woman on couch (102x76cm-40x30in) s. painted c.1954. 22-Feb-3 Bunte, Elgin #1151
£745 $1200 €1088 The string (86x61cm-34x24in) s.d.1940 canvas on board. 22-Feb-3 Bunte, Elgin #1155
£1125 $1800 €1643 Young woman (102x76cm-40x30in) s. 17-May-3 Bunte, Elgin #1201 est:2000-3000
£2484 $4000 €3627 Sidewalk improvisation (61x51cm-24x20in) s. 22-Feb-3 Bunte, Elgin #1153

CRINO (19th C) ?
Works on paper
£1050 $1985 €1533 Valetta harbour at night with Gozoan fishing boats (20x38cm-8x15in) s.d.1883 W/C htd bodycol. 18-Feb-4 John Bellman, Billingshurst #1844/R est:300-400

CRIPPA, Luigi (1921-) Italian
£280 $502 €409 Untitled (37x57cm-15x22in) s.d.1963 i. verso. 12-May-4 Dobiaschofsky, Bern #3506/R (S.FR 650)

CRIPPA, Roberto (1921-1972) Italian
£326 $535 €450 Still life (40x50cm-16x20in) s. 29-May-3 Galleria Pace, Milan #12
£811 $1427 €1200 Spirals (50x70cm-20x28in) s. acrylic paper on masonite. 19-May-4 Il Ponte, Milan #1122
£973 $1800 €1450 Spiral (70x50cm-28x20in) s. acrylic painted 1971. 11-Mar-4 Galleria Pace, Milan #33/R est:1800-2400
£1192 $2170 €1800 Spirals (63x90cm-25x35in) s. acrylic paper. 17-Jun-4 Galleria Pananti, Florence #421/R est:1000-1500
£1267 $2331 €1900 Spiral (70x50cm-28x20in) s. acrylic cardboard painted 1970. 10-Jun-4 Galleria Pace, Milan #21/R est:2200-3000
£1342 $2483 €2000 Spiral (50x70cm-20x28in) s. acrylic cardboard on canvas. 13-Mar-4 Meeting Art, Vercelli #104 est:2000
£1399 $2336 €2000 Spirals (70x50cm-28x20in) s. acrylic board. 26-Jun-3 Sant Agostino, Torino #210/R est:1500-2000
£1449 $2377 €2000 Spirals (32x40cm-13x16in) s.verso painted 1952. 29-May-3 Galleria Pace, Milan #73/R est:3000
£1469 $2497 €2100 Landscape (46x55cm-18x22in) s.i.d.1971 verso cork board. 20-Nov-3 Finarte Semenzato, Milan #1/R est:1500-2000
£1565 $2801 €2300 Landscape (53x65cm-21x26in) s.i.d.1971 oil cork board prov. 16-Mar-4 Finarte Semenzato, Milan #397/R est:2000
£1667 $3067 €2500 Falling star (92x73cm-36x29in) s.i.d.1971 verso asbestos on board. 8-Jun-4 Finarte Semenzato, Milan #365/R est:2500-3000
£1812 $2971 €2500 Geometry (70x25cm-28x10in) s.d.51 verso prov. 27-May-3 Sotheby's, Milan #48/R est:3500
£2000 $3680 €3000 Totem (100x60cm-39x24in) s.d.1970. 12-Jun-4 Meeting Art, Vercelli #474/R est:3000
£2041 $3714 €3000 Untitled (77x60cm-30x24in) s.verso oil collage board. 6-Feb-4 Galleria Rosenberg, Milan #38/R est:3000
£2069 $3455 €3000 Sun (81x66cm-32x26in) s.i.verso oil cork board. 17-Nov-3 Sant Agostino, Torino #301/R est:3000-4000
£2113 $3697 €3000 Composition (35x25cm-14x10in) s.d.50 board prov. 16-Dec-3 Porro, Milan #26/R est:3000-5000
£2276 $3641 €3300 Totem (100x50cm-39x20in) s.i.verso oil collage paper on canvas. 13-Mar-3 Galleria Pace, Milan #23/R
£2333 $4293 €3500 Spirals (60x70cm-24x28in) s.d.51 verso tempera paper on canvas. 8-Jun-4 Finarte Semenzato, Milan #346/R est:2000-2500
£2465 $4092 €3500 Spirals (50x60cm-20x24in) s.d.1952. 11-Jun-3 Finarte Semenzato, Milan #559/R
£2533 $4661 €3800 Spirals (45x53cm-18x21in) s.d.51 verso. 8-Jun-4 Finarte Semenzato, Milan #345/R est:2500-3000
£2667 $4907 €4000 Totem (100x50cm-39x20in) s.i.d.1959 oil collage. 12-Jun-4 Meeting Art, Vercelli #831/R est:4000
£2958 $5176 €4200 Spirals (40x65cm-16x26in) s.d.1951 verso prov. 16-Dec-3 Finarte Semenzato, Milan #316/R est:2300-2700
£3032 $5154 €4427 Untitled (50x60cm-20x24in) s.d.48 verso panel prov. 22-Nov-3 Burkhard, Luzern #100/R est:4000-5000 (S.FR 6700)
£3043 $4991 €4200 Untitled (70x70cm-28x28in) s.d.953 verso. 27-May-3 Sotheby's, Milan #49/R est:3000-4000
£3103 $4966 €4500 Totem (70x60cm-28x24in) s.d. 13-Mar-3 Galleria Pace, Milan #111/R est:4000-5000
£3239 $5669 €4600 Spirals (59x69cm-23x27in) s. 16-Dec-3 Finarte Semenzato, Milan #315/R est:2800-3200
£3557 $6581 €5300 Composition (60x73cm-24x29in) s.d.1970 mixed media collage cork lit. 13-Mar-4 Meeting Art, Vercelli #326 est:2500
£3800 $6992 €5700 Half horse half bird (97x130cm-38x51in) s.i.d.56 verso. 8-Jun-4 Finarte Semenzato, Milan #364/R est:5000-6000
£3819 $6035 €5500 Spirals (60x80cm-24x31in) painted 1951. 6-Sep-3 Meeting Art, Vercelli #599 est:5000
£3986 $6776 €5700 Spirals (60x70cm-24x28in) s.d.1951 verso. 20-Nov-3 Finarte Semenzato, Milan #3/R est:6000-6500
£4167 $7083 €6000 Totem (70x40cm-28x16in) on wax on masonite prov. 28-Oct-3 Il Ponte, Milan #247/R
£4167 $6583 €6000 Totem (99x80cm-39x31in) painted 1956. 6-Sep-3 Meeting Art, Vercelli #603 est:5000
£4196 $7133 €6000 Untitled (59x79cm-23x31in) s.d.1951 verso acrylic board. 24-Nov-3 Christie's, Milan #216/R est:4000-6000
£4200 $7644 €6132 Geometric (40x130cm-16x51in) s.i.verso board sold with another by same hand two. 4-Feb-4 Sotheby's, Olympia #204/R est:1500-2000
£4362 $7809 €6500 Eclipse (130x97cm-51x38in) s.i.d.1966 tempera board. 28-May-4 Farsetti, Prato #316/R est:5200-6200
£5245 $8916 €7500 Spiral (80x99cm-31x39in) s.d.949-50 verso. 25-Nov-3 Sotheby's, Milan #14/R est:3500-4000
£5600 $10304 €8400 Spiral (70x60cm-28x24in) s.i.d.1952 verso. 12-Jun-4 Meeting Art, Vercelli #505/R est:5000
£6081 $10703 €9000 Untitled (100x100cm-39x39in) s.d.53 prov. 24-May-4 Christie's, Milan #234/R est:5000-7000
£6294 $10699 €9000 Figures (130x110cm-51x43in) s.i.d.55 verso masonite. 24-Nov-3 Christie's, Milan #243/R est:10000-15000
£7667 $14107 €11500 Spirals (80x100cm-31x39in) s.d.1951 verso. 8-Jun-4 Finarte Semenzato, Milan #344/R est:5000-6000
Sculpture
£1533 $2760 €2300 Untitled (100cm-39in) pat bronze. 22-Apr-4 Finarte Semenzato, Rome #236a/R est:3000-4000
Works on paper
£267 $480 €400 Totem (31x23cm-12x9in) s. frottage. 22-Apr-4 Finarte Semenzato, Rome #117/R
£345 $576 €500 Spiral (27x20cm-11x8in) s. pastel exec.1962. 17-Nov-3 Sant Agostino, Torino #55/R
£347 $590 €500 Composition (48x34cm-19x13in) s.d.1960 mixed media over eau forte. 28-Oct-3 Il Ponte, Milan #231
£667 $1227 €1000 Untitled (40x30cm-16x12in) s. collage cardboard. 12-Jun-4 Meeting Art, Vercelli #83/R
£942 $1545 €1300 Spirals (24x17cm-9x7in) s.d.54 gouache chl Chinese ink set of 3. 27-May-3 Sotheby's, Milan #46/R est:1500
£986 $1725 €1400 Spirals (49x70cm-19x28in) mixed media paper on canvas. 16-Dec-3 Finarte Semenzato, Milan #314/R est:1300-1700
£1014 $1784 €1500 Totem (70x50cm-28x20in) s.d.1953 mixed media cardboard. 19-May-4 Il Ponte, Milan #1124 est:1600-1800
£1333 $2453 €2000 Spiral (35x49cm-14x19in) s.d.1952 mixed media cardboard. 12-Jun-4 Meeting Art, Vercelli #354/R est:2000
£1600 $2944 €2400 Flight (33x40cm-13x16in) s.i.verso collage cork board. 12-Jun-4 Meeting Art, Vercelli #716/R est:2000
£1701 $3044 €2500 Composition (60x55cm-24x22in) s.d.1963 verso mixed media cork board prov. 16-Mar-4 Finarte Semenzato, Milan #107/R est:1200
£1712 $2911 €2500 Untitled (65x54cm-26x21in) s.verso collage cork board. 7-Nov-3 Galleria Rosenberg, Milan #95/R est:2500
£1761 $2923 €2500 Untitled (60x49cm-24x19in) cork mixed media board. 11-Jun-3 Finarte Semenzato, Milan #578/R
£1812 $2971 €2500 Untitled (61x80cm-24x31in) s.d.61 verso cork collage panel. 27-May-3 Sotheby's, Milan #47/R est:3000
£2027 $3568 €3000 Untitled (54x65cm-21x26in) s.d.71 mixed media cork board. 24-May-4 Christie's, Milan #84/R est:3000-3500
£2069 $3310 €3000 Untitled (73x60cm-29x24in) s.i.verso collage panel. 13-Mar-3 Galleria Pace, Milan #83/R est:3500-5000
£2069 $3455 €3000 Untitled (60x73cm-24x29in) s.verso collage board. 13-Nov-3 Galleria Pace, Milan #132/R est:4500
£2083 $3292 €3000 Sun (92x73cm-36x29in) collage cork board. 6-Sep-3 Meeting Art, Vercelli #546 est:3000
£2276 $3641 €3300 Soleil (72x93cm-28x37in) s.i.verso cork on panel. 13-Mar-3 Galleria Pace, Milan #156/R est:4000-5000
£2535 $4208 €3600 Untitled (73x60cm-29x24in) s.d.1970 verso collage cork panel. 14-Jun-3 Meeting Art, Vercelli #284/R est:3000
£2600 $4498 €3796 Untitled (68x52cm-27x20in) s.d.961 wax crayon gouache gold paint collage paper on canvas. 11-Dec-3 Christie's, Kensington #220/R est:800-1200
£2759 $4607 €4000 Marilyn (78x103cm-31x41in) s.d.1964 verso collage mixed media board exhib.lit. 17-Nov-3 Sant Agostino, Torino #285/R est:2500-3500

£3087 $5711 €4600 Falling star (81x100cm-32x39in) s.i.verso collage on cork exec.1969. 11-Mar-4 Galleria Pace, Milan #65/R est:5500-7000
£3147 $5350 €4500 Untitled (54x65cm-21x26in) cork collage board. 28-Nov-3 Farsetti, Prato #275/R est:4000-5000
£3217 $5469 €4600 Eclypse (116x89cm-46x35in) s.verso collage cork board. 28-Nov-3 Farsetti, Prato #266/R est:3600-4000
£5594 $9510 €8000 Icarus (130x130cm-51x51in) s.i.d.1964 verso cok mixed media collage board prov. 25-Nov-3 Sotheby's, Milan #42/R est:8000-10000
£5705 $10211 €8500 Landscape (130x97cm-51x38in) s.i.d.1961 verso mixed media collage cork board. 30-May-4 Meeting Art, Vercelli #31 est:8000
£6159 $10101 €8500 Totem (146x113cm-57x44in) s.i.d.64 verso cork collage lead board. 30-May-3 Farsetti, Prato #518/R
£7047 $12614 €10500 Person (200x200cm-79x79in) s.d.1962 verso cork collage board. 28-May-4 Farsetti, Prato #94/R est:8000-10000
£7333 $13493 €11000 Figure machine (200x200cm-79x79in) s.i.verso cork collage board exec.1962. 11-Jun-4 Farsetti, Prato #364/R est:8000-10000
£7718 $13815 €11500 Earth gravity (200x200cm-79x79in) s.d.1962 verso cork collage board. 28-May-4 Farsetti, Prato #288/R est:8000-10000
£9058 $14855 €12500 No exit (200x200cm-79x79in) s.d.1960 verso cork collage board. 30-May-3 Farsetti, Prato #357/R est:12000
£10490 $17832 €15000 I died innocent (162x130cm-64x51in) i.verso cork collage exec.1960. 28-Nov-3 Farsetti, Prato #340/R est:8500-10500

CRISCITO, di (19th C) Italian
£6040 $11114 €9000 Animals and farmers at Vesta's Temple (60x103cm-24x41in) s. 24-Mar-4 Finarte Semenzato, Rome #5/R est:10000-12000

CRISCONIO, Luigi (1893-1946) Italian
£315 $526 €450 Boats in harbour (28x36cm-11x14in) s. cardboard. 24-Jun-3 Finarte Semenzato, Rome #132
£1000 $1840 €1500 Railway (30x40cm-12x16in) s. board. 8-Jun-4 Sotheby's, Milan #14/R est:1500-2500
£1056 $1827 €1500 Street in Naples (35x43cm-14x17in) s. board. 11-Dec-3 Christie's, Rome #25 est:1600-1800
£1197 $2071 €1700 Terrace in Capri (65x46cm-26x18in) s. board. 10-Dec-3 Finarte Semenzato, Rome #225/R est:1800-2000
£1333 $2453 €2000 Naples harbour (16x24cm-6x9in) s. 8-Jun-4 Sotheby's, Milan #11/R est:2000-4000
£2535 $4208 €3600 Granatello (45x58cm-18x23in) s.d.39 prov. 11-Jun-3 Christie's, Rome #218/R est:3800-4200
£2958 $4910 €4200 Ragazzo con cilindro (66x57cm-26x22in) s. prov.exhib.lit. 11-Jun-3 Christie's, Rome #232/R est:3800-4200

CRISCONIO, Luigi (attrib) (1893-1946) Italian
£333 $613 €500 Street in Naples (35x43cm-14x17in) board. 10-Jun-4 Christie's, Rome #40

CRISCUOLO, Giovan Filippo (circle) (1495-1584) Italian
£28521 $45634 €40500 Holy Family with angel and Saints (43x59cm-17x23in) board triptych. 21-Sep-3 Finarte, Venice #51/R

CRISP, George (19/20th C) British
£280 $476 €400 Still life with fruit and lemon (20x30cm-8x12in) s.d.1905. 20-Nov-3 Dorotheum, Salzburg #174/R
£300 $552 €438 Primroses and moss covered blackbird's nest on a grassy bank (19x24cm-7x9in) s. 23-Jun-4 Cheffins, Cambridge #500/R
£380 $616 €551 Still life of strawberries on a bank (23x30cm-9x12in) s.d.75. 30-Jul-3 Hamptons Fine Art, Godalming #270
£520 $837 €754 Still life of grapes, peaches and strawberries on a mossy bank (30x41cm-12x16in) s.d.90. 15-Aug-3 Keys, Aylsham #680/R

CRISP, James A (1879-1962) Australian
£810 $1304 €1183 In the goat paddock (29x45cm-11x18in) s.d.22 canvas on board. 13-Oct-3 Joel, Victoria #414 est:1500-2500 (A.D 2000)

CRISS, Francis (1901-1973) American
£37736 $60000 €55095 Factory girl (97x74cm-38x29in) 14-Sep-3 Susanin's, Chicago #6089/R est:3000-5000

CRISTALL, Joshua (1767-1847) British
Works on paper
£260 $476 €380 View over a river inlet (16x23cm-6x9in) s. W/C. 27-Jan-4 Bonhams, Knightsbridge #169/R
£300 $474 €435 Welsh river (10x18cm-4x7in) W/C. 2-Sep-3 Bonhams, Oxford #47
£400 $668 €584 Young boy on a track (27x18cm-11x7in) pencil W/C. 16-Oct-3 Christie's, Kensington #81/R
£750 $1253 €1095 Bridge near Harrow (12x19cm-5x7in) pencil W/C. 16-Oct-3 Christie's, Kensington #38/R
£860 $1548 €1256 Diana with attendant Zephyrs (18x26cm-7x10in) s.d.1837 W/C sold with a W/C by George Jones. 22-Apr-4 Lawrence, Crewkerne #742
£880 $1628 €1285 Study of weeds (14x23cm-6x9in) pencil W/C sold with three W/C by other artists four. 10-Mar-4 Sotheby's, Olympia #124/R est:800-1200
£2200 $3740 €3212 Nant Guinion, Caernarvonshire, North Wales (24x37cm-9x15in) s.d.1821 pencil W/C scratching out. 20-Nov-3 Christie's, London #69/R est:1500-2000

CRISTESCO, Constantin (fl.1911) French
Sculpture
£3000 $5400 €4380 Two jumping horses (35x35cm-14x14in) s. brown pat bronze st.f.Susse. 21-Apr-4 Sotheby's, London #97/R est:3000-5000

CRISTIANI, Mateo (1860-?) German
£336 $624 €500 Nude in wood (63x54cm-25x21in) bears sig. panel. 6-Mar-4 Arnold, Frankfurt #706

CRISTIANO, Renato (1926-) Italian
Works on paper
£7190 $13013 €10497 Girl carrying fruit (73x40cm-29x16in) s. pastel lit. 3-Apr-4 Glerum, Singapore #21/R est:8000-11000 (S.D 22000)

CRISTINA, Joelle (20th C) French
£315 $535 €450 Voyage avec les Gnaouas (100x100cm-39x39in) s. acrylic pastel canvas. 29-Nov-3 Neret-Minet, Paris #198/R

CRISTOFARO, Giuseppe Maria (20th C) Italian
£241 $449 €360 Ploughing (26x35cm-10x14in) s. board painted 1940-50 exhib. 4-Mar-4 Babuino, Rome #527

CRITCHER, Catherine Carter (1868-1964) American
£40107 $75000 €58556 Indian portrait (30x25cm-12x10in) s. canvas on board prov. 24-Jul-4 Coeur d'Alene, Hayden #160/R est:8000-12000

CRITE, Allan Rohan (1910-) American
Sculpture
£894 $1600 €1305 Virgin enthroned (14x7cm-6x3in) s.d.1940 paint pressed metal. 14-May-4 Skinner, Boston #402/R est:300-350

CRITTALL, Ariel (1914-) British
£250 $463 €365 Mysterious Plants (51x46cm-20x18in) s.i.d.1999 verso linen on board. 13-Feb-4 Sworder & Son, Bishops Stortford #131/R

CRIVELLI, Angelo Maria (17/18th C) Italian
£6525 $10897 €9200 Heron et canards dans un paysage lacustre (65x125cm-26x49in) 17-Oct-3 Tajan, Paris #5/R est:4500-6000
£30000 $54000 €43800 Wooded landscapes, ducks in a pond, and pheasants and rabbits (104x110cm-41x43in) pair prov. 22-Apr-4 Sotheby's, London #95/R est:12000-18000

CRIVELLI, Angelo Maria (attrib) (17/18th C) Italian
£2817 $4930 €4000 Oiseaux picorant des poissons (67x90cm-26x35in) 19-Dec-3 Delvaux, Paris #114/R est:4000-6000

CRIVELLI, Angelo Maria (style) (17/18th C) Italian
£15000 $27450 €21900 Still lifes with gamebirds in parkland landscapes (58x99cm-23x39in) pair. 6-Jul-4 Sotheby's, Olympia #565/R est:6000-8000

CRIVELLI, Giovanni (?-1760) Italian
£3333 $5967 €5000 Dead games (58x73cm-23x29in) pair. 12-May-4 Finarte Semenzato, Milan #14/R est:5000-7000
£10563 $18486 €15000 Bull attacked by dogs (179x235cm-70x93in) 17-Dec-3 Christie's, Rome #429/R est:4000-6000
£17333 $31027 €26000 Dead game. Turkeys (58x73cm-23x29in) pair. 12-May-4 Finarte Semenzato, Milan #15/R est:5000-7000
£17606 $30810 €25000 Wolf attacked by dogs (179x238cm-70x94in) 17-Dec-3 Christie's, Rome #430/R est:4000-6000

CRIVELLI, Vittorio (1440-1502) Italian
£18667 $34160 €28000 Pieta' (63x25cm-25x10in) tempera board exhib. 1-Jun-4 Sotheby's, Milan #146/R est:20000-30000

CROATTO, Bruno (1875-1945) Italian
£2533 $4535 €3800 Roses and glass (66x65cm-26x26in) s.d.1943. 12-May-4 Stadion, Trieste #811/R est:4000-5000
£2676 $4630 €3800 Still life (50x40cm-20x16in) s.d.1945 canvas on cardboard. 11-Dec-3 Christie's, Rome #117/R est:2800-3500
£3846 $6423 €5500 Still life with lobster (55x55cm-22x22in) s.i. i.verso board painted 1929. 26-Jun-3 Sant Agostino, Torino #294/R est:4500-5500
£5000 $8950 €7500 Flowers in Oriental vase (65x50cm-26x20in) s.d.1926. 12-May-4 Stadion, Trieste #839/R est:3500-4500
£7333 $13126 €11000 Vase with white roses (66x65cm-26x26in) s.i.d.1941. 13-May-4 Babuino, Rome #521/R est:2000-2500

CROCE, Luigi Scarpa (1901-) Italian
£922 $1494 €1300 Pagliaccetto (44x29cm-17x11in) s.d.1932 s.i.d.1932 verso panel. 22-May-3 Stadion, Trieste #184/R est:700-1000

CROCETTI, Venanzo (1913-) Italian
Works on paper
£915 $1602 €1300 Nudes (31x21cm-12x8in) s. ChineseiInk. 16-Dec-3 Finarte Semenzato, Milan #108/R

CROCIANI, Émile (1902-1979) French
£550 $1040 €803 Barque au port de ville, France (50x65cm-20x26in) s. i.verso board. 19-Feb-4 Christie's, Kensington #139
£1329 $2285 €1900 Le cirque (65x51cm-26x20in) s. s.i.verso panel. 3-Dec-3 Tajan, Paris #174/R est:2000-2500

CROCICCHI, Luca (1958-) Italian
£867 $1595 €1300 Seated figure (36x22cm-14x9in) init. board. 11-Jun-4 Farsetti, Prato #497/R

CROCIFISSI, Simone dei (1330-1399) Italian
£92958 $154310 €132000 Crucifixion (48x27cm-19x11in) tempera gold panel. 11-Jun-3 Semenzato, Florence #169/R est:150000-170000

CROCKER, John Denison (1823-1907) American

£625	$1000	€913	Landscape with stag (46x71cm-18x28in) s. 20-Sep-3 Nadeau, Windsor #207/R
£2875	$4600	€4198	Landscape with hunter and dogs (58x94cm-23x37in) s. 20-Sep-3 Nadeau, Windsor #83/R

CROCKET, Douglas G (fl.1901-1909) British

£600	$1110	€876	Mother and children outside a cottage (43x36cm-17x14in) s. 9-Mar-4 Bonhams, Knightsbridge #203/R

CROCKFORD, Duncan (1920-1991) Canadian

£246	$417	€359	Harvest time, Black Diamond (30x41cm-12x16in) s. i.verso prov. 6-Nov-3 Heffel, Vancouver #34/R (C.D 550)
£267	$437	€390	Pigeon Mountain near Exshaw, Alberta (51x61cm-20x24in) s. board. 28-May-3 Maynards, Vancouver #76 (C.D 600)
£289	$524	€422	Cliffside trail nr. Cavendish Beach, P.E.I (30x41cm-12x16in) s.d.1973 i.d.verso canvasboard. 18-Apr-4 Levis, Calgary #27/R (C.D 700)
£402	$683	€587	Golden harvest, scene near Caroline, Alberta (41x51cm-16x20in) s. i.verso canvasboard prov. 6-Nov-3 Heffel, Vancouver #33/R (C.D 900)
£413	$748	€603	Autumn, Bow Valley (30x41cm-12x16in) s. s.i.d.1958 verso canvasboard. 18-Apr-4 Levis, Calgary #26/R est:1000-1200 (C.D 1000)
£543	$907	€793	Assinoboine, mountain and Marvel Lake (40x50cm-16x20in) s.i. board. 17-Nov-3 Hodgins, Calgary #53/R est:1200-1800 (C.D 1200)
£1267	$2116	€1850	Off the western coast (69x85cm-27x33in) s.d.1969. 17-Nov-3 Hodgins, Calgary #117/R est:2000-2500 (C.D 2800)

CRODEL, Charles (1894-1973) French

£467	$845	€700	Woman's head with flowers and bird (35x61cm-14x24in) s. 2-Apr-4 Winterberg, Heidelberg #843/R
£629	$1051	€900	Apple harvest (32x45cm-13x18in) s. mixed media. 11-Oct-3 Dr Fritz Nagel, Leipzig #4048/R
£972	$1624	€1400	Early spring (33x46cm-13x18in) s. s.i. verso panel. 25-Oct-3 Dr Lehr, Berlin #114/R
£1133	$2040	€1700	Children's carousel in Halle (33x47cm-13x19in) s. panel. 24-Apr-4 Dr Lehr, Berlin #89/R est:1800

CRODEL, Paul Eduard (1862-1928) German

£772	$1436	€1150	Winter river landscape with houses on the edge of the forest (92x127cm-36x50in) s. 5-Mar-4 Wendl, Rudolstadt #3609/R

CROEGAERT, Georges (1848-1923) Belgian

£1200	$2172	€1800	Dame faisant de la musique (34x24cm-13x9in) s. panel. 30-Mar-4 Campo & Campo, Antwerp #53/R est:6000-8000
£1200	$2208	€1800	La jeune Orientale aux bijoux (32x24cm-13x9in) s.i.d.1883 panel. 14-Jun-4 Gros & Delettrez, Paris #580/R est:1500-1800
£3000	$5460	€4380	Stroll by the coast, Trouville sur mer (27x22cm-11x9in) s.i. 16-Jun-4 Christie's, Kensington #37/R est:3000-5000
£5000	$9200	€7300	Cardinal reading a letter (41x33cm-16x13in) s.i. panel. 25-Mar-4 Christie's, Kensington #124/R est:5000-7000
£5882	$10000	€8588	Ball of string (27x22cm-11x9in) s.i. panel. 29-Oct-3 Christie's, Rockefeller NY #44/R est:12000-18000
£8000	$14400	€11680	Feeding time (35x27cm-14x11in) s. panel. 21-Jan-4 Sotheby's, Olympia #465/R est:6000-9000
£9486	$16980	€13850	Leisure hours (24x32cm-9x13in) panel prov. 15-May-4 Christie's, Sydney #409/R est:20000-30000 (A.D 24000)
£13500	$21870	€19710	Connoisseur. Inspiration (36x27cm-14x11in) s.i. panel pair. 30-Jul-3 Hamptons Fine Art, Godalming #223/R est:5000-7000
£16000	$29120	€23360	Le gouter (41x32cm-16x13in) s.i. panel. 15-Jun-4 Sotheby's, London #195/R est:15000-20000
£17000	$30940	€24820	Le gourmand (41x32cm-16x13in) s. panel. 15-Jun-4 Sotheby's, London #197/R est:15000-20000

CROFT, Arthur (1828-?) British

Works on paper

£400	$740	€584	Aiguille Verte, from near the Pierre Pointue, France (49x28cm-19x11in) s.d.1874 W/C. 9-Mar-4 Bonhams, Knightsbridge #59/R
£750	$1275	€1095	Alpine village scene with figures, and mountains shrouded in mist (76x54cm-30x21in) s.d.1892. 29-Oct-3 Edgar Horn, Eastbourne #347
£1500	$2805	€2190	Monaco and Monte Carlo from Cape St Martin (11x38cm-4x15in) s. W/C. 24-Feb-4 Canterbury Auctions, UK #167/R est:750-1000
£9200	$15640	€13432	Fragment of Nature's architecture, Tintagel, Cornwall (229x142cm-90x56in) s.d.1885 W/C over pencil htd bodycol exhib. 27-Nov-3 Sotheby's, London #312/R est:5000-7000

CROFT, Richard (1935-) British

£320	$550	€467	At Sliddery Ford (40x40cm-16x16in) s. 3-Dec-3 John Ross, Belfast #96
£855	$1574	€1300	Still life (75x92cm-30x36in) s. 22-Jun-4 De Veres Art Auctions, Dublin #16/R

CROFTS, Ernest (1847-1911) British

£3050	$5582	€4453	Prince Rupert at Marston Moor (34x26cm-13x10in) s.d.93. 10-Jul-4 Windibank, Dorking #303/R est:2500-3000
£5500	$10120	€8030	Boscobel oak (46x63cm-18x25in) s.d.1889 exhib. 11-Jun-4 Christie's, London #201/R est:6000-8000
£8500	$15640	€12410	George II at the Battle of Dettingen, George dismounted, drew his sword and put himself at the head (70x128cm-28x50in) s.d.1881 prov.exhib.lit. 11-Jun-4 Christie's, London #200/R est:7000-10000
£9231	$15877	€13477	Deplacement de Cavalerie (50x79cm-20x31in) s.d.1883. 3-Dec-3 AB Stockholms Auktionsverk #2586/R est:35000-40000 (S.KR 120000)
£10000	$18200	€14600	Before Naseby (59x113cm-23x44in) s.d.78 prov. 16-Jun-4 Bonhams, New Bond Street #56/R est:10000-15000

CROIN, Joseph (1894-1949) Dutch

£400	$732	€600	Clay pot with thistles (94x66cm-37x26in) s.d.1939 prov. 7-Jun-4 Glerum, Amsterdam #36/R

CROISSANT, August (1870-?) German

£795	$1400	€1161	Village landscape with figures (79x58cm-31x23in) s. 20-May-4 American Auctioneer #474983/R

CROISSANT, Michael (1928-) German

Sculpture

£2937	$4993	€4200	Head and shoulders (15x19x9cm-6x7x4in) mono.i.d.99 gold brown pat.bronze prov.lit. 27-Nov-3 Lempertz, Koln #95/R est:2800

CROISY, Aristide-Onesime (1840-1899) French

Sculpture

£1379	$2303	€2000	Profils de jeunes filles (75x75cm-30x30in) marble bas relief. 12-Nov-3 Chassaing Rivet, Toulouse #40

CROIX, Antoine de la (19th C) French

Works on paper

£288	$460	€400	Trompe-l'oeil (24x20cm-9x8in) i. pen blk ink W/C. 16-May-3 Tajan, Paris #110

CROIX, Benedicto (20th C) ?

£625	$1019	€900	Venetian landscape (42x89cm-17x35in) s. panel. 16-Jul-3 Durán, Madrid #94/R

CROLA, Georg Heinrich (1804-1879) German

£839	$1427	€1200	Artist's house in Ilsenburg (35x26cm-14x10in) i.d.55 paper on board. 27-Nov-3 Bassenge, Berlin #5546

CROMBEKE, Cecile (20th C) British

£260	$473	€380	Crows in a ploughed field, with dandelion (79x107cm-31x42in) s. board. 21-Jun-4 Bonhams, Bath #452
£400	$736	€584	Dandelion clocks (70x51cm-28x20in) s. board. 29-Mar-4 Bonhams, Bath #49/R

CROME, John (1768-1821) British

£353	$650	€515	Norfolk pool (30x48cm-12x19in) canvas on board. 26-Jun-4 Susanin's, Chicago #6120/R
£1100	$2024	€1606	Twilight on the River Winson (30x43cm-12x17in) 25-Mar-4 Scarborough Perry Fine Arts, Hove #616
£2000	$3620	€2920	Twilight on the River Wison (30x43cm-12x17in) 16-Apr-4 Keys, Aylsham #683 est:2000-3000
£12676	$21930	€18000	Paysage avec paysan rentrant son troupeau (138x197cm-54x78in) mono.d.1816. 10-Dec-3 Maigret, Paris #55/R est:9000-12000

Works on paper

£525	$903	€767	Norfolk river landscape with figure on bridge, cattle and sheep by cottages (28x48cm-11x19in) W/C prov. 5-Dec-3 Keys, Aylsham #565

CROME, John (attrib) (1768-1821) British

£275	$514	€413	Thatched buildings amidst trees (30x38cm-12x15in) panel. 21-Jul-4 John Nicholson, Haslemere #184
£484	$867	€707	Farm near Norwich (44x34cm-17x13in) board prov. 12-May-4 Dunbar Sloane, Wellington #75/R est:1000-2000 (NZ.D 1400)
£663	$1100	€968	Wooded landscape with faggot gatherers (76x63cm-30x25in) prov. 30-Sep-3 Christie's, Rockefeller NY #346/R

Works on paper

£300	$552	€438	Figures one with a dog in a wooded lane (13x11cm-5x4in) W/C. 11-Jun-4 Keys, Aylsham #541

CROME, John Berney (1794-1842) British

£280	$484	€409	Boats by the windmill on a moonlit river (22x20cm-9x8in) board. 10-Dec-3 Bonhams, Bury St Edmunds #573

CROME, John Berney (attrib) (1794-1842) British

£300	$555	€438	Wooton Point, the wash (26x37cm-10x15in) board. 10-Feb-4 Bonhams, Knightsbridge #35/R
£700	$1281	€1022	Windmill at Mousehold Heath, Norwich (13x21cm-5x8in) i.verso panel. 8-Apr-4 Christie's, Kensington #98/R
£1400	$2520	€2044	Moonlight river scene (62x77cm-24x30in) i.verso panel. 21-Jan-4 Sotheby's, Olympia #95/R est:1500-2000
£4800	$8832	€7008	Wooded landscape with a shepherd and sheep on a path (71x92cm-28x36in) 11-Jun-4 Christie's, London #59/R est:4000-6000

CROME, William Henry (1806-1873) British

£800	$1264	€1160	Near Aix-la-Chapelle (51x61cm-20x24in) i. on stretcher prov. 4-Sep-3 Christie's, Kensington #201/R
£2400	$4464	€3504	Chelsea Old Church at moonlight (71x91cm-28x36in) s. indis d. 4-Mar-4 Christie's, Kensington #246/R est:3000-4000

CROME, William Henry (attrib) (1806-1873) British

£546	$1000	€819	Cottage landscape (76x64cm-30x25in) 9-Jul-4 Du Mouchelle, Detroit #2078/R

CROMEK, Thomas Hartley (1809-1873) British

Works on paper

£350	$644	€511	View of the Hercules, Egypt (20x32cm-8x13in) pencil black ink W/C. 25-Mar-4 Christie's, Kensington #90/R
£900	$1638	€1314	The Basilica San Marco (16x30cm-6x12in) pencil black ink W/C. 1-Jul-4 Christie's, Kensington #372/R

£1200	$2004	€1752	Gateway to an Italian town, a church beyond (19x27cm-7x11in) pencil W/C prov. 16-Oct-3 Christie's, Kensington #53/R est:600-800
£2000	$3400	€2920	San Giorgio Maggiore from the Piazza San Marco, Italy (23x33cm-9x13in) s.i.d.1839 pencil pen brown in, W/C htd bodycol. 20-Nov-3 Christie's, London #116/R est:2000-3000

CROMMELYNCK, Robert (1895-1968) Belgian

£293	$540	€440	Sapins dans les fagnes sous la neige (70x100cm-28x39in) s. 14-Jun-4 Horta, Bruxelles #8

CROMWELL, Joane (1889-1966) American

£467	$850	€682	Laguna shores (20x25cm-8x10in) canvasboard prov. 15-Jun-4 John Moran, Pasadena #1
£1324	$2250	€1933	Tanglewood (61x76cm-24x30in) s. i.verso. 18-Nov-3 John Moran, Pasadena #131 est:2000-3000

CRONE, David (20th C) Irish

£400	$732	€584	Abstract head (35x38cm-14x15in) s. board. 2-Jun-4 John Ross, Belfast #5
£450	$774	€657	Renatrated forms (45x35cm-18x14in) s.verso board. 3-Dec-3 John Ross, Belfast #100
£450	$824	€657	Heads (28x28cm-11x11in) s.d.1982 verso board. 2-Jun-4 John Ross, Belfast #47
£750	$1373	€1095	Island (38x48cm-15x19in) s.verso board. 2-Jun-4 John Ross, Belfast #142
£800	$1376	€1168	Garden (45x61cm-18x24in) s.d. March 1976 verso. 3-Dec-3 John Ross, Belfast #184
Works on paper			
£915	$1465	€1300	Intimate view (50x56cm-20x22in) mixed media prov.exhib. 16-Sep-3 Whyte's, Dublin #133/R
£979	$1664	€1400	Street (74x52cm-29x20in) s.i.d.1983 gouache exhib.lit. 18-Nov-3 Whyte's, Dublin #150/R

CRONE, Ulrik Lichtenberg (1964-) Danish?

Works on paper			
£329	$549	€480	Sugar High V (130x130cm-51x51in) s.d.1996 mixed media. 7-Oct-3 Rasmussen, Copenhagen #296/R (D.KR 3500)

CRONER, Ted (1922-) American

Photographs			
£1916	$3200	€2797	Central Park South (39x48cm-15x19in) s.verso i.d.1947-48 verso gelatin silver print one of 10 prov.lit. 17-Oct-3 Phillips, New York #133/R est:2000-3000

CRONQVIST, Lena (1938-) Swedish

£1026	$1815	€1498	Green landscape, Koster (35x35cm-14x14in) s.d.1968. 27-Apr-4 AB Stockholms Auktionsverk #911/R est:20000-25000 (S.KR 14000)
£1160	$2088	€1694	Inges mountain (41x46cm-16x18in) s.d.1970 prov. 26-Apr-4 Bukowskis, Stockholm #506/R est:15000-18000 (S.KR 16000)
£1172	$2075	€1711	Thistles (39x44cm-15x17in) s.d.1979 exhib. 27-Apr-4 AB Stockholms Auktionsverk #910/R est:15000-18000 (S.KR 16000)
£1586	$2696	€2316	Coastal landscape (39x44cm-15x17in) s.d.1989. 4-Nov-3 Bukowskis, Stockholm #642/R est:25000-30000 (S.KR 21000)
£1926	$3274	€2812	Coastal landscape (36x35cm-14x14in) s.d.1967. 5-Nov-3 AB Stockholms Auktionsverk #988/R est:15000-20000 (S.KR 25500)
£2644	$4494	€3860	Autumn in town, man raking leaves (91x86cm-36x34in) s.d.1966. 5-Nov-3 AB Stockholms Auktionsverk #1055/R est:20000-25000 (S.KR 35000)
£4305	$7319	€6285	Girl in glass bubble (46x40cm-18x16in) s.d.1999. 5-Nov-3 AB Stockholms Auktionsverk #992/R est:40000-50000 (S.KR 57000)
£4683	$7961	€6837	Heat - Interior scene with bed (32x30cm-13x12in) s.d.1966 exhib.lit. 4-Nov-3 Bukowskis, Stockholm #548/R est:50000-70000 (S.KR 62000)
£5665	$9630	€8271	Girl swimming with rubber duck (39x43cm-15x17in) s.d.1999. 5-Nov-3 AB Stockholms Auktionsverk #991/R est:40000-50000 (S.KR 75000)
£10989	$19451	€16044	Girl in bath tub with daddy clown doll (152x145cm-60x57in) s.d.1997 verso prov.exhib.lit. 27-Apr-4 AB Stockholms Auktionsverk #980/R est:175000-200000 (S.KR 150000)
£23568	$42422	€34409	Which hand? - girl with cat and dog (136x90cm-54x35in) tempera oil painted 1990 prov.exhib.lit. 26-Apr-4 Bukowskis, Stockholm #477/R est:350000-400000 (S.KR 325000)
Works on paper			
£363	$653	€530	Inside the minister's gaze (27x21cm-11x8in) s.d.1972 pencil. 26-Apr-4 Bukowskis, Stockholm #523/R (S.KR 5000)

CRONSTEDT, Margaretha Hedvig (attrib) (1763-1816) Swedish

£554	$992	€809	Landscape with bridge (44x56cm-17x22in) 28-May-4 Uppsala Auktionskammare, Uppsala #51/R (S.KR 7500)

CROOK, Pamela Jane (1945-) British

£7000	$12040	€10220	American (98x132cm-39x52in) s.i.d.1997 verso acrylic. 3-Dec-3 Christie's, Kensington #653/R est:3000-5000

CROOKE, Ray Austin (1922-) Australian

£455	$841	€664	Landscape (25x35cm-10x14in) canvas on board. 10-Mar-4 Deutscher-Menzies, Melbourne #508/R (A.D 1100)
£562	$939	€815	Fishing dinghy (20x25cm-8x10in) s. 30-Jun-3 Australian Art Auctions, Sydney #74 (A.D 1400)
£684	$1278	€1026	Sydney harbour scene (15x20cm-6x8in) canvasboard. 21-Jul-4 Goodman, Sydney #168 (A.D 1750)
£1021	$1736	€1491	Island interior nocturne (22x29cm-9x11in) s. board. 25-Nov-3 Christie's, Melbourne #322 (A.D 2400)
£1036	$1626	€1513	Near Coen, Queenslands (30x39cm-12x15in) s. board. 24-Nov-2 Goodman, Sydney #19 est:3000-5000 (A.D 2900)
£1049	$1930	€1532	Islander in a hut (30x41cm-12x16in) s. 28-Jun-4 Australian Art Auctions, Sydney #128 (A.D 2800)
£1107	$1793	€1616	Island interior (22x30cm-9x12in) s. board. 30-Jul-3 Goodman, Sydney #6/R (A.D 2700)
£1220	$2183	€1781	Ferntree Gully (45x60cm-18x24in) s.d.58 board prov. 10-May-4 Joel, Victoria #245 est:2000-3000 (A.D 3000)
£1298	$2362	€1895	Queensland landscape (28x39cm-11x15in) s. board. 16-Jun-4 Deutscher-Menzies, Melbourne #319/R est:3000-5000 (A.D 3400)
£1301	$2328	€1899	Stockman's camp W A (30x45cm-12x18in) s. acrylic board prov. 10-May-4 Joel, Victoria #250 est:2500-3500 (A.D 3200)
£1322	$2446	€1930	Island village (23x30cm-9x12in) s. board. 10-Mar-4 Deutscher-Menzies, Melbourne #339 est:2200-2800 (A.D 3200)
£1417	$2281	€2069	Ferntree gully (58x73cm-23x29in) s.d.58 board prov. 13-Oct-3 Joel, Victoria #351 est:3500-4500 (A.D 3500)
£1526	$2549	€2213	Island morning (37x46cm-15x18in) s. 30-Jun-3 Australian Art Auctions, Sydney #88 (A.D 3800)
£1538	$2477	€2245	Dawn, North Queensland (37x49cm-15x19in) s. bears i.verso. 25-Aug-3 Sotheby's, Paddington #453/R est:3500-5500 (A.D 3800)
£1639	$2656	€2393	Fijian (24x28cm-9x11in) s. board prov. 30-Jul-3 Goodman, Sydney #155/R est:2000-3000 (A.D 4000)
£1685	$3101	€2460	Island morning (40x50cm-16x20in) s. 28-Jun-4 Australian Art Auctions, Sydney #137 (A.D 4500)
£1721	$2789	€2513	Stockman (30x37cm-12x15in) s. 30-Jul-3 Goodman, Sydney #151/R est:2500-3500 (A.D 4200)
£1807	$3018	€2620	Islander with basket of flowers (35x46cm-14x18in) s. 30-Jun-3 Australian Art Auctions, Sydney #137 (A.D 4500)
£2024	$3259	€2955	Thursday Island (29x36cm-11x14in) s. canvasboard prov. 25-Aug-3 Sotheby's, Paddington #288 est:3000-5000 (A.D 5000)
£2128	$3617	€3107	Botanical Gardens (36x45cm-14x18in) s. prov. 25-Nov-3 Christie's, Melbourne #141/R est:5000-7000 (A.D 5000)
£2290	$4168	€3343	Card players (41x51cm-16x20in) s. canvas on board. 16-Jun-4 Deutscher-Menzies, Melbourne #131/R est:7000-9000 (A.D 6000)
£2459	$3984	€3590	Two figures in a river landscape (59x89cm-23x35in) s. board. 30-Jul-3 Goodman, Sydney #152/R est:6000-10000 (A.D 6000)
£2664	$4209	€3889	Islanders (40x51cm-16x20in) s. 2-Sep-3 Deutscher-Menzies, Melbourne #163/R est:7000-9000 (A.D 6500)
£2686	$4969	€3922	Mornington Island group (30x45cm-12x18in) s. i.verso board. 10-Mar-4 Deutscher-Menzies, Melbourne #348/R est:5000-8000 (A.D 6500)
£2754	$4682	€4021	Sydney Harbour (22x29cm-9x11in) s. composition board prov. 24-Nov-3 Sotheby's, Melbourne #173/R est:3000-5000 (A.D 6500)
£2846	$4467	€4127	North Queensland (90x121cm-35x48in) s. painted c.1971 prov. 27-Aug-3 Christie's, Sydney #582/R est:15000-20000 (A.D 7000)
£2979	$5064	€4349	Deighton river crossing III (60x75cm-24x30in) s. i.verso. 25-Nov-3 Christie's, Melbourne #75/R (A.D 7000)
£3306	$6116	€4827	Islanders in the jungle (75x59cm-30x23in) s. board prov. 10-Mar-4 Deutscher-Menzies, Melbourne #173/R est:14000-18000 (A.D 8000)
£3320	$5544	€4980	Untitled (44x59cm-17x23in) s. board. 27-Oct-3 Goodman, Sydney #19/R est:8000-10000 (A.D 8000)
£3602	$6123	€5259	Island Village (24x34cm-9x13in) board. 24-Nov-3 Sotheby's, Melbourne #98/R est:4000-6000 (A.D 8500)
£3830	$6510	€5592	Woman cutting stencil, Vatulele (122x91cm-48x36in) s.d.94 i.verso. 26-Nov-3 Deutscher-Menzies, Melbourne #37a/R est:14000-18000 (A.D 9000)
£4016	$6507	€5863	Conversation (29x34cm-11x13in) s. board prov. 30-Jul-3 Goodman, Sydney #15/R est:5000-7000 (A.D 9800)
£4043	$6872	€5903	Livai, raking outside his hut, Toberua (76x61cm-30x24in) s.i. 26-Nov-3 Deutscher-Menzies, Melbourne #12/R est:12000-16000 (A.D 9500)
£4098	$6475	€5983	Palmer River, Queensland (61x76cm-24x30in) s. prov. 2-Sep-3 Deutscher-Menzies, Melbourne #142/R est:12000-16000 (A.D 10000)
£4453	$7170	€6501	Island boy (79x59cm-31x23in) s. 13-Oct-3 Joel, Victoria #320/R est:14000-16000 (A.D 11000)
£4959	$8777	€7240	Islander (50x60cm-20x24in) s. 3-May-4 Christie's, Melbourne #148/R est:12000-16000 (A.D 12000)
£5285	$8297	€7663	Rural landscape (60x75cm-24x30in) s. board prov. 26-Aug-3 Christie's, Sydney #126/R est:8000-12000 (A.D 13000)
£5394	$9008	€8091	Island scene (60x46cm-24x18in) s. 27-Oct-3 Goodman, Sydney #20/R est:10000-14000 (A.D 13000)
£5785	$10702	€8446	Arrival toberua (122x122cm-48x48in) s. prov. 10-Mar-4 Deutscher-Menzies, Melbourne #113/R est:20000-25000 (A.D 14000)
£5785	$10702	€8446	Islanders in the shade (92x122cm-36x48in) s. i.verso. 10-Mar-4 Deutscher-Menzies, Melbourne #126/R est:14000-18000 (A.D 14000)
£6489	$11809	€9474	Island woman (61x76cm-24x30in) s. canvas on board. 16-Jun-4 Deutscher-Menzies, Melbourne #115/R est:20000-30000 (A.D 17000)
£6911	$10850	€10021	Sleeping boy, Thursday Island (22x29cm-9x11in) s. canvas on board prov. 26-Aug-3 Christie's, Sydney #128/R est:10000-12000 (A.D 17000)
£7025	$12996	€10257	Thursday Island (30x38cm-12x15in) canvas on board painted c.1965 prov. 10-Mar-4 Deutscher-Menzies, Melbourne #147/R est:18000-24000 (A.D 17000)
£7377	$11656	€10770	Island girl (61x91cm-24x36in) s. board prov. 2-Sep-3 Deutscher-Menzies, Melbourne #84/R est:24000-28000 (A.D 18000)
£7438	$13760	€10859	Island serenade (46x61cm-18x24in) s. i.verso canvas on board prov.exhib. 10-Mar-4 Deutscher-Menzies, Melbourne #213/R est:10000-15000 (A.D 18000)
£7520	$13461	€10979	Afternoon walk (55x139cm-22x55in) s. 4-May-4 Sotheby's, Melbourne #46/R est:18000-28000 (A.D 18500)
£7724	$12126	€11200	Sleeping figure, Thursday Island (45x101cm-18x40in) s. board. 27-Aug-3 Christie's, Sydney #514/R est:20000-30000 (A.D 19000)
£8051	$13686	€11754	Thursday Island Passage (75x99cm-30x39in) s. composition board prov.exhib. 24-Nov-3 Sotheby's, Melbourne #59/R est:18000-25000 (A.D 19000)
£8130	$12764	€11789	Chillagoe (75x100cm-30x39in) s. canvas on board prov. 27-Aug-3 Christie's, Sydney #547/R est:18000-25000 (A.D 20000)
£8163	$15020	€11918	Island interior (45x61cm-18x24in) s. board. 29-Mar-4 Goodman, Sydney #5/R est:12000-18000 (A.D 20000)
£8475	$14407	€12374	Boy with still life (60x75cm-24x30in) s. prov. 24-Nov-3 Sotheby's, Melbourne #20/R est:20000-30000 (A.D 20000)
£8511	$14468	€12426	Two islanders (75x75cm-30x30in) s. canvas on board prov. 25-Nov-3 Christie's, Melbourne #16/R est:20000-30000 (A.D 20000)
£9756	$15317	€14146	Waterfall (121x91cm-48x36in) s. exhib. 26-Aug-3 Christie's, Sydney #39/R est:20000-30000 (A.D 24000)
£10593	$18008	€15466	Islanders with poinsettias (60x75cm-24x30in) s. board prov.exhib. 24-Nov-3 Sotheby's, Melbourne #2/R est:22000-28000 (A.D 25000)
£11336	$18251	€16551	Morning - Normanton (62x92cm-24x36in) s. composition board prov. 25-Aug-3 Sotheby's, Paddington #137/R est:25000-35000 (A.D 28000)
£11885	$19254	€17352	Island girls (61x91cm-24x36in) s. canvasboard prov. 30-Jul-3 Goodman, Sydney #72a est:25000-35000 (A.D 29000)
£12295	$19918	€17951	Man with spear - Native family (58x73cm-23x29in) s.d.65 board prov. 30-Jul-3 Goodman, Sydney #27/R est:18000-22000 (A.D 30000)
£13765	$22162	€20097	Island Garden, Fiji (92x122cm-36x48in) s. island scene verso double-sided prov. 25-Aug-3 Sotheby's, Paddington #213/R est:28000-38000 (A.D 34000)
£14876	$27521	€21719	Girls with hibiscus (91x122cm-36x48in) s. board prov. 10-Mar-4 Deutscher-Menzies, Melbourne #14/R est:35000-45000 (A.D 36000)
£16794	$30565	€24519	Islanders (91x122cm-36x48in) s. 16-Jun-4 Deutscher-Menzies, Melbourne #104/R est:30000-40000 (A.D 44000)

Works on paper
£579 $1070 €845 Gippsland landscape (39x49cm-15x19in) gouache paper on board. 10-Mar-4 Deutscher-Menzies, Melbourne #471 est:800-1200 (A.D 1400)
£766 $1302 €1118 Study for Island View (22x30cm-9x12in) s.i. W/C synthetic polymer paint paper on board. 26-Nov-3 Deutscher-Menzies, Melbourne #253/R (A.D 1800)
£840 $1528 €1226 North Queensland building (14x19cm-6x7in) s. gouache. 16-Jun-4 Deutscher-Menzies, Melbourne #401/R est:2000-3000 (A.D 2200)
£1186 $2017 €1732 Outstation, Cape York Peninsula (10x15cm-4x6in) s. gouache prov. 24-Nov-3 Sotheby's, Melbourne #230 est:1200-1500 (A.D 2800)
£2300 $3841 €3358 Farmstead (61x91cm-24x36in) s. 14-Oct-3 Sotheby's, London #181/R est:2500-3500

CROOKE, Ray Austin (attrib) (1922-) Australian
£620 $1054 €930 Islander portrait (44x34cm-17x13in) canvas on board. 28-Oct-3 Goodman, Sydney #363/R (A.D 1500)

CROOKS, Ron (1925-) American
£266 $425 €388 Gambler's demise (61x76cm-24x30in) s. masonite. 22-Sep-3 O'Gallerie, Oregon #205/R
£449 $750 €656 Bottom deal (61x76cm-24x30in) masonite. 18-Oct-3 David Dike, Dallas #115/R

CROOMES, Irncee (20th C) ?
Works on paper
£291 $475 €425 Guitar player (61x43cm-24x17in) s. crayon. 27-Sep-3 Charlton Hall, Columbia #509/R

CROOS, Anthony Jansz van der (1606-1662) Dutch
£5479 $9315 €8000 Wooded landscape with a sportsman and his dog on a sandy road, view of The Hague in the distance (54x58cm-21x23in) s.d.1658. 5-Nov-3 Christie's, Amsterdam #42/R est:6000-8000
£11173 $20000 €16313 Wooded landscape with figures thatching a barn (40x34cm-16x13in) s.d.1651 prov. 27-May-4 Sotheby's, New York #109/R est:20000-30000
£26846 $49396 €40000 Wooded river landscape with cattle and figures (135x164cm-53x65in) s.d.1657. 25-Mar-4 Dr Fritz Nagel, Stuttgart #611/R est:8000

CROOS, Jacob van der (17th C) Dutch
£7800 $13494 €11388 River landscape with fishermen before the walls of a town, possibly a view of Rhenen (49x40cm-19x16in) indis sig. panel prov. 9-Dec-3 Sotheby's, Olympia #342/R est:4000-6000

CROPSEY, Jasper Francis (1823-1900) American
£6471 $11000 €9448 Figure fishing in a wooded river landscape (15x20cm-6x8in) s. board. 18-Nov-3 John Moran, Pasadena #52 est:6000-8000
£14365 $26000 €20973 Island in the Hudson (16x27cm-6x11in) s.d.1864 oil pencil prov. 31-Mar-4 Sotheby's, New York #85/R est:10000-15000
£14535 $25000 €21221 Study of boat and lobster pots, West Lulworth (32x49cm-13x19in) s.d.1857 s.i.d.verso prov.lit. 3-Dec-3 Sotheby's, New York #118/R est:20000-30000
£14773 $26000 €21569 Summer landscape (17x23cm-7x9in) init.d.1853 paper on board prov.exhib. 18-May-4 Christie's, Rockefeller NY #2/R est:15000-25000
£15217 $28000 €22217 Landscape near Greenwood Lake, New Jersey (55x76cm-22x30in) prov. 27-Jun-4 Freeman, Philadelphia #90/R est:30000-50000
£18919 $35000 €27622 Waterfall (53x36cm-21x14in) s.d.1884 oil en grisaille exhib. 11-Mar-4 Christie's, Rockefeller NY #7/R est:20000-30000
£24148 $42500 €35256 Autumn (25x18cm-10x7in) s.d.1886 prov. 19-May-4 Sotheby's, New York #105/R est:20000-30000
£29940 $50000 €43712 Fisherman in a fall landscape (33x25cm-13x10in) s.d.1881 prov. 23-Oct-3 Shannon's, Milford #143/R est:40000-60000
£40698 $70000 €59419 Lake scene with hikers in vale (15x25cm-6x10in) s.d.1875 prov. 3-Dec-3 Sotheby's, New York #113/R est:20000-30000
£69767 $120000 €101860 Greenwood lake (46x76cm-18x30in) s.d.1875 prov.exhib. 4-Dec-3 Christie's, Rockefeller NY #4/R
£99432 $175000 €145171 Lake George (33x53cm-13x21in) s.d.1866 prov.exhib.lit. 19-May-4 Sotheby's, New York #104/R est:60000-80000
£130682 $230000 €190796 Wawayanda river in Warwick (51x76cm-20x30in) s.d.1884. 19-May-4 Sotheby's, New York #53/R est:200000-300000
£244186 $420000 €356512 Niagara Falls (91x64cm-36x25in) s.d.1860 prov.exhib.lit. 3-Dec-3 Sotheby's, New York #28/R est:300000-500000
Works on paper
£1761 $2800 €2571 Autumn landscape (30x45cm-12x18in) s.d.1899 W/C. 13-Sep-3 Weschler, Washington #743/R est:3000-5000
£8380 $15000 €14070 Hudson River landscape, with sailboats and cows along bank (25x43cm-10x17in) s.d.1892 W/C. 20-Mar-4 Pook & Pook, Downington #559/R est:20000-30000
£11250 $18000 €16425 Early snow on Mt. Washington, New Hampshire (41x66cm-16x26in) s.d.1891 W/C. 20-Sep-3 Bunte, Elgin #1457 est:10000-15000

CROPSEY, Jasper Francis (attrib) (1823-1900) American
£1381 $2500 €2016 Highlands (61x91cm-24x36in) 16-Apr-4 James Julia, Fairfield #775/R est:3000-5000

CROPSEY, John (20th C) American
£1900 $2983 €2755 Buying flowers on the banks of the Seine (91x122cm-36x48in) s. 28-Aug-3 Christie's, Kensington #336/R est:1000-1500

CROSATO, Giovanni Battista (1697-1756) Italian
£11184 $20579 €17000 Etude por plafond (29x36cm-11x14in) prov. 24-Jun-4 Christie's, Paris #78/R est:6000-8000

CROSBIE, William (1915-1999) British
£270 $494 €394 A cockatiel on a branch (22x45cm-9x18in) s.i.d.LXII verso board. 29-Jan-4 Bonhams, Edinburgh #317
£460 $768 €672 Wine bottle, stoneware jar and apple (25x30cm-10x12in) s. 11-Oct-3 Shapes, Edinburgh #359
£650 $1086 €949 House boats on Loch Lomond (30x49cm-12x19in) s. board. 16-Oct-3 Bonhams, Edinburgh #11
£950 $1767 €1387 Asters (34x24cm-13x9in) s.d.LXVII board prov. 4-Mar-4 Christie's, Kensington #181/R
£1000 $1790 €1460 Garden retreat (27x37cm-11x15in) s. board. 28-May-4 Lyon & Turnbull, Edinburgh #41 est:1000-1500
£1300 $2041 €1885 Still life with fruit and flowers (61x45cm-24x18in) s. indis d. 27-Aug-3 Sotheby's, London #1156/R est:1500-2000
£2300 $3979 €3358 Autumn flowers (90x70cm-35x28in) s. s.i.verso. 11-Dec-3 Lyon & Turnbull, Edinburgh #12/R est:1500-2000
£2400 $3768 €3480 Still life with irises tulips, daisies and marsh marigolds (76x51cm-30x20in) s. 27-Aug-3 Sotheby's, London #1162/R est:2000-3000
£6000 $9420 €8700 Adam and Eve (84x118cm-33x46in) s. board prov.exhib. 27-Aug-3 Sotheby's, London #1155/R est:6000-8000
Works on paper
£540 $902 €788 Sp. (37x49cm-15x19in) s.d.1943 pen ink wash dr. 16-Oct-3 Lawrence, Crewkerne #671
£1200 $1884 €1740 Gracie (39x30cm-15x12in) s.i. gouache pastel pencil. 27-Aug-3 Sotheby's, London #1152/R est:1000-1500
£1900 $3059 €2755 Tabletop still life (39x52cm-15x20in) s.d.47 ink pastel. 21-Aug-3 Bonhams, Edinburgh #1186 est:1500-2000
£5800 $9860 €8468 Within the music we beget (53x33cm-21x13in) s.i.d.42 pen brush ink W/C bodycol. 30-Oct-3 Christie's, London #152/R est:4000-6000

CROSBY, Frederick Gordon (1885-1943) British
Works on paper
£3000 $5400 €4380 Amiens (42x28cm-17x11in) s. chl pencil monochrome wash. 26-Apr-4 Bonhams, New Bond Street #259 est:3000-3500

CROSBY, William (1830-1910) British
£450 $851 €657 Comedy, a portrait (30x25cm-12x10in) i.d.1867 verso oval. 19-Feb-4 Richardson & Smith, Whitby #405

CROSHAW, Thomas (?) British
£420 $773 €613 Fishing on the Rhine (56x86cm-22x34in) s. 14-Jun-4 Bonhams, Bath #2

CROSIO, Luigi (1835-1915) Italian
£1724 $2862 €2500 Portrait of officer (62x49cm-24x19in) s. oval. 1-Oct-3 Della Rocca, Turin #234/R
£25333 $46107 €38000 Scene in the old part of Pompeii (52x78cm-20x31in) s. 1-Jul-4 Van Ham, Cologne #1252/R est:2500

CROSMAN, Rose (20th C) American
£656 $1200 €958 Flowers and vase on a table (69x64cm-27x25in) s. exhib. 5-Jun-4 Treadway Gallery, Cincinnati #626/R est:1000-2000

CROSS, Bernice (1912-1996) American
£375 $600 €548 Magician with rabbit in hat (81x51cm-32x20in) i. 20-Sep-3 Sloans & Kenyon, Bethesda #675/R
£375 $600 €548 Mother and children. Night street scene with figures (48x41cm-19x16in) s.verso two. 20-Sep-3 Sloans & Kenyon, Bethesda #676/R

CROSS, Dorothy (1956-) Irish
Works on paper
£1284 $2426 €1900 Three figures (76x57cm-30x22in) s.d.1981 mixed media prov. 17-Feb-4 Whyte's, Dublin #211/R est:2000-3000
£1818 $3091 €2600 Krapp's last tape I. Krapp's last tape II (53x53cm-21x21in) s.i.d.1981 ink pair prov. 18-Nov-3 Whyte's, Dublin #82/R est:3000-5000

CROSS, Frederick George (1881-1941) Canadian
Works on paper
£385 $642 €562 Cowichan Bay (30x38cm-12x15in) s.i. W/C. 17-Nov-3 Hodgins, Calgary #120/R (C.D 850)

CROSS, Henri Edmond (1856-1910) French
£136363 $234545 €195000 Canale Ponte Lungo (48x65cm-19x26in) s. prov.exhib.lit. 8-Dec-3 Artcurial Briest, Paris #28/R est:250000-300000
£400000 $728000 €584000 Rio San TRovaso, Venice (73x92cm-29x36in) s. i.on stretcher painted 1903-04 prov.exhib.lit. 21-Jun-4 Sotheby's, London #38/R est:400000-600000
£405882 $690000 €592588 La sieste au bord de la mer (65x81cm-26x32in) s. painted c.1903 prov.exhib.lit. 5-Nov-3 Christie's, Rockefeller NY #219/R est:400000-600000
Prints
£2235 $4000 €3263 La promenade (28x41cm-11x16in) color lithograph. 6-May-4 Swann Galleries, New York #270/R est:5000-8000
Works on paper
£267 $485 €400 Jardiniers (25x27cm-10x11in) st.init. chl col crayon. 4-Jul-4 Eric Pillon, Calais #120/R
£268 $494 €400 Anges (16x12cm-6x5in) studio st. col crayon lead pencil. 24-Mar-4 Joron-Derem, Paris #72
£436 $807 €650 Voiliers pres de rivage (23x33cm-9x13in) st.init. dr. 14-Mar-4 Eric Pillon, Calais #180/R
£533 $971 €800 Oliviers (7x12cm-3x5in) init. W/C. 4-Jul-4 Eric Pillon, Calais #119/R
£633 $1153 €950 Eglise en bord de riviere (15x20cm-6x8in) init. W/C. 4-Jul-4 Eric Pillon, Calais #118/R
£704 $1218 €1000 Nu de femme de dos (23x16cm-9x6in) studio st. chl estompe. 10-Dec-3 Millon & Associes, Paris #76
£1310 $2410 €1913 Fragments de ciel et mer (17x25cm-7x10in) i. w/C. 14-Jun-4 Philippe Schuler, Zurich #4408/R est:3000-5000 (S.FR 3000)
£2727 $4636 €3900 Femme a la lyre (12x18cm-5x7in) st.mono. W/C. 21-Nov-3 Lombrail & Teucquam, Paris #119 est:3000-4000
£3043 $5570 €4443 L'ecume (12x17cm-5x7in) mono. W/C. 4-Jun-4 Zofingen, Switzerland #2439/R est:2000 (S.FR 7000)

£3478 $6365 €5078 Cote Provencale (12x17cm-5x7in) s. W/C. 4-Jun-4 Zofingen, Switzerland #2438/R est:2000 (S.FR 8000)
£3478 $6365 €5078 Perouse-La-Terrasse (27x44cm-11x17in) W/C. 4-Jun-4 Zofingen, Switzerland #2441 est:2000 (S.FR 8000)
£4348 $7957 €6348 Paysage Provencal (17x12cm-7x5in) s. W/C. 4-Jun-4 Zofingen, Switzerland #2440 est:2000 (S.FR 10000)
£5298 $9642 €8000 Cheval au bord de mer (12x17cm-5x7in) init. W/C prov. 18-Jun-4 Piasa, Paris #88/R est:8000-10000
£8000 $14720 €11680 Eglise de La Salute, Venise (17x22cm-7x9in) s. W/C pencil lit. 22-Jun-4 Sotheby's, London #408/R est:5000-7000
£14570 $26662 €22000 Paysage de Provence (37x44cm-15x17in) init. W/C exhib. 7-Apr-4 Piasa, Paris #64/R est:10000-15000
£16000 $29440 €23360 Provence. Lavandou. Chemin fleuri. Hamac pres de la mer. Etude d'arbre (10x17cm-4x7in) W/C two double-sided five. 24-Jun-4 Christie's, London #317/R est:15000-20000
£33520 $60000 €48939 Femme cousant (18x26cm-7x10in) st.mono.verso W/C pencil prov. 6-May-4 Sotheby's, New York #204/R est:10000-15000

CROSS, Henry H (1837-1918) American
£1130 $2000 €1650 Sioux indian under attack (30x40cm-12x16in) s.d.1862 board. 28-Apr-4 Christie's, Los Angeles #32/R est:3000-5000

CROSS, Mark (1955-) New Zealander
£1696 $3121 €2476 Tide markers (51x70cm-20x28in) s.d.1994 board. 25-Mar-4 International Art Centre, Auckland #133/R est:4500-6500 (NZ.D 4750)

CROSS, Peter (1645-1724) British
Miniatures
£2800 $4760 €4088 Mr Scroop Howe (9cm-4in) W/C oval prov. 18-Nov-3 Bonhams, New Bond Street #25/R est:2000-3000

CROSS, Sally (1874-1950) American
£206 $350 €301 Still life with hollyhocks, fruit and cockatoos (69x119cm-27x47in) s. 21-Nov-3 Skinner, Boston #390/R

CROSSE, Malcolm (20th C) British
Works on paper
£320 $512 €467 St Peters Port, Guernsey (23x36cm-9x14in) s.i. 16-Sep-3 Capes Dunn, Manchester #873
£2300 $3910 €3358 St Peter's Port, Guernsey (24x35cm-9x14in) s.i. W/C htd bodycol. 25-Nov-3 Bonhams, Knightsbridge #1/R est:500-700

CROSSE, Peter Lawrence (c.1645-1724) British
Miniatures
£10270 $19000 €14994 Anne Sotheby (8x5cm-3x2in) exec.c.1700 oval. 12-Mar-4 Du Mouchelle, Detroit #2035/R est:2000-3000

CROSSE, Richard (1742-1810) British
Miniatures
£1000 $1730 €1460 Young lady (5cm-2in) mono.verso gold frame oval. 9-Dec-3 Christie's, London #68/R est:1000-1500
£1500 $2595 €2190 Gentleman (5cm-2in) silver-gilt frame oval prov. 9-Dec-3 Christie's, London #69/R est:1500-2500
£3000 $5400 €4380 Gentleman wearing a high collared green coat (3cm-1in) gold frame oval exhib.lit. 22-Apr-4 Bonhams, New Bond Street #59/R est:2000-3000
£11000 $19800 €16060 European gentleman at an Ottoman Court (10cm-4in) pearwood frame oval exhib. 22-Apr-4 Bonhams, New Bond Street #101/R est:8000-12000

CROSSLAND, J H (1852-1939) British
£360 $644 €526 View of Yewdale, near Coniston (49x75cm-19x30in) s. 11-May-4 Bonhams, Knightsbridge #138/R

CROSSLAND, James Henry (1852-1939) British
£420 $697 €613 Highland loch scene (19x29cm-7x11in) s. 1-Oct-3 Woolley & Wallis, Salisbury #292/R
£420 $769 €613 Derwent at Whatstandwell, Derbyshire (48x75cm-19x30in) s.d.87. 10-Jun-4 Neales, Nottingham #600
£1105 $1900 €1613 Highland landscape (62x102cm-24x40in) s. 3-Dec-3 Naón & Cia, Buenos Aires #39/R
£1497 $2500 €2186 River landscape with figures on the shore (41x66cm-16x26in) s. sold with a companion. 26-Oct-3 Bonhams & Butterfields, San Francisco #6444/R

CROSSMAN, William (1896-?) American
£427 $700 €619 Winter evening landscape (76x102cm-30x40in) prov. 31-May-3 Brunk, Ashville #585/R

CROSTHWAITE, Paul (20th C) American
£274 $450 €397 Landscape with waterfall and figures below (61x46cm-24x18in) s. masonite. 4-Jun-3 Alderfer's, Hatfield #333

CROSVEN, Thomas (?) American?
£261 $425 €381 River landscape. 28-Sep-3 Bonhams & Butterfields, Los Angeles #7003a

CROTCH, Dr William (1775-1847) British
Works on paper
£1300 $2379 €1898 View of Windsor Castle from Clewer Lane (13x22cm-5x9in) i.d.1832 pencil W/C prov. 3-Jun-4 Christie's, London #106/R est:800-1200

CROTTI, Jean (1878-1958) French
£297 $550 €434 Le voilier rouge (56x46cm-22x18in) s. d.1936 verso. 10-Mar-4 Doyle, New York #18/R
£1208 $2162 €1800 Homme rouge (32x25cm-13x10in) s. panel. 30-May-4 Eric Pillon, Calais #219/R
£1879 $3364 €2800 Portrait et masque (42x27cm-17x11in) s. panel. 30-May-4 Eric Pillon, Calais #218/R
£4150 $7552 €6100 Sans titre (55x46cm-22x18in) s.d.43 panel. 8-Feb-4 Anaf, Lyon #162/R est:4000-5000
£4525 $7692 €6607 L'homme dans la foule (65x54cm-26x21in) s.d.1930 prov. 25-Nov-3 Germann, Zurich #15/R est:8000-10000 (S.FR 10000)
£7383 $13510 €11000 Nu et son double (65x54cm-26x21in) s.d.31 i. verso. 7-Jul-4 Artcurial Briest, Paris #67/R est:6000-8000
£18667 $34160 €28000 Femme au long cou (61x46cm-24x18in) s. d.20 novembre 1923 stretcher lit. 7-Jun-4 Artcurial Briest, Paris #35/R est:25000-35000
£25875 $44504 €37000 Femmes aux longs cous (61x50cm-24x20in) s. painted c.1925. 8-Dec-3 Artcurial Briest, Paris #70/R est:15000-20000
Works on paper
£338 $639 €500 Tete de femme et profile d'homme (28x21cm-11x8in) s.d.1954 black crayon prov. 21-Feb-4 Cornette de St.Cyr, Paris #190/R
£629 $1070 €900 Portrait de Salvador Dali (13x11cm-5x4in) s. graphite prov. 23-Nov-3 Cornette de St.Cyr, Paris #72

CROUCH, William (fl.1817-1850) British
Works on paper
£750 $1380 €1095 View of Stately House. Romantic architectural view. View towards a city (9x14cm-4x6in) W/C set of three. 22-Jun-4 Bonhams, Knightsbridge #196/R

CROUPPEN, Carol (20th C) American
£235 $400 €343 DHS Drifting 3 (119x142cm-47x56in) oil stick oil pastel. 7-Nov-3 Selkirks, St. Louis #435

CROUSE, H Max (?) British?
Works on paper
£580 $998 €847 Ripon Cathedral (30x48cm-12x19in) s. W/C. 5-Dec-3 Keys, Aylsham #437/R
£1100 $2035 €1606 Ripon Cathedral with figures by River Ure (30x48cm-12x19in) s.d.1885. 12-Feb-4 Andrew Hartley, Ilkley #792/R est:700-900

CROVELLO, William (20th C) ?
Sculpture
£1059 $1800 €1546 Untitled (51x43cm-20x17in) marble. 9-Nov-3 Wright, Chicago #435 est:1500-2000

CROWE, Victoria (1945-) British
Works on paper
£320 $586 €467 Medallion and painting angel (12x16cm-5x6in) s. mixed media. 8-Apr-4 Bonhams, Edinburgh #40

CROWLEY, Deidre (20th C) Irish?
Works on paper
£403 $632 €580 Beside the quiet lake (40x56cm-16x22in) s.d.96 mixed media. 26-Aug-3 James Adam, Dublin #142/R

CROWLEY, Nicholas Joseph (attrib) (1813-1857) British
£2000 $3620 €3000 Fortune telling by cup tossing (22x28cm-9x11in) init. board. 31-Mar-4 James Adam, Dublin #16/R est:2000-3000

CROWN PRINCE RUDOLF OF AUSTRIA (19th C) Austrian
Works on paper
£805 $1426 €1200 Bird of prey (23x24cm-9x9in) s.d.22.1.1870 W/C. 29-Apr-4 Dorotheum, Vienna #160/R

CROWQUILL, Alfred (1804-1872) British
Works on paper
£650 $1125 €949 Phantasmagoria (19x35cm-7x14in) s.d.1872 ink W/C prov.exhib. 11-Dec-3 Sotheby's, London #183/R

CROWTHER, Henry (19/20th C) British
£243 $450 €355 Delaware Peggy, in landscape (30x38cm-12x15in) s.i.d.1907. 10-Feb-4 Doyle, New York #169/R
£248 $450 €362 Pomeranian in a landscape (31x38cm-12x15in) s.d.1916. 30-Mar-4 Bonhams & Butterfields, San Francisco #115/R
£380 $680 €555 Flashaway Rip - an Irish setter (24x29cm-9x11in) s.i.d.1928 canvas on board. 17-Mar-4 Bonhams, Chester #388
£400 $680 €584 Irish terrier (18x23cm-7x9in) panel. 27-Nov-3 Christie's, Kensington #297/R
£760 $1360 €1110 Haulstone Dipper (30x37cm-12x15in) s.i.d.1930. 17-Mar-4 Bonhams, Chester #387
£800 $1432 €1168 Scottish Terrier before a landscape (28x38cm-11x15in) s.d.1910. 17-Mar-4 Bonhams, Chester #386
£865 $1600 €1263 Ospringe Bugler in a landscape (30x38cm-12x15in) s.d.1921 prov. 10-Feb-4 Doyle, New York #173/R est:1000-1500
£900 $1656 €1314 Underbank startler, a terrier (30x38cm-12x15in) s.i.d.1920. 10-Jun-4 Christie's, Kensington #387/R

CROWTHER, Stephen (1922-) British
£290 $528 €423 Another World, amusement arcade at Seaton Carew (70x90cm-28x35in) s.d.1996. 29-Jun-4 Anderson & Garland, Newcastle #297

£300	$546	€438	Village store (50x75cm-20x30in) s. 29-Jun-4 Anderson & Garland, Newcastle #304
£310	$564	€453	Harbour wall, low tide (60x90cm-24x35in) s.d.98. 29-Jun-4 Anderson & Garland, Newcastle #306
£340	$619	€496	Compression Deck, Hartlepool Docks (75x100cm-30x39in) s.d.93. 29-Jun-4 Anderson & Garland, Newcastle #292
£340	$619	€496	Self portrait against the headland (40x50cm-16x20in) s.d.1985. 29-Jun-4 Anderson & Garland, Newcastle #301/R
£350	$637	€511	Seahouses harbour (60x105cm-24x41in) s.d.1960. 29-Jun-4 Anderson & Garland, Newcastle #296
£360	$655	€526	Early Days - when we were young (101x125cm-40x49in) s.d.1959 board. 29-Jun-4 Anderson & Garland, Newcastle #357/R
£380	$692	€555	Flying Flag, Edinburgh (75x100cm-30x39in) s.d.2000. 29-Jun-4 Anderson & Garland, Newcastle #295
£380	$692	€555	Mending the nets, Brixham Harbour (60x91cm-24x36in) s.d.97 exhib. 29-Jun-4 Anderson & Garland, Newcastle #335/R
£490	$892	€715	Sheltered waters, Hartlepool Marina (60x91cm-24x36in) s.d.91. 29-Jun-4 Anderson & Garland, Newcastle #294/R
£520	$946	€759	After the shower, Seaton Carew (60x75cm-24x30in) s.d.91. 29-Jun-4 Anderson & Garland, Newcastle #300/R
£520	$946	€759	First light, Hartlepool Bay. Winter gold (69x89cm-27x35in) s.d.94 s.d.76 board two. 29-Jun-4 Anderson & Garland, Newcastle #329

CROXFORD, William Edwards (19/20th C) British
Works on paper

£250	$418	€365	Quayside (13x25cm-5x10in) s.d.1889 W/C. 14-Oct-3 David Lay, Penzance #123
£350	$595	€511	Amberley, Sussex (28x46cm-11x18in) s. 5-Nov-3 John Nicholson, Haslemere #521
£1350	$2133	€1971	Stoke, Nr Hartland, north Devon (45x65cm-18x26in) s.d.95 W/C. 23-Jul-3 Hampton & Littlewood, Exeter #400/R est:1500-2000

CROZER, Aspasie (19th C) French
Works on paper

£989	$1800	€1444	N'Oubliez Pas. A lover at a tree (42x35cm-17x14in) s.d.1810 s.d.1811 gouache paper on board pair. 4-Feb-4 Christie's, Rockefeller NY #117/R est:800-1200

CROZET, Marquis Roger du (fl.1869-1880) French
Sculpture

£1950	$3100	€2847	Horse with saddle (23x33cm-9x13in) s. exec.c.1890 bronze. 4-May-3 William Jenack, New York #367 est:2000-3000

CROZIER, George (?-1915) British
Works on paper

£340	$544	€496	Cattle by the sea. W/C. 16-Sep-3 Bonhams, Ipswich #232

CROZIER, Robert (1815-1891) British

£1300	$2171	€1898	Lady with feathered hat (79x53cm-31x21in) s.d.1883 after Rubens. 8-Oct-3 Halls, Shrewsbury #90/R est:1500-2500
£1700	$2703	€2482	Three children feeding cage birds (53x41cm-21x16in) s.d.1895. 9-Sep-3 Gorringes, Lewes #1819/R est:1200-1500

CROZIER, William (1930-) British

£540	$977	€788	Cliff face, Ayreshire, No 2 (76x52cm-30x20in) s.d.1960 oil paper. 2-Apr-4 Moore Allen & Innocent, Cirencester #423/R
£1100	$1837	€1606	Landscape (78x72cm-31x28in) board. 11-Oct-3 Shapes, Edinburgh #386 est:800-1200
£1141	$2019	€1700	Landscape with yellow sky (56x38cm-22x15in) s.d.1960 oil paper sold with a catalogue. 27-Apr-4 Whyte's, Dublin #95/R est:1800-2200
£1200	$2172	€1800	Untitled (74x47cm-29x19in) s. oil paper. 30-Mar-4 De Veres Art Auctions, Dublin #88/R est:2000-3000
£2000	$3580	€2920	Essex wilderness II (67x87cm-26x34in) board prov. 14-May-4 Christie's, Kensington #473/R est:2000-3000
£2819	$4989	€4200	Colin's field, west Cork (36x46cm-14x18in) s. 27-Apr-4 Whyte's, Dublin #93/R est:4000-6000
£3490	$6177	€5200	Island (46x51cm-18x20in) s.i.verso prov.exhib. 27-Apr-4 Whyte's, Dublin #170/R est:5000-7000
£4118	$7000	€6012	Red field (152x152cm-60x60in) s. 9-Nov-3 Bonhams & Butterfields, Los Angeles #4087/R est:3000-5000
£4698	$8409	€7000	Blue foxgloves in interior (55x65cm-22x26in) s. s.verso prov. 26-May-4 James Adam, Dublin #66/R est:5000-7000
£6084	$10343	€8700	Rode to Ballydehob (36x46cm-14x18in) s. exhib. 25-Nov-3 De Veres Art Auctions, Dublin #24/R est:4000-6000

CRUICKSHANK, Frederick (1800-1868) British
Miniatures

£1600	$2864	€2336	John Gibson Reeves (10x8cm-4x3in) init.d.1833 rec. gilt metal frame. 25-May-4 Christie's, London #220/R est:1000-1500

CRUICKSHANK, Grace (fl.1860-1894) British
Miniatures

£1600	$2944	€2336	Lady Canning and her daughter, in a landscape (17cm-7in) painted porcelain. 24-Jun-4 Bonhams, New Bond Street #147/R est:500-700

CRUICKSHANK, William (1848-1922) British

£650	$1190	€949	Larder still life with hare and pheasant (20x13cm-8x5in) s. ivory. 8-Apr-4 Bonhams, Edinburgh #109

Works on paper

£320	$592	€467	Still life of grapes and apples on a bank (12x9cm-5x4in) s. W/C ivory oval. 14-Jul-4 Bonhams, Chester #519
£350	$550	€508	Still life of rabbits on a bank (13x18cm-5x7in) s. W/C ivorine. 15-Dec-2 Desmond Judd, Cranbrook #852
£350	$550	€508	Still life of ducks on a bank (10x15cm-4x6in) s. W/C ivorine. 15-Dec-2 Desmond Judd, Cranbrook #853
£350	$602	€511	Still life of flowers in a jug (15x10cm-6x4in) s. W/C ivory. 3-Dec-3 Andrew Hartley, Ilkley #1052
£350	$602	€511	Still life with blossoms (23x30cm-9x12in) W/C. 3-Dec-3 Andrew Hartley, Ilkley #1045
£400	$728	€584	Still life of game hanging on a ledge (15x8cm-6x3in) s. W/C. 4-Feb-4 John Nicholson, Haslemere #45
£400	$716	€584	Winters blessing, still life (38x53cm-15x21in) W/C. 5-May-4 John Nicholson, Haslemere #434
£450	$765	€657	Still life of dead game, fruit and pottery (12x19cm-5x7in) s. W/C ivory. 19-Nov-3 Tennants, Leyburn #921/R
£480	$874	€701	Convolvulus and a bird's nest on a mossy bank (24x38cm-9x15in) s. pencil W/C htd white oval. 1-Jul-4 Christie's, Kensington #265/R
£500	$910	€730	Game and an ale flagon beneath a tree (12x19cm-5x7in) s. W/C ivory. 1-Jul-4 Mellors & Kirk, Nottingham #714
£520	$837	€754	Still life with birds nest (8x10cm-3x4in) s. W/C oval. 13-Aug-3 Andrew Hartley, Ilkley #768
£550	$875	€803	Still life jug of flowers on a ledge (14x10cm-6x4in) W/C. 13-Sep-3 Windibank, Dorking #169/R
£560	$1036	€818	Still life of birds nest and blossom branch on a mossy bank (25x40cm-10x16in) s. W/C. 14-Jul-4 Bonhams, Chester #517
£580	$986	€847	Still life with bird's nest and apple blossom on a bank (29x49cm-11x19in) s. W/C. 18-Nov-3 Bonhams, Leeds #72
£600	$1122	€876	Bird's nest and white dog rose against a bank. Bird's nest and flowers (21x25cm-8x10in) one init. W/C bodycol pair. 24-Feb-4 Bonhams, Knowle #41
£650	$1105	€949	Bird's nest with eggs and fruit beneath a mossy bank (16x27cm-6x11in) s. W/C bodycol sold with a companion. 1-Dec-3 Bonhams, Bath #68/R
£650	$1105	€949	Still life of dead game and a cat (12x22cm-5x9in) s. W/C ivory. 19-Nov-3 Tennants, Leyburn #920/R
£750	$1275	€1095	Day's bag, hare and peasant. Day's bag, blackcock (12x19cm-5x7in) s. W/C scratching out pair. 27-Nov-3 Christie's, Kensington #202/R
£920	$1463	€1343	Studies of dead game in a larder (20x12cm-8x5in) s. gouache ivory panel pair. 18-Mar-3 Anderson & Garland, Newcastle #321/R

CRUIKSHANK, George (1792-1878) British
Works on paper

£250	$430	€365	Design for a title page (28x19cm-11x7in) s.d.1884 pencil brown ink. 3-Dec-3 Christie's, Kensington #246a/R
£400	$668	€584	Cured cripple (24x18cm-9x7in) s.d. June 3 1832 W/C pencil. 14-Oct-3 Bonhams, New Bond Street #233/R
£815	$1500	€1190	Long Vacation (44x56cm-17x22in) init.i. ink sold with eight companions mounted on a sheet nine. 27-Jun-4 Freeman, Philadelphia #54/R est:2000-3000

CRUIKSHANK, Isaac (1756-1811) British
Works on paper

£1600	$2944	€2336	Hebrew pedler. Tam O'shanter and souter Johnny. Refreshment at an inn on going to town (18x28cm-7x11in) s.i. pen ink W/C over pencil set of three. 26-Mar-4 Sotheby's, London #96/R est:1500-2000

CRUISE, Boyd (1909-1988) American
Works on paper

£739	$1300	€1079	Rosemary, young girl (43x33cm-17x13in) s. W/C. 22-May-4 New Orleans Auction, New Orleans #772/R est:500-800
£3343	$5750	€4881	Pomegranate (28x18cm-11x7in) s. W/C. 6-Dec-3 Neal Auction Company, New Orleans #565/R est:4000-6000

CRUTE, Harry E (20th C) British

£300	$501	€438	Oddicombe Beach, Torquay (23x28cm-9x11in) s. i.verso board. 14-Oct-3 David Lay, Penzance #413

CRUYL, Lieven (c.1640-1720) Belgian
Works on paper

£15541	$27351	€23000	View of the Capitol, Rome (15x21cm-6x8in) bears i. pen col ink col wash prov.exhib. 19-May-4 Sotheby's, Amsterdam #39/R est:6500-7500

CRUZ HERRERA, Jose Herrerilla (1890-1972) Spanish

£646	$1157	€950	Andalucian beauty (34x26cm-13x10in) s. canvas on cardboard. 22-Mar-4 Durán, Madrid #106/R
£839	$1401	€1200	Lady with shawl (29x23cm-11x9in) s.d.1910 canvas on board. 30-Jun-3 Ansorena, Madrid #322/R
£1497	$2724	€2200	Studying Cervantes (70x50cm-28x20in) s.d.1927. 3-Feb-4 Segre, Madrid #122/R est:2200
£2797	$4671	€4000	Gypsy woman reading a letter (60x50cm-24x20in) s. painted c.1920. 30-Jun-3 Ansorena, Madrid #329/R
£3191	$5330	€4500	Beaute marocaine (46x38cm-18x15in) s. 16-Jun-3 Gros & Delettrez, Paris #201/R est:3500-4500
£4138	$6869	€6000	Florist (64x53cm-25x21in) s. 30-Sep-3 Ansorena, Madrid #65/R est:5500
£6042	$10090	€8700	Personnages pres d'un oued (46x55cm-18x22in) s. 25-Oct-3 Dianous, Marseille #445
£6338	$10141	€9000	Nue a Rabat (46x33cm-18x13in) s. 20-Sep-3 Compagnie Marocaine des Objets d'Art, Casablanca #101/R
£11972	$19155	€17000	Jeune fille a la rose (64x52cm-25x20in) s. 20-Sep-3 Compagnie Marocaine des Objets d'Art, Casablanca #78/R
£26408	$42254	€37500	Nue a Rabat (147x48cm-58x19in) s. panel. 20-Sep-3 Compagnie Marocaine des Objets d'Art, Casablanca #177/R

CRUZ, Pedro (?) ?

£268	$481	€400	Flowers (33x44cm-13x17in) s.d.1961 canvas on board. 31-May-4 Cabral Moncada Leiloes, Lisbon #96/R

CRUZ-DIEZ, Carlos (1923-) Venezuelan

£4245	$7810	€6368	Untitled (80x80cm-31x31in) s.verso acrylic on aluminium in 6 parts. 27-Jun-4 Subastas Odalys, Caracas #6/R
£4525	$7692	€6607	Induction chromatique (120x120cm-47x47in) s.i.d.1975 ac canvas on panel. 22-Nov-3 Burkhard, Luzern #166/R est:8000-10000 (S.FR 10000)

£7095 $12487 €10500 Physichromie No. 297 (61x83cm-24x33in) s.i.d.1966 verso paint plastic panel prov. 18-May-4 Tajan, Paris #94/R est:3000-4000
£7821 $14000 €11419 Physicrome 493 (61x82cm-24x32in) s.i.d.70 acrylic panel prov. 26-May-4 Sotheby's, New York #183/R est:10000-15000
£11312 $19231 €16516 Physiochromology (100x100cm-39x39in) s.i.d.Oct 73 acrylic panel. 22-Nov-3 Burkhard, Luzern #168/R est:15000-20000 (S.FR 25000)
Sculpture
£3021 $5136 €4411 Physichromie No.1133 (50x50cm-20x20in) s.d.1979 optic metal relief prov. 5-Nov-3 AB Stockholms Auktionsverk #940/R est:30000-40000 (S.KR 40000)
Works on paper
£385 $700 €578 Interference (30x30cm-12x12in) s.verso mixed media exec.1978. 21-Jun-4 Subastas Odalys, Caracas #3/R
£2903 $4500 €4238 Physicromie 920 (50x50cm-20x20in) s.verso mixed media. 29-Sep-2 Subastas Odalys, Caracas #68/R
£5008 $9115 €7512 Colour. s.verso mixed media exec.1982 in 6 parts. 21-Jun-4 Subastas Odalys, Caracas #9/R

CSAKY, Josef (1888-1971) French/Hungarian
Sculpture
£1042 $1740 €1500 Femme a l'enfant (32cm-13in) num.EA/2 brown pat bronze Cast Blanchet. 25-Oct-3 Cornette de St.Cyr, Paris #490 est:1500-2000
£2013 $3725 €3000 Femme a l'enfant (33cm-13in) s.st.f.Blanchet pat bronze. 14-Mar-4 St-Germain-en-Laye Encheres #127/R est:4000
£3356 $6242 €5000 Femme agenouillee (27x25x15cm-11x10x6in) s. plaster exec.c.1929. 2-Mar-4 Artcurial Briest, Paris #146/R est:4500-5000
£4803 $8837 €7300 Tete ovoide version II (27x18x15cm-11x7x6in) s. num.HC1 pat bronze Cast Blanchet. 24-Jun-4 Credit Municipal, Paris #69/R est:3000-4000
£5000 $9100 €7500 Adam et Eve (50x30cm-20x12in) s. num.7/8 pat bronze Cast Blanchet. 4-Jul-4 Eric Pillon, Calais #294/R
£5034 $9363 €7500 Figure abstraite (79cm-31in) s.num.4/8 black pat bronze marble socle. 2-Mar-4 Artcurial Briest, Paris #145/R est:8000-12000
£9155 $15838 €13000 L'architecture (72x22x14cm-28x9x6in) s.num.1/8 silver bronze Cast Blanchet prov.lit. 13-Dec-3 Martinot & Savignat, Pontoise #92/R est:11000-12000
Works on paper
£1111 $1855 €1600 Mere et ses enfants (49x30cm-19x12in) s.d.66 lead pencil. 21-Oct-3 Artcurial Briest, Paris #102 est:1000-1500

CSATO (19/20th C) Hungarian
£1127 $1949 €1600 Composition (46x55cm-18x22in) s.d.1949 prov. 14-Dec-3 Versailles Encheres #43/R est:1000-1200

CSEREPES, Istvan (1901-1944) Hungarian
Works on paper
£738 $1335 €1077 Bathing (37x26cm-15x10in) s. W/C. 16-Apr-4 Mu Terem Galeria, Budapest #162/R (H.F 280000)

CSERNUS, Tibor (1927-) Hungarian
£4324 $8000 €6313 Sacrifice of Isaac (230x175cm-91x69in) s.d.1987 verso prov. 12-Feb-4 Sotheby's, New York #331/R est:4000-6000
£5034 $8910 €7500 Paysage (140x180cm-55x71in) s.d.1978 verso prov. 28-Apr-4 Artcurial Briest, Paris #522/R est:2000-3000
Works on paper
£1757 $3250 €2565 Maquettes d'Avions (72x121cm-28x48in) init. pastel prov. 12-Feb-4 Sotheby's, New York #336/R est:2000-3000

CSERY, Miklos (20th C) Hungarian
£594 $1010 €850 Reclining female nude (55x95cm-22x37in) s.d.1927 i.verso. 28-Nov-3 Schloss Ahlden, Ahlden #1551/R

CSILLAG, Yozsef (1894-1977) Hungarian
£475 $750 €694 Figures in field harvesting hay (61x91cm-24x36in) s. i.on stretcher. 6-Sep-3 Brunk, Ashville #142
£698 $1200 €1019 Peasants in the field (41x51cm-16x20in) s. painted c.1930 sold with another similar. 7-Dec-3 Treadway Gallery, Cincinnati #478/R

CSOK, Istvan (1865-1961) Hungarian
£1175 $2032 €1716 Portrait of a boy - Sandorka (51x41cm-20x16in) s. painted c.1900. 12-Dec-3 Kieselbach, Budapest #164/R (H.F 450000)
£2138 $3784 €3121 Girl with a chain of pearls (50x40cm-20x16in) s. 28-Apr-4 Kieselbach, Budapest #171/R (H.F 800000)
£3741 $6622 €5462 Zuzu is sewing (60x50cm-24x20in) s. 28-Apr-4 Kieselbach, Budapest #172/R (H.F 1400000)
£8352 $14449 €12194 By the window (63x50cm-25x20in) s. 12-Dec-3 Kieselbach, Budapest #136/R (H.F 3200000)
£8551 $15135 €12484 Thamar (60x50cm-24x20in) s. painted 1906. 28-Apr-4 Kieselbach, Budapest #150/R (H.F 3200000)
£9620 $17027 €14045 Corner of the studio (37x50cm-15x20in) s.d.904. 28-Apr-4 Kieselbach, Budapest #17/R (H.F 3600000)
£16289 $27040 €23782 Thamar (60x50cm-24x20in) s. 4-Oct-3 Kieselbach, Budapest #117/R (H.F 6000000)
£17126 $30998 €25004 Still life with spring flowers (101x80cm-40x31in) s. 16-Apr-4 Mu Terem Galeria, Budapest #139/R (H.F 6500000)
£90856 $160815 €132650 The awakening of spring (102x183cm-40x72in) s. 28-Apr-4 Kieselbach, Budapest #99/R (H.F 34000000)

CSUK, Jeno (1887-1927) Hungarian
£280 $467 €400 Girl (53x40cm-21x16in) s. panel. 26-Jun-3 Weidler, Nurnberg #4591/R

CUBELLS Y RUIZ, Enrique Martinez (1874-1947) Spanish
£369 $661 €550 Study for soldier (36x28cm-14x11in) prov. 25-May-4 Durán, Madrid #652/R
£1897 $3167 €2750 Landscape (61x45cm-24x18in) s. 17-Nov-3 Durán, Madrid #176/R est:1200
£2837 $4596 €4000 Barca de pesca (33x23cm-13x9in) 20-May-3 Ansorena, Madrid #175/R est:4000
£3147 $5255 €4500 Interior (44x34cm-17x13in) s. 30-Jun-3 Ansorena, Madrid #437/R est:4500
£6711 $12013 €10000 Troy fall (182x252cm-72x99in) s. board. 25-May-4 Durán, Madrid #191/R est:4000
£11644 $19795 €17000 Boys bathing on the beach (50x61cm-20x24in) s. 4-Nov-3 Ansorena, Madrid #142/R est:17000
£18000 $30600 €26280 Fisherwoman (84x104cm-33x41in) s. s.i.verso. 18-Nov-3 Sotheby's, London #218/R
£25362 $41594 €35000 Sacando la barca (82x66cm-32x26in) s. 27-May-3 Durán, Madrid #240/R est:25000

CUBELLS Y RUIZ, Enrique Martinez (attrib) (1874-1947) Spanish
£272 $487 €400 Landscape (28x45cm-11x18in) 22-Mar-4 Durán, Madrid #588/R
£395 $726 €600 Study for gallant scene (39x49cm-15x19in) 22-Jun-4 Durán, Madrid #562/R

CUBELLS, Salvador Martinez (1845-1914) Spanish
£7586 $13655 €11000 Fruit market (84x52cm-33x20in) s.d.1894. 26-Jan-4 Durán, Madrid #210/R est:11000

CUBILLO, Gustavo (20th C) Spanish
£278 $442 €400 Galerias (114x146cm-45x57in) s.d.89 s.i.d.verso acrylic. 29-Apr-3 Durán, Madrid #10/R

CUBITT, Ted (20th C) Canadian
£249 $416 €364 Untitled - sunlight on the snow (55x75cm-22x30in) s.d.1970. 17-Nov-3 Hodgins, Calgary #144/R (C.D 550)

CUBLEY, Henry Hadfield (fl.1882-1904) British
£250 $398 €363 Morning, Whitby (28x44cm-11x17in) s. board. 9-Sep-3 David Duggleby, Scarborough #308/R
£280 $504 €409 Cattle watering in a highland landscape (28x48cm-11x19in) s. 22-Apr-4 Locke & England, Leamington Spa #114/R
£280 $515 €409 Near Gare Loch (76x63cm-30x25in) s. s.i.verso. 8-Jun-4 Bonhams, Knightsbridge #141/R
£284 $500 €415 By the shores of Loch Nell Argyllshire (51x76cm-20x30in) s.d.1896. 23-May-4 Treadway Gallery, Cincinnati #509/R
£290 $539 €423 Cattle watering, castle beyond (29x35cm-11x14in) s.d.96 i.verso board. 2-Mar-4 Bamfords, Derby #442/R
£350 $655 €511 Morning near Barmouth (48x74cm-19x29in) s.d.1921 i.verso. 24-Feb-4 Rogers Jones, Clwyd #158/R
£360 $673 €526 Morning near Arrochar, Loch Long (30x46cm-12x18in) s.i.d.99 panel. 20-Jul-4 Sworder & Son, Bishops Stortford #767/R
£400 $652 €584 Mussel gatherers at Whitby (61x36cm-24x14in) s.i.d.1919. 27-Sep-3 Hogben, Folkstone #211
£460 $856 €672 Cafel Carey, Wales (50x75cm-20x30in) s.d.1911. 2-Mar-4 Bamfords, Derby #445
£500 $815 €730 Old Whitby scene with buildings and young children on the shore (30x41cm-12x16in) s.i.d.1919 board. 27-Sep-3 Hogben, Folkstone #207
£500 $815 €730 Old houses, Arthoy NY (58x43cm-23x17in) i. 27-Sep-3 Hogben, Folkstone #209
£500 $895 €730 By the shores of Loch Gil, Invernesshire (76x51cm-30x20in) s. indis d. s.i.d.verso. 11-May-4 Bonhams, Knightsbridge #144/R
£550 $897 €803 Old Welsh village with thatched cottage, figures, horse and cart (61x43cm-24x17in) s.i.d.1917. 27-Sep-3 Hogben, Folkstone #210
£550 $990 €803 Near Barmouth, North Wales (51x76cm-20x30in) s. i.d.1916 verso. 21-Apr-4 Tennants, Leyburn #1168
£600 $978 €876 Highland drover on Skye (58x89cm-23x35in) s.d.1880 verso. 28-Sep-3 Lots Road Auctions, London #354
£700 $1141 €1022 Cows in a Scottish landscape (61x41cm-24x16in) s.i.d.1920 pair. 27-Sep-3 Hogben, Folkstone #208
£1800 $3060 €2628 Highland cattle with girls on horseback, a dog, and mountains (61x91cm-24x36in) s.d.1897. 5-Nov-3 John Nicholson, Haslemere #664/R est:800-1500
£2200 $4092 €3212 Head of Loch Long (51x76cm-20x30in) s. i.verso. 4-Mar-4 Christie's, Kensington #52/R est:1500-2000
£3200 $5728 €4672 Lane near Dovedale (61x91cm-24x36in) s.d.80 s.i.d.1880 verso. 27-May-4 Christie's, Kensington #162/R est:1800-2000

CUCARO, Pascal (1915-) American
£568 $1000 €829 Washington Square Park, San Francisco (66x84cm-26x33in) s. 22-May-4 Harvey Clar, Oakland #2254

CUCCHI, Enzo (1949-) Italian
£9649 $17754 €14088 Untitled (55x22cm-22x9in) s.d.1980 verso. 23-Jun-4 Koller, Zurich #3125/R est:3000-4000 (S.FR 22000)
£12000 $21840 €17520 Untitled, age of Jesus (76x111cm-30x44in) s.d.1986 verso oil tempera paper on wood prov.exhib. 6-Feb-4 Sotheby's, London #244/R est:12000-15000
£41333 $76467 €62000 Wild stroll (172x88cm-68x35in) s.i.d.1982 oil tubes mixed media prov. 18-Jul-4 Sotheby's, Paris #235/R est:20000-30000
Works on paper
£1149 $2056 €1700 Drawing cathedral (13x25cm-5x10in) s.i.d.1993 verso crayon chl. 4-May-4 Calmels Cohen, Paris #244/R est:1200-1500
£1176 $1965 €1717 Untitled (29x30cm-11x12in) s.d.1982 verso Indian ink gouache. 24-Jun-3 Germann, Zurich #53/R est:3000-4000 (S.FR 2600)
£2334 $4294 €3500 Untitled (26x21cm-10x8in) s.d.24.2.1987 verso ball pen prov.lit. 9-Jun-4 Artcurial Briest, Paris #524/R est:2500-3500
£2400 $4392 €3600 Furrows of Europe 85 (16x24cm-6x9in) s.i.d.1985 chl prov.exhib.lit. 4-Jun-4 Lempertz, Koln #101/R est:3000
£8772 $16140 €12807 Il sentimento di un ricordo (39x30cm-15x12in) s.verso chl pencil prov. 23-Jun-4 Koller, Zurich #3149/R est:1200-2500 (S.FR 20000)

CUCUEL, Edward (1875-1951) American
£1625 $2600 €2373 Spring ride (30x41cm-12x16in) s.i.verso masonite. 19-Sep-3 Freeman, Philadelphia #122/R est:2000-3000
£1678 $2887 €2400 Portrait of Elizabeth Meinhold (69x50cm-27x20in) s.i.d.30 board. 3-Dec-3 Neumeister, Munich #546/R est:2500
£3106 $5000 €4535 Still life with teacups and round tray (20x36cm-8x14in) s. panel prov. 20-Aug-3 James Julia, Fairfield #1411/R est:8000-10000

£6000 $10320 €8760 Starnberger See (41x50cm-16x20in) s. i.verso plywood. 4-Dec-3 Christie's, Kensington #46/R est:4000-10000
£6000 $10800 €9000 Beschneite Buchen (65x79cm-26x31in) s. s.i.verso. 20-Apr-4 Sotheby's, Amsterdam #226/R est:10000-15000
£10000 $18000 €15000 Frozen lake in a mountainous winter landscape (80x80cm-31x31in) s. 20-Apr-4 Sotheby's, Amsterdam #232/R est:15000-20000
£13542 $21531 €19500 Young woman with green garter (64x46cm-25x18in) s. verso. 11-Sep-3 Weidler, Nurnberg #312/R
£20000 $34000 €29200 Young woman (80x65cm-31x26in) s.verso. 18-Nov-3 Sotheby's, London #346/R
£20979 $36084 €30000 Summer dream (44x55cm-17x22in) s. prov. 5-Dec-3 Ketterer, Munich #25/R est:30000-40000
£22093 $38000 €32256 Afternoon on the lake (54x81cm-21x32in) s. 4-Dec-3 Christie's, Rockefeller NY #78/R est:30000-50000
£24648 $44120 €35000 Two nude females sitting at a table in a private booth (61x74cm-24x29in) s. lit. 8-Jan-4 Allgauer, Kempten #2364/R est:35000
£30769 $52923 €44000 Journey (72x57cm-28x22in) s. painted 1914/18 prov. 5-Dec-3 Ketterer, Munich #29/R est:30000-40000
£34091 $60000 €49773 Wood Nymph - Baumnixe (99x99cm-39x39in) s. s.i.stretcher. 19-May-4 Sotheby's, New York #15/R est:40000-60000
£34667 $62053 €52000 Girl on shore picking blossom (80x80cm-31x31in) s. s. i. stretcher. 13-May-4 Neumeister, Munich #317/R est:35000-40000
£37162 $66520 €55000 On the jetty (54x67cm-21x26in) s. board prov.lit. 8-May-4 Schloss Ahlden, Ahlden #809/R est:56000
£45000 $77400 €65700 Im yacht club, Starnberg (80x80cm-31x31in) s. s.i.stretcher. 3-Dec-3 Christie's, London #34/R est:35000-45000
£46196 $85000 €67446 East wind (70x48cm-28x19in) s. i. stretcher prov. 27-Jun-4 Freeman, Philadelphia #112/R est:50000-80000
£48000 $88320 €72000 At Lake Starnberg (98x97cm-39x38in) s. prov. 11-Jun-4 Villa Grisebach, Berlin #7/R est:60000-80000
£48295 $85000 €70511 Villa by the Lake - Villa am See (109x99cm-43x39in) s. i.stretcher. 19-May-4 Sotheby's, New York #14/R est:50000-70000
£52326 $90000 €76396 Wildflowers (80x80cm-31x31in) s.i.on stretcher. 3-Dec-3 Sotheby's, New York #30/R est:60000-80000
Works on paper
£1367 $2487 €2050 Two girls at the river's edge about to go rowing (34x39cm-13x15in) s. W/C. 1-Jul-4 Van Ham, Cologne #1254/R est:4400
£3000 $5370 €4380 Under the chestnut tree (24x33cm-9x13in) s. W/C. 26-May-4 Sotheby's, Olympia #348/R est:3000-5000
£4000 $7160 €5840 Afternoon on the Stanberger see (35x28cm-14x11in) s. W/C. 26-May-4 Sotheby's, Olympia #350/R est:4000-6000
£5000 $8950 €7400 Picnic (34x37cm-13x15in) s. W/C lit. 8-May-4 Schloss Ahlden, Ahlden #810/R est:6000
£5000 $8950 €7400 On the jetty (34x39cm-13x15in) s. W/C lit. 8-May-4 Schloss Ahlden, Ahlden #811/R est:6500

CUDENNEC, Patrice (1952-) French
£493 $863 €700 Locronan, le porteur de banniere (46x38cm-18x15in) s. 21-Dec-3 Thierry & Lannon, Brest #381
£500 $895 €750 Brehat entre les pins (60x20cm-24x8in) s. 16-May-4 Thierry & Lannon, Brest #208
£599 $1048 €850 Figures au port de Brigneau (73x60cm-29x24in) s. 21-Dec-3 Thierry & Lannon, Brest #380
£634 $1109 €900 Village Breton sous la neige (35x27cm-14x11in) s. 21-Dec-3 Thierry & Lannon, Brest #379
£733 $1313 €1100 Trois pecheurs au retour de peche (65x54cm-26x21in) s. 16-May-4 Thierry & Lannon, Brest #206/R
£845 $1479 €1200 Composition au retour de peche (65x54cm-26x21in) s. 21-Dec-3 Thierry & Lannon, Brest #382

CUDWORTH, Jack (1930-) British
£550 $913 €803 Hunt (33x25cm-13x10in) s. board. 1-Oct-3 John Ross, Belfast #87
£850 $1411 €1241 Corn field (25x30cm-10x12in) s.d.73 board. 1-Oct-3 John Ross, Belfast #102
£867 $1560 €1300 Evening on the river (40x32cm-16x13in) s. board. 20-Apr-4 James Adam, Dublin #12/R
£1014 $1723 €1480 Man and sheep (45x40cm-18x16in) s. s.i.verso acrylic prov. 27-Nov-3 Heffel, Vancouver #5/R est:2000-2500 (C.D 2250)
£1067 $1920 €1600 Fox hunters in landscape with church background (35x28cm-14x11in) s. board. 20-Apr-4 James Adam, Dublin #46/R est:1000-1500
£1690 $2704 €2400 Dublin mountains (30x71cm-12x28in) i.verso board prov. 16-Sep-3 Whyte's, Dublin #186/R est:1200-1500

CUECO, Henri (1929-) French
£738 $1321 €1100 Nature morte (45x61cm-18x24in) s. 30-May-4 Eric Pillon, Calais #117/R
£833 $1392 €1200 Plage (61x46cm-24x18in) s. s.i.d.1967 verso acrylic prov. 21-Oct-3 Artcurial Briest, Paris #561/R
£8000 $14400 €12000 Claustra (130x162cm-51x64in) s. painted 1975. 25-Apr-4 Versailles Encheres #145 est:10000-12000

CUENCA MUNOZ, Rafael (1894-?) Spanish
£517 $864 €750 Ball (46x38cm-18x15in) s. 17-Nov-3 Durán, Madrid #91/R

CUENI, August (1883-1966) Swiss
£339 $577 €495 Alpine huts in the snow (45x55cm-18x22in) s.d.1937. 19-Nov-3 Fischer, Luzern #2045/R (S.FR 750)
£452 $769 €660 Anenomes and gentian (30x35cm-12x14in) s.d.1952. 28-Nov-3 Zofingen, Switzerland #2954 (S.FR 1000)
£545 $905 €790 Gentian (23x27cm-9x11in) s.d.1941 panel. 13-Jun-3 Zofingen, Switzerland #2813 (S.FR 1200)
£870 $1591 €1270 Group of houses in a winter landscape. Still life with flowers (31x37cm-12x15in) s.d.38 double-sided. 4-Jun-4 Zofingen, Switzerland #2771 (S.FR 2000)
£1304 $2387 €1904 Village scene with a church near Basle (38x47cm-15x19in) s.d.1936 cardboard. 4-Jun-4 Zofingen, Switzerland #2772 est:3500 (S.FR 3000)
£1448 $2462 €2114 Thierstein I (71x90cm-28x35in) s.d.1937. 19-Nov-3 Fischer, Luzern #2044/R est:1500-1800 (S.FR 3200)
£2818 $4678 €4086 Laufen valley village - Breitenbach (50x61cm-20x24in) s.d.1940 hessian. 13-Jun-3 Zofingen, Switzerland #2812 est:7000 (S.FR 6200)

CUERDA, Abel (1943-) Spanish?
£274 $466 €400 Shadow versus light (54x65cm-21x26in) s.d.72 sid.verso. 4-Nov-3 Ansorena, Madrid #999/R
£274 $466 €400 Untitled (65x54cm-26x21in) s.d.1972. 4-Nov-3 Ansorena, Madrid #997/R
£276 $458 €400 Composition (54x65cm-21x26in) s.d.72. 1-Oct-3 Ansorena, Madrid #634/R
£282 $487 €400 Open record to future generations (116x89cm-46x35in) s.d.1989. 15-Dec-3 Ansorena, Madrid #1012/R
£296 $512 €420 Dream landscape (100x81cm-39x32in) s.d.1973. 15-Dec-3 Ansorena, Madrid #999/R
£303 $548 €460 Homage to Chagall (97x130cm-38x51in) s.d.1989 s.d.verso. 14-Apr-4 Ansorena, Madrid #334/R
£324 $560 €460 Abstract (81x65cm-32x26in) s.d.1972. 15-Dec-3 Ansorena, Madrid #930/R
£347 $573 €500 Open door to wealth (92x70cm-36x28in) s.d.89 s.i.verso. 2-Jul-3 Ansorena, Madrid #834/R
£362 $594 €500 Origen (54x65cm-21x26in) s.i.d.1973 verso. 27-May-3 Durán, Madrid #691/R
£377 $640 €550 Scales (81x100cm-32x39in) s.d.1963 s.d.verso. 4-Nov-3 Ansorena, Madrid #955/R
£387 $670 €550 Stones in interior (100x81cm-39x32in) s.d.1973. 15-Dec-3 Ansorena, Madrid #998/R
£451 $745 €650 Abstract (81x130cm-32x51in) s.d.1973. 2-Jul-3 Ansorena, Madrid #947/R
£461 $747 €650 Homenaje a Frida Kahlo (89x116cm-35x46in) s.d.89 verso. 20-May-3 Ansorena, Madrid #353/R

CUERVO HERRERO, Andres (1863-1933) Spanish
£805 $1442 €1200 Malaga beach (24x33cm-9x13in) s. board. 25-May-4 Durán, Madrid #155/R

CUEVAS, Jose Luis (1934-) Mexican
Works on paper
£236 $425 €345 Retrato del Pintor M S (15x11cm-6x4in) s.i.d.1967 pen ink wash. 22-Jan-4 Swann Galleries, New York #148
£344 $550 €502 Autorretrato en una fiesta (15x25cm-6x10in) s.i.d.1968 ink wash prov. 19-Sep-3 Freeman, Philadelphia #29/R
£359 $575 €524 Woman with guitar (23x15cm-9x6in) s.i. pen ink. 20-Sep-3 Sloans & Kenyon, Bethesda #1009/R
£632 $1075 €923 Figure (30x20cm-12x8in) s.d.1982 gouache ink. 30-Oct-3 Louis Morton, Mexico #18/R (M.P 12000)
£1857 $3250 €2711 Autorretrato con prostituta (70x55cm-28x22in) s.i.d.1978 ink wash prov. 19-Dec-3 Sotheby's, New York #1221/R est:3000-4000
£6145 $11000 €8972 Circus family. Meat market. Self-portrait with wizard (41x42cm-16x17in) s.i.d.73 W/C ink pencil set of 3. 26-May-4 Sotheby's, New York #163/R est:10000-15000

CUGNOTET, Edgard (19th C) French
£414 $757 €600 Bords de mer (36x60cm-14x24in) d.1880. 1-Feb-4 Teitgen, Nancy #32

CUI RUZUO (1944-) Chinese
Works on paper
£7112 $12802 €10384 Landscape in snow (82x49cm-32x19in) s.i.d.2002 ink col hanging scroll. 25-Apr-4 Christie's, Hong Kong #97/R est:80000-100000 (HK.D 100000)
£8535 $15363 €12461 Flower (176x95cm-69x37in) s.i.d.2003 ink col hanging scroll. 25-Apr-4 Christie's, Hong Kong #103/R est:120000-150000 (HK.D 120000)
£11583 $19344 €16911 Flowers and birds (179x95cm-70x37in) s.d.2002 ink col hanging scroll. 26-Oct-3 Christie's, Hong Kong #358/R est:100000-120000 (HK.D 150000)

CUI ZIFAN (1915-) Chinese
Works on paper
£350 $585 €511 Insect flight above trailing flowers (69x46cm-27x18in) s. ink col. 14-Nov-3 Christie's, Kensington #270/R
£1991 $3585 €2907 Lotus pond (68x68cm-27x27in) s.d.1990 ink col hanging scroll. 25-Apr-4 Christie's, Hong Kong #130/R est:30000-50000 (HK.D 28000)

CUIXART, Modest (1925-) Spanish
£567 $919 €800 Bailadero (25x21cm-10x8in) s.d.2000 acrylic paper. 20-May-3 Ansorena, Madrid #280/R
£567 $919 €800 Oratefrater (25x21cm-10x8in) s.d.2000 acrylic paper. 20-May-3 Ansorena, Madrid #281/R
£603 $977 €850 Acrobatina (25x21cm-10x8in) s.d.2000 acrylic paper. 20-May-3 Ansorena, Madrid #282/R
£878 $1546 €1300 Portrait of lady (71x50cm-28x20in) s.d.1984 oil over lithograph. 18-May-4 Segre, Madrid #253/R
£942 $1545 €1300 Veredictus (25x21cm-10x8in) s. s.i.d.2000 acrylic paper. 27-May-3 Durán, Madrid #124/R
£3873 $6778 €5500 Untitled 14 (81x31cm-32x12in) s.i.d.1958 verso oil marble powder. 16-Dec-3 Segre, Madrid #138/R est:5500
Works on paper
£1133 $2051 €1700 Gaudi as a young man (41x31cm-16x12in) s.i.d.1981 chl ink wax crayon. 30-Mar-4 Segre, Madrid #242/R est:450
£4027 $7450 €6000 Composition (81x65cm-32x26in) s.d.79 s.i.verso mixed media. 15-Mar-4 Blanchet, Paris #180/R est:5000-7000
£6419 $11297 €9500 Composition (116x89cm-46x35in) s.d.1960 verso mixed media on canvas prov. 24-May-4 Christie's, Milan #193/R est:5000-8000

CULL, A B (fl.1906-1927) British
Works on paper
£550 $886 €798 HMS Southampton (33x51cm-13x20in) s.i. W/C. 20-Aug-3 Brightwells, Leominster #873

CULL, Alma Burlton (fl.1906-1927) British
£1303 $2358 €1902 Three battleships. Battleships at anchor (49x20cm-19x8in) s.d.05 pair. 30-Mar-4 Stephan Welz, Johannesburg #404 est:6000-10000 (SA.R 15500)

Works on paper

£280 $510 €409 An irrawaddy during a monsoon (16x27cm-6x11in) s.d.1927 W/C scratching out exhib. 1-Jul-4 Christie's, Kensington #181

£850 $1522 €1241 Union Castle liner in coastal waters at dusk (28x51cm-11x20in) s.d.1927 pencil W/C scratching out prov. 26-May-4 Christie's, Kensington #470/R

£900 $1611 €1314 Arundel Castle in the Solent off the Isle of Wight (18x32cm-7x13in) s.d.1921 pencil W/C scratching out prov. 26-May-4 Christie's, Kensington #469/R

£1730 $3200 €2526 HMS Ships, Iron Duke, Empress of India, Marlborough and Benbow (33x53cm-13x21in) s.d.1928 W/C prov. 10-Feb-4 Christie's, Rockefeller NY #136/R est:3000-5000

CULLAM, C (?) British?

£2400 $4368 €3600 Venetian canal scene (71x127cm-28x50in) s. 15-Jun-4 Rosebery Fine Art, London #503/R est:400-600

CULLBERG, Erland (1931-) Swedish

£916 $1621 €1337 Frightened tradesman (116x87cm-46x34in) s. 27-Apr-4 AB Stockholms Auktionsverk #1046/R (S.KR 12500)

£1246 $2119 €1819 Figure composition (129x100cm-51x39in) s. prov. 4-Nov-3 Bukowskis, Stockholm #534/R est:12000-15000 (S.KR 16500)

CULLEN, Charles (1939) Irish

£1189 $2021 €1700 Emer and Veronica, Berlin (52x76cm-20x30in) s.i.d.1983 acrylic chl paper prov. 18-Nov-3 Whyte's, Dublin #147/R est:2000-3000

Works on paper

£397 $723 €600 Warrior (75x51cm-30x20in) s. mixed media. 15-Jun-4 James Adam, Dublin #176/R

CULLEN, Maurice Galbraith (1866-1934) Canadian

£6306 $10721 €9207 Montmorency River near a bridge (38x45cm-15x18in) s. i.verso prov. 27-Nov-3 Heffel, Vancouver #185/R est:15000-18000 (C.D 14000)

£6458 $11819 €9429 Laurentian farmstead (38x68cm-15x27in) s.d.96. 27-Jan-4 Iegor de Saint Hippolyte, Montreal #11 (C.D 15500)

£10135 $17230 €14797 Mount Rundle from Bow River (38x45cm-15x18in) s.d.1930 i.verso board prov.exhib.lit. 27-Nov-3 Heffel, Vancouver #103/R est:15000-20000 (C.D 22500)

£11607 $19964 €16946 Country Home, winter (37x45cm-15x18in) s.d.14. 2-Dec-3 Joyner Waddington, Toronto #88j/R est:10000-12000 (C.D 26000)

£18018 $30631 €26306 Cache River, Quebec (38x46cm-15x18in) s. prov. 18-Nov-3 Sotheby's, Toronto #160/R est:30000-50000 (C.D 40000)

£58559 $99550 €85496 Quebec city from Levis (45x55cm-18x22in) s.d.1904 prov. 27-Nov-3 Heffel, Vancouver #100/R est:50000-60000 (C.D 130000)

£73171 $130976 €106830 View of Quebec from Levis (77x102cm-30x40in) s. painted 1920 prov.exhib.lit. 27-May-4 Heffel, Vancouver #29/R est:150000-200000 (C.D 180000)

Works on paper

£1727 $3092 €2521 Twilight landscape (30x40cm-12x16in) s. pastel paper on board prov. 27-May-4 Heffel, Vancouver #99/R est:4000-6000 (C.D 4250)

£7143 $12286 €10429 March afternoon on the Cache river (44x58cm-17x23in) s. pastel prov. 2-Dec-3 Joyner Waddington, Toronto #24/R est:15000-20000 (C.D 16000)

CULLEN, Michael (1946-) Irish

£1184 $2179 €1800 Untitled (33x41cm-13x16in) s.d.1992. 22-Jun-4 De Veres Art Auctions, Dublin #68/R est:3000-4000

£1538 $2615 €2200 Mediterranean still life with fruits (36x45cm-14x18in) s.i.verso oil on linen. 25-Nov-3 De Veres Art Auctions, Dublin #130/R est:1500-2000

Works on paper

£604 $1081 €900 Las Vegas (35x45cm-14x18in) s.d.1995 mixed media. 31-May-4 Hamilton Osborne King, Dublin #227

CULLEN, Stephen (20th C) Irish?

£387 $696 €580 Crafton Street (58x41cm-23x16in) s. 20-Apr-4 James Adam, Dublin #125/R

£1007 $1802 €1500 Colliemore Harbour, winter (40x60cm-16x24in) s. 31-May-4 Hamilton Osborne King, Dublin #49/R est:800-1400

CULLEN, Tom (1934-2001) British

£369 $661 €550 Killiney beach from Killiney hill, and Sugarloaf beyond (48x70cm-19x28in) s.d.1974. 31-May-4 Hamilton Osborne King, Dublin #22

£387 $678 €550 St Ann's hill (51x35cm-20x14in) s.d.1990. 16-Dec-3 James Adam, Dublin #154/R

CULLIN, Isaac (fl.1881-1920) British

Works on paper

£1800 $3096 €2628 Lemberg and Greenback before the race. Lemberg and Greenback leading the parade (16x23cm-6x9in) i.d.1910-11 W/C pair. 3-Dec-3 Bonhams, Knightsbridge #122/R est:1500-2000

CULLIN, Isaac and WHEELER, John Arnold (19th C) British

Works on paper

£600 $954 €876 Loeden, winner of the 1883 Grand National (36x46cm-14x18in) s.i. W/C prov. 12-Sep-3 Gardiner & Houlgate, Bath #79/R

CULMER, Henry L A (1854-1914) American

£7386 $13000 €10784 Pillars of the Wasatch (76x51cm-30x20in) init. 22-May-4 Harvey Clar, Oakland #2432a

Works on paper

£3235 $5500 €4723 Panoramic southwest landscape (13x21cm-5x8in) s. W/C. 18-Nov-3 John Moran, Pasadena #111a est:2000-3000

CULVER, Dennis (20th C) American?

£335 $600 €489 Monument to pure water source (122x152cm-48x60in) i. 13-May-4 Dallas Auction Gallery, Dallas #267/R

CULVERHOUSE, Johann Mongels (1820-1892) Dutch

£1022 $1850 €1492 Wedding (25x20cm-10x8in) s. panel. 16-Apr-4 James Julia, Fairfield #746/R est:2000-4000

£1299 $2325 €1897 Night market in Dutch town (44x54cm-17x21in) s.d.1850. 22-Mar-4 Philippe Schuler, Zurich #4396 est:4000-5000 (S.FR 3000)

£1333 $2413 €2000 Early morning market in Dutch town (30x40cm-12x16in) s. panel. 1-Apr-4 Van Ham, Cologne #1329/R est:2200

£1676 $2900 €2447 Vegetable market at night (53x43cm-21x17in) s.d.69. 13-Dec-3 Sloans & Kenyon, Bethesda #789/R est:4000-6000

£2113 $3380 €3000 First market customers of the morning (29x40cm-11x16in) i. verso panel. 19-Sep-3 Sigalas, Stuttgart #371/R est:3000

£3810 $6819 €5600 Marche de nuit (40x60cm-16x24in) s.i.d.1877. 17-Mar-4 Hotel des Ventes Mosan, Brussels #94 est:2800-3200

£6077 $11000 €8872 Ice skating in the sunset (61x97cm-24x38in) s.d.1874 prov. 31-Mar-4 Sotheby's, New York #81/R est:3000-4000

CULWELL, Ben L (1918-1992) American

Works on paper

£599 $1000 €875 Untitled (18x8cm-7x3in) W/C. 18-Oct-3 David Dike, Dallas #258/R

CUMAN, Fabio (1972-) Italian

Works on paper

£333 $613 €500 Secret nightmare (90x127cm-35x50in) s.d.2001 mixed media board. 12-Jun-4 Meeting Art, Vercelli #445

CUMBERWORTH, Charles (1811-1852) French

Sculpture

£3448 $5724 €5000 Charite (29cm-11in) s.st.f.Susse brown pat bronze. 2-Oct-3 Sotheby's, Paris #6/R est:7500

CUMBERWORTH, Charles (after) (1811-1852) French

Sculpture

£11184 $20579 €17000 Jongleur. Charmeur de serpentes (197cm-78in) black pat bronze pair. 23-Jun-4 Millon & Associes, Paris #124/R est:20000-25000

CUMBO, E Hove (18/19th C) ?

£500 $815 €730 Women gathering reeds at sunset (97x157cm-38x62in) s.d.1819. 25-Sep-3 Gorringes, Worthing #684

CUMBO, Ettore (1833-1899) Italian

£282 $487 €400 View of stream (13x23cm-5x9in) board prov. 9-Dec-3 Pandolfini, Florence #266/R

£331 $603 €500 Vase with primroses (31x20cm-12x8in) 21-Jun-4 Pandolfini, Florence #112/R

£845 $1462 €1200 Alps (67x45cm-26x18in) init. s.d.1871 verso. 9-Dec-3 Pandolfini, Florence #271/R

£849 $1494 €1240 Landscape from hilltop (13x17cm-5x7in) s. 23-May-4 Agra, Warsaw #43/R (P.Z 6000)

£915 $1584 €1300 Shoe makers in Florence (53x45cm-21x18in) 9-Dec-3 Pandolfini, Florence #220/R

£1223 $2006 €1700 Sunset on the lake (24x43cm-9x17in) cardboard. 10-Jun-3 Pandolfini, Florence #121 est:1200-1400

£1367 $2242 €1900 Mountainous landscape (46x68cm-18x27in) 10-Jun-3 Pandolfini, Florence #86/R

£6475 $10619 €9000 Marble quarry, Carrara (117x78cm-46x31in) s. 10-Jun-3 Pandolfini, Florence #78/R est:9000-10000

CUMBRAE-STEWART, Janet Agnes (1883-1960) Australian

£828 $1291 €1201 Hobart harbour (20x25cm-8x10in) board. 1-Aug-2 Joel, Victoria #246 est:2000-3000 (A.D 2400)

£828 $1291 €1201 Jones cottage by the beach (40x27cm-16x11in) 1-Aug-2 Joel, Victoria #251 est:1500-2500 (A.D 2400)

£897 $1399 €1301 Hot day at Garfield, 1910 (20x28cm-8x11in) s. s.i.verso. 1-Aug-2 Joel, Victoria #248 est:2000-3000 (A.D 2600)

£1172 $1829 €1699 Lower paddock Montrose, Brighton (16x31cm-6x12in) painted c.1915. 1-Aug-2 Joel, Victoria #250 est:2000-3000 (A.D 3400)

£1724 $2690 €2500 Regatta at the Anderson Street Bridge (21x29cm-8x11in) s. i.verso board. 1-Aug-2 Joel, Victoria #245 est:6000-8000 (A.D 5000)

£2069 $3228 €3000 Henley on the Yarra (22x29cm-9x11in) board. 1-Aug-2 Joel, Victoria #249 est:6000-8000 (A.D 6000)

£2241 $3496 €3249 Gathering wildflowers (37x54cm-15x21in) 1-Aug-2 Joel, Victoria #247 est:5000-7000 (A.D 6500)

£2273 $3864 €3319 Girl with a fan (37x27cm-15x11in) s.d.20 pastel. 29-Oct-3 Lawson Menzies, Sydney #92/R est:6000-8000 (A.D 5500)

Works on paper

£344 $625 €502 Trees (38x31cm-15x12in) s.d.13 W/C. 16-Jun-4 Deutscher-Menzies, Melbourne #544/R (A.D 900)

£681 $1157 €994 Unloading at a Wharf (36x44cm-14x17in) s. pastel. 26-Nov-3 Deutscher-Menzies, Melbourne #281/R (A.D 1600)

£2024 $3259 €2955 Child study (36x26cm-14x10in) s. pastel. 13-Oct-3 Joel, Victoria #333/R est:3500-4000 (A.D 5000)

£3534 $5514 €5124 Woman with green urn (54x37cm-21x15in) s. pastel. 1-Aug-2 Joel, Victoria #154 est:8000-12000 (A.D 10250)

£6883 $11081 €10049 Frog Prince (54x36cm-21x14in) s.d.24 i.verso pastel prov. 25-Aug-3 Sotheby's, Paddington #171/R est:12000-15000 (A.D 17000)

CUMELIN, Johan Peter (1764-1820) Swedish

Works on paper

£495 $892 €723 Romantic park landscape (17x24cm-7x9in) s. W/C Indian ink prov. 26-Jan-4 Lilla Bukowskis, Stockholm #84 (S.KR 6600)

CUMING, Frederick G R (1930-) British

£260	$481	€380	Beach scene (26x40cm-10x16in) s. board. 11-Feb-4 Sotheby's, Olympia #201/R
£260	$478	€380	Folkestone Harbour (19x27cm-7x11in) s. board. 14-Jun-4 Bonhams, Bath #161
£340	$626	€496	Promenade Arachon avec hommes et dames (20x25cm-8x10in) indis.s. board. 14-Jun-4 Bonhams, Bath #160
£420	$777	€613	Beach scene, Sandgate (15x20cm-6x8in) s. board prov. 11-Mar-4 Christie's, Kensington #246
£550	$974	€803	Listening post (32x42cm-13x17in) s. board. 27-Apr-4 Bonhams, Knightsbridge #157
£750	$1275	€1095	Chatham Pier (41x58cm-16x23in) s. i.verso board. 26-Nov-3 Sotheby's, Olympia #91/R
£900	$1665	€1314	Still life with flowers and blue cloth (51x61cm-20x24in) s. board. 11-Mar-4 Christie's, Kensington #312/R
£950	$1587	€1387	Vaporetti of Piazzo de San Marco (51x61cm-20x24in) s. board. 16-Oct-3 Christie's, Kensington #434/R
£1400	$2338	€2044	Funfair, Brighton Pier (25x46cm-10x18in) s. board exhib. 16-Oct-3 Christie's, Kensington #425/R est:1500-2000
£1550	$2728	€2263	Hastings Pier, Romeo and Juliet (28x51cm-11x20in) s. board. 18-May-4 Woolley & Wallis, Salisbury #59/R est:500-700
£1800	$3168	€2628	Stormy beach, Kent (29x34cm-11x13in) s. board. 18-May-4 Woolley & Wallis, Salisbury #60/R est:500-700
£2800	$4928	€4088	Sailing into Venice (46x76cm-18x30in) s. board. 19-May-4 Sotheby's, Olympia #237/R est:3000-5000
£4400	$7744	€6424	Still life and window (152x101cm-60x40in) s.d.72 prov. 18-May-4 Woolley & Wallis, Salisbury #61/R est:3000-5000
£5800	$10208	€8468	Entry to Rye Harbour II (61x61cm-24x24in) 18-May-4 Woolley & Wallis, Salisbury #62/R est:2500-3500
£6200	$10912	€9052	Fairground, sunset (91x91cm-36x36in) s. 18-May-4 Woolley & Wallis, Salisbury #78/R est:3000-5000

CUMMING, James (1922-1991) British

Works on paper

£300	$501	€438	The chairs (74x58cm-29x23in) s. gouache prov. 18-Jun-3 John Nicholson, Haslemere #620/R
£400	$668	€584	Abstract on pink paper (23x33cm-9x13in) s. gouache. 18-Jun-3 John Nicholson, Haslemere #630

CUMMING, Liz (1956-) Australian

£703	$1315	€1055	Wilpena moment (122x206cm-48x81in) s.d.97 i.verso. 21-Jul-4 Shapiro, Sydney #163/R (A.D 1800)

CUMMING, William Skeoch (fl.1885-1906) British

Works on paper

£2600	$4186	€3770	Royal Scottish Dragoons (74x110cm-29x43in) W/C. 21-Aug-3 Bonhams, Edinburgh #1119/R est:2500-3500

CUMMINGS, Bertha E (19th C) American

£401	$650	€585	View of Mt Monadnock from a farmstead (38x58cm-15x23in) s.d.95. 10-Aug-3 Skinner, Bolton #371/R

CUMMINGS, Edward Estlin (1894-1962) American

£2391	$4400	€3491	Self portrait (38x28cm-15x11in) d.1938 verso canvas on board. 10-Jun-4 Swann Galleries, New York #72/R est:1000-1500
£2935	$5400	€4285	Portrait of the artist's wife (41x30cm-16x12in) d.1937 verso canvas on board. 10-Jun-4 Swann Galleries, New York #71/R est:1000-1500

CUMMINGS, George R (20th C) British

£600	$1074	€876	Shakleton's Endurance entering the Weddell Sea 1914 (61x121cm-24x48in) s.i.d.2003 board. 26-May-4 Christie's, Kensington #745/R

CUMMINGS, Vera (1891-1949) New Zealander

£543	$924	€793	Portrait of a Maori chief with Moko (24x19cm-9x7in) s. 4-Nov-3 Peter Webb, Auckland #148/R est:1500-2000 (NZ.D 1500)
£551	$1031	€804	Maori Chief (20x15cm-8x6in) 24-Feb-4 Peter Webb, Auckland #27/R (NZ.D 1500)
£714	$1293	€1042	Maori chief (19x13cm-7x5in) s. 30-Mar-4 Stephan Welz, Johannesburg #166 est:2000-3000 (SA.R 8500)
£752	$1278	€1098	Maori woman with pipe and moko (26x22cm-10x9in) 27-Nov-3 International Art Centre, Auckland #96/R (NZ.D 2000)
£761	$1293	€1111	Portrait of Maori woman with pipe and ear pendant (26x210cm-10x83in) s. 4-Nov-3 Peter Webb, Auckland #147/R est:2000-2500 (NZ.D 2100)
£970	$1678	€1416	Portrait of Patara Te Tuhi (29x24cm-11x9in) s. 9-Dec-3 Peter Webb, Auckland #166/R est:2500-3500 (NZ.D 2600)
£1029	$1925	€1502	Sad thought (24x20cm-9x8in) 24-Feb-4 Peter Webb, Auckland #100/R (NZ.D 2800)

CUMMINGS, Vera (attrib) (1891-1949) New Zealander

£543	$875	€793	Maori portrait (22x17cm-9x7in) board. 20-Aug-3 Dunbar Sloane, Auckland #43/R est:2000-3000 (NZ.D 1500)

CUMMINGS, Will (?) New Zealander?

£1359	$2160	€1984	Kahikatea tree. s. acrylic board. 9-Sep-3 Watson's, Christchurch #16 (NZ.D 3750)

CUNAEUS, Conradyn (1828-1895) Dutch

£3061	$5571	€4500	Proud catch (42x58cm-17x23in) s. panel. 3-Feb-4 Christie's, Amsterdam #86/R est:3000-5000
£4000	$7200	€6000	Greyhound and shepherd dog. King Charles Spaniel and a Drentse partridge dog (24x34cm-9x13in) one s.d.1858 panel pair. 20-Apr-4 Sotheby's, Amsterdam #30/R est:3000-5000
£4667	$8493	€7000	Rest from the ride (58x72cm-23x28in) s. prov. 1-Jul-4 Christie's, Amsterdam #584/R est:3000-5000

CUNDA, Claude (20th C) French?

£265	$485	€400	Composition abstraite (100x32cm-39x13in) s. panel. 7-Apr-4 Fraysse & Associes, Paris #9/R

CUNDALL, Charles (1890-1971) British

£300	$549	€438	Dead tree (45x32cm-18x13in) s.i. 6-Jul-4 Bonhams, Knightsbridge #46/R
£360	$634	€526	Royal vidit to South Africa, HMS Vanguard (27x52cm-11x20in) s.d.1947 oil on paper. 19-May-4 Sotheby's, Olympia #104/R
£550	$968	€803	Jumieges Abbey, Normandy (24x33cm-9x13in) s.d.1920 panel. 19-May-4 Sotheby's, Olympia #105/R
£900	$1665	€1314	Summer morning, Littlebury, Essex (27x36cm-11x14in) s. board. 11-Feb-4 Sotheby's, Olympia #139/R est:800-1200
£1300	$2405	€1898	Summer morning, Sussex (33x56cm-13x22in) s. 11-Feb-4 Sotheby's, Olympia #138/R est:1000-1500
£1600	$2768	€2336	Concours de Pecheurs, Paris with Notre Dame in the background (45x75cm-18x30in) s. 9-Dec-3 Bonhams, Oxford #121/R est:800-1200
£2000	$3680	€2920	Moscow in the snow (29x49cm-11x19in) s. board. 23-Jun-4 Bonhams, Bury St Edmunds #357/R est:1500-2500
£3400	$6290	€4964	Amalfi (40x31cm-16x12in) s. s.i.verso panel. 11-Feb-4 Sotheby's, Olympia #137/R est:2500-3500
£6500	$12025	€9490	Dieppe, August (35x46cm-14x18in) s.d.1939 exhib. 11-Feb-4 Sotheby's, Olympia #141/R est:2500-3500

Works on paper

£450	$832	€657	Perth (21x37cm-8x15in) s.d.1947 W/C exhib. 11-Feb-4 Sotheby's, Olympia #140/R
£650	$1105	€949	Verona (29x43cm-11x17in) s. W/C. 26-Nov-3 Hamptons Fine Art, Godalming #36

CUNDIN, Jose Maria (1938-) Spanish

£227	$400	€331	Untitled (20x15cm-8x6in) s.d.1970. 22-May-4 New Orleans Auction, New Orleans #842
£2585	$4705	€3800	Figures (130x130cm-51x51in) s. prov. 3-Feb-4 Segre, Madrid #131/R est:400

CUNEO, Jose (1887-1977) Uruguayan

£941	$1600	€1374	Cagnes-sur-Mer (33x41cm-13x16in) s. board. 20-Nov-3 Galeria y Remates, Montevideo #25/R
£958	$1600	€1399	Roses (53x48cm-21x19in) s.d.1939. 7-Oct-3 Galeria y Remates, Montevideo #33/R
£3529	$6000	€5152	El Rosario farm (50x66cm-20x26in) s. cardboard lit. 25-Nov-3 Galeria y Remates, Montevideo #147/R
£3533	$6500	€5158	Dusk (54x65cm-21x26in) s. cardboard lit. 22-Jun-4 Galeria y Remates, Montevideo #53/R est:6000-9000
£4118	$7000	€6012	Pine trees (50x65cm-20x26in) s.d.1951. 25-Nov-3 Galeria y Remates, Montevideo #44/R
£4891	$9000	€7141	Dusk on the estate (65x50cm-26x20in) cardboard prov. 22-Jun-4 Galeria y Remates, Montevideo #51/R est:12000-15000
£5588	$9500	€8158	Landscape in Cerro Largo (82x100cm-32x39in) s. lit. 25-Nov-3 Galeria y Remates, Montevideo #146/R
£6000	$10200	€8760	Landscape in Punta del Este (61x50cm-24x20in) s. 25-Nov-3 Galeria y Remates, Montevideo #148/R
£9375	$16500	€13688	Ranch (49x65cm-19x26in) s.d.46 cardboard prov. 5-Jan-4 Galeria y Remates, Montevideo #70/R est:18000-22000
£9412	$16000	€13742	Ranch (60x73cm-24x29in) s. lit. 25-Nov-3 Galeria y Remates, Montevideo #42

Works on paper

£924	$1700	€1349	Salto harbour (49x64cm-19x25in) s.d.1946 W/C. 22-Jun-4 Galeria y Remates, Montevideo #56/R est:2000-3000
£1136	$2000	€1659	Cagnes (46x61cm-18x24in) s. pastel exec.1930. 5-Jan-4 Galeria y Remates, Montevideo #93/R est:2800

CUNEO, Rinaldo (1877-1935) American

£958	$1600	€1399	Trees and hills (27x31cm-11x12in) canvas on board. 26-Oct-3 Bonhams & Butterfields, San Francisco #6498/R
£1589	$2750	€2320	Panamint Valley. Italian rooftops (28x30cm-11x12in) s. first paper board second paper laid on paper board pair prov. 10-Dec-3 Bonhams & Butterfields, San Francisco #6324/R est:3000-5000
£1734	$3000	€2532	Mt Whitney and the Alabama Hills (27x30cm-11x12in) paper board prov. 10-Dec-3 Bonhams & Butterfields, San Francisco #6323/R est:3000-5000
£4046	$7000	€5907	Country Road through the trees (77x66cm-30x26in) s. panel prov. 10-Dec-3 Bonhams & Butterfields, San Francisco #6325/R est:3000-5000
£8696	$16000	€12696	Belle View, France (59x73cm-23x29in) s.i.d.1913 prov.exhib. 8-Jun-4 Bonhams & Butterfields, San Francisco #4207/R est:6000-8000

CUNEO, Terence (1907-1996) British

£350	$648	€511	Still life (26x30cm-10x12in) s. 13-Feb-4 Sworder & Son, Bishops Stortford #67/R
£1100	$1837	€1606	Venetian canal (25x35cm-10x14in) s.d.Jan 1989. 16-Oct-3 Christie's, Kensington #444/R est:800-1200
£1274	$2191	€1860	Domingo, figures and donkeys in a street (60x50cm-24x20in) s. 3-Dec-3 Stephan Welz, Johannesburg #15/R est:12000-18000 (SA.R 14000)
£1800	$3096	€2628	Broomyard foundry (76x102cm-30x40in) s. 2-Dec-3 Bonhams, New Bond Street #57/R est:2000-3000
£2002	$3443	€2923	Old Customs House, Fowey, Cornwall (60x50cm-24x20in) s. 3-Dec-3 Stephan Welz, Johannesburg #14/R est:12000-18000 (SA.R 22000)
£2800	$4816	€4088	Construction the Hoover Dam (76x102cm-30x40in) s.d.July 56. 2-Dec-3 Bonhams, New Bond Street #56/R est:3000-5000
£3000	$5460	€4380	Scenes depicting Vickers earth-moving tractors and a bulldozer (75x62cm-30x24in) s.d.1952 1953 three. 29-Jun-4 Anderson & Garland, Newcastle #391/R est:600-900
£3800	$7030	€5548	Venice (30x46cm-12x18in) s.d.December 88. 11-Feb-4 Sotheby's, Olympia #180/R est:3000-5000
£6200	$11098	€9052	Bryce Canyon, Utah, USA (41x51cm-16x20in) s. s.i.verso. 16-Mar-4 Bonhams, New Bond Street #71/R est:4000-6000
£7000	$11060	€10220	Segrave on the Sunbeam on his way to victory at San Sebastian (52x32cm-20x13in) s. 5-Sep-3 Bonhams, Knightsbridge #4/R
£14000	$24080	€20440	At the throttle of the Flying Scotsman (51x63cm-20x25in) s.d.June 1969 prov. 2-Dec-3 Bonhams, New Bond Street #58/R est:5000-7000

Works on paper
£3500 $6370 €5110 Various sketches (31x39cm-12x15in) s.i. pencil ten. 1-Jul-4 Christie's, Kensington #31/R est:3000-5000

CUNHA, Hector da (1915-1996) Spanish/Uruguayan
£276 $461 €400 Untitled (21x31cm-8x12in) s. paper. 11-Nov-3 Castellana, Madrid #210/R
£276 $461 €400 Untitled (21x31cm-8x12in) s. paper. 11-Nov-3 Castellana, Madrid #225/R
£310 $518 €450 Untitled (21x31cm-8x12in) s. paper. 11-Nov-3 Castellana, Madrid #25/R

CUNLIFF, Horatio (19th C) British?
£554 $992 €809 Scene from the peasants war (63x91cm-25x36in) s.d.1882. 28-May-4 Uppsala Auktionskammare, Uppsala #94/R (S.KR 7500)

CUNNINGHAM, Benjamin Frazier (1904-1975) American
£559 $1000 €816 Design for a tapestry (91x51cm-36x20in) prov. 16-May-4 Wright, Chicago #243/R

CUNNINGHAM, Earl (1893-1977) American
£3488 $6000 €5092 Harbour Scene (51x61cm-20x24in) s. masonite. 7-Dec-3 Freeman, Philadelphia #142 est:6000-8000

CUNNINGHAM, Edward Francis (c.1742-1795) British
£5000 $9150 €7300 Equestrian portrait of Fredrick II of Prussia (103x93cm-41x37in) 9-Jul-4 Christie's, Kensington #121/R est:6000-8000

CUNNINGHAM, George (?) British
£480 $826 €701 And to think I could have gone on the stage (49x59cm-19x23in) s. board. 5-Dec-3 ELR Auctions, Sheffield #469/R
Works on paper
£350 $557 €508 Birch Lea, Hollow Meadows, Manchester Road, Sheffield (37x55cm-15x22in) s. W/C sold with photos. 12-Sep-3 ELR Auctions, Sheffield #284/R
£370 $588 €537 Shooting party at the Round House at Ringinglow, Sheffield (18x26cm-7x10in) s. W/C. 12-Sep-3 ELR Auctions, Sheffield #285/R
£450 $774 €657 Michael Road (18x13cm-7x5in) s. W/C. 5-Dec-3 ELR Auctions, Sheffield #720
£500 $935 €730 Parade of shops in a snow storm (15x26cm-6x10in) s. W/C. 20-Jul-4 Sworder & Son, Bishops Stortford #740/R
£550 $875 €798 Snow covered street scene at Ranmoor, Sheffield with figures (20x26cm-8x10in) s. W/C. 12-Sep-3 ELR Auctions, Sheffield #286/R
£550 $946 €803 Tenter Street, Sunday morning (15x20cm-6x8in) s. W/C. 5-Dec-3 ELR Auctions, Sheffield #721
£580 $1067 €847 Main Street, Grenoside (36x564cm-14x222in) s. W/C ink. 26-Mar-4 ELR Auctions, Sheffield #319/R
£640 $1018 €928 Bassett Lane, snowy landscape with figure and dog (20x42cm-8x17in) s. W/C. 12-Sep-3 ELR Auctions, Sheffield #277/R
£650 $1034 €943 Monyash, snowy landscape with van on a rural lane (24x36cm-9x14in) s. W/C. 12-Sep-3 ELR Auctions, Sheffield #276/R
£800 $1272 €1160 Earl of Arundel, Surrey, winter scene with figures (17x24cm-7x9in) s. i.d.1987 verso W/C. 12-Sep-3 ELR Auctions, Sheffield #287
£1550 $2666 €2263 Rustlings Road, snowplough (22x27cm-9x11in) s.i. W/C. 5-Dec-3 ELR Auctions, Sheffield #719/R est:300-500
£3400 $5406 €4930 Lansdowne Picture Palace, London Rd, Sheffield with figures and trams (35x45cm-14x18in) s. W/C. 12-Sep-3 ELR Auctions, Sheffield #288/R est:600-800

CUNNINGHAM, Imogen (1883-1976) American
Photographs
£1695 $3000 €2475 In the marina, San Francisco, 1950 (20x19cm-8x7in) s.d.1950 gelatin silver print. 27-Apr-4 Christie's, Rockefeller NY #210/R est:4000-6000
£1934 $3500 €2824 Yucca plant (23x18cm-9x7in) gelatin silver print exec. late 1920's. 19-Apr-4 Daniel Cooney, Brooklyn #469054/R
£3743 $6250 €5465 Magnolia blossom (26x34cm-10x13in) s.d.1936 gelatin silver print. 21-Oct-3 Bonhams & Butterfields, San Francisco #1481/R
£4143 $7500 €6049 Triangles (10x8cm-4x3in) s.d. gelatin silver print 1928/printed later lit. 19-Apr-4 Bonhams & Butterfields, San Francisco #394/R est:6000-8000
£8982 $15000 €13114 Magnolia blossom (27x35cm-11x14in) s.d.1925 photo printed later. 17-Oct-3 Sotheby's, New York #3/R est:12000-18000
£14493 $23768 €20000 Frida Kahlo Rivera (32x24cm-13x9in) silver gelatin lit. 30-May-3 Villa Grisebach, Berlin #1137/R est:7000-9000

CUNNINGHAM, John (1926-1999) British
£5800 $10498 €8468 Barra Castle (45x56cm-18x22in) s. 19-Apr-4 Sotheby's, London #145/R est:3000-4000
£11500 $19780 €16790 Grigadale Bay, Ardnamurchan (80x126cm-31x50in) s. 4-Dec-3 Bonhams, Edinburgh #14/R est:7000-10000

CUNNINGHAM, Vera (1897-1955) British
£300 $561 €438 Venetian fantasy (61x51cm-24x20in) s. exhib. 24-Feb-4 Bonhams, Knowle #135
Works on paper
£450 $752 €657 River running through the mountains (35x45cm-14x18in) s.d.45 pen black ink W/C sold with more by the same hand. 16-Oct-3 Christie's, Kensington #273

CUNNINGHAM, William (?) British?
£400 $664 €584 Music session (35x35cm-14x14in) s. board. 1-Oct-3 John Ross, Belfast #134
£437 $764 €620 Twelve Pins, Connemara (35x45cm-14x18in) s. 16-Dec-3 James Adam, Dublin #91/R
£867 $1560 €1300 Evening harvest, Connemara (42x42cm-17x17in) s. board. 20-Apr-4 James Adam, Dublin #8686/R

CUNZ, Martha (1876-1961) Swiss
Works on paper
£679 $1154 €991 Florence (17x35cm-7x14in) s. col chk. 18-Nov-3 Hans Widmer, St Gallen #1043 est:1200-2500 (S.FR 1500)

CUPRIEN, Frank W (1871-1948) American
£978 $1800 €1428 Remains of an old pier (38x51cm-15x20in) s. masonite prov. 27-Jun-4 Bonhams & Butterfields, San Francisco #3832/R est:3000-5000
£1406 $2250 €2053 Sails at the sunset (61x89cm-24x35in) s.d.36 i.verso masonite. 18-May-3 Auctions by the Bay, Alameda #1067/R
£2500 $4250 €3650 Golden sunset, California coast (41x51cm-16x20in) s.i. painted c.1910. 18-Nov-3 John Moran, Pasadena #93 est:3000-4500
£6936 $12000 €10127 Golden sunset, Laguna Beach, California (30x41cm-12x16in) s. i.verso prov. 10-Dec-3 Bonhams & Butterfields, San Francisco #6206/R est:3000-5000

CURCIO, Edgardo (1881-1923) Italian
Works on paper
£493 $908 €750 Straw hat (17x15cm-7x6in) s.d.1922 W/C. 23-Jun-4 Finarte Semenzato, Rome #20/R

CURDES, Richard (1891-1974) Polish
£255 $392 €400 Low tide near Cuxhaven (70x50cm-28x20in) s. board. 4-Sep-2 Schopman, Hamburg #128/R

CURDIE, John (19th C) British
£300 $477 €438 Linn at Cray Mill (75x62cm-30x24in) s.d.1883. 18-Mar-3 Anderson & Garland, Newcastle #403/R

CURIE, Parvine (20th C) French?
Sculpture
£2013 $3685 €3000 Morada (46x43x33cm-18x17x13in) s. num.1/8 base brown pat bronze st.f.Clementi exec 1983. 7-Jul-4 Artcurial Briest, Paris #241 est:3000-4000

CURIONI, Alessandro (19th C) Italian
£699 $1168 €1000 Landscape with figures (70x104cm-28x41in) s.d.1883. 26-Jun-3 Sant Agostino, Torino #125/R
£1049 $1752 €1500 Landscape with figures (70x104cm-28x41in) s.d.1883. 26-Jun-3 Sant Agostino, Torino #135/R est:1000-1400

CURLING, Peter (1955-) Irish
£3289 $6053 €5000 Adjusting leathers (44x36cm-17x14in) s. board. 22-Jun-4 De Veres Art Auctions, Dublin #53/R est:5000-6000
£9155 $15838 €13000 Summer sales (70x90cm-28x35in) s. 10-Dec-3 Bonhams & James Adam, Dublin #135/R est:12000-15000
£15333 $27753 €23000 Bumper horses going to the post (60x92cm-24x36in) s. prov. 31-Mar-4 James Adam, Dublin #99/R est:8000-12000
£17450 $31235 €26000 Grand Canal from the Academia Bridge, Venice (76x91cm-30x36in) s. 26-May-4 James Adam, Dublin #96/R est:25000-30000
£35000 $62650 €51100 At the races (102x152cm-40x60in) 14-May-4 Christie's, London #203/R est:12000-18000
Works on paper
£599 $1036 €850 Horse going away on a left hand course (38x51cm-15x20in) W/C prov. 10-Dec-3 Bonhams & James Adam, Dublin #183/R
£738 $1358 €1100 Horse and rider (30x43cm-12x17in) s.d. W/C. 23-Mar-4 Mealy's, Castlecomer #1149/R est:800-1200
£1007 $1782 €1500 Greville Starkey on Downstown Charley (28x36cm-11x14in) s.i. pencil prov. 27-Apr-4 Whyte's, Dublin #221/R est:1500-1800
£1056 $1827 €1500 Hauling timber (33x39cm-13x15in) s.d.75 W/C prov. 10-Dec-3 Bonhams & James Adam, Dublin #79/R est:1500-2000
£2113 $3380 €3000 Study of a jockey (54x67cm-21x26in) s.i.d.1974 W/C. 16-Sep-3 Whyte's, Dublin #218/R est:1800-2200
£2676 $4282 €3800 Horses exercising (43x61cm-17x24in) s. W/C pen ink. 16-Sep-3 Whyte's, Dublin #217/R est:3000-4000
£6690 $11574 €9500 Away from the last, Punchestown (42x73cm-17x29in) s. W/C prov. 10-Dec-3 Bonhams & James Adam, Dublin #182/R est:8000-12000
£10563 $18275 €15000 Tape start, Clonmel (53x74cm-21x29in) s. W/C sold with a catalogue prov. 10-Dec-3 Bonhams & James Adam, Dublin #80/R est:8000-12000

CURNIER, Venance (1885-1971) French?
£267 $485 €400 Untitled (38x46cm-15x18in) s.d.1907. 29-Jun-4 Chenu & Scrive, Lyon #57/R

CURNOCK, James (1812-1862) British
£1347 $2250 €1967 Young anglers (31x26cm-12x10in) s.d.1851 board prov. 7-Oct-3 Sotheby's, New York #104 est:1000-1500

CURNOCK, James Jackson (1839-1891) British
£731 $1155 €1067 Couple by pond (30x23cm-12x9in) s.d.1861. 24-Jul-3 Louis Morton, Mexico #104/R (M.P 12000)
£811 $1378 €1184 Lane at Walton near Bristol (46x61cm-18x24in) s.d.1863 s.i.verso exhib. 21-Nov-3 Walker's, Ottawa #257/R est:2000-3000 (C.D 1800)
Works on paper
£260 $476 €380 Cattle by a river in a summer landscape (25x39cm-10x15in) s.d.1864 W/C htd. bodycol. 8-Jul-4 Lawrence, Crewkerne #1537
£400 $740 €584 Old Farm near Windermere, old cottage with figure and chickens (41x33cm-16x13in) W/C. 14-Feb-4 Hogben, Folkstone #119
£425 $693 €621 Llyn Llydaw, Snowdonia (28x46cm-11x18in) W/C. 27-Sep-3 Rogers Jones, Clwyd #37/R
£1850 $2923 €2683 Summertime wooded glen with rocky stream (61x44cm-24x17in) s. W/C. 2-Sep-3 Bristol Auction Rooms #576/R est:1800-2200

CURNOE, Greg (1936-) Canadian
Works on paper
£482 $896 €704 Hugh and Sheila (44x56cm-17x22in) i.d.Feb 1 1969 ink exhib. 2-Mar-4 Ritchie, Toronto #163/R (C.D 1200)

CUROS, Jordi (1930-) Spanish
£276 $461 €400 Can Figueras, Rambla, Barcelona (66x54cm-26x21in) s. s.i.d.89 verso. 17-Nov-3 Durán, Madrid #1170/R
£276 $461 €400 Paris (60x73cm-24x29in) s. 17-Nov-3 Durán, Madrid #1281/R
£306 $548 €450 Beach (60x73cm-24x29in) s. 22-Mar-4 Durán, Madrid #1231/R
£428 $774 €650 Grand Canal (60x74cm-24x29in) s. 14-Apr-4 Ansorena, Madrid #193/R

CURRADI, Francesco (1570-1661) Italian
£23333 $41767 €35000 Madonna and Child enthroned (214x278cm-84x109in) 12-May-4 Finarte Semenzato, Milan #29/R est:25000-30000

CURRADI, Francesco (attrib) (1570-1661) Italian
£1972 $3175 €2800 San Franceso (82x70cm-32x28in) octagonal. 8-May-3 Farsetti, Prato #789/R est:4000-5000
£6500 $11895 €9490 Head of a young boy in a brown coat (36x24cm-14x9in) oil paper on canvas. 7-Jul-4 Bonhams, New Bond Street #124/R est:2000-3000

CURRAN, Charles Courtney (1861-1942) American
£275 $500 €402 Portrait of William Dana Ewart (76x61cm-30x24in) s.d.1936. 1-Jul-4 Dan Ripley, Indianapolis #146
£2514 $4500 €3670 In the kitchen (51x30cm-20x12in) s. prov. 6-May-4 Shannon's, Milford #157/R est:5000-7000
£3144 $5250 €4590 Cloud filled landscapes (41x48cm-16x19in) s. masonite pair. 16-Nov-3 CRN Auctions, Cambridge #1/R
£3315 $6000 €4840 Girl in white (22x30cm-9x12in) s. i.verso canvasboard prov. 31-Mar-4 Sotheby's, New York #51/R est:10000-15000
£5882 $10000 €8588 Watching the clouds roll by (63x76cm-25x30in) s. 21-Nov-3 Skinner, Boston #457/R est:7000-9000
£26163 $45000 €38198 Seat on the summit (63x76cm-25x30in) s.i.d.1920 canvas on masonite prov.exhib. 3-Dec-3 Sotheby's, New York #29/R est:30000-50000
£63953 $110000 €93371 Blueberries and ferns (56x46cm-22x18in) s.d.1911 exhib. 4-Dec-3 Christie's, Rockefeller NY #60/R est:120000-180000
Works on paper
£844 $1350 €1232 Portrait of a young lady (43x36cm-17x14in) s.d.1916 pastel. 20-Sep-3 Sloans & Kenyon, Bethesda #1190a/R est:1750-2250

CURRAN, Oliver (20th C) Irish?
£347 $566 €500 Eviction (66x78cm-26x31in) s. 23-Sep-3 De Veres Art Auctions, Dublin #343

CURREY, Fanny W (fl.1880-1897) British
£320 $534 €467 Azaleas in a glass dish (35x60cm-14x24in) s.d.1897. 20-Oct-3 Bonhams, Bath #52
£880 $1470 €1285 Artist in her studio at the Hall House, Lismore (21x12cm-8x5in) i.verso panel. 20-Oct-3 Bonhams, Bath #54
£1550 $2589 €2263 Flowers in a cottage garden (35x22cm-14x9in) mono. 20-Oct-3 Bonhams, Bath #55 est:100-150
Works on paper
£420 $701 €613 Dusk over a city river. Moorland view (17x25cm-7x10in) W/C pair. 20-Oct-3 Bonhams, Bath #60
£500 $835 €730 Girl on a river bank (23x34cm-9x13in) s. W/C. 20-Oct-3 Bonhams, Bath #59
£600 $1002 €876 Bazaar in Tangier. Street in Tangier (39x24cm-15x9in) s. W/C pair. 20-Oct-3 Bonhams, Bath #53
£620 $1035 €905 Dog asleep in an orchard (32x22cm-13x9in) s. W/C. 20-Oct-3 Bonhams, Bath #57
£700 $1169 €1022 Lismore Castle an hour before the storm, looking out over Blackwater (25x35cm-10x14in) mono. W/C. 20-Oct-3 Bonhams, Bath #58
£950 $1587 €1387 Girls sewing in a street. Breton women at a stile (26x17cm-10x7in) one s.d.1880 W/C bodycol over pencil pair. 20-Oct-3 Bonhams, Bath #56

CURRIE, Ken (20th C) ?
Works on paper
£2800 $4676 €4088 Bound worker with scythe (126x98cm-50x39in) s. chl. 16-Oct-3 Christie's, Kensington #558 est:300-500
£3800 $6346 €5548 Bound worker (124x98cm-49x39in) s.d.79 chl. 16-Oct-3 Christie's, Kensington #560 est:300-500

CURRIE, Sue (20th C) New Zealander
£294 $526 €429 Nelson Wharf (61x89cm-24x35in) s.d.79 board. 11-May-4 Watson's, Christchurch #127/R (NZ.D 850)

CURRIER and IVES (19th C) American
Prints
£1429 $2700 €2086 American field sports: flush'd (23x30cm-9x12in) i. col lithograph. 22-Feb-4 Skinner, Boston #34/R est:1500-2500
£1429 $2700 €2086 Central Park, Winter (33x43cm-13x17in) i. col lithograph. 22-Feb-4 Skinner, Boston #62/R est:600-800
£1535 $2900 €2241 The life of a fireman (24x32cm-9x13in) i. col lithograph. 22-Feb-4 Skinner, Boston #37/R est:2000-3000
£2116 $4000 €3089 A good chance (24x31cm-9x12in) i. col lithograph. 22-Feb-4 Skinner, Boston #2/R est:2500-3500
£2116 $4000 €3089 The Grand Drive, Central Park, NY (21x31cm-8x12in) i. col lithograph. 22-Feb-4 Skinner, Boston #40/R est:1000-1500
£2381 $4500 €3476 Life on the prairie (21x29cm-8x11in) i. col lithograph. 22-Feb-4 Skinner, Boston #22/R est:7500-9500
£2910 $5500 €4249 New England winter scene (20x27cm-8x11in) i. col lithograph. 22-Feb-4 Skinner, Boston #28/R est:3000-4000
£2910 $5500 €4249 Snowed up (18x24cm-7x9in) i. col lithograph. 22-Feb-4 Skinner, Boston #33/R est:2000-2500
£3175 $6000 €4636 Life on the prairie: The trappers defence, 'Fire fight fire' (58x79cm-23x31in) i. col lithograph. 22-Feb-4 Skinner, Boston #61/R est:2000-3000
£3968 $7500 €5793 The whale fishery (20x27cm-8x11in) i. col lithograph exhib. 22-Feb-4 Skinner, Boston #21/R est:7500-9500
£3968 $7500 €5793 Winter in the country (23x29cm-9x11in) i. col lithograph. 22-Feb-4 Skinner, Boston #30/R est:2500-3500
£4762 $9000 €6953 Taking the back track (20x28cm-8x11in) i. col lithograph. 22-Feb-4 Skinner, Boston #24/R est:3000-4000
£5027 $9500 €7339 Midnight race on the Mississippi (21x30cm-8x12in) i. col lithograph. 22-Feb-4 Skinner, Boston #15/R est:4000-6000
£5114 $9000 €7466 Home to thanksgiving (45x71cm-18x28in) hand col lithograph after G H Durrie. 18-May-4 Sotheby's, New York #187/R est:8000-12000
£5291 $10000 €7725 Trolling for blue fish (24x33cm-9x13in) i. col lithograph exhib. 22-Feb-4 Skinner, Boston #5/R est:3000-4000
£5820 $11000 €8497 Autumn in New England (21x28cm-8x11in) i. col lithograph. 22-Feb-4 Skinner, Boston #19/R est:3000-5000
£6349 $12000 €9270 Home to Thanksgiving (20x28cm-8x11in) i. col lithograph. 22-Feb-4 Skinner, Boston #9/R est:6000-8000
£6878 $13000 €10042 Mink trapping (23x30cm-9x12in) i. col lithograph. 22-Feb-4 Skinner, Boston #3/R est:4000-6000
£7407 $14000 €10814 Husking (26x32cm-10x13in) i. col lithograph. 22-Feb-4 Skinner, Boston #16/R est:10000-14000
£7937 $15000 €11588 Winter in the country (22x30cm-9x12in) i. col lithograph. 22-Feb-4 Skinner, Boston #27/R est:6000-8000
£9524 $18000 €13905 The Rocky Mountains, emigrants crossing the plains (23x29cm-9x11in) i. col lithograph. 22-Feb-4 Skinner, Boston #14/R est:18000-26000
£9524 $18000 €13905 Central Park, winter (22x30cm-9x12in) i. col lithograph. 22-Feb-4 Skinner, Boston #42/R est:1000-1500
£10053 $19000 €14677 The great fire at Chicago, Oct.r 8th 1871 (22x28cm-9x11in) i. col lithograph exhib. 22-Feb-4 Skinner, Boston #38/R est:2000-3000
£11640 $22000 €16994 The 'Lightning Express' trains (24x32cm-9x13in) i. col lithograph exhib. 22-Feb-4 Skinner, Boston #7/R est:6000-8000
£12698 $24000 €18539 Across the continent (23x30cm-9x13in) i. col lithograph. 22-Feb-4 Skinner, Boston #8/R est:6000-8000
£19841 $37500 €28968 The life of a hunter (24x31cm-9x12in) i. col lithograph exhib. 22-Feb-4 Skinner, Boston #4/R est:15000-25000
£34392 $65000 €50212 Baseball game (24x33cm-9x13in) i. col lithograph. 22-Feb-4 Skinner, Boston #6/R est:8000-12000

CURRIER, Cyrus Bates (1868-1946) American
£1061 $1900 €1549 Eucalyptus and clouds (51x41cm-20x16in) s.d.46. 16-Mar-4 Matthew's, Oregon #95/R est:1200-1800

CURRIER, J Frank (1843-1909) American
£1359 $2500 €1984 Landscape with approaching storm (64x51cm-25x20in) s.verso board. 25-Jun-4 Freeman, Philadelphia #235/R est:1500-2500
Works on paper
£221 $400 €323 Studio model (48x33cm-19x13in) W/C en grisaille. 31-Mar-4 Sotheby's, New York #56/R
£541 $1000 €790 Road to Schlessheim (23x36cm-9x14in) chl. 13-Mar-4 Susanin's, Chicago #6063/R

CURRIER, Nathaniel (1813-1888) American
Prints
£1376 $2600 €2009 American winter sports (20x26cm-8x10in) i. col lithograph. 22-Feb-4 Skinner, Boston #31/R est:2500-3500
£1376 $2600 €2009 Awful conflagration of the steamboat, Lexington (22x13cm-9x5in) col lithograph. 22-Feb-4 Skinner, Boston #48/R est:600-800
£1376 $2600 €2009 Preparing for market (22x29cm-9x11in) i. col lithograph. 22-Feb-4 Skinner, Boston #50/R est:1500-2000
£1535 $2900 €2241 Camping out (24x32cm-9x13in) i. col lithograph. 22-Feb-4 Skinner, Boston #18/R est:2000-3000
£1535 $2900 €2241 American winter scenes (19x26cm-7x10in) i. col lithograph. 22-Feb-4 Skinner, Boston #35/R est:1500-2000
£1720 $3250 €2511 The last war whoop (23x30cm-9x12in) i. col lithograph. 22-Feb-4 Skinner, Boston #43/R est:2000-3000
£1720 $3250 €2511 Catching a trout (22x29cm-9x11in) i. col lithograph exhib. 22-Feb-4 Skinner, Boston #1/R est:3000-5000
£2116 $4000 €3089 Peytona and fashion (20x30cm-8x12in) i. col lithograph. 22-Feb-4 Skinner, Boston #23/R est:8000-12000
£2249 $4250 €3284 American winter sports (22x29cm-9x11in) i. col lithograph. 22-Feb-4 Skinner, Boston #17/R est:3000-4000
£2249 $4250 €3284 Clipper ship, 'Red Jacket' (20x27cm-8x11in) i. col lithograph. 22-Feb-4 Skinner, Boston #39/R est:2000-3000
£2249 $4250 €3284 Surrender of General Burgoyne at Saratoga NY Oct 17th 1777 (21x28cm-8x11in) i. col lithograph. 22-Feb-4 Skinner, Boston #44/R est:2500-3500
£2381 $4500 €3476 Surrender of Lord Cornwallis at Yorktown VA Oct 19th 1781 (21x28cm-8x11in) i. col lithograph. 22-Feb-4 Skinner, Boston #45/R est:2600-3000
£3704 $7000 €5408 American farm scenes, No 4 (22x28cm-9x11in) i. col lithograph. 22-Feb-4 Skinner, Boston #20/R est:5500-7500
£4233 $8000 €6180 American winter scenes (19x25cm-7x10in) i. col lithograph. 22-Feb-4 Skinner, Boston #29/R est:2000-2500
£8995 $17000 €13133 American forest scene (24x32cm-9x13in) i. col lithograph. 22-Feb-4 Skinner, Boston #11/R est:8000-10000
£11640 $22000 €16994 The road, winter (20x29cm-8x11in) i. col lithograph. 22-Feb-4 Skinner, Boston #10/R est:6000-8000

CURRIN, Garry (20th C) New Zealander
£1598 $2716 €2333 Johnny Jones the whaler (54x180cm-21x71in) s.d.1997 board. 27-Nov-3 International Art Centre, Auckland #150/R est:2800-3800 (NZ.D 4250)

CURRIN, John (1962-) American
£212291 $380000 €309945 The Optimist (81x66cm-32x26in) exec 1996 prov. 12-May-4 Sotheby's, New York #5/R est:400000-600000
Works on paper
£3593 $6000 €5246 Untitled (28x20cm-11x8in) s.d.92 graphite acrylic on paper prov. 14-Nov-3 Phillips, New York #218/R est:8000-12000

£7821	$14000	€11419	Braless (29x19cm-11x7in) s.d.92 verso ink pencil prov. 13-May-4 Sotheby's, New York #314/R est:8000-12000
£9000	$16380	€13140	Untitled (21x28cm-8x11in) s.i.cover various media 60 sketchbook. 21-Jun-4 Bonhams, New Bond Street #127/R est:8000-10000
£10180	$17000	€14863	Untitled (30x22cm-12x9in) s.d.91 gouache graphite prov.lit. 14-Nov-3 Phillips, New York #219/R est:15000-20000
£22346	$40000	€32625	Model (36x28cm-14x11in) s. ink prov. 12-May-4 Christie's, Rockefeller NY #350/R est:20000-30000

CURRY, Adolf (1879-1939) Austrian

£500	$900	€750	Walk (24x27cm-9x11in) s. panel. 21-Apr-4 Dorotheum, Vienna #23/R

CURRY, Ethel Luella (1902-2000) Canadian

£1364	$2223	€1991	Fish cleaning (29x34cm-11x13in) s.verso panel. 23-Sep-3 Ritchie, Toronto #103/R est:1000-1500 (C.D 3000)

CURRY, John Steuart (1897-1946) American

£37791	$65000	€55175	Homestead (72x150cm-28x59in) s.i. 4-Dec-3 Christie's, Rockefeller NY #103/R est:30000-50000
Prints			
£1902	$3500	€2777	Horses running before a storm (25x36cm-10x14in) s.i.d.1930 lithograph. 26-Jun-4 Sloans & Kenyon, Bethesda #217/R est:2000-2500
£2059	$3500	€3006	John Brown. s. lithograph. 28-Nov-3 Thomaston Place, Thomaston #15
Works on paper			
£3352	$6000	€4894	Leaping figures, study for the Flying Cadonas (48x33cm-19x13in) s.d.1932 pastel pencil ink. 16-May-4 Wright, Chicago #150/R est:4000-6000

CURRY, Robert F (1872-1945) American

£333	$603	€500	Oberstdorf in the Allgau in winter (62x73cm-24x29in) s. board lit. 1-Apr-4 Frank Peege, Freiburg #1195/R
£352	$609	€500	Mountain landscape (74x60cm-29x24in) s. 10-Dec-3 Hugo Ruef, Munich #2401/R
£411	$641	€600	River landscape in late summer (62x80cm-24x31in) s. board. 10-Apr-3 Weidler, Nurnberg #391
£414	$691	€600	Mountain village in winter (60x75cm-24x30in) s. board. 9-Jul-3 Hugo Ruef, Munich #74
£538	$839	€850	River Isar (49x69cm-19x27in) s. i. verso board. 18-Oct-2 Von Zezschwitz, Munich #61/R
£600	$1098	€900	Castle park in early spring (80x100cm-31x39in) s. 5-Jun-4 Arnold, Frankfurt #558/R
£667	$1200	€1000	Cloudy Oberstdorf mountains (74x60cm-29x24in) s. 22-Apr-4 Allgauer, Kempten #3510/R
£667	$1200	€1000	Mittenwald in the snow (75x86cm-30x34in) s. 22-Apr-4 Weidler, Nurnberg #314/R
£753	$1281	€1100	Autumnal wood (79x98cm-31x39in) s. 5-Nov-3 Hugo Ruef, Munich #950
£972	$1604	€1400	Steinach am Brenner in winter (66x88cm-26x35in) s. 2-Jul-3 Neumeister, Munich #620/R
£979	$1664	€1400	Snow covered Tyrolean Alps (100x120cm-39x47in) s. 20-Nov-3 Van Ham, Cologne #1523/R est:900
£1000	$1800	€1500	Rubihorn in evening sun (74x62cm-29x24in) s. panel lit. 22-Apr-4 Allgauer, Kempten #3507/R est:1500
£1164	$1979	€1700	Allgau spring landscape with snow covered mountains (55x69cm-22x27in) s. board lit. 6-Nov-3 Allgauer, Kempten #3402/R est:1300
£1301	$2212	€1900	On the Kramer near Garmish - alpine peaks and Waxenstein (61x74cm-24x29in) s. i. verso canvas on board. 6-Nov-3 Allgauer, Kempten #3403/R est:1350
£1301	$2212	€1900	Lermoos in winter (80x101cm-31x40in) s. 6-Nov-3 Allgauer, Kempten #3404/R est:1600
£1333	$2400	€2000	Winter's day in mountain village (63x75cm-25x30in) s. 22-Apr-4 Allgauer, Kempten #3509/R est:1600
£1497	$2500	€2186	Winter landscape (79x99cm-31x39in) s. 23-Oct-3 Shannon's, Milford #193/R est:2000-3000
£1549	$2773	€2200	A winter's day in a village in Oberbayern (61x74cm-24x29in) s. lit. 8-Jan-4 Allgauer, Kempten #2365/R est:2200
£2096	$3500	€3060	Winter in the Tyrol (76x86cm-30x34in) s.i.verso prov. 7-Oct-3 Sotheby's, New York #180 est:3000-5000
£2545	$4250	€3716	Snowy river (101x126cm-40x50in) s. 7-Oct-3 Sotheby's, New York #184 est:5000-7000
£2759	$4607	€4000	Winter's day in village (60x80cm-24x31in) s. lit. 10-Jul-3 Allgauer, Kempten #2456 est:1500

CURSITER, Stanley (1887-1976) British

£1000	$1730	€1460	Still life of red and yellow roses (40x44cm-16x17in) s.d.1958 board. 11-Dec-3 Lyon & Turnbull, Edinburgh #11/R est:1000-1500
£2119	$3602	€3094	Portrait of the artist's sister-in-law (47x47cm-19x19in) s. prov. 24-Nov-3 Sotheby's, Melbourne #267/R est:5000-7000 (A.D 5000)
£2400	$3864	€3480	View of Aryshire (24x34cm-9x13in) s. 21-Aug-3 Bonhams, Edinburgh #1116/R est:1000-1500
£3390	$5763	€4949	Sea crashing on the rocks (50x60cm-20x24in) s.d.1930 prov. 24-Nov-3 Sotheby's, Melbourne #264/R est:8000-12000 (A.D 8000)
£3800	$6954	€5548	Cliffs and surf, Orkney (29x39cm-11x15in) s.d.1951 canvasboard. 8-Apr-4 Bonhams, Edinburgh #164/R est:3000-5000
£13559	$23051	€19796	Orkney Landscape (85x100cm-33x39in) s.d.1954 prov. 24-Nov-3 Sotheby's, Melbourne #269/R est:15000-25000 (A.D 32000)
£14407	$24492	€21034	Misty West Coast, Hoy Bay, Orkney (85x100cm-33x39in) s. prov. 24-Nov-3 Sotheby's, Melbourne #262/R est:25000-30000 (A.D 34000)
Works on paper			
£1695	$2881	€2475	Rousay Cliffs, Blue Sea, Orkney (35x50cm-14x20in) s. i.verso W/C prov. 24-Nov-3 Sotheby's, Melbourne #263/R est:4000-6000 (A.D 4000)
£1800	$3096	€2628	Orcadian coast (35x50cm-14x20in) s.d.1926 W/C. 4-Dec-3 Bonhams, Edinburgh #104a est:2000-3000
£2034	$3458	€2970	Orkney Landscape (23x34cm-9x13in) s.d.1920 W/C prov. 24-Nov-3 Sotheby's, Melbourne #265/R est:4000-6000 (A.D 4800)
£2542	$4322	€3711	Orkney Landscape (34x49cm-13x19in) s.d.1928 W/C prov. 24-Nov-3 Sotheby's, Melbourne #266/R est:6000-10000 (A.D 6000)

CURTIS, David Jan (1948-) British

£2000	$3140	€2900	San dunes and sea, Arisaig, Scotland (61x76cm-24x30in) s.d.91. 28-Aug-3 Christie's, Kensington #320/R est:800-1200
Works on paper			
£1600	$2512	€2320	Red flag markers, Whitby (52x70cm-20x28in) s. pencil W/C bodycol. 28-Aug-3 Christie's, Kensington #319/R est:800-1200

CURTIS, Edward S (1868-1952) American

Photographs			
£1796	$3000	€2622	Vanishing race (20x25cm-8x10in) with sig. orotone. 21-Oct-3 Swann Galleries, New York #71/R est:4000-6000
£1796	$3000	€2622	An oasis in the Bad Lands (30x40cm-12x16in) i.d.1905 verso photogravure. 21-Oct-3 Swann Galleries, New York #73/R est:2500-3500
£1799	$3400	€2627	The vanishing race (15x20cm-6x8in) s.i. platinum. 17-Feb-4 Swann Galleries, New York #27/R est:2500-3500
£1850	$3200	€2701	Chief and his staff (32x44cm-13x17in) with sig. silver print. 9-Dec-3 Swann Galleries, New York #442/R est:2000-3000
£1852	$3000	€2685	Oasis in the Badlands' (30x41cm-12x16in) s.d.1905 silver gelatin print. 26-Jul-3 Thomaston Place, Thomaston #112/R
£1946	$3250	€2841	Canon del Muerto (34x28cm-13x11in) s. orotone exec.1900-1905. 21-Oct-3 Bonhams & Butterfields, San Francisco #1484/R
£2059	$3500	€3006	Apache women fording river (15x20cm-6x8in) s. gelatin silver print prov. 1-Nov-3 Santa Fe Art, Santa Fe #115/R est:2000-4000
£2260	$4000	€3300	Fisherman, Wishham (34x27cm-13x11in) s. photo. 28-Apr-4 Sotheby's, New York #92/R est:5000-7000
£2434	$4600	€3554	Canon de Chelly (16x20cm-6x8in) s. platinum. 17-Feb-4 Swann Galleries, New York #26/R est:3000-4000
£2540	$4800	€3708	Prayer to the stars (25x20cm-10x8in) s. orotone. 17-Feb-4 Christie's, Rockefeller NY #177/R est:3500-4500
£2542	$4500	€3711	Maid of dreams. 1904 (9x7cm-4x3in) s. orotone. 27-Apr-4 Christie's, Rockefeller NY #309/R est:2000-3000
£2825	$5000	€4125	Maid of dreams, 1904 (25x20cm-10x8in) s. orotone. 27-Apr-4 Christie's, Rockefeller NY #308/R est:5000-7000
£2994	$5000	€4371	Oasis in the Badlands, Red Hawk, Ogalada Sioux (27x35cm-11x14in) s. toned gelatin silver print lit. 21-Oct-3 Bonhams & Butterfields, San Francisco #1490/R
£3593	$6000	€5246	Scout, Apache (28x36cm-11x14in) s. orotone lit. 20-Oct-3 Christie's, Rockefeller NY #16/R est:6000-8000
£3892	$6500	€5682	Maid of dreams (25x20cm-10x8in) s. orotone. 17-Oct-3 Sotheby's, New York #115/R est:5000-7000
£4237	$7500	€6186	Prayer to the stars, 1909 (35x28cm-14x11in) s. orotone. 27-Apr-4 Christie's, Rockefeller NY #307/R est:7000-9000
£4491	$7500	€6557	Native from the Great Plains (39x21cm-15x8in) s.num.70 gold toned printing-out print exec.c.1900 exhib. 20-Oct-3 Christie's, Rockefeller NY #21/R est:8000-10000
£4790	$8000	€6993	Oasis in the Badlands, Sioux, Chief Red Hawk (20x25cm-8x10in) s. orotone lit. 20-Oct-3 Christie's, Rockefeller NY #17/R est:7000-9000
£5090	$8500	€7431	An oasis in the Badlands, Sioux, Chief Red Hawk (28x35cm-11x14in) s. orotone lit. 20-Oct-3 Christie's, Rockefeller NY #19/R est:1000-15000
£5389	$9000	€7868	Rush gatherer, Kutenai (20x25cm-8x10in) s. orotone prov.lit. 20-Oct-3 Christie's, Rockefeller NY #18/R est:7000-9000
£7059	$12000	€10306	Canyon de Chelly (28x36cm-11x14in) orotone photograph. 1-Nov-3 Altermann Galleries, Santa Fe #73
£7186	$12000	€10492	Shot in the hand, Apsaroke (40x26cm-16x10in) i. photogravure. 20-Oct-3 Christie's, Rockefeller NY #23/R est:7000-9000
£9239	$17000	€13489	Canyon de Chelley (48x40cm-19x16in) gold-toned photograph. 24-Jun-4 Sotheby's, New York #200/R est:8000-12000
£9581	$16000	€13988	Hopi man (44x30cm-17x12in) sepia toned photo. 17-Oct-3 Sotheby's, New York #114/R est:10000-15000
£11377	$19000	€16610	Canon de Chelley, Arizona (28x35cm-11x14in) s. orotone lit. 20-Oct-3 Christie's, Rockefeller NY #15/R est:15000-20000
£11413	$21000	€16663	Son of the Desert (48x41cm-19x16in) gold-toned photograph. 24-Jun-4 Sotheby's, New York #199/R est:8000-12000
£13043	$24000	€19043	Canyon del Muerto (48x40cm-19x16in) gold-toned photograph. 24-Jun-4 Sotheby's, New York #201/R est:6000-10000

CURTIS, Elizabeth (1873-?) American

£559	$1000	€816	York River sunset (61x81cm-24x32in) burlap. 10-Jan-4 Harvey Clar, Oakland #1454
£1294	$2200	€1889	Adobe garden (61x81cm-24x32in) s. 29-Oct-3 Christie's, Los Angeles #11/R est:2500-3500
£1536	$2750	€2243	Florist at work (61x81cm-24x32in) burlap. 10-Jan-4 Harvey Clar, Oakland #1228

CURTIS, George Carroll (19/20th C) American

£300	$549	€438	Nude bathing in woodland (65x53cm-26x21in) indis sig.i. 8-Apr-4 Christie's, Kensington #25/R

CURTIS, J W (1839-1901) Australian

£1322	$2446	€1930	Wattle in blossom and pine plantation (30x51cm-12x20in) s.d.95 i.verso prov.exhib. 10-Mar-4 Deutscher-Menzies, Melbourne #379/R est:3200-4500 (A.D 3200)
£1374	$2501	€2006	Escaping the blaze (44x73cm-17x29in) s.d.95-96 canvas on board. 16-Jun-4 Deutscher-Menzies, Melbourne #257/R est:4000-6000 (A.D 3600)
Works on paper			
£723	$1230	€1056	Droving Horses (33x65cm-13x26in) W/C. 26-Nov-3 Deutscher-Menzies, Melbourne #220/R (A.D 1700)

CURTIS, James Waltham (1839-1901) Australian

£2033	$3638	€2968	Farmyard (29x49cm-11x19in) s.d.89. 10-May-4 Joel, Victoria #298 est:3600-4200 (A.D 5000)

CURTIS, Leland (1897-?) American

£1786	$3250	€2608	Grand Teton and Mt Owen (61x81cm-24x32in) s. prov. 15-Jun-4 John Moran, Pasadena #97 est:3000-4000
£2473	$4500	€3611	High Sierras landscape (30x41cm-12x16in) s. canvasboard prov. 15-Jun-4 John Moran, Pasadena #101 est:1500-2500
£2800	$4564	€4088	USS Bear in Neny Fjord, Antarctica (71x98cm-28x39in) s.i.d.1957 i. stretcher. 24-Sep-3 Christie's, London #375/R est:3000-5000

CURTIS, Louis (20th C) American

£625	$1000	€913	View from Oakland Hills. s.d.1928. 20-Sep-3 Harvey Clar, Oakland #1331

CURTIS, Ralph W (1854-1902) American
Works on paper
£10795 $19000 €15761 White Lotus (51x36cm-20x14in) W/C pencil exec c.1890-1900 prov.exhib. 18-May-4 Christie's, Rockefeller NY #71/R est:12000-18000

CURTIS, Robert Emerson (1899-1996) Australian
Works on paper
£319 $542 €466 Woollen mill factory (24x35cm-9x14in) s.d.1937 pastel pencil. 26-Nov-3 Deutscher-Menzies, Melbourne #146/R (A.D 750)
£340 $579 €496 Power house, Mount Lyell, Tasmania (23x35cm-9x14in) s.d.1934 pencil. 26-Nov-3 Deutscher-Menzies, Melbourne #147/R (A.D 800)

CURTIS, Roy Jupurrula (c.1942-) Australian
Works on paper
£1953 $3652 €2930 Ngarlajiyi-yala, bush carrot and bush potato (106x60cm-42x24in) bears name.verso synthetic polymer paint linen prov. 26-Jul-4 Sotheby's, Melbourne #418/R est:5000-7000 (A.D 5000)

CURTIS, Sarah (?-1743) British
£785 $1452 €1146 Good and bad government (167x137cm-66x54in) s.d.89 i.verso prov. 15-Mar-4 Sotheby's, Melbourne #172 est:800-1200 (A.D 1900)

CURTIS, William Fuller (1873-?) American
£5028 $9000 €7341 Underwater fish scene (46x109cm-18x43in) s. panel. 10-Jan-4 Pook & Pook, Downington #431/R

CURZON, Paul Alfred de (1820-1895) French
£280 $504 €420 Woodland path (12x17cm-5x7in) panel. 26-Apr-4 Rieber, Stuttgart #1114/R
£1375 $2200 €2008 Landscape with peasants resting (56x46cm-22x18in) s. 20-Sep-3 New Orleans Auction, New Orleans #545/R
£22059 $37500 €32206 Young girl of Galinero (104x70cm-41x28in) s. exhib.lit. 28-Oct-3 Sotheby's, New York #32/R est:15000-20000

CUSACHS Y CUSACHS, Jose (1851-1908) Spanish
£13793 $24828 €20000 Ready for the battle (27x46cm-11x18in) s. 26-Jan-4 Durán, Madrid #168/R est:10000
£31915 $53298 €45000 Donkey (60x120cm-24x47in) s. exhib. 20-Oct-3 Durán, Madrid #245/R
Works on paper
£1690 $2924 €2400 Soldier (27x15cm-11x6in) s.d.1889 mixed media. 15-Dec-3 Ansorena, Madrid #350/R est:2400

CUSACK, Ralph (1912-) British?
£1250 $2300 €1900 The family bed (69x54cm-27x21in) s.d.43 i.verso. 22-Jun-4 De Veres Art Auctions, Dublin #31/R est:1500-2000

CUSATELLI, Vittorio (1912-) Italian
£396 $649 €550 Female nude (40x50cm-16x20in) 5-Jun-3 Adma, Formigine #740

CUSHING, Barbara (20th C) American
£232 $425 €339 Mohawk preserve - Catskill Farm (38x56cm-15x22in) oil on paper. 10-Jul-4 Hindman, Chicago #103/R

CUSNER, Robert (19/20th C) Belgian
£222 $408 €324 Chapel courtyard (46x60cm-18x24in) s. 14-Jun-4 Waddingtons, Toronto #37/R (C.D 550)

CUSSOL, Beatrice (1970-) ?
Works on paper
£608 $1070 €900 Untitled No. 215 (60x80cm-24x31in) W/C ink exec 1998. 18-May-4 Tajan, Paris #185/R est:1000-1200

CUSTIS, Eleanor Parke (1897-1983) American
Photographs
£3107 $5500 €4536 Decorative frieze (16x36cm-6x14in) s.i. gelatin silver print. 27-Apr-4 Christie's, Rockefeller NY #19/R est:3000-5000
Works on paper
£279 $475 €407 Procession (54x44cm-21x17in) s. W/C. 21-Nov-3 Skinner, Boston #483/R
£2096 $3500 €3060 At the beach (33x28cm-13x11in) init. gouache prov. 23-Oct-3 Shannon's, Milford #24/R est:2500-3500

CUTHBERT, David (1951-) British
£250 $455 €365 Evening near St. Ives (71x51cm-28x20in) s.d.99 acrylic. 15-Jun-4 David Lay, Penzance #681

CUTHBERT, Jane (?) British?
Works on paper
£290 $476 €423 Study of an old coaching inn (30x36cm-12x14in) s. W/C. 28-May-3 Brightwells, Leominster #1043

CUTHBERTSON, William A (fl.1920s) British
£280 $515 €409 In the shallows (26x36cm-10x14in) s. 23-Jun-4 Bonhams, Bury St Edmunds #428

CUTLER, Cecil (?-1934) British
Works on paper
£400 $680 €584 Portrait of Edward VII smoking a cigar (21x16cm-8x6in) s. pencil W/C. 19-Nov-3 Tennants, Leyburn #938a
£820 $1468 €1197 Dinner party (42x21cm-17x8in) s. W/C bodycol sold with a landscape by another hand. 22-Mar-4 Bonhams & Brooks, Norfolk #174/R

CUTRONE, Ronnie (1948-) American
£326 $600 €476 Blood of the lamb (178x229cm-70x90in) s.i.d.1981 overlap acrylic prov. 10-Jun-4 Phillips, New York #694/R
Works on paper
£309 $546 €460 Freedom fighter (105x75cm-41x30in) s.d. W/C chl collage. 30-Apr-4 Dr Fritz Nagel, Stuttgart #84/R
£309 $546 €460 Balinese morning (105x75cm-41x30in) s.d. WC chl. 30-Apr-4 Dr Fritz Nagel, Stuttgart #85/R
£367 $650 €536 Untitled, ants (76x306cm-30x120in) s.d.1981 verso mixed media triptych prov. 2-May-4 Bonhams & Butterfields, Los Angeles #3048/R
£395 $700 €577 Giant unbreakable Cowboys and Indians (213x178cm-84x70in) s.i.d.1981 verso mixed media canvas. 2-May-4 Bonhams & Butterfields, Los Angeles #3049/R

CUTTICA, Eugenio (1957-) Argentinian
£261 $425 €381 Armonias implacables III (89x89cm-35x35in) s. 28-Sep-3 Bonhams & Butterfields, Los Angeles #7059

CUTTS, Gertrude Spurr (1858-1941) Canadian
£1044 $1942 €1524 Netley Farm, Gomshall, Surrey (30x61cm-12x24in) s.d.98 s.i.verso. 2-Mar-4 Ritchie, Toronto #52/R est:700-1000 (C.D 2600)

CUYCK VAN MIERHOP, Franz (c.1640-1690) Flemish
£6207 $10303 €9000 Hunting life with duck, wild birds and dog (66x85cm-26x33in) bears sig. prov. 1-Oct-3 Dorotheum, Vienna #146/R est:9000-14000

CUYCK, Michel van (1797-1875) Belgian
£467 $835 €700 Marine (60x90cm-24x35in) s. 11-May-4 Vanderkindere, Brussels #180

CUYLENBORCH, Abraham van (1620-1658) Dutch
£6294 $10699 €9000 Diana with followers in grotto (49x87cm-19x34in) mono. panel. 20-Nov-3 Van Ham, Cologne #1302/R est:13000
£6667 $12067 €10000 Allegory of the fertility of the Goddess Ceres (49x88cm-19x35in) bears mono.d.1659 panel prov. 1-Apr-4 Van Ham, Cologne #1173/R est:13000

CUYLENBORCH, Abraham van (attrib) (1620-1658) Dutch
£1200 $2076 €1752 Interior of a grotto with figures amongst classical ruins and fountains (55x75cm-22x30in) panel. 12-Dec-3 Christie's, Kensington #60/R est:1500-2000
£1600 $2864 €2336 Nymphs in a cave (60x50cm-24x20in) panel. 11-May-4 Bonhams, Knightsbridge #98/R est:1500-2000

CUYLENBURGH, Cornelis van (1758-1827) Dutch
£1944 $3247 €2800 At the grocery shop (47x43cm-19x17in) s.d.1826 panel prov. 21-Oct-3 Sotheby's, Amsterdam #51/R est:3000-5000
Works on paper
£1467 $2625 €2200 Portrait of Adrianus Hartevelt, his wife Helena Johanna van Niel and children (34x47cm-13x19in) s.i.d.1788 mixed media. 17-May-4 Glerum, Amsterdam #61/R est:1200-1600

CUYLENBURGH, Cornelis van (attrib) (1758-1827) Dutch
£2113 $3697 €3000 Le festin des Dieux (27x32cm-11x13in) 17-Dec-3 Rabourdin & Choppin de Janvry, Paris #38/R est:1800-2200

CUYP, Aelbert (1620-1691) Dutch
£4375 $7000 €6388 Hay harvest (51x66cm-20x26in) wood panel. 20-Sep-3 Bunte, Elgin #1452 est:10000-15000
Works on paper
£524 $954 €765 Young woman with horse and boy (16x18cm-6x7in) i. verso chk htd. 17-Jun-4 Kornfeld, Bern #25 (S.FR 1200)
£7000 $12810 €10220 Study of two cows (9x15cm-4x6in) blk chk blk grey wash prov. 8-Jul-4 Sotheby's, London #87/R est:10000-15000

CUYP, Aelbert (circle) (1620-1691) Dutch
£8108 $14270 €12000 Portrait of boy with parrot (117x72cm-46x28in) 22-May-4 Lempertz, Koln #1035/R est:10000-12000

CUYP, Aelbert (studio) (1620-1691) Dutch
£16000 $28640 €24000 Barn interior with cattle and maid fetching vegetables (70x90cm-28x35in) s. panel prov. 17-May-4 Christie's, Amsterdam #75/R est:10000-15000

CUYP, Aelbert (style) (1620-1691) Dutch
£10000 $18200 €15000 Ships by Papendrecht (190x146cm-75x57in) panel lit. 29-Jun-4 Sotheby's, Paris #36/R est:10000-15000

CUYP, Benjamin Gerritsz (1612-1652) Dutch
£3125 $5094 €4500 Proclamation to the shepherds (65x78cm-26x31in) panel. 25-Sep-3 Dr Fritz Nagel, Stuttgart #1241/R est:7000

£4500 $7785 €6570 Kitchen interior with two men and a young boy preparing food (25x34cm-10x13in) s. panel oval. 10-Dec-3 Bonhams, New Bond Street #12/R est:2000-3000
£8400 $14532 €12264 Barn interior with Boors smoking and drinking (37x50cm-15x20in) bears sig panel oval prov. 9-Dec-3 Sotheby's, Olympia #346/R est:7000-10000

CUYP, Jacob Gerritsz (1594-1651) Dutch
£5667 $10143 €8500 Portrait of a gentleman, aged 47, with flat white lace collar (74x59cm-29x23in) s.i.d.1645 panel prov.lit. 17-May-4 Christie's, Amsterdam #17/R est:5000-7000
£7000 $12810 €10220 Double portrait of father and son (110x76cm-43x30in) s.i. panel. 9-Jul-4 Christie's, Kensington #56/R est:8000-12000
£20548 $34932 €30000 Moses and the seven daughters of Jethro (72x109cm-28x43in) s.d.1635 prov.exhib.lit. 4-Nov-3 Sotheby's, Amsterdam #113/R est:30000-40000

CUYP, Jacob Gerritsz (attrib) (1594-1651) Dutch
£8869 $15876 €12949 Girl with spring flowers (68x52cm-27x20in) panel. 26-May-4 AB Stockholms Auktionsverk #2512/R est:80000-100000 (S.KR 120000)

CUYP, Jacob Gerritsz and MOMMERS, Hendrik (17th C) Dutch
£1399 $2336 €2000 A maid milking a cow (47x33cm-19x13in) s.d.1645 panel. 30-Jun-3 Sotheby's, Amsterdam #29/R

CUYPER, Alfons de (1887-1950) Belgian
£526 $968 €800 City view of a canal in winter (45x61cm-18x24in) s.d.22. 28-Jun-4 Sotheby's, Amsterdam #123/R

CUZCO SCHOOL (18th C) South American
£27933 $50000 €40782 Virgin of the Rosary (162x110cm-64x43in) 26-May-4 Sotheby's, New York #67/R est:15000-20000

CUZIN, Christophe (1956-) French
£486 $812 €700 Sans titre (185x135cm-73x53in) acrylic prov. 25-Oct-3 Cornette de St.Cyr, Paris #397
£625 $1044 €900 Sans titre, 311 891 (185x135cm-73x53in) s.verso acrylic prov. 25-Oct-3 Cornette de St.Cyr, Paris #396/R

CWIERTNIEWICZ, Wojciech (1955-) Polish
£372 $640 €543 Untitled (100x80cm-39x31in) s.d.89. 4-Dec-3 Agra, Warsaw #4/R (P.Z 2500)
£459 $761 €670 Untitled (100x80cm-39x31in) painted 1989. 2-Oct-3 Agra, Warsaw #71/R (P.Z 3000)
£706 $1278 €1031 Untitled (139x139cm-55x55in) s.d.89. 4-Apr-4 Agra, Warsaw #39/R (P.Z 5000)

CYBIS, Jan (1897-1972) Polish
£1477 $2732 €2200 Sous-bois (38x38cm-15x15in) s. 15-Mar-4 Claude Boisgirard, Paris #24/R est:2800-3200
£2031 $3392 €2965 Afternoon nap (60x197cm-24x78in) 19-Oct-3 Agra, Warsaw #32/R est:5000 (P.Z 13000)
Works on paper
£692 $1279 €1010 Boats (32x40cm-13x16in) W/C. 14-Mar-4 Agra, Warsaw #72/R (P.Z 5000)
£883 $1465 €1289 Landscape with meadow and red houses (30x48cm-12x19in) s.d.67 W/C. 15-Jun-3 Agra, Warsaw #40/R (P.Z 5500)

CYNCIC, Menci C (20th C) ?
£3664 $6558 €5349 Lake in summer mountain landscape (43x56cm-17x22in) s. 13-May-4 Stuker, Bern #570 est:500-800 (S.FR 8500)

CYR, Georges (1880-1964) French
£324 $538 €470 Honfleur (46x55cm-18x22in) s. 1-Oct-3 Millon & Associes, Paris #180
£839 $1427 €1200 La Seine a Croisset (50x65cm-20x26in) s.d.1929. 30-Nov-3 Salle des ventes Pillet, Lyon la Foret #115

CZACHORSKI, Ladislaus von (1850-1911) Polish
£73306 $135615 €107027 Lady at her toilet (65x43cm-26x17in) 14-Mar-4 Agra, Warsaw #17/R (P.Z 530000)
£85072 $141220 €124205 At the piano (37x50cm-15x20in) s.d.1902. 15-Jun-3 Agra, Warsaw #1/R est:390000 (P.Z 530000)

CZAJKOWSKI, Stanislaw (1878-1954) Polish
£627 $978 €915 Crucifix in front of a church (45x35cm-18x14in) s. cardboard. 30-Mar-3 Agra, Warsaw #51/R (P.Z 4000)
£1284 $2132 €1875 Grey day (25x35cm-10x14in) s. cardboard. 15-Jun-3 Agra, Warsaw #29/R est:8000 (P.Z 8000)

CZAPLA, Marian (20th C) Polish
£306 $508 €447 Tulips in a vase (55x46cm-22x18in) acrylic painted 1999. 2-Oct-3 Agra, Warsaw #54/R (P.Z 2000)

CZARTORYSKA, Anna (20th C) ?
£380 $700 €555 Portrait of Rabbi reading a book (33x23cm-13x9in) s. panel. 26-Jun-4 Susanin's, Chicago #6002/R

CZECH, Emil (1862-1929) Austrian
£349 $615 €510 Autumn river landscape (49x39cm-19x15in) s.d.1909 canvas on board prov. 22-May-4 Galerie Gloggner, Luzern #24/R (S.FR 800)
Works on paper
£403 $741 €600 Girl in blue dress reading (85x67cm-33x26in) s.d.1913 W/C. 26-Mar-4 Dorotheum, Vienna #343/R

CZENE, Apatfalvi (20th C) Hungarian
£421 $670 €615 Still life of books and objects (58x89cm-23x35in) s. 12-Sep-3 Aspire, Cleveland #79

CZENE, Bela (1911-) Hungarian
£854 $1400 €1238 Cultivating the plants (122x58cm-48x23in) s. board painted c.1960. 7-Jun-3 Treadway Gallery, Cincinnati #1503

CZERMAK, Jaroslav (1831-1878) Czechoslovakian
£5435 $10000 €7935 Lady in waiting (137x86cm-54x34in) s.i.d.1878. 27-Jun-4 Freeman, Philadelphia #43/R est:4000-6000

CZERNOTZKY, Ernst (1869-1939) Austrian
£884 $1583 €1300 Still life (70x100cm-28x39in) s. lit. 20-Mar-4 Bergmann, Erlangen #1077
£900 $1593 €1314 Ivory tankard, silver and gilt chalice on a Oriental rug. Chinese lacquer cabinet (25x19cm-10x7in) s. panel pair. 27-Apr-4 Bonhams, Knowle #74/R
£1528 $2597 €2200 Still life with books and nautilus vase (28x22cm-11x9in) s. panel. 28-Oct-3 Dorotheum, Vienna #169/R est:1200-1600

CZIGANY, Dezso (1883-1937) Hungarian
£1765 $2929 €2577 Bearded man (45x34cm-18x13in) s. canvas on cardboard. 4-Oct-3 Kieselbach, Budapest #192/R (H.F 650000)
£3952 $7153 €5770 Woman portrait (62x50cm-24x20in) s. panel. 16-Apr-4 Mu Terem Galeria, Budapest #169/R (H.F 1500000)
£18443 $33383 €26927 Still life with handwoven (67x56cm-26x22in) canvas on card. 16-Apr-4 Mu Terem Galeria, Budapest #37/R (H.F 7000000)
£23490 $40638 €34295 Woman in the garden (57x47cm-22x19in) s. canvas on cardboard. 12-Dec-3 Kieselbach, Budapest #94/R (H.F 9000000)

CZIMRA, Gyula (1901-1966) Hungarian
£1449 $2623 €2116 Sunlit city (60x72cm-24x28in) s. 16-Apr-4 Mu Terem Galeria, Budapest #120/R (H.F 550000)

CZOBEL, Bela (1883-1974) Hungarian
£6264 $10837 €9145 Young girl (81x60cm-32x24in) s. 12-Dec-3 Kieselbach, Budapest #75/R (H.F 2400000)
£6948 $12298 €10144 Still life with flowers in interior (60x47cm-24x19in) s. 28-Apr-4 Kieselbach, Budapest #134/R (H.F 2600000)
£8667 $15687 €13000 La plage de Fecamp (47x60cm-19x24in) s. canvas on board painted 1906. 5-Apr-4 Marie & Robert, Paris #75/R est:12000-15000
£11047 $19000 €16129 Still life with blue glass (92x73cm-36x29in) s.i.d.1963 verso prov.exhib. 3-Dec-3 Doyle, New York #41/R est:5000-7000
£14931 $24786 €21799 In the park (79x65cm-31x26in) s. 4-Oct-3 Kieselbach, Budapest #60/R (H.F 5500000)
Works on paper
£522 $903 €762 Still life of Lilies of the valley (47x30cm-19x12in) s. mixed media. 12-Dec-3 Kieselbach, Budapest #3/R (H.F 200000)
£580 $1049 €847 Woman portrait (58x40cm-23x16in) s. pencil. 16-Apr-4 Mu Terem Galeria, Budapest #166/R (H.F 220000)
£731 $1264 €1067 Still life of flowers (63x48cm-25x19in) s. mixed media. 12-Dec-3 Kieselbach, Budapest #150/R (H.F 280000)
£748 $1324 €1092 Flowers by the window (52x37cm-20x15in) s. pastel. 28-Apr-4 Kieselbach, Budapest #103/R (H.F 280000)
£887 $1535 €1295 Girl with bow in her hair (52x41cm-20x16in) s.d.42 pastel. 12-Dec-3 Kieselbach, Budapest #74/R (H.F 340000)
£1566 $2709 €2286 Girl with a bow (53x40cm-21x16in) s. pastel. 12-Dec-3 Kieselbach, Budapest #216/R (H.F 600000)
£2036 $3380 €2973 Girl (43x28cm-17x11in) s. pastel. 4-Oct-3 Kieselbach, Budapest #133/R (H.F 750000)
£9620 $17027 €14045 Studio still life (65x56cm-26x22in) s. mixed media. 28-Apr-4 Kieselbach, Budapest #27/R (H.F 3600000)

DAALHOFF, Hermanus Antonius van (1867-1953) Dutch
£403 $745 €600 Pinkstermorgen (25x35cm-10x14in) s. i.verso. 15-Mar-4 Sotheby's, Amsterdam #170/R
£510 $929 €750 Horse riders on a beach (21x26cm-8x10in) s. s.i.d.16.8.1918 plywood. 3-Feb-4 Christie's, Amsterdam #522
£612 $1114 €900 Bridge over a ditch (13x18cm-5x7in) s. panel sold with W/C by C J Lanooy. 3-Feb-4 Christie's, Amsterdam #410
£1711 $3147 €2600 Mother with children (21x27cm-8x11in) s. panel. 28-Jun-4 Sotheby's, Amsterdam #136/R est:1000-1500

DAAMEN, Theo (20th C) Dutch
£400 $732 €600 Problem child (56x39cm-22x15in) s.d.1970 board prov. 7-Jun-4 Glerum, Amsterdam #336/R

DABADIE, Henri (1867-1949) French
£1000 $1830 €1500 Meknes (46x56cm-18x22in) s.i. 3-Jun-4 Tajan, Paris #218/R est:1500-2000
£1712 $2911 €2500 Petit chemin a Sidi Bou SAid (65x54cm-26x21in) s. i.verso. 9-Nov-3 Eric Pillon, Calais #113/R
£2687 $4568 €3923 Le jardin de la Bayia Marrakech (72x54cm-28x21in) s. 5-Nov-3 Dobiaschofsky, Bern #458/R est:1800 (S.FR 6100)
£4366 $7554 €6200 View of Fez (34x74cm-13x29in) s.i.d.1907. 15-Dec-3 Gros & Delettrez, Paris #507/R est:6000-8000
£7234 $12081 €10200 Rabat au crepuscule (70x146cm-28x57in) s.d.1920. 19-Oct-3 Rabourdin & Choppin de Janvry, Paris #104/R est:12000-15000

DABIN, Joel (1933-) French
£1118 $2058 €1700 Le marche vendeen II (100x100cm-39x39in) s. s.i.verso. 22-Jun-4 Christie's, Amsterdam #356/R est:600-800

DABIT, Eugène (1898-1936) French
£633 $1165 €950 Le bal (60x72cm-24x28in) s. i.verso painted 1925. 9-Jun-4 Piasa, Paris #42/R

£933 $1717 €1400 Grand nu assis sur une chaise. Une cour d'ecole (73x54cm-29x21in) double-sided. 9-Jun-4 Piasa, Paris #40
£933 $1717 €1400 Interieur (43x53cm-17x21in) s. i.verso painted 1925. 9-Jun-4 Piasa, Paris #41/R

DABO, Leon (1868-1960) American
£568 $1000 €829 Saint Tropez (33x41cm-13x16in) s.d.40 canvas on board. 23-May-4 Bonhams & Butterfields, Los Angeles #7042/R
£2045 $3600 €2986 After the Rain at Woodstock (61x76cm-24x30in) s. prov. 23-May-4 Hindman, Chicago #172/R est:3000-5000
£3049 $5000 €4421 Sunset (56x76cm-22x30in) s. painted c.1900. 7-Jun-3 Treadway Gallery, Cincinnati #1337 est:8000-10000
£3352 $6000 €4894 Sailing at dusk (30x41cm-12x16in) mono. i.stretcher prov. 26-May-4 Doyle, New York #79/R est:6000-8000
£5031 $8000 €7345 Still life of flowers (51x51cm-20x20in) mono. 12-Sep-3 Skinner, Boston #331/R
£5405 $10000 €7891 Landscape with pines (41x50cm-16x20in) s.d.52 mono.d.verso board prov. 11-Mar-4 Christie's, Rockefeller NY #56/R est:5000-7000

DABOS, Laurent (1761-1835) French
£6667 $12000 €9734 Head of Napoleon surrounded by a laurel wreath in a sunburst (49cm-19in circular) prov.exhib.lit. 23-Jan-4 Christie's, Rockefeller NY #112/R est:2000-3000

DABOUR, John (1837-1905) American/Turkish
£376 $650 €549 Boston Gardens, depicting a formal garden with birdhouse (43x69cm-17x27in) s.d.1876. 15-Dec-3 Winter Associates, Plainville #34/R

D'ACCARDI, Gian Rodolfo (1906-1993) Italian
£268 $497 €400 Little horses in autumn (24x30cm-9x12in) s. s.verso. 13-Mar-4 Meeting Art, Vercelli #16
£274 $466 €400 Autumn (60x70cm-24x28in) s. 7-Nov-3 Galleria Rosenberg, Milan #46/R
£300 $552 €450 Horses in the wood (40x50cm-16x20in) s. 12-Jun-4 Meeting Art, Vercelli #300
£333 $613 €500 Horses in the wood (60x70cm-24x28in) s. 12-Jun-4 Meeting Art, Vercelli #691/R
£380 $699 €570 Hunting in autumn (40x50cm-16x20in) s. cardboard on canvas. 12-Jun-4 Meeting Art, Vercelli #646
£445 $695 €650 Wooded landscape with horses (40x50cm-16x20in) s. 8-Apr-3 Il Ponte, Milan #1005
£467 $859 €700 Horses in autumn (60x70cm-24x28in) s. s.verso. 12-Jun-4 Meeting Art, Vercelli #572
£503 $931 €750 Horses in the wood (70x60cm-28x24in) s. 13-Mar-4 Meeting Art, Vercelli #440
£507 $892 €750 Venice (60x70cm-24x28in) s. prov. 19-May-4 Il Ponte, Milan #1131
£1056 $1754 €1500 Cavalli nel bosco (100x170cm-39x67in) s. 14-Jun-3 Meeting Art, Vercelli #713/R est:1500

DACHINGER, Hugo (1908-1995) British/Austrian
Works on paper
£300 $519 €438 Do I want him? (29x42cm-11x17in) mono.d.1989 W/C ink prov. 11-Dec-3 Lane, Penzance #286
£1200 $2004 €1752 Kiss. mono.d.1989 pastel sold quantity of painting by same hand. 21-Oct-3 Bonhams, Knightsbridge #58/R est:400-600

DADA GROUP (20th C) ?
Prints
£8000 $14320 €12000 Festival Dada. print. 15-May-4 Renaud, Paris #311/R

DADAMAINO (1935-2004) Italian
£1867 $3435 €2800 Interactions of colours (27x35cm-11x14in) s.i. tempera paper. 12-Jun-4 Meeting Art, Vercelli #852/R est:1000
£6993 $11888 €10000 Untitled (20x200cm-8x79in) s.i. acrylic canvas on board. 24-Nov-3 Christie's, Milan #180/R est:5000-7000
Sculpture
£1707 $2800 €2492 Ottico dynamico (28x28cm-11x11in) s.i.d.61/64 verso aluminium on board diagonal prov. 28-May-3 Sotheby's, Amsterdam #5/R est:2000-3000
£6133 $11285 €9200 Dynamic optical object (70x50cm-28x20in) s.i.d.1961 verso wood aluminium prov. 8-Jun-4 Finarte Semenzato, Milan #443/R est:6000-7000
Works on paper
£1761 $3081 €2500 Untitled (100x116cm-39x46in) Chinese ink. 16-Dec-3 Finarte Semenzato, Milan #246/R est:2800-3200

DADD, Frank (1851-1929) British
£5000 $8500 €7300 Parson's pets (51x41cm-20x16in) s.d.1925. 27-Nov-3 Christie's, Kensington #411/R est:2000-3000
Works on paper
£430 $679 €624 Well dressed gentlemen and ladies watching riders and oxen (43x34cm-17x13in) init. gouache. 2-Sep-3 Rasmussen, Copenhagen #1876 (D.KR 4600)
£1000 $1850 €1460 First try (41x32cm-16x13in) s.d.87 W/C. 10-Mar-4 Sotheby's, Olympia #166/R est:1000-1500
£2800 $5152 €4088 Captain of the Troop (61x122cm-24x48in) s. W/C. 8-Jun-4 Bonhams, New Bond Street #108/R est:3000-5000

DADDI, Bernardo (1312-1350) Italian
£1400000 $2562000 €2044000 Coronation of the Vergin (112x65cm-44x26in) tempera panel gold ground prov.exhib.lit. 7-Jul-4 Sotheby's, London #38/R est:1400000-1800000

DADE, Ernest (1864-1935) British
£340 $568 €496 Stormy weather, Yorkshire coast (22x38cm-9x15in) i.verso. 22-Oct-3 Cheffins, Cambridge #545
Works on paper
£250 $458 €365 Low tide (34x52cm-13x20in) s.d.99 W/C. 6-Jun-4 Lots Road Auctions, London #343
£300 $477 €435 Fishing boats by the quayside (23x27cm-9x11in) s.d.88 W/C. 9-Sep-3 David Duggleby, Scarborough #153
£340 $615 €496 Concarneau (17x26cm-7x10in) s. W/C. 30-Mar-4 David Duggleby, Scarborough #136/R
£900 $1449 €1305 Yorkshire cobbles (23x33cm-9x13in) s.d.94 W/C. 15-Aug-3 Keys, Aylsham #526/R

DADE, Frederick (1874-1908) British
Works on paper
£580 $986 €847 Calais (22x65cm-9x26in) s.i. W/C htd white. 18-Nov-3 Bonhams, Leeds #14
£750 $1380 €1095 End of the voyage (40x56cm-16x22in) s.i. W/C. 24-Mar-4 Hamptons Fine Art, Godalming #268/R
£800 $1448 €1168 Whitby from Upgang (18x47cm-7x19in) s. W/C. 30-Mar-4 David Duggleby, Scarborough #181/R

DADIE-ROBERG, Dagmars (1897-?) Swedish
Sculpture
£1241 $2297 €1800 Tete de femme Art Deco (22cm-9in) s.d.1925 pat bronze st.f.Valsuani. 19-Jan-4 Horta, Bruxelles #95 est:1800-2200

DADO, Miodrag Djuric (1933-) Yugoslavian
£336 $625 €500 Untitled (48x31cm-19x12in) s.d.1984 col crayon ink W/C. 3-Mar-4 Tajan, Paris #239
£1477 $2643 €2200 Composition (60x60cm-24x24in) s.d.70 prov. 26-May-4 Christie's, Paris #89/R est:1500-2000
£2098 $3566 €3000 Personnage fantastique (168x72cm-66x28in) s.d.97 verso panel. 27-Nov-3 Millon & Associes, Paris #239 est:1000-1500
£2639 $4354 €3800 Composition (113x195cm-44x77in) 2-Jul-3 Cornette de St.Cyr, Paris #15/R est:4000-6000
£3061 $5480 €4500 Untitled (81x65cm-32x26in) 21-Mar-4 Calmels Cohen, Paris #123/R est:3000-4000
£3147 $5255 €4500 Tyran cruel (162x130cm-64x51in) s.d.1985. 29-Jun-3 Versailles Encheres #181/R
£10000 $18200 €15000 Personnages (163x130cm-64x51in) s.d.1965 prov. 5-Jul-4 Le Mouel, Paris #80/R est:5000-6000
£11667 $21583 €17500 Rebellion de Pancraisse (130x197cm-51x78in) s.i.d.68 prov.exhib. 18-Jul-4 Sotheby's, Paris #238/R est:10000-15000
Works on paper
£333 $607 €500 Pret-a-porter feminin de luxe (40x30cm-16x12in) s.d.1987 chl pastel gouache. 29-Jun-4 Cornette de St.Cyr, Paris #147/R
£533 $960 €800 Untitled (50x34cm-20x13in) s.d.1984 gouache graphite col crayon double-sided. 24-Apr-4 Cornette de St.Cyr, Paris #504/R
£556 $878 €800 Bebes (37x53cm-15x21in) crayon dr prov. 27-Apr-3 Versailles Encheres #61
£738 $1358 €1100 Untitled (49x64cm-19x25in) s. gouache. 24-Mar-4 Joron-Derem, Paris #87
£1400 $2548 €2100 Composition - Hospi (196x147cm-77x58in) s.d.1980 pastel col crayons prov. 5-Jul-4 Le Mouel, Paris #81/R est:1500-2000
£1538 $2569 €2200 Westhampton (77x38cm-30x15in) s.i.d.78 gouache exhib. 25-Jun-3 Digard, Paris #136/R est:2000-3000
£2000 $3640 €3000 Figure (50x65cm-20x26in) s.verso gouache paper on canvas. 29-Jun-4 Cornette de St.Cyr, Paris #149/R est:3000-4000
£3467 $6309 €5200 Bread (73x92cm-29x36in) s.d.1990 smoke on canvas prov. 29-Jun-4 Cornette de St.Cyr, Paris #159/R est:4000
£4067 $7401 €6100 Saint Hubert (115x166cm-45x65in) s.d.1974 gouache W/C ink collage prov. 29-Jun-4 Cornette de St.Cyr, Paris #151/R est:5000-7000

DADO, Rini (20th C) Dutch?
Sculpture
£1449 $2377 €2000 Nude (36cm-14in) i. num.II/V bronze. 27-May-3 Sotheby's, Amsterdam #528/R est:2000-3000

DADSWELL, Lyndon (1908-1986) Australian
Sculpture
£1220 $2183 €1781 Mother and child (87x45x31cm-34x18x12in) stone prov. 10-May-4 Joel, Victoria #337 est:3000-5000 (A.D 3000)

DADURE, A (19th C) ?
£847 $1558 €1237 After the battle of Naseby (109x136cm-43x54in) s.d.1848. 14-Jun-4 Waddingtons, Toronto #361/R est:1500-2000 (C.D 2100)

DAEGE, Eduard (1805-1883) German
£313 $560 €460 Monk (32x26cm-13x10in) mono. metal on panel lit. 20-Mar-4 Bergmann, Erlangen #1070

DAEHLIN, Gitte (1956-) Norwegian
Works on paper
£241 $441 €352 Kneeling figure (98x68cm-39x27in) s. pastel. 2-Feb-4 Blomqvist, Lysaker #1048/R (N.KR 3000)

DAEL, Jan Frans van (1764-1840) Dutch
£52778 $95000 €77056 Still life of roses in glass vase (46x37cm-18x15in) mono. panel prov. 22-Jan-4 Sotheby's, New York #105/R est:70000-100000
£55172 $91586 €80000 Composition with flowers and fruit (93x69cm-37x27in) s. 30-Sep-3 Ansorena, Madrid #32/R est:80000
£143357 $246573 €205000 Still life of mixed flowers in an earthenware pot on a marble table (73x60cm-29x24in) s. prov.exhib.lit. 2-Dec-3 Christie's, Paris #220/R est:150000-200000

DAELEN, Eduard (1848-?) German
£1733 $3103 €2600 Venus grotto (73x61cm-29x24in) s. i.d.1875 verso lit. 14-May-4 Schloss Ahlden, Ahlden #2891/R est:1800

DAEMS, P (1911-1982) ?
Works on paper
£436 $811 €650 Farmer in the city (64x50cm-25x20in) s.d.1936 W/C. 4-Mar-4 Auction Maastricht #1091/R

DAENS, Antoine (1871-1946) Belgian
£533 $981 €800 Ferme au bord de l'etang (49x60cm-19x24in) s.d.1917. 14-Jun-4 Horta, Bruxelles #212

DAEPP, Arnold Hans (1886-1949) Swiss
£617 $1048 €901 Lake Geneva (64x81cm-25x32in) s.d.46. 7-Nov-3 Dobiaschofsky, Bern #97/R (S.FR 1400)

DAFFARN, William George (fl.1872-1904) British
£260 $424 €380 Cornfield scene with figures (23x33cm-9x13in) s.d.1880 i.verso. 27-Sep-3 Rogers Jones, Clwyd #92

DAFFINGER, Moritz Michael (1790-1849) Austrian
Miniatures
£3472 $5903 €5000 Portrait of man (7x5cm-3x2in) s. book. 28-Oct-3 Wiener Kunst Auktionen, Vienna #25/R est:4000-10000
£4000 $7200 €5840 Grafin Henrietta Hunyady (8cm-3in) gild mount rec. velvet mount oval easel leather case exhib.lit. 22-Apr-4 Bonhams, New Bond Street #151/R est:6000-8000
£6500 $11245 €9490 Count Mikhail Semenovich Vorontsov (15x11cm-6x4in) s. ormolu frame prov. 9-Dec-3 Christie's, London #264/R est:3000-5000
£13423 $24027 €20000 Beautiful Viennese lady (9x8cm-4x3in) s. W/C ivory gold frame lit. 27-May-4 Hassfurther, Vienna #36/R est:12000-18000
£22222 $37778 €32000 Double portrait (7x6cm-3x2in) s. ivory two in one leather case. 28-Oct-3 Wiener Kunst Auktionen, Vienna #26/R est:10000-25000
£42000 $72660 €61320 Countess Elisaveta Ksaver'evna Vorontsova (9x8cm-4x3in) s. ormolu frame prov. 9-Dec-3 Christie's, London #263/R est:15000-20000
Works on paper
£695 $1266 €1050 Portrait of a gentleman (22x16cm-9x6in) s.d.1841 W/C ink pencil. 19-Jun-4 Quittenbaum, Hamburg #14
£944 $1700 €1378 Portrait of a young officer (24x18cm-9x7in) s. indis i. W/C on card. 21-Jan-4 Doyle, New York #10/R est:1000-1500

D'AGAR, Charles (1669-1723) French
£3500 $6440 €5110 Portrait of a boy in a lilac coat and red cloak (71x64cm-28x25in) 11-Jun-4 Christie's, London #7/R est:3000-5000

D'AGAR, Charles (attrib) (1669-1723) French
£3500 $6265 €5110 Portrait of a gentleman (136x101cm-54x40in) 26-May-4 Sotheby's, Olympia #14/R est:4000-6000
£16000 $27200 €23360 Portrait of Lady Elizabeth Germaine, daughter of Charles, 2nd Early of Berkeley (178x105cm-70x41in) i. prov. 25-Nov-3 Christie's, London #7/R est:6000-9000

D'AGAR, Jacob (attrib) (1642-1715) French
£13233 $22892 €19320 Small noble girl seated on terrace with her King Charles' spaniel (140x112cm-55x44in) prov. 9-Dec-3 Rasmussen, Copenhagen #1208/R est:150000-200000 (D.KR 140000)
£17905 $32766 €26141 Double portrait of Charlotte Amalie and Sophie Goye (126x103cm-50x41in) prov. 9-Jun-4 Rasmussen, Copenhagen #1406/R est:150000-200000 (D.KR 200000)

DAGIU, Francesco (1714-1784) Italian
£10067 $18523 €15000 St Lawrence (97x70cm-38x28in) prov. 24-Mar-4 Dorotheum, Vienna #62/R est:15000-20000

DAGNAC-RIVIERE, Charles (1864-1945) French
£532 $888 €750 Scene du rue (22x27cm-9x11in) s. 19-Jun-3 Millon & Associes, Paris #200/R
£638 $1066 €900 Une porte a Rabat (18x24cm-7x9in) s. panel. 19-Jun-3 Millon & Associes, Paris #201
£851 $1421 €1200 Rue de la mosquee au Caire (23x32cm-9x13in) s. st.mono.i.verso panel. 12-Oct-3 St-Germain-en-Laye Encheres #26/R

DAGNAN-BOUVERET, Pascal Adolphe Jean (1852-1929) French
£2123 $3610 €3100 Portrait de A J Meuneir Jeune (24x16cm-9x6in) st.sig.verso panel. 6-Nov-3 Rabourdin & Choppin de Janvry, Paris #31/R est:400-500
Works on paper
£329 $605 €500 Portrait de jeune femme (59x48cm-23x19in) s. pastel. 22-Jun-4 Ribeyre & Baron, Paris #42
£514 $873 €750 Madame Muenier (29x22cm-11x9in) s.i. crayon. 6-Nov-3 Rabourdin & Choppin de Janvry, Paris #66

DAGNAUX, Albert Marie (1861-1933) French
£350 $595 €511 Market day (35x25cm-14x10in) s. canvasboard. 6-Nov-3 Christie's, Kensington #838/R

DAGUERRE, Louis Jacques Mande (1787-1851) French
Works on paper
£6644 $11095 €9500 Ruines antiques dans un paysage imaginaire (5x11cm-2x4in) s. wash lit. 10-Oct-3 Tajan, Paris #1/R est:4500-5500

D'AGUILAR, Michael (20th C) ?
£231 $425 €337 Beach scene (38x53cm-15x21in) s. 27-Jun-4 Hindman, Chicago #903/R
£280 $518 €409 In the garden (46x61cm-18x24in) init. 15-Jan-4 Christie's, Kensington #995/R
£300 $555 €438 At the seaside (46x61cm-18x24in) init. s.d.verso board. 15-Jan-4 Christie's, Kensington #996/R
£550 $919 €803 At the dining room table (24x50cm-9x20in) s. s.d.1976 verso board. 16-Oct-3 Christie's, Kensington #332/R

DAHAN, Marc Alain (?) French?
£490 $832 €700 Night-mare court (64x80cm-25x31in) acrylic collage wood. 27-Nov-3 Calmels Cohen, Paris #63

DAHL, Anton (19th C) Scandinavian
£1000 $1700 €1460 Danish landscape (91x130cm-36x51in) 29-Nov-3 Carlsen Gallery, Greenville #634/R

DAHL, Carl (1813-1862) German
£3025 $5233 €4417 Copenhagen Harbour (17x25cm-7x10in) 9-Dec-3 Rasmussen, Copenhagen #1574/R est:10000 (D.KR 32000)
£3133 $5734 €4574 Sailing ship at anchor by a warehouse (37x50cm-15x20in) prov. 9-Jun-4 Rasmussen, Copenhagen #1828/R est:30000-40000 (D.KR 35000)
Works on paper
£561 $886 €813 View through gate to Gjorslev Manor, hunter with gun in foreground (35x33cm-14x13in) s.d.1/48 pen grey wash. 2-Sep-3 Rasmussen, Copenhagen #2018/R (D.KR 6000)

DAHL, Hans (1849-1937) Norwegian
£257 $471 €375 Portrait of woman (38x41cm-15x16in) s. 2-Feb-4 Blomqvist, Lysaker #1038/R (N.KR 3200)
£591 $1058 €863 Sunset at Sognefjord (24x41cm-9x16in) s.d.aug.87 panel. 28-May-4 Uppsala Auktionskammare, Uppsala #141/R (S.KR 8000)
£601 $1052 €877 Boat by shore (25x21cm-10x8in) s. panel. 16-Dec-3 Grev Wedels Plass, Oslo #145/R (N.KR 7000)
£901 $1622 €1315 Cottages by the sea (62x89cm-24x35in) s.d.1899. 26-Jan-4 Lilla Bukowskis, Stockholm #236 (S.KR 12000)
£1552 $2778 €2266 Sailing dinghy at sea (42x54cm-17x21in) s. 25-May-4 Bukowskis, Stockholm #334/R est:30000-35000 (S.KR 21000)
£2039 $3650 €2977 Lady wearing straw hat (39x25cm-15x10in) s.d.18 Mai 75 canvas on panel. 25-May-4 Grev Wedels Plass, Oslo #4/R est:30000 (N.KR 25000)
£2039 $3650 €2977 Two small girls by Stryns Lake (29x44cm-11x17in) s. canvas on panel. 25-May-4 Grev Wedels Plass, Oslo #5/R est:30000-40000 (N.KR 25000)
£2432 $4281 €3600 Mountain landscape with fortress (55x90cm-22x35in) s.d.82 prov. 22-May-4 Lempertz, Koln #1492/R est:6000
£2692 $4631 €3930 Mountain landscape with country girl (49x66cm-19x26in) s. 2-Dec-3 Bukowskis, Stockholm #265/R est:30000-40000 (S.KR 35000)
£3433 $6009 €5012 A pleasant trip - figures in boat on fjord (56x39cm-22x15in) s. i. stretcher. 16-Dec-3 Grev Wedels Plass, Oslo #345/R est:40000 (N.KR 40000)
£3763 $7000 €5494 Portrait of girl in alpine meadow holding scythe (109x81cm-43x32in) s. 3-Mar-4 Alderfer's, Hatfield #312/R est:4000-6000
£4500 $8190 €6570 Young harvester at a sunlit fjord (109x81cm-43x32in) s. 16-Jun-4 Christie's, Kensington #193/R est:4000-6000
£6818 $12000 €9954 In the fjords of Norway (66x99cm-26x39in) s. 18-May-4 Bonhams & Butterfields, San Francisco #90/R est:6000-8000
£7042 $12183 €10000 Carefree youth (99x66cm-39x26in) s. 10-Dec-3 Christie's, Amsterdam #676/R est:5000-7000
£8741 $14598 €12500 Peasant girls flirting on shore of fjord (100x66cm-39x26in) i. stretcher. 28-Jun-3 Bolland & Marotz, Bremen #630/R est:4500
£10000 $18000 €14600 Last rays of the sun (56x92cm-22x36in) s. 22-Apr-4 Christie's, Rockefeller NY #2/R est:15000-20000
£10052 $17993 €14676 Rowing to church (90x144cm-35x57in) s. 26-May-4 AB Stockholms Auktionsverk #2390/R est:175000-200000 (S.KR 136000)
£11209 $20064 €16365 By the estuary, western Norway (66x99cm-26x39in) s.i. i.stretcher. 22-Mar-4 Blomqvist, Oslo #331/R est:120000-150000 (N.KR 140000)
£15500 $28210 €22630 Summer day on a Norwegian fjord (99x67cm-39x26in) s.i. 15-Jun-4 Sotheby's, London #368/R est:10000-15000
£52000 $94640 €75920 Upon sunny waters (113x188cm-44x74in) s.i. prov. 15-Jun-4 Sotheby's, London #355/R est:30000-50000
Works on paper
£488 $898 €732 Sailing on the fjord. s. W/C. 14-Jun-4 Blomqvist, Lysaker #1064 (N.KR 6000)

DAHL, Hans Andreas (1881-1919) Norwegian
£620 $1035 €905 View of Fjord. Sketch of shed (28x39cm-11x15in) s. one d.1905 canvas on board pair. 12-Nov-3 Sotheby's, Olympia #206/R
£1500 $2685 €2190 Sunny day, Sogne Fjord, Norway (30x40cm-12x16in) s. board. 26-May-4 Sotheby's, Olympia #329/R est:2000-4000
£1500 $2685 €2190 Glimpse of Naro fjord, Norway (40x30cm-16x12in) s. 26-May-4 Sotheby's, Olympia #332/R est:2000-4000
£1959 $3370 €2860 Winter's day, North Vestlandet (39x50cm-15x20in) s. panel. 8-Dec-3 Blomqvist, Oslo #445/R est:20000-25000 (N.KR 23000)
£2217 $3969 €3237 Girl and man by beached rowing boat in fjord landscape (31x46cm-12x18in) s. panel. 28-May-4 Uppsala Auktionskammare, Uppsala #157/R est:20000-25000 (S.KR 30000)
£2600 $4654 €3796 Geiranger fjord, Norway (41x30cm-16x12in) s. 26-May-4 Sotheby's, Olympia #331/R est:2000-4000
£3416 $5705 €4987 On the fjord in a boat (79x54cm-31x21in) s. 13-Oct-3 Blomqvist, Oslo #272/R est:60000-70000 (N.KR 40000)

DAHL, I C (19th C) Danish
£2516 $4679 €3673 Landscape in Oberlausitz, storm approaching (27x40cm-11x16in) prov. 2-Mar-4 Rasmussen, Copenhagen #1326/R est:20000 (D.KR 28000)

DAHL, Ingerid (1861-1944) Norwegian
£555 $927 €810 Interior scene with two figures (42x32cm-17x13in) s. indist.i.d.17 verso. 13-Oct-3 Blomqvist, Oslo #250/R (N.KR 6500)

DAHL, J (1825-1890) Danish
£890 $1451 €1299 Ship's portrait of Jylland af Assens (55x73cm-22x29in) s.d.1889. 28-Sep-3 Hindemae, Ullerslev #135/R (D.KR 9500)

DAHL, J C C (1788-1857) Norwegian
Works on paper
£412 $709 €602 Study of pine tree on edge of cliff (19x12cm-7x5in) mono.i.d.1828 pencil. 3-Dec-3 Museumsbygningen, Copenhagen #129/R (D.KR 4400)
£2246 $4178 €3279 Seascape with vessels (20x32cm-8x13in) s.d.1824 pen W/C. 2-Mar-4 Rasmussen, Copenhagen #1688/R est:25000 (D.KR 25000)

DAHL, Johan Christian Clausen (1788-1857) Norwegian
£3691 $6792 €5500 Seascapes (16x30cm-6x12in) cardboard pair. 27-Mar-4 Farsetti, Prato #283/R est:6500
£4054 $7135 €6000 Villa Quisisana and Gulf of Naples (72x11cm-28x4in) board prov.lit. 22-May-4 Lempertz, Koln #1493/R est:7000
£4895 $8322 €7000 Romantic river landscape (44x50cm-17x20in) panel lit. 28-Nov-3 Schloss Ahlden, Ahlden #1386/R est:3200
£6165 $11035 €9001 Landscape with sawmill, Kaupanger (7x11cm-3x4in) s.d.1847 prov.exhib.lit. 22-Mar-4 Blomqvist, Oslo #302/R est:45000-55000 (N.KR 77000)
£10764 $17545 €15500 Shipwreck (39x66cm-15x26in) s. bears d.823 paper on panel. 24-Sep-3 Neumeister, Munich #409/R est:8000
£11209 $20064 €16365 Norwegian landscape (27x24cm-11x9in) s.d.1815 lit. 22-Mar-4 Blomqvist, Oslo #319/R est:150000-170000 (N.KR 140000)
£14518 $24244 €21196 Coastal landscape with Moen's Klint (10x16cm-4x6in) s.d.1828 paper on canvas prov.lit. 13-Oct-3 Blomqvist, Oslo #256/R est:110000-130000 (N.KR 170000)
£15436 $28711 €23000 Mountainous landscape with figures on bridge (78x62cm-31x24in) s.d.1814. 8-Mar-4 Bernaerts, Antwerp #82/R est:15000-20000
£18000 $32760 €26280 Nordic landscape with a lake (24x17cm-9x7in) s.d.1821 paper on canvas prov.lit. 15-Jun-4 Sotheby's, London #303/R est:15000-20000
£19165 $32964 €27981 River landscape (21x35cm-8x14in) s.d.1851 paper on paper prov.exhib.lit. 8-Dec-3 Blomqvist, Oslo #436/R est:100000-120000 (N.KR 225000)
£20000 $36400 €29200 View from Krokkleiva, Norway (31x24cm-12x9in) s.d.1828 prov.exhib.lit. 15-Jun-4 Sotheby's, London #304/R est:20000-30000
£33000 $60060 €48180 Ruins near Baia (26x37cm-10x15in) indis.s. d.1822 i.verso lit. 15-Jun-4 Sotheby's, London #302/R est:20000-30000
£33333 $61000 €48666 Study with brook (31x36cm-12x14in) s.i.d.Octbr.1832 prov.exhib.lit. 7-Jun-4 Blomqvist, Oslo #354/R est:150000-200000 (N.KR 410000)
£36111 $65000 €52722 Figure in a morning coat and top hat, seen from behind (20x16cm-8x6in) s.d.20 Januar 1821 oil paper on board prov.exhib.lit. 22-Jan-4 Christie's, Rockefeller NY #151/R est:20000-30000
£39024 $71415 €56975 Shipwreck by the coast at Kullen (21x31cm-8x12in) s.d.1829 prov.exhib.lit. 7-Jun-4 Blomqvist, Oslo #319/R est:250000-350000 (N.KR 480000)
Works on paper
£1016 $1860 €1483 Man lying down (13x20cm-5x8in) s.d.1819 Indian ink. 7-Jun-4 Blomqvist, Oslo #321/R (N.KR 12500)

DAHL, Johan Christian Clausen (attrib) (1788-1857) Norwegian
Works on paper
£268 $494 €400 Norwegian landscape (28x44cm-11x17in) pencil. 26-Mar-4 Bolland & Marotz, Bremen #394/R

DAHL, Jorgen (1825-1890) Danish
£1522 $2785 €2222 Sailing vessels off Skagen's new lighthouse (58x83cm-23x33in) s.d.1885 prov. 9-Jun-4 Rasmussen, Copenhagen #1813/R est:20000-25000 (D.KR 17000)
£3279 $6000 €4787 Danish barque Maria Aistrup of Frederikshavn under reduced sail (57x84cm-22x33in) s.i.d.1881. 29-Jul-4 Christie's, Rockefeller NY #250/R est:7000-9000

DAHL, Michael (1656-1743) Swedish
£1223 $1969 €1786 Portrait of Sir Thomas Bootle (125x99cm-49x39in) 25-Aug-3 Lilla Bukowskis, Stockholm #744 est:20000-25000 (S.KR 16000)
£1478 $2646 €2158 Portrait of an English vicar (127x103cm-50x41in) s.d.1734 prov. 25-May-4 Bukowskis, Stockholm #516/R est:20000-25000 (S.KR 20000)
£2198 $4000 €3209 Portrait of Sir Cholmeley Dering, M P for Kent, wearing a green jacket (127x102cm-50x40in) 4-Feb-4 Christie's, Rockefeller NY #113/R est:5000-7000
£2686 $4915 €3922 Nobel gentleman wearing wig (127x102cm-50x40in) s. 9-Jun-4 Rasmussen, Copenhagen #1549/R est:30000 (D.KR 30000)
£5846 $10055 €8535 Charles Duke of Marlborough white Earl of Sunderland (233x145cm-92x57in) bears i. prov.lit. 3-Dec-3 AB Stockholms Auktionsverk #2729/R est:40000-50000 (S.KR 76000)
£6000 $10740 €8760 Portrait of Admiral Sir Thomas Hardy with a telescope in his right hand (127x112cm-50x44in) prov. 26-May-4 Christie's, Kensington #574/R est:3000-5000
£7800 $14274 €11388 Portrait of a young lady, said to be Lady Anne, daughter of Archibald Campbell (123x101cm-48x40in) prov. 8-Jul-4 Lawrence, Crewkerne #1596/R est:7500-10000
£15363 $27500 €22430 Portrait of Queen Anne (128x102cm-50x40in) prov. 27-May-4 Sotheby's, New York #218/R est:15000-20000

DAHL, Michael (after) (1656-1743) Swedish
£6000 $10200 €8760 Portrait of Henrietta Hobart, Countess of Suffolk (71x59cm-28x23in) 27-Nov-3 Sotheby's, London #137/R est:2000-3000

DAHL, Michael (attrib) (1656-1743) Swedish
£1600 $2928 €2336 Portrait of Mr Grosvenor (76x63cm-30x25in) oval lit. 8-Jul-4 Sotheby's, London #221/R est:2000-3000
£1900 $3477 €2774 Portrait of Mrs Mostyn (76x63cm-30x25in) oval lit. 8-Jul-4 Sotheby's, London #223/R est:2000-3000
£2000 $3600 €2920 Portrait of William Harvey, Mayor of Norwich (73x61cm-29x24in) prov. 21-Jan-4 Sotheby's, Olympia #13/R est:2000-3000
£2200 $4026 €3212 Portrait of Mrs Mostyn (76x63cm-30x25in) oval lit. 8-Jul-4 Sotheby's, London #222/R est:2000-3000
£4200 $7686 €6132 Portrait of a lady, said to be Elizabeth Gurney (123x103cm-48x41in) 7-Jul-4 Bonhams, New Bond Street #52/R est:3000-4000

DAHL, Michael (circle) (1656-1743) Swedish
£6500 $10270 €9425 Portrait of a lady, thought to be Mrs Levinz, seated in a blue dress (127x102cm-50x40in) 4-Sep-3 Christie's, Kensington #26/R est:2000-3000

DAHL, Peter (1934-) Swedish/Norwegian
£430 $701 €628 Landscape with white house (54x65cm-21x26in) s.d.59. 29-Sep-3 Lilla Bukowskis, Stockholm #933 (S.KR 5600)
£1888 $3210 €2756 Moonlight (67x73cm-26x29in) s.d.56. 4-Nov-3 Bukowskis, Stockholm #596/R est:20000-25000 (S.KR 25000)
£2956 $5292 €4316 Against the red wallpaper - from an inn with beer bottles and figures (146x194cm-57x76in) s.d.76. 28-May-4 Uppsala Auktionskammare, Uppsala #325/R est:50000-60000 (S.KR 40000)
£3097 $5264 €4522 Papuan shoes (65x54cm-26x21in) s.d.65 oil tempera. 5-Nov-3 AB Stockholms Auktionsverk #1058/R est:35000-40000 (S.KR 41000)
£10574 $17976 €15438 The triumph II (73x100cm-29x39in) s.d.74 exhib.lit. 4-Nov-3 Bukowskis, Stockholm #599/R est:150000-175000 (S.KR 140000)
£14286 $25286 €20858 Do we dare to greet all the elegant visitors? (91x100cm-36x39in) s.d.70 exhib. 27-Apr-4 AB Stockholms Auktionsverk #1078/R est:125000-150000 (S.KR 195000)
Works on paper
£1160 $2088 €1694 Untitled (41x30cm-16x12in) s. W/C. 26-Apr-4 Bukowskis, Stockholm #592/R est:12000-15000 (S.KR 16000)
£1284 $2183 €1875 Woman (39x30cm-15x12in) s. W/C. 5-Nov-3 AB Stockholms Auktionsverk #1044/R est:15000-20000 (S.KR 17000)
£2115 $3595 €3088 Nude study (72x53cm-28x21in) s. W/C. 4-Nov-3 Bukowskis, Stockholm #597/R est:15000-20000 (S.KR 28000)
£2341 $3980 €3418 The embrace (72x46cm-28x18in) s. W/C. 4-Nov-3 Bukowskis, Stockholm #598/R est:15000-20000 (S.KR 31000)

DAHL, Sigwald Johannes (1827-1902) Norwegian
£1987 $3636 €3000 Parrot on perch with monkey stealing seeds (36x27cm-14x11in) s.d.10. Januar 1865 board. 8-Apr-4 Dorotheum, Vienna #267/R est:2000-2300
£2079 $3597 €3035 Injured stag on woodland ground (84x99cm-33x39in) s.d.1852 prov. 9-Dec-3 Rasmussen, Copenhagen #1423/R est:20000-30000 (D.KR 22000)
£8098 $13928 €11823 Birds on sheaf of oats (82x67cm-32x26in) s. 8-Dec-3 Blomqvist, Oslo #434/R est:120000-150000 (N.KR 95070)
£21739 $37609 €31739 Patrie aus Telemarken in Norwegen (86x112cm-34x44in) s.d.1865 prov. 9-Dec-3 Rasmussen, Copenhagen #1227/R est:100000-150000 (D.KR 230000)
Works on paper
£2273 $3773 €3296 Fox in winter landscape (36x51cm-14x20in) s.d.1870 W/C. 13-Jun-3 Zofingen, Switzerland #2435/R est:2000 (S.FR 5000)

DAHL, Sigwald Johannes (attrib) (1827-1902) Norwegian
£486 $792 €700 Italian landscape (22x30cm-9x12in) i. verso panel. 25-Sep-3 Dr Fritz Nagel, Stuttgart #1300/R

DAHL-WOLFE, Louise (1895-1989) American
Photographs
£2515 $4200 €3672 Hammamet, Bazaar, Tunisie (34x26cm-13x10in) i.d.1950 verso gelatin silver print printed later prov.lit. 20-Oct-3 Christie's, Rockefeller NY #87/R est:3000-5000
£2695 $4500 €3935 Jacqueline and John Kennedy (27x30cm-11x12in) gelatin silver print exec.c.1958 prov. 20-Oct-3 Christie's, Rockefeller NY #69/R est:3000-5000

DAHLAGER, Jules (20th C) American
£4011 $7500 €5856 Home of a sourdough (30x23cm-12x9in) s. board prov. 24-Jul-4 Coeur d'Alene, Hayden #148/R est:4000-6000

DAHLBERG, Brian (20th C) New Zealander?
£906 $1458 €1323 Body, mind and spirit (64x121cm-25x48in) s.i.verso canvas on board. 12-Aug-3 Peter Webb, Auckland #171/R (NZ.D 2500)

DAHLBERG, Jens Edward (1813-1897) Danish
£1968 $3385 €2873 Standing genius (73x49cm-29x19in) after Berthel Thorvaldsen prov. 3-Dec-3 Museumsbygningen, Copenhagen #122/R est:12000-15000 (D.KR 21000)

DAHLBOM, Wilhelm (1855-1928) Swedish
£276 $496 €414 Coastal landscape with boat houses and boats (33x50cm-13x20in) s.i.d.1909. 25-Apr-4 Goteborg Auktionsverk, Sweden #204/R (S.KR 3800)
£351 $657 €512 Landscape with cows by lake (69x88cm-27x35in) s.d.1896. 29-Feb-4 Uppsala Auktionskammare, Uppsala #344 (S.KR 4800)
£676 $1209 €1000 Cattle watering (70x90cm-28x35in) s.d.1896. 8-May-4 Bukowskis, Helsinki #372/R

DAHLEN, Reiner (1836-1874) German
£550 $875 €798 Man in an extensive winter landscape (25x44cm-10x17in) s. panel. 9-Sep-3 Bonhams, Knightsbridge #239/R

DAHLGREN, Carl Christian (1841-1920) American
£294 $550 €429 Sunset amongst the redwoods (112x76cm-44x30in) s.indis.i. 29-Feb-4 Bonhams & Butterfields, San Francisco #4531
£586 $950 €856 Sunlight on a wooded river landscape (51x36cm-20x14in) s. 9-Aug-3 Auctions by the Bay, Alameda #1485/R
£652 $1200 €952 Path through the eucalyptus trees (30x40cm-12x16in) s. 8-Jun-4 Auctions by the Bay, Alameda #1082/R

DAHLIN, Dorte (1955-) Danish
£733 $1333 €1070 Dracula (100x205cm-39x81in) s.d.1988 verso oil asphalt lit.prov. 7-Feb-4 Rasmussen, Havnen #4226 (D.KR 8000)

DAHLING, Heinrich Anton (1773-1850) German
£93960 $172886 €140000 Entrance of Napoleon I in Berlin through Brandenburg Gate (48x68cm-19x27in) two prov. 24-Mar-4 Dorotheum, Vienna #280/R

DAHLMAN, Helge (1924-1979) Finnish
£417 $696 €600 Town (46x55cm-18x22in) s.d.1960. 23-Oct-3 Hagelstam, Helsinki #826/R
£671 $1248 €1000 Day in spring (10x17cm-4x7in) s. 7-Mar-4 Bukowskis, Helsinki #306/R
£743 $1330 €1100 Autumn landscape, Kylaniemi (18x22cm-7x9in) s.d.71 board. 8-May-4 Bukowskis, Helsinki #79/R
£810 $1296 €1150 Folis Island (20x29cm-8x11in) s. 18-Sep-3 Hagelstam, Helsinki #846
£946 $1693 €1400 Coastal landscape, Edeviken, Helsingfors (22x27cm-9x11in) s.d.70 board. 8-May-4 Bukowskis, Helsinki #136/R
£1056 $1827 €1500 Landscape (27x33cm-11x13in) s.d.1966 board. 13-Dec-3 Hagelstam, Helsinki #165/R est:1000
£1081 $1935 €1600 Winter landscape (27x35cm-11x14in) s.d.70 board. 8-May-4 Bukowskis, Helsinki #42/R est:1500-1700
£1081 $1935 €1600 A calm day (24x36cm-9x14in) s.d.66 board. 8-May-4 Bukowskis, Helsinki #121/R est:1500-1800
£1127 $1803 €1600 Still life (46x55cm-18x22in) s. 18-Sep-3 Hagelstam, Helsinki #856/R est:1000
£1200 $2208 €1800 The jetty (22x27cm-9x11in) s.d.74 i.verso. 9-Jun-4 Bukowskis, Helsinki #366/R est:1800
£1972 $3411 €2800 Landscape from Brunnsparken (19x33cm-7x13in) s. panel. 13-Dec-3 Hagelstam, Helsinki #164/R est:1500

DAHLSKOG, Evald (1894-1950) Swedish
£2341 $3980 €3418 Palermo (73x92cm-29x36in) s.i.d.1927. 4-Nov-3 Bukowskis, Stockholm #83/R est:25000-30000 (S.KR 31000)
£3550 $6035 €5183 Landscape (70x80cm-28x31in) s.d.18. 4-Nov-3 Bukowskis, Stockholm #82/R est:30000-35000 (S.KR 47000)

DAHLSTROM, Carl Andreas (1806-1869) Swedish
£1037 $1690 €1514 Review of troops at Ladugardsgardet with Carl XIV Johan (61x94cm-24x37in) panel. 29-Sep-3 Lilla Bukowskis, Stockholm #196 (S.KR 13500)

DAHM, H P C (1787-1844) Danish
Works on paper
£2033 $3720 €2968 Ship's portrait Varig Vennskap of Tonsberg (47x65cm-19x26in) s. gouache. 7-Jun-4 Blomqvist, Oslo #288/R est:30000-40000 (N.KR 25000)

DAHM, Helen (1878-1968) Swiss
£1086 $1738 €1586 Landscape with woman and foal (54x54cm-21x21in) s. paper on board. 16-Sep-3 Philippe Schuler, Zurich #3232/R est:1600-2000 (S.FR 2400)
£1835 $3064 €2661 Blue, black angel (107x91cm-42x36in) s. 23-Jun-3 Philippe Schuler, Zurich #3385 est:4000-5000 (S.FR 4000)
Works on paper
£181 $308 €264 Lilies and poppies (52x33cm-20x13in) s.d. mixed media col lithograph. 18-Nov-3 Hans Widmer, St Gallen #1280 (S.FR 400)
£339 $567 €495 Easter - still life (54x40cm-21x16in) s.d.1954 pastel. 24-Jun-3 Germann, Zurich #936/R (S.FR 750)
£362 $579 €529 Nun (33x26cm-13x10in) s. chl pencil col pen. 16-Sep-3 Philippe Schuler, Zurich #3141 (S.FR 800)
£452 $756 €660 Woman with dog (25x26cm-10x10in) s.d.1915 chk. 24-Jun-3 Germann, Zurich #934/R (S.FR 1000)
£568 $1045 €829 Candles with Christmas tree baubles (29x17cm-11x7in) s.i.d. pastel chk. 14-Jun-4 Philippe Schuler, Zurich #4123 (S.FR 1300)
£742 $1366 €1083 Still life with tulips, fruit and cat (62x48cm-24x19in) s. pastel chk. 14-Jun-4 Philippe Schuler, Zurich #4121/R (S.FR 1700)
£749 $1273 €1094 Still life of flowers (64x51cm-25x20in) s.d.1944 mixed media. 7-Nov-3 Dobiaschofsky, Bern #166/R (S.FR 1700)
£1048 $1676 €1520 Animal (17x21cm-7x8in) W/C pencil. 15-May-3 Stuker, Bern #1137/R (S.FR 2200)
£1704 $2846 €2488 Still life with twigs of blossom in vase (115x68cm-45x27in) s. mixed media. 24-Oct-3 Hans Widmer, St Gallen #15/R est:3500-6500 (S.FR 3800)
£2412 $4439 €3522 Lilies on blue table (99x69cm-39x27in) s. mixed media. 23-Jun-4 Koller, Zurich #3100/R est:6000-8000 (S.FR 5500)

DAHMEN, Karl-Fred (1917-1981) German
£2958 $5117 €4200 Terrestrial (52x45cm-20x18in) s. s.d.1960 mixed media hessian. 13-Dec-3 Lempertz, Koln #125/R est:3000
£3200 $5728 €4800 Untitled (46x62cm-18x24in) s. oil W/C dispersion sand paper on board collage prov. 14-May-4 Ketterer, Munich #240/R est:2800-3000
£3800 $6042 €5510 Ohne titel (81x72cm-32x28in) s. s.d.1963 verso oil wax crayon metal fabric collage on canvas p. 11-Sep-3 Christie's, Kensington #221/R est:4000-6000
£5667 $10370 €8500 Earthlike composition III (95x80cm-37x31in) s.d.57 s.i.d. stretcher oil sand exhib.lit. 4-Jun-4 Lempertz, Koln #102/R est:5500-6000
Sculpture
£1467 $2699 €2200 Reduction of a landscape (35x28cm-14x11in) s.i.d.1974 verso objects in frame. 12-Jun-4 Villa Grisebach, Berlin #704/R est:1200-1500
£1538 $2615 €2200 Tied up (29x25x7cm-11x10x3in) s. s.i.d.1976 verso cushion panel leather canvas col. 27-Nov-3 Lempertz, Koln #99/R est:2000
£4000 $7160 €6000 Composition (71x46x11cm-28x18x4in) s.i.d. verso. 15-May-4 Van Ham, Cologne #536/R est:6000
Works on paper
£694 $1160 €1000 Untitled (27x21cm-11x8in) s.i.d.25.4.80 verso sand oil pastel chk panel prov. 24-Oct-3 Ketterer, Hamburg #310/R
£2238 $3849 €3200 Untitled (61x48cm-24x19in) s. collage mixed media exec.1962 lit. 4-Dec-3 Van Ham, Cologne #110/R est:3800
£2667 $4880 €4000 Untitled (44x37cm-17x15in) s.d.1978 mixed media panel. 4-Jun-4 Lempertz, Koln #103/R est:3800
£4667 $8587 €7000 Ultramarine (74x84cm-29x33in) s.d.56 s.i.d.verso mixed media panel prov. 12-Jun-4 Villa Grisebach, Berlin #349/R est:7000-9000
£4895 $8322 €7000 Black gorge (96x70cm-38x28in) s. s.d.1960 verso mixed media oil sand canvas. 29-Nov-3 Arnold, Frankfurt #114/R est:6000

DAHMS, Paul W (1913-1988) Swedish
£255 $392 €400 Pheasants by stream in winter (24x30cm-9x12in) 4-Sep-2 Schopman, Hamburg #89/R
£322 $570 €480 Three pheasants (40x50cm-16x20in) s. lit. 30-Apr-4 Auktionhaus Georg Rehm, Augsburg #8012

DAHN, Walter (1954-) German
£302 $535 €450 Ivy annulus (110x114cm-43x45in) st.sig. acrylic. 30-Apr-4 Dr Fritz Nagel, Stuttgart #88/R
£369 $653 €550 Untitled (145x99cm-57x39in) st.sig. linen. 30-Apr-4 Dr Fritz Nagel, Stuttgart #89/R
£5000 $9150 €7500 Accident with curtain - for George Condo (260x220cm-102x87in) s.d.1984 acrylic cotton prov.exhib.lit. 4-Jun-4 Lempertz, Koln #106/R est:8000-10000
£6000 $10980 €9000 Composition (200x150cm-79x59in) s.d.86 verso prov. 4-Jun-4 Lempertz, Koln #107/R est:6000
Works on paper
£293 $519 €428 Saturn phase II (20x14cm-8x6in) s.d.85 W/C. 27-Apr-4 AB Stockholms Auktionsverk #1088/R (S.KR 4000)
£452 $756 €660 Untitled (29x21cm-11x8in) s.d.1987 mixed media. 24-Jun-3 Germann, Zurich #937/R (S.FR 1000)

DAHN, Walter and DOKOUPIL, Jiri Georg (20th C) German/Czech
£4333 $7930 €6500 Untitled (160x135cm-63x53in) s.d.81 acrylic prov. 4-Jun-4 Lempertz, Koln #108/R est:5000

DAI BENXIAO (1621-1693) Chinese
Works on paper
£90734 $151525 €132472 Landscapes in the styles of ancient masters (28x17cm-11x7in) eight s. i.d.1686 ink col ten leaves album. 27-Oct-3 Sotheby's, Hong Kong #320/R est:900000-1200000 (HK.D 1175000)

DAI JUN (18th C) Chinese
Works on paper
£490 $842 €700 River landscape with farm houses in the foreground (37x47cm-15x19in) s.i.d.1737 or 1797 hanging scroll. 5-Dec-3 Lempertz, Koln #240

DAILLION, Horace (1854-1937) French
Sculpture
£1523 $2772 €2300 The source (65cm-26in) s.st.f. Medaille d'Or pat bronze exec. painted 1900. 19-Jun-4 Hans Stahl, Hamburg #357/R est:2000
£3800 $6460 €5548 Triomphe (126cm-50in) s. pat bronze lit. 28-Oct-3 Sotheby's, London #182/R est:4000-6000

DAINGERFIELD, Elliott (1859-1932) American
£915 $1500 €1327 Portrait of a black man (66x51cm-26x20in) i.verso. 2-Jun-3 Grogan, Boston #647/R
£5294 $9000 €7729 Sunrise (25x30cm-10x12in) s. board. 22-Nov-3 New Orleans Auction, New Orleans #1070/R est:6000-9000
£7182 $13000 €10486 Straw girl (43x41cm-17x16in) indis.sig. 31-Mar-4 Sotheby's, New York #50/R est:2500-3500
£7821 $14000 €11419 Goose girl (30x41cm-12x16in) s. board prov. 6-May-4 Shannon's, Milford #29/R est:6000-8000
£12784 $22500 €18665 Spirit of the night (51x41cm-20x16in) s. prov. 19-May-4 Sotheby's, New York #87/R est:10000-15000
£17045 $30000 €24886 Grand Canyon, moonlight (91x76cm-36x30in) s. prov. 19-May-4 Sotheby's, New York #88/R est:30000-50000

DAINI, Augusto (1860-1920) Italian
£400 $664 €584 Good news (41x30cm-16x12in) s. 1-Oct-3 Woolley & Wallis, Salisbury #178/R
£1173 $2100 €1713 His proposal (70x46cm-28x18in) s. 14-May-4 Skinner, Boston #55/R est:2000-3000
Works on paper
£500 $885 €730 Goatherder's courtship (74x54cm-29x21in) s.i. pencil W/C. 29-Apr-4 Christie's, Kensington #64

DAINI, Rita (1954-) Venezuelan
Sculpture
£625 $1119 €913 Striding male nude (46cm-18in) s. num.1/6 base dark brown pat bronze. 22-Mar-4 Waddingtons, Toronto #618/R est:400-600 (C.D 1500)

DAINTREY, Adrian (1902-1988) British
£280 $476 €409 Summer garden, Bermuda (35x45cm-14x18in) canvasboard. 4-Nov-3 Bonhams, New Bond Street #129a
£380 $684 €555 Margaretta Terrace, Chelsea (78x75cm-31x30in) s.d.1946 board prov.exhib. 21-Apr-4 Cheffins, Cambridge #516
£550 $990 €803 Oakley Street, Chelsea (40x50cm-16x20in) s.d.1946 prov.exhib. 21-Apr-4 Cheffins, Cambridge #515
£750 $1350 €1095 Power station (64x76cm-25x30in) s. 20-Jan-4 Bonhams, Knightsbridge #60/R
£750 $1320 €1095 On the beach (26x76cm-10x30in) s. board. 18-May-4 Bonhams, Knightsbridge #68/R
£750 $1403 €1095 Le Havre (54x67cm-21x26in) 21-Jul-4 Bonhams, New Bond Street #171/R
£2400 $4080 €3504 Bothy, Culham Court, Henley-on-Thames (33x41cm-13x16in) panel painted c.1938-40 prov. 21-Nov-3 Christie's, London #53/R est:1000-1500

DAINVILLE, Maurice (1856-1930) French
£352 $567 €500 Andresselles (27x46cm-11x18in) s.i. 11-May-3 Versailles Encheres #107
£366 $656 €534 Two obelisks in harem (41x32cm-16x13in) s.i.d.1881. 12-May-4 Dobiaschofsky, Bern #3511 (S.FR 850)
£387 $624 €550 Untitled (27x46cm-11x18in) s. 11-May-3 Versailles Encheres #106

DAIWAILLE, Alexander Joseph (1818-1888) Dutch
£12162 $21405 €18000 Snowy landscape. Mountain landscape (23x27cm-9x11in) s.d.1848 panel two. 22-May-4 Lempertz, Koln #1496/R est:22000
£17450 $31235 €26000 Patineurs dans un paysage d'hiver (50x72cm-20x28in) s. 25-May-4 Campo & Campo, Antwerp #51/R est:6000-10000

DAIWAILLE, Alexander Joseph and VERBOECKHOVEN, Eugène (19th C) Dutch/Belgian
£10056 $18000 €14682 Tending the herd (53x79cm-21x31in) s. prov. 6-May-4 Shannon's, Milford #146/R est:20000-30000
£14118 $24000 €20612 Pastoral scene (74x102cm-29x40in) s. 29-Oct-3 Christie's, Rockefeller NY #9/R est:30000-40000

DAKE, Carel Lodewijk (jnr) (1886-1946) Dutch
£263 $476 €400 Shepherd with a flock of sheep (56x67cm-22x26in) s. 19-Apr-4 Glerum, Amsterdam #238/R
£342 $582 €500 Paddy field (58x72cm-23x28in) s. board. 5-Nov-3 Vendue Huis, Gravenhage #541/R
£408 $731 €600 Houses at the foot of a mountain (18x30cm-7x12in) s. cardboard. 16-Mar-4 Christie's, Amsterdam #42
£2381 $4262 €3500 Entrance to a temple complex (51x82cm-20x32in) s. panel. 16-Mar-4 Christie's, Amsterdam #31/R est:1500-2000

DAKEN, Sidney Tilden (1876-1935) American
£313 $500 €457 Indians exploring Yosemite. s. 20-Sep-3 Harvey Clar, Oakland #1274

DAKON (?) ?
Sculpture
£2000 $3180 €2920 Head of lady (30cm-12in) s. bronze exec.c.1930 marble plinth. 9-Sep-3 Sotheby's, Olympia #380/R est:1200-1500

DAL BO, Zaccaria (1872-1935) Italian
£7183 $12427 €10200 Venetian view (73x93cm-29x37in) s. 9-Dec-3 Finarte Semenzato, Milan #78/R est:10500-11000

DAL, Harald (1901-1972) Norwegian
£492 $905 €718 Rapids with timber (67x61cm-26x24in) s. 29-Mar-4 Blomqvist, Lysaker #1037 (N.KR 6200)
£3415 $6249 €4986 Landscape (102x140cm-40x55in) s.d.47 s.i.stretcher prov.exhib.lit. 7-Jun-4 Blomqvist, Oslo #420/R est:20000-25000 (N.KR 42000)
£3833 $6593 €5596 Old landslip (100x130cm-39x51in) s.i.d.1959-66 verso. 8-Dec-3 Blomqvist, Oslo #510/R est:40000-50000 (N.KR 45000)

DALBANNE, Claude (1877-1964) French
£336 $617 €500 Composition (22x27cm-9x11in) s.verso cardboard. 28-Mar-4 Anaf, Lyon #17
£872 $1605 €1300 Autoportrait (40x32cm-16x13in) cardboard lit. 28-Mar-4 Anaf, Lyon #8/R
£1745 $3211 €2600 Descente de croix (46x55cm-18x22in) 28-Mar-4 Anaf, Lyon #11/R est:2000-2500
Works on paper
£336 $617 €500 Composition (19x19cm-7x7in) collage exec.c.1923. 28-Mar-4 Anaf, Lyon #14
£470 $864 €700 Nature morte au bouquet de fleurs (31x21cm-12x8in) s. W/C. 28-Mar-4 Anaf, Lyon #13
£470 $864 €700 Composition (19x19cm-7x7in) collage exec.c.1923. 28-Mar-4 Anaf, Lyon #15/R
£604 $1111 €900 Composition (59x46cm-23x18in) collage exec.c.1925. 28-Mar-4 Anaf, Lyon #16
£671 $1235 €1000 Mise au tombeau (24x30cm-9x12in) s.d.1924 bistre wash W/C. 28-Mar-4 Anaf, Lyon #12

DALBERG, Ake (1910-) Swedish
£399 $718 €599 Interior scene with woman and cats (52x68cm-20x27in) s. 25-Apr-4 Goteborg Auktionsverk, Sweden #333/R (S.KR 5500)

DALBERG, G (19th C) German
£1300 $2457 €1898 Favourable reading (36x58cm-14x23in) s. panel. 19-Feb-4 Christie's, Kensington #84/R est:1500-2000

D'ALBISSOLA, Tullio (20th C) ?
Sculpture
£8112 $13790 €11600 Fifteen-year-old sphynx (16x50x20cm-6x20x8in) s. bronze exec.c.1930. 19-Nov-3 Cambi, Genoa #47/R est:10000-11000

DALBONO, Eduardo (1843-1915) Italian
£775 $1286 €1100 Naples Bay (10x17cm-4x7in) s. card. 13-Jun-3 Farsetti, Prato #502
£1056 $1754 €1500 La terrazza (17x15cm-7x6in) panel. 11-Jun-3 Christie's, Rome #103/R est:1800-2500
£1871 $3068 €2600 Blessing of the donkey (26x48cm-10x19in) s. paper on canvas. 10-Jun-3 Pandolfini, Florence #38/R est:1000-1200
£2394 $4142 €3400 Nymphs (21x28cm-8x11in) s. cardboard. 10-Dec-3 Finarte Semenzato, Rome #163/R est:2000-2500
£2667 $4907 €4000 Seascapes (18x29cm-7x11in) s. canvas on cardboard. 8-Jun-4 Sotheby's, Milan #33/R est:2000-4000
£3357 $5606 €4800 Figures on a boat (14x23cm-6x9in) s. card. 24-Jun-3 Finarte Semenzato, Rome #136/R
Works on paper
£709 $1184 €1000 Seated peasant woman (22x16cm-9x6in) s.d.1882 pencil. 14-Oct-3 Finarte Semenzato, Milan #150/R

DALBY OF YORK, David (1794-1836) British
£2414 $4031 €3500 Acteon beating Memnon (51x71cm-20x28in) s.i.d.1821. 11-Nov-3 Castellana, Madrid #181/R est:2500
£2900 $4930 €4234 Full cry (26x38cm-10x15in) s. 18-Nov-3 Bonhams, Leeds #250/R est:3000-5000
£4000 $6680 €5840 Portrait of Lieutenant Colonel Standish Derby O'Grady, later 2nd Viscount Guillamore, on charger (61x74cm-24x29in) 14-Oct-3 Sotheby's, London #489/R est:4000-6000
£4800 $8832 €7008 Acteon beating Memnon (51x75cm-20x30in) s.i.d.1831. 10-Jun-4 Christie's, Kensington #13/R est:4000-6000
£5172 $8638 €7500 Farrer (75x94cm-30x37in) s.i.d.1833. 11-Nov-3 Castellana, Madrid #180/R est:4250
£6000 $10560 €8760 Over the fence (23x30cm-9x12in) s. board. 21-May-4 Christie's, London #77/R est:6000-8000
£8721 $15000 €12733 Cock Robin, a chestnut hunter in a wooded landscape (61x76cm-24x30in) indis sig. prov. 5-Dec-3 Christie's, Rockefeller NY #16/R est:15000-20000
£19000 $31730 €27740 Portrait of Captain Percy Burrell Williams of the 9th Light Dragoons Lancers, with his charger Penin (100x125cm-39x49in) 14-Oct-3 Sotheby's, London #484/R est:20000-30000

DALBY, John (fl.1826-1853) British
£1700 $2992 €2482 A Chestnut hunter in an extensive landscape with a white dog (59x75cm-23x30in) s.d.1838. 18-May-4 Woolley & Wallis, Salisbury #101/R est:2500-3500
£1800 $3060 €2628 Bay in a stable (31x41cm-12x16in) s.i.d.1839 i.verso. 27-Nov-3 Christie's, Kensington #80/R est:2000-3000
£4469 $8000 €6525 Anxious moment (30x43cm-12x17in) s. prov. 27-May-4 Sotheby's, New York #202/R est:5000-7000

DALE, Robert and HAVELL, Robert (19th C) British
Prints
£13000 $21710 €18980 Panoramic view of King George's Sound (21x277cm-8x109in) hand-coloured aquatint strip. 13-Nov-3 Sotheby's, London #196/R est:8000-10000

DALEN, Patricia van (1955-) Venezuelan
£774 $1200 €1130 Untitled (70x100cm-28x39in) s. 29-Sep-2 Subastas Odalys, Caracas #6/R

DALENA, Danilo (1943-) Asian
£2431 $4059 €3549 Sto Nino (61x85cm-24x33in) s.d.85. 12-Oct-3 Sotheby's, Singapore #61/R est:7000-9000 (S.D 7000)

DALENS, Dirk II (1659-1688) Dutch
Works on paper
£15068 $25616 €22000 Herders in a landscape, with a man on a bridge (29x38cm-11x15in) s.d.1685 black chk col ink wash prov. 4-Nov-3 Sotheby's, Amsterdam #65/R est:10000-15000

DALESSI, Giovanni (1964-) Italian?
£1200 $2208 €1800 Mother and child (80x70cm-31x28in) s.d.98 verso oil sold with oil by same artist two. 8-Jun-4 Sotheby's, Amsterdam #166/R est:2000-3000

DALGARNO, Roy Frederick Leslie (1910-2001) Australian
£1736 $3211 €2535 Pont Charles, Prague (51x77cm-20x30in) s.d.52 board prov. 10-Mar-4 Deutscher-Menzies, Melbourne #62/R est:2000-4000 (A.D 4200)

DALGAS, Carlo (1820-1851) Danish
£1164 $2130 €1699 Summer idyll with thatched house by fjord (49x69cm-19x27in) s.i. verso. 9-Jun-4 Rasmussen, Copenhagen #1637/R est:10000 (D.KR 13000)

DALGLISH, Andrew Adie (19/20th C) British
Works on paper
£500 $900 €730 Ruined castle (40x60cm-16x24in) s. W/C. 22-Apr-4 Bonhams, Edinburgh #354

D'ALHEIM, Jean (1840-1894) Russian
£1268 $2104 €1800 Venetian vedute (54x72cm-21x28in) s. 16-Jun-3 Dorotheum, Vienna #2/R est:1500-2000
£1322 $2247 €1930 Sunnyu canal in Venice (53x64cm-21x25in) s. 5-Nov-3 Dobiaschofsky, Bern #304/R est:3000 (S.FR 3000)
£2980 $5454 €4500 Sunny canal in Venice (53x64cm-21x25in) s. 8-Apr-4 Dorotheum, Vienna #115/R est:3800-4200

DALI, Louis (20th C) French?
£223 $400 €326 Rue de Paris (41x51cm-16x20in) s. board. 8-May-4 Susanin's, Chicago #6083/R
£407 $650 €594 French winter street scene (23x28cm-9x11in) s. painted c.1950's. 20-Sep-3 Bunte, Elgin #1441a

DALI, Salvador (1904-1989) Spanish
£30000 $54600 €43800 Scene dans un patio du harem (35x30cm-14x12in) s.d.1965 oil gouache W/C paper prov.lit. 5-Feb-4 Christie's, London #389/R est:12000-15000
£30000 $55200 €43800 Study for the Trilogy of the Desert (36x46cm-14x18in) gouache pencil exec 1946 prov. 24-Jun-4 Christie's, London #436/R est:30000-40000
£83799 $150000 €122347 Picador (145x115cm-57x45in) painted 1969 prov.exhib. 6-May-4 Sotheby's, New York #358/R est:150000-200000
£88235 $150000 €128823 Le triomphe de Nautilus (30x35cm-12x14in) s.i.d.1941 prov.exhib.lit. 5-Nov-3 Christie's, Rockefeller NY #323/R est:150000-200000
£360000 $662400 €525600 Portrait de Mme Philips avec agneau et ange (108x80cm-43x31in) s.d.1953 exhib. 23-Jun-4 Christie's, London #265/R est:220000-280000
£620000 $1128400 €905200 Grenade (50x59cm-20x23in) s.d.1948 prov. 21-Jun-4 Sotheby's, London #58/R est:300000-400000

Prints			
£1613	$3000	€2355	Fantastic beach scene (24x30cm-9x12in) etching sanguine. 2-Mar-4 Swann Galleries, New York #147/R est:4000-6000
£1882	$3200	€2748	Don Quixote (45x57cm-18x22in) s.i.d.1966 i.d.verso col etching. 6-Nov-3 Swann Galleries, New York #535/R est:1500-2500
£2365	$4234	€3500	Enlisement d'Horus (63x48cm-25x19in) s. num.11/250 col eau forte lithograph. 4-May-4 Calmels Cohen, Paris #52a est:1200-1500
£2621	$4717	€3800	Moise et le monotheisme (50x65cm-20x26in) lithograph exec 1974. 25-Jan-4 Chayette & Cheval, Paris #120 est:800-1000
£2632	$4842	€3843	La divine comedie. Departure for a grand travel (25x21cm-10x8in) s. lithograph double-sided. 23-Jun-4 Koller, Zurich #3229b est:6000-9000 (S.FR 6000)
£5220	$9500	€7621	St. George and the Dragon (43x28cm-17x11in) s.d.1947 etching. 19-Jun-4 Rachel Davis, Shaker Heights #471 est:10000-15000
£5988	$10000	€8742	Saint George and the dragon (46x28cm-18x11in) s.d.1947 etching one of 250. 25-Oct-3 Rachel Davis, Shaker Heights #389/R
£12429	$22000	€18146	Andre Parinaud, after 50 years of surrealism, Fribourg, Switzerland (68x54cm-27x21in) s.num. col drypoint pochoir 12 with an additional suite album. 28-Apr-4 Christie's, Rockefeller NY #27/R est:8000-10000
£15642	$28000	€22837	Divine comedie (32x25cm-13x10in) wood engraving portfolio of 100. 6-May-4 Swann Galleries, New York #447/R est:30000-50000
Sculpture			
£823	$1472	€1202	Rhinoceros (12cm-5in) s. green pat.bronze gilded cast.Airaindor Valsuam, Paris. 22-Mar-4 Philippe Schuler, Zurich #4078/R (S.FR 1900)
£898	$1500	€1311	Minotaur (18cm-7in) s.num.200/350 bronze. 29-Jun-3 William Jenack, New York #127 est:1000-1500
£1042	$1740	€1500	Menorah (44cm-17in) d.1980 num.198/250 multiple gilt bronze. 23-Oct-3 Credit Municipal, Paris #130 est:1000-1500
£1056	$1827	€1500	Venus a la giraffe (57x28cm-22x11in) s.i. pat.bronze Cast.Venturi Arte Bologna Italia. 13-Dec-3 Lempertz, Koln #302/R est:1800
£1192	$2170	€1800	Venus a la girafe (56x27x9cm-22x11x4in) s. num.471/1500 black pat bronze Cast Venturi. 18-Jun-4 Charbonneaux, Paris #192/R est:1500-2000
£1221	$2038	€1783	Anthropomorphic cabinet (16cm-6in) s.num.140/330 bronze incl.polished marble base Cast Mibrosa Foner. 7-Oct-3 Rasmussen, Copenhagen #257/R est:15000 (D.KR 13000)
£1231	$2117	€1797	Le cabinet antropomorphe (22cm-9in) s.num.137/330 bronze Cast.Mibrosa. 7-Dec-3 Uppsala Auktionskammare, Uppsala #360/R est:20000-25000 (S.KR 16000)
£1233	$2096	€1800	Christo de San Juan de la cRuz (33cm-13in) s. num.144/150 silver. 9-Nov-3 Eric Pillon, Calais #255/R
£1329	$2259	€1900	Rhinoceros (9cm-4in) i. gilded bronze Cast.Airaindor VM. 26-Nov-3 Lempertz, Koln #631/R est:750
£1333	$2453	€2000	Cristo de San Juan de la Cruz (55cm-22in) s.num. gilt 24K bronze sold with marble socle. 14-Jun-4 Tajan, Paris #231/R est:2000-2500
£1343	$2376	€2000	L'anti-fleur (38cm-15in) s.d.70 num.84/150 verso glass lit. 27-Apr-4 Artcurial Briest, Paris #209/R est:2200-2800
£1456	$2300	€2126	Rhinoceros (13x15cm-5x6in) s.num.200/350 bronze exec.c.1980. 6-Apr-3 William Jenack, New York #64 est:2000-3000
£1467	$2625	€2200	Surreal eyes (34x22x5cm-13x9x2in) s.i. silver pat.bronze artificial eyes Cast.Venturi. 13-May-4 Neumeister, Munich #318/R est:800-1200
£1533	$2821	€2300	Venus aux tiroirs (42cm-17in) s. num.180/850 pate-de-verre metal Cast Daum lit. 8-Jun-4 Artcurial Briest, Paris #188 est:1000-1500
£1549	$2711	€2200	Venus a la girafe (56cm-22in) s. num.14/1500 dark pat bronze Cast Venturi Arte. 19-Dec-3 Dorotheum, Vienna #238/R est:2000-2500
£1656	$3013	€2500	Venus aux tiroirs (36cm-14in) s.d.1983 num.205/499 green pat bronze cire perdue Cast Valsuani. 18-Jun-4 Charbonneaux, Paris #191/R est:2500-3000
£1760	$2852	€2500	Untitled (20x20cm-8x8in) s. carreaux de faience 12. 5-Aug-3 Tajan, Paris #80/R est:2000-3000
£1879	$3439	€2800	Ying et le Yang (13cm-5in) s. num.EA polished bronze three parts on socle lit. 7-Jul-4 Artcurial Briest, Paris #146 est:3000-4000
£1888	$3210	€2756	Venus a la giraffe (57cm-22in) s.num.1169/1500 pat.bronze prov. 4-Nov-3 Bukowskis, Stockholm #259/R est:20000-25000 (S.KR 25000)
£1964	$3338	€2867	Persistance de la Memoire (37cm-15in) s.num.193/350 gold pat.bronze Cast Venturi Arte. 4-Nov-3 Bukowskis, Stockholm #260/R est:25000-30000 (S.KR 26000)
£2000	$3680	€3000	Cabinet (24x12x6cm-9x5x2in) i. num.106/330 f.Mibrosa solid sterling silver. 8-Jun-4 Sotheby's, Amsterdam #69/R est:3500-4000
£2013	$3564	€3000	Le minotaure (45cm-18in) s.num.16/99 brown pat bronze Cast C. Valsuant. 29-Apr-4 Claude Aguttes, Neuilly #159/R est:3000-3200
£2254	$3944	€3200	Venus and giraffe (57x27x9cm-22x11x4in) s.st.f.Euroart num.1046/1500 pat bronze. 16-Dec-3 Segre, Madrid #145/R est:3200
£2333	$4293	€3500	Minotaure (44cm-17in) i. num.12/99 f.Valsuani bronze lit. 8-Jun-4 Sotheby's, Amsterdam #67/R est:2500-3000
£2414	$4466	€3500	Venus aux neuf tiroirs (36cm-14in) s.d.1985 num.196/499 green pat bronze st.f.Valsuani. 13-Feb-4 Charbonneaux, Paris #127/R est:3000-4000
£2500	$4125	€3600	Christ of Saint John of the Cross (61cm-24in) s. num.234/250 bronze marble base. 2-Jul-3 Ansorena, Madrid #1180/R
£2542	$4500	€3711	La persistance de la memoire (36cm-14in) s.num.36/350 gold pat bronze marble base. 2-May-4 Bonhams & Butterfields, Los Angeles #3018/R est:2000-4000
£2551	$4744	€3800	Hommage a Newton, sans bras, etude (28cm-11in) s.num.6/8 gilt brown pat bronze st.f.Valsuani lit. 2-Mar-4 Artcurial Briest, Paris #262a est:2500-3000
£2797	$4755	€4000	Menorah (45x35x6cm-18x14x2in) s. pat bronze limited edition of 300. 27-Nov-3 Calmels Cohen, Paris #80/R est:3500-4000
£2800	$5152	€4200	Homme oiseau (20cm-8in) s. pat bronze cire perdue Cast Valsuani. 9-Jun-4 Beaussant & Lefèvre, Paris #127 est:4500-5000
£2817	$4563	€4000	Untitled (20x20cm-8x8in) s. carreaux de faience wood four parts. 5-Aug-3 Tajan, Paris #79/R est:4000-6000
£2817	$4873	€4000	Unicorne (57cm-22in) s.st.f.Venturi num.164/350 pat bronze. 9-Dec-3 Artcurial Briest, Paris #315/R est:6000-8000
£2819	$4989	€4200	Persistance de la memoire (37cm-15in) s.d.1980 num.161/350 green pat bronze gold lit. 27-Apr-4 Artcurial Briest, Paris #211/R est:2000-3000
£2825	$5000	€4125	Hommage a Newton (35cm-14in) s.num.347/350 brown green pat bronze marble base. 2-May-4 Bonhams & Butterfields, Los Angeles #3017/R est:3000-5000
£3028	$5056	€4391	Rhinoceros (12cm-5in) s.i. green pat.bronze gilded. 23-Jun-3 Philippe Schuler, Zurich #3113/R est:3000-4000 (S.FR 6600)
£3133	$5609	€4700	Cubist angel (56x19x12cm-22x7x5in) i. gold pat.bronze. 15-May-4 Van Ham, Cologne #549/R est:5000
£3211	$5362	€4656	Venus a la giraffe (57cm-22in) s.i. bronze silvered. 23-Jun-3 Philippe Schuler, Zurich #3112/R est:8000-10000 (S.FR 7000)
£3356	$5940	€5000	Birdman. s.i. green gold pat.bronze. 28-Apr-4 Wiener Kunst Auktionen, Vienna #321/R est:5000-8000
£3370	$5965	€4920	Surrealistic angel (57cm-22in) s.num.1123/1500 pat.bronze. 27-Apr-4 AB Stockholms Auktionsverk #1163/R est:35000-40000 (S.KR 46000)
£3493	$6428	€5100	Cabinet anthropomorphique (31x60x20cm-12x24x8in) i. bronze Cast.Fonderia Mibrosa, Barcelona. 8-Jun-4 Germann, Zurich #70/R est:10000-14000 (S.FR 8000)
£3500	$5845	€5110	L'escargot et l'ange (46cm-18in) i.st.num.103/350 bronze conceived 1977 lit. 22-Oct-3 Sotheby's, Olympia #172/R est:4000-6000
£3521	$5705	€5000	Hommage a terpsichore (44x23x70cm-17x9x28in) bronze edition of 350. 5-Aug-3 Tajan, Paris #45/R est:4000-6000
£3597	$5899	€5000	Le cabinet antropomorphique (31x63x20cm-12x25x8in) i. dark brown pat.bronze. 4-Jun-3 Ketterer, Hamburg #295/R est:6000-8000
£4000	$6360	€5800	Elephant spatial (98x39cm-39x15in) with sig.num.298/350 blue green gold pat. bronze perspex pyramid. 11-Sep-3 Christie's, Kensington #97/R est:4000-6000
£4000	$7240	€5840	La vision de l'ange (44x36x34cm-17x14x13in) gold brown pat bronze 241 from edition of 350 conceived 1977. 1-Apr-4 Christie's, Kensington #79/R est:4000-6000
£4029	$7132	€5882	Femme en Flammes (85cm-33in) s.num.214/350 polished bronze Cast.Venturi Arte. 27-Apr-4 AB Stockholms Auktionsverk #1164/R est:35000-40000 (S.KR 55000)
£4225	$7310	€6000	Noblesse du temps (60cm-24in) s.st.f.Venturi num.135/350 green pat bronze. 9-Dec-3 Artcurial Briest, Paris #312/R est:8000-10000
£4225	$7310	€6000	Cheva a la montre molle (44cm-17in) s.st.f.Camblest num.334/350 pat bronze. 9-Dec-3 Artcurial Briest, Paris #314/R est:5000-7000
£4310	$7155	€6250	Venus a la tete de rose (77cm-30in) s. bronze. 5-Oct-3 Lombrail & Teucquam, Paris #154
£4437	$7676	€6300	Saint Georges et le dragon (46cm-18in) s.st.f.Venturi num.128/350 pat bronze. 9-Dec-3 Artcurial Briest, Paris #318/R est:8000-10000
£4483	$8069	€6500	Woman climbing stairs (12cm-5in) s.d.1974 num.289 gold. 26-Jan-4 Durán, Madrid #1320/R est:6500
£4578	$7416	€6500	Space Venus (35x32x65cm-14x13x26in) bronze edition of 350. 5-Aug-3 Tajan, Paris #43/R est:4000-6000
£4800	$8592	€7008	Cabinet Anthromorphique (64cm-25in) s. num.162/330 base st.f.Foneria Mibrosa. 16-Mar-4 Bonhams, Knightsbridge #46/R est:5000-7000
£4800	$8832	€7008	L'escargot et l'ange (44cm-17in) i.num.212/350 bronze lit. 24-Mar-4 Sotheby's, Olympia #191/R est:4000-6000
£5000	$8350	€7300	Licorne (58cm-23in) i.st.num.198/350 bronze conceived 1977 prov. 22-Oct-3 Sotheby's, Olympia #165/R est:5000-7000
£5000	$8650	€7300	Alice au pays des merveilles (90x44cm-35x17in) s.d.1984 num.215/350 green gold pat bronze conceived 1977 st.f. 11-Dec-3 Christie's, Kensington #135/R est:5000-7000
£5034	$8910	€7500	Jeune vierge autosodomisee par sa propre chastete (71x61x0cm-28x24x0in) s.i. num.5/8 bas relief metal silver mounted plexiglass lit. 27-Apr-4 Artcurial Briest, Paris #210/R est:2500-3000
£5034	$8909	€7500	Femme en flammes (84cm-33in) s.i. verso gold pat.bronze. 30-Apr-4 Dr Fritz Nagel, Stuttgart #763/R est:8500
£5282	$8557	€7500	Space elephant (43x14x94cm-17x6x37in) bronze edition of 350. 5-Aug-3 Tajan, Paris #44/R est:4000-6000
£5333	$9600	€8000	Venus spatiale (65cm-26in) s.num.31/350 dark pat bronze st.f. 20-Apr-4 Galerie Moderne, Brussels #1501/R est:8000-10000
£5500	$9515	€8030	Cabinet anthropomorphique (79x23cm-31x9in) s.num.163/330 brown pat bronze st.f.Foneira Mibrosa. 11-Dec-3 Christie's, Kensington #118/R est:6000-8000
£5600	$9352	€8176	Cabinet anthropomorphique (58cm-23in) i. num.97/330 bronze st.f.Mibrosa conceived 1973. 22-Oct-3 Sotheby's, Olympia #159/R est:6000-8000
£6000	$9540	€8700	Hommage a terpsichore (70x44cm-28x17in) with sig.num.236/350 gold green pat. bronze st.f.Jemelton. 11-Sep-3 Christie's, Kensington #95/R est:4000-6000
£6000	$10380	€8760	Femme en flammes (84x28cm-33x11in) s.d.1981 num.254/350 gold pat bronze conceived 1980 st.f. 11-Dec-3 Christie's, Kensington #126/R est:6000-8000
£6000	$11040	€9000	Cabinet anthropomorphique (31x63x20cm-12x25x8in) i. num.149/330 f.Mibrosa bronze lit. 8-Jun-4 Sotheby's, Amsterdam #72/R est:9000-12000
£6333	$11526	€9500	Rhinoceros cosmique (88cm-35in) s. num.1/25 partly gilded bronze st.f.Valsuani cire perdue. 30-Jun-4 Calmels Cohen, Paris #70a est:20000-30000
£6333	$11526	€9500	Venus au cygne (68x59cm-27x23in) s. num. 57/150 bronze Cast Airaindor. 30-Jun-4 Calmels Cohen, Paris #70b est:4000-6000
£6500	$11245	€9490	Saint Georges et le dragon (46x45cm-18x18in) s.d.1984 num.167/350 green gold pat bronze conceived 1977 st.f. 11-Dec-3 Christie's, Kensington #125/R est:5000-7000
£6500	$11960	€9490	Cabinet anthropomorphique (64cm-25in) i.num.146/330 bronze st.f.Foneria Mibrosa. 24-Mar-4 Sotheby's, Olympia #188/R est:6000-8000
£7000	$12670	€10220	Cabinet anthropomorphique (77x23cm-30x9in) s.num.106/330 brown pat bronze st.f.Foneria Mibrosa. 1-Apr-4 Christie's, Kensington #74/R est:6000-8000
£7021	$11374	€9900	Minotaurus (46cm-18in) s. base num.14/99 C.Valsuani cire perdue. 20-May-3 Ansorena, Madrid #810/R est:9900
£7500	$11925	€10875	Le profil du temps (51cm-20in) with sig.num.228/350 green gold pat. bronze st.f.Jemelton. 11-Sep-3 Christie's, Kensington #93/R est:3000-4000
£7500	$12525	€10950	Venus spatiale (63cm-25in) i.st.num.295/350 bronze conceived 1977 prov.lit. 22-Oct-3 Sotheby's, Olympia #169/R est:6000-8000
£8000	$14480	€11680	Femme a la tete de rose (82cm-32in) s.num.71/99 gold pat bronze plexiglass metal base. 1-Apr-4 Christie's, Kensington #64/R est:4000-6000
£8000	$14480	€11680	La persistance de la memoire (41x9x21cm-16x4x8in) s.d.1981 num.161/350 gold green pat bronze st.f.Venturiarte. 1-Apr-4 Christie's, Kensington #82/R est:4000-6000
£8500	$14195	€12410	Persistance de la memoire (59cm-23in) i. st.1984 num.237/350 bronze cire perdue prov.lit. 22-Oct-3 Sotheby's, Olympia #150/R est:5000-7000
£8500	$15640	€12410	Le cheval a la montre Molle (44cm-17in) i.num.272/350 bronze lit. 24-Mar-4 Sotheby's, Olympia #189/R est:4000-6000
£8500	$15640	€12410	Profil du temps (51cm-20in) s.num.254/350 bronze lit. 24-Mar-4 Sotheby's, Olympia #190/R est:5000-7000
£9000	$16290	€13140	Venus spatiale (65x32x35cm-26x13x14in) gold green pat bronze 267 from edition of 350 conceived 1977. 1-Apr-4 Christie's, Kensington #78/R est:6000-8000
£9000	$16560	€13140	Homage a terpsichore (70cm-28in) i.num.318/350 bronze two lit. 24-Mar-4 Sotheby's, Olympia #192/R est:4000-6000
£49296	$79860	€70000	Alice au pays des Merveilles (227x46x111cm-89x18x44in) s.num.6/7 bronze Cast Tesconi exhib. 5-Aug-3 Tajan, Paris #41/R est:80000-120000
£52818	$85565	€75000	Profil du temps (150x100x60cm-59x39x24in) s.num.3/3 bronze Cast Tesconi exhib. 5-Aug-3 Tajan, Paris #42/R est:80000-120000
£55882	$95000	€81588	Objet surrealiste a fonctionnement symbolique (48x27x10cm-19x11x4in) s. num.1/8 assemblage shoe white marble prov.lit. 5-Nov-3 Christie's, Rockefeller NY #325/R est:80000-100000
£60000	$109800	€90000	Venus a la girafe (240cm-94in) s. num.1/3 brown pat. bronze exec.1973 lit. 7-Jun-4 Artcurial Briest, Paris #49/R est:80000-120000
£81006	$145000	€118269	Femme a la tete de roses (188cm-74in) s.st.f.Bonvincini num.1/4 gold pat bronze excl base prov.exhib. 5-May-4 Christie's, Rockefeller NY #354/R est:70000-90000
£85000	$154700	€124100	L'unicorne (183cm-72in) s. num.1/7 st.f.Perseo green gold pat bronze exec. 1984 prov.exhib. 3-Feb-4 Christie's, London #233/R est:70000-90000
Works on paper			
£1000	$1730	€1460	Sans titre (25x20cm-10x8in) s. pencil double-sided. 11-Dec-3 Christie's, Kensington #114/R est:1200-1800
£1067	$1931	€1600	Trotteur aux papillons (78x120cm-31x47in) s. num.74/150 mixed media photo lithograph exec 1972. 2-Apr-4 Coutau Begarie, Paris #40/R est:1000-1500
£1200	$2184	€1800	Don Quichote (42x58cm-17x23in) s.i. pen ink. 2-Jul-4 Bloomsbury, London #297/R est:700-900
£1400	$2534	€2044	Study for Le crane de Zurbaran (35x20cm-14x8in) pencil ballpoint pen black ink double-sided prov. 1-Apr-4 Christie's, Kensington #73/R est:1200-1800

£1800 $2862 €2610 Cornes de rhinoceros dynamiques dans un paysage. Night club a Acapulco (9x14cm-4x6in) ballpoint pen ink gouache double-sided. 11-Sep-3 Christie's, Kensington #79/R est:2000-3000
£1800 $3312 €2628 Sana titre (28x23cm-11x9in) s.d.1975 felt-tip pen prov. 24-Mar-4 Sotheby's, Olympia #164/R est:2000-3000
£2000 $3680 €2920 Architecture paranoiaque (20x18cm-8x7in) i. pencil executed 1949 prov. 24-Mar-4 Sotheby's, Olympia #165/R est:2000-3000
£2000 $3640 €3000 Estudio de rostro para la Madonna de Port (8x6cm-3x2in) ink drawing oval. 29-Jun-4 Segre, Madrid #134/R est:4500
£2294 $3830 €3326 Au tribunal (27x20cm-11x8in) s. crayon prov. 21-Jun-3 Galerie du Rhone, Sion #512/R est:4500-5500 (S.FR 5000)
£2550 $4667 €3800 Nu assis (32x24cm-13x9in) lead pencil prov. 7-Jul-4 Artcurial Briest, Paris #178/R est:4000-5000
£3000 $5520 €4380 Etudes de nus (23x31cm-9x12in) s. pencil double-sided executed 1923 prov. 24-Mar-4 Sotheby's, Olympia #160/R est:1500-2000
£4054 $7662 €6000 Composition (19x15cm-7x6in) graphite double-sided exec.c.1934 prov. 21-Feb-4 Cornette de St.Cyr, Paris #193/R est:5000-7000
£4061 $7310 €5929 Sketch for The formation of monsters (23x15cm-9x6in) Indian ink exec.c.1938 exhib.prov. 26-Apr-4 Bukowskis, Stockholm #244/R est:25000-30000 (S.KR 56000)
£4362 $8114 €6500 Don Juan Tenorio (19x28cm-7x11in) s. W/C dr. 2-Mar-4 Ansorena, Madrid #840/R est:6500
£5263 $9526 €8000 Homme assis (38x29cm-15x11in) sanguine dr. 14-Apr-4 Ansorena, Madrid #274d/R est:8000
£5705 $10611 €8500 Nu de face (37x27cm-15x11in) s. graphite dr. 2-Mar-4 Ansorena, Madrid #861/R est:7500
£5845 $9352 €8300 Nu de dos (30x28cm-12x11in) s. biro sketch text. 19-Sep-3 Sigalas, Stuttgart #296/R est:8000
£6000 $10380 €8760 Siete de copas (32x21cm-13x8in) s. gouache collage card. 11-Dec-3 Christie's, Kensington #130/R est:6000-8000
£6000 $10920 €8760 Les apotres, etude pour la bible (35x47cm-14x19in) s. brush ink wash exec.c.1965. 4-Feb-4 Sotheby's, London #527/R est:6000-8000
£6159 $10101 €8500 Elephant (30x56cm-12x22in) collage ink exec.c.1972. 29-May-3 Galleria Pace, Milan #146/R est:12500
£6500 $11960 €9490 A regarder la loupe (15x23cm-6x9in) gouache pencil card exec.c.1960-61. 22-Jun-4 Sotheby's, London #488/R est:7000-9000
£6623 $12053 €10000 Le couple a la commode (21x16cm-8x6in) s. ink wash exec. c.1923 prov. 18-Jun-4 Piasa, Paris #188/R est:3000-4000
£6944 $11319 €10000 Don Quixote and Sancho Panca (39x37cm-15x15in) s.d.1959 Indian ink prov. 27-Sep-3 Dr Fritz Nagel, Stuttgart #9516/R est:8000
£7487 $14000 €10931 Dessin pour bijoux de Coco Chanel (56x38cm-22x15in) s.d.1966 ball point pen W/C prov. 25-Feb-4 Christie's, Rockefeller NY #125/R est:12000-16000
£8000 $14480 €12000 Study for 'Monarchy time' (35x45cm-14x18in) W/C pencil. 30-Mar-4 Segre, Madrid #123/R est:15000
£8000 $14720 €11680 Regne du mou, le regne du dur (19x9cm-7x4in) s.i.d.1946 pen ink prov.lit. 24-Jun-4 Christie's, London #430/R est:8000-12000
£8000 $14720 €11680 Dalinien manner to paint the finest details (21x22cm-8x9in) s. pen India ink exec c.1947 prov.lit. 24-Jun-4 Christie's, London #434/R est:7000-9000
£8531 $14674 €12200 Bishop's blessing over Port Lligat (34x73cm-13x29in) s.i. biro. 2-Dec-3 Hauswedell & Nolte, Hamburg #117/R est:12500
£9500 $15105 €13775 Monogramme - Galasalvadordali (28x34cm-11x13in) s. pencil pen ink on card executed c.1946. 11-Sep-3 Christie's, Kensington #108/R est:10000-15000
£9868 $17862 €15000 Surrealist figure (47x34cm-19x13in) pencil dr. 14-Apr-4 Ansorena, Madrid #274c/R est:15000
£10000 $18400 €14600 Way to wash abdomen, sleeve trimmed with shells and crutch for little finger (10x18cm-4x7in) s.d. pen India ink exec 1947 prov.lit. 24-Jun-4 Christie's, London #431/R est:7000-9000
£12000 $22080 €17520 Flesh wheel barrow (15x9cm-6x4in) mono.i. pen ink exec c.1947 prov.lit. 24-Jun-4 Christie's, London #437/R est:12000-15000
£12000 $22080 €17520 Eye glass of the painter (16x16cm-6x6in) s.i. pen India ink exec c.1947 prov.lit. 24-Jun-4 Christie's, London #440/R est:12000-15000
£12570 $22500 €18352 Oiel et figure (23x33cm-9x13in) s.i.d.1939 W/C pen ink prov. 6-May-4 Sotheby's, New York #377/R est:15000-20000
£13423 $24027 €20000 Salt woman (47x35cm-19x14in) s.d.1965 W/C pastel card. 29-May-4 Farsetti, Prato #426/R est:20000-25000
£14667 $26547 €22000 Circuits de la memoire (43x30cm-17x12in) s.d.1969 W/C ink. 1-Apr-4 Credit Municipal, Paris #56/R est:30000-35000
£14706 $25000 €21471 Untitled - mythology (65x49cm-26x19in) s.d.1963 W/C ink. 9-Nov-3 Bonhams & Butterfields, Los Angeles #4019/R
£15000 $27600 €21900 Saint George and the dragon (30x25cm-12x10in) s.i.d.1969 ball-point pen prov. 24-Jun-4 Christie's, London #439/R est:8000-12000
£15000 $27600 €21900 Portrait de femme d'apres Leonard. Nu (20x25cm-8x10in) s.d.65 ball-point pencil double-sided. 24-Jun-4 Christie's, London #442/R est:14000-18000
£17000 $30940 €24820 Moise, illustration pour la Sainte Bible (49x34cm-19x13in) W/C brush India ink chl exec 1964 prov. 5-Feb-4 Christie's, London #390/R est:12000-15000
£17000 $30940 €24820 Etude pour les chants de Maldoror (28x21cm-11x8in) s.i. ball-point pen ink exec.1933 prov. 4-Feb-4 Sotheby's, London #496/R est:12000-18000
£17000 $30940 €24820 Les trois graces (26x19cm-10x7in) s.i. pen ink exec.c.1930 prov.exhib. 4-Feb-4 Sotheby's, London #508/R est:15000-20000
£19000 $34580 €27740 Illustration pour La Sainte Bible (49x34cm-19x13in) s.d.1964 W/C pen ink paper prov. 5-Feb-4 Christie's, London #388/R est:15000-20000
£19719 $34113 €28000 Untitled (48x63cm-19x25in) s.d.1969 gouache crayon ink wash. 9-Dec-3 Artcurial Briest, Paris #316/R est:15000-20000
£20000 $36800 €29200 Wood of Birnam - La foret de Birnam (20x17cm-8x7in) mono. pen India ink exec 1946 prov.exhib.lit. 24-Jun-4 Christie's, London #432/R est:20000-30000
£22000 $40260 €32120 Untitled (55x75cm-22x30in) s.d.1939 pen brush ink prov. 2-Feb-4 Christie's, London #67/R est:24000-28000
£26000 $47840 €37960 Couverts a poisson. Esquisses (18x24cm-7x9in) mono.d.1959 gouache ink wash pencil board double-sided prov.exhib. 24-Jun-4 Christie's, London #438/R est:10000-15000
£27933 $50000 €40782 Andromeda (70x53cm-28x21in) s.d.1931 pencil prov.exhib. 5-May-4 Christie's, Rockefeller NY #158/R est:35000-45000
£30726 $55000 €44860 Gault Prize (118x79cm-46x31in) s. gouache brush India ink board exec c.1966 prov. 5-May-4 Christie's, Rockefeller NY #157/R est:60000-80000
£52000 $94640 €75920 Vanitas (63x47cm-25x19in) s.i.d.1933 pen ink sanguine prov. 5-Feb-4 Christie's, London #386/R est:25000-35000
£52000 $94640 €75920 Flores y toreros (52x38cm-20x15in) s.d.1967 gouache pen ink W/C prov.exhib. 5-Feb-4 Christie's, London #393/R est:30000-40000
£59000 $108560 €86140 Femme nue sur arc-en-ciel (77x56cm-30x22in) s. gouache pen ink chl prov. 22-Jun-4 Sotheby's, London #487/R est:40000-60000
£60000 $110400 €87600 Meuniere Frasquita (49x34cm-19x13in) s.d.1959 W/C red ball-point pen ink board prov. 24-Jun-4 Christie's, London #433/R est:40000-60000
£72626 $130000 €106034 Horse and rider (99x72cm-39x28in) s.d.1935 pen India ink prov. 6-May-4 Sotheby's, New York #376/R est:80000-120000
£100000 $184000 €146000 Six dessins de cartes a jouer (50x31cm-20x12in) s.d.67 felt-tip pen pencil pen ink six prov. 24-Jun-4 Christie's, London #441/R est:25000-35000
£170000 $309400 €248200 Vase of flowers (102x76cm-40x30in) s.i.d.1956 gouache W/C board prov. 5-Feb-4 Christie's, London #391/R est:75000-100000
£200000 $366000 €292000 Tour des heares aux papillons (143x53cm-56x21in) s. gouache pencil on board executed 1964 prov.exhib. 2-Feb-4 Christie's, London #84/R est:120000-180000
£247059 $420000 €360706 Figure aux tiroirs (75x56cm-30x22in) s.d.1937 ink pencil prov.exhib.lit. 5-Nov-3 Sotheby's, New York #51/R est:350000-450000

DALI, Salvador (attrib) (1904-1989) Spanish

Works on paper
£333 $550 €483 Untitled, circus horses, riders and performer (28x38cm-11x15in) W/C ink. 7-Jul-3 Schrager Galleries, Milwaukee #1148

DALIFARD, Raymond (1901-1976) French

£280 $468 €409 Paysage du midi (32x41cm-13x16in) s. panel. 22-Oct-3 Sotheby's, Olympia #119/R
£480 $802 €701 Still life (32x41cm-13x16in) s. panel. 22-Oct-3 Sotheby's, Olympia #121/R

DALIGE DE FONTENAY, Leonard Alexis (1813-1892) French

£2340 $3909 €3300 Pres du couvent (45x65cm-18x26in) s. i.d.1849 verso. 12-Oct-3 St-Germain-en-Laye Encheres #30/R est:2000-2500
£4067 $7442 €6100 Vue de village anime (41x34cm-16x13in) s. 6-Jun-4 Osenat, Fontainebleau #263/R est:4000-4500

DALL, Hans (1862-1920) Danish

£269 $484 €393 Landscape with avenue (33x82cm-13x32in) s. 24-Apr-4 Rasmussen, Havnen #2201 (D.KR 3000)

DALLAIRE, Jean Guy (1943-) Canadian

Sculpture
£1389 $2319 €2000 La tendresse (26x31x17cm-10x12x7in) s.i.d. brown pat.bronze marble socle. 24-Oct-3 Ketterer, Hamburg #314/R est:2500-3500

DALLAIRE, Jean Philippe (1916-1965) Canadian

£6250 $10750 €9125 Two figures with parasols (20x20cm-8x8in) s.d.58 board. 2-Dec-3 Joyner Waddington, Toronto #5/R est:5000-7000 (C.D 14000)
£8130 $14553 €11870 Coq, rooster (38x46cm-15x18in) s.d.57 s.i.d.verso. 31-May-4 Sotheby's, Toronto #162/R est:30000-40000 (C.D 20000)
Works on paper
£289 $500 €422 Jacques Legendre, Quebec (35x32cm-14x13in) s.d.50 pencil. 9-Dec-3 Pinneys, Montreal #169 (C.D 650)
£1321 $2365 €1929 Bouquet (40x25cm-16x10in) s.d.1952 i.d.verso gouache prov. 27-May-4 Heffel, Vancouver #87/R est:3000-5000 (C.D 3250)
£1696 $2833 €2459 Nature morte (14x18cm-6x7in) s.d.51 gouache. 17-Jun-3 Pinneys, Montreal #126 est:3000-4000 (C.D 3800)
£4472 $8004 €6529 San Pietro (30x22cm-12x9in) s.i.d.1952 gouache prov.lit. 27-May-4 Heffel, Vancouver #110/R est:12000-15000 (C.D 11000)
£4800 $8784 €7008 Personnage fantaisie (24x16cm-9x6in) s.d.1952 gouache prov.lit. 1-Jun-4 Joyner Waddington, Toronto #80/R est:12000-15000 (C.D 12000)
£4911 $8446 €7170 Standing figure (31x22cm-12x9in) s.d.1958 W/C gouache. 2-Dec-3 Joyner Waddington, Toronto #134/R est:8000-12000 (C.D 11000)
£5357 $9214 €7821 Adolescence (50x35cm-20x14in) s.i.d.1946 gouache. 2-Dec-3 Joyner Waddington, Toronto #30/R est:4000-6000 (C.D 12000)
£6400 $11712 €9344 Still life with ham (49x59cm-19x23in) s. gouache exec 1953 prov.lit. 1-Jun-4 Joyner Waddington, Toronto #33/R est:12000-15000 (C.D 16000)
£7600 $13908 €11096 Who is guilty (29x25cm-11x10in) s.d.51 i. verso gouache. 1-Jun-4 Joyner Waddington, Toronto #175/R est:8000-12000 (C.D 19000)

DALLE-ORE, Corinne (20th C) French

Works on paper
£385 $654 €550 Mercerie, coton (92x73cm-36x29in) s. mixed media canvas. 29-Nov-3 Neret-Minet, Paris #69/R

DALLEVES, Raphy (1878-1940) Swiss

Works on paper
£696 $1273 €1016 Jeune heremensarde assise (24x30cm-9x12in) s. crayon prov. 5-Jun-4 Galerie du Rhone, Sion #310/R (S.FR 1600)
£22624 $39140 €33031 Heremensarde au missel (60x47cm-24x19in) s.d.1909 crayon W/C gouache lit. 12-Dec-3 Galerie du Rhone, Sion #646/R est:50000-70000 (S.FR 50000)
£36697 $61284 €53211 Vue du village d'Heremence (41x81cm-16x32in) s. crayon ink W/C exec.c.1906. 21-Jun-3 Galerie du Rhone, Sion #470/R est:25000-35000 (S.FR 80000)

DALLIN, Cyrus Edwin (1861-1944) American

Sculpture
£2500 $4250 €3650 Pretty eagle (74x51x51cm-29x20x20in) i.num.4/21 bronze prov. 1-Nov-3 Santa Fe Art, Santa Fe #40/R est:10000-15000

DALLINGER VON DALLING, Johann Baptist (1782-1868) Austrian

£1389 $2361 €2000 Animals in meadow (37x48cm-15x19in) s.d.1845 panel. 28-Oct-3 Dorotheum, Vienna #14/R est:2500-2800
£1806 $2979 €2600 Peasant with cattle (69x57cm-27x22in) s.d.1836 panel. 2-Jul-3 Neumeister, Munich #621/R est:2500
£4698 $8409 €7000 Horses in the meadow (72x99cm-28x39in) s. 27-May-4 Dorotheum, Vienna #196/R est:7000-9000

DALL'OCA BIANCA, Angelo (1858-1942) Italian

£514 $873 €750 Children playing in garden (19x28cm-7x11in) s. panel. 8-Nov-3 Geble, Radolfzell #764/R
£1972 $3273 €2800 Il colle del pollaio (30x34cm-12x13in) s. canvas on board. 11-Jun-3 Christie's, Rome #193/R est:1500-2000
£4333 $7843 €6500 Harvest (49x31cm-19x12in) s. board lit. 30-Mar-4 Babuino, Rome #390/R est:6000
£4342 $7989 €6600 Spring on the lake (19x28cm-7x11in) s. board. 23-Jun-4 Finarte Semenzato, Rome #121/R est:1800-2200

£5298 $9642 €8000 Battistero in Siena (94x68cm-37x27in) s. prov. 21-Jun-4 Pandolfini, Florence #144/R est:8500-9500
£5333 $9813 €8000 Strolling in the park (60x33cm-24x13in) s.board. 8-Jun-4 Sotheby's, Milan #79/R est:8000-12000
Works on paper
£2319 $3803 €3200 Portrait of lady (61x40cm-24x16in) s. mixed media. 27-May-3 Il Ponte, Milan #926
£3041 $5351 €4500 Paradiso Bridge (50x70cm-20x28in) s.d.1936 pastel cardboard. 19-May-4 Il Ponte, Milan #624 est:3800-4000

DALMBERT, Daniel (1918-) French
£278 $458 €400 Composition abstraite en rouge (73x116cm-29x46in) s. 1-Jul-3 Lemoine & Ferrando, Paris #57

DALOU, Aime Jules (1838-1902) French
Sculpture
£900 $1530 €1314 Porteuse de paille (12cm-5in) s.st.f.Susse pat bronze. 28-Oct-3 Sotheby's, London #217/R
£927 $1697 €1400 Paysan la pelle sur l'Epaule (13cm-5in) s. dark brown pat. bronze. 6-Apr-4 Sotheby's, Olympia #139/R est:1000-1500
£989 $1800 €1444 Pensive nude (8cm-3in) s.st.f.A.A. Hebrard brown pat bronze. 7-Feb-4 Sloans & Kenyon, Bethesda #1206/R est:800-1200
£993 $1818 €1500 Terassier levant sa pelle horizontalement (12cm-5in) s.i. dark brown pat. bronze i.f.Susse. 6-Apr-4 Sotheby's, Olympia #136/R est:1000-1500
£993 $1818 €1500 Paysan a la binette (9cm-4in) s. green brown pat. bronze i.f.Susse. 6-Apr-4 Sotheby's, Olympia #137/R est:1000-1500
£993 $1808 €1500 Paveur au repos (12cm-5in) s.st.f.Susse pat bronze. 19-Jun-4 St-Germain-en-Laye Encheres #115/R est:1500
£993 $1808 €1500 Botteleur (10x10cm-4x4in) s.st.f.Susse pat bronze. 19-Jun-4 St-Germain-en-Laye Encheres #117/R est:1500
£993 $1808 €1500 Retour des champs (13cm-5in) s.st.f.Susse pat bronze. 19-Jun-4 St-Germain-en-Laye Encheres #118/R est:1500
£993 $1808 €1500 Botteleuse (10x9cm-4x4in) s.st.f.Susse pat bronze. 19-Jun-4 St-Germain-en-Laye Encheres #128/R est:1500
£993 $1808 €1500 Paysan, mains sur les hanches (12cm-5in) st.f.Susse s.verso pat bronze. 19-Jun-4 St-Germain-en-Laye Encheres #141/R est:1500
£1060 $1939 €1600 Casseur de Pierre Courbe (9cm-4in) s. dark brown pat. bronze i.f.Susse. 6-Apr-4 Sotheby's, Olympia #138/R est:1000-1500
£1100 $1870 €1606 Bineur debout (14cm-6in) s.st.f.Susse pat bronze. 28-Oct-3 Sotheby's, London #216/R
£1103 $1843 €1600 The reaper (43cm-17in) pat.bronze Cast. Susse Paris. 9-Jul-3 Hugo Ruef, Munich #1832 est:600
£1126 $2049 €1700 Faneuse (12cm-5in) s.st.f.Susse pat bronze. 19-Jun-4 St-Germain-en-Laye Encheres #113/R est:1500
£1192 $2170 €1800 Rebatteur de faux (12x16x11cm-5x6x4in) s.st.f.Susse pat bronze. 19-Jun-4 St-Germain-en-Laye Encheres #126/R est:1800
£1192 $2170 €1800 Retour de l'herbe (8cm-3in) s.st.f.Susse pat bronze. 19-Jun-4 St-Germain-en-Laye Encheres #139/R est:1200
£1258 $2290 €1900 Homme a la pioche (15cm-6in) s.st.f.Susse pat bronze. 19-Jun-4 St-Germain-en-Laye Encheres #129/R est:1800
£1325 $2424 €2000 Batteur de faux. s. bronze st.f.Susse. 6-Apr-4 Sotheby's, Olympia #116/R est:1500-2000
£1391 $2531 €2100 Terrassier au manteau (13cm-5in) s.st.f.Susse pat bronze. 19-Jun-4 St-Germain-en-Laye Encheres #131/R est:1500
£1391 $2531 €2100 Foreur (15cm-6in) s.st.f.Susse pat bronze. 19-Jun-4 St-Germain-en-Laye Encheres #134/R est:2000
£1400 $2380 €2044 Porteuse de lait (11cm-4in) s.st.f.Susse pat bronze. 28-Oct-3 Sotheby's, London #209/R
£1523 $2772 €2300 Porteur de corbeille (11cm-4in) s.st.f.Hebrard pat bronze. 19-Jun-4 St-Germain-en-Laye Encheres #122/R est:3000
£1549 $2572 €2200 La verite meconnue (14cm-6in) s.i. brownish pat. bronze. 11-Jun-3 Sotheby's, Amsterdam #355/R est:500-700
£1656 $3030 €2500 Le grand paysan (29cm-11in) s.i. dark brown pat. bronze. 6-Apr-4 Sotheby's, Olympia #135/R est:2500-3500
£1656 $3013 €2500 Travaux des champs (22x18cm-9x7in) s.st.f.Hebrard pat bronze relief. 19-Jun-4 St-Germain-en-Laye Encheres #123/R est:2500
£1656 $3013 €2500 Tanneur aiguisant ses outils (22cm-9in) s.st.f.Susse pat bronze. 19-Jun-4 St-Germain-en-Laye Encheres #136/R est:2500
£2148 $3802 €3200 Desespoir (19cm-7in) s. num.9 pat bronze Cast Susse lit. 30-Apr-4 Tajan, Paris #55/R est:2000-3000
£2222 $3711 €3200 Le desespoir (20x8x13cm-8x3x5in) green brown pat bronze Cast Susses. 23-Oct-3 Credit Municipal, Paris #112/R est:1000-1500
£2324 $4020 €3300 Paysan relevant ses manches (42cm-17in) s. pat bronze Cast Susse. 14-Dec-3 Eric Pillon, Calais #40/R
£2914 $5303 €4400 Badigeonneur (31cm-12in) s.st.f.Susse pat bronze. 19-Jun-4 St-Germain-en-Laye Encheres #125/R est:5000
£3345 $5787 €4750 Baigneuse assise s'essuyant le pied (18cm-7in) s. num.2 brown pat bronze Cast A A Hebrard cire perdue. 14-Dec-3 St-Germain-en-Laye Encheres #101/R est:4500-6000
£3709 $6750 €5600 Desespoir (20x14x8cm-8x6x3in) s.st.f.Susse pat bronze. 19-Jun-4 St-Germain-en-Laye Encheres #107/R est:6000
£3712 $6755 €5420 Buste de jeune femme (36cm-14in) s. bronze. 17-Jun-4 Kornfeld, Bern #302/R est:5000 (S.FR 8500)
£4336 $7371 €6200 Buste d'enfant endormi (20cm-8in) s. pat bronze st.f. Hebrard cire perdue lit. 28-Nov-3 Doutrebente, Paris #49/R est:3000-4000
£4444 $8000 €6488 Antoine-Laurent Lavoisier seated (51cm-20in) s.st.f.Susse bronze reduction. 23-Apr-4 Christie's, Rockefeller NY #138/R est:10000-15000
£4932 $7742 €7200 Miroir brise (19x12cm-7x5in) s.st.f.Susse pat bronze lit. 20-Apr-3 Deauville, France #91/R est:5500-6000
£5000 $9150 €7300 Antoine Laurent Lavoisier (28cm-11in) s.st.f.Susse pat bronze. 9-Jul-4 Sotheby's, London #155/R est:3000-5000
£6000 $10980 €8760 Grand paysan (78cm-31in) s.st.f.Susse pat bronze lit. 9-Jul-4 Sotheby's, London #158/R est:6000-8000
£7000 $12740 €10220 Etude pour une femme nue s'essuyant le pied (26cm-10in) s.st.f.Dalou brown pat bronze. 3-Feb-4 Christie's, London #112/R est:7000-9000
£10333 $18703 €15500 La brodeuse (29x24cm-11x9in) s. num.B2 black pat bronze cire perdue lit. 31-Mar-4 Sotheby's, Paris #246/R est:12000-18000
£11000 $19800 €16060 Nude bather drying her feet (40cm-16in) s.st.f.Susse brown pat bronze. 21-Apr-4 Sotheby's, London #130/R est:10000-15000
£21000 $35700 €30660 Baigneuse (52cm-20in) s. gres earthenware. 28-Oct-3 Sotheby's, London #208/R
£26207 $43503 €38000 Buste de jeune fille (54cm-21in) s.st.f.Hebrard green pat bronze lit. 2-Oct-3 Sotheby's, Paris #141/R est:25000

DALOU, Aime Jules (after) (1838-1902) French
Sculpture
£3333 $6033 €5000 Grand paysan (29cm-11in) s.st.f.Susse i. bronze. 30-Mar-4 Christie's, Amsterdam #205/R est:1800-2800

DALPAYRAT, Pierre Adrien (1844-?) French
Sculpture
£5319 $8883 €7500 Un couple d'orang-outang, tenant l'un (23x30x26cm-9x12x10in) s. sandstone col lit. 17-Jun-3 Camard, Paris #14/R est:5000-7000

DALSGAARD, Christen (1824-1907) Danish
£478 $894 €698 Woodland road in winter (17x23cm-7x9in) init.indis.d.82 or 87 panel. 25-Feb-4 Museumsbygningen, Copenhagen #185 (D.KR 5300)
£682 $1159 €996 Danish autumn landscape with figures (17x30cm-7x12in) mono,. 10-Nov-3 Rasmussen, Vejle #61/R (D.KR 7400)
£766 $1240 €1111 Coastal landscape from Lundeborg (33x43cm-13x17in) s.d.31/7 1891. 4-Aug-3 Rasmussen, Vejle #303/R (D.KR 8000)
£902 $1668 €1317 Landscape with farmer and hare (24x32cm-9x13in) init.d.1851. 15-Mar-4 Rasmussen, Vejle #486/R (D.KR 10000)

DALSGAARD, Sven (1914-1999) Danish
£362 $648 €529 The cheat (27x22cm-11x9in) s.d.1968 verso. 10-May-4 Rasmussen, Vejle #798 (D.KR 4000)
£542 $996 €791 Recipe, 10-1-78 (60x60cm-24x24in) s.d.1978 oil mixed media exhib.prov. 29-Mar-4 Rasmussen, Copenhagen #370/R (D.KR 6000)
£1033 $1725 €1508 Mother and child. in two parts tied together with rope exhib. 7-Oct-3 Rasmussen, Copenhagen #1654/R (D.KR 11000)
£1422 $2275 €2062 Evening (80x56cm-31x22in) s.d.1958 panel relief in iron exhib. 17-Sep-3 Kunsthallen, Copenhagen #34/R est:10000 (D.KR 15000)
Sculpture
£1354 $2491 €1977 Figure with circle. gilded iron. 29-Mar-4 Rasmussen, Copenhagen #347a est:15000 (D.KR 15000)
£2817 $4704 €4113 The sun rider - Man on horseback (350x200x70cm-138x79x28in) large painted iron sold with photo exec.c.1955 prov.lit. 7-Oct-3 Rasmussen, Copenhagen #233/R est:40000-60000 (D.KR 30000)
Works on paper
£287 $516 €419 Twin II (55x41cm-22x16in) s.i.d.1963 Indian ink crayon. 24-Apr-4 Rasmussen, Havnen #4062 (D.KR 3200)
£407 $729 €594 Composition (56x44cm-22x17in) s.d.1980 mixed media. 10-May-4 Rasmussen, Vejle #787/R (D.KR 4500)

DALTON, Dave (1952-) American
£377 $600 €550 Molokai Channel (76x61cm-30x24in) s.d.1980 s.i.d.verso. 23-Mar-3 Auctions by the Bay, Alameda #852/R

DALVIT, Oskar (1911-1975) Swiss
£173 $310 €253 Instrument (29x19cm-11x7in) s.d. board. 22-Mar-4 Philippe Schuler, Zurich #6007 (S.FR 400)
Works on paper
£298 $498 €432 Underwater (40x28cm-16x11in) s.d.1958 mixed media board. 23-Jun-3 Philippe Schuler, Zurich #8212 (S.FR 650)
£452 $783 €660 Two stones (49x59cm-19x23in) s.d.1946 s.i.d.1946 verso wax oil tempera. 9-Dec-3 Sotheby's, Zurich #128/R (S.FR 1000)

DALY, Matthew A (1860-1937) American
£759 $1200 €1108 Mount Lefroy and Victor Glacier, Alberta (51x61cm-20x24in) s. 7-Sep-3 Treadway Gallery, Cincinnati #580/R

DALZELL, Stuart (20th C) British
£2200 $4092 €3212 Flamenco (150x120cm-59x47in) lacquer pastel gold leaf on canvas. 8-Mar-4 Christie's, London #1

DAM VAN ISSELT, Lucie van (1871-1949) Dutch
£1399 $2406 €2000 Still life of flowers (36x33cm-14x13in) s. panel. 8-Dec-3 Glerum, Amsterdam #85/R est:500-700
£1711 $3147 €2600 Flower still life (24x25cm-9x10in) s. panel. 28-Jun-4 Sotheby's, Amsterdam #133/R est:2500-3000
£1905 $3467 €2800 Chrysanthemums in a jug by a tiled wall (41x31cm-16x12in) s. plywood. 3-Feb-4 Christie's, Amsterdam #166/R est:2000-3000
£3472 $5486 €5000 Eiersnoer - quail's eggs string (31x47cm-12x19in) s. panel. 2-Sep-3 Christie's, Amsterdam #385/R est:5000-6000
£3497 $6014 €5000 White roses (30x41cm-12x16in) s. panel. 8-Dec-3 Glerum, Amsterdam #86/R est:1500-1800

DAM, Jan van (1857-?) Dutch
£1447 $2620 €2200 Figures leaving Petrus Church of Leiden (41x31cm-16x12in) s. board. 19-Apr-4 Glerum, Amsterdam #155/R est:800-1000

DAM, Wouter (1726-1786) Dutch
£2447 $4087 €3500 Elegant lady in a garden setting (83x88cm-33x35in) s.d.1758. 30-Jun-3 Sotheby's, Amsterdam #54

DAMANE-DEMARTRAIS, Michel François (1763-1827) French
£909 $1545 €1300 Vue du marche et de la Fontaine des Saints Innocents a Paris (36x56cm-14x22in) 1-Dec-3 Rieunier, Paris #5/R

DAMAS, Eugène (1848-?) French
£1946 $3601 €2900 Couple de paysans (53x65cm-21x26in) s. 14-Mar-4 St-Germain-en-Laye Encheres #50/R est:3000

DAMAVE, Poppe (1921-1988) Dutch
Works on paper
£470 $869 €700 Diner time (67x84cm-26x33in) s.d.52 W/C. 15-Mar-4 Sotheby's, Amsterdam #182/R

DAMBADARJAA, Enkhbold (20th C) ?
£417 $654 €600 Racing at Leopardstown (40x59cm-16x23in) s. board. 26-Aug-3 James Adam, Dublin #189/R

DAMBREVILLE, Claude (20th C) Haitian
£433 $776 €650 Elegante au chapeau (60x30cm-24x12in) s. 17-May-4 Rogeon, Paris #37

DAMERON, Émile Charles (1848-1908) French
£563 $935 €800 Lavandiere au bord de l'eau (54x37cm-21x15in) s. 15-Jun-3 Peron, Melun #126a
£1033 $1860 €1550 Woman with flowers in meadow (29x15cm-11x6in) s. panel. 26-Apr-4 Rieber, Stuttgart #1002/R est:1680
£2467 $4440 €3700 Beach (13x22cm-5x9in) s. panel. 26-Apr-4 Rieber, Stuttgart #1001/R est:2500
£2754 $4516 €3800 Le gardien du troupeau (38x55cm-15x22in) s. 11-May-3 Osenat, Fontainebleau #43/R est:3500-4000

DAMGAARD-SORENSEN, Henning (1928-) Danish
£722 $1329 €1054 Composition with circles (110x146cm-43x57in) masonite. 29-Mar-4 Rasmussen, Copenhagen #381/R (D.KR 8000)

DAMIAN, Horia (1922-) Rumanian
Works on paper
£308 $514 €440 Blue composition (64x49cm-25x19in) s.d.65 mixed media board prov. 11-Oct-3 De Vuyst, Lokeren #83/R
£352 $609 €500 La cite (73x102cm-29x40in) s.i. gouache prov. 14-Dec-3 Versailles Encheres #15
£533 $960 €800 Composition (63x48cm-25x19in) s.d.verso mixed media. 25-Apr-4 Versailles Encheres #18

DAMIANI, Jorge (1931-) Italian
£354 $580 €517 Composition woth woman (30x30cm-12x12in) s.d.81. 3-Jun-3 Galeria y Remates, Montevideo #51
£647 $1100 €945 Doves (50x60cm-20x24in) s.d.74. 25-Nov-3 Galeria y Remates, Montevideo #24
£882 $1500 €1288 Bad light (60x73cm-24x29in) s. 25-Nov-3 Galeria y Remates, Montevideo #126/R
£1164 $2200 €1699 Landscape (38x46cm-15x18in) s.d.86. 22-Feb-4 Galeria y Remates, Montevideo #125/R est:2000
£1189 $1950 €1736 Moon and huge tree (38x46cm-15x18in) s. prov. 3-Jun-3 Galeria y Remates, Montevideo #107
£1250 $2300 €1825 Patio (50x61cm-20x24in) s.d.76 acrylic. 22-Jun-4 Galeria y Remates, Montevideo #91/R est:2800-3500
£1647 $2800 €2405 Psychograms (60x60cm-24x24in) s.d.1982. 25-Nov-3 Galeria y Remates, Montevideo #127
£2588 $4400 €3778 Compartments (108x78cm-43x31in) s.d.1986. 25-Nov-3 Galeria y Remates, Montevideo #125/R
Works on paper
£398 $700 €581 Abstract (65x84cm-26x33in) s.d.60 mixed media. 5-Jan-4 Galeria y Remates, Montevideo #17/R
£556 $1050 €812 Couple and walls (60x73cm-24x29in) s. collage prov. 22-Feb-4 Galeria y Remates, Montevideo #127/R
£1005 $1900 €1467 Boat (72x92cm-28x36in) s.d.73 collage. 22-Feb-4 Galeria y Remates, Montevideo #124/R est:3500

DAMIANO, Bernard (1926-2000) Italian
£267 $483 €400 Outils du peintre devant la fenetre (92x73cm-36x29in) s. 30-Mar-4 Gioffredo, Nice #106/R
£322 $570 €480 La danse (65x49cm-26x19in) paper on canvas. 29-Apr-4 Claude Aguttes, Neuilly #97
£537 $950 €800 La cafetiere bleue (73x60cm-29x24in) s.d.1994. 29-Apr-4 Claude Aguttes, Neuilly #239/R
£604 $1069 €900 Paysage de Nice (80x120cm-31x47in) s. cardboard. 29-Apr-4 Claude Aguttes, Neuilly #162/R

DAMIANOS, Constantin (1869-1953) Austrian
£420 $722 €600 Snow covered village street (31x23cm-12x9in) s. fibreboard. 4-Dec-3 Dorotheum, Graz #7/R
£634 $1052 €900 Mountain landscape in summer (31x44cm-12x17in) s. canvas on board. 12-Jun-3 Dorotheum, Graz #3/R
£1477 $2643 €2200 Donau ships (33x46cm-13x18in) s.d.21 canvas on board. 27-May-4 Dorotheum, Graz #11/R est:1100

DAMINI, Pietro (1592-1631) Italian
Works on paper
£559 $934 €800 Apollo as reinsman with figures (23x30cm-9x12in) pen htd white wash. 28-Jun-3 Bolland & Marotz, Bremen #569/R

DAMIOLI, Aldo (1952-) Italian
£2333 $4293 €3500 Venice, New York (40x40cm-16x16in) s.i.verso painted 1999. 8-Jun-4 Finarte Semenzato, Milan #459/R est:2200-2500
£2465 $4313 €3500 Venice New York (70x90cm-28x35in) s.i.d.1998 acrylic. 16-Dec-3 Finarte Semenzato, Milan #220/R est:3300-3700
£3169 $5546 €4500 Venice, New York (70x90cm-28x35in) s.i.d.1997 verso acrylic prov. 16-Dec-3 Finarte Semenzato, Milan #221/R est:3300-3700
£5102 $9133 €7500 Venice, New York, Milan (130x180cm-51x71in) s.i.verso. 16-Mar-4 Finarte Semenzato, Milan #378/R est:8000

DAMIS Y CORTES, Joaquin (19th C) Spanish
£4762 $8524 €7000 Confidences (76x58cm-30x23in) s. 22-Mar-4 Durán, Madrid #223/R est:6500

DAMISCH, Gunter (1958-) Austrian
£1931 $3534 €2800 Untitled (110x70cm-43x28in) 27-Jan-4 Dorotheum, Vienna #269/R est:5000-7000
£5594 $9510 €8000 Spash-back for my Grandmother (69x203cm-27x80in) oil mixed media. 28-Nov-3 Wiener Kunst Auktionen, Vienna #683/R est:8000-12000
£6040 $10812 €9000 Meeting with large man (150x110cm-59x43in) s.i.d. verso. 25-May-4 Dorotheum, Vienna #366/R est:9000-12000
£6040 $10812 €9000 Handing over the shield (110x70cm-43x28in) s.i.d.1990/91 verso. 25-May-4 Dorotheum, Vienna #388/R est:9000-12000
£6250 $10625 €9000 Composition (150x160cm-59x63in) s.i.d.2000/2001 verso. 28-Oct-3 Wiener Kunst Auktionen, Vienna #279/R est:7500-10000
£6711 $11879 €10000 Lonely in the night (200x160cm-79x63in) s.i.d. verso. 28-Apr-4 Wiener Kunst Auktionen, Vienna #318/R est:7000-12000
£6993 $11888 €10000 Four movements (200x200cm-79x79in) prov. 26-Nov-3 Dorotheum, Vienna #98/R est:10000-13000
Works on paper
£300 $540 €450 Untitled (48x62cm-19x24in) s.d.82 verso ink wash Indian ink sepia. 21-Apr-4 Dorotheum, Vienna #287
£467 $859 €700 Untitled (33x25cm-13x10in) s.d.88 mixed media. 9-Jun-4 Dorotheum, Salzburg #754/R
£629 $1070 €900 Untitled (98x68cm-39x27in) s.d.90/3 chl pencil W/C. 26-Nov-3 Dorotheum, Vienna #324/R

DAMM, Rudolf (attrib) (19th C) German
£387 $696 €580 Coastal town (29x37cm-11x15in) 26-Apr-4 Rieber, Stuttgart #977/R

DAMME, Emile van (1885-?) Belgian?
£1342 $2376 €2000 Vachere (45x66cm-18x26in) d. 27-Apr-4 Campo & Campo, Antwerp #230/R est:2250-2750

DAMME, Frans van (1860-1925) Belgian
£304 $575 €450 Fermette au bord de l'eau (75x45cm-30x18in) s. 17-Feb-4 Galerie Moderne, Brussels #178/R
£445 $757 €650 Barques (35x57cm-14x22in) s. panel. 10-Nov-3 Horta, Bruxelles #447
£451 $718 €650 Vue du vieux quai a Ostende (54x73cm-21x29in) s. 9-Sep-3 Vanderkindere, Brussels #38
£552 $1021 €800 Barque de peche sur la plage (57x50cm-22x20in) s. 19-Jan-4 Horta, Bruxelles #342
£567 $948 €800 Summer landscape (50x44cm-20x17in) s.d.1881. 20-Oct-3 Bernaerts, Antwerp #54/R
£769 $1308 €1100 Bateau rouge dans le port d'Ostende (50x75cm-20x30in) s. 18-Nov-3 Galerie Moderne, Brussels #838/R
£845 $1462 €1200 View of Scheldt (55x100cm-22x39in) s. 13-Dec-3 De Vuyst, Lokeren #329
£1000 $1840 €1500 Bateaux dans le port d'Ostende (50x75cm-20x30in) 14-Jun-4 Amberes, Antwerp #132

DAMME, Jacobus Johannes (1877-1956) Dutch
£400 $716 €600 Polder landscape with cow (39x59cm-15x23in) s.d.1944. 11-May-4 Vendu Notarishuis, Rotterdam #61/R

DAMME, Suzanne van (1901-1986) Belgian
£278 $442 €400 Nature morte aux fruits et au vase (60x71cm-24x28in) s.d.1925 verso. 9-Sep-3 Vanderkindere, Brussels #54
£393 $727 €570 La mer du Nord, vue de balcon (67x85cm-26x33in) s. 16-Feb-4 Horta, Bruxelles #340
£1141 $2099 €1700 Vase garni de fleurs (90x66cm-35x26in) s. 23-Mar-4 Galerie Moderne, Brussels #219/R est:1000-1500
Works on paper
£467 $845 €700 Composition (130x90cm-51x35in) s. mixed media. 30-Mar-4 Palais de Beaux Arts, Brussels #710

DAMME-SYLVA, Émile van (1853-1935) Belgian
£350 $662 €511 Cows in pasture, windmill beyond (25x35cm-10x14in) s. 19-Feb-4 Christie's, Kensington #333/R
£387 $670 €550 Porteuse de lait (20x26cm-8x10in) s. panel. 9-Dec-3 Vanderkindere, Brussels #147
£390 $651 €550 Vaches au pre (38x31cm-15x12in) s. canvas on panel. 17-Jun-3 Vanderkindere, Brussels #29
£417 $663 €600 Vaches au paturage (65x54cm-26x21in) s. 9-Sep-3 Palais de Beaux Arts, Brussels #280
£872 $1614 €1300 Cow herder with cows on the heather of Kalmthout (39x69cm-15x27in) s. 13-Mar-4 De Vuyst, Lokeren #330/R

DAMMERON, C (?) ?
Works on paper
£1277 $2132 €1800 Jeune marocaine (71x53cm-28x21in) s. pastel. 19-Oct-3 Rabourdin & Choppin de Janvry, Paris #10/R est:2200

DAMOYE, Pierre Emmanuel (1847-1916) French
£559 $951 €800 La fileuse (34x27cm-13x11in) s.d.82 panel. 27-Nov-3 Millon & Associes, Paris #119
£937 $1481 €1350 Bords de riviere (33x60cm-13x24in) s.d.76 panel prov. 2-Sep-3 Christie's, Amsterdam #235/R est:1500-2000
£1629 $2818 €2378 Plage aux rochers (33x60cm-13x24in) s.d.85 panel. 12-Dec-3 Galerie du Rhone, Sion #181/R (S.FR 3600)
£1667 $3050 €2500 Marais (34x61cm-13x24in) s. panel. 6-Jun-4 Osenat, Fontainebleau #258/R est:3000-3500
£1973 $3295 €2881 Landscape with cornfield (33x62cm-13x24in) s. panel. 24-Oct-3 Hans Widmer, St Gallen #93/R est:1800-4500 (S.FR 4400)

£2406 $4500 €3513 Landscape with cottages (36x56cm-14x22in) s.d.91. 24-Feb-4 Arthur James, Florida #125
£2808 $4774 €4100 Landscape (47x86cm-19x34in) 4-Nov-3 Ansorena, Madrid #51/R est:4100
£3050 $4940 €4300 Landscape (47x86cm-19x34in) 20-May-3 Ansorena, Madrid #172/R est:4100
£3229 $5392 €4714 Early spring landscape by small lake (58x82cm-23x32in) s.d.83. 24-Oct-3 Hans Widmer, St Gallen #92/R est:1800-4500 (S.FR 7200)
£3261 $5348 €4500 Paysage au moulin (50x73cm-20x29in) s.d.1904 prov. 11-May-3 Osenat, Fontainebleau #99/R est:5500-6000
£3333 $6033 €5000 Bord de riviere animee (33x61cm-13x24in) s. panel. 5-Apr-4 Deburaux, Boulogne #81/R est:1500-1800
£4225 $7014 €6000 Voilier et barques (46x73cm-18x29in) s.d.86. 15-Jun-3 Peron, Melun #195
£5000 $8000 €7250 Au bord du lac (37x55cm-15x22in) s. panel. 18-Sep-3 Christie's, Kensington #16/R est:5000-7000
£7778 $14000 €11356 Coucher de soleil sur l'etang (32x60cm-13x24in) s.d.87 panel prov. 22-Apr-4 Christie's, Rockefeller NY #112/R est:10000-15000

DAMSCHROEDER, Jan Jac Matthys (1825-1905) German
£778 $1300 €1136 Mother and children (38x30cm-15x12in) s. 19-Jun-3 Shelley, Hendersonville #1405
£2148 $3801 €3200 Interior scene (60x50cm-24x20in) s. lit. 30-Apr-4 Auktionhaus Georg Rehm, Augsburg #8013/R est:5500

DAN, Lars (1960-) Danish
£358 $645 €523 Composition with heads (150x165cm-59x65in) s.d.1985 verso. 24-Apr-4 Rasmussen, Havnen #4240/R (D.KR 4000)
£406 $759 €593 Composition (110x70cm-43x28in) s.d.89-1990 verso. 25-Feb-4 Kunsthallen, Copenhagen #74 (D.KR 4500)
£542 $996 €791 Figure composition (165x125cm-65x49in) s.d.99 paper prov. 29-Mar-4 Rasmussen, Copenhagen #399/R (D.KR 6000)
£751 $1254 €1096 Figure composition (165x125cm-65x49in) s.d.99 paper prov. 7-Oct-3 Rasmussen, Copenhagen #249/R (D.KR 8000)
Works on paper
£1033 $1725 €1508 Yellow and black composition (150x237cm-59x93in) s.d.98-99 mixed media W/C gouache. 7-Oct-3 Rasmussen, Copenhagen #161/R (D.KR 11000)

DAN, Virginia (20th C) American
Works on paper
£373 $600 €545 Frolic (79x99cm-31x39in) s. pastel. 20-Aug-3 James Julia, Fairfield #1736/R

DANBY, Francis (1793-1861) British
£1620 $2802 €2300 Moonlit view of a ruined castle (25x38cm-10x15in) panel prov. 10-Dec-3 Bonhams & James Adam, Dublin #22/R est:2000-4000
£9000 $15300 €13140 Figures by a village stream with figures by a terraced houses (40x50cm-16x20in) s. prov. 25-Nov-3 Christie's, London #69/R est:10000-15000
Works on paper
£620 $1141 €905 Norweigan landscape (13x20cm-5x8in) W/C pencil prov.exhib. 8-Jun-4 Bonhams, New Bond Street #37/R
£629 $1070 €900 Extensive landscape (9x13cm-4x5in) s. W/C. 27-Nov-3 Bassenge, Berlin #5548
£658 $1211 €1000 Port Abergnotslyn with figures fishing from rocks (31x43cm-12x17in) s. W/C ink. 22-Jun-4 Mealy's, Castlecomer #773/R est:1000-1500
£750 $1275 €1095 Pont Aberglaslyn (31x43cm-12x17in) s. W/C ink. 18-Nov-3 Sotheby's, Olympia #180/R

DANBY, Francis (attrib) (1793-1861) British
£756 $1300 €1104 Nymphs before a lake at dusk (71x99cm-28x39in) s.indis.d.31. 6-Dec-3 Neal Auction Company, New Orleans #1096/R

DANBY, James Francis (1816-1875) British
£3800 $7030 €5548 Douglas, Isle of Man (28x44cm-11x17in) s.d.1866 i.verso. 10-Mar-4 Sotheby's, Olympia #197/R est:2000-3000

DANBY, Ken (1940-) Canadian
Works on paper
£982 $1689 €1434 October Sun (48x67cm-19x26in) s.d.68 W/C prov. 2-Dec-3 Joyner Waddington, Toronto #455 est:2000-2500 (C.D 2200)
£1118 $2001 €1632 The scraper (33x54cm-13x21in) s.d.1969 W/C prov.exhib. 27-May-4 Heffel, Vancouver #182/R est:2500-3500 (C.D 2750)

DANBY, Thomas (1818-1886) British
£2035 $3500 €2971 Beautiful Vista (41x61cm-16x24in) s. prov. 7-Dec-3 Freeman, Philadelphia #35 est:2000-3000
£2568 $4750 €3749 Farmstead in Sussex (66x127cm-26x50in) s.i. 14-Jan-4 Dallas Auction Gallery, Dallas #459/R est:3000-5000
Works on paper
£250 $468 €365 Girl fetching water, a stone bridge, cattle and hills beyond (42x64cm-17x25in) s. W/C. 20-Jul-4 Bearnes, Exeter #508

DANCASTER, Barbara W (20th C) American
Works on paper
£230 $425 €336 Lake in winter (48x74cm-19x29in) s.d.1985 W/C. 13-Mar-4 Auctions by the Bay, Alameda #398/R

DANCE, Nathaniel (1734-1811) British
£3600 $6624 €5256 Portrait of Robert Marsh of the East India Company (127x102cm-50x40in) prov. 11-Jun-4 Christie's, London #30/R est:3000-5000

DANCE, Nathaniel (attrib) (1734-1811) British
£16000 $29440 €23360 Portrait of Elizabeth Balguy nee Gould (76x64cm-30x25in) prov. 24-Jun-4 Ewbank, Send #534/R est:5000-8000

DANCHIN, Leon (1887-1939) French
Sculpture
£1773 $2961 €2500 Deux setters en arret (18x37cm-7x15in) s. num.29/50 green pat bronze Cast Susse. 14-Oct-3 Vanderkindere, Brussels #140/R est:1000-1500
Works on paper
£699 $1189 €1000 Etudes de setter gordon et spagniel (31x46cm-12x18in) s. gouache pair. 20-Nov-3 Millon & Associes, Paris #124/R

D'ANCONA, Vito (1825-1884) Italian
£13406 $21986 €18500 Woman in profile (25x18cm-10x7in) prov.lit. 27-May-3 Finarte Semenzato, Milan #77/R est:16000-18000

D'ANCONA, Vito (attrib) (1825-1884) Italian
£1079 $1770 €1500 Madonna and Child (60x33cm-24x13in) 10-Jun-3 Pandolfini, Florence #18/R est:700-800

DANDELOT, Elisabeth (20th C) French
Works on paper
£629 $1083 €900 Fes (63x47cm-25x19in) s.i.d.1928 W/C. 8-Dec-3 Tajan, Paris #252/R

DANDINI, Cesare (1595-1658) Italian
£29371 $50517 €42000 Madonna and Child (77x62cm-30x24in) 2-Dec-3 Sotheby's, Milan #109/R est:20000-30000

DANDINI, Ottaviano (attrib) (18th C) Italian
Works on paper
£2361 $4250 €3447 Evangelist Saint Mark (23x20cm-9x8in) red black chk. 21-Jan-4 Doyle, New York #42/R est:3000-5000

DANDINI, Pietro (1646-1712) Italian
£3600 $6480 €5256 Diana the huntress (43x34cm-17x13in) 21-Apr-4 Bonhams, New Bond Street #62/R est:3000-5000
£8803 $14173 €12500 Santa Caterine d'Alessandria (70x56cm-28x22in) 8-May-3 Farsetti, Prato #611/R est:13000-16000

DANDOY, Auguste (1839-1893) Belgian
£921 $1695 €1400 River landscape with fishermen (44x72cm-17x28in) s.d.90. 22-Jun-4 Palais de Beaux Arts, Brussels #218

DANDRE BARDON, Michel (1700-1778) French
Works on paper
£1020 $1827 €1500 Etudes de soldats, dont un a terre (23x18cm-9x7in) i.verso red chk pen brown ink prov. 18-Mar-4 Christie's, Paris #283/R est:1500-2000
£1389 $2500 €2028 Dispersion of the Dacians (15x26cm-6x10in) i. pen ink wash over black chk. 21-Jan-4 Sotheby's, New York #108/R est:3000-3500
£2500 $4600 €3800 Figure d'homme, bras tendus (15x25cm-6x10in) s. sangine. 23-Jun-4 Sotheby's, Paris #12/R est:3000-4000
£5578 $9985 €8200 Deux scenes avec des soldats romains (38x21cm-15x8in) black pencil brown wash 2 in one frame. 19-Mar-4 Piasa, Paris #61/R est:4000-5000

DANDRE BARDON, Michel (attrib) (1700-1778) French
Works on paper
£699 $1168 €1000 Pelerind d'Emmaus (45x31cm-18x12in) pen ink htd gouache. 30-Jun-3 Bailly Pommery, Paris #6

DANDRIDGE, Bartholomew (17/18th C) British
£154321 $250000 €225309 Portrait of Lord Carnarvon and Lady Caroline Leigh as children with dog (132x152cm-52x60in) s.d.1738 prov. 3-Aug-3 North East Auctions, Portsmouth #1663/R est:50000-70000

DANDRIDGE, Bartholomew (attrib) (17/18th C) British
£8800 $14960 €12848 Portrait of a boy a member of the Nicolini family (163x112cm-64x44in) 27-Nov-3 Sotheby's, London #133/R est:7000-10000

DANE, David F (20th C) British
£280 $468 €409 Two wherries (56x81cm-22x32in) s. 17-Oct-3 Keys, Aylsham #622

DANEDI, Stefano (1608-1689) Italian
£11258 $20490 €17000 Madonna and Child with lamb in landscape (105x80cm-41x31in) 16-Jun-4 Christie's, Rome #487/R est:15000-20000

DANEK-SEDLACEK, Frantisek (1892-?) Czechoslovakian
£282 $504 €400 Still life with fruit (22x47cm-9x19in) i. lit. 8-Jan-4 Allgauer, Kempten #2367

DANEO, Renato (1908-1978) Italian
£629 $1145 €950 Mare (73x54cm-29x21in) s. 18-Jun-4 Stadion, Trieste #375

DANERI, Eugenio (1881-1970) Argentinian
£12363 $22500 €18050 Little harbour (50x60cm-20x24in) s.d.59 cardboard on canvas. 29-Jun-4 Arroyo, Buenos Aires #81/R est:11000

DANET, Albert (?) French?
£267 $477 €400 Chaumiere (46x55cm-18x22in) s. panel. 16-May-4 Renault-Aubry, Pontivy #435b

DANGEL, Miguel von (1946-) Venezuelan/German
£975 $1560 €1424 Map Series (80x70cm-31x28in) mixed media exec.1991. 21-Sep-3 Subastas Odalys, Caracas #78/R
Works on paper
£253 $405 €369 Crucifixion (56x38cm-22x15in) s. mixed media exec.1989. 21-Sep-3 Subastas Odalys, Caracas #66
£992 $1825 €1488 Figures with shawls (87x68cm-34x27in) s. mixed media exec.1990. 27-Jun-4 Subastas Odalys, Caracas #173
£1029 $1750 €1502 Untitled (73x101cm-29x40in) mixed media exec.1989. 23-Nov-3 Subastas Odalys, Caracas #121/R

DANGELO, Sergio (1931-) Italian
£544 $974 €800 For the seagulls (50x70cm-20x28in) s. oil collage prov. 16-Mar-4 Finarte Semenzato, Milan #110/R
£748 $1339 €1100 Meshes of the afternoon (20x37cm-8x15in) s.i.verso. 16-Mar-4 Finarte Semenzato, Milan #112/R
£775 $1356 €1100 Composition with table and lamp (40x30cm-16x12in) s.i.d.1954 verso. 16-Dec-3 Finarte Semenzato, Milan #232/R
£909 $1545 €1300 Abandoned garden (50x60cm-20x24in) s.i.d.55 verso prov.exhib. 26-Nov-3 Pandolfini, Florence #59/R
£1014 $1784 €1500 Remains (70x100cm-28x39in) s. s.i.d.1963 on stretcher. 24-May-4 Christie's, Milan #88/R est:1200-1800
£1020 $1827 €1500 Mirage ofthe sand castle (39x69cm-15x27in) s.d.1957. 16-Mar-4 Finarte Semenzato, Milan #431 est:1700
£1119 $1902 €1600 Cinemascope (60x120cm-24x47in) s.d.1958. 25-Nov-3 Sotheby's, Milan #50/R est:1000-1500
£1678 $3003 €2500 Pour connaitre mon amour (50x70cm-20x28in) s.i.d.1955 enamel mixed media paper on canvas three. 25-May-4 Sotheby's, Milan #82/R est:2000
£2238 $3804 €3200 White town. Climbing sign (25x55cm-10x22in) s.i.d.57 verso tempera cardboard two. 25-Nov-3 Sotheby's, Milan #53/R est:1000-1500
£2568 $4519 €3800 Armed vegetables (79x60cm-31x24in) init. s.i.d.1952 verso exhib. 24-May-4 Christie's, Milan #83/R est:1500-2000

D'ANGELO, Sergio (20th C) Italian
£667 $1213 €1000 Composition (70x100cm-28x39in) s.d.1964. 12-Jul-4 Il Ponte, Milan #1018
Works on paper
£473 $832 €700 Composition (30x40cm-12x16in) s. mixed media on canvas exec.1967. 19-May-4 Il Ponte, Milan #1142

DANGER, Henri (1857-1937) French
£839 $1427 €1200 Le village pres de la riviere (65x81cm-26x32in) s.i. 24-Nov-3 Boscher, Cherbourg #832/R
£11111 $20000 €16222 Venus and Cupid (200cm-79in circular) s. prov. 21-Jan-4 Sotheby's, New York #179/R est:10000-15000

D'ANGERS, David (after) (19th C) ?
Sculpture
£4698 $8315 €7000 Philopomene (90cm-35in) bears sig.d.1837 pat bronze. 29-Apr-4 Sotheby's, Paris #206/R est:5000-6000

DANHAUSER, Josef (1805-1845) Austrian
£486 $768 €700 Newborn (18x22cm-7x9in) s. 6-Sep-3 Schopman, Hamburg #658/R
£5369 $9503 €8000 Wellwishers (31x26cm-12x10in) lit. 28-Apr-4 Wiener Kunst Auktionen, Vienna #7/R est:5000-20000
£147651 $261342 €220000 Reading the will (94x112cm-37x44in) s.d.1844 panel prov.lit. 28-Apr-4 Wiener Kunst Auktionen, Vienna #17/R est:180000-350000
Works on paper
£310 $515 €450 Old man (16x12cm-6x5in) s. i. verso pencil. 30-Sep-3 Dorotheum, Vienna #120
£403 $741 €600 Important letter (21x27cm-8x11in) W/C pencil. 26-Mar-4 Dorotheum, Vienna #119/R
£2838 $5166 €4143 Half figure of a young girl, facing right, with sketch of a head (29x21cm-11x8in) pencil htd white prov.exhib.lit. 17-Jun-4 Kornfeld, Bern #6/R est:7500 (S.FR 6500)

DANIEL, Abraham (?-1806) British
Miniatures
£2200 $3960 €3212 Blue eyed child in a coat with frilled collar (4cm-2in) bracelet clasp mount oval exhib.lit. 22-Apr-4 Bonhams, New Bond Street #57/R est:2000-3000
£2800 $5040 €4088 Blue eyed child in a white dress and bonnet (5cm-2in) gold frame oval exhib. 22-Apr-4 Bonhams, New Bond Street #60/R est:1000-1500
£3000 $5400 €4380 John Mackie junior, as a boy (6cm-2in) gold frame oval prov.exhib. 22-Apr-4 Bonhams, New Bond Street #72/R est:2000-3000
£7500 $13500 €10950 Lady wearing a dress with fringed shoulder caps (5cm-2in) gold fausse-montre locket col enamel oval exhib.lit. 22-Apr-4 Bonhams, New Bond Street #53/R est:4000-6000
£14000 $25200 €20440 Child, traditionally called Princess Charlotte Augusta (5cm-2in) pearl glass enamel gold frame oval red case prov.exhib.lit. 22-Apr-4 Bonhams, New Bond Street #69/R est:6000-8000

DANIEL, Henry Wilkinson (fl.1909-1936) British
£300 $516 €438 View of Rye (51x76cm-20x30in) 2-Dec-3 Gorringes, Lewes #2341

DANIEL, Joseph (1760-1803) British
Miniatures
£5500 $9900 €8030 Officer, probably a member of the Vincent family (7cm-3in) gold frame oval prov.exhib.lit. 22-Apr-4 Bonhams, New Bond Street #119/R est:3000-5000

DANIEL, William Swift (1865-1933) American
£882 $1500 €1288 Atmospheric coastal (41x61cm-16x24in) s. prov. 18-Nov-3 John Moran, Pasadena #155 est:1200-1800

DANIELL, Samuel (1775-1811) British
Works on paper
£1800 $2934 €2628 Female Kudu (19x21cm-7x8in) pencil prov. 25-Sep-3 Christie's, London #450 est:1000-1500
£2200 $3586 €3212 Waterfall in Ceylon with deer resting in the foreground (33x43cm-13x17in) pencil W/C prov.exhib. 24-Sep-3 Christie's, London #22/R est:2500-3500
£2800 $4564 €4088 African Korah chieftain's daughter, in an animal skin, crouching by a river (30x23cm-12x9in) pencil W/C prov. 25-Sep-3 Christie's, London #447/R est:3000-5000
£3000 $4890 €4380 African figure studies (24x16cm-9x6in) two i. pencil grey wash seven folio. 25-Sep-3 Christie's, London #449 est:3500-4500
£9500 $16150 €13870 Native women bathing in a river, Ceylon (36x45cm-14x18in) pencil W/C. 4-Nov-3 Bonhams, New Bond Street #50/R est:8000-10000
£10000 $17000 €14600 Bird from east, bird studies (36x39cm-14x15in) W/C album of nineteen. 4-Nov-3 Bonhams, New Bond Street #52/R est:8000-12000

DANIELL, Thomas (1749-1840) British
£26000 $42380 €37960 Zenana Scene (46x36cm-18x14in) prov.exhib.lit. 24-Sep-3 Christie's, London #12 est:15000-25000
£65000 $105950 €94900 Hill House, former residence of Augustus Cleveland at Bhagalpore (58x81cm-23x32in) panel prov.lit. 24-Sep-3 Christie's, London #4/R est:40000-60000
£68000 $120360 €99280 South east view of Fort St. George, Madras, storm approaching (71x91cm-28x36in) prov.lit. 27-Apr-4 Bonhams, New Bond Street #38/R est:30000-50000
£90000 $146700 €131400 View of Panchganga Ghat, Benares (56x64cm-22x25in) init.d.1802 panel prov.lit. 24-Sep-3 Christie's, London #71/R est:30000-50000
Works on paper
£460 $842 €672 Friends curry near Chatham (18x28cm-7x11in) pen ink wash over pencil prov. 8-Jul-4 Duke & Son, Dorchester #85/R
£480 $816 €701 Hindu temple against a giant boulder (32x39cm-13x15in) i.verso grey wash W/C prov. 26-Nov-3 Hamptons Fine Art, Godalming #48
£1600 $2608 €2336 Drawing for Oriental Scenery (41x58cm-16x23in) pencil grey wash two prov.lit. 24-Sep-3 Christie's, London #19/R est:2000-3000
£1700 $2771 €2482 Three studies of animals (23x28cm-9x11in) pencil prov.exhib.lit. three. 24-Sep-3 Christie's, London #11/R est:1200-1800
£2600 $4238 €3796 Drawings for Oriental Scenery (48x69cm-19x27in) i. pencil prov. 24-Sep-3 Christie's, London #18/R est:3000-5000
£3800 $6194 €5548 Great rock near Tatcul (36x53cm-14x21in) i.verso pencil grey brown blue wash prov.exhib. 24-Sep-3 Christie's, London #6/R est:2500-3500
£3800 $6194 €5548 Drawings for Oriental Scenery (43x58cm-17x23in) pencil pen brown ink brown wash two prov. 24-Sep-3 Christie's, London #17/R est:2000-3000
£5500 $8965 €8030 Young elephant with his Indian trainer (23x36cm-9x14in) pencil prov.exhib. 24-Sep-3 Christie's, London #9/R est:2500-3500

DANIELL, Thomas and William (18th C) British
Prints
£4000 $6520 €5840 Mausoleum of Sultan Chusero. Entrance to the Mausoleums (49x65cm-19x26in) hand col aquatint pair. 24-Sep-3 Christie's, London #243/R est:2000-3000
Works on paper
£1600 $2608 €2336 Drawings for Oriental Scenery (43x61cm-17x24in) pencil two prov. 24-Sep-3 Christie's, London #16/R est:2000-3000
£1600 $2832 €2336 South-east view of Nancul, Madras (34x54cm-13x21in) i.d.85 d.June 4th 1792 verso pencil grey wash exhib. 29-Apr-4 Christie's, Kensington #97 est:1500-2000
£1700 $2771 €2482 Standing Indian girl, with details of ornaments. A Maharatta (23x18cm-9x7in) both i. pencil prov.exhib.lit. two. 24-Sep-3 Christie's, London #13/R est:1500-2000
£1800 $2934 €2628 Four studies of Indian male servants (18x10cm-7x4in) i. pencil prov.lit. 24-Sep-3 Christie's, London #14/R est:1000-1500
£2800 $4564 €4088 Papanasam (43x56cm-17x22in) i. pencil brown grey wash prov. 24-Sep-3 Christie's, London #7/R est:2000-3000
£4500 $7335 €6570 Four studies of elephants (23x33cm-9x13in) one i. pencil four prov. 24-Sep-3 Christie's, London #8/R est:2500-3500
£17000 $27710 €24820 Hindu temple in the Fort of Rohtas, Bihar (36x53cm-14x21in) i. pencil W/C prov.exhib. 24-Sep-3 Christie's, London #73/R est:12000-18000
£24000 $39120 €35040 View on the Chitpore Road, Calcutta (43x61cm-17x24in) pencil pen brown ink W/C prov.exhib. 24-Sep-3 Christie's, London #72/R est:20000-30000
£28000 $45640 €40880 Gateway of the Taj Mahal, Agra (51x69cm-20x27in) i. pencil W/C prov.exhib. 24-Sep-3 Christie's, London #75/R est:25000-35000
£110000 $179300 €160600 Entrance to the Khusrau Bagh at Allahabad (48x69cm-19x27in) pencil W/C prov.lit. 24-Sep-3 Christie's, London #74/R est:35000-45000

DANIELL, William (1769-1837) British
£8500 $15470 €12410 Fire pheasant of the Island of Java (23x30cm-9x12in) i. verso board painted 1831. 1-Jul-4 Sotheby's, London #159/R est:8000-12000
£8500 $15470 €12410 Musk deer and birds of paradise (23x30cm-9x12in) i. verso board. 1-Jul-4 Sotheby's, London #160/R est:8000-12000
£21000 $38220 €30660 View of Newcastle on the river Tyne from St Ann's (94x184cm-37x72in) exhib. 1-Jul-4 Sotheby's, London #137/R est:15000-20000
Works on paper
£280 $476 €409 Ship off shore (18x14cm-7x6in) i.d.88 pencil wash. 19-Nov-3 Christie's, Kensington #323/R
£400 $708 €584 Old Fort Ghaut, Calcutta (20x30cm-8x12in) pencil laid paper. 29-Apr-4 Christie's, Kensington #90
£450 $806 €657 Nabob's Trooper, Lucknow (16x9cm-6x4in) i. pencil prov. 25-May-4 Bonhams, Knightsbridge #16/R
£1050 $1785 €1533 Arcot Gate, Vellore (46x66cm-18x26in) pencil grey wash prov. 26-Nov-3 Hamptons Fine Art, Godalming #64 est:250-400
£1100 $2013 €1606 Tomb of Sher Shah, Sasseraf (46x58cm-18x23in) pencil wash exhib. 8-Jul-4 Duke & Son, Dorchester #87/R
£1900 $3477 €2774 Mosque at Rajimahl (43x66cm-17x26in) pencil wash exhib. 8-Jul-4 Duke & Son, Dorchester #86/R

£3600 $6120 €5256 Windsor Castle from the playground, Eton (30x50cm-12x20in) s.d.1827 W/C over pencil scratching out prov.exhib. 4-Nov-3 Bonhams, New Bond Street #42/R est:4000-6000
£4200 $6846 €6132 Purdah Cars (18x28cm-7x11in) i. prov.exhib. 24-Sep-3 Christie's, London #10/R est:1200-1800
£5000 $8150 €7300 Rich Mohammedan (10x15cm-4x6in) i.verso pencil W/C prov.exhib.lit. 24-Sep-3 Christie's, London #78/R est:2500-3500
£9000 $16470 €13140 Estuary of the River Leven near Ulverston, Cumbria (156x24cm-61x9in) init. i.verso pencil W/C gum arabic htd bodycol prov.exhib. 3-Jun-4 Christie's, London #142/R est:2000-3000
£22000 $35860 €32120 View of the Ganges and the Barna Temple, Benares (43x41cm-17x16in) pencil pen ink W/C scratching out prov.lit. 24-Sep-3 Christie's, London #5/R est:25000-35000

DANIELL, William (studio) (1769-1837) British
£10588 $18000 €15458 Egyptian scene with pyramids, an obelisk and a Mosque (74x93cm-29x37in) 19-Nov-3 Bonhams & Butterfields, San Francisco #127/R

DANIELS, Alfred (1924-) British
£400 $728 €584 Rowers by the river (20x25cm-8x10in) s.d.03 acrylic board. 15-Jun-4 Bonhams, Knightsbridge #96/R
£420 $739 €613 Highland cattle, Glenmorangie (38x45cm-15x18in) s. acrylic. 18-May-4 Woolley & Wallis, Salisbury #209/R
£600 $1092 €876 Fisherman in the harbour (53x63cm-21x25in) s.d.03 board. 15-Jun-4 Bonhams, Knightsbridge #4/R
£650 $1183 €949 Thames Tug, Cherry Tree Wharf (30x61cm-12x24in) s.d.1969 board. 1-Jul-4 Christie's, Kensington #251/R
£1900 $3458 €2774 In the pet shop (91x117cm-36x46in) s.d.1954 board. 1-Jul-4 Christie's, Kensington #250/R est:800-1200
Works on paper
£400 $704 €584 Red deer, Dalwhinnie (29x40cm-11x16in) s. W/C htd white. 18-May-4 Woolley & Wallis, Salisbury #283/R

DANIELS, Andries (attrib) (c.1580-1640) Flemish
£1901 $3327 €2700 Buste de Vierge dans un guirlande de fleurs (21x16cm-8x6in) copper. 19-Dec-3 Delvaux, Paris #94/R est:1200-1500
£3974 $7232 €6000 Virgin and Child surrounded by a floral wreath (91x70cm-36x28in) i. panel. 16-Jun-4 Dorotheum, Vienna #91/R est:8000-12000

DANIELS, Bernie (1916-) Australian
£393 $711 €574 Honey and dreaming (45x60cm-18x24in) 4-Apr-4 International Art Centre, Auckland #202/R (NZ.D 1100)

DANIELS, Dolly Nampitjinpa (1931-) Australian
Works on paper
£1875 $3506 €2813 Warlukurlangu jukurrpa (121x91cm-48x36in) bears name.verso synthetic polymer paint canvasboard prov. 26-Jul-4 Sotheby's, Melbourne #420/R est:5000-8000 (A.D 4800)

DANIELS, Fred H (1872-) American
£350 $625 €511 Early November Waltham, Mass (30x41cm-12x16in) s.d.1934 init.i.verso board. 8-Jan-4 James Julia, Fairfield #1012/R

DANIELS, George Fisher (1821-?) American
£449 $750 €656 White mountains with grazing cows in foreground (13x18cm-5x7in) s. s.i.d.1865 verso board. 16-Nov-3 CRN Auctions, Cambridge #21/R

DANIELS, William (1813-1880) British
£706 $1200 €1031 Flowers girls (39x30cm-15x12in) s. panel. 21-Nov-3 Skinner, Boston #243/R est:1200-1600

DANIELS, William (attrib) (1813-1880) British
£320 $544 €467 Portrait of brigand wearing feather plumed hat (46x36cm-18x14in) 22-Nov-3 Bonhams, Chester #348

DANIELSEN, Steffan (20th C) Scandinavian
£1264 $2325 €1845 Rural district in evening, Nolsoy (68x68cm-27x27in) s. 29-Mar-4 Rasmussen, Copenhagen #255 est:4000 (D.KR 14000)
£1264 $2325 €1845 Coastal landscape, Nolsoy, Faroe Islands (47x100cm-19x39in) 29-Mar-4 Rasmussen, Copenhagen #265 est:3500 (D.KR 14000)

DANIELSON, Carl Johan (1866-1945) Finnish
£490 $911 €730 Apple-tree in blossom (45x63cm-18x25in) s.d.1916. 7-Mar-4 Bukowskis, Helsinki #307/R

DANIELSON-GAMBOGI, Elin (1861-1919) Finnish
£4133 $7399 €6200 Flowering begonia (23x14cm-9x6in) s. board. 15-May-4 Hagelstam, Helsinki #64/R est:5000
£4412 $7500 €6442 Red gate (41x61cm-16x24in) s. i.verso. 22-Nov-3 Jackson's, Cedar Falls #7/R est:7500-10000
£6643 $11294 €9500 Sunset (22x43cm-9x17in) s. 29-Nov-3 Bukowskis, Helsinki #71/R est:7000-9000
£8389 $15604 €12500 The red gate (43x61cm-17x24in) s. 7-Mar-4 Bukowskis, Helsinki #308/R est:7000
£13986 $23776 €20000 Southern sunshine (40x50cm-16x20in) s.d.1901 canvas on board. 29-Nov-3 Bukowskis, Helsinki #96/R est:20000-25000
£15035 $25559 €21500 Two children in corn field (70x53cm-28x21in) 29-Nov-3 Bukowskis, Helsinki #99/R est:15000-18000
£16901 $29239 €24000 Daisies in meadow (36x24cm-14x9in) s. canvas on board. 13-Dec-3 Hagelstam, Helsinki #82/R est:15000
£23649 $42331 €35000 Apple-tree in blossom (54x82cm-21x32in) s. 8-May-4 Bukowskis, Helsinki #98/R est:40000-50000
£43662 $75535 €62000 Girl in field of rye (60x50cm-24x20in) s.d.1899 exhib. 13-Dec-3 Hagelstam, Helsinki #80/R est:50000
£43662 $75535 €62000 Winter in Montmartre (46x61cm-18x24in) s.d.1892 exhib. 13-Dec-3 Hagelstam, Helsinki #81/R est:35000
£74324 $133041 €110000 About to go to bed (69x49cm-27x19in) s.d.1897 exhib. 8-May-4 Bukowskis, Helsinki #60/R est:50000-60000

DANIELSSON, Emil (1882-1967) Finnish
£479 $766 €680 The woodsman (68x52cm-27x20in) init.d.1908. 18-Sep-3 Hagelstam, Helsinki #1008/R

DANIOTH, Heinrich (1896-1953) German
£441 $749 €644 Portrait of bearded man (39x27cm-15x11in) mono.d.14 paper. 5-Nov-3 Dobiaschofsky, Bern #459/R (S.FR 1000)
£16594 $30201 €24227 Goscheneralp (70x56cm-28x22in) s.d.1920 lit. 16-Jun-4 Fischer, Luzern #1334/R est:16000-18000 (S.FR 38000)
£23581 $41502 €34428 Margritli (65x53cm-26x21in) s.d.48 masonite prov.exhib.lit. 22-May-4 Galerie Gloggner, Luzern #26/R est:23000-25000 (S.FR 54000)
Works on paper
£262 $477 €383 Peasants taking an oath (56x33cm-22x13in) d.13/V 1936 chl. 16-Jun-4 Fischer, Luzern #2738 (S.FR 600)
£480 $845 €701 Nicco and the actor (37x25cm-15x10in) s.i. pencil pen prov.exhib.lit. 22-May-4 Galerie Gloggner, Luzern #25/R (S.FR 1100)
£498 $846 €727 Painter and young woman (19x18cm-7x7in) mono. wash Indian ink brush htd white. 19-Nov-3 Fischer, Luzern #2606/R (S.FR 1100)
£1448 $2462 €2114 Peasant wearing hood (50x44cm-20x17in) s.i. pencil lit. 19-Nov-3 Fischer, Luzern #2605/R est:900-1300 (S.FR 3200)
£2036 $3462 €2973 Rutli oath (63x27cm-25x11in) Indian ink lit. 19-Nov-3 Fischer, Luzern #2604/R est:1500-2000 (S.FR 4500)

DANISH SCHOOL, 19th C
£5398 $9500 €7881 Cello player (81x61cm-32x24in) board painted c.1880. 23-May-4 Treadway Gallery, Cincinnati #539/R est:10000-15000
Sculpture
£20805 $36826 €31000 Cupidon (142cm-56in) st.f.Rasmussen pat bronze. 29-Apr-4 Sotheby's, Paris #115/R est:8000-12000

DANKMEYER, Carel Bernardus (1861-1923) Dutch
£336 $578 €480 View of a landscape (12x35cm-5x14in) s. board. 7-Dec-3 Sotheby's, Amsterdam #651/R
£361 $650 €527 Profile portrait of a child (30x25cm-12x10in) init. canvas on panel. 23-Jan-4 Freeman, Philadelphia #161/R
£753 $1281 €1100 City view of Amsterdam with Lutheran church (37x46cm-15x18in) s. 5-Nov-3 Vendue Huis, Gravenhage #159/R
£816 $1486 €1200 Impression of summer (32x43cm-13x17in) s. cardboard on plywood. 3-Feb-4 Christie's, Amsterdam #213 est:500-700
£890 $1514 €1300 Amersfoort bridge (43x34cm-17x13in) s. marouflе. 5-Nov-3 Vendue Huis, Gravenhage #158
£952 $1733 €1400 View of the Grote Kerk, Maassluis (37x54cm-15x21in) s. 3-Feb-4 Christie's, Amsterdam #370/R est:1000-1500
£1224 $2229 €1800 Avondstemming noordzee, sailing vessels on the Northsea at sunset (60x91cm-24x36in) s. i.on stretcher. 3-Feb-4 Christie's, Amsterdam #291/R est:1200-1600
£1250 $2300 €1900 Windmills by a river (61x83cm-24x33in) s. 22-Jun-4 Christie's, Amsterdam #179/R est:1500-2000
£1293 $2352 €1900 Polder landscape (25x38cm-10x15in) s. plywood. 3-Feb-4 Christie's, Amsterdam #262/R est:1200-1600
£1769 $3219 €2600 De lekpoort, Vianen, city gate by the river Lek (60x85cm-24x33in) s. 3-Feb-4 Christie's, Amsterdam #358/R est:1200-1600
£1781 $3027 €2600 Peasant in kitchen garden (49x65cm-19x26in) s. exhib. 5-Nov-3 Vendue Huis, Gravenhage #110/R est:2000-3000

DANLER, Herbert (1928-) Austrian
£1560 $2606 €2200 Tyrolean village (28x42cm-11x17in) mono.d.1979 panel. 16-Oct-3 Dorotheum, Salzburg #726/R est:1200-1800
£1702 $2843 €2400 Fendels village (27x42cm-11x17in) mono.d.1978 panel. 16-Oct-3 Dorotheum, Salzburg #727/R est:1200-1800
£1745 $3228 €2600 Gallstein (27x44cm-11x17in) mono. s.i.d.1999 verso panel. 9-Mar-4 Dorotheum, Vienna #259/R est:1500-2000
£1986 $3316 €2800 Schnalser Hofe (29x62cm-11x24in) mono. s.i.d.1997 verso panel. 14-Oct-3 Dorotheum, Vienna #296/R est:1500-2000

DANLOUX, Henri Pierre (1753-1809) French
£279 $500 €407 Portrait of a lady (84x66cm-33x26in) s. 16-May-4 CRN Auctions, Cambridge #50/R
£1655 $3013 €2500 Portrait d'un ecclesiastique (72x61cm-28x24in) oval. 21-Jun-4 Tajan, Paris #107/R est:3000-4000
£21053 $38737 €32000 Portrait du violoniste Henri-Joseph Perignon (15x13cm-6x5in) mono.d.1783 panel prov. 24-Jun-4 Christie's, Paris #103/R est:15000-20000
£1229050 $2200000 €1794413 Baron de Besenval (46x37cm-18x15in) 27-May-4 Sotheby's, New York #35/R est:1000000-1500000
Works on paper
£7237 $13316 €11000 Portraits de Don Luis et Don Antonio (12x15cm-5x6in) i. i.verso crayon chl chk htd gouache oval prov. 23-Jun-4 Sotheby's, Paris #20/R est:8000-12000

DANLOUX, Henri Pierre (attrib) (1753-1809) French
£775 $1286 €1100 Portrait de Garat l'Aine, de Bordeaux (22x17cm-9x7in) i.verso canvas on cardboard oval. 13-Jun-3 Ferri, Paris #49/R
£1931 $3225 €2800 Portrait d'une fillette (29x24cm-11x9in) 17-Nov-3 Delorme & Bocage, Paris #82/R est:3000-4000
£3356 $6175 €5000 Portrait de jeune femme, portant une guirlande de fleurs (21x18cm-8x7in) 24-Mar-4 Tajan, Paris #137/R est:2000-3000

DANLOUX, Henri Pierre (school) (1753-1809) French
£9790 $16350 €14000 Portrait de la Marquise de Pange (73x60cm-29x24in) oval. 29-Jun-3 St-Germain-en-Laye Encheres #3/R est:3000-3500

DANN, Frode N (1892-?) American/Danish
£385 $700 €562 Nudes in California landscape (26x32cm-10x13in) s.d.1942. 7-Feb-4 Sloans & Kenyon, Bethesda #898/R

DANN, Johanna (1878-?) German
£1092 $1746 €1550 Roses in glass vase (23x33cm-9x13in) s. 18-Sep-3 Rieber, Stuttgart #802/R est:120

D'ANNA, Alessandro (18th C) Italian
£4054 $7135 €6000 Coastal landscape (22x32cm-9x13in) s.d.1784 tempera paper. 18-May-4 Sotheby's, Milan #158/R est:5000-7000
Works on paper
£800 $1280 €1168 Shepherd and flock resting by a road. Shepherd and flock resting by a waterfall (12x17cm-5x7in) both s. one d.1801 bodycol oval pair. 16-Sep-3 Bonhams, Knowle #77/R
£1556 $2800 €2272 Gentleman and his wife in a landscape (26x19cm-10x7in) s.i.d.1782 bodycol. 22-Jan-4 Christie's, Rockefeller NY #264/R est:2000-3000

DANNEMANN, Karl (1896-) German
£403 $741 €600 Nobleman showing off his puppet, Olympia (68x89cm-27x35in) s.i.d.20. 26-Mar-4 Bolland & Marotz, Bremen #323/R

DANNER, Sara Kolb (1894-1969) American
£435 $800 €635 Impressionist landscape, riverside village with steepled church (51x61cm-20x24in) s. 9-Jun-4 Alderfer's, Hatfield #396/R
£751 $1300 €1096 Wooded path with trees (63x77cm-25x30in) s. 10-Dec-3 Bonhams & Butterfields, San Francisco #6317/R est:3000-5000
£1087 $2000 €1587 View of Philadelphia (40x50cm-16x20in) s. canvasboard prov. 8-Jun-4 Bonhams & Butterfields, San Francisco #4375/R est:3000-5000

DANS, Maria Antonia (1932-1988) Spanish
£3741 $6810 €5500 Mountains in Galicia (50x61cm-20x24in) s. double-sided prov. 3-Feb-4 Segre, Madrid #172/R est:5000
Works on paper
£1560 $2606 €2200 Recollection (50x70cm-20x28in) s. pastel card exhib. 20-Oct-3 Durán, Madrid #84/R
£1733 $3137 €2600 Boats (49x68cm-19x27in) s.d.1976 gouache wax crayon board. 30-Mar-4 Segre, Madrid #138/R est:1800

DANSAERT, Léon (1830-1909) Belgian
£1316 $2421 €2000 Reading over her shoulder (31x24cm-12x9in) s. panel. 22-Jun-4 Christie's, Amsterdam #126/R est:2500-3500
£1342 $2483 €2000 The audience (61x86cm-24x34in) s. 13-Mar-4 De Vuyst, Lokeren #89/R est:2000-3000

DANTAN, Edouard Joseph (1848-1897) French
£3100 $5580 €4526 Vase de fleurs (62x56cm-24x22in) s.d.1883. 21-Jan-4 Sotheby's, Olympia #497/R est:2500-3500

DANTI, Gino (1881-1968) Italian
£900 $1548 €1314 Piazza Santa Maria Novella, Florence (20x30cm-8x12in) s. panel. 4-Dec-3 Christie's, Kensington #70/R

DANTON, Ferdinand (19/20th C) American
£210 $350 €307 Landscape with birch trees (79x102cm-31x40in) s. 14-Nov-3 Aspire, Cleveland #78

D'ANTONIO, Francesco (15th C) Italian
£60000 $109800 €87600 Madonna and Child with music-making angels (148x128cm-58x50in) tempera panel gold ground prov.lit. 7-Jul-4 Sotheby's, London #39/R est:60000-80000

DANTU, Georges (19/20th C) French
Works on paper
£1182 $2235 €1750 Lever de lune sous les glycines au Japon (35x26cm-14x10in) s. i.d.1926 verso W/C. 17-Feb-4 Vanderkindere, Brussels #91 est:125-175

D'ANTY, Henry (1910-1998) French
£261 $477 €381 Cheval blanc (46x38cm-18x15in) s. 4-Jun-4 Zofingen, Switzerland #2416 (S.FR 600)
£352 $609 €500 Trois comperes (46x55cm-18x22in) s. 10-Dec-3 Rossini, Paris #45
£383 $700 €575 French village scene (46x53cm-18x21in) 9-Jul-4 Du Mouchelle, Detroit #2047/R
£423 $731 €600 Neige (50x100cm-20x39in) s. 10-Dec-3 Rossini, Paris #43
£423 $739 €600 Maisons aux toits rouges (50x100cm-20x39in) s. 19-Dec-3 Delvaux, Paris #61
£533 $965 €800 Village (81x100cm-32x39in) s. 3-Apr-4 Gerard, Besancon #33
£543 $923 €793 Bouquet de fleurs (108x50cm-43x20in) s. 28-Nov-3 Zofingen, Switzerland #2539 (S.FR 1200)
£600 $1086 €900 Folklore (92x73cm-36x29in) s. s.i.verso. 1-Apr-4 Credit Municipal, Paris #51
£621 $1117 €900 Pecheurs en Bretagne (65x81cm-26x32in) s. studio st.s.i. verso. 25-Jan-4 Chayette & Cheval, Paris #261
£671 $1235 €1000 Clown (131x97cm-52x38in) s. 24-Mar-4 Joron-Derem, Paris #199
£671 $1235 €1000 Paysage enneige (81x112cm-32x44in) s. 24-Mar-4 Joron-Derem, Paris #200
£944 $1605 €1378 Nature morte (81x100cm-32x39in) s. 4-Nov-3 Bukowskis, Stockholm #279/R (S.KR 12500)

DANZIGER, Itzhak (1916-1977) Israeli
Sculpture
£22892 $38000 €33422 Ein Gedi (45cm-18in) brown pat bronze conceived 1950s prov.lit. 2-Oct-3 Christie's, Tel Aviv #67/R est:40000-60000

DAPHNIS, Nassos (1914-) Greek
Works on paper
£6145 $11000 €8972 No 4 (114x165cm-45x65in) s.i.verso liquitex acrylic prov.exhib. 16-May-4 Wright, Chicago #270/R est:10000-15000

DAPRAI, Jean (1929-) French/Italian
£530 $964 €800 Trois dimensions (73x60cm-29x24in) s. 15-Jun-4 Rossini, Paris #183

DARBOUR, Marguerite Mary (19/20th C) French
£480 $874 €701 Under the arcades in San Marco Square in Venice (24x31cm-9x12in) s. cardboard. 16-Jun-4 Fischer, Luzern #2055/R (S.FR 1100)

DARBOVEN, Hanne (1941-) German
Works on paper
£9000 $16380 €13140 59 variante (31x23cm-12x9in) i.num.1-15 ink printed paper collage 16 parts prov.exhib.lit. 6-Feb-4 Sotheby's, London #131/R est:5000-7000
£43575 $78000 €63620 Untitled. graphite eight elements prov. 12-May-4 Christie's, Rockefeller NY #418/R est:90000-120000

DARBY, Brendan (?) Australian?
£412 $745 €602 Gorge. 1-Apr-4 Joel, Victoria #121 (A.D 1000)

DARBY, Elizabeth Clorinda (?-1906) American
Works on paper
£734 $1300 €1072 Floral arrangement in a Chinese vase (74x56cm-29x22in) s. W/C gouache. 2-May-4 William Jenack, New York #199

D'ARCANGELO, Allan (1930-) American
£2473 $4500 €3611 Niagara extension and double overpass (122x122cm-48x48in) s.d.1965 i.verso acrylic collage prov. 29-Jun-4 Sotheby's, New York #432/R est:3000-5000
£3892 $6500 €5682 Landscape (137x122cm-54x48in) s.i.d.1969 verso acrylic prov. 7-Oct-3 Sotheby's, New York #399 est:2500-3500

D'ARCEVIA, Bruno (20th C) Italian
£237 $425 €346 Mythological god (30x23cm-12x9in) s. canvasboard. 21-Mar-4 Bonhams & Butterfields, Los Angeles #7131/R
£1006 $1800 €1469 Classical figures by a temple (338x240cm-133x94in) s. 21-Mar-4 Bonhams & Butterfields, Los Angeles #7126/R est:1000-1500

D'ARCY, David (20th C) American
Works on paper
£301 $550 €452 Down hidden paths (81x102cm-32x40in) pastel on 2ply board. 10-Jul-4 Hindman, Chicago #108/R

DARCY, Ernest (20th C) American
Works on paper
£1138 $1900 €1661 Couple in passionate embrace at foot of a bed (53x38cm-21x15in) init. gouache ink W/C. 15-Nov-3 Illustration House, New York #21/R est:1500-2500

DARDARI, Alfano (20th C) Italian
£211 $350 €308 Fruit cellar (41x51cm-16x20in) s. 4-Oct-3 Neal Auction Company, New Orleans #914

DARDEL, Fritz von (1817-1901) Swedish
Works on paper
£330 $595 €482 Chased by wolves (19x29cm-7x11in) s. W/C. 26-Jan-4 Lilla Bukowskis, Stockholm #27 (S.KR 4400)
£350 $644 €525 Generals (16x20cm-6x8in) W/C. 14-Jun-4 Lilla Bukowskis, Stockholm #412 (S.KR 4800)
£405 $730 €591 Flirting on the toboggan slide (22x29cm-9x11in) s.i.d.1851. 26-Jan-4 Lilla Bukowskis, Stockholm #28 (S.KR 5400)
£654 $1125 €955 By the steamboat's jetty - entrance to Stockholm (22x31cm-9x12in) init.d.1881 W/C. 3-Dec-3 AB Stockholms Auktionsverk #2442/R (S.KR 8500)

DARDEL, Nils (1888-1943) Swedish
Works on paper
£982 $1699 €1434 Model study (46x60cm-18x24in) s.d.1926 mixed media. 15-Dec-3 Lilla Bukowskis, Stockholm #569 (S.KR 12500)
£1160 $2088 €1694 The dandy - possibly Murice Rosland (34x24cm-13x9in) mixed media exhib.prov. 26-Apr-4 Bukowskis, Stockholm #56/R est:80000-100000 (S.KR 16000)

DARDENNE, Milo (1938-) Belgian
£436 $772 €650 Deux chevaux dans la neige (100x80cm-39x31in) s. 27-Apr-4 Campo & Campo, Antwerp #50

DARDOIZE, Émile (1826-1901) French
£1479 $2455 €2100 Chemin pres du village (57x35cm-22x14in) s. 15-Jun-3 Peron, Melun #172
£1739 $2852 €2400 Le remassage des foins a l'oree du bois (38x60cm-15x24in) s. 11-May-3 Osenat, Fontainebleau #208/R est:3000-3500

DARET, Jean (1613-1668) Flemish
£17450 $32108 €26000 La Vierge a l'Enfant (33x27cm-13x11in) s. panel prov. 24-Mar-4 Tajan, Paris #96/R est:15000-20000

DAREY, Louis (1863-1914) French
£856 $1600 €1250 Portrait of a woman astride her horse with her dog (23x15cm-9x6in) s. panel. 25-Feb-4 Doyle, New York #63/R est:800-1200

DARGE, Fred (1900-1979) American
£719 $1200 €1050 Rocky stream (20x25cm-8x10in) canvasboard. 18-Oct-3 David Dike, Dallas #179/R
£778 $1300 €1136 Cowboy on horseback (30x41cm-12x16in) canvasboard. 18-Oct-3 David Dike, Dallas #113/R
£838 $1400 €1223 Incoming showers (20x25cm-8x10in) canvasboard. 18-Oct-3 David Dike, Dallas #176/R
£898 $1500 €1311 Paint horse Texas (30x41cm-12x16in) canvasboard. 18-Oct-3 David Dike, Dallas #114/R est:1000-2000
£1946 $3250 €2841 Hunter (46x61cm-18x24in) canvasboard. 18-Oct-3 David Dike, Dallas #111/R est:2500-5000

DARGELAS, Andre Henri (1828-1906) French
£6000 $11040 €8760 Blindman's buff (19x27cm-7x11in) s. panel. 25-Mar-4 Christie's, Kensington #75/R est:5000-8000
£21719 $36271 €31710 The playroom (37x46cm-15x18in) s. panel. 17-Nov-3 Waddingtons, Toronto #238/R est:35000-40000 (C.D 48000)

DARGIE, Sir William (1912-2003) Australian
£494 $894 €721 Fruit pickers (51x61cm-20x24in) s. prov. 31-Mar-4 Goodman, Sydney #403 (A.D 1200)
£607 $978 €886 Evening, the Finke River, Central Australia (38x49cm-15x19in) s. board. 13-Oct-3 Joel, Victoria #425 est:1000-1500 (A.D 1500)
£697 $1101 €1018 The millrack (51x61cm-20x24in) s. i. verso. 2-Sep-3 Deutscher-Menzies, Melbourne #363/R est:1500-2000 (A.D 1700)
£810 $1304 €1183 Back road, Old Beechworth (38x48cm-15x19in) s. canvasboard. 13-Oct-3 Joel, Victoria #369 est:800-1200 (A.D 2000)
£1087 $1750 €1587 Springvale, central Otago (70x90cm-28x35in) s. 20-Aug-3 Peter Webb, Auckland #2040/R est:2000-3000 (NZ.D 3000)
£1178 $1896 €1720 Filly by Mallay (78x100cm-31x39in) s. board. 20-Aug-3 Peter Webb, Auckland #2031/R est:2000-3000 (NZ.D 3250)

D'ARIENZO, Miguel A (1950-) Argentinian
£7059 $12000 €10306 Topless toba bizantino o el imperio de la mirada del nuevo orden sexual (228x169cm-90x67in) init.d.95-96 tempera prov. 18-Nov-3 Christie's, Rockefeller NY #175/R est:12000-18000
£10588 $18000 €15458 La novia del coronel - The colonel's girlfriend (196x180cm-77x71in) s.d.2000 tempera prov. 18-Nov-3 Christie's, Rockefeller NY #174/R est:15000-20000

DARKING, Harry Frederick (1911-1999) British
£260 $434 €377 Morning sparkle, Llandudno (46x57cm-18x22in) s.d.63 s.i.verso board. 26-Jun-3 Mellors & Kirk, Nottingham #869/R

DARLEY, Felix O C (1822-1888) American
Works on paper
£389 $650 €568 Illustration for The Spy, J F Cooper (23x28cm-9x11in) s.d.1850 graphite gouache. 29-Jun-3 William Jenack, New York #160
£598 $1100 €873 Watching a parade with a clown (36x43cm-14x17in) s.i.d.1886 col pastel crayon. 10-Jun-4 Swann Galleries, New York #73/R
£1080 $1900 €1577 Harvesting and railroad (25x41cm-10x16in) s. ink wash dr prov. 3-Jan-4 Collins, Maine #49/R est:900-1200
£2695 $4500 €3935 The wreckers (23x23cm-9x9in) s.d.1841 W/C. 15-Nov-3 Illustration House, New York #10/R est:4000-6000

DARLING, Wilder M (1856-1933) American
£377 $600 €547 Exterior scene with fence (38x33cm-15x13in) s. 12-Sep-3 Aspire, Cleveland #67

DARLING, William S (1882-1963) American
£486 $900 €710 Before the rain (25x36cm-10x14in) s. i.verso canvas on board. 13-Mar-4 Auctions by the Bay, Alameda #401/R
£492 $900 €718 Zinnias (51x61cm-20x24in) s. canvas on board. 10-Apr-4 Auctions by the Bay, Alameda #1656/R
£1374 $2500 €2006 Spring on the ranch (46x56cm-18x22in) s. canvasboard. 15-Jun-4 John Moran, Pasadena #107 est:2000-3000

DARMER, Jane (19th C) ?
£550 $919 €803 Temple of Venus castle of Bauli. St Sebastian Island of Santa Clara (26x37cm-10x15in) i.d.1848 verso pair. 9-Jul-3 Peter Wilson, Nantwich #51

DARNAUT, Hugo (1851-1937) Austrian
£338 $595 €500 Castle steps (18x26cm-7x10in) s. board. 22-May-4 Lempertz, Koln #1497/R
£759 $1259 €1100 Landscape with figures (29x24cm-11x9in) s.d.1873 pencil. 30-Sep-3 Dorotheum, Vienna #164/R
£764 $1177 €1200 Viennese Prater, Heustadlwasser (25x20cm-10x8in) s. 4-Sep-2 Schopman, Hamburg #10/R
£1126 $2049 €1700 Autumn landscape with farmhouse (43x40cm-17x16in) s.d.1913 canvas on board. 21-Jun-4 Dorotheum, Vienna #310/R est:2400-3000
£3147 $5350 €4500 Landscape with stream (25x20cm-10x8in) s.d.1899 canvas on board. 24-Nov-3 Dorotheum, Vienna #119/R est:3000-4000
£3497 $5944 €5000 Village track (36x55cm-14x22in) s. 24-Nov-3 Dorotheum, Vienna #87/R est:5000-7000
£4027 $7208 €6000 Late autumn in Hungary (33x46cm-13x18in) s. s.i.verso cardboard lit. 27-May-4 Hassfurther, Vienna #38/R est:5000-7000
£5034 $9010 €7500 A summer day (28x42cm-11x17in) s.d.1896 board. 27-May-4 Dorotheum, Vienna #175/R est:3800-4500
£5766 $10725 €8418 Old mill. s.d.1882. 6-Mar-4 Dorotheum, Prague #26/R est:80000-120000 (C.KR 280000)
£5839 $10452 €8700 Autumn scene of Grafenegg (34x48cm-13x19in) s. s.i.verso cardboard lit. 27-May-4 Hassfurther, Vienna #37/R est:6000-8000
£12570 $22500 €18352 View through the trees (111x83cm-44x33in) s. 6-May-4 Doyle, New York #56/R est:25000-35000
£18792 $33262 €28000 Waidhofen a d Ybbs (32x40cm-13x16in) s.d.1882 panel prov. 28-Apr-4 Wiener Kunst Auktionen, Vienna #54/R est:18000-35000
£20979 $35664 €30000 Plankenberg (82x121cm-32x48in) s. 24-Nov-3 Dorotheum, Vienna #142/R est:30000-36000
£48611 $82639 €70000 Working in the forest (83x120cm-33x47in) s.d.1889. 28-Oct-3 Wiener Kunst Auktionen, Vienna #42/R est:20000-50000

DARNAUT, Hugo (attrib) (1851-1937) Austrian
£1208 $2162 €1800 Front garden (45x38cm-18x15in) i. 27-May-4 Dorotheum, Graz #12/R est:1800

DARPY, Lucien Gilbert (1875-?) French
£901 $1424 €1315 Soucis a pieds d'alouette - marigolds and delphiniums (73x60cm-29x24in) s. exhib. 2-Sep-3 Deutscher-Menzies, Melbourne #454/R est:2500-4000 (A.D 2200)

DARRAH, Ann Sophia Towne (1819-1881) American
£4324 $8000 €6313 Glass Head, Manchester, Massachusetts (23x33cm-9x13in) init. s.d.June 28 1872 verso panel prov. 11-Mar-4 Christie's, Rockefeller NY #18/R est:4000-6000

DARROCH, Duncan (1888-1967) New Zealander
£340 $619 €496 Mount Cook, New Zealand (65x83cm-26x33in) s. 3-Jul-4 Shapes, Edinburgh #438/R

DARROW, Whitney (jnr) (1909-1999) American
£267 $500 €390 Fashionable woman and young son seated on couch (33x25cm-13x10in) s. board en grisaille painted c.1940. 26-Feb-4 Illustration House, New York #50

D'ARTHOIS, Jacques (1613-1686) Flemish
£8725 $15617 €13000 Lisiere de bois animee de voyageurs (85x113cm-33x44in) 25-May-4 Palais de Beaux Arts, Brussels #66/R est:8500-10000
£20000 $36000 €29200 Wooded landscape with huntsmen, drovers and cattle on a track (101x144cm-40x57in) 22-Apr-4 Sotheby's, London #87/R est:15000-20000
£23973 $40753 €35000 Landscape with trees and figures (68x93cm-27x37in) 4-Nov-3 Ansorena, Madrid #47/R est:35000
£28369 $45957 €40000 Pastores jugando a las cartas (84x117cm-33x46in) d.1644 prov.lit. 20-May-3 Ansorena, Madrid #94b/R est:40000

D'ARTHOIS, Jacques (attrib) (1613-1686) Flemish
£1848 $3307 €2698 Italian landscape with figures (64x76cm-25x30in) prov. 25-May-4 Bukowskis, Stockholm #451/R est:20000-25000 (S.KR 25000)
£9220 $15397 €13000 Cavaliers dans une allee bordee d'arbres (93x132cm-37x52in) 17-Oct-3 Tajan, Paris #76/R est:6000-8000
Works on paper
£524 $892 €750 Paysage boise de la Foret des Soignes (27x43cm-11x17in) pierre noire white chk. 18-Nov-3 Galerie Moderne, Brussels #722/R

D'ARTHOIS, Jacques (style) (1613-1686) Flemish
£5689 $9500 €8306 Extensive landscape with travellers and a town in the distance (132x183cm-52x72in) 7-Oct-3 Sotheby's, New York #52/R est:7000-9000

DARTIGNENARY, Alfred (?) ?
Works on paper
£280 $476 €409 Portrait of a young gentleman in military uniform (43x36cm-17x14in) col chk. 30-Oct-3 Duke & Son, Dorchester #26/R

DARTIGUENAVE, Paul (1862-1918) French/American
£344 $550 €502 Landscape with river and houses (38x30cm-15x12in) s. 20-Sep-3 Pook & Pook, Downington #388/R
£587 $1050 €857 Spring blossoms (64x76cm-25x30in) s. 8-Jan-4 James Julia, Fairfield #727/R

DARTIGUENAVE, Prosper Guillaume (1815-1885) French
£420 $713 €600 Portrait of two sisters, one holding flowers, one holding a canary (49x38cm-19x15in) 18-Nov-3 Mealy's, Castlecomer #1306/R

DARWIN, Sir Robin (1910-1974) British
£250 $430 €365 Portrait of a lady (40x30cm-16x12in) s. board. 3-Dec-3 Christie's, Kensington #444
£360 $569 €522 Provencal townscape (25x35cm-10x14in) s. prov. 3-Sep-3 Bonhams, Bury St Edmunds #409
£400 $728 €584 Woodland in autumn (76x63cm-30x25in) s. indis.d. 1-Jul-4 Christie's, Kensington #74
£750 $1388 €1095 Rehearsal (76x63cm-30x25in) s.d.26 p. 11-Mar-4 Christie's, Kensington #7/R
£2200 $3740 €3212 Ascot Heath (64x76cm-25x30in) s.d.55. 30-Oct-3 Duke & Son, Dorchester #252/R est:1000-2000

DAS, Arup (1927-) Indian
£2717 $5000 €3967 Seduce of Rishasringa (132x106cm-52x42in) s.d.91. 25-Mar-4 Christie's, Rockefeller NY #225/R est:5000-7000

£3414 $6145 €4984 Untitled (106x106cm-42x42in) s. 25-Apr-4 Christie's, Hong Kong #615/R est:40000-45000 (HK.D 48000)

DAS, Sunil (1939-) Indian

£1000 $1670 €1460 Untitled (81x81cm-32x32in) s.d.97 s.verso. 17-Oct-3 Christie's, Kensington #513/R est:1000-1200
£1000 $1670 €1460 Untitled (80x80cm-31x31in) s.d.97 s.verso. 17-Oct-3 Christie's, Kensington #514/R est:1000-1200

DASBURG, Andrew (1887-1979) American

Works on paper
£361 $650 €527 Standing female nude (43x23cm-17x9in) s. graphite. 23-Jan-4 Freeman, Philadelphia #68/R
£1029 $1750 €1502 Church and tree (43x53cm-17x21in) s.d.66 pen ink prov. 1-Nov-3 Santa Fe Art, Santa Fe #148/R est:2500-3500
£1324 $2250 €1933 Spring trees (46x58cm-18x23in) s.d.66 pen ink prov. 1-Nov-3 Santa Fe Art, Santa Fe #149/R est:2000-3000
£4118 $7000 €6012 Study for Zuni pueblo (43x58cm-17x23in) s. chl conte crayon prov. 1-Nov-3 Santa Fe Art, Santa Fe #150/R est:15000-20000
£7514 $13000 €10970 Still life (38x56cm-15x22in) s.d.31 ink W/C exhib.lit. 10-Dec-3 Bonhams & Butterfields, San Francisco #6075/R est:15000-20000

D'ASCENZO, Nicola (1871-1954) American/Italian

£404 $650 €590 The lacemaker (121x61cm-48x24in) s.d.95 bears i. 17-Aug-3 Bonhams & Butterfields, San Francisco #5791/R
Works on paper
£588 $1000 €858 Mural designs (18x10cm-7x4in) W/C three in one frame. 21-Nov-3 Skinner, Boston #377/R est:800-1200

D'ASCENZO, Victor (20th C) American

£313 $500 €457 Cherub and satyr (112x71cm-44x28in) 19-Sep-3 Freeman, Philadelphia #74/R

DASH, Robert (1934-) American

£1946 $3600 €2919 Roses at the gate. Spring. Pink sundown (25x25cm-10x10in) s. i.verso acrylic panel three. 14-Jul-4 American Auctioneer #490197/R est:500-800

DASHWOOD, Jeffrey (1947-) British

Sculpture
£1389 $2500 €2028 Shelduck (25x43cm-10x17in) bronze. 24-Jan-4 Skinner, Boston #639/R est:2500-4000
£5200 $9152 €7592 Goshawk (26x47cm-10x19in) s. num.11/12. 18-May-4 Woolley & Wallis, Salisbury #376/R est:3000-5000

DASIO, Maximilian (1865-1932) German

£400 $720 €600 Street gathering in Munich (36x30cm-14x12in) s.d.1942 panel. 26-Apr-4 Rieber, Stuttgart #888/R

DASNOY, Albert (1901-1992) Belgian

£528 $914 €750 Head of a child (32x26cm-13x10in) s. panel. 13-Dec-3 De Vuyst, Lokeren #78
£1348 $2250 €1900 Toilette (51x60cm-20x24in) s. exhib. 14-Oct-3 Vanderkindere, Brussels #90/R est:1750-2500

DASPHER, Julian (20th C) New Zealander

£1087 $1750 €1587 Subaru factory at Tip Top Corner (76x76cm-30x30in) s. i.d.1985 verso. 20-Aug-3 Dunbar Sloane, Auckland #117/R est:2000-3000 (NZ.D 3000)

D'ASSIA, Enrico (20th C) ?

£556 $944 €800 Winter games (32x80cm-13x31in) s. tempera card. 28-Oct-3 Il Ponte, Milan #211
£1042 $1771 €1500 Akhenaton and Nefertitis. Time glass (25x41cm-10x16in) s. tempera paper painted 1975 pair prov. 28-Oct-3 Il Ponte, Milan #234/R est:500-600
Works on paper
£3333 $5667 €4800 Coliseum. Cathedral (55x90cm-22x35in) s.d.1971 W/C pair. 28-Oct-3 Il Ponte, Milan #235/R est:1000-1200

D'ASTE, Joseph (20th C) Italian

Sculpture
£1258 $2290 €1900 Couple de jeunes fermiers (44cm-17in) s.st.f. Chardon gold pat bronze incl. marble base. 15-Jun-4 Vanderkindere, Brussels #177/R est:2000-3000
£1259 $2102 €1800 Enfants a l'ecole (38cm-15in) s. gilt pat bronze. 13-Oct-3 Horta, Bruxelles #486 est:500-600

D'ASTINIERES, Comte Eugène Nicolas (1841-1918) French

Sculpture
£1000 $1840 €1460 Boy holding a fish (48cm-19in) s. brown pat. bronze st.f.Susse. 12-Jun-4 Finan Watkins & Co, Mere #21/R

DASTUGUE, Maxime (19th C) French

£1200 $2220 €1752 Harem dancer (73x59cm-29x23in) s. 14-Jul-4 Christie's, Kensington #865/R est:700-1000

DASVELDT, Jan (1770-1855) Dutch

£1769 $3219 €2600 Hounds fighting over a hare in an extensive landscape (132x199cm-52x78in) init. 3-Feb-4 Christie's, Amsterdam #59/R est:1500-2000

DATSENKO, Lidya (1946-) Russian

£275 $448 €402 Still life with apples, plums and flowers (50x55cm-20x22in) s. 28-Sep-3 John Nicholson, Haslemere #101/R

DAUBIGNY (18/19th C) French

£5389 $9000 €7868 Landscape with cows (46x77cm-18x30in) s.d.1873 laid down on board. 19-Oct-3 Bonhams & Butterfields, Los Angeles #7050 est:1000-1500

DAUBIGNY (attrib) (18/19th C) French

£1135 $1895 €1600 Vaches au bord de la mare au clair de lune (38x62cm-15x24in) bears sig. 17-Jun-3 Vanderkindere, Brussels #42 est:600-800

DAUBIGNY, Charles François (1817-1878) French

£1133 $2051 €1700 Interieur de ferme ou portrait presume de Ravier (22x31cm-9x12in) s. panel lit. 30-Mar-4 Rossini, Paris #298/R est:1000-1500
£1500 $2490 €2175 Paturage au crepuscule (15x22cm-6x9in) s. panel. 13-Jun-3 Zofingen, Switzerland #2352/R est:3000 (S.FR 3300)
£2156 $3600 €3148 Forest scene with lake beyond (18x36cm-7x14in) s. board. 19-Oct-3 Susanin's, Chicago #6034/R est:2000-4000
£3667 $6637 €5500 Plaine aux Rochers, Vallon au Crepuscule (46x55cm-18x22in) s. panel lit. 30-Mar-4 Rossini, Paris #297/R est:5000-8000
£4000 $7360 €5840 River landscape, possibly les bords de L'Oise (35x59cm-14x23in) s. panel. 23-Mar-4 Bonhams, New Bond Street #99/R est:2000-30000
£5800 $10034 €8468 Bords de l'Oise (15x26cm-6x10in) s.d.1869 p. 11-Dec-3 Lyon & Turnbull, Edinburgh #49/R est:2000-3000
£6522 $11935 €9522 Chevaux sous les arbres (54x117cm-21x46in) s. prov. 5-Jun-4 Galerie du Rhone, Sion #529/R est:15000-20000 (S.FR 15000)
£6944 $11806 €10000 River landscape (33x43cm-13x17in) s. 28-Oct-3 Wiener Kunst Auktionen, Vienna #44/R est:7000-15000
£7042 $12183 €10000 Lake in evening (24x47cm-9x19in) s.d.1873 panel. 13-Dec-3 Lempertz, Koln #12/R est:8000
£8939 $16000 €13051 Riviere avec six canards (20x32cm-8x13in) s. panel prov.lit. 6-May-4 Doyle, New York #38/R est:8000-12000
£9200 $16836 €13800 Levee de lune (25x38cm-10x15in) s. panel. 6-Jun-4 Osenat, Fontainebleau #170/R est:12000-15000
£9797 $18517 €14500 Bord de l'Oise (38x67cm-15x26in) s. panel. 17-Feb-4 Vanderkindere, Brussels #14/R est:6000-8000
£10000 $18100 €15000 Claire de lune sur l'etang (110x65cm-43x26in) s.d.1865 exhib.lit. 30-Mar-4 Rossini, Paris #300/R est:12000-18000
£10870 $17826 €15000 Soleil couchant a Kerity, Bretagne (27x58cm-11x23in) s.d.1861. 11-May-3 Osenat, Fontainebleau #91/R est:12000-15000
£11333 $20513 €17000 Le plateau de Valmondois (40x56cm-16x22in) s.d.1873 lit. 30-Mar-4 Rossini, Paris #296/R est:5000-8000
£11561 $20000 €16879 River landscape (33x56cm-13x22in) s. sold with a letter. 10-Dec-3 Boos Gallery, Michigan #533/R est:40000-60000
£14706 $25000 €21471 Bord de la Seine (39x67cm-15x26in) s. panel prov.lit. 28-Oct-3 Sotheby's, New York #16/R est:30000-40000
£20833 $37500 €30416 Les pecheurs d'anguilles (17x30cm-7x12in) s.d.1864 panel prov.exhib.lit. 23-Apr-4 Sotheby's, New York #149/R est:15000-20000
£25000 $45000 €36500 Bord de riviere (41x73cm-16x29in) s.d.1868 panel prov. 23-Apr-4 Sotheby's, New York #7/R est:50000-70000
Works on paper
£493 $853 €700 Arbres au bord d'un cours d'eau (29x40cm-11x16in) studio st. black crayon. 12-Dec-3 Artus Associes, Paris #65
£612 $1096 €900 Paysage de bord de mer (30x46cm-12x18in) mono. sanguine. 17-Mar-4 Tajan, Paris #140
£1027 $1747 €1500 Paysage en bord de mer (31x48cm-12x19in) studio st. chl. 6-Nov-3 Tajan, Paris #66
£1304 $2139 €1800 Vaches au bord de la riviere (22x31cm-9x12in) s. sanguine. 11-May-3 Osenat, Fontainebleau #90/R est:1200-1500
£3233 $5917 €4850 Bord de l'Oise (42x57cm-17x22in) s. chl dr. 6-Jun-4 Osenat, Fontainebleau #168/R est:5000-5500

DAUBIGNY, Charles François (attrib) (1817-1878) French

£271 $462 €396 River landscape (15x19cm-6x7in) i. board. 19-Nov-3 Fischer, Luzern #2047 (S.FR 600)
£661 $1123 €965 Evening river landscape (25x40cm-10x16in) i. panel. 5-Nov-3 Dobiaschofsky, Bern #462/R (S.FR 1500)
£2335 $4250 €3409 Evening by the river (23x41cm-9x16in) s. panel. 7-Feb-4 Sloans & Kenyon, Bethesda #1276/R est:3000-5000
£6098 $10000 €8842 Landscape with cottages and distant hills (28x53cm-11x21in) indis.sig. panel prov. 31-May-3 Brunk, Ashville #340/R est:5000-10000
Works on paper
£1000 $1810 €1500 Lapins pres du terrier (29x16cm-11x6in) black pencil lit. 30-Mar-4 Rossini, Paris #299 est:150-250

DAUBIGNY, Karl (1846-1886) French

£1267 $2318 €1900 Bord de Seine (33x60cm-13x24in) s. panel. 6-Jun-4 Osenat, Fontainebleau #61/R est:1800-2000
£1900 $3174 €2774 River landscape (30x52cm-12x20in) s.d.1871. 24-Jun-3 Germann, Zurich #161/R est:4000-6000 (S.FR 4200)
£2797 $4811 €4000 Promenade en barque sur le lac (25x40cm-10x16in) s. 7-Dec-3 Osenat, Fontainebleau #114 est:4000-4500
£3333 $6100 €5000 Bord de l'Oise (54x86cm-21x34in) s. 6-Jun-4 Osenat, Fontainebleau #60/R est:6000-8000
£3623 $5942 €5000 Ramasseuses de coquillages en Normandie (29x63cm-11x25in) s.d.1883 panel. 11-May-3 Osenat, Fontainebleau #94/R est:6000-6500
£3779 $6500 €5517 Preparatifs de peche (32x46cm-13x18in) s. board. 3-Dec-3 Naón & Cia, Buenos Aires #42/R est:4000-6000
£3846 $6538 €5500 River landscape with figures (22x44cm-9x17in) s. panel. 24-Nov-3 Dorotheum, Vienna #145/R est:3000-3500
£4305 $8050 €6500 Bord de Loire (27x56cm-11x22in) s.d.1877 panel. 20-Jul-4 Gioffredo, Nice #24
£6522 $10696 €9000 Peniches sur la Seine, le canal St Martin, le quai de l'Arsenal (29x46cm-11x18in) s.i. 11-May-3 Osenat, Fontainebleau #95/R est:9000-10000
£7246 $11884 €10000 Les laveuses a Auvers-sur-Oise (50x90cm-20x35in) s.d.1884. 11-May-3 Osenat, Fontainebleau #96/R est:7500-8500
£8108 $15000 €11838 Sur la plage (28x43cm-11x17in) s.d.1881 panel. 13-Feb-4 David Rago, Lambertville #31/R est:7000-9000

DAUBIGNY, Karl (attrib) (1846-1886) French
£2533 $4636 €3800 Bord de riviere (31x55cm-12x22in) s. canvas on panel. 6-Jun-4 Osenat, Fontainebleau #59 est:4000-4500

DAUBIGNY, Pierre (1793-1858) French
Miniatures
£2000 $3680 €2920 Jean Francois Ducis (7cm-3in) s. set in to gold lined red lacquered snuff box. 24-Jun-4 Bonhams, New Bond Street #76/R est:2000-3000

DAUCHEZ, Andre (1870-1943) French
£464 $867 €700 Maison bord de riviere (22x32cm-9x13in) s. 24-Jul-4 Thierry & Lannon, Brest #360
£567 $1014 €850 Village au pays bigouden (24x34cm-9x13in) s. panel. 16-May-4 Thierry & Lannon, Brest #303/R
£704 $1232 €1000 Les bord de l'Odet (24x33cm-9x13in) s. panel. 21-Dec-3 Thierry & Lannon, Brest #302
£1200 $2184 €1752 On the wooded shore (37x46cm-15x18in) s. i.verso. 16-Jun-4 Christie's, Kensington #20/R est:1500-2000
£1958 $3270 €2800 Estuaire en Bretagne (60x92cm-24x36in) s. 29-Jun-3 Eric Pillon, Calais #141/R
£2676 $4683 €3800 Lumiere d'orage (91x65cm-36x26in) s. 21-Dec-3 Thierry & Lannon, Brest #149/R est:3000-4000
£2700 $4833 €4050 L'embouchure de l'Odet (61x91cm-24x36in) s. 16-May-4 Thierry & Lannon, Brest #132/R est:4000-5000
Works on paper
£795 $1486 €1200 Marins en barque (53x66cm-21x26in) s. chl. 24-Jul-4 Thierry & Lannon, Brest #31

DAUCHOT, Gabriel (1927-) French
£235 $425 €343 Wedding (18x28cm-7x11in) s. 3-Apr-4 Susanin's, Chicago #5076/R
£268 $481 €400 Portrait d'homme au bouquet de violettes (80x40cm-31x16in) s. 27-May-4 Christie's, Paris #129/R
£308 $524 €450 Bal masque sur la plage (19x47cm-7x19in) s. 9-Nov-3 Eric Pillon, Calais #236/R
£333 $597 €500 Paysage anime sous la neige (38x46cm-15x18in) s. 16-May-4 Osenat, Fontainebleau #74
£343 $631 €501 Le parc (40x80cm-16x31in) s. 14-Jun-4 Waddingtons, Toronto #266/R (C.D 850)
£366 $634 €520 Les voiles blanches (33x48cm-13x19in) s. 13-Dec-3 Touati, Paris #89/R
£374 $670 €550 Paysage de neige (40x81cm-16x32in) s. 19-Mar-4 Ribeyre & Baron, Paris #93
£387 $670 €550 Les regates (19x47cm-7x19in) s. 13-Dec-3 Touati, Paris #88/R
£436 $781 €650 Arlequin (80x40cm-31x16in) s. prov. 27-May-4 Christie's, Paris #128/R
£493 $853 €700 La maitre d'hotel (47x19cm-19x7in) s. s.i.verso. 13-Dec-3 Touati, Paris #85/R
£951 $1645 €1350 L'Aubade sous la neige (19x47cm-7x19in) s. s.i.verso. 13-Dec-3 Touati, Paris #86/R
Works on paper
£599 $1036 €850 Dans l'atelier (47x61cm-19x24in) s. W/C. 13-Dec-3 Touati, Paris #87/R

DAUDELIN, Charles (1920-) Canadian
£3556 $5902 €5192 Untitled, fruits imaginaires (63x109cm-25x43in) s.d.1943 sold with a catalogue exhib. 5-Oct-3 Levis, Calgary #24/R est:14000-16000 (C.D 8000)

DAUFIN, Jacques (1930-) French
£739 $1353 €1079 Nature morte (73x99cm-29x39in) s. 4-Jun-4 Zofingen, Switzerland #2442/R (S.FR 1700)

DAUGHERTY, James (1889-1974) American
Works on paper
£367 $660 €550 Magic garden (29x33cm-11x13in) mono. pastel. 24-Apr-4 Cornette de St.Cyr, Paris #505
£670 $1200 €978 Untitled (46x58cm-18x23in) s. chl. 16-May-4 Wright, Chicago #181/R
£1630 $3000 €2380 Upward and onward (18x99cm-7x39in) W/C pen ink pencil exec. c.1935. 10-Jun-4 Swann Galleries, New York #78/R est:2000-3000

DAUGHTERS, Robert (1929-) American
£236 $425 €345 Man from Alcalde (30x40cm-12x16in) s.i. 25-Apr-4 Bonhams & Butterfields, San Francisco #5565/R
£1216 $2250 €1775 Horses foraging in the snow (36x46cm-14x18in) s. 15-Jul-4 Sotheby's, New York #55/R est:2000-3000
£2027 $3750 €2959 Village in snow (61x91cm-24x36in) s. 15-Jul-4 Sotheby's, New York #65/R est:2500-3500
£2050 $3300 €2973 Vermillion Needles (51x76cm-20x30in) 22-Aug-3 Altermann Galleries, Santa Fe #159
£2162 $4000 €3157 Chief (91x61cm-36x24in) s.d.74. 15-Jul-4 Sotheby's, New York #54/R est:2000-3000
£6471 $11000 €9448 Ranchos de Taos Church (91x71cm-36x28in) s. prov. 1-Nov-3 Santa Fe Art, Santa Fe #78/R est:8000-12000

DAUMIER, Honore (1808-1879) French
Prints
£5479 $9315 €8000 Enfonce lafayette !. lithograph. 6-Nov-3 Piasa, Paris #75/R
£6704 $12000 €9788 Les bas bleus (23x18cm-9x7in) lithographs set of 40. 6-May-4 Swann Galleries, New York #271/R est:7000-10000
Sculpture
£2333 $4247 €3500 Buste de parlementaire (13cm-5in) st.f.MLG num.9/25 pat bronze. 2-Jul-4 Binoche, Paris #21/R est:4000-5000
£2513 $4498 €3669 Le fat, le Comte Sebastiani - from Les Bustes (13cm-5in) num.7/25 pat.bronze lit. 26-May-4 AB Stockholms Auktionsverk #2473/R est:30000-40000 (S.KR 34000)
£2797 $4671 €4000 Caricature presumee de l'Amiral Verhuel (13cm-5in) brown pat bronze. 29-Jun-3 St-Germain-en-Laye Encheres #15/R
£5389 $9000 €7868 Le rodeur, le ramasseur de bouts de cigares (15cm-6in) init.num.16/30 brown pat bronze st.f.Valsuani lit. 7-Oct-3 Sotheby's, New York #246 est:10000-15000
Works on paper
£5298 $9642 €8000 Interior of a Paris art salon with figures (35x25cm-14x10in) mono.i. chl prov. 17-Jun-4 Frank Peege, Freiburg #1209/R est:10000
£14118 $24000 €20612 Tete d'homme (12x9cm-5x4in) pen ink ink wash prov.lit. 6-Nov-3 Sotheby's, New York #118/R est:10000-15000
£15556 $28000 €22712 Lawyer pointing to a defendant in a courtroom (8x14cm-3x6in) s. black chk pen grey ink wash. 22-Jan-4 Christie's, Rockefeller NY #140/R est:20000-30000
£50000 $92000 €73000 Avocat pathetique (22x15cm-9x6in) s. pen ink wash chl pencil prov.lit. 22-Jun-4 Sotheby's, London #412/R est:30000-40000
£126638 $230480 €184891 Deux buveurs (21x27cm-8x11in) mono. pen ink W/C exec. c.1855 prov. 18-Jun-4 Kornfeld, Bern #22/R est:275000 (S.FR 290000)
£179310 $297655 €260000 Plaideur mecontent (23x19cm-9x7in) s. chk pen ink wash gouache htd white prov.exhib.lit. 30-Sep-3 Christie's, Paris #17/R est:200000-300000

DAUMIER, Honore (after) (1808-1879) French
Prints
£4000 $7360 €6000 Hotel des Ventes (22x16cm-9x6in) engraving exec.1863 lit. 10-Jun-4 Piasa, Paris #65/R

DAUPHIN de FRANCE, Louis (?) French
Works on paper
£423 $739 €600 Caricature d'homme en buste, habille en moine Franciscain (14x10cm-6x4in) black chk pen brown ink prov. 17-Dec-3 Christie's, Paris #56/R

DAUPHIN, Eugène Baptiste Emile (1857-1930) French
£476 $852 €695 Coastal landscape with fishing boats (46x65cm-18x26in) s. 22-Mar-4 Philippe Schuler, Zurich #6135 (S.FR 1100)

D'AURIA, Vincenzo (1872-1939) Italian
£870 $1600 €1270 Fisherman's return (51x69cm-20x27in) s. 9-Jun-4 Doyle, New York #3018/R est:1000-1500

DAUZATS, Adrien (1804-1868) French
£775 $1340 €1100 Crique rocheuse (33x27cm-13x11in) init. prov. 12-Dec-3 Piasa, Paris #75
£1400 $2534 €2100 L'Abbaye de Jumieges (31x46cm-12x18in) s. oil paper on canvas exhib. 30-Mar-4 Rossini, Paris #207/R est:3000-5000
£2533 $4585 €3800 La Madeleine a Troyes (38x46cm-15x18in) s.i. cardboard sold with a dr of the same subject exhib. 30-Mar-4 Rossini, Paris #208/R est:3000-5000
£24476 $42098 €35000 View of a courtyard in Cairo (72x54cm-28x21in) s. panel. 2-Dec-3 Christie's, Paris #430/R est:30000-50000
Works on paper
£221 $400 €323 Yard in northern France (20x25cm-8x10in) ink W/C. 16-Apr-4 American Auctioneer #82/R

DAVELOOZE, Jean Baptiste (1807-1886) Belgian
£3046 $5544 €4600 Paysage anime (71x94cm-28x37in) s. 16-Jun-4 Hotel des Ventes Mosan, Brussels #152 est:5000-6000

DAVENPORT, Ian (1966-) British
£2500 $4175 €3650 Untitled (120x120cm-47x47in) s.d.1996 verso household paint MDF prov. 21-Oct-3 Sotheby's, London #447/R est:3000-4000
£3200 $5728 €4672 Untitled (46x46cm-18x18in) s.verso prov. 16-Mar-4 Bonhams, New Bond Street #108/R est:1000-1500
£8000 $14560 €11680 Poured painting, black, red, black (183x183cm-72x72in) s.i.d.1998 verso household gloss paint fibreboard prov.exhib. 21-Jun-4 Bonhams, New Bond Street #158/R est:8000-12000

DAVENPORT, J G (19th C) British
£2158 $3540 €3000 Nona. panel. 6-Jun-3 Chochon-Barre & Allardi, Paris #41b

DAVENPORT, Leslie (1905-) British
Works on paper
£300 $552 €438 Study of a sunflower (29x20cm-11x8in) s.d.71 pastel. 11-Jun-4 Keys, Aylsham #527

DAVENPORT, Rebecca (1943-) American
£559 $1000 €816 Bare breasted woman (102x104cm-40x41in) mono.d.1985. 7-May-4 Sloans & Kenyon, Bethesda #1741/R
£594 $950 €867 Mae Sommers (168x183cm-66x72in) s.i.d.1973 verso. 20-Sep-3 Sloans & Kenyon, Bethesda #1185/R
£1563 $2500 €2282 Luis Lastra (168x183cm-66x72in) mono.d.1976. 20-Sep-3 Sloans & Kenyon, Bethesda #1184/R est:2500-3500

DAVENPORT, William Slocum (1868-?) American
£351 $650 €527 Landscape (36x43cm-14x17in) s. 14-Jul-4 American Auctioneer #490531/R

DAVEY, Philip (1949-) Australian
£496 $917 €724 Victoria Docks (91x91cm-36x36in) s.i.verso. 15-Mar-4 Sotheby's, Melbourne #186 est:400-600 (A.D 1200)

DAVEY, Randall (1887-1964) American
£279 $500 €407 European city scene (53x84cm-21x33in) s. 8-Jan-4 James Julia, Fairfield #894/R
£9659 $17000 €14102 After a race at Rolling Rock (66x81cm-26x32in) s. masonite exhib. 19-May-4 Sotheby's, New York #185/R est:20000-30000
Prints
£1765 $3000 €2577 Winter pasture (20x23cm-8x9in) s.i. monotype prov. 1-Nov-3 Santa Fe Art, Santa Fe #225/R est:4000-6000

DAVEY, Rosaleen (20th C) Irish?
Works on paper
£805 $1442 €1200 Study of cones and cubes (50x42cm-20x17in) s.d.94 pastel. 31-May-4 Hamilton Osborne King, Dublin #198/R
£909 $1545 €1300 Obscured blue (48x46cm-19x18in) s.d.92 pastel. 25-Nov-3 De Veres Art Auctions, Dublin #41/R est:800-1200

DAVID, Andre (?) French
£288 $472 €400 Femme de Pont Labbe (36x30cm-14x12in) s. panel. 3-Jun-3 Livinec, Gaudcheau & Jezequel, Rennes #69

DAVID, Cyril (20th C) American
Works on paper
£552 $1000 €828 Boat dock (41x64cm-16x25in) pencil. 16-Apr-4 American Auctioneer #83/R
£552 $1000 €828 Century Hotel (23x33cm-9x13in) pencil. 16-Apr-4 American Auctioneer #84/R

DAVID, Euphemide Therese (1823-?) French
£247 $450 €361 Feeding the song birds (23x13cm-9x5in) s. panel. 19-Jun-4 Jackson's, Cedar Falls #248/R

DAVID, Giovanni (1743-1790) Italian
Works on paper
£4934 $9079 €7500 Allegory from the Bible (17x13cm-7x5in) s. gouache on vellum. 22-Jun-4 Sotheby's, Milan #124/R est:4000-6000

DAVID, Giovanni (attrib) (1743-1790) Italian
Works on paper
£1367 $2187 €1900 Portrait of man (26x21cm-10x8in) pencil pen W/C. 14-May-3 Finarte Semenzato, Milan #513/R est:1200-1600

DAVID, Hermine (1886-1971) French
£403 $721 €600 Conversion de Saint Paul (54x65cm-21x26in) s. panel. 30-May-4 Eric Pillon, Calais #158/R
£458 $792 €650 Dejeuner au jardin (64x54cm-25x21in) s. 9-Dec-3 Chambelland & Giafferi, Paris #41/R
£704 $1218 €1000 Saint-Vaaste-la-Hougue (41x33cm-16x13in) s.d.1914. 15-Dec-3 Charbonneaux, Paris #74/R
£867 $1551 €1300 Nature morte a la campagne. Route le long de la Marne (46x55cm-18x22in) s. panel pair prov. 17-May-4 Chayette & Cheval, Paris #145
£867 $1551 €1300 Paysage du midi (37x45cm-15x18in) s.d.1951 panel pair prov. 17-May-4 Chayette & Cheval, Paris #149
Works on paper
£276 $510 €400 Paysage, la bergere et son troupeau (25x36cm-10x14in) s.d.1957 W/C prov. 13-Feb-4 Charbonneaux, Paris #38
£282 $487 €400 La Caleche a Palma (22x29cm-9x11in) s.d.1930 dr. 15-Dec-3 Charbonneaux, Paris #70
£282 $487 €400 Promenade dans le parc (22x29cm-9x11in) s.d.1920 W/C. 15-Dec-3 Charbonneaux, Paris #151
£282 $487 €400 Dans le port de Saint-Vaast-la-Hougue (30x34cm-12x13in) s.i. W/C. 15-Dec-3 Charbonneaux, Paris #168
£296 $512 €420 Dourgne (25x21cm-10x8in) s.i.d.1938 W/C. 15-Dec-3 Charbonneaux, Paris #98
£352 $609 €500 Paysage cubain (13x18cm-5x7in) s.i. W/C. 15-Dec-3 Charbonneaux, Paris #92
£352 $609 €500 Paysage (24x30cm-9x12in) s.d.1918 W/C. 15-Dec-3 Charbonneaux, Paris #178
£387 $670 €550 Aquarelle de Floride (23x24cm-9x9in) s. W/C exec. c.1917. 15-Dec-3 Charbonneaux, Paris #181
£423 $731 €600 Retour de peche, rue a Saint-Vaast (41x29cm-16x11in) s.i.d.1960 W/C. 15-Dec-3 Charbonneaux, Paris #62/R
£423 $731 €600 La cote de Miami (23x32cm-9x13in) s.i. W/C. 15-Dec-3 Charbonneaux, Paris #149
£423 $731 €600 La Caleche a Sevres (17x23cm-7x9in) s.i.d.1923 W/C. 15-Dec-3 Charbonneaux, Paris #179
£458 $792 €650 Sur la route de Chateauneuf-de-Gadagne (22x30cm-9x12in) s.i.d.1951 W/C. 15-Dec-3 Charbonneaux, Paris #145
£458 $792 €650 Bord de plage a Miami (29x34cm-11x13in) s.d.1916 W/C. 15-Dec-3 Charbonneaux, Paris #172
£493 $853 €700 Le village de Utelle dans les Alpes-Maritimes (41x30cm-16x12in) s.d.1932 W/C. 15-Dec-3 Charbonneaux, Paris #111
£563 $975 €800 Les femmes tunisiennes (20x27cm-8x11in) s.i.d.1924 W/C. 15-Dec-3 Charbonneaux, Paris #137
£800 $1456 €1200 Paysage a Miami (29x34cm-11x13in) s.i.d.1915 W/C. 4-Jul-4 Eric Pillon, Calais #123/R

DAVID, Jacques-Louis (1748-1825) French
Works on paper
£1042 $1646 €1500 French officer on horseback (10x19cm-4x7in) s. W/C lit. 19-Sep-3 Schloss Ahlden, Ahlden #1544/R est:950
£4801 $8738 €7250 Tete de femme de profil (17x13cm-7x5in) s. black crayon prov. 16-Jun-4 Piasa, Paris #163/R est:3000-4000
£15000 $27450 €21900 View of along the Tiber with the Castel Sant'Angelo and St Peter's (13x19cm-5x7in) i. pen brown ink grey wash over blk chk double-sided prov. 8-Jul-4 Sotheby's, London #136/R est:15000-20000
£19048 $34095 €28000 Portrait du General Andoche Junot, Duc d'Abrantes (20x13cm-8x5in) s.i. black chk. 18-Mar-4 Christie's, Paris #142/R est:7000-10000

DAVID, Jacques-Louis (circle) (1748-1825) French
£16484 $30000 €24067 Abduction of Briseis (227x161cm-89x63in) prov.exhib. 4-Feb-4 Christie's, Rockefeller NY #34/R est:6000-8000
£45455 $78182 €65000 Portrait of a young man (80x65cm-31x26in) prov. 2-Dec-3 Christie's, Paris #713/R est:12000-18000
Works on paper
£9310 $15548 €13500 Death of Lucretia (52x77cm-20x30in) Indian ink brush. 15-Nov-3 Lempertz, Koln #1284/R est:9000

DAVID, Jacques-Louis (studio) (1748-1825) French
£15172 $25186 €22000 Napoleon on St Bernhard (137x116cm-54x46in) prov. 1-Oct-3 Dorotheum, Vienna #257/R est:10000-14000

DAVID, Jean (1908-) Rumanian
£638 $1180 €950 Composition (46x38cm-18x15in) s. 15-Mar-4 Claude Boisgirard, Paris #27/R

DAVID, Jean-Louis (1792-1868) French
Works on paper
£420 $713 €600 Militaire a cheval (34x27cm-13x11in) s.d.1854 W/C. 18-Nov-3 Vanderkindere, Brussels #101

DAVID, Jose Maria (1944-) ?
Sculpture
£3600 $6012 €5256 Cheetah (69x127cm-27x50in) s.d.14 Nov 2000 dark brown pat. bronze. 14-Oct-3 Sotheby's, Olympia #33/R est:3000-4000

DAVID, Jules (1808-1892) French
£360 $666 €526 Le depart pour la ville (7x15cm-3x6in) panel. 14-Jan-4 Lawrence, Crewkerne #1398
£733 $1327 €1100 Maison rose (35x71cm-14x28in) s.d.1868. 4-Apr-4 St-Germain-en-Laye Encheres #6/R

DAVID, Michael (1954-) American
Works on paper
£324 $600 €473 Skirt (24x15cm-9x6in) init. W/C wax collage exec 1992 prov. 12-Feb-4 Sotheby's, New York #300/R
£541 $1000 €790 Marsyus (183x152cm-72x60in) s.i.d. overlap encaustic canvas exec 1983. 15-Jul-4 Sotheby's, New York #101

DAVID, Nurit (1952-) Israeli
£6145 $11000 €8972 Landscape no 3 (150x165cm-59x65in) s.d.2000 i.verso exhib. 18-Mar-4 Sotheby's, New York #62/R est:12000-15000

DAVID, Pierre Jean (1788-1856) French
Sculpture
£16000 $27680 €23360 Philopoemen (66cm-26in) s.d.1837 brown pat bronze base lit. 12-Dec-3 Sotheby's, London #233/R est:7000-10000

DAVIDEK, Stefan (1924-) American
£219 $400 €320 Blue mix no.6 (102x76cm-40x30in) s.d.75. 5-Jun-4 Susanin's, Chicago #5118/R

DAVIDSEN, Finn (1903-1964) Norwegian
£344 $575 €502 From Akers river (81x100cm-32x39in) s. 20-Oct-3 Blomqvist, Lysaker #1053/R (N.KR 4000)

DAVIDSON, A (19th C) British
Works on paper
£750 $1253 €1095 Old letters, interior with young lady at a desk (61x91cm-24x36in) s.d.1852 pencil W/C. 11-Jul-3 Jim Railton, Durham #875/R

DAVIDSON, Alexander (1838-1887) British
£2000 $3640 €2920 Learning their lines (77x100cm-30x39in) s.d.1875. 5-Feb-4 Mellors & Kirk, Nottingham #560/R

DAVIDSON, Alexander (attrib) (1838-1887) British
£280 $493 €409 Awaiting the fleet (36x25cm-14x10in) 19-May-4 Dreweatt Neate, Newbury #101/R

DAVIDSON, Allan Douglas (1873-1932) British
£260 $432 €380 Standing female nude (16x11cm-6x4in) s. board. 2-Oct-3 Lane, Penzance #213
£350 $627 €511 Portrait of Cecil Lay (35x30cm-14x12in) s.d.1925 board. 22-Mar-4 Bonhams & Brooks, Norfolk #338/R
£610 $1000 €885 Woman in black dress with red rose in her hair (30x25cm-12x10in) s. artist board prov. 31-May-3 Brunk, Ashville #478/R
£625 $1150 €950 Vision du faune (25x23cm-10x9in) s. board. 28-Jun-4 Joron-Derem, Paris #105
£1800 $3348 €2628 Tipple (34x24cm-13x9in) s. board. 4-Mar-4 Christie's, Kensington #637/R est:1200-1800

£4500 $8055 €6570 Bather (115x89cm-45x35in) s. exhib. 26-May-4 Sotheby's, Olympia #201/R est:2500-3500
£5500 $9350 €8030 Reclining nude beside a tree (20x23cm-8x9in) s. board. 19-Nov-3 Bonhams, New Bond Street #110/R est:1000-1500

DAVIDSON, Allen (1913-1988) American
£588 $1100 €858 Even tide (51x61cm-20x24in) painted c.1940. 29-Feb-4 Grogan, Boston #66/R

DAVIDSON, Bessie (1879-1965) Australian
£500 $835 €730 Grenoble (17x22cm-7x9in) s. s.o.d.1943 verso board. 20-Oct-3 Stephan Welz, Johannesburg #472 est:2000-3000 (SA.R 5800)

DAVIDSON, Bruce (1933-) American
Photographs
£63333 $114000 €92466 East 100Th Street, maquette (20x25cm-8x10in) album 124 gelatin silver print. 24-Apr-4 Phillips, New York #91/R est:100000-150000

DAVIDSON, Charles (1824-1902) British
Works on paper
£270 $427 €392 Ullswater with cattle on path (18x23cm-7x9in) s. W/C. 27-Jul-3 Desmond Judd, Cranbrook #1104
£300 $558 €438 Gathering shellfish, low tide (28x44cm-11x17in) s. W/C over pencil. 2-Mar-4 Bearnes, Exeter #393
£340 $626 €496 Early spring, Red Hill (23x28cm-9x11in) W/C. 8-Jun-4 Gorringes, Lewes #1985/R

DAVIDSON, Charles Topham (1848-?) British
Works on paper
£280 $512 €409 Loch Ranza (13x22cm-5x9in) s.i. W/C. 27-Jan-4 Bonhams, Knightsbridge #361/R
£700 $1281 €1022 Kenack, Cornwall (30x48cm-12x19in) s. W/C bodycol. 27-Jan-4 Bonhams, Knightsbridge #355/R
£1400 $2562 €2044 Harvester's lunch (28x45cm-11x18in) s. W/C. 27-Jan-4 Bonhams, Knightsbridge #353/R est:1500-2000

DAVIDSON, Colin (1968-) Irish
£2950 $5399 €4307 Bridge near Lough Corrib (76x96cm-30x38in) s. board. 2-Jun-4 John Ross, Belfast #115 est:1500-1800
£3026 $5568 €4600 Hooker (97x71cm-38x28in) s.d.2002 verso prov. 22-Jun-4 De Veres Art Auctions, Dublin #137/R est:5000-6000

DAVIDSON, Daniel (20th C) American?
£273 $500 €399 Ping pong (163x163cm-64x64in) 5-Jun-4 Susanin's, Chicago #5031/R

DAVIDSON, George (19/20th C) British
£1000 $1850 €1460 Showery evening, figures in a Scottish street at twilight (61x43cm-24x17in) s. 13-Feb-4 Keys, Aylsham #709/R est:1000-1500

DAVIDSON, Herb (20th C) American
£1486 $2600 €2170 Illustration to Jack Kerouac's before the road (79x60cm-31x24in) s.stretcher painted 1959. 17-Dec-3 Christie's, Rockefeller NY #38/R est:3000-4000
£1829 $3200 €2670 Telly loves ya (66x71cm-26x28in) painted 1978 exhib. 17-Dec-3 Christie's, Rockefeller NY #207/R est:3000-5000
£2400 $4200 €3504 All she needs is love (76x61cm-30x24in) painted 1970 exhib.lit. 17-Dec-3 Christie's, Rockefeller NY #206/R est:3000-5000

DAVIDSON, Herbert (?) ?
£1311 $2400 €1914 At the window (91x56cm-36x22in) 10-Jul-4 Hindman, Chicago #111/R est:1500-2000

DAVIDSON, J Stuart (?) British?
£550 $946 €803 Highland cattle on a hillside (102x152cm-40x60in) s. 2-Dec-3 Gorringes, Lewes #2430

DAVIDSON, Jeremiah (attrib) (1695-1745) British
£34000 $61880 €49640 Portrait of a gentleman, possibly one of the Campbell family of Breadalbane (242x152cm-95x60in) 1-Jul-4 Sotheby's, London #119/R est:12000-18000

DAVIDSON, Jerry (1935-) Canadian
£813 $1455 €1187 Don't go near the water (61x81cm-24x32in) s. i.d.1993 verso acrylic board. 6-May-4 Heffel, Vancouver #49/R est:2000-2500 (C.D 2000)

DAVIDSON, Jim (20th C) American
Sculpture
£2000 $3580 €3000 Le combat de coqs (76x128cm-30x50in) bears sig. brown pat bronze. 12-May-4 Coutau Begarie, Paris #237/R est:5000-6000

DAVIDSON, Jo (1883-1952) American
Sculpture
£1081 $2000 €1578 Bust of Abraham Lincoln (64cm-25in) with sig.d.1943 brown pat bronze incl marble base. 15-Jul-4 Sotheby's, New York #84 est:800-1200

DAVIDSON, Kristian (20th C) Danish?
£3791 $6975 €5535 Figure composition with heads and blue background (105x105cm-41x41in) 29-Mar-4 Rasmussen, Copenhagen #271/R est:20000 (D.KR 42000)

DAVIDSON, Lilian Lucy (1879-1954) Irish
£13333 $24133 €20000 Going to the fiar (45x35cm-18x14in) mono. 30-Mar-4 De Veres Art Auctions, Dublin #44/R est:10000-15000
£13380 $23148 €19000 West of Ireland village scene with boy (63x43cm-25x17in) prov. 10-Dec-3 Bonhams & James Adam, Dublin #82/R est:8000-12000
£21333 $38613 €32000 Hanging out the washing, Rathmines back streets (52x42cm-20x17in) mono. board. 31-Mar-4 James Adam, Dublin #44/R est:10000-15000
£26000 $46540 €37960 Here is the news (46x61cm-18x24in) mono. 13-May-4 Sotheby's, London #65/R est:20000-30000
Works on paper
£700 $1148 €1022 Duck pond (25x30cm-10x12in) mono. W/C. 4-Jun-3 John Ross, Belfast #52
£915 $1465 €1300 Rosbeg, County Donegal (28x38cm-11x15in) mono. i.verso W/C. 16-Sep-3 Whyte's, Dublin #115/R
£979 $1664 €1400 The duck pond (25x30cm-10x12in) mono. i.verso W/C gouache. 18-Nov-3 Whyte's, Dublin #185/R
£1250 $2037 €1800 Courtyard, Friars Hill (37x24cm-15x9in) mono. W/C prov.exhib. 24-Sep-3 James Adam, Dublin #143/R est:1500-2500

DAVIDSON, Maria (1926-) Russian
£1000 $1800 €1460 Zhar Ptitsa ballet (44x52cm-17x20in) oil on paper. 24-Apr-4 Shishkin Gallery, Moscow #94/R est:1200-1600

DAVIDSON, Morris (1898-?) American
£279 $475 €407 Sailboats (30x41cm-12x16in) s. painted c.1949. 9-Nov-3 Outer Cape Auctions, Provincetown #48/R

DAVIDSON, Rowland (20th C) British
£340 $612 €496 Catching crabs on the seashore (31x41cm-12x16in) s. 20-Apr-4 Rosebery Fine Art, London #383
£600 $1116 €876 At the horse fair, Ballyclare (35x25cm-14x10in) s. 3-Mar-4 John Ross, Belfast #70
£650 $1118 €949 Feeding the hens (30x35cm-12x14in) s. 3-Dec-3 John Ross, Belfast #253
£650 $1190 €949 Piper (30x25cm-12x10in) s. 2-Jun-4 John Ross, Belfast #27
£700 $1204 €1022 The session (61x45cm-24x18in) s. 3-Dec-3 John Ross, Belfast #34
£750 $1373 €1095 Robinson's Bar, Belfast (46x35cm-18x14in) s. board. 2-Jun-4 John Ross, Belfast #34
£820 $1410 €1197 Christmas shopping (40x30cm-16x12in) s. 3-Dec-3 John Ross, Belfast #218
£950 $1577 €1387 Stitch in time (45x55cm-18x22in) s. 1-Oct-3 John Ross, Belfast #30
£950 $1739 €1387 Interior girl in a kitchen (45x35cm-18x14in) s. 2-Jun-4 John Ross, Belfast #105a
£1100 $2046 €1606 Reading time (50x40cm-20x16in) s. 3-Mar-4 John Ross, Belfast #166 est:1200-1400
£1500 $2490 €2190 Benches at the city hall, Belfast (40x56cm-16x22in) s. 1-Oct-3 John Ross, Belfast #67 est:1000-1200
£1600 $2752 €2336 Irish dancers (101x127cm-40x50in) s. 3-Dec-3 John Ross, Belfast #105 est:2000-2500
£3490 $6177 €5200 Local feis (102x127cm-40x50in) s. board. 27-Apr-4 Whyte's, Dublin #242/R est:4000-6000

DAVIDSON, Thomas (19th C) British
£1500 $2505 €2190 Grand arrival (63x76cm-25x30in) s. 13-Nov-3 Christie's, Kensington #283/R est:1500-2000
£3293 $5500 €4808 Lord Horation Nelson returning from voyage (112x86cm-44x34in) s.d.1886. 15-Nov-3 Illustration House, New York #8/R est:2000-3000

DAVIE, Alan (1920-) British
£3600 $6120 €5256 Mystical seascape (27x29cm-11x11in) s.i.d.86 board prov. 26-Nov-3 Sotheby's, Olympia #168/R est:2500-3500
£3623 $5942 €5000 Surprise for the emperor's daughter. Untitled (42x53cm-17x21in) s.d.59 acrylic card on board two. 27-May-3 Sotheby's, Milan #51/R est:5000-7000
£5500 $10230 €8030 Receptical for sighs no.7 (122x152cm-48x60in) s.i.d.April 75 prov. 4-Mar-4 Christie's, Kensington #274/R est:6000-10000
£7000 $12040 €10220 Surprise for the Emperor's daughter (42x53cm-17x21in) s.d.59 board. 3-Dec-3 Sotheby's, London #87/R est:4000-6000
£12000 $21840 €17520 Monkey love (152x122cm-60x48in) s.i.d.Mar 60 verso board prov.lit. 6-Feb-4 Sotheby's, London #213/R est:10000-12000

DAVIE, Karen (1965-) American
£6145 $11000 €8972 In out in out drawing num 22 and num 23 (112x76cm-44x30in) s.i.d.94 verso acrylic diptych prov. 14-May-4 Phillips, New York #138/R est:8000-12000
£14525 $26000 €21207 Interior ghosts no 5 (183x244cm-72x96in) s.i.d.2000 verso prov. 14-May-4 Phillips, New York #141/R est:15000-20000

DAVIES, Albert Webster (1890-1967) American
£1242 $2000 €1813 Old colonial Williamsburg (43x61cm-17x24in) s. masonite panel painted c.1930. 22-Feb-3 Bunte, Elgin #1298 est:400-600

DAVIES, Arthur B (1862-1928) American
£244 $400 €354 Landscape (25x30cm-10x12in) s. gouache. 4-Jun-3 Alderfer's, Hatfield #272
£815 $1500 €1190 Seated figure (41x33cm-16x13in) i. 9-Jun-4 Alderfer's, Hatfield #397 est:1500-2500
£838 $1350 €1223 Frolicking nudes (23x30cm-9x12in) s. i. verso board oval. 20-Aug-3 James Julia, Fairfield #1568/R est:2000-3000
£1257 $2250 €1835 Girl with flower (30x20cm-12x8in) s. panel. 6-May-4 Shannon's, Milford #239/R est:2000-3000
£1705 $3000 €2489 Dancing Bacchantes (25x30cm-10x12in) s. prov. 23-May-4 Hindman, Chicago #180/R est:4000-6000
£1714 $3000 €2502 Autumn Rockland Lake (14x24cm-6x9in) i.verso panel two. 19-Dec-3 Sotheby's, New York #1005/R est:1000-1500
£1796 $3250 €2622 Wild wind of vision (46x76cm-18x30in) s. 31-Mar-4 Sotheby's, New York #136/R est:5000-7000

£1934 $3500 €2824 Indian enchantment (76x46cm-30x18in) s. 31-Mar-4 Sotheby's, New York #14/R est:2500-3500
£1984 $3750 €2897 Nudes bathing with swans in a neoclassical setting (53x64cm-21x25in) estate st.verso canvas on board. 21-Feb-4 Jeffery Burchard, Florida #39/R
£2386 $4200 €3484 Fleecy Arcady (20x41cm-8x16in) prov. 23-May-4 Hindman, Chicago #176/R est:3000-5000
£3125 $5000 €4563 River god (58x71cm-23x28in) 20-Sep-3 Bunte, Elgin #1270 est:10000-15000
£3495 $6500 €5103 Little Mattie (20x29cm-8x11in) prov. 3-Mar-4 Christie's, Rockefeller NY #15/R est:2000-3000
£3977 $7000 €5806 Mountain landscape with village (66x102cm-26x40in) prov. 23-May-4 Hindman, Chicago #177/R est:8000-12000
£4595 $8500 €6709 Home (36x26cm-14x10in) s. 11-Mar-4 Christie's, Rockefeller NY #73/R est:4000-6000
£7558 $13000 €11035 Figures in a landscape (59x72cm-23x28in) s. painted c.1912 exhib. 3-Dec-3 Sotheby's, New York #52/R est:15000-25000
Prints
£2044 $3250 €2984 Various nude figures (28x41cm-11x16in) s. monoprint. 10-Sep-3 Alderfer's, Hatfield #456/R est:800-1000
Works on paper
£290 $475 €421 Reclining nude (30x38cm-12x15in) s. chl chk prov. 31-May-3 Brunk, Ashville #172/R
£297 $550 €434 Landscape with clouds (27x34cm-11x13in) s.d.195 W/C. 18-Jul-4 Bonhams & Butterfields, Los Angeles #7030/R
£353 $650 €515 Study of a female nude (41x30cm-16x12in) i.verso crayon prov. 25-Jun-4 Freeman, Philadelphia #17/R
£359 $600 €524 Lago Trasimeno (20x30cm-8x12in) gouache. 17-Oct-3 Du Mouchelle, Detroit #2019/R
£400 $700 €584 Toledo II (24x31cm-9x12in) i. W/C prov. 19-Dec-3 Sotheby's, New York #1113/R
£419 $700 €612 Carrara mountains (20x30cm-8x12in) W/C gouache. 17-Oct-3 Du Mouchelle, Detroit #2018/R
£513 $950 €749 Landscape with clouds (25x30cm-10x12in) s.indis.d.1901 pastel. 18-Jul-4 Bonhams & Butterfields, Los Angeles #7031/R
£514 $900 €750 Blue sky (24x31cm-9x12in) W/C prov. 19-Dec-3 Sotheby's, New York #1114/R est:800-1200
£659 $1200 €962 Chateau, Spain (24x31cm-9x12in) e. executed c.1928 prov.exhib. 29-Jun-4 Sotheby's, New York #294/R est:1500-2000
£659 $1200 €962 Mountain rhythms (30x24cm-12x9in) W/C executed c.1928 prov.exhib. 29-Jun-4 Sotheby's, New York #295/R est:1500-2000
£659 $1200 €962 Gray skies and passing clouds (24x31cm-9x12in) W/C two executed c.1928 prov.exhib. 29-Jun-4 Sotheby's, New York #296/R est:1500-2500
£698 $1200 €1019 Study of female nudes (31x26cm-12x10in) s. pencil chk gouache paper on board. 2-Dec-3 Christie's, Rockefeller NY #88/R
£811 $1500 €1184 Dancing figures (74x127cm-29x50in) chk prepared blk cardboard. 15-Jul-4 Sotheby's, New York #76/R est:1500-2000
£1136 $2000 €1659 Mountain landscape (30x23cm-12x9in) s. W/C. 23-May-4 Hindman, Chicago #182/R est:3000-5000
£2429 $4250 €3546 Sea and hills and mist and mountains (23x30cm-9x12in) W/C two prov. 19-Dec-3 Sotheby's, New York #1111/R est:900-1200
£3039 $5500 €4437 Mountain pass (31x24cm-12x9in) W/C exec.c.1928 prov.exhib. 31-Mar-4 Sotheby's, New York #141/R est:1500-2500
£3591 $6500 €5243 Mountains, Italy (32x23cm-13x9in) W/C exec.c.1928 prov.exhib. 31-Mar-4 Sotheby's, New York #138/R est:1500-2500
£4802 $8500 €7011 Composition with figures (40x33cm-16x13in) init. s.verso gouache board exhib. 28-Apr-4 Christie's, Los Angeles #75/R est:2500-3500

DAVIES, Arthur E (1893-1988) British
£280 $465 €409 Marlingford Mill, Norfolk (20x25cm-8x10in) s. panel. 12-Nov-3 Gardiner & Houlgate, Bath #730
Works on paper
£260 $419 €377 Morning mist, Runham (28x38cm-11x15in) s. W/C. 15-Aug-3 Keys, Aylsham #626
£260 $419 €377 Salthouse Church (30x41cm-12x16in) s. W/C. 15-Aug-3 Keys, Aylsham #629
£260 $419 €377 On the Alde, Suffolk 1985 (28x38cm-11x15in) s. W/C. 15-Aug-3 Keys, Aylsham #632
£260 $478 €380 Horstead of Buxton Mill (11x15cm-4x6in) s. W/C. 11-Jun-4 Keys, Aylsham #586/R
£270 $435 €392 Lowestoft harbour, 1985 (28x36cm-11x14in) s. W/C. 15-Aug-3 Keys, Aylsham #625
£280 $451 €406 Nasturtiums in a glass bowl (43x48cm-17x19in) s.d.1973 W/C. 15-Aug-3 Keys, Aylsham #628
£280 $451 €406 Wells next the sea 1985 (28x38cm-11x15in) s. W/C. 15-Aug-3 Keys, Aylsham #631
£280 $507 €409 On the Deben, Suffolk (25x36cm-10x14in) s. pen ink. 16-Apr-4 Keys, Aylsham #642
£280 $515 €409 View of Salthouse Church across the broads (11x15cm-4x6in) s. W/C. 11-Jun-4 Keys, Aylsham #584
£300 $483 €435 Ebb tide, Brancaster (25x36cm-10x14in) s. W/C. 15-Aug-3 Keys, Aylsham #627/R
£300 $483 €435 Ely Cathedral (36x28cm-14x11in) s. W/C. 15-Aug-3 Keys, Aylsham #630
£300 $477 €438 Old Quayside, Norwich (29x42cm-11x17in) s. W/C. 10-Sep-3 Cheffins, Cambridge #448
£350 $644 €511 Golden Ball Inn, Norwich (10x15cm-4x6in) s. W/C. 11-Jun-4 Keys, Aylsham #588
£360 $572 €526 Misty afternoon, Norwich Cathedral (38x50cm-15x20in) s. W/C. 10-Sep-3 Cheffins, Cambridge #449/R
£520 $957 €759 Morning mist, Beccles (10x15cm-4x6in) s. W/C. 11-Jun-4 Keys, Aylsham #585
£540 $902 €788 Old mill, Cley (28x38cm-11x15in) s. W/C. 17-Oct-3 Keys, Aylsham #665/R

DAVIES, Brian (20th C) ?
£800 $1456 €1168 Bread, lemon and oysters (39x59cm-15x23in) s. 15-Jun-4 Dreweatt Neate, Newbury #651/R
£1150 $1990 €1679 Still life of peaches, grapes, wine and pewter flagon on a ledge (36x30cm-14x12in) s. 14-Dec-3 Desmond Judd, Cranbrook #1022
£1300 $2249 €1898 Still life of peaches, pears, grapes, nuts and wine on a ledge (30x25cm-12x10in) s. 14-Dec-3 Desmond Judd, Cranbrook #1087
£3300 $6171 €4818 Still life of a loaf of bread and quails eggs (41x61cm-16x24in) s. 20-Jul-4 Sworder & Son, Bishops Stortford #739/R est:800-1000

DAVIES, Charles W (19th C) British
£950 $1739 €1387 Officer, horse and dog in a stable (44x62cm-17x24in) init.d.1849. 7-Apr-4 Woolley & Wallis, Salisbury #285/R

DAVIES, David (1864-1939) Australian
£4580 $8336 €6687 St. Ives (21x26cm-8x10in) s.d.93 board. 16-Jun-4 Deutscher-Menzies, Melbourne #154/R est:15000-20000 (A.D 12000)
£7252 $13198 €10588 St. Ives (28x61cm-11x24in) s.i. prov. 16-Jun-4 Deutscher-Menzies, Melbourne #86/R est:15000-20000 (A.D 19000)
Works on paper
£1660 $2772 €2490 Sketch at Berneval (28x22cm-11x9in) s. W/C. 27-Oct-3 Goodman, Sydney #110/R est:4000-6000 (A.D 4000)

DAVIES, Gregory (20th C) British
£360 $659 €526 Grass Rhythms, a summer landscape (59x105cm-23x41in) s. board. 6-Jul-4 Bearnes, Exeter #478/R

DAVIES, Ivor (1935-) British
£260 $406 €377 Yalta meeting (25x20cm-10x8in) s.d.1980. 20-Oct-2 Desmond Judd, Cranbrook #926

DAVIES, J N (?) Australian?
Works on paper
£10163 $15955 €14838 Antarctic birds of Australia and New Zealand. W/C gouache W/C sixty-eight album. 27-Aug-3 Christie's, Sydney #840/R est:25000-35000 (A.D 25000)

DAVIES, James Hey (1844-1930) British
£1300 $2171 €1898 Harvesting (51x76cm-20x30in) s.d.1906. 12-Nov-3 Sotheby's, Olympia #113/R est:1000-1200

DAVIES, John (1946-) British
£9600 $16320 €14016 Ale tasters (71x91cm-28x36in) 18-Nov-3 Bonhams, Leeds #175/R est:4000-6000
Sculpture
£6000 $10980 €8760 Head TP (32cm-13in) painted polyester prov. 2-Jun-4 Sotheby's, London #118/R est:5000-7000
Works on paper
£3200 $5856 €4672 Couple (48x40cm-19x16in) chk pen exec.1980 exhib. 2-Jun-4 Sotheby's, London #128/R est:2500-3500

DAVIES, John R (1899-1985) British
£559 $1000 €816 Cotswold landscape (51x61cm-20x24in) s. board. 7-May-4 Sloans & Kenyon, Bethesda #1672/R

DAVIES, Norman Prescott (1862-1915) British
£1227 $2270 €1791 Spirit of the south wind (90x59cm-35x23in) s.d.1905. 9-Mar-4 Watson's, Christchurch #76 est:3500-5000 (NZ.D 3350)
£3000 $5520 €4380 Azalias (38x28cm-15x11in) s.d.1898. 8-Jun-4 Bonhams, Knightsbridge #270/R est:1500-2500

DAVIES, Roland (1904-1993) British
£280 $496 €409 On the beach at Great Yarmouth (30x41cm-12x16in) s. 27-Apr-4 Bonhams, Knightsbridge #44

DAVIES, William (1826-1910) British
£500 $910 €730 Penllech Bay Carmarthenshire (32x47cm-13x19in) s.d.1903 s.i.d.verso. 1-Jul-4 Mellors & Kirk, Nottingham #838
£3490 $6421 €5200 Flock grazing in mountain landscape (33x49cm-13x19in) s.d.1901. 27-Mar-4 L & B, Essen #78/R est:500

DAVILA, Daniel (1843-1924) Mexican
£263 $448 €384 Chicks (18x24cm-7x9in) s.d.1876. 29-Oct-3 Louis Morton, Mexico #37/R est:6000-8000 (M.P 5000)

DAVILA, Jose Antonio (1935-) Venezuelan
£593 $935 €866 Traveller (90x100cm-35x39in) s. 27-Apr-3 Subastas Odalys, Caracas #83
£878 $1615 €1317 Beach (81x91cm-32x36in) s. painted c.1970. 27-Jun-4 Subastas Odalys, Caracas #8/R

DAVILA, Juan (1946-) Chilean
£8264 $15289 €12065 Nothing 1987 (257x242cm-101x95in) s. i.d.1987 verso oil on 14 panel prov.exhib. 10-Mar-4 Deutscher-Menzies, Melbourne #12/R est:35000-55000 (A.D 20000)
£10744 $19876 €15686 My birthday (200x200cm-79x79in) s. i.d.1988 verso prov. 10-Mar-4 Deutscher-Menzies, Melbourne #138 est:30000-40000 (A.D 26000)

DAVIS, Amee (1893-1973) American
£494 $850 €721 Gloucester harbour (41x51cm-16x20in) s. canvasboard painted c.1940. 7-Dec-3 Treadway Gallery, Cincinnati #620/R

DAVIS, Arthur A (fl.1877-1905) British
£1000 $1570 €1450 Hounds jumping a gate (91x61cm-36x24in) s.d.1900. 28-Aug-3 Christie's, Kensington #119 est:1200-1800
£1050 $1900 €1533 Running into him. Any port in a storm (51x76cm-20x30in) s.d.1904 i.verso pair. 30-Mar-4 Christie's, Rockefeller NY #46/R est:4000-6000
Works on paper
£280 $501 €409 Rabbiting (24x36cm-9x14in) s.d.1910 W/C. 17-Mar-4 Bonhams, Chester #390

DAVIS, Arthur H (fl.1871-1894) British
£550 $1007 €803 Salisbury Cathedral from Longbridge, Fisherton (46x77cm-18x30in) s.d.81 i.verso. 7-Apr-4 Woolley & Wallis, Salisbury #256/R

DAVIS, Brad (1942-) American
Works on paper
£278 $500 €406 Eggplant (17x14cm-7x6in) s.d.1974 pen ink W/C metallic paint paper on fabric prov. 24-Apr-4 David Rago, Lambertville #281/R

DAVIS, Charles F (19/20th C) British
£380 $646 €555 Study of a hunter in a stable interior (41x51cm-16x20in) s.d.08. 19-Nov-3 Tennants, Leyburn #1189

DAVIS, Charles Harold (1856-1933) American
£1497 $2500 €2186 Birds over a field (20x36cm-8x14in) s.d.1888. 23-Oct-3 Shannon's, Milford #192/R est:2500-3500
£2031 $3250 €2965 Landscape with trees (30x46cm-12x18in) s. 19-Sep-3 Freeman, Philadelphia #121/R est:2000-3000
£2512 $4500 €3668 On the marshes (33x41cm-13x16in) s.d.1887 prov. 6-May-4 Shannon's, Milford #186/R est:5000-7000
£4042 $6750 €5901 Evening, winter sky (18x30cm-7x12in) s.d.1884. 7-Oct-3 Sotheby's, New York #176 est:2500-3500

DAVIS, Dorothy (1910-1991) American
£235 $400 €343 Woman cooking a pie on a wood stove while children play (51x66cm-20x26in) s. 21-Nov-3 Eldred, East Dennis #212e/R

DAVIS, Edward Thompson (1833-1867) British
£14371 $24000 €20982 Kissing grandpa (46x35cm-18x14in) s.d.1860 panel. 7-Oct-3 Sotheby's, New York #101 est:8000-12000
£28144 $47000 €41090 Crochet lesson (46x35cm-18x14in) s.d.1885 panel. 7-Oct-3 Sotheby's, New York #124 est:8000-12000

DAVIS, Frederick (fl.1850-1892) British
Works on paper
£300 $516 €438 West End Farm, Pinner (27x47cm-11x19in) s.d.1865 W/C. 4-Dec-3 Hobbs Parker, Ashford #388

DAVIS, Frederick William (1862-1919) British
£1399 $2378 €2000 In the village tavern (71x91cm-28x36in) s.d.1889 exhib.lit. 28-Nov-3 Schloss Ahlden, Ahlden #1425/R est:2300

DAVIS, Gene (1920-1985) American
£2703 $5000 €3946 Untitled - 152 (245x7cm-96x3in) acrylic painted 1971 prov. 12-Feb-4 Sotheby's, New York #192/R est:1500-2000
£2973 $5500 €4341 Untitled - 150 (244x7cm-96x3in) acrylic painted 1971 prov. 12-Feb-4 Sotheby's, New York #194/R est:1500-2000
£3988 $6500 €5822 Pumpkin (36x51cm-14x20in) s.i.d.1959 verso acrylic pencil. 23-Sep-3 Christie's, Rockefeller NY #112/R est:3000-5000
£4054 $7500 €5919 Untitled - 156 (7x305cm-3x120in) acrylic painted 1971 prov. 12-Feb-4 Sotheby's, New York #198/R est:1500-2000
£4601 $7500 €6717 Pocono (72x352cm-28x139in) init.i.d.1984 verso acrylic. 23-Sep-3 Christie's, Rockefeller NY #111/R est:7000-9000
£10056 $18000 €14682 Mohawk (171x176cm-67x69in) s.i.d.1970 acrylic prov. 12-May-4 Christie's, Rockefeller NY #158/R est:20000-30000

DAVIS, Gerald (1938-) Irish?
£278 $506 €420 Landscape with memories of an ancient fort. s.d.71 board. 15-Jun-4 James Adam, Dublin #236/R
£563 $1025 €850 Soft painting (35x50cm-14x20in) s.d.72 board. 15-Jun-4 James Adam, Dublin #133/R

DAVIS, Gladys Rockmore (1901-1967) American
£542 $900 €791 Sea shell (66x41cm-26x16in) init. 4-Oct-3 Neal Auction Company, New Orleans #608/R
£625 $1100 €913 Portrait of a young gil seated, holding a dachshund (76x64cm-30x25in) init. 22-May-4 Selkirks, St. Louis #549/R

DAVIS, H (?) ?
£1023 $1800 €1494 Hilly Connecticut summer landscape with partly cloudy sky (43x51cm-17x20in) s. 1-Jan-4 Nadeau, Windsor #140/R est:2000-3000

DAVIS, Harry A (?) American
£994 $1800 €1451 Group of boys flying kites (48x74cm-19x29in) s. 3-Apr-4 David Rago, Lambertville #84/R est:2500-3000

DAVIS, Henry William Banks (1833-1914) British
£1600 $2976 €2336 Moorland pasture (30x46cm-12x18in) init.d.1912. 4-Mar-4 Christie's, Kensington #454/R est:1200-1800
£4500 $8190 €6570 Harvest scene, Boulogne (28x50cm-11x20in) s. 16-Jun-4 Bonhams, New Bond Street #41/R est:2000-4000
£5000 $8300 €7300 Pair of prize longhorn cattle (51x97cm-20x38in) s.d.1856. 2-Oct-3 Neales, Nottingham #753/R est:4000-5000

DAVIS, Jack (1924-) American
Works on paper
£1371 $2400 €2002 Now smile (42x27cm-17x11in) s. ink W/C ills board exec Feb 1961. 17-Dec-3 Christie's, Rockefeller NY #192/R est:2000-3000
£2571 $4500 €3754 Yes ? (48x41cm-19x16in) s. ink W/C illus board exec Oct 1961 exhib. 17-Dec-3 Christie's, Rockefeller NY #62/R est:2000-3000
£2857 $5000 €4171 Go ahead and putt, it'll be a few minutes before the shock wave reaches us (43x35cm-17x14in) s. ink W/C ills board exec Sept 1962. 17-Dec-3 Christie's, Rockefeller NY #194/R est:2000-3000
£3429 $6000 €5006 Take me to your leader (51x41cm-20x16in) s.i. W/C illus board exec 1959 exhib. 17-Dec-3 Christie's, Rockefeller NY #31/R est:2000-3000

DAVIS, John Scarlett (attrib) (1804-1845) British
£669 $1150 €977 Interior of a room in Hampton Court Palace (64x76cm-25x30in) s. 6-Dec-3 Selkirks, St. Louis #109

DAVIS, Joseph H (fl.1832-1837) American
Works on paper
£926 $1500 €1352 Portrait of Warren Smith, aged 22 (25x20cm-10x8in) i. W/C. 1-Aug-3 North East Auctions, Portsmouth #604/R
£1543 $2500 €2253 Portrait of Matilda Smith, aged 19 (25x20cm-10x8in) i. W/C. 1-Aug-3 North East Auctions, Portsmouth #605/R
£42614 $75000 €62216 David and Hannah York (27x38cm-11x15in) i. W/C pen ink. 18-May-4 Sotheby's, New York #103/R est:20000-30000

DAVIS, Leonard M (1864-1938) American
£223 $400 €326 Lake in the mountains, sunset (23x30cm-9x12in) s. 14-May-4 Skinner, Boston #77/R
£932 $1500 €1361 Alaskan landscape (15x23cm-6x9in) s. board. 20-Aug-3 James Julia, Fairfield #1744/R est:1400-1800

DAVIS, Louis B (1861-1941) British
Works on paper
£1400 $2324 €2044 Aries (53x20cm-21x8in) s. W/C. 1-Oct-3 Sotheby's, Olympia #164/R est:500-700
£4698 $8128 €6859 Tears of heaven falling from a circle of angels (171x59cm-67x23in) chl. 12-Dec-3 Kieselbach, Budapest #185/R (H.F 1800000)
£6516 $10816 €9513 Saint George (137x50cm-54x20in) s. mixed media paper on canvas. 4-Oct-3 Kieselbach, Budapest #101/R (H.F 2400000)

DAVIS, Lucien (1860-1941) British
Works on paper
£550 $919 €803 Savouring the scent (19x12cm-7x5in) s. W/C gouache. 12-Nov-3 Sotheby's, Olympia #136/R
£580 $986 €847 Young lady in a rose trimmed hat (38cm-15in circular) s. W/C bodycol sold with a companion. 1-Dec-3 Bonhams, Bath #63/R

DAVIS, Lynn (1944-) American
Photographs
£3175 $6000 €4636 Bent Pyramid, Dashur, Cairo, Egypt (103x103cm-41x41in) s.d.1997 num.4/10 gelatin silver print. 17-Feb-4 Christie's, Rockefeller NY #286/R est:4000-6000
£7345 $13000 €10724 Iceberg no.7, Disko Bay, Greenland (71x71cm-28x28in) s.i.d.1989 num.6/10 gelatin silver print. 27-Apr-4 Christie's, Rockefeller NY #363/R est:6000-8000

DAVIS, Noel Denholm (fl.1899-1939) British
£650 $1040 €943 Portrait of a lady (30x23cm-12x9in) board. 16-Sep-3 Bonhams, Knightsbridge #68/R
Works on paper
£700 $1274 €1022 Young woman in dappled sunlight (54x43cm-21x17in) s pastel. 1-Jul-4 Mellors & Kirk, Nottingham #703/R

DAVIS, Paul (1938-) American
Works on paper
£514 $900 €750 Lore of Roulette (42x42cm-17x17in) s. pencil gouache ink shaped board round exec Jan 1967. 17-Dec-3 Christie's, Rockefeller NY #158/R

DAVIS, Richard Barrett (1782-1854) British
£650 $1196 €949 Sporting sweep (30x40cm-12x16in) i.stretcher. 10-Jun-4 Christie's, Kensington #5/R
£14000 $24640 €20440 Richard Davis, huntsman to King George III's harriers, with hounds (108x143cm-43x56in) prov. 21-May-4 Christie's, London #51/R est:10000-15000

DAVIS, Richard Barrett (attrib) (1782-1854) British
£978 $1800 €1428 T. Winfield, huntsman to the Bucknell Hounds (43x56cm-17x22in) 27-Jun-4 Hindman, Chicago #857a/R est:300-500

DAVIS, Rose (20th C) British
Works on paper
£260 $432 €380 Life models (44x27cm-17x11in) s. i.verso chl. 2-Oct-3 Lane, Penzance #122

DAVIS, Samuel (1757-1819) British
Works on paper
£23000 $37490 €33580 Kotwali Gate, Gaur, Bengal (53x71cm-21x28in) pencil W/C prov.exhib.lit. 24-Sep-3 Christie's, London #24/R est:10000-15000

DAVIS, Sarah (attrib) (19th C) British
£667 $1200 €974 Portrait of a woman (76x63cm-30x25in) painted c.1850. 21-Jan-4 Doyle, New York #130 est:800-1200

DAVIS, Stan (1942-) American
£1125 $1800 €1643 Warm light of summer (23x30cm-9x12in) oil on linen. 19-Sep-3 Altermann Galleries, Santa Fe #2
£1188 $1900 €1734 Spooked (28x25cm-11x10in) oil on linen. 19-Sep-3 Altermann Galleries, Santa Fe #1
£5000 $8500 €7300 When leadership weighs (51x51cm-20x20in) oil on linen. 1-Nov-3 Altermann Galleries, Santa Fe #9

DAVIS, Stark (1885-?) American
£475 $850 €694 Crane with outstretched wings (97x58cm-38x23in) s. board. 21-Mar-4 Hindman, Chicago #857/R est:1000-2000
£1063 $1700 €1552 Cat with Oriental screen (91x61cm-36x24in) s. 21-Sep-3 William Jenack, New York #158 est:800-1200

DAVIS, Steven (20th C) American
£250 $455 €365 Anvil (213x152cm-84x60in) acrylic painted 1984 prov. 4-Feb-4 Sotheby's, Olympia #244/R

DAVIS, Stuart (1894-1964) American
£15988 $27500 €23342 Lady on the beach (75x46cm-30x18in) s.d.1917 prov.exhib. 3-Dec-3 Sotheby's, New York #48/R est:30000-50000
£110465 $190000 €161279 Cigarette papers (30x32cm-12x13in) s. s.d.1933 verso prov.exhib.lit. 4-Dec-3 Christie's, Rockefeller NY #113/R est:200000-300000
£319767 $550000 €466860 Sunrise (25x36cm-10x14in) s. painted 1933 prov.exhib.lit. 4-Dec-3 Christie's, Rockefeller NY #96/R est:250000-350000
Prints
£2793 $5000 €4078 Hotel de France (36x28cm-14x11in) s.num.25/30 lithograph. 4-May-4 Doyle, New York #157/R est:2500-3500
£6471 $11000 €9448 Arch No. I (23x33cm-9x13in) s. num.11/30 lithograph. 4-Nov-3 Christie's, Rockefeller NY #5/R est:7000-9000
Works on paper
£4857 $8500 €7091 From the fishing boat (25x37cm-10x15in) pencil prov. 19-Dec-3 Sotheby's, New York #1016/R est:6000-9000
£18466 $32500 €26960 Poolroom. Figures outside a tavern (36x28cm-14x11in) s.d.1911 W/C pencil double-sided prov.lit. 19-May-4 Sotheby's, New York #108/R est:20000-30000
£23256 $40000 €33954 Grade A (30x22cm-12x9in) s.d.26 gouache ink chl collage board prov.exhib. 3-Dec-3 Sotheby's, New York #72/R est:30000-50000

DAVIS, Vestie E (1904-1978) American
£2794 $4750 €4079 Coney Island boardwalk (30x61cm-12x24in) s.d.1960 prov. 18-Nov-3 Doyle, New York #19/R est:5000-7000

DAVIS, W H (19th C) British
£2500 $4650 €3650 Shorthorn cow and bull calf of roan colour, in a landscape (64x76cm-25x30in) 3-Mar-4 Brightwells, Leominster #906 est:2500-3000

DAVIS, Warren B (1865-1928) American
£1571 $2750 €2294 Sidelon-sun (41x46cm-16x18in) s. s.i. on stretcher. 19-Dec-3 Sotheby's, New York #1066/R est:3000-5000
£1676 $3000 €2447 Rest stop (66x51cm-26x20in) s. 26-May-4 Doyle, New York #86/R est:3000-5000
Works on paper
£341 $600 €498 Dancer (13x10cm-5x4in) s. i.verso gouache exec.c.1910. 23-May-4 Treadway Gallery, Cincinnati #493/R

DAVIS, William (1812-1873) British
£17000 $28900 €24820 Field of corn (30x48cm-12x19in) init. board prov. 25-Nov-3 Christie's, London #177/R est:5000-8000

DAVIS, William Henry (?-1865) British
£1366 $2200 €1994 Prize bull in a landscape (56x69cm-22x27in) s.d.1845. 14-Jan-4 Christie's, Rockefeller NY #56/R est:3000-5000
£1600 $2720 €2336 Hereford sow in a meadow (67x91cm-26x36in) s.d.1851 exhib. 26-Nov-3 Hamptons Fine Art, Godalming #200/R est:1500-2000
£2000 $3720 €2920 Mr Sam Wiley's van Dunck, a prize bull in a field (56x68cm-22x27in) s.d.1850 i.on stretcher. 4-Mar-4 Christie's, Kensington #535/R est:2000-3000
£2300 $4209 €3358 A hunter and a dog in a landscape (51x76cm-20x30in) s.d.1826. 7-Apr-4 Woolley & Wallis, Salisbury #286/R est:800-1200
£3400 $6324 €4964 Prize heffer and a prize cow (53x99cm-21x39in) s.d.1856. 4-Mar-4 Christie's, Kensington #540/R est:6000-8000
£4200 $7812 €6132 Prize bull in a field (46x61cm-18x24in) s.d.1851 prov. 4-Mar-4 Christie's, Kensington #539/R est:2000-3000
£6000 $11160 €8760 Prize Hereford cow (66x91cm-26x36in) s.d.1851 prov.exhib. 4-Mar-4 Christie's, Kensington #534/R est:3000-5000

DAVIS, William M (1829-1920) American
£6145 $11000 €8972 Close shave (30x36cm-12x14in) s. canvasboard prov. 6-May-4 Shannon's, Milford #54/R est:10000-15000
Works on paper
£307 $575 €448 Pastoral scene with three cows streamside (30x43cm-12x17in) s. W/C board. 28-Feb-4 Thomaston Place, Thomaston #92/R

DAVIS, William Triplett (1884-1961) American
£244 $400 €356 Edge of town (61x51cm-24x20in) s. board painted c.1929. 4-Jun-3 Alderfer's, Hatfield #292/R

DAVISON, Nora (fl.1881-1905) British
£1317 $2239 €1923 Landscape with cattle (30x37cm-12x15in) s. cardboard double-sided. 29-Nov-3 Dorotheum, Prague #20/R est:15000-23000 (C.KR 60000)
Works on paper
£250 $395 €363 Tall ships and tugs in a harbour (20x33cm-8x13in) s. W/C. 27-Jul-3 Desmond Judd, Cranbrook #1034

DAVISON, W H (19th C) British
£4372 $8000 €6383 Auxiliary steamer Tycho Brahe off the South Stack Lighthouse, Anglesey (79x134cm-31x53in) s.d.10/6/69. 29-Jul-4 Christie's, Rockefeller NY #252/R est:6000-8000

DAVISSON, Homer Gordon (1866-1957) American
£1018 $1700 €1486 Autumn landscape (41x48cm-16x19in) s. board. 20-Jun-3 Freeman, Philadelphia #169/R est:1000-1500

DAVRINGHAUSEN, Heinrich Maria (1894-1970) German
£483 $806 €700 Untitled (25x28cm-10x11in) mono. s.verso. 13-Nov-3 Neumeister, Munich #296/R
£700 $1253 €1050 Untitled (57x43cm-22x17in) s.i.d. 13-May-4 Neumeister, Munich #321/R
£1133 $2029 €1700 Composition (25x28cm-10x11in) mono. s. verso. 15-May-4 Van Ham, Cologne #550/R est:1600
£1259 $2140 €1800 Untitled (50x61cm-20x24in) s. 29-Nov-3 Villa Grisebach, Berlin #527/R
£2222 $3711 €3200 Church in Kornelimunster (62x62cm-24x24in) i. lit. 25-Oct-3 Auktionhaus Herr, Cologne #327/R est:2700-5400
£18182 $30909 €26000 Female nude against architecture (199x100cm-78x39in) prov. 26-Nov-3 Lempertz, Koln #632/R est:30000-35000
Works on paper
£276 $461 €400 Untitled (30x43cm-12x17in) s.d.1960 gouache. 13-Nov-3 Neumeister, Munich #299/R
£290 $484 €420 Composition in green and black (34x52cm-13x20in) s.d.1955 gouache pencil. 13-Nov-3 Neumeister, Munich #297/R
£300 $537 €450 Untitled (34x51cm-13x20in) mono.i. verso gouache. 13-May-4 Neumeister, Munich #324/R
£333 $597 €500 Untitled (26x41cm-10x16in) s.d. gouache pencil. 13-May-4 Neumeister, Munich #323/R
£504 $826 €700 Composition (60x43cm-24x17in) mono. pastel. 4-Jun-3 Ketterer, Hamburg #308/R
£567 $1014 €850 Untitled (41x59cm-16x23in) s.d. gouache pencil. 13-May-4 Neumeister, Munich #322/R

DAVY, George (20th C) British
£550 $1029 €803 Horse in a landscape (75x100cm-30x39in) s.d.1964. 21-Jul-4 Lyon & Turnbull, Edinburgh #149

DAWBARN, Joseph Yelverton (fl.1890-1930) British
Works on paper
£600 $1038 €876 Coming from Mass - Sunday in a Dutch fishing village. W/C. 9-Dec-3 Lawrences, Bletchingley #1652

DAWE, Georg (1781-1829) British
£340000 $608600 €496400 Portrait of Tasr Alexander I (236x148cm-93x58in) s.d.1820 prov. 26-May-4 Sotheby's, London #13/R est:120000-180000

DAWE, Georg (circle) (1781-1829) British
£14000 $23380 €20440 Portrait of Major General Sir Henry Floyd, BT, wearing uniform (124x102cm-49x40in) 14-Oct-3 Sotheby's, London #464 est:8000-12000

DAWES, Edwin M (1872-1945) American
£610 $1000 €885 Autumn lake (41x51cm-16x20in) s. board painted c.1910. 7-Jun-3 Treadway Gallery, Cincinnati #1391

DAWIS, Germaine (19th C) French
£680 $1218 €1000 Jeune femme en buste a demi-nue (74x54cm-29x21in) s.d.1913. 20-Mar-4 Binoche, Orleans #44

DAWNAY, Adrian (20th C) British
Works on paper
£550 $935 €803 Pugs asleep. Baby pugs (29x39cm-11x15in) s.i.d.2003 pen ink chk two. 27-Nov-3 Christie's, Kensington #409/R
£750 $1275 €1095 Pug (30x38cm-12x15in) s.d.2003 pen ink chk two. 27-Nov-3 Christie's, Kensington #405/R

DAWNAY, F (?) British?
£1600 $2864 €2336 Children playing in a stream (69x105cm-27x41in) s. 18-Mar-4 Neales, Nottingham #794 est:300-500

DAWNEY, Ada (?) British?
£950 $1672 €1387 Continental landscape with flowering shrubs and butterflies. Asiatic pheasants (87x122cm-34x48in) pair. 19-May-4 Dreweatt Neate, Newbury #76

DAWS, Frederick Thomas (1878-?) British
£260 $475 €380 Lion in the desert (41x51cm-16x20in) s. 31-Jul-4 Sloans & Kenyon, Bethesda #1223/R
£773 $1400 €1129 Boxer puppy (43x33cm-17x13in) s.d.11. 30-Mar-4 Bonhams & Butterfields, San Francisco #129/R est:800-1200

DAWS, Lawrence (1927-) Australian
£519 $866 €779 J M at Mount Cotton (26x29cm-10x11in) s. i.verso mixed media board. 27-Oct-3 Goodman, Sydney #57/R (A.D 1250)
£551 $936 €804 Purple landscape (50x57cm-20x22in) s.d.64 bears i.verso board prov. 24-Nov-3 Sotheby's, Melbourne #244 (A.D 1300)
£638 $1085 €931 White structure II (56x76cm-22x30in) s. acrylic paper on board. 25-Nov-3 Christie's, Melbourne #126/R (A.D 1500)
£690 $1076 €1001 Anakiey (56x53cm-22x21in) s. board. 1-Aug-2 Joel, Victoria #240 est:2000-2500 (A.D 2000)

£810 $1304 €1183 Pilbara (56x56cm-22x22in) s. board. 13-Oct-3 Joel, Victoria #332 est:2000-3000 (A.D 2000)
£1626 $2911 €2374 Mandala and landscape (51x61cm-20x24in) oil collage board prov. 4-May-4 Sotheby's, Melbourne #259/R est:4000-6000 (A.D 4000)
£2024 $3259 €2955 Field of poppies (66x89cm-26x35in) s. board. 13-Oct-3 Joel, Victoria #236/R est:3000-5000 (A.D 5000)
£3659 $5744 €5306 Nude in landscape (74x63cm-29x25in) s. cardboard prov.exhib. 26-Aug-3 Christie's, Sydney #258/R est:3000-4000 (A.D 9000)
£3719 $6880 €5430 Outcast (152x127cm-60x50in) s. painted c.1956 prov.exhib. 10-Mar-4 Deutscher-Menzies, Melbourne #205/R est:10000-15000 (A.D 9000)
£6098 $9573 €8842 Owl creek landscape, Glasshouse mountains (100x120cm-39x47in) s. i.stretcher. 27-Aug-3 Christie's, Sydney #609/R est:8000-15000 (A.D 15000)
£10213 $17362 €14911 Lily pool (153x152cm-60x60in) s. i.d.1985 verso. 25-Nov-3 Christie's, Melbourne #10/R est:15000-20000 (A.D 24000)
£11271 $17808 €16456 Gold mine (68x91cm-27x36in) s. board prov. 2-Sep-3 Deutscher-Menzies, Melbourne #100/R est:25000-35000 (A.D 27500)
Works on paper
£1577 $2633 €2366 Himalayas from Glass House Mountains (100x128cm-39x50in) s. mixed media. 27-Oct-3 Goodman, Sydney #89/R est:2500-3500 (A.D 3800)
£2869 $4533 €4189 Landscape (84x84cm-33x33in) s. synthetic polymer. 2-Sep-3 Deutscher-Menzies, Melbourne #155/R est:5500-7000 (A.D 7000)
£3607 $5698 €5266 Figure on beach IV (59x59cm-23x23in) s.d.64 gouache W/C chl collage prov. 2-Sep-3 Deutscher-Menzies, Melbourne #138/R est:9000-12000 (A.D 8800)

DAWS, Philip (fl.1873-1879) British
£450 $819 €657 Netley Mill, Shere (39x54cm-15x21in) s.d.1872 i.d.verso. 16-Jun-4 Rupert Toovey, Partridge Green #118/R

DAWSON, Alfred (fl.1860-1894) British
£1150 $1990 €1679 On the Thames, near Kew, mist on the river with figures and barge (38x58cm-15x23in) s.d.76 i.verso. 11-Dec-3 Neales, Nottingham #668/R est:500-800

DAWSON, Arthur (1858-1922) British
£438 $700 €639 Summer landscape with shepherd and flock of sheep (36x43cm-14x17in) s.d.1902 i.verso panel. 20-Sep-3 Pook & Pook, Downington #139
Works on paper
£282 $450 €412 Figures on a boat (36x51cm-14x20in) s. W/C exec. c.1885. 20-Sep-3 Bunte, Elgin #310

DAWSON, Charles Clarence (1889-?) American
Works on paper
£1512 $2600 €2208 Broom vendor (38x25cm-15x10in) s. W/C exec.c.1930. 7-Dec-3 Treadway Gallery, Cincinnati #596/R est:1500-2500

DAWSON, Henry (1811-1878) British
£680 $1258 €993 River scene with girl rowing a boat (30x41cm-12x16in) 14-Jan-4 Brightwells, Leominster #847
£1000 $1830 €1460 Wilford near Nottingham (52x87cm-20x34in) init. 10-Jun-4 Neales, Nottingham #609 est:600-800
£2400 $3840 €3504 Cattle watering by a shaded river bank (75x98cm-30x39in) s.d.67. 16-Sep-3 Bonhams, Knowle #85/R est:4000-6000
£2600 $4238 €3796 Scene on the Grantham canal (49x75cm-19x30in) s.d.1860. 25-Sep-3 Mellors & Kirk, Nottingham #751/R est:2500-3000
£4800 $8160 €7008 Frigate (61cm-24in circular) init.d.59 prov. 19-Nov-3 Christie's, Kensington #511/R
£4800 $8592 €7008 Three-decker lying in the river at dusk (51x77cm-20x30in) d.1873. 26-May-4 Christie's, Kensington #601/R est:1500-2500
Prints
£9259 $15000 €13518 Benjamin Lay (20x18cm-8x7in) i. engraving. 1-Aug-3 North East Auctions, Portsmouth #396/R est:6000-9000

DAWSON, Henry Thomas (fl.1860-1896) British
£1900 $3268 €2774 Fishing on the Trent (29x44cm-11x17in) s.d. 2-Dec-3 Sotheby's, London #146/R est:2000-3000
£3200 $5056 €4640 Ullswater (25x32cm-10x13in) s.d.1860 panel. 4-Sep-3 Christie's, Kensington #179/R est:2000-3000

DAWSON, Janet (1935-) Australian
£785 $1452 €1146 Potatoes and onions with painting gear 2 (40x45cm-16x18in) s.d.8.89 i.verso. 15-Mar-4 Sotheby's, Melbourne #179 est:800-1200 (A.D 1900)
£1322 $2446 €1930 Potatoes and onions with painting gear I (40x45cm-16x18in) s.d.8.89 i.verso. 15-Mar-4 Sotheby's, Melbourne #178 est:800-1200 (A.D 3200)

DAWSON, John (20th C) American
£269 $450 €393 Two Stars tidal pool on Big Sur (25x81cm-10x32in) s.d. 11-Oct-3 Nadeau, Windsor #104/R
£898 $1500 €1311 Sea otters (61x122cm-24x48in) s.d. acrylic. 11-Oct-3 Nadeau, Windsor #103/R est:3000-4000

DAWSON, Lucy (20th C) British
Works on paper
£497 $900 €726 Don't be long (25x30cm-10x12in) s. col chk. 30-Mar-4 Bonhams & Butterfields, San Francisco #84/R

DAWSON, Montague (1895-1973) British
£1500 $2550 €2190 H.M.S. Norfolk (24x64cm-9x25in) s. board en grisaille prov. 19-Nov-3 Christie's, Kensington #607/R
£3593 $6000 €5246 Whales ahoy (34x53cm-13x21in) s. board prov. 7-Oct-3 Sotheby's, New York #165 est:10000-15000
£7222 $13000 €10544 Full sail (107x72cm-42x28in) s. prov. 23-Apr-4 Sotheby's, New York #212/R est:20000-30000
£7500 $12000 €10950 Off the storm bound horn (30x41cm-12x16in) board. 19-Sep-3 Du Mouchelle, Detroit #2017/R est:8000-12000
£13115 $24000 €19148 Catching the breeze on the open ocean (71x107cm-28x42in) s. 29-Jul-4 Christie's, Rockefeller NY #316/R est:25000-35000
£14970 $25000 €21856 Thermopylae (53x91cm-21x36in) s. panel prov. 23-Oct-3 Shannon's, Milford #140a/R est:30000-50000
£15000 $24000 €21900 Charles H Lunt in fair weather (51x76cm-20x30in) s. prov. 16-Sep-3 Bonhams, New Bond Street #31/R est:15000-20000
£15000 $24000 €21900 The Mayflower (51x76cm-20x30in) s. 16-Sep-3 Bonhams, New Bond Street #83/R est:6000-8000
£15385 $25692 €22462 HMS Dreadnought (50x61cm-20x24in) s. prov. 17-Nov-3 Waddingtons, Toronto #135/R est:25000-50000 (C.D 34000)
£16043 $30000 €23423 Fair weather, fine voyage, The White Star (61x91cm-24x36in) s. 24-Jul-4 Coeur d'Alene, Hayden #96/R est:30000-50000
£22059 $37500 €32206 Under sail (61x92cm-24x36in) s. 28-Oct-3 Sotheby's, New York #175/R est:30000-40000
£29891 $55000 €43641 Droadnought (51x61cm-20x24in) 11-Jun-4 Du Mouchelle, Detroit #2012/R est:50000-70000
£30000 $51600 €43800 HRH Prince Philip, Duke of Edinburgh's dragon class yacht Bluebittle off Cowes (77x56cm-30x22in) s. 2-Dec-3 Sotheby's, London #117/R est:20000-30000
£38922 $65000 €56826 The clipper salutes the Admiral's ship (71x107cm-28x42in) 14-Nov-3 Du Mouchelle, Detroit #2009/R est:40000-50000
£40541 $75000 €59190 The Flying Cloud, running before the wind (61x92cm-24x36in) s. prov. 10-Feb-4 Christie's, Rockefeller NY #253/R est:30000-50000
£40984 $75000 €59837 Skimming the wave crests on a sunlit sea (51x76cm-20x30in) s. 29-Jul-4 Christie's, Rockefeller NY #318/R est:30000-50000
£46448 $85000 €67814 Downwind and running free (61x91cm-24x36in) s. 29-Jul-4 Christie's, Rockefeller NY #319/R est:50000-70000
£49180 $90000 €71803 Yankee packet - Dreadnought (61x51cm-24x20in) s. prov. 29-Jul-4 Christie's, Rockefeller NY #317/R est:30000-50000
£55000 $94600 €80300 Winging on the clipper ship Geart Republic (71x104cm-28x41in) s. 2-Dec-3 Sotheby's, London #121/R est:50000-70000
£56757 $105000 €82865 The Lightning, on high seas (101x127cm-40x50in) s. prov.lit. 10-Feb-4 Christie's, Rockefeller NY #254/R est:120000-180000
£64171 $120000 €93690 Decks awash (69x104cm-27x41in) s. 24-Jul-4 Coeur d'Alene, Hayden #95/R est:60000-90000
£64865 $120000 €94703 Seventeenth Century English Privateers at their Caribbean anchorage (61x91cm-24x36in) s. prov. 10-Feb-4 Christie's, Rockefeller NY #255/R est:90000-120000
£90909 $170000 €132727 Rough weather, U.S.S. Constitution (102x127cm-40x50in) s. 24-Jul-4 Coeur d'Alene, Hayden #94/R est:80000-120000
£145946 $270000 €213081 Night anchorage at Whampoa (102x127cm-40x50in) s. prov. 10-Feb-4 Christie's, Rockefeller NY #256/R est:150000-200000
Works on paper
£3800 $6802 €5548 On patrol (30x45cm-12x18in) s. pencil W/C htd white scratching out prov. 26-May-4 Christie's, Kensington #477/R est:4000-6000
£5000 $8950 €7300 Shoreham fishing smack in a stiff breeze (41x67cm-16x26in) s. W/C bodycol. 26-May-4 Christie's, Kensington #472/R est:4000-6000
£5587 $10000 €8157 Full sail (48x74cm-19x29in) s. W/C paperboard prov. 14-May-4 Skinner, Boston #134/R est:7000-9000
£7784 $13000 €11365 A light wind (41x66cm-16x26in) W/C. 14-Nov-3 Du Mouchelle, Detroit #2008/R est:12000-15000
£12000 $20640 €17520 With the wind (29x44cm-11x17in) s. W/C gouache. 2-Dec-3 Sotheby's, London #116/R est:6000-8000

DAWSON, Neil (1948-) New Zealander
£1083 $1765 €1581 Abstract composition (34x32cm-13x13in) s. board aluminium. 23-Sep-3 Peter Webb, Auckland #11/R est:3000-5000 (NZ.D 3000)
Sculpture
£2500 $4525 €3650 Hole - rock, sunset construction (45x50cm-18x20in) painted aluminium wire mesh prov. 30-Mar-4 Peter Webb, Auckland #21/R est:5000-7000 (NZ.D 7000)
£4821 $8727 €7039 Switch (100x96cm-39x38in) painted wire mesh. 30-Mar-4 Peter Webb, Auckland #22/R est:6000-8000 (NZ.D 13500)

DAWSON, Nelson (1859-1941) British
£300 $531 €438 Preussen ashore Dover cliffs (64x76cm-25x30in) s. 29-Apr-4 Gorringes, Lewes #2430

DAWSON, Septimus (19th C) British
£700 $1106 €1015 Card game (71x91cm-28x36in) s. 4-Sep-3 Christie's, Kensington #264/R

DAWSON, Verne (20th C) American?
£23952 $40000 €34970 Manhattan (183x183cm-72x72in) painted 1998 prov. 12-Nov-3 Christie's, Rockefeller NY #503/R est:12000-18000

DAWSON, William (1901-?) American
Sculpture
£833 $1500 €1216 Woman in yellow dress (41cm-16in) carved painted wood articulated arm. 24-Apr-4 Slotin Folk Art, Buford #343/R est:1000-2000
£1111 $2000 €1622 Six headed totem (13x10cm-5x4in) caved painted wood prov. 24-Apr-4 Slotin Folk Art, Buford #342/R est:3000-5000
Works on paper
£389 $700 €568 White horse (38x48cm-15x19in) W/C. 24-Apr-4 Slotin Folk Art, Buford #345/R

DAWSON-WATSON, Dawson (1864-1939) American/British
£2322 $4250 €3390 End of an autumn day (61x46cm-24x18in) s.d.1916. 5-Jun-4 Treadway Gallery, Cincinnati #522/R est:5000-7000
£5063 $8000 €7392 Little cow girl (56x79cm-22x31in) s. 27-Jul-3 Simpson's, Houston #400
£5389 $9000 €7868 Sunlight through the Dunes (46x66cm-18x26in) s.d.98 prov. 23-Oct-3 Shannon's, Milford #41/R est:6000-8000
£14970 $25000 €21856 Governor's Palace, San Antonio, Texas (102x76cm-40x30in) 18-Oct-3 David Dike, Dallas #208/R est:20000-30000

DAX, Adrien (1913-) French
£680 $1217 €1000 Untitled (59x44cm-23x17in) s. isorel. 21-Mar-4 Calmels Cohen, Paris #80/R
Works on paper
£612 $1096 €900 Untitled (14x9cm-6x4in) s.d.1962 collage gilded sheet double-sided two prov. 21-Mar-4 Calmels Cohen, Paris #89/R

£816 $1461 €1200 Untitled (19x17cm-7x7in) ink paper on board prov. 21-Mar-4 Calmels Cohen, Paris #82
£1020 $1827 €1500 Untitled (24x17cm-9x7in) s.d.23/1/51 gouache three prov. 21-Mar-4 Calmels Cohen, Paris #91/R est:1000-1200

DAXHELET, Paul (1905-1993) Belgian
£218 $350 €318 African wedding (51x61cm-20x24in) 22-Feb-3 Bunte, Elgin #1237
£298 $497 €420 Le buisson sacre (24x36cm-9x14in) s. panel. 15-Oct-3 Hotel des Ventes Mosan, Brussels #263
£331 $603 €500 Thailande, les deux dragons et les deux bronzes (40x60cm-16x24in) s. i.verso. 16-Jun-4 Hotel des Ventes Mosan, Brussels #277
£378 $650 €552 Et des fleurs jailli rend du sol (51x102cm-20x40in) s. painted c.1960. 7-Dec-3 Treadway Gallery, Cincinnati #717/R
£430 $783 €650 Tanger, les Berberes (40x60cm-16x24in) s. i.verso. 16-Jun-4 Hotel des Ventes Mosan, Brussels #289
£461 $770 €650 Polynesie Bora-Bora (40x60cm-16x24in) s. 15-Oct-3 Hotel des Ventes Mosan, Brussels #265
£563 $1025 €850 Danseuses Balinaises (20x40cm-8x16in) s. panel. 16-Jun-4 Hotel des Ventes Mosan, Brussels #279
£603 $1007 €850 Scene Africaine (50x60cm-20x24in) s. 15-Oct-3 Hotel des Ventes Mosan, Brussels #247
£603 $1007 €850 Settat, marche aux chameaux (50x100cm-20x39in) s. 15-Oct-3 Hotel des Ventes Mosan, Brussels #276
£748 $1339 €1100 Danseuses balinaises (80x100cm-31x39in) s. 17-Mar-4 Hotel des Ventes Mosan, Brussels #166
£1208 $2235 €1800 Fantasia (20x60cm-8x24in) s. panel. 15-Mar-4 Gros & Delettrez, Paris #285/R est:1800-2000
£4255 $7106 €6000 Le vieux quai a Hong-Kong et la nouvelle ville (114x194cm-45x76in) s.d.1978. 15-Oct-3 Hotel des Ventes Mosan, Brussels #271/R est:3000-4000
Works on paper
£374 $670 €550 La feria (53x70cm-21x28in) s. chl sanguine. 17-Mar-4 Hotel des Ventes Mosan, Brussels #167
£1200 $2208 €1800 Marche Africain (35x50cm-14x20in) s.i. W/C pen. 14-Jun-4 Gros & Delettrez, Paris #280/R est:2000-3000

DAY, Basil (19/20th C) British
Works on paper
£850 $1445 €1241 Admiral's visit, Macau (25x36cm-10x14in) init.d.1909 W/C. 4-Nov-3 Bonhams, New Bond Street #21/R

DAY, Foreshaw (1837-1903) Canadian
£400 $732 €584 Halifax Rifles camped at Bedford range (32x47cm-13x19in) s. 1-Jun-4 Joyner Waddington, Toronto #394/R (C.D 1000)
Works on paper
£543 $907 €793 Untitled - mountain valley (24x33cm-9x13in) s.d.1888 W/C. 17-Nov-3 Hodgins, Calgary #113/R est:1400-1600 (C.D 1200)

DAY, Francis (1863-1925) American
£6818 $12000 €10227 Bedtime melody or an old song (107x81cm-42x32in) s. 21-May-4 North East Auctions, Portsmouth #992/R

DAY, Harvey (20th C) American
£1505 $2800 €2197 Wagon train through the desert (51x61cm-20x24in) s. painted c.1940. 7-Mar-4 Treadway Gallery, Cincinnati #563/R est:500-700

DAY, Herbert J (20th C) American
£369 $650 €539 Brown County landscape (41x51cm-16x20in) s. board painted c.1925. 23-May-4 Treadway Gallery, Cincinnati #565/R
£369 $650 €539 Hunter in a landscape (61x76cm-24x30in) s. exhib. 28-May-4 Aspire, Cleveland #24/R

DAY, Horace Talmage (1909-1984) American
Works on paper
£552 $1000 €828 Sunset over city (36x53cm-14x21in) W/C. 16-Apr-4 American Auctioneer #86/R
£1105 $2000 €1658 Corner store, Augusta, Georgia (51x64cm-20x25in) W/C. 16-Apr-4 American Auctioneer #85/R est:1000-1500

DAY, James Francis (1863-1942) American
£2486 $4500 €3630 Portrait of Georgette Borland (66x51cm-26x20in) s. prov. 31-Mar-4 Sotheby's, New York #62/R est:2500-3500

DAY, John (19th C) British
£580 $998 €847 Enniskillen, Ireland (33x41cm-13x16in) 5-Dec-3 Keys, Aylsham #596/R

DAY, Larry (1921-1997) American
£419 $700 €612 Abstract (91x91cm-36x36in) s. prov. 20-Jun-3 Freeman, Philadelphia #125/R
Works on paper
£281 $450 €410 Break (51x51cm-20x20in) s. chl prov. 19-Sep-3 Freeman, Philadelphia #8/R

DAY, Mabel K (1884-1959) American
£2045 $3600 €2986 Sand dunes, Nova Scotia (74x84cm-29x33in) s. 1-Jan-4 Quinn's, Falls Church #273/R

DAY, Maurice (1892-1983) American
Works on paper
£214 $400 €312 Three red and white sailboats racing (18x25cm-7x10in) s. W/C. 28-Feb-4 Thomaston Place, Thomaston #107a/R
£428 $800 €625 Reconstruction drawing carbon pencil logging camp. s. graphite. 28-Feb-4 Thomaston Place, Thomaston #108a/R
£802 $1500 €1171 Treats (33x48cm-13x19in) s. i.d.1979 verso W/C. 28-Feb-4 Thomaston Place, Thomaston #108/R
£856 $1600 €1250 Afternoon gossip (23x25cm-9x10in) s. W/C. 28-Feb-4 Thomaston Place, Thomaston #107/R
£882 $1650 €1288 Bracket sprite (23x33cm-9x13in) s. W/C. 28-Feb-4 Thomaston Place, Thomaston #109a/R
£1070 $2000 €1562 Ecstasy (23x18cm-9x7in) W/C. 28-Feb-4 Thomaston Place, Thomaston #109/R
£1073 $1900 €1567 Little brown church, Round Pond, Maine. d.1945 verso. 1-May-4 Thomaston Place, Thomaston #600/R

DAY, Melvin (1923-) New Zealander
£2595 $4645 €3789 INITIVM (121x151cm-48x59in) s.d.81. 12-May-4 Dunbar Sloane, Wellington #36/R est:4000-8000 (NZ.D 7500)
Works on paper
£655 $1028 €950 Monument (52x65cm-20x26in) i.verso mixed media board. 27-Aug-3 Dunbar Sloane, Wellington #6 (NZ.D 1800)

DAY, Thomas (attrib) (18th C) British
Miniatures
£2200 $3960 €3212 Rev Archibald Alison (4cm-2in) i.verso gold frame oval exhib.lit. 22-Apr-4 Bonhams, New Bond Street #36 est:400-600

DAY, W Percy (fl.1905-1922) British
£600 $1104 €876 Portrait of a young boy, Murray Penfold (61x50cm-24x20in) s.d.1920 i.verso. 23-Jun-4 Bonhams, Bury St Edmunds #398/R

DAY, William Cave (1862-1924) British
£450 $819 €657 Sand stretches to the sea, boats on a beach at low tide (76x45cm-30x18in) s. 15-Jun-4 Bonhams, Oxford #89

DAYES, Edward (1763-1804) British
Works on paper
£4600 $8464 €6716 View of the town of Thorshaven and the harbour of Frederickswaag, Faroe Island (27x38cm-11x15in) s.i. W/C over pencil prov. 26-Mar-4 Sotheby's, London #103/R est:3000-4000

DAYEZ, Georges (1907-1991) French
£250 $450 €365 Seated female (33x18cm-13x7in) 23-Jan-4 Freeman, Philadelphia #204/R
£2113 $3507 €3000 Nature morte aux feuilles de lierre (67x75cm-26x30in) s.i.d.60 verso. 13-Jun-3 Renaud, Paris #47/R est:3800

DAYNES, Edmond (1895-1986) French
£438 $700 €639 Chalutier noir (73x100cm-29x39in) s. 21-Sep-3 Bonhams & Butterfields, San Francisco #2805/R

D'AZEGLIO, Massimo (1798-1866) Italian
£1042 $1771 €1500 Tree (31x23cm-12x9in) s. cardboard. 1-Nov-3 Meeting Art, Vercelli #293 est:1500
Works on paper
£426 $711 €600 Genre scene (11x18cm-4x7in) pencil. 20-Oct-3 Sant Agostino, Torino #2/R
£845 $1462 €1200 Landscapes. s.d.1823 pencil series. 9-Dec-3 Pandolfini, Florence #175/R

DAZZI, Arturo (1882-1966) Italian
Sculpture
£3262 $5448 €4600 Genesis (67x63cm-26x25in) plaster relief pair. 14-Oct-3 Finarte Semenzato, Rome #6/R est:3000-3500

D'COSTA, Rhett (20th C) Australian
£372 $658 €543 Blue stripe (137x184cm-54x72in) oil pigment prov. 3-May-4 Christie's, Melbourne #264/R (A.D 900)

DE, Biren (1926-) Indian
£4076 $7500 €5951 Untitled (122x76cm-48x30in) s.d.July 77 verso. 24-Mar-4 Sotheby's, New York #195/R est:6000-8000
£4891 $9000 €7141 July '93 (117x81cm-46x32in) s.d.93 i.July 93 verso. 25-Mar-4 Christie's, Rockefeller NY #240/R est:5000-7000

DEACON, A G (20th C) British?
£450 $828 €657 Going out (61x91cm-24x36in) s.d.1966. 10-Jun-4 Christie's, Kensington #132/R

DEACON, Rachel (20th C) British
£600 $1110 €876 Woman with lilies (90x74cm-35x29in) s. prov. 11-Feb-4 Cheffins, Cambridge #461/R

DEACON, Richard (1949-) British
Sculpture
£10056 $18000 €14682 Art for other people num 48 (30x160x165cm-12x63x65in) beachwood prov.exhib. 12-May-4 Christie's, Rockefeller NY #422/R est:18000-22000

DEAK EBNER, Lajos (1850-1934) Hungarian
£685 $1240 €1000 Girl with basket (38x19cm-15x7in) s. canvas on card. 16-Apr-4 Mu Terem Galeria, Budapest #40/R (H.F 260000)
£869 $1442 €1269 Parisian girl (20x12cm-8x5in) 4-Oct-3 Kieselbach, Budapest #71/R (H.F 320000)
£1265 $2289 €1847 Returning caravan (44x69cm-17x27in) s. 16-Apr-4 Mu Terem Galeria, Budapest #43/R (H.F 480000)

DEAK, Adrienne (1890-1956) Hungarian
£420 $701 €600 Still life with watermelon (52x74cm-20x29in) cardboard. 10-Oct-3 Stadion, Trieste #54/R
£850 $1386 €1241 Still life with a vase of peonies and other flowers (69x98cm-27x39in) s. canvas on board. 24-Sep-3 Dreweatt Neate, Newbury #87/R
£962 $1703 €1405 Spring bucket of flowers (80x60cm-31x24in) s. 28-Apr-4 Kieselbach, Budapest #77/R (H.F 360000)

DEAK, Nandor (1883-1953) Hungarian
£224 $375 €327 Picking flowers, three young ladies (71x61cm-28x24in) s.d.1934. 14-Nov-3 Aspire, Cleveland #52

DEAKIN, Edwin (1838-1923) American
£1556 $2582 €2272 Monastery (41x61cm-16x24in) 2-Oct-3 Heffel, Vancouver #13 (C.D 3500)
£1556 $2582 €2272 Castle on the river (76x51cm-30x20in) 2-Oct-3 Heffel, Vancouver #12 (C.D 3500)
£13587 $25000 €19837 The Santa Ines Mission (41x61cm-16x24in) s. i. stretcher prov. 8-Jun-4 Bonhams & Butterfields, San Francisco #4219/R est:25000-35000

DEAKIN, Peter (fl.1855-1879) British
Works on paper
£440 $735 €642 Cattle at sunset (39x61cm-15x24in) s. W/C. 14-Oct-3 Bearnes, Exeter #344/R

DEAN, Frank (1865-1946) British
Works on paper
£380 $635 €555 Egyptian market (46x55cm-18x22in) s.i. pencil W/C. 8-Oct-3 Christie's, Kensington #1106
£950 $1701 €1387 Lady reading on a window seat (60x45cm-24x18in) s. pastel. 25-May-4 Bonhams, Knightsbridge #13/R

DEAN, Walter Lofthouse (1854-1912) American
£894 $1600 €1305 Docked boats (61x35cm-24x14in) s. canvasboard. 14-May-4 Skinner, Boston #285/R est:1200-1800
£1635 $2600 €2387 Hammock (31x46cm-12x18in) s.d.79. 12-Sep-3 Skinner, Boston #275/R est:2000

DEAN, William Edward James (19/20th C) British
Works on paper
£270 $424 €394 Quiet waters, meandering river in hilly landscape (18x28cm-7x11in) s. W/C. 10-Dec-2 Bamfords, Derby #731

DEANE, Charles (fl.1815-1855) British
£95000 $161500 €138700 View of Chelsea from the river (83x129cm-33x51in) i. prov.exhib. 26-Nov-3 Christie's, London #10/R est:100000-150000

DEANE, Emmeline (fl.1879-1934) British
Works on paper
£300 $552 €438 Portrait of a lady, in a white ball gown (74x61cm-29x24in) s.d.1893 pastel col chk. 25-Mar-4 Christie's, Kensington #222

DEANE, William Wood (1825-1873) British
£2059 $3500 €3006 Van Dyck and Frans Hals in a studio (91x122cm-36x48in) s.d.1854 canvas on board. 19-Nov-3 Bonhams & Butterfields, San Francisco #137/R
Works on paper
£1700 $2975 €2482 Charles Cathedral with many figures outside on the steps (97x69cm-38x27in) s.d.1871 W/C. 18-Dec-3 John Nicholson, Haslemere #1053/R est:1500-2500

DEANES, Edward (fl.1860-1893) British
£1800 $3294 €2628 Violin mender (61x51cm-24x20in) s. 7-Apr-4 Bonhams, Bury St Edmunds #483 est:600-800
Works on paper
£650 $1203 €949 Portrait of Miss Mabel Rimell (130x69cm-51x27in) s.d.1895 W/C. 9-Mar-4 Bonhams, Knightsbridge #64/R

DEANGELIS, P A (19th C) Italian
Works on paper
£2600 $4238 €3796 Palace Square, Malta (25x39cm-10x15in) s.i.d.1851 bodycol. 24-Sep-3 Christie's, London #200/R est:2000-3000

DEANS, A A (1915-) New Zealander
Works on paper
£1993 $3168 €2910 Lake Kaniere, Westlands (47x65cm-19x26in) s.d.1992 W/C. 9-Sep-3 Watson's, Christchurch #81 (NZ.D 5500)
£2589 $4789 €3780 Cattle moving, Morven (27x58cm-11x23in) s. W/C. 13-Jul-4 Watson's, Christchurch #25/R est:5000-6500 (NZ.D 7300)

DEANS, Austin A (1915-) New Zealander
£465 $799 €679 The Gates, Matukituki Ranges (44x53cm-17x21in) s.d.1976 board. 7-Dec-3 International Art Centre, Auckland #357/R (NZ.D 1250)
£1692 $2876 €2470 Glendhu Bay, Lake Wanaka (95x98cm-37x39in) s.d.1961 board. 27-Nov-3 International Art Centre, Auckland #142 est:4000-6000 (NZ.D 4500)
Works on paper
£297 $512 €434 Landscape with mountains (26x35cm-10x14in) s.d.1938 W/C. 7-Dec-3 International Art Centre, Auckland #306/R (NZ.D 800)
£364 $571 €528 Twelve Mile beach, Westland (34x54cm-13x21in) s.d.1988 W/C. 27-Aug-3 Dunbar Sloane, Wellington #105/R (NZ.D 1000)
£376 $639 €549 Autumn at Queenstown (27x38cm-11x15in) s.d.1991 W/C. 27-Nov-3 International Art Centre, Auckland #153/R (NZ.D 1000)
£1241 $2197 €1812 Kowai creek, Timaru (47x67cm-19x26in) s.d.1974 W/C. 28-Apr-4 Dunbar Sloane, Auckland #81/R est:4000-6000 (NZ.D 3500)

DEARN, Dora (19th C) British?
Works on paper
£950 $1492 €1387 Stealing the nest, peasant boy with nest and chicks (45x31cm-18x12in) s.d.1890 W/C. 16-Apr-3 Bamfords, Derby #586/R

DEARN, Raymond (19/20th C) British
£1000 $1790 €1460 Old buildings at Ballamenach, Sulby, Isle of Man (46x61cm-18x24in) s.i. verso. 7-May-4 Chrystals Auctions, Isle of Man #291 est:1200-1500
£1000 $1790 €1460 Summer afternoon (46x61cm-18x24in) s.d.1901 i.verso. 7-May-4 Chrystals Auctions, Isle of Man #292 est:1200-1500
£1000 $1790 €1460 Scene at Ballamenaugh, Sulby, Isle of Man (46x61cm-18x24in) s.d.1901 i. verso. 7-May-4 Chrystals Auctions, Isle of Man #293 est:1200-1500
£1500 $2685 €2190 Cottage at Ballamenauch, Isle of Man. Summer Ballamenauch, Isle of Man (46x61cm-18x24in) s. i.verso pair. 7-May-4 Chrystals Auctions, Isle of Man #284 est:3000-4000
£2200 $3520 €3212 Cottage in Sulby Glen (51x76cm-20x30in) s.d.1902 i.verso. 16-Sep-3 Bonhams, Knowle #86 est:500-800
£2500 $4300 €3650 Cottage in Sulby Glen (61x76cm-24x30in) s.i. verso. 5-Dec-3 Chrystals Auctions, Isle of Man #237/R est:2500-3500
Works on paper
£600 $1032 €876 Farm Ballamenagh. Carrick Cottage Ballamenagh (25x38cm-10x15in) s. W/C pair. 5-Dec-3 Chrystals Auctions, Isle of Man #240/R

D'EAUBONNE, Louis Lucien (1834-1894) French
Works on paper
£493 $863 €700 Femme couronnee (23x16cm-9x6in) s.d.1895 graphite pen ink wash htd white. 16-Dec-3 Christie's, Paris #272/R

DEBAT-PONSAN, Edouard-Bernard (1847-1913) French
£800 $1456 €1200 Retour du troupeau (20x27cm-8x11in) s. panel. 4-Jul-4 Eric Pillon, Calais #27/R
£1300 $2041 €1885 Rest in the meadow (32x50cm-13x20in) s.d.96 panel. 28-Aug-3 Christie's, Kensington #77/R est:1200-1800

DEBATTY, Georges (1927-) Belgian
£621 $1148 €900 Paysage fantastique (93x125cm-37x49in) s. panel. 16-Feb-4 Horta, Bruxelles #24

DEBAY, Auguste Hyacinth (1804-1865) French
Sculpture
£7931 $13166 €11500 Berceau primitif (44cm-17in) s. brown pat bronze lit. 2-Oct-3 Sotheby's, Paris #42/R est:9000

DEBEQUE, Alex (19th C) French
Sculpture
£3172 $5710 €4600 Henri IV et Charles X en pied (27cm-11in) s.i.d.1820 gold pat bronze socle pair. 26-Jan-4 Gros & Delettrez, Paris #197/R est:800-1200

DEBERITZ, Per (1880-1945) Norwegian
£569 $1047 €854 Windy day in summer (40x47cm-16x19in) s. panel. 14-Jun-4 Blomqvist, Lysaker #1069 (N.KR 7000)
£952 $1751 €1390 House behind trees. s. 29-Mar-4 Blomqvist, Lysaker #1042/R (N.KR 12000)
£2647 $4421 €3865 Archipelago from Skaatoy (38x45cm-15x18in) s.d.38 panel. 13-Oct-3 Blomqvist, Oslo #300/R est:12000-15000 (N.KR 31000)

DEBIAGGI, Casimiro (1855-1939) Italian
Sculpture
£1700 $2941 €2482 Fishing interrupted (27x35cm-11x14in) s.d.1883 brown pat bronze black marble base lit. 12-Dec-3 Sotheby's, London #263/R est:2000-3000

DEBON, Edmond (1846-1922) French
£7778 $14000 €11356 Quiet afternoon (89x115cm-35x45in) s.d.1885. 23-Apr-4 Sotheby's, New York #172/R est:18000-25000

DEBORD, Marjorie (1910-1987) American
£898 $1500 €1311 Despondence (76x61cm-30x24in) 18-Oct-3 David Dike, Dallas #163/R est:2000-4000

DEBOURG, Edouard (20th C) French
£600 $1038 €876 Breton street (49x65cm-19x26in) indis.sig. 11-Dec-3 Christie's, Kensington #41/R

DEBRE, Olivier (1920-1999) French

£909	$1545	€1300	Signe pecheur (73x60cm-29x24in) s.d.1948 s.i.d.verso prov. 25-Nov-3 Tajan, Paris #2/R est:1500-2000
£921	$1667	€1400	Nature morte aux ceramiques (32x40cm-13x16in) s. cardboard. 19-Apr-4 Boscher, Cherbourg #719/R
£1268	$2193	€1800	Composition (16x10cm-6x4in) mono.d.1990 verso. 14-Dec-3 Versailles Encheres #26/R est:1000-1200
£1333	$2453	€2000	Bleu pale (22x27cm-9x11in) s.d.1978. 11-Jun-4 Pierre Berge, Paris #57 est:2000-2500
£1399	$2547	€2100	Still life with vases (33x41cm-13x16in) s. board painted c.1950. 30-Jun-4 Calmels Cohen, Paris #73/R est:2000-3000
£1469	$2452	€2100	Composition (23x36cm-9x14in) s.d.1948 panel. 29-Jun-3 Versailles Encheres #46/R
£1597	$2668	€2300	Composition (22x33cm-9x13in) s.verso. 21-Oct-3 Artcurial Briest, Paris #391/R est:2500-3000
£1611	$3012	€2400	Composition (23x36cm-9x14in) s.d.1948 panel. 29-Feb-4 Versailles Encheres #219a/R est:2000-3000
£1806	$2979	€2600	Italie (24x33cm-9x13in) s.i.verso painted c.1974. 2-Jul-3 Cornette de St.Cyr, Paris #47/R est:2500-3000
£2222	$3712	€3200	Interieur rose (24x33cm-9x13in) mono.d.58 s.i.d.verso prov. 21-Oct-3 Artcurial Briest, Paris #390/R est:2500-3000
£2817	$4704	€4113	Green composition (60x73cm-24x29in) s.indis.i.d.64. 7-Oct-3 Rasmussen, Copenhagen #104/R est:30000-40000 (D.KR 30000)
£2961	$5359	€4500	Verre et bleu (54x65cm-21x26in) init.i.d.74 s.verso paint. 19-Apr-4 Boscher, Cherbourg #718/R est:4000
£3158	$5811	€4800	Petite rouge du jardin (34x46cm-13x18in) s.i.d.1988 verso prov. 28-Jun-4 Joron-Derem, Paris #213/R est:3000-3500
£3169	$5482	€4500	Sans titre (53x81cm-21x32in) mono.d.1948 prov. 14-Dec-3 Versailles Encheres #67/R est:5000-6000
£3200	$5888	€4800	Composition (41x33cm-16x13in) painted 1972. 9-Jun-4 Artcurial Briest, Paris #459/R est:3000-4000
£3610	$6643	€5271	Autumn Tou. (100x100cm-39x39in) init.d.69 s.d.69 verso. 29-Mar-4 Rasmussen, Copenhagen #167/R est:50000-75000 (D.KR 40000)
£3800	$6042	€5510	Pale jaune (100x100cm-39x39in) s.i.d.76 verso. 11-Sep-3 Christie's, Kensington #204/R est:2000-3000
£4040	$7352	€6100	Fond vert (60x73cm-24x29in) s.d.75 verso. 18-Jun-4 Piasa, Paris #230/R est:2500-3000
£4342	$7989	€6600	Untitled (54x73cm-21x29in) s.i.d.70 verso. 23-Jun-4 Maigret, Paris #38/R est:2500-3000
£4430	$8106	€6600	Ocre rose de Loire (100x100cm-39x39in) s.i.d.83-84 verso exhib. 7-Jul-4 Artcurial Briest, Paris #246 est:6000-8000
£4441	$7416	€6484	Composition (73x91cm-29x36in) init. s.indis.i.d.74 verso. 13-Oct-3 Blomqvist, Oslo #333/R est:25000-35000 (N.KR 52000)
£4500	$7155	€6525	Royau bleu - vert (60x63cm-24x25in) init. s.i.d.73 verso prov. 11-Sep-3 Christie's, Kensington #209/R est:1000-1500
£4789	$8285	€6800	Tout vert paysage (100x100cm-39x39in) mono. s.i.d.1959 verso. 14-Dec-3 Versailles Encheres #115/R est:6000-8000
£4895	$8322	€7000	Vent jaune tache vert et rouge (100x100cm-39x39in) s.i.d.1991 verso. 25-Nov-3 Tajan, Paris #49/R est:8000-10000
£5000	$8650	€7300	Touraine automne, jaune rose (60x73cm-24x29in) init.d.76 s.i.d.76 verso prov. 11-Dec-3 Christie's, Kensington #241/R est:1000-1500
£5034	$8910	€7500	Royan clair taches vivies (100x100cm-39x39in) s.i.d.84 verso prov. 28-Apr-4 Artcurial Briest, Paris #280/R est:8000-10000
£5315	$8876	€7600	Gris vertical des tilleuls d'hiver a la tache jaune (120x120cm-47x47in) s.i.d.1988 verso prov. 11-Oct-3 Cornette de St.Cyr, Paris #12/R est:8000-10000
£5333	$9706	€8000	Vallee coloree (100x100cm-39x39in) s.i.d.1993 verso. 30-Jun-4 Calmels Cohen, Paris #78/R est:8000-10000
£5395	$9926	€8200	Composition (120x94cm-47x37in) mono.d.1947. 28-Jun-4 Joron-Derem, Paris #199/R est:10000-12000
£5500	$8745	€7975	Untitled (100x100cm-39x39in) init.d.71 s.i.d.verso exhib. 11-Sep-3 Christie's, Kensington #206/R est:2000-3000
£5500	$8745	€7975	Rouge l'automne touraine (99x99cm-39x39in) s.i.d.95 verso. 11-Sep-3 Christie's, Kensington #207/R est:1000-1500
£5595	$9511	€8000	Norvege brune (100x100cm-39x39in) s.i.d.1978 verso prov. 25-Nov-3 Tajan, Paris #47/R est:7000-8000
£5595	$9511	€8000	Gris clair coule aux taches vives (100x100cm-39x39in) s.d.1989 verso prov. 25-Nov-3 Tajan, Paris #48/R est:5000-6000
£6250	$10438	€9000	Verte a la tache rose (100x100cm-39x39in) s.i.d. i.verso acrylic. 25-Oct-3 Cornette de St.Cyr, Paris #652/R est:8000-10000
£6333	$11527	€9500	Amsterdam (81x100cm-32x39in) s. s.i.d.1950. 5-Jul-4 Le Mouel, Paris #51/R est:10000-12000
£6713	$11211	€9600	Coulante bleue, tache rouge (100x100cm-39x39in) s.d.81 i.verso prov.exhib. 11-Oct-3 Cornette de St.Cyr, Paris #9/R est:6000-8000
£8553	$15737	€13000	Bleu leger aux taches lourdes (100x100cm-39x39in) mono. s.i.d.1965 verso. 27-Jun-4 Versailles Encheres #100/R est:12000-15000
£10667	$19200	€16000	Still life (60x72cm-24x28in) s.d.1955 s.i.d.verso prov. 25-Apr-4 Versailles Encheres #95 est:10000-12000
£12000	$22080	€18000	Bleu tache rose, Touraine - Loire (185x185cm-73x73in) s.d.1979/80 i. verso prov. 8-Jun-4 Artcurial Briest, Paris #270/R est:20000-25000
£12817	$20635	€18200	Figure jaune (195x114cm-77x45in) s. painted 1957. 22-Aug-3 Deauville, France #126/R est:20000-25000
£13423	$24698	€20000	Still life (50x65cm-20x26in) mono. s.i.d.1956 verso. 29-Mar-4 Cornette de St.Cyr, Paris #6/R est:8000-10000
£17450	$31235	€26000	Grande bleue (220x195cm-87x77in) s.i.d.64 verso exhib. 26-May-4 Christie's, Paris #88/R est:18000-20000

Works on paper

£596	$1085	€900	Composition (64x48cm-25x19in) s.d.56 ink. 18-Jun-4 Charbonneaux, Paris #80/R
£699	$1189	€1000	Sans titre (49x31cm-19x12in) s.d.1951 Indian ink prov. 25-Nov-3 Tajan, Paris #3/R
£699	$1202	€1000	Grand signe noir (80x30cm-31x12in) s. black ink acrylic. 3-Dec-3 Tajan, Paris #449/R
£1000	$1800	€1500	Composition (49x32cm-19x13in) s. gouache. 25-Apr-4 Versailles Encheres #78 est:1000-1200
£1014	$1784	€1500	Untitled (122x80cm-48x31in) s. ink prov.exhib. 18-May-4 Tajan, Paris #151/R est:1500-2000
£1711	$3147	€2600	Composition (75x55cm-30x22in) s.d.1981 ink gouache prov. 27-Jun-4 Versailles Encheres #54/R est:1500-1800
£1761	$3046	€2500	Musiciens chanteurs (14x23cm-6x9in) mono.d.1949 i.d.nov.1949 verso gouache prov. 14-Dec-3 Versailles Encheres #66/R est:2000-2500
£2254	$3899	€3200	Composition (180x60cm-71x24in) s. ink. 14-Dec-3 Versailles Encheres #100/R est:2500-3000
£2600	$4680	€3900	Signe vertical (120x80cm-47x31in) s. Chinese ink exhib. 24-Apr-4 Cornette de St.Cyr, Paris #506/R est:1500-2000

DEBRE, Olivier and MATHIEU, Georges (20th C) French

Works on paper

£1000	$1840	€1500	Sans titre (26x40cm-10x16in) one s. ink felt collage one ink diptych. 14-Jun-4 Tajan, Paris #191 est:1800-2000

DEBRET, François (attrib) (1777-1850) ?

Works on paper

£3169	$5546	€4500	Projet pour pavillon de jardin (31x52cm-12x20in) pierre noire pen ink W/C. 19-Dec-3 Pierre Berge, Paris #27/R est:2000-2500

DEBRET, Jean Baptist (1768-1848) French

Works on paper

£16117	$29495	€24176	Chameleon and two snakes (24x39cm-9x15in) W/C. 6-Jul-4 Bolsa de Arte, Rio de Janeiro #59/R (B.R 88000)

DEBRET, Jean Baptist (attrib) (1768-1848) French

£10490	$17832	€15000	La bataille d'Eylau (97x129cm-38x51in) 1-Dec-3 Coutau Begarie, Paris #257/R est:20000-30000

DEBUCOURT, Philibert Louis (1755-1832) French

£4490	$7139	€6600	Jeu de colin-maillard dans une grange (21x27cm-8x11in) mono. panel. 23-Mar-3 St-Germain-en-Laye Encheres #24/R
£10067	$18724	€15000	Une procession dans un village des environs de Paris (47x58cm-19x23in) s.d.1817 panel prov.exhib. 8-Mar-4 Artcurial Briest, Paris #29/R est:12000

Prints

£2533	$4661	€3800	Les deux baisers (38x43cm-15x17in) col pen. 11-Jun-4 Hauswedell & Nolte, Hamburg #935/R est:5000
£6376	$11285	€9500	Promenade publique (65x48cm-26x19in) col eau forte aquatint exec.1792. 29-Apr-4 Piasa, Paris #52/R est:7500-8000

DEBUCOURT, Philibert Louis (attrib) (1755-1832) French

£2098	$3566	€3000	Femme surprise a sa toilette (43x33cm-17x13in) mono. panel. 1-Dec-3 Millon & Associes, Paris #53/R est:3000-4000

DEBUT, Jean-Didier (1824-1893) French

Sculpture

£766	$1317	€1118	Janissaire (53cm-21in) s. brown bronze prov. 3-Dec-3 Koller, Zurich #1282/R est:1500-2500 (S.FR 1700)
£1000	$1830	€1500	Porteur d'eau tunisien (32cm-13in) i. pat bronze. 3-Jun-4 Tajan, Paris #219/R est:1500-2000
£1200	$2184	€1752	Amour mendiant (38cm-15in) s. brown pat bronze marble base. 15-Jun-4 Sotheby's, Olympia #101/R est:800-1200

DEBUT, Marcel (1865-1933) French

Sculpture

£1064	$1777	€1500	Le triomphe du chasseur (88cm-35in) s. brown pat bronze. 17-Jun-3 Galerie Moderne, Brussels #1528 est:1800-2400
£1129	$2055	€1648	Le forgeron (38cm-15in) s. green brown pat. bronze. 15-Jun-4 Waddingtons, Toronto #704/R est:700-1000 (C.D 2800)
£1409	$2607	€2100	Chasseur a l'olifan (87cm-34in) s. pat bronze. 14-Mar-4 St-Germain-en-Laye Encheres #55/R est:2000-2500
£2000	$3740	€2920	Perseus rescuing Andromeda (41cm-16in) s. relief cast bronze vase tin liner exec.c.1900. 24-Feb-4 Sotheby's, Olympia #74/R est:2000-3000
£3617	$6040	€5100	Chanson de la mer (111cm-44in) s. brown pat bronze. 12-Oct-3 St-Germain-en-Laye Encheres #54/R est:3500-4000

DECAMPS, Alexandre Gabriel (1803-1860) French

£2133	$3861	€3200	Attelage au chariot (17x22cm-7x9in) mono. 30-Mar-4 Rossini, Paris #934/R est:1200-1800
£5594	$9622	€8000	Souvenir de Fontainebleau (61x102cm-24x40in) mono. oil paper on canvas. 7-Dec-3 Osenat, Fontainebleau #118

Works on paper

£400	$728	€600	Tete de femme-singe (11x10cm-4x4in) pen ink wash prov. 30-Jun-4 Delvaux, Paris #124
£667	$1207	€1000	La jeune femme couchee (17x25cm-7x10in) mono. pierre noire sanguine. 30-Mar-4 Rossini, Paris #935
£691	$1271	€1050	Combattant grec observant au loin une ville en flamme (26x21cm-10x8in) s. W/C. 25-Jun-4 Rossini, Paris #26
£765	$1400	€1117	An Arab on a camel (33x50cm-13x20in) black chk. 29-Jan-4 Swann Galleries, New York #259/R
£922	$1540	€1300	Hamall, portefaix a Smyrne (25x17cm-10x7in) mono.i. W/C. 16-Jun-3 Gros & Delettrez, Paris #111/R
£1064	$1723	€1500	Paysage Oriental anime (15x23cm-6x9in) mono. W/C varnish. 21-May-3 Daguerre, Paris #79/R est:1500
£1333	$2413	€2000	La vagabonde aux deux chiens (21x16cm-8x6in) W/C exhib.lit. 30-Mar-4 Rossini, Paris #936 est:600-1000
£1769	$3166	€2600	Etude pour la bataille des Cimbres (20x43cm-8x17in) W/C chl htd oil varnish. 19-Mar-4 Piasa, Paris #125/R est:5000

DECAMPS, Alexandre Gabriel (attrib) (1803-1860) French

£569	$1046	€854	Knife-grinder (44x35cm-17x14in) panel. 14-Jun-4 Lilla Bukowskis, Stockholm #123 (S.KR 7800)

Works on paper

£317	$548	€450	Soldat turc devant la porte (15x10cm-6x4in) W/C. 15-Dec-3 Gros & Delettrez, Paris #536

DECAMPS, Eugene (attrib) (?) French?

Works on paper

£336	$577	€480	Scene de rue orientaliste (8x13cm-3x5in) W/C. 5-Dec-3 Maigret, Paris #45

DECAMPS, Jean (?) French?
Sculpture
£2148 $3801 €3200 Musicienne et faune (36x62x17cm-14x24x7in) bronze marble base Cast Cardoni Mabille. 28-Apr-4 Marc Kohn, Paris #235/R est:3000-3500

DECAMPS, Maurice (1892-1953) French
£400 $628 €580 Villeneure (38x46cm-15x18in) s. prov. 28-Aug-3 Christie's, Kensington #178
£1300 $2210 €1898 Mixed flowers with michaelmas daisies (46x56cm-18x22in) s. 30-Oct-3 Duke & Son, Dorchester #194 est:400-700

DECANIS, M (?) ?
£2270 $3790 €3200 Flowers (92x67cm-36x26in) s. 20-Oct-3 Sant Agostino, Torino #307/R est:1200-1600

DECANIS, Theophile (1847-1917) French
£500 $900 €750 Paysage du Midi (28x37cm-11x15in) s. 20-Apr-4 Chenu & Scrive, Lyon #69/R

DECARAVA, Roy (1919-) American
Photographs
£2096 $3500 €3060 Two women (23x34cm-9x13in) s. s.i.verso gelatin silver print. 16-Oct-3 Phillips, New York #139/R est:3000-4000
£2695 $4500 €3935 Self-portrait (28x36cm-11x14in) s. gelatin silver print on board. 16-Oct-3 Phillips, New York #140/R est:2000-3000

DECARIS, Albert (1901-1988) French
£537 $961 €800 Personnages dan sun chemin (33x42cm-13x17in) s. 27-May-4 Christie's, Paris #111/R
Works on paper
£284 $474 €400 Venise, Le Rialto (49x63cm-19x25in) s. W/C. 12-Oct-3 St-Germain-en-Laye Encheres #212
£336 $540 €500 Le minotaure (57x71cm-22x28in) studio st. chl dr. 23-Feb-3 St-Germain-en-Laye Encheres #149/R

DECARIS, Albert (attrib) (1901-1988) French
£1837 $2920 €2700 Kore (135x100cm-53x39in) 21-Mar-3 Bailly Pommery, Paris #133/R est:3000-5000

DECHAR, Peter (1942-) American
£1511 $2750 €2206 Pears no.2 (91x132cm-36x52in) s.d.67 prov. 29-Jun-4 Sotheby's, New York #433/R est:2000-3000

DECHELETTE, Louis Auguste (1894-1964) French
£280 $504 €420 La famille (24x21cm-9x8in) s. panel. 26-Apr-4 Tajan, Paris #386
£633 $1140 €950 Les pigeonniers (24x41cm-9x16in) s. 26-Apr-4 Tajan, Paris #292/R

DECK, Leo (1908-1997) Swiss
£280 $502 €409 Railway bridge in Bern (80x108cm-31x43in) s.d.60 board. 12-May-4 Dobiaschofsky, Bern #423/R (S.FR 650)
£280 $502 €409 Schlosswil (46x55cm-18x22in) s. i.verso panel. 12-May-4 Dobiaschofsky, Bern #3518 (S.FR 650)
£306 $556 €447 Flowers in springtime (56x46cm-22x18in) s. masonite. 16-Jun-4 Fischer, Luzern #2057 (S.FR 700)
£323 $579 €472 Paris with Seine bridge (35x48cm-14x19in) s. 12-May-4 Dobiaschofsky, Bern #3514 (S.FR 750)
£345 $617 €504 Seine quay (38x46cm-15x18in) s.d.57 panel. 12-May-4 Dobiaschofsky, Bern #3523 (S.FR 800)
£655 $1192 €956 Sunflowers (47x56cm-19x22in) s. masonite. 16-Jun-4 Fischer, Luzern #2058/R (S.FR 1500)
£690 $1234 €1007 Walk in the spring (45x55cm-18x22in) s. panel. 12-May-4 Dobiaschofsky, Bern #424 est:1200 (S.FR 1600)

DECKEN, van de (19th C) ?
£560 $1019 €840 Still life of flowers in vase (21x25cm-8x10in) s. oak panel. 19-Jun-4 Rasmussen, Havnen #2189/R (D.KR 6300)

DECKER, Anja (1908-1995) German
£392 $674 €560 Composition (59x42cm-23x17in) s. oil varnish. 3-Dec-3 Hauswedell & Nolte, Hamburg #755/R
£1067 $1963 €1600 Composition (53x49cm-21x19in) 11-Jun-4 Hauswedell & Nolte, Hamburg #1233/R est:1800
Works on paper
£267 $491 €400 Composition (30x40cm-12x16in) s. Indian ink. 11-Jun-4 Hauswedell & Nolte, Hamburg #1237/R

DECKER, Cornelis (1651-1709) Dutch
£5282 $9137 €7500 Wooded landscape with angler by stream (53x71cm-21x28in) mono. panel prov. 13-Dec-3 Lempertz, Koln #205/R est:8000

DECKER, Cornelis Gerritsz (1625-1678) Dutch
£5822 $9897 €8500 Weaver's workshop with couple eating at a table (31x43cm-12x17in) d.1652 panel. 4-Nov-3 Sotheby's, Amsterdam #91/R est:3000-5000
£12162 $21405 €18000 Farmstead near a stream, with fisherman in a rowing boat (65x82cm-26x32in) s. 18-May-4 Sotheby's, Amsterdam #85/R est:20000-30000

DECKER, Cornelis Gerritsz (attrib) (1625-1678) Dutch
£1399 $2378 €2000 Paysage lacustre anime (47x39cm-19x15in) panel. 18-Nov-3 Vanderkindere, Brussels #23 est:2000-3000

DECKER, Georg (1818-1894) Hungarian
£764 $1299 €1100 Portrait of young woman wearing rose in hair (55x45cm-22x18in) s. 28-Oct-3 Dorotheum, Vienna #66/R
£820 $1369 €1197 Portrait of mother and child (29x23cm-11x9in) s. board. 12-Nov-3 Sotheby's, Olympia #177/R

DECKER, Jos de (1912-2000) Belgian
Sculpture
£2308 $3854 €3300 Small fountain (39cm-15in) s. num.IV/IV dark brown pat bronze St.f.De Grove one of 12. 11-Oct-3 De Vuyst, Lokeren #103/R est:3000-4000
£5034 $9312 €7500 Adolescence (165x52cm-65x20in) s. brown pat plaster lit. 13-Mar-4 De Vuyst, Lokeren #492/R est:5000-7000
£5245 $8759 €7500 Ballerina with pony tail (79x13cm-31x5in) s.num.ii/iii St.f.Nevele brown pat bronze black marble base lit. 11-Oct-3 De Vuyst, Lokeren #567/R est:6000-8000

DECKER, Luc de (1907-1982) Belgian
£426 $711 €600 Roses (80x100cm-31x39in) s. 17-Jun-3 Galerie Moderne, Brussels #177

DECKER, Paul (younger) (1685-1742) German
Works on paper
£1500 $2745 €2190 Allegory of faith (34x21cm-13x8in) s. red chk exhib. 7-Jul-4 Bonhams, Knightsbridge #11/R est:1500-2000

DECKER, Robert M (1847-1921) American
£284 $500 €415 Scene outside bull ring in Texas (38x48cm-15x19in) s. 1-Jan-4 Quinn's, Falls Church #202/R
£368 $600 €534 Country landscape mill and babbling brook (43x30cm-17x12in) s. 20-Jul-3 Jeffery Burchard, Florida #62
£7784 $13000 €11365 White Birches - a winter study (30x38cm-12x15in) s. prov. 23-Oct-3 Shannon's, Milford #75/R est:9000-12000

DECKER, Robert M (attrib) (1847-1921) American
£874 $1625 €1276 Great landscape (51x74cm-20x29in) 6-Mar-4 Page, Batavia #126

DECKERS, Edouard (1873-1956) Belgian
Sculpture
£3800 $6840 €5548 Le charmeur (75cm-30in) s.i. brown pat bronze lit. 21-Apr-4 Sotheby's, London #114/R est:3000-5000

DECKERS, Émile (1885-1968) Belgian
£420 $722 €600 Alger-Vase fleuri (73x60cm-29x24in) s.i.d.1955. 8-Dec-3 Tajan, Paris #258/R
£1189 $2045 €1700 Sauvageonne (35x27cm-14x11in) s.i.d.1955 board. 8-Dec-3 Tajan, Paris #256/R est:1600-1800
£2658 $4571 €3800 Algerienne au tatouage (40x30cm-16x12in) s.i.d.1956. 8-Dec-3 Tajan, Paris #254/R est:3800-4200
£2658 $4571 €3800 Jeune Algerienne au collier d'emeraudes (40x30cm-16x12in) s.i.d.1955. 8-Dec-3 Tajan, Paris #257/R est:3800-4200
£4610 $7699 €6500 Muraille de Fes (53x64cm-21x25in) s.i.d.1952. 16-Jun-3 Gros & Delettrez, Paris #318/R est:4500-6000
£5674 $9475 €8000 Trois visages d'Algerienne (84x55cm-33x22in) s.i.d.1961. 16-Jun-3 Gros & Delettrez, Paris #345/R est:9000-12000
£6028 $10067 €8500 Les Touaregs (83x55cm-33x22in) s.i.d.1962. 16-Jun-3 Gros & Delettrez, Paris #95/R est:6500-8000
Works on paper
£352 $609 €500 Portrait de berbere (50x38cm-20x15in) sanguine dr. 15-Dec-3 Gros & Delettrez, Paris #452
£3067 $5612 €4600 Jeune arabe souriant (73x54cm-29x21in) mono. pastel. 7-Jun-4 Palais de Beaux Arts, Brussels #249/R est:2000-3000
£16000 $29120 €23360 Study of three Algerian women (55x85cm-22x33in) s.i.d.1933 pastel chk. 17-Jun-4 Christie's, London #107/R est:15000-20000

DECKERS, Jan (?) Belgian
£733 $1320 €1100 Still life with melon, nuts and grapes (45x64cm-18x25in) s. 26-Apr-4 Bernaerts, Antwerp #244/R

DECRIND, Paul (1916-1995) French
£533 $965 €800 Saint-Jacut de la Mer, Cotes du Nord (27x41cm-11x16in) s. canvas on panel. 3-Apr-4 Gerard, Besancon #43

DEDINI, Eldon (1921-) American
Works on paper
£1829 $3200 €2670 And yet Kitty, in many, many ways I'm very poor (43x34cm-17x13in) s. gouache ills board exec Dec 1963 exhib. 17-Dec-3 Christie's, Rockefeller NY #138/R est:2000-3000
£2571 $4500 €3754 Of course there's someone else (50x37cm-20x15in) s. gouache W/C exec May 1961 lit. 17-Dec-3 Christie's, Rockefeller NY #65/R est:3000-4000
£2571 $4500 €3754 Notice how the eyes follow you around the room (43x32cm-17x13in) s. gouache ills board exec Nov 1965 exhib. 17-Dec-3 Christie's, Rockefeller NY #197/R est:3000-4000

DEEL, Guy (1933-) American
£4076 $7500 €6114 Last chance (35x45cm-14x18in) s. i.verso board lit. 8-Jun-4 Bonhams & Butterfields, San Francisco #4150/R est:3000-5000

DEEM, George (1932-) American
£2000 $3640 €2920 Frans Hals postcards series (183x122cm-72x48in) s.i.d.1964 verso prov. 30-Jun-4 Christie's, Kensington #102/R est:3000-4000

DEENY, Gillian (20th C) Irish
£296 $518 €420 Summer garden (66x76cm-26x30in) s. board. 16-Dec-3 James Adam, Dublin #235/R

DEERING, Roger (1904-) American
£430 $800 €628 Spring by the sea (55x76cm-22x30in) s. 5-Mar-4 Skinner, Boston #580/R

DEFAUX, Alexandre (1826-1900) French
£598 $1100 €873 Farmyard (23x33cm-9x13in) s. 9-Jun-4 Doyle, New York #3019
£707 $1300 €1032 Barnyard (25x46cm-10x18in) s. panel. 25-Jun-4 Freeman, Philadelphia #316/R est:1000-1500
£1200 $2196 €1800 Bouleaux (61x50cm-24x20in) s. 6-Jun-4 Osenat, Fontainebleau #137 est:2000-2200
£1285 $2300 €1876 Barbizon landscape with figure (66x91cm-26x36in) s.d.18. 20-Mar-4 Sloans & Kenyon, Bethesda #1185/R est:1800-2500
£1538 $2646 €2200 Moutons au pre (59x84cm-23x33in) s. 8-Dec-3 Cornette de St.Cyr, Paris #60/R est:1000-1500
£1619 $2655 €2250 Pommiers en fleurs dans les champs (33x52cm-13x20in) s. panel. 3-Jun-3 Livinec, Gaudcheau & Jezequel, Rennes #50/R
£1700 $3043 €2482 Study of cows and chickens (54x65cm-21x26in) s. 26-May-4 Sotheby's, Olympia #259/R est:800-1200
£1921 $3130 €2900 Promeneur et son chien au pied d'un arbre (50x30cm-20x12in) s. 1-Feb-3 Dubee & Berron, Vernou en Sologne #41
£2098 $3608 €3000 Vaches au pre (59x84cm-23x33in) s. 8-Dec-3 Cornette de St.Cyr, Paris #61/R est:1000-1500
£2200 $3982 €3300 Fontainebleau (65x51cm-26x20in) s. 30-Mar-4 Segre, Madrid #42/R est:2300
£2536 $4159 €3500 Le lavoir de Creteil (32x46cm-13x18in) s. i.verso. 11-May-3 Osenat, Fontainebleau #105 est:4500-5000
£2752 $4926 €4100 Bateaux de peche a Yport (33x53cm-13x21in) s. panel. 25-May-4 Chambelland & Giafferi, Paris #112/R est:3000-4000
£3262 $5448 €4600 Ferme sous les arbres (51x69cm-20x27in) s.d.1883 prov. 19-Oct-3 Anaf, Lyon #102/R est:4000-5000
£4000 $7320 €6000 Basse-cour (45x35cm-18x14in) s. panel. 6-Jun-4 Osenat, Fontainebleau #121/R est:5000-5500
£4145 $7626 €6300 Mare aux canards (58x84cm-23x33in) s. 22-Jun-4 Adjug'art, Brest #341/R est:1200-1800
£4366 $7248 €6200 Vaches et poules au bord de l'eau (40x67cm-16x26in) s.i. 15-Jun-3 Peron, Melun #129
£4955 $8523 €7234 Ma maison a Montigny (40x68cm-16x27in) s. s.i.verso. 8-Dec-3 Philippe Schuler, Zurich #3400/R est:7000-9000 (S.FR 11000)
£7059 $12000 €10306 Printemps, poules sous le pommier en fleurs (58x84cm-23x33in) s. 29-Oct-3 Christie's, Rockefeller NY #109/R est:12000-16000
£10667 $19520 €16000 Poules. Canards (41x33cm-16x13in) s. s.d.verso pair. 6-Jun-4 Osenat, Fontainebleau #135/R est:12000-14000
£10870 $17826 €15000 Coqs, poules et canards sous les pommieres en fleurs (101x83cm-40x33in) s. painted c.1873-1875. 11-May-3 Osenat, Fontainebleau #109/R est:12000-13000
Works on paper
£839 $1443 €1200 Coqs et poules pres du puit (13x30cm-5x12in) s. wax crayon htd white chk. 7-Dec-3 Osenat, Fontainebleau #49

DEFER, Jean Baptiste (attrib) (1674-?) French
Sculpture
£49296 $86268 €70000 Louis XIV (51cm-20in) i. bronze prov.lit. 16-Dec-3 Christie's, Paris #312/R est:50000-80000

DEFESCHE, Pieter (1921-) Dutch
£541 $1000 €790 Landscape (79x60cm-31x24in) s.d.1986. 13-Jul-4 Christie's, Rockefeller NY #62/R est:2000-3000
£635 $1200 €927 Rorotonga Muri Beach. Rorotonga II. Maui (49x64cm-19x25in) s. W/C set of three different sizes. 22-Feb-4 Bonhams & Butterfields, Los Angeles #7066 est:600-800
£2000 $3680 €3000 Untitled (65x85cm-26x33in) s.d.62. 8-Jun-4 Sotheby's, Amsterdam #260/R est:3000-4000
£2400 $4392 €3600 White moonlight (94x90cm-37x35in) s.d.68 exhib. 7-Jun-4 Glerum, Amsterdam #305/R est:2500-3500
£2754 $4516 €3800 Romantic intermezzo (80x90cm-31x35in) s.d.60 exhib. 27-May-3 Sotheby's, Amsterdam #540/R est:1800-2500
£2867 $5275 €4300 Ardennen offensief (99x130cm-39x51in) s.d.59 s.i.stretcher prov.exhib. 8-Jun-4 Sotheby's, Amsterdam #280/R est:4500-5500
Works on paper
£1497 $2724 €2200 Composition (47x56cm-19x22in) s.d.65 gouache crayon collage. 3-Feb-4 Christie's, Amsterdam #608 est:800-1200

DEFOSSEZ, Alfred (1932-) French
£267 $483 €400 Paysage (31x39cm-12x15in) s. 1-Apr-4 Credit Municipal, Paris #81
£307 $549 €460 Fleurs vertes (130x81cm-51x32in) s. s.i.verso. 17-May-4 Chayette & Cheval, Paris #202

DEFRANCE, Leonard (1735-1805) Flemish
Works on paper
£704 $1218 €1000 Dispute conjugale (22x28cm-9x11in) i.verso. 10-Dec-3 Hotel des Ventes Mosan, Brussels #132

DEFREGGER, Franz von (1835-1921) German
£2162 $3870 €3200 Peasant smoking pipe (28x24cm-11x9in) s.d.86. 8-May-4 Dawo, Saarbrucken #33/R est:3500
£2685 $4940 €4000 Peasant girl (27x21cm-11x8in) s. 24-Mar-4 Hugo Ruef, Munich #949/R est:3000
£3125 $5094 €4500 Gaislerspitzen at dusk (31x19cm-12x7in) i.verso panel. 23-Sep-3 Wiener Kunst Auktionen, Vienna #26/R est:2000-3000
£3209 $6000 €4685 Bauern (33x23cm-13x9in) s. board on panel. 25-Feb-4 Doyle, New York #2/R est:3000-5000
£3289 $5954 €5000 Der Thalerwirt (120x97cm-47x38in) bears sig. lit. 19-Apr-4 Glerum, Amsterdam #297/R est:4000-6000
£3378 $5946 €5000 Portrait of small girl (13x13cm-5x5in) s. panel. 22-May-4 Lempertz, Koln #1499/R est:6000
£3472 $5729 €5000 Girl wearing hat (16x12cm-6x5in) s. panel lit. 2-Jul-3 Neumeister, Munich #62/R est:6000
£5903 $9740 €8500 Portrait of young girl wearing scarf and black headband (32x25cm-13x10in) s. panel. 3-Jul-3 Van Ham, Cologne #1102/R est:11000
£8725 $16054 €13000 Peasant boy (25x18cm-10x7in) s. bears d.95 panel. 24-Mar-4 Hugo Ruef, Munich #948/R est:4000
£9934 $18079 €15000 Portrait of a young girl (36x29cm-14x11in) s.d.1877. 16-Jun-4 Hugo Ruef, Munich #944/R est:3800
£10490 $17832 €15000 Portrait of a Tyroler (34x26cm-13x10in) s.d.75. 25-Nov-3 Hassfurther, Vienna #29/R est:8000-10000
£11806 $19243 €17000 Portrait of young peasant with pipe (38x30cm-15x12in) s. panel lit. 24-Sep-3 Neumeister, Munich #411/R est:7500
£11921 $21695 €18000 Half portrait of a young girl wearing a shawl (30x22cm-12x9in) s. 16-Jun-4 Hugo Ruef, Munich #943/R est:4500
£17365 $29000 €25353 At the pub (30x38cm-12x15in) s.d.1890 i.verso. 7-Oct-3 Sotheby's, New York #133 est:15000-20000
£19718 $34113 €28000 Portrait of Defregger's daughter (50x37cm-20x15in) s.d.98. 13-Dec-3 Lempertz, Koln #13/R est:15000
£26573 $45175 €38000 Monks with peasants (100x74cm-39x29in) s. 19-Nov-3 Dorotheum, Klagenfurt #7/R est:30000
Works on paper
£851 $1379 €1200 Portrait of young woman looking at book (20x15cm-8x6in) s. pencil lit. 23-May-3 Karlheinz Kaupp, Staufen #1927/R
£1042 $1698 €1500 Man sitting (46x39cm-18x15in) s.verso pencil double-sided. 23-Sep-3 Wiener Kunst Auktionen, Vienna #19/R est:1500-3000
£1793 $2977 €2600 Girl in Tyrolean costume (30x21cm-12x8in) s.d.1885 W/C pen. 30-Sep-3 Dorotheum, Vienna #190/R est:2000-2300

DEFREGGER, Franz von (attrib) (1835-1921) German
£1278 $2300 €1866 Portrait of a man smoking a pipe (29x16cm-11x6in) mono. i.verso canvas on panel. 24-Apr-4 Weschler, Washington #569/R est:1000-2000
Works on paper
£467 $835 €700 Mother and child on bench (23x14cm-9x6in) pencil W/C. 14-May-4 Bassenge, Berlin #6158

DEGAS, Edgar (1834-1917) French
£25333 $46613 €38000 Fille de Jephte (52x76cm-20x30in) oil sketch prov.lit. 9-Jun-4 Le Roux & Morel, Paris #31/R est:40000-50000
£2178771 $3900000 €3181006 Promenade des chevaux (39x89cm-15x35in) painted c.1892 pel. 5-May-4 Sotheby's, New York #18/R est:5000000-7000000
£2178771 $3900000 €3181006 Avant la course (30x48cm-12x19in) s. paper on panel painted c.1882-88 prov.exhib.lit. 5-May-4 Sotheby's, New York #20/R est:5000000-7000000
£3700000 $6734000 €5402000 Chevaux de courses (32x40cm-13x16in) s. panel prov.exhib.lit. 21-Jun-4 Sotheby's, London #14/R est:2800000-3500000
Photographs
£4333 $7887 €6500 Portrait d'Henry Lerolle et de sa femme (28x39cm-11x15in) photograph prov. 2-Jul-4 Beaussant & Lefèvre, Paris #215/R est:8000-10000
£28667 $52173 €43000 Portrait des filles d'Henry Lerolle (39x28cm-15x11in) photograph prov. 2-Jul-4 Beaussant & Lefèvre, Paris #216/R est:8000-10000
£48667 $88573 €73000 Portrait de Madeleine Lerolle (29x39cm-11x15in) photograph prov. 2-Jul-4 Beaussant & Lefèvre, Paris #214/R est:8000-10000
£58667 $106773 €88000 Portrait au miroir d'Henry Lerolle (29x36cm-11x14in) photograph prov. 2-Jul-4 Beaussant & Lefèvre, Paris #213/R est:15000-20000
£113333 $206267 €170000 Self-portrait with Henry Lerolle's daughters (37x29cm-15x11in) photograph prov. 2-Jul-4 Beaussant & Lefèvre, Paris #212/R est:25000-30000
Prints
£5034 $9312 €7500 Ludovic Halevy parlant a Madame Cardinal (21x16cm-8x6in) monotype. 15-Mar-4 Blanchet, Paris #57/R est:8000-10000
Sculpture
£2500 $4175 €3600 Danseuse regardant son pied (42cm-17in) bronze. 21-Oct-3 Campo, Vlaamse Kaai #408a
£11111 $20000 €16222 Danse Espagnole (46cm-18in) s. num.2/3 brown pat bronze marble base st.f.AA Hebrard prov.lit. 20-Jan-4 Arthur James, Florida #107
£41899 $75000 €61173 Arabesque ouverte sur la jambe droite, le bras gauche en avant (22cm-9in) s. num.14 blk pat bronze exec 1882-1895 st.f.AA Hebrard prov.lit. 5-May-4 Christie's, Rockefeller NY #217/R est:50000-70000
£45882 $78000 €66988 Danseuse au tambourin (28cm-11in) s. num.12 st.f.A.A.Hebrard brown pat bronze prov.exhib.lit. 5-Nov-3 Christie's, Rockefeller NY #207/R est:40000-60000
£89385 $160000 €130502 Danseuse s'avancant les bras leves la jambe droite en avant (65cm-26in) st.num.72/Q st.f.Hebrard brown pat bronze prov.exhib.lit. 6-May-4 Sotheby's, New York #233/R est:80000-120000
£150000 $276000 €219000 Cheval sautant un obstacle (30cm-12in) st.sig.st.f.Hebrard brown pat bronze prov.lit. 22-Jun-4 Christie's, London #21/R est:140000-180000
£170000 $309400 €248200 Danseuse regardant la plante de son pied droit (48cm-19in) st.sig.st.f.Hebrard bronze prov.lit. 21-Jun-4 Sotheby's, London #2/R est:120000-160000
£294118 $500000 €429412 Grande arabesque, deuxieme temps (43x62cm-17x24in) s.num.15/C brown pat. bronze cire perdue A.A. Hebrard prov.lit. 5-Nov-3 Sotheby's, New York #1/R est:500000-700000
£4500000 $8190000 €6570000 Petite danseuse de quatorze ans (98cm-39in) st.f.Hebrard bronze muslin satin wooden base prov.exhib.lit. 3-Feb-4 Sotheby's, London #37/R est:5000000-7000000
Works on paper
£550 $919 €798 Egyptian relief (19x31cm-7x12in) pencil. 19-Jun-3 Kornfeld, Bern #313 (S.FR 1200)
£1399 $2378 €2000 Egyptian relief (22x34cm-9x13in) pencil. 26-Nov-3 Dorotheum, Vienna #109/R est:2000-2400
£5882 $10000 €8588 Etude de cheval de dos. Cheval et cavalier (6x6cm-2x2in) first studio st. both pencil prov.exhib. pair. 6-Nov-3 Sotheby's, New York #104/R est:10000-15000
£10564 $18486 €15000 Etude d'homme a cheval (31x24cm-12x9in) studio st. crayon stump dr double-sided prov.lit. 18-Dec-3 Tajan, Paris #2/R est:15000-20000
£11119 $18569 €15900 Cavalier (20x12cm-8x5in) studio st. graphite dr prov.exhib. 29-Jun-3 Eric Pillon, Calais #111/R

£11888	$20447	€17000	Etude pour la fille de Jephthah (31x24cm-12x9in) studio st. graphite dr prov. 8-Dec-3 Artcurial Briest, Paris #8/R est:20000-30000
£15000	$25050	€21900	Apres la course (25x32cm-10x13in) st.sig. black crayon prov. 21-Oct-3 Sotheby's, London #3/R est:10000-15000
£15000	$27600	€21900	Etude de nu (28x21cm-11x8in) st.sig. d.1856 pencil prov.exhib. 24-Jun-4 Christie's, London #305/R est:10000-15000
£18341	$33380	€26778	Olinde et Sophronie sur le bucher (55x43cm-22x17in) pastel exec. 1859-1861 prov. 18-Jun-4 Kornfeld, Bern #23/R est:40000 (S.FR 42000)
£21667	$39650	€32500	Cheval monte par une amazone (24x19cm-9x7in) st.sig. pencil prov. 5-Jun-4 Lempertz, Koln #659/R est:3000-35000
£28000	$51520	€40880	Cheval s'enlevant au galop (32x23cm-13x9in) st.sig. chl prov.exhib. 24-Jun-4 Christie's, London #334/R est:15000-20000
£35000	$63700	€51100	Nude study (54x36cm-21x14in) st.sig. chl over chl counter proof on paper prov. 5-Feb-4 Christie's, London #305/R est:35000-45000
£36000	$65520	€52560	Femme a sa toilette (84x49cm-33x19in) st.sig. chl brown chk exec.c.1892 prov. 4-Feb-4 Sotheby's, London #416/R est:25000-35000
£53073	$95000	€77487	Grandstand - Study for Le Faux Depart (23x36cm-9x14in) studio st. verso pencil exec c.1869-1871 prov.exhib.lit. 6-May-4 Sotheby's, New York #201/R est:10000-15000
£65493	$113303	€93000	Apres le bain (46x29cm-18x11in) st.sig. chl exec. c.1896 prov. 14-Dec-3 Rabourdin & Choppin de Janvry, Paris #45/R est:100000-110000
£67039	$120000	€97877	Bain (63x50cm-25x20in) st. counter impression chl grey chk exec c.1890 prov. 6-May-4 Sotheby's, New York #217/R est:80000-120000
£94406	$162378	€135000	Femme a sa toilette penchee vers la droite (40x27cm-16x11in) chl tracing paper exec.c.1890 prov.exhib. 3-Dec-3 Beaussant & Lefèvre, Paris #28/R est:30000
£100000	$182000	€146000	Danseuse vue de profil (46x59cm-18x23in) st.sig. chl pastel exec c.1880-81 prov.lit. 5-Feb-4 Christie's, London #320/R est:140000-180000
£150838	$270000	€220223	Danseuse vue en buste (100x70cm-39x28in) st.sig. chl paper on board prov.exhib.lit. 6-May-4 Sotheby's, New York #346/R est:140000-180000
£167598	$300000	€244693	Cheval de selle (32x18cm-13x7in) st.sig. pencil prov.exhib.lit. 5-May-4 Sotheby's, New York #1/R est:80000-120000
£170000	$309400	€248200	Sortie du bain (90x78cm-35x31in) chl pastel joined sheets of paper exec c.1895-98 prov.exhib.lit. 5-Feb-4 Christie's, London #321/R est:180000-240000
£251397	$450000	€367040	Groupe de danseuses (57x69cm-22x27in) st.sig. chl pastel paper on board exec.c.1900 prov.lit. 6-May-4 Sotheby's, New York #124/R est:500000-600000
£280000	$509600	€408800	Femme a sa toilette (105x75cm-41x30in) studio st. chl pastel exec.c.1895-1903 prov.exhib. 3-Feb-4 Sotheby's, London #38/R est:150000-200000

DEGENHARDT, Gertrude (1940-) German

Works on paper

£267	$480	€400	Woman wearing hat (35x34cm-14x13in) s.d. mixed media board. 24-Apr-4 Dr Lehr, Berlin #93/R

DEGGENDORFER, Alfred (1899-1975) Austrian

£333	$613	€500	High mountains (21x31cm-8x12in) mono. tempera. 9-Jun-4 Dorotheum, Salzburg #610/R

DEGLE, Franz Joseph (1724-1812) German

£430	$783	€650	Portrait of the mayor of Augsburg Johannes Nikolaus Bischoff (100x79cm-39x31in) i.d.1773 verso. 17-Jun-4 Frank Peege, Freiburg #1088/R
£3750	$6000	€5475	Portrait of Maria Anna Mozart (94x76cm-37x30in) s.d.1763 prov. 20-Sep-3 New Orleans Auction, New Orleans #211/R est:12000-18000

DEGLE, Franz Joseph (attrib) (1724-1812) German

£915	$1584	€1300	Representation of a sculptor's workshop (45x56cm-18x22in) i.verso canvas on canvas. 10-Dec-3 Hugo Ruef, Munich #2369

DEGLUME, Henri (1865-1940) Belgian

£349	$639	€520	Sous-bois a l'etang (50x75cm-20x30in) s. 8-Jul-4 Campo, Vlaamse Kaai #93
£400	$724	€600	Bord d'etang ensoleille (52x74cm-20x29in) s. 30-Mar-4 Palais de Beaux Arts, Brussels #513

DEGNER, Artur (1887-1972) German

£350	$601	€500	Still life with flowers (49x69cm-19x27in) s. cardboard. 6-Dec-3 Quittenbaum, Hamburg #83/R

DEGODE, Wilhelm (1862-1931) German

£1467	$2669	€2200	Hilly landscape with flowering bushes (79x59cm-31x23in) s.d.1898 board. 1-Jul-4 Van Ham, Cologne #1257/R est:1000
£2400	$4368	€3504	Stroll along a sunlit avenue (100x150cm-39x59in) s.i.d.97. 16-Jun-4 Christie's, Kensington #79/R est:4000-6000

DEGOTARDI, John (1823-1882) Australian?

Photographs

£4545	$8409	€6636	Sydney and Port Jackson, from Myles buildings (37x175cm-15x69in) albumen silver photograph. 10-Mar-4 Deutscher-Menzies, Melbourne #164/R est:4000-6000 (A.D 11000)

DEGOTTEX, Jean (1918-1988) French

£1469	$2452	€2100	Media IX (100x75cm-39x30in) s.d.73 s.i.d.verso acrylic paper on canvas prov. 29-Jun-3 Versailles Encheres #203/R
£1656	$3013	€2500	Les Pavots (27x18cm-11x7in) s.i.d.1954 verso. 18-Jun-4 Charbonneaux, Paris #142/R est:2500-3000
£1972	$3411	€2800	Chemin de Crete (17x100cm-7x39in) s.d.1953 s.i.d.verso prov. 14-Dec-3 Versailles Encheres #64/R est:3000-4000
£2013	$3705	€3000	Papier plein no.13 (80x60cm-31x24in) st.i.d.1976 verso acrylic torn paper. 29-Mar-4 Cornette de St.Cyr, Paris #20/R est:2500-3000
£2517	$4580	€3800	Composition (45x37cm-18x15in) s.d.1951. 18-Jun-4 Charbonneaux, Paris #141/R est:4000-4500
£3803	$6655	€5400	Meta SEII (80x52cm-31x20in) s.d.1961 panel. 18-Dec-3 Cornette de St.Cyr, Paris #69/R est:6000-8000
£4196	$7133	€6000	Terre a ciel (130x161cm-51x63in) s.d.54. 28-Nov-3 Blanchet, Paris #216/R est:6000-8000
£4333	$7973	€6500	Media IX (150x100cm-59x39in) s.i.d.9.2.73 verso acrylic paper on canvas prov. 9-Jun-4 Artcurial Briest, Paris #530/R est:7000-9000

Works on paper

£304	$535	€450	Untitled (25x26cm-10x10in) felt pen wax crayon gouache collage paper on board. 18-May-4 Tajan, Paris #153/R
£333	$607	€500	Apres l'encre-acte (48x62cm-19x24in) s.i.d.74 ink pen. 30-Jun-4 Delvaux, Paris #57
£764	$1245	€1100	Les pavots (36x25cm-14x10in) studio st. W/C Indian ink. 29-Sep-3 Charbonneaux, Paris #202
£780	$1303	€1100	Les pavots (36x25cm-14x10in) s.d.1954 Indian ink. 19-Oct-3 Charbonneaux, Paris #113/R
£833	$1358	€1200	Les pavots (36x24cm-14x9in) studio st. W/C Indian ink. 18-Jul-3 Charbonneaux, Paris #167
£1250	$2300	€1900	TSHET Rouge II (64x50cm-25x20in) s.i. gouache three prov. 22-Jun-4 Christie's, Amsterdam #329/R est:700-900
£1389	$2194	€2000	Entre-acte (50x64cm-20x25in) s.i.d.74 Chinese ink prov.exhib.lit. 27-Apr-3 Versailles Encheres #112
£1538	$2615	€2200	Metasphere one (64x49cm-25x19in) s.d.1966 W/C white gouache scratching out. 28-Nov-3 Blanchet, Paris #210/R est:2500-3000
£1800	$3312	€2700	Suite Serto V (64x50cm-25x20in) s.d.1957 india ink. 11-Jun-4 Pierre Berge, Paris #84/R est:2000-3000
£1812	$3334	€2700	Metasphere (64x49cm-25x19in) s.d.31.10.1966 Indian ink wash. 29-Mar-4 Cornette de St.Cyr, Paris #23/R est:1800-2000
£1812	$3334	€2700	Suite Jshet (103x75cm-41x30in) s.d.25.11.62 Indian ink col ink. 29-Mar-4 Cornette de St.Cyr, Paris #15/R est:2000-3000
£1812	$3207	€2700	Horsphere (104x75cm-41x30in) s.d.12.65 Indian ink red paper. 28-Apr-4 Artcurial Briest, Paris #258/R est:3000-4000
£1818	$3036	€2600	Papier plein (80x120cm-31x47in) s.i.d.1975 mixed media paper on canvas prov. 29-Jun-3 Versailles Encheres #204/R
£1880	$3458	€2800	Suite Serto (64x50cm-25x20in) s.d.18.3.1957 st.i.verso Indian ink lit. 29-Mar-4 Cornette de St.Cyr, Paris #22/R est:2200-2500
£1986	$3316	€2800	Blanc et noir (46x55cm-18x22in) s. s.d.1958 verso peinture cardboard. 19-Oct-3 Anaf, Lyon #103/R est:3000-4000
£2416	$4446	€3600	Signe de la fleur (55x75cm-22x30in) s.d.1959 col ink Indian ink. 29-Mar-4 Cornette de St.Cyr, Paris #21/R est:2000-2500
£3611	$5958	€5200	Suite la rose III (50x65cm-20x26in) s.d.1959 Indian ink col ink prov.exhib.lit. 2-Jul-3 Cornette de St.Cyr, Paris #31/R est:5000-6000

DEGRAVE, Jules Alex (19th C) French

£1220	$2000	€1769	Group of young children awaiting their lesson (41x33cm-16x13in) s. panel painted c.1880. 7-Jun-3 Treadway Gallery, Cincinnati #1317 est:3000-4000

DEGREEF, Amedee (1878-1968) Belgian

£289	$500	€422	Cloudy Day (30x61cm-12x24in) s. 9-Dec-3 Pinneys, Montreal #33 (C.D 650)

DEGREEF, Jean (1852-1894) Belgian

£272	$487	€400	Cheval tirant une charette dans les pres (29x40cm-11x16in) s. canvas on panel. 16-Mar-4 Vanderkindere, Brussels #28
£303	$561	€440	Vue de Rouge-Cloitre (38x55cm-15x22in) 19-Jan-4 Horta, Bruxelles #322
£493	$893	€750	Chemin de campagne (39x33cm-15x13in) s. canvas on panel. 19-Apr-4 Horta, Bruxelles #308
£528	$914	€750	Chemin creux (30x49cm-12x19in) s. panel. 13-Dec-3 De Vuyst, Lokeren #105
£537	$983	€800	Le chemin du Rouge-Cloitre (38x55cm-15x22in) s. 8-Jul-4 Campo, Vlaamse Kaai #75
£669	$1157	€950	Ruelle d'Overijse animee (37x55cm-15x22in) s. 9-Dec-3 Vanderkindere, Brussels #27
£1014	$1814	€1500	Meunier arrivant au moulin (43x64cm-17x25in) s. s.d.1884 verso. 10-May-4 Horta, Bruxelles #410 est:2200-2800
£1200	$2172	€1800	Matin gris (54x67cm-21x26in) s. 30-Mar-4 Palais de Beaux Arts, Brussels #515/R est:1600-2400
£1589	$2893	€2400	Le premier etang du Rouge-Cloitre (84x129cm-33x51in) s.d.1884. 15-Jun-4 Vanderkindere, Brussels #172/R est:2500-3500
£7042	$12183	€10000	Rue de village a Woluwe (97x130cm-38x51in) s. exhib. 9-Dec-3 Campo, Vlaamse Kaai #280/R est:10000-12500

DEHN, Adolf (1895-1968) American

£959	$1525	€1391	Three Haitian girls (94x61cm-37x24in) s. board painted c.1955. 12-Sep-3 Aspire, Cleveland #52 est:800-1600
£1105	$2000	€1613	Italian hill top (41x61cm-16x24in) board. 16-Apr-4 American Auctioneer #93/R est:1500-2000
£1196	$2200	€1746	Inlet (30x41cm-12x16in) board. 28-Mar-4 Carlsen Gallery, Greenville #558/R
£1301	$2250	€1899	Pennsylvania winter (46x91cm-18x36in) s. d.1956 verso masonite. 10-Dec-3 Alderfer's, Hatfield #367/R est:1700-2000
£2793	$5000	€4078	Central park (56x76cm-22x30in) s.d.50 board. 26-May-4 Doyle, New York #131/R est:6000-8000
£4945	$9000	€7220	Central Park in winter (29x70cm-11x28in) s. init.verso masonite. 29-Jun-4 Sotheby's, New York #283/R est:2000-9000

Works on paper

£246	$425	€359	Victorian house in a hilly landscape (35x51cm-14x20in) s. ink. 13-Dec-3 Weschler, Washington #579
£324	$520	€473	Town park (25x33cm-10x13in) s. W/C. 20-Aug-3 James Julia, Fairfield #1607/R
£442	$800	€645	Alpine landscape (51x71cm-20x28in) W/C. 16-Apr-4 American Auctioneer #94/R
£818	$1300	€1194	Scientist and his demons (76x51cm-30x20in) s.d.1941 W/C. 14-Sep-3 Susanin's, Chicago #6090/R est:1000-1500
£838	$1500	€1223	Lake Atitlan (51x71cm-20x28in) s. W/C. 11-Jan-4 William Jenack, New York #52 est:800-1200
£1242	$2000	€1813	Sunbathing on the beach (43x58cm-17x23in) s. W/C. 20-Aug-3 James Julia, Fairfield #1606/R est:2000-3000
£3757	$6500	€5485	Overture (54x36cm-21x14in) s.d.1940 pencil W/C prov. 10-Dec-3 Bonhams & Butterfields, San Francisco #6066/R est:3000-5000

DEHN, Georg (1843-1904) German

£403	$741	€600	Village (30x25cm-12x10in) s. canvas on panel. 24-Mar-4 Hugo Ruef, Munich #950/R
£940	$1729	€1400	Washerwomen under bridge (50x41cm-20x16in) s. 24-Mar-4 Hugo Ruef, Munich #947/R

DEHNER, Dorothy (1901-1994) American
Sculpture
£2096 $3500 €3060 Untitled (30cm-12in) s.d.1972 bronze. 25-Oct-3 Rachel Davis, Shaker Heights #540/R
Works on paper
£659 $1100 €962 Untitled (15x11cm-6x4in) s.d.1950 ink W/C prov. 11-Nov-3 Christie's, Rockefeller NY #116/R est:800-1200

DEHODENCQ, Alfred (1822-1882) French
£944 $1605 €1350 Portrait d'homme (81x65cm-32x26in) s.i. 27-Nov-3 Millon & Associes, Paris #110/R
Works on paper
£288 $460 €400 Two studies of Saints (21x12cm-8x5in) studio st. pen brown ink blue paper. 16-May-3 Tajan, Paris #112
£352 $609 €500 L'arrestation de Charlotte Corday (18x28cm-7x11in) pen black ink. 12-Dec-3 Renaud, Paris #67
£367 $664 €550 Portrait d'Edmond, fils de l'artiste et etudes de bateaux et cavalier (21x31cm-8x12in) brown ink wash W/C exec. c.1871. 31-Mar-4 Sotheby's, Paris #136/R
£867 $1569 €1300 Etudes d'hommes et de femmes (21x34cm-8x13in) black crayon. 31-Mar-4 Sotheby's, Paris #135/R est:600-800
£867 $1569 €1300 Etude pour deux enfants jouant avec une tortue (20x31cm-8x12in) pen brown ink black crayon sold with another. 31-Mar-4 Sotheby's, Paris #139/R est:500-700
£1000 $1810 €1500 Etude pour la justice du Pacha (55x51cm-22x20in) pen brown ink black crayon sold with two others. 31-Mar-4 Sotheby's, Paris #133/R est:1000-1500
£1067 $1931 €1600 Etude pour les adieux de Boabdil a Grenade (30x20cm-12x8in) pen brown ink sold with three others. 31-Mar-4 Sotheby's, Paris #134/R est:700-900
£1267 $2293 €1900 Etudes de femme arabe et de bohemienne. pen brown ink graphite sold with two others. 31-Mar-4 Sotheby's, Paris #141/R est:700-900
£1667 $3017 €2500 Etude pour la danse des negres a Tanger (14x20cm-6x8in) pen brown ink. 31-Mar-4 Sotheby's, Paris #138/R est:400-600
£1867 $3379 €2800 Deux etudes pour la fete juive a Tanger. Deux etudes pour l'execution de la juive (30x22cm-12x9in) two pen brown ink two graphite four. 31-Mar-4 Sotheby's, Paris #140/R est:500-700

DEHOY, Charles (1872-1940) Belgian
£384 $652 €560 Nu couche (12x15cm-5x6in) s. cardboard. 10-Nov-3 Horta, Bruxelles #264
£486 $773 €700 Bord de Meuse (50x60cm-20x24in) s. 9-Sep-3 Palais de Beaux Arts, Brussels #210/R
£2797 $4755 €4000 Nature morte, statue enfant et oranges (73x70cm-29x28in) s.d.1921 verso. 1-Dec-3 Palais de Beaux Arts, Brussels #48/R est:4000-5000
Works on paper
£664 $1129 €950 Peniches sur le canal (28x31cm-11x12in) s.d.1913 W/C. 1-Dec-3 Palais de Beaux Arts, Brussels #247/R

DEHRENS, Frank (19/20th C) ?
£381 $610 €552 Nude (90x80cm-35x31in) s. 15-May-3 Stuker, Bern #1143 (S.FR 800)
£1143 $1829 €1657 Carnations (106x85cm-42x33in) i. 15-May-3 Stuker, Bern #1142 est:1200-1500 (S.FR 2400)

DEIERLING, Heinrich Harry (1894-1989) German
£1667 $2783 €2400 Coastal landscape - Baltic (40x53cm-16x21in) s.d. 25-Oct-3 Dr Lehr, Berlin #117/R est:500

DEIKE, Clara (1881-1964) American
£1760 $3150 €2570 Landscape (64x53cm-25x21in) s.d.31 exhib. 19-Mar-4 Aspire, Cleveland #70 est:800-1200

DEIKER, Carl (1879-1958) German
£278 $464 €400 Deer by stream in wood (40x51cm-16x20in) s.i.d. 24-Oct-3 Ketterer, Hamburg #155/R
£574 $930 €832 The poor child - child in bed, dog on quilt with baby's bottle (24x36cm-9x14in) s.d.06. 4-Aug-3 Rasmussen, Vejle #130/R (D.KR 6000)

DEIKER, Carl Friedrich (1836-1892) German
£1538 $2569 €2200 Hares in snowy field (27x20cm-11x8in) s. panel. 9-Oct-3 Michael Zeller, Lindau #543/R est:2200
£1867 $3397 €2800 Pheasants in wood (18x31cm-7x12in) s. 30-Jun-4 Neumeister, Munich #528/R est:1200
£2657 $4438 €3800 Four dogs barking at cat on signpost (35x23cm-14x9in) s.d.1885 panel. 9-Oct-3 Michael Zeller, Lindau #542/R est:2900
£2667 $4827 €4000 Deer in clearing in early morning (52x66cm-20x26in) s.d.1882. 1-Apr-4 Van Ham, Cologne #1332 est:1100
£2667 $4853 €4000 Flowers in a clearing in the morning light (52x66cm-20x26in) s.d.1882. 1-Jul-4 Van Ham, Cologne #1258 est:3000

DEIKER, Johannes Christian (1822-1895) German
£367 $675 €550 Young deer (49x54cm-19x21in) s.d.31/8/66 cardboard. 12-Jun-4 Karlheinz Kaupp, Staufen #1044/R
£3824 $6500 €5583 Spaniel (27x21cm-11x8in) s. panel. 21-Nov-3 Skinner, Boston #74/R est:2500-3500

DEINEKA, Alexander (1899-1969) Russian
£5000 $8950 €7500 Sailors on ship (34x51cm-13x20in) s. 13-May-4 Neumeister, Munich #327/R est:3000-3500
£90000 $161100 €131400 Ode to spring (99x99cm-39x39in) s. 26-May-4 Sotheby's, London #303/R est:60000-80000

DEINEKA, Alexander (attrib) (1899-1969) Russian
Works on paper
£726 $1300 €1060 Sketches for the envelopes and posters (31x44cm-12x17in) W/C exec. 1940's. 29-May-4 Shishkin Gallery, Moscow #4/R

DEIRA, Ernesto (1928-1986) Argentinian
£1977 $3400 €2886 Figures (54x64cm-21x25in) s. mixed media. 3-Dec-3 Naón & Cia, Buenos Aires #89/R est:3000-5000
£7692 $14000 €11230 Figure (70x50cm-28x20in) s. s.i.d.1963 verso. 29-Jun-4 Arroyo, Buenos Aires #86/R est:14000
£11732 $21000 €17129 Hotspur's end (114x147cm-45x58in) s.d.1963 verso. 26-May-4 Sotheby's, New York #130/R est:12000-18000
Works on paper
£1955 $3500 €2854 Untitled (50x70cm-20x28in) mixed media. 11-May-4 Arroyo, Buenos Aires #30

DEITERS, Hans (1868-?) German
£299 $536 €440 Young beauty (60x40cm-24x16in) s. 18-Mar-4 Neumeister, Munich #2658
Works on paper
£268 $494 €400 Spring (43x64cm-17x25in) gouache. 27-Mar-4 L & B, Essen #255/R

DEITERS, Heinrich (1840-1916) German
£1645 $3026 €2500 Landscape with grazing sheep (63x93cm-25x37in) s.d.84. 25-Jun-4 Michael Zeller, Lindau #507/R est:2500

DEIX, Manfred (1949-) Austrian
Works on paper
£400 $720 €600 Holiday tour (32x27cm-13x11in) s. mixed media. 21-Apr-4 Dorotheum, Vienna #255/R
£500 $900 €750 Bundeskanzler Herbert Fux (20x26cm-8x10in) s.i. mixed media. 21-Apr-4 Dorotheum, Vienna #256/R

DEJEAN, Louis (1872-1953) French
Sculpture
£4054 $7135 €6000 Torse feminin (61cm-24in) s.i. pat bronze. 18-May-4 Christie's, Paris #28/R est:6000-8000

DEJOINER, Luther Evans (1886-1954) American
£1766 $3250 €2578 Sunlight on a wooded path (56x67cm-22x26in) s.d.04. 8-Jun-4 Bonhams & Butterfields, San Francisco #4188/R est:4000-6000

DEKEN, Albert de (1915-2003) Belgian
£473 $847 €700 Summer landscape (60x70cm-24x28in) double-sided. 10-May-4 Amberes, Antwerp #257
£594 $993 €850 Seascape (31x45cm-12x18in) s. 11-Oct-3 De Vuyst, Lokeren #104
£845 $1462 €1200 Petit pont a Merksem (50x70cm-20x28in) s. 9-Dec-3 Campo, Vlaamse Kaai #276/R
£1042 $1740 €1500 Nature morte a la bouteille de genievre (70x80cm-28x31in) s. 21-Oct-3 Campo, Vlaamse Kaai #402 est:2000-2500
£1408 $2437 €2000 Petite auberge dans le Morvan, France (60x80cm-24x31in) s. 9-Dec-3 Campo, Vlaamse Kaai #275/R est:1200-1500
Works on paper
£319 $533 €460 Sur la digue de mer (36x53cm-14x21in) s. W/C. 21-Oct-3 Campo, Vlaamse Kaai #404

DEKKER, Henk (1897-1974) Dutch
£280 $512 €420 Tregastel, Brittany (40x50cm-16x20in) s. 7-Jun-4 Glerum, Amsterdam #88/R
£428 $787 €650 At sea (50x70cm-20x28in) s. 22-Jun-4 Christie's, Amsterdam #286/R
£436 $750 €637 Sailboats in a harbour (58x99cm-23x39in) s. 7-Dec-3 Hindman, Chicago #746/R
£445 $757 €650 Fishing boat by breakwater (28x38cm-11x15in) s. 5-Nov-3 Vendue Huis, Gravenhage #172
£500 $915 €750 Fishing boat near the quay in front of a village (29x39cm-11x15in) s. 7-Jun-4 Glerum, Amsterdam #64/R
£748 $1362 €1100 View of Terschelling (30x40cm-12x16in) s. 3-Feb-4 Christie's, Amsterdam #353 est:500-700
£759 $1267 €1100 Sailing ships in the mist (39x49cm-15x19in) s. 11-Nov-3 Vendu Notarishuis, Rotterdam #125/R
£822 $1397 €1200 The Katwijk 23 on the sea (78x58cm-31x23in) s. 5-Nov-3 Vendue Huis, Gravenhage #174/R
£987 $1816 €1500 Opkomende nevel Volendam (40x50cm-16x20in) s. i. stretcher. 28-Jun-4 Sotheby's, Amsterdam #172/R est:1000-1500
£987 $1816 €1500 Sailing vessels at sea (60x80cm-24x31in) s. 28-Jun-4 Sotheby's, Amsterdam #173/R est:2000-3000
£1259 $2102 €1800 Sailing vessels off shore (40x60cm-16x24in) s.d.36. 30-Jun-3 Sotheby's, Amsterdam #332/R
£1888 $3247 €2700 Shell-fisher on the beach (60x80cm-24x31in) s. 7-Dec-3 Sotheby's, Amsterdam #655/R

DEKKERS, Ad (1938-) Dutch
£2793 $5000 €4078 Vier begransde vierkanten in vierkant (60x60cm-24x24in) s.i.d.1973 verso oil incised panel prov. 14-May-4 Phillips, New York #283/R est:5000-7000
£5028 $9000 €7341 Two cirkelvormige freeslijnen in een cirkel (60cm-24in circular) s.i.d.1973 verso oil incised wooden panel prov. 14-May-4 Phillips, New York #282/R est:5000-7000
£6294 $10699 €9000 Vierkant gefreesd in Vierkant (120x120cm-47x47in) s.i.d.1972 verso white painted wood prov.lit. 25-Nov-3 Christie's, Amsterdam #319/R est:9000-12000

DEKKERT, Eugène (1865-1956) German
£433 $789 €650 Florian Square in Garmisch (51x71cm-20x28in) s. 1-Jul-4 Van Ham, Cologne #1261

£500 $925 €730 Figure outside a cottage before a river (33x37cm-13x15in) s. 14-Jul-4 Christie's, Kensington #1152/R
£684 $1121 €950 St Monance harbour, Scotland (51x40cm-20x16in) s.d. s.i.d. verso prov. 4-Jun-3 Ketterer, Hamburg #3/R
£814 $1385 €1188 Poultry in snowy yard (40x45cm-16x18in) s. 19-Nov-3 Fischer, Luzern #2053/R (S.FR 1800)
£1678 $3087 €2500 Children by lake (82x72cm-32x28in) s. 27-Mar-4 L & B, Essen #79/R est:150
£1900 $3268 €2774 Continental harbour (65x80cm-26x31in) s. canvas on board. 4-Dec-3 Bonhams, Edinburgh #99/R est:2000-3000
£4000 $6800 €5840 St Monans harbour, Fife (51x41cm-20x16in) s.d.14 s.i.d.stretcher. 30-Oct-3 Christie's, London #136/R est:2000-3000

DELABANO, Barney (1926-1997) American
£1557 $2600 €2273 Suburbia (51x81cm-20x32in) masonite. 18-Oct-3 David Dike, Dallas #78/R est:2000-4000

DELABRIERE, Paul Edouard (1829-1912) French
Sculpture
£1020 $1827 €1500 Coq faisan surpris par un rongeur (36cm-14in) s. brown pat bronze marble socle. 20-Mar-4 Binoche, Orleans #98 est:800-900
£1088 $1948 €1600 Chien braque et epagneul sur faisin (54cm-21in) s. brown pat bronze. 20-Mar-4 Binoche, Orleans #99 est:800-900
£1156 $2070 €1700 Lion du Senegal et antilope (48x80cm-19x31in) green pat bronze exhib. 19-Mar-4 Ribeyre & Baron, Paris #110/R est:1500-2000
£1271 $2250 €1856 Two hounds chained to a post (36x36x18cm-14x14x7in) s. bronze. 1-May-4 Thomaston Place, Thomaston #103/R
£1294 $2200 €1889 Pair of sandpipers (25cm-10in) s. pat bronze prov. 28-Oct-3 Christie's, Rockefeller NY #245/R
£1515 $2500 €2212 Untitled, pair of hunting dogs chained to a post (56x56x25cm-22x22x10in) s. bronze. 7-Jul-3 Schrager Galleries, Milwaukee #1403
£1517 $2807 €2200 La parade du faisan (40cm-16in) s. brown pat bronze. 13-Jan-4 Vanderkindere, Brussels #129 est:1000-1500
£2059 $3500 €3006 Snipe family (29cm-11in) s. pat bronze prov. 28-Oct-3 Christie's, Rockefeller NY #246/R
£2100 $3423 €3066 Study of a pheasant and chick with a small lizard and fallen oak branch (38x43cm-15x17in) golden brown pat bronze green maurin scotia stand. 28-Sep-3 Wilkinson, Doncaster #5/R
£4500 $7650 €6570 Spanish haberdier (57cm-22in) s. pat bronze. 28-Oct-3 Sotheby's, London #93/R
£8000 $14400 €11680 Huntsman with two hounds (50x40cm-20x16in) s. brown pat bronze lit. 21-Apr-4 Sotheby's, London #92/R est:8000-12000

DELACHAUX, Léon (1850-1918) Swiss
£2000 $3620 €3000 Jeune femme lisant (41x32cm-16x13in) s.d.87. 31-Mar-4 Sotheby's, Paris #95/R est:2000-3000
£5464 $10000 €7977 Broken doll (60x74cm-24x29in) s.d.1885. 3-Jun-4 Christie's, Rockefeller NY #658/R est:4000-6000

DELACHAUX, Marcelin (?-1902) French?
£1361 $2163 €2000 Presentation du perroquet (32x24cm-13x9in) s. panel. 23-Mar-3 St-Germain-en-Laye Encheres #32/R est:900-1000

DELACHAUX, Theodore (1879-1949) Swiss
£1591 $2641 €2307 Le bain (80x80cm-31x31in) i. verso. 13-Jun-3 Zofingen, Switzerland #2818/R est:4500 (S.FR 3500)

DELACOU, Yvonne (20th C) French?
Sculpture
£1268 $2218 €1800 Elisa (45cm-18in) green pat bronze cire perdue Cast F.Cappeli Paris. 21-Dec-3 Thierry & Lannon, Brest #38 est:2000-2500

DELACROIX, Andre (?-1934) French
£496 $829 €700 Maisons aux environs de Tunis (33x41cm-13x16in) s. cardboard. 16-Jun-3 Gros & Delettrez, Paris #94

DELACROIX, Auguste (1809-1868) French
£500 $915 €730 Study of a monastery, with figures beyond (24x32cm-9x13in) s.d.1836. 8-Apr-4 Christie's, Kensington #186/R
£1831 $3168 €2600 Ramasseuses de coquillages surprises par la maree (65x55cm-26x22in) s.i.d.1852. 10-Dec-3 Rossini, Paris #66/R
£3400 $6290 €4964 In the boudoir (60x48cm-24x19in) s.i.d.1853 indis.s.i.verso panel. 14-Jul-4 Sotheby's, Olympia #182/R est:1000-2000
Works on paper
£265 $485 €400 L'heure du the (33x23cm-13x9in) s. W/C gouache. 7-Apr-4 Doutrebente, Paris #33

DELACROIX, Eugène (1798-1863) French
£7083 $11829 €10200 Le Christ portant sa croix (28x41cm-11x16in) st.init. oil pen prov. 26-Oct-3 Feletin, Province #95
£10667 $19307 €16000 Palette (32x43cm-13x17in) wood. 30-Mar-4 Rossini, Paris #245/R est:3000-5000
£26490 $48212 €40000 Un Forgeron (32x24cm-13x9in) prov.exhib.lit. 15-Jun-4 Artcurial Briest, Paris #246/R est:40000-60000
£49669 $90894 €75000 Jeune Raphael meditant dans son atelier (35x27cm-14x11in) s. exhib.lit. 7-Apr-4 Piasa, Paris #25/R est:75000-85000
£98592 $170563 €140000 Etude de veste orientale (50x61cm-20x24in) prov.exhib.lit. 10-Dec-3 Beaussant & Lefèvre, Paris #64/R est:180000-220000
£129252 $231361 €190000 Clorinde a Cheval (65x49cm-26x19in) i.d.1859 prov.lit. 17-Mar-4 Tajan, Paris #105/R est:25000-30000
£281690 $487324 €400000 Hamlet and Horatio in the graveyard (31x24cm-12x9in) s. paper on canvas painted 1844 prov.exhib.lit. 10-Dec-3 Beaussant & Lefèvre, Paris #63/R est:450000-500000
Works on paper
£340 $609 €500 Etude d'un groupe de figures (21x34cm-8x13in) s. black crayon. 17-Mar-4 Maigret, Paris #98/R
£362 $666 €550 Etude d'ane, chien et angelots (24x19cm-9x7in) graphite. 28-Jun-4 Rossini, Paris #10
£437 $800 €638 Studies of the head of a horse (14x20cm-6x8in) artist st. pencil. 29-Jan-4 Swann Galleries, New York #253/R
£528 $914 €750 Etude pour le commerce, caisson du plafond du salon du roi (12x30cm-5x12in) bears mono. black crayon tracing paper. 12-Dec-3 Libert, Castor, Paris #20
£800 $1464 €1200 Etude (40x26cm-16x10in) graphite dr. 3-Jun-4 E & Eve, Paris #20/R
£933 $1689 €1400 Etudes pur le massacre de Scio (27x21cm-11x8in) st.mono. graphite. 30-Mar-4 Rossini, Paris #246/R
£984 $1800 €1437 Studies of figures from the Antique (17x27cm-7x11in) artist st. pen brown ink card stock. 29-Jan-4 Swann Galleries, New York #254/R est:2000-3000
£1088 $1948 €1600 Etude de personnage et reprise des jambes (14x18cm-6x7in) black crayon. 17-Mar-4 Tajan, Paris #122 est:400
£1119 $1902 €1600 Study of a Moroccan landscape (17x27cm-7x11in) i.verso pencil htd white lit. 28-Nov-3 Schloss Ahlden, Ahlden #1632/R est:1600
£1119 $1902 €1600 Study of a woman on a roof terrace (17x27cm-7x11in) i.verso pencil col crayon htd white lit. 28-Nov-3 Schloss Ahlden, Ahlden #1633/R est:1600
£1867 $3397 €2800 Chasse aux sangliers (20x34cm-8x13in) pen ink. 30-Jun-4 Delvaux, Paris #119/R est:4000
£1879 $3495 €2800 Etude d'un homme agenouille les mains jointes (23x12cm-9x5in) studio st. pen brown ink after Raphael. 2-Mar-4 Artcurial Briest, Paris #1/R est:2000-3000
£1905 $3029 €2800 Projet de decor (29x36cm-11x14in) mono. crayon dr. 21-Mar-3 Bailly Pommery, Paris #46
£3000 $5400 €4380 Battle of the amazons (18x34cm-7x13in) pen ink after Rubens prov. 21-Jan-4 Sotheby's, New York #141/R est:5000-7000
£4218 $7550 €6200 Feuille d'etudes pour un decor (18x24cm-7x9in) pen brown ink. 19-Mar-4 Piasa, Paris #121/R est:5000
£4218 $7550 €6200 Etude pour la Reception du comte de Mornay par le sultan du Maroc (16x23cm-6x9in) black pencil prov. 19-Mar-4 Piasa, Paris #122/R est:5000
£5000 $7850 €7800 Mahmoud II, empereur des turcs (26x22cm-10x9in) st.sig. pen red ink W/C. 15-Dec-2 St-Germain-en-Laye Encheres #43/R est:2500-3000
£7778 $14000 €11356 Study of a tiger (15x23cm-6x9in) s. pencil ink wash. 23-Apr-4 Sotheby's, New York #45/R est:8000-12000
£8000 $14560 €11680 Marocain assis (18x25cm-7x10in) init. sepia wash pencil exec. 1832 prov.lit. 15-Jun-4 Sotheby's, London #162/R est:8000-12000
£8000 $14560 €11680 L'academicien a l'etude (24x17cm-9x7in) init. pen ink sepia wash exec. late 1820's prov. 15-Jun-4 Sotheby's, London #163/R est:8000-12000
£8389 $15520 €12500 Tigre couche (12x19cm-5x7in) i.indis.d.18 oct 59 pen brown ink prov. 15-Mar-4 Blanchet, Paris #60/R est:15000-20000
£9934 $18079 €15000 Etude de lionne allongee sur le dos, deux reprises de la tete (19x27cm-7x11in) black crayon prov.exhib. 16-Jun-4 Piasa, Paris #171/R est:15000
£13087 $24211 €19500 Tigre assis (15x24cm-6x9in) s. pen brown ink. 15-Mar-4 Blanchet, Paris #59/R est:20000-25000
£14126 $24297 €20200 Etudes de chevaux, cavaliers et lions (25x41cm-10x16in) pen india ink exec. c.1824-1826 prov.exhib. 3-Dec-3 Blanchet, Paris #3/R est:12000-15000
£94444 $170000 €137888 Chevalier en armure (25x18cm-10x7in) s. graphite W/C gum arabic htd white prov. 21-Jan-4 Sotheby's, New York #118/R est:180000-220000

DELACROIX, Eugène (attrib) (1798-1863) French
£467 $859 €700 Study of a female nude (25x34cm-10x13in) 11-Jun-4 Wendl, Rudolstadt #3991/R
Works on paper
£464 $850 €677 Studies for Apollo overcoming the serpent python (31x20cm-12x8in) i.verso pen col ink. 29-Jan-4 Swann Galleries, New York #255/R

DELACROIX, Eugène (style) (1798-1863) French
£10959 $18630 €16000 Sanson and Dalila (118x139cm-46x55in) 4-Nov-3 Ansorena, Madrid #137/R est:16000

DELACROIX, Michel (?) ?
£699 $1202 €1000 Du cote de chez manet (22x30cm-9x12in) s. 3-Dec-3 Tajan, Paris #236/R

DELAHAUT, Jo (1911-1992) Belgian
£1342 $2483 €2000 Juxtaposition number 2 (41x60cm-16x24in) s.i.d.1971 verso panel. 13-Mar-4 De Vuyst, Lokeren #100/R est:2000-2400
£2416 $4470 €3600 Composition (53x71cm-21x28in) s.d.79 acrylic paper. 13-Mar-4 De Vuyst, Lokeren #102/R est:3500-4000
£2553 $4264 €3600 Composition (130x30cm-51x12in) panel. 20-Oct-3 Bernaerts, Antwerp #235 est:1250-1500
£2937 $4905 €4200 Composition (27x36cm-11x14in) s. 11-Oct-3 De Vuyst, Lokeren #107/R est:3000-4000
£3200 $5856 €4800 Composition (27x38cm-11x15in) s.d.62 panel. 7-Jun-4 Palais de Beaux Arts, Brussels #358/R est:1500-2000
£3490 $6456 €5200 Echappee number 4 (130x96cm-51x38in) s.d.82 s.i.d.82 verso. 13-Mar-4 De Vuyst, Lokeren #101/R est:3500-4500
£4333 $7930 €6500 Cinquante quatre VIII vert-rouge (55x73cm-22x29in) s.d.54. 7-Jun-4 Palais de Beaux Arts, Brussels #357/R est:3000-4000
£4397 $7343 €6200 Composition (73x54cm-29x21in) 20-Oct-3 Bernaerts, Antwerp #231/R est:1250-1500
Sculpture
£1958 $3270 €2800 Composition (44x62cm-17x24in) s.verso oil metal prov. 11-Oct-3 De Vuyst, Lokeren #108/R est:2000-2500
Works on paper
£461 $847 €700 Composition (21x17cm-8x7in) s.d.88 pastel. 22-Jun-4 Palais de Beaux Arts, Brussels #223
£604 $1069 €900 Composition (49x34cm-19x13in) s.d.1966 collage. 27-Apr-4 Campo, Vlaamse Kaai #390
£1600 $2864 €2400 Composition (38x30cm-15x12in) s.d.55 gouache. 15-May-4 De Vuyst, Lokeren #91/R est:1500-2000

DELAHOGUE, Alexis-Auguste (1867-1936) French
£780 $1303 €1100 Canal a Venise (23x31cm-9x12in) s.i.d.1904 panel. 20-Jun-3 Drouot Estimations, Paris #36
£1596 $2665 €2250 Scene de village du Sud, Afrique du Nord. Personnages (33x24cm-13x9in) s.d.1906 double-sided. 20-Jun-3 Drouot Estimations, Paris #37 est:1500-1800
£1958 $3368 €2800 Cortege de la Mariee (38x56cm-15x22in) s. 8-Dec-3 Tajan, Paris #260/R est:2500-3500

£4546 $7819 €6500 Kairouan (50x65cm-20x26in) s.i.d.1914. 8-Dec-3 Tajan, Paris #259/R est:5000-6000
£4583 $7654 €6600 Rue animee (55x39cm-22x15in) s. 25-Oct-3 Dianous, Marseille #397
£4795 $8151 €7000 Rue animee en Tunisie (50x65cm-20x26in) s. 10-Nov-3 Horta, Bruxelles #85/R

DELAHOGUE, Eugène Jules (1867-1934) French
£944 $1605 €1350 Nice, le quartier St Philippe (24x19cm-9x7in) d.1924 cardboard. 20-Nov-3 Gioffredo, Nice #255
£1277 $2132 €1800 Aux portes de la ville (19x24cm-7x9in) s. canvas on panel. 16-Jun-3 Gros & Delettrez, Paris #470 est:1200-2000
£2168 $3620 €3100 View of the Royal Palace in Tangier (38x55cm-15x22in) s.i. 30-Jun-3 Ansorena, Madrid #432/R

DELAIGUE, Victor Constantin (19/20th C) French
Sculpture
£3073 $5500 €4487 Dante inferno (76cm-30in) s. bronze ivory. 20-Mar-4 Selkirks, St. Louis #566/R est:6500-7500

DELAMAIN, Paul (1821-1882) French
£8451 $14620 €12000 Guerrier et cheval (65x54cm-26x21in) s. 15-Dec-3 Gros & Delettrez, Paris #90/R est:12000-18000

DELAMARRE, Raymond (1890-?) French
Sculpture
£3333 $6133 €5000 David a la fronde (73cm-29in) s. green pat bronze. 10-Jun-4 Camard, Paris #75/R est:7000-8000

DELAMOTTE, Jean François (attrib) (17th C) French
£9859 $17254 €14000 Trompe l'oeil aux gravures (86x98cm-34x39in) exhib. 17-Dec-3 Piasa, Paris #81/R est:15000

DELAMOTTE, William (1775-1863) British
£1000 $1860 €1460 Anglers in an extensive landscape (42x61cm-17x24in) d.19.Jan.1831. 4-Mar-4 Christie's, Kensington #421/R est:1200-1800
£8869 $15876 €12949 Dutch canal landscape (98x125cm-39x49in) s.d.1819 prov. 26-May-4 AB Stockholms Auktionsverk #2382/R est:30000-40000 (S.KR 120000)
Works on paper
£280 $515 €409 Castle Square, Brighton (20x46cm-8x18in) s.i.d.1855 pencil col chk. 25-Mar-4 Christie's, Kensington #38

DELANE, Solomon (1727-1784) British
£47000 $84130 €68620 Italianate landscape with figures in the foreground and buildings beyond (99x136cm-39x54in) init.d.1772 prov.exhib. 14-May-4 Christie's, London #72/R est:20000-30000

DELANEY, Arthur (1927-1987) British
£1800 $3150 €2628 Northern industrial townscape with mill buildings, chimneys and figures (36x15cm-14x6in) s. 16-Dec-3 Capes Dunn, Manchester #707a
£4000 $7280 €5840 Viaducts, Stockport (25x23cm-10x9in) s. exhib. 29-Jun-4 Capes Dunn, Manchester #710/R
£4839 $9000 €7065 Houses near Bolton (36x41cm-14x16in) s. s.i.verso masonite. 5-Mar-4 Skinner, Boston #513/R est:4000-6000
£5000 $8950 €7300 Trams in Albert Square, Manchester (23x16cm-9x6in) s. board. 17-Mar-4 Bonhams, Chester #271/R est:5000-7000
£6000 $11340 €8760 Albert Square (26x34cm-10x13in) s. board prov. 18-Feb-4 Peter Wilson, Nantwich #16
£6200 $10540 €9052 Piccadilly, Manchester (30x40cm-12x16in) s. board prov. 29-Oct-3 Bonhams, Chester #364 est:6000-8000
£7200 $12240 €10512 Deansgate, Manchester (34x25cm-13x10in) s. board. 29-Oct-3 Bonhams, Chester #365/R est:7000-10000

DELANEY, Beauford (1901-1979) American
£3908 $6762 €5550 Composition jaune (55x38cm-22x15in) s.i.d.1964. 9-Dec-3 Chambelland & Giafferi, Paris #40/R est:5000-6000
£5986 $10356 €8500 Composition vert d'eau (65x54cm-26x21in) s.i.d.1965. 9-Dec-3 Chambelland & Giafferi, Paris #39/R est:6000-8000

DELANEY, Edward (?) ?
Sculpture
£1538 $2615 €2200 Untitled (47cm-19in) bronze marble base. 25-Nov-3 De Veres Art Auctions, Dublin #100h/R est:1500-2000
£1944 $3169 €2800 Figure beside a tree (34cm-13in) bronze prov. 24-Sep-3 James Adam, Dublin #90/R est:1500-2000
£2533 $4585 €3800 Horse (28cm-11in) bronze marble base. 30-Mar-4 De Veres Art Auctions, Dublin #63/R est:3000-4000
£2632 $4842 €4000 The shepherd Jesus holding a lamb (54cm-21in) bronze unique. 22-Jun-4 De Veres Art Auctions, Dublin #51/R est:4000-5000

DELANEY, Joseph (1904-1981) American
£776 $1250 €1133 The American road (61x18cm-24x7in) pair masonite. 20-Aug-3 James Julia, Fairfield #1436/R
£1553 $2500 €2267 Factory town (61x38cm-24x15in) s. verso masonite. 20-Aug-3 James Julia, Fairfield #1435/R est:1750-2500

DELANGHE, Jean Jacques (1800-1865) Belgian
£464 $844 €700 Portrait d'une dame de qualite (83x70cm-33x28in) s.d.1835. 15-Jun-4 Vanderkindere, Brussels #8
£3239 $5669 €4600 Portrait de couple (125x113cm-49x44in) s. 16-Dec-3 Galerie Moderne, Brussels #642/R est:5000-7000

DELANGLE, Anatole Alfred Theodore (?-1901) French
£5556 $10000 €8112 La fenaison (51x73cm-20x29in) s.d.IXXI. 23-Apr-4 Sotheby's, New York #157/R est:8000-12000

DELANO, Gerard Curtis (1890-1972) American
£2941 $5000 €4294 Portrait of an Indian man (51x41cm-20x16in) board. 1-Nov-3 Altermann Galleries, Santa Fe #63
£2941 $5000 €4294 Portrait of an Indian woman (51x41cm-20x16in) canvasboard. 1-Nov-3 Altermann Galleries, Santa Fe #63a
£4706 $8000 €6871 The hunt (36x66cm-14x26in) s. board prov.lit. 1-Nov-3 Santa Fe Art, Santa Fe #222/R est:20000-30000
£4813 $9000 €7027 Whiteface country (33x48cm-13x19in) s. board prov. 24-Jul-4 Coeur d'Alene, Hayden #197/R est:3000-5000
£5294 $9000 €7729 Land of enchantment (41x51cm-16x20in) canvasboard. 1-Nov-3 Altermann Galleries, Santa Fe #64
£93332 $158665 €136265 Pueblo ceremonial dance, no 107 (76x91cm-30x36in) s. i.verso prov.lit. 1-Nov-3 Santa Fe Art, Santa Fe #209/R est:100000-150000
Works on paper
£5882 $10000 €8588 Tending the flock (48x33cm-19x13in) s. W/C prov.lit. 1-Nov-3 Santa Fe Art, Santa Fe #211/R est:20000-25000
£7647 $13000 €11165 Woman on horse with dog and child (33x43cm-13x17in) W/C. 1-Nov-3 Altermann Galleries, Santa Fe #61

DELANOY, Jacques (1820-1890) French
£1131 $1889 €1651 Apples, plums and pears in landscape. peaches, grapes and berries with autumn leaves (27x45cm-11x18in) one s.d.1878 one s. pair. 17-Nov-3 Waddingtons, Toronto #195/R (C.D 2500)

DELANY, Mary (attrib) (?-1788) British
Works on paper
£5988 $10000 €8742 Flowers (25x16cm-10x6in) collage pair lit. 20-Oct-3 Sotheby's, New York #455/R est:5000-7000

DELAP, Tony (1927-) American
Sculpture
£1000 $1630 €1460 Klabberjess (188x188x10cm-74x74x4in) wood canvas acrylic prov. 23-Sep-3 John Nicholson, Haslemere #165/R est:500-1000

DELAPLANCHE, Eugène (1836-1891) French
Sculpture
£2201 $3566 €3191 Woman playing violin (67cm-26in) s. pat.bronze Cast.F Barbedienne. 4-Aug-3 Rasmussen, Vejle #1079/R est:25000 (D.KR 23000)
£5200 $8996 €7592 Bust of a girl (52cm-20in) s.d.1878 white marble. 12-Dec-3 Sotheby's, London #253/R est:3000-4000

DELAPUENTE, Fernando (1909-1975) Spanish
£833 $1417 €1200 Still life with bottle (41x31cm-16x12in) s.d.1957 board. 28-Oct-3 Segre, Madrid #183/R
£986 $1725 €1400 Notre-Dame, Paris. s.d.1952 cardboard on board. 16-Dec-3 Segre, Madrid #257/R

DELARGE, Jim (1965-) French
Works on paper
£1867 $3435 €2800 We used to drink and fight used to like ooh (100x100cm-39x39in) s.i.d.2003 verso mixed media panel. 9-Jun-4 Artcurial Briest, Paris #345 est:1500-1800
£2000 $3680 €3000 Procter and Gamble (100x100cm-39x39in) s.i.d.2003 verso mixed media panel. 9-Jun-4 Artcurial Briest, Paris #346/R est:1500-1800

DELARGERE, E (19th C) Italian
£4336 $7457 €6200 Business trip to Milan (59x79cm-23x31in) 3-Dec-3 Stadion, Trieste #1022/R est:2500-3500

DELARIVA, Nicolas Louis Albert (1755-1818) French
£1447 $2663 €2200 Docteur ambulant (27x20cm-11x8in) s. panel. 24-Jun-4 Christie's, Paris #132/R

DELAROCHE, Paul (1797-1856) French
Works on paper
£336 $571 €480 Etudes (26x20cm-10x8in) crayon prov. 21-Nov-3 Coutau Begarie, Paris #121/R

DELAROCHE, Paul (attrib) (1797-1856) French
Works on paper
£440 $800 €642 Portrait of Napoleon Bonaparte (27x22cm-11x9in) graphite. 29-Jun-4 Sotheby's, New York #86/R

DELAROQUE, Guy (?) French?
£385 $654 €550 Sagesse 18 (110x75cm-43x30in) s. oil paper on canvas. 29-Nov-3 Neret-Minet, Paris #171/R

DELATOUSCHE, Germain (1898-?) French
£1043 $1700 €1523 Rue de la Glaciere, Paris (64x81cm-25x32in) s.d.1938 i.verso prov.exhib. 24-Sep-3 Doyle, New York #22 est:2000-3000
£1223 $2250 €1786 Rue de la Glaciere, Paris (64x81cm-25x32in) s.d.1938 i.verso prov.exhib. 9-Jun-4 Doyle, New York #3021 est:2000-3000

DELATTRE, Henri (1801-1876) French

£563 $986 €800 Vache dans un paysage (24x32cm-9x13in) s.d.1860 board. 16-Dec-3 Adjug'art, Brest #395/R

DELATTRE, Joseph (1858-1912) French

£5734 $9576 €8200 Rouen, brume (32x55cm-13x22in) s. prov. 7-Oct-3 Livinec, Gaudcheau & Jezequel, Rennes #98/R
£7203 $12029 €10300 Rouen (38x46cm-15x18in) s. prov. 7-Oct-3 Livinec, Gaudcheau & Jezequel, Rennes #99/R

DELAUNAY, Jules (?-1906) French

£262 $483 €393 The cavalrist (35x27cm-14x11in) s. panel. 14-Jun-4 Lilla Bukowskis, Stockholm #629 (S.KR 3600)

DELAUNAY, Marcel (1876-1959) French

£733 $1349 €1100 Pichet de fleur (35x26cm-14x10in) s. panel prov. 11-Jun-4 Pierre Berge, Paris #255

DELAUNAY, Robert (1885-1941) French

£9000 $16290 €13140 Paysage, le rocher devant la mer (46x65cm-18x26in) painted c.1904 prov.lit. 1-Apr-4 Christie's, Kensington #35/R est:5000-7000
£16000 $29120 €23360 Fleurs (54x35cm-21x14in) s. 4-Feb-4 Sotheby's, London #241/R est:12000-15000
£100000 $182000 €146000 Vue du Quai de Louvre (65x54cm-26x21in) s.d.1928 prov.exhib. 3-Feb-4 Christie's, London #161/R est:100000-150000
Prints
£3356 $5940 €5000 Saint-Severin (52x72cm-20x28in) col lithograph. 29-Apr-4 Piasa, Paris #170/R est:5000-6000
Works on paper
£11409 $20423 €17000 Paris, Tour Eiffel (23x46cm-9x18in) gouache lit. 30-May-4 Eric Pillon, Calais #231/R

DELAUNAY, Sonia (1885-1979) French/Russian

£80000 $147200 €116800 Rythme colore (89x116cm-35x46in) painted 1954-1957 prov.exhib. 23-Jun-4 Christie's, London #243/R est:80000-120000
Sculpture
£2098 $3566 €3000 Lighter (10cm-4in) hand painted metal. 30-Nov-3 Anaf, Lyon #261/R est:3000-4000
Works on paper
£333 $600 €500 Projet de tissu (7x5cm-3x2in) mono. gouache. 24-Apr-4 Cornette de St.Cyr, Paris #352
£367 $660 €550 Projet de tissu (31x24cm-12x9in) mono. gouache. 24-Apr-4 Cornette de St.Cyr, Paris #354
£690 $1276 €1000 Projet de tissu, Lyon no 14 (18x19cm-7x7in) gouache. 13-Feb-4 Charbonneaux, Paris #39/R
£933 $1671 €1400 Projet de tissus (27x21cm-11x8in) gouache prov. 15-May-4 De Vuyst, Lokeren #92
£1300 $2353 €1898 Etude de robe (30x22cm-12x9in) init.d.1922 pencil brush black ink W/C prov. 1-Apr-4 Christie's, Kensington #48/R est:1200-1800
£1520 $2873 €2250 Projet de tissu (24x10cm-9x4in) gouache. 21-Feb-4 Cornette de St.Cyr, Paris #196/R est:2200-2500
£1538 $2646 €2200 Composition geometrique, projet de tissu (42x35cm-17x14in) gouache prov.exhib. 4-Dec-3 Piasa, Paris #102/R est:2000-3000
£2083 $3479 €3000 Maquette pour la couverture de Album Sonia Delaunay (33x25cm-13x10in) i. gouache lead pencil prov. 21-Oct-3 Artcurial Briest, Paris #101/R est:2500-3500
£2667 $4907 €4000 Rythme couleur (55x35cm-22x14in) s. gouache prov. 14-Jun-4 Porro, Milan #14/R est:4200-6000
£3357 $5706 €4800 Rythmes contrastes (25x20cm-10x8in) init.d.1923-51 pen col gouache prov.lit. 23-Nov-3 Cornette de St.Cyr, Paris #88/R est:600-800
£3521 $5845 €5000 Rythme et coulour (25x16cm-10x6in) s. Indian ink gouache exec 1956. 14-Jun-3 Meeting Art, Vercelli #579/R est:5000
£3893 $6968 €5800 Rythme couleur (39x29cm-15x11in) s.i. gouache exec.1962. 26-May-4 Christie's, Paris #54/R est:4000-6000
£4000 $7360 €6000 Projet de costume pour Jacqueline Chaumont (42x28cm-17x11in) s. num.678 W/C exec. 1923 exhib.lit. 8-Jun-4 Artcurial Briest, Paris #185/R est:6000-7000
£4072 $6801 €5945 Chocolat (26x20cm-10x8in) s.i.d.1914 pastel silk paper prov. 24-Jun-3 Germann, Zurich #44/R est:13000-18000 (S.FR 9000)
£4333 $7973 €6500 Projet de costume pour Rene Crevel (39x27cm-15x11in) s. i.verso num.676 W/C crayon exec.1923 exhib.lit. 8-Jun-4 Artcurial Briest, Paris #186/R est:6000-7000
£7000 $11130 €10150 Rythme couleur (56x40cm-22x16in) s.d.76 pencil gouache prov. 11-Sep-3 Christie's, Kensington #212/R est:4000-6000
£7895 $14526 €11527 Composition F 1917 (50x28cm-20x11in) s.d.1972 pencil gouache. 23-Jun-4 Koller, Zurich #3103/R est:5000-8000 (S.FR 18000)
£8500 $14705 €12410 Projet de couverture pour l'album (23x23cm-9x9in) wax crayon gouache prov.exhib. 11-Dec-3 Christie's, Kensington #90/R est:6000-8000
£9091 $15636 €13000 Montreux aux Rochers de Naye (27x20cm-11x8in) s.i. col crayon. 2-Dec-3 Calmels Cohen, Paris #4/R est:8000-10000
£10564 $18275 €15000 Danseuse (55x38cm-22x15in) s.i. gouache crayon prov. 9-Dec-3 Artcurial Briest, Paris #248/R est:15000-20000
£18000 $32760 €26280 Rythme couleur (43x56cm-17x22in) s.d.1967 gouache chl prov. 5-Feb-4 Christie's, London #439/R est:20000-30000
£19231 $33077 €27500 Composition, rythme colore (56x76cm-22x30in) s.d.57 gouache collage. 4-Dec-3 Piasa, Paris #95/R est:20000-30000
£20667 $37613 €31000 Zenith - Study (29x45cm-11x18in) mono.i.d.14 wax painting exhib. 30-Jun-4 Calmels Cohen, Paris #5/R est:30000-35000
£26000 $47840 €37960 Composition simultanee (27x22cm-11x9in) s.d.1942 gouache prov. 24-Jun-4 Christie's, London #452/R est:10000-15000

DELAVAL, Pierre Louis (1790-?) French

£3239 $5669 €4600 Portrait du Comte Louis Nicolas Lemercier (65x54cm-26x21in) s.d.1823 exhib. 17-Dec-3 Piasa, Paris #111/R est:3000-4000

DELAVAL, Pierre Louis (attrib) (1790-?) French

£1479 $2588 €2100 Portrait de la Comtesse Marie-Anne Lemercier (64x51cm-25x20in) 17-Dec-3 Piasa, Paris #112 est:1200-1500

DELAVALLEE, Henri (1862-1943) French

£2649 $4954 €4000 Paysage anime a la chaumiere (49x64cm-19x25in) s. board. 24-Jul-4 Thierry & Lannon, Brest #145/R est:4000-4500
£3169 $5546 €4500 Chaumiere en Bretagne par temps d'orage (55x73cm-22x29in) s. 21-Dec-3 Thierry & Lannon, Brest #151/R est:4600-5600
Works on paper
£986 $1725 €1400 Paysage anime de Turquie (37x54cm-15x21in) s. pastel. 21-Dec-3 Thierry & Lannon, Brest #84
£4930 $8627 €7000 Les chenes tetards sur les bords de l'Aven (42x58cm-17x23in) s. pastel. 21-Dec-3 Thierry & Lannon, Brest #85/R est:6000-8000

DELAVALLEE, Paul Savigny (?) French

£333 $613 €500 Ramasseurs de goemon (53x64cm-21x25in) s. panel. 8-Jun-4 Livinec, Gaudcheau & Jezequel, Rennes #112

DELAVIGNE (?) French

Sculpture
£1118 $1900 €1632 Cupid (71cm-28in) s. white marble. 22-Nov-3 Jackson's, Cedar Falls #195/R est:2500-3500

DELAWARR, Val (19th C) Australian

£483 $753 €700 Mountain stream (43x58cm-17x23in) s.d.94 board. 1-Aug-2 Joel, Victoria #347 est:1500-2500 (A.D 1400)
£600 $1062 €876 Mouth of the Hawkesbury river from along island (23x36cm-9x14in) s.i.verso board. 27-Apr-4 Bonhams, New Bond Street #10/R

DELAY, Alexandre (1941-) Swiss

Works on paper
£333 $606 €500 Etude de nu, femme couchee sur le cote (120x80cm-47x31in) s.i. mixed media board exec 1986 prov. 30-Jun-4 Calmels Cohen, Paris #89/R

DELBECKE, Louis Auguste Corneille (attrib) (1821-1891) Belgian

£897 $1614 €1300 L'eveque Jean Baptiste Vandermersch (140x100cm-55x39in) s.d.1870. 20-Jan-4 Galerie Moderne, Brussels #153

DELBOS, Julius (1879-1967) American

£262 $475 €383 Anchored boats (51x60cm-20x24in) s. masonite. 18-Apr-4 Bonhams & Butterfields, Los Angeles #7089
£385 $700 €562 Sailboats at dock (10x12cm-4x5in) s. 7-Feb-4 Sloans & Kenyon, Bethesda #895/R

DELCAMBRE (20th C) French

Sculpture
£1389 $2319 €2000 Alpha (164x40x38cm-65x16x15in) s.num.1/8 green pat bronze prov. 25-Oct-3 Cornette de St.Cyr, Paris #398/R est:4000-6000

DELCOUR, Jean (attrib) (c.1627-1707) Flemish

Sculpture
£2041 $3653 €3000 St Joseph with Infant St Joseph (43cm-17in) terracotta. 17-Mar-4 Neumeister, Munich #179/R est:2000

DELCOUR, Pierre (19th C) French

£300 $540 €450 La pluie a Londres (35x55cm-14x22in) s.verso canvas laid down. 20-Apr-4 Galerie Moderne, Brussels #382

DELCROIX, Giacomo (attrib) (1894-1972) Italian

£352 $609 €500 View of Tuscan villa (30x40cm-12x16in) card on canvas. 9-Dec-3 Pandolfini, Florence #364/R

DELDEN, Jan Wessel van (attrib) (1820-1848) Dutch

£1148 $2100 €1676 Fishing boats in harbour (25x46cm-10x18in) s. 10-Apr-4 Brunk, Ashville #655/R est:500-1000

DELDERENE, Léon (1864-1921) Belgian

£433 $793 €650 Running river in autumn with island and farm (75x90cm-30x35in) s.d.1903. 5-Jun-4 Arnold, Frankfurt #559
£467 $859 €700 Mere et enfant au centre du village (50x35cm-20x14in) s.d.1908. 14-Jun-4 Horta, Bruxelles #213
£537 $961 €800 Route de campagne borde de fermes (70x100cm-28x39in) s. 25-May-4 Campo & Campo, Antwerp #60
£671 $1201 €1000 Chemin rural vers l'eglise (50x66cm-20x26in) s. 25-May-4 Campo & Campo, Antwerp #62
£1224 $2192 €1800 Vue portuaire (40x59cm-16x23in) panel. 22-Mar-4 Amberes, Antwerp #196
£1389 $2361 €2000 The little village (90x60cm-35x24in) s.d.1900. 28-Oct-3 Christie's, Amsterdam #58/R est:2000-3000
£1477 $2643 €2200 Vaches au bord d'un ruisseau (130x106cm-51x42in) s. 25-May-4 Campo & Campo, Antwerp #61/R est:1500-2000
£2517 $4605 €3800 Woodland with stream (99x130cm-39x51in) s.d.1900. 8-Apr-4 Dorotheum, Vienna #265/R est:3800-4200

DELEN, Dirk van (1605-1671) Dutch

£6500 $11700 €9490 Architectural capriccio with elegant company (70x94cm-28x37in) s. panel. 23-Apr-4 Christie's, Kensington #82/R est:5000-7000
£8276 $13738 €12000 Interior scene in a church (49x65cm-19x26in) board. 30-Sep-3 Ansorena, Madrid #60/R est:10000
£9220 $14936 €13000 Interior scene of a church (49x65cm-19x26in) 20-May-3 Ansorena, Madrid #146/R est:13000
£86111 $155000 €125722 Solomon receiving the Queen of Sheba (114x169cm-45x67in) s.d.1642 panel prov.lit. 22-Jan-4 Sotheby's, New York #108/R est:100000-150000

DELESCLUZE, Edmond (1905-1993) Belgian
£319 $533 €450 Bord de mer anime a Rabat (44x55cm-17x22in) s. canvas on panel. 14-Oct-3 Vanderkindere, Brussels #41
£355 $592 €500 Ruelle de Rabat animee (45x55cm-18x22in) s. canvas on panel. 14-Oct-3 Vanderkindere, Brussels #43
£420 $713 €600 Ruelle de la Medina de Sale, Maroc, animee (45x54cm-18x21in) s. canvas on panel painted c.1937-38. 18-Nov-3 Vanderkindere, Brussels #91
£455 $773 €650 Ruelle de la Medina de Rabat anime (44x55cm-17x22in) s. canvas on panel painted c.1937-38. 18-Nov-3 Vanderkindere, Brussels #90
£486 $773 €700 Vue animee de Rabat (45x55cm-18x22in) s. canvas on panel. 9-Sep-3 Vanderkindere, Brussels #125
£493 $853 €700 Spectateurs a la foire (55x65cm-22x26in) s. 9-Dec-3 Vanderkindere, Brussels #108
£729 $1159 €1050 Medina de marrakech animee (44x54cm-17x21in) s. canvas on panel. 9-Sep-3 Vanderkindere, Brussels #123
£748 $1339 €1100 La grace (160x125cm-63x49in) s. 16-Mar-4 Vanderkindere, Brussels #74
£2000 $3340 €2920 Reclining female nude (100x90cm-39x35in) s.d.1938. 12-Nov-3 Sotheby's, Olympia #237/R est:1000-1500
Works on paper
£278 $442 €400 Nu (64x48cm-25x19in) s.d.1938 pastel gouache. 9-Sep-3 Vanderkindere, Brussels #107
£347 $552 €500 Moissons (35x47cm-14x19in) s.d.1932 W/C. 9-Sep-3 Vanderkindere, Brussels #119
£629 $1145 €950 La resurrection de Lazare (64x79cm-25x31in) s. W/C. 15-Jun-4 Vanderkindere, Brussels #27

DELESSARD, Auguste Joseph (1827-1890) French
£1000 $1840 €1500 Paysage au crepuscule (29x48cm-11x19in) s. 9-Jun-4 Oger, Dumont, Paris #49 est:1500-2000

DELESTRE, Eugène (1862-1919) French
£890 $1450 €1299 Haystacks. painted 1902. 28-Sep-3 Carlsen Gallery, Greenville #569/R

DELETANG, Robert Adrien (1874-1951) French
£533 $981 €800 Pays basque, la fete du village (38x53cm-15x21in) s.d.1941. 9-Jun-4 Beaussant & Lefèvre, Paris #135
Works on paper
£367 $675 €550 Scene de l'exode (55x69cm-22x27in) s.d.1940 gouache. 9-Jun-4 Beaussant & Lefèvre, Paris #133
£433 $797 €650 Le sardiniere de Pontarabie, Hendaye (63x48cm-25x19in) s.i.d.1941 chl stump htd white. 9-Jun-4 Beaussant & Lefèvre, Paris #131
£733 $1349 €1100 Hermanie. Sur la place du village (26x31cm-10x12in) s.d.38 one i. chl htd col two. 9-Jun-4 Beaussant & Lefèvre, Paris #134/R est:400-500

DELFF, Cornelis Jacobsz (1571-1643) Dutch
£5369 $9611 €8000 Couple dans un interieur de cuisine avec poissons, viande, legumes et fruits (102x146cm-40x57in) 25-May-4 Palais de Beaux Arts, Brussels #533/R est:6600-9000

DELFF, Jacob Willemsz (younger) (1619-1661) Dutch
£5500 $9515 €8030 Portrait of a gentleman, indentified as the artist (57x48cm-22x19in) s. panel. 10-Dec-3 Bonhams, New Bond Street #5/R est:5000-7000

DELFGAAUW, Gerard Johannes (1882-1947) Dutch
£461 $847 €700 Feeding the goat (30x24cm-12x9in) s. 22-Jun-4 Christie's, Amsterdam #314/R
£625 $1150 €950 A cargo ship in the harbour, Rotterdam (30x40cm-12x16in) s. 22-Jun-4 Christie's, Amsterdam #198/R
£658 $1211 €1000 Watering cows by a windmill (50x70cm-20x28in) s. 22-Jun-4 Christie's, Amsterdam #298/R
£909 $1564 €1300 Dromedary (30x40cm-12x16in) s. 8-Dec-3 Glerum, Amsterdam #68/R
£1000 $1830 €1460 Dutch town on a river bridge (39x79cm-15x31in) s. 6-Jul-4 Bonhams, Knightsbridge #185/R est:1200-1800
£1064 $1777 €1500 Small village on the water (29x39cm-11x15in) s. 20-Oct-3 Glerum, Amsterdam #132/R est:1500-2000
£1135 $1895 €1600 Cairo street (60x50cm-24x20in) s. 20-Oct-3 Glerum, Amsterdam #175/R est:2000-2500
£1379 $2303 €2000 Harbour view (58x99cm-23x39in) s. 11-Nov-3 Vendu Notarishuis, Rotterdam #108/R est:1500-2000
£1560 $2606 €2200 View of Rotterdam harbour (40x80cm-16x31in) s. 20-Oct-3 Glerum, Amsterdam #107/R est:2000-2500
£2953 $5463 €4400 Ships in Rotterdam harbour (60x100cm-24x39in) s. 13-Mar-4 De Vuyst, Lokeren #106/R est:4500-5500
£3618 $6549 €5500 View of Nicholas Church seen from side of the Central Station, Amsterdam (79x98cm-31x39in) s. 19-Apr-4 Glerum, Amsterdam #157/R est:3000-4000
£7986 $13337 €11500 View of Alkmaar (60x80cm-24x31in) s. prov. 21-Oct-3 Sotheby's, Amsterdam #144/R est:4000-6000

DELFOSSE, Auguste (19th C) Belgian
£1538 $2615 €2200 Les joueurs de des dans un interieur de cafe (80x102cm-31x40in) s. 1-Dec-3 Palais de Beaux Arts, Brussels #49/R est:4000-5000

DELGADO RAMOS, Alvaro (1922-) Spanish
£370 $600 €537 Still life (40x50cm-16x20in) s. 29-Jul-3 Galeria y Remates, Montevideo #9/R
£1678 $3003 €2500 Nude (35x27cm-14x11in) s. board lit. 25-May-4 Durán, Madrid #116/R est:2000
£1702 $2757 €2400 Ramera (35x27cm-14x11in) s. masonite. 20-May-3 Ansorena, Madrid #333/R est:2250
£1773 $2961 €2500 Landscape in Navia (38x46cm-15x18in) s. board. 20-Oct-3 Durán, Madrid #82/R
£2069 $3455 €3000 Holy face (46x38cm-18x15in) s. board lit. 17-Nov-3 Durán, Madrid #118/R est:2850
£3356 $6275 €5000 Still life with fish (80x100cm-31x39in) s. exhib. 24-Feb-4 Durán, Madrid #232/R est:3500
£4577 $7324 €6500 Peasant (70x50cm-28x20in) s.d.1970 board el. 16-Sep-3 Segre, Madrid #122/R
£4698 $8738 €7000 View of village (51x53cm-20x21in) s. 2-Mar-4 Ansorena, Madrid #85/R est:6000
Works on paper
£533 $971 €800 Retrato de Caballero (48x38cm-19x15in) s. chl brown wash. 29-Jun-4 Segre, Madrid #287/R
£604 $1130 €900 Peasant man (65x43cm-26x17in) s. col dr. 24-Feb-4 Durán, Madrid #60/R
£704 $1127 €1000 Hare (44x62cm-17x24in) s. col wax crayon. 16-Sep-3 Segre, Madrid #122a/R
£1293 $2352 €1900 Peasants (70x50cm-28x20in) s. wash wax crayon exhib.lit. 3-Feb-4 Segre, Madrid #134/R est:1100

DELGADO, Gerardo (1942-) Spanish
£733 $1327 €1100 Still life (60x78cm-24x31in) s.d.1983 paper prov. 30-Mar-4 Segre, Madrid #189/R

DELGADO, Guillermo (1930-) Spanish
£1549 $2680 €2200 Landscape (120x90cm-47x35in) 15-Dec-3 Ansorena, Madrid #1031/R est:1700

DELILLE, François (1817-?) French
£250 $468 €375 Coastal scene (38x61cm-15x24in) s. 21-Jul-4 John Nicholson, Haslemere #174

DELIOTTI, Walter (1925-) Uruguayan
£222 $420 €324 Factory (20x25cm-8x10in) s. cardboard. 22-Feb-4 Galeria y Remates, Montevideo #150
£265 $500 €387 Harbour (24x33cm-9x13in) s. cardboard. 22-Feb-4 Galeria y Remates, Montevideo #148
£276 $461 €400 Untitled (20x25cm-8x10in) s. cardboard. 11-Nov-3 Castellana, Madrid #7/R
£276 $461 €400 Untitled (20x25cm-8x10in) s. cardboard. 11-Nov-3 Castellana, Madrid #53/R
£276 $461 €400 Untitled (20x25cm-8x10in) s. cardboard. 11-Nov-3 Castellana, Madrid #201/R
£326 $600 €476 Harbour and buildings (20x25cm-8x10in) s. cardboard. 22-Jun-4 Galeria y Remates, Montevideo #133
£341 $600 €498 Omnibus (20x25cm-8x10in) s. cardboard. 5-Jan-4 Galeria y Remates, Montevideo #10
£369 $650 €539 Harbour (24x33cm-9x13in) s. cardboard. 5-Jan-4 Galeria y Remates, Montevideo #9
£398 $700 €581 Harbour with figure (24x33cm-9x13in) s. canvas on cardboard. 5-Jan-4 Galeria y Remates, Montevideo #8
£414 $691 €600 Untitled (24x33cm-9x13in) s. 11-Nov-3 Castellana, Madrid #3/R
£426 $750 €622 Boat (20x25cm-8x10in) s. cardboard. 5-Jan-4 Galeria y Remates, Montevideo #11
£516 $950 €753 Boat (33x25cm-13x10in) s.d.92 oil collage. 22-Jun-4 Galeria y Remates, Montevideo #131/R
£525 $850 €761 The 'Virazon' (32x43cm-13x17in) s. board. 29-Jul-3 Galeria y Remates, Montevideo #122/R
£707 $1300 €1032 Harbour with figure (33x41cm-13x16in) s. cardboard. 22-Jun-4 Galeria y Remates, Montevideo #130/R
£909 $1600 €1327 Harbour with clock (46x38cm-18x15in) s. 5-Jan-4 Galeria y Remates, Montevideo #61/R est:1500-2000
£1005 $1900 €1467 Landscape in Buenos Aires (50x60cm-20x24in) s.d68. 22-Feb-4 Galeria y Remates, Montevideo #100/R est:3000
£1051 $1850 €1534 Harbour with sailing boat (50x65cm-20x26in) s. 5-Jan-4 Galeria y Remates, Montevideo #60/R est:2000-3000
£1059 $1800 €1546 Harbour (47x57cm-19x22in) s.d.80. 25-Nov-3 Galeria y Remates, Montevideo #71/R
£1304 $2400 €1904 Today he plays (50x61cm-20x24in) s.d.92. 22-Jun-4 Galeria y Remates, Montevideo #128/R est:2500-3000

DELITZ, Leo (attrib) (1882-1966) Yugoslavian
£385 $654 €550 Village square (35x46cm-14x18in) s. canvas on panel. 19-Nov-3 Dorotheum, Klagenfurt #9/R

DELL, Etheline (fl.1885-1923) British
£550 $935 €803 Suffolk cottage (25x33cm-10x13in) s. panel. 19-Nov-3 Tennants, Leyburn #1232
Works on paper
£400 $680 €584 Figures on a footbridge before a county cottage (23x33cm-9x13in) W/C. 18-Nov-3 Bonhams, Leeds #53
£400 $728 €584 At the cottage gate (20x24cm-8x9in) s. pencil W/C htd white. 1-Jul-4 Christie's, Kensington #477/R

DELL, John H (1836-1888) British
£659 $1200 €962 Knife Grinder (23x20cm-9x8in) mono.d.60 board. 7-Feb-4 Neal Auction Company, New Orleans #458
£1000 $1860 €1460 Countryman's cottage (35x27cm-14x11in) mono.d.68. 2-Mar-4 Bearnes, Exeter #445/R
£1700 $3128 €2482 Feeding rabbits (20x25cm-8x10in) mono. panel. 23-Mar-4 Bonhams, New Bond Street #117/R est:1000-1500
£3000 $5010 €4380 Milking time (32x48cm-13x19in) mono.d.63 panel. 13-Nov-3 Christie's, Kensington #291/R est:3000-5000

DELL'ACQUA, Cesare Felix Georges (1821-1904) Italian
£367 $656 €550 Jeune femme en priere (57x45cm-22x18in) s. canvas on panel. 11-May-4 Vanderkindere, Brussels #144
£979 $1635 €1400 Les honneurs au peintre (60x38cm-24x15in) s. 13-Oct-3 Horta, Bruxelles #227
Works on paper
£1119 $1902 €1600 La bucentaure. s. W/C. 18-Nov-3 Galerie Moderne, Brussels #810/R est:1000-1500
£1200 $1920 €1752 Disorderly class (45x60cm-18x24in) s.d.1867 W/C over pencil. 16-Sep-3 Bonhams, Knowle #50/R est:800-1200

DELLAR, Roger (20th C) British
Works on paper
£360 $634 €526 The Watercress Line 1. Through the market (23x32cm-9x13in) s. one W/C one pastel two. 18-May-4 Woolley & Wallis, Salisbury #288/R

DELLEANI, Lorenzo (1840-1908) Italian
£1965 $3576 €2869 Lago de Mucrone (23x33cm-9x13in) mono.d.10/11/97 s.i.verso panel. 16-Jun-4 Fischer, Luzern #1098/R est:8000-10000 (S.FR 4500)
£2759 $4579 €4000 Pasture (31x45cm-12x18in) board. 1-Oct-3 Della Rocca, Turin #305/R
£4681 $7817 €6600 Saint Michel's celebration (15x23cm-6x9in) d.80 board lit. 20-Oct-3 Sant Agostino, Torino #287/R est:5500-6500
£5369 $9611 €8000 Storm on the Mucrone (31x45cm-12x18in) d.82 board. 25-May-4 Finarte Semenzato, Milan #203/R est:8000-10000
£5442 $9741 €8000 Sunset on the ice (31x45cm-12x18in) board. 22-Mar-4 Sant Agostino, Torino #261/R est:10000
£6333 $11463 €9500 Dusk on the Lys (152x126cm-60x50in) s.d.1908 i.on stretcher. 30-Mar-4 Babuino, Rome #375/R est:7000
£7639 $12986 €11000 Landscape (32x45cm-13x18in) d.1907 board. 1-Nov-3 Meeting Art, Vercelli #238/R est:10000
£8054 $14416 €12000 Landscape (37x26cm-15x10in) d.1901 board. 25-May-4 Finarte Semenzato, Milan #155/R est:8000-10000
£8667 $15947 €13000 Stream in the field (45x31cm-18x12in) s.d.99 board prov.exhib. 14-Jun-4 Sant Agostino, Torino #301/R est:13000-16000
£8725 $15443 €13000 Washerwomen at stream (31x44cm-12x17in) d.08 verso board. 1-May-4 Meeting Art, Vercelli #118 est:12000
£9028 $15347 €13000 Dusk (44x31cm-17x12in) s.i.d.1897 board. 1-Nov-3 Meeting Art, Vercelli #449/R est:12000
£9396 $16819 €14000 Storm on the Mucrone (45x31cm-18x12in) d.89 board lit. 25-May-4 Finarte Semenzato, Milan #206/R est:12000-13000
£10667 $19627 €16000 Landscape with figures (31x45cm-12x18in) d.1888 board prov.exhib.lit. 14-Jun-4 Sant Agostino, Torino #302/R est:16000-20000
£10667 $19627 €16000 Alpine landscape (31x44cm-12x17in) d.86 board exhib.lit. 10-Jun-4 Christie's, Rome #97/R est:6000-9000
£11409 $20423 €17000 Studio of the Festa die Santa Barnaba (45x31cm-18x12in) panel. 27-May-4 Dorotheum, Vienna #148/R est:7000-8000
£11888 $19853 €17000 Mountainous landscape (39x26cm-15x10in) s.d.97 board. 24-Jun-3 Finarte Semenzato, Rome #159/R est:12000
£12752 $22570 €19000 Along the Tiber (44x30cm-17x12in) s.d.1898 board lit. 1-May-4 Meeting Art, Vercelli #257 est:15000
£12752 $22826 €19000 Ave Maria (60x40cm-24x16in) s. i.verso. 25-May-4 Finarte Semenzato, Milan #179/R est:20000-22000
£21277 $35532 €30000 Ponte dei Sospiri, Venice (137x104cm-54x41in) painted 1887. 20-Oct-3 Sant Agostino, Torino #289/R est:30000-40000

DELLEANI, Lorenzo (attrib) (1840-1908) Italian
£650 $1164 €949 Landscape with clouds (25x37cm-10x15in) d.14.7.86 i.verso panel. 11-May-4 Bonhams, Knightsbridge #216/R

DELLEANI, Nina (1868-?) Italian
£278 $472 €400 Trees (30x44cm-12x17in) s.d.1935 board. 1-Nov-3 Meeting Art, Vercelli #8

DELLEPIANE, David (1866-c.1932) French/Italian
£993 $1818 €1500 Bord de mer (9x18cm-4x7in) s. panel. 9-Apr-4 Claude Aguttes, Neuilly #83/R est:1300-1500
£1854 $3375 €2800 Boy fishing (165x62cm-65x24in) s. 17-Jun-4 Finarte Semenzato, Milan #256/R est:2000-3000
£2797 $4811 €4000 Projet d'affiche pour le train de Chamonix-Montervers (34x26cm-13x10in) s. painted c.1910-1920. 5-Dec-3 Chochon-Barre & Allardi, Paris #73/R est:5000-5500
Works on paper
£300 $537 €450 Retour du marche (17x18cm-7x7in) s. crayon. 16-May-4 Thierry & Lannon, Brest #45b
£600 $1074 €900 Le couple pres du moulin (22x30cm-9x12in) s. W/C chl. 16-May-4 Thierry & Lannon, Brest #44/R

DELL'ERA, Giovan Battista (1765-1798) Italian
Works on paper
£385 $654 €550 Diana meeting Apollo (26x40cm-10x16in) ink. 19-Nov-3 Finarte Semenzato, Milan #505/R

DELL'ERA, Giovan Battista (attrib) (1765-1798) Italian
Works on paper
£600 $1038 €876 Maidens bringing offerings to an altar dedicated to Jupiter (34x37cm-13x15in) black chk pen brown ink grey wash. 12-Dec-3 Christie's, Kensington #413/R

DELMOTTE, Marcel (1901-1984) Belgian
£367 $667 €550 Adolescente (50x40cm-20x16in) s.d.1983 panel. 4-Jul-4 MonsAntic, Maisieres #416
£400 $724 €600 Job (60x43cm-24x17in) s. panel. 30-Mar-4 Palais de Beaux Arts, Brussels #522
£400 $724 €600 Vase bleu (60x43cm-24x17in) s. panel. 30-Mar-4 Palais de Beaux Arts, Brussels #523
£490 $832 €700 La femme en bleu (30x40cm-12x16in) s.d.1941 paper on canvas. 27-Nov-3 Millon & Associes, Paris #233
£526 $968 €800 Portrait of a girl (60x50cm-24x20in) s. verso board. 28-Jun-4 Sotheby's, Amsterdam #229/R
£526 $968 €800 Paon (70x50cm-28x20in) s.d.1961 panel. 22-Jun-4 Palais de Beaux Arts, Brussels #225
£533 $965 €800 La paresse (80x60cm-31x24in) s. panel. 30-Mar-4 Palais de Beaux Arts, Brussels #520
£537 $988 €800 Paysage (50x84cm-20x33in) s. panel. 28-Mar-4 MonsAntic, Maisieres #379
£603 $1007 €850 Paysage aux femmes (36x24cm-14x9in) s. panel. 14-Oct-3 Vanderkindere, Brussels #107
£634 $1096 €900 Le reveil de l'orient (60x50cm-24x20in) s.d.1969 panel. 9-Dec-3 Campo, Vlaamse Kaai #290
£733 $1327 €1100 La prudence (60x80cm-24x31in) s. panel. 30-Mar-4 Palais de Beaux Arts, Brussels #519/R
£753 $1281 €1100 Porte ouverte sur le vide (88x68cm-35x27in) s.d.1974 panel. 10-Nov-3 Horta, Bruxelles #186
£800 $1440 €1200 Composition fantastique (44x55cm-17x22in) s.d.1967 panel. 26-Apr-4 Bernaerts, Antwerp #555/R
£839 $1427 €1200 Scene de famille (441x29cm-174x11in) s.d.1934 cardboard. 27-Nov-3 Millon & Associes, Paris #234/R
£933 $1689 €1400 Il n'y a pas de verite (80x100cm-31x39in) s.d.1974 panel. 30-Mar-4 Palais de Beaux Arts, Brussels #518/R
£959 $1630 €1400 Mort d'Orphee (92x122cm-36x48in) s.d.1976 panel lit. 10-Nov-3 Horta, Bruxelles #185
£1200 $2148 €1800 Ainsi naissent et meurent les civilisations (70x90cm-28x35in) s. d.1963 verso panel. 11-May-4 Vanderkindere, Brussels #37 est:1000-1250
£1200 $2184 €1800 Le dernier refuge de l'esprit au XXe siecle (60x42cm-24x17in) s.d.1983 panel. 4-Jul-4 MonsAntic, Maisieres #415 est:1000-1500
£1267 $2267 €1900 Autoportrait de l'artiste (135x115cm-53x45in) s.d.1969. 16-May-4 MonsAntic, Maisieres #400 est:1000-1500
£1678 $2803 €2400 Arbres fantastiques (170x105cm-67x41in) panel double-sided. 13-Oct-3 Horta, Bruxelles #154 est:3000-4000
£1733 $3103 €2600 Composition surrealiste (90x125cm-35x49in) s.d.1976. 16-May-4 MonsAntic, Maisieres #399 est:1800-2200
£1800 $3222 €2700 Un jour se leve (91x122cm-36x48in) s. panel. 11-May-4 Vanderkindere, Brussels #92/R est:3000-4000
£1958 $3270 €2800 Le chapeau jaune (124x92cm-49x36in) s. panel. 13-Oct-3 Horta, Bruxelles #153 est:3500-4500
£2378 $4042 €3400 L'humanite et la science (91x122cm-36x48in) s.d.1958 panel. 1-Dec-3 Palais de Beaux Arts, Brussels #50 est:3200-4500
£2603 $4425 €3800 Femme a la fenetre (122x93cm-48x37in) s. panel lit. 10-Nov-3 Horta, Bruxelles #184
Works on paper
£4965 $8291 €7000 Paravent (121x246cm-48x97in) s.d.1959 mixed media four panel folding screen. 15-Oct-3 Hotel des Ventes Mosan, Brussels #286 est:8000-10000

DELOBBE, François Alfred (1835-1920) French
£5183 $8500 €7515 Portrait of a young girl seated on floor cushion with cats (56x46cm-22x18in) s.d.1877. 4-Jun-3 Alderfer's, Hatfield #246/R est:4000-6000
£5369 $9504 €8000 Scene galante (66x55cm-26x22in) s. 30-Apr-4 Tajan, Paris #119/R est:8000-12000

DELOBEL, Christian (1934-) French
£690 $1152 €1000 Plage a Ouistreham Riva Bella (80x101cm-31x40in) s. 11-Nov-3 Lesieur & Le Bars, Le Havre #140

DELOOPER, William (1932-) American
£344 $550 €502 Untitled III (183x173cm-72x68in) s.i.d.78 acrylic. 20-Sep-3 Sloans & Kenyon, Bethesda #986/R
Works on paper
£503 $900 €734 Blue field (38x51cm-15x20in) s.d.2/73 W/C. 7-May-4 Sloans & Kenyon, Bethesda #1738/R

DELORME, Raphael (1886-1962) French
£5480 $9316 €8000 Tireuse d'arc (100x80cm-39x31in) s. 5-Nov-3 Tajan, Paris #15/R

DELORMOZ, Paul (1895-1980) French
£330 $562 €482 Old town of Annecy (50x65cm-20x26in) s. board. 5-Nov-3 Dobiaschofsky, Bern #473 (S.FR 750)
£1690 $2958 €2400 Pardon a Notre Dame de Tronoen, la procession (27x42cm-11x17in) s. panel. 21-Dec-3 Thierry & Lannon, Brest #153/R est:2000-2500
Works on paper
£389 $728 €580 Matin sur la jetee des sables d'olonne (28x36cm-11x14in) s. W/C. 24-Feb-4 Thierry & Lannon, Brest #292/R

DELORT, Charles Edouard (1841-1895) French
£2333 $4293 €3500 Le retour (70x99cm-28x39in) s. 9-Jun-4 Oger, Dumont, Paris #44/R est:2000-3000
£3275 $6026 €4782 Little pickpocket (41x33cm-16x13in) s. 14-Jun-4 Philippe Schuler, Zurich #4266/R est:8000-12000 (S.FR 7500)

DELOYE, Jean Baptiste Gustave (1848-1899) French
Sculpture
£1974 $3632 €3000 Hercule et Anthee (29cm-11in) s.d.1858 terracotta lit. 23-Jun-4 Sotheby's, Paris #112/R est:3000-4000

DELPORTE, Charles (1928-) Belgian
£265 $482 €400 Paysage cosmique (80x100cm-31x39in) s. s.i.d.1979 verso. 16-Jun-4 Hotel des Ventes Mosan, Brussels #273
£268 $475 €400 Chromatisme 2 (100x155cm-39x61in) s. panel. 27-Apr-4 Campo, Vlaamse Kaai #399
£282 $487 €400 Champs magnetiques (60x80cm-24x31in) s. panel. 9-Dec-3 Campo, Vlaamse Kaai #291
£313 $522 €450 Variation (84x100cm-33x39in) s. d.1971 verso panel. 21-Oct-3 Campo & Campo, Antwerp #76
£313 $522 €450 J'ai vu le soleil (100x80cm-39x31in) s. s.verso panel. 21-Oct-3 Campo & Campo, Antwerp #77/R
£352 $616 €500 Le Christ astronaute (213x285cm-84x112in) s. panel triptych. 16-Dec-3 Galerie Moderne, Brussels #793
£369 $653 €550 L'amour maternel (104x165cm-41x65in) s. panel. 27-Apr-4 Campo, Vlaamse Kaai #398
£374 $670 €550 Celle qui lancera sa fusee pyramidale (39cm-15in) s. s.i.d.73 verso oval prov. 21-Mar-4 Calmels Cohen, Paris #126/R
£403 $713 €600 Visage pennigerien (70x50cm-28x20in) s.d.1968 panel. 27-Apr-4 Campo, Vlaamse Kaai #401

DELPRAT, Paul Ashton (1942-) Australian

£285	$450	€413	Portrait of a young man (110x90cm-43x35in) s. board. 22-Jul-3 Lawson Menzies, Sydney #205/R (A.D 700)
£407	$638	€590	Nude swimmers (90x136cm-35x54in) s. board. 26-Aug-3 Christie's, Sydney #220 (A.D 1000)
£650	$1021	€943	Untitled, red landscape (181x136cm-71x54in) s. board. 27-Aug-3 Christie's, Sydney #702 est:800-1200 (A.D 1600)

DELPY, Hippolyte Camille (1842-1910) French

£1348	$2250	€1900	Paysage a l'etang (14x24cm-6x9in) s. panel. 19-Jun-3 Millon & Associes, Paris #116 est:1000-1500
£2899	$4754	€4000	Bord de riviere (23x40cm-9x16in) s. panel. 11-May-3 Osenat, Fontainebleau #100/R est:5000-5500
£3073	$5500	€4487	Sunrise along a river (33x60cm-13x24in) s. panel. 6-May-4 Doyle, New York #32/R est:8000-12000
£3521	$5845	€5000	Pommiers en fleurs (29x53cm-11x21in) s.d.69. 15-Jun-3 Peron, Melun #199
£3946	$7063	€5800	Bords de riviere au soleil couchant (28x46cm-11x18in) s. panel. 19-Mar-4 Millon & Associes, Paris #40/R est:4000-4500
£4333	$7843	€6500	Paysan bechant son jardin (66x47cm-26x19in) s. 31-Mar-4 Sotheby's, Paris #105/R est:8000-10000
£4336	$7457	€6200	Bord de riviere, soleil couchant (28x47cm-11x19in) s. panel. 5-Dec-3 Gros & Delettrez, Paris #48/R est:3000-5000
£4545	$7818	€6500	Paysage de neige en Hollande (50x100cm-20x39in) s. 7-Dec-3 Osenat, Fontainebleau #82 est:7000-9000
£4832	$8891	€7200	Lavandieres et pecheurs au bord de la riviere. Un chien endormi (32x56cm-13x22in) s.d.1874 panel double-sided. 24-Mar-4 Binoche, Paris #79/R est:8000-10000
£5430	$9231	€7928	River landscape with washerwoman (40x71cm-16x28in) s.d.1901 panel prov. 19-Nov-3 Fischer, Luzern #1073/R est:12000-15000 (S.FR 12000)
£5594	$9622	€8000	Le pont d'Asnieres (35x51cm-14x20in) s.i.d.Aout 1871 panel. 7-Dec-3 Osenat, Fontainebleau #81 est:7000-8000
£5797	$9507	€8000	Bord de riviere au soleil couchant (41x71cm-16x28in) s. panel. 11-May-3 Osenat, Fontainebleau #101/R est:9000-10000
£5882	$10000	€8588	Potato gatherers (55x45cm-22x18in) s.i.d.1880. 28-Oct-3 Sotheby's, New York #135/R est:10000-15000
£5978	$11000	€8728	Approaching storm (38x64cm-15x25in) s. panel. 27-Mar-4 New Orleans Auction, New Orleans #594/R est:12000-18000
£6159	$10101	€8500	Bord de riviere (45x75cm-18x30in) s. painted c.1900. 11-May-3 Osenat, Fontainebleau #102/R est:9000-10000
£6294	$10825	€9000	Bords de l'Yvonne (47x80cm-19x31in) s.d.1907 i.verso panel. 7-Dec-3 Osenat, Fontainebleau #80 est:9000-10000
£6623	$12119	€10000	Lavandieres au bord de la riviere (50x80cm-20x31in) s.d.1897 panel. 9-Apr-4 Claude Aguttes, Neuilly #10/R est:6000-8000
£6667	$12000	€9734	La lavandiere (40x70cm-16x28in) s.d.1901 panel. 23-Apr-4 Sotheby's, New York #144/R est:12000-15000
£6977	$12000	€10186	Washerwoman along the banks of a river (44x71cm-17x28in) init. panel. 3-Dec-3 Doyle, New York #98/R est:10000-15000
£7647	$13000	€11165	Washerwomen on a riverbank (39x70cm-15x28in) s.d.1900 init.verso panel. 28-Oct-3 Sotheby's, New York #122/R est:12000-15000
£7667	$14107	€11500	Lavandieres au bord de l'Oise (40x71cm-16x28in) s.d.1902 panel. 9-Jun-4 Oger, Dumont, Paris #48/R est:10000-12000
£8000	$13760	€11680	Washing on the banks of the river (41x71cm-16x28in) s.d.04 panel. 3-Dec-3 Christie's, London #25/R est:8000-12000
£8145	$13846	€11892	River landscape with washerwomen (60x100cm-24x39in) s.d.72 prov. 19-Nov-3 Fischer, Luzern #1075/R est:15000-18000 (S.FR 18000)
£8824	$15000	€12883	Lavandiere et Barques, soleil couchant (44x70cm-17x28in) s. init.verso. 28-Oct-3 Sotheby's, New York #121/R est:15000-20000
£10000	$17000	€14600	Rue Pavoisee a Dieppe (35x61cm-14x24in) s. prov. 28-Oct-3 Sotheby's, New York #124/R est:12000-18000
£10556	$19000	€15412	River landscape, summer (43x70cm-17x28in) s. panel prov. 22-Apr-4 Christie's, Rockefeller NY #118/R est:15000-20000
£13529	$23000	€19752	Lavandieres au bord de l'eau (30x53cm-12x21in) s. panel. 28-Oct-3 Sotheby's, New York #123/R est:15000-25000

DELPY, Hippolyte Camille (attrib) (1842-1910) French

£559	$1029	€850	Peniche au soleil couchant (22x32cm-9x13in) s. panel. 22-Jun-4 Calmels Cohen, Paris #32
£900	$1665	€1314	River landscape at sunset (39x56cm-15x22in) bears sig. 10-Mar-4 Sotheby's, Olympia #246/R est:1000-1500

DELPY, J H (1877-1957) French

£1156	$2070	€1700	Paysage avec lavandieres (34x61cm-13x24in) panel. 21-Mar-4 Teitgen, Nancy #16

DELPY, Jacques-Henry (1877-1957) French

£334	$600	€500	Coquelicots dans un vase (54x81cm-21x32in) s. 26-Apr-4 Tajan, Paris #177
£408	$649	€600	Bord de Seine anime d'une barque (34x55cm-13x22in) s. board. 23-Mar-3 Mercier & Cie, Lille #208
£559	$962	€800	Lavandiere au bord de la riviere (27x35cm-11x14in) s. 7-Dec-3 Feletin, Province #92
£600	$1092	€900	Bord de riviere (18x32cm-7x13in) s. panel. 4-Jul-4 Eric Pillon, Calais #8/R
£695	$1273	€1050	Mere et enfant au bord de la riviere, soleil couchant (35x63cm-14x25in) s. panel. 7-Apr-4 Piasa, Paris #66
£739	$1323	€1079	Landscape at sunset (24x35cm-9x14in) s. panel. 26-May-4 AB Stockholms Auktionsverk #2414/R (S.KR 10000)
£786	$1431	€1148	River landscape at sunset (46x64cm-18x25in) s. 16-Jun-4 Fischer, Luzern #2060/R (S.FR 1800)
£919	$1700	€1342	Sunset (36x61cm-14x24in) s. panel. 17-Jul-4 New Orleans Auction, New Orleans #752/R est:1800-2500
£1184	$2143	€1800	Chaumiere au bord de la riviere (24x41cm-9x16in) s. panel. 19-Apr-4 Boscher, Cherbourg #707 est:1000-2000
£1408	$2338	€2000	Lavandieres au bord de l'eau (38x55cm-15x22in) s. 15-Jun-3 Peron, Melun #182
£1500	$2400	€2190	Lavandieres au bord de riviere (46x25cm-18x10in) s. panel. 20-Sep-3 New Orleans Auction, New Orleans #543/R
£1500	$2400	€2190	Figure solitaire (28x41cm-11x16in) s. 20-Sep-3 New Orleans Auction, New Orleans #544/R
£2035	$3500	€2971	River landscape (33x56cm-13x22in) s. masonite. 6-Dec-3 Neal Auction Company, New Orleans #234/R est:4000-5000
£3333	$6000	€4866	Autumn sunset on the river (37x60cm-15x24in) s. panel. 23-Apr-4 Sotheby's, New York #146/R est:8000-12000
£6667	$12000	€9734	Washerwoman at the riverbank (37x60cm-15x24in) s.d.1909 panel. 23-Apr-4 Sotheby's, New York #145/R est:8000-12000

DELPY, Lucien Victor (1898-1966) French

£954	$1727	€1450	Paris, Place de la Concorde (53x63cm-21x25in) s.d.1947. 18-Apr-4 Rouillac, Vendome #121
£1667	$2983	€2500	Thoniers sous voiles a quai (50x61cm-20x24in) s. 16-May-4 Thierry & Lannon, Brest #306 est:2000-2300
£2000	$3660	€2920	Yachts in a calm (73x95cm-29x37in) s. 7-Apr-4 Woolley & Wallis, Salisbury #199/R est:800-1200
£2057	$3250	€2900	Entree de la rade de Lorient (75x92cm-30x36in) s. 24-Jul-3 Adjug'art, Brest #300/R
£2119	$3963	€3200	Bretonnes le vent dans le dos, Ouessant (71x120cm-28x47in) s. 24-Jul-4 Thierry & Lannon, Brest #148/R est:3000-4000
£2676	$4683	€3800	Retour de peche (73x92cm-29x36in) s. 21-Dec-3 Thierry & Lannon, Brest #162/R est:3000-4000
Works on paper			
£600	$1098	€876	Yachts off a headland (47x61cm-19x24in) s. gouache. 7-Apr-4 Woolley & Wallis, Salisbury #133/R
£800	$1432	€1200	Le port de Colombo (23x32cm-9x13in) s.i. gouache. 16-May-4 Thierry & Lannon, Brest #240
£1325	$2477	€2000	Ouessant (48x63cm-19x25in) s.d.37 gouache. 24-Jul-4 Thierry & Lannon, Brest #96 est:1200-1500
£1333	$2387	€2000	Concarneau. s.d.1841 W/C pastel. 16-May-4 Osenat, Fontainebleau #17/R est:1500-2000

DELSENE, Henri (?) ?

£521	$828	€750	Scene galante (37x28cm-15x11in) s. panel. 9-Sep-3 Vanderkindere, Brussels #19

DELTEIL, Joseph (1894-1978) French

Works on paper			
£300	$552	€450	Silhouette dansante (21x13cm-8x5in) s. blue biro. 9-Jun-4 Piasa, Paris #45

DELTOMBE, Paul (1878-1971) French

£2168	$3620	€3100	Corniche a Villefranche (50x65cm-20x26in) s. 25-Jun-3 Blanchet, Paris #10/R

DELUC, Gabriel (1850-1916) French

£260	$479	€390	Morning in the harbour (38x65cm-15x26in) s. 14-Jun-4 Blomqvist, Lysaker #1070/R (N.KR 3200)

DELUERMOZ, Henri (1876-1943) French

£1862	$3408	€2700	Ecuyere (17x17cm-7x7in) s. oil paper. 31-Jan-4 Gerard, Besancon #25
£2345	$4291	€3400	Elephant (44x58cm-17x23in) s. cardboard. 31-Jan-4 Gerard, Besancon #26
£12414	$22717	€18000	Tigre (109x60cm-43x24in) s. canvas on panel. 31-Jan-4 Gerard, Besancon #27

DELUOL, Andre (1909-2003) French

Sculpture			
£1533	$2821	€2300	Naissance de Venus (66x100x4cm-26x39x2in) s. marble relief. 11-Jun-4 Piasa, Paris #26 est:2500-3000

DELUSSE, Jean Jacques Theresa (1757-1833) French

Miniatures			
£2200	$3740	€3212	Officer, half-length (6cm-2in) s.d.1792 oval prov. 18-Nov-3 Bonhams, New Bond Street #74/R est:1500-2000

DELVAL, Robert (20th C) French

£461	$847	€700	Jeune femme assise (80x40cm-31x16in) s.d.1952. 28-Jun-4 Joron-Derem, Paris #236
£615	$1100	€898	Catherine a la blousse bleue (36x28cm-14x11in) s. s.i.verso. 7-May-4 Sloans & Kenyon, Bethesda #1664/R

DELVAUX, Edouard (attrib) (1806-1862) Belgian

£349	$636	€510	Landscape with a small waterfall (24x19cm-9x7in) panel. 16-Jun-4 Fischer, Luzern #2061/R (S.FR 800)

DELVAUX, Jacques (20th C) Belgian

£369	$653	€550	Paysage ensoleille (80x100cm-31x39in) s.d.1993. 27-Apr-4 Campo & Campo, Antwerp #62

DELVAUX, Paul (1897-1994) Belgian

£2817	$4873	€4000	Sommeil (46x65cm-18x26in) s.i. col lithograph. 15-Dec-3 Bailly Pommery, Paris #143/R est:3000
£8000	$13360	€11680	Vue des environs (79x100cm-31x39in) s.d.10-25 painted 1925. 22-Oct-3 Sotheby's, Olympia #37/R est:4000-6000
£40000	$73600	€58400	Deux femmes couchees (16x46cm-6x18in) s.d.1967 i. verso panel prov.exhib.lit. 22-Jun-4 Sotheby's, London #191/R est:40000-60000
£250000	$457500	€365000	Nu au lever - le lever (113x89cm-44x35in) s.d.11.32 prov.exhib.lit. 2-Feb-4 Christie's, London #80/R est:250000-300000
£550000	$1001000	€803000	L'offrande (140x111cm-55x44in) s.d.12-63 d.1963 verso panel prov.exhib.lit. 3-Feb-4 Sotheby's, London #62/R est:300000-500000
Prints			
£1467	$2699	€2200	The fan (64x47cm-25x19in) s. lithograph exec. 1968 one of 75. 11-Jun-4 Villa Grisebach, Berlin #1598/R est:1000-1500
£2000	$3320	€2920	Anne lost in thought (65x51cm-26x20in) s.num.22/75 col lithograph. 6-Oct-3 Sotheby's, London #79/R est:2500-3500
£2128	$3553	€3000	La chambre (44x55cm-17x22in) s.d.6-69 etching. 15-Oct-3 Hotel des Ventes Mosan, Brussels #206/R est:3000-4000

£2254	$3899	€3200	Plage (69x90cm-27x35in) s.i. col lithograph exec.1972. 15-Dec-3 Bailly Pommery, Paris #147/R est:2500
£2297	$4043	€3400	Azalee (36x29cm-14x11in) s. num.60/75 lt. 18-May-4 Galerie Moderne, Brussels #227/R est:3000-4000
£2333	$4293	€3500	The lover (53x68cm-21x27in) s. num.56/75 lithograph exec. 1971. 9-Jun-4 Christie's, Amsterdam #105/R est:3000-5000
£2817	$4873	€4000	Eventail (76x56cm-30x22in) s.i. col lithograph exec.1968. 15-Dec-3 Bailly Pommery, Paris #137 est:1200
£2817	$4873	€4000	Locomobile (60x80cm-24x31in) s.i. lithograph exec.1970. 15-Dec-3 Bailly Pommery, Paris #142/R est:3500
£2817	$4873	€4000	Voyante (68x100cm-27x39in) s.i. col lithograph exec.1974. 15-Dec-3 Bailly Pommery, Paris #150/R est:4000
£2958	$5117	€4200	Voute (70x92cm-28x36in) s.i. col lithograph exec.1973. 15-Dec-3 Bailly Pommery, Paris #153/R est:2500
£3147	$5412	€4500	Anne lost in thoughts (64x49cm-25x19in) s.num.3/75 col lithograph. 3-Dec-3 Sotheby's, Amsterdam #379/R est:4000-6000
£3239	$5604	€4600	Anne songeuse (65x51cm-26x20in) s.i. col lithograph exec.1966. 15-Dec-3 Bailly Pommery, Paris #135/R est:3000
£3497	$5944	€5000	The fan (65x48cm-26x19in) s. col lithograph. 29-Nov-3 Villa Grisebach, Berlin #300/R est:5000-6000
£3663	$6484	€5348	The rivals (65x50cm-26x20in) s.num.24/75 col lithograph lit. 27-Apr-4 AB Stockholms Auktionsverk #1278/R est:60000-65000 (S.KR 50000)
£3732	$6457	€5300	Fenetre (68x93cm-27x37in) s.i. col lithograph exec.1952. 15-Dec-3 Bailly Pommery, Paris #144/R est:4000-5000
£3873	$6701	€5500	Silence (68x100cm-27x39in) s.i. col lithograph exec.1972. 15-Dec-3 Bailly Pommery, Paris #149/R est:4500
£4789	$8285	€6800	Jardin (65x90cm-26x35in) s.i. col lithograph exec. 1971. 15-Dec-3 Bailly Pommery, Paris #145/R est:5000-7000
£8500	$15470	€12410	Le jardin (66x91cm-26x36in) one s.num.48/75 one s.num.45/50 col lithograph pair. 1-Jul-4 Sotheby's, London #170/R est:5000-7000

Works on paper

£333	$603	€500	Entree de foret au Rouge-Cloitre (26x17cm-10x7in) crayon exhib. 30-Mar-4 Palais de Beaux Arts, Brussels #525
£604	$1117	€900	Jeune femme nue de face (25x17cm-10x7in) graphite prov. 15-Mar-4 Horta, Bruxelles #314
£699	$1189	€1000	Paysanne a la fontaine (16x9cm-6x4in) graphite prov. 18-Nov-3 Pierre Berge, Paris #90
£795	$1446	€1200	Torero (30x14cm-12x6in) s. W/C pencil. 19-Jun-4 Bergmann, Erlangen #890
£1208	$2223	€1800	Young man (22x14cm-9x6in) lead pencil prov. 24-Mar-4 Joron-Derem, Paris #97 est:2000-3000
£1325	$2411	€2000	Nu feminin (26x17cm-10x7in) dr. 15-Jun-4 Galerie Moderne, Brussels #194 est:1800-2200
£1678	$2853	€2400	Les paveurs (35x24cm-14x9in) gouache. 1-Dec-3 Palais de Beaux Arts, Brussels #47/R est:2000-2500
£2133	$3904	€3200	Vue de la gare du Quartier Leopold (30x22cm-12x9in) s. crayon lit. 7-Jun-4 Palais de Beaux Arts, Brussels #253/R est:2500-3500
£2500	$3975	€3625	Maternite (32x24cm-13x9in) pen brush ink executed c.1932. 11-Sep-3 Christie's, Kensington #62/R est:3000-4000
£2500	$4550	€3650	Petite etude de nu couche (17x13cm-7x5in) pen ink exec.c.1936 exhib. 4-Feb-4 Sotheby's, London #503/R est:2500-3500
£3020	$5618	€4500	Femmes devant le temple (24x34cm-9x13in) i.verso Indian ink ink wash prov. 2-Mar-4 Artcurial Briest, Paris #75/R est:6000-8000
£3200	$5088	€4640	Composition avec nus (26x35cm-10x14in) init.d.30 pencil wax crayon. 11-Sep-3 Christie's, Kensington #64/R est:3500-4500
£3200	$5728	€4800	San Peyre (36x44cm-14x17in) s.i.d.62 W/C pencil Indian ink prov. 15-May-4 De Vuyst, Lokeren #483/R est:5000-6000
£3776	$6420	€5400	Tete de jeune femme (20x16cm-8x6in) s.d.1945 wash. 1-Dec-3 Palais de Beaux Arts, Brussels #248/R est:4000-6000
£4000	$6360	€5800	Trois femme. Maison a nuit and tete de femme (21x29cm-8x11in) brown felt tip pen double-sided. 11-Sep-3 Christie's, Kensington #65/R est:5000-7000
£4000	$7280	€5840	Etude pour le viol (17x13cm-7x5in) pen ink exec.c.1936 exhib. 4-Feb-4 Sotheby's, London #499/R est:4000-6000
£4000	$7280	€5840	Etude pour le viol (17x13cm-7x5in) pen ink exec.c.1936 exhib. 4-Feb-4 Sotheby's, London #500/R est:4000-6000
£4000	$7280	€5840	Etude de personnage avec chapeau (17x13cm-7x5in) i. pen ink exec.1936 exhib. 4-Feb-4 Sotheby's, London #502/R est:4000-6000
£4000	$7280	€5840	Etude de femme devetue couchee (13x17cm-5x7in) pen ink exec.c.1935-36 exhib. 4-Feb-4 Sotheby's, London #504/R est:4000-6000
£4000	$7280	€5840	Etude de personnages et architectures et cariiatides (13x17cm-5x7in) pen ink exec.c.1936 exhib. 4-Feb-4 Sotheby's, London #505/R est:4000-6000
£4000	$7160	€6000	Study for the green sofa (14x21cm-6x8in) crayon dr. 15-May-4 Renaud, Paris #66/R
£4200	$7644	€6132	Nus feminins enlaces (13x17cm-5x7in) i. pen ink exec.c.1935-40 exhib. 4-Feb-4 Sotheby's, London #506/R est:4000-6000
£4800	$8736	€7008	Etude pour la rose (17x13cm-7x5in) pen ink exec.c.1936 exhib. 4-Feb-4 Sotheby's, London #507/R est:4000-6000
£6000	$10920	€8760	Young girls (30x25cm-12x10in) s.d.1965 W/C India ink prov. 5-Feb-4 Christie's, London #384/R est:8000-12000
£6000	$9540	€8700	Stoumont (55x72cm-22x28in) s.i.d.31 pen brush ink W/C. 11-Sep-3 Christie's, Kensington #89/R est:3000-5000
£6081	$11493	€9000	Huy (53x72cm-21x28in) s.d.10-33 W/C ink. 17-Feb-4 Galerie Moderne, Brussels #246/R est:8000-12000
£6667	$11933	€10000	Accoudee (38x49cm-15x19in) s. Indian ink prov.exhib. 15-May-4 De Vuyst, Lokeren #484/R est:7500-10000
£6761	$11696	€9600	Egyptian lady (34x48cm-13x19in) s. W/C Indian ink prov. 13-Dec-3 De Vuyst, Lokeren #489/R est:8000-10000
£9091	$15182	€13000	Paysage a St Idesbald (55x66cm-22x26in) W/C Indian ink exhib.lit. 11-Oct-3 De Vuyst, Lokeren #465/R est:14000-16000
£10067	$18523	€15000	Femme et temple (24x33cm-9x13in) mono. Indian ink exec c.1949 prov.exhib. 24-Mar-4 Joron-Derem, Paris #93/R est:15000-18000
£10135	$18142	€15000	Miami beach (53x71cm-21x28in) s.i.d.39 Chinese ink wash W/C. 4-May-4 Calmels Cohen, Paris #197/R est:12000-15000
£10500	$19320	€15330	Architectural and figure studies (16x25cm-6x10in) pencil album prov. 24-Mar-4 Sotheby's, Olympia #16/R est:3000-4000
£12000	$21840	€17520	Nude (60x41cm-24x16in) s.d.7-30 gouache W/C pen ink buff paper prov. 5-Feb-4 Christie's, London #387/R est:12000-15000
£13427	$23094	€19200	Deux jeunes femmes (39x50cm-15x20in) s.i.d.10-11-51 Chinese ink W/C. 2-Dec-3 Sotheby's, Amsterdam #60/R est:20000-25000
£15000	$27300	€21900	Farewell (27x36cm-11x14in) s.d.1966 pen India ink prov. 5-Feb-4 Christie's, London #385/R est:20000-30000
£15000	$27600	€21900	Two women (36x28cm-14x11in) s.indis.i.d.1942 pen ink wash prov. 24-Jun-4 Christie's, London #443/R est:10000-15000
£16779	$30872	€25000	Rideau rouge (47x60cm-19x24in) s. W/C Indian ink. 24-Mar-4 Joron-Derem, Paris #99/R est:28000-30000
£18000	$32760	€26280	Young girl (30x24cm-12x9in) s.i.d.1970 W/C pen ink prov. 5-Feb-4 Christie's, London #383/R est:12000-18000
£18000	$32760	€26280	Femme a la fleur (35x26cm-14x10in) s.d.12-75 W/C India ink prov. 5-Feb-4 Christie's, London #382/R est:15000-20000
£20979	$35664	€30000	Femme pensive a la robe bleue (70x52cm-28x20in) s. Indian ink W/C. 1-Dec-3 Palais de Beaux Arts, Brussels #52/R est:30000-40000
£26000	$47840	€37960	Feux (43x56cm-17x22in) s.d.1949 pen ink W/C exhib. 22-Jun-4 Sotheby's, London #486/R est:20000-25000
£40000	$66800	€58400	Phryne devant ses juges (46x38cm-18x15in) s.d.13-7-63 W/C pen brush ink gouache prov.exhib. 21-Oct-3 Sotheby's, London #77/R est:40000-60000
£94972	$170000	€138659	Le bain des dames chez Georges Grard (56x75cm-22x30in) i.d.19-8-47 W/C pen in pencil prov.exhib. 6-May-4 Sotheby's, New York #347/R est:150000-200000
£200000	$366000	€292000	Squelette (80x55cm-31x22in) s.i.d.25-3-44 mixed media board prov.exhib.lit. 2-Feb-4 Christie's, London #81/R est:220000-280000

DELVEAUX, Guillaume (19th C) Belgian

£843	$1375	€1231	La Britto de Somneville (87x64cm-34x25in) s. prov. 28-Sep-3 Hindemae, Ullerslev #75/R (D.KR 9000)

DELVECCHIO, Maurizio (1962-) Swiss

£336	$621	€500	Dance-poster (100x60cm-39x24in) s. s.i.d.2003 verso. 13-Mar-4 Meeting Art, Vercelli #169

DELVILLE, Jean (1867-1953) Belgian

£30000	$51600	€43800	L'homme-dieu (158x169cm-62x67in) s.i.d.1900 prov.exhib. 3-Dec-3 Christie's, London #60/R est:30000-50000

Works on paper

£2676	$4630	€3800	Portrait de jeune enfant (38x29cm-15x11in) s.d.1940 pastel pencil. 13-Dec-3 De Vuyst, Lokeren #113/R est:3000-4000
£8671	$15000	€12660	Study for les kramoros (108x56cm-43x22in) s.i. pencil pastel crayon prov. 11-Dec-3 Sotheby's, New York #35/R est:15000-20000
£23776	$40420	€34000	Parisfal (66x49cm-26x19in) s. pastel. 27-Nov-3 Millon & Associes, Paris #152/R est:10000-15000

DELVIN, Jean Joseph (1853-1922) Belgian

£2517	$4280	€3600	Jeune cavaliere au levrier sur la plage (45x55cm-18x22in) s. 1-Dec-3 Palais de Beaux Arts, Brussels #53/R est:2000-3000

DELVOYE, Wim (1965-) Dutch?

Photographs

£3352	$6000	€4894	Untitled, marble floor no 11 (59x76cm-23x30in) s.d.98 num. of one verso cibachrome prov.exhib.lit. 14-May-4 Phillips, New York #153/R est:6000-8000
£3352	$6000	€4894	Untitled, marble floor no 23 (59x76cm-23x30in) cibachrome prov.exhib.lit. 14-May-4 Phillips, New York #155/R est:6000-8000
£4225	$7310	€6000	Marble floor (86x101cm-34x40in) col photograph prov. 9-Dec-3 Artcurial Briest, Paris #464/R est:4000-6000

Sculpture

£44910	$75000	€65569	St. Stephanus II (211x316x110cm-83x124x43in) stained glass enamel paint steel executed 1990 prov.exhib.lit. 13-Nov-3 Phillips, New York #41/R est:50000-70000

DELYEN, Jean-François (attrib) (1684-1761) French

£2695	$4501	€3800	Portrait de Madame de Dampierre de Greny (82x65cm-32x26in) 17-Oct-3 Tajan, Paris #91/R est:3000-4000

DEMACHY, Robert (19/20th C) American

Photographs

£2500	$4500	€3650	Symbolist study of sleeping woman in woods (16x23cm-6x9in) gum bichromate print prov.lit. 22-Apr-4 Phillips, New York #45/R est:8000-12000

DEMAN, Albert (1929-) French

£387	$670	€550	Coquelicots et fleurs variees (73x50cm-29x20in) s.d.56. 13-Dec-3 Touati, Paris #69
£400	$736	€600	La ferme (46x92cm-18x36in) s.d.55 prov. 14-Jun-4 Tajan, Paris #106
£420	$756	€613	Rendez vous Manque (54x73cm-21x29in) s. s.i.verso. 20-Jan-4 Bonhams, Knightsbridge #120/R
£570	$1050	€850	Vase fleuri (46x33cm-18x13in) s. 26-Mar-4 Neret-Minet, Paris #5
£915	$1584	€1300	Bouquet de fleurs des champs (80x46cm-31x18in) s.d.55. 13-Dec-3 Touati, Paris #70
£1162	$2010	€1650	Le poisson (32x91cm-13x36in) s.d.56. 13-Dec-3 Touati, Paris #71 est:300
£1241	$2272	€1800	Fleurs (92x73cm-36x29in) s. 1-Feb-4 Feletin, Province #112/R

DEMAND, Thomas (1964-) German

Photographs

£26000	$47320	€37960	Grube (229x167cm-90x66in) C-print on Diasec exec 1999 prov.lit. 5-Feb-4 Sotheby's, London #47/R est:30000-40000
£32000	$58880	€46720	Liege (166x209cm-65x82in) s. verso c-print mounted onto diasec executed 1993 prov. 25-Jun-4 Christie's, London #238/R est:20000-30000
£39106	$70000	€57095	Rasen, lawn (122x170cm-48x67in) chromogenic print plexiglas edition 3 of 6 prov.exhib.lit. 12-May-4 Christie's, Rockefeller NY #430/R est:50000-70000
£42000	$75180	€63000	Desk (96x184cm-38x72in) s.i.d. verso col photo diasec prov. 14-May-4 Ketterer, Munich #271/R est:35000-45000
£50279	$90000	€73407	Podium (300x180cm-118x71in) s.d.2000 num.5/6 verso cibachrome print prov.exhib.lit. 11-May-4 Christie's, Rockefeller NY #1/R est:70000-90000

DEMANGE, Adolphe (1857-1927) French

£621	$1037	€900	Elegante lors de l'Exposition Universelle (33x46cm-13x18in) s.d.1900. 11-Jul-3 Rabourdin & Choppin de Janvry, Paris #2

DEMARCHELIER, Patrick (1943-) ?

Photographs

£2395	$4000	€3497	Claudia Schiffer, St. Barthelemy, West Indies, 1991. s.i.d.1991 num.20 gelatin silver print prov. 14-Nov-3 Phillips, New York #298/R est:4000-6000

£2994	$5000	€4371	Cindy Crawford, Leh, India, 1989 (61x51cm-24x20in) s.i.d.1989 gelatin silver print prov. 14-Nov-3 Phillips, New York #296/R est:4000-6000

DEMARCO, Hugo Rodolfo (1932-1995) Argentinian

£1351	$2378	€2000	Colour (24x24cm-9x9in) s.d.1969 acrylic cardboard. 22-May-4 Galleria Pananti, Florence #322/R est:2200-2500
£2535	$4208	€3600	Rotation (60x60cm-24x24in) i.d.1974 verso acrylic prov. 11-Jun-3 Finarte Semenzato, Milan #573/R est:2000-3000

DEMARNE, Jean Louis (1744-1829) French

£3830	$6396	€5400	Bergers et bergeres (43x52cm-17x20in) s. prov.lit. 19-Oct-3 Anaf, Lyon #104/R est:5000-6000
£3947	$7263	€6000	Paysans et leur troupeau pres de moulin a eau (30x38cm-12x15in) i.verso. 24-Jun-4 Tajan, Paris #69/R est:6000-8000
£33566	$57734	€48000	Shepherdess and her dog on a bridge. Peasant woman on a path (202x170cm-80x67in) both s. pair. 2-Dec-3 Christie's, Paris #104/R est:30000-50000
£40000	$73200	€58400	Village fair (55x82cm-22x32in) panel prov.exhib.lit. 8-Jul-4 Sotheby's, London #175/R est:40000-60000
Works on paper			
£2113	$3697	€3000	La rencontre a l'abreuvoir. Les activites portuaires (15x11cm-6x4in) W/C ink wash two in one frame. 17-Dec-3 Delorme & Bocage, Paris #19/R est:3000-4000

DEMARTEAU, Gilles (elder) (1722-1776) Flemish

Works on paper			
£367	$664	€550	Le satyre amoureux (25x30cm-10x12in) 2-Apr-4 Winterberg, Heidelberg #277

DEMARTEAU, Gilles (elder-attrib) (1722-1776) Flemish

Works on paper			
£302	$556	€450	Tete de jeune femme (32x15cm-13x6in) sanguine. 28-Mar-4 Versailles Encheres #31/R

DEMARTINI, Eduard (1892-1961) Czechoslovakian

£438	$727	€639	Morning toilette (75x65cm-30x26in) mono.d.1936. 4-Oct-3 Dorotheum, Prague #131/R est:20000-30000 (C.KR 20000)

DEMARTINI, Joe (1927-) American

Works on paper			
£535	$1000	€781	Salome with severed head of John the Baptist (46x69cm-18x27in) s. W/C exec.c.1970. 26-Feb-4 Illustration House, New York #54
£1337	$2500	€1952	Soaring woman holding dove of peace and promise of nuclear future (56x38cm-22x15in) s. W/C airbrush. 26-Feb-4 Illustration House, New York #55 est:2000-3000

DEMAY, Germain (19th C) French

Sculpture			
£1549	$2680	€2200	Chien de chasse aboyant (12x29cm-5x11in) brown pat bronze. 14-Dec-3 St-Germain-en-Laye Encheres #95/R est:2000-2200

DEMAY, Jean François (attrib) (1798-1850) French

£3521	$6162	€5000	Une caleche devant un relais de poste (32x40cm-13x16in) 18-Dec-3 Tajan, Paris #133/R est:3000-4000

DEMEL, Franz (1878-1947) Austrian

£430	$783	€650	Winter landscape (31x47cm-12x19in) s. 21-Jun-4 Dorotheum, Vienna #162/R
Works on paper			
£397	$727	€600	Schloss Trautenfels/Grimming (16x23cm-6x9in) s. W/C. 8-Apr-4 Dorotheum, Vienna #250
£1241	$2061	€1800	Sunny autumn day in the country (36x52cm-14x20in) s. 30-Sep-3 Dorotheum, Vienna #337/R est:1800-2000

DEMESTER, Eugène (?) French?

£400	$732	€600	Brittany harbour scene (60x72cm-24x28in) s. 27-Jul-4 Henry Adams, Chichester #433
£500	$945	€730	Pont Aven, Brittany. Bourvaise en Vendee (27x34cm-11x13in) s. i.verso pair. 19-Feb-4 Christie's, Kensington #147/R

DEMETZ, Karl (1909-1986) German

£302	$565	€450	Shepherd with flock (59x77cm-23x30in) s. 27-Feb-4 Weidler, Nurnberg #8701/R
£699	$1203	€1000	Grain harvest on the Swabian Alp (70x80cm-28x31in) s. 5-Dec-3 Bolland & Marotz, Bremen #695/R

DEMIANY, Carl Theodor (1801-1840) German

£800	$1456	€1200	Portraits of a couple (65x57cm-26x22in) one s.d.1832 one i. pair. 1-Jul-4 Van Ham, Cologne #1262

DEMING, Adelaide (1864-?) American

£611	$1100	€892	Verdant landscape (20x25cm-8x10in) s. 23-Jan-4 Freeman, Philadelphia #234/R

DEMING, Edwin Willard (1860-1942) American

£294	$500	€429	Portrait of War Arrow (22x18cm-9x7in) s. i.verso board prov. 18-Nov-3 John Moran, Pasadena #119c
£435	$800	€635	Hunt (71x132cm-28x52in) 13-Jun-4 Bonhams & Butterfields, Los Angeles #7039/R
£2454	$4000	€3583	Great swamp battle (61x178cm-24x70in) s. board. 19-Jul-3 Outer Cape Auctions, Provincetown #70/R
Sculpture			
£1628	$2800	€2377	Indian brave with wildcat (35cm-14in) i. pat bronze. 2-Dec-3 Christie's, Rockefeller NY #75/R est:2000-3000
Works on paper			
£417	$750	€609	Two Indians by a teepee (13x15cm-5x6in) s. gouache. 23-Jan-4 Freeman, Philadelphia #43/R
£581	$1000	€848	Hunting wild moose (41x29cm-16x11in) s.d.1899 W/C gouache. 2-Dec-3 Christie's, Rockefeller NY #81/R

DEMMIN, Erich (1911-) German

£268	$502	€400	Amsterdam scene with figures (19x16cm-7x6in) s. panel. 27-Feb-4 Altus, Berlin #446/R
£280	$467	€400	Shallow waters (60x80cm-24x31in) s. i. verso. 28-Jun-3 Dannenberg, Berlin #662/R
£282	$505	€420	North Sea beach (60x80cm-24x31in) s. 28-May-4 Altus, Berlin #602/R

DEMONCHY, Andre (1914-) French

£466	$840	€700	Le chateau et la ville de Foix (61x50cm-24x20in) s. i.d.1968 verso. 26-Apr-4 Tajan, Paris #342/R

DEMONT-BRETON, Virginie (1859-1935) French

£2013	$3564	€3000	Fillette sur la plage (32x24cm-13x9in) s. panel. 27-Apr-4 Artcurial Briest, Paris #131/R est:4000-6000
£4126	$6890	€5900	Les enfants dans les vagues a Wissant (26x35cm-10x14in) s.i. panel. 29-Jun-3 Eric Pillon, Calais #92/R
£8235	$14000	€12023	After the storm (50x62cm-20x24in) s.i. 28-Oct-3 Sotheby's, New York #119/R est:10000-15000

DEMOTT, John (1954-) American

£683	$1100	€990	Mountain music (61x46cm-24x18in) 22-Aug-3 Altermann Galleries, Santa Fe #69
£2298	$3700	€3332	Slicker weather at sunrise (74x51cm-29x20in) 22-Aug-3 Altermann Galleries, Santa Fe #71

DEMOUSSY, Augustin Louis (1809-1880) French

£861	$1567	€1300	Jeune femme pensive (66x55cm-26x22in) mono. 21-Jun-4 Tajan, Paris #156 est:800-1200

D'EMPAIRE, Gabriel (?) Venezuelan

£255	$470	€372	Copy (26x30cm-10x12in) s. canvas on masonite. 28-Mar-4 Subastas Odalys, Caracas #12
£272	$490	€397	Tanaguarena (30x40cm-12x16in) s. 25-Apr-4 Subastas Odalys, Caracas #33
£296	$545	€432	Anauco (35x50cm-14x20in) s. 28-Mar-4 Subastas Odalys, Caracas #57
£340	$625	€496	Simon Bolivar (22x14cm-9x6in) s. masonite. 28-Mar-4 Subastas Odalys, Caracas #118
£516	$800	€753	Seascape (50x60cm-20x24in) s. 3-Nov-2 Subastas Odalys, Caracas #18/R
£547	$875	€799	Still life (78x100cm-31x39in) s. 21-Sep-3 Subastas Odalys, Caracas #3/R
£710	$1100	€1037	Untitled (40x30cm-16x12in) s. masonite. 3-Nov-2 Subastas Odalys, Caracas #97/R
£1488	$2530	€2172	Study for Carlota Corday (35x27cm-14x11in) s. 23-Nov-3 Subastas Odalys, Caracas #119/R est:400
£2976	$5060	€4345	Simon Bolivar (60x50cm-24x20in) s. 23-Nov-3 Subastas Odalys, Caracas #52/R est:700

DEMPSEY, John (19th C) British

Works on paper			
£286	$500	€418	You really hate the guy don't you ? (45x37cm-18x15in) ink W/C illus board taped to cardboard exec Feb 1956 exhib. 17-Dec-3 Christie's, Rockefeller NY #32/R
£400	$700	€584	If he wants to play this 69 you mentioned, my dear, play it (42x35cm-17x14in) s. W/C paper on ills board exec 1971 exhib. 17-Dec-3 Christie's, Rockefeller NY #245/R
£914	$1600	€1334	Man reading Playboy (37x29cm-15x11in) s. W/C illus board exec c.1974. 17-Dec-3 Christie's, Rockefeller NY #64/R est:2000-3000
£914	$1600	€1334	Damn it, Lorenzo, not so romantic (44x34cm-17x13in) s. W/C paper on illus board exec Sept 1960. 17-Dec-3 Christie's, Rockefeller NY #63/R est:1000-1500
£914	$1600	€1334	No, he hasn't yet, mama (42x31cm-17x12in) s. W/C paper on illus board exec June 1962. 17-Dec-3 Christie's, Rockefeller NY #68/R est:1500-2000
£2000	$3500	€2920	You certainly look different without your dictation pad, Miss Bloom (40x33cm-16x13in) s. W/C paper on illus board exec Jan 1969. 17-Dec-3 Christie's, Rockefeller NY #66/R est:1500-2500

DEMPSEY, Richard W (1909-1987) American

£1117	$2000	€1631	Carnival (48x58cm-19x23in) s. acrylic paper. 7-May-4 Sloans & Kenyon, Bethesda #1626/R est:500-700

DEMSKI, J (?) ?

£993	$1808	€1500	Cossacks resting (20x26cm-8x10in) panel. 21-Jun-4 Dorotheum, Vienna #128/R est:1700-1900
£993	$1808	€1500	Outpost (20x26cm-8x10in) panel. 21-Jun-4 Dorotheum, Vienna #129/R est:1700-1900

DEMUTH, Charles (1883-1935) American

Works on paper			
£1381	$2500	€2016	Flowers (18x23cm-7x9in) W/C. 16-Apr-4 Du Mouchelle, Detroit #2074/R est:3000-5000
£4696	$8500	€6856	Time out at the track (23x13cm-9x5in) s.d.1919 W/C. 3-Apr-4 Neal Auction Company, New Orleans #515/R est:8000-12000

£5588 $9500 €8158 Pansies (11x14cm-4x6in) init. s.d.1905 verso W/C prov. 30-Oct-3 Phillips, New York #82/R est:10000-15000
£7386 $13000 €10784 Flowers (20x28cm-8x11in) s. W/C pencil exec c.1915-16 prov.exhib.lit. 19-May-4 Sotheby's, New York #130/R est:15000-25000
£9143 $16000 €13349 Two women and a child on the beach (21x28cm-8x11in) W/C pencil prov. 19-Dec-3 Sotheby's, New York #1013/R est:12000-18000

DENAILLY, Louise Hector Francois (1879-1942) French
£1439 $2360 €2000 Portrait of gentleman (100x82cm-39x32in) s. 10-Jun-3 Pandolfini, Florence #130/R est:2200-2400
£1439 $2360 €2000 Portrait of lady (100x82cm-39x32in) s. 10-Jun-3 Pandolfini, Florence #131/R est:2200-2400

DENARIE, Paul (1859-1942) French
£400 $728 €600 Bord de l'Oise (33x23cm-13x9in) s.i.d.1922. 30-Jun-4 Delvaux, Paris #32
£901 $1550 €1315 Market place in Rouen (68x77cm-27x30in) s. 8-Dec-3 Philippe Schuler, Zurich #3401/R (S.FR 2000)
£1176 $2000 €1717 Vente aux encheres - the auction sale (58x91cm-23x36in) s. 22-Nov-3 New Orleans Auction, New Orleans #666/R est:2500-4000
£1333 $2427 €2000 Jetee de roses et vase en porcelaine sur entablement (50x65cm-20x26in) s.d.1908. 30-Jun-4 Delvaux, Paris #29/R

DENBY, Jacquie (20th C) British
£400 $636 €584 Kettleness (73x78cm-29x31in) s. board painted c.1997. 9-Sep-3 David Duggleby, Scarborough #301/R

DENDAL, Andre (1901-1979) Belgian
£306 $548 €450 Nature morte aux fruits (80x90cm-31x35in) s. 16-Mar-4 Vanderkindere, Brussels #40

DENEUX, Gabriel Charles (1856-?) French
Works on paper
£1467 $2684 €2200 Kairouan (26x37cm-10x15in) s.i.d.1909 W/C. 3-Jun-4 Tajan, Paris #217/R est:1500-2000

DENEUX, Jean Dieudonne (1749-1786) Flemish
£4366 $7554 €6200 Nature morte aux fleurs (88x54cm-35x21in) s. 10-Dec-3 Hotel des Ventes Mosan, Brussels #136 est:4000-5000

DENEW, Richard (fl.1827-1858) British
£2000 $3320 €2920 Capriccios (58x48cm-23x19in) s. pair. 2-Oct-3 Neales, Nottingham #759/R est:2000-3000

DENG FEN (1892-1968) Chinese
Works on paper
£1565 $2817 €2285 Night at Port Shelter (18x51cm-7x20in) s.i.d.1963 ink col fan leaf. 25-Apr-4 Christie's, Hong Kong #58/R est:18000-22000 (HK.D 22000)
£2134 $3841 €3116 Horse (18x50cm-7x20in) s.i.d.1961 ink col fan sold with one calligraphy. 26-Apr-4 Sotheby's, Hong Kong #677/R est:20000-30000 (HK.D 30000)
£3089 $5158 €4510 Fish watching (85x29cm-33x11in) s.d.1960 ink col scroll. 26-Oct-3 Christie's, Hong Kong #251/R est:30000-40000 (HK.D 40000)
£6950 $11606 €10147 Gathering in a pavilion (85x33cm-33x13in) s.i. ink col scroll. 26-Oct-3 Christie's, Hong Kong #250/R est:35000-40000 (HK.D 90000)

DENGYEL, Tibor (1913-2000) Belgian/Hungarian
£461 $834 €700 Le bal masque (65x100cm-26x39in) s.d.1960 verso. 19-Apr-4 Horta, Bruxelles #411

DENIES, Isaak (1647-1690) Dutch
£5263 $9684 €8000 Peches, noix et raisins sur entablement (49x39cm-19x15in) 22-Jun-4 Palais de Beaux Arts, Brussels #161/R est:10000-15000
£9155 $15838 €13000 Still life of flowers (65x49cm-26x19in) s.d.1676. 11-Dec-3 Dr Fritz Nagel, Stuttgart #461/R est:24000

DENIS, Jose (19th C) Spanish
£2887 $5053 €4100 Goyan figures (48x34cm-19x13in) s. 16-Dec-3 Segre, Madrid #70/R est:2700

DENIS, Maurice (1870-1943) French
£795 $1454 €1200 Paysage d'automne vu du jardin du Musee du Prieure (46x61cm-18x24in) s.d.15 cardboard. 7-Apr-4 Fraysse & Associes, Paris #1/R
£4901 $8919 €7400 Lecture sur la terrasse (29x39cm-11x15in) mono. canvas on cardboard. 15-Jun-4 Rossini, Paris #33/R est:3000-5000
£5282 $8557 €7500 Nu pour Nausicaa (55x44cm-22x17in) mono.d.1913 prov.lit. 5-Aug-3 Tajan, Paris #25/R est:8000-10000
£6704 $12000 €9788 Ruins in Lebanon (26x18cm-10x7in) s.d.1929 panel. 6-May-4 Shannon's, Milford #102/R est:12000-18000
£12676 $21042 €18000 Berger brebis (84x62cm-33x24in) s.d.1921 cardboard. 16-Jun-3 E & Eve, Paris #85
£14000 $25760 €21000 Allegorie de l'art (145x223cm-57x88in) mono. paper on canvas prov.lit. 8-Jun-4 Artcurial Briest, Paris #126/R est:15000-20000
£17000 $28390 €24820 Plage au yacht (55x46cm-22x18in) s. board painted 1938 prov.exhib.lit. 21-Oct-3 Sotheby's, London #28/R est:18000-25000
£80000 $147200 €116800 Danse - Eternel ete, Wiesbaden (146x83cm-57x33in) s. painted c.1905 prov.exhib. 22-Jun-4 Sotheby's, London #138/R est:80000-120000
£120000 $218400 €175200 Porte de Concarneau (65x92cm-26x36in) s.d.1924 prov.exhib.lit. 4-Feb-4 Sotheby's, London #246/R est:50000-70000
Prints
£1867 $3435 €2800 Sur le canape d'argent pale (42x29cm-17x11in) col lithograph exec. 1892-99 one of 100. 11-Jun-4 Villa Grisebach, Berlin #1508/R est:1200-1500
£3631 $6500 €5301 Sur le canape d'argent pale (42x28cm-17x11in) lithograph. 6-May-4 Swann Galleries, New York #279/R est:5000-8000
Works on paper
£2365 $4233 €3500 Etude de jeune Bretonne (34x25cm-13x10in) st.mono. crayon prov. 7-May-4 Millon & Associes, Paris #101/R est:4000-5000
£3334 $6134 €5000 Paysage de foret (29x22cm-11x9in) mono.d.1888 W/C prov. 9-Jun-4 Tajan, Paris #2/R est:6000-8000

DENIS, Simon Joseph Alexander Clement (1755-1813) Flemish
£306 $547 €450 Belier et moutons (15x20cm-6x8in) i.mono.verso paper. 17-Mar-4 Tajan, Paris #98
£1184 $2179 €1800 Vues des Cascades de Tivoli (39x58cm-15x23in) paper on cardboard. 25-Jun-4 Rossini, Paris #53 est:2000-3000
£5443 $9742 €8000 Bovin dans un etable (19x29cm-7x11in) s.verso paper. 17-Mar-4 Tajan, Paris #72/R est:2000
£20833 $37500 €30416 River landscape with an approaching storm, figures running in the foreground (57x70cm-22x28in) s.d.1791. 22-Jan-4 Sotheby's, New York #230/R est:30000-40000

DENIS, Simon Joseph Alexander Clement (attrib) (1755-1813) Flemish
£1333 $2427 €2000 Paysage de campagne italienne (32x46cm-13x18in) panel. 30-Jun-4 Delvaux, Paris #150a/R est:2000-3000
Works on paper
£750 $1298 €1095 Roman Campagna views and church and monastery at Ariccia. indis.sig.verso black chk pen grey ink col wash 3 in 1 mount prov. 12-Dec-3 Christie's, Kensington #462/R
£3741 $6697 €5500 Vue de port de Naples avec le chateau de l'oeuf (35x51cm-14x20in) brown wash black crayon. 17-Mar-4 Tajan, Paris #75/R est:3000-4000

DENISON, Stephen (1909-) British
£400 $720 €584 Sleningford Mill, on the Ure (63x76cm-25x30in) s.d.46 i.verso. 21-Apr-4 Tennants, Leyburn #1239

DENISSOV, Youri (?) Russian
£272 $495 €400 Rue de St Petersbourg. s. 8-Feb-4 Lesieur & Le Bars, Le Havre #32
£578 $1052 €850 La patinoire. s. 8-Feb-4 Lesieur & Le Bars, Le Havre #78
£714 $1300 €1050 Scene de la gare. s. 8-Feb-4 Lesieur & Le Bars, Le Havre #123
£918 $1671 €1350 Classe de ballet. s. 8-Feb-4 Lesieur & Le Bars, Le Havre #122/R

DENMARK (1950-) Belgian
Works on paper
£9500 $17290 €13870 Time Magazine (112x303cm-44x119in) paper copper wire. 21-Jun-4 Bonhams, New Bond Street #105/R est:10000-12000

DENNEHY, Douglas Manson (1927-) Irish
£872 $1544 €1300 Farmstead, west of Ireland (30x61cm-12x24in) s. i.verso board. 27-Apr-4 Whyte's, Dublin #232/R
£1690 $2704 €2400 Village scene, County Kerry (30x61cm-12x24in) s. i.verso board. 16-Sep-3 Whyte's, Dublin #184/R est:1800-2200

DENNER, Balthasar (1685-1749) German
£1678 $3087 €2500 Portrait de dame au besicle tenant un livre (54x40cm-21x16in) 24-Mar-4 Tajan, Paris #84 est:2000-3000
£2200 $3960 €3212 Portrait of an elderly lady wearing a headscarf (38x32cm-15x13in) 20-Apr-4 Sotheby's, Olympia #346/R est:1500-2000
£2376 $4300 €3469 Portrait of a gentleman in blue coat (76x64cm-30x25in) s. 16-Apr-4 James Julia, Fairfield #652/R est:4000-6000

DENNER, Balthasar (attrib) (1685-1749) German
£709 $1149 €1000 Portrait of old bearded man (62x53cm-24x21in) i. verso lit. 23-May-3 Karlheinz Kaupp, Staufen #1728/R

DENNER, Esther (18th C) German
Works on paper
£268 $494 €400 Putti fishing (15x35cm-6x14in) i. Indian ink. 26-Mar-4 Ketterer, Hamburg #232/R

DENNERY, Gustave Lucien (1863-?) French
£333 $610 €500 Lady in the garden (46x60cm-18x24in) s. 5-Jun-4 Arnold, Frankfurt #560/R

DENNIS, Margery (1922-) Australian
£859 $1607 €1289 Near Adelong, N S W (85x121cm-33x48in) s.d.88 board prov. 21-Jul-4 Shapiro, Sydney #148/R est:2000-3000 (A.D 2200)

DENNIS, Morgan (1892-1960) American
Works on paper
£216 $400 €315 Untitled (38x28cm-15x11in) s. W/C. 15-Feb-4 Outer Cape Auctions, Provincetown #75a/R
£245 $400 €358 Low tide, Turbot's Creek (28x41cm-11x16in) s. W/C. 19-Jul-3 Outer Cape Auctions, Provincetown #173/R
£249 $450 €364 Black and white Scotties under an apple tree (25x18cm-10x7in) pencil. 3-Apr-4 Outer Cape Auctions, Provincetown #68/R
£307 $500 €448 Two wire Fox Terriers on porch (25x33cm-10x13in) s. graphite htd white. 19-Jul-3 Outer Cape Auctions, Provincetown #147/R
£324 $600 €473 Why bury that? (20x20cm-8x8in) pencil. 15-Feb-4 Outer Cape Auctions, Provincetown #80a/R

DENNIS, Roger Wilson (1902-1996) American
£222 $400 €324 Shoreline and dunes (38x48cm-15x19in) s.d.84 i.verso canvasboard. 26-Apr-4 Winter Associates, Plainville #141/R
£2245 $3750 €3278 Repairs (51x61cm-20x24in) s.i.verso. 23-Oct-3 Shannon's, Milford #86/R est:3000-5000

DENNY, Gideon Jacques (1830-1886) American
£4891 $9000 €7141 Sailing boat with larger vessels in distance (50x91cm-20x36in) mono. prov. 8-Jun-4 Bonhams & Butterfields, San Francisco #4225/R est:3000-5000

DENNY, Robin (1930-) British
£1300 $2327 €1898 Apart, Here and then series (239x188cm-94x74in) s.d.68-72 stretcher s.i.d.verso. 16-Mar-4 Bonhams, New Bond Street #106/R est:1000-1500
£1800 $3222 €2628 Aside, Here and then series (239x188cm-94x74in) 16-Mar-4 Bonhams, New Bond Street #107/R est:1000-1500

DENON, Vivant Dominique (1747-1825) French
Works on paper
£775 $1340 €1100 Couple eclaire par une bougie (10x16cm-4x6in) pen black ink grey wash htd white gouache. 12-Dec-3 Renaud, Paris #100

DENONNE, Alexander (1879-1953) Belgian
£267 $477 €400 Parc anime (35x25cm-14x10in) s. 11-May-4 Vanderkindere, Brussels #57
£336 $624 €500 The reading (100x70cm-39x28in) s. 8-Mar-4 Bernaerts, Antwerp #101/R
£374 $670 €550 Le peintre et son modele. s. canvas on panel. 16-Mar-4 Vanderkindere, Brussels #86
£517 $957 €750 Vue animee du Parc de Bruxelles (80x60cm-31x24in) s. 13-Jan-4 Vanderkindere, Brussels #2
£524 $892 €750 Allee animee (80x60cm-31x24in) s. 18-Nov-3 Vanderkindere, Brussels #242
£633 $1159 €950 Le verger (80x70cm-31x28in) s. 7-Jun-4 Palais de Beaux Arts, Brussels #57/R
£1722 $3134 €2600 Ruelle marchande animee (50x60cm-20x24in) s. 15-Jun-4 Galerie Moderne, Brussels #135/R est:400-600

DENT, John (1951-) Australian
£732 $1149 €1061 Victorian gothic (99x89cm-39x35in) prov.exhib. 27-Aug-3 Christie's, Sydney #559/R est:1800-2500 (A.D 1800)

DENTON, Kenneth (1932-) British
£400 $720 €584 St. Benet's Abbey, Norfolk (34x54cm-13x21in) s. i.verso board. 22-Apr-4 Lawrence, Crewkerne #952
£450 $810 €657 Trafalgar Square (41x61cm-16x24in) s. board. 20-Jan-4 Bonhams, Knightsbridge #182/R

DENTON, Lois C (1887-1980) American
£509 $850 €743 Hueco tanks (61x76cm-24x30in) canvasboard. 18-Oct-3 David Dike, Dallas #278/R
£539 $900 €787 Blossoming desert off Sandhills road (41x51cm-16x20in) canvasboard. 18-Oct-3 David Dike, Dallas #236/R
£569 $950 €831 Landscape (46x61cm-18x24in) canvasboard. 18-Oct-3 David Dike, Dallas #270/R
£599 $1000 €875 Cabin interior (61x76cm-24x30in) canvasboard. 18-Oct-3 David Dike, Dallas #300/R

DENTON, Ray (1939-) British
£950 $1777 €1387 In the harbour St Ives (80x90cm-31x35in) s. prov. 26-Feb-4 Lane, Penzance #27

DENTON, Troy (1949-) American
£326 $600 €476 Cattle driving (91x122cm-36x48in) s. 27-Jun-4 Bonhams & Butterfields, San Francisco #3841/R

D'ENTRAYGUES, Charles Bertrand (1851-?) French
£7200 $12024 €10512 French farmyard with poultry and children (100x81cm-39x32in) s. 12-Nov-3 Sotheby's, Olympia #212/R est:6000-8000

DENTZEL, Gustav A (attrib) (19/20th C) American
Sculpture
£58011 $105000 €84696 Standing giraffe (170cm-67in) painted wood glass leather brass iron. 3-Apr-4 Nadeau, Windsor #50/R est:15000-20000

DENZEL, Anton (1888-1962) German
£336 $617 €500 Boy leading cows across river (51x69cm-20x27in) s.d.21 lit. 25-Mar-4 Karlheinz Kaupp, Staufen #2411/R
£433 $780 €650 Two sheep (36x50cm-14x20in) s.d.1938 panel. 26-Apr-4 Rieber, Stuttgart #814/R
£486 $871 €720 Spring day in Upper Swabia (31x37cm-12x15in) s.d.1920 canvas on board. 6-May-4 Michael Zeller, Lindau #642/R

DEPARIS, Daniel Gustave Jean (20th C) French
£1243 $2250 €1815 Dachshund, a place in the sun (38x55cm-15x22in) s. 30-Mar-4 Bonhams & Butterfields, San Francisco #130/R est:2200-3300

DEPAULIS, Alexis Joseph (1792-1867) French
Sculpture
£1294 $2200 €1889 Loui-Philippe (24x24cm-9x9in) s.i. marble relief. 28-Oct-3 Christie's, Rockefeller NY #123/R

DEPERO, Fortunato (1892-1960) Italian
£906 $1676 €1350 Season (50x60cm-20x24in) s. s.i.verso. 13-Mar-4 Meeting Art, Vercelli #530
£7042 $12324 €10000 Study for Vogue (36x22cm-14x9in) s.d.1929 tempera paper prov. 16-Dec-3 Porro, Milan #5/R est:5000-7000
£13287 $22587 €19000 Three heads (89x68cm-35x27in) s. tempera paper. 29-Nov-3 Farsetti, Prato #462/R est:18000-22000
£13514 $23784 €20000 Rural view (71x77cm-28x30in) s. board lit. 24-May-4 Christie's, Milan #281/R est:20000-30000
£15436 $27631 €23000 Face of woman and flowers (35x24cm-14x9in) s.d.1917 verso canvas on cardboard. 25-May-4 Sotheby's, Milan #238/R est:18000-22000
£17568 $32500 €25649 Succulent plants (110x75cm-43x30in) s.i.d.1946 panel. 12-Feb-4 Sotheby's, New York #44/R est:8000-12000
Works on paper
£1007 $1862 €1500 Study for carving (27x21cm-11x8in) init. pencil lit. 13-Mar-4 Meeting Art, Vercelli #476 est:1500
£1074 $1987 €1600 Study for interior (49x39cm-19x15in) pencil. 13-Mar-4 Meeting Art, Vercelli #38 est:1000
£1074 $1922 €1600 Study (25x15cm-10x6in) s. cgi. exec.1944-45. 25-May-4 Sotheby's, Milan #108/R est:1500
£1429 $2557 €2100 Dog (21x15cm-8x6in) s.d.1946 ink W/C exhib.lit. 16-Mar-4 Finarte Semenzato, Milan #117/R est:1700
£1678 $2853 €2400 Study for advertising (20x13cm-8x5in) s.d.1922 col Chinese ink. 25-Nov-3 Sotheby's, Milan #24/R
£1701 $3044 €2500 Study for composition (26x17cm-10x7in) s.d.1949 pencil pen W/C. 16-Mar-4 Finarte Semenzato, Milan #434/R est:2200
£1812 $2971 €2500 Study (21x18cm-8x7in) s.d.1948 Chinese ink W/C pencil. 27-May-3 Sotheby's, Milan #59/R est:2500
£2027 $3568 €3000 Campari (12x9cm-5x4in) s.i. W/C pencil ink paper on card exec.c.1927. 24-May-4 Christie's, Milan #137/R est:3000-4000
£2027 $3568 €3000 Alpine landscape (36x35cm-14x14in) pencil ink exec.1935-36. 24-May-4 Christie's, Milan #135/R est:3000-4000
£2238 $3804 €3200 Bedroom gymnastics (46x37cm-18x15in) s. chl exec.c.1951. 25-Nov-3 Sotheby's, Milan #21/R est:2500-3000
£2483 $4445 €3700 Study (20x19cm-8x7in) s.d.1922 chl Chinese ink. 25-May-4 Sotheby's, Milan #110/R est:1700
£2536 $4159 €3500 Study (20x16cm-8x6in) s. pencil ink exec.c.1917. 27-May-3 Sotheby's, Milan #60/R est:4000
£2797 $4755 €4000 Alpine flowers (61x49cm-24x19in) s. chl exec.c.1953. 25-Nov-3 Sotheby's, Milan #23/R est:3500-4000
£2817 $4676 €4000 Spinning head (20x32cm-8x13in) s.d.946 i.verso chl. 11-Jun-3 Finarte Semenzato, Milan #502/R est:2400-3000
£3020 $5406 €4500 Study (31x14cm-12x6in) s.i.d.1948 chl pencil. 25-May-4 Sotheby's, Milan #109/R est:2000
£4545 $7727 €6500 Dog and reflections (27x14cm-11x6in) s. pencil. 26-Nov-3 Pandolfini, Florence #20/R est:6500-7500
£5634 $9352 €8000 Figura (60x50cm-24x20in) s.d.1940 mixed media. 14-Jun-3 Meeting Art, Vercelli #233/R est:8000
£8392 $14266 €12000 Plough man (15x23cm-6x9in) d.1914 ink W/C prov.exhib. 24-Nov-3 Christie's, Milan #304/R est:10000-13000
£9790 $16643 €14000 Little match (50x51cm-20x20in) s. wool collage exec.1924. 25-Nov-3 Sotheby's, Milan #178/R est:13000-18000
£11189 $19021 €16000 Shrink (14x18cm-6x7in) s. Chinese ink lit. 25-Nov-3 Sotheby's, Milan #20/R est:3500-4000
£12081 $21624 €18000 Jugglers (177x93cm-70x37in) pencil paper on canvas exec.1920. 25-May-4 Sotheby's, Milan #113/R est:18000-25000
£14765 $26430 €22000 Venice, Pola, Florence (97x135cm-38x53in) Chinese ink tempera paper on canvas. 25-May-4 Sotheby's, Milan #112/R est:28000

DEPERTHES, Jacques (1936-) French?
£300 $537 €438 After the snow storm (70x70cm-28x28in) s. s.i.verso. 18-Mar-4 Christie's, Kensington #700/R
£428 $800 €625 Provence (74x91cm-29x36in) s. s.i.d.1968 verso. 24-Feb-4 Arthur James, Florida #126
£877 $1465 €1280 La rue (55x46cm-22x18in) s. 16-Nov-3 Koller, Geneva #1217/R (S.FR 2000)

DEPETRIS, Giovanni (1890-1940) Italian
£1448 $2404 €2100 Vegetable garden in Villa Bonomino (19x26cm-7x10in) s.d.920 board. 1-Oct-3 Della Rocca, Turin #23/R est:1500-2000

D'EPINAY, Prosper (1830-1914) French
Sculpture
£12368 $22758 €18800 Ceinture doree (96cm-38in) white marble. 24-Jun-4 Claude Boisgirard, Paris #102/R est:18000-20000
£22000 $39600 €32120 Standing nude (97cm-38in) s.d.1873 white marble lit. 21-Apr-4 Sotheby's, London #102/R est:20000-25000

DEPREY, A (18/19th C) French
Works on paper
£814 $1385 €1188 Landscapes (13x18cm-5x7in) one s.d.1803 verso gouache two. 1-Dec-3 Koller, Zurich #6449 est:1800-2500 (S.FR 1800)

DEPYPERE, Michel (1923-1978) Belgian
£347 $580 €500 Promeneurs a la plage (60x70cm-24x28in) s. 21-Oct-3 Campo & Campo, Antwerp #90

DERAIN, Andre (1880-1954) French
£1923 $3019 €3000 Au parc (14x19cm-6x7in) 15-Dec-2 St-Germain-en-Laye Encheres #4 est:4000-5000
£2051 $3221 €3200 Bobby de trois-quart (18x17cm-7x7in) studio st.verso. 15-Dec-2 St-Germain-en-Laye Encheres #7/R est:3000-5000
£2349 $4205 €3500 Portrait de femme (18x16cm-7x6in) 25-May-4 Karl & Faber, Munich #256/R est:7000
£2980 $5454 €4500 Scene mythologique (19x19cm-7x7in) s. exhib. 7-Apr-4 Fraysse & Associes, Paris #2/R est:4000-6000
£3200 $5088 €4640 Nature morte (59x33cm-23x13in) s. 11-Sep-3 Christie's, Kensington #40/R est:2500-3500

£3205	$5032	€5000	Bobby a la palette (39x20cm-15x8in) 15-Dec-2 St-Germain-en-Laye Encheres #2 est:8000-10000
£3352	$6000	€4894	Panier de fleurs (37x46cm-15x18in) with sig. panel prov. 6-May-4 Doyle, New York #106/R est:12000-18000
£3476	$6500	€5075	Rose (20x18cm-8x7in) s. canvas on board. 25-Feb-4 Christie's, Rockefeller NY #21/R est:4000-6000
£3819	$6378	€5500	Nymphes dans un paysage (22x38cm-9x15in) s. painted c.1946-1950. 21-Oct-3 Artcurial Briest, Paris #224a/R est:6000-8000
£4161	$7740	€6200	Paysage a Ousson (30x36cm-12x14in) s. paper on canvas. 3-Mar-4 Tajan, Paris #117/R est:6500-7500
£4444	$7378	€6488	Still life with grapes and pears (29x38cm-11x15in) 2-Oct-3 Heffel, Vancouver #14 (C.D 10000)
£4564	$8534	€6800	Nu assis (33x27cm-13x11in) s. prov. 29-Feb-4 Versailles Encheres #124/R est:5000-6000
£4828	$8690	€7000	Paysage aux deux arbres (23x35cm-9x14in) s. painted 1928 prov.lit. 25-Jan-4 Chayette & Cheval, Paris #242/R est:7000-7500
£5689	$9500	€8306	Portrait de Maria Lani (46x38cm-18x15in) s. prov.exhib.lit. 7-Oct-3 Sotheby's, New York #263 est:10000-15000
£6000	$10380	€8760	Young girl with a red bow (28x18cm-11x7in) s. prov. 11-Dec-3 Christie's, Kensington #58/R est:3000-5000
£7500	$13725	€10950	Shepherd and flock in a landscape (27x50cm-11x20in) s. prov. 7-Apr-4 Woolley & Wallis, Salisbury #326/R est:7500-10000
£8242	$15000	€12033	Foret de fontainbleau (40x49cm-16x19in) s. painted c.1935-36. 29-Jun-4 Sotheby's, New York #335/R est:10000-15000
£8334	$13917	€12000	Portrait de femme (35x27cm-14x11in) trace sig. lit. 21-Oct-3 Artcurial Briest, Paris #224/R est:12000-15000
£10667	$19627	€16000	Jeune fille au chapeau (38x55cm-15x22in) s. painted c.1931 prov.exhib.lit. 9-Jun-4 Tajan, Paris #46/R est:10000-12000
£10897	$17109	€17000	Portrait de femme au collier de perles (55x46cm-22x18in) studio st.verso painted c.1950 lit. 15-Dec-2 St-Germain-en-Laye Encheres #3/R est:15000-18000
£11765	$20000	€17177	Bagneuse debout de dos dans un paysage (74x57cm-29x22in) s. painted c.1925 prov.exhib.lit. 6-Nov-3 Sotheby's, New York #354/R est:25000-35000
£12667	$23307	€19000	Nus autour d'un repas champetre (30x30cm-12x12in) s. exec. c.1946-1950 lit. 8-Jun-4 Artcurial Briest, Paris #152/R est:15000-20000
£13000	$23660	€18980	Nu au bord de la mer (37x22cm-15x9in) s. painted c.1924 prov. 4-Feb-4 Sotheby's, London #252/R est:7000-10000
£13497	$22000	€19706	L'eglise de Crecy-en-Brie (54x55cm-21x22in) s. painted c.1910 prov.exhib.lit. 25-Sep-3 Christie's, Rockefeller NY #522/R est:20000-30000
£13816	$25421	€21000	Portrait (45x28cm-18x11in) st.sig. cardboard painted c.1913 prov. 23-Jun-4 Maigret, Paris #28/R est:8000-12000
£13986	$24056	€20000	Paysage de Provence (37x46cm-15x18in) s. prov.lit. 8-Dec-3 Artcurial Briest, Paris #27/R est:22000-28000
£14667	$26547	€22000	Buste de jeune garcon (73x60cm-29x24in) s. prov. 1-Apr-4 Credit Municipal, Paris #55/R est:20000-25000
£18543	$33748	€28000	Vase de fleurs (55x46cm-22x18in) s. painted c.1945-48. 16-Jun-4 Renaud, Paris #54/R est:18000-20000
£19005	$32308	€42000	Bord de Seine a Carrieres-sur-Seine (46x55cm-18x22in) s. painted 1913 prov. 25-Nov-3 Pierre Berge, Paris #12/R est:20000-25000
£22000	$40040	€32120	Le village (65x81cm-26x32in) painted c.1912 prov.exhib. 3-Feb-4 Christie's, London #157/R est:15000-20000
£22059	$37500	€32206	Nu allonge s'appuyant sur un bras (72x185cm-28x73in) s. prov.exhib.lit. 6-Nov-3 Sotheby's, New York #337/R est:35000-45000
£25000	$42500	€36500	Paysage de Sainte-Maxime (33x41cm-13x16in) s. painted c.1930 prov.exhib.lit. 6-Nov-3 Sotheby's, New York #335/R est:25000-35000
Prints			
£4412	$7500	€6442	Tete de femme (32x22cm-13x9in) s. drypoint exec.c.1910. 6-Nov-3 Swann Galleries, New York #538/R est:4000-6000
Sculpture			
£1000	$1840	€1500	Tete primitive (5x2x3cm-2x1x1in) bronze. 10-Jun-4 Hauswedell & Nolte, Hamburg #132/R est:1800
£2000	$3180	€2900	Tete (13cm-5in) i.num.6/11 brown pat. bronze lit. 11-Sep-3 Christie's, Kensington #42/R est:2500-3500
£2013	$3604	€3000	Personnage au bras gauche leve (13x10x2cm-5x4x1in) s. num.3/11 pat bronze prov.lit. 26-May-4 Christie's, Paris #32/R est:3000-5000
£2349	$4370	€3500	Personnage a la fleur (13x10x3cm-5x4x1in) i.num.00 verso bas relief brown pat bronze exhib.lit. 2-Mar-4 Artcurial Briest, Paris #157/R est:3000-4000
£23529	$40000	€34352	Femme au long cou (32cm-13in) i. num.11/11 brown red pat bronze conceived 1930s prov.exhib.lit. 6-Nov-3 Sotheby's, New York #310/R est:12000-18000
Works on paper			
£243	$406	€350	Jeune femme (32x25cm-13x10in) studio st. lead pencil. 21-Oct-3 Artcurial Briest, Paris #49
£256	$403	€400	Bobby, etude du nu. violette ink dr double-sided. 15-Dec-2 St-Germain-en-Laye Encheres #32
£268	$494	€400	Tete d'homme (20x18cm-8x7in) studio st. chl. 24-Mar-4 Joron-Derem, Paris #44
£278	$464	€400	Jeune femme a la chevelure (32x25cm-13x10in) studio st. lead pencil drawing. 21-Oct-3 Artcurial Briest, Paris #50
£300	$543	€438	Femme a genoux (49x37cm-19x15in) studio st. pencil tracing paper. 1-Apr-4 Christie's, Kensington #7/R
£334	$600	€500	Nu allonge (19x26cm-7x10in) graphite. 26-Apr-4 Tajan, Paris #31/R
£336	$617	€500	Raymonde allongee (18x27cm-7x11in) bears studio st. black crayon. 28-Mar-4 Anaf, Lyon #102
£345	$572	€500	Deux jeunes femmes (22x28cm-9x11in) studio st. graphite. 1-Oct-3 Millon & Associes, Paris #33
£347	$566	€500	Le Romain (29x17cm-11x7in) st. crayon. 18-Jul-3 Feletin, Province #155
£369	$687	€550	Cheval stylise (30x37cm-12x15in) graphite blue crayon. 2-Mar-4 Artcurial Briest, Paris #38
£370	$618	€530	Paysage anime (20x29cm-8x11in) studio st. crayon drawing. 21-Oct-3 Artcurial Briest, Paris #58
£372	$584	€580	Le dieu Pan (21x13cm-8x5in) violette ink dr. 15-Dec-2 St-Germain-en-Laye Encheres #28
£430	$788	€650	Modele assis le buste decouvert (25x19cm-10x7in) studio st. black crayon stump. 7-Apr-4 Doutrebente, Paris #35
£449	$704	€700	Tete de Bobby (27x21cm-11x8in) pastel dr. 15-Dec-2 St-Germain-en-Laye Encheres #5
£451	$754	€650	Tete (28x28cm-11x11in) studio st. graphite. 23-Oct-3 Credit Municipal, Paris #52
£462	$725	€720	Vieille paysanne (22x17cm-9x7in) gouache. 15-Dec-2 St-Germain-en-Laye Encheres #37/R
£466	$840	€700	L'homme au fouet (18x23cm-7x9in) ink wash prov. 26-Apr-4 Tajan, Paris #28
£470	$864	€700	Nu les jambes croisees (19x29cm-7x11in) bears studio st. black crayon. 28-Mar-4 Anaf, Lyon #101
£486	$812	€700	Nu en mouvement (48x36cm-19x14in) studio st. chl tracing paper. 21-Oct-3 Artcurial Briest, Paris #57
£486	$812	€700	Etude de nu (26x20cm-10x8in) bears studio st. graphite. 23-Oct-3 Credit Municipal, Paris #94
£486	$812	€700	Nu allonge (26x41cm-10x16in) s.i. graphite. 23-Oct-3 Credit Municipal, Paris #95
£513	$805	€800	Tete d'homme (27x21cm-11x8in) violette ink dr. 15-Dec-2 St-Germain-en-Laye Encheres #31/R
£541	$968	€800	Visage (15x15cm-6x6in) crayon. 5-May-4 Coutau Begarie, Paris #34/R
£541	$968	€800	Les baigneuses (28x18cm-11x7in) crayon. 5-May-4 Coutau Begarie, Paris #35
£550	$990	€803	Cantrice (23x18cm-9x7in) studio st. W/C. 20-Jan-4 Bonhams, Knightsbridge #62/R
£581	$1000	€848	Standing female nude (30x20cm-12x8in) ink prov. 7-Dec-3 Freeman, Philadelphia #56
£583	$1050	€875	Personnage a la cape (28x20cm-11x8in) gouache prov. 26-Apr-4 Tajan, Paris #25/R
£590	$986	€850	Etude de nu (24x20cm-9x8in) bears studio st. graphite. 23-Oct-3 Credit Municipal, Paris #93
£592	$1089	€900	Nu assis (42x30cm-17x12in) studio st. graphite. 22-Jun-4 Ribeyre & Baron, Paris #58/R
£595	$1023	€850	La colline bleue (21x16cm-8x6in) bears studio st. W/C prov. 3-Dec-3 Tajan, Paris #53/R
£600	$1002	€876	Nude seated (14x22cm-6x9in) pencil prov. 22-Oct-3 Sotheby's, Olympia #7/R
£600	$1104	€876	Femme debout (23x20cm-9x8in) pencil prov. 24-Mar-4 Sotheby's, Olympia #17/R
£600	$1080	€900	Le porte etendard (25x22cm-10x9in) ink gouache double-sided prov. 26-Apr-4 Tajan, Paris #23/R est:1000-1500
£600	$1080	€900	Etude pour une reine (26x22cm-10x9in) gouache prov. 26-Apr-4 Tajan, Paris #26/R
£600	$1080	€900	Femme provencale portant un panier de fleurs (23x14cm-9x6in) s. W/C. 26-Apr-4 Tajan, Paris #27/R
£604	$1069	€900	Tete de faune (19x20cm-7x8in) lead pencil. 27-Apr-4 Artcurial Briest, Paris #102
£608	$1149	€900	Nu allonge (38x48cm-15x19in) studio st. graphite. 21-Feb-4 Cornette de St.Cyr, Paris #197/R
£641	$1006	€1000	Monsieur, Madame, et leur chien (21x27cm-8x11in) black crayon dr. 15-Dec-2 St-Germain-en-Laye Encheres #27/R
£662	$1212	€1000	Visage (25x19cm-10x7in) studio st. black crayon. 7-Apr-4 Doutrebente, Paris #34/R
£667	$1200	€1000	Personnage du moyen-age (14x15cm-6x6in) col wash. 26-Apr-4 Tajan, Paris #30/R
£671	$1188	€1000	Profil de jeune femme (51x40cm-20x16in) studio st. felt pen. 27-Apr-4 Artcurial Briest, Paris #100
£738	$1358	€1100	Visages (31x25cm-12x10in) bears studio st. black crayon estompe. 28-Mar-4 Anaf, Lyon #100/R
£750	$1380	€1095	Femme nue (23x16cm-9x6in) black crayon prov. 24-Mar-4 Sotheby's, Olympia #18/R
£777	$1469	€1150	Nu debout (32x25cm-13x10in) studio st. graphite double-sided. 21-Feb-4 Cornette de St.Cyr, Paris #198/R
£795	$1446	€1200	Nu feminin au collier (29x19cm-11x7in) studio st. crayon dr. 15-Jun-4 Rossini, Paris #161/R
£800	$1440	€1200	Le hallebardier (25x17cm-10x7in) W/C prov. 26-Apr-4 Tajan, Paris #22/R est:1200-1500
£800	$1440	€1200	Etude pour la citadelle (18x28cm-7x11in) gouache prov. 26-Apr-4 Tajan, Paris #24/R est:1000-1500
£833	$1308	€1300	Arlequin et colombine (22x17cm-9x7in) ink dr. 15-Dec-2 St-Germain-en-Laye Encheres #24/R
£872	$1605	€1300	Nu debout (41x29cm-16x11in) s. sanguine. 28-Mar-4 Anaf, Lyon #103
£872	$1605	€1300	Dans l'atelier (29x39cm-11x15in) bears studio st. black crayon. 28-Mar-4 Anaf, Lyon #104
£872	$1605	€1300	Chevalier et son ecuyer (35x31cm-14x12in) bears studio st. black crayon. 28-Mar-4 Anaf, Lyon #106
£894	$1600	€1305	Reclining nude (32x48cm-13x19in) s. pencil brush W/C wash prov. 6-May-4 Doyle, New York #103/R est:2000-3000
£933	$1699	€1400	Femme au pied de la statue (35x27cm-14x11in) s. ink graphite dr. 4-Jul-4 Eric Pillon, Calais #170/R
£934	$1680	€1400	Le chapeau tricolore (34x26cm-13x10in) gouache. 26-Apr-4 Tajan, Paris #21/R est:1500-2000
£1000	$1840	€1500	Femme au chapeau a plume (23x17cm-9x7in) W/C gouache. 10-Jun-4 Camard, Paris #160 est:1500-1800
£1000	$1840	€1500	Femme a la jupe bleue (23x15cm-9x6in) W/C gouache ink. 10-Jun-4 Camard, Paris #161 est:1500-1800
£1026	$1610	€1600	Bobby en colere (30x26cm-12x10in) pastel. 15-Dec-2 St-Germain-en-Laye Encheres #9/R est:1500-2000
£1042	$1740	€1500	La danse (22x25cm-9x10in) studio st. Indian ink. 25-Oct-3 Cornette de St.Cyr, Paris #494 est:1500-2000
£1056	$1828	€1500	Jeune femme accroupie (32x24cm-13x9in) studio st. graphite dr. 9-Dec-3 Artcurial Briest, Paris #197 est:1500-2000
£1067	$1963	€1600	Portrait de femme brune (65x54cm-26x21in) s. pastel. 10-Jun-4 Camard, Paris #157 est:1600-1800
£1067	$1963	€1600	Le modele nu assis (59x42cm-23x17in) s. sanguin. 14-Jun-4 Tajan, Paris #37/R est:1200-1500
£1100	$1837	€1606	Femme nue (22x16cm-9x6in) pencil prov. 22-Oct-3 Sotheby's, Olympia #1/R est:600-800
£1154	$1812	€1800	Tete de Bobby (27x34cm-11x13in) pastel. 15-Dec-2 St-Germain-en-Laye Encheres #12/R est:1200-1500
£1200	$2160	€1752	Captain (20x18cm-8x7in) studio st. W/C. 20-Jan-4 Bonhams, Knightsbridge #65/R est:500-800
£1200	$2160	€1800	View of village with bell tower (30x24cm-12x9in) s.pencil. 22-Apr-4 Finarte Semenzato, Rome #137/R
£1245	$2204	€1818	Landscape (21x34cm-8x13in) init. pencil prov. 27-Apr-4 AB Stockholms Auktionsverk #1217/R est:12000-15000 (S.KR 17000)
£1250	$2088	€1800	Les ruines (31x48cm-12x19in) s. ink wash sepia exec. c.1930. 21-Oct-3 Christie's, Paris #63/R est:1000-1500
£1310	$2359	€1900	Seated nude (44x58cm-17x23in) s. chl drawing prov. 25-Jan-4 Chayette & Cheval, Paris #271/R est:2000-2500
£1477	$2717	€2200	Fruits, pichet et bouteille (15x22cm-6x9in) bears studio st. gouache. 28-Mar-4 Anaf, Lyon #107/R est:1800-2000
£1477	$2717	€2200	Cruches, raisin et poires (14x19cm-6x7in) bears studio st. gouache. 28-Mar-4 Anaf, Lyon #108 est:1800-2000
£1500	$2715	€2190	Femme nue (26x21cm-10x8in) studio st. pencil sold with another by the same hand. 1-Apr-4 Christie's, Kensington #5/R est:1200-1800
£1538	$2415	€2400	Bobby au collier de perles (27x21cm-11x8in) pastel. 15-Dec-2 St-Germain-en-Laye Encheres #11/R est:1000-1200
£1571	$2466	€2450	Visages (27x22cm-11x9in) black crayon one double-sided five. 15-Dec-2 St-Germain-en-Laye Encheres #22 est:1500-2000
£1800	$3114	€2628	La foret (42x57cm-17x22in) s. pencil. 11-Dec-3 Christie's, Kensington #51/R est:2000-3000

£1800 $3258 €2628 Nue au repos (25x30cm-10x12in) studio st. pencil. 1-Apr-4 Christie's, Kensington #2/R est:600-800
£1879 $3495 €2800 Etude pur un portrait (63x48cm-25x19in) studio st. graphite. 2-Mar-4 Artcurial Briest, Paris #40/R est:3000-3500
£1974 $3632 €3000 Paysage du midi (35x45cm-14x18in) s. ink ink wash. 28-Jun-4 Joron-Derem, Paris #90/R est:3000-4000
£2361 $3943 €3400 Paysage aux deux clochers (36x57cm-14x22in) s. brown ink wash. 21-Oct-3 Artcurial Briest, Paris #51/R est:2000-3000
£2436 $3824 €3800 Portrait de Bobby (27x21cm-11x8in) chl drs one double-sided nine. 15-Dec-2 St-Germain-en-Laye Encheres #10 est:5000-6000
£2465 $4265 €3500 Nu de dos (60x42cm-24x17in) s. sanguine dr. 9-Dec-3 Artcurial Briest, Paris #198/R
£2800 $4452 €4060 La dans (44x37cm-17x15in) s. bodycol. 11-Sep-3 Christie's, Kensington #41/R est:3000-4000
£2800 $5040 €4088 Sarabande (16x23cm-6x9in) st.sig. W/C gouache prov. 21-Apr-4 Tennants, Leyburn #978/R est:1800-2200
£2817 $4873 €4000 Ballerine (58x43cm-23x17in) s. crayon dr. 9-Dec-3 Artcurial Briest, Paris #196/R est:3000-5000
£2838 $5223 €4143 Femme nue de dos (43x40cm-17x16in) s. pencil. 8-Jun-4 Germann, Zurich #18/R est:3000-4500 (S.FR 6500)
£3467 $6240 €5200 Modele nu assis (65x50cm-26x20in) s. sanguine. 26-Apr-4 Tajan, Paris #36/R est:1000-1200
£3846 $6038 €6000 Bobby, portraits (21x27cm-8x11in) chl estompe drs seven. 15-Dec-2 St-Germain-en-Laye Encheres #16/R est:1800-2000
£4000 $7280 €5840 Femme allongee (27x22cm-11x9in) s. gouache pen black ink prov. 21-Jun-4 Bonhams, New Bond Street #68/R est:2000-3000
£4762 $7619 €6905 Bathers (23x22cm-9x9in) s. W/C over pencil. 15-May-3 Stuker, Bern #1145/R est:3000-3500 (S.FR 10000)
£6989 $13000 €10204 Carnivale (41x70cm-16x28in) s. gouache. 2-Mar-4 Swann Galleries, New York #162/R est:4000-6000
£6993 $12028 €10000 La danse (42x35cm-17x14in) s. gouache. 3-Dec-3 Tajan, Paris #47/R est:10000-12000

DERBAR, James (20th C) American
£400 $732 €584 Marine battle scene with a Dutch vessels (76x102cm-30x40in) s. 27-Jan-4 Peter Francis, Wales #1/R

DERBY, William (1786-1847) British
£1450 $2552 €2117 Extensive wooded landscape with men undressing, diving into a river (76x64cm-30x25in) s.d.1814. 30-Dec-3 British Auctioneer #793 est:1500-1800
Works on paper
£260 $458 €380 Portrait of a little girl holding a basket of flowers, with a small dog (23x15cm-9x6in) s.d.1814. 30-Dec-3 British Auctioneer #833

DEREK, John (1926-1998) American
Photographs
£5714 $10000 €8342 Bo Derek (34x27cm-13x11in) colour coupler print exec 1980 lit. 17-Dec-3 Christie's, Rockefeller NY #262/R est:5000-7000

DEREUSE-POURBAIX, Helene (20th C) Belgian
£600 $1062 €876 Le banc en bord de mer (32x42cm-13x17in) s. canvasboard prov. 29-Apr-4 Christie's, Kensington #217/R

DEREUX, Philippe (1918-) French
Works on paper
£1162 $2010 €1650 Femme au chapeau fleuri (52x34cm-20x13in) mono.d.1973 mixed media collage paper on cardboard. 14-Dec-3 Versailles Encheres #215/R est:1500-1800
£3200 $5888 €4800 Mulatre (53x34cm-21x13in) mono.d.75.5.9 collage mixed media. 9-Jun-4 Artcurial Briest, Paris #317 est:2500-3000
£3466 $6378 €5200 Venus aux Bigoudis (73x35cm-29x14in) mono.d.7-74 s.i.d. verso collage mixed media board. 9-Jun-4 Artcurial Briest, Paris #316/R est:4000-5000

DERFLA, R (19th C) ?
£1996 $3572 €2914 Bedouin camps (18x32cm-7x13in) s. pair. 26-May-4 AB Stockholms Auktionsverk #2338/R est:15000-18000 (S.KR 27000)

DERGES, Susan (1955-) British
Photographs
£3593 $6000 €5246 Ice (169x61cm-67x24in) cibachrome photogram exec. 1997 prov.lit. 17-Oct-3 Phillips, New York #273/R est:5000-7000
£4000 $6680 €5840 Ice (169x59cm-67x23in) cibachrome photogram exec 1997 prov.lit. 21-Oct-3 Sotheby's, London #451/R est:4000-6000
£5090 $8500 €7431 The river Taw (128x61cm-50x24in) s.verso cibachrome photogram aluminium exec.1998 prov. 17-Oct-3 Phillips, New York #18/R est:6000-8000

DERICKX, Louis (1835-1895) Belgian
£1000 $1840 €1500 Chariot attele traversant le fleuve (26x60cm-10x24in) s.d.1874 panel. 14-Jun-4 Horta, Bruxelles #82 est:1800-2200

DERIEUX, Roger (1922-) French
£542 $996 €791 Field landscape (27x41cm-11x16in) s. prov. 29-Mar-4 Rasmussen, Copenhagen #395 (D.KR 6000)
£1127 $1882 €1645 Nature morte aux oranges (92x73cm-36x29in) s. 7-Oct-3 Rasmussen, Copenhagen #156/R est:15000 (D.KR 12000)

DERKERT, Siri (1888-1973) Swedish
£906 $1541 €1323 Tora (30x23cm-12x9in) s. exhib. 4-Nov-3 Bukowskis, Stockholm #134/R (S.KR 12000)
£1088 $1958 €1588 Girl with flower (76x51cm-30x20in) s. d.37 verso canvas on panel. 26-Apr-4 Bukowskis, Stockholm #86/R est:20000-25000 (S.KR 15000)
£1595 $2872 €2329 Trees (30x42cm-12x17in) s. panel. 26-Apr-4 Bukowskis, Stockholm #87/R est:15000-20000 (S.KR 22000)
£3810 $6743 €5563 Leffe and Greta (61x86cm-24x34in) s. d.31 verso panel. 27-Apr-4 AB Stockholms Auktionsverk #831/R est:30000-35000 (S.KR 52000)

DERKOVITS, Gyula (1894-1934) Hungarian
Works on paper
£1900 $3155 €2774 Bedding out the plants (37x48cm-15x19in) s.d.1924 mixed media. 4-Oct-3 Kieselbach, Budapest #106/R (H.F 700000)

DERMODY, Grace (20th C) American
£242 $450 €353 Texas landscape with bluebonnets (20x25cm-8x10in) s. board painted c.1930. 7-Mar-4 Treadway Gallery, Cincinnati #598/R

DEROME, Albert Thomas (1885-1959) American
£3179 $5500 €4641 Carmel Valley at Los Laureles (25x36cm-10x14in) s. painted 1940 canvasboard prov.lit. 10-Dec-3 Bonhams & Butterfields, San Francisco #6223/R est:4000-6000

DEROY, Isidore (1797-1886) French
Works on paper
£445 $757 €650 Vue de la facade de l'eglise de Gisors (39x24cm-15x9in) s.i.d.1845 W/C gouache over crayon. 6-Nov-3 Tajan, Paris #107

DEROY, L C (?) ?
£993 $1658 €1400 Landscape (54x73cm-21x29in) s. board. 14-Oct-3 Finarte Semenzato, Milan #86/R est:800-1000

DERPAPAS, Georgios (1937-) Greek
£30000 $53700 €43800 Surrealist landscape (106x122cm-42x48in) s.d. panel prov. 10-May-4 Sotheby's, Olympia #85/R est:20000-30000

DERRICK, W Marsten (19th C) Dutch
£447 $800 €653 Sailing ships on coast (30x46cm-12x18in) s. board. 7-May-4 Sloans & Kenyon, Bethesda #1140/R
£720 $1195 €1051 Portrait of a border terrier (27x20cm-11x8in) s.d.1894 board. 30-Sep-3 Bristol Auction Rooms #585/R

DERRICK, William R (1857-1941) American
£297 $550 €434 Landscape with sheep (20x28cm-8x11in) s. canvasboard. 18-Jul-4 William Jenack, New York #293/R
£578 $1000 €844 Two sheep grazing (33x48cm-13x19in) W/C. 12-Dec-3 Du Mouchelle, Detroit #2257/R

DERRICKS, Maurice (20th C) Australian?
Sculpture
£1106 $1914 €1615 Bull and bear (29x19x49cm-11x7x19in) i. bronze. 10-Dec-3 Shapiro, Sydney #87/R est:1500-2500 (A.D 2600)

DERUET, Claude (attrib) (1588-1662) French
£4196 $7007 €6000 Portrait d'un jeune couple (51x62cm-20x24in) 26-Jun-3 Artcurial Briest, Paris #493 est:2300-2500

DERUET, Claude (circle) (1588-1662) French
£24000 $43200 €35040 Portrait of a nobleman in red and gold embroidered suit with the cross of Malta (213x143cm-84x56in) prov. 21-Apr-4 Christie's, London #64/R est:7000-10000

DERVAL, Gaston (19th C) French
£1892 $3386 €2800 Self portrait of glass and fruit bowl (46x63cm-18x25in) s. 8-May-4 Schloss Ahlden, Ahlden #696/R est:2800

DERVELOOSE, J B (19th C) ?
£1745 $3246 €2600 Country lane with shepherd and herd (48x72cm-19x28in) s. 8-Mar-4 Bernaerts, Antwerp #66/R est:1000-1500

DESATNICK, Mike (1943-) American?
£1242 $2000 €1813 Pueblo portrait, reflected light (41x30cm-16x12in) board. 22-Aug-3 Altermann Galleries, Santa Fe #46
£2514 $4500 €3670 Day of the corn dance (51x41cm-20x16in) board. 15-May-4 Altermann Galleries, Santa Fe #20/R
£4412 $7500 €6442 Northern pueblo corn dance (91x61cm-36x24in) board. 1-Nov-3 Altermann Galleries, Santa Fe #140

DESBOIS, Jules (1851-1935) French
Sculpture
£1724 $2862 €2500 Femme (48cm-19in) s. pat terracotta lit. 2-Oct-3 Sotheby's, Paris #44/R
£3862 $6411 €5600 Comedie (30cm-12in) s.st.f.Hebrard brown pat bronze lit. 2-Oct-3 Sotheby's, Paris #43/R
£4200 $7140 €6132 Source (27cm-11in) s. terracotta lit. 28-Oct-3 Sotheby's, London #201/R
£22069 $36634 €32000 Misere (42cm-17in) s.i. terracotta marble base. 2-Oct-3 Sotheby's, Paris #37/R est:25000

DESBOUTIN, Marcelin Gilbert (1823-1902) French
£265 $485 €400 Mere et enfants (27x22cm-11x9in) s. 7-Apr-4 Piasa, Paris #41
Works on paper
£647 $1100 €945 Portrait of the artist's two sons with their puppet theatre (20x25cm-8x10in) s. pen blk ink gouache. 28-Oct-3 Sotheby's, New York #104/R est:1000-1500

DESBROSSES, Jean-Alfred (1835-1906) French
£500 $905 €750 Le ruisseau de la grande cascade du Mont Dore, soleil du matin (56x35cm-22x14in) s. 30-Mar-4 Rossini, Paris #945

DESCALS PUJOL, Ernest (1956-) Spanish
£326 $535 €450 Terraza de un cafe de Paris (72x94cm-28x37in) s.d.86. 27-May-3 Durán, Madrid #681/R
£448 $807 €650 Cafe in Paris (72x94cm-28x37in) s. 26-Jan-4 Durán, Madrid #589/R

DESCAMPS, Henri (1898-1990) Belgian
£369 $679 €550 Travaux de route a Boitsfort (70x85cm-28x33in) s.d.1961. 23-Mar-4 Galerie Moderne, Brussels #321

DESCAMPS, Joseph (19/20th C) French
Sculpture
£2162 $3870 €3200 Nu (18cm-7in) s. ivory marble socle. 10-May-4 Horta, Bruxelles #125 est:1200-1500

DESCAMPS-SABOURET, Louise (1855-?) French
£979 $1684 €1400 Nature morte aux oiseaux de chasse (73x92cm-29x36in) 3-Dec-3 Coutau Begarie, Paris #202/R

DESCARSIN, Remi-Furcy (18th C) French
£6711 $11879 €10000 Portrait du Garde National et de sa femme (90x73cm-35x29in) s.i.d.1791 lit. 29-Apr-4 David Kahn, Paris #168/R est:4500-6000

DESCHAMPS, Gabriel (1919-) French
£973 $1800 €1421 Wandering figure amongst colourful fields (51x61cm-20x24in) s. s.on stretcher. 17-Jan-4 New Orleans Auction, New Orleans #504/R est:2000-4000
£1600 $2672 €2336 Vue de Provence (65x80cm-26x31in) s. 21-Oct-3 Bonhams, Knightsbridge #47/R est:1500-2000
£2400 $4440 €3504 Maganosc, Campagne de Grasse (58x71cm-23x28in) s. bears i.stretcher. 10-Feb-4 Bonhams, Knightsbridge #342/R est:2000-3000
£2500 $4600 €3650 Near Antibes (44x53cm-17x21in) s. 24-Jun-4 Locke & England, Leamington Spa #147/R est:800-1200
£4000 $6640 €5840 Vue de cap nege (71x91cm-28x36in) s. 1-Oct-3 Woolley & Wallis, Salisbury #216/R est:4000-6000

DESCHAMPS, Gerard (1937-) French
Sculpture
£12162 $21406 €18000 Kahawa Chuma (86x101x16cm-34x40x6in) s.i.d.1961 verso handkerchiefs on canvas wood case prov. 18-May-4 Tajan, Paris #77/R est:12000-15000
Works on paper
£7733 $14229 €11600 Assemblage, un jour a Amsterdam (103x122cm-41x48in) s.verso stretcher mixed media canvas plexiglass. 11-Jun-4 Pierre Berge, Paris #93/R est:3000-4000
£11333 $20627 €17000 Plastique au miroir (78x97cm-31x38in) s.d.1963 collage wax plastic on canvas prov. 29-Jun-4 Cornette de St.Cyr, Paris #56/R est:15000-18000

DESCHAMPS, Louis Henri (1846-1902) French
£1800 $2988 €2628 Tambour de basque (36x53cm-14x21in) s. 2-Oct-3 Biddle & Webb, Birmingham #910

DESCHWANDEN, Melchior Paul von (1811-1881) Swiss
£1572 $2767 €2295 Three angels (126x104cm-50x41in) s.d.1861 prov. 22-May-4 Galerie Gloggner, Luzern #105/R est:2800-3500 (S.FR 3600)

DESCLABISSAC, Alexander (1868-?) German
£756 $1309 €1104 Afternoon tea (37x41cm-15x16in) s. painted c.1900. 14-Dec-3 Agra, Warsaw #54/R est:5000 (P.Z 5000)
Works on paper
£336 $561 €480 Woman combing hair (46x42cm-18x17in) mono.d.08 chk. 28-Jun-3 Bolland & Marotz, Bremen #824

DESCOMPS, Joe (1869-1950) French
Sculpture
£1100 $1870 €1606 Female nude figure (18cm-7in) s. ivory. 25-Nov-3 Sotheby's, Olympia #129/R est:1000-1200
£1348 $2250 €1900 Danseuse Orientale (46cm-18in) s. gold pat bronze black marble socle. 12-Oct-3 St-Germain-en-Laye Encheres #60/R est:2000-2500
£1389 $2319 €2000 Jeune femme drapee ecoutant satyre (60cm-24in) s. pat bronze Cast Barbedienne. 21-Oct-3 Galerie Moderne, Brussels #1540/R
£1946 $3250 €2822 Russian dancer (46cm-18in) i. cold painted bronze ivory. 13-Jul-3 Butterfields, Los Angeles #1030/R est:3000-5000
£2654 $4750 €3875 Seated nude with rose (43x56cm-17x22in) s. silver pat bronze. 20-Mar-4 Freeman, Philadelphia #592/R est:2500-3500
£14493 $23768 €20000 Exotic ballerina (42cm-17in) s. ivory marble base. 27-May-3 Durán, Madrid #309/R est:11000

DESCOURS, Michel Hubert (1707-1775) French
£1135 $2089 €1657 Portrait of elegant woman (78x63cm-31x25in) s.d.1749 verso. 14-Jun-4 Philippe Schuler, Zurich #4267/R (S.FR 2600)

DESCOURTILZ, C (19th C) French
Works on paper
£4000 $6680 €5840 Fleur et fruits du bannier ou figuier d'Adam (32x24cm-13x9in) s.d.1824 W/C drawing. 13-Nov-3 Sotheby's, London #33/R est:3000-4000

DESFRICHES, Aignan (1715-1800) French
£822 $1397 €1200 Landscapes (6cm-2in circular) pair. 5-Nov-3 Beaussant & Lefèvre, Paris #9
£7042 $12183 €10000 Chatreux lisant devant les ruines de l'Abbaye de Micy (182x139cm-72x55in) painted c.1764 lit. 12-Dec-3 Libert, Castor, Paris #51/R
£16197 $28021 €23000 Famille aupres des ruines de l'Abbaye de Micy (181x133cm-71x52in) lit. 12-Dec-3 Libert, Castor, Paris #53/R
Works on paper
£658 $1211 €1000 Paysage fluvial (18x25cm-7x10in) graphite chk. 24-Jun-4 Claude Boisgirard, Paris #4
£662 $1212 €1000 Voyageur pres des ruines d'une forteresse (9x14cm-4x6in) s.d.177 gouache en grisaille. 7-Apr-4 Doutrebente, Paris #9/R
£759 $1267 €1100 Eglise de la chapelle (14x19cm-6x7in) pierre noire. 12-Nov-3 Chassaing Rivet, Toulouse #130c
£951 $1645 €1350 Route de campagne (26x31cm-10x12in) pierre noire ink wash exhib. 12-Dec-3 Libert, Castor, Paris #13
£1049 $1752 €1500 Paysages de bords de rivieres animes de personnages (9x14cm-4x6in) one s.d.1782 drs pair. 25-Jun-3 Digard, Paris #1/R est:800-1000
£1192 $2181 €1800 Le moulin d'Yvre (9x14cm-4x6in) s.d.1775 i.verso gouache en grisaille exhib. 7-Apr-4 Doutrebente, Paris #8/R est:800-1000
£2113 $3655 €3000 Un anAchorete au pied d'un chapelle fortifiee (27x44cm-11x17in) s.d.1786 graphite grattoir. 12-Dec-3 Libert, Castor, Paris #12/R est:3000-4000

DESFRICHES, Aignan (attrib) (1715-1800) French
£272 $487 €400 Paysage anime de personnages et animaux (16x24cm-6x9in) peinture. 20-Mar-4 Binoche, Orleans #55

DESGOFFE, Alexandre (1805-1885) French
£1799 $2950 €2500 Paysage classique anime (34x52cm-13x20in) mono. 6-Jun-3 Maigret, Paris #106/R est:2400-2800

DESGOFFE, Blaise (1830-1901) French
£559 $1029 €850 Etude de la fusee d'une epee (26x13cm-10x5in) s. panel. 25-Jun-4 Millon & Associes, Paris #56/R
£1055 $1900 €1540 Still life (41x28cm-16x11in) s. panel. 25-Jan-4 Bonhams & Butterfields, San Francisco #3568/R est:2000-3000
£5389 $9000 €7868 Still life with objects of vertu (65x46cm-26x18in) s. prov.exhib. 7-Oct-3 Sotheby's, New York #76/R est:7000-10000

DESGRANGES, Gerard (20th C) French
£655 $1094 €950 Neige a Reigneville (46x61cm-18x24in) s. 11-Nov-3 Lesieur & Le Bars, Le Havre #16

DESHAYES, Charles Felix Edouard (1831-1895) French
£1172 $1958 €1700 Cows by water (37x55cm-15x22in) s.d.1889 panel. 9-Jul-3 Hugo Ruef, Munich #76/R est:800
£1333 $2413 €2000 Nature morte aux fruits (30x50cm-12x20in) s.d.1890. 5-Apr-4 Deburaux, Boulogne #116/R est:3000-3500

DESHAYES, Eugène (1828-1890) French
£352 $609 €500 Village oriental (11x26cm-4x10in) s.i.d. panel. 15-Dec-3 Gros & Delettrez, Paris #304
£881 $1400 €1286 At work, mill scene (28x54cm-11x21in) s. panel. 12-Sep-3 Skinner, Boston #239/R
£942 $1545 €1300 Chaumiere a Barbizon (19x25cm-7x10in) s. panel. 11-May-3 Osenat, Fontainebleau #209/R
£1049 $1804 €1500 Paysage de Kabylie (22x50cm-9x20in) s. panel. 5-Dec-3 Maigret, Paris #93 est:1600-1800
£1678 $2887 €2400 Les ponts sur le torrent (32x22cm-13x9in) s. 7-Dec-3 Osenat, Fontainebleau #154 est:2500-2800
£1701 $3044 €2500 Cotes africaines. s. 19-Mar-4 Millon & Associes, Paris #45/R est:3000-4000
£1812 $2971 €2500 Bord de mer en Normandie (33x5cm-13x2in) s. panel. 11-May-3 Osenat, Fontainebleau #168/R est:2500-3000
£1888 $3248 €2700 Campement dans la Palmeraie (25x75cm-10x30in) s. panel. 8-Dec-3 Tajan, Paris #263/R est:1500-1800
£1958 $3368 €2800 Caravane dans l'atlas (50x73cm-20x29in) s.d.1916. 8-Dec-3 Tajan, Paris #261/R est:2800-3000
£2333 $4293 €3500 Attatich dans le Sud algerois (22x55cm-9x22in) s. panel. 14-Jun-4 Gros & Delettrez, Paris #244/R est:2500-3000
£2518 $4330 €3600 Scene de campement (25x100cm-10x39in) s. panel. 8-Dec-3 Tajan, Paris #266/R est:1500-1800
£4133 $7605 €6200 Les roches rouges, cote Djidjellienne, Algerie (65x81cm-26x32in) s. 14-Jun-4 Gros & Delettrez, Paris #461/R est:4000-6000
£14184 $23688 €20000 Jardins de la villa Abd el Tif (73x100cm-29x39in) s. 19-Oct-3 Rabourdin & Choppin de Janvry, Paris #114/R est:8500-9500

DESHAYES, Eugène (attrib) (1828-1890) French
£1035 $1728 €1500 Vue d'un village (29x19cm-11x7in) bears sig. panel. 17-Nov-3 Tajan, Paris #150/R est:1000-1200

DESHAYES, Frederic Léon (1883-1970) French
£733 $1349 €1100 Paysages Algeriens (41x24cm-16x9in) s. one d.1929 pair. 14-Jun-4 Gros & Delettrez, Paris #223

DESHAYS DE COLLEVILLE, Jean Baptiste (1729-1765) French
£2500 $4500 €3650 Blessing of a child (36x46cm-14x18in) grisaille prov. 23-Jan-4 Christie's, Rockefeller NY #106/R est:2000-3000
£4000 $7320 €6000 Resurrection (55x45cm-22x18in) prov. 3-Jun-4 E & Eve, Paris #30/R est:6000-8000

DESHAYS DE COLLEVILLE, Jean Baptiste (attrib) (1729-1765) French
£1000 $1790 €1500 Assumption (45x37cm-18x15in) en grisaille lit. 11-May-4 Christie's, Paris #184/R est:2000-4000

DESHONG, Drew (20th C) American?
£269 $450 €393 Seated figure (86x66cm-34x26in) 18-Oct-3 David Dike, Dallas #107/R

DESIDE, Ramon (1935-) Spanish
£483 $869 €700 Composition (74x104cm-29x41in) s. s.d.82. 26-Jan-4 Durán, Madrid #51/R

DESIDERIO DA FIRENZE (attrib) (16th C) Italian
Sculpture
£72000 $131760 €105120 Pan, seated (25x21x11cm-10x8x4in) bronze lit. 9-Jul-4 Sotheby's, London #37/R est:80000-120000

DESIDERIO, Vincent (1955-) American?
£12432 $23000 €18151 Father of us all (32x87cm-13x34in) panel on canvas triptych painted 1992 prov.exhib.lit. 12-Feb-4 Sotheby's, New York #169/R est:1000-2000

DESIRE-LUCAS, Louis-Marie (1869-1949) French
£537 $999 €800 Une rue a Montpezat (44x65cm-17x26in) s. 3-Mar-4 Ferri, Paris #166/R
£671 $1248 €1000 L'Eglise Saint-Jean-des-Rois a Tolede (53x64cm-21x25in) s. 3-Mar-4 Ferri, Paris #167
£1111 $1800 €1611 Concepcion Church, Menton (37x46cm-15x18in) s. 29-Jul-3 Galeria y Remates, Montevideo #29/R est:1500-1800
£1111 $1800 €1611 Winter's Afternoon (38x46cm-15x18in) s. prov. 29-Jul-3 Galeria y Remates, Montevideo #30/R est:1400-1700
£1656 $3096 €2500 Le pont de Millau (46x38cm-18x15in) s. 24-Jul-4 Thierry & Lannon, Brest #153/R est:2500-3000
£1788 $3344 €2700 La Tour d'Auguste, la Turbie (38x46cm-15x18in) s. 24-Jul-4 Thierry & Lannon, Brest #152/R est:2000-3000
£1867 $3360 €2800 Port d'Arenas (36x44cm-14x17in) 24-Apr-4 Hotel des Ventes de Vienne, Vienne #185
£1879 $3495 €2800 Le port (65x54cm-26x21in) s. 3-Mar-4 Ferri, Paris #165 est:3000-4000
£1987 $3715 €3000 Interieur breton (91x71cm-36x28in) 24-Jul-4 Thierry & Lannon, Brest #156/R est:2500-3000
£2000 $3600 €3000 Scene intimiste (53x44cm-21x17in) 24-Apr-4 Hotel des Ventes de Vienne, Vienne #184
£2053 $3839 €3100 Treboul, la baie de Dourarnenez (65x54cm-26x21in) s.d.1949. 24-Jul-4 Thierry & Lannon, Brest #441
£2550 $4744 €3800 Vue de Quimperle (81x65cm-32x26in) s. 3-Mar-4 Ferri, Paris #168/R est:4000-5000
£2676 $4683 €3800 L'Anse de Pouldavid (59x73cm-23x29in) s. 21-Dec-3 Thierry & Lannon, Brest #159 est:3000-4000
£2715 $5077 €4100 Les Plomarc'h (81x65cm-32x26in) s. 24-Jul-4 Thierry & Lannon, Brest #154/R est:4000-5000
£3113 $5821 €4700 Espalion pecheur en barque, effet de lumiere (53x64cm-21x25in) 24-Jul-4 Thierry & Lannon, Brest #155/R est:3000-4000
£3333 $6067 €5000 Village mediterraneen (54x65cm-21x26in) s. 4-Jul-4 Eric Pillon, Calais #207/R

DESJARDIN, Martin (after) (1640-1694) Dutch
Sculpture
£8966 $16138 €13000 L'enlevement d'Europe (35x28cm-14x11in) black pat bronze marble socle prov. 26-Jan-4 Gros & Delettrez, Paris #200/R est:8000-12000
£10588 $18000 €15458 Edouard Colbert, Marquis de Villacerf (107x79x40cm-42x31x16in) marble prov.lit. 25-Nov-3 Christie's, Rockefeller NY #80/R est:20000-30000
£21127 $36549 €30000 Grand Dauphin (63x45x23cm-25x18x9in) pat bronze prov.exhib. 11-Dec-3 Binoche, Paris #41/R est:12000-18000

DESJARDIN, Martin (attrib) (1640-1694) Dutch
Sculpture
£36620 $63352 €52000 Louis XIV (56x43x22cm-22x17x9in) pat bronze. 11-Dec-3 Binoche, Paris #70/R est:8000-10000

DESMARE, Lucien (20th C) Belgian
£403 $741 €600 Marins a quai (90x70cm-35x28in) s. 23-Mar-4 Galerie Moderne, Brussels #232/R
£2200 $3938 €3300 Festival day (95x200cm-37x79in) s.d.1938. 15-May-4 De Vuyst, Lokeren #104/R est:2700-3500

DESMAREES, George (1697-1776) Swedish
£2800 $5096 €4200 Portrait of an important lady wearing grey satin dress and red velvet cape (81x65cm-32x26in) 20-Jun-4 Wilkinson, Doncaster #346 est:2000-4000

DESMAREES, George (attrib) (1697-1776) Swedish
£833 $1308 €1200 Young man wearing rococo wig (63x54cm-25x21in) oval. 30-Aug-3 Hans Stahl, Toestorf #103
£2692 $4631 €3930 Portrait of physician Herman Schutzercrantz (78x62cm-31x24in) lit. 2-Dec-3 Bukowskis, Stockholm #306/R est:25000-30000 (S.KR 35000)

DESMAREES, George (school) (1697-1776) Swedish
£878 $1572 €1300 Maria Anna Grafin Holnstein in salon (22x17cm-9x7in) tin. 8-May-4 Hans Stahl, Toestorf #98

DESMARQUAIS, Charles Hippolyte (1823-?) French
£765 $1408 €1148 Landscape with waterway (91x127cm-36x50in) s.d.1887. 14-Jun-4 Lilla Bukowskis, Stockholm #222 (S.KR 10500)

D'ESMENARD, Ines (fl.1814-1851) French
£2797 $4671 €4000 Jeune femme dans un escalier (31x33cm-12x13in) s.d.1822. 30-Jun-3 Bailly Pommery, Paris #82/R est:4000

DESMIDT, Jeanne (19th C) Belgian
£1293 $2315 €1888 Still life with lilac (100x73cm-39x29in) s. 12-May-4 Dobiaschofsky, Bern #429/R est:4000 (S.FR 3000)
£1293 $2315 €1888 Still life with dahlias and chrysanthemums (100x73cm-39x29in) s.d.1895. 12-May-4 Dobiaschofsky, Bern #430/R est:4000 (S.FR 3000)

DESMOND, Nerine (1908-1993) South African
£259 $432 €378 Autumn roses (60x48cm-24x19in) s. board. 20-Oct-3 Stephan Welz, Johannesburg #834 est:1200-1800 (SA.R 3000)
Works on paper
£353 $639 €515 Gaggle of geese in a farmyard (31x45cm-12x18in) s. W/C. 30-Mar-4 Stephan Welz, Johannesburg #237 est:1500-2000 (SA.R 4200)

DESMONS, Iluchar (1903-?) Brazilian?
Works on paper
£2747 $5027 €4121 The supper of Dr Cochrane of Rio de Janeiro (19x26cm-7x10in) s.d.1855 mixed media. 6-Jul-4 Bolsa de Arte, Rio de Janeiro #39/R (B.R 15000)

DESNOS, Ferdinand (1901-1958) French
£385 $662 €550 La sortie de la messe (33x24cm-13x9in) s. panel. 3-Dec-3 Tajan, Paris #286/R
£757 $1392 €1150 Singes (30x86cm-12x34in) s. s.verso panel. 24-Jun-4 Credit Municipal, Paris #51
£1000 $1800 €1500 A l'ami Chalgalo (55x46cm-22x18in) s.i.d.1953 panel double-sided. 26-Apr-4 Tajan, Paris #264/R est:1800-2000
£1534 $2760 €2300 Amboise, le pecheur. Le pecheur (50x65cm-20x26in) s.d.1956 double-sided. 26-Apr-4 Tajan, Paris #376/R est:2700-2800
£1748 $3007 €2500 Les mouettes (42x130cm-17x51in) s. 3-Dec-3 Tajan, Paris #242/R est:2900-3000
£2013 $3685 €3000 Adam and Eve (46x38cm-18x15in) s.d.1925 exhib. 7-Jul-4 Artcurial Briest, Paris #80/R est:3000-4000
Works on paper
£245 $421 €350 Paysage Tourangeau (20x26cm-8x10in) s. s.i.d.1931 verso ink wash. 3-Dec-3 Tajan, Paris #231/R

DESNOS, Robert (1900-1945) French
Works on paper
£467 $859 €700 Paysage sous la neige, profil d'homme fumant, decor de bistrot (13x20cm-5x8in) pen crayon. 9-Jun-4 Piasa, Paris #46
£600 $1104 €900 Detournement pornographique d'un dessin de Cocteau (25x11cm-10x4in) pen over print. 9-Jun-4 Piasa, Paris #48
£800 $1472 €1200 Une girafe, une maison et une carafe (26x20cm-10x8in) s. pen. 9-Jun-4 Piasa, Paris #50
£833 $1533 €1250 Amusante image pornographique (16x16cm-6x6in) pen crayon. 9-Jun-4 Piasa, Paris #47
£1733 $3189 €2600 Rue Meurt (32x21cm-13x8in) s. crayon. 9-Jun-4 Piasa, Paris #49/R est:1000-1200

DESNOYER, François (1894-1972) French
£800 $1456 €1200 View of village (24x34cm-9x13in) st.sig. panel. 4-Jul-4 Eric Pillon, Calais #149/R
£993 $1818 €1500 Paysage de Stavnika (25x50cm-10x20in) s. cardboard. 9-Apr-4 Bailly Pommery, Paris #95 est:800-1500
£1745 $3228 €2600 Eglise du village (61x50cm-24x20in) s.d.1940 panel. 14-Mar-4 Eric Pillon, Calais #177/R
£2349 $4370 €3500 Paysage du Midi (46x65cm-18x26in) s. 2-Mar-4 Artcurial Briest, Paris #246 est:2500-3000
£2550 $4718 €3800 Port (33x65cm-13x26in) s. panel. 14-Mar-4 Eric Pillon, Calais #147/R
£4082 $7306 €6000 Bateau grec (53x65cm-21x26in) s. lit. 19-Mar-4 Millon & Associes, Paris #109/R est:3000-4000
£4899 $9015 €7300 Sleeping on the hammock (46x54cm-18x21in) s. painted c.1945 prov.lit. 24-Mar-4 Joron-Derem, Paris #74/R est:7000-8000
Works on paper
£10000 $18000 €15000 Patineurs (115x85cm-45x33in) s.d.1932. 24-Apr-4 Cornette de St.Cyr, Paris #356/R est:25000

DESOUTTER, Roger (1923-) British
£520 $936 €759 Brigantine in a following sea (59x75cm-23x30in) s.d.Jan 78 on overlap. 22-Apr-4 Lawrence, Crewkerne #953

D'ESPAGNAT, Georges (1870-1950) French
£2183 $3777 €3100 Nu allonge (46x31cm-18x12in) mono. cardboard. 10-Dec-3 Millon & Associes, Paris #81/R est:1800-2000
£2349 $4205 €3500 Nu allonge dans la prairie (24x33cm-9x13in) s. panel. 30-May-4 Eric Pillon, Calais #37/R
£3020 $5406 €4500 Nature morte aux pommes et aux poires (27x41cm-11x16in) init. 26-May-4 Christie's, Paris #15/R est:4000-6000
£3600 $6012 €5256 Vase de fleurs (46x38cm-18x15in) init. prov. 22-Oct-3 Sotheby's, Olympia #39/R est:2000-3000
£4324 $8000 €6313 Quai de Seine (38x55cm-15x22in) init. prov. 11-Feb-4 Sotheby's, New York #20/R est:10000-15000
£5369 $9933 €8000 Thonniers a Saint-Gilles (49x60cm-19x24in) mono. i.verso prov. 13-Mar-4 De Vuyst, Lokeren #442/R est:8500-10000
£5486 $9162 €7900 Nature morte aux fleurs et la coupe de fruits (38x46cm-15x18in) mono. 21-Oct-3 Artcurial Briest, Paris #307/R est:5500-6500
£5882 $10000 €8588 Femme au foulard (55x47cm-22x19in) init. prov. 5-Nov-3 Christie's, Rockefeller NY #270/R est:12000-16000
£6400 $10688 €9344 Scene de plage (46x61cm-18x24in) init. prov. 22-Oct-3 Sotheby's, Olympia #47/R est:4000-6000
£7285 $13331 €11000 Voiliers (33x55cm-13x22in) s. 9-Apr-4 Claude Aguttes, Neuilly #16/R est:6000-7000
£8803 $15405 €12500 Woman and child (92x73cm-36x29in) s. 18-Dec-3 Cornette de St.Cyr, Paris #1/R est:10000-15000
£9497 $17000 €13866 Anemones et oeillets (61x51cm-24x20in) init. 14-May-4 Skinner, Boston #360/R est:3000-5000

£9938 $16000 €14509 Still life with roses (74x61cm-29x24in) s. 20-Aug-3 James Julia, Fairfield #626/R est:12000-15000
£10067 $18624 €15000 Bouquet et pommes (65x54cm-26x21in) mono. prov. 13-Mar-4 De Vuyst, Lokeren #439/R est:10000-12000
£10738 $19221 €16000 Vase de fleurs (73x60cm-29x24in) s. 30-May-4 Eric Pillon, Calais #27/R
£12270 $20000 €17914 Maison a Saint-Veran (60x74cm-24x29in) init. painted c.1900 prov. 25-Sep-3 Christie's, Rockefeller NY #524/R est:20000-30000
£13514 $25000 €19730 Tango (46x38cm-18x15in) init. lit. 11-Feb-4 Sotheby's, New York #27/R est:10000-15000
£13966 $25000 €20390 Grande jette de fleurs (90x81cm-35x32in) init. prov. 6-May-4 Sotheby's, New York #434/R est:15000-20000
£19117 $32500 €27911 Playtime (73x91cm-29x36in) init. 19-Nov-3 Bonhams & Butterfields, San Francisco #155/R
£20000 $36800 €29200 Jeune fille a la corbeille de roses (163x84cm-64x33in) init. painted 1923 prov.exhib.lit. 23-Jun-4 Christie's, London #148/R est:18000-24000
£22378 $37371 €32000 Hamac dans le parc fleuri (65x54cm-26x21in) init. prov. 29-Jun-3 Eric Pillon, Calais #102/R
£25140 $45000 €36704 La lecture (45x55cm-18x22in) init. prov. 6-May-4 Sotheby's, New York #427/R est:15000-20000
Works on paper
£361 $650 €527 Le chaplain (10x15cm-4x6in) init. W/C. 23-Jan-4 Freeman, Philadelphia #72/R
£599 $1091 €900 Promenade sur le port (19x23cm-7x9in) mono. W/C paper on board. 30-Jun-4 Calmels Cohen, Paris #128
£733 $1334 €1100 Port (22x31cm-9x12in) mono. W/C paper on board. 30-Jun-4 Calmels Cohen, Paris #126/R
£799 $1455 €1200 Plage (18x23cm-7x9in) mono. W/C paper on board. 30-Jun-4 Calmels Cohen, Paris #129
£1074 $1987 €1600 Femme nue appuyee (57x39cm-22x15in) mono. crayon dr. 14-Mar-4 St-Germain-en-Laye Encheres #124/R est:1500
£1250 $2088 €1800 Port de Concarneau (23x21cm-9x8in) mono. W/C ink traces crayon. 21-Oct-3 Artcurial Briest, Paris #41/R est:1800-2200

D'ESPARBES, Jean (1898-1968) French
£276 $458 €400 Nu allonge (24x33cm-9x13in) s. 1-Oct-3 Millon & Associes, Paris #107/R
£403 $749 €600 Promenade a cheval (54x65cm-21x26in) s. 7-Mar-4 Lesieur & Le Bars, Le Havre #42

DESPIAU, Charles (1874-1946) French
Sculpture
£2941 $5500 €4294 Danseuse (61x15x14cm-24x6x6in) pat bronze prov.lit. 25-Feb-4 Christie's, Rockefeller NY #66/R est:4000-6000
£3514 $6500 €5130 Tete de jeune femme (25cm-10in) i. green pat bronze exec c.1930 st.f.Valsuani cire perdue. 12-Feb-4 Sotheby's, New York #13/R est:4000-6000
£4054 $7500 €5919 Portrait of the actress Maria Lani (36cm-14in) i. num.8/8 dark green pat bronze exec 1929 st.f.Valsuani. 12-Feb-4 Sotheby's, New York #16/R est:8000-12000
£4730 $8324 €7000 Nenette (31cm-12in) s. num.8/8 pat bronze. 18-May-4 Christie's, Paris #46/R est:4000-6000
£6897 $11448 €10000 Buste de jeune fille. s. num.5/6 brown pat bronze. 2-Oct-3 Sotheby's, Paris #147/R est:8000
£17483 $29720 €25000 Cra-cra (38cm-15in) s. brown green pat bronze incl blk granite base Cast A.Rudier lit. 1-Dec-3 Camard, Paris #35 est:25000-30000
Works on paper
£300 $540 €450 L'homme au baton (34x21cm-13x8in) s. chl htd. 26-Apr-4 Tajan, Paris #40
£420 $701 €600 Nu assis (36x23cm-14x9in) sanguine dr. 27-Jun-3 Doutrebente, Paris #28/R
£480 $893 €701 Seated nude (31x22cm-12x9in) s. brown pencil. 4-Mar-4 Christie's, London #311/R
£759 $1267 €1100 Nu assis appuye (36x25cm-14x10in) s. sanguine. 17-Nov-3 Charbonneaux, Paris #121
£764 $1276 €1100 Nu assis (33x25cm-13x10in) s. brown pencil. 21-Oct-3 Christie's, Paris #66/R

DESPIAU, Charles and MAYODON, Jean (20th C) French
Sculpture
£7639 $12757 €11000 Assia (86x25x20cm-34x10x8in) s. mono num.1/10 terracotta. 21-Oct-3 Christie's, Paris #65/R est:5000-7000

DESPIERRE, Jacques (1912-1995) French
£634 $1096 €900 Deux roses blanches (27x22cm-11x9in) 10-Dec-3 Ferri, Paris #35/R
£764 $1276 €1100 Peronnage au bord d'un quai (65x81cm-26x32in) s. 21-Oct-3 Artcurial Briest, Paris #345 est:1200-1500
£986 $1706 €1400 Jardin a Septzai (60x120cm-24x47in) s. d.1969 verso. 10-Dec-3 Claude Boisgirard, Paris #15
£1184 $2179 €1800 Toits bleus, arbres rouges (65x81cm-26x32in) s. s.i. verso painted 1961. 28-Jun-4 Joron-Derem, Paris #238 est:1800-2000

DESPOIS, Eugenie (1795-?) French
Miniatures
£1100 $1969 €1606 Young lady in a black dress (8cm-3in) s.d.1817 rec. 25-May-4 Christie's, London #225 est:600-800

DESPORTES, Alexandre-François (1661-1743) French
£34211 $62947 €52000 Epagneul gardant trophee de chasse (80x64cm-31x25in) prov. 25-Jun-4 Piasa, Paris #46/R est:32000-40000
£55556 $100000 €81112 Still life of grapes, peaches in blue and white porcelain bowl (89x119cm-35x47in) s.d.1726. 22-Jan-4 Sotheby's, New York #95/R est:80000-120000
£144737 $266316 €220000 Cerf aux abois (102x135cm-40x53in) s.d.1729 prov.lit. 24-Jun-4 Christie's, Paris #87/R est:100000-150000

DESPORTES, Alexandre-François (attrib) (1661-1743) French
£10526 $19368 €16000 Portrait de Monsieur Paris (146x113cm-57x44in) 25-Jun-4 Piasa, Paris #45/R est:18000-22000

DESPORTES, Alexandre-François (circle) (1661-1743) French
£10000 $17300 €14600 Plums in a Chinese porcelain bowl on a table ledge (13x31cm-5x12in) prov. 12-Dec-3 Christie's, Kensington #159/R est:6000-8000

DESPORTES, Nicolas (attrib) (1718-1787) French
£2632 $4842 €4000 Nature morte a la brioche (37x46cm-15x18in) 25-Jun-4 Piasa, Paris #101/R est:4000-6000

D'ESPOSITO (19/20th C) ?
Works on paper
£1200 $1992 €1752 Steam yacht, Sunbeam, off the Maltese coast (33x53cm-13x21in) s.d.1891 i.verso gouache. 1-Oct-3 Bonhams, Knightsbridge #106/R est:300-500

D'ESPOSITO, G (19/20th C) ?
Works on paper
£1000 $1820 €1460 British steam sailing ship in Valletta Harbour (38x65cm-15x26in) s. gouache. 17-Jun-4 Clevedon Sale Rooms #1032/R est:400-600

D'ESPOSITO, Leopoldo (attrib) (19th C) Italian
Works on paper
£7237 $13316 €11000 Ischia island seen from the sea (47x93cm-19x37in) gouache. 22-Jun-4 Sotheby's, Milan #154/R est:13000-15000

DESPOULAIN, Jean Claude (1945-) French
Sculpture
£1135 $1838 €1600 Oie de Toulouse (19x14cm-7x6in) s.num.1/8 black brown pat bronze st.f.Serralheiro. 24-May-3 Martinot & Savignat, Pontoise #117/R est:1600-1800

DESPREZ, Louis Jean (1743-1804) French
Prints
£1974 $3632 €3000 Temple de Serapis (47x69cm-19x27in) engraving W/C. 23-Jun-4 Sotheby's, Paris #23/R est:2000-3000
Works on paper
£533 $955 €800 Adoration of the shepherds (29x21cm-11x8in) i. pen wash. 13-May-4 Bassenge, Berlin #5379
£5000 $8650 €7300 View of the Gulf of Mare Piano, with village beyond (22x33cm-9x13in) black chk pen black ink col wash prov.lit. 12-Dec-3 Christie's, Kensington #455/R est:2500-3500
£22000 $40260 €32120 Capriccio view of the Colosseum, Rome with pilgrims gathering before altars (50x89cm-20x35in) W/C pen ink framing lines. 7-Jul-4 Bonhams, Knightsbridge #37/R est:15000-20000

DESPREZ, Louis Jean (attrib) (1743-1804) French
Prints
£7200 $13104 €10512 Triumphe des Art Modernes ou Carnaval de Jupiter (22x36cm-9x14in) init. i.verso etching prov. 1-Jul-4 Sotheby's, London #23/R est:3000-5000
Works on paper
£355 $592 €500 Cavalcade en foret (11x16cm-4x6in) pen black ink beige wash. 23-Jun-3 Ribeyre & Baron, Paris #6/R

DESPREZ, Marguerite (19th C) French
Works on paper
£455 $773 €650 Vue de monastere et son parc (18x27cm-7x11in) gouache. 24-Nov-3 E & Eve, Paris #133/R

DESRAIS, Claude Louis (1746-1816) French
Works on paper
£286 $511 €420 La mort de Seneque (17x26cm-7x10in) red chk pen brown ink col wash. 18-Mar-4 Christie's, Paris #316/R
£340 $609 €500 Bataille de Nazaret, 19 Floreal An 7 (8cm-3in circular) pen black ink brown wash. 19-Mar-4 Piasa, Paris #120
£2606 $4508 €3700 Jeu de cendrillon (40x46cm-16x18in) i. pen ink wash. 15-Dec-3 Bailly Pommery, Paris #25/R est:2000-2500
£33566 $57734 €48000 Album representing studies of hairstyles, bonnets and hats (27x22cm-11x9in) s.d.1777 1778 1788 137 drawings blk chk pen ink brown wash. 2-Dec-3 Christie's, Paris #519/R est:5000-7000

DESROSIERS, Jean Guy (1934-) Canadian
£357 $614 €521 Temps de jeunesse (75x25cm-30x10in) s. 2-Dec-3 Joyner Waddington, Toronto #546 (C.D 800)

DESSAR, Louis Paul (1867-1952) American
£1229 $2200 €1794 Sheep in fall woodland setting (61x74cm-24x29in) s. 29-May-4 Brunk, Ashville #533/R

DESSENIS, Alfons (1874-1950) Belgian
£268 $499 €400 Inner court (92x72cm-36x28in) s.d.1901. 8-Mar-4 Bernaerts, Antwerp #607

DESSERPRIT, Roger (1923-1985) French

£523	$978	€790	Composition (50x71cm-20x28in) s.d.49 panel. 25-Jul-4 Feletin, Province #65
£828	$1531	€1200	Composition (60x92cm-24x36in) s.d.1957 oil mixed media panel. 13-Feb-4 Charbonneaux, Paris #76/R
£4255	$7106	€6000	Composition sanguine (164x108cm-65x43in) s.d.1954 verso oil copper aluminium wood. 19-Oct-3 Charbonneaux, Paris #142/R est:10000
Sculpture			
£2917	$4871	€4200	Le couple (55cm-22in) num.1/8 bronze Cast Delval. 25-Oct-3 Cornette de St.Cyr, Paris #656/R est:4500-5000
£3103	$5183	€4500	Entrelacs (76cm-30in) s.d.1916 num.1/8 brown pat bronze. 17-Nov-3 Charbonneaux, Paris #239/R est:4500-5000

DESSI, Gianni (1955-) Italian

£700	$1141	€1022	Quadretto (119x89cm-47x35in) s.i.verso canvas on panel painted 1987 prov. 23-Sep-3 John Nicholson, Haslemere #163/R
£1946	$3620	€2900	Doorstep (130x140cm-51x55in) s.d.1980 verso. 4-Mar-4 Babuino, Rome #400 est:1000-1500
£4200	$7644	€6132	Hortus Conclusus (257x282cm-101x111in) s.i.d.1986 verso oil wood paper collage. 4-Feb-4 Sotheby's, Olympia #180/R est:700-1000

DESSONS, Pierre (1936-) French

Works on paper			
£280	$476	€400	L'instruction (27x22cm-11x9in) s.verso mixed media canvas. 29-Nov-3 Neret-Minet, Paris #196/R
£733	$1327	€1100	Le clown blanc (73x60cm-29x24in) s. mixed media canvas. 3-Apr-4 Neret-Minet, Paris #167
£874	$1486	€1250	Regard parallele (92x73cm-36x29in) s. mixed media canvas. 29-Nov-3 Neret-Minet, Paris #113
£1333	$2413	€2000	La derniere sardine (116x89cm-46x35in) s. mixed media. 3-Apr-4 Neret-Minet, Paris #109 est:2600-3000

DESSOULAVY, Georges (1898-1952) Swiss

£543	$923	€793	Contre jour (45x65cm-18x26in) st.sig. verso. 18-Nov-3 Hans Widmer, St Gallen #1045 (S.FR 1200)

DESSY, Stanislao (1900-?) Italian

£2500	$4600	€3800	Portrait of man (50x40cm-20x16in) s.d.1933. 23-Jun-4 Finarte Semenzato, Rome #99/R est:1500-1600

DESTAPPE, Francois Jacques Marie Maurice (19th C) French

£724	$1209	€1057	Fishing boats and fishermen on rocky beach (66x94cm-26x37in) s. 17-Nov-3 Waddingtons, Toronto #186/R (C.D 1600)

D'ESTE, Baldassare (style) (?) ?

£5263	$9684	€8000	Portrait of general in profile (30x23cm-12x9in) panel. 24-Jun-4 Christie's, Paris #65/R est:8000-12000

D'ESTIENNE, Henri (1872-1949) French

£599	$1048	€850	Ouessant cote Rocheuse (32x55cm-13x22in) s. panel. 21-Dec-3 Thierry & Lannon, Brest #311
£810	$1417	€1150	Lecture pendant la sieste de bebe (50x65cm-20x26in) s. board. 21-Dec-3 Thierry & Lannon, Brest #310
£1667	$3000	€2500	Girl with yellow flowers (46x33cm-18x13in) s. 21-Apr-4 Christie's, Amsterdam #60/R est:3000-5000
£2057	$3435	€2900	L'Amiraute d'Alger (35x76cm-14x30in) s. cardboard. 16-Jun-3 Gros & Delettrez, Paris #416/R est:1500-2300
£5000	$8650	€7100	Bassin de l'Amiraute, Alger (50x67cm-20x26in) s. cardboard on panel. 15-Dec-3 Gros & Delettrez, Paris #355/R est:6000-8000
Works on paper			
£284	$474	€400	Pavillon d'Angkor Vat, Exposition Coloniale (45x62cm-18x24in) gouache. 16-Jun-3 Gros & Delettrez, Paris #555
£319	$533	€450	Le temple d'Angkor Vat, l'Exposition Coloniale, la nuit (73x103cm-29x41in) s. W/C gouache prov. 16-Jun-3 Gros & Delettrez, Paris #552
£709	$1184	€1000	Le temple d'Angkor Vat, l'Exposition Coloniale (73x103cm-29x41in) s. W/C gouache prov. 16-Jun-3 Gros & Delettrez, Paris #553/R
£3667	$6747	€5500	Femme Ouled Nail (30x25cm-12x10in) s. pastel. 14-Jun-4 Gros & Delettrez, Paris #185/R est:5000-6000

DESTREE, J J (1827-1888) Belgian

£1034	$1728	€1500	City on the river (49x61cm-19x24in) d.1877. 11-Nov-3 Vendu Notarishuis, Rotterdam #162 est:1500-2000

DESTREE, Johannes Josephus (1827-1888) Belgian

£552	$1021	€800	Vue de campagne (41x61cm-16x24in) s. 19-Jan-4 Horta, Bruxelles #297
£1301	$2212	€1900	Village, probably Voorschoten (38x58cm-15x23in) s. 5-Nov-3 Vendue Huis, Gravenhage #46/R est:2000-2500
£1316	$2382	€2000	Woman and child on a path in a river landscape, a castle on the rocks (41x30cm-16x12in) s. panel. 19-Apr-4 Glerum, Amsterdam #33/R est:2000-3000
Works on paper			
£1748	$2972	€2500	Vue de la maison de campagne de leurs Altesses Royales (16x24cm-6x9in) s.i.d.1847 W/C. 27-Nov-3 Bassenge, Berlin #5551/R est:3000

DESUBLEO, Michele (1601-1676) Flemish

£23490	$42047	€35000	Europa kidnapped (156x200cm-61x79in) prov.lit. 26-May-4 Porro, Milan #30/R est:45000-50000

DESUBLEO, Michele (attrib) (1601-1676) Flemish

£11111	$20000	€16222	Sea nymph (74x61cm-29x24in) prov. 22-Jan-4 Sotheby's, New York #40/R est:20000-30000

DESVALLIERES, Georges (1861-1950) French

£461	$770	€650	Etude (22x40cm-9x16in) mono. cardboard. 19-Jun-3 Millon & Associes, Paris #166

DESVARREUX, Raymond (1876-1963) French

£1000	$1790	€1500	Soldats au front durant la premiere guerre (38x55cm-15x22in) s.d.1918. 11-May-4 Vanderkindere, Brussels #137 est:1400-1800
£2685	$4966	€4000	Depart pour la chasse. Chasse (46x54cm-18x21in) s. panel pair. 14-Mar-4 St-Germain-en-Laye Encheres #19/R est:2000-2500

DESVERNOIS, Joseph Eugene (1790-1872) Swiss

Works on paper			
£350	$594	€500	Montreux on Lake Geneva (40x58cm-16x23in) i. verso pen brush. 27-Nov-3 Bassenge, Berlin #5552

DETAILLE, Edouard (1848-1912) French

£6250	$11500	€9500	Militaire a cheval (33x24cm-13x9in) s.d.1877. 22-Jun-4 Ribeyre & Baron, Paris #39 est:4000-5000
£11173	$20000	€16313	Glaneuse on racecourse (54x65cm-21x26in) s.d.1869 prov. 27-May-4 Sotheby's, New York #303/R est:20000-30000
Works on paper			
£222	$400	€324	Soldiers gathered in a winter landscape (29x23cm-11x9in) s. crayon pencil. 24-Apr-4 Weschler, Washington #562/R
£315	$536	€460	Officiers a la terrasse d'un cafe (21x15cm-8x6in) s. W/C gouache. 4-Nov-3 Servarts Themis, Bruxelles #542
£373	$600	€545	Military officers playing cards (27x20cm-11x8in) bears sig.d.1895 pencil W/C htd white. 17-Aug-3 Bonhams & Butterfields, San Francisco #5789
£524	$892	€750	Bonaparte en 1er Consul. mono.d.1868 crayon. 1-Dec-3 Coutau Begarie, Paris #158/R
£629	$1082	€900	Soldier in full ornate (33x21cm-13x8in) s.d.1899 W/C gouache. 7-Dec-3 Sotheby's, Amsterdam #620
£987	$1816	€1500	Sixieme regiment de chasseur a cheval (47x38cm-19x15in) s.d.1900 W/C. 24-Jun-4 Claude Boisgirard, Paris #11/R est:1500-1800
£2177	$3897	€3200	Etude de militaires (43x24cm-17x9in) mono. gouache. 22-Mar-4 Digard, Paris #117/R est:200-300
£2198	$4000	€3209	Cavalry solider (52x37cm-20x15in) s.d.1883 col chk W/C prov. 29-Jun-4 Sotheby's, New York #102/R est:4000-5000
£2957	$5500	€4317	Military review (38x64cm-15x25in) s.d.1874 W/C. 3-Mar-4 Alderfer's, Hatfield #279 est:6000-8000
£4422	$7915	€6500	Etude de militaires (54x66cm-21x26in) mono. chl gouache triptych. 22-Mar-4 Digard, Paris #116/R est:200-300

DETANGER, Germain (1846-1902) French

£2267	$4080	€3400	Corbeille de fleurs et fruit (125x78cm-49x31in) d.1893. 24-Apr-4 Hotel des Ventes de Vienne, Vienne #183

DETERT, Harry (20th C) ?

£1060	$1928	€1600	Self portrait (83x66cm-33x26in) s.d.30. 18-Jun-4 Bolland & Marotz, Bremen #808/R est:550
£1788	$3254	€2700	Washerwoman (91x115cm-36x45in) s.d.34. 18-Jun-4 Bolland & Marotz, Bremen #807/R est:1800

DETHOMAS, Maxime (1867-1929) French

Works on paper			
£461	$847	€700	Projet de costume I (49x31cm-19x12in) s. pastel. 28-Jun-4 Joron-Derem, Paris #118
£526	$968	€800	Projet de costume II (48x31cm-19x12in) s. pastel. 28-Jun-4 Joron-Derem, Paris #119
£592	$1089	€900	Vroubleski, projet de costume (49x30cm-19x12in) mono.i. pastel. 28-Jun-4 Joron-Derem, Paris #117

DETILLEUX, Servais (1874-1940) Belgian

£1745	$3228	€2600	Elegant lady (54x34cm-21x13in) s. 15-Mar-4 Sotheby's, Amsterdam #56/R est:1500-2000

DETMOLD, Charles Maurice (1883-1908) British

Works on paper			
£560	$969	€818	Cormorant (19x14cm-7x6in) s. W/C. 11-Dec-3 Sotheby's, London #185/R

DETMOLD, Edward Julian (1883-1957) British

Works on paper			
£450	$779	€657	Osprey (18x14cm-7x6in) s. W/C. 11-Dec-3 Sotheby's, London #187
£500	$915	€730	Hawfinch (21x14cm-8x6in) W/C. 28-Jul-4 Bonhams, Knightsbridge #42/R
£1000	$1730	€1460	Humble bee and marsh orchid (21x13cm-8x5in) s. W/C prov.exhib. 11-Dec-3 Sotheby's, London #191/R est:1200-1600
£1200	$2076	€1752	Venus flytrap (21x12cm-8x5in) s. W/C prov.exhib. 11-Dec-3 Sotheby's, London #195 est:1500-2000

DETMOLD, Henry E (1854-1924) British

£1259	$2140	€1800	Le retour des pecheurs (41x31cm-16x12in) 24-Nov-3 Boscher, Cherbourg #784/R est:2000-2500
£1769	$3166	€2600	Depart de la caravane de la mariee (34x52cm-13x20in) s. 19-Mar-4 Millon & Associes, Paris #51/R est:2000-2500
£3667	$6747	€5500	Le depart de la caravane de la mariee devant Marrakech (34x52cm-13x20in) s. 14-Jun-4 Gros & Delettrez, Paris #521/R est:4000-6000

DETREVILLE, Richard (1864-1929) American

£297	$475	€434	View of the Pacific coastline from a flowering hillside (58x46cm-23x18in) s. canvasboard. 18-May-3 Auctions by the Bay, Alameda #1136/R

£419	$750	€612	Mallard (30x46cm-12x18in) s. 8-May-4 Auctions by the Bay, Alameda #442/R

DETROY, Léon (1857-1955) French

£379	$702	€550	Jardin au lever du soleil (84x108cm-33x43in) s. 19-Jan-4 Horta, Bruxelles #401
£1334	$2454	€2000	Paysage de la cote mediterraneenne (47x57cm-19x22in) s. prov. 8-Jun-4 Artcurial Briest, Paris #145/R est:1500-2000
£3000	$5010	€4380	Grand bouquet de fleurs (74x99cm-29x39in) s. board. 22-Oct-3 Sotheby's, Olympia #122/R est:4000-6000
£3380	$5476	€4800	Venise (35x37cm-14x15in) s. 11-Aug-3 Boscher, Cherbourg #732 est:4500-5000

DETRY, Arsene (1897-1981) Belgian

£633	$1134	€950	Les roulottes (40x50cm-16x20in) s.d.1949. 16-May-4 MonsAntic, Maisieres #405
£667	$1213	€1000	Paysage (120x90cm-47x35in) s. 4-Jul-4 MonsAntic, Maisieres #419
£733	$1335	€1100	Paturages, le temps gris (52x61cm-20x24in) s. 4-Jul-4 MonsAntic, Maisieres #421
£940	$1663	€1400	Ruelle (73x116cm-29x46in) s. 27-Apr-4 Campo, Vlaamse Kaai #405

DETTHOW, Eric (1888-1952) Swedish

£290	$522	€435	French landscape with canal boat (38x46cm-15x18in) s. panel. 25-Apr-4 Goteborg Auktionsverk, Sweden #388/R (S.KR 4000)
£319	$574	€479	Peonies in vase (75x60cm-30x24in) s. 25-Apr-4 Goteborg Auktionsverk, Sweden #1266/R (S.KR 4400)
£491	$835	€717	Italian woman with man (39x30cm-15x12in) s. panel exhib. 4-Nov-3 Bukowskis, Stockholm #8/R (S.KR 6500)
£614	$1002	€896	View of Grundsund (88x115cm-35x45in) s. 29-Sep-3 Lilla Bukowskis, Stockholm #298 (S.KR 8000)
£906	$1541	€1323	Reclining model (56x92cm-22x36in) s.d.1912. 5-Nov-3 AB Stockholms Auktionsverk #890/R (S.KR 12000)
£1192	$2170	€1800	Saint-Tropez (33x41cm-13x16in) s. panel. 16-Jun-4 Claude Boisgirard, Paris #41/R est:1200-1500
£1813	$3263	€2647	Orange grove, South of France (81x100cm-32x39in) s.d.1935 exhib. 26-Apr-4 Bukowskis, Stockholm #19/R est:18000-20000 (S.KR 25000)

DETTI, Cesare Auguste (1847-1914) Italian

£2038	$3750	€2975	Standard bearer (60x46cm-24x18in) s.i.d.87. 27-Jun-4 Freeman, Philadelphia #49/R est:4000-6000
£2973	$5322	€4400	Marie Pauline, duchesse de honneur (47x37cm-19x15in) s.d.1872 panel lit. 8-May-4 Schloss Ahlden, Ahlden #779/R est:4500
£4670	$8500	€6818	La chasse (55x45cm-22x18in) s. prov. 29-Jun-4 Sotheby's, New York #104/R est:6000-8000
£5882	$10000	€8588	Light entertainment (36x28cm-14x11in) s.d.1895 prov. 29-Oct-3 Christie's, Rockefeller NY #205/R est:10000-15000
£7059	$12000	€10306	Elegant lady reading music (55x38cm-22x15in) s.d.1887. 29-Oct-3 Christie's, Rockefeller NY #206/R est:12000-18000
£7059	$12000	€10306	Les Amiants (66x46cm-26x18in) s. 28-Oct-3 Sotheby's, New York #150/R est:15000-20000
£12752	$22826	€19000	Ladies and gentlemen in the park (27x41cm-11x16in) s.d.80 board. 25-May-4 Finarte Semenzato, Milan #215/R est:20000-21000
Works on paper			
£1284	$2145	€1862	Latest news (26x37cm-10x15in) st.sig. W/C. 23-Jun-3 Philippe Schuler, Zurich #3881/R est:2500-3000 (S.FR 2800)

DETTMANN, Ludwig Julius Christian (1865-1944) German

Works on paper			
£382	$603	€550	New York harbour entrance (21x30cm-8x12in) s. pastel lit. 19-Sep-3 Schloss Ahlden, Ahlden #1643/R

DETTMANN, Ludwig Julius Christian (attrib) (1865-1944) German

£270	$484	€400	Sheep (9x14cm-4x6in) board oval. 8-May-4 Hans Stahl, Toestorf #51

DEUCHERT, Heinrich (1840-?) German

Works on paper			
£343	$572	€490	Villa S Majestat on Worth island in Starnberger See (23x27cm-9x11in) i.d.24. Juli 1863 w/C pencil. 10-Oct-3 Winterberg, Heidelberg #560

DEUEL, Austin (1939-) American

Works on paper			
£369	$650	€539	Spotted signs (56x76cm-22x30in) s. W/C gouache. 23-May-4 Hindman, Chicago #183/R

DEUNHOUWER, Piet (1928-) Dutch

£1042	$1646	€1500	Passage (57x71cm-22x28in) s. panel. 26-Apr-3 Auction Maastricht #39/R est:2000-3000

DEURS, Caroline van (1860-1932) Danish

£1348	$2507	€1968	Playing patience (82x62cm-32x24in) s. 2-Mar-4 Rasmussen, Copenhagen #1663/R est:15000 (D.KR 15000)

DEUSS, Hans (1948-) Dutch

£4348	$7130	€6000	A fragile past (60x40cm-24x16in) s.d.94 prov. 27-May-3 Sotheby's, Amsterdam #352/R est:6000-9000

DEUSSER, August (1870-1942) German

£700	$1267	€1050	Prussian cavalry riders in summer landscape (51x61cm-20x24in) s. 1-Apr-4 Van Ham, Cologne #1334
£1800	$3294	€2700	Cologne (50x67cm-20x26in) prov.exhib. 5-Jun-4 Lempertz, Koln #663/R est:1400

DEUTSCH, Boris (1892-1978) American

Works on paper			
£706	$1200	€1031	Woman in blue reading (70x56cm-28x22in) s.d.1959 pencil pastel. 20-Nov-3 Auctions by the Bay, Alameda #1106/R

DEUTSCH, Ernst (1883-?) Austrian

Works on paper			
£1189	$2021	€1700	Title page for - The Woman (58x35cm-23x14in) s.i. gouache. 26-Nov-3 Dorotheum, Vienna #145/R

DEUTSCH, Ludwig (1855-1935) French

£62162	$111270	€92000	Palace guard (172x130cm-68x51in) s.d.1927 lit. 8-May-4 Schloss Ahlden, Ahlden #799/R est:85000

DEUX, Fred (1924-) French

Works on paper			
£235	$437	€350	Composition (36x16cm-14x6in) s.d.64 graphite. 3-Mar-4 Artcurial Briest, Paris #355
£302	$561	€450	Reflet du village dans la tete d'une oiseau (49x64cm-19x25in) s.i.d.1.51 ink oil. 3-Mar-4 Artcurial Briest, Paris #354
£490	$832	€700	Don du gris (17x9cm-7x4in) s.d.1986 graphite prov. 23-Nov-3 Cornette de St.Cyr, Paris #97/R
£604	$1124	€900	Paysage abstrait (50x65cm-20x26in) s.d.16.5.1954 W/C graphite ink wash. 3-Mar-4 Artcurial Briest, Paris #356
£699	$1189	€1000	Composition (50x39cm-20x15in) s.d.1962 pen wash prov. 23-Nov-3 Cornette de St.Cyr, Paris #96
£800	$1440	€1200	Untitled (36x26cm-14x10in) s.d.1969 ink dr. 25-Apr-4 Versailles Encheres #54
£933	$1680	€1400	Petit acte (32x50cm-13x20in) s. graphite. 25-Apr-4 Versailles Encheres #9

DEVAL, Pierre (1897-1993) French

Works on paper			
£1854	$3375	€2800	La belle endormie (29x47cm-11x19in) s. pastel. 15-Jun-4 Blanchet, Paris #234/R est:2500-3000

DEVAMBEZ, Andre (1867-1943) French

£1724	$3155	€2500	Le colereux (35x23cm-14x9in) s. panel. 31-Jan-4 Gerard, Besancon #36
£1793	$3281	€2600	Poilus dans une rue enneigee (9x13cm-4x5in) s. panel. 31-Jan-4 Gerard, Besancon #29
£1931	$3534	€2800	Le solitaire (10x12cm-4x5in) s. panel. 31-Jan-4 Gerard, Besancon #31
£2000	$3660	€2900	Petits ecoliers sur la place (11x15cm-4x6in) s. panel. 31-Jan-4 Gerard, Besancon #28
£2000	$3660	€2900	Jeune ecolier a ses devoirs (12x10cm-5x4in) s. panel. 31-Jan-4 Gerard, Besancon #32
£2241	$4102	€3250	La serenade (12x10cm-5x4in) s. panel. 31-Jan-4 Gerard, Besancon #30
£2414	$4417	€3500	Scene d'interieur, soldat assis, le sabre pose sur ses genoux (26x21cm-10x8in) s. panel. 31-Jan-4 Gerard, Besancon #35
£2621	$4796	€3800	Interieur de taverne, gentilhomme essuyant la lame de son epee (20x29cm-8x11in) s. panel. 31-Jan-4 Gerard, Besancon #34
£2632	$4842	€4000	Lutin des Collines (15x19cm-6x7in) s. wood. 28-Jun-4 Joron-Derem, Paris #138/R est:4000-5000
£3586	$6563	€5200	Village anime sous la neige (21x15cm-8x6in) s.i. panel. 31-Jan-4 Gerard, Besancon #33
£4225	$7310	€6000	Yport plage (11x14cm-4x6in) s.i. panel. 10-Dec-3 Neret-Minet, Paris #48/R est:1300-1500
£4225	$7310	€6000	Yport, plage (11x14cm-4x6in) s.i. panel. 10-Dec-3 Remi Ader, Paris #48/R est:1300-1500
£14539	$24280	€20500	Scene de plage (20x40cm-8x16in) s. 15-Oct-3 Claude Aguttes, Neuilly #25/R est:10000-12000
Works on paper			
£1200	$2160	€1800	Avant l'attaque (29x35cm-11x14in) s.d.Septembre 1915 gouache. 20-Apr-4 Chenu & Scrive, Lyon #74/R est:1500-2000

DEVAS, Anthony (1911-1958) British

£1000	$1790	€1460	Thistles (25x35cm-10x14in) s. exhib. 14-May-4 Christie's, Kensington #515/R est:1000-1500
£1300	$2366	€1898	Portrait of Nicolette Paulton the artist's wife (51x41cm-20x16in) s. prov. 1-Jul-4 Christie's, Kensington #44/R est:1500-2000

DEVAULX, François Theodore (1808-1870) French

Sculpture			
£1882	$3200	€2748	George Washington (45cm-18in) i. brown pat bronze prov. 28-Oct-3 Christie's, Rockefeller NY #18/R est:3000-5000

DEVEDEUX, Louis (1820-1874) French

£1745	$3246	€2600	Enfant au chapeau (65x54cm-26x21in) s.d.1852 oval. 7-Mar-4 Lesieur & Le Bars, Le Havre #29/R
£2684	$4939	€4000	Portrait d'une jeune fille tenant un cerceau (150x117cm-59x46in) s.d.1845. 24-Mar-4 Tajan, Paris #183/R est:4000-6000
£6593	$12000	€9626	Birth of Venus (130x97cm-51x38in) s. 19-Jun-4 Jackson's, Cedar Falls #46/R est:10000-15000

DEVELLY, Charles (1783-1849) French
Works on paper
£13265 $23745 €19500 Patineurs sur le bassin de la Villette, hiver (31x42cm-12x17in) s.d.1821 pen brown ink wash black pencil htd gouache. 19-Mar-4 Piasa, Paris #173/R est:3000-4000

DEVENTER, Willem Anthonie van (1824-1893) Dutch
Works on paper
£548 $932 €800 Scavengers on beach (31x43cm-12x17in) s. W/C lit. 6-Nov-3 Allgauer, Kempten #3272/R

DEVENYNS, Steve (1953-) American
£621 $1000 €900 Tough trip thru paradise (33x76cm-13x30in) 22-Aug-3 Altermann Galleries, Santa Fe #15

DEVERIA, Achille (1800-1857) French
Works on paper
£544 $974 €800 Portrait d'un Lieutenant des Cuirassiers de la Garde Royale (34x26cm-13x10in) s.d.1824 graphite htd white two joined sheets. 18-Mar-4 Christie's, Paris #307/R
£851 $1379 €1200 Couple enlace pres d'une chaumiere (18x15cm-7x6in) s. W/C. 21-May-3 Daguerre, Paris #77
£2800 $4676 €4088 Turkish gentleman and lady seated in an interior (47x59cm-19x23in) s. black white chk. 14-Oct-3 Sotheby's, London #18/R est:3000-5000

DEVERIA, Achille (attrib) (1800-1857) French
£346 $620 €505 Mlle Henriette - Eleve de Conservatoire (33x25cm-13x10in) mono.i.d. pencil. 22-Mar-4 Philippe Schuler, Zurich #6340 (S.FR 800)

DEVERIA, Eugène (1808-1865) French
£2649 $4821 €4000 Portrait de Marie-Eugenie Deveria, fille de l'artiste (48x35cm-19x14in) s. panel painted c.1850-55 prov. 18-Jun-4 Piasa, Paris #47/R est:4000-6000

DEVERIA, Eugène (attrib) (1808-1865) French
£339 $543 €495 Henri IV with cleric (41x33cm-16x13in) s. 16-Sep-3 Philippe Schuler, Zurich #5436 (S.FR 750)

DEVERIA, Henri-Victor (1829-1897) French
£1127 $1949 €1600 Children picking cherries (31x22cm-12x9in) s. panel prov. 13-Dec-3 Lempertz, Koln #209/R est:2000

DEVERIA, Luis (19/20th C) Spanish
£3517 $6331 €5100 Theatre figure (45x37cm-18x15in) s.d.1914. 26-Jan-4 Ansorena, Madrid #70/R est:5100

DEVERY, David (20th C) American?
Works on paper
£542 $900 €786 Red chaps (147x122cm-58x48in) 13-Jun-3 Du Mouchelle, Detroit #2095/R

DEVETTA, Edoardo (1912-1993) Italian
£355 $592 €500 Sappada (40x50cm-16x20in) s. s.i.d.1958 verso cartone telato. 21-Jun-3 Stadion, Trieste #238/R
£385 $642 €550 Cathedral (60x50cm-24x20in) s. s.d.1971. 10-Oct-3 Stadion, Trieste #436/R
£420 $701 €600 Composition (70x50cm-28x20in) s. s.i.verso. 10-Oct-3 Stadion, Trieste #388/R

DEVILLE, Jean (1872-?) French
£897 $1488 €1300 Berger sur la falaise (54x65cm-21x26in) s. 5-Oct-3 Lombrail & Teucquam, Paris #303

DEVILLE, Joseph Henri (1803-1857) Swiss
£1154 $1927 €1650 Girl from Wallis feeding goat in front of shed (31x40cm-12x16in) s. panel. 27-Jun-3 Michael Zeller, Lindau #514/R est:1400

DEVILLE-CHABROLLE, Marie Paule (1952-) French
Sculpture
£2951 $4929 €4250 Jeune femme (34x30x20cm-13x12x8in) bronze. 26-Oct-3 Feletin, Province #78

DEVILLIE, Charles (1850-1905) French
£433 $789 €650 Portrait d'homme a la mandoline (81x73cm-32x29in) s. 29-Jun-4 Chenu & Scrive, Lyon #59/R

DEVIS, A (18th C) British
£451 $754 €650 Portrait of a boy (21x17cm-8x7in) s.d.1769. 23-Oct-3 Hagelstam, Helsinki #857

DEVIS, Anthony (1729-1817) British
Works on paper
£250 $443 €365 View of Windermere and the Langdale Pykes (28x41cm-11x16in) ink wash drawing prov. 28-Apr-4 Halls, Shrewsbury #488/R
£260 $411 €377 Landscape with rabbits (13x20cm-5x8in) pencil pn wash. 3-Sep-3 Bonhams, Bury St Edmunds #365
£260 $460 €380 Ullswater (28x41cm-11x16in) ink wash drawing prov. 28-Apr-4 Halls, Shrewsbury #487
£320 $586 €467 Donkeys in a field (20x28cm-8x11in) W/C. 27-Jan-4 Bonhams, Knightsbridge #142
£360 $623 €526 Neath River, figure under trees by a river with shipping in the distance (13x19cm-5x7in) pencil W/C. 9-Dec-3 Bonhams, Oxford #46
£450 $832 €657 Cattle in a landscape (13x19cm-5x7in) pen ink wash pair. 10-Mar-4 Sotheby's, Olympia #29/R
£800 $1360 €1168 Landscape with figures (14x20cm-6x8in) pen ink wash pair. 4-Nov-3 Bonhams, New Bond Street #60/R
£800 $1464 €1168 Sunbury on Thames (10x12cm-4x5in) pencil grey ink prov. 3-Jun-4 Christie's, London #105/R

DEVIS, Anthony (attrib) (1729-1817) British
£556 $1000 €812 Travellers, man afoot, woman on donkey, rural road with four sheep and cow (20x28cm-8x11in) s. wood panel. 26-Jan-4 Schrager Galleries, Milwaukee #1442
£600 $948 €870 Briton ferry in Glamorganshire (37x58cm-15x23in) i.d.1763 verso panel. 4-Sep-3 Christie's, Kensington #102/R

DEVIS, Arthur (1711-1787) British
£6000 $10020 €8760 Portrait of a gentleman and his wife (14x12cm-6x5in) canvas on panel pair. 14-Oct-3 Sotheby's, London #435/R est:4000-6000
£12000 $20040 €17520 Portrait of a lady seated, wearing a white dress, her bonnet on a table by a window (60x40cm-24x16in) prov. 14-Oct-3 Sotheby's, London #442/R est:10000-15000
£15000 $25050 €21900 Portrait of a lady of the Lister family seated by a table, child on her lap (48x34cm-19x13in) panel prov.lit. 14-Oct-3 Sotheby's, London #436/R est:10000-15000
£20000 $33400 €29200 Portrait of a gentleman, possibly the Reverend William Digby seated by rocks (74x61cm-29x24in) prov.lit. 14-Oct-3 Sotheby's, London #441/R est:12000-18000
£45000 $82800 €65700 Portrait of Thomas Bateman Lane (60x42cm-24x17in) s.d.1755 prov.exhib.lit. 9-Jun-4 Christie's, London #1/R est:40000-60000
£55000 $91850 €80300 Portrait of a gentleman, possibly John Wallop, Ist Earl of Portsmouth holding a hunter in landscape (74x62cm-29x24in) prov.exhib.lit. 14-Oct-3 Sotheby's, London #437/R est:40000-60000
Miniatures
£6000 $10800 €8760 John Tennan (4cm-2in) s.i.d.1747 i.verso oil ivory gold frame oval exhib.lit. 22-Apr-4 Bonhams, New Bond Street #25/R est:2000-3000
Works on paper
£300 $519 €438 Cottage near Wembley (13x20cm-5x8in) ink W/C prov. 11-Dec-3 Bruton Knowles, Cheltenham #78
£6500 $11895 €9490 Study of a portrait of an elegant couple (46x30cm-18x12in) blk chk blue paper prov. 3-Jun-4 Christie's, London #51/R est:3000-5000

DEVIS, Arthur (circle) (1711-1787) British
£31250 $55000 €45625 Tennis players (48x37cm-19x15in) prov. 18-May-4 Sotheby's, New York #210/R est:20000-25000

DEVIS, Arthur William (1763-1822) British
£8500 $13855 €12410 Hindu girl seated cross-legged spinning watched by a parrot (20x28cm-8x11in) with sig.indis.d. prov.lit. 24-Sep-3 Christie's, London #76/R est:8000-12000

DEVIS, Arthur William (attrib) (1763-1822) British
£1229 $2200 €2063 Landscape with young boy and his two dogs (74x61cm-29x24in) 20-Mar-4 Pook & Pook, Downington #368/R est:2500-3500
£1700 $3043 €2482 Portrait of Harriet Leonard (62x51cm-24x20in) 27-May-4 Christie's, Kensington #52/R est:1500-2000

DEVIS, Pierre (?) ?
£313 $509 €450 Auderghem (45x33cm-18x13in) s. 23-Sep-3 Galerie Moderne, Brussels #932

DEVLIN, John (1950-) Irish
Works on paper
£533 $960 €800 Pax et bonum (58x38cm-23x15in) s.d.1978 pencil W/C. 20-Apr-4 James Adam, Dublin #22/R

DEVOS, Albert (1868-1950) Belgian
£625 $1150 €950 Pecheur de crevettes (82x101cm-32x40in) s. 22-Jun-4 Palais de Beaux Arts, Brussels #226
£890 $1514 €1300 Fishing port (69x108cm-27x43in) s. 5-Nov-3 Vendue Huis, Gravenhage #269/R

DEVOS, Léon (1897-1974) Belgian
£267 $483 €400 Le petit fosse (50x60cm-20x24in) s. 30-Mar-4 Campo, Vlaamse Kaai #43
£267 $483 €400 Porcelaines, fleurs, chandelier et cadran emaille sur une table (80x70cm-31x28in) s.d.1926. 30-Mar-4 Palais de Beaux Arts, Brussels #528
£272 $487 €400 Vase de fleurs (35x22cm-14x9in) s. 16-Mar-4 Vanderkindere, Brussels #287
£372 $665 €550 Dunes (65x80cm-26x31in) s. panel. 10-May-4 Horta, Bruxelles #486
£490 $832 €700 Nature morte aux perdrix grises (60x61cm-24x24in) s. 30-Nov-3 Salle des ventes Pillet, Lyon la Foret #116
£556 $872 €800 Nature morte aux pommes (38x60cm-15x24in) s. 26-Aug-3 Galerie Moderne, Brussels #326/R
£638 $1066 €900 Delphinium (50x70cm-20x28in) s. 17-Jun-3 Galerie Moderne, Brussels #186/R
£667 $1193 €1000 Port de Nieuport (50x60cm-20x24in) s. 16-May-4 MonsAntic, Maisieres #406
£671 $1188 €1000 Deux femmes dans un paysage (92x70cm-36x28in) s. 27-Apr-4 Campo, Vlaamse Kaai #408
£959 $1630 €1400 Port mediterraneen (50x65cm-20x26in) s. 10-Nov-3 Horta, Bruxelles #396
£972 $1624 €1400 Still life with bread (65x80cm-26x31in) s. 21-Oct-3 Campo & Campo, Antwerp #104

Works on paper
£1600 $2944 €2400 Seated nude (92x65cm-36x26in) s. W/C. 9-Jun-4 Christie's, Amsterdam #83/R est:2500-3500

DEVOS, Pierre (1917-1972) Belgian
£909 $1518 €1300 Jeune Fille (80x60cm-31x24in) s.d.61. 11-Oct-3 De Vuyst, Lokeren #122

DEVRIEZ, Philippe (?) ?
Sculpture
£1333 $2427 €2000 Danseuse (55cm-22in) s. pat bronze marble base. 12-Jul-4 Il Ponte, Milan #965 est:1800-2000

DEVROEY, Jozef (1908-1997) Belgian
£390 $651 €550 Couple mowing (101x123cm-40x48in) s.d.1925 canvas on panel. 20-Oct-3 Bernaerts, Antwerp #260/R

DEWAR, William Jesmond (attrib) (19/20th C) British
£420 $769 €613 Lunch at Goodwood (55x64cm-22x25in) i.verso board prov. 8-Apr-4 Christie's, Kensington #205/R

DEWASNE, Jean (1921-1999) French
£6803 $12177 €10000 Composition geometrique (97x130cm-38x51in) s.d.1958 mixed media aluminium. 19-Mar-4 Millon & Associes, Paris #172/R est:6000-8000

DEWEY, Charles Melville (1849-1937) American
£3672 $6500 €5361 Boat at low tide (11x18cm-4x7in) s. 2-May-4 Bonhams & Butterfields, San Francisco #1086/R est:500-700

DEWEY, Edward H (1850-1939) American
£973 $1800 €1421 Portrait of a recumbent English setter (30x43cm-12x17in) s.d.09 board. 10-Feb-4 Doyle, New York #196/R est:2000-3000

DEWHURST, Wynford (1864-1941) British
£600 $1002 €876 Austrian village (36x27cm-14x11in) s. board. 16-Oct-3 Christie's, Kensington #383/R
£650 $1170 €949 French river scene with a water mill beside trees (73x60cm-29x24in) s. 21-Apr-4 Tennants, Leyburn #1148

DEWHURST, Wynford (attrib) (1864-1941) British
£750 $1253 €1095 Evening near Avignon (36x48cm-14x19in) indis.i.verso. 19-Oct-3 Desmond Judd, Cranbrook #1022

DEWING, Amy Flemming Bronson (20th C) American
£261 $475 €392 Two nudes (76x64cm-30x25in) s.d.1945. 19-Jun-4 Harvey Clar, Oakland #2224

DEWING, Thomas W (1851-1938) American
£4324 $8000 €6313 Reclining nude (15x27cm-6x11in) indis.sig.d.1878 panel. 11-Mar-4 Christie's, Rockefeller NY #23/R est:5000-7000
Works on paper
£245 $450 €358 Victorian woman (30x20cm-12x8in) s. pastel. 11-Jun-4 David Rago, Lambertville #266/R
£1700 $2924 €2482 Elegant lady, in a pink dress, seated in an interior (53x39cm-21x15in) s. pastel. 3-Dec-3 Christie's, Kensington #53/R est:200-400
£26816 $48000 €39151 Girl with red hair (23x13cm-9x5in) s. pastel prov. 6-May-4 Shannon's, Milford #35/R est:10000-15000

DEWITT, J (?) ?
£1192 $2170 €1800 Cherubins et angelots (21x33cm-8x13in) panel. 17-Jun-4 Marie & Robert, Paris #33 est:800-1000

DEWS, J Steven (1949-) British
£3000 $5370 €4380 Great Eastern laying cable (51x76cm-20x30in) s. 26-May-4 Christie's, Kensington #741/R est:3500-5000
£23000 $39560 €33580 Columbia to windward of Shamrock, off New York, America's Cup 1899 (61x91cm-24x36in) s. i.on stretcher. 2-Dec-3 Sotheby's, London #131a/R est:25000-35000
£36000 $61920 €52560 Hard beat to the West Lymington Town sailing club j-class regatta (102x152cm-40x60in) s. 2-Dec-3 Sotheby's, London #120/R est:40000-60000

DEXEL, Walter (1890-1973) German
£3620 $6154 €5285 Waterfall I (39x30cm-15x12in) s.d.1913 s.i.d. verso board exhib. 25-Nov-3 Germann, Zurich #128/R est:5000-6000 (S.FR 8000)
£4299 $7179 €6277 Sketch for diagonals (42x30cm-17x12in) s.i.d.1963 verso panel exhib. 24-Jun-3 Germann, Zurich #66/R est:10000-12000 (S.FR 9500)
£6061 $10848 €8849 Big black L (65x65cm-26x26in) si. verso 1929 prov. 22-Mar-4 Philippe Schuler, Zurich #4443/R est:10000-14000 (S.FR 14000)
£6294 $10825 €9000 Composition with two vertical white stripes (80x62cm-31x24in) s.d.1968 s.i.d. verso. 2-Dec-3 Hauswedell & Nolte, Hamburg #135/R est:12000
£6993 $11888 €10000 Pulverturm in Meran (41x68cm-16x27in) s.i.d.12 verso board exhib.lit. 26-Nov-3 Lempertz, Koln #635/R est:10000
£8451 $14620 €12000 1924 V - Variante (53x36cm-21x14in) s. i. verso board. 13-Dec-3 Lempertz, Koln #126/R est:5000
Works on paper
£433 $793 €650 Composition 1922 1/32 (21x16cm-8x6in) i. pencil. 5-Jun-4 Lempertz, Koln #664/R
£559 $951 €800 Sketch for signpost: Naumberg - Jena (14x20cm-6x8in) s.i. gouache Indian ink lit. 26-Nov-3 Lempertz, Koln #638/R
£1100 $1837 €1606 Geometric design (34x25cm-13x10in) st.d.1920/21 pencil prov. 22-Oct-3 Sotheby's, Olympia #137/R est:500-700
£2657 $4571 €3800 Town scene (33x26cm-13x10in) s. W/C. 6-Dec-3 Hans Stahl, Toestorf #364 est:900

DEXTER, Walter (1876-1958) British
£340 $626 €496 Landscape (9x11cm-4x4in) s. 11-Jun-4 Keys, Aylsham #573
Works on paper
£260 $478 €380 Lady Chapel, King's Lynn (6x9cm-2x4in) s. W/C. 11-Jun-4 Keys, Aylsham #572

DEXTER, William (1818-1860) Australian
£350 $585 €511 Sparrows and mistletoe on a mossy bank (25x30cm-10x12in) s. board feigned oval. 8-Oct-3 Christie's, Kensington #967/R
Works on paper
£690 $1076 €1001 Birds nest (22x33cm-9x13in) s.i. W/C exhib. 1-Aug-2 Joel, Victoria #145 est:2000-3000 (A.D 2000)

DEY, John William (1912-1978) American
£359 $600 €524 Flamingo (41x33cm-16x13in) paint board. 15-Nov-3 Slotin Folk Art, Buford #364/R

DEYDIER, René (1882-1942) French
£748 $1190 €1100 Port du Guilvinec (54x65cm-21x26in) s. 18-Mar-3 Adjug'art, Brest #106

DEYGAS, Regis (1876-?) French
£1343 $2497 €2000 Moment in time (50x65cm-20x26in) s. 3-Mar-4 Tajan, Paris #6/R est:800-1000

DEYMONAZ, Andre (1946-) French
£1361 $2476 €2000 Le pique-nique (46x55cm-18x22in) s. 8-Feb-4 Anaf, Lyon #164/R est:1500-1600

DEYROLLE, Jean (1911-1967) French
£1200 $2148 €1800 Untitled (87x61cm-34x24in) s.i. 13-May-4 Neumeister, Munich #571/R est:1800-2000
£1878 $3136 €2742 Composition (76x56cm-30x22in) s.d.264 paper on canvas. 7-Oct-3 Rasmussen, Copenhagen #79/R est:20000-25000 (D.KR 20000)
£2333 $4200 €3500 Eloy, Opus 552 (60x73cm-24x29in) s. s.i.verso tempera exhib.lit. 25-Apr-4 Versailles Encheres #49 est:3000-4000
£2349 $4158 €3500 Gens (65x54cm-26x21in) s. s.i.verso painted c.1958 prov. 28-Apr-4 Artcurial Briest, Paris #261/R est:4000-5000
£2400 $4320 €3600 Lunien (81x54cm-32x21in) s. i.verso. 24-Apr-4 Cornette de St.Cyr, Paris #509/R est:1500
£3041 $5351 €4500 Rival (100x50cm-39x20in) s. i. verso tempera prov.exhib.lit. 18-May-4 Tajan, Paris #27/R est:5000-6000

DEYROLLE, Theophile-Louis (1844-1923) French
£537 $951 €800 Lecture au jardin (36x36cm-14x14in) s.i.d.80. 30-Apr-4 Tajan, Paris #177
£570 $1061 €850 Portrait de ma grand-mere Lucie Fossey (13x18cm-5x7in) d.1893. 3-Mar-4 Ferri, Paris #385/R
£1067 $1909 €1600 Nature morte au pichet (46x33cm-18x13in) s. 16-May-4 Thierry & Lannon, Brest #137/R est:1500-1800
£1275 $2346 €1900 Children playing on farmstead path in Brittany (49x60cm-19x24in) s.i.d.1879. 27-Mar-4 Dannenberg, Berlin #546/R est:1200
£2000 $3580 €3000 Repas des chasseurs (73x100cm-29x39in) s. 16-May-4 Thierry & Lannon, Brest #136/R est:3000-4000
£2318 $4334 €3500 Le retour du troupeau (31x41cm-12x16in) s. 24-Jul-4 Thierry & Lannon, Brest #157/R est:3000-3500
£2817 $4930 €4000 Jeune Bretonne et sa fillette sur le chemin du moulin (172x124cm-68x49in) s. 21-Dec-3 Thierry & Lannon, Brest #163/R est:4000-5000
£4667 $8353 €7000 Noce en Bretagne (90x120cm-35x47in) s. 16-May-4 Renault-Aubry, Pontivy #439
£11333 $20287 €17000 Fete du cidre (71x102cm-28x40in) s. 16-May-4 Renault-Aubry, Pontivy #440

DEZAUNAY, Émile (1854-1940) French
£384 $703 €580 Bord de mer (32x40cm-13x16in) s. 7-Apr-4 Piasa, Paris #102
£1329 $2285 €1900 Sortie du port du Pouliguen (26x35cm-10x14in) s. panel. 7-Dec-3 Livinec, Gaudcheau & Jezequel, Rennes #66/R
£1733 $3103 €2600 La chapelle de Golguen a Tregastel (54x65cm-21x26in) s. 16-May-4 Thierry & Lannon, Brest #139 est:2500-3000
£1800 $3276 €2700 Portrait de jeune fille (55x46cm-22x18in) s. 4-Jul-4 Eric Pillon, Calais #94/R
£2042 $3574 €2900 Riviere du Belon (46x55cm-18x22in) s. 21-Dec-3 Thierry & Lannon, Brest #154/R est:2000-2500
£9467 $16945 €14200 La moisson pres de Pont-Aven (88x115cm-35x45in) s. painted 1891. 16-May-4 Thierry & Lannon, Brest #138/R est:10000-12000
Works on paper
£533 $955 €800 Moisson en Bretagne (32x50cm-13x20in) s. chl. 16-May-4 Thierry & Lannon, Brest #30
£795 $1486 €1200 Sortie de messe a Ste Anne d'Auray (31x41cm-12x16in) s. W/C. 24-Jul-4 Thierry & Lannon, Brest #313
£1424 $2663 €2150 Bretonne a la gerbe d'or (40x34cm-16x13in) s. W/C. 24-Jul-4 Thierry & Lannon, Brest #56 est:1800-2000
£1933 $3519 €2900 Les enfants (30x38cm-12x15in) s.d.1930 W/C. 4-Jul-4 Eric Pillon, Calais #160/R

DEZENTJE, Ernest (1885-1972) ?
£250 $443 €365 Mt. Salak, Java, Indonesia (39x63cm-15x25in) s. 29-Apr-4 Christie's, Kensington #301
£408 $731 €600 Indonesian landscape with sawahs at the foot of a mountain (47x60cm-19x24in) s.d.28 canvasboard. 16-Mar-4 Christie's, Amsterdam #47
£411 $699 €600 Pnd di Tjipajung (36x79cm-14x31in) s.d.52. 5-Nov-3 Vendue Huis, Gravenhage #540

£442 $791 €650 People working on the sawah (30x47cm-12x19in) s. board. 16-Mar-4 Christie's, Amsterdam #27
£503 $931 €750 Tropenweelde (30x36cm-12x14in) s.i.d.49 sold with another. 15-Mar-4 Sotheby's, Amsterdam #164/R
£578 $1035 €850 Indonesian landscape (50x75cm-20x30in) s. 16-Mar-4 Christie's, Amsterdam #111
£1522 $2359 €2222 Padi fields (74x119cm-29x47in) s.d.26. 6-Oct-2 Sotheby's, Singapore #58/R est:3000-4000 (S.D 4200)
£1961 $3549 €2863 Flowers (60x100cm-24x39in) s. 3-Apr-4 Glerum, Singapore #67/R est:3000-3600 (S.D 6000)
£3105 $5619 €4533 Landscape (64x91cm-25x36in) s.d.48. 4-Apr-4 Sotheby's, Singapore #25/R est:2000-3000 (S.D 9500)
£3741 $6697 €5500 Herinnering aan de Kali Besar, Batavia (105x85cm-41x33in) s.d.23 s.i.d.stretcher. 16-Mar-4 Christie's, Amsterdam #24/R est:3000-5000

DEZEUZE, Daniel (1942-) French
Works on paper
£567 $1014 €850 Sans titre (76x56cm-30x22in) s. ink chk. 12-May-4 Chochon-Barre & Allardi, Paris #81

D'HAESE, Reinhoud (1928-) Belgian
Sculpture
£1818 $3200 €2654 Insecte (58cm-23in) welded sheet bronze grey marble cube suppor prov. 22-May-4 Selkirks, St. Louis #799/R est:2000-3000
£2174 $3565 €3000 Fetard (32cm-13in) welded pewter stone base prov.exhib. 27-May-3 Sotheby's, Amsterdam #421/R est:3500-4500
£4000 $7160 €6000 Paponide (54x38cm-21x15in) i.d.1999 verso copper stone base. 15-May-4 De Vuyst, Lokeren #599/R est:6000-7000
£4667 $8353 €7000 S'exposer a etre c'est se condamner a n'etre rien d'autre (60x65cm-24x26in) i.verso brass stone base lit. 15-May-4 De Vuyst, Lokeren #526/R est:6500-8000

D'HAESE, Roel (1921-) Belgian
Sculpture
£2595 $4800 €3789 Sphinx (64cm-25in) s.i.d.1974 base dark brown pat bronze. 13-Jul-4 Christie's, Rockefeller NY #170/R est:2000-3000

D'HASTREL, Adolphe (1805-1874) French
Prints
£3297 $5835 €4946 Rio de Janeiro, Dessirre du sommet du Corcovado (42x65cm-17x26in) Lithograph W/C. 27-Apr-4 Bolsa de Arte, Rio de Janeiro #3/R (B.R 18000)
Works on paper
£2353 $4000 €3435 Montevideo harbour and cathedral (19x24cm-7x9in) s. W/C. 25-Nov-3 Galeria y Remates, Montevideo #173/R

D'HAUCOURT, Genevieve (20th C) French
£289 $500 €422 Figures by a castle (36x46cm-14x18in) init. board. 13-Dec-3 Sloans & Kenyon, Bethesda #780/R

D'HONT, Piet (1917-1997) Dutch
Sculpture
£1119 $1902 €1600 Bison (23cm-9in) bronze incl bronze base conceived 1967 edn of 5 prov.exhib.lit. 25-Nov-3 Christie's, Amsterdam #135/R est:1800-2200

DHURANDHAR, Mahadev Viswanath (1867-1944) Indian
£1400 $2380 €2044 Female nude (40x56cm-16x22in) canvas on board. 4-Nov-3 Bonhams, New Bond Street #43/R est:1500-2000
Works on paper
£750 $1275 €1095 Offering (26x15cm-10x6in) s.d.1910 pencil. 4-Nov-3 Bonhams, New Bond Street #44/R
£750 $1275 €1095 Mharastrian girl (26x12cm-10x5in) s.d.20/12/11 pencil W/C. 4-Nov-3 Bonhams, New Bond Street #45/R
£780 $1326 €1139 Veil (27x23cm-11x9in) chl. 4-Nov-3 Bonhams, New Bond Street #46/R

DIAL, Thornton (1928-) American
£958 $1600 €1399 Lady with a bird (124x94cm-49x37in) 15-Nov-3 Slotin Folk Art, Buford #159/R est:3000-5000
£1167 $2100 €1704 Man with fish (56x76cm-22x30in) oil on paper. 24-Apr-4 Slotin Folk Art, Buford #368/R est:1000-2000
Works on paper
£958 $1600 €1399 Cat (53x56cm-21x22in) mixed media metal prov. 15-Nov-3 Slotin Folk Art, Buford #162/R est:300-500

DIAMANDOPOULOS, Diamantis (1914-1995) Greek
£6000 $10200 €8760 Playtime (20x26cm-8x10in) prov. 18-Nov-3 Sotheby's, London #65/R est:6000-8000
£8000 $14000 €11680 Head of a woman (42x30cm-17x12in) s. exhib. 16-Dec-3 Bonhams, New Bond Street #92/R est:8000-12000
£24000 $42960 €35040 The candelabrum (53x33cm-21x13in) s. canvas on hardboard painted c.1950 exhib. 11-May-4 Bonhams, New Bond Street #94/R est:15000-20000

DIAMANT, Lazar Mikhajlowitsch (1874-1922) German?
£2113 $3655 €3000 At monastery (39x53cm-15x21in) s. Cyrillic masonite. 10-Dec-3 Dorotheum, Vienna #81/R est:3200-3500

DIAMOND, Carrie (20th C) British
£400 $668 €584 Red poppies (90x70cm-35x28in) s. 21-Oct-3 Bonhams, Knightsbridge #76/R

DIANO, Giacinto (1730-1803) Italian
£17333 $31373 €26000 L'Apotheose des heros de l'Antiquite, projet de plafond (95x147cm-37x58in) 30-Mar-4 Millon & Associes, Paris #16/R est:10000-15000

DIARACK, Paul (19th C) British
£600 $936 €876 Anchored sailing craft and figures, Italianate coastal scene beyond (20x25cm-8x10in) indis.sig. d.1842 verso. 22-Sep-2 Desmond Judd, Cranbrook #863

DIAS, Antonio (1944-) Brazilian
£16300 $28852 €24450 The day as a prisoner (120x120cm-47x47in) i. s.i.verso. 27-Apr-4 Bolsa de Arte, Rio de Janeiro #94/R (B.R 89000)

DIAS, Cicero (1907-) ?
£13370 $23665 €20055 Woman with an apple (60x92cm-24x36in) s. 27-Apr-4 Bolsa de Arte, Rio de Janeiro #52/R (B.R 73000)
Works on paper
£27473 $48626 €41210 Untitled (43x46cm-17x18in) s. W/C seven. 27-Apr-4 Bolsa de Arte, Rio de Janeiro #72/R (B.R 150000)
£56667 $104267 €85000 Dance (53x73cm-21x29in) s.d.1928 W/C prov.exhib. 10-Jun-4 Christie's, Paris #12/R est:40000-60000

DIAZ CANEJA, Juan Manuel (1905-1988) Spanish
£14765 $27463 €22000 Landscape (64x54cm-25x21in) s.d.1974 verso. 2-Mar-4 Ansorena, Madrid #844/R est:12000

DIAZ CARRENO, Francisco (c.1840-1903) Spanish
£805 $1498 €1200 Snack (65x84cm-26x33in) 2-Mar-4 Ansorena, Madrid #130/R est:1050

DIAZ CASTILLA, Luciano (1940-) Spanish
£764 $1215 €1100 Atardecer (30x50cm-12x20in) s. 29-Apr-3 Durán, Madrid #123/R
£764 $1260 €1100 I left (41x51cm-16x20in) s. i.verso. 2-Jul-3 Ansorena, Madrid #923/R
£839 $1401 €1200 Landscape (38x46cm-15x18in) s. 30-Jun-3 Ansorena, Madrid #218/R
£851 $1421 €1200 Pastor y arboles sobre fondo blanco (37x48cm-15x19in) s. 23-Jun-3 Durán, Madrid #152/R
£1056 $1849 €1500 Rocks and goats (65x81cm-26x32in) s. 16-Dec-3 Durán, Madrid #115/R est:1500
£1275 $2283 €1900 To work (73x92cm-29x36in) s. 25-May-4 Durán, Madrid #111/R est:1900
£1300 $2366 €1950 Carros (82x97cm-32x38in) s. 29-Jun-4 Segre, Madrid #303/R est:1950
£1327 $2414 €1950 Poppies (73x100cm-29x39in) s. 3-Feb-4 Segre, Madrid #141/R est:1950
£1449 $2377 €2000 Restful bull (81x100cm-32x39in) s. 27-May-3 Durán, Madrid #98/R est:1800
£1510 $2824 €2250 Men and cattle (73x100cm-29x39in) s. 24-Feb-4 Durán, Madrid #186/R est:2000
£1510 $2673 €2250 Village in autumn (81x100cm-32x39in) s. 27-Apr-4 Durán, Madrid #138/R est:2100

DIAZ DE LA PENA (19th C) French
£400 $748 €600 Figure in woodland (33x41cm-13x16in) s. board. 22-Jul-4 Gorringes, Lewes #1973
£872 $1623 €1300 Woman in wood (40x50cm-16x20in) s.d.1864. 8-Mar-4 Bernaerts, Antwerp #870
£2500 $4175 €3600 Fleurs (50x65cm-20x26in) s. 21-Oct-3 Campo, Vlaamse Kaai #409 est:3000-4000

DIAZ DE LA PENA, Narcisse-Virgile (1807-1876) French
£845 $1462 €1200 Paysage a l'etang (14x26cm-6x10in) mono. 12-Dec-3 Libert, Castor, Paris #61
£1182 $2117 €1750 Nature morte a la grappe de raisin (40x33cm-16x13in) s. 5-May-4 Coutau Begarie, Paris #58/R est:2000-3000
£1200 $2172 €1800 Sous-bois (46x38cm-18x15in) l'essence painted c.1855 exhib. 30-Mar-4 Rossini, Paris #285/R est:1000-1500
£1338 $2221 €1900 Roses et giroflees (17x11cm-7x4in) s.verso panel. 15-Jun-3 Peron, Melun #7
£1422 $2546 €2076 Forest clearing (53x40cm-21x16in) s. i. verso. 13-May-4 Stuker, Bern #92/R est:4000-6000 (S.FR 3300)
£1533 $2775 €2300 La jeune femme au chien (23x17cm-9x7in) peinture a l'essence exhib. 30-Mar-4 Rossini, Paris #281/R est:1000-1500
£1587 $3000 €2317 Angel with nude in a landscape (36x25cm-14x10in) s. panel. 21-Feb-4 Jeffery Burchard, Florida #30
£1800 $3186 €2628 Faggot gatherer (20x25cm-8x10in) s. panel. 28-Apr-4 Halls, Shrewsbury #526/R est:2000-3000
£1882 $3500 €2748 Into the woods (49x68cm-19x27in) panel. 5-Mar-4 Skinner, Boston #240/R est:4000-6000
£2000 $3680 €3000 Odalisque et ses servantes (21x16cm-8x6in) s. 14-Jun-4 Gros & Delettrez, Paris #105/R est:3000-4000
£2067 $3741 €3100 Baigneuse assise au Rocher (23x17cm-9x7in) s. painted c.1860-1865. 30-Mar-4 Rossini, Paris #283/R est:1200-2000
£2093 $3600 €3056 Foret a Fontainebleau (27x36cm-11x14in) s. board. 3-Dec-3 Naón & Cia, Buenos Aires #30/R est:3000-4000
£2098 $3608 €3000 Les baigneuses (16x26cm-6x10in) s. painted c.1850-1855. 7-Dec-3 Osenat, Fontainebleau #125 est:3500-4000
£2533 $4636 €3800 Bouquet de roses et fleurs des champs (21x16cm-8x6in) s. painted c.1870 oval. 6-Jun-4 Osenat, Fontainebleau #141/R est:4000-4500
£2667 $4827 €4000 Madeleine repentante (21x16cm-8x6in) s. painted c.1860 exhib.lit. 30-Mar-4 Rossini, Paris #282/R est:1500-2500
£2667 $4880 €4000 Environs du Jean de Paris a Fontainebleau (32x44cm-13x17in) s. panel. 6-Jun-4 Osenat, Fontainebleau #124/R est:4000-4500
£3020 $5406 €4500 L'anneau d'amethyste (45x23cm-18x9in) s.d.61 panel prov. 25-May-4 Chambelland & Giafferi, Paris #61/R est:5000-6000
£3108 $5470 €4600 Landscape near Barbizon (43x55cm-17x22in) s. 22-May-4 Lempertz, Koln #1505/R est:4000
£3194 $5047 €4600 Venus and Cupid (22x17cm-9x7in) s. panel lit. 19-Sep-3 Schloss Ahlden, Ahlden #1540/R est:3200

£3704 $6000 €5371 Fagoteuse en foret de fontainebleau (56x76cm-22x30in) s. panel. 8-Aug-3 Barridorf, Portland #48/R est:7000-9000
£4000 $7280 €6000 Forest scene with a woman collecting twigs in a clearing (23x28cm-9x11in) s. panel lit. 1-Jul-4 Van Ham, Cologne #1297/R est:4500
£4167 $7500 €6084 L'amour puni (30x48cm-12x19in) s. prov. 23-Apr-4 Sotheby's, New York #141/R est:7000-10000
£4348 $7130 €6000 Sous-bois a Fontainebleau (40x32cm-16x13in) panel. 11-May-3 Osenat, Fontainebleau #110/R est:6500-7000
£4722 $8500 €6894 Les baigneuses (23x34cm-9x13in) s. panel. 23-Apr-4 Sotheby's, New York #142/R est:8000-12000
£4762 $8524 €7000 Ramasseuse de fagots au bord de la mare (23x29cm-9x11in) s. panel. 19-Mar-4 Millon & Associes, Paris #17/R est:4000-6000
£5245 $9021 €7500 Nymphes dans un sous bois (29x46cm-11x18in) s. panel. 5-Dec-3 Maigret, Paris #72/R est:1000-1200
£5500 $10010 €8030 L'orage (24x32cm-9x13in) s. panel prov. 15-Jun-4 Sotheby's, London #171/R est:6000-8000
£5667 $10370 €8500 Jeunes femmes en sous-bois (41x33cm-16x13in) s. panel painted c.1870. 6-Jun-4 Osenat, Fontainebleau #122/R est:9000-10000
£6000 $10320 €8760 Le foret de Barbizon (20x26cm-8x10in) s. panel. 4-Dec-3 Christie's, Kensington #25/R est:3000-5000
£6333 $11590 €9500 Bohemiennes (32x24cm-13x9in) s. panel. 6-Jun-4 Osenat, Fontainebleau #125/R est:12000-15000
£6500 $11830 €9490 Bathers at a woodland pool (41x32cm-16x13in) panel prov. 16-Jun-4 Christie's, Kensington #26/R est:5000-7000
£7092 $11844 €10000 Les baigneuses (41x26cm-16x10in) s. panel. 17-Jun-3 Christie's, Paris #39/R est:10000-15000
£8333 $15000 €12166 Etang dans un bois (30x40cm-12x16in) s. panel. 23-Apr-4 Sotheby's, New York #143/R est:10000-15000
£9441 $16238 €13500 Broisiere dans la clairiere, foret de Fontainebleau (27x35cm-11x14in) s. 7-Dec-3 Osenat, Fontainebleau #122
£9500 $16340 €13870 Young family (34x23cm-13x9in) s. panel. 3-Dec-3 Christie's, London #28/R est:8000-12000
£10000 $18100 €15000 Paysage de Barbizon, plaine d'Apremont (19x24cm-7x9in) s. painted c.1865-1870 panel lit. 30-Mar-4 Rossini, Paris #280/R est:2500-3500
£10556 $19000 €15412 Nymphs and putti in an Arcadian landscape (54x68cm-21x27in) s.d.70 prov. 22-Apr-4 Christie's, Rockefeller NY #109/R est:15000-20000
£12000 $20640 €17520 Foret de Fontainebleau (45x56cm-18x22in) s.d.74 panel prov. 3-Dec-3 Christie's, London #26/R est:15000-20000
£13529 $23000 €19752 Fagotiere en foret de Fontainebleau (105x71cm-41x28in) s. prov. 28-Oct-3 Sotheby's, New York #18/R est:20000-30000
Works on paper
£533 $965 €800 Arbre (35x23cm-14x9in) mono. pen brown ink lit. 30-Mar-4 Rossini, Paris #284
£915 $1584 €1300 Wooded landscape (15x22cm-6x9in) mono. en blk ink W/C traces blk crayon. 10-Dec-3 Piasa, Paris #115

DIAZ DE LA PENA, Narcisse-Virgile (attrib) (1807-1876) French
£333 $600 €486 In the woods (48x61cm-19x24in) bears sig.d.70. 24-Apr-4 Skinner, Boston #169
£450 $824 €657 Clearing (13x22cm-5x9in) panel prov. 8-Apr-4 Bonhams, Edinburgh #91
£694 $1132 €1000 Landscape with cows (38x46cm-15x18in) 23-Sep-3 Wiener Kunst Auktionen, Vienna #5/R
£1101 $1872 €1607 Party in the wood (65x49cm-26x19in) 5-Nov-3 Dobiaschofsky, Bern #490/R est:5000 (S.FR 2500)
£1408 $2437 €2000 In Fontainebleau wood (64x47cm-25x19in) i. panel. 13-Dec-3 Lempertz, Koln #210/R est:2000
£1719 $2923 €2510 Landscape with four children (19x31cm-7x12in) panel. 1-Dec-3 Koller, Zurich #6496 est:4000-6000 (S.FR 3800)
£1810 $3077 €2643 Two girls in the undergrowth (26x19cm-10x7in) s. panel. 1-Dec-3 Koller, Zurich #6495 est:4000-6000 (S.FR 4000)
£2697 $4963 €4100 Paysanne devant la mare (19x25cm-7x10in) bears sig panel. 22-Jun-4 Ribeyre & Baron, Paris #44 est:1000-1200

DIAZ DE LA PENA, Narcisse-Virgile and MONTICELLI, Adolphe (19th C) French
£10667 $19307 €16000 Bouquet sur un entablement (42x33cm-17x13in) s. panel oval lit. 30-Mar-4 Rossini, Paris #318/R est:8000-12000

DIAZ DOMINGUEZ, Angel (1881-1952) Spanish
£655 $1179 €950 Landscape with bridge (43x61cm-17x24in) s. cardboard. 26-Jan-4 Ansorena, Madrid #164/R

DIAZ FERRER, Jose (1922-) Spanish
£355 $574 €500 Rincon rural (45x37cm-18x15in) 20-May-3 Ansorena, Madrid #12/R

DIAZ GONZALEZ, Vicente (1889-1941) Spanish
£921 $1667 €1400 Man reading (92x53cm-36x21in) s.i.d.1896. 14-Apr-4 Ansorena, Madrid #173/R

DIAZ, Cesario (20th C) Spanish
£379 $683 €550 Woman (32x34cm-13x13in) s. board. 26-Jan-4 Ansorena, Madrid #931/R

DIAZ, Claudio (1939-) Spanish
£503 $841 €720 Puerta (100x73cm-39x29in) s.d.1985 prov. 24-Jun-3 Segre, Madrid #200/R

DIBBETS, Jan (1941-) Dutch
Photographs
£5594 $9510 €8000 3-30 Sea (60x125cm-24x49in) ten photographs on paper on board exec 1973 prov.lit. 25-Nov-3 Christie's, Amsterdam #318/R est:15000-20000
£9497 $17000 €13866 From ten windows (52x52cm-20x20in) s. num.IV 28/40 VIII 24/40 VI 22/40 colour photos three prov. 13-May-4 Sotheby's, New York #380/R est:10000-15000
Works on paper
£855 $1574 €1300 Untitled (33x42cm-13x17in) s.d.1969 mixed media. 28-Jun-4 Sotheby's, Amsterdam #234/R

DIBBLE, Paul (20th C) New Zealander
Sculpture
£2347 $3825 €3427 Study for the orator (56cm-22in) s.d.1999 bronze. 23-Sep-3 Peter Webb, Auckland #12/R est:3000-4000 (NZ.D 6500)

DIBDIN, Thomas Colman (1810-1893) British
Works on paper
£236 $425 €345 Fishing by the old mill (20x30cm-8x12in) s.d.1857 W/C gouache. 24-Apr-4 Skinner, Boston #77
£400 $668 €584 Resting rustics (32x22cm-13x9in) s.d.1838 W/C over pencil htd bodycol. 14-Oct-3 Sotheby's, London #506
£450 $752 €657 View of Greenwich Conservatory, with the Thames in the distance (25x36cm-10x14in) s. pastel gouache. 7-Oct-3 Bonhams, Knightsbridge #18/R
£580 $945 €841 Countryside in autumn (50x71cm-20x28in) s.d.1861 W/C bodycol. 23-Sep-3 Bonhams, Knightsbridge #30/R
£600 $1002 €876 Country cottage. Farmer and his wife (19x28cm-7x11in) W/C over pencil two. 14-Oct-3 Sotheby's, London #511
£700 $1169 €1022 Country woman on a lane (37x53cm-15x21in) s. W/C over pencil bodycol. 14-Oct-3 Sotheby's, London #508
£750 $1365 €1095 On Stock Gill, Ambleside (28x38cm-11x15in) s.i.d.1854 pencil W/C htd white scratching out prov. 1-Jul-4 Christie's, Kensington #197/R
£800 $1336 €1168 Waterfall (50x34cm-20x13in) s. W/C over pencil htd bodycol. 14-Oct-3 Sotheby's, London #509
£1200 $2220 €1752 Cathedral exterior (51x37cm-20x15in) s.d.1871 W/C bodycol. 14-Jul-4 Sotheby's, Olympia #92/R est:800-1200
£1800 $3006 €2628 Windsor Castle from the Thames (53x76cm-21x30in) s. W/C over pencil htd bodycol. 14-Oct-3 Sotheby's, London #505/R est:1000-1500
£1800 $3006 €2628 Rouen cathedral (102x67cm-40x26in) s.d.1883 W/C over pencil htd bodycol. 14-Oct-3 Sotheby's, London #510 est:800-1200
£2800 $4676 €4088 Country lane (69x53cm-27x21in) s.d.1862 W/C over pencil htd bodycol. 14-Oct-3 Sotheby's, London #507/R est:800-1200
£10000 $16300 €14600 Illustrations of the Rock Cut Temples of India (36x28cm-14x11in) pencil W/C gum arabic eight htd white nine. 24-Sep-3 Christie's, London #84/R est:10000-15000

DICHTL, Erich (1890-1955) Austrian
£634 $1135 €900 Roebuck in a winter woodland scene (56x50cm-22x20in) s. lit. 8-Jan-4 Allgauer, Kempten #2369/R
£1267 $2267 €1900 Deer in forest clearing (80x100cm-31x39in) s. 13-May-4 Dorotheum, Linz #487/R est:1600-2200
Works on paper
£333 $597 €500 Marten with first bird (54x41cm-21x16in) s. chl. 13-May-4 Dorotheum, Linz #613/R

DICHTL, Martin (fl.1660-1690) German
£1273 $2113 €1846 Old woman with hen (95x76cm-37x30in) s.d.1668. 13-Jun-3 Zofingen, Switzerland #2354 est:1500 (S.FR 2800)

DICIERVO, Jorge (1947-) Argentinian
Works on paper
£495 $900 €723 Figure (34x24cm-13x9in) s. pencil. 5-Jul-4 Arroyo, Buenos Aires #37/R

DICK, Cecil (1915-) American
Works on paper
£1176 $2000 €1717 Buffalo hunt (53x74cm-21x29in) s. gouache prov. 1-Nov-3 Santa Fe Art, Santa Fe #68/R est:2000-3000

DICK, Ernesto (1889-1959) Italian
£300 $537 €450 Cottages in the mountains (48x62cm-19x24in) s. 12-May-4 Stadion, Trieste #658/R
£420 $722 €600 Fishermen in the harbour (62x70cm-24x28in) s. 3-Dec-3 Stadion, Trieste #1146/R

DICK, George (1916-1978) American
£311 $500 €454 Mocking bird (18x13cm-7x5in) board. 22-Aug-3 Altermann Galleries, Santa Fe #232
£311 $500 €454 Hermit thrush (18x13cm-7x5in) board. 22-Aug-3 Altermann Galleries, Santa Fe #231
£621 $1000 €907 Red bird (13x18cm-5x7in) board. 22-Aug-3 Altermann Galleries, Santa Fe #230
£870 $1400 €1270 Ready to trade (14x18cm-6x7in) board. 22-Aug-3 Altermann Galleries, Santa Fe #136

DICK, Jessie Alexandra (fl.1920-1940) British
£290 $493 €423 Still life of jug with eucalyptus and Penguin paperback (75x100cm-30x39in) s. 10-Nov-3 Thomson Roddick & Medcalf, Edinburgh #266

DICK, Karl Theophil (1884-1967) German
£302 $540 €441 Southern landscape with figures (53x68cm-21x27in) s.d.13. 13-May-4 Stuker, Bern #594 (S.FR 700)
£431 $772 €629 Standing female nude on lakeshore (96x65cm-38x26in) s.d.35. 12-May-4 Dobiaschofsky, Bern #445/R (S.FR 1000)
£455 $755 €660 Jura landscape with houses (56x69cm-22x27in) s.d.1938. 13-Jun-3 Zofingen, Switzerland #2822 (S.FR 1000)
£478 $875 €698 Peasant girl with a cow (60x65cm-24x26in) s.d.1949. 4-Jun-4 Zofingen, Switzerland #2777 (S.FR 1100)
£682 $1132 €989 Last snows in wood (80x90cm-31x35in) s.d.1940. 13-Jun-3 Zofingen, Switzerland #2821 est:1800 (S.FR 1500)
£727 $1207 €1054 Female nude with red cloth (90x75cm-35x30in) s.d.1922. 13-Jun-3 Zofingen, Switzerland #2820 est:1500 (S.FR 1600)

DICK, Rudolf (20th C) Austrian

Works on paper

£338	$595	€500	Stephansplatz in Vienna (46x33cm-18x13in) mono. W/C paper on board. 19-May-4 Dorotheum, Klagenfurt #38/R

DICK, Sir William Reid (1879-1961) British

Sculpture

£2000	$3600	€2920	Catapult (34cm-13in) s. bronze. 21-Apr-4 Lyon & Turnbull, Edinburgh #231/R est:2000-3000
£4500	$8280	€6570	Catapult of slingboy (31cm-12in) s. brown green pat. bronze green marble plinth. 11-Jun-4 Christie's, London #86/R est:4000-6000
£7500	$13800	€10950	Femina Victrix of the struggle (21cm-8in) s. brown pat. marble plinth prov.lit. 11-Jun-4 Christie's, London #85/R est:4000-6000
£9800	$17542	€14308	Sir Winston Churchill (28cm-11in) s.d.1942 plaster prov. 16-Mar-4 Bonhams, New Bond Street #5/R est:2000-3000

DICKE, Otto Dingeman (1918-1984) Dutch

Works on paper

£267	$488	€400	Female nude sitting (64x48cm-25x19in) s.i.d.75 black chk. 7-Jun-4 Glerum, Amsterdam #198/R

DICKERHOF, Urs (1941-) Swiss

£388	$694	€566	Faraway soldier (85x65cm-33x26in) s.i.d.1968-51 verso. 12-May-4 Dobiaschofsky, Bern #446/R (S.FR 900)

DICKERSON, Robert (1924-) Australian

£1909	$3188	€2864	The drinking bowl (35x24cm-14x9in) s. pastel. 27-Oct-3 Goodman, Sydney #148/R est:3000-3500 (A.D 4600)
£3036	$4889	€4433	Seducer (25x30cm-10x12in) canvas on board prov.exhib. 25-Aug-3 Sotheby's, Paddington #296/R est:5000-7000 (A.D 7500)
£5372	$9938	€7843	Blue face (56x45cm-22x18in) s. board. 10-Mar-4 Deutscher-Menzies, Melbourne #336/R est:10000-15000 (A.D 13000)
£5785	$10702	€8446	Boys in the street (46x61cm-18x24in) s. board. 10-Mar-4 Deutscher-Menzies, Melbourne #116/R est:15000-20000 (A.D 14000)
£8936	$15191	€13047	Dancers (75x100cm-30x39in) s. i.d.1973 verso. 26-Nov-3 Deutscher-Menzies, Melbourne #47/R est:22000-28000 (A.D 21000)
£12397	$22934	€18100	Children with fawn (122x91cm-48x36in) s. board prov. 10-Mar-4 Deutscher-Menzies, Melbourne #122/R est:38000-48000 (A.D 30000)
£16260	$25528	€23577	Mother and child (121x90cm-48x35in) s. enamel board lit. 26-Aug-3 Christie's, Sydney #3/R est:30000-40000 (A.D 40000)
£17814	$28680	€26008	Island children (120x151cm-47x59in) s. composition board painted c.1962 prov. 25-Aug-3 Sotheby's, Paddington #215/R est:50000-60000 (A.D 44000)
£21277	$36170	€31064	Paper Boy, Paddington (91x121cm-36x48in) s. composition board painted 1968 prov.exhib. 26-Nov-3 Deutscher-Menzies, Melbourne #37c/R est:50000-65000 (A.D 50000)

Works on paper

£537	$913	€806	The gaze (33x25cm-13x10in) s. chl. 28-Oct-3 Goodman, Sydney #344a (A.D 1300)
£661	$1124	€965	Strawberry pickers 1993 (26x38cm-10x15in) s. chl. 29-Oct-3 Lawson Menzies, Sydney #159/R est:2000-3000 (A.D 1600)
£810	$1304	€1183	Head of a girl (35x27cm-14x11in) s. pastel. 13-Oct-3 Joel, Victoria #276 est:2000-3000 (A.D 2000)
£813	$1455	€1187	Head of a child (25x17cm-10x7in) s. prov. 4-May-4 Sotheby's, Melbourne #178 est:2000-3000 (A.D 2000)
£820	$1328	€1197	Train station (26x18cm-10x7in) s. chl. 30-Jul-3 Goodman, Sydney #14/R (A.D 2000)
£1025	$1660	€1497	Lone figure in street (28x38cm-11x15in) s. chl. 30-Jul-3 Goodman, Sydney #162/R est:1500-2000 (A.D 2500)
£1113	$1793	€1625	Wondering (17x13cm-7x5in) s. pastel. 13-Oct-3 Joel, Victoria #254/R est:2500-3500 (A.D 2750)
£1145	$2084	€1672	Boy with pony (30x35cm-12x14in) s. chl. 16-Jun-4 Deutscher-Menzies, Melbourne #372/R est:2500-4500 (A.D 3000)
£1162	$1940	€1743	Face (27x18cm-11x7in) s. chl. 27-Oct-3 Goodman, Sydney #205/R (A.D 2800)
£1215	$1955	€1774	Children playing in the street (54x75cm-21x30in) s. chl prov. 25-Aug-3 Sotheby's, Paddington #362/R est:3000-3500 (A.D 3000)
£1240	$2194	€1810	Young boy (38x28cm-15x11in) s. pastel chl. 3-May-4 Christie's, Melbourne #350/R est:3000-4000 (A.D 3000)
£1276	$2170	€1863	Child (40x30cm-16x12in) s. chl. 26-Nov-3 Deutscher-Menzies, Melbourne #189/R est:2000-4000 (A.D 3000)
£1348	$2481	€1968	Receptionist (37x28cm-15x11in) s. chl. 28-Jun-4 Australian Art Auctions, Sydney #92 (A.D 3600)
£1388	$2553	€2026	Man with beret (37x27cm-15x11in) s. pastel. 29-Mar-4 Goodman, Sydney #61/R est:2500-3500 (A.D 3400)
£1423	$2233	€2063	Young girl (36x29cm-14x11in) s. pastel. 26-Aug-3 Christie's, Sydney #305 est:3500-5000 (A.D 3500)
£1423	$2547	€2078	Lone man (29x37cm-11x15in) s. pastel. 10-May-4 Joel, Victoria #401 est:2000-3000 (A.D 3500)
£1450	$2640	€2117	Henry (37x27cm-15x11in) s. chl. 16-Jun-4 Deutscher-Menzies, Melbourne #402/R est:2000-3000 (A.D 3800)
£1506	$2515	€2184	Louisa (38x28cm-15x11in) s. pastel. 30-Jun-3 Australian Art Auctions, Sydney #130 (A.D 3750)
£1527	$2779	€2229	Portrait of man (76x53cm-30x21in) s. chl. 16-Jun-4 Deutscher-Menzies, Melbourne #234/R est:5000-7000 (A.D 4000)
£1531	$2816	€2235	Child in the street (37x27cm-15x11in) s. i.verso chl. 29-Mar-4 Goodman, Sydney #193/R est:2500-5000 (A.D 3750)
£1545	$2765	€2256	Nude study (54x37cm-21x15in) s. chl. 10-May-4 Joel, Victoria #330 est:2500-3000 (A.D 3800)
£1577	$2633	€2366	Paris hat (37x27cm-15x11in) s. chl. 27-Oct-3 Goodman, Sydney #204/R est:3800-4800 (A.D 3800)
£1679	$3056	€2451	Portrait of a woman (75x55cm-30x22in) s. chl. 16-Jun-4 Deutscher-Menzies, Melbourne #291/R est:5000-7000 (A.D 4400)
£1702	$2894	€2485	Girl and Cat (54x36cm-21x14in) s. chl. 26-Nov-3 Deutscher-Menzies, Melbourne #190/R est:3000-5000 (A.D 4000)
£1702	$2894	€2485	Portrait (100x64cm-39x25in) s. chl. 26-Nov-3 Deutscher-Menzies, Melbourne #231/R est:1500-2500 (A.D 4000)
£1707	$2850	€2475	Anticipation (38x27cm-15x11in) s. pastel. 30-Jun-3 Australian Art Auctions, Sydney #91 (A.D 4250)
£1707	$2680	€2475	Young boy (56x37cm-22x15in) s. chl. 26-Aug-3 Christie's, Sydney #316 est:1200-1500 (A.D 4200)
£1779	$3273	€2597	Young beauty (32x27cm-13x11in) s. pastel. 28-Jun-4 Australian Art Auctions, Sydney #82 (A.D 4750)
£1803	$2921	€2632	Profile of a figure (37x26cm-15x10in) s. chl pastel. 30-Jul-3 Goodman, Sydney #13/R est:2500-3500 (A.D 4400)
£1829	$2872	€2652	Young girl (56x37cm-22x15in) s. chl. 26-Aug-3 Christie's, Sydney #276/R est:1200-1500 (A.D 4500)
£1829	$2872	€2652	Thinking children (37x55cm-15x22in) s. chl. 26-Aug-3 Christie's, Sydney #283 est:1200-1500 (A.D 4500)
£1832	$3334	€2675	Portrait of a young girl (38x28cm-15x11in) s. pastel. 16-Jun-4 Deutscher-Menzies, Melbourne #406/R est:2000-3000 (A.D 4800)
£1860	$3440	€2716	Jockeys (32x36cm-13x14in) s. pastel. 10-Mar-4 Deutscher-Menzies, Melbourne #371/R est:4500-5500 (A.D 4500)
£1915	$3255	€2796	The man (76x55cm-30x22in) s. pastel. 25-Nov-3 Christie's, Melbourne #320 est:4000-6000 (A.D 4500)
£1942	$3593	€2835	Far away (54x36cm-21x14in) s. pastel chl. 10-Mar-4 Deutscher-Menzies, Melbourne #503/R est:2000-3000 (A.D 4700)
£2013	$3422	€2939	Portrait of a young boy (58x39cm-23x15in) s. pastel paper on board. 24-Nov-3 Sotheby's, Melbourne #171/R est:5000-7000 (A.D 4750)
£2024	$3259	€2955	Resentful (55x38cm-22x15in) s. pastel prov. 13-Oct-3 Joel, Victoria #240 est:7000-8000 (A.D 5000)
£2033	$3191	€2948	Two girls (37x55cm-15x22in) s. chl. 26-Aug-3 Christie's, Sydney #341/R est:1200-1500 (A.D 5000)
£2066	$3512	€3016	Serious boy (55x36cm-22x14in) s. pastel. 29-Oct-3 Lawson Menzies, Sydney #20/R est:5000-7000 (A.D 5000)
£2127	$3617	€3105	Sydney showgirl (52x36cm-20x14in) s. chl executed c.1960. 26-Nov-3 Deutscher-Menzies, Melbourne #155/R est:5500-7500 (A.D 5000)
£2128	$3681	€3107	Untitled (55x38cm-22x15in) s. pastel board. 10-Dec-3 Shapiro, Sydney #88/R est:3000-5000 (A.D 5000)
£2479	$4215	€3619	Happy talk (37x27cm-15x11in) s. pastel. 29-Oct-3 Lawson Menzies, Sydney #19/R est:4000-6000 (A.D 6000)
£2553	$4340	€3727	Girl with daffodils (76x56cm-30x22in) s. i.verso pastel. 26-Nov-3 Deutscher-Menzies, Melbourne #13/R est:6000-9000 (A.D 6000)
£2586	$4034	€3750	Female face (75x54cm-30x21in) s. chl. 1-Aug-2 Joel, Victoria #303 est:6000-8000 (A.D 7500)
£2686	$4754	€3922	Study for two faces (36x26cm-14x10in) s. pastel. 3-May-4 Christie's, Melbourne #334/R est:3000-5000 (A.D 6500)
£2774	$5187	€4161	Sisters (53x35cm-21x14in) s. chl pastel. 20-Jul-4 Goodman, Sydney #118/R est:4000-6000 (A.D 7100)
£2893	$5351	€4224	Face (54x36cm-21x14in) s. chl. 10-Mar-4 Deutscher-Menzies, Melbourne #384/R est:5000-8000 (A.D 7000)
£2893	$5351	€4224	Innocence (54x36cm-21x14in) s. i.verso pastel prov. 10-Mar-4 Deutscher-Menzies, Melbourne #221/R est:5000-7000 (A.D 7000)
£2979	$5064	€4349	Woman at a table (76x56cm-30x22in) s. i.verso pastel. 26-Nov-3 Deutscher-Menzies, Melbourne #89/R est:6000-9000 (A.D 7000)
£2979	$5064	€4349	Russian woman (75x55cm-30x22in) s. pastel prov. 25-Nov-3 Christie's, Melbourne #124/R est:7000-10000 (A.D 7000)
£3099	$5733	€4525	Red room (75x55cm-30x22in) s. pastel. 10-Mar-4 Deutscher-Menzies, Melbourne #294/R est:6500-8500 (A.D 7500)
£3099	$5733	€4525	Mother and child (39x28cm-15x11in) s. chl prov. 10-Mar-4 Deutscher-Menzies, Melbourne #385/R est:3500-4500 (A.D 7500)
£3252	$5106	€4715	Boy on a street corner (51x47cm-20x19in) s. pastel prov. 26-Aug-3 Christie's, Sydney #306/R est:7000-10000 (A.D 8000)
£3279	$5311	€4787	Salt, vinegar and pepper (132x78cm-52x31in) s. chl paper on board. 30-Jul-3 Goodman, Sydney #12/R est:6000-9000 (A.D 8000)
£3390	$5763	€4949	Portrait of Anna (76x54cm-30x21in) s. chl prov. 24-Nov-3 Sotheby's, Melbourne #170/R est:8000-12000 (A.D 8000)
£3404	$5787	€4970	The three barristers (74x54cm-29x21in) s. pastel prov. 25-Nov-3 Christie's, Melbourne #159/R est:8000-12000 (A.D 8000)
£3719	$6880	€5430	Mrs Bassett in Windsor Street (76x101cm-30x40in) s. pastel paper on board. 10-Mar-4 Deutscher-Menzies, Melbourne #127/R est:10000-15000 (A.D 9000)
£3776	$6947	€5513	Young girl (56x37cm-22x15in) s. pastel. 29-Mar-4 Goodman, Sydney #191/R est:4000-6000 (A.D 9250)
£3776	$6947	€5513	Mother and daughter (75x55cm-30x22in) s. pastel prov. 29-Mar-4 Goodman, Sydney #192/R est:6000-9000 (A.D 9250)
£4043	$6872	€5903	Spring day, Regent Park (65x100cm-26x39in) s. i.verso pastel. 25-Nov-3 Christie's, Melbourne #122/R est:7000-10000 (A.D 9500)
£4098	$6639	€5983	Champagne bar (76x56cm-30x22in) s. pastel. 30-Jul-3 Goodman, Sydney #21/R est:7000-9000 (A.D 10000)
£4494	$8270	€6561	Twins (56x77cm-22x30in) s. pastel. 28-Jun-4 Australian Art Auctions, Sydney #139 (A.D 12000)
£5344	$9725	€7802	Young cleric (91x76cm-36x30in) s. i.verso synthetic polymer on canvas. 16-Jun-4 Deutscher-Menzies, Melbourne #108/R est:15000-25000 (A.D 14000)
£10526	$16947	€15368	At the Taxi Rank 8pm (110x73cm-43x29in) s. pastel prov.exhib. 25-Aug-3 Sotheby's, Paddington #187/R est:18000-28000 (A.D 26000)
£10656	$16836	€15558	Boy running at Bundanon (118x148cm-46x58in) s. synthetic polymer prov. 2-Sep-3 Deutscher-Menzies, Melbourne #106/R est:30000-40000 (A.D 26000)

DICKINSON, Edwin (1891-1978) American

£2374	$4250	€3466	Portrait of Eugene Bernald (32x38cm-13x15in) s.d.1957 masonite prov. 6-May-4 Doyle, New York #95/R est:7000-9000
£6044	$11000	€8824	East side street (40x41cm-16x16in) indis sig. s.verso board painted 1917 prov.exhib.lit. 29-Jun-4 Sotheby's, New York #304/R est:15000-25000
£7059	$12000	€10306	House Nantucket Sound (41x61cm-16x24in) s. 21-Nov-3 Eldred, East Dennis #828/R est:5000-10000

Works on paper

£3779	$6500	€5517	Trees (31x24cm-12x9in) s.d.1933 chl pencil prov. 2-Dec-3 Christie's, Rockefeller NY #85/R est:3000-5000

DICKINSON, J (19th C) British

£41000	$69700	€59860	Ormonde, cantering to the post prior to winning the Derby (122x178cm-48x70in) s. 19-Nov-3 Sotheby's, Olympia #37/R est:25000-35000

DICKINSON, J Reed (fl.1867-1881) British

Works on paper

£400	$688	€584	Spring bonnet (24x20cm-9x8in) s. pencil W/C bodycol. 3-Dec-3 Christie's, Kensington #64/R

DICKINSON, Jeremy (20th C) German

£1196	$2200	€1746	Auto stack no 3 (51x51cm-20x20in) s.i.d.1999 overlap oil acrylic prov. 10-Jun-4 Phillips, New York #480/R est:2500-3000

DICKINSON, Preston (1891-1930) American
Works on paper
£2270 $4200 €3314 Union Square in winter (25x20cm-10x8in) s. gouache paperboard. 11-Mar-4 Christie's, Rockefeller NY #47/R est:4000-6000
£3409 $6000 €4977 Still life with flowers (25x16cm-10x6in) s. gouache pencil. 18-May-4 Christie's, Rockefeller NY #125/R est:15000-25000
£5398 $9500 €7881 Harlem River Bridge (44x55cm-17x22in) s.d.22 chl pastel gouache. 18-May-4 Christie's, Rockefeller NY #139/R est:20000-30000
£9143 $16000 €13349 Still life with bananas. Study of grain silos (33x43cm-13x17in) pastel pencil double-sided. 19-Dec-3 Sotheby's, New York #1018/R est:15000-25000

DICKMAN, Charles John (1863-1943) American
£1359 $2500 €1984 Woman walking in a village at dusk (31x45cm-12x18in) s. board prov. 8-Jun-4 Bonhams & Butterfields, San Francisco #4230/R est:3000-5000
£2235 $4000 €3263 Etaples, nocturne with boats on the beach. s.i.d.99. 10-Jan-4 Harvey Clar, Oakland #1565

DICKMANN, Oskar (1896-1972) Austrian
£362 $615 €529 Ascona (30x25cm-12x10in) s.i.d.1940 verso panel. 28-Nov-3 Zofingen, Switzerland #2962 (S.FR 800)

DICKSEE, Frank (1853-1928) British
£414 $691 €604 Studying the script (50x39cm-20x15in) s. 20-Oct-3 Stephan Welz, Johannesburg #433 est:4000-6000 (SA.R 4800)
£1300 $2171 €1898 Marshes (39x53cm-15x21in) init.d.1920 canvasboard prov. 13-Nov-3 Christie's, Kensington #172/R est:600-800
£1514 $2800 €2210 Juliet (33x23cm-13x9in) init. board. 13-Mar-4 Susanin's, Chicago #6124/R est:800-1200
£1900 $3534 €2774 Portrait of Mrs Ralph Vivian in a white lace trimmed dress (71x61cm-28x24in) init.d.1912 painted oval. 4-Mar-4 Christie's, Kensington #394/R est:400-600
Works on paper
£520 $827 €759 Sword fight (18x23cm-7x9in) s.d.1871 indis.i.verso W/C. 12-Sep-3 Gardiner & Houlgate, Bath #120/R
£1500 $2490 €2190 Within the shadows of the Church, the vows (20x15cm-8x6in) s. gouache. 1-Oct-3 Sotheby's, Olympia #175/R est:1500-2000

DICKSEE, Herbert (1862-1942) British
£5000 $8800 €7300 A lion (86x70cm-34x28in) s. 18-May-4 Woolley & Wallis, Salisbury #309/R est:800-1200
Works on paper
£280 $476 €409 Albatross (29x22cm-11x9in) s.i.d.dec 26th 89 W/C. 25-Nov-3 Bonhams, Knightsbridge #224

DICKSEE, Margaret Isabel (1808-1903) British
£25000 $45000 €36500 Sheridan at the Linleys (91x122cm-36x48in) s.d.1899 exhib. 21-Jan-4 Sotheby's, Olympia #306/R est:10000-15000

DICKSEE, Thomas Francis (1819-1895) British
£3800 $7030 €5548 Grief of Constance (34x27cm-13x11in) mono.d.1865 board. 10-Mar-4 Sotheby's, Olympia #183/R est:3000-5000

DICKSON, J A C (19th C) British
£611 $1100 €892 Inverlochie Castle, West Highlands, Scotland (76x152cm-30x60in) 24-Apr-4 Skinner, Boston #359 est:1000-1500

DICKSON, Tom (1949-) Canadian
£2033 $3638 €2968 December evening, Peggy's Cove (53x68cm-21x27in) s. i.verso board prov. 27-May-4 Heffel, Vancouver #61/R est:2000-3000 (C.D 5000)

DICKSTEIN, Alvin (20th C) American
£382 $650 €558 Untitled (86x86cm-34x34in) prov. 9-Nov-3 Wright, Chicago #393

DICORCIA, Philip Lorca (1953-) American
Photographs
£2800 $5152 €4088 Brent booth, 21 years old, Des Moines, Iowa, 30 dollars (38x58cm-15x23in) s.verso col coupler print edition of 20 prov. 24-Jun-4 Sotheby's, Olympia #629/R est:2000-3000
£3704 $7000 €5408 New York, 1993 (63x94cm-25x37in) s.verso color coupler print. 17-Feb-4 Christie's, Rockefeller NY #174/R est:6000-8000
£3892 $6500 €5682 William Charles Everlove (38x57cm-15x22in) s.i.verso chromogenic col print. 16-Oct-3 Phillips, New York #262/R est:8000-12000
£3892 $6500 €5682 New York (63x95cm-25x37in) s.verso chromogenic col print board exec.1996 one of 15 prov. 17-Oct-3 Phillips, New York #181/R est:10000-15000
£4000 $6680 €5840 London (66x95cm-26x37in) s.verso ektacolor professional print exec 1995 prov.lit. 21-Oct-3 Sotheby's, London #457/R est:4000-6000
£4601 $7500 €6717 Hong Kong (65x95cm-26x37in) s.verso col coupler print edition of 15 prov. 23-Sep-3 Christie's, Rockefeller NY #144/R est:9000-12000
£5090 $8500 €7431 Paris (65x97cm-26x38in) s.verso chromogenic col print board one of 15 prov.lit. 17-Oct-3 Phillips, New York #182/R est:7000-10000
£5389 $9000 €7868 Mexico, 1998 (76x102cm-30x40in) s.verso cibachrome mounted on board prov.lit. 14-Nov-3 Phillips, New York #238/R est:8000-12000
£5650 $10000 €8249 Mexico City, 1998 (65x95cm-26x37in) s. color coupler print. 27-Apr-4 Christie's, Rockefeller NY #199/R est:9000-12000
£5689 $9500 €8306 Tokyo (64x96cm-25x38in) s.verso chromogenic col print board one of 15 prov.lit. 17-Oct-3 Phillips, New York #180/R est:10000-15000
£7186 $12000 €10492 Brian (42x59cm-17x23in) s.verso chromogenic col print lit. 16-Oct-3 Phillips, New York #265/R est:8000-12000
£8380 $15000 €12235 New York (76x101cm-30x40in) s.verso col coupler print board edition of 15 prov. 12-May-4 Christie's, Rockefeller NY #462/R est:9000-12000
£8475 $15000 €12374 Tokyo, 1998 (96x142cm-38x56in) s. color coupler print. 27-Apr-4 Christie's, Rockefeller NY #198/R est:10000-15000
£11377 $19000 €16610 Mario (40x58cm-16x23in) s.i.verso chromogenic col print lit. 16-Oct-3 Phillips, New York #266/R est:8000-12000
£12291 $22000 €17945 Head num 3 (122x152cm-48x60in) s.verso Fujicolor crystal print plexiglas edition of 10 prov. 12-May-4 Christie's, Rockefeller NY #459/R est:15000-20000
£12291 $22000 €17945 Head num 1 (122x152cm-48x60in) s.verso Fujicolor crystal print plexiglas edition of 10 prov. 12-May-4 Christie's, Rockefeller NY #460/R est:15000-20000

DIDAY, François (1802-1877) Swiss
£345 $617 €504 Fortified harbour with breaking waves (20x27cm-8x11in) s. panel. 12-May-4 Dobiaschofsky, Bern #447 (S.FR 800)
£733 $1312 €1070 La Tour du Poussin a Ponte Molle (20x29cm-8x11in) s. paper on canvas. 12-May-4 Dobiaschofsky, Bern #448/R est:1200 (S.FR 1700)
£870 $1591 €1270 Au bord du lac (28x37cm-11x15in) s. paper on canvas. 4-Jun-4 Zofingen, Switzerland #2340/R (S.FR 2000)
£1810 $3241 €2643 Mountains in summer (17x24cm-7x9in) mono. 14-May-4 Dobiaschofsky, Bern #3/R est:4500 (S.FR 4200)
£1826 $3342 €2666 Promenade dans les Alpes (31x42cm-12x17in) i.verso panel. 5-Jun-4 Galerie du Rhone, Sion #198/R est:1000-1500 (S.FR 4200)
£3846 $6654 €5615 Village en montagnes (27x45cm-11x18in) s. paper on panel. 9-Dec-3 Sotheby's, Zurich #14/R est:5000-8000 (S.FR 8500)
£5482 $9156 €8004 Torrent dans la montagne (71x58cm-28x23in) s.d.1852. 16-Nov-3 Koller, Geneva #1220 est:15000-25000 (S.FR 12500)
£12217 $20769 €17837 Mouth of the Versoix on Lake Geneva with Mont Blanc (62x88cm-24x35in) s.d.1853 lit.prov. 19-Nov-3 Fischer, Luzern #1255/R est:20000-24000 (S.FR 27000)
Works on paper
£352 $599 €514 Lauterbrunnen valley with Jungfrau (27x21cm-11x8in) mono. W/C. 5-Nov-3 Dobiaschofsky, Bern #491/R (S.FR 800)

DIDAY, François (attrib) (1802-1877) Swiss
£346 $620 €505 Mountain landscape with stream (27x21cm-11x8in) canvas on panel. 22-Mar-4 Philippe Schuler, Zurich #4320 (S.FR 800)

DIDERON, Louis Jules (1901-) French
Works on paper
£387 $670 €550 Nu assis (64x49cm-25x19in) s. sanguine. 10-Dec-3 Ferri, Paris #36

DIDIER, Clovis François Auguste (1858-?) French
£900 $1665 €1314 Waiting game (41x34cm-16x13in) s.d.1899. 14-Jul-4 Christie's, Kensington #897/R

DIDIER, Emile (1890-1960) French
£800 $1440 €1200 Paysage, pres de Grenoble (54x73cm-21x29in) s.d.1927. 20-Apr-4 Chenu & Scrive, Lyon #75/R

DIDIER, Jules (1831-1892) French
£360 $601 €526 Design for an interior (72x85cm-28x33in) 7-Oct-3 Bonhams, Knightsbridge #238/R
£1343 $2470 €2000 Paysans traversant un pont dans la campagne Italienne (46x38cm-18x15in) s. 24-Mar-4 Tajan, Paris #166/R est:4000-6000
£15882 $27000 €23188 Depart pour la chasse (120x160cm-47x63in) s. 28-Oct-3 Sotheby's, New York #173/R est:30000-40000

DIDIER, Luc (1954-) French
£1644 $2795 €2400 Somme a Abbeville (46x61cm-18x24in) s. 9-Nov-3 Eric Pillon, Calais #227/R
£2118 $3600 €3092 Le jardin fleuri de Madame Caran (51x66cm-20x26in) s.i. 22-Nov-3 New Orleans Auction, New Orleans #672/R est:1800-2500

DIDIER-POUGET, William (1864-1959) French
£430 $783 €650 Vallee du Lot le matin (46x38cm-18x15in) s. i.verso. 18-Jun-4 Piasa, Paris #165
£552 $1010 €800 Bruyeres en fleurs un matin en Franche-Comte (55x46cm-22x18in) s. 1-Feb-4 Feletin, Province #129
£1093 $2000 €1596 Brume du martin bruyeres en fleurs, Vallee de la Dordogne (51x64cm-20x25in) s. i.v. 5-Jun-4 Neal Auction Company, New Orleans #99/R est:3000-4000
£1193 $1992 €1730 Le matin, Bruyeres en fleurs, Vallee de Doubs (60x81cm-24x32in) s. mono.i.d.verso prov. 21-Jun-3 Galerie du Rhone, Sion #508/R est:3000-5000 (S.FR 2600)

DIDIONI, Francesco (1859-1895) Italian
£298 $498 €432 Portrait of Lina Wenger (39x27cm-15x11in) s. i. verso board. 23-Jun-3 Philippe Schuler, Zurich #8585 (S.FR 650)
£1549 $2711 €2200 Portrait of woman (60x44cm-24x17in) 17-Dec-3 Finarte Semenzato, Milan #53/R est:2000-3000
£3662 $6408 €5200 Portrait of woman (60x46cm-24x18in) s. 17-Dec-3 Finarte Semenzato, Milan #52/R est:5000-6000

DIEBENKORN, Richard (1922-1993) American
£698324 $1250000 €1019553 Untitled - Ocean park (96x63cm-38x25in) init.d.87 acrylic gouache oil crayon pencil on cut pastel prov.ex. 12-May-4 Sotheby's, New York #25/R est:400000-500000
£1061453 $1900000 €1549721 Ocean Park 73 (206x160cm-81x63in) init.d.74 s.i.d.verso prov.exhib. 11-May-4 Christie's, Rockefeller NY #25/R est:2000000-3000000
Prints
£1765 $3000 €2577 Passage II (36x31cm-14x12in) s.num.22/25 aquatint. 21-Nov-3 Swann Galleries, New York #33/R est:1000-1500
£1796 $3000 €2622 Untitled (89x66cm-35x26in) init.d.1978 num.14/35 aquatint drypoint. 21-Oct-3 Bonhams & Butterfields, San Francisco #1301/R
£1933 $3500 €2822 Seated woman (64x50cm-25x20in) init.d.1965 num.9/100 lithograph. 19-Apr-4 Bonhams & Butterfields, San Francisco #250/R est:4000-6000
£2162 $4000 €3157 Two way (61x38cm-24x15in) init.d.1982 num.16/35 etching. 12-Feb-4 Christie's, Rockefeller NY #46/R est:2000-3000
£2353 $4000 €3435 Seated woman no.13 (30x19cm-12x7in) init.d.1964-65 num.23/25 etching drypoint. 21-Nov-3 Swann Galleries, New York #32/R est:1000-1500
£2581 $4800 €3768 Softground cross (67x101cm-26x40in) init.d.1982 num.62/68 soft ground etching drypoint. 2-Mar-4 Swann Galleries, New York #163/R est:2000-3000

£2695 $4500 €3935 Untitled, no 1 (60x45cm-24x18in) init.d.77 num.18/25 drypoint. 7-Oct-3 Sotheby's, New York #370 est:3000-5000
£2712 $4800 €3960 Construct, red (28x24cm-11x9in) init.i.d.1980 col etching aquatint. 28-Apr-4 Christie's, Rockefeller NY #263/R est:4000-6000
£3955 $7000 €5774 Seated woman (64x49cm-25x19in) init.d.1965 num.84/100 lithograph. 30-Apr-4 Sotheby's, New York #314a/R est:3000-4000
£6215 $11000 €9074 Tr-color II (48x46cm-19x18in) init.i.d.1981 col etching aquatint edition of 35. 28-Apr-4 Christie's, Rockefeller NY #264/R est:6000-8000
£18079 $32000 €26395 Ochre (63x91cm-25x36in) init.d.1983 num.118/200 col lithograph. 30-Apr-4 Sotheby's, New York #315/R est:20000-30000
£28249 $50000 €41244 Blue (103x64cm-41x25in) init.d.1984 num.126/200 col woodcut. 28-Apr-4 Christie's, Rockefeller NY #265/R est:25000-35000
Works on paper
£3823 $6500 €5582 Untitled - seated lady (43x36cm-17x14in) init.d.65 i.d.verso ink pencil prov. 9-Nov-3 Bonhams & Butterfields, Los Angeles #4049/R est:5000-7000
£17647 $30000 €25765 Untitled - seated woman (43x32cm-17x13in) init.d.63 ink. 9-Nov-3 Bonhams & Butterfields, Los Angeles #4050/R est:10000-15000
£83799 $150000 €122347 Untitled (59x48cm-23x19in) init.d.70 chl gouache W/C prov. 13-May-4 Sotheby's, New York #148/R est:80000-100000

DIEDEREN, Jef (1920-) Dutch
£979 $1664 €1400 Little bird flying home (80x60cm-31x24in) s.d.91 acrylic. 24-Nov-3 Glerum, Amsterdam #306/R
£1329 $2259 €1900 Composition (44x50cm-17x20in) s.d.57 board. 25-Nov-3 Christie's, Amsterdam #44/R est:2000-3000
£1399 $2378 €2000 Pillar I. Pillar II. Pillar III (225x21cm-89x8in) s.d.93 acrylic tryptych prov. 24-Nov-3 Glerum, Amsterdam #274/R est:3000-5000
£1399 $2378 €2000 Cezanne III (78x100cm-31x39in) s.d.90 verso acrylic collage lit. 24-Nov-3 Glerum, Amsterdam #275/R est:3000-5000
£2533 $4661 €3800 Mont Mirail (205x138cm-81x54in) s.d.99 verso acrylic. 9-Jun-4 Christie's, Amsterdam #380/R est:2000-3000
£5944 $10105 €8500 Summer (131x184cm-52x72in) s.d.55 exhib. 25-Nov-3 Christie's, Amsterdam #311/R est:5000-7000
Works on paper
£594 $1010 €850 Le jardin de M Jubain (56x76cm-22x30in) s.d.85 gouache acrylic prov.exhib.lit. 24-Nov-3 Glerum, Amsterdam #300/R
£594 $1010 €850 Composition with red, blue and yellow (56x76cm-22x30in) s.d.87 gouache prov. 24-Nov-3 Glerum, Amsterdam #301/R

DIEFENBACH, Lucidus (attrib) (1886-1958) German
£400 $720 €600 Bathers on Chiemsee shore (40x49cm-16x19in) i. panel lit. 22-Apr-4 Allgauer, Kempten #3513/R

DIEFFENBACH, Anton Heinrich (1831-1914) German
£5369 $9933 €8000 Fillette nourrissant des poussins (58x42cm-23x17in) s. 15-Mar-4 Horta, Bruxelles #229/R est:7000-9000

DIEFFENBRUNNER, Johann Georg (attrib) (1718-1786) German
£1711 $3147 €2600 Assumption (87x62cm-34x24in) i. verso. 24-Jun-4 Dr Fritz Nagel, Stuttgart #676/R est:1200

DIEGHEM, Jacob van (19th C) Dutch
£540 $967 €788 Sheep and chickens in landscape (28x38cm-11x15in) s.d.1895. 6-May-4 Biddle & Webb, Birmingham #885
£1000 $1700 €1460 Landscape studies of yews and lambs (16x23cm-6x9in) s. board pair. 30-Oct-3 Bracketts, Tunbridge Wells #1100/R
£1400 $2338 €2044 Sheep resting (18x25cm-7x10in) s.d.87 panel pair. 12-Nov-3 Sotheby's, Olympia #197/R est:1500-2000

DIEGHEM, Joseph van (1843-1885) Belgian
£680 $1068 €993 Sheep, poultry and dog by the coast (22x30cm-9x12in) s. panel. 30-Aug-3 Rasmussen, Havnen #2013/R (D.KR 7300)
£764 $1245 €1100 Sheep in meadow (17x24cm-7x9in) s.d.80 panel. 24-Sep-3 Neumeister, Munich #414/R
£795 $1454 €1200 Sheep in meadow (16x26cm-6x10in) s. panel. 8-Apr-4 Dorotheum, Vienna #63/R
£979 $1664 €1400 Sheep in meadow (40x29cm-16x11in) s.d.1881 panel. 20-Nov-3 Van Ham, Cologne #1540/R est:2000

DIEGO, Julio de (1900-1979) Spanish
£2059 $3500 €3006 Aztec Indian (89x58cm-35x23in) s.verso painted c.1940. 9-Nov-3 Wright, Chicago #206 est:4000-5000
£2647 $4500 €3865 Victorian Hotel (69x46cm-27x18in) s.d.1941 masonite. 9-Nov-3 Wright, Chicago #205 est:5000-7000
£4412 $7500 €6442 Deconstruction of Santos (119x89cm-47x35in) s.d.1945. 9-Nov-3 Wright, Chicago #207 est:6000-8000
Works on paper
£447 $800 €653 Archaic faces (41x48cm-16x19in) s. mixed media. 8-May-4 Susanin's, Chicago #6091/R
£625 $1044 €906 Women carrying baskets of fish (72x53cm-28x21in) s.d.1936 W/C. 17-Jun-3 Pinneys, Montreal #42 est:1400-1800 (C.D 1400)

DIEHL, Arthur (1870-1929) American
£243 $450 €355 Untitled (28x46cm-11x18in) s. board. 17-Jul-4 Outer Cape Auctions, Provincetown #52/R
£503 $900 €734 Coastal dunes (17x28cm-7x11in) s. board. 14-May-4 Skinner, Boston #235/R
£552 $900 €806 Full mast ship at sea (76x46cm-30x18in) s. board. 19-Jul-3 Outer Cape Auctions, Provincetown #102/R
£586 $950 €856 Sand dunes (10x11cm-4x4in) s. board. 31-Jul-3 Eldred, East Dennis #1124/R
£588 $1000 €858 Venetian view (31x41cm-12x16in) s.d.Aug 23 1916 canvasboard. 21-Nov-3 Skinner, Boston #324/R est:700-900
£749 $1250 €1094 Unloading the daily catch (36x25cm-14x10in) s. board. 12-Jul-3 Auctions by the Bay, Alameda #411/R
£755 $1200 €1102 Woman descending a staircase with water jugs (15x25cm-6x10in) s. prov. 13-Sep-3 Weschler, Washington #772/R
£765 $1300 €1117 Venetian canal (33x40cm-13x16in) board. 21-Nov-3 Skinner, Boston #322/R est:700-900
£765 $1300 €1117 Dunes (33x40cm-13x16in) s. 21-Nov-3 Skinner, Boston #551/R est:700-900
£864 $1400 €1261 Landscape with horse and rider (51x30cm-20x12in) s. board. 31-Jul-3 Eldred, East Dennis #846/R est:1400-1600
£943 $1500 €1377 Sand dunes (30x38cm-12x15in) s.d.1928 board. 23-Mar-3 Auctions by the Bay, Alameda #872/R
£950 $1700 €1387 Dock workers (27x30cm-11x12in) s. s.i.d.Aug 24 1924 verso board. 14-May-4 Skinner, Boston #276/R est:700-900
£1049 $1700 €1532 Fishing boat at dock (25x20cm-10x8in) s. 31-Jul-3 Eldred, East Dennis #847/R est:1500-2000
£1111 $1800 €1622 Due scene (30x61cm-12x24in) s. 31-Jul-3 Eldred, East Dennis #848/R est:2000-3000
£1118 $1800 €1632 Cape Cod beach (30x61cm-12x24in) s. 20-Aug-3 James Julia, Fairfield #1641/R est:1000-1500
£1189 $2200 €1736 Ship at sea (38x46cm-15x18in) s. board. 17-Jul-4 Outer Cape Auctions, Provincetown #19/R
£2077 $3800 €3032 Docks (41x75cm-16x30in) s.d.1925 board. 29-Jul-4 Christie's, Rockefeller NY #285/R est:4000-6000
£2235 $4000 €3263 Boat houses, Provincetown (46x76cm-18x30in) s.d.1928 board prov. 6-May-4 Shannon's, Milford #75/R est:5000-7000

DIEHL, Cal (?) ?
£457 $850 €667 Winter landscape with horse-drawn cart and figures (41x53cm-16x21in) s. 3-Mar-4 Alderfer's, Hatfield #331

DIEHL, Gosta (1899-1964) Finnish
£634 $1096 €900 Village (60x50cm-24x20in) s.d.1940. 13-Dec-3 Hagelstam, Helsinki #161/R
£2267 $4057 €3400 Harvesting time (60x100cm-24x39in) s.d.1954. 15-May-4 Hagelstam, Helsinki #208/R est:4000
£2838 $5080 €4200 Fishermen (80x100cm-31x39in) s.d.1953. 8-May-4 Bukowskis, Helsinki #303/R est:3000-3500

DIEKER, Carl Friedrich (19th C) ?
£838 $1400 €1223 Dog and roosters (36x48cm-14x19in) s. sold with another by European School, 19thC. 20-Jun-3 Freeman, Philadelphia #219/R

DIELMAN, Marguerite (1880-?) Belgian
£1575 $2678 €2300 Vase de fleurs (101x68cm-40x27in) s. 10-Nov-3 Horta, Bruxelles #319 est:800-1200

DIELMAN, Pierre Emmanuel (1800-1858) Belgian
£699 $1300 €1021 Sheep (21x29cm-8x11in) s. i.verso panel. 5-Mar-4 Skinner, Boston #245/R est:1000-1500

DIELMANN, Jakob Furchtegott (1809-1885) German
£625 $1019 €900 Stoning (33x45cm-13x18in) s.d.18.Marx 1880. 26-Sep-3 Bolland & Marotz, Bremen #513/R
Works on paper
£694 $1097 €1000 Flower girls from Schwalm (7x3cm-3x1in) W/C over pencil. 6-Sep-3 Arnold, Frankfurt #541

DIELMANN, Julius Theodor (1862-1931) German
£533 $976 €800 Taunus landscape in spring with farm and village (66x95cm-26x37in) canvas on canvas. 5-Jun-4 Arnold, Frankfurt #562/R

DIELS, Herman (?) ?
£676 $1189 €1000 Nursing the sick in Geel (100x100cm-39x39in) s. 24-May-4 Bernaerts, Antwerp #700/R

DIELS, Jef (1952-) Belgian
£2000 $3620 €3000 Dora (80x80cm-31x31in) s.d.1989 panel. 30-Mar-4 Campo, Vlaamse Kaai #56/R est:3500-4500

DIEMEN, Jan van (20th C) Dutch?
£578 $1052 €850 American football (100x100cm-39x39in) s.d.79 s.verso. 3-Feb-4 Christie's, Amsterdam #571/R

DIEMER, Michael Zeno (1867-1939) German
£537 $988 €800 Athos mountain at night (46x130cm-18x51in) panel. 24-Mar-4 Hugo Ruef, Munich #952/R
£800 $1360 €1168 Cresting wave (71x96cm-28x38in) s. 19-Nov-3 Christie's, Kensington #590/R
£814 $1400 €1188 Ship approaching the shore, Lake Garda, Italy (69x89cm-27x35in) s.d.1907. 7-Dec-3 Grogan, Boston #103/R
£1425 $2594 €2081 Monastery under moonlight, mount Athos, Greece (47x131cm-19x52in) s. canvas on board. 16-Jun-4 Christie's, Kensington #134/R est:1500-2000
£1500 $2580 €2190 Sailing at sunset (60x83cm-24x33in) s. 2-Dec-3 Sotheby's, London #51/R est:1500-2000
£1500 $2685 €2190 Windjammer in the Mediterranean (71x95cm-28x37in) s. 26-May-4 Christie's, Kensington #671/R est:1500-2000
£1958 $3368 €2800 Three-master on a stormy sea (110x144cm-43x57in) s. 3-Dec-3 Neumeister, Munich #556/R est:2500
£2013 $3705 €3000 Dutch schooner of Cap Tindaro, Sicily (58x83cm-23x33in) s. i. verso. 26-Mar-4 Ketterer, Hamburg #8/R est:4000-5000
£2254 $3899 €3200 Four-masted barque in open water (70x95cm-28x37in) s. 10-Dec-3 Christie's, Amsterdam #677/R est:3500-4500
£2857 $5114 €4200 Sailing ship off mountainous coastline (100x144cm-39x57in) s.d.1920. 17-Mar-4 Neumeister, Munich #437/R est:4000
£3176 $5684 €4700 Three master off Italian coast (61x81cm-24x32in) s. lit. 8-May-4 Dawo, Saarbrucken #50/R est:3800
£3691 $6755 €5500 Sailing ship in front of southern coastal town (56x76cm-22x30in) s. lit. 8-Jul-4 Allgauer, Kempten #2082/R est:5000
£9372 $16120 €13683 Bosphorus - entrance to Constantinople (82x110cm-32x43in) s. 3-Dec-3 Museumsbygningen, Copenhagen #211/R est:100000-150000 (D.KR 100000)

£23649 $42331 €35000 After the Kiel sailing regatta 1904 (170x281cm-67x111in) s.d.1904 lit. 8-May-4 Schloss Ahlden, Ahlden #756/R est:18500
Works on paper
£302 $556 €450 Ursula church in Munich (33x24cm-13x9in) s. w/C. 24-Mar-4 Hugo Ruef, Munich #1173
£567 $919 €800 Street - possibly Munich (20x12cm-8x5in) mono. wash Indian ink board. 23-May-3 Paul Kieffer, Pforzhiem #5538/R

DIENER-DENOS, Rudolph (1889-1956) Hungarian
£738 $1335 €1077 Coast of Brittany (30x40cm-12x16in) s. 16-Apr-4 Mu Terem Galeria, Budapest #18/R (H.F 280000)
£1086 $1803 €1586 Combing (99x78cm-39x31in) s. 4-Oct-3 Kieselbach, Budapest #201/R (H.F 400000)
£1107 $2003 €1616 Still life with a can (50x71cm-20x28in) s. 16-Apr-4 Mu Terem Galeria, Budapest #188/R (H.F 420000)

DIENES, Andre de (1913-1985) American
Photographs
£5429 $9500 €7926 Marilyn Monroe (23x22cm-9x9in) i.d.1960 verso gelatin silver print two. 17-Dec-3 Christie's, Rockefeller NY #61/R est:300-5000

DIENZ, Herm (1891-1980) German
£2657 $4517 €3800 Landscape (48x36cm-19x14in) s. board. 26-Nov-3 Lempertz, Koln #642/R est:4000-5000

DIEPENBECK, Abraham van (1596-1675) Flemish
Works on paper
£483 $801 €700 Predication. Moise et les Dix Commandements (20x15cm-8x6in) wash double-sided. 6-Oct-3 Amberes, Antwerp #277
£507 $892 €750 Portrait of St John of Matha (15x10cm-6x4in) pen brown ink wash black chk lit. 19-May-4 Sotheby's, Amsterdam #51/R
£890 $1514 €1300 Death of Socrates (10x16cm-4x6in) i.verso brush brown ink brown wash col chk prov.exhib. 4-Nov-3 Sotheby's, Amsterdam #47/R

DIEPENBECK, Abraham van (attrib) (1596-1675) Flemish
Works on paper
£433 $797 €650 St Michael with dragon (23x16cm-9x6in) chk wash. 11-Jun-4 Hauswedell & Nolte, Hamburg #832/R

DIEPRAAM, Abraham (attrib) (1622-1670) Dutch
£640 $1100 €934 Boy with bowl (30x23cm-12x9in) 7-Dec-3 Grogan, Boston #24/R
£1275 $2346 €1900 Deux fumeurs (26x18cm-10x7in) panel. 26-Mar-4 Piasa, Paris #12/R est:1800-2200

DIERCK, Ken (?) American?
Sculpture
£884 $1600 €1291 Whimsical figural. two parts. 3-Apr-4 Harvey Clar, Oakland #1321

DIERCKX, Pierre Jacques (1854-1947) Belgian
£1399 $2378 €2000 Chez le marchand de volailles au temps passe (83x103cm-33x41in) s. exhib. 18-Nov-3 Vanderkindere, Brussels #92 est:1500-2000
£1867 $3341 €2800 Ferry house of Thielrode (83x101cm-33x40in) s.d.1901. 15-May-4 De Vuyst, Lokeren #111/R est:1500-2000

DIERCKXSEN, F J (19th C) Dutch
£1412 $2400 €2062 Landscape with cattle grazing, windmill and farm beyond (61x86cm-24x34in) s.d.1838 panel. 22-Nov-3 New Orleans Auction, New Orleans #314/R est:3000-5000

DIERICKX, Karel (1940-) Belgian
£382 $638 €550 De lepe despoot (90x70cm-35x28in) s.d.1968 verso. 21-Oct-3 Campo, Vlaamse Kaai #798
Works on paper
£524 $876 €750 Composition (44x35cm-17x14in) s.d.1988 mixed media. 11-Oct-3 De Vuyst, Lokeren #125

DIERICKX, Omer (1862-1939) Belgian
£302 $556 €450 Portrait d'homme (100x70cm-39x28in) s.d.1918 panel. 23-Mar-4 Galerie Moderne, Brussels #163

DIERICKX, Raymond (1904-1978) Belgian
£567 $1014 €850 Fishing at the quay (67x89cm-26x35in) s. panel. 15-May-4 De Vuyst, Lokeren #112/R

DIERS, Ed (?) American?
Works on paper
£244 $400 €354 Landscape (15x15cm-6x6in) s. W/C. 7-Jun-3 Treadway Gallery, Cincinnati #518
£366 $600 €531 Landscape (23x18cm-9x7in) s. mixed media dr. 7-Jun-3 Treadway Gallery, Cincinnati #517

DIERS, Thierry (1954-) French
£828 $1531 €1200 Ecriture musicale (100x100cm-39x39in) s.d.1985. 13-Feb-4 Charbonneaux, Paris #95/R

DIERX, Léon (1841-1912) French
Works on paper
£500 $920 €750 Vieille ville au bord d'une riviere au crepuscule (8x16cm-3x6in) s.i. pen wash. 9-Jun-4 Piasa, Paris #53/R

DIES, Albert-Christophe (1755-1822) German
Works on paper
£600 $1080 €876 Mother and infant in a cave with figure watching. Angle delivering infant (23x29cm-9x11in) s.i. i.verso pen col ink col wash black chk double-sided. 20-Apr-4 Sotheby's, Olympia #163/R
£929 $1700 €1356 Le Temple de la Concorde (51x74cm-20x29in) s.i. pen brown ink wash. 29-Jan-4 Swann Galleries, New York #313/R est:2000-3000

DIESNER, Gerhild (1915-1995) Austrian
£4167 $7083 €6000 Still life (39x49cm-15x19in) s.d.69. 28-Oct-3 Wiener Kunst Auktionen, Vienna #217/R est:6000-12000
£6040 $10812 €9000 Flowers (70x50cm-28x20in) s.d.71. 25-May-4 Dorotheum, Vienna #224/R est:10000-14000
£10067 $17819 €15000 Still life (70x56cm-28x22in) s.d.1976. 28-Apr-4 Wiener Kunst Auktionen, Vienna #225/R est:19000-25000
£10738 $19221 €16000 Autumn in Torbole - Lake Garda (69x69cm-27x27in) s. i. stretcher. 25-May-4 Dorotheum, Vienna #223/R est:10000-14000

DIEST, Adriaen van (1655-1704) Dutch
£70000 $127400 €102200 English fleet at sea (133x100cm-52x39in) mono. 1-Jul-4 Sotheby's, London #149/R est:15000-20000

DIEST, Adriaen van (attrib) (1655-1704) Dutch
£4196 $7133 €6000 Calm lake on Dutch coast with figures and boats (50x70cm-20x28in) panel. 21-Nov-3 Reiss & Sohn, Konigstein #9/R est:8000
£4500 $7650 €6570 Italianate landscape with drovers and cattle beside a waterfall (127x107cm-50x42in) 29-Oct-3 Bonhams, New Bond Street #54/R est:5000-7000

DIEST, Frans van (19th C) Belgian
£1067 $1909 €1600 Pedestrian concourse on the quay of Antwerp (88x136cm-35x54in) s. 15-May-4 De Vuyst, Lokeren #348/R est:1700-2000

DIEST, Hieronymus van (1631-1673) Dutch
£3000 $5370 €4500 Seascape (40x60cm-16x24in) 12-May-4 Finarte Semenzato, Milan #78/R est:2000-3000

DIESTE, Hermann (20th C) German
£293 $525 €440 View of the valley (80x70cm-31x28in) s. 14-May-4 Behringer, Furth #1604

DIETER, Hans (1881-1968) German
£658 $1211 €1000 Landscape of Lake Constance (35x45cm-14x18in) s.i. masonite. 26-Jun-4 Karrenbauer, Konstanz #1714
£851 $1379 €1200 Bodensee landscape (50x62cm-20x24in) s. panel lit. 23-May-3 Karlheinz Kaupp, Staufen #1863
£1111 $1833 €1600 Bodensee (75x65cm-30x26in) s. board. 5-Jul-3 Geble, Radolfzell #457/R est:1600
£1600 $2912 €2400 On the lake shore, Uberlinger (79x90cm-31x35in) s. masonite. 3-Jul-4 Geble, Radolfzell #393/R est:2000
£2081 $3828 €3100 Bodensee (52x60cm-20x24in) s. 27-Mar-4 Geble, Radolfzell #713/R est:2600

DIETERICH, Johann Friedrich (1787-1846) German
£625 $1031 €900 Portrait of Friedrich Christoph Mayer (86x72cm-34x28in) s.i.d.1829. 3-Jul-3 Dr Fritz Nagel, Stuttgart #485/R

DIETERLE, Marie (1856-1935) French
£938 $1500 €1369 Cattle and sheep on a pathway with drover beyond (46x66cm-18x26in) i.verso. 19-Sep-3 Freeman, Philadelphia #132/R est:1500-2500
£1324 $2250 €1933 Cattle watering by a bridge (36x25cm-14x10in) s. 31-Oct-3 North East Auctions, Portsmouth #1200
£2232 $3839 €3259 Cattle near the water's edge (78x103cm-31x41in) s. 2-Dec-3 Ritchie, Toronto #101/R est:6000-9000 (C.D 5000)

DIETERLE, Martin (1935-) French
£704 $1232 €1000 Couleurs du soir (60x73cm-24x29in) s. s.i.d.76 verso. 17-Dec-3 Delorme & Bocage, Paris #34/R
£1549 $2711 €2200 Porquerolles (60x73cm-24x29in) s. s.i.d.1972 verso. 17-Dec-3 Delorme & Bocage, Paris #35/R est:1000-1200

DIETLER, Johann Friedrich (1804-1874) Swiss
£409 $733 €597 Portrait of Abraham Hunzigker (29x24cm-11x9in) i.d.1839 verso board. 13-May-4 Stuker, Bern #97/R (S.FR 950)
£1408 $2465 €2000 Portrait of gentleman. Portrait of lady (27x21cm-11x8in) i.d.verso pair. 17-Dec-3 Il Ponte, Milan #602 est:2200-2300
Works on paper
£407 $692 €594 Anna Maria Bischoff-Preiswerk (33x24cm-13x9in) s.d.1851 i. verso W/C. 19-Nov-3 Fischer, Luzern #2457/R (S.FR 900)

DIETMANN, Erik (1937-2002) Swedish
Sculpture
£1127 $1882 €1645 Untitled (75cm-30in) s. wooden box lead lid with hat and three small bronze men. 7-Oct-3 Rasmussen, Copenhagen #173/R est:15000 (D.KR 12000)
£1208 $2139 €1800 Cuisinieres (30x35x0cm-12x14x0in) s. green pat bronze metal prov. 28-Apr-4 Artcurial Briest, Paris #432/R est:1800-2200
£1400 $2576 €2100 Poil (28x60x22cm-11x24x9in) num.9/10 iron bone soapstone exec 1989 prov. 9-Jun-4 Artcurial Briest, Paris #487/R est:2500-3000

DIETRICH, Adolf (1877-1957) Swiss

£6987 $12716 €10201 Flowers in a vase with a yellow bird (25x18cm-10x7in) s.d.54 cardboard prov. 18-Jun-4 Kornfeld, Bern #29/R est:17500 (S.FR 16000)
£8621 $15431 €12587 Blue tit in flight (20x20cm-8x8in) s.d.1949 lit. 17-May-4 Beurret, Zurich #38/R est:18000-22000 (S.FR 20000)
£8734 $15895 €12752 Portrait of Mr Luthy (50x41cm-20x16in) s.d.1948 panel prov.exhib. 18-Jun-4 Kornfeld, Bern #27/R est:20000 (S.FR 20000)
£8734 $15895 €12752 Portrait of a child (34x28cm-13x11in) s.d.1930 i.verso cardboard prov.exhib. 18-Jun-4 Kornfeld, Bern #24/R est:20000 (S.FR 20000)
£9955 $16923 €14534 Bodensee (27x34cm-11x13in) s.d.1932 s. verso prov. 25-Nov-3 Germann, Zurich #47/R est:10000-15000 (S.FR 22000)
£12227 $22253 €17851 Portrait of a woman with tiled stove behind (50x41cm-20x16in) s.d.1932 cardboard prov.exhib. 18-Jun-4 Kornfeld, Bern #26/R est:20000 (S.FR 28000)
£13575 $21719 €19820 Rauhreif near Sandegg (38x54cm-15x21in) s.d.1925 board lit.exhib.prov. 16-Sep-3 Philippe Schuler, Zurich #3233/R est:30000-40000 (S.FR 30000)
£13974 $25013 €20402 Summer morning at Entersee (28x37cm-11x15in) s.d.1930 board exhib.lit. 26-May-4 Sotheby's, Zurich #88/R est:35000-55000 (S.FR 32000)
£14480 $25050 €21141 Bullfinch on window sill (21x25cm-8x10in) s.d.1941 board lit. 9-Dec-3 Sotheby's, Zurich #87/R est:35000-40000 (S.FR 32000)
£15721 $28611 €22953 Chaffinch on a blossom branch (27x22cm-11x9in) s.d.1951 cardboard prov. 18-Jun-4 Kornfeld, Bern #28/R est:40000 (S.FR 36000)
£15909 $26409 €23068 Bird on window ledge (20x25cm-8x10in) i. verso board prov.lit. 13-Jun-3 Zofingen, Switzerland #2823/R est:40000 (S.FR 35000)
£16594 $30201 €24227 Yellow flowering cactus in a landscape near Untersee (47x64cm-19x25in) s.d.1950 cardboard prov.exhib. 18-Jun-4 Kornfeld, Bern #25/R est:40000 (S.FR 38000)
£18341 $33380 €26778 Three chaffinches on a window sill (19x31cm-7x12in) s.d.1948 panel prov. 18-Jun-4 Kornfeld, Bern #30/R est:40000 (S.FR 42000)
£20175 $37123 €29456 Berlingen in 1800 (20x30cm-8x12in) s.i.d.1917 board on plywood prov.lit. 23-Jun-4 Koller, Zurich #3055/R est:40000-60000 (S.FR 46000)
£29412 $50882 €42942 Fieldfare (24x20cm-9x8in) s.d.1937 board lit. 9-Dec-3 Sotheby's, Zurich #94/R est:65000-75000 (S.FR 65000)
£30172 $54009 €44051 Zinnia (68x42cm-27x17in) s.d.1941 board lit. 17-May-4 Beurret, Zurich #40/R est:70000-90000 (S.FR 70000)
£30435 $55696 €44435 Two bunches of carnations (47x36cm-19x14in) s.d.1941 board prov.lit. 7-Jun-4 Christie's, Zurich #117/R est:80000-120000 (S.FR 70000)
£47826 $87522 €69826 Eppenberg near Eschenz (31x48cm-12x19in) s.d.1930 board prov.lit. 7-Jun-4 Christie's, Zurich #116/R est:70000-90000 (S.FR 110000)
£78261 $143217 €114261 Berlingen from Juhe (57x100cm-22x39in) s.d.1936 panel prov.lit. 7-Jun-4 Christie's, Zurich #123/R est:200000-250000 (S.FR 180000)
£108597 $187873 €158552 Still life with lady's slipper and salamander (50x50cm-20x20in) s.i.d.1928 board prov.exhib.lit. 9-Dec-3 Sotheby's, Zurich #41/R est:50000-80000 (S.FR 240000)
£130435 $238696 €190435 Small still life of grapes (48x50cm-19x20in) s.d.1933 panel prov.exhib.lit. 7-Jun-4 Christie's, Zurich #111/R est:80000-120000 (S.FR 300000)
Works on paper
£1310 $2345 €1913 View from Hegauer mountain in winter from See-Rucken (18x26cm-7x10in) mono. pencil exhib. 26-May-4 Sotheby's, Zurich #87/R est:3000-5000 (S.FR 3000)
£3521 $5634 €5000 Flowers in round vase (43x33cm-17x13in) s.d.1954 i. verso lit. 19-Sep-3 Karlheinz Kaupp, Staufen #2195/R est:5000
£6726 $10964 €9820 Untersee in evening (24x34cm-9x13in) col chk prov.exhib. 29-Sep-3 Christie's, Zurich #69/R est:18000-25000 (S.FR 15000)

DIETRICH, Christian Wilhelm Ernst (1712-1774) German

£704 $1218 €1000 Bearded apostles (8x7cm-3x3in) panel pair prov. 13-Dec-3 Lempertz, Koln #211
£898 $1671 €1311 A Russian nobleman (21x16cm-8x6in) s. 2-Mar-4 Rasmussen, Copenhagen #1312/R (D.KR 10000)
£1100 $2035 €1606 A philosopher holding his staff (40x31cm-16x12in) board. 11-Feb-4 Cheffins, Cambridge #423 est:1200-1500
£1538 $2646 €2245 Old man - Charitas (54x38cm-21x15in) 2-Dec-3 Bukowskis, Stockholm #401/R est:15000-18000 (S.KR 20000)
£5607 $8860 €8130 Jesus Healing the Sick (55x73cm-22x29in) s.i.stretcher. 2-Sep-3 Rasmussen, Copenhagen #1591/R est:75000-100000 (D.KR 60000)
£7692 $13077 €11000 The Good Samaritan (80x68cm-31x27in) s. 20-Nov-3 Van Ham, Cologne #1312/R est:8000
£20833 $34375 €30000 Proclamation to the shepherds (84x100cm-33x39in) s.d.1758. 3-Jul-3 Dr Fritz Nagel, Stuttgart #431/R
£27000 $46710 €39420 Italianate landscapes (56x66cm-22x26in) both s.d.1762 pair. 11-Dec-3 Sotheby's, London #205/R est:15000-20000
Works on paper
£1300 $2379 €1898 Farmhouse among ruins (21x29cm-8x11in) pen ink wash over pencil. 7-Jul-4 Bonhams, Knightsbridge #21/R est:1500-2000
£3930 $7153 €5738 Proclamation to the herdsmen (37x28cm-15x11in) i.verso pen brush ink prov. 17-Jun-4 Kornfeld, Bern #7/R est:7500 (S.FR 9000)

DIETRICH, Christian Wilhelm Ernst (attrib) (1712-1774) German

£1000 $1800 €1460 Head of an old man (52x38cm-20x15in) 23-Apr-4 Christie's, Kensington #155/R est:1200-1800
£2113 $3697 €3000 Portrait d'un jeune Turc (48x36cm-19x14in) 18-Dec-3 Tajan, Paris #109/R est:3000-5000
£3028 $4845 €4300 Landscape with river and distant town (36x43cm-14x17in) lit. 19-Sep-3 Karlheinz Kaupp, Staufen #1900/R est:800
£4934 $9079 €7500 Portrait of young woman with venetian mask (82x62cm-32x24in) 24-Jun-4 Dr Fritz Nagel, Stuttgart #643/R est:2900
Works on paper
£704 $1218 €1000 Portrait of the wife of the artist Joseph Brecheisen (28x20cm-11x8in) chl htd white. 11-Dec-3 Dr Fritz Nagel, Stuttgart #369/R

DIETRICH, Fritz (19th C) German

£293 $528 €440 Cardinal playing chess (70x100cm-28x39in) s.i. 21-Apr-4 Neumeister, Munich #2630

DIETRICH, Henryk (1889-1948) Polish

£424 $747 €636 Landscape with field (23x32cm-9x13in) board. 23-May-4 Agra, Warsaw #49/R (P.Z 3000)

DIETRICH, Keith Hamilton (1950-) South African?

Works on paper
£403 $730 €588 Anonymous man (36x47cm-14x19in) s.i.d.1986 airbrush. 30-Mar-4 Stephan Welz, Johannesburg #236 est:2500-3000 (SA.R 4800)

DIETRICH, Michael H (1940-) German

£845 $1352 €1200 Nights on the Ecke (60x50cm-24x20in) s.d.1982 oil gold leaf. 18-Sep-3 Rieber, Stuttgart #965

DIETRICHSON, Mathilde (1837-1921) Norwegian

£1629 $2916 €2378 Interior scene with woman reading (22x16cm-9x6in) s. panel. 10-May-4 Rasmussen, Vejle #326/R est:10000-12000 (D.KR 18000)

DIETSCH, C Percival (?) ?

Sculpture
£1216 $2250 €1775 Nude female (37cm-15in) bronze. 11-Mar-4 Sotheby's, New York #122/R est:2500-3500

DIETSCHI, Peter (1935-) Swiss

£524 $954 €765 Untitled (100x99cm-39x39in) s.d.62. 16-Jun-4 Fischer, Luzern #2078/R (S.FR 1200)

DIETZ, Jakob (?) ?

£671 $1201 €1000 Village street in winter (41x45cm-16x18in) s.d.42. 27-May-4 Dorotheum, Graz #13/R

DIETZSCH, Barbara Regina (1706-1783) German

Works on paper
£1215 $1920 €1762 Pastoral landscapes with figures and animals (7x9cm-3x4in) bears sig.verso gouache pair. 2-Sep-3 Rasmussen, Copenhagen #1869/R est:8000-10000 (D.KR 13000)

DIETZSCH, Barbara Regina (attrib) (1706-1783) German

Works on paper
£2000 $3600 €2920 Flower studies, tied with coloured ribbons (29x20cm-11x8in) gouache vellum pair. 20-Apr-4 Sotheby's, Olympia #182/R est:2000-3000

DIETZSCH, Georg Friedrich (1717-1755) German

Works on paper
£900 $1557 €1314 Seated hunter with two hounds and the day's bag. Deer hunt (16x22cm-6x9in) init. bodycol vellum pair. 12-Dec-3 Christie's, Kensington #556/R

DIETZSCH, Johann Christoph (1710-1769) German

Works on paper
£528 $950 €771 Extensive landscape with two figures by a stream (16x21cm-6x8in) bodycol vellum. 22-Jan-4 Christie's, Rockefeller NY #233/R
£1844 $3080 €2600 Marines (11x17cm-4x7in) s.verso gouache pair. 17-Oct-3 Tajan, Paris #47 est:2500-3500
£13000 $24050 €18980 Botanical drawings (29x21cm-11x8in) W/C board pair by members of the Dietzch family of Nuremburg. 15-Jul-4 Bonhams, New Bond Street #13/R est:8000-12000

DIEU, Antoine (1662-1727) French

Works on paper
£2568 $4519 €3800 Fishermen hauling in nets (10x19cm-4x7in) s. i.verso pen black ink grey wash red chk prov.exhib.lit. 19-May-4 Sotheby's, Amsterdam #135/R est:1400-1800

DIEU, Antoine (attrib) (1662-1727) French

Works on paper
£494 $919 €721 Religious scene (34x22cm-13x9in) pen brown wash. 2-Mar-4 Rasmussen, Copenhagen #1679/R (D.KR 5500)
£2192 $3726 €3200 Venus commandant aux amours de toucher Amphitrite et Diane de leurs fleches (28x47cm-11x19in) pen ink wash htd gouache. 6-Nov-3 Tajan, Paris #55/R

DIEUDONNE, E de (19th C) French

£1146 $1914 €1650 Madame Angot (65x55cm-26x22in) s.d.1880. 27-Oct-3 Giraudeau, Tours #17

DIEUDONNE, Emmanuel de (19th C) French

£4085 $7148 €5800 Entree de la mosquee (60x39cm-24x15in) s. panel. 16-Dec-3 Claude Aguttes, Neuilly #56/R est:6000-8000

DIEUDONNE, Jacques Augustin (19th C) French?

Sculpture
£16084 $27664 €23000 Buste representant J E J A Macdonald, Marechal de France (70cm-28in) s.i.d.1824 brown pat bronze piedouche prov.lit. 2-Dec-3 Sotheby's, Paris #70/R est:7000-9000

DIEVENBACH, Hendricus Anthonius (1872-1946) Dutch

£789 $1429 €1200 Mother doing handwork and her two small children in an interior (34x44cm-13x17in) s.i. 19-Apr-4 Glerum, Amsterdam #241/R

DIEY, Yves (1892-1984) French

£800 $1432 €1200 Deux chiens de chasse (96x128cm-38x50in) 12-May-4 Coutau Begarie, Paris #214/R

DIEZ, Anton (1914-1992) Belgian

£486 $812 €700 Femme nue (60x40cm-24x16in) s. 21-Oct-3 Campo & Campo, Antwerp #496

Works on paper

£278	$464	€400	Portrait de femme en profil (49x33cm-19x13in) s. pastel. 21-Oct-3 Campo & Campo, Antwerp #498

DIEZ, Joaquin (19th C) Spanish

£690	$1241	€1000	Shepherd resting (60x40cm-24x16in) s. 26-Jan-4 Ansorena, Madrid #261/R
£690	$1241	€1000	Shepherd smoking (60x40cm-24x16in) s. 26-Jan-4 Ansorena, Madrid #260/R

DIEZ, Sylvain (20th C) French

£333	$603	€500	La surprise (65x92cm-26x36in) s. acrylic. 3-Apr-4 Neret-Minet, Paris #223
£385	$654	€550	Une vieille histoire (73x54cm-29x21in) s. acrylic. 29-Nov-3 Neret-Minet, Paris #117/R
£433	$784	€650	Un bon programme (74x54cm-29x21in) s. acrylic. 3-Apr-4 Neret-Minet, Paris #171/R

DIEZ, Wilhelm von (1839-1907) German

£1259	$2140	€1800	Saddled brown horse in stable (21x25cm-8x10in) i. board. 20-Nov-3 Dorotheum, Salzburg #181/R est:2800-3500

DIEZLER, Jakob (1789-1855) German

£5986	$10356	€8500	Rhine landscape with view of Koblenz (37x58cm-15x23in) prov. 13-Dec-3 Lempertz, Koln #212/R est:3000

DIGGELMANN, Alex Walter (1902-1987) Swiss

Works on paper

£323	$585	€472	Scheidegg, Eiger in winter (50x37cm-20x15in) s. W/C. 31-Mar-4 Zurichsee Auktionen, Erlenbach #60/R (S.FR 750)

DIGHTON, Denis (1792-1827) British

£220000	$374000	€321200	Greeks and Turks (182x244cm-72x96in) s.d.1823 prov.exhib.lit. 18-Nov-3 Sotheby's, London #28/R est:200000-300000

Works on paper

£1000	$1670	€1460	Prussian army officers - Dragoon of Guards (37x26cm-15x10in) W/C over pencil. 14-Oct-3 Sotheby's, London #496/R est:800-1200

DIGHTON, Joshua (fl.1820-1840) British

£1000	$1700	€1460	Group of three huntsmen and jockeys (23x20cm-9x8in) three. 29-Oct-3 Mallams, Oxford #695 est:250-350

Works on paper

£900	$1656	€1314	Fagan, in the colours of H Robertson Esq. Jockey (20x16cm-8x6in) W/C two. 10-Jun-4 Christie's, Kensington #143/R
£2200	$3740	€3212	Portraits of jockeys in owners colours (25x18cm-10x7in) W/C six. 29-Oct-3 Mallams, Oxford #696/R est:900-1100
£5800	$10672	€8468	Seven jockeys. Two huntsmen (24x20cm-9x8in) one i. pencil W/C bodycol set of nine. 10-Jun-4 Christie's, Kensington #142/R est:5000-7000

DIGHTON, Richard (1785-1880) British

Works on paper

£700	$1288	€1022	Family group by a parkland bench (29x36cm-11x14in) s.d.1812 W/C pen black ink. 23-Mar-4 Rosebery Fine Art, London #724

DIGHTON, Robert (1752-1814) British

Works on paper

£462	$800	€675	Portrait of standing gentleman (25x20cm-10x8in) s. W/C. 10-Dec-3 Alderfer's, Hatfield #296
£2400	$4008	€3504	Puppy's dress. Choice fruit. Harmony of courtship. Discord of matrimony (14x11cm-6x4in) s.i. W/C set of four. 14-Oct-3 Bonhams, New Bond Street #104/R est:1200-1800

DIGHTON, William Edward (1822-1853) British

Works on paper

£2800	$5096	€4088	Arabs by the ruins at Luxor (35x55cm-14x22in) W/C over pencil. 1-Jul-4 Sotheby's, London #235/R est:3000-4000

DIGNAM, Mary Ella Williams (1860-1938) Canadian

£560	$1025	€818	Old man's garden (45x60cm-18x24in) s. lit. 1-Jun-4 Joyner Waddington, Toronto #366/R (C.D 1400)

DIGNIMONT, Andre (1891-1965) French

Works on paper

£243	$406	€350	L'odalisque turque (49x63cm-19x25in) st.sig. W/C. 21-Oct-3 Artcurial Briest, Paris #44
£276	$458	€400	Decor de theatre (34x48cm-13x19in) s.i. gouache. 6-Oct-3 Blanchet, Paris #288/R
£315	$526	€450	Femme aux seins nus (65x50cm-26x20in) s. gouache. 7-Oct-3 Livinec, Gaudcheau & Jezequel, Rennes #140
£336	$594	€500	Modele au canape bleu (47x63cm-19x25in) s. W/C crayon. 27-Apr-4 Artcurial Briest, Paris #102a
£347	$580	€500	Jeune femme a la cigarette (57x52cm-22x20in) s.i. W/C prov. 21-Oct-3 Christie's, Paris #88/R
£470	$874	€700	Paysage de neige (64x49cm-25x19in) s. W/C. 3-Mar-4 Ferri, Paris #356
£503	$936	€750	Femme denudee aux boucles rousses (54x41cm-21x16in) s. gouache. 7-Mar-4 Lesieur & Le Bars, Le Havre #31
£671	$1248	€1000	Femme au collier de perles noires (64x49cm-25x19in) s. gouache. 7-Mar-4 Lesieur & Le Bars, Le Havre #30/R
£674	$1125	€950	Modele a l'atelier (48x64cm-19x25in) s. W/C. 12-Oct-3 St-Germain-en-Laye Encheres #109/R
£1007	$1883	€1500	Innocente mariette (65x50cm-26x20in) st.sig. W/C. 29-Feb-4 Versailles Encheres #125/R est:1200-1500
£1458	$2435	€2100	Nu de dos au chapeau (40x28cm-16x11in) s. ink drawing ink wash htd pastel. 21-Oct-3 Artcurial Briest, Paris #43 est:800-1000
£2933	$5397	€4400	Le bar a matelots (35x35cm-14x14in) s.d.26 gouache W/C graphite prov. 8-Jun-4 Artcurial Briest, Paris #123/R est:3000-4000

DIJKSTRA, Rineke (1959-) Dutch

Photographs

£6293	$10824	€9000	Accra, Ghana (62x52cm-24x20in) s.num.1/15 verso C print prov. 3-Dec-3 Sotheby's, Amsterdam #484/R est:6000-8000
£8800	$15488	€12848	Portugal, May 1st 1994. Portugal May 8th 1994 (25x20cm-10x8in) s.verso num.14/20 dye coupler prints two. 18-May-4 Bonhams, New Bond Street #541/R est:8000-12000
£9581	$16000	€13988	Evora, Portugal May 1 1994. Villa Franca, Portugal May 1994 (26x20cm-10x8in) s.i.d.May 1 1994 num.20 two col photograph. 14-Nov-3 Phillips, New York #109/R est:18000-25000
£10056	$18000	€14682	Zilvitis, Lithuania July 28 2000 (139x102cm-55x40in) s.d.December 9, 2000 verso c-print edition of 10 prov. 14-May-4 Phillips, New York #156/R est:25000-35000
£11976	$20000	€17485	Amit, Golani Bridge, Elyacim, Israel (180x150cm-71x59in) cibachrome print mounted to plexiglass exec 1999 prov.exhib. 12-Nov-3 Christie's, Rockefeller NY #584/R est:20000-30000
£15569	$26000	€22731	Abigael, Herzliya, Israel. Abigael, Palmahim Israeli Air Force Base (126x108cm-50x43in) cibachrome prints exec 1999 diptych prov.exhib. 12-Nov-3 Christie's, Rockefeller NY #583583/R est:20000-30000
£17877	$32000	€26100	Hilton Head, South Carolina, USA (40x31cm-16x12in) s.i. 24 Juni 1992 verso col photo edition of 15 prov.exhib.lit. 14-May-4 Phillips, New York #159/R est:25000-35000
£19553	$35000	€28547	Kolobrzeg, Poland (40x32cm-16x13in) s.i.26 Juli 92 verso col photo edition of 15 prov.exhib.lit. 14-May-4 Phillips, New York #160/R est:25000-35000
£32934	$55000	€48084	Tecla, Amsterdam, Netherlands, May 16 1994 (124x104cm-49x41in) s. num.6 verso colour photograph prov. 14-Nov-3 Phillips, New York #116/R est:60000-80000
£95808	$160000	€139880	Odessa. Ukraine, August 4 1993 (124x104cm-49x41in) s.num.6 verso c-print executed 1993 prov.exhib.lit. 13-Nov-3 Phillips, New York #8/R est:150000-200000

DIJSSELHOF, Gerrit Willem (1866-1924) Dutch

£276	$500	€420	A nasty smelly snappy fish (21x30cm-8x12in) mono. panel. 19-Apr-4 Glerum, Amsterdam #274/R
£276	$500	€420	A fish near the bottom of the sea (13x18cm-5x7in) mono. panel. 19-Apr-4 Glerum, Amsterdam #275/R
£395	$726	€600	Carps (27x39cm-11x15in) 28-Jun-4 Sotheby's, Amsterdam #140/R
£1312	$2191	€1916	Goldfish in a rocky pool (18x23cm-7x9in) mono. 17-Nov-3 Waddingtons, Toronto #151/R est:600-800 (C.D 2900)
£3061	$5571	€4500	Underwater (31x45cm-12x18in) 3-Feb-4 Christie's, Amsterdam #154/R est:700-900
£4452	$7568	€6500	Fish in aquarium (47x68cm-19x27in) mono. 5-Nov-3 Vendue Huis, Gravenhage #388/R est:2000-3000

DIK, Peter (1943-1984) Dutch

£268	$494	€400	Ducks flying over meadow (80x100cm-31x39in) s. 26-Mar-4 Ketterer, Hamburg #235/R

DIKE, Philip Latimer (1906-1990) American

Works on paper

£5294	$9000	€7729	Afternoon gathering (53x36cm-21x14in) s. i.verso W/C prov. 18-Nov-3 John Moran, Pasadena #84 est:3000-4000
£8235	$14000	€12023	Figures at beach umbrella stand (36x56cm-14x22in) s.d.55 W/C prov. 18-Nov-3 John Moran, Pasadena #88a est:2500-3500

DILASSER, Francois (1926-) French

£800	$1472	€1200	Untitled 5 (27x40cm-11x16in) s.d.87 acrylic paper prov. 8-Jun-4 Livinec, Gaudcheau & Jezequel, Rennes #81

DILETTO, Charles (1911-1989) American

£246	$425	€359	Harbour scene (41x51cm-16x20in) s. 10-Dec-3 Alderfer's, Hatfield #373

DILGER, Josef (1899-1972) German

£333	$600	€500	Still life of flowers (60x50cm-24x20in) mono. 24-Apr-4 Dr Lehr, Berlin #95/R

DILGER, Stella (1900-?) Australian

£287	$453	€419	Sailor (49x31cm-19x12in) s. board prov.exhib. 2-Sep-3 Deutscher-Menzies, Melbourne #372/R (A.D 700)

DILL, Guy (20th C) American

Sculpture

£1117	$1900	€1631	Untitled (203x61cm-80x24in) stone concrete prov. 9-Nov-3 Bonhams & Butterfields, Los Angeles #4104/R est:3000-5000

DILL, Ludwig (1848-1940) German

£281	$504	€410	The Lagoon (28x37cm-11x15in) s. oil study board. 22-Mar-4 Philippe Schuler, Zurich #6137 (S.FR 650)
£403	$741	€600	Sailing boats (33x21cm-13x8in) s. board. 25-Mar-4 Dr Fritz Nagel, Stuttgart #701/R
£441	$749	€630	Autumn evening (62x45cm-24x18in) i. verso board. 20-Nov-3 Weidler, Nurnberg #319/R

£447 $823 €680 Fishing boats in calm waters (32x56cm-13x22in) s. i. verso board. 24-Jun-4 Dr Fritz Nagel, Stuttgart #700/R
£775 $1387 €1100 Fishing boat (35x25cm-14x10in) s. board lit. 8-Jan-4 Allgauer, Kempten #2370/R
£872 $1623 €1300 Birch trees (54x38cm-21x15in) s. 6-Mar-4 Arnold, Frankfurt #714/R est:600
£903 $1472 €1300 Birch trees by pond in evening (36x51cm-14x20in) s. panel. 25-Sep-3 Dr Fritz Nagel, Stuttgart #1342/R
£940 $1729 €1400 Fishing boats off Chioggia (60x80cm-24x31in) s. lit. 25-Mar-4 Karlheinz Kaupp, Staufen #2416/R
£1111 $1811 €1600 Riverside wood (74x94cm-29x37in) s.indis.d. s.i. verso tempera board. 27-Sep-3 Dr Fritz Nagel, Stuttgart #9511/R est:1200
£1200 $2184 €1800 Fishing boats in the Lagoon (74x92cm-29x36in) s. i. verso board. 30-Jun-4 Neumeister, Munich #537/R est:2000
£1250 $2313 €1825 Venetian canal (33x46cm-13x18in) s. panel. 10-Feb-4 David Lay, Penzance #582/R est:400-600
£1467 $2655 €2200 Fishing in the Lagoon (25x20cm-10x8in) s. board. 3-Apr-4 Hans Stahl, Hamburg #21/R est:1900
£1467 $2640 €2200 Juniper tree in the snow (37x40cm-15x16in) s.i.d.1910 tempera. 26-Apr-4 Rieber, Stuttgart #1294/R est:2400
£1736 $2865 €2500 Birch trees by lake in evening light (34x49cm-13x19in) s. board. 3-Jul-3 Dr Fritz Nagel, Stuttgart #482/R est:3500
£1958 $3329 €2800 River landscape with trees (35x49cm-14x19in) s. i. verso board. 20-Nov-3 Weidler, Nurnberg #334/R
£3000 $5010 €4380 Bringing home the catch (57x44cm-22x17in) s.d.80. 12-Nov-3 Sotheby's, Olympia #191/R est:2000-3000
Works on paper
£336 $617 €500 Crane by water (28x19cm-11x7in) s. 26-Mar-4 Ketterer, Hamburg #236/R
£1600 $2912 €2400 October evening (66x50cm-26x20in) s. gouache. 30-Jun-4 Neumeister, Munich #408/R est:2000

DILL, Otto (1884-1957) German
£282 $487 €400 Cows in meadow (23x33cm-9x13in) s. chl. 13-Dec-3 Lempertz, Koln #128/R
£1119 $1902 €1600 Peasant with three cows (19x30cm-7x12in) mono.d.14 canvas on board. 20-Nov-3 Dorotheum, Salzburg #208/R est:2000-3000
£2148 $3952 €3200 Man on horse with dogs (48x68cm-19x27in) s. lit. 26-Mar-4 Karrenbauer, Konstanz #1709/R est:1000
£2345 $3916 €3400 Horse racing (35x49cm-14x19in) s. board. 13-Nov-3 Neumeister, Munich #304/R est:3000-4000
£2667 $4800 €4000 Two tigers resting (36x50cm-14x20in) s. board lit. 22-Apr-4 Allgauer, Kempten #3514/R est:6000
£3067 $5581 €4600 Peasant with horses (50x68cm-20x27in) s. board. 30-Jun-4 Neumeister, Munich #538/R est:3000
£3125 $5094 €4500 Horse racing (44x59cm-17x23in) s. paper on canvas. 27-Sep-3 Dr Fritz Nagel, Stuttgart #9513/R est:7500
£3333 $6100 €5000 Horses (63x74cm-25x29in) s.d.1943. 5-Jun-4 Lempertz, Koln #669/R est:5500
£3691 $6792 €5500 Two lions in the Savannah (49x59cm-19x23in) s.d.1915 lit. 25-Mar-4 Karlheinz Kaupp, Staufen #2417/R est:1500
£3953 $7075 €5850 Stable boy (46x54cm-18x21in) s. board. 8-May-4 Dawo, Saarbrucken #83/R est:6500
£4167 $6792 €6000 Lion taming in the circus (60x80cm-24x31in) s.d.1939. 27-Sep-3 Dr Fritz Nagel, Stuttgart #9512/R est:9500
£4527 $8103 €6700 At the races (40x46cm-16x18in) s. lit. 8-May-4 Schloss Ahlden, Ahlden #823/R est:6500
£4527 $8103 €6700 At the races (40x44cm-16x17in) s. lit. 8-May-4 Schloss Ahlden, Ahlden #824/R est:6500
£4577 $7919 €6500 Race horses before the start (45x53cm-18x21in) s. board. 13-Dec-3 Lempertz, Koln #127/R est:4000
£5518 $10152 €8056 Avenue (48x68cm-19x27in) s. canvas on board prov. 23-Jun-4 Koller, Zurich #3015a est:16000-22000 (S.FR 12580)
£5594 $9510 €8000 Rose garden in park (61x80cm-24x31in) s.d.1925. 20-Nov-3 Van Ham, Cologne #1541/R est:11000
£5986 $10356 €8500 Resting outside country house (70x80cm-28x31in) s.d.1943 st.sig. verso. 13-Dec-3 Lempertz, Koln #304/R est:4000
£12000 $21840 €17520 At the races (60x80cm-24x31in) s. prov. 15-Jun-4 Sotheby's, London #56/R est:10000-15000
Works on paper
£278 $453 €400 Jockey (23x32cm-9x13in) s. pencil typing paper. 27-Sep-3 Dr Fritz Nagel, Stuttgart #9087/R
£278 $453 €400 Polo player (24x35cm-9x14in) s. pencil. 27-Sep-3 Dr Fritz Nagel, Stuttgart #9088/R
£313 $509 €450 Jockey with horse (24x31cm-9x12in) s. W/C Indian ink. 27-Sep-3 Dr Fritz Nagel, Stuttgart #9085/R
£331 $603 €500 River landscape with town, seated woman in foreground (28x37cm-11x15in) s. W/C. 19-Jun-4 Hans Stahl, Hamburg #30/R
£451 $736 €650 Tiger in enclosure (28x38cm-11x15in) s. W/C Indian ink paper on board. 27-Sep-3 Dr Fritz Nagel, Stuttgart #9089/R
£464 $844 €700 Planting fruit (46x36cm-18x14in) s. i.verso W/C. 19-Jun-4 Quittenbaum, Hamburg #78/R
£621 $1148 €900 Horse's head (45x31cm-18x12in) s. W/C. 12-Feb-4 Weidler, Nurnberg #6506/R
£625 $1019 €900 Peasant in horse drawn cart (40x49cm-16x19in) s. W/C. 27-Sep-3 Dr Fritz Nagel, Stuttgart #9086/R
£634 $1014 €900 Leopard (27x39cm-11x15in) s. W/C. 18-Sep-3 Rieber, Stuttgart #1059

DILLARD, Emily (1879-1968) American
£479 $800 €699 Still life (76x61cm-30x24in) 18-Oct-3 David Dike, Dallas #88/R

DILLENS, Adolphe Alexander (1821-1877) Belgian
£350 $594 €500 Portrait de femme (22x16cm-9x6in) s. panel. 18-Nov-3 Galerie Moderne, Brussels #819/R
£2937 $4993 €4200 Le cadeau (66x52cm-26x20in) panel. 1-Dec-3 Amberes, Antwerp #297/R

DILLENS, Albert (1844-?) Belgian
£470 $864 €700 Chaumieres (24x30cm-9x12in) s. panel. 23-Mar-4 Galerie Moderne, Brussels #330

DILLENS, Hendrick Joseph (1812-1872) Belgian
£385 $642 €550 Mere et enfant (20x13cm-8x5in) s.d.68 panel. 13-Oct-3 Horta, Bruxelles #128
£1342 $2483 €2000 La conversation (28x20cm-11x8in) s.d.1849 panel. 15-Mar-4 Horta, Bruxelles #179 est:1200-1800
£2000 $3680 €2920 Group of children defending a kitten from a terrier (43x56cm-17x22in) s.d.1857 panel. 23-Mar-4 Wotton Auction Rooms, Wotton #805 est:2000-2500
£4167 $6625 €6000 Peasant family (46x61cm-18x24in) s.i.d.1856 panel. 13-Sep-3 Quittenbaum, Hamburg #17/R est:7000
£4624 $8000 €6751 Blind man's bluff (63x55cm-25x22in) s.d.1858. 13-Dec-3 Weschler, Washington #501 est:3000-5000
£9441 $15766 €13500 Trois enfants jouant au soldat (40x32cm-16x13in) s.d.1857 panel. 13-Oct-3 Horta, Bruxelles #127/R est:8000-12000
£10000 $17200 €14600 Wedding party (91x77cm-36x30in) s.indis.i.d.1850 panel. 3-Dec-3 Christie's, London #6/R est:10000-15000

DILLER, Burgoyne (1906-1965) American
£15094 $24000 €22037 First theme (61x61cm-24x24in) s.d.1964 verso masonite relief exhib.lit. 14-Sep-3 Wright, Chicago #133/R est:25000-35000
Works on paper
£2358 $3750 €3443 First theme (23x20cm-9x8in) init.d.61 graphite col pencil prov. 14-Sep-3 Wright, Chicago #132/R est:5000-7000
£2717 $5000 €3967 Two studies for wall construction (28x20cm-11x8in) col pencil. 10-Jun-4 Swann Galleries, New York #75/R est:6000-9000

DILLER, Fritz (20th C) German
Sculpture
£1007 $1872 €1500 Hunting dogs (27x45x27cm-11x18x11in) s. bronze marble socle. 6-Mar-4 Arnold, Frankfurt #385/R est:600

DILLER, Richard (1890-) ?
£267 $477 €400 Small fox (35x31cm-14x12in) s. i. verso. 13-May-4 Dorotheum, Linz #488

DILLEY, Ramon (1933-) French
Works on paper
£300 $540 €450 Amies du kech (40x23cm-16x9in) s.i. gouache exec.1993. 24-Apr-4 Cornette de St.Cyr, Paris #357/R

D'ILLIERS, Gaston (1876-1952) French
Sculpture
£1497 $2380 €2200 Dolly (26cm-10in) brown pat bronze. 23-Mar-3 St-Germain-en-Laye Encheres #94/R est:2000

DILLIS, Cantius (1779-1856) German
Works on paper
£403 $721 €600 Nosslauerthal (23x30cm-9x12in) i.d.1832 chk htd white. 25-May-4 Karl & Faber, Munich #84/R
£541 $951 €800 Cave in woodland (23x29cm-9x11in) W/C on pen double-sided prov. 22-May-4 Lempertz, Koln #1405/R

DILLIS, Johann Georg von (1759-1841) German
£6250 $10188 €9000 Kochelsee (19x25cm-7x10in) board on canvas lit. 24-Sep-3 Neumeister, Munich #416/R est:3000
£11111 $18111 €16000 Hunters in upper Bavarian landscape (51x67cm-20x26in) 24-Sep-3 Neumeister, Munich #415/R est:12000
Works on paper
£268 $481 €400 River landscape (8x7cm-3x3in) pen over pencil. 25-May-4 Karl & Faber, Munich #87
£320 $573 €480 Landscape (21x29cm-8x11in) mono.i.d.1839 pen wash. 13-May-4 Bassenge, Berlin #5542
£621 $1037 €900 Mountain landscape with bridge (32x23cm-13x9in) s. Indian ink brush. 15-Nov-3 Lempertz, Koln #1459/R
£699 $1272 €1021 River landscape (22x33cm-9x13in) black chk htd white blue paper prov.exhib. 17-Jun-4 Kornfeld, Bern #10/R (S.FR 1600)
£738 $1321 €1100 Extensive valley view (17x21cm-7x8in) sepia pen over pencil. 25-May-4 Karl & Faber, Munich #86/R
£1096 $1863 €1600 Mountainous river landscape with wooden bridge (20x26cm-8x10in) s. pen brush wash. 4-Nov-3 Hartung & Hartung, Munich #3024/R est:1000
£1208 $2223 €1800 Landscape with trees and figures near Tivoli (22x31cm-9x12in) mono.i.d.1805 pen on pencil. 26-Mar-4 Venator & Hansten, Koln #1549/R est:1500
£1310 $2384 €1913 Village street in Ebersberg (12x17cm-5x7in) i. W/C over pencil. 17-Jun-4 Kornfeld, Bern #11/R est:3000 (S.FR 3000)

DILLMANN, Hilmar (1940-) German
£265 $482 €400 Roman baths in Potsdam-Sanssouci (11x25cm-4x10in) s. panel i.verso. 19-Jun-4 Bergmann, Erlangen #850
£306 $548 €450 Paris, boulevard le soir (13x20cm-5x8in) s. i. verso panel. 20-Mar-4 Bergmann, Erlangen #1141

DILLON, Frank (1823-1909) British
Works on paper
£397 $727 €600 Arabe se reposant derriere des ruines (28x46cm-11x18in) s. W/C. 7-Apr-4 Piasa, Paris #156
£497 $909 €750 Village anime (31x48cm-12x19in) init.i. W/C htd white. 7-Apr-4 Piasa, Paris #155

DILLON, Gerard (1917-1971) Irish
£800 $1408 €1168 Burial (23x16cm-9x6in) s. oil pencil. 18-May-4 Fellows & Sons, Birmingham #85/R
£1736 $2830 €2500 Boats entering harbour (26x36cm-10x14in) s.d.44 oil paper. 23-Sep-3 De Veres Art Auctions, Dublin #167/R est:900-1200

£2113	$3380	€3000	Sand fly (48x74cm-19x29in) s. oil sand board. 16-Sep-3 Whyte's, Dublin #69/R est:3000-4000
£2254	$3606	€3200	Portrait of James Maguire in National Service uniform, Hammersmith (48x41cm-19x16in) s. board prov. 16-Sep-3 Whyte's, Dublin #25/R est:2000-3000
£4336	$7371	€6200	Lips (53x36cm-21x14in) s. oil collage board prov.exhib. 18-Nov-3 Whyte's, Dublin #73/R est:5000-7000
£12000	$21720	€18000	Bathers on the beach, Malaga (34x45cm-13x18in) s. board prov. 30-Mar-4 De Veres Art Auctions, Dublin #67/R est:20000-30000
£17500	$31325	€25550	Cat in the cane chair (35x19cm-14x7in) s. i.verso board prov. 14-May-4 Christie's, London #147/R est:12000-18000
£30726	$55000	€44860	Corpus Christi, Roundstone (41x49cm-16x19in) board prov. 6-May-4 Doyle, New York #136/R est:6000-8000
£39437	$68225	€56000	Soft hills (97x114cm-38x45in) s.i.verso board. 10-Dec-3 Bonhams & James Adam, Dublin #109/R est:40000-50000
£45000	$80550	€65700	Artist's studio, Abbey Road (65x67cm-26x26in) s.verso board. 14-May-4 Christie's, London #146/R est:25000-35000
£70000	$125300	€102200	Roundstone (46x61cm-18x24in) s. board exhib. 14-May-4 Christie's, Kensington #419/R est:40000-60000
Prints			
£2617	$4633	€3900	Family in the countryside (25x33cm-10x13in) s. monotype W/C prov. 27-Apr-4 Whyte's, Dublin #1/R est:2000-3000
Works on paper			
£389	$697	€580	Abstract studies (23x33cm-9x13in) s. W/C. 31-May-4 Hamilton Osborne King, Dublin #37/R
£400	$656	€584	Abstract (22x30cm-9x12in) mono. W/C. 4-Jun-3 John Ross, Belfast #93
£599	$1036	€850	Harvest (27x38cm-11x15in) s. mixed media. 10-Dec-3 Bonhams & James Adam, Dublin #157/R
£667	$1207	€1000	Nativity scene (15x8cm-6x3in) i.verso ink wash. 30-Mar-4 De Veres Art Auctions, Dublin #133/R
£1189	$2021	€1700	Abstract. Man in an arran sweater (10x18cm-4x7in) one s. pen wash one init. lithograph W/C two. 18-Nov-3 Whyte's, Dublin #6/R est:1500-2000
£2000	$3620	€3000	Wonder of two people (44x56cm-17x22in) mixed media prov. 31-Mar-4 James Adam, Dublin #80/R est:3000-5000
£2282	$4039	€3400	Gypsied by a fire (20x20cm-8x8in) W/C prov. 27-Apr-4 Whyte's, Dublin #5/R est:3000-4000
£2282	$4085	€3400	Wood carver (39x49cm-15x19in) s. mixed media prov. 26-May-4 James Adam, Dublin #143/R est:3000-5000
£2378	$4042	€3400	Collage Street, Dublin (27x37cm-11x15in) s. W/C exhib. 25-Nov-3 De Veres Art Auctions, Dublin #15/R est:2000-3000
£2416	$4277	€3600	Young couple standing amidst a forest (27x38cm-11x15in) s. W/C prov. 27-Apr-4 Whyte's, Dublin #7/R est:3000-4000
£2703	$5108	€4000	West of Ireland homestead with figures and animals (24x29cm-9x11in) s. W/C prov. 17-Feb-4 Whyte's, Dublin #8/R est:1500-2000
£2746	$4394	€3900	Galway farmer (17x12cm-7x5in) init. W/C artist's board exhib. 16-Sep-3 Whyte's, Dublin #27/R est:3500-4500
£3067	$5551	€4600	Weeds from deep (91x122cm-36x48in) s.i.verso mixed media. 30-Mar-4 De Veres Art Auctions, Dublin #192/R est:4000-6000
£3944	$6823	€5600	Inishlacken (24x33cm-9x13in) s. mixed media collage prov. 10-Dec-3 Bonhams & James Adam, Dublin #108/R est:5000-8000
£4167	$6792	€6000	Farmyard with chickens (37x49cm-15x19in) s.d.43 i.verso W/C. 24-Sep-3 James Adam, Dublin #145/R est:2000-3000
£7000	$12670	€10500	Wonder of two people (44x56cm-17x22in) mixed media prov. 31-Mar-4 James Adam, Dublin #79/R est:3000-5000

DIMAI, Rudolf (1899-1964) Austrian

£319	$533	€450	Still life of cherries (16x24cm-6x9in) s.d.1921 board. 16-Oct-3 Dorotheum, Salzburg #645/R

DIMAS, Manuel (1959-) Venezuelan

£952	$1733	€1400	Asterix (130x98cm-51x39in) s.verso acrylic prov.exhib. 3-Feb-4 Segre, Madrid #268/R

DINAN, John (?) ?

£567	$1026	€850	Still life (25x30cm-10x12in) s. 30-Mar-4 De Veres Art Auctions, Dublin #141/R
£1867	$3379	€2800	French scene landscape (41x51cm-16x20in) s. board. 30-Mar-4 De Veres Art Auctions, Dublin #225/R est:1500-2000

DINCKEL, George W (1890-1978) American

Works on paper			
£250	$400	€365	Bass rocks, Cape Ann (43x56cm-17x22in) s. gouache. 21-Sep-3 Grogan, Boston #85/R

DINE, Jim (1935-) American

£11377	$19000	€16610	Heart and scull one (117x85cm-46x33in) s.d.1984 oil pastel chl collage paper prov. 13-Nov-3 Sotheby's, New York #253/R est:12000-18000
£12000	$22080	€17520	Robin (152x88cm-60x35in) s.d.1980 gouache pastel chl prov. 25-Jun-4 Christie's, London #198/R est:15000-20000
£15000	$27300	€21900	In the French forest (247x130cm-97x51in) s. i.d.1991 verso prov.exhib. 6-Feb-4 Sotheby's, London #251/R est:20000-30000
£72000	$131040	€105120	Jewel (168x122cm-66x48in) s.i.d.1992 verso prov.exhib. 6-Feb-4 Sotheby's, London #233/R est:80000-120000
Prints			
£1796	$3000	€2622	To the lake (121x97cm-48x38in) s.d.1998 num.25/30 col woodcut. 21-Oct-3 Bonhams & Butterfields, San Francisco #1307/R
£1935	$3600	€2825	Red, white and blue Venus for Mondale (76x46cm-30x18in) s.num.83/150 col screenprint. 2-Mar-4 Swann Galleries, New York #164/R est:2000-3000
£1963	$3200	€2866	Robe against the desert sky (106x75cm-42x30in) s.d.1979 num.12/20 lithograph screenprint on Arches. 24-Sep-3 Christie's, Rockefeller NY #225/R est:2000-3000
£2059	$3500	€3006	Desire in primary colours (76x164cm-30x65in) col aquatint. 31-Oct-3 Sotheby's, New York #527/R
£2260	$4000	€3300	Bathrobe (91x61cm-36x24in) s.d.1975 num.40/60 col woodcut lithograph. 28-Apr-4 Christie's, Rockefeller NY #267/R est:5000-7000
£2353	$4000	€3435	Heart at the Opera (127x97cm-50x38in) s.d.1983 col lithograph. 4-Nov-3 Christie's, Rockefeller NY #230/R est:4000-6000
£2353	$4000	€3435	Yellow robe (128x89cm-50x35in) s.d.1980 col lithograph. 4-Nov-3 Christie's, Rockefeller NY #229/R est:5000-7000
£2353	$4000	€3435	Self in the Ocean (138x101cm-54x40in) s.d.1991 et aquatint. 4-Nov-3 Christie's, Rockefeller NY #232/R est:3000-4000
£2401	$4250	€3505	Viennese hearts II (88x79cm-35x31in) s.d.1990 num.37/40 hand col screenprint etching. 30-Apr-4 Sotheby's, New York #323/R est:5000-7000
£2500	$4300	€3650	Two red hearts (56x89cm-22x35in) s.d.1993 woodcut photo-engraving on two sheet. 2-Dec-3 Christie's, London #132/R est:4000-6000
£2642	$4730	€3857	Olympic robe (88x68cm-35x27in) s.d.88 num.102/300 col lithograph. 31-May-4 Stephan Welz, Johannesburg #443/R est:18000-24000 (SA.R 32000)
£2647	$4500	€3865	Two red hearts (76x109cm-30x43in) col woodcut photoengraving. 31-Oct-3 Sotheby's, New York #531/R
£2800	$4816	€4088	The world, for Diane Waldman (76x102cm-30x40in) s.i.d.1971 num.70/100 col lithograph. 4-Dec-3 Sotheby's, London #233/R est:3000-3500
£2800	$5096	€4088	Red and black diptych robe (96x75cm-38x30in) s.num.14/20 col lithograph diptych. 1-Jul-4 Sotheby's, London #359/R est:2500-3000
£2945	$4800	€4300	Heart and the Wall (227x177cm-89x70in) s.d.1983 num.28/28 etching drypoint sanding wove paper. 24-Sep-3 Christie's, Rockefeller NY #227/R est:4000-6000
£3000	$5460	€4380	Viennese hearts II (86x79cm-34x31in) s.d.1990 num.32/40 col silkscreen etching aquatint. 1-Jul-4 Sotheby's, London #363/R est:3000-4000
£3000	$5460	€4380	Viennese hearts V (85x70cm-33x28in) s.d.1990 num.32/40 col silkscreen etching aquatint. 1-Jul-4 Sotheby's, London #364/R est:3000-4000
£3107	$5500	€4536	Behind the thicket (32x54cm-13x21in) s.d.1993 num.34/75 woodcut etching soft ground. 30-Apr-4 Sotheby's, New York #324/R est:4000-6000
£3235	$5500	€4723	Woodcut self (105x84cm-41x33in) col woodcut. 31-Oct-3 Sotheby's, New York #530/R
£3672	$6500	€5361	Viennese hearts III (87x65cm-34x26in) s.d.1987-90 col hand col screenprint etching aquatint. 28-Apr-4 Christie's, Rockefeller NY #268/R est:4000-6000
£3672	$6500	€5361	Paintbrush (53x50cm-21x20in) s.d.1971 num.44/75 etching. 30-Apr-4 Sotheby's, New York #316/R est:3000-4000
£3672	$6500	€5361	Double Venus in the sky at night (99x71cm-39x28in) s.d.1984 num.12/50 col screenprint lithograph. 30-Apr-4 Sotheby's, New York #319/R est:6000-8000
£3672	$6500	€5361	Nine views of winter (133x94cm-52x37in) s.d.1985 num.8/24 hand col woodcut. 30-Apr-4 Sotheby's, New York #322/R est:4000-6000
£3824	$6500	€5583	Red etching robe (90x60cm-35x24in) s. col etching. 31-Oct-3 Sotheby's, New York #524/R
£3824	$6500	€5583	Beautiful heart (80x65cm-31x26in) s.d.1996 etching aquatint. 4-Nov-3 Christie's, Rockefeller NY #233/R est:8000-10000
£3955	$7000	€5774	Nine views of winter (133x94cm-52x37in) s.d.1985 num.12/24 black grey woodcut screenprint. 30-Apr-4 Sotheby's, New York #321/R est:3000-4000
£4000	$6880	€5840	Colourful Venus and Neptune (170x94cm-67x37in) s.d.1992 col woodcut on two sheets. 2-Dec-3 Christie's, London #133/R est:4000-6000
£4118	$7000	€6012	Two hearts in the forest (91x152cm-36x60in) s. col lithograph woodcut. 31-Oct-3 Sotheby's, New York #525/R
£4118	$7000	€6012	World (76x100cm-30x39in) s.d.1972 lithograph woodcut screenprint collage pencil. 4-Nov-3 Christie's, Rockefeller NY #226/R est:6000-9000
£4138	$6910	€6041	Lemon and moon 2000 (55x90cm-22x35in) s.i.num.4/15 woodcut hand colouring on two sheets. 20-Oct-3 Stephan Welz, Johannesburg #221/R est:20000-30000 (SA.R 48000)
£4200	$7644	€6132	Five paintbrushes (52x69cm-20x27in) s.d.1973 num.27/28 etching. 1-Jul-4 Sotheby's, London #361/R est:2500-3500
£4237	$7500	€6186	Tools and dreams (59x98cm-23x39in) s.d.1985 num.23/50 drypoint aquatint. 30-Apr-4 Sotheby's, New York #320/R est:3000-5000
£4412	$7500	€6442	LA eye works (128x110cm-50x43in) col etching aquatint carborundum. 31-Oct-3 Sotheby's, New York #526/R
£4412	$7500	€6442	Two Danish red robes (75x120cm-30x47in) col aquatint drypoint. 31-Oct-3 Sotheby's, New York #529/R
£4706	$8000	€6871	Six hearts (79x57cm-31x22in) s.i. col lithograph collage. 31-Oct-3 Sotheby's, New York #522/R
£5000	$8500	€7300	Hand painting (126x102cm-50x40in) s.d.1986 engraving. 4-Nov-3 Christie's, Rockefeller NY #231/R est:10000-15000
£5000	$8500	€7300	Woodcut bathrobe (91x61cm-36x24in) s.d.1975 col lithograph woodcut. 4-Nov-3 Christie's, Rockefeller NY #228/R est:5000-7000
£5294	$9000	€7729	Five paintbrushes (75x90cm-30x35in) s.d.1973 etching. 4-Nov-3 Christie's, Rockefeller NY #227/R est:5000-8000
£5588	$9500	€8158	Handkerchief (69x56cm-27x22in) col woodcut etching. 31-Oct-3 Sotheby's, New York #532/R
£5594	$9621	€8000	Yellow watercolours (146x106cm-57x42in) s.d.1993 num.12/24 hand col woodcut prov. 3-Dec-3 Sotheby's, Amsterdam #383/R est:7000-9000
£5650	$10000	€8249	Heart called Paris spring (59x49cm-23x19in) s.d.1982 num.52/90 col etching. 30-Apr-4 Sotheby's, New York #317/R est:8000-12000
£5650	$10000	€8249	Kindergarten (152x187cm-60x74in) s.d.1983 num.44/75 col woodcut. 30-Apr-4 Sotheby's, New York #318/R est:8000-12000
£6200	$11284	€9052	Kindergarten robes (139x91cm-55x36in) s.i. col woodcut edition of 75. 1-Jul-4 Sotheby's, London #366/R est:4000-6000
£10588	$18000	€15458	Dutch hearts (41x51cm-16x20in) col lithograph album. 31-Oct-3 Sotheby's, New York #521/R
Sculpture			
£23952	$40000	€34970	Walla Walla Robe (116x93x6cm-46x37x2in) sig.i. d.1984 num.2/6 verso wall relief painted bronze prov. 12-Nov-3 Christie's, Rockefeller NY #404/R est:60000-80000
Works on paper			
£1227	$2000	€1791	Basil in black leather (44x29cm-17x11in) s. ink crayon on transparency over lithograph. 23-Sep-3 Christie's, Rockefeller NY #48/R est:1000-1500
£3243	$6000	€4735	Seattle Family - Connie (128x69cm-50x27in) s.d.1996 chl pastel enamel graphite prov. 12-Feb-4 Sotheby's, New York #324/R est:5000-7000
£3352	$6000	€4894	Two boots above a landscape. s.i. W/C. 13-May-4 Dallas Auction Gallery, Dallas #241/R est:6000-8000
£10180	$17000	€14863	Crommelynk gate, red grease (120x158cm-47x62in) s.d.1984 chl oil stick pastel prov. 13-Nov-3 Sotheby's, New York #252/R est:18000-25000
£11000	$18370	€16060	Coming home hearts for N 1 (47x58cm-19x23in) s.i.d.1969 W/C. 21-Oct-3 Sotheby's, London #351/R est:4000-6000
£12587	$21021	€18000	Grey palette (160x97cm-63x38in) s.i.d.1963 verso pastel chl gouache. 11-Oct-3 Cornette de St.Cyr, Paris #112/R est:18000-22000
£13265	$23745	€19500	Chelsea-Anthurin (84x63cm-33x25in) s.d.91 mixed media prov.exhib. 22-Mar-4 Digard, Paris #124/R est:16000-26000
£40000	$74000	€60000	Study for Four Continents (122x107cm-48x42in) chl oil gouache paper set of 4 prov.exhib. 18-Jul-4 Sotheby's, Paris #234/R est:60000-80000

DINET, Étienne (1861-1929) French

£3000	$5490	€4500	Cavalier a Mehari (19x16cm-7x6in) cardboard prov. 3-Jun-4 Tajan, Paris #224/R est:4500-5500
£3472	$5486	€5000	Etude pour un guerrier arbe. s. cardboard. 25-Apr-3 Etude de Provence, Marseille #233 est:4500-5000
£5745	$9594	€8100	Caravane a El Grara, pres de Ghardaia (26x35cm-10x14in) s.i. panel painted c.1891. 20-Jun-3 Drouot Estimations, Paris #34 est:6000-7500
£11620	$20102	€16500	Chasseur a l'affut (33x41cm-13x16in) s. cardboard. 15-Dec-3 Gros & Delettrez, Paris #281/R est:10000-12000
£16000	$27520	€23360	Berbers at an oasis well (81x57cm-32x22in) s. 3-Dec-3 Christie's, London #97/R est:20000-30000

£26667 $48801 €40000 Jeune danseuse au voile vert (58x68cm-23x27in) s.d.1908. 3-Jun-4 Tajan, Paris #273/R est:25000-35000
£29655 $49228 €43000 Portrait de Jeanne Dinet (154x123cm-61x48in) s.d.1883 exhib.lit. 2-Oct-3 Sotheby's, Paris #116/R est:45000
£59859 $103556 €85000 Sous les lauriers roses (63x82cm-25x32in) s. prov.exhib.lit. 14-Dec-3 St-Germain-en-Laye Encheres #50/R est:70000-75000
£80000 $147200 €120000 Jeunes Berbers etendant le linge en bord de riviere (100x80cm-39x31in) s. lit. 11-Jun-4 Claude Aguttes, Neuilly #141/R est:100000-120000
Works on paper
£317 $548 €450 Chien de chasse (12x18cm-5x7in) s. W/C. 15-Dec-3 Gros & Delettrez, Paris #278
£1208 $2247 €1800 Portrait de jeune garcon (14x10cm-6x4in) s. W/C graphite. 2-Mar-4 Artcurial Briest, Paris #48/R est:2000-2500
£1268 $2193 €1800 Etude de pieds (13x13cm-5x5in) gouache graphite. 15-Dec-3 Gros & Delettrez, Paris #280/R est:1200-1800
£1549 $2680 €2200 Etude de genoux (20x14cm-8x6in) gouache graphite. 15-Dec-3 Gros & Delettrez, Paris #276/R est:1200-1800
£1761 $3046 €2500 Etude de mains (11x19cm-4x7in) gouache graphite. 15-Dec-3 Gros & Delettrez, Paris #277/R est:1200-2000
£2113 $3655 €3000 Etude de bras (11x11cm-4x4in) gouache graphite lit. 15-Dec-3 Gros & Delettrez, Paris #279/R est:1200-2000
£2639 $4169 €3800 Paysage Orientaliste. s. W/C. 25-Apr-3 Etude de Provence, Marseille #281 est:3800-4200
£3750 $6262 €5400 Jeune femme Orientale (32x25cm-13x10in) ink W/C htd gouache. 23-Oct-3 Credit Municipal, Paris #55/R est:2500-3000

DINET, Étienne (attrib) (1861-1929) French
Works on paper
£915 $1520 €1300 Paysage au mur et palmiers (14x25cm-6x10in) s.i.d.1919 W/C. 16-Jun-3 E & Eve, Paris #177

DINETTO, Lino (1927-) South American
£1412 $2400 €2062 Ladies on the beach (74x93cm-29x37in) s. 25-Nov-3 Galeria y Remates, Montevideo #90/R
£1941 $3300 €2834 Figure (130x96cm-51x38in) s. lit. 25-Nov-3 Galeria y Remates, Montevideo #89/R

DING GUANPENG (fl.1742-1754) Chinese
Works on paper
£4247 $7093 €6201 Street hawker (40x24cm-16x9in) s. ink col. 26-Oct-3 Christie's, Hong Kong #449/R (HK.D 55000)

DING YANYONG (1902-1978) Chinese
£18533 $30950 €27058 Fish in a jar (45x31cm-18x12in) s.d.April 10 1971 board prov. 27-Oct-3 Sotheby's, Hong Kong #365/R est:50000-70000 (HK.D 240000)
£29872 $53770 €43613 Portrait of an artist. Portrait of a lady (61x45cm-24x18in) one s.d.1965 one s.d.1967 canvas on board double-sided exhib.lit. 26-Apr-4 Sotheby's, Hong Kong #523/R est:300000-400000 (HK.D 420000)
Works on paper
£559 $962 €800 A burning candle with a rat sitting on the candle holder (34x42cm-13x17in) s.d.1971 ink. 5-Dec-3 Lempertz, Koln #259/R
£640 $1152 €934 Figures (46x34cm-18x13in) s.d.1973 ink col scroll. 25-Apr-4 Christie's, Hong Kong #8/R est:10000-12000 (HK.D 9000)
£2703 $4514 €3946 Flowers and birds (149x63cm-59x25in) s.d.1971 ink hanging scroll. 26-Oct-3 Christie's, Hong Kong #211/R est:40000-50000 (HK.D 35000)
£3707 $6190 €5412 Eagle (138x61cm-54x24in) s.i.d.1975 ink col hanging scroll. 26-Oct-3 Christie's, Hong Kong #247/R est:50000-60000 (HK.D 48000)

DING YUNPENG (fl.1584-1638) Chinese
£2148 $3844 €3200 Landscape. s.d.1600 paint. 27-May-4 Beaussant & Lefevre, Paris #267/R est:3500-4000

DING, Henri Marius (1844-1898) French
Sculpture
£1103 $2041 €1600 La confidence (44cm-17in) s.d.1882 brown pat bronze. 16-Feb-4 Horta, Bruxelles #127 est:1500-2000

DINGEMANS, Jan (1921-2001) South African
£342 $581 €499 Group of Congolese women on a hillside (35x60cm-14x24in) s. board. 4-Nov-3 Stephan Welz, Johannesburg #637 est:3000-4000 (SA.R 4000)
£454 $813 €663 Congolese women in a landscape (30x60cm-12x24in) s. board. 31-May-4 Stephan Welz, Johannesburg #358 (SA.R 5500)

DINGEMANS, Waalko Jans (jnr) (1901-1991) Dutch
£362 $655 €550 Blaricum (48x58cm-19x23in) s.d.1940 i.verso. 19-Apr-4 Glerum, Amsterdam #174

DINGER, Otto (1860-?) German
£2639 $4486 €3800 Resting during work in the fields (37x63cm-15x25in) s. i. verso board. 28-Oct-3 Dorotheum, Vienna #39/R est:4000-4600

DINGLE, Adrian (1911-1974) Canadian
£227 $370 €331 Sand painter (61x46cm-24x18in) s. masonite. 23-Sep-3 Ritchie, Toronto #123/R (C.D 500)
£455 $823 €664 Farm in the foothills (41x51cm-16x20in) s. hard board prov. 18-Apr-4 Levis, Calgary #29/R est:800-1000 (C.D 1100)
£579 $1053 €845 Early Catch, Ingonish, Cape Breton Island (44x76cm-17x30in) s. prov. board. 5-Feb-4 Heffel, Vancouver #24/R (C.D 1400)

DINGLE, Edward von Siebold (20th C) American
Works on paper
£471 $800 €688 Cardinal (51x37cm-20x15in) s. gouache prov. 21-Nov-3 Skinner, Boston #344/R

DINGLE, Kim (1951-) American?
£5028 $9000 €7341 Wild girls rabbit puppet (183x152cm-72x60in) s.i.d.1993 verso oil linen prov. 12-May-4 Christie's, Rockefeller NY #481/R est:10000-15000

DINGLE, Thomas (jnr) (19th C) British
£620 $1035 €905 Evening (29x44cm-11x17in) s. 16-Oct-3 Lawrence, Crewkerne #742/R

DINGLI, Robert Caruana (attrib) (1881-1940) Maltese
Works on paper
£2600 $4316 €3796 View of steps and buildings in Mediterranean town, possibly Malta (23x28cm-9x11in) s. W/C. 10-Jun-3 Canterbury Auctions, UK #140 est:100-150

DINGLINGER, Georg Friedrich (1666-1720) German
Miniatures
£1800 $3114 €2628 Augustus the Strong, King of Poland (3cm-1in) on copper oval. 9-Dec-3 Christie's, London #13 est:1000-1500

DINKLAGE, Erna (1895-?) German
£7333 $13127 €11000 Fasching (65x50cm-26x20in) s. panel triptych. 13-May-4 Neumeister, Munich #332/R est:14000-18000

DINNERSTEIN, Harvey (1928-) American
£326 $600 €476 Portrait of a young woman (48x33cm-19x13in) s. oval. 25-Jun-4 Freeman, Philadelphia #239/R
£761 $1400 €1111 Reclining nude (36x64cm-14x25in) s.d.1966 prov. 25-Jun-4 Freeman, Philadelphia #218/R est:600-1000
£2245 $3750 €3278 Clinton Square, Newburgh, New York (41x51cm-16x20in) s. exhib. 23-Oct-3 Shannon's, Milford #11/R est:1200-1800
Works on paper
£924 $1700 €1349 Seated female nude (43x30cm-17x12in) s.d.1966 pastel prov. 25-Jun-4 Freeman, Philadelphia #91/R est:250-400
£1257 $2200 €1835 The Fight Part I - The Dead are dying of thirst - George Foreman (60x62cm-24x24in) s. pastel ink wash board exec May 1975. 17-Dec-3 Christie's, Rockefeller NY #215/R est:1200-1800
£2286 $4000 €3338 The fight part I - the Dead are dying of thirst - Mohammed Ali (51x40cm-20x16in) s.verso pastel ink wash board exec May 1975. 17-Dec-3 Christie's, Rockefeller NY #216/R est:1200-1800

DINSDALE, John Bentham (19th C) British
£540 $967 €788 U.S.S. Constitution (21x26cm-8x10in) s. panel. 17-Mar-4 Bonhams, Chester #374
£600 $1074 €876 Kaisow (21x26cm-8x10in) s. panel. 17-Mar-4 Bonhams, Chester #376
£680 $1217 €993 Norris at full sail (21x26cm-8x10in) s. panel. 17-Mar-4 Bonhams, Chester #375
£720 $1289 €1051 Loss of the Packet - Townsend - during the Anglo-American War (21x26cm-8x10in) s. panel painted 1812. 17-Mar-4 Bonhams, Chester #377
£1000 $1840 €1460 Nightingale (75x100cm-30x39in) s. s.i.verso. 8-Jun-4 Bonhams, Knightsbridge #353/R est:1000-1500
£1100 $1969 €1606 Indefatigable and Amazon (76x101cm-30x40in) s. i.verso. 17-Mar-4 Bonhams, Chester #378 est:900-1200
£1700 $2890 €2482 Engagement (76x102cm-30x40in) s. 19-Nov-3 Christie's, Kensington #588/R
£1800 $2988 €2628 Skirmish (71x91cm-28x36in) s.i.verso. 1-Oct-3 Bonhams, Knightsbridge #116/R est:2000-3000

DIODATI, Francesco Paolo (1864-?) Italian
£2465 $4092 €3500 Vita al paese (103x106cm-41x42in) s.d.1897. 11-Jun-3 Christie's, Rome #194/R est:3300-3800

DIOMEDE, Miguel (1902-1974) Argentinian
£2541 $4600 €3710 White jug (22x27cm-9x11in) canvas on cardboard. 30-Mar-4 Arroyo, Buenos Aires #97
£3956 $7200 €5776 Perdrix (40x30cm-16x12in) i.d.1969 verso canvas on cardboard. 29-Jun-4 Arroyo, Buenos Aires #64/R est:6500
£3978 $7200 €5808 Oranges (41x37cm-16x15in) board. 30-Mar-4 Arroyo, Buenos Aires #63

DION, Mark (1961-) American
Sculpture
£934 $1700 €1364 Coke, hamburger with fries (104cm-41in) tar glass place met table three pieces. 29-Jun-4 Sotheby's, New York #618/R est:2000-3000

DIORIA, V O (19th C) Italian
£2113 $3655 €3000 Fishermen in the bay (60x119cm-24x47in) s. 10-Dec-3 Sotheby's, Milan #15/R est:3000-5000

DIPINJE, Carlo Talcini (19th C) Italian
£2800 $4396 €4060 Madonna della sedia (76x76cm-30x30in) s.i.d.1838 verso panel after Raphael. 28-Aug-3 Christie's, Kensington #1/R est:1800-2200

DIRCKINCK-HOLMFELD, Helmuth (1835-1912) Danish
£15294 $26000 €22329 Ludvig Dahl's children playing in Kongens Have Park (82x137cm-32x54in) s.d.1883 prov. 29-Oct-3 Christie's, Rockefeller NY #27/R est:30000-40000

DIRCKX, Anton (1878-1927) Dutch

£345 $576 €500 Ships on the River Dordrecht (48x73cm-19x29in) s. 11-Nov-3 Vendu Notarishuis, Rotterdam #30
£570 $1055 €850 Moored boats, Rotterdam (40x60cm-16x24in) s.d.19. 15-Mar-4 Sotheby's, Amsterdam #129/R est:800-1200

DIRIKS, Edvard Karl (1855-1930) Norwegian

£238 $438 €347 After dinner rest (54x46cm-21x18in) s. panel. 29-Mar-4 Blomqvist, Lysaker #1049 (N.KR 3000)
£333 $613 €486 Wooded landscape in winter (25x35cm-10x14in) s. panel. 29-Mar-4 Blomqvist, Lysaker #1046 (N.KR 4200)
£363 $602 €526 House and figures by water (27x34cm-11x13in) s. panel. 16-Jun-3 Blomqvist, Lysaker #1022/R (N.KR 4200)
£383 $662 €559 From Lofoten (44x53cm-17x21in) s. 13-Dec-3 Blomqvist, Lysaker #1065 (N.KR 4400)
£397 $730 €580 Seamstress (55x46cm-22x18in) s. 29-Mar-4 Blomqvist, Lysaker #1048 (N.KR 5000)
£565 $978 €825 Landscape (73x54cm-29x21in) s. 13-Dec-3 Blomqvist, Lysaker #1066/R (N.KR 6500)
£601 $1052 €877 Chickens in France (55x46cm-22x18in) s.d.1914 i.verso. 16-Dec-3 Grev Wedels Plass, Oslo #148/R (N.KR 7000)
£804 $1471 €1174 French landscape (46x55cm-18x22in) s. 2-Feb-4 Blomqvist, Lysaker #1047/R (N.KR 10000)
£872 $1605 €1273 Regatta (240x148cm-94x58in) s. 29-Mar-4 Blomqvist, Lysaker #1050 (N.KR 11000)
£1549 $2494 €2262 Winter's day in Drobak (60x73cm-24x29in) s. 25-Aug-3 Blomqvist, Lysaker #1040/R est:20000-25000 (N.KR 18000)

DIRKS, Andreas (1866-1922) German

£486 $802 €700 Peasant crofts by canal in Friesland (91x122cm-36x48in) s. 3-Jul-3 Van Ham, Cologne #1146/R
£600 $1080 €900 Sailing ship (50x66cm-20x26in) s. 26-Apr-4 Rieber, Stuttgart #1189/R
£1267 $2267 €1900 Fishing boats on beach (85x138cm-33x54in) s. lit. 14-May-4 Schloss Ahlden, Ahlden #2921/R est:1400

DIRKX, Piet (1953-) Dutch?

Works on paper
£2029 $3328 €2800 Dame Blanche, Astoria Palace (200x55cm-79x22in) s.i.d.1974-1995 verso ecaustic panel prov. 27-May-3 Sotheby's, Amsterdam #572/R est:1000-1500

DISCART, Jean (19th C) French

£45000 $81900 €65700 L'aiguiseur (64x48cm-25x19in) s.i. panel. 17-Jun-4 Christie's, London #101/R est:50000-70000

DISCEPOLI, Giovanni Battista (1590-1660) Italian

£34899 $65262 €52000 Saint Thomas incredulous (87x105cm-34x41in) exhib.lit. 29-Feb-4 Finarte, Venice #30/R est:65000-69000

DISCEPOLI, Giovanni Battista (attrib) (1590-1660) Italian

Works on paper
£510 $913 €750 Le sacrifice d'Isaac (31x19cm-12x7in) bears sig. mono. graphite htd white. 17-Mar-4 Maigret, Paris #50

DISCHLER, Hermann (1866-1935) German

£775 $1239 €1100 Evening (30x38cm-12x15in) s.d.1920 board lit. 19-Sep-3 Karlheinz Kaupp, Staufen #1941/R
£993 $1609 €1400 Autumn track (27x40cm-11x16in) mono. lit. 23-May-3 Karlheinz Kaupp, Staufen #1775/R
£1087 $1989 €1587 Country house in the Black Forest with a peasant and geese (33x40cm-13x16in) s.d.1918. 4-Jun-4 Zofingen, Switzerland #2445 est:1500 (S.FR 2500)
£1509 $2700 €2203 Farmstead, Hinterzarten (23x40cm-9x16in) s.d.18 canvas on board. 12-May-4 Dobiaschofsky, Bern #451/R est:2700 (S.FR 3500)

DISCOVOLO, Antonio (1874-1956) Italian

£3020 $5648 €4500 Nun (55x45cm-22x18in) board. 26-Feb-4 Cambi, Genoa #467/R est:3000-4000

DISDERI, Andre Adolphe Eugène (1819-1889) French

Photographs
£10490 $17518 €15000 Portraits de musiciens et peintres. photograph album. 10-Oct-3 Tajan, Paris #50/R est:18000-20000

DISEN, Andreas (1845-1923) Norwegian

£504 $873 €736 High mountains (9x14cm-4x6in) s. panel. 13-Dec-3 Blomqvist, Lysaker #1069 (N.KR 5800)
£688 $1150 €1004 Cabin in the woods (33x48cm-13x19in) s. 20-Oct-3 Blomqvist, Lysaker #1060/R (N.KR 8000)
£732 $1346 €1098 Mountain landscape with pine trees at sunrise (20x27cm-8x11in) s. 14-Jun-4 Blomqvist, Lysaker #1072/R (N.KR 9000)

DISLER, Martin (1949-1996) Swiss

£3379 $5946 €5000 Untitled (203x190cm-80x75in) s.d.1983 acrylic prov. 18-May-4 Tajan, Paris #124/R est:6000-8000
£3493 $6253 €5100 Triptych (90x64cm-35x25in) s.d.1979/80 verso exhib. 26-May-4 Sotheby's, Zurich #152/R est:8000-15000 (S.FR 8000)
£4299 $7308 €6277 Untitled (160x205cm-63x81in) acrylic spray pavatex exhib. 25-Nov-3 Germann, Zurich #109/R est:7000-9000 (S.FR 9500)
£4977 $8462 €7266 Untitled (96x126cm-38x50in) s.d.1982 acrylic chl gouache. 25-Nov-3 Germann, Zurich #25/R est:5000-7000 (S.FR 11000)
£5944 $10105 €8500 Untitled (153x400cm-60x157in) acrylic gouache paper on canvas. 26-Nov-3 Dorotheum, Vienna #91/R est:11000-17000
£6114 $11249 €8926 Untitled (248x208cm-98x82in) s.d.1989 verso prov. 8-Jun-4 Germann, Zurich #4/R est:15000-20000 (S.FR 14000)
£6114 $11249 €8926 Untitled (161x249cm-63x98in) s.d.1982 acrylic prov. 8-Jun-4 Germann, Zurich #25/R est:10000-15000 (S.FR 14000)

Works on paper
£452 $769 €660 Composition (57x46cm-22x18in) s.i.d.1971 Indian ink col pen. 28-Nov-3 Zofingen, Switzerland #2964/R (S.FR 1000)
£468 $767 €650 Untitled (32x24cm-13x9in) s.d. Indian ink W/C. 4-Jun-3 Ketterer, Hamburg #315/R
£541 $952 €800 Untitled (50x70cm-20x28in) s.d.1984 W/C prov. 18-May-4 Tajan, Paris #126/R
£543 $923 €793 Untitled (32x24cm-13x9in) s.d.1982 gouache. 25-Nov-3 Germann, Zurich #769 (S.FR 1200)
£588 $982 €858 Untitled (76x56cm-30x22in) s.d.1983 gouache. 24-Jun-3 Germann, Zurich #100/R (S.FR 1300)
£633 $1058 €924 Untitled (70x50cm-28x20in) s.d.1985. 24-Jun-3 Germann, Zurich #99/R (S.FR 1400)
£769 $1285 €1123 Untitled (56x75cm-22x30in) s.d.1983 gouache. 24-Jun-3 Germann, Zurich #939 est:1500-2000 (S.FR 1700)
£933 $1671 €1400 Composition (89x59cm-35x23in) s.d. W/C oil crayon prov. 14-May-4 Ketterer, Munich #305/R est:1000-1500
£995 $1662 €1453 Composition (110x84cm-43x33in) s.d.1986 gouache. 24-Jun-3 Germann, Zurich #938 est:2200-2600 (S.FR 2200)
£1048 $1928 €1530 Untitled (69x49cm-27x19in) s.d. gouache. 8-Jun-4 Germann, Zurich #785 est:2000-3000 (S.FR 2400)
£1223 $2250 €1786 Untitled (76x56cm-30x22in) s.d.1982 chl gouache. 8-Jun-4 Germann, Zurich #784 est:2800-3200 (S.FR 2800)
£1486 $2616 €2200 Untitled (100x70cm-39x28in) s.d.1983 gouache prov. 18-May-4 Tajan, Paris #125/R est:800-1000

DISMORR, Jessica (1885-1939) British

£700 $1169 €1022 Portrait of a lady, with a red scarf (51x38cm-20x15in) 16-Oct-3 Christie's, Kensington #587/R
£850 $1420 €1241 Interior (61x47cm-24x19in) board. 16-Oct-3 Christie's, Kensington #590/R
£1300 $2171 €1898 Portrait of a young lady (62x47cm-24x19in) board. 16-Oct-3 Christie's, Kensington #588/R est:400-600
£2200 $3674 €3212 Portrait of a young girl (76x61cm-30x24in) 16-Oct-3 Christie's, Kensington #589/R est:1000-1500

DITSCHEINER, Adolf (1846-1904) Austrian

£3125 $5313 €4500 Melk on the Donau (34x58cm-13x23in) s.d.1901. 28-Oct-3 Dorotheum, Vienna #182/R est:2400-2600

DITSCHER, Otto (1903-?) Austrian?

£282 $487 €400 Still life of flowers (60x40cm-24x16in) panel. 12-Dec-3 Berlinghof, Heidelberg #1160/R

DITTEN, Bertha von (?) Norwegian

£648 $1075 €940 Mountain village, possibly Vaagaa (61x79cm-24x31in) s. 16-Jun-3 Blomqvist, Lysaker #1025 (N.KR 7500)

DITTEN, Johannes van (1848-1924) Norwegian

£341 $545 €494 Drying hay (35x51cm-14x20in) s. 22-Sep-3 Blomqvist, Lysaker #1036/R (N.KR 4000)
£358 $572 €519 From Svolvaer (35x51cm-14x20in) s. 22-Sep-3 Blomqvist, Lysaker #1037 (N.KR 4200)
£648 $1075 €940 From Lofoten (32x52cm-13x20in) mono. 16-Jun-3 Blomqvist, Lysaker #1307/R (N.KR 7500)
£2563 $4100 €3742 Mountain landscape with harbour (13x18cm-5x7in) s.d.1893 prov. 21-Sep-3 William Jenack, New York #139 est:2500-4000

DITTLINGER, Marinus Bonifacius Willem (1864-1943) Dutch

£651 $1106 €950 Still life with roquefort (24x32cm-9x13in) init. 5-Nov-3 Vendue Huis, Gravenhage #325/R

DITTMANN, Bruno (1870-?) German

£285 $510 €416 Rounding up the flock (58x77cm-23x30in) s. canvasboard. 18-Mar-4 Christie's, Kensington #567

DITZLER, Anton (1811-1845) German

£2667 $4853 €4000 Rhine panorama, near Nonnenwerth (10x56cm-4x22in) s. i.verso board. 1-Jul-4 Van Ham, Cologne #1302 est:400

DIULGHEROFF, Nicolas (1901-1982) Italian/Bulgarian

£915 $1520 €1300 Sinfonia Astrale (26x40cm-10x16in) s. 14-Jun-3 Meeting Art, Vercelli #74/R
£1611 $2883 €2400 Untitled (38x56cm-15x22in) s. tempera card on canvas painted 1973. 28-May-4 Farsetti, Prato #69/R est:2100-2400

Works on paper
£364 $663 €550 Composition (5x17cm-2x7in) s.d.1928 gouache. 17-Jun-4 Galleria Pananti, Florence #433/R
£1014 $1784 €1500 Untitled (40x40cm-16x16in) s. s.i.d.1974 verso collage card prov. 24-May-4 Christie's, Milan #70/R est:1800-2500

DIVITA, Frank (?) American

Sculpture
£1706 $2900 €2491 Graceful descent (43cm-17in) bronze. 1-Nov-3 Altermann Galleries, Santa Fe #180

DIX, Otto (1891-1969) German

£8865 $14362 €12500 Paul Andre Duerr (36x28cm-14x11in) mono.d.46 panel lit. 23-May-3 Karlheinz Kaupp, Staufen #2051/R est:12500
£44521 $75685 €65000 Hegau landscape (70x100cm-28x39in) mono.d.44 canvas on masonite. 8-Nov-3 Geble, Radolfzell #774/R est:65000
£50000 $91000 €73000 Strasse der bordelle - the street of brothels (55x57cm-22x22in) s.d.1914 oil paper on board prov.exhib.lit. 4-Feb-4 Sotheby's, London #268/R est:50000-70000

£77181	$138154	€115000	Moon over street (65x47cm-26x19in) s. paper. 25-May-4 Karl & Faber, Munich #261/R est:140000-160000
£101399	$174406	€145000	Forest in the evening (100x75cm-39x30in) mono.d.1940 oil plywood prov.exhib. 5-Dec-3 Ketterer, Munich #96/R est:150000-250000

Prints

£1899	$3400	€2773	Lustmord I (27x35cm-11x14in) s.i. num.39/50 drypoint. 6-May-4 Swann Galleries, New York #455/R est:3000-5000
£1958	$3329	€2800	Sex murder (28x35cm-11x14in) s. etching drypoint prov. 29-Nov-3 Villa Grisebach, Berlin #186/R est:3000-5000
£2183	$3974	€3187	Frau Otto Mueller. s.i. lithograph. 17-Jun-4 Kornfeld, Bern #318/R est:4000 (S.FR 5000)
£2200	$4004	€3212	Amerikanischer reitakt (44x36cm-17x14in) s.i.num.48/50 tone drypoint. 1-Jul-4 Sotheby's, London #166 est:2500-3000
£2267	$4171	€3400	Technical personnel (30x20cm-12x8in) s.i drypoint etching. 10-Jun-4 Hauswedell & Nolte, Hamburg #146/R est:4500
£2333	$4293	€3500	International riding act (40x29cm-16x11in) s.i.d.1922 drypoint etching. 10-Jun-4 Hauswedell & Nolte, Hamburg #145/R est:5000
£2333	$4293	€3500	Church yard in Dresden (47x64cm-19x25in) s.i.d.1955 col lithograph. 12-Jun-4 Villa Grisebach, Berlin #331/R est:4000-5000
£2416	$4446	€3600	Bodensee landscape - with swans (48x65cm-19x26in) s.i.d. lithograph. 26-Mar-4 Ketterer, Hamburg #377/R est:2500-3000
£2600	$4784	€3900	Sketch (39x29cm-15x11in) s. drypoint exec. 1922 one of 50. 11-Jun-4 Villa Grisebach, Berlin #1567/R est:3000-5000
£2667	$4800	€4000	Roman woman (57x36cm-22x14in) s.i.d. col lithograph. 24-Apr-4 Dr Lehr, Berlin #98/R est:5000
£2667	$4907	€4000	Saul and David (55x44cm-22x17in) s.i.d.1958 col lithograph. 10-Jun-4 Hauswedell & Nolte, Hamburg #157/R est:6000
£2797	$4811	€4000	Soldier in Brussels (29x20cm-11x8in) s.i. etching. 2-Dec-3 Hauswedell & Nolte, Hamburg #142/R est:3000
£2800	$5152	€4200	Dresden church (48x66cm-19x26in) s.i.d.1955 col lithograph. 10-Jun-4 Hauswedell & Nolte, Hamburg #155/R est:3000
£2933	$5397	€4400	Saul and David (55x44cm-22x17in) s.i.d.1958 col lithograph one of 76. 12-Jun-4 Villa Grisebach, Berlin #330/R est:4000-6000
£3217	$5469	€4600	Cat (39x51cm-15x20in) s.d. col lithograph. 26-Nov-3 Lempertz, Koln #650/R est:5000
£3333	$6000	€5000	Bettina with flowers (63x47cm-25x19in) s.d.1953 col lithograph. 26-Apr-4 Rieber, Stuttgart #4444/R est:12800
£3636	$6255	€5200	Lake in autumn (47x63cm-19x25in) s.i. col lithograph. 2-Dec-3 Hauswedell & Nolte, Hamburg #148/R est:6000
£3691	$6607	€5500	Red haired girl (53x44cm-21x17in) s.i.d. col lithograph. 25-May-4 Karl & Faber, Munich #262/R est:8000-10000
£3846	$6538	€5500	Cockerel in front of barn (71x51cm-28x20in) s.i.d. col lithograph. 29-Nov-3 Bassenge, Berlin #6683/R est:7000
£4000	$7320	€6000	Cat and cockerel (43x62cm-17x24in) s.d. col lithograph. 5-Jun-4 Lempertz, Koln #676/R est:6000-7000
£4196	$7217	€6000	Crime of passion (28x35cm-11x14in) s.i.d.1922 drypoint etching. 2-Dec-3 Hauswedell & Nolte, Hamburg #141/R est:8000
£4452	$7568	€6500	Cat and hen (57x75cm-22x30in) s.i.d.1966 col lithograph. 8-Nov-3 Geble, Radolfzell #858/R est:6500
£4514	$7448	€6500	Saul and David (55x44cm-22x17in) s.i.d.58 col lithograph lit. 5-Jul-3 Geble, Radolfzell #523/R est:4500
£5245	$8759	€7500	Schloss Randegg (15x20cm-6x8in) s.i.d. drypoint etching. 10-Oct-3 Winterberg, Heidelberg #1143/R est:9200
£5963	$9959	€8646	Apotheosis. s.d.1919 woodcut. 19-Jun-3 Kornfeld, Bern #324/R est:8000 (S.FR 13000)
£6667	$12267	€10000	Crime of passion (30x26cm-12x10in) s.i. etching. 10-Jun-4 Hauswedell & Nolte, Hamburg #144/R est:12000
£13333	$24533	€20000	Leonie (48x37cm-19x15in) s.i.d.1923 col lithograph one of 65 prov. 11-Jun-4 Villa Grisebach, Berlin #38/R est:20000-25000
£14667	$26987	€22000	Matchmaker (48x36cm-19x14in) s.d.1923 col lithograph one of 65 prov. 11-Jun-4 Villa Grisebach, Berlin #40/R est:22000-24000

Works on paper

£524	$902	€750	Portrait of a man (23x20cm-9x8in) s.d.1919 crayon. 5-Dec-3 Maigret, Paris #52
£839	$1401	€1200	Portrait of a girl (56x42cm-22x17in) s.d.27 pencil prov. 11-Oct-3 De Vuyst, Lokeren #129
£839	$1427	€1200	High mountains (37x51cm-15x20in) mono.d.42 i. verso pencil. 29-Nov-3 Villa Grisebach, Berlin #532/R est:2000-3000
£1379	$2524	€2000	Sweet foreplay (30x21cm-12x8in) pencil ink prov. 27-Jan-4 Dorotheum, Vienna #176/R est.2000-2200
£1745	$3211	€2600	Olevano (26x40cm-10x16in) s.d. pencil. 26-Mar-4 Ketterer, Hamburg #375/R est:2600-3000
£2000	$3680	€3000	Male nude, rear view (53x39cm-21x15in) s.d.1913 chl white chk prov.exhib.lit. 12-Jun-4 Villa Grisebach, Berlin #249/R est:3000-4000
£2667	$4907	€4000	Erna II (52x44cm-20x17in) mono.d.1932 silver pen. 10-Jun-4 Hauswedell & Nolte, Hamburg #142/R est:6000
£2740	$4658	€4000	Bodensee landscape near Langenargen (42x54cm-17x21in) s. W/C lit. 8-Nov-3 Geble, Radolfzell #819/R est:4000
£2797	$4755	€4000	Erna (48x31cm-19x12in) s. pencil prov. 29-Nov-3 Villa Grisebach, Berlin #203/R est:4000-5000
£2897	$4837	€4200	Children on the beach (18x24cm-7x9in) s. W/C col chk over pencil paperboard. 13-Nov-3 Neumeister, Munich #307/R est:4000-4500
£3147	$5350	€4500	Bodensee (18x25cm-7x10in) s. W/C Indian ink on chk. 29-Nov-3 Villa Grisebach, Berlin #272/R est:3500-4500
£3357	$5706	€4800	Bodensee reeds (18x25cm-7x10in) s. W/C on pencil. 29-Nov-3 Villa Grisebach, Berlin #270/R est:3500-4500
£3472	$5799	€5000	Study for a self-portrait (48x35cm-19x14in) s.d. pencil board double-sided. 25-Oct-3 Dr Lehr, Berlin #123/R est:6000
£4196	$7133	€6000	Horn church (18x26cm-7x10in) s.d.55 W/C on pencil. 29-Nov-3 Villa Grisebach, Berlin #271/R est:4000-5000
£4333	$7757	€6500	Sailing ships on Bodensee (17x24cm-7x9in) s. W/C on pencil. 13-May-4 Neumeister, Munich #334/R est:5600-5800
£4333	$7973	€6500	Portrait de jeune fille (55x42cm-22x17in) mono.d.27 graphite prov. 8-Jun-4 Artcurial Briest, Paris #113/R est:4000-5000
£4333	$7973	€6500	Old Anna (65x36cm-26x14in) s. i.verso pencil exec. 1920. 12-Jun-4 Villa Grisebach, Berlin #250/R est:7000-9000
£7667	$14107	€11500	Landscape with birds flying overhead (35x50cm-14x20in) mono.d.35 i.verso ink silverpoint card prov. 11-Jun-4 Villa Grisebach, Berlin #1576/R est:7000-9000
£8392	$14434	€12000	View of Steckborn from Hemmenhofen (50x59cm-20x23in) s.d.1952 pastel. 2-Dec-3 Hauswedell & Nolte, Hamburg #139/R est:12000
£12000	$22080	€18000	Pregnant woman (60x46cm-24x18in) s. i.verso pencil prov. 11-Jun-4 Villa Grisebach, Berlin #37/R est:14000-18000
£15500	$28210	€22630	Portrat von Marga Kummer - Portrait of Marga Kummer (42x31cm-17x12in) s.i. chl prov. 4-Feb-4 Sotheby's, London #539/R est:6000-8000
£16084	$27343	€23000	Sitting nude (41x58cm-16x23in) s. pencil lit. 29-Nov-3 Farsetti, Prato #421/R est:22000-28000
£16667	$30000	€25000	Evening fog (49x37cm-19x15in) s.d i. verso W/C gouache on ink graphite board. 24-Apr-4 Dr Lehr, Berlin #97/R est:30000
£21678	$36853	€31000	Composition (26x28cm-10x11in) s. i. verso gouache exhib.lit. 26-Nov-3 Lempertz, Koln #644/R est:25000
£22000	$40040	€32120	Portrat einer frau in blauer bluse - Portrait of a woman in a blue blouse (58x47cm-23x19in) s.i.d.1926 gouache prov. 4-Feb-4 Sotheby's, London #540/R est:12000-15000
£32168	$54685	€46000	Out of work (62x49cm-24x19in) s.i.d.24/413 W/C on pencil i. verso prov.exhib.lit. 28-Nov-3 Villa Grisebach, Berlin #51/R est:25000-30000
£60000	$110400	€87600	Karton xu Melancholie (120x88cm-47x35in) mono.d.1930 chl white sanguine brown chk prov.exhib.lit. 24-Jun-4 Christie's, London #382/R est:60000-80000
£110000	$200200	€160600	Dame - Lady (52x37cm-20x15in) s.i.verso W/C brush ink executed 1923 prov. 3-Feb-4 Sotheby's, London #17/R est:120000-160000
£155000	$282100	€226300	Herren und damen - Gentlemen and ladies (56x46cm-22x18in) s.d.22 i.verso W/C pencil prov.exhib.lit. 3-Feb-4 Sotheby's, London #19/R est:120000-160000

DIXON, Alec R (20th C) ?

£350	$627	€511	Reclining female nude (51x41cm-20x16in) s.d.1933 board. 18-Mar-4 Christie's, Kensington #450/R

DIXON, Alfred (1842-1919) British

£1000	$1700	€1460	Lina Susan Penelope Norman (47x39cm-19x15in) 29-Oct-3 Bonhams, Chester #421 est:1000-1500

DIXON, Charles Edward (1872-1934) British

£284	$475	€415	Painted in seven minutes. s.i. 18-Oct-3 Harvey Clar, Oakland #1220
£2800	$5292	€4088	French North Atlantic liner Ile de France clearing Plymouth (30x122cm-12x48in) s.d.1930. 17-Feb-4 Bonhams, New Bond Street #58/R est:3000-5000
£4324	$8000	€6313	Bombardment of Lowestoft (36x99cm-14x39in) s.d.1918 pair. 10-Feb-4 Christie's, Rockefeller NY #144/R est:10000-15000

Works on paper

£320	$586	€467	Frolic II on the Wroxham Broads (35x52cm-14x20in) s.d.1922 W/C. 7-Apr-4 Bonhams, Bury St Edmunds #410/R
£400	$688	€584	Tilbury of today (19x27cm-7x11in) s.d.1911 pen ink W/C prov. 2-Dec-3 Sotheby's, London #114/R
£420	$769	€613	Schooner and a steam vessel in a slight swell with other shipping beyond (20x43cm-8x17in) s. indis d. W/C htd white. 8-Jul-4 Duke & Son, Dorchester #100/R
£520	$837	€754	Fully rigged brigantine on swell (13x15cm-5x6in) s.i.d.1931 W/C. 23-Feb-3 Desmond Judd, Cranbrook #1077
£520	$946	€759	Panoramic view of Durham City across the roof tops towards the Castle (44x79cm-17x31in) s.d.1891 W/C. 29-Jun-4 Anderson & Garland, Newcastle #193/R
£552	$1010	€800	Quatre mats carre tout dessus. s.d.29 W/C gouache. 31-Jan-4 Neret-Minet, Paris #166/R
£759	$1200	€1108	Harbour scene with moored ships, possibly the Thames (33x61cm-13x24in) s. W/C htd bodycol. 6-Sep-3 Brunk, Ashville #677
£903	$1471	€1318	Shipping scene, London (19x35cm-7x14in) s.d.1889 W/C. 23-Sep-3 Peter Webb, Auckland #158/R (NZ.D 2500)
£903	$1471	€1318	Shipping scene, London (19x35cm-7x14in) s.d.1889 W/C. 23-Sep-3 Peter Webb, Auckland #159/R (NZ.D 2500)
£950	$1701	€1387	Hulks and other shipping moored at a wharf (30x60cm-12x24in) s.d.94 pencil W/C htd white. 26-May-4 Christie's, Kensington #449/R
£1200	$2208	€1752	Shipping on the River Thames (36x58cm-14x23in) s. W/C. 24-Mar-4 Hamptons Fine Art, Godalming #254
£1200	$2184	€1800	Otway leaving Gibralter (27x76cm-11x30in) s.i.d.1910 W/C. 15-Jun-4 Rosebery Fine Art, London #578/R est:1500-2000
£1500	$2550	€2190	Off Gravesend (55x35cm-22x14in) s.i.d.98 W/C bodycol. 19-Nov-3 Christie's, Kensington #384/R
£1800	$3402	€2628	At Lisbon (18x54cm-7x21in) s.i. pen ink W/C. 17-Feb-4 Bonhams, New Bond Street #66/R est:2000-3000
£1923	$3500	€2808	Tower Bridge (46x76cm-18x30in) s.i.d.1925 W/C. 29-Jun-4 Peter Webb, Auckland #109/R est:6000-8000 (NZ.D 5500)
£2159	$3800	€3152	Harbour scene (36x56cm-14x22in) W/C. 23-May-4 Hindman, Chicago #44/R est:2000-2500
£2159	$3800	€3152	Hotel with Palms (36x56cm-14x22in) W/C. 23-May-4 Hindman, Chicago #45/R est:2000-2500
£2213	$3496	€3231	The Lower Pool (24x60cm-9x24in) s.i.d.09 W/C. 2-Sep-3 Deutscher-Menzies, Melbourne #441/R est:4000-6000 (A.D 5400)
£2254	$3562	€3291	Above Greenwich (24x60cm-9x24in) s.i.d.09 w/C. 2-Sep-3 Deutscher-Menzies, Melbourne #440/R est:4000-6000 (A.D 5500)
£2857	$5171	€4171	In dock (55x38cm-22x15in) s.i.d.1902 W/C. 30-Mar-4 Peter Webb, Auckland #120/R est:6000-8000 (NZ.D 8000)
£3000	$5100	€4380	Spithead (27x76cm-11x30in) s.i.d.02 W/C prov. 27-Nov-3 Sotheby's, London #398/R est:3000-5000
£3512	$6217	€5128	Greenwich reach (27x47cm-11x19in) s.i.d.09 W/C. 3-May-4 Christie's, Melbourne #373/R est:4000-6000 (A.D 8500)
£3600	$6480	€5256	RMS Majestic on the Mersey. Above Woolwich (18x27cm-7x11in) s.i. pencil W/C htd white pair. 22-Apr-4 Mellors & Kirk, Nottingham #993/R est:1000-1400
£3600	$6444	€5256	Off Tilbury (42x63cm-17x25in) s.i.d.1900 brown in, W/C bodycol. 26-May-4 Christie's, Kensington #448/R est:3000-5000
£3800	$6954	€5548	Shipping on the Thames (33x67cm-13x26in) s.d.06 W/C bodycol prov. 27-Jan-4 Holloways, Banbury #344/R est:1200-1800
£3819	$6073	€5576	Off Tilbury (27x77cm-11x30in) s.i.d.1902 W/C. 1-May-3 Dunbar Sloane, Wellington #75/R est:12000-15000 (NZ.D 11000)
£4000	$6800	€5840	Beating down (26x70cm-10x28in) s.i.d.1913 pencil ink W/C. 19-Nov-3 Christie's, Kensington #381/R
£4525	$7557	€6607	Barking Reach (38x100cm-15x39in) s.i.d.03 W/C prov. 17-Nov-3 Waddingtons, Toronto #74/R est:3000-4000 (C.D 10000)
£5000	$8500	€7300	Pool of London (26x76cm-10x30in) s.i.d.01 W/C htd bodycol prov. 27-Nov-3 Sotheby's, London #399/R est:3000-4000
£5000	$8500	€7300	Barges beating up off Gravesend (28x76cm-11x30in) s.i.d.09 W/C bodycol. 30-Oct-3 Duke & Son, Dorchester #35/R
£5200	$8840	€7592	Off Albert Docks (28x76cm-11x30in) s.i.d.03 W/C bodycol. 30-Oct-3 Duke & Son, Dorchester #34/R
£5200	$9724	€7592	City pool (49x74cm-19x29in) s.i.d.1906 W/C. 20-Jul-4 Dreweatt Neate, Newbury #200/R est:3000-5000
£5500	$9350	€8030	Departure of RMS Orontes from Tilbury (28x79cm-11x31in) s.i.d.02 W/C htd bodycol prov. 27-Nov-3 Sotheby's, London #397/R est:3000-5000
£7000	$11200	€10220	Canadian Pacific liner, Empress of Australia, in Hong Kong harbour (36x53cm-14x21in) s.i.d.28 pen ink W/C htd white. 16-Sep-3 Bonhams, New Bond Street #6/R est:8000-10000
£7000	$11900	€10220	Shipping off (46x75cm-18x30in) s.i.d.1925 pencil W/C. 19-Nov-3 Christie's, Kensington #382/R
£8000	$13600	€11680	H.M.S. Victory (69x119cm-27x47in) s.d.98 pen ink W/C bodycol. 19-Nov-3 Christie's, Kensington #385/R

DIXON, Francis Stillwell (1872-1967) American

£295	$475	€431	December afternoon (20x25cm-8x10in) masonite. 20-Aug-3 James Julia, Fairfield #1726/R
£484	$900	€707	Early snow (51x66cm-20x26in) s. painted c.1920. 7-Mar-4 Treadway Gallery, Cincinnati #632/R
£860	$1600	€1256	Evening (53x66cm-21x26in) s.i.stretcher painted c.1920. 7-Mar-4 Treadway Gallery, Cincinnati #631/R est:1000-2000

DIXON, Geoff (20th C) New Zealander

£414	$703	€604	Kangaroo in a wooly hat (27x20cm-11x8in) s. i.d.March 1993 verso enamel on board. 26-Nov-3 Dunbar Sloane, Wellington #137 est:500-1000 (NZ.D 1100)

DIXON, Harry (1861-1942) British

£300	$552	€438	Rural landscape with pond and cattle drinking (18x23cm-7x9in) s. exhib. 12-Jun-4 Dickins, Middle Claydon #55
£380	$695	€555	Highland cattle (60x44cm-24x17in) s. 7-Apr-4 Woolley & Wallis, Salisbury #321/R
£4800	$8928	€7008	Tiger, tiger burning bright (62x108cm-24x43in) s. 4-Mar-4 Christie's, Kensington #600/R est:1500-2000

DIXON, James (1887-1970) British?

£1200	$2196	€1752	Present for Miss Jill Clark (54x37cm-21x15in) i. paper. 8-Jul-4 Lawrence, Crewkerne #1668/R est:1200-1800
£6419	$12132	€9500	View of the west end village, Tory Island, after finishing the herring season (43x66cm-17x26in) s.i.d.17 October 1960 oil paper on board. 17-Feb-4 Whyte's, Dublin #110/R est:6000-8000
Works on paper			
£2917	$4754	€4200	Greenland Hawk (54x33cm-21x13in) s.i.d.18/10/1964 mixed media. 24-Sep-3 James Adam, Dublin #112/R est:2500-4000
£3067	$5551	€4600	Girl Pat coming home through the Seven Seas (56x76cm-22x30in) s.i. mixed media. 30-Mar-4 De Veres Art Auctions, Dublin #108/R est:5000-8000
£3600	$6012	€5256	Tory Islan (43x66cm-17x26in) i.d.1966 mixed media. 14-Oct-3 David Lay, Penzance #165/R est:1200-1800

DIXON, Leng (1916-1968) South African

Works on paper			
£274	$465	€400	Old cathedral, Cape Town (54x41cm-21x16in) s.d.52 pen ink gouache W/C. 4-Nov-3 Stephan Welz, Johannesburg #667 est:3500-5000 (SA.R 3200)
£470	$799	€686	Cape Malay quarter (31x23cm-12x9in) s.i. pen ink W/C. 4-Nov-3 Stephan Welz, Johannesburg #670 est:2500-4000 (SA.R 5500)

DIXON, Maynard (1875-1946) American

£19022	$35000	€27772	Barn and poplars, Carson City, Nevada (39x48cm-15x19in) s.i.d.Oct 1935 canvas on board prov.exhib.lit. 8-Jun-4 Bonhams & Butterfields, San Francisco #4131/R est:40000-60000
£29412	$55000	€42942	Black mesa, Navajo Reservation, Arizona (25x33cm-10x13in) s. canvasboard prov. 24-Jul-4 Coeur d'Alene, Hayden #165/R est:15000-25000
£29976	$50960	€43765	I call myself s soldier (76x51cm-30x20in) board. 1-Nov-3 Altermann Galleries, Santa Fe #74
£34392	$65000	€50212	Cowboy on horseback with cattle in landscape (30x41cm-12x16in) s.i.d.Oct 1940 canvasboard prov. 17-Feb-4 John Moran, Pasadena #75/R est:30000-50000
£96257	$180000	€140535	Cut bank, Tucson (51x41cm-20x16in) s.d.1942 board prov. 24-Jul-4 Coeur d'Alene, Hayden #97/R est:50000-75000
£267380	$500000	€390375	Cattle drive (157x198cm-62x78in) s. prov. 24-Jul-4 Coeur d'Alene, Hayden #140/R est:500000-750000
Works on paper			
£982	$1700	€1434	Colorado Desert, Arizona (11x15cm-4x6in) mono.i.d.August 02 pencil col chk prov. 10-Dec-3 Bonhams & Butterfields, San Francisco #6089/R est:2000-3000
£1049	$1700	€1521	Bear in western landscape (20x18cm-8x7in) s. ink dr. 8-Aug-3 Barridorf, Portland #220/R est:2000-3000
£2206	$3750	€3221	Old adobe by moonlight, Tucson (11x15cm-4x6in) i. i.d.Aug 07 verso graphite chk. 18-Nov-3 John Moran, Pasadena #117c est:5000-7000
£2601	$4500	€3797	Old women of Taos, Robe Studies, Taos (12x18cm-5x7in) init.i.d.1932 pencil prov. 10-Dec-3 Bonhams & Butterfields, San Francisco #6090/R est:3000-5000
£3743	$7000	€5465	No-lah-no-mah (36x28cm-14x11in) init. pen ink lit. 24-Jul-4 Coeur d'Alene, Hayden #235/R est:6000-9000
£3824	$6500	€5583	Cattle drive through the desert (16x20cm-6x8in) init.d.1941 col pencil. 20-Nov-3 Auctions by the Bay, Alameda #1060/R
£5085	$9000	€7424	Lesson. Herald. Prayer (13x8cm-5x3in) init.i. ink graphite htd white three prov.lit. 28-Apr-4 Christie's, Los Angeles #27/R est:8000-12000
£5348	$10000	€7808	Me-no-kan (36x28cm-14x11in) init. pen ink lit. 24-Jul-4 Coeur d'Alene, Hayden #236/R est:6000-9000
£13369	$25000	€19519	Poplars of Carson (41x30cm-16x12in) s.d.1937 W/C prov. 24-Jul-4 Coeur d'Alene, Hayden #98/R est:20000-30000

DIXON, Percy (1862-1924) British

Works on paper			
£300	$489	€438	Scottish estuary scene (17x26cm-7x10in) W/C. 25-Sep-3 Clevedon Sale Rooms #222
£320	$554	€467	Moray Firth, (15x36cm-6x14in) sig. W/C. 11-Dec-3 Neales, Nottingham #537
£350	$595	€511	Figures by a pond in a moorland landscape (31x48cm-12x19in) s.d.86 W/C over pencil. 25-Nov-3 Bonhams, Knowle #184
£420	$722	€613	Loch Lubnaig, Strathyre (23x37cm-9x15in) studio st. pencil W/C. 3-Dec-3 Christie's, Kensington #185/R
£600	$978	€876	Estuary landscape with highlands in background (44x69cm-17x27in) s. 25-Sep-3 Clevedon Sale Rooms #227

DIXON, Robert (1780-1815) British

Works on paper			
£280	$515	€409	Cottage at Diss, Norfolk (7x11cm-3x4in) W/C prov. 11-Jun-4 Keys, Aylsham #592

DIXON, Samuel (?-1769) British

Works on paper			
£2824	$4800	€4123	Georgian scenes (40x46cm-16x18in) embossed gouache three sold with one by W Hayes. 25-Nov-3 Christie's, Rockefeller NY #147/R est:3000-5000
£5882	$10000	€8588	Birds (37x47cm-15x19in) embossed gouache two sold with other two. 25-Nov-3 Christie's, Rockefeller NY #149/R est:5000-8000
£5988	$10000	€8742	Flower. Peahen. Flower (23x18cm-9x7in) embossed gouache lit. three. 20-Oct-3 Sotheby's, New York #449/R est:6000-8000
£10000	$17000	€14600	Birds (39x50cm-15x20in) embosesed gouache pair. 25-Nov-3 Christie's, Rockefeller NY #148/R est:3000-5000
£10778	$18000	€15736	Flowers (23x19cm-9x7in) embossed gouache set of 4 lit. 20-Oct-3 Sotheby's, New York #450/R est:8000-12000

DIXON, Samuel (attrib) (?-1769) British

Works on paper			
£7784	$13000	€11365	Bird and flower (35x45cm-14x18in) embossed gouache. 20-Oct-3 Sotheby's, New York #448/R est:5000-7000

DIXON, Willard (20th C) American

£601	$1100	€877	Kern River Powerhouse (86x124cm-34x49in) 10-Jul-4 Hindman, Chicago #121/R est:300-500

D'IZARNY, Francois (1952-) French

£1127	$1949	€1600	Atelier au rideau rouge (54x65cm-21x26in) s. 9-Dec-3 Chambelland & Giafferi, Paris #43/R est:2500-3000

DIZIANI, Antonio (1737-1797) Italian

£16783	$28028	€24000	Lake landscape with anglers (97x132cm-38x52in) 7-Oct-3 Pandolfini, Florence #573 est:28000

DIZIANI, Antonio (attrib) (1737-1797) Italian

£12000	$21960	€18000	River landscape with figures and farms (97x135cm-38x53in) 1-Jun-4 Sotheby's, Milan #177/R est:18000-22000
£21000	$38430	€30660	Bacchanal scene in a pastoral landscape (46x59cm-18x23in) prov. 6-Jul-4 Sotheby's, Olympia #543/R est:6000-8000

DIZIANI, Antonio (circle) (1737-1797) Italian

£9396	$17289	€14000	River landscape (45x80cm-18x31in) prov. 24-Mar-4 Dorotheum, Vienna #63/R est:4000-6000

DIZIANI, Gaspare (1689-1767) Italian

Works on paper			
£260	$475	€380	Seated scholar holding an open book. Crucifixion studies (20x28cm-8x11in) indis.i. pen brown ink wash pencil double-sided. 29-Jan-4 Swann Galleries, New York #108/R
£719	$1151	€1000	Study of putto and dogs (11x20cm-4x8in) pen W/C. 14-May-3 Finarte Semenzato, Milan #503/R
£1200	$2160	€1752	Three putti bearing garlands (17x22cm-7x9in) bears i.verso pen brown ink wash red chk. 20-Apr-4 Sotheby's, Olympia #102/R est:700-900
£1200	$2196	€1752	Diana. Standing female figure with a shield (26x14cm-10x6in) pen ink wash over red chk double-sided arched top. 7-Jul-4 Bonhams, Knightsbridge #77/R est:1500-2000
£1421	$2600	€2075	Satan tempting Christ to change stones into bread (21x15cm-8x6in) i. pen brown ink wash red chk. 29-Jan-4 Swann Galleries, New York #109/R est:3000-5000
£1905	$3409	€2800	Bacchanale de putti (21x34cm-8x13in) i. pen brown ink grey wash. 17-Mar-4 Tajan, Paris #35/R est:3000

DIZIANI, Gaspare (attrib) (1689-1767) Italian

£1141	$2122	€1700	Harvest scene (39x28cm-15x11in) 5-Mar-4 Wendl, Rudolstadt #3619/R est:1700
£4965	$8291	€7000	Mose e il serpente di bronzo (55x70cm-22x28in) 18-Jun-3 Christie's, Rome #446/R est:8000-10000
£5172	$8586	€7500	Melchisedek offering bread and wine to Abraham (61x79cm-24x31in) prov. 1-Oct-3 Dorotheum, Vienna #46/R est:5000-7000
£10667	$19413	€16000	Solomon and the Queen of Sheba (105x84cm-41x33in) prov. 1-Jul-4 Van Ham, Cologne #1089/R est:13000
Works on paper			
£592	$1089	€900	Pentecost (52x28cm-20x11in) pen ink W/C over pencil. 22-Jun-4 Sotheby's, Milan #81/R
£1549	$2680	€2200	Une Reine en priere (17x12cm-7x5in) i. pen brown ink sanguine brown wash. 12-Dec-3 Renaud, Paris #13/R est:1500

DIZIANI, Gaspare (circle) (1689-1767) Italian

£8741	$14598	€12500	Joseph sold byhis brothers (90x112cm-35x44in) 7-Oct-3 Pandolfini, Florence #579/R est:12000-14000

DIZIANI, Gaspare and NAZZARI, Bartolomeo (18th C) Italian

£29371	$50517	€42000	Portrait of the officer Count Johann Matthias von der Schulemburg (150x115cm-59x45in) 2-Dec-3 Sotheby's, Milan #122/R est:15000-20000

DJAMIN, Nasjah (1924-1997) Indonesian

£2431	$4059	€3549	Pewrahu-Perahu (59x84cm-23x33in) s. prov.lit. 12-Oct-3 Sotheby's, Singapore #174/R est:6000-8000 (S.D 7000)

DJANIRA (1914-1979) Brazilian

£6227	$11022	€9341	Entrance to the artist's house in Santa Teresa (57x69cm-22x27in) s. 27-Apr-4 Bolsa de Arte, Rio de Janeiro #58/R (B.R 34000)
Works on paper			
£4304	$7876	€6456	Girl and angels (46x33cm-18x13in) s.d.1951 gouache. 6-Jul-4 Bolsa de Arte, Rio de Janeiro #67/R (B.R 23500)

DJAWA (attrib) (1905-1980) Australian
Works on paper
£1563 $2922 €2345 Ceremonial canoe (25x121cm-10x48in) earth pigments eucalyptus bark cane bush string exec.c.1960 prov. 26-Jul-4 Sotheby's, Melbourne #151/R est:4000-6000 (A.D 4000)

DJAYKURRNGA, George (1930-) Australian
Works on paper
£1563 $2922 €2345 Namarrkon the lightning man (108x49cm-43x19in) earth pigments eucalyptus bark exec.c.1970 prov. 26-Jul-4 Sotheby's, Melbourne #292/R est:4000-6000 (A.D 4000)

DJENEEF, Ivan (20th C) Russian
£2654 $4750 €3875 Portrait of Lois Fisher (152x102cm-60x40in) 20-Mar-4 Sloans & Kenyon, Bethesda #1188/R est:5000-7000

DJIRNA, I Made (1957-) Balinese
£1505 $2409 €2197 Termenung (70x60cm-28x24in) s.d.1997. 18-May-3 Sotheby's, Singapore #187/R est:2000-3000 (S.D 4200)
£1736 $2899 €2535 Boss (100x130cm-39x51in) s.i.d.1999/2000 verso mixed media canvas. 12-Oct-3 Sotheby's, Singapore #187/R est:5000-7000 (S.D 5000)
£2581 $4129 €3768 Woman and cat (100x90cm-39x35in) s.d.90. 18-May-3 Sotheby's, Singapore #186/R est:4000-6000 (S.D 7200)
£3442 $5335 €5025 Animale (90x140cm-35x55in) s.d.1997 s.i.d.verso. 6-Oct-2 Sotheby's, Singapore #184/R est:7000-9000 (S.D 9500)
Works on paper
£2083 $3479 €3041 Cockerels (70x100cm-28x39in) s.d.1996 mixed media canvas. 12-Oct-3 Sotheby's, Singapore #192/R est:4000-6000 (S.D 6000)

DJOMA, Freddy (1920-?) Australian
Works on paper
£1133 $2118 €1700 Fire at the sacred Gumaidja Nara ground at Biranybirany (92x30cm-36x12in) earth pigments eucalyptus bark exec.c.1965 prov. 26-Jul-4 Sotheby's, Melbourne #529/R (A.D 2900)

DJULWARAK, Dawidi (1921-1970) Australian
Works on paper
£1220 $1927 €1769 Hollow log ceremony (52x23cm-20x9in) earth pigments eucalyptus bark exec.c.1960 prov. 28-Jul-3 Sotheby's, Paddington #344/R est:2000-4000 (A.D 3000)
£1789 $2826 €2584 Wagilag sisters (87x50cm-34x20in) i.verso earth pigments eucalyptus bark exec.c.1965 prov. 28-Jul-3 Sotheby's, Paddington #336/R est:3000-5000 (A.D 4400)

DJUMPURBUR, Tom (20th C) Australian
Works on paper
£407 $642 €590 Untitled, body paint (121x51cm-48x20in) i.verso earth pigments eucalyptus bark exec.c.1993 prov. 28-Jul-3 Sotheby's, Paddington #472 (A.D 1000)

DLOUHY, Benno (1893-1926) Czechoslovakian
£288 $536 €420 Winter mood (83x57cm-33x22in) s. board. 6-Mar-4 Dorotheum, Prague #70 est:8000-12000 (C.KR 14000)

DMITRIENKO, Pierre (1925-1974) French
£1141 $2123 €1700 Composition (33x55cm-13x22in) s.d.1953. 3-Mar-4 Artcurial Briest, Paris #358 est:800-1000
£1479 $2559 €2100 Composition (81x65cm-32x26in) s. s.d.1957 verso prov. 9-Dec-3 Artcurial Briest, Paris #502/R est:2000-2500
£1513 $2784 €2300 Composition (54x65cm-21x26in) s.d.1952. 27-Jun-4 Versailles Encheres #30/R est:1500-2000
£1878 $3136 €2742 Pluie doree (120x150cm-47x59in) s.d.1960 exhib. 7-Oct-3 Rasmussen, Copenhagen #76/R est:20000-30000 (D.KR 20000)
Works on paper
£278 $464 €400 Composition - pluie (46x34cm-18x13in) s.d.1950 W/C. 21-Oct-3 Artcurial Briest, Paris #651
£280 $476 €400 Variante plume noire (53x44cm-21x17in) s. china ink gouache. 29-Nov-3 Neret-Minet, Paris #167b

DMITRIEV-ORENBURGSKY, Nikolai (1838-1898) Russian
£828 $1382 €1200 La route de montagne (15x22cm-6x9in) s. oil paper. 17-Nov-3 Claude Boisgirard, Paris #18

DMITRIEVSKY, Lydia (1895-1967) Russian
£16260 $29106 €23740 Self-portrait (74x92cm-29x36in) exhib. 28-May-4 Uppsala Auktionskammare, Uppsala #271/R est:20000-25000 (S.KR 220000)

DOBASHI, Jun (1910-1975) Japanese
£278 $500 €406 Untitled (56x46cm-22x18in) s.i.d.55. 25-Jan-4 Bonhams & Butterfields, San Francisco #3627/R
£537 $950 €800 Village (27x35cm-11x14in) s. i.d.1957 verso oil sable panel prov. 28-Apr-4 Artcurial Briest, Paris #500
£537 $950 €800 Composition - Village (22x27cm-9x11in) s. i.d.1957 verso oil sable panel prov. 28-Apr-4 Artcurial Briest, Paris #496
£537 $950 €800 Poussiere d'etoiles. Village (18x31cm-7x12in) s.d.1957 1958 oil sable panel two prov. 28-Apr-4 Artcurial Briest, Paris #497
£872 $1544 €1300 Paysage (41x51cm-16x20in) s. s.i.d.1957 verso oil sable panel prov. 28-Apr-4 Artcurial Briest, Paris #494/R est:800-1000
£1103 $1986 €1600 Raison d'une fantaisie (96x130cm-38x51in) s.d.1958 s.i.d.verso exhib. 25-Jan-4 Chayette & Cheval, Paris #233 est:1500-2000
£1448 $2607 €2100 Nebuleuse (89x130cm-35x51in) s.d.1960 exhib. 25-Jan-4 Chayette & Cheval, Paris #232/R est:1500-2000
Works on paper
£268 $475 €400 Composition (17x23cm-7x9in) s.d.64 mixed media collage. 28-Apr-4 Charbonneaux, Paris #146

DOBAY, Anton (1906-1986) German
Works on paper
£1007 $1802 €1500 Woman (40x30cm-16x12in) s.d.21.11.1973 wax chk broad prov. 25-May-4 Dorotheum, Vienna #278/R est:2000-3000
£1745 $3123 €2600 Fruit tree after van Gogh (40x30cm-16x12in) s.d.27.6.1975 pencil wax chk board prov. 25-May-4 Dorotheum, Vienna #277/R est:3000-4000

DOBBIE, Beatrice (?) ?
£1795 $3250 €2621 Pekingese (50x61cm-20x24in) s. 30-Mar-4 Bonhams & Butterfields, San Francisco #114/R est:3500-5000

DOBBIN, John (1815-1888) British
Works on paper
£600 $1104 €876 Dunblane, Scotland (33x45cm-13x18in) s.d.1872 W/C. 23-Mar-4 Bonhams, Knightsbridge #70/R
£800 $1264 €1168 Church of St Peters viewed from across the river (41x56cm-16x22in) s.d.1856 W/C. 23-Jul-3 Hampton & Littlewood, Exeter #420/R
£1400 $2576 €2044 View of Venice (33x91cm-13x36in) s.d.1881 W/C. 8-Jun-4 Bonhams, Knightsbridge #33/R est:1200-1800
£2600 $4134 €3796 Busy continental town scene with numerous figures, Loudoun, France (61x79cm-24x31in) s.i.d.1856 W/C. 1-May-3 John Nicholson, Haslemere #666/R est:1000-1500

DOBBIN, Lady Kate (1868-c.1948) Irish
Works on paper
£739 $1183 €1050 Dahlias in a blue lustreware vase (64x48cm-25x19in) i.verso W/C artist's board. 16-Sep-3 Whyte's, Dublin #96/R
£1806 $2943 €2600 Wooded path (34x23cm-13x9in) s. W/C. 28-Sep-3 Hamilton Osborne King, Dublin #152/R est:2500-3000

DOBBS, John Barnes (1931-) American
£468 $750 €683 Carnival in Nancy (66x81cm-26x32in) s. 17-May-3 Bunte, Elgin #1295

DOBELI, Johann Othmar (1874-1922) Swiss
£264 $449 €385 Farmstead near Zofingen (28x33cm-11x13in) s.d.1912 i. verso board. 5-Nov-3 Dobiaschofsky, Bern #493/R (S.FR 600)
£357 $571 €518 Aargau farmstead (25x31cm-10x12in) s.d.1915 board. 15-May-3 Stuker, Bern #1154 (S.FR 750)
£409 $679 €593 Soldier's portrait (60x50cm-24x20in) s.d.1917. 13-Jun-3 Zofingen, Switzerland #2826 (S.FR 900)
£452 $769 €660 Summer landscape with farmstead (29x90cm-11x35in) s.d.1918. 19-Nov-3 Fischer, Luzern #2073/R (S.FR 1000)
£455 $755 €660 Character head (47x57cm-19x22in) s.d.1913. 13-Jun-3 Zofingen, Switzerland #2825 (S.FR 1000)
£543 $923 €793 Old Schloss Wikon (48x58cm-19x23in) s.d.1917. 28-Nov-3 Zofingen, Switzerland #2967 (S.FR 1200)
£545 $905 €790 Postman Muller from Vordemwald (60x50cm-24x20in) s.d.1906. 13-Jun-3 Zofingen, Switzerland #2824 (S.FR 1200)
£724 $1231 €1057 Oftringen (35x90cm-14x35in) s.d.1908. 28-Nov-3 Zofingen, Switzerland #2966 est:1500 (S.FR 1600)

DOBELL, Sir William (1899-1970) Australian
£2542 $4322 €3711 Folk singer (11x10cm-4x4in) s. board prov. 24-Nov-3 Sotheby's, Melbourne #162/R est:2000-4000 (A.D 6000)
£3557 $6368 €5336 Portrait of a woman reading (12x8cm-5x3in) s. board. 17-May-4 Sotheby's, Melbourne #584/R est:3000-5000 (A.D 9000)
£3688 $5828 €5384 Koki, Beach, New Guinea (22x29cm-9x11in) s. board prov.exhib. 2-Sep-3 Deutscher-Menzies, Melbourne #96/R est:14000-18000 (A.D 9000)
£3894 $6152 €5685 Wangi beach (9x12cm-4x5in) s. board prov.exhib. 2-Sep-3 Deutscher-Menzies, Melbourne #202/R est:5500-7500 (A.D 9500)
£4065 $6382 €5894 Kings cross (31x45cm-12x18in) s. board. 26-Aug-3 Christie's, Sydney #268/R est:9000-12000 (A.D 10000)
£4743 $8490 €7115 Landscape with cows and children (17x24cm-7x9in) s. board. 17-May-4 Sotheby's, Melbourne #558/R est:5000-7000 (A.D 12000)
£6504 $10211 €9431 Study for the portrait of Dr McMahon (14x14cm-6x6in) board. 26-Aug-3 Christie's, Sydney #321/R est:10000-12000 (A.D 16000)
£7724 $13825 €11277 Scene at Wangi-boats at high wind (60x72cm-24x28in) s. composition board prov.exhib. 4-May-4 Sotheby's, Melbourne #81/R est:20000-30000 (A.D 19000)
£11570 $21405 €16892 London Bridge, Hungerford Bridge (40x51cm-16x20in) s. board prov.exhib. 10-Mar-4 Deutscher-Menzies, Melbourne #51/R est:25000-35000 (A.D 28000)
£15702 $29050 €22925 Portrait of Hedley R Marston (121x91cm-48x36in) s. board prov. 10-Mar-4 Deutscher-Menzies, Melbourne #52/R est:40000-60000 (A.D 38000)
£19835 $36694 €28959 White Horse Inn, Dorking 1935 (29x36cm-11x14in) s. board prov.exhib. 10-Mar-4 Deutscher-Menzies, Melbourne #41/R est:40000-50000 (A.D 48000)
Works on paper
£691 $1085 €1002 Theatre study (13x16cm-5x6in) gouache prov. 27-Aug-3 Christie's, Sydney #530 est:1200-1500 (A.D 1700)
£711 $1274 €1038 Seated woman (12x12cm-5x5in) s.i.d.1961 pencil prov. 15-May-4 Christie's, Sydney #78 est:1500-2000 (A.D 1800)
£894 $1404 €1296 Study (16x23cm-6x9in) indis.sig.i.d.1941 ink. 26-Aug-3 Christie's, Sydney #282/R est:1500-2500 (A.D 2200)
£992 $1686 €1448 Self portrait, smoking (16x22cm-6x9in) pencil prov. 29-Oct-3 Lawson Menzies, Sydney #169/R est:3000-5000 (A.D 2400)
£1500 $2655 €2190 New Guinea Tribesmen (15x23cm-6x9in) s. gouache. 28-Apr-4 Halls, Shrewsbury #446/R est:700-1000
£1829 $2872 €2652 Portrait of a young man (38x28cm-15x11in) s. pencil. 26-Aug-3 Christie's, Sydney #365/R est:2500-3500 (A.D 4500)
£6122 $11265 €8938 Study for Irish youth (32x22cm-13x9in) pencil. 29-Mar-4 Goodman, Sydney #155/R est:10000-12000 (A.D 15000)

DOBKOWSKI, Jan (20th C) Polish

£268	$486	€391	Composition (38x28cm-15x11in) s.d.1971/72. 4-Apr-4 Agra, Warsaw #89/R (P.Z 1900)
£1379	$2303	€2000	Red and green composition (76x61cm-30x24in) s.i.d.1971/72 verso. 16-Nov-3 Agra, Warsaw #78/R est:1000
£2276	$3801	€3300	Love (199x147cm-78x58in) s.i.d.1970 verso. 16-Nov-3 Agra, Warsaw #94/R est:1000

DOBNER, Josef (1898-1972) Austrian

Sculpture

£1049	$1783	€1500	Dancer (31cm-12in) s.d.1924 verso limewood one of four. 25-Nov-3 Dorotheum, Vienna #364/R est:1600-2000
£1049	$1783	€1500	Dancer (32cm-13in) s.d.1924 verso limewood one of four. 25-Nov-3 Dorotheum, Vienna #365/R est:1600-2000
£1049	$1783	€1500	Dancer (31cm-12in) s.d.1924 verso limewood one of four. 25-Nov-3 Dorotheum, Vienna #366/R est:1600-2000
£1049	$1783	€1500	Dancer (31cm-12in) s.d.1924 verso limewood one of four. 25-Nov-3 Dorotheum, Vienna #367/R est:1600-2000

DOBOUJINSKY, Mstislav (1875-1957) Russian

Works on paper

£1800	$3222	€2628	Costume design for Persian dancer (22x33cm-9x13in) s.i. W/C pair. 26-May-4 Sotheby's, Olympia #446/R est:800-1000
£2000	$3400	€3000	Costume designs (37x25cm-15x10in) s.d. pencil gouache chl set of 3. 25-Nov-3 Christie's, London #212/R est:1500-2000
£12000	$21480	€17520	Theatre stage design (21x29cm-8x11in) s. s.i.verso W/C gouache. 26-May-4 Sotheby's, Olympia #450/R est:800-1200

DOBREE, Valentine (19/20th C) British?

Works on paper

£420	$773	€613	Cubist still life with a violin (36x67cm-14x26in) s. collage board. 23-Mar-4 Rosebery Fine Art, London #907

DOBRINSKY, Yitzhak (1891-1973) Russian

£436	$811	€650	Fillette en rouge (41x27cm-16x11in) s. panel painted c.1965. 2-Mar-4 Artcurial Briest, Paris #163
£3497	$5944	€5000	Portrait de jeune fille a Maison Lafitte (55x38cm-22x15in) s.d.53. 27-Nov-3 Calmels Cohen, Paris #47/R est:2000-2500

DOBROWOLSKI, Odo (1883-1917) Polish

Works on paper

£1135	$1963	€1657	Cathedral (62x47cm-24x19in) s.d.913 pastel chk. 14-Dec-3 Agra, Warsaw #50/R est:7000 (P.Z 7500)

DOBROWSKY, Josef (1889-1964) Austrian

£1560	$2606	€2200	Portrait of girl wearing red hat (63x52cm-25x20in) s.d.33 board. 14-Oct-3 Dorotheum, Vienna #89/R est:2800-5500
£2685	$4805	€4000	Portrait of a lady (100x75cm-39x30in) s.d.45 board. 27-May-4 Hassfurther, Vienna #41/R est:5000-6000
£3356	$6007	€5000	Reclining female nude (46x56cm-18x22in) s.d.46 panel. 25-May-4 Dorotheum, Vienna #216/R est:6000-8000
£4196	$7133	€6000	Reclining female nude (36x47cm-14x19in) mono. board prov. 26-Nov-3 Dorotheum, Vienna #162/R est:9000-12000
£4895	$8322	€7000	Vase of flowers (70x51cm-28x20in) s.d.43 board. 28-Nov-3 Wiener Kunst Auktionen, Vienna #512/R est:3000-6000
£4899	$8770	€7300	Traunstein (50x60cm-20x24in) momo. 27-May-4 Hassfurther, Vienna #40/R est:8000-11000
£10638	$17766	€15000	Village street in winter (50x60cm-20x24in) s.d.1937. 16-Oct-3 Dorotheum, Salzburg #619/R est:3600-4500
£12081	$21624	€18000	Aggstein ruins (46x70cm-18x28in) s.d.25 cardboard. 27-May-4 Hassfurther, Vienna #39/R est:18000-22000
£12587	$21399	€18000	Ybbs (50x60cm-20x24in) s.d.1929 prov. 26-Nov-3 Dorotheum, Vienna #152/R est:14000-20000
£34722	$59028	€50000	The prodigal son (142x99cm-56x39in) s. panel lit. 28-Oct-3 Wiener Kunst Auktionen, Vienna #81/R est:35000-70000

Works on paper

£284	$474	€400	Girl nude in landscape (40x32cm-16x13in) bears d. chk Indian ink brush. 14-Oct-3 Dorotheum, Vienna #37/R
£431	$772	€629	Summer mountain landscape (34x42cm-13x17in) s.d.37 W/C. 12-May-4 Dobiaschofsky, Bern #454/R (S.FR 1000)
£535	$850	€781	Figures in a winter landscape (39x52cm-15x20in) s.d.33 gouache pair. 13-Sep-3 Weschler, Washington #694/R
£600	$1080	€900	Reclining female nude (37x49cm-15x19in) i.d.Dezember 1913 pencil. 21-Apr-4 Dorotheum, Vienna #11/R
£634	$1109	€900	Portrait of a lady (61x47cm-24x19in) s.d.59 pastel. 19-Dec-3 Dorotheum, Vienna #155/R
£658	$1211	€1000	Nude (41x55cm-16x22in) chl. 22-Jun-4 Wiener Kunst Auktionen, Vienna #129/R
£658	$1211	€1000	Female nude viewed from the back (59x39cm-23x15in) mono.d.47 col chk. 22-Jun-4 Wiener Kunst Auktionen, Vienna #111/R
£709	$1184	€1000	Portrait of woman (61x45cm-24x18in) mono.d.9.3.56 pastel. 14-Oct-3 Dorotheum, Vienna #169/R
£1208	$2138	€1800	Still life of flowers (60x47cm-24x19in) s.d. W/C. 30-Apr-4 Dr Fritz Nagel, Stuttgart #120/R est:500
£1329	$2259	€1900	Reclining nude (62x84cm-24x33in) s.d.35 pastel graphite. 26-Nov-3 Dorotheum, Vienna #164/R est:1900-2400
£1645	$3026	€2500	Peonies (58x46cm-23x18in) s.d.1961 gouache. 22-Jun-4 Wiener Kunst Auktionen, Vienna #115/R est:2500
£2335	$4250	€3503	Village in a landscape (49x68cm-19x27in) s.d.1950 lit. 1-Jul-4 Ben-Ami, Tel Aviv #4914/R est:4500-6000
£2685	$4752	€4000	Flowers in jug (60x46cm-24x18in) s. W/C. 28-Apr-4 Wiener Kunst Auktionen, Vienna #72/R est:3000-6000
£2778	$4528	€4000	Flowers in a jug (62x48cm-24x19in) s.d.35 mixed media. 23-Sep-3 Wiener Kunst Auktionen, Vienna #88/R est:3500-5000

DOBROWSKY, Josef (attrib) (1889-1964) Austrian

£333	$597	€500	Weir (45x68cm-18x27in) i. stretcher. 13-May-4 Dorotheum, Linz #467/R

Works on paper

£694	$1132	€1000	Landscape (27x30cm-11x12in) W/C. 23-Sep-3 Wiener Kunst Auktionen, Vienna #100/R

DOBRZYCKI, Zygmunt (1895-1970) Belgian/Polish

£987	$1816	€1500	Femme au jardin (59x72cm-23x28in) s. 28-Jun-4 Joron-Derem, Paris #164 est:800-1000
£1074	$1965	€1600	Paysage de Paris (81x100cm-32x39in) s. 7-Jul-4 Artcurial Briest, Paris #115 est:1200-1800
£1074	$1965	€1600	Cavaliers (81x100cm-32x39in) s.d.1953. 7-Jul-4 Artcurial Briest, Paris #116 est:1200-1800
£1342	$2456	€2000	Femme a sa toilette (100x81cm-39x32in) s. 7-Jul-4 Artcurial Briest, Paris #113/R est:1500-2000
£1342	$2456	€2000	Nu assis (73x60cm-29x24in) s.d.1932. 7-Jul-4 Artcurial Briest, Paris #114 est:1500-2000

DOBSON, Cowan (1893-1980) British

£294	$550	€429	Portrait of Dorothy Lamour (61x51cm-24x20in) s.d.43. 29-Feb-4 Bonhams & Butterfields, San Francisco #4549
£800	$1488	€1168	Ann Isobela Peck, half length portrait (75x62cm-30x24in) s. 6-Mar-4 Shapes, Edinburgh #402/R
£1450	$2683	€2117	Reclining nude (51x66cm-20x26in) init. 11-Mar-4 Christie's, Kensington #19/R est:1000-1500

DOBSON, Frank (1886-1963) British

£325	$517	€475	Seated nude (61x51cm-24x20in) board. 1-May-3 John Nicholson, Haslemere #694
£550	$919	€803	Nude young girl with blonde hair (58x48cm-23x19in) board. 18-Jun-3 John Nicholson, Haslemere #621
£1000	$1670	€1460	Mary Leah (25x20cm-10x8in) panel. 16-Oct-3 Christie's, Kensington #319/R est:800-1200
£1000	$1850	€1460	Two seated girls in a meadow (25x35cm-10x14in) board. 11-Mar-4 Christie's, Kensington #37/R est:800-1200
£1600	$2672	€2336	Mary Leah lying down (20x25cm-8x10in) s.d.14 oil pencil panel. 16-Oct-3 Christie's, Kensington #317/R est:800-1200
£1700	$2924	€2482	Mother and child (32x41cm-13x16in) s.d.14 board. 3-Dec-3 Christie's, Kensington #632/R est:1200-1800

Sculpture

£5500	$10175	€8030	Female torso (45cm-18in) s. plaster. 11-Mar-4 Christie's, Kensington #51/R est:800-1200

Works on paper

£300	$519	€438	Red crested cardinals (35x48cm-14x19in) s.i.d.46 pastel W/C. 9-Dec-3 Bonhams, Oxford #31
£320	$531	€467	Baby cradled in mother's arms (31x27cm-12x11in) s. pencil. 6-Oct-3 David Duggleby, Scarborough #243
£360	$623	€526	Sulphur and white breasted Toucans (35x48cm-14x19in) s.i.d.46 pastel W/C. 9-Dec-3 Bonhams, Oxford #82/R
£450	$752	€657	Seated female nude (38x18cm-15x7in) s.d.20 pencil. 16-Oct-3 Christie's, Kensington #242
£650	$1086	€949	Crouching nude (25x34cm-10x13in) s. red chk. 16-Oct-3 Christie's, Kensington #248/R
£700	$1274	€1022	Seated female nude (51x35cm-20x14in) s.d.30 pencil W/C. 1-Jul-4 Christie's, Kensington #19/R
£800	$1456	€1168	Nude (51x35cm-20x14in) s.d.35 ink chl. 15-Jun-4 Bonhams, New Bond Street #45/R
£850	$1386	€1241	Standing nude (48x31cm-19x12in) s. col chks. 24-Sep-3 Dreweatt Neate, Newbury #17
£900	$1638	€1314	Female nude torso (51x35cm-20x14in) s. red chk. 1-Jul-4 Christie's, Kensington #20/R
£1000	$1720	€1460	Portrait of a man (39x25cm-15x10in) pencil W/C. 3-Dec-3 Christie's, Kensington #637/R est:1200-1800
£1500	$2775	€2190	Seated nude (25x35cm-10x14in) s.d.36 red chk prov. 11-Mar-4 Christie's, Kensington #54/R est:700-900
£1700	$3094	€2482	Nude (35x24cm-14x9in) s.d.31 red chk W/C. 15-Jun-4 Bonhams, New Bond Street #42/R est:1500-2000
£1800	$3276	€2628	Coastal scene with boats (34x49cm-13x19in) W/C prov. 15-Jun-4 Bonhams, New Bond Street #41/R est:2000-2500

DOBSON, Henry John (1858-1928) British

£300	$501	€438	Drawing water (45x35cm-18x14in) s.d.97. 16-Oct-3 Bonhams, Edinburgh #143
£400	$680	€584	Village scene with a lady standing beside a figure on a horse and cart (25x30cm-10x12in) init. prov. 19-Nov-3 Tennants, Leyburn #1086
£900	$1503	€1314	Her ain fireside (29x39cm-11x15in) s. 16-Oct-3 Bonhams, Edinburgh #130/R
£1000	$1720	€1460	His first steps (45x60cm-18x24in) s. 4-Dec-3 Bonhams, Edinburgh #91 est:1200-1800
£1014	$1693	€1450	Interior (35x46cm-14x18in) s.i. 10-Oct-3 Winterberg, Heidelberg #561/R
£1049	$1752	€1500	The Belfry (46x36cm-18x14in) s.i. 28-Jun-3 Bolland & Marotz, Bremen #633/R est:1600
£2000	$3620	€2920	Belfry (46x35cm-18x14in) s.i. 19-Apr-4 Sotheby's, London #11/R est:2500-3000
£2800	$4816	€4088	Reading by the grate (45x60cm-18x24in) s. 4-Dec-3 Bonhams, Edinburgh #54/R est:3000-5000
£2800	$4816	€4088	Spinning (50x60cm-20x24in) s. 4-Dec-3 Bonhams, Edinburgh #37/R est:3000-5000
£3000	$5430	€4380	Hot porridge (35x45cm-14x18in) s. 19-Apr-4 Sotheby's, London #16/R est:2500-3000
£4600	$7222	€6670	Stoking the coals (25x30cm-10x12in) s. 27-Aug-3 Sotheby's, London #932/R est:1500-2000
£5000	$7850	€7250	Feeding the cat (41x30cm-16x12in) s. 27-Aug-3 Sotheby's, London #933/R est:3000-5000
£5200	$8476	€7592	Pride of her heart (45x60cm-18x24in) s.i. two. 25-Sep-3 Mellors & Kirk, Nottingham #745/R est:2000-2500

Works on paper

£350	$584	€500	The donkey ride (25x17cm-10x7in) mono.d.1901 W/C. 28-Jun-3 Bolland & Marotz, Bremen #634/R

DOBSON, Henry Raeburn (1901-) British
£280 $529 €409 Still life of chrysanthemums (61x51cm-24x20in) s. 19-Feb-4 Lyon & Turnbull, Edinburgh #111/R

DOBSON, Raeburn (20th C) British
£300 $561 €438 Banff. s. 22-Jul-4 Bonhams, Edinburgh #352

DOBSON, Robert (fl.1860-1901) British
Works on paper
£360 $644 €526 Extensive river landscape with figures on a bank (47x74cm-19x29in) s. W/C. 17-Mar-4 Bonhams, Chester #245
£900 $1422 €1314 River landscape with autumnal foliage (69x112cm-27x44in) s. 23-Jul-3 Grant, Worcester #434/R

DOBSON, William (attrib) (1610-1646) British
£709 $1255 €1035 Portrait of Edward Pierce (72x60cm-28x24in) board. 28-Apr-4 Dunbar Sloane, Auckland #56/R (NZ.D 2000)
£1854 $3393 €2800 Portrait presume de Lady Elizabeth Pickering (77x63cm-30x25in) oval. 7-Apr-4 Libert, Castor, Paris #17/R est:2000-3000

DOBSON, William Charles Thomas (1817-1898) British
Works on paper
£850 $1522 €1241 Gathering flowers (48x35cm-19x14in) s.d.1876 W/C. 25-May-4 Bonhams, Knightsbridge #207/R
£4769 $8203 €6963 Nursery tales (70x56cm-28x22in) mono.d.1874 W/C. 2-Dec-3 Bukowskis, Stockholm #272/R est:30000-40000 (S.KR 62000)

DOBYASCHOFSKY, Franz Joseph (1818-1867) Austrian
Works on paper
£2013 $3705 €3000 Herders resting in landscape with trees (45x60cm-18x24in) wash brush over pen. 26-Mar-4 Dorotheum, Vienna #64/R est:1000-1500

DOCHARTY, A Brownlie (1862-1940) British
£594 $950 €867 Scottish mountain scene (51x74cm-20x29in) 16-Sep-3 Maynards, Vancouver #370 est:2000-3000 (C.D 1300)
£1200 $2040 €1752 Salmon Pool (51x70cm-20x28in) s. exhib. 30-Oct-3 Christie's, London #118/R est:1500-2000
£1400 $2576 €2044 Shady nook (40x49cm-16x19in) s. 8-Jun-4 Bonhams, Knightsbridge #273/R est:1200-1800
£1500 $2355 €2175 Grazing sheep in a pasture (71x91cm-28x36in) s. 27-Aug-3 Sotheby's, London #1110/R est:2000-3000
£1604 $3000 €2342 Woodland stream, autumn (127x102cm-50x40in) s. 25-Feb-4 Doyle, New York #69/R est:3000-4000
£2000 $3740 €2920 Pigeons on a roof of a Lowland cottage with garden in foreground (15x30cm-6x12in) s.d.1930. 25-Feb-4 Mallams, Oxford #141/R est:2000-3000

DOCHARTY, James (1829-1878) British
£450 $810 €657 Landscape with loch and trees (42x62cm-17x24in) prov. 21-Apr-4 Tennants, Leyburn #1138
£620 $1085 €905 Spate on the Dochart, Kilin (64x89cm-25x35in) s.d.1872. 18-Dec-3 Bonhams, Edinburgh #359
£2300 $4163 €3358 Mountain torrent (73x103cm-29x41in) s.d.77 s.i.verso. 19-Apr-4 Sotheby's, London #31/R est:2500-3000

DOCKER, Edward (1858-1932) British
£2400 $4008 €3504 Feeding pigeons at the well (90x71cm-35x28in) s. 8-Oct-3 Christie's, Kensington #915/R est:800-1200

DOCKING, Shay (1928-) Australian
£954 $1737 €1393 Edge of the lake (91x137cm-36x54in) s.d.59 s.i.verso board. 16-Jun-4 Deutscher-Menzies, Melbourne #364/R est:3000-5000 (A.D 2500)

DOCKREE, Mark Edwin (1858-1890) British
£1200 $2148 €1752 Morning on sands near Aberystwith. Afternoon on the coast at Borth (18x42cm-7x17in) s. pair. 26-May-4 Christie's, Kensington #634/R est:600-800

DODD, Arthur Charles (fl.1878-1890) British
£1049 $1900 €1532 Bobby (25x35cm-10x14in) s.i. panel. 30-Mar-4 Bonhams & Butterfields, San Francisco #29/R est:1800-2500

DODD, Charles Tattershall (jnr) (fl.1892-1929) British
£620 $992 €905 At Quimperle, Finisterre (54x36cm-21x14in) s. i.stretcher. 16-Sep-3 Bonhams, Knowle #117

DODD, Charles Tattershall (snr) (1815-1878) British
£5556 $10000 €8112 Landscape in Wales (69x102cm-27x40in) s.d.1854. 22-Apr-4 Christie's, Rockefeller NY #50/R est:12000-18000

DODD, Francis (1874-1949) British
£400 $728 €584 Blackheath street scene with figures, carts, cars etc (58x48cm-23x19in) s. painted c.1930. 3-Feb-4 Gorringes, Bexhill #1030
£950 $1634 €1387 Morning light (60x48cm-24x19in) s.d.1913 canvas on board. 3-Dec-3 Christie's, Kensington #188/R
Works on paper
£350 $602 €511 Whitehall (11x15cm-4x6in) s. pencil brown ink W/C. 3-Dec-3 Christie's, Kensington #93/R
£360 $666 €526 Gravesend (28x30cm-11x12in) s.d.1921 W/C. 9-Mar-4 Gorringes, Lewes #2217
£650 $1118 €949 Portrait of Muirhead Bone at his desk (31x26cm-12x10in) s.i.d.1931 pencil. 3-Dec-3 Christie's, Kensington #458

DODD, Harvey (20th C) American
Works on paper
£255 $400 €372 Untitled, house (69x104cm-27x41in) s. pastel exec.c.1990. 20-Apr-3 Outer Cape Auctions, Provincetown #85/R

DODD, Hugh (20th C) British
Works on paper
£480 $802 €701 Sizing up a filly (39x29cm-15x11in) s.i. W/C bodycol. 14-Oct-3 Bonhams, New Bond Street #259/R

DODD, Joseph Josiah (1809-1880) British
Works on paper
£250 $465 €365 Taj Mahal, Agra (56x39cm-22x15in) s.d.1869 W/C. 2-Mar-4 Bamfords, Derby #393/R

DODD, Lamar (?) ?
£1463 $2400 €2136 New York City scape (61x91cm-24x36in) s.i.d.1952 prov.exhib. 1-Jun-3 William Jenack, New York #56 est:2000-3000

DODD, Robert (1748-1816) British
£280 $518 €409 Trefruw Mill, near Llanrwst (32x37cm-13x15in) s.i. panel oval. 14-Jul-4 Christie's, Kensington #846/R
£12000 $19200 €17520 Ships of the fleet with a 74-gun Third Rate heading out of Portsmouth Harbour (55x21cm-22x8in) s. 16-Sep-3 Bonhams, New Bond Street #80/R est:12000-18000
£20000 $35800 €29200 Close action between HMS Eurotas and the French Frigate Clorinde 1814 (53x76cm-21x30in) s.d.1814 three prov.exhib. 26-May-4 Christie's, Kensington #580/R est:20000-30000
£240000 $384000 €350400 Battle of Trafalgar, the British columns. French Squadron (63x152cm-25x60in) one s.d.1805 pair. 16-Sep-3 Bonhams, New Bond Street #85/R est:100000-150000

DODD, Robert (attrib) (1748-1816) British
£7947 $14464 €12000 View of the action between HMS Amethyst, capturing the French frigate Neiman (79x58cm-31x23in) i. pair. 17-Jun-4 Hamilton Osborne King, Dublin #158/R est:3000-5000
£19000 $32680 €27740 Lord Howe's victory, the glorious 1st. June, 1784, English fleet bearing down on the French (137x199cm-54x78in) 2-Dec-3 Sotheby's, London #7/R est:10000-15000
£23000 $39560 €33580 Lord Howe's victory, the glorious 1st. June, 1794, Queen Charlotte in close action (137x187cm-54x74in) 2-Dec-3 Sotheby's, London #8/R est:10000-15000

DODEIGNE, Eugène (1923-) French
£3741 $6697 €5500 Femme allongee (97x130cm-38x51in) s. 19-Mar-4 Millon & Associes, Paris #174/R est:1500-2000
Sculpture
£1232 $2020 €1700 Figure (23cm-9in) init. num.4/6 bronze prov. 27-May-3 Sotheby's, Amsterdam #575/R est:500-700
£7483 $13395 €11000 Femme (150cm-59in) mono.base stone. 19-Mar-4 Millon & Associes, Paris #173/R est:4000-5000
£9441 $15766 €13500 Couchee (201x40cm-79x16in) mono. Cast Pierre de Soignies wood base prov.exhib.lit. 11-Oct-3 De Vuyst, Lokeren #479/R est:12000-15000
£9859 $17056 €14000 Figure (148x75cm-58x30in) stone freestone base Cast Pierre de Soignies. 13-Dec-3 De Vuyst, Lokeren #498/R est:13000-16000
£39860 $66566 €57000 Comme une colonne (225x58x58cm-89x23x23in) mono. Cast Pierre de Soignies prov. 11-Oct-3 De Vuyst, Lokeren #495/R
Works on paper
£667 $1193 €1000 Man walking (107x75cm-42x30in) s. chl. 15-May-4 De Vuyst, Lokeren #116

DODEL, Wilhelm (1907-1944) Russian
£17333 $31200 €26000 Rosemarie (125x840cm-49x331in) s.d. panel. 24-Apr-4 Dr Lehr, Berlin #99/R est:10000

DODENHOFF, Heinz (1889-?) German
£350 $601 €500 View from Weyerberg to Bremen (50x70cm-20x28in) s. i.verso board. 5-Dec-3 Bolland & Marotz, Bremen #357/R

DODGE, Frances Farrand (1878-?) American
£192 $350 €280 Landscape with stone wall (51x41cm-20x16in) s. board. 19-Jun-4 Jackson's, Cedar Falls #31/R

DODGSON, George Haydock (1811-1880) British
Works on paper
£600 $1080 €876 Wooded country house scene with figures by water front (31x24cm-12x9in) s.d.1845 W/C. 20-Apr-4 Hutchinson, Boroughbridge #302/R

DODSON, John (20th C) British
£400 $652 €584 Northern Memory 1 (61x86cm-24x34in) s.d.1994 i.verso. 24-Sep-3 Dreweatt Neate, Newbury #130

DODSON, Tom (1910-1991) British
£920 $1564 €1343 Northern street scene (44x33cm-17x13in) s.d.1977. 29-Oct-3 Bonhams, Chester #371/R
£1000 $1700 €1460 Northern street scene with figures at a bus stop (44x34cm-17x13in) s.d.1877. 29-Oct-3 Bonhams, Chester #372 est:900-1200

£1350 $2417 €1971 In the parlour (46x61cm-18x24in) s.d.1974 canvasboard. 17-Mar-4 Bonhams, Chester #255/R est:1200-1800
Works on paper
£350 $613 €511 Newsboy at a street corner (25x13cm-10x5in) s.i.d.74 pencil. 16-Dec-3 Capes Dunn, Manchester #711

DODT, Frants Martin (1775-1819) Danish
£281 $484 €410 Sleigh ride on Holmen's Canal (11x14cm-4x6in) s. cardboard oval. 2-Dec-3 Kunsthallen, Copenhagen #521/R (D.KR 3000)

DODWELL, Edward (1767-1832) British
Prints
£26000 $46540 €37960 Views in Greece (52x34cm-20x13in) i. hand col aquatint card 30 album. 13-May-4 Sotheby's, London #189/R est:25000-30000

DOELEMAN, Johan Hendrik (1848-1913) Dutch
£638 $1066 €900 Landscape with farm and peasants on a country path (23x32cm-9x13in) s.d.08 cardboard. 20-Oct-3 Glerum, Amsterdam #142/R

DOELL, Ludwig (1789-1863) German
£738 $1358 €1100 Willem Burchgraeff (62x52cm-24x20in) lit. 25-Mar-4 Karlheinz Kaupp, Staufen #2419/R

DOEMLING, John Carl (1892-?) American
£847 $1600 €1237 Seated lady holding red rose (76x66cm-30x26in) s. 17-Feb-4 John Moran, Pasadena #77/R est:3000-4000

DOERELL, E G (19th C) German
£470 $864 €700 Mountains with fortress (16x24cm-6x9in) s.d.76 panel. 27-Mar-4 Dannenberg, Berlin #547/R
£503 $926 €750 Winter landscape (16x24cm-6x9in) s. i. verso panel. 27-Mar-4 Dannenberg, Berlin #548/R

DOERR, Charles Augustin Victor (1815-1894) French
£5000 $8950 €7500 Julius Caesar on the Rubicone (94x126cm-37x50in) s. 17-May-4 Finarte Semenzato, Rome #84/R est:5000-6000

DOES, Jacob van der (attrib) (17th C) Dutch
£537 $988 €800 Herders with horse, sheep, cow and goats in Italian Campagna (32x44cm-13x17in) 26-Mar-4 Bolland & Marotz, Bremen #442/R

DOES, Willem van der (1889-1966) Dutch
£267 $477 €400 Winter near Overschie (48x68cm-19x27in) s. panel. 11-May-4 Vendu Notarishuis, Rotterdam #173
£489 $817 €700 Steamship (32x41cm-13x16in) s. 30-Jun-3 Sotheby's, Amsterdam #204
£884 $1583 €1300 Three Magi (43x31cm-17x12in) s. canvas on board prov. 16-Mar-4 Christie's, Amsterdam #50/R est:800-1200
£884 $1583 €1300 Achter mijm huis te Lawang bij het eerste ochtendgloren (49x33cm-19x13in) s. i.verso canvas on board prov. 16-Mar-4 Christie's, Amsterdam #51 est:600-800
£1088 $1948 €1600 Junk in the harbour of Soerabaja at night (50x75cm-20x30in) s.d.29. 16-Mar-4 Christie's, Amsterdam #54 est:800-1200
£1905 $3410 €2800 Zonsondergang achter den kawi (33x44cm-13x17in) s. canvas on board prov. 16-Mar-4 Christie's, Amsterdam #52 est:800-1200
£2951 $4929 €4308 Landscape. Street scene in Bandung (50x80cm-20x31in) s.d.33 two. 12-Oct-3 Sotheby's, Singapore #48/R est:5000-7000 (S.D 8500)
£4898 $8767 €7200 Dinogo bij batoe (70x100cm-28x39in) s.d.32 i.stretcher prov. 16-Mar-4 Christie's, Amsterdam #49/R est:2500-3500

DOESBURG, Theo van and SCHWITTERS, Kurt (20th C) Dutch
Prints
£2941 $5000 €4294 Kleine Dada soiree (30x31cm-12x12in) offset lithograph exec.1922. 31-Oct-3 Sotheby's, New York #460/R est:2000-3000

DOESER, Jacobus (1884-1969) Dutch
£294 $499 €420 Still life of flowers with roses (74x59cm-29x23in) s. 24-Nov-3 Glerum, Amsterdam #104/R
£336 $621 €500 Flowers in a vase (60x80cm-24x31in) s. 15-Mar-4 Sotheby's, Amsterdam #196/R
£340 $619 €500 Still life with zinnias in a vase (80x60cm-31x24in) s. sold with etching. 3-Feb-4 Christie's, Amsterdam #427
£541 $1000 €790 Mountain landscape (84x104cm-33x41in) 13-Feb-4 Du Mouchelle, Detroit #2014/R
£898 $1500 €1311 Portrait of a woman (76x61cm-30x24in) 17-Oct-3 Du Mouchelle, Detroit #2170/R est:1600-2000

DOEUS, Cora (?) French
Works on paper
£563 $975 €800 Portrait de Sara Bernard (40x35cm-16x14in) graphite. 12-Dec-3 Renaud, Paris #61b

DOEVE, Eppo (1907-) Dutch
Works on paper
£544 $990 €800 Picking pears (42x42cm-17x17in) s. gouache. 3-Feb-4 Christie's, Amsterdam #418

DOFFO, Juan (20th C) Argentinian
£2473 $4500 €3611 Sky composition (60x60cm-24x24in) s.i.d.1997 verso acrylic. 29-Jun-4 Arroyo, Buenos Aires #66/R est:4500
£3297 $6000 €4814 Bridge (50x150cm-20x59in) s.i.d.1999 verso acrylic. 5-Jul-4 Arroyo, Buenos Aires #58/R est:4000

DOGARTH, Erich Josef (1927-) Austrian
£379 $700 €569 Floral still life with beetle and butterfly (30x23cm-12x9in) s. 17-Jul-4 Skinner, Boston #330/R

DOGNON-SCHMIDT, Gerard (20th C) ?
£420 $752 €613 Portrait of Yehudi Menuhin (91x72cm-36x28in) s.d.1988. 11-May-4 Sotheby's, Olympia #561/R

DOHAN, Kaigetsudo (fl.1710-1720) Japanese
Prints
£17391 $32000 €25391 Standing courtesan (58x32cm-23x13in) s.col print. 23-Mar-4 Christie's, Rockefeller NY #1/R est:35000-45000

DOHANOS, Stevan (1907-1994) American
Works on paper
£695 $1300 €1015 Expedition members using shortwave radio (66x51cm-26x20in) s. casein. 26-Feb-4 Illustration House, New York #56
£815 $1500 €1190 Maine fishermen at shore (20x25cm-8x10in) s. black ink white gouache. 10-Jun-4 Swann Galleries, New York #76/R est:2000-3000

DOHLMANN, Augusta (1847-1914) Austrian
£944 $1605 €1350 Vase de fleurs (51x47cm-20x19in) indis.s.d. 18-Nov-3 Vanderkindere, Brussels #29

DOHM, Heinrich (1875-1940) Danish
£516 $877 €753 Coastal landscape with beached fishing boats (48x61cm-19x24in) s.d.1929. 10-Nov-3 Rasmussen, Vejle #439 (D.KR 5600)

DOHNALEK, K (20th C) Hungarian
£427 $682 €623 Landscape with girl wearing national costume, Eastern Europe (74x100cm-29x39in) s. 22-Sep-3 Rasmussen, Vejle #53/R (D.KR 4500)

DOHRS, Marjorie (20th C) American
Works on paper
£2794 $4750 €4079 Untitled - foundry laborers (43x33cm-17x13in) s.d.1934 verso gouache. 9-Nov-3 Wright, Chicago #157 est:700-900

DOIG, Peter (1959-) British
£5000 $9100 €7300 Untitled (30x21cm-12x8in) s.d.99 oil W/C paper prov. 5-Feb-4 Christie's, London #215/R est:6000-8000
£11173 $20000 €16313 Untitled, American house (42x60cm-17x24in) s.d.99 verso oil paper prov.exhib. 14-May-4 Phillips, New York #125/R est:10000-15000
£13000 $23530 €18980 Ski mountain (27x21cm-11x8in) s.i.d.1995 verso panel prov. 1-Apr-4 Christie's, Kensington #348/R est:4000-6000
£36000 $60120 €52560 Reflection (31x36cm-12x14in) s.i.d.97 verso prov. 21-Oct-3 Sotheby's, London #308/R est:25000-35000
£39106 $70000 €57095 Hitch-hiker, reflected (63x99cm-25x39in) s.i.d.1990 verso prov. 12-May-4 Christie's, Rockefeller NY #352/R est:80000-120000
£95808 $160000 €139880 Figure in the surf (137x98cm-54x39in) s. i.d.2000 verso prov. 12-Nov-3 Sotheby's, New York #35/R est:100000-150000
£130000 $217100 €189800 Winter landscape - backyard (91x76cm-36x30in) s.i.d.96/97 i.verso prov.exhib. 21-Oct-3 Sotheby's, London #306/R est:70000-90000
£191617 $320000 €279761 White Creep (290x199cm-114x78in) s.i.d.95-1996 verso prov. 11-Nov-3 Christie's, Rockefeller NY #51/R est:200000-300000
Prints
£3000 $5520 €4380 One hundred years ago (96x60cm-38x24in) s.num.21/46 col etching prov. 24-Jun-4 Sotheby's, Olympia #424/R est:2500-3500

DOIGNEAU, Edouard Edmond de (1865-1954) French
£734 $1320 €1100 Le cirque (54x65cm-21x26in) s. exhib. 26-Apr-4 Tajan, Paris #174 est:600-800
£1477 $2761 €2200 Veneur landais (40x32cm-16x13in) panel. 1-Mar-4 Coutau Begarie, Paris #211/R est:1200-1400
Works on paper
£284 $474 €400 Berger Marocain appuye sur un baton (36x25cm-14x10in) crayon gouache W/C. 16-Jun-3 Gros & Delettrez, Paris #301/R
£319 $533 €450 Caravane aux abords d'une ville (22x30cm-9x12in) crayon gouache W/C. 16-Jun-3 Gros & Delettrez, Paris #309/R
£352 $609 €500 Etude pour cavalier (32x17cm-13x7in) crayon gouache W/C. 15-Dec-3 Gros & Delettrez, Paris #12/R
£355 $592 €500 Femme pres d'une mosquee (22x30cm-9x12in) crayon gouache W/C. 16-Jun-3 Gros & Delettrez, Paris #297/R
£367 $675 €550 L'homme au burnous, Meknes (34x24cm-13x9in) i.d.29 crayon gouache W/C. 14-Jun-4 Gros & Delettrez, Paris #14/R
£367 $675 €550 Berger dans l'Atlas (17x28cm-7x11in) crayon gouache W/C. 14-Jun-4 Gros & Delettrez, Paris #27/R
£400 $736 €600 Le marchand d'agrumes, Bab el Hart, Rabat (35x24cm-14x9in) i. crayon gouache W/C. 14-Jun-4 Gros & Delettrez, Paris #2/R
£400 $736 €600 Chameau au repos, Rabat (24x35cm-9x14in) i. crayon gouache W/C. 14-Jun-4 Gros & Delettrez, Paris #5/R
£400 $736 €600 La caravane devant le Tombeau des Mamelouks, Le Caire (22x30cm-9x12in) crayon gouache W/C. 14-Jun-4 Gros & Delettrez, Paris #9/R
£400 $736 €600 Au marche, Maroc (24x35cm-9x14in) crayon gouache W/C. 14-Jun-4 Gros & Delettrez, Paris #12/R
£400 $736 €600 Femme de Marrakech (32x23cm-13x9in) i. crayon gouache W/C. 14-Jun-4 Gros & Delettrez, Paris #17/R
£400 $736 €600 Femme assise devant une maison (34x24cm-13x9in) crayon gouache W/C. 14-Jun-4 Gros & Delettrez, Paris #18/R
£423 $731 €600 Cavalier quittant Meknes (25x35cm-10x14in) i. crayon gouache W/C. 15-Dec-3 Gros & Delettrez, Paris #4/R
£423 $731 €600 Porteuse d'eau (35x25cm-14x10in) i. crayon gouache W/C. 15-Dec-3 Gros & Delettrez, Paris #15/R

£423	$731	€600	Jeune femme a la robe rose (32x21cm-13x8in) crayon gouache W/C. 15-Dec-3 Gros & Delettrez, Paris #13/R
£426	$711	€600	Femme de Bou-Saada (31x22cm-12x9in) i. crayon gouache W/C. 16-Jun-3 Gros & Delettrez, Paris #283/R
£426	$711	€600	Deux dromadaires sur les bords nu Nil (22x30cm-9x12in) crayon W/C gouache. 16-Jun-3 Gros & Delettrez, Paris #291/R
£432	$708	€600	Chasse a courre (39x31cm-15x12in) studio st. W/C gouache. 3-Jun-3 Livinec, Gaudcheau & Jezequel, Rennes #16/R
£433	$797	€650	Chameaux dans les souks de Marrakech (24x53cm-9x21in) i. crayon gouache W/C. 14-Jun-4 Gros & Delettrez, Paris #19/R
£433	$797	€650	Marche a Marrakech (24x35cm-9x14in) i. crayon gouache W/C. 14-Jun-4 Gros & Delettrez, Paris #24/R
£433	$797	€650	Felouk sur les bords du Nil (22x30cm-9x12in) crayon gouache W/C. 14-Jun-4 Gros & Delettrez, Paris #25/R
£467	$859	€700	Deux cavaliers, Maroc (25x34cm-10x13in) crayon gouache W/C two sheets. 14-Jun-4 Gros & Delettrez, Paris #1/R
£467	$859	€700	Caravane s'abreuvant sur les bords du Nil (22x30cm-9x12in) i. crayon gouache W/C. 14-Jun-4 Gros & Delettrez, Paris #8/R
£467	$859	€700	Cavalier Marocain (31x23cm-12x9in) crayon gouache W/C. 14-Jun-4 Gros & Delettrez, Paris #10/R
£470	$869	€700	Homme assis (32x20cm-13x8in) pencil gouache W/C. 15-Mar-4 Gros & Delettrez, Paris #3/R
£470	$869	€700	Femmes faisant de la vannerie a Ghise (22x30cm-9x12in) i. pencil gouache W/C. 15-Mar-4 Gros & Delettrez, Paris #8/R
£496	$829	€700	Le petit Algerien El Hamel (32x22cm-13x9in) crayon gouache W/C. 16-Jun-3 Gros & Delettrez, Paris #285/R
£496	$829	€700	Femme de Bou-Saada (45x32cm-18x13in) crayon gouache W/C. 16-Jun-3 Gros & Delettrez, Paris #286/R
£496	$829	€700	Marchand devant son echopee a Brousse, Turquie (22x30cm-9x12in) crayon W/C gouache. 16-Jun-3 Gros & Delettrez, Paris #296/R
£496	$829	€700	Portrait de Mohamed (32x24cm-13x9in) i. crayon gouache. 16-Jun-3 Gros & Delettrez, Paris #302/R
£496	$829	€700	Cheval arabe (23x30cm-9x12in) crayon gouache W/C. 16-Jun-3 Gros & Delettrez, Paris #305/R
£500	$920	€750	Deux cavaliers devant une casbah (24x35cm-9x14in) crayon gouache W/C. 14-Jun-4 Gros & Delettrez, Paris #4/R
£533	$981	€800	Marchand de legumes, Maroc (25x34cm-10x13in) crayon gouache W/C. 14-Jun-4 Gros & Delettrez, Paris #6/R
£533	$981	€800	Cavalier et deux chevaux, sur les hauteurs de Fes (24x35cm-9x14in) mono.i. crayon gouache W/C. 14-Jun-4 Gros & Delettrez, Paris #13/R
£537	$993	€800	Vue de Rabat-Sale (22x29cm-9x11in) pencil gouache W/C. 15-Mar-4 Gros & Delettrez, Paris #2/R
£537	$993	€800	Cavaliers devant une casbah de l'Atlas (15x20cm-6x8in) pencil gouache W/C. 15-Mar-4 Gros & Delettrez, Paris #11/R
£563	$975	€800	Fontaine de Fes (34x24cm-13x9in) s.i.d.29 crayon gouache W/C. 15-Dec-3 Gros & Delettrez, Paris #3/R
£563	$975	€800	Jeune fille de Marrakech (31x23cm-12x9in) i. crayon gouache W/C. 15-Dec-3 Gros & Delettrez, Paris #9/R
£563	$975	€800	CHasseur marocain (32x19cm-13x7in) crayon gouache. 15-Dec-3 Gros & Delettrez, Paris #10/R
£563	$975	€800	Cavalier et cheval s'abreuvant (32x25cm-13x10in) crayon gouache W/C. 15-Dec-3 Gros & Delettrez, Paris #17/R
£563	$975	€800	Cavalier de fantasia (32x25cm-13x10in) crayon gouache W/C. 15-Dec-3 Gros & Delettrez, Paris #16/R
£563	$975	€800	Cavalier devant le marabout (24x31cm-9x12in) crayon gouache W/C. 15-Dec-3 Gros & Delettrez, Paris #18/R
£563	$975	€800	Cavalier de fantasia (32x22cm-13x9in) crayon gouache W/C. 15-Dec-3 Gros & Delettrez, Paris #25/R
£563	$975	€800	Cavalier et paysan (24x34cm-9x13in) crayon gouache W/C. 15-Dec-3 Gros & Delettrez, Paris #29/R
£567	$948	€800	Jeune mere et son enfant sur le chemin (31x24cm-12x9in) crayon gouache W/C. 16-Jun-3 Gros & Delettrez, Paris #284/R
£567	$948	€800	Famille de nomades et leurs dromadaires (22x30cm-9x12in) crayon W/C gouache. 16-Jun-3 Gros & Delettrez, Paris #290/R
£567	$948	€800	Chamelier sur une place, Le Caire (22x30cm-9x12in) crayon W/C gouache. 16-Jun-3 Gros & Delettrez, Paris #292/R
£567	$948	€800	Etudes de chevaux et personnages (25x36cm-10x14in) crayon gouache W/C. 16-Jun-3 Gros & Delettrez, Paris #306/R
£567	$1043	€850	Cactus et aloes aux environs de Rabat (26x35cm-10x14in) crayon gouache W/C. 14-Jun-4 Gros & Delettrez, Paris #28/R
£600	$1104	€900	Vue de Fortassa, envirn de Meknes (34x24cm-13x9in) i. crayon gouache W/C. 14 Jun 4 Gros & Delettrez, Paris #11/R
£600	$1104	€900	Entree de palais, Meknes (34x24cm-13x9in) i. crayon gouache W/C. 14-Jun-4 Gros & Delettrez, Paris #26/R
£604	$1117	€900	Dromadaires et femme portant un panier (21x29cm-8x11in) pencil gouache W/C. 15-Mar-4 Gros & Delettrez, Paris #5/R
£634	$1096	€900	Chamelier et troupeau (22x30cm-9x12in) crayon gouache W/C. 15-Dec-3 Gros & Delettrez, Paris #33/R
£634	$1096	€900	Tombeaux des Califes (22x30cm-9x12in) i.d.1913 crayon gouache W/C. 15-Dec-3 Gros & Delettrez, Paris #32/R
£634	$1096	€900	Caravane. Jeune fille et dromadaires (22x30cm-9x12in) crayon gouache W/C double-sided. 15-Dec-3 Gros & Delettrez, Paris #30/R
£634	$1096	€900	Marchand de courges (24x34cm-9x13in) crayon gouache W/C. 15-Dec-3 Gros & Delettrez, Paris #26/R
£634	$1096	€900	Repos a l'ombre des agaves (25x35cm-10x14in) crayon gouache W/C. 15-Dec-3 Gros & Delettrez, Paris #28/R
£634	$1096	€900	Rivages du Caire (22x30cm-9x12in) i. crayon gouache W/C. 15-Dec-3 Gros & Delettrez, Paris #35/R
£638	$1066	€900	Pur sang, selle et etrier. Scene de rue animee (25x36cm-10x14in) crayon gouache W/C double-sided. 16-Jun-3 Gros & Delettrez, Paris #307/R
£638	$1066	€900	Paysage marocain (32x44cm-13x17in) gouache. 19-Oct-3 Rabourdin & Choppin de Janvry, Paris #148/R
£667	$1227	€1000	Le repos de la caravane (22x30cm-9x12in) crayon gouache W/C. 14-Jun-4 Gros & Delettrez, Paris #31/R
£671	$1242	€1000	Cavalier (34x24cm-13x9in) pencil gouache W/C. 15-Mar-4 Gros & Delettrez, Paris #7/R
£671	$1242	€1000	La caravane (19x26cm-7x10in) mono.d.1913 pencil gouache W/C. 15-Mar-4 Gros & Delettrez, Paris #13/R
£704	$1218	€1000	Cour de palais a Rabat (35x25cm-14x10in) i. crayon gouache W/C. 15-Dec-3 Gros & Delettrez, Paris #1/R
£704	$1218	€1000	Cavalier de fantasia (36x25cm-14x10in) crayon gouache W/C. 15-Dec-3 Gros & Delettrez, Paris #23/R
£704	$1218	€1000	Felouks (13x16cm-5x6in) crayon gouache W/C. 15-Dec-3 Gros & Delettrez, Paris #31
£704	$1218	€1000	Barbouk (22x30cm-9x12in) i.d.1913 crayon gouache W/C. 15-Dec-3 Gros & Delettrez, Paris #27/R
£709	$1184	€1000	Cavalier devant Bab Guenoua (36x25cm-14x10in) crayon gouache W/C. 16-Jun-3 Gros & Delettrez, Paris #299/R
£709	$1184	€1000	Sur le chemin (22x30cm-9x12in) crayon W/C gouache. 16-Jun-3 Gros & Delettrez, Paris #310/R
£775	$1340	€1100	Porte de Filala, Fes (35x25cm-14x10in) s.i. crayon gouache W/C. 15-Dec-3 Gros & Delettrez, Paris #2/R
£775	$1340	€1100	Campement dans le desert (38x46cm-15x18in) crayon gouache W/C. 15-Dec-3 Gros & Delettrez, Paris #8/R
£775	$1340	€1100	Campement (31x46cm-12x18in) crayon gouache W/C. 15-Dec-3 Gros & Delettrez, Paris #5/R
£775	$1340	€1100	Cavalier marocain (31x24cm-12x9in) crayon gouache W/C. 15-Dec-3 Gros & Delettrez, Paris #24/R
£805	$1490	€1200	Cavalier (29x23cm-11x9in) pencil gouache W/C. 15-Mar-4 Gros & Delettrez, Paris #4/R
£805	$1490	€1200	Marabout a Fes (24x35cm-9x14in) i. pencil gouache W/C. 15-Mar-4 Gros & Delettrez, Paris #15/R
£845	$1462	€1200	Scene de marche (25x35cm-10x14in) i. crayon gouache.w. 15-Dec-3 Gros & Delettrez, Paris #11/R
£845	$1462	€1200	Reservoir de Bir et Bey (31x46cm-12x18in) i. crayon gouache W/C. 15-Dec-3 Gros & Delettrez, Paris #7
£845	$1462	€1200	Marchand de chevaux (25x35cm-10x14in) crayon gouache W/C. 15-Dec-3 Gros & Delettrez, Paris #6/R
£845	$1479	€1200	Depar pour la chasse, la meute (36x28cm-14x11in) s. W/C gouache. 21-Dec-3 Thierry & Lannon, Brest #223
£845	$1479	€1200	Bas Pouldu (31x46cm-12x18in) s. pastel W/C. 21-Dec-3 Thierry & Lannon, Brest #250
£851	$1421	€1200	Le cheval et l'enfant, Tunisie (23x30cm-9x12in) crayon gouache W/C. 16-Jun-3 Gros & Delettrez, Paris #308/R
£922	$1540	€1300	Cavaliers de fantasia, Maroc (36x25cm-14x10in) crayon gouache W/C. 16-Jun-3 Gros & Delettrez, Paris #287/R
£940	$1738	€1400	Chamelier et dromadaires, Marrakech (24x34cm-9x13in) i. pencil gouache W/C. 15-Mar-4 Gros & Delettrez, Paris #6/R
£940	$1738	€1400	Vue de Rabat (25x35cm-10x14in) i. pencil gouache W/C. 15-Mar-4 Gros & Delettrez, Paris #9/R
£951	$1645	€1350	Chamelle et son petit. Bac de Gizeh (22x31cm-9x12in) i. crayon gouache W/C double-sided. 15-Dec-3 Gros & Delettrez, Paris #36/R
£993	$1658	€1400	Cheval et jeune cavalier a la fontaine (22x30cm-9x12in) crayon W/C gouache. 16-Jun-3 Gros & Delettrez, Paris #311/R
£1064	$1777	€1500	Cavalier pres de Meknes (25x36cm-10x14in) i. crayon gouache W/C. 16-Jun-3 Gros & Delettrez, Paris #280/R est:600-900
£1074	$1987	€1600	Cheval et cavalier (25x36cm-10x14in) pencil gouache W/C. 15-Mar-4 Gros & Delettrez, Paris #12/R est:750-1000
£1074	$1987	€1600	Cavalier avec deux chevaux (25x35cm-10x14in) pencil gouache W/C. 15-Mar-4 Gros & Delettrez, Paris #1/R est:600-900
£1135	$1895	€1600	Deux cavaliers (31x23cm-12x9in) crayon gouache W/C. 16-Jun-3 Gros & Delettrez, Paris #298/R est:1000-1500
£1208	$2235	€1800	Cavalier (30x16cm-12x6in) pencil gouache W/C. 15-Mar-4 Gros & Delettrez, Paris #10/R est:750-1000
£1333	$2453	€2000	Le marche marocain (31x41cm-12x16in) s. W/C. 11-Jun-4 Claude Aguttes, Neuilly #121/R est:2000-3000
£1348	$2250	€1900	Vue de Fes (24x36cm-9x14in) crayon gouache W/C. 16-Jun-3 Gros & Delettrez, Paris #281/R est:800-1000
£1489	$2487	€2100	Meknes, la halte (24x35cm-9x14in) crayon gouache W/C. 16-Jun-3 Gros & Delettrez, Paris #279/R est:1200-1800
£1489	$2487	€2100	Cavalier du Maroc (31x23cm-12x9in) crayon gouache W/C. 16-Jun-3 Gros & Delettrez, Paris #289/R est:1000-1500
£1560	$2606	€2200	Cavalier de fantasia (36x25cm-14x10in) crayon gouache W/C. 16-Jun-3 Gros & Delettrez, Paris #288/R est:1200-1800
£1611	$2980	€2400	Cavalier et sa monture (24x35cm-9x14in) pencil gouache W/C. 15-Mar-4 Gros & Delettrez, Paris #14/R est:600-900
£1702	$2843	€2400	Felouque a Gizeh (45x30cm-18x12in) i.d.1913 crayon gouache W/C. 16-Jun-3 Gros & Delettrez, Paris #293/R est:750-1100
£1773	$2961	€2500	Cavalier devant une porte a Fes (25x36cm-10x14in) crayon gouache W/C. 16-Jun-3 Gros & Delettrez, Paris #282/R est:1500-2300
£2042	$3533	€2900	Cavalier au bord de l'oued (47x47cm-19x19in) s. W/C gouache. 15-Dec-3 Gros & Delettrez, Paris #22/R est:2000-3000

DOISNEAU, Robert (1912-1994) French

Photographs

£1587	$3000	€2317	La dame Indignee (24x30cm-9x12in) s. init.i.d.1981 verso gelatin silver print. 17-Feb-4 Christie's, Rockefeller NY #242/R est:2000-3000
£1647	$2750	€2405	Un regard oblique (40x50cm-16x20in) s. gelatin silver print exec.1948 lit. 21-Oct-3 Bonhams & Butterfields, San Francisco #1530/R
£1693	$3200	€2472	Le Fox Terrier du pont des arts (28x23cm-11x9in) s. init.i.d.1980 verso gelatin silver print. 17-Feb-4 Christie's, Rockefeller NY #3/R est:2000-3000
£1695	$3000	€2475	La Dame Indignee, 1948 (24x30cm-9x12in) s.verso gelatin silver print. 27-Apr-4 Christie's, Rockefeller NY #274/R est:2000-3000
£1796	$3000	€2622	La stricte intimite (25x20cm-10x8in) i. studio st. verso gelatin silver print exec.1945 prov.lit. 17-Oct-3 Phillips, New York #123/R est:3000-4000
£1932	$3400	€2821	Les animaux superierus (23x34cm-9x13in) with sig. i.d.1954 verso silver print. 20-May-4 Swann Galleries, New York #451/R est:2500-3500
£2116	$4000	€3089	Un regard oblique (24x29cm-9x11in) s. init.d.verso gelatin silver print. 17-Feb-4 Christie's, Rockefeller NY #11/R est:3000-5000
£2147	$3800	€3135	L'information scolaire, 1956 (22x34cm-9x13in) s.i.d. num.3/3 verso gelatin silver print. 27-Apr-4 Christie's, Rockefeller NY #275/R est:2500-3500
£2260	$4000	€3300	Le baiser de l'hotel de Ville, 1950 (24x30cm-9x12in) s. init.i.d.verso gelatin silver print. 27-Apr-4 Christie's, Rockefeller NY #276/R est:4000-6000
£2381	$4500	€3476	Le baiser de l'Hotel de Ville (24x30cm-9x12in) s. i.d.1950 verso gelatin silver print. 17-Feb-4 Christie's, Rockefeller NY #1/R est:4000-6000
£2517	$4330	€3600	Jacques Prevert a la buvette du pont, pres de son chien (24x21cm-9x8in) s. photo. 6-Dec-3 Renaud, Paris #275/R
£2874	$4800	€4196	Le Baiser de l'Htmtel de Ville (24x27cm-9x11in) s. init.d.1950 verso gelatin silver print printed c.1980 lit. 20-Oct-3 Christie's, Rockefeller NY #93/R est:3000-5000
£2963	$5600	€4326	Un regard oblique (30x39cm-12x15in) silver print. 17-Feb-4 Swann Galleries, New York #74/R est:3500-4500
£4333	$7973	€6500	Couple doing the Bebop in night club in Saint Germain des Pres, Paris (60x49cm-24x19in) silver gelatin lit.exhib. 10-Jun-4 Villa Grisebach, Berlin #1061/R est:2000-3000

DOK-HI KIM (20th C) Oriental

£10417	$17396	€15000	Night reflection (152x152cm-60x60in) s.d.2002 verso. 25-Oct-3 Cornette de St.Cyr, Paris #728 est:15000-20000

DOKKUM, Gerard Willem Pieter van (1870-1931) Dutch

£540	$950	€788	Peasant on a county road (25x36cm-10x14in) s. 22-May-4 Harvey Clar, Oakland #2194

DOKOUPIL, Jiri Georg (1954-) Czechoslovakian
£436 $750 €637 Boy with calculator (30x30cm-12x12in) s.d.2034 acrylic painted 1985 prov. 3-Dec-3 Doyle, New York #66/R
£6711 $11879 €10000 Untitled (210x324cm-83x128in) s. verso lit. 28-Apr-4 Wiener Kunst Auktionen, Vienna #314/R est:10000-15000
Works on paper
£699 $1168 €1000 Poire (105x75cm-41x30in) s.d.1990 W/C. 11-Oct-3 Cornette de St.Cyr, Paris #148/R
£700 $1288 €1022 Apfel und birne - die neue ordnung (43x42cm-17x17in) chl prov. 24-Jun-4 Sotheby's, Olympia #601/R
£700 $1288 €1022 Korper und geist - die neue orgnung (55x42cm-22x17in) chl prov. 24-Jun-4 Sotheby's, Olympia #602/R
£900 $1656 €1350 Composition (56x42cm-22x17in) mono.d.83 pastel. 12-Jun-4 Villa Grisebach, Berlin #705/R est:1200-1500
£1133 $2063 €1700 Untitled (70x51cm-28x20in) s.d.1989 dr prov. 29-Jun-4 Cornette de St.Cyr, Paris #158/R est:1500-2000
£2500 $4525 €3650 Tronco de brasil (100x81cm-39x32in) s.d.1989 verso i.stretcher soot on canvas. 1-Apr-4 Christie's, Kensington #264/R est:3000-4000

DOLAN, Patrick (1926-1980) British
£380 $703 €555 Abstract in black and white (65x46cm-26x18in) 13-Jul-4 Bonhams, Knightsbridge #53/R
£1338 $2141 €1900 Substrata echo (102x91cm-40x36in) s.i. oil mixed media hessian prov. 16-Sep-3 Whyte's, Dublin #47/R est:2000-3000

DOLANDE, Jean (20th C) French?
£1267 $2267 €1900 Composition (60x92cm-24x36in) 16-May-4 Osenat, Fontainebleau #77/R est:1500-2000
£1275 $2385 €1900 Composition (80x80cm-31x31in) s.d.2003 verso oil acrylic. 29-Feb-4 Versailles Encheres #223 est:1200-1500

DOLANYI BENCZUR, Ida (1876-1970) Hungarian
£1086 $1803 €1586 Still life of flowers (101x81cm-40x32in) s. 4-Oct-3 Kieselbach, Budapest #16/R (H.F 400000)
£1581 $2861 €2308 Flower still life with pinks (84x68cm-33x27in) s. 16-Apr-4 Mu Terem Galeria, Budapest #45/R (H.F 600000)
£1581 $2861 €2308 Still life with peony (80x60cm-31x24in) s. 16-Apr-4 Mu Terem Galeria, Budapest #101/R (H.F 600000)

DOLBY, Edwin (fl.1849-1865) British
Works on paper
£320 $534 €467 Victoria tower (22x15cm-9x6in) mono.d.1884 W/C pencil gouache. 7-Oct-3 Bonhams, Knightsbridge #35c/R
£400 $700 €584 Louvier (66x43cm-26x17in) s.i. W/C. 16-Dec-3 Capes Dunn, Manchester #769
£694 $1181 €1000 View of Burgos (16x24cm-6x9in) s.d.1893 W/C. 28-Oct-3 Segre, Madrid #1/R
£1500 $2430 €2175 Blackfriar's Bridge. Temple bar in 1878. London Bridge. Lambeth Palace (16x24cm-6x9in) mono.d.1884 W/C set of four. 30-Jul-3 Hamptons Fine Art, Godalming #118/R est:700-1000

DOLBY, Tim (1954-) British
£340 $537 €496 Tenby harbour with the arches (46x71cm-18x28in) s. board. 22-Jul-3 Peter Francis, Wales #23/R

DOLCI, Carlo (1616-1686) Italian
£6944 $11319 €10000 Allegory of poetry (57x44cm-22x17in) i. verso. 25-Sep-3 Dr Fritz Nagel, Stuttgart #1215/R est:6000
£9400 $17202 €13724 Madonna and Child (65x49cm-26x19in) with sig. stretcher. 9-Jun-4 Rasmussen, Copenhagen #1536/R est:30000 (D.KR 105000)
£234899 $432215 €350000 Tobiolo and Sara getting married (88x69cm-35x27in) prov.lit. 24-Mar-4 Finarte Semenzato, Rome #218/R est:320000-350000
Works on paper
£3000 $5490 €4380 Reclining draped man (20x31cm-8x12in) black red white chk prov. 7-Jul-4 Bonhams, Knightsbridge #59a/R est:3000-5000

DOLCI, Carlo (attrib) (1616-1686) Italian
Works on paper
£1056 $1827 €1500 Homme vu de trois-quarts (25x17cm-10x7in) i. col crayon. 12-Dec-3 Renaud, Paris #10/R est:1500-2000

DOLENA, James E (?) ?
£280 $450 €406 Japanese tea ceremony (58x38cm-23x15in) s. 23-Aug-3 Harvey Clar, Oakland #1228

DOLEZEL, Jenny (1964-) New Zealander
£735 $1375 €1073 Upside down (69x87cm-27x34in) s.i.d.1988 oil stick paper. 24-Feb-4 Peter Webb, Auckland #99/R (NZ.D 2000)
£1449 $2348 €2101 Ship of fools (50x79cm-20x31in) s.i.d.1991 oil on paper. 31-Jul-3 International Art Centre, Auckland #7/R est:5500-7500 (NZ.D 4000)
£1786 $3232 €2608 Days at home (48x67cm-19x26in) s.i.d.1994 oil pastel pencil. 30-Mar-4 Peter Webb, Auckland #137/R est:5000-6000 (NZ.D 5000)
£6320 $10870 €9227 Escape (152x183cm-60x72in) s.d.1996 prov. 3-Dec-3 Dunbar Sloane, Auckland #23/R est:15000-20000 (NZ.D 17000)
Works on paper
£2068 $3515 €3019 Wild days, wild ways (34x60cm-13x24in) s.i.d.1992 pastel. 27-Nov-3 International Art Centre, Auckland #58/R est:4000-6000 (NZ.D 5500)
£2321 $4271 €3389 Dont worry, it only TV (50x95cm-20x37in) s.d.1988 mixed media. 25-Mar-4 International Art Centre, Auckland #46/R est:5500-7500 (NZ.D 6500)

DOLHART, Oskar (20th C) German
£800 $1448 €1200 Cruiser Konigsberg off Kiel (47x58cm-19x23in) s.i.d.34 board. 3-Apr-4 Hans Stahl, Hamburg #147/R

DOLICE, Leon (1892-1960) American
£629 $1145 €950 New York harbour scene (33x53cm-13x21in) s. cardboard. 19-Jun-4 Quittenbaum, Hamburg #79/R
Works on paper
£412 $700 €602 New York Street views, winter (30x20cm-12x8in) s. pastel two. 21-Nov-3 Skinner, Boston #583/R

D'OLIVIER, Louis Camille (1827-1870) French
Photographs
£14686 $24525 €21000 Etude de nu (16x21cm-6x8in) salt print lit. 10-Oct-3 Tajan, Paris #100/R est:15000-20000

DOLL, Anton (1826-1887) German
£1528 $2490 €2200 Snowy winter landscape with horse cart and figures (20x40cm-8x16in) s.i. 25-Sep-3 Dr Fritz Nagel, Stuttgart #1345/R est:3900
£1965 $3576 €2869 Enjoying the cold weather on the banks of the Laar, Tirol (15x25cm-6x10in) s. panel. 16-Jun-4 Fischer, Luzern #1220/R est:5000-7000 (S.FR 4500)
£3356 $6174 €5000 Dachau (41x66cm-16x26in) s. i. stretcher. 26-Mar-4 Bolland & Marotz, Bremen #502/R est:5500
£4636 $8437 €7000 Village on Lake Zurich (58x86cm-23x34in) s. 16-Jun-4 Hugo Ruef, Munich #948/R est:6500
£5102 $9133 €7500 Enjoying the ice outside village (30x58cm-12x23in) s.i. 17-Mar-4 Neumeister, Munich #440/R est:7000
£5671 $9811 €8280 Figures on frozen river in village, The Alps in background (67x87cm-26x34in) s.i. 9-Dec-3 Rasmussen, Copenhagen #1278/R est:60000-75000 (D.KR 60000)
£9790 $16839 €14000 Winter landscape with farm houses, near Alt-Gauting (63x88cm-25x35in) s.i. 3-Dec-3 Neumeister, Munich #557/R est:13000
Works on paper
£408 $731 €600 Washerwomen by river in city (20x15cm-8x6in) mono.d.53. 17-Mar-4 Neumeister, Munich #281
£420 $722 €600 Castle in hilly landscape with river (16x23cm-6x9in) s.i.d.59 W/C. 3-Dec-3 Neumeister, Munich #384
£3221 $5928 €4800 Wilhelm arch on Maxburg (26x23cm-10x9in) s. W/C. 24-Mar-4 Hugo Ruef, Munich #1174/R est:3500
£3356 $6174 €5000 Pagerie on the Maxburgstrasse (26x23cm-10x9in) s. W/C. 24-Mar-4 Hugo Ruef, Munich #1175/R est:3500

DOLL, Anton (attrib) (1826-1887) German
£533 $971 €800 Woodcutters in a winter woodland scene (16x23cm-6x9in) paper on board. 1-Jul-4 Van Ham, Cologne #1303/R
£1111 $1833 €1600 Winter landscape with farmstead on edge of frozen lake (39x49cm-15x19in) 2-Jul-3 Neumeister, Munich #631/R
£2958 $5117 €4200 Winter landscape with figures (27x34cm-11x13in) s. 13-Dec-3 Hagelstam, Helsinki #35/R est:3000

DOLL, Auguste (1871-1955) Austrian
Works on paper
£403 $741 €600 Trees in landscape (31x43cm-12x17in) s. pen Indian ink W/C. 26-Mar-4 Dorotheum, Vienna #309/R

DOLLA, Noel (1945-) French
£1338 $2315 €1900 Silences de la fumee (100x100cm-39x39in) mono.d.90 acrylic smoke prov. 9-Dec-3 Artcurial Briest, Paris #433/R est:2500-3000
£1538 $2615 €2200 Untitled - Tartalanes (172x179cm-68x70in) s.i.d.12/1973. 27-Nov-3 Lempertz, Koln #108/R est:2500
£1867 $3435 €2800 Untitled (240x143cm-94x56in) s.d.1973 verso acrylic prov.exhib. 9-Jun-4 Artcurial Briest, Paris #534/R est:3000-4000

DOLLMAN, Herbert P (1856-?) British
£950 $1767 €1387 Which hand will you have ? (36x30cm-14x12in) s.d.1880. 4-Mar-4 Christie's, Kensington #595/R

DOLLMAN, John Charles (1851-1934) British
£7200 $13104 €10512 London York stage outside the Black Swan (71x102cm-28x40in) s.d.1906. 16-Jun-4 Bonhams, New Bond Street #55/R est:8000-12000
Works on paper
£450 $832 €657 Leopard (34x25cm-13x10in) init. W/C gouache. 10-Mar-4 Sotheby's, Olympia #217/R

DOLLMAN, Ruth (fl.1905-1928) British
Works on paper
£320 $586 €467 Sheep grazing on the Downs (27x44cm-11x17in) s.d.1907 W/C. 6-Jul-4 Bearnes, Exeter #433/R

DOLLOND, W Anstey (fl.1880-1911) British
Works on paper
£550 $1012 €803 Distant thoughts (43x20cm-17x8in) s. pencil W/C. 25-Mar-4 Christie's, Kensington #224/R
£586 $979 €850 Women (44x20cm-17x8in) s. W/C pair. 17-Nov-3 Durán, Madrid #182/R
£600 $1020 €876 Classical maiden on a terrace (41x28cm-16x11in) s. W/C. 26-Nov-3 Hamptons Fine Art, Godalming #67/R
£800 $1456 €1168 Distant thoughts (44x20cm-17x8in) s. pencil W/C. 1-Jul-4 Christie's, Kensington #149/R
£950 $1729 €1387 Dancing classical maiden (38x20cm-15x8in) s. W/C. 4-Jul-4 Lots Road Auctions, London #336
£1000 $1630 €1460 Roman slave girl (44x20cm-17x8in) s. W/C. 23-Sep-3 Anderson & Garland, Newcastle #151/R
£1111 $1811 €1600 Women (44x20cm-17x8in) s. W/C pair. 23-Sep-3 Durán, Madrid #74/R

DOLPH, John Henry (1835-1903) American

£419	$750	€612	Best friends (25x46cm-10x18in) s. board. 8-Jan-4 James Julia, Fairfield #451/R
£1243	$2300	€1815	Kittens (25x20cm-10x8in) s. panel. 13-Mar-4 DeFina, Austinburg #785/R est:2000-3000
£3226	$6000	€4710	Game birds and their chicks (15x25cm-6x10in) s.d.74 panel pair. 6-Mar-4 North East Auctions, Portsmouth #1114/R est:3000-5000
£3226	$6000	€4710	Mother tabby cat and three kittens at their dish (28x38cm-11x15in) s. 6-Mar-4 North East Auctions, Portsmouth #1115/R est:3000-5000
£6216	$11500	€9075	Basket of puppies (46x61cm-18x24in) init. 10-Feb-4 Doyle, New York #274/R est:12000-18000

DOLPHIN, Willem (1935-) Belgian

£524	$902	€750	Nature morte aux fruits (46x52cm-18x20in) s.d.1962. 2-Dec-3 Campo & Campo, Antwerp #124
£1888	$3248	€2700	Nature morte a la cruche et aux legumes (50x60cm-20x24in) s.d.1977 panel. 2-Dec-3 Campo & Campo, Antwerp #123/R est:3000-3500
£2013	$3564	€3000	Mature morte (50x60cm-20x24in) s.d.1989 panel. 27-Apr-4 Campo & Campo, Antwerp #87/R est:2750-3250

DOLPHYN, Victor (1909-1992) Belgian

£355	$592	€500	Still life with pears (37x47cm-15x19in) s.d.75. 20-Oct-3 Bernaerts, Antwerp #182/R
£355	$592	€500	Still life with lobster (47x60cm-19x24in) s.d.75. 20-Oct-3 Bernaerts, Antwerp #184/R

DOLRON, Desiree (1963-) Dutch

Photographs

£4000	$7360	€6000	Gaze, Bridget (119x119cm-47x47in) s.i.d.97/98 num.2/6 verso cibachrome print. 8-Jun-4 Sotheby's, Amsterdam #163/R est:2000-4000
£4667	$8587	€7000	Gaze (120x120cm-47x47in) s.i.d.97/98 verso cibachrome print edn of 6 prov. 8-Jun-4 Sotheby's, Amsterdam #164/R est:2000-4000
£5667	$10427	€8500	Gaze (120x120cm-47x47in) s.i.d.97/98 verso cibachrome print edn of 6 prov. 8-Jun-4 Sotheby's, Amsterdam #165/R est:2000-4000

DOM, Elise (1913-) Dutch

£342	$582	€500	Puss (33x45cm-13x18in) s. board. 5-Nov-3 Vendue Huis, Gravenhage #409/R

DOM, Paulus Ludovicus Carolus (1885-?) Dutch

£1042	$1646	€1500	Ladies in blue (61x47cm-24x19in) s. 2-Sep-3 Christie's, Amsterdam #368/R est:500-700
£2740	$4658	€4000	Autumn in the Luxembourg Gardens (39x54cm-15x21in) s.i. board. 5-Nov-3 Vendue Huis, Gravenhage #509/R est:1500-2000

DOMARADZKI, Stefan (1897-1983) Polish

£321	$533	€469	Landscape with haystacks (21x42cm-8x17in) s.d.1930. 15-Jun-3 Agra, Warsaw #46/R (P.Z 2000)

DOMBARD, Rene (20th C) Belgian

£355	$592	€500	Venise (50x60cm-20x24in) s. i.verso. 15-Oct-3 Hotel des Ventes Mosan, Brussels #256

DOMBROWSKI, Carl Ritter von (1872-1951) German

£379	$702	€550	Deer (60x80cm-24x31in) s. 12-Feb-4 Weidler, Nurnberg #341/R
£733	$1320	€1100	Goats in snowy mountains (86x66cm-34x26in) s. 21-Apr-4 Neumeister, Munich #2631
£3970	$6868	€5796	Winter landscape with brown bear (143x100cm-56x39in) s. 9-Dec-3 Rasmussen, Copenhagen #1525/R est:20000 (D.KR 42000)

DOMELA, Cesar (1900-1992) Dutch

£213333	$392533	€320000	Composition neo-plastique 5a (58x58cm-23x23in) mono. s.d.1924 verso prov.exhib.lit. 9-Jun-4 Christie's, Amsterdam #239/R est:80000-120000

Works on paper

£769	$1323	€1100	Composition (32x24cm-13x9in) s.d.1956 ink pencil. 4-Dec-3 Van Ham, Cologne #123/R
£1800	$3312	€2700	Composition (61x46cm-24x18in) s. s.d.Nov 1963 verso gouache collage. 8-Jun-4 Sotheby's, Amsterdam #18/R est:3000-4000
£2000	$3680	€3000	Lutas (63x49cm-25x19in) s.d.54 gouache prov.exhib. 9-Jun-4 Christie's, Amsterdam #243/R est:3000-5000
£2222	$3667	€3200	Composition (54x35cm-21x14in) s.verso gouache pastel. 2-Jul-3 Cornette de St.Cyr, Paris #51/R est:3500-4000
£2533	$4661	€3800	Untitled (48x70cm-19x28in) s.d.1958 verso gouache. 9-Jun-4 Christie's, Amsterdam #240/R est:3000-5000
£2533	$4661	€3800	Untitled (66x50cm-26x20in) s.d.Janvier 1972 verso gouache collage. 8-Jun-4 Sotheby's, Amsterdam #19/R est:3000-4000
£2667	$4907	€4000	Complementaires (65x50cm-26x20in) s.d.1956 s.i.verso gouache prov. 9-Jun-4 Christie's, Amsterdam #241/R est:3000-5000
£2917	$4871	€4200	Composition (53x36cm-21x14in) s.d.1949 s.d.Aout 49 verso gouache col wax pastel prov. 21-Oct-3 Artcurial Briest, Paris #396a/R est:2500-3000

DOMENCHIN DE CHAVANNE, Pierre Salomon (attrib) (1673-1744) French

£1678	$3087	€2500	Paysages de riviere dans la campagne Romaine (27x43cm-11x17in) pair. 24-Mar-4 Tajan, Paris #90 est:2400-3000

DOMENECH Y VICENTE, Luis (19th C) Spanish

Sculpture

£4333	$7757	€6500	Sirenes (27x77cm-11x30in) s.i. pat bronze. 17-May-4 Sotheby's, Paris #70/R est:7000-9000

DOMENICHINI, Apollonio (18th C) Italian

£27586	$45793	€40000	View from the Dogana across the Basin of St Mark (34x55cm-13x22in) 1-Oct-3 Dorotheum, Vienna #41/R est:20000-30000
£41379	$68690	€60000	Grand Canal in Venice (72x54cm-28x21in) pair. 1-Oct-3 Dorotheum, Vienna #43/R est:65000-75000

DOMENICHINO (1581-1641) Italian

Works on paper

£105634	$184859	€150000	Le martyre de Saint Andre (19x23cm-7x9in) i. black chk pen brown ink wash prov.lit. 17-Dec-3 Christie's, Paris #4/R est:100000-150000

DOMENICHINO (circle) (1581-1641) Italian

£8389	$15017	€12500	Giaele (75x56cm-30x22in) i.on stretcher. 27-May-4 Semenzato, Florence #180/R est:12000-15000

DOMENICHINO (style) (1581-1641) Italian

£259	$463	€378	Ressurection (12x8cm-5x3in) copper. 13-May-4 Stuker, Bern #392 (S.FR 600)
£5278	$9500	€7706	Portrait of a muse (74x66cm-29x26in) 21-Jan-4 Doyle, New York #101/R est:15000-25000

DOMENICI, Carlo (1898-1981) Italian

£347	$590	€500	Shepherd (35x25cm-14x10in) s. board. 1-Nov-3 Meeting Art, Vercelli #84
£521	$885	€750	By the stable (35x50cm-14x20in) s. board lit. 1-Nov-3 Meeting Art, Vercelli #21
£599	$994	€850	Seascape (33x50cm-13x20in) s. board. 13-Jun-3 Farsetti, Prato #404/R
£634	$1096	€900	Tuscan cowboy (50x35cm-20x14in) s. i.verso. 10-Dec-3 Finarte Semenzato, Rome #286/R
£671	$1188	€1000	Oxen (35x50cm-14x20in) s. board. 1-May-4 Meeting Art, Vercelli #195
£791	$1298	€1100	Beached boats (30x49cm-12x19in) s. 10-Jun-3 Pandolfini, Florence #270
£800	$1440	€1200	Peasants with horses on country road (35x50cm-14x20in) s. panel lit. 22-Apr-4 Allgauer, Kempten #3517/R
£800	$1432	€1200	Village street (50x70cm-20x28in) s. board. 12-May-4 Stadion, Trieste #668
£805	$1426	€1200	Cart with oxen (35x50cm-14x20in) s. masonite. 1-May-4 Meeting Art, Vercelli #415
£872	$1544	€1300	Horses (35x50cm-14x20in) s. d.56 verso masonite. 1-May-4 Meeting Art, Vercelli #319
£1056	$1827	€1500	Farm (35x50cm-14x20in) s. i.verso masonite. 9-Dec-3 Pandolfini, Florence #276/R
£1119	$1869	€1600	Tuscan cowboys on horseback (48x69cm-19x27in) s. board. 26-Jun-3 Sant Agostino, Torino #66/R est:2000
£1127	$1870	€1600	Gore di Collinaia (30x45cm-12x18in) s.i. board. 13-Jun-3 Farsetti, Prato #569/R
£1151	$1888	€1600	Tuscan cowboys (32x41cm-13x16in) s. board. 10-Jun-3 Pandolfini, Florence #232/R est:800-1000
£1333	$2453	€2000	Oxen in the fields (49x69cm-19x27in) s. cardboard. 8-Jun-4 Sotheby's, Milan #61/R est:2000-4000
£1333	$2387	€2000	Farm (51x70cm-20x28in) s. 12-May-4 Stadion, Trieste #670/R est:1200-1600
£1338	$2221	€1900	Farmhouse (37x42cm-15x17in) s. board. 13-Jun-3 Farsetti, Prato #465/R
£1467	$2699	€2200	Village street (23x35cm-9x14in) s. board. 10-Jun-4 Christie's, Rome #165/R est:1600-1800
£1517	$2534	€2200	Oxen with cart (57x81cm-22x32in) s. bo. 14-Nov-3 Farsetti, Prato #404/R est:2000-2500
£1523	$2772	€2300	Maremma (65x110cm-26x43in) s. s.i.verso board. 17-Jun-4 Galleria Pananti, Florence #595/R est:2800-3000
£1549	$2680	€2200	Street near Montenero (45x60cm-18x24in) s. i.verso board. 9-Dec-3 Pandolfini, Florence #380/R est:2200-2400
£1600	$2896	€2400	Maremma (35x50cm-14x20in) s. s.i.verso board. 2-Apr-4 Farsetti, Prato #404/R est:1600-1900
£1600	$2896	€2400	Seashore (50x75cm-20x30in) s. board. 2-Apr-4 Farsetti, Prato #493 est:1200-1400
£1761	$2923	€2500	Horseride in Maremma (50x70cm-20x28in) s. cardboard. 13-Jun-3 Farsetti, Prato #480/R
£1761	$3046	€2500	Seashore (34x50cm-13x20in) s. board. 9-Dec-3 Pandolfini, Florence #275/R est:2300-2400
£1831	$3168	€2600	Harvest (30x69cm-12x27in) s. board. 10-Dec-3 Sotheby's, Milan #85/R est:1000-2000
£2113	$3655	€3000	Ploughing (34x50cm-13x20in) s. cardboard exhib. 11-Dec-3 Christie's, Rome #107/R est:1800-2200
£2254	$3899	€3200	Hunting in the Maremma (34x50cm-13x20in) s. cardboard exhib. 11-Dec-3 Christie's, Rome #108/R est:1800-2200
£2446	$4012	€3400	Quercianella (39x69cm-15x27in) s. s.d.31 board. 10-Jun-3 Pandolfini, Florence #231/R est:2700-2900
£2600	$4706	€3900	Back from work (69x100cm-27x39in) s. board. 2-Apr-4 Farsetti, Prato #456/R est:2500-3000

DOMENICI, Carlo (attrib) (1898-1981) Italian

£333	$597	€500	Farm (28x38cm-11x15in) cardboard. 12-May-4 Stadion, Trieste #799

DOMERGUE, Emile Jean (1879-?) French

£535	$850	€781	Goose girl (30x48cm-12x19in) s.d.1905 board. 14-Sep-3 Susanin's, Chicago #6113/R

DOMERGUE, Jean Gabriel (1889-1962) French

£1000	$1600	€1450	Nude (33x24cm-13x9in) s. board. 15-May-3 Stuker, Bern #1155/R (S.FR 2100)
£1135	$1895	€1600	Elegante (50x45cm-20x18in) s. 17-Jun-3 Galerie Moderne, Brussels #334/R est:1300-1800
£1418	$2369	€2000	Portrait de jeune homme (17x12cm-7x5in) cardboard gold. 19-Jun-3 Millon & Associes, Paris #220/R est:1000-1200
£1631	$2724	€2300	Portrait de jeune femme (24x19cm-9x7in) s. panel. 15-Oct-3 Claude Aguttes, Neuilly #1/R est:1800-2000
£1656	$3030	€2500	Joelle (24x19cm-9x7in) s. i.verso isorel panel. 7-Apr-4 Fraysse & Associes, Paris #3/R est:2500-3500

£1674	$2846	€2444	Nina (24x19cm-9x7in) s. i. verso panel. 5-Nov-3 Dobiaschofsky, Bern #496/R est:4000 (S.FR 3800)
£1773	$2961	€2500	Jeune femme au foulard turquoise (23x17cm-9x7in) s. 12-Oct-3 St-Germain-en-Laye Encheres #107/R est:2000-2500
£1905	$3410	€2800	Portrait de Baba (34x24cm-13x9in) s. isorel. 19-Mar-4 Millon & Associes, Paris #99/R est:2500-3000
£1953	$3360	€2851	Jeune fille blonde (80x60cm-31x24in) s. 3-Dec-3 Naón & Cia, Buenos Aires #41/R est:3000-4000
£2013	$3604	€3000	Portrait de jeune fille au foulard orange et au bibi (24x19cm-9x7in) s. panel. 30-May-4 Eric Pillon, Calais #92/R
£2098	$3503	€3000	Nu (33x24cm-13x9in) s. panel. 27-Jun-3 Calmels Cohen, Paris #27/R est:3000-4000
£2098	$3503	€3000	Corinne au balcon (33x24cm-13x9in) s. panel. 29-Jun-3 Eric Pillon, Calais #161/R
£2098	$3608	€3000	Feerie (27x22cm-11x9in) s. cardboard. 3-Dec-3 Tajan, Paris #412/R est:3000-4000
£2109	$3353	€3100	Jeune femme a la voilette (24x18cm-9x7in) s. 21-Mar-3 Bailly Pommery, Paris #117/R
£2128	$3553	€3000	Gabi (22x17cm-9x7in) s. i.verso masonite. 15-Oct-3 Neret-Minet, Paris #11/R
£2148	$3844	€3200	Portrait d'Anita (24x19cm-9x7in) s. panel. 30-May-4 Eric Pillon, Calais #96/R
£2192	$3726	€3200	Jeune fille nue en buste (33x23cm-13x9in) s. panel. 9-Nov-3 Eric Pillon, Calais #135/R
£2215	$4075	€3300	Gloria (24x19cm-9x7in) s.i. board. 29-Mar-4 Lombrail & Teucquam, Paris #115/R
£2215	$3964	€3300	Portrait de Maussia (24x19cm-9x7in) s. panel. 30-May-4 Eric Pillon, Calais #95/R
£2215	$3964	€3300	Portrait dE nina (24x19cm-9x7in) s. panel. 30-May-4 Eric Pillon, Calais #93/R
£2252	$4098	€3400	Jeune femme au foulard jaune (51x45cm-20x18in) s. isorel. 18-Jun-4 Piasa, Paris #168/R est:3500-4000
£2252	$4211	€3400	Femme au cabaret (35x27cm-14x11in) s. panel. 20-Jul-4 Gioffredo, Nice #5/R
£2282	$4085	€3400	Jeune femme au chapeau blanc (24x19cm-9x7in) s. panel. 30-May-4 Eric Pillon, Calais #91/R
£2550	$4565	€3800	Portrait de Lili (33x24cm-13x9in) s. panel. 30-May-4 Eric Pillon, Calais #103/R
£2667	$4907	€4000	Robe blanche a pois noirs (55x46cm-22x18in) s. 9-Jun-4 Beaussant & Lefèvre, Paris #136/R est:4000-4500
£2676	$4630	€3800	Portrait de Gaby (24x19cm-9x7in) s. panel. 14-Dec-3 Eric Pillon, Calais #143/R
£2695	$4501	€3800	Modele nu, Liliane (46x38cm-18x15in) s. isorel. 21-Jun-3 Peron, Melun #45
£2797	$4671	€4000	Nu debout au miroir (46x38cm-18x15in) s. panel. 29-Jun-3 Eric Pillon, Calais #170/R
£2817	$4535	€4000	Portrait de Flossie (24x19cm-9x7in) s. i.verso panel. 22-Aug-3 Deauville, France #113/R est:3500-4000
£2819	$5046	€4200	Portrait de Nadine (33x24cm-13x9in) s. isorel. 25-May-4 Chambelland & Giafferi, Paris #104/R est:3000-4000
£2917	$4871	€4200	Yasmine au bar (33x24cm-13x9in) s. 25-Oct-3 Dianous, Marseille #419
£3147	$5255	€4500	Portrait de Flossy (24x19cm-9x7in) s. panel. 29-Jun-3 Eric Pillon, Calais #169/R
£3169	$5134	€4500	Femme Orientale (52x45cm-20x18in) s.d.1918 panel. 5-Aug-3 Tajan, Paris #19/R est:5000-7000
£3221	$5766	€4800	Couple dans la loge a l'Opera (33x24cm-13x9in) s. panel. 30-May-4 Eric Pillon, Calais #100/R
£3333	$6133	€5000	Portrait de Cora (33x24cm-13x9in) s. isorel. 9-Jun-4 Le Roux & Morel, Paris #46/R est:4000-5000
£3497	$5839	€5000	Carita (24x19cm-9x7in) s. panel. 29-Jun-3 Eric Pillon, Calais #168/R
£3521	$6092	€5000	Portrait de Lady Y (24x19cm-9x7in) s. panel. 14-Dec-3 Eric Pillon, Calais #142/R
£3533	$6501	€5300	Danseuse a sa toilette (26x21cm-10x8in) s. i.d.1939 verso panel. 11-Jun-4 Pierre Berge, Paris #174/R est:5300-5500
£3636	$6073	€5200	Portrait de Jacqueline (24x19cm-9x7in) s. panel. 29-Jun-3 Eric Pillon, Calais #166/R
£3667	$6747	€5500	La boule de verre (83x52cm-33x20in) s. isorel prov. 8-Jun-4 Artcurial Briest, Paris #161/R est:6000-8000
£3691	$6607	€5500	Baigneuse (32x41cm-13x16in) s. panel. 30-May-4 Eric Pillon, Calais #94/R
£3893	$6968	€5800	Portrait de jeune femme (61x50cm-24x20in) s. prov. 26-May-4 Christie's, Paris #62/R est:6000-8000
£4392	$8301	€6500	Deux femmes dans un interieur (136x172cm-54x68in) s.d.1907. 21-Feb-4 Cornette de St.Cyr, Paris #199/R est:5000-6000
£4895	$8175	€7000	Au pongeoir (27x22cm-11x9in) s. i.verso panel. 29-Jun-3 Eric Pillon, Calais #160/R
£5208	$8698	€7500	Chez la modiste (41x33cm-16x13in) s. panel. 25-Oct-3 Cornette de St.Cyr, Paris #196/R est:6000-8000
£5634	$9746	€8000	Jeune femme dans la loge (46x38cm-18x15in) s. panel. 14-Dec-3 Eric Pillon, Calais #119/R
£6711	$12013	€10000	Midinette (46x38cm-18x15in) s. i.verso panel. 30-May-4 Eric Pillon, Calais #99/R
£7047	$12614	€10500	Couple dans la loge a l'Opera (55x46cm-22x18in) s. panel. 30-May-4 Eric Pillon, Calais #101/R
£7801	$13028	€11000	Maryse en tenue de soiree (81x63cm-32x25in) s. 20-Jun-3 Drouot Estimations, Paris #201/R est:7000-8000
£9396	$16819	€14000	Nu assis (73x60cm-29x24in) s. panel. 30-May-4 Eric Pillon, Calais #98/R
Works on paper			
£276	$458	€400	Elegante (30x40cm-12x16in) s. gouache. 6-Oct-3 Blanchet, Paris #159
£276	$458	€400	Elegante au chapeau (30x40cm-12x16in) s. gouache. 6-Oct-3 Blanchet, Paris #160
£276	$458	€400	Femme Art Deco (30x40cm-12x16in) s. gouache. 6-Oct-3 Blanchet, Paris #161
£310	$515	€450	Elegante a l'ombrelle (30x40cm-12x16in) s. gouache. 6-Oct-3 Blanchet, Paris #162
£448	$744	€650	Andalouse (30x40cm-12x16in) s. gouache. 6-Oct-3 Blanchet, Paris #158
£10000	$18100	€15000	Danseuse a la robe de lame (156x118cm-61x46in) s.d.23 gouache paper on canvas. 30-Mar-4 Rossini, Paris #342/R est:2500-4000

DOMICENT, Martin (1823-1898) Flemish

£544	$995	€810	Interior scene (21x27cm-8x11in) mono. panel. 9-Jul-4 Dawo, Saarbrucken #27/R
£725	$1326	€1080	The broken plate (21x27cm-8x11in) s. panel. 9-Jul-4 Dawo, Saarbrucken #28/R

DOMINGO Y FALLOLA, Roberto (1867-1956) Spanish

£1800	$3276	€2628	Leading the herd into corral (33x41cm-13x16in) s. 16-Jun-4 Christie's, Kensington #148/R est:2000-3000
Works on paper			
£276	$497	€400	Pepe Dominguin (16x21cm-6x8in) s. ink dr. 26-Jan-4 Durán, Madrid #183/R
£276	$497	€400	Bull scene (16x22cm-6x9in) s. ink dr. 26-Jan-4 Durán, Madrid #180/R
£276	$497	€400	Bull scene (16x20cm-6x8in) s. ink dr. 26-Jan-4 Durán, Madrid #178/R
£285	$511	€425	Bull scene (20x28cm-8x11in) s. dr. 25-May-4 Durán, Madrid #33/R
£302	$565	€450	Horses (12x16cm-5x6in) s. mixed media. 24-Feb-4 Durán, Madrid #89/R
£328	$547	€475	Bull scene (16x21cm-6x8in) s. ink dr. 17-Nov-3 Durán, Madrid #16/R
£331	$573	€470	Bull scene (14x19cm-6x7in) s. ink col crayon dr. 15-Dec-3 Ansorena, Madrid #370/R
£345	$621	€500	Bull scene (15x22cm-6x9in) s. ink dr. 26-Jan-4 Durán, Madrid #182/R
£379	$633	€550	Bullfight (23x15cm-9x6in) s. ink dr. 17-Nov-3 Durán, Madrid #17/R
£379	$630	€550	Woman playing guitar (10x10cm-4x4in) s. ink dr. 1-Oct-3 Ansorena, Madrid #504/R
£379	$633	€550	Pilin (15x21cm-6x8in) s. ink dr. 17-Nov-3 Durán, Madrid #18/R
£379	$683	€550	Sunday in Madrid (16x22cm-6x9in) s. pen dr. 26-Jan-4 Durán, Madrid #190/R
£403	$721	€600	Bad people (20x29cm-8x11in) s. dr. 25-May-4 Durán, Madrid #36/R
£436	$781	€650	Bull scene (16x22cm-6x9in) s. dr. 25-May-4 Durán, Madrid #19/R
£448	$807	€650	Bull scene (16x22cm-6x9in) s. ink dr. 26-Jan-4 Durán, Madrid #184/R
£470	$841	€700	Bull scene (15x20cm-6x8in) s. dr double-sided. 25-May-4 Durán, Madrid #16/R
£483	$869	€700	Carlos Arruza (15x21cm-6x8in) s. ink dr. 26-Jan-4 Durán, Madrid #187/R
£503	$901	€750	Bull scene (16x22cm-6x9in) s. dr. 25-May-4 Durán, Madrid #20/R
£503	$901	€750	Bull scene (15x20cm-6x8in) s. dr double-sided. 25-May-4 Durán, Madrid #18/R
£503	$901	€750	Bull scene (15x20cm-6x8in) s. dr double-sided. 25-May-4 Durán, Madrid #26/R
£503	$901	€750	Rodolfo Gaona (15x20cm-6x8in) s. dr. 25-May-4 Durán, Madrid #25/R
£537	$961	€800	Toast (21x14cm-8x6in) s. dr. 25-May-4 Durán, Madrid #15/R
£537	$961	€800	Bull scene (15x20cm-6x8in) s. dr. 25-May-4 Durán, Madrid #21/R
£570	$1021	€850	Bull scene (15x20cm-6x8in) s. dr double-sided. 25-May-4 Durán, Madrid #23/R
£570	$1021	€850	Bull scene (15x20cm-6x8in) s. dr double-sided. 25-May-4 Durán, Madrid #22/R
£604	$1081	€900	Bull scene (15x20cm-6x8in) s. dr double-sided. 25-May-4 Durán, Madrid #27/R
£604	$1081	€900	Domingo Ortega (15x20cm-6x8in) s. dr double-sided. 25-May-4 Durán, Madrid #24/R
£604	$1081	€900	Bull scene (19x27cm-7x11in) s. dr. 25-May-4 Durán, Madrid #34/R
£738	$1321	€1100	Bull scene (15x21cm-6x8in) s. dr double-sided. 25-May-4 Durán, Madrid #28/R
£872	$1562	€1300	Bull scene (21x30cm-8x12in) s. dr. 25-May-4 Durán, Madrid #29/R
£1007	$1802	€1500	Valencia Square (20x29cm-8x11in) s. dr. 25-May-4 Durán, Madrid #35/R est:400
£1342	$2403	€2000	Bull scene (32x49cm-13x19in) s. dr. 25-May-4 Durán, Madrid #37/R est:600
£1630	$2674	€2250	Puerto (48x65cm-19x26in) s. gouache. 27-May-3 Durán, Madrid #85/R est:1800
£2174	$3565	€3000	Tauromaquia (24x17cm-9x7in) each s.i. pen drawings six. 27-May-3 Durán, Madrid #87/R est:1200
£2897	$4808	€4200	Fair (65x50cm-26x20in) s. gouache. 30-Sep-3 Ansorena, Madrid #12/R est:4200
£3103	$5183	€4500	Every year (64x50cm-25x20in) s. gouache. 17-Nov-3 Durán, Madrid #160/R est:2500
£8966	$14972	€13000	Dance (87x72cm-34x28in) s. gouache board. 17-Nov-3 Durán, Madrid #214/R est:8500

DOMINGO Y MARQUES, Francisco (1842-1920) Spanish

£390	$651	€550	Dama fumando junto a la chimenea (17x13cm-7x5in) s. panel. 23-Jun-3 Durán, Madrid #100/R
£669	$1171	€950	Portrait of woman (46x37cm-18x15in) s. 16-Dec-3 Durán, Madrid #70
£1974	$3572	€3000	Clown (22x14cm-9x6in) s. board. 14-Apr-4 Ansorena, Madrid #70/R est:3000
£2600	$4706	€3900	Hunt scene (27x22cm-11x9in) s. board. 30-Mar-4 Segre, Madrid #101/R est:3900
£3947	$7145	€6000	Old man with walking stick (40x23cm-16x9in) board. 14-Apr-4 Ansorena, Madrid #67/R est:6000
Works on paper			
£276	$497	€400	Majo (13x19cm-5x7in) s. chl dr. 26-Jan-4 Durán, Madrid #196/R
£313	$575	€475	Mosquetaires. Study of figures (11x20cm-4x8in) s. dr double-sided. 22-Jun-4 Durán, Madrid #632/R
£315	$526	€450	Caballero (35x18cm-14x7in) gouache. 24-Jun-3 Segre, Madrid #26/R
£533	$981	€800	Mountainous landscape (30x40cm-12x16in) s.d.1893 pastel card. 10-Jun-4 Christie's, Rome #125/R
£638	$1034	€900	Mosquetero (15x25cm-6x10in) s.d.1898 drawing sanguine. 20-May-3 Ansorena, Madrid #415/R
£1379	$2303	€2000	Spanish beauties (21x31cm-8x12in) s. gouache. 17-Nov-3 Durán, Madrid #192/R est:1600

DOMINGO, Roberto (1883-1956) Spanish
£764 $1299 €1100 Painter (16x12cm-6x5in) s. cardboard lit. 28-Oct-3 Segre, Madrid #62/R
£2254 $3606 €3200 Gentlemen in the garden (9x13cm-4x5in) s.d.1908 card. 16-Sep-3 Segre, Madrid #74/R
£26000 $44200 €37960 Sunset (75x101cm-30x40in) s. s.i.verso. 18-Nov-3 Sotheby's, London #226/R
Works on paper
£1538 $2569 €2200 Llevando al toro (14x25cm-6x10in) gouache prov. 24-Jun-3 Segre, Madrid #29/R est:1000
£2378 $3971 €3400 Acoso y derribo (30x47cm-12x19in) s. gouache. 24-Jun-3 Segre, Madrid #30/R est:1300
£3401 $6190 €5000 Difficult bull (34x53cm-13x21in) s.d.1917 i.verso gouache. 3-Feb-4 Segre, Madrid #57/R est:4000
£7500 $12000 €10875 Conduccion de una corrida, Castilla. Una estocada de mataquito (49x65cm-19x26in) s. gouache pair. 18-Sep-3 Christie's, Kensington #118/R est:8000-12000

DOMINGO, Roberto (attrib) (1883-1956) Spanish
£1300 $2379 €1898 Bringing out the bulls (33x41cm-13x16in) s. 1-Feb-4 Lots Road Auctions, London #356 est:300-500

DOMINGUEZ BECQUER, Joaquin (1819-1879) Spanish
£11000 $18700 €16060 Hunter. Dandy. Woman praying (38x28cm-15x11in) s.d.1844 three prov. 18-Nov-3 Sotheby's, London #264a/R

DOMINGUEZ PEREZ, Fiz (1970-) Spanish
£671 $1255 €1000 Maternity (73x92cm-29x36in) s. 24-Feb-4 Durán, Madrid #145/R

DOMINGUEZ SALAZAR, Luis (1931-) Venezuelan
£260 $435 €380 Untitled (50x40cm-20x16in) s. acrylic painted 1988. 19-Oct-3 Subastas Odalys, Caracas #30

DOMINGUEZ Y SANCHEZ, Manuel (1839-1906) Spanish
£1644 $2795 €2400 Escape (45x28cm-18x11in) s.d.99 cardboard. 4-Nov-3 Ansorena, Madrid #57/R est:2400
Works on paper
£284 $460 €400 Personaje medieval (52x33cm-20x13in) s. W/C. 20-May-3 Ansorena, Madrid #959/R
£2241 $3743 €3250 Praying (86x58cm-34x23in) s. W/C. 17-Nov-3 Durán, Madrid #217/R est:1200

DOMINGUEZ, Goyo (1960-) Spanish
£1096 $1863 €1600 Garden (38x46cm-15x18in) s.d.90 s.i.verso. 4-Nov-3 Ansorena, Madrid #437/R est:1200

DOMINGUEZ, Oscar (1906-1958) Spanish
£302 $535 €450 Composition (50x65cm-20x26in) s. 27-Apr-4 Campo, Vlaamse Kaai #409
£1589 $2893 €2400 La ville III (22x14cm-9x6in) i.verso stretcher. 15-Jun-4 Blanchet, Paris #185/R est:2500-3000
£1892 $3329 €2800 Trois figures, decalomanie interpretee (18x12cm-7x5in) prov. 18-May-4 Tajan, Paris #3/R est:1350-1500
£17219 $31338 €26000 Composition au taureau (32x40cm-13x16in) s. 15-Jun-4 Blanchet, Paris #184/R est:6000-8000
£18000 $32760 €26280 Le coq (73x100cm-29x39in) s.d.47 prov. 3-Feb-4 Christie's, London #284/R est:25000-35000
£55000 $100650 €80300 El quinque y la paloma (80x100cm-31x39in) s.d.42 prov.exhib.lit. 2-Feb-4 Christie's, London #90/R est:60000-90000
£122449 $219184 €180000 Constructions (130x162cm-51x64in) s.d.14.2.56 i.d verso prov.exhib. 21-Mar-4 Calmels Cohen, Paris #54/R est:120000-150000
£141844 $229787 €200000 Personages (95x120cm-37x47in) s. painted 1947. 20-May-3 Ansorena, Madrid #319/R est:200000
£189531 $348736 €276715 Cosmic fantasy (147x97cm-58x38in) s.d.1938 prov.lit. 29-Mar-4 Rasmussen, Copenhagen #26/R est:800000-1200000 (D.KR 2100000)
Works on paper
£993 $1808 €1500 Composition a l'epi de ble (31x21cm-12x8in) s.i.d.28/12/53 pen india ink prov. 15-Jun-4 Blanchet, Paris #182 est:1500-2000
£1049 $1783 €1500 L'oeil (30x24cm-12x9in) s. Indian ink prov. 23-Nov-3 Cornette de St.Cyr, Paris #101 est:300-400
£1189 $2021 €1700 Marye el O mas (15x27cm-6x11in) s.i. ballpoint pen prov. 23-Nov-3 Cornette de St.Cyr, Paris #98/R est:300-400
£1189 $2021 €1700 Animal fantastique (23x17cm-9x7in) s. ink prov. 23-Nov-3 Cornette de St.Cyr, Paris #99 est:300-400
£1400 $2422 €2044 L'enclume a la rose (31x20cm-12x8in) pencil prov.exhib. 11-Dec-3 Christie's, Kensington #133/R est:1500-2000
£1496 $2679 €2200 Untitled (16x17cm-6x7in) s.i.d.1941 ink. 21-Mar-4 Calmels Cohen, Paris #15/R est:1000-1500
£1897 $3395 €2770 Abstract figure (31x24cm-12x9in) s. pen W/C. 13-May-4 Stuker, Bern #100/R est:4000-6000 (S.FR 4400)
£2333 $4293 €3500 Composition (26x36cm-10x14in) s.i.d.48 ink prov. 8-Jun-4 Sotheby's, Amsterdam #50/R est:3000-5000
£2658 $4571 €3800 Bisonte de altamira (42x51cm-17x20in) s.d.56 gouache. 3-Dec-3 Tajan, Paris #136/R est:3500-4000
£3046 $5544 €4600 Deux taureaux dans l'arene (32x24cm-13x9in) s. W/C. 15-Jun-4 Blanchet, Paris #181/R est:1500-3000
£3169 $5482 €4500 Composition au taureau (30x40cm-12x16in) s. Indian ink exec.c.1947. 14-Dec-3 Versailles Encheres #144/R est:5000-6000
£3497 $6014 €5000 Untitled (24x34cm-9x13in) s. transfer htd green gouache exec.c.1940. 6-Dec-3 Renaud, Paris #90/R
£3846 $6538 €5500 Paysage cosmique (22x27cm-9x11in) s. gouache panel prov. 23-Nov-3 Cornette de St.Cyr, Paris #100 est:600-800
£3867 $7115 €5800 Jeune fille au dinosaure (27x39cm-11x15in) s. ink wash gouache collage exec. c.1935 prov. 8-Jun-4 Artcurial Briest, Paris #182/R est:6000-8000
£4196 $7007 €6000 Sp. (30x21cm-12x8in) s. ink wash prov. 29-Jun-3 Versailles Encheres #133/R
£4200 $7728 €6132 Eve et serpent (23x15cm-9x6in) s.d.35 pencil. 24-Mar-4 Sotheby's, Olympia #161/R est:1000-2000
£4400 $8096 €6424 Bisonte de altamira (43x52cm-17x20in) s.d.56 gouache. 24-Mar-4 Sotheby's, Olympia #169/R est:4000-6000
£5762 $10486 €8700 Le taureau dans l'arene (31x22cm-12x9in) s. W/C. 15-Jun-4 Blanchet, Paris #183/R est:2500-3000
£6000 $10919 €9000 Femmes (19x24cm-7x9in) s.d.55 mixed media canvasboard prov. 30-Jun-4 Calmels Cohen, Paris #55/R est:8000-10000
£6667 $11933 €10000 Untitled (27x29cm-11x11in) Chinese ink dr. 15-May-4 Renaud, Paris #76/R
£6667 $11933 €10000 Untitled (28x38cm-11x15in) s.i.d.1951 Chinese ink dr. 15-May-4 Renaud, Paris #75/R
£7823 $14003 €11500 Untitled (31x24cm-12x9in) s.d.1944 decalcomonaie gouache. 21-Mar-4 Calmels Cohen, Paris #43/R est:8000-10000

DOMINICIS, Achille de (19th C) Italian
Works on paper
£252 $450 €368 Peasant girl (34x23cm-13x9in) s.d.79 W/C. 18-Mar-4 Skinner, Bolton #608a

DOMINICIS, Gino de (1947-1998) Italian
Works on paper
£12500 $20875 €18250 Untitled (63x60cm-25x24in) s.d.1987 verso pencil chalkboard prov.exhib. 22-Oct-3 Christie's, London #44/R est:8000-12000

DOMINIK, Tadeusz (1928-) Polish
£791 $1432 €1155 Natura (54x60cm-21x24in) s.d.1970 acrylic. 4-Apr-4 Agra, Warsaw #69/R (P.Z 5600)
£917 $1523 €1339 Fruit, III (56x70cm-22x28in) acrylic painted 1974. 2-Oct-3 Agra, Warsaw #72/R est:2000 (P.Z 6000)
£1059 $1917 €1546 Landscape (67x91cm-26x36in) s.d.1978 acrylic. 4-Apr-4 Agra, Warsaw #67/R (P.Z 7500)
£1116 $1920 €1629 Landscape (65x94cm-26x37in) s.i.d.1984 acrylic. 4-Dec-3 Agra, Warsaw #6/R est:7000 (P.Z 7500)
Works on paper
£398 $660 €581 Composition (38x56cm-15x22in) gouache. 2-Oct-3 Agra, Warsaw #20/R (P.Z 2600)

DOMINIQUE, John August (1893-1984) American
£215 $400 €314 Green hills, Ojai (30x36cm-12x14in) s.d.1975 masonite. 6-Mar-4 Harvey Clar, Oakland #1303
£223 $400 €326 Matilija Creek (25x30cm-10x12in) d.1959 canvasboard. 10-Jan-4 Harvey Clar, Oakland #1217
£269 $450 €393 California river. s.d.1952 canvasboard. 15-Nov-3 Harvey Clar, Oakland #1234
£344 $550 €502 Matilija Creek. s.d.1956. 20-Sep-3 Harvey Clar, Oakland #1335
£419 $700 €612 Laguna coast. s.d.1977 canvasboard. 15-Nov-3 Harvey Clar, Oakland #1233
£419 $750 €612 Mountainous landscape (25x36cm-10x14in) s.d.1928 board. 16-Mar-4 Matthew's, Oregon #86/R
£552 $1000 €806 California landscape (41x51cm-16x20in) s.d.1945. 3-Apr-4 Harvey Clar, Oakland #1235
£1190 $2250 €1737 Landscape - summer in Montecito (64x76cm-25x30in) s. i.d.July 1927 verso. 17-Feb-4 John Moran, Pasadena #48/R est:2000-3000
£1589 $2750 €2320 Hills near Santa Barbara (61x76cm-24x30in) s.d.1948. 10-Dec-3 Bonhams & Butterfields, San Francisco #6226/R est:4000-6000

DOMMERSEN, Cornelis Christian (1842-1928) Dutch
£544 $990 €800 Duingezicht la panne - guiding the flock through the dunes (30x39cm-12x15in) s.i.d.1901 s.i.d.verso. 3-Feb-4 Christie's, Amsterdam #52/R
£987 $1816 €1500 Phare at the end of the North Breakwater, tide coming in - Hoek van Holland (50x67cm-20x26in) s.d.93 s.i. verso. 28-Jun-4 Sotheby's, Amsterdam #63/R est:2000-3000
£1974 $3572 €3000 View of dry-dock of Amsterdam, from the direction of the Ruyterhuis (27x37cm-11x15in) s.indis.d. 19-Apr-4 Glerum, Amsterdam #5/R est:2400-2600
£2083 $3396 €3000 Fishermen in a calm (35x48cm-14x19in) init.d.1857 panel. 29-Sep-3 Sotheby's, Amsterdam #92/R
£4392 $7730 €6500 Marine par gros temps (90x130cm-35x51in) s. 18-May-4 Galerie Moderne, Brussels #256/R est:5000-6000
£9000 $15300 €13140 Entrance to Ymuiden harbour (76x127cm-30x50in) s.d.1880. 19-Nov-3 Christie's, Kensington #569/R
£11806 $20069 €17000 View of a canal in a Dutch town (61x76cm-24x30in) s.d.1875 lit. 28-Oct-3 Christie's, Amsterdam #224/R est:20000-30000
£21053 $38105 €32000 Many ships in front of the Dutch coast, close to the train station of Hook of Holland (108x177cm-43x70in) s.i.d.1907. 19-Apr-4 Glerum, Amsterdam #19/R est:27000-30000
Works on paper
£1250 $2088 €1800 Fishermen by a windmill (34x53cm-13x21in) s.d.1900 W/C. 21-Oct-3 Sotheby's, Amsterdam #42/R est:2000-3000

DOMMERSEN, Louis (20th C) Dutch
£600 $1098 €876 Street scene, Ultrecht (40x50cm-16x20in) s.i. board. 8-Apr-4 Christie's, Kensington #188/R

DOMMERSEN, P C (1834-1908) Dutch
£724 $1296 €1057 Coastal landscape with figures, boats and houses (43x57cm-17x22in) panel. 10-May-4 Rasmussen, Vejle #480/R (D.KR 8000)

DOMMERSEN, Pieter Christian (1834-1908) Dutch
£1041 $1697 €1500 Stormy weather off the coast (15x20cm-6x8in) init.d.86 panel. 29-Sep-3 Sotheby's, Amsterdam #93/R
£1319 $2203 €1900 River landscape (50x76cm-20x30in) s. 24-Oct-3 Ketterer, Hamburg #58/R est:2000-2500
£1800 $3330 €2628 Artist and companions beside an estuary (30x35cm-12x14in) s.d.1894. 10-Mar-4 Sotheby's, Olympia #257/R est:1500-2000
£1900 $3401 €2774 Blustery day on the Scheldt (27x38cm-11x15in) s.d.1883 panel. 26-May-4 Christie's, Kensington #653/R est:1200-1800

£2041 $3714 €3000 Sailing boat entering a Dutch harbour (25x32cm-10x13in) s. panel. 3-Feb-4 Christie's, Amsterdam #79/R est:3000-5000
£2098 $3566 €3000 Off Marken Island in Ijsselmeer (30x40cm-12x16in) s.d.1898 panel. 20-Nov-3 Van Ham, Cologne #1543/R est:5800
£2500 $4175 €3600 Shipping in a calm (27x38cm-11x15in) s.d.1884 prov. 21-Oct-3 Sotheby's, Amsterdam #19/R est:4000-6000
£2500 $4600 €3650 Family boat trip (20x25cm-8x10in) s.d.1897. 25-Mar-4 Christie's, Kensington #167/R est:1500-2000
£3401 $6190 €5000 Figures in a rowing boat on a river near Dutch town (51x76cm-20x30in) s.d.1901. 3-Feb-4 Christie's, Amsterdam #93/R est:8000-12000
£3600 $6624 €5256 Boats entering harbour in the face of a storm (50x80cm-20x31in) s.d.1863 prov. 29-Mar-4 Bonhams, Bath #58/R est:4000-6000
£3957 $6489 €5500 Street scene in Winschoten, Groningen (51x40cm-20x16in) s.d. i. verso panel. 4-Jun-3 Ketterer, Hamburg #43/R est:7000-9000
£4000 $6800 €5840 Entering harbour, stormy weather (51x81cm-20x32in) s.d.1872. 19-Nov-3 Bonhams, New Bond Street #8/R est:4000-6000
£4800 $8688 €7200 Grand marche a Cologne (39x31cm-15x12in) s.d.1877. 30-Mar-4 Campo & Campo, Antwerp #87/R est:4000-6000
£5000 $9250 €7300 Harderwyck on the Zuider Zee (25x36cm-10x14in) s.d.1893 i.verso panel prov. 11-Mar-4 Duke & Son, Dorchester #208/R
£5500 $8800 €8030 Harderwykon the Zuider Zee (39x60cm-15x24in) s.d.1882 i.verso panel prov. 16-Sep-3 Bonhams, New Bond Street #68/R est:2500-3500
£5932 $10085 €8661 Evening before Brouwershaven (76x126cm-30x50in) s.d.1880 s.i.d.verso prov. 24-Nov-3 Sotheby's, Melbourne #340/R est:12000-18000 (A.D 14000)
£6333 $11337 €9500 Old-Dutch town scene with canal, many figures and barge carrier (60x90cm-24x35in) s.d.1875. 11-May-4 Vendu Notarishuis, Rotterdam #100/R est:10000-15000
£6500 $11180 €9490 Dutch sailing boats off shore in a flat calm (27x38cm-11x15in) init. panel. 4-Dec-3 Christie's, Kensington #191/R est:5000-8000
£6944 $11597 €10000 Market day in Winschoten (51x40cm-20x16in) s.d.1889 panel. 21-Oct-3 Sotheby's, Amsterdam #46/R est:10000-15000
£8000 $15120 €11680 Shipping before a Dutch harbour town (61x91cm-24x36in) s.d.1887 panel. 17-Feb-4 Bonhams, New Bond Street #74/R est:8000-12000
£14500 $26680 €21170 View of Amsterdam from the Isslemeer, with shipping in the foreground (61x91cm-24x36in) s.d.1887 panel. 23-Jun-4 Cheffins, Cambridge #491/R est:15000-25000
£14815 $24000 €21482 Hotel de Ville Vere Zeeland. Hotel de Violle Alkemaar Holland (38x29cm-15x11in) s.i. pair. 8-Aug-3 Barridorf, Portland #101/R est:20000-30000

DOMMERSEN, W (1850-1927) Dutch
£1150 $2059 €1679 Street scene (45x35cm-18x14in) s. indis i.verso. 16-Mar-4 Bonhams, Oxford #62 est:200-300

DOMMERSEN, William (1850-1927) Dutch
£550 $875 €798 Continental townscape with figures (41x31cm-16x12in) mono. i.verso. 9-Sep-3 Bonhams, Knightsbridge #294/R
£550 $919 €803 Rue de Bac, Rouen (23x15cm-9x6in) init. init.i.verso panel. 7-Oct-3 Bonhams, Knightsbridge #158/R
£600 $1110 €876 Italian coastal view (30x41cm-12x16in) s. 13-Jan-4 Bonhams, Knightsbridge #146/R
£850 $1522 €1241 On the Amstel, boats and figures on a quayside (28x41cm-11x16in) s. 7-May-4 Christopher Matthews, Yorkshire #311/R
£850 $1573 €1241 Figures by a coastal ruin off the Moselle (30x41cm-12x16in) s.i. verso. 14-Jul-4 Christie's, Kensington #951/R
£1000 $1800 €1460 Italian coastal scene (51x76cm-20x30in) s. 21-Jan-4 Sotheby's, Olympia #403/R est:800-1200
£1154 $1962 €1685 Modena, Italy (49x75cm-19x30in) s. i.verso. 4-Nov-3 Stephan Welz, Johannesburg #573 est:8000-12000 (SA.R 13500)
£1176 $1965 €1717 Peasants by a canal (50x76cm-20x30in) s. 17-Nov-3 Waddingtons, Toronto #162/R est:2000-3000 (C.D 2600)
£1300 $2405 €1898 Cattaro. Taranto (25x40cm-10x16in) s. i.verso pair. 10-Mar-4 Sotheby's, Olympia #250/R est:1200-1800
£1420 $2500 €2073 Village street scene (46x36cm-18x14in) s. 18-May-4 Bonhams & Butterfields, San Francisco #76/R est:3000-5000
£1500 $2595 €2190 Mother catching lobsters with her daughter (25x20cm-10x8in) s. 14-Dec-3 Desmond Judd, Cranbrook #1047
£1500 $2775 €2190 Modena. Chiusi (30x51cm-12x20in) s. i.verso pair. 10-Mar-4 Sotheby's, Olympia #248/R est:1500-2000
£1562 $2750 €2281 View of a church in Dordrecht with figures in a boat in the foreground (51x39cm-20x15in) s. 18-May-4 Bonhams & Butterfields, San Francisco #78/R est:3000-5000
£1736 $2951 €2500 On the riverbank (30x39cm-12x15in) s. canvas on plywood. 28-Oct-3 Christie's, Amsterdam #106/R est:2500-3500
£1800 $3312 €2628 Italianate coastal scene (40x61cm-16x24in) s. 25-Mar-4 Christie's, Kensington #93/R est:2000-3000
£1800 $3312 €2628 On the Zuider Zee (28x38cm-11x15in) s.d.1899. 8-Jun-4 Bonhams, Knightsbridge #357/R est:2000-3000
£1888 $3210 €2700 Vue de Bruges anime (51x41cm-20x16in) s. 18-Nov-3 Vanderkindere, Brussels #27 est:2000-3000
£2000 $3740 €2920 Ruins of Rento Castle on the Tiber. On the Amstel, Holland (35x46cm-14x18in) s. mono.i.verso pair. 24-Feb-4 Bonhams, Knowle #94/R est:2000-3000
£2000 $3540 €2920 On the Amstel. Shiedam, Holland (28x38cm-11x15in) s. pair. 29-Apr-4 Gorringes, Lewes #2330 est:3000-4000
£2200 $4026 €3212 Living along the river (51x76cm-20x30in) s. 7-Apr-4 Gardiner & Houlgate, Bath #238/R est:2400-3600
£2600 $4342 €3796 Schiedam on the Sheldt (41x61cm-16x24in) s. i.verso pair. 12-Nov-3 Sotheby's, Olympia #184/R est:1500-2000
£3000 $5370 €4380 Street scene in Rouen with market traders and horse drawn carts (61x91cm-24x36in) s. 7-May-4 Christopher Matthews, Yorkshire #310/R est:1500-2000

DOMOND, Wilmino (20th C) ?
£467 $850 €682 Villagers (51x41cm-20x16in) s. masonite. 6-Feb-4 Freeman, Philadelphia #323/R

DOMOTO, Hisao (1928-) Japanese
£3217 $5372 €4600 Composition (81x116cm-32x46in) s.d.1958 prov. 29-Jun-3 Versailles Encheres #41/R
£5369 $9503 €8000 Instantaneite (162x114cm-64x45in) s.d.62 s.i.d.verso exhib. 28-Apr-4 Artcurial Briest, Paris #273/R est:8000-10000

DOMSAITIS, Pranas (1880-1965) South African
£345 $576 €504 Standing figure (48x26cm-19x10in) mono. board. 20-Oct-3 Stephan Welz, Johannesburg #574 est:2500-4000 (SA.R 4000)
£462 $837 €675 Ploughing beside a country bridge (53x69cm-21x27in) s. canvas on board. 30-Mar-4 Stephan Welz, Johannesburg #470/R est:6000-9000 (SA.R 5500)
£546 $989 €797 Flowers in a vase (49x40cm-19x16in) mono. board. 30-Mar-4 Stephan Welz, Johannesburg #534/R est:7000-10000 (SA.R 6500)
£924 $1673 €1349 Anenomes in a white vase (62x45cm-24x18in) s.d.53 canvas on board. 30-Mar-4 Stephan Welz, Johannesburg #532/R est:6000-9000 (SA.R 11000)
£924 $1673 €1349 Blumen posen (59x62cm-23x24in) s. s.i.verso. 30-Mar-4 Stephan Welz, Johannesburg #536/R est:9000-12000 (SA.R 11000)
£966 $1749 €1410 Two figures (62x36cm-24x14in) s. board. 30-Mar-4 Stephan Welz, Johannesburg #482/R est:6000-8000 (SA.R 11500)

DOMSCHEIT, Franz (1880-?) German
£1400 $2520 €2100 Wooded landscape with lake (63x51cm-25x20in) s. 24-Apr-4 Dr Lehr, Berlin #100/R est:2000

DON, Martino del (19th C) Italian?
Works on paper
£700 $1204 €1022 Lecture in Venice (28x38cm-11x15in) s. pencil W/C bodycol. 3-Dec-3 Christie's, Kensington #168/R

DONADONI, Stefano (1844-1911) Italian
Works on paper
£395 $726 €600 View of the Castel Sant'Angelo, Rome (37x55cm-15x22in) s. pencil pen ink W/C. 22-Jun-4 Christie's, Amsterdam #215/R
£420 $714 €613 View of the Roman Forum (28x37cm-11x15in) s. pencil W/C scratching out. 6-Nov-3 Christie's, Kensington #980/R

DONALD, Elizabeth (20th C) British
£406 $750 €593 Portrait of an elderly gentleman (66x56cm-26x22in) s. 17-Jan-4 New Orleans Auction, New Orleans #414/R

DONALD, George (1943-) British
Works on paper
£440 $810 €642 Lilies considered (51x60cm-20x24in) s.d.03 mixed media. 29-Mar-4 Thomson Roddick & Medcalf, Edinburgh #265/R

DONALD, John Milne (1819-1866) British
£820 $1451 €1197 View of a loch with figures in a boat. 27-Apr-4 Lawrences, Bletchingley #1571
£1200 $2148 €1752 Children fishing by a stream (52x78cm-20x31in) s. 26-May-4 Sotheby's, Olympia #215/R est:1000-1500

DONALD, Tom (1853-1883) British
£450 $805 €657 Landscape with cattle (24x34cm-9x13in) init. board. 26-May-4 Sotheby's, Olympia #239/R

DONALDSON, Andrew Benjamin (1840-1919) British
£1600 $2960 €2336 Empty fountain (45x62cm-18x24in) mono.d.1866. 14-Jul-4 Sotheby's, Olympia #127/R est:1000-1500

DONALDSON, David Abercrombie (1916-1996) British
£700 $1253 €1022 Still life of mixed flowers in a vase (37x46cm-15x18in) s.verso panel. 28-May-4 Lyon & Turnbull, Edinburgh #30
£2500 $3925 €3625 Bride's toast (30x30cm-12x12in) s. 27-Aug-3 Sotheby's, London #1148/R est:1500-2000
£3600 $6012 €5256 Table top still life (62x75cm-24x30in) s. 16-Oct-3 Bonhams, Edinburgh #7/R est:3000-5000
£4000 $6440 €5800 Japanese girl (102x94cm-40x37in) s. 21-Aug-3 Bonhams, Edinburgh #1161/R est:4000-6000
£5200 $8840 €7592 Christine in Black (102x86cm-40x34in) s. prov. 30-Oct-3 Christie's, London #234/R est:5000-7000
£8800 $14960 €12848 Young girl in an interior (124x99cm-49x39in) s. indis.i. 30-Oct-3 Christie's, London #232/R est:5000-8000
Works on paper
£340 $537 €493 Brittany I (16x21cm-6x8in) s. chl chk pastel prov. 3-Sep-3 Bonhams, Bury St Edmunds #377

DONALDSON, Kim (1952-) Zimbabwean
£269 $497 €393 Foreign passage (75x136cm-30x54in) s.verso prov. 15-Mar-4 Sotheby's, Melbourne #148 (A.D 650)
Works on paper
£700 $1141 €1022 Gemsbok (35x53cm-14x21in) s. pastel. 24-Sep-3 Dreweatt Neate, Newbury #68/R

DONALDSON, Marysia (20th C) British?
£280 $468 €409 Still life of Hyacinth (51x35cm-20x14in) s. 16-Oct-3 Lyon & Turnbull, Edinburgh #59

DONAT, Friederich Reginald (1830-1907) Belgian
£336 $628 €500 First letter - beach with fisherman and woman reading letter (53x41cm-21x16in) s. i. verso panel. 27-Feb-4 Altus, Berlin #548/R
£987 $1816 €1500 Conversing on a quay (52x40cm-20x16in) s. panel. 22-Jun-4 Christie's, Amsterdam #124/R est:1500-1800
£1338 $2315 €1900 Fisherman on the beach. Fisherman's wife (47x26cm-19x10in) s. panel pair. 10-Dec-3 Christie's, Amsterdam #682/R est:1500-2000
£1818 $3091 €2600 Couple de pecheurs sur la plage (52x41cm-20x16in) s. panel. 1-Dec-3 Palais de Beaux Arts, Brussels #250/R est:2000-3000

DONAT, Johann Daniel (1744-1830) Austrian
£1871 $3311 €2732 Young girl in blue empire dress (57x43cm-22x17in) s. 28-Apr-4 Kieselbach, Budapest #155/R (H.F 700000)

DONATI, Enrico (1909-) American/Italian

£1816	$3250	€2651	Polaris (91x81cm-36x32in) s. s.i.d.1968 verso oil sand on canvas prov. 6-May-4 Doyle, New York #118/R est:1500-2500
£3073	$5500	€4487	Luxor noon (91x81cm-36x32in) s. s.i.d.1980 stretcher oil sand on canvas. 6-May-4 Doyle, New York #87/R est:2500-3500
£3352	$6000	€4894	Rosetta (102x107cm-40x42in) s.i.d.1983 i.d.stretcher oil sand lit. 6-May-4 Doyle, New York #129/R est:2500-3500
£5814	$10000	€8488	Excalibur 2 (76x91cm-30x36in) s.d.1966 s.i.d.verso oil sand prov. 3-Dec-3 Doyle, New York #84/R est:2000-3000
£11173	$20000	€16313	San Gimignano XVIII (128x152cm-50x60in) oil sand on canvas prov. 6-May-4 Doyle, New York #86/R est:3000-4000
£14535	$25000	€21221	Red ice (122x152cm-48x60in) s.i.d.1961 oil sand prov. 3-Dec-3 Doyle, New York #42/R est:4000-6000
£15116	$26000	€22069	Ibam forte via appia (112x145cm-44x57in) s. s.i.d.1962 on stretcher oil sand prov. 3-Dec-3 Doyle, New York #53/R est:3000-4000
£16279	$28000	€23767	Chambre a pression osmotique II (76x63cm-30x25in) s.d.1948 on stretcher oil pen ink prov.exhib. 3-Dec-3 Doyle, New York #57/R est:3000-5000
£17442	$30000	€25465	Homage a faraday (61x101cm-24x40in) s.d.1948 i.verso oil pen ink prov. 3-Dec-3 Doyle, New York #58/R est:3000-5000
£19632	$32000	€28663	Ego et l'Aurore (76x122cm-30x48in) s. painted c.1945 prov.exhib. 23-Sep-3 Christie's, Rockefeller NY #9/R est:20000-30000
£20000	$36600	€29200	Floating peninsula (51x61cm-20x24in) s.d.45 prov.exhib. 2-Feb-4 Christie's, London #94/R est:10000-15000
Works on paper			
£516	$950	€753	Noel (20x28cm-8x11in) s.i.d.1945-6 pen ink. 10-Jun-4 Swann Galleries, New York #77/R

DONATI, Lazzaro (1926-) Italian

£269	$450	€390	Porto la Speranza (71x48cm-28x19in) s. board. 12-Jul-3 Susanin's, Chicago #5040/R
£284	$475	€412	Eva (71x48cm-28x19in) s. board. 12-Jul-3 Susanin's, Chicago #5041
£299	$475	€437	Figura dal Cielo Viola (71x48cm-28x19in) s.d.1966 verso board. 10-Sep-3 Alderfer's, Hatfield #331
£707	$1300	€1032	Firenze (69x51cm-27x20in) s. i.d.1960 verso panel. 23-Jun-4 Doyle, New York #5026/R est:200-300

DONCKER, Herman Mijnerts (17th C) Dutch

£4139	$7409	€6043	Elegant company in interior (48x74cm-19x29in) init.d.34 pa prov. 25-May-4 Bukowskis, Stockholm #491/R est:50000-60000 (S.KR 56000)

DONCRE, Guillaume-Dominique (1743-1820) French

£1163	$2000	€1698	Lady with a lace bonnet (81x66cm-32x26in) s.d.177. 6-Dec-3 Neal Auction Company, New Orleans #183/R est:4000-6000
£2483	$4146	€3500	Deux jeunes femmes preparant un bouquet dans un interieur (46x37cm-18x15in) panel. 17-Oct-3 Tajan, Paris #122/R est:4000-6000

DONCRE, Guillaume-Dominique (attrib) (1743-1820) French

£5467	$9895	€8200	Allegories (79x108cm-31x43in) en grisaille canvas on panel pair. 4-Apr-4 Salle des ventes Pillet, Lyon la Foret #23/R est:4500-5000

DONDUCCI, Giovanni Andrea (1575-1655) Italian

£56338	$90141	€80000	Landscape with the good Samaritan (130x169cm-51x67in) lit. 21-Sep-3 Finarte, Venice #47/R

DONDUCCI, Giovanni Andrea (attrib) (1575-1655) Italian

£6593	$12000	€9626	Camillus and Brennus the Gaul (192x287cm-76x113in) 29-Jun-4 Sotheby's, New York #25/R est:15000-20000
Works on paper			
£5395	$9926	€8200	La Sainte Famille avec Sainte Marguerite, un Eveque, Marie-Madeleine et un ange (27x24cm-11x9in) brown wash htd white. 25-Jun-4 Rossini, Paris #13 est.500-600

DONG GAO (1740-1818) Chinese

Works on paper			
£4623	$8321	€6750	Birds and flowers (13x10cm-5x4in) s.i. ink col leaves silk twelve album. 25-Apr-4 Christie's, Hong Kong #412/R est:40000-50000 (HK.D 65000)

DONG MING LI (20th C) Chinese

£329	$550	€480	Under the apple tree (71x109cm-28x43in) s. 11-Oct-3 Nadeau, Windsor #25/R

DONG QICHANG (1555-1636) Chinese

Works on paper			
£4267	$7681	€6230	Light snow over Tongguan (126x48cm-50x19in) s.i. ink col hanging scroll. 25-Apr-4 Christie's, Hong Kong #341/R est:80000-100000 (HK.D 60000)
£5690	$10242	€8307	Landscape of Mount Lingyan (110x57cm-43x22in) s.i.d.1621 ink hanging scroll silk prov. 25-Apr-4 Christie's, Hong Kong #348/R est:80000-100000 (HK.D 80000)
£11380	$20484	€16615	Landscape (30x121cm-12x48in) s.i.d.1615 ink handscroll. 25-Apr-4 Christie's, Hong Kong #332/R est:120000-150000 (HK.D 160000)
£23166	$38687	€33822	Mountain temple in mist after the rain (145x47cm-57x19in) s. ink on silk lit. 26-Oct-3 Christie's, Hong Kong #435/R (HK.D 300000)

DONG SHOUPING (1904-) Chinese

Works on paper			
£14865	$26162	€22000	Landscape with mountains and waterfall (136x295cm-54x116in) s.d.1973 seals Indian ink scroll. 21-May-4 Dr Fritz Nagel, Stuttgart #1186/R est:2800

DONGEN, Dionys van (1748-1819) Dutch

£5800	$10614	€8468	Dutch man-o-war and smalschip off a coastline (49x64cm-19x25in) s.d.1775 panel. 7-Jul-4 Bonhams, New Bond Street #25/R est:2000-3000

DONGEN, Kees van (1877-1968) French/Dutch

£10563	$18486	€15000	Nu de dos (44x26cm-17x10in) s. chl htd white chk prov. 18-Dec-3 Cornette de St.Cyr, Paris #6/R est:15000-18000
£14789	$23958	€21000	Deauville, canoe (48x60cm-19x24in) s. oil paper prov. 5-Aug-3 Tajan, Paris #10/R est:10000-15000
£29412	$50000	€42942	L'oiseau solitaire (46x38cm-18x15in) s. i.d.1908 verso. 6-Nov-3 Sotheby's, New York #170/R est:50000-70000
£30000	$55201	€45000	La Bohemienne (65x50cm-26x20in) s. prov.lit. 8-Jun-4 Artcurial Briest, Paris #160/R est:25000-35000
£35294	$60000	€51529	Portrait de Dora (54x46cm-21x18in) s. s.d.1935 stretcher prov. 6-Nov-3 Sotheby's, New York #169/R est:60000-80000
£36364	$61818	€52000	Remorqueur sur la Meuse (46x55cm-18x22in) s.i.d.1949 verso exhib. 28-Nov-3 Drouot Estimations, Paris #199/R est:40000-60000
£42000	$76440	€61320	Fleurs (27x22cm-11x9in) s. prov. 3-Feb-4 Christie's, London #183/R est:30000-40000
£65000	$119600	€94900	Femme aux boucles d'oreilles bleues (48x41cm-19x16in) s. oil W/C paper on canvas prov.exhib. 22-Jun-4 Sotheby's, London #442/R est:55000-75000
£97765	$175000	€142737	Place Vendome (53x65cm-21x26in) s. exhib. 6-May-4 Sotheby's, New York #278/R est:120000-180000
£129252	$231361	€190000	Buste de femme (65x50cm-26x20in) s. painted c.1920 prov. 21-Mar-4 Calmels Cohen, Paris #170/R est:70000-90000
£140000	$257600	€204400	Femme a l'orchidee (65x54cm-26x21in) painted c.1928 prov. 22-Jun-4 Sotheby's, London #163/R est:140000-180000
£231333	$425653	€347000	Le facteur (81x65cm-32x26in) s. painted 1923 prov.exhib.lit. 9-Jun-4 Beaussant & Lefèvre, Paris #218/R est:80000-100000
£247059	$420000	€360706	Sur la plage (100x81cm-39x32in) s. painted 1921 prov.lit. 5-Nov-3 Christie's, Rockefeller NY #288/R est:250000-350000
£588235	$1000000	€858823	Grand bouquet de fleurs (196x130cm-77x51in) s. s.verso painted c.1908-10 pel. 5-Nov-3 Sotheby's, New York #32/R est:1000000-1800000
£660927	$1202887	€998000	Portrait d'une blonde (41x27cm-16x11in) s. 16-Jun-4 Claude Boisgirard, Paris #43/R est:70000-80000
£949721	$1700000	€1386593	Les amies (74x59cm-29x23in) s. s.i.verso painted c.1922 prov.exhib.lit. 6-May-4 Sotheby's, New York #149/R est:800000-1200000
£1300000	$2379000	€1898000	Danseuse aux bijoux (129x97cm-51x38in) s. painted c.1905 prov.exhib.lit. 2-Feb-4 Christie's, London #25/R est:1200000-1600000
Works on paper			
£933	$1708	€1400	Ships on the River Maas (12x19cm-5x7in) s. black chk prov. 7-Jun-4 Glerum, Amsterdam #2/R
£2632	$4842	€4000	Woman writing at a desk (20x15cm-8x6in) s. blk chk brown ink. 28-Jun-4 Sotheby's, Amsterdam #119/R est:1000-1200
£3217	$5469	€4600	La coiffeuse. s. W/C. 18-Nov-3 Galerie Moderne, Brussels #588 est:600-800
£3662	$5932	€5200	Elegante debout (32x23cm-13x9in) mono. ink dr prov. 5-Aug-3 Tajan, Paris #16/R est:3000-4000
£3867	$6960	€5800	Le Nil a Assouan (45x31cm-18x12in) s.i. black crayon htd W/C prov.exhib.lit. 26-Apr-4 Tajan, Paris #20/R est:6000-7000
£4172	$7593	€6300	Les terrassiers (26x37cm-10x15in) s. chl htd gouache. 20-Jun-4 Versailles Encheres #29/R est:3000-3500
£4552	$7556	€6600	Danseuse de revue (22x14cm-9x6in) mono.i. col crayon dr. 6-Oct-3 Blanchet, Paris #249/R
£5000	$8350	€7300	A Bas le rue laffitte ! (46x32cm-18x13in) s.i. col crayons gouache brush ink chl. 21-Oct-3 Sotheby's, London #11/R est:6000-8000
£5333	$9813	€8000	Deauville aux courses (26x35cm-10x14in) s.i. ballpoint pen col crayon three prov. 9-Jun-4 Christie's, Amsterdam #34/R est:4000-6000
£5594	$9510	€8000	Peche aux singes (27x19cm-11x7in) s. ink W/C. 20-Nov-3 Finarte Semenzato, Milan #39/R est:8000-8500
£6593	$12000	€9626	Portrait de Pierre Laffitte (40x29cm-16x11in) s.i. W/C pencil. 29-Jun-4 Sotheby's, New York #331/R est:12000-15000
£8621	$14397	€12500	Portrait de Pierre Lafitte (38x27cm-15x11in) s.i. W/C pencil. 17-Nov-3 Delorme & Bocage, Paris #117/R est:8000-10000
£11268	$18254	€16000	La plage (62x47cm-24x19in) s. W/C prov. 5-Aug-3 Tajan, Paris #15/R est:12000-15000
£12676	$20536	€18000	Personnage et cheval (47x61cm-19x24in) s. W/C prov. 5-Aug-3 Tajan, Paris #11/R est:8000-12000
£13195	$22035	€19000	Femme se penchant (40x32cm-16x13in) s. white chk htd green pastel brown paper prov. 21-Oct-3 Artcurial Briest, Paris #4/R est:12000-15000
£18056	$30153	€26000	Femme arabe, le Caire (40x28cm-16x11in) s.i. india ink ink wash exhib. 21-Oct-3 Christie's, Paris #85/R est:7000-9000
£18156	$32500	€26508	Nu debout (48x30cm-19x12in) s. brush ink W/C prov. 6-May-4 Sotheby's, New York #326/R est:15000-20000
£20000	$36400	€29200	Sortie de l'opera (45x27cm-18x11in) init.i. chl gouache W/C paper on paper exec.1901 prov.exhib. 4-Feb-4 Sotheby's, London #419/R est:16000-22000
£23973	$40754	€35000	Bicyclette sous la pluie (23x15cm-9x6in) s.d.47 W/C oil paper on cardboard. 6-Nov-3 Tajan, Paris #247/R
£32123	$57500	€46900	L'ecuyer (63x48cm-25x19in) s. gouache pencil. 6-May-4 Sotheby's, New York #281/R est:60000-80000
£33333	$61333	€50000	Portrait of a woman (44x35cm-17x14in) s. W/C. 8-Jun-4 Sotheby's, Amsterdam #61/R est:5000-70000
£33803	$54761	€48000	Deauville, la plage (61x47cm-24x19in) s. W/C prov. 5-Aug-3 Tajan, Paris #12/R est:25000-30000
£35212	$57043	€50000	L'ecuyer (64x48cm-25x19in) s. gouache prov. 5-Aug-3 Tajan, Paris #17/R est:30000-40000
£36000	$66240	€52560	Le Nil (41x51cm-16x20in) s. W/C prov. 22-Jun-4 Sotheby's, London #436/R est:35000-45000
£45334	$83415	€68000	Elegante devant un miroir (64x49cm-25x19in) s. ink wash W/C pastel prov.lit. 9-Jun-4 Tajan, Paris #10/R est:50000-60000
£45776	$74156	€65000	Aquaplane (49x60cm-19x24in) s. W/C prov. 5-Aug-3 Tajan, Paris #13/R est:15000-20000
£52818	$85565	€75000	Deauville, la plage (60x48cm-24x19in) s. W/C prov. 5-Aug-3 Tajan, Paris #9/R est:30000-40000
£54226	$87847	€77000	Deauville, trois personnages (61x47cm-24x19in) s. W/C prov. 5-Aug-3 Tajan, Paris #14/R est:18000-25000

DONGEN, L van (?) ?

£433	$780	€650	Mother and child (79x69cm-31x27in) s. 26-Apr-4 Bernaerts, Antwerp #175a/R
£2933	$5280	€4400	Seated Chinese woman (121x80cm-48x31in) s.d.1937 gilt panel. 26-Apr-4 Bernaerts, Antwerp #176/R est:1500-2000
£3333	$6000	€5000	Standing nude (150x59cm-59x23in) s.d.1941. 26-Apr-4 Bernaerts, Antwerp #177 est:3000-4000
Works on paper			
£280	$504	€420	Farmer at work (22x15cm-9x6in) s. W/C. 26-Apr-4 Bernaerts, Antwerp #175b

DONGEN, von (20th C) ?
£1796 $3000 €2622 Capture of inspiration (107x76cm-42x30in) s.verso painted c.1930. 15-Nov-3 Illustration House, New York #67/R est:2500-3500

DONGES, Langley Thomas (1901-1992) Canadian
£267 $437 €390 Autumn landscape (61x76cm-24x30in) s. board. 28-May-3 Maynards, Vancouver #156 (C.D 600)

DONGHI, Antonio (1897-1963) Italian
£26667 $48000 €40000 Making of Rome (40x50cm-16x20in) s.d.40 exhib. 22-Apr-4 Finarte Semenzato, Rome #342/R est:38000-40000

DONINI, Emilio (1825-?) Italian
£2013 $3765 €3000 Landscape (75x110cm-30x43in) painted 1872. 26-Feb-4 Cambi, Genoa #514/R est:900-1000
£2113 $3507 €3000 Coastal landscape with fishermen (40x59cm-16x23in) s. 11-Jun-3 Christie's, Rome #155/R est:2300-2800

DONNA, Porfirio di (1942-1986) American
£667 $1200 €974 Untitled (17x17cm-7x7in) s.d.1972 verso acrylic graphite. 24-Apr-4 David Rago, Lambertville #102/R
Works on paper
£1167 $2100 €1704 Untitled (41x29cm-16x11in) 2 mixed media exec.1979 1 W/C exec.1983 three 2 prov. 24-Apr-4 David Rago, Lambertville #103/R est:300-600

DONNAY, Auguste (1862-1921) Belgian
£496 $829 €700 Paysage (9x14cm-4x6in) mono. i.verso panel. 15-Oct-3 Hotel des Ventes Mosan, Brussels #141
Works on paper
£284 $474 €400 La carriere (30x40cm-12x16in) pastel panel. 15-Oct-3 Hotel des Ventes Mosan, Brussels #122
£567 $948 €800 Untitled (15x16cm-6x6in) s. W/C pair. 15-Oct-3 Hotel des Ventes Mosan, Brussels #128

DONNAY, Jean (1897-1992) Belgian
£578 $1035 €850 Trouville (21x32cm-8x13in) s.i.d.30 panel. 17-Mar-4 Hotel des Ventes Mosan, Brussels #107

DONNE, Col Henry Richard Beadon (fl.1906-1939) British
Works on paper
£850 $1505 €1241 In the Erin Valley, Kashmir (31x63cm-12x25in) s. W/C. 29-Apr-4 Christie's, Kensington #105/R

DONNE, Walter J (1867-?) British
£2200 $3498 €3190 Burford High Street (39x42cm-15x17in) s. board. 9-Sep-3 Bonhams, Knightsbridge #275b/R est:1000-1500
Works on paper
£300 $555 €438 Montreuil sur Mer (20x28cm-8x11in) s. W/C. 9-Mar-4 Gorringes, Lewes #2138

DONNELLY, Anne (20th C) Irish
£1842 $3389 €2800 Houses in the south (28x37cm-11x15in) s. paper exhib. 22-Jun-4 De Veres Art Auctions, Dublin #189 est:3000-4000

DONNER VON RICHTER, Otto (1828-1911) German
£839 $1427 €1200 Goethe in Airolo Mountains resting during walk (65x42cm-26x17in) s. 21-Nov-3 Reiss & Sohn, Konigstein #10/R est:1000
£6000 $11040 €8760 Sacred kiss (44x29cm-17x11in) s.i. panel. 25-Mar-4 Christie's, Kensington #123/R est:6000-8000

DONNER, Carl (?) ?
Works on paper
£270 $489 €394 Pheasants in snowy woodland (25x36cm-10x14in) s. W/C. 16-Apr-4 Keys, Aylsham #608
£300 $501 €438 Grouse in highland landscape (36x25cm-14x10in) s. W/C. 17-Oct-3 Keys, Aylsham #539
£380 $654 €555 Secluded widgeon on the wintry washes (36x51cm-14x20in) s. W/C. 5-Dec-3 Keys, Aylsham #513/R
£400 $668 €584 Garden fantail pigeons (46x36cm-18x14in) s.d.02 W/C. 17-Oct-3 Keys, Aylsham #543
£400 $644 €580 Blackgame in highland landscape (36x48cm-14x19in) s. W/C. 15-Aug-3 Keys, Aylsham #662/R
£460 $768 €672 Duckwing game-fowl (41x28cm-16x11in) s. W/C. 17-Oct-3 Keys, Aylsham #542
£500 $860 €730 Winter woodland woodcock (36x51cm-14x20in) s. W/C. 5-Dec-3 Keys, Aylsham #514/R
£560 $1036 €818 Red-lag partridge in winter (36x56cm-14x22in) s. W/C. 13-Feb-4 Keys, Aylsham #628/R
£600 $1110 €876 Stag and hen bronze turkeys in farmyard (36x56cm-14x22in) s. W/C. 13-Feb-4 Keys, Aylsham #629

DONNER, Diego (1959-) Uruguayan
£347 $580 €507 Abstract (61x73cm-24x29in) s.d.1998 fabric relief. 7-Oct-3 Galeria y Remates, Montevideo #78/R
Works on paper
£305 $500 €445 Untitled (75x90cm-30x35in) s.d.2000 mixed media panel. 3-Jun-3 Galeria y Remates, Montevideo #55

DONNY, Desire (1798-1861) Flemish
£894 $1627 €1350 Clair de lune sur le port de Bruges (35x44cm-14x17in) s.d.1839 panel. 15-Jun-4 Vanderkindere, Brussels #7
£1507 $2562 €2200 Beached sailing ship (26x36cm-10x14in) s.d.53 panel. 5-Nov-3 Hugo Ruef, Munich #957/R est:900
£2500 $4525 €3800 River view by moonlight (28x40cm-11x16in) s. panel. 19-Apr-4 Glerum, Amsterdam #7/R
£6597 $10490 €9500 Le suavetage du trois-mats (104x141cm-41x56in) s. 15-Sep-3 Horta, Bruxelles #129/R est:10000-12000

DONO, Heri (1960-) Indonesian
£2934 $4900 €4284 Kapal terbang buatari sendiri - self made plane (60x80cm-24x31in) s.d.1990 acrylic collage. 26-Oct-3 Christie's, Hong Kong #88/R est:30000-60000 (HK.D 38000)
£3125 $5219 €4563 Mimpi Dapat Lotere (60x80cm-24x31in) s.d.2001 s.i.d.verso. 12-Oct-3 Sotheby's, Singapore #179/R est:9000-12000 (S.D 9000)
£4348 $6739 €6348 Main Petak Umpet (96x96cm-38x38in) s.i.d.1984 verso. 6-Oct-2 Sotheby's, Singapore #186/R est:12000-15000 (S.D 12000)

DONOGHUE, James (20th C) ?
£260 $484 €380 Maritime scene with sailing vessels off coast (42x57cm-17x22in) s. board. 5-Mar-4 Moore Allen & Innocent, Cirencester #339

DONOGHUE, John (1853-1903) American
Sculpture
£13295 $23000 €19411 Sophocles celebrsting the victory at Salamis (113x66x38cm-44x26x15in) bronze st.f.F.Barbedienne. 11-Dec-3 Sotheby's, New York #42/R est:25000-35000
Works on paper
£250 $418 €365 Goose girl (23x37cm-9x15in) s.d.1886 W/C. 16-Oct-3 Lyon & Turnbull, Edinburgh #124

DONOHO, Gaines Ruger (1857-1916) American
£700 $1288 €1022 Jetty, Gretz (23x18cm-9x7in) i.d.1883 stretcher verso. 8-Jun-4 Bonhams, Knightsbridge #174/R
£2825 $5000 €4125 Landscape with hay stacks (56x76cm-22x30in) s. 2-May-4 Grogan, Boston #102/R

DONOVAN, Phoebe (1902-1998) British
£403 $721 €600 Alpes Maritimes (25x35cm-10x14in) s. board. 31-May-4 Hamilton Osborne King, Dublin #203
£700 $1253 €1022 Returning home (51x61cm-20x24in) s. board. 14-May-4 Christie's, Kensington #370/R
£1944 $3169 €2800 At the market (60x51cm-24x20in) s. 23-Sep-3 De Veres Art Auctions, Dublin #220/R est:3000-4000
Works on paper
£320 $576 €480 Tied up boats (23x34cm-9x13in) s. W/C. 20-Apr-4 James Adam, Dublin #214/R
£599 $1036 €850 Portraits of two terriers (45x36cm-18x14in) s. pastel pair. 10-Dec-3 Bonhams & James Adam, Dublin #112/R

DONZE, Numa (1885-1952) Swiss
£655 $1172 €956 In Elsass (74x90cm-29x35in) s. 26-May-4 Sotheby's, Zurich #32/R (S.FR 1500)

DONZELLI, Bruno (1941-) Italian
£268 $497 €400 Italian serenade (30x40cm-12x16in) s. mixed media board. 13-Mar-4 Meeting Art, Vercelli #306
£347 $549 €500 Print (90x100cm-35x39in) s.i.d.1987 verso mixed media on canvas prov. 27-Apr-3 Versailles Encheres #159
£347 $549 €500 Morandiana (100x100cm-39x39in) s.d.1987 i.d.verso acrylic prov. 27-Apr-3 Versailles Encheres #156
£352 $585 €500 Specchio Picassiano (50x40cm-20x16in) s. s.i.verso oil mixed media. 14-Jun-3 Meeting Art, Vercelli #32
£367 $675 €550 Fruit salad (40x50cm-16x20in) s. s.i.verso. 12-Jun-4 Meeting Art, Vercelli #465/R
£433 $797 €650 Following De Chirico (70x60cm-28x24in) s.i. s.i.verso acrylic. 12-Jun-4 Meeting Art, Vercelli #697/R
£528 $877 €750 Finestra con depero (50x70cm-20x28in) s. s.i.verso. 14-Jun-3 Meeting Art, Vercelli #489/R
£1042 $1646 €1500 Art heart (90x100cm-35x39in) oil mixed media nails. 6-Sep-3 Meeting Art, Vercelli #322 est:1500
£1056 $1754 €1500 Colazione da Burri (100x100cm-39x39in) s. s.i.verso oil mixed media collage. 14-Jun-3 Meeting Art, Vercelli #64/R est:1500
Works on paper
£467 $859 €700 Futuristic night scene (40x50cm-16x20in) s.i. mixed media collage on canvas. 12-Jun-4 Meeting Art, Vercelli #795/R

DOODY OF DRUMCONDERA, Dennis O (18/19th C) Irish?
Prints
£2300 $3841 €3358 Triumphal entry of the union into London (157x25cm-62x10in) soft ground etching. 14-Oct-3 Bonhams, New Bond Street #132/R est:1500-2000

DOOL, Reinier Arie (1933-) Dutch
£822 $1397 €1200 Feeding the ducks (90x80cm-35x31in) s.d.71. 5-Nov-3 Vendue Huis, Gravenhage #426/R

DOOLAARD, Cornelis Jans (1944-) Dutch
£567 $1037 €850 Greetings out of the new world (25x25cm-10x10in) mono. exhib.lit. 7-Jun-4 Glerum, Amsterdam #347/R

DOOLIN, James (1932-) American
£356 $637 €520 Still life (29x44cm-11x17in) s.d.1970 verso board. 15-May-4 Christie's, Sydney #312/R (A.D 900)

DOOLITTLE, Warren Ford (jnr) (1911-1987) American

£829 $1500 €1210 Leda and the Swan (56x91cm-22x36in) s. 3-Apr-4 Neal Auction Company, New Orleans #672/R est:2000-3000

DOOMER, Lambert (1623-1700) Dutch

Works on paper

£14000 $25620 €20440 Village street with a bridge over a stream (23x42cm-9x17in) s.d.1645 verso pen brown ink grey wash prov.exhib.lit. 8-Jul-4 Sotheby's, London #83/R est:7000-9000

DOOMS, J (?) ?

£972 $1546 €1400 Still life with birds (80x100cm-31x39in) s. panel. 15-Sep-3 Bernaerts, Antwerp #760
£1111 $1767 €1600 Still life with shoes (40x50cm-16x20in) s. panel. 15-Sep-3 Bernaerts, Antwerp #759 est:100-150
£1528 $2429 €2200 Landscape at Latem (40x50cm-16x20in) s. panel. 15-Sep-3 Bernaerts, Antwerp #758 est:100-150

DOOMS, Vic (1912-1994) Belgian

£764 $1276 €1100 Bateau (40x30cm-16x12in) s. s.verso panel. 21-Oct-3 Campo & Campo, Antwerp #501
£1389 $2319 €2000 Spek met eieren (55x45cm-22x18in) s. panel. 21-Oct-3 Campo, Vlaamse Kaai #422 est:800-1000
£1678 $2853 €2400 La chaise (70x60cm-28x24in) s. panel. 1-Dec-3 Palais de Beaux Arts, Brussels #54 est:1250-1750
£1958 $3329 €2800 Vue de la Lys en hiver (40x50cm-16x20in) s. panel. 1-Dec-3 Palais de Beaux Arts, Brussels #55/R est:1250-1750

DOORDT, Jacob van (17th C) German

Miniatures

£14376 $26739 €20989 Portrait of Christian IV and his Queen Anna Cathrine (3x2cm-1x1in) gouache oval pair exec.c.1610-1611. 2-Mar-4 Rasmussen, Copenhagen #1301/R est:100000 (D.KR 160000)

DOOREN, Edmond van (1895-1965) Belgian

£533 $960 €800 Awakening of the earth (50x64cm-20x25in) s. prov. 26-Apr-4 Bernaerts, Antwerp #558/R
£867 $1569 €1300 Hiver (80x90cm-31x35in) s. 30-Mar-4 Campo, Vlaamse Kaai #191
£1200 $2172 €1800 La ville (80x100cm-31x39in) s. 30-Mar-4 Campo, Vlaamse Kaai #192/R est:1700-2200
£1600 $2896 €2400 Le Prince Carnaval (110x150cm-43x59in) s.d.1951. 30-Mar-4 Campo, Vlaamse Kaai #194/R est:2500-3400

Works on paper

£282 $487 €400 Old city (46x62cm-18x24in) s. Indian ink. 13-Dec-3 De Vuyst, Lokeren #338
£1200 $2172 €1800 Belgian coast (81x121cm-32x48in) s. 1-Apr-4 Van Ham, Cologne #1349/R est:1600

DOORN, Tinus van (1905-1940) Dutch

£514 $873 €750 Still life with skull (14x19cm-6x7in) mono.d.36. 5-Nov-3 Vendue Huis, Gravenhage #373
£753 $1281 €1100 Still life with pear (17x23cm-7x9in) mono.d.38. 5-Nov-3 Vendue Huis, Gravenhage #375
£1333 $2453 €2000 Still life with lemon and bird skeleton (40x54cm-16x21in) indis.s.d.37. 8-Jun-4 Sotheby's, Amsterdam #233/R est:2500-3500
£1370 $2329 €2000 Still life with lemons and bird (40x54cm-16x21in) 5-Nov-3 Vendue Huis, Gravenhage #378 est:700-800
£2740 $4658 €4000 Still life with flowers and lemons (24x29cm-9x11in) s.d.36. 5-Nov-3 Vendue Huis, Gravenhage #377/R est:500-700
£5822 $9897 €8500 Still life with the boat Fortune (31x39cm-12x15in) mono.d.52 panel. 5-Nov-3 Vendue Huis, Gravenhage #376/R est:400-600
£9091 $15455 €13000 Reclining nude (55x74cm-22x29in) mono.d.39. 25-Nov-3 Christie's, Amsterdam #1/R est:3500-4500
£18116 $29710 €25000 Two calves (100x100cm-39x39in) s.d.30 prov. 27-May-3 Sotheby's, Amsterdam #328/R est:8000-12000

DOOYEWAARD, Jacob (1876-1969) Dutch

£408 $743 €600 Snowy mountain range at sunrise (20x27cm-8x11in) s.d.41 canvas on plywood. 3-Feb-4 Christie's, Amsterdam #228
£603 $1008 €880 Ingeslapen model (33x24cm-13x9in) s. board. 20-Oct-3 Stephan Welz, Johannesburg #208/R est:4000-6000 (SA.R 7000)
£1078 $1800 €1574 De kimono (37x17cm-15x7in) s.d.1952 i.d.verso board. 20-Oct-3 Stephan Welz, Johannesburg #207/R est:7000-10000 (SA.R 12500)

DOOYEWAARD, Willem (1892-1980) Dutch

£1552 $2591 €2266 Ballet dancer (39x20cm-15x8in) s. board. 20-Oct-3 Stephan Welz, Johannesburg #206/R est:18000-24000 (SA.R 18000)
£1806 $2943 €2600 View of a temple, Kyoto (65x53cm-26x21in) s.i.d.1930. 29-Sep-3 Sotheby's, Amsterdam #251/R
£3401 $6088 €5000 Geisha bij draagstoel - Geisha by sedan chair (100x50cm-39x20in) s.i.d.1930. 16-Mar-4 Christie's, Amsterdam #106/R est:4000-6000
£6463 $11568 €9500 Japansche dame - Japanese lady (100x50cm-39x20in) s.i.d.31 i.stretcher. 16-Mar-4 Christie's, Amsterdam #110/R est:4000-6000
£12245 $21918 €18000 Balinese man with a fighting cock (75x55cm-30x22in) s. prov. 16-Mar-4 Christie's, Amsterdam #12/R est:8000-12000
£31660 $52873 €46224 Balinese girl dancing (99x54cm-39x21in) s. prov. 26-Oct-3 Christie's, Hong Kong #22/R est:200000-280000 (HK.D 410000)

Works on paper

£544 $974 €800 Geisha, Kyoto (46x26cm-18x10in) s.i.d.1931 gouache. 16-Mar-4 Christie's, Amsterdam #75
£1307 $2366 €1908 Man (42x20cm-17x8in) s.d.Sept 22 pencil lit. 4-Apr-4 Sotheby's, Singapore #31/R est:4000-6000 (S.D 4000)
£3200 $5824 €4800 Rookende Japansche, Geisha smoking (65x50cm-26x20in) s. W/C bodycol. 1-Jul-4 Christie's, Amsterdam #445/R est:2000-3000

DORAZIL, F (19th C) ?

£1208 $2138 €1800 Leopold Graf Sternberg (63x50cm-25x20in) s.d.1887. 29-Apr-4 Dorotheum, Vienna #210/R est:700-900

DORAZIO, Piero (1927-) Italian

£1067 $1963 €1600 Geova I (25x35cm-10x14in) s.i.d.1999 verso. 11-Jun-4 Farsetti, Prato #201/R est:1600-1900
£1081 $1903 €1600 Abstract (27x34cm-11x13in) s.d.2000 paper. 22-May-4 Galleria Pananti, Florence #402/R est:1600-1800
£1081 $1903 €1600 Unphaios I (25x30cm-10x12in) s.i.d.2002 verso. 22-May-4 Galleria Pananti, Florence #430/R est:1600-2000
£1103 $1766 €1600 Ompnalos V (25x30cm-10x12in) s.i.verso. 13-Mar-3 Galleria Pace, Milan #106/R est:1750-2250
£1111 $1756 €1600 Form III (30x24cm-12x9in) card on canvas oval. 6-Sep-3 Meeting Art, Vercelli #582
£1268 $2104 €1800 Lumi 1 (35x25cm-14x10in) s.i.verso. 14-Jun-3 Meeting Art, Vercelli #84/R est:1500
£1351 $2378 €2000 Fotinos IV (30x24cm-12x9in) s.i.d.2001 verso. 22-May-4 Galleria Pananti, Florence #387/R est:1200-1500
£1379 $2303 €2000 Light red (25x35cm-10x14in) s.d.2001. 13-Nov-3 Finarte Semenzato, Rome #333 est:1800-2400
£1379 $2207 €2000 Zophoe I (30x24cm-12x9in) s.i.verso painted 2001. 13-Mar-3 Galleria Pace, Milan #134/R est:2800-3500
£1467 $2699 €2200 Siris III (24x30cm-9x12in) s.i.d.1998. 12-Jun-4 Meeting Art, Vercelli #90/R est:2000
£1517 $2534 €2200 Friends colours I (22x35cm-9x14in) s.i.verso. 13-Nov-3 Galleria Pace, Milan #95/R est:2800
£1549 $2572 €2200 Nighting I (40x30cm-16x12in) s.i.d.1998 verso. 11-Jun-3 Finarte Semenzato, Milan #577/R
£1701 $3095 €2500 Untitled (25x35cm-10x14in) s.verso oval. 6-Feb-4 Galleria Rosenberg, Milan #68/R
£1701 $3095 €2500 Always green (25x35cm-10x14in) s.verso. 6-Feb-4 Galleria Rosenberg, Milan #108/R est:2500
£1933 $3480 €2900 Fleu du quai (68x23cm-27x9in) s.i.d.1989 verso acrylic. 25-Apr-4 Versailles Encheres #177 est:800-1000
£2183 $3624 €3100 Illusione II (35x40cm-14x16in) s.i.verso. 14-Jun-3 Meeting Art, Vercelli #333/R est:2500
£2215 $4097 €3300 Hit and miss (35x50cm-14x20in) s.i.verso painted 2003. 13-Mar-4 Meeting Art, Vercelli #367 est:3000
£2381 $4262 €3500 Tour (45cm-18in circular) s.i.d.1999 verso canvas on board. 16-Mar-4 Finarte Semenzato, Milan #121/R est:1000-1200
£2414 $3862 €3500 Telikos VII (350x50cm-138x20in) s.i.verso painted 2001. 13-Mar-3 Galleria Pace, Milan #143/R est:4000-5000
£2500 $3950 €3600 Eye and cross IV (35x50cm-14x20in) painted 2003. 6-Sep-3 Meeting Art, Vercelli #362 est:3000
£2587 $4399 €3700 Composition (49x69cm-19x27in) s.d.1987 masonite prov. 20-Nov-3 Finarte Semenzato, Milan #118/R est:3700-4300
£2617 $4842 €3900 Lab Gamma (25x35cm-10x14in) s.i.verso painted 2002. 11-Mar-4 Galleria Pace, Milan #85/R est:3000-4000
£2690 $4303 €3900 Milos VI (45x60cm-18x24in) studio st.i.d.1998 verso. 13-Mar-3 Galleria Pace, Milan #34/R est:4400-5700
£2690 $4303 €3900 Untitled (50x70cm-20x28in) s.d.1987 acrylic paper on board. 13-Mar-3 Galleria Pace, Milan #155/R est:4800-6200
£2899 $4754 €4000 Criss Cross (40x60cm-16x24in) s.i.verso. 29-May-3 Galleria Pace, Milan #105/R est:6500
£3020 $5406 €4500 Mende (40x60cm-16x24in) s.i.d.1999. 30-May-4 Meeting Art, Vercelli #22 est:3000
£3020 $5406 €4500 Untitled (56x76cm-22x30in) s.d.1981 tempera paper on cardboard. 28-May-4 Farsetti, Prato #156/R est:4500-5500
£3020 $5406 €4500 Dogon I (50x35cm-20x14in) s.i.d.1994 verso. 28-May-4 Farsetti, Prato #285/R est:4200-4700
£3103 $5183 €4500 Golden VI (50x30cm-20x12in) s.d.1985 verso. 13-Nov-3 Finarte Semenzato, Rome #347/R est:3800-4500
£3103 $5183 €4500 Corinth (60x75cm-24x30in) s.i.verso. 13-Nov-3 Galleria Pace, Milan #70/R est:6500
£3356 $6208 €5000 Tantun. s.i.d.200 verso oval. 11-Mar-4 Galleria Pace, Milan #76/R est:5000-7000
£3356 $6007 €5000 Strict (80x40cm-31x16in) s.i.d.1999 verso. 28-May-4 Farsetti, Prato #163/R est:4200-4700
£3380 $5611 €4800 Four suns (70x50cm-28x20in) s.i.d.1989 verso. 13-Jun-3 Farsetti, Prato #318/R
£3623 $5942 €5000 MM II (60x75cm-24x30in) s.i.verso painted 2001. 29-May-3 Galleria Pace, Milan #131/R est:6800
£3733 $6869 €5600 Donan (40x60cm-16x24in) s.i.d.2002 verso. 12-Jun-4 Meeting Art, Vercelli #827/R est:4000
£4000 $7320 €6000 Altrove II (42x34cm-17x13in) s.i.d.1977 prov. 4-Jun-4 Lempertz, Koln #114/R est:5000
£4082 $7306 €6000 Untitled (50x32cm-20x13in) s.d.1957. 22-Mar-4 Sant Agostino, Torino #479/R est:4200
£4225 $7014 €6000 Alcatraz (60x75cm-24x30in) s.i. 14-Jun-3 Meeting Art, Vercelli #528/R est:5000
£4467 $8085 €6700 Composition (50x32cm-20x13in) s.d.1957 tempera card. 2-Apr-4 Farsetti, Prato #366/R est:6700-7700
£4533 $8341 €6800 Temptation I (45x65cm-18x26in) s.i.d. 12-Jun-4 Meeting Art, Vercelli #467/R est:4000
£4757 $7516 €6850 Corynth (60x75cm-24x30in) painted 2002. 6-Sep-3 Meeting Art, Vercelli #604 est:5000
£5072 $8319 €7000 Fragments (63x42cm-25x17in) s.i.d.1978 verso. 27-May-3 Sotheby's, Milan #66/R est:9000
£5797 $9507 €8000 Pagan (50x70cm-20x28in) s.i.d.1974 verso. 27-May-3 Sotheby's, Milan #65/R est:7000
£7333 $13200 €11000 Net (20x30cm-8x12in) s.d.1963 verso. 22-Apr-4 Finarte Semenzato, Rome #197/R est:4800-5200
£8392 $14266 €12000 Borealis A (95x75cm-37x30in) s.i.d.1986 verso. 24-Nov-3 Christie's, Milan #201/R est:10000-12000
£9986 $16976 €14280 Copy I (50x100cm-20x39in) s.i.d.1973 verso prov.lit. 18-Nov-3 Babuino, Rome #475/R est:5000-7000
£10839 $18427 €15500 Flash back I (96x120cm-38x47in) s.i.d.1991-92 verso acrylic. 20-Nov-3 Finarte Semenzato, Milan #218/R est:14000-16000
£10976 $18000 €16025 Progres rythmique (51x61cm-20x24in) s.d.63 s.i.d.1963 on stretcher prov. 28-May-3 Sotheby's, Amsterdam #126/R est:10000-12000
£12162 $21405 €18000 Doric II (200x50cm-79x20in) s.i.d.1971 verso prov.exhib.lit. 24-May-4 Christie's, Milan #161/R est:20000-30000
£12162 $21405 €18000 Doric I (200x50cm-79x20in) s.i.d.1971 verso prov.exhib.lit. 24-May-4 Christie's, Milan #160/R est:20000-30000
£12162 $21405 €18000 Fin de siecle (220x80cm-87x31in) s.i.d.1988-89 verso. 22-May-4 Galleria Pananti, Florence #480/R est:20000-22000

£12973	$24000	€18941	Streak II (50x180cm-20x71in) s.i.d.1975 verso acrylic prov. 12-Feb-4 Sotheby's, New York #337a/R est:6000-8000
£13333	$24000	€20000	Spotted II (90x65cm-35x26in) s. painted 1968. 22-Apr-4 Finarte Semenzato, Rome #286/R est:20000-22000
£20280	$34476	€29000	Four or five times (151x200cm-59x79in) s.i.d.1986 verso acrylic. 28-Nov-3 Farsetti, Prato #87/R est:28000-32000
£21333	$39253	€32000	Piccolo tic tac rosso (41x33cm-16x13in) s.d.60. 12-Jun-4 Villa Grisebach, Berlin #354/R est:10000-12000
£21477	$38443	€32000	Miss Bleu (46x39cm-18x15in) s.i.d.1962. 28-May-4 Farsetti, Prato #317/R est:32000-36000
£22183	$38377	€31500	Reveil R (73x60cm-29x24in) s.d.59 s.i.d.1959 stretcher. 13-Dec-3 Lempertz, Koln #130/R est:15000
£24476	$41608	€35000	Composition (70x90cm-28x35in) s.d.55 exhib. 28-Nov-3 Farsetti, Prato #371/R est:35000-45000
£29371	$49930	€42000	Odd blue (79x100cm-31x39in) s.i.d.1960 verso prov.exhib.lit. 25-Nov-3 Sotheby's, Milan #215/R est:45000-65000
£32168	$54685	€46000	Green land (70x280cm-28x110in) s.i.d.1963-64 verso. 20-Nov-3 Finarte Semenzato, Milan #216/R est:50000-60000
£34667	$63440	€52000	Sospetto di forma (146x113cm-57x44in) s.i.d.58 s.i.d. verso prov.exhib. 4-Jun-4 Lempertz, Koln #112/R est:40000-50000
£35135	$61838	€52000	Din-don (200x200cm-79x79in) s.i.d.1966 lit. 24-May-4 Christie's, Milan #162/R est:40000-60000
Sculpture			
£1149	$2022	€1700	Untitled (9x17x2cm-4x7x1in) s.d.54 bronze prov. 24-May-4 Christie's, Milan #99/R est:2500-3500
Works on paper			
£1297	$2400	€1894	Untitled (65x65cm-26x26in) s. W/C exec 1980 prov. 13-Jul-4 Christie's, Rockefeller NY #14/R est:2000-3000
£1399	$2378	€2000	Untitled (24x32cm-9x13in) s.d.1962 pastel. 20-Nov-3 Finarte Semenzato, Milan #78/R est:2000-2500
£1600	$2880	€2400	Untitled (37x56cm-15x22in) s.d.1986 pastel. 22-Apr-4 Finarte Semenzato, Rome #196/R est:1800-2400
£1761	$2923	€2500	Doric (88x68cm-35x27in) s.d.1971 verso pastel. 14-Jun-3 Meeting Art, Vercelli #80/R est:2500
£2000	$3600	€3000	Untitled (43x54cm-17x21in) s. W/C exec.1984 exhib. 22-Apr-4 Finarte Semenzato, Rome #108/R est:2800-3500
£2215	$4097	€3300	Untitled (75x105cm-30x41in) s.d.1989 mixed media collage card. 13-Mar-4 Meeting Art, Vercelli #118 est:3000
£2439	$4000	€3561	Doppelzeichnung - double drawing (32x49cm-13x19in) s.d.61 wax crayon prov. 28-May-3 Sotheby's, Amsterdam #17/R est:4000-5000
£3287	$5587	€4700	Untitled (61x48cm-24x19in) s.i.d.62 col chk. 27-Nov-3 Lempertz, Koln #109/R est:4000
£4698	$8409	€7000	Nets (25x70cm-10x28in) s.d.61 pe felt-tip pen prov. 25-May-4 Sotheby's, Milan #104/R est:10000
£5705	$10211	€8500	Net (74x54cm-29x21in) s.d.59 gouache pastel prov. 25-May-4 Sotheby's, Milan #157/R est:4000-5000

DORCHY, Henry (1920-) Belgian

£537	$993	€800	Grande Dame Marine (65x100cm-26x39in) s.i.d.52 verso paper on canvas. 13-Mar-4 De Vuyst, Lokeren #124
£694	$1104	€1000	Le chant de la sirene (80x54cm-31x21in) s.verso. 9-Sep-3 Palais de Beaux Arts, Brussels #218

DORDA RODRIGUEZ, Enrique (1869-1944) Spanish

£387	$678	€550	Self-portrait (25x19cm-10x7in) s.d.1892 board. 16-Dec-3 Segre, Madrid #61/R

DORE, Gustave (1832-1883) French

£2552	$4721	€3700	L'Olympe (23x18cm-9x7in) studio stamp panel. 11-Feb-4 Beaussant & Lefèvre, Paris #20/R est:1500
£4348	$8000	€6348	At prayer (38x30cm-15x12in) s.i.d.1849 prov. 25-Jun-4 Freeman, Philadelphia #340/R est:400-600
£6447	$11863	€9800	Coucher de soleil sur l'etang (90x57cm-35x22in) s. 28-Jun-4 Joron-Derem, Paris #77/R est:8000-10000
£7500	$13800	€10950	Sarah Bernhardt (65x54cm-26x21in) s.d.1870. 25-Mar-4 Christie's, Kensington #64/R est:6000-8000
£10277	$18395	€15004	Mother and Child, London Bridge (71x55cm-28x22in) painted 1871 prov.lit. 15-May-4 Christie's, Sydney #18/R est:30000-50000 (A.D 26000)
£18341	$33380	€26778	Le revendeur de Whitechapel (95x76cm-37x30in) s.d.1878 prov.exhib. 18-Jun-4 Kornfeld, Bern #31/R est:30000 (S.FR 42000)
Sculpture			
£3310	$6124	€4800	Nu allonge et amour (8cm-3in) s. pat bronze Cast Thiebaut prov. 11-Feb-4 Beaussant & Lefèvre, Paris #22/R est:2500
£3448	$6379	€5000	La parque et l'amour (57cm-22in) s. terracotta prov.exhib.lit. 11-Feb-4 Beaussant & Lefèvre, Paris #24/R est:1500
£6552	$12121	€9500	Saute-mouton (35cm-14in) s. pat bronze exec.c.1880 prov.lit. 11-Feb-4 Beaussant & Lefèvre, Paris #23/R est:3000
Works on paper			
£268	$494	€400	Figure studies for Les Chasseurs (23x30cm-9x12in) pencil. 26-Mar-4 Venator & Hansten, Koln #1550
£345	$638	€500	L'arbre arrache (28x20cm-11x8in) ink wash. 11-Feb-4 Beaussant & Lefèvre, Paris #14/R
£350	$594	€500	Barbu marchant (18x11cm-7x4in) Indian ink exec.c.1865. 23-Nov-3 Cornette de St.Cyr, Paris #102
£410	$750	€599	Study of a mountainous landscape (27x20cm-11x8in) artist st. pencil brush blue ink wash. 29-Jan-4 Swann Galleries, New York #268/R
£458	$792	€650	Woman in front of a mirror (44x36cm-17x14in) studio st. W/C traces blk crayon. 10-Dec-3 Piasa, Paris #116
£483	$893	€700	Le cuirasse (46x29cm-18x11in) s.d.13 janvier 1855 W/C ink. 11-Feb-4 Beaussant & Lefèvre, Paris #11
£533	$955	€800	Homme a mi-corps (14x14cm-6x6in) s.i. pen ink. 11-May-4 Christie's, Paris #125/R
£655	$1212	€950	Scene de bataille. Les ames damnees (30x46cm-12x18in) chl pair. 11-Feb-4 Beaussant & Lefèvre, Paris #18
£656	$1200	€958	Street scene with man accosting a woman before a crowd (22x26cm-9x10in) s. pen blue ink. 29-Jan-4 Swann Galleries, New York #269/R
£724	$1332	€1100	L'ermite (57x42cm-22x17in) chl htd white chk. 28-Jun-4 Joron-Derem, Paris #76/R
£789	$1453	€1200	Lecon de violon. Etude de personnages (26x44cm-10x17in) lead pencil double-sided. 28-Jun-4 Joron-Derem, Paris #67/R
£993	$1658	€1400	Le Christ au jardin des oliviers (37x50cm-15x20in) ink wash gouache. 20-Jun-3 Drouot Estimations, Paris #58/R
£1069	$1978	€1550	Mephistopheles. Scene de rue. Lettre (27x20cm-11x8in) pencil ink three. 11-Feb-4 Beaussant & Lefèvre, Paris #15 est:200-300
£1126	$2060	€1700	Scene allegorique (46x36cm-18x14in) bears studio st. W/C. 7-Apr-4 Piasa, Paris #5 est:1200-1500
£1127	$1870	€1600	A la sortie de l'eglise (16x25cm-6x10in) s. W/C. 15-Jun-3 Peron, Melun #58
£1361	$2435	€2000	Portrait de Madame Dore (16x12cm-6x5in) black pencil ink wash paper on cardboard. 19-Mar-4 Piasa, Paris #166/R est:1000
£1467	$2655	€2200	Paysage d'Ecosse (31x23cm-12x9in) s. wash. 5-Apr-4 Deburaux, Boulogne #73/R est:2500-3000
£1645	$3026	€2500	Traversee du Styx (41x58cm-16x23in) s.d.1846 gouache W/C lead pencil. 28-Jun-4 Joron-Derem, Paris #70/R est:2500-3000
£2098	$3608	€3000	L'annonciation (141x83cm-56x33in) s. chl htd white chk. 5-Dec-3 Chochon-Barre & Allardi, Paris #81/R est:3000-4000
£2449	$4384	€3600	Christ quittant le pretoire (35x49cm-14x19in) brush brown wash htd white gouache. 17-Mar-4 Tajan, Paris #133/R est:1500
£2500	$4250	€3650	Christ entering Jerusalem (52x81cm-20x32in) chl graphite gouache. 21-Nov-3 Skinner, Boston #208/R est:800-1200
£2600	$4498	€3796	Extensive landscape with ruins of a castle (16x20cm-6x8in) s. W/C. 12-Dec-3 Christie's, Kensington #488/R est:400-600
£2781	$5062	€4200	Cavalier abreuvant son cheval (23x33cm-9x13in) s.d.1879 W/C black crayon. 16-Jun-4 Piasa, Paris #186/R est:2500-3000
£3537	$6332	€5200	Femme au bord du lac Lemanau soleil couchant (32x46cm-13x18in) i. W/C gouache traces black crayon. 17-Mar-4 Tajan, Paris #135/R est:1300
£4444	$8000	€6488	Nymphs in a landscape (53x67cm-21x26in) black chk pen brown ink W/C bodycol prov. 22-Jan-4 Christie's, Rockefeller NY #148/R est:5000-8000
£5172	$9569	€7500	Tete de Christ a la couronne d'epines (57x46cm-22x18in) s. ink black crayon. 11-Feb-4 Beaussant & Lefèvre, Paris #19/R est:4000
£5882	$10000	€8588	Jeremiah preaching to his followers (70x53cm-28x21in) s.i. pencil chl htd white paper on card. 29-Oct-3 Christie's, Rockefeller NY #158/R est:8000-12000
£9524	$17048	€14000	Persee et Andromede (31x25cm-12x10in) s. chl brown ink wash htd gouache. 19-Mar-4 Piasa, Paris #164 est:800
£15436	$27322	€23000	Songe d'une nuit d'ete (65x81cm-26x32in) W/C gouache pair oval prov. 30-Apr-4 Tajan, Paris #138/R est:20000-30000

DORE, Gustave (attrib) (1832-1883) French

Works on paper			
£291	$468	€425	Girl on balcony, Seville. wash prov. 25-Aug-3 Lilla Bukowskis, Stockholm #784 (S.KR 3800)

DORE, Jacques (?) French

£2133	$3861	€3200	Africain en costume tradionnel (44x36cm-17x14in) s. 30-Mar-4 Campo & Campo, Antwerp #88/R est:500-650
Works on paper			
£900	$1656	€1314	At the dressing table (73x58cm-29x23in) s.i. pastel. 25-Mar-4 Christie's, Kensington #225

DORE, Joseph (1805-1878) Czechoslovakian

£470	$869	€700	Travellers with donkey resting next to stream (68x55cm-27x22in) s. lit. 12-Mar-4 Zadick, Uberlingen #4082

DORELLA, Aldo (1925-) Italian

£268	$497	€400	Dancers in a theatre (70x50cm-28x20in) s. s.i.verso. 13-Mar-4 Meeting Art, Vercelli #174

DOREN, Émile van (1865-1949) Belgian

£667	$1220	€1000	Landscape (27x36cm-11x14in) s. panel prov. 5-Jun-4 Lempertz, Koln #681/R
£2083	$3312	€3000	Paysage de Campine (90x150cm-35x59in) s. 9-Sep-3 Vanderkindere, Brussels #24/R

DORESTE, Angel (1933-) Spanish

£1528	$2597	€2200	Beach in Berria (31x75cm-12x30in) s.d.1986 acrylic board. 28-Oct-3 Segre, Madrid #326/R est:2100

DORFFMEISTER, Josef (1764-1814) Hungarian

£9444	$17000	€13788	Portrait of a young boy and girl (114x84cm-45x33in) s.d. 22-Jan-4 Sotheby's, New York #240/R est:18000-22000

DORFLER, Roland (1926-) German

£333	$600	€500	Composition (100x120cm-39x47in) s.d.1959 panel. 26-Apr-4 Rieber, Stuttgart #831/R

D'ORGEIX, Christian (20th C) French

£347	$580	€500	Composition (60x75cm-24x30in) s. panel. 21-Oct-3 Campo, Vlaamse Kaai #733
£839	$1427	€1200	Le Sabbah des sorcieres (33x41cm-13x16in) s. prov. 23-Nov-3 Cornette de St.Cyr, Paris #103/R
£1199	$2183	€1800	Untitled (91x73cm-36x29in) s. acrylic painted c.1953 prov. 30-Jun-4 Calmels Cohen, Paris #85/R est:1000-1500
Works on paper			
£559	$1029	€850	Untitled (29x24cm-11x9in) s. crayon dr prov. 27-Jun-4 Versailles Encheres #198

DORIE, Dominique (1958-) French

£241	$425	€362	Fleurs au vase Ttransparent (99x99cm-39x39in) s.i. stretcher prov. 18-May-4 Arthur James, Florida #156

DORIGNAC, Georges (1879-1925) French

£759	$1259	€1100	Nature morte au poisson (73x93cm-29x37in) s. 1-Oct-3 Millon & Associes, Paris #54
Works on paper			
£507	$907	€750	Tete de jeune homme (32x27cm-13x11in) s.d.1912 sanguine black chk. 7-May-4 Millon & Associes, Paris #122

DORIGNY, Michel (1617-1665) French
Works on paper
£7042 $12324 €10000 Venus et Adonis (15x20cm-6x8in) black chk oval after Simon Vouet prov. 17-Dec-3 Christie's, Paris #36/R est:10000-15000

DORING, Adam Lude (1925-) German
£451 $736 €650 Violine (25x25cm-10x10in) s.d.1973 s.i. verso masonite. 27-Sep-3 Dr Fritz Nagel, Stuttgart #9097/R

DORING, Willi (19th C) German
£874 $1486 €1250 Paysage au chateau (80x120cm-31x47in) s. 18-Nov-3 Vanderkindere, Brussels #50

DORION, Charles S (?) American?
£535 $850 €781 Moonlight sail (46x76cm-18x30in) s. 12-Sep-3 Skinner, Boston #287/R

D'ORLEANS, Marie (1865-1907) French
Works on paper
£479 $815 €700 Etude de champignons (29x54cm-11x21in) s. W/C over crayon. 6-Nov-3 Tajan, Paris #238
£685 $1164 €1000 Etude de courges (38x55cm-15x22in) s. W/C over crayon. 6-Nov-3 Tajan, Paris #237

DORMAEL, Simone van (20th C) ?
£295 $546 €440 La venitienne au masque noir (72x60cm-28x24in) s. 15-Mar-4 Horta, Bruxelles #301

DORNBERGER, Karl Johannes (1864-1940) Norwegian
£426 $681 €618 Winter landscape with woman and child (52x75cm-20x30in) s. 22-Sep-3 Blomqvist, Lysaker #1039/R (N.KR 5000)
£691 $1147 €1002 Red house with flowering trees (54x50cm-21x20in) s. panel. 16-Jun-3 Blomqvist, Lysaker #1027/R (N.KR 8000)
£2044 $3516 €2984 Lilacs in bloom, Soon (50x60cm-20x24in) s.d.1915 i.verso panel. 8-Dec-3 Blomqvist, Oslo #482/R est:25000-30000 (N.KR 24000)
Works on paper
£261 $451 €381 Battle scene (72x58cm-28x23in) s. mixed media. 13-Dec-3 Blomqvist, Lysaker #1071/R (N.KR 3000)

DORNER, Helmut (1952-) German
£900 $1656 €1314 PC (48x38cm-19x15in) s.i.d.1988 verso oil wood prov.exhib. 24-Jun-4 Sotheby's, Olympia #578/R est:1000-1500
£1300 $2392 €1898 Decs (32x30cm-13x12in) s.i.d.1991 verso canvas on wood prov.exhib. 24-Jun-4 Sotheby's, Olympia #577/R est:1200-1500
£1667 $3066 €2500 FLS (29x34cm-11x13in) s.i.d.89 verso canvas on wood prov.exhib. 9-Jun-4 Artcurial Briest, Paris #547/R est:3000-3800
£3911 $7000 €5710 Schlzschrk (118x147cm-46x58in) s.i.d.2002 verso oil resin canvas on panel prov. 14-May-4 Phillips, New York #279/R est:8000-12000
£7263 $13000 €10604 Three. s.i.verso oil lacquer three parts prov.exhib. 14-May-4 Phillips, New York #278/R est:15000-20000

DORNER, Johann Jakob (elder) (1741-1813) German
£3103 $5152 €4500 Encounter with blind Belisar (57x50cm-22x20in) copper. 1-Oct-3 Dorotheum, Vienna #222/R est:4500-6000

DORNER, Johann Jakob (younger) (1775-1852) German
£4698 $8644 €7000 Bavarian mountain landscape with houses and stone bridge (57x51cm-22x20in) mono. prov.exhib. 24-Mar-4 Dorotheum, Vienna #258/R est:8000-10000
Works on paper
£2800 $5124 €4088 Study of a clump of trees. Study of a birch tree (31x21cm-12x8in) bears i. W/C gouache two joined sheets double-sided prov. 8-Jul-4 Sotheby's, London #155/R est:2000-3000

DORNER, Johann Jakob (younger-attrib) (1775-1852) German
£1477 $2717 €2200 Mountain stream with jetty and walker (36x42cm-14x17in) 24-Mar-4 Hugo Ruef, Munich #967/R est:1500
Works on paper
£1133 $2051 €1700 Small mountain stream near alpine farmstead (29x42cm-11x17in) i. verso W/C pencil. 2-Apr-4 Winterberg, Heidelberg #401/R est:2200

DORNER, Max (1870-1939) German
£625 $1150 €950 Spring landscape (69x59cm-27x23in) s.d.1905. 25-Jun-4 Michael Zeller, Lindau #579/R

DORNY, Bertrand (1931-) French
Works on paper
£403 $753 €600 Composition (35x36cm-14x14in) s.d.1988 collage. 29-Feb-4 Versailles Encheres #225/R

DORPH, Anton (1831-1914) Danish
£1432 $2621 €2091 Eagerness for work - twin girls in the dunes knitting (31x41cm-12x16in) s. 9-Jun-4 Rasmussen, Copenhagen #1650/R est:10000-15000 (D.KR 16000)
£4000 $7160 €5840 Figures amongst classical ruins (26x34cm-10x13in) init. 10-May-4 Sotheby's, Olympia #141/R est:2000-3000

DORPH, Bertha (attrib) (1875-1960) Danish
£1607 $2780 €2346 Young girl wearing yellow dress and large hat in landscape (68x56cm-27x22in) 9-Dec-3 Rasmussen, Copenhagen #1654/R est:6000-8000 (D.KR 17000)

DORR, Harry (fl.1930-1940) British
£800 $1432 €1168 Figure resting on a log with a fence and chestnut trees (54x75cm-21x30in) s. 16-Mar-4 Gildings, Market Harborough #449

DORRIES, Bernhard (1898-1978) German
£5000 $9200 €7500 Portrait of a young woman (31x21cm-12x8in) s. panel. 11-Jun-4 Villa Grisebach, Berlin #1577/R est:1000-2000

DORSCH, Ferdinand (1875-1938) German
£667 $1193 €1000 Visit (74x63cm-29x25in) s.d.1916 i. stretcher. 13-May-4 Neumeister, Munich #335/R
Works on paper
£308 $529 €440 Snowy street in small town (61x47cm-24x19in) s.i. mixed media. 4-Dec-3 Neumeister, Munich #2594
£486 $768 €700 Two houses with a garden (52x37cm-20x15in) s.d.1904 mixed media. 5-Sep-3 Wendl, Rudolstadt #3326/R
£600 $1074 €900 View over the roofs of Schloss Weesenstein in Sachsen (33x46cm-13x18in) s.d.1912 i. verso bodycol W/C pastel board. 15-May-4 Bassenge, Berlin #6798

DORSCHFELDT, Georg Albert (1898-1979) German
£352 $630 €500 Vase of spring flowers (70x60cm-28x24in) s. 8-Jan-4 Allgauer, Kempten #2372/R
£541 $968 €800 Sunlit birch avenue (70x84cm-28x33in) s.d.1932. 6-May-4 Michael Zeller, Lindau #646/R
£915 $1639 €1300 Vase of spring flowers (100x70cm-39x28in) s. board lit. 8-Jan-4 Allgauer, Kempten #2371/R

DORSEY, William (1942-) American
£345 $650 €504 Eucalyptus trees, Santa Barbara (41x30cm-16x12in) s. 22-Feb-4 Bonhams & Butterfields, Los Angeles #7003
£486 $900 €710 Trees near Ojai (30x41cm-12x16in) s. canvasboard. 18-Jan-4 Bonhams & Butterfields, Los Angeles #7002/R
£529 $900 €772 Cypress trees in coastal landscape (28x36cm-11x14in) s. prov. 18-Nov-3 John Moran, Pasadena #6
£529 $1000 €772 Stream in Sycamore Canyon (23x30cm-9x12in) s. prov. 17-Feb-4 John Moran, Pasadena #193/R
£582 $1100 €850 Red roofs beyond the advocado and orange trees (71x56cm-28x22in) s. prov. 17-Feb-4 John Moran, Pasadena #191/R
£582 $1100 €850 California landscape (20x30cm-8x12in) s. masonite prov. 17-Feb-4 John Moran, Pasadena #192/R
£941 $1600 €1374 Flower field and eucalyptus landscape (76x61cm-30x24in) s. 18-Nov-3 John Moran, Pasadena #18 est:2500-3500
£1324 $2250 €1933 Eucalyptus landscape (46x61cm-18x24in) s. masonite prov. 18-Nov-3 John Moran, Pasadena #164 est:1500-2500
£1359 $2500 €1984 The Santa Ynez Valley in bloom (61x91cm-24x36in) s. 8-Jun-4 Bonhams & Butterfields, San Francisco #4390/R est:3000-5000
£1445 $2500 €2110 Solitude (61x76cm-24x30in) s. 10-Dec-3 Bonhams & Butterfields, San Francisco #6344/R est:3000-5000
£1587 $3000 €2317 Flower field in eucalyptus landscape (61x76cm-24x30in) s. 17-Feb-4 John Moran, Pasadena #25/R est:2500-3500
£1648 $3000 €2406 Flower field (41x51cm-16x20in) s. 15-Jun-4 John Moran, Pasadena #36c est:1500-2000
£1923 $3500 €2808 Eucalyptus coastal scene (76x102cm-30x40in) s. 15-Jun-4 John Moran, Pasadena #103 est:3000-5000
£2116 $4000 €3089 Flower field in eucalyptus coastal (91x122cm-36x48in) s. 17-Feb-4 John Moran, Pasadena #98/R est:3500-5000
£3439 $6500 €5021 Mountains and flower fields in eucalyptus landscape (122x183cm-48x72in) s. prov. 17-Feb-4 John Moran, Pasadena #146a/R est:5000-7000
£5978 $11000 €8728 Wildflowers on the dunes (36x48cm-14x19in) s. 8-Jun-4 Bonhams & Butterfields, San Francisco #4391/R est:4000-6000

D'ORSI, Achille (1845-1929) Italian
Sculpture
£4000 $6920 €5840 Neapolitan fisherboy smoking a pipe (56cm-22in) s. brown pat bronze lit. 12-Dec-3 Sotheby's, London #262/R est:4000-6000

DOSAMANTES, Francisco (1911-) Mexican
Works on paper
£211 $335 €308 Landscape (29x40cm-11x16in) s. pencil. 29-Apr-3 Louis Morton, Mexico #70/R (M.P 3500)

DOSHIN, Kaigetsudo (fl.1700-1716) Japanese
Prints
£10000 $18400 €14600 Standing courtesan (55x31cm-22x12in) s. print exec. early 1710's lit. 8-Jun-4 Sotheby's, London #25/R est:10000-15000

DOSSENA, Alceo (1878-1937) Italian
Sculpture
£3873 $6701 €5500 Madonna and Child (46x33cm-18x13in) s.d.1934 marble relief. 9-Dec-3 Pandolfini, Florence #108 est:3000-4000
£8000 $14480 €12000 Madonna and Child with Saint John (79x50cm-31x20in) s.d.34 marble relief. 31-Mar-4 Finarte Semenzato, Milan #256/R est:8000-9000

DOSSI, Battista (attrib) (1474-1548) Italian
£34000 $58820 €49640 The Visitation (75x63cm-30x25in) 11-Dec-3 Sotheby's, London #180/R est:15000-20000

D'OTEMAR, Marie Adolphe Edouard (19th C) French
£803 $1332 €1172 Portrait of a girl with flowers in her hair (123x73cm-48x29in) s. 15-Jun-3 Agra, Warsaw #43/R (P.Z 5000)

DOTREMONT, Christian (1922-1979) Belgian

Works on paper

£6000	$10740	€9000	Logogram, texte incertain (55x76cm-22x30in) st.sig. pencil Indian ink. 15-May-4 De Vuyst, Lokeren #586/R est:10000-12000
£30047	$50178	€43869	Calligraphy signs (76x166cm-30x65in) s.d.1976 dr. triptych prov. 7-Oct-3 Rasmussen, Copenhagen #12/R est:300000-350000 (D.KR 320000)

DOTTORI, Gerardo (1884-1977) Italian

£3667	$6747	€5500	Landscape in Umbria (36x29cm-14x11in) s. board painted 1946. 11-Jun-4 Farsetti, Prato #331/R est:5200-6200
£8333	$13167	€12000	Landscape (22x61cm-9x24in) board. 6-Sep-3 Meeting Art, Vercelli #491 est:12000
£12752	$22826	€19000	Landscape in Umbria. s.d.61 s.i.d.verso tempera board. 29-May-4 Farsetti, Prato #521/R est:12000-15000

Works on paper

£1042	$1646	€1500	PO. of General Armani (62x45cm-24x18in) chl card exec.1917. 6-Sep-3 Meeting Art, Vercelli #642 est:1500
£1831	$3039	€2600	Composition (25x35cm-10x14in) s.d.1929 water pencil. 14-Jun-3 Meeting Art, Vercelli #658/R est:2000
£3401	$6088	€5000	Abstract (21x21cm-8x8in) s.d.1925 Chinese ink. 16-Mar-4 Finarte Semenzato, Milan #462/R est:6000
£3448	$5759	€5000	Portrait of the writer Alberto Presenzini Mattoli (60x42cm-24x17in) s.d.1929 pastel graphite lit. 13-Nov-3 Finarte Semenzato, Rome #208/R est:3500-3800

DOTY, John Warren (1870-1959) American

£546	$1000	€797	Matterhorn (215x117cm-85x46in) painted c.1923. 10-Jul-4 Auctions by the Bay, Alameda #479/R

DOU, Gerard (1613-1675) Dutch

£890	$1514	€1300	Old woman wearing brown coat and leather gloves (19x15cm-7x6in) panel lit. 6-Nov-3 Allgauer, Kempten #3406/R est:1200

DOU, Gerard (attrib) (1613-1675) Dutch

£40000	$73200	€58400	Interior with woman holding candle (19x14cm-7x6in) panel. 8-Jul-4 Sotheby's, London #274/R est:15000-20000

DOU, Gerard (circle) (1613-1675) Dutch

£5500	$9900	€8030	Portrait of a lady, in a black velvet dress (31x25cm-12x10in) s.d.1641 panel feigned oval. 23-Apr-4 Christie's, Kensington #23/R est:2000-4000
£13287	$22853	€19000	Le charlatan (104x84cm-41x33in) 3-Dec-3 Palais de Beaux Arts, Brussels #1254/R est:16000-24000

DOU, S V (17/18th C) Dutch

£809	$1504	€1181	Soldiers on horseback in front of village church (52x44cm-20x17in) s. panel. 2-Mar-4 Rasmussen, Copenhagen #1474/R (D.KR 9000)
£1402	$2215	€2033	Soldiers on horseback in battle in front of village church (52x44cm-20x17in) s. panel. 2-Sep-3 Rasmussen, Copenhagen #1841/R est:5000 (D.KR 15000)

DOUARD, Cecile (1866-1946) French

£1467	$2669	€2200	Still life with a vase of flowers (105x74cm-41x29in) s.d.1896. 1-Jul-4 Van Ham, Cologne #1304/R est:2700

DOUBA, Josef (1866-1928) German

£1427	$2425	€2083	Comforter (100x70cm-39x28in) s. 29-Nov-3 Dorotheum, Prague #30/R est:40000-60000 (C.KR 65000)

DOUBIGNY, Francoise (attrib) (?) ?

£935	$1534	€1300	Landscape with trees (32x64cm-13x25in) 10-Jun-3 Pandolfini, Florence #67/R est:1200-1400

DOUBLEDAY, Matthew (?) ?

Works on paper

£400	$716	€584	Dovedale, Derbyshire (34x49cm-13x19in) s. W/C bodycol pair. 18-Mar-4 Neales, Nottingham #706/R

DOUCET, Henri (1883-1915) French

£374	$700	€546	Chinese scene (71x61cm-28x24in) s.d.1935. 29-Feb-4 Grogan, Boston #6/R

DOUCET, Jacques (1924-1994) French

£1895	$3544	€2767	Flore des rocs (60x60cm-24x24in) s. i. exhib.prov. 25-Feb-4 Kunsthallen, Copenhagen #80/R est:20000 (D.KR 21000)
£2491	$4409	€3637	Untitled (81x65cm-32x26in) s. 27-Apr-4 AB Stockholms Auktionsverk #1185/R est:20000-25000 (S.KR 34000)
£3169	$5483	€4500	Porte d'Orient (61x38cm-24x15in) s. prov.lit. 9-Dec-3 Artcurial Briest, Paris #507/R est:5000-6000
£4895	$8175	€7000	Composition (60x40cm-24x16in) s. 25-Jun-3 Digard, Paris #104/R est:2500-3000
£7433	$13305	€11000	Untitled (81x60cm-32x24in) s. 4-May-4 Calmels Cohen, Paris #173/R est:10000-12000
£8054	$14819	€12000	French Graffiti (195x97cm-77x38in) s. s.i.verso painted 1984. 23-Mar-4 Joron-Derem, Paris #131/R est:15000-18000
£8741	$14598	€12500	Composition (60x81cm-24x32in) s. d.1955 verso prov.lit. 29-Jun-3 Versailles Encheres #85/R

Works on paper

£604	$1130	€900	Sans titre (40x26cm-16x10in) s. gouache prov.lit. 29-Feb-4 Versailles Encheres #228
£604	$1069	€900	Composition (24x24cm-9x9in) s. mixed media collages exec c.1957-58. 28-Apr-4 Artcurial Briest, Paris #274a
£671	$1255	€1000	Sans titre (37x24cm-15x9in) s. gouache exec.c.1965 prov. 29-Feb-4 Versailles Encheres #229
£800	$1432	€1200	Composition (64x49cm-25x19in) s. gouache lit. 15-May-4 De Vuyst, Lokeren #118
£845	$1462	€1200	Sans titre (38x24cm-15x9in) s. gouache prov.lit. 14-Dec-3 Versailles Encheres #53/R
£880	$1523	€1250	Sans titre (53x37cm-21x15in) s. pastel prov.lit. 14-Dec-3 Versailles Encheres #62/R
£915	$1584	€1300	Sans titre (50x37cm-20x15in) s. pastel prov.lit. 14-Dec-3 Versailles Encheres #61/R
£940	$1757	€1400	Sans titre (37x23cm-15x9in) s. gouache prov.lit. 29-Feb-4 Versailles Encheres #230/R
£1014	$1784	€1500	Untitled (15x15cm-6x6in) s. collage exec 1963-64 lit. 18-May-4 Tajan, Paris #101/R est:1500-1800
£1067	$1920	€1600	Untitled (59x45cm-23x18in) s. collage prov.lit. 25-Apr-4 Versailles Encheres #68 est:2000-2500
£1812	$3371	€2700	Composition (44x25cm-17x10in) s. mixed media collage exhib. 3-Mar-4 Artcurial Briest, Paris #361/R est:2200-3000
£1879	$3495	€2800	Composition (43x28cm-17x11in) s. mixed media collage exhib.lit. 3-Mar-4 Artcurial Briest, Paris #360/R est:2200-3000
£2254	$3899	€3200	Mur miroir (73x60cm-29x24in) s. i.verso collage prov.exhib.lit. 14-Dec-3 Versailles Encheres #87/R est:5000-6000
£2333	$4293	€3500	Untitled (47x33cm-19x13in) s. gouache exec. 1963 lit. 10-Jun-4 Camard, Paris #156/R est:2000-3000
£2448	$4161	€3500	Composition (79x58cm-31x23in) s. mixed media. 23-Nov-3 Cornette de St.Cyr, Paris #604/R est:3000-4000
£3958	$6254	€5700	Composition (34x54cm-13x21in) s. gouache prov. 27-Apr-3 Versailles Encheres #8

DOUDIJNS, Willem (1630-1697) Dutch

£2953	$5434	€4400	Scene de sacrifice (122x121cm-48x48in) mono. 26-Mar-4 Piasa, Paris #21 est:3000-4000

DOUDIJNS, Willem (attrib) (1630-1697) Dutch

Works on paper

£473	$832	€700	Dionysos finds Ariadne abandoned by Theseus on Naxos (35x28cm-14x11in) brush wash htd bodycol prov. 22-May-4 Lempertz, Koln #1252

DOUGHERTY (20th C) American?

£434	$750	€634	Portrait of a seated man nude (76x53cm-30x21in) s. 10-Dec-3 Alderfer's, Hatfield #382/R

DOUGHERTY, James (20th C) American?

Works on paper

£950	$1700	€1387	Synchronist study of bathers at the beach. init. gouache prov. 16-May-4 Wright, Chicago #121/R est:1500-2000

DOUGHERTY, Parke Custis (1867-?) American

£283	$450	€413	Moonlit landscape (66x81cm-26x32in) s.d.07. 4-May-3 William Jenack, New York #231
£1512	$2600	€2208	Harbour scene with church in the background (64x79cm-25x31in) s. board. 6-Dec-3 Pook & Pook, Downington #281/R est:2500-3500
£2647	$4500	€3865	French village in moonlight (64x81cm-25x32in) s. 31-Oct-3 North East Auctions, Portsmouth #1728

DOUGHERTY, Paul (1877-1947) American

£806	$1500	€1177	Landscape with shepherd and flock along road (66x81cm-26x32in) s. 3-Mar-4 Alderfer's, Hatfield #398 est:2000-3000
£1059	$1800	€1546	Cornish headland (33x39cm-13x15in) s. board. 20-Nov-3 Auctions by the Bay, Alameda #1087/R
£1099	$2000	€1605	Cabin in landscape (41x30cm-16x12in) s. board. 15-Jun-4 John Moran, Pasadena #59 est:2000-3000
£1156	$2000	€1688	Approaching fog (38x46cm-15x18in) i.verso panel. 10-Dec-3 Bonhams & Butterfields, San Francisco #6202/R est:3000-5000
£1323	$2500	€1932	Coastal - Monhegan Island (30x41cm-12x16in) s. board prov. 17-Feb-4 John Moran, Pasadena #114/R est:2000-3000
£1324	$2250	€1933	Mountain landscape (33x41cm-13x16in) estate st. wood panel. 18-Nov-3 John Moran, Pasadena #104 est:2000-3000
£2206	$3750	€3221	Crashing waves on rocks (46x51cm-18x20in) s. canvas on board. 18-Nov-3 John Moran, Pasadena #144 est:3000-5000
£2245	$3750	€3278	Sunlit peaks (33x41cm-13x16in) s. i.verso board prov. 23-Oct-3 Shannon's, Milford #254/R est:1500-2500
£5163	$9500	€7538	The Carmel Coast (50x76cm-20x30in) s. prov. 8-Jun-4 Bonhams & Butterfields, San Francisco #4267/R est:6000-8000

DOUGHTEN, Alice B (1880-?) American

£223	$400	€326	Brown jug (36x25cm-14x10in) s. board. 20-Mar-4 Selkirks, St. Louis #151

DOUGHTY, Thomas (1793-1856) American

£4190	$7500	€6117	Romantic landscape (28x23cm-11x9in) panel prov. 21-Mar-4 Hindman, Chicago #773/R est:10000-15000
£4469	$8000	€6525	Young woman by a brook (28x23cm-11x9in) prov. 21-Mar-4 Hindman, Chicago #774/R est:10000-15000
£25000	$44000	€36500	Landscape (49x42cm-19x17in) s.d.1832. 18-May-4 Christie's, Rockefeller NY #1/R est:20000-30000

DOUGHTY, Thomas (attrib) (1793-1856) American

£1017	$1800	€1485	View Hudson (43x36cm-17x14in) bears sig.d.1841 i.d.1841 stretcher oval prov. 27-Apr-4 Doyle, New York #13 est:2000-3000

DOUGLAS, Andrew A (1870-1935) British

£600	$1020	€876	Cattle resting beneath a tree (25x36cm-10x14in) s.i.d.1835 verso. 4-Nov-3 Rowley Fine Art, Newmarket #415/R
£750	$1395	€1095	Cattle fording a river (27x34cm-11x13in) s.i. board exhib. 4-Mar-4 Christie's, Kensington #145/R
£1152	$1959	€1682	Mountain landscape with cattle and lake, Scotland (57x79cm-22x31in) s. exhib. 10-Nov-3 Rasmussen, Vejle #355/R est:6000-8000 (D.KR 12500)

Works on paper
£3000 $5100 €4380 View of Edinburgh from Calton Hill, looking down Princes Street (54x76cm-21x30in) s. W/C bodycol. 30-Oct-3 Christie's, London #134/R est:2000-3000

DOUGLAS, Cameron (1957-) Canadian
Sculpture
£424 $729 €619 Lyra (46cm-18in) s.d.99 num.2/6 bronze. 2-Dec-3 Joyner Waddington, Toronto #122/R (C.D 950)

DOUGLAS, David (19/20th C) ?
£321 $575 €469 Mountain river (51x76cm-20x30in) s. 20-Mar-4 Selkirks, St. Louis #147

DOUGLAS, Edward Algernon Stuart (1850-c.1920) British
£1075 $2000 €1570 On the hunt (40x55cm-16x22in) s.d.1879. 5-Mar-4 Skinner, Boston #229/R est:4000-6000
£1600 $2832 €2336 Hunting of hounds (15x10cm-6x4in) s. pair. 28-Apr-4 British Auctioneer #659/R est:1500-2000
£1600 $2832 €2336 Hunting scene (15x18cm-6x7in) s. 28-Apr-4 British Auctioneer #660/R est:1500-2000
£2400 $4248 €3504 Hunting of hounds (15x10cm-6x4in) s. pair. 28-Apr-4 British Auctioneer #658/R est:1500-2000
£2800 $5124 €4088 Portrait of a bloodhound (90x75cm-35x30in) s. 8-Jul-4 Lawrence, Crewkerne #1636/R est:1500-2500
Works on paper
£1400 $2562 €2044 Bloodhounds picking up a scent (41x72cm-16x28in) s. W/C pencil. 8-Jul-4 Lawrence, Crewkerne #1534/R est:800-1200

DOUGLAS, Edwin (1848-1914) British
£2100 $3843 €3066 Portrait of Comrade, favourite hound of the Surrey Union Hunt Master (36x28cm-14x11in) zinc panel. 27-Jan-4 Gorringes, Lewes #1568/R est:2000-3000
£3867 $7000 €5646 Collie in a winter landscape (61x51cm-24x20in) s. 30-Mar-4 Bonhams & Butterfields, San Francisco #73/R est:8000-12000
£4600 $8418 €6716 Portrait of Old Iris, the Lawbrook Pet, a Jersey cow (30x25cm-12x10in) mono. 27-Jan-4 Gorringes, Lewes #1570/R est:2000-3000
£5600 $10584 €8176 Milking time (143x92cm-56x36in) mono. 18-Feb-4 Peter Wilson, Nantwich #3
£22000 $37400 €32120 Waiting for master (61x74cm-24x29in) mono. 27-Nov-3 Christie's, Kensington #289/R est:4000-6000

DOUGLAS, Edwin (attrib) (1848-1914) British
£480 $883 €701 Awaiting his master - a dog standing eagerly in a hallway (23x32cm-9x13in) panel. 23-Mar-4 Anderson & Garland, Newcastle #355/R

DOUGLAS, Hope Toulmin (1883-?) British
£400 $732 €584 Old pensioner, white horse in a gateway (24x34cm-9x13in) s. i.verso. 3-Jun-4 Lane, Penzance #197

DOUGLAS, James (1858-1911) British
Works on paper
£417 $663 €600 Changing pastures (17x24cm-7x9in) s.d.1886 W/C. 10-Sep-3 James Adam, Dublin #31/R

DOUGLAS, Jessie (fl.1903-1928) British
Works on paper
£2254 $3606 €3200 Brittany maid (28x20cm-11x8in) s. W/C. 16-Sep-3 Whyte's, Dublin #85/R est:2000-3000

DOUGLAS, Sir William Fettes (1822-1891) British
£270 $473 €394 Two young men (15x11cm-6x4in) 18-Dec-3 Bonhams, Edinburgh #307
£5800 $9860 €8468 Mother and child seated holding a miniature and letter, her son reading (41x57cm-16x22in) s.cypher. 8-Nov-3 Shapes, Edinburgh #511/R est:3000-4000
Works on paper
£300 $483 €435 Man's head (7x6cm-3x2in) mono. pencil. 21-Aug-3 Bonhams, Edinburgh #1024

DOUGLAS, William (1780-1832) British
Works on paper
£56000 $103600 €81760 Portrait of Robert Wauchope (29x23cm-11x9in) s.d.1803 W/C. 14-Jan-4 Lawrence, Crewkerne #1310 est:5000-7000

DOUGLAS-HAMILTON, A M R (19/20th C) American
£2791 $4800 €4075 Breaking the record, Waldorf to Morris Park, New York (46x81cm-18x32in) s.d.1900 prov. 5-Dec-3 Christie's, Rockefeller NY #28/R est:5000-7000

DOUJU, Alain (20th C) French
£265 $482 €400 Plage a Deauville (38x55cm-15x22in) s. s.verso. 20-Jun-4 Imberdis, Pont Audemer #72

DOUKAS, Hector (1885-1969) Greek
£950 $1701 €1387 Street in Edessa (60x45cm-24x18in) s. 11-May-4 Bonhams, New Bond Street #62/R
£1600 $2864 €2336 Children playing (17x22cm-7x9in) s. hardboard. 11-May-4 Bonhams, New Bond Street #65/R est:800-1200
£1800 $3060 €2628 Still life with anemones (60x50cm-24x20in) s. 18-Nov-3 Sotheby's, London #144/R est:1200-1800
£2000 $3500 €2920 English garden, Munich (50x60cm-20x24in) s. 16-Dec-3 Bonhams, New Bond Street #24/R est:2000-3000
£2500 $4475 €3650 Playtime (40x50cm-16x20in) s. 10-May-4 Sotheby's, Olympia #132/R est:2500-3000
£3400 $5950 €4964 Seascape (61x81cm-24x32in) s. 16-Dec-3 Bonhams, New Bond Street #46/R est:3000-5000
£3500 $5950 €5110 Fruit basket (50x61cm-20x24in) s. prov. 18-Nov-3 Sotheby's, London #118/R est:2000-3000
£3800 $6460 €5548 Sailboats at sunset (60x81cm-24x32in) s. prov. 18-Nov-3 Sotheby's, London #91/R est:2000-3000
£7000 $12530 €10220 Sheep grazing in a pasture (100x133cm-39x52in) s. 11-May-4 Bonhams, New Bond Street #10/R est:7000-9000

DOUMET, Zacharie Felix (1761-1818) French
Works on paper
£280 $493 €409 L'Alarme Corse (13x16cm-5x6in) s.i. gouache. 18-May-4 Fellows & Sons, Birmingham #206/R

DOUMICHAUD DE LA CHASSAGNE-GROSSE, Laetitia (19/20th C) French
Works on paper
£329 $605 €500 Portrait de petit garcon (53x42cm-21x17in) s.d.1924 pastel oval. 25-Jun-4 Millon & Associes, Paris #150/R

DOURLENS, Xavier Jules (1826-1888) French
£952 $1514 €1400 Woman in the alley (36x20cm-14x8in) s. panel. 23-Mar-3 Mercier & Cie, Lille #262

DOUST, Jan van (?) ?
£270 $500 €394 Mixed garden flowers (80x60cm-31x24in) s. 16-Feb-4 Bonhams, Bath #96

DOUST, W H (19th C) British
£1815 $3250 €2650 Brig of the British Government's Revenue Service in pursuit (46x61cm-18x24in) s.d.1854. 16-Mar-4 Bonhams & Butterfields, San Francisco #6135/R est:2500-3500

DOUTHWAITE, Patricia (1939-2002) British
Works on paper
£260 $429 €380 Still life with vase on a table (63x44cm-25x17in) pastel. 5-Jul-3 Shapes, Edinburgh #332/R
£260 $429 €380 Tree composition (39x28cm-15x11in) s.d.1990 pastel. 5-Jul-3 Shapes, Edinburgh #334
£280 $468 €409 Jug and cat (74x55cm-29x22in) chk. 16-Oct-3 Bonhams, Edinburgh #29
£280 $512 €409 Shire bull (54x75cm-21x30in) s.d.89 conte. 8-Apr-4 Bonhams, Edinburgh #19
£280 $510 €409 Naked figure and yellow band (64x49cm-25x19in) s.d.72 pastel. 3-Jul-4 Shapes, Edinburgh #439/R
£290 $525 €423 Female head (63x49cm-25x19in) s.d.87 chl. 3-Apr-4 Shapes, Edinburgh #460
£300 $549 €438 Self portrait with ringlets (64x51cm-25x20in) s.d.90 conte. 8-Apr-4 Bonhams, Edinburgh #2
£400 $668 €584 Two dancers (55x82cm-22x32in) i. col chk. 16-Oct-3 Bonhams, Edinburgh #27/R
£440 $735 €642 Vase of flowers (29x19cm-11x7in) s.d.87 pastel pair. 16-Oct-3 Bonhams, Edinburgh #40
£440 $801 €642 Fossil design (60x47cm-24x19in) s.d.70 pastel. 3-Jul-4 Shapes, Edinburgh #440/R
£520 $952 €759 Happy face (57x81cm-22x32in) s.d.89 col chk. 8-Apr-4 Bonhams, Edinburgh #13/R
£620 $1023 €905 Female head and shoulders (64x49cm-25x19in) s.d.1980 pastel. 5-Jul-3 Shapes, Edinburgh #331/R
£800 $1456 €1168 Manderin (82x58cm-32x23in) s.d.90 pastel. 3-Jul-4 Shapes, Edinburgh #442/R
£1100 $1815 €1606 Female head and shoulders (40x29cm-16x11in) s.d.1989 pastel. 5-Jul-3 Shapes, Edinburgh #333/R est:200-300
£1350 $2322 €1971 Barra, two portrait heads and two birds (62x47cm-24x19in) s.d.87 chl four. 6-Dec-3 Shapes, Edinburgh #429 est:300-500

DOUTRELEAU, Pierre (1938-) French
£3893 $7123 €5800 Marine (60x92cm-24x36in) s. prov. 7-Jul-4 Artcurial Briest, Paris #165 est:1000-1500

DOUTRELEAU, Valentin Louis (1814-?) French
£2800 $5152 €4200 Sacre de Godefroy Brossais de Saint-Marc en la cathedrale de Rennes (73x94cm-29x37in) s.i.d.1841 verso. 8-Jun-4 Livinec, Gaudcheau & Jezequel, Rennes #94/R

DOUVEN, Jan Frans van (1656-1727) German
£4000 $7320 €6000 Portrait of Giovanni Guglielmo von der Pfalz. Anna Maria Luisa Medici (52x41cm-20x16in) pair oval. 1-Jun-4 Sotheby's, Milan #85/R est:6000-8000

DOUW, Simon Johannes van (1630-1677) Flemish
£1600 $2816 €2336 Shoeing the gentleman's horse (36x49cm-14x19in) s. panel. 19-May-4 Dreweatt Neate, Newbury #63/R est:2000-3000
£2098 $3503 €3000 Choc de cavalerie sur un pont (48x64cm-19x25in) panel. 27-Jun-3 Millon & Associes, Paris #22/R est:3000-4000
£7200 $12456 €10512 Cavalry engagement between Turks and Christians (58x83cm-23x33in) prov. 9-Dec-3 Sotheby's, Olympia #363/R est:5000-8000

DOUZETTE, Louis (1834-1924) German
£1074 $1965 €1600 Sailing boat and lighthouse out at sea in full moon (30x40cm-12x16in) s. 9-Jul-4 Dawo, Saarbrucken #38/R est:1900
£1081 $1903 €1600 Full moon over harbour town (25x39cm-10x15in) s.d.95 panel. 22-May-4 Lempertz, Koln #1508/R est:1500
£1159 $2109 €1750 Peasant hut in moonlight (33x41cm-13x16in) s. board prov. 19-Jun-4 Dannenberg, Berlin #552/R est:1200
£1319 $2085 €1900 Harbour scene in north Germany (80x120cm-31x47in) s. 5-Sep-3 Wendl, Rudolstadt #3328/R est:1900

£1400 $2534 €2100 Summer wood with girl (24x38cm-9x15in) s. board. 3-Apr-4 Hans Stahl, Hamburg #2/R est:1800
£1810 $3241 €2643 Moonlit Dutch harbour (70x100cm-28x39in) s. 13-May-4 Stuker, Bern #104/R est:5000-7000 (S.FR 4200)
£2553 $4136 €3600 Sailing boat on moonlit lake (25x36cm-10x14in) s. lit. 23-May-3 Karlheinz Kaupp, Staufen #2004 est:300
£3221 $5928 €4800 Water near Koserow by moonlight (49x75cm-19x30in) s. i. verso board. 26-Mar-4 Bolland & Marotz, Bremen #503a/R est:1700
£4362 $8027 €6500 Baltic harbour town by moonlight (80x120cm-31x47in) s.d.1914. 26-Mar-4 Bolland & Marotz, Bremen #503/R est:2700

DOUZON, Theodore (1829-?) French
£474 $849 €692 Children bathing in wood (59x77cm-23x30in) s. 12-May-4 Dobiaschofsky, Bern #461/R (S.FR 1100)

DOVA, Gianni (1925-1991) Italian
£968 $1800 €1413 Woman in an interior (43x51cm-17x20in) s.d.1957. 7-Mar-4 Treadway Gallery, Cincinnati #705/R est:400-600
£979 $1664 €1400 Study for fabric (97x70cm-38x28in) s.verso tempera paper. 26-Nov-3 Pandolfini, Florence #518/R est:1500-1700
£1088 $1948 €1600 Composition (45x35cm-18x14in) s.d.1950 oil tempera board. 22-Mar-4 Sant Agostino, Torino #339/R est:2000
£1467 $2699 €2200 Nuclear composition (80x70cm-31x28in) s.d.1953 enamel. 8-Jun-4 Finarte Semenzato, Milan #343/R est:2000-2500
£1538 $2615 €2200 Bird on branch in the evening (29x25cm-11x10in) s. s.i.verso. 28-Nov-3 Farsetti, Prato #201/R est:1200-1600
£1724 $2879 €2500 Untitled (25x19cm-10x7in) s. board. 13-Nov-3 Finarte Semenzato, Rome #361/R est:2000-3000
£2014 $3182 €2900 Bird (94x68cm-37x27in) tempera paper on canvas. 6-Sep-3 Meeting Art, Vercelli #313 est:2500
£2148 $3844 €3200 Untitled (35x60cm-14x24in) s. board. 25-May-4 Sotheby's, Milan #91/R est:2000
£2254 $3944 €3200 Two birds and the moon (40x50cm-16x20in) s. s.i.d.1956 verso. 17-Dec-3 Il Ponte, Milan #1117/R est:2500-3000
£2414 $4031 €3500 Untitled (55x40cm-22x16in) s.d.50 tempera. 13-Nov-3 Finarte Semenzato, Rome #364/R est:3500-4500
£2517 $4280 €3600 Little bull (25x30cm-10x12in) s. s.i.verso. 20-Nov-3 Finarte Semenzato, Milan #155/R est:2000-2500
£2817 $4676 €4000 Shores (50x40cm-20x16in) s. enamel. 11-Jun-3 Finarte Semenzato, Milan #564/R
£2897 $4837 €4200 Roses (60x50cm-24x20in) s.s.verso. 13-Nov-3 Finarte Semenzato, Rome #436 est:3800-4500
£2973 $5232 €4400 Figure (105x60cm-41x24in) s.i.d.60 verso paper on canvas. 24-May-4 Christie's, Milan #72/R est:4000-6000
£3200 $5888 €4800 Two birds, the moon and the sea (40x50cm-16x20in) s. s.i.d.1956 verso. 12-Jun-4 Meeting Art, Vercelli #855/R est:4000
£4225 $7014 €6000 Aranceti alle maldive (70x90cm-28x35in) s. s.i.verso enamel. 14-Jun-3 Meeting Art, Vercelli #352/R est:5000
£4514 $7674 €6500 Agressive figure (70x60cm-28x24in) s.d.1958 prov. 28-Oct-3 Il Ponte, Milan #241/R
£4600 $8326 €6900 All blue (116x89cm-46x35in) s. painted 1975 lit. 2-Apr-4 Farsetti, Prato #304/R est:4100-4600
£4730 $8324 €7000 Composition (80x100cm-31x39in) oil mixed media painted c.1953 prov. 24-May-4 Christie's, Milan #194/R est:7000-10000
£4762 $8524 €7000 Untitled (60x92cm-24x36in) painted 1950. 16-Mar-4 Finarte Semenzato, Milan #438/R est:6000
£6040 $10812 €9000 Unreal composition (100x130cm-39x51in) painted c.1965 exhib. 25-May-4 Sotheby's, Milan #89/R est:10000
£6643 $11294 €9500 Resting on the branches (145x115cm-57x45in) s. painted 1972 prov.exhib.lit. 24-Nov-3 Christie's, Milan #200/R est:8000-12000
£7333 $13493 €11000 Composition (120x119cm-47x47in) s.d.52 exhib. 8-Jun-4 Finarte Semenzato, Milan #363/R est:8000-12000
£7692 $13077 €11000 Trap (81x64cm-32x25in) s.d.64 lit. 20-Nov-3 Finarte Semenzato, Milan #143/R est:11000-12000
£8725 $16141 €13000 Nuclear (80x90cm-31x35in) s.d.1951. 11-Mar-4 Galleria Pace, Milan #144/R est:15000-20000
£8784 $15459 €13000 Big carnival (148x186cm-58x73in) s.i.d.52 paper on canvas prov. 24-May-4 Christie's, Milan #227/R est:10000-15000
Works on paper
£525 $892 €750 Howl (27x34cm-11x13in) s.d.71 mixed media paper on canvas prov. 26-Nov-3 Pandolfini, Florence #81/R
£646 $1157 €950 Composition (70x100cm-28x39in) s. chl prov. 16-Mar-4 Finarte Semenzato, Milan #123/R
£897 $1497 €1300 Composition (50x37cm-20x15in) s. hydropaint paper on canvas. 14-Nov-3 Farsetti, Prato #41/R
£1074 $1987 €1600 Composition (50x64cm-20x25in) s.i.d.1962 felt-tip pen. 13-Mar-4 Meeting Art, Vercelli #338 est:1500
£1113 $2015 €1670 Composition (75x48cm-30x19in) s.d.1945 mixed media paper on board. 2-Apr-4 Farsetti, Prato #130/R est:1600-1900
£1329 $2259 €1900 Drawing for fabric (103x74cm-41x29in) s.verso mixed media. 26-Nov-3 Pandolfini, Florence #507/R est:1500-1700
£1408 $2338 €2000 Uccelli e fiori in giardino (62x50cm-24x20in) mixed media cardboard on canvas. 14-Jun-3 Meeting Art, Vercelli #285/R est:2000
£2069 $3310 €3000 Untitled (143x76cm-56x30in) s. mixed media paper on canvas prov. 13-Mar-3 Galleria Pace, Milan #75/R
£2113 $3507 €3000 Composition (65x89cm-26x35in) s. mixed media. 14-Jun-3 Meeting Art, Vercelli #551/R est:3000

DOVASTON, Margaret (1884-1955) British
£9000 $15300 €13140 Good song (51x41cm-20x16in) s. prov. 27-Nov-3 Sotheby's, London #431/R est:10000-15000
£16260 $29106 €23740 After dinner, rest awhile (46x61cm-18x24in) s. i.verso. 4-May-4 Ritchie, Toronto #31/R est:20000-30000 (C.D 40000)
£20000 $34400 €29200 Toast (44x59cm-17x23in) s. prov. 3-Dec-3 Cheffins, Cambridge #614/R est:10000-15000
£25000 $45000 €36500 Tea at the vicarage (49x67cm-19x26in) s. prov. 21-Apr-4 Cheffins, Cambridge #507/R est:15000-20000

DOVE, Arthur G (1880-1946) American
£397727 $700000 €580681 Windy morning (51x71cm-20x28in) panel painted 1936 prov.exhib.lit. 19-May-4 Sotheby's, New York #126/R est:700000-900000
£639535 $1100000 €933721 Snowstorm (35x51cm-14x20in) s. painted 1935 prov.exhib.lit. 3-Dec-3 Sotheby's, New York #64/R est:700000-900000
Works on paper
£6587 $11000 €9617 Sun drawing water (12x17cm-5x7in) s. W/C pencil executed 1932 prov.exhib. 11-Nov-3 Christie's, Rockefeller NY #118/R est:7000-9000
£8649 $16000 €12628 Fall Brook railroad tracks (12x18cm-5x7in) s. W/C prov.exhib. 11-Mar-4 Christie's, Rockefeller NY #92/R est:10000-15000
£8982 $15000 €13114 Abstraction (22x27cm-9x11in) s. W/C. 9-Oct-3 Christie's, Rockefeller NY #107/R est:7000-10000
£11364 $20000 €16591 St Peter's (13x18cm-5x7in) s. W/C prov. 18-May-4 Christie's, Rockefeller NY #121/R est:20000-30000
£12784 $22500 €18665 Barns (10x15cm-4x6in) s. W/C prov.exhib. 19-May-4 Sotheby's, New York #132/R est:25000-35000
£20000 $35000 €29200 Wind (49x61cm-19x24in) ink W/C prov. 19-Dec-3 Sotheby's, New York #1048/R est:5000-7000

DOVE, Benjamin (20th C) American
£503 $900 €734 Moonlight (61x46cm-24x18in) s.d.1970. 14-May-4 Skinner, Boston #178/R

DOVE, Stanley (20th C) British
Sculpture
£2800 $4928 €4088 First horseman of the Apocalypse number 4 (56x58cm-22x23in) s. num.2/4. 18-May-4 Woolley & Wallis, Salisbury #382/R est:1000-1500

DOVERA, Achille (1838-1895) Italian
£1060 $1928 €1600 Cart (31x52cm-12x20in) s. 17-Jun-4 Finarte Semenzato, Milan #280/R est:1000-1500
Works on paper
£1087 $1783 €1500 Old Milan (35x50cm-14x20in) s. W/C. 27-May-3 Il Ponte, Milan #949/R
£1088 $1948 €1600 Market (22x52cm-9x20in) s. W/C cardboard. 22-Mar-4 Sant Agostino, Torino #264/R est:2000

DOVERI, A (19th C) Italian
£6643 $11427 €9500 View of Lake Como (45x61cm-18x24in) s.d.1870. 3-Dec-3 Stadion, Trieste #1012/R est:2000-3000
£7133 $12269 €10200 Town on Lake Como (45x61cm-18x24in) s.d.1870. 3-Dec-3 Stadion, Trieste #1013/R est:2000-3000

DOVIANE, Auguste (1825-1887) Swiss
£517 $926 €755 Swiss soldier (24x15cm-9x6in) s. panel. 12-May-4 Dobiaschofsky, Bern #462/R (S.FR 1200)
£2969 $5404 €4335 The slaughter at Waterloo (54x73cm-21x29in) s. 16-Jun-4 Fischer, Luzern #1108/R est:7000-9000 (S.FR 6800)

DOW, Arthur W (1857-1922) American
£8982 $15000 €13114 Autumn Sketch (36x51cm-14x20in) s.i.verso. 23-Oct-3 Shannon's, Milford #92/R est:20000-30000
Prints
£3390 $6000 €4949 Clam house (11x16cm-4x6in) s. s.i.d.1914 verso col woodcut. 30-Apr-4 Sotheby's, New York #10/R est:3000-4000

DOW, Nell P (1893-1976) American
Works on paper
£269 $450 €393 Bluebonnets (30x46cm-12x18in) W/C. 18-Oct-3 David Dike, Dallas #164/R

DOW, Thomas Millie (1848-1919) British
£620 $1066 €905 Barges by a bridge (21x31cm-8x12in) init. canvas on board painted c.1880. 4-Dec-3 Bonhams, Edinburgh #87
£800 $1488 €1168 Italian vineyard (18x32cm-7x13in) panel. 4-Mar-4 Christie's, Kensington #74/R
£1700 $2669 €2465 Late autumn at Barbazon (50x65cm-20x26in) s.d.79 exhib. 27-Aug-3 Sotheby's, London #1025/R est:2000-3000
£2600 $4420 €3796 Moonlight in the Alps (63x77cm-25x30in) init. s.i.d.verso. 25-Nov-3 Christie's, London #178/R est:3000-5000

DOW, William J (1891-1973) American
Works on paper
£276 $500 €403 Peggy's Cove (33x48cm-13x19in) s. W/C. 16-Apr-4 James Julia, Fairfield #852b/R

DOWD, John (1960-) American
£605 $950 €883 Dunes (36x46cm-14x18in) s. 20-Apr-3 Outer Cape Auctions, Provincetown #95/R
£838 $1550 €1223 Untitled, house (51x61cm-20x24in) s. 17-Jul-4 Outer Cape Auctions, Provincetown #78/R
£865 $1600 €1263 Untitled, landscape with house (51x61cm-20x24in) s. 17-Jul-4 Outer Cape Auctions, Provincetown #31a/R
£1720 $2700 €2511 Untitled (61x91cm-24x36in) s. 20-Apr-3 Outer Cape Auctions, Provincetown #58/R

DOWLING, Jane (1925-) British
Works on paper
£300 $528 €438 The drawing school, Royal Academy (23x30cm-9x12in) init. pencil tempera. 18-May-4 Woolley & Wallis, Salisbury #280/R

DOWLING, Julie (1969-) Australian
Works on paper
£2099 $3821 €3065 Stolen 1998 (35x28cm-14x11in) synthetic polymer on four canvas exhib. 16-Jun-4 Deutscher-Menzies, Melbourne #2/R est:4000-6000 (A.D 5500)

£2930 $5479 €4395 Sunday best (100x75cm-39x30in) s.i.d.2001 verso synthetic polymer paint red ochre canvas prov. 26-Jul-4 Sotheby's, Melbourne #144/R est:10000-15000 (A.D 7500)

£7634 $13893 €11146 Warru - fire (120x100cm-47x39in) s. i.d.June 1999 verso synthetic polymer ochre gold on canvas exh. 16-Jun-4 Deutscher-Menzies, Melbourne #200/R est:9000-12000 (A.D 20000)

DOWLING, Robert (1827-1886) British

£992 $1806 €1448 Portrait (49x40cm-19x16in) s.d.1863 verso. 16-Jun-4 Deutscher-Menzies, Melbourne #206/R est:4000-6000 (A.D 2600)

£1000 $1830 €1460 Portrait of Willoughby Trevelyan, Veteran of the Charge of the Light Brigade (90x70cm-35x28in) s. prov. 8-Jul-4 Lawrence, Crewkerne #1608 est:300-500

£15574 $24607 €22738 Portrait of the Reverend Henry Dowling (76x63cm-30x25in) prov. 2-Sep-3 Deutscher-Menzies, Melbourne #31/R est:35000-40000 (A.D 38000)

DOWLING, William J (1907-1980) Irish

£263 $484 €400 View of Lambay Island (21x33cm-8x13in) s. canvasboard. 22-Jun-4 De Veres Art Auctions, Dublin #216/R

£333 $603 €500 Coastal landscape, Co Kerry (36x46cm-14x18in) s. board. 30-Mar-4 De Veres Art Auctions, Dublin #185

DOWNES, Purlta Mary Anne (1945-) Australian

Works on paper

£610 $963 €891 Ngarriyili (76x112cm-30x44in) i.verso synthetic polymer paint prov. 28-Jul-3 Sotheby's, Paddington #494 est:1500-2500 (A.D 1500)

DOWNES, Rackstraw (1939-) American

£21605 $35000 €31327 U.S Scrap metal gets shipped for reprocessing in Southeast Asia (41x305cm-16x120in) s. prov. 8-Aug-3 Barridorf, Portland #241/R est:30000-50000

DOWNIE, Kate (1958-) British

£300 $540 €438 Coalman (151x197cm-59x78in) s.d.88 acrylic coaldust. 22-Apr-4 Bonhams, Edinburgh #316

DOWNIE, Patrick (1854-1945) British

£450 $792 €657 Moorland scene with cattle (29x44cm-11x17in) 18-May-4 Patersons, Paisley #547

£750 $1358 €1095 Lana cathedral before restoration, sheep in foreground (13x23cm-5x9in) 16-Apr-4 Keys, Aylsham #750

£950 $1672 €1387 Village street scene with church, shepherd and sheep (24x34cm-9x13in) 18-May-4 Patersons, Paisley #548

£1800 $2826 €2610 Ducks pond (30x23cm-12x9in) s. board prov. 27-Aug-3 Sotheby's, London #1143/R est:1500-2000

£1900 $3344 €2774 Clyde coast with horse and cart and figures (50x75cm-20x30in) 18-May-4 Patersons, Paisley #544

£2000 $3140 €2900 Isle of Arran from Portincross (35x25cm-14x10in) s. panel. 27-Aug-3 Sotheby's, London #1077/R est:1500-2000

£2000 $3720 €2920 Silvery noonday, Tarbert, Loch Fyne (30x46cm-12x18in) s. 4-Mar-4 Christie's, Kensington #134/R est:2000-3000

£2200 $4092 €3212 Bathers, Firth of Clyde (17x25cm-7x10in) s. s.i.d.1921 verso canvasboard. 4-Mar-4 Christie's, Kensington #135/R est:700-1000

Works on paper

£420 $752 €613 Fishing boats in an offshore breeze (18x26cm-7x10in) s. pencil W/C scratching out. 26-May-4 Christie's, Kensington #435/R

£1000 $1860 €1460 Vennel from Buchluch St. Greenock (30x24cm-12x9in) s.d.1938 s.i.d.verso W/C bodycol on board. 4-Mar-4 Christie's, Kensington #170/R est:600-800

£2200 $3982 €3212 Fresh breeze of Gourock (36x53cm-14x21in) s.d.1918 W/C bodycol scratching. 19-Apr-4 Sotheby's, London #119/R est:1500-2000

DOWNING, Delapoer (fl.1886-1902) British

£740 $1258 €1080 Court jester with a child and puppet (39x28cm-15x11in) s. 29-Oct-3 Bonhams, Chester #501

£2923 $5028 €4268 On the way to church (77x53cm-30x21in) s. 3-Dec-3 AB Stockholms Auktionsverk #2551/R est:50000-60000 (S.KR 38000)

DOWNING, Joe (1925-) ?

£503 $891 €750 Composition (46x55cm-18x22in) s. oil acrylic. 28-Apr-4 Artcurial Briest, Paris #490a

Works on paper

£526 $968 €800 Composition (14x21cm-6x8in) s. collage mixed media. 28-Jun-4 Joron-Derem, Paris #214

DOWNING, Thomas (1928-) American

£601 $1100 €877 First rideau rouge (234x117cm-92x46in) s.d.80 verso acrylic. 31-Jul-4 Sloans & Kenyon, Bethesda #297/R

£870 $1600 €1270 Ring One (46x46cm-18x18in) s.i.d.9/68 verso. 26-Jun-4 Sloans & Kenyon, Bethesda #289/R est:800-1200

DOWNMAN, John (1750-1824) British

£1400 $2604 €2044 Portrait of a gentleman in a brown jacket and white cravat (23x19cm-9x7in) s.d.1778 copper oval. 4-Mar-4 Christie's, Kensington #329/R est:1200-1800

£2000 $3720 €2920 Portrait of a gentleman in a blue coat with red collar (23x18cm-9x7in) s. indis d. copper oval. 4-Mar-4 Christie's, Kensington #328/R est:1500-2000

£3056 $5500 €4462 Elizabeth Inchbald (37x47cm-15x19in) s. 21-Jan-4 Sotheby's, New York #159/R est:1200-1800

Miniatures

£18000 $32400 €26280 Elizabeth Farren, later Countess of Derby (8cm-3in) gold frame oval prov.exhib.lit. 22-Apr-4 Bonhams, New Bond Street #92/R est:10000-15000

Works on paper

£300 $552 €438 Portrait of a lady (9x7cm-4x3in) pencil. 22-Jun-4 Bonhams, Knightsbridge #133

£320 $560 €467 Portrait of a lady (20x15cm-8x6in) init.d.1778 pencil. 19-Dec-3 Mallams, Oxford #84/R

£500 $925 €730 Portrait of Mrs John Hunter, bust length wearing a white lace cap (23x17cm-9x7in) s.i.d.1777 pencil sketch oval. 14-Jul-4 Bonhams, Chester #512

£760 $1391 €1110 Portrait of Mr Ives as a young gentleman (20x17cm-8x7in) mono.d.1780 W/C oval. 7-Apr-4 Bonhams, Bury St Edmunds #386/R

£900 $1665 €1314 Portrait of Judge Lushington and his mother (27x36cm-11x14in) s. W/C oval. 10-Mar-4 Sotheby's, Olympia #15/R est:1000-1500

£900 $1656 €1314 Portrait of an elegant dressed lady (19cm-7in) init.d.17 black chk pair. 23-Jun-4 Bonhams, Bury St Edmunds #311/R

£1300 $2210 €1898 Portrait of a lady (20x17cm-8x7in) col chk htd white oval prov. 27-Nov-3 Sotheby's, London #224/R est:700-1000

£1400 $2380 €2044 Portrait of John Mortlock of Cambridge, half length, in a black jacket (16x14cm-6x6in) s.d.1777 pencil blk chk stump htd white. 20-Nov-3 Christie's, London #26/R est:1000-1500

£1600 $2720 €2336 Portrait of Master Twisden, in a blue coat and white coat beside a whippet (21x20cm-8x8in) s.d.1794 blk chk prov. 20-Nov-3 Christie's, London #28/R est:1000-1500

£2000 $3400 €2920 Portrait of Countess Tyrconnell (22x18cm-9x7in) s. col chk oval. 27-Nov-3 Sotheby's, London #222/R est:1000-1500

£2000 $3400 €2920 Portrait of Admiral John Gell (21x17cm-8x7in) s.i. col chk W/C prov.exhib.lit. 27-Nov-3 Sotheby's, London #223/R est:1000-1500

£2500 $4250 €3650 Portrait of Mrs Sarah Anne King with her daughter (30x25cm-12x10in) s. W/C over pencil htd bodycol. 27-Nov-3 Sotheby's, London #221/R est:2500-3500

£3200 $5440 €4672 Portrait of Miss Ellis, half-length in a white dress and headscarf (20x16cm-8x6in) s.d.1797 pencil blk chk blue pink wash stump oval prov. 20-Nov-3 Christie's, London #25/R est:1200-1800

£3800 $6460 €5548 Portrait of Major Shuttleworth. Portrait of Mrs Shuttleworth (19x16cm-7x6in) s. s.d.1784 blk chk W/C pair. 20-Nov-3 Christie's, London #27/R est:2000-3000

DOWNMAN, John (attrib) (1750-1884) British

£500 $900 €730 Portrait of Robert Atkins (25x20cm-10x8in) panel oval. 21-Jan-4 Sotheby's, New York #139/R est:1200-1800

DOWNS, Edgar (1876-1963) British

£300 $552 €438 Horse plough (34x44cm-13x17in) s. 24-Jun-4 Locke & England, Leamington Spa #159/R

DOWNS, Jarinyanu David (c.1925-1995) Australian

Works on paper

£1172 $2191 €1758 Jesus preach'im all people (76x51cm-30x20in) synthetic polymer paint canvasboard prov. 26-Jul-4 Sotheby's, Melbourne #449/R est:3000-4000 (A.D 3000)

£1176 $2106 €1717 Kurtal with head-dress of Radiating Wuring (84x106cm-33x42in) natural earth pigments linen exec 1990 prov. 25-May-4 Lawson Menzies, Sydney #160/R est:6000-9000 (A.D 3000)

£1563 $2922 €2345 Genesis in Juwanticountry (91x61cm-36x24in) s.i.verso earth pigment synthetic polymer paint canvasboard prov. 26-Jul-4 Sotheby's, Melbourne #450 est:4000-6000 (A.D 4000)

£1641 $3068 €2462 Jawanti and the Nyapuru Women (91x61cm-36x24in) s.verso earth pigments bush gum canvasboard prov. 26-Jul-4 Sotheby's, Melbourne #126/R est:5000-7000 (A.D 4200)

£1875 $3506 €2813 Jakarra reunited with himself (61x73cm-24x29in) s.verso earth pigments bush gum prov. 26-Jul-4 Sotheby's, Melbourne #125/R est:6000-8000 (A.D 4800)

£2734 $5113 €4101 Untitled (97x67cm-38x26in) s. synthetic polymer paint canvas exec.c.1984 prov. 26-Jul-4 Sotheby's, Melbourne #451/R est:7000-10000 (A.D 7000)

£6250 $11688 €9375 Dance of Kurtal (228x136cm-90x54in) s.verso earth pigments bush gum linen prov.exhib. 26-Jul-4 Sotheby's, Melbourne #127/R est:20000-30000 (A.D 16000)

£6504 $10276 €9431 Yellow cloud gurdarl with kutu kutu clouds and falling rain (121x91cm-48x36in) s.i.verso earth pigments synthetic polymer paint canvas prov. 28-Jul-3 Sotheby's, Paddington #197/R est:18000-25000 (A.D 16000)

DOWNS, Johnny Gordon (1940-) Australian

Works on paper

£1172 $2191 €1758 Mimintilli (100x75cm-39x30in) bears name.verso synthetic polymer paint canvas prov.exhib.lit. 26-Jul-4 Sotheby's, Melbourne #424/R est:4000-6000 (A.D 3000)

DOYEN, Gustave (1837-?) French

£5988 $10000 €8742 Untitled, woman with kittens and bird on her shoulder (117x79cm-46x31in) 14-Nov-3 Du Mouchelle, Detroit #2011/R est:20000-25000

£35294 $60000 €51529 Grande soeur (66x40cm-26x16in) s. prov.lit. 28-Oct-3 Sotheby's, New York #39/R est:40000-60000

DOYLE, Charles Altamont (1832-1893) British

Works on paper

£1800 $3222 €2628 The faction fight (14x32cm-6x13in) pencil black ink W/C. 14-May-4 Christie's, London #70/R est:2000-3000

DOYLE, D'Arcy (1932-2001) Australian

£1377 $2216 €2010 Misty morning (45x54cm-18x21in) s. board. 13-Oct-3 Joel, Victoria #424 est:2000-3000 (A.D 3400)

£1639 $2590 €2393 Twin sentinels (30x38cm-12x15in) s. board prov. 2-Sep-3 Deutscher-Menzies, Melbourne #268/R est:3000-4000 (A.D 4000)

£2282 $3811 €3423 Running the storm (25x30cm-10x12in) s. 27-Oct-3 Goodman, Sydney #193/R est:3000-5000 (A.D 5500)

£2459 $3984 €3590 Cricket match (25x30cm-10x12in) s. board prov. 30-Jul-3 Goodman, Sydney #154/R est:4000-5000 (A.D 6000)

£2653 $4882 €3873 Loging team (39x49cm-15x19in) s. board. 29-Mar-4 Goodman, Sydney #181/R est:6000-8000 (A.D 6500)

£2697 $4504 €4046 Big match (25x30cm-10x12in) s. board. 27-Oct-3 Goodman, Sydney #163/R est:3000-5000 (A.D 6500)

£3279 $5311 €4787 Bush homestead (60x90cm-24x35in) s. board. 30-Jul-3 Goodman, Sydney #148/R est:8000-10000 (A.D 8000)

£3558 $6547 €5195 Street cricket (46x61cm-18x24in) s. board. 28-Jun-4 Australian Art Auctions, Sydney #101/R (A.D 9500)

£3734 $6237 €5601 Logging camp (45x58cm-18x23in) s. board. 27-Oct-3 Goodman, Sydney #198/R est:4000-6000 (A.D 9000)
£4959 $8430 €7240 Old stockman (59x49cm-23x19in) s. i.verso. 29-Oct-3 Lawson Menzies, Sydney #116/R est:10000-15000 (A.D 12000)
£6504 $10211 €9431 Spectators advice (59x89cm-23x35in) s. prov. 26-Aug-3 Christie's, Sydney #122/R est:16000-24000 (A.D 16000)
£8299 $13859 €12449 Cobb and Co Royal Mail (61x92cm-24x36in) s. board. 27-Oct-3 Goodman, Sydney #160/R est:20000-28000 (A.D 20000)
£9350 $16736 €13651 Off to the pictures (59x89cm-23x35in) s.i. board. 4-May-4 Sotheby's, Melbourne #261/R est:10000-15000 (A.D 23000)
£15319 $26043 €22366 Famous Australian Sporting Heroes. composition board painted 1967 seventeen. 26-Nov-3 Deutscher-Menzies, Melbourne #193/R est:40000-50000 (A.D 36000)

DOYLE, John (1928-) British
Works on paper
£650 $1183 €949 View of Green Court and the dark entry looking towards Bell Harry Tower, Canterbury Cathedral (41x58cm-16x23in) s.d.1975 W/C. 15-Jun-4 Canterbury Auctions, UK #123

DOYLE, Richard (1824-1883) British
Works on paper
£600 $1104 €876 Derby day (18x25cm-7x10in) pencil grey wash prov. 10-Jun-4 Christie's, Kensington #68/R

DOYLE, Sam (1906-1985) American
£1944 $3500 €2838 We we (102x89cm-40x35in) latex paint on window shade prov. 24-Apr-4 Slotin Folk Art, Buford #283/R est:4000-6000
£2500 $4500 €3650 Christ of Holy figure (109x69cm-43x27in) paint on tin prov. 24-Apr-4 Slotin Folk Art, Buford #281/R est:5000-8000
£2778 $5000 €4056 Wise man riding camel (81x69cm-32x27in) housepaint on tin. 24-Apr-4 Slotin Folk Art, Buford #282/R est:5000-8000
£4167 $7500 €6084 Sammy Davis Jr. (114x74cm-45x29in) housepaint on tin. 24-Apr-4 Slotin Folk Art, Buford #279/R est:10000-15000
£4167 $7500 €6084 Rockin Mary (104x64cm-41x25in) paint on tin prov. 24-Apr-4 Slotin Folk Art, Buford #280/R est:10000-15000
£5389 $9000 €7868 Try me (124x71cm-49x28in) Roofing tin prov.lit. 15-Nov-3 Slotin Folk Art, Buford #136/R est:8000-12000
£7186 $12000 €10492 Joe (119x71cm-47x28in) roofing tin prov.lit. 15-Nov-3 Slotin Folk Art, Buford #135/R est:8000-12000

DOYLE, William M S (1769-1828) American
Miniatures
£1486 $2750 €2170 John Clark (5x5cm-2x2in) oval. 12-Mar-4 Du Mouchelle, Detroit #2027/R est:1000-2000

D'OYLY, Maj Gen Sir Charles Walters (1822-1900) British
Works on paper
£300 $510 €438 St Paul's Cathedral, Calcutta, India (28x28cm-11x11in) s. W/C htd white. 4-Nov-3 Bonhams, New Bond Street #61
£750 $1275 €1095 Lighthouse at Point de Galle, Ceylon. Above Landour, Himalayas (22x34cm-9x13in) W/C htd white two. 4-Nov-3 Bonhams, New Bond Street #54

DOYLY-JOHN, C R (1906-1993) British
£260 $434 €380 Harbour scene South of France (35x48cm-14x19in) s. board. 21-Oct-3 Sworder & Son, Bishops Stortford #296/R
£260 $486 €390 San Sebastian (46x66cm-18x26in) s. 22-Jul-4 Gorringes, Lewes #1997
£280 $504 €409 Fisherman coming ashore (40x76cm-16x30in) bears sig. 20-Jan-4 Bonhams, Knightsbridge #193/R
£300 $477 €438 Mediterranean harbour scene (36x71cm-14x28in) s. 9-Sep-3 Gorringes, Lewes #1862
£320 $579 €467 Venice, off Place Marco, side street (38x74cm-15x29in) s. 16-Apr-4 Keys, Aylsham #401/R
£320 $566 €467 St. Tropez (45x66cm-18x26in) s. i.verso. 27-Apr-4 Bonhams, Knightsbridge #8/R
£320 $566 €467 Mediterranean Harbour (23x33cm-9x13in) s. 28-Apr-4 Halls, Shrewsbury #509
£320 $544 €467 Santa Margherita near Portofino, Italy (50x76cm-20x30in) s. i.verso. 29-Oct-3 Edgar Horn, Eastbourne #359
£320 $586 €467 Juan-les-Pins (45x64cm-18x25in) s. 7-Jul-4 Cheffins, Cambridge #105
£340 $622 €496 Eze, hill village near Monte Carlo, South of France (34x70cm-13x28in) s. i.verso. 6-Apr-4 Bonhams, Chester #975
£350 $581 €511 St Tropez near St Maxime, French Riviera (36x71cm-14x28in) s. 10-Jun-3 Canterbury Auctions, UK #116
£360 $598 €526 On coast 3km from Monte-Carlo (41x56cm-16x22in) s.i. 30-Sep-3 Andrew Smith, Winchester #142/R
£360 $670 €526 St Tropez (35x71cm-14x28in) s. 2-Mar-4 Bearnes, Exeter #425/R
£380 $707 €555 Santa Margarite (35x71cm-14x28in) s. 2-Mar-4 Bearnes, Exeter #430/R
£380 $646 €555 French coastline near Eden Roc (36x70cm-14x28in) i.verso. 29-Oct-3 Edgar Horn, Eastbourne #358
£420 $743 €613 St. Jihn near Antibes (43x54cm-17x21in) s. board. 27-Apr-4 Bonhams, Knightsbridge #90/R
£640 $1190 €934 Sunset, Cannes (24x35cm-9x14in) s. 2-Mar-4 Bearnes, Exeter #431

DOZIER, Otis (1904-1987) American
£5090 $8500 €7431 Rocks (91x102cm-36x40in) 18-Oct-3 David Dike, Dallas #183/R est:8000-10000
Prints
£2096 $3500 €3060 Roadrunner (23x33cm-9x13in) lithograph. 18-Oct-3 David Dike, Dallas #64/R est:3000-6000
£2395 $4000 €3497 Crows in melon patch (25x30cm-10x12in) lithograph. 18-Oct-3 David Dike, Dallas #63/R est:2000-4000

DRACHMANN, Holger (1846-1908) Danish
£561 $886 €813 Moens Klint (17x22cm-7x9in) s.d.1868 verso prov. 2-Sep-3 Rasmussen, Copenhagen #1897 (D.KR 6000)
£607 $960 €880 Coastal landscape (20x17cm-8x7in) init.i.d.7/6 82. 2-Sep-3 Rasmussen, Copenhagen #1893 (D.KR 6500)
£611 $1040 €892 Coastal landscape with dinghy, cattle in background (33x55cm-13x22in) s.i.d.Maj 91. 29-Nov-3 Rasmussen, Havnen #2113 (D.KR 6500)
£687 $1250 €1003 View of Venice (9x16cm-4x6in) s.i.d.1905 panel. 7-Feb-4 Rasmussen, Havnen #2300 (D.KR 7500)
£729 $1152 €1057 Vaade ovn, Bornholm (17x24cm-7x9in) prov. 2-Sep-3 Rasmussen, Copenhagen #1902 (D.KR 7800)
£1028 $1624 €1491 Sailing vessels off Kronborg (16x24cm-6x9in) s.d.74 prov. 2-Sep-3 Rasmussen, Copenhagen #1638/R (D.KR 11000)
£1040 $1799 €1518 From Gibraltar (19x31cm-7x12in) mono. 9-Dec-3 Rasmussen, Copenhagen #1520/R (D.KR 11000)
£1374 $2500 €2006 Mid Summer evening at Skagen Strand (30x47cm-12x19in) init.i.d.79. 7-Feb-4 Rasmussen, Havnen #2240/R est:8000-10000 (D.KR 15000)
£1399 $2616 €2043 Seascape with sailing vessels in rough seas off the coast (25x36cm-10x14in) s.i.d.1876 paper on board. 25-Feb-4 Museumsbygningen, Copenhagen #143 est:4000 (D.KR 15500)
£1418 $2453 €2070 French fishermen in the Channel (38x52cm-15x20in) init.d.67. 9-Dec-3 Rasmussen, Copenhagen #1458/R est:20000-25000 (D.KR 15000)
£1797 $3342 €2624 Seascape with boats off the coast of Skagen at sunset (24x31cm-9x12in) s.i.d.Sept.1904. 2-Mar-4 Rasmussen, Copenhagen #1330/R est:20000 (D.KR 20000)
£2430 $3839 €3524 Ship wreck on edge of water (41x61cm-16x24in) s.i.d.Novb.02. 2-Sep-3 Rasmussen, Copenhagen #1757/R est:25000 (D.KR 26000)
£2765 $4700 €4037 Seascape with vessels on rough seas (48x66cm-19x26in) s.i.d.1900. 10-Nov-3 Rasmussen, Vejle #272/R est:30000-40000 (D.KR 30000)
£3427 $6339 €5003 Fishing boats off the coast at Vlissingen (60x92cm-24x36in) s.i.d.1883. 15-Mar-4 Rasmussen, Vejle #68/R est:40000 (D.KR 38000)
£3781 $6541 €5520 Vessels off the coast at Halifax (40x65cm-16x26in) s.i.d.Septr.1899. 9-Dec-3 Rasmussen, Copenhagen #1490/R est:40000-50000 (D.KR 40000)

DRACHMANN, Jens (1880-1929) American/Danish
£287 $516 €419 Seascape with vessels (28x45cm-11x18in) s.i.d.03. 24-Apr-4 Rasmussen, Havnen #2331 (D.KR 3200)

DRAGHI, Giovan Battista (attrib) (1657-1712) Italian
Works on paper
£490 $817 €700 Trombonist (22x16cm-9x6in) chk htd white. 28-Jun-3 Bolland & Marotz, Bremen #571/R

DRAGON, David (20th C) American
£1143 $2000 €1669 Humphrey Bogart. John Wayne (46x46cm-18x18in) each s.d.1974 prov. two. 17-Dec-3 Christie's, Rockefeller NY #228/R est:2000-3000

DRAGONETTE, Cooper (1970-C) American
£221 $400 €323 Off Bradford Street, Provincetown (25x36cm-10x14in) s.d.2004 verso. 3-Apr-4 Outer Cape Auctions, Provincetown #51/R

DRAHONET, Alexandre Jean Dubois (1791-1834) French
£1944 $3500 €2838 Wedding portraits (65x55cm-26x22in) s.d.1820 one mono.d.1820 pair. 21-Jan-4 Sotheby's, New York #166/R est:5000-7000
Works on paper
£1400 $2338 €2044 Portrait of Lieutenant Bouverie of Delapre Abbey, Northampton (24x17cm-9x7in) d.1812 W/C over pencil. 14-Oct-3 Sotheby's, London #477a est:1000-1500

DRAHONET, Alexandre Jean Dubois (attrib) (1791-1834) French
Works on paper
£867 $1595 €1300 Portrait de deux freres (44x37cm-17x15in) chl stump velin. 9-Jun-4 Oger, Dumont, Paris #24/R

DRAHOSCH, Ludwig (1969-) Austrian
£800 $1472 €1200 Angel fight (60x40cm-24x16in) s.i.d.96 verso. 9-Jun-4 Dorotheum, Salzburg #737/R

DRAKE, Dewitt (c.1891-1979) Canadian
£181 $336 €264 Three houses (23x27cm-9x11in) s. board. 2-Mar-4 Ritchie, Toronto #128/R (C.D 450)
£220 $402 €321 Farm building, figure, hills tree and road (22x26cm-9x10in) st.sig. board prov. 1-Jun-4 Joyner Waddington, Toronto #539 (C.D 550)
£245 $422 €358 House in winter (22x26cm-9x10in) s. board. 2-Dec-3 Joyner Waddington, Toronto #542 (C.D 550)

DRAKE, E D (19/20th C) New Zealander?
£781 $1242 €1140 Paddle steamer Wairere on the Wanganui River (27x38cm-11x15in) s.d.1892. 1-May-3 Dunbar Sloane, Wellington #11/R est:2000-4000 (NZ.D 2250)
£1859 $3197 €2714 Wairere steamer on Wanganui River (28x39cm-11x15in) s.d.1892. 3-Dec-3 Dunbar Sloane, Auckland #91/R est:5000-7000 (NZ.D 5000)

DRAMARD, Georges de (1839-1900) ?
£723 $1200 €1056 Hounds in battle (33x46cm-13x18in) s. 4-Oct-3 Neal Auction Company, New Orleans #146/R est:1500-2500

DRAPELL, Joseph (20th C) American
£804 $1382 €1174 Security No 2 (102x145cm-40x57in) acrylic painted 1985. 2-Dec-3 Joyner Waddington, Toronto #498 est:1200-1800 (C.D 1800)

DRAPER, Charles F (19th C) British
£1850 $3349 €2701 Moie de Mouton, Sark (96x66cm-38x26in) mono.d.1902. 1-Apr-4 Martel Maides, Guernsey #231/R est:800-1200

DRAPER, Herbert James (1864-1920) British
£544 $886 €794 Portrait of young woman (32x24cm-13x9in) s. panel. 27-Sep-3 Rasmussen, Havnen #2228/R (D.KR 5800)
£1600 $2944 €2336 Midsummer Eve (22cm-9in circular) canvas on board fragment lit. 23-Mar-4 Bonhams, New Bond Street #76/R est:1000-1500
£2000 $3600 €2920 Portrait of Teddy, son of Lieutenant BWG Oates (133x67cm-52x26in) s. prov.exhib.lit. 21-Jan-4 Sotheby's, Olympia #299/R est:2000-3000
£3250 $5135 €4713 Golden rays (140x100cm-55x39in) 4-Sep-3 Christie's, Kensington #253/R est:4000-6000
£8500 $15640 €12410 Study for day and the dawnstar (30x22cm-12x9in) s. board prov.lit. 11-Jun-4 Christie's, London #99/R est:3000-5000
£18000 $30600 €26280 Day and the dawn star (43x32cm-17x13in) prov.exhib.lit. 25-Nov-3 Christie's, London #153/R est:20000-30000
£20000 $36400 €29200 For Saint Dorothea's day (79x119cm-31x47in) s. exhib.lit. 16-Jun-4 Bonhams, New Bond Street #70/R est:25000-30000
£30000 $55200 €43800 Wrath of the Sea God (58x102cm-23x40in) s. prov.exhib.lit. 11-Jun-4 Christie's, London #161/R est:40000-60000
Works on paper
£12500 $22750 €18250 Study of Florrie Bird for a water nymph (46x61cm-18x24in) s.i. blk white chk grey paper prov.exhib.lit. 1-Jul-4 Sotheby's, London #278/R est:6000-8000

DRAPER, J (19th C) ?
£719 $1337 €1050 Interior scene with gentleman reading letter (52x42cm-20x17in) s.indis.d. 2-Mar-4 Rasmussen, Copenhagen #1529/R (D.KR 8000)

DRATHMANN, Christopher (1856-1931) German
£278 $442 €400 Two cows on shore (30x26cm-12x10in) s.d.1882 panel. 11-Sep-3 Weidler, Nurnberg #328/R
£496 $804 €700 Deer at wood's edge (83x110cm-33x43in) s. lit. 23-May-3 Karlheinz Kaupp, Staufen #1790

DRATZ, Jean (1905-1967) Belgian
£473 $894 €700 Pas dans la neige (50x60cm-20x24in) s. 17-Feb-4 Galerie Moderne, Brussels #149/R

DRAVER, Orrin (1895-1964) American
£472 $750 €689 Red barn (30x41cm-12x16in) s. 23-Mar-3 Auctions by the Bay, Alameda #851/R
£1351 $2500 €1972 Winter landscape (51x61cm-20x24in) s. 13-Mar-4 DeFina, Austinburg #912/R est:1800-2200

DRAWBRIDGE, John (1930-) New Zealander
£480 $802 €701 Element no.3 (72x102cm-28x40in) s.d.1962 exhib. 21-Oct-3 Bonhams, Knightsbridge #137a
Works on paper
£623 $1115 €910 Redscape (73x53cm-29x21in) s.d.1974 W/C. 12-May-4 Dunbar Sloane, Wellington #135/R est:2000-4000 (NZ.D 1800)

DREBER, Heinrich (1822-1875) German
£3378 $5946 €5000 Odysseus with the nymph Kalypso on the Island of Ogygia (142x115cm-56x45in) s. prov.lit. 22-May-4 Lempertz, Koln #1509/R est:6000-8000
Works on paper
£873 $1590 €1275 Tree trunk on hilly ground entwined with plants (22x27cm-9x11in) pencil brush wash light brown paper. 17-Jun-4 Kornfeld, Bern #12/R (S.FR 2000)

DRECHSLER, Johann Baptist (1756-1811) Austrian
£3662 $6335 €5200 Still life of roses in glass vase, grapes and butterfly (53x42cm-21x17in) 13-Dec-3 Hagelstam, Helsinki #22/R est:4000
£32000 $57600 €46720 Still life of flowers, fruit, basket, walnut and birds nest on a ledge (49x38cm-19x15in) s.d.1811 panel prov. 22-Apr-4 Sotheby's, London #111/R est:20000-30000
£33077 $56892 €48292 Still life of flowers (64x54cm-25x21in) s.d.1797 panel pair. 2-Dec-3 Bukowskis, Stockholm #398/R est:250000-300000 (S.KR 430000)

DREESEN, Willi (20th C) Swiss
£326 $597 €476 Trois Valaisannes (59x88cm-23x35in) s.d.64 oil plaster pavatex. 5-Jun-4 Galerie du Rhone, Sion #314 (S.FR 750)

DREGELY, Laszlo (1932-) Hungarian
£340 $619 €500 Attendant le miracle - waiting for wonder (229x110cm-90x43in) s. prov. 3-Feb-4 Christie's, Amsterdam #632

DREGER, Tom von (1868-1949) Austrian
£1042 $1771 €1500 Reclining male nude (64x93cm-25x37in) s.d.1891. 28-Oct-3 Dorotheum, Vienna #174/R est:1300-1600
Works on paper
£336 $621 €500 Child (50x40cm-20x16in) s.mono.d.1941 mixed media. 9-Mar-4 Dorotheum, Vienna #74

DREHER, Franz (?) German
£363 $650 €530 Three kittens playing (18x24cm-7x9in) s. panel. 21-Mar-4 Bonhams & Butterfields, Los Angeles #7352/R

DREHER, Peter (1932-) German
£282 $519 €420 Porcelain cup on white table (16x18cm-6x7in) s.i.d.1975 verso board. 25-Mar-4 Karlheinz Kaupp, Staufen #2815/R
£338 $541 €480 Key hanging from nail (12x7cm-5x3in) s.d.15.9.83 board. 19-Sep-3 Karlheinz Kaupp, Staufen #2197/R
£1067 $1952 €1600 Day by day is a good day (25x20cm-10x8in) i. s.i.d.4.3.87 verso two. 4-Jun-4 Lempertz, Koln #116/R est:1600

DREIBHOLZ, Cristiaan Lodewyck Willem (1799-1874) Dutch
£1319 $2085 €1900 Sailing vessels by a coast (20x28cm-8x11in) s. panel. 2-Sep-3 Christie's, Amsterdam #316/R est:2000-3000
Works on paper
£470 $864 €700 Ships on choppy seas in front of rocky coast (46x64cm-18x25in) pencil brown brush. 29-Mar-4 Glerum, Amsterdam #12
£5944 $10105 €8500 Harbour with sailing boats (27x33cm-11x13in) s.W/C. 27-Nov-3 Bassenge, Berlin #5563/R est:3000

DRENDEL, Graeme (1953-) Australian?
£1429 $2629 €2086 Breather (106x74cm-42x29in) s.d.98 prov. 29-Mar-4 Goodman, Sydney #153/R est:3500-4500 (A.D 3500)
Works on paper
£371 $671 €542 Preliminaries (18x30cm-7x12in) s.d.97 s.i.d.verso W/C. 31-Mar-4 Goodman, Sydney #285 (A.D 900)

DRENKHAHN, Reinhard (20th C) German
£1946 $3581 €2900 Beach runner, red (100x50cm-39x20in) masonite prov. 26-Mar-4 Ketterer, Hamburg #381/R est:1700-2000

DREONI, Arrigo (1911-1987) Italian
£252 $413 €350 Landscape (56x71cm-22x28in) s. 10-Jun-3 Pandolfini, Florence #407
£432 $708 €600 Wooden bridge (52x64cm-20x25in) s.d.45. 10-Jun-3 Pandolfini, Florence #225/R

DREOSSI, Alice (1882-1967) Dutch
£455 $782 €650 Market at the Lido (46x56cm-18x22in) board. 3-Dec-3 Stadion, Trieste #957/R

DRESDEN SCHOOL (18th C) German
£5903 $9622 €8500 Konigstein fortress (58x127cm-23x50in) 25-Sep-3 Dr Fritz Nagel, Stuttgart #1296/R est:3800

DRESSE, Fernand (1916-) Belgian
£340 $609 €500 Nature morte a la perruche (18x24cm-7x9in) s.d.45 panel. 17-Mar-4 Hotel des Ventes Mosan, Brussels #160

DRESSLER, A (19th C) ?
Sculpture
£1438 $2445 €2100 Roman emperor standing (74cm-29in) i. bronze black marble. 5-Nov-3 Vendue Huis, Gravenhage #4020/R est:800-1200

DRESSLER, Adolf (1833-1881) German
£2000 $3640 €3000 Forest stream in summer (34x27cm-13x11in) s. 1-Jul-4 Van Ham, Cologne #1305 est:1000
£10204 $18265 €15000 Stream in wood (167x131cm-66x52in) s. 17-Mar-4 Neumeister, Munich #443/R est:10000

DRESSLER, Alberto (20th C) Italian
Works on paper
£350 $584 €500 Portrait of bearded man (50x50cm-20x20in) s. chl. 10-Oct-3 Stadion, Trieste #749/R

DRESSLER, August Wilhelm (1886-1970) German
£600 $1104 €900 Reflections (75x45cm-30x18in) s.d.1946. 8-Jun-4 Della Rocca, Turin #313/R est:800-1200
£600 $1104 €900 Reflections (51x31cm-20x12in) s.d.1944. 8-Jun-4 Della Rocca, Turin #319/R
£600 $1104 €900 At the well (40x50cm-16x20in) s.d.1938 board. 8-Jun-4 Della Rocca, Turin #317/R
£600 $1104 €900 Sunset in the wood (73x44cm-29x17in) s.acrylic1941 board. 8-Jun-4 Della Rocca, Turin #335/R
£600 $1104 €900 Rural (74x54cm-29x21in) s.d.1940 board. 8-Jun-4 Della Rocca, Turin #341/R
£633 $1165 €950 Along the river (65x43cm-26x17in) s.d.1942. 8-Jun-4 Della Rocca, Turin #309/R
£3007 $5112 €4300 Italian theatre box (85x70cm-33x28in) 29-Nov-3 Bassenge, Berlin #6684/R est:1500

DRESSLER, Franz (1918-) Austrian
£294 $500 €429 St Nikola in Strudengau (48x38cm-19x15in) s. board. 28-Nov-3 Zofingen, Switzerland #2574 (S.FR 650)

DREUX, Alfred de (1810-1860) French
£2733 $4947 €4100 Les cavaliers (32x23cm-13x9in) s. 5-Apr-4 Deburaux, Boulogne #72 est:2000-2500
£8597 $13756 €12552 Rider with dogs (19x33cm-7x13in) s. panel. 19-Sep-3 Koller, Zurich #3071/R est:20000-25000 (S.FR 19000)
£11806 $19715 €17000 Cheval selle (24x32cm-9x13in) s. lit. 21-Oct-3 Fraysse & Associes, Paris #13/R
£18605 $32000 €27163 Hunting in the forest (33x46cm-13x18in) s. 5-Dec-3 Christie's, Rockefeller NY #72/R est:20000-30000
£18605 $32000 €27163 Coming out of the forest (33x46cm-13x18in) s. 5-Dec-3 Christie's, Rockefeller NY #73/R est:20000-30000
£47887 $83802 €68000 La lettre (64x81cm-25x32in) s.d.1860 exhib. 16-Dec-3 Artcurial Briest, Paris #242/R est:80000-100000
£173184 $310000 €252849 Cheval blanc effraye par l'orage (55x45cm-22x18in) painted c.1840 prov.exhib.lit. 5-May-4 Sotheby's, New York #16/R est:200000-300000

Works on paper
£4500 $8235 €6570 La rencontre evitee - Galloping horsemen avoiding a horse and cart (31x40cm-12x16in) s. black lead W/C bodycol htd gum arabic prov. 6-Jul-4 Christie's, London #197/R est:5000-7000

DREUX, Alfred de (attrib) (1810-1860) French
Works on paper
£816 $1461 €1200 Cavalier tenant par la bridge deux chevaux (22x29cm-9x11in) black pencil brown wash htd gouache. 19-Mar-4 Piasa, Paris #161/R

DREVES, Arnold (19th C) German
£1702 $2843 €2400 Moorland (106x148cm-42x58in) s.i. 17-Oct-3 Berlinghof, Heidelberg #1018/R est:2200

DREVET, Jean Baptiste (1854-1940) French
£399 $650 €583 La bourrasque (36x51cm-14x20in) s. 27-Sep-3 Charlton Hall, Columbia #303/R
Works on paper
£280 $510 €420 View of the village of Monetier (16x24cm-6x9in) s.i. W/C. 29-Jun-4 Chenu & Scrive, Lyon #62/R
£567 $1031 €850 Village covered in snow with figures (16x26cm-6x10in) s. W/C. 29-Jun-4 Chenu & Scrive, Lyon #64/R

DREW, Clement (1806-1889) American
£353 $600 €515 Harbour seascape with lighthouse on point and sailing ships (10x15cm-4x6in) i.verso board. 8-Nov-3 Van Blarcom, South Natick #46/R
£373 $600 €545 Moonlit coastal scene (18x25cm-7x10in) s. board. 20-Aug-3 James Julia, Fairfield #935/R
£726 $1300 €1060 Ship in full sail. s. wood panel. 8-Jan-4 James Julia, Fairfield #552/R
£820 $1500 €1230 Gurnet Lights, Plymouth Harbour (20x30cm-8x12in) s.d.1886 s.i.d.verso. 29-Jul-4 Eldred, East Dennis #437/R est:2000-3000
£820 $1500 €1230 Mount Desert Rock Light (23x30cm-9x12in) i.verso board. 29-Jul-4 Eldred, East Dennis #481/R est:2000-3000
£894 $1600 €1305 Braces rock from Persian Head, East Gloucester (20x30cm-8x12in) s. s.d.1885 verso board. 16-May-4 CRN Auctions, Cambridge #23/R
£1117 $2000 €1631 Land's End, Coast of England (51x76cm-20x30in) s.i.d.1878 verso. 16-Mar-4 Bonhams & Butterfields, San Francisco #6131/R est:3000-5000
£1366 $2500 €2049 Gurnet Lights (15x25cm-6x10in) s.d.1888 verso board. 29-Jul-4 Eldred, East Dennis #436/R est:2000-3000
£1396 $2500 €2038 Eddystone Lighthouse (51x76cm-20x30in) s.i.d.1878 verso. 16-Mar-4 Bonhams & Butterfields, San Francisco #6130/R est:3000-5000
£1676 $3000 €2447 Brig near rocky cliffs (36x56cm-14x22in) s. s.i.d.1878 verso. 16-Mar-4 Bonhams & Butterfields, San Francisco #6132/R est:1500-2000

DREW, Clement (attrib) (1806-1889) American
£443 $700 €647 View of a lighthouse possibly Minot's Light (10x15cm-4x6in) panel. 25-Jul-3 Eldred, East Dennis #291e/R
£1236 $2100 €1805 Isle of Shoals Light (23x28cm-9x11in) s.i.d.1839 verso. 1-Nov-3 Skinner, Boston #137/R est:800-1200

DREW, Dudley (1924-) Australian
£586 $914 €850 Lilac (79x59cm-31x23in) s. 1-Aug-2 Joel, Victoria #297 est:800-1200 (A.D 1700)

DREW, George W (1875-1968) American
£588 $1000 €858 Still life with apples (28x41cm-11x16in) s. exhib. 21-Nov-3 Eldred, East Dennis #816/R est:500-1000
£938 $1500 €1369 Landscape with cottage and figures (51x76cm-20x30in) s. 17-May-3 Bunte, Elgin #1266 est:1500-2500

DREWES, Werner (1899-1985) American
£1676 $3000 €2447 Untitled (23x15cm-9x6in) s. prov. 16-May-4 Wright, Chicago #245/R est:3000-4000
£2151 $4000 €3140 Sunday morning in Rhone valley (56x81cm-22x32in) s.d.1959. 7-Mar-4 Treadway Gallery, Cincinnati #695/R est:5000-7000
Works on paper
£327 $575 €477 Coastal scene (28x43cm-11x17in) s. W/C. 22-May-4 Selkirks, St. Louis #553/R
£462 $850 €675 Lyrical abstract (23x36cm-9x14in) s.d.1944 gouache on board. 11-Jun-4 David Rago, Lambertville #222/R
£540 $950 €788 Coastal scene (43x58cm-17x23in) s. W/C. 22-May-4 Selkirks, St. Louis #552/R

DREWES, Werner (attrib) (1899-1985) American
£486 $792 €700 Dusseldorf harbour in evening (94x135cm-37x53in) i. stretcher. 26-Sep-3 Bolland & Marotz, Bremen #732/R

DREWS, Kaj (1884-1964) Danish
£275 $500 €402 Norwegian fjord landscape (67x97cm-26x38in) s. 7-Feb-4 Rasmussen, Havnen #2020 (D.KR 3000)
£549 $1000 €802 Wooded landscape (95x135cm-37x53in) s. 7-Feb-4 Rasmussen, Havnen #2068 (D.KR 6000)
£820 $1500 €1197 Danish moor landscape (69x99cm-27x39in) s.d.1936. 5-Jun-4 Treadway Gallery, Cincinnati #681/R est:2500-3500

DREWS, Svend (1919-) Danish
£300 $500 €438 Coastal landscape with sailing boat (66x56cm-26x22in) s. 25-Oct-3 Rasmussen, Havnen #2124 (D.KR 3200)
£429 $673 €626 Landscape with waterfall (51x41cm-20x16in) s. 30-Aug-3 Rasmussen, Havnen #2009 (D.KR 4600)

DREXEL, Hans Christoph (1886-1979) German
£293 $528 €440 Harlequin and woman (25x24cm-10x9in) s. canvas on panel. 24-Apr-4 Dr Lehr, Berlin #103/R

DREXEL, Norbert (1933-) Austrian
Works on paper
£390 $651 €550 Still life of fruit (24x39cm-9x15in) s. mixed media. 16-Oct-3 Dorotheum, Salzburg #807/R
£467 $859 €700 Cafe (35x50cm-14x20in) s.d.86 pastel mixed media. 9-Jun-4 Dorotheum, Salzburg #797/R
£496 $829 €700 Paris with view of Notre Dame (35x50cm-14x20in) s.d.1988 pastel. 16-Oct-3 Dorotheum, Salzburg #953/R
£567 $948 €800 Cafe III (23x32cm-9x13in) s.d.91 pastel mixed media. 16-Oct-3 Dorotheum, Salzburg #955/R
£567 $1043 €850 Pont Neuf - Paris (35x50cm-14x20in) s.d.1988 pastel. 9-Jun-4 Dorotheum, Salzburg #798/R

DREYBERG, Charles (?) Belgian?
£738 $1307 €1100 Maritza (150x130cm-59x51in) s. 27-Apr-4 Campo, Vlaamse Kaai #410

DREYER, Dankvart (1816-1852) Danish
£289 $534 €422 River (14x34cm-6x13in) study. 15-Mar-4 Rasmussen, Vejle #349 (D.KR 3200)
£302 $541 €441 After the duel (31x35cm-12x14in) 12-Jan-4 Rasmussen, Vejle #208 (D.KR 3200)
£1258 $1975 €1837 Bishop Absalon (39x24cm-15x9in) one s.d.1851 panel pair lit.prov. 30-Aug-3 Rasmussen, Havnen #2048/R est:6000-8000 (D.KR 13500)
£3970 $6868 €5796 Bushes and plants by stone wall on outskirts of wood (23x34cm-9x13in) 9-Dec-3 Rasmussen, Copenhagen #1386/R est:30000-50000 (D.KR 42000)

DREYER, Paul Uwe (1939-) German
£354 $577 €510 Composition (79x80cm-31x31in) s.i. verso canvas on masonite. 27-Sep-3 Dr Fritz Nagel, Stuttgart #9518/R
£775 $1340 €1100 Emblem pose for T (95x100cm-37x39in) s.i.d. Nov/Dez 1970. 13-Dec-3 Lempertz, Koln #131/R

DRGAC, Uncle Pete (?) American?
£659 $1100 €962 Flowers and animals (36x30cm-14x12in) tempera cardboard. 15-Nov-3 Slotin Folk Art, Buford #242/R

DRIAN (20th C) French
£3667 $6747 €5500 Le lion de l'Atlas (70x50cm-28x20in) s. 14-Jun-4 Gros & Delettrez, Paris #537/R est:3000-4000

DRIAN, Étienne (1885-1961) French
£2200 $4048 €3300 Singeries habilles (31x28cm-12x11in) s. pair. 9-Jun-4 Oger, Dumont, Paris #51/R est:1500-2000

DRIBEN, Peter (c.1903-1968) American
£1678 $3003 €2500 Untitled (82x61cm-32x24in) s. cardboard painted c.1943-1955 lit. 27-May-4 Sotheby's, Paris #103/R est:2500-3000
£2013 $3604 €3000 Beauty parade (80x60cm-31x24in) s. cardboard. 27-May-4 Sotheby's, Paris #104/R est:3000-5000
£3691 $6607 €5500 Have you any hearts? (89x68cm-35x27in) s. cardboard painted c.1960. 27-May-4 Sotheby's, Paris #107/R est:2500-3000
£5369 $9611 €8000 No swimming allowed (83x63cm-33x25in) s. cardboard painted c.1950. 27-May-4 Sotheby's, Paris #106/R est:5000-7000
£7383 $13215 €11000 Beauty parade magazine (87x68cm-34x27in) s. cardboard painted c.1950. 27-May-4 Sotheby's, Paris #105/R est:5000-7000

DRIELST, Egbert van (1746-1818) Dutch
Works on paper
£510 $913 €750 Deux chaumieres dans un paysage (24x37cm-9x15in) mono. i.verso graphite grey wash. 17-Mar-4 Maigret, Paris #31/R
£2270 $3790 €3200 Wooded landscape. s.d.1794 verso W/C gouache arabic gum prov. 15-Oct-3 Sotheby's, Paris #134/R

DRIES, Jean (1905-1973) French
£1056 $1849 €1500 Deauville (27x46cm-11x18in) s. 19-Dec-3 Delvaux, Paris #45 est:1500-2000

DRIESSCHE, Ernest van den (1894-1985) Belgian
£909 $1545 €1300 Nativite (28x24cm-11x9in) s. panel. 1-Dec-3 Palais de Beaux Arts, Brussels #193
£1733 $3103 €2600 Village festival (104x123cm-41x48in) s. panel. 15-May-4 De Vuyst, Lokeren #340/R est:2000-2500
Works on paper
£280 $476 €400 La balancoire (34x24cm-13x9in) s. pastel. 1-Dec-3 Palais de Beaux Arts, Brussels #174/R
£280 $476 €400 Couple (35x26cm-14x10in) mono. W/C. 1-Dec-3 Palais de Beaux Arts, Brussels #180
£308 $523 €440 Personnages (34x26cm-13x10in) s. felt. 1-Dec-3 Palais de Beaux Arts, Brussels #179
£322 $547 €460 Couple entoure de personnages (35x27cm-14x11in) s. mixed media. 1-Dec-3 Palais de Beaux Arts, Brussels #175
£350 $594 €500 Personnages (26x23cm-10x9in) s. felt. 1-Dec-3 Palais de Beaux Arts, Brussels #183/R
£350 $594 €500 Vierge entouree d'enfants (36x28cm-14x11in) s. felt. 1-Dec-3 Palais de Beaux Arts, Brussels #184/R
£420 $713 €600 Personnage distribuant des pains (25x35cm-10x14in) s. pastel. 1-Dec-3 Palais de Beaux Arts, Brussels #176/R
£490 $832 €700 Personnages carnavalesques (45x60cm-18x24in) s. pastel. 1-Dec-3 Palais de Beaux Arts, Brussels #182

£524 $892 €750 Le cortege (45x60cm-18x24in) s. pastel. 1-Dec-3 Palais de Beaux Arts, Brussels #188/R
£664 $1129 €950 La nativite (50x69cm-20x27in) s. pastel. 1-Dec-3 Palais de Beaux Arts, Brussels #186
£664 $1129 €950 Personnages carnavalesques (49x67cm-19x26in) s. pastel. 1-Dec-3 Palais de Beaux Arts, Brussels #187
£664 $1129 €950 L'adoration (50x70cm-20x28in) s. pastel. 1-Dec-3 Palais de Beaux Arts, Brussels #189/R
£664 $1129 €950 Personnages carnavalesques (51x70cm-20x28in) s. pastel. 1-Dec-3 Palais de Beaux Arts, Brussels #191/R
£664 $1129 €950 Personnages carnavalesques (50x68cm-20x27in) s. pastel. 1-Dec-3 Palais de Beaux Arts, Brussels #192/R
£699 $1189 €1000 Eine Kapiteins Kapelleke (50x44cm-20x17in) s. pastel. 1-Dec-3 Palais de Beaux Arts, Brussels #185/R

DRIESSCHE, Lucien van den (1926-1991) Belgian
£347 $566 €500 Ete en Flandres (100x120cm-39x47in) s. panel. 23-Sep-3 Galerie Moderne, Brussels #927
£451 $754 €650 Temps de pluie (100x120cm-39x47in) s. panel. 21-Oct-3 Campo, Vlaamse Kaai #592
£470 $832 €700 Maisons (80x100cm-31x39in) s. panel. 27-Apr-4 Campo, Vlaamse Kaai #611

DRIESSCHE, Marcel van (1925-) Belgian
£267 $480 €400 Rode zon (57x81cm-22x32in) s.d.69 oil paper. 26-Apr-4 Bernaerts, Antwerp #537/R

DRIESTEN, Arend Jan van (1878-1969) Dutch
£658 $1191 €1000 Village house by the water (24x34cm-9x13in) s. canvas on panel. 19-Apr-4 Glerum, Amsterdam #134/R
£674 $1125 €950 Landscape with farmers ploughing, spring sowing time (34x52cm-13x20in) s. panel. 20-Oct-3 Glerum, Amsterdam #11/R
£805 $1490 €1200 Boerenwoning in de peel (60x92cm-24x36in) s. 15-Mar-4 Sotheby's, Amsterdam #143/R est:1200-1500
£1528 $2414 €2200 Early spring (70x51cm-28x20in) s. 2-Sep-3 Christie's, Amsterdam #264/R est:1500-2000
£3221 $5960 €4800 Afgebroken molen te nieuwkoop (50x70cm-20x28in) s. 15-Mar-4 Sotheby's, Amsterdam #142/R est:1000-1500
Works on paper
£667 $1193 €1000 Farm on a lake (19x28cm-7x11in) s. W/C. 11-May-4 Vendu Notarishuis, Rotterdam #257
£1974 $3572 €3000 Walkers on the dyke (48x70cm-19x28in) s. W/C. 19-Apr-4 Glerum, Amsterdam #140/R est:1500-2000
£2237 $4049 €3400 Farmer in a punt in front of a farm in a polder landscape (44x69cm-17x27in) s. W/C. 19-Apr-4 Glerum, Amsterdam #139/R est:1500-2000
£2368 $4287 €3600 Farmer in a punt in a polder landscape (50x77cm-20x30in) s. W/C. 19-Apr-4 Glerum, Amsterdam #138/R est:1500-2000

DRIGGS, Elsie (1898-1992) American
£342 $550 €499 Passenger Figure (91x56cm-36x22in) s. painted c.1970. 22-Feb-3 Bunte, Elgin #1205
£406 $650 €593 Calligraphy (91x109cm-36x43in) s. 17-May-3 Bunte, Elgin #1309

DRING, William (1904-1990) British
£1800 $3096 €2628 At the coal face (77x60cm-30x24in) s.d.74. 3-Dec-3 Christie's, Kensington #650/R est:1000-1500
£8800 $15752 €12848 Portrait of Nicky Gargano (76x63cm-30x25in) s. 16-Mar-4 Bonhams, New Bond Street #67/R est:5000-7000
Works on paper
£250 $463 €365 Portrait of a lady (45x32cm-18x13in) s.d.76 pastel. 11-Mar-4 Christie's, Kensington #41

DRINKARD, David (1948-) American
£683 $1100 €997 Flush (41x51cm-16x20in) acrylic board. 22-Aug-3 Altermann Galleries, Santa Fe #226
£1553 $2500 €2252 Back Bay duck hunt (51x76cm-20x30in) acrylic board. 22-Aug-3 Altermann Galleries, Santa Fe #227
£2353 $4000 €3435 Full flush (61x91cm-24x36in) board. 1-Nov-3 Altermann Galleries, Santa Fe #179
£2514 $4500 €3670 Bird's up (61x91cm-24x36in) acrylic board. 15-May-4 Altermann Galleries, Santa Fe #157/R

DRINKWATER, Milton (19/20th C) British
£1000 $1700 €1460 Fishing in a mountain landscape (76x127cm-30x50in) s.d.1905. 5-Nov-3 Doyle, New York #23/R est:500-700
Works on paper
£280 $484 €409 Summer in the Highlands, sheep on the banks of a loch (13x43cm-5x17in) s. W/C bodycol. 11-Dec-3 Neales, Nottingham #545/R
£280 $518 €409 Loch Katrin, Ben Nevis beyond (29x43cm-11x17in) s. pencil W/C. 14-Jul-4 Christie's, Kensington #1147

DRISCOLL, H A (1872-1944) American
£647 $1100 €945 Taking the fly (40x56cm-16x22in) s. prov. 21-Nov-3 Skinner, Boston #349/R est:800-1200

DRIVER, Don (1930-) New Zealander
£362 $587 €525 City (51x90cm-20x35in) s.d.1960 board. 31-Jul-3 International Art Centre, Auckland #9/R est:1000-2000 (NZ.D 1000)
£761 $1233 €1103 Garden (90x90cm-35x35in) s. board. 31-Jul-3 International Art Centre, Auckland #4/R est:1000-3000 (NZ.D 2100)
Works on paper
£1042 $1656 €1521 Relief with pleats (127x85cm-50x33in) s. i.d.1969 verso mixed media exhib. 1-May-3 Dunbar Sloane, Wellington #13/R est:3000-5000 (NZ.D 3000)
£1306 $2259 €1907 Salt bags (122x89cm-48x35in) s.i.d.1985 verso mixed media. 9-Dec-3 Peter Webb, Auckland #162/R est:2000-4000 (NZ.D 3500)

DRIVIER, Leon-Ernest (1878-1951) French
Sculpture
£1931 $3225 €2800 La baigneuse (52x22cm-20x9in) s. platre d'atelier exec.c.1930. 16-Nov-3 Muizon & Le Coent, Paris #105/R
£2759 $4607 €4000 Madeleine (37cm-15in) polychrome plaster exec.c.1920. 16-Nov-3 Muizon & Le Coent, Paris #92/R
£2759 $4607 €4000 Femme emportant un homme sur un cheval aile (67x40cm-26x16in) platre d'atelier exec. 1910-1920. 16-Nov-3 Muizon & Le Coent, Paris #104/R
£3862 $6450 €5600 Le deluge (62x50cm-24x20in) platre d'atelier exec. 1910-1920. 16-Nov-3 Muizon & Le Coent, Paris #102/R
£3931 $6565 €5700 Les bacchantes (76x30x30cm-30x12x12in) s. platre d'atelier patine exec. 1910-1920. 16-Nov-3 Muizon & Le Coent, Paris #99/R
£4483 $7486 €6500 Les lutteuses (28x51cm-11x20in) s. platre d'atelier patine exec. 1910-1920. 16-Nov-3 Muizon & Le Coent, Paris #100/R
£4552 $7601 €6600 L'ombre de la lumiere (58x60x30cm-23x24x12in) s. platre d'atelier patine exec. 1910-1920. 16-Nov-3 Muizon & Le Coent, Paris #101/R
£7586 $12669 €11000 Femme a l'enfant ou frere et soeur (65x30x28cm-26x12x11in) s. platre d'atelier pat exec. 1910-1920. 16-Nov-3 Muizon & Le Coent, Paris #98/R
£13103 $21883 €19000 La baiser (38x100cm-15x39in) platre d'atelier pat exec. 1910-1920. 16-Nov-3 Muizon & Le Coent, Paris #97/R
£30000 $55200 €45000 L'archer (140cm-55in) s. green brown pat. bronze st.f. Rudier. 10-Jun-4 Camard, Paris #82/R est:15000-18000
Works on paper
£638 $1173 €950 Couturiere (41x30cm-16x12in) s. wax pastel. 24-Mar-4 Joron-Derem, Paris #59

DROCCO, Guido and MELLO, Franco (20th C) Italian
Sculpture
£1678 $3003 €2500 Cactus (170x70cm-67x28in) st.Gufram d.2000 polyurethane paint. 25-May-4 Sotheby's, Milan #197/R est:2500-3000

DROEGE, Anthony (20th C) American
£519 $950 €779 Black swan (178x157cm-70x62in) 10-Jul-4 Hindman, Chicago #125/R est:500-700

DROEGE, Oskar (1898-1983) German
£278 $439 €400 Eiderstedt landscape (35x50cm-14x20in) s. panel. 6-Sep-3 Schopman, Hamburg #749/R
£278 $439 €400 Dune landscape with gathering storm (35x50cm-14x20in) s. panel. 6-Sep-3 Schopman, Hamburg #837/R
£318 $490 €500 Wohldorf, Alster on winter evening (34x50cm-13x20in) s. panel one of pair. 4-Sep-2 Schopman, Hamburg #129/R
£478 $736 €750 Landscape (34x50cm-13x20in) s. panel pair. 4-Sep-2 Schopman, Hamburg #130/R

DROESE, Felix (1950-) German
Works on paper
£378 $642 €540 Duck (30x21cm-12x8in) s.i.d.1981 verso Indian ink W/C. 29-Nov-3 Villa Grisebach, Berlin #758/R
£2349 $4158 €3500 Untitled (150x100cm-59x39in) s.d. verso bitumen earth water board. 30-Apr-4 Dr Fritz Nagel, Stuttgart #760/R est:6500

DROGUE, Jean Jacques (1858-1901) French
Works on paper
£485 $824 €708 Female nude near water (55x33cm-22x13in) s. pastel. 5-Nov-3 Dobiaschofsky, Bern #497/R (S.FR 1100)

DROIT, Jean (20th C) French
Works on paper
£345 $638 €500 Elegante de profil sur fon japonisant (36x27cm-14x11in) s. oval. 19-Jan-4 Horta, Bruxelles #407
£587 $981 €840 Les boutons et les roses. Le manteau de loutre (29x24cm-11x9in) mixed media pair. 13-Oct-3 Horta, Bruxelles #415

DROLLING, Martin (1752-1817) French
£3497 $5944 €5000 Le cireur de bottes (32x22cm-13x9in) prov. 1-Dec-3 Rieunier, Paris #13/R est:6000-8000
£3947 $7263 €6000 Portrait de jeune garcon (46x37cm-18x15in) s.d.1805. 23-Jun-4 Sotheby's, Paris #56/R est:6000-8000
£5000 $9000 €7300 Portrait of a little boy placing a coral necklace on a dog, both seated in parkland setting (32x24cm-13x9in) s.d.1804 prov. 22-Jan-4 Sotheby's, New York #265/R est:10000-150000
£13158 $24211 €20000 Portrait de Louis XVI (73x60cm-29x24in) s.indis.d. prov.lit. 24-Jun-4 Christie's, Paris #104/R est:20000-30000

DROLLING, Martin (attrib) (1752-1817) French
£993 $1659 €1400 Portrait d'un peintre (11x8cm-4x3in) cardboard. 17-Oct-3 Tajan, Paris #111 est:1200-1500

DRONSART, Alexandre (19th C) French
£897 $1497 €1300 Le berger (65x81cm-26x32in) s. 17-Nov-3 Delorme & Bocage, Paris #133/R

DROOCHSLOOT, Cornelis (1630-1673) Dutch
£2245 $4018 €3300 Village street with peasants resting (26x34cm-10x13in) mono. panel. 17-Mar-4 Neumeister, Munich #341/R est:2000
£2980 $5424 €4500 Paysans et promeneurs sur un chemin en bordure de foret (32x45cm-13x18in) s. panel. 21-Jun-4 Tajan, Paris #41/R est:4000-6000

DROOCHSLOOT, Cornelis (attrib) (1630-1673) Dutch
£7616 $13861 €11500 Rue de village anime de marchands et de saltimbanques (46x68cm-18x27in) indis.mono. panel. 21-Jun-4 Tajan, Paris #66/R est:6000-8000

DROOCHSLOOT, Joost Cornelisz (1586-1666) Dutch
£4452 $7568 €6500 Landscape with figures conversing near ruins (23x27cm-9x11in) mono.d.1641 panel. 4-Nov-3 Sotheby's, Amsterdam #53/R est:3000-4000
£5944 $9927 €8500 Village street with figures (69x106cm-27x42in) panel. 30-Jun-3 Bailly Pommery, Paris #42/R
£7359 $13173 €10744 Busy village (48x72cm-19x28in) mono.d.1654 panel prov. 22-Mar-4 Philippe Schuler, Zurich #4398/R est:25000-30000 (S.FR 17000)
£13986 $23357 €20000 La rue d'un village Flamand (49x70cm-19x28in) panel. 26-Jun-3 Artcurial Briest, Paris #474 est:20000-25000
£14765 $27168 €22000 View into Dutch village with Seven Works of Charity (52x74cm-20x29in) panel prov. 24-Mar-4 Dorotheum, Vienna #132/R est:20000-30000
£18000 $30600 €26280 Wooded landscape with a cavalry skirmish (77x108cm-30x43in) s.d.1641. 29-Oct-3 Christie's, London #39/R est:12000-18000
£28966 $48083 €42000 Scene in Flemish village (50x66cm-20x26in) board. 30-Sep-3 Ansorena, Madrid #56/R est:40000
£30000 $54900 €43800 Village street with maypole and figures drinking (80x100cm-31x39in) mono.d.1646 prov. 8-Jul-4 Sotheby's, London #103/R est:20000-30000
£35000 $60550 €51100 Parable of the Wise and Foolish virgins (99x155cm-39x61in) s.d.1616 prov. 11-Dec-3 Sotheby's, London #132/R est:30000-50000
£38000 $68400 €55480 Village street with peasant (33x44cm-13x17in) init. panel. 21-Apr-4 Christie's, London #29/R est:12000-18000
£39150 $67730 €57159 Scene (100x152cm-39x60in) s.d.1642 46. 12-Dec-3 Kieselbach, Budapest #182/R (H.F 15000000)

DROOCHSLOOT, Joost Cornelisz (attrib) (1586-1666) Dutch
£2238 $3737 €3200 Bettesba pool (51x73cm-20x29in) bears mono. panel. 30-Jun-3 Sotheby's, Amsterdam #36/R
£3357 $5706 €4800 La collation devant l'auberge (40x35cm-16x14in) panel. 30-Nov-3 Anaf, Lyon #112/R est:3000-3500

DROUAIS, François Hubert (1727-1775) French
£23026 $42368 €35000 Portrait de Herault de Sechelles (70x59cm-28x23in) oval prov. 25-Jun-4 Piasa, Paris #49/R est:25000-30000

DROUAIS, Hubert (1699-1767) French
£2042 $3533 €2900 Portrait de Madame de la Roquette Buisson Durpaire (76x67cm-30x26in) s.d.1731 oval. 10-Dec-3 Maigret, Paris #19/R est:2800-3200

DROUANT, Armand (1898-) French
£352 $609 €500 Le port (60x73cm-24x29in) s.d.1955. 13-Dec-3 Touati, Paris #95/R

DROUET-CORDIER, Suzanne (1885-1973) French
£621 $1136 €900 Fin de journee, bedouins assis au bord de l'eau (22x27cm-9x11in) s. panel. 31-Jan-4 Gerard, Besancon #37

DROUILLET, Gerard (20th C) French
£1933 $3557 €2900 Composition africaine (200x180cm-79x71in) mono.d.90. 10-Jun-4 Camard, Paris #206/R est:2700-3000

DROUOT, E (1859-1945) French
Sculpture
£3129 $5695 €4600 Lopers. brown pat bronze. 9-Feb-4 Amberes, Antwerp #607

DROUOT, Edouard (1859-1945) French
Sculpture
£934 $1708 €1400 Decrotteur arabe (34cm-13in) i. pat bronze lit. 3-Jun-4 Tajan, Paris #221/R est:1500-1800
£1060 $1939 €1600 Quarry worker (42cm-17in) s. greenish brown pat. bronze. 6-Apr-4 Sotheby's, Amsterdam #327/R est:1000-1500
£1189 $1985 €1700 Cheval de trait au travail (36x53cm-14x21in) s. brown pat bronze green marble base. 11-Oct-3 De Vuyst, Lokeren #130/R est:1700-1900
£1284 $2259 €1900 Sur les cimes (78x62cm-31x24in) s.i. brown pat.bronze. 24-May-4 Bernaerts, Antwerp #437/R est:2000-3000
£1400 $2268 €2030 Hercules wrestling with the Nemean Lion (43cm-17in) s. bronze. 26-Jan-3 Desmond Judd, Cranbrook #613
£1477 $2613 €2200 Pousse-pousse (34cm-13in) s. pat bronze exhib. 28-Apr-4 Beaussant & Lefèvre, Paris #216 est:400
£1565 $2488 €2300 Vers la source (96cm-38in) s. brown pat bronze. 23-Mar-3 Mercier & Cie, Lille #77/R est:2000-2500
£1626 $2911 €2374 Cloches Noel (75cm-30in) s. pat.bronze lit. 26-May-4 AB Stockholms Auktionsverk #2476/R est:8000-10000 (S.KR 22000)
£1667 $2983 €2434 Night (89cm-35in) s. pat bronze. 22-Mar-4 Waddingtons, Toronto #752/R est:4000-6000 (C.D 4000)
£1803 $3227 €2650 Gladiateur sur son char (40x70cm-16x28in) s. gold pat. bronze. 21-Mar-4 Muizon & Le Coent, Paris #69/R
£2000 $3680 €3000 Amour (66cm-26in) s. pat bronze golden base. 9-Jun-4 Beaussant & Lefèvre, Paris #227/R est:1000-1200
£2069 $3455 €3000 Reverie Orientale (86cm-34in) s. gilt pat bronze. 17-Nov-3 Tajan, Paris #80/R est:1200-1500
£2600 $4732 €3900 Man wrestling with a lion (69cm-27in) s. brown pat. bronze. 20-Jun-4 Wilkinson, Doncaster #55 est:3000-4000
£2817 $4676 €4000 La fortune - female figure of fortune (91cm-36in) bronze marble base. 11-Jun-3 Sotheby's, Amsterdam #367/R est:3000-4000
£3194 $5431 €4600 Jeune femme Orientale tenant un sabre (80cm-31in) medaille pat bronze. 28-Oct-3 Rabourdin & Choppin de Janvry, Paris #74/R est:5800-6000
£8123 $15190 €11860 Le Jour. La Nuit (93cm-37in) pat.bronze square sandstone base pair prov. 24-Feb-4 Rasmussen, Copenhagen #48/R est:50000-75000 (D.KR 90000)

DROWN, William Staples (?-1915) American
£255 $475 €372 The village street (25x35cm-10x14in) s. canvasboard. 5-Mar-4 Skinner, Boston #285/R
£299 $475 €437 Ireland (28x38cm-11x15in) s. i.verso. 12-Sep-3 Skinner, Boston #397/R
£503 $800 €734 Warwickshire cottage (25x36cm-10x14in) s.i.d.98 i.verso. 12-Sep-3 Skinner, Boston #250/R

DROZDOVA, Elena (1960-) Russian?
£336 $628 €500 Russian winter (25x55cm-10x22in) s. 24-Feb-4 Durán, Madrid #722/R
£403 $753 €600 Fair in the village (30x60cm-12x24in) s. 24-Feb-4 Durán, Madrid #723/R

DRTIKOL, Frantisek (1883-1961) Czechoslovakian
£285 $472 €416 Landscape with two trees (27x26cm-11x10in) s.d.1941 board. 4-Oct-3 Dorotheum, Prague #77/R est:10000-15000 (C.KR 13000)
£417 $709 €609 Landscape (28x33cm-11x13in) s.d.1946 plywood. 29-Nov-3 Dorotheum, Prague #79/R est:10000-15000 (C.KR 19000)
£1317 $2239 €1923 Apparition (21x14cm-8x6in) s.d.1942 plywood. 29-Nov-3 Dorotheum, Prague #80/R est:15000-23000 (C.KR 60000)
Photographs
£2174 $3565 €3000 Untitled (24x30cm-9x12in) vintage photograph. 30-May-3 Farsetti, Prato #412/R
£4237 $7500 €6186 Untitled - seated nude with drapery (22x30cm-9x12in) gelatin silver print prov. 27-Apr-4 Christie's, Rockefeller NY #63/R est:6000-8000
£6587 $11000 €9617 Upward thrust (29x23cm-11x9in) st.sig. photo. 17-Oct-3 Sotheby's, New York #231/R est:7000-10000
£10169 $18000 €14847 Untitled - nude seated on cube (28x23cm-11x9in) pigment print. 27-Apr-4 Christie's, Rockefeller NY #64/R est:22000-28000
£10667 $19627 €16000 Study - cactus (22x29cm-9x11in) s.d. i. verso vintage pigment print. 10-Jun-4 Villa Grisebach, Berlin #1063/R est:16000-18000
£11111 $20000 €16222 Untitled, sitting nude (28x23cm-11x9in) st. platinum print. 24-Apr-4 Collins, Maine #5/R est:5000-7000
£11594 $19014 €16000 The release (24x22cm-9x9in) vintage bromide silver gelatin. 30-May-3 Villa Grisebach, Berlin #1146/R est:14000-16000
£13174 $22000 €19234 Untitled, nude (29x22cm-11x9in) pigment print lit. 20-Oct-3 Christie's, Rockefeller NY #35/R est:25000-35000
£13873 $24000 €20255 Tranquil descent (22x29cm-9x11in) pigment print. 9-Dec-3 Swann Galleries, New York #458/R est:25000-35000
£24444 $44000 €35688 Untitled (22x29cm-9x11in) pigment print executed c.1927-29 prov.lit. 23-Apr-4 Phillips, New York #17/R est:40000-60000
£25150 $42000 €36719 Etude (28x22cm-11x9in) with sig.i.d.1926 verso num XXXIV pigment print. 21-Oct-3 Swann Galleries, New York #110/R est:40000-60000

DRUCK, Hermann (1856-1931) German
£333 $600 €500 Riverside town (38x60cm-15x24in) s. 26-Apr-4 Rieber, Stuttgart #1306/R
£524 $892 €750 Landscape in Necktartailfingen (63x89cm-25x35in) s. 29-Nov-3 Sigalas, Stuttgart #271/R
£596 $1085 €900 June landscape (70x199cm-28x78in) s. 18-Jun-4 Bolland & Marotz, Bremen #609/R
£667 $1200 €1000 Neckar valley near Nurtingen (50x80cm-20x31in) s. 26-Apr-4 Rieber, Stuttgart #813/R
£669 $1070 €950 Leonberg, evening (50x80cm-20x31in) s. 18-Sep-3 Rieber, Stuttgart #799/R

DRUCKENMILLER, John (20th C) American
Works on paper
£289 $500 €422 Batting practice, forbes field, Pittsburgh (36x30cm-14x12in) s. W/C. 10-Dec-3 Alderfer's, Hatfield #493/R

DRUMAUX, Angelina (1881-1959) Luxembourger
£430 $783 €650 Nature morte aux clementines (16x24cm-6x9in) s. 16-Jun-4 Hotel des Ventes Mosan, Brussels #216
£439 $830 €650 Vue de Venise (32x41cm-13x16in) s. panel. 17-Feb-4 Vanderkindere, Brussels #544
£966 $1786 €1400 Vue de Menton (50x65cm-20x26in) s. 19-Jan-4 Horta, Bruxelles #302
£1312 $2191 €1850 Nature morte aux fleurs (66x50cm-26x20in) s. 15-Oct-3 Hotel des Ventes Mosan, Brussels #234 est:1500-1800
£2817 $4873 €4000 Bouquet de pivoines (100x80cm-39x31in) s. 10-Dec-3 Hotel des Ventes Mosan, Brussels #201/R est:4000-5000

DRUMMOND, Arthur (1871-1951) British
£2400 $3768 €3480 Startled pheasants (81x74cm-32x29in) s.d.95. 27-Aug-3 Sotheby's, London #1006/R est:3000-5000

DRUMMOND, J (19th C) British
£1700 $2703 €2482 Fisher girls and boys playing among rock pools (19x15cm-7x6in) s.d.80 pair. 18-Mar-3 Anderson & Garland, Newcastle #437/R est:450-650

DRUMMOND, J Nelson (fl.1882-1896) British
Works on paper
£260 $442 €380 Fishing huts, Fiji (17x23cm-7x9in) s. pastel. 4-Nov-3 Woolley & Wallis, Salisbury #289/R
£300 $489 €438 Moonlit tree lined lake scene (122x89cm-48x35in) s. W/C. 23-Sep-3 John Nicholson, Haslemere #87
£300 $540 €438 Softening twilight of an autumn eve (49x74cm-19x29in) s. pastel. 22-Apr-4 Lawrence, Crewkerne #782

DRUMMOND, James (1816-1877) British
£3500 $6545 €5110 Departure of the bride, Scottish wedding (55x42cm-22x17in) s.d.1850. 21-Jul-4 Bonhams, New Bond Street #172/R est:4000-6000
Works on paper
£560 $1002 €818 Fisherman and fisherwoman, head and shoulders (32x25cm-13x10in) s.d.68 W/C pair oval. 17-Mar-4 Bonhams, Chester #350

£780 $1295 €1139 Storm coming (66x48cm-26x19in) s.d.1873 W/C. 1-Oct-3 Sotheby's, Olympia #99/R
£1150 $1852 €1668 Grandfather's birthday (77x56cm-30x22in) s. W/C. 21-Aug-3 Bonhams, Edinburgh #1127/R est:800-1200
£1500 $2685 €2190 Gathering cockles (50x69cm-20x27in) s.d.60 W/C. 17-Mar-4 Bonhams, Chester #348/R est:1500-2000

DRUMMOND, Julian E (19/20th C) British
Works on paper
£450 $828 €657 Having a good natter (33x44cm-13x17in) s.d.1909 W/C. 23-Mar-4 Bonhams, Knightsbridge #68/R

DRUMMOND, Samuel (1765-1844) British
£18000 $30600 €26280 Battle of the Nile (44x71cm-17x28in) prov. 19-Nov-3 Christie's, Kensington #454/R

DRUMMOND-FISH, Captain George (fl.1906-1938) British
Works on paper
£800 $1448 €1200 Upper Lough Corrib (26x37cm-10x15in) s.i. W/C. 31-Mar-4 James Adam, Dublin #26/R

DRYER, Moira (1957-1992) American
£5521 $9000 €8061 Card (117x122cm-46x48in) s.i.d.1989 verso acrylic wood prov.exhib. 23-Sep-3 Christie's, Rockefeller NY #66/R est:8000-12000

DRYSDALE, A J (1870-1934) American
Works on paper
£726 $1300 €1060 River landscape. s. W/C pastel. 13-May-4 Dallas Auction Gallery, Dallas #118/R est:2000-4000

DRYSDALE, Alexander John (1870-1934) American
£581 $1000 €848 Louisiana Bayou (51x76cm-20x30in) s. oil wash board. 6-Dec-3 Neal Auction Company, New Orleans #572/R
£649 $1200 €948 Bayou landscape (30x81cm-12x32in) s. oil wash on board. 17-Jan-4 New Orleans Auction, New Orleans #742/R est:1500-2500
£765 $1300 €1117 Louisiana cypress and swamp (74x23cm-29x9in) s. oil wash on board. 22-Nov-3 New Orleans Auction, New Orleans #1068/R est:1000-1500
£864 $1400 €1261 Louisiana bayou (36x48cm-14x19in) s. oil wash board. 2-Aug-3 Neal Auction Company, New Orleans #412/R est:2000-3000
£984 $1800 €1437 Louisiana bayou scene (13x48cm-5x19in) s. oil wash board. 5-Jun-4 Neal Auction Company, New Orleans #818/R est:1500-2500
£984 $1800 €1437 Louisiana bayou scene (13x48cm-5x19in) s. oil wash board. 5-Jun-4 Neal Auction Company, New Orleans #819/R est:1500-2500
£1050 $1900 €1533 Live Oak, city park (61x23cm-24x9in) s. oil wash board. 3-Apr-4 Neal Auction Company, New Orleans #871/R est:1000-1500
£1099 $2000 €1605 Loisana Bayou at dawn (36x81cm-14x32in) s.d.1922 oil wash board. 7-Feb-4 Neal Auction Company, New Orleans #475/R est:3000-5000
£1105 $2000 €1613 Louisiana bayou scene (15x48cm-6x19in) s. oil wash on board. 3-Apr-4 Neal Auction Company, New Orleans #420/R est:1500-2000
£1279 $2200 €1867 Louisiana bayou with water lilies (51x76cm-20x30in) s. oil wash painted c.1910. 7-Dec-3 Treadway Gallery, Cincinnati #558/R est:3000-5000
£1294 $2200 €1889 Bayou landscape with grove of oaks and cypress (48x74cm-19x29in) s. 22-Nov-3 New Orleans Auction, New Orleans #1067/R est:1800-2500
£1381 $2500 €2016 Louisiana live oaks (15x48cm-6x19in) s. board. 3-Apr-4 Neal Auction Company, New Orleans #419/R est:1500-2000
£1506 $2500 €2199 Louisiana Bayou scene (13x74cm-5x29in) s. oil wash board prov. 4-Oct-3 Neal Auction Company, New Orleans #1085/R est:800-1200
£1530 $2800 €2234 Louisiana Bayou scene (36x48cm-14x19in) s. oil wash board. 5-Jun-4 Neal Auction Company, New Orleans #392/R est:2500-3500
£1566 $2600 €2286 Oaks on Louisiana Bayou (48x15cm-19x6in) s. oil wash board prov. 4-Oct-3 Neal Auction Company, New Orleans #1086 est:800-1200
£1705 $3000 €2489 Louisiana bayou (48x66cm-19x26in) s. oil wash painted c.1910. 23-May-4 Treadway Gallery, Cincinnati #612/R est:3000-4000
£1765 $3000 €2577 Bayou landscape with oak (38x51cm-15x20in) s. oil wash on board. 22-Nov-3 New Orleans Auction, New Orleans #1066/R est:1500-2500
£1955 $3500 €2933 Bayou landscapes (46x61cm-18x24in) s.d.1912 pair. 16-May-4 Abell, Los Angeles #419/R
£2160 $3500 €3154 Louisiana bayou (48x71cm-19x28in) s.d.1921 oil wash board. 2-Aug-3 Neal Auction Company, New Orleans #415/R est:2500-3500
£2285 $4250 €3336 Swamplands (46x61cm-18x24in) s.d.1914 board. 5-Mar-4 Skinner, Boston #442/R est:3000-5000
£2596 $4750 €3790 Louisiana bayou (38x99cm-15x39in) s. oil wash board. 5-Jun-4 Neal Auction Company, New Orleans #393/R est:3000-5000
£2651 $4400 €3870 Louisiana Bayou in Autumn colours (38x102cm-15x40in) s. oil wash board. 4-Oct-3 Neal Auction Company, New Orleans #585/R est:2500-3500
£2793 $5000 €4078 Bayou landscape (61x79cm-24x31in) s.d.1918 board. 21-Mar-4 Jeffery Burchard, Florida #52/R
Works on paper
£254 $425 €371 Landscape with bayou and waterlilies (51x76cm-20x30in) s. W/C gouache. 27-Oct-3 O'Gallerie, Oregon #745/R
£976 $1600 €1415 Louisiana bayou (20x28cm-8x11in) s.d. W/C. 7-Jun-3 Treadway Gallery, Cincinnati #1378 est:800-1200
£1341 $2200 €1944 Louisiana bayou (20x28cm-8x11in) s. ink W/C exec.c.1910. 7-Jun-3 Treadway Gallery, Cincinnati #1381 est:800-1200

DRYSDALE, Sir George Russell (1912-1981) Australian
£9756 $15317 €14146 Sketch for Drought series (14x19cm-6x7in) s. s.i. verso board painted c.1948 prov. 26-Aug-3 Christie's, Sydney #4/R est:15000-20000 (A.D 24000)
£21277 $36170 €31064 Untitled (76x127cm-30x50in) studio stamp sold with easel prov. 25-Nov-3 Christie's, Melbourne #43/R est:60000-80000 (A.D 50000)
£40984 $64754 €59837 Men mixing concrete (50x60cm-20x24in) s.d.1937 board prov.exhib. 2-Sep-3 Deutscher-Menzies, Melbourne #45/R est:90000-120000 (A.D 100000)
£67073 $105305 €97256 Desert nomad (60x50cm-24x20in) s. painted c.1970 prov. 26-Aug-3 Christie's, Sydney #115/R est:140000-180000 (A.D 165000)
£91603 $166718 €133740 Mother and child (126x76cm-50x30in) s. s.i.verso prov.exhib. 16-Jun-4 Deutscher-Menzies, Melbourne #26/R est:140000-180000 (A.D 240000)
£148936 $253192 €217447 Yard Builder (61x46cm-24x18in) s. s.i.verso painted c.1965 prov. 26-Nov-3 Deutscher-Menzies, Melbourne #23/R est:300000-400000 (A.D 350000)
£227273 $386364 €331819 Red landscape 1958 (76x102cm-30x40in) s. exhib.lit. 29-Oct-3 Lawson Menzies, Sydney #31/R (A.D 550000)
£307377 $485656 €448770 Country child (76x61cm-30x24in) s. prov.exhib. 2-Sep-3 Deutscher-Menzies, Melbourne #33/R est:700000-900000 (A.D 750000)
Works on paper
£579 $1070 €845 Clown. Clown and swan (14x11cm-6x4in) init. pen ink double-sided. 10-Mar-4 Deutscher-Menzies, Melbourne #538/R est:1000-1500 (A.D 1400)
£826 $1463 €1206 Aboriginal stockman (15x20cm-6x8in) init. ink prov. 3-May-4 Christie's, Melbourne #211 est:1800-2200 (A.D 2000)
£909 $1545 €1327 Farmer remembered (14x21cm-6x8in) s.i. pen ink prov. 29-Oct-3 Lawson Menzies, Sydney #181/R est:2500-3500 (A.D 2200)
£909 $1609 €1327 Tropical night (13x18cm-5x7in) studio st.i. ink prov. 3-May-4 Christie's, Melbourne #333/R est:3000-4000 (A.D 2200)
£931 $1499 €1359 Reclining nude (24x30cm-9x12in) ink prov. 25-Aug-3 Sotheby's, Paddington #244 (A.D 2300)
£1215 $1955 €1774 Country child (20x17cm-8x7in) s. bears i.verso ink wash prov. 25-Aug-3 Sotheby's, Paddington #291/R est:4000-6000 (A.D 3000)
£1446 $2560 €2111 Three figures (20x17cm-8x7in) s. ink prov. 3-May-4 Christie's, Melbourne #360 est:2000-3500 (A.D 3500)
£1570 $2905 €2292 Children blowing bubbles (12x19cm-5x7in) s.i. pen ink wash prov. 10-Mar-4 Deutscher-Menzies, Melbourne #215/R est:3500-4500 (A.D 3800)
£1610 $2737 €2351 Men at the bar (25x33cm-10x13in) s. ink. 24-Nov-3 Sotheby's, Melbourne #181/R est:3000-5000 (A.D 3800)
£1619 $2607 €2364 Watching telly (35x27cm-14x11in) s.i. ink wash. 25-Aug-3 Sotheby's, Paddington #261/R est:2500-4500 (A.D 4000)
£1653 $2810 €2413 Studies of soldiers (25x20cm-10x8in) s. pen ink. 29-Oct-3 Lawson Menzies, Sydney #172/R est:4000-6000 (A.D 4000)
£1653 $3058 €2413 Maisie in chair (22x17cm-9x7in) s. pen ink executed c.1960 prov. 10-Mar-4 Deutscher-Menzies, Melbourne #219/R est:4500-6000 (A.D 4000)
£1679 $3056 €2451 Stockman (24x18cm-9x7in) pen ink. 16-Jun-4 Deutscher-Menzies, Melbourne #375/R est:3000-5000 (A.D 4400)
£1702 $2894 €2485 Seated girl (31x24cm-12x9in) studio stamp pencil exec.c.1939 lit. 25-Nov-3 Christie's, Melbourne #167/R est:4000-6000 (A.D 4000)
£1707 $2680 €2475 Whiskey drinker (13x12cm-5x5in) s.i.d.70 ink W/C. 26-Aug-3 Christie's, Sydney #271/R est:2000-3000 (A.D 4200)
£1707 $2680 €2475 Nude study (40x26cm-16x10in) s.d.57 ink wash. 26-Aug-3 Christie's, Sydney #368/R est:3000-5000 (A.D 4200)
£1787 $3038 €2609 Mother and child (19x14cm-7x6in) s. ink. 25-Nov-3 Christie's, Melbourne #181/R est:3000-5000 (A.D 4200)
£1787 $3038 €2609 Study for Portrait of young boy (27x20cm-11x8in) s.i.d.66 pencil. 25-Nov-3 Christie's, Melbourne #183/R est:4000-6000 (A.D 4200)
£1860 $3440 €2716 Cottage interior (22x25cm-9x10in) s. pen ink exhib. 10-Mar-4 Deutscher-Menzies, Melbourne #216/R est:5000-7000 (A.D 4500)
£1901 $3517 €2775 Seated man (21x16cm-8x6in) s.i.d.1976 pen ink prov. 10-Mar-4 Deutscher-Menzies, Melbourne #217/R est:4500-6000 (A.D 4600)
£1949 $3314 €2846 Companions (24x15cm-9x6in) s. ink. 24-Nov-3 Sotheby's, Melbourne #86/R est:3000-5000 (A.D 4600)
£1949 $3314 €2846 Mother and Child (47x30cm-19x12in) s.d.5.VI.57 ink wash prov. 24-Nov-3 Sotheby's, Melbourne #111/R est:5000-8000 (A.D 4600)
£2043 $3472 €2983 Near Cullabonna (13x20cm-5x8in) s.i.d.67 ink W/C. 25-Nov-3 Christie's, Melbourne #127/R est:3500-5500 (A.D 4800)
£2127 $3617 €3105 Stockman (36x20cm-14x8in) s. pen ink. 26-Nov-3 Deutscher-Menzies, Melbourne #232/R est:3000-4000 (A.D 5000)
£2227 $3585 €3251 Crying Babe (11x16cm-4x6in) s. ink W/C prov. 25-Aug-3 Sotheby's, Paddington #258/R est:4000-6000 (A.D 5500)
£2449 $4506 €3576 Outback (17x22cm-7x9in) s. W/C. 29-Mar-4 Goodman, Sydney #151/R est:1500-2500 (A.D 6000)
£2593 $4331 €3890 The drinker (23x20cm-9x8in) s. ink wash. 27-Oct-3 Goodman, Sydney #25/R est:6000-8000 (A.D 6250)
£2642 $4148 €3831 Aboriginal man (36x24cm-14x9in) s. s.i.verso ink wash prov. 26-Aug-3 Christie's, Sydney #346/R est:4000-5000 (A.D 6500)
£2686 $4969 €3922 Study for the cricketers (15x20cm-6x8in) s.i. pencil prov. 10-Mar-4 Deutscher-Menzies, Melbourne #220/R est:3000-4000 (A.D 6500)
£2686 $4754 €3922 Stockman (20x12cm-8x5in) s. W/C ink prov. 3-May-4 Christie's, Melbourne #306/R est:5000-6000 (A.D 6500)
£2766 $4702 €4038 Two children (22x14cm-9x6in) s.i.d.Xmas 1977 ink wash. 25-Nov-3 Christie's, Melbourne #145/R est:4000-6000 (A.D 6500)
£2979 $5064 €4349 The sisters (28x21cm-11x8in) s.i.d.Xmas 1978 ink wash. 25-Nov-3 Christie's, Melbourne #144/R est:4000-6000 (A.D 7000)
£3049 $4786 €4421 On the verandah (21x19cm-8x7in) s. ink W/C prov. 26-Aug-3 Christie's, Sydney #379b/R est:5000-7000 (A.D 7500)
£3191 $5426 €4659 Girl in pink dress (23x14cm-9x6in) s. pencil col wash. 25-Nov-3 Christie's, Melbourne #143/R est:4000-6000 (A.D 7500)
£3455 $5425 €5010 Soldiers (30x20cm-12x8in) studio st. W/C ink exec.c.1942 prov. 27-Aug-3 Christie's, Sydney #579/R est:6000-8000 (A.D 8500)
£4065 $6382 €5894 Figure studies (39x29cm-15x11in) s. ink prov. 26-Aug-3 Christie's, Sydney #358a/R est:10000-12000 (A.D 10000)
£4472 $7020 €6484 Old couple (26x20cm-10x8in) s. ink W/C prov. 26-Aug-3 Christie's, Sydney #379a/R est:5000-7000 (A.D 11000)
£4898 $9012 €7151 Outback landscape (25x35cm-10x14in) W/C ink prov. 29-Mar-4 Goodman, Sydney #14/R est:12000-15000 (A.D 12000)
£8943 $14041 €12967 Children on the beach (30x29cm-12x11in) s. W/C prov. 26-Aug-3 Christie's, Sydney #379c/R est:8000-10000 (A.D 22000)
£13740 $25008 €20060 Grandma's Sunday walk (32x49cm-13x19in) s. W/C pen ink executed c.1971 prov.exhib. 16-Jun-4 Deutscher-Menzies, Melbourne #75/R est:25000-35000 (A.D 36000)

DUARTE, Angel (1930-) Spanish
£352 $609 €500 C.29 Equipo 57 (49x49cm-19x19in) s.i.d.1972 verso masonite prov. 13-Dec-3 Lempertz, Koln #305/R
£791 $1298 €1100 C32 - Equipo 57 (49x49cm-19x19in) s.i. stretcher masonite. 4-Jun-3 Ketterer, Hamburg #318/R

DUARTE, Jose (1928-) Spanish
£671 $1255 €1000 View of the sea (81x60cm-32x24in) s. s.i.d.82 verso. 24-Feb-4 Durán, Madrid #63/R
£2695 $4366 €3800 Indiana (74x101cm-29x40in) s.d.1971. 20-May-3 Ansorena, Madrid #312/R est:3600
£2796 $5145 €4250 Women in the fields (72x101cm-28x40in) s.d.74 s.i.d.verso. 22-Jun-4 Durán, Madrid #141/R est:4000

DUASSUT, Curtius (fl.1889-1903) British
Works on paper
£1733 $3137 €2600 Extensive moor landscape with grazing sheep (40x67cm-16x26in) s.d.1900 W/C gouache. 1-Apr-4 Van Ham, Cologne #1350/R est:2000

DUBACH, Margaretha (1938-) Swiss
£261 $477 €381 Composition (60x120cm-24x47in) s.i.d.1967 oil mixed media. 4-Jun-4 Zofingen, Switzerland #2781 (S.FR 600)

DUBASTY, Adolphe Henri (1814-1884) French
£1700 $2703 €2465 Femme a sa toilette (33x24cm-13x9in) s.d.1831 panel. 9-Sep-3 Bonhams, Knightsbridge #170/R est:1500-2000

DUBASTY, Joseph (19th C) French
Miniatures
£1000 $1840 €1460 Officer in uniform of chasseurs-a-cheval style (4cm-2in) s. set in to tortoiseshell snuff box. 24-Jun-4 Bonhams, New Bond Street #75/R est:1000-1500

DUBAUT, Pierre (1886-1968) French
Works on paper
£315 $541 €450 Trot attele (24x32cm-9x13in) studio st. ink wash W/C. 3-Dec-3 Coutau Begarie, Paris #92/R
£336 $628 €500 Trot monte (26x36cm-10x14in) W/C. 1-Mar-4 Coutau Begarie, Paris #92/R
£354 $577 €510 Amazone (19x28cm-7x11in) W/C. 29-Sep-3 Coutau Begarie, Paris #122/R
£369 $690 €550 Sulkys au champ de course (40x30cm-16x12in) ink wash htd gouache. 1-Mar-4 Coutau Begarie, Paris #90/R
£382 $600 €550 Chevaux de halage (22x16cm-9x6in) s. W/C. 29-Aug-3 Deauville, France #123/R
£406 $698 €580 Les joueurs de polo (23x21cm-9x8in) studio st. ink wash. 3-Dec-3 Coutau Begarie, Paris #90/R
£411 $699 €600 Le cheval pret a l'embarquement avec son lad anglais (19x23cm-7x9in) s. W/C. 7-Nov-3 Coutau Begarie, Paris #103
£470 $879 €700 Sulkys en course (31x47cm-12x19in) W/C. 1-Mar-4 Coutau Begarie, Paris #93
£500 $895 €750 Scene d'attelage, le virage (23x33cm-9x13in) W/C ink. 12-May-4 Coutau Begarie, Paris #166/R
£503 $866 €720 Le rendez-vous (30x23cm-12x9in) studio st. W/C. 3-Dec-3 Coutau Begarie, Paris #91
£524 $902 €750 Trotteurs (31x47cm-12x19in) studio st. pen wash. 3-Dec-3 Coutau Begarie, Paris #89
£559 $962 €800 Les joueurs de polo (21x36cm-8x14in) studio st. ink wash. 3-Dec-3 Coutau Begarie, Paris #95/R
£629 $1083 €900 Le pansage (23x29cm-9x11in) s. ink wash. 3-Dec-3 Coutau Begarie, Paris #94/R
£639 $1041 €920 A l'ecurie (20x27cm-8x11in) W/C. 29-Sep-3 Coutau Begarie, Paris #123/R
£658 $1230 €980 L'entrainement aux sulkys (23x29cm-9x11in) W/C ink. 1-Mar-4 Coutau Begarie, Paris #91/R
£734 $1263 €1050 Scene de polo, la charge (34x34cm-13x13in) W/C. 3-Dec-3 Coutau Begarie, Paris #93
£753 $1281 €1100 Avant la partie de polo (38x52cm-15x20in) st.sig. W/C. 7-Nov-3 Coutau Begarie, Paris #106
£764 $1245 €1100 Course de galop (47x61cm-19x24in) W/C. 29-Sep-3 Coutau Begarie, Paris #124/R
£903 $1417 €1300 Grand Prix 64. s.i. W/C. 29-Aug-3 Deauville, France #128/R
£1562 $2453 €2250 Avant la partie de polo (25x36cm-10x14in) s.d.1923 W/C. 29-Aug-3 Deauville, France #122/R est:2400-2600

DUBAUT, Pierre (attrib) (1886-1968) French
£1111 $1833 €1600 Jockeys on horses before race (63x80cm-25x31in) bears sig. 3-Jul-3 Dr Fritz Nagel, Stuttgart #484/R est:1800

DUBBELS, Hendrik (1620-1676) Dutch
£6897 $11448 €10000 Ships anchoring in calm sea (33x44cm-13x17in) lit. 1-Oct-3 Dorotheum, Vienna #94/R est:12000-16000

DUBBELS, Hendrik (circle) (1620-1676) Dutch
£10274 $17466 €15000 Man-of-war in calm waters, with other boats moored at a quay (48x93cm-19x37in) bears sig. Aelbert Cuyp panel prov.lit. 4-Nov-3 Sotheby's, Amsterdam #61/R est:15000-20000

DUBE, Louis Theodore (20th C) French
£408 $750 €596 Portrait of gentleman (61x51cm-24x20in) s.i. sold with portrait of his wife by Mattie Dube. 27-Jun-4 Bonhams & Butterfields, San Francisco #3828/R
£580 $969 €841 Immaculate conception (147x96cm-58x38in) s.d.1890 after Murillo. 17-Jun-3 Pinneys, Montreal #140 est:1500-2000 (C.D 1300)

DUBIEL, Evelyn S (c.1922-) American
£511 $900 €746 The Sabbath (51x41cm-20x16in) 1-Jan-4 Fallon, Copake #236/R
Works on paper
£216 $400 €324 Morning visit (13x23cm-5x9in) W/C exec. c.2004. 17-Jul-4 Fallon, Copake #151a/R
£241 $400 €349 Folk art floral. W/C. 14-Jun-3 Fallon, Copake #215/R
£256 $450 €374 Quiet life (46x36cm-18x14in) 1-Jan-4 Fallon, Copake #244/R
£313 $550 €457 Fishing the Penna countryside (23x18cm-9x7in) W/C. 1-Jan-4 Fallon, Copake #241/R
£398 $700 €581 Friends (23x20cm-9x8in) W/C. 1-Jan-4 Fallon, Copake #242/R
£398 $700 €581 Haying at a Pomfret CT farm (33x23cm-13x9in) W/C. 1-Jan-4 Fallon, Copake #240/R
£459 $850 €689 Gone fishing (20x28cm-8x11in) W/C exec. c.2004. 17-Jul-4 Fallon, Copake #148a/R
£540 $950 €788 Skating on a long pond (33x23cm-13x9in) W/C. 1-Jan-4 Fallon, Copake #237/R
£543 $1000 €793 Day at the sea (23x33cm-9x13in) W/C. 27-Mar-4 Fallon, Copake #180
£595 $1100 €869 Summertime in New England (23x33cm-9x13in) W/C exec. c.2003. 17-Jul-4 Fallon, Copake #146a/R
£670 $1200 €978 Elizabeth Park (23x33cm-9x13in) W/C. 15-May-4 Fallon, Copake #84/R

DUBIEZ, Claudius (19/20th C) French
Works on paper
£3867 $7076 €5800 Nature morte a la carafe et au verre de vin (64x50cm-25x20in) s.d.1857 pastel oval. 6-Jun-4 Anaf, Lyon #93/R est:5000-6000

DUBIN, Ralph (1927-1988) American
£245 $450 €368 Weekend at Newport (61x89cm-24x35in) s. i.verso. 11-Jun-4 David Rago, Lambertville #120/R

DUBINI (19th C) ?
Sculpture
£6738 $11252 €9500 Jeune homme et une jeune fille Arabes (57cm-22in) s. marble pat bronze piedouche exec.c.1880 pair. 17-Jun-3 Christie's, Paris #142/R est:5000-8000

DUBLIN, Jacques (1901-1978) Swiss
£304 $557 €444 Young girl with flowers (33x21cm-13x8in) s.d.1934. 4-Jun-4 Zofingen, Switzerland #2784 (S.FR 700)

DUBOC, Ferdinand (19th C) French
£704 $1218 €1000 Campement au bord de la mer, Algerie (65x98cm-26x39in) s. 15-Dec-3 Gros & Delettrez, Paris #133/R

DUBOIS, Albert (c.1831-?) American/German
£629 $1145 €950 Still life of flowers (40x54cm-16x21in) s. chipboard. 19-Jun-4 Bergmann, Erlangen #835

DUBOIS, Ambroise (studio) (1543-1614) French
£22535 $39437 €32000 Scene de l'histoire de Theagene et Chariclee (152x230cm-60x91in) prov. 17-Dec-3 Piasa, Paris #68/R est:30000-40000
£22535 $39437 €32000 Scene de l'histoire de Theagene et Chariclee (152x230cm-60x91in) prov. 17-Dec-3 Piasa, Paris #69/R est:30000-40000

DUBOIS, Antoine Benoit (attrib) (1619-1680) French
Works on paper
£1638 $2932 €2391 River landscape with boat and figures (19x29cm-7x11in) gouache two. 17-May-4 Beurret, Zurich #1/R est:3000-4000 (S.FR 3800)

DUBOIS, Charles-Edouard (1847-1885) French
£271 $462 €396 Alpine landscape with gathering storm (35x45cm-14x18in) s. 19-Nov-3 Fischer, Luzern #2074/R (S.FR 600)
£2162 $4000 €3243 Evening at East Hampton (61x74cm-24x29in) s. 14-Jul-4 American Auctioneer #490330/R est:400-600

DUBOIS, Ernest (1863-1931) French
Sculpture
£1267 $2267 €1900 Mansart debout un plan a la main (76cm-30in) i. pat. terracotta. 16-May-4 Lombrail & Teucquam, Paris #134
£1361 $2163 €2000 Mr Lebreton (79cm-31in) s.d.1904 white marble. 23-Mar-3 Salle des ventes Pillet, Lyon la Foret #241
£1667 $3000 €2434 Unititled - Return of the Prodigal Son (53x38x28cm-21x15x11in) s. bronze. 26-Jan-4 Schrager Galleries, Milwaukee #1227
£2956 $5292 €4316 Le Pardon (73cm-29in) s. pat.bronze Cast Jollet and Colin. 26-May-4 AB Stockholms Auktionsverk #2481/R est:30000-35000 (S.KR 40000)

DUBOIS, Ernest (after) (1863-1931) French
Sculpture
£5674 $9475 €8000 Le fauconnier a cheval (69cm-27in) st. copper pat bronze. 16-Jun-3 Gros & Delettrez, Paris #88/R est:6000-8000

DUBOIS, Ferdinand (19th C) French
£296 $480 €429 Castle, road and villagers (30x46cm-12x18in) s. 29-Jul-3 Galeria y Remates, Montevideo #35/R

DUBOIS, François (1790-1871) French
£13287 $22853 €19000 Napoleon sur son cheval Marengo (46x38cm-18x15in) s.d.1815. 2-Dec-3 Sotheby's, Paris #17/R est:2000-3000

DUBOIS, Gaston (19th C) French
£851 $1421 €1200 Combat de coqs (50x40cm-20x16in) s. 16-Jun-3 Gros & Delettrez, Paris #509/R
£1293 $2314 €1900 Shepherdess (79x118cm-31x46in) s. 22-Mar-4 Durán, Madrid #146/R est:1900
£3600 $6624 €5400 L'essayage (49x33cm-19x13in) s. 14-Jun-4 Gros & Delettrez, Paris #577/R est:3200-4500

DUBOIS, Henri Pierre Hippolyte (1837-1909) French
£474 $872 €720 View in North Africa (24x32cm-9x13in) 22-Jun-4 Mealy's, Castlecomer #143

DUBOIS, Jean (1923-1990) French
£268 $475 €400 Cercles rouges dans le vert (100x160cm-39x63in) s. wood. 27-Apr-4 Campo & Campo, Antwerp #88

DUBOIS, Jules (1864-1957) Belgian
£324 $600 €473 Landscape (48x69cm-19x27in) s. 14-Jan-4 Dallas Auction Gallery, Dallas #443b
£342 $582 €500 Barques echouees (35x50cm-14x20in) s. 10-Nov-3 Horta, Bruxelles #351

DUBOIS, Louis (1830-1880) Belgian
£909 $1564 €1300 Dans l'atelier du peintre (85x62cm-33x24in) s.d.1855. 2-Dec-3 Campo & Campo, Antwerp #125
£986 $1706 €1400 Personnages dans un paysage (30x62cm-12x24in) s. 9-Dec-3 Campo, Vlaamse Kaai #298

DUBOIS, Maria (?) French
Works on paper
£521 $823 €750 Desert horsemen (36x47cm-14x19in) s. pastel board lit. 19-Sep-3 Schloss Ahlden, Ahlden #1534/R

DUBOIS, Paul (1829-1905) French
Sculpture
£1034 $1728 €1500 Portrait de Marie Jules Parrot (48x28x30cm-19x11x12in) s. i.verso plaster exec.c.1870. 16-Nov-3 Muizon & Le Coent, Paris #82/R
£1059 $1832 €1546 Mandolin player (48cm-19in) s.d.1865 pat bronze st.f. Barbedienne lit. 14-Dec-3 Agra, Warsaw #22/R est:7000 (P.Z 7000)
£1351 $2378 €2000 Maternite (46cm-18in) s.st.f.Barbedienne pat bronze. 18-May-4 Galerie Moderne, Brussels #1501 est:1500-2000
£1457 $2666 €2200 Le petit porteur d'eau (41cm-16in) s. brown pat. bronze. 6-Apr-4 Sotheby's, Amsterdam #329/R est:2500-3000
£1800 $3060 €2628 Charite (35cm-14in) s.st.f.Barbedienne pat bronze. 28-Oct-3 Sotheby's, London #198/R
£1976 $3538 €2885 Courage Militaire (52cm-20in) s.num.42 parcel gilt bronze f.Barbedienne prov. 15-May-4 Christie's, Sydney #420/R est:4000-6000 (A.D 5000)
£3000 $5100 €4380 Courage militaire (68cm-27in) s.st.f.Barbedienne pat bronze. 28-Oct-3 Sotheby's, London #174/R est:3000-5000
£3448 $5724 €5000 Charite (80cm-31in) s.st.f.Barbedienne brown pat bronze. 2-Oct-3 Sotheby's, Paris #158/R est:7500-10000
£3529 $6000 €5152 Louis Pasteur (69cm-27in) st.f.Rudier i. brown pat bronze. 28-Oct-3 Christie's, Rockefeller NY #102/R est:4000-6000
£3824 $6500 €5583 Chanteur florentin (92cm-36in) s.st.f.Barbedienne brown pat bronze. 28-Oct-3 Christie's, Rockefeller NY #103/R
£3911 $7000 €5710 Male harlequin. Female harlequine (86cm-34in) s. brown pat bronze pair. 20-Mar-4 Freeman, Philadelphia #558/R est:1500-2500
£4000 $7200 €5840 Le courage militaire (68cm-27in) s.st.f.F. Barbedienne dark brown pat bronze. 21-Apr-4 Sotheby's, London #44/R est:3000-5000
£5882 $10000 €8588 Charity (79cm-31in) s. bronze wooden plinth Cast Barbedienne. 28-Oct-3 Christie's, Rockefeller NY #101/R est:10000-15000
£6383 $10660 €9000 Le chanteur Florentin (115cm-45in) s.d.1865 brown pat bronze Cast Barbedienne. 19-Jun-3 Millon & Associes, Paris #84/R est:7000-8000

DUBOIS, Paul-Elie (1886-1949) French
£373 $623 €545 Landscape near Figuig (24x30cm-9x12in) s.i. board prov. 15-Nov-3 Galerie Gloggner, Luzern #36/R (S.FR 850)
£570 $952 €832 North African landscape (27x35cm-11x14in) s. canvas on board prov. 15-Nov-3 Galerie Gloggner, Luzern #32/R (S.FR 1300)
£570 $952 €832 North African landscape with red hill (27x35cm-11x14in) s. canvas on board prov. 15-Nov-3 Galerie Gloggner, Luzern #35/R (S.FR 1300)
£614 $1025 €896 North African landscape with camel (26x35cm-10x14in) s. canvas on board prov. 15-Nov-3 Galerie Gloggner, Luzern #34 (S.FR 1400)
£729 $1152 €1050 Femme berbere. panel. 25-Apr-3 Etude de Provence, Marseille #254
£1200 $2196 €1800 Dans l'Oasis a Bou-Saada (46x55cm-18x22in) s. i.verso. 3-Jun-4 Tajan, Paris #231/R est:2000-2500
£1228 $2051 €1793 L'Oasis de Bou-Saada (46x55cm-18x22in) s. i. stretcher prov. 15-Nov-3 Galerie Gloggner, Luzern #31/R est:1200-1500 (S.FR 2800)
£1316 $2197 €1921 Oasis de Figuig (61x50cm-24x20in) s.i.d.24 i. verso prov. 15-Nov-3 Galerie Gloggner, Luzern #29/R est:1400-1600 (S.FR 3000)
£1389 $2194 €2000 Paysage. d.1928. 25-Apr-3 Etude de Provence, Marseille #262 est:2200-2500
£2412 $4029 €3522 Le Golfe de Carthage - Sidi Bou Said (50x61cm-20x24in) s.i.d.25 i. verso prov. 15-Nov-3 Galerie Gloggner, Luzern #30/R est:1400-1600 (S.FR 5500)
£3289 $6084 €4900 Sidi-Bou-Said, Tunisie (46x61cm-18x24in) s.i. 15-Mar-4 Gros & Delettrez, Paris #209/R est:5000-6000
Works on paper
£556 $878 €800 La traite des chevres. d.1928 W/C. 25-Apr-3 Etude de Provence, Marseille #258
£604 $1117 €900 Le Touareg (20x13cm-8x5in) s.i. chl. 15-Mar-4 Gros & Delettrez, Paris #40/R
£769 $1323 €1100 Jeune Orientale (45x38cm-18x15in) s. chl htd white gouache. 5-Dec-3 Chochon-Barre & Allardi, Paris #82/R
£937 $1481 €1350 Touaregs dans le desert. W/C. 25-Apr-3 Etude de Provence, Marseille #235
£1200 $2208 €1800 Noble touareg du Hoggar (53x32cm-21x13in) s.i.d.1928 W/C. 11-Jun-4 Claude Aguttes, Neuilly #122/R est:1500-2000
£1631 $2724 €2300 La traite des chevres (65x49cm-26x19in) s.i. W/C. 16-Jun-3 Gros & Delettrez, Paris #78/R est:1500-2000
£1986 $3316 €2800 Les trois Targui (49x66cm-19x26in) s.i.d.1928 i.verso W/C gouache. 16-Jun-3 Gros & Delettrez, Paris #81/R est:1200-1800
£2013 $3725 €3000 La mere de l'Amenokal, Hoggar (62x47cm-24x19in) s. pastel chl. 15-Mar-4 Gros & Delettrez, Paris #90/R est:3000-3500

DUBOIS, Raphael (1888-?) Belgian
£255 $475 €372 Un coin de Montmartre (40x49cm-16x19in) s. board. 5-Mar-4 Skinner, Boston #514/R
£272 $487 €400 Un trois mats a quai (70x91cm-28x36in) s. panel. 16-Mar-4 Vanderkindere, Brussels #54
£397 $723 €600 Le parc anime (40x30cm-16x12in) s. 15-Jun-4 Vanderkindere, Brussels #123
£411 $699 €600 Vue de Bruxelles (60x50cm-24x20in) s. 4-Nov-3 Servarts Themis, Bruxelles #544
£493 $853 €700 The open window (65x51cm-26x20in) s. 13-Dec-3 De Vuyst, Lokeren #126
£612 $1096 €900 Verger au printemps (65x80cm-26x31in) s. 17-Mar-4 Hotel des Ventes Mosan, Brussels #120
£1119 $1924 €1600 Composition a la table dressee (80x60cm-31x24in) s.d.1917. 8-Dec-3 Horta, Bruxelles #30 est:1200-1500
£1429 $2557 €2100 Foire animee (40x50cm-16x20in) s. 16-Mar-4 Vanderkindere, Brussels #285 est:1200-1800
£1748 $2920 €2500 Retour des oies (52x77cm-20x30in) s. 13-Oct-3 Horta, Bruxelles #145 est:2000-2500

DUBOIS-PILLET, Albert (1845-1890) French
£6294 $10699 €9000 Southern French coastal landscape (48x61cm-19x24in) s. 20-Nov-3 Van Ham, Cologne #1544/R est:1900
Works on paper
£7000 $12880 €10220 Quai Montebello (21x14cm-8x6in) s. pen ink exec.c.1885-86 prov. 22-Jun-4 Sotheby's, London #404/R est:8000-10000
£14000 $25760 €20440 Bord de Marne a l'aube (16x22cm-6x9in) s. W/C exec.c.1886 prov. 22-Jun-4 Sotheby's, London #402/R est:15000-20000
£17000 $31280 €24820 Clocher dans la campagne (16x19cm-6x7in) W/C exec.c.1886 oval prov. 22-Jun-4 Sotheby's, London #401/R est:12000-15000

DUBORD, Jean Pierre (1949-) French
£405 $750 €591 Maisons au Bretagne (51x61cm-20x24in) s. i.verso. 10-Mar-4 Doyle, New York #19/R
£412 $700 €602 La route en bord de Seine (53x64cm-21x25in) s. 5-Nov-3 Doyle, New York #25/R
£435 $800 €635 Le fleur de la campagne Normande (25x51cm-10x20in) s. s.i.verso. 23-Jun-4 Doyle, New York #5028/R
£435 $800 €635 Les bateaux sur la Seine (25x51cm-10x20in) s. s.i.verso. 23-Jun-4 Doyle, New York #5029/R
£500 $850 €730 La fete de la mer (53x66cm-21x26in) s. 5-Nov-3 Doyle, New York #24/R
£521 $850 €761 Bord de Seine (25x51cm-10x20in) s. s.i.verso. 17-Jul-3 Doyle, New York #24/R
£530 $964 €800 Automne a Saint-Martin de Boscherville (46x55cm-18x22in) s. s.verso. 20-Jun-4 Imberdis, Pont Audemer #71
£559 $1000 €816 La marche aux fleurs au Bretagne (58x74cm-23x29in) s. s.i.verso. 8-Jan-4 Doyle, New York #18/R
£595 $1100 €869 Le marche en Bretagne (61x76cm-24x30in) s. 15-Jul-4 Doyle, New York #27/R est:1500-2500
£598 $1100 €873 La cote Normande dans lew calvados (61x76cm-24x30in) s. i.verso. 25-Mar-4 Doyle, New York #19 est:2000-3000
£815 $1500 €1190 Le plage dans le Calvados (51x61cm-20x24in) s. 9-Jun-4 Doyle, New York #3027 est:2500-3500
£859 $1400 €1254 Les fleurs dans le jardin (76x89cm-30x35in) s. i.verso. 17-Jul-3 Doyle, New York #23/R
£872 $1623 €1300 Paysage d'eau a Jumieges (60x73cm-24x29in) s. 7-Mar-4 Lesieur & Le Bars, Le Havre #163
£1104 $1800 €1612 La cote dans le calvados (61x76cm-24x30in) s. i.verso. 17-Jul-3 Doyle, New York #22/R est:1500-2500
£1744 $3000 €2546 Les fleurs dans la Campagne Normande (61x76cm-24x30in) s. i.verso. 3-Dec-3 Doyle, New York #158/R est:3000-4000
£1766 $3250 €2578 Les hauteurs de Rouen en automne (61x76cm-24x30in) s. s.i.verso. 23-Jun-4 Doyle, New York #5027/R est:2000-3000
£1890 $3250 €2759 La sortie des bateaux (61x76cm-24x30in) s. i.verso. 3-Dec-3 Doyle, New York #157/R est:3000-4000

DUBOULOZ, Jean-Auguste (1800-1870) French
£428 $787 €650 Sortie clandestine (22x27cm-9x11in) s. 25-Jun-4 Millon & Associes, Paris #65

DUBOURG, Alexandre (?) French?
Works on paper
£1701 $3044 €2500 Plage a maree basse (13x24cm-5x9in) mono. pastel. 19-Mar-4 Piasa, Paris #145/R est:1000-1200

DUBOURG, Augustin (fl.1790-1800) French
Miniatures
£1469 $2526 €2100 Portrait de jeune femme assise avec un livre (7cm-3in circular) s. 4-Dec-3 E & Eve, Paris #30/R

DUBOURG, Louis Alexandre (c.1825-1891) French
£385 $700 €562 Fisherboy (7x5cm-3x2in) s. panel. 7-Feb-4 Sloans & Kenyon, Bethesda #874a/R
£10615 $19000 €15498 La fenaison (55x96cm-22x38in) s. exhib. 6-May-4 Doyle, New York #36/R est:3000-5000
Works on paper
£1096 $1863 €1600 Barques (11x19cm-4x7in) mono. pastel. 6-Nov-3 Tajan, Paris #236

DUBOVSKOY, Nicolay Nikanorovich (1859-1918) Russian
£12162 $21770 €18000 Stooks (28x37cm-11x15in) s. board. 8-May-4 Bukowskis, Helsinki #425/R est:8000-12000

DUBOYS, Paul (attrib) (fl.c.1610) Flemish
£1127 $1972 €1600 Saint Catherine of Alexandria (43x32cm-17x13in) panel. 17-Dec-3 Piasa, Paris #84 est:3000-5000

DUBREUIL, Cheri François (1828-1880) French
£611 $1113 €892 French warship Jupiter on rough southern seas (48x65cm-19x26in) s. 16-Jun-4 Fischer, Luzern #2081/R (S.FR 1400)
£3217 $5469 €4600 Combat naval (90x150cm-35x59in) s.d.1871. 24-Nov-3 Boscher, Cherbourg #760/R est:4500-5000
£3357 $5706 €4800 Le vaisseau l'Ocean sortant de la Manche. Rade de Toulon (74x98cm-29x39in) pair. 23-Nov-3 Claude Boisgirard, Paris #195/R est:5000-5600

DUBREUIL, Jean Francois (1946-) French
£367 $660 €550 Le Quotidien de Paris 3211 (90x139cm-35x55in) s.i.verso canvas laid down. 20-Apr-4 Galerie Moderne, Brussels #243/R

DUBREUIL, Toussaint (1561-1602) French
Works on paper
£2111 $3800 €3082 Lot's wife looking back at the destruction of Sodom and Gomorrah (21x27cm-8x11in) black chk pen brown ink wash prov. 22-Jan-4 Christie's, Rockefeller NY #83a/R est:4000-6000

DUBRUCQ, Guido Denis (?) ?
£483 $893 €700 Vase fleuri de pivoines (70x110cm-28x43in) s. 19-Jan-4 Horta, Bruxelles #466

DUBSKY, Mario (1939-) ?
Works on paper
£250 $430 €365 Still life (71x54cm-28x21in) s.indis.i.d.57 chl. 3-Dec-3 Christie's, Kensington #618

DUBUC, Jean Louis (1946-) French
£302 $535 €450 Promenade sur la jetee (55x46cm-22x18in) s. 29-Apr-4 Claude Aguttes, Neuilly #86

DUBUC, Roland (1924-1998) Swiss
£638 $1066 €900 Paysage anime sous la neige (27x35cm-11x14in) s. 19-Oct-3 Charbonneaux, Paris #151
£828 $1382 €1200 Les toits (27x35cm-11x14in) s. 17-Nov-3 Charbonneaux, Paris #199
£1342 $2497 €2000 Montmartre sous la neige (46x55cm-18x22in) s. 7-Mar-4 Lesieur & Le Bars, Le Havre #33
£1544 $2871 €2300 Le parvis de la cathedrale (65x54cm-26x21in) s. 7-Mar-4 Lesieur & Le Bars, Le Havre #32
£2000 $3340 €2900 Clowns musiciens (65x48cm-26x19in) s. cardboard. 11-Nov-3 Lesieur & Le Bars, Le Havre #18
£2759 $4607 €4000 Petit manege (65x81cm-26x32in) s. 11-Nov-3 Lesieur & Le Bars, Le Havre #17
Works on paper
£369 $683 €550 Peniches en Normandie (40x55cm-16x22in) s. W/C. 14-Mar-4 St-Germain-en-Laye Encheres #180
£389 $689 €580 Bords de Seine (47x61cm-19x24in) s. W/C. 28-Apr-4 Charbonneaux, Paris #147
£496 $829 €700 Paris, Montmartre (63x48cm-25x19in) s. gouache. 19-Oct-3 Charbonneaux, Paris #105
£528 $856 €750 Concert (36x47cm-14x19in) s. W/C. 11-Aug-3 Boscher, Cherbourg #786
£552 $921 €800 Place de Paris animee sous la neige (47x62cm-19x24in) s. gouache. 17-Nov-3 Charbonneaux, Paris #125

DUBUCAND, Alfred (1828-1894) French
Sculpture
£900 $1665 €1314 Group of partridges with their chicks (36cm-14in) s. brown pat bronze. 13-Jan-4 Sotheby's, Olympia #83/R est:1500-2200
£1007 $1862 €1500 Bouquetin perche (31cm-12in) s. pat bronze. 14-Mar-4 St-Germain-en-Laye Encheres #16/R
£1200 $2172 €1800 Chamois en bronze (30x20cm-12x8in) s. brown pat. bronze. 31-Mar-4 Sotheby's, Paris #284/R est:1800-2500
£1250 $2000 €1825 Hunter on horseback with dogs (25cm-10in) bronze. 17-May-3 Bunte, Elgin #1095 est:2000-3000
£1600 $2896 €2400 Braque (25x32cm-10x13in) s. brown pat. bronze. 31-Mar-4 Sotheby's, Paris #278/R est:1500-2000
£1972 $3411 €2800 Anier egyptien (21x18cm-8x7in) s. num.EV1851 pat bronze. 15-Dec-3 Gros & Delettrez, Paris #176/R est:2500-3500
£2067 $3803 €3100 Horse (37x30cm-15x12in) s.i. terrasse brown pat bronze. 9-Jun-4 Le Roux & Morel, Paris #172 est:2000
£2096 $3500 €3060 Hunter (28x23cm-11x9in) s. brown pat. bronze on marble plinth. 16-Nov-3 Simpson's, Houston #303/R
£2400 $3768 €3480 Stag and doe (43x43cm-17x17in) s.d.1870 brown pat. bronze. 27-Aug-3 Sotheby's, London #979/R est:2500-3500
£4000 $6800 €5840 Anier du Caire (34x26cm-13x10in) s. pat bronze. 28-Oct-3 Sotheby's, London #103/R
£7693 $13231 €11000 Chasse a la Gazelle au Guepard Perse (65cm-26in) i.base brown pat gilded bronze incl base lit. 8-Dec-3 Tajan, Paris #267/R est:12000-14000

DUBUFE, Claude Marie (1790-1864) French
£5333 $9653 €8000 Mademoiselle Georges, la rupture (65x54cm-26x21in) exhib. 30-Mar-4 Rossini, Paris #252/R est:8000-12000
£8000 $14320 €11680 Portrait of Lady Menuhin's grandfather and great grandmother (148x116cm-58x46in) s. 11-May-4 Sotheby's, Olympia #557/R est:6000-8000
£11000 $20240 €16060 Portrait de la Comtesse de Kergolay (115x86cm-45x34in) i. 25-Mar-4 Christie's, Kensington #45/R est:4000-6000
£16000 $29121 €24000 Portrait de Gerard Gould et de sa mere (148x116cm-58x46in) s. 30-Jun-4 Pierre Berge, Paris #58/R est:25000-30000

DUBUFE, Edouard Marie Guillaume (1853-1909) French
£12500 $22500 €18250 Diane sortant de son bain (220x105cm-87x41in) s. 23-Apr-4 Sotheby's, New York #203/R est:20000-30000

DUBUFFET, Jean (1901-1985) French
£2346 $4200 €3425 Resille no 21 (22x12cm-9x5in) s.d.59 verso black oil imprint prov.exhib.lit. 14-May-4 Phillips, New York #288/R est:6000-8000
£20000 $36400 €29200 Site avec 7 personnages (67x50cm-26x20in) init.d.81 acrylic paper on canvas prov.lit. 5-Feb-4 Christie's, London #163/R est:24000-28000
£20000 $36800 €29200 Mire G 90 - Kowloon (67x100cm-26x39in) init.d.83 acrylic paper on canvas prov.exhib.lit. 24-Jun-4 Sotheby's, London #166/R est:20000-30000
£20958 $35000 €30599 Topographie aux composites (67x89cm-26x35in) s.d.59 s.i.d.verso oil gouache collage canvas prov.exhib.lit. 12-Nov-3 Christie's, Rockefeller NY #347/R est:30000-40000
£22000 $36740 €32120 Sequence XXVIII (35x25cm-14x10in) init.d.79 acrylic cut-out paper collage paper prov.lit. 21-Oct-3 Sotheby's, London #387/R est:10000-15000
£23077 $38538 €33000 Site avec trois figures (50x67cm-20x26in) mono.d.1981 acrylic paper on canvas prov.lit. 29-Jun-3 Versailles Encheres #125/R
£23952 $40000 €34970 Sequence X (35x25cm-14x10in) init.d.79 acrylic gouache paper collage paper prov.exhib.lit. 13-Nov-3 Sotheby's, New York #234/R est:15000-20000
£25000 $41250 €36000 Paysage tavele aux arbres (30x49cm-12x19in) s.i.d. s.i.d.janvier 54 verso oil paper lit. 2-Jul-3 Cornette de St.Cyr, Paris #6/R est:40000-60000
£27465 $48063 €39000 Site avec quatre personnages (67x50cm-26x20in) s.d.1981 acrylic paper on canvas prov.lit. 18-Dec-3 Cornette de St.Cyr, Paris #80/R est:40000-50000
£28000 $51520 €40880 Site avec trois personnages (68x50cm-27x20in) init.d.81 acrylic paper on canvas prov.exhib.lit. 25-Jun-4 Christie's, London #124/R est:25000-35000
£42000 $76440 €61320 Chevaux a la lune (50x60cm-20x24in) s.d.43 prov.lit. 5-Feb-4 Christie's, London #117/R est:25000-35000
£52870 $89879 €77190 Pierre Philosophique (65x81cm-26x32in) s.d.51 oil on isorel stones prov.lit. 4-Nov-3 Bukowskis, Stockholm #278/R est:1000000-1500000 (S.KR 700000)
£59880 $100000 €87425 Le pain de la terre (73x92cm-29x36in) s.d.53 s.i.d.avril 53 verso prov.exhib.lit. 13-Nov-3 Sotheby's, New York #176/R est:80000-120000
£65000 $119600 €94900 Texturologie XX (81x100cm-32x39in) s.d.58 s.i.d. verso prov.lit. 24-Jun-4 Sotheby's, London #231/R est:50000-70000
£72626 $130000 €106034 Site avec 3 personnages (74x105cm-29x41in) init.d.82 acrylic paper collage prov.lit. 13-May-4 Sotheby's, New York #207/R est:80000-120000
£80000 $133600 €116800 Petit tour de piste (73x92cm-29x36in) s.d.58 s.i.d.octobre 58 verso prov.lit. 21-Oct-3 Sotheby's, London #389/R est:80000-120000
£80000 $145600 €116800 Paysage eclectique (114x48cm-45x19in) s.d.57 s.i.d.verso oil canvas collage prov.lit. 4-Feb-4 Christie's, London #15/R est:100000-150000
£90000 $163800 €131400 Paysage aux Griffures (89x116cm-35x46in) s.d.53 prov.exhib.lit. 5-Feb-4 Sotheby's, London #36/R est:100000-150000
£105000 $193200 €153300 Table venerable (114x146cm-45x57in) s.d.57 i.d.verso prov.lit. 23-Jun-4 Sotheby's, London #21/R est:100000-150000
£161111 $265833 €232000 Personnage levant les bras dans un paysage (50x61cm-20x24in) s.d.1949 isorel prov.lit. 2-Jul-3 Cornette de St.Cyr, Paris #8 est:200000-300000
£191617 $320000 €279761 Scene episodique a deux protagonistes (203x130cm-80x51in) init.d.74 s.i.d.verso vinyl prov.exhib.lit. 12-Nov-3 Christie's, Rockefeller NY #350/R est:200000-300000
£200000 $360000 €300000 Esclave (81x100cm-32x39in) s.d.1951 i.versopel. 25-Apr-4 Versailles Encheres #131 est:300000-350000
£263473 $440000 €384671 Fenetre sur le ciel (74x91cm-29x36in) s.d.55 s.i.d.verso prov.lit. 12-Nov-3 Sotheby's, New York #5/R est:500000-700000
£280000 $509600 €408800 Paysage sautant sur son petit arpent (130x97cm-51x38in) painted 1947 prov.exhib.lit. 5-Feb-4 Sotheby's, London #13/R est:250000-350000
£307263 $550000 €448604 La Liquidite du monde (130x162cm-51x64in) s.d.52 s.i.d.verso isorel prov.exhib.lit. 11-May-4 Christie's, Rockefeller NY #63/R est:400000-600000
£480000 $873600 €700800 Petit homme beige dore (55x46cm-22x18in) s.i.d.1945 verso oil soil pebbles glue canvas prov.exhib.lit. 5-Feb-4 Sotheby's, London #11/R est:250000-350000
£628743 $1050000 €917965 Le soleil les decolore (130x97cm-51x38in) painted 1947 canvasboard prov.exhib.lit. 11-Nov-3 Christie's, Rockefeller NY #39/R est:600000-800000
£726257 $1300000 €1060335 Ancien combattant (91x66cm-36x26in) s.d.45 prov.exhib.lit. 11-May-4 Christie's, Rockefeller NY #20/R est:1500000-2500000
£1061453 $1900000 €1549721 Cow with the beautiful muzzle (116x89cm-46x35in) s.d.54 s.i.d.November 54 verso. 12-May-4 Sotheby's, New York #19/R est:2000000-3000000
£1731844 $3100000 €2528492 Vache tachetee (89x111cm-35x44in) s.d.54 s.i.d.verso prov.exhib.lit. 11-May-4 Christie's, Rockefeller NY #29/R est:2500000-3500000
Prints
£2096 $3500 €3060 From Fables, lion heraldique (71x89cm-28x35in) init.d.7/50 col silkscreen. 21-Oct-3 Bonhams & Butterfields, San Francisco #1177/R
£2400 $3984 €3504 Assemblages d'empreintes, les herboristes (27x49cm-11x19in) s.num.5/20 col lithograph. 6-Oct-3 Sotheby's, London #127a est:1500-2000
£2793 $5000 €4078 Villa duplex (74x43cm-29x17in) init.d.76 num.28/50 col silkscreen. 7-May-4 Sloans & Kenyon, Bethesda #1751/R est:4000-5000
£2941 $5000 €4294 Parade nuptiale (39x34cm-15x13in) init.d.1973 num.42/85 col screenprint. 4-Nov-3 Christie's, Rockefeller NY #88/R est:3000-5000
£3000 $5460 €4380 Vacations (18x25cm-7x10in) s.i. col lithograph. 1-Jul-4 Sotheby's, London #165/R est:2000-3000
£3500 $5810 €5110 Parcours (10x27cm-4x11in) init.d.1981 num.44/80 silkscreen silk on paper two batons. 6-Oct-3 Sotheby's, London #127/R est:3500-4500
£3672 $6500 €5361 L'homme au chapeau (52x38cm-20x15in) s.d.1961 num.1/50 col lithograph. 28-Apr-4 Christie's, Rockefeller NY #35/R est:8000-10000
£3824 $6500 €5583 Faits memorables (75x98cm-30x39in) init. col screenprint exec.1978. 4-Nov-3 Christie's, Rockefeller NY #89/R est:6000-10000
£4412 $7500 €6442 Parcours (51x58cm-20x23in) s. screenprint. 31-Oct-3 Sotheby's, New York #533/R
£6000 $10920 €8760 Fougere au chapeau (51x40cm-20x16in) s.i.d.1954 col lithograph. 1-Jul-4 Sotheby's, London #163/R est:3000-4000
£14689 $26000 €21446 Nez carotte (60x38cm-24x15in) s.i.d.1962 num.14/50 col lithograph. 28-Apr-4 Christie's, Rockefeller NY #36/R est:30000-50000
Sculpture
£55000 $100100 €80300 Sorciere (17cm-7in) root and stones executed July 1954 prov.exhib.lit. 4-Feb-4 Christie's, London #7/R est:60000-80000
£68862 $115000 €100539 Borne au logos I (99x52x51cm-39x20x20in) init.d.66 epoxy paint on polyurethane prov.exhib.lit. 12-Nov-3 Christie's, Rockefeller NY #343/R est:120000-180000
£101333 $186453 €152000 Arbre, Livre et Gite (120x80x60cm-47x31x24in) polyester 8 parts exec 1969 prov.lit. 8-Jun-4 Artcurial Briest, Paris #2226/R est:120000-150000
£137725 $230000 €201079 Buste a la cravate (92x56x35cm-36x22x14in) init.i.d.72 num.345 polyurethane paint epoxy resin prov.exhib.lit. 13-Nov-3 Sotheby's, New York #244/R est:150000-200000
Works on paper
£3409 $6000 €4977 Untitled (25x46cm-10x18in) init.d.67 marker pen. 20-May-4 American Auctioneer #474987/R
£6135 $10000 €8957 Motif (21x23cm-8x9in) init.d.73 ink paper collage board prov.lit. 23-Sep-3 Christie's, Rockefeller NY #7/R est:4000-6000

£6667 $11933 €10000 Untitled (29x50cm-11x20in) collage felt pen board prov. 15-May-4 Van Ham, Cologne #559/R est:20000
£6667 $12267 €10000 Paysage avec deux personnages (35x25cm-14x10in) mono.d.80 India ink prov.lit. 9-Jun-4 Artcurial Briest, Paris #417/R est:10000-14000
£6704 $12000 €9788 Personnage XXI (28x22cm-11x9in) init.d.64 i.verso col blk marker pen lit. 13-May-4 Sotheby's, New York #120/R est:8000-12000
£6780 $12000 €9899 Le meteore (27x39cm-11x15in) init.d.71 i.verso marker pen prov.lit. 2-May-4 Bonhams & Butterfields, Los Angeles #3031/R est:15000-20000
£7718 $14124 €11500 J Dubuffet salue le Professeur E Tosatti (29x24cm-11x9in) s.i.d.29.5.69 col felt crayon lit. 7-Jul-4 Artcurial Briest, Paris #253/R est:12000-15000
£8054 $14255 €12000 Paysage avec un personnage (35x25cm-14x10in) mono.d.80 blk felt pen collage prov.exhib.lit. 28-Apr-4 Artcurial Briest, Paris #321/R est:8000-12000
£8667 $15947 €13000 Situation XCVI (35x25cm-14x10in) black felt pen exec 1979 prov.lit. 9-Jun-4 Artcurial Briest, Paris #416/R est:12000-15000
£9790 $16839 €14000 Escalier coupe d'un parlier (50x22cm-20x9in) mono.d.1967 i.verso felt-tip pen over pencil cardboard prov. 5-Dec-3 Ketterer, Munich #131/R est:15000-20000
£9859 $17056 €14000 Paysage (36x25cm-14x10in) mono.i.d.21 septembre 1974 col crayon felt pen prov.lit. 14-Dec-3 Versailles Encheres #156/R est:12000-15000
£10000 $18400 €14600 Palmeraie aux quatre oiseaux (21x26cm-8x10in) init. verso gouache ink exec 1949 prov.exhib.lit. 24-Jun-4 Sotheby's, London #194/R est:10000-15000
£10056 $18000 €14682 Le Maitre d'Hotel (39x19cm-15x7in) init.d.73 i.verso col marker paper collage on cardboard prov.lit. 13-May-4 Sotheby's, New York #206/R est:12000-18000
£11000 $18370 €16060 Empreinte V (49x66cm-19x26in) s.d.57 china ink prov.exhib.lit. 21-Oct-3 Sotheby's, London #400/R est:8000-12000
£16760 $30000 €24470 Personnage dans un paysage (32x25cm-13x10in) init.d.mai 60 i.verso ink prov.lit. 13-May-4 Sotheby's, New York #121/R est:30000-40000
£24496 $45073 €36500 Le Cadastre (44x69cm-17x27in) s.i. paper on card felt pen exec 1973. 29-Mar-4 Cornette de St.Cyr, Paris #2/R est:25000-30000
£24648 $40915 €35000 Paysage azux nuages tachetes (50x62cm-20x24in) s.d.1955 W/C ink collage. 13-Jun-3 Hauswedell & Nolte, Hamburg #598/R est:45000
£25000 $46000 €36500 Poires sur la cheminee (46x65cm-18x26in) s.d.octobre 42 gouache card lit. 24-Jun-4 Sotheby's, London #195/R est:10000-15000
£26316 $48421 €40000 Dame abondante (44x27cm-17x11in) s.d.54 gouache collage prov.lit. 27-Jun-4 Versailles Encheres #132/R est:40000-45000
£34014 $60885 €50000 Theatrale rencontre (99x47cm-39x19in) s.i.d.55 ink prov.lit. 21-Mar-4 Calmels Cohen, Paris #167/R est:50000-60000
£34637 $62000 €50570 Vache (32x43cm-13x17in) s.d.54 ink exec 1954 prov.lit. 12-May-4 Christie's, Rockefeller NY #125/R est:40000-50000
£35928 $60000 €52455 Polymorphie X (39x68cm-15x27in) init.d.71 marker paper on board prov.lit. 12-Nov-3 Christie's, Rockefeller NY #346/R est:25000-35000
£42000 $70140 €61320 Untitled (25x19cm-10x7in) s.d.46 gouache ink prov. 21-Oct-3 Sotheby's, London #388/R est:20000-30000
£53892 $90000 €78682 Vegetation sauvage (71x67cm-28x26in) s.d.57 ink cut-out paper collage prov.exhib.lit. 13-Nov-3 Sotheby's, New York #103/R est:40000-50000
£92814 $155000 €135508 Dentiste (35x32cm-14x13in) s.i.d.47 gesso ink prov.exhib.lit. 11-Nov-3 Christie's, Rockefeller NY #63/R est:150000-250000
£100000 $184000 €146000 Jardin austere (22x31cm-9x12in) s.d.55 butterfly wing collage W/C ink prov.exhib.lit. 23-Jun-4 Sotheby's, London #10/R est:80000-120000
£140000 $257600 €204400 Homme au chapeau (24x26cm-9x10in) s.i.d.1951 gouache Swedish putty oil on board prov.exhib.lit. 24-Jun-4 Christie's, London #12/R est:140000-180000

DUBUIS, Anna (1878-1929) Swiss
£769 $1331 €1123 Valere et Tourbillon (50x90cm-20x35in) s.d.1916. 12-Dec-3 Galerie du Rhone, Sion #486/R (S.FR 1700)

DUBUIS, Fernand (1908-1991) Swiss
£1762 $2996 €2573 Murs (81x54cm-32x21in) s.d.57 i. stretcher. 7-Nov-3 Dobiaschofsky, Bern #279/R est:4800 (S.FR 4000)

DUBUISSON, Alexandre (1805-1870) French
£2133 $3840 €3200 Paturage (54x78cm-21x31in) s.d.1841. 20-Apr-4 Chenu & Scrive, Lyon #80/R est:3000-3500

DUCAIRE, Maryse (20th C) French
£216 $400 €315 Seated female nude (18x15cm-7x6in) s. 18-Jul-4 Bonhams & Butterfields, Los Angeles #7073/R
£310 $568 €450 Nu de dos (24x14cm-9x6in) s. 1-Feb-4 Feletin, Province #187
£310 $568 €450 Nu allonge (22x27cm-9x11in) s. 1-Feb-4 Feletin, Province #188
£699 $1300 €1021 Reclining nude (46x61cm-18x24in) s. painted c.1960. 7-Mar-4 Treadway Gallery, Cincinnati #709/R est:1500-2000

DUCAROIR, Claudine (?) French?
Works on paper
£420 $713 €600 Untitled (60x81cm-24x32in) s. ink acrylic canvas. 29-Nov-3 Neret-Minet, Paris #66/R

DUCASSE, Ralph (1916-) American
£471 $800 €688 Flora (41x28cm-16x11in) 9-Nov-3 Wright, Chicago #258

DUCATE, Marie (1957-) French
Works on paper
£237 $425 €346 Untitled (56x56cm-22x22in) s.d.1988 gouache prov. 16-May-4 Wright, Chicago #362/R
£251 $450 €366 Untitled (76x64cm-30x25in) s.d.1985 gouache prov. 16-May-4 Wright, Chicago #361/R

DUCATILLION, Fernand Georges (1888-?) Belgian
£1862 $3445 €2700 Femme Grecque lors de la guerre d'Independance (100x800cm-39x315in) s.d.1888. 13-Jan-4 Vanderkindere, Brussels #65 est:625-875

DUCE, Alberto (1919-) Spanish
£379 $633 €550 Maternity (36x25cm-14x10in) s. board. 17-Nov-3 Durán, Madrid #567/R
£414 $691 €600 Painter and model (50x67cm-20x26in) s. board. 17-Nov-3 Durán, Madrid #566
£638 $1034 €900 Painter and model (50x67cm-20x26in) s. panel. 20-May-3 Ansorena, Madrid #349/R
£655 $1088 €950 Three graces (45x56cm-18x22in) s. board. 1-Oct-3 Ansorena, Madrid #667/R

DUCE, Scott (20th C) American
£464 $850 €677 Faults now visible (109x74cm-43x29in) acrylic on paper. 10-Jul-4 Hindman, Chicago #129/R

DUCHAMP, Marcel (1887-1968) French
Prints
£2059 $3500 €3006 Bride (33x25cm-13x10in) s. num.19/30 etching exec.1965. 4-Nov-3 Christie's, Rockefeller NY #90/R est:2000-3000
Sculpture
£2800 $4648 €4088 Bouche-evier (62x62cm-24x24in) s.d.num.80/100 verso silver multiple. 6-Oct-3 Sotheby's, London #224/R est:1000-2000
£7333 $13567 €11000 Eau et gaz a tous les etages (35x26x5cm-14x10x2in) init.i. cardboard collage lit. 18-Jul-4 Sotheby's, Paris #296/R est:10000-15000
£10667 $19733 €16000 Mariee mise a nu (33x28x2cm-13x11x1in) s.i.d.1934 box dr photograph lit. 18-Jul-4 Sotheby's, Paris #295/R est:10000-15000
£19214 $34969 €28052 La boite en valise (40x37x9cm-16x15x4in) s.i.d.1958 suitcase containing 67 works by Duchamp prov. 18-Jun-4 Kornfeld, Bern #32/R est:40000 (S.FR 44000)
Works on paper
£7110 $11874 €10310 La mariee mise a nu par ses celibataires meme. cassette. 19-Jun-3 Kornfeld, Bern #329 est:3000 (S.FR 15500)

DUCHAMP, Marcel and VILLON, Jacques (20th C) French
Prints
£5650 $10000 €8249 The bride (49x31cm-19x12in) s. by both artists i.num.82/200 col aquatint. 28-Apr-4 Christie's, Rockefeller NY #37/R est:15000-20000
£8383 $14000 €12239 Bride (49x31cm-19x12in) s.i. col aquatint. 11-Nov-3 Christie's, Rockefeller NY #119/R est:15000-20000

DUCHAMP, Suzanne (1889-1963) French
£546 $1000 €797 Fille en jardin (53x64cm-21x25in) s. painted c.1940. 5-Jun-4 Treadway Gallery, Cincinnati #745/R est:1500-2000

DUCHANEE, Thawan (1939-) Thai
£7742 $12387 €11303 Fish (122x152cm-48x60in) s.d.64 board prov. 18-May-3 Sotheby's, Singapore #91/R est:20000-30000 (S.D 21600)
£14624 $23398 €21351 Reclining nudes with cockerel (122x213cm-48x84in) s.d.67 board prov. 18-May-3 Sotheby's, Singapore #90/R est:25000-35000 (S.D 40800)

DUCHATEAU, Hugo (1938-) Belgian
Works on paper
£300 $555 €438 White circle (30x29cm-12x11in) s. d.1984 mixed media. 13-Jul-4 Bonhams, Knightsbridge #52/R

DUCHESNE DE GISORS, Jean Baptiste Joseph (1770-1856) French
Miniatures
£1208 $2138 €1800 King Karl X of France (8x11cm-3x4in) s.d.1817 enamel oval. 29-Apr-4 Dorotheum, Vienna #233/R est:1200-1600
£7800 $14040 €11388 Jean Baptiste Duchesne, the artist's father (6cm-2in circular) s.d.1798 square gilt metal frame leather case prov.exhib. 22-Apr-4 Bonhams, New Bond Street #153/R est:2000-3000
£60000 $108000 €87600 Caroline Ferdinande Louise, Duchess of Berry (15cm-6in) s.d.1827 ormolu frame octagonal leather case prov.exhib.lit. 22-Apr-4 Bonhams, New Bond Street #152/R est:4000-6000

DUCHIN, Eddy (20th C) American
£1081 $2000 €1622 South Pacific Atol (61x46cm-24x18in) s. canvasboard. 18-Jul-4 William Jenack, New York #389 est:150-300

DUCK, Jacob (1600-1660) Dutch
£12308 $21169 €17970 Interior scene with card playing figures (57x74cm-22x29in) panel. 2-Dec-3 Bukowskis, Stockholm #383/R est:175000-200000 (S.KR 160000)
£59212 $108949 €90000 Soldiers resting (51x67cm-20x26in) s.d.1657 panel prov. 24-Jun-4 Tajan, Paris #23/R est:100000-120000

DUCK, Jan le (attrib) (1630-1676) Dutch
£45775 $79190 €65000 White whippet (125x156cm-49x61in) 11-Dec-3 Dr Fritz Nagel, Stuttgart #428/R est:12000

DUCKER, Eugène Gustav (1841-1916) German
£455 $773 €650 Sandy beach with boats and figures (19x27cm-7x11in) s. panel. 22-Nov-3 Arnold, Frankfurt #492/R
£833 $1375 €1200 Painter working on seashore (46x31cm-18x12in) s. board. 3-Jul-3 Van Ham, Cologne #1151/R
£1748 $2920 €2500 Boat leaving shore (43x65cm-17x26in) s.d.1884. 27-Jun-3 Michael Zeller, Lindau #517/R est:900
Works on paper
£280 $476 €400 Rocky coastline in evening (14x19cm-6x7in) s. W/C. 27-Nov-3 Bassenge, Berlin #5564
£420 $713 €600 Grey day on the Baltic (40x50cm-16x20in) s. i. verso gouache board. 20-Nov-3 Van Ham, Cologne #1545/R

DUCKER, Jack M (fl.1910-1930) British
£300 $549 €438 Falls of Dochart (40x61cm-16x24in) s. s.i.d.1929 verso. 6-Jul-4 Bonhams, Knightsbridge #22

DUCKETT, Charles H (fl.1905-1940) British
£750 $1275 €1095 Maidens relaxing by a pool in an Arcadian landscape (61x76cm-24x30in) 6-Nov-3 Christie's, Kensington #749/R

DUCKETT, Georgina (1966-) Australian
£610 $957 €891 Untitled (167x137cm-66x54in) s.i.d.1995 verso. 27-Aug-3 Christie's, Sydney #703 est:600-1000 (A.D 1500)

DUCLAUX, Jean Antoine (1783-1868) French
£2041 $3653 €3000 L'arrivee a l'ecurie (32x41cm-13x16in) panel. 19-Mar-4 Oger, Dumont, Paris #34/R est:4000-5000
£95238 $170476 €140000 Paysage des bords de la Saone (66x103cm-26x41in) s.d.1822 prov.exhib. 19-Mar-4 Beaussant & Lefèvre, Paris #84/R est:120000-150000
Works on paper
£500 $900 €750 Sous le grand chene (25x43cm-10x17in) chl htd white chk. 20-Apr-4 Chenu & Scrive, Lyon #9/R

DUCLERE, Teodoro (1816-1867) Italian
£8042 $13430 €11500 Taormina theatre (35x55cm-14x22in) s.i. 24-Jun-3 Finarte Semenzato, Rome #196/R est:13000-15000

DUCLOS, Cristina (1943-) Argentinian
£2355 $3862 €3250 La comoda (60x73cm-24x29in) s.d.81. 27-May-3 Durán, Madrid #292/R est:3000

DUCLOU, Pierre (20th C) French
Works on paper
£490 $832 €700 Rencontre (41x62cm-16x24in) s. mixed media. 29-Nov-3 Neret-Minet, Paris #132

DUCMELIC, Zdravko (1923-) Argentinian
£2186 $4000 €3192 Figure and space (28x22cm-11x9in) cardboard. 1-Jun-4 Arroyo, Buenos Aires #96
£2842 $5200 €4149 Study for mural (39x100cm-15x39in) cardboard. 1-Jun-4 Arroyo, Buenos Aires #46
Works on paper
£330 $600 €482 Jockey (36x23cm-14x9in) s. ink. 5-Jul-4 Arroyo, Buenos Aires #28/R
£670 $1200 €978 Fishermen (27x21cm-11x8in) W/C. 11-May-4 Arroyo, Buenos Aires #33

DUCOMMUN, Jean Felix (1920-1958) Swiss
£1092 $1987 €1594 Harbour scene with bathers (54x65cm-21x26in) s. 16-Jun-4 Fischer, Luzern #1324/R est:2600-2800 (S.FR 2500)

DUCREUX, Joseph (1735-1802) French
Works on paper
£2000 $3660 €2920 Portrait of a man in a hat, head and shoulders (41x33cm-16x13in) blk white chk blue paper prov.exhib. 8-Jul-4 Sotheby's, London #129/R est:2000-3000

DUCREUX, Joseph (attrib) (1735-1802) French
£704 $1232 €1000 Etude de tete d'homme (45x36cm-18x14in) 17-Dec-3 Piasa, Paris #96

DUCROS, Abraham Louis Rodolphe (1748-1810) Swiss
Works on paper
£2222 $4000 €3244 Rocky landscape with figures by a river (62x41cm-24x16in) W/C over black chk. 21-Jan-4 Sotheby's, New York #142/R est:4000-6000
£3061 $5480 €4500 Les marais Pontains. La grotte de Palazzuolo sur le lac d'Albano (23x34cm-9x13in) i. W/C pair. 19-Mar-4 Piasa, Paris #196/R est:3000

DUCROS, Abraham Louis Rodolphe (attrib) (1748-1810) Swiss
Works on paper
£2800 $4844 €4088 Tomb of Caecilia Metella (51x66cm-20x26in) i. bodycol. 12-Dec-3 Christie's, Kensington #473/R est:1500-2000

DUDA GRACZ, Jerzy (1941-) Polish
£1059 $1917 €1546 Obraz 2871 (39x50cm-15x20in) s.d.2003 o. 4-Apr-4 Agra, Warsaw #83/R (P.Z 7500)
£2684 $4857 €3919 Obraz 2867 (49x39cm-19x15in) s.d.2003. 4-Apr-4 Agra, Warsaw #82/R (P.Z 19000)
£2759 $4607 €4000 Polish motive, crucifix over the ruins of a town (49x70cm-19x28in) s.d.1872/95 d.6/VII/95 verso oil collage board. 16-Nov-3 Agra, Warsaw #56/R est:4000
Works on paper
£459 $761 €670 Paris (40x26cm-16x10in) ink pen wash gouache exec.1969. 2-Oct-3 Agra, Warsaw #31/R (P.Z 3000)

DUDANT, Roger (1929-1991) Belgian
£313 $560 €460 Abstraction (77x47cm-30x19in) s.d.66 panel. 17-Mar-4 Hotel des Ventes Mosan, Brussels #174
£382 $638 €550 Composition (73x100cm-29x39in) s.d.1964. 21-Oct-3 Campo, Vlaamse Kaai #425
£448 $829 €650 Composition (92x64cm-36x25in) s.d.63. 19-Jan-4 Horta, Bruxelles #7
£486 $763 €700 Composition (45x65cm-18x26in) s.d.1963. 26-Aug-3 Galerie Moderne, Brussels #364/R
£800 $1472 €1200 Compositions (53x80cm-21x31in) s. one d.75 one d.86 verso two. 14-Jun-4 Horta, Bruxelles #315
£1000 $1830 €1500 Composition (81x116cm-32x46in) s.d.73. 7-Jun-4 Palais de Beaux Arts, Brussels #360/R est:1500

DUDGEON, James (19th C) British
£279 $475 €407 Equine portrait Tom Hal with the dog Cash (48x58cm-19x23in) s.d.1883. 22-Nov-3 New Orleans Auction, New Orleans #325

DUDLEY, Arthur (fl.1890-1907) British
Works on paper
£300 $489 €438 Still life of grapes, cherries, oranges, melons and earthenware jar (66x26cm-26x10in) s. W/C. 23-Sep-3 Anderson & Garland, Newcastle #252
£320 $566 €467 Still life of fruit (25x76cm-10x30in) s. W/C. 29-Apr-4 Gorringes, Lewes #2504
£600 $1104 €876 Still life of fruit (27x75cm-11x30in) s. W/C pair. 23-Mar-4 Bonhams, Knightsbridge #291/R

DUDLEY, Charles (19/20th C) British
£1100 $1760 €1606 Group portrait of Pug, Jack Russell and Retriever. Group portrait of three Jack Russells (35x46cm-14x18in) s. pair. 16-Sep-3 Rosebery Fine Art, London #469/R est:500-700

DUDLEY, Frank V (1868-1957) American
£23952 $40000 €34970 At the beach (69x76cm-27x30in) s. 7-Oct-3 Sotheby's, New York #242 est:7000-10000

DUDOT, Rene (fl.1653-1659) French
£4934 $9079 €7500 Resting during the Flight to Egypt (27x19cm-11x7in) canavs on panel prov.exhib. 24-Jun-4 Christie's, Paris #125/R est:2000-4000

DUDOVICH, Marcello (1878-1962) Italian
£927 $1687 €1400 Farewell freedom (39x24cm-15x9in) s. tempera paper. 18-Jun-4 Stadion, Trieste #391
£2797 $4755 €4000 Portrait of lady (55x36cm-22x14in) tempera. 19-Nov-3 Cambi, Genoa #400/R est:800-1000
Works on paper
£315 $535 €450 Lady and solicitor (34x50cm-13x20in) chl lead dr. 19-Nov-3 Cambi, Genoa #435
£1408 $2437 €2000 Bathing costume (45x32cm-18x13in) s. pencil. 10-Dec-3 Finarte Semenzato, Rome #187/R est:200-2200

DUDREVILLE, Leonardo (1885-1974) Italian
£1159 $1901 €1600 Landscape in Besnate on the Adda (25x39cm-10x15in) init.d.940 s.i.verso board. 27-May-3 Finarte Semenzato, Milan #8/R
£1522 $2496 €2100 Landscape in Borgotaro (25x39cm-10x15in) s.d.938 s.i.verso board prov. 27-May-3 Finarte Semenzato, Milan #7/R
£1558 $2790 €2275 Washerwomen on shore (26x36cm-10x14in) s.d.919 s.i.d. verso. 22-Mar-4 Philippe Schuler, Zurich #4444/R est:3000-3500 (S.FR 3600)
£2371 $4244 €3462 Evening coast (25x35cm-10x14in) s. panel. 12-May-4 Dobiaschofsky, Bern #463/R est:4000 (S.FR 5500)

DUE, Ole (1875-?) Danish
£379 $607 €553 Landscape at sunset (25x38cm-10x15in) s. 22-Sep-3 Rasmussen, Vejle #340 (D.KR 4000)

DUECKER, Otto (1948-) American
£2514 $4500 €3670 Old Justin's. Old Levis. s.i. masonite pair. 13-May-4 Dallas Auction Gallery, Dallas #329/R est:2000-4000

DUEZ, Ernest Ange (1846-1896) French
£3944 $6546 €5600 Singe volant une pomme (80x151cm-31x59in) s.i.d.1870. 10-Jun-3 Renaud, Paris #18/R est:4000-5000

DUFAUR, Comte Raoul de Pilbrac (1852-1937) French
£2119 $3602 €3094 Study of the scriptures (76x98cm-30x39in) s. prov.exhib. 24-Nov-3 Sotheby's, Melbourne #330/R est:2500-3500 (A.D 5000)

DUFAUX, F (?) ?
£714 $1143 €1035 Le marabou (24x38cm-9x15in) s. i. verso canvas on board. 15-May-3 Stuker, Bern #1164/R (S.FR 1500)

DUFAUX, Frederic II (1852-1943) Swiss
£349 $636 €510 Silvaplana (24x18cm-9x7in) s.i.d.14/7/1928 cardboard prov. 16-Jun-4 Fischer, Luzern #2083/R (S.FR 800)
£837 $1423 €1222 Lago Maggiore (15x23cm-6x9in) s.i.d.1919 panel prov. 7-Nov-3 Dobiaschofsky, Bern #98/R est:2400 (S.FR 1900)
£1127 $1949 €1600 Port de Bastia (36x22cm-14x9in) s.i.d.911 canva on cardboard. 9-Dec-3 Artcurial Briest, Paris #89/R est:2000-3000
£1301 $2042 €1899 Untitled, passing glance (61x46cm-24x18in) s. 1-Sep-3 Shapiro, Sydney #367/R est:3000-5000 (A.D 3200)
£1552 $2778 €2266 Bords du Lac de Geneve. Cabanes de pecheurs, Belotte-Geneve (16x23cm-6x9in) s.i.d.17.aout 1917 board two. 12-May-4 Dobiaschofsky, Bern #464/R est:2400 (S.FR 3600)
£1760 $3046 €2500 Elegante a sa toilette (33x22cm-13x9in) s. canvas on cardboard. 9-Dec-3 Artcurial Briest, Paris #88/R est:2500-3500
£2895 $4834 €4227 Jetee des Paquis (38x55cm-15x22in) s.d.24 avril 909. 16-Nov-3 Koller, Geneva #1300/R est:400-700 (S.FR 6600)

£6190	$9905	€8976	Returning from the market (106x169cm-42x67in) s.d.1890. 15-May-3 Stuker, Bern #1165/R est:10000-12000 (S.FR 13000)

DUFAUX, Frederic II (attrib) (1852-1943) Swiss

£431	$772	€629	Southern hilly landscape with tower and buildings (14x24cm-6x9in) 12-May-4 Dobiaschofsky, Bern #465 (S.FR 1000)

DUFEU, Edouard (1840-1900) French

£620	$1147	€905	View of a port (50x61cm-20x24in) s. 10-Mar-4 Sotheby's, Olympia #252/R
£1206	$2013	€1700	Mosquee ottomane sur la Corne d'Or (18x26cm-7x10in) s. panel. 16-Jun-3 Gros & Delettrez, Paris #494/R est:1700-2500
£1325	$2411	€2000	In front of the gate to an oriental city (54x65cm-21x26in) s. 21-Jun-4 Dorotheum, Vienna #173/R est:2000-2400
£1500	$2730	€2250	View of Rome (65x81cm-26x32in) s. 4-Jul-4 Eric Pillon, Calais #59/R
£1718	$2800	€2508	Procession in the cathedral (61x51cm-24x20in) s. 24-Sep-3 Doyle, New York #26 est:2000-4000
Works on paper			
£863	$1416	€1200	Le cirque (100x78cm-39x31in) s. W/C gouache pencil. 3-Jun-3 Livinec, Gaudcheau & Jezequel, Rennes #107/R

DUFFAUT, Prefete (1923-) Haitian

£240	$400	€350	Street in mountains with bridge (51x41cm-20x16in) s. masonite. 16-Nov-3 Bonhams & Butterfields, Los Angeles #7077/R
£254	$425	€371	River with ships and mountains (61x41cm-24x16in) s. 16-Nov-3 Bonhams & Butterfields, Los Angeles #7079/R
£300	$537	€450	La pont de la baie d'azur (41x51cm-16x20in) s.d.93. 17-May-4 Rogeon, Paris #161
£333	$597	€500	Animation au bord de lac (29x40cm-11x16in) panel. 17-May-4 Rogeon, Paris #33
£1133	$2029	€1700	Village en spirale (59x78cm-23x31in) s.d.78. 17-May-4 Rogeon, Paris #81

DUFFELEN, Gerrit van (1889-1967) Dutch

£317	$576	€475	Sailing ship at anchor in port (99x79cm-39x31in) s. 30-Jun-4 Vendue Huis, Gravenhage #545
£467	$835	€700	Still life with flowers (37x29cm-15x11in) s. 11-May-4 Vendu Notarishuis, Rotterdam #227/R

DUFFIELD, M E (1819-1914) British

Works on paper			
£500	$915	€730	Still life with a rose on a rock (23x21cm-9x8in) s. W/C oval. 7-Apr-4 Woolley & Wallis, Salisbury #74/R

DUFFIELD, Mary Elizabeth (1819-1914) British

Works on paper			
£260	$442	€380	Roses and raspberries (16x47cm-6x19in) s. W/C. 25-Nov-3 Bonhams, Knightsbridge #132
£280	$504	€409	Still life with spray of yellow roses and cornflowers (38x28cm-15x11in) s. 20-Apr-4 Canterbury Auctions, UK #171
£480	$878	€701	Roses and a butterfly (23x30cm-9x12in) s.d.1863 W/C. 27-Jan-4 Bonhams, Knightsbridge #314/R
£1200	$2004	€1740	Roses and pansies in a jardiniere (57cm-22in circular) s. W/C. 26-Jun-3 Ambrose, Loughton #785/R est:1200-1500

DUFFIELD, William (1816-1863) British

£2000	$3580	€2920	Pigeon, songbirds, stoneware flask on a wooden ledge (36x48cm-14x19in) s.d.1852. 27-May-4 Christie's, Kensington #349/R est:1500-2000

DUFFIN, John (1965-) British

£500	$925	€730	We have lift off (56x38cm-22x15in) s. s.i.d.1995-2002 verso. 13-Jul-4 Bonhams, Knightsbridge #55/R

DUFFY, Ailleen Plaskett (1905-) Canadian

£645	$1200	€942	Frozen Delaware (38x38cm-15x15in) s.i.verso board. 3-Mar-4 Alderfer's, Hatfield #332 est:200-300

DUFFY, Bill and Phyllis (20th C) American

Sculpture			
£2500	$4500	€3650	Noah's Ark (64x74cm-25x29in) carved painted wood. 24-Apr-4 Slotin Folk Art, Buford #400/R est:1000-3000
£3194	$5750	€4663	Animal kingdom (74x89cm-29x35in) caved painted wood. 24-Apr-4 Slotin Folk Art, Buford #401/R est:1000-3000

DUFFY, Phyllis (?) American

£278	$500	€406	Side show by the seashore (58x69cm-23x27in) acrylic. 24-Apr-4 Slotin Folk Art, Buford #267/R

DUFFY, Rita (20th C) Irish?

£1329	$2259	€1900	Frolic (61x61cm-24x24in) s.i. s.d.1997 verso board prov. 25-Nov-3 De Veres Art Auctions, Dublin #132/R est:1000-1500

DUFLOS, Robert Louis Raymond (1898-?) French

£881	$1498	€1286	Reclining female nude on bed (38x61cm-15x24in) s. 5-Nov-3 Dobiaschofsky, Bern #499/R (S.FR 2000)
Works on paper			
£290	$536	€420	Jeune femme nue en buste (44x36cm-17x14in) s. 19-Jan-4 Horta, Bruxelles #404
£380	$653	€555	Zinnias (46x56cm-18x22in) s. col chk prov.exhib. 2-Dec-3 Ritchie, Toronto #102/R (C.D 850)

DUFNER, Edward (1872-1957) American

£7186	$12000	€10492	Portrait of the Artist's wife, Boothbay Harbour, Maine (23x18cm-9x7in) s.i.d.1938 board prov. 23-Oct-3 Shannon's, Milford #116/R est:12000-18000
Works on paper			
£2174	$3500	€3174	Summer sailing days (28x38cm-11x15in) s. W/C. 20-Aug-3 James Julia, Fairfield #1619/R est:2500-3000
£4190	$7500	€6117	Summer evening (64x76cm-25x30in) s. W/C prov.exhib. 6-May-4 Shannon's, Milford #156/R est:8000-12000

DUFOUR, Bernard (1922-) French

£412	$750	€602	Les gardiens de la villa (131x195cm-52x77in) s. painted c.1959. 29-Jun-4 Sotheby's, New York #443/R
£467	$850	€682	Untitled (97x78cm-38x31in) s.d.56. 29-Jun-4 Sotheby's, New York #441/R
£5333	$9867	€8000	Self-portrait, winter (130x195cm-51x77in) s.i.d.67 verso prov.exhib.lit. 18-Jul-4 Sotheby's, Paris #275/R est:8000-12000

DUFOUR, Camille (1841-?) French

£340	$612	€496	Scene on the Eure at Auteuil, France (36x59cm-14x23in) s. prov. 22-Apr-4 Lawrence, Crewkerne #895/R
£420	$777	€613	Lavacourt en face l'eteuil Mantes Hte Isle (24x36cm-9x14in) s.i.verso board. 10-Feb-4 Bonhams, Knightsbridge #155/R
£806	$1484	€1177	Shepherdess and flock by a stream (50x65cm-20x26in) s. 9-Jun-4 Walker's, Ottawa #317/R est:2000-2500 (C.D 2000)

DUFRENE, François (1930-1992) French

£3267	$5880	€4900	Composition (36x56cm-14x22in) s.d.1962 torn posters on canvas. 24-Apr-4 Cornette de St.Cyr, Paris #512/R est:2000-3000
Works on paper			
£1829	$3000	€2670	Untitled (26x18cm-10x7in) s.d.62 paper collage prov.exhib. 28-May-3 Sotheby's, Amsterdam #87/R est:3000-4000
£2317	$3800	€3383	Untitled (24x24cm-9x9in) s.i.d.59 paper collage on card prov.exhib. 28-May-3 Sotheby's, Amsterdam #83/R est:3000-4000
£3611	$5958	€5200	Dessous d'affiche a la paysanne II (81x53cm-32x21in) s.d.1970 s.i.d.verso torn poster on canvas. 2-Jul-3 Cornette de St.Cyr, Paris #61/R est:6000-8000
£3944	$6823	€5600	Dessous d'affiches a la paysanne II (81x54cm-32x21in) s.d.1970 s.i.d.verso torn poster. 14-Dec-3 Versailles Encheres #176/R est:5000-6000

DUFRENOY, Georges (1870-1942) French

£1678	$3121	€2500	Rue Animee (105x74cm-41x29in) s. panel. 3-Mar-4 Tajan, Paris #101 est:2500-3000
£3800	$6992	€5700	Paris, scene de rue (28x36cm-11x14in) s. 8-Jun-4 Artcurial Briest, Paris #142/R est:3000-4000

DUFRESNE, Annette (20th C) American

£316	$500	€461	Portrait of a woman (61x46cm-24x18in) s.verso prov. 7-Sep-3 Treadway Gallery, Cincinnati #678/R
£378	$650	€552	Portrait of a woman (46x36cm-18x14in) s.verso painted c.1940 prov. 7-Dec-3 Treadway Gallery, Cincinnati #695/R

DUFRESNE, Charles (1876-1938) French

£699	$1202	€1000	Trois figures et un crocodile (40x32cm-16x13in) s. canvas on cardboard. 3-Dec-3 Tajan, Paris #67/R
£707	$1300	€1032	Descent from the cross (23x18cm-9x7in) s. 9-Jun-4 Doyle, New York #3028
£933	$1671	€1400	La crucifixion (66x54cm-26x21in) exhib. 16-May-4 Osenat, Fontainebleau #78/R
£940	$1729	€1400	La Rade de Toulon (21x48cm-8x19in) s. oil paper painted c.1937. 24-Mar-4 Binoche, Paris #76
£1227	$2000	€1791	Nu couche de dos (73x100cm-29x39in) s. prov. 25-Sep-3 Christie's, Rockefeller NY #602/R est:3000-5000
£1259	$2102	€1800	Personnage dans la foret (16x22cm-6x9in) paint paper on canvas. 25-Jun-3 Blanchet, Paris #39 est:2500
£1748	$2920	€2500	Pastoral (24x33cm-9x13in) prov. 25-Jun-3 Blanchet, Paris #41/R
£2000	$3320	€2900	Le repos, ou trois femmes dans un paysage (32x33cm-13x13in) s. peinture a l'essence paper. 30-Sep-3 Blanchet, Paris #252 est:2500-3000
£3067	$5643	€4600	Chasseurs a cheval tirant sur un lionne (40x48cm-16x19in) s. 14-Jun-4 Tajan, Paris #25/R est:4000-6000
£10000	$18200	€15000	Grande crucifixion (150x150cm-59x59in) s. painted 1931 exhib.lit. 2-Jul-4 Binoche, Paris #22/R est:15000-18000
Works on paper			
£1176	$2200	€1717	Petit bain (18x23cm-7x9in) gouache pen Chinese ink. 25-Feb-4 Christie's, Rockefeller NY #82/R est:1800-2200
£1577	$2902	€2350	Orchestre algerois (17x25cm-7x10in) s. W/C exec.c.1911. 24-Mar-4 Binoche, Paris #75/R est:500-700

DUFRESNE, Charles (attrib) (1876-1938) French

£556	$906	€800	Composition with seated woman (72x59cm-28x23in) s. 26-Sep-3 Bolland & Marotz, Bremen #733/R

DUFRESNOY, Charles Alphonse (attrib) (1611-1668) French

£8333	$15000	€12166	Portrait of a man holding a portrait (107x91cm-42x36in) 22-Jan-4 Sotheby's, New York #206/R est:20000-30000

DUFY, Jean (1888-1964) French

£1399	$2378	€2000	Promenade (43x54cm-17x21in) s.i. bister. 26-Nov-3 Dorotheum, Vienna #146/R est:2000-2500
£1744	$3000	€2546	Paysage (28x38cm-11x15in) s. 7-Dec-3 Susanin's, Chicago #6083/R est:3000-5000
£2551	$4744	€3800	Vallon au pied d'un village (50x20cm-20x8in) s. exec c.1943-44. 3-Mar-4 Tajan, Paris #64 est:3000-4500
£3200	$5664	€4672	Jeune femme au collier de perles (27x22cm-11x9in) s.d.30. 27-Apr-4 Bonhams, Knightsbridge #145/R est:1000-1500

£4054 $7500 €5919 Sous-bois - la foret (85x47cm-33x19in) s.d.29 prov. 12-Feb-4 Sotheby's, New York #14/R est:7000-9000
£4360 $7500 €6366 Clowns musicians (24x19cm-9x7in) s. 3-Dec-3 Doyle, New York #139/R est:10000-15000
£5000 $9100 €7300 Nature morte aux vases de fleurs (27x35cm-11x14in) s. 3-Feb-4 Christie's, London #194/R est:5000-7000
£5595 $9623 €8000 Le cirque (36x27cm-14x11in) s. 3-Dec-3 Tajan, Paris #378/R est:4500-6000
£6593 $12000 €9626 Clowns musiciens (24x19cm-9x7in) s. 29-Jun-4 Sotheby's, New York #353/R est:10000-15000
£6993 $11888 €10000 Circus (38x46cm-15x18in) s. 29-Nov-3 Arnold, Frankfurt #141/R est:6000
£8982 $15000 €13114 Orchestra with clown guitarist (38x46cm-15x18in) s. 7-Oct-3 Sotheby's, New York #271 est:18000-25000
£9497 $17000 €13866 Bouquet de fleurs (40x33cm-16x13in) s. canvas on masonite. 6-May-4 Doyle, New York #73/R est:10000-15000
£12752 $22826 €19000 Baux de Provence (50x73cm-20x29in) s.i.d.1948. 26-May-4 Christie's, Paris #41/R est:14000-18000
£12883 $21000 €18809 Le Jardin de Tuileries (33x55cm-13x22in) s. prov. 25-Sep-3 Christie's, Rockefeller NY #589/R est:15000-20000
£14973 $28000 €21861 Vue du jardin par la fenetre (49x59cm-19x23in) s.d.1927 W/C paper on board. 25-Feb-4 Christie's, Rockefeller NY #60/R est:10000-15000
£15141 $25134 €21500 Medrano, cavaliers a l'obstacle (61x46cm-24x18in) s. lit. 11-Jun-3 Delorme & Bocage, Paris #55/R est:6000-8000
£19118 $32500 €27912 Course d'obstacles (33x46cm-13x18in) s. 6-Nov-3 Sotheby's, New York #345/R est:20000-25000
£22819 $42444 €34000 Moulin a Eau, Preuilly sur Claisse (100x73cm-39x29in) s. painted c.1943-45 lit. 3-Mar-4 Tajan, Paris #65/R est:35000-40000
£23464 $42000 €34257 Place de la Concorde (65x46cm-26x18in) s. 5-May-4 Christie's, Rockefeller NY #350/R est:40000-60000
£23529 $40000 €34352 Port de peche (100x75cm-39x30in) s. panted c.1945-50 prov. 6-Nov-3 Sotheby's, New York #328/R est:30000-40000
£25175 $42797 €36000 Seine with Ile de France (54x73cm-21x29in) s. 29-Nov-3 Arnold, Frankfurt #142/R est:8000
£27941 $47500 €40794 Voiliers dans l'avant-port du Havre (58x65cm-23x26in) s.d.27. 6-Nov-3 Sotheby's, New York #317/R est:25000-35000
£27941 $47500 €40794 Chevaliers aux courses (46x55cm-18x22in) s. painted c.1960 prov. 6-Nov-3 Sotheby's, New York #315/R est:25000-35000
£33520 $60000 €48939 Parade equestre (39x46cm-15x18in) s. 6-May-4 Sotheby's, New York #452/R est:25000-35000

Works on paper

£268 $491 €400 Maison Provencale (39x26cm-15x10in) sig.apocryphe blue ink drawing. 7-Jul-4 Artcurial Briest, Paris #24
£268 $491 €400 Feuillage (24x31cm-9x12in) studio st. ink ink wash. 7-Jul-4 Artcurial Briest, Paris #25
£274 $430 €400 Moulin (29x45cm-11x18in) s. graphite. 20-Apr-3 Deauville, France #5
£274 $430 €400 Paysage (28x48cm-11x19in) s. graphite. 20-Apr-3 Deauville, France #6
£331 $606 €500 Modele assis (61x47cm-24x19in) bears st.sig. Indian ink drawing. 7-Apr-4 Piasa, Paris #173
£331 $606 €500 Salzburg (25x40cm-10x16in) bears st.sig.i. ball pen. 7-Apr-4 Piasa, Paris #176
£364 $667 €550 Repos du modele (43x56cm-17x22in) bears studio st. Indian ink drawing. 7-Apr-4 Piasa, Paris #174
£403 $737 €600 Caleche a Cintra (25x39cm-10x15in) st.sig.i. ball point pen. 7-Jul-4 Artcurial Briest, Paris #30
£420 $701 €600 Rue animee (32x47cm-13x19in) st.sig. pencil. 13-Oct-3 Horta, Bruxelles #308
£467 $835 €700 Le cirque (27x45cm-11x18in) graphite. 16-May-4 Thierry & Lannon, Brest #385
£563 $1030 €850 Athenes (25x40cm-10x16in) bears st.sig. black crayon. 7-Apr-4 Piasa, Paris #175
£604 $1105 €900 Montmartre, le Sacre-Coeur (30x39cm-12x15in) st.sig. lead pencil drawing. 7-Jul-4 Artcurial Briest, Paris #27
£604 $1105 €900 Paris, la Tour Eiffel (25x37cm-10x15in) st.sig. lead pencil drawing. 7-Jul-4 Artcurial Briest, Paris #28
£800 $1432 €1200 Composition au vase de fleurs (25x18cm-10x7in) s. pen. 16-May-4 Thierry & Lannon, Brest #386
£839 $1427 €1200 Le paddock a Deauville (40x28cm-16x11in) studio st. pencil. 27-Nov-3 Calmels Cohen, Paris #40/R
£1067 $1920 €1600 Bouquet de fleurs (49x34cm-19x13in) st.sig. blue biro. 26-Apr-4 Tajan, Paris #74/R est:1200-1500
£1216 $2250 €1775 Landscape with trees (48x31cm-19x12in) st.sig. W/C prov. 12-Feb-4 Sotheby's, New York #10/R est:2500-3500
£1268 $2193 €1800 Poissons (28x38cm-11x15in) st.sig. W/C gouache. 14-Dec-3 Eric Pillon, Calais #131/R
£1650 $2673 €2409 Etoile with L'Arc de Triomphe, horses and carriages in foreground (27x37cm-11x15in) s. W/C. 27-Jan-3 Bristol Auction Rooms #449 est:500-700
£1867 $3397 €2800 Bouquet of flowers (45x39cm-18x15in) s.d.1920 W/C paper on board. 30-Jun-4 Calmels Cohen, Paris #1/R est:3000-4000
£1958 $3368 €2800 Fruits, bouquet de fleurs et tube de couleur (50x40cm-20x16in) s. W/C. 3-Dec-3 Tajan, Paris #43 est:3000-5000
£3145 $5000 €4592 Bouquet de fleurs un interieur (58x51cm-23x20in) s. W/C prov. 9-Sep-3 Arthur James, Florida #106
£3356 $6141 €5000 Scene de Cirque (44x58cm-17x23in) s.d.1925 W/C ink lit. 7-Jul-4 Artcurial Briest, Paris #22/R est:5000-7000
£3662 $6335 €5200 Bouquet de fleurs (51x37cm-20x15in) s. W/C gouache. 10-Dec-3 Remi Ader, Paris #43/R est:4000-5000
£3662 $6335 €5200 Bouquet de fleurs (51x37cm-20x15in) s. W/C gouache. 10-Dec-3 Neret-Minet, Paris #43/R est:4000-5000
£4545 $7818 €6500 Circus (48x60cm-19x24in) s.d.26 W/C gouache. 2-Dec-3 Christie's, Paris #366/R est:4600-6000
£5215 $8500 €7614 Les fleurs (55x41cm-22x16in) s.d.24 W/C. 25-Sep-3 Christie's, Rockefeller NY #596/R est:7000-9000
£6145 $11000 €8972 Still life (37x39cm-15x15in) s.d.1913 pastel. 6-May-4 Sotheby's, New York #416/R est:5000-7000
£6486 $12000 €9470 Jardin public mediterraneen (48x61cm-19x24in) s.d.26 W/C. 11-Feb-4 Sotheby's, New York #77/R est:15000-20000
£6593 $12000 €9626 Clowns musiciens (31x44cm-12x17in) s. gouache W/C prov. 29-Jun-4 Sotheby's, New York #348/R est:10000-15000
£6952 $13000 €10150 Voiliers d'Ile d'Yeu (46x60cm-18x24in) s.i.d.1928 W/C. 25-Feb-4 Christie's, Rockefeller NY #97/R est:7000-9000
£8108 $15000 €11838 Trapeziste (59x44cm-23x17in) s. W/C gouache paper on canvas prov. 11-Feb-4 Sotheby's, New York #69/R est:18000-25000
£9000 $16560 €13140 Bouquet de dahlias (50x36cm-20x14in) s. W/C gouache. 24-Mar-4 Sotheby's, Olympia #31/R est:5000-7000
£10270 $19000 €14994 Jardin des Tuileries (48x64cm-19x25in) s. W/C gouache. 11-Feb-4 Sotheby's, New York #67/R est:20000-30000
£11173 $20000 €16313 Bouquet de fleurs au coquillage (61x46cm-24x18in) s. gouache paper on board prov. 5-May-4 Christie's, Rockefeller NY #119/R est:14000-18000
£11628 $20000 €16977 Le bois de Boulogne (45x60cm-18x24in) s. gouache W/C. 3-Dec-3 Doyle, New York #138/R est:15000-25000
£14054 $26000 €20519 Honfleur (45x60cm-18x24in) s. W/C gouache prov. 11-Feb-4 Sotheby's, New York #74/R est:15000-20000
£14437 $24975 €20500 Paddock (44x62cm-17x24in) s. W/C gouache. 14-Dec-3 Eric Pillon, Calais #102/R
£14865 $27500 €21703 Chevaux en liberte (45x59cm-18x23in) s. W/C gouache prov. 11-Feb-4 Sotheby's, New York #68/R est:12000-18000
£15363 $27500 €22430 Port du Havre (46x60cm-18x24in) s. gouache W/C paper on canvas. 6-May-4 Sotheby's, New York #457/R est:15000-20000
£20321 $38000 €29669 Scene de cirque (65x50cm-26x20in) s. gouache paper on canvas prov. 25-Feb-4 Christie's, Rockefeller NY #99/R est:15000-20000
£24324 $45000 €35513 Institut de France (49x65cm-19x26in) s. gouache paper on canvas prov. 11-Feb-4 Sotheby's, New York #59/R est:20000-30000

DUFY, Raoul (1877-1953) French

£11173 $20000 €16313 Entree musicale (37x27cm-15x11in) s. 6-May-4 Sotheby's, New York #460/R est:15000-20000
£17647 $30000 €25765 Chopin (22x27cm-9x11in) s.i. painted 1941 prov.exhib.lit. 5-Nov-3 Christie's, Rockefeller NY #356/R est:30000-40000
£22887 $36849 €32500 Peintre et son epouse (16x23cm-6x9in) s.d.1941 panel. 22-Aug-3 Deauville, France #78/R est:30000-40000
£25503 $45141 €38000 Decoration florale pour une porte (250x97cm-98x38in) st.sig. panel painted 1912 prov.exhib. 27-Apr-4 Artcurial Briest, Paris #174/R est:40000-60000
£26471 $45000 €38648 Violon bleu (24x33cm-9x13in) s.i. painted c.1950 prov.exhib.lit. 5-Nov-3 Christie's, Rockefeller NY #355/R est:30000-40000
£27941 $47500 €40794 St James's Palace (34x41cm-13x16in) s.i.d.1935. 6-Nov-3 Sotheby's, New York #243/R est:50000-70000
£31788 $57854 €48000 La jetee de Sainte-Adresse (38x46cm-15x18in) s. painted c.1907 prov.exhib. 18-Jun-4 Piasa, Paris #26/R est:50000-60000
£35000 $64400 €51100 La voie ferree (38x45cm-15x18in) s. painted 1940 prov.lit. 23-Jun-4 Christie's, London #184/R est:35000-45000
£38462 $66154 €55000 L'avenue de bois de Boulogne a Paris (46x55cm-18x22in) s. lit. 2-Dec-3 Calmels Cohen, Paris #50/R est:60000-80000
£39106 $70000 €57095 Sacre-Coeur du Montmartre, Rue Pavoise (27x19cm-11x7in) s.d.1902 prov.lit. 6-May-4 Sotheby's, New York #444/R est:70000-90000
£45000 $81900 €65700 Les canotiers sur la marne (60x73cm-24x29in) s. painted c,1922-25 prov. 4-Feb-4 Sotheby's, London #225/R est:50000-70000
£47059 $80000 €68706 Saint-Paul de Vence (54x65cm-21x26in) s. painted c.1925 prov.lit. 6-Nov-3 Sotheby's, New York #191/R est:100000-150000
£48000 $88320 €70080 Port (38x46cm-15x18in) s. prov. 22-Jun-4 Sotheby's, London #161/R est:50000-70000
£55000 $100100 €80300 Deauville, le paddock (54x64cm-21x25in) s. painted 1930-1935 prov. 3-Feb-4 Christie's, London #246/R est:70000-100000
£56579 $104105 €86000 Clair de lune a Nice (33x41cm-13x16in) s. prov. 22-Jun-4 Ribeyre & Baron, Paris #66/R est:35000-45000
£63758 $114128 €95000 Peintre et modele (81x65cm-32x26in) s. s.verso painted 1909 exhib.lit. 29-May-4 Farsetti, Prato #517/R est:90000-110000
£64706 $110000 €94471 La place d'Hyeres l'obelisque et le kiosque a musique (37x46cm-15x18in) s. painted 1927 prov.exhib.lit. 5-Nov-3 Christie's, Rockefeller NY #255/R est:80000-100000
£64706 $110000 €94471 Courses a Deauville (28x35cm-11x14in) s. painted c.1941 prov.exhib. 6-Nov-3 Sotheby's, New York #197/R est:80000-120000
£65000 $119600 €94900 Forban (33x82cm-13x32in) s.d.1935 lit. 22-Jun-4 Sotheby's, London #162/R est:70000-100000
£68000 $123760 €99280 L'avenue du bois (61x73cm-24x29in) s.d.1908 exhib.lit. 3-Feb-4 Christie's, London #158/R est:60000-80000
£78488 $135000 €114592 Langres (81x101cm-32x40in) s. painted 1935 prov.exhib.lit. 3-Dec-3 Doyle, New York #39/R est:140000-180000
£88235 $150000 €128823 Canotiers (60x70cm-24x28in) s. painted c.1923 prov.exhib.lit. 6-Nov-3 Sotheby's, New York #171a/R est:90000-120000
£98000 $178360 €143080 Voiliers a Deauville (28x73cm-11x29in) s.d.1935 prov. 4-Feb-4 Sotheby's, London #249/R est:70000-90000
£100000 $170000 €146000 14 Juillet a Antibes (46x54cm-18x21in) s. painted 1912. 5-Nov-3 Christie's, Rockefeller NY #251/R est:180000-220000
£117483 $202070 €168000 L'estacade des bains (65x81cm-26x32in) s. prov. 5-Dec-3 Maigret, Paris #97/R est:55000-65000
£135000 $225450 €197100 La rentree des regattes (46x55cm-18x22in) s. painted 1930 prov.exhib.lit. 21-Oct-3 Sotheby's, London #63/R est:120000-150000
£139665 $250000 €203911 Nu debout aux tableaux (65x54cm-26x21in) s. painted 1944 prov.exhib.lit. 6-May-4 Sotheby's, New York #284/R est:20000-250000
£140000 $254800 €204400 Les voiles au sec (46x55cm-18x22in) s. painted 1932 prov.exhib.lit. 3-Feb-4 Christie's, London #248/R est:140000-180000
£150000 $276000 €219000 La jetee (65x81cm-26x32in) s. painted 1906 prov.lit. 23-Jun-4 Christie's, London #150/R est:150000-200000
£176471 $300000 €257648 Barques aux Martigues (46x54cm-18x21in) s. painted 1907 prov.exhib. 5-Nov-3 Christie's, Rockefeller NY #244/R est:280000-350000
£180000 $327600 €262800 Fete nautique (65x81cm-26x32in) s. painted c.1920-22 prov.exhib.lit. 4-Feb-4 Sotheby's, London #236/R est:150000-200000
£180000 $331200 €262800 Le marche a Falaise (45x54cm-18x21in) s. painted 1905 prov.lit. 23-Jun-4 Christie's, London #145/R est:130000-180000
£211268 $365493 €300000 Saint-Tropez (60x73cm-24x29in) s. prov.exhib.lit. 12-Dec-3 Piasa, Paris #18/R est:150000-200000
£1564246 $2800000 €2283799 Fete a Sainte-Adresse (63x79cm-25x31in) s. painted 1906 prov.exhib.lit. 5-May-4 Sotheby's, New York #6/R est:1800000-2200000

Prints

£3169 $5482 €4500 La grande baigneuse (68x52cm-27x20in) s.num. col lithograph vellum edition of 40 exec.c.1928. 11-Dec-3 Piasa, Paris #32/R

Works on paper

£260 $434 €380 Design for Bianchini-Ferier (47x33cm-19x13in) gouache. 21-Oct-3 Bonhams, Knightsbridge #152/R
£280 $481 €400 Etude de coquillage (65x50cm-26x20in) s. Indian ink. 3-Dec-3 Tajan, Paris #42
£302 $553 €450 Personnage assis (16x11cm-6x4in) st.init. crayon drawing. 7-Jul-4 Artcurial Briest, Paris #33
£352 $609 €500 Moissons (20x26cm-8x10in) s. crayon conte. 10-Dec-3 Remi Ader, Paris #61
£352 $609 €500 Moissons (20x26cm-8x10in) s. crayon conte. 10-Dec-3 Neret-Minet, Paris #61
£420 $701 €600 Portrait de jeune garcon (51x33cm-20x13in) s. crayon dr. 27-Jun-3 Doutrebente, Paris #30/R
£462 $850 €675 Epson (25x20cm-10x8in) s.i. gouache W/C. 11-Jun-4 David Rago, Lambertville #298/R

£470	$869	€700	Deux fleurs sur fond orange (14x9cm-6x4in) st.init. gouache decoupe lit. 15-Mar-4 Blanchet, Paris #86
£503	$921	€750	Deux Marguerites (7x10cm-3x4in) init. verso gouache. 7-Jul-4 Artcurial Briest, Paris #32
£655	$1212	€950	Le repas des moissonneurs (31x50cm-12x20in) st.sig. pencil prov. 13-Feb-4 Charbonneaux, Paris #42
£679	$1154	€991	Composition avec danseuses (56x42cm-22x17in) st.mono. ink gouache. 22-Nov-3 Burkhard, Luzern #95/R (S.FR 1500)
£699	$1168	€1000	Naiades (50x66cm-20x26in) ink gouache. 25-Jun-3 Blanchet, Paris #31/R
£750	$1328	€1095	La vendage (29x23cm-11x9in) s. pencil prov. 27-Apr-4 Bonhams, Knightsbridge #113/R
£900	$1593	€1314	Etude de textile - chevaux, Voiliers, Fontaines (58x61cm-23x24in) collage W/C. 27-Apr-4 Bonhams, Knightsbridge #75/R
£972	$1624	€1400	Vue d'une ville (19x19cm-7x7in) st.mono. pencil double-sided. 24-Oct-3 Ketterer, Hamburg #325/R
£973	$1800	€1421	Fontaine (34x27cm-13x11in) studio st. pencil exec 1909-10. 12-Feb-4 Sotheby's, New York #12/R est:2500-3500
£986	$1706	€1400	Paysage aux vaches (29x46cm-11x18in) graphite dr lit. 9-Dec-3 Artcurial Briest, Paris #210 est:1300-1600
£1100	$1837	€1606	Roses (51x46cm-20x18in) gouache over pencil prov. 22-Oct-3 Sotheby's, Olympia #130/R est:800-1200
£1119	$1924	€1600	Etude des arbres (24x30cm-9x12in) s. W/C pencil prov. 2-Dec-3 Sotheby's, Amsterdam #82/R est:2500-3500
£1189	$2045	€1700	Personnages (27x22cm-11x9in) bears studio st. ink wash lit. 3-Dec-3 Tajan, Paris #41/R est:1800-2000
£1250	$2088	€1800	Les roses (43x33cm-17x13in) gouache. 24-Oct-3 Ketterer, Hamburg #323/R est:1800-2000
£1259	$2065	€1750	Portrait de Monsieur Geissmar (78x60cm-31x24in) bears studio st. Indian ink. 6-Jun-3 David Kahn, Paris #34 est:2200
£1283	$2400	€1873	Voiliers (39x51cm-15x20in) s. W/C pen ink exec.1922-24 prov. 25-Feb-4 Christie's, Rockefeller NY #98/R est:3000-5000
£1736	$2899	€2500	Rayure roses florales (52x37cm-20x15in) i. gouache. 24-Oct-3 Ketterer, Hamburg #322/R est:2500-3500
£1765	$3000	€2577	Design for wallpaper (58x45cm-23x18in) init. gouache pencil prov.exhib. 9-Nov-3 Bonhams & Butterfields, Los Angeles #4021/R
£1846	$3433	€2750	Regates (30x46cm-12x18in) graphite. 2-Mar-4 Artcurial Briest, Paris #42/R est:2800-3200
£1946	$3581	€2900	Baccara (34x25cm-13x10in) mono. ink exhib.lit. 24-Mar-4 Joron-Derem, Paris #46/R est:3500-4000
£2028	$3387	€2900	Paysage (25x48cm-10x19in) st.sig. graphite dr. 25-Jun-3 Digard, Paris #100/R est:2500-3000
£2109	$3775	€3100	Le kiosque a musique (48x63cm-19x25in) s. ink. 19-Mar-4 Oger, Dumont, Paris #11/R est:3000
£2530	$4200	€3694	Le Paddock (35x54cm-14x21in) s.d.1931 pen ink htd gouache prov.exhib. 2-Oct-3 Christie's, Tel Aviv #39/R est:4000-6000
£2651	$4400	€3870	La plage (15x31cm-6x12in) s. gouache W/C exec 1951 prov. 2-Oct-3 Christie's, Tel Aviv #40/R est:4000-6000
£2700	$4509	€3942	Sitting nude (65x49cm-26x19in) s.d.1929 pen ink prov. 22-Oct-3 Sotheby's, Olympia #132/R est:2500-3500
£2703	$5000	€3946	Danseuse jaune (44x33cm-17x13in) studio st. pencil W/C laid paper exec 1922. 12-Feb-4 Sotheby's, New York #15/R est:7000-9000
£2892	$4800	€4222	Notre orchester a Guaymas. Old Tuscan square dancers. Portrait of Charlotte Bergman (21x28cm-8x11in) s.i. s.i.d.Avril 1951 s.i. pen ink pencil three prov.exhib. 2-Oct-3 Christie's, Tel Aviv #38/R est:5000-7000
£2937	$5462	€4375	Passerelle du Queen Mary (50x65cm-20x26in) i. ink htd white chk. 3-Mar-4 Tajan, Paris #62/R est:5000-6000
£2958	$5176	€4200	Compositions. st.sig. gouache pair. 19-Dec-3 Delvaux, Paris #46 est:2000-2500
£3304	$5617	€4824	La peniche (30x23cm-12x9in) s. W/C lit. 5-Nov-3 Dobiaschofsky, Bern #501/R est:7500 (S.FR 7500)
£3333	$6133	€5000	Baigneuse au coquillage (61x47cm-24x19in) ink dr exec. c.1930 prov. 11-Jun-4 Pierre Berge, Paris #230/R est:5000-6000
£3380	$5915	€4800	Compositions (66x48cm-26x19in) st.sig. gouache pair. 19-Dec-3 Delvaux, Paris #47/R est:3000-3500
£3800	$6346	€5548	Trumpet player (65x50cm-26x20in) s. pen ink gouache exec 1942 prov. 22-Oct-3 Sotheby's, Olympia #133/R est:4000-6000
£4192	$7000	€6120	Le basin a Deauville (50x65cm-20x26in) st.sig. ink. 7-Oct-3 Sotheby's, New York #260 est:7000-9000
£4200	$7728	€6132	Semis de fleurs et d'epis de ble (60x46cm-24x18in) gouache. 24-Mar-4 Sotheby's, Olympia #136/R est:1000-1500
£4518	$7500	€6596	J S Bach (50x62cm-20x24in) s. mono.i. pen ink htd gouache exec 1950 prov.exhib. 2-Oct-3 Christie's, Tel Aviv #37/R est:3000-4000
£5521	$9000	€8061	Petite eglise dans la campagne et charrette de foin (47x63cm-19x25in) s. W/C exec.c.1930. 25-Sep-3 Christie's, Rockefeller NY #552/R est:10000-15000
£5594	$9622	€8000	Nice, la baie des anges (54x46cm-21x18in) s. pencil ink executed c.1926 prov. 2-Dec-3 Sotheby's, Amsterdam #77/R est:8000-12000
£6000	$10380	€8760	Vue de Sainte-Addresse (46x21cm-18x8in) s. chl brush black ink W/C exec.c.1949 prov. 11-Dec-3 Christie's, Kensington #191/R est:6000-8000
£9396	$16631	€14000	Olivier en provence (49x64cm-19x25in) s. W/C. 29-Apr-4 Claude Aguttes, Neuilly #175/R
£9412	$16000	€13742	Une charrette (43x53cm-17x21in) s. W/C brush brown ink pencil prov. 5-Nov-3 Christie's, Rockefeller NY #156/R est:18000-22000
£9412	$16000	€13742	Cour de ferme (50x65cm-20x26in) s. gouache exec 1943 lit. 6-Nov-3 Sotheby's, New York #346/R est:20000-30000
£9639	$16000	€14073	Le Paddock (29x44cm-11x17in) s.i.d.27 gouache W/C pen ink pencil prov.exhib.lit. 2-Oct-3 Christie's, Tel Aviv #41/R est:10000-15000
£9718	$16813	€13800	Canards (51x65cm-20x26in) s. W/C exec.1927. 15-Dec-3 Marc Kohn, Paris #92/R est:24000
£10811	$20000	€15784	Anemones (40x40cm-16x16in) st.sig. gouache oil paper on canvas prov.lit. 11-Feb-4 Sotheby's, New York #35/R est:12000-18000
£11000	$20240	€16060	Baccara (45x55cm-18x22in) s. pen ink prov.exhib.lit. 22-Jun-4 Sotheby's, London #437/R est:8000-12000
£11894	$20220	€17365	Le promeneur au bord de mer, au Havre (50x65cm-20x26in) s. gouache prov. 5-Nov-3 Dobiaschofsky, Bern #500/R est:20000 (S.FR 27000)
£12000	$20040	€17520	Nu a la Renoir (50x66cm-20x26in) st.sig. pastel executed c.1930-31 prov. 21-Oct-3 Sotheby's, London #103/R est:14000-18000
£12941	$22000	€18894	L'orchestre Mexicain (176x220cm-69x87in) woven sig. num.2/6 verso wool tapestry prov. 6-Nov-3 Sotheby's, New York #372/R est:25000-35000
£13408	$24000	€19576	Voiliers (44x55cm-17x22in) s. W/C. 5-May-4 Christie's, Rockefeller NY #143/R est:18000-22000
£13637	$22773	€19500	Pont au pecheur (20x65cm-8x26in) s. W/C gouache. 30-Jun-3 Artcurial Briest, Paris #723/R est:20000-25000
£15363	$27500	€22430	Promeneur au bord de mer au Havre (50x64cm-20x25in) s. W/C exec c.1924 prov.lit. 6-May-4 Sotheby's, New York #456/R est:20000-30000
£16760	$30000	€24470	Feu d'artifice (50x65cm-20x26in) gouache W/C pencil paper on board exec 1950 prov.exhib. 5-May-4 Christie's, Rockefeller NY #139/R est:30000-40000
£16784	$28868	€24000	Bateau au large des cotes normandes (20x43cm-8x17in) studio st. gouache prov. 8-Dec-3 Artcurial Briest, Paris #38/R est:25000-30000
£18000	$32760	€26280	Manoir du Vallon, le vent dans les arbres (50x65cm-20x26in) s. gouache exec 1932 prov.exhib. 5-Feb-4 Christie's, London #334/R est:12000-16000
£18000	$32940	€27000	Le marche du Havre (45x48cm-18x19in) s. W/C crayon exec. c.1900 lit. 7-Jun-4 Artcurial Briest, Paris #19/R est:30000-40000
£18000	$33120	€26280	London (51x66cm-20x26in) s.i.d.1929 W/C pencil prov.lit. 24-Jun-4 Christie's, London #253/R est:20000-30000
£18824	$32000	€27483	Paysage a Vallauris (51x65cm-20x26in) s. W/C paper on board. 5-Nov-3 Christie's, Rockefeller NY #120/R est:25000-35000
£20000	$33400	€29200	Paysage aux troncs d'arbres (50x66cm-20x26in) s. gouache W/C prov.lit. 21-Oct-3 Sotheby's, London #116/R est:18000-20000
£21678	$36853	€31000	Projet pour le Palais des Lumieres (50x119cm-20x47in) s. gouache paper on cardboard prov.lit. 28-Nov-3 Doutrebente, Paris #21/R est:45000
£21769	$38966	€32000	Waterloo Bridge (50x64cm-20x25in) s. W/C exec. c.1928-1930. 21-Mar-4 Calmels Cohen, Paris #178/R est:30000-40000
£22000	$40040	€32120	Hyde Park (50x65cm-20x26in) s. gouache W/C exec c.1930 prov. 5-Feb-4 Christie's, London #333/R est:10000-15000
£23077	$39231	€33000	Corrida (47x62cm-19x24in) s. W/C graphite. 28-Nov-3 Drouot Estimations, Paris #181/R est:20000-25000
£25000	$45500	€36500	Le 14 juillet a Aspet (50x65cm-20x26in) s. gouache W/C over pencil exec.1943 prov. 4-Feb-4 Sotheby's, London #446/R est:25000-35000
£26471	$45000	€38648	Paysage (50x65cm-20x26in) s. gouache W/C over pencil paper on board prov. 5-Nov-3 Christie's, Rockefeller NY #137/R est:30000-40000
£27972	$47552	€40000	Port de Marseille (49x64cm-19x25in) s.d.1924 W/C. 18-Nov-3 Vanderkindere, Brussels #127/R est:40000-60000
£30000	$55200	€43800	Petit paddock (29x43cm-11x17in) s.i. W/C gouache pen ink exec 1928 prov.exhib.lit. 24-Jun-4 Christie's, London #359/R est:22000-28000
£32000	$58880	€46720	Trio casals (49x63cm-19x25in) s. gouache W/C exec 1946. 24-Jun-4 Christie's, London #356/R est:30000-50000
£32000	$58880	€46720	Bateaux en mer (51x66cm-20x26in) s. gouache W/C exec c.1925 prov. 24-Jun-4 Christie's, London #360/R est:15000-20000
£35000	$64400	€51100	Regates a Fecamp. L'estacade (23x35cm-9x14in) W/C pencil double-sided exec 1905 prov. 24-Jun-4 Christie's, London #332/R est:35000-45000
£35000	$64400	€51100	Roses (50x66cm-20x26in) s.d.1941 gouache W/C prov.lit. 24-Jun-4 Christie's, London #361/R est:35000-45000
£35000	$64400	€51100	Enfants dans le parc a Hardancourt (50x65cm-20x26in) s.d.1932 W/C prov.lit. 22-Jun-4 Sotheby's, London #432/R est:35000-45000
£36000	$65520	€52560	Courses a Goodwood (38x28cm-15x11in) studio st. gouache brush ink pencil black crayon exec.c.1935 prov. 4-Feb-4 Sotheby's, London #447/R est:35000-45000
£38000	$69160	€55480	Reception chez le Pacha de Marrakech (50x65cm-20x26in) s. gouache W/C pencil exec 1926 prov. 5-Feb-4 Christie's, London #335/R est:40000-60000
£38000	$69920	€55480	Corrida (59x64cm-23x25in) s.d.1920 W/C pencil. 24-Jun-4 Christie's, London #342/R est:40000-60000
£38000	$69920	€55480	Ecuries a Pont-l'Eveque (50x64cm-20x25in) s. W/C prov.lit. 22-Jun-4 Sotheby's, London #430/R est:35000-50000
£40268	$74094	€60000	Deauville, le depart (50x65cm-20x26in) s.i.d.1929 W/C exhib.lit. 29-Mar-4 Rieunier, Paris #60/R est:50000-60000
£43296	$77500	€63212	Bouquet de fleurs (48x64cm-19x25in) s. W/C prov.lit. 6-May-4 Sotheby's, New York #280/R est:40000-60000
£44000	$80080	€64240	Leda et le cygne (48x64cm-19x25in) s. gouache exec 1928 prov.lit. 5-Feb-4 Christie's, London #339/R est:50000-70000
£44118	$75000	€64412	Grand Canal a Venise (48x63cm-19x25in) s.d.1938 W/C prov. 6-Nov-3 Sotheby's, New York #348/R est:50000-70000
£47486	$85000	€69330	Fenetre ouverte, sur La Madeleine (66x50cm-26x20in) s. W/C gouache over pencil exec 1925 prov. 5-May-4 Christie's, Rockefeller NY #152/R est:40000-60000
£48000	$88320	€70080	Deauville, le depart (50x66cm-20x26in) s.i.d.1929 gouache W/C prov.lit. 24-Jun-4 Christie's, London #343/R est:50000-60000
£54585	$99345	€79694	Champ de courses de Deauville (50x65cm-20x26in) s. W/C exec. c.1930. 18-Jun-4 Kornfeld, Bern #34/R est:80000 (S.FR 125000)
£67039	$120000	€97877	Nu debout dans l'atelier de l'impasse de Guelma (50x65cm-20x26in) s.d.1930 gouache exec 1930 prov.lit. 5-May-4 Christie's, Rockefeller NY #120/R est:80000-120000
£90000	$165600	€131400	Promenade des Anglais a Nice (50x66cm-20x26in) s. studio st. gouache prov. 24-Jun-4 Christie's, London #341/R est:55000-75000
£130000	$239200	€189800	Tour Eiffel (74x57cm-29x22in) s.i. gouache pencil card exec c.1929-30 prov.lit. 24-Jun-4 Christie's, London #352/R est:120000-180000
£195531	$350000	€285475	Jockeys et turfistes a Epsom (50x64cm-20x25in) s. gouache W/C exec.1939 prov.exhib.lit. 5-May-4 Sotheby's, New York #29/R est:200000-300000

DUGDALE, Thomas Cantrell (1880-1952) British

£1000	$1820	€1460	Reclining female nude (63x76cm-25x30in) s. 1-Jul-4 Christie's, Kensington #46/R est:1000-1500
£2500	$4650	€3650	Portrait of a gentleman in a white doublet and red breeches, in a landscape (127x102cm-50x40in) s.i. 4-Mar-4 Christie's, Kensington #388/R est:3000-5000
£5000	$8350	€7300	Gentleman with his pipe standing in a doorway (91x72cm-36x28in) s. 16-Oct-3 Christie's, Kensington #305/R est:3000-5000

DUGDALE, Thomas Cantrell (attrib) (1880-1952) British

£750	$1298	€1095	Academic female nude studies from the rear (76x51cm-30x20in) i. two. 11-Dec-3 Scarborough Perry Fine Arts, Hove #656

DUGGINS, James Edward (1881-1968) British

£1000	$1720	€1460	Fishing boats by a coastal village (31x39cm-12x15in) s. board. 4-Dec-3 Locke & England, Leamington Spa #139/R est:100-150

DUGHET, Gaspard (1615-1675) French

£1042	$1698	€1500	Southern landscape with water fall and figures (37x55cm-15x22in) 24-Sep-3 Neumeister, Munich #341/R est:2200
£8075	$13000	€11790	Panoramic landscape with castle and city (84x117cm-33x46in) canvas on panel. 20-Aug-3 James Julia, Fairfield #651/R est:20000-30000
£16448	$30264	€25000	Village fortifie (74x97cm-29x38in) 24-Jun-4 Tajan, Paris #49/R est:25000-35000
£22000	$40260	€32120	Italianate river landscape with a villa and shepherds resting with their flock (78x111cm-31x44in) prov.lit. 7-Jul-4 Christie's, London #69/R est:12000-18000

Works on paper

£1338	$2315	€1900	Sujet biblique (27x21cm-11x8in) black crayon. 12-Dec-3 Renaud, Paris #24/R est:1500
£2113	$3655	€3000	La vocation des apotres (18x43cm-7x17in) black crayon. 12-Dec-3 Renaud, Paris #25/R est:2000-3000

DUGHET, Gaspard (attrib) (1615-1675) French

£1081	$1859	€1578	Landscape with figures and fort (36x28cm-14x11in) 8-Dec-3 Philippe Schuler, Zurich #3403/R (S.FR 2400)

£6704 $12000 €9788 Arcadian landscape with classical figures on path (99x94cm-39x37in) 27-May-4 Sotheby's, New York #91/R est:15000-20000
Works on paper
£1000 $1800 €1460 Landscape with river and classical buildings in the background (31x21cm-12x8in) bears i.verso pen brown ink wash prov.lit. 20-Apr-4 Sotheby's, Olympia #23/R est:1200-1800

DUGHET, Gaspard (circle) (1615-1675) French
£5200 $8996 €7592 Classical landscape with peasants resting beside a track (61x73cm-24x29in) 12-Dec-3 Christie's, Kensington #149/R est:4000-6000

DUGHET, Gaspard (school) (1615-1675) French
£9333 $16707 €14000 River landscape with figures (118x174cm-46x69in) 17-May-4 Finarte Semenzato, Rome #78/R est:14000-16000

DUGHET, Gaspard (style) (1615-1675) French
£5500 $10065 €8030 Temple of Concorde, Rome (93x136cm-37x54in) 9-Jul-4 Christie's, Kensington #103/R est:4000-6000
£5800 $10440 €8468 Classical landscape with Arcadian figures (73x99cm-29x39in) 20-Apr-4 Sotheby's, Olympia #375/R est:5000-7000

DUGOURC, Jean Demosthene (attrib) (1749-1825) French
Works on paper
£479 $815 €700 Trophees militaires (31x49cm-12x19in) i. sanguine. 6-Nov-3 Tajan, Paris #68

DUGUID, Henry G (fl.1831-1860) British
£3000 $4830 €4350 Melrose Abbey, Vale of the Tweed, moonlight. Kilchurn Castle (25x31cm-10x12in) s.d.56 i.verso board feigned pair. 21-Aug-3 Bonhams, Edinburgh #1076/R est:2000-3000
£3000 $5100 €4380 View of Edinburgh from the Braid Hills (51x76cm-20x30in) exhib. 30-Oct-3 Christie's, London #11/R est:3000-5000

DUHEM, Henri Aime (1860-1941) French
£298 $542 €450 Bord de riviere (36x46cm-14x18in) s. 20-Jun-4 Imberdis, Pont Audemer #47
£349 $642 €530 Automne (33x41cm-13x16in) s. 23-Jun-4 Maigret, Paris #96
£615 $1100 €898 In the hay fields (23x33cm-9x13in) s.verso panel prov. 14-May-4 Skinner, Boston #29/R

DUINEN, Jacob Hendrik van (1840-1885) Dutch
£1053 $1905 €1600 Ships in the inner harbour (19x30cm-7x12in) s.d.73 panel. 19-Apr-4 Glerum, Amsterdam #12/R est:1200-1400

DUIZ, Giovanni (1923-) Italian
£769 $1323 €1100 Boats and wrecks (50x97cm-20x38in) s.d.74 s.i.verso board. 3-Dec-3 Stadion, Trieste #958/R

DUJARDIN, Karel (1622-1678) Dutch
£1313 $2100 €1917 Picnic day (41x30cm-16x12in) 21-Sep-3 Grogan, Boston #3/R

DUJARDIN, Karel (attrib) (1622-1678) Dutch
£898 $1500 €1311 Portrait of a nobleman (71x53cm-28x21in) 19-Oct-3 Susanin's, Chicago #6029/R est:2000-4000
£2222 $3667 €3200 Rider with horse, dogs and dead hare (24x19cm-9x7in) panel. 3-Jul-3 Van Ham, Cologne #970/R est:5800
£2657 $4250 €3879 Portrait of a man half-length (76x61cm-30x24in) 20-Sep-3 Bunte, Elgin #1408 est:10000-15000
£5500 $9900 €8030 Southern landscape with a boy fording a stream on a pony (35x46cm-14x18in) 22-Apr-4 Sotheby's, London #80/R est:6000-8000

DUJARDIN, Victoire Augustine (19th C) French
Works on paper
£625 $1150 €950 Portrait de Charlotte Corday (125x69cm-49x27in) s.d.1879 chl crayon. 24-Jun-4 Credit Municipal, Paris #37/R

DUKE FRANZ FERDINAND (1863-1914) Austrian
Works on paper
£805 $1426 €1200 House (26x17cm-10x7in) s.d.1884 Indian ink. 29-Apr-4 Dorotheum, Vienna #168/R

DUKE, A (19th C) British
£6200 $11284 €9052 The Squire (43x53cm-17x21in) s.d.97. 29-Jun-4 Beeston Castle Salerooms, Tarporley #417/R est:2000-3000

DUKE, A C (19/20th C) British
£1200 $2040 €1752 Fisherfolk gossiping on the shore (36x119cm-14x47in) s.i. 19-Nov-3 Christie's, Kensington #564/R est:800-1200

DUKE, Alfred (?-1905) British
£500 $920 €730 Terriers ratting (35x46cm-14x18in) s. 10-Jun-4 Christie's, Kensington #383/R
£700 $1281 €1022 Unwelcome dinner guest (34x42cm-13x17in) s. 8-Apr-4 Christie's, Kensington #135/R
£2143 $3686 €3129 Hounds on the scent (46x76cm-18x30in) s. 2-Dec-3 Ritchie, Toronto #56/R est:4000-6000 (C.D 4800)
£3400 $6188 €4964 Two setters (29x39cm-11x15in) s. 5-Feb-4 Mellors & Kirk, Nottingham #592/R est:2000-3000
£3600 $6552 €5256 Otter hounds and a Fox Terrier (40x29cm-16x11in) s. 5-Feb-4 Mellors & Kirk, Nottingham #593/R est:2000-3000
£8000 $13600 €11680 English setter and a pointer (61x76cm-24x30in) s. 27-Nov-3 Christie's, Kensington #415/R est:8000-12000

DUKE, Peder (1938-) Swedish
£616 $1109 €899 Composition - formskynken. s.d.1999 verso. 26-Apr-4 Bukowskis, Stockholm #515/R (S.KR 8500)
£616 $1108 €899 The flower (100x89cm-39x35in) s.d.1995. 26-Jan-4 Lilla Bukowskis, Stockholm #722 (S.KR 8200)
£729 $1341 €1094 The night's shelter (93x102cm-37x40in) s.d.1995 verso. 14-Jun-4 Lilla Bukowskis, Stockholm #277 (S.KR 10000)

DULAC, Edmund (1882-1953) British/French
Works on paper
£380 $692 €555 Portrait of a seated gentleman (24x16cm-9x6in) s.i.d.1907 W/C. 15-Jun-4 Bonhams, Knightsbridge #91/R
£1400 $2548 €2100 Programme for Stravinsky's L'oiseau de Feu (32x24cm-13x9in) W/C htd gold silver ink five exec.c.1909 slipcase. 2-Jul-4 Bloomsbury, London #303/R est:1200-1500
£1450 $2320 €2117 A castle (23x30cm-9x12in) s.i.d.1905 W/C bodycol. 16-Sep-3 Rosebery Fine Art, London #414 est:1500-2000
£3889 $7000 €5678 Friar and the song (44x28cm-17x11in) s.i.d.16 W/C pencil ink. 21-Jan-4 Sotheby's, New York #218/R est:7000-10000
£7222 $13000 €10544 Tempest - book design (38x25cm-15x10in) s.d.08 W/C pencil prov.exhib.lit. 21-Jan-4 Sotheby's, New York #215/R est:4000-6000
£7778 $14000 €11356 Tempest - design for a book (43x28cm-17x11in) s.i.d.08 W/C pencil prov.lit. 21-Jan-4 Sotheby's, New York #220/R est:5000-7000
£8889 $16000 €12978 Buried moon (44x38cm-17x15in) s.i.d.16 W/C ink bodycol. 21-Jan-4 Sotheby's, New York #219/R est:6000-9000
£15000 $27450 €21900 Nuptial dance of Aladdin and the Lady Bedr-el-Budur (32x25cm-13x10in) s.d.14 pencil W/C. 8-Jul-4 Sotheby's, London #332/R est:8000-10000

DULAC, Edmund (attrib) (1882-1953) British/French
Works on paper
£400 $728 €584 Oh plagued no more with human or divine (25x19cm-10x7in) pen brown ink W/C. 15-Jun-4 Rosebery Fine Art, London #477/R
£400 $728 €584 Here with a little bread beneath the bough (25x18cm-10x7in) pen brown ink W/C. 15-Jun-4 Rosebery Fine Art, London #478
£500 $850 €730 Eastern lady reclining on a bed with peacocks on the balcony. Lady in a floral garden with temple (22x17cm-9x7in) W/C pair. 31-Oct-3 Moore Allen & Innocent, Cirencester #543
£727 $1207 €1054 Oriental woman playing music (28x22cm-11x9in) i. W/C. 13-Jun-3 Zofingen, Switzerland #2439/R est:800 (S.FR 1600)

DULDIG, Karl (?) ?
Sculpture
£2066 $3822 €3016 Female figure (63cm-25in) s.d.1969 bronze. 10-Mar-4 Deutscher-Menzies, Melbourne #296/R est:1500-3000 (A.D 5000)

DULER, Émile Henri (1902-1981) French
Sculpture
£987 $1816 €1500 Trois Graces (239cm-94in) wood. 22-Jun-4 Chassaing Rivet, Toulouse #101

DULL, John J (1859-1949) American
Works on paper
£245 $450 €358 Philadelphia scene (30x23cm-12x9in) s. W/C. 25-Jun-4 Freeman, Philadelphia #10/R
£258 $475 €377 Paddle steamer (23x30cm-9x12in) s. W/C scratching out. 25-Jun-4 Freeman, Philadelphia #29/R

DULLAERT, Heiman (1636-1684) Dutch
£21000 $38430 €30660 Trompe-l'oeil with plumes in ink bottle, letter, seal stamp and bottle (25x37cm-10x15in) indis.sig. panel prov.lit. 8-Jul-4 Sotheby's, London #282/R est:15000-20000

DULLAH (1919-1996) Javanese
£1376 $2202 €2009 Portrait of a man (58x48cm-23x19in) s. canvas on board. 18-May-3 Sotheby's, Singapore #161/R est:3000-5000 (S.D 3840)
£1458 $2435 €2129 Old Man (58x48cm-23x19in) s. 12-Oct-3 Sotheby's, Singapore #154/R est:3000-5000 (S.D 4200)
£1769 $3166 €2600 Portrait of a woman (60x49cm-24x19in) s.d.1976. 16-Mar-4 Christie's, Amsterdam #62/R est:3000-5000
£2317 $3869 €3383 Farmers working in the rice field (37x49cm-15x19in) s. 26-Oct-3 Christie's, Hong Kong #65/R est:35000-55000 (HK.D 30000)
£2431 $4059 €3549 Red flowers (51x46cm-20x18in) s. 12-Oct-3 Sotheby's, Singapore #166/R est:4000-6000 (S.D 7000)
£2585 $4627 €3800 Girl with butterflies (78x67cm-31x26in) s. 16-Mar-4 Christie's, Amsterdam #65/R est:4000-6000
£2604 $4349 €3802 Bunga Alamanda (50x60cm-20x24in) s.d.90 lit. 12-Oct-3 Sotheby's, Singapore #168/R est:4000-6000 (S.D 7500)
£2717 $4212 €3967 Alamanda (61x41cm-24x16in) s.d.92. 6-Oct-2 Sotheby's, Singapore #170/R est:5000-7000 (S.D 7500)
£2778 $5028 €4056 Alamanda (60x40cm-24x16in) s.d.1978 s.verso. 3-Apr-4 Glerum, Singapore #68/R est:6000-8000 (S.D 8500)
£3243 $5416 €4735 Portrait of a girl with flowers in her hair (39x35cm-15x14in) s. 26-Oct-3 Christie's, Hong Kong #62/R est:25000-35000 (HK.D 42000)
£4247 $7093 €6201 Portraits of old ladies (35x32cm-14x13in) s.d.1968 one s.d.1970 pair. 26-Oct-3 Christie's, Hong Kong #63/R est:22000-32000 (HK.D 55000)

£5556 $10056 €8112 Old lady (60x50cm-24x20in) s.d.1973 canvas on board. 4-Apr-4 Sotheby's, Singapore #168/R est:6000-8000 (S.D 17000)
£5882 $10647 €8588 Seated lady (150x90cm-59x35in) s.d.61. 4-Apr-4 Sotheby's, Singapore #165/R est:18000-25000 (S.D 18000)
£10425 $17409 €15221 Kampung in Bali (59x90cm-23x35in) s. 26-Oct-3 Christie's, Hong Kong #53/R est:55000-80000 (HK.D 135000)
£29872 $53770 €43613 Balinese procession (140x123cm-55x48in) s. 25-Apr-4 Christie's, Hong Kong #573/R est:400000-480000 (HK.D 420000)
£50193 $83822 €73282 Barong dance (68x139cm-27x55in) s. 26-Oct-3 Christie's, Hong Kong #52/R est:110000-220000 (HK.D 650000)

DULMEN KRUMPELMAN, Erasmus Bernardus van (1832-1909) Dutch
£1119 $1869 €1600 Figures in front of a church (56x94cm-22x37in) s. prov. 30-Jun-3 Sotheby's, Amsterdam #233/R
£2238 $3737 €3200 Cyclists crossing a bridge in a Dutch town (66x97cm-26x38in) prov. 30-Jun-3 Sotheby's, Amsterdam #232/R
Works on paper
£699 $1168 €1000 A view of Hoorn. A landscape (51x70cm-20x28in) s.d.51 W/C double-sided. 30-Jun-3 Sotheby's, Amsterdam #234/R

DULMEN KRUMPELMAN, Erasmus Bernhard van (1897-1987) Dutch
£952 $1733 €1400 French church (57x95cm-22x37in) s. 3-Feb-4 Christie's, Amsterdam #430/R est:1000-1500
£3618 $6658 €5500 Boys playing in the river Aa (73x106cm-29x42in) s.d.40. 22-Jun-4 Christie's, Amsterdam #582/R est:6000-8000
£7237 $13316 €11000 The Westerhaven, Groningen, in winter (66x94cm-26x37in) s.d.1941. 22-Jun-4 Christie's, Amsterdam #569/R est:7000-9000
Works on paper
£490 $832 €700 Two woman in the alley (37x21cm-15x8in) s. chk W/C. 24-Nov-3 Glerum, Amsterdam #146/R
£594 $1022 €850 Beziers (47x58cm-19x23in) s.i. W/C. 7-Dec-3 Sotheby's, Amsterdam #696/R
£2500 $4600 €3800 Figures n a street near a drawbridge (48x64cm-19x25in) s. W/C. 28-Jun-4 Sotheby's, Amsterdam #201/R est:800-1200

DUMA, William (1936-) Canadian
£249 $416 €364 Fall stream (30x40cm-12x16in) s.i. board. 17-Nov-3 Hodgins, Calgary #356/R (C.D 550)
£280 $512 €409 Lake Superior glow (30x40cm-12x16in) s.i. board. 1-Jun-4 Hodgins, Calgary #461/R (C.D 700)
£294 $491 €429 Kananaskis Hills (30x40cm-12x16in) s.i.d.1989 board. 17-Nov-3 Hodgins, Calgary #124/R (C.D 650)
£315 $536 €460 Large veranda (61x76cm-24x30in) s. s.i.verso. 23-Nov-3 Levis, Calgary #30/R (C.D 700)
£317 $529 €463 Foothills farm (30x40cm-12x16in) s.i. board. 17-Nov-3 Hodgins, Calgary #4/R (C.D 700)
£338 $574 €493 Bright autumn day (23x30cm-9x12in) s. s.i.verso acrylic board prov. 23-Nov-3 Levis, Calgary #32/R (C.D 750)
£362 $605 €529 Night scene (30x40cm-12x16in) s.i.d.1988 board. 17-Nov-3 Hodgins, Calgary #251/R (C.D 800)
£407 $680 €594 Light shaft (23x30cm-9x12in) s.i. board. 17-Nov-3 Hodgins, Calgary #9/R (C.D 900)
£450 $766 €657 Mountain patterns (30x41cm-12x16in) s. s.i.verso acrylic prov. 23-Nov-3 Levis, Calgary #31/R (C.D 1000)
£452 $756 €660 From the hills (30x40cm-12x16in) s.i. board. 17-Nov-3 Hodgins, Calgary #5/R est:500-700 (C.D 1000)
£676 $1149 €987 Kluane Lake (61x76cm-24x30in) s. s.i.verso acrylic prov. 23-Nov-3 Levis, Calgary #29/R (C.D 1500)

DUMAIGE, Étienne-Henri (1830-1888) French
Sculpture
£1109 $1984 €1619 Jeanne d'Arc (72cm-28in) s. polished pat.bronze lit. 26-May-4 AB Stockholms Auktionsverk #2483/R est:15000-18000 (S.KR 15000)
£2235 $4000 €3263 Daphni (43cm-17in) s. gilt silver brown pat bronze socle. 20-Mar-4 Freeman, Philadelphia #519/R est:2000-3000
£2500 $3950 €3625 Seated young Graeco-Romano beauty with a lamp (61cm-24in) s. bronze exec.c.1870-1880. 17-Nov-2 Desmond Judd, Cranbrook #599
£3200 $5760 €4672 Camille Desmoulins (96cm-38in) s.i.d.1789 brown pat bronze. 21-Apr-4 Sotheby's, London #99/R est:3000-5000
£4600 $8464 €6716 Avant le combat, Volontaire, and Apres le combat, Grenadier (66cm-26in) s. brown pat bronze plinth pair. 10-Jun-4 Morphets, Harrogate #45/R est:3000-4000

DUMAS, Antoine (1932-) Canadian
£691 $1237 €1009 Benevolat (61x76cm-24x30in) s.d.1979. 6-May-4 Heffel, Vancouver #51/R (C.D 1700)

DUMAS, Marlene (1953-) Dutch
£4601 $7500 €6717 Distorted mirror image of a child (21x10cm-8x4in) i. s.d.1991 verso ink pencil prov.exhib. 23-Sep-3 Christie's, Rockefeller NY #166/R est:3500-4500
£48000 $87360 €70080 Lying (49x60cm-19x24in) s.i.d.87 verso prov. 5-Feb-4 Christie's, London #232/R est:35000-50000
£71856 $120000 €104910 Spread (60x45cm-24x18in) s.i.d.1999 verso prov.exhib. 12-Nov-3 Christie's, Rockefeller NY #565/R est:100000-150000
£90000 $163800 €131400 Male stripper (60x50cm-24x20in) s.i.d.1999 verso prov.exhib.lit. 4-Feb-4 Christie's, London #43/R est:60000-80000
£111732 $200000 €163129 Annunciation (180x89cm-71x35in) s.i.d.1988 verso acrylic prov. 12-May-4 Christie's, Rockefeller NY #325/R est:120000-180000
£120000 $220800 €175200 Peeping tom (60x50cm-24x20in) s.i.d.1994 prov. 24-Jun-4 Christie's, London #48/R est:60000-80000
£130000 $236600 €189800 Over Lyken Lopen (90x70cm-35x28in) s.i. stretcher painted 1993 prov.exhib. 5-Feb-4 Sotheby's, London #4/R est:60000-80000
£173653 $290000 €253533 Wet Dreams (110x130cm-43x51in) s.d.87 stretcher i.verso prov.exhib.lit. 11-Nov-3 Christie's, Rockefeller NY #3/R est:120000-160000
£312849 $560000 €456760 The Dance (89x180cm-35x71in) s.i.d.1992 stretcher prov.exhib.lit. 11-May-4 Christie's, Rockefeller NY #59/R est:250000-350000
£491620 $880000 €717765 Young boys (100x300cm-39x118in) s.i.d.1993 verso prov.exhib.lit. 13-May-4 Phillips, New York #14/R est:250000-350000
Works on paper
£2667 $4907 €4000 Pappa (23x31cm-9x12in) s.d.1990 W/C prov. 9-Jun-4 Christie's, Amsterdam #369/R est:4000-6000
£4000 $7360 €6000 Sensory deprivation (29x20cm-11x8in) init.i.d.1992 W/C blk ink pencil prov. 9-Jun-4 Christie's, Amsterdam #371/R est:6000-8000
£4333 $7973 €6500 Mamma (23x31cm-9x12in) s.i.d.1989 W/C pencil prov. 9-Jun-4 Christie's, Amsterdam #374/R est:4000-6000
£4790 $8000 €6993 Untitled (19x18cm-7x7in) gouache W/C exec 1992 prov. 12-Nov-3 Christie's, Rockefeller NY #568/R est:10000-15000
£4895 $8420 €7000 Standing nude (20x14cm-8x6in) s.verso ink executed c.1994. 2-Dec-3 Sotheby's, Amsterdam #186/R est:4000-6000
£5000 $9200 €7300 Unsuited couple (42x29cm-17x11in) s.i.d.1985 W/C oilstick executed 1985. 25-Jun-4 Christie's, London #245/R est:5000-7000
£5000 $9200 €7300 Pathetic ballerina (38x21cm-15x8in) s.d.1989 gouache W/C chl prov. 25-Jun-4 Christie's, London #248/R est:6000-8000
£5333 $9813 €8000 Ask me no questions and I'll tell you no lies (21x10cm-8x4in) s.i.d.1991 ink lit. 12-Jun-4 Villa Grisebach, Berlin #416/R est:3500-4500
£6000 $11040 €9000 Ghost (22x27cm-9x11in) s.i.d.86 W/C blk ink wax crayon prov. 9-Jun-4 Christie's, Amsterdam #376/R est:4000-6000
£7000 $12880 €10220 Breaking of a human body - on the sidewalk (21x29cm-8x11in) s.i.d.1987 chl ink three. 25-Jun-4 Christie's, London #249/R est:8000-12000
£7263 $13000 €10604 Binding factor (32x24cm-13x9in) s.i.d.1990 W/C prov. 12-May-4 Christie's, Rockefeller NY #327/R est:10000-15000
£7667 $14030 €11500 Old fears are still valid (30x24cm-12x9in) s.i.d.87 Indian ink pastel chk. 4-Jun-4 Lempertz, Koln #119/R est:6000
£8000 $13360 €11680 Dead man dreaming (26x40cm-10x16in) s.i.d.2003 pencil ink prov. 22-Oct-3 Christie's, London #123/R est:3000-5000
£10333 $18910 €15500 Strong woman (31x22cm-12x9in) s.i.d.87 Indian ink W/C. 4-Jun-4 Lempertz, Koln #120/R est:12000
£13408 $24000 €19576 Same story told a 3rd time (19x33cm-7x13in) s.i.d.1991 ink three sheets prov. 12-May-4 Christie's, Rockefeller NY #328/R est:12000-18000
£16000 $29120 €23360 Couple (22x17cm-9x7in) one i. second s.i.d.1993 ink two prov. 5-Feb-4 Christie's, London #225/R est:8000-12000
£21229 $38000 €30994 Artist with hidden agenda (28x24cm-11x9in) s.i.d.1994 gouache W/C prov. 12-May-4 Christie's, Rockefeller NY #326/R est:12000-18000
£65000 $119600 €94900 Passion (61x49cm-24x19in) s.d.94 gouache ink prov.exhib. 25-Jun-4 Christie's, London #250/R est:25000-35000

DUMAX, Ernest Joachim (1811-?) French
£726 $1335 €1060 River landscape (26x40cm-10x16in) s. indis i. stretcher. 14-Jun-4 Waddingtons, Toronto #279/R est:2000-2500 (C.D 1800)

DUMBRELL, Lesley (1941-) Australian
Works on paper
£2686 $4969 €3922 Oia (152x305cm-60x120in) s.d.1989 i.verso synthetic polymer liquitex prov.exhib. 15-Mar-4 Sotheby's, Melbourne #57 est:5000-8000 (A.D 6500)

DUMINIL, Frank (1933-) French
£734 $1248 €1050 Paralleles des brumes X (100x81cm-39x32in) s. 29-Nov-3 Neret-Minet, Paris #96

DUMITRESCO, Natalie (1915-1997) French
£265 $485 €400 Voyage bleu (63x25cm-25x10in) d.1980. 7-Apr-4 Le Roux & Morel, Paris #98
£331 $606 €500 Composition (46x55cm-18x22in) d.1973 verso. 7-Apr-4 Le Roux & Morel, Paris #59
£331 $606 €500 Composition (12x18cm-5x7in) s.d.1968. 7-Apr-4 Le Roux & Morel, Paris #48
£364 $667 €550 Composition (14x18cm-6x7in) d.1974. 7-Apr-4 Le Roux & Morel, Paris #50
£364 $667 €550 Composition (136x28cm-54x11in) 7-Apr-4 Le Roux & Morel, Paris #52
£364 $667 €550 Cite satellite (38x55cm-15x22in) s.d.1968 s.verso exhib. 7-Apr-4 Le Roux & Morel, Paris #70
£364 $667 €550 Composition (30x60cm-12x24in) s. s.d.1965 verso. 7-Apr-4 Le Roux & Morel, Paris #91
£397 $727 €600 Composition (22x14cm-9x6in) d.1974 verso. 7-Apr-4 Le Roux & Morel, Paris #47
£397 $727 €600 Composition (60x60cm-24x24in) 7-Apr-4 Le Roux & Morel, Paris #103
£397 $727 €600 Composition (60x29cm-24x11in) s. 7-Apr-4 Le Roux & Morel, Paris #97
£397 $727 €600 Composition (16x22cm-6x9in) s. s.d.1950 verso. 7-Apr-4 Le Roux & Morel, Paris #90
£430 $788 €650 Composition (14x18cm-6x7in) s.d.1976. 7-Apr-4 Le Roux & Morel, Paris #49
£464 $848 €700 En longueur (65x24cm-26x9in) s. s.d.1984 verso. 7-Apr-4 Le Roux & Morel, Paris #62
£464 $848 €700 Pendant ce temps-la (38x55cm-15x22in) s.d.1971 s.d.verso. 7-Apr-4 Le Roux & Morel, Paris #60
£464 $848 €700 Composition (22x16cm-9x6in) 7-Apr-4 Le Roux & Morel, Paris #44
£464 $848 €700 Composition (33x24cm-13x9in) s. s.d.1990 verso. 7-Apr-4 Le Roux & Morel, Paris #45
£464 $848 €700 Composition (46x55cm-18x22in) d.1980 verso. 7-Apr-4 Le Roux & Morel, Paris #88
£494 $850 €721 Untitled (55x38cm-22x15in) s. s.d.1960 verso prov. 3-Dec-3 Doyle, New York #76/R
£497 $909 €750 Composition (94x34cm-37x13in) paint on fabric. 7-Apr-4 Le Roux & Morel, Paris #104
£530 $970 €800 Composition (35x40cm-14x16in) d.1963 verso. 7-Apr-4 Le Roux & Morel, Paris #57
£530 $970 €800 Composition (14x18cm-6x7in) d.1950 verso. 7-Apr-4 Le Roux & Morel, Paris #42
£530 $970 €800 Composition (19x24cm-7x9in) s.on stretcher. 7-Apr-4 Le Roux & Morel, Paris #51
£530 $970 €800 Composition (41x33cm-16x13in) s. s.d.1968 verso exhib. 7-Apr-4 Le Roux & Morel, Paris #73
£563 $1030 €850 Composition (22x16cm-9x6in) s.d.1953 s.verso. 7-Apr-4 Le Roux & Morel, Paris #58
£596 $1091 €900 Composition (46x38cm-18x15in) s.d.1979 s.d.verso. 7-Apr-4 Le Roux & Morel, Paris #61
£596 $1091 €900 Composition (16x22cm-6x9in) s.d.176 verso. 7-Apr-4 Le Roux & Morel, Paris #46
£662 $1212 €1000 Composition (46x55cm-18x22in) s. s.d.1970 verso. 7-Apr-4 Le Roux & Morel, Paris #55/R

£662	$1212	€1000	Composition (73x92cm-29x36in) s. s.d.1958 verso. 7-Apr-4 Le Roux & Morel, Paris #77
£662	$1212	€1000	Bleu, rouge, jaune (43x62cm-17x24in) s. s.d.1974 verso. 7-Apr-4 Le Roux & Morel, Paris #94
£694	$1160	€1000	Sans titre (24x33cm-9x13in) s. 25-Oct-3 Cornette de St.Cyr, Paris #668/R
£728	$1333	€1100	Composition (73x92cm-29x36in) s. s.d.89 verso. 7-Apr-4 Le Roux & Morel, Paris #78/R
£728	$1333	€1100	Mon soleil (73x92cm-29x36in) s. s.d.92-93 verso. 7-Apr-4 Le Roux & Morel, Paris #84/R
£738	$1374	€1100	Danse (92x73cm-36x29in) s.d.1978 s.i.d.verso. 3-Mar-4 Artcurial Briest, Paris #364
£762	$1394	€1150	Composition (27x46cm-11x18in) s. s.d.1965 verso. 7-Apr-4 Le Roux & Morel, Paris #87
£795	$1454	€1200	Composition (37x46cm-15x18in) d.1953 verso. 7-Apr-4 Le Roux & Morel, Paris #89
£833	$1392	€1200	10 000 fenetres (73x92cm-29x36in) s. s.i.d.IV-IX 1967 verso prov. 21-Oct-3 Artcurial Briest, Paris #420 est:2000-2500
£833	$1392	€1200	Composition - jaune (40x80cm-16x31in) s. 21-Oct-3 Artcurial Briest, Paris #435
£861	$1575	€1300	Composition geometrique (38x46cm-15x18in) s. 7-Apr-4 Le Roux & Morel, Paris #71
£894	$1636	€1350	Compositions (12x16cm-5x6in) s.d.1949 pair. 7-Apr-4 Le Roux & Morel, Paris #93
£972	$1624	€1400	Composition - grey (80x40cm-31x16in) d.1959 verso. 21-Oct-3 Artcurial Briest, Paris #436 est:1500-1800
£987	$1816	€1500	Composition (40x23cm-16x9in) s. panel. 28-Jun-4 Joron-Derem, Paris #209/R est:1500-2000
£993	$1818	€1500	Composition (16x22cm-6x9in) d.1953 verso. 7-Apr-4 Le Roux & Morel, Paris #43
£993	$1818	€1500	Grande ville (89x116cm-35x46in) s. s.d.1965 verso. 7-Apr-4 Le Roux & Morel, Paris #69 est:300-350
£993	$1818	€1500	Constellation Venus (97x130cm-38x51in) s. s.d.1989 verso. 7-Apr-4 Le Roux & Morel, Paris #79/R est:550-700
£1042	$1740	€1500	Apres la pluie (89x116cm-35x46in) s.i.d.1X-89 verso exhib. 21-Oct-3 Artcurial Briest, Paris #414/R est:2000-2500
£1060	$1939	€1600	Rouge (195x130cm-77x51in) s. 7-Apr-4 Le Roux & Morel, Paris #82/R est:1300-1700
£1086	$1846	€1586	Composition (75x94cm-30x37in) s. 25-Nov-3 Germann, Zurich #108/R est:1500-1800 (S.FR 2400)
£1192	$2181	€1800	Mood Indigo (80x80cm-31x31in) s. s.d.1968 verso exhib. 7-Apr-4 Le Roux & Morel, Paris #75 est:550-700
£1192	$2181	€1800	Composition V 90 (97x130cm-38x51in) s.d.90 s.d.verso exhib. 7-Apr-4 Le Roux & Morel, Paris #85/R est:550-700
£1325	$2424	€2000	Page d'ecriture (92x73cm-36x29in) s.d.1964 exhib. 7-Apr-4 Le Roux & Morel, Paris #68 est:450-600
£1325	$2424	€2000	Composition (38x46cm-15x18in) s. s.verso. 7-Apr-4 Le Roux & Morel, Paris #72
£1389	$2320	€2000	Eugene Ionesco et sa legion d'Honnneur (145x114cm-57x45in) s. s.i.d.1984 verso. 21-Oct-3 Artcurial Briest, Paris #446/R est:3000-4000
£1391	$2545	€2100	Composition releif (46x38cm-18x15in) s.d.1968 verso. 7-Apr-4 Le Roux & Morel, Paris #66/R est:200-260
£1391	$2545	€2100	Composition (40x80cm-16x31in) d.1956 verso. 7-Apr-4 Le Roux & Morel, Paris #92 est:300-350
£1523	$2787	€2300	Apiaw (185x114cm-73x45in) s. d.1967 verso. 7-Apr-4 Le Roux & Morel, Paris #74 est:1100-1400
£1523	$2787	€2300	Epaisseurs transparentes. s. s.verso exhib. 7-Apr-4 Le Roux & Morel, Paris #81/R est:650-800
£1528	$2551	€2200	Constellation en bleu (92x73cm-36x29in) s. s.i.d.IV 57 verso exhib. 21-Oct-3 Artcurial Briest, Paris #422/R est:2500-3000
£1589	$2909	€2400	Composition (50x61cm-20x24in) s. s.d.50 verso. 7-Apr-4 Le Roux & Morel, Paris #64/R est:180-200
£1623	$2969	€2450	Constellation en vert (61x50cm-24x20in) s. s.d.1955 verso. 7-Apr-4 Le Roux & Morel, Paris #56/R est:150-200
£1722	$3151	€2600	Fete au village (116x89cm-46x35in) s. s.d.1968 verso exhib. 7-Apr-4 Le Roux & Morel, Paris #80/R est:650-850
£1944	$3247	€2800	Claire Comana (200x200cm-79x79in) s.d.1975-IX s.i.d.17-VIII-1975 verso exhib. 21-Oct-3 Artcurial Briest, Paris #457/R est:3500-4500
£2083	$3479	€3000	Sonder les profondeurs (200x200cm-79x79in) s. s.i.d.1962 verso exhib. 21-Oct-3 Artcurial Briest, Paris #458/R est:4000-5000
£2252	$4121	€3400	Composition jaune (72x100cm-28x39in) s.d.1952 verso. 7-Apr-4 Le Roux & Morel, Paris #65/R est:300-350
£2450	$4484	€3700	Bleu fiac (97x130cm-38x51in) s.d.1980 s.d.verso. 7-Apr-4 Le Roux & Morel, Paris #67/R est:400-500
£2450	$4484	€3700	Gris rose (73x92cm-29x36in) s. s.verso exhib. 7-Apr-4 Le Roux & Morel, Paris #86/R est:350-400
£2568	$4519	€3800	Untitled (92x65cm-36x26in) s.d.1956 prov. 18-May-4 Tajan, Paris #35/R est:4000-5000
£2649	$4821	€4000	Composition (89x116cm-35x46in) s. s.d.1959 prov. 18-Jun-4 Charbonneaux, Paris #144/R est:2500-3000
£3444	$6302	€5200	Mur des marronniers (114x162cm-45x64in) s. s.d.1959-60 verso exhib. 7-Apr-4 Le Roux & Morel, Paris #76/R est:1800-2200
£4702	$8605	€7100	Composition geometrique. s. s.d.50-51 verso exhib. 7-Apr-4 Le Roux & Morel, Paris #83/R est:1300-1700
Works on paper			
£265	$485	€400	Composition (30x40cm-12x16in) s.d.1968 gouache. 7-Apr-4 Le Roux & Morel, Paris #63
£364	$667	€550	Composition (26x34cm-10x13in) s.d.1963 gouache. 7-Apr-4 Le Roux & Morel, Paris #54
£629	$1151	€950	Composition (176x48cm-69x19in) gouache W/C. 7-Apr-4 Le Roux & Morel, Paris #95
£671	$1248	€1000	Composition (58x77cm-23x30in) s.d.1968 gouache ink prov. 3-Mar-4 Artcurial Briest, Paris #362
£699	$1189	€1000	Composition striee (36x51cm-14x20in) s. Indian ink gouache prov. 23-Nov-3 Cornette de St.Cyr, Paris #105/R
£1042	$1740	€1500	Composition (89x116cm-35x46in) s. ink gouache collage paper on canvas. 21-Oct-3 Artcurial Briest, Paris #415 est:800-1000

DUMONCEAU DE BERGENDAEL, Comtesse Mathilde (1877-1952) Belgian

£709	$1184	€1000	Barque au bord de l'etange au nenuphars. Nature morte (50x60cm-20x24in) s. panel double-sided. 17-Jun-3 Vanderkindere, Brussels #34
£814	$1385	€1188	Woman with basket in front of a house (50x61cm-20x24in) s.indis.d.1914. 1-Dec-3 Koller, Zurich #6572/R est:1500-1800 (S.FR 1800)

DUMOND, Frank Vincent (1865-1951) American

£1728	$2800	€2506	Fence (30x41cm-12x16in) s. board. 8-Aug-3 Barridorf, Portland #357/R est:3000-5000

DUMONT, Alfred (1828-1894) Swiss

£1086	$1879	€1586	Interieur du Chateau de Valere (38x46cm-15x18in) s. i.on stretcher. 12-Dec-3 Galerie du Rhone, Sion #450/R est:2500-3500 (S.FR 2400)
£4495	$7507	€6518	Jeune couple d'Evolene chevauchant un mulet (74x60cm-29x24in) s.d. prov. 21-Jun-3 Galerie du Rhone, Sion #456/R est:10000-15000 (S.FR 9800)

DUMONT, Claude (?) French

£333	$597	€500	L'arlequin musicien (61x38cm-24x15in) 16-May-4 Feletin, Province #235

DUMONT, F (18/19th C) ?

£1111	$1889	€1600	Flower token (58x41cm-23x16in) s.d.1874 panel. 28-Oct-3 Dorotheum, Vienna #241/R est:2000-2300

DUMONT, François (1850-?) Belgian

£340	$609	€500	Paysage Orientaliste (51x62cm-20x24in) s.d.1893 after Franz Vinck. 17-Mar-4 Hotel des Ventes Mosan, Brussels #88
£867	$1560	€1300	Galant company in Old Antwerp (56x41cm-22x16in) s.d.73. 26-Apr-4 Bernaerts, Antwerp #44/R

DUMONT, François (1751-1831) French

Miniatures			
£2703	$5000	€3946	The De Montiers (3x3cm-1x1in) oval pair. 12-Mar-4 Du Mouchelle, Detroit #2026/R est:800-1200
£20500	$37720	€29930	Lady wearing blue dress with gold trim (6cm-2in) s.d.set rose cut diamonds mounted in silver. 24-Jun-4 Bonhams, New Bond Street #127/R est:8000-12000
£24000	$41520	€35040	Monsieur de Damas seated in aubergine-coloured coat (8cm-3in circular) s. gilt-metal frame exhib.lit. 9-Dec-3 Christie's, London #131/R est:8000-12000

DUMONT, Henri Julien (1859-?) French

£2715	$4942	€4100	Jardin a Giverny (82x65cm-32x26in) s. 19-Jun-4 St-Germain-en-Laye Encheres #108/R est:4000
£3401	$6088	€5000	Mon beau miroir (116x112cm-46x44in) s. 19-Mar-4 Millon & Associes, Paris #73/R est:6000-8000

DUMONT, P (1884-1936) French

£503	$891	€750	Old south German harbour town (52x40cm-20x16in) s. panel one of pair. 28-Apr-4 Schopman, Hamburg #661/R
£503	$891	€750	Fish market with landing stage (53x41cm-21x16in) s. panel one of pair. 28-Apr-4 Schopman, Hamburg #662/R

DUMONT, Pierre (1884-1936) French

£517	$859	€750	Maison (38x46cm-15x18in) s. 1-Oct-3 Millon & Associes, Paris #117/R
£699	$1189	€1000	Lac de Saint-Cucufa (60x73cm-24x29in) s. 21-Nov-3 Coutau Begarie, Paris #2/R
£699	$1189	€1000	Maison de campagne (65x80cm-26x31in) s. 23-Nov-3 Cornette de St.Cyr, Paris #605/R
£839	$1401	€1200	Village sous la neige (38x55cm-15x22in) s. 25-Jun-3 Maigret, Paris #60
£1049	$1783	€1500	Nature morte a la coupe de fruits (61x80cm-24x31in) s. 23-Nov-3 Cornette de St.Cyr, Paris #606/R est:1000-1500
£1105	$1900	€1613	Rouen Harbour (28x33cm-11x13in) s. 7-Dec-3 Susanin's, Chicago #6087/R est:700-1000
£1325	$2411	€2000	Bouquet de fleurs (92x73cm-36x29in) s. 18-Jun-4 Piasa, Paris #96/R est:2000-3000
£1457	$2652	€2200	Bateaux de peche a quai a Honfleur (65x81cm-26x32in) s. exhib. 18-Jun-4 Piasa, Paris #97/R est:2000-3000
£2400	$4416	€3504	Au centre ville (65x81cm-26x32in) s. 24-Mar-4 Sotheby's, Olympia #89/R est:800-1200
£2828	$4694	€4100	Etang (46x55cm-18x22in) s. 1-Oct-3 Millon & Associes, Paris #118/R
£3893	$7240	€5800	Rouen (65x81cm-26x32in) s. 3-Mar-4 Tajan, Paris #69/R est:6000-8000

DUMONT, Pierre (attrib) (1884-1936) French

£604	$1111	€900	Mounted jockeys ready to race (60x80cm-24x31in) i. lit. 27-Mar-4 Sigalas, Stuttgart #246/R

DUMORTIER, Jean Felix (?) Belgian?

£1389	$2319	€2000	Scenes de la vie de Christ (104x50cm-41x20in) set of 4. 21-Oct-3 Galerie Moderne, Brussels #219/R est:1500-2000

DUMORTIER, Prosper (1805-1879) Flemish

£313	$522	€450	Femme aux anglaises (39x32cm-15x13in) s. 21-Oct-3 Galerie Moderne, Brussels #273

DUMOUCHEL, Albert (1916-) Canadian

£356	$615	€520	La Chambre (53x45cm-21x18in) s.i.verso board. 9-Dec-3 Pinneys, Montreal #22 (C.D 800)

DUMOUCHEL, Georges (20th C) French

£345	$576	€500	Port de Honfleur a maree haute (61x43cm-24x17in) s. 11-Nov-3 Lesieur & Le Bars, Le Havre #19

DUMOULIN, Louis (1860-1924) French

£1227	$2000	€1779	Village fair scene in France (33x46cm-13x18in) s.indis.i. 20-Jul-3 Jeffery Burchard, Florida #16

DUMOULIN, Romeo (1883-1944) Belgian

£559	$951	€800	Dans le jardin, la cueillette des renoncules. s. s.i.verso cardboard. 27-Nov-3 Millon & Associes, Paris #221a/R

£638	$1066	€900	La visite. s. cardboard. 17-Jun-3 Vanderkindere, Brussels #3
£1399	$2378	€2000	Vieille Maison Rue Cheravoi a Liege (50x40cm-20x16in) s. panel. 18-Nov-3 Galerie Moderne, Brussels #877/R est:3000-5000
£1611	$2996	€2400	The greengrocer (40x50cm-16x20in) s. 8-Mar-4 Bernaerts, Antwerp #831/R est:1250-1500
£2297	$4112	€3400	La sortie du bain de mer (26x34cm-10x13in) s. panel. 10-May-4 Horta, Bruxelles #175 est:2200-2500
£3472	$5521	€5000	Enfants au pre (40x50cm-16x20in) s. 15-Sep-3 Horta, Bruxelles #133/R est:5000-7000
£4305	$7834	€6500	Elegante sur la digue (27x35cm-11x14in) s. panel. 15-Jun-4 Galerie Moderne, Brussels #389/R est:800-1000
Works on paper			
£233	$420	€350	Le tramway (17x25cm-7x10in) s.d.1909 W/C. 26-Apr-4 Tajan, Paris #4
£528	$914	€750	Procession to the Scherpen hill (17x14cm-7x6in) s. W/C. 13-Dec-3 De Vuyst, Lokeren #128
£878	$1572	€1300	Le chariot du briquetier (28x44cm-11x17in) s. mixed media. 10-May-4 Horta, Bruxelles #176
£4138	$7655	€6000	Repos (68x84cm-27x33in) s. s.i.verso. 19-Jan-4 Horta, Bruxelles #155/R est:6000-8000

DUN, Nicholas François (1764-1832) French

Miniatures			
£4500	$8100	€6570	Prince Achille Murat as a young man (6cm-2in) s. gilt metal mount oval exhib.lit. 22-Apr-4 Bonhams, New Bond Street #128/R est:1500-2500

DUNAND, Jean (1877-1942) Swiss

£6711	$12013	€10000	L'homme a l'oiseau (17x11cm-7x4in) s. col lacquer wood prov.exhib.lit. 27-May-4 Tajan, Paris #55/R est:10000-12000
£9061	$16219	€13500	Eglise d'Estaing (120x76cm-47x30in) s.d.1942 lacquer eggshell wood prov.lit. 27-May-4 Tajan, Paris #39/R est:5000-7000
£21676	$37500	€31647	La peche (61x57cm-24x22in) s. lacquered on wood prov.lit. 11-Dec-3 Sotheby's, New York #105/R est:15000-20000
Sculpture			
£148649	$261622	€220000	Lac bleu (156x194cm-61x76in) painted panel. 18-May-4 Christie's, Paris #12/R est:80000-100000
Works on paper			
£3846	$6615	€5500	Arborescences cubistes, stylisees (180x35cm-71x14in) s. lacquer silver granite htd col grey anthracite panel lit. 3-Dec-3 Beaussant & Lefèvre, Paris #84/R est:3000-3500
£5245	$9021	€7500	Arborescences cubistes, stylisees (167x43cm-66x17in) s. lacquer silver granite htd col grey anthracite panel lit. 3-Dec-3 Beaussant & Lefèvre, Paris #83/R est:3000-3500
£46154	$78462	€66000	Untitled (178x164cm-70x65in) s. lacquer. 26-Nov-3 Christie's, Paris #28/R est:22000-25000
£76923	$132308	€110000	Jeune archer (180x122cm-71x48in) s. col laque de Chine htd silver black laquer panel lit. 3-Dec-3 Beaussant & Lefèvre, Paris #82/R est:50000-60000

DUNAND, Pierre (20th C) French

Works on paper			
£16108	$29961	€24000	Pantheres s'abreuvant (150x150cm-59x59in) s. lacquered col Indian inks black gilded panel lit. 4-Mar-4 Tajan, Paris #55/R est:20000-25000

DUNBAR, George (20th C) American

Works on paper			
£9239	$17000	€13489	Torso (102x142cm-40x56in) s. clay on board. 27-Mar-4 New Orleans Auction, New Orleans #947/R est:18000-25000

DUNBAR, Harold (1882-1953) American

£339	$600	€495	Wooded landscape (30x23cm-12x9in) s. 2-May-4 Grogan, Boston #78/R
£894	$1600	€1305	Flying clouds (66x91cm-26x36in) s. 8-Jan-4 James Julia, Fairfield #969/R est:2000-3000
£1436	$2600	€2097	Windmill by the sea (28x36cm-11x14in) s.d.1921 board. 2-Apr-4 Eldred, East Dennis #45/R est:500-800

DUNBAR, Patrick (?) ?

£615	$1100	€898	Out for a sail (71x102cm-28x40in) s. 8-Jan-4 James Julia, Fairfield #682/R

DUNBAR, R B (19/20th C) British?

£260	$484	€380	Fisherman in a stream with figures on a bank (50x60cm-20x24in) s.d.1918. 6-Mar-4 Shapes, Edinburgh #412

DUNBIER, Augustus W (1888-1977) American

£223	$400	€326	Floral still life (41x51cm-16x20in) s. canvasboard. 15-May-4 Jeffery Burchard, Florida #164
£302	$550	€441	Lake Manawa (61x51cm-24x20in) s. i.d.1967 verso board. 19-Jun-4 Jackson's, Cedar Falls #173/R
£391	$700	€571	Park scene with figures seated at benches (51x61cm-20x24in) s. canvasboard. 15-May-4 Jeffery Burchard, Florida #163

DUNCAN, Edward (1803-1882) British

Works on paper			
£203	$340	€296	Breaker of hearts (29x18cm-11x7in) mono s.verso W/C prov. 17-Nov-3 Waddingtons, Toronto #39/R (C.D 450)
£243	$450	€365	View of a castle and town from the sea (15x30cm-6x12in) pencil W/C prov. 14-Jul-4 American Auctioneer #490479/R
£400	$736	€584	Cattle in a rural landscape (33x50cm-13x20in) s.d.1878 W/C. 22-Jun-4 Bonhams, Knightsbridge #168b/R
£490	$833	€715	Beach scene (33x49cm-13x19in) s.d.1857 W/C over pencil. 28-Oct-3 Bonhams, Knowle #301
£800	$1456	€1168	A lazy day at the water's edge (33x47cm-13x19in) s.d.1874 pencil W/C bodycol. 1-Jul-4 Christie's, Kensington #106/R
£920	$1693	€1343	Rialto Bridge, Venice (24x34cm-9x13in) s. W/C. 22-Jun-4 Bonhams, Knightsbridge #168a/R
£1300	$2340	€1898	Bassenthwaite Water, Cumberland (23x36cm-9x14in) s.i. W/C. 21-Jan-4 Sotheby's, Olympia #177/R est:500-700
£1800	$3060	€2628	Harvesters in a country village (22x31cm-9x12in) s. W/C over pencil htd bodycol prov. 27-Nov-3 Sotheby's, London #295/R est:1000-1500
£1879	$3477	€2800	Boats in harbour (37x58cm-15x23in) s.d.1877 W/C. 10-Mar-4 James Adam, Dublin #14/R est:1000-1500
£2000	$3680	€2920	Shipping off the coast (32x48cm-13x19in) W/C over pencil htd bodycol. 26-Mar-4 Sotheby's, London #135/R est:2500-3500
£3000	$5550	€4380	Luggers and ship wreck in stormy seas, with rocky coastline (34x51cm-13x20in) s.d.1879 W/C. 16-Jul-4 Charterhouse, Sherborne #494/R
£4200	$7728	€6132	Ship in distress, with figures on the shore firing a rocket (37x67cm-15x26in) s. W/C over pencil htd scratching out prov.exhib. 26-Mar-4 Sotheby's, London #137/R est:5000-7000

DUNCAN, George Bernard (1904-1974) New Zealander

£234	$438	€351	Pymble pastoral (61x68cm-24x27in) s. board. 20-Jul-4 Goodman, Sydney #22/R (A.D 600)
£579	$1070	€845	Yellow house (40x51cm-16x20in) s. oil on hessian. 10-Mar-4 Deutscher-Menzies, Melbourne #475/R est:1500-2500 (A.D 1400)
£1157	$2140	€1689	Flower market (28x35cm-11x14in) s. 10-Mar-4 Deutscher-Menzies, Melbourne #474/R est:2500-3500 (A.D 2800)

DUNCAN, Jean (1900-) American

£549	$900	€796	Rural structures (46x61cm-18x24in) s. painted c.1940. 7-Jun-3 Treadway Gallery, Cincinnati #1485

DUNCAN, John (1866-1945) British

£450	$720	€653	Bridge, Killin (29x39cm-11x15in) init. canvasboard. 16-Sep-3 Bonhams, Knightsbridge #119/R
£2000	$3720	€2920	Goddess Innana, The Queen of Heaven and Earth (41x30cm-16x12in) s. board. 6-Mar-4 Shapes, Edinburgh #312/R est:2000-3000

DUNCAN, John McKirdy (1866-1945) British

£1850	$2923	€2701	After the storm, western Isles (30x40cm-12x16in) s. 6-Sep-3 Shapes, Edinburgh #339/R est:1000-1500
£2900	$4582	€4234	Iona, summer's day (38x46cm-15x18in) board. 6-Sep-3 Shapes, Edinburgh #338/R est:1000-1500
Works on paper			
£1450	$2422	€2117	Mythological frieze of naked figures and unicorns (34x66cm-13x26in) s. pen oil board. 11-Oct-3 Shapes, Edinburgh #324 est:1500-2000

DUNCAN, Laurence (fl.1860-1891) British

Works on paper			
£1300	$2366	€1898	The toy yacht (35x30cm-14x12in) s.d.1867 pencil W/C bodycol. 1-Jul-4 Christie's, Kensington #165/R est:800-1200

DUNCAN, Mary (1885-1964) British

£313	$538	€457	In Montreal, first still life (34x46cm-13x18in) s.d.1939. 2-Dec-3 Joyner Waddington, Toronto #531 (C.D 700)
£446	$768	€651	Beatrice (60x44cm-24x17in) s.d.1941 canvasboard prov. 2-Dec-3 Joyner Waddington, Toronto #363/R (C.D 1000)
£480	$878	€701	Summer reading (82x60cm-32x24in) s.d.1954 i. verso prov. 1-Jun-4 Joyner Waddington, Toronto #369/R (C.D 1200)
£1000	$1870	€1500	Mousehold garden (43x53cm-17x21in) s. board. 22-Jul-4 Gorringes, Lewes #1967 est:300-500
£1133	$2051	€1700	June sunshine (35x22cm-14x9in) s. 30-Mar-4 De Veres Art Auctions, Dublin #220/R est:1400-1800
£1500	$2490	€2190	Polperro fisherman mending nets (25x18cm-10x7in) s.d.1923 oil on paper. 4-Oct-3 Finan Watkins & Co, Mere #142
Works on paper			
£643	$1195	€939	Seated nude (56x45cm-22x18in) s.d.1966 pastel. 2-Mar-4 Ritchie, Toronto #160/R (C.D 1600)

DUNCAN, Robert (1952-) American

£14706	$27500	€21471	Rough start (71x102cm-28x40in) s. 24-Jul-4 Coeur d'Alene, Hayden #247/R est:15000-25000

DUNCAN, Thomas (1807-1845) British

£480	$802	€701	Portrait of the Countess of Caithness (23x18cm-9x7in) oil sketch panel. 14-Oct-3 David Lay, Penzance #295

DUNCAN, Walter (fl.1880-c.1910) British

Works on paper			
£260	$413	€380	Hampton Court gardens (18x28cm-7x11in) s. W/C. 10-Sep-3 Cheffins, Cambridge #473
£260	$476	€380	Mansion house (18x13cm-7x5in) s. W/C. 27-Jan-4 Bonhams, Knightsbridge #213/R
£275	$500	€402	Courtship Scene (15x25cm-6x10in) s.d.1878 W/C. 7-Feb-4 Harvey Clar, Oakland #1310
£280	$512	€409	Walk through a snowy woodland (27x19cm-11x7in) s.d.1904 W/C bodycol. 27-Jan-4 Bonhams, Knightsbridge #287
£340	$622	€496	View of the Houses of parliament from the Thames (19x27cm-7x11in) s. W/C. 27-Jan-4 Bonhams, Knightsbridge #332/R
£820	$1468	€1197	Thames at Marlow (19x27cm-7x11in) s. W/C over pencil htd bodycol. 26-May-4 Sotheby's, Olympia #162/R

DUNCANSON, Robert S (1821-1872) American
£153409 $270000 €223977 Landscape (76x127cm-30x50in) s.d.1870 prov. 18-May-4 Christie's, Rockefeller NY #5/R est:150000-250000
£195122 $320000 €282927 View of Asheville, North Carolina (58x89cm-23x35in) s.d.1850 prov. 31-May-3 Brunk, Ashville #50/R est:100000-150000

DUNDAS, Douglas Robert (1900-1981) Australian
£289 $535 €422 Landscape, mountains near Canberra (40x51cm-16x20in) s.d.50 prov. 10-Mar-4 Deutscher-Menzies, Melbourne #552/R (A.D 700)
£361 $604 €523 Great Moon Bay, Georges river (60x76cm-24x30in) s. 30-Jun-3 Australian Art Auctions, Sydney #114 (A.D 900)
£826 $1405 €1206 Rain in the hills (63x85cm-25x33in) s. 29-Oct-3 Lawson Menzies, Sydney #164/R est:2000-3000 (A.D 2000)

DUNET, Alfred (20th C) French
£530 $970 €800 La place (32x45cm-13x18in) s.d.35 cardboard. 9-Apr-4 Claude Aguttes, Neuilly #21

DUNHAM, Carroll (1949-) American
£8000 $14480 €11680 Character study No.1 (84x61cm-33x24in) init.d.Dec 97 acrylic pencil W/C on linen prov. 1-Apr-4 Christie's, Kensington #328/R est:8000-12000
£8000 $14480 €11680 Character study No.2 (86x74cm-34x29in) init.d.Dec 97 acrylic pencil W/C on linen prov. 1-Apr-4 Christie's, Kensington #329/R est:8000-12000
£20950 $37500 €30587 Integrated painting no 6 (152x216cm-60x85in) oil mixed media linen painted 1992 prov. 13-May-4 Sotheby's, New York #472/R est:18000-22000
£21229 $38000 €30994 Mound C (164x229cm-65x90in) s.d.Jan Mar April May 1992 oil acrylic linen prov.exhib. 12-May-4 Christie's, Rockefeller NY #386/R est:30000-40000
Works on paper
£2610 $4750 €3811 Red patches (91x43cm-36x17in) s.d.1986 gouache ink crayon pencil two joined sheets. 29-Jun-4 Sotheby's, New York #571/R est:4000-6000
£7821 $14000 €11419 Untitled (22x28cm-9x11in) s.d.95 96 pencil four parts prov. 13-May-4 Sotheby's, New York #471/R est:10000-15000
£12000 $20040 €17520 Portrait, red head (120x145cm-47x57in) s.d.Feb, March April 1999 chl household paint canvas prov.exhib. 22-Oct-3 Christie's, London #90/R est:15000-20000
£16467 $27500 €24042 Character study no 3 (81x61cm-32x24in) init.d.Dec 97 mixed media oil linen prov. 13-Nov-3 Sotheby's, New York #602/R est:15000-20000

DUNIGAN, Martha (1934-2002) American
Works on paper
£216 $400 €315 Storm shadows (69x104cm-27x41in) d.1989 pastel chl. 15-Feb-4 Outer Cape Auctions, Provincetown #56a/R

DUNIKOWSKI, Xaver (1875-1964) Polish
Sculpture
£24503 $44596 €37000 Maternite (89x41x27cm-35x16x11in) s.d.1919 pat bronze cire perdue Cast Valsuani lit. 16-Jun-4 Claude Boisgirard, Paris #44/R est:25000-30000

DUNINGTON, A (1860-c.1928) British
£1000 $1670 €1460 Blacksmith shoeing horse with donkey and dog looking on (69x89cm-27x35in) s. 15-Nov-3 Nigel Ward, Hereford #1418/R

DUNINGTON, Albert (1860-c.1928) British
£480 $850 €701 Nr Malling, Kent (61x92cm-24x36in) s.d.78. 27-Apr-4 Bonhams, Knowle #95
£550 $985 €803 Highland cattle by a river, near Brodick, Arran. On the slopes of Ben Venue (51x41cm-20x16in) s. i.verso pair. 27-May-4 Christie's, Kensington #219/R
£640 $1171 €934 Barton Old Aqueduct. The 1st vessel to Manchester SS Snowdrop (33x49cm-13x19in) s.i. one d.1893 one d.1894 pair. 6-Apr-4 Bonhams, Chester #964
£850 $1522 €1241 Cattle on the waters edge at Brodick, Arran (51x76cm-20x30in) s. i.verso. 27-May-4 Christie's, Kensington #206/R
£950 $1701 €1387 Red sky at night, Loch Fadh (76x102cm-30x40in) s.d.1899 i.verso. 27-May-4 Christie's, Kensington #217/R
£1200 $2148 €1752 Highland cattle by the Beauly River, Invernesshire. Highland cattle near Dunkelt (41x61cm-16x24in) s. i.verso pair. 27-May-4 Christie's, Kensington #216/R est:500-800
Works on paper
£700 $1239 €1022 East Hendred Berks, village street scene (42x60cm-17x24in) s.i.d.1916. 28-Apr-4 Peter Wilson, Nantwich #152

DUNKEL, Joachim (1925-) German
Sculpture
£1389 $2319 €2000 Standing female figure (57x14x10cm-22x6x4in) brown pat.bronze marble socle. 24-Oct-3 Ketterer, Hamburg #327/R est:2800-3000

DUNKER, Balthasar Anton (1746-1807) German
Works on paper
£396 $674 €578 Landscape with woman and goat (23x19cm-9x7in) s.d.1790 W/C. 5-Nov-3 Dobiaschofsky, Bern #1303/R (S.FR 900)
£733 $1312 €1070 Hunter with dog in river landscape with ruins (32x25cm-13x10in) i. W/C. 13-May-4 Stuker, Bern #9150/R est:2400-3000 (S.FR 1700)
£867 $1595 €1300 Figures in medieval dress under trees (39x31cm-15x12in) s. brush W/C. 11-Jun-4 Hauswedell & Nolte, Hamburg #947/R

D'UNKER, Carl (1829-1866) Swedish
£461 $751 €673 Portrait of Elise Selmer (83x62cm-33x24in) s.d.1853 lit. 29-Sep-3 Lilla Bukowskis, Stockholm #136 (S.KR 6000)
£1075 $1753 €1570 Organ-grinders and singers at an inn (42x50cm-17x20in) s. s.d.1855 verso prov.lit. 29-Sep-3 Lilla Bukowskis, Stockholm #138 (S.KR 14000)
£1467 $2655 €2200 Violinist (40x33cm-16x13in) s.d.1859. 1-Apr-4 Van Ham, Cologne #1675/R est:1600
£2797 $4755 €4000 Three city musicians playing (77x52cm-30x20in) s.d.1853. 20-Nov-3 Van Ham, Cologne #1892/R est:6000
£5391 $10027 €7871 Dinner party at a German inn (64x85cm-25x33in) s.d.1857. 2-Mar-4 Rasmussen, Copenhagen #1251/R est:60000 (D.KR 60000)

DUNLAP, Eugene (1916-) American
£248 $400 €360 Monterey coast (81x127cm-32x50in) s. 24-Aug-3 Bonhams & Butterfields, Los Angeles #7000

DUNLAP, Helena (1876-1955) American
£4348 $8000 €6348 Hindu temple, Bombay. Church at Cherebance, Mexico. Temple in North Africa. two s. i. three various sizes. 8-Jun-4 Bonhams & Butterfields, San Francisco #4356/R est:5000-7000
£9412 $16000 €13742 Taos mother and child (27x24cm-11x9in) canvas on canvas painted c.1918. 18-Nov-3 John Moran, Pasadena #124 est:10000-15000

DUNLAP, Hope (1881-?) American
Works on paper
£321 $600 €469 Woman with fairy (41x28cm-16x11in) s. pen ink W/C. 26-Feb-4 Illustration House, New York #60

DUNLAP, William (attrib) (1766-1839) American
£1148 $2100 €1676 Portrait of a young boy (43x41cm-17x16in) s.verso. 10-Apr-4 Brunk, Ashville #93/R est:800-1500

DUNLOP, Brian James (1938-) Australian
£2672 $4863 €3901 Reclining nude (67x95cm-26x37in) s. s.i.verso canvas on board prov.exhib. 16-Jun-4 Deutscher-Menzies, Melbourne #41/R est:9000-12000 (A.D 7000)
£2766 $4702 €4038 Interior still life (71x56cm-28x22in) s. prov. 26-Nov-3 Deutscher-Menzies, Melbourne #133/R est:6500-8500 (A.D 6500)
£4752 $8791 €6938 Parsnips (78x120cm-31x47in) s. prov.exhib. 15-Mar-4 Sotheby's, Melbourne #121/R est:9000-12000 (A.D 11500)
£4878 $7659 €7073 Studio with figure (90x60cm-35x24in) s. prov. 26-Aug-3 Christie's, Sydney #112/R est:12000-15000 (A.D 12000)
£7438 $13760 €10859 Interior, Port Fairy 1990 (147x242cm-58x95in) s. diptych prov.exhib. 10-Mar-4 Deutscher-Menzies, Melbourne #23/R est:30000-40000 (A.D 18000)
Works on paper
£638 $1085 €931 Adolescent (53x64cm-21x25in) s.d.87 pencil W/C. 25-Nov-3 Christie's, Melbourne #319 (A.D 1500)
£1736 $2950 €2535 Girl reading at window (55x47cm-22x19in) s. W/C prov. 29-Oct-3 Lawson Menzies, Sydney #132/R est:2000-3000 (A.D 4200)

DUNLOP, Ronald Ossory (1894-1973) British
£400 $736 €584 Kings Collage Chapel (50x40cm-20x16in) s. 23-Jun-4 Bonhams, Bury St Edmunds #391/R
£400 $736 €584 Self portrait (45x34cm-18x13in) s. 23-Jun-4 Bonhams, Bury St Edmunds #392
£480 $859 €701 Autumn by the Tweed at Peebles (39x49cm-15x19in) s. i.stretcher. 17-Mar-4 Bonhams, Chester #354
£500 $915 €730 Autumn landscape (40x49cm-16x19in) s. prov. 3-Jun-4 Lane, Penzance #214
£600 $960 €870 Cows going to drink (26x36cm-10x14in) s. board prov. 16-Sep-3 Bonhams, Knightsbridge #7/R
£600 $1002 €876 View down a shantytown street (61x51cm-24x20in) s. 16-Oct-3 Christie's, Kensington #469/R
£650 $1164 €949 Portrait of (56x41cm-22x16in) s. 14-May-4 Christie's, Kensington #318/R
£694 $1132 €1000 Figures in landscape (23x28cm-9x11in) s. board. 24-Sep-3 James Adam, Dublin #96/R est:1000-1500
£700 $1295 €1022 Bus stop (61x51cm-24x20in) s. 11-Mar-4 Christie's, Kensington #95/R
£700 $1239 €1022 Boatyard (36x46cm-14x18in) s. board. 28-Apr-4 Halls, Shrewsbury #550s/R
£700 $1232 €1022 Paxos Island, Corfu (40x30cm-16x12in) s. 19-May-4 Sotheby's, Olympia #122/R
£800 $1336 €1168 Young woman seated on a sofa with a cat in her lap (46x35cm-18x14in) s. 26-Jun-3 Greenslade Hunt, Taunton #558/R
£850 $1573 €1241 Path to the Downs (41x51cm-16x20in) s. 9-Mar-4 Gorringes, Lewes #2300
£850 $1505 €1241 Sussex landscape (76x91cm-30x36in) s. 27-Apr-4 Bonhams, Knightsbridge #291/R
£850 $1522 €1241 Still life (30x25cm-12x10in) s.verso. 14-May-4 Christie's, Kensington #386/R
£850 $1547 €1241 Dark trees under a stormy sky (63x76cm-25x30in) s. 15-Jun-4 Bonhams, Knightsbridge #115/R
£900 $1593 €1314 Sussex Downs near Arundel (39x49cm-15x19in) s.i.verso. 28-Apr-4 Peter Wilson, Nantwich #13
£950 $1672 €1387 Marina (40x52cm-16x20in) s. 19-May-4 Sotheby's, Olympia #140/R
£960 $1738 €1402 Donegal coast (33x43cm-13x17in) s. prov. 16-Apr-4 Keys, Aylsham #738/R
£1046 $1893 €1527 Street in Chichester, Sussex (50x61cm-20x24in) s. i.verso prov. 1-Apr-4 Heffel, Vancouver #22/R est:1500-2000 (C.D 2500)
£1100 $1936 €1606 Farmyard, Guernsey (40x56cm-16x22in) s. 19-May-4 Sotheby's, Olympia #126/R est:1200-1800
£1127 $1803 €1600 Cattle being herded through a farmyard (46x43cm-18x17in) s.d.1938 panel. 16-Sep-3 Whyte's, Dublin #214/R est:2000-3000
£1127 $1803 €1600 Irish critics, the bar Paris (225x30cm-89x12in) s. canvasboard prov. 16-Sep-3 Whyte's, Dublin #223/R est:1500-2000
£1259 $2140 €1800 Cattle watering (25x36cm-10x14in) s. board painted c.1967. 18-Nov-3 Whyte's, Dublin #98/R est:2000-3000
£1300 $2236 €1898 Little Hampton harbour (41x51cm-16x20in) s. 2-Dec-3 Bonhams, New Bond Street #55/R est:1200-1800
£1400 $2562 €2044 Fishing on a river (45x56cm-18x22in) s.d.1931 board. 2-Jun-4 John Ross, Belfast #108 est:1500-1800
£1408 $2437 €2000 Port of Martiques, Bouche de Rhone (38x49cm-15x19in) s. board. 10-Dec-3 Bonhams & James Adam, Dublin #113/R est:2000-3000
£1469 $2497 €2100 Wooded path in autumn with glimpse of water beyond (34x46cm-13x18in) s. board. 18-Nov-3 Whyte's, Dublin #178/R est:1800-2200
£1600 $2720 €2336 Ferry at Sunbury (49x60cm-19x24in) s. 1-Dec-3 Bonhams, Bath #37/R est:800-1200

£1678	$2853	€2400	Landscape with farm buildings and church (41x51cm-16x20in) s. 18-Nov-3 Whyte's, Dublin #102/R est:2000-3000
£1700	$3043	€2482	Harbour (40x51cm-16x20in) s. 16-Mar-4 Bonhams, New Bond Street #70/R est:1000-1500
£1700	$3060	€2482	Estuary scene with yachts and other boats (41x51cm-16x20in) s. 21-Apr-4 Tennants, Leyburn #1255 est:600-800
£1700	$2992	€2482	Itchenor (40x51cm-16x20in) s. 19-May-4 Sotheby's, Olympia #123/R est:1500-2000
£1879	$3364	€2800	Le Plage (50x60cm-20x24in) s. board. 31-May-4 Hamilton Osborne King, Dublin #197a est:3000-5000
£1900	$3496	€2774	Kingston upon Thames (39x50cm-15x20in) s. 24-Mar-4 Hamptons Fine Art, Godalming #318/R
£1958	$3329	€2800	Park scene with figures (41x51cm-16x20in) s. 18-Nov-3 Whyte's, Dublin #202/R est:2000-3000
£2000	$3640	€2920	Backwater of the Thames, Trowlock Island (63x76cm-25x30in) indis.s. prov. 29-Jun-4 Bonhams, Knowle #89 est:2000-3000
£2000	$3740	€2920	Portrait of Miss Caroline Besley, seated (66x51cm-26x20in) s. i.d.1959 verso. 22-Jul-4 Tennants, Leyburn #799 est:1400-1600
£2200	$3938	€3212	River landscape (63x75cm-25x30in) s. 14-May-4 Christie's, Kensington #381/R est:1500-2000
£2500	$4075	€3600	Street in Dublin (39x50cm-15x20in) s. 24-Sep-3 James Adam, Dublin #131/R est:2000-3000
£2500	$4625	€3650	Beached boats (41x51cm-16x20in) s. 11-Feb-4 Sotheby's, Olympia #153/R est:2500-3500
£2600	$4238	€3796	Boats at the quayside, Honfleur (46x36cm-18x14in) s. painted 1960. 23-Sep-3 John Nicholson, Haslemere #207/R est:500-1000
£2800	$4564	€4060	Village near Martigues (47x59cm-19x23in) s. 23-Sep-3 Bonhams, Leeds #143 est:2800-3500
£3800	$6688	€5548	Looking up river at Littlehampton (63x76cm-25x30in) s. 19-May-4 Sotheby's, Olympia #121/R est:3000-5000
£3846	$6538	€5500	Workhorse (41x51cm-16x20in) s. 18-Nov-3 Whyte's, Dublin #101/R est:2000-3000
£4000	$7160	€5840	Dun Laoghaire Harbour, Co Dublin (51x61cm-20x24in) s. prov. 13-May-4 Sotheby's, London #92/R est:4000-6000

Works on paper

£260	$434	€380	Arch on Constitution Hill (38x56cm-15x22in) s. W/C. 21-Oct-3 Bonhams, Knightsbridge #101/R
£520	$962	€759	Portrait of a young lady (23x13cm-9x5in) s. pencil dr. 13-Feb-4 Keys, Aylsham #491
£650	$1086	€949	Old Mill Road. Chichester (32x52cm-13x20in) s. W/C pair. 21-Oct-3 Bonhams, Knightsbridge #98/R
£750	$1328	€1095	Paris street (56x43cm-22x17in) s. mixed media. 1-May-4 Hamptons Fine Art, Godalming #29

DUNN, David (19/20th C) American

£824	$1500	€1203	Barn and cattle in California landscape (28x36cm-11x14in) s. canvasboard. 15-Jun-4 John Moran, Pasadena #13 est:800-1200

DUNN, Delphine (20th C) American

£226	$400	€330	Fishing boat moored at a dock (20x18cm-8x7in) s. 2-May-4 Bonhams & Butterfields, San Francisco #1099/R
£311	$550	€454	Untitled (22x26cm-9x10in) s. 2-May-4 Bonhams & Butterfields, San Francisco #1136/R

DUNN, George (?) British?

£380	$623	€555	Bit of a session (22x25cm-9x10in) s. board. 4-Jun-3 John Ross, Belfast #54
£450	$738	€657	Still life (45x40cm-18x16in) s. board. 4-Jun-3 John Ross, Belfast #97
£600	$996	€876	Cafe interior (81x71cm-32x28in) s. 1-Oct-3 John Ross, Belfast #11

DUNN, Harvey (1884-1952) American

£5435	$10000	€7935	The little Indian boy (102x76cm-40x30in) s.d.1920 lit. 8-Jun-4 Bonhams & Butterfields, San Francisco #4122/R est:10000-15000
£10000	$17000	€14600	Lincoln surveying the landscape (75x206cm-30x81in) s.d.1929. 21-Nov-3 Skinner, Boston #507/R est:3000-5000
£33824	$57500	€49383	Cowboys going up defile (66x97cm-26x38in) s.d.17 prov.lit. 1-Nov-3 Santa Fe Art, Santa Fe #108/R est:45000-65000

DUNN, Harvey (attrib) (1884-1952) American

£10165	$18500	€14841	Sailing ship (119x89cm-47x35in) s.d. 1-Jul-4 Dan Ripley, Indianapolis #141

DUNN, Joseph (1806-1860) British

£2400	$4416	€3504	Two pointers in a rural landscape (56x76cm-22x30in) s.d.53. 25-Mar-4 Mallams, Cheltenham #289/R est:2000-3000

DUNNE, George (?) British?

£280	$465	€409	Tactices (23x25cm-9x10in) s. board. 1-Oct-3 John Ross, Belfast #246
£300	$516	€438	A bit of a session (23x25cm-9x10in) s. board. 3-Dec-3 John Ross, Belfast #16
£322	$577	€480	Figures sitting in a window (45x50cm-18x20in) s. 31-May-4 Hamilton Osborne King, Dublin #16/R
£338	$592	€480	Winter meeting (43x39cm-17x15in) s.i.d.91 board. 16-Dec-3 James Adam, Dublin #109/R
£436	$781	€650	Cafe scene (40x45cm-16x18in) s. 31-May-4 Hamilton Osborne King, Dublin #15/R
£567	$1026	€850	Bar chat (47x51cm-19x20in) s. 30-Mar-4 De Veres Art Auctions, Dublin #176
£570	$1021	€850	Leopardstown races (40x45cm-16x18in) s. 31-May-4 Hamilton Osborne King, Dublin #16a
£592	$1089	€900	Musicians (54x44cm-21x17in) s. 22-Jun-4 De Veres Art Auctions, Dublin #224/R
£600	$996	€876	Circus (81x71cm-32x28in) s. 1-Oct-3 John Ross, Belfast #178
£625	$1019	€900	Sharing secrets (46x51cm-18x20in) s. prov. 23-Sep-3 De Veres Art Auctions, Dublin #273
£625	$1019	€900	Word in your ear (46x51cm-18x20in) s. prov. 23-Sep-3 De Veres Art Auctions, Dublin #274
£933	$1689	€1400	Jazz band (47x51cm-19x20in) s. 30-Mar-4 De Veres Art Auctions, Dublin #142/R

DUNNE, Joe (1957-) Irish

Works on paper

£423	$739	€600	Landscape (28x38cm-11x15in) mono. pastel. 16-Dec-3 James Adam, Dublin #128/R

DUNNING, Robert Spear (1829-1905) American

£4620	$8500	€6745	Sailboat at a bend in the river. Cattle watering at a bend in the river (10x14cm-4x6in) s.d.1870 verso canvas on board pair. 8-Jun-4 Bonhams & Butterfields, San Francisco #4027/R est:3000-5000
£18994	$34000	€27731	Still life with grapes, peach and other fruits (20x30cm-8x12in) s.d.90 verso. 16-May-4 CRN Auctions, Cambridge #20/R
£129412	$220000	€188942	Opulent still life with peaches and honeycomb (77x65cm-30x26in) s.d.1871. 21-Nov-3 Skinner, Boston #303/R est:75000-125000

DUNOUY, Alexandre Hyacinthe (1757-1841) French

£102778	$185000	€150056	Bay of Naples with Vesuvius erupting beyond (45x37cm-18x15in) indis.sig. i.stretcher oil paper on canvas. 22-Jan-4 Sotheby's, New York #283/R est:40000-60000

DUNOUY, Alexandre Hyacinthe (attrib) (1757-1841) French

£3600	$6228	€5256	Italianate landscape with figures and their donkey on a road before a copse (42x55cm-17x22in) 9-Dec-3 Sotheby's, Olympia #449/R est:3000-5000

DUNOYER DE SEGONZAC, Andre (1884-1974) French

£1310	$2424	€1900	Passerelle de Creteil (53x73cm-21x29in) s. ink wash dr lit. 16-Feb-4 Giraudeau, Tours #17
£2500	$4400	€3650	Nature morte a la bouteille rouge (20x25cm-8x10in) init. s.verso panel prov.exhib. 19-May-4 Dreweatt Neate, Newbury #80/R est:4000-6000
£2978	$5480	€4348	Interior scene with female figure (65x46cm-26x18in) s. prov. 29-Mar-4 Rasmussen, Copenhagen #198/R est:40000-50000 (D.KR 33000)
£9396	$16819	€14000	Anemones et livre (65x81cm-26x32in) s. prov.exhib. 26-May-4 Christie's, Paris #27/R est:14000-18000

Works on paper

£268	$494	€400	Vendangeuse a Saint Tropez (17x26cm-7x10in) s.i. Indian ink. 24-Mar-4 Joron-Derem, Paris #57
£278	$525	€406	Meandering stream with distant buildings (30x48cm-12x19in) s. pen ink. 23-Feb-4 Winter Associates, Plainville #186/R
£300	$540	€450	Maryse (16x18cm-6x7in) s. ink dr. 24-Apr-4 Cornette de St.Cyr, Paris #403
£470	$874	€700	Vue de village (25x33cm-10x13in) s. brown ink paper on cardboard. 2-Mar-4 Artcurial Briest, Paris #50
£506	$800	€739	Campagne de Seine (33x48cm-13x19in) s.d. graphite. 27-Jul-3 Simpson's, Houston #257
£604	$1124	€900	Paysage d'hiver, fermes pres de Provins (35x48cm-14x19in) s. Indian ink. 2-Mar-4 Artcurial Briest, Paris #51
£621	$1148	€900	Vieux provencal (32x29cm-13x11in) s.d.1930 ink wash dr lit. 16-Feb-4 Giraudeau, Tours #19
£726	$1335	€1060	Seated nude (25x47cm-10x19in) s. pen ink grisaille W/C wash. 14-Jun-4 Waddingtons, Toronto #263/R est:1500-2000 (C.D 1800)
£743	$1405	€1100	Quai de la Seine a Paris (35x47cm-14x19in) s. ink. 21-Feb-4 Cornette de St.Cyr, Paris #201/R
£833	$1392	€1200	Lake (31x51cm-12x20in) W/C Indian ink. 24-Oct-3 Ketterer, Hamburg #328/R
£903	$1507	€1300	Baigneurs a Saint-Tropez (45x61cm-18x24in) s. ink ink wash. 21-Oct-3 Artcurial Briest, Paris #42 est:800-1000
£1100	$1749	€1595	Paysage agricole (31x48cm-12x19in) s. pen brush ink prov.exhib. 11-Sep-3 Christie's, Kensington #54/R est:600-800
£1200	$2112	€1752	La charette (23x31cm-9x12in) s. pen ink prov. 19-May-4 Dreweatt Neate, Newbury #94/R est:1500-2000
£1275	$2359	€1900	Paysage (28x46cm-11x18in) s. W/C. 14-Mar-4 Eric Pillon, Calais #144/R
£1528	$2551	€2200	Jeune fille allongee (32x49cm-13x19in) s. ink wash ink exhib. 21-Oct-3 Christie's, Paris #62/R est:2500-3500
£1935	$3600	€2825	Femme en repose (32x49cm-13x19in) s. pen ink wash. 2-Mar-4 Swann Galleries, New York #617/R est:2000-3000
£2148	$3844	€3200	Eglise de Davron (58x79cm-23x31in) s. chk ink wash prov. 26-May-4 Christie's, Paris #8/R est:2500-3000
£2489	$4156	€3634	La montagne San Pelire, vue du Plan de la Tour (56x75cm-22x30in) s. WC over Indian ink prov. 24-Jun-3 Germann, Zurich #164 est:5000-8000 (S.FR 5500)
£2500	$4600	€3650	Route de foret (49x38cm-19x15in) s. W/C pen ink prov. 24-Mar-4 Sotheby's, Olympia #6/R est:3000-4000
£2778	$5000	€4056	Country scene (56x76cm-22x30in) W/C. 24-Apr-4 Du Mouchelle, Detroit #3100/R est:2500-4500
£3514	$6500	€5130	Baie de Saint-Tropez (48x62cm-19x24in) s. W/C pen ink prov. 11-Feb-4 Sotheby's, New York #46/R est:7000-9000
£5000	$7950	€7250	Schale mit apfein (35x48cm-14x19in) s. pencil ink W/C. 11-Sep-3 Christie's, Kensington #53/R est:4000-6000
£5667	$10200	€8500	Paysage de Provence (55x75cm-22x30in) s. W/C exhib. 26-Apr-4 Tajan, Paris #37/R est:10000-12000
£7821	$14000	€11419	Nature morte avec des fleurs et des fruits sur une table (58x79cm-23x31in) s. W/C gouache brush India ink prov. 6-May-4 Sotheby's, New York #435/R est:15000-20000
£8500	$15470	€12410	Nature morte au parapluie (48x66cm-19x26in) s. W/C pen brush ink prov.exhib.lit. 4-Feb-4 Sotheby's, London #554/R est:8000-12000
£9211	$16947	€14000	Nature morte aux fleurs et citrons (56x77cm-22x30in) s. W/C ink prov. 22-Jun-4 Ribeyre & Baron, Paris #61/R est:8000-10000
£17000	$31280	€24820	Bouteille de vin rose (58x79cm-23x31in) s. gouache W/C pen ink exec 1963 prov. 24-Jun-4 Christie's, London #346/R est:10000-15000
£19118	$32500	€27912	Vase d'aneomones, citrons et panier sur la table (57x78cm-22x31in) s. W/C pen ink. 6-Nov-3 Sotheby's, New York #342/R est:20000-25000
£24500	$45080	€35770	Tomatoes (59x79cm-23x31in) s. gouache W/C wash pen ink pencil exec 1973 prov. 24-Jun-4 Christie's, London #347/R est:15000-20000
£30726	$55000	€44860	Chapeau de paille d'Italie (56x78cm-22x31in) s. W/C pen India ink exec c.1959 prov. 5-May-4 Christie's, Rockefeller NY #257/R est:30000-40000

DUNSMORE, John Ward (1856-1945) British

£226	$400	€330	Pastoral scene with church in background, cows grazing in foreground (20x28cm-8x11in) s. panel. 1-May-4 Thomaston Place, Thomaston #351/R

DUNSTAN, Bernard (1920-) British

£600	$1002	€876	Beach at Friog (23x29cm-9x11in) init. board. 16-Oct-3 Christie's, Kensington #423/R
£978	$1800	€1428	Kitchen (23x28cm-9x11in) init.i.d.17-9-68 verso board prov. 27-Jun-4 Freeman, Philadelphia #58/R est:1500-2500
£1100	$1837	€1606	Tea table (28x20cm-11x8in) s.i.verso board prov. 16-Oct-3 Christie's, Kensington #320/R est:1200-1800
£1100	$1892	€1606	Girl putting on her nightdress (30x19cm-12x7in) init. board prov. 3-Dec-3 Christie's, Kensington #413/R est:1200-1800
£1100	$1936	€1606	Negligee (17x29cm-7x11in) init. canvasboard. 19-May-4 Sotheby's, Olympia #251/R est:1200-1800
£1300	$2210	€1898	Siesta, resting (16x33cm-6x13in) init. board. 26-Nov-3 Hamptons Fine Art, Godalming #134/R est:1500-1800
£1304	$2400	€1904	Green bedroom (27x27cm-11x11in) init. board painted 1965-66 prov. 27-Jun-4 Freeman, Philadelphia #57/R est:1500-2500
£1400	$2380	€2044	Nude at a door (32x20cm-13x8in) init.i.d.4, 2000 board. 26-Nov-3 Hamptons Fine Art, Godalming #124 est:1500-1800
£1400	$2380	€2044	Barmouth Beach (25x32cm-10x13in) board. 25-Nov-3 Outhwaite & Litherland, Liverpool #471
£1400	$2548	€2044	Open Bathroom door (25x25cm-10x10in) init. board. 1-Jul-4 Christie's, Kensington #252/R est:800-1200
£1600	$2816	€2336	Nude girl going into a bathroom (28x34cm-11x13in) init. canvas on board. 18-May-4 Bonhams, Knightsbridge #138/R est:1000-1500
£1900	$3268	€2774	Verona, in the arena (25x25cm-10x10in) init. board prov. 2-Dec-3 Bonhams, New Bond Street #90/R est:800-1200
£2600	$4342	€3796	At the National Gallery (31x25cm-12x10in) init. i.verso board. 7-Oct-3 Bonhams, Knightsbridge #54/R est:2500-3500
£2600	$4420	€3796	Hotel room (27x30cm-11x12in) init. i.d.98 verso canvas on board. 26-Nov-3 Sotheby's, Olympia #93/R est:2000-3000
£2600	$4654	€3796	Siesta (25x25cm-10x10in) init. board prov. 16-Mar-4 Bonhams, New Bond Street #15/R est:1500-2000
Works on paper			
£280	$510	€409	Nude getting into bath (39x24cm-15x9in) init. red chk prov. 1-Jul-4 Christie's, Kensington #289
£300	$531	€438	Fan design (18x36cm-7x14in) init. pastel. 27-Apr-4 Bonhams, Knightsbridge #173
£650	$1164	€949	Reclining female nude (28x38cm-11x15in) init. red chk. 14-May-4 Christie's, Kensington #563
£800	$1360	€1168	Slumber (24x32cm-9x13in) init. pastel. 26-Nov-3 Hamptons Fine Art, Godalming #127/R
£800	$1480	€1168	Dark bedroom (19x18cm-7x7in) init. pastel exhib. 11-Mar-4 Christie's, Kensington #313/R
£850	$1420	€1241	The bathroom (24x20cm-9x8in) init. pastel. 16-Oct-3 Christie's, Kensington #321/R
£850	$1547	€1241	Pizetta, Morning (19x19cm-7x7in) init. pastel prov.exhib. 1-Jul-4 Christie's, Kensington #274/R

DUNTON, W Herbert (1878-1936) American

£5988	$10000	€8742	Elk, spike bull and cow (13x20cm-5x8in) canvasboard. 18-Oct-3 David Dike, Dallas #80/R est:6000-8000
£54729	$93040	€79904	Lookout (51x41cm-20x16in) 1-Nov-3 Altermann Galleries, Santa Fe #60

DUNTZE, Johannes Bertholomaus (1823-1895) German

£1100	$2024	€1606	Unwelcome companions (32x43cm-13x17in) mono.d.45. 25-Mar-4 Christie's, Kensington #189/R est:1200-1800
£1389	$2264	€2000	Rhine landscape with steamer in moonlight (23x36cm-9x14in) s.d. panel. 26-Sep-3 Bolland & Marotz, Bremen #517/R est:2700
£4800	$8736	€7008	Winter twilight (22x36cm-9x14in) s.d.1874 panel. 16-Jun-4 Bonhams, New Bond Street #18/R est:2000-3000
£5500	$10010	€8030	Norwegian fjord landscape (84x137cm-33x54in) s.d.1874. 16-Jun-4 Christie's, Kensington #195/R est:5000-8000
£5594	$9510	€8000	River landscape in winter (80x110cm-31x43in) s.d.1862. 20-Nov-3 Van Ham, Cologne #1547/R est:5000
£6000	$10200	€8760	Skating on a frozen river (64x96cm-25x38in) s.d.1884. 19-Nov-3 Bonhams, New Bond Street #30/R est:6000-8000
£22222	$40000	€32444	Village on the Rhine in winter (97x138cm-38x54in) s.d.1880. 23-Apr-4 Sotheby's, New York #33/R est:18000-25000

DUNZ, Alfred (1865-1932) Swiss

£345	$617	€504	River landscapes (21x28cm-8x11in) s. two. 13-May-4 Stuker, Bern #107 (S.FR 800)

DUNZ, Johannes (1645-1736) Swiss

£393	$715	€574	Portrait of Johann Heinrich Hummel (29x21cm-11x8in) i. panel. 16-Jun-4 Fischer, Luzern #2082/R (S.FR 900)

DUNZENDORFER, Albrecht (1907-1980) Austrian

£280	$476	€400	Iron foundry (84x63cm-33x25in) s. panel. 27-Nov-3 Dorotheum, Linz #474/R
£839	$1427	€1200	Muhlviertler landscape (50x60cm-20x24in) s. panel. 27-Nov-3 Dorotheum, Linz #476/R
£1189	$2021	€1700	View of Linz through the Haselgraben (60x50cm-24x20in) mono.d.47 board. 27-Nov-3 Dorotheum, Linz #469/R est:3000-4000
£1200	$2148	€1800	Muhlviertel landscape (43x58cm-17x23in) s. d.1972 verso panel. 13-May-4 Dorotheum, Linz #472/R est:3000-3600
£1259	$2140	€1800	Muhlviertler landscape at sunset (50x70cm-20x28in) s. panel. 27-Nov-3 Dorotheum, Linz #472/R est:3200-3800
£1329	$2259	€1900	The three Zinnen (78x57cm-31x22in) s. panel. 27-Nov-3 Dorotheum, Linz #475/R est:2800-3000
£1538	$2615	€2200	Winter landscape with farmhouse (50x70cm-20x28in) s. d.1980 verso panel. 27-Nov-3 Dorotheum, Linz #471/R est:4000-4400
£1818	$3091	€2600	Muhlviertler landscape (68x82cm-27x32in) s. panel. 27-Nov-3 Dorotheum, Linz #470/R est:3600-3800

DUODO, Giuseppe (19th C) Italian?

£405	$632	€600	Girl (33x24cm-13x9in) board. 30-Mar-3 Adma, Formigine #151
£1000	$1790	€1500	Portrait of young Venetian woman (77x50cm-30x20in) s. cardboard. 12-May-4 Stadion, Trieste #728/R est:900-1200

DUPAGNE, Adrien (1889-1980) Belgian

£355	$592	€500	Maternite (60x44cm-24x17in) s. panel. 15-Oct-3 Hotel des Ventes Mosan, Brussels #175
£397	$723	€600	Leda et la cygne (78x90cm-31x35in) s. 15-Jun-4 Vanderkindere, Brussels #117
£3427	$5825	€4900	Le cirque (74x92cm-29x36in) s.d.1951. 18-Nov-3 Vanderkindere, Brussels #120/R est:2500-3500
Works on paper			
£324	$560	€460	Buste de femme (43x33cm-17x13in) s. mixed media. 10-Dec-3 Hotel des Ventes Mosan, Brussels #241

DUPAGNE, Arthur (1895-1961) Belgian

Sculpture			
£1702	$2843	€2400	Africain sur pirogue (36cm-14in) s. pat bronze. 14-Oct-3 Vanderkindere, Brussels #153/R
£2013	$3745	€3000	Bust of man (50x45cm-20x18in) brown pat.plaster. 8-Mar-4 Bernaerts, Antwerp #89/R est:500-600

DUPAIN, Max Spencer (1911-1992) Australian

Photographs			
£1885	$2978	€2752	Flinders Street Station, Melbourne (45x40cm-18x16in) s.d.1946 i. verso silver gelatin. 2-Sep-3 Deutscher-Menzies, Melbourne #147/R est:5000-5500 (A.D 4600)
£2000	$3460	€2920	Mother and child, Cronulla (34x35cm-13x14in) s.d.1937 gelatin silver print. 10-Dec-3 Shapiro, Sydney #122a/R est:5000-7000 (A.D 4700)
£2033	$3638	€2968	Burning the sugar cane (40x49cm-16x19in) s. silver gelatin print. 4-May-4 Sotheby's, Melbourne #209/R est:3000-4000 (A.D 5000)
£2119	$3602	€3094	Monstera (48x38cm-19x15in) s. silver gelatin print. 24-Nov-3 Sotheby's, Melbourne #92/R est:2500-4500 (A.D 5000)
£2254	$3562	€3291	Main shells, Sydney Opera House (37x47cm-15x19in) s.d.1972 s. verso silver gelatin. 2-Sep-3 Deutscher-Menzies, Melbourne #148/R est:6000-6500 (A.D 5500)
£2600	$4576	€3796	Solarised Jean with wire mesh (28x21cm-11x8in) gelatin silver print. 18-May-4 Bonhams, New Bond Street #297/R est:2500-3300
£3239	$5215	€4729	Jean with mesh (37x25cm-15x10in) s.d.38 gelatin silver print. 25-Aug-3 Sotheby's, Paddington #315/R est:3000-5000 (A.D 8000)
£3320	$5544	€4980	Pamela's hour (38x39cm-15x15in) s.i.d.36 gelatin silver photograph. 27-Oct-3 Goodman, Sydney #92/R est:8000-10000 (A.D 8000)
£3602	$6123	€5259	Silos (40x44cm-16x17in) s. silver gelatin print. 24-Nov-3 Sotheby's, Melbourne #93/R est:3000-5000 (A.D 8500)
£4098	$6475	€5983	Sunbaker (37x42cm-15x17in) s.d.37 s.i.d.37 verso silver gelatin. 2-Sep-3 Deutscher-Menzies, Melbourne #9/R est:14000-18000 (A.D 10000)
£4580	$8336	€6687	Jean with wire mesh (50x36cm-20x14in) s. gelatin silver print. 16-Jun-4 Deutscher-Menzies, Melbourne #191/R est:7000-10000 (A.D 12000)
£20000	$35200	€29200	Sydney Opera House (30x30cm-12x12in) gelatin silver print collection of 178. 18-May-4 Bonhams, New Bond Street #299/R est:20000-30000

DUPAS, Jean (1882-1964) French

£1267	$2267	€1900	Les grands voiliers (38x46cm-15x18in) s. 16-May-4 Thierry & Lannon, Brest #140 est:1000-1200
£18786	$32500	€27428	Figural panel from birth of Aphrodite mural for the Grand lounge of the S.S. Normandie (124x77cm-49x30in) painted glass executed 1935 prov.lit. 11-Dec-3 Sotheby's, New York #106/R est:20000-30000
Prints			
£4865	$9000	€7103	Xvme salon des artistes decorateurs (76x71cm-30x28in) with sig.d.1924 lithograph. 11-Mar-4 Sotheby's, New York #198/R est:7000-10000
Works on paper			
£2072	$3750	€3025	Femme (61x43cm-24x17in) s.d.1932 ink chl pencil crayon prov. 30-Mar-4 Sotheby's, New York #357/R est:5000-7000
£5944	$10105	€8500	La navire (31x25cm-12x10in) s.i.d.1929 Indian ink ombre crayon. 24-Nov-3 Tajan, Paris #24/R est:8000-10000

DUPASQUIER, Antoine Leonard (1748-1831) French

Works on paper			
£319	$533	€450	Hercule et le lion Neme. i.d.1777 pen Chinese ink prov. 15-Oct-3 Sotheby's, Paris #93/R

DUPAU, Louise (1874-1966) French

£260	$478	€380	Martigues (52x73cm-20x29in) s. board. 10-Jun-4 Lyon & Turnbull, Edinburgh #120
£260	$478	€380	Mediterranean fishing village (52x73cm-20x29in) s. board. 10-Jun-4 Lyon & Turnbull, Edinburgh #12

DUPERREUX, Alexandre Louis Robert Millin (1764-1843) French

£3667	$6563	€5500	View of castle (26x38cm-10x15in) s.d.1820. 11-May-4 Christie's, Paris #207/R est:1000-1500
£4610	$7468	€6500	Wide river (73x110cm-29x43in) s.d.1808 lit. 23-May-3 Karlheinz Kaupp, Staufen #1771/R est:800
£6643	$11294	€9500	Pyrennean landscapes (27x37cm-11x15in) s.d.1803 two. 20-Nov-3 Van Ham, Cologne #1548/R est:3500
£12222	$22000	€17844	Nobles disembarking along the banks of a river (75x110cm-30x43in) s.d.1808. 22-Jan-4 Sotheby's, New York #229/R est:20000-30000

DUPIN, F (?) French

£1342	$2510	€2000	Figures in garden (70x104cm-28x41in) s. 24-Feb-4 Dorotheum, Vienna #124/R est:2800-3000

DUPLAIN, Albert (1890-1978) Swiss

£617	$1048	€901	Grandvaux (50x80cm-20x31in) s. i.d.2/3 6 41 verso. 7-Nov-3 Dobiaschofsky, Bern #99/R (S.FR 1400)

DUPLESSI-BERTAUX, Jean (1747-1819) French

£2685	$4940	€4000	La halte des cavaliers (46x39cm-18x15in) s. panel. 23-Mar-4 Galerie Moderne, Brussels #325/R est:4000-5000

Works on paper
£1000 $1800 €1460 Studies of horses and their riders (15x13cm-6x5in) one s. black chk pair. 20-Apr-4 Sotheby's, Olympia #142/R est:1500-2000

DUPLESSIS, J V (18th C) ?
£18531 $31503 €26500 Philippe-Norbert, comte van der Stegen, accompagnant son oncle (134x158cm-53x62in) s. 18-Nov-3 Vanderkindere, Brussels #200/R est:15000-20000

DUPLESSIS, Joseph Siffrede (1725-1802) French
£11667 $21467 €17500 Portrait presume de Monsieur de Boullongne, intendant des finances (79x59cm-31x23in) oval prov.exhib.lit. 11-Jun-4 Maigret, Paris #61/R est:17000-20000

DUPLESSIS, Michel (18th C) French
£4363 $8027 €6500 Halte de cavaliers devant des ruines antiques (46x38cm-18x15in) s. 24-Mar-4 Tajan, Paris #129/R est:4000-6000

DUPLESSIS, Michel (attrib) (18th C) French
£851 $1421 €1200 Paysage d'asie mineure avec campement Turc (12x20cm-5x8in) panel. 17-Oct-3 Tajan, Paris #118

DUPON, Josue (1864-1935) Belgian
Sculpture
£2800 $5040 €4088 Condor (32cm-13in) s.st.f. dark brown green pat bronze sold with marble base. 21-Apr-4 Sotheby's, London #74/R est:3500-4500
£4000 $6800 €5840 King Albert I (60x42cm-24x17in) s.d.1931 tinted plaster. 28-Oct-3 Sotheby's, London #109/R
£7092 $11844 €10000 Farmer's wife with flowers and fruit on a horse (66x71x25cm-26x28x10in) s.i. black pat bronze col marble socle st.f. Nle des Bronzes. 20-Oct-3 Bernaerts, Antwerp #37 est:10000-15000

DUPONT, Gainsborough (attrib) (1755-1797) British
£1400 $2212 €2030 Portrait of a boy in a brown jacket and white shirt (73x62cm-29x24in) painted oval prov. 4-Sep-3 Christie's, Kensington #28 est:800-1200

DUPONT, Paul (19/20th C) ?
Prints
£1622 $3000 €2368 Olympia, Grand Ballet, Brighton (122x76cm-48x30in) s. col lithograph exec.c.1900. 9-Mar-4 Christie's, Rockefeller NY #241/R est:1800-2400

DUPONT, Pieter (1870-1911) Dutch
£667 $1213 €1000 Cattle drinking at the river's edge (61x51cm-24x20in) s. 1-Jul-4 Van Ham, Cologne #1317/R
Works on paper
£1513 $2739 €2300 Ploughing oxen (30x72cm-12x28in) s. chl pastel. 19-Apr-4 Glerum, Amsterdam #282/R est:150-200

DUPONT, Richard John Munro (19/20th C) British
£400 $748 €584 Falls of Clyde, Newmarket (61x76cm-24x30in) s.i.d.July 1947. 22-Jul-4 Tennants, Leyburn #865

DUPONT, Victor (1875-?) French
£753 $1281 €1100 Fileuse. Homme au chaudron (80x60cm-31x24in) s.d.1909 pair. 10-Nov-3 Horta, Bruxelles #513

DUPOUY, Georgette (20th C) French
£269 $450 €393 Paysage fleuri (51x61cm-20x24in) s. 18-Jun-3 Doyle, New York #26/R

DUPRAT, Albert Ferdinand (1882-?) Italian
£839 $1443 €1200 Canal a Venise (55x45cm-22x18in) s.d.1904 panel. 3-Dec-3 Beaussant & Lefèvre, Paris #32/R
£862 $1560 €1259 Canal in Venice (46x33cm-18x13in) panel. 31-Mar-4 Zurichsee Auktionen, Erlenbach #16/R est:2500-3000 (S.FR 2000)
£2778 $4528 €4000 Gondoles dans la lagune de Venise (54x73cm-21x29in) s. 26-Sep-3 Rabourdin & Choppin de Janvry, Paris #55/R est:5000-5500
£5629 $10301 €8500 Vue de Venise (93x132cm-37x52in) s. panel prov. 9-Apr-4 Claude Aguttes, Neuilly #75/R est:7000-8000

DUPRAY, Henry-Louis (1841-1909) French
£559 $1000 €816 Untitled - scene with French cavalry (38x30cm-15x12in) s. prov. 21-Mar-4 Hindman, Chicago #775/R est:1500-2500
£921 $1695 €1400 Hussards de la garde (34x27cm-13x11in) s. panel. 25-Jun-4 Millon & Associes, Paris #41/R
£1119 $1902 €1600 La pose des soldats au cafe de Monsieur Arnaud (26x34cm-10x13in) s. panel painted c.1870. 18-Nov-3 Vanderkindere, Brussels #61 est:1500-2500
£1196 $2200 €1746 Untitled scene with French cavalry (38x30cm-15x12in) s. prov. 27-Jun-4 Hindman, Chicago #872/R est:1500-2500
£1818 $3091 €2600 Officier napoleonien a cheval (27x21cm-11x8in) s. panel. 18-Nov-3 Vanderkindere, Brussels #68 est:2000-3000

DUPRE, Amalia (1845-1928) Italian
Sculpture
£2958 $4762 €4200 Bust of a woman (44cm-17in) marble. 8-May-3 Farsetti, Prato #709/R est:5000-6000

DUPRE, Daniel (1752-1817) Dutch
£460 $768 €672 Dutch wagoners and other figures in a landscape (18x23cm-7x9in) 21-Oct-3 Gorringes, Lewes #2171/R
£2667 $4773 €4000 Mountainous Italianate landscape with peasant woman and child (41x54cm-16x21in) s.d.1810 panel prov. 17-May-4 Christie's, Amsterdam #117/R est:5000-7000
Works on paper
£1892 $3330 €2800 View at Civita Castellana (34x42cm-13x17in) i.verso brush brown ink wash black chk exhib. 19-May-4 Sotheby's, Amsterdam #330/R est:3500-4500
£2397 $4075 €3500 Extensive mountainous landscape with waterfalls, peasants and their flock (53x46cm-21x18in) bears d.1672 s.i.d.1796 verso pen brown ink W/C after J Hackert. 4-Nov-3 Sotheby's, Amsterdam #110/R est:3500-4500

DUPRE, Geoffroy (19/20th C) ?
£3400 $6222 €5100 Etudes d'enfants (41x27cm-16x11in) one s.i.d.1901 two. 3-Jun-4 Tajan, Paris #232/R est:4000-5000

DUPRE, Guillaume and PRIEUR, Barthelemy (after) (17th C) French
Sculpture
£55245 $95021 €79000 Busts of Henri IV, King of France and Navarre and Marie de Medici (25cm-10in) bronze base bronze grey marble plinth exec c.1600 lit. 2-Dec-3 Christie's, Paris #699/R est:20000-30000

DUPRE, Jules (1811-1889) French
£704 $1218 €1000 Chaumieres (26x36cm-10x14in) s. panel. 10-Dec-3 Maigret, Paris #72
£780 $1303 €1100 Chemin creux sous la neige (25x30cm-10x12in) mono.d.78. 15-Oct-3 Hotel des Ventes Mosan, Brussels #113
£800 $1464 €1200 Granges et chaumieres (26x35cm-10x14in) s. panel. 6-Jun-4 Osenat, Fontainebleau #133
£1087 $1783 €1500 Paysage au moulin (12x16cm-5x6in) panel. 11-May-3 Osenat, Fontainebleau #119 est:1600-1800
£1200 $2004 €1752 Cottage in a landscape (14x26cm-6x10in) panel. 7-Oct-3 Bonhams, Knightsbridge #258/R est:1000-1500
£1333 $2427 €2000 Fisher boats on stormy seas (21x32cm-8x13in) s. board. 1-Jul-4 Van Ham, Cologne #1319/R est:3500
£1748 $2920 €2500 Vaches pres de la mare (24x35cm-9x14in) s. 29-Jun-3 Eric Pillon, Calais #45/R
£1767 $3233 €2650 Pecheur sur la mare (19x29cm-7x11in) s. paper on canvas. 6-Jun-4 Osenat, Fontainebleau #128/R est:3000-3500
£1831 $3168 €2600 Troupeau dans un paysage (16x25cm-6x10in) s. panel. 14-Dec-3 Eric Pillon, Calais #10/R
£1884 $3090 €2600 Le petit pecheur (33x24cm-13x9in) init. panel. 11-May-3 Osenat, Fontainebleau #120/R est:3000-3500
£1902 $3500 €2777 Hamlet (23x33cm-9x13in) s. 26-Jun-4 Selkirks, St. Louis #422/R est:2000-3000
£2203 $3744 €3216 Autumn landscape (17x31cm-7x12in) s.i. panel. 5-Nov-3 Dobiaschofsky, Bern #505/R est:6000 (S.FR 5000)
£2215 $4097 €3300 Vaches pres de la mare (22x33cm-9x13in) s. 14-Mar-4 Eric Pillon, Calais #24/R
£2400 $3840 €3480 Cows in a meadow (37x45cm-15x18in) s.d.1881. 18-Sep-3 Christie's, Kensington #8/R est:1500-1800
£2400 $4392 €3600 Trois pommes sur assiette (24x32cm-9x13in) s.verso paper on canvas lit. 6-Jun-4 Osenat, Fontainebleau #126/R est:2200-2500
£2600 $4472 €3796 Cattle grazing in a meadow (29x23cm-11x9in) s.d.1873 panel. 4-Dec-3 Christie's, Kensington #13/R est:2000-3000
£3333 $6033 €5000 Troupeau a la mare (22x31cm-9x12in) exhib.lit. 30-Mar-4 Rossini, Paris #267/R est:1800-2500
£3467 $6275 €5200 Crepuscule (27x40cm-11x16in) s. panel painted c.1860-1865 exhib.lit. 30-Mar-4 Rossini, Paris #266/R est:1800-2500
£3497 $6014 €5000 Vaches au paturage (38x46cm-15x18in) s. 7-Dec-3 Osenat, Fontainebleau #137 est:5000-6000
£3623 $5942 €5000 Chaumiere pres de la mare (20x31cm-8x12in) s. panel. 11-May-3 Osenat, Fontainebleau #122/R est:5000-5200
£4000 $7240 €6000 Terrain eboule en foret de Compiegne (33x41cm-13x16in) painted c.1870 exhib.lit. 30-Mar-4 Rossini, Paris #271/R est:2000-3000
£4348 $7130 €6000 Chaumieres en bordure de la mare (34x54cm-13x21in) s. panel painted c.1885-86. 11-May-3 Osenat, Fontainebleau #125/R est:8000-9000
£4965 $8291 €7000 Une route pres de Champagne, Seine et Oise (58x45cm-23x18in) s. prov.lit. 12-Oct-3 St-Germain-en-Laye Encheres #45/R est:3000-4000
£5090 $8500 €7431 Bathers in the stream (46x56cm-18x22in) s. 19-Oct-3 Susanin's, Chicago #6049/R est:3000-5000
£6395 $11000 €9337 Bucolic River landscape (50x92cm-20x36in) s. 3-Dec-3 Doyle, New York #94/R est:8000-12000
£6466 $11897 €9440 Boats by lakeshore (28x42cm-11x17in) s. panel. 26-Mar-4 Koller, Zurich #517/R est:12000-16000 (S.FR 15000)
£10333 $18703 €15500 Le chemin creux (101x81cm-40x32in) exhib. 30-Mar-4 Rossini, Paris #265/R est:14000-20000
£10333 $18703 €15500 Claire de lune sur la mer, environs de Cailleux (73x60cm-29x24in) s. painted c.1870 exhib.lit. 30-Mar-4 Rossini, Paris #269/R est:5000-8000
£15278 $27500 €22306 Pleine mer (24x32cm-9x13in) s. painted c.1868-69. 23-Apr-4 Sotheby's, New York #2/R est:10000-15000
Works on paper
£267 $483 €400 La vieille tour du chateau (35x23cm-14x9in) st.mono. grahpite htd white. 30-Mar-4 Rossini, Paris #270
£800 $1448 €1200 Les bucherons (18x29cm-7x11in) mono. black crayon exec.c.1845. 30-Mar-4 Rossini, Paris #268/R
£2098 $3503 €3000 Sailing boats at anchor (28x30cm-11x12in) mono. pencil. 10-Oct-3 Winterberg, Heidelberg #564/R est:2600
£7746 $12859 €11000 Abreuvoir (20x34cm-8x13in) s. W/C lit. 15-Jun-3 Peron, Melun #53

DUPRE, Jules (attrib) (1811-1889) French
£396 $674 €578 Evening landscape (29x41cm-11x16in) 5-Nov-3 Dobiaschofsky, Bern #507/R (S.FR 900)
£400 $636 €584 River landscape (33x23cm-13x9in) s. 9-Sep-3 Gorringes, Lewes #2073
£873 $1607 €1275 Landscape with pond (13x10cm-5x4in) s. panel. 14-Jun-4 Philippe Schuler, Zurich #4270/R (S.FR 2000)
£2215 $4075 €3300 River landscape in evening (61x74cm-24x29in) s. 25-Mar-4 Dr Fritz Nagel, Stuttgart #697/R est:1800

DUPRE, Julien (1851-1910) French

£800	$1336	€1168	Woman on a track in a river landscape (33x46cm-13x18in) s. 8-Oct-3 Christie's, Kensington #801/R
£890	$1514	€1300	Travaux des champs (19x25cm-7x10in) s. panel. 9-Nov-3 Eric Pillon, Calais #60/R
£3889	$7000	€5678	Cows at pasture (39x46cm-15x18in) s. prov. 21-Jan-4 Sotheby's, New York #186/R est:10000-15000
£4670	$8500	€6818	Cows in pasture with figure (64x81cm-25x32in) s. 7-Feb-4 Sloans & Kenyon, Bethesda #1280/R est:7000-9000
£7394	$12275	€10500	Bergere et ses moutons (35x27cm-14x11in) s. 15-Jun-3 Peron, Melun #90
£8333	$14167	€12166	Lady feeding the chickens (34x26cm-13x10in) s. canvas on canvas prov. 23-Nov-3 Levis, Calgary #203/R est:1200-1500 (C.D 18500)
£18056	$32500	€26362	La laitiere (54x81cm-21x32in) s. 23-Apr-4 Sotheby's, New York #17/R est:40000-60000
£19444	$35000	€28388	Un berger et son troupeau (65x34cm-26x13in) s. prov. 23-Apr-4 Sotheby's, New York #16/R est:40000-60000
£20588	$35000	€30058	Laitiere (65x81cm-26x32in) s. 28-Oct-3 Sotheby's, New York #31/R est:40000-60000

DUPRE, Victor (1816-1879) French

£329	$605	€500	Pecheur au bord d'un etang (27x45cm-11x18in) board on canvas. 28-Jun-4 Joron-Derem, Paris #141
£1027	$1747	€1500	Vaches s'abreuvant dans une mare (16x23cm-6x9in) s. panel. 8-Nov-3 Gerard, Besancon #47
£1119	$1924	€1600	Vaches au paturage (21x46cm-8x18in) s. panel. 7-Dec-3 Osenat, Fontainebleau #136 est:2800-3000
£1538	$2615	€2200	Vaches paissant autour d'une mare (21x41cm-8x16in) s. 24-Nov-3 Boscher, Cherbourg #723/R est:2000-2500
£2267	$4148	€3400	Paysage au moulin (16x22cm-6x9in) s. panel. 6-Jun-4 Osenat, Fontainebleau #132/R est:2500-3000
£2319	$3803	€3200	Vaches a la mare (19x28cm-7x11in) s. panel. 11-May-3 Osenat, Fontainebleau #121 est:3500-4000
£2817	$4873	€4000	Paysage en bord de riviere (21x40cm-8x16in) s. 12-Dec-3 Piasa, Paris #52/R est:5000-6000
£3200	$5824	€4800	Extensive French river landscape with a cowherd (36x59cm-14x23in) s.d.1854 panel. 1-Jul-4 Van Ham, Cologne #1320/R est:4200
£3403	$5887	€4968	La mare pres des chaumieres (18x35cm-7x14in) s. panel exhib.prov. 9-Dec-3 Rasmussen, Copenhagen #1596/R est:30000 (D.KR 36000)
£3873	$6430	€5500	Pecheurs au bord de l'eau (31x40cm-12x16in) s. 15-Jun-3 Peron, Melun #68
£4133	$7564	€6200	Village lointain (21x41cm-8x16in) s. panel. 6-Jun-4 Osenat, Fontainebleau #131/R est:6500-7000
£4710	$7725	€6500	Paturage pres de la mare (33x47cm-13x19in) s. 11-May-3 Osenat, Fontainebleau #123 est:7000-7500
£4800	$8784	€7200	Vaches devant la mare (50x61cm-20x24in) s. 6-Jun-4 Osenat, Fontainebleau #130/R est:10000-12000
£5435	$8913	€7500	Le repos du troupeau (33x46cm-13x18in) s.d.1856. 11-May-3 Osenat, Fontainebleau #127/R est:10000-11000
£6522	$10696	€9000	Pauturage dans le Berry (20x43cm-8x17in) s.d.1867 panel. 11-May-3 Osenat, Fontainebleau #124/R est:8000-8500
£9091	$15636	€13000	Les vaches a la mare (51x85cm-20x33in) s. 7-Dec-3 Osenat, Fontainebleau #135 est:12000-15000

DUPRE, Victor (attrib) (1816-1879) French

£359	$650	€524	River landscape with a figure in a boat (32x46cm-13x18in) with sig. 30-Mar-4 Christie's, Rockefeller NY #93/R
£662	$1205	€1000	Le Bas de Breau (16x23cm-6x9in) s. panel. 20-Jun-4 Versailles Encheres #34/R

DUPRES (?) French?

£1027	$1900	€1499	Messenger (20x30cm-8x12in) s. 18-Jan-4 Carlsen Gallery, Greenville #266/R

DUPUICH, Jean Alfred (?) French

Works on paper

£267	$477	€400	Mastiff (9x13cm-4x5in) W/C. 12-May-4 Coutau Begarie, Paris #109/R
£267	$477	€400	Batard anglo-saintongeois (9x13cm-4x5in) W/C. 12-May-4 Coutau Begarie, Paris #110/R
£267	$477	€400	Braque saint-germain (9x13cm-4x5in) W/C. 12-May-4 Coutau Begarie, Paris #111/R
£267	$477	€400	Levrier afghan (9x13cm-4x5in) W/C. 12-May-4 Coutau Begarie, Paris #113/R
£367	$656	€550	Basset Ardennais (9x13cm-4x5in) W/C. 12-May-4 Coutau Begarie, Paris #106/R
£367	$656	€550	Chien de Saint-Hubert (9x13cm-4x5in) W/C. 12-May-4 Coutau Begarie, Paris #114/R
£389	$728	€580	Levrier Russe ou Barzoi (9x13cm-4x5in) studio st.verso W/C. 1-Mar-4 Coutau Begarie, Paris #80a/R
£467	$835	€700	Cocker noir Francais (8x13cm-3x5in) W/C. 12-May-4 Coutau Begarie, Paris #105/R
£570	$1067	€850	Bouledougue francais (9x13cm-4x5in) studio st.verso W/C. 1-Mar-4 Coutau Begarie, Paris #80b/R

DUPUIS, Louis Francois Joseph (1842-1921) Belgian

£897	$1659	€1300	L'apprentissage de la lecture (40x32cm-16x13in) s. 19-Jan-4 Horta, Bruxelles #370

Sculpture

£1170	$1954	€1650	Seated Archimedes (32cm-13in) s. brown pat bronze Cast L.Dupuis. 20-Oct-3 Bernaerts, Antwerp #39 est:1200-1500
£2500	$3975	€3600	L'etalon maintenu (53x76cm-21x30in) s.d.1884 dark pat bronze Cast Henri Bellens. 15-Sep-3 Horta, Bruxelles #169/R est:2000-3000

DUPUIS, Maurice (1882-1959) French

£263	$476	€400	Rose rouge (18x21cm-7x8in) s.d.30 panel. 19-Apr-4 Horta, Bruxelles #275
£1389	$2319	€2000	Retour des pecheurs (73x100cm-29x39in) s. 21-Oct-3 Galerie Moderne, Brussels #223/R

DUPUIS, Pierre (1610-1682) French

£184211	$338947	€280000	Corbeille de prunes et grenade sur entablement sculpte (51x60cm-20x24in) s. prov.exhib.lit. 24-Jun-4 Christie's, Paris #47/R est:250000-350000

DUPUIS, Pierre (attrib) (1610-1682) French

£48000	$83040	€70080	White iris, carnation and other flowers in porcelain vase with plums on ledge (58x72cm-23x28in) prov. 10-Dec-3 Christie's, London #67/R est:20000-30000

DUPUY, L (19th C) French

£1702	$2843	€2400	Maison au bord de l'etang (92x74cm-36x29in) s. 20-Jun-3 Drouot Estimations, Paris #94 est:1500-2000

DUPUY, Louis (19/20th C) French

£300	$543	€438	Figure in lane with village in distance (30x38cm-12x15in) s. 16-Apr-4 Keys, Aylsham #831
£769	$1285	€1100	Moulin a Aube (24x33cm-9x13in) s. panel. 29-Jun-3 Eric Pillon, Calais #48/R
£2660	$4441	€3750	Lavour aux environs de Barbizon (46x65cm-18x26in) s. 23-Jun-3 Ribeyre & Baron, Paris #39/R est:1200-1800

DUPUY, Paul Michel (1869-1949) French

£1000	$1790	€1500	Port breton (42x55cm-17x22in) s. cardboard. 16-May-4 Lombrail & Teucquam, Paris #155/R
£1067	$1909	€1600	Villa au jardin fleuri (64x91cm-25x36in) st.sig. 16-May-4 Lombrail & Teucquam, Paris #156/R
£1831	$3168	€2600	Elegantes montant l'escalier (14x13cm-6x5in) s. panel. 14-Dec-3 Rabourdin & Choppin de Janvry, Paris #17/R est:3000-3500
£2667	$4907	€4000	La promenade au parc (31x25cm-12x10in) s. panel. 11-Jun-4 Claude Aguttes, Neuilly #19/R est:4000-6000
£2900	$5220	€4234	Parc Monceau (38x55cm-15x22in) s. 21-Jan-4 Sotheby's, Olympia #525/R est:1800-2400
£3200	$5760	€4672	Promenade en Barque (50x65cm-20x26in) s. 21-Jan-4 Sotheby's, Olympia #527/R est:3000-4000
£3800	$6840	€5548	Parc Monceau, Paris (33x46cm-13x18in) s.i. board. 21-Jan-4 Sotheby's, Olympia #526/R est:1800-2500
£6738	$11252	€9500	La cueillette du raisin (60x80cm-24x31in) s. 19-Jun-3 Millon & Associes, Paris #190/R est:6000-8000
£20000	$36400	€29200	Bal masque (120x241cm-47x95in) s. 17-Jun-4 Christie's, London #25/R est:20000-30000

DUQUE, Adonay (20th C) ?

£2484	$4520	€3726	Queen III (168x149cm-66x59in) s. acrylic painted 1998. 21-Jun-4 Subastas Odalys, Caracas #119/R est:6000
£3679	$6770	€5519	Anarchic work 1930 II (205x164cm-81x65in) s. acrylic painted 1998. 27-Jun-4 Subastas Odalys, Caracas #24/R est:5000

DUQUESNOY, François (attrib) (1594-1643) Flemish

Works on paper

£1972	$3411	€2800	Etudes d'angelots (25x19cm-10x7in) i. black crayon white chk. 12-Dec-3 Renaud, Paris #112/R est:3000

DUQUESNOY, J (18th C) Flemish

Sculpture

£3873	$6778	€5500	Christ en croix (42cm-17in) ivory col wood bas relief. 16-Dec-3 Galerie Moderne, Brussels #2033/R est:2000-3000

DUQUETTE, Elizabeth (20th C) American

Works on paper

£8197	$15000	€11968	Two women in a landscape (85x71cm-33x28in) s. gouache on board. 3-Jun-4 Christie's, Rockefeller NY #1268/R est:1000-1500

DUQUETTE, Tony (20th C) American

Sculpture

£3552	$6500	€5186	Horses (99x95cm-39x37in) bronze pair prov. 3-Jun-4 Christie's, Rockefeller NY #216/R est:3000-5000

DURA, Alberto (1888-1971) Uruguayan

£1667	$2700	€2417	Wall with bushes (40x47cm-16x19in) s.d.1958. 29-Jul-3 Galeria y Remates, Montevideo #91/R est:2200-2800
£3235	$5500	€4723	Prado (74x70cm-29x28in) s.d.1924. 25-Nov-3 Galeria y Remates, Montevideo #139/R
£3529	$6000	€5152	View of the Cerro (100x131cm-39x52in) s. 25-Nov-3 Galeria y Remates, Montevideo #41
£4000	$6800	€5840	Spring (53x48cm-21x19in) s. 25-Nov-3 Galeria y Remates, Montevideo #140/R
£4412	$7500	€6442	River lights (58x73cm-23x29in) s.d.1938 lit. 25-Nov-3 Galeria y Remates, Montevideo #138/R
£13235	$22500	€19323	Landscape with plum trees (67x78cm-26x31in) s. 25-Nov-3 Galeria y Remates, Montevideo #39/R

DURACK, Elizabeth (1915-2000) Australian

Works on paper

£611	$1111	€892	Seated girl (42x20cm-17x8in) s. W/C. 16-Jun-4 Deutscher-Menzies, Melbourne #381/R est:1000-1500 (A.D 1600)
£621	$968	€900	Woman and children gathering food (43x58cm-17x23in) s. W/C. 1-Aug-2 Joel, Victoria #193 est:1200-1500 (A.D 1800)
£687	$1250	€1003	Aboriginal children near Laverton, Western Australia (41x52cm-16x20in) s.i. pen ink. 16-Jun-4 Deutscher-Menzies, Melbourne #382/R est:2000-3000 (A.D 1800)
£729	$1173	€1064	Ice cream - Lolly water, Meekatharra W.A. (47x53cm-19x21in) s.i.d.58 chl pastel. 25-Aug-3 Sotheby's, Paddington #340/R (A.D 1800)
£813	$1455	€1187	After the hunt (44x54cm-17x21in) s. W/C. 10-May-4 Joel, Victoria #326 est:2000-3000 (A.D 2000)

£936 $1591 €1367 Chameleons (54x74cm-21x29in) s. i.verso W/C pen ink. 26-Nov-3 Deutscher-Menzies, Melbourne #120/R est:1400-1800 (A.D 2200)
£1660 $2772 €2490 The wanderers (43x59cm-17x23in) s. W/C. 27-Oct-3 Goodman, Sydney #40/R est:3500-4500 (A.D 4000)

DURAN, Carolus (1837-1917) French
£268 $499 €400 Portrait de femme (55x46cm-22x18in) s. 3-Mar-4 Ferri, Paris #65
£2000 $3180 €2900 Portrait of a lady (64x53cm-25x21in) s.d.1908 panel. 9-Sep-3 Bonhams, Knightsbridge #47/R est:700-900
£2318 $4242 €3500 Etude autour d'une amazone (21x22cm-8x9in) canvas on cardboard. 9-Apr-4 Claude Aguttes, Neuilly #55/R est:2000-3000
Works on paper
£710 $1300 €1037 Portrait of a woman (25x20cm-10x8in) s.i.d.18 Janvier 1870 pencil sold with a study by English School. 29-Jan-4 Swann Galleries, New York #271/R

DURAN, Jean (?) ?
Works on paper
£1333 $2387 €2000 Panthere sur un rocher (47x64cm-19x25in) s.i. chl dr. 17-May-4 Sotheby's, Paris #4/R est:2000-3000

DURAN, Robert (1927-) French
£867 $1560 €1300 Cadastre (100x80cm-39x31in) s. 20-Apr-4 Chenu & Scrive, Lyon #81/R

DURAN, Santa (1909-) American
£240 $400 €350 Yesterdays smoke house at Belverde Rd (23x30cm-9x12in) canvasboard. 18-Oct-3 David Dike, Dallas #267/R

DURAN, Silvia (20th C) ?
£330 $538 €482 Lioness and cubs walking in landscape (71x103cm-28x41in) i.verso. 28-Sep-3 Wilkinson, Doncaster #315
£600 $1020 €876 Siberian tigers (69x102cm-27x40in) s. 30-Oct-3 Chrystals Auctions, Isle of Man #274
£660 $1122 €964 Siberian tiger (48x102cm-19x40in) s. 30-Oct-3 Chrystals Auctions, Isle of Man #273

DURANCAMPS, Rafael (1891-1979) Spanish
£458 $801 €650 Church interior (24x17cm-9x7in) s.i. cardboard. 16-Dec-3 Durán, Madrid #38/R
£1233 $2096 €1800 Still life with cards and bread (21x26cm-8x10in) s. board. 4-Nov-3 Ansorena, Madrid #91/R est:1800
£3624 $6741 €5400 Asparagus (35x45cm-14x18in) s. board. 2-Mar-4 Ansorena, Madrid #80/R est:4500
£6200 $10106 €9052 Riverside landscape with figures and yachts in foreground (38x46cm-15x18in) s. 25-Sep-3 Clevedon Sale Rooms #230/R est:4000-6000
£8054 $14980 €12000 View of Berga (39x61cm-15x24in) s. s.i.verso canvas on board. 2-Mar-4 Ansorena, Madrid #72/R est:10800
£8500 $15640 €12410 Libro abierto - open book (65x100cm-26x39in) s. board exhib. 24-Mar-4 Sotheby's, Olympia #177/R est:3000-5000
£9868 $17862 €15000 Still life with book and brushes (61x73cm-24x29in) s. 14-Apr-4 Ansorena, Madrid #78/R est:12000
£10780 $17464 €15200 Boats on the beach (44x44cm-17x17in) s. 20-May-3 Ansorena, Madrid #157/R est:13200
£12081 $22470 €18000 My life's essentials (54x80cm-21x31in) s. s.i.verso. 2-Mar-4 Ansorena, Madrid #57/R est:16800
£12245 $22286 €18000 Bull fight (37x45cm-15x18in) s. board. 3-Feb-4 Segre, Madrid #363/R est:4500
£12676 $21930 €18000 Reading (54x65cm-21x26in) s. 15-Dec-3 Ansorena, Madrid #37/R est:17000
Works on paper
£458 $801 €650 Bull scenes (24x32cm-9x13in) s. dr. 16-Dec-3 Durán, Madrid #13/R
£483 $806 €700 Fish (19x25cm-7x10in) s. gouache. 11-Nov-3 Castellana, Madrid #166/R
£674 $1125 €950 Bailando la sardana (11x13cm-4x5in) s. pastel. 23-Jun-3 Durán, Madrid #132

DURAND, Andre (1807-1867) French
£27384 $47100 €39981 Resting on the way to Mendoza (85x121cm-33x48in) s. painted 1858. 3-Dec-3 Naón & Cia, Buenos Aires #2/R est:40000-60000

DURAND, Asher Brown (1796-1886) American
£506 $905 €739 Portrait of a young girl (38x46cm-15x18in) 11-May-4 Roland's, New York #473258/R
£6471 $11000 €9448 Hill, dale and bracken (51x76cm-20x30in) init. canvas on masonite prov. 30-Oct-3 Phillips, New York #18/R est:10000-15000
£25926 $42000 €37593 Rocks in Oearson's Ravine (61x47cm-24x19in) i. 8-Aug-3 Barridorf, Portland #58/R est:20000-30000
£37037 $60000 €53704 View from the woodlands (46x61cm-18x24in) s. 8-Aug-3 Barridorf, Portland #62/R est:60000-90000

DURAND, Francois (20th C) French
£450 $828 €657 Portrait of a bewigged lady arranging flowers (23x17cm-9x7in) s. 8-Jun-4 Bonhams, Knightsbridge #220/R

DURAND, Godefroy (1832-?) French
Works on paper
£578 $1035 €850 La sentinelle (28x33cm-11x13in) i.d.1872 ink W/C. 17-Mar-4 Maigret, Paris #103/R

DURAND, Jean (1894-1977) French
£30770 $52924 €44000 Touaregs dans le desert (81x116cm-32x46in) s. 8-Dec-3 Tajan, Paris #268/R est:30000-32000

DURAND, Jean Nicolas Louis (1760-1834) French
Works on paper
£680 $1218 €1000 La place des Victoires (21x26cm-8x10in) i. graphite pen grey ink wash W/C oval sold with an engraving. 18-Mar-4 Christie's, Paris #163/R
£952 $1705 €1400 La barriere Sainte-Jacques. La barriere d'Orleans (18x26cm-7x10in) i. graphite pen grey ink wash W/C pair. 18-Mar-4 Christie's, Paris #168/R
£1020 $1827 €1500 La place Vendome (21x26cm-8x10in) i. graphite pen grey ink wash W/C oval sold with an engraving. 18-Mar-4 Christie's, Paris #161/R est:1500-2000
£1020 $1827 €1500 La place de la Concorde, Place Louis XV (21x26cm-8x10in) i. graphite pen grey ink wash W/C oval sold with an engraving. 18-Mar-4 Christie's, Paris #162/R est:1500-2000
£1020 $1827 €1500 Le Pont de la Concorde, avec une vue panoramique de Paris (19x27cm-7x11in) graphite pen grey ink wash W/C sold with an engraving. 18-Mar-4 Christie's, Paris #169/R est:1500-2000
£1156 $2070 €1700 L'eglise des Invalides (20x26cm-8x10in) i. graphite pen grey ink wash W/C oval two sold with an engraving. 18-Mar-4 Christie's, Paris #158/R est:1500-2000
£1156 $2070 €1700 L'Ecole Militaire vue du Champ de Mars (18x26cm-7x10in) i. graphite pen grey ink wash W/C sold with 2 engravings. 18-Mar-4 Christie's, Paris #166/R est:800-1200
£1224 $2192 €1800 L'eglise de la Sorbonne du cote de la place. La Sorbonne du cote de la cour (21x26cm-8x10in) i. graphite pen grey ink wash W/C oval two sold with 2 engravings. 18-Mar-4 Christie's, Paris #153/R est:2000-3000
£1293 $2314 €1900 L'interieurs des eglises des Invalides et de la Sorbonne (26x21cm-10x8in) i. graphite pen grey ink wash W/C oval two sold with 2 engravings. 18-Mar-4 Christie's, Paris #172/R est:1000-1500
£1361 $2435 €2000 La place des Vosges, Place Royale (21x26cm-8x10in) i. graphite pen grey ink wash W/C oval sold with an engraving. 18-Mar-4 Christie's, Paris #160/R est:2000-3000
£1361 $2435 €2000 L'interieurs des eglises Saint Philippe du Roule et du Val-de-Grace (26x21cm-10x8in) i. graphite pen grey ink W/C oval pair sold with 3 engravings. 18-Mar-4 Christie's, Paris #171/R est:1200-1600
£2041 $3653 €3000 Le Palais du Louvre depuis la Seine (20x26cm-8x10in) i. graphite pen grey ink W/C htd white oval pair. 18-Mar-4 Christie's, Paris #147/R est:2000-3000
£2041 $3653 €3000 L'Hotel des Invalides du cote de la Seine. La cour de l'Hotel des Invalides (20x26cm-8x10in) i. graphite pen grey ink wash W/C oval two sold with 2 engravings. 18-Mar-4 Christie's, Paris #159/R est:2000-3000
£2041 $3653 €3000 L'Institut, le College Mazarin. L'Interieur de l'Institut (21x26cm-8x10in) i. graphite pen grey ink W/C oval pair sold with 2 engravings. 18-Mar-4 Christie's, Paris #170/R est:3000-5000
£2177 $3897 €3200 Monument a la gloire de la Nation. L'Arc de Triomphe de Saint Antoine (18x27cm-7x11in) s.i. graphite pen grey ink W/C pair sold with 2 engravings. 18-Mar-4 Christie's, Paris #164/R est:2000-3000
£2381 $4262 €3500 L'entree du Palais-Bourbon. La cour du Palais-Bourbon (19x27cm-7x11in) graphite pen grey ink wash W/C pair sold with 2 engravings. 18-Mar-4 Christie's, Paris #150/R est:2000-3000
£2721 $4871 €4000 L'Hotel des Invalides a vol d'oiseau (20x26cm-8x10in) i. graphite pen grey ink wash W/C oval two sold with an engraving. 18-Mar-4 Christie's, Paris #157/R est:2000-3000

DURAND, L (?) ?
£1807 $3000 €2638 Portrait of Adele Frick (152x84cm-60x33in) s. 4-Oct-3 Neal Auction Company, New Orleans #145/R est:3000-5000

DURAND, Louis (18th C) French
Miniatures
£10563 $18486 €15000 Portrait du Marquis de Calviere. Une allegorie des Arts (7cm-3in circular) s. one i.verso mother of pearl black frame pair prov. 17-Dec-3 Christie's, Paris #65/R est:15000-20000

DURAND, Simon (1838-1896) Swiss
£811 $1395 €1184 Seated man and girl (41x29cm-16x11in) mono. panel. 2-Dec-3 Koller, Zurich #3002/R est:2000-3000 (S.FR 1800)

DURAND-BRAGER, Jean Baptiste Henri (1814-1879) French
£903 $1508 €1300 Entree du port (16x33cm-6x13in) s. panel. 26-Oct-3 Lesieur & Le Bars, Le Havre #90
£1088 $1948 €1600 Voilier sur le rivage (27x20cm-11x8in) mono. wood. 22-Mar-4 Digard, Paris #91/R est:1500-2200
£1974 $3632 €3000 Marine (49x39cm-19x15in) s. 23-Jun-4 Sotheby's, Paris #61/R est:3000-5000
£2199 $3672 €3100 Vue de Cap en Afrique de Sud (28x41cm-11x16in) s. 19-Jun-3 Millon & Associes, Paris #155/R est:1500-2000
£9302 $16000 €13581 Alabama and the Kearsarge, battle at sea. s. prov. 7-Dec-3 Hindman, Chicago #738/R est:3000-5000

DURAND-HENRIOT, Jacques (1922-1997) French
£455 $782 €650 Paysage de Provence (38x46cm-15x18in) s. 7-Dec-3 Livinec, Gaudcheau & Jezequel, Rennes #88

DURANTE, Conte Giorgio (attrib) (1685-1755) Italian
£2098 $3566 €3000 Dindon au-dessus d'une cage a oiseaux (131x97cm-52x38in) 1-Dec-3 Millon & Associes, Paris #61/R est:2000-3000

DURANTE, Domenico Maria (1879-1944) Italian

£2211	$3957	€3250	Amalia (30x26cm-12x10in) s.d.1934 exhib. 22-Mar-4 Sant Agostino, Torino #503/R est:4000

DURANTINI, Luigi (attrib) (1791-1857) Italian

£420	$722	€600	Christ with crown of thorns (47x38cm-19x15in) s. 5-Dec-3 Bolland & Marotz, Bremen #535/R

DURANTON, Andre (1905-) French

£979	$1684	€1400	La partie de billard (59x56cm-23x22in) s. 3-Dec-3 Tajan, Paris #184/R est:1500-1800
£1119	$1924	€1600	Quai de la gare (38x55cm-15x22in) s. 3-Dec-3 Tajan, Paris #246 est:1500-1800

DURAY, Tibor (1912-1988) Hungarian?

£950	$1577	€1387	Winter (100x120cm-39x47in) s. 4-Oct-3 Kieselbach, Budapest #124/R (H.F 350000)

DURBAN, Arne (1912-1993) Norwegian

Sculpture

£1107	$1905	€1616	Two deer (135x15x25cm-53x6x10in) s. bronze incl.socle. 8-Dec-3 Blomqvist, Oslo #527/R est:12000-15000 (N.KR 13000)
£1193	$2051	€1742	Kaare Espolin Johnsson (39x22x26cm-15x9x10in) indis.sig. bronze. 8-Dec-3 Blomqvist, Oslo #529/R est:10000-12000 (N.KR 14000)
£3251	$5526	€4746	Seated nude (39cm-15in) s. bronze. 19-Nov-3 Grev Wedels Plass, Oslo #20/R est:20000-30000 (N.KR 38000)
£4962	$8435	€7245	Woman kneeling (35x26x17cm-14x10x7in) s. bronze. 19-Nov-3 Grev Wedels Plass, Oslo #21/R est:30000-40000 (N.KR 58000)

DURDEN, James (1878-1964) British

£3800	$6688	€5548	Silver dress (215x137cm-85x54in) s. painted c.1930 prov.exhib. 19-May-4 Sotheby's, Olympia #116/R est:3000-5000

DUREAU, George (1930-) American

£469	$750	€685	Sam (91x76cm-36x30in) s. oil chl paper. 20-Sep-3 New Orleans Auction, New Orleans #888/R
£1358	$2200	€1983	Louisiana landscape (107x127cm-42x50in) s.verso prov. 2-Aug-3 Neal Auction Company, New Orleans #404/R est:2500-3500
£2035	$3500	€2971	New Orleans porch (38x25cm-15x10in) s. prov. 6-Dec-3 Neal Auction Company, New Orleans #591 est:800-1200

Works on paper

£741	$1200	€1082	Still life of fruit (71x51cm-28x20in) s. W/C prov. 2-Aug-3 Neal Auction Company, New Orleans #403 est:1000-1500

DURELLI, Francesco (18/19th C) Italian

Works on paper

£486	$826	€700	Interior (26x38cm-10x15in) s.d.1832 Chinese ink dr. 29-Oct-3 Il Ponte, Milan #583

DUREN, Terence Romaine (1907-1968) American

Works on paper

£193	$350	€282	Primitive home (48x36cm-19x14in) s. W/C. 16-Apr-4 James Julia, Fairfield #1035/R
£376	$700	€549	Backyard in Shelby (23x30cm-9x12in) s. pencil W/C. 3-Mar-4 Christie's, Rockefeller NY #48/R

DURENCEAU, Andre (20th C) ?

Works on paper

£316	$500	€461	Eurydice from Orpheus (46x18cm-18x7in) s.d.1929 pencil col. 7-Sep-3 Treadway Gallery, Cincinnati #712/R

DURER, Albrecht (1471-1528) German

Prints

£1711	$3147	€2600	Saint Bartholomew (12x7cm-5x3in) burin. 22-Jun-4 Sotheby's, Milan #240/R est:800-1200
£1724	$2879	€2500	Le Christ aux limbes, Pl de la grande passion (39x28cm-15x11in) woodcut. 9-Jul-3 Tajan, Paris #22 est:2000-2500
£1788	$3200	€2610	St. Simon (12x7cm-5x3in) engraving. 6-May-4 Swann Galleries, New York #126/R est:1500-2500
£1871	$2993	€2600	Mourning of Christ (39x28cm-15x11in) xilograph. 14-May-3 Finarte Semenzato, Milan #348/R est:2500-3500
£1899	$3400	€2773	Bath house (41x28cm-16x11in) woodcut executed c.1498. 6-May-4 Swann Galleries, New York #14/R est:3000-5000
£2000	$3440	€2920	Cannon (22x32cm-9x13in) etching. 2-Dec-3 Christie's, London #27 est:1800-2200
£2000	$3400	€2920	Joachim and the angel (30x21cm-12x8in) woodcut executed c.1504. 6-Nov-3 Swann Galleries, New York #9/R est:2500-3500
£2000	$3400	€2920	Virgin surrounded by many angels (30x21cm-12x8in) woodcut. 6-Nov-3 Swann Galleries, New York #14/R est:5000-8000
£2000	$3640	€2920	Penance of St John Chrysostom (18x12cm-7x5in) engraving exec.c.1497 prov. 1-Jul-4 Sotheby's, London #30/R est:2000-3000
£2013	$3705	€3000	Portrait of King Maximilian I (58x41cm-23x16in) woodcut. 26-Mar-4 Dorotheum, Vienna #44/R est:1000-1500
£2055	$3493	€3000	Circumcision of Christ (29x21cm-11x8in) woodcut. 4-Nov-3 Hartung & Hartung, Munich #3028/R est:4000
£2059	$3500	€3006	Visitation (30x21cm-12x8in) woodcut. 6-Nov-3 Swann Galleries, New York #8/R est:5000-8000
£2081	$3724	€3100	Mary with monkey (42x30cm-17x12in) copperplate. 25-May-4 Karl & Faber, Munich #20/R est:3000
£2083	$3396	€3000	Cloth held by two angels (10x14cm-4x6in) copperplate. 26-Sep-3 Venator & Hansten, Koln #635/R est:4500
£2098	$3566	€3000	The dream (18x12cm-7x5in) copperplate. 28-Nov-3 Bassenge, Berlin #5831/R est:2200
£2098	$3566	€3000	In Egypt (40x21cm-16x8in) woodcut. 27-Nov-3 Bassenge, Berlin #5086/R est:2400
£2133	$3819	€3200	Carrying the cross (39x28cm-15x11in) woodcut. 13-May-4 Bassenge, Berlin #5118 est:1800
£2183	$3974	€3187	The prodigal son. copperplate. 17-Jun-4 Kornfeld, Bern #29 est:5000 (S.FR 5000)
£2200	$3784	€3212	Peasant and his wife (11x8cm-4x3in) engraving exec.c.1497-98 prov. 4-Dec-3 Sotheby's, London #29/R est:2000-3000
£2200	$3982	€3300	Crown of thorns (12x7cm-5x3in) mono.d. copperplate. 2-Apr-4 Winterberg, Heidelberg #134/R est:2550
£2200	$3938	€3300	Kiss of St Chrysostomus (18x12cm-7x5in) copperplate. 14-May-4 Bassenge, Berlin #5833/R est:2400
£2200	$3938	€3300	St Christopher facing left (12x7cm-5x3in) engraving. 27-May-4 Bloomsbury, London #61/R est:1200-1800
£2235	$3800	€3263	Christ in limbo (40x29cm-16x11in) woodcut. 6-Nov-3 Swann Galleries, New York #136/R est:3000-5000
£2300	$3910	€3358	Whore of Babylon (39x28cm-15x11in) woodcut exec.1597. 1-Dec-3 Bonhams, New Bond Street #40/R est:2000-3000
£2333	$4223	€3500	Christ saying farewell to his mother (13x10cm-5x4in) woodcut. 2-Apr-4 Winterberg, Heidelberg #140/R est:2800
£2353	$4000	€3435	Virgin and Child with a par (14x10cm-6x4in) engraving. 6-Nov-3 Swann Galleries, New York #138/R est:6000-9000
£2445	$4451	€3570	Babylonian woman. woodcut. 17-Jun-4 Kornfeld, Bern #49 est:6000 (S.FR 5600)
£2500	$4300	€3650	Melencolia I (24x18cm-9x7in) engraving. 4-Dec-3 Sotheby's, London #30/R est:2000-3000
£2533	$4610	€3698	Angel fight. woodcut. 17-Jun-4 Kornfeld, Bern #46 est:5500 (S.FR 5800)
£2533	$4610	€3698	The seven angels. woodcut. 17-Jun-4 Kornfeld, Bern #45 est:6000 (S.FR 5800)
£2570	$4600	€3752	Vision of the seven candlesticks (38x30cm-15x12in) woodcut executed c.1497. 6-May-4 Swann Galleries, New York #13/R est:4000-6000
£2620	$4769	€3825	Adam and Eve. copperplate. 17-Jun-4 Kornfeld, Bern #28 est:2000 (S.FR 6000)
£2657	$4517	€3800	Fuite en Egypte (30x21cm-12x8in) print. 28-Nov-3 Tajan, Paris #24 est:2000
£2751	$5007	€4016	Virgin with Infant Jesus on crescent moon. woodcut. 17-Jun-4 Kornfeld, Bern #50/R est:7500 (S.FR 6300)
£2797	$4755	€4000	Holy Trinity (39x28cm-15x11in) woodcut. 27-Nov-3 Bassenge, Berlin #5093 est:5000
£2800	$4816	€4088	Sudarium held by two angels (10x14cm-4x6in) engraving prov. 4-Dec-3 Sotheby's, London #27/R est:2500-3500
£2800	$4816	€4088	Virgin with the Infant Christ with St Anne (11x7cm-4x3in) engraving exec.c.1500 prov. 4-Dec-3 Sotheby's, London #28/R est:2000-3000
£2800	$4816	€4088	Hercules at the crossroads (32x22cm-13x9in) engraving. 2-Dec-3 Christie's, London #23/R est:2500-3500
£2867	$5131	€4300	Small pleasure (11x6cm-4x2in) copperplate. 13-May-4 Bassenge, Berlin #5132/R est:1800
£3000	$5160	€4380	Ecce homo (39x28cm-15x11in) woodcut prov. 4-Dec-3 Sotheby's, London #7/R est:1000-1500
£3017	$5400	€4405	Holy Family with the butterfly (25x20cm-10x8in) engraving executed c.1495. 6-May-4 Swann Galleries, New York #10/R est:6000-9000
£3057	$5563	€4463	Melancholy. copperpalte. 17-Jun-4 Kornfeld, Bern #35 est:5000 (S.FR 7000)
£3200	$5504	€4672	Flagellation (39x27cm-15x11in) woodcut prov. 4-Dec-3 Sotheby's, London #14/R est:3000-5000
£3200	$5504	€4672	Deposition (38x27cm-15x11in) woodcut prov. 4-Dec-3 Sotheby's, London #16/R est:3000-5000
£3200	$5824	€4672	Holy Family with the butterfly (24x18cm-9x7in) engraving exec.c.1495. 1-Jul-4 Sotheby's, London #29/R est:3500-4000
£3200	$5824	€4672	Virgin nursing the Child (12x7cm-5x3in) engraving prov. 1-Jul-4 Sotheby's, London #31/R est:3000-4000
£3200	$5824	€4672	Peasant couple dancing (12x7cm-5x3in) d.1514 engraving. 1-Jul-4 Sotheby's, London #34/R est:2500-3000
£3310	$5528	€4800	Saint Hubert ou Saint Eustache (35x26cm-14x10in) engraving. 9-Jul-3 Tajan, Paris #25 est:4000
£3357	$5706	€4800	Cook and wife (11x8cm-4x3in) copperplate. 27-Nov-3 Bassenge, Berlin #5103/R est:3000
£3600	$6192	€5256	Joachim and Saint Anne at the Golden Gate (29x21cm-11x8in) woodcut. 2-Dec-3 Christie's, London #32/R est:2000-3000
£3667	$6563	€5500	St Christopher looking back (12x7cm-5x3in) copperplate. 13-May-4 Bassenge, Berlin #5126/R est:5000
£3667	$6563	€5500	Satyr family (11x7cm-4x3in) copperplate. 13-May-4 Bassenge, Berlin #5131/R est:2000
£3793	$6334	€5500	Jealousy effects. engraving. 11-Jul-3 Rabourdin & Choppin de Janvry, Paris #39/R
£3800	$6536	€5548	Dream of the doctor (19x12cm-7x5in) engraving. 2-Dec-3 Christie's, London #26/R est:2000-3000
£3800	$6916	€5548	Circumcision (30x21cm-12x8in) woodcut exec.c.1505. 1-Jul-4 Sotheby's, London #33/R est:3000-4000
£3843	$6994	€5611	Woman with seven headed dragon. woodcut. 17-Jun-4 Kornfeld, Bern #48 est:6000 (S.FR 8800)
£4000	$6880	€5840	Crucifixion (39x28cm-15x11in) woodcut prov. 4-Dec-3 Sotheby's, London #10/R est:2000-3000
£4000	$6880	€5840	Lamentation (39x28cm-15x11in) woodcut prov. 4-Dec-3 Sotheby's, London #12/R est:3000-5000
£4190	$7500	€6117	Knot with a white disk (28x20cm-11x8in) woodcut. 6-May-4 Swann Galleries, New York #17/R est:4000-6000
£4267	$7637	€6400	The Holy Family with scarecrow (23x18cm-9x7in) copperplate. 14-May-4 Bassenge, Berlin #5832/R est:3000
£4333	$7757	€6500	St Anthony outside city (10x14cm-4x6in) copperplate. 13-May-4 Bassenge, Berlin #5128 est:4000
£4412	$7500	€6442	Saint Jerome in his study (24x18cm-9x7in) engraving pair. 31-Oct-3 Sotheby's, New York #138/R
£4469	$8000	€6525	Peasant couple at market (10x8cm-4x3in) engraving. 6-May-4 Swann Galleries, New York #20/R est:8000-12000
£4800	$8256	€7008	Kiss of Judas (40x28cm-16x11in) woodcut prov. 4-Dec-3 Sotheby's, London #13/R est:4000-6000
£4800	$8256	€7008	Melencolia (24x19cm-9x7in) engraving two. 2-Dec-3 Christie's, London #25/R est:3000-5000
£4803	$8742	€7012	Mary breast feeding Child. copperplate. 17-Jun-4 Kornfeld, Bern #31/R est:7500 (S.FR 11000)
£4895	$8322	€7000	Offres d'amour (15x14cm-6x6in) burin. 28-Nov-3 Tajan, Paris #25/R
£5240	$9537	€7650	Woman with seven headed dragon. woodcut. 17-Jun-4 Kornfeld, Bern #47/R est:10000 (S.FR 12000)
£5333	$9547	€8000	Animal with lamb's horns (39x28cm-15x11in) woodcut. 13-May-4 Bassenge, Berlin #5119/R est:4500

£5667	$10257	€8500	Messe de Saint Gregoire (30x20cm-12x8in) print. 31-Mar-4 Tajan, Paris #25/R est:1500
£6000	$10920	€8760	Small horse (16x11cm-6x4in) engraving prov. 1-Jul-4 Sotheby's, London #26/R est:5000-6000
£6040	$11114	€9000	Mary sitting on wall with Child (15x10cm-6x4in) mono.d. copperplate prov. 26-Mar-4 Ketterer, Hamburg #81/R est:12000-15000
£6114	$11127	€8926	Little messenger. copperplate. 17-Jun-4 Kornfeld, Bern #36/R est:15000 (S.FR 14000)
£6333	$11337	€9500	Maria with monkey (19x12cm-7x5in) copperplate. 13-May-4 Bassenge, Berlin #5124/R est:2500
£6333	$11337	€9500	Apollo and Diana (11x7cm-4x3in) copperplate. 13-May-4 Bassenge, Berlin #5130 est:1500
£6987	$12716	€10201	Flag waver. copperplate. 17-Jun-4 Kornfeld, Bern #38/R est:15000 (S.FR 16000)
£7059	$12000	€10306	Dream of the doctor (19x12cm-7x5in) engraving. 6-Nov-3 Swann Galleries, New York #4/R est:10000-15000
£7424	$13511	€10839	Penitence of St John Chrysostomus. copperplate. 17-Jun-4 Kornfeld, Bern #34/R est:20000 (S.FR 17000)
£8000	$14560	€11680	Abduction of Proserpine (31x21cm-12x8in) d.1516 etching iron prov. 1-Jul-4 Sotheby's, London #37/R est:10000-15000
£8200	$14104	€11972	Christ in limbo (39x28cm-15x11in) woodcut prov. 4-Dec-3 Sotheby's, London #5/R est:4000-6000
£8235	$14000	€12023	Nemesis (33x23cm-13x9in) engraving executed c.1501-02. 6-Nov-3 Swann Galleries, New York #7/R est:15000-20000
£8500	$14620	€12410	Resurrection (39x27cm-15x11in) woodcut prov. 4-Dec-3 Sotheby's, London #6/R est:4000-6000
£8800	$15136	€12848	Last supper (40x29cm-16x11in) woodcut prov. 4-Dec-3 Sotheby's, London #11/R est:4000-6000
£8800	$15136	€12848	Christ on the mount (39x28cm-15x11in) woodcut prov. 4-Dec-3 Sotheby's, London #15/R est:4000-6000
£9333	$16707	€14000	Bagpipe player (12x7cm-5x3in) copperplate. 13-May-4 Bassenge, Berlin #5134 est:3000
£10000	$17200	€14600	St Jerome in his cell (24x16cm-9x6in) woodcut. 4-Dec-3 Sotheby's, London #24/R est:4000-6000
£10000	$17900	€15000	Maria with sceptre and crown (12x7cm-5x3in) copperplate. 13-May-4 Bassenge, Berlin #5123/R est:6000
£10044	$18279	€14664	Flag waver. copperplate. 17-Jun-4 Kornfeld, Bern #37/R est:20000 (S.FR 23000)
£11888	$20210	€17000	Coat of arms with skull (22x16cm-9x6in) copperplate. 27-Nov-3 Bassenge, Berlin #5105/R est:9000
£16000	$27520	€23360	Virgin and Child with the pear (16x10cm-6x4in) engraving prov. 4-Dec-3 Sotheby's, London #25/R est:10000-12000
£36000	$61920	€52560	Saint Jerome in penitence (32x22cm-13x9in) engraving exec.c.1497. 4-Dec-3 Sotheby's, London #26/R est:20000-25000
£44693	$80000	€65252	St. Eustace (36x25cm-14x10in) engraving executed c.1501. 6-May-4 Swann Galleries, New York #15/R est:30000-50000
£95000	$163400	€138700	Samson rending the lion (38x28cm-15x11in) woodcut executed c.1496. 2-Dec-3 Christie's, London #28/R est:60000-80000
£213974	$389432	€312402	Adam and Eve. copperplate. 17-Jun-4 Kornfeld, Bern #27/R est:200000 (S.FR 490000)
Works on paper			
£11034	$18317	€16000	St Eustachius (35x16cm-14x6in) mono. copperplate. 30-Sep-3 Dorotheum, Vienna #62/R est:16000-18000

DURET, Andre (1921-) French

£276	$505	€400	Hammamet (97x130cm-38x51in) s. 2-Feb-4 Millon & Associes, Paris #313/R
£276	$505	€400	Fitou, Corbieres (81x100cm-32x39in) s. 2-Feb-4 Millon & Associes, Paris #300/R
£276	$505	€400	Retour de carnaval (97x130cm-38x51in) s. 2-Feb-4 Millon & Associes, Paris #316/R
£290	$530	€420	La fille au bouquet (97x130cm-38x51in) s. 2-Feb-4 Millon & Associes, Paris #315
£310	$568	€450	La Rochelle (73x92cm-29x36in) s. 2-Feb-4 Millon & Associes, Paris #287/R
£310	$568	€450	Port Maliguen (51x60cm-20x24in) s. 2-Feb-4 Millon & Associes, Paris #246
£310	$568	€450	Bords de l'Ourcq a La Ferte-Milon (81x100cm-32x39in) s. 2-Feb-4 Millon & Associes, Paris #290/R
£455	$833	€660	Le marche aux fleurs (146x114cm-57x45in) s. 2-Feb-4 Millon & Associes, Paris #318
£469	$858	€680	Retour de carnaval (97x130cm-38x51in) s. 2-Feb-4 Millon & Associes, Paris #317/R

DURET, Francisque-Joseph (1804-1864) French

Sculpture			
£1074	$1901	€1600	Joueur a la mandoline (55cm-22in) s. pat bronze. 29-Apr-4 Sotheby's, Paris #200/R est:2000-3000
£1333	$2413	€2000	L'improvisator (56cm-22in) s. pat. bronze Cast Delafontaine. 5-Apr-4 Deburaux, Boulogne #55/R est:4000-5000
£1600	$2912	€2336	Figure of Improvvisatore (54cm-21in) s.i. brown pat. bronze. 29-Jun-4 Bonhams, Knightsbridge #262/R est:1200-1500
£1944	$3306	€2800	Danseur jouant la tarentelle (53x21x15cm-21x8x6in) brown pat bronze exec.c.1860. 28-Oct-3 Rabourdin & Choppin de Janvry, Paris #35/R est:2800-3000
£2013	$3745	€3000	Danseur jouant la tarentelle (21x53cm-8x21in) brown pat bronze exec.c.1860. 7-Mar-4 Lesieur & Le Bars, Le Havre #206/R
£2017	$3671	€2945	Improvisatore (56cm-22in) s. pat bronze exec 1839. 20-Jun-4 Agra, Warsaw #6/R (P.Z 14000)
£2500	$4250	€3650	Danseurs napolitains (46cm-18in) s. pat bronze pair lit. 28-Oct-3 Sotheby's, London #99/R
£2639	$4486	€3800	Danseur au tambourin (5x5x5cm-2x2x2in) brown pat bronze exec.c.1860. 28-Oct-3 Rabourdin & Choppin de Janvry, Paris #36/R est:3600-4000
£3333	$5567	€4700	Danseur napolitain (94x39cm-37x15in) s. bronze Cast Delafontaine. 17-Oct-3 Renaud, Paris #59/R est:4000-4500

DURET, Pierre Andre (20th C) French

£862	$1560	€1259	Nude (100x65cm-39x26in) s. 31-Mar-4 Zurichsee Auktionen, Erlenbach #143/R (S.FR 2000)

DURET-DUJARRIC, Isabelle (1949-) French

£5500	$9955	€8030	La chapelle de campagne (24x30cm-9x12in) s.d.03 oil paper. 1-Apr-4 Christie's, Kensington #147/R est:4000-5000
£15232	$27722	€23000	Roses (50x32cm-20x13in) s.d.92 paper. 19-Jun-4 Gerard, Besancon #52
Works on paper			
£4000	$6360	€5800	Plage (26x35cm-10x14in) s.i.d.2000 pencil pastel brush col ink. 11-Sep-3 Christie's, Kensington #162/R est:3000-5000
£4000	$7240	€6000	Corbeille fleurie (36x51cm-14x20in) s.d.2000 W/C. 3-Apr-4 Gerard, Besancon #13

DUREUIL, Michel (1929-) French

£360	$659	€526	Sous-bois (30x38cm-12x15in) s.d.59. 28-Jul-4 Mallams, Oxford #325/R
£400	$732	€584	Study of a girl on a sofa (15x15cm-6x6in) s.i. panel. 28-Jul-4 Mallams, Oxford #335
£420	$769	€613	La route du village (36x43cm-14x17in) 28-Jul-4 Mallams, Oxford #324/R
£460	$842	€672	Au bord de la riviere (30x36cm-12x14in) s. 28-Jul-4 Mallams, Oxford #326
£540	$967	€788	An open gateway leading to a paddock (23x30cm-9x12in) s.d.31. 7-May-4 Mallams, Oxford #297/R
£680	$1217	€993	La peniche (23x30cm-9x12in) s.d.53. 7-May-4 Mallams, Oxford #295/R
£700	$1099	€1015	Au bord la riviere (51x61cm-20x24in) s.d.51. 28-Aug-3 Christie's, Kensington #110
£700	$1253	€1022	Sous les Ponts de Paris (20x25cm-8x10in) s.d.54. 7-May-4 Mallams, Oxford #298

DUREY, René (1890-1959) French

£250	$463	€365	Apples, a knife and a bowl on a draped table (38x55cm-15x22in) s. 15-Jan-4 Christie's, Kensington #1060
£360	$601	€526	View of St Paul's and Blackfriars bridge (38x55cm-15x22in) s.i.d.1950. 7-Oct-3 Bonhams, Knightsbridge #78/R
£486	$812	€700	Maison dans un paysage (54x65cm-21x26in) s. 21-Oct-3 Artcurial Briest, Paris #184

DURHAM, Cornelius Bevis (fl.1825-1865) British

Works on paper			
£1000	$1700	€1460	Sophia Georgina Bigland of Bigland Hall, Lancashire (30x22cm-12x9in) s. W/C ivorine. 1-Dec-3 Bonhams, Bath #87/R est:1000-1500

DURHAM, Mary Edith (attrib) (1963-1944) British

£450	$765	€657	Portrait of a small girl seated beneath a tree holding a posy of flowers (102x76cm-40x30in) init.d.1893. 19-Nov-3 Tennants, Leyburn #1164

DURHEIM, Johann Ludwig Rudolf (1811-1895) Swiss

£6643	$11294	€9500	Ceremonie religieuse dans l'eglise du Saint-Sepulcre a Jerusalem (70x91cm-28x36in) mono. 27-Nov-3 Millon & Associes, Paris #146/R est:12000-15000

DURIEUX, Emile (?) French

£596	$1085	€900	Paysage ardennais avec village et ferme au bord de l'eau (40x60cm-16x24in) s. pair. 21-Jun-4 Bernaerts, Antwerp #71

DURIG, Rolf (1926-) Swiss

£690	$1234	€1007	Femme au chapeau (56x47cm-22x19in) s.d.43 board. 14-May-4 Dobiaschofsky, Bern #281/R est:2400 (S.FR 1600)
£897	$1498	€1310	Black rose (100x65cm-39x26in) s.d.61 s.i.d. stretcher exhib. 24-Oct-3 Hans Widmer, St Gallen #49/R est:1200-2800 (S.FR 2000)
£1293	$2315	€1888	Composition (102x58cm-40x23in) s.d.1956 i. stretcher. 14-May-4 Dobiaschofsky, Bern #283/R est:4800 (S.FR 3000)

DURING, Diederick (1917-) South African

Works on paper			
£248	$443	€362	Guitar player (40x30cm-16x12in) s. pastel. 31-May-4 Stephan Welz, Johannesburg #387 (SA.R 3000)

DURING, H (19th C) ?

£1549	$2680	€2200	Tramp (38x20cm-15x8in) s.d.1836. 13-Dec-3 Lempertz, Koln #16/R est:1500

DURINGER, Daniel (1720-1786) French?

Works on paper			
£349	$636	€510	View over Lake Lucerne (30x40cm-12x16in) s.i.d.1749 black pen W/C. 16-Jun-4 Fischer, Luzern #2866/R (S.FR 800)

DURKIN, Tom (1928-1990) British

Works on paper			
£400	$720	€584	Two fashionable ladies promenading (34x17cm-13x7in) s. pencil chl oil. 21-Apr-4 Tennants, Leyburn #1238

DURNBAUER, Ludwig (1860-1895) Austrian

Sculpture			
£1135	$2066	€1657	Young woman with a lute (70cm-28in) i. pat bronze. 16-Jun-4 Fischer, Luzern #1561/R est:1400-1600 (S.FR 2600)

DURNO, James (c.1745-1795) British

£4435	$7938	€6475	The Ascension (127x83cm-50x33in) painted 1794. 26-May-4 AB Stockholms Auktionsverk #2502/R est:50000-60000 (S.KR 60000)

DURR, Louis (1896-1973) Swiss

£323	$579	€472	Shore of Bielersee (58x58cm-23x23in) s.d.38. 12-May-4 Dobiaschofsky, Bern #473/R (S.FR 750)

£323	$579	€472	Mountain lake in morning light (60x70cm-24x28in) s.d.33. 13-May-4 Stuker, Bern #109 (S.FR 750)
£370	$676	€540	View of Lake Brienz (49x54cm-19x21in) s.d.1936. 4-Jun-4 Zofingen, Switzerland #2785 (S.FR 850)
£374	$637	€546	Lake Brienz landscape (54x64cm-21x25in) s.d.60 i. verso. 5-Nov-3 Dobiaschofsky, Bern #514/R (S.FR 850)
£396	$674	€578	View from Schynige Platte (42x58cm-17x23in) s.d.42 i. stretcher. 5-Nov-3 Dobiaschofsky, Bern #511/R (S.FR 900)
£455	$755	€660	Niesen in summer light (36x44cm-14x17in) s.d.59. 13-Jun-3 Zofingen, Switzerland #2831 (S.FR 1000)
£474	$849	€692	Brienzersee in the morning (38x46cm-15x18in) s.d.44 i. verso. 12-May-4 Dobiaschofsky, Bern #470 (S.FR 1100)
£862	$1543	€1259	Eiger, Monch and Jungfrau (32x80cm-13x31in) s.d.61 i. verso. 12-May-4 Dobiaschofsky, Bern #469/R est:1500 (S.FR 2000)
£948	$1697	€1384	Eiger from the Jungrau (70x60cm-28x24in) s.d.53 i. stretcher. 14-May-4 Dobiaschofsky, Bern #198/R est:3800 (S.FR 2200)
£1055	$1856	€1583	Lake (45x60cm-18x24in) s.d.41. 22-May-4 Dorotheum, Prague #53/R est:26000-40000 (C.KR 50000)

DURR, Wilhelm (elder) (1815-1890) German

£884	$1583	€1300	Holy Family with angels making music (96x75cm-38x30in) s.d.1879. 17-Mar-4 Neumeister, Munich #445/R
£1020	$1827	€1500	Christ with Peter and other followers (36x57cm-14x22in) s.d.1879 and 1878 board two. 17-Mar-4 Neumeister, Munich #444/R est:1700

DURRANT, Roy Turner (1925-1998) British

£300	$528	€438	Effigy at Olney (61x60cm-24x24in) s.d.74 acrylic board. 18-May-4 Bonhams, Knightsbridge #173/R
£380	$646	€555	Still life (25x20cm-10x8in) s.d.55 board. 26-Nov-3 Sotheby's, Olympia #176/R
£450	$752	€657	Landscape under moonlight (40x50cm-16x20in) s.d.69 W/C pencil on card sold with three others by same hand. 21-Oct-3 Bonhams, Knightsbridge #60/R
£500	$850	€730	Landscape (26x36cm-10x14in) s.d.55 exhib. 26-Nov-3 Sotheby's, Olympia #174/R
£1250	$2200	€1825	Harvest apples (32x39cm-13x15in) s.i.d.1950 verso board sold with a W/C by same hand. 19-May-4 Sotheby's, Olympia #254/R est:800-1200
Works on paper			
£250	$425	€365	Autumnal landscape (12x20cm-5x8in) s.i. W/C pencil ink. 26-Nov-3 Sotheby's, Olympia #173/R
£250	$448	€365	Composition (63x51cm-25x20in) s.d.1963 i.verso gouache. 16-Mar-4 Bonhams, Knightsbridge #51/R
£260	$458	€380	Untitled (21x30cm-8x12in) s.d.1966 gouache. 18-May-4 Bonhams, Knightsbridge #209/R
£280	$504	€409	Flowers (35x25cm-14x10in) s.d.56 gouache W/C. 20-Jan-4 Bonhams, Knightsbridge #68/R
£300	$555	€438	Abstract (42x34cm-17x13in) indis. sig.d.10.7.63 W/C bodycol. 11-Mar-4 Christie's, Kensington #331
£550	$985	€803	Abstract in black, white and brown (61x48cm-24x19in) s.d.76 mixed media. 16-Mar-4 Bonhams, Knightsbridge #52/R
£550	$1018	€803	Sideways in morning (86x75cm-34x30in) s.d.75 gouache acrylic board. 13-Jul-4 Bonhams, Knightsbridge #57
£700	$1169	€1022	Untitled (46x36cm-18x14in) s.d.75 gouache on board. 21-Oct-3 Bonhams, Knightsbridge #66/R
£700	$1295	€1022	Still life with bottle (20x33cm-8x13in) s.i.d.56 W/C pen ink sold with another by the same hand. 11-Feb-4 Sotheby's, Olympia #261/R
£700	$1232	€1022	Abstract head (25x20cm-10x8in) init.d.58 gouache black crayon sold with W/C by same hand. 19-May-4 Sotheby's, Olympia #317/R
£750	$1388	€1095	An autumn sound (20x24cm-8x9in) s.i.d.1956 W/C gouache ink sold with another by the same hand. 11-Feb-4 Sotheby's, Olympia #262/R
£1200	$2112	€1752	Winged figure (32x25cm-13x10in) s.d.52 W/C gouache pencil ink. 19-May-4 Sotheby's, Olympia #287/R est:800-1200

DURRELL, Lawrence (1912-1990) ?

£500	$920	€750	Voilier sur la mer (35x102cm-14x40in) panel prov. 9-Jun-4 Piasa, Paris #57/R
£533	$981	€800	Paysage mediterraneen, port avec barques (50x73cm-20x29in) s.d.70 prov. 9-Jun-4 Piasa, Paris #55/R
Works on paper			
£267	$491	€400	Composition abstraite et tachiste (43x32cm-17x13in) s. gouache pen prov. 9-Jun-4 Piasa, Paris #61
£333	$613	€500	Village de Grece (23x30cm-9x12in) s. pen htd gouache. 9-Jun-4 Piasa, Paris #60
£333	$613	€500	Composition abstraite evoquant des portes, des toits et des maisons (43x31cm-17x12in) s.d.1963 wash ink W/C. 9-Jun-4 Piasa, Paris #62
£367	$675	€550	Composition abstraite (43x31cm-17x12in) s. gouache prov. 9-Jun-4 Piasa, Paris #58/R

DURRIE, George Henry (1820-1863) American

£1023	$1800	€1494	Landscape with figures and wagon approaching a small lakeside town (33x43cm-13x17in) oil on tin. 22-May-4 Pook & Pook, Downington #486/R est:2000-3000
£13750	$22000	€20075	Autumnal landscape with house, barn, animals and family haying the fields (36x61cm-14x24in) init. 20-Sep-3 Pook & Pook, Downington #460/R est:10000-15000

DURRIE, George Henry (after) (1820-1863) American

Prints			
£4321	$7000	€6309	Autumn in New England - cider making. col lithograph lit. 1-Aug-3 North East Auctions, Portsmouth #382/R est:6000-9000

DURRIE, George Henry (attrib) (1820-1863) American

£21591	$38000	€31523	Winter landscape with figures working around stone home, barn and outbuildings (30x38cm-12x15in) panel. 21-May-4 Pook & Pook, Downington #299/R est:10000-15000

DURRILA, Larry (20th C) Australian

Works on paper			
£813	$1276	€1187	Untitled (73x43cm-29x17in) natural pigments bark. 27-Aug-3 Christie's, Sydney #771 est:500-800 (A.D 2000)

DURSCHKE, Max (1875-?) German

£756	$1309	€1104	Still life with porcelain figures (65x80cm-26x31in) s. painted c.1920. 14-Dec-3 Agra, Warsaw #45/R (P.Z 5000)
£1009	$1836	€1473	Still life with porcelain figures (70x80cm-28x31in) s. 20-Jun-4 Agra, Warsaw #7/R (P.Z 7000)

DURU, Jean Baptiste (attrib) (18th C) French

£6338	$10965	€9000	Grey hunter before the city of Calais. Grey hunter in a landscape (53x64cm-21x25in) one indis.sig.i.d.1694 one i.d.1704 pair. 10-Dec-3 Christie's, Amsterdam #869/R est:10000-15000

DURY-VASSELON, Hortense (19th C) French

£592	$1089	€900	Jetee de fleurs (49x61cm-19x24in) s.d.1913 panel. 25-Jun-4 Daguerre, Paris #158/R
£1333	$2413	€2000	Nature morte aux faisans (73x92cm-29x36in) s. 2-Apr-4 Rossini, Paris #61/R est:2500-3000
£2000	$3620	€3000	Panier de fleurs, fruits et eventail (73x92cm-29x36in) s. 2-Apr-4 Rossini, Paris #60/R est:2500-3000

DUSA, Ferdis (1888-1958) German

£316	$557	€474	Bunch of flowers (96x67cm-38x26in) s. 22-May-4 Dorotheum, Prague #96/R est:15000-23000 (C.KR 15000)
£316	$557	€474	Prayer (38x28cm-15x11in) s. plywood. 22-May-4 Dorotheum, Prague #98/R est:15000-23000 (C.KR 15000)

DUSART, Cornelis (1660-1704) Dutch

£1700	$2890	€2482	Tavern interior with couple sat by fire (32x28cm-13x11in) s. 23-Nov-3 Wilkinson, Doncaster #236/R
Prints			
£3000	$5160	€4380	Hurdy-gurdy player with his dancing doll (17x15cm-7x6in) etching. 4-Dec-3 Sotheby's, London #78/R est:3000-4000
£3500	$6020	€5110	Large village fair (26x34cm-10x13in) etching prov. 4-Dec-3 Sotheby's, London #77/R est:4000-6000
Works on paper			
£1200	$2160	€1752	Partial study of a seated man (18x11cm-7x4in) bears i.verso col chk sold with two Dutch drs prov. 20-Apr-4 Sotheby's, Olympia #77/R est:1500-2000
£2055	$3493	€3000	Tavern with peasants drinking (25x38cm-10x15in) s.d.1690 black chk ink wash framing lines. 5-Nov-3 Christie's, Amsterdam #110/R est:1500-2000
£2432	$4281	€3600	Caricature head of a woman, calling to the right (9cm-4in circular) s. black red chk vellum prov.exhib. 19-May-4 Sotheby's, Amsterdam #79/R est:4500-6000
£2703	$4757	€4000	Caricature head of a man with a pipe in his hat (10cm-4in circular) s. black red chk W/C prov.exhib. 19-May-4 Sotheby's, Amsterdam #78/R est:4500-6000
£5068	$8919	€7500	Caricature head of a woman (10cm-4in circular) s. black red chk W/C vellum prov.exhib. 19-May-4 Sotheby's, Amsterdam #77/R est:4500-6000
£5743	$10108	€8500	Caricature head of a leering man, a recorder tucked into his hat (10cm-4in circular) s.d.1690 red black chk W/C vellum prov.exhib. 19-May-4 Sotheby's, Amsterdam #80/R est:4500-6000
£20408	$36531	€30000	Un paysan assis regardant en bas a droite, tenant un pichet (25x23cm-10x9in) col chk prov. 18-Mar-4 Christie's, Paris #193/R est:8000-12000
£23288	$39589	€34000	Tinker walking down a village street (20x16cm-8x6in) s. pen brown ink wash over black chk prov.lit. 4-Nov-3 Sotheby's, Amsterdam #73/R est:25000-35000

DUSART, Cornelis (attrib) (1660-1704) Dutch

£1000	$1820	€1500	Two peasants smoking and drinking in an interior (21x18cm-8x7in) init. panel. 1-Jul-4 Christie's, Amsterdam #594 est:2500-3500

DUSAULCHOY, Charles (1781-1852) French

£296	$545	€450	Portrait d'homme en redingote grise et gillet brun (64x54cm-25x21in) s. 25-Jun-4 Rossini, Paris #64

DUSAUTOY, Jacques Léon (1817-1894) French

Works on paper			
£11620	$20335	€16500	Jeune turque au chapeau bleu (98x79cm-39x31in) s.d.1871 pastel cardboard oval. 16-Dec-3 Claude Aguttes, Neuilly #81a/R est:8000-10000

DUSCHEK, Richard (1884-1959) German

£304	$557	€444	Roses in a ceramic vase (53x44cm-21x17in) s. 4-Jun-4 Zofingen, Switzerland #2446 (S.FR 700)
Works on paper			
£272	$487	€400	Construction d'un pont (23x33cm-9x13in) s. gouache. 21-Mar-4 St-Germain-en-Laye Encheres #58
£286	$511	€420	Mission de Karena (23x33cm-9x13in) s. gouache. 21-Mar-4 St-Germain-en-Laye Encheres #59
£354	$633	€520	Lever du jour (23x33cm-9x13in) s. mono. 21-Mar-4 St-Germain-en-Laye Encheres #54/R
£395	$706	€580	Porteurs au coucher de soleil a Zanzibar (33x46cm-13x18in) s. i.verso gouache. 21-Mar-4 St-Germain-en-Laye Encheres #46/R
£422	$755	€620	Cote a Tanga, Tanzanie (33x45cm-13x18in) s. gouache. 21-Mar-4 St-Germain-en-Laye Encheres #47/R
£422	$755	€620	Chasseur de lion (29x20cm-11x8in) s. gouache. 21-Mar-4 St-Germain-en-Laye Encheres #48/R
£510	$913	€750	Chef du village (23x33cm-9x13in) s. gouache. 21-Mar-4 St-Germain-en-Laye Encheres #50/R
£531	$950	€780	Preparation du piege (23x33cm-9x13in) gouache. 21-Mar-4 St-Germain-en-Laye Encheres #51/R
£531	$950	€780	Village makonde (33x45cm-13x18in) s. gouache. 21-Mar-4 St-Germain-en-Laye Encheres #57/R
£544	$974	€800	Battage au village (23x33cm-9x13in) s. gouache. 21-Mar-4 St-Germain-en-Laye Encheres #52/R
£612	$1096	€900	Pileuses de mil a Wagoga (23x33cm-9x13in) s. gouache. 21-Mar-4 St-Germain-en-Laye Encheres #64/R

DUSI, Cosroe (1808-1859) Italian

£59155 $95239 €84000 Ninfa e satiri (160x213cm-63x84in) 8-May-3 Farsetti, Prato #686/R est:95000-105000

DUSSEK, Eduard Adrian (1871-1930) Hungarian

£3846 $6423 €5500 Portrait of young woman on stone seat (111x170cm-44x67in) s.i.d.1914. 9-Oct-3 Michael Zeller, Lindau #550/R est:5500

DUTCH SCHOOL

£6500 $10725 €9490 Still life study of flowers in a classical style vase (114x89cm-45x35in) 1-Jul-3 Tayler & Fletcher, Cheltenham #7

DUTCH SCHOOL, 16th C

£5819 $10416 €8496 Maria lactans (47x35cm-19x14in) panel. 12-May-4 Dobiaschofsky, Bern #831/R est:17000 (S.FR 13500)

DUTCH SCHOOL, 17th C

£5629 $10245 €8500 Crucifixion scene (55x74cm-22x29in) 17-Jun-4 Frank Peege, Freiburg #1097/R est:10000

£5629 $10245 €8500 Jesus carrying the cross to Calvary (54x75cm-21x30in) 17-Jun-4 Frank Peege, Freiburg #1098/R est:10000

£5822 $9897 €8500 Portrait of a young man, said to Johann de Witt (66x54cm-26x21in) prov. 5-Nov-3 Christie's, Amsterdam #10/R est:1200-1600

£6250 $10313 €9000 Still life of fruit (49x73cm-19x29in) 2-Jul-3 Neumeister, Munich #565/R est:2000

£6338 $11092 €9000 Ship battle (88x131cm-35x52in) 17-Dec-3 Il Ponte, Milan #281/R est:8000-9000

£6579 $12105 €10000 Rural fair (84x105cm-33x41in) 22-Jun-4 Durán, Madrid #181/R est:10000

£6667 $12133 €10000 Alexander the Great giving away Campespe to Apeles (150x255cm-59x100in) 1-Jul-4 Van Ham, Cologne #1138/R est:2500

£7308 $12569 €10670 Landscape with soldiers (51x67cm-20x26in) copper. 7-Dec-3 Uppsala Auktionskammare, Uppsala #34/R est:50000-60000 (S.KR 95000)

£8500 $15215 €12410 Portrait of Queen Elizabeth of Bohemia as a child (76x63cm-30x25in) i. 22-Mar-4 Bonhams & Brooks, Norfolk #201/R est:500-700

£8784 $15459 €13000 Kitchen interior with a maid, still life of pots and pans (50x63cm-20x25in) panel. 18-May-4 Sotheby's, Amsterdam #86/R est:4000-6000

£13333 $24133 €20000 Enjoying the ice (43x63cm-17x25in) bears sig.d.1648 panel. 1-Apr-4 Van Ham, Cologne #1227/R est:12000

£13793 $23034 €20000 Enjoying the ice (52x100cm-20x39in) panel prov. 15-Nov-3 Lempertz, Koln #1105/R est:5000

£14626 $26180 €21500 Un cavalier vu de face (15x9cm-6x4in) indis.sig. oil paper. 18-Mar-4 Christie's, Paris #332/R est:1000-1500

£15000 $27000 €21900 Hand holding a bouquet of flowers (21x19cm-8x7in) copper. 22-Jan-4 Sotheby's, New York #267/R est:12000-15000

£16000 $28960 €24000 Travellers outside woodland tavern (36x48cm-14x19in) panel. 1-Apr-4 Van Ham, Cologne #1229/R est:7000

£20000 $33400 €29000 Granida and Daifilo (98x124cm-39x49in) panel. 15-Nov-3 Lempertz, Koln #1106/R est:20000

Works on paper

£374 $670 €550 Farmstead by river (21x17cm-8x7in) i. chk wash. 17-Mar-4 Neumeister, Munich #271/R

£120000 $207600 €175200 Conflict between the English fleet and the Spanish Armada (14x35cm-6x14in) i. gouache vellum on panel exhib.lit. 10-Dec-3 Bonhams, New Bond Street #48/R est:30000-40000

DUTCH SCHOOL, 17th/18th C

£5903 $9740 €8500 Stil life of flowers with roses, tulips and carnations (98x68cm-39x27in) panel. 2-Jul-3 Neumeister, Munich #567/R est:3000

£6413 $11352 €9363 In front of an inn (37x30cm-15x12in) 28-Apr-4 Kieselbach, Budapest #129/R (H.F 2400000)

£31034 $55552 €45310 Winter river landscape with figures (73x95cm-29x37in) 12-May-4 Dobiaschofsky, Bern #618/R est:6000 (S.FR 72000)

DUTCH SCHOOL, 18th C

£4790 $8000 €6993 Traveling musicians (56x43cm-22x17in) init. board. 19-Oct-3 Susanin's, Chicago #6032/R est:1000-1500

£5195 $9299 €7585 Village landscape with peasants making merry. Enjoying the ice (21x25cm-8x10in) one bears i. copper pair. 22-Mar-4 Philippe Schuler, Zurich #4411/R est:3000-4000 (S.FR 12000)

£5517 $9214 €8000 Still life of flowers and fruit (54x41cm-21x16in) 11-Nov-3 Castellana, Madrid #149/R est:11000

£5667 $10257 €8500 Extensive landscape with travellers (86x110cm-34x43in) 1-Apr-4 Van Ham, Cologne #1232/R est:8000

£6993 $11678 €10000 Paysage au chateau avec personnages au premier plan (62x77cm-24x30in) 13-Oct-3 Pierre Berge, Paris #17/R est:6000-7000

£9000 $15570 €13140 Winter landscape with skaters on a frozen river (36x52cm-14x20in) bears sig.d.1652 prov. 9-Dec-3 Sotheby's, Olympia #344/R est:4000-6000

£10056 $18000 €14682 Still life of fruit and flowers in basket on marble ledge with butterfly and snail (43x54cm-17x21in) i. prov. 27-May-4 Sotheby's, New York #71/R est:20000-30000

£12000 $21960 €17520 Rowing boats and sailing boats heading towards French men-of-war (53x72cm-21x28in) 10-Jul-4 Windibank, Dorking #290/R est:3000-5000

DUTCH SCHOOL, 18th/19th C

£6944 $11458 €10000 Seascape (37x54cm-15x21in) panel. 3-Jul-3 Van Ham, Cologne #1000/R est:2000

DUTCH SCHOOL, 19th C

£6338 $11092 €9000 Patineurs sur une riviere gelee (38x51cm-15x20in) bears mono.d. panel. 17-Dec-3 Rabourdin & Choppin de Janvry, Paris #87 est:1300-1500

£10500 $17535 €15330 Battle of Camperdown (113x157cm-44x62in) 11-Nov-3 Bonhams, Knightsbridge #252a/R est:3000-4000

Sculpture

£6719 $12028 €9810 Bust of a Dutch girl (41cm-16in) marble bronze marble base exec c.1880 prov. 15-May-4 Christie's, Sydney #170/R est:6000-8000 (A.D 17000)

DUTEIL, Jean Claude (1950-) French

£320 $592 €480 La plage de Dinard (22x47cm-9x19in) s. 14-Jul-4 Livinec, Gaudcheau & Jezequel, Rennes #137

DUTEURTRE, Pierre Eugène (1911-) French

£284 $475 €415 Mother with her two children (65x55cm-26x22in) s. i.verso. 19-Oct-3 Bonhams & Butterfields, Los Angeles #7040

£291 $500 €425 Nu. s. 6-Dec-3 Harvey Clar, Oakland #1163

£297 $550 €434 Sisters (56x46cm-22x18in) s. 12-Mar-4 Jackson's, Cedar Falls #1018/R

£493 $853 €700 Femme a sa toilette (55x46cm-22x18in) s. 14-Dec-3 Eric Pillon, Calais #207/R

£1347 $2250 €1967 Four figures in the Tuilleries gardens. Figures lunching. Woman with flowers. Woman with bouquet (46x55cm-18x22in) s. set of four different sizes. 16-Nov-3 Bonhams & Butterfields, Los Angeles #7062/R est:400-600

DUTEURTRE, Pierre Eugène (attrib) (1911-) French

£280 $524 €420 Portrait of a French girl holding bouquet of flowers (45x37cm-18x15in) s. 22-Jul-4 Tennants, Leyburn #797

DUTILLEUX, Constant (1807-1865) French

£775 $1340 €1100 La scarpe a Saint-Nicolas-les-Arras (28x46cm-11x18in) s. 12-Dec-3 Piasa, Paris #74

DUTILLIEU, Jef (1876-1960) Belgian

£500 $920 €750 Vue du ruisseau (38x67cm-15x26in) s. 14-Jun-4 Horta, Bruxelles #311

£578 $1035 €850 Bord de canal anime en Flandres (85x115cm-33x45in) s. 16-Mar-4 Vanderkindere, Brussels #228

DUTTON, John Frederick Harrison (fl.1893-c.1916) British

£1000 $1800 €1460 Portrait of Mrs France-Hayhurst, standing three-quarter length (149x100cm-59x39in) s.d. 21-Apr-4 Christie's, Kensington #190/R est:500-800

£1000 $1800 €1460 Portrait of Captain W H France-Hayhurst, standing three-quarter length (150x100cm-59x39in) s.d.1918. 21-Apr-4 Christie's, Kensington #191/R est:400-600

£4000 $7200 €5840 Portrait of Colonel France-Hayhurst, seated half length (103x82cm-41x32in) s. 21-Apr-4 Christie's, Kensington #186/R est:400-600

DUTTON, Thomas G (c.1819-1891) British

£800 $1432 €1168 HM brig Sea Lark running inshore (25x31cm-10x12in) init. panel. 26-May-4 Christie's, Kensington #621/R

DUTTON, Thomas G (attrib) (c.1819-1891) British

£2400 $3840 €3504 American emigrant ship Ocean Monarch ablaze off Great Orme's Head (76x112cm-30x44in) prov. 16-Sep-3 Bonhams, New Bond Street #86/R est:1500-2000

DUURSMA, Djurre Pieter (1888-1965) Dutch

£1041 $1697 €1500 Self portrait (61x82cm-24x32in) prov. 29-Sep-3 Sotheby's, Amsterdam #198/R

DUVAL, Alix (1848-?) French

£805 $1490 €1200 Man with dog. Smoker (18x13cm-7x5in) s. panel two. 13-Mar-4 De Vuyst, Lokeren #127

DUVAL, Edward J (fl.1876-1916) British

Works on paper

£700 $1169 €1022 Largo, coast of Fife (44x69cm-17x27in) s.d.1878 W/C htd white. 14-Oct-3 Bearnes, Exeter #329/R

DUVAL, Georges (20th C) French

£382 $607 €550 Table garnie de fleurs et de fruits (65x92cm-26x36in) s. 15-Sep-3 Horta, Bruxelles #435

DUVAL, Jean Charles (20th C) French

£1818 $3128 €2600 Ceremonie dans le Chouf au Liban (44x35cm-17x14in) s. i.verso board. 8-Dec-3 Tajan, Paris #271/R est:3000-4000

DUVAL, Louis Étienne (1824-1914) Swiss

£317 $538 €463 Albano pres Rome (24x35cm-9x14in) mono.i. board. 28-Nov-3 Zofingen, Switzerland #2972 (S.FR 700)

£1761 $3081 €2500 Personnages pres d'une fontaine (22x28cm-9x11in) s. 16-Dec-3 Claude Aguttes, Neuilly #52/R est:2000-3000

£8370 $14229 €12220 Resting Polyphem on Sicily (116x202cm-46x80in) s.d.1887 i. stretcher. 5-Nov-3 Dobiaschofsky, Bern #515/R est:22000 (S.FR 19000)

DUVAL, Louis Étienne (attrib) (1824-1914) Swiss

£805 $1482 €1200 Scene de cour de ferme devant un paysage panoramique (24x34cm-9x13in) 24-Mar-4 Tajan, Paris #179

DUVAL-CARRIE, Edouard (1954-) Haitian

£867 $1595 €1300 Apparition dans la foret (60x60cm-24x24in) s.i.d.89. 9-Jun-4 Beaussant & Lefevre, Paris #139/R

DUVAL-GOZLAN, Léon (1853-1941) French

£1133 $2029 €1700 Chaumiere en Bretagne (48x65cm-19x26in) s. 16-May-4 Thierry & Lannon, Brest #309 est:2000-2500

DUVAL-LECAMUS, Pierre (1790-1854) French
£3733 $6832 €5600 Recompense (32x24cm-13x9in) s. prov.exhib. 6-Jun-4 Rouillac, Vendome #32/R

DUVALL, Charles William (1864-1966) American
£539 $900 €787 Autumnal river landscape, probably Ohio (56x69cm-22x27in) s. 19-Oct-3 Jeffery Burchard, Florida #82

DUVALL, Fannie Eliza (1861-1934) American
£4420 $8000 €6453 Field of poppies (51x91cm-20x36in) s. 31-Mar-4 Sotheby's, New York #105/R est:5000-7000

DUVALL, John (1816-1892) British
£2800 $4452 €4088 Coming to the meet. s. prov. 10-Sep-3 Cheffins, Cambridge #519/R est:800-1200

DUVALL, John (attrib) (1816-1892) British
£750 $1350 €1095 Chestnut mare and foal (41x56cm-16x22in) 21-Apr-4 Cheffins, Cambridge #474/R

DUVANEL, Joseph Edward (1933-1993) Swiss
£302 $540 €441 Wedding (80x70cm-31x28in) s.d.67. 12-May-4 Dobiaschofsky, Bern #476/R (S.FR 700)
£413 $756 €603 In the artist's studio (75x61cm-30x24in) s. 4-Jun-4 Zofingen, Switzerland #2783 (S.FR 950)
£452 $724 €660 Carousel (79x70cm-31x28in) s. 16-Sep-3 Philippe Schuler, Zurich #5611 (S.FR 1000)
Works on paper
£294 $500 €429 Nude (29x39cm-11x15in) s.d.1972 W/C. 28-Nov-3 Zofingen, Switzerland #2973 (S.FR 650)

DUVANNES, Albert (1881-1962) American
£1058 $2000 €1545 Landscape (48x76cm-19x30in) s. prov. 17-Feb-4 John Moran, Pasadena #50/R est:800-1200

DUVENECK, Frank (1848-1919) American
£2043 $3800 €2983 Harlequin (43x42cm-17x17in) init.d.81 canvas on board prov. 3-Mar-4 Christie's, Rockefeller NY #13/R est:3000-5000

DUVERGER, Theophile Emmanuel (1821-1886) French
£2817 $4676 €4000 Mere et deux enfants (65x53cm-26x21in) s. 15-Jun-3 Peron, Melun #138
£3250 $5915 €4745 Evening prayers (23x18cm-9x7in) s. panel prov. 4-Feb-4 John Nicholson, Haslemere #155/R est:3000-4000
£5800 $9976 €8468 Mother and child at home (22x17cm-9x7in) s. panel prov. 4-Dec-3 Christie's, Kensington #144/R est:4000-6000
£10588 $18000 €15458 Best friends (35x27cm-14x11in) s. panel prov. prov. 29-Oct-3 Christie's, Rockefeller NY #119/R est:20000-30000

DUVERNE, Henri (?) French
£800 $1432 €1200 Jour de fete en Bretagne (56x46cm-22x18in) s. 16-May-4 Thierry & Lannon, Brest #311

DUVIDAL DE MONTFERRIER, Louise-Rose-Julie (1797-1869) French
£5862 $9789 €8265 Portrait d'un sapeur de profil (32x28cm-13x11in) s. paper on canvas. 17-Oct-3 Tajan, Paris #126/R est:4000-6000

DUVIEUX, Henri (?-1882) French
£600 $1080 €900 Oriental harbour (18x25cm-7x10in) bears sig. board. 26-Apr-4 Rieber, Stuttgart #1054/R
£933 $1689 €1400 Bord de mer aux baigneuses (17x29cm-7x11in) s. exhib. 30-Mar-4 Rossini, Paris #336/R
£945 $1635 €1380 Sunset over Venice (38x54cm-15x21in) s. 9-Dec-3 Rasmussen, Copenhagen #1521/R (D.KR 10000)
£1141 $2099 €1700 Tartanes sur le Bosphore (20x29cm-8x11in) bears sig. panel. 28-Mar-4 Anaf, Lyon #110 est:2500-3000
£1200 $2160 €1800 Oriental scene outside town (18x30cm-7x12in) s. panel. 26-Apr-4 Rieber, Stuttgart #1053/R est:3900
£1233 $2097 €1800 Sailing ships on the Lagoon, Venice (40x65cm-16x26in) s. 5-Nov-3 Dobiaschofsky, Bern #516/R est:5000 (S.FR 2800)
£1233 $2097 €1800 Sunset over Venice (35x60cm-14x24in) s. 5-Nov-3 Dobiaschofsky, Bern #517/R est:5000 (S.FR 2800)
£1389 $2361 €2000 Cappriccio of Venice (18x30cm-7x12in) s. panel. 28-Oct-3 Dorotheum, Vienna #62/R est:2200-2800
£1888 $3210 €2700 Vue presumee du Bosphore (16x22cm-6x9in) s. panel. 21-Nov-3 Lombrail & Teucquam, Paris #118/R
£2199 $3672 €3100 La halte de la caravane (14x24cm-6x9in) s. 23-Jun-3 Ribeyre & Baron, Paris #38/R est:1200-1800
£2273 $4250 €3319 Venice, evening. Venice, dawn (28x46cm-11x18in) s. panel pair. 25-Feb-4 Doyle, New York #1/R est:8000-12000
£2603 $4425 €3800 Venise, vue du jardin francais (14x23cm-6x9in) s. cardboard on canvas. 9-Nov-3 Eric Pillon, Calais #11/R
£3688 $6159 €5200 Vue d'Istanbul (22x32cm-9x13in) s. 15-Oct-3 Claude Aguttes, Neuilly #53/R est:5000-7000
£3841 $7029 €5800 View of La Salute, Venice (40x65cm-16x26in) s. 9-Apr-4 Bailly Pommery, Paris #73/R est:4000-6000
£4967 $9089 €7500 View of Venice (40x65cm-16x26in) s. 9-Apr-4 Bailly Pommery, Paris #74/R est:4000-6000

DUVILLIER, René (1919-2002) French
£294 $499 €420 Sensation interne XVIII (61x50cm-24x20in) s. s.i.d.1971 verso prov. 23-Nov-3 Cornette de St.Cyr, Paris #110
£470 $860 €700 Joussance de l'espace (73x92cm-29x36in) s. s.i.d.13.1.75. 7-Jul-4 Artcurial Briest, Paris #255
£567 $1031 €850 Cycle aerien (60x100cm-24x39in) s. s.i.d.65 verso. 5-Jul-4 Neret-Minet, Paris #68
£700 $1274 €1050 Composition (89x116cm-35x46in) s. s.i.d.12/64 verso. 5-Jul-4 Neret-Minet, Paris #69/R
£1007 $1883 €1500 Tourbillon no 3 (92x73cm-36x29in) s. s.i.d.1959 prov.exhib. 29-Feb-4 Versailles Encheres #232/R est:2000-3000
£1620 $2802 €2300 Luminaire orange (73x100cm-29x39in) s. s.i.d.1963 verso prov. 14-Dec-3 Versailles Encheres #59/R est:2000-2500

DUVIVIER, Ignaz (1758-1832) French
Works on paper
£1800 $3294 €2628 Hippodrome, Constantinople (32x47cm-13x19in) s.i. pen grey ink brown grey wash over blk chk. 8-Jul-4 Sotheby's, London #157/R est:2000-3000

DUVOISIN, Henri (1877-1959) Swiss
£498 $846 €727 Dans le jardin des Tuileries (27x35cm-11x14in) s.d.1902. 28-Nov-3 Zofingen, Switzerland #2974 (S.FR 1100)

DUWE, Harald (1926-1984) German
£510 $785 €800 Elbe (54x64cm-21x25in) s.i. panel. 4-Sep-2 Schopman, Hamburg #131/R
£1632 $2578 €2350 Hamburg harbour (65x84cm-26x33in) s. panel. 6-Sep-3 Schopman, Hamburg #750/R est:2500

DUXA, Carl (1871-1937) Austrian
£702 $1173 €1025 Dutch winter scene with figures by coast (40x60cm-16x24in) s. panel. 25-Oct-3 Rasmussen, Havnen #2050/R (D.KR 7500)

DUYCKINCK, Gerret (attrib) (1660-1715) American
£924 $1700 €1349 Portrait of Abiah Franlin (41x30cm-16x12in) 26-Jun-4 Susanin's, Chicago #6047/R est:2000-4000

DUYK, F (?) ?
£5333 $9653 €8000 Les carrosses (80x100cm-31x39in) s. 30-Mar-4 Palais de Beaux Arts, Brussels #536/R est:2000-3000

DUYK, Frans (19/20th C) Belgian
£594 $993 €850 Le gardien et sa meute (50x65cm-20x26in) s. 13-Oct-3 Horta, Bruxelles #452

DUYSTER, Willem Cornelisz (attrib) (1600-1635) Dutch
£27933 $50000 €40782 Soldiers in guardroom (42x47cm-17x19in) panel prov.exhib.lit. 27-May-4 Sotheby's, New York #31/R est:50000-70000

DUYTS, Gustave den (1850-1897) Belgian
£433 $793 €650 Paysage aux saules (18x28cm-7x11in) s.d.78 panel. 7-Jun-4 Palais de Beaux Arts, Brussels #254/R
£3077 $5231 €4400 Allee du par animee de promeneurs (25x41cm-10x16in) s. panel. 1-Dec-3 Palais de Beaux Arts, Brussels #254/R est:3600-5000
Works on paper
£704 $1218 €1000 Petits canaux autour de l'eglise (14x25cm-6x10in) s. W/C. 9-Dec-3 Campo, Vlaamse Kaai #294
£2237 $4049 €3400 Paysage hivernal anime (73x52cm-29x20in) s. W/C. 19-Apr-4 Horta, Bruxelles #439 est:1000-1500

DUYVER, Alberic Victor (1859-?) Belgian
£331 $569 €483 Portrait of dog (45x37cm-18x15in) s. 7-Dec-3 Uppsala Auktionskammare, Uppsala #131 (S.KR 4300)

DVORAK, Anton (1817-1881) Bohemian
£1097 $1866 €1602 Lady Brauner with toddler (44x31cm-17x12in) i.verso. 29-Nov-3 Dorotheum, Prague #35/R (C.KR 50000)

DVORAK, Franz (1862-1927) Austrian
£394 $654 €575 Dreaming (25x15cm-10x6in) s. board. 4-Oct-3 Dorotheum, Prague #28/R est:8000-12000 (C.KR 18000)
£458 $834 €669 Peasants in landscape (55x75cm-22x30in) s. 16-Jun-4 Deutscher-Menzies, Melbourne #209/R est:1500-2500 (A.D 1200)
£464 $817 €696 Portrait of a child (33x24cm-13x9in) s. 22-May-4 Dorotheum, Prague #51 est:22000-35000 (C.KR 22000)

DVORETSKIJ, Jurij (1927-1991) Russian
£2113 $3507 €3000 Manifestazione nella Piazza Rossa (90x128cm-35x50in) s,d,1958. 14-Jun-3 Meeting Art, Vercelli #654/R est:3000

DWIGGINS, Clare Victor (1874-1959) American
Works on paper
£201 $360 €293 Summer fun (58x109cm-23x43in) s. W/C. 19-Mar-4 Aspire, Cleveland #76

DWIGHT, Ed (1933-) American
Sculpture
£11364 $20000 €16591 Miles Davis (114x69x51cm-45x27x20in) s.d.93 num.2/25 bronze marble base. 22-May-4 New Orleans Auction, New Orleans #832/R est:25000-40000

DWORSCHAK, Franz (1882-1954) Austrian
Works on paper
£629 $1070 €900 View of Steyr (35x45cm-14x18in) s.d.1960 W/C. 27-Nov-3 Dorotheum, Linz #554/R

DWURNIK, Edward (1943-) Polish
£703 $1168 €1026 Woman chopping off a man's head (81x65cm-32x26in) painted 1974. 2-Oct-3 Agra, Warsaw #35/R (P.Z 4600)
£1147 $1904 €1675 Busy city square with traffic (92x73cm-36x29in) 2-Oct-3 Agra, Warsaw #53/R est:2000 (P.Z 7500)
£1271 $2301 €1856 Landscape (81x102cm-32x40in) s.d.66. 4-Apr-4 Agra, Warsaw #32/R (P.Z 9000)

DWYER, James (1898-1973) American
Works on paper
£1564 $2800 €2283 Horse and rider leaving town (64x38cm-25x15in) s. gouache. 15-May-4 Illustration House, New York #34/R est:1500-2500

DWYER, Nancy (1954-) American
Sculpture
£1486 $2750 €2170 The Me Block (34x34x32cm-13x13x13in) Honduran mahogany exec 1989 prov. 12-Feb-4 Sotheby's, New York #234/R est:1000-1500
£1730 $3200 €2526 The ME block (34x32x34cm-13x13x13in) Honduran mahogany edition of 40. 12-Feb-4 Christie's, Rockefeller NY #55/R est:1000-1500
£1816 $3250 €2651 ART 2 (38x51cm-15x20in) s.d.1993 num.2/20 prov. 16-May-4 Wright, Chicago #429/R est:700-900

DYCE, William (1806-1864) British
Works on paper
£5800 $9860 €8468 Culver Cliffs, Isle of Wight (16x26cm-6x10in) i. pencil W/C bodycol. col chks scratching prov.exhib.lit. 20-Nov-3 Christie's, London #47/R est:5000-8000

DYCK, Alphonsus Josephus van (1894-1979) Dutch
£855 $1574 €1300 View of Veere (57x45cm-22x18in) s. 28-Jun-4 Sotheby's, Amsterdam #116/R
Works on paper
£385 $662 €550 View of Veere (43x38cm-17x15in) s.d.1922 gouache. 7-Dec-3 Sotheby's, Amsterdam #690/R

DYCK, Paul (1917-) American
£1902 $3500 €2777 Canyons of Memories (122x91cm-48x36in) sold with another oil on canvas. 24-Jun-4 Sotheby's, New York #203/R est:4000-6000
£4118 $7000 €6012 Sun river lodges (28x58cm-11x23in) s. panel prov. 1-Nov-3 Santa Fe Art, Santa Fe #19/R est:5000-9000
£7487 $14000 €10931 White buffalo (91x122cm-36x48in) s. board. 24-Jul-4 Coeur d'Alene, Hayden #154/R est:15000-25000

DYCK, Philip van (1680-1753) Flemish
£8500 $14110 €12410 Portrait of a gentleman in an interior wearing blue coat and pink waistcoat (84x62cm-33x24in) s.d.1743 prov. 30-Sep-3 Sotheby's, London #122/R est:6000-8000

DYCK, Sir Anthony van (1599-1641) Flemish
£23288 $39589 €34000 Head of man (117x143cm-46x56in) board. 4-Nov-3 Ansorena, Madrid #131/R est:25000
£40000 $69200 €58400 Portrait of a gentleman, half-length, in black with a white ruff (81x60cm-32x24in) prov. 11-Dec-3 Sotheby's, London #47/R est:50000-70000
£139860 $240559 €200000 Portrait of Lord John Belasyse (99x79cm-39x31in) prov. 2-Dec-3 Sotheby's, Milan #127/R est:200000-250000
£195946 $344865 €290000 Portrait of thirty-seven year old man in dark clothing (126x100cm-50x39in) d.Aet.37, Anno 1639. 22-May-4 Lempertz, Koln #1043/R est:300000-400000
Works on paper
£533 $971 €800 Holy Family with Saint Anne and Saint John (28x22cm-11x9in) W/C pencil. 4-Jul-4 Finarte, Venice #7/R

DYCK, Sir Anthony van (after) (1599-1641) Flemish
£560 $1003 €818 Lamentation of Christ (75x57cm-30x22in) panel. 13-May-4 Stuker, Bern #111 (S.FR 1300)
£9800 $15876 €14210 Thomas Wentworth, holding a document and dictating the reply (30x25cm-12x10in) i. 26-Jan-3 Desmond Judd, Cranbrook #825

DYCK, Sir Anthony van (attrib) (1599-1641) Flemish
£55556 $100000 €81112 Portrait of monk of the Benedictine order, holding skull (112x88cm-44x35in) prov.exhib. 22-Jan-4 Sotheby's, New York #111/R est:100000-150000
£66667 $120000 €97334 Profile study of bearded old man (32x41cm-13x16in) i.verso paper on canvas on panel prov. 22-Jan-4 Sotheby's, New York #21/R est:40000-60000

DYCK, Sir Anthony van (circle) (1599-1641) Flemish
£18000 $32400 €26280 Study of a head of a bearded man (37x30cm-15x12in) canvas on panel prov. 22-Apr-4 Sotheby's, London #46/R est:8000-12000

DYCK, Sir Anthony van (studio) (1599-1641) Flemish
£6000 $11040 €8760 Portrait of Lord Bernard Stuart, later Earl of Lichfield (73x62cm-29x24in) prov. 26-Mar-4 Sotheby's, London #2/R est:6000-8000
£22173 $39690 €32373 Portrait of a burgomaster (114x82cm-45x32in) prov.exhib.lit. 25-May-4 Bukowskis, Stockholm #465/R est:300000-400000 (S.KR 300000)
£46980 $86443 €70000 Infant Jesus as Salvator Mundi (121x84cm-48x33in) lit.prov. 24-Mar-4 Dorotheum, Vienna #104/R est:15000-20000
£61111 $110000 €89222 Double portrait of the Countess of Manchester and her daughter, Lady Rich in a landscape (131x149cm-52x59in) prov.lit. 23-Jan-4 Christie's, Rockefeller NY #134/R est:40000-60000

DYCK, Sir Anthony van (style) (1599-1641) Flemish
£5278 $9500 €7706 Portrait of a man (52x42cm-20x17in) 21-Jan-4 Sotheby's, New York #164/R est:3000-5000
£6500 $11895 €9490 Assumption of the Virgin (62x41cm-24x16in) panel. 6-Jul-4 Sotheby's, Olympia #431/R est:2000-3000
£7639 $12451 €11000 Twelve apostles (10x8cm-4x3in) 25-Sep-3 Dr Fritz Nagel, Stuttgart #1235/R est:11000
£10667 $19520 €16000 Family portrait (153x169cm-60x67in) i. 1-Jun-4 Sotheby's, Milan #79/R est:8000-12000
£12022 $22000 €17552 Portrait of a lady wearing a gold dress with pink wrap (127x102cm-50x40in) i. prov. 3-Jun-4 Christie's, Rockefeller NY #428/R est:10000-15000
£17000 $30430 €24820 Portrait of Sir Arthur Hopton, being handed a letter from a gentleman said to be his brother (115x134cm-45x53in) i. 22-Mar-4 Bonhams & Brooks, Norfolk #352/R est:7000-10000

DYDYSCHKO, Konstantin (?-1932) ?
£336 $617 €500 Winter (50x34cm-20x13in) s. 25-Mar-4 Hagelstam, Helsinki #1046
£627 $1147 €915 Street scene in Florence (49x35cm-19x14in) s.i.indis.d.1919. 9-Jun-4 Rasmussen, Copenhagen #1854/R (D.KR 7000)

DYE, Charlie (1906-1972) American
£16760 $30000 €24470 Robes for trade (61x91cm-24x36in) board. 15-May-4 Altermann Galleries, Santa Fe #45/R
£19553 $35000 €28547 Villa at Zacatecas (74x119cm-29x47in) board. 15-May-4 Altermann Galleries, Santa Fe #46/R
Works on paper
£529 $900 €772 Study for Slicker in the Wind (46x61cm-18x24in) st.init. graphite prov. 1-Nov-3 Santa Fe Art, Santa Fe #203/R
£765 $1300 €1117 Study for gate count (58x86cm-23x34in) s. graphite. 1-Nov-3 Santa Fe Art, Santa Fe #93/R est:1500-2500
£1059 $1800 €1546 Study for Mustangs, Mules and Men (56x86cm-22x34in) s. graphite prov. 1-Nov-3 Santa Fe Art, Santa Fe #91/R est:1500-2500
£1059 $1800 €1546 Study for frosty dawn (61x86cm-24x34in) graphite prov. 1-Nov-3 Santa Fe Art, Santa Fe #92/R est:1000-2000
£1176 $2000 €1717 Study for Old Blue in the Lead (56x102cm-22x40in) init.i. graphite prov. 1-Nov-3 Santa Fe Art, Santa Fe #204/R est:2000-3000
£1324 $2250 €1933 Study for Roundup in the Rockies (58x74cm-23x29in) st.sig.i. graphite prov. 1-Nov-3 Santa Fe Art, Santa Fe #202/R est:1000-2000
£1912 $3250 €2792 Study for Trailing Them North (58x122cm-23x48in) st.sig.i. graphite graphite prov. 1-Nov-3 Santa Fe Art, Santa Fe #205/R est:2000-3000

DYE, Clarkson (1869-1955) American
£3179 $5500 €4641 Two women gathering flowers outside of the Santa Barbara Mission (51x76cm-20x30in) s. 10-Dec-3 Bonhams & Butterfields, San Francisco #6313/R est:4000-6000

DYER, Charles Gifford (1846-1912) American
£1457 $2652 €2200 Bridge of Sighs in Venice (36x19cm-14x7in) s.d.1873 i.verso board. 21-Jun-4 Dorotheum, Vienna #54/R est:2000-2600

DYER, Geoff (1947-) Australian
£830 $1386 €1245 Tasmanian river scene (91x122cm-36x48in) s. 27-Oct-3 Goodman, Sydney #242/R (A.D 2000)

DYER, H Anthony (1872-1943) American
Works on paper
£941 $1600 €1374 Naples illuminated (20x26cm-8x10in) gouache. 21-Nov-3 Skinner, Boston #523/R est:400-600

DYER, Lowell (19th C) British
£600 $948 €870 Angel of the annunciation (44x35cm-17x14in) s.verso. 4-Sep-3 Christie's, Kensington #233/R

DYER, Marion (?) American?
£245 $400 €358 Winter landscape (43x48cm-17x19in) s. artist board. 26-Sep-3 York Town, York #871
Works on paper
£261 $425 €381 Winter scene of the Rebecca at the Well Fountain in Penn Park in snowstorm (48x33cm-19x13in) s. 26-Sep-3 York Town, York #870
£291 $475 €425 Nice barnyard scene with sheep and chickens (53x38cm-21x15in) s. 26-Sep-3 York Town, York #879

DYER, Ted (20th C) British
£320 $534 €467 Snow and cligga head (51x76cm-20x30in) s. 14-Oct-3 David Lay, Penzance #545
£350 $585 €511 Snow flurry over the fields (41x51cm-16x20in) s. 14-Oct-3 David Lay, Penzance #543/R
£540 $988 €788 Boats on their moorings Cowlands Creek (23x34cm-9x13in) s. 3-Jun-4 Lane, Penzance #13/R

DYF, Marcel (1899-1985) French
£1000 $1800 €1460 Portrait of a young girl in a blue shawl (61x51cm-24x20in) s. 20-Jan-4 Bonhams, Knightsbridge #262/R est:2000-3000
£1958 $3368 €2800 Le peuple du voyage (38x46cm-15x18in) s. 3-Dec-3 Tajan, Paris #405/R est:3000-4600
£2162 $4000 €3157 Portrait of Claudine (56x46cm-22x18in) 12-Mar-4 Du Mouchelle, Detroit #2142/R est:4000-6000
£2400 $4008 €3504 En Provence (37x45cm-15x18in) s.d.1945. 22-Oct-3 Sotheby's, Olympia #105/R est:3000-4000
£2431 $4059 €3500 Voiliers par temps calme (26x32cm-10x13in) s. 22-Oct-3 Ribeyre & Baron, Paris #40/R est:1200-2000

£2431	$4059	€3500	Le campanile de Venise (25x33cm-10x13in) s. 22-Oct-3 Ribeyre & Baron, Paris #41/R est:1200-2000
£2639	$4407	€3800	Voiliers au port (36x45cm-14x18in) s. 22-Oct-3 Ribeyre & Baron, Paris #37/R est:1500-2000
£2752	$5091	€4100	Jeune fille devant sa coiffeuse (55x46cm-22x18in) s. 14-Mar-4 Eric Pillon, Calais #146/R
£2797	$4755	€4000	Bouquet sur une table. s. isorel panel. 27-Nov-3 Millon & Associes, Paris #197/R est:4500-6000
£2800	$5040	€4200	Le modele au buste denude (46x38cm-18x15in) s. 26-Apr-4 Tajan, Paris #185/R est:2000-3000
£2837	$4738	€4000	Champ de ble (80x100cm-31x39in) s. 15-Oct-3 Rabourdin & Choppin de Janvry, Paris #13/R est:6000-8000
£2837	$4596	€4000	Vase de fleurs (54x46cm-21x18in) s. 23-May-3 Sotheby's, Paris #54/R est:5000-7000
£2900	$5104	€4234	Port d'Amsterdam (63x53cm-25x21in) s. 18-May-4 Fellows & Sons, Birmingham #83/R est:3000-5000
£2994	$5000	€4371	Le Mont Sainte Victoire (37x46cm-15x18in) estate st. board prov. 7-Oct-3 Sotheby's, New York #277 est:5000-7000
£3200	$5888	€4672	Vase de fleurs (33x24cm-13x9in) s. 24-Mar-4 Sotheby's, Olympia #66/R est:2000-3000
£3412	$5800	€4982	La rue principale, Marnes-la-Coquette (46x53cm-18x21in) s. 22-Nov-3 New Orleans Auction, New Orleans #667/R est:7000-10000
£3500	$6440	€5110	Les danseurs Espagnols (55x46cm-22x18in) s. 24-Mar-4 Sotheby's, Olympia #59/R est:2000-3000
£3571	$6500	€5214	Dahlias simples (55x46cm-22x18in) s. painted 1968 prov. 29-Jun-4 Sotheby's, New York #371/R est:8000-12000
£3600	$6660	€5256	Le manege de chevaux de bois (44x53cm-17x21in) s. 14-Jan-4 Lawrence, Crewkerne #1404/R est:3000-5000
£3757	$6500	€5485	Good morning (46x53cm-18x21in) prov. 9-Dec-3 Arthur James, Florida #107
£3800	$6992	€5548	Vase de fleurs (46x38cm-18x15in) s. 24-Mar-4 Sotheby's, Olympia #67/R est:2000-3000
£3819	$6378	€5500	Jeune femme assise dans la campagne (56x46cm-22x18in) s. 22-Oct-3 Ribeyre & Baron, Paris #38/R est:3000-3800
£3826	$7077	€5700	Plage animee (38x46cm-15x18in) s. 14-Mar-4 Eric Pillon, Calais #154/R
£3889	$7000	€5678	Fishing boats on a beach (46x61cm-18x24in) s. 20-Jan-4 Arthur James, Florida #151
£3977	$7000	€5806	Figures strolling on la Croisette, Cannes (38x46cm-15x18in) s. 18-May-4 Bonhams & Butterfields, San Francisco #193/R est:4000-6000
£4000	$6680	€5840	La Sonnet (55x46cm-22x18in) s. prov. 22-Oct-3 Sotheby's, Olympia #106/R est:4000-5000
£4056	$6773	€5800	Marche (46x55cm-18x22in) s. 29-Jun-3 Eric Pillon, Calais #184/R
£4070	$7000	€5942	Claudine reading (46x55cm-18x22in) s. 3-Dec-3 Doyle, New York #148/R est:5000-7000
£4200	$7602	€6132	Les pecheurs sur la jetee (46x55cm-18x22in) s. painted c.1981. 1-Apr-4 Christie's, Kensington #148/R est:4000-6000
£4200	$7602	€6132	La jetee (46x55cm-18x22in) s. painted c.1981. 1-Apr-4 Christie's, Kensington #150/R est:4000-6000
£4333	$7887	€6500	Port (54x65cm-21x26in) s. 4-Jul-4 Eric Pillon, Calais #134/R
£4400	$7568	€6424	French landscape (58x71cm-23x28in) s. 3-Dec-3 Andrew Hartley, Ilkley #1177 est:2000-3000
£4500	$7920	€6570	Jeune Gitane (58x71cm-23x28in) s. 18-May-4 Fellows & Sons, Birmingham #82/R est:4500-5500
£4577	$8011	€6500	Place de la Concorde (54x65cm-21x26in) s. painted c.1940. 19-Dec-3 Delvaux, Paris #39/R est:4500-5500
£4861	$8118	€7000	Vase de fleurs (55x45cm-22x18in) s. 22-Oct-3 Ribeyre & Baron, Paris #43/R est:3000-5000
£5000	$8350	€7200	Voiliers dans la baie (36x45cm-14x18in) s. 22-Oct-3 Ribeyre & Baron, Paris #36/R est:1500-2000
£5200	$9464	€7592	Portrait of a lady at her dressing table (74x60cm-29x24in) s. prov. 15-Jun-4 Bonhams, Knightsbridge #32/R est:4000-6000
£5215	$8500	€7614	Bouquet de roses et de marguerites (55x46cm-22x18in) s. painted c.1970. 25-Sep-3 Christie's, Rockefeller NY #517/R est:7000-9000
£5294	$9000	€7729	Still life with roses, irises and other flowers in a vase (55x46cm-22x18in) s. 19-Nov-3 Bonhams & Butterfields, San Francisco #163/R
£5369	$9987	€8000	Jardin potager aux arbres en fleur (60x74cm-24x29in) s. 3-Mar-4 Tajan, Paris #177/R est:8000-10000
£5500	$9185	€8030	Village de Plouharnel, Bretagne (44x54cm-17x21in) 11-Nov-3 John Taylors, Louth #389
£5600	$9912	€8176	Arzon vu du croisty, Bretagne (47x55cm-19x22in) s. prov. 27-Apr-4 Bonhams, Knightsbridge #2/R est:4000-6000
£5634	$9746	€8000	Venise, La Salute (61x74cm-24x29in) s. 15-Dec-3 Bailly Pommery, Paris #127/R est:4000-6000
£5694	$9510	€8200	Paysage de campagne (45x92cm-18x36in) s. 22-Oct-3 Ribeyre & Baron, Paris #39/R est:1800-2500
£5800	$9976	€8468	Femme s'habillant (74x58cm-29x23in) s. 2-Dec-3 Gorringes, Lewes #2310/R est:6000-8000
£5814	$10000	€8488	Bouquet of wild flowers (73x60cm-29x24in) s.i.stretcher. 3-Dec-3 Doyle, New York #147/R est:6000-8000
£6294	$10510	€9000	Vase de fleurs (54x47cm-21x19in) s. 29-Jun-3 Eric Pillon, Calais #172/R
£6395	$11000	€9337	Village de Kerjouano (46x53cm-18x21in) s. 7-Dec-3 Hindman, Chicago #825/R est:8000-10000
£6500	$11765	€9490	La Sarthe pres de Malicorne (59x72cm-23x28in) s. painted c.1967 prov. 1-Apr-4 Christie's, Kensington #151/R est:7000-9000
£6944	$11597	€10000	Vase de fleurs (55x45cm-22x18in) s. 22-Oct-3 Ribeyre & Baron, Paris #44/R est:3000-5000
£7000	$12110	€10220	Bouquet de fleurs (53x45cm-21x18in) s. 11-Dec-3 Christie's, Kensington #96/R est:4000-6000
£7609	$14000	€11109	Peonies in a Corean vase (65x54cm-26x21in) s. painted c.1970. 27-Jun-4 Freeman, Philadelphia #62/R est:3000-5000
£7639	$12757	€11000	Marche en Provence (45x57cm-18x22in) s. 22-Oct-3 Ribeyre & Baron, Paris #42/R est:3000-4000
£7740	$13158	€11300	Vase de fleurs (46x38cm-18x15in) s. 9-Nov-3 Eric Pillon, Calais #125/R
£8000	$14080	€11680	Danseuse au miroir (58x71cm-23x28in) s. 18-May-4 Fellows & Sons, Birmingham #84/R est:5000-6000
£8125	$13000	€11863	Untitled (46x53cm-18x21in) 19-Sep-3 Du Mouchelle, Detroit #2108/R est:6000-9000
£9000	$14310	€13050	Locmariaquer (45x54cm-18x21in) s. prov. 11-Sep-3 Christie's, Kensington #76/R est:4000-6000
£9000	$14220	€13140	Neauphle le Vieux (44x53cm-17x21in) s. 2-Sep-3 Gildings, Market Harborough #431/R
£9783	$18000	€14283	Fruits fleurs et bourgogne devant les volets (60x73cm-24x29in) s. 27-Jun-4 Freeman, Philadelphia #64/R est:5000-8000
£11000	$17490	€15950	Port Navalo (46x55cm-18x22in) s. prov. 11-Sep-3 Christie's, Kensington #78/R est:4000-6000
£11250	$18000	€16425	Landscape (61x74cm-24x29in) 19-Sep-3 Du Mouchelle, Detroit #2107/R est:8000-12000
£12000	$19080	€17400	Claudine en ballerine (72x58cm-28x23in) s. 11-Sep-3 Christie's, Kensington #71/R est:6000-8000
£17000	$27030	€24650	La riviere a bercheres (60x73cm-24x29in) s. prov. 11-Sep-3 Christie's, Kensington #83/R est:6000-8000

Works on paper

£278	$464	€400	Jeune femme (31x24cm-12x9in) s. crayon W/C. 22-Oct-3 Ribeyre & Baron, Paris #35/R
£451	$754	€650	Bord de riviere (23x30cm-9x12in) s. crayon ink W/C. 22-Oct-3 Ribeyre & Baron, Paris #34/R

DYKE, Kryn van (1910-1980) Dutch

£267	$477	€400	Man near empty bottle (59x39cm-23x15in) s.d.44. 11-May-4 Vendu Notarishuis, Rotterdam #71/R

DYKMAN, Christoffel Hendrik (1879-1954) Dutch

£420	$722	€600	Blacksmith in The Hague (30x40cm-12x16in) s. 8-Dec-3 Glerum, Amsterdam #123/R

DYKMAN, Henry J (1893-1972) South African

£259	$432	€378	Still life of roses in a vase (60x75cm-24x30in) s. canvas on board. 20-Oct-3 Stephan Welz, Johannesburg #878 est:3000-5000 (SA.R 3000)
£274	$465	€400	Iceland poppies in a vase (45x35cm-18x14in) s. board. 4-Nov-3 Stephan Welz, Johannesburg #391 est:2000-3000 (SA.R 3200)
£328	$547	€479	Still life of flowers in a bowl and ceramic figure (61x81cm-24x32in) s. board. 20-Oct-3 Stephan Welz, Johannesburg #887 est:2500-3500 (SA.R 3800)
£347	$621	€507	Still life of hibiscus in a brass bowl (66x99cm-26x39in) s. board. 31-May-4 Stephan Welz, Johannesburg #178 (SA.R 4200)
£991	$1774	€1447	Proteas in a copper bowl and a lighted candle (60x49cm-24x19in) s. board. 25-May-4 Cannon & Cannon, Pietermaritzburg #422 (SA.R 12000)

DYKSTRA, Evert (1948-) Dutch

£411	$699	€600	Still life with bottle and lemons (42x34cm-17x13in) s.d.1991. 5-Nov-3 Vendue Huis, Gravenhage #292

DYKSTRA, Johan (1896-1978) Dutch

£7333	$13420	€11000	Gronings landscape with Blauw Borgje in the background (50x70cm-20x28in) s. 7-Jun-4 Glerum, Amsterdam #108/R est:12000-16000

Works on paper

£442	$805	€650	Ballet dancer (33x21cm-13x8in) init. red chk htd white. 3-Feb-4 Christie's, Amsterdam #434
£987	$1816	€1500	Cows in a landscape, Groningen (31x40cm-12x16in) st.studio pen black ink W/C. 22-Jun-4 Christie's, Amsterdam #563/R est:1000-1500
£1399	$2378	€2000	Landscape with cows. (35x55cm-14x22in) s. W/C. 25-Nov-3 Christie's, Amsterdam #36/R est:1000-1500
£1600	$2928	€2400	Children in the corn field (24x38cm-9x15in) studio st. col pencil. 7-Jun-4 Glerum, Amsterdam #105/R est:2000-3000

DYONNET, Edmond (1859-1954) Canadian

£313	$538	€457	Les Bouleaux Blancs (21x16cm-8x6in) s. paper prov. 2-Dec-3 Joyner Waddington, Toronto #480 (C.D 700)

DYSON, Julian (1936-2003) British

£250	$458	€365	Early years - Self portrait (51x41cm-20x16in) s.i. acrylic. 4-Jun-4 David Lay, Penzance #168
£250	$458	€365	Whitemoor 2 (112x81cm-44x32in) s.d.1990. 4-Jun-4 David Lay, Penzance #251
£250	$458	€365	Two men (76x61cm-30x24in) s.d.1983 acrylic. 4-Jun-4 David Lay, Penzance #266
£250	$458	€365	Van Gogh brothers (33x53cm-13x21in) s.d.1999 acrylic. 4-Jun-4 David Lay, Penzance #275
£250	$458	€365	Zoe (51x13cm-20x5in) s.i.d.2002 acrylic. 4-Jun-4 David Lay, Penzance #297
£250	$458	€365	On a walk (41x51cm-16x20in) s.i.d.2001 acrylic. 4-Jun-4 David Lay, Penzance #309
£250	$458	€365	Dancing to balloons (51x30cm-20x12in) s.i.d.2000 acrylic. 4-Jun-4 David Lay, Penzance #320
£250	$458	€365	Sun bathing (41x28cm-16x11in) s.d.2001 acrylic. 4-Jun-4 David Lay, Penzance #358
£250	$458	€365	On the ward (51x36cm-20x14in) s.d.2001 acrylic. 4-Jun-4 David Lay, Penzance #511
£250	$458	€365	China clay country (84x84cm-33x33in) s.d.1991 acrylic. 4-Jun-4 David Lay, Penzance #517
£280	$512	€409	Birds (28x43cm-11x17in) s.d.2002 acrylic. 4-Jun-4 David Lay, Penzance #50
£280	$512	€409	Cliff (71x81cm-28x32in) 4-Jun-4 David Lay, Penzance #116
£280	$512	€409	King (46x43cm-18x17in) s.i.d.2002 acrylic chl. 4-Jun-4 David Lay, Penzance #49
£280	$512	€409	Meeting in the park (76x66cm-30x26in) s.d.1989. 4-Jun-4 David Lay, Penzance #142
£280	$512	€409	Walking by the harbour wall (61x71cm-24x28in) s.d.1988 verso acrylic. 4-Jun-4 David Lay, Penzance #252
£280	$512	€409	Family (53x41cm-21x16in) s.d.1999 acrylic. 4-Jun-4 David Lay, Penzance #335
£280	$512	€409	Earth bound (51x38cm-20x15in) s.i.d.2001 acrylic. 4-Jun-4 David Lay, Penzance #356
£280	$512	€409	Boat aground (33x28cm-13x11in) s.d.1988. 4-Jun-4 David Lay, Penzance #372
£280	$512	€409	Untitled (84x81cm-33x32in) s. acrylic. 4-Jun-4 David Lay, Penzance #384
£280	$512	€409	Dog - golf (51x76cm-20x30in) s.d.2002 acrylic. 4-Jun-4 David Lay, Penzance #397
£280	$512	€409	Fledgling (53x61cm-21x24in) s.i.d.2003 acrylic. 4-Jun-4 David Lay, Penzance #466
£280	$512	€409	Reclining nude (51x76cm-20x30in) s.d.2001 acrylic. 4-Jun-4 David Lay, Penzance #515
£300	$549	€438	Interior (81x81cm-32x32in) s.d.1994 verso acrylic chl. 4-Jun-4 David Lay, Penzance #112

£300	$549	€438	Snooker players (66x66cm-26x26in) s.d.1990 acrylic. 4-Jun-4 David Lay, Penzance #127
£300	$549	€438	Sheep on a hill (61x61cm-24x24in) s.d.2003 acrylic. 4-Jun-4 David Lay, Penzance #200
£300	$549	€438	Sennen (74x74cm-29x29in) s.i.d.2002 acrylic. 4-Jun-4 David Lay, Penzance #247/R
£300	$549	€438	Doll (51x38cm-20x15in) s.i.d.2003 acrylic chl. 4-Jun-4 David Lay, Penzance #250
£300	$549	€438	Bird (51x36cm-20x14in) s.d.2002 acrylic. 4-Jun-4 David Lay, Penzance #322
£300	$549	€438	Reclining nude (61x91cm-24x36in) s.d.2002 acrylic. 4-Jun-4 David Lay, Penzance #448
£300	$549	€438	On the nest (58x48cm-23x19in) s.d.2003 acrylic. 4-Jun-4 David Lay, Penzance #468
£320	$586	€467	King (41x28cm-16x11in) s.i.d.2001 acrylic. 4-Jun-4 David Lay, Penzance #292/R
£320	$586	€467	Bird in a cage (41x48cm-16x19in) s.d.2000 acrylic. 4-Jun-4 David Lay, Penzance #328
£320	$586	€467	Young camel (53x38cm-21x15in) s.i.d.1999 acrylic. 4-Jun-4 David Lay, Penzance #345
£320	$586	€467	Dog (41x51cm-16x20in) acrylic. 4-Jun-4 David Lay, Penzance #261
£320	$586	€467	Shopping (30x20cm-12x8in) s.i.d.2000 acrylic. 4-Jun-4 David Lay, Penzance #365
£320	$586	€467	Cow (28x41cm-11x16in) s.d.2001 acrylic. 4-Jun-4 David Lay, Penzance #460
£350	$641	€511	Clay pit (76x122cm-30x48in) s.d.1991. 4-Jun-4 David Lay, Penzance #124/R
£350	$641	€511	White House (91x91cm-36x36in) s.d.1985. 4-Jun-4 David Lay, Penzance #149
£350	$641	€511	Chase (36x51cm-14x20in) s.i.d.2000 acrylic. 4-Jun-4 David Lay, Penzance #308
£350	$641	€511	Three figures (76x66cm-30x26in) s.d.1997 verso acrylic. 4-Jun-4 David Lay, Penzance #443
£350	$641	€511	Sheep. s.d.1998 acrylic. 4-Jun-4 David Lay, Penzance #469
£380	$695	€555	Bird taking a worm (25x48cm-10x19in) s.d.1991 verso acrylic. 4-Jun-4 David Lay, Penzance #63
£380	$695	€555	Coastal landscape (61x81cm-24x32in) s.d.1992 acrylic. 4-Jun-4 David Lay, Penzance #257
£380	$695	€555	Dog (25x33cm-10x13in) init.d.1999 acrylic. 4-Jun-4 David Lay, Penzance #311
£380	$695	€555	Spotty bow tie (46x53cm-18x21in) s.d.2000 acrylic. 4-Jun-4 David Lay, Penzance #336
£380	$695	€555	Tropical holiday (51x38cm-20x15in) s.d.2001 i. verso acrylic. 4-Jun-4 David Lay, Penzance #340
£380	$695	€555	Black Bull (48x79cm-19x31in) s.i.d.2002 acrylic. 4-Jun-4 David Lay, Penzance #396/R
£400	$732	€584	Our leader (51x30cm-20x12in) s.d.1999 i.verso acrylic. 4-Jun-4 David Lay, Penzance #321
£400	$732	€584	Flightless birds (25x36cm-10x14in) s.i.d.1999 acrylic. 4-Jun-4 David Lay, Penzance #338
£400	$732	€584	Dog - golf (30x51cm-12x20in) s.d.2002 acrylic. 4-Jun-4 David Lay, Penzance #344
£400	$732	€584	Pass at Greensplat (58x71cm-23x28in) s.i.d.2002 acrylic. 4-Jun-4 David Lay, Penzance #394
£420	$769	€613	Cat on a mat (53x74cm-21x29in) s.d.2002 acrylic. 4-Jun-4 David Lay, Penzance #236/R
£420	$769	€613	West Gunheath (46x51cm-18x20in) s.i. acrylic. 4-Jun-4 David Lay, Penzance #278
£420	$769	€613	Walking (36x51cm-14x20in) s.i.d.2000 acrylic. 4-Jun-4 David Lay, Penzance #302/R
£420	$769	€613	Circling birds (23x36cm-9x14in) acrylic. 4-Jun-4 David Lay, Penzance #312/R
£420	$769	€613	Fledgling (48x74cm-19x29in) s.i.d.2003 acrylic. 4-Jun-4 David Lay, Penzance #393/R
£450	$824	€657	Happy dog (25x36cm-10x14in) s.i.d.2000 acrylic. 4-Jun-4 David Lay, Penzance #326
£450	$824	€657	Out walking (86x76cm-34x30in) s.i.d.2002. 4-Jun-4 David Lay, Penzance #453
£480	$878	€701	Red tractor (89x69cm-35x27in) s.d.1981. 4-Jun-4 David Lay, Penzance #253
£480	$878	€701	Cat (41x48cm-16x19in) s.d.2001 acrylic. 4-Jun-4 David Lay, Penzance #313
£500	$915	€730	Low tide (81x112cm-32x44in) 4-Jun-4 David Lay, Penzance #77/R
£500	$915	€730	Water wheel (84x51cm-33x20in) s. acrylic. 4-Jun-4 David Lay, Penzance #400
£500	$915	€730	Cow (76x91cm-30x36in) s.d.1998 verso acrylic. 4-Jun-4 David Lay, Penzance #455
£520	$952	€759	By birthday - Betty (71x33cm-28x13in) s.i.d.2002 acrylic. 4-Jun-4 David Lay, Penzance #346
£520	$952	€759	Cow (61x64cm-24x25in) s.d.2003 acrylic. 4-Jun-4 David Lay, Penzance #446/R
£520	$952	€759	Tanker (74x61cm-29x24in) s.d.2003 acrylic. 4-Jun-4 David Lay, Penzance #634
£550	$1007	€803	China clay works (81x86cm-32x34in) s.d.2002 acrylic. 4-Jun-4 David Lay, Penzance #58
£550	$1007	€803	Holiday 2 (76x51cm-30x20in) s.d.2001 acrylic chl. 4-Jun-4 David Lay, Penzance #255/R
£550	$1007	€803	Puffer fish (46x66cm-18x26in) s.d.1991 acrylic. 4-Jun-4 David Lay, Penzance #287/R
£550	$1007	€803	Cat (43x53cm-17x21in) s.d.1999 acrylic. 4-Jun-4 David Lay, Penzance #347/R
£550	$1007	€803	Out of Africa (64x91cm-25x36in) s.d.2002 acrylic. 4-Jun-4 David Lay, Penzance #514
£600	$1098	€876	Rag doll (53x38cm-21x15in) s.d.1998. 4-Jun-4 David Lay, Penzance #181
£600	$1098	€876	Bird (91x61cm-36x24in) s.d.2003 acrylic. 4-Jun-4 David Lay, Penzance #202/R
£650	$1190	€949	King (76x51cm-30x20in) s.d.2002 acrylic chl. 4-Jun-4 David Lay, Penzance #23
£700	$1281	€1022	Figure by the sea (91x66cm-36x26in) s.d.1995. 4-Jun-4 David Lay, Penzance #246
£720	$1318	€1051	Nude (91x61cm-36x24in) s.d.2002 acrylic. 4-Jun-4 David Lay, Penzance #201
£750	$1373	€1095	Watchful bird (102x91cm-40x36in) s.d.1996. 4-Jun-4 David Lay, Penzance #97/R
£750	$1373	€1095	Galleon (51x41cm-20x16in) s.d.1997 acrylic. 4-Jun-4 David Lay, Penzance #172
£800	$1464	€1168	Cat (58x91cm-23x36in) s.d.2002 acrylic. 4-Jun-4 David Lay, Penzance #106/R
£820	$1501	€1197	Greensplat chapel (64x84cm-25x33in) s.i.d.2002 acrylic. 4-Jun-4 David Lay, Penzance #248/R
£850	$1556	€1241	Open Boat (46x71cm-18x28in) s.d.1989. 4-Jun-4 David Lay, Penzance #22/R
£920	$1684	€1343	Tanker (38x58cm-15x23in) s.d.1997 acrylic. 4-Jun-4 David Lay, Penzance #173
£950	$1739	€1387	Birds (61x69cm-24x27in) s.d.2003 acrylic. 4-Jun-4 David Lay, Penzance #2543/R
£950	$1739	€1387	Tanker off Falmouth (66x91cm-26x36in) s.i.d.2002 verso acrylic. 4-Jun-4 David Lay, Penzance #272/R
£980	$1793	€1431	Doll (53x38cm-21x15in) s.i.d.98 acrylic. 4-Jun-4 David Lay, Penzance #171/R
£1400	$2562	€2044	One, two and then kick (152x168cm-60x66in) s.i.d.1999 acrylic. 4-Jun-4 David Lay, Penzance #66 est:500-800
£1900	$3477	€2774	Tanker and gulls (152x168cm-60x66in) s.d.1998. 4-Jun-4 David Lay, Penzance #314/R est:2000-3000
Works on paper			
£250	$458	€365	Bird takes worm (25x36cm-10x14in) s.d.2003 mixed media. 4-Jun-4 David Lay, Penzance #342
£300	$549	€438	Nude dancing (38x25cm-15x10in) s.d.1999 mixed media. 4-Jun-4 David Lay, Penzance #283
£320	$586	€467	Dog and fly (36x25cm-14x10in) s.d.2003 mixed media. 4-Jun-4 David Lay, Penzance #277
£480	$878	€701	Watching cow (41x58cm-16x23in) s.i.d.1997 mixed media. 4-Jun-4 David Lay, Penzance #243/R
£550	$1007	€803	Concert (76x51cm-30x20in) s.i.d.2001 mixed media. 4-Jun-4 David Lay, Penzance #267

DZAMA, Marcel (1974-) American

Works on paper			
£1271	$2250	€1856	Untitled (28x36cm-11x14in) s. mixed media wood. 2-May-4 Bonhams & Butterfields, Los Angeles #3093/R est:1500-2000
£2275	$3800	€3322	Untitled (311x25cm-122x10in) s. pen ink W/C set of eight prov. 14-Nov-3 Phillips, New York #259/R est:4000-6000

DZBANSKI, Sixtus von (1874-?) Polish

£385	$642	€550	Peasant with ox cart (93x124cm-37x49in) s.d.1937. 26-Jun-3 Weidler, Nurnberg #6513/R

DZIGURSKI, Alex (1911-1995) American

£437	$800	€656	Seascape (58x89cm-23x35in) s. 7-Jun-4 Everard, Savannah #476388/R
£471	$750	€683	Glacier stream (61x76cm-24x30in) s. painted c.1973. 12-Sep-3 Aspire, Cleveland #111
£473	$875	€691	Coastal landscape at sunset (64x91cm-25x36in) s. 16-Jan-4 Aspire, Cleveland #53/R
£491	$800	€717	Positano, Italy (62x91cm-24x36in) s.i.verso. 28-Sep-3 Bonhams & Butterfields, Los Angeles #7000
£514	$950	€750	California Pacific ocean seascape (46x61cm-18x24in) s. 19-Jan-4 O'Gallerie, Oregon #724/R
£604	$1100	€882	Seascape (64x76cm-25x30in) s.d.1950. 15-Jun-4 John Moran, Pasadena #188a
£695	$1300	€1015	California coast (61x91cm-24x36in) s. 25-Feb-4 Doyle, New York #56/R
£718	$1300	€1048	California coastal landscape with rolling surf (61x91cm-24x36in) s. 3-Apr-4 Nadeau, Windsor #75/R est:2000-3000
£756	$1300	€1104	Over the sunset sea (61x91cm-24x36in) s.d.1960 sold with a book. 7-Dec-3 Hindman, Chicago #748/R est:1000-1500
£769	$1400	€1123	Sunset coastal scene (61x91cm-24x36in) s. 15-Jun-4 John Moran, Pasadena #188 est:2000-3000
£824	$1500	€1203	Quiet waters (61x76cm-24x30in) s.d.1950. 19-Jun-4 Jackson's, Cedar Falls #12/R est:1500-2500
£833	$1500	€1216	Rolling breakers (61x91cm-24x36in) s. 25-Apr-4 Bonhams & Butterfields, San Francisco #5558/R est:2000-3000
£898	$1500	€1311	Spring landscape in the snowy Sierras with rushing mountain stream (61x76cm-24x30in) s. 27-Oct-3 O'Gallerie, Oregon #784/R est:900-1200
£1018	$1700	€1486	Surf at dusk (61x91cm-24x36in) s. 20-Jun-3 Freeman, Philadelphia #95/R est:1000-1500
£1078	$1800	€1563	Green surf (61x91cm-24x36in) s. 13-Jul-3 Butterfields, San Francisco #2034/R est:1500-2000
£1099	$2000	€1605	Crashing waves (61x91cm-24x36in) s. 29-Jun-4 Sotheby's, New York #255/R est:3000-5000
£1163	$2000	€1698	Ocean grandeur (61x91cm-24x36in) s. 7-Dec-3 Susanin's, Chicago #6058/R est:1000-1500
£1243	$2250	€1815	Seascape (62x93cm-24x37in) s. 18-Apr-4 Bonhams & Butterfields, Los Angeles #7022 est:2000-3000
£1250	$2000	€1825	Seascape at sunset (61x91cm-24x36in) 19-Sep-3 Du Mouchelle, Detroit #2238/R est:2000-2500
£1389	$2500	€2028	Waves at sunset (61x121cm-24x48in) s. 25-Apr-4 Bonhams & Butterfields, San Francisco #5559/R est:3000-4000
£1398	$2250	€2041	Coastal scene with surf and waves (61x91cm-24x36in) s. painted c.1960. 22-Feb-3 Bunte, Elgin #1278 est:1500-2500
£1497	$2500	€2186	Pacific Ocean seascape at sunset (61x122cm-24x48in) s. 14-Jul-3 O'Gallerie, Oregon #801/R est:1000-1500
£1647	$2750	€2405	Seacape near san Francisco Bay at sunset (61x122cm-24x48in) s. 14-Jul-3 O'Gallerie, Oregon #131/R est:1000-1500
£1702	$2843	€2400	Veduta de Trieste dal Castello di Miramare (70x100cm-28x39in) s. 21-Jun-3 Stadion, Trieste #400/R est:2500-3500

DZUBAS, Friedel (1915-1994) American/German

£2454	$4000	€3583	Maelstream (102x102cm-40x40in) s.i.d.1976 verso acrylic prov. 23-Sep-3 Christie's, Rockefeller NY #119/R est:7000-9000
£4945	$9000	€7220	Dos rios (102x102cm-40x40in) s.d.1975 i.verso acrylic prov. 29-Jun-4 Sotheby's, New York #493/R est:3000-5000

EADE, Edward Douglas (1911-1984) British

£800	$1360	€1168	Parrots at the zoo (36x42cm-14x17in) s.i.on overlap. 26-Nov-3 Sotheby's, Olympia #92/R
£1400	$2282	€2030	Thames barge (29x39cm-11x15in) s. board. 23-Sep-3 Bonhams, Leeds #169/R est:1400-1600

EADIE, Ian A M (?) British
£340 $554 €496 Silver sands of Morar (75x136cm-30x54in) s.d.58. 23-Sep-3 Anderson & Garland, Newcastle #322/R

EADIE, Robert (1877-1954) British
£800 $1256 €1160 Watergate, Perth, Gable of old Gowrie House (35x61cm-14x24in) s.i.d.1840 board. 27-Aug-3 Sotheby's, London #1067/R
£2800 $4396 €4060 Perth High Street, looking from John Street (35x61cm-14x24in) s.i.d.1840 board. 27-Aug-3 Sotheby's, London #1066/R est:1500-2000
Works on paper
£212 $390 €310 Gardener's bouquet (25x39cm-10x15in) s. W/C. 14-Jun-4 Waddingtons, Toronto #67/R (C.D 525)
£260 $434 €380 Feeding chickens (29x37cm-11x15in) s. W/C. 16-Oct-3 Bonhams, Edinburgh #191
£300 $567 €438 East coast fishing harbour (27x38cm-11x15in) s. W/C. 19-Feb-4 Lyon & Turnbull, Edinburgh #134/R
£320 $586 €467 On the quayside (32x45cm-13x18in) s. W/C. 29-Jan-4 Bonhams, Edinburgh #336
£350 $651 €511 Durham (37x54cm-15x21in) s. pen ink W/C. 4-Mar-4 Christie's, Kensington #155a/R
£400 $668 €584 Dunure, Ayrshire. s. W/C. 13-Nov-3 Bonhams, Edinburgh #308
£400 $736 €584 Church interior (54x39cm-21x15in) s. W/C. 10-Jun-4 Lyon & Turnbull, Edinburgh #80
£480 $797 €701 Feeding the chickens (29x37cm-11x15in) s. W/C. 13-Jun-3 Jacobs & Hunt, Petersfield #194/R
£520 $936 €759 Coullins skye, two horses at water trough in front of a barn (45x56cm-18x22in) W/C. 20-Apr-4 Rowley Fine Art, Newmarket #421/R
£550 $974 €803 St Abbs harbour (38x56cm-15x22in) s. W/C. 1-May-4 Shapes, Edinburgh #413
£800 $1376 €1168 Edinburgh street scene (38x25cm-15x10in) s.d.42 W/C pencil. 2-Dec-3 Gorringes, Lewes #2544/R

EAGER, Helen (1952-) Australian
£2479 $4587 €3619 Performance (167x256cm-66x101in) s.d.88 verso oilstick paper on canvas. 15-Mar-4 Sotheby's, Melbourne #123/R est:2000-3000 (A.D 6000)

EAGER, Wayne (1957-) Australian
£391 $708 €571 Logging track (113x94cm-44x37in) s.i.verso. 30-Mar-4 Lawson Menzies, Sydney #10 est:1200-1500 (A.D 950)
£535 $968 €781 Untitled (111x84cm-44x33in) 30-Mar-4 Lawson Menzies, Sydney #66a/R est:1500-2500 (A.D 1300)
£988 $1788 €1442 Night watch (134x108cm-53x43in) with sig. i.d.1989 verso. 30-Mar-4 Lawson Menzies, Sydney #40 est:3000-5000 (A.D 2400)
Works on paper
£412 $745 €602 Untitled I 1989 (74x54cm-29x21in) i.verso synthetic polymer. 30-Mar-4 Lawson Menzies, Sydney #20/R est:800-1000 (A.D 1000)

EAKINS, Susan (1851-1938) American
£1744 $3000 €2546 Artist and Model (38x30cm-15x12in) prov.exhib. 7-Dec-3 Freeman, Philadelphia #159a est:3000-5000

EAKINS, Thomas (style) (1844-1916) American
£5556 $9000 €8112 Grey bearded man with long hair. panel. 26-Jul-3 Thomaston Place, Thomaston #81/R

EANDI, Fernando (1926-) Italian
£433 $797 €650 Landscape covered in snow (40x34cm-16x13in) s.d.1964 board. 12-Jun-4 Meeting Art, Vercelli #522
£897 $1497 €1300 Diva from my fence (30x25cm-12x10in) s. s.i.d.1978 verso. 17-Nov-3 Sant Agostino, Torino #109/R
£1020 $1827 €1500 Fence and tree (70x60cm-28x24in) s. s.i.d.1975 verso. 22-Mar-4 Sant Agostino, Torino #513/R est:1000-1400
£1119 $1869 €1600 Beach on the Adriatic (70x60cm-28x24in) s.d.1985 acrylic. 26-Jun-3 Sant Agostino, Torino #271/R est:1200-1600
Works on paper
£340 $609 €500 Fence and target (51x35cm-20x14in) s.d.1969 mixed media cardboard exhib. 22-Mar-4 Sant Agostino, Torino #324/R

EANES, Frances S (1885-1974) American
£307 $550 €448 Zinnias, tiger lilies, daisies in a green porcelain vase (61x56cm-24x22in) 7-May-4 Sloans & Kenyon, Bethesda #1191/R
£307 $550 €448 Yellow and white daisies with autumn leaves (76x91cm-30x36in) 7-May-4 Sloans & Kenyon, Bethesda #1198/R
£335 $600 €489 Peonies and iris in a white vase with fan (61x51cm-24x20in) 7-May-4 Sloans & Kenyon, Bethesda #1189/R
£335 $600 €489 White peonies and iris in a white vase with pansies (46x61cm-18x24in) s. 7-May-4 Sloans & Kenyon, Bethesda #1196/R
£363 $650 €530 Still life with green pitcher and apples (48x33cm-19x13in) s. 7-May-4 Sloans & Kenyon, Bethesda #1194/R
£363 $650 €530 Orange poppies in a tall blue vase with two bottles (71x66cm-28x26in) 7-May-4 Sloans & Kenyon, Bethesda #1197/R
£419 $750 €612 Mums, daisies, phlox in a yellow vase (61x51cm-24x20in) mono. 7-May-4 Sloans & Kenyon, Bethesda #1190/R
£447 $800 €653 Zinnias in sunlight on green table (66x56cm-26x22in) 7-May-4 Sloans & Kenyon, Bethesda #1193/R
£475 $850 €694 Red and orange zinnias in a cobalt vase (61x51cm-24x20in) init. 7-May-4 Sloans & Kenyon, Bethesda #1192/R
£503 $900 €734 Still life with yellow pitcher (46x36cm-18x14in) 7-May-4 Sloans & Kenyon, Bethesda #1188/R
£503 $900 €734 Spray of mums, yellow and white daisies on green tablecloth (58x66cm-23x26in) 7-May-4 Sloans & Kenyon, Bethesda #1195/R
£894 $1600 €1305 Red and orange zinnias in an Indian vase (71x89cm-28x35in) 7-May-4 Sloans & Kenyon, Bethesda #1199/R est:1000-1500

EARDLEY, Joan (1921-1963) British
£7800 $12558 €11310 Stormy sea IV (32x56cm-13x22in) s. board exhib. 21-Aug-3 Bonhams, Edinburgh #1042/R est:5000-8000
£8000 $13760 €11680 Haystacks - Catterline (35x60cm-14x24in) s. prov. 4-Dec-3 Bonhams, Edinburgh #30/R est:10000-15000
£13000 $23790 €18980 Drying salmon nets (69x99cm-27x39in) board exhib. 28-Jul-4 Mallams, Oxford #285/R est:10000-15000
Works on paper
£900 $1530 €1314 Portrait of an old lady (20x13cm-8x5in) s. pastel. 30-Oct-3 Christie's, London #219/R
£2000 $3720 €2920 Stobcross Crane and rotunda, Glasgow (22x25cm-9x10in) pastel pen ink executed c.1960. 4-Mar-4 Christie's, Kensington #226/R est:2000-3000
£2200 $3740 €3212 Farmyard Buildings (10x21cm-4x8in) pastel. 30-Oct-3 Christie's, London #221/R est:1500-2000
£2500 $4525 €3650 Portrait of Andrew Sampson (14x14cm-6x6in) pencil pastel. 19-Apr-4 Sotheby's, London #133/R est:2000-3000
£4000 $6800 €5840 Three girls, Samson family (13x16cm-5x6in) blk chk pastel prov. 30-Oct-3 Christie's, London #225/R est:2000-3000
£4800 $8688 €7008 Study of a reclining girl (14x14cm-6x6in) pastel pencil. 19-Apr-4 Sotheby's, London #134/R est:1500-2000
£6800 $11560 €9928 Head of a boy (20x19cm-8x7in) pastel buff paper. 30-Oct-3 Christie's, London #224/R est:3000-5000
£7000 $11900 €10220 Close Mouth (22x20cm-9x8in) s. i.backboard pencil gouache pen blk ink exhib. 30-Oct-3 Christie's, London #218/R est:4000-6000
£9000 $15300 €13140 Pat (17x16cm-7x6in) s. pastel prov.exhib. 30-Oct-3 Christie's, London #223/R est:3000-5000
£9200 $15640 €13432 Samson children (27x22cm-11x9in) pastel. 30-Oct-3 Christie's, London #222/R est:4000-6000
£14000 $22540 €20300 Pat Samson in a red jersey (17x17cm-7x7in) s. pastel exhib. 21-Aug-3 Bonhams, Edinburgh #1040/R est:3000-5000

EARL, George (1824-1908) British
£800 $1336 €1168 Dog holding a rabbit (66x66cm-26x26in) 7-Oct-3 Bonhams, Knightsbridge #113/R
£800 $1472 €1168 Bob, a black horse in a stable (37x51cm-15x20in) init.i. 10-Jun-4 Christie's, Kensington #72/R

EARL, George (attrib) (1824-1908) British
£600 $972 €870 At an otter hunt (66x79cm-26x31in) 30-Jul-3 Hamptons Fine Art, Godalming #218/R
£2700 $4293 €3942 Portrait of terriers head (23cm-9in circular) panel. 9-Sep-3 Gorringes, Lewes #2061/R est:700-1000

EARL, Louis (19th C) British?
Works on paper
£491 $850 €717 Sketch of landscape with fort in distance (20x30cm-8x12in) s. pencil. 13-Dec-3 Charlton Hall, Columbia #656/R

EARL, Maud (1863-1943) British
£1060 $1939 €1600 Dinner time (43x35cm-17x14in) panel. 8-Apr-4 Dorotheum, Vienna #292/R est:1200-1400
£1450 $2668 €2117 Retriever with cock pheasant (60x45cm-24x18in) s.d.1904. 29-Mar-4 Thomson Roddick & Medcalf, Edinburgh #227/R
£3500 $6265 €5110 Lilies and doves (153x61cm-60x24in) s. board. 27-May-4 Christie's, Kensington #341/R est:1500-2000
£4412 $7500 €6442 Portrait of a Jack Russell (63x53cm-25x21in) s. 21-Nov-3 Skinner, Boston #168/R est:7000-9000
£5000 $8500 €7300 Champion Dinette, French bulldog (51x61cm-20x24in) s. 27-Nov-3 Christie's, Kensington #318/R est:5000-7000
£7500 $13800 €10950 Retriever (61x46cm-24x18in) s.d.1904 prov. 10-Jun-4 Christie's, Kensington #406/R est:2500-3500
£10227 $18000 €14931 Two Sealyham dogs (66x56cm-26x22in) s.d.95. 18-May-4 Sotheby's, New York #31/R est:8000-12000
£16393 $30000 €23934 German Shepherd and parrot (119x145cm-47x57in) s.d.1917 prov. 3-Jun-4 Christie's, Rockefeller NY #670/R est:40000-60000
£31977 $55000 €46686 What we have we'll hold, portrait of Dimboola the chmpion bull dog (77x102cm-30x40in) s.d.96 lit. 5-Dec-3 Christie's, Rockefeller NY #58/R est:30000-50000

EARL, Percy (fl.1909-1930) British
£2500 $4250 €3650 Exhibitionist (61x76cm-24x30in) 19-Nov-3 Sotheby's, Olympia #117/R est:2500-3500

EARL, Thomas (attrib) (19th C) British
£1400 $2576 €2044 Skye terrier with a hare (71x91cm-28x36in) 10-Jun-4 Christie's, Kensington #366/R est:800-1200

EARLE, Charles (1832-1893) British
Works on paper
£380 $695 €555 Le Palais des Papes, Avignon (39x67cm-15x26in) s. W/C. 27-Jan-4 Bonhams, Knightsbridge #307/R
£400 $732 €584 Downland landscape with windmills (36x53cm-14x21in) s. W/C. 8-Jul-4 Duke & Son, Dorchester #53
£1400 $2380 €2044 View from the Palatine Hill, Rome (37x54cm-15x21in) s. W/C. 4-Nov-3 Bonhams, New Bond Street #83/R est:800-1200

EARLE, Lawrence Carmichael (1845-1921) American
£321 $600 €469 Portrait of a woman with a striped head scarf (26x20cm-10x8in) s.d.84 panel. 26-Feb-4 Skinner, Bolton #351a/R
£2545 $4250 €3716 Young girl with doll (30x23cm-12x9in) s.d.87 panel prov. 23-Oct-3 Shannon's, Milford #20/R est:3000-5000
£5689 $9500 €8306 Young girl with fan (30x23cm-12x9in) s.d.87 panel prov. 23-Oct-3 Shannon's, Milford #19/R est:3000-5000

EARLE, Paul Barnard (1872-1955) Canadian
£422 $692 €616 Cottage in the Laurentians (25x36cm-10x14in) s.d.1932 panel. 28-May-3 Maynards, Vancouver #28 (C.D 950)
£580 $998 €847 Summer landscape (26x34cm-10x13in) s.indis.d. panel prov. 2-Dec-3 Joyner Waddington, Toronto #369/R (C.D 1300)

£580 $998 €847 Farmhouse in winter (26x34cm-10x13in) d.1920 verso prov. 2-Dec-3 Joyner Waddington, Toronto #491 (C.D 1300)

£714 $1229 €1042 Church, Ile d'Orleans (26x34cm-10x13in) s. panel painted 1934. 2-Dec-3 Joyner Waddington, Toronto #318/R (C.D 1600)

EARLE, Stephen (1942-) Australian

£345 $542 €504 View from up here (112x112cm-44x44in) s.d.2.70 s.verso acrylic prov.exhib. 26-Aug-3 Christie's, Sydney #389 (A.D 850)

Works on paper

£289 $535 €422 No.6 (121x120cm-48x47in) s.d.May 72 i.verso synthetic polymer. 15-Mar-4 Sotheby's, Melbourne #225 (A.D 700)

EARNSHAW, M (19/20th C) British

Works on paper

£1200 $2160 €1752 Portrait of two girls with a terrier (69x56cm-27x22in) s. pastel. 20-Apr-4 Clarke Gammon, Guildford #38/R est:500-800

EARP, H (snr) (1831-1914) British

£320 $554 €467 Landscape with horses and figure by a pond (23x43cm-9x17in) s.d.1897. 11-Dec-3 Scarborough Perry Fine Arts, Hove #627

£340 $588 €496 River landscape with cattle and figure (23x28cm-9x11in) s. 11-Dec-3 Scarborough Perry Fine Arts, Hove #626

£767 $1372 €1150 Fishermen at the river's edge (25x30cm-10x12in) s. 14-May-4 Behringer, Furth #1570/R

EARP, Henry (19th C) British

£700 $1281 €1022 Figure and horses on a country track, haystacks a farm and spire in distance (45x60cm-18x24in) s. 6-Jul-4 Bearnes, Exeter #509/R

Works on paper

£400 $668 €584 Sunset over the Downs with horse and wagon on path, windmill beyond (20x25cm-8x10in) s. W/C. 16-Nov-3 Desmond Judd, Cranbrook #1111

£420 $676 €609 Cattle and drover on path in English landscape (33x25cm-13x10in) s. W/C exec.c.1860-1890. 23-Feb-3 Desmond Judd, Cranbrook #1022

EARP, Henry (snr) (1831-1914) British

£380 $692 €555 Figures on a woodland path (23x18cm-9x7in) s. board. 17-Jun-4 Gorringes, Worthing #762/R

£400 $664 €584 Bramber Castle (25x36cm-10x14in) painted c.1890. 2-Oct-3 Heffel, Vancouver #15 (C.D 900)

£420 $701 €613 Shere Common, Guildford (30x46cm-12x18in) s.d.1897 i.verso. 14-Oct-3 David Lay, Penzance #436

£460 $782 €672 Cattle on a wooded country lane (20x40cm-8x16in) s. 1-Dec-3 Bonhams, Bath #107/R

£620 $1054 €905 Cattle grazing on Salisbury meadows (18x29cm-7x11in) s. panel. 1-Dec-3 Bonhams, Bath #106

£1100 $1870 €1606 Landscape and cattle (30x40cm-12x16in) s. board. 19-Nov-3 Tennants, Leyburn #1065/R est:700-900

£1500 $2685 €2190 Homeward bound (76x63cm-30x25in) s. 27-May-4 Christie's, Kensington #164/R est:1500-2000

£2600 $4420 €3796 River landscape with cattle, sheep and figures nearby (91x127cm-36x50in) s.d.1887. 19-Nov-3 Tennants, Leyburn #1064/R est:2500-3000

Works on paper

£260 $413 €380 Cart horse team in a summer wood (35x25cm-14x10in) s. W/C. 9-Sep-3 Bonhams, Leeds #155

£480 $850 €701 Rural scene, workers with their horse and cart on a lane (25x50cm-10x20in) s. W/C. 28-Apr-4 Peter Wilson, Nantwich #148

£900 $1683 €1314 Drover and cattle on a lane. Travellers resting (24x48cm-9x19in) s. W/C over pencil pair. 24-Feb-4 Bonhams, Knowle #17

£9000 $16200 €13140 Hauling timber in Calke Park, Derbyshire (49x74cm-19x29in) s. pencil W/C htd white. 22-Apr-4 Mellors & Kirk, Nottingham #1038/R est:3000-4000

EARP, William Henry (19th C) British

Works on paper

£250 $463 €365 Clipper ship Aristides (16x22cm-6x9in) s. i.verso W/C bodycol. 16-Feb-4 Bonhams, Bath #84

£260 $465 €380 Off Filey Brigg, Yorkshire (23x48cm-9x19in) s. 13-May-4 Grant, Worcester #333/R

EASON, Thomas (20th C) American?

Works on paper

£578 $1000 €844 Figures in a Middle Eastern landscape at nightfall (69x44cm-27x17in) s. gouache. 13-Dec-3 Weschler, Washington #535

EAST, H (?) British

£1200 $1920 €1752 Evening glow, Surrey (50x75cm-20x30in) s. 18-Sep-3 Bonhams, Edinburgh #366/R est:1000-1500

EAST, Henry (?) British?

£420 $777 €613 River landscape (30x40cm-12x16in) s. 13-Jan-4 Bonhams, Knightsbridge #299/R

EAST, Sir Alfred (1849-1913) British

£360 $666 €526 Italian lake (23x33cm-9x13in) prov. 10-Feb-4 David Lay, Penzance #1

£622 $1076 €908 In the hayfields, Kettering (41x61cm-16x24in) s.d.1896. 9-Dec-3 Pinneys, Montreal #73 (C.D 1400)

£750 $1253 €1095 Shady glade. prov. 14-Oct-3 Rosebery Fine Art, London #476

£1023 $1800 €1494 On the River (30x46cm-12x18in) s. prov. 23-May-4 Hindman, Chicago #40/R est:2000-3000

£1200 $2004 €1752 Across the meadow (30x41cm-12x16in) s.d.1888. 13-Nov-3 Christie's, Kensington #170/R est:800-1200

£1326 $2400 €1936 View at Kettering (23x41cm-9x16in) s. panel. 3-Apr-4 Charlton Hall, Columbia #104/R est:500-800

£1500 $2745 €2190 Angler on his way home (15x23cm-6x9in) s. 7-Apr-4 Gardiner & Houlgate, Bath #200/R est:800-1200

£2000 $3720 €2920 Shady glade (71x91cm-28x36in) s. canvasboard prov. 4-Mar-4 Christie's, Kensington #500/R est:1000-1500

£2200 $3938 €3212 Brook (53x72cm-21x28in) s. exhib. 26-May-4 Sotheby's, Olympia #192/R est:2500-3500

£3400 $6086 €4964 Dignity of autumn (127x107cm-50x42in) s. prov.exhib. 26-May-4 Sotheby's, Olympia #193/R est:2000-3000

£3600 $6588 €5256 Sheep in a water meadow (74x105cm-29x41in) s.d.1906 s.verso. 6-Jul-4 Bonhams, Knightsbridge #267/R est:3000-4000

£5000 $8500 €7300 Provencale dance (107x125cm-42x49in) 27-Nov-3 Sotheby's, London #419/R est:5000-7000

Works on paper

£250 $430 €365 Gate to Shinto Shrine with figures (30x46cm-12x18in) W/C. 3-Dec-3 Brightwells, Leominster #1212/R

£600 $1104 €876 Scarborough (50x65cm-20x26in) W/C prov. 23-Jun-4 Cheffins, Cambridge #453/R

£620 $1147 €905 Valley of The Lambourne (29x39cm-11x15in) s.i. ink. 16-Jul-4 Charterhouse, Sherborne #544/R

£650 $1151 €949 Couple on a country lane (23x34cm-9x13in) s. prov. 2-May-4 Lots Road Auctions, London #365

£700 $1169 €1022 Landscape with mountains and lake (35x52cm-14x20in) s.d.1883 W/C. 21-Oct-3 Bonhams, Knightsbridge #54/R

£1300 $2236 €1898 Fugi-San, early morning (34x24cm-13x9in) s.i. W/C prov. 3-Dec-3 Christie's, Kensington #189/R est:600-800

£1400 $2408 €2044 Island of Ye-no-Shima, Japan (24x34cm-9x13in) init. pencil W/C. 3-Dec-3 Christie's, Kensington #187/R est:300-500

£1800 $3006 €2628 An eastern bazaar (39x28cm-15x11in) W/C. 21-Oct-3 Bruton Knowles, Cheltenham #427/R est:800-1000

EAST, Sir Alfred (attrib) (1849-1913) British

£1800 $3330 €2628 In the hayfields Kettering (38x53cm-15x21in) bears sig.d.1896. 13-Feb-4 Keys, Aylsham #660/R est:1000-1500

EASTLAKE, Sidney (19th C) British

£420 $777 €613 Coastal scene with sand dunes (59x90cm-23x35in) s. 14-Jul-4 Bonhams, Chester #438

£569 $1019 €831 Dunes (61x91cm-24x36in) s. 4-May-4 Ritchie, Toronto #43/R est:1000-1500 (C.D 1400)

EASTLAKE, Sir Charles Lock (1793-1865) British

Works on paper

£317 $529 €463 Portrait of a lady in ruffled hat (19x14cm-7x6in) s. pencil dr. 17-Nov-3 Waddingtons, Toronto #36/R (C.D 700)

EASTLAKE, Sir Charles Lock (attrib) (1793-1865) British

£1300 $2418 €1898 Abelard and Heloise on a terrace (135x104cm-53x41in) with sig. 4-Mar-4 Christie's, Kensington #609/R est:1000-1500

EASTMAN, Emily (19th C) American

Works on paper

£3241 $5250 €4732 Girl in blue dress (25x20cm-10x8in) W/C prov. 1-Aug-3 North East Auctions, Portsmouth #852/R est:3000-5000

EASTMAN, Seth (1808-1875) American

Works on paper

£1257 $2250 €1835 Sioux Chief (36x28cm-14x11in) mono. gouache W/C oval. 8-Jan-4 James Julia, Fairfield #692b/R est:1500-2500

£7027 $13000 €10259 Indian encampment (42x70cm-17x28in) s. W/C paper on linen. 11-Mar-4 Christie's, Rockefeller NY #14/R est:12000-18000

EASTON, Craig (1961-) Australian

Works on paper

£909 $1682 €1327 V'S sister - liquid walls (152x244cm-60x96in) s.d.95 verso synthetic polymer in 2 parts. 15-Mar-4 Sotheby's, Melbourne #26/R est:2500-3500 (A.D 2200)

£909 $1682 €1327 V'S sister - liquid walls (152x244cm-60x96in) s.d.95 synthetic polymer two panel. 15-Mar-4 Sotheby's, Melbourne #109/R est:2500-3500 (A.D 2200)

EASTON, Timothy (1943-) British

£280 $501 €409 Evening primrose and butterfly bush (25x20cm-10x8in) s.d.1992 i.d.verso. 22-Mar-4 Bonhams & Brooks, Norfolk #366/R

EASTWOOD, Raymond James (1898-1987) American

£2186 $4000 €3192 Ridge (64x76cm-25x30in) s. painted c.1935. 5-Jun-4 Treadway Gallery, Cincinnati #687/R est:2000-3000

EASTWOOD, Walter (attrib) (1867-1943) British

Works on paper

£1100 $2013 €1606 Peel Harbour, Isle of Man (23x33cm-9x13in) s. W/C. 8-Jul-4 Duke & Son, Dorchester #102/R est:300-600

EATON, Charles Harry (1850-1901) American

£7500 $12000 €10950 Marshlands. s.d.1887 board. 20-Sep-3 Harvey Clar, Oakland #1538

EATON, Charles Warren (1857-1937) American

£387 $700 €565 Flemish village at night (76x71cm-30x28in) s. 16-Apr-4 James Julia, Fairfield #937/R

£1117 $2000 €1631 Landscape with haystack (41x61cm-16x24in) s. 6-May-4 Shannon's, Milford #241/R est:2000-3000

£1765	$3000	€2577	Bruges (61x51cm-24x20in) s.i.d.1903. 21-Nov-3 Skinner, Boston #527/R est:3000-5000
£1796	$3000	€2622	Water Gate, Vavenna (61x76cm-24x30in) s. i.verso. 23-Oct-3 Shannon's, Milford #224/R est:4000-6000
£2326	$4000	€3396	Sunset (40x55cm-16x22in) s.d.1896. 3-Dec-3 Doyle, New York #182/R est:6000-8000
£2358	$3750	€3419	Near going to the sun camp (48x58cm-19x23in) s. 12-Sep-3 Aspire, Cleveland #39 est:5000-8000
£2616	$4500	€3819	Evening glow (25x20cm-10x8in) s. board painted c.1910. 7-Dec-3 Treadway Gallery, Cincinnati #607/R est:2000-4000
£2654	$4750	€3875	Spring landscape sunset (30x41cm-12x16in) s. board. 14-May-4 Skinner, Boston #59/R est:1500-3000
£2957	$5500	€4317	Through the woods, Glacier Park, Montana (61x51cm-24x20in) s. i.v, painted c.1910. 7-Mar-4 Treadway Gallery, Cincinnati #548/R est:4000-6000
£3468	$6000	€5063	Enchanted sunset (46x41cm-18x16in) board. 12-Dec-3 Du Mouchelle, Detroit #2006/R est:1500-2000
£4144	$7500	€6050	Close of day (51x61cm-20x24in) s. canvas on masonite. 18-Apr-4 Jeffery Burchard, Florida #98/R
£5028	$9000	€7341	Forest interior (61x51cm-24x20in) s. prov. 6-May-4 Shannon's, Milford #60/R est:9000-12000
Works on paper			
£470	$850	€686	Rocky New England field landscape (28x38cm-11x15in) s. W/C. 3-Apr-4 Nadeau, Windsor #293

EATON, Michael (20th C) New Zealander?

Works on paper			
£1099	$2033	€1605	North view to Porter Heights (34x45cm-13x18in) s.i.d.88 W/C. 9-Mar-4 Watson's, Christchurch #59 est:2000-3000 (NZ.D 3000)

EATON, Valoy (20th C) American

£1941	$3300	€2834	Early spring (46x61cm-18x24in) masonite. 1-Nov-3 Altermann Galleries, Santa Fe #162

EATON, William Raymond (1848-1922) American

£404	$650	€590	No way to start the morning (71x61cm-28x24in) s. 17-Aug-3 Bonhams & Butterfields, San Francisco #5800

EATON, Wyant (1849-1896) American

£313	$522	€454	Waterfall (23x31cm-9x12in) s.i.verso board. 17-Jun-3 Pinneys, Montreal #121 (C.D 700)

EBATARINJA, Arnulf (1931-) Australian

Works on paper			
£303	$552	€442	Ranges. W/C. 5-Feb-4 Joel, Victoria #200 (A.D 725)
£372	$688	€543	Central Australian landscape (33x48cm-13x19in) s. W/C prov. 10-Mar-4 Deutscher-Menzies, Melbourne #573/R (A.D 900)

EBATARINJA, Walter (1915-1969) Australian

Works on paper			
£611	$1111	€892	Central Australian landscape (44x36cm-17x14in) s. W/C. 16-Jun-4 Deutscher-Menzies, Melbourne #380/R est:1200-1500 (A.D 1600)
£649	$1181	€948	Central Australian landscape (36x41cm-14x16in) s. W/C. 16-Jun-4 Deutscher-Menzies, Melbourne #379/R est:1200-1500 (A.D 1700)

EBBE, Axel (1868-1941) Swedish

Sculpture			
£1385	$2382	€2022	Jumping into the water (70cm-28in) s.d.1912 dark pat.bronze. 3-Dec-3 AB Stockholms Auktionsverk #2511/R est:8000-10000 (S.KR 18000)

EBBESEN, Torben (1945-) Danish

£293	$533	€428	Blind picture (79x79cm-31x31in) s.d.1990 verso. 7-Feb-4 Rasmussen, Havnen #4235 (D.KR 3200)
£1408	$2352	€2056	Brain landscape (110x170cm-43x67in) s.d.1986 verso panel. 7-Oct-3 Rasmussen, Copenhagen #178/R est:15000 (D.KR 15000)

EBEL, Fritz Carl Werner (1835-1895) German

£417	$679	€600	Mountain landscape (23x33cm-9x13in) s. canvas on board. 26-Sep-3 Bolland & Marotz, Bremen #518
£2027	$3568	€3000	Woodland with figures (67x92cm-26x36in) s.d.1873. 22-May-4 Lempertz, Koln #1513/R est:4000
£2138	$3955	€3100	Extensive wooded landscape with pond (33x47cm-13x19in) s.d.79. 14-Feb-4 Hans Stahl, Hamburg #18/R est:2800
£6383	$10660	€9000	Hessen landscape with herder and cows (107x160cm-42x63in) s.d.1890. 21-Jun-3 Hans Stahl, Hamburg #20/R est:9000

EBEL, Richard (1885-1919) German

£434	$750	€634	Winter landscape (61x79cm-24x31in) 12-Dec-3 Du Mouchelle, Detroit #2390/R est:800-1000

EBELMANN, Johannes (17th C) German

Works on paper			
£4054	$7135	€6000	Allegory of fortune with two river Gods (11x29cm-4x11in) s.d.1624 pen black ink col wash col chk prov.exhib. 19-May-4 Sotheby's, Amsterdam #4/R est:2400-2800

EBENSPERGER, Hans (1929-1971) ?

£690	$1234	€1007	Ships (63x79cm-25x31in) mono. 13-May-4 Stuker, Bern #112 est:1500-2000 (S.FR 1600)

EBERHARD, Heinrich (1884-1973) German

£302	$535	€450	Still life of flowers with fruit (47x33cm-19x13in) s. board. 30-Apr-4 Dr Fritz Nagel, Stuttgart #121/R
£382	$623	€550	Peterskirche in Wurzburg (97x70cm-38x28in) s.d.1931. 27-Sep-3 Dr Fritz Nagel, Stuttgart #9102/R
£417	$679	€600	Neuburg an der Donau (65x75cm-26x30in) s.d.1931 i. verso. 27-Sep-3 Dr Fritz Nagel, Stuttgart #9103/R

EBERL, François (1887-1962) French

£530	$964	€800	Buste d'homme (65x54cm-26x21in) s.i. 15-Jun-4 Blanchet, Paris #206
£671	$1188	€1000	Vase de fleurs et chat (61x50cm-24x20in) s. 27-Apr-4 Artcurial Briest, Paris #145
£986	$1706	€1400	L'odalisque montmartroise (42x65cm-17x26in) s.d.1947. 10-Dec-3 Rossini, Paris #68/R
£1469	$2497	€2100	La plage (35x27cm-14x11in) s.d.1950. 27-Nov-3 Millon & Associes, Paris #187/R est:800-1000
£1724	$2862	€2500	Garconne (35x25cm-14x10in) s. 1-Oct-3 Millon & Associes, Paris #87
£1724	$2862	€2500	Portrait de femme (32x27cm-13x11in) s. panel. 1-Oct-3 Millon & Associes, Paris #86
£1905	$3410	€2800	Portrait de femme (35x27cm-14x11in) s. 19-Mar-4 Millon & Associes, Paris #97/R est:1500-2000
£1931	$3476	€2800	Nu couche (46x55cm-18x22in) s. panel painted c.1950. 25-Jan-4 Chayette & Cheval, Paris #179 est:2000-2500
£2517	$4280	€3600	Portrait de femme (35x27cm-14x11in) s. 27-Nov-3 Millon & Associes, Paris #186/R est:1800-2200
£2551	$4744	€3800	Portrait de femme a la robe rouge (46x38cm-18x15in) s. painted c.1925-1930. 2-Mar-4 Artcurial Briest, Paris #207/R est:3500-4000
£2759	$4579	€4000	Femme au poudrier (55x46cm-22x18in) s. 1-Oct-3 Millon & Associes, Paris #85/R
£2797	$4755	€4000	Nu assis (73x54cm-29x21in) s.d.23. 27-Nov-3 Millon & Associes, Paris #182/R est:2500-3000

EBERL, Josef (1792-1880) Austrian?

Works on paper			
£2207	$3663	€3200	Mountain lake in Austria (36x52cm-14x20in) s.i. W/C. 30-Sep-3 Dorotheum, Vienna #205/R est:2400-3000

EBERL, Z (20th C) ?

£1118	$2058	€1700	Resting (122x96cm-48x38in) s. 25-Jun-4 Millon & Associes, Paris #151/R est:1500-2000

EBERLE, Adolf (1843-1914) German

£2235	$3800	€3263	After hunt meal (56x69cm-22x27in) s.i. panel. 22-Nov-3 Jackson's, Cedar Falls #6/R est:6000-8000
£5594	$9622	€8000	Getting ready for the hunt (48x54cm-19x21in) s.i. panel. 3-Dec-3 Neumeister, Munich #560/R est:7000
£11111	$18556	€16000	Watching the hunter (61x71cm-24x28in) s.i. panel. 21-Oct-3 Sotheby's, Amsterdam #80/R est:8000-12000

EBERLE, Richard (1918-2001) German

£946	$1693	€1400	View of garden through terrace door (80x65cm-31x26in) s.d. 8-May-4 Dawo, Saarbrucken #227/R

EBERLE, Robert (1815-1860) Swiss

£4200	$7770	€6132	Return of the Herd (51x61cm-20x24in) s. 10-Mar-4 Sotheby's, Olympia #275/R est:2000-3000

EBERLE, Todd (1963-) American

Photographs			
£2333	$4200	€3406	Congress IV (63x76cm-25x30in) num.4/6 chromogenic print prov.exhib. 23-Apr-4 Phillips, New York #101/R est:3000-5000

EBERLEIN, G H (1847-1926) German

Sculpture			
£3846	$6423	€5500	Labourers (102cm-40in) s. pat bronze pair. 7-Oct-3 Sotheby's, Amsterdam #187 est:4000-6000

EBERS, Emil (1807-1884) Polish

£459	$766	€666	Trip to England (28x39cm-11x15in) s.d.1847. 23-Jun-3 Philippe Schuler, Zurich #8587 (S.FR 1000)

EBERSBACH, Hartwig (1940-) German

£1389	$2319	€2000	Menu 3 - Section 21 (83x125cm-33x49in) mono.d. s.i.d. verso panel. 25-Oct-3 Dr Lehr, Berlin #132/R est:3000
£1799	$2950	€2500	Bouquet X (125x84cm-49x33in) mono.d. s.i. verso oil collage masonite. 4-Jun-3 Ketterer, Hamburg #322/R est:2500-3000
£2333	$4293	€3500	Dragon's head (129x89cm-51x35in) mono.d.91 oil paint tubes masonite exhib. 12-Jun-4 Villa Grisebach, Berlin #420/R est:3000-4000

EBERSTEIN, H (?) ?

£1049	$1804	€1500	Venice Lagoon (51x83cm-20x33in) s. 3-Dec-3 Stadion, Trieste #1107/R est:1500-2000

EBERSTEIN, Herman (?) ?

£1745	$3228	€2600	Venice carnival (81x76cm-32x30in) s. 13-Mar-4 De Vuyst, Lokeren #129/R est:2500-3000

EBERT, Albert (1906-1976) German

£1958	$3329	€2800	Flowers (25x17cm-10x7in) s.d.1952 panel exhib. 29-Nov-3 Villa Grisebach, Berlin #759/R est:2000-3000

£2400	$4320	€3600	Still life with asters (25x18cm-10x7in) s.d. panel. 24-Apr-4 Dr Lehr, Berlin #105/R est:3000
£2797	$4755	€4000	Lantern festival (25x19cm-10x7in) s.d.1954 oil ashphalt panel. 29-Nov-3 Villa Grisebach, Berlin #363/R est:3500-4500

EBERT, Anton (1845-1896) German

£1812	$3334	€2700	Portrait de femme au ruban bleu (54x42cm-21x17in) s.i. panel oval. 29-Mar-4 Lombrail & Teucquam, Paris #45/R
£2550	$4565	€3800	Girl with coral necklace and Japanese fan (34x26cm-13x10in) s. panel. 27-May-4 Dorotheum, Vienna #66/R est:2800-3400
£6294	$10699	€9000	Surprise (63x50cm-25x20in) i.d.1872 panel. 24-Nov-3 Dorotheum, Vienna #41/R est:10000-14000
£7500	$13725	€10950	Broken pitcher (105x76cm-41x30in) s. after Jean Baptiste Greuze. 6-Jul-4 Sotheby's, Olympia #580/R est:4000-6000

EBERT, Anton (attrib) (1845-1896) German

£2933	$5250	€4400	Portrait of lady (43x58cm-17x23in) 16-May-4 Abell, Los Angeles #175

EBERT, Carl (1821-1885) German

£921	$1695	€1400	Extensive landscape with peasants harvesting (22x40cm-9x16in) mono. i.d.1854 verso panel. 24-Jun-4 Dr Fritz Nagel, Stuttgart #697/R

EBERT, Castel (19th C) Belgian?

£621	$1148	€900	Cabines au bord de la mer (8x17cm-3x7in) s.d.1888 verso. 19-Jan-4 Horta, Bruxelles #388

EBERT, Charles H (1873-1959) American

£3911	$7000	€5710	Monhegan cove (20x25cm-8x10in) s. plaster board prov. 6-May-4 Shannon's, Milford #73/R est:2500-3500

EBERZ, Josef (1880-1942) German

Prints			
£2083	$3479	€3000	Cacti field (43x35cm-17x14in) s.i.d. W/C lithograph. 24-Oct-3 Ketterer, Hamburg #330/R est:3000-4000

EBIHARA (20th C) Japanese

Works on paper			
£1639	$3000	€2393	Sleeping fox (28x41cm-11x16in) s. ink W/C prov. 3-Jun-4 Christie's, Rockefeller NY #729/R est:100-150

EBLE, Theo (1899-1974) Swiss

£987	$1648	€1441	Rhein harbour, Basle (59x80cm-23x31in) s.d.37. 24-Oct-3 Hans Widmer, St Gallen #87/R est:1500-3500 (S.FR 2200)
£1256	$2097	€1834	Memory (42x32cm-17x13in) s.d.33 tempera exhib. 24-Oct-3 Hans Widmer, St Gallen #85/R est:1500-3500 (S.FR 2800)

EBNER, Richard (1911-) German

£800	$1480	€1168	Beggar (42x66cm-17x26in) s. 10-Mar-4 Sotheby's, Olympia #281/R

EBNETH, Lajos von (1902-1982) Hungarian

£3125	$5000	€4563	Untitled - red ball (81x107cm-32x42in) s. 20-Sep-3 Sloans & Kenyon, Bethesda #1032/R est:5000-7000
Works on paper			
£1566	$2709	€2286	Composition (45x31cm-18x12in) s.d.28 mixed media. 12-Dec-3 Kieselbach, Budapest #159/R (H.F 600000)

ECHALOOK, Luccassie (1942-) North American

Sculpture			
£811	$1378	€1184	Inuit hunter in a skin boat (41cm-16in) mottled dark soapstone. 3-Nov-3 Waddingtons, Toronto #149/R est:2000-3000 (C.D 1800)

ECHAURRI, Miguel Angel (1927-) Spanish

£1647	$2800	€2405	Still life (65x85cm-26x33in) s.d.1960. 25-Nov-3 Galeria y Remates, Montevideo #192/R
£3169	$5482	€4500	Landscape with castle (93x97cm-37x38in) s. painted 1927. 10-Dec-3 Castellana, Madrid #69/R
Works on paper			
£408	$743	€600	Woman (48x34cm-19x13in) s. pencil dr exhib.lit. 3-Feb-4 Segre, Madrid #162/R

ECHAUZ, Francisco (1927-) Spanish

Works on paper			
£276	$500	€420	Three colours (50x44cm-20x17in) s. mixed media. 14-Apr-4 Ansorena, Madrid #330/R
£479	$815	€700	Prado Museum (30x30cm-12x12in) s. mixed media. 4-Nov-3 Ansorena, Madrid #887/R

ECHEVERRIA, Federico de (1911-) Spanish?

Works on paper			
£309	$574	€460	Untitled (59x17cm-23x7in) s. mixed media collage board. 2-Mar-4 Ansorena, Madrid #893
£521	$859	€750	Untitled (59x17cm-23x7in) s. mixed media collage board. 2-Jul-3 Ansorena, Madrid #840/R

ECHEVERRIA, Santos (20th C) Spanish?

£1042	$1656	€1500	Landscape of Lezo (65x54cm-26x21in) s. 29-Apr-3 Durán, Madrid #127/R est:1500
£1042	$1656	€1500	Landscape of Guevara (65x54cm-26x21in) s. 29-Apr-3 Durán, Madrid #128/R est:1500

ECHTERMEYER, Curt (20th C) German

£331	$603	€500	The unlikely couple (60x49cm-24x19in) s.d.1925 board sketch verso. 19-Jun-4 Quittenbaum, Hamburg #80/R

ECK, Adam (attrib) (?-1664) Hungarian

Sculpture			
£4138	$6869	€6000	Orpheus and other figures playing musical instruments (53x53x600cm-21x21x236in) box lid wood. 30-Sep-3 Dorotheum, Vienna #142/R est:12000-14000

ECK, Rudolf (20th C) Austrian

£699	$1203	€1000	View over Leoben (63x79cm-25x31in) s. 4-Dec-3 Dorotheum, Graz #44/R

ECKARDT, Aloys (1845-1906) German

£529	$899	€772	Lake in the evening (74x100cm-29x39in) s. 5-Nov-3 Dobiaschofsky, Bern #521/R (S.FR 1200)
£1695	$3000	€2475	Still life with apples, grapes and pitcher with wasps in (46x58cm-18x23in) s. prov. 2-May-4 Bonhams & Butterfields, San Francisco #1049/R est:3000-5000

ECKARDT, Christian (1832-1914) Danish

£267	$485	€401	Storm by the entrance to Korssor (29x48cm-11x19in) init. 19-Jun-4 Rasmussen, Havnen #2326/R (D.KR 3000)
£337	$550	€492	Coastal landscape, Italy (31x51cm-12x20in) s.d.74. 27-Sep-3 Rasmussen, Havnen #2068/R (D.KR 3600)
£466	$732	€680	Harbour scene in evening (86x134cm-34x53in) s.d.1882. 30-Aug-3 Rasmussen, Havnen #2288 (D.KR 5000)
£467	$738	€677	View towards the manor farm Wedelsborg (43x57cm-17x22in) s. 2-Sep-3 Rasmussen, Copenhagen #1980/R (D.KR 5000)
£562	$967	€821	Boats at low tide (22x31cm-9x12in) s. panel. 2-Dec-3 Kunsthallen, Copenhagen #534/R (D.KR 6000)
£629	$1170	€918	Fishing boats off Korsor, afternoon (29x48cm-11x19in) s. 2-Mar-4 Rasmussen, Copenhagen #1408/R (D.KR 7000)
£762	$1371	€1113	The property Henriettelyst at Fyn (41x55cm-16x22in) s.d.1868. 24-Apr-4 Rasmussen, Havnen #2277/R (D.KR 8500)
£839	$1317	€1225	The attractive property Henriettelyst at Fyn (41x55cm-16x22in) s.d.1868. 30-Aug-3 Rasmussen, Havnen #2261/R (D.KR 9000)
£1087	$1946	€1587	Southern coastal landscape with sailing boats (37x59cm-15x23in) s.i.d.75. 12-Jan-4 Rasmussen, Vejle #41/R (D.KR 11500)
£1438	$2674	€2099	Coastal landscape with view towards a town (31x49cm-12x19in) s.d.73. 2-Mar-4 Rasmussen, Copenhagen #1358/R est:10000-12000 (D.KR 16000)
£1611	$2578	€2352	Seascape with Greek fishermen (60x94cm-24x37in) s.d.1875 exhib. 22-Sep-3 Rasmussen, Vejle #280/R est:15000-20000 (D.KR 17000)
£1617	$3008	€2361	Danish and Dutch vessels off the coast (75x123cm-30x48in) s.d.1891. 2-Mar-4 Rasmussen, Copenhagen #1446/R est:12000-15000 (D.KR 18000)
£2344	$4337	€3422	Seascape with sailing vessels (38x58cm-15x23in) s.d.1870. 15-Mar-4 Rasmussen, Vejle #69/R est:30000 (D.KR 26000)
£3055	$5682	€4460	Seascape with frigates in fresh breeze (61x84cm-24x33in) s.d.1851. 2-Mar-4 Rasmussen, Copenhagen #1406/R est:30000 (D.KR 34000)
£3514	$6500	€5130	Latvian coastal craft and paddle steamer in the Bay of Riga (60x97cm-24x38in) s.d.1877 indis.i.stretcher prov. 10-Feb-4 Christie's, Rockefeller NY #221/R est:7000-9000
£4029	$7372	€5882	Seascape with sailing vessels and steamer by entrance to Copenhagen Harbour (25x35cm-10x14in) s.d.1859 prov. 9-Jun-4 Rasmussen, Copenhagen #1812/R est:30000-35000 (D.KR 45000)

ECKART, Christian (1959-) Canadian

Sculpture			
£4945	$9000	€7220	White painting no.610 (245x259cm-96x102in) s.i.d.1988 verso formica birch plywood 23 carat gold leaf prov. 29-Jun-4 Sotheby's, New York #530/R est:4000-6000

ECKENBRECHER, Themistocles von (1842-1921) German

£805	$1442	€1200	Vue de fjord en Norvege (66x90cm-26x35in) s. 25-May-4 Palais de Beaux Arts, Brussels #374/R
£839	$1401	€1200	Lofos in Valders, Norway (33x44cm-13x17in) mono.d.6.Juli 1901 i. verso board. 28-Jun-3 Bolland & Marotz, Bremen #637/R
£839	$1427	€1200	Sunset over the water with Spitzbergen in background (24x33cm-9x13in) mono.i.d.18/8/05 cardboard lit. 28-Nov-3 Schloss Ahlden, Ahlden #1485/R
£1342	$2470	€2000	Mediterranean landscape (16x26cm-6x10in) mono.d. panel. 26-Mar-4 Ketterer, Hamburg #181/R est:2200-2500
£1399	$2378	€2000	Waterfall in Norway (75x116cm-30x46in) s.d.87. 20-Nov-3 Van Ham, Cologne #1549/R est:3200
£1497	$2679	€2200	Fishing harbour on the Lofoten (45x66cm-18x26in) s.i.d.13.8.1895 i. verso canvas on board. 17-Mar-4 Neumeister, Munich #446/R est:2300
£1747	$3074	€2551	Welcome to the Rosenlaui glacier (84x71cm-33x28in) s.d.88 i. stretcher prov. 22-May-4 Galerie Gloggner, Luzern #106/R est:1800-2500 (S.FR 4000)
£2000	$3680	€3000	At the water's edge (38x63cm-15x25in) s.d.1860 s.i.d.verso stretcher. 12-Jun-4 Villa Grisebach, Berlin #111/R est:3000-4000
£2587	$4399	€3700	Fjord landscape with small steamer (64x94cm-25x37in) s.d.1913 lit. 28-Nov-3 Schloss Ahlden, Ahlden #1490/R est:3500
£2587	$4399	€3700	View towards the Skaala (60x91cm-24x36in) s.i.d.1907 lit. 28-Nov-3 Schloss Ahlden, Ahlden #1491/R est:3500
£3194	$5207	€4600	Norwegian fjord landscape with boats (100x144cm-39x57in) s.d.899 s.i. stretcher. 27-Sep-3 Dannenberg, Berlin #534/R est:3000
£10000	$18700	€14600	Dutch frozen river landscape with figures skating besides boats (73x116cm-29x46in) s.d.67 prov. 22-Jul-4 Tennants, Leyburn #830/R est:6000-8000
Works on paper			
£455	$759	€650	Two figures, one in Greek dress (33x44cm-13x17in) mono. htd white pencil. 10-Oct-3 Winterberg, Heidelberg #566
£2200	$3740	€3212	Bab el Metwali, Cairo (36x25cm-14x10in) s.i.d.89 W/C. 4-Nov-3 Bonhams, New Bond Street #97/R est:2000-3000

£3500 $6370 €5110 Old Galatea Bridge connecting Karakoy to Eminonu over the Golden Horn (37x27cm-15x11in) s.i.d.89 pencil blk ink W/C htd white paper on card. 17-Jun-4 Christie's, London #116/R est:4000-6000

ECKENER, Alexander (1870-1944) German
£676 $1209 €1000 Priele near Bongsiel (54x44cm-21x17in) s.d.22. 8-May-4 Hans Stahl, Toestorf #52/R
Works on paper
£878 $1572 €1300 Freight steamer in Flensburg harbour (22x34cm-9x13in) s. W/C. 8-May-4 Hans Stahl, Toestorf #53/R

ECKENFELDER, Friedrich (1861-1938) German
£500 $905 €750 Balingen (21x47cm-8x19in) s. lit. 1-Apr-4 Frank Peege, Freiburg #1218/R
£500 $905 €750 Two carthorses (37x54cm-15x21in) s.d.1881 lit. 1-Apr-4 Frank Peege, Freiburg #1219/R
£667 $1207 €1000 Balingen (27x55cm-11x22in) s. lit. 1-Apr-4 Frank Peege, Freiburg #1217/R
£1257 $2300 €1835 Hose cart and peasant (53x41cm-21x16in) 31-Jan-4 South Bay, Long Island #92
£1357 $2308 €1981 Horse and cart in field (40x58cm-16x23in) s. 28-Nov-3 Zofingen, Switzerland #2576 est:3500 (S.FR 3000)
£1399 $2378 €2000 Post coach pulled by two black horses with Alps in background (60x80cm-24x31in) s. 22-Nov-3 Arnold, Frankfurt #494/R est:1600
£1600 $2912 €2400 Horses (16x21cm-6x8in) s. panel. 30-Jun-4 Neumeister, Munich #541/R est:2000
£1761 $3046 €2500 Workhorses at rest (65x91cm-26x36in) s. 10-Dec-3 Christie's, Amsterdam #849a/R est:2500-3500

ECKER, Franz (1943-1999) Austrian
£315 $535 €450 Abstract (80x100cm-31x39in) s.d.1982. 27-Nov-3 Dorotheum, Linz #535/R
£350 $594 €500 Shark in sight (104x64cm-41x25in) s.i.d.77 verso. 27-Nov-3 Dorotheum, Linz #533/R
£420 $713 €600 The glass ball (90x80cm-35x31in) s.i.d.77 verso. 27-Nov-3 Dorotheum, Linz #532/R
£769 $1308 €1100 Untitled (85x85cm-33x33in) s. panel. 27-Nov-3 Dorotheum, Linz #537/R

ECKERLER, Karl (19th C) German
£458 $732 €650 Flowers at window (97x73cm-38x29in) s. panel. 18-Sep-3 Rieber, Stuttgart #1288/R

ECKERSBERG, C W (1783-1853) Danish
Works on paper
£284 $491 €415 Figure of man symbolising Father Time (15x12cm-6x5in) pen wash prov. 9-Dec-3 Rasmussen, Copenhagen #1718/R (D.KR 3000)
£806 $1474 €1177 Man flirting with young woman (15x10cm-6x4in) s.d.1807-1809 pen pencil prov. 9-Jun-4 Rasmussen, Copenhagen #2073/R (D.KR 9000)
£1970 $3604 €2876 Young couples flirting (16x20cm-6x8in) init. pencil pair. 9-Jun-4 Rasmussen, Copenhagen #2074/R est:20000 (D.KR 22000)

ECKERSBERG, Christoffer Wilhelm (1783-1853) Danish
£3781 $6541 €5520 Study for Groser Smith (25x25cm-10x10in) exhib. 9-Dec-3 Rasmussen, Copenhagen #1340/R est:30000 (D.KR 40000)
£4693 $8776 €6852 Portrait of young gentleman (40x31cm-16x12in) prov.lit. 25-Feb-4 Kunsthallen, Copenhagen #548/R est:50000 (D.KR 52000)
£5482 $9484 €8004 Portrait of a gentleman (36x28cm-14x11in) s. oval exhib. 9-Dec-3 Rasmussen, Copenhagen #1203/R est:50000-75000 (D.KR 58000)
£44763 $81916 €65354 Another part of Nordfeldt's garden (37x44cm-15x17in) painted 1809 exhib.prov. 9-Jun-4 Rasmussen, Copenhagen #1430/R est:500000-600000 (D.KR 500000)
£118147 $204395 €172495 Danish frigates during spring 1849 (60x79cm-24x31in) exhib.prov. 9-Dec-3 Rasmussen, Copenhagen #1217/R est:1200000-1500000 (D.KR 1250000)
£465533 $851925 €679678 Seascape with many sailing ships and a Danish man-o-war (58x86cm-23x34in) init.d.1827 exhib.prov. 9-Jun-4 Rasmussen, Copenhagen #1434/R est:5000000 (D.KR 5200000)
Works on paper
£2336 $3692 €3387 From the gate at The Stock Exchange with four figures (13x12cm-5x5in) init.i. pen pencil grey wash prov. 2-Sep-3 Rasmussen, Copenhagen #2021/R est:30000-40000 (D.KR 25000)
£4486 $7088 €6505 Street scene with two gentlemen discussing outside entrance to park (22x34cm-9x13in) pen pencil grey wash exec.c.c.1838-40 prov. 2-Sep-3 Rasmussen, Copenhagen #2020/R est:30000-40000 (D.KR 48000)
£4500 $8190 €6570 Marines (23x31cm-9x12in) one s.d.1830 one s.d.1844 pen ink wash pair. 15-Jun-4 Sotheby's, London #300/R est:5000-7000
£5674 $9475 €8000 Sculptures. s.d.1826 pierre noire set of 3 prov. 15-Oct-3 Sotheby's, Paris #211/R est:12000
£14178 $24527 €20700 View of Zahlkammer gate towards Palace Square (31x24cm-12x9in) init.d.1809 W/C pencil lit. 9-Dec-3 Rasmussen, Copenhagen #1216/R est:100000-150000 (D.KR 150000)

ECKERSBERG, Hansine (1826-1860) Danish
£1340 $2170 €1943 Roses on ledge (28x40cm-11x16in) s.d.1839 panel. 4-Aug-3 Rasmussen, Vejle #139/R est:15000 (D.KR 14000)
£2778 $4389 €4000 Roses and citrus leaves (21x29cm-8x11in) s. panel. 6-Sep-3 Schopman, Hamburg #672/R est:3800

ECKERSBERG, Johan Fredrik (1822-1870) Norwegian
£7520 $13762 €10979 Norwegian fjord landscape with boat returning home with hay (62x88cm-24x35in) s.d.1864. 9-Jun-4 Rasmussen, Copenhagen #1841/R est:75000-100000 (D.KR 84000)
£10675 $17827 €15586 Coastal landscape with figures (66x94cm-26x37in) s.d.1868. 13-Oct-3 Blomqvist, Oslo #284/R est:150000-180000 (N.KR 125000)
£13458 $24091 €19649 Mountain landscape with figures under Romsdalshorn (26x32cm-10x13in) s.indis.d.1860 i.stretcher paper on canvas. 25-May-4 Grev Wedels Plass, Oslo #38/R est:70000-90000 (N.KR 165000)
£13687 $23268 €19983 Mountain landscape from Romsdalen (62x79cm-24x31in) s.d.1850. 19-Nov-3 Grev Wedels Plass, Oslo #51/R est:150000-200000 (N.KR 160000)
Works on paper
£1008 $1855 €1472 Artist resting at a waterfall (22x32cm-9x13in) s.d.1854 W/C. 14-Jun-4 Waddingtons, Toronto #345/R est:1000-1500 (C.D 2500)

ECKERT, Georg Maria (1828-1903) German
£1667 $3017 €2500 Ruins of tower of Heidelberg Castle (69x66cm-27x26in) mono.d. 2-Apr-4 Winterberg, Heidelberg #402/R est:3200

ECKHARDT, Georg Ludwig (1770-1794) German
£750 $1222 €1095 Scene with green-grocer (36x29cm-14x11in) s.d.1764. 28-Sep-3 Hindemae, Ullerslev #118/R (D.KR 8000)

ECKHART, Gerry (1902-1984) ?
Works on paper
£296 $473 €420 Abstract (38x29cm-15x11in) s.d.1978 W/C wash. 16-Sep-3 Segre, Madrid #252/R

ECKHOUT, Albert (attrib) (1610-1666) Dutch
£33333 $60000 €48666 Head of a boy (22x19cm-9x7in) i. oil on paper exhib. 21-Jan-4 Sotheby's, New York #62/R est:8000-12000

ECKL, Vilma (1892-1982) Austrian
Works on paper
£600 $1074 €900 House entrance with small girl in doorway (58x39cm-23x15in) s.d. W/Cs. col chk prov. 13-May-4 Dorotheum, Linz #566/R
£1986 $3316 €2800 Picking potatoes (39x46cm-15x18in) s. col chk. 14-Oct-3 Dorotheum, Vienna #141/R est:3200-4500

ECKMANN, Otto (attrib) (1865-1902) German
£957 $1750 €1397 Damoiselle aux colombes (106x40cm-42x16in) 5-Jun-4 Galerie du Rhone, Sion #497 (S.FR 2200)

ECONOMOU, Ioannis (1860-1931) Greek
£3700 $6475 €5402 Still life with quinces (46x31cm-18x12in) s.d.1916 hardboard. 16-Dec-3 Bonhams, New Bond Street #32/R est:3000-5000
£4000 $7000 €5840 Still life with fruit (28x40cm-11x16in) s.d.1915 panel. 16-Dec-3 Bonhams, New Bond Street #42/R est:4000-5000

ECONOMOU, Michalis (1888-1933) Greek
£40000 $68000 €58400 House with tree (39x55cm-15x22in) s. linen on board prov.lit. 18-Nov-3 Sotheby's, London #31/R est:25000-35000

ECUADORIAN SCHOOL
£4471 $7600 €6528 Saint Raphael (76x57cm-30x22in) canvas on panel. 23-Nov-3 Subastas Odalys, Caracas #178/R est:7000

EDDY, Henry Brevoort (1872-1935) American
£223 $400 €326 Indian (15x10cm-6x4in) s. board. 7-May-4 Sloans & Kenyon, Bethesda #1215/R

EDE, Basil (1931-) British
Works on paper
£260 $471 €380 Chance meeting (16x25cm-6x10in) s.d.1956 gouache. 31-Mar-4 Bonhams, Knightsbridge #11/R
£310 $533 €453 Lesser spotted woodpecker (30x20cm-12x8in) s. W/C bodycol. 4-Dec-3 Richardson & Smith, Whitby #455/R
£435 $800 €635 Red grouse (33x28cm-13x11in) s. gouache. 25-Jun-4 Freeman, Philadelphia #90/R

EDE, Frederick Charles Vipond (1865-1943) American
£1339 $2304 €1955 Shepherdess and her flock (47x64cm-19x25in) s.d.92. 2-Dec-3 Joyner Waddington, Toronto #232/R est:3000-4000 (C.D 3000)
£1667 $3000 €2434 Ducks by a stream (32x44cm-13x17in) s. canvasboard. 24-Apr-4 Weschler, Washington #624/R est:3000-5000
£1750 $2800 €2555 Riverside in Moret-sur-Long, France (56x66cm-22x26in) s.d.1928. 20-Sep-3 Sloans & Kenyon, Bethesda #1194/R est:3000-5000
£5500 $10010 €8030 Aux bords du Lumain (60x73cm-24x29in) s.d.85. 16-Jun-4 Christie's, Kensington #12/R est:2000-3000
Works on paper
£181 $302 €264 The goat girl (27x41cm-11x16in) s. W/C. 17-Nov-3 Waddingtons, Toronto #1/R (C.D 400)

EDEFALK, Cecilia (1954-) Swedish?
£2417 $4109 €3529 Man and girl (49x54cm-19x21in) s.d.1995. 5-Nov-3 AB Stockholms Auktionsverk #923/R est:20000-25000 (S.KR 32000)
£87745 $157941 €128108 Dad (242x135cm-95x53in) s.d.87/88 verso two parts prov.exhib.lit. 26-Apr-4 Bukowskis, Stockholm #532/R est:200000-250000 (S.KR 1210000)

EDEL, Albert (20th C) American
£279 $475 €407 Sunset at railroad wharf (30x41cm-12x16in) s.verso board. 9-Nov-3 Outer Cape Auctions, Provincetown #108/R
£338 $625 €493 Pier and Provincetown (41x56cm-16x22in) s. board. 15-Feb-4 Outer Cape Auctions, Provincetown #74/R

EDELFELT, Albert (1854-1905) Finnish

£5594	$9510	€8000	Interior from Haiko farm (25x30cm-10x12in) 29-Nov-3 Bukowskis, Helsinki #60/R est:8000-10000
£8846	$15215	€12915	Femme au parapluie (28cm-11in circular) s. leather. 3-Dec-3 AB Stockholms Auktionsverk #2544/R est:80000-100000 (S.KR 115000)
£39437	$68225	€56000	Summer's day at Haiko (42x66cm-17x26in) s.d.1897. 13-Dec-3 Hagelstam, Helsinki #90/R est:70000
£54054	$96757	€80000	Portrait of Madame Cohen (58x44cm-23x17in) s.d.1890. 8-May-4 Bukowskis, Helsinki #183/R est:80000-120000
£132867	$225874	€190000	Anchored off Haiko jetty (44x38cm-17x15in) s. canvas on board prov.lit. 29-Nov-3 Bukowskis, Helsinki #25c/R est:150000-180000
Works on paper			
£537	$988	€800	Dance (33x22cm-13x9in) i. pencil. 25-Mar-4 Hagelstam, Helsinki #811
£1088	$1958	€1632	Ship's portrait of Amfion near Svensksund (18x26cm-7x10in) s. W/C wash htd white. 25-Apr-4 Goteborg Auktionsverk, Sweden #206/R est:20000 (S.KR 15000)
£1154	$1985	€1685	Portrait of gentleman (30x24cm-12x9in) s. W/C htd white. 3-Dec-3 AB Stockholms Auktionsverk #2639/R est:15000-20000 (S.KR 15000)
£1689	$3024	€2500	Nightly meeting (21x17cm-8x7in) s. gouache. 8-May-4 Bukowskis, Helsinki #184/R est:3000-3500
£3662	$5859	€5200	Baroness Anna Bennet (51x33cm-20x13in) s. gouache lit. 18-Sep-3 Hagelstam, Helsinki #783 est:4500
£4930	$8528	€7000	Monte Carlo (32x26cm-13x10in) d.25 Mars 1886 W/C. 13-Dec-3 Hagelstam, Helsinki #91/R est:8000
£11538	$19615	€16500	Portrait of young girl (34x37cm-13x15in) study W/C prov.lit. 29-Nov-3 Bukowskis, Helsinki #159/R est:6000-8000

EDELMANN, Charles Auguste (1879-1950) French

£1987	$3616	€3000	Jeune femme devant une boutique (41x33cm-16x13in) s. 18-Jun-4 Piasa, Paris #131 est:400-600

EDELMANN, Hanno (1923-) German

£299	$550	€437	Die Loge (130x160cm-51x63in) s.d.65. 26-Jun-4 Sloans & Kenyon, Bethesda #288/R
£1146	$1766	€1800	Hamburg bridge (70x100cm-28x39in) s.d.59. 4-Sep-2 Schopman, Hamburg #132/R est:2400

EDELMANN, Yrjo (1941-) Swedish

£1268	$2028	€1800	Still life of wine glass (66x53cm-26x21in) s.d.1972. 18-Sep-3 Hagelstam, Helsinki #773/R est:2000
£1435	$2440	€2095	Jeans (81x90cm-32x35in) s.d.76. 5-Nov-3 AB Stockholms Auktionsverk #1068/R est:12000-15000 (S.KR 19000)
£2930	$5187	€4278	Night object (100x85cm-39x33in) s.d.81. 27-Apr-4 AB Stockholms Auktionsverk #1130/R est:40000-50000 (S.KR 40000)
£9155	$15838	€13000	All together (120x140cm-47x55in) s.d.1983. 13-Dec-3 Hagelstam, Helsinki #197/R est:8000
Works on paper			
£1473	$2504	€2151	A child disappears (49x37cm-19x15in) s.d.66 verso mixed media. 4-Nov-3 Bukowskis, Stockholm #536/R est:10000-12000 (S.KR 19500)

EDEN, Emily (1797-1869) British

Prints			
£40000	$65200	€58400	Portraits of the Princes and Peoples of India. Hand-coloured lithographic title with 27 lithographic plates. 24-Sep-3 Christie's, London #70/R est:22000-28000

EDEN-SILLENSTEDE, Arthur (1899-1977) German

£833	$1317	€1200	Neuharlingersiel (48x71cm-19x28in) s. 6-Sep-3 Schopman, Hamburg #751/R

EDENS, Henning (1885-1943) German

£537	$1004	€800	Blankenese house (36x40cm-14x16in) s.d. canvas on board. 28-Feb-4 Quittenbaum, Hamburg #66/R
£556	$917	€800	Hamburg harbour (31x41cm-12x16in) s.d.37 board. 3-Jul-3 Van Ham, Cologne #1158/R
£1000	$1810	€1500	Beach (35x46cm-14x18in) s.d.1921 board. 3-Apr-4 Hans Stahl, Hamburg #150/R est:1700

EDER, A (19th C) ?

£1389	$2361	€2000	Genre scene (73x100cm-29x39in) s. 28-Oct-3 Dorotheum, Vienna #144/R est:2500-2800

EDER, Gyula (1875-1945) Hungarian

£938	$1500	€1369	Bacchus and maiden (76x56cm-30x22in) s. 19-Sep-3 Freeman, Philadelphia #179/R est:600-1000

EDERER, Carl (1875-1951) German

£403	$749	€600	Cattle out at pasture (33x42cm-13x17in) s. i.verso. 5-Mar-4 Wendl, Rudolstadt #3627/R
Works on paper			
£1007	$1842	€1500	Portrait of a young lady with a black hat (63x42cm-25x17in) s.d.95 pastel lit. 8-Jul-4 Allgauer, Kempten #1960/R est:1500

EDGAR, Edmund (1801-?) Australian

Works on paper			
£7000	$11410	€10220	Portrait of a gentleman, on board ship, Sydney (13x11cm-5x4in) i.d.1842 verso W/C over pencil lit. 25-Sep-3 Christie's, London #482/R est:6000-8000

EDGAR, James R (fl.1860-1870) British

£2500	$4175	€3650	Happy as a king. Boyhood troubles (20x30cm-8x12in) s. pair. 13-Nov-3 Christie's, Kensington #126/R est:3000-5000

EDGAR, Norman (?) ?

£850	$1445	€1241	Still life with carnation and tulips (66x66cm-26x26in) s. 4-Nov-3 Dreweatt Neate, Newbury #132/R
£1300	$2171	€1898	Still life of azaleas and fruit (75x90cm-30x35in) s. 16-Oct-3 Bonhams, Edinburgh #68/R est:1500-2000
£2300	$3979	€3358	Soup tureen (71x91cm-28x36in) s. 11-Dec-3 Lyon & Turnbull, Edinburgh #41/R est:1500-2000
Works on paper			
£360	$601	€526	Fishing boats (54x76cm-21x30in) s. gouache. 19-Jun-3 Bonhams, Edinburgh #331

EDIE, Stuart Carson (1908-) American

£245	$450	€358	Sunday morning (20x25cm-8x10in) s. i.d.1945 verso. 10-Jun-4 Swann Galleries, New York #79/R
£719	$1200	€1050	Red, white and blue (63x115cm-25x45in) s. s.i.d.1946 verso prov.exhib.lit. 7-Oct-3 Sotheby's, New York #233

EDLICH, Stephen (1944-) American

Works on paper			
£295	$475	€431	Untitled (61x46cm-24x18in) mixed media exec. c.1978. 22-Feb-3 Bunte, Elgin #1166
£1421	$2600	€2075	84 Transports Jean Chatel (137x91cm-54x36in) mixed media. 10-Apr-4 Cobbs, Peterborough #92/R

EDLINGER, Gunther (1958-) Austrian

Works on paper			
£993	$1658	€1400	Karajan portrait (80x80cm-31x31in) s.d.2003 verso mixed media graphic. 16-Oct-3 Dorotheum, Salzburg #757/R

EDLINGER, Johann Georg von (1741-1819) Austrian

£544	$974	€800	Woman's portrait (51x41cm-20x16in) 17-Mar-4 Neumeister, Munich #447/R

EDLINGER, Johann Georg von (attrib) (1741-1819) Austrian

£596	$1085	€900	Portrait of a gentleman (60x45cm-24x18in) 16-Jun-4 Hugo Ruef, Munich #889

EDMONDS, Francis William (1806-1863) American

£36932	$65000	€53921	Sammy the tailor (25x30cm-10x12in) painted 1836 prov.exhib.lit. 18-May-4 Christie's, Rockefeller NY #11/R est:20000-30000

EDMONDSON, Simon (1955-) British

£1200	$2004	€1752	Great Austerity (221x195cm-87x77in) s. i.d.1986-87 verso. 21-Oct-3 Bonhams, Knightsbridge #215/R est:1500-2000

EDMONDSON, William (c.1870-1951) American

Sculpture			
£28533	$52500	€41658	Woman engaged in domestic activity (36x15x18cm-14x6x7in) limestone lit. 10-Jun-4 Sotheby's, New York #231/R est:6000-8000
£35135	$65000	€51297	Girl with braided hair (27x8x15cm-11x3x6in) limestone driftwood prov.lit. 15-Jan-4 Sotheby's, New York #323/R est:50000-80000

EDMONDSON, William J (1868-1966) American

£539	$900	€787	Landscape with cattle, farmhouse and stream (33x56cm-13x22in) s. 14-Nov-3 Aspire, Cleveland #43 est:1000-2000

EDMONSTON, Samuel (1825-?) British

£320	$586	€467	A future warrior (30x25cm-12x10in) s. board. 29-Jan-4 Bonhams, Edinburgh #326

EDOUARD, Albert Jules (1845-?) French

£6167	$11347	€9250	Judith (100x62cm-39x24in) s. 14-Jun-4 Tajan, Paris #19/R est:6000-8000

EDOUART, Augustin (1789-1861) French

Miniatures			
£4620	$8500	€6745	Reverend Dr John Jacob Robertson and family (38x74cm-15x29in) i.d.1st May 1845 silhouette sold with rocking chair. 26-Jun-4 Selkirks, St. Louis #416/R est:9000-12000
Works on paper			
£304	$550	€444	Silhouette of seated lady (18x28cm-7x11in) W/C. 2-Apr-4 Douglas, South Deerfield #40
£414	$750	€604	Silhouette of man with dog (18x28cm-7x11in) W/C. 2-Apr-4 Douglas, South Deerfield #41

EDRIDGE, Henry (1769-1821) British

Miniatures			
£1000	$1800	€1460	Gentleman of the Vanhomrigh family (6cm-2in) gold frame oval exhib. 22-Apr-4 Bonhams, New Bond Street #66/R est:600-800
£1800	$3240	€2628	Marmaduke Sealy (8cm-3in) init.i.verso card gold frame oval exhib.lit. 22-Apr-4 Bonhams, New Bond Street #138/R est:1200-1800
£2621	$4377	€3800	Gentleman (6cm-2in) oval. 12-Nov-3 Sotheby's, Milan #28/R est:1600-2000
£4324	$8000	€6313	Male portrait (5x5cm-2x2in) exec.c.1780 oval. 12-Mar-4 Du Mouchelle, Detroit #2029/R est:1000-2000

Works on paper

£280	$442	€406	Portrait of a young man (15x13cm-6x5in) s.d.1806 verso. 24-Jul-3 Dominic Winter, Swindon #142
£550	$990	€803	Chateau of Hougoumont at Waterloo (22x28cm-9x11in) i.d.August 20th 1817 W/C over pencil. 21-Jan-4 Sotheby's, Olympia #133/R
£650	$1190	€949	Portrait, possibly of Sir Charles Farnaby and of a female of the same family (18x13cm-7x5in) one d.1807 pencil wash pair. 7-Apr-4 Gardiner & Houlgate, Bath #145
£900	$1503	€1314	Portrait of an officer of the 19th Light Dragoons standing in a landscape (40x28cm-16x11in) s. grey wash pencil. 14-Oct-3 Sotheby's, London #477/R est:1000-1500
£1100	$2013	€1606	Portrait of 1st Lord Stanley of Alderley, three quarter length seated (29x24cm-11x9in) s.d.1811 pencil W/C gum arabic htd white prov. 3-Jun-4 Christie's, London #111/R est:1200-1800
£1200	$2040	€1752	Portrait of Miss Morice the younger, in a dress and sash holding a bird (19x14cm-7x6in) s.d.1797 pencil grey wash buff paper prov. 20-Nov-3 Christie's, London #21/R est:800-1200
£4400	$7480	€6424	Full length portrait of cavalry officer standing on a terrace (43x30cm-17x12in) s.d.1808 pencil W/C pair. 27-Nov-3 Greenslade Hunt, Taunton #948/R est:800-1200

EDRIDGE, Henry (attrib) (1769-1821) British

Works on paper

£260	$481	€380	Brighton beach with fishing boats (15x35cm-6x14in) W/C. 10-Mar-4 Sotheby's, Olympia #38/R
£2200	$4048	€3212	William Duke of Clarence in naval uniform (40x30cm-16x12in) pencil W/C. 29-Mar-4 Bonhams, Bath #1/R est:600-800

EDSBERG, Knud (1911-) Danish

£309	$504	€451	Stable interior with children (79x65cm-31x26in) s. 27-Sep-3 Rasmussen, Havnen #2080 (D.KR 3300)
£391	$615	€571	Cows and horses in field (40x50cm-16x20in) s. 30-Aug-3 Rasmussen, Havnen #2062 (D.KR 4200)
£394	$642	€575	Cows in meadow (70x100cm-28x39in) s. 27-Sep-3 Rasmussen, Havnen #2133 (D.KR 4200)

EDSBERG, Soren (20th C) Danish

£284	$518	€426	Feeding the horses (54x75cm-21x30in) s.d.45. 19-Jun-4 Rasmussen, Havnen #2346 (D.KR 3200)

EDSON, Allan (1846-1888) Canadian

£361	$672	€527	Stream in the woods (61x91cm-24x36in) 2-Mar-4 Ritchie, Toronto #56/R (C.D 900)
£1116	$1920	€1629	Homestead with picnickers (35x52cm-14x20in) s. 2-Dec-3 Joyner Waddington, Toronto #262/R est:1500-2000 (C.D 2500)
£2009	$3455	€2933	Forest scene with farmhouse (60x45cm-24x18in) s. 2-Dec-3 Joyner Waddington, Toronto #187/R est:3000-5000 (C.D 4500)

Works on paper

£181	$336	€264	Forest brook (14x22cm-6x9in) s. W/C. 2-Mar-4 Ritchie, Toronto #57/R (C.D 450)
£289	$500	€422	Matapedia Valley (27x37cm-11x15in) mono.i. W/C. 9-Dec-3 Pinneys, Montreal #188 (C.D 650)
£680	$1244	€993	Wood gatherers in a glade (34x49cm-13x19in) s.d.1880 W/C. 1-Jun-4 Hodgins, Calgary #397/R (C.D 1700)
£804	$1382	€1174	Woodsmen returning to the log cabin (24x34cm-9x13in) s.i.d.XX. 2-Dec-3 Joyner Waddington, Toronto #429 est:1000-1500 (C.D 1800)

EDSON, Enid (20th C) American

Works on paper

£235	$400	€343	East River and Brooklyn Navy Yard (41x52cm-16x20in) s. W/C executed c.1945. 21-Nov-3 Skinner, Boston #582/R

EDWARDS, Howard Arden (1884-1953) American

£7647	$13000	€11165	Peaceful valley, Eagle Rock, CA (69x86cm-27x34in) s. i.verso exhib. 18-Nov-3 John Moran, Pasadena #149 est:2000-3000

EDWARDS, James (1820-1888) British

£640	$1146	€934	Quiet stream, sunlit summer landscape (61x51cm-24x20in) s. 18-Mar-4 Neales, Nottingham #792

EDWARDS, John (19th C) British

£320	$573	€467	Study of an otter leaving its lair (25x33cm-10x13in) s. 13-May-4 Grant, Worcester #378
£500	$895	€730	Lambing time (58x46cm-23x18in) s. 13-May-4 Grant, Worcester #379/R
£1100	$2002	€1606	Winter afternoon (59x49cm-23x19in) s. s.i.verso. 5-Feb-4 Mellors & Kirk, Nottingham #557/R est:600-800

EDWARDS, Lionel (1878-1966) British

£10465	$18000	€15279	15 miles from the Marble Arch (51x76cm-20x30in) s. indis d.1935 prov. 5-Dec-3 Christie's, Rockefeller NY #71/R est:20000-30000

Works on paper

£300	$501	€438	Sheet of sketches showing farm labourers at work (9x11cm-4x4in) indis.init. pencil. 9-Oct-3 Greenslade Hunt, Taunton #571
£300	$549	€438	Original illustration for Black Arrow (22x15cm-9x6in) i. pen ink brush over pencil two. 8-Jul-4 Lawrence, Crewkerne #1564
£900	$1656	€1314	After all handsome is as handsome does (20x25cm-8x10in) init.i.d.23 pen ink panel. 10-Jun-4 Christie's, Kensington #135/R
£900	$1656	€1314	Down the side of Dunkerry, the Devon and Somerset (22x29cm-9x11in) i. pencil ink prov. 10-Jun-4 Christie's, Kensington #138/R
£1200	$2148	€1752	Lovely Cottage over Beechers Brook 1946 Grand National Winder (13x25cm-5x10in) s. W/C exec 1946. 7-May-4 Chrystals Auctions, Isle of Man #283 est:1000-1500
£1800	$3060	€2628	An unexpected dip (21x57cm-8x22in) s.d.05 pencil W/C. 27-Nov-3 Christie's, Kensington #33/R est:2000-3000
£2209	$3800	€3225	Scarteen country, Cromhill, looking towards the Galtee mountains (23x36cm-9x14in) mono. black chk pen ink htd white. 5-Dec-3 Christie's, Rockefeller NY #113/R est:2500-3500
£2700	$4914	€3942	Hind hunting above weir water (48x34cm-19x13in) s.i.d.1936 W/C bodycol. 21-Jun-4 Bonhams, Bath #437/R est:2500-3000
£2800	$5096	€4088	Hind hunting, Webbers Post, Exmoor (34x50cm-13x20in) s.d.1936 W/C bodycol. 21-Jun-4 Bonhams, Bath #440/R est:2500-3000
£2950	$5487	€4307	Hunting a hind, Withypool (23x35cm-9x14in) s.i.d.1936 W/C bodycol. 2-Mar-4 Bearnes, Exeter #322/R est:1500-2000
£2950	$5310	€4307	No cause for alarm, Norwich stag hounds near Pulham St Mary (41x56cm-16x22in) s. W/C. 20-Apr-4 Wotton Auction Rooms, Wotton #905 est:3000-3500
£3000	$5460	€4380	Hind and calf at Cussacombe Post, Exmoor (34x50cm-13x20in) s.i.d.1936 W/C bodycol. 21-Jun-4 Bonhams, Bath #436/R est:2500-3000
£3488	$6000	€5092	Earth stopper (28x32cm-11x13in) s. pencil chl htd white. 5-Dec-3 Christie's, Rockefeller NY #114/R est:2000-3000
£3779	$6500	€5517	Grey hunter in a landscape (36x51cm-14x20in) s. indis d. pencil W/C htd white paper on card. 5-Dec-3 Christie's, Rockefeller NY #69/R est:4000-6000
£3800	$6916	€5548	Gone to sea, Glenthorne (50x34cm-20x13in) s.d.1936 W/C bodycol. 21-Jun-4 Bonhams, Bath #441/R est:2500-3000
£4000	$6800	€5840	Mist (31x35cm-12x14in) s.i.d.26 W/C gouache. 19-Nov-3 Sotheby's, Olympia #69/R est:2000-3000
£5000	$9100	€7300	Stag hunting on the North Devon coast (34x50cm-13x20in) s.d.1936 W/C bodycol. 21-Jun-4 Bonhams, Bath #439/R est:2500-3000
£6000	$10920	€8760	Huntsman and hounds on a clifftop (50x34cm-20x13in) s. W/C bodycol. 21-Jun-4 Bonhams, Bath #438/R est:2500-3000
£13000	$22880	€18980	Prairie Waltz. Bucking Bronco (32x22cm-13x9in) s.i.d.1903 W/C bodycol prov. two. 21-May-4 Christie's, London #69/R est:4000-6000
£16279	$28000	€23767	Ditch, Newmarket (36x51cm-14x20in) s.indis d.1932 W/C gouache htd white paper on card exhib. 5-Dec-3 Christie's, Rockefeller NY #1/R est:10000-15000

EDWARDS, Mary A (1894-1988) Australian

£304	$479	€444	Javanese child in pink (35x30cm-14x12in) s.indis.d. 1-Sep-3 Shapiro, Sydney #335 (A.D 750)
£760	$1194	€1110	Untitled, portrait of a girl holding an orange (58x57cm-23x22in) s.d.38 canvasboard. 1-Sep-3 Shapiro, Sydney #332/R (A.D 1870)
£760	$1194	€1110	Lakomololo (48x48cm-19x19in) s.d.36 canvasboard exhib. 1-Sep-3 Shapiro, Sydney #333/R (A.D 1870)
£2195	$3446	€3205	Untitled, Tjawan of Bali (56x48cm-22x19in) s.d.39 s.i.verso canvasboard. 1-Sep-3 Shapiro, Sydney #334/R est:2000-4000 (A.D 5400)

EDWARDS, McLean (1972-) Australian

£486	$782	€710	Head of a man (41x30cm-16x12in) s.d.2001 verso. 25-Aug-3 Sotheby's, Paddington #272/R est:1200-1500 (A.D 1200)
£1057	$1659	€1533	Whiskey bottle (90x70cm-35x28in) prov. 26-Aug-3 Christie's, Sydney #230/R est:2500-3500 (A.D 2600)
£2049	$3237	€2992	Silly boy (38x38cm-15x15in) s.d.1996 verso. 2-Sep-3 Deutscher-Menzies, Melbourne #250/R est:2500-3500 (A.D 5000)
£3099	$5269	€4525	For Elanor (76x60cm-30x24in) i.d.1999 verso. 29-Oct-3 Lawson Menzies, Sydney #6/R est:2500-4500 (A.D 7500)
£3617	$6149	€5281	Portrait with still life (51x40cm-20x16in) s.d.95 verso prov. 25-Nov-3 Christie's, Melbourne #4/R est:7000-10000 (A.D 8500)
£3894	$6152	€5685	Head - hotel (79x60cm-31x24in) s.i.d.1997 verso prov. 2-Sep-3 Deutscher-Menzies, Melbourne #2/R est:5000-8000 (A.D 9500)
£4979	$8315	€7469	Man with camera and still life (121x84cm-48x33in) s.verso. 27-Oct-3 Goodman, Sydney #30/R est:16000-20000 (A.D 12000)
£7627	$12966	€11135	Mother and Son (100x100cm-39x39in) exhib. 24-Nov-3 Sotheby's, Melbourne #23/R est:18000-22000 (A.D 18000)
£9787	$16638	€14289	Border guard (183x122cm-72x48in) s.i.verso board exhib.prov. 25-Nov-3 Christie's, Melbourne #26/R est:15000-20000 (A.D 23000)
£10744	$19876	€15686	Man with beast 2000 (120x180cm-47x71in) board diptych prov.exhib. 10-Mar-4 Deutscher-Menzies, Melbourne #10/R est:12000-16000 (A.D 26000)
£11382	$17870	€16504	Lamplight (147x96cm-58x38in) s.i.d.98 verso prov.exhib. 26-Aug-3 Christie's, Sydney #53/R est:15000-20000 (A.D 28000)
£13617	$23149	€19881	Rent (180x250cm-71x98in) painted 2001 prov. 26-Nov-3 Deutscher-Menzies, Melbourne #6/R est:18000-24000 (A.D 32000)

EDWARDS, Melvin (1937-) American

Sculpture

£4294	$7000	€6269	Song that comes to mind (38x28x20cm-15x11x8in) s.i.d.92 verso welded steel prov.exhib. 23-Sep-3 Christie's, Rockefeller NY #30/R est:4000-6000

EDWARDS, Shirley (20th C) Canadian

£356	$615	€520	Female nude (58x91cm-23x36in) 9-Dec-3 Maynards, Vancouver #264 (C.D 800)

EDWARDS, Simon (20th C) New Zealander?

£797	$1291	€1156	Early evening, Arthurs Pass (54x36cm-21x14in) s.d.2002 board. 31-Jul-3 International Art Centre, Auckland #95/R est:1000-2000 (NZ.D 2200)
£815	$1321	€1182	Peninsula (53x72cm-21x28in) s.d.2001 canvasboard exhib. 31-Jul-3 International Art Centre, Auckland #11/R est:2500-3500 (NZ.D 2250)
£1429	$2629	€2086	Light plain (91x121cm-36x48in) s.d.2001 acrylic oil prov. 25-Mar-4 International Art Centre, Auckland #93/R est:3800-4800 (NZ.D 4000)

EDWARDS, T (fl.1816) ?

£3400	$6358	€5100	Ware Reform Festival, 25th July 1832 (56x69cm-22x27in) i.verso. 22-Jul-4 Gorringes, Lewes #2018/R est:1000-1500

EDWARDSON, Laurence C (1904-1995) American

£663	$1200	€968	Lanesville, Rockport (46x61cm-18x24in) s. s.i.d.1960 verso masonite. 3-Apr-4 Neal Auction Company, New Orleans #923/R est:1200-1800
£872	$1500	€1273	December in Georgia (58x74cm-23x29in) s. s.i.d.1964 verso masonite. 6-Dec-3 Neal Auction Company, New Orleans #594/R est:1200-1800
£872	$1500	€1273	Eastern Point Light, Gloucester, Massachusetts (48x28cm-19x11in) s. s.i.verso. 6-Dec-3 Neal Auction Company, New Orleans #596 est:1200-1800
£1512	$2600	€2208	Spring, Westwego Canal, New Orleans (58x74cm-23x29in) s. s.i.verso masonite. 6-Dec-3 Neal Auction Company, New Orleans #595 est:1200-1800

EDY-LEGRAND, Edouard Léon Louis (1892-1970) French

£2867	$5189	€4300	Marocains pres d'une table verte (52x65cm-20x26in) s.i.d.31 or 34 cardboard prov. 31-Mar-4 Sotheby's, Paris #149/R est:2000-3000

£4577 $8011 €6500 Retour de peche (56x69cm-22x27in) i. s.verso peint lacquer gold engraved panel. 19-Dec-3 Delvaux, Paris #36/R est:3800-4000
£4698 $8315 €7000 Femme blonde a poitrine nue (73x60cm-29x24in) s. 27-Apr-4 Artcurial Briest, Paris #141/R est:4000-5000
£14184 $23688 €20000 La halte des cavaliers (65x100cm-26x39in) s. cardboard. 16-Jun-3 Gros & Delettrez, Paris #40/R est:15000-18000
£16549 $26479 €23500 Femme assise (100x80cm-39x31in) s. 20-Sep-3 Compagnie Marocaine des Objets d'Art, Casablanca #152/R
£18310 $29296 €26000 La famille a la terrasse (60x105cm-24x41in) s. panel. 20-Sep-3 Compagnie Marocaine des Objets d'Art, Casablanca #127/R
£19366 $30986 €27500 Kasbah (75x105cm-30x41in) s. panel. 20-Sep-3 Compagnie Marocaine des Objets d'Art, Casablanca #97/R
Works on paper
£2128 $3553 €3000 Portrait de Folle (27x20cm-11x8in) s.d.31 mars 1953 pen W/C dr prov.exhib. 16-Jun-3 Gros & Delettrez, Paris #20/R est:3000-4000
£2979 $4974 €4200 Casbahs de l'Atlas (64x33cm-25x13in) studio st. W/C dr exec.c.1939 prov.exhib. 16-Jun-3 Gros & Delettrez, Paris #19/R est:3000-4000

EDZARD, Dietz (1893-1963) German
£419 $700 €612 New hat (15x10cm-6x4in) s. canvasboard. 16-Nov-3 William Jenack, New York #250
£539 $900 €787 Jeune femme a la cravatte (46x38cm-18x15in) st.sig. i.d.1932 verso prov. 7-Oct-3 Sotheby's, New York #297
£599 $1000 €875 Portrait (38x30cm-15x12in) s. 19-Oct-3 Bonhams & Butterfields, Los Angeles #7057/R
£738 $1358 €1100 Dancer in wardrobe (43x33cm-17x13in) s. board. 26-Mar-4 Bolland & Marotz, Bremen #663/R
£898 $1500 €1311 Liliane (46x38cm-18x15in) s.d.30 i.d.1929 verso prov. 7-Oct-3 Sotheby's, New York #296 est:2500-3500
£919 $1700 €1342 Serveuse II (25x12cm-10x5in) init. canvas on panel prov. 12-Feb-4 Sotheby's, New York #87/R est:500-700
£919 $1700 €1342 Maria Lani (36x23cm-14x9in) s.i.d.1930 verso prov. 15-Jul-4 Sotheby's, New York #92 est:600-900
£1022 $1900 €1492 Still life of roses and calla lily in white vase (69x43cm-27x17in) s. 3-Mar-4 Alderfer's, Hatfield #314/R est:3000-5000
£1078 $1800 €1574 Etude pour Le Bar (58x44cm-23x17in) st.sig. i.d.1930 verso prov. 7-Oct-3 Sotheby's, New York #298 est:3000-5000
£1227 $2000 €1791 Femme masquee portant une fleur (81x48cm-32x19in) s. prov. 25-Sep-3 Christie's, Rockefeller NY #533/R est:3000-4000
£1800 $2862 €2610 Jeune garcon aux cheveux noirs (24x19cm-9x7in) init.i.d.26 prov. 11-Sep-3 Christie's, Kensington #46/R est:1500-2000
£2654 $4750 €3875 Lady on a Parisian balcony (60x74cm-24x29in) s. 21-Mar-4 Bonhams & Butterfields, Los Angeles #7332/R est:2500-3500
£3667 $6747 €5500 Lady with a pink umbrella (86x66cm-34x26in) s. 9-Jun-4 Christie's, Amsterdam #74/R est:4000-6000
£4000 $7240 €5840 Promenade du matin (61x45cm-24x18in) prov. 1-Apr-4 Christie's, Kensington #40/R est:4000-6000
£6135 $10000 €8957 Danseuses et harlequin (65x81cm-26x32in) s. 25-Sep-3 Christie's, Rockefeller NY #516/R est:10000-15000
£7000 $12670 €10220 Chanteuse (84x52cm-33x20in) s. prov. 1-Apr-4 Christie's, Kensington #42/R est:4000-6000
£9000 $16560 €13140 Angelica au theatre (60x73cm-24x29in) s. prov. 24-Mar-4 Sotheby's, Olympia #55/R est:5000-7000
£10270 $19000 €14994 Place de la Concorde (81x64cm-32x25in) s. 12-Feb-4 Sotheby's, New York #39/R est:12000-18000

EECHAUT, C (19th C) ?
£1500 $2355 €2175 Cooking the catch (49x41cm-19x16in) s.d.1855 panel. 28-Aug-3 Christie's, Kensington #71/R est:1500-2000

EECKHOUDT, Jean van den (1875-1946) Belgian
£476 $852 €700 Nature morte aux poires (58x50cm-23x20in) mono.d.45. 16-Mar-4 Vanderkindere, Brussels #37
£1119 $1902 €1600 Vase de roses (43x34cm-17x13in) mono.d.1938 cardboard. 1-Dec-3 Palais de Beaux Arts, Brussels #328/R est:1000-1500
£1867 $3416 €2800 Autoportrait (117x79cm-46x31in) mono.d.43 prov. 7-Jun-4 Palais de Beaux Arts, Brussels #317/R est:3000-4000
Works on paper
£1333 $2387 €2000 Deux enfants (34x36cm-13x14in) s.d.1909 pastel. 15-May-4 De Vuyst, Lokeren #342/R est:2200-2400

EECKHOUT, Gerbrand van den (1621-1674) Dutch
£27778 $50000 €40556 Volumnia pleading with her son to spare Rome (207x170cm-81x67in) s.d.1674 prov.lit. 22-Jan-4 Sotheby's, New York #8/R est:60000-80000
£36000 $64440 €54000 Portrait of man (81x65cm-32x26in) s.d.1646. 16-May-4 other European Auctioneer #22

EECKHOUT, Gerbrand van den (attrib) (1621-1674) Dutch
£2685 $4940 €4000 Drummer (62x48cm-24x19in) panel lit. 25-Mar-4 Karlheinz Kaupp, Staufen #2238/R est:4000

EECKHOUT, Jakob Joseph (1793-1861) Flemish
£720 $1224 €1051 Fisherfolk on the shore (99x77cm-39x30in) 29-Oct-3 Bonhams, Chester #493

EECKHOUT, Jakob Joseph and SCHELFHOUT, Andreas (19th C) Flemish/Dutch
£14000 $23800 €20440 Wedding feast (53x66cm-21x26in) s.d.1826 panel. 4-Nov-3 Bristol Auction Rooms #532/R est:2000-3000

EECKHOUT, Victor (1821-1879) Flemish
£867 $1551 €1300 Interieur d'auberge anime (39x53cm-15x21in) s. panel. 11-May-4 Vanderkindere, Brussels #162
Works on paper
£537 $993 €800 Ruelles a Tanger (19x28cm-7x11in) one s.i.d.21 sept 1869 W/C pair. 15-Mar-4 Gros & Delettrez, Paris #32/R
£738 $1366 €1100 La priere du soir, Tanger, Maroc (18x25cm-7x10in) s.i.d.1879 graphite. 15-Mar-4 Gros & Delettrez, Paris #187/R

EEDEN, Frits van (1944-) Dutch
£342 $582 €500 Composition with heads of horses (100x120cm-39x47in) s. d.1979 verso panel. 5-Nov-3 Vendue Huis, Gravenhage #456/R
£1189 $2045 €1700 Composition (150x120cm-59x47in) s. 8-Dec-3 Glerum, Amsterdam #160/R est:1200-1500

EEDEN, Marcel van (1965-) Dutch
Works on paper
£385 $662 €550 Petrol station (18x14cm-7x6in) s.d.1993 pencil prov. 8-Dec-3 Glerum, Amsterdam #415/R

EEKERKIK, Romeo (1923-1983) North American
Sculpture
£1712 $2910 €2500 Igloo with Inuit dogs, Inuk, komatik with seal, harpoon and gun (30cm-12in) antler whalebone base exec.c.1960. 3-Nov-3 Waddingtons, Toronto #369/R est:3000-4000 (C.D 3800)

EEKMAN, Nicolaas (1889-1973) Belgian
£533 $955 €800 L'homme roux (32x19cm-13x7in) s. s.i.verso panel. 15-May-4 De Vuyst, Lokeren #122
£933 $1671 €1400 Les hommes (73x52cm-29x20in) s. 16-May-4 MonsAntic, Maisieres #411
£1064 $1777 €1500 Les roches bleues (33x41cm-13x16in) s. panel. 20-Oct-3 Bernaerts, Antwerp #269/R est:2000-2500
£1333 $2440 €2000 Pecheur d'anguilles (41x33cm-16x13in) s.d.49. 7-Jun-4 Palais de Beaux Arts, Brussels #59/R est:1500-2000
£1600 $2880 €2400 Seated nude (55x33cm-22x13in) s. panel. 26-Apr-4 Bernaerts, Antwerp #800 est:2000-3000
£1793 $3317 €2600 Au coin du poele (64x52cm-25x20in) s.d. paper on board. 19-Jan-4 Horta, Bruxelles #72 est:2000-3000
£1818 $3091 €2600 Village de pecheurs (54x73cm-21x29in) s. 1-Dec-3 Palais de Beaux Arts, Brussels #60/R est:2500-3500
Works on paper
£268 $497 €400 Vieil homme a la canne et deux chats (39x24cm-15x9in) s.d.43 pen W/C. 13-Mar-4 De Vuyst, Lokeren #130
£347 $580 €500 Pecheur (58x44cm-23x17in) s. W/C. 21-Oct-3 Campo, Vlaamse Kaai #428
£537 $993 €800 Monniken (40x40cm-16x16in) s.d.16 pastel. 15-Mar-4 Sotheby's, Amsterdam #191/R
£667 $1227 €1000 Mere et enfant dans un interieur (53x36cm-21x14in) s.d.1927 graphite col crayon. 14-Jun-4 Horta, Bruxelles #362
£1133 $2029 €1700 Trois estropies (76x98cm-30x39in) s.d.19 black chk. 15-May-4 De Vuyst, Lokeren #121 est:1300-1500

EEL, Knud (1914-1967) Danish
£543 $972 €793 Rainbow (110x136cm-43x54in) init.d.1966 exhib. 10-May-4 Rasmussen, Vejle #693/R (D.KR 6000)
£833 $1349 €1208 Coastal landscape with shipwreck, women and children in foreground (90x121cm-35x48in) s.d.1957 exhib. 4-Aug-3 Rasmussen, Vejle #600/R (D.KR 8700)

EELKEMA, Elke Jelles (1788-1839) Dutch
£15000 $24000 €21750 Summer flowers in a vase on a ledge. Fruit on a marble ledge (57x46cm-22x18in) s. pair. 18-Sep-3 Christie's, Kensington #43/R est:15000-20000

EELSINGH, Stien (1903-1964) Dutch
Works on paper
£2667 $4880 €4000 Young female farmer by two grazing horses (48x63cm-19x25in) gouache. 7-Jun-4 Glerum, Amsterdam #101/R est:3000-4000

EEMANS, Marc (1907-1998) Belgian
£284 $460 €400 Friendship of the sea (33x46cm-13x18in) s.d.69. 23-May-3 Altus, Berlin #524/R
£629 $1051 €900 Composition (26x17cm-10x7in) board. 11-Oct-3 De Vuyst, Lokeren #136
£3132 $5418 €4573 Composition (46x54cm-18x21in) s.d.24 fibreboard. 12-Dec-3 Kieselbach, Budapest #109/R (H.F 1200000)
£9396 $16255 €13718 Leaves - the frameof the flesh (60x72cm-24x28in) s.d.28. 12-Dec-3 Kieselbach, Budapest #104/R (H.F 3600000)
£13050 $22577 €19053 Variations of a masked ball (81x100cm-32x39in) s.d.1971 verso. 12-Dec-3 Kieselbach, Budapest #105/R (H.F 5000000)
£54000 $99360 €78840 La veste de Hans Arp (61x50cm-24x20in) s.d.28 i.verso board. 24-Mar-4 Sotheby's, Olympia #154/R est:4000-6000
Works on paper
£2400 $4392 €3600 Composition surrealiste (55x44cm-22x17in) s.d.29 mixed media. 7-Jun-4 Palais de Beaux Arts, Brussels #60/R est:800-1200

EEMONT, Adrien van (attrib) (c.1627-1662) Dutch
£2333 $4247 €3500 Landscape with shepherds and their flocks (42x65cm-17x26in) panel. 1-Jul-4 Van Ham, Cologne #1093/R est:3500
£5040 $8719 €7358 Italianate landscape with drovers and travelers resting beside a well (73x62cm-29x24in) 9-Dec-3 Sotheby's, Olympia #358/R est:4000-6000

EERELMAN, Otto (1839-1926) Dutch
£1316 $2421 €2000 Study of boxers (67x80cm-26x31in) s.d.1872 canvas on board. 28-Jun-4 Sotheby's, Amsterdam #34/R est:2000-3000
£1800 $3276 €2628 Knock at the cottage door (55x38cm-22x15in) s. indis d. panel. 16-Jun-4 Christie's, Kensington #219/R est:2000-3000
£2013 $3725 €3000 Dog (22x30cm-9x12in) s. panel. 15-Mar-4 Sotheby's, Amsterdam #63/R est:800-1200
£5333 $9600 €8000 Duitse dwerg pinchers (29x45cm-11x18in) s. i.stretcher. 21-Apr-4 Christie's, Amsterdam #226/R est:8000-12000
£6000 $10200 €8760 Bianco, a hound at a kennel door (46x37cm-18x15in) s.i. 27-Nov-3 Christie's, Kensington #387/R est:6000-8000

£7746 $13401 €11000 Dog sitting (100x74cm-39x29in) s. 13-Dec-3 De Vuyst, Lokeren #537/R est:12000-15000
£11111 $18889 €16000 Two pointers - Hans and Spot on the heath (60x90cm-24x35in) s. 28-Oct-3 Christie's, Amsterdam #49/R est:6000-8000
£14667 $26400 €22000 Saint Bernard puppy (27x35cm-11x14in) s. 20-Apr-4 Sotheby's, Amsterdam #167/R est:20000-30000
Works on paper
£526 $968 €800 Studies of horses in motion (32x48cm-13x19in) init.i.d.3 pencil. 22-Jun-4 Christie's, Amsterdam #30/R
£738 $1358 €1100 Dog's head (6x9cm-2x4in) s.d.79 W/C. 29-Mar-4 Glerum, Amsterdam #164
£1316 $2421 €2000 Amalia Carre-Salamonskye (35x52cm-14x20in) init. pencil black chk chl pastel. 22-Jun-4 Christie's, Amsterdam #40/R est:2000-3000
£6250 $10438 €9000 At the circus (39x49cm-15x19in) s. W/C prov.exhib.lit. 21-Oct-3 Sotheby's, Amsterdam #48/R est:10000-15000

EFFINGER VON WILDEGG, Ludwig Rudolf (1803-1872) Swiss
Works on paper
£300 $519 €438 Bust of a woman (50x38cm-20x15in) s.d.1823 black lead brown wash after the Antique. 12-Dec-3 Christie's, Kensington #566

EFRAT, Beni (1936-) Israeli
Sculpture
£1816 $3250 €2651 Broadcast (22cm-9in) s.d.1976 num.5/5 steel painted aluminum. 18-Mar-4 Sotheby's, New York #64/R est:3000-4000

EGAN, Felim (1952-) British?
£1267 $2293 €1900 Painting with blue triangles (40x40cm-16x16in) s.d.89 verso acrylic mixed media prov. 31-Mar-4 James Adam, Dublin #89/R est:2000-3000
£1733 $3137 €2600 Woodnote (48x48cm-19x19in) s.d.03 verso board. 31-Mar-4 James Adam, Dublin #88/R est:2000-3000
£2000 $3620 €3000 Squarings (61x61cm-24x24in) s.d.89 verso acrylic mixed media prov. 31-Mar-4 James Adam, Dublin #90/R est:3000-5000
£2000 $3620 €3000 Dance series VIII (51x51cm-20x20in) s.d.88 acrylic paper prov. 30-Mar-4 De Veres Art Auctions, Dublin #73/R est:3000-4000
£2148 $3801 €3200 Woodnote (48x48cm-19x19in) s.d.2003 verso acrylic mixed media wood prov. 27-Apr-4 Whyte's, Dublin #181/R est:2000-3000
£2676 $4282 €3800 Grey diptych with four lines (81x41cm-32x16in) s.d.1983 verso acrylic diptych exhib. 16-Sep-3 Whyte's, Dublin #48/R est:3000-4000
£2703 $5108 €4000 Blue painting (75x75cm-30x30in) s.d.2003 verso. 17-Feb-4 Whyte's, Dublin #35/R est:4000-5000
£3289 $6053 €5000 Composition (75x77cm-30x30in) s.d.2001 verso acrylic. 22-Jun-4 De Veres Art Auctions, Dublin #133/R est:5000-6000
£4133 $7481 €6200 Woodnote (48x48cm-19x19in) s.d.03 verso board. 31-Mar-4 James Adam, Dublin #91/R est:2000-3000
Works on paper
£467 $845 €700 Untitled (54x99cm-21x39in) s.d.81 mixed media. 30-Mar-4 De Veres Art Auctions, Dublin #207
£811 $1532 €1200 Six red lines (46x38cm-18x15in) s.d.1991 W/C. 17-Feb-4 Whyte's, Dublin #89/R est:1000-1500
£4133 $7481 €6200 Untitled (77x77cm-30x30in) s.d.96 verso mixed media prov. 30-Mar-4 De Veres Art Auctions, Dublin #145/R est:4000-6000
£5035 $8559 €7200 Intertidal note (85x85cm-33x33in) s.i. d.1995 verso mixed media. 25-Nov-3 De Veres Art Auctions, Dublin #147/R est:4000-6000

EGAN, Orla (?) Irish
£461 $847 €700 Cutting the corn, Church Hill, County Donegal (21x24cm-8x9in) s.i.verso board. 22-Jun-4 De Veres Art Auctions, Dublin #180/R

EGE, Mogens (1892-1946) Danish
£473 $846 €691 Stranded at Skagen's point (100x138cm-39x54in) s. 12-Jan-4 Rasmussen, Vejle #48/R (D.KR 5000)

EGEDIUS, Ambrosius (20th C) Norwegian?
£307 $491 €445 Two goats at the cheese farm (66x71cm-26x28in) s,. 22-Sep-3 Blomqvist, Lysaker #1040 (N.KR 3600)

EGEDIUS, Halfdan (1877-1899) Norwegian
£4003 $7166 €5844 Interior scene with girl (51x36cm-20x14in) exhib. 22-Mar-4 Blomqvist, Oslo #323/R est:80000-100000 (N.KR 50000)
£6117 $10950 €8931 Stabbur - storehouse on pillars (24x30cm-9x12in) init.d.92 paper on panel. 25-May-4 Grev Wedels Plass, Oslo #65/R est:80000-100000 (N.KR 75000)

EGELI, Arthur (20th C) American
£270 $475 €394 Blue boating, Provincetown Harbour (25x46cm-10x18in) s. 3-Jan-4 Outer Cape Auctions, Provincetown #122/R
£500 $850 €730 Sunset over Provincetown harbour (74x91cm-29x36in) s. 9-Nov-3 Outer Cape Auctions, Provincetown #95/R

EGGEMEYER, Maude (1877-1934) American
£3380 $6050 €4935 House on Red Bud Hill (41x51cm-16x20in) init.d.1915. 19-Mar-4 Aspire, Cleveland #16/R est:2000-3000

EGGENHOFER, Nick (1897-1985) American
£2515 $4200 €3672 Buffalo hunt (30x43cm-12x17in) s. W/C gouache pencil board. 9-Oct-3 Christie's, Rockefeller NY #78/R est:4000-6000
Works on paper
£1765 $3000 €2577 Trail diver (41x33cm-16x13in) gouache. 1-Nov-3 Altermann Galleries, Santa Fe #46
£2118 $3600 €3092 Montana cowboy (30x23cm-12x9in) gouache W/C. 1-Nov-3 Altermann Galleries, Santa Fe #47
£2674 $5000 €3904 Plains scout (28x25cm-11x10in) s. gouache. 24-Jul-4 Coeur d'Alene, Hayden #223/R est:3000-5000

EGGENSCHWILER, Franz (1930-) Swiss
Sculpture
£2752 $4596 €3990 Untitled (28x38x28cm-11x15x11in) stone bronze wood iron. 19-Jun-3 Kornfeld, Bern #333/R est:7500 (S.FR 6000)

EGGER, Hans (1908-) Swiss
£857 $1371 €1243 Two clowns and female acrobat (76x30cm-30x12in) s. 15-May-3 Stuker, Bern #1168/R (S.FR 1800)

EGGER, Jean (1897-1934) Austrian
£52448 $89161 €75000 St Martin am Silberberg, Karnten (81x65cm-32x26in) s. prov. 26-Nov-3 Dorotheum, Vienna #41/R est:70000-100000

EGGER, John Konstantin (1908-) Swiss
£345 $624 €504 Sleeping woman (60x100cm-24x39in) panel prov. 31-Mar-4 Zurichsee Auktionen, Erlenbach #126/R (S.FR 800)

EGGER, Joseph (1897-1969) French
£271 $462 €396 Peonies (52x6cm-20x2in) s. 28-Nov-3 Zofingen, Switzerland #2978 (S.FR 600)

EGGER-LIENZ, Albin (1868-1926) Austrian
£6040 $10691 €9000 Sketch for Corpus Christi procession (17x28cm-7x11in) s.i.d.1906 board lit. 28-Apr-4 Wiener Kunst Auktionen, Vienna #111/R est:5000-12000
£22378 $38042 €32000 In front of the mirror (57x37cm-22x15in) s. prov. 28-Nov-3 Wiener Kunst Auktionen, Vienna #459/R est:25000-50000
Works on paper
£1053 $1937 €1600 Study of a house (20x12cm-8x5in) s. pencil double-sided. 22-Jun-4 Wiener Kunst Auktionen, Vienna #47/R est:1200
£1447 $2663 €2200 Josef Speckbacher (24x17cm-9x7in) s.i.d.1897 pencil. 22-Jun-4 Wiener Kunst Auktionen, Vienna #46/R est:1000
£8725 $15443 €13000 Man stoking flames watched by women (46x69cm-18x27in) s.d.05 pastel lit. 28-Apr-4 Wiener Kunst Auktionen, Vienna #112/R est:10000-20000
£14685 $24965 €21000 Cherso (47x66cm-19x26in) pastel. 25-Nov-3 Hassfurther, Vienna #30/R est:8000-10000
£41958 $71329 €60000 Man sharpening scythe (51x62cm-20x24in) s. W/C paper on board prov. 26-Nov-3 Dorotheum, Vienna #40/R est:20000-28000

EGGERS, George William (1883-1958) American
£215 $400 €314 Landscape with stream (41x51cm-16x20in) s. painted c.1930. 7-Mar-4 Treadway Gallery, Cincinnati #622/R

EGGERS, Peter (1855-1907) Swedish
£375 $625 €548 Seascape with sailing vessel by rocks and lighthouse (58x97cm-23x38in) s.d.1885. 25-Oct-3 Rasmussen, Havnen #2545/R (D.KR 4000)

EGGINTON, Frank (1908-1990) British
£1800 $3366 €2700 Irish lakeland scene (51x74cm-20x29in) s. 21-Jul-4 John Nicholson, Haslemere #121/R est:1800-2000
£2685 $4805 €4000 Near Gortahork, Co. Donegal (61x92cm-24x36in) s. 26-May-4 James Adam, Dublin #112/R est:4000-6000
Works on paper
£338 $574 €493 Dumanus Bay (20x27cm-8x11in) s. i.verso W/C. 21-Nov-3 Walker's, Ottawa #238/R (C.D 750)
£500 $800 €730 Landscape with house (38x51cm-15x20in) s. W/C exec. c.1960. 20-Sep-3 Bunte, Elgin #1298
£563 $975 €800 Mullaghberg Strand, Co Donegal (37x53cm-15x21in) s. W/C prov. 10-Dec-3 Bonhams & James Adam, Dublin #191/R
£699 $1189 €1000 Still life of flowers (25x37cm-10x15in) s. W/C prov. 18-Nov-3 Whyte's, Dublin #47/R
£699 $1189 €1000 A Connemara Lough, near Oughterard, County Galway (38x53cm-15x21in) s.d.1981 i.verso W/C. 18-Nov-3 Whyte's, Dublin #192/R
£800 $1360 €1168 Bog near Parke, County Mayo (36x52cm-14x20in) s. W/C. 1-Dec-3 Bonhams, Bath #49/R
£800 $1376 €1168 Cabbage patch near Kilkeel, County Down (28x35cm-11x14in) s. W/C. 3-Dec-3 John Ross, Belfast #112
£800 $1456 €1168 Dunfanaghy Strand and Muckish, Donegal (37x53cm-15x21in) s.d.75 pencil W/C prov. 1-Jul-4 Christie's, Kensington #446/R
£839 $1427 €1200 Lough Salt Mountain from Ards, County Donegal (38x55cm-15x22in) s.d.1980 i.verso W/C. 18-Nov-3 Whyte's, Dublin #194/R
£850 $1394 €1241 Connemara, County Galway (36x26cm-14x10in) s. i.verso W/C. 3-Jun-3 Fellows & Sons, Birmingham #176/R
£946 $1788 €1400 Castle coole bridge, County Fermanagh (25x36cm-10x14in) s.d.1935 i.verso W/C. 17-Feb-4 Whyte's, Dublin #174 est:1000-1200
£950 $1758 €1387 Winter trees (38x56cm-15x22in) s. W/C. 11-Mar-4 John Ross, Belfast #831
£1000 $1810 €1500 Soft day near Falcarragh, Co Donnegal (35x52cm-14x20in) s.i.verso W/C prov. 31-Mar-4 James Adam, Dublin #111/R est:1500-2000
£1000 $1810 €1500 Landscape, possibly west of Ireland (38x54cm-15x21in) s. W/C. 30-Mar-4 De Veres Art Auctions, Dublin #121/R est:1400-1800
£1000 $1830 €1460 Turnip field, early morning, Co. Down (35x50cm-14x20in) s. W/C. 2-Jun-4 John Ross, Belfast #212 est:1250-1500
£1007 $1802 €1500 Gap of Dunloe, Killarney (53x74cm-21x29in) s. W/C. 26-May-4 James Adam, Dublin #97/R est:1500-2500
£1050 $1806 €1533 Coastal inlet, County Mayo (38x50cm-15x20in) s. W/C. 3-Dec-3 John Ross, Belfast #31 est:1200-1400
£1067 $1931 €1600 Among the Sperrins, Co Londonderry (35x52cm-14x20in) s.d.April 1980 verso W/C prov. 31-Mar-4 James Adam, Dublin #56/R est:1200-1800
£1100 $2035 €1606 Lough Agher river, County Donegal (38x53cm-15x21in) s. W/C. 11-Mar-4 John Ross, Belfast #832
£1100 $1969 €1606 Quarterland Bay, Strangford Lough, Co Down (37x52cm-15x20in) s. pencil W/C. 14-May-4 Christie's, Kensington #344/R est:1000-1500
£1100 $1969 €1606 Near Kilkeel, Co Down (26x35cm-10x14in) s. pencil W/C. 14-May-4 Christie's, Kensington #346/R est:800-1200
£1100 $2002 €1606 Ploughed field Co. Tyrone (36x52cm-14x20in) s. pencil W/C prov. 1-Jul-4 Mellors & Kirk, Nottingham #672/R est:800-1000

£1200	$2172	€1800	Cottage near Ballinrobe, Co Mayo (38x54cm-15x21in) s. W/C. 31-Mar-4 James Adam, Dublin #98/R est:1000-1500
£1200	$2148	€1752	Cottage pool, Cashla River, Co Galway (26x36cm-10x14in) s. pencil W/C. 14-May-4 Christie's, Kensington #345/R est:800-1200
£1300	$2405	€1898	Black face sheep, Connemara (37x53cm-15x21in) s.d.85 W/C. 14-Jul-4 Bonhams, Chester #468/R est:1400-1800
£1300	$2431	€1898	Going to the market on autumn day (37x52cm-15x20in) s. W/C. 22-Jul-4 Martel Maides, Guernsey #227
£1458	$2377	€2100	Melmore, from Horn Head, Co Donegal (37x53cm-15x21in) s. W/C. 24-Sep-3 James Adam, Dublin #140/R est:1750-2200
£1486	$2809	€2200	Dundonald, County Down (37x53cm-15x21in) s. W/C. 17-Feb-4 Whyte's, Dublin #137/R est:1800-2200
£1500	$2505	€2190	Scrabo and Ballydrain, Co. Down (37x53cm-15x21in) s. W/C. 16-Oct-3 Bonhams, Edinburgh #127 est:1000-1500
£1611	$2883	€2400	Donegal cottage (37x53cm-15x21in) s. W/C. 26-May-4 James Adam, Dublin #113/R est:1500-2000
£1800	$3276	€2628	Snow scene, Dumfanaghy, Co Donegal (36x53cm-14x21in) s. W/C prov. 16-Jun-4 John Nicholson, Haslemere #708/R est:2000-3000
£2000	$3260	€2920	Wet day near Belmullet Co. Mayo (37x53cm-15x21in) s. pencil W/C prov. 25-Sep-3 Mellors & Kirk, Nottingham #707/R est:1500-2000
£2013	$3604	€3000	Drive and lodge of a country estate (53x76cm-21x30in) s. indis d. W/C. 26-May-4 James Adam, Dublin #115/R est:3500-4500
£2083	$3396	€3000	Laragh, Kenmare River, Co Kerry (53x75cm-21x30in) s. W/C. 24-Sep-3 James Adam, Dublin #99/R est:2000-3000
£2100	$3906	€3066	Landscape with cottage and figure standing beside a hayrick (52x75cm-20x30in) s.verso W/C. 4-Mar-4 Clevedon Sale Rooms #110/R est:1200-1800
£2133	$3861	€3200	Glengarriff (53x74cm-21x29in) s. W/C. 31-Mar-4 James Adam, Dublin #97/R est:2500-3500
£2200	$4114	€3212	Above Cookstown, Co Tyrone (14x20cm-6x8in) s. W/C. 25-Feb-4 Mallams, Oxford #107/R est:2000-3000
£2238	$3804	€3200	Bengorm, near Westport, Co. Mayo (54x77cm-21x30in) s.i. W/C. 25-Nov-3 De Veres Art Auctions, Dublin #218/R est:2000-3000
£2400	$4296	€3504	Cottage and peat gatherer (24x34cm-9x13in) s.d.1933 pencil W/C. 14-May-4 Christie's, Kensington #347/R est:1500-2500
£2400	$4392	€3504	Showery day, Connemara (36x51cm-14x20in) s. W/C over traces pencil. 8-Jul-4 Lawrence, Crewkerne #1583/R est:800-1200
£2550	$4565	€3800	Mountain landscape with sheep (53x76cm-21x30in) s. W/C prov. 26-May-4 James Adam, Dublin #190/R est:2000-3000
£2600	$4654	€3796	Cromane, Co Kerry (26x36cm-10x14in) s. i.verso W/C bodycol. 14-May-4 Christie's, Kensington #343/R est:800-1200
£2900	$4727	€4234	Cottage in Co. Mayo (38x53cm-15x21in) s. pencil W/C prov. 25-Sep-3 Mellors & Kirk, Nottingham #706/R est:2000-3000
£3356	$5940	€5000	Waterville Lake, County Kerry. Meenish Island, Connemara (38x53cm-15x21in) one s. W/C prov.exhib. 27-Apr-4 Whyte's, Dublin #223/R est:4000-6000

EGGINTON, Robert (?) British?

£250	$415	€365	Rannoch Moor (40x76cm-16x30in) s. board. 1-Oct-3 John Ross, Belfast #94

EGGINTON, W (1875-1951) British

Works on paper

£540	$902	€788	Panoramic scene with folk on horse back. W/C. 18-Oct-3 Hogben, Folkstone #223

EGGINTON, Wycliffe (1875-1951) British

£450	$806	€657	In quiet solitude, Shetland Isles (36x51cm-14x20in) s.d.1899 i.verso. 11-May-4 Bonhams, Knightsbridge #158/R
£460	$842	€672	Devonshire country cottage (55x76cm-22x30in) s. 28-Jul-4 Hampton & Littlewood, Exeter #620/R

Works on paper

£280	$512	€409	Moorland scene (18x26cm-7x10in) s. W/C. 27-Jan-4 Bonhams, Knightsbridge #171/R
£310	$564	€453	Near Snowdon (24x34cm-9x13in) s. W/C. 21-Jun-4 Bonhams, Bath #329
£320	$582	€467	On the moors near Teignmouth (25x35cm-10x14in) s. W/C. 21-Jun-4 Bonhams, Bath #392
£320	$589	€467	In the Lledr Valley, North Wales (35x52cm-14x20in) s. W/C. 9-Jun-4 Wingetts, Wrexham #258
£400	$740	€584	End of a stormy day (18x25cm-7x10in) s. W/C. 10-Feb-4 David Lay, Penzance #234
£400	$728	€584	Off to new pastures (25x38cm-10x15in) s. pencil W/C. 1-Jul-4 Christie's, Kensington #444/R
£420	$727	€613	Cloudy day, Dartmoor, Devon (36x53cm-14x21in) s. s.i.verso W/C. 10-Dec-3 Bonhams, Bury St Edmunds #527/R
£500	$915	€730	Perthshire Loch on a summer day (36x51cm-14x20in) s. W/C. 28-Jul-4 Mallams, Oxford #195
£570	$1010	€850	Mounted shepherd and flock (29x39cm-11x15in) s. W/C pencil. 27-Apr-4 Whyte's, Dublin #217/R
£600	$996	€876	Shrimpers on the beach, south Devon (34x53cm-13x21in) s. W/C. 2-Oct-3 Lane, Penzance #236
£620	$1066	€905	Cattle grazing (25x35cm-10x14in) s. W/C. 3-Dec-3 John Ross, Belfast #43
£633	$1146	€950	Glen Shee (36x52cm-14x20in) s. W/C. 31-Mar-4 James Adam, Dublin #120/R
£650	$1079	€949	Near Achsasheen (25x35cm-10x14in) s. W/C. 1-Oct-3 John Ross, Belfast #129
£650	$1209	€949	Mountain and river, Blackmount (36x53cm-14x21in) s. W/C prov. 4-Mar-4 Christie's, Kensington #164/R
£650	$1190	€949	Lough Arkraig (35x50cm-14x20in) s. W/C. 2-Jun-4 John Ross, Belfast #13
£700	$1281	€1022	Still life, pansies (35x50cm-14x20in) s. W/C. 2-Jun-4 John Ross, Belfast #203
£720	$1318	€1051	Bishopsteignton (53x73cm-21x29in) s.i.verso W/C. 28-Jul-4 Hampton & Littlewood, Exeter #586/R
£750	$1388	€1095	Driving sheep near Killin, Perthshire (35x53cm-14x21in) s. i.verso W/C. 14-Jul-4 Sotheby's, Olympia #115/R
£764	$1245	€1100	Cattle watering (35x54cm-14x21in) s. W/C. 24-Sep-3 James Adam, Dublin #21/R est:1000-1500
£900	$1611	€1314	Beach view (35x52cm-14x20in) s. W/C. 26-May-4 Sotheby's, Olympia #198/R est:1000-1500
£940	$1663	€1400	Horseman herding cattle along a bog road. Bogland with horse and foal (14x23cm-6x9in) s. W/C pair. 27-Apr-4 Whyte's, Dublin #218/R
£950	$1558	€1387	Sheep on the moor (35x50cm-14x20in) s. W/C. 4-Jun-3 John Ross, Belfast #129
£950	$1729	€1387	Beauly River. View from Beaufort Castle (36x53cm-14x21in) s. W/C pair ex. 1-Jul-4 Christie's, Kensington #445/R
£1338	$2315	€1900	Asking the way. Marshes (27x36cm-11x14in) s. W/C pair. 10-Dec-3 Bonhams & James Adam, Dublin #45/R est:2000-3000
£1812	$3244	€2700	Wild ponies. Gathering peat (51x76cm-20x30in) s. W/C pair. 26-May-4 James Adam, Dublin #114/R est:2500-3500

EGGLESTON, Benjamin (1867-1937) American

£296	$550	€432	Woodland landscape with birch trees (11x17cm-4x7in) board. 5-Mar-4 Skinner, Boston #470/R
£457	$850	€667	The plough horses (20x30cm-8x12in) board. 5-Mar-4 Skinner, Boston #472/R
£484	$900	€707	Coming winter (20x30cm-8x12in) panel. 5-Mar-4 Skinner, Boston #468/R
£1796	$3000	€2622	Landscape (41x61cm-16x24in) s.d.1915 prov. 23-Oct-3 Shannon's, Milford #189/R est:3000-5000
£5108	$9500	€7458	On the beach (25x33cm-10x13in) board. 5-Mar-4 Skinner, Boston #541/R est:300-500

EGGLESTON, William (1939-) American

Photographs

£1667	$3000	€2434	Untitled (20x30cm-8x12in) s.verso chromogenic print prov. 23-Apr-4 Phillips, New York #173/R est:3000-5000
£1739	$3200	€2539	Untitled, dark sky with blue ring (58x76cm-23x30in) Iris pring prov. 10-Jun-4 Phillips, New York #552/R est:3000-5000
£2065	$3800	€3015	Untitled, clouds, Kentucky (56x76cm-22x30in) Iris print prov. 10-Jun-4 Phillips, New York #550/R est:3000-5000
£2222	$4000	€3244	Vizcaya, Miami (34x51cm-13x20in) s.d.1985 chromogentic colour print prov.lit. 23-Apr-4 Phillips, New York #189/R est:4000-6000
£2800	$5152	€4088	51 Sign on phone poll (45x30cm-18x12in) s. dye transfer print exec 1965-74 edn 6/7 prov.lit. 24-Jun-4 Sotheby's, London #101/R est:3000-4000
£2800	$5152	€4088	Tall Cloud - Los Alamos (45x30cm-18x12in) s. dye transfer print exec 1965-74 edn 6/7 prov.lit. 24-Jun-4 Sotheby's, London #102/R est:3000-4000
£2874	$4800	€4196	St Simons Island, Georgia (25x37cm-10x15in) s. chromogenic col print exec.1978 prov.lit. 17-Oct-3 Phillips, New York #178/R est:4000-6000
£3778	$6800	€5516	Untitled (28x40cm-11x16in) s.i. num.4/10 dye transfer print prov.lit. 23-Apr-4 Phillips, New York #213/R est:6000-8000
£3778	$6800	€5516	Near the river at Greenville, Mississippi (30x45cm-12x18in) s. dye transfer print prov.lit. 23-Apr-4 Phillips, New York #218/R est:6000-8000
£4444	$8000	€6488	Untitled (23x35cm-9x14in) s. dye transfer print prov. 23-Apr-4 Phillips, New York #199/R est:8000-10000
£4889	$8800	€7138	Washington, D.C (37x56cm-15x22in) s. dye transfer print prov.lit. 23-Apr-4 Phillips, New York #215/R est:5000-7000
£5000	$9000	€7300	Untitled (37x55cm-15x22in) s. dye transfer print prov. 23-Apr-4 Phillips, New York #217/R est:9000-12000
£5689	$9500	€8306	Near Greenwood, Mississippi (30x45cm-12x18in) s.i. num.76.371 verso dye transfer print exec. 1979 prov. 17-Oct-3 Phillips, New York #28/R est:8000-12000
£6587	$11000	€9617	Eguin Palntation, near Minter City, Mississippi (31x46cm-12x18in) s.i.d.Spring 1973 verso num.4 dye transfer print prov. 17-Oct-3 Phillips, New York #31/R est:10000-15000
£7222	$13000	€10544	Memphis (43x29cm-17x11in) s. dye transfer print prov.lit. 23-Apr-4 Phillips, New York #40/R est:15000-20000
£8000	$14720	€11680	Webb Mississippi (36x55cm-14x22in) s. dye transfer print exec 1969 edn 7/9 prov. 24-Jun-4 Sotheby's, London #105/R est:8000-12000
£10180	$17000	€14863	Memphis, Tennessee (33x48cm-13x19in) s.verso dye transfer print exec.1971 prov.lit. 17-Oct-3 Phillips, New York #27/R est:10000-15000
£14444	$26000	€21088	Biloxi, Mississippi (31x46cm-12x18in) init.i.verso dye transfer print prov.lit. 23-Apr-4 Phillips, New York #39/R est:10000-15000
£17964	$30000	€26227	Southern suite (31x46cm-12x18in) s.i. num.76.325 verso dye transfer print exec.1979 prov.lit. 17-Oct-3 Phillips, New York #30/R est:12000-18000
£21469	$38000	€31345	Morton, Mississippi (34x23cm-13x9in) s. dye-transfer print printed c.1974 prov. 28-Apr-4 Sotheby's, New York #159/R est:1000-15000
£22599	$40000	€32995	Sumner, Mississippi, Cassidy Bayou (27x43cm-11x17in) s.d.1971 dye transfer print printed 1986 lit. 28-Apr-4 Sotheby's, New York #233/R est:20000-30000
£33898	$60000	€49491	Trouble waters (29x44cm-11x17in) s. num.30 15 dye transfer print prov.lit. 27-Apr-4 Christie's, Rockefeller NY #165/R est:50000-70000
£39548	$70000	€57740	Greenwood, Mississippi, red ceiling (29x45cm-11x18in) s.i.d.1980 verso photo lit. 28-Apr-4 Sotheby's, New York #234/R est:70000-100000
£52778	$95000	€77056	Graceland (37x56cm-15x22in) s. 11 dye transfer prints portfolio num.11 prov. 23-Apr-4 Phillips, New York #42/R est:90000-120000
£103889	$187000	€151678	Greenwood, Mississippi (31x47cm-12x19in) s.verso dye transfer print mounted on board prov.lit. 23-Apr-4 Phillips, New York #41/R est:100000-150000
£107784	$180000	€157365	Memphis (30x43cm-12x17in) s.d.1970 verso dye transfer print prov.lit. 17-Oct-3 Phillips, New York #29/R est:90000-120000

EGGLI, Johann Jakob (1812-1880) Swiss

Works on paper

£1719	$2923	€2510	Ossingen (36x49cm-14x19in) gouache. 19-Nov-3 Fischer, Luzern #2725/R est:3100-3300 (S.FR 3800)

EGGLI, Johann Jakob (attrib) (1812-1880) Swiss

Works on paper

£313	$509	€450	Rheinfall at Schaffhausen (24x37cm-9x15in) s. bears i. mixed media. 25-Sep-3 Dr Fritz Nagel, Stuttgart #1140/R

EGL, Herbert (1953-) German

£805	$1426	€1200	Untitled (160x200cm-63x79in) s.d. 1985. 30-Apr-4 Dr Fritz Nagel, Stuttgart #122/R

EGLAU, Max (1825-?) American

£4070	$7000	€5942	Industry on the Hudson (30x50cm-12x20in) s. painted c.1865 prov. 3-Dec-3 Doyle, New York #173/R est:8000-10000
£9259	$15000	€13426	Mt. Holyoke (66x102cm-26x40in) s. 8-Aug-3 Barridorf, Portland #134/R est:10000-15000

EGLAU, Otto (1917-) German
Works on paper
£280 $515 €420 Landscape (43x57cm-17x22in) s.d.80 W/C. 12-Jun-4 Villa Grisebach, Berlin #706/R

EGLER, Willi (1887-?) German
£254 $425 €371 River landscape with man fishing (79x110cm-31x43in) s.d.1919 sold with three others by various artists. 26-Oct-3 Bonhams & Butterfields, San Francisco #6468/R

EGLEY, William (1798-1870) British
Miniatures
£1400 $2506 €2044 Master Hornblow, in blue silk dress (5cm-2in) s.d.1861 silver gilt frame prov. 25-May-4 Christie's, London #163/R est:400-600

EGLEY, William (attrib) (1798-1870) British
Miniatures
£1103 $1843 €1600 Officer (5cm-2in) exec.c.1840. 12-Nov-3 Sotheby's, Milan #33/R est:1600-2000
£1800 $2988 €2628 Portrait of a lady seated on a green upholstered arm chair and holding a small dog (16cm-6in) giltwood frame. 2-Oct-3 Sotheby's, Olympia #26/R est:600-800

EGLEY, William Maw (c.1827-1916) British
£2200 $3938 €3212 Aurora (28x25cm-11x10in) mono.d.1863 i.verso painted oval. 27-May-4 Christie's, Kensington #324/R est:2000-3000
£3000 $5580 €4380 Awaiting her loves return (36x25cm-14x10in) s.d.1872. 4-Mar-4 Christie's, Kensington #624/R est:4000-6000
£4878 $8732 €7122 To disiplin the vixen - Act 4, scene 3 (93x74cm-37x29in) s.d.1856. 26-May-4 AB Stockholms Auktionsverk #2370/R est:50000-60000 (S.KR 66000)
£12195 $21829 €17805 Preparing for Christmas (62x47cm-24x19in) s.d.1868 i.verso. 4-May-4 Ritchie, Toronto #29/R est:30000-40000 (C.D 30000)

EGLINGTON, Samuel (fl.1830-1856) British
£900 $1647 €1314 Still life of a hare, oysters and a jug of celery in larder (49x39cm-19x15in) s.d.1841 panel. 6-Jul-4 Bonhams, Knightsbridge #161/R

EGMONT, Justus van (attrib) (1601-1674) Flemish
£699 $1203 €1000 Adoration of the Magi (25x20cm-10x8in) panel. 8-Dec-3 Claude Aguttes, Neuilly #21/R
£987 $1816 €1500 Portrait du Grand Conde (70x57cm-28x22in) oval. 25-Jun-4 Piasa, Paris #72 est:2000-3000

EGNER, Marie (1850-1940) Austrian
£3497 $5944 €5000 Animals and landscapes (11x21cm-4x8in) canvas on panel six. 28-Nov-3 Wiener Kunst Auktionen, Vienna #488/R est:5000-10000
£6040 $10691 €9000 Stillfried an der March (14x23cm-6x9in) mono.i. verso panel prov. 28-Apr-4 Wiener Kunst Auktionen, Vienna #50/R est:7000-15000
£6250 $10625 €9000 Wind damaged tree on the Koralpe (39x44cm-15x17in) board lit. 28-Oct-3 Wiener Kunst Auktionen, Vienna #51/R est:8000-18000
£6711 $12013 €10000 The Fortress from Ragusa (13x23cm-5x9in) s. panel. 27-May-4 Dorotheum, Vienna #92/R est:12000-16000
£11538 $19615 €16500 Vintage collection (28x18cm-11x7in) s. canvas on board. 25-Nov-3 Hassfurther, Vienna #31/R est:25000-30000
£11552 $18830 €16866 Village scene - children at festival time (40x55cm-16x22in) s. board. 23-Sep-3 Peter Webb, Auckland #151/R est:10000-15000 (NZ.D 32000)
£13889 $23611 €20000 Rambling roses in Sirmione (57x79cm-22x31in) s. i. verso prov.lit. 28-Oct-3 Wiener Kunst Auktionen, Vienna #52/R est:18000-38000
£18667 $34347 €28000 Still life with fruit (102x64cm-40x25in) s. 11-Jun-4 Villa Grisebach, Berlin #1585/R est:8000-12000
Works on paper
£414 $687 €600 Sailing boat on beach (27x37cm-11x15in) i.d.88 W/C. 30-Sep-3 Dorotheum, Vienna #329/R
£470 $864 €700 Oaks on hillside (24x30cm-9x12in) i.d.76 pen lit. 26-Mar-4 Dorotheum, Vienna #104/R
£1141 $2099 €1700 Village street in Topolscan (20x30cm-8x12in) s.i. verso W/C. 26-Mar-4 Dorotheum, Vienna #238/R est:2000-2500
£1379 $2290 €2000 City wall in early morning light (16x23cm-6x9in) W/C. 30-Sep-3 Dorotheum, Vienna #328/R est:2600-3000
£1611 $2964 €2400 Boats in canal, Venice (19x24cm-7x9in) s. i. verso pen Indian ink grisaille W/C lit. 26-Mar-4 Dorotheum, Vienna #237/R est:2000-2200
£3497 $5944 €5000 Summer day (25x30cm-10x12in) st.sig. W/C. 28-Nov-3 Wiener Kunst Auktionen, Vienna #476/R est:2500-5000

EGNER, Marie (attrib) (1850-1940) Austrian
£872 $1562 €1300 Front garden in bloom (24x33cm-9x13in) i. verso board. 27-May-4 Dorotheum, Graz #15/R

EGOROFF, Marie (20th C) Russian
Works on paper
£493 $908 €750 Homme casque de profil (58x44cm-23x17in) s. lead pencil. 28-Jun-4 Joron-Derem, Paris #121
£493 $908 €750 Homme Barbu de profil (58x44cm-23x17in) s. lead pencil. 28-Jun-4 Joron-Derem, Paris #122

EGOROV, Andrey Simonoviev (1861-1924) Russian
Works on paper
£2400 $4296 €3504 Fetching water from the river (32x46cm-13x18in) s. gouache. 26-May-4 Sotheby's, Olympia #379/R est:1000-1500

EGRY, Jozsef (1883-1951) Hungarian
£1201 $2077 €1753 In the Hall (18x24cm-7x9in) s. panel. 12-Dec-3 Kieselbach, Budapest #86/R (H.F 460000)
£2539 $4493 €3707 Self portrait (48x31cm-19x12in) s. cardboard. 28-Apr-4 Kieselbach, Budapest #21/R (H.F 950000)
Works on paper
£1044 $1806 €1524 Homewards (30x43cm-12x17in) s. mixed media. 12-Dec-3 Kieselbach, Budapest #84/R (H.F 400000)
£1086 $1803 €1586 Fisherman by lake Balaton (30x43cm-12x17in) s. pencil. 4-Oct-3 Kieselbach, Budapest #14/R (H.F 400000)
£1096 $1896 €1600 Fisherman by the Lake Balaton Netting (22x31cm-9x12in) s. mixed media. 12-Dec-3 Kieselbach, Budapest #48/R (H.F 420000)
£1122 $1987 €1638 Lake Balaton (21x29cm-8x11in) s. W/C. 28-Apr-4 Kieselbach, Budapest #107/R (H.F 420000)
£2172 $3605 €3171 Man sitting in a boat, Golden Gate on lake Balaton (35x54cm-14x21in) s. mixed media. 4-Oct-3 Kieselbach, Budapest #61/R (H.F 800000)
£2308 $3831 €3370 Reed and cows by lake Balaton (30x40cm-12x16in) s. pastel. 4-Oct-3 Kieselbach, Budapest #113/R (H.F 850000)
£3162 $5723 €4617 Gentle slopes in Badacsony (33x39cm-13x15in) s. pastel. 16-Apr-4 Mu Terem Galeria, Budapest #179/R (H.F 1200000)
£9230 $15322 €13476 Badascony (48x66cm-19x26in) s. pastel. 4-Oct-3 Kieselbach, Budapest #15/R (H.F 3400000)
£15660 $27092 €22864 Evening lights by the Lake Balaton (62x85cm-24x33in) s. mixed media. 12-Dec-3 Kieselbach, Budapest #85/R (H.F 6000000)

EGUSQUIZA, Rogelio (1845-1913) Spanish
£845 $1479 €1200 Femme a l'eventail (16x10cm-6x4in) s.i. panel. 17-Dec-3 Delorme & Bocage, Paris #39
£2013 $3765 €3000 Guard (37x25cm-15x10in) s. 24-Feb-4 Durán, Madrid #204/R est:2500
£2536 $4159 €3500 De Ronda (37x25cm-15x10in) s. 27-May-3 Durán, Madrid #189/R est:3000

EHLERS, Oskar (attrib) (?) ?
£633 $1000 €924 Three men in a Herreshoff design gaff rigged catboat in heavy seas (102x150cm-40x59in) 25-Jul-3 Eldred, East Dennis #291c/R est:800-1000

EHLINGER, Maurice Ambrose (1896-1981) French
£288 $489 €420 Jeune fille nue se regardant dans un miroir (73x60cm-29x24in) s. 8-Nov-3 Gerard, Besancon #55
£445 $757 €650 Jeune fille nue (60x73cm-24x29in) s. 8-Nov-3 Gerard, Besancon #54
£548 $932 €800 Coupe de pommes et bouquet de fleurs (81x65cm-32x26in) s. 8-Nov-3 Gerard, Besancon #52
£738 $1307 €1100 La lecture (46x61cm-18x24in) s. 29-Apr-4 Claude Aguttes, Neuilly #85
£1100 $1837 €1606 Big bouquet of flowers (73x60cm-29x24in) s. 22-Oct-3 Sotheby's, Olympia #190/R est:700-1000
£1172 $2110 €1700 Jeune fill nue endormie dans un hamac (65x81cm-26x32in) s. 25-Jan-4 Chayette & Cheval, Paris #182 est:1200-1500
£1645 $3026 €2500 Nu au chat (65x81cm-26x32in) s. 22-Jun-4 Chassaing Rivet, Toulouse #279
£3333 $6033 €5000 Jeune fille nue allongee de dos (81x100cm-32x39in) s. 3-Apr-4 Gerard, Besancon #46
£3356 $6007 €5000 Sieste au soleil (60x73cm-24x29in) s. 30-May-4 Eric Pillon, Calais #58/R

EHMSEN, Heinrich (1886-1964) German
£382 $638 €550 Joueur de petanque (19x23cm-7x9in) s. 21-Oct-3 Christie's, Paris #177/R
Works on paper
£285 $518 €430 Female nude standing (56x41cm-22x16in) st.sig. pastel. 19-Jun-4 Bergmann, Erlangen #891

EHNINGER, John W (1827-1889) American
£1377 $2300 €2010 Catch of the day (13x20cm-5x8in) s. panel. 16-Nov-3 William Jenack, New York #431 est:1500-2500
£1645 $3026 €2500 Portrait of rider in landscape (63x76cm-25x30in) mono.d.63. 24-Jun-4 Christie's, Paris #133/R est:5000-7000

EHREN, Julius von (1864-?) German
£2657 $4438 €3800 Bahrenfeld market (50x70cm-20x28in) i. verso. 11-Oct-3 Hans Stahl, Hamburg #95/R est:3800

EHRENBERG, Wilhelm von (1630-1676) Dutch
£2500 $4500 €3650 Interior of St Charles Borromeo, Antwerp, with elegant company (41x47cm-16x19in) indis.i. panel. 23-Apr-4 Christie's, Kensington #73/R est:3000-5000

EHRENGRANAT, Carl Adam (18th C) Danish?
Works on paper
£542 $1013 €791 Romantic landscape with Roman triumph arch (33x44cm-13x17in) i.d.1792 pencil chl. 25-Feb-4 Museumsbygningen, Copenhagen #138/R (D.KR 6000)

EHRENHAFT, Wesely (19/20th C) German?
£436 $816 €650 Cart by house (42x46cm-17x18in) s.d.11 board. 24-Feb-4 Dorotheum, Vienna #145/R

EHRENSTRAHL, Anna Maria Klocker von (1666-1729) Swedish
£9978 $17860 €14568 Horses (40x59cm-16x23in) canvas on panel prov. 25-May-4 Bukowskis, Stockholm #401/R est:75000-100000 (S.KR 135000)

EHRENSTRAHL, David Klocker von (studio) (1629-1698) German
£8846 $15215 €12915 Portrait of Karl XI, ca.15 years old (140x109cm-55x43in) prov.lit. 3-Dec-3 AB Stockholms Auktionsverk #2456/R est:80000-100000 (S.KR 115000)
£11923 $20508 €17408 The truth discovered by time and wisdom (185x152cm-73x60in) lit. 2-Dec-3 Bukowskis, Stockholm #302/R est:100000-150000 (S.KR 155000)

EHRENSVARD, Carl August (1745-1800) Swedish
Works on paper
£1183 $2117 €1727 My journey to Finnland (14x25cm-6x10in) Indian ink wash. 26-May-4 AB Stockholms Auktionsverk #2135/R est:4000-5000 (S.KR 16000)
£3991 $7144 €5827 Lovers (19x19cm-7x7in) Indian ink wash W/C prov. 25-May-4 Bukowskis, Stockholm #539/R est:25000-30000 (S.KR 54000)

EHRENSVARD, Carl August (attrib) (1745-1800) Swedish
Works on paper
£634 $1096 €900 Lady with coffee cup. Man reading book (22x18cm-9x7in) i.verso Indian ink pair. 13-Dec-3 Hagelstam, Helsinki #52/R

EHRENTRAUT, J (1841-1923) German
£1119 $1924 €1600 Country man with wine glass (26x18cm-10x7in) s. i. verso panel. 4-Dec-3 Neumeister, Munich #2725/R est:700

EHRET, Georg Dyonis (1710-1770) British
Works on paper
£1600 $2960 €2336 Bladder-nut (51x34cm-20x13in) s. pencil W/C. 15-Jul-4 Bonhams, New Bond Street #22/R est:1500-2000
£2400 $4440 €3504 St John's Wort (26x17cm-10x7in) s.i.d.1765 pencil W/C vellum. 15-Jul-4 Bonhams, New Bond Street #21/R est:2000-3000
£2800 $5180 €4088 Cherry laurel (51x34cm-20x13in) init. pencil W/C. 15-Jul-4 Bonhams, New Bond Street #23/R est:2500-3500
£2800 $5180 €4088 Field rose (34x27cm-13x11in) s. pencil W/C. 15-Jul-4 Bonhams, New Bond Street #24/R est:2000-3000
£3200 $5920 €4672 Guava (51x34cm-20x13in) s.i. pencil W/C. 15-Jul-4 Bonhams, New Bond Street #25/R est:2000-3000
£3400 $6290 €4964 Pelargonium aculeatum (26x17cm-10x7in) s.i.d.1764 pencil W/C vellum. 15-Jul-4 Bonhams, New Bond Street #19/R est:3000-4000
£3500 $6475 €5110 Turnera biglandulosis (27x19cm-11x7in) s.i.d.1761 pencil W/C vellum. 15-Jul-4 Bonhams, New Bond Street #20/R est:3500-4500
£3600 $6660 €5256 Cistus ladanifer (51x34cm-20x13in) s.i. pencil W/C. 15-Jul-4 Bonhams, New Bond Street #26/R est:2500-3500
£36000 $64440 €52560 Palma Americana foliis polygonati brevioribus (23x37cm-9x15in) s.d.1742 W/C bodycol vellum. 13-May-4 Sotheby's, London #12/R est:35000-45000
£44000 $73480 €64240 Glory Lily (47x33cm-19x13in) s.d.1758 W/C bodycol. gold bronze hightening. 13-Nov-3 Sotheby's, London #50/R est:35000-45000

EHRHARDT, Alfred (1901-1984) German
Photographs
£2308 $3923 €3300 Patterns on sand made by water, North Sea (49x30cm-19x12in) s.i. verso bromide silver gelatin. 27-Nov-3 Villa Grisebach, Berlin #1152/R est:2500-3000

EHRHARDT, Curt (1895-1972) Swiss
£483 $806 €700 Devil (43x36cm-17x14in) s. i.verso board. 13-Nov-3 Neumeister, Munich #314/R
£833 $1392 €1200 Pursuit (29x39cm-11x15in) s. s.i. verso board. 24-Oct-3 Ketterer, Hamburg #335/R
£897 $1497 €1300 Circus (44x47cm-17x19in) s. i.d.1921 verso board. 13-Nov-3 Neumeister, Munich #315/R
£909 $1564 €1300 Dream (30x40cm-12x16in) s. s.i.d.1920 verso board. 4-Dec-3 Van Ham, Cologne #134/R
£979 $1684 €1400 Pregnant (30x40cm-12x16in) s. s.i.d.1920 verso board. 4-Dec-3 Van Ham, Cologne #133/R
£1389 $2264 €2000 Circus show (40x50cm-16x20in) s. i.d.1921 verso board. 26-Sep-3 Bolland & Marotz, Bremen #735/R est:3300
£1533 $2745 €2300 Hand grenade thrower (42x50cm-17x20in) mono.d. s.i.d. verso prov. 14-May-4 Ketterer, Munich #14/R est:2000-3000
£5944 $10105 €8500 Les promeneurs (79x60cm-31x24in) s. s.i. verso bears d.1921 verso board. 29-Nov-3 Villa Grisebach, Berlin #179/R est:3000-4000

EHRHARDT, Paul W (1872-?) German
£526 $968 €800 The Biedermeier boudoir (53x44cm-21x17in) s. 22-Jun-4 Christie's, Amsterdam #67/R

EHRIG, William Columbus (1892-1969) American
£950 $1700 €1387 Sunlit splendour (91x122cm-36x48in) s. s.i.verso. 8-Jan-4 James Julia, Fairfield #681/R est:1000-2000
£3073 $5500 €4487 Breakers (76x102cm-30x40in) s.d.1957. 20-Mar-4 Sloans & Kenyon, Bethesda #1200/R est:5000-6000

EHRLICH, Franz (1907-1984) German
Works on paper
£533 $960 €800 Saboteur (36x25cm-14x10in) mono.d. W/C col chk board. 24-Apr-4 Dr Lehr, Berlin #111/R

EHRMANN, François Emile (1833-1910) French
£1667 $3017 €2500 La triere (34x54cm-13x21in) s.d.1865 exhib. 30-Mar-4 Rossini, Paris #335/R est:2500-3500

EHRMANNS, Theodor von (1846-1923) Austrian
£694 $1181 €1000 Hohen Goll (23x29cm-9x11in) s.d.865. 28-Oct-3 Dorotheum, Vienna #24/R

EIBISCH, Eugeniusz (1896-1987) Polish
£4173 $6928 €6093 Portrait of a man (45x38cm-18x15in) s. painted c.1960. 15-Jun-3 Agra, Warsaw #10/R est:25000 (P.Z 26000)

EIBLER, Emma (1868-1958) Swiss
£322 $602 €480 Nikolai fleet in Hamburg (50x62cm-20x24in) panel. 28-Feb-4 Bolland & Marotz, Bremen #278/R

EICH, Johann Friedrich (attrib) (1748-1807) German
£2617 $4868 €3900 Portrait of Friedrich Heinrich Jacobi (53x45cm-21x18in) 5-Mar-4 Wendl, Rudolstadt #3953/R est:550

EICHBERG, Carl Kayser (?) German
£282 $487 €400 Rowing boat in the reeds (34x44cm-13x17in) 15-Dec-3 Dr Fritz Nagel, Stuttgart #7054/R
£352 $609 €500 Cows in the moonlight (67x80cm-26x31in) 15-Dec-3 Dr Fritz Nagel, Stuttgart #7057/R

EICHBERGER, Sepp (20th C) German?
Sculpture
£1126 $2049 €1700 Horse and chariot (31cm-12in) s.d.1929 brown pat. bronze incl. wooden base. 16-Jun-4 Hugo Ruef, Munich #1753/R est:900

EICHELBERGER, Robert A (19th C) American
£455 $800 €664 Landscape of a winter marsh (71x46cm-28x18in) s. 3-Jan-4 Cobbs, Peterborough #3/R

EICHHORN, Gustav (1857-1928) German
£267 $480 €400 Farmstead by stream in wooded pre-alpine landscape (13x22cm-5x9in) s.d.1919 panel. 22-Apr-4 Allgauer, Kempten #3519/R
£290 $484 €420 Figuers in field in pre alpine landscape (8x10cm-3x4in) s.d.1923 board. 10-Jul-3 Allgauer, Kempten #2467/R
£290 $484 €420 Figures working in the fields in Chiemgau (8x10cm-3x4in) s.d.1922 board. 10-Jul-3 Allgauer, Kempten #2468/R
£345 $576 €500 Returning home from the harvest (8x10cm-3x4in) s.d.1922 board. 10-Jul-3 Allgauer, Kempten #2470/R
£414 $691 €600 Farmstead in trees on shore (11x18cm-4x7in) s.d.1922 board. 10-Jul-3 Allgauer, Kempten #2464/R
£759 $1267 €1100 Farmstead on lake shore (11x21cm-4x8in) s.d.1922 board. 10-Jul-3 Allgauer, Kempten #2465/R
£897 $1497 €1300 Autumn shore of Fraueninsel (16x26cm-6x10in) s.d.1923 panel lit. 10-Jul-3 Allgauer, Kempten #2463/R

EICHHORN, Peter (1877-1960) German
£317 $538 €463 Outside tavern (9x10cm-4x4in) s.i. panel. 19-Nov-3 Fischer, Luzern #2076/R (S.FR 700)

EICHHORST, Franz (1885-?) German
£1000 $1790 €1500 Peasant market (52x62cm-20x24in) s. canvas on board. 13-May-4 Neumeister, Munich #336/R est:1000-1200

EICHINGER, Erwin (1892-1950) Austrian
£500 $835 €730 Pipe smoker (27x20cm-11x8in) s. board. 12-Nov-3 Sotheby's, Olympia #221/R
£775 $1340 €1100 In the monastery kitchen (41x52cm-16x20in) s. panel. 10-Dec-3 Dorotheum, Vienna #14/R
£1800 $3096 €2628 Cardinal examining drawings (26x32cm-10x13in) s.i. panel prov. 4-Dec-3 Christie's, Kensington #113/R est:2000-3000
£2200 $3784 €3212 Captain examining his charts (32x26cm-13x10in) s. panel prov. 4-Dec-3 Christie's, Kensington #115/R est:2500-3500
£4000 $7360 €5840 Lucky throw (38x44cm-15x17in) s.i. panel. 25-Mar-4 Christie's, Kensington #197/R est:2500-3500

EICHINGER, Otto (1922-) Austrian
£740 $1280 €1080 Good Wine - Portrait of a gentleman wearing a hat. board. 9-Dec-3 Lawrences, Bletchingley #1842
£852 $1500 €1244 The card players (24x30cm-9x12in) s. 23-May-4 Bonhams & Butterfields, San Francisco #6591/R
£1676 $3000 €2447 Portrait of a Rabbi (19x26cm-7x10in) s. panel. 18-Mar-4 Sotheby's, New York #267/R est:3000-5000

EICHINGER, Ulrich (20th C) Austrian
£1000 $1850 €1460 Portrait of a Rabbi (27x21cm-11x8in) s. board. 10-Mar-4 Sotheby's, Olympia #300/R est:1200-1800
£1600 $2656 €2336 Portrait of a Rabbi (27x21cm-11x8in) s. board. 1-Oct-3 Sotheby's, Olympia #217/R est:800-1200

EICHLER, Antoine (19th C) German
£267 $480 €400 Portrait of Pauline Grumpelt aged 20 (59x47cm-23x19in) oval. 26-Apr-4 Rieber, Stuttgart #1275/R

EICHLER, Gottfried (elder) (1677-1757) German
£7000 $12600 €10500 Portraits of the artist's children (66x61cm-26x24in) 26-Apr-4 Rieber, Stuttgart #1200/R est:2500

EICHLER, Johann Gottfried (younger) (1715-1770) German
Works on paper
£373 $676 €560 St Joannes de Deo (16x10cm-6x4in) wash pen. 2-Apr-4 Winterberg, Heidelberg #285/R

EICHLER, Reinhold Max (1872-1947) German
£3200 $5728 €4800 Still life of flowers (62x51cm-24x20in) s. 13-May-4 Neumeister, Munich #337/R est:4000-4500

EICHLER, Victor (1893-?) German
Sculpture
£1074 $1901 €1600 Crouching figure (53cm-21in) i. brown pat.bronze. 28-Apr-4 Schopman, Hamburg #327/R est:1700

EICHSTAEDT, Rudolf (1857-c.1924) German
£1656 $2550 €2600 Rose time (64x81cm-25x32in) s. i. stretcher. 4-Sep-2 Schopman, Hamburg #11/R est:1400

EICKE, Paula (20th C) German
£296 $545 €450 Abstract interior with cup on a table (46x54cm-18x21in) s.i.verso canvas on panel. 25-Jun-4 Von Zezschwitz, Munich #321/R

EICKELBERG, Willem Hendrik (1845-1920) Dutch
£556 $878 €800 Sunset over snow-covered polder landscape (43x61cm-17x24in) s. 2-Sep-3 Christie's, Amsterdam #288

EICKEN, Elisabeth von (1862-1940) German
£1391 $2531 €2100 Autumn evening (62x74cm-24x29in) s. 18-Jun-4 Bolland & Marotz, Bremen #610/R est:1200

EIDRIGEVICIUS, Stasys (20th C) Polish
Works on paper
£256 $436 €374 Abstract character (30x24cm-12x9in) s.d.1981 pencil. 19-Nov-3 Agra, Warsaw #7/R (P.Z 1700)

EIEBAKKE, August (1867-1938) Norwegian
£374 $688 €561 Sketch of farm in Ostfold (22x28cm-9x11in) s. panel. 14-Jun-4 Blomqvist, Lysaker #1075/R (N.KR 4600)

EIELSON, Jorge (1924-) Peruvian
£4196 $7133 €6000 Quipus 33 T-1 (120x120cm-47x47in) s.i.d.66 verso canvas on board. 28-Nov-3 Farsetti, Prato #11/R est:3200-4200
Sculpture
£2308 $3854 €3300 Quipus 29.Bouquet1 (100x100x20cm-39x39x8in) s.i.d.66-72 verso fabric on panel prov.lit. 29-Jun-3 Versailles Encheres #206 est:500-600
£2308 $3923 €3300 Amazone (60x60cm-24x24in) s.i.d.1994 verso fel board. 20-Nov-3 Finarte Semenzato, Milan #20/R est:2000-2500
£8392 $14266 €12000 Quipus 30 T-1 (150x78x22cm-59x31x9in) s.i.d.71 verso canvas on board. 28-Nov-3 Farsetti, Prato #240/R est:3200-4200

EIJSDEN, Theo van (1900-1980) Dutch
£753 $1281 €1100 Composition, hommage to Emily Bronte (79x65cm-31x26in) s.d.67. 5-Nov-3 Vendue Huis, Gravenhage #458

EIKAAS, Ludvig (1920-) Norwegian
£684 $1163 €999 White interior (46x55cm-18x22in) s. i.verso panel. 19-Nov-3 Grev Wedels Plass, Oslo #102/R (N.KR 8000)
£688 $1108 €1004 Interior scene with figures (50x60cm-20x24in) s. panel. 25-Aug-3 Blomqvist, Lysaker #1042/R (N.KR 8000)
£979 $1752 €1429 Country court yard, rainy day (80x53cm-31x21in) s. i.stretcher. 25-May-4 Grev Wedels Plass, Oslo #94/R (N.KR 12000)
£2170 $3972 €3168 Still life of vase and bowl (73x86cm-29x34in) s. 2-Feb-4 Blomqvist, Lysaker #1051/R est:18000-22000 (N.KR 27000)

EILERS, Conrad (1845-1914) German
£235 $400 €343 Docked (30x24cm-12x9in) s. 21-Nov-3 Skinner, Boston #514/R

EILERSEN, Eiler Rasmussen (1827-1912) Danish
£295 $501 €431 Woodland lake (98x100cm-39x39in) mono.d.86 exhib. 10-Nov-3 Rasmussen, Vejle #448 (D.KR 3200)
£331 $592 €483 Woodland lake with swallows in flight (26x38cm-10x15in) mono.d.1864. 12-Jan-4 Rasmussen, Vejle #69/R (D.KR 3500)
£403 $726 €588 Prospect view of a manor farm, Fyn (40x60cm-16x24in) mono.d.1855. 24-Apr-4 Rasmussen, Havnen #2374 (D.KR 4500)
£452 $810 €660 Wooded landscape with lake and deer (64x92cm-25x36in) s.d.1871. 10-May-4 Rasmussen, Vejle #91/R (D.KR 5000)
£468 $782 €683 Wooded landscape with deer (47x67cm-19x26in) mono.d.98. 25-Oct-3 Rasmussen, Havnen #2228 (D.KR 5000)
£719 $1337 €1050 Moonlight at Brobyvaerk, Odense river (42x60cm-17x24in) s. exhib. 2-Mar-4 Rasmussen, Copenhagen #1369/R (D.KR 8000)
£1527 $2841 €2229 Young man fishing in Sus river, summer (90x122cm-35x48in) mono.d.1869. 2-Mar-4 Rasmussen, Copenhagen #1398/R est:8000-10000 (D.KR 17000)
£5035 $8408 €7200 Pompei, Campania felix (65x114cm-26x45in) s.d.1884 exhib. 24-Jun-3 Finarte Semenzato, Rome #195/R

EILSHEMIUS, Louis M (1864-1941) American
£240 $400 €350 Landscape with nude bathing (23x33cm-9x13in) s. board. 19-Oct-3 Jeffery Burchard, Florida #50
£380 $700 €555 Bathers by a waterfall (20x25cm-8x10in) s.d.1922 oil on paper. 23-Jun-4 Doyle, New York #5030/R
£447 $800 €653 October rhapsody (72x107cm-28x42in) s. 14-May-4 Skinner, Boston #185/R
£523 $900 €764 Misty lake (48x76cm-19x30in) board. 6-Dec-3 South Bay, Long Island #168a/R
£524 $876 €750 Evening (31x43cm-12x17in) s. i. verso. 28-Jun-3 Bolland & Marotz, Bremen #638
£599 $1000 €875 Beach scene (51x76cm-20x30in) masonite. 17-Oct-3 Du Mouchelle, Detroit #2016/R
£615 $1100 €898 Dawn (43x51cm-17x20in) s.d.1919 composition board prov. 26-May-4 Doyle, New York #74/R
£688 $1100 €1004 Echo (76x51cm-30x20in) s. exhib. 17-May-3 Bunte, Elgin #1292 est:1500-2500
£722 $1300 €1054 Female nude in landscape (20x41cm-8x16in) s. board. 23-Jan-4 Freeman, Philadelphia #197/R
£894 $1600 €1305 Christmas afternoon (56x66cm-22x26in) s.d.1916 board on board prov. 26-May-4 Doyle, New York #75/R est:3000-4000
Works on paper
£250 $400 €365 Landscape with birch trees (23x33cm-9x13in) s.d.1891 W/C. 21-Sep-3 William Jenack, New York #92

EINBECK, Georg (1870-1951) French
£2941 $5000 €4294 Iris (59x49cm-23x19in) s.d.1927 tempera board lit. 28-Nov-3 Zofingen, Switzerland #2979/R est:4500 (S.FR 6500)
Works on paper
£284 $500 €415 La Baie de Garavan (31x47cm-12x19in) s. gouache prov.lit. 22-May-4 Galerie Gloggner, Luzern #29/R (S.FR 650)

EINBECK, Walter (1890-?) German
£850 $1505 €1241 Allegory of beauty (127x100cm-50x39in) s.d.1921. 29-Apr-4 Christie's, Kensington #296/R

EINBERGER, Andreas (1878-1953) Austrian
£368 $659 €537 Goat (40x51cm-16x20in) s. 22-Mar-4 Philippe Schuler, Zurich #6138 (S.FR 850)

EINBERGER, Leopold (1955-) Austrian
£467 $859 €700 Still life with flowers in vase (60x50cm-24x20in) s. i.d.2003 verso board. 9-Jun-4 Dorotheum, Salzburg #734/R

EINERSSEN, John (1949-) Canadian
£744 $1354 €1086 Power and Gold (51x61cm-20x24in) s. 5-Feb-4 Heffel, Vancouver #026/R (C.D 1800)

EINHART, Karl (1885-1959) German
£347 $631 €520 View of Constance (38x45cm-15x18in) s. cardboard. 3-Jul-4 Geble, Radolfzell #396/R
£436 $803 €650 Untersee with Hori (50x60cm-20x24in) s. lit. 27-Mar-4 Geble, Radolfzell #719/R

EINSLE, Anton (1801-1871) Austrian
£1549 $2572 €2200 Portrait of Baron Drasche-Wartinberg (78x63cm-31x25in) s. i. verso canvas on panel. 16-Jun-3 Dorotheum, Vienna #56/R est:3000-3500
£2265 $4213 €3307 Sleeping child (62x75cm-24x30in) s.d.1869. 6-Mar-4 Dorotheum, Prague #34/R est:40000-80000 (C.KR 110000)

EINSLE, Anton (attrib) (1801-1871) Austrian
£1049 $1783 €1500 Holy Family with Infant St John (18x15cm-7x6in) i.d.820 verso panel oval. 20-Nov-3 Dorotheum, Salzburg #4/R est:1200-1800
£3667 $6600 €5500 Portrait of Franz Joseph I (68x55cm-27x22in) prov. 20-Apr-4 Sotheby's, Amsterdam #66/R est:6000-8000

EIRI, Hosoda (fl.c.1790-1800) Japanese
Prints
£3000 $5520 €4380 Mitate of a Daimyo's procession entering a castle (37x120cm-15x47in) s. print pentaptych exec. c.1790's lit. 8-Jun-4 Sotheby's, London #289/R est:3000-4000
£4000 $7360 €5840 Procession of a young nobleman and his suite (38x130cm-15x51in) s. print pentaptych exec. c.1796 lit. 8-Jun-4 Sotheby's, London #297/R est:3500-4500
£6800 $12512 €9928 Travellers in snowclad landscape (38x76cm-15x30in) s. print triptych lit. 8-Jun-4 Sotheby's, London #299/R est:3000-5000
£7693 $13078 €11000 Courtisane Karatsuchi de Echizen-ya. s. print. 25-Nov-3 Tajan, Paris #367/R est:14000-15000

EIRIZ, Antonia (1929-1995) Cuban
£10000 $17000 €14600 En la coba (151x126cm-59x50in) s. s.i.verso prov. 18-Nov-3 Christie's, Rockefeller NY #176/R est:5000-7000

EISE, Ida (1894-1978) New Zealander
£839 $1527 €1225 Landscape Whangarei (30x37cm-12x15in) s. canvasboard exhib. 29-Jun-4 Peter Webb, Auckland #95/R est:1800-2500 (NZ.D 2400)

EISEL, Fritz (1929-) German
£420 $722 €600 On the footpath (70x100cm-28x39in) hessian. 5-Dec-3 Bolland & Marotz, Bremen #799/R

EISEN and HIROSHIGE (19th C) Japanese
Works on paper
£3357 $5706 €4800 Soixante-neuf relais de la grande route de Kiso (26x37cm-10x15in) W/C dr set of 10 exhib. 25-Nov-3 Sotheby's, Paris #173/R est:1000-1400

EISEN, Charles (18th C) French
Works on paper
£476 $852 €700 Jeune homme offrant une guilande de fleurs a une bergere (14x20cm-6x8in) blk crayon. 18-Mar-4 Peschetau-Badin Godeau & Leroy, Paris #5/R

EISEN, Charles (attrib) (18th C) French
Works on paper
£909 $1545 €1300 Etude pour un Plafond, scene de la Vie du Christ (45x30cm-18x12in) i.verso pen grey wash. 18-Nov-3 Galerie Moderne, Brussels #726/R

EISEN, Charles-Dominique-Joseph (1720-1778) French
Works on paper
£743 $1308 €1100 Shepherdess leading against a rock. Young man near a spring (9x5cm-4x2in) s. pen grey ink brown wash pair prov.exhib.lit. 19-May-4 Sotheby's, Amsterdam #158/R
£1831 $3204 €2600 Persee et Andormede (13x9cm-5x4in) s.d.1750 graphite vellum prov. 17-Dec-3 Christie's, Paris #49/R est:1500-2000

EISEN, Charles-Dominique-Joseph (attrib) (1720-1778) French
Works on paper
£845 $1462 €1200 Frise de putti jouant (4x36cm-2x14in) pen brown ink. 10-Dec-3 Piasa, Paris #39
£4762 $8524 €7000 Jeune homme surpris dans un jardin (17x11cm-7x4in) pen blk ink grey wash blk crayon. 17-Mar-4 Tajan, Paris #43/R est:1500

EISEN, Keisai (1790-1848) Japanese
Works on paper
£4348 $8000 €6348 Beauty after the bath (119x42cm-47x17in) s.i. col ink hanging scroll. 23-Mar-4 Christie's, Rockefeller NY #123/R est:10000-15000

EISEN, Louis (18th C) ?
£3356 $6174 €5000 Leda et la cygne. Diane et Endymion (64x74cm-25x29in) s.d.1786 pair. 26-Mar-4 Piasa, Paris #44/R est:3000-4000

EISENBERG, Yaacov (1897-1966) Israeli
£495 $900 €743 Sunset on Jerusalem mountains (26x34cm-10x13in) s. i.d.1940 verso canvas on cardboard. 1-Jul-4 Ben-Ami, Tel Aviv #4991/R
£522 $950 €783 Alley in Jerusalem (26x34cm-10x13in) s.d.1946. 1-Jul-4 Ben-Ami, Tel Aviv #4989/R
£549 $1000 €824 Sharon Valley (25x35cm-10x14in) s. i.verso canvas on cardboard. 1-Jul-4 Ben-Ami, Tel Aviv #4988/R
£710 $1300 €1037 Figure in an alley in Jerusalem (46x33cm-18x13in) s.d.1960. 1-Jun-4 Ben-Ami, Tel Aviv #4874/R est:1200-1600
£856 $1600 €1250 Zaffed (46x31cm-18x12in) s.i.d.1959 prov. 1-Mar-4 Ben-Ami, Tel Aviv #4699/R est:1800-2400
£884 $1600 €1291 Alley in the Old City of Jerusalem (38x55cm-15x22in) s. i.verso painted c.1946. 1-Apr-4 Ben-Ami, Tel Aviv #4760/R est:1600-2400
£1038 $1900 €1515 Landscape of Ein Karem in Jerusalem (50x65cm-20x26in) s. 1-Jun-4 Ben-Ami, Tel Aviv #4894/R est:2000-3000
£1073 $1900 €1567 Landscape of Jerusalem from Mount Hatzofim (50x65cm-20x26in) s. i.d.verso prov. 1-May-4 Ben-Ami, Tel Aviv #4775/R est:2200-3000
£1080 $1900 €1577 Figures in Abu-Tur neighbourhood in Jerusalem (38x55cm-15x22in) s.i. painted c.1950. 1-Jan-4 Ben-Ami, Tel Aviv #4386/R est:1500-2000
£1093 $2000 €1596 Alley in Jerusalem (45x33cm-18x13in) s. canvas on board painted c.1950 prov. 1-Feb-4 Ben-Ami, Tel Aviv #4659/R est:1800-2400
£1118 $1900 €1632 An alley in Jerusalem (55x37cm-22x15in) s.d.1959. 1-Dec-3 Ben-Ami, Tel Aviv #4337/R est:1200-1600
£1229 $2250 €1794 Landscape of Abu Tor in Jerusalem (38x55cm-15x22in) s. painted c.1950. 1-Feb-4 Ben-Ami, Tel Aviv #4639/R est:2000-3000
£1524 $2850 €2225 Courtyard of the Bezalel Academy of Arts and Crafts in Jerusalem (54x37cm-21x15in) s. i.verso painted c.1950 prov. 1-Mar-4 Ben-Ami, Tel Aviv #4700/R est:1800-2400
Works on paper
£197 $360 €288 Landscape around the Jerusalem Mountains (22x28cm-9x11in) s.i. chl pastel exec.c.1920 prov. 1-Feb-4 Ben-Ami, Tel Aviv #4620/R
£198 $350 €289 Young Jewish man from Jerusalem playing the flute (34x23cm-13x9in) s.i. chl pastel prov. 1-May-4 Ben-Ami, Tel Aviv #4795/R
£213 $390 €311 Portrait of a young Jewish boy from Jerusalem (32x22cm-13x9in) s.i. chl pastel exec.c.1920 prov. 1-Feb-4 Ben-Ami, Tel Aviv #4607/R
£225 $420 €329 Portrait of a Jewish boy from Jerusalem (26x17cm-10x7in) s.d.1917 chl pastel prov. 1-Mar-4 Ben-Ami, Tel Aviv #4679/R
£464 $850 €677 Portrait of Boris Schatz (42x29cm-17x11in) s.i.d.1929 prov. 1-Feb-4 Ben-Ami, Tel Aviv #4592/R

EISENBERGER, Ludwig (fl.1895-1920) ?
Sculpture
£1176 $2200 €1717 Victorious warrior on horseback (56cm-22in) s. bronze marble base. 29-Feb-4 Grogan, Boston #91/R

EISENDIECK, Suzanne (1908-1998) German
£884 $1600 €1291 Jardin a apremont (41x33cm-16x13in) s. prov. 18-Apr-4 Bonhams & Butterfields, Los Angeles #7027a est:1500-2000
£884 $1583 €1300 Portrait of Joula (24x16cm-9x6in) s. i. verso. 20-Mar-4 Bergmann, Erlangen #1149
£1216 $2177 €1800 Girl's portrait (52x40cm-20x16in) s. lit. 8-May-4 Schloss Ahlden, Ahlden #860/R est:1700
£1357 $2267 €1981 Charmille in St Jean (45x38cm-18x15in) s. i.verso. 17-Nov-3 Waddingtons, Toronto #208/R est:3000-3500 (C.D 3000)
£1648 $3000 €2472 Dancer in front of a mirror (65x46cm-26x18in) s. 1-Jul-4 Ben-Ami, Tel Aviv #4932/R est:4000-5000

EISENHUT, Ferencz (1857-1903) Hungarian
£1701 $3044 €2500 Standing armed Albanian (50x34cm-20x13in) s.d.02 board lit. 20-Mar-4 Bergmann, Erlangen #1109 est:2200-2500

EISENLOHR, Friedrich (1805-1856) German
Works on paper
£453 $821 €680 Ruins of Marienthal near Johannisberg (23x34cm-9x13in) s.i. pencil. 2-Apr-4 Winterberg, Heidelberg #411/R
£643 $1074 €920 Ruins in Rome (26x34cm-10x13in) s. i. verso Indian ink. 10-Oct-3 Winterberg, Heidelberg #568/R
£664 $1109 €950 Family round table (10x16cm-4x6in) i. pencil two. 10-Oct-3 Winterberg, Heidelberg #573
£667 $1207 €1000 Ruins of the Colosseum, Rome (26x19cm-10x7in) i.d.Decembre 27 pencil. 2-Apr-4 Winterberg, Heidelberg #405
£867 $1569 €1300 Interior cloister of S Croce church (15x20cm-6x8in) s.i.d.29 Juli 28 pencil. 2-Apr-4 Winterberg, Heidelberg #406/R
£2098 $3503 €3000 Cocumella grotto with view of Sorrento Bay (20x26cm-8x10in) i. pencil. 10-Oct-3 Winterberg, Heidelberg #571/R est:1200
£2448 $4087 €3500 Medieval gateway in Perugia (38x26cm-15x10in) s.i.d.Agusto 27 pencil. 10-Oct-3 Winterberg, Heidelberg #569/R est:1200
£3007 $5022 €4300 Moonlit Nemi Lake in Albanian mountains (30x26cm-12x10in) i.d.ottobre 26 wash brush sepia over pencil. 10-Oct-3 Winterberg, Heidelberg #567/R est:1480

EISENMANN, Georg (attrib) (18th C) German
£662 $1205 €1000 Mountainous landscape in a rising thunderstorm (22x28cm-9x11in) panel. 16-Jun-4 Dorotheum, Vienna #411/R

EISENMENGER, Rudolf Hermann (1902-) Austrian
Works on paper
£867 $1560 €1300 Papageno, Salzburg beyond (27x26cm-11x10in) s.d.1956 mixed media. 21-Apr-4 Dorotheum, Vienna #155/R

EISENSCHER, Yaacov (1896-1980) Israeli
£549 $1000 €824 Ships in Jaffa harbour (38x46cm-15x18in) s. 1-Jul-4 Ben-Ami, Tel Aviv #4929/R
£706 $1200 €1031 The red house (35x25cm-14x10in) s. canvas on board painted 1950's. 1-Dec-3 Ben-Ami, Tel Aviv #4350/R
£1530 $2800 €2234 Painter and the model (46x55cm-18x22in) s. 1-Jun-4 Ben-Ami, Tel Aviv #4858/R est:3500-4500

EISENSCHITZ, Willy (1889-1974) French
£1467 $2625 €2200 Vue d'Ibiza (60x73cm-24x29in) s. 16-May-4 Lombrail & Teucquam, Paris #169/R
£1761 $3046 €2500 Bord de mer (38x54cm-15x21in) s. cardboard. 12-Dec-3 Renaud, Paris #155 est:2000
£6040 $10691 €9000 Landscape in Provence (48x60cm-19x24in) s. double-sided. 28-Apr-4 Wiener Kunst Auktionen, Vienna #89/R est:9000-15000
£8844 $15830 €13000 Vue de la Seine a Paris (60x73cm-24x29in) s.d.1926. 21-Mar-4 Muizon & Le Coent, Paris #56/R
£14474 $26632 €22000 Paysage aux collines (65x100cm-26x39in) s.d.1925. 22-Jun-4 Calmels Cohen, Paris #53/R est:5000-6000
£23027 $42369 €35000 Paysage de la Drome, les vignes (100x135cm-39x53in) s. 22-Jun-4 Calmels Cohen, Paris #52/R est:10000-15000
Works on paper
£400 $736 €600 Landscape (37x52cm-15x20in) WC. 9-Jun-4 Dorotheum, Vienna #63
£532 $888 €750 Rue au reverbere (26x34cm-10x13in) s. chl pastel. 14-Oct-3 Millon & Associes, Paris #78/R
£733 $1313 €1100 Naples (34x46cm-13x18in) s.i.d.1928 W/C. 16-May-4 Lombrail & Teucquam, Paris #170/R
£1049 $1783 €1500 Paysage (31x43cm-12x17in) s. pastel. 27-Nov-3 Calmels Cohen, Paris #48/R est:1200-1500

EISENSCHOLZ, Wolfried (20th C) Dutch?
£307 $549 €460 Mountain landscape (50x70cm-20x28in) s.d.1926 prov. 11-May-4 Vendu Notarishuis, Rotterdam #22/R

EISENSTAEDT, Alfred (1898-1995) American
Photographs
£1693 $3200 €2472 Marlene Dietrich (48x38cm-19x15in) s.d.1929 gelatin silver print. 17-Feb-4 Christie's, Rockefeller NY #217/R est:4000-6000
£1705 $3000 €2489 Marilyn Monroe (34x44cm-13x17in) with sig. num.51/250 silver print. 20-May-4 Swann Galleries, New York #444/R est:4000-6000
£2536 $4159 €3500 Sharecropper Lonnie Fair's daughter dressing for church (25x20cm-10x8in) i. vintage silver gelatin. 30-May-3 Villa Grisebach, Berlin #1151/R est:4000-5000
£2778 $4722 €4000 Marilyn Monroe (35x44cm-14x17in) s.i. i.d. verso gelatin silver lit. 31-Oct-3 Lempertz, Koln #101/R est:4000-4500
£2800 $4760 €4088 VJ Day, Times Square, New York City, August 15 1945 (25x20cm-10x8in) st.i.d.verso silver print exec.1945 printed later. 19-Nov-3 Sotheby's, Olympia #81/R est:1000-1500
£3672 $6500 €5361 Drum major and children, University of Michigan (41x54cm-16x21in) s.num.62/250 i.d.1951 verso photo printed 1991. 28-Apr-4 Sotheby's, New York #200/R est:5000-7000
£3672 $6500 €5361 Premiere at La Scala, Milan (32x23cm-13x9in) s.num.9/50 i.d.1933 verso photo printed 1979. 28-Apr-4 Sotheby's, New York #201/R est:5000-7000
£7345 $13000 €10724 Farewell to servicement, Penn Station (44x34cm-17x13in) s.num.124/250 i.verso photo printed 1991. 28-Apr-4 Sotheby's, New York #207/R est:8000-12000
£9040 $16000 €13198 V J Day, Times Square, New York City (44x30cm-17x12in) s.num.94/250 i.d.1945 verso photo printed 1991. 28-Apr-4 Sotheby's, New York #203/R est:10000-20000
£11299 $20000 €16497 Children at a puppet theatre, Paris (37x54cm-15x21in) s.num.80/250 i.d.1963 verso photo printed 1991. 28-Apr-4 Sotheby's, New York #202/R est:15000-25000

EISERMANN, Richard (1853-1927) German
Works on paper
£5879 $10406 €8583 Children with bucket of spring flowers (170x95cm-67x37in) s. pastel. 28-Apr-4 Kieselbach, Budapest #182/R (H.F 2200000)

EISHI, Chobunsai (1756-1827) Japanese
Prints
£1818 $3091 €2600 Courtisan Morokoshi de Echizen ya assise devant une table a ecrire. s. print. 25-Nov-3 Tajan, Paris #361 est:1800-2000

EISHI, Hosoda (1756-1829) Japanese
Prints
£5245 $8916 €7500 Morokoshi (35x25cm-14x10in) s. col print prov.lit. 25-Nov-3 Sotheby's, Paris #4/R est:9000-12000
£5594 $9510 €8000 Matsukaze (38x25cm-15x10in) s. col print triptych lit. 25-Nov-3 Sotheby's, Paris #5/R est:9000-12000

EISHO, Chokosai (fl.1790s) Japanese
Prints
£2657 $4517 €3800 Naniwya Okita (39x25cm-15x10in) s. col print exec.1795 lit. 25-Nov-3 Sotheby's, Paris #7/R est:4500-5500
£3000 $5520 €4380 Noble lady and her attendants on a verandah of a Yashiki overlooking a river (37x75cm-15x30in) s. print triptych prov. 8-Jun-4 Sotheby's, London #292/R est:3000-4000

EISHUN, Kano (1769-1816) Japanese
Works on paper
£1200 $2004 €1752 Pine tree, maple and calligraphy (104x41cm-41x16in) s. ink col silk. 12-Nov-3 Christie's, London #50/R

EISLER, Georg (1928-1998) Austrian
£1408 $2465 €2000 In cafe (36x45cm-14x18in) s.d.80. 19-Dec-3 Dorotheum, Vienna #383/R est:3200-4000
£1831 $3204 €2600 Landscape with figures (60x80cm-24x31in) s.d.60 lit. 19-Dec-3 Dorotheum, Vienna #257/R est:4000-5500
Works on paper
£2013 $3564 €3000 Untitled (48x61cm-19x24in) s.d.1985 pastel chk. 28-Apr-4 Wiener Kunst Auktionen, Vienna #210/R est:3000-6000

EISMANN, Johann Anton (1604-1698) German
£8333 $14167 €12000 View of harbour with figures (58x158cm-23x62in) 29-Oct-3 Il Ponte, Milan #810/R

EISMANN, Johann Anton (circle) (1604-1698) German
£6081 $10703 €9000 Roman ruins by harbour (98x135cm-39x53in) 22-May-4 Lempertz, Koln #1045/R est:10000

EISNER, Ib (1925-) Danish
£284 $518 €426 Mid Summer Night's bonfire on the shore (35x40cm-14x16in) s. 19-Jun-4 Rasmussen, Havnen #4234 (D.KR 3200)
£341 $613 €498 Autumn landscape with figure (35x41cm-14x16in) s. 24-Apr-4 Rasmussen, Havnen #4215 (D.KR 3800)
£373 $585 €545 At Sjopromenaden, Tivoli (40x50cm-16x20in) s. 30-Aug-3 Rasmussen, Havnen #4015/R (D.KR 4000)
£430 $774 €628 Figures by bonfire, Mid Summer Night (40x50cm-16x20in) s. 24-Apr-4 Rasmussen, Havnen #4214/R (D.KR 4800)
£2151 $3871 €3140 Rainy day (70x80cm-28x31in) s. 24-Apr-4 Rasmussen, Havnen #4026 est:3000 (D.KR 24000)
Works on paper
£321 $583 €469 Head of a joker (42x50cm-17x20in) s. mixed media panel. 7-Feb-4 Rasmussen, Havnen #4298/R (D.KR 3500)
£641 $1167 €936 Crucifixion. Christ. s. mixed media panel pair. 7-Feb-4 Rasmussen, Havnen #4196 (D.KR 7000)

EISNER, Jeppe (1952-) Danish
£348 $633 €508 Self-portrait, Roskilde Cathedral in background (60x50cm-24x20in) s. 7-Feb-4 Rasmussen, Havnen #4199/R (D.KR 3800)
£672 $1210 €981 Surrealistic composition with figures (70x80cm-28x31in) s. 24-Apr-4 Rasmussen, Havnen #4046/R (D.KR 7500)
£687 $1250 €1003 Gudhjem graveyard (60x70cm-24x28in) s. 7-Feb-4 Rasmussen, Havnen #4207 (D.KR 7500)
£733 $1333 €1070 Composition with fantasy animal in front of mill (60x55cm-24x22in) s. 7-Feb-4 Rasmussen, Havnen #4174/R (D.KR 8000)
£733 $1333 €1070 Scarecrow. Composition with figures. s. pair. 7-Feb-4 Rasmussen, Havnen #4177 (D.KR 8000)
£1007 $1833 €1470 Composition with gentleman and clown painting. s. two. 7-Feb-4 Rasmussen, Havnen #4184 (D.KR 11000)
£1190 $2167 €1737 Landscape with unicorn and figures (70x80cm-28x31in) s. 7-Feb-4 Rasmussen, Havnen #4192 est:2000 (D.KR 13000)
£1374 $2500 €2006 Surrealistic beach composition (105x120cm-41x47in) s. 7-Feb-4 Rasmussen, Havnen #4200 est:3000 (D.KR 15000)
£2015 $3667 €2942 Carnival mood in front of the Royal Theatre (70x80cm-28x31in) s. 7-Feb-4 Rasmussen, Havnen #4190/R est:2000 (D.KR 22000)

EISUI, Ichirakutei (fl.1789-1804) Japanese
Prints
£1818 $3091 €2600 Courtisane Komurasuki de tamaya. s. print. 25-Nov-3 Tajan, Paris #364/R est:1800-2000
£4500 $8280 €6570 Yoyoharu of the Matsubaya (36x24cm-14x9in) s. print exec. c.1796. 8-Jun-4 Sotheby's, London #301/R est:4500-5500

EISUKE, Miyao (19/20th C) Japanese
Sculpture
£8904 $15137 €13000 Boys with flags making music (21cm-8in) s. bronze gold. 8-Nov-3 Dr Fritz Nagel, Stuttgart #1889/R est:9500
£17808 $30274 €26000 Falconer and servant (28cm-11in) s. bronze gold. 8-Nov-3 Dr Fritz Nagel, Stuttgart #1891/R est:19000

EITNER, Ernst (1867-1955) German
£759 $1403 €1100 Boberg dunes (33x40cm-13x16in) s. i. verso. 14-Feb-4 Hans Stahl, Hamburg #138/R
£1135 $1895 €1600 On the Alster (32x38cm-13x15in) s. board. 16-Oct-3 Dorotheum, Salzburg #574/R est:1300-1700
£1844 $3079 €2600 Winter landscape (37x49cm-15x19in) s. board. 16-Oct-3 Dorotheum, Salzburg #575/R est:1000-1400
£2361 $3943 €3400 Park (80x60cm-31x24in) s. s.i. stretcher. 24-Oct-3 Ketterer, Hamburg #336/R est:3500-4000
£2797 $4811 €4000 Hamburg (38x46cm-15x18in) s. i.d.1896 verso board. 4-Dec-3 Schopman, Hamburg #724/R est:4800
Works on paper
£313 $494 €450 Ekensund (21x27cm-8x11in) s. W/C. 6-Sep-3 Schopman, Hamburg #752/R
£352 $563 €500 Winter landscape (29x45cm-11x18in) s. W/C. 19-Sep-3 Altus, Berlin #504/R

EIU, Hosoda (fl.c.1793-1797) Japanese
Prints
£2500 $4600 €3650 Komurasaki of the Kadotamaya (36x24cm-14x9in) s. print lit. 8-Jun-4 Sotheby's, London #294/R est:2500-3000

EIZAN, Kikugawa (1787-1867) Japanese
Prints
£2200 $4048 €3212 Mitate of a Daimyo procession by beauties crossing a river by boat (37x124cm-15x49in) s. print pentaptych exec. mid 1810's lit. 8-Jun-4 Sotheby's, London #386/R est:1500-2000

EJSTRUP, Kaj (1902-1956) Danish
£847 $1439 €1237 View of fields with fruit tree in blossom in foreground (70x90cm-28x35in) init.d.44. 26-Nov-3 Kunsthallen, Copenhagen #299 (D.KR 9000)
£1703 $3065 €2486 Hilly summer landscape (65x85cm-26x33in) init.d.44 exhib. 24-Apr-4 Rasmussen, Havnen #4137 est:2000 (D.KR 19000)

EKAGINA, Peggy (1919-) North American
Sculpture
£1441 $2450 €2104 Sedna with truncated hands as the Inuit myth depicts (33cm-13in) s. mottled dark soapstone. 3-Nov-3 Waddingtons, Toronto #48/R (C.D 3200)

EKDAWI, Mounir (1930-) Egyptian
£1000 $1770 €1460 Two ways to go. Gift (74x61cm-29x24in) s. board two. 29-Apr-4 Bonhams, New Bond Street #590/R est:800-1200

EKEGARDH, Hans (1891-1962) Swedish
£455 $738 €664 Women bathing (40x55cm-16x22in) i.verso panel. 9-Aug-3 Hindemae, Ullerslev #1085/R (D.KR 4800)

EKELAND, Arne (1908-1995) Norwegian
£937 $1612 €1368 The night (34x42cm-13x17in) s. i.verso paper on panel. 8-Dec-3 Blomqvist, Oslo #543/R (N.KR 11000)
£3080 $5235 €4497 Seated nude (50x42cm-20x17in) s.d.57. 19-Nov-3 Grev Wedels Plass, Oslo #103/R est:30000 (N.KR 36000)
Works on paper
£650 $1197 €975 Composition with figures (31x39cm-12x15in) s. gouache. 14-Jun-4 Blomqvist, Lysaker #1080 (N.KR 8000)

EKELS, Jan (younger) (1759-1793) Dutch
£6897 $11448 €10000 Young gentleman in elegant interior with hunting utensils (47x42cm-19x17in) 1-Oct-3 Dorotheum, Vienna #179/R est:10000-14000

EKELUND, Poul (1920-1976) Danish
£316 $581 €461 Field landscape with horses (75x83cm-30x33in) s. 29-Mar-4 Rasmussen, Copenhagen #496 (D.KR 3500)
£317 $567 €463 Interior scene with woman (56x46cm-22x18in) init. s.verso. 10-May-4 Rasmussen, Vejle #553 (D.KR 3500)
£452 $810 €660 Landscape with houses (50x60cm-20x24in) s.d.50. 10-May-4 Rasmussen, Vejle #661/R (D.KR 5000)
£493 $789 €715 Field landscape (56x78cm-22x31in) s. 17-Sep-3 Kunsthallen, Copenhagen #272/R (D.KR 5200)
£498 $806 €722 Road through field landscape (34x48cm-13x19in) s. canvas on masonite. 4-Aug-3 Rasmussen, Vejle #646 (D.KR 5200)
£533 $971 €800 Field landscape (39x49cm-15x19in) s. 19-Jun-4 Rasmussen, Havnen #4023/R (D.KR 6000)
£533 $971 €800 Landscape with cattle (46x55cm-18x22in) s. 19-Jun-4 Rasmussen, Havnen #4052 (D.KR 6000)
£657 $1098 €959 Girl wearing yellow top (53x76cm-21x30in) s. prov. 7-Oct-3 Rasmussen, Copenhagen #324/R (D.KR 7000)
£677 $1266 €988 Landscape with horse, St Ejstrup (60x65cm-24x26in) i.stretcher exhib. 25-Feb-4 Kunsthallen, Copenhagen #252/R (D.KR 7500)
£706 $1199 €1031 Seated girl (61x50cm-24x20in) s. exhib. 26-Nov-3 Kunsthallen, Copenhagen #355/R (D.KR 7500)
£812 $1519 €1186 Figures in park (46x58cm-18x23in) init. 25-Feb-4 Kunsthallen, Copenhagen #287/R (D.KR 9000)

EKELUND, Ragnar (1892-1960) Finnish
£694 $1160 €1000 Port in France (61x73cm-24x29in) s. 23-Oct-3 Hagelstam, Helsinki #959/R
£775 $1239 €1100 Field (46x55cm-18x22in) s. 18-Sep-3 Hagelstam, Helsinki #922
£1600 $2864 €2400 Street (60x50cm-24x20in) s. 15-May-4 Hagelstam, Helsinki #172/R est:2500
£2133 $3819 €3200 Chatillon (50x65cm-20x26in) s. 15-May-4 Hagelstam, Helsinki #171/R est:2500
£2238 $3804 €3200 View from Tallinn (61x65cm-24x26in) s. 29-Nov-3 Bukowskis, Helsinki #121/R est:3000-3500

Works on paper

£282	$451	€400	Bures sur Yvette (18x20cm-7x8in) s. dr. 21-Sep-3 Bukowskis, Helsinki #332/R

EKENAES, Jahn (1847-1920) Norwegian

£6966	$12468	€10170	Man sitting on sledge fishing from hole in the ice (31x51cm-12x20in) s.d.1891. 22-Mar-4 Blomqvist, Oslo #346/R est:60000-80000 (N.KR 87000)

EKLUND, Anders (1734-1802) Swedish

£730	$1189	€1066	Portrait of Jacob Palm Svensson (74x54cm-29x21in) s.d.1783 verso. 29-Sep-3 Lilla Bukowskis, Stockholm #131/R (S.KR 9500)
£1239	$2230	€1809	Portraits of Sven Roos Jnr and his wife Charlotta (65x51cm-26x20in) oval pair. 26-Jan-4 Lilla Bukowskis, Stockholm #450 est:15000-20000 (S.KR 16500)
£7538	$12966	€11005	Elisabeth Palm wearing Turkish outfit (79x63cm-31x25in) s.d.1768 verso prov. 2-Dec-3 Bukowskis, Stockholm #307/R est:75000-100000 (S.KR 98000)

EKLUND, Sten (1942-) Swedish

Works on paper

£616	$1109	€899	Untitled (43x42cm-17x17in) s.d.1966 gouache. 26-Apr-4 Bukowskis, Stockholm #490/R (S.KR 8500)
£4532	$7704	€6617	Purifying plant (53x71cm-21x28in) init.d.69 s.verso mixed media glass. 4-Nov-3 Bukowskis, Stockholm #529/R est:18000-20000 (S.KR 60000)

EKLUNDH, Claes (1944-) Swedish

Works on paper

£831	$1412	€1213	Head (60x48cm-24x19in) init. W/C prov. 5-Nov-3 AB Stockholms Auktionsverk #972/R (S.KR 11000)

EKMAN, Emil (1880-1951) Swedish

£1521	$2585	€2221	Fishing boats in morning light off the Swedish skerries (75x110cm-30x43in) s.d.1939. 10-Nov-3 Rasmussen, Vejle #302/R est:4000 (D.KR 16500)

EKMAN, Harry (20th C) American?

£2819	$5046	€4200	Knitting (76x64cm-30x25in) s. painted c.1958 lit. 27-May-4 Sotheby's, Paris #113/R est:1500-2000

EKMAN, Robert Wilhelm (1808-1873) Finnish

£1154	$1985	€1685	Portrait of Sophia Catarina Scharp seated in interior (45x37cm-18x15in) 3-Dec-3 AB Stockholms Auktionsverk #2576/R est:25000-30000 (S.KR 15000)
£2432	$4354	€3600	Regina von Emmeritz (73x90cm-29x35in) 8-May-4 Bukowskis, Helsinki #135/R est:4000-6000
£3378	$6047	€5000	Finlander's cot in Savolax (47x60cm-19x24in) s. cardboard lit. 8-May-4 Bukowskis, Helsinki #105/R est:5000-6000
£5811	$10401	€8600	Regina von Emmeritz (73x90cm-29x35in) 8-May-4 Bukowskis, Helsinki #31/R est:10000-13000
£7042	$12183	€10000	Peasant boy smoking (56x46cm-22x18in) s.d.1868 lit. 13-Dec-3 Hagelstam, Helsinki #95/R est:10000

EKMARCK, Mathilda (1822-1905) Swedish?

£3030	$5424	€4424	Still life of fruit (50x68cm-20x27in) s.d.1858. 26-May-4 AB Stockholms Auktionsverk #2275/R est:18000-20000 (S.KR 41000)

EKSTEDT, Sven (1894-1950) Swedish

£989	$1751	€1444	Walking in the Botanical garden, Copenhagen (34x26cm-13x10in) s.indis.d.19 panel exhib. 27-Apr-4 AB Stockholms Auktionsverk #844/R (S.KR 13500)

EKSTROM, Per (1844-1935) Swedish

£692	$1274	€1038	Landscape at sunset (46x72cm-18x28in) i.verso canvas on panel. 14-Jun-4 Lilla Bukowskis, Stockholm #241 (S.KR 9500)
£943	$1631	€1377	Hazy sunshine landscape (44x55cm-17x22in) s. 15-Dec-3 Lilla Bukowskis, Stockholm #486 (S.KR 12000)
£1000	$1720	€1460	Flooded landscape with farm (39x48cm-15x19in) s. panel. 7-Dec-3 Uppsala Auktionskammare, Uppsala #183/R (S.KR 13000)
£1163	$2011	€1698	Landscape (36x55cm-14x22in) s. 15-Dec-3 Lilla Bukowskis, Stockholm #364 est:10000-12000 (S.KR 14800)
£1769	$3043	€2583	Sunset (46x55cm-18x22in) s. 3-Dec-3 AB Stockholms Auktionsverk #2315/R est:25000-30000 (S.KR 23000)
£1968	$3621	€2952	Flooded landscape (37x63cm-15x25in) s. panel. 14-Jun-4 Lilla Bukowskis, Stockholm #1083 est:12000-15000 (S.KR 27000)
£2041	$3755	€3062	Sunset (38x63cm-15x25in) s. 14-Jun-4 Lilla Bukowskis, Stockholm #402/R est:15000-18000 (S.KR 28000)
£2154	$3705	€3145	Sunset over the sea (48x79cm-19x31in) s. 3-Dec-3 AB Stockholms Auktionsverk #2413/R est:15000-18000 (S.KR 28000)
£2231	$3837	€3257	Landscape from Saro (72x134cm-28x53in) s.d.1892. 2-Dec-3 Bukowskis, Stockholm #30/R est:40000-50000 (S.KR 29000)
£2402	$4324	€3507	Landscape at dusk (43x84cm-17x33in) s.d.1895. 26-Jan-4 Lilla Bukowskis, Stockholm #480 est:25000-30000 (S.KR 32000)
£2809	$5027	€4101	Landscape view of Mjorn Lake (76x101cm-30x40in) s.d.1901 canvas on panel. 25-May-4 Bukowskis, Stockholm #61/R est:35000-40000 (S.KR 38000)
£3231	$5557	€4717	Sunset (67x106cm-26x42in) s. 7-Dec-3 Uppsala Auktionskammare, Uppsala #182/R est:30000-40000 (S.KR 42000)
£3692	$6351	€5390	Flooded landscape at sunset (150x100cm-59x39in) s. 3-Dec-3 AB Stockholms Auktionsverk #2281/R est:50000-60000 (S.KR 48000)
£3695	$6615	€5395	Sunset in the woodland glade (102x68cm-40x27in) s. 25-May-4 Bukowskis, Stockholm #62/R est:45000-50000 (S.KR 50000)
£3846	$6615	€5615	Flooded landscape (70x96cm-28x38in) s. s.d.1879 verso. 2-Dec-3 Bukowskis, Stockholm #31/R est:60000-80000 (S.KR 50000)
£4769	$8203	€6963	Houses at Oland with hazy sunshine (70x110cm-28x43in) s/. 2-Dec-3 Bukowskis, Stockholm #29/R est:40000-50000 (S.KR 62000)
£4846	$8335	€7075	French garden, Barbizon (51x91cm-20x36in) s.i.d.1879 canvas on panel prov.lit. 2-Dec-3 Bukowskis, Stockholm #163/R est:50000-60000 (S.KR 63000)
£5322	$9525	€7770	Wooded landscape at dusk (94x155cm-37x61in) s.i.d.1879. 28-May-4 Uppsala Auktionskammare, Uppsala #211/R est:80000-100000 (S.KR 72000)
£5395	$9658	€7877	Sunrise over Segerstad (70x131cm-28x52in) s.d.1890 exhib.lit. 28-May-4 Uppsala Auktionskammare, Uppsala #212/R est:70000-80000 (S.KR 73000)
£5543	$9922	€8093	Evening with Segerstad's church, Oland (80x117cm-31x46in) s. 26-May-4 AB Stockholms Auktionsverk #2138/R est:75000-100000 (S.KR 75000)
£6800	$12171	€9928	Hazy flooded landscape (10x152cm-4x60in) s.d.1895 prov. 26-May-4 AB Stockholms Auktionsverk #2351/R est:70000-80000 (S.KR 92000)
£8130	$14553	€11870	Flooded landscape in sunlight (93x66cm-37x26in) s. 26-May-4 AB Stockholms Auktionsverk #2184/R est:50000-75000 (S.KR 110000)
£9615	$16538	€14038	Winter landscape at sunset (100x150cm-39x59in) s.d.1901. 3-Dec-3 AB Stockholms Auktionsverk #2412/R est:125000-150000 (S.KR 125000)
£10717	$19183	€15647	Night light at the entrance to Stockholm (54x36cm-21x14in) s.d.1895 exhib. 25-May-4 Bukowskis, Stockholm #63/R est:100000-125000 (S.KR 145000)

Works on paper

£628	$1125	€917	Boys fishing (32x54cm-13x21in) s.i.d.1890 mixed media. 28-May-4 Uppsala Auktionskammare, Uppsala #215 (S.KR 8500)
£813	$1455	€1187	Beach huts (32x53cm-13x21in) s.i.d.1890 mixed media. 28-May-4 Uppsala Auktionskammare, Uppsala #216 (S.KR 11000)

EKSTROM, Per (attrib) (1844-1935) Swedish

£1089	$1959	€1590	French landscape with woman (36x66cm-14x26in) i.verso. 26-Jan-4 Lilla Bukowskis, Stockholm #669 (S.KR 14500)

EKVALL, Emma (1838-1925) Swedish

£665	$1191	€971	Still life of flowers (51x36cm-20x14in) s. canvas on panel. 25-May-4 Bukowskis, Stockholm #49/R (S.KR 9000)
£1147	$1846	€1675	Portraits of Edward and Mathilda Owen (63cm-25in circular) s.d.1917 pair. 25-Aug-3 Lilla Bukowskis, Stockholm #608 est:20000-25000 (S.KR 15000)

EKVALL, Knut (1843-1912) Swedish

£4923	$8468	€7188	Block caused by snow (112x151cm-44x59in) s.d.1872. 3-Dec-3 AB Stockholms Auktionsverk #2258/R est:60000-80000 (S.KR 64000)

EL-BACHA, Amin (1932-) Lebanese

Works on paper

£1300	$2301	€1898	Garden of earthy delights. Symbols (38x26cm-15x10in) s. two. 29-Apr-4 Bonhams, New Bond Street #556/R est:1200-1500

EL-GLAOUI, Hassan (1924-) ?

£1200	$2208	€1800	Chevaux et poulain (50x61cm-20x24in) s. 9-Jun-4 Oger, Dumont, Paris #53/R est:1500-2000

EL-HANANI, Jacob (1947-) American

Works on paper

£3374	$5500	€4926	Reshet (48x48cm-19x19in) s.verso ink prov.exhib. 23-Sep-3 Christie's, Rockefeller NY #60/R est:6000-8000

EL-RAMALY, Bou Zian (19th C) Algerian

Works on paper

£600	$1098	€900	Combat naval (37x55cm-15x22in) i. W/C lit. 3-Jun-4 Tajan, Paris #210/R

ELAND, John Shenton (1872-?) British

£6600	$12210	€9636	Portrait of Doris Una Seth-Smith (145x99cm-57x39in) s.d.97. 14-Jan-4 Lawrence, Crewkerne #1426/R est:1500-2000

ELAND, Leonardus Joseph (1884-1952) Dutch

£274	$466	€400	Boat on the sea by moonlight (43x36cm-17x14in) s. board. 5-Nov-3 Vendue Huis, Gravenhage #535
£347	$549	€500	Planting season in the sawahs (64x100cm-25x39in) s. 2-Sep-3 Christie's, Amsterdam #263
£377	$640	€550	Red coast (58cm-23in) s. 5-Nov-3 Vendue Huis, Gravenhage #534/R
£395	$726	€600	Harbour in India (32x47cm-13x19in) s. panel. 28-Jun-4 Sotheby's, Amsterdam #57/R
£442	$791	€650	Fishermen at sunset (35x55cm-14x22in) s. 16-Mar-4 Christie's, Amsterdam #85/R
£486	$768	€700	Harvesting at the foot of a volcano (33x44cm-13x17in) s. panel. 2-Sep-3 Christie's, Amsterdam #248
£748	$1339	€1100	View on a lake (30x40cm-12x16in) s. 16-Mar-4 Christie's, Amsterdam #71/R est:500-700
£1634	$2615	€2386	Landscape (40x60cm-16x24in) s. 18-May-3 Sotheby's, Singapore #22/R est:4000-4500 (S.D 4560)
£1739	$2696	€2539	Landscape (45x35cm-18x14in) s. board. 6-Oct-2 Sotheby's, Singapore #59/R est:1500-2000 (S.D 4800)
£2124	$3845	€3101	Padi fields (50x70cm-20x28in) s. 4-Apr-4 Sotheby's, Singapore #23/R est:2000-3000 (S.D 6500)
£2151	$3441	€3140	Landscape. River landscape (40x60cm-16x24in) s. pair. 18-May-3 Sotheby's, Singapore #54/R est:2000-3000 (S.D 6000)
£2257	$3769	€3295	River landscape. Moonlit village (60x80cm-24x31in) s. two. 12-Oct-3 Sotheby's, Singapore #4/R est:4500-5500 (S.D 6500)
£2451	$4436	€3578	Rice fields at dawn (50x70cm-20x28in) s. 4-Apr-4 Sotheby's, Singapore #24/R est:3000-5000 (S.D 7500)
£2585	$4627	€3800	Indonesian landscape with figures, ox-carts in the distance (91x60cm-36x24in) s. 16-Mar-4 Christie's, Amsterdam #37/R est:800-1200
£2614	$4732	€3816	View of a lake (81x101cm-32x40in) s. 4-Apr-4 Sotheby's, Singapore #4/R est:5000-7000 (S.D 8000)
£2778	$4639	€4056	Forest landscape (150x100cm-59x39in) s. 12-Oct-3 Sotheby's, Singapore #42/R est:5000-7000 (S.D 8000)

ELBO, Jose (1804-1846) Spanish

£14493	$23768	€20000	La Venta de La Trinidad (66x93cm-26x37in) s.d.1841. 27-May-3 Durán, Madrid #258/R est:20000

ELDER, Ethel Harriet (?) British?

£300	$489	€438	Portrait of May Elder (66x56cm-26x22in) s. i.on stretcher. 25-Sep-3 Mellors & Kirk, Nottingham #739

ELDER, Will and KURTZMAN, Harvey (20th C) American

Works on paper			
£3429	$6000	€5006	Little Annie Fanny (57x42cm-22x17in) gouache ills board two separate caption sheets exec May 1963. 17-Dec-3 Christie's, Rockefeller NY #201/R est:7000-9000
£5143	$9000	€7509	Little Annie Fanny alone on a Desert Isle (56x42cm-22x17in) s. gouache ills board with Will Elder and Paul Coker five. 17-Dec-3 Christie's, Rockefeller NY #120/R est:5000-7000
£6286	$11000	€9178	Little Annie Fanny (51x35cm-20x14in) gouache ills board four exec Sept 1963. 17-Dec-3 Christie's, Rockefeller NY #146/R est:6000-8000
£13714	$24000	€20022	Little Annie Fanny - The Surfers (53x38cm-21x15in) gouache ills board with Jack Davis and Frank Franzetta five. 17-Dec-3 Christie's, Rockefeller NY #121/R est:15000-20000

ELDERSHAW, John Roy (1892-1973) Australian

£821	$1290	€1199	Yacandanda Valley (60x80cm-24x31in) s. 24-Nov-2 Goodman, Sydney #75/R est:2200-4200 (A.D 2300)
Works on paper			
£458	$834	€669	Southern tablelands (35x51cm-14x20in) s. W/C. 16-Jun-4 Deutscher-Menzies, Melbourne #346/R est:1000-1500 (A.D 1200)

ELDH, Albert (1878-1955) Swedish

£595	$1070	€893	Landscape from Grebbestad (110x85cm-43x33in) s.d.44. 25-Apr-4 Goteborg Auktionsverk, Sweden #318/R (S.KR 8200)

ELDH, Carl (1873-1955) Swedish

Sculpture			
£1154	$1985	€1685	From the street, mother and child (25cm-10in) s. pat.bronze lit. 3-Dec-3 AB Stockholms Auktionsverk #2513/R est:10000-15000 (S.KR 15000)
£1774	$3175	€2590	Ariadne (26cm-10in) s.i.d.1899 bronze Cast H Berman lit. 25-May-4 Bukowskis, Stockholm #296/R est:15000-18000 (S.KR 24000)
£2308	$3969	€3370	Young girl (25cm-10in) s.i.d.1904 dark pat.bronze Cast Bergman. 2-Dec-3 Bukowskis, Stockholm #230/R est:10000-12000 (S.KR 30000)

ELDRED, Lemeul D (1848-1921) American

£2469	$4000	€3605	Rocky coastal scene with shipping (10x20cm-4x8in) s. board. 31-Jul-3 Eldred, East Dennis #839/R est:2500-3500

ELDRED, Thomas Brownell (1903-1993) American

Works on paper			
£647	$1100	€945	Untitled (30x23cm-12x9in) s.d.1941 W/C. 9-Nov-3 Wright, Chicago #263 est:1200-1500
£706	$1200	€1031	Untitled (48x33cm-19x13in) s.d.1941 W/C. 9-Nov-3 Wright, Chicago #264 est:1500-2000

ELDRIDGE, Charles Henry (1869-?) British

£480	$888	€701	Venetian canal scene (63x90cm-25x35in) s.i.verso after Turner. 13-Jan-4 Bonhams, Knightsbridge #285/R

ELDRIDGE, Mildred E (1909-1991) British

Works on paper			
£320	$506	€467	Goldfinch, bluetit, wren and chaffinch (19x23cm-7x9in) s.d.1972 W/C over pencil prov. 3-Sep-3 Bonhams, Bury St Edmunds #366

ELENBERG, Joel (1948-1980) Australian

Works on paper			
£1191	$2061	€1739	Untitled, river series (185x60cm-73x24in) s.d.74 W/C ink six partitions prov. 10-Dec-3 Shapiro, Sydney #28/R est:3000-5000 (A.D 2800)

ELESZKIEWICZ, Stanislas (1900-1963) Polish

£350	$594	€500	Le marechal-ferrand (32x21cm-13x8in) mono. oil paper on cardboard. 20-Nov-3 Claude Aguttes, Neuilly #90
£795	$1446	€1200	Homme assoupi sur table (50x65cm-20x26in) s. cardboard. 19-Jun-4 St-Germain-en-Laye Encheres #203/R
£1062	$1805	€1550	Partie de des (46x55cm-18x22in) s. cardboard on canvas. 9-Nov-3 Eric Pillon, Calais #99/R

ELFORD, Victor (?) ?

£300	$549	€438	Land's End (61x91cm-24x36in) s. 8-Apr-4 Christie's, Kensington #104

ELGOOD, George Samuel (1851-1943) British

£650	$1190	€949	Fountain, Rome (26x41cm-10x16in) s.i.d.1882. 27-Jan-4 Bonhams, Knightsbridge #71/R
Works on paper			
£1000	$1660	€1460	Italian garden (24x36cm-9x14in) s.d.1897 W/C. 1-Oct-3 Sotheby's, Olympia #103/R est:1000-2000
£1000	$1600	€1460	Larkspur (20x18cm-8x7in) s.d.1906 i.verso W/C. 16-Sep-3 Gorringes, Bexhill #1556/R est:1000-1500
£1150	$1921	€1679	Garden at Harwick (20x36cm-8x14in) s.d.1897 w/. 14-Oct-3 Canterbury Auctions, UK #119/R est:800-1000
£1200	$2208	€1752	Chrysanthemums (21x16cm-8x6in) s.d.1906 W/C exhib. 8-Jun-4 Bonhams, New Bond Street #119/R est:1200-1800
£1700	$2890	€2482	Stocks in a garden (24x18cm-9x7in) s.d.1902 W/C. 1-Dec-3 Bonhams, Bath #56/R est:600-800
£2400	$4368	€3504	The ornamental garden, Hardwick Hall (24x36cm-9x14in) s. pencil W/C. 1-Jul-4 Christie's, Kensington #135/R est:1200-1800
£2400	$4368	€3504	The Parterre, Villa Garzoni (33x52cm-13x20in) s.d.1898 pencil W/C prov.exhib. 1-Jul-4 Christie's, Kensington #136/R est:1000-1200

ELHAFEN, Ignaz (1658-1715) German

Sculpture			
£71689	$126173	€106100	Rape of the Sabine women (12x19x3cm-5x7x1in) i. ivory lit.prov. 22-May-4 Lempertz, Koln #1202/R est:38000

ELHANANI, Jacob (20th C) ?

£1342	$2510	€2000	No 7 36x36 (92x92cm-36x36in) s.d. s.i.d.verso prov. 29-Feb-4 Versailles Encheres #233 est:800-1000

ELIAERTS, Jean François (1761-1848) Belgian

£29605	$54474	€45000	Still life of fruit. Still life of flowers (53x45cm-21x18in) s.d.1838 pair. 25-Jun-4 Piasa, Paris #29/R est:45000-60000

ELIAS, Alfred (19th C) British

£278	$464	€400	Sheep (36x52cm-14x20in) s. s. verso canvas on masonite. 24-Oct-3 Ketterer, Hamburg #165/R

ELIAS, Étienne (1936-) Belgian

£490	$817	€700	Titane in Amsterdam (90x100cm-35x39in) s. s.i.verso. 11-Oct-3 De Vuyst, Lokeren #138
£524	$876	€750	Oostend boy (100x90cm-39x35in) s. s.i.verso. 11-Oct-3 De Vuyst, Lokeren #139
£2083	$3479	€3000	Raveel dans son jardin (100x100cm-39x39in) s. 21-Oct-3 Campo, Vlaamse Kaai #429/R est:2000-2400

ELIASSON, Olafur (1967-) Danish

£6137	$11292	€8960	Composition (40x60cm-16x24in) s.d.1992 verso prov. 29-Mar-4 Rasmussen, Copenhagen #240/R est:60000 (D.KR 68000)
Photographs			
£4121	$7500	€6017	Untitled (60x90cm-24x35in) s.d.1998 num.1/1 col photograph prov. 29-Jun-4 Sotheby's, New York #643/R est:2500-3500
£5500	$9185	€8030	Untitled, from the Island series (60x90cm-24x35in) c-print prov. 22-Oct-3 Christie's, London #111/R est:2000-3000
£6500	$11960	€9490	Untitled (60x90cm-24x35in) s.d.1997 c-print prov. 25-Jun-4 Christie's, London #224/R est:4000-6000
£9000	$15030	€13140	Untitled, from the Iceland series (60x90cm-24x35in) s.d.1995 num.1/1 verso c-print prov. 22-Oct-3 Christie's, London #110/R est:3000-5000
Sculpture			
£2395	$4000	€3497	3D five fold symmetry (34x38x38cm-13x15x15in) cut paper adhesive executed 2000 prov. 14-Nov-3 Phillips, New York #293/R est:4000-6000

ELIESON, Chr (19th C) Norwegian

£260	$479	€390	Sailing vessels (33x45cm-13x18in) s. 14-Jun-4 Blomqvist, Lysaker #1082 (N.KR 3200)

ELIM, Frank (20th C) French

£500	$865	€730	Soldiers in a trench before no-man's land. 9-Dec-3 Lawrences, Bletchingley #1712
£680	$1082	€1000	Duke of Anjou (21x27cm-8x11in) s.d.1932 panel. 23-Mar-3 Mercier & Cie, Lille #244 est:1000-1200
£1479	$2455	€2100	Sortie du port de Trouville (22x27cm-9x11in) s. panel. 15-Jun-3 Peron, Melun #128a
£1615	$2600	€2358	Before the start (27x41cm-11x16in) s. 14-Jan-4 Christie's, Rockefeller NY #63/R est:1500-2000

ELINK-STERK, Isaac Cornelis (1808-1871) Dutch

£1111	$1811	€1600	Interior of Dutch church (23x17cm-9x7in) panel. 26-Sep-3 Bolland & Marotz, Bremen #521/R est:1700

ELIOT, C (19th C) ?

£1757	$3250	€2565	It's a chicks life (30x41cm-12x16in) s. pair. 15-Jul-4 Sotheby's, New York #26/R est:2500-3500

ELIOT, Ruth (1913-2001) Canadian

£315	$536	€460	Autumn leaves (30x41cm-12x16in) board. 23-Nov-3 Levis, Calgary #34/R (C.D 700)
£378	$627	€552	Untitled, fishing boat in dry dock (30x40cm-12x16in) wood board double-sided prov. 5-Oct-3 Levis, Calgary #28/R (C.D 850)
£413	$748	€603	Untitled - fall splendor (30x41cm-12x16in) wood board double-sided. 18-Apr-4 Levis, Calgary #31/R est:900-1200 (C.D 1000)

ELIOTT, Harry (1882-1959) ?

£2828	$5231	€4100	Sanglier courant. Cerf bat l'eau (53x80cm-21x31in) s. panel pair. 11-Feb-4 Beaussant & Lefèvre, Paris #175/R est:3000
Works on paper			
£449	$737	€620	La panique au marche (42x76cm-17x30in) pochoir col. 28-May-3 Coutau Begarie, Paris #176
£733	$1342	€1100	Scene de chasse a courre (20x18cm-8x7in) s.d.1916 W/C prov. 6-Jun-4 Rouillac, Vendome #47
£733	$1342	€1100	Chasseur tirant un lapin (20x18cm-8x7in) s.d.1916 W/C prov. 6-Jun-4 Rouillac, Vendome #46
£2657	$4571	€3800	After a days' hunting (46x63cm-18x25in) W/C exec.c.1920. 3-Dec-3 Coutau Begarie, Paris #86/R est:4000-5000

ELISCU, Frank (1912-1996) American

Sculpture			
£2326	$4000	€3396	Swimming nude with fish (62cm-24in) i. brown pat bronze marble base. 2-Dec-3 Christie's, Rockefeller NY #93/R est:1500-2500

ELKINS, Henry Arthur (1847-1884) American
£1100 $1947 €1606 Rocky river landscape (91x61cm-36x24in) s. 29-Apr-4 Christie's, Kensington #177/R est:1000-1500
£1730 $3200 €2526 Western landscape (51x76cm-20x30in) s. 24-Jan-4 Jeffery Burchard, Florida #50/R

ELLAGA, Barney (c.1931-) Australian
Works on paper
£1569 $2808 €2291 Alawa Country (76x196cm-30x77in) synthetic polymer paint canvas exec 1994 prov. 25-May-4 Lawson Menzies, Sydney #298/R est:4000-6000 (A.D 4000)

ELLE, Edouard (1854-1911) Belgian
£439 $830 €650 Bateau a maree basse (18x21cm-7x8in) s. panel. 17-Feb-4 Galerie Moderne, Brussels #134/R

ELLE, Louis (elder-attrib) (1612-1689) French
£2448 $4210 €3500 Portrait presume de Monsieur, frere du roi (100x79cm-39x31in) 3-Dec-3 Fraysse & Associes, Paris #112/R est:3000-4000

ELLEBY, William A (19th C) British
£231 $425 €337 Untitled - field with haystacks (18x30cm-7x12in) s. canvas on board. 27-Jun-4 Hindman, Chicago #1001/R

ELLENRIEDER, Maria (1791-1863) Swiss
£2837 $4596 €4000 St John the Baptist as a child in landscape (106x59cm-42x23in) s.d.1830 verso prov.lit. 23-May-3 Karlheinz Kaupp, Staufen #1754/R est:2500
Works on paper
£496 $804 €700 Young couple sitting on rocks with old woman (14x16cm-6x6in) s.d.1832 pencil. 23-May-3 Paul Kieffer, Pforzhiem #5276/R
£699 $1168 €1000 Infant Jesus on cloud (72x55cm-28x22in) lit. 27-Jun-3 Karrenbauer, Konstanz #1717/R
£2837 $4596 €4000 Santa Rosa da Lima (51x38cm-20x15in) s.d.1828 verso pastel htd gold prov.lit. 23-May-3 Karlheinz Kaupp, Staufen #1756/R est:2000

ELLER, Lucien Roudier (1894-1940) French
£414 $687 €600 Elegante des rues (54x30cm-21x12in) s. panel. 1-Oct-3 Millon & Associes, Paris #167
£2414 $4007 €3500 Figures du cinema de Pagnol (93x73cm-37x29in) 1-Oct-3 Millon & Associes, Paris #166/R est:1200-1500

ELLIGER, Ottmar I (1633-1679) Swedish
£72222 $130000 €105444 Still life with sprigs of guelder-rose and forget-me-not (24x19cm-9x7in) s.d.1666 panel prov. 22-Jan-4 Sotheby's, New York #61/R est:100000-150000

ELLIGER, Ottmar I (attrib) (1633-1679) Swedish
£19956 $35721 €29136 Still life of grapes and peaches in mountainous landscape (105x79cm-41x31in) 25-May-4 Bukowskis, Stockholm #477/R est:100000-125000 (S.KR 270000)

ELLIGER, Ottmar II (1666-1735) German
£5921 $10895 €9000 Allegory of Autumn (49x41cm-19x16in) s. 24-Jun-4 Christie's, Paris #74/R est:5000-7000

ELLINGER, David (1913-2003) American
£1250 $2000 €1825 Bird perched atop a basket of fruit (36x43cm-14x17in) s. velvet theorem. 20-Sep-3 Pook & Pook, Downington #61/R est:1500-2500
£1359 $2500 €1984 Grace (104x91cm-41x36in) s. i.verso. 22-Jun-4 Sotheby's, New York #199/R est:2500-3000
£1563 $2500 €2282 Rooster (33x33cm-13x13in) s. velvet theorem. 20-Sep-3 Pook & Pook, Downington #312/R est:1000-1500
£1902 $3500 €2777 Mixed flowers in an urn (44x47cm-17x19in) s. i. on velvet. 27-Jun-4 Freeman, Philadelphia #147/R est:1500-2500
£2174 $4000 €3174 Wash day (71x57cm-28x22in) s. i.verso. 22-Jun-4 Sotheby's, New York #200/R est:5000
£2326 $4000 €3396 Overflowing basket of fruit and bird on marbleised table (61x74cm-24x29in) s. velvet theorem. 6-Dec-3 Pook & Pook, Downington #342/R est:2500-3500
£3282 $5250 €4792 Amish woman working on a quilt (89x69cm-35x27in) i.verso. 20-Sep-3 Pook & Pook, Downington #539/R est:3500-5500
£4688 $7500 €6844 Amish farm scene (71x81cm-28x32in) s.i. 20-Sep-3 Pook & Pook, Downington #540/R est:8000-12000
Prints
£2500 $4000 €3650 Amish auction scene (48x66cm-19x26in) silkscreen. 20-Sep-3 Pook & Pook, Downington #463 est:1000-1500
Works on paper
£483 $850 €705 Fraktur of a bird resting on the leaf of a flower (13x10cm-5x4in) s.i. W/C. 21-May-4 Pook & Pook, Downington #254
£966 $1700 €1410 Fraktur of a bird perched atop of a branch (15x20cm-6x8in) s.i. W/C. 21-May-4 Pook & Pook, Downington #253 est:400-700
£1250 $2200 €1825 Basket of fruit (30x38cm-12x15in) s. W/C. 21-May-4 Pook & Pook, Downington #390/R est:1200-1800

ELLINGER, David (attrib) (1913-2003) American
£233 $400 €340 Winter landscape with horse drawn sled (30x41cm-12x16in) board. 6-Dec-3 Pook & Pook, Downington #399/R
£320 $550 €467 Farm scene with two buildings, figures and animals (28x38cm-11x15in) board. 6-Dec-3 Pook & Pook, Downington #412/R

ELLIOT, Charles Loring (1812-1868) American
£872 $1500 €1273 Portrait of Pierre Van Cortlandt IV as a young boy (58x48cm-23x19in) oval. 6-Dec-3 Neal Auction Company, New Orleans #343/R est:2000-3000
£900 $1629 €1314 Portrait of a lady (60x50cm-24x20in) i.verso painted c.1846. 4-Apr-4 Lots Road Auctions, London #355/R

ELLIOT, Charles Loring (attrib) (1812-1868) American
£1017 $1750 €1485 Portrait of Theodoric Romeyn Van Cortlandt (53x43cm-21x17in) oval. 6-Dec-3 Neal Auction Company, New Orleans #344/R est:2000-3000

ELLIOT, Thomas (fl.1790-1800) British
£82000 $146780 €119720 Panorama of Portsmouth harbour with a flagship of the Red Squadron (86x140cm-34x55in) s. 26-May-4 Christie's, Kensington #587/R est:15000-25000

ELLIOT, William (1909-2001) American
Works on paper
£299 $500 €437 Old water grist mill Bandera, TX (38x56cm-15x22in) W/C. 18-Oct-3 David Dike, Dallas #296/R

ELLIOTT, Douglas Ferguson (1916-) Canadian
£203 $344 €296 Fog at Prospect, Nova Scotia (41x66cm-16x26in) s. acrylic board prov. 23-Nov-3 Levis, Calgary #449/R (C.D 450)
£203 $344 €296 Hazy afternoon, Nova Scotia (41x66cm-16x26in) s. acrylic board prov. 23-Nov-3 Levis, Calgary #450/R (C.D 450)

ELLIOTT, Emily Louise Orr (1867-1952) Canadian
£200 $366 €292 Ship at a wharf (22x17cm-9x7in) s.d.1908 canvas on board prov. 1-Jun-4 Joyner Waddington, Toronto #481 (C.D 500)
£402 $747 €587 Centre Island (23x27cm-9x11in) panel. 2-Mar-4 Ritchie, Toronto #120/R (C.D 1000)
£560 $1025 €818 Toronto Harbour (35x30cm-14x12in) s. panel. 1-Jun-4 Joyner Waddington, Toronto #514 (C.D 1400)

ELLIOTT, Frederick James (1864-1949) Australian
Works on paper
£1564 $2830 €2283 Ship passing the cliff (57x83cm-22x33in) s. W/C. 31-Mar-4 Goodman, Sydney #347/R est:1500-2500 (A.D 3800)

ELLIOTT, Grace L M (fl.1900-1918) British
£500 $835 €730 Cattle in a meadow with estuary beyond (61x91cm-24x36in) s.d.1910. 12-Nov-3 Halls, Shrewsbury #315/R

ELLIOTT, Grace L M (attrib) (fl.1900-1918) British
Works on paper
£290 $461 €423 Unloading the catch on Newquay beach (25x64cm-10x25in) s. W/C exec.c.1870-1890. 23-Mar-3 Desmond Judd, Cranbrook #1078

ELLIOTT, Larry (20th C) American
£459 $850 €670 Rabbits (36x28cm-14x11in) s. panel. 16-Jan-4 Aspire, Cleveland #68/R

ELLIOTT, Ric (1933-1995) Australian
£319 $552 €466 Historic shop, Hunters Hill (40x70cm-16x28in) s. masonite board prov. 10-Dec-3 Shapiro, Sydney #12/R (A.D 750)
£332 $621 €485 Black opal country (60x90cm-24x35in) s. board. 27-Feb-4 Lawson Menzies, Sydney #2131/R (A.D 800)
£372 $688 €543 Glebe (23x15cm-9x6in) s. board prov. 10-Mar-4 Deutscher-Menzies, Melbourne #558/R (A.D 900)
£402 $671 €583 Overlooking the spit (61x91cm-24x36in) s. board. 30-Jun-3 Australian Art Auctions, Sydney #128 (A.D 1000)
£763 $1389 €1114 Street scene (20x33cm-8x13in) s. canvas on board. 16-Jun-4 Deutscher-Menzies, Melbourne #609/R est:800-1200 (A.D 2000)
£802 $1459 €1171 Historic shop, Hunter's Hill (40x71cm-16x28in) s. canvasboard. 16-Jun-4 Deutscher-Menzies, Melbourne #306/R est:1600-2400 (A.D 2100)
£992 $1806 €1448 Street scene (25x84cm-10x33in) board. 16-Jun-4 Deutscher-Menzies, Melbourne #514/R est:3000-4000 (A.D 2600)

ELLIOTT, Richard (20th C) Irish?
Works on paper
£724 $1332 €1100 The St Stephen's Green Club (56x71cm-22x28in) s. W/C. 22-Jun-4 De Veres Art Auctions, Dublin #228/R

ELLIOTT, Robinson (1814-1894) British
£900 $1665 €1314 Fisher children - the expected return (44x35cm-17x14in) s.i. verso. 14-Jul-4 Bonhams, Chester #408/R
Works on paper
£320 $582 €467 Fisherman resting on the banks of the North Tyne (35x54cm-14x21in) s.d.1882 W/C. 29-Jun-4 Anderson & Garland, Newcastle #267/R

ELLIS, Arthur (1856-?) British
£400 $724 €584 Portrait of a woman (52x42cm-20x17in) s. 15-Apr-4 Hobbs Parker, Ashford #690/R

ELLIS, Dean (1920-) American
£1229 $2200 €1794 Martian Chronicles (64x41cm-25x16in) acrylic. 15-May-4 Illustration House, New York #6/R est:2500-3500

ELLIS, Edwin (1841-1895) British
£500 $815 €730 Crofters cottage (33x48cm-13x19in) s. 23-Sep-3 John Nicholson, Haslemere #325
£600 $1098 €900 Lakeland scene at dusk with rowing boat tied up against a wall (106x152cm-42x60in) s. 12-Jul-4 Mullucks Wells, Bishop's Stortford #396
£680 $1238 €993 Marine scene (58x114cm-23x45in) s. 15-Jun-4 Canterbury Auctions, UK #81/R

£1050 $1712 €1533 Fisherman making for shore in a dingy (45x84cm-18x33in) s. 24-Sep-3 Dreweatt Neate, Newbury #96/R est:500-700

ELLIS, Ernest F (19th C) American
£245 $450 €358 Seascape (20x41cm-8x16in) s.verso. 26-Jun-4 Susanin's, Chicago #6095/R

ELLIS, Frederick Vincent (1892-1961) New Zealander
£284 $502 €415 Portrait of a Spanish lady (98x85cm-39x33in) s.d.57. 28-Apr-4 Dunbar Sloane, Auckland #100 (NZ.D 800)
£290 $467 €423 Shell tanker, Evans Bay 1960 (32x39cm-13x15in) board prov. 20-Aug-3 Dunbar Sloane, Auckland #81/R (NZ.D 800)
£833 $1325 €1216 South road, Waiwera S.I (54x63cm-21x25in) s.d.1939 board. 1-May-3 Dunbar Sloane, Wellington #66/R est:600-1200 (NZ.D 2400)
£1090 $1853 €1591 City marina and St. Gerards (35x40cm-14x16in) s.d.1952 board. 26-Nov-3 Dunbar Sloane, Wellington #139/R est:500-1000 (NZ.D 2900)

ELLIS, Fremont F (1897-1985) American
£2206 $3750 €3221 Afternoon at el Zaguan (25x20cm-10x8in) s. i.verso masonite. 18-Nov-3 John Moran, Pasadena #19 est:4000-6000
£2235 $4000 €3263 Sketch for trout lake (28x36cm-11x14in) s. i.verso canvas on board prov. 6-May-4 Shannon's, Milford #199/R est:4000-6000
£5556 $9000 €8056 Aspens (61x51cm-24x20in) s. 8-Aug-3 Barridorf, Portland #261/R est:9000-12000
£5882 $10000 €8588 Bicycle rider (41x51cm-16x20in) s. s.i.verso canvas on board prov.lit. 1-Nov-3 Santa Fe Art, Santa Fe #61/R est:10000-15000
£6630 $12000 €9680 Aspens at Mill Creek (56x71cm-22x28in) s.d.63 i.verso prov. 31-Mar-4 Sotheby's, New York #107/R est:8000-10000
£7059 $12000 €10306 Adobe, numero de dias (63x76cm-25x30in) s. prov. 29-Oct-3 Christie's, Los Angeles #22/R est:12000-18000
£9040 $16000 €13198 Summer cottonwoods on the Pecos (55x76cm-22x30in) s. s.i.verso canvasboard. 28-Apr-4 Christie's, Los Angeles #3/R est:20000-30000
£14706 $25000 €21471 Aspen Santa Fe Canyon (56x76cm-22x30in) board. 1-Nov-3 Altermann Galleries, Santa Fe #155
£15294 $26000 €22329 El vaquero (61x51cm-24x20in) board. 1-Nov-3 Altermann Galleries, Santa Fe #156
Works on paper
£1818 $3000 €2636 Santuario at Chimmayo (25x33cm-10x13in) s. i.verso W/C. 7-Jul-3 Schrager Galleries, Milwaukee #1267

ELLIS, Gordon (1920-1978) British
£750 $1418 €1095 High water - London Bridge 1600 (91x152cm-36x60in) s. i.on stretcher. 19-Feb-4 Christie's, Kensington #154/R
£2000 $3580 €2920 Mersey shipping - Deck Cargo. Mersey shipping - Waiting for the tide (31x54cm-12x21in) both s. board pair. 17-Mar-4 Bonhams, Chester #258 est:1000-1500
£2700 $4860 €3942 Return of the Wanderer. SS Clan Matheson (37x48cm-15x19in) s. canvas on board sold with 2 others by G Shaw and S R Fever. 21-Jan-4 Sotheby's, Olympia #383/R est:600-800

ELLIS, Joseph F (1783-1848) British
£320 $586 €467 On the Winnien, Dolgelly (47x73cm-19x29in) s.d.1879 i.verso. 28-Jul-4 Hampton & Littlewood, Exeter #628/R

ELLIS, Nicholas Edwin John (?) British
£550 $875 €803 Reclining nude (54x81cm-21x32in) 9-Sep-3 Bonhams, Knightsbridge #136/R

ELLIS, Paul H (fl.1882-1908) British
£1050 $1785 €1533 Peasants and wagon on a track in a mountainous landscape (62x91cm-24x36in) i.verso. 26-Nov-3 Hamptons Fine Art, Godalming #145 est:300-500

ELLIS, Ray G (1921-) American
£1173 $2100 €1713 Lester Pigott, English Derby (28x20cm-11x8in) s. board. 7-May-4 Sloans & Kenyon, Bethesda #1706/R est:2500-3000

ELLIS, Robert (1929-) New Zealander
£765 $1300 €1117 Lugar, place (53x74cm-21x29in) s.d.1960. 9-Nov-3 Wright, Chicago #282 est:2000-3000
£882 $1500 €1288 Crying woman (66x61cm-26x24in) s. masonite. 9-Nov-3 Wright, Chicago #286 est:3000-4000
£1250 $2263 €1825 Arepa omeka (33x29cm-13x11in) s.i.d.1984 board. 30-Mar-4 Peter Webb, Auckland #3/R est:3000-5000 (NZ.D 3500)
£4348 $7000 €6348 8 Maehe (59x59cm-23x23in) s.i.d.1992 board. 20-Aug-3 Dunbar Sloane, Auckland #53/R est:12000-15000 (NZ.D 12000)
£5903 $9385 €8618 Motorway journey (89x89cm-35x35in) s.d.1970 board exhib. 1-May-3 Dunbar Sloane, Wellington #27/R est:10000-20000 (NZ.D 17000)
£5957 $9709 €8697 Motorway journey (70x90cm-28x35in) s.d.1970 s.i.d.verso board. 23-Sep-3 Peter Webb, Auckland #34/R est:10000-15000 (NZ.D 16500)
£6993 $12727 €10210 River winding through the city (122x122cm-48x48in) s.d.1965 s.i.d.verso board exhib. 29-Jun-4 Peter Webb, Auckland #53/R est:16000-25000 (NZ.D 20000)
Works on paper
£692 $1239 €1010 Rakaumangamanga (75x57cm-30x22in) s.i.d.19 November 1984 mixed media. 12-May-4 Dunbar Sloane, Wellington #13/R est:3500-7000 (NZ.D 2000)
£706 $1200 €1031 Mujer - woman (43x74cm-17x29in) s.d.1960 casein. 9-Nov-3 Wright, Chicago #285 est:1000-1500
£1083 $1765 €1581 City and fertile plain (63x50cm-25x20in) s.d.1962 wax crayon W/C. 23-Sep-3 Peter Webb, Auckland #13/R est:3000-5000 (NZ.D 3000)

ELLIS, Tristram (1844-1922) British
Works on paper
£250 $403 €363 View in Corfu (15x20cm-6x8in) s. W/C. 15-Aug-3 Keys, Aylsham #548/R
£520 $941 €759 Maderia (18x36cm-7x14in) s.d.1908 W/C. 31-Mar-4 Brightwells, Leominster #941
£760 $1366 €1110 Molde, Norway (23x52cm-9x20in) s.i.d.1898 W/C sold with another by the same hand. 21-Jan-4 Sotheby's, Olympia #211/R
£1000 $1700 €1460 Public Gardens, Athens (18x35cm-7x14in) s.d.1890 W/C over pencil. 18-Nov-3 Sotheby's, London #135/R est:1200-1800
£1200 $2148 €1752 The Erectheion (26x37cm-10x15in) s.i. W/C pencil. 11-May-4 Bonhams, New Bond Street #18/R est:1200-1800
£3800 $6080 €5548 Cyprus (24x35cm-9x14in) s.i.d.1879 W/C over pencil htd bodycol. 16-Sep-3 Bonhams, Knowle #55 est:300-500

ELLIS, William (attrib) (fl.1863-1864) British
£400 $680 €584 Cottage at Barmouth, North Wales (31x51cm-12x20in) s. i.verso. 29-Oct-3 Bonhams, Chester #318

ELLIS, William (1747-1810) British
£350 $616 €511 Cornfields at Hampstead, Staffordshire (43x67cm-17x26in) i.verso. 18-May-4 Bonhams, Knowle #354

ELLISON, John (1912-1957) Canadian
Works on paper
£322 $557 €470 Cargo Vessel (56x72cm-22x28in) s.i. W/C. 9-Dec-3 Pinneys, Montreal #190 (C.D 725)

ELLISON, Thomas (1866-c.1942) British
Works on paper
£260 $465 €380 Evening on the LLedr (50x74cm-20x29in) s. W/C. 11-May-4 Bonhams, Ipswich #295
£300 $516 €438 Autumnal river scene (43x58cm-17x23in) s. W/C. 3-Dec-3 Andrew Hartley, Ilkley #1087
£580 $969 €847 Nefyn coast with figures and rowing boats (44x59cm-17x23in) s. W/C. 9-Jul-3 Peter Wilson, Nantwich #67
£750 $1373 €1095 Marche de poisson, Bruges (37x53cm-15x21in) s. W/C exhib. 7-Apr-4 Bonhams, Bury St Edmunds #403/R

ELLMINGER, Ignaz (1843-1894) Austrian
£884 $1610 €1300 Shepherding couple with flock in landscape (26x53cm-10x21in) s. lit. 3-Feb-4 Sigalas, Stuttgart #492/R
£2098 $3566 €3000 Market on the main square of Krems (37x58cm-15x23in) s.d.1889 panel. 20-Nov-3 Dorotheum, Salzburg #180/R est:6000-9000

ELLRICK, A J M (20th C) American
£2312 $4000 €3376 Otsego Lake (64x117cm-25x46in) s. 10-Dec-3 Alderfer's, Hatfield #347/R est:2000-3000

ELLSWORTH, Clarence (1885-1961) American
£989 $1800 €1444 Indian ambush (18x23cm-7x9in) init. canvasboard prov. 15-Jun-4 John Moran, Pasadena #127c est:1800-2200
£1852 $3500 €2704 Fringe of the herd - indian/buffalo (41x61cm-16x24in) s.d.1949 i. verso board prov. 17-Feb-4 John Moran, Pasadena #126/R est:4000-6000
£4497 $8500 €6566 Last cartridge, dispatch bearer (36x51cm-14x20in) s.d.1948 i. stretcher prov. 17-Feb-4 John Moran, Pasadena #127/R est:4000-6000

ELLWOOD, G S (19/20th C) British?
Works on paper
£667 $1153 €974 Doven cottage (25x33cm-10x13in) d.1904 W/C. 9-Dec-3 Maynards, Vancouver #126 (C.D 1500)

ELMER, Stephen (1717-1796) British
£3000 $5400 €4380 Spaniel guarding game (101x127cm-40x50in) 21-Jan-4 Sotheby's, Olympia #96/R est:800-1200
£3700 $6919 €5550 Flock of partridge with a lake and swallows (37x45cm-15x18in) s. sold with a companion. 26-Jul-4 Bonhams, Bath #54/R est:3000-4000

ELMER, Stephen (attrib) (1717-1796) British
£2794 $4750 €4079 Pair of pheasants in an extensive landscape with ruins (102x127cm-40x50in) 31-Oct-3 North East Auctions, Portsmouth #1208

ELMIGER, Franz Jakob (1882-1934) Swiss
£262 $461 €383 Cow in bay near Ennethorw (36x49cm-14x19in) i. canvas on panel prov. 22-May-4 Galerie Gloggner, Luzern #33 (S.FR 600)
£262 $461 €383 Garden landscape (28x58cm-11x23in) canvas on board prov. 22-May-4 Galerie Gloggner, Luzern #35 (S.FR 600)
£452 $769 €660 Standing female nude (72x44cm-28x17in) mono. board on panel. 19-Nov-3 Fischer, Luzern #2084/R (S.FR 1000)
£452 $769 €660 Village stream in winter (35x49cm-14x19in) mono. board on panel. 19-Nov-3 Fischer, Luzern #2081 (S.FR 1000)
£568 $1033 €829 Ermensee in winter (39x34cm-15x13in) canvas on cardboard. 16-Jun-4 Fischer, Luzern #2087 (S.FR 1300)
£746 $1245 €1089 Two dead birds (52x41cm-20x16in) s. i. verso canvas on board prov.lit. 15-Nov-3 Galerie Gloggner, Luzern #39/R (S.FR 1700)
£873 $1537 €1275 Old mill on wintery Ermensee (47x53cm-19x21in) s.d.1911 prov.lit. 22-May-4 Galerie Gloggner, Luzern #32/R (S.FR 2000)
£1041 $1769 €1520 Two cows in shade of fruit tree (57x84cm-22x33in) s.d.17 i. verso. 19-Nov-3 Fischer, Luzern #2086/R est:1800-2500 (S.FR 2300)
£1310 $2306 €1913 Chestnut tree in front of house (36x48cm-14x19in) mono. i. verso canvas on board prov. 22-May-4 Galerie Gloggner, Luzern #34/R est:1000-1200 (S.FR 3000)
£1579 $2637 €2305 Barn in field (46x63cm-18x25in) i. panel prov. 15-Nov-3 Galerie Gloggner, Luzern #38 est:3000-3600 (S.FR 3600)
£2851 $4761 €4162 Autumn meadow (98x135cm-39x53in) s. i. stretcher prov.lit. 15-Nov-3 Galerie Gloggner, Luzern #37/R est:5500-6000 (S.FR 6500)

ELMORE, Alfred (1815-1881) British
£1500 $2490 €2190 Religious debate (30x45cm-12x18in) s.d.1850-1852. 1-Oct-3 Sotheby's, Olympia #120/R est:1500-2000

ELMORE, Richard (fl.1852-1892) British
£4025 $6843 €5877 Harvesters (88x129cm-35x51in) s.d.1872.3 prov. 24-Nov-3 Sotheby's, Melbourne #290/R est:8000-12000 (A.D 9500)

ELOFF, Zakkie (1925-) South African
£413 $739 €603 Rooihaartebeest (45x60cm-18x24in) s. 31-May-4 Stephan Welz, Johannesburg #228 (SA.R 5000)
£504 $913 €736 Pair of black backed jackals (31x44cm-12x17in) s. canvasboard. 30-Mar-4 Stephan Welz, Johannesburg #243 est:2500-4000 (SA.R 6000)
£546 $989 €797 Woman hoeing in a rural landscape (38x57cm-15x22in) s.d.53 board. 30-Mar-4 Stephan Welz, Johannesburg #469 est:4000-6000 (SA.R 6500)
Works on paper
£264 $473 €385 Herd of impala running (49x66cm-19x26in) s. brush ink. 31-May-4 Stephan Welz, Johannesburg #222 (SA.R 3200)
£264 $473 €385 Herd of zebra running (49x66cm-19x26in) s. brush ink. 31-May-4 Stephan Welz, Johannesburg #223 (SA.R 3200)
£302 $504 €441 Five elephants (48x65cm-19x26in) s. W/C. 20-Oct-3 Stephan Welz, Johannesburg #821 est:2000-3000 (SA.R 3500)
£328 $547 €479 Impalas (45x62cm-18x24in) s. W/C. 20-Oct-3 Stephan Welz, Johannesburg #819 est:2000-3000 (SA.R 3800)

ELRICK, Thomas K (1906-1960) American
£1058 $2000 €1545 The old stone wall (30x41cm-12x16in) s. 17-Feb-4 John Moran, Pasadena #69/R est:2000-3000

ELSEN, Alfred (1850-1900) Belgian
£676 $1189 €1000 Landscape (70x100cm-28x39in) s. 24-May-4 Bernaerts, Antwerp #545/R

ELSEVIER, Louwys-Aernouts (1617-1675) Dutch
£2500 $4500 €3650 Allegory of art, putti disporting with a portrait of the artist (86x122cm-34x48in) s.d. en grisaille. 23-Apr-4 Christie's, Kensington #71/R est:3000-5000

ELSHEIMER, Adam (1574-1620) German
Prints
£2267 $4057 €3400 Tobias and angel (16x10cm-6x4in) etching. 13-May-4 Bassenge, Berlin #5139/R est:1200

ELSHEIMER, Adam (attrib) (1574-1620) German
£894 $1600 €1305 Fight into Egypt (20x15cm-8x6in) copper. 20-Mar-4 Sloans & Kenyon, Bethesda #1149/R est:900-1200

ELSLEY, Arthur John (1861-1952) British
£70588 $120000 €103058 False alarm/Christmas morning (92x68cm-36x27in) s.d.1894 exhib.lit. 28-Oct-3 Sotheby's, New York #74/R est:150000-200000
£83333 $150000 €121666 This little pig went to market (95x69cm-37x27in) s. painted c.1911 prov.lit. 22-Apr-4 Christie's, Rockefeller NY #64/R est:180000-220000
£135000 $245700 €197100 Baby's turn (109x142cm-43x56in) s.d.1905 lit. 16-Jun-4 Bonhams, New Bond Street #68/R est:80000-120000
£164706 $280000 €240471 Hide and seek (92x73cm-36x29in) s.d.1908 prov.lit. 29-Oct-3 Christie's, Rockefeller NY #75/R est:300000-400000

ELSNER, Karl (1865-1935) Austrian
Works on paper
£805 $1482 €1200 Perchtoldsdorf tower (30x24cm-12x9in) s.d. W/C. 26-Mar-4 Dorotheum, Vienna #292/R

ELSWORTH, Alfred (19th C) British
£2200 $3740 €3212 Head of a mastiff (46x36cm-18x14in) s.d.1884. 27-Nov-3 Christie's, Kensington #319/R est:800-1200

ELTEN, Hendrik Dirk Kruseman van (1829-1904) Dutch
£289 $500 €422 Nocturnal landscape with boaters on lake, house and windmill beyond (53x76cm-21x30in) s. 10-Dec-3 Alderfer's, Hatfield #284
£1317 $2200 €1923 Landscape (33x58cm-13x23in) s. 18-Jun-3 Doyle, New York #46/R est:1500-2500
£1800 $2880 €2610 Evening stroll (29x39cm-11x15in) s. panel. 18-Sep-3 Christie's, Kensington #51/R est:2000-3000
£1852 $3000 €2685 Red roofs (36x58cm-14x23in) s. 8-Aug-3 Barridorf, Portland #146/R est:2500-3500
£1905 $3467 €2800 After the storm, travelers on a path in a landscape (49x63cm-19x25in) init.d.1849. 3-Feb-4 Christie's, Amsterdam #61/R est:2000-3000

ELTTES, Renee (attrib) (19th C) French?
£1014 $1693 €1450 Africaine (58x41cm-23x16in) s.d.40. 7-Oct-3 Livinec, Gaudcheau & Jezequel, Rennes #101/R

ELTYSHEV, Nikolai Ivanovich (1922-) Russian
£380 $692 €555 Fun by the river (70x80cm-28x31in) s.d.1999. 20-Jun-4 Lots Road Auctions, London #336/R

ELUARD, Paul (1895-1952) French
Works on paper
£667 $1227 €1000 Monstres, personnage nu dansant, fleurs (26x20cm-10x8in) s. pen. 9-Jun-4 Piasa, Paris #63
£738 $1307 €1100 Untitled (29x21cm-11x8in) s.d.1910 Chinese ink wash. 29-Apr-4 Christie's, Paris #84/R
£918 $1644 €1350 Istamboul (31x23cm-12x9in) s.d.21 W/C. 16-Mar-4 Vanderkindere, Brussels #113

ELVGREN, Gil (1914-1980) American
£3235 $5500 €4723 Girl with soda bottle (30x69cm-12x27in) s. prov. 29-Oct-3 Christie's, Los Angeles #76/R est:6000-8000
£10180 $17000 €14863 Figures don't lie (91x76cm-36x30in) 15-Nov-3 Illustration House, New York #141/R est:9000-15000
£12081 $21624 €18000 Up and cunning (77x61cm-30x24in) s. painted 1955. 27-May-4 Sotheby's, Paris #132/R est:12000-15000
£13423 $24027 €20000 Cornered (77x61cm-30x24in) s. painted 1955. 27-May-4 Sotheby's, Paris #112/R est:12000-15000
£14525 $26000 €21207 Woman playing with three kittens (76x61cm-30x24in) s. 15-May-4 Illustration House, New York #125/R est:25000-40000
£14765 $26430 €22000 Gents prefer (76x61cm-30x24in) s. painted 1963 lit. 27-May-4 Sotheby's, Paris #134/R est:15000-20000
£16779 $30034 €25000 I gave him brushoff (77x66cm-30x26in) s. i.verso painted 1947 lit. 27-May-4 Sotheby's, Paris #109/R est:12000-15000
£18792 $33638 €28000 Modest manouvre (77x61cm-30x24in) s. painted 1969 lit. 27-May-4 Sotheby's, Paris #111/R est:12000-15000
£18792 $33638 €28000 Ruffled feathers (77x61cm-30x24in) s. painted 1967 lit. 27-May-4 Sotheby's, Paris #131/R est:12000-15000
£18792 $33638 €28000 What do you think (77x61cm-30x24in) s. i.stretcher painted 1961 lit. 27-May-4 Sotheby's, Paris #135/R est:12000-15000
£20134 $36040 €30000 The right number (77x61cm-30x24in) s. painted 1961 lit. 27-May-4 Sotheby's, Paris #110/R est:12000-15000
£29530 $52859 €44000 Cover up (76x66cm-30x26in) s. painted 1955 lit. 27-May-4 Sotheby's, Paris #108/R est:20000-25000
£29530 $52859 €44000 Skirts ahoy (77x61cm-30x24in) s. painted 1967 lit. 27-May-4 Sotheby's, Paris #133/R est:20000-25000
£36242 $64872 €54000 Lucky dog (77x61cm-30x24in) s. painted 1958 lit. 27-May-4 Sotheby's, Paris #136/R est:15000-20000
£39106 $70000 €57095 Secretary with spilled ink (76x61cm-30x24in) s. 15-May-4 Illustration House, New York #124/R est:25000-40000

ELWELL, Frederick William (1870-1958) British
£650 $1105 €949 Mountainous continental scenes (15x20cm-6x8in) s.d. Christmas 1939 on white metal pair. 21-Nov-3 Dee Atkinson & Harrison, Driffield #716/R
£750 $1328 €1095 Continental valley scene (28x38cm-11x15in) artist's board. 30-Apr-4 Dee Atkinson & Harrison, Driffield #773
£2400 $4320 €3504 Portrait of a man with a pint of beer (90x70cm-35x28in) board. 20-Jan-4 Bonhams, Knightsbridge #114/R est:1000-1500
£6500 $11505 €9490 Another man with a pint (89x69cm-35x27in) board. 30-Apr-4 Dee Atkinson & Harrison, Driffield #776/R est:6000-8000
£8000 $14320 €11680 Breakfast time (114x81cm-45x32in) s. 27-May-4 Christie's, Kensington #338/R est:5000-7000

ELWELL, Mary (1874-1952) British
£250 $425 €365 River scene mountains in the background (23x33cm-9x13in) s. 21-Nov-3 Dee Atkinson & Harrison, Driffield #715
£2300 $4071 €3358 Thorpe Hall, Rudston, East Yorkshire (25x36cm-10x14in) s.d.1927. 30-Apr-4 Dee Atkinson & Harrison, Driffield #772 est:1000-1500

ELWELL, Robert Farrington (1874-1962) American
£2415 $4250 €3526 Southwestern scene of cowboys around the chuck wagon with a cattle heard (74x102cm-29x40in) s. 3-Jan-4 Cobbs, Peterborough #144/R
Works on paper
£1118 $1800 €1621 Cowboys on horses (39x62cm-15x24in) s.i.d.1908 mixed media. 24-Aug-3 Bonhams & Butterfields, Los Angeles #7021 est:1000-1500

ELWES, Helen (1958-) British
Works on paper
£340 $598 €496 Interior at Warwick (35x25cm-14x10in) W/C gouache. 18-May-4 Woolley & Wallis, Salisbury #7/R

ELWES, Robert (fl.1840-1880) British
£800 $1496 €1168 Mountain gorge with a camel. Mountain gorge with two Arabs (170x122cm-67x48in) mono.i.d.1873 two. 20-Jul-4 Sworder & Son, Bishops Stortford #96/R

ELWYN, John (1916-1997) British
£1450 $2712 €2117 In mid Cardiganshire (9x13cm-4x5in) s. board. 25-Feb-4 Mallams, Oxford #211/R est:500-800
Works on paper
£1600 $2912 €2336 Mid Wales farm (35x45cm-14x18in) gouache. 21-Jun-4 Bonhams, Bath #334/R est:800-1200

ELYARD, Samuel (1817-1910) Australian
Works on paper
£537 $913 €806 Bush at my back (51x30cm-20x12in) s. W/C. 28-Oct-3 Goodman, Sydney #499a (A.D 1300)

ELZER, Hendrik Jacob (1808-1866) Dutch
£940 $1757 €1400 Vaisseaux Hollandais dans la tempete (25x32cm-10x13in) s. panel. 29-Feb-4 Osenat, Fontainebleau #201

ELZER, Ruud (1915-1995) Dutch
£5944 $10105 €8500 Seated nude (80x60cm-31x24in) s.d.59. 25-Nov-3 Christie's, Amsterdam #3/R est:2000-3000

EMANUEL, Frank Lewis (1865-1948) British
£300 $555 €438 Near the water's edge, Collioure, France (27x36cm-11x14in) s.i.d.1933 board. 15-Jan-4 Christie's, Kensington #985/R
£360 $666 €526 La Rochelle harbour (25x33cm-10x13in) panel. 9-Mar-4 Gorringes, Lewes #2230
£2168 $3729 €3100 Fuques old port (90x110cm-35x43in) s. 3-Dec-3 Stadion, Trieste #1011/R est:3000-4000

EMANUEL, John (?) ?
£260 $450 €380 Seated nude (80x57cm-31x22in) s.d.1978 board. 11-Dec-3 Lane, Penzance #318

EMBLEMA, Salvatore (1929-) Italian?
£500 $920 €750 Untitled (14x15cm-6x6in) s.d.1989 verso. 12-Jun-4 Meeting Art, Vercelli #758

EMBRY, Norris (20th C) ?
£719 $1200 €1050 Gathering at the dock (76x86cm-30x34in) s. 20-Jun-3 Freeman, Philadelphia #208/R

EMERSON, David (20th C) British
£500 $935 €730 Blue interior with figure (77x92cm-30x36in) board prov. 24-Feb-4 Bonhams, Knowle #130

EMERSON, Edith (1888-1981) American
£274 $450 €397 Portrait of a redheaded woman (33x25cm-13x10in) s. canvasboard. 4-Jun-3 Alderfer's, Hatfield #335

EMERSON, Peter Henry (1856-1936) British
Photographs
£3000 $5280 €4380 During the Reed (22x29cm-9x11in) platinum print lit. 19-May-4 Christie's, London #77/R est:2000-3000
£12222 $22000 €17844 Gathering water lilies (20x29cm-8x11in) platinum print lit. 22-Apr-4 Phillips, New York #7/R est:12000-18000

EMERSON, William C (1865-?) American
£330 $600 €482 Seclusion (28x33cm-11x13in) s. tempera board. 7-Feb-4 Dan Ripley, Indianapolis #14
£380 $600 €555 Autumn landscape (46x61cm-18x24in) s. tempera. 7-Sep-3 Treadway Gallery, Cincinnati #610/R
£795 $1400 €1161 Woodland nymphs (53x74cm-21x29in) s. board painted c.1910. 23-May-4 Treadway Gallery, Cincinnati #531/R
£1075 $2000 €1570 Spring landscape with maiden (61x61cm-24x24in) s. painted c.1910. 7-Mar-4 Treadway Gallery, Cincinnati #504/R est:1500-2000

EMERSON, William C (attrib) (1865-?) American
£235 $400 €343 Spring landscape (51x69cm-20x27in) i. board. 22-Nov-3 Jackson's, Cedar Falls #79/R

EMERY, Lin (1926-) American
Sculpture
£3022 $5500 €4412 Icarus (122x25x30cm-48x10x12in) welded bronze. 7-Feb-4 Neal Auction Company, New Orleans #497/R est:5000-7000

EMERY, Sergio (1928-) Swiss
£271 $462 €396 Composition (49x69cm-19x27in) s.d.86. 28-Nov-3 Zofingen, Switzerland #2981 (S.FR 600)
£341 $566 €494 Composition (50x70cm-20x28in) s.d.1986. 13-Jun-3 Zofingen, Switzerland #2836 (S.FR 750)
£433 $775 €632 Composition (141x74cm-56x29in) s.d.9.X.83 acrylic paper. 22-Mar-4 Philippe Schuler, Zurich #4162 (S.FR 1000)

EMETT, Rowland (1906-1990) British
Works on paper
£2900 $5104 €4234 Takes a bit of getting used to. Aye, the afternoon slow is always an 'elp with top meadow. ink col wash two cartoons. 18-May-4 Woolley & Wallis, Salisbury #132/R est:400-600
£4800 $8448 €7008 Cartoons. five. 18-May-4 Woolley & Wallis, Salisbury #137/R est:300-500

EMILIAN SCHOOL (14th C) Italian
£16000 $29280 €24000 Crucifixion (23x35cm-9x14in) tempera gold ground. 1-Jun-4 Sotheby's, Milan #127/R est:20000-30000

EMILIAN SCHOOL (16th C) Italian
£25140 $45000 €36704 Portrait of bearded man (28x22cm-11x9in) panel. 27-May-4 Sotheby's, New York #88a/R est:30000-50000

EMILIAN SCHOOL (17th C) Italian
£5298 $9642 €8000 Christ and Joseph of Arimathaea (116x91cm-46x36in) 16-Jun-4 Dorotheum, Vienna #330/R est:8000-12000
£9333 $17080 €14000 David and Goliath (98x76cm-39x30in) 1-Jun-4 Sotheby's, Milan #140/R est:8000-12000
£12000 $21840 €18000 Field labour (132x190cm-52x75in) 29-Jun-4 Pandolfini, Florence #2/R est:32000-34000
£12000 $21840 €18000 Building the house (132x190cm-52x75in) 29-Jun-4 Pandolfini, Florence #11/R est:32000-34000
£18000 $31140 €26280 Madonna and Child with the Infant Saint John the Baptist and a Franciscan Monk (99x106cm-39x42in) 10-Dec-3 Christie's, London #86/R est:15000-20000
£19595 $34486 €29000 Dalila and Sansone (115x145cm-45x57in) 18-May-4 Sotheby's, Milan #433/R est:25000-35000
£20270 $35676 €30000 Charity (184x129cm-72x51in) 18-May-4 Sotheby's, Milan #445/R est:15000-25000

EMILIAN SCHOOL (17th/18th C) Italian
£4698 $8644 €7000 Saint Paul's conversion (67x87cm-26x34in) 29-Mar-4 Pandolfini, Florence #738/R est:10000

EMILIAN SCHOOL (18th C) Italian
£4362 $7809 €6500 Roast chicken with mortar and fruit (50x99cm-20x39in) 26-May-4 Semenzato, Florence #213/R est:6000-8000
£8562 $14555 €12500 River view (131x186cm-52x73in) tempera. 7-Nov-3 Finarte, Venice #49/R est:12000-16000
£8562 $14555 €12500 Arcade and figures (213x183cm-84x72in) tempera. 7-Nov-3 Finarte, Venice #51/R est:16000-22000
£9932 $16884 €14500 Building. Arcade along river (79x143cm-31x56in) tempera pair. 7-Nov-3 Finarte, Venice #52/R est:12000-16000
£15753 $26781 €23000 River landscape with figures. Figures and soldiers (211x152cm-83x60in) pair. 7-Nov-3 Finarte, Venice #29/R est:25000-32000
£20000 $36600 €30000 Cleopatra's banquet (145x230cm-57x91in) 1-Jun-4 Sotheby's, Milan #43/R est:10000-15000
£23630 $40171 €34500 Arch and ruins. Ruins and figures. Arcade and figures (172x190cm-68x75in) tempera set of 3. 7-Nov-3 Finarte, Venice #50/R est:38000-48000

EMIN, Tracey (1963-) British
£4000 $7400 €5840 Figures at a table (69x113cm-27x44in) board. 13-Jul-4 Bonhams, Knightsbridge #59/R est:3000-4000
Photographs
£3352 $6000 €4894 Sometimes I feel beautiful (123x84cm-48x33in) cibachrome print on foamcore exec 2000 edn 3/6 prov. 13-May-4 Sotheby's, New York #364/R est:6000-8000
£15642 $28000 €22837 Monument Valley (122x183cm-48x72in) c-print mounted on vinyl prov.exhib.lit. 13-May-4 Phillips, New York #1/R est:20000-30000
Sculpture
£2000 $3340 €2920 Sleep (50x73cm-20x29in) s.i.d.1996 monoprint stitched label pillowcase prov.exhib. 21-Oct-3 Sotheby's, London #329/R est:2000-3000
£25000 $46000 €36500 Legal sex anal ?. Anal sex legal? (34x158x10cm-13x62x4in) pink neons dimmer switches two executed 1998 prov. 25-Jun-4 Christie's, London #266/R est:10000-15000
£70000 $128800 €102200 My coffin (42x183x59cm-17x72x23in) casket mattress ink on four sheets prov.exhib. 23-Jun-4 Sotheby's, London #40/R est:40000-60000
Works on paper
£550 $985 €803 Brids on a branch (29x20cm-11x8in) s.d.1999 pen ink prov. 16-Mar-4 Bonhams, Knightsbridge #54
£900 $1638 €1314 Birds (29x20cm-11x8in) s.d.1999 pen ink. 21-Jun-4 Bonhams, New Bond Street #143/R
£1267 $2267 €1900 Jester mill (74x51cm-29x20in) d.93 collage crayons. 12-May-4 Chochon-Barre & Allardi, Paris #44 est:1000-1500

EMMENEGGER, Hans (1866-1940) Swiss
£3057 $5380 €4463 Landscape in late summer (43x62cm-17x24in) i. i. stretcher prov. 22-May-4 Galerie Gloggner, Luzern #39/R est:3800-4500 (S.FR 7000)
£4167 $6958 €6084 Still life with two vases of flowers (61x50cm-24x20in) s.d.11 prov.lit. 15-Nov-3 Galerie Gloggner, Luzern #41/R est:4500-5500 (S.FR 9500)

EMMENEGGER, Hans (attrib) (1866-1940) Swiss
£407 $692 €594 Trees (24x33cm-9x13in) s.i.d.1892 stretcher. 28-Nov-3 Zofingen, Switzerland #2982 (S.FR 900)

EMMERIK, G van (1808-1882) Dutch
£1348 $2481 €2022 Seascapes. s.d.1852 pair. 14-Jun-4 Lilla Bukowskis, Stockholm #672 est:20000-30000 (S.KR 18500)

EMMERIK, Govert van (1808-1882) Dutch
£957 $1550 €1388 Seascape with sailing vessels off the coast (53x80cm-21x31in) s. 4-Aug-3 Rasmussen, Vejle #34/R (D.KR 10000)
£1180 $1924 €1700 Shipping in calm at sunset (19x24cm-7x9in) init. board. 29-Sep-3 Sotheby's, Amsterdam #67/R
£1842 $3389 €2800 Ships on rough seas (30x40cm-12x16in) s.d.1850. 28-Jun-4 Sotheby's, Amsterdam #15/R est:1000-1500
£2177 $3962 €3200 Shipping on a choppy sea by a coast (58x74cm-23x29in) s.d.1856. 3-Feb-4 Christie's, Amsterdam #63/R est:3000-5000
£2667 $4827 €4000 Fishing boat and cutter in stormy sea (71x95cm-28x37in) s. 1-Apr-4 Van Ham, Cologne #1354/R est:2400

EMMERIK, Govert van (attrib) (1808-1882) Dutch
£676 $1189 €1000 Steam boat in the storm (57x73cm-22x29in) 19-May-4 Il Ponte, Milan #664
£1447 $2663 €2200 A rough sea with a Dutch hoy leaving port, a threemaster on the horizon (58x74cm-23x29in) sold with painting by another hand. 22-Jun-4 Christie's, Amsterdam #11/R est:1500-1900

EMMERSON, Henry H (1831-1895) British
£4000 $7400 €5840 First bathe (50x25cm-20x10in) s. board exhib. 13-Jan-4 Bonhams, Knightsbridge #273/R est:2000-3000
Works on paper
£950 $1644 €1387 Cattle grazing by a path in summer with a view of Durham City and Cathedral (36x53cm-14x21in) s.d.1886 W/C. 9-Dec-3 Anderson & Garland, Newcastle #331/R

EMMS, John (1843-1912) British
£580 $1056 €847 Country courtship (31x49cm-12x19in) s. 5-Feb-4 Mellors & Kirk, Nottingham #582/R
£1800 $3312 €2628 Pigs in a wood (28x38cm-11x15in) s. 10-Jun-4 Christie's, Kensington #99/R est:2000-3000
£1900 $3458 €2774 Portraits of dogs heads (18x15cm-7x6in) s. board. 16-Jun-4 John Nicholson, Haslemere #768/R est:500-1000
£2000 $3680 €2920 Donkey and foal (35x30cm-14x12in) s.d.76. 10-Jun-4 Christie's, Kensington #98/R est:1500-2000
£2267 $4103 €3400 Horse in a stable (69x92cm-27x36in) s.d.1896. 30-Mar-4 De Veres Art Auctions, Dublin #245/R est:4000-6000
£2442 $4200 €3565 Donkey (21x26cm-8x10in) s. canvas on card. 5-Dec-3 Christie's, Rockefeller NY #40/R est:5000-7000

£2907 $5000 €4244 Grouse shooting (25x36cm-10x14in) s. 5-Dec-3 Christie's, Rockefeller NY #94/R est:5000-7000
£3038 $5500 €4435 Jack Russell (35x43cm-14x17in) s. 30-Mar-4 Bonhams & Butterfields, San Francisco #55a/R est:6000-8000
£3200 $5824 €4672 Tomboy (27x36cm-11x14in) s.i.d.1906 board. 16-Jun-4 Bonhams, New Bond Street #59/R est:2000-3000
£3500 $5950 €5110 Where's my letter? (52x68cm-20x27in) s. 27-Nov-3 Sotheby's, London #367/R est:3000-5000
£3784 $7000 €5525 Foxhounds (38x33cm-15x13in) s. 10-Feb-4 Doyle, New York #247/R est:6000-8000
£3867 $7000 €5646 Zoe, a Jack Russel in a barn (40x51cm-16x20in) s.i.d.1896. 30-Mar-4 Bonhams & Butterfields, San Francisco #53/R est:3700-5500
£4054 $7500 €5919 Borzoi in landscape (51x66cm-20x26in) s. 10-Feb-4 Doyle, New York #246/R est:7000-9000
£4143 $7500 €6049 Brindle greyhound in a landscape (28x34cm-11x13in) s.d.90. 30-Mar-4 Bonhams & Butterfields, San Francisco #59/R est:2200-3300
£4800 $8880 €7008 New Forest buckhounds, Guider and Druid (75x62cm-30x24in) s.d.77. 10-Mar-4 Sotheby's, Olympia #214/R est:3000-4000
£5000 $8500 €7300 Highland lad with collies in the snow (36x46cm-14x18in) s.d.85. 19-Nov-3 Sotheby's, Olympia #55/R est:5000-7000
£5000 $9250 €7300 St. Bernards (45cm-18in circular) s. prov. 14-Jan-4 Lawrence, Crewkerne #1419/R est:4000-6000
£5000 $9250 €7300 Guard dog (53x38cm-21x15in) s. prov. 11-Mar-4 Duke & Son, Dorchester #215/R est:4000-6000
£6000 $10200 €8760 Hounds in the snow (46x61cm-18x24in) s. 19-Nov-3 Sotheby's, Olympia #54/R est:5000-7000
£6077 $11000 €8872 Beauty (40x51cm-16x20in) s.i.d.93. 30-Mar-4 Bonhams & Butterfields, San Francisco #51/R est:6000-8000
£6500 $11960 €9490 Countess, a deerhound (29x29cm-11x11in) s.i. 10-Jun-4 Christie's, Kensington #422/R est:7000-10000
£6500 $11895 €9490 Portrait of a horse in a stable (69x89cm-27x35in) s.d.1896. 28-Jul-4 Bonhams, Knightsbridge #136/R est:6000-8000
£7027 $13000 €10259 Bowstring (33x43cm-13x17in) init.i.d.78 prov. 10-Feb-4 Doyle, New York #249/R est:8000-12000
£7200 $11376 €10440 Head studies of two terriers, Jock and Rose (22cm-9in circular) s.d.82 pair prov. 24-Jul-3 Lawrence, Crewkerne #951/R est:2500-3500
£11050 $20000 €16133 Hester Sorrel (41x51cm-16x20in) s.i.d.96. 30-Mar-4 Bonhams & Butterfields, San Francisco #54/R est:6000-8000
£30000 $51000 €43800 Day's bag (60x79cm-24x31in) s. prov. 27-Nov-3 Sotheby's, London #370/R est:30000-40000
£75000 $132000 €109500 Otter hounds and a terrier by a bridge - tired out (91x130cm-36x51in) s.d.81 prov. 21-May-4 Christie's, London #16/R est:60000-80000
£350000 $616000 €511000 House of idleness - hounds and terrier in a kennel (102x127cm-40x50in) s.d.1899 prov.exhib. 21-May-4 Christie's, London #46/R est:180000-250000
Works on paper
£5200 $8944 €7592 At the end of the day (44x37cm-17x15in) s. W/C. 3-Dec-3 Bonhams, Knightsbridge #173/R est:4000-6000

EMPI, Maurice (1932-) ?
£467 $849 €700 Paddock (46x56cm-18x22in) s. 4-Jul-4 Eric Pillon, Calais #247/R
£537 $999 €800 Voiliers (61x73cm-24x29in) s. 2-Mar-4 Artcurial Briest, Paris #266
£537 $993 €800 Paddock (50x61cm-20x24in) s. 14-Mar-4 Eric Pillon, Calais #264/R
£630 $1071 €920 Baigneurs sur la plage (52x66cm-20x26in) s. 8-Nov-3 Gerard, Besancon #58
£630 $1071 €920 La fanfare municipale (52x66cm-20x26in) s. 8-Nov-3 Gerard, Besancon #59
£734 $1226 €1050 Plage de la cote d'Azur (27x22cm-11x9in) s. 7-Oct-3 Livinec, Gaudcheau & Jezequel, Rennes #144
£836 $1421 €1220 Le bal chez Gegene (52x66cm-20x26in) s. 8-Nov-3 Gerard, Besancon #61
£925 $1572 €1350 La plage en ete (52x66cm-20x26in) s. 8-Nov-3 Gerard, Besancon #60
Works on paper
£268 $499 €400 La course cycliste (48x62cm-19x24in) s. gouache. 7-Mar-4 Lesieur & Le Bars, Le Havre #40
£336 $624 €500 A la terrasse de cafe (48x59cm-19x23in) s.gouache. 7-Mar-4 Lesieur & Le Bars, Le Havre #39
£428 $727 €625 At the race track (48x62cm-19x24in) s. gouache prov. 23-Nov-3 Levis, Calgary #204/R (C.D 950)

EMPRIN, Giuliano (1902-1991) Italian
£268 $475 €400 Tuileries (30x26cm-12x10in) s. painted 1969. 1-May-4 Meeting Art, Vercelli #10
£347 $590 €500 Largo Garibaldi (50x40cm-20x16in) s. i.verso. 1-Nov-3 Meeting Art, Vercelli #388

EMSLIE, Alfred Edward (1848-1918) British
£5156 $8250 €7528 Harvesting (36x58cm-14x23in) s. 17-May-3 Bunte, Elgin #1224 est:3000-5000

ENAULT, Alex (?-1913) French
£1014 $1814 €1500 Le regard evocateur (29x21cm-11x8in) s. panel oval. 10-May-4 Horta, Bruxelles #32 est:1000-1500

ENAULT, François (?-1918) French
£822 $1488 €1250 Taillis a Varenguebec (35x25cm-14x10in) s. i.verso panel. 19-Apr-4 Boscher, Cherbourg #760

ENCKELL, Magnus (1870-1925) Finnish
£1081 $1935 €1600 Man on verandah (47x46cm-19x18in) s.d.1919 board. 8-May-4 Bukowskis, Helsinki #111/R est:1500-1800
£5068 $9071 €7500 Still life of vase (66x55cm-26x22in) s.d.1915 exhib. 8-May-4 Bukowskis, Helsinki #108/R est:8000-10000
Works on paper
£375 $626 €540 View of farm (22x32cm-9x13in) s. mixed media. 26-Oct-3 Bukowskis, Helsinki #317/R
£420 $713 €600 Coastal landscape (30x37cm-12x15in) s.d.1915 W/C. 29-Nov-3 Bukowskis, Helsinki #109/R
£604 $1123 €900 Florence. Self-portrait (28x44cm-11x17in) s. W/C double-sided exhib.prov. 7-Mar-4 Bukowskis, Helsinki #316/R
£1146 $1914 €1650 By the mirror (43x32cm-17x13in) s.d.1916 W/C. 26-Oct-3 Bukowskis, Helsinki #318/R est:700

ENCKELL, Torger (1901-1991) Finnish
£306 $557 €450 Lady wearing black hat (65x54cm-26x21in) s.d.24. 8-Feb-4 Bukowskis, Helsinki #337/R
£380 $608 €540 Seated woman (81x65cm-32x26in) s.d.58 exhib. 21-Sep-3 Bukowskis, Helsinki #335/R
£451 $754 €650 Self-portrait (85x70cm-33x28in) s.d.60 exhib. 26-Oct-3 Bukowskis, Helsinki #321/R
£500 $835 €720 Seated model (65x54cm-26x21in) s/d/58. 26-Oct-3 Bukowskis, Helsinki #319/R

ENDE, Edgar (1901-1965) German
£10738 $19007 €16000 Der Ausbruch (71x91cm-28x36in) s.d.33 lit. 27-Apr-4 Artcurial Briest, Paris #181/R est:4000-6000

ENDE, Hans am (1864-1918) German
£1678 $2853 €2400 Three birches in a landscape (69x50cm-27x20in) i. lit. 28-Nov-3 Schloss Ahlden, Ahlden #707/R est:850
£1748 $3007 €2500 Evening time in forest at Weyerberg (53x39cm-21x15in) mono. canvas on board. 5-Dec-3 Bolland & Marotz, Bremen #360/R est:3500
£2980 $5424 €4500 Country landscape with blue skies (36x48cm-14x19in) mono. canvas on board. 18-Jun-4 Bolland & Marotz, Bremen #340/R est:4500
£5960 $10848 €9000 Cornfield (65x45cm-26x18in) mono. canvas on board. 18-Jun-4 Bolland & Marotz, Bremen #338/R est:13000
Works on paper
£313 $509 €450 Birch trees by moorland croft (8x11cm-3x4in) mono. chk. 26-Sep-3 Bolland & Marotz, Bremen #314
£313 $522 €450 House in landscape (7x17cm-3x7in) mono. pencil. 24-Oct-3 Ketterer, Hamburg #166/R
£556 $906 €800 Trees on moor (7x13cm-3x5in) mono. chk. 26-Sep-3 Bolland & Marotz, Bremen #315
£590 $962 €850 Snowy wood (41x60cm-16x24in) s.i. chl mixed media. 26-Sep-3 Bolland & Marotz, Bremen #312
£1724 $2879 €2500 Sunshine (27x20cm-11x8in) s.d.1902 pen W/C. 15-Nov-3 Von Zezschwitz, Munich #24/R est:2500

ENDE-PICHLER, Gabriele (1944-) German
£567 $1014 €850 Spring awakening (100x120cm-39x47in) s.d. 13-May-4 Neumeister, Munich #578/R

ENDER, Anton (20th C) Swiss
£317 $538 €463 Female nude (69x50cm-27x20in) s.d.38 board. 18-Nov-3 Hans Widmer, St Gallen #1048 (S.FR 700)
£452 $769 €660 Two buildings between trees in hilly landscape (41x31cm-16x12in) s.d.47 board. 18-Nov-3 Hans Widmer, St Gallen #1047/R (S.FR 1000)

ENDER, Axel Hjalmar (1853-1920) Norwegian
£2462 $4234 €3595 Lady wearing blue dress by church pew (42x28cm-17x11in) s.i.d.1881 panel. 3-Dec-3 AB Stockholms Auktionsverk #2601/R est:25000-26000 (S.KR 32000)
£3407 $5860 €4974 An outing - woman and child with horse and cart (45x66cm-18x26in) s. 8-Dec-3 Blomqvist, Oslo #453/R est:50000-60000 (N.KR 40000)
£4259 $7325 €6218 Girl seated on large stone in landscape (64x52cm-25x20in) s.d.1881. 8-Dec-3 Blomqvist, Oslo #446/R est:70000-90000 (N.KR 50000)
£15385 $26462 €22462 Winter landscape with figures tobogganing (60x90cm-24x35in) s/d/1915. 7-Dec-3 Uppsala Auktionskammare, Uppsala #138/R est:100000-150000 (S.KR 200000)
£26405 $45417 €38551 Sleigh ride on frozen lake, possibly Mjosa (65x90cm-26x35in) s. lit. 8-Dec-3 Blomqvist, Oslo #409/R est:180000-220000 (N.KR 310000)

ENDER, Boris (20th C) Russian
Works on paper
£270 $476 €400 Untitled (26x34cm-10x13in) s.verso W/C. 19-May-4 Camard, Paris #32

ENDER, Eduard (1822-1883) Austrian
£973 $1800 €1421 Portrait of a boy in a red suit (137x109cm-54x43in) s.d.1869. 15-Jul-4 Sotheby's, New York #21/R est:2000-4000

ENDER, Johann Nepomuk (1793-1854) Austrian
Works on paper
£540 $945 €788 Portrait of a Grecian girl holding a book (18x14cm-7x6in) W/C over pencil. 16-Dec-3 Bonhams, New Bond Street #4/R

ENDER, Thomas (1793-1875) Austrian
£903 $1490 €1300 Ship in stormy seas off rocky coast (43x57cm-17x22in) bears sig. 3-Jul-3 Van Ham, Cologne #1160/R
£10417 $17708 €15000 Riva on Lake Garda (40x50cm-16x20in) s. 28-Oct-3 Wiener Kunst Auktionen, Vienna #15/R est:14000-28000
Works on paper
£294 $499 €420 Houses on edge of Berchtesgaden (26x37cm-10x15in) s.i.d.1834 pencil. 21-Nov-3 Reiss & Sohn, Konigstein #186/R
£455 $773 €650 Extensive landscape (8x23cm-3x9in) bears sig. W/C. 27-Nov-3 Bassenge, Berlin #5566
£521 $849 €750 Wooded landscape with lake (13x17cm-5x7in) s. chl. 26-Sep-3 Venator & Hansten, Koln #809/R
£1747 $3179 €2551 Southern harbour town (32x47cm-13x19in) W/C over pencil prov.exhib. 17-Jun-4 Kornfeld, Bern #14/R est:3000 (S.FR 4000)
£2013 $3705 €3000 Ruins of Aggstein an der Donau (10x15cm-4x6in) s. i. verso W/C. 26-Mar-4 Dorotheum, Vienna #178/R est:3600-4000
£2685 $4940 €4000 Tyrolean castle (30x47cm-12x19in) s. W/C. 26-Mar-4 Dorotheum, Vienna #174/R est:3000-3500

£4861 $8264 €7000 Walkers in mountains (33x51cm-13x20in) bears i. W/C. 28-Oct-3 Wiener Kunst Auktionen, Vienna #19/R est:5000-15000
£5556 $9444 €8000 Burg Rangweil (25x31cm-10x12in) i. verso W/C. 28-Oct-3 Wiener Kunst Auktionen, Vienna #20/R est:4000-12000
£5556 $9444 €8000 Kaun valley with Gepatschferner (33x50cm-13x20in) i. verso W/C. 28-Oct-3 Wiener Kunst Auktionen, Vienna #17/R est:5000-15000
£5705 $10211 €8500 View over Molloger alpine hut in Langtauferstal (31x81cm-12x32in) W/C. 27-May-4 Hassfurther, Vienna #43/R est:7000-9000
£5862 $9731 €8500 Amalfitana (33x50cm-13x20in) s. W/C. 30-Sep-3 Dorotheum, Vienna #229/R est:8000-10000
£5944 $10105 €8500 Eiger and Monch (35x55cm-14x22in) i. i.verso W/C. 28-Nov-3 Wiener Kunst Auktionen, Vienna #430/R est:3000-10000
£6040 $11114 €9000 Pfitzgrundl in Zemthale, Tyrol (30x24cm-12x9in) s.i. verso W/C. 26-Mar-4 Dorotheum, Vienna #185/R est:10000-12000
£6250 $10625 €9000 Nasserein with Gepatschferner (33x50cm-13x20in) i. W/C. 28-Oct-3 Wiener Kunst Auktionen, Vienna #18/R est:5000-15000
£6944 $11806 €10000 Ysper valley (24x36cm-9x14in) s. verso W/C. 28-Oct-3 Wiener Kunst Auktionen, Vienna #16/R est:4000-10000
£9091 $15455 €13000 Nassfeld (24x34cm-9x13in) s. W/C. 28-Nov-3 Wiener Kunst Auktionen, Vienna #429/R est:5000-12000

ENDER, Thomas (attrib) (1793-1875) Austrian
Works on paper
£1493 $2538 €2180 Landscape with glacier (27x44cm-11x17in) i. verso W/C. 19-Nov-3 Fischer, Luzern #2458/R est:600-800 (S.FR 3300)

ENDERLE, Johann Baptist (attrib) (1725-1798) German
£1888 $3248 €2700 Birth of Christ with kings (30x22cm-12x9in) one of pair. 5-Dec-3 Michael Zeller, Lindau #532/R est:1500
£1923 $3308 €2750 Birth of Christ with shepherds (30x22cm-12x9in) one of pair. 5-Dec-3 Michael Zeller, Lindau #531/R est:1500

ENDERS, Jean Joseph (1862-?) French
£1200 $2184 €1800 View of the Seine and the Pont Alexandre III, Paris (66x93cm-26x37in) s. 1-Jul-4 Van Ham, Cologne #1328/R est:2800

ENDERSBY, Frank (20th C) British
Works on paper
£300 $549 €438 What makes me smile, study of circus performers under the big top. s.d.04 W/C. 9-Jul-4 Moore Allen & Innocent, Cirencester #960/R

ENDRES, Charles (19th C) French
£530 $991 €800 Jeune femme a la couture (55x38cm-22x15in) s. 20-Jul-4 other European Auctioneer #115
£1987 $3715 €3000 Jeune femme au chevalet (61x35cm-24x14in) s.d.87. 20-Jul-4 other European Auctioneer #117
Works on paper
£298 $557 €450 Jeune fille ecrivant (35x31cm-14x12in) s. pastel. 20-Jul-4 other European Auctioneer #116

ENDSTORFER, Anton (1880-?) Austrian
Sculpture
£1186 $2123 €1732 Fishing boy (44cm-17in) s. bronze prov. 15-May-4 Christie's, Sydney #153/R est:3000-5000 (A.D 3000)

ENFANTIN, Augustin (1793-1827) French
£1842 $3389 €2800 Promeneur dans la foret de Fontainebleau (40x47cm-16x19in) 24-Jun-4 Christie's, Paris #146/R est:2000-3000

ENFIELD, Henry (1849-1908) British
£280 $515 €420 Lake landscape (60x90cm-24x35in) s. 9-Jun-4 Bukowskis, Helsinki #594/R
£467 $845 €700 Norwegian fjord (53x87cm-21x34in) s. 1-Apr-4 Van Ham, Cologne #1355
£541 $843 €800 Landscape with Sogne-Fhord with steamer and boats (55x101cm-22x40in) s. i. verso. 28-Mar-3 Altus, Berlin #540/R
£701 $1079 €1100 Esefjord b Balholm, Norway (70x120cm-28x47in) s. 4-Sep-2 Schopman, Hamburg #246/R
£845 $1462 €1200 Aardal, Sognefjord (52x88cm-20x35in) s.i.verso. 10-Dec-3 Dorotheum, Vienna #203/R
£1405 $2600 €2051 Ship (71x117cm-28x46in) s. 13-Mar-4 Susanin's, Chicago #6117/R est:1500-2000
£1600 $2864 €2336 Naero fjord (72x117cm-28x46in) s. s.i.stretcher. 18-Mar-4 Christie's, Kensington #507/R est:800-1200

ENGAERTH, Eduard von (1818-1897) German
£728 $1333 €1100 Portrait of young girl with roses in hair (72x60cm-28x24in) s.d.1868. 8-Apr-4 Dorotheum, Vienna #204/R

ENGALIERE, Marius (1824-1857) French
£1382 $2542 €2100 Couvent en Espagne (24x38cm-9x15in) s. canvas on cardboard. 22-Jun-4 Calmels Cohen, Paris #37/R est:2000-3000

ENGBARTH, Otto (1935-) German
£769 $1308 €1100 Games field (38x45cm-15x18in) s.d.80 panel. 29-Nov-3 Sigalas, Stuttgart #629/R

ENGBERG, Gabriel Karl (1872-1953) Finnish
£417 $696 €600 Landscape (50x35cm-20x14in) s. 23-Oct-3 Hagelstam, Helsinki #848
£800 $1472 €1200 Desert (59x41cm-23x16in) s.d.1930. 9-Jun-4 Bukowskis, Helsinki #380/R

ENGEL VON DER RABENAU, Carl (1817-1870) German
£6014 $10224 €8600 The artist friends (49x59cm-19x23in) mono.d.1841 lit. 28-Nov-3 Schloss Ahlden, Ahlden #1403/R est:8500

ENGEL, Adolphe Charles Maximilien (1801-1833) Belgian
£1382 $2542 €2100 Mountainous landscape with cattle bathing (38x50cm-15x20in) s.d.1826 panel. 28-Jun-4 Sotheby's, Amsterdam #4/R est:1800-2500

ENGEL, Johann Friedrich (1844-?) German
£3125 $5313 €4500 Kinderzeit (70x100cm-28x39in) s.i. prov. 28-Oct-3 Christie's, Amsterdam #70/R est:5000-7000
£4800 $8832 €7008 Portrait of a young boy in liederhosen (34x25cm-13x10in) s.i. panel. 25-Mar-4 Christie's, Kensington #208/R est:4000-6000

ENGEL, Jules (1915-) Hungarian
£368 $600 €537 Untitled (94x94cm-37x37in) 28-Sep-3 Bonhams & Butterfields, Los Angeles #7053
£590 $950 €856 Untitled (85x71cm-33x28in) 24-Aug-3 Bonhams & Butterfields, Los Angeles #7054 est:800-1200
£807 $1300 €1170 Untitled (85x99cm-33x39in) 24-Aug-3 Bonhams & Butterfields, Los Angeles #7048 est:800-1200
Works on paper
£307 $500 €448 Untitled (97x97cm-38x38in) mixed media. 28-Sep-3 Bonhams & Butterfields, Los Angeles #7054
£387 $700 €565 Front yard (56x23cm-22x9in) s. gouache. 18-Apr-4 Bonhams & Butterfields, Los Angeles #7075
£497 $800 €721 Untitled (61x51cm-24x20in) s.i.verso pencil. 24-Aug-3 Bonhams & Butterfields, Los Angeles #7040

ENGEL, Nissan (20th C) American
£240 $400 €350 Landscape (79x119cm-31x47in) s. prov. 15-Nov-3 Sloans & Kenyon, Bethesda #86/R

ENGEL, Otto Heinrich (1866-1949) German
£3846 $6423 €5500 Flensburg landscape (36x61cm-14x24in) s. i. verso canvas on board. 28-Jun-3 Bolland & Marotz, Bremen #640/R est:3800
£6597 $10753 €9500 Friesian interior (45x53cm-18x21in) s. panel. 26-Sep-3 Bolland & Marotz, Bremen #522/R est:5500
Works on paper
£338 $605 €500 Chat between the houses (32x23cm-13x9in) mono. bears d. W/C pen. 8-May-4 Hans Stahl, Toestorf #55/R
£694 $1090 €1000 Small North Sea harbour (20x28cm-8x11in) s. W/C gouache. 30-Aug-3 Hans Stahl, Toestorf #68/R
£1370 $2329 €2000 Fohr landscape (70x89cm-28x35in) mono. i. verso pastel. 8-Nov-3 Hans Stahl, Toestorf #62/R est:2900

ENGEL, Werner Emil (1880-1941) Swiss
£862 $1543 €1259 Sailing boats on Lake Thun (50x70cm-20x28in) s.d.40. 13-May-4 Stuker, Bern #113 est:2500-3000 (S.FR 2000)

ENGEL-PAK, Ernest (1885-1965) Belgian
£347 $580 €500 Papillons, desnos, chatillon (56x47cm-22x19in) s. 25-Oct-3 Cornette de St.Cyr, Paris #774
£664 $1129 €950 Composition fond orange (57x37cm-22x15in) s.d.1951 cardboard prov. 23-Nov-3 Cornette de St.Cyr, Paris #470/R

ENGELBACH, Florence (1872-1951) British
£280 $482 €409 Still life of flowers in a vase (61x51cm-24x20in) s. 2-Dec-3 Gorringes, Lewes #2304
£300 $540 €438 Portrait of Master Engelbach, son of the artist (44x36cm-17x14in) prov. 21-Apr-4 Cheffins, Cambridge #520/R
£800 $1472 €1168 Anemones in a blue vase (43x28cm-17x11in) s. 11-Jun-4 Halls, Shrewsbury #795/R
£5400 $9990 €7884 Portrait of a lady (133x104cm-52x41in) s.d.1906. 10-Mar-4 Sotheby's, Olympia #218/R est:2000-3000

ENGELEN, Louis van (1856-1940) Belgian
£302 $562 €450 Girl with doll (50x40cm-20x16in) s.d.1882 panel. 8-Mar-4 Bernaerts, Antwerp #1050
£621 $1030 €900 Etang (45x60cm-18x24in) panel. 6-Oct-3 Amberes, Antwerp #278
£867 $1569 €1300 Homme pres de l'atre (31x52cm-12x20in) panel. 30-Mar-4 Campo & Campo, Antwerp #305/R
£1000 $1800 €1500 Animated coast view in Italy (32x59cm-13x23in) s.d.1883. 26-Apr-4 Bernaerts, Antwerp #1004 est:1000-1250

ENGELEN, Piet van (1863-1923) Belgian
£473 $832 €700 Hunting dog (37x45cm-15x18in) s. 24-May-4 Bernaerts, Antwerp #481/R
£1206 $2207 €1761 Donkeys on beach (109x149cm-43x59in) s. 2-Feb-4 Blomqvist, Lysaker #1052/R est:20000-30000 (N.KR 15000)
£8054 $14899 €12000 Donkeys on the beach of Blankenberghe (109x149cm-43x59in) s.i. 13-Mar-4 De Vuyst, Lokeren #420/R est:6000-8000

ENGELHARD, Otmar (20th C) German
£278 $442 €400 Still life with pot plant (71x56cm-28x22in) s.d.1947. 11-Sep-3 Weidler, Nurnberg #4655

ENGELHARDT, Edna (20th C) American
£407 $700 €594 Autumnal landscape with ducks rising from the lake (69x89cm-27x35in) s. i.verso. 6-Dec-3 Pook & Pook, Downington #103
£472 $750 €689 Winter river scene (64x76cm-25x30in) s. 10-Sep-3 Alderfer's, Hatfield #357

£566 $900 €826 Winter landscape with river, snowy banks and pine trees (36x51cm-14x20in) s. canvasboard. 10-Sep-3 Alderfer's, Hatfield #355
£597 $950 €872 Still life with vase of flowers beside window (61x76cm-24x30in) s. 10-Sep-3 Alderfer's, Hatfield #356/R
£659 $1100 €962 Stream in winter (41x51cm-16x20in) s. 20-Jun-3 Freeman, Philadelphia #211/R
£875 $1400 €1278 Winter landscape (76x91cm-30x36in) s. 19-Sep-3 Freeman, Philadelphia #151 est:1500-2500
£1047 $1800 €1529 Winter wooded landscape with stream (69x89cm-27x35in) s. 6-Dec-3 Pook & Pook, Downington #102 est:800-1200

ENGELHARDT, Georg-Hermann (1855-?) German
£342 $534 €500 Otztal alpine plateau with flock of sheep (36x46cm-14x18in) s. panel. 10-Apr-3 Weidler, Nurnberg #360

ENGELHARDT, William (20th C) American
£323 $600 €472 Flowering desert (51x61cm-20x24in) s. painted c.1940. 7-Mar-4 Treadway Gallery, Cincinnati #628/R

ENGELHARDT-KYFFHAUSER, Otto (1884-?) German
£284 $499 €420 Rhine (79x59cm-31x23in) s. lit. 21-May-4 Mehlis, Plauen #15101/R
£467 $835 €700 1915 in Flanders (80x100cm-31x39in) s. i. verso panel lit. 14-May-4 Schloss Ahlden, Ahlden #2926/R
£2025 $3159 €3200 Silence of infinity (82x100cm-32x39in) s. 18-Oct-2 Von Zezschwitz, Munich #9/R est:1800

ENGELMULLER, Ferdinand (1867-1924) Czechoslovakian
£1687 $2970 €2531 Forest interior (91x69cm-36x27in) s. 22-May-4 Dorotheum, Prague #65/R est:80000-120000 (C.KR 80000)

ENGELS, Leo (1882-1952) Belgian
£333 $597 €500 In front of the window (70x53cm-28x21in) s.d.1908. 15-May-4 De Vuyst, Lokeren #125

ENGELS, Lisl (1916-) Austrian
£1133 $2085 €1700 Still life with flowers in blue vase (85x74cm-33x29in) s.d.1988. 9-Jun-4 Dorotheum, Salzburg #677/R est:1400-1800
Works on paper
£352 $616 €500 Mountain landscape (27x37cm-11x15in) s.d.1947 gouache. 19-Dec-3 Dorotheum, Vienna #158
£658 $1211 €1000 Still life (42x62cm-17x24in) s.d.1933 mixed media. 22-Jun-4 Wiener Kunst Auktionen, Vienna #222/R

ENGELSEN, Hakon (1933-) Norwegian
Works on paper
£273 $500 €399 Storm approaching in Lofoten (53x71cm-21x28in) s. W/C exhib. 2-Feb-4 Blomqvist, Lysaker #1053 (N.KR 3400)

ENGELSTED, Malthe (1852-1930) Danish
£2624 $4698 €3831 Street scene with figures looking at window display in evening (61x80cm-24x31in) init.d.1902 exhib. 10-May-4 Rasmussen, Vejle #391/R est:30000 (D.KR 29000)

ENGELUND, Svend (1908-) Danish
£325 $527 €471 Landscape (20x28cm-8x11in) init. paper on panel. 4-Aug-3 Rasmussen, Vejle #591/R (D.KR 3400)
£548 $981 €800 Model study of female nude (25x19cm-10x7in) init. panel. 12-Jan-4 Rasmussen, Vejle #490 (D.KR 5800)
£633 $1134 €924 Interior scene with girl by window (25x34cm-10x13in) mono. 10-May-4 Rasmussen, Vejle #670/R (D.KR 7000)
£662 $1184 €967 Landscape with yellow fields and buildings (23x37cm-9x15in) init. 12-Jan-4 Rasmussen, Vejle #504/R (D.KR 7000)
£1129 $1919 €1648 Field landscape (38x55cm-15x22in) init.d.66 masonite. 29-Nov-3 Rasmussen, Havnen #4204/R est:8000-10000 (D.KR 12000)
£1218 $2242 €1778 Station scene with figures waiting for train (32x49cm-13x19in) init.d.55 masonite. 29-Mar-4 Rasmussen, Copenhagen #439/R est:15000-20000 (D.KR 13500)
£1229 $2199 €1794 Still life of female nude and jug (53x34cm-21x13in) letter verso. 12-Jan-4 Rasmussen, Vejle #503/R est:4000 (D.KR 13000)
£1538 $2754 €2245 Street scene with houses (71x80cm-28x31in) mono.d.41. 10-May-4 Rasmussen, Vejle #667/R est:18000-20000 (D.KR 17000)
£1627 $2635 €2359 View across landscape (50x66cm-20x26in) init.d.76. 4-Aug-3 Rasmussen, Vejle #593/R est:8000-10000 (D.KR 17000)
£2457 $4399 €3587 Green landscape (60x81cm-24x32in) init.d.69 exhib. 12-Jan-4 Rasmussen, Vejle #500/R est:15000-20000 (D.KR 26000)
£2888 $5314 €4216 View of Randers River in winter (55x94cm-22x37in) init. 29-Mar-4 Rasmussen, Copenhagen #489/R est:20000-25000 (D.KR 32000)
£3781 $6767 €5520 View across landscape (98x120cm-39x47in) init.d.57. 12-Jan-4 Rasmussen, Vejle #501/R est:15000-20000 (D.KR 40000)

ENGER, Erling (1899-1990) Norwegian
£285 $524 €416 Winter landscape with houses (27x39cm-11x15in) init. panel. 10-Jun-4 Grev Wedels Plass, Oslo #167/R (N.KR 3500)
£310 $517 €453 Landscape (22x29cm-9x11in) s. 20-Oct-3 Blomqvist, Lysaker #1068/R (N.KR 3600)
£473 $790 €691 Land (38x46cm-15x18in) s. 20-Oct-3 Blomqvist, Lysaker #1067 (N.KR 5500)
£1022 $1635 €1482 Wooded landscape in Spring (66x73cm-26x29in) 22-Sep-3 Blomqvist, Lysaker #1047 (N.KR 12000)
£1223 $2190 €1786 Winter landscape with birch grove (38x47cm-15x19in) s. 25-May-4 Grev Wedels Plass, Oslo #88/R est:20000-30000 (N.KR 15000)
£1301 $2380 €1899 Wooded landscape (50x62cm-20x24in) init.d.70. 7-Jun-4 Blomqvist, Oslo #422/R est:20000-25000 (N.KR 16000)
£1366 $2282 €1994 Pine forest (47x55cm-19x22in) s.d.69. 13-Oct-3 Blomqvist, Oslo #310/R est:15000-20000 (N.KR 16000)
£1540 $2618 €2248 Winter landscape with house (46x55cm-18x22in) init.d.69. 19-Nov-3 Grev Wedels Plass, Oslo #80/R est:20000-30000 (N.KR 18000)
£2195 $4039 €3205 Winter landscape (73x92cm-29x36in) s.d.64. 10-Jun-4 Grev Wedels Plass, Oslo #168/R est:30000-40000 (N.KR 27000)
Works on paper
£344 $575 €502 Wooded landscape (21x28cm-8x11in) s. W/C. 20-Oct-3 Blomqvist, Lysaker #1069/R (N.KR 4000)

ENGESTROM, Georg (1921-) Finnish
£680 $1238 €1000 Landscape with hill (90x90cm-35x35in) s. 8-Feb-4 Bukowskis, Helsinki #339/R

ENGL, Hugo (1852-?) Austrian
£811 $1451 €1200 Mountain lake (15x21cm-6x8in) s. board. 6-May-4 Michael Zeller, Lindau #649
£811 $1451 €1200 Landscape with chamois (18x18cm-7x7in) s. panel. 6-May-4 Michael Zeller, Lindau #650

ENGLAND, E S (19/20th C) ?
£665 $1224 €971 Startled by a hedgehog (41x61cm-16x24in) s. 14-Jun-4 Waddingtons, Toronto #104/R est:700-900 (C.D 1650)
£1100 $1980 €1606 Study of a prize sow standing in a country landscape (45x60cm-18x24in) s.d.1900. 21-Apr-4 Tennants, Leyburn #1187 est:400-500

ENGLAND, Paul Grady (1918-) American
Works on paper
£484 $900 €707 Bathers. Male nude with blazing sun (28x38cm-11x15in) one s. W/C pair. 7-Mar-4 Treadway Gallery, Cincinnati #669/R

ENGLE, Harry Leon (1870-?) American
£1250 $2200 €1825 Heralds of summer at Yorkville, Illinois (51x61cm-20x24in) s.i.d.1922. 23-May-4 Treadway Gallery, Cincinnati #577/R est:2000-3000

ENGLEHART, J J (1867-1915) American
£565 $1000 €825 Mountain landscape with Indians on the shore and on footpath (127x76cm-50x30in) s. 3-May-4 O'Gallerie, Oregon #130/R est:1500-2000

ENGLEHART, John Joseph (1867-1915) American
£272 $500 €397 Mountain landscape with Indian encampment (23x30cm-9x12in) init. panel. 29-Mar-4 O'Gallerie, Oregon #23
£300 $500 €438 Mount Lassen from Manzanita lake (30x63cm-12x25in) s. 26-Oct-3 Bonhams & Butterfields, San Francisco #6485/R
£351 $650 €512 View along the Merced River (49x71cm-19x28in) 18-Jan-4 Bonhams & Butterfields, Los Angeles #7009/R
£449 $750 €656 View of Yosemite Valley (20x41cm-8x16in) s. 26-Oct-3 Bonhams & Butterfields, San Francisco #6484/R
£559 $900 €816 Mt Shasta from McCloud River, California (18x32cm-7x13in) s. i. verso. 17-Aug-3 Bonhams & Butterfields, San Francisco #5799
£566 $900 €826 Mt Hood from high mountain lake with Indian encampment (86x46cm-34x18in) s.pseudonym C N Doughty. 5-May-3 O'Gallerie, Oregon #801/R
£898 $1500 €1311 Emerald Bay (76x127cm-30x50in) s. 11-Oct-3 Auctions by the Bay, Alameda #1632/R
£9040 $16000 €13198 Yosemite Valley (111x162cm-44x64in) s. exhib. 28-Apr-4 Christie's, Los Angeles #8/R est:10000-15000

ENGLEHEART, George (1752-1829) British
Miniatures
£1216 $2250 €1775 Portrait of a gentleman (8x8cm-3x3in) hand painted rec. 12-Mar-4 Du Mouchelle, Detroit #2003/R est:2000-3000
£1300 $2392 €1898 Portrait of a lady in profile, wearing a lace collar (6cm-2in) rectangular. 24-Jun-4 Bonhams, New Bond Street #4/R est:1000-1500
£1400 $2548 €2044 Lady, wearing lilac dress with white fichu, black choker and powdered hair (4cm-2in) i.d.1787 verso gold frame later brooch clasp oval. 3-Feb-4 Bonhams, New Bond Street #81/R est:1500-2500
£1486 $2750 €2170 Portrait of a gentleman (5x5cm-2x2in) exec.c.1785 oval. 12-Mar-4 Du Mouchelle, Detroit #2008/R est:1000-2000
£1700 $3128 €2482 Gentleman, wearing brown coat (5cm-2in) gilt metal mount with blue enamel border. 24-Jun-4 Bonhams, New Bond Street #59/R est:800-1200
£1757 $3250 €2565 Lady Robinson (8x5cm-3x2in) rec. 12-Mar-4 Du Mouchelle, Detroit #2004/R est:2000-3000
£2100 $3822 €3066 Gentleman wearing a red coat with blue lapels (4cm-2in) gilt metal frame oval exec.c.1785. 29-Jun-4 Sotheby's, Olympia #321/R est:800-1200
£2200 $3960 €3212 Miss Canning (7cm-3in) gilt metal frame oval prov.exhib.lit. 22-Apr-4 Bonhams, New Bond Street #133/R est:2000-3000
£2600 $4472 €3796 Young gentleman, in a blue coat (8cm-3in) rectangulat black frame. 2-Dec-3 Christie's, Kensington #80/R est:600-800
£2703 $5000 €3946 Portrait of a lady (8x5cm-3x2in) exec.c.1800 oval. 12-Mar-4 Du Mouchelle, Detroit #2002/R est:2000-3000
£3000 $5190 €4380 Young lady seated (8cm-3in) metal frame oval. 9-Dec-3 Christie's, London #72/R est:3000-5000
£3200 $5536 €4672 John Weir (4cm-2in) silver-gilt frame oval. 9-Dec-3 Christie's, London #73/R est:800-1200
£3200 $5888 €4672 Thomas Seward Beachcroft (7cm-3in) set in leather travelling case prov. 24-Jun-4 Bonhams, New Bond Street #115/R est:2500-3500
£3200 $5888 €4672 Gentleman, wearing blue coat, cream waistcoat (9cm-4in) s. s.d.1809 verso silver gilt frame. 24-Jun-4 Bonhams, New Bond Street #131/R est:3000-5000
£3243 $6000 €4735 W M Dawson (5cm-2in) exec.c.1780 oval. 12-Mar-4 Du Mouchelle, Detroit #2007/R est:1000-2000
£3243 $6000 €4735 Portrait of a lady (3x3cm-1x1in) oval. 12-Mar-4 Du Mouchelle, Detroit #2010/R est:1000-2000
£3400 $6120 €4964 Gentleman in a black coat (9cm-4in) s.d.1812 verso gilded wood frame rec. exhib. 22-Apr-4 Bonhams, New Bond Street #157/R est:1000-1500
£3600 $6480 €5256 Gentleman, in a blue coat with black velvet collar (8cm-3in) init.verso gilt frame oval exhib. 22-Apr-4 Bonhams, New Bond Street #96/R est:1500-2500
£3600 $6624 €5256 John Turner wearing blue coat (8cm-3in) gold frame set in red leather case prov.exhib.lit. 24-Jun-4 Bonhams, New Bond Street #116/R est:2500-3500
£3784 $7000 €5525 Portrait of a lady (5x5cm-2x2in) exec.c.1785 oval. 12-Mar-4 Du Mouchelle, Detroit #2009/R est:1000-2000
£3800 $6840 €5548 Lady, in a white dress with ribbon waistband (8cm-3in) d.Feb 14th verso gold frame oval exhib.lit. 22-Apr-4 Bonhams, New Bond Street #98/R est:2000-3000

£4200 $7014 €6132 Portrait of young man (8x6cm-3x2in) init.i.d.1813 verso W/C. 16-Oct-3 Lawrence, Crewkerne #104/R
£4400 $8096 €6424 Naval officer called Admiral Byron (5cm-2in) gold frame plaited hair border. 24-Jun-4 Bonhams, New Bond Street #62/R est:1500-2500
£4500 $8100 €6570 Mrs Catherine Inglis (5cm-2in) gold frame oval prov.exhib.lit. 22-Apr-4 Bonhams, New Bond Street #50/R est:2000-3000
£4595 $8500 €6709 Untitled, young man (8x8cm-3x3in) oval. 12-Mar-4 Du Mouchelle, Detroit #2001/R est:1000-2000
£4595 $8500 €6709 Edward Lockwood Percival (5x5cm-2x2in) exec.c.1800 oval. 12-Mar-4 Du Mouchelle, Detroit #2011/R est:1000-2000
£4865 $9000 €7103 Portrait of a gentleman (5x5cm-2x2in) exec.c.1785 oval. 12-Mar-4 Du Mouchelle, Detroit #2005/R est:1000-2000
£5000 $8950 €7300 Mr Uthoff, wearing a blue coat with gold buttons (9cm-4in) init. gilt metal frame prov.lit. 25-May-4 Christie's, London #145/R est:2500-3500
£5200 $8840 €7592 Gentleman (7cm-3in) s. oval. 18-Nov-3 Bonhams, New Bond Street #124/R est:3000-5000
£5200 $9360 €7592 Young gentleman in a dark coat (8cm-3in) s. mono.verso oval exhib.lit. 22-Apr-4 Bonhams, New Bond Street #135/R est:2500-3500
£5405 $10000 €7891 Portrait of a lady (5x3cm-2x1in) exec.c.1780 oval. 12-Mar-4 Du Mouchelle, Detroit #2006/R est:2000-3000
£5500 $9900 €8030 Mrs Samuel Stephens (7cm-3in) i.d.1790 verso gilt metal frame oval easel stand prov.exhib.lit. 22-Apr-4 Bonhams, New Bond Street #89/R est:3000-5000
£6000 $10800 €8760 Margaret Scott (4cm-2in) blue glass gold frame oval exhib. 22-Apr-4 Bonhams, New Bond Street #62/R est:3000-5000
£6000 $11040 €8760 Lady wearing white dress and bonnet trimmed with blue ribbon (6cm-2in) mono. 24-Jun-4 Bonhams, New Bond Street #85/R est:2000-3000
£6200 $11160 €9052 Double portrait of ladies, possibly sisters (4cm-2in) gold fausse-montre frame oval two in one exhib.lit. 22-Apr-4 Bonhams, New Bond Street #52/R est:6000-8000
£6500 $11700 €9490 Luke Gardiner, later Lord Mountjoy (5cm-2in) gold fausse-montre locket frame oval prov.exhib.lit. 22-Apr-4 Bonhams, New Bond Street #56/R est:5000-7000
£6500 $11635 €9490 Helen Malcolm, wearing a white dress (9cm-4in) init. gilt metal frame prov. 25-May-4 Christie's, London #144/R est:5000-7000
£7000 $12110 €10220 Sophia White (8cm-3in) s.d.1803 oval prov.exhib. 9-Dec-3 Christie's, London #117/R est:3000-5000
£7000 $12600 €10220 Lady, wearing white dress with blue ribbon (5cm-2in) gold frame oval exhib.lit. 22-Apr-4 Bonhams, New Bond Street #48/R est:4000-6000
£7500 $12975 €10950 Mary Ann Tennison (9cm-4in) s.d.1803 oval prov.exhib. 9-Dec-3 Christie's, London #118/R est:2500-3500
£7500 $13500 €10950 Lady wearing a black dress and hat with feathers (5cm-2in) gold frame oval prov.exhib.lit. 22-Apr-4 Bonhams, New Bond Street #68/R est:4000-6000
£7500 $13500 €10950 Lady wearing a white dress with open fichu (7cm-3in) gilt metal mount oval prov.exhib.lit. 22-Apr-4 Bonhams, New Bond Street #87/R est:3000-5000
£9500 $16435 €13870 John Weir (8cm-3in) init. oval. 9-Dec-3 Christie's, London #114/R est:4000-6000
£9500 $17100 €13870 Portraits of Sir John and Lady Davis (4cm-2in) gold frame oval pair exhib.lit. 22-Apr-4 Bonhams, New Bond Street #67/R est:5000-7000
£9800 $17640 €14308 Portrait of Mr and Mrs Flint (8cm-3in) s. one i.verso one s.d.1802 verso oval pair exhib.lit. 22-Apr-4 Bonhams, New Bond Street #134/R est:6000-8000
£26000 $46800 €37960 Child in a large black hat with rosette and feathers (6cm-2in) silver frame oval exhib.lit. 22-Apr-4 Bonhams, New Bond Street #70/R est:12000-18000

ENGLEHEART, John Cox Dillman (1782-1862) British

Miniatures

£1400 $2576 €2044 Miss Elizabeth Pyne (10cm-4in) gilt metal frame. 24-Jun-4 Bonhams, New Bond Street #168/R est:1000-1500
£2000 $3680 €2920 Portrait of a husband and wife (8cm-3in) ormolu frames pair. 24-Jun-4 Bonhams, New Bond Street #172/R est:2000-3000
£2000 $3680 €2920 Portrait of a husband and wife (7cm-3in) pierced brass fames pair. 24-Jun-4 Bonhams, New Bond Street #171/R est:2000-3000
£2300 $4186 €3358 An officer (8cm-3in) s.d.1813 verso gilt metal frame oval. 29-Jun-4 Sotheby's, Olympia #328/R est:1400-1800
£2600 $4420 €3796 Young lady (8cm-3in) oval. 18-Nov-3 Bonhams, New Bond Street #164/R est:1000-1500
£4200 $6972 €6132 Portrait of a lady wearing a pink dress and plum shawl (9cm-4in) Fitted in a red leather case prov. 2-Oct-3 Sotheby's, Olympia #23/R est:1200-1800
£6000 $10800 €8760 Three sisters (15cm-6in) gilt metal mount gilded woodframe rec. exhib.lit. 22-Apr-4 Bonhams, New Bond Street #156/R est:4000-6000

ENGLEHEART, John Cox Dillman (attrib) (1782-1862) British

Miniatures

£811 $1500 €1184 Portrait of a lady (8x5cm-3x2in) oval. 12-Mar-4 Du Mouchelle, Detroit #2012/R est:1000-2000

ENGLISH NAIVE SCHOOL, 18th C

£26000 $46540 €37960 View of Purley Hall, Berkshire with Warren Hastings and his menagerie of exotic animals (76x107cm-30x42in) 22-Mar-4 Bonhams & Brooks, Norfolk #284/R est:10000-15000

ENGLISH PROVINCIAL SCHOOL, 18th C

£3552 $6500 €5186 Portrait of a lady (74x68cm-29x27in) d.1768 prov. 7-Apr-4 Sotheby's, New York #75/R est:8000-12000

ENGLISH PROVINCIAL SCHOOL, 19th C

£5500 $9845 €8030 Shepherd with ram and sheepdog in a landscape (46x61cm-18x24in) i. 16-Mar-4 Bonhams, Oxford #73/R est:2000-3000

ENGLISH SCHOOL, 16th C

£550000 $1012000 €803000 Portrait of King Edward VI in red doublet (70x52cm-28x20in) panel prov.exhib.lit. 9-Jun-4 Christie's, London #6/R est:400000-600000

ENGLISH SCHOOL, 17th C

£10366 $17000 €15031 Portrait of Mary Kytson holding a pair of gloves (112x94cm-44x37in) i. panel prov. 31-May-3 Brunk, Ashville #366/R est:3000-6000
£12291 $22000 €17945 Portrait of mariner aged 38 (91x70cm-36x28in) i.d.1615 prov. 27-May-4 Sotheby's, New York #209/R est:10000-15000
£38000 $68020 €55480 Portrait of a lady and her children in court costume, she seated in a armchair (160x145cm-63x57in) prov. 22-Mar-4 Bonhams & Brooks, Norfolk #332/R est:20000-30000

Sculpture

£9000 $16110 €13140 Portrait of Henry Purcell (22x17cm-9x7in) white marble relief. 11-May-4 Sotheby's, Olympia #413/R est:3000-5000

ENGLISH SCHOOL, 17th/18th C

£6711 $12013 €10000 La Vierge, l'Enfant et Saint Jean Baptiste (124x102cm-49x40in) 25-May-4 Palais de Beaux Arts, Brussels #70/R est:8000-10000
£7000 $11060 €10220 Half length portrait of a young boy dressed in a red jacket and white cravat (77x63cm-30x25in) oval. 27-Apr-3 Wilkinson, Doncaster #340/R
£24000 $40800 €35040 View of Old Palace yard, Westminster, east end of Westminster Abbey with the Chapel of King Henry (58x93cm-23x37in) 25-Nov-3 Christie's, London #57/R est:15000-25000

ENGLISH SCHOOL, 18th C

£5000 $8600 €7300 Ship sailing towards Holland (65x48cm-26x19in) painted on glass. 2-Dec-3 Sotheby's, London #257/R est:2000-3000
£5322 $9525 €7770 Sailing vessel by the English coast (92x147cm-36x58in) 25-May-4 Bukowskis, Stockholm #510/R est:40000-50000 (S.KR 72000)
£5750 $10350 €8395 Three masted naval merchant vessel, Blenheim off the South Coast (63x106cm-25x42in) 20-Apr-4 Rowley Fine Art, Newmarket #428/R
£7237 $13316 €11000 Portrait of two Russian noblemen (60x79cm-24x31in) prov. 22-Jun-4 Mealy's, Castlecomer #365/R est:2500-3500
£7400 $13838 €10804 An English setter, in a wooded landscape (102x127cm-40x50in) 20-Jul-4 Sworder & Son, Bishops Stortford #106/R est:2000-3000
£8500 $15640 €12410 Extensive wooded landscape with cowherds and cattle (73x122cm-29x48in) 11-Jun-4 Christie's, London #41/R est:5000-7000
£10811 $19027 €16000 Portrait of officer (99x72cm-39x28in) 18-May-4 Sotheby's, Milan #502/R est:10000-15000
£28000 $47600 €40880 Equestrian portrait of an Indian nobleman in a white tunic, holding a hawk on his right hand (127x102cm-50x40in) 25-Nov-3 Christie's, London #18/R est:5000-8000

Sculpture

£98000 $175420 €143080 Figures of shepherd and shepherdess (218cm-86in) lead on stone base pair. 25-May-4 Sotheby's, Billingshurst #462/R est:30000-50000

Works on paper

£5500 $10010 €8030 View of Chirk Castle (94x128cm-37x50in) pen ink oil on linen paper. 21-Jun-4 Christie's, London #25/R est:1000-2000

ENGLISH SCHOOL, 18th/19th C

£10000 $18300 €15000 La fete foraine (103x141cm-41x56in) 5-Jun-4 Gros & Delettrez, Paris #65/R est:15000-20000

ENGLISH SCHOOL, 19th C

£3631 $6500 €5301 British full-rigger - Slieve Donard passing the South Stack (61x91cm-24x36in) canvas laid down. 16-Mar-4 Bonhams & Butterfields, San Francisco #6150/R est:3000-5000
£3823 $6500 €5582 Approaching storm (132x179cm-52x70in) 19-Nov-3 Bonhams & Butterfields, San Francisco #129/R
£4268 $7000 €6189 Red haired boy leaning against rocks with a hammer (91x71cm-36x28in) prov. 31-May-3 Brunk, Ashville #333/R est:1500-2500
£5000 $8350 €7300 Battle of Copenhagen (84x114cm-33x45in) 14-Oct-3 Sotheby's, London #449 est:2000-3000
£5114 $9000 €7466 Portrait of a young family taking tea (101x79cm-40x31in) 18-May-4 Sotheby's, New York #100/R est:15000-20000
£5333 $9707 €8000 Rider and horse in landscape (58x71cm-23x28in) 29-Jun-4 Sotheby's, Paris #41/R est:3000-4000
£5369 $9879 €8000 Leaving for hunting (55x89cm-22x35in) 24-Mar-4 Finarte Semenzato, Rome #3/R est:10000
£5400 $9882 €7884 The meet (68x89cm-27x35in) 7-Apr-4 Woolley & Wallis, Salisbury #273/R est:400-600
£5800 $10034 €8468 Election celebrations in Swaffham Market Place (24x35cm-9x14in) panel. 10-Dec-3 Bonhams, Bury St Edmunds #599/R est:3000-5000
£6704 $12000 €9788 British Racing Cutter towing a yawl off Margate (61x89cm-24x35in) indis.s. 16-Mar-4 Bonhams & Butterfields, San Francisco #6147/R est:4000-6000
£7500 $12750 €10950 Grouse shooting. Partridge shooting. Woodcock shooting. Pheasant shooting (27x38cm-11x15in) board set of four prov. 25-Nov-3 Christie's, London #93/R est:8000-12000
£7600 $13832 €11400 French port scene (137x178cm-54x70in) 20-Jun-4 Wilkinson, Doncaster #347 est:8000-10000
£8667 $15947 €13000 Famille de notables dans un paysage vallonne (187x280cm-74x110in) 14-Jun-4 Horta, Bruxelles #171/R est:15000-18000
£9000 $17010 €13140 Portsmouth (61x94cm-24x37in) indis.init.d.185. 17-Feb-4 Bonhams, New Bond Street #48/R est:1500-2000
£9000 $16110 €13140 Great Exhibition of Industrial and decorative Art, 1861 (44x63cm-17x25in) 27-May-4 Christie's, Kensington #273/R est:7000-10000
£10563 $18275 €15000 Paysage aux grands arbres avec une halte de Turcs (152x287cm-60x113in) 10-Dec-3 Maigret, Paris #54/R est:7000-10000
£16000 $28640 €23360 Portrait of Niccolo Paganini (78x48cm-31x19in) 11-May-4 Sotheby's, Olympia #562/R est:12000-18000
£26490 $48477 €40000 Portrait presume de Mrs Ainslie et de son fils (73x63cm-29x25in) 7-Apr-4 Libert, Castor, Paris #20/R est:800-1000
£75000 $132750 €109500 Planter's homestead. Landing the barrels (63x102cm-25x40in) pair. 27-Apr-4 Bonhams, New Bond Street #125/R est:20000-40000

Photographs

£12000 $21120 €17520 Mrs Susannah Mostyn's family album (33x28cm-13x11in) salt albument print album prov. 19-May-4 Christie's, London #59/R est:2000-3000

Sculpture

£6500 $10790 €9490 Admiral Lord Nelson (234cm-92in) stone stepped base. 1-Oct-3 Bonhams, Knightsbridge #285/R est:10000-15000
£8500 $14705 €12410 Bust of Shakespeare (69cm-27in) white marble socle. 12-Dec-3 Sotheby's, London #226/R est:6000-8000

Miniatures

£4865 $9000 €7103 Portrait of a gentleman (8x5cm-3x2in) exec.c.1825 oval. 12-Mar-4 Du Mouchelle, Detroit #2049/R est:900-1500

Works on paper

£3401	$6088	€5000	Vaches dans la campagne anglaise (37x55cm-15x22in) s.d.1851 or 1854 W/C exhib. 17-Mar-4 Maigret, Paris #12/R est:600-800
£5000	$8150	€7300	Fort William, from the River Hoogly, Calcutta (147x229cm-58x90in) pencil W/C. 24-Sep-3 Christie's, London #83/R est:7000-10000

ENGLISH, F F (1854-1922) American

Works on paper

£495	$900	€723	Along the river (51x33cm-20x13in) s. W/C. 19-Jun-4 Jackson's, Cedar Falls #21/R
£5031	$8000	€7345	Crossing (38x79cm-15x31in) s. W/C. 10-Sep-3 Alderfer's, Hatfield #434/R est:4000-6000

ENGLISH, Frank F (1854-1922) American

Works on paper

£289	$500	€422	Road and house with stone wall (18x25cm-7x10in) W/C. 10-Dec-3 Alderfer's, Hatfield #429
£318	$550	€464	Houses with picket fence (15x23cm-6x9in) W/C. 10-Dec-3 Alderfer's, Hatfield #428
£323	$550	€472	Hay wagon (33x66cm-13x26in) s. W/C gouache. 21-Nov-3 Skinner, Boston #262/R
£353	$650	€515	Dutch street, after the rain (46x81cm-18x32in) s. W/C board. 9-Jun-4 Doyle, New York #3030
£407	$700	€594	Wagon on a country road (25x48cm-10x19in) s. W/C exec.c.1900. 7-Dec-3 Treadway Gallery, Cincinnati #476/R
£419	$700	€612	Village scene with mother and daughter by the shore (48x76cm-19x30in) s. W/C. 20-Jun-3 Freeman, Philadelphia #3/R
£419	$750	€612	Pastoral landscape (23x35cm-9x14in) s. W/C gouache paperboard. 14-May-4 Skinner, Boston #72/R
£659	$1200	€962	Farmscape with sheep (33x51cm-13x20in) s. W/C. 19-Jun-4 Jackson's, Cedar Falls #22/R
£898	$1500	€1311	Shower creek (28x56cm-11x22in) s. W/C gouache paper on paperboard. 20-Jun-3 Freeman, Philadelphia #13/R est:1200-1800
£1087	$2000	€1587	Hay wagon (33x67cm-13x26in) s. W/C. 27-Jun-4 Freeman, Philadelphia #169/R est:2000-3000
£1163	$2000	€1698	Haywagon (33x53cm-13x21in) s. W/C. 7-Dec-3 Freeman, Philadelphia #224 est:1000-1500
£1220	$2000	€1769	House by the marsh with figures and animals (48x76cm-19x30in) s. W/C gouache. 4-Jun-3 Alderfer's, Hatfield #411/R est:1800-2200
£1375	$2200	€2008	Horse and carriage on a path (36x66cm-14x26in) s. W/C exec. c.1890. 20-Sep-3 Bunte, Elgin #1434 est:1200-1800
£1453	$2600	€2438	Figures and horses walking down country road beside a cottage (43x66cm-17x26in) s. W/C. 20-Mar-4 Pook & Pook, Downington #394/R est:2000-2500
£1564	$2800	€2627	Two figures and horse standing on country road beside cottage (43x66cm-17x26in) s. W/C. 20-Mar-4 Pook & Pook, Downington #393/R est:2000-2500
£1590	$2750	€2321	Landscape of scene along a Delaware with figures (43x79cm-17x31in) s. W/C. 10-Dec-3 Alderfer's, Hatfield #426/R est:3000-4000
£1747	$3250	€2551	Midsummer in New England (33x64cm-13x25in) s. W/C. 3-Mar-4 Alderfer's, Hatfield #400/R est:3000-3250
£2601	$4500	€3797	Canadian village (46x74cm-18x29in) s. W/C executed c.1900. 10-Dec-3 Alderfer's, Hatfield #425/R est:5000-8000
£3763	$7000	€5494	Farm landscape with figures and chickens near barn (61x91cm-24x36in) s. W/C. 3-Mar-4 Alderfer's, Hatfield #399 est:8000-10000

ENGLISH, Grace (1891-1956) British

£700	$1141	€1022	London window (66x56cm-26x22in) s. 24-Sep-3 Dreweatt Neate, Newbury #120/R

ENGLISH, James (1916-1988) British

£270	$483	€394	Heading for water (32x45cm-13x18in) s. board. 30-May-4 Lots Road Auctions, London #348/R

ENGLISH, James (1946-) Irish

£280	$476	€400	Connemara lakes, from top of mountain near Clifden (24x35cm-9x14in) s. i.verso board. 18-Nov-3 Mealy's, Castlecomer #1410
£500	$920	€760	Stone cairn with thornbush (31x26cm-12x10in) s. i.verso exhib. 22-Jun-4 De Veres Art Auctions, Dublin #148/R
£2685	$4805	€4000	Beach boats Tabarca, Spain (34x44cm-13x17in) s. 26-May-4 James Adam, Dublin #101/R est:4000-6000

ENGLISH, Mabel Bacon Plimpton (1861-?) American

£299	$500	€437	Landscape with trees (43x28cm-17x11in) s. 20-Jun-3 Freeman, Philadelphia #126/R

ENGLUND, Lars (1933-) Swedish

£769	$1362	€1123	Painting - Untitled (5x21cm-2x8in) s.d.67 prov. 27-Apr-4 AB Stockholms Auktionsverk #972/R (S.KR 10500)
£4762	$8429	€6953	Mirror for the galleries (190x170cm-75x67in) s.d.1991 verso tempera shaped panel prov. 27-Apr-4 AB Stockholms Auktionsverk #973/R est:40000-60000 (S.KR 65000)

Sculpture

£2051	$3631	€2994	Plaited basket work (72cm-28in) s.d.1989 black steel. 27-Apr-4 AB Stockholms Auktionsverk #970/R est:30000-35000 (S.KR 28000)

Works on paper

£513	$908	€749	Rubbish bubble (39x36cm-15x14in) s. polyurethane. 27-Apr-4 AB Stockholms Auktionsverk #971/R (S.KR 7000)

ENGMAN, Harald (1903-1968) Danish

£268	$494	€400	Street at night (51x41cm-20x16in) s.d.1941. 25-Mar-4 Hagelstam, Helsinki #917
£489	$890	€734	Street in Copenhagen (46x69cm-18x27in) s. 19-Jun-4 Rasmussen, Havnen #4035/R (D.KR 5500)
£1043	$1668	€1512	Evening at Nyboder (34x48cm-13x19in) s.d.1930. 17-Sep-3 Kunsthallen, Copenhagen #270/R (D.KR 11000)
£1534	$2869	€2240	When the night is falling (45x35cm-18x14in) s.d.1942 lit. 25-Feb-4 Kunsthallen, Copenhagen #265/R est:18000 (D.KR 17000)
£1805	$3375	€2635	The Heroes of our time (49x40cm-19x16in) s.d.1938. 25-Feb-4 Kunsthallen, Copenhagen #266/R est:16000 (D.KR 20000)
£4139	$7037	€6043	Mother Denmark (37x30cm-15x12in) s.d.41 masonite. 26-Nov-3 Kunsthallen, Copenhagen #328/R est:25000 (D.KR 44000)

ENGONOPOULOS, Nikos (1910-1985) Greek

Works on paper

£5200	$8840	€7592	Artist and model (23x16cm-9x6in) s.d.36 W/C pen ink prov. 18-Nov-3 Sotheby's, London #66/R est:3500-4500
£7000	$12530	€10220	Divine couple. Poet in Ferrara (32x24cm-13x9in) s. one d.40 ink pencil two. 11-May-4 Bonhams, New Bond Street #71/R est:5000-7000

ENGSTFELD, Albert (1876-?) German

£909	$1545	€1300	At the market (38x28cm-15x11in) s. cardboard lit. 28-Nov-3 Schloss Ahlden, Ahlden #1548/R

ENGSTROM, Albert (1869-1940) Swedish

Works on paper

£510	$939	€765	Hare in the skerries (36x63cm-14x25in) s. mixed media. 14-Jun-4 Lilla Bukowskis, Stockholm #340 (S.KR 7000)

ENGSTROM, Leander (1886-1927) Swedish

£1662	$2825	€2427	Mountain brook. Southern woman (33x41cm-13x16in) s. double-sided. 4-Nov-3 Bukowskis, Stockholm #173/R est:30000-40000 (S.KR 22000)
£2175	$3916	€3176	Foaming waterfall (54x65cm-21x26in) s. panel. 26-Apr-4 Bukowskis, Stockholm #121/R est:30000-40000 (S.KR 30000)
£2735	$4895	€3993	Evening landscape, Torne trask (53x67cm-21x26in) s.d.1925. 28-May-4 Uppsala Auktionskammare, Uppsala #262 est:30000-40000 (S.KR 37000)
£3046	$5482	€4447	Still life of pansies (33x26cm-13x10in) s. canvas on board. 26-Apr-4 Bukowskis, Stockholm #25/R est:35000-40000 (S.KR 42000)
£3058	$4924	€4465	Landscape with whirling rapids (71x76cm-28x30in) s.d.1924. 25-Aug-3 Lilla Bukowskis, Stockholm #441 est:25000-30000 (S.KR 40000)
£6042	$10272	€8821	View of Ragunda (38x46cm-15x18in) s.i.d.1915. 4-Nov-3 Bukowskis, Stockholm #88/R est:60000-80000 (S.KR 80000)
£6526	$11748	€9528	View from Fjallgatan towards Djurgarden (47x38cm-19x15in) s. 26-Apr-4 Bukowskis, Stockholm #53a/R est:100000-125000 (S.KR 90000)
£12462	$21186	€18195	Palsundet, Stockholm (36x48cm-14x19in) s. lit. 4-Nov-3 Bukowskis, Stockholm #120/R est:100000-125000 (S.KR 165000)
£19260	$32742	€28120	Rottle Mill, Grenna (61x44cm-24x17in) s.d.1913 prov.exhib.lit. 4-Nov-3 Bukowskis, Stockholm #175/R est:150000-175000 (S.KR 255000)
£20513	$36308	€29949	Landscape from Nuolja Hill, Abisko (72x62cm-28x24in) panel painted 1917 prov.exhib.lit. 27-Apr-4 AB Stockholms Auktionsverk #751/R est:300000-350000 (S.KR 280000)
£46073	$78323	€67267	Lofoten - landscape from Salangen (97x80cm-38x31in) s.d.1916 panel. 5-Nov-3 AB Stockholms Auktionsverk #665/R est:400000-500000 (S.KR 610000)
£64199	$109139	€93731	From the deer park, Stockholm (72x54cm-28x21in) s. verso painted 1914 prov. 4-Nov-3 Bukowskis, Stockholm #11/R est:300000-350000 (S.KR 850000)
£99710	$179478	€145577	Landscape from the Arno by Compiobbi (52x72cm-20x28in) s.i.d.1922 prov.exhib.lit. 26-Apr-4 Bukowskis, Stockholm #27/R est:1000000-1200000 (S.KR 1375000)

Works on paper

£14728	$25038	€21503	Norwegian coast (73x52cm-29x20in) s. W/C exec.c.1918 prov.lit. 5-Nov-3 AB Stockholms Auktionsverk #850/R est:60000-80000 (S.KR 195000)
£18882	$32100	€27568	View of Florence (88x64cm-35x25in) s.i.d.Maj 1920 mixed media. 5-Nov-3 AB Stockholms Auktionsverk #755/R est:150000-200000 (S.KR 250000)

ENGSTROM, Martin (1952-) Swedish

£403	$713	€588	Untitled (45x35cm-18x14in) s.d.90 oil gold leaf panel prov. 27-Apr-4 AB Stockholms Auktionsverk #991/R (S.KR 5500)

ENGUIEUX, Alfredo (20th C) Spanish?

£241	$403	€349	Los bigotes (50x62cm-20x24in) s.d.77. 24-Jun-3 Louis Morton, Mexico #319 (M.P 4200)
£344	$575	€499	Caballo (60x70cm-24x28in) s. 24-Jun-3 Louis Morton, Mexico #171 (M.P 6000)

ENJOLRAS, D (1857-1945) French

Works on paper

£1060	$1981	€1600	Jeune fille cueillant des fleurs (71x31cm-28x12in) s. crayon pastel. 25-Jul-4 Versailles Encheres #46/R

ENJOLRAS, Delphin (1857-1945) French

£2128	$3553	€3000	Jeune femme assis pres d'une cheminee (55x38cm-22x15in) s. 20-Jun-3 Drouot Estimations, Paris #74/R est:3500-4000
£4500	$8190	€6570	Nude by the fire (35x27cm-14x11in) s. 16-Jun-4 Christie's, Kensington #256/R est:2000-3000
£4832	$8940	€7200	Brodeuse (55x38cm-22x15in) s. 14-Mar-4 Eric Pillon, Calais #14/R
£5000	$9000	€7300	Roses by candlelight (46x33cm-18x13in) s. 21-Jan-4 Sotheby's, New York #181/R est:6000-8000
£6500	$11050	€9490	Femme dans son boudoir (73x54cm-29x21in) s. 18-Nov-3 Sotheby's, London #348/R
£6800	$12172	€9928	Flower bouquet (44x31cm-17x12in) s. 26-May-4 Sotheby's, Olympia #333/R est:4000-6000
£13333	$24400	€20000	Le boudoir (46x33cm-18x13in) s. 6-Jun-4 Anaf, Lyon #95/R est:12000-15000

Works on paper

£2252	$4098	€3400	Nu a la lampe (37x27cm-15x11in) s. mixed media. 16-Jun-4 Hotel des Ventes Mosan, Brussels #233 est:1500-2000
£2381	$3786	€3500	Fete venitienne (38x46cm-15x18in) s. i.verso pastel. 23-Mar-3 St-Germain-en-Laye Encheres #63/R est:2200
£2684	$4751	€4000	Jeune enfant au ruban (55x46cm-22x18in) s. pastel. 30-Apr-4 Tajan, Paris #172/R est:4000-6000

£4000 $7400 €5840 Bouquet (72x52cm-28x20in) s. pastel. 14-Jul-4 Sotheby's, Olympia #264/R est:4000-6000
£4200 $7140 €6132 Jeune femme arrangeant les roses (60x60cm-24x24in) s. pastel. 4-Nov-3 Bonhams, New Bond Street #7/R est:4000-6000
£4300 $7611 €6278 Young woman reading (53x36cm-21x14in) s. pastel. 27-Apr-4 Bonhams, Knowle #145/R est:2000-3000
£5379 $8984 €7800 Femme rousse au chale de cachemire (72x60cm-28x24in) s. pastel. 17-Nov-3 Tajan, Paris #117/R est:7000-8000
£7000 $12740 €10220 La belle arome (51x70cm-20x28in) s. pastel. 16-Jun-4 Christie's, Kensington #257/R est:3000-5000
£8392 $14266 €12000 Lecture a la lampe (71x52cm-28x20in) s. pastel. 21-Nov-3 Lombrail & Teucquam, Paris #121/R est:12000-13000
£9100 $16107 €13286 Letter (70x51cm-28x20in) s. pastel prov. 27-Apr-4 Bonhams, Knowle #144 est:3000-5000
£19500 $35490 €28470 La lecture au clair de la lampe (54x73cm-21x29in) s. pastel. 15-Jun-4 Sotheby's, London #214/R est:6000-8000

ENKAOUA, Daniel (1962-) Israeli
£8434 $14000 €12314 Untitled (92x76cm-36x30in) jute prov. 2-Oct-3 Christie's, Tel Aviv #112/R est:18000-24000
£13966 $25000 €20390 Interior (131x100cm-52x39in) s.d.90-91. 18-Mar-4 Sotheby's, New York #59/R est:18000-25000

ENKOK, Davidee (20th C) North American
Sculpture
£1111 $1800 €1622 Kneeling woman with two children on her back (25x18x25cm-10x7x10in) grey soapstone. 26-Jul-3 Thomaston Place, Thomaston #564/R

ENMAN, Thomas K (20th C) American
£240 $400 €350 Back Bay, Newport. s.d.1986. 15-Nov-3 Harvey Clar, Oakland #1223
£254 $425 €371 Santa Rosa Creek Road, Cambria, California (30x46cm-12x18in) s. 14-Jul-3 O'Gallerie, Oregon #794/R

ENNEKING, John J (1841-1916) American
£829 $1500 €1210 Wooded landscape at sunset (25x41cm-10x16in) s. 3-Apr-4 Nadeau, Windsor #86 est:1800-2500
£1078 $1800 €1574 Sheep grazing (25x36cm-10x14in) s. panel. 23-Oct-3 Shannon's, Milford #216/R est:2500-3500
£1397 $2500 €2040 Landscape with mountains (23x33cm-9x13in) s. board. 6-May-4 Shannon's, Milford #216/R est:2500-3500
£1412 $2500 €2062 Autumnal landscape under a cloudy sky (8x12cm-3x5in) s. board. 2-May-4 Bonhams & Butterfields, San Francisco #1111/R est:3000-5000
£1564 $2800 €2283 Storm approaching, an autumnal landscape (51x61cm-20x24in) s. 14-May-4 Skinner, Boston #190/R est:2000-4000
£1582 $2800 €2310 Cattle grazing at sunset (12x10cm-5x4in) s.indis.d. 2-May-4 Bonhams & Butterfields, San Francisco #1124/R est:3000-5000
£1613 $3000 €2355 Autumn's Glory (30x51cm-12x20in) s. 3-Mar-4 Christie's, Rockefeller NY #9/R est:4000-6000
£3235 $5500 €4723 Sunset autumn landscape (12x18cm-5x7in) s.d.98 board prov. 18-Nov-3 John Moran, Pasadena #109 est:5000-7000
£5028 $9000 €7341 Summer cottage with hollyhocks (30x46cm-12x18in) s.d.88 board. 26-May-4 Doyle, New York #47/R est:8000-12000
£5091 $8500 €7433 Oak tree (25x36cm-10x14in) s. i.verso board prov. 23-Oct-3 Shannon's, Milford #188/R est:4000-6000
£5091 $8500 €7433 Landscape (25x30cm-10x12in) init.d.82 prov. 23-Oct-3 Shannon's, Milford #210/R est:4000-6000
£5938 $9500 €8669 Springtime landscape (25x36cm-10x14in) s. board prov. 21-Sep-3 Grogan, Boston #51/R
£6215 $11000 €9074 Pond at twilight (30x40cm-12x16in) s.d.84. 2-May-4 Bonhams & Butterfields, San Francisco #1123/R est:6000-8000
£7910 $14000 €11549 Wooded stream in autumn. Waterfall (25x30cm-10x12in) s.d.09 pair. 2-May-4 Bonhams & Butterfields, San Francisco #1117/R est:12000-18000
£8939 $16000 €13051 Evening glow (25x30cm-10x12in) s. 6-May-4 Shannon's, Milford #67/R est:4000-6000
£10056 $18000 €14682 New England landscape (46x61cm-18x24in) s.d.89. 6-May-4 Shannon's, Milford #82/R est:10000-15000
£10686 $18915 €15602 Rolling river landscape with sheep under the apple blossoms (22x30cm-9x12in) s. 2-May-4 Bonhams & Butterfields, San Francisco #1110/R est:20000-30000
£11176 $19000 €16317 Impressionistic wooded scene with house (46x61cm-18x24in) s. 21-Nov-3 Eldred, East Dennis #834/R est:15000-20000
£13408 $24000 €19576 Autumn landscape (46x66cm-18x26in) s.d.86 prov. 6-May-4 Shannon's, Milford #32/R est:15000-25000

ENNEKING, John J (attrib) (1841-1916) American
£1059 $1800 €1546 Grazing sheep in sunset pasture (25x36cm-10x14in) board. 21-Nov-3 Skinner, Boston #480/R est:2000-4000
£1705 $3000 €2489 Autumn landscape at sunset (25x30cm-10x12in) 1-Jan-4 Nadeau, Windsor #191/R est:800-1200
£3955 $7000 €5774 Snow capped mountain in late autumn, New England (24x30cm-9x12in) 2-May-4 Bonhams & Butterfields, San Francisco #1118/R est:2000-3000

ENNESS, Augustus William (1876-1948) British
£260 $478 €380 Tranquil landscape with a pool and woodland (39x49cm-15x19in) s. canvas on panel. 23-Mar-4 Rosebery Fine Art, London #945/R
£270 $451 €394 Barmouth estuary. s.i. on stretcher. 14-Oct-3 Rosebery Fine Art, London #570
£290 $534 €423 North country river landscape in spring (16x19cm-6x7in) s. 11-Jun-4 Keys, Aylsham #661
£300 $501 €438 Children playing by a beached fishing boat, castle beyond (24x34cm-9x13in) s.d.1907. 26-Jun-3 Greenslade Hunt, Taunton #548
£350 $585 €511 Waves breaking on the coast (64x76cm-25x30in) s. 14-Oct-3 David Lay, Penzance #550
£350 $585 €511 River scene (40x51cm-16x20in) s. 12-Nov-3 Sotheby's, Olympia #132/R
£360 $572 €526 Near Coniston (15x20cm-6x8in) s. board. 10-Sep-3 Sotheby's, Olympia #173/R
£403 $742 €588 Concarneau, France (26x38cm-10x15in) s. canvas on panel. 14-Jun-4 Waddingtons, Toronto #109/R est:1000-1500 (C.D 1000)
£420 $701 €613 Cattle grazing in a riverside meadow, church tower beyond (37x49cm-15x19in) s.d.28 indis.i.verso. 26-Jun-3 Greenslade Hunt, Taunton #549/R
£480 $864 €701 Still life of red and yellow flowers in a decorated vase (41x51cm-16x20in) s. 21-Apr-4 Tennants, Leyburn #1201
£500 $930 €730 Village duck pond, Dalham, Suffolk (38x49cm-15x19in) s. canvasboard. 4-Mar-4 Christie's, Kensington #473/R
£700 $1288 €1022 River in summer time (37x51cm-15x20in) s.d.1929 panel. 24-Mar-4 Hamptons Fine Art, Godalming #300/R
£750 $1343 €1095 Wooded landscapes (38x48cm-15x19in) s. pair. 5-May-4 John Nicholson, Haslemere #452
£800 $1336 €1168 Entrance to the Guidecca Canal, Venice (36x49cm-14x19in) s.d.27 i.stretcher. 26-Jun-3 Greenslade Hunt, Taunton #551/R
£880 $1470 €1285 Martiques, France (35x51cm-14x20in) s. board. 26-Jun-3 Greenslade Hunt, Taunton #552/R
£950 $1587 €1387 Martiques, France (38x51cm-15x20in) s. canvas on board. 16-Oct-3 Christie's, Kensington #390/R

ENNION, Eric (1900-1981) British
Works on paper
£720 $1145 €1051 Pochards and tufted ducks on flood water (27x34cm-11x13in) s. W/C. 30-Apr-3 Peter Wilson, Nantwich #93/R

ENNIS, George Pearse (1884-1936) American
£870 $1600 €1270 Muir woods (51x61cm-20x24in) s. 11-Jun-4 David Rago, Lambertville #235/R est:1500-2500
Works on paper
£335 $600 €489 Maine coastal scene with rowboat (18x23cm-7x9in) s. W/C. 8-Jan-4 James Julia, Fairfield #937/R
£376 $700 €549 Coastal cliff (38x49cm-15x19in) s. W/C. 5-Mar-4 Skinner, Boston #544/R

ENOCK, Arthur Henry (fl.1869-1910) British
Works on paper
£630 $1052 €920 Ships on the Dart (33x51cm-13x20in) s. W/C. 13-Nov-3 Rendalls, Ashburton #1995
£780 $1295 €1139 Fishing on a moorland river (48x69cm-19x27in) s. W/C. 2-Oct-3 Lane, Penzance #87
£860 $1436 €1256 Sheep in a valley (49x79cm-19x31in) s. W/C. 14-Oct-3 Bearnes, Exeter #318/R
£900 $1701 €1314 Near Ely, twilight (74x49cm-29x19in) s.d.1883 W/C. 17-Feb-4 Fellows & Sons, Birmingham #144/R
£2100 $3507 €3066 Twilight at Totnes (33x51cm-13x20in) s. W/C. 13-Nov-3 Rendalls, Ashburton #1996

ENOTRIO (1920-1989) Argentinian
£411 $736 €600 Paesaggio mediterraneo (100x70cm-39x28in) s. s.i.d.1961 verso. 22-Mar-4 Philippe Schuler, Zurich #6139 (S.FR 950)
£552 $921 €800 Landscape in Calabria (50x70cm-20x28in) s. s.i.verso. 13-Nov-3 Finarte Semenzato, Rome #269
£667 $1227 €1000 Olive trees on the Tirrenian Sea (50x60cm-20x24in) s. s.i.verso. 12-Jun-4 Meeting Art, Vercelli #938/R
£733 $1349 €1100 Still life (50x70cm-20x28in) s. i.verso board. 11-Jun-4 Farsetti, Prato #48
£884 $1583 €1300 Landscape in Calabria (50x70cm-20x28in) s. board. 22-Mar-4 Sant Agostino, Torino #465/R
£1000 $1800 €1500 Landscape on the Tirreno (60x90cm-24x35in) s. s.i.verso. 22-Apr-4 Finarte Semenzato, Rome #158 est:800-1000
£3067 $5643 €4600 Railway (70x100cm-28x39in) s. s.i.verso board prov. 10-Jun-4 Galleria Pace, Milan #59/R est:7000

ENRIQUEZ FERRER, Francisco (20th C) Spanish
£345 $576 €500 Portrait of boy (55x42cm-22x17in) s.d.1839. 11-Nov-3 Castellana, Madrid #179/R

ENRIQUEZ, Carlos (1900-1957) Cuban
£6855 $12613 €10008 Tilin Garcia on horseback (51x40cm-20x16in) s.d.46. 14-Jun-4 Waddingtons, Toronto #200/R est:20000-30000 (C.D 17000)
£10081 $18548 €14718 Horses in a landscape (60x73cm-24x29in) s.d.53. 14-Jun-4 Waddingtons, Toronto #201/R est:30000-50000 (C.D 25000)
£20588 $35000 €30058 Mujer - Woman (61x46cm-24x18in) panel painted c.1945 prov. 18-Nov-3 Christie's, Rockefeller NY #149/R est:25000-30000

ENROTH, Erik (1917-1975) Finnish
£676 $1209 €1000 Still life of bottle and glass (78x55cm-31x22in) s.d.63 board. 8-May-4 Bukowskis, Helsinki #253/R

ENSLIN, George (1919-1972) South African
£714 $1293 €1042 Old harbour, Hermanus (49x60cm-19x24in) s.d.56 board. 30-Mar-4 Stephan Welz, Johannesburg #433 est:5000-8000 (SA.R 8500)
£1111 $1889 €1622 Landscape with houses and poplar trees (29x45cm-11x18in) s. board. 4-Nov-3 Stephan Welz, Johannesburg #314 est:1600-2000 (SA.R 13000)
£1121 $1872 €1637 Malay quarter (60x90cm-24x35in) s.d.62. 20-Oct-3 Stephan Welz, Johannesburg #254 est:5000-7000 (SA.R 13000)

ENSOR, James (1860-1949) Belgian
£10490 $18042 €15000 Accessoires (26x33cm-10x13in) s.d.81 panel prov.exhib.lit. 2-Dec-3 Sotheby's, Amsterdam #47/R est:6000-8000
£10667 $19627 €16000 Cuvette (23x18cm-9x7in) s. verso board painted c.1880. 8-Jun-4 Sotheby's, Amsterdam #35/R est:6000-8000
£47059 $80000 €68706 Bateaux au soleil (55x67cm-22x26in) s. painted c.1923-30 prov.exhib.lit. 6-Nov-3 Sotheby's, New York #184/R est:70000-90000
£55000 $101200 €80300 Nuit de Walpurgis (51x61cm-20x24in) s.d.28 prov.exhib.lit. 22-Jun-4 Sotheby's, London #174/R est:60000-80000
£65000 $118300 €94900 La charge des Walkyries (56x68cm-22x27in) s. s.i.d.13 fevrier 1938 verso prov. 3-Feb-4 Christie's, London #226/R est:70000-100000
£91549 $158380 €130000 Lievre et corbeau (72x88cm-28x35in) s. prov.exhib.lit. 13-Dec-3 De Vuyst, Lokeren #444/R
£125000 $227500 €182500 Chou rouge et masques (65x81cm-26x32in) s. painted c.1925-1930 prov.exhib.lit. 3-Feb-4 Christie's, London #156/R est:100000-150000
£220000 $404800 €321200 Verre de vin rouge, fraises et cerises (18x24cm-7x9in) s.d.92 panel prov.exhib.lit. 22-Jun-4 Christie's, London #19/R est:100000-150000

£650000	$1189500	€949000	Bons juges (38x46cm-15x18in) s.d.91 panel prov.exhib.lit. 2-Feb-4 Christie's, London #33/R est:500000-700000
Prints			
£1875	$3000	€2738	Combat de Pouilleux Desir et Rissole (23x28cm-9x11in) drypoint. 18-Sep-3 Swann Galleries, New York #225/R est:2000-3000
£2000	$3400	€2920	La cathedrale (24x18cm-9x7in) s.d.1886 etching. 6-Nov-3 Swann Galleries, New York #354/R est:5000-8000
£2200	$4004	€3212	View of Ostende to the east (24x30cm-9x12in) s.i. s.verso hand col etching. 1-Jul-4 Sotheby's, London #167/R est:2500-3000
£2235	$3800	€3263	Les patineurs (17x24cm-7x9in) s.i.d.1889 s.verso etching. 6-Nov-3 Swann Galleries, New York #351/R est:3500-5000
£2477	$4137	€3592	Demons me turlupinant - affiche de la plume. s. col lithograph. 19-Jun-3 Kornfeld, Bern #336/R est:2500 (S.FR 5400)
£2517	$4280	€3600	Les mauvais medecins. etching. 1-Dec-3 Palais de Beaux Arts, Brussels #5/R est:2000-3000
£2550	$4693	€3800	La cathedrale (23x17cm-9x7in) s.d.1886 print. 28-Mar-4 MonsAntic, Maisieres #383 est:4000-6000
£2625	$4200	€3833	Cathedrale (24x18cm-9x7in) s.i.d.1886 etching two parts. 18-Sep-3 Swann Galleries, New York #228/R est:3000-5000
£2797	$4755	€4000	La kermesse au moulin (14x18cm-6x7in) s.d. i. verso. 27-Nov-3 Bassenge, Berlin #5572 est:2500
£2800	$5124	€4200	La cathedrale. s.d.1886 eau forte. 7-Jun-4 Palais de Beaux Arts, Brussels #209/R est:3500-5000
£2905	$5200	€4241	Les mauvias medecins (17x25cm-7x10in) etching. 6-May-4 Swann Galleries, New York #282/R est:5000-8000
£3378	$6385	€5000	La cathedrale (24x18cm-9x7in) s.i. etching. 17-Feb-4 Galerie Moderne, Brussels #271/R est:2000-2600
£3490	$6456	€5200	La kermesse au moulin (14x18cm-6x7in) s.d.1889 s.i.verso hand-col etching lit. 13-Mar-4 De Vuyst, Lokeren #428/R est:5500-6500
£3495	$6500	€5103	La cathedrale, 1re planche (24x18cm-9x7in) s.d.1886 etching. 2-Mar-4 Swann Galleries, New York #172/R est:4000-6000
£3824	$6500	€5583	La cathedrale (24x18cm-9x7in) s.d.1896 i.verso etching. 6-Nov-3 Swann Galleries, New York #353/R est:7000-10000
£3944	$6823	€5600	La mort poursuivant le troupeau des humains (24x18cm-9x7in) s.d.1895 s.i.verso etching lit. 13-Dec-3 De Vuyst, Lokeren #540/R est:6000-7000
£4000	$7280	€5840	La mort poursuivant le troupeau humain (45x35cm-18x14in) s.i.d.1896 s.i.verso etching. 1-Jul-4 Sotheby's, London #168/R est:4000-5000
£4366	$7554	€6200	Les bons juges (18x24cm-7x9in) s.d.1894 s.i.verso etching lit. 13-Dec-3 De Vuyst, Lokeren #442/R est:5000-6000
£4667	$8587	€7000	La Cathedrale (25x19cm-10x7in) s.d.1886 i. verso etching. 10-Jun-4 Hauswedell & Nolte, Hamburg #184/R est:7500
£4706	$8000	€6871	Entry of Christ (24x36cm-9x14in) s. etching. 31-Oct-3 Sotheby's, New York #260
£4895	$8420	€7000	Les peches capitaux domines par lamort (9x14cm-4x6in) s.i.d.1904 s.i.d. verso col etching drypoint. 2-Dec-3 Hauswedell & Nolte, Hamburg #154/R est:2000
£5000	$8500	€7300	Lust (9x13cm-4x5in) s.d.1888 etching. 31-Oct-3 Sotheby's, New York #251/R
£5800	$9976	€8468	Death pursuing the flock of humans (32x22cm-13x9in) s.i. etching. 4-Dec-3 Sotheby's, London #146/R est:5000-7000
£6333	$11653	€9500	L'entree du Christ a Bruxelles (24x36cm-9x14in) s. i. verso etching drypoint. 10-Jun-4 Hauswedell & Nolte, Hamburg #185/R est:10000
£8333	$15250	€12500	La vengeance de Hop-Frog. s. eau forte. 7-Jun-4 Palais de Beaux Arts, Brussels #210/R est:4500-6000
Works on paper			
£5667	$10427	€8500	Mercury (24x16cm-9x6in) s.i.d.1906 blk chk. 9-Jun-4 Christie's, Amsterdam #93/R est:4000-6000
£8392	$14266	€12000	La vente (21x16cm-8x6in) s. blk chk exec c.1885-1888. 25-Nov-3 Christie's, Amsterdam #233/R est:1500-2000

ENSOR, James (attrib) (1860-1949) Belgian

£2000	$3640	€3000	Two young men in a boat (26x16cm-10x6in) panel prov. 3-Jul-4 Geble, Radolfzell #397/R est:3000

ENSOR, Mary (fl.1863-1897) British

£260	$476	€380	Still life with bird's nest and poppies and lilies (22x29cm-9x11in) s. board. 7-Apr-4 Woolley & Wallis, Salisbury #322/R

ENTRAIGUES, Rafael Julia (19th C) Spanish

£395	$726	€600	Children singing (32x18cm-13x7in) s. 22-Jun-4 Durán, Madrid #9/R

ENTZ, Loren (1949-) American

£7219	$13500	€10540	In the cool of the evening (91x122cm-36x48in) s. 24-Jul-4 Coeur d'Alene, Hayden #22/R est:25000-50000

ENWRIGHT, J J (?) ?

£1180	$1900	€1723	Fishing port, Maine (51x66cm-20x26in) s. 20-Aug-3 James Julia, Fairfield #893/R est:1500-2500
£1676	$3000	€2447	Rockport, docked fishing boats (71x97cm-28x38in) s. 16-May-4 CRN Auctions, Cambridge #34/R

ENZINGER, Hans (1889-1972) Austrian

£267	$480	€400	Untitled (7x11cm-3x4in) s.d.16 panel. 21-Apr-4 Dorotheum, Vienna #33/R
£470	$879	€700	Hay harvest (9x11cm-4x4in) s. panel. 24-Feb-4 Dorotheum, Vienna #93
£532	$888	€750	Working in the fields (8x11cm-3x4in) s. panel. 16-Oct-3 Dorotheum, Salzburg #625/R
£604	$1117	€900	Sleigh ride (8x9cm-3x4in) s. panel. 9-Mar-4 Dorotheum, Vienna #96/R
£828	$1514	€1200	Suburb (12x18cm-5x7in) s. panel. 27-Jan-4 Dorotheum, Vienna #84/R
Works on paper			
£828	$1374	€1200	Freyung, Vienna (12x18cm-5x7in) s. W/C. 30-Sep-3 Dorotheum, Vienna #308/R
£940	$1729	€1400	Market day in Stockerau (12x14cm-5x6in) s.i. gouache board. 26-Mar-4 Dorotheum, Vienna #321/R

ENZLER, Albert (1882-1974) Swiss

Works on paper			
£1448	$2462	€2114	Travel in the Alps (23x29cm-9x11in) s.i. gouache lacquer board prov. 28-Nov-3 Falk & Falk, Zurich #389/R est:1200 (S.FR 3200)

EOCH, Barbara Ab (18th C) Swiss

£2649	$4848	€4000	Christ en gloire entoure de la Vierge et des Apotres (72x52cm-28x20in) i.d.1769. 9-Apr-4 Bailly Pommery, Paris #32/R est:4000-6000

EPP, Rudolf (1834-1910) German

£1389	$2292	€2000	Portrait of young Tyrolean woman in costume (67x51cm-26x20in) s. 3-Jul-3 Dr Fritz Nagel, Stuttgart #486/R est:2900
£2431	$3962	€3500	Young woman knitting (37x27cm-15x11in) s. 24-Sep-3 Neumeister, Munich #420/R est:4000
£3767	$6404	€5500	Boy playing zither to family (67x50cm-26x20in) s. 5-Nov-3 Hugo Ruef, Munich #960 est:1500

EPP, Rudolf (attrib) (1834-1910) German

£523	$900	€764	Portrait of a man opening a gift (51x41cm-20x16in) s.d.1875. 6-Dec-3 Selkirks, St. Louis #654/R
£988	$1700	€1442	Father arriving home (53x66cm-21x26in) s.d.1875. 6-Dec-3 Selkirks, St. Louis #653 est:1000-1500

EPPENS, William H (1885-?) American

£625	$1100	€913	Autumn stream (76x91cm-30x36in) s. painted c.1930. 23-May-4 Treadway Gallery, Cincinnati #570/R
Works on paper			
£246	$410	€359	Winter scene with cabin with a stream running alongside (25x36cm-10x14in) s.d.1934 W/C. 14-Nov-3 Aspire, Cleveland #157

EPPER, Ignaz (1892-1969) Swiss

Works on paper			
£413	$689	€599	Study of man's head (49x40cm-19x16in) i. verso chl study verso. 23-Jun-3 Philippe Schuler, Zurich #3226 (S.FR 900)
£498	$846	€727	Landscape (23x27cm-9x11in) s. ink. 22-Nov-3 Burkhard, Luzern #67/R (S.FR 1100)
£543	$923	€793	Corrida (33x48cm-13x19in) s.i.d.1953 Indian ink on chl. 25-Nov-3 Germann, Zurich #776 (S.FR 1200)
£550	$919	€798	Sailing boat with two figures (19x27cm-7x11in) s. chl. 23-Jun-3 Philippe Schuler, Zurich #3225 (S.FR 1200)
£588	$1018	€858	Fishing boat in harbour, Southern France (21x31cm-8x12in) s. ink W/C prov. 9-Dec-3 Sotheby's, Zurich #62/R (S.FR 1300)
£742	$1329	€1083	Back view of reclining female nude (25x33cm-10x13in) s. chl prov. 26-May-4 Sotheby's, Zurich #97/R est:1800-2200 (S.FR 1700)
£849	$1375	€1240	Harbour landscape (30x38cm-12x15in) s. i.d.23 Juni 1919 verso col pen. 24-May-3 Burkhard, Luzern #37/R (S.FR 1800)
£877	$1465	€1280	Portrait of young woman (51x41cm-20x16in) s. chl prov. 15-Nov-3 Galerie Gloggner, Luzern #42/R est:2500-2800 (S.FR 2000)
£917	$1532	€1330	Untitled (34x40cm-13x16in) i. verso chl. 23-Jun-3 Philippe Schuler, Zurich #3222 (S.FR 2000)
£948	$1697	€1384	Harbour with fishing boats (434x54cm-171x21in) s. col chk. 14-May-4 Dobiaschofsky, Bern #219/R est:2600 (S.FR 2200)
£1055	$1762	€1530	Man and woman in interior (44x31cm-17x12in) mono. i. verso chl. 23-Jun-3 Philippe Schuler, Zurich #3223/R est:2000-3000 (S.FR 2300)
£1081	$1859	€1578	Sleeping person in a bed next to a heater (26x20cm-10x8in) chl over pencil. 8-Dec-3 Philippe Schuler, Zurich #3183 (S.FR 2400)
£1096	$1831	€1600	Portrait of young woman (48x37cm-19x15in) s. chl prov. 15-Nov-3 Galerie Gloggner, Luzern #44/R est:2800-3500 (S.FR 2500)
£1667	$2783	€2434	Couple in interior (49x40cm-19x16in) s. chl prov. 15-Nov-3 Galerie Gloggner, Luzern #43/R est:2500-2800 (S.FR 3800)
£1937	$3332	€2828	View of Zurich (25x33cm-10x13in) s. chl. 8-Dec-3 Philippe Schuler, Zurich #3180/R est:1500-2000 (S.FR 4300)
£2262	$3914	€3303	Three people (45x47cm-18x19in) s. chl. 9-Dec-3 Sotheby's, Zurich #46/R est:4000-6000 (S.FR 5000)
£2838	$5081	€4143	Barque with three men (25x21cm-10x8in) s. chl prov. three. 26-May-4 Sotheby's, Zurich #121/R est:5000-7000 (S.FR 6500)
£4148	$7426	€6056	Self portrait (39x28cm-15x11in) s. chl prov. 26-May-4 Sotheby's, Zurich #126/R est:2000-2500 (S.FR 9500)
£4167	$6958	€6084	Nine figures in boat - lifeboat (57x38cm-22x15in) s. pastel chk prov. 15-Nov-3 Galerie Gloggner, Luzern #45/R est:2500-2800 (S.FR 9500)
£5046	$8427	€7317	Interior with woman (86x47cm-34x19in) mono. i. chl. 23-Jun-3 Philippe Schuler, Zurich #3224/R est:2000-3000 (S.FR 11000)

EPPS, Ellen (fl.1873) British

£11000	$20240	€16060	Portrait of Laura, Lady Alma-Tadema, entering the Dutch room at Townshend House (77x63cm-30x25in) s.i.d.1873 prov. 11-Jun-4 Christie's, London #163/R est:10000-15000

EPSTEIN, Henri (1892-1944) Polish/French

£759	$1267	€1100	Village sous arbre (48x70cm-19x28in) s.d.1924. 17-Nov-3 Claude Boisgirard, Paris #25/R
£1391	$2531	€2100	Voiliers au port (27x41cm-11x16in) s. 15-Jun-4 Rossini, Paris #109/R est:2000-3000
£2185	$3977	€3300	On the beach (33x46cm-13x18in) s.d.1930. 15-Jun-4 Rossini, Paris #113/R est:2500-4000
£2349	$4370	€3500	Nature morte au gibier (73x54cm-29x21in) s. 2-Mar-4 Artcurial Briest, Paris #167/R est:3000-4000
£2624	$4382	€3700	Nature morte (50x61cm-20x24in) s. 20-Jun-3 Drouot Estimations, Paris #162 est:2000-2200
£2649	$4821	€4000	Interieur de maison close (33x41cm-13x16in) s. 15-Jun-4 Rossini, Paris #121/R est:2500-4000
£2886	$5339	€4300	Nature morte aux fruits (50x65cm-20x26in) s. 15-Mar-4 Claude Boisgirard, Paris #35 est:4000-5000
£3103	$5586	€4500	Maisons du village (60x73cm-24x29in) s. 25-Jan-4 Chayette & Cheval, Paris #176/R est:4500-5000
£3691	$6866	€5500	Scene de marche (60x73cm-24x29in) s. 2-Mar-4 Artcurial Briest, Paris #168 est:6000-7000
£3974	$7232	€6000	Paysage aux grands arbres (54x65cm-21x26in) s. 15-Jun-4 Rossini, Paris #105/R est:5000-8000

£4000	$6680	€5800	Paysage au arbres (72x54cm-28x21in) s. painted c.1925. 17-Nov-3 Claude Boisgirard, Paris #24/R est:6000-8000
£4106	$7473	€6200	Deux femmes a l'oiseau (61x50cm-24x20in) s. 15-Jun-4 Rossini, Paris #98/R est:5000-8000
£4577	$7919	€6500	Eglise de Saint-Jean-Pied-de-Port (60x80cm-24x31in) s.d.1929. 15-Dec-3 Bailly Pommery, Paris #126/R est:4000-7000
£4610	$7468	€6500	Avenue of trees in country (50x65cm-20x26in) s. lit. 23-May-3 Karlheinz Kaupp, Staufen #1897 est:6500
£6250	$10438	€9125	Still life with flowers and pineapples (46x61cm-18x24in) s. painted c.1930. 19-Oct-3 Agra, Warsaw #10/R est:40000 (P.Z 40000)
Works on paper			
£464	$844	€700	Barque aux animaux (19x26cm-7x10in) s. gouache. 15-Jun-4 Rossini, Paris #99/R
£464	$844	€700	Beach scene (22x30cm-9x12in) s. W/C. 15-Jun-4 Rossini, Paris #118/R
£497	$904	€750	Maquignons (25x32cm-10x13in) s. W/C. 15-Jun-4 Rossini, Paris #102/R
£530	$964	€800	Paysans au marche (24x35cm-9x14in) s. W/C. 15-Jun-4 Rossini, Paris #114/R
£530	$964	€800	Marche aux bestiaux (23x30cm-9x12in) s. W/C. 15-Jun-4 Rossini, Paris #127/R
£563	$1025	€850	Arbre au-dessus du village (24x35cm-9x14in) s. W/C. 15-Jun-4 Rossini, Paris #128/R
£795	$1446	€1200	Paysage d'hiver (40x54cm-16x21in) s. W/C. 15-Jun-4 Rossini, Paris #126/R
£795	$1446	€1200	Danseur au cabaret (23x30cm-9x12in) s. W/C. 15-Jun-4 Rossini, Paris #108/R
£828	$1382	€1200	Paysage de Corse (19x31cm-7x12in) s. W/C. 17-Nov-3 Claude Boisgirard, Paris #23
£861	$1567	€1300	Deux filles sur le port (41x54cm-16x21in) s. W/C. 15-Jun-4 Rossini, Paris #101/R
£927	$1687	€1400	Voiliers echoues (42x61cm-17x24in) s. W/C. 15-Jun-4 Rossini, Paris #125/R
£1457	$2652	€2200	Filles du port (50x38cm-20x15in) s. W/C gouache. 15-Jun-4 Rossini, Paris #112/R est:1200-1800
£2098	$3566	€3000	Paysage de Provence (38x46cm-15x18in) s. W/C. 27-Nov-3 Calmels Cohen, Paris #52/R est:1500-2000

EPSTEIN, Jehudo (1870-1946) Polish

£1268	$2218	€1800	Bridge (61x94cm-24x37in) s. 19-Dec-3 Dorotheum, Vienna #31/R est:1300-1900
£1972	$3451	€2800	Railway station in Rome (111x150cm-44x59in) s.d.1901 exhib. 19-Dec-3 Dorotheum, Vienna #28/R est:4500-6000
Works on paper			
£1206	$2013	€1700	Portrait of Jewish man (40x31cm-16x12in) s.d.1926 chk ochre. 14-Oct-3 Dorotheum, Vienna #35/R est:1000-1300

EPSTEIN, Jehudo (attrib) (1870-1946) Polish

£769	$1400	€1123	Barge along river (41x61cm-16x24in) 8-Feb-4 William Jenack, New York #258

EPSTEIN, Sir Jacob (1880-1959) British/American

Sculpture			
£1104	$1800	€1612	Eighth portrait of Peggy Jean (26cm-10in) green pat bronze conceived 1921 prov.lit. 25-Sep-3 Christie's, Rockefeller NY #621/R est:2500-3500
£1900	$3477	€2774	Nan - the dreamer, head and shoulders (12cm-5in) bronze marble plinth conceived c.1911. 8-Jul-4 Lawrence, Crewkerne #1575 est:800-1200
£2054	$3800	€2999	Portrait of Annabel Freud (20cm-8in) bronze exec 1949 prov. 13-Jul-4 Christie's, Rockefeller NY #173/R est:3000-5000
£2162	$4000	€3157	Portrait of Ann Freud (18cm-7in) dark brown verdigris pat bronze exec 1949 prov. 13-Jul-4 Christie's, Rockefeller NY #172/R est:3000-5000
£2500	$4400	€3650	Lucifer, Belial and Beelzebub (23x32cm-9x13in) brown pat. bronze sold with a photograph. 19-May-4 Sotheby's, Olympia #165/R est:1200-1800
£2500	$4400	€3650	Ian, Ossian (34cm-13in) brown pat. bronze stone base lit. 19-May-4 Sotheby's, Olympia #168/R est:2500-3500
£2800	$5180	€4088	Portland Mason (25cm-10in) brown pat. bronze conceived 1952 lit. 11-Mar-4 Christie's, Kensington #50/R est:3000-5000
£2844	$4750	€4152	Lucifer, Belial and Beelzebub (22x30cm-9x12in) s. brown pat bronze lit. 7-Oct-3 Sotheby's, New York #288 est:1500-2500
£3000	$5160	€4380	Dolores (33cm-13in) green pat. bronze lit. 2-Dec-3 Bonhams, New Bond Street #59/R est:3000-5000
£4192	$7000	€6120	Italian peasant woman with a shawl (34cm-13in) brown pat bronze prov.exhib.lit. 7-Oct-3 Sotheby's, New York #286 est:3000-5000
£4400	$7744	€6424	Portrait of Jackie, laughing, 3rd portrait (32cm-13in) brown green pat. bronze marble base lit. 19-May-4 Sotheby's, Olympia #167/R est:2500-3500
£4800	$8160	€7008	Ellen Jansen - smiling head (33cm-13in) green pat. bronze conceived 1931 prov.lit. 21-Nov-3 Christie's, London #174/R est:4000-6000
£6000	$10560	€8760	Rani Rama (74cm-29in) green pat. bronze marble base lit. 19-May-4 Sotheby's, Olympia #169/R est:5000-7000
£6500	$11180	€9490	Victor (17cm-7in) green brown pat. bronze lit. 2-Dec-3 Bonhams, New Bond Street #61/R est:2000-3000
£7143	$13000	€10429	Morna (63x42x26cm-25x17x10in) i.sig. green pat. bronze lit. 29-Jun-4 Sotheby's, New York #358/R est:8000-12000
£7800	$13962	€11388	Portrait of Rabindranath Tagore (50cm-20in) s. green pat bronze lit. 16-Mar-4 Bonhams, New Bond Street #22/R est:2500-3500
Works on paper			
£380	$669	€555	Sleeping woman (20x13cm-8x5in) s. W/C. 18-May-4 Bonhams, Knightsbridge #159
£659	$1100	€962	Sleeping nude (43x53cm-17x21in) pencil. 17-Oct-3 Du Mouchelle, Detroit #2026/R
£780	$1396	€1139	Study of a child sucking his thumb (56x43cm-22x17in) s. pencil drawing. 7-May-4 Mallams, Oxford #153
£1000	$1830	€1460	Sanita (54x43cm-21x17in) s. pencil. 8-Jul-4 Lawrence, Crewkerne #1574/R est:1000-1500
£1200	$2184	€1752	Reclining nude (40x51cm-16x20in) s. pencil. 15-Jun-4 Bonhams, New Bond Street #47/R est:1000-1500
£1250	$2338	€1875	Irises (58x44cm-23x17in) s. W/C bodycol. 26-Jul-4 Bonhams, Bath #30/R est:1500-2000
£1400	$2506	€2044	Reclining nude (47x54cm-19x21in) s. pencil. 16-Mar-4 Bonhams, New Bond Street #18/R est:1000-1500
£1500	$2775	€2190	Jackie (54x42cm-21x17in) s. pencil. 11-Feb-4 Sotheby's, Olympia #101/R est:600-800
£1600	$2960	€2336	Landscape with trees from the Epping Forest series (56x43cm-22x17in) s.verso W/C bodycol prov. 11-Mar-4 Duke & Son, Dorchester #90/R est:1500-3000
£1900	$3458	€2774	Reclining negress (43x56cm-17x22in) s. pencil prov.lit. 1-Jul-4 Christie's, Kensington #25/R est:800-1200
£2000	$3700	€2920	Sunflowers (56x43cm-22x17in) s.i.d.1963 W/C bodycol. 11-Mar-4 Duke & Son, Dorchester #92 est:1000-2000
£2000	$3700	€2920	Daisies (58x43cm-23x17in) s.i.d.1936 W/C bodycol over pencil. 11-Mar-4 Duke & Son, Dorchester #93 est:1000-2000
£2000	$3640	€2920	Epping Forest (43x56cm-17x22in) s. W/C bodycol. 1-Jul-4 Christie's, Kensington #105/R est:2000-3000
£2200	$4026	€3212	Two women in bed (48x56cm-19x22in) s. chl. 7-Apr-4 Gardiner & Houlgate, Bath #121/R est:2500-3750
£2400	$4128	€3504	Tulips (56x433cm-22x170in) s. W/C bodycol exhib. 3-Dec-3 Christie's, Kensington #541/R est:1800-2500
£2600	$4654	€3796	Reclining nude (40x51cm-16x20in) s. pencil. 16-Mar-4 Bonhams, New Bond Street #19/R est:1000-1500
£2800	$4816	€4088	Peonies (56x44cm-22x17in) s. W/C bodycol prov.exhib. 3-Dec-3 Christie's, Kensington #543/R est:1800-2500
£3000	$5280	€4380	Camelias (57x44cm-22x17in) gouache W/C prov. 18-May-4 Woolley & Wallis, Salisbury #329/R est:2500-3500

EPSTEIN-HEFTER, Elisabeth (1879-1956) Swiss

£769	$1285	€1100	Paysage (46x37cm-18x15in) s. panel. 25-Jun-3 Rabourdin & Choppin de Janvry, Paris #100
£1064	$1723	€1500	Portrait of woman with bare shoulders (33x27cm-13x11in) s. canvas on board lit. 23-May-3 Karlheinz Kaupp, Staufen #1918/R est:1500

EQUIPO CRONICA (20th C) Spanish

Sculpture			
£3169	$5546	€4500	Spears and flags (40x34x40cm-16x13x16in) s. num.11/25 serigraph cardboard plexiglass lit. 16-Dec-3 Segre, Madrid #146/R est:5000
£3448	$6207	€5000	Spectator (127x41x75cm-50x16x30in) painted cardboard. 26-Jan-4 Ansorena, Madrid #762/R est:5000

ERARD, Charles II (attrib) (1606-1689) French

£7333	$13493	€11000	Tobie et Sara (125x125cm-49x49in) round. 9-Jun-4 Le Roux & Morel, Paris #4/R est:5000-7000

ERASMO, Jean (attrib) (18th C) ?

£307	$550	€448	Jesus with Pontius (6x10cm-2x4in) wood panel. 9-Jan-4 Du Mouchelle, Detroit #2070/R

ERASSI, Mikhail (1823-1898) Russian

£16000	$27200	€23360	Crimean view (35x48cm-14x19in) s. 19-Nov-3 Sotheby's, London #9/R est:3000-4000

ERAWAN, Nyoman (1958-) Indonesian

£1319	$2203	€1926	Balad (95x137cm-37x54in) s.d.1997. 12-Oct-3 Sotheby's, Singapore #195/R est:3000-4000 (S.D 3800)
£1449	$2246	€2116	Fishes (106x80cm-42x31in) s.d.90. 6-Oct-2 Sotheby's, Singapore #178/R est:4000-6000 (S.D 4000)

ERB, Erno (1878-1943) Polish?

£486	$792	€700	Market women in Lemberg (25x35cm-10x14in) s. board. 26-Sep-3 Bolland & Marotz, Bremen #645

ERB, Leo (1928-) German

Sculpture			
£2465	$4264	€3500	Untitled (54x54x25cm-21x21x10in) s.i.d.69 wood. 13-Dec-3 Lempertz, Koln #306/R est:500

ERBA, Carlo (1884-1917) Italian

Works on paper			
£533	$981	€800	Figures (20x18cm-8x7in) s. pencil. 14-Jun-4 Sant Agostino, Torino #361/R
£800	$1472	€1200	Futiristic figure (34x23cm-13x9in) s. chl. 14-Jun-4 Sant Agostino, Torino #362/R
£833	$1533	€1250	Speed (26x15cm-10x6in) s. chl. 14-Jun-4 Sant Agostino, Torino #363/R

ERBACH, Alois (1880-1972) German

£4533	$8115	€6800	Industrial landscape by river (45x58cm-18x23in) s. prov. 14-May-4 Ketterer, Munich #16/R est:2500-3500
Works on paper			
£733	$1313	€1100	Still life (25x28cm-10x11in) s.i.d. i. verso W/C over pencil prov. 14-May-4 Ketterer, Munich #15/R

ERBE, Paul (1894-1972) German

£486	$812	€700	Ducks by pond (61x80cm-24x31in) s. 22-Oct-3 Neumeister, Munich #685/R

ERBSLOH, Adolf (1881-1947) German

£1342	$2403	€2000	Madonna with child (59x35cm-23x14in) 25-May-4 Karl & Faber, Munich #270/R est:4000-6000
£3020	$5406	€4500	Portrait of Anna Hirzel-Langenhan (54x42cm-21x17in) 25-May-4 Karl & Faber, Munich #271/R est:8000-10000
£10000	$18400	€15000	Triptych with naked female figures under trees (27x57cm-11x22in) prov.exhib. 11-Jun-4 Villa Grisebach, Berlin #14/R est:15000-20000
Works on paper			
£800	$1432	€1200	Positano (23x31cm-9x12in) i.d.Juni 23 pencil. 15-May-4 Bassenge, Berlin #6803/R
£1200	$2148	€1800	Female nude (18x14cm-7x6in) col chk. 15-May-4 Bassenge, Berlin #6801/R est:1200

ERDELY, Francis de (1904-1959) American/Hungarian
£340 $609 €500 Paysanne (69x54cm-27x21in) s.d.1922. 16-Mar-4 Vanderkindere, Brussels #556
£563 $900 €822 Portrait of a woman (30x23cm-12x9in) painted 1941. 19-Sep-3 Du Mouchelle, Detroit #2208/R
£839 $1443 €1200 Femme a la jarre (80x63cm-31x25in) s.i.d.1928. 8-Dec-3 Horta, Bruxelles #24
£1737 $3074 €2536 By the table (100x120cm-39x47in) s.d.1924. 28-Apr-4 Kieselbach, Budapest #124/R (H.F 650000)
£2098 $3608 €3000 Fertilite (90x100cm-35x39in) s. 2-Dec-3 Campo & Campo, Antwerp #134/R est:3250-3750
£3221 $5960 €4800 Fertilite (90x100cm-35x39in) s. 15-Mar-4 Claude Boisgirard, Paris #36/R est:5000-6000
£6425 $11500 €9381 Tender years (102x56cm-40x22in) s. 16-Mar-4 Matthew's, Oregon #85/R est:6000-8000
Works on paper
£1695 $3000 €2475 Mardi gras (63x50cm-25x20in) s. W/C gouache. 28-Apr-4 Christie's, Los Angeles #78/R est:2500-3500

ERDELYI, Bela (20th C) Hungarian?
£1135 $1895 €1600 Ox drawn plough (75x102cm-30x40in) s.d. 14-Oct-3 Dorotheum, Vienna #123/R est:1600-2000

ERDELYI, Vojtech (1891-1955) Czechoslovakian
£438 $727 €639 Summer (85x68cm-33x27in) s. board. 4-Oct-3 Dorotheum, Prague #109/R est:20000-30000 (C.KR 20000)

ERDMANN, Axel (1873-1954) Swedish
£373 $698 €545 Fishing harbour, Stockholm (40x50cm-16x20in) s.indis.d.1906. 29-Feb-4 Uppsala Auktionskammare, Uppsala #81 (S.KR 5100)

ERDMANN, Ludwig (attrib) (1820-?) German
£470 $864 €700 Girl with donkey pulling milk cart (42x56cm-17x22in) lit. 25-Mar-4 Karlheinz Kaupp, Staufen #2424/R

ERDMANN, Moritz (1845-1919) German
£1266 $1975 €2000 Haycart passing village church (38x27cm-15x11in) board. 18-Oct-2 Von Zezschwitz, Munich #12/R est:2400
£1538 $2646 €2245 Alpine landscape with farm (90x125cm-35x49in) s. 7-Dec-3 Uppsala Auktionskammare, Uppsala #106/R est:15000-18000 (S.KR 20000)

ERDMANN, Otto (1834-1905) German
£1347 $2250 €1967 Unexpected letter (70x52cm-28x20in) s.d.1870. 7-Oct-3 Sotheby's, New York #86/R est:4000-6000

ERDMANN, Robert (20th C) German
£367 $675 €550 Seated female nude (90x70cm-35x28in) s. 11-Jun-4 Wendl, Rudolstadt #4012/R

ERDTMANN, Elias (1862-1945) Swedish
£923 $1588 €1348 Feeding chickens (53x80cm-21x31in) s. 7-Dec-3 Uppsala Auktionskammare, Uppsala #198/R (S.KR 12000)

ERENTXUN, Eloy (20th C) Spanish
£350 $584 €500 Garden, mountains in background (66x50cm-26x20in) s. 30-Jun-3 Ansorena, Madrid #278/R

ERFMANN, Ferdinand (1901-1968) Dutch
£658 $1211 €1000 Sahara landscape with mosque (23x38cm-9x15in) s. board exhib. 28-Jun-4 Sotheby's, Amsterdam #148/R
£2533 $4661 €3800 Sunbathing at the beach (50x71cm-20x28in) i. stretcher. 8-Jun-4 Sotheby's, Amsterdam #229/R est:3000-4000
£6993 $12028 €10000 Aan het raam (51x40cm-20x16in) s.d.1940. 2-Dec-3 Sotheby's, Amsterdam #31/R est:12000-16000
£17483 $29720 €25000 Floorshow at the new Karseboom (61x40cm-24x16in) init.d.1967 prov. 25-Nov-3 Christie's, Amsterdam #175/R est:10000-15000
Works on paper
£4408 $8111 €6700 Femme du Crystal Palace (16x12cm-6x5in) s.i.d.1938 ink W/C together with three drawings four. 28-Jun-4 Sotheby's, Amsterdam #146/R est:1500-2500

ERFURTH, Hugo (1874-1948) German?
Photographs
£4545 $7727 €6500 Otto Dix with brush (23x18cm-9x7in) i. verso silver gelatin lit.exhib. 27-Nov-3 Villa Grisebach, Berlin #1160/R est:5000-7000

ERGANIAN, Sarkis (1870-1950) American/Turkish
£334 $575 €488 Bust-length portrait of a woman (46x38cm-18x15in) s. 6-Dec-3 Selkirks, St. Louis #199/R

ERHARDT, Johann Christoph (attrib) (1795-1822) German
Works on paper
£290 $475 €400 Trees in landscape (10x13cm-4x5in) pen. 30-May-3 Bassenge, Berlin #7847

ERHARDT, L V (19th C) German
£2685 $5020 €4000 Rocky coast near Nervi (110x150cm-43x59in) s. 24-Feb-4 Dorotheum, Vienna #37/R est:4500-5000

ERHARDT, Wilhelm (1815-1890) Czechoslovakian
£1049 $1783 €1500 Panorama (57x21cm-22x8in) s.d.1879. 20-Nov-3 Van Ham, Cologne #1560/R est:1500
£1879 $3514 €2800 Salzkammergut landscape (59x90cm-23x35in) s.d.1879. 24-Feb-4 Dorotheum, Vienna #211/R est:2500-2800

ERICHSEN, Thorvald (1868-1939) Norwegian
£1220 $2244 €1781 Red mountain (32x41cm-13x16in) init.indis.d.1917 i.verso exhib. 10-Jun-4 Grev Wedels Plass, Oslo #169/R est:15000-20000 (N.KR 15000)
£1288 $2253 €1880 Landscape from Telemark (25x32cm-10x13in) i.verso canvas on panel. 16-Dec-3 Grev Wedels Plass, Oslo #152/R est:15000-20000 (N.KR 15000)
£1537 $2567 €2244 After the rain (41x46cm-16x18in) init. i.stretcher exhib.prov. 13-Oct-3 Blomqvist, Oslo #299/R est:25000-30000 (N.KR 18000)
£1540 $2618 €2248 Coastal landscape from Holmsbu (32x41cm-13x16in) init.d.1917 s.i.d.verso panel. 19-Nov-3 Grev Wedels Plass, Oslo #78/R est:15000-20000 (N.KR 18000)
£2033 $3720 €2968 Coastal landscape from Holmsbu (32x40cm-13x16in) init.d.1917 i.verso panel. 7-Jun-4 Blomqvist, Oslo #368/R est:28000-32000 (N.KR 25000)
£2033 $3720 €2968 Landscape from Tjome (32x41cm-13x16in) init.d.21 panel exhib.prov. 7-Jun-4 Blomqvist, Oslo #385/R est:30000-40000 (N.KR 25000)
£2447 $4380 €3573 Landscape (38x46cm-15x18in) init.d.30. 25-May-4 Grev Wedels Plass, Oslo #69/R est:20000-30000 (N.KR 30000)
£3407 $5860 €4974 From Oia (60x73cm-24x29in) i.verso. 8-Dec-3 Blomqvist, Oslo #488/R est:70000-90000 (N.KR 40000)
£25619 $42784 €37404 The church and the bank at Lillehammer (60x73cm-24x29in) s.d.33 i.stretcher lit. 13-Oct-3 Blomqvist, Oslo #298/R est:325000-375000 (N.KR 300000)

ERICHSEN-BROWN, Frank (1878-1967) Canadian
£982 $1689 €1434 Go-Home Bay (52x65cm-20x26in) s. 2-Dec-3 Joyner Waddington, Toronto #357/R est:2000-3000 (C.D 2200)

ERICKSON, Norman (20th C) American
£949 $1500 €1386 Winterlands (51x61cm-20x24in) s. 7-Sep-3 Treadway Gallery, Cincinnati #662/R est:600-800

ERICKSON, Oscar B (1883-1968) American
£441 $750 €644 Winter stream (41x33cm-16x13in) s. 22-Nov-3 Jackson's, Cedar Falls #97/R
Works on paper
£494 $850 €721 Autumn landscape (36x41cm-14x16in) s.d.1937 pastel. 7-Dec-3 Treadway Gallery, Cincinnati #547/R

ERICSON, David (1869-1946) American
£1576 $2900 €2301 View of the French Riviera (58x71cm-23x28in) s. canvas on board painted c.1928. 26-Jun-4 Sloans & Kenyon, Bethesda #1095/R est:2500-3500
£3261 $6000 €4761 An evening in a French port (73x83cm-29x33in) s. 8-Jun-4 Bonhams & Butterfields, San Francisco #4047/R est:5000-7000

ERICSON, Johan (1849-1925) Swedish
£731 $1257 €1067 View of the harbour in Concarneau (38x54cm-15x21in) s.d.1889 panel. 7-Dec-3 Uppsala Auktionskammare, Uppsala #137/R (S.KR 9500)
£841 $1354 €1228 Moonlight over the shore (59x49cm-23x19in) s.d.1892. 25-Aug-3 Lilla Bukowskis, Stockholm #443 (S.KR 11000)
£923 $1588 €1348 Town scene, Concarneau (36x55cm-14x22in) s.d.88 panel. 7-Dec-3 Uppsala Auktionskammare, Uppsala #136/R (S.KR 12000)
£924 $1654 €1349 Coastal landscape from Concarneau (37x55cm-15x22in) s.i.d.1882 panel. 26-May-4 AB Stockholms Auktionsverk #2244/R (S.KR 12500)
£1018 $1700 €1486 Village in autumn (31x47cm-12x19in) s.d.8 Aug 78. 7-Oct-3 Sotheby's, New York #114 est:2000-3000
£1231 $2117 €1797 Children playing by waterway (70x100cm-28x39in) s.i.d.1885. 3-Dec-3 AB Stockholms Auktionsverk #2294/R est:20000-25000 (S.KR 16000)
£1478 $2646 €2158 Skepparkroken, landscape with man resting (29x47cm-11x19in) s.d.4.8.78. 28-May-4 Uppsala Auktionskammare, Uppsala #165/R est:12000-15000 (S.KR 20000)
£1538 $2646 €2245 Moonlight over harbour on the west coast (75x120cm-30x47in) s.d.1918. 2-Dec-3 Bukowskis, Stockholm #182/R est:20000-25000 (S.KR 20000)
£1996 $3572 €2914 Harbour in Marstrand (59x81cm-23x32in) s.i.d.14.8.1902. 26-May-4 AB Stockholms Auktionsverk #2117/R est:20000-25000 (S.KR 27000)
£2000 $3440 €2920 Coastal landscape from Marstrandsfjord (35x55cm-14x22in) s.d.1897. 3-Dec-3 AB Stockholms Auktionsverk #2256/R est:25000-30000 (S.KR 26000)
£2103 $3785 €3155 Summer landscape with figures in meadow (68x105cm-27x41in) s.d.1892. 25-Apr-4 Goteborg Auktionsverk, Sweden #176/R est:25000 (S.KR 29000)
£2187 $4023 €3281 Fishing village (82x117cm-32x46in) s.d.1916. 14-Jun-4 Lilla Bukowskis, Stockholm #657 est:30000-35000 (S.KR 30000)
£3104 $5557 €4532 Twilight on the west coast (75x113cm-30x44in) s.d.1889. 25-May-4 Bukowskis, Stockholm #171/R est:30000-35000 (S.KR 42000)
£3104 $5557 €4532 Fishing boats in harbour (37x52cm-15x20in) s.d.1918. 25-May-4 Bukowskis, Stockholm #172/R est:20000-25000 (S.KR 42000)
£5322 $9525 €7770 Selling fish on the quay (100x150cm-39x59in) s.d.1907. 25-May-4 Bukowskis, Stockholm #170/R est:50000-70000 (S.KR 72000)

ERIKSEN, Bjarne (1882-1970) Norwegian
£344 $554 €502 Cabin by the sea (55x66cm-22x26in) s. 25-Aug-3 Blomqvist, Lysaker #1060 (N.KR 4000)
£609 $1053 €889 Street in Soon (53x51cm-21x20in) s. 13-Dec-3 Blomqvist, Lysaker #1081 (N.KR 7000)

ERIKSEN, Gorm (1940-) Danish
£300 $500 €438 Forest demon (100x101cm-39x40in) init. 25-Oct-3 Rasmussen, Havnen #4167 (D.KR 3200)

ERIKSEN, Sigurd (1884-1976) Norwegian
£258 $416 €377 Trees by the sea (64x83cm-25x33in) s. 25-Aug-3 Blomqvist, Lysaker #1063 (N.KR 3000)
£258 $431 €377 By the fjord (54x66cm-21x26in) s. 20-Oct-3 Blomqvist, Lysaker #1074/R (N.KR 3000)
£366 $673 €534 Summer landscape (50x55cm-20x22in) s. 10-Jun-4 Grev Wedels Plass, Oslo #172/R (N.KR 4500)
£397 $659 €576 Cabin by water with jetty (32x42cm-13x17in) s. panel. 16-Jun-3 Blomqvist, Lysaker #1309 (N.KR 4600)
£538 $968 €785 Interior scene with gentleman playing patience (75x87cm-30x34in) s. 24-Apr-4 Rasmussen, Havnen #2017/R (D.KR 6000)

£687 $1202 €1003 Coastal landscape with woman and child by boat (66x73cm-26x29in) s.d.1959. 16-Dec-3 Grev Wedels Plass, Oslo #153/R (N.KR 8000)

£732 $1346 €1069 Coastal landscape (56x66cm-22x26in) s. 10-Jun-4 Grev Wedels Plass, Oslo #171/R (N.KR 9000)

£1521 $2723 €2221 Coastal landscape with bay (66x73cm-26x29in) s/. 22-Mar-4 Blomqvist, Oslo #387/R est:15000-18000 (N.KR 19000)

£3263 $5840 €4764 Lokke farm in Sandvika (100x120cm-39x47in) s.i.d.1941. 25-May-4 Grev Wedels Plass, Oslo #67/R est:40000-60000 (N.KR 40000)

£3928 $6560 €5735 Oslo town with The Palace and Akershus Fort (70x86cm-28x34in) s.d.1922. 13-Oct-3 Blomqvist, Oslo #302/R est:20000-25000 (N.KR 46000)

ERIKSSON, Andreas (1975-) Swedish

£1511 $2568 €2206 Untitled - Links 3B (150x120cm-59x47in) s. verso oil acrylic prov. 5-Nov-3 AB Stockholms Auktionsverk #1052/R est:10000-12000 (S.KR 20000)

ERIKSSON, Christian (1858-1935) Swedish

Sculpture

£1552 $2778 €2266 Seated Laplander (22cm-9in) s.d.1909 brown pat.bronze Cast H Bergman. 25-May-4 Bukowskis, Stockholm #289/R est:12000-15000 (S.KR 21000)

£1615 $2778 €2358 Elof (20cm-8in) s.i.1901 dark pat.bronze Cast Bergman. 2-Dec-3 Bukowskis, Stockholm #233/R est:10000-12000 (S.KR 21000)

£1615 $2778 €2358 Elof - small nude boy standing (19cm-7in) s.i.d.1901 dark pat.bronze Cast.Meyer lit. 3-Dec-3 AB Stockholms Auktionsverk #2455/R est:15000-18000 (S.KR 21000)

£1700 $3043 €2482 Elof - small boy standing (19cm-7in) s.i.d.1901 gold bp. Cast H Bergman lit. 26-May-4 AB Stockholms Auktionsverk #2156/R est:15000-18000 (S.KR 23000)

ERIKSSON, Ernst Elis (1906-) Swedish

Sculpture

£2248 $4046 €3282 692 (22x23x5cm-9x9x2in) s.d.mars 63 mixed media in wooded box. 26-Apr-4 Bukowskis, Stockholm #529/R est:15000-20000 (S.KR 31000)

£2784 $4927 €4065 Box with contents (21x30cm-8x12in) objects collage executed 1962. 27-Apr-4 AB Stockholms Auktionsverk #907/R est:12000-15000 (S.KR 38000)

£3771 $6788 €5506 Berries (58x88x9cm-23x35x4in) s.d.27.7.64 assemblage in wooden box. 26-Apr-4 Bukowskis, Stockholm #527/R est:25000-30000 (S.KR 52000)

Works on paper

£1342 $2415 €1959 Untitled (52x78cm-20x31in) d.61 mixed media pa,. 26-Apr-4 Bukowskis, Stockholm #528/R est:20000-25000 (S.KR 18500)

ERIKSSON, Liss (1919-2000) Swedish

Sculpture

£1473 $2504 €2151 Mother and child (40cm-16in) s.d.1956 brown pat.bronze Cast.Valsuani cire perdue on stone socle. 4-Nov-3 Bukowskis, Stockholm #78/R est:8000-10000 (S.KR 19500)

£2198 $3890 €3209 Lovers (55cm-22in) s.num.3/5 pat.bronze sold with wood socle Cast Bergman cire perdue. 27-Apr-4 AB Stockholms Auktionsverk #1123/R est:18000-20000 (S.KR 30000)

ERIXSON, Sven (1899-1970) Swedish

£627 $1009 €915 Fisherman (37x46cm-15x18in) 25-Aug-3 Lilla Bukowskis, Stockholm #143 (S.KR 8200)

£638 $1149 €931 Coastal landscape with pine trees (38x45cm-15x18in) s. panel. 26-Jan-4 Lilla Bukowskis, Stockholm #561 (S.KR 8500)

£922 $1502 €1346 Garden with flowers and butterflies (38x57cm-15x22in) s. 29-Sep-3 Lilla Bukowskis, Stockholm #795 (S.KR 12000)

£943 $1631 €1377 Ida and Emma gets a new roof, Sondrum (38x46cm-15x18in) s. cardboard exhib. 15-Dec-3 Lilla Bukowskis, Stockholm #539 (S.KR 12000)

£982 $1669 €1434 God has in his photo studio a dark-room called Getsemane (80x75cm-31x30in) s.d.68 enamel lit. 5-Nov-3 AB Stockholms Auktionsverk #869/R (S.KR 13000)

£1070 $1723 €1562 Limestone quarry (33x42cm-13x17in) s. panel. 25-Aug-3 Lilla Bukowskis, Stockholm #124 (S.KR 14000)

£1133 $1926 €1654 View from Sondrum (38x46cm-15x18in) s. 5-Nov-3 AB Stockholms Auktionsverk #643/R est:15000-18000 (S.KR 15000)

£1208 $2054 €1764 Market day in Tunis (43x58cm-17x23in) s.d.35 panel. 5-Nov-3 AB Stockholms Auktionsverk #644/R est:20000-25000 (S.KR 16000)

£1231 $2117 €1797 Windy day, Majorca (55x73cm-22x29in) s.d.29. 7-Dec-3 Uppsala Auktionskammare, Uppsala #247/R est:20000-25000 (S.KR 16000)

£1360 $2311 €1986 The stone quarry, moonlight (38x46cm-15x18in) s.d.44 cardboard exhib. 4-Nov-3 Bukowskis, Stockholm #136/R est:12000-15000 (S.KR 18000)

£1511 $2568 €2206 Girl by tree (51x38cm-20x15in) s.d.30. 5-Nov-3 AB Stockholms Auktionsverk #852/R est:25000-30000 (S.KR 20000)

£1692 $2911 €2470 A show in the old town (45x54cm-18x21in) s. panel. 7-Dec-3 Uppsala Auktionskammare, Uppsala #241/R est:25000-30000 (S.KR 22000)

£1888 $3210 €2756 From the weaving studio - weaving of Melodies from the Market (73x100cm-29x39in) s.prov.lit. 5-Nov-3 AB Stockholms Auktionsverk #857/R est:30000-35000 (S.KR 25000)

£2030 $3655 €2964 Still life of hyacinth (55x46cm-22x18in) s. 26-Apr-4 Bukowskis, Stockholm #95/R est:18000-20000 (S.KR 28000)

£2341 $3980 €3418 Southern garden with woman and donkey (46x55cm-18x22in) s. 4-Nov-3 Bukowskis, Stockholm #137/R est:20000-25000 (S.KR 31000)

£2611 $4699 €3812 Landscape view of Sondrum (73x93cm-29x37in) s. 26-Apr-4 Bukowskis, Stockholm #96/R est:30000-35000 (S.KR 36000)

£2683 $4830 €3917 Skiers in winter landscape (108x75cm-43x30in) s.d.61. 26-Apr-4 Bukowskis, Stockholm #97/R est:30000-35000 (S.KR 37000)

£2901 $5221 €4235 The angler (66x77cm-26x30in) s.i.d.1937. 26-Apr-4 Bukowskis, Stockholm #89/R est:50000-70000 (S.KR 40000)

£3021 $5136 €4411 Landscape from Majorca (52x63cm-20x25in) s.d.27. 4-Nov-3 Bukowskis, Stockholm #153/R est:50000-60000 (S.KR 40000)

£3399 $5778 €4963 Bonfires in spring, Tumba (42x52cm-17x20in) s. panel. 5-Nov-3 AB Stockholms Auktionsverk #672/R est:40000-50000 (S.KR 45000)

£3927 $6677 €5733 Still life of flowers (61x48cm-24x19in) s. 5-Nov-3 AB Stockholms Auktionsverk #770/R est:50000-60000 (S.KR 52000)

£4305 $7319 €6285 Still life of blue vase (73x60cm-29x24in) s.d.50. 5-Nov-3 AB Stockholms Auktionsverk #771/R est:50000-60000 (S.KR 57000)

£5076 $9137 €7411 Joy (71x55cm-28x22in) s. panel. 26-Apr-4 Bukowskis, Stockholm #90/R est:65000-70000 (S.KR 70000)

£5128 $9077 €7487 The pass (80x100cm-31x39in) s.d.42. 27-Apr-4 AB Stockholms Auktionsverk #845/R est:50000-60000 (S.KR 70000)

£6193 $10529 €9042 The Easter tree (81x60cm-32x24in) s.d.1950 exhib. 5-Nov-3 AB Stockholms Auktionsverk #815/R est:60000-80000 (S.KR 82000)

£6949 $11813 €10146 The bird tree (35x27cm-14x11in) s.d.24 exhib.lit. 5-Nov-3 AB Stockholms Auktionsverk #645/R est:80000-100000 (S.KR 92000)

£7252 $13053 €10588 Summer's day (61x73cm-24x29in) s. 26-Apr-4 Bukowskis, Stockholm #101a/R est:50000-60000 (S.KR 100000)

£7326 $12455 €10696 Funeral in Handelop (66x81cm-26x32in) s.i.d.1932. 4-Nov-3 Bukowskis, Stockholm #135/R est:60000-80000 (S.KR 97000)

£19579 $35243 €28585 Winter in Stockholm (89x117cm-35x46in) s.d.dec.1932 prov.exhib.lit. 26-Apr-4 Bukowskis, Stockholm #93b/R est:250000-300000 (S.KR 270000)

Works on paper

£292 $503 €426 Composition with boat (18x22cm-7x9in) s. W/C. 7-Dec-3 Uppsala Auktionskammare, Uppsala #242 (S.KR 3800)

£326 $587 €476 In the garden (16x13cm-6x5in) s.i. W/C. 26-Apr-4 Bukowskis, Stockholm #99/R (S.KR 4500)

£500 $860 €730 Still life in blue (40x30cm-16x12in) s.d.26 i.verso gouache. 7-Dec-3 Uppsala Auktionskammare, Uppsala #215 (S.KR 6500)

£656 $1207 €984 Nils Holgersson in Lapland (47x30cm-19x12in) s.i.d.32 mixed media. 14-Jun-4 Lilla Bukowskis, Stockholm #455 (S.KR 9000)

£725 $1305 €1088 The blue grotto, Capri (32x41cm-13x16in) s. W/C. 25-Apr-4 Goteborg Auktionsverk, Sweden #419/R (S.KR 10000)

£1676 $3085 €2514 In Paris (29x35cm-11x14in) s.d.26 gouache exhib. 14-Jun-4 Lilla Bukowskis, Stockholm #296 est:15000-20000 (S.KR 23000)

£1905 $3371 €2781 Sverre in the sandbox (46x55cm-18x22in) s. mixed media panel. 27-Apr-4 AB Stockholms Auktionsverk #717/R est:12000-15000 (S.KR 26000)

£3626 $6526 €5294 Theatre performance in old town (46x55cm-18x22in) s. mixed media panel. 26-Apr-4 Bukowskis, Stockholm #94/R est:50000-60000 (S.KR 50000)

£3916 $7049 €5717 Girl with bicycle having a drink (62x55cm-24x22in) s.d.45 gouache. 26-Apr-4 Bukowskis, Stockholm #101/R est:20000-22000 (S.KR 54000)

£4206 $7571 €6141 Girl with refreshing drinks (126x88cm-50x35in) s. gouache. 26-Apr-4 Bukowskis, Stockholm #98/R est:50000-55000 (S.KR 58000)

ERKELENS, Anthonie (1774-1804) Dutch

Works on paper

£541 $951 €800 Shed, with church and windmill in the background (17x21cm-7x8in) pen brown ink W/C prov. 19-May-4 Sotheby's, Amsterdam #307/R

ERKSERGIAN, Carnig (1855-1931) American/Armenian

£406 $650 €593 Portrait of a man with moustache (76x64cm-30x25in) s.d.1888. 20-Sep-3 Sloans & Kenyon, Bethesda #152/R

ERLEBACHER, Martha Mayer (1937-) American

£1195 $1900 €1745 Woman in chair with red cuschions (36x28cm-14x11in) mono. board. 12-Sep-3 Skinner, Boston #384/R est:1800-2200

ERLER, Fritz (1868-1940) German

£1139 $1777 €1800 Winter walk (40x54cm-16x21in) s. 18-Oct-2 Von Zezschwitz, Munich #28/R est:1800

£2700 $4833 €4050 Summer solstice (70x60cm-28x24in) s. lit. 14-May-4 Von Zezschwitz, Munich #286/R est:4800

£4267 $7637 €6400 Springtime (60x40cm-24x16in) s. i.verso lit. 14-May-4 Von Zezschwitz, Munich #285/R est:4200

£6962 $10861 €11000 Female nude (118x103cm-46x41in) s. panel silver. 18-Oct-2 Von Zezschwitz, Munich #21/R est:12000

Works on paper

£506 $790 €800 Swordsman (72x45cm-28x18in) s. chk ochre pencil htd white. 18-Oct-2 Von Zezschwitz, Munich #23/R

ERLER, Max (1888-1958) Austrian

£759 $1388 €1100 Kitzbuhl (35x49cm-14x19in) s. board. 27-Jan-4 Dorotheum, Vienna #33/R

ERLER-SAMADEN, Erich (1870-1946) German

£592 $1089 €900 Stable in Engadin (19x30cm-7x12in) 25-Jun-4 Michael Zeller, Lindau #558/R

£607 $1014 €880 Winter's day in Munich (61x45cm-24x18in) s. panel. 15-Nov-3 Von Zezschwitz, Munich #39/R

£1049 $1804 €1500 Exploring the glacier (50x71cm-20x28in) s.d.1910 tempera mixed media card. 3-Dec-3 Stadion, Trieste #1047/R est:1200-1600

£1176 $2081 €1717 Girl with grapes (66x48cm-26x19in) s. 28-Apr-4 Kieselbach, Budapest #49/R (H.F 440000)

£1333 $2387 €2000 Mountain church in the snow (60x50cm-24x20in) s. 13-May-4 Neumeister, Munich #341/R est:600-800

£1958 $3368 €2800 Drinking from the water trough (95x95cm-37x37in) s. 4-Dec-3 Van Ham, Cologne #136/R est:2000

£2621 $4377 €3800 Peasant woman (94x101cm-37x40in) s. exhib. 13-Nov-3 Neumeister, Munich #317/R est:4500-5000

£5517 $9214 €8000 At the high valley (80x80cm-31x31in) s. exhib. 13-Nov-3 Neumeister, Munich #316/R est:9000-10000

Works on paper

£268 $494 €400 Standing female nude (63x46cm-25x18in) s. cohre. 24-Mar-4 Hugo Ruef, Munich #1224

ERMAKOVA, Irina (1931-) Russian

£320 $582 €467 Portrait of a girl (34x29cm-13x11in) s. painted 1959. 20-Jun-4 Lots Road Auctions, London #364/R

ERMELS, Johann Franciscus (1641-1693) German

£10000 $17300 €14600 Wooded landscape with travelers resting amongst classical ruins, cattle, sheep nearby (63x67cm-25x26in) s. 10-Dec-3 Christie's, London #114/R est:10000-15000

Works on paper

£537 $988 €800 Rocky woodland (30x20cm-12x8in) i. verso pen over chk wash. 26-Mar-4 Venator & Hansten, Koln #1348/R

ERNECKE, Hermann (1817-1894) German

£11000	$19910	€16500	Portrait de jeune homme au chechia (60x47cm-24x19in) s. 31-Mar-4 Sotheby's, Paris #97/R est:7000-9000

ERNESTI, Richard (1856-1946) American

£430	$800	€628	Mountain landscape (41x61cm-16x24in) s. canvas on board painted c.1930. 7-Mar-4 Treadway Gallery, Cincinnati #595/R

ERNI, Hans (1909-) Swiss

£278	$509	€406	Doves (18x14cm-7x6in) 4-Jun-4 Zofingen, Switzerland #2791 (S.FR 640)
£873	$1607	€1275	Youth and queen bee (32x24cm-13x9in) s.d. tempera. 14-Jun-4 Philippe Schuler, Zurich #4131/R (S.FR 2000)
£1448	$2679	€2100	La chataigne (17x27cm-7x11in) s.d.45 panel prov. 11-Feb-4 Beaussant & Lefèvre, Paris #178/R est:800-1000
£1681	$3009	€2454	Nomad with cattle (65x50cm-26x20in) s.d.Jan 73 i. verso tempera. 14-May-4 Dobiaschofsky, Bern #241/R est:7500 (S.FR 3900)
£1957	$3580	€2857	Fille debout (58x31cm-23x12in) s.d.68 s.i.d.verso prov. 5-Jun-4 Galerie du Rhone, Sion #566/R est:3500-4500 (S.FR 4500)
£2009	$3535	€2933	Rencontre dans l'etable (65x44cm-26x17in) s.d.10 8 71 tempera pen prov. 22-May-4 Galerie Gloggner, Luzern #40 est:3800-4500 (S.FR 4600)
£4367	$8035	€6376	Two horses (135x138cm-53x54in) s.d.1972 fresco tempera scratching plaster on panel prov. 8-Jun-4 Germann, Zurich #127/R est:15000-20000 (S.FR 10000)
£5172	$9259	€7551	Peasant woman resting (47x92cm-19x36in) s.d.3.V.63 i. verso. 14-May-4 Dobiaschofsky, Bern #212/R est:14000 (S.FR 12000)
£9050	$15656	€13213	More cultivation or hunger (45x52cm-18x20in) tempera panel lit. 9-Dec-3 Sotheby's, Zurich #64/R est:6000-9000 (S.FR 20000)
Works on paper			
£263	$439	€384	Horse (34x24cm-13x9in) s.i.d.65 Indian ink prov. 15-Nov-3 Galerie Gloggner, Luzern #46 (S.FR 600)
£266	$444	€386	Nu assis (18x17cm-7x7in) s. ink. 21-Jun-3 Galerie du Rhone, Sion #358 (S.FR 580)
£284	$522	€415	Icarus skirting the sun (33x35cm-13x14in) s.i.d. W/C pencil. 14-Jun-4 Philippe Schuler, Zurich #4132/R (S.FR 650)
£291	$483	€422	The couple (20x14cm-8x6in) s.d.8.11.67. 13-Jun-3 Zofingen, Switzerland #2838 (S.FR 640)
£306	$562	€447	Portrait of woman and man (26x37cm-10x15in) s.d. Indian ink wash. 14-Jun-4 Philippe Schuler, Zurich #4134 (S.FR 700)
£389	$700	€568	Seated figure (41x51cm-16x20in) s.d.55 ink W/C. 23-Jan-4 Freeman, Philadelphia #22/R
£431	$772	€629	Horse with wings above fish (24x20cm-9x8in) s.i.d.31.3.82 chl. 13-May-4 Stuker, Bern #617 (S.FR 1000)
£517	$926	€755	Seated female nude (28x20cm-11x8in) s.i. Indian ink col chk W/C. 12-May-4 Dobiaschofsky, Bern #1571/R (S.FR 1200)
£647	$1157	€945	Mother and child (28x20cm-11x8in) s.i.d.58 Indian ink. 12-May-4 Dobiaschofsky, Bern #1570/R est:1600 (S.FR 1500)
£659	$1094	€956	Female nude (32x25cm-13x10in) s.d.1970 W/C Indian ink. 13-Jun-3 Zofingen, Switzerland #2839/R (S.FR 1450)
£724	$1158	€1057	Couple on beach (39x28cm-15x11in) s.d.1954 W/C Indian ink. 16-Sep-3 Philippe Schuler, Zurich #3146 est:900-1200 (S.FR 1600)
£950	$1615	€1387	Two men carrying nude woman (32x46cm-13x18in) s.d.26.11.65 W/C Indian ink. 19-Nov-3 Fischer, Luzern #2615/R est:2000-3000 (S.FR 2100)
£1009	$1685	€1463	Fish (35x37cm-14x15in) s.d. W/C. 23-Jun-3 Philippe Schuler, Zurich #3235/R (S.FR 2200)
£1478	$2705	€2158	Les trois ages (50x30cm-20x12in) s.d.14/4/71 gouache. 5-Jun-4 Galerie du Rhone, Sion #319/R est:2500-3500 (S.FR 3400)
£1834	$3338	€2678	Greek theatre with masks (53x69cm-21x27in) s.d.60 ink wash. 16-Jun-4 Fischer, Luzern #2746/R est:4400-4800 (S.FR 4200)
£2036	$3258	€2973	Horse (36x48cm-14x19in) s.d.1969 gouache. 16-Sep-3 Philippe Schuler, Zurich #3145 est:4000-5000 (S.FR 4500)
£3333	$5333	€4833	Horse and bull (65x45cm-26x18in) s.d.20 Okt 65 W/C. 15-May-3 Stuker, Bern #1175 est:4000-4500 (S.FR 7000)

ERNST, Elizabeth (1909-1997) Australian

£622	$1039	€933	Mirage (60x91cm-24x36in) s.d.59 board. 27-Oct-3 Goodman, Sydney #250/R (A.D 1500)
£747	$1247	€1121	Still life (62x50cm-24x20in) s. board. 27-Oct-3 Goodman, Sydney #254/R (A.D 1800)

ERNST, Helge (1916-1990) Danish

£271	$500	€396	Coastal landscape with vessels (54x73cm-21x29in) mono. 15-Mar-4 Rasmussen, Vejle #667/R (D.KR 3000)
£362	$648	€529	Blue composition (33x46cm-13x18in) init. 10-May-4 Rasmussen, Vejle #509/R (D.KR 4000)
£406	$759	€593	Ornamental (41x73cm-16x29in) init. 25-Feb-4 Kunsthallen, Copenhagen #54/R (D.KR 4500)
£724	$1296	€1057	Red composition (33x41cm-13x16in) init. 10-May-4 Rasmussen, Vejle #508/R (D.KR 8000)
£767	$1412	€1120	Still life (60x92cm-24x36in) init. s.d.1989 verso. 29-Mar-4 Rasmussen, Copenhagen #313/R (D.KR 8500)
£800	$1359	€1168	Composition (101x65cm-40x26in) init. 29-Nov-3 Rasmussen, Havnen #4151 (D.KR 8500)
£857	$1603	€1251	Self-portrait (146x89cm-57x35in) s. i.verso exhib. 25-Feb-4 Kunsthallen, Copenhagen #111/R (D.KR 9500)
£1127	$1882	€1645	Summer picture (73x116cm-29x46in) s. s.d.1969 verso. 7-Oct-3 Rasmussen, Copenhagen #289/R est:15000 (D.KR 12000)
£1173	$2194	€1713	Circulation (97x130cm-38x51in) s. 25-Feb-4 Kunsthallen, Copenhagen #126/R est:10000 (D.KR 13000)
£1401	$2382	€2045	Still life (73x90cm-29x35in) init. s.i.d.1987/88 verso. 10-Nov-3 Rasmussen, Vejle #601/R est:12000 (D.KR 15200)
£1448	$2592	€2114	Town fragment, Paris (100x90cm-39x35in) s. d.1984 verso. 10-May-4 Rasmussen, Vejle #515/R est:15000 (D.KR 16000)
£1674	$2997	€2444	The small table (82x55cm-32x22in) init. d.1975 verso. 10-May-4 Rasmussen, Vejle #516/R est:20000 (D.KR 18500)
£1810	$3240	€2643	Composition (130x97cm-51x38in) s. d.1989 verso. 10-May-4 Rasmussen, Vejle #517/R est:20000 (D.KR 20000)
£2076	$3882	€3031	Studio (114x162cm-45x64in) s.d.74. 25-Feb-4 Kunsthallen, Copenhagen #133/R est:15000 (D.KR 23000)
£2299	$4254	€3357	Still life in yellow (73x100cm-29x39in) s. d.1987 verso. 15-Mar-4 Rasmussen, Vejle #549/R est:20000 (D.KR 25500)

ERNST, Jimmy (1920-1984) American/German

£1529	$2600	€2232	Mineral n.27 (20x15cm-8x6in) s.d.1952 board prov. 9-Nov-3 Wright, Chicago #290 est:2000-3000
£1796	$3000	€2622	Cirque d'hiver (63x91cm-25x36in) s.d.52 prov.exhib.lit. 7-Oct-3 Sotheby's, New York #236 est:5000-7000
£2273	$4000	€3319	About to be (86x124cm-34x49in) s.d.1960. 22-May-4 Selkirks, St. Louis #555/R est:2500-3500
£3529	$6000	€5152	Phoenix near the sun (122x76cm-48x30in) s.d.1964 board prov. 9-Nov-3 Wright, Chicago #289 est:7000-9000
£4706	$8000	€6871	Antiworld (127x165cm-50x65in) s.d.1966 s.i.d.verso prov. 9-Nov-3 Wright, Chicago #291 est:9000-12000
Works on paper			
£435	$800	€635	Abstraction composition (56x76cm-22x30in) s.d.1952 brush ink. 10-Jun-4 Swann Galleries, New York #80/R
£503	$800	€734	Luruillo. Holiday wishes (15x8cm-6x3in) one s.i.d.69 one s.i. W/C ink pair. 13-Sep-3 Weschler, Washington #800/R
£879	$1600	€1283	Nebula III (26x61cm-10x24in) s.d.54 gouache paper on masonite. 29-Jun-4 Sotheby's, New York #452/R est:1000-1500
£1176	$2000	€1717	Abstract composition (76x56cm-30x22in) s.d.1951 W/C brush wash ink gouache. 21-Nov-3 Swann Galleries, New York #44/R est:2500-3500
£2180	$3750	€3183	White Space (33x43cm-13x17in) s.d.51 gouache prov. 7-Dec-3 Freeman, Philadelphia #148 est:800-1200

ERNST, Max (1891-1976) German

£8000	$14720	€11680	Grand ignorant (184x113cm-72x44in) oil collage lithograph three screen panel lit. 24-Mar-4 Sotheby's, Olympia #155/R est:3000-4000
£19728	$35313	€29000	Mandala pour Alain (27x22cm-11x9in) s.i.d.1961 oil W/C collage wood prov.lit. 21-Mar-4 Calmels Cohen, Paris #153/R est:30000-40000
£27586	$51034	€40000	Composition au ciel rouge (41x33cm-16x13in) s. panel. 16-Feb-4 Giraudeau, Tours #48
£33333	$61333	€50000	La foret (25x19cm-10x7in) s.d.51 paper prov.exhib. 11-Jun-4 Villa Grisebach, Berlin #65/R est:70000-90000
£33557	$60067	€50000	Paysage d'Arizona, printemps (23x28cm-9x11in) s. i.on stretcher paper on canvas prov.exhib. 26-May-4 Christie's, Paris #47/R est:40000-60000
£34000	$62560	€49640	Mandala pour Alain (27x21cm-11x8in) s.d.61 s.i.d.verso oil collage W/C panel prov.lit. 23-Jun-4 Christie's, London #250/R est:35000-45000
£36912	$67919	€55000	Untitled (41x33cm-16x13in) s. panel painted c.1960. 29-Mar-4 Cornette de St.Cyr, Paris #26/R est:60000-80000
£41176	$70000	€60117	Untitled (55x18cm-22x7in) s. panel mounted card painted c.1961 prov.lit. 6-Nov-3 Sotheby's, New York #261/R est:80000-120000
£42000	$76860	€61320	Untitled (33x24cm-13x9in) s. oil gouache paper collage on panel prov. 2-Feb-4 Christie's, London #79/R est:40000-60000
£48000	$88320	€70080	Oiseau (24x19cm-9x7in) s. sandpaper on canvas painted 1925 prov.lit. 22-Jun-4 Sotheby's, London #194/R est:50000-70000
£50279	$90000	€73407	Untitled (17x25cm-7x10in) s. i.verso painted 1948 prov.lit. 5-May-4 Christie's, Rockefeller NY #300/R est:40000-60000
£54423	$97417	€80000	Visages en gris (45x38cm-18x15in) s. painted 1950 prov.exhib. 21-Mar-4 Calmels Cohen, Paris #51/R est:80000-100000
£55000	$100650	€80300	Madame D (55x46cm-22x18in) s.d.55 s.i.d.verso prov.lit. 2-Feb-4 Christie's, London #89/R est:50000-70000
£55882	$95000	€81588	Arizona rouge (24x33cm-9x13in) s. panel painted 1955 prov.lit. 5-Nov-3 Christie's, Rockefeller NY #322/R est:100000-150000
£85000	$155550	€124100	Muschelblume (24x19cm-9x7in) s. painted 1928 prov.exhib.lit. 2-Feb-4 Christie's, London #53/R est:35000-55000
£85294	$145000	€124529	Window with flowers and dog (31x22cm-12x9in) s.i.d.48 verso prov.exhib.lit. 6-Nov-3 Sotheby's, New York #265/R est:50000-70000
£89520	$162926	€130699	Arizona night (36x56cm-14x22in) s.d.44 prov.exhib. 18-Jun-4 Kornfeld, Bern #35/R est:225000 (S.FR 205000)
£223529	$380000	€326352	La vie des animaux (130x163cm-51x64in) s.d.64 s.i.verso prov.exhib. 4-Nov-3 Christie's, Rockefeller NY #34/R est:450000-650000
£250000	$457500	€365000	Portrait of a girl with Mexican earrings (46x38cm-18x15in) s. masonite painted c.1946 prov.exhib.lit. 2-Feb-4 Christie's, London #66/R est:300000-400000
£320000	$585600	€467200	Le chant de la grenouille (76x91cm-30x36in) s.d.57 s.i.verso prov.lit. 2-Feb-4 Christie's, London #70/R est:160000-240000
£530000	$969900	€773800	Fleurs (80x65cm-31x26in) s. painted 1928 prov.exhib.lit. 2-Feb-4 Christie's, London #61/R est:300000-500000
£559567	$1029603	€816968	La conversion du feu. Aux Antipodes du paysage (38x55cm-15x22in) s. painted 1937 prov.exhib.lit. 29-Mar-4 Rasmussen, Copenhagen #14/R est:2000000-2500000 (D.KR 6200000)
£880000	$1610400	€1284800	Le fuite (92x73cm-36x29in) s. painted 1940 prov.exhib.lit. 2-Feb-4 Christie's, London #58/R est:350000-450000
Prints			
£1613	$3000	€2355	Un poeme dans chaque livre (13x15cm-5x6in) s.i.num.28/40 col etching aquatint. 2-Mar-4 Swann Galleries, New York #180/R est:2000-3000
£1867	$3435	€2800	To, Max Ernst, the outspoken pair (24x18cm-9x7in) s. etching col aquatint one of 30. 12-Jun-4 Villa Grisebach, Berlin #711/R est:2000-3000
£2000	$3680	€3000	Masks (33x50cm-13x20in) s. col lithograph one of 302. 12-Jun-4 Villa Grisebach, Berlin #710/R est:1800-2400
£2183	$3974	€3187	For: Max Ernst, Paramythen. s.i. col etching. 17-Jun-4 Kornfeld, Bern #331 est:4000 (S.FR 5000)
£3007	$5172	€4300	Rhythms (42x27cm-17x11in) col lithograph exec. 1950. 4-Dec-3 Van Ham, Cologne #137/R est:4500
Sculpture			
£3497	$5944	€5000	Cheri Bibi (34x16cm-13x6in) s.st.f.Valsuani pat bronze. 21-Nov-3 Lombrail & Teucquam, Paris #87/R est:5000-6000
£4667	$8587	€7000	Cheri Bibi (34cm-13in) i. num.85/175 st.f.Valsuani exec 1975 lit. 8-Jun-4 Sotheby's, Amsterdam #66/R est:7000-10000
£5405	$9297	€7891	Cherie Bibi (34cm-13in) s. green brown pat.bronze Cast. Valsuani prov.lit. 2-Dec-3 Koller, Zurich #3325/R est:10000-14000 (S.FR 12000)
£5405	$10000	€7891	Cheri Bibi (34cm-13in) st.f.Valsuani num.111/175 green pat bronze prov.lit. 11-Feb-4 Sotheby's, New York #44/R est:10000-15000
£6884	$11290	€9500	Petite torture sur socle (32cm-13in) i.num.128/150 marble exec.1975 lit. 27-May-3 Sotheby's, Amsterdam #375/R est:8000-10000
£8511	$14213	€12000	Objet mobile recommande aux familles (99cm-39in) s.d.num.000/9 wood fibres conceived 1936 prov.lit. 19-Oct-3 Anaf, Lyon #137 est:12000-15000
£9052	$16203	€13216	Tete de minotaure (86x44x31cm-34x17x12in) num.2/8 bronze Cast Susse exec. 1991. 13-May-4 Pierre Berge, Paris #56/R est:10500-15000 (S.FR 21000)
£11765	$20000	€17177	Grande tete (14cm-6in) i. num.2/6 cast gold Cast 1971 prov.lit. 6-Nov-3 Sotheby's, New York #254/R est:25000-35000
£14480	$24615	€32000	Turtle (96x110x82cm-38x43x32in) s. num.5/8 pat bronze Cast Susse lit. 3-Nov-3 Pierre Berge, Paris #25/R est:50000-70000
£14706	$25000	€21471	Tete (8cm-3in) i.d.48 num.5/VI st.RAF brown pat bronze lit. 6-Nov-3 Sotheby's, New York #264/R est:30000-40000
£14765	$26430	€22000	Masque aux grands yeux ronds (74x31x31cm-29x12x12in) s.st.f.Susse num.7/8 pat bronze. 26-May-4 Christie's, Paris #50/R est:15000-20000

£15517 $27776 €22655 Masque aux yeux ronds (76x33x32cm-30x13x13in) num.2/8 bronze Cast Susse exec. 1991. 13-May-4 Pierre Berge, Paris #54/R est:10500-15000 (S.FR 36000)
£16379 $29319 €23913 Masque aux yeux invisibles (89x36x45cm-35x14x18in) num.2/8 bronze Cast Susse exec. 1991. 13-May-4 Pierre Berge, Paris #55/R est:10500-15000 (S.FR 38000)
£16760 $30000 €24470 Masque aux yeux invisibles (88cm-35in) i.num.4/8 st.f.Susse Freres green pat bronze conceived 1938-39. 6-May-4 Sotheby's, New York #359/R est:30000-40000
£20474 $36649 €29892 La femme demi-tete (178x36x35cm-70x14x14in) num.2/8 bronze Cast Susse exec. 1991. 13-May-4 Pierre Berge, Paris #53/R est:22500-27000 (S.FR 47500)
£24324 $41838 €35513 Janus (44cm-17in) s. black brown pat.bronze Cast.Valsuani prov. 2-Dec-3 Koller, Zurich #3326/R est:40000-50000 (S.FR 54000)
£26174 $48423 €39000 Janus, Giano (45cm-18in) s. brown pat bronze edition of 18 Cast Valsuani lit. 15-Mar-4 Blanchet, Paris #123/R est:30000-40000
£30726 $55000 €44860 Tortue (25x27x16cm-10x11x6in) s.i. num.6/9 brown pat bronze conceived 1944 prov.exhib.lit. 6-May-4 Sotheby's, New York #334/R est:30000-40000
£83799 $150000 €122347 Un chinois egare (74cm-29in) i. num.E.A 2/3 st.f.Susse blk pat bronze conceived 1960 lit. 6-May-4 Sotheby's, New York #378/R est:15000-200000
£122905 $220000 €179441 Apaisement (68cm-27in) i. num.I/V st.f.Valsuani green pat bronze prov.exhib.lit. 6-May-4 Sotheby's, New York #372/R est:140000-180000
£153846 $261538 €340000 Grand genie (182x226x82cm-72x89x32in) s. num.5/8 pat bronze Cast Susse. 25-Nov-3 Pierre Berge, Paris #26/R est:150000-200000
Works on paper
£1485 $2702 €2168 Bonheur nouveau (11x20cm-4x8in) i. Indian ink. 17-Jun-4 Kornfeld, Bern #324/R est:2500 (S.FR 3400)
£1517 $2534 €2200 Portrait de Paul Eluard (20x11cm-8x4in) init. Chinese ink. 17-Nov-3 Sant Agostino, Torino #189/R est:1200-1600
£3211 $5362 €4656 Untitled (48x34cm-19x13in) s.i. frottage. 19-Jun-3 Kornfeld, Bern #339/R est:8000 (S.FR 7000)
£4585 $8345 €6694 Rosier millenaire. Nain en courte chemise (17x10cm-7x4in) frottage two. 17-Jun-4 Kornfeld, Bern #326/R est:12500 (S.FR 10500)
£5000 $9250 €7300 Mer (27x21cm-11x8in) s.i. pencil frottage exec 1926 prov. 12-Feb-4 Sotheby's, New York #48/R est:10000-15000
£7343 $12483 €10500 Les chiens ont soif (43x31cm-17x12in) s. Indian ink brush pastel chk prov.lit. 26-Nov-3 Lempertz, Koln #652/R est:8000
£11888 $20210 €17000 Microbe (16x9cm-6x4in) s. Indian ink W/C prov. 29-Nov-3 Villa Grisebach, Berlin #304/R est:12000-15000
£14224 $25461 €20767 Le soleil (23x16cm-9x6in) s.d.1976 collage frottage prov. 13-May-4 Pierre Berge, Paris #58/R est:30000-40000 (S.FR 33000)

ERNST, Max (after) (1891-1976) German
Sculpture
£6690 $11574 €9500 Masque aux yeux ronds (73x32x32cm-29x13x13in) s.num.7/8 bronze Cast Susse. 12-Dec-3 Artus Associes, Paris #165
£13028 $22539 €18500 Loplop ailee (248x111x50cm-98in) s.num.6/8 bronze Cast Susse. 12-Dec-3 Artus Associes, Paris #166

ERNST, Max (attrib) (1891-1976) German
£2568 $4750 €3749 Untitled (91x23cm-36x9in) s. board. 14-Jan-4 Dallas Auction Gallery, Dallas #132/R est:10000-15000

ERNST, Otto (1884-1967) Swiss
£370 $676 €540 Spring in Asp (45x60cm-18x24in) s.i.verso cardboard. 4-Jun-4 Zofingen, Switzerland #2792 (S.FR 850)

ERNST, Rudolph (1854-1932) Austrian
£21739 $40000 €31739 In the Mosque (61x49cm-24x19in) s.d.88 panel. 27-Jun-4 Freeman, Philadelphia #45/R est:25000-40000
£35000 $63700 €51100 Reverie du soir dans les jardins du Harem (61x49cm-24x19in) s. panel exhib. 17-Jun-4 Christie's, London #137/R est:35000-45000
£35000 $63700 €51100 Merchant (61x49cm-24x19in) s.d.86 panel. 17-Jun-4 Christie's, London #138/R est:20000-30000
£37425 $62500 €54641 Reading the Koran (48x36cm-19x14in) s.i. panel prov. 23-Oct-3 Shannon's, Milford #118/R est:25000-35000
£44118 $75000 €64412 Preparing the Hookah (71x92cm-28x36in) s. panel. 29-Oct-3 Christie's, Rockefeller NY #53/R est:80000-120000
£48649 $87081 €72000 Oriental man with tiger (98x131cm-39x52in) s. lit. 8-May-4 Schloss Ahlden, Ahlden #800/R est:65000
£48667 $89547 €73000 La cueillette de roses (61x49cm-24x19in) s. panel. 10-Jun-4 Camard, Paris #53/R est:75000-95000
£50000 $85000 €73000 The Couple (76x64cm-30x25in) s. panel. 28-Oct-3 Sotheby's, New York #92/R est:60000-80000
£52000 $94640 €75920 Jeunes femmes sur la terrasse (64x82cm-25x32in) s. panel exhib. 17-Jun-4 Christie's, London #125/R est:40000-60000
£53334 $97602 €80000 Orientale alanguie a la rose (61x49cm-24x19in) s. panel. 3-Jun-4 Tajan, Paris #258/R est:60000-80000
£70000 $119000 €102200 Perfume makers (101x79cm-40x31in) s. panel prov. 18-Nov-3 Sotheby's, London #339/R
£90000 $165600 €135000 Le fumeur de narghile au palais (72x92cm-28x36in) s. panel. 14-Jun-4 Gros & Delettrez, Paris #130/R est:15000-200000
Works on paper
£3389 $6100 €4948 Harem musician (50x33cm-20x13in) s. W/C prov. 21-Jan-4 Sotheby's, New York #255/R est:3000-5000

ERNST, Rudolph (style) (1854-1932) Austrian
£7021 $12568 €10251 Harem interior (46x35cm-18x14in) 26-May-4 AB Stockholms Auktionsverk #2449/R est:25000-30000 (S.KR 95000)

ERRI, Bartolomeo (15th C) Italian
£157895 $290526 €240000 Saint Thomas at the table with King Saint Louis (44x31cm-17x12in) panel prov.lit. 25-Jun-4 Piasa, Paris #31/R est:120000-150000

ERRO, Gudmundur (1932-) Icelandic
£764 $1276 €1100 Il Fenisottero (57x37cm-22x15in) s. oil paper on canvas lit. 25-Oct-3 Cornette de St.Cyr, Paris #670/R
£1056 $1849 €1500 Untitled (60x44cm-24x17in) s.d.2001 enamel. 18-Dec-3 Cornette de St.Cyr, Paris #153/R est:1200-1500
£1133 $2063 €1700 Diagonal destruction (150x150cm-59x59in) s.i.verso painted 2001 prov. 29-Jun-4 Cornette de St.Cyr, Paris #97/R
£1208 $2139 €1800 Hyman bloom slaughtered animal (64x125cm-25x49in) s.i.d.1966 prov. 28-Apr-4 Artcurial Briest, Paris #399 est:2000-3000
£1513 $2784 €2300 Untitled (76x40cm-30x16in) s.d.2001 verso acrylic. 27-Jun-4 Versailles Encheres #136/R est:2000-3000
£1620 $2835 €2300 Hommage a Fernand Leger (38x56cm-15x22in) s.d.1999 verso. 18-Dec-3 Cornette de St.Cyr, Paris #156/R est:2500-3000
£1745 $3088 €2600 Hommage a Picasso et Baudelaire (33x46cm-13x18in) s.d.86 verso acrylic. 28-Apr-4 Artcurial Briest, Paris #400/R est:1500-2000
£1867 $3360 €2800 Untitled (33x46cm-13x18in) s.d.1996 verso acrylic lit. 24-Apr-4 Cornette de St.Cyr, Paris #514/R est:3000-4000
£2000 $3600 €3000 Strike is perfectly legal (100x65cm-39x26in) s.d.1991 acrylic prov.lit. 25-Apr-4 Versailles Encheres #144 est:3500-4500
£2000 $3640 €3000 Hommage allegee (55x38cm-22x15in) s.d.1997 verso acrylic paper. 5-Jul-4 Le Mouel, Paris #77/R est:3000-4000
£2222 $3667 €3200 Sans titre (38x45cm-15x18in) s.d.1999 verso acrylic panel. 2-Jul-3 Cornette de St.Cyr, Paris #137/R est:2000-2500
£2292 $3781 €3300 Hommage a Fernand Leger et Pablo Picasso (38x55cm-15x22in) s.d.2001 verso acrylic. 2-Jul-3 Cornette de St.Cyr, Paris #138/R est:3000-4500
£2292 $3896 €3300 Composition (73x54cm-29x21in) s.d.1960 prov.lit. 28-Oct-3 Il Ponte, Milan #248/R
£2684 $4751 €4000 Hommage a Miro et Leger (33x25cm-13x10in) s.d.1994 verso acrylic wood prov. 28-Apr-4 Artcurial Briest, Paris #411a est:2000-3000
£2778 $4583 €4000 Oh look, I found my book (73x98cm-29x39in) s.i.d.2001 verso acrylic. 2-Jul-3 Cornette de St.Cyr, Paris #141/R est:5000-6000
£2937 $4993 €4200 Untitled (97x130cm-38x51in) acrylic prov. 27-Nov-3 Lempertz, Koln #113/R est:5000
£3819 $6302 €5500 Pere Tanguy (101x74cm-40x29in) s.d.1969 verso prov.lit. 2-Jul-3 Cornette de St.Cyr, Paris #126/R est:6000-8000
£3846 $6538 €5500 Reserve de 199 personnalites (50x100cm-20x39in) s. s.i.d.1961 verso lit. 25-Nov-3 Tajan, Paris #42/R est:5000-6000
£4196 $7007 €6000 Elvira au chapeau (70x100cm-28x39in) s. s.d.1966 verso lit. 11-Oct-3 Cornette de St.Cyr, Paris #98/R est:5000-7000
£4196 $7217 €6000 Brainwashing of rainbow trout (89x102cm-35x40in) s.i.d.1968 verso prov.lit. 3-Dec-3 Beaussant & Lefèvre, Paris #15/R est:6000-8000
£5034 $8910 €7500 Black canary (80x80cm-31x31in) s.d.1997 d.verso acrylic. 28-Apr-4 Artcurial Briest, Paris #397/R est:6000-8000
£5986 $10475 €8500 L'artiste et le nu chaste (50x100cm-20x39in) s.verso prov.lit. 18-Dec-3 Cornette de St.Cyr, Paris #120/R est:7000-8000
£6667 $12267 €10000 France serie Russian public propagande (97x130cm-38x51in) s.i.d.1976 acrylic. 10-Jun-4 Camard, Paris #203/R est:8000-10000
£7986 $13177 €11500 Amazon woman is under my control (130x97cm-51x38in) s.d.1999 verso acrylic. 2-Jul-3 Cornette de St.Cyr, Paris #134/R est:10000-12000
£7986 $13177 €11500 How, who (98x77cm-39x30in) s.d.2000 verso acrylic. 2-Jul-3 Cornette de St.Cyr, Paris #143/R est:8000-10000
£8333 $15167 €12500 Rawhide kid (127x66cm-50x26in) s.d.1982 verso lit. 29-Jun-4 Cornette de St.Cyr, Paris #95/R est:10000-12000
£8742 $14861 €12500 Sans titre, serie des Leger (146x89cm-57x35in) s.d.1997 verso prov. 25-Nov-3 Tajan, Paris #43/R est:6000-8000
£9790 $16350 €14000 The painter's paradise (100x65cm-39x26in) s.d.1962 verso prov.lit. 11-Oct-3 Cornette de St.Cyr, Paris #91/R est:8000-10000
£9890 $18000 €14439 Mao in the harbour (95x150cm-37x59in) s.d.1974 verso prov. 29-Jun-4 Sotheby's, New York #494/R est:3000-5000
£10564 $18275 €15000 I am your new host (195x97cm-77x38in) s.d.1995 verso prov.exhib. 9-Dec-3 Artcurial Briest, Paris #381/R est:20000-25000
£10738 $19758 €16000 Familien Idylle- of the Berlin Series (97x130cm-38x51in) painted 1971 prov.lit. 29-Mar-4 Cornette de St.Cyr, Paris #73/R est:12000-15000
£12000 $21840 €18000 Voyage desert (81x100cm-32x39in) painted 1972 prov.lit. 29-Jun-4 Cornette de St.Cyr, Paris #84/R est:18000-22000
Sculpture
£3000 $5460 €4500 Decor (62x64cm-24x25in) s.i.d.1959 verso assemblage wood lit. 29-Jun-4 Cornette de St.Cyr, Paris #88/R est:4500-5000
Works on paper
£278 $464 €400 Lenine et buste d'homme en marbre (42x33cm-17x13in) s.d.1975 collage. 25-Oct-3 Cornette de St.Cyr, Paris #673
£336 $614 €500 Who are they (24x20cm-9x8in) s.d.75 collage lit. 7-Jul-4 Artcurial Briest, Paris #257
£524 $892 €750 Sans titre (17x11cm-7x4in) s.d.1973 collage. 23-Nov-3 Cornette de St.Cyr, Paris #111
£590 $986 €850 Sans titre (32x44cm-13x17in) s.d.71 verso collage. 21-Oct-3 Artcurial Briest, Paris #484/R
£604 $1069 €900 Personnages (30x40cm-12x16in) s.d.1998 verso gouache. 28-Apr-4 Artcurial Briest, Paris #400a
£700 $1260 €1050 Untitled (22x11cm-9x4in) s.d.1973 collage. 25-Apr-4 Versailles Encheres #182
£921 $1695 €1400 Conducteur (77x58cm-30x23in) s.d.1989 W/C lit. 28-Jun-4 Joron-Derem, Paris #190
£1111 $1856 €1600 Guerrier (55x75cm-22x30in) s.d.1990 verso W/C. 25-Oct-3 Cornette de St.Cyr, Paris #672 est:1800-2000
£1267 $2280 €1900 Chanteuse de la Traviata (57x76cm-22x30in) s.verso W/C lit. 24-Apr-4 Cornette de St.Cyr, Paris #513/R est:2000-3000
£1333 $2440 €2000 The green bottle (57x77cm-22x30in) s.d.1982 verso W/C. 4-Jun-4 Lempertz, Koln #122/R est:1800-2000
£1622 $2854 €2400 Conference de desarmement (77x58cm-30x23in) s.d.1991 verso W/C prov.lit. 18-May-4 Tajan, Paris #162/R est:1500-2000
£3691 $6792 €5500 Speed of monkey spacemen (57x45cm-22x18in) collage lit. 24-Mar-4 Joron-Derem, Paris #204/R est:2000-2500

ERSKINE, W C C (fl.1870s) British
Works on paper
£750 $1418 €1095 Group of curlers, hooray he's dang ott the minister (25x34cm-10x13in) init.d.72 W/C. 19-Feb-4 Lyon & Turnbull, Edinburgh #142

ERTE, Romain de Tirtoff (1892-1990) Russian
Prints
£3500 $6300 €5110 Fountain (53x22cm-21x9in) s. col drypoint aquatint. 22-Apr-4 Christie's, Kensington #451/R est:2000-3000
Sculpture
£1049 $1900 €1532 Triumph (55x18cm-22x7in) i.num.AP6/37 polychrome bronze. 18-Apr-4 Bonhams & Butterfields, Los Angeles #7111 est:1200-1800
£1087 $2000 €1587 Twilight. polychrome bronze. 13-Jun-4 Bonhams & Butterfields, Los Angeles #7073/R est:1200-1800
£1222 $2250 €1784 Kiss of fire (48x46cm-19x18in) sid.num.199/300 polychrome bronze. 13-Jun-4 Bonhams & Butterfields, Los Angeles #7072/R est:1200-1800
£1519 $2750 €2218 Globe (60x18cm-24x7in) i. polychrome bronze. 18-Apr-4 Bonhams & Butterfields, Los Angeles #7113 est:1200-1800

£1796	$3250	€2622	Le soleil (45x19cm-18x7in) i. ploychrome bronze. 18-Apr-4 Bonhams & Butterfields, Los Angeles #7112 est:1500-2000
£1946	$3600	€2841	Belle de nuit (43cm-17in) num.293/375 bronze. 17-Jul-4 New Orleans Auction, New Orleans #899/R est:4000-7000

Works on paper

£300	$528	€438	Stage design (11x15cm-4x6in) st. ink W/C. 18-May-4 Bonhams, Knightsbridge #27
£460	$847	€700	Rose Marie (37x27cm-15x11in) s. i. verso gouache. 25-Jun-4 Tajan, Paris #13
£600	$960	€876	Costume design (30x23cm-12x9in) s.i.verso W/C. 18-Sep-3 Scarborough Perry Fine Arts, Hove #660
£629	$1083	€900	Costume for Manhattan Mary (30x14cm-12x6in) s. mixed media. 2-Dec-3 Hauswedell & Nolte, Hamburg #161/R
£638	$1186	€950	Composition - E (38x28cm-15x11in) s. mixed media. 7-Mar-4 Bukowskis, Helsinki #488/R
£683	$1100	€997	Costume designs (38x28cm-15x11in) s. gouache pair. 21-Aug-3 Doyle, New York #22a/R
£719	$1200	€1050	Woman standing in red, white and black costume - costume design (25x36cm-10x14in) s. gouache W/C. 14-Jul-3 O'Gallerie, Oregon #830/R est:1500-2000
£780	$1412	€1139	Costume design for a lady - Grey jewelled dress with open midriff (38x28cm-15x11in) s. g. 17-Apr-4 Dickins, Middle Claydon #69
£800	$1464	€1168	Costume study (36x26cm-14x10in) s. gouache executed c.1923. 1-Feb-4 Lots Road Auctions, London #337
£800	$1448	€1168	Costume design for a lady - pink jewelled dress with cut away slit to the side (36x25cm-14x10in) s. gouache. 17-Apr-4 Dickins, Middle Claydon #60
£800	$1448	€1168	Costume designs for men in grey with gloves (36x25cm-14x10in) s. i.verso gouache. 17-Apr-4 Dickins, Middle Claydon #75
£820	$1484	€1197	Costume design for a lady (36x25cm-14x10in) s. gouache. 17-Apr-4 Dickins, Middle Claydon #57
£820	$1484	€1197	Costume design for a lady - Pamela Austin, Beauty and the Beast (36x25cm-14x10in) s. gouache double-sided. 17-Apr-4 Dickins, Middle Claydon #68
£820	$1484	€1197	Costume designs - grey tutu (36x25cm-14x10in) s.i. gouache. 17-Apr-4 Dickins, Middle Claydon #74
£833	$1317	€1200	Danseuse (29x23cm-11x9in) gouache htd gold silver. 25-Apr-3 Etude de Provence, Marseille #150
£840	$1520	€1226	Costume design for a lady - long blue dress for a Hispanic dancer (25x15cm-10x6in) s. gouache. 17-Apr-4 Dickins, Middle Claydon #59
£840	$1520	€1226	Costume design for a lady - Long blue dress with bow bustle and train (36x25cm-14x10in) s. gouache. 17-Apr-4 Dickins, Middle Claydon #62
£840	$1520	€1226	Costume design for a lady - Grey off the shoulder dress (38x28cm-15x11in) s. gouache pencil sketch verso double-sided. 17-Apr-4 Dickins, Middle Claydon #71
£840	$1520	€1226	Costume design for a lady - Grey dress having gypsy style skirt (36x25cm-14x10in) s.i. gouache. 17-Apr-4 Dickins, Middle Claydon #72
£840	$1520	€1226	Costume designs - 4 tap dancers having grey top and bottoms (36x25cm-14x10in) s.i. gouache. 17-Apr-4 Dickins, Middle Claydon #73
£850	$1539	€1241	Costume design for a lady, bodice with violin and lace gloves (36x28cm-14x11in) indis.i. gouache. 17-Apr-4 Dickins, Middle Claydon #56
£850	$1539	€1241	Costume design for a lady - These Foolish Kings Showgirls (36x28cm-14x11in) s.i. gouache. 17-Apr-4 Dickins, Middle Claydon #66
£872	$1623	€1300	Composition - D (37x27cm-15x11in) s. mixed media. 7-Mar-4 Bukowskis, Helsinki #487/R
£880	$1593	€1285	Costume design for a lady - Long lilac dress with long gloves and lilac vale (33x25cm-13x10in) s i.verso gouache. 17-Apr-4 Dickins, Middle Claydon #61
£880	$1593	€1285	Costume design for a lady - For These Foolish Kings (36x28cm-14x11in) s. i.verso gouache. 17-Apr-4 Dickins, Middle Claydon #65
£880	$1593	€1285	Costume design for a lady - These Foolish Kings Showgirls (36x28cm-14x11in) s.i. gouache. 17-Apr-4 Dickins, Middle Claydon #67
£880	$1593	€1285	Costume design for a man - grey suit with bow tie, blue cape and top hat (38x25cm-15x10in) s. gouache. 17-Apr-4 Dickins, Middle Claydon #76
£900	$1647	€1314	Costume study (32x23cm-13x9in) s.i. gouache. 1-Feb-4 Lots Road Auctions, London #336
£900	$1629	€1314	Costume design for a Lady Joy Corbett, peacock butterfly design (38x28cm-15x11in) s. gouache. 17-Apr-4 Dickins, Middle Claydon #55
£900	$1629	€1314	Costume design for a man - Texan cowboy with Stetson (36x25cm-14x10in) s. gouache. 17-Apr-4 Dickins, Middle Claydon #77
£960	$1700	€1402	Beautiful woman standing in a long gown (25x36cm-10x14in) s. W/C gouache. 3-May-4 O'Gallerie, Oregon #813/R est:1200-1800
£1000	$1800	€1460	Quintette girl (38x28cm-15x11in) s. i.verso gouache. 20-Jan-4 Arthur James, Florida #14
£1000	$1810	€1460	Costume design for a lady - Long yellow dress for a Hispanic dancer (25x20cm-10x8in) s. gouache. 17-Apr-4 Dickins, Middle Claydon #58
£1042	$1646	€1500	Danseuse (29x23cm-11x9in) gouache htd gold silver. 25-Apr-3 Etude de Provence, Marseille #149 est:1000-1200
£1080	$1955	€1577	Costume design for a lady - For These Foolish Kings (36x28cm-14x11in) s. gouache. 17-Apr-4 Dickins, Middle Claydon #63
£1080	$1955	€1577	Costume design for a lady - For These Foolish King (36x28cm-14x11in) s. gouache. 17-Apr-4 Dickins, Middle Claydon #64
£1111	$1756	€1600	Femme au parfum (29x23cm-11x9in) gouache htd gold silver. 25-Apr-3 Etude de Provence, Marseille #148 est:1000-1200
£1120	$2027	€1635	Costume design for a lady - Grey jewelled dress with open midriff (38x28cm-15x11in) s. gouache. 17-Apr-4 Dickins, Middle Claydon #70
£1200	$2160	€1752	Scandal paper (18x22cm-7x9in) s.i. gouache paper on paper lit. 22-Apr-4 Christie's, Kensington #440/R est:800-1200
£1290	$2400	€1883	Tete de femme (5x17cm-2x7in) s. gouache. 2-Mar-4 Swann Galleries, New York #183/R est:2000-3000
£1333	$2453	€2000	Egyptian costume - Hatora (34x23cm-13x9in) gouache gold silver. 10-Jun-4 Hauswedell & Nolte, Hamburg #195/R est:800
£1500	$2775	€2190	Series of four costume design for the Tiller Girls (36x25cm-14x10in) s. bodycol ink set of four. 10-Feb-4 David Lay, Penzance #529/R est:1500-2000
£1875	$3000	€2738	Le lotus (36x27cm-14x11in) s. gouache. 18-Sep-3 Swann Galleries, New York #233/R est:2500-3500
£2000	$3600	€2920	Manteau de diamants (27x37cm-11x15in) s.i. gouache. 22-Apr-4 Christie's, Kensington #439/R est:1000-1500
£9500	$17005	€13870	Monkey. Its a baby!. Motor car (37x27cm-15x11in) s. i.verso gouache set of eight. 26-May-4 Sotheby's, London #257/R est:8000-12000

ERTZ, Bruno (1873-1956) American

Works on paper

£479	$800	€699	Kingfisher (30x51cm-12x20in) s.d.42 W/C. 27-Oct-3 Schrager Galleries, Milwaukee #1383/R

ERWIN, Jack (1920-) American

£599	$1000	€875	Filling station, Grapevine Highway, Dallas TX (30x41cm-12x16in) masonite. 18-Oct-3 David Dike, Dallas #118/R
£838	$1400	€1223	Katy Freight Depot, Record Street, Dallas TX (46x61cm-18x24in) masonite. 18-Oct-3 David Dike, Dallas #120/R

ERWITT, Elliott (1928-) American

Photographs

£1916	$3200	€2797	New York (11x9cm-4x4in) s. s.i.d.1974 verso gelatin silver print prov.lit. 17-Oct-3 Phillips, New York #137/R est:2500-3500
£3107	$5500	€4536	New York City, 1974 (21x31cm-8x12in) s. s.i.d.1974 verso gelatin silver print. 27-Apr-4 Christie's, Rockefeller NY #162/R est:3000-5000

ERZIA, Stephan (1876-1960) Russian

Sculpture

£5140	$9200	€7504	Head of woman (34cm-13in) painted wood exec.c.1935 exhib.lit. 4-May-4 Arroyo, Buenos Aires #34/R est:8000
£7821	$14000	€11419	Head of woman (32cm-13in) painted wood exec.c.1930 exhib.lit. 4-May-4 Arroyo, Buenos Aires #35/R est:10000

ESAM, Arthur (1850-c.1910) Australian

Works on paper

£851	$1447	€1242	Watering the horses (33x48cm-13x19in) i.verso W/C. 25-Nov-3 Christie's, Melbourne #225 (A.D 2000)

ESCALONA, Julio (20th C) Venezuelan?

£258	$400	€377	Plain (71x100cm-28x39in) s. 3-Nov-2 Subastas Odalys, Caracas #71

ESCHARD, Charles (1748-1810) French

Works on paper

£408	$731	€600	Le jeune ecailler (22x16cm-9x6in) crayon htd W/C. 17-Mar-4 Maigret, Paris #54/R
£612	$1096	€900	Paysage avec voyageurs. s.d.1805 gouache. 19-Mar-4 Beaussant & Lefèvre, Paris #33/R
£669	$1157	€950	Moutons et vache au repos (26x28cm-10x11in) i. pen brown ink brown wash htd gouache. 10-Dec-3 Piasa, Paris #68

ESCHBACH, Paul Andre Jean (1881-1961) French

£400	$716	€600	Pecheur en barque (50x61cm-20x24in) s. 16-May-4 Renault-Aubry, Pontivy #443
£599	$1048	€850	Chaumiere sous la neige (50x61cm-20x24in) s. 21-Dec-3 Thierry & Lannon, Brest #309
£662	$1238	€1000	Retour de peche, barques sous voiles (24x33cm-9x13in) s. panel. 24-Jul-4 Thierry & Lannon, Brest #163
£894	$1672	€1350	Marine en Bretagne (38x46cm-15x18in) s. 24-Jul-4 Thierry & Lannon, Brest #366/R
£915	$1602	€1300	Marine retour de peche (40x80cm-16x31in) s. 21-Dec-3 Thierry & Lannon, Brest #164/R
£1200	$2148	€1800	Matin a Douarnenez (45x54cm-18x21in) s. 16-May-4 Thierry & Lannon, Brest #313 est:1000-1500
£1788	$3344	€2700	Bateaux au repos a Douarnenez (46x55cm-18x22in) s. 24-Jul-4 Thierry & Lannon, Brest #162/R est:2000-2500
£1987	$3715	€3000	Le dechargement des thoniers au port de Douarnenez (65x81cm-26x32in) s. 24-Jul-4 Thierry & Lannon, Brest #160/R est:3000-4000
£3046	$5697	€4600	Voiliers sous le soleil de Concarneau (62x73cm-24x29in) s. 24-Jul-4 Thierry & Lannon, Brest #161/R est:4500-5000

ESCHER, Maurits Cornelis (1898-1972) Dutch

Prints

£1808	$3200	€2640	Sea shells (16x11cm-6x4in) s.i. mezzotint laid paper. 28-Apr-4 Christie's, Rockefeller NY #45/R est:2500-3500
£2147	$3800	€3135	Grasshopper (18x24cm-7x9in) s.i. wood engraving. 28-Apr-4 Christie's, Rockefeller NY #42/R est:3500-4500
£2600	$4732	€3796	Plane filling I (19x24cm-7x9in) s.i.num.27/50 mezzotint. 1-Jul-4 Sotheby's, London #174/R est:3000-4000
£3261	$5348	€4500	Three worlds, Locher 405 (360x247cm-142x97in) s.i. lithograph paper on cardboard. 27-May-3 Sotheby's, Amsterdam #600/R est:2300-3000
£3390	$6000	€4949	Mummified frog (14x17cm-6x7in) s.i.num.18/24 mezzotint laid paper. 28-Apr-4 Christie's, Rockefeller NY #44/R est:4500-5500
£3529	$6000	€5152	Plane filling II (42x47cm-17x19in) s. num.38/56 lithograph exec.1957. 4-Nov-3 Christie's, Rockefeller NY #93/R est:6000-8000
£3593	$6000	€5246	Other world (32x26cm-13x10in) s.i. col woodcut. 21-Oct-3 Bonhams & Butterfields, San Francisco #1179/R
£3667	$6747	€5500	Lucht en water (43x44cm-17x17in) s.i. woodcut exec 1938 prov. 8-Jun-4 Sotheby's, Amsterdam #320/R est:6000-9000
£3955	$7000	€5774	Rippled surface (26x32cm-10x13in) s.i. col linocut. 28-Apr-4 Christie's, Rockefeller NY #46/R est:5000-7000
£4236	$7074	€6100	Other world. s. etching. 23-Oct-3 Credit Municipal, Paris #43/R est:2000-2500
£4237	$7500	€6186	Old houses in Positano (24x29cm-9x11in) s.num.19/20 lithograph. 28-Apr-4 Christie's, Rockefeller NY #41/R est:4000-5000
£4667	$8587	€7000	Andere Wereld (317x260cm-125x102in) s. woodcut exec 1947. 8-Jun-4 Sotheby's, Amsterdam #319/R est:7000-9000
£4700	$8554	€6862	Sky and water I (44x44cm-17x17in) s.i. woodcut. 1-Jul-4 Sotheby's, London #173/R est:4000-6000
£4802	$8500	€7011	Horseman (24x45cm-9x18in) s.i. col woodcut. 28-Apr-4 Christie's, Rockefeller NY #43/R est:5000-7000
£5000	$8500	€7300	Doppelplanetoid (37cm-15in circular) s.i. col engraving exec.1949. 1-Dec-3 Bonhams, New Bond Street #166/R est:5000-7000
£5085	$9000	€7424	Rind (35x24cm-14x9in) s.i. col wood engraving woodcut. 28-Apr-4 Christie's, Rockefeller NY #47/R est:8000-12000
£5333	$9813	€8000	Sky and water I (43x43cm-17x17in) s. wood engraving exec. 1938. 9-Jun-4 Christie's, Amsterdam #228/R est:8000-12000
£6000	$10920	€8760	Day and night (41x70cm-16x28in) s.i. col woodcut. 1-Jul-4 Sotheby's, London #171/R est:6000-8000
£6780	$12000	€9899	Ascending and descending (36x29cm-14x11in) s.num.45/52 lithograph. 28-Apr-4 Christie's, Rockefeller NY #48/R est:15000-20000
£7059	$12000	€10306	Other world (39x33cm-15x13in) s.i. woodcut wood engraving. 4-Nov-3 Christie's, Rockefeller NY #91/R est:8000-10000
£9040	$16000	€13198	The bridge (53x37cm-21x15in) s.num.5/60 lithograph. 28-Apr-4 Christie's, Rockefeller NY #39/R est:5000-8000

£9259 $15000 €13426 Day and night (39x67cm-15x26in) s.i. woodcut. 8-Aug-3 Barridorf, Portland #354/R est:15000-25000
£28235 $48000 €41223 Drawing hands (38x45cm-15x18in) s. num.2/17 lithograph exec.1948. 4-Nov-3 Christie's, Rockefeller NY #92/R est:40000-50000

ESCHKE, Hermann (1823-1900) German
£1186 $2017 €1732 Freshwater Bay, Isle of Wight, sunrise (69x88cm-27x35in) s.d.1877 i.verso prov. 24-Nov-3 Sotheby's, Melbourne #310/R est:3000-5000 (A.D 2800)

ESCHKE, Richard-Hermann (1859-1944) German
£604 $1130 €900 Summer's day by the lake (21x34cm-8x13in) s. board on canvas. 24-Feb-4 Dorotheum, Vienna #272/R
£1259 $2140 €1800 Summer coast in Mecklenburg (91x112cm-36x44in) s. 20-Nov-3 Van Ham, Cologne #1561/R est:1900

ESCHWEGE, Elmar von (1856-1935) German
£450 $752 €657 In the midst of a melee (56x45cm-22x18in) 8-Oct-3 Christie's, Kensington #836
£570 $1061 €850 Forest stream (59x44cm-23x17in) s. 5-Mar-4 Wendl, Rudolstadt #3633/R
£927 $1687 €1400 Coach arriving in front of a castle (70x96cm-28x38in) s.d.29. 19-Jun-4 Hans Stahl, Hamburg #37

ESCOMBE, Anne (fl.1869-1875) British
£600 $1080 €876 Lyme Regis (42x85cm-17x33in) s.i. 22-Apr-4 Lawrence, Crewkerne #925

ESCUELA, Juan (20th C) ?
Sculpture
£2599 $4600 €3795 Le Baton de Vieillesse (34cm-13in) copper pat bronze exec.c.1900. 2-May-4 Bonhams & Butterfields, San Francisco #1523/R est:3000-4000

ESHUYS, Hendrikus Jacobus (1888-1967) Dutch
£280 $476 €400 Cat (60x69cm-24x27in) s. 24-Nov-3 Glerum, Amsterdam #140/R

ESKILSON, Per (1820-1872) Swedish
£813 $1455 €1187 Cottage interior (42x48cm-17x19in) s. 25-May-4 Bukowskis, Stockholm #132/R (S.KR 11000)

ESKOLA, Kalle (1912-) Finnish
£278 $464 €400 House (65x52cm-26x20in) s.d.1955. 23-Oct-3 Hagelstam, Helsinki #1004
£306 $510 €440 Still life of jug and apple (42x58cm-17x23in) s.d.70. 26-Oct-3 Bukowskis, Helsinki #324/R
£333 $597 €500 Interior scene with girl standing by grand piano (54x46cm-21x18in) s.d.1944. 15-May-4 Hagelstam, Helsinki #194/R
£868 $1450 €1250 Cafe interior (55x45cm-22x18in) s.d.44. 26-Oct-3 Bukowskis, Helsinki #323/R

ESMERALDO, Servulo (20th C) Brazilian
£769 $1231 €1123 E 6901 (152x102cm-60x40in) 16-Sep-3 Philippe Schuler, Zurich #3016 est:1500-2000 (S.FR 1700)

ESPALIU, Pepe (1955-1993) Spanish
Works on paper
£2200 $3982 €3300 Pinocchio (51x38cm-20x15in) s. i.verso chl sanguine dr prov. 30-Mar-4 Segre, Madrid #310/R est:3300

ESPINA Y CAPO, Juan (1848-1933) Spanish
£671 $1201 €1000 Path (28x52cm-11x20in) s.d.97 board. 25-May-4 Durán, Madrid #178/R
£1232 $2020 €1700 Landscape (37x67cm-15x26in) s. 27-May-3 Durán, Madrid #285/R est:1500
£2238 $3737 €3200 Autumn at the villa (30x40cm-12x16in) s. 30-Jun-3 Ansorena, Madrid #215/R

ESPINASSE, Raymond (1897-1985) French
£579 $1065 €880 Pecheur a Sete (22x26cm-9x10in) s. panel painted 1950. 22-Jun-4 Chassaing Rivet, Toulouse #283
Works on paper
£395 $726 €600 Barques a Sete (40x49cm-16x19in) s. s.i.d.1949 verso W/C gouache. 22-Jun-4 Chassaing Rivet, Toulouse #284

ESPINOSA, Juan Bautista de (attrib) (fl.1616-1626) Spanish
£23611 $42500 €34472 Still life of fruits and a plate of olives (50x67cm-20x26in) 22-Jan-4 Sotheby's, New York #243/R est:20000-30000

ESPINOSA, Manuel (?) Argentinian
£1955 $3500 €2854 Er-Rahman (60x60cm-24x24in) 11-May-4 Arroyo, Buenos Aires #34
£3516 $6400 €5133 Paintings (68x48cm-27x19in) s.d.1972 verso acrylic paper pair. 29-Jun-4 Arroyo, Buenos Aires #24/R est:2000

ESPINOZA, Manuel (1937-) Venezuelan
Works on paper
£367 $675 €551 Untitled (57x76cm-22x30in) s. mixed media card exec.1991. 27-Jun-4 Subastas Odalys, Caracas #30/R

ESPLANDIU, Juan (1901-1978) Spanish
£288 $489 €420 Gran Via, Madrid (36x28cm-14x11in) s.d.58. 4-Nov-3 Ansorena, Madrid #396/R

ESPLIN, Clarke (20th C) New Zealander
Works on paper
£275 $509 €402 Street busker (37x24cm-15x9in) s. W/C executed c.1985. 9-Mar-4 Watson's, Christchurch #171 (NZ.D 750)
£311 $557 €454 Black cat in coat of arms (38x28cm-15x11in) s. ink drawing. 11-May-4 Watson's, Christchurch #60/R (NZ.D 900)
£326 $518 €476 Coursan, France (27x35cm-11x14in) s. W/C. 9-Sep-3 Watson's, Christchurch #57 (NZ.D 900)
£358 $569 €523 Village in Burgundy, France (27x36cm-11x14in) s. W/C. 9-Sep-3 Watson's, Christchurch #75 (NZ.D 990)
£709 $1312 €1035 Outdoor cafe scene, Evora Portugal (55x72cm-22x28in) s. W/C. 13-Jul-4 Watson's, Christchurch #10/R (NZ.D 2000)

ESPLIN, Tom (1915-) New Zealander
£1786 $3036 €2608 Venice, Little Canal (34x21cm-13x8in) s. board. 27-Nov-3 International Art Centre, Auckland #121/R est:3500-4500 (NZ.D 4750)
£1974 $3355 €2882 Hill town (49x62cm-19x24in) s. board. 26-Nov-3 Dunbar Sloane, Wellington #115 est:1500-2500 (NZ.D 5250)
£2174 $3457 €3174 Monastry in Lombardy (19x30cm-7x12in) board. 9-Sep-3 Watson's, Christchurch #10 (NZ.D 6000)
£2538 $4314 €3705 Bohinj, Yogoslavia (27x42cm-11x17in) s. i.d.1984 verso board. 26-Nov-3 Dunbar Sloane, Wellington #93/R est:2000-4000 (NZ.D 6750)
£2714 $4913 €3962 Canal (36x46cm-14x18in) s. board. 30-Mar-4 Peter Webb, Auckland #168/R est:2500-5000 (NZ.D 7600)
£2857 $5257 €4171 Andalusian hill village (27x42cm-11x17in) s. board. 25-Mar-4 International Art Centre, Auckland #153/R est:5000-8000 (NZ.D 8000)
£3114 $5574 €4546 Spick Market, Singapore (29x39cm-11x15in) s. board. 11-May-4 Watson's, Christchurch #55/R est:10000-14000 (NZ.D 9000)
£3195 $5432 €4665 East Budleigh village (28x45cm-11x18in) s. board. 27-Nov-3 International Art Centre, Auckland #89/R est:4000-6000 (NZ.D 8500)
£3546 $6560 €5177 Hamlet (35x52cm-14x20in) s. board. 13-Jul-4 Watson's, Christchurch #45/R est:10000-12000 (NZ.D 10000)
£3663 $6777 €5348 Souvenir of Cefalu, Sicily (39x26cm-15x10in) s. board. 9-Mar-4 Watson's, Christchurch #62 est:10000-12000 (NZ.D 10000)
£3806 $6813 €5557 Staithes, England (29x41cm-11x16in) s. board. 11-May-4 Watson's, Christchurch #6/R est:10000-15000 (NZ.D 11000)
£3818 $5995 €5536 Old walls of Italy (34x51cm-13x20in) s. board. 27-Aug-3 Dunbar Sloane, Wellington #99/R est:3000-5000 (NZ.D 10500)

ESPOSITO, Enzo (1946-) Italian
£414 $662 €600 Untitled (26x33cm-10x13in) s.verso painted 1988. 13-Mar-3 Galleria Pace, Milan #20/R
Sculpture
£1141 $2111 €1700 Untitled (90x60x15cm-35x24x6in) s.d.1991 verso painted wood. 11-Mar-4 Galleria Pace, Milan #104/R est:1300-1700
Works on paper
£608 $1070 €900 Untitled (70x80cm-28x31in) s.d.84 verso collage glass mixed media card on canvas prov. 24-May-4 Christie's, Milan #47/R
£830 $1527 €1212 Untitled (72x79cm-28x31in) s.d.1984 verso mixed media collage canvas prov. 8-Jun-4 Germann, Zurich #77/R (S.FR 1900)

ESPOSITO, Gaetano (1858-1911) Italian
£470 $879 €700 Boatyard in Gulf of Naples (51x60cm-20x24in) s. panel. 28-Feb-4 Bolland & Marotz, Bremen #290/R
£2113 $3655 €3000 Choir boy (160x100cm-63x39in) s. 9-Dec-3 Pandolfini, Florence #222/R est:2100-2300
£3333 $6133 €5000 Naples Bay (22x34cm-9x13in) board. 8-Jun-4 Sotheby's, Milan #5/R est:5000-7000

ESPOSITO, Vincenzo (fl.1890-1920) Maltese
Works on paper
£500 $815 €725 Vessel entering Marsamaxett harbour, Valetta, Malta (23x53cm-9x21in) s.i. gouache. 23-Sep-3 Bonhams, Knightsbridge #52/R
£500 $850 €730 Cruisers (10x28cm-4x11in) W/C bodycol pair. 19-Nov-3 Christie's, Kensington #345/R
£520 $936 €759 Valetta harbour, Malta, by moonlight. Fishing boats off Valetta (11x23cm-4x9in) s. W/C gouache htd white pair. 21-Apr-4 Tennants, Leyburn #974
£550 $974 €803 Vessels in the Grand Harbour (11x23cm-4x9in) s. gouache. 27-Apr-4 Bonhams, New Bond Street #80
£683 $1100 €997 Break in the weather (36x48cm-14x19in) s. gouache prov. 20-Aug-3 James Julia, Fairfield #1020/R

ESPOY, Angel (1879-1963) American
£765 $1300 €1117 Cowboy on horseback in western landscape (16x20cm-6x8in) s. masonite. 18-Nov-3 John Moran, Pasadena #118
£852 $1500 €1244 Rider beside a river (41x51cm-16x20in) s. 23-May-4 Bonhams & Butterfields, San Francisco #6611/R
£989 $1800 €1444 Matador at a doorway (30x23cm-12x9in) s. board prov. 15-Jun-4 John Moran, Pasadena #200 est:1500-2000
£1000 $1700 €1460 Crashing waves and rocks (41x51cm-16x20in) s. prov. 18-Nov-3 John Moran, Pasadena #178 est:2000-3000
£1044 $1900 €1524 Coastal scene with sailboat in distance (46x61cm-18x24in) s. prov. 15-Jun-4 John Moran, Pasadena #77a est:2500-3500
£1058 $2000 €1545 Cattle in meadow (25x30cm-10x12in) s. prov. 17-Feb-4 John Moran, Pasadena #108/R est:1500-2000
£1099 $2000 €1605 Seascape (41x51cm-16x20in) s. prov. 15-Jun-4 John Moran, Pasadena #199 est:1000-2000
£1223 $2250 €1786 Two men fishing in the California surf (63x76cm-25x30in) s. prov. 8-Jun-4 Bonhams & Butterfields, San Francisco #4277/R est:3000-5000
£1323 $2500 €1932 Seascape - crashing waves and rocks (61x86cm-24x34in) s. prov. 17-Feb-4 John Moran, Pasadena #59/R est:1500-3500
£1852 $3500 €2704 Seascape (3x36cm-1x14in) s. prov. 17-Feb-4 John Moran, Pasadena #141/R est:2500-3500
£1902 $3500 €2777 California desert landscape (61x76cm-24x30in) s. 8-Jun-4 Auctions by the Bay, Alameda #1105/R

£2312	$4000	€3376	Crashing waves at sunset (61x91cm-24x36in) s. 10-Dec-3 Bonhams & Butterfields, San Francisco #6209/R est:4000-6000
£2312	$4000	€3376	California desert (61x76cm-24x30in) s. i.stretcher i.verso. 10-Dec-3 Bonhams & Butterfields, San Francisco #6336/R est:4000-6000
£2646	$5000	€3863	Landscape - snow capped mountain with flower field (76x91cm-30x36in) s. 17-Feb-4 John Moran, Pasadena #35/R est:5000-7000
£2941	$5000	€4294	Sunset seascape (61x91cm-24x36in) s. prov. 18-Nov-3 John Moran, Pasadena #53a est:3000-4000
£2951	$4750	€4308	Palm Springs desert scene (61x76cm-24x30in) s. 22-Feb-3 Bunte, Elgin #1273 est:2000-3000
£3529	$6000	€5152	Cattle and wild flowers in a landscape (51x61cm-20x24in) s. canvas on canvas. 18-Nov-3 John Moran, Pasadena #53 est:4500-6500
£3804	$7000	€5554	California wildflowers (50x61cm-20x24in) s. 8-Jun-4 Bonhams & Butterfields, San Francisco #4292/R est:5000-7000
£4620	$8500	€6745	California landscape with poppies and oaks (63x76cm-25x30in) s. prov. 8-Jun-4 Bonhams & Butterfields, San Francisco #4293/R est:4000-6000
£4945	$9000	€7220	Eucalyptus and flower field (76x102cm-30x40in) s. prov. 15-Jun-4 John Moran, Pasadena #77 est:10000-15000

ESQUIVEL, Antonio Maria de (1806-1857) Spanish

£1812	$2971	€2500	Female portrait (82x65cm-32x26in) s. 27-May-3 Durán, Madrid #94/R est:2500
£1993	$3268	€2750	Male portrait (82x65cm-32x26in) s. 27-May-3 Durán, Madrid #93/R est:2500
£2641	$4621	€3750	Portrait of gentleman (46x37cm-18x15in) s. 16-Dec-3 Durán, Madrid #156/R est:3750
£5245	$8759	€7500	Portrait of gentleman (83x56cm-33x22in) s.d.1846. 30-Jun-3 Ansorena, Madrid #332/R est:6000

ESQUIVEL, Antonio Maria de (attrib) (1806-1857) Spanish

£290	$521	€420	Portrait of gentleman (21x16cm-8x6in) s.d.1842. 26-Jan-4 Ansorena, Madrid #90/R

ESQUIVEL, Vicente (19th C) Spanish

£4100	$7667	€5986	Abbot's visit (41x55cm-16x22in) s. panel. 24-Feb-4 Bonhams, Knowle #65/R est:3000-5000

ESSCHE, Maurice van (1906-1977) South African

£2353	$4259	€3435	Congolese watercarriers in a forest (40x32cm-16x13in) s. 30-Mar-4 Stephan Welz, Johannesburg #511/R est:12000-16000 (SA.R 28000)
£2642	$4730	€3857	Portrait of a woman in a black dress (62x55cm-24x22in) s. board. 31-May-4 Stephan Welz, Johannesburg #572/R est:10000-15000 (SA.R 32000)
Works on paper			
£252	$456	€368	Near Durbanville (25x46cm-10x18in) s. i.verso crayon W/C. 30-Mar-4 Stephan Welz, Johannesburg #198 est:1800-2400 (SA.R 3000)

ESSELENS, Jacob (1626-1687) Dutch

Works on paper			
£1633	$2922	€2400	Un paysage pres de Arnhem, le long du Rhin (20x26cm-8x10in) i. pen brown ink grey wash prov. 18-Mar-4 Christie's, Paris #320/R est:2000-3000

ESSELENS, Jacob (circle) (1626-1687) Dutch

£12583	$22901	€19000	Woodpickers in the dunes of a beach (41x49cm-16x19in) panel. 16-Jun-4 Dorotheum, Vienna #46/R est:16000-24000

ESSEN, Didrik von (19th C) Swedish

£280	$500	€409	Going to town (25x42cm-10x17in) s. 14-May-4 Skinner, Boston #23/R

ESSEN, Ebba von (20th C) Irish?

£373	$676	€560	Landscape (46x59cm-18x23in) mono. 30-Mar-4 De Veres Art Auctions, Dublin #238

ESSEN, Johannes Cornelis (1854-1936) Dutch

£642	$1200	€963	River landscape with figure on the bank (45x59cm-18x23in) s. 25-Jul-4 Bonhams & Butterfields, San Francisco #6039/R
Works on paper			
£700	$1190	€1022	Farmyard (34x51cm-13x20in) s. W/C. 4-Nov-3 Bonhams, New Bond Street #2/R

ESSENHIGH, Inka (1969-) American

£5028	$9000	€7341	Untitled, study for thieves (65x57cm-26x22in) enamel paper prov. 12-May-4 Christie's, Rockefeller NY #347/R est:10000-15000
£23952	$40000	€34970	Bloodsuckers (122x122cm-48x48in) s.i.d.1999 verso oil enamel prov. 13-Nov-3 Sotheby's, New York #475/R est:40000-60000

ESSER, Elgar (1967-) German

Photographs			
£5500	$9185	€8030	Choule, Frankreich (103x144cm-41x57in) c-print on Diasec edition 3 of 4. 22-Oct-3 Christie's, London #112/R est:2500-3500
£5667	$10427	€8500	Foci del Po, Italy (90x128cm-35x50in) C-print diasec face exec 1998 edn of 5. 8-Jun-4 Sotheby's, Amsterdam #157/R est:6000-8000
£5988	$10000	€8742	Saint Briare 1999 Frankreich (124x162cm-49x64in) c-print executed 1999 prov. 14-Nov-3 Phillips, New York #245/R est:10000-15000
£10000	$18400	€15000	Morbihan, France (90x128cm-35x50in) C-print on diasec face exec 1998 edn of 5 prov. 8-Jun-4 Sotheby's, Amsterdam #158/R est:6000-8000
£10778	$18000	€15736	Chartressac I and II, France (124x162cm-49x64in) d.1997 num.5/5 chromogenic col print diasec two prov.lit. 17-Oct-3 Phillips, New York #1/R est:18000-22000
£16760	$30000	€24470	Chaptoceaux Frankreich 2000 (123x159cm-48x63in) cibachrome print Diasec face exec 2000 1 edn 5 prov. 13-May-4 Sotheby's, New York #379/R est:8000-12000
£19553	$35000	€28547	Blois Frankreich (189x236cm-74x93in) col coupler print edition 1 of 5 prov.exhib.lit. 12-May-4 Christie's, Rockefeller NY #444/R est:10000-15000

ESSEX, Richard Hamilton (1802-1855) British

£2800	$5040	€4088	Old London Bridge (68x116cm-27x46in) 21-Jan-4 Sotheby's, Olympia #94/R est:3000-5000

ESSEX, William (1784-1869) British

Miniatures			
£1000	$1840	€1460	Anne Lucy Poulett, Lady Nugent (14cm-6in) s.i. rectangular. 24-Jun-4 Bonhams, New Bond Street #27/R est:1000-1500

ESSFELD, Alexander (20th C) German

£333	$603	€500	Sailing boats in harbour (70x90cm-28x35in) s. 1-Apr-4 Van Ham, Cologne #1363

ESSIG, George E (1838-1926) American

Works on paper			
£318	$550	€464	Seascape with sailboats (41x69cm-16x27in) s. W/C. 10-Dec-3 Alderfer's, Hatfield #460
£324	$600	€473	Ship at sea (33x66cm-13x26in) gouache cardboard. 13-Mar-4 DeFina, Austinburg #798/R
£409	$650	€597	Fishing boats with sails raised in tree-lined cove on sunny day (38x64cm-15x25in) s. W/C. 10-Sep-3 Alderfer's, Hatfield #265
£419	$700	€612	Steamboat with buoy (33x58cm-13x23in) s. W/C. 20-Jun-3 Freeman, Philadelphia #29/R
£438	$700	€639	Sunset coastal landscape with sailboats (28x48cm-11x19in) s. W/C. 20-Sep-3 Pook & Pook, Downington #477/R
£503	$800	€734	Boat at full sail on choppy seas with other sailboats in distance (38x64cm-15x25in) s. W/C. 10-Sep-3 Alderfer's, Hatfield #264/R
£625	$1000	€913	Sunset coastal landscape with sailboat (28x48cm-11x19in) s. W/C. 20-Sep-3 Pook & Pook, Downington #478/R
£670	$1200	€1126	Coastal scene (30x61cm-12x24in) s. W/C. 20-Mar-4 Pook & Pook, Downington #114/R
£699	$1300	€1021	Portrait of fishing boats (38x66cm-15x26in) s. W/C. 3-Mar-4 Alderfer's, Hatfield #298 est:700-900
£726	$1300	€1219	Bay scene (28x61cm-11x24in) s. W/C. 20-Mar-4 Pook & Pook, Downington #113/R

ESTALELLA PUJOLA, Ramon (1895-1986) Spanish

£1908	$3453	€2900	Still life of flowers (59x65cm-23x26in) s. 14-Apr-4 Ansorena, Madrid #79/R est:2300

ESTALELLA, Ramon (20th C) Spanish

£319	$564	€475	Landscape (61x50cm-24x20in) s. board. 27-Apr-4 Durán, Madrid #128/R
£915	$1602	€1300	Still life (89x116cm-35x46in) s. s.d.1969 verso. 16-Dec-3 Durán, Madrid #117/R

ESTE, Gaudi (1947-) Venezuelan

£939	$1530	€1371	Figures (92x65cm-36x26in) s. painted 1973. 28-Sep-3 Subastas Odalys, Caracas #1/R
Sculpture			
£2060	$3750	€3090	Untitled (30x28x9cm-12x11x4in) s. wood exec.1984. 21-Jun-4 Subastas Odalys, Caracas #108/R
£2650	$4185	€3869	Untitled (73x97x37cm-29x38x15in) s.verso bronze. 27-Apr-3 Subastas Odalys, Caracas #60

ESTELLES HERRERO, Jose (1930-) Spanish

Works on paper			
£328	$590	€475	Landscape covered in snow (72x101cm-28x40in) s.d.88 W/C. 26-Jan-4 Durán, Madrid #617/R

ESTERL, Felix (1904-1941) German

£6993	$11888	€10000	Larkspur and fruit (63x46cm-25x18in) prov. 25-Nov-3 Hassfurther, Vienna #32/R est:5000-7000

ESTES, Richard (1932-) American

£17284	$28000	€25062	Mt. Desert VII (51x41cm-20x16in) s.d.96 oil on wood prov. 8-Aug-3 Barridorf, Portland #240/R est:25000-35000
£26816	$48000	€39151	Sandwiches - Hamburgers - Frankfurters (51x76cm-20x30in) s.i. acrylic board painted 1970 prov.lit. 12-May-4 Christie's, Rockefeller NY #166/R est:35000-45000
£52000	$95680	€75920	Staten island ferry with view of east river (45x40cm-18x16in) s.d.93 prov. 24-Jun-4 Sotheby's, London #273/R est:35000-45000
£206704	$370000	€301788	Baby doll lounge (92x152cm-36x60in) init.d.78 prov.exhib.lit. 11-May-4 Christie's, Rockefeller NY #65/R est:350000-450000
£279330	$500000	€407822	34th Street - Manhattan looking east (231x231cm-91x91in) s.d.82 prov.exhib.lit. 12-May-4 Sotheby's, New York #45/R est:400000-600000
Prints			
£1912	$3250	€2792	Arch saint-Louis (37x61cm-15x24in) s. col screenprint. 31-Oct-3 Sotheby's, New York #534/R
£5978	$11000	€8728	D-train (91x183cm-36x72in) col silkscreen edition of 125 prov. 10-Jun-4 Phillips, New York #556/R est:15000-20000
£7182	$13000	€10486	Holland Hotel (118x193cm-46x76in) s.num.34/100 col silkscreen. 19-Apr-4 Bonhams & Butterfields, San Francisco #252/R est:10000-15000
Works on paper			
£1618	$2800	€2362	Wake. Mount Desert (14x9cm-6x4in) s.i.d.96 gouache two prov. 10-Dec-3 Phillips, New York #637/R est:2000-3000
£28188	$50456	€42000	Airstream (35x53cm-14x21in) s. gouache exec.1974 prov.lit. 27-May-4 Sotheby's, Paris #259/R est:20000-30000

ESTEVAN, Hermengildo (1851-1945) Spanish

£922	$1540	€1300	Landscape (37x25cm-15x10in) s.i. palette. 20-Oct-3 Durán, Madrid #166/R
£1206	$2013	€1700	Landscape (15x23cm-6x9in) s. board. 20-Oct-3 Durán, Madrid #164/R est:500

£2553	$4136	€3600	Figure in red (79x57cm-31x22in) s. 20-May-3 Ansorena, Madrid #68/R est:3600

ESTEVE, Agustin (attrib) (1753-1809) Spanish

£1342	$2470	€2000	Portrait d'homme a la redingote noire (68x56cm-27x22in) 26-Mar-4 Piasa, Paris #50 est:1800-2000

ESTEVE, Maurice (1904-2001) French

£3472	$5486	€5000	Fields of colour (25x34cm-10x13in) mono. i.d.61 verso lit. 19-Sep-3 Schloss Ahlden, Ahlden #1680/R est:5800
£4698	$8738	€7000	Table au vase de fleurs (66x50cm-26x20in) s. prov. 3-Mar-4 Tajan, Paris #108/R est:8000-12000
£6769	$12658	€9883	Composition (39x22cm-15x9in) s.d.82 W/C. 25-Feb-4 Kunsthallen, Copenhagen #76/R est:75000 (D.KR 75000)
£14000	$25760	€20440	Goudes (27x35cm-11x14in) s.d.54 prov.lit. 24-Jun-4 Sotheby's, London #186/R est:15000-20000
£15000	$27600	€21900	Pilotis (27x41cm-11x16in) s.d.57 s.i.d.verso prov.exhib.lit. 24-Jun-4 Sotheby's, London #169/R est:10000-15000
£17372	$29532	€25363	Composition (24x14cm-9x6in) s. d.1952 verso prov. 5-Nov-3 AB Stockholms Auktionsverk #1088/R est:60000-80000 (S.KR 230000)
£22000	$40040	€33000	Scaphandriers (50x65cm-20x26in) s.d.47 s.i.d. verso prov.exhib.lit. 30-Jun-4 Calmels Cohen, Paris #62/R est:35000-40000
£30000	$54600	€43800	Favourite (46x32cm-18x13in) s.d.54 s.i.d.54 verso prov.lit. 6-Feb-4 Sotheby's, London #159/R est:20000-30000
£30556	$51028	€44000	Bourdin (38x55cm-15x22in) s.d.64 s.i.d.verso prov.lit. 21-Oct-3 Christie's, Paris #200/R est:30000-40000
£35000	$63700	€51100	Forge (33x55cm-13x22in) s. s.i.d.53 verso prov.lit. 5-Feb-4 Christie's, London #103/R est:15000-20000
£43357	$72406	€62000	Sabotier (65x54cm-26x21in) s.d.1949 s.i.d.verso prov.exhib.lit. 29-Jun-3 Versailles Encheres #60a/R est:75000
Works on paper			
£2028	$3387	€2900	Peintre (31x38cm-12x15in) s.d.1944 chl prov. 29-Jun-3 Versailles Encheres #49/R
£3147	$5255	€4500	Sans titre (31x24cm-12x9in) s.d.1982 chl crayon. 11-Oct-3 Cornette de St.Cyr, Paris #63/R est:4500-5000
£3610	$6643	€5271	Composition (49x40cm-19x16in) s.d.83 chl pastel. 29-Mar-4 Rasmussen, Copenhagen #137/R est:80000 (D.KR 40000)
£4305	$7319	€6285	Composition (18x13cm-7x5in) s. W/C prov. 5-Nov-3 AB Stockholms Auktionsverk #1177/R est:18000-20000 (S.KR 57000)
£4513	$8303	€6589	Composition (46x36cm-18x14in) s.d.89 prov. 29-Mar-4 Rasmussen, Copenhagen #123/R est:60000-80000 (D.KR 50000)
£5000	$9100	€7300	108-D (32x43cm-13x17in) s. chl col crayon prov.exhib. 6-Feb-4 Sotheby's, London #161/R est:5000-7000
£7040	$12953	€10278	Composition (49x61cm-19x24in) s.d.70 crayon W/C prov. 29-Mar-4 Rasmussen, Copenhagen #110/R est:80000 (D.KR 78000)
£7333	$13493	€11000	Composition No 1988 (48x53cm-19x21in) s.d.77 pastel W/C prov.exhib. 8-Jun-4 Artcurial Briest, Paris #202/R est:6000-8000
£8108	$14271	€12000	Composition blue, orange Juan et verge (50x65cm-20x26in) s. W/C chl prov. 18-May-4 Tajan, Paris #37/R est:12000-15000
£11458	$18104	€16500	Composition 733.A (49x40cm-19x16in) s.d.1961 W/C prov. 27-Apr-3 Versailles Encheres #38
£15278	$25514	€22000	Composition (62x51cm-24x20in) s.d.70 W/C pencil prov. 21-Oct-3 Christie's, Paris #199/R est:10000-12000
£17333	$31894	€26000	Composition No 1012 (62x49cm-24x19in) s.d.69 W/C prov.exhib. 8-Jun-4 Artcurial Briest, Paris #201/R est:8000-12000
£18000	$32760	€26280	Untitled (37x50cm-15x20in) s.d.60 i.verso W/C exec.1960. 5-Feb-4 Christie's, London #102/R est:12000-16000
£20805	$37242	€31000	Untitled (62x50cm-24x20in) s.d.70 W/C prov.exhib. 26-May-4 Christie's, Paris #66/R est:8000-12000

ESTEVEZ, Antonio (1910-1983) American

£333	$600	€486	Lady (51x41cm-20x16in) panel. 24-Apr-4 Slotin Folk Art, Buford #651/R

ESTLER, Georg Gustav (1860-1954) German

£625	$987	€900	River landscape in early morning in Erbtal (40x60cm-16x24in) s. 5-Sep-3 Wendl, Rudolstadt #3342/R
£1056	$1827	€1500	Spreewald landscape with boat in water (97x73cm-38x29in) s. i. verso. 12-Dec-3 Altus, Berlin #581/R est:1800

ESTRADA, Adolfo (1927-) Spanish?

£671	$1255	€1000	French woman (41x33cm-16x13in) s. 24-Feb-4 Durán, Madrid #18/R

ESTRADA, Angel (1933-) Spanish

£303	$530	€430	Still life with apples and cheese (22x27cm-9x11in) s.d.1973. 16-Dec-3 Segre, Madrid #264/R

ESTRADA, Juan de (1717-1792) Spanish

£403	$713	€600	Virgin (30x21cm-12x8in) i.d.1755 verso. 27-Apr-4 Durán, Madrid #40/R

ESTRADA, Mari Pepa (1915-) Spanish

£352	$563	€500	Mother, what does the coloured man want ? (38x46cm-15x18in) s.d.1984 prov. 16-Sep-3 Segre, Madrid #264/R

ESTRUGA, Oscar (1933-) Spanish

£517	$864	€750	I want to teach (46x55cm-18x22in) s. 17-Nov-3 Durán, Madrid #97/R
£638	$1192	€950	Landscape after Velazquez (65x81cm-26x32in) s. 24-Feb-4 Durán, Madrid #169/R

ESTVAD, Leo (1902-) Danish

£672	$1210	€981	Coastal landscape from Bornholm (81x102cm-32x40in) s,. 24-Apr-4 Rasmussen, Havnen #4028 (D.KR 7500)

ESVAL, Aasmund (1889-1971) Norwegian

£417	$722	€609	Female nude (80x65cm-31x26in) s. 13-Dec-3 Blomqvist, Lysaker #1085 (N.KR 4800)

ETCHEVERRY, Denis (1867-1950) French

£318	$579	€480	Vase de roses (35x27cm-14x11in) s. 19-Jun-4 Binoche, Orleans #23
£490	$896	€710	Vase de fleurs roses et mauves (41x33cm-16x13in) s. 31-Jan-4 Gerard, Besancon #43
£493	$908	€750	Modele des Beaux-Arts (80x64cm-31x25in) s.d.1893. 25-Jun-4 Millon & Associes, Paris #54
£524	$959	€760	Vase de pensees (35x27cm-14x11in) s. 31-Jan-4 Gerard, Besancon #39
£697	$1275	€1010	Vase de fleurs blanches, roses et mauves (35x27cm-14x11in) s. 31-Jan-4 Gerard, Besancon #40
£724	$1325	€1050	Vase de rhododendrons (24x19cm-9x7in) s. 31-Jan-4 Gerard, Besancon #42
£828	$1514	€1200	Vase de pensees (35x27cm-14x11in) s. 31-Jan-4 Gerard, Besancon #41
£1093	$1989	€1650	Plage des Basques a Biarritz (31cm-12in) s. i.verso panel oval. 19-Jun-4 Binoche, Orleans #22
£1310	$2398	€1900	Vase de roses blanches (41x33cm-16x13in) s. 31-Jan-4 Gerard, Besancon #44
£1600	$2944	€2400	Femme assise au bouquet de roses (110x100cm-43x39in) s.d.1925 prov.exhib.lit. 9-Jun-4 Beaussant & Lefèvre, Paris #150/R est:2000-2500
£2414	$4417	€3500	Roses blanches dans un vase de porcelaine blanche et or (24x19cm-9x7in) s. 31-Jan-4 Gerard, Besancon #45
£2649	$4848	€4000	Nature morte de la medecine (54x73cm-21x29in) s.d.1886. 9-Apr-4 Bailly Pommery, Paris #72/R est:4000-6000

ETERNOD, Marcel Victor (1891-1971) Swiss

£405	$697	€591	Seascape (46x55cm-18x22in) s. 8-Dec-3 Philippe Schuler, Zurich #3326 (S.FR 900)
£705	$1198	€1029	Souvenir du Maroc (26x40cm-10x16in) s. i.d.1922 verso. 5-Nov-3 Dobiaschofsky, Bern #530/R (S.FR 1600)

ETEROVICH, Anthony W (1916-) American

£239	$380	€349	Creators (76x119cm-30x47in) s. 12-Sep-3 Aspire, Cleveland #90

ETEVE, Felix Raoul (20th C) French

£380	$608	€555	Notre Dame (45x53cm-18x21in) s. 21-Sep-3 Lots Road Auctions, London #347

ETEX, Antoine (1808-1888) French

Sculpture			
£2759	$4579	€4000	Olympia (18x40cm-7x16in) s.i. gilt bronze. 2-Oct-3 Sotheby's, Paris #154/R est:4500-7500

ETHOFER, Theodor J (1849-1915) Austrian

£1127	$1870	€1600	Flower girl (54x29cm-21x11in) s. panel. 12-Jun-3 Dorotheum, Graz #7/R est:1100
£1549	$2572	€2200	Girl in traditional costume knitting (55x32cm-22x13in) s. panel. 12-Jun-3 Dorotheum, Graz #5/R est:1500
£1549	$2572	€2200	Cairo bazar (50x31cm-20x12in) s. panel. 12-Jun-3 Dorotheum, Graz #6/R est:1500
£6000	$10920	€8760	Courtyard in the Alhambra, Granada (77x42cm-30x17in) s.i. 16-Jun-4 Christie's, Kensington #284/R est:6000-8000

ETIENNE, Maxen (20th C) Haitian

£219	$400	€320	Appel au loa (61x71cm-24x28in) s.i. board. 3-Jun-4 Christie's, Rockefeller NY #1123/R
£874	$1600	€1276	Cows and peasant (61x71cm-24x28in) s. board. 3-Jun-4 Christie's, Rockefeller NY #1120/R est:500-700

ETIENNE, W (19th C) ?

£9302	$16000	€13581	Harem scene (107x81cm-42x32in) s.i. 3-Dec-3 Doyle, New York #110/R est:8000-12000
£10000	$18200	€14600	La couture orientaliste (107x80cm-42x31in) s.i. 15-Jun-4 Sotheby's, London #132/R est:10000-15000

ETIENNE-MARTIN (1913-1995) French

Sculpture			
£3356	$6007	€5000	Claude a long cou (34cm-13in) s. bronze. 25-May-4 Chambelland & Giafferi, Paris #57/R est:5000-6000
£10564	$18275	€15000	Femme (120cm-47in) wood prov.exhib. 9-Dec-3 Arcurial Briest, Paris #400/R est:18000-20000

ETKIN, Susan (1955-) American

Works on paper			
£399	$718	€583	Dry-clean Series No.1 (57x76cm-22x30in) s.i.d.1990 mixed media. 26-Apr-4 Bukowskis, Stockholm #517/R (S.KR 5500)

ETNIER, Stephen (1903-1984) American

£1955	$3500	€2854	Bell bouy (38x48cm-15x19in) board. 8-Jan-4 James Julia, Fairfield #19/R est:2000-4000
£2945	$4800	€4300	Northwester, Old Cove, S Harpswell ME (79x28cm-31x11in) s. 26-Sep-3 York Town, York #909 est:4800
£3039	$5500	€4437	Fishing shacks in winter (41x61cm-16x24in) s. masonite prov. 16-Apr-4 James Julia, Fairfield #559/R est:2500-4000
£3416	$5500	€4987	Clothes line (30x51cm-12x20in) s. 20-Aug-3 James Julia, Fairfield #1356/R est:7000-9000
£3580	$5800	€5191	Winter Casco Bay (53x102cm-21x40in) s. 8-Aug-3 Barridorf, Portland #213/R est:6000-9000
£3704	$6000	€5371	Boatyard (61x79cm-24x31in) s. board prov.exhib. 8-Aug-3 Barridorf, Portland #211/R est:6000-9000

£3827	$6200	€5549	Race day, Bermuda (51x41cm-20x16in) s.i. s.verso masonite prov. 8-Aug-3 Barridorf, Portland #364/R est:4000-6000
£4286	$7500	€6258	On the terrace (40x61cm-16x24in) s.d.48. 19-Dec-3 Sotheby's, New York #1057/R est:2500-3500
£4491	$7500	€6557	Vieux carre (60x82cm-24x32in) s.d.46 masonite prov.exhib.lit. 7-Oct-3 Sotheby's, New York #217 est:4000-6000
£4630	$7500	€6714	Stiff breeze, Nassau (56x91cm-22x36in) 8-Aug-3 Barridorf, Portland #185/R est:6000-9000
£4938	$8000	€7160	From the New Windsor Hotel, Bermuda (76x71cm-30x28in) s. 8-Aug-3 Barridorf, Portland #171/R est:8000-12000
£9259	$15000	€13426	Whistle and gong (61x91cm-24x36in) s. masonite. 8-Aug-3 Barridorf, Portland #172/R est:10000-15000
£9259	$15000	€13426	On Winnegance Bay (51x91cm-20x36in) s. s.i.verso prov. 8-Aug-3 Barridorf, Portland #176/R est:12000-18000
£9259	$15000	€13426	Inside Haskells (56x91cm-22x36in) s. masonite. 8-Aug-3 Barridorf, Portland #196/R est:9000-12000
£18519	$30000	€26853	Boulder (56x91cm-22x36in) s.i.verso prov.exhib. 8-Aug-3 Barridorf, Portland #182/R est:30000-50000
Works on paper			
£3580	$5800	€5191	Harbour, St. Croix (57x79cm-22x31in) s.i. W/C prov.exhib. 8-Aug-3 Barridorf, Portland #212/R est:4000-6000

ETROG, Sorel (1933-) Canadian/Rumanian

Sculpture			
£884	$1643	€1291	Bashota (34cm-13in) s.num.2/10 bronze. 2-Mar-4 Ritchie, Toronto #202a/R est:2000-3000 (C.D 2200)
£2252	$3829	€3288	Episode (53cm-21in) s. num.1/7 bronze prov.exhib. 18-Nov-3 Sotheby's, Toronto #75/R est:4000-6000 (C.D 5000)
£2941	$5000	€4294	Sabal (53x36cm-21x14in) s.d.1967 bronze prov. 9-Nov-3 Wright, Chicago #372 est:5000-7000
£4400	$8052	€6424	Don Giovanni (70cm-28in) s. num.2/7 bronze prov. 1-Jun-4 Joyner Waddington, Toronto #57/R est:6000-8000 (C.D 11000)
£9412	$16000	€13742	Queen. s.num.7 bronze prov. 9-Nov-3 Wright, Chicago #374 est:10000-15000
Works on paper			
£241	$448	€352	Figure composition (47x47cm-19x19in) s. pastel gouache. 2-Mar-4 Ritchie, Toronto #203/R (C.D 600)
£400	$732	€584	Study figure no.2 (42x56cm-17x22in) s. pastel prov. 1-Jun-4 Joyner Waddington, Toronto #464 (C.D 1000)

ETTING, Emlen (1905-1992) American

£272	$500	€397	Male nude (58x43cm-23x17in) paper. 25-Jun-4 Freeman, Philadelphia #147/R
£333	$600	€486	Icarus (53x64cm-21x25in) s.i.d.1936 verso. 23-Jan-4 Freeman, Philadelphia #187/R
£419	$700	€612	Portrait of a gentleman (48x38cm-19x15in) s.i.stretcher. 20-Jun-3 Freeman, Philadelphia #118/R
£578	$1000	€844	Portrait of a standing man (37x24cm-15x9in) s. board prov. 11-Dec-3 Sotheby's, New York #221/R est:1200-1800
£806	$1500	€1177	Still life with exotic flowers (82x61cm-32x24in) s. 3-Mar-4 Christie's, Rockefeller NY #57/R est:2000-3000
Works on paper			
£190	$350	€277	Wine glass (33x41cm-13x16in) s. W/C. 25-Jun-4 Freeman, Philadelphia #18/R

ETTINGER, Churchill (1903-) American

£6145	$11000	€8972	Winter hunt (64x51cm-25x20in) s. masonite prov. 6-May-4 Shannon's, Milford #207/R est:9000-12000
£9581	$16000	€13988	Southern style (51x61cm-20x24in) s. canvasboard prov. 23-Oct-3 Shannon's, Milford #213/R est:3000-5000

ETTINGSHAUSEN, Andreas Ritter von (1796-1878) Austrian

Photographs			
£120000	$211200	€175200	Section of clematis. i.d.1840 daguerrotype prov.exhib.lit. 19-May-4 Christie's, London #7/R est:90000-120000

ETTY, William (1787-1849) British

£380	$707	€555	Nymph and young faun dancing (13x8cm-5x3in) i.verso panel prov. 4-Mar-4 Christie's, Kensington #620
£850	$1530	€1241	Study of a female nude (62x44cm-24x17in) oil paper on board. 21-Jan-4 Sotheby's, Olympia #271/R est:600-800
£1657	$3000	€2419	Friends (76x61cm-30x24in) 30-Mar-4 Christie's, Rockefeller NY #58/R est:6000-8000
£5000	$8500	€7300	Andromeda chained to the rocks (89x57cm-35x22in) 27-Nov-3 Sotheby's, London #204/R est:6000-8000
£5500	$10175	€8030	Toilet of Venus (60x50cm-24x20in) 9-Mar-4 Bonhams, Knightsbridge #202a/R est:5000-7000
£22346	$40000	€32625	Day dreams (51x77cm-20x30in) board prov. 27-May-4 Sotheby's, New York #285/R est:30000-40000
Works on paper			
£473	$832	€700	Figure of a female nude (37x25cm-15x10in) i. chl htd white. 19-May-4 James Adam, Dublin #27

ETTY, William (attrib) (1787-1849) British

£350	$581	€511	Female nude (22cm-9in circular) circular. 5-Oct-3 Lots Road Auctions, London #341
£350	$585	€511	Young lady reading (30x24cm-12x9in) board oval. 13-Nov-3 Christie's, Kensington #243
£1400	$2590	€2044	Aphrodite (59x49cm-23x19in) prov. 11-Feb-4 Cheffins, Cambridge #442/R est:300-400

ETTY, William (studio) (1787-1849) British

£5500	$9130	€8030	Bacchante reclining on a panther's skin (61x74cm-24x29in) 30-Sep-3 Sotheby's, London #78/R est:3000-4000

ETUNGAT, Abraham (1911-) ?

Sculpture			
£1351	$2297	€1972	Crouching Inuit hunter with harpoon (43cm-17in) mottled green soapstone hide. 3-Nov-3 Waddingtons, Toronto #96/R est:2500-3500 (C.D 3000)

EUBANK, Ann Bell (20th C) American

£223	$400	€326	Floral still life (64x51cm-25x20in) s.d.67. 7-May-4 Sloans & Kenyon, Bethesda #1203/R

EUBANKS, Tony (1939-) American

£3851	$6200	€5584	Warriors of the dog society (76x86cm-30x34in) 22-Aug-3 Altermann Galleries, Santa Fe #6
£5587	$10000	€8157	24 degrees in Taos (71x127cm-28x50in) 15-May-4 Altermann Galleries, Santa Fe #15/R

EUGEN (1865-1947) Swedish

£1807	$3126	€2638	Still life of vegetables (50x65cm-20x26in) s.i.d.1888. 15-Dec-3 Lilla Bukowskis, Stockholm #218 est:15000-20000 (S.KR 23000)
£2154	$3705	€3145	Mountain landscape, St Remy (48x61cm-19x24in) s.d.1936 panel exhib. 2-Dec-3 Bukowskis, Stockholm #186/R est:25000-30000 (S.KR 28000)
£2385	$4102	€3482	Landscape from Osterlen, Kivik (51x71cm-20x28in) mono.d.1931 panel. 2-Dec-3 Bukowskis, Stockholm #92/R est:30000-40000 (S.KR 31000)
£3178	$5689	€4640	Rolling landscape (51x61cm-20x24in) s. 25-May-4 Bukowskis, Stockholm #98/R est:30000-40000 (S.KR 43000)
£4462	$7674	€6515	Study for Hoare frost (29x47cm-11x19in) s.d.1908 verso panel lit. 3-Dec-3 AB Stockholms Auktionsverk #2270/R est:60000-70000 (S.KR 58000)
£8846	$15215	€12915	The bay, Waldemarsudde (48x57cm-19x22in) s.d.1945 panel. 3-Dec-3 AB Stockholms Auktionsverk #2239/R est:60000-70000 (S.KR 115000)
Works on paper			
£671	$1234	€1007	The express (30x37cm-12x15in) s. d.34 verso chk mixed media. 14-Jun-4 Lilla Bukowskis, Stockholm #297 (S.KR 9200)
£826	$1486	€1206	View of Tyreso Palace (34x41cm-13x16in) s. 26-Jan-4 Lilla Bukowskis, Stockholm #364 (S.KR 11000)
£1822	$3353	€2733	Landscape with clouds (28x44cm-11x17in) mono.d.1930 W/C. 14-Jun-4 Lilla Bukowskis, Stockholm #109 est:8000-10000 (S.KR 25000)

EUGEN (attrib) (1865-1947) Swedish

£605	$1083	€883	Sailing boat in moonlight (80x106cm-31x42in) 12-Jan-4 Rasmussen, Vejle #402 (D.KR 6400)

EULENBURG, Olga (1848-?) German

Works on paper			
£1467	$2669	€2200	Lady sitting on the beach (31x42cm-12x17in) s. pastel W/C lit. 3-Jul-4 Badum, Bamberg #33/R est:1900

EULER, Carl (1815-?) German

£533	$976	€800	Farm with cattle on an alpine meadow (46x62cm-18x24in) s.d.1865 canvas on canvas. 5-Jun-4 Arnold, Frankfurt #569/R

EULER, Emilie (1796-1850) German

Works on paper			
£699	$1189	€1000	Five peaches (19x22cm-7x9in) W/C gouache. 20-Nov-3 Van Ham, Cologne #1562/R

EULER, H (?) ?

£5208	$8490	€7500	Country garden (100x65cm-39x26in) s. 25-Sep-3 Neumeister, Munich #2755 est:300

EUN NIM RO (1946-) Korean

Works on paper			
£667	$1227	€1000	Composition (100x70cm-39x28in) s.d. gouache W/C chk. 11-Jun-4 Hauswedell & Nolte, Hamburg #1503/R

EURICH, Richard (1903-1992) British

£700	$1295	€1022	River Wharfe, Ilkley (18x28cm-7x11in) s.d.88 board prov. 11-Feb-4 Sotheby's, Olympia #147/R
£1200	$2004	€1752	Rainy day, Isle of Wight (41x51cm-16x20in) s.d.65 board prov. 21-Oct-3 Bonhams, Knightsbridge #15/R est:1000-1500
£1500	$2730	€2190	New Forest, passing shower (20x34cm-8x13in) s.d.3.12.73 board prov.exhib. 1-Jul-4 Christie's, Kensington #339/R est:700-1000
£1600	$2816	€2336	Dark sea with storm clouds (23x29cm-9x11in) s. board exhib. 18-May-4 Woolley & Wallis, Salisbury #14/R est:800-1200
£1800	$3330	€2628	Toys with sextant (51x61cm-20x24in) s.d.37 s.i.stretcher. 11-Feb-4 Sotheby's, Olympia #163/R est:1500-2000
£4800	$8016	€7008	Head of a girl (22x18cm-9x7in) s.indis.d.193 board exhib. 16-Oct-3 Christie's, Kensington #581/R est:700-1000
£9000	$15030	€13140	Girl by a window (41x31cm-16x12in) s.d.1930 exhib. 16-Oct-3 Christie's, Kensington #577/R est:3000-5000
£9500	$17575	€13870	Harbour scene, Penzance (37x45cm-15x18in) s. panel. 11-Feb-4 Sotheby's, Olympia #164/R est:2000-3000
£11000	$20130	€16060	Northumbrian sword dance (30x61cm-12x24in) s.d.73 s.i.d.verso board prov. 4-Jun-4 Christie's, London #1/R est:4000-6000

EUROPEAN SCHOOL, 16th C

Sculpture			
£15000	$27600	€21900	Seated cat with rat in its mouth (18cm-7in) black brown pat bronze red marble plinth lit. 10-Jun-4 Christie's, London #19/R est:12000-18000

EUROPEAN SCHOOL, 17th C

£16107	$29638	€24000	Prince dressed for hunting (125x102cm-49x40in) 25-Mar-4 Karlheinz Kaupp, Staufen #2264/R est:2500

EUROPEAN SCHOOL, 17th/18th C
£4000 $7400 €6000 Figures and sheep under large trees by a stream (104x145cm-41x57in) 14-Jul-4 American Auctioneer #490268/R est:2000-3000

EUROPEAN SCHOOL, 18th/19th C
£6294 $10699 €9000 Risen Christ with Mary Magdalen (65x49cm-26x19in) 20-Nov-3 Weidler, Nurnberg #327/R est:400
Sculpture
£16000 $28800 €23360 Figure of Mercury (73cm-29in) gilding dark pat bronze marble base lit. 21-Apr-4 Sotheby's, London #39/R est:3000-5000
£56291 $102450 €85000 Venus (170cm-67in) carved marble. 17-Jun-4 Hamilton Osborne King, Dublin #378/R est:30000-50000

EUROPEAN SCHOOL, 19th C
£4747 $7500 €6931 St. Agnes, seated female with nimbus, crown and flowers, lamb on her lap (76x61cm-30x24in) 6-Sep-3 Brunk, Ashville #879
£5435 $10000 €7935 Tonalist scene of Venice at night with carnival lights (91x76cm-36x30in) 11-Jun-4 David Rago, Lambertville #307/R est:500-800
£6122 $11265 €9183 Flora (118x84cm-46x33in) oval. 14-Jun-4 Lilla Bukowskis, Stockholm #896 est:10000-12000 (S.KR 84000)
£6643 $11294 €9500 Southern coast (32x43cm-13x17in) 22-Nov-3 Arnold, Frankfurt #675/R est:1000
£10703 $17232 €15626 Mirror, mirror. (130x135cm-51x53in) indis.sig. 25-Aug-3 Lilla Bukowskis, Stockholm #577 est:25000-30000 (S.KR 140000)
£19333 $35573 €29000 Under the blooming trees (114x91cm-45x36in) 10-Jun-4 Christie's, Rome #134/R est:23000-28000

EUROPEAN SCHOOL, 20th C
£6452 $12000 €9420 Fishing boats at rest (33x46cm-13x18in) s.d.1918 board. 3-Mar-4 Alderfer's, Hatfield #320 est:700-900
Sculpture
£9722 $16042 €14000 Lady with dogs. ivory bronze marble base ec.1920. 2-Jul-3 Ansorena, Madrid #1212/R est:14000

EUSTACE, A W (1820-1907) Australian
£992 $1806 €1448 Droving (23x30cm-9x12in) s. board prov. 16-Jun-4 Deutscher-Menzies, Melbourne #557/R est:800-1500 (A.D 2600)

EUSTACHE, Robert (19th C) French
£2857 $5114 €4200 Felouques sur le Nil a Boulac (45x65cm-18x26in) s.i. 21-Mar-4 St-Germain-en-Laye Encheres #32/R est:3200-3500

EUSTON, Jacob Howard (1892-1965) American
£587 $1050 €857 Clearing up Indiana dunes (61x8cm-24x3in) s. 8-Jan-4 James Julia, Fairfield #1019/R

EVANGELINE, Margaret Wirstrom (20th C) American
£302 $550 €441 Southern Crossn (102x102cm-40x40in) os.i.verso board. 7-Feb-4 Neal Auction Company, New Orleans #800

EVANS OF ETON, William (1798-1877) British
Works on paper
£500 $835 €730 On the Brocas, Eton (25x36cm-10x14in) s.d.1845 W/C. 14-Oct-3 Bonhams, Knightsbridge #56/R
£550 $1007 €803 Eton College from Flexon's field (29x38cm-11x15in) i.d.1824 pencil prov. 3-Jun-4 Christie's, London #108/R

EVANS, Bernard (1848-1922) British
Works on paper
£250 $450 €365 Figure ploughing in a rural landscape (36x53cm-14x21in) s. 24-Jan-4 British Auctioneer #270/R
£250 $450 €365 Dales landscape with wooded river valley and hills beyond (52x36cm-20x14in) s.i. W/C. 21-Apr-4 Tennants, Leyburn #1054
£450 $828 €657 On the way home (33x51cm-13x20in) s. pencil W/C. 25-Mar-4 Christie's, Kensington #151/R

EVANS, David (1929-1988) British
Works on paper
£680 $1285 €993 Dog office, midnight (88x118cm-35x46in) s.d.1987 W/C. 19-Feb-4 Lyon & Turnbull, Edinburgh #95

EVANS, De Scott (1847-1898) American
£3911 $7000 €5710 Mandolin and roses (61x51cm-24x20in) s. i.verso prov.exhib. 6-May-4 Shannon's, Milford #161/R est:8000-12000
£7186 $12000 €10492 Hanging pears (30x25cm-12x10in) s. 23-Oct-3 Shannon's, Milford #79/R est:12000-18000
£13953 $24000 €20371 Irish question (30x25cm-12x10in) s. 4-Dec-3 Christie's, Rockefeller NY #49/R est:20000-30000
Works on paper
£1257 $2250 €1835 Picking wildflowers (58x41cm-23x16in) s. W/C pencil exec.c.1891 prov. 26-May-4 Doyle, New York #50/R est:3000-5000

EVANS, Frederick Henry (1853-1943) British
Photographs
£1500 $2700 €2190 Theydon Bois, Epping Forest (15x11cm-6x4in) platinum print prov. 22-Apr-4 Phillips, New York #191/R est:4000-6000
£1796 $3000 €2622 Chateau Amboise (24x15cm-9x6in) s.i. platinum print pencil W/C exec.c.1900 prov. 17-Oct-3 Sotheby's, New York #137/R est:2000-3000
£3593 $6000 €5246 Across the nave, Durham Cathedral (24x13cm-9x5in) s.i. platinum print exec.c.1900. 17-Oct-3 Sotheby's, New York #190/R est:8000-12000

EVANS, Frederick M (1859-1929) British
Works on paper
£680 $1244 €993 Mending the quilt (29x24cm-11x9in) s. W/C. 6-Jul-4 Bearnes, Exeter #454/R
£1200 $2184 €1800 Grandfather's little helper (33x25cm-13x10in) s. W/C. 1-Jul-4 Christie's, Kensington #173/R est:300-400

EVANS, J (19th C) American?
Works on paper
£2315 $3750 €3380 Portrait of child in red with whip and straw hat (25x20cm-10x8in) W/C lit. 1-Aug-3 North East Auctions, Portsmouth #851/R est:3000-5000

EVANS, J R (19th C) American
£1229 $2200 €1794 Landscapes with figures at a river (18x38cm-7x15in) s. pair prov. 20-Mar-4 Pook & Pook, Downington #556/R est:1000-2000

EVANS, Jane (1946-) Australian
£347 $552 €507 Portrait of a man with cap (61x48cm-24x19in) s.d.1981 canvas on board. 1-May-3 Dunbar Sloane, Wellington #56 est:1000-3000 (NZ.D 1000)
£1449 $2348 €2101 Girl in cloche hat (55x37cm-22x15in) s.d.1982 acrylic on paper. 31-Jul-3 International Art Centre, Auckland #25/R est:2500-3500 (NZ.D 4000)
£4167 $6750 €6042 Waiting for the train (90x105cm-35x41in) s.d.1974 board. 31-Jul-3 International Art Centre, Auckland #14/R est:7000-10000 (NZ.D 11500)
Works on paper
£290 $470 €421 Head of boy II (59x39cm-23x15in) s.d.1988 W/C. 31-Jul-3 International Art Centre, Auckland #189 (NZ.D 800)
£906 $1458 €1323 Hibiscus with chair II (75x56cm-30x22in) s.d.1984 s.i.d.1984 verso gouache. 12-Aug-3 Peter Webb, Auckland #195/R (NZ.D 2500)
£1000 $1570 €1450 Small blue rooster (39x30cm-15x12in) s.d.1998 gouache W/C. 27-Aug-3 Dunbar Sloane, Wellington #124 (NZ.D 2750)
£1389 $2208 €2028 Untitled (78x58cm-31x23in) s.d.1992 W/C. 1-May-3 Dunbar Sloane, Wellington #55/R est:4000-6000 (NZ.D 4000)
£1504 $2556 €2196 Larks in parks 1 (54x73cm-21x29in) s.d.Dec.1980 gouache. 27-Nov-3 International Art Centre, Auckland #40/R est:5000-7000 (NZ.D 4000)

EVANS, Kirby Royston (20th C) Canadian
Works on paper
£271 $453 €396 Imagined English village (53x72cm-21x28in) s.i.d.1991 W/C. 17-Nov-3 Hodgins, Calgary #2/R (C.D 600)

EVANS, Lindsay A (1891-1976) Canadian
£203 $370 €296 Dark alley (50x39cm-20x15in) s.i. board prov.exhib. 1-Jul-4 Heffel, Vancouver #7/R (C.D 500)
£203 $370 €296 Home guard, London (55x40cm-22x16in) s.i. board prov. 1-Jul-4 Heffel, Vancouver #8/R (C.D 500)
£203 $370 €296 Sapper's (60x51cm-24x20in) s.i. board prov. 1-Jul-4 Heffel, Vancouver #10/R (C.D 500)
£224 $407 €327 Seg T.C. Poelger Cdn. Engineers (77x49cm-30x19in) s.i.d.1945 s.i.verso board prov. 1-Jul-4 Heffel, Vancouver #12/R (C.D 550)

EVANS, Lucille (1894-?) American
£269 $450 €393 Raininess (89x58cm-35x23in) s. oil collage masonite. 25-Oct-3 David Rago, Lambertville #1012
£958 $1600 €1399 Abstract composition (61x86cm-24x34in) s. 25-Oct-3 David Rago, Lambertville #1013 est:500-700

EVANS, Mary Paige (20th C) American
£751 $1300 €1096 Still life with apple (135x104cm-53x41in) s. prov. 13-Dec-3 Sloans & Kenyon, Bethesda #810/R

EVANS, Minnie (1892-1987) American
Works on paper
£1722 $3100 €2514 Picture I painted at Anlie Gate (38x56cm-15x22in) col pencil wax crayon on poster paper prov. 24-Apr-4 Slotin Folk Art, Buford #274/R est:5000-8000
£2814 $4700 €4108 My home, my home (38x56cm-15x22in) crayon col pencil prov. 15-Nov-3 Slotin Folk Art, Buford #134/R est:5000-8000

EVANS, Nick (1907-) British
£800 $1456 €1168 Miners strike - fair day pay for a fair day's work (122x122cm-48x48in) s.d.1978 board exhib. 21-Jun-4 Bonhams, Bath #327/R

EVANS, Patricia (20th C) American
£556 $1000 €812 Bridge (43x48cm-17x19in) s. masonite. 23-Jan-4 Freeman, Philadelphia #132

EVANS, Powys (1899-?) British
Works on paper
£750 $1388 €1095 Portrait of of John Drinkwater. Caricature of John Masefield (30x30cm-12x12in) pen ink two prov. 10-Mar-4 Sotheby's, Olympia #122/R

EVANS, Ray (1920-) British
£550 $968 €803 Fishermen at Roundstone (26x29cm-10x11in) s. acrylic. 18-May-4 Woolley & Wallis, Salisbury #299/R

EVANS, Walker (1903-1975) American

Photographs

£1467	$2700	€2142	Untitled, branching arrows (11x9cm-4x4in) Polaroid prov. 10-Jun-4 Phillips, New York #557/R est:3000-5000
£1796	$3000	€2622	Alabama tenant farmer family singing hymns (14x21cm-6x8in) num.I-22 photo exec.1936 printed later prov. 17-Oct-3 Sotheby's, New York #131/R est:6000-8000
£1808	$3200	€2640	Arkansas flood refugee, Forrest City, 1937 (25x20cm-10x8in) gelatin silver print prov.lit. 27-Apr-4 Christie's, Rockefeller NY #214/R est:4000-6000
£1852	$3500	€2704	Bowery lunchroom, New York (16x21cm-6x8in) gelatin silver print. 17-Feb-4 Christie's, Rockefeller NY #188/R est:3000-5000
£1878	$3400	€2742	Barber shop (23x18cm-9x7in) s.d.1936 num.56/100 gelatin silver print. 19-Apr-4 Daniel Cooney, Brooklyn #469209/R
£2000	$3580	€3000	Fisherman's house (19x19cm-7x7in) s.i. silver print prov. 13-May-4 Le Mouel, Paris #240/R est:3000-4000
£2096	$3500	€3060	Untitled, one way (7x7cm-3x3in) col polaroid exec.1973 or 1974 prov. 17-Oct-3 Phillips, New York #169/R est:4000-6000
£2174	$4000	€3174	Untitled, now open (11x9cm-4x4in) Polaroid prov. 10-Jun-4 Phillips, New York #555/R est:3000-5000
£2395	$4000	€3497	Bud Fields, tenant farmer in cotton field, Hale County, Alabama (24x19cm-9x7in) i.d.1936 num. III 325 verso gelatin silver print printed c.1969. 20-Oct-3 Christie's, Rockefeller NY #142/R est:3000-5000
£2395	$4000	€3497	Robert Frank, Nova Scotia (19x19cm-7x7in) s.d.1971 gelatin silver print. 20-Oct-3 Christie's, Rockefeller NY #206/R est:5000-7000
£2500	$4400	€3650	South End, Boston (15x11cm-6x4in) with sig.i. silver print. 20-May-4 Swann Galleries, New York #348/R est:4000-5000
£2667	$4773	€4000	Communist Party (15x22cm-6x9in) s.i. silver print prov. 13-May-4 Le Mouel, Paris #106/R est:4000-5000
£2695	$4500	€3935	Detail, Main Street of Pennsylvania town (22x10cm-9x4in) i.d.1935 gelatin silver print lit. 11-Nov-3 Christie's, Rockefeller NY #195/R est:7000-9000
£2994	$5000	€4371	Barber shop, Southern Town (19x24cm-7x9in) i.d.1936 num.verso gelatin silver print printed c.1960 prov. 20-Oct-3 Christie's, Rockefeller NY #13/R est:3000-5000
£2994	$5000	€4371	Alabama tenant farmer, Bud Fields (18x17cm-7x7in) gelatin silver print lit. 20-Oct-3 Christie's, Rockefeller NY #140/R est:8000-10000
£3107	$5500	€4536	Massachusetts Town, 1934 (15x20cm-6x8in) i.d.1934 gelatin silver print prov. 27-Apr-4 Christie's, Rockefeller NY #215/R est:3000-5000
£3672	$6500	€5361	Penny picture display, Savannah, 1936 (32x27cm-13x11in) gelatin silver print prov.lit. 27-Apr-4 Christie's, Rockefeller NY #219/R est:8000-10000
£4192	$7000	€6120	Berenice Abbott (17x12cm-7x5in) i.num.V6 verso gelatin silver print exec.c.1930 prov. 20-Oct-3 Christie's, Rockefeller NY #62/R est:10000-15000
£4790	$8000	€6993	Untitled, Cuban girl looking through window bars (18x24cm-7x9in) num.XVIII 16 verso gelatin silver print prov.lit. 20-Oct-3 Christie's, Rockefeller NY #188/R est:9000-12000
£5090	$8500	€7431	Breakfast room, Bellegrove Plantation (25x32cm-10x13in) s. num.7/75 gelatin silver print board exec.1935 prov.lit. 17-Oct-3 Phillips, New York #256/R est:5000-7000
£5389	$9000	€7868	Detail, American Legionnaire (23x19cm-9x7in) i.d.1936 gelatin silver print. 11-Nov-3 Christie's, Rockefeller NY #200/R est:7000-9000
£5556	$10000	€8112	Houses in the negro quarter, Vicksburg, Mississippi (20x25cm-8x10in) s.i.verso gelatin silver print prov.lit. 23-Apr-4 Phillips, New York #38/R est:10000-15000
£5689	$9500	€8306	Factory Street in Amsterdam, New York (14x19cm-6x7in) gelatin silver print lit. 11-Nov-3 Christie's, Rockefeller NY #188/R est:7000-9000
£5988	$10000	€8742	Birmingham boarding houses (18x24cm-7x9in) i.d.1936 gelatin silver print. 11-Nov-3 Christie's, Rockefeller NY #198/R est:5000-7000
£6250	$11000	€9125	Main street, Saratoga spring N.Y (30x24cm-12x9in) with sig. silver print. 20-May-4 Swann Galleries, New York #347/R est:3000-5000
£7186	$12000	€10492	Manhattan (11x6cm-4x2in) d.num.XIV verso photo exec.c.1929. 17-Oct-3 Sotheby's, New York #209/R est:8000-12000
£7186	$12000	€10492	New York City (11x8cm-4x3in) gelatin silver print lit. 20-Oct-3 Christie's, Rockefeller NY #7/R est:15000-20000
£7186	$12000	€10492	Bowery Lunchroom, New York (15x20cm-6x8in) s.d.1933-34/1955 gelatin silver print exec.c.1965 prov.lit. 20-Oct-3 Christie's, Rockefeller NY #217/R est:15000-20000
£7784	$13000	€11365	Company houses, Scott's Run, West Virginia (19x24cm-7x9in) i.d.1935 gelatin silver print lit. 11-Nov-3 Christie's, Rockefeller NY #197/R est:10000-15000
£8000	$14080	€11680	Sidewalk and shopfront, New Orleans (24x19cm-9x7in) s. gelatin silver print lit. 19-May-4 Christie's, London #186/R est:5000-7000
£8383	$14000	€12239	Houses in the Negro quarter of Tupelo, Mississippi (19x24cm-7x9in) gelatin silver print lit. 11-Nov-3 Christie's, Rockefeller NY #196/R est:15000-20000
£10778	$18000	€15736	Dock workers, Havana (13x16cm-5x6in) i.d.1932 gelatin silver print lit. 11-Nov-3 Christie's, Rockefeller NY #193/R est:10000-15000
£12429	$22000	€18146	Country store and gas station (13x24cm-5x9in) photo lit. 28-Apr-4 Sotheby's, New York #119/R est:15000-20000
£15569	$26000	€22731	Posed portraits, New York (20x15cm-8x6in) i.d.1931 lit. 11-Nov-3 Christie's, Rockefeller NY #191/R est:12000-18000
£15569	$26000	€22731	New Orleans boarding house (17x16cm-7x6in) s.d.1935 gelatin silver print prov.lit. 20-Oct-3 Christie's, Rockefeller NY #12/R est:10000-15000
£16766	$28000	€24478	Minstrel showbill (20x17cm-8x7in) i.d.1936 gelatin silver print lit. 11-Nov-3 Christie's, Rockefeller NY #201/R est:10000-15000
£16766	$28000	€24478	Walker Evans (24x19cm-9x7in) s.i.num.50/100 photos 14 portfolio prov. 17-Oct-3 Sotheby's, New York #130/R est:15000-20000
£18563	$31000	€27102	Country store and gas station, Alabama (17x24cm-7x9in) i.verso photo. 17-Oct-3 Sotheby's, New York #211/R est:20000-30000
£22754	$38000	€33221	Hotel porch, Saratoga Springs, New York (15x20cm-6x8in) gelatin silver print lit. 11-Nov-3 Christie's, Rockefeller NY #19/R est:15000-25000
£25150	$42000	€36719	Alabama tenant farmer, Floyd Burroughs (23x9cm-9x4in) s.i.d.1936 gelatin silver print prov.lit. 20-Oct-3 Christie's, Rockefeller NY #138/R est:30000-50000
£38922	$65000	€56826	Farmer's kitchen, Hale County, Alabama (24x15cm-9x6in) i.d.1936 gelatin silver print lit. 11-Nov-3 Christie's, Rockefeller NY #199/R est:30000-40000
£41916	$70000	€61197	Alabama tenant farmer family, Fields family (19x24cm-7x9in) s.i.d.1936 gelatin silver print prov.lit. 20-Oct-3 Christie's, Rockefeller NY #143/R est:40000-60000
£71856	$120000	€104910	Alabama tenant farmer wife, Allie Mae Burroughs (23x18cm-9x7in) s.i.d.1936 gelatin silver print prov.lit. 20-Oct-3 Christie's, Rockefeller NY #139/R est:70000-90000
£96045	$170000	€140226	Negro barbershop interior, Atlanta (19x24cm-7x9in) i.d.1936 num.I/6 verso photo board prov.exhib.lit. 27-Apr-4 Sotheby's, New York #22/R est:80000-120000
£101796	$170000	€148622	Penny picture display, Savannah (23x18cm-9x7in) s.i.d.1936 gelatin silver print prov.lit. 20-Oct-3 Christie's, Rockefeller NY #14/R est:100000-150000

EVE, Jean (1900-1968) French

£649	$1200	€948	Eygalieres le mas du chatueau (28x36cm-11x14in) s.i. 18-Jul-4 William Jenack, New York #231/R est:800-1200
£703	$1300	€1026	Paysage a fourges (23x33cm-9x13in) s.i. prov. 18-Jul-4 William Jenack, New York #339 est:800-1200
£1958	$3368	€2800	Petite neige a Dampmesnil (27x22cm-11x9in) s.d.1955. 3-Dec-3 Tajan, Paris #271/R est:3000-4000
£2797	$4811	€4000	Maison dans un sous-bois (32x40cm-13x16in) s. 3-Dec-3 Tajan, Paris #237 est:6000-8000
£2797	$4811	€4000	Entree au village, St Clairs/Epte (46x55cm-18x22in) s. s.i.d.1948 verso. 3-Dec-3 Tajan, Paris #241/R est:4100-4200

EVEN, Andre (1918-) French

£276	$461	€400	Campagne pres de Pont-Aven (46x65cm-18x26in) s. 11-Nov-3 Lesieur & Le Bars, Le Havre #27

EVEN, Jean (19th C) French

£647	$1157	€945	Avant le depart (92x73cm-36x29in) s. i. verso. 12-May-4 Dobiaschofsky, Bern #480/R est:2000 (S.FR 1500)
£3846	$6615	€5500	Giverny au printemps, chemin de la matine (41x33cm-16x13in) s. d.verso. 3-Dec-3 Tajan, Paris #240/R est:6000-7000

Works on paper

£775	$1356	€1100	Jour de regates (48x63cm-19x25in) s. W/C gouache. 21-Dec-3 Thierry & Lannon, Brest #49

EVENEPOEL, Henri (1872-1899) Belgian

£3521	$6092	€5000	Les pelerins d'Emmaus (27x41cm-11x16in) s.i.verso copy of van Veronese prov.lit. 13-Dec-3 De Vuyst, Lokeren #541/R est:5000-6000
£65333	$119560	€98000	Le jeune peintre (28x23cm-11x9in) mono. prov.exhib.lit. 7-Jun-4 Palais de Beaux Arts, Brussels #256/R est:20000-30000

Works on paper

£338	$585	€480	Profile of a woman (15x9cm-6x4in) st.mono. pencil prov. 13-Dec-3 De Vuyst, Lokeren #147
£458	$792	€650	Bed (17x26cm-7x10in) st.mono. pencil prov. 13-Dec-3 De Vuyst, Lokeren #143
£567	$1014	€850	Study of three girls (19x11cm-7x4in) pencil. 15-May-4 De Vuyst, Lokeren #127
£704	$1218	€1000	Portrait d'Arthur Pougin (18x14cm-7x6in) s. black chk exhib. 13-Dec-3 De Vuyst, Lokeren #137/R
£738	$1351	€1100	Figures parisiennes. i.verso dr. three various sizes prov. 8-Jul-4 Campo, Vlaamse Kaai #102/R
£915	$1584	€1300	Isola Bella (17x11cm-7x4in) W/C prov.lit. 13-Dec-3 De Vuyst, Lokeren #140/R
£986	$1706	€1400	Bellagio (11x17cm-4x7in) W/C prov. 13-Dec-3 De Vuyst, Lokeren #141
£993	$1808	€1500	Projet d'affiche (45x34cm-18x13in) mono. W/C. 16-Jun-4 Hotel des Ventes Mosan, Brussels #181 est:300-400
£1549	$2680	€2200	Portrait of Maurice Evenpoel, brother of the artist (25x21cm-10x8in) sanguine prov.exhib.lit. 13-Dec-3 De Vuyst, Lokeren #138/R est:2200-2500

EVERARD, Bertha King (1873-1965) South African

£1034	$1728	€1510	Fishing boats, St Ives (44x34cm-17x13in) lit. 20-Oct-3 Stephan Welz, Johannesburg #411/R est:10000-15000 (SA.R 12000)

EVERARD-HADEN, Ruth (1904-1992) South African

£320	$582	€467	Landscape with fence (46x55cm-18x22in) s. 15-Jun-4 Bonhams, Knightsbridge #49

EVERBROECK, Frans van (attrib) (17th C) Flemish

£12838	$22595	€19000	Still life with a pink roses, white rose and other flowers in a glass vase with orange tip, snail an (35x25cm-14x10in) panel. 18-May-4 Sotheby's, Amsterdam #93/R est:6000-8000

EVERDINGEN, Adriaen van (1832-1912) Dutch

£714	$1313	€1042	Man on path and cattle grazing (27x39cm-11x15in) s, panel painted c.1858. 29-Mar-4 Blomqvist, Lysaker #1060/R (N.KR 9000)
£2550	$4718	€3800	Summer landscape. Winter landscape (21x28cm-8x11in) indis sig. panel pair. 15-Mar-4 Sotheby's, Amsterdam #78/R est:2000-3000

Works on paper

£369	$683	€550	Farm in a polder landscape (37x60cm-15x24in) s. W/C. 15-Mar-4 Sotheby's, Amsterdam #79/R
£414	$687	€600	Landscape with mill (24x37cm-9x15in) s.d.60 W/C. 1-Oct-3 Ansorena, Madrid #343/R
£445	$757	€650	Landscape with cows near a pool (23x36cm-9x14in) init. brush brown wash. 4-Nov-3 Sotheby's, Amsterdam #164/R

EVERDINGEN, Allart (1621-1675) Dutch

Works on paper

£301	$550	€439	Landscape with group of trees on a rock ledge (30x24cm-12x9in) brush ink wash. 29-Jan-4 Swann Galleries, New York #173/R
£2600	$4758	€3796	Wooded mountain landscape with a fallen pine and a distant castle (11x14cm-4x6in) init. pen brown ink W/C prov. 8-Jul-4 Sotheby's, London #79/R est:3000-5000

EVERDINGEN, Allart (attrib) (1621-1675) Dutch

£3819	$6226	€5500	Ships in distress (85x72cm-33x28in) 25-Sep-3 Dr Fritz Nagel, Stuttgart #1244/R est:2000

EVERDINGEN, Pieter van (c.1651-1739) Dutch

Works on paper

£2568	$4519	€3800	Choppy sea with boats near the coast (10x14cm-4x6in) mono. pen grey ink wash prov.lit. 19-May-4 Sotheby's, Amsterdam #67/R est:2000-3000

EVERETT, Charles (19th C) British
Works on paper
£338 $595 €500 Interior of the Church of St Jacques, Bruges (33x46cm-13x18in) W/C gouache black lead prov. 19-May-4 Sotheby's, Amsterdam #186/R

EVERETT, Edwin E (fl.1880-1884) British
Works on paper
£300 $537 €438 Shepherd by a ruined castle (33x48cm-13x19in) s. W/C. 5-May-4 John Nicholson, Haslemere #402

EVERGOOD, Phillip (1901-1973) American
£284 $500 €415 Reminiscence of a dance (89x53cm-35x21in) painted c.1967. 23-May-4 Treadway Gallery, Cincinnati #674/R
£1899 $3000 €2773 Marketplace (48x41cm-19x16in) s. 7-Sep-3 Treadway Gallery, Cincinnati #688/R est:3000-5000
£2471 $4250 €3608 It'd better not rain (38x28cm-15x11in) s.d.1966 board. 7-Dec-3 Treadway Gallery, Cincinnati #633/R est:6000-8000
£3763 $7000 €5494 Children and very giant squash (61x51cm-24x20in) s.d.1962. 7-Mar-4 Treadway Gallery, Cincinnati #721/R est:5000-7000
£34091 $60000 €49773 Dog bite clinic (102x128cm-40x50in) s. painted c.1933 prov.exhib.lit. 18-May-4 Christie's, Rockefeller NY #115/R est:25000-35000
Works on paper
£380 $700 €555 Woman at a window (61x48cm-24x19in) s. chl wash. 10-Jun-4 Swann Galleries, New York #82/R
£601 $1100 €877 Glorification of flowers (76x56cm-30x22in) s.d.1965 W/C chl. 5-Jun-4 Treadway Gallery, Cincinnati #742/R est:2000-3000
£971 $1700 €1418 Seated woman with pipe (73x54cm-29x21in) s.d.1964 ink inkwash chl prov. 19-Dec-3 Sotheby's, New York #1025/R est:1200-1800

EVERHART, Jane (20th C) American
Works on paper
£260 $475 €390 Jonkman's backyard, Michigan (99x61cm-39x24in) pastel gouache. 10-Jul-4 Hindman, Chicago #139/R

EVERINGHAM, Rick (1945-) Australian
£407 $638 €590 Roundabout (59x59cm-23x23in) s. board. 26-Aug-3 Christie's, Sydney #385 (A.D 1000)
£453 $820 €661 Life is too important to take seriously (46x38cm-18x15in) s. board. 31-Mar-4 Goodman, Sydney #513 (A.D 1100)

EVERITT, Allen Edward (1824-1882) British
£498 $831 €727 King James I Chamber, Knoxton Abbey (31x40cm-12x16in) panel. 17-Nov-3 Waddingtons, Toronto #82/R (C.D 1100)

EVERITT, Allen Edward (attrib) (1824-1882) British
Works on paper
£280 $468 €409 Aston Hall, Birmingham (25x16cm-10x6in) i.verso W/C sold with a lithograph. 7-Oct-3 Fellows & Sons, Birmingham #455/R

EVERS, Carl (19/20th C) ?
Works on paper
£1257 $2100 €1835 Cruise ship leaving port, native fisherman trading with women (43x69cm-17x27in) s. W/C gouache exec.c.1950. 15-Nov-3 Illustration House, New York #158/R est:2000-3000

EVERSDYCK, Willem (?-1671) Dutch
£3147 $5350 €4500 Scholar reading (92x69cm-36x27in) i. panel. 20-Nov-3 Van Ham, Cologne #1318/R est:5000

EVERSEN, Adrianus (1818-1897) Dutch
£675 $1100 €986 Dutch street (28x36cm-11x14in) bears sig. board. 24-Sep-3 Doyle, New York #28/R
£1736 $2743 €2500 Figures on the bridge by the Bikkereiland, Amsterdam (21x25cm-8x10in) s. panel. 2-Sep-3 Christie's, Amsterdam #155/R est:2500-3500
£2148 $3995 €3200 Bikkerstraat in Amsterdam (20x25cm-8x10in) s. panel. 4-Mar-4 Auction Maastricht #1110/R est:4000-5000
£3400 $6256 €4964 Antwerp (22x18cm-9x7in) panel prov. 25-Mar-4 Christie's, Kensington #165/R est:2000-3000
£4762 $8667 €7000 Figures conversing in a Dutch town in winter (19x15cm-7x6in) mono. panel. 3-Feb-4 Christie's, Amsterdam #51/R est:4000-6000
£4861 $7681 €7000 Village life (32x39cm-13x15in) mono. 2-Sep-3 Christie's, Amsterdam #161/R est:5000-7000
£6667 $12000 €10000 Figures by a town gate (13x11cm-5x4in) init. panel. 21-Apr-4 Christie's, Amsterdam #238/R est:10000-15000
£10000 $18000 €15000 Daily activities in a sunlit Dutch town (36x31cm-14x12in) s. panel. 21-Apr-4 Christie's, Amsterdam #228/R est:15000-20000
£11111 $18889 €16000 Hattem in winter (32x39cm-13x15in) s.i. 28-Oct-3 Christie's, Amsterdam #6/R est:8000-12000
£12500 $20875 €18000 Villagers in a Dutch town (17x26cm-7x10in) mono. panel. 21-Oct-3 Sotheby's, Amsterdam #181/R est:15000-20000
£12500 $22500 €18250 Villagers in a Dutch town (44x34cm-17x13in) s. 23-Apr-4 Sotheby's, New York #34/R est:25000-35000
£13194 $22431 €19000 Figures on a bridge in a Dutch town (36x27cm-14x11in) s. panel. 28-Oct-3 Christie's, Amsterdam #227/R est:16000-20000
£16667 $30000 €25000 View of the Dijkpoort, Hattem (39x30cm-15x12in) s. panel. 20-Apr-4 Sotheby's, Amsterdam #164/R est:12000-15000
£17361 $29514 €25000 Figures by a canal in a sunlit Dutch town (23x30cm-9x12in) s. panel. 28-Oct-3 Christie's, Amsterdam #211/R est:25000-35000
£18500 $33115 €27010 Dutch town scene (34x41cm-13x16in) mono. indis d.18. 26-May-4 Sotheby's, Olympia #267/R est:8000-12000
£19444 $33056 €28000 Numerous figures on a sunlit town square (23x28cm-9x11in) s. panel prov. 28-Oct-3 Christie's, Amsterdam #219/R est:20000-30000
£41667 $69583 €60000 Villagers in the streets of a Dutch town (57x47cm-22x19in) s. 21-Oct-3 Sotheby's, Amsterdam #190/R est:60000-80000

EVERSEN, Johannes Hendrik (1906-1995) Dutch
£1053 $1937 €1600 Still life with snowdrops and other winter flowers (23x18cm-9x7in) s.d.1951 panel. 22-Jun-4 Christie's, Amsterdam #494/R est:1200-1600
£8000 $14800 €11680 Still life with ham (51x72cm-20x28in) s. prov. 14-Jul-4 Sotheby's, Olympia #242/R est:4000-6000
£9500 $17575 €13870 Still life of celery with bread and carafe of wine (39x29cm-15x11in) s.d.60 prov. 14-Jul-4 Sotheby's, Olympia #240/R est:4000-6000
£11500 $20700 €16790 Still life of a lobster and lemon upon a pewter plate (50x70cm-20x28in) s.d.1962 prov. 22-Apr-4 Lawrence, Crewkerne #899/R est:10000-15000
£18000 $33300 €26280 Still life of oysters and prawns with wine and lemon (50x39cm-20x15in) s.d.1975 prov. 14-Jul-4 Sotheby's, Olympia #243/R est:4000-6000
£20381 $37500 €29756 Tabletop still life with books, pewter tankard, candlestand and pipe (51x71cm-20x28in) s.d.1963. 27-Jun-4 Freeman, Philadelphia #27/R est:8000-12000
£22000 $40700 €32120 Still life with cheese and wine (41x51cm-16x20in) s.d.1959 prov. 14-Jul-4 Sotheby's, Olympia #241/R est:4000-6000

EVES, Reginald Grenville (1876-1941) British
£800 $1264 €1160 Portrait of a lady in a white dress and fur shawl (137x84cm-54x33in) s.d.1920. 4-Sep-3 Christie's, Kensington #75/R
£800 $1432 €1168 Portrait of a lady (124x99cm-49x39in) s.d.1912. 26-May-4 Sotheby's, Olympia #191/R

EVESSON, Willie (20th C) ?
£265 $482 €400 Clontarf morning light (37x49cm-15x19in) s. board. 15-Jun-4 James Adam, Dublin #191/R

EVRARD, G (20th C) ?
£1100 $1727 €1595 Carnations in a basket (51x61cm-20x24in) s. 28-Aug-3 Christie's, Kensington #302/R est:700-1000

EVRARD, Paula (1876-1927) Belgian
£439 $786 €650 Still life of flowers (105x46cm-41x18in) 10-May-4 Amberes, Antwerp #263

EVRARD, Perpette (1662-1727) Flemish
Miniatures
£2000 $3600 €2920 Lady, wearing a white dress with gold stripes (7cm-3in) s.d.1720 verso vellum playing card oval fishskin case exhib. 22-Apr-4 Bonhams, New Bond Street #26/R est:2000-3000

EWALD, Reinhold (1890-1974) German
£2083 $3292 €3000 Woman (36x25cm-14x10in) s. board sold with pencil sketch. 6-Sep-3 Arnold, Frankfurt #550/R est:600
£3472 $5486 €5000 Women skating (45x36cm-18x14in) s.d.22 board. 6-Sep-3 Arnold, Frankfurt #549/R est:900

EWART, Peter (1918-2001) Canadian
£223 $379 €326 North of Clinton (25x30cm-10x12in) s. board. 6-Nov-3 Heffel, Vancouver #41/R (C.D 500)
£379 $645 €553 Near Black Canyon, Ashcroft district (51x61cm-20x24in) s. board prov. 6-Nov-3 Heffel, Vancouver #40/R (C.D 850)
£520 $952 €759 Roger's Pass, from Mt Abbott (45x60cm-18x24in) s.i. board. 1-Jun-4 Hodgins, Calgary #104/R (C.D 1300)
£580 $987 €847 High Country, Bonaparte River canyon (51x61cm-20x24in) s. i.verso board prov. 6-Nov-3 Heffel, Vancouver #39/R est:1000-1200 (C.D 1300)

EWBANK, John Wilson (1799-1847) British
£350 $655 €511 Figures on a path overlooking a highland lake scene at sunset (46x61cm-18x24in) s. 24-Feb-4 Bonhams, Knowle #115
£541 $1000 €812 Harbourscape (58x76cm-23x30in) 17-Jul-4 Fallon, Copake #162/R

EWBANK, John Wilson (attrib) (1799-1847) British
£290 $528 €423 Figures on the Black Middens Rocks, Tynemouth (16x19cm-6x7in) indis.s. board. 29-Jun-4 Anderson & Garland, Newcastle #492

EWEN, William Paterson (1925-2002) Canadian
£482 $896 €704 Fields near Ospringe, Ont (20x25cm-8x10in) s. s.i.d.July 17/69 verso canvasboard. 2-Mar-4 Ritchie, Toronto #150/R (C.D 1200)
£20325 $36382 €29675 Full moon (122x127cm-48x50in) s. i.d.1984 verso acrylic on gouged plywood prov. 31-May-4 Sotheby's, Toronto #181/R est:30000-40000 (C.D 50000)

EWER, Louis C (19/20th C) American
£1173 $2100 €1713 Brook trout (46x76cm-18x30in) s. 8-Jan-4 James Julia, Fairfield #433/R est:2500-4000

EWERT, Per Jon Tage (1869-1894) Swedish
£251 $450 €366 The path to the lake (79x58cm-31x23in) s. 10-Jan-4 Harvey Clar, Oakland #1154

EWING, Leckie (19/20th C) British
Works on paper
£320 $592 €467 Harbour scene, St Andrews (28x36cm-11x14in) s. 12-Feb-4 Andrew Hartley, Ilkley #741
£380 $703 €555 St Andrews, Scotland (25x33cm-10x13in) s. 12-Feb-4 Andrew Hartley, Ilkley #740

EWORTH, Hans (style) (?-1574) Flemish
£6000 $10800 €8760 Portrait of Mary Queen of Scots (82x72cm-32x28in) 21-Jan-4 Sotheby's, Olympia #1/R est:2000-3000

EXIL, Levoy (20th C) Haitian
£367 $656 €550 Maternite a la colombe (86x43cm-34x17in) s. 17-May-4 Rogeon, Paris #165
£500 $895 €750 Danse sacree (89x63cm-35x25in) s. 17-May-4 Rogeon, Paris #63

EXNER, Antoine (1922-) ?
£293 $528 €440 Sailing ships going to sea (59x89cm-23x35in) s. 22-Apr-4 Weidler, Nurnberg #4607

EXNER, Julius (1825-1910) Danish
£362 $648 €529 Room in the loft (16x23cm-6x9in) init.d.1845. 10-May-4 Rasmussen, Vejle #474/R (D.KR 4000)
£374 $591 €542 The Rev. Nielsen, Copenhagen (39x30cm-15x12in) i.verso. 2-Sep-3 Rasmussen, Copenhagen #1888 (D.KR 4000)
£375 $625 €548 Portrait of young gentleman (29x21cm-11x8in) i.verso. 25-Oct-3 Rasmussen, Havnen #2217/R (D.KR 4000)
£1797 $3342 €2624 Interior from cottage with chair, table and red sofa (16x24cm-6x9in) s. panel. 2-Mar-4 Rasmussen, Copenhagen #1220/R est:8000 (D.KR 20000)
£1869 $2953 €2710 A proposal (39x33cm-15x13in) s. 2-Sep-3 Rasmussen, Copenhagen #1693/R est:15000-20000 (D.KR 20000)
£2470 $3877 €3606 Interior scene with young woman and her child (64x57cm-25x22in) init.d.1873. 30-Aug-3 Rasmussen, Havnen #2087/R est:30000 (D.KR 26500)
£9848 $18021 €14378 Small girl wearing purple dress seated on stone steps (127x96cm-50x38in) init.d.1851. 9-Jun-4 Rasmussen, Copenhagen #1832/R est:125000 (D.KR 110000)
Works on paper
£378 $654 €552 The artist's finished work admired by the family (23x28cm-9x11in) s.i.d.1899 pen wash. 9-Dec-3 Rasmussen, Copenhagen #1753/R (D.KR 4000)

EXNER, Karl (20th C) Austrian
£950 $1492 €1378 Satyr playing pipe music to Sybils in a garden (69x128cm-27x50in) s. board oval. 28-Aug-3 Christie's, Kensington #267/R

EXTER, Alexandra (1882-1949) Russian
£8333 $15250 €12500 Projet de costume (48x37cm-19x15in) s. board prov.lit. 5-Jun-4 Lempertz, Koln #705/R est:6000-8000
£48000 $81600 €72000 Still life of fruit, vegetables, bowl of eggs and bottle of milk (82x54cm-32x21in) lit. 25-Nov-3 Christie's, London #207/R est:35000-45000
Works on paper
£6711 $12416 €10000 Projet de costume (56x36cm-22x14in) s. gouache. 15-Mar-4 Claude Boisgirard, Paris #37/R est:5000-6000
£12838 $22595 €19000 Projet de costume (47x30cm-19x12in) s.d.1924 verso gouache lit. 19-May-4 Camard, Paris #87/R est:15000-20000
£13423 $23758 €20000 Projet de costume pour Salome d'apres Oscar Wile (52x38cm-20x15in) s. gouache. 27-Apr-4 Artcurial Briest, Paris #114/R est:7000-8000
£13514 $23784 €20000 Projet pour decor de Don Juan (37x52cm-15x20in) s. gouache exec.1929. 19-May-4 Camard, Paris #88/R est:20000-25000
£13514 $23784 €20000 Projet de decor (43x56cm-17x22in) s. gouache lit. 19-May-4 Camard, Paris #85/R est:12000-15000
£14865 $26162 €22000 Projet de costume (49x38cm-19x15in) s.d.1924 gouache lit. 19-May-4 Camard, Paris #90/R est:15000-20000
£14865 $26162 €22000 Projet de costume (56x36cm-22x14in) s.d.24 gouache lit. 19-May-4 Camard, Paris #91/R est:15000-20000
£15541 $27351 €23000 Projet de costume (52x40cm-20x16in) s.d.1926 gouache lit. 19-May-4 Camard, Paris #89/R est:15000-20000
£20946 $36865 €31000 Projet de costume (57x42cm-22x17in) s.verso gouache lit. 19-May-4 Camard, Paris #86/R est:15000-20000
£22222 $40000 €32444 Costume design for the seven against Thebes (51x33cm-20x13in) s.i. pencil gouache. 23-Apr-4 Sotheby's, New York #103/R est:30000-40000

EXTER, Julius (1863-1939) German
£3620 $5792 €5285 Portrait of young woman wearing white headscarf (30x32cm-12x13in) s.d.1903. 16-Sep-3 Philippe Schuler, Zurich #3357/R est:1500-2000 (S.FR 8000)

EYBL, Franz (1806-1880) Austrian
£4895 $8322 €7000 Woman's portrait (27x22cm-11x9in) i.d.831 panel prov. 24-Nov-3 Dorotheum, Vienna #73/R est:3000-3400

EYCK, Charles (1897-1983) Dutch
£1361 $2435 €2000 Children playing in the woods (114x100cm-45x39in) 17-Mar-4 De Zwann, Amsterdam #4637/R est:2000-3000
£1819 $3310 €2729 Town scene in France (79x64cm-31x25in) s.d.28. 16-Jun-4 Wolf's, New York #486708/R est:600-800
£1837 $3288 €2700 Suburb of Paris (30x38cm-12x15in) d.1943. 17-Mar-4 De Zwann, Amsterdam #4641/R est:2000-3000
£12000 $21960 €18000 Tuscany (80x59cm-31x23in) s.i.d.1925 s.verso. 7-Jun-4 Glerum, Amsterdam #12/R est:5000-7000
Works on paper
£268 $499 €400 Nude (52x35cm-20x14in) s.d.Sept 1951 W/C sketch. 4-Mar-4 Auction Maastricht #1017/R
£420 $722 €600 Neptune (64x50cm-25x20in) s.i. gouache. 3-Dec-3 Auction Maastricht #962/R
£420 $722 €600 Landscape in Provence (34x42cm-13x17in) s.d.82 pen. 3-Dec-3 Auction Maastricht #963/R
£664 $1143 €950 Le pecheur de Bonaire (49x38cm-19x15in) s.d.54 gouache. 3-Dec-3 Auction Maastricht #906/R
£872 $1614 €1300 L'automme (45x54cm-18x21in) s.i.d.1953 gouache. 15-Mar-4 Sotheby's, Amsterdam #156/R est:750-850

EYCK, Charles (attrib) (1897-1983) Dutch
£420 $701 €600 Pollard willows along the Geul river (45x60cm-18x24in) s.d.2-2-76 gouache. 10-Oct-3 Vendue Huis, Gravenhage #814
Works on paper
£280 $467 €400 Piazza in Roma (24x27cm-9x11in) s. pen. 10-Oct-3 Vendue Huis, Gravenhage #832
£385 $642 €550 Boulevard St Denis in Paris (26x32cm-10x13in) s.d.1973 gouache. 10-Oct-3 Vendue Huis, Gravenhage #829
£420 $722 €600 Neptune (64x50cm-25x20in) s.i. gouache. 4-Dec-3 Vendue Huis, Gravenhage #692
£420 $722 €600 Provence, France (34x42cm-13x17in) s.d.82 pen. 4-Dec-3 Vendue Huis, Gravenhage #693
£455 $759 €650 Grote Looiersstraat in Maastricht (24x31cm-9x12in) s.d.65 pen. 10-Oct-3 Vendue Huis, Gravenhage #887
£490 $817 €700 Sketch from Spain (31x27cm-12x11in) s. pastel. 10-Oct-3 Vendue Huis, Gravenhage #815
£664 $1143 €950 Le pecheur de Bonaire (49x38cm-19x15in) s.d.54 gouache. 4-Dec-3 Vendue Huis, Gravenhage #906

EYCK, Jan Karel van (17th C) Flemish
£5500 $9350 €8030 Crowded village scene with a messenger reading a proclamation (99x138cm-39x54in) s.d.1686. 30-Oct-3 Sotheby's, Olympia #61/R est:4000-6000

EYCKEN, Alphonse van der (19th C) Belgian
£660 $1102 €964 Three quarter length portrait of a woman stood in front of a mirror (27x21cm-11x8in) board. 22-Jun-3 Wilkinson, Doncaster #261/R

EYCKEN, Charles van den (19th C) Belgian
£1042 $1656 €1500 Les petits chapardeurs (50x36cm-20x14in) s. panel. 15-Sep-3 Horta, Bruxelles #219 est:1200-1800
£1284 $2426 €1900 Chien sur une chaise, attendant sa maitresse (60x50cm-24x20in) s.d.1921. 17-Feb-4 Vanderkindere, Brussels #32 est:1200-1800
£2203 $3744 €3216 Two sheep and goat by old tree and lake (20x25cm-8x10in) s.d.1845 panel. 5-Nov-3 Dobiaschofsky, Bern #532/R est:4500 (S.FR 5000)
£2685 $4966 €4000 Chien et chat devant les armoiries (22x28cm-9x11in) s.d.1884 panel. 15-Mar-4 Horta, Bruxelles #137/R est:3000-5000
£5333 $9813 €8000 Trois chatons a la boite a bijoux (33x44cm-13x17in) s.d.1896. 14-Jun-4 Horta, Bruxelles #83 est:3500-5000
£6993 $12028 €10000 Deux chiens decouvrant un cageot de homards vivants (65x71cm-26x28in) s.d.1889. 8-Dec-3 Horta, Bruxelles #138/R est:8000-12000
£8000 $14400 €12000 Cat in the kitchen (44x57cm-17x22in) s.d.1919. 21-Apr-4 Christie's, Amsterdam #182/R est:7000-9000
£14679 $24514 €21285 Cats playing in artist's studio (69x95cm-27x37in) s.d.1903. 23-Jun-3 Philippe Schuler, Zurich #3515/R est:14000-18000 (S.FR 32000)
£21333 $38400 €32000 Taste for treasures (39x59cm-15x23in) s. prov. 21-Apr-4 Christie's, Amsterdam #191/R est:15000-20000
£26389 $44861 €38000 In the artist's studio - a mischievous game (69x94cm-27x37in) s.d.1903. 28-Oct-3 Christie's, Amsterdam #197/R est:40000-60000

EYCKEN, Charles van den (jnr) (1859-1923) Belgian
£993 $1658 €1400 Tete de chien (21x17cm-8x7in) s. panel. 14-Oct-3 Vanderkindere, Brussels #59/R
£1100 $2035 €1606 Happy family (33x45cm-13x18in) s. panel. 15-Jan-4 Christie's, Kensington #809/R est:1000-1500
£1972 $3411 €2800 Chiens et charue (35x45cm-14x18in) s.d.1880. 10-Dec-3 Hotel des Ventes Mosan, Brussels #156 est:2200-2400
£3514 $6641 €5200 Les chiens de cirque (49x38cm-19x15in) s. panel. 17-Feb-4 Vanderkindere, Brussels #86/R est:5000-7000
£3826 $7077 €5700 Cat playing (33x24cm-13x9in) s. board. 13-Mar-4 De Vuyst, Lokeren #517/R est:6500-7500

EYCKEN, Charles van den (snr) (1809-1891) Belgian
£2192 $3726 €3200 Jeu de chatons (35x27cm-14x11in) s. panel. 10-Nov-3 Horta, Bruxelles #374
£3046 $5544 €4600 Le petit espiegle (22x31cm-9x12in) s. panel. 16-Jun-4 Hotel des Ventes Mosan, Brussels #178 est:3000-3200

EYCKEN, Felix van den (19th C) Belgian
£897 $1659 €1300 Chien et lapin. Chien sur son tapis (16x20cm-6x8in) one s. panel pair. 19-Jan-4 Horta, Bruxelles #28/R
£900 $1548 €1314 Children and cats playing in a barn (43x61cm-17x24in) s. 5-Dec-3 Chrystals Auctions, Isle of Man #298
£940 $1758 €1372 Teasing (41x58cm-16x23in) s. 24-Feb-4 Bonhams, Knowle #106
£1329 $2285 €1900 Apres un bon repas (34x44cm-13x17in) s. 8-Dec-3 Horta, Bruxelles #71 est:1800-2200
£1342 $2483 €2000 Le secours aux naufrages (48x66cm-19x26in) s. 15-Mar-4 Horta, Bruxelles #138 est:1800-2200
£2000 $3660 €3000 Interieur de cuisine avec personnages attables (45x56cm-18x22in) s. 7-Jun-4 Palais de Beaux Arts, Brussels #312/R est:2800-3500

EYCKERMANS, Lode (20th C) Belgian?
Sculpture
£3333 $5967 €5000 Mother and child (72x62cm-28x24in) s. dark brown pat bronze marble base prov. 15-May-4 De Vuyst, Lokeren #128/R est:4000-5000

EYDEN, William A (1893-1982) American
£259 $425 €376 Mountain lake (20x25cm-8x10in) s. board painted c.1925. 7-Jun-3 Treadway Gallery, Cincinnati #1408
£280 $500 €409 Beech trees (56x81cm-22x32in) s. board. 14-May-4 Skinner, Boston #187/R
£3481 $5500 €5082 Broadway, New York City (76x102cm-30x40in) s. 7-Sep-3 Treadway Gallery, Cincinnati #684/R est:6000-8000
Works on paper
£214 $400 €312 Autumnal landscape (53x69cm-21x27in) s. gouache. 26-Feb-4 Skinner, Bolton #608a/R
£320 $550 €467 Indiana beech trees (46x61cm-18x24in) s. gouache board exec.c.1930. 7-Dec-3 Treadway Gallery, Cincinnati #609/R

EYERS, J J (19th C) ?
£1705 $3000 €2489 Trompe l'oeil of hanging game birds (66x48cm-26x19in) s. pair. 21-May-4 Pook & Pook, Downington #297/R est:3000-4000

EYMER, Arnoldus Johannes (1803-1863) Dutch
£403 $745 €600 Travelers in a mountainous landscape (28x23cm-11x9in) s. board. 15-Mar-4 Sotheby's, Amsterdam #84/R
£4000 $7200 €6000 River Spaarne, Haarlem in the distance (44x60cm-17x24in) s.d.49 panel. 21-Apr-4 Christie's, Amsterdam #37/R est:3000-5000

EYNDE, Louis van den (1881-1966) Belgian?
£699 $1189 €1000 Vase de roses, chapeau, parasol et livres sur une table drapee (80x100cm-31x39in) s. 1-Dec-3 Palais de Beaux Arts, Brussels #139/R est:500-700

EYNDEN, Jacobus van (younger) (1733-1824) Dutch
Works on paper
£608 $1070 €900 Stone curlew (28x20cm-11x8in) s.d.1785 W/C black chk. 19-May-4 Sotheby's, Amsterdam #304/R

EYRE, Donald (?) British
Works on paper
£300 $540 €438 Fishing on the River Dove (58x46cm-23x18in) pencil W/C htd white. 22-Apr-4 Mellors & Kirk, Nottingham #1042

EYRE, Gladstone (1863-1933) Australian
£262 $482 €383 Home at dark (61x105cm-24x41in) s. 28-Jun-4 Australian Art Auctions, Sydney #154 (A.D 700)
Works on paper
£382 $684 €558 Coastal scene with ship. W/C. 28-May-4 Lawson Menzies, Sydney #2204 (A.D 975)
£813 $1276 €1179 South Head from the Spit (27x76cm-11x30in) s.i. W/C. 26-Aug-3 Christie's, Sydney #386 est:1000-1500 (A.D 2000)

EYRE, Ivan Kenneth (1935-) Canadian
£6532 $11104 €9537 Pavan II (142x111cm-56x44in) s. d.1979 verso acrylic prov. 27-Nov-3 Heffel, Vancouver #206/R est:20000-25000 (C.D 14500)
Works on paper
£301 $560 €439 Self portrait (31x24cm-12x9in) s.d.1976 conte pencil prov.lit. 4-Mar-4 Heffel, Vancouver #12/R (C.D 750)

EYSEN, Louis (1843-1899) German
£2667 $4853 €4000 Landscape with trees (20x30cm-8x12in) mono. board. 30-Jun-4 Neumeister, Munich #543/R est:1000

EYSKENS, Felix (1882-1968) Belgian
£322 $596 €480 Boats on the River Schelde in Amsterdam (24x34cm-9x13in) s. canvas on panel. 13-Mar-4 De Vuyst, Lokeren #133
£333 $600 €500 City view near the water (80x125cm-31x49in) s. 26-Apr-4 Bernaerts, Antwerp #276/R
£600 $1080 €900 City view with women at the market (60x90cm-24x35in) s. 26-Apr-4 Bernaerts, Antwerp #278/R

EYTON, Anthony (1923-) British
£300 $486 €438 Children playing (120x106cm-47x42in) s. 27-Jan-3 Bristol Auction Rooms #489
£400 $708 €584 Landscape in Greece (64x77cm-25x30in) s. 27-Apr-4 Bonhams, Knightsbridge #24/R
£1900 $3515 €2774 South London garden (148x137cm-58x54in) s. s.i.d.1988 verso prov. 11-Feb-4 Sotheby's, Olympia #186/R est:1200-1800
£2700 $4833 €3942 Beach and sea (93x52cm-37x20in) prov. 14-May-4 Christie's, Kensington #621/R est:2000-3000
£5200 $9308 €7592 Bathing in the Ganges (148x174cm-58x69in) 16-Mar-4 Bonhams, New Bond Street #69/R est:3000-5000
Works on paper
£300 $555 €438 Beach, Swanage (35x42cm-14x17in) s.i.d.90 pastel. 11-Mar-4 Christie's, Kensington #268/R
£350 $602 €511 London Bridge (35x32cm-14x13in) chl. 3-Dec-3 Christie's, Kensington #698
£400 $728 €584 Seated nude (72x48cm-28x19in) pastel. 1-Jul-4 Christie's, Kensington #199/R
£420 $773 €613 Figures on a beach (53x69cm-21x27in) s.d.95 W/C. 24-Mar-4 Hamptons Fine Art, Godalming #244/R
£550 $990 €803 Lido, Worthing (60x80cm-24x31in) s. pastel sold with another by same hand two. 20-Jan-4 Bonhams, Knightsbridge #32
£900 $1503 €1314 Woman with a towel (75x54cm-30x21in) s.d.1994 pastel. 16-Oct-3 Christie's, Kensington #322/R
£900 $1665 €1314 Spring garden (109x80cm-43x31in) s.d.1991 pastel. 11-Mar-4 Christie's, Kensington #273/R

EZCURRA, Agustin (1880-1958) South American
£1698 $2750 €2462 Dance of the Negroes (135x210cm-53x83in) s.d.34-35 prov. 29-Jul-3 Galeria y Remates, Montevideo #100/R est:3500-4500

EZDORF, Christian (1801-1851) German
£2797 $4755 €4000 Rock archway in the sea off coast of Iceland (61x85cm-24x33in) i. stretcher. 27-Nov-3 Bassenge, Berlin #5575/R est:6000

FAABORG, Finn (1902-1995) Norwegian
£739 $1279 €1079 Two figures (37x44cm-15x17in) s. panel. 13-Dec-3 Blomqvist, Lysaker #1089 (N.KR 8500)

FABARIUS, Friedrich Wilhelm (1815-1900) German
£594 $1010 €850 Fishing boats on beach (20x29cm-8x11in) s.d.1877. 22-Nov-3 Arnold, Frankfurt #500

FABBI, Alberto (1858-1906) Italian
£3329 $5659 €4760 Love scene (69x103cm-27x41in) 1-Dec-3 Babuino, Rome #295/R est:4000-5000

FABBI, Fabio (1861-1946) Italian
£1831 $3039 €2600 Algerian street musician (33x18cm-13x7in) s. panel. 16-Jun-3 Dorotheum, Vienna #136/R est:2600-3000
£2967 $5370 €4450 Slave sale (14x10cm-6x4in) s. panel lit. 3-Apr-4 Badum, Bamberg #278/R est:3800
£3521 $6092 €5000 Wedding (37x47cm-15x19in) s. 10-Dec-3 Sotheby's, Milan #100/R est:5000-7000
£12752 $23463 €19000 Le charmeur de serpent (71x40cm-28x16in) s. 28-Mar-4 Anaf, Lyon #111/R est:18000-20000
£17647 $30000 €25765 Slave market (77x77cm-30x30in) s. 19-Nov-3 Bonhams & Butterfields, San Francisco #46/R
£18000 $32760 €26280 La passeggiata (50x73cm-20x29in) s. 15-Jun-4 Sotheby's, London #114/R est:15000-20000
£21667 $39000 €31634 Abduction (100x55cm-39x22in) s. 22-Apr-4 Christie's, Rockefeller NY #199/R est:20000-30000
£22222 $40000 €32444 Orange seller (70x55cm-28x22in) s. prov. 22-Apr-4 Christie's, Rockefeller NY #201/R est:40000-60000
£28409 $50000 €41477 Wedding procession (88x143cm-35x56in) s. 18-May-4 Bonhams & Butterfields, San Francisco #64/R est:50000-70000
£39007 $65142 €55000 La presentation des esclaves dans un port oriental (76x60cm-30x24in) s. 16-Jun-3 Gros & Delettrez, Paris #458/R est:60000-80000
Works on paper
£1667 $2733 €2300 Odalisks (30x45cm-12x18in) s. W/C cardboard. 27-May-3 Finarte Semenzato, Milan #38/R
£3553 $6537 €5400 Odalisk (51x36cm-20x14in) s.d.09 W/C. 23-Jun-4 Finarte Semenzato, Rome #22/R est:5500-6000
£5000 $8600 €7300 Arabic dancing girl (44x30cm-17x12in) s. pencil W/C. 4-Dec-3 Christie's, Kensington #227/R est:5000-7000

FABBI, Romolo (20th C) Italian
£1560 $2528 €2200 Aeroplani in cabrata (50x37cm-20x15in) s.d.35. 22-May-3 Stadion, Trieste #351/R est:2000-3000
£2376 $3849 €3350 Ritorno della squadriglia vittoriosa (80x80cm-31x31in) s. i.verso. 22-May-3 Stadion, Trieste #350/R est:4000-5000

FABBIANI, Juan Vicente (1910-) Venezuelan
£228 $415 €342 Portrait (49x39cm-19x15in) s. painted 1928. 21-Jun-4 Subastas Odalys, Caracas #177
£313 $575 €470 Woman (46x38cm-18x15in) s. painted 1978. 27-Jun-4 Subastas Odalys, Caracas #135
£330 $600 €495 Seascape (46x55cm-18x22in) s. painted 1988. 21-Jun-4 Subastas Odalys, Caracas #179
£340 $625 €510 Still life (21x31cm-8x12in) s. painted 1976. 27-Jun-4 Subastas Odalys, Caracas #108/R
£367 $675 €551 Still life (38x46cm-15x18in) s. painted 1984. 27-Jun-4 Subastas Odalys, Caracas #81/R
£387 $600 €565 Still life (33x46cm-13x18in) s. 29-Sep-2 Subastas Odalys, Caracas #76
£441 $750 €644 Nude (55x42cm-22x17in) s. painted 1986. 23-Nov-3 Subastas Odalys, Caracas #35
£454 $835 €681 Still life (45x57cm-18x22in) s. painted 1979. 27-Jun-4 Subastas Odalys, Caracas #144
£519 $965 €758 Nude (91x71cm-36x28in) s. painted 1972. 14-Mar-4 Subastas Odalys, Caracas #45/R
£581 $900 €848 Landscape (46x56cm-18x22in) s. 29-Sep-2 Subastas Odalys, Caracas #4/R
£635 $1060 €927 Still life of fruit (38x46cm-15x18in) s. painted 1987. 13-Jul-3 Subastas Odalys, Caracas #82/R
£659 $1225 €962 Still life (36x46cm-14x18in) s. painted 1971. 14-Mar-4 Subastas Odalys, Caracas #77/R
£784 $1310 €1145 Dolls (70x60cm-28x24in) s. painted 1979. 19-Oct-3 Subastas Odalys, Caracas #5/R
£1397 $2375 €2040 Still life (41x61cm-16x24in) s. masonite painted 1945. 23-Nov-3 Subastas Odalys, Caracas #151/R
£1876 $3190 €2739 Still life (43x56cm-17x22in) s. masonite painted 1947. 23-Nov-3 Subastas Odalys, Caracas #148/R

FABBRI, Agenore (1911-1998) Italian
£290 $475 €400 Untitled (70x50cm-28x20in) s. tempera Chinese ink prov. 27-May-3 Sotheby's, Milan #67
£733 $1349 €1100 L (44x40cm-17x16in) s.i.d.verso prov. 10-Jun-4 Galleria Pace, Milan #57/R
£986 $1637 €1400 Laceration (40x30cm-16x12in) s.d.1962 verso acrylic board. 11-Jun-3 Finarte Semenzato, Milan #672/R
Sculpture
£2297 $4043 €3400 Composition (58cm-23in) s.d.1952 painted terracotta. 19-May-4 Il Ponte, Milan #1086 est:1800-2000
£3667 $6747 €5500 Seated figure (30x14x12cm-12x6x5in) s.verso terracotta. 12-Jun-4 Meeting Art, Vercelli #93/R est:5000
£3804 $7000 €5554 Nastro di gala (33x165x41cm-13x65x16in) enameled steel lit. 28-Mar-4 Wright, Chicago #178/R est:7000-9000
£6597 $11215 €9500 Composition (116cm-46in) s. bronze exec.1958 prov.exhib.lit. 28-Oct-3 Il Ponte, Milan #246/R
£7042 $12324 €10000 Man in space (133cm-52in) s. bronze. 16-Dec-3 Porro, Milan #28/R est:5000-7000
Works on paper
£233 $429 €350 Men (50x35cm-20x14in) s. W/C paper on canvas prov. 8-Jun-4 Finarte Semenzato, Milan #121/R
£369 $683 €550 Don Milani (50x70cm-20x28in) s.verso mixed media card prov. 11-Mar-4 Galleria Pace, Milan #11/R
£471 $772 €650 Untitled (24x34cm-9x13in) s.d.60 Chinese ink pastel card prov. 27-May-3 Sotheby's, Milan #170/R

£738 $1366 €1100 Horses (63x44cm-25x17in) s.d.1945 mixed media. 13-Mar-4 Meeting Art, Vercelli #475
£769 $1308 €1100 Untitled (48x34cm-19x13in) s. Chinese ink gouache. 25-Nov-3 Sotheby's, Milan #114

FABBRI, V (19th C) Italian?
£2324 $4020 €3300 Regatta on the GRand Canal. View of Venice (60x90cm-24x35in) s. pair. 14-Dec-3 Finarte, Venice #28/R est:1000-1100

FABBRICOTTI, Emanuela (1887-?) Italian
Works on paper
£1399 $2336 €2000 Young woman in white (70x50cm-28x20in) s.d.1936 pastel. 24-Jun-3 Finarte Semenzato, Rome #104/R

FABBRINI, Giuseppe (1740-?) Italian
Works on paper
£503 $926 €750 Caritas (33x15cm-13x6in) s.i. chk htd white. 26-Mar-4 Venator & Hansten, Koln #1464

FABBU, Umberto (20th C) Italian?
Sculpture
£1800 $3060 €2628 Figure of a boy at the beach playing with a snail (66cm-26in) s.d.1932 white marble bronze. 5-Nov-3 John Nicholson, Haslemere #1026 est:3000-4000

FABELO, Roberto (1950-) Cuban
£8380 $15000 €12235 Big blue cock (91x128cm-36x50in) s.d.1997 s.d.verso prov. 26-May-4 Sotheby's, New York #155/R est:18000-22000

FABER DU FAUR, Christian Wilhelm von (1780-1857) German
Works on paper
£408 $731 €600 Desert rider (18x24cm-7x9in) W/C over pencil htd white pencil sketch verso. 17-Mar-4 Neumeister, Munich #284/R

FABER DU FAUR, Hans von (1863-1949) German
£1057 $1871 €1575 Women riding in park (81x89cm-32x35in) s. board. 28-Apr-4 Schopman, Hamburg #531/R est:1680
£1057 $1871 €1575 Elegant riders (85x99cm-33x39in) s. 28-Apr-4 Schopman, Hamburg #533/R est:1700
Works on paper
£300 $537 €450 Riders on beach (11x21cm-4x8in) s. Indian ink W/C. 13-May-4 Neumeister, Munich #345/R

FABER DU FAUR, Otto von (1828-1901) German
£366 $656 €534 Study of Oriental head (45x34cm-18x13in) board prov. 12-May-4 Dobiaschofsky, Bern #481/R (S.FR 850)
£903 $1472 €1300 French artillery (21x46cm-8x18in) s. i. verso board. 25-Sep-3 Dr Fritz Nagel, Stuttgart #1349/R
Works on paper
£333 $613 €500 Wild horses in the Hungarian Steppe (16x19cm-6x7in) s. gouache exec. c.1880. 11-Jun-4 Wendl, Rudolstadt #4014/R

FABER, Christoffer (1800-1869) Danish
£379 $701 €553 The Resurrection (157x109cm-62x43in) s.d.1845. 15-Mar-4 Rasmussen, Vejle #244/R (D.KR 4200)

FABER, Christoffcr (attrib) (1800-1869) Danish
£404 $752 €590 Figures in front of St Knud's church, Odense (74x95cm-29x37in) 2-Mar-4 Rasmussen, Copenhagen #1547/R (D.KR 4500)

FABER, Johann Joachim (1778-1846) German
Works on paper
£352 $563 €500 Borghetto c Valle del Tevere (23x40cm-9x16in) i.d.1807 pencil htd white lit. 19-Sep-3 Karlheinz Kaupp, Staufen #2017

FABER, John (elder) (c.1650-1721) Dutch
£3200 $5536 €4672 Military skirmish in a wooded pass (85x114cm-33x45in) s.d.16. 12-Dec-3 Christie's, Kensington #167/R est:2000-3000

FABER, John (younger) (1684-1756) Dutch
Works on paper
£387 $692 €580 Portrait of the Duke of Marlborough (10x10cm-4x4in) i. pen. 13-May-4 Bassenge, Berlin #5384/R

FABER, Karl (1885-1962) German
£461 $847 €700 Autumn day (83x60cm-33x24in) s. panel. 25-Jun-4 Michael Zeller, Lindau #634/R

FABER, Karl Gottfried Traugott (1786-1863) German
£15972 $25236 €23000 Dresden from the right bank of the Elbe below the August Bridge (108x153cm-43x60in) with sig.indis d. 2-Sep-3 Christie's, Amsterdam #156/R est:8000-10000

FABERT, Jean (20th C) French
£209 $375 €305 Cirque Bouglione, Paris (46x56cm-18x22in) s. s.i.verso. 8-Jan-4 James Julia, Fairfield #149/R

FABI-ALTINI, Francesco (attrib) (1830-1906) Italian
Sculpture
£13333 $23867 €20000 Kidnapping of Proserpina (214cm-84in) s.d.1898 white marble. 17-May-4 Finarte Semenzato, Rome #892/R est:18000-20000

FABIANO, Fabien (1883-1962) French
£264 $450 €385 Still life with pitcher and flowers (61x48cm-24x19in) s.d.65 prov. 22-Nov-3 Jackson's, Cedar Falls #413/R

FABIEN, Henri Zotique (1876-1936) Canadian
£268 $447 €389 Le Fleuve St. Laurent, Quebec (30x41cm-12x16in) s. board. 17-Jun-3 Pinneys, Montreal #13 (C.D 600)

FABIEN, Louis (1924-) Belgian
£250 $400 €365 Le sommeil (33x25cm-13x10in) s.d.1967. 20-Sep-3 Bunte, Elgin #1275
£283 $450 €413 La plage (38x56cm-15x22in) s.d.72 s.i.d.verso prov. 9-Sep-3 Arthur James, Florida #46
£470 $869 €700 Reclining nude (35x27cm-14x11in) s.d.71. 15-Mar-4 Sotheby's, Amsterdam #204/R

FABISCH, Joseph Hugues (1812-1886) French
Sculpture
£3488 $6000 €5092 Woman in long dress (112cm-44in) s. white marble. 6-Dec-3 Selkirks, St. Louis #692/R est:8000-10000

FABIUS, Jan (1820-1889) Dutch
£890 $1514 €1300 Children playing on a see-saw (49x59cm-19x23in) s. 5-Nov-3 Vendue Huis, Gravenhage #88/R
£1316 $2421 €2000 A harmonious family (78x103cm-31x41in) s.indis.i. 22-Jun-4 Christie's, Amsterdam #13/R est:2000-3000

FABRE, François-Xavier (1766-1837) French
£3133 $5765 €4700 Princess Dortoa Barbara Jablonwwska (31x25cm-12x10in) s.d. panel. 11-Jun-4 Hauswedell & Nolte, Hamburg #1015/R est:7000

FABRE, François-Xavier (attrib) (1766-1837) French
Works on paper
£544 $974 €800 Quatre hommes dont un avec un genou a terre (30x26cm-12x10in) pen col ink grey wash. 18-Mar-4 Christie's, Paris #249

FABRE, Jan (1958-) Belgian
Sculpture
£1329 $2300 €1940 Untitled (16x12x21cm-6x5x8in) synthetic resin skull organic material prov. 10-Dec-3 Phillips, New York #590/R est:3000-4000

FABREGAS, Francisco (20th C) Spanish
£966 $1738 €1400 Frenc Can-can (61x50cm-24x20in) s. s.i.d.1939 verso. 26-Jan-4 Ansorena, Madrid #878/R
£1034 $1862 €1500 Two female friends (61x50cm-24x20in) s. s.i.d.1939 verso. 26-Jan-4 Ansorena, Madrid #883/R est:1000

FABRES Y COSTA, Antonio (1854-1936) Spanish
£5765 $10319 €8417 A good smoke - man with pipe (67x44cm-26x17in) s.i.d.6-94 panel exhib. 26-May-4 AB Stockholms Auktionsverk #2439/R est:20000-25000 (S.KR 78000)
Works on paper
£815 $1500 €1190 Too hot! (48x30cm-19x12in) s. W/C. 27-Jun-4 Hindman, Chicago #868/R est:300-500

FABRI, Pompeo (1874-1959) Italian
£667 $1227 €1000 Old walls. Roman countryside (14x23cm-6x9in) s. board pair. 10-Jun-4 Christie's, Rome #21

FABRI, Robert (1839-1909) Italian
£819 $1368 €1196 Sword grinder (35x28cm-14x11in) s.d.1871 panel. 20-Oct-3 Stephan Welz, Johannesburg #191/R est:8000-12000 (SA.R 9500)

FABRI-CANTI, Jose (1910-1994) French
£221 $375 €323 Street view (60x74cm-24x29in) s. board. 21-Nov-3 Skinner, Boston #516/R

FABRICATORE, Nicola (1889-?) Italian
£915 $1584 €1300 Quiet time. Under the arcades (15x18cm-6x7in) s. cardboard pair. 11-Dec-3 Christie's, Rome #78

FABRICIUS, Richard D (1863-?) German
Sculpture
£2013 $3705 €3000 Female nude balancing on tortoise (77cm-30in) pat.bronze marble socle. 26-Mar-4 Bolland & Marotz, Bremen #730/R est:4000

FABRIS, Pietro (18th C) Italian
£10989 $20000 €16044 Cobbler's shop. Cooper's shop (48x41cm-19x16in) pair. 17-Jun-4 Christie's, Rockefeller NY #63/R est:30000-50000
£28966 $48372 €42000 Pozzuoli Bay (28x49cm-11x19in) s.d.1776 tempera paper prov.exhib.lit. 12-Nov-3 Sotheby's, Milan #151/R est:25000-35000

FABRIS, Pietro (attrib) (18th C) Italian
Works on paper
£2013 $3705 €3000 Moines distribuant la soupe (20x16cm-8x6in) gouache. 24-Mar-4 Tajan, Paris #31 est:1000-1500
£37500 $67500 €54750 Charles II departing from Naples for Spain (51x66cm-20x26in) gouache. 21-Jan-4 Sotheby's, New York #105/R est:30000-40000

FABRIS, Pietro (style) (18th C) Italian
£8333 $13750 €12000 Tuna fishing in Gulf of Naples (82x130cm-32x51in) 2-Jul-3 Neumeister, Munich #634/R est:7000

FABRITIUS, Chillian (?-1633) German
£16107 $29638 €24000 Holy Family with St Catherine and noble donor (99x73cm-39x29in) s. panel. 24-Mar-4 Dorotheum, Vienna #431/R est:24000-32000

FABRIZIO, Paola (1964-) Italian
£1241 $1986 €1800 Bush (80x80cm-31x31in) s. 13-Mar-3 Galleria Pace, Milan #105/R est:1650-2200

FABRO, Luciano (1936-) Italian
Sculpture
£5000 $9200 €7300 De Italia (99x90cm-39x35in) s.i.d.72 num.43/50 verso leather prov. 24-Jun-4 Sotheby's, London #236/R est:6000-8000
Works on paper
£4500 $7515 €6570 Effimero 3 (100x60cm-39x24in) s.i.d.86 verso pencil cut-out paper cardboard blade prov. 22-Oct-3 Christie's, London #43/R est:4000-6000

FABRO, Rosina del (1874-1946) Austrian
£451 $745 €650 Naked girl seated (67x46cm-26x18in) s.d.18 board. 3-Jul-3 Neumeister, Munich #2827

FABRON, Luigi (1855-1905) Italian
£563 $935 €800 Interno di cortile (37x47cm-15x19in) s. 11-Jun-3 Christie's, Rome #99
£838 $1500 €1223 Portraits of gentlemen (38x48cm-15x19in) s.d.1870 two. 20-Mar-4 Sloans & Kenyon, Bethesda #1180/R est:2500-3000

FABRY, Ana (1963-) Argentinian
Works on paper
£3297 $6000 €4814 E.R.S.A Leccion, Salvese quien Oueda (147x139cm-58x55in) s.d.98 i.verso mixed media. 29-Jun-4 Sotheby's, New York #690/R est:7000-9000

FABRY, Elisee (1882-1949) Belgian
£340 $609 €500 Vue de Borgoumont (49x59cm-19x23in) s. i.d.Aout 1927 verso. 17-Mar-4 Hotel des Ventes Mosan, Brussels #140
£629 $1051 €900 Vieux coin a clervaux (79x99cm-31x39in) s. s.i.d.1946. 11-Oct-3 De Vuyst, Lokeren #144
£1064 $1777 €1500 Horizon (82x100cm-32x39in) s. 15-Oct-3 Hotel des Ventes Mosan, Brussels #160 est:1200-1500

FABRY, Émile (1865-1966) Belgian
£265 $482 €400 Le Christ, homme et la femme (37x66cm-15x26in) s. canvas on panel. 15-Jun-4 Vanderkindere, Brussels #101
£340 $609 €500 Trois visages (54x48cm-21x19in) s. canvas on panel. 16-Mar-4 Vanderkindere, Brussels #19
£530 $964 €800 La crucifixion (92x62cm-36x24in) s.d.1920 verso stretcher. 15-Jun-4 Vanderkindere, Brussels #50
£596 $1085 €900 Deux visages ou la tendresse (38x40cm-15x16in) s. canvas on panel. 15-Jun-4 Vanderkindere, Brussels #87
£629 $1145 €950 Etudes pour la decoration de la salle des Papillons au Musee Royal (37x38cm-15x15in) exec. c.1909 two. 15-Jun-4 Vanderkindere, Brussels #30/R
£880 $1523 €1250 Tete d'Hypnos (70x47cm-28x19in) s.d.1954. 9-Dec-3 Vanderkindere, Brussels #50
£1241 $2297 €1800 Compositions symbolistes (31x47cm-12x19in) s. cardboard pair. 16-Feb-4 Horta, Bruxelles #487 est:800-1000
£2177 $3897 €3200 Les emblemes de l'ideal (78x53cm-31x21in) s.indis.i. 16-Mar-4 Vanderkindere, Brussels #55/R est:1000-1500
£13574 $22533 €19818 Samson and Delila (131x101cm-52x40in) s.d.1926. 4-Oct-3 Kieselbach, Budapest #151/R (H.F 5000000)
£14931 $24786 €21799 Goddesses, parks (106x131cm-42x52in) s. 4-Oct-3 Kieselbach, Budapest #138/R (H.F 5500000)
£19004 $31546 €27746 Women on the shore (83x117cm-33x46in) s. 4-Oct-3 Kieselbach, Budapest #163/R (H.F 7000000)
Works on paper
£528 $914 €750 Projet de decoration pour la facade de l'Universite de Cardiff (35x49cm-14x19in) s.d.mars 1915 chl. 9-Dec-3 Vanderkindere, Brussels #63
£586 $1084 €850 Profil d'homme. Portrait de femme. s.d.1918 one pastel one col crayon pair. 13-Jan-4 Vanderkindere, Brussels #104
£586 $1084 €850 Untitled. Ange. one d.1913 one s.d.1919 col crayon pair. 13-Jan-4 Vanderkindere, Brussels #107
£739 $1279 €1050 Devant les Parques de la vie, l'homme est etendu. (48x56cm-19x22in) s.d.1911 chl htd pastel board. 9-Dec-3 Vanderkindere, Brussels #125
£894 $1627 €1350 Homme nu (25x13cm-10x5in) s.d.92 crayon. 15-Jun-4 Vanderkindere, Brussels #82
£1088 $1948 €1600 Profil de femme (20x17cm-8x7in) s.d.92 graphite ink. 16-Mar-4 Vanderkindere, Brussels #57 est:200-300

FABRY, Émile (attrib) (1865-1966) Belgian
£862 $1595 €1250 Deux nus (71x56cm-28x22in) canvas on panel prov. 13-Jan-4 Vanderkindere, Brussels #82
£1172 $2169 €1700 Homme et femme nus (101x84cm-40x33in) canvas on panel prov. 13-Jan-4 Vanderkindere, Brussels #68 est:600-800

FABRY, Jaro (1912-1953) American
Works on paper
£950 $1700 €1387 Hollywood cast party (46x61cm-18x24in) s. W/C gouache litho pencil. 15-May-4 Illustration House, New York #143/R est:1500-2500

FACCHINETTI, Nicolau Antonio (1824-1900) Italian
£45000 $69750 €65700 Bay of Rio seen from the road to Petropolis (56x80cm-22x31in) s.d.1869 i.on stretcher. 26-Sep-2 Christie's, London #116/R est:25000-35000
Works on paper
£3480 $6368 €5220 Souvenir de la rue Paissandu (26x35cm-10x14in) s.i.d.1880 graphite. 6-Jul-4 Bolsa de Arte, Rio de Janeiro #50/R (B.R 19000)

FACCINCANI, Athos (1951-) Italian
£340 $626 €510 Vase of flowers (50x35cm-20x14in) s. paper on canvas. 12-Jun-4 Meeting Art, Vercelli #151
£379 $633 €550 Dream and magnolia (25x35cm-10x14in) s. gouache oil. 13-Nov-3 Galleria Pace, Milan #74/R
£433 $797 €650 Garden in bloom on the lake (20x30cm-8x12in) s. 12-Jun-4 Meeting Art, Vercelli #661/R
£443 $819 €660 Vase of flowers (50x35cm-20x14in) s. paper on canvas. 13-Mar-4 Meeting Art, Vercelli #460
£467 $859 €700 Broom (45x25cm-18x10in) s.i. paper on canvas. 10-Jun-4 Galleria Pace, Milan #96/R
£500 $920 €750 Landscape (35x45cm-14x18in) s. painted 1996. 12-Jun-4 Meeting Art, Vercelli #554/R
£633 $1165 €950 Fragments of light and colours (20x30cm-8x12in) s. 12-Jun-4 Meeting Art, Vercelli #296/R
£638 $1180 €950 Landscape (20x30cm-8x12in) s. 11-Mar-4 Galleria Pace, Milan #95/R
£638 $1180 €950 Villa at the sea (40x30cm-16x12in) s. 13-Mar-4 Meeting Art, Vercelli #212
£733 $1327 €1100 Landscape (35x50cm-14x20in) s. 2-Apr-4 Farsetti, Prato #145/R
£1067 $1963 €1600 Quays on the Grand Canal (60x60cm-24x24in) s. s.i.verso. 12-Jun-4 Meeting Art, Vercelli #243/R est:1500
£1172 $1876 €1700 Lake tale (50x50cm-20x20in) s. s.verso. 13-Mar-3 Galleria Pace, Milan #110/R est:2000-2600
£1241 $2073 €1800 Lake landscape (60x60cm-24x24in) s. 13-Nov-3 Galleria Pace, Milan #87/R est:2800
£1342 $2483 €2000 Cortina (50x70cm-20x28in) s. painted 1998. 13-Mar-4 Meeting Art, Vercelli #501 est:1500
£1408 $2338 €2000 Positano (90x100cm-35x39in) s. 14-Jun-3 Meeting Art, Vercelli #625/R est:2000
£1611 $2980 €2400 Landscape (6x80cm-2x31in) s. 11-Mar-4 Galleria Pace, Milan #96/R est:2800-3500
Works on paper
£382 $603 €550 Thinking around a little table (25x45cm-10x18in) gouache paper on canvas. 6-Sep-3 Meeting Art, Vercelli #658
£400 $736 €600 Santorini (35x50cm-14x20in) s. gouache paper on canvas. 12-Jun-4 Meeting Art, Vercelli #189/R
£500 $920 €750 Spring tale (50x70cm-20x28in) s. i.verso gouache oil paper on canvas. 12-Jun-4 Meeting Art, Vercelli #932/R
£521 $823 €750 Pink drean in Santorini (44x64cm-17x25in) gouache paper on canvas. 6-Sep-3 Meeting Art, Vercelli #728
£528 $877 €750 Ortensie tra i fiori gialli e le rose (44x64cm-17x25in) s. i.verso gouache oil paper on canvas. 14-Jun-3 Meeting Art, Vercelli #182/R

FACCIOLA, G (?) ?
Works on paper
£933 $1671 €1400 View from Pincio to Rome (28x47cm-11x19in) s. W/C. 13-May-4 Bassenge, Berlin #5549/R

FACCIOLI, Giovanni (1729-1809) Italian
£1200 $2172 €1800 Monks working (52x74cm-20x29in) 3-Apr-4 Badum, Bamberg #186/R est:3000
£1200 $2172 €1800 Monks working in garden (52x74cm-20x29in) lit. 3-Apr-4 Badum, Bamberg #187/R est:3000

FACKERE, Jef van de (1879-1946) Belgian
Works on paper
£3557 $6581 €5300 Flower arranger (93x75cm-37x30in) s. pastel. 13-Mar-4 De Vuyst, Lokeren #331/R est:6000-7000

FACKERT, Jurgen (1943-) German
£1528 $2490 €2200 Untitled (81x79cm-32x31in) s. verso dispersion spray pigment acrylic varnish iron. 27-Sep-3 Dr Fritz Nagel, Stuttgart #9527/R est:2900

FADER, Fernando (1882-1935) Argentinian
£25683 $47000 €37497 Exit from Mass (100x70cm-39x28in) 1-Jun-4 Arroyo, Buenos Aires #62
£30601 $56000 €44677 Pirca (55x78cm-22x31in) 1-Jun-4 Arroyo, Buenos Aires #72

FADINE, Igor (1939-) Russian
£398 $700 €581 Children playing in the snow (48x58cm-19x23in) mono. i.d.1985. 18-May-4 Arthur James, Florida #187/R

FAED, James (19/20th C) British
£350 $595 €511 Chillingham cattle in the park (28x23cm-11x9in) s.d.1881 s.i. verso board. 27-Nov-3 Greenslade Hunt, Taunton #1014

FAED, James (jnr) (1856-1920) British
£1000 $1860 €1460 Rocks and heather (13x23cm-5x9in) panel. 4-Mar-4 Christie's, Kensington #66/R est:500-800
£1000 $1870 €1500 On the hills at Laggan (15x23cm-6x9in) s. panel. 21-Jul-4 John Nicholson, Haslemere #185
£2000 $3340 €2920 Scottish landscape with heather covered valley (31x46cm-12x18in) s.indis.d. panel. 17-Nov-3 Trembath Welch, Great Dunmow #495/R est:600-800
£2700 $4347 €3915 On the Almond (28x39cm-11x15in) s.d.May 1886 i.on stretcher. 21-Aug-3 Bonhams, Edinburgh #1074/R est:1500-2000

FAED, John (1820-1902) British
£2200 $3938 €3212 Portrait of a seated gentleman (14x12cm-6x5in) i.verso panel. 16-Mar-4 Gildings, Market Harborough #450/R est:1500-2200
£7500 $12075 €10875 Blenheim and then the old man shook his head (60x78cm-24x31in) s. exhib. 21-Aug-3 Bonhams, Edinburgh #1209/R est:7000-10000
£15000 $27600 €21900 Boaz and Ruth (21x27cm-8x11in) mono. board prov.exhib.lit. 11-Jun-4 Christie's, London #150/R est:15000-20000
Works on paper
£1150 $1852 €1668 Scene from Burn's Cottar's Saturday night (18x23cm-7x9in) W/C en grisaille. 21-Aug-3 Bonhams, Edinburgh #1220 est:400-600

FAED, John (attrib) (1820-1902) British
£2300 $4117 €3358 Serving the enlistment papers (76x61cm-30x24in) 11-Jan-4 Desmond Judd, Cranbrook #690

FAED, Thomas (1826-1900) British
£6800 $10676 €9860 Fisher girl (53x41cm-21x16in) s.d.1859. 27-Aug-3 Sotheby's, London #913/R est:6000-8000
£7500 $11775 €10875 Orange seller (78x51cm-31x20in) s.d.1884 prov. 27-Aug-3 Sotheby's, London #911/R est:6000-8000
£19048 $34095 €28000 Coming events cast their shadows before (72x48cm-28x19in) s.d.1857. 17-Mar-4 Maigret, Paris #1/R est:10000-15000
Works on paper
£500 $945 €730 Loch scene by moonlight (12x20cm-5x8in) init. sepia. 19-Feb-4 Lyon & Turnbull, Edinburgh #153
£580 $934 €841 Portrait of Sandy Home (11x10cm-4x4in) s.d.1852 pencil ink W/C. 21-Aug-3 Bonhams, Edinburgh #1016

FAED, Thomas (attrib) (1826-1900) British
£462 $794 €675 Interior scene with family (31x26cm-12x10in) s. panel. 3-Dec-3 AB Stockholms Auktionsverk #2612/R (S.KR 6000)
£633 $1140 €950 Man and girl by oven (61x45cm-24x18in) 26-Apr-4 Rieber, Stuttgart #966/R

FAELDMAN, Joshua (19/20th C) ?
£260 $475 €390 Fullness of summer (38x56cm-15x22in) s.d.1867. 31-Jul-4 Sloans & Kenyon, Bethesda #1218/R

FAFARD, Joseph (1942-) Canadian
Sculpture
£1250 $2150 €1825 Jason (24cm-9in) s.d.93 num.7/7 bronze prov. 2-Dec-3 Joyner Waddington, Toronto #40/R est:1200-1500 (C.D 2800)
£4241 $7295 €6192 Often Morris bullied his mother (17x36cm-7x14in) s.d.87 num.1/3 bronze with glass table top. 2-Dec-3 Joyner Waddington, Toronto #162/R est:5000-8000 (C.D 9500)
£5691 $10187 €8309 Lescaux (71x61x30cm-28x24x12in) s.d.1988 num.2/5 bronze. 27-May-4 Heffel, Vancouver #122/R est:8000-12000 (C.D 14000)
£6306 $10721 €9207 Benoit (48x58x24cm-19x23x9in) s.d.1991 num.3/5 bronze. 27-Nov-3 Heffel, Vancouver #51/R est:5000-7000 (C.D 14000)
Works on paper
£1829 $3274 €2670 Hicks (81x102cm-32x40in) i.d.1989 pastel prov. 31-May-4 Sotheby's, Toronto #179/R est:3000-5000 (C.D 4500)

FAGAN, Robert (attrib) (1745-1816) British
£2667 $4827 €4000 Young boy with basket of apples (62x74cm-24x29in) 31-Mar-4 James Adam, Dublin #29a/R est:3000-4000

FAGER, F de (17th C) ?
£1800 $3240 €2628 Portrait of a gentleman, in armour (125x96cm-49x38in) s.d.16. 23-Apr-4 Christie's, Kensington #76/R est:1500-2000

FAGERKVIST, Thor (1884-1960) Swedish
£281 $503 €410 Passionerna (64x55cm-25x22in) s. exhib.prov. 28-May-4 Uppsala Auktionskammare, Uppsala #350 (S.KR 3800)

FAGERLIN, Ferdinand (1825-1907) Swedish
£424 $734 €619 Kitchen interior with woman (32x42cm-13x17in) s. 15-Dec-3 Lilla Bukowskis, Stockholm #101 (S.KR 5400)
£428 $689 €625 The last drop (32x26cm-13x10in) s. 25-Aug-3 Lilla Bukowskis, Stockholm #859 (S.KR 5600)
£437 $805 €656 Interior scene with fisherman in kitchen (32x42cm-13x17in) mono. panel. 14-Jun-4 Lilla Bukowskis, Stockholm #829 (S.KR 6000)
£739 $1323 €1079 Girl with red scarf (41x34cm-16x13in) s. 26-May-4 AB Stockholms Auktionsverk #2191/R (S.KR 10000)
£917 $1477 €1339 Idyllic interior (57x64cm-22x25in) s. 25-Aug-3 Lilla Bukowskis, Stockholm #492 (S.KR 12000)
£1626 $2911 €2374 Palms outside town wall, Rome (41x29cm-16x11in) d.Juli 1856 s.i.d.1856 verso. 26-May-4 AB Stockholms Auktionsverk #2238/R est:8000-10000 (S.KR 22000)
£12000 $21840 €17520 Wishing it were she (85x103cm-33x41in) s.i. prov. 15-Jun-4 Sotheby's, London #307/R est:12000-18000
£12565 $22491 €18345 Devotion at home - or The recovery (81x100cm-32x39in) s.i.d.68 prov.lit. 26-May-4 AB Stockholms Auktionsverk #2318/R est:75000-100000 (S.KR 170000)

FAGERLUND, Mikael (1955-) Swedish
£453 $770 €661 Untitled (37x30cm-15x12in) s.d.95 verso panel prov. 5-Nov-3 AB Stockholms Auktionsverk #997/R (S.KR 6000)

FAGET-GERMAIN, Pierre (1903-1961) French
£292 $481 €420 Trois-mats au portant (77x99cm-30x39in) panel. 5-Jul-3 Neret-Minet, Paris #148/R
£638 $1066 €900 Pointe Pescade (21x32cm-8x13in) s. panel. 19-Oct-3 Rabourdin & Choppin de Janvry, Paris #102/R

FAGGIOLI, Juan Carlos (19/20th C) Argentinian
£670 $1200 €978 Moulin de la Galette, Paris (25x34cm-10x13in) 11-May-4 Arroyo, Buenos Aires #36
£1648 $3000 €2406 Fisherman's fair (60x90cm-24x35in) s.i.d.1956. 5-Jul-4 Arroyo, Buenos Aires #25/R est:3000
£1923 $3500 €2808 Still life (97x130cm-38x51in) s.d.1949. 29-Jun-4 Arroyo, Buenos Aires #20/R est:3500
£2155 $3900 €3146 Plaza de Mayo, 1890 (90x66cm-35x26in) 30-Mar-4 Arroyo, Buenos Aires #35

FAGUAYS, Pierre le (1892-1935) French
Sculpture
£1034 $1728 €1500 Combat de coqs (19x69cm-7x27in) silver pat bronze black marble socle lit. 14-Nov-3 Claude Boisgirard, Paris #61/R est:1200-1500
£1200 $2196 €1752 Vestal (35cm-14in) i. bronze onyx base. 3-Jun-4 Sotheby's, Olympia #267/R est:1000-1500
£1414 $2587 €2050 Femme au bouclier (56cm-22in) green pat bronze marble socle. 31-Jan-4 Gerard, Besancon #246
£1800 $3006 €2628 Art Deco figure of a muscular athlete (34x55cm-13x22in) s. pat bronze granite sold with base. 11-Nov-3 Rosebery Fine Art, London #115 est:1800-2200
£2000 $3740 €2920 Message of love (44cm-17in) s. silvered bronze marble pedestal exec.c.1925. 24-Feb-4 Sotheby's, Olympia #260/R est:2000-3000
£12139 $21000 €17723 Figural relief (48x134x18cm-19x53x7in) bronze onyx marble. 11-Dec-3 Sotheby's, New York #43/R est:8000-12000
£14525 $26000 €21207 Archer (61cm-24in) s. silver brown pat bronze ivory marble base. 20-Mar-4 Freeman, Philadelphia #600/R est:5000-8000

FAGUAYS, Pierre le (after) (1892-1935) French
Sculpture
£4396 $8000 €6594 Pierrot and Columbine (41cm-16in) i. pat bronze marble base exec. 1925 prov. 16-Jun-4 Sotheby's, New York #262/R est:6000-8000

FAHEY, Edward Henry (1844-1907) British
£600 $1110 €876 Entrance to Wroxham Broad (30x48cm-12x19in) s.d.1886. 13-Feb-4 Keys, Aylsham #459/R
£750 $1388 €1095 Street scene in Lai-alia, Italy (23x14cm-9x6in) s.d.89 panel pair. 9-Mar-4 Bonhams, Knightsbridge #154/R
Works on paper
£1800 $3294 €2628 River view outside Oxford (25x35cm-10x14in) s.d.73 W/C. 27-Jan-4 Bonhams, Knightsbridge #380/R est:1500-2000

FAHEY, James (1804-1885) British
Works on paper
£280 $468 €409 Bassenthwiate lake, Cumbria (42x76cm-17x30in) s. W/C. 14-Oct-3 Bonhams, Knightsbridge #189/R

FAHLCRANTZ, Carl Johan (1774-1861) Swedish
£591 $1058 €863 Landscape with waterfall (78x60cm-31x24in) prov.lit. 25-May-4 Bukowskis, Stockholm #418/R (S.KR 8000)
£917 $1477 €1339 View towards Gripsholm's Palace (59x76cm-23x30in) s.d.1819. 25-Aug-3 Lilla Bukowskis, Stockholm #164 (S.KR 12000)
£1330 $2381 €1942 Pastoral landscape (40x51cm-16x20in) s.d.1821 prov. 25-May-4 Bukowskis, Stockholm #419/R est:10000-12000 (S.KR 18000)
£2513 $4498 €3669 Romantic mountain and river landscape (62x82cm-24x32in) 25-May-4 Bukowskis, Stockholm #417/R est:15000-18000 (S.KR 34000)
£6923 $11908 €10108 Landscape with castle (124x170cm-49x67in) 3-Dec-3 AB Stockholms Auktionsverk #2392/R est:25000-30000 (S.KR 90000)

FAHLCRANTZ, Carl Johan (attrib) (1774-1861) Swedish
£628 $1125 €917 Southern landscape with sailing vessel on river (26x35cm-10x14in) i.verso. 26-May-4 AB Stockholms Auktionsverk #2335/R (S.KR 8500)

FAHLGREN, Carl August (1819-1905) Swedish
£541 $968 €800 Archipelago, summer (51x75cm-20x30in) s.d.1883. 8-May-4 Bukowskis, Helsinki #371/R

FAHLSTROM, Oyvind (1928-1976) Swedish
£19260 $32742 €28120 Il Dono di Casalpusterlengo (50x65cm-20x26in) varnish chk paper on canvas prov.exhib.lit. 4-Nov-3 Bukowskis, Stockholm #577/R est:175000-200000 (S.KR 255000)
Works on paper
£378 $642 €552 Untitled (20x14cm-8x6in) pastel prov. 5-Nov-3 AB Stockholms Auktionsverk #1060/R (S.KR 5000)
£378 $642 €552 Untitled (20x14cm-8x6in) pastel prov. 5-Nov-3 AB Stockholms Auktionsverk #1061/R (S.KR 5000)
£755 $1284 €1102 Untitled (26x34cm-10x13in) Indian ink prov. 5-Nov-3 AB Stockholms Auktionsverk #1063/R (S.KR 10000)
£906 $1541 €1323 Untitled (34x26cm-13x10in) pastel prov. 5-Nov-3 AB Stockholms Auktionsverk #1062/R (S.KR 12000)

FAHNLE, Hans (1903-1968) German
£451 $736 €650 Still life of fruit (42x52cm-17x20in) s.d.1943 masonite. 27-Sep-3 Dr Fritz Nagel, Stuttgart #9110/R

FAHRBACH, Carl Ludwig (1835-1902) German
£952 $1705 €1400 River landscape with stone bridge (37x51cm-15x20in) s. 17-Mar-4 Neumeister, Munich #450/R
£1118 $2058 €1700 Stony stream in autumn wood (30x24cm-12x9in) mono. board. 24-Jun-4 Dr Fritz Nagel, Stuttgart #705/R est:1400
£1118 $2058 €1700 Extensive wooded landscape (79x131cm-31x52in) s.d.1870. 24-Jun-4 Dr Fritz Nagel, Stuttgart #706/R est:400
£2083 $3396 €3000 Deer in forest (85x112cm-33x44in) s.d.1899. 25-Sep-3 Dr Fritz Nagel, Stuttgart #1347/R est:1100
£5556 $9056 €8000 Forest near Bensberg (112x85cm-44x33in) s. 25-Sep-3 Dr Fritz Nagel, Stuttgart #1348/R est:8900

FAHRENKROG, Ludwig (1867-?) German
£1507 $2562 €2200 Portrait of a lady (129x88cm-51x35in) s. 5-Nov-3 Vendue Huis, Gravenhage #121 est:2200-2500

FAHRI, Jean Claude (1940-) ?
Sculpture
£2657 $4571 €3800 Disque (66x66cm-26x26in) s. plexiglas. 4-Dec-3 Piasa, Paris #48/R est:400-500

FAHRINGER, Carl (1874-1952) Austrian
£800 $1456 €1200 Oriental summer (34x49cm-13x19in) indis.mono. lit. 3-Jul-4 Badum, Bamberg #80/R
£979 $1664 €1400 Farmer's market (56x79cm-22x31in) s. 25-Nov-3 Hassfurther, Vienna #33
£1200 $2148 €1800 Eagle (50x37cm-20x15in) s. 13-May-4 Dorotheum, Linz #485/R est:2400-2800
£1690 $2958 €2400 Black poodle (41x52cm-16x20in) s.d.48. 19-Dec-3 Dorotheum, Vienna #132/R est:2200-3200
Works on paper
£855 $1574 €1300 Fishermen on the quay near the Hoofdtoren, Hoorn (59x43cm-23x17in) s.d.34 gouache. 22-Jun-4 Christie's, Amsterdam #203/R
£921 $1695 €1400 Pelican (40x26cm-16x10in) Gouache. 22-Jun-4 Wiener Kunst Auktionen, Vienna #89/R
£2585 $4627 €3800 Stone cutters at a temple site (50x42cm-20x17in) s.i. gouache W/C. 16-Mar-4 Christie's, Amsterdam #35/R est:2500-3500
£3401 $6088 €5000 Klung Kung (32x45cm-13x18in) s.i.d.27 W/C gouache. 16-Mar-4 Christie's, Amsterdam #30/R est:2500-3500
£5229 $9464 €7634 Pasar scene (32x47cm-13x19in) s.d.29 mixed media board prov. 3-Apr-4 Glerum, Singapore #11/R est:7000-10000 (S.D 16000)

FAIGENBAUM, Patrick (1954-) ?
Photographs
£2013 $3705 €3000 Famille Carpegna Falconieri, Rome (47x48cm-19x19in) s.d.1987 num.5/8 verso gelatin silver print prov. 29-Mar-4 Cornette de St.Cyr, Paris #100/R est:3000-4000

FAILLA, Fabio (1917-1987) Italian
£559 $951 €800 Seminar pupil (70x38cm-28x15in) s.d.1949 s.i.d.verso board. 24-Nov-3 Christie's, Milan #106
£811 $1427 €1200 Authentic books (45x70cm-18x28in) s. s.i.verso prov. 24-May-4 Christie's, Milan #131
£1486 $2616 €2200 Books (50x84cm-20x33in) s. s.i.d.1961 verso prov. 24-May-4 Christie's, Milan #128/R est:2200-2800

FAILLY, Baron Oscar de (19th C) French
£1230 $2300 €1796 Traditional landscape (41x51cm-16x20in) 25-Feb-4 Dallas Auction Gallery, Dallas #429/R

FAINI, Virgilio (1872-?) Italian
Works on paper
£468 $767 €650 Back from mowing (13x27cm-5x11in) s. W/C. 10-Jun-3 Pandolfini, Florence #209

FAIOLA, Viviana (1950-) Italian
£400 $736 €600 Composition (70x60cm-28x24in) s.verso. 12-Jun-4 Meeting Art, Vercelli #398
£433 $797 €650 Untitled (70x50cm-28x20in) s.i.verso painted 1998 lit. 12-Jun-4 Meeting Art, Vercelli #38

FAIR, Fraser Grant (1949-) Australian
£1736 $3211 €2535 Giekie Gorge (196x181cm-77x71in) s.d.89 prov. 15-Mar-4 Sotheby's, Melbourne #152 est:600-800 (A.D 4200)

FAIRBAIRN, Hilda (fl.1893) British
£300 $537 €438 The Beech Avenue (41x51cm-16x20in) s.d.1913. 7-Jan-4 George Kidner, Lymington #208/R

FAIRBAIRN, Ida M (fl.1923-1939) British
£300 $558 €438 Still life of primula in blue vase (26x21cm-10x8in) s. board. 2-Mar-4 Bearnes, Exeter #452

FAIRHURST, Enoch (1874-?) British
Works on paper
£320 $586 €467 Admiring glances (36x22cm-14x9in) s. W/C. 27-Jan-4 Bonhams, Knightsbridge #78/R

FAIRHURST, Ernest (19th C) British
£260 $476 €380 Her Majesty Queen Elizabeth II taking the salute at the trooping of the colour (43x76cm-17x30in) s. 8-Jul-4 Duke & Son, Dorchester #178

FAIRLEY, Barker (1887-1986) Canadian
£785 $1429 €1146 Eleanora Prokos (51x41cm-20x16in) s. s.i.d.1978 verso board prov. 5-Feb-4 Heffel, Vancouver #29/R (C.D 1900)
£1210 $2226 €1767 Portrait of Almuth Lutkenhaus (61x50cm-24x20in) s.i.d.1975 verso board prov. 9-Jun-4 Walker's, Ottawa #41/R est:2000-3000 (C.D 3000)
£1760 $3221 €2570 White shed (40x50cm-16x20in) board painted 1978 prov. 1-Jun-4 Joyner Waddington, Toronto #386/R est:3000-4000 (C.D 4400)
£2621 $4823 €3827 Muskoka Lake (50x61cm-20x24in) s. s.i.d.1970 verso board prov. 9-Jun-4 Walker's, Ottawa #40/R est:2000-3000 (C.D 6500)
Works on paper
£440 $805 €642 Back yard view (22x28cm-9x11in) W/C exec 1938. 1-Jun-4 Joyner Waddington, Toronto #515 (C.D 1100)

FAIRLIE, John (fl.1845) British
£419 $700 €612 Highlands landscape with castle (51x76cm-20x30in) s.d.94. 16-Nov-3 William Jenack, New York #221

FAIRMAN, Frances C (1836-1923) British
£1500 $2550 €2190 Head of a bulldog (46x38cm-18x15in) s. 27-Nov-3 Christie's, Kensington #357/R est:1500-2000
£3243 $6000 €4735 Monkeyano (66x51cm-26x20in) s.i.d.1909 prov.lit. 10-Feb-4 Doyle, New York #175/R est:4000-6000
Works on paper
£950 $1739 €1387 Tibetan spaniels (5x12cm-2x5in) s.d.1902 W/C. 28-Jul-4 Bonhams, Knightsbridge #167/R

FAIRWEATHER, Ian (1891-1974) Australian
£7000 $12810 €10220 Mother and child (36x36cm-14x14in) canvasboard prov. 8-Jul-4 Duke & Son, Dorchester #170/R
£16529 $30579 €24132 Dutch barge, The Haque (29x42cm-11x17in) board painted c.1917-18 prov.exhib. 10-Mar-4 Deutscher-Menzies, Melbourne #87/R est:30000-40000 (A.D 40000)
£49180 $77705 €71803 Family group (52x38cm-20x15in) s. oil gouache card prov. 2-Sep-3 Deutscher-Menzies, Melbourne #34/R est:45000-65000 (A.D 120000)
£198347 $351074 €289587 Tea garden, Peking (88x90cm-35x35in) compressed card prov.exhib.lit. 3-May-4 Christie's, Melbourne #23/R est:120000-180000 (A.D 480000)
Works on paper
£33058 $61157 €48265 Roundabout (106x76cm-42x30in) synthetic polymer on board executed c.1971-74 prov.exhib. 10-Mar-4 Deutscher-Menzies, Melbourne #31/R est:90000-120000 (A.D 80000)
£33058 $58512 €48265 Market scene, peking (37x40cm-15x16in) s. gouache pencil exec.c.1945 prov.exhib.lit. 3-May-4 Christie's, Melbourne #85/R est:50000-60000 (A.D 80000)
£54878 $86159 €79573 Composition in orange and yellow (95x136cm-37x54in) synthetic polymer paint gouache cardboard on hardboard prov.exhib. 26-Aug-3 Christie's, Sydney #17/R est:120000-160000 (A.D 135000)

FAISTAUER, Anton (1887-1930) Austrian
£38000 $69920 €55480 Blumenstrauss in Henkelvase - Flowers in a vase (50x40cm-20x16in) s.d.24/1/18 canvasboard prov. 23-Jun-4 Christie's, London #164/R est:15000-20000
£40000 $73600 €58400 Blumenstrauss in Vase - Flowers in a vase (50x40cm-20x16in) s.d.1917 canvasboard prov. 23-Jun-4 Christie's, London #163/R est:15000-20000
£41667 $70833 €60000 Still life with apples and bottle (47x61cm-19x24in) prov.lit. 28-Oct-3 Wiener Kunst Auktionen, Vienna #80/R est:25000-55000
Works on paper
£3147 $5350 €4500 Portrait of young woman - possibly Hilda Geiringer (63x49cm-25x19in) s.d.1924 pastel gouache prov. 26-Nov-3 Dorotheum, Vienna #150/R est:2000-3000

FAISTENBERGER, Anton and ROTTMAYR, Johann Michael (17th C) Austrian
£16552 $27476 €24000 Mountainous landscape in evening light (143x108cm-56x43in) prov.lit. 1-Oct-3 Dorotheum, Vienna #246/R est:20000-30000

FAIVRE, Jules-Abel (1867-1945) French
£385 $654 €562 Seated woman with fan (46x33cm-18x13in) s. 19-Nov-3 Fischer, Luzern #2092 (S.FR 850)

FAIVRE, Jules-Abel (attrib) (1867-1945) French
Works on paper
£1300 $2106 €1898 Flower girl (53x43cm-21x17in) with sig. pastel paer on canvas. 30-Jul-3 Hamptons Fine Art, Godalming #151/R est:700-900

FAIVRE, Justin (1902-) American
£739 $1300 €1079 Magnolia cone (46x38cm-18x15in) s.d.1940. 22-May-4 Harvey Clar, Oakland #2252

FAIVRE, Léon Maxim (1856-1914) French
Works on paper
£300 $540 €450 Jeune femme au foulard rose (45x26cm-18x10in) pastel. 25-Apr-4 Daniel Herry, Beaune #88
£300 $540 €450 Jeune fille au ruban rouge (32x20cm-13x8in) gouache. 25-Apr-4 Daniel Herry, Beaune #89

FAIVTSOVNOU, F (20th C) ?
£3691 $6607 €5500 En gare (170x270cm-67x106in) s.i.d.1987 verso prov. 27-May-4 Sotheby's, Paris #257/R est:2000-3000

FALARDEAU, A S (1822-1889) Canadian
£2000 $3580 €3000 L'ange de l'Annonciation (75x59cm-30x23in) i.d.1866 verso. 11-May-4 Vanderkindere, Brussels #33/R est:2000-3000

FALAT, Antoni (1942-) Polish
£432 $787 €631 Three nude women. s.d.1981. 20-Jun-4 Agra, Warsaw #9/R (P.Z 3000)
£720 $1311 €1051 Dog with buildings and figures in the background (75x67cm-30x26in) s.d.11.XII.79. 20-Jun-4 Agra, Warsaw #8/R (P.Z 5000)

FALAT, Julian (1853-1929) Polish
£4167 $6875 €6000 Extensive polish winter landscape with hut by river (35x96cm-14x38in) s.i. board. 2-Jul-3 Neumeister, Munich #635/R est:1500
£6563 $10959 €9582 Winter in Osieku (35x96cm-14x38in) s. cardboard painted c.1920. 19-Oct-3 Agra, Warsaw #9/R est:40000 (P.Z 42000)
£25682 $42632 €37496 Krakow in the fog (39x100cm-15x39in) s.d.98. 15-Jun-3 Agra, Warsaw #3/R est:160000 (P.Z 160000)
£29501 $51036 €43071 Troops camped under the trees in a winter landscape (81x160cm-32x63in) s. lit. 14-Dec-3 Agra, Warsaw #30/R est:190000 (P.Z 195000)
Works on paper
£2161 $3934 €3155 Women praying at a shrine (65x45cm-26x18in) s. W/C pastel cardboard exec 1910-1915. 20-Jun-4 Agra, Warsaw #10/R (P.Z 15000)
£2572 $4449 €3755 Under the pine trees (75x54cm-30x21in) W/C cardboard exec. before 1909. 14-Dec-3 Agra, Warsaw #31/R est:17000 (P.Z 17000)
£2656 $4436 €3878 View of Kosciol Sw Anny (53x72cm-21x28in) s.d.1919 W/C. 19-Oct-3 Agra, Warsaw #22/R est:13000 (P.Z 17000)
£5658 $9958 €8261 Landscape covered in snow (50x95cm-20x37in) W/C. 23-May-4 Agra, Warsaw #12/R (P.Z 40000)
£6051 $10469 €8834 Winter in Poland (38x94cm-15x37in) s. W/C cardboard exec. c.1910-1920. 14-Dec-3 Agra, Warsaw #27/R est:35000 (P.Z 40000)

FALCH, Ivar (20th C) Norwegian
£267 $446 €390 Outside the smithy (52x69cm-20x27in) s. 17-Nov-3 Blomqvist, Lysaker #1056 (N.KR 3200)

FALCHETTI, Alberto (1878-1952) Italian
£1528 $2597 €2200 Frassinetto mountains (33x44cm-13x17in) s. cardboard. 1-Nov-3 Meeting Art, Vercelli #191/R est:2000
£1867 $3435 €2800 Landscape (34x45cm-13x18in) s. cardboard. 14-Jun-4 Sant Agostino, Torino #279/R est:2800-3200
£1879 $3326 €2800 In the mountains (34x45cm-13x18in) s. cardboard lit. 1-May-4 Meeting Art, Vercelli #82 est:1500
£1946 $3445 €2900 Riva del Carbon, Venice (34x44cm-13x17in) s. s.i.verso cardboard. 1-May-4 Meeting Art, Vercelli #362 est:2500
£1958 $3270 €2800 Still life with grapes (56x28cm-22x11in) s.d.1898. 26-Jun-3 Sant Agostino, Torino #92/R est:3000

FALCHETTI, G (1843-1918) Italian
£2400 $4440 €3600 Landscape near Turin (50x80cm-20x31in) s. 16-Jul-4 Charterhouse, Sherborne #548/R

FALCHETTI, Giuseppe (1843-1918) Italian
£800 $1472 €1200 Back from pasture (9x14cm-4x6in) cardboard prov. 14-Jun-4 Sant Agostino, Torino #129/R
£1733 $3172 €2600 Coast and fishing boat (38x47cm-15x19in) s.d.87. 5-Jun-4 Arnold, Frankfurt #570/R est:1200
£2797 $4671 €4000 Still life (41x31cm-16x12in) s. cardboard on canvas. 26-Jun-3 Sant Agostino, Torino #90/R est:4500
£3357 $5606 €4800 Still life of fruit (40x26cm-16x10in) s.d.1893 cardboard. 26-Jun-3 Sant Agostino, Torino #89/R est:5500
£5333 $9813 €8000 Still life (90x60cm-35x24in) s.d.1894. 14-Jun-4 Sant Agostino, Torino #307/R est:8000-10000
£5674 $9475 €8000 Still life of fruit (47x33cm-19x13in) s.d.1882. 20-Oct-3 Sant Agostino, Torino #297/R est:8500
£5797 $9507 €8000 View of Lake Como (65x88cm-26x35in) s.d.1887. 27-May-3 Finarte Semenzato, Milan #89/R est:10000
£6944 $11806 €10000 View of Lake Como (65x88cm-26x35in) s.d.1887 lit. 1-Nov-3 Meeting Art, Vercelli #339/R est:10000

FALCHI, Ange (1913-) French
£541 $968 €800 Untitled (62x75cm-24x30in) s.d.53. 4-May-4 Calmels Cohen, Paris #187a

FALCHI, Ettore (1913-) Italian
£3309 $5427 €4600 Abstract (128x88cm-50x35in) 5-Jun-3 Adma, Formigine #864 est:3200-3400

FALCIATORE, Filippo (style) (18th C) Italian
£13000 $22490 €18980 Figures selling various objects to passers by. Figures around a table (41x63cm-16x25in) pair. 11-Dec-3 Sotheby's, London #213/R est:8000-12000

FALCK, Jarl (1901-1983) Finnish
£336 $617 €500 Landscape (18x27cm-7x11in) s. 25-Mar-4 Hagelstam, Helsinki #1011

FALCO PUJOL, Joaquim (1958-) Spanish
£1192 $2170 €1800 Baba (98x130cm-39x51in) s.i.d.1984 verso. 17-Jun-4 Galleria Pananti, Florence #32/R est:2000

FALCO, Joaquim (1958-) Spanish
£417 $663 €600 El dit al'ull (10x81cm-4x32in) s.d.2001 s.i.d.verso. 29-Apr-3 Durán, Madrid #57/R
£500 $920 €750 Salad (65x81cm-26x32in) s.d.2002 acrylic. 12-Jun-4 Meeting Art, Vercelli #48/R
£503 $931 €750 Angels (92x73cm-36x29in) s. enamel acrylic painted 2002. 13-Mar-4 Meeting Art, Vercelli #28

FALCONE, Aniello (1607-1656) Italian
Works on paper
£546 $1000 €797 Cavalry skirmish. Portrait study (12x20cm-5x8in) pen brown ink red chk double-sided. 29-Jan-4 Swann Galleries, New York #49/R
£900 $1557 €1314 Five women. Kneeling man (19x14cm-7x6in) red chk double-sided prov. 12-Dec-3 Christie's, Kensington #365/R

FALCONE, Aniello (attrib) (1607-1656) Italian
£4605 $8474 €7000 Choc de cavalerie (36cm-14in circular) canvas on panel. 23-Jun-4 Millon & Associes, Paris #24/R est:7500-8000
£19217 $34398 €28057 Battle outside a besieged town (125x177cm-49x70in) prov. 25-May-4 Bukowskis, Stockholm #444/R est:150000-200000 (S.KR 260000)
£25868 $46305 €37767 Battle outside a besieged town (125x177cm-49x70in) prov. 25-May-4 Bukowskis, Stockholm #445/R est:150000-200000 (S.KR 350000)

FALCONER, Douglas (?) British
£420 $785 €630 Loch Nevis, North Scotland (23x33cm-9x13in) s. board. 22-Jul-4 Gorringes, Lewes #1737
£480 $763 €701 Loch Leven (41x61cm-16x24in) s. board. 9-Sep-3 Gorringes, Lewes #2083

FALCONET, Étienne Maurice (1716-1791) French
Sculpture
£2500 $4550 €3650 La baigneuse (81cm-32in) s. brown green pat. bronze. 16-Jun-4 Andrew Hartley, Ilkley #331/R est:1000-1500
£12937 $22252 €18500 L'amour aux colombes, jeune fille a la corbeille de fleurs (17cm-7in) one s.d.1753 terracotta wood socle pair. 3-Dec-3 Oger, Dumont, Paris #185/R est:10000-12000

FALCONET, Étienne Maurice (circle) (1716-1791) French
Sculpture
£14000 $24220 €20440 Group of Bacchantes (63cm-25in) brown pat. bronze pair. 11-Dec-3 Christie's, London #74/R est:8000-12000

FALCONI, Walter (1935-) Italian
£359 $599 €520 Reclining female nude (70x50cm-28x20in) s.i.d.1975 verso acrylic. 17-Nov-3 Sant Agostino, Torino #78/R
£448 $749 €650 Old good things (70x70cm-28x28in) s.i.d.1975 acrylic exhib. 17-Nov-3 Sant Agostino, Torino #96/R

FALCONNIER, Leon (1811-1876) French
Sculpture
£1324 $2250 €1933 Abraham Lincoln's emancipation of the slaves (53cm-21in) s. bronze. 18-Nov-3 Doyle, New York #20 est:4000-6000

FALENS, Carel van (1683-1733) Dutch
£2292 $3781 €3300 La halte des cavaliers (30x44cm-12x17in) panel. 1-Jul-3 Lemoine & Ferrando, Paris #38/R est:3000-4000
£8000 $14640 €12000 Fete de village, le magicien. Chasse a courre, le cerf (24x34cm-9x13in) panel two panel. 5-Jun-4 Gros & Delettrez, Paris #62/R est:12000-18000
£12414 $22345 €18000 Hunting scenes (42x51cm-17x20in) board pair. 26-Jan-4 Ansorena, Madrid #61/R est:18000
£15248 $25465 €21500 Le depart pour la chasse au faucon (45x56cm-18x22in) copper. 15-Oct-3 Rabourdin & Choppin de Janvry, Paris #49/R est:18000-20000

FALENS, Carel van (attrib) (1683-1733) Dutch
£1560 $2605 €2262 Returning after falcon hunt (30x38cm-12x15in) 23-Jun-3 Philippe Schuler, Zurich #3516/R est:4000-6000 (S.FR 3400)
£1950 $3042 €2847 Hunting party, the rest after the chase (36x44cm-14x17in) board. 11-Apr-3 Jacobs & Hunt, Petersfield #254/R est:800-1200
£20408 $32449 €30000 Cavaliers, baigneurs et promeneurs (90x127cm-35x50in) 23-Mar-3 Mercier & Cie, Lille #165/R est:27000-33000

FALERO, Emilio (1947-) Cuban
£234 $425 €342 Selene no 1 (61x76cm-24x30in) s.i.d.1972. 6-Feb-4 Freeman, Philadelphia #330/R

FALERO, Luis Riccardo (1851-1896) Spanish
£11765 $20000 €17177 Witches Sabbath (74x41cm-29x16in) s.d.1880 prov. 28-Oct-3 Sotheby's, New York #86/R est:18000-25000
£19118 $32500 €27912 Reve de Falero (81x150cm-32x59in) s.d.1880 prov. 28-Oct-3 Sotheby's, New York #87/R est:40000-60000
£52941 $90000 €77294 Vision de Faust (145x118cm-57x46in) s.d.1878 exhib.lit. 28-Oct-3 Sotheby's, New York #85/R est:100000-150000

FALES, Douglas (1929-) Canadian
Works on paper
£248 $421 €362 Buffalo helmet, Stony Chiefs, Plains, Canada (61x51cm-24x20in) s.i.d.1990 pastel prov. 23-Nov-3 Levis, Calgary #454/R (C.D 550)

FALETTI, Franco (1935-) Italian
£336 $621 €500 Homage to Michelangelo (50x100cm-20x39in) s. i.verso acrylic. 13-Mar-4 Meeting Art, Vercelli #422

FALGUIERE, Alexandre (1831-1900) French
£1852 $3000 €2685 Moments reflection (38x46cm-15x18in) s. 8-Aug-3 Barridorf, Portland #169/R est:3000-5000
Sculpture
£834 $1500 €1218 Winner of the cock fight (58cm-23in) incised sig. bronze. 24-Apr-4 Skinner, Boston #244/R est:2000-3000
£1069 $1785 €1550 Buste de Diane (35x22x16cm-14x9x6in) pat bronze sold with base. 11-Jul-3 Rabourdin & Choppin de Janvry, Paris #152/R
£1312 $2191 €1850 Le vainqueur au coq (82cm-32in) s.st.f.Thiebaut medaille pat bronze. 20-Jun-3 Drouot Estimations, Paris #202 est:1500-2000
£2200 $3740 €3212 Vainqueur au coq (79cm-31in) s.st.f.Thiebaut pat bronze. 28-Oct-3 Sotheby's, London #168/R
£2448 $4161 €3500 Torch bearer (90cm-35in) i. bronze. 20-Nov-3 Van Ham, Cologne #1230/R est:2400
£5800 $10034 €8468 Bust of Diana (62cm-24in) s.i. brown pat bronze red marble socle st.f.Thiebaut Freres. 12-Dec-3 Sotheby's, London #268/R est:4000-6000
£5929 $10613 €8656 Bust of Diana (60cm-24in) s. marble. 15-May-4 Christie's, Sydney #468/R est:10000-15000 (A.D 15000)
£7500 $12975 €10950 Fame (48cm-19in) s.st.f.Susse brown pat bronze red marble base. 12-Dec-3 Sotheby's, London #260/R est:3000-5000

FALGUIERE, Alexandre (attrib) (1831-1900) French
£800 $1448 €1200 Baigneuse en buste (75x54cm-30x21in) s. 30-Mar-4 Rossini, Paris #797/R

FALILEEVA, Ekaterina Nicolaevna (1886-1948) Russian
£12179 $19000 € Mother and child in front of the Kremlin (109x83cm-43x33in) s. 11-Apr-3 Christie's, Rockefeller NY #25/R est:15000-20000

FALK, Gathie (1928-) Canadian
£3049 $5457 €4452 Venice sink with postcards from Marco Polo, number 13 (106x106cm-42x42in) s.d.1990 i.verso prov. 27-May-4 Heffel, Vancouver #191/R est:8000-12000 (C.D 7500)

FALK, Hans (1918-2002) Swiss
£961 $1768 €1403 Container, New York (25x36cm-10x14in) s.i.d.1984 acrylic tempera collage. 8-Jun-4 Germann, Zurich #790 (S.FR 2200)
Works on paper
£284 $522 €415 Horse in stable (33x30cm-13x12in) s. mixed media. 8-Jun-4 Germann, Zurich #789 (S.FR 650)
£317 $538 €463 Untitled (43x54cm-17x21in) s. mixed media. 25-Nov-3 Germann, Zurich #779 (S.FR 700)
£431 $780 €629 Still life with bottle (34x49cm-13x19in) s. mixed media exhib. 31-Mar-4 Zurichsee Auktionen, Erlenbach #169/R (S.FR 1000)
£441 $749 €644 Circus tent in village (20x28cm-8x11in) s.i.d.1980 W/C Indian ink. 5-Nov-3 Dobiaschofsky, Bern #1564 (S.FR 1000)
£633 $1058 €924 Composition (39x42cm-15x17in) s. collage mixed media over lithograph. 24-Jun-3 Germann, Zurich #956 (S.FR 1400)
£633 $1058 €924 Stromboli (21x27cm-8x11in) s. mixed media exhib. 24-Jun-3 Germann, Zurich #957 (S.FR 1400)
£633 $1058 €924 Grey helmet (24x28cm-9x11in) s. mixed media. 24-Jun-3 Germann, Zurich #958 (S.FR 1400)
£769 $1308 €1123 Untitled (38x42cm-15x17in) s. mixed media collage on lithograph. 25-Nov-3 Germann, Zurich #778 est:1000-1200 (S.FR 1700)
£1086 $1814 €1586 Stromboli (100x69cm-39x27in) s. collage acrylic oil chk over col lithograph. 24-Jun-3 Germann, Zurich #955 est:2500-3000 (S.FR 2400)
£1267 $2154 €1850 Reclining female nude (23x39cm-9x15in) s.d.1967 mixed media oil pencil tempera. 22-Nov-3 Burkhard, Luzern #7/R est:2200-2600 (S.FR 2800)

FALK, Lars-Erik (1922-) Swedish
£1133 $1926 €1654 Untitled (41x28cm-16x11in) init. panel. 5-Nov-3 AB Stockholms Auktionsverk #703/R est:12000-15000 (S.KR 15000)
£2568 $4366 €3749 Untitled (72x45cm-28x18in) s.d.1950-83 verso prov. 5-Nov-3 AB Stockholms Auktionsverk #702/R est:25000-30000 (S.KR 34000)
Sculpture
£1099 $1945 €1605 The cathedral (34cm-13in) s.d.1949-90 num.II.VI white painted metal prov. 27-Apr-4 AB Stockholms Auktionsverk #1957/R est:10000-12000 (S.KR 15000)
£1160 $2088 €1694 Window-sash II (100x63cm-39x25in) s.d.1956-1977 metal. 26-Apr-4 Bukowskis, Stockholm #284/R est:20000-25000 (S.KR 16000)
£1813 $3082 €2647 White sculpture (49cm-19in) s.d.1957 num.I/IV white marble. 5-Nov-3 AB Stockholms Auktionsverk #704/R est:30000-40000 (S.KR 24000)
Works on paper
£317 $539 €463 Composition in blue (10x28cm-4x11in) s.d.1968 gouache. 5-Nov-3 AB Stockholms Auktionsverk #782/R (S.KR 4200)

FALK, Ragnar (1903-1977) Swedish
£305 $548 €458 Coastal landscape (46x43cm-18x17in) s. 25-Apr-4 Goteborg Auktionsverk, Sweden #344/R (S.KR 4200)

FALK, Robert Rafailovich (1886-1958) Russian
£8667 $15513 €13000 Seated figure in garden (48x43cm-19x17in) mono.cyrillic. 13-May-4 Neumeister, Munich #348/R est:2000-3000
£17931 $32276 €26000 Arbres et maisons (68x44cm-27x17in) s. s.i.d.1929 verso. 21-Jan-4 Tajan, Paris #86/R est:12000-15000
£21034 $35128 €30500 Nature morte a la bouteille et au poisson (91x64cm-36x25in) s.d.1922. 17-Nov-3 Claude Boisgirard, Paris #26/R est:10000-12000
£36486 $65311 €54000 The house behind the forest (53x81cm-21x32in) s. 8-May-4 Bukowskis, Helsinki #435/R est:8000-9000

FALK, T J (19th C) American
£1235 $2000 €1803 Table top with red currants in white glass footed compote (36x48cm-14x19in) s. board prov. 1-Aug-3 North East Auctions, Portsmouth #955/R est:1000-1500

FALKENSTEIN, Claire (1908-1997) American
£1341 $2400 €1958 Untitled (46x33cm-18x13in) s.d.1947 verso board prov. 16-May-4 Wright, Chicago #252/R est:2000-3000
£1397 $2500 €2040 Untitled (56x46cm-22x18in) s. linen on board prov. 16-May-4 Wright, Chicago #253/R est:2500-3500
Sculpture
£12568 $23000 €18349 Untitled, fusion (122x41x84cm-48x16x33in) copper Murano glass exec.c.1968. 6-Jun-4 Wright, Chicago #345/R est:15000-20000
£14674 $27000 €21424 Untitled (213x107x30cm-84x42x12in) copper pat. glass. 28-Mar-4 Wright, Chicago #581/R est:10000-15000

FALL, George (c.1848-1925) British
£950 $1720 €1387 The Mount, looking towards Micklegate Bar, York (42x53cm-17x21in) s. 30-Mar-4 David Duggleby, Scarborough #13/R
Works on paper
£320 $544 €467 Barges on the river Ouse, back of Coney Street, York (24x19cm-9x7in) s. pencil W/C vignette. 19-Nov-3 Tennants, Leyburn #893
£360 $612 €526 Marygate tower (23x32cm-9x13in) s.i. W/C. 18-Nov-3 Bonhams, Leeds #114
£360 $612 €526 Back of Coney Street (29x22cm-11x9in) s.i. i.verso pencil W/C. 18-Nov-3 Bonhams, Leeds #111
£360 $612 €526 Bootham Bar (32x24cm-13x9in) s.i. W/C. 18-Nov-3 Bonhams, Leeds #112
£360 $648 €526 Old Guildhall, Ouse Bridge, York (18x26cm-7x10in) s.i. pencil W/C htd white. 21-Apr-4 Tennants, Leyburn #947
£400 $680 €584 York Minster (18x23cm-7x9in) s. W/C. 18-Nov-3 Bonhams, Leeds #110
£420 $714 €613 Barges on the river Ouse with buildings in the distance (23x17cm-9x7in) s. i.verso pencil W/C. 19-Nov-3 Tennants, Leyburn #890a/R
£450 $810 €657 View of York Minster from the river Ouse, figures and hay barge in foreground (16x22cm-6x9in) s. pencil W/C. 21-Apr-4 Tennants, Leyburn #945
£520 $884 €759 Bootham bar (23x17cm-9x7in) s. i.verso pencil W/C vignette. 19-Nov-3 Tennants, Leyburn #890/R
£520 $936 €759 View of River Ouse with figures and boats in foreground (20x45cm-8x18in) s.d.82 pencil W/C. 21-Apr-4 Tennants, Leyburn #948
£550 $935 €803 Scene on the river Ouse at York, with the Guildhall nearby (18x25cm-7x10in) pencil W/C vignette. 19-Nov-3 Tennants, Leyburn #892
£550 $990 €803 York Minster. Canterbury Cathedral (16x23cm-6x9in) s. pencil W/C pair prov. 21-Apr-4 Tennants, Leyburn #944/R

FALLER, Louis-Clement (1819-1901) French
£333 $613 €500 Danseuses sur fond de lac (40x51cm-16x20in) s.d.1914. 14-Jun-4 Horta, Bruxelles #456

FALLIES, Maurice (20th C) French
£881 $1400 €1286 Pont-Neuf, Paris (33x40cm-13x16in) s. board. 12-Sep-3 Skinner, Boston #473/R

FALSARIO DEL GUERCINO (18th C) Italian
Works on paper
£600 $1038 €876 Landscape with figures attending to cannon, ships in a bay beyond (21x29cm-8x11in) pen brown ink wash. 12-Dec-3 Christie's, Kensington #343

FALTER, John P (1910-1982) American
£621 $1000 €907 Crossing the plate (10x15cm-4x6in) s. board. 20-Aug-3 James Julia, Fairfield #1794/R

FALTER, John P (attrib) (1910-1982) American
Works on paper
£307 $550 €448 The artist and his model (38x28cm-15x11in) gouache. 11-Jan-4 William Jenack, New York #223

FALTER, Marcel (1866-?) French
£10350 $17284 €14800 Ecuyere (65x81cm-26x32in) s. 7-Oct-3 Livinec, Gaudcheau & Jezequel, Rennes #125/R

FALZI, Ignaz Peter (?) German?
£336 $594 €500 Fishermen in a moonlit landscape (15x30cm-6x12in) s. panel. 30-Apr-4 Auktionhaus Georg Rehm, Augsburg #7519

FALZONI, Giulio (1900-1978) Italian
£369 $683 €550 Running horses (35x50cm-14x20in) s. cardboard on canvas. 13-Mar-4 Meeting Art, Vercelli #451
£450 $833 €657 Grand Canal, Venice (49x69cm-19x27in) s. 14-Jul-4 Christie's, Kensington #1153/R
Works on paper
£362 $594 €500 Carnival in Paris (25x35cm-10x14in) s. s.i.verso W/C card. 29-May-3 Galleria Pace, Milan #18/R
£367 $667 €550 Gypsies walking (50x70cm-20x28in) s. i.verso W/C. 12-Jul-4 Il Ponte, Milan #1048
£377 $640 €550 Happy riders (50x33cm-20x13in) s. W/C cardboard. 7-Nov-3 Tuttarte, Modena #608
£586 $938 €850 Venezia, Ponte di Rialto (50x70cm-20x28in) s. W/C cardboard. 13-Mar-3 Galleria Pace, Milan #9/R

FAN ZENG (1938-) Chinese
Works on paper
£541 $951 €800 Ge Hong holding pill (69x45cm-27x18in) s. Indian ink col. 21-May-4 Dr Fritz Nagel, Stuttgart #1098/R

FANART, Clement-Alphonse-Antonin (1831-1903) French
£479 $815 €700 Vue de Langres (28x39cm-11x15in) s. 8-Nov-3 Gerard, Besancon #66

£1096 $1863 €1600 Village au bord de la riviere (44x66cm-17x26in) s. paper on canvas. 8-Nov-3 Gerard, Besancon #65

FANCOURT, E (?) ?
£1050 $1880 €1533 Portrait of Reverend Thomas Mills, holding a book (79x63cm-31x25in) s.i.d.1845 verso. 22-Mar-4 Bonhams & Brooks, Norfolk #271/R est:400-600

FANFANI, Enrico (19th C) Italian
£1875 $3000 €2738 Haggar and Ishmael (79x53cm-31x21in) s. 17-May-3 Bunte, Elgin #122 est:3000-5000
£1996 $3572 €2914 Woman at the well (80x55cm-31x22in) s. 26-May-4 AB Stockholms Auktionsverk #2375/R est:15000-18000 (S.KR 27000)
£2079 $3597 €3035 Female artist in front of easel with palette in her hand (73x57cm-29x22in) s. oval. 9-Dec-3 Rasmussen, Copenhagen #1638/R est:15000-20000 (D.KR 22000)

FANG CONGYI (1301-c.1378) Chinese
Works on paper
£17070 $30725 €24922 Landscape in mist (62x32cm-24x13in) s. ink hanging scroll prov. 25-Apr-4 Christie's, Hong Kong #317/R est:240000-300000 (HK.D 240000)

FANG HENGXIAN (fl.1647-1678) Chinese
Works on paper
£22760 $40967 €33230 Landscape (186x50cm-73x20in) s.i.d.1669 ink hanging scroll satin. 25-Apr-4 Christie's, Hong Kong #401/R est:50000-60000 (HK.D 320000)

FANG JUNBI (1898-1986) Chinese
£19915 $35846 €29076 Peonies (46x91cm-18x36in) prov. 25-Apr-4 Christie's, Hong Kong #711/R est:280000-360000 (HK.D 280000)
£54054 $90270 €78919 Portrait of a lady in pink (116x81cm-46x32in) painted c.1925-28 exhib. 26-Oct-3 Christie's, Hong Kong #140/R est:650000-850000 (HK.D 700000)

FANG RENDING (1901-1975) Chinese
Works on paper
£7722 $12896 €11274 Crossing the river on a buffalo's back (169x94cm-67x37in) s.d.1946 ink col hanging scroll. 27-Oct-3 Sotheby's, Hong Kong #258/R est:55000-75000 (HK.D 100000)
£10669 $19203 €15577 Milkmaid (170x96cm-67x38in) s.d.1941 ink col hanging scroll. 26-Apr-4 Sotheby's, Hong Kong #566/R est:100000-150000 (HK.D 150000)

FANG SHISHU (1692-1751) Chinese
Works on paper
£11380 $20484 €16615 Landscape (133x62cm-52x24in) s.i. ink col hanging scroll. 25-Apr-4 Christie's, Hong Kong #400/R est:40000-50000 (HK.D 160000)

FANGE, Jens (1965-) Swedish
£2795 $4751 €4081 Large pink painter (130x160cm-51x63in) s.d.2002 verso exhib.prov. 5-Nov-3 AB Stockholms Auktionsverk #981/R est:40000-45000 (S.KR 37000)
Works on paper
£601 $1063 €877 Black profile (40x28cm-16x11in) s. W/C. 27-Apr-4 AB Stockholms Auktionsverk #951/R (S.KR 8200)

FANGEL, Maud Tousey (1881-1968) American
Works on paper
£243 $450 €355 Wirehaired fox terrier (23x30cm-9x12in) s. chk paper on board. 10-Feb-4 Doyle, New York #189/R

FANGH, Desiderius (1876-?) Austrian
Works on paper
£470 $864 €700 Mill (40x49cm-16x19in) s.d.1929 W/C exhib. 26-Mar-4 Dorotheum, Vienna #312/R
£533 $960 €800 Harbour (23x30cm-9x12in) s.d.1940 gouache double-sided. 21-Apr-4 Dorotheum, Vienna #130/R
£1074 $1976 €1600 Lake (33x43cm-13x17in) s.d.1938 mixed media. 26-Mar-4 Dorotheum, Vienna #322/R est:1400-1500

FANGOR, Wojciech (1922-) Polish
£3636 $6182 €5200 B 112 (71x71cm-28x28in) s.i.d.1966 verso acrylic prov. 27-Nov-3 Lempertz, Koln #114/R est:1400-1600
£5282 $9137 €7500 B 111 (71x71cm-28x28in) s.i.d.1966 verso tempera prov. 13-Dec-3 Lempertz, Koln #308/R est:1500
£5594 $9510 €8000 No 35 (129x97cm-51x38in) s.i.d.1963 verso prov.lit. 29-Nov-3 Villa Grisebach, Berlin #323/R est:3000-4000
£6000 $10980 €9000 B 2 (100x100cm-39x39in) s.i.d.1964 verso prov. 4-Jun-4 Lempertz, Koln #129/R est:4500

FANNEN, J (fl.1890-1900) British
£1000 $1790 €1460 British full-rigger Wiltshire and other shipping at sea (53x86cm-21x34in) 26-May-4 Christie's, Kensington #626/R est:1000-1500
£1500 $2550 €2190 Brigantine Henry of Guernsey (51x79cm-20x31in) s.d.1866. 25-Nov-3 Martel Maides, Guernsey #203/R est:1000-1200

FANNER, Alice (1865-1930) British
£932 $1500 €1361 The balustrade, Luxembourg gardens (20x28cm-8x11in) s. panel. 20-Aug-3 James Julia, Fairfield #959/R est:2000-3000

FANSHAW, Samuel Raymond (1814-1888) American
£2516 $4000 €3673 Still life of fruit (46x57cm-18x22in) s.d.1866. 12-Sep-3 Skinner, Boston #262/R est:700-900

FANTACCHIOTTI, Cesare (1844-1922) Italian
Sculpture
£815 $1500 €1190 Bust of a lady (51cm-20in) s. marble. 9-Jun-4 Doyle, New York #3229 est:3000-4000

FANTAZAS, Henryk (20th C) American
£307 $550 €448 Zeppelin eaters (76x91cm-30x36in) s.i. 7-May-4 Sloans & Kenyon, Bethesda #1736/R

FANTIN-LATOUR, Henri (1836-1904) French
£728 $1333 €1100 Diana au repos (19x29cm-7x11in) s. prov. 7-Apr-4 Piasa, Paris #7/R
£3693 $6500 €5392 Baigneuse effrayee (22x27cm-9x11in) indis sig. prov. 18-May-4 Bonhams & Butterfields, San Francisco #128/R est:6000-8000
£4667 $8400 €7000 Petite orientale couchee (11x16cm-4x6in) s. canvas on panel painted 1904 prov.lit. 20-Apr-4 Sotheby's, Amsterdam #93/R est:3000-5000
£6466 $11573 €9440 Nu couche (30x47cm-12x19in) s. 12-May-4 Dobiaschofsky, Bern #483/R est:18000 (S.FR 15000)
£129412 $220000 €188942 Panier de raisins blancs et de peches (46x62cm-18x24in) s.d.95 prov.lit. 5-Nov-3 Christie's, Rockefeller NY #215/R est:250000-350000
£145251 $260000 €212066 Fleurs: oeillets et jacynthe dans une flute a champagne (38x27cm-15x11in) s.d.72 prov.lit. 4-May-4 Christie's, Rockefeller NY #2/R est:200000-300000
£167598 $300000 €244693 Roses (34x33cm-13x13in) s. painted 1903 prov.lit. 5-May-4 Sotheby's, New York #3/R est:200000-300000
£823529 $1400000 €1202352 Vase de fleurs avec une tasse de cafe (48x39cm-19x15in) s.d.1865 prov.exhib. 4-Nov-3 Christie's, Rockefeller NY #3/R est:1400000-1800000
Works on paper
£331 $606 €500 Nus feminins. bears st.i.d.83 black crayon chl stomping tracing paper prov. 7-Apr-4 Piasa, Paris #8
£510 $913 €750 Etude d'homme (17x8cm-7x3in) crayon. 21-Mar-4 Muizon & Le Coent, Paris #29
£1042 $1771 €1490 Study of women (17x26cm-7x10in) s. pencil. 18-Nov-3 Babuino, Rome #139/R

FANTIN-LATOUR, Theodore (1805-1872) French
£3000 $5100 €4380 Reve du poete (60x73cm-24x29in) indis.sig. prov.lit. 18-Nov-3 Sotheby's, London #313/R

FANTIN-LATOUR, Victoria (1840-1926) French
£5882 $10000 €8588 Bouquet de Narcisses (17x24cm-7x9in) 28-Oct-3 Sotheby's, New York #169/R est:10000-15000
£15500 $28365 €22630 Nasturtiums (34x44cm-13x17in) s.d.1912. 7-Apr-4 Woolley & Wallis, Salisbury #301/R est:6000-8000

FANTINI, Tiziana (1923-) Italian
£384 $699 €580 View of Trieste (23x114cm-9x45in) s. board. 18-Jun-4 Stadion, Trieste #494

FANTJE, I (1931-2002) Indonesian?
£1042 $1740 €1521 Seruni (94x64cm-37x25in) s. 12-Oct-3 Sotheby's, Singapore #165/R est:3000-4000 (S.D 3000)

FANTONI, Francesco (fl.1509-1530) Italian
£40845 $67803 €58000 Annunciation, Saint Sebastian and Saint Catherine (150x137cm-59x54in) board lit. 11-Jun-3 Semenzato, Florence #174/R est:60000-65000

FANTUZZI, Antonio (16th C) Italian
Prints
£2000 $3580 €3000 Jupiter giving the three goddesses the judgement of Paris (35x50cm-14x20in) copperpalte after Primaticcio. 13-May-4 Bassenge, Berlin #5143/R est:3500

FANTUZZI, Eliano (1909-1987) Italian
£302 $561 €450 Landscape covered in snow (50x60cm-20x24in) s. s.i.verso. 4-Mar-4 Babuino, Rome #501
£336 $624 €500 Lonely (65x54cm-26x21in) s. s.verso. 4-Mar-4 Babuino, Rome #447
£350 $594 €500 Figure and cow (30x40cm-12x16in) enamel painted 1954. 19-Nov-3 Cambi, Genoa #430
£367 $675 €550 Woman on a bench (50x40cm-20x16in) s. painted 1978. 11-Jun-4 Farsetti, Prato #277
£403 $749 €600 Woman on the grass (60x80cm-24x31in) s. painted 1980. 4-Mar-4 Babuino, Rome #20
£470 $874 €700 Watching TV (60x70cm-24x28in) s. painted 1979. 4-Mar-4 Babuino, Rome #180
£503 $936 €750 Woman with flowers in Venice (70x50cm-28x20in) s. s.i.verso. 4-Mar-4 Babuino, Rome #382
£537 $999 €800 Fishing at night (60x80cm-24x31in) s. painted 1978. 4-Mar-4 Babuino, Rome #520
£570 $1061 €850 Friends at bar (65x55cm-26x22in) s. s.i.verso. 4-Mar-4 Babuino, Rome #54
£690 $1152 €1000 Venetian souvenir (90x60cm-35x24in) s. s.i.verso. 13-Nov-3 Finarte Semenzato, Rome #267
£699 $1189 €1000 Flower market (60x80cm-24x31in) s. s.i.verso painted 1980. 18-Nov-3 Babuino, Rome #362/R
£897 $1497 €1300 Picnic in the suburbs (100x150cm-39x59in) s. 13-Nov-3 Finarte Semenzato, Rome #308 est:1300-1500
£1034 $1728 €1500 Venice (50x70cm-20x28in) s. cardboard. 13-Nov-3 Finarte Semenzato, Rome #232 est:1200-1500

FANVOL, G (19th C) British
£5233 $9000 €7640 Bassett hounds (117x81cm-46x32in) s. prov. 5-Dec-3 Christie's, Rockefeller NY #80/R est:6000-8000

FARA, Teresio (1929-1986) Argentinian
£1086 $1846 €1586 Composition (90x120cm-35x47in) s.d.1968 s.i.d. verso prov. 25-Nov-3 Germann, Zurich #133/R est:2000-3000 (S.FR 2400)
£1117 $2000 €1631 House in the suburbs (57x70cm-22x28in) s.d.54. 4-May-4 Arroyo, Buenos Aires #50/R est:1700
£1366 $2500 €1994 White flower (50x40cm-20x16in) 1-Jun-4 Arroyo, Buenos Aires #3
£1676 $3000 €2447 Small still life (18x24cm-7x9in) 11-May-4 Arroyo, Buenos Aires #37
£2486 $4500 €3630 Still life (40x51cm-16x20in) board. 30-Mar-4 Arroyo, Buenos Aires #99
£3315 $6000 €4840 Trigales (32x40cm-13x16in) board. 30-Mar-4 Arroyo, Buenos Aires #16
£16575 $30000 €24200 Interior (120x90cm-47x35in) 30-Mar-4 Arroyo, Buenos Aires #74
Works on paper
£824 $1500 €1203 Garconne (29x23cm-11x9in) s.d.74 pastel collage. 5-Jul-4 Arroyo, Buenos Aires #9/R est:1000

FARAGO, Geza (1877-1928) Hungarian
£10689 $18919 €15606 Expectation by moonlight (47x44cm-19x17in) s. 28-Apr-4 Kieselbach, Budapest #44/R (H.F 4000000)

FARALLI, Gianpaolo (1955-) Italian
£272 $487 €400 Sunset (50x30cm-20x12in) s. s.i.d.2003 verso. 22-Mar-4 Sant Agostino, Torino #381/R
£390 $651 €550 Silence (30x50cm-12x20in) s. on forex. 20-Oct-3 Sant Agostino, Torino #179/R
£839 $1552 €1250 Town lights (80x100cm-31x39in) s.d.2001 lit. 13-Mar-4 Meeting Art, Vercelli #471

FARAONI, Enzo (1920-) Italian
£367 $664 €550 Still life (40x50cm-16x20in) s. painted 1978. 2-Apr-4 Farsetti, Prato #467
£528 $914 €750 Woman reading (50x70cm-20x28in) s. s.i.d.1971 card. 9-Dec-3 Pandolfini, Florence #412/R

FARASYN, Edgard (1858-1938) Belgian
£563 $975 €800 Jeune fille au tricot (24x32cm-9x13in) s. mahogany panel. 9-Dec-3 Vanderkindere, Brussels #1
£625 $1018 €900 Shell-gatherer at the beach (20x35cm-8x14in) s. 29-Sep-3 Sotheby's, Amsterdam #142/R
£2617 $4816 €3900 Sculptor in studio (65x55cm-26x22in) s. 26-Mar-4 Bolland & Marotz, Bremen #510a/R est:2200
£3356 $6007 €5000 Pecheur de crevettes a Oostduinkerke (85x54cm-33x21in) s. 25-May-4 Campo & Campo, Antwerp #95/R est:1800-2400

FARDEL, Robert (1867-1931) French
£372 $665 €550 Summer landscape with stream and boathouse (59x81cm-23x32in) s. panel. 6-May-4 Michael Zeller, Lindau #655

FARDOULYS, James Nicholas (1900-1975) Australian
£1235 $2235 €1803 Animal decotion - Down Sydney Town (40x55cm-16x22in) s.d.14.4.1966 i.verso canvas on board. 30-Mar-4 Lawson Menzies, Sydney #143 est:1000-1500 (A.D 3000)

FARE, Arthur Cecil (?) British
Works on paper
£325 $562 €475 Bristol Baptist College (44x80cm-17x31in) i. W/C over pencil. 9-Dec-3 Bristol Auction Rooms #401/R

FARE, Arthur Charles (1876-1958) British
Works on paper
£420 $777 €613 The Roman Baths, Bath (31x41cm-12x16in) s.d.1928 W/C. 16-Feb-4 Bonhams, Bath #100

FARGHER, J (?) ?
Works on paper
£620 $1035 €905 Morning. Grey morning (18x53cm-7x21in) init. i.verso pair. 20-Jun-3 Chrystals Auctions, Isle of Man #208/R

FARGHER, Tim (1952-) British
£2800 $5292 €4088 Floribunda, Hacheston, Suffolk (86x89cm-34x35in) s.d.1988 s.i.d.verso. 19-Feb-4 Christie's, Kensington #249/R est:300-500

FARGUE, Paulus Constantin la (1732-1782) Dutch
£4444 $8000 €6488 Hunters resting in a village (37x29cm-15x11in) panel. 23-Jan-4 Christie's, Rockefeller NY #143/R est:10000-15000
£18000 $32220 €27000 Westerkerk, Amsterdam, seen from the Prinsengracht (28x39cm-11x15in) panel. 17-May-4 Christie's, Amsterdam #106/R est:12000-16000
Works on paper
£21622 $38054 €32000 Beach at Katwijk, with figures, boats and carts (21x36cm-8x14in) s.d.1776 i.verso pen brown ink wash black chk prov.exhib.lit. 19-May-4 Sotheby's, Amsterdam #249/R est:6000-8000
£27027 $47568 €40000 View of Voorschoten, with figures skating on the Kerksloot (17x28cm-7x11in) s.d.1771 pen brown ink wash black chk prov.exhib.lit. 19-May-4 Sotheby's, Amsterdam #266/R est:6500-8000

FARHAT, Ammar (1911-c.1986) Tunisian
£4225 $7310 €6000 Jeunes femmeSeine prenant le the (46x32cm-18x13in) s.d.51 i.verso. 15-Dec-3 Gros & Delettrez, Paris #101/R est:6000-7000
£5461 $9120 €7700 Au cafe, Tunis. Nature morte au pichet (50x62cm-20x24in) s.d.66 double-sided. 16-Jun-3 Gros & Delettrez, Paris #91/R est:7500-10000

FARHI, Jean Claude (1940-) French
Sculpture
£1208 $2211 €1800 Colonne (74x19x19cm-29x7x7in) s.d.87 plexiglas prov. 7-Jul-4 Artcurial Briest, Paris #260 est:2000-2500
£1800 $3276 €2628 Dissemination (57cm-22in) i. base mixed media sculpture elec lights exec 1988. 4-Feb-4 Sotheby's, Olympia #250/R est:1800-2200
£3160 $5277 €4550 Colonne (170cm-67in) s.d.1982 plexiglas. 25-Oct-3 Cornette de St.Cyr, Paris #674/R est:1200-1500
£14000 $25900 €21000 Table de jeu (72x119x64cm-28x47x25in) plexiglas exec.1985 prov. 18-Jul-4 Sotheby's, Paris #196/R est:20000-25000

FARINA, Ernesto (1912-) Argentinian
£503 $900 €734 Still life (22x32cm-9x13in) 11-May-4 Arroyo, Buenos Aires #39

FARINATI, Giambattista Zelotti (attrib) (1526-1578) Italian
Works on paper
£2400 $4152 €3504 Legend of Jason (16x35cm-6x14in) black chk pen brown ink wash sold with 8 by other artists prov. 12-Dec-3 Christie's, Kensington #310/R est:700-1000

FARINATI, Orazio (1559-c.1616) Italian
£6000 $10200 €8760 Lementation (33x28cm-13x11in) slate. 29-Oct-3 Christie's, London #92/R est:6000-8000

FARINATI, Paolo (attrib) (1524-1606) Italian
Works on paper
£2192 $3726 €3200 Study of angel (32x22cm-13x9in) pen ink wash htd gouache. 6-Nov-3 Tajan, Paris #4/R

FARINATI, Paolo (circle) (1524-1606) Italian
£32000 $55360 €46720 Rape of Europa (198x96cm-78x38in) 10-Dec-3 Bonhams, New Bond Street #32/R est:4000-6000

FARINELLI, Ezio (1937-) Italian
£273 $503 €410 Figure in landscape (50x70cm-20x28in) s. s.i.d.1995 verso. 12-Jun-4 Meeting Art, Vercelli #629
£369 $683 €550 Rome at dusk (50x40cm-20x16in) s. 13-Mar-4 Meeting Art, Vercelli #184
£500 $920 €750 Lady (100x80cm-39x31in) s. 12-Jun-4 Meeting Art, Vercelli #952/R

FARINGTON, Joseph (1747-1821) British
£1678 $2853 €2400 Woodland scene with figures (29x39cm-11x15in) s. panel lit. 28-Nov-3 Schloss Ahlden, Ahlden #1387/R est:2600
£12000 $20400 €17520 Gatehouse on the bridge over the River Severn at Bridgnorth, Shropshire (69x113cm-27x44in) s.d.1791 prov.exhib.lit. 25-Nov-3 Christie's, London #60/R est:15000-20000
Works on paper
£380 $711 €570 East end of the remains of the Cathedral of St Andrews (32x38cm-13x15in) s.d.1788 pen ink wash. 22-Jul-4 Dominic Winter, Swindon #188/R
£550 $1029 €825 West view of the remains of the Castle of St Andrews (24x49cm-9x19in) s.i.d.1788 pen ink wash. 22-Jul-4 Dominic Winter, Swindon #189/R
£560 $885 €818 Lodore waterfall (30x33cm-12x13in) s. W/C ink. 23-Jul-3 Hampton & Littlewood, Exeter #379/R
£600 $1110 €876 Linlithgow Palace (30x54cm-12x21in) i.d.August 3rd 1788 W/C pencil. 9-Mar-4 Bonhams, New Bond Street #33/R

FARKASHAZY, Nicolas (1895-1964) Hungarian
Works on paper
£1159 $2098 €1692 Street detail from bird's eye view (62x88cm-24x35in) s. pastel. 16-Apr-4 Mu Terem Galeria, Budapest #182/R (H.F 440000)
£1258 $2290 €1900 Strolling (48x69cm-19x27in) s. mixed media cardboard lit. 18-Jun-4 Stadion, Trieste #79/R est:1200-1600

FARLEY, Richard Blossom (1875-1951) American
£366 $600 €531 Seascape (15x23cm-6x9in) s. panel. 4-Jun-3 Alderfer's, Hatfield #404/R
£488 $800 €708 Lowlands at Eddington, PA (15x23cm-6x9in) s. panel. 4-Jun-3 Alderfer's, Hatfield #403/R

FARLEY, Richard Blossom (attrib) (1875-1951) American
£406 $650 €593 Portrait of William Henry Fry (91x71cm-36x28in) s. indis d.1927 i.verso. 19-Sep-3 Freeman, Philadelphia #191/R

FARM, Gerald (1935-) American
£435 $700 €631 Just passing through (61x76cm-24x30in) board. 22-Aug-3 Altermann Galleries, Santa Fe #68
£2353 $4000 €3435 New day (61x76cm-24x30in) 1-Nov-3 Altermann Galleries, Santa Fe #111
Works on paper
£248 $400 €360 Old Bob (30x41cm-12x16in) chl. 22-Aug-3 Altermann Galleries, Santa Fe #66

FARMER, Edna (20th C) American

Works on paper

£383 $700 €559 At the opera (71x46cm-28x18in) W/C executed c.1930. 5-Jun-4 Susanin's, Chicago #6002/R

FARMER, Emily (1826-1905) British

Works on paper

£860 $1539 €1256 Children bird-nesting (32x39cm-13x15in) s. W/C. 17-Mar-4 Bonhams, Chester #330

£2600 $4732 €3796 Necklace maker (31x39cm-12x15in) s. W/C htd white arched top. 1-Jul-4 Sotheby's, London #267/R est:3000-5000

FARMER, Fannie (attrib) (19th C) American

£4620 $8500 €6745 United States Military Academy: west Point from the opposite shore (59x81cm-23x32in) 22-Jun-4 Sotheby's, New York #179/R est:5000-7000

FARMER, Josephus (1894-?) American

£1667 $3000 €2434 7000 years of Human history (122x76cm-48x30in) s.d.1985 latex paint window shade. 24-Apr-4 Slotin Folk Art, Buford #291/R est:4000-6000

Sculpture

£1083 $1950 €1581 Auction of blck people (28x61cm-11x24in) painted wood relief. 24-Apr-4 Slotin Folk Art, Buford #292/R est:3000-5000

FARNBACHER, Emanuel (20th C) German?

£599 $1071 €850 Winter's day in a mountain village in Tirol with figures (40x30cm-16x12in) s. 8-Jan-4 Allgauer, Kempten #2378/R

FARNDON, Walter (1876-1964) American

£806 $1500 €1177 Figures on a path in a wooded landscape (36x46cm-14x18in) s. board. 3-Mar-4 Christie's, Rockefeller NY #38/R est:2000-3000

£1720 $3200 €2511 Boats at dock (36x46cm-14x18in) s. board. 3-Mar-4 Christie's, Rockefeller NY #39/R est:3000-5000

£1747 $3250 €2551 Band concert (36x25cm-14x10in) s. panel painted c.1920. 7-Mar-4 Treadway Gallery, Cincinnati #530/R est:3000-5000

£2093 $3600 €3056 Houses along dam (35x45cm-14x18in) s. board. 3-Dec-3 Doyle, New York #201/R est:3000-5000

£2174 $4000 €3174 Sailbots in the harbour, summer. Winter sunrise (45x35cm-18x14in) s.i. board double-sided. 8-Jun-4 Bonhams & Butterfields, San Francisco #4058/R est:4000-6000

£2994 $5000 €4371 Afternoon reflections (36x46cm-14x18in) s. 23-Oct-3 Shannon's, Milford #89/R est:4000-6000

£3591 $6500 €5243 Green river (35x46cm-14x18in) s. s.i.d.1931 verso canvasboard prov. 31-Mar-4 Sotheby's, New York #27/R est:3000-5000

£3911 $7000 €5710 Village by a bay (64x76cm-25x30in) s. prov. 6-May-4 Shannon's, Milford #240/R est:5000-7000

£5249 $9500 €7664 Commercial Street, Provincetown, Massachusetts (35x46cm-14x18in) s. s.i.d.1931 verso prov. 31-Mar-4 Sotheby's, New York #28/R est:3000-5000

FARNESE (1926-1996) ?

Works on paper

£4029 $7374 €6044 Censorship (102x73cm-40x29in) gouache mixed media. 6-Jul-4 Bolsa de Arte, Rio de Janeiro #89/R (B.R 22000)

FARNHAM, Ammi Merchant (1846-1922) American

£2198 $4000 €3209 San Diego coastal scene (36x61cm-14x24in) s. prov. 15-Jun-4 John Moran, Pasadena #172a est:3000-4000

FARNHAM, Sally James (1876-1943) American

Sculpture

£20053 $37500 €29277 Horse and rider (20x33x15cm-8x13x6in) bronze prov.lit. 24-Jul-4 Coeur d'Alene, Hayden #188/R est:8000-12000

FARNSWORTH, Alfred Villiers (1858-1908) American

Works on paper

£941 $1600 €1374 Cows in pastoral landscape (18x25cm-7x10in) s. W/C. 18-Nov-3 John Moran, Pasadena #15 est:1000-2000

FARNSWORTH, Jerry (1895-?) American

£1946 $3250 €2841 Truro Child (46x38cm-18x15in) s. s.i.verso prov. 23-Oct-3 Shannon's, Milford #256/R est:1500-2500

£5389 $9000 €7868 Calypso (193x101cm-76x40in) s.d.1933 s.i.d.1933 verso canvas on board prov.exhib. 7-Oct-3 Sotheby's, New York #243 est:1500-2000

FARNUM, H Cyrus (1886-?) American

£252 $400 €368 Mill (33x46cm-13x18in) s. 12-Sep-3 Skinner, Boston #446/R

£588 $1000 €858 Gathering in the marketplace of Biskra (41x56cm-16x22in) s.i. 31-Oct-3 North East Auctions, Portsmouth #1731

FARNY, Henry F (1847-1916) American

Works on paper

£5978 $11000 €8728 Indian frontiersmen, dogsled and team (15x27cm-6x11in) s. pen ink. 8-Jun-4 Bonhams & Butterfields, San Francisco #4121/R est:6000-8000

£18717 $35000 €27327 Minnechiga, Ogalalah Sioux (20x15cm-8x6in) s.d.1890 W/C prov. 24-Jul-4 Coeur d'Alene, Hayden #201/R est:20000-30000

£41176 $70000 €60117 Apache water carrier (22x14cm-9x6in) s.d.99 gouache prov. 29-Oct-3 Christie's, Los Angeles #38/R est:80000-120000

FARQUHARSON, David (1839-1907) British

£1500 $2775 €2190 Grouse in flight over a cornfield (61x92cm-24x36in) s.d.1905. 9-Mar-4 Bonhams, Knightsbridge #357/R est:1500-2000

£1700 $2737 €2465 On the sands at Portobello (33x61cm-13x24in) init.d.1873 arched top. 21-Aug-3 Bonhams, Edinburgh #1185 est:1000-1500

£1800 $3312 €2628 By a woodland stream (30x51cm-12x20in) s. 24-Mar-4 Hamptons Fine Art, Godalming #270/R

£1983 $3372 €2975 Kilchurn Castle (61x42cm-24x17in) s.d.1898 i.verso. 28-Oct-3 Goodman, Sydney #491a est:2500-3500 (A.D 4800)

£2000 $3140 €2900 Washing at the stream (51x77cm-20x30in) s. 27-Aug-3 Sotheby's, London #1132/R est:2000-3000

£2043 $3472 €2983 Loading (35x52cm-14x20in) init.d.1876 i.d.verso. 25-Nov-3 Christie's, Melbourne #194/R est:4000-6000 (A.D 4800)

£4000 $6280 €5800 Summer day (38x28cm-15x11in) s.d.1878 s.i.d.verso. 27-Aug-3 Sotheby's, London #923/R est:3000-5000

£4800 $8160 €7008 Seedtime (23x31cm-9x12in) s.d.1878 s.i.d.1877 verso. 30-Oct-3 Christie's, London #92/R est:5000-8000

£6600 $12078 €9636 Home from the harvest (35x60cm-14x24in) s.d.1887 prov. 8-Apr-4 Bonhams, Edinburgh #180 est:3000-4000

Works on paper

£391 $700 €571 Wayside Inn at twilight (13x15cm-5x6in) W/C. 20-Mar-4 Sloans & Kenyon, Bethesda #1138/R

£1000 $1660 €1460 River above Rouen (41x60cm-16x24in) s.d.84 W/C bodycol. 1-Oct-3 Sotheby's, Olympia #149/R est:1000-2000

£1150 $1852 €1668 Old shepherd (25x34cm-10x13in) s.d.1879 W/C. 21-Aug-3 Bonhams, Edinburgh #1146 est:500-800

FARQUHARSON, John (1865-1931) British

Works on paper

£300 $501 €438 Sennen Cove fog clearing, Lands End (25x36cm-10x14in) s. i.verso W/C. 15-Nov-3 Nigel Ward, Hereford #1449/R

FARQUHARSON, Joseph (1846-1935) British

£2250 $4072 €3285 The shepherd of the Nile (42x59cm-17x23in) s. 3-Apr-4 British Auctioneer #252

£2300 $3910 €3358 Surrey lane with pheasants on a track (32x24cm-13x9in) s. board. 8-Nov-3 Shapes, Edinburgh #420/R est:1000-2000

£2600 $4420 €3796 Moonlight on the Feugh (30x47cm-12x19in) s. 30-Oct-3 Christie's, London #91/R est:2500-3500

£6500 $11050 €9490 Sheep grazing by a river (30x57cm-12x22in) board prov. 25-Nov-3 Christie's, London #103/R est:7000-10000

£10000 $17900 €14600 The woodcutter's return (91x71cm-36x28in) s. 28-May-4 Lyon & Turnbull, Edinburgh #16/R est:8000-12000

£17000 $31790 €24820 Fisherwoman on a deserted sandy beach (55x91cm-22x36in) s. 21-Jul-4 Lyon & Turnbull, Edinburgh #127/R est:6000-9000

£20000 $31400 €29000 In deep mid winter (76x51cm-30x20in) s. prov. 27-Aug-3 Sotheby's, London #1183/R est:20000-30000

£35000 $59500 €51100 Evening's Last and sweetest hour (151x100cm-59x39in) s. 30-Oct-3 Christie's, London #95/R est:20000-30000

£50000 $78500 €72500 Day was sloping towards his western bower (51x76cm-20x30in) s. exhib. 27-Aug-3 Sotheby's, London #1184/R est:50000-70000

£60000 $94200 €87000 Blow, blow, thou wintry wind (63x51cm-25x20in) s. prov.exhib. 27-Aug-3 Sotheby's, London #1185/R est:50000-70000

FARQUHARSON, Joseph (circle) (1846-1935) French

£13000 $22100 €18980 Salmon fishing (128x87cm-50x34in) 30-Oct-3 Christie's, London #60/R est:10000-15000

FARR, Charles Griffin (1908-) American

£2762 $5000 €4033 Protrero hillside (102x140cm-40x55in) 16-Apr-4 American Auctioneer #118/R est:15000-20000

£2762 $5000 €4033 Rose garden (91x122cm-36x48in) 16-Apr-4 American Auctioneer #119/R est:11000-15000

£3315 $6000 €4840 Iris and wild poppies (61x76cm-24x30in) 16-Apr-4 American Auctioneer #117/R est:9000-12000

FARR, Ellen B (1840-1907) American

£1323 $2500 €1932 Pepper tree berries and foliage (30x20cm-12x8in) s. canvasboard prov. 17-Feb-4 John Moran, Pasadena #188/R est:1000-1500

£1923 $3500 €2808 Pepper tree branch (46x30cm-18x12in) s. 15-Jun-4 John Moran, Pasadena #46 est:3000-4000

£7514 $13000 €10970 Blossoming pepper tree (81x112cm-32x44in) s.i. prov. 10-Dec-3 Bonhams & Butterfields, San Francisco #6276/R est:3000-5000

FARRAR, Betty Binkly (1914-1979) American

Sculpture

£3529 $6000 €5152 St Francis, artist's proof (163x30x41cm-64x12x16in) s.d.1975 num.1/2 bronze fountain prov. 1-Nov-3 Santa Fe Art, Santa Fe #259/R est:2000-4000

FARRELL, Micheal (1945-2000) Irish

£4667 $8447 €7000 Famine series, nature morte Irlande 1846 (115x174cm-45x69in) s. i.d.1996 verso. 30-Mar-4 De Veres Art Auctions, Dublin #83/R est:8000-10000

Works on paper

£1400 $2506 €2044 Cafe Triste (75x105cm-30x41in) s.d.81 pencil W/C prov.exhib. 14-May-4 Christie's, London #94/R est:1000-1500

£2105 $3874 €3200 Shorter history of Ireland (76x56cm-30x22in) s.d.80 W/C pencil prov. 22-Jun-4 De Veres Art Auctions, Dublin #139/R est:1500-2000

FARREN, Robert (1832-?) British

£1200 $2220 €1752 The farmer's daughter (47x32cm-19x13in) s. paper on canvas prov. 11-Feb-4 Cheffins, Cambridge #436/R est:1400-1800

FARRER, Henry (1843-1903) American/British

£3025 $4900 €4417 Still life with three eggs (13x25cm-5x10in) s.d.1868 paper. 31-Jul-3 Eldred, East Dennis #845/R est:1000-1500

Works on paper
£452 $800 €660 Trees by a pond at sunset (7x11cm-3x4in) s. pencil W/C sold with another by a different hand. 2-May-4 Bonhams & Butterfields, San Francisco #1115/R
£1677 $2800 €2448 November day, view on Long island, NY (30x43cm-12x17in) s.i.verso W/C exec.c.1860-65. 20-Jun-3 Freeman, Philadelphia #10a/R est:800-1200
£1744 $3000 €2546 Autumn afternoon (45x62cm-18x24in) s.d.1902 W/C paper on board exhib. 3-Dec-3 Doyle, New York #165/R est:3000-5000
£1796 $3000 €2622 Path to the inlet (46x64cm-18x25in) s. W/C prov. 23-Oct-3 Shannon's, Milford #157/R est:4000-6000

FARRERAS, Francisco (1927-) Spanish
£1408 $2465 €2000 Coudrage 27 (31x31cm-12x12in) s.d.1984 s.i.d.verso paint collage wood. 16-Dec-3 Segre, Madrid #158/R est:1200
£5282 $8451 €7500 Perseus (120x100cm-47x39in) s.i.d.73 verso oil collage board prov.lit. 16-Sep-3 Segre, Madrid #141/R est:5500
Works on paper
£884 $1610 €1300 Collage (25x20cm-10x8in) s.d.1994 collage paint board prov. 3-Feb-4 Segre, Madrid #201/R
£915 $1602 €1300 Collage 600 (30x30cm-12x12in) s.i.d.1973 collage panel lit. 16-Dec-3 Segre, Madrid #157/R
£1127 $1972 €1600 Collage 587 (30x30cm-12x12in) s.i.d.1973 verso collage panel lit. 16-Dec-3 Segre, Madrid #156/R est:1000
£1333 $2427 €2000 Collage (40x26cm-16x10in) s.d.1983 collage ink wash. 29-Jun-4 Segre, Madrid #222/R est:2000
£4196 $7007 €6000 Collage no.236 (91x74cm-36x29in) s.i.d.1965 verso collage mixed media panel prov. 24-Jun-3 Segre, Madrid #119/R est:5000

FARRIER, Robert (1796-1879) British
£7000 $12600 €10220 Who shall serve the king ? - the recruit (50x62cm-20x24in) board prov. 21-Apr-4 Cheffins, Cambridge #492/R est:6000-8000

FARRINGTON, Ruth (?) American?
£268 $500 €391 Floral still life. 26-Feb-4 Skinner, Bolton #711/R

FARRUGGIO, Remo (1904-1981) American/Italian
£353 $600 €515 Portrait (25x20cm-10x8in) s. board painted c.1948. 9-Nov-3 Outer Cape Auctions, Provincetown #54/R
£370 $600 €537 Untitled (43x51cm-17x20in) s. 8-Aug-3 Barridorf, Portland #334/R
£378 $700 €552 Almond grove (64x99cm-25x39in) s. 15-Feb-4 Outer Cape Auctions, Provincetown #72/R
£399 $650 €583 Untitled abstract (25x36cm-10x14in) s. board. 19-Jul-3 Outer Cape Auctions, Provincetown #138/R
£405 $750 €591 Earth tones (25x36cm-10x14in) s. oil on paper. 15-Feb-4 Outer Cape Auctions, Provincetown #48/R
£455 $800 €664 Cubist townscape (20x20cm-8x8in) s. paper painted c.1938. 3-Jan-4 Outer Cape Auctions, Provincetown #27/R
£514 $950 €750 Modules to the moon (61x76cm-24x30in) s. 17-Jul-4 Outer Cape Auctions, Provincetown #30a/R
£757 $1400 €1105 Hamlet (64x97cm-25x38in) s.d.1962. 17-Jul-4 Outer Cape Auctions, Provincetown #60a/R
£1080 $1900 €1577 Townscape, waterside (58x79cm-23x31in) s. paper. 3-Jan-4 Outer Cape Auctions, Provincetown #77/R
£1081 $2000 €1578 Untitled, people (48x41cm-19x16in) s.verso board. 17-Jul-4 Outer Cape Auctions, Provincetown #99/R
£1543 $2500 €2237 Poet and the moon (41x51cm-16x20in) s.d.1937 masonite. 8-Aug-3 Barridorf, Portland #333/R est:900-1200

FARSKY, Otto (19/20th C) American
£465 $800 €679 Soldier (41x25cm-16x10in) s. board painted c.1890. 7-Dec-3 Treadway Gallery, Cincinnati #480/R

FARTHING, Stephen (1950-) British
Works on paper
£260 $486 €390 Sao Paulo by night (68x47cm-27x19in) s. W/C collage. 22-Jul-4 Dominic Winter, Swindon #314

FARULLI, Fernando (1923-1997) Italian
£364 $663 €550 Motorway bridge (50x70cm-20x28in) s. s.verso. 17-Jun-4 Galleria Pananti, Florence #464/R
£396 $649 €550 Piombino factories (55x75cm-22x30in) s. 10-Jun-3 Pandolfini, Florence #441
£662 $1205 €1000 Composition (130x130cm-51x51in) s. i.verso. 17-Jun-4 Galleria Pananti, Florence #473/R

FASANELLA, Ralph (1914-1997) American
£172973 $320000 €252541 New York City (138x279cm-54x110in) s. painted 1956-57 exhib.lit. 15-Jan-4 Sotheby's, New York #322/R est:100000-150000

FASANOTTI, Gaetano (1831-1882) Italian
£1454 $2471 €2123 Coast (32x51cm-13x20in) s.d.1874. 5-Nov-3 Dobiaschofsky, Bern #534/R est:4800 (S.FR 3300)
£4895 $8175 €7000 Seascape (44x73cm-17x29in) s.d.1874. 26-Jun-3 Sant Agostino, Torino #306/R est:7000-9000

FASCIOTTI, Titta (1927-1993) South African
£259 $432 €378 Landscape with houses (29x39cm-11x15in) s. board. 20-Oct-3 Stephan Welz, Johannesburg #884 est:2000-3000 (SA.R 3000)
£259 $432 €378 Three figures in conversation (22x17cm-9x7in) s. board. 20-Oct-3 Stephan Welz, Johannesburg #938 est:800-1200 (SA.R 3000)
£294 $532 €429 Sunrise over a beach (38x54cm-15x21in) s. canvas on board. 30-Mar-4 Stephan Welz, Johannesburg #182 est:2000-3000 (SA.R 3500)
£302 $504 €441 Watsonias in colour, Northern Cape (16x24cm-6x9in) s.d.82 canvasboard. 20-Oct-3 Stephan Welz, Johannesburg #902 est:2000-3000 (SA.R 3500)
£336 $608 €491 Landscape (29x39cm-11x15in) s.d.73 board. 30-Mar-4 Stephan Welz, Johannesburg #209 est:2000-3000 (SA.R 4000)
£353 $639 €515 Red blossoms (29x34cm-11x13in) s.d.73 board. 30-Mar-4 Stephan Welz, Johannesburg #257 est:2500-4000 (SA.R 4200)
£385 $654 €562 Dry river, Drakensburg, Natal (24x34cm-9x13in) s.d.88 board. 4-Nov-3 Stephan Welz, Johannesburg #301 est:1800-2400 (SA.R 4500)
£504 $913 €736 Rose on a window sill (50x34cm-20x13in) s. board. 30-Mar-4 Stephan Welz, Johannesburg #262 est:2500-4000 (SA.R 6000)
£603 $1008 €880 Houses beneath a mountain (35x50cm-14x20in) s. board. 20-Oct-3 Stephan Welz, Johannesburg #879 est:4000-6000 (SA.R 7000)
£756 $1369 €1104 Alleyway. Up the stairs (34x24cm-13x9in) s. board pair. 30-Mar-4 Stephan Welz, Johannesburg #503 est:4000-6000 (SA.R 9000)

FASINI, Alexandre (1892-1982) Russian
£580 $1056 €847 Figure studies with red, yellow and green (54x65cm-21x26in) s.d.1931. 15-Jun-4 Bonhams, Knightsbridge #95/R
Works on paper
£600 $1074 €876 Composition with figures (21x17cm-8x7in) s.d.1921 pencil pen W/C. 26-May-4 Sotheby's, Olympia #474/R
£700 $1253 €1022 Two studies of nudes (27x22cm-11x9in) s.d.1925-26 gouache two. 26-May-4 Sotheby's, Olympia #475/R

FASNACHT, Heide Ann (1951-) American
Sculpture
£1081 $2000 €1578 Untitled (61x75cm-24x30in) painted wood construction exec 1987 prov.exhib. 12-Feb-4 Sotheby's, New York #209/R est:2500-3000

FASSBENDER, Adolf (20th C) American?
Photographs
£5000 $9000 €7300 Crashing wave (37x48cm-15x19in) chlorobromide print. 22-Apr-4 Phillips, New York #55/R est:5000-7000

FASSBENDER, Josef (1903-1974) German
£10490 $17832 €15000 Old city of Cologne (102x90cm-40x35in) 26-Nov-3 Lempertz, Koln #660/R est:18000-20000

FASSETT, Cornelia Adele Strong (1831-1898) American
£539 $900 €787 Portraits (61x51cm-24x20in) s. pair. 19-Jun-3 Shelley, Hendersonville #1113

FASSIANOS, Alecos (1935-) Greek
£1689 $3023 €2500 Personnage (21x26cm-8x10in) s. paper on canvas. 4-May-4 Calmels Cohen, Paris #236/R est:2000-3000
£3667 $6673 €5500 Man in blue (50x50cm-20x20in) s. 5-Jul-4 Le Mouel, Paris #78/R est:6000-8000
£4467 $8040 €6700 Woman (50x64cm-20x25in) s. prov. 25-Apr-4 Versailles Encheres #142 est:3500-4500
£4532 $7704 €6617 Le baiser (66x77cm-26x30in) s.d.76 prov. 5-Nov-3 AB Stockholms Auktionsverk #1098/R est:50000-60000 (S.KR 60000)
£6000 $10200 €8760 Thoughts of home (65x46cm-26x18in) s. 18-Nov-3 Sotheby's, London #58/R est:4000-6000
£6000 $10740 €8760 Les Cerfs volants (129x97cm-51x38in) s.d.1963 i.verso prov. 10-May-4 Sotheby's, Olympia #41/R est:6000-8000
£7400 $12950 €10804 Man (80x65cm-31x26in) s. s.i.verso prov. 16-Dec-3 Bonhams, New Bond Street #136/R est:4000-6000
£11458 $18104 €16500 Untitled (161x128cm-63x50in) s.d.1987 acrylic prov. 27-Apr-3 Versailles Encheres #98
£12000 $21480 €17520 Baiser (68x78cm-27x31in) s.d.76. 10-May-4 Sotheby's, Olympia #37/R est:6000-8000
£16000 $27200 €23360 Red man (145x114cm-57x45in) s.d.73 prov.exhib. 18-Nov-3 Sotheby's, London #59/R est:10000-15000
£35000 $62650 €51100 Red men (189x279cm-74x110in) s.d.1974. 10-May-4 Sotheby's, Olympia #76/R est:18000-25000
Works on paper
£235 $437 €350 Jeune homme (17x12cm-7x5in) s.i. col crayon. 3-Mar-4 Tajan, Paris #206
£296 $545 €450 Femme a la cigarette (135x22cm-53x9in) s. ink dr prov. 27-Jun-4 Versailles Encheres #139/R
£300 $546 €450 Femme dans un interieur (32x22cm-13x9in) s. conte. 30-Jun-4 Delvaux, Paris #58
£313 $522 €450 Nu (23x32cm-9x13in) s.d.5 novembre 1970 graphite. 25-Oct-3 Cornette de St.Cyr, Paris #675
£705 $1297 €1050 Nu allonge sur le lit (49x62cm-19x24in) s.d.1974 wax pastel. 24-Mar-4 Joron-Derem, Paris #155/R
£738 $1374 €1100 Tranche de pasteque (19x18cm-7x7in) s. gouache collage. 3-Mar-4 Tajan, Paris #205/R
£816 $1461 €1200 Etude d'homme de profil tenant des fleurs et des fruits (49x34cm-19x13in) s. col crayon. 19-Mar-4 Piasa, Paris #212a
£900 $1656 €1350 Baigneurs et personnage fumant (33x50cm-13x20in) s.d.1969 col crayon. 13-Jun-4 Lombrail & Teucquam, Paris #114/R
£1284 $2259 €1900 Jeune homme bleu (26x22cm-10x9in) s. gouache prov. 18-May-4 Tajan, Paris #161/R est:2000-3000
£1476 $2746 €2200 Cycliste (29x22cm-11x9in) s. wax crayon brown paper. 3-Mar-4 Tajan, Paris #204/R est:2000-2500
£1600 $2864 €2336 Spring (31x28cm-12x11in) s. crayon pencil prov. 11-May-4 Bonhams, New Bond Street #111/R est:500-700
£1800 $3222 €2628 Woman (26x23cm-10x9in) s. col crayons. 10-May-4 Sotheby's, Olympia #126/R est:1000-1500
£2600 $4654 €3796 Promenade (29x27cm-11x11in) s.i. go paper on canvas exec. 1996 prov. 11-May-4 Bonhams, New Bond Street #122/R est:1500-2000
£3800 $6650 €5548 Two friends (65x50cm-26x20in) s. W/C. 16-Dec-3 Bonhams, New Bond Street #134/R est:2500-3500
£3800 $6802 €5548 Man (42x34cm-17x13in) s. mixed media paper on canvas. 10-May-4 Sotheby's, Olympia #80/R est:2000-3000

FASSIN, Nicholas de (1728-1811) Flemish
£4200 $7560 €6132 Italianate landscape with drovers watering their animals (57x77cm-22x30in) mono.d.1791. 20-Apr-4 Sotheby's, Olympia #288/R est:4000-6000

FASSIN, Nicholas de (attrib) (1728-1811) Flemish

£3357 $5773 €4800 Paysage Italianisant avec bergers et troupeau se reposant pres d'une ruine (70x87cm-28x34in) mono. 3-Dec-3 Palais de Beaux Arts, Brussels #655/R est:5000-7000

FATHI, Hassan (1957-) Egyptian

£667 $1227 €1000 Thought container (100x100cm-39x39in) s.i.d.1998 verso oil mixed media. 12-Jun-4 Meeting Art, Vercelli #486/R

FATTAH, Ismail (1934-) Iraqi

Works on paper

£1900 $3363 €2774 Various forms. Two figures (35x45cm-14x18in) s.d.1966 gouache acrylic W/C pen ink two. 29-Apr-4 Bonhams, New Bond Street #586/R est:1500-2000

FATTORI, Giovanni (1825-1908) Italian

£4525 $7828 €6607 Officer on horseback (17x12cm-7x5in) s. panel prov. 12-Dec-3 Galerie du Rhone, Sion #182/R est:9000-12000 (S.FR 10000)

£8389 $15017 €12500 Man with moustaches (26x35cm-10x14in) lit. 25-May-4 Finarte Semenzato, Milan #219/R est:15000-16000

£14118 $24000 €20612 Soldati in marcia (17x25cm-7x10in) s. panel prov.exhib.lit. 29-Oct-3 Christie's, Rockefeller NY #214/R est:30000-40000

£22000 $40480 €33000 Stream in Maremma (15x23cm-6x9in) s. board prov.exhib.lit. 10-Jun-4 Christie's, Rome #182/R est:23000-28000

£26667 $49067 €40000 Soldier on horseback with two horses (29x16cm-11x6in) s. 10-Jun-4 Christie's, Rome #183/R est:25000-35000

£28169 $46761 €40000 Lanciere a cavallo (59x67cm-23x26in) s. prov. 11-Jun-3 Christie's, Rome #186/R est:40000-60000

£36914 $65337 €55000 Roman peasants in the village (31x15cm-12x6in) s. panel prov.lit. 30-Apr-4 Tajan, Paris #158/R est:25000-30000

Prints

£2042 $3533 €2900 Oxen (24x41cm-9x16in) eau forte lit. 9-Dec-3 Pandolfini, Florence #180/R est:400-450

Works on paper

£403 $741 €600 Portrait d'homme. s.d.1883 dr. 23-Mar-4 Galerie Moderne, Brussels #116

£1745 $3211 €2600 Three soldiers with horses (37x49cm-15x19in) s. ochre one of pair. 26-Mar-4 Dorotheum, Vienna #153/R est:1600-1800

£1879 $3458 €2800 Resting soldier with horse (38x49cm-15x19in) s. i. verso ochre one of pair. 26-Mar-4 Dorotheum, Vienna #155/R est:1600-1800

£2158 $3540 €3000 Horses (29x22cm-11x9in) s.i. Chinese ink. 10-Jun-3 Pandolfini, Florence #35/R est:3000-3200

£6338 $10521 €9000 Capre al pascolo (360x150cm-142x59in) s.i.d.1873 verso W/C. 11-Jun-3 Christie's, Rome #159/R est:4000-6000

FATTORINI, Eliseo Tuderte (1830-1887) Italian

Works on paper

£596 $1085 €900 Birth of the Virgin (34x58cm-13x23in) s.i.d.1877 W/C. 21-Jun-4 Pandolfini, Florence #12/R

FAUBERT, Jean (1946-) French

£282 $487 €400 L'homme a la pipe (33x23cm-13x9in) s. 15-Dec-3 Charbonneaux, Paris #191

FAUCHE, Léon (1868-?) French

£1600 $2944 €2336 Ile Saint Louis, Paris (50x61cm-20x24in) s. 25-Mar-4 Christie's, Kensington #33/R est:1000-1500

FAUCHEUR, Jean (1956-) French?

Works on paper

£533 $960 €800 Untitled (130x97cm-51x38in) s.d.2003 s.verso spray paint. 24-Apr-4 Cornette de St.Cyr, Paris #517

FAUCONNIER, Henri le (1881-1946) French

£2536 $4159 €3500 Landscape (32x40cm-13x16in) s. board prov. 27-May-3 Sotheby's, Amsterdam #479/R est:3000-4000

Works on paper

£537 $988 €800 Woman's portrait (102x70cm-40x28in) mono. W/C. 26-Mar-4 Ketterer, Hamburg #394/R

£671 $1201 €1000 Still life with pot plant on blue table (99x61cm-39x24in) mono. mixed media. 25-May-4 Karl & Faber, Munich #380/R

£1064 $1777 €1500 Village view with church (75x56cm-30x22in) s. W/C. 20-Oct-3 Bernaerts, Antwerp #52/R est:1500-2000

£1074 $1901 €1600 Vue a travers la fenetre (73x52cm-29x20in) mono. W/C. 27-Apr-4 Campo, Vlaamse Kaai #484 est:1700-2000

£1594 $2614 €2200 A view of Sloten (55x75cm-22x30in) s. W/C. 27-May-3 Sotheby's, Amsterdam #474/R est:2500-3500

FAUCONNIER, le (19/20th C) French

£1958 $3329 €2800 Jeune fille en rouge (73x50cm-29x20in) s.i.d.1922 verso. 23-Nov-3 Cornette de St.Cyr, Paris #612 est:1000-1200

FAUERHOLDT, Viggo (1832-1883) Danish

£469 $764 €685 Seascape with sailing vessels, Fyn (24x32cm-9x13in) s. 28-Sep-3 Hindemae, Ullerslev #134/R (D.KR 5000)

£588 $940 €858 Entrance to a town in the Norwegian skerries (35x48cm-14x19in) s.d.1860. 22-Sep-3 Rasmussen, Vejle #299/R (D.KR 6200)

£716 $1311 €1045 Calm summer's day, Hven in background (21x30cm-8x12in) init.d.1857. 9-Jun-4 Rasmussen, Copenhagen #1807/R (D.KR 8000)

£898 $1671 €1311 View of town on hillside by lake (35x48cm-14x19in) s.d.1860. 2-Mar-4 Rasmussen, Copenhagen #1435/R (D.KR 10000)

£1769 $3219 €2600 Moored sailing vessels by a coast at dusk (40x61cm-16x24in) s.i.d.1870. 3-Feb-4 Christie's, Amsterdam #105/R est:2500-3500

£2363 $4088 €3450 Coastal landscape with sailing boats crossing the breakwater (88x132cm-35x52in) s.d.1862. 9-Dec-3 Rasmussen, Copenhagen #1494/R est:30000-40000 (D.KR 25000)

£3403 $5887 €4968 Entrance to Oslo (59x92cm-23x36in) s.d.1859. 9-Dec-3 Rasmussen, Copenhagen #1445/R est:40000 (D.KR 36000)

£12287 $21257 €17939 Busy traffic at Knippelsbro (66x97cm-26x38in) s.d.1861. 9-Dec-3 Rasmussen, Copenhagen #1279/R est:150000 (D.KR 130000)

£12534 $22936 €18300 Entrance to Copenhagen's customs house (47x63cm-19x25in) s.d.1855 prov. 9-Jun-4 Rasmussen, Copenhagen #1455/R est:150000 (D.KR 140000)

FAUERHOLDT, Viggo (attrib) (1832-1883) Danish

£1528 $2551 €2200 Fishing boats at sea (80x94cm-31x37in) 24-Oct-3 Ketterer, Hamburg #8/R est:2500-3000

FAULCONER, Mary (1912-) American

Works on paper

£2582 $4750 €3770 244 East 49th Street (18x15cm-7x6in) s. gouache set of three. 10-Jun-4 Sotheby's, New York #129/R est:2000-3000

FAULKENBERRY, Gay (1952-) American

£1176 $2000 €1717 Northlight arrangement (23x38cm-9x15in) s. canvas on panel painted c.1987 prov. 1-Nov-3 Santa Fe Art, Santa Fe #48/R est:1000-2000

FAULKNER, Amanda (1953-) British

Works on paper

£480 $864 €701 Untitled (75x52cm-30x20in) s.d.84 pastel chl. 20-Jan-4 Bonhams, Knightsbridge #270/R

FAULKNER, Benjamin (1787-1849) British

£2200 $3938 €3212 Portrait of a gentleman (75x63cm-30x25in) s.d.1831 verso. 11-May-4 Sotheby's, Olympia #597/R est:1500-2000

FAULKNER, Frank (1946-) American

£989 $1800 €1444 Caparison (150x91cm-59x36in) s.d.1968 verso acrylic embossed vinyl exhib. 29-Jun-4 Sotheby's, New York #472/R est:3000-5000

FAULKNER, John (c.1830-1888) British

£750 $1275 €1095 Mountainous landscape with drover, dog and sheep (78x121cm-31x48in) s. 19-Nov-3 Tennants, Leyburn #1109

£1867 $3379 €2800 Figure in extensive lake and mountain landscape (77x120cm-30x47in) s. 31-Mar-4 James Adam, Dublin #58/R est:2000-3000

Works on paper

£300 $537 €438 Cattle watering at a river with farm house in the background (36x25cm-14x10in) s. W/C. 7-May-4 Mallams, Oxford #232/R

£392 $650 €572 Village church near Coventry (44x76cm-17x30in) s.i. W/C. 30-Sep-3 Christie's, Rockefeller NY #430/R

£450 $819 €675 A drover and cattle in a Scottish landscape (41x46cm-16x18in) s.indis.i. pencil W/C htd white. 1-Jul-4 Christie's, Kensington #100/R

£500 $800 €730 Rocky coastal landscape (41x71cm-16x28in) s. W/C. 20-Sep-3 Nadeau, Windsor #168

£528 $914 €750 Drover with cattle (23x34cm-9x13in) s. W/C. 10-Dec-3 Bonhams & James Adam, Dublin #8/R

£704 $1218 €1000 Roadside, Bagington, Warickshire (40x64cm-16x25in) s. W/C. 10-Dec-3 Bonhams & James Adam, Dublin #37/R

£820 $1501 €1197 On Loch Shiel, Argyllshire (74x125cm-29x49in) s.i. W/C scratching out. 29-Jan-4 Bonhams, Edinburgh #305

£1060 $1928 €1600 Summer landscape (48x96cm-19x38in) s. W/C. 17-Jun-4 Hamilton Osborne King, Dublin #341/R est:2000-3000

£1181 $1924 €1700 Fishing smacks and other shipping in a breeze (64x100cm-25x39in) s. W/C. 28-Sep-3 Hamilton Osborne King, Dublin #209 est:1200-1500

£1192 $2170 €1800 Watering cattle by trees and a windmill (45x97cm-18x38in) s. W/C. 17-Jun-4 Hamilton Osborne King, Dublin #343/R est:2000-3000

£1300 $2210 €1898 On the Avon near Stoneleigh. In the open country (48x99cm-19x39in) s.i. W/C pair. 25-Nov-3 Bonhams, Knightsbridge #70/R

£2200 $3938 €3212 On Loch Shiel, Argyllshire (76x127cm-30x50in) s.i. pencil W/C. 14-May-4 Christie's, Kensington #310/R est:1500-2500

£2500 $4475 €3650 Shipping off a rocky coastline, Dublin Bay (69x102cm-27x40in) s. pencil W/C. 14-May-4 Christie's, Kensington #309/R est:2500-3500

£5500 $9845 €8030 Crookhaven, Co Cork (27x46cm-11x18in) s.i. pencil W/C htd bodycol scratching out prov. 14-May-4 Christie's, London #88/R est:2000-3000

FAULKNER, Sarah (1959-) Australian

£309 $559 €451 Untitled (27x35cm-11x14in) s.d.86 acrylic on paper. 30-Mar-4 Lawson Menzies, Sydney #1/R (A.D 750)

£620 $1147 €905 Man with olive sack (94x65cm-37x26in) s.d.89 i.verso prov. 15-Mar-4 Sotheby's, Melbourne #149 est:500-700 (A.D 1500)

£2273 $4205 €3319 Stable hand (182x121cm-72x48in) s.d.88 board prov. 15-Mar-4 Sotheby's, Melbourne #63/R est:2000-3000 (A.D 5500)

FAUQUAND (20th C) ?

£2183 $3820 €3100 Barques et thoniers sous voiles a quai (85x100cm-33x39in) s. 21-Dec-3 Thierry & Lannon, Brest #312/R est:2000-2200

FAURE, Amandus (1874-1931) German

£347 $566 €500 Oriental dance scene (34x44cm-13x17in) s. i. verso board. 27-Sep-3 Dr Fritz Nagel, Stuttgart #9112/R

£369 $653 €550 Variety artiste (127x87cm-50x34in) s. 30-Apr-4 Dr Fritz Nagel, Stuttgart #130/R

£548 $932 €800 Still life - spring flowers in green vase (86x66cm-34x26in) s.d.17 lit. 6-Nov-3 Allgauer, Kempten #3412/R

£567 $919 €800 Spring flowers in green ceramic vase (72x68cm-28x27in) s.d.18 lit. 23-May-3 Karlheinz Kaupp, Staufen #1839

£738 $1358 €1100 Circus scene (105x124cm-41x49in) s.d.17. 25-Mar-4 Dr Fritz Nagel, Stuttgart #704/R

£833 $1317 €1200 In the harem (28x33cm-11x13in) s.d.18 board lit. 19-Sep-3 Schloss Ahlden, Ahlden #1524/R
£1127 $1972 €1600 Still life of flowers (90x100cm-35x39in) s.d.23. 19-Dec-3 Dorotheum, Vienna #33/R est:1500-2000

FAURE, Elisabeth (1906-1964) French
£2333 $4293 €3500 Le marchand de fruits (50x65cm-20x26in) s. panel. 14-Jun-4 Gros & Delettrez, Paris #292/R est:4000-6000
Works on paper
£567 $1043 €850 Repas de Mariage a Fort Lamy (30x48cm-12x19in) s. gouache. 14-Jun-4 Gros & Delettrez, Paris #278/R

FAURE, Eugène (1822-1879) French
£14000 $22400 €20300 Woodland idyll (218x123cm-86x48in) s. prov. 18-Sep-3 Christie's, Kensington #184/R est:8000-12000

FAURE, M (19/20th C) French?
Sculpture
£1615 $2600 €2358 Standing bull (21cm-8in) i. bronze. 14-Jan-4 Christie's, Rockefeller NY #305/R est:1500-2500

FAURER, Louis (1916-2001) American
Photographs
£1695 $3000 €2475 Robert and Mary Frank, NYC, 1950 (25x16cm-10x6in) s.i.d. gelatin silver print executed c.1980. 27-Apr-4 Christie's, Rockefeller NY #158/R est:2500-3500
£2825 $5000 €4125 Bowing for the Vogue collection, Paris (31x24cm-12x9in) s.i.d.1972 gelatin silver print prov.lit. 27-Apr-4 Christie's, Rockefeller NY #317/R est:5000-7000
£3892 $6500 €5682 Street peddler (25x18cm-10x7in) s.d.1952 gelatin silver print. 16-Oct-3 Phillips, New York #141/R est:6000-8000
£5556 $10000 €8112 Theatre goers, New York (23x34cm-9x13in) s.d.1949 gelatin silver print lit. 23-Apr-4 Phillips, New York #20/R est:6000-8000
£10778 $18000 €15736 52nd St Pier looking toward United Nations building (33x22cm-13x9in) st.sig.verso num.13 verso gelatin silver print exec.1951 prov.exh. 17-Oct-3 Phillips, New York #37/R est:10000-15000

FAUSETT, Dean (1913-) American
Works on paper
£950 $1700 €1387 Forest of Savernake, England. s.i. W/C. 13-May-4 Dallas Auction Gallery, Dallas #334/R est:600-1000

FAUST, Joseph (1868-?) French
£4161 $7366 €6200 Scene de la vie de Dante (145x114cm-57x45in) s. 30-Apr-4 Tajan, Paris #139/R est:4000-6000

FAUSTIN, Celestin (1948-1981) Haitian
£234 $375 €342 Voodoo (91x61cm-36x24in) s.d.1977. 17-May-3 Bunte, Elgin #670

FAUSTMAN, Mollie (1883-1966) Swedish
£290 $522 €435 The stone well (77x85cm-30x33in) init. exhib. 25-Apr-4 Goteborg Auktionsverk, Sweden #351/R (S.KR 4000)
£1312 $2414 €1968 Woman with book (41x33cm-16x13in) s. 14-Jun-4 Lilla Bukowskis, Stockholm #292 est:6000-8000 (S.KR 18000)

FAUSTNER, Luitpold (attrib) (1845-1924) German
£414 $691 €600 Sunday hunter (38x26cm-15x10in) i.d.1879 panel. 10-Jul-3 Allgauer, Kempten #2479/R

FAUTRIER, Jean (1898-1964) French
£3467 $6379 €5200 Composition (48x61cm-19x24in) s.d.1959 tempera pastel paper prov.lit. 11-Jun-4 Pierre Berge, Paris #68y/R est:6000-8000
£3497 $5944 €5000 Manhattan (26x34cm-10x13in) s.d.1951 oil gouache lithograph lit. 28-Nov-3 Wiener Kunst Auktionen, Vienna #604/R est:5000-8000
£13000 $23660 €18980 Portrait (29x27cm-11x11in) s. painted c.1926-27 prov. 6-Feb-4 Sotheby's, London #151/R est:10000-15000
£24000 $43680 €35040 Nature morte au raisin (50x61cm-20x24in) indis.sig. prov.exhib. 6-Feb-4 Sotheby's, London #152/R est:25000-35000
£30000 $54600 €43800 Composition (19x24cm-7x9in) indis.sig. prov. 6-Feb-4 Sotheby's, London #167/R est:15000-20000
£58000 $106720 €84680 Composition (46x61cm-18x24in) s.d.61 oil pigment paper on canvas prov. 25-Jun-4 Christie's, London #116/R est:40000-60000
£68028 $121769 €100000 Wavy lines 2 (50x73cm-20x29in) s.d.60 paper on canvas prov. 16-Mar-4 Finarte Semenzato, Milan #422/R est:130000-140000
£85333 $153600 €128000 Tete (27x22cm-11x9in) oil pigment paper on canvas painted c.1954 prov.lit. 25-Apr-4 Versailles Encheres #98 est:100000-120000
£190000 $345800 €277400 Ile be happy (90x147cm-35x58in) s.d.60 i.on stretcher oil paper on canvas prov.exhib. 4-Feb-4 Christie's, London #16/R est:200000-300000
Prints
£2349 $4393 €3500 Boite en fer blanc (27x35cm-11x14in) s. print prov. 1-Mar-4 Artcurial Briest, Paris #100/R est:3000-4000
Sculpture
£14350 $24396 €20951 Tete striee (27cm-11in) s.num.2/9 pat.bronze incl.black stone socle prov.lit. Cast Esse. 5-Nov-3 AB Stockholms Auktionsverk #1083/R est:60000-70000 (S.KR 190000)
Works on paper
£870 $1566 €1270 Composition (14x23cm-6x9in) s. W/C. 26-Apr-4 Bukowskis, Stockholm #246/R (S.KR 12000)
£1007 $1852 €1500 Griffures (28x50cm-11x20in) chl. 24-Mar-4 Joron-Derem, Paris #140 est:1600-1800
£1049 $1783 €1500 Griffure (29x48cm-11x19in) mono. chl graphite. 23-Nov-3 Cornette de St.Cyr, Paris #638/R est:1500-2000
£1119 $1924 €1600 Untitled (32x50cm-13x20in) chl. 2-Dec-3 Calmels Cohen, Paris #34/R est:1600-1800
£1594 $2614 €2200 Untitled (33x50cm-13x20in) init.d.59 pencil dr. 30-May-3 Farsetti, Prato #232/R
£2013 $3604 €3000 Untitled (32x49cm-13x19in) init.d.62 chl tempera. 28-May-4 Farsetti, Prato #154/R est:2800-3200
£2083 $3479 €3000 Ne de dos (37x24cm-15x9in) s. crayon stumping thin paper on board lit. 21-Oct-3 Artcurial Briest, Paris #117/R est:2000-2500
£2200 $4004 €3212 Otage (20x32cm-8x13in) s.i.d.44 pen ink. 4-Feb-4 Sotheby's, Olympia #174/R est:2500-3500
£2797 $4755 €4000 Composition (32x24cm-13x9in) s.d.1963 W/C gouache paper on canvas. 23-Nov-3 Cornette de St.Cyr, Paris #639/R est:4000-6000
£2800 $5096 €4088 Untitled (50x64cm-20x25in) s.d.61 W/C gouache. 4-Feb-4 Sotheby's, Olympia #184/R est:3000-4000
£3497 $6014 €5000 Composition (49x64cm-19x25in) init.d.61 gouache W/C blotting paper. 4-Dec-3 Piasa, Paris #63/R est:3000-4000
£3846 $6538 €5500 Abstract (50x64cm-20x25in) s. W/C prov. 25-Nov-3 Sotheby's, Milan #138/R est:4000-5000
£5594 $9510 €8000 Untitled (49x64cm-19x25in) init.d.55 W/C tempera prov. 25-Nov-3 Sotheby's, Milan #140/R est:4000-5000

FAUVEL, Georges (1890-?) French
£638 $1186 €950 Barques au sec (38x55cm-15x22in) s.d.1891. 7-Mar-4 Lesieur & Le Bars, Le Havre #43

FAUVELET, Jean Baptiste (1819-1883) French
£1887 $3509 €2755 Young couple conversing (20x25cm-8x10in) s. panel. 2-Mar-4 Rasmussen, Copenhagen #1638/R est:6000-8000 (D.KR 21000)

FAUVILLE, Daniel (1953-) Belgian
£533 $976 €800 Composition (200x200cm-79x79in) s.d.87-88 verso. 7-Jun-4 Palais de Beaux Arts, Brussels #362

FAVAI, Gennaro (1882-?) Italian?
£588 $1100 €858 Palace of Desdemona (48x41cm-19x16in) s. panel painted c.1937. 25-Feb-4 Doyle, New York #26/R

FAVEN, Antti (1882-1948) Finnish
£521 $870 €750 Birches (27x28cm-11x11in) s. 23-Oct-3 Hagelstam, Helsinki #905
£1748 $2972 €2500 Autumn colours (39x33cm-15x13in) s.d.1912 board. 29-Nov-3 Bukowskis, Helsinki #63/R est:1500-2000
£2400 $4296 €3600 Autumn landscape (60x47cm-24x19in) s.d.1927. 15-May-4 Hagelstam, Helsinki #62/R est:4000
£3200 $5728 €4800 Landscape (38x29cm-15x11in) s. canvas on board. 15-May-4 Hagelstam, Helsinki #61/R est:3000
£4895 $8322 €7000 View from Brunnsparken towards the ocean (91x131cm-36x52in) s.d.1931. 29-Nov-3 Bukowskis, Helsinki #200/R est:7000-9000
Works on paper
£1533 $2745 €2300 Ville Vallgren (36x31cm-14x12in) s.d.1921 mixed media. 15-May-4 Hagelstam, Helsinki #63/R est:1800

FAVIER, Philippe (1957-) French
Works on paper
£2334 $4294 €3500 L'Archipel des Pacotilles (27x27cm-11x11in) s.d.21/9/92 collage paint under glass prov.exhib. 9-Jun-4 Artcurial Briest, Paris #557/R est:4000-5000
£3125 $5219 €4500 Roma Capriciosa (37x37cm-15x15in) s.d.15/9/93 mixed media under glass prov. 21-Oct-3 Artcurial Briest, Paris #563/R est:5000-7000
£14085 $24648 €20000 Lieu dit (24x24cm-9x9in) s.i. W/C collage ink crayon prov. 18-Dec-3 Cornette de St.Cyr, Paris #42/R est:1200-1500

FAVIER, Pierre (1899-?) French
£400 $680 €584 La Zone a la porte de Saint Cloud (29x40cm-11x16in) s.d.mars 1926 board. 29-Oct-3 Hampton & Littlewood, Exeter #551/R

FAVORIN, Ellen (1853-1919) Finnish
£704 $1127 €1000 Punkaharju (13x15cm-5x6in) s. 18-Sep-3 Hagelstam, Helsinki #1043
£839 $1560 €1250 The bathing hut (5x12cm-2x5in) s. 7-Mar-4 Bukowskis, Helsinki #319/R
£915 $1584 €1300 Cottage by shore (14x18cm-6x7in) s. board. 13-Dec-3 Hagelstam, Helsinki #100/R
£1127 $1803 €1600 Winter evening (16x22cm-6x9in) s. 18-Sep-3 Hagelstam, Helsinki #1050 est:1500
£1267 $2267 €1900 Landscape from Oritsaari in Ruokolax (9x15cm-4x6in) s. 15-May-4 Hagelstam, Helsinki #137/R est:1500
£1268 $2028 €1800 Korpijoki (17x13cm-7x5in) s. 18-Sep-3 Hagelstam, Helsinki #1007 est:1000
£1620 $2592 €2300 Coastal landscape with jetty (14x23cm-6x9in) s. 18-Sep-3 Hagelstam, Helsinki #897/R est:1200
£1892 $3386 €2800 Walking along the coastal road (41x50cm-16x20in) s. 8-May-4 Bukowskis, Helsinki #191/R est:2500-2800
£4476 $7608 €6400 Rowing boat on Lojo Lake (80x130cm-31x51in) s.d.1897. 29-Nov-3 Bukowskis, Helsinki #28/R est:4000-5000

FAVORY, Andre (1888-1937) French
£400 $708 €584 Boats moored on a calm river (43x61cm-17x24in) s. 29-Apr-4 Christie's, Kensington #230/R
£733 $1335 €1100 Oliviers en Provence (46x56cm-18x22in) s. 4-Jul-4 Eric Pillon, Calais #211/R
£839 $1427 €1200 L'aqueduc (60x73cm-24x29in) s. 23-Nov-3 Cornette de St.Cyr, Paris #607/R
£1049 $1783 €1500 Les baigneuses au pre (73x54cm-29x21in) s. 20-Nov-3 Claude Aguttes, Neuilly #216/R est:1600-2000

Works on paper
£2400 $4464 €3504 Reclining female nude (48x62cm-19x24in) s. pastel paper on board. 4-Mar-4 Christie's, London #475/R est:1000-1500

FAVRAY, Antoine de (1706-1791) French
£183099 $316761 €260000 Portrait de Charles Gravier, Comte de Vergennes (140x112cm-55x44in) s.i.d.1766 prov.exhib.lit. 10-Dec-3 Beaussant & Lefèvre, Paris #29/R est:250000-300000
£204225 $353310 €290000 Portrait de la Comtesse de Vergennes en costume oriental (129x93cm-51x37in) s.i.d.1768 prov.exhib.lit. 10-Dec-3 Beaussant & Lefèvre, Paris #30/R est:200000-300000

FAVRE, Maurice (1875-1919) French
Sculpture
£1733 $3155 €2600 Horse jumping over a gate (46cm-18in) i. bronze marble base. 1-Jul-4 Van Ham, Cologne #1027/R est:1100
£1860 $3200 €2716 Medieval warrior in full metal male and full length robe with cross on chest (76cm-30in) s.i. pat bronze. 6-Dec-3 Selkirks, St. Louis #683/R est:1800-2600
£1972 $3175 €2800 Le saut dans la mare (43x44cm-17x17in) s.i. brown pat bronze. 6-May-3 Coutau Begarie, Paris #77 est:3000-4000

FAVRE, Valerie (20th C) ?
Works on paper
£5282 $9243 €7500 Balls and tunnels (175x120cm-69x47in) s.i.d.1996 verso ink acrylic prov. 18-Dec-3 Cornette de St.Cyr, Paris #175/R est:2000-3000

FAVREAU, Marcel (?) Canadian?
£444 $769 €648 Paysage d'ete (30x41cm-12x16in) s. 9-Dec-3 Pinneys, Montreal #159 (C.D 1000)

FAVRETTO, Giacomo (1849-1887) Italian
£1438 $2300 €2099 Initiation (13x15cm-5x6in) s. board. 21-Sep-3 Grogan, Boston #33/R
£4310 $7716 €6293 Young flower girl (59x36cm-23x14in) s. 12-May-4 Dobiaschofsky, Bern #484/R est:18000 (S.FR 10000)
£275862 $460690 €400000 Confidences (65x95cm-26x37in) s. 14-Nov-3 Farsetti, Prato #541/R
Works on paper
£797 $1307 €1100 Gentleman (26x17cm-10x7in) s. W/C card. 29-May-3 Galleria Pace, Milan #97 est:1700

FAVRETTO, Giacomo (circle) (1849-1887) Italian
£14789 $24549 €21000 Sogni disturbati (47x67cm-19x26in) s. panel. 11-Jun-3 Christie's, Rome #261/R est:10000-15000

FAWCETT, John (1952-) American
£2706 $4600 €3951 Sacred water (61x51cm-24x20in) masonite. 1-Nov-3 Altermann Galleries, Santa Fe #7
Works on paper
£1676 $3000 €2447 Job well done (43x58cm-17x23in) W/C. 15-May-4 Altermann Galleries, Santa Fe #5/R

FAWCETT, Robert (1903-1967) American
Works on paper
£642 $1200 €937 Couple relaxing on sand dune (30x41cm-12x16in) mono.i. ink W/C gouache exec.c.1950. 26-Feb-4 Illustration House, New York #66

FAXON, Richard (19th C) French
£3133 $5797 €4700 Barque en difficulte dans l'estuaire de la Gironde (49x73cm-19x29in) s. 14-Jul-4 Livinec, Gaudcheau & Jezequel, Rennes #145/R

FAY, Hans (1888-1957) German
Works on paper
£338 $605 €500 Still life of tulips (63x43cm-25x17in) s. gouache lit. 8-May-4 Dawo, Saarbrucken #181/R
£473 $847 €700 Four youngsters with horses (77x54cm-30x21in) s. gouache lit. 8-May-4 Dawo, Saarbrucken #180/R

FAY, Ludwig Benno (1859-1906) German
£5933 $10799 €8900 Grandfather and his grandson riding together on a horse-drawn sleigh (64x96cm-25x38in) s. 1-Jul-4 Van Ham, Cologne #1337/R est:9000

FAY, Theodora (19/20th C) Norwegian?
£561 $932 €813 Mountain farm with children (33x45cm-13x18in) s. 16-Jun-3 Blomqvist, Lysaker #1040 (N.KR 6500)

FAYOLLE, Amelie (19th C) French
Works on paper
£1351 $2419 €2000 Allegory of music, painting and sculpture (39x30cm-15x12in) s. gouache lit. 8-May-4 Schloss Ahlden, Ahlden #703/R est:1900

FAZZINI, Pericle (1913-1987) Italian
Sculpture
£1350 $2200 €1971 Nu (20cm-8in) gold pat bronze prov. 25-Sep-3 Christie's, Rockefeller NY #623/R est:1500-2000
£5556 $9444 €8000 Cat scratching itself (28x138cm-11x54in) s.d.1954 bronze. 28-Oct-3 Il Ponte, Milan #273/R

FEARING, Kelly (1918-) American
£1676 $3000 €2447 St. Jerome. s. 13-May-4 Dallas Auction Gallery, Dallas #61/R est:800-1200
Works on paper
£599 $1000 €875 Untitled (66x41cm-26x16in) mixed media. 18-Oct-3 David Dike, Dallas #139/R

FEARNLEY, Thomas (1802-1842) Norwegian
£3336 $5672 €4871 The Golf of Naples (14x24cm-6x9in) init.indis.i.d.33 s.i.d.1/7/33 verso paper on panel. 19-Nov-3 Grev Wedels Plass, Oslo #23/R est:20000-30000 (N.KR 39000)
Works on paper
£584 $975 €853 Landscape (30x41cm-12x16in) s. W/C pencil. 17-Nov-3 Blomqvist, Lysaker #1057/R (N.KR 7000)

FEARNSMITH, George (attrib) (19/20th C) British
£280 $521 €409 Two girls in orchard (25x19cm-10x7in) canvas on panel. 2-Mar-4 Bearnes, Exeter #459

FEATHER, Yan Kel (1920-) British
£520 $962 €759 Family (41x51cm-16x20in) s. i.d.1980 verso. 10-Feb-4 David Lay, Penzance #325

FEBURE, Edouard (20th C) French
£740 $1339 €1080 French River scene (46x61cm-18x24in) s.d.1923 board sold with another. 17-Apr-4 Dickins, Middle Claydon #36

FEBVRE, Edouard (20th C) French
£517 $859 €750 Cambement de Bohemiens en hiver (54x65cm-21x26in) s. panel. 1-Oct-3 Millon & Associes, Paris #75/R

FECHHELM, Carl Traugott (1748-1819) German
£6507 $11062 €9500 CArrosse devant un palai (54x92cm-21x36in) s.i.d.1782. 6-Nov-3 Sotheby's, Paris #114/R est:4000-6000

FECHIN, Nicolai (1881-1955) American/Russian
£20053 $37500 €29277 Portrait of a young girl (20x15cm-8x6in) s. prov. 24-Jul-4 Coeur d'Alene, Hayden #61/R est:20000-30000
£105882 $180000 €154588 Old church of Ranchos (24x30cm-9x12in) s. i.verso prov. 18-Nov-3 John Moran, Pasadena #110 est:175000-225000
£167598 $300000 €244693 Taos Indian (61x51cm-24x20in) 15-May-4 Altermann Galleries, Santa Fe #64/R
Works on paper
£4891 $9000 €7141 Portrait of a native American elder (40x29cm-16x11in) s. blk crayon. 8-Jun-4 Bonhams & Butterfields, San Francisco #4157/R est:3000-5000
£7542 $13500 €11011 Gypsy (41x30cm-16x12in) chl. 15-May-4 Altermann Galleries, Santa Fe #63/R

FECHIN, Nicolai (attrib) (1881-1955) American/Russian
Works on paper
£320 $550 €467 Portrait of a young girl (41x30cm-16x12in) chl. 7-Dec-3 William Jenack, New York #302

FECHNER, Eduard Clemens (1799-1861) Russian
Works on paper
£1067 $1909 €1600 Mere entouree de ses quatre fils (63x52cm-25x20in) s.d.1843 graphite W/C htd white. 11-May-4 Christie's, Paris #374/R est:400-600

FECHTER, Emerich (1854-1912) Austrian
£350 $594 €500 Summer meadow in the pre-Alps (72x86cm-28x34in) s.d.1897. 20-Nov-3 Van Ham, Cologne #1565

FECTEAU, Marcel (1927-) Canadian
£269 $489 €393 Ciel d'or (25x30cm-10x12in) s.d.1979 i.verso masonite prov. 5-Feb-4 Heffel, Vancouver #30/R (C.D 650)
£289 $526 €422 Artist and his canoe (25x30cm-10x12in) s.d.1979 masonite prov. 5-Feb-4 Heffel, Vancouver #31/R (C.D 700)

FEDDEN, Mary (1915-) British
£280 $518 €409 Tuscany (64x43cm-25x17in) s.i. 10-Feb-4 David Lay, Penzance #445
£600 $1062 €876 Esch sur sure (32x40cm-13x16in) s.d.1999 verso board. 27-Apr-4 Bonhams, Knightsbridge #225/R
£900 $1638 €1314 Cats in Turkey (23x18cm-9x7in) s.d.1983. 21-Jun-4 Bonhams, Bath #427/R
£1900 $3458 €2774 Sheep (23x15cm-9x6in) s.d.1986 board prov. 1-Jul-4 Christie's, Kensington #366/R est:2000-3000
£1950 $3432 €2847 Eggs in a basket (19x25cm-7x10in) s.d.1997 tempera board. 18-May-4 Woolley & Wallis, Salisbury #150/R est:600-1000
£1950 $3549 €2847 Cat with a vase of flower (29x39cm-11x15in) s.d.1991 board. 21-Jun-4 Bonhams, Bath #429/R est:800-1200
£2000 $3200 €2920 Two girls in red (38x24cm-15x9in) s.i.d.1983 verso. 19-May-3 Bruton Knowles, Cheltenham #204/R est:1200-1800
£2200 $3784 €3212 Greens palms (25x24cm-10x9in) s.d.1972 board. 2-Dec-3 Bonhams, New Bond Street #149/R est:1200-1800
£2400 $4440 €3504 Night boat (15x19cm-6x7in) s. board. 11-Mar-4 Christie's, Kensington #350/R est:2000-3000
£2800 $4676 €4088 Cat in a flowerbed (19x14cm-7x6in) s. board. 16-Oct-3 Christie's, Kensington #606/R est:1000-1500

£2800	$4480	€4088	Sheep by moonlight (39x49cm-15x19in) s.d.1989. 20-Sep-3 Lacy Scott, Bury St.Edmunds #466/R
£3000	$5160	€4380	Still life with flowers and porcelain dog (41x23cm-16x9in) s.d.48. 3-Dec-3 Christie's, Kensington #724/R est:2000-3000
£3200	$5728	€4672	Milk jug (37x34cm-15x13in) s.d.1987 board. 16-Mar-4 Bonhams, New Bond Street #75/R est:3000-5000
£3600	$6192	€5256	Oasis (51x61cm-20x24in) s.d.1989 prov. 2-Dec-3 Bonhams, New Bond Street #146/R est:4000-6000
£3700	$6845	€5402	Quinces and vegetables (41x51cm-16x20in) s.d.2003. 10-Feb-4 David Lay, Penzance #443/R est:3000-4000
£3800	$6536	€5548	Julian Trevelyan looking out to sea (15x20cm-6x8in) s.d.1985 board exhib. 3-Dec-3 Christie's, Kensington #729/R est:1500-2000
£4000	$6880	€5840	Pansies (24x26cm-9x10in) s.d.59 board. 3-Dec-3 Christie's, Kensington #719/R est:1500-2000
£4200	$7014	€6132	Portrait of a lady with a cat (21x15cm-8x6in) s. board. 16-Oct-3 Christie's, Kensington #609/R est:1500-2000
£4200	$7770	€6132	Still life with a camellia (41x51cm-16x20in) s.d.1985. 11-Mar-4 Christie's, Kensington #343/R est:4000-6000
£4500	$8325	€6570	Still life with jug, lemon and fish (30x61cm-12x24in) s.d.1996. 11-Feb-4 Sotheby's, Olympia #204/R est:3000-5000
£5200	$8840	€7592	Fruit (31x41cm-12x16in) s.d.00 board. 26-Nov-3 Sotheby's, Olympia #104/R est:3000-4000
£5500	$10065	€8030	Still life of summer flowers in a vase (43x41cm-17x16in) s.d.1950 panel. 8-Jul-4 Duke & Son, Dorchester #181/R
£6000	$10020	€8760	Still life with fruit and primula (42x51cm-17x20in) s.d.1999 board. 16-Oct-3 Christie's, Kensington #681/R est:4000-6000
£6000	$10800	€8760	A basket of lemons (51x41cm-20x16in) s.d.1972. 21-Apr-4 Tennants, Leyburn #1248/R est:6000-8000
£6500	$11830	€9490	Potted polyanthus, avocados, corn cob on a garden wall (60x50cm-24x20in) s.d.1997. 21-Jun-4 Bonhams, Bath #425/R est:5000-7000
£7000	$12530	€10220	Still life, Merindol (61x51cm-24x20in) s.d.1970 board exhib. 14-May-4 Christie's, Kensington #588/R est:5000-8000
£8000	$14800	€11680	Still life with fruit (51x61cm-20x24in) s.d.1997 board. 11-Mar-4 Christie's, Kensington #345/R est:6000-8000
£8000	$14800	€11680	Still life by the sea (51x51cm-20x20in) s.d.1998. 11-Mar-4 Christie's, Kensington #346/R est:6000-8000
£8000	$13600	€11680	Barbara's bunch (51x76cm-20x30in) s.d.1977 prov.exhib. 30-Oct-3 Duke & Son, Dorchester #216/R est:5000-10000
£9000	$15480	€13140	Arranging flowers (61x91cm-24x36in) s.d.1989 prov. 3-Dec-3 Sotheby's, London #50/R est:10000-15000
£9000	$16380	€13140	Zechariah's Dream (51x61cm-20x24in) s.d.1951 prov. 1-Jul-4 Christie's, Kensington #365/R est:8000-12000
£20500	$37310	€29930	Still life with lemons (46x61cm-18x24in) s.d.60 board. 1-Jul-4 Christie's, Kensington #367/R est:6000-8000

Works on paper

£300	$540	€438	Moonlit scene with characters and horses in a landscape (15x38cm-6x15in) s.d.1974 W/C ink. 20-Apr-4 Wotton Auction Rooms, Wotton #880
£370	$629	€540	Study of a cuckoo (54x75cm-21x30in) s.d.1970 pencil. 25-Nov-3 Bonhams, Knowle #162
£550	$1001	€803	Country house with a church (16x23cm-6x9in) s.d.1985 gouache. 21-Jun-4 Bonhams, Bath #426/R
£650	$1086	€949	Still life at Corbes (48x64cm-19x25in) s.d.1970 pencil. 14-Oct-3 David Lay, Penzance #282/R
£720	$1310	€1051	Cat and mouse beneath an orange chair (12x12cm-5x5in) s.d.1991 pastel gouache. 21-Jun-4 Bonhams, Bath #428/R
£820	$1312	€1197	Bird in the snow (17x15cm-7x6in) s.d.1984 W/C. 19-May-3 Bruton Knowles, Cheltenham #176/R
£1100	$2035	€1606	Kitten (18x16cm-7x6in) s.d.1975 pencil W/C. 11-Mar-4 Christie's, Kensington #341/R est:1000-1500
£1500	$2730	€2190	Mediterranean still life with fruit (59x49cm-23x19in) s.d.1970 pencil. 1-Jul-4 Christie's, Kensington #363/R est:1500-2000
£1600	$2672	€2336	Crow (18x24cm-7x9in) s.d.1990 W/C. 16-Oct-3 Christie's, Kensington #612/R est:600-800
£1600	$2960	€2336	Landscape with sheep (15x11cm-6x4in) s.d.91 W/C bodycol. 11-Mar-4 Christie's, Kensington #340/R est:800-1200
£1600	$2816	€2336	Still life at Corbes (47x60cm-19x24in) s.d.1970 pencil black crayon. 19-May-4 Sotheby's, Olympia #263/R est:1500-2000
£1600	$2912	€2336	Lemon still life (14x11cm-6x4in) s.d.1991 W/C bodycol. 1-Jul-4 Christie's, Kensington #361/R est:1000-1500
£1650	$2838	€2409	Pears (24x33cm-9x13in) s. gouache. 2-Dec-3 Bonhams, New Bond Street #151/R est:800-1200
£1800	$3330	€2628	Still life with fruit and bottle (37x54cm-15x21in) s.d.1977 pencil W/C. 11-Mar-4 Christie's, Kensington #351/R est:2000-3000
£1800	$3330	€2628	Simone Boccanegra, Glyndebourne (43x56cm-17x22in) s.d.1998 pencil W/C board. 11-Mar-4 Christie's, Kensington #352/R est:2000-3000
£1900	$3097	€2774	Still life with pineapple and bottle. Still life with onions and bottle (37x55cm-15x22in) both s.d.1977 pencil monochromatic W/C two. 24-Sep-3 Dreweatt Neate, Newbury #51/R est:600-800
£1900	$3173	€2774	Song thrush (12x13cm-5x5in) s.d.1993 W/C bodycol prov. 16-Oct-3 Christie's, Kensington #608/R est:600-800
£2000	$3700	€2920	Eskdale (24x17cm-9x7in) s.d.1981 W/C bodycol. 11-Mar-4 Christie's, Kensington #344/R est:2000-3000
£2000	$3540	€2920	Moroccan moon (33x22cm-13x9in) s.d.1970 W/C gouache. 27-Apr-4 Bonhams, Knightsbridge #114/R est:1000-1500
£2000	$3540	€2920	Green palms (25x24cm-10x9in) s.i.d.1972 W/C gouache. 27-Apr-4 Bonhams, Knightsbridge #143/R est:2000-2500
£2200	$3784	€3212	Black cat on the table (22x29cm-9x11in) s.d.1991 W/C bodycol. 3-Dec-3 Christie's, Kensington #733/R est:800-1200
£2200	$3784	€3212	Blackbird (14x14cm-6x6in) s.d.1991 W/C bodycol. 3-Dec-3 Christie's, Kensington #735/R est:700-1000
£2200	$3784	€3212	Bird in the undergrowth (14x21cm-6x8in) s.d.1981 W/C bodycol. 3-Dec-3 Christie's, Kensington #736/R est:700-1000
£2400	$4440	€3504	Still life with pineapple and jar (37x55cm-15x22in) s.d.1977 W/C pencil black crayon. 11-Feb-4 Sotheby's, Olympia #221/R est:2000-3000
£2400	$4368	€3504	Two cats with a basket containing a pineapple, apples and a lemon (76x54cm-30x21in) s.d.1985 W/C. 21-Jun-4 Bonhams, Bath #421/R est:2000-3000
£2500	$4625	€3650	Still life with grapes (15x23cm-6x9in) s.d.1991 W/C bodycol. 11-Mar-4 Christie's, Kensington #339/R est:2500-3500
£2600	$4654	€3796	Makropulos case I (47x56cm-19x22in) s.d.1998 mixed media collage. 16-Mar-4 Bonhams, New Bond Street #86/R est:2000-3000
£2600	$4810	€3796	Cat along the shore (17x22cm-7x9in) s.d.1993 W/C bodycol. 11-Mar-4 Christie's, Kensington #337/R est:1500-2000
£2600	$4836	€3796	Two fruit (20x20cm-8x8in) gouache. 8-Mar-4 Christie's, London #5
£2800	$4816	€4088	Looking out to sea (14x19cm-6x7in) s.d.1989 W/C bodycol. 3-Dec-3 Christie's, Kensington #731/R est:700-1000
£3000	$5460	€4380	Still life with fig and flower (18x20cm-7x8in) s.d.1990 W/C bodycol. 1-Jul-4 Christie's, Kensington #362/R est:1500-2000
£3200	$5824	€4672	Church yard by the sea (23x28cm-9x11in) s.d.1994 W/C bodycol. 1-Jul-4 Christie's, Kensington #364/R est:1500-2000
£3500	$5845	€5110	Tabby cat (17x12cm-7x5in) s.d.1986 W/C bodycol. 16-Oct-3 Christie's, Kensington #610/R est:800-1200
£3800	$7030	€5548	Man and zebra (13x19cm-5x7in) s.d.1988 W/C board prov. 11-Mar-4 Christie's, Kensington #348/R est:1500-2000
£3800	$6688	€5548	Julian in Italy (19x15cm-7x6in) s.d.1982 W/C gouache prov. 19-May-4 Sotheby's, Olympia #274/R est:2500-3500
£4200	$7644	€6132	Fishermen on a sea wall with a dog and a woman knitting (20x25cm-8x10in) s.d.1996 mixed media. 21-Jun-4 Bonhams, Bath #423/R est:1500-2000
£4400	$8008	€6424	Sheep under the moon and stars (24x19cm-9x7in) s.d.1985 W/C. 21-Jun-4 Bonhams, Bath #422/R est:1200-1600
£4400	$8008	€6424	Tabby cat and the moon (19x23cm-7x9in) s.d.1985 W/C. 21-Jun-4 Bonhams, Bath #424/R est:1400-1600
£4500	$7740	€6570	Seated tabby in a landscape (23x15cm-9x6in) s.d.1982 W/C bodycol. 3-Dec-3 Christie's, Kensington #737/R est:1000-1500
£4800	$8016	€7008	Girl by the sea (19x13cm-7x5in) s.d.1988 W/C bodycol prov. 16-Oct-3 Christie's, Kensington #613/R est:800-1200
£5500	$9185	€8030	Collecting seaweed (19x23cm-7x9in) s.d.1988 W/C bodycol. 16-Oct-3 Christie's, Kensington #616/R est:1000-1500
£6000	$10320	€8760	Thrush (17x12cm-7x5in) s.d.1985 i.d.3/7/85 mount W/C bodycol. 3-Dec-3 Christie's, Kensington #739/R est:700-1000

FEDDER, Otto (1873-1919) German

£374	$670	€550	Peasant family with horse cart (14x16cm-6x6in) s. board. 17-Mar-4 Neumeister, Munich #451
£867	$1551	€1300	Coach in front of an inn (16x14cm-6x6in) s. board. 14-May-4 Behringer, Furth #1567/R est:1000
£867	$1551	€1300	Peasants riding in a wagon along a snowy path (16x12cm-6x5in) s. panel. 14-May-4 Behringer, Furth #1568/R est:1000
£1000	$1790	€1500	Mountain landscape with farmers and coach in front of a house (14x17cm-6x7in) s. board. 14-May-4 Behringer, Furth #1566/R est:1000
£1074	$1976	€1600	Hunters returning home in winter landscape (10x10cm-4x4in) s. panel. 24-Mar-4 Hugo Ruef, Munich #958 est:600
£2778	$4389	€4000	Chiemsee - fishermen (28x37cm-11x15in) s. lit. 19-Sep-3 Schloss Ahlden, Ahlden #1494/R est:4200

Works on paper

£313	$509	€450	Winter evening by pond (29x50cm-11x20in) s. W/C. 24-Sep-3 Neumeister, Munich #271

FEDELER, Carl Justus Harmen (1799-1858) German

£5705	$10497	€8500	Brig - Germania (53x77cm-21x30in) s.d.1851. 26-Mar-4 Bolland & Marotz, Bremen #513/R est:7000

FEDER, Adolphe (1886-1940) French

£922	$1540	€1300	Place du gouvernement (50x61cm-20x24in) s. 19-Oct-3 Rabourdin & Choppin de Janvry, Paris #129/R
£2013	$3564	€3000	Nature morte a la statue (81x100cm-32x39in) s.i.d.1915. 27-Apr-4 Artcurial Briest, Paris #151/R est:3000-4000
£3311	$6026	€5000	Bouquet (81x65cm-32x26in) s. 15-Jun-4 Rossini, Paris #86/R est:1200-1800

Works on paper

£464	$844	€700	Rue aux deux passantes (23x30cm-9x12in) s. W/C. 15-Jun-4 Rossini, Paris #87

FEDERICI, Gino (1888-1973) Italian

£1000	$1840	€1500	Herd at pasture (70x100cm-28x39in) s. 14-Jun-4 Sant Agostino, Torino #214/R est:1200-1600

FEDERICO, Cavalier Michele (1884-1966) Italian

£280	$468	€406	Waves crashing on the cliffs, Capri (38x48cm-15x19in) s.i. 21-Jun-3 Lacy Scott, Bury St.Edmunds #453/R
£362	$605	€529	Morning, Capri (38x50cm-15x20in) s. 17-Nov-3 Waddingtons, Toronto #259/R (C.D 800)
£400	$732	€584	Figures in a rowing boat off Capri (64x42cm-25x17in) s.i. 6-Jul-4 Bonhams, Knightsbridge #86/R
£452	$756	€660	The harbour at Capri (49x63cm-19x25in) s. i.verso. 17-Nov-3 Waddingtons, Toronto #266/R (C.D 1000)
£464	$844	€700	Capri (30x40cm-12x16in) s.i. board. 21-Jun-4 Pandolfini, Florence #197/R
£524	$965	€765	Coast of Capri (78x112cm-31x44in) s. 14-Jun-4 Waddingtons, Toronto #330/R est:2000-3000 (C.D 1300)
£653	$1150	€953	Seascape (53x69cm-21x27in) s. 1-Jan-4 Nadeau, Windsor #239
£729	$1350	€1064	Sunset afternoon, Capri (46x64cm-18x25in) s.i. 16-Jan-4 Aspire, Cleveland #45/R est:1000-1500
£850	$1420	€1241	Early morning at Capri (55x70cm-22x28in) s.i. i.verso. 11-Nov-3 Bonhams, Knightsbridge #117/R
£860	$1436	€1256	Evening approaching, Capri (54x71cm-21x28in) s. 17-Nov-3 Waddingtons, Toronto #265/R est:1000-1500 (C.D 1900)
£905	$1511	€1321	Pounding surf, Capri (50x71cm-20x28in) s. 17-Nov-3 Waddingtons, Toronto #260/R est:1000-1500 (C.D 2000)
£1229	$2200	€1794	Seascape (58x74cm-23x29in) s. 8-Jan-4 Doyle, New York #21/R est:2000-3000
£1400	$2506	€2100	Fishermen coming back (53x40cm-21x16in) s. 12-May-4 Stadion, Trieste #653/R est:900-1200

FEDERLE, Helmut (1944-) Swiss

£8939	$16000	€13051	Siedlung Korea II (50x35cm-20x14in) s.i.d.88 verso prov. 14-May-4 Phillips, New York #286/R est:8000-12000
£16667	$30667	€25000	Untitled (186x140cm-73x55in) s.i.d.1982 verso prov.exhib. 12-Jun-4 Villa Grisebach, Berlin #440/R est:18000-24000
£40223	$72000	€58726	Drei formen, 1/4, 1/8, 1/16 (280x440cm-110x173in) col dispersion prov.exhib.lit. 14-May-4 Phillips, New York #239/R est:30000-40000

Works on paper

£385	$642	€562	Untitled (14x20cm-6x8in) mono.i.d. verso pencil W/C gouache gold pen. 24-Jun-3 Germann, Zurich #960 (S.FR 850)
£905	$1538	€1321	Untitled (26x18cm-10x7in) mono.d.1982 verso ink prov. 22-Nov-3 Burkhard, Luzern #208/R (S.FR 2000)
£1719	$2871	€2510	Mountain lake (70x100cm-28x39in) s.i.d.1973 verso pencil gouache. 24-Jun-3 Germann, Zurich #959/R est:1500-2000 (S.FR 3800)

FEDI, Pio (1816-1892) Italian
Sculpture
£1205 $2000 €1759 Portrait of bust of a gentleman (64x53x25cm-25x21x10in) i.d.1868 verso marble. 4-Oct-3 Neal Auction Company, New Orleans #280/R est:3000-5000

FEDIER, Franz (1922-) Swiss
£819 $1466 €1196 Relief (90x50cm-35x20in) s.d.68 verso exhib. 14-May-4 Dobiaschofsky, Bern #278/R est:2200 (S.FR 1900)

FEDOROVA, Maria (1859-1934) Russian
£590 $986 €850 The water carrier (21x28cm-8x11in) s/. 26-Oct-3 Bukowskis, Helsinki #557/R

FEDOROVITCH, Vladimir (20th C) Russian
£32000 $57280 €46720 Landscape (105x155cm-41x61in) s. 26-May-4 Sotheby's, London #78/R est:10000-15000

FEDOTOV, Pavel Andreevich (after) (1815-1852) Russian
£5000 $9000 €7300 Marriage proposal (59x88cm-23x35in) 23-Apr-4 Sotheby's, New York #29/R est:8000-12000

FEDOTOV, Pavel Andreevich (attrib) (1815-1852) Russian
Works on paper
£521 $850 €761 Portrait of a woman (23x18cm-9x7in) bears sig. pencil. 24-Sep-3 Doyle, New York #103

FEDRIANI Y RAMIREZ, Tomas (19th C) Spanish
£1519 $2750 €2218 Senorita and her suitor (61x46cm-24x18in) s.d.1854. 3-Apr-4 Neal Auction Company, New Orleans #971/R est:2500-3500

FEELEY, Paul (1913-1966) American
£5278 $9500 €7706 Etamin (60x60cm-24x24in) s.i.d.1965 stretcher enamel prov.exhib. 24-Apr-4 David Rago, Lambertville #289/R est:3000-6000
£7547 $12000 €11019 Maia (76x64cm-30x25in) oil-based enamel exhib. 14-Sep-3 Wright, Chicago #150/R est:15000-20000
£13497 $22000 €19706 Untitled (152x122cm-60x48in) prov.exhib. 23-Sep-3 Christie's, Rockefeller NY #56/R est:18000-25000

FEENEY, Jacinta (20th C) Irish?
£1842 $3389 €2800 Stillest hour (148x119cm-58x47in) s.i.verso board. 22-Jun-4 De Veres Art Auctions, Dublin #170/R est:3000-4000

FEER, Anneke van der (1902-1956) Dutch
£267 $485 €400 Portrait of a lady (45x35cm-18x14in) s. 30-Jun-4 Vendue Huis, Gravenhage #515

FEHDMER, Richard (1860-?) German
£676 $1209 €1000 Vachere (97x80cm-38x31in) 10-May-4 Amberes, Antwerp #264
£719 $1200 €1050 Birkenwald (69x91cm-27x36in) s. 20-Jun-3 Freeman, Philadelphia #108/R
£743 $1330 €1100 Chariot attele dans un paysage enneige (70x100cm-28x39in) s.i.d.1847. 10-May-4 Horta, Bruxelles #386/R

FEHER, Georges (1929-) French
£300 $540 €450 Composition (66x82cm 26x32in) s. painted 1955. 24-Apr-4 Cornette de St.Cyr, Paris #518

FEHR, Friedrich (1862-1927) German
£1333 $2413 €2000 Chess players (86x119cm-34x47in) s.d.1901 panel. 1-Apr-4 Van Ham, Cologne #1364/R est:1800
£2657 $4517 €3800 Nude on Moroccan divan (41x57cm-16x22in) s. 20-Nov-3 Dorotheum, Salzburg #176/R est:2000-3000

FEHR, Julius (1860-1900) German
£1448 $2462 €2114 Table and bench under trees in park (55x50cm-22x20in) s.d.19. 18-Nov-3 Hans Widmer, St Gallen #1049 est:1500-3200 (S.FR 3200)

FEHRLE, Jakob Wilhelm (1884-1974) German
Sculpture
£1611 $2851 €2400 Angel bringing Mary good news (80x94cm-31x37in) mono.d. clay. 30-Apr-4 Dr Fritz Nagel, Stuttgart #785/R est:2000
£1667 $2717 €2400 Nude woman stepping into bath (35cm-14in) mono.d.1922 brown pat.bronze. 27-Sep-3 Dr Fritz Nagel, Stuttgart #9521/R est:1800
£1736 $2899 €2500 Standing female figure (27x7x6cm-11x3x2in) mono. verso dark pat.bronze. 24-Oct-3 Ketterer, Hamburg #338/R est:2700-3500
£12752 $22570 €19000 The four seasons (120x70cm-47x28in) mono.d. clay. 30-Apr-4 Dr Fritz Nagel, Stuttgart #786/R
Works on paper
£694 $1132 €1000 Adam and Eve (43x53cm-17x21in) mono.d.1919 gouache board. 27-Sep-3 Dr Fritz Nagel, Stuttgart #9118/R
£764 $1245 €1100 Three female nudes (25x31cm-10x12in) mono.d.1915 gouache panel. 27-Sep-3 Dr Fritz Nagel, Stuttgart #9116/R

FEIBUSCH, Hans (1898-1998) German
£600 $954 €876 French street scene with figures and motor cars (64x48cm-25x19in) 1-May-3 John Nicholson, Haslemere #693
£800 $1272 €1168 French street scene (51x69cm-20x27in) mono. 1-May-3 John Nicholson, Haslemere #692/R
£5245 $8916 €7500 Telephone kiosk (71x86cm-28x34in) mono. exhib. 29-Nov-3 Villa Grisebach, Berlin #263/R est:6000-8000
Works on paper
£320 $576 €467 Figures with laurel wreath (14x12cm-6x5in) init.d.54 gouache. 20-Jan-4 Bonhams, Knightsbridge #70/R
£500 $815 €725 Christ in glory (108x75cm-43x30in) init.d.61 gouache. 23-Sep-3 Bonhams, Leeds #164/R
£600 $954 €876 Biplane and Greek Gods (38x26cm-15x10in) s.d.49 gouache board sold with another by same hand and a slogan. 10-Sep-3 Sotheby's, Olympia #71/R
£780 $1420 €1139 Garden flowers (36x51cm-14x20in) s.i. W/C gouache. 21-Jun-4 Bonhams, Bath #353
£1500 $2385 €2190 Architects prefer Shell (39x55cm-15x22in) mono. gouache paper on cardboard lit. 10-Sep-3 Sotheby's, Olympia #74/R est:400-600

FEID, Josef (1806-1870) Austrian
£3521 $5845 €5000 Wooded landscape (103x139cm-41x55in) s.d.1859. 16-Jun-3 Dorotheum, Vienna #196/R est:6000-8000
£3873 $6430 €5500 Cows in meadow (44x55cm-17x22in) s.d.1852 panel. 16-Jun-3 Dorotheum, Vienna #103/R est:2500-3000

FEID, Josef (attrib) (1806-1870) Austrian
£1167 $2112 €1750 Return home (29x40cm-11x16in) lit. 3-Apr-4 Badum, Bamberg #9/R est:1750
£1538 $2615 €2200 Resting by woodland path (42x45cm-17x18in) d.856. 20-Nov-3 Dorotheum, Salzburg #171/R est:2000-3000

FEIFFER, Jules (1929-) American?
Works on paper
£267 $500 €390 Standing man with hands in his pockets (86x48cm-34x19in) s. marker exec.c.1970. 26-Feb-4 Illustration House, New York #67

FEIGL, Friedrich (1884-1965) German
£260 $434 €380 Haverstock Hill (61x88cm-24x35in) s. canvasboard prov. 21-Oct-3 Bonhams, Knightsbridge #59/R
£300 $501 €438 Figures in a summer landscape (51x72cm-20x28in) s. prov. 21-Oct-3 Bonhams, Knightsbridge #61/R
Works on paper
£400 $668 €584 Figures on a bridge over the river (35x55cm-14x22in) s. gouache. 21-Oct-3 Bonhams, Knightsbridge #53/R

FEILER, Paul (1918-) British
£750 $1328 €1095 Quiet village (54x76cm-21x30in) mono.d.45. 27-Apr-4 Bonhams, Knightsbridge #160
£4000 $7400 €5840 Orbis L1 (25x25cm-10x10in) s.i.d.1970. 11-Mar-4 Christie's, Kensington #375/R est:1500-2000
£13000 $23790 €18980 Boskenna (40x40cm-16x16in) s.i.d.1962 verso. 2-Jun-4 Sotheby's, London #101/R est:5000-7000
Works on paper
£2000 $3340 €2920 Untitled, window study (23x22cm-9x9in) s.d.52 pencil chl bodycol col chk prov. 16-Oct-3 Christie's, Kensington #714/R est:1000-1500

FEIN, Nat (20th C) American
Photographs
£7186 $12000 €10492 Babe bows out (27x33cm-11x13in) s. ferrotyped. 17-Oct-3 Sotheby's, New York #237/R est:6000-9000

FEINGERSH, Oded (1938-) Israeli
£656 $1200 €958 Landscape of Rosh Pina (65x89cm-26x35in) s.d.2003. 1-Jun-4 Ben-Ami, Tel Aviv #4893/R est:1300-1700
£663 $1200 €968 Landscape of Rosh Pina (65x90cm-26x35in) s.d.2003. 1-Apr-4 Ben-Ami, Tel Aviv #4747/R
£791 $1400 €1155 Landscape of rosh pina (65x90cm-26x35in) s. 1-May-4 Ben-Ami, Tel Aviv #4777/R est:1200-1600

FEININGER, Andreas (1906-1999) French
Photographs
£2222 $4000 €3244 New York (27x34cm-11x13in) s.i.d.1950 gelatin silver print prov. 23-Apr-4 Phillips, New York #197/R est:4000-6000
£2333 $4293 €3500 Empire State Building (29x24cm-11x9in) s. silver gelatin. 10-Jun-4 Villa Grisebach, Berlin #1075/R est:3000-4000
£2373 $4200 €3465 Lunch rush on 5th Avenue, 1950 (48x38cm-19x15in) s.verso gelatin silver print. 27-Apr-4 Christie's, Rockefeller NY #201/R est:3000-5000
£2500 $4500 €3650 Hotel de Savoie, Paris (34x26cm-13x10in) s.i.verso gelatin silver print prov. 23-Apr-4 Phillips, New York #102/R est:5000-7000
£2639 $4486 €3800 Empire State Building (30x24cm-12x9in) s. gelatin silver. 31-Oct-3 Lempertz, Koln #104/R est:2300
£3056 $5500 €4462 Stockholm (27x34cm-11x13in) s.i.d.1937 gelatin silver print prov.lit. 23-Apr-4 Phillips, New York #242/R est:5000-7000
£3293 $5500 €4808 Statue of Liberty with traces of moving stars in the sky (23x19cm-9x7in) s.i. gelatin silver print exec.c.1940 prov. 20-Oct-3 Christie's, Rockefeller NY #194/R est:3000-5000
£3955 $7000 €5774 Queen Elizabeth in New York Harbour, 1958 (43x32cm-17x13in) s. i.d.1958 verso num.6/40 gelatin silver print. 27-Apr-4 Christie's, Rockefeller NY #204/R est:3000-5000
£4000 $7360 €6000 Downtown skyport on East River, Cities Service building in back (25x20cm-10x8in) s.i.d. verso silver gelatin lit.exhib. 10-Jun-4 Villa Grisebach, Berlin #1076/R est:5000-7000
£4491 $7500 €6557 Brooklyn Bridge (37x51cm-15x20in) s. d.1948 verso ferrotyped. 17-Oct-3 Sotheby's, New York #233/R est:5000-7000
£5085 $9000 €7424 Times Square at 42nd St (28x32cm-11x13in) s.i.d.1950 num.AF818 ferrotyped. 28-Apr-4 Sotheby's, New York #196/R est:5000-7000

£8333	$15000	€12166	Wild white marguerites (23x18cm-9x7in) gelatin silver print set of three prov.lit. 23-Apr-4 Phillips, New York #57/R est:40000-60000

FEININGER, Lyonel (1871-1956) American/German

£9170	$16690	€13388	Composition (20x25cm-8x10in) s.i.d.5 Mai 1915 black chl. 18-Jun-4 Kornfeld, Bern #36/R est:20000 (S.FR 21000)
£614525	$1100000	€897207	Norman village I (80x100cm-31x39in) s.d.18 prov.exhib.lit. 6-May-4 Sotheby's, New York #102/R est:700000-900000
£900000	$1638000	€1314000	Gables III (108x88cm-43x35in) s.d.29 s.i.d.on stretcher prov.exhib.lit. 21-Jun-4 Sotheby's, London #40/R est:500000-700000
£980000	$1783600	€1430800	Diabolospielerinnen I - Diabolo players I (39x66cm-15x26in) s.d.1909 d.verso prov.exhib.lit. 3-Feb-4 Sotheby's, London #12/R est:1200000-1600000
£2200000	$4026000	€3212000	Newspaper readers II (104x93cm-41x37in) painted 1916 prov.exhib.lit. 2-Feb-4 Christie's, London #21/R est:2500000-3500000
Photographs			
£2273	$4000	€3319	Bauhaus at night (18x23cm-7x9in) init.i. silver print. 20-May-4 Swann Galleries, New York #317/R est:3000-4000
Prints			
£1761	$2800	€2571	Gelmeroda village and church (10x8cm-4x3in) s. woodcut. 14-Sep-3 Susanin's, Chicago #6124/R est:3000-5000
£1765	$3000	€2577	Sunset (16x24cm-6x9in) s.i.d.1911 etching. 31-Oct-3 Sotheby's, New York #261/R
£1765	$3000	€2577	Gelmeroda (22x17cm-9x7in) s.i.d.1918 woodcut. 31-Oct-3 Sotheby's, New York #262
£1800	$3312	€2700	Sunrise (19x23cm-7x9in) s. drypoint exec. 1911 one of 130. 12-Jun-4 Villa Grisebach, Berlin #268/R est:3000-4000
£1916	$3200	€2797	Town hall (11x11cm-4x4in) s. woodcut. 11-Nov-3 Christie's, Rockefeller NY #127/R est:2500-3500
£1916	$3200	€2797	Anglers (10x14cm-4x6in) s. woodcut. 11-Nov-3 Christie's, Rockefeller NY #128/R est:2000-3000
£1948	$3487	€2844	Sunrise/small town (15x23cm-6x9in) s.i.d. etching lit.prov. 22-Mar-4 Philippe Schuler, Zurich #4013/R est:4000-5300 (S.FR 4500)
£2000	$3680	€3000	Zottelstedt town hall (11x13cm-4x5in) s.i.d.1918 woodcut one of 55. 12-Jun-4 Villa Grisebach, Berlin #177/R est:3000-4000
£2000	$3680	€3000	Three sailing boats (24x28cm-9x11in) s.i. woodcut exec. 1919 prov. 12-Jun-4 Villa Grisebach, Berlin #264/R est:4000-6000
£2000	$3680	€3000	Sunrise (15x23cm-6x9in) s.i.d.1911 etching one of 130. 11-Jun-4 Villa Grisebach, Berlin #1553/R est:3000-4000
£2059	$3500	€3006	Gelmeroda (41x28cm-16x11in) s. woodcut. 31-Oct-3 Sotheby's, New York #266/R
£2118	$3600	€3092	Melligen church (12x16cm-5x6in) s.i.d.1918 woodcut. 6-Nov-3 Swann Galleries, New York #540/R est:2500-3500
£2133	$3904	€3200	Lehnstedt (26x31cm-10x12in) s.i. woodcut. 5-Jun-4 Lempertz, Koln #712/R est:3000
£2588	$4400	€3778	Zottelstedt, 2 (23x28cm-9x11in) s.i. woodcut. 6-Nov-3 Swann Galleries, New York #539/R est:3500-5000
£2647	$4500	€3865	Vorstadt (24x38cm-9x15in) s. woodcut. 31-Oct-3 Sotheby's, New York #267/R
£2667	$4773	€4000	Harz village 1 (18x18cm-7x7in) s.i. woodcut prov. 14-May-4 Ketterer, Munich #376/R est:4000-4500
£3000	$5520	€4500	Lehnstedt (25x30cm-10x12in) s.i. woodcut exec. 1919. 12-Jun-4 Villa Grisebach, Berlin #265/R est:5000-7000
£3357	$5606	€4800	Church with houses, tree, star (6x7cm-2x3in) s.i. W/C woodcut. 10-Oct-3 Winterberg, Heidelberg #1209/R est:5800
£3497	$6014	€5000	The gate (27x20cm-11x8in) s.i.d.1912 etching drypoint. 2-Dec-3 Hauswedell & Nolte, Hamburg #171/R est:8000
£3800	$6916	€5548	Villa am strande, 4 (36x51cm-14x20in) s.i. woodcut exec.c.1920. 1-Jul-4 Sotheby's, London #175/R est:4000-6000
£4895	$8322	€7000	Merry boat trip (14x17cm-6x7in) s.i. woodcut. 26-Nov-3 Lempertz, Koln #663/R est:6500
£5333	$9547	€8000	Green bridge (27x20cm-11x8in) s. etching. 15-May-4 Bassenge, Berlin #6807a/R est:7500
£6294	$10699	€9000	War fleet 2 (33x44cm-13x17in) s.i. woodcut prov. 28-Nov-3 Villa Grisebach, Berlin #56/R est:9000-12000
£7333	$13493	€11000	Village with a church (28x36cm-11x14in) s.i.d.1970 woodcut one of five. 12-Jun-4 Villa Grisebach, Berlin #263/R est:6000-8000
Sculpture			
£7784	$13000	€11365	Characters from Wee Willie Winkie (10x14x11cm-4x6x4in) hand carved painted wood. 11-Nov-3 Christie's, Rockefeller NY #121/R est:8000-12000
Works on paper			
£1400	$2576	€2100	Walkers on beach (14x21cm-6x8in) d.7 6 24 pencil. 10-Jun-4 Hauswedell & Nolte, Hamburg #198/R est:1800
£2793	$5000	€4078	St. Quenole, Brittany (30x48cm-12x19in) s.d.1943 s.d.verso black chk ink W/C double-sided. 6-May-4 Doyle, New York #107/R est:10000-15000
£2886	$5310	€4300	Ghosties (9x15cm-4x6in) s.d. Indian ink over pencil prov. 26-Mar-4 Ketterer, Hamburg #396/R est:3500-4500
£3293	$5500	€4808	Sailboat (28x19cm-11x7in) s.d.vii.6.39 Indian ink gouache. 7-Oct-3 Sotheby's, New York #290 est:4000-6000
£3390	$6000	€4949	Der Markplatz in Halle, nach einem alten Stiche (16x22cm-6x9in) s.i.d.Sept 1923 ink. 2-May-4 Bonhams & Butterfields, Los Angeles #3003/R est:3000-5000
£3533	$6501	€5300	Bridge in upper Weimar (16x20cm-6x8in) d.19.IX.13 col chk. 10-Jun-4 Hauswedell & Nolte, Hamburg #196/R est:8000
£3593	$6000	€5246	Distance harbor (29x48cm-11x19in) s.d.13 Aug 1945 pen ink wash prov.exhib. 11-Nov-3 Christie's, Rockefeller NY #120/R est:10000-15000
£4196	$7217	€6000	Paris (17x12cm-7x5in) bears sig.i.d.1907 pencil. 2-Dec-3 Hauswedell & Nolte, Hamburg #162/R est:8000
£4312	$7201	€6252	Figures on shore with steamer beyond (20x24cm-8x9in) Indian ink. 19-Jun-3 Kornfeld, Bern #376/R est:7500 (S.FR 9400)
£4491	$7500	€6557	Merry Xmas (10x14cm-4x6in) s.i.d.1955 W/C pen ink prov. 11-Nov-3 Christie's, Rockefeller NY #123/R est:7000-9000
£4500	$8280	€6570	Promenade (19x23cm-7x9in) d.7.VII pen ink prov. 24-Mar-4 Sotheby's, Olympia #34/R est:4000-6000
£4861	$8118	€7000	Country road (21x24cm-8x9in) d.Sep 20 10 col chk prov.exhib. 24-Oct-3 Ketterer, Hamburg #340/R est:7000-9000
£4895	$8322	€7000	Ouville-la-Riviere, Normandy (24x31cm-9x12in) s.i.d.Sept. 28th 1953 chl col chk prov.exhib. 29-Nov-3 Villa Grisebach, Berlin #159/R est:7000-9000
£5594	$9622	€8000	Fishing boat in the rain (16x20cm-6x8in) s.d.1914 col pen. 2-Dec-3 Hauswedell & Nolte, Hamburg #165/R est:10000
£5828	$9500	€8509	Vier Abbildungen (12x16cm-5x6in) s. W/C over pen Indian ink prov. 25-Sep-3 Christie's, Rockefeller NY #613/R est:7000-9000
£6000	$11040	€9000	Church (23x31cm-9x12in) s.i.d.1911 pen ink. 12-Jun-4 Villa Grisebach, Berlin #176/R est:9000-12000
£6000	$11040	€9000	Isle of mystery (25x34cm-10x13in) s.i.d.52 ink W/C. 12-Jun-4 Villa Grisebach, Berlin #269/R est:9000-12000
£6000	$10980	€9000	Street in Terptow on the Rega (47x37cm-19x15in) s.i.d.9.9.1932 chl prov.exhib. 5-Jun-4 Lempertz, Koln #708/R est:12000-15000
£6587	$11000	€9617	Art committe. Spirits of compunction (12x17cm-5x7in) s.i. W/C pen ink two. 11-Nov-3 Christie's, Rockefeller NY #125/R est:14000-18000
£6667	$12267	€10000	Sunlit village (30x47cm-12x19in) s.d.7. Xi. 50 W/C Indian ink chk. 10-Jun-4 Hauswedell & Nolte, Hamburg #203/R est:7000
£6690	$11574	€9500	Rocky peaks (17x24cm-7x9in) s.d.1954 W/C Indian ink over pencil. 13-Dec-3 Lempertz, Koln #132/R est:9000
£7500	$13650	€10950	Meerlandschaft in blau - Seascape in blue (29x46cm-11x18in) init.d.45 W/C brush ink prov. 4-Feb-4 Sotheby's, London #543/R est:9000-12000
£7784	$13000	€11365	I should worry ! (20x28cm-8x11in) s.i.d.1946 W/C pen ink prov. 11-Nov-3 Christie's, Rockefeller NY #122/R est:12000-16000
£8725	$16054	€13000	Steamer under sail near island (19x26cm-7x10in) s.d. W/C Indian ink. 26-Mar-4 Ketterer, Hamburg #395/R est:14000-16000
£8939	$16000	€13051	Untitled (30x46cm-12x18in) s.d.318 32 W/C pen India ink brush grey wash prov. 5-May-4 Christie's, Rockefeller NY #127/R est:20000-30000
£9500	$17290	€13870	Street with houses (23x31cm-9x12in) s.d.5.viii.51 W/C pen ink prov.exhib.lit. 5-Feb-4 Christie's, London #365/R est:8000-12000
£10056	$18000	€14682	Mondschein auf see (23x25cm-9x10in) s.i.d.1918 W/C pen India ink prov. 5-May-4 Christie's, Rockefeller NY #124/R est:22000-28000
£10067	$18523	€15000	Paris. s.i. mixed media Indian ink chl htd col chk pen. 26-Mar-4 Karrenbauer, Konstanz #1711/R est:5000
£10490	$18042	€15000	Waterway mists (31x48cm-12x19in) s.d.1950 W/C pen ink col chk prov. 5-Dec-3 Ketterer, Munich #104/R est:15000-18000
£10667	$19627	€16000	Village street with a large tree (20x24cm-8x9in) d.10 col chk black chk prov.exhib. 12-Jun-4 Villa Grisebach, Berlin #178/R est:15000-20000
£11173	$20000	€16313	Gay Child (24x31cm-9x12in) initi.d.1943 W/C pen India ink brush grey wash prov. 5-May-4 Christie's, Rockefeller NY #126/R est:20000-30000
£11189	$19245	€16000	Heringsdorf beach (16x20cm-6x8in) s.i.d.11 col chk over pencil. 5-Dec-3 Ketterer, Munich #44/R est:8000-12000
£12000	$21480	€18000	Sailing ship off yellow coast (22x32cm-9x13in) s.d.8 4 33 W/C Indian ink. 15-May-4 Dr Sturies, Dusseldorf #47/R
£12667	$23307	€19000	Town scene (31x24cm-12x9in) s.d.June 1952 ink W/C prov. 12-Jun-4 Villa Grisebach, Berlin #259/R est:20000-25000
£14000	$25060	€21000	Fishing cutter from Swinemund (25x40cm-10x16in) s.i.d. W/C Indian ink prov. 14-May-4 Ketterer, Munich #377/R est:8000-12000
£14667	$26987	€22000	The cloud (32x48cm-13x19in) s.i.d.July W/C Indian ink chl. 10-Jun-4 Hauswedell & Nolte, Hamburg #201/R est:20000
£14970	$25000	€21856	Four figures. Three figures (15x9cm-6x4in) s.i.d.1955 W/C pen ink two prov. 11-Nov-3 Christie's, Rockefeller NY #124/R est:9000-12000
£15569	$26000	€22731	Seven figures. Three figures. Little outcast (15x24cm-6x9in) s.d.1954 s.i.d.verso W/C pen ink set of three. 11-Nov-3 Christie's, Rockefeller NY #126/R est:18000-22000
£16000	$29440	€24000	Ship and tuck (25x43cm-10x17in) s.i.d.1946 W/C pen chl. 10-Jun-4 Hauswedell & Nolte, Hamburg #202/R est:35000
£23333	$42933	€35000	Barque arriving (18x29cm-7x11in) s.i.d.1934 W/C ink prov. 12-Jun-4 Villa Grisebach, Berlin #260/R est:20000-30000
£26573	$45706	€38000	Steam engine (24x31cm-9x12in) s.i.d.1915 Indian ink W/C. 2-Dec-3 Hauswedell & Nolte, Hamburg #166/R est:36000
£26667	$49067	€40000	Northern bay (25x42cm-10x17in) s.i.d.6.8.34 W/C wash Indian ink pen. 10-Jun-4 Hauswedell & Nolte, Hamburg #200/R est:40000
£35808	$65170	€52280	Red ocean and yellow ship (25x35cm-10x14in) s.d.1935 W/C pen ink prov.exhib.lit. 18-Jun-4 Kornfeld, Bern #37/R est:50000 (S.FR 82000)

FEININGER, Theodore Lux (1910-) American

Photographs			
£2000	$3680	€3000	Self portrait with Xanti Schwinsky (11x8cm-4x3in) s.i. verso silver gelatin prov. 10-Jun-4 Villa Grisebach, Berlin #1079/R est:2000-2500
£3333	$6133	€5000	Members of the Bauhaus band - Ernst Egeler, Clemens Roseler (24x18cm-9x7in) s.i. bromide silver gelatin prov. 10-Jun-4 Villa Grisebach, Berlin #1080/R est:5000-7000
£4000	$7360	€6000	Bauhaus student (11x8cm-4x3in) s.i. verso silver gelatin prov. 10-Jun-4 Villa Grisebach, Berlin #1078/R est:2000-2500
£6294	$10699	€9000	Two heads (17x24cm-7x9in) s.i. verso silver gelatin lit.exhib. 27-Nov-3 Villa Grisebach, Berlin #1168/R est:7000-9000
£6884	$11290	€9500	In the sun (24x18cm-9x7in) s.i.d. verso vintage silver gelatin. 30-May-3 Villa Grisebach, Berlin #1165/R est:2800-3200

FEINT, Adrian (1894-1971) Australian

£305	$556	€445	Vase of flowers (14x11cm-6x4in) s.d.1965 board. 16-Jun-4 Deutscher-Menzies, Melbourne #567/R (A.D 800)
£314	$562	€458	Still life of flowers in a jug. s. board. 28-May-4 Lawson Menzies, Sydney #2230 (A.D 800)
£334	$597	€488	Still life flowers in a jug. s. board. 28-May-4 Lawson Menzies, Sydney #2171 (A.D 850)
£455	$773	€683	Green glass and hydrangeas (29x16cm-11x6in) s.d.1963 board. 28-Oct-3 Goodman, Sydney #477/R (A.D 1100)
£458	$834	€669	Study for floral adventure (16x19cm-6x7in) s. i.verso board. 16-Jun-4 Deutscher-Menzies, Melbourne #568/R est:800-1200 (A.D 1200)
£471	$842	€688	Still life flowers in decorative jug. s. 28-May-4 Lawson Menzies, Sydney #2119 (A.D 1200)
£486	$782	€710	Basket of hibiscus at Pittwater (15x15cm-6x6in) s.d.1964 board. 13-Oct-3 Joel, Victoria #347 est:1200-1500 (A.D 1200)
£725	$1320	€1059	Gardenias on the Hawkesbury (25x20cm-10x8in) s.d.1955 board. 16-Jun-4 Deutscher-Menzies, Melbourne #414/R est:2000-3000 (A.D 1900)
£732	$1310	€1069	Outback (32x29cm-13x11in) s.d.1945 i.verso board. 4-May-4 Sotheby's, Melbourne #165/R (A.D 1800)
£1719	$3214	€2579	Untitled (47x41cm-19x16in) s.d.1940 prov. 21-Jul-4 Shapiro, Sydney #155/R est:3000-5000 (A.D 4400)
£2331	$3962	€3403	Banksias in a jug (45x24cm-18x9in) s.d.1959. 24-Nov-3 Sotheby's, Melbourne #156/R est:4000-6000 (A.D 5500)

FEISTEL, B (20th C) German

£1200	$2148	€1800	Winter in Thiessow (86x115cm-34x45in) s.d.29 s.i.verso. 14-May-4 Von Zezschwitz, Munich #930/R est:650

FEITH, Gustav (1875-1951) Austrian

Works on paper			
£530	$970	€800	October blossom (17x12cm-7x5in) s.i.d.1925 W/C. 8-Apr-4 Dorotheum, Vienna #169/R
£759	$1259	€1100	Meadow flowers (35x26cm-14x10in) s.d.1950 W/C paper on board. 30-Sep-3 Dorotheum, Vienna #368/R

FEITO, Luis (1929-) Spanish

£1000 $1820 €1500 Untitled (22x15cm-9x6in) s.d.2000. 29-Jun-4 Segre, Madrid #158/R est:1500
£1027 $1747 €1500 Untitled (11x17cm-4x7in) s. tempera cardboard. 7-Nov-3 Galleria Rosenberg, Milan #130/R
£4276 $7868 €6500 Composition (26x34cm-10x13in) s.d.1957. 28-Jun-4 Joron-Derem, Paris #225/R est:1500-2000
£4333 $7887 €6500 Composition in diptych (56x92cm-22x36in) s. s.d.1970 verso diptych exhib. 5-Jul-4 Le Mouel, Paris #62/R est:6000-8000
£5000 $9100 €7500 Composition black and yellow (100x81cm-39x32in) s.d.1970 verso. 5-Jul-4 Le Mouel, Paris #63/R est:8000-10000
£5172 $9310 €7500 1071 (73x92cm-29x36in) s. s.i.d.1974 verso. 26-Jan-4 Durán, Madrid #202/R est:5000
£5369 $10040 €8000 Composition (73x92cm-29x36in) s.i.verso. 24-Feb-4 Durán, Madrid #19/R est:5000
£5500 $10010 €8030 Pintura No 879 (80x80cm-31x31in) s.i.d.1971 verso acrylic. 4-Feb-4 Sotheby's, Olympia #202/R est:6000-8000
£5634 $9859 €8000 Havi (25x40cm-10x16in) s.i.d.1960 verso. 16-Dec-3 Segre, Madrid #129/R est:5000
£5689 $9500 €8306 Four one four (58x71cm-23x28in) s. s.i.d.1963 verso. 25-Oct-3 Rachel Davis, Shaker Heights #598/R
£5814 $10000 €8488 Pintura no (168x112cm-66x44in) s.i.d.1991 verso acrylic prov. 3-Dec-3 Doyle, New York #15/R est:4000-6000
£8383 $14000 €12239 Untitled (61x91cm-24x36in) s. 25-Oct-3 Rachel Davis, Shaker Heights #597/R
£14000 $25480 €20440 Pintura (59x90cm-23x35in) s. s.d.1957 verso oil mixed media prov. 6-Feb-4 Sotheby's, London #187/R est:10000-15000
£17606 $30458 €25000 Composition (81x100cm-32x39in) s.d.1963 verso. 9-Dec-3 Artcurial Briest, Paris #409/R est:10000-12000

Works on paper

£265 $482 €400 Composition (32x23cm-13x9in) s.i. ink wash exec. 1972 prov. 15-Jun-4 Blanchet, Paris #261
£1400 $2520 €2100 Composition (52x74cm-20x29in) s.d.1961 ink prov. 25-Apr-4 Versailles Encheres #50 est:1000-1200
£1645 $3026 €2500 Composition (34x49cm-13x19in) s.i.d.1954 gouache. 28-Jun-4 Joron-Derem, Paris #218/R est:800-1000
£2165 $3874 €3161 Untitled (50x70cm-20x28in) i. i. verso gouache prov. 22-Mar-4 Philippe Schuler, Zurich #4014/R est:2000-2600 (S.FR 5000)
£5500 $10120 €8030 Composition (75x108cm-30x43in) gouache paperboard exec.c.1950 prov. 24-Jun-4 Sotheby's, Olympia #584/R est:1500-2000
£6500 $11830 €9490 Pintura 467-A (24x33cm-9x13in) s. s.i.d.1963 verso mixed media canvas. 21-Jun-4 Bonhams, New Bond Street #82/R est:800-1200
£14190 $24974 €21000 Untitled (60x93cm-24x37in) s.d.1957 mixed media prov. 18-May-4 Tajan, Paris #33/R est:15000-20000
£17000 $30940 €24820 Pintura 383 (89x116cm-35x46in) s. s.i.d.1963 verso mixed media canvas. 21-Jun-4 Bonhams, New Bond Street #81/R est:3000-5000

FEKETE, Janos (19th C) Hungarian

£369 $679 €550 View along stream to thatched farmstead (55x74cm-22x29in) s.d.1873. 25-Mar-4 Karlheinz Kaupp, Staufen #2428/R

FELBER, Carl (1880-1932) Swiss

£459 $766 €666 Herbstmorgen am Riffelsee (72x102cm-28x40in) s.d. 21-Jun-3 Galerie du Rhone, Sion #362/R (S.FR 1000)
£909 $1509 €1318 Bernina Hospice (60x85cm-24x33in) s.i.d.1918. 13-Jun-3 Zofingen, Switzerland #2841 est:2500 (S.FR 2000)

FELBIER, Maurice (1903-1991) Belgian

£282 $487 €400 Fleurs des bois (85x60cm-33x24in) s. 9-Dec-3 Campo, Vlaamse Kaai #309
£1111 $1856 €1600 Roses et pivoines (85x75cm-33x30in) s.d.1944. 21-Oct-3 Campo, Vlaamse Kaai #818 est:600-700

FELBINGER, Andreas (19th C) German?

£533 $960 €800 Tegernsee (36x61cm-14x24in) s. i. verso. 22-Apr-4 Allgauer, Kempten #3523/R

FELDBAUER, Max (1869-1948) German

£3472 $5799 €5000 Horse portrait (65x79cm-26x31in) s. i. verso panel. 25-Oct-3 Bergmann, Erlangen #964/R
£4375 $7306 €6300 Girl's portrait (54x40cm-21x16in) mono.d.05 lit. 25-Oct-3 Bergmann, Erlangen #963/R

FELDBERG-EBER, Lore (1895-1966) German

£590 $939 €850 Portrait of girl (73x60cm-29x24in) s. 13-Sep-3 Quittenbaum, Hamburg #91/R

FELDHUTTER, Ferdinand (1842-1898) German

£1458 $2435 €2100 Starnberger See (16x27cm-6x11in) s.d.1881 panel lit. 25-Oct-3 Bergmann, Erlangen #927/R est:1800
£1892 $3386 €2800 Waterfall near Bad Gastein (48x41cm-19x16in) s. 6-May-4 Michael Zeller, Lindau #656/R est:2800
£2685 $4940 €4000 Alpine view with lake (80x110cm-31x43in) s.d.1896. 27-Mar-4 L & B, Essen #103/R est:1500

FELDHUTTER, Ferdinand (attrib) (1842-1898) German

£1648 $3000 €2406 Mountain Lake (89x132cm-35x52in) s. 7-Feb-4 Neal Auction Company, New Orleans #588/R est:3000-4000

FELDMAN, Andres (1921-) ?

£588 $1000 €858 Cafe (100x120cm-39x47in) s. 25-Nov-3 Galeria y Remates, Montevideo #76/R

FELDMAN, Dorit (20th C) Israeli?

Works on paper

£699 $1189 €1000 Yard stick (76x56cm-30x22in) s. mixed media metal. 27-Nov-3 Calmels Cohen, Paris #117/R

FELDMANN, Wilhelm (1859-1932) German

£667 $1207 €1000 Flensburg harbour (35x58cm-14x23in) s.d.1917 board. 3-Apr-4 Hans Stahl, Hamburg #151/R
£986 $1706 €1400 Landscape with farm building (64x83cm-25x33in) s. 10-Dec-3 Dorotheum, Vienna #158/R

FELDT, A (19th C) ?

£473 $846 €691 Mountain landscape with figures and houses, Austria (31x47cm-12x19in) s. 12-Jan-4 Rasmussen, Vejle #408/R (D.KR 5000)

FELGENTREFF, Paul (1854-1933) German

£2273 $4000 €3319 Einkehr (68x56cm-27x22in) s.i. 18-May-4 Bonhams & Butterfields, San Francisco #105/R est:4000-6000

FELGUEREZ, Manuel (1928-) Mexican

£1264 $2150 €1845 Untitled (29x48cm-11x19in) s. panel. 30-Oct-3 Louis Morton, Mexico #144 est:11000-15000 (M.P 24000)
£3583 $6091 €5231 Untitled (122x160cm-48x63in) s.d.1975 panel. 30-Oct-3 Louis Morton, Mexico #95/R est:80000-90000 (M.P 68000)

Sculpture

£800 $1400 €1168 Merry go round (61x31cm-24x12in) s. painted steel. 19-Dec-3 Sotheby's, New York #1225/R est:2000-2500

FELIPE, Antonio de (1965-) Spanish

£1361 $2435 €2000 Cowboy (50x50cm-20x20in) s. acrylic lit. 22-Mar-4 Durán, Madrid #153/R est:1500

FELISARI, Enrico (1897-1981) Italian

£733 $1349 €1100 Model resting (75x60cm-30x24in) s.d.1977. 12-Jun-4 Meeting Art, Vercelli #993/R
£2000 $3680 €3000 Portrait of woman with hat (66x46cm-26x18in) s.d.1940 exhib. 8-Jun-4 Sotheby's, Milan #114/R est:3000-5000

FELIX, Eugen (1837-1906) Austrian

£2378 $4042 €3400 Water source in wood (45x23cm-18x9in) s.d.1902 panel. 24-Nov-3 Dorotheum, Vienna #181/R est:2800-3200

FELIX, Léon Pierre (1869-1940) French

£2007 $3472 €2850 L'Amiraute d'Alger (41x33cm-16x13in) s. panel. 14-Dec-3 St-Germain-en-Laye Encheres #67/R est:3000-3500

FELIX, Luis (1868-1950) Spanish

£1986 $3377 €2900 Piano concert (68x100cm-27x39in) s. 4-Nov-3 Ansorena, Madrid #60/R est:2500

FELIXMULLER, Conrad (1897-1977) German

£3667 $6600 €5500 Grandmother with grandchildren in courtyard (58x67cm-23x26in) s.d. 24-Apr-4 Dr Lehr, Berlin #114/R est:6000
£5944 $10105 €8500 Self portrait of head with brush in hand (40x50cm-16x20in) s.d.51-52 prov. 29-Nov-3 Villa Grisebach, Berlin #184/R est:9000-12000
£50000 $92000 €73000 Flower girl. Praising the model (80x85cm-31x33in) s.d.25 s.d.34 verso double-sided prov.exhib.lit. 22-Jun-4 Sotheby's, London #178/R est:60000-80000
£119718 $207113 €170000 Spring evening walk (98x61cm-39x24in) s. i. verso lit. 13-Dec-3 Lempertz, Koln #133/R est:150000-180000

Prints

£2098 $3608 €3000 Man and woman (40x48cm-16x19in) s.mono.i.d.1917 woodcut. 2-Dec-3 Hauswedell & Nolte, Hamburg #180/R est:3000
£2238 $3849 €3200 Figures in wood (25x30cm-10x12in) s.mono. col woodcut. 2-Dec-3 Hauswedell & Nolte, Hamburg #181/R est:3000
£2308 $3923 €3300 Friends (35x20cm-14x8in) s.i.d.1919/21. 26-Nov-3 Lempertz, Koln #666/R est:3500
£2500 $4075 €3600 Figures in world (75x50cm-30x20in) s.i.d.1919 lithograph. 27-Sep-3 Dr Fritz Nagel, Stuttgart #9522/R est:1800
£2667 $4907 €4000 Rainy day (56x46cm-22x18in) s.i.d.1921 lithograph. 10-Jun-4 Hauswedell & Nolte, Hamburg #210/R est:1600
£6000 $10980 €9000 People above the world (69x50cm-27x20in) s.i.d. lithograph. 5-Jun-4 Lempertz, Koln #717/R est:9000-10000

Works on paper

£13986 $23776 €20000 Mother and child - tony Kirchhoff with daughter (59x47cm-23x19in) s.i.d. W/C gouache on pencil lit. 28-Nov-3 Villa Grisebach, Berlin #53/R est:20000-25000

FELKEL, Johannes (17th C) ?

Works on paper

£940 $1729 €1400 Jupiter and Io (22x17cm-9x7in) s.d.1687 W/C paper on panel. 26-Mar-4 Dorotheum, Vienna #168/R

FELL, Sheila (1931-1979) British

£7200 $11376 €10512 Potato pickers, Aspatria (51x61cm-20x24in) prov. 24-Jul-3 Mitchells, Cockermouth #853/R est:3000-4000
£17000 $28390 €24820 Wheat harvest at Mechi Farm, Cumberland I (51x61cm-20x24in) s. s.i.d.1968 stretcher. 16-Oct-3 Christie's, Kensington #647/R est:5000-7000

Works on paper

£660 $1221 €964 Landscape with houses (20x28cm-8x11in) i. ink wash sketch. 15-Jul-4 Mitchells, Cockermouth #512/R
£1800 $3006 €2628 Farm amongst hills (34x45cm-13x18in) s. chl. 16-Oct-3 Christie's, Kensington #643/R est:800-1200
£6800 $11764 €9928 Cockermouth in snow (20x25cm-8x10in) s. board exhib. 11-Dec-3 Mitchells, Cockermouth #921/R est:3000-5000

FELLER-BRAND, Walter (1917-) Swiss
£259 $463 €378 Summer in Schwarzburgerland (30x40cm-12x16in) s. i. verso board. 12-May-4 Dobiaschofsky, Bern #485 (S.FR 600)

FELLINGER, Leo (1884-1975) Austrian
£738 $1321 €1100 Flowers in jug (73x45cm-29x18in) mono. jute. 27-May-4 Dorotheum, Graz #17/R
£1408 $2338 €2000 Still life with flowers (47x37cm-19x15in) mono. 12-Jun-3 Dorotheum, Graz #8/R est:1300
£1972 $3273 €2800 Flowers in jug (81x62cm-32x24in) mono. 12-Jun-3 Dorotheum, Graz #9/R est:2000

FELLINGER, Matthaus (1924-) Austrian
Works on paper
£385 $654 €550 On the Danube near Obermuhl (46x65cm-18x26in) s.i.d.82 W/C. 27-Nov-3 Dorotheum, Linz #567/R

FELLINI, Federico (1920-1993) Italian
Works on paper
£759 $1267 €1100 Untitled (27x21cm-11x8in) s. felt-tip pen. 14-Nov-3 Farsetti, Prato #242/R
£897 $1497 €1300 Untitled (27x21cm-11x8in) s. ball-point pen felt-tip pen. 14-Nov-3 Farsetti, Prato #117

FELLINI, Giulio Cesare (?-c.1660) Italian
Works on paper
£671 $1235 €1000 Goddesses holding wreaths (34x39cm-13x15in) mono. pen Indian ink brush pencil. 26-Mar-4 Venator & Hansten, Koln #1349/R

FELLNER, Ferdinand (1799-1859) German
Works on paper
£733 $1320 €1100 Greek fighter (28x19cm-11x7in) pencil. 24-Apr-4 Reiss & Sohn, Konigstein #5482/R

FELLOWES, James (18th C) British
£1400 $2212 €2030 Portrait of Thomas Aldersey of Aldersey (91x76cm-36x30in) i. 4-Sep-3 Christie's, Kensington #34/R est:1500-2000
£1600 $2528 €2320 Portrait of a lady in a blue dress (76x63cm-30x25in) s.d.1738. 4-Sep-3 Christie's, Kensington #31/R est:1000-1500
£1900 $3002 €2755 Portrait of a young boy in Roman costume (76x63cm-30x25in) 4-Sep-3 Christie's, Kensington #33/R est:1000-1500
£3500 $5530 €5075 Portrait of Margaret Aldersey in a yellow dress and blue wrap (91x76cm-36x30in) 4-Sep-3 Christie's, Kensington #32/R est:2000-3000

FELLOWS, Fred (1934-) American
£2890 $5000 €4219 Guarding the winter camp (61x91cm-24x36in) s.i.d.79 masonite prov. 10-Dec-3 Bonhams & Butterfields, San Francisco #6127/R est:6000-8000
£4118 $7000 €6012 Welcome committee (61x91cm-24x36in) masonite. 1-Nov-3 Altermann Galleries, Santa Fe #129
Sculpture
£994 $1600 €1441 Men to match mountains (58x33x18cm-23x13x7in) num.13/35 bronze. 22-Aug-3 Altermann Galleries, Santa Fe #72
£6587 $11000 €9617 No easy way out (191x66x41cm-75x26x16in) bronze incl. base. 11-Oct-3 Nadeau, Windsor #47/R est:16000-20000
£12849 $23000 €18760 No easy way out (107cm-42in) bronze edn of 50. 15-May-4 Altermann Galleries, Santa Fe #89/R

FELON, Joseph (1818-1896) French
Works on paper
£900 $1494 €1314 Female nude (44x27cm-17x11in) s.i. red chk. 30-Sep-3 Sotheby's, London #14

FELS, Carolyn (1941-) Australian
Works on paper
£269 $497 €393 Time/now (183x122cm-72x48in) s.d.May 1996 i.verso mixed media on canvas prov.exhib. 15-Mar-4 Sotheby's, Melbourne #131 (A.D 650)

FELSKI, Albina (1916-) American
Works on paper
£215 $400 €314 Girl in chicken yard (56x69cm-22x27in) s. gouache acrylic panel. 6-Mar-4 Susanin's, Chicago #5001/R

FEMIAN, F (18th C) French
£1448 $2462 €2114 Portrait of Charles Etienne de Loys (51x41cm-20x16in) s.i.d. verso oval. 19-Nov-3 Fischer, Luzern #1225/R est:2000-2500 (S.FR 3200)

FENCER, Lorna Napurrula (20th C) Australian
Works on paper
£1328 $2484 €1992 Caterpillar dreaming (130x95cm-51x37in) bears name.i.d.1995 verso synthetic polymer paint canvas prov. 26-Jul-4 Sotheby's, Melbourne #271/R est:4000-6000 (A.D 3400)
£1367 $2557 €2051 Untitled (184x122cm-72x48in) i.verso synthetic polymer canvas exec. 1999 prov. 21-Jul-4 Shapiro, Sydney #100/R est:3500-5000 (A.D 3500)

FENDI, Peter (1796-1842) Austrian
Works on paper
£448 $744 €650 Portrait of a man (10x8cm-4x3in) s. pen htd white red. 30-Sep-3 Dorotheum, Vienna #141/R
£552 $916 €800 The Annunciation (18x15cm-7x6in) mono.i. pencil. 30-Sep-3 Dorotheum, Vienna #147/R
£1034 $1717 €1500 The diver (7x10cm-3x4in) W/C. 30-Sep-3 Dorotheum, Vienna #207/R
£1119 $1902 €1600 Warden boy (10x8cm-4x3in) s. pencil. 27-Nov-3 Dorotheum, Linz #597/R est:2400-2800

FENETTY, Frederick M (1854-1915) American/Italian
£323 $600 €472 Floral still life in orange and yellow (45x35cm-18x14in) s. 5-Mar-4 Skinner, Boston #358/R
£457 $850 €667 Still life with roses (45x35cm-18x14in) s. 5-Mar-4 Skinner, Boston #356/R
£645 $1200 €942 Still life with apple blossoms (36x45cm-14x18in) s. 5-Mar-4 Skinner, Boston #357/R
£968 $1800 €1413 Chrysanthemums (45x76cm-18x30in) s. 5-Mar-4 Skinner, Boston #265/R est:400-600
£1075 $2000 €1570 Floral still life with peonies (50x40cm-20x16in) s. 5-Mar-4 Skinner, Boston #371/R est:400-600
£3352 $6000 €4894 Flowers in a green vase (46x36cm-18x14in) s. prov. 6-May-4 Shannon's, Milford #225/R est:4000-6000

FENG CHANGJIANG (1943-) Chinese
Works on paper
£7722 $12896 €11274 Birthday (91x82cm-36x32in) s. ink col scroll. 26-Oct-3 Christie's, Hong Kong #267/R est:110000-130000 (HK.D 100000)
£11380 $20484 €16615 Prayer (91x84cm-36x33in) s. ink col scroll. 25-Apr-4 Christie's, Hong Kong #101/R est:160000-180000 (HK.D 160000)

FENG CHAORAN (1882-1954) Chinese
Works on paper
£4623 $8321 €6750 Lady beside a willow tree (19x56cm-7x22in) s.i. i.verso ink col folding fan. 25-Apr-4 Christie's, Hong Kong #84/R est:30000-40000 (HK.D 65000)
£35562 $64011 €51921 Flower goddesses (140x78cm-55x31in) s.i.d.1921 ink col hanging scroll. 26-Apr-4 Sotheby's, Hong Kong #619/R est:100000-200000 (HK.D 500000)

FENG LINZHANG (1943-) Chinese
Works on paper
£8494 $14185 €12401 Early spring (59x177cm-23x70in) s.i. ink col scroll. 26-Oct-3 Christie's, Hong Kong #265/R est:120000-150000 (HK.D 110000)

FENG ZIKAI (1898-1975) Chinese
Works on paper
£1027 $1747 €1500 Spring walk (43x32cm-17x13in) s.i. seal Indian ink col hanging scroll. 7-Nov-3 Dr Fritz Nagel, Stuttgart #954/R est:1500
£1849 $3329 €2700 Birds (32x24cm-13x9in) s.i. ink col scroll. 25-Apr-4 Christie's, Hong Kong #106/R est:10000-20000 (HK.D 26000)
£1849 $3329 €2700 Cat (31x35cm-12x14in) s.i. ink scroll lit. 25-Apr-4 Christie's, Hong Kong #107/R est:25000-35000 (HK.D 26000)
£2134 $3841 €3116 Flying a kite (17x49cm-7x19in) s. i.verso ink col folding fan. 25-Apr-4 Christie's, Hong Kong #105/R est:15000-20000 (HK.D 30000)
£2134 $3841 €3116 Caring for others (18x48cm-7x19in) s.i. ink col fan calligraphy verso. 26-Apr-4 Sotheby's, Hong Kong #680/R est:28000-35000 (HK.D 30000)
£2471 $4127 €3608 Sunrise (34x22cm-13x9in) s.i. ink col. 27-Oct-3 Sotheby's, Hong Kong #203/R est:20000-30000 (HK.D 32000)
£2703 $4865 €3946 Cartoons (21x16cm-8x6in) s.i. one d.1947 ink two one frame. 26-Apr-4 Sotheby's, Hong Kong #681/R est:20000-30000 (HK.D 38000)
£2934 $4900 €4284 Family (31x35cm-12x14in) s.i. ink scroll lit. 26-Oct-3 Christie's, Hong Kong #301/R est:20000-30000 (HK.D 38000)
£2934 $4900 €4284 Fishing boat and calligraphy (33x27cm-13x11in) s.i. ink col scrolls set of two. 26-Oct-3 Christie's, Hong Kong #303/R est:40000-60000 (HK.D 38000)
£2934 $4900 €4284 Scholar under pine tree (42x31cm-17x12in) s.i. ink scroll. 26-Oct-3 Christie's, Hong Kong #304/R est:20000-30000 (HK.D 38000)
£2934 $4900 €4284 Feeding a horse (35x24cm-14x9in) s.i. ink col scroll. 26-Oct-3 Christie's, Hong Kong #306/R est:25000-30000 (HK.D 38000)
£3089 $5158 €4510 Planting melon (20x47cm-8x19in) s.d.1949 ink col scroll. 26-Oct-3 Christie's, Hong Kong #302/R est:15000-20000 (HK.D 40000)
£3089 $5158 €4510 Parenthood (33x36cm-13x14in) s. ink. 27-Oct-3 Sotheby's, Hong Kong #205/R est:15000-20000 (HK.D 40000)
£3414 $6145 €4984 Lend a helping hand (33x35cm-13x14in) s.i. ink lit. 26-Apr-4 Sotheby's, Hong Kong #682/R est:18000-25000 (HK.D 48000)
£3861 $6448 €5637 Various works (26x36cm-10x14in) s.i. ink col set of four. 27-Oct-3 Sotheby's, Hong Kong #212/R est:50000-70000 (HK.D 50000)
£4247 $7093 €6201 Living in the country side (57x30cm-22x12in) s.i. ink col scroll. 26-Oct-3 Christie's, Hong Kong #305/R est:30000-35000 (HK.D 55000)
£4324 $7222 €6313 Longevity (48x34cm-19x13in) s.i.d.1961 ink hanging scroll. 27-Oct-3 Sotheby's, Hong Kong #204/R est:12000-18000 (HK.D 56000)
£4623 $8321 €6750 Gathering by the shore (71x38cm-28x15in) s.i.d.1947 ink col. 26-Apr-4 Sotheby's, Hong Kong #684/R est:40000-60000 (HK.D 65000)
£5019 $8382 €7328 Buddha (44x33cm-17x13in) s. ink col scroll. 26-Oct-3 Christie's, Hong Kong #307/R est:22000-25000 (HK.D 65000)
£6950 $11606 €10147 Returning home (44x32cm-17x13in) s.i. ink col hanging scroll. 26-Oct-3 Christie's, Hong Kong #212/R est:25000-35000 (HK.D 90000)
£9266 $15475 €13528 Green hills with figures (62x48cm-24x19in) s.i.d.1942 ink col hanging scroll. 27-Oct-3 Sotheby's, Hong Kong #211/R est:25000-35000 (HK.D 120000)
£9957 $17923 €14537 Goddess of mercy (65x29cm-26x11in) s.i. ink col hanging scroll. 26-Apr-4 Sotheby's, Hong Kong #685/R est:30000-50000 (HK.D 140000)
£49787 $89616 €72689 Amitabha, the eternal Buddha (131x66cm-52x26in) s.i.d.1948 ink col lit. 26-Apr-4 Sotheby's, Hong Kong #679/R est:200000-300000 (HK.D 700000)

FENGER, Hans (?) German
£317 $507 €450 Sleeping vintner in cellar (60x50cm-24x20in) s. panel. 19-Sep-3 Sigalas, Stuttgart #373/R

FENGER, W (?) ?
£1050 $1817 €1533 Mohammed Ali - Pasha of Egypt (35x27cm-14x11in) bears i.verso board. 12-Dec-3 Moore Allen & Innocent, Cirencester #364/R est:300-500

FENN, George (1810-1879) British
£1081 $2000 €1578 Prize cow (48x61cm-19x24in) s.d.1839. 10-Feb-4 Doyle, New York #236/R est:3000-5000

FENN, Harry (1845-1911) American
Works on paper
£228 $425 €333 The gate (20x17cm-8x7in) s. W/C grisaille. 5-Mar-4 Skinner, Boston #277/R

FENOSA, Apelles (1899-1989) Spanish
Sculpture
£940 $1663 €1400 Centaure (24cm-9in) s. num.4/5 pat bronze. 30-Apr-4 Tajan, Paris #72 est:2000
£1399 $2336 €2000 Femme debout. bronze. 27-Jun-3 Calmels Cohen, Paris #43/R est:1500-2000
£1538 $2569 €2200 La violoniste. bronze. 27-Jun-3 Calmels Cohen, Paris #42/R est:1500-2000
£2098 $3503 €3000 Centaure. bronze. 27-Jun-3 Calmels Cohen, Paris #41/R est:1500-2000
£2260 $3842 €3300 Petite violoniste (15cm-6in) s. bronze. 9-Nov-3 Eric Pillon, Calais #77/R

FENSON, Robert (19/20th C) British
£360 $666 €526 Highland loch view, with rowing boat in the foreground (50x75cm-20x30in) s.d.95. 13-Jan-4 Bonhams, Knightsbridge #27
£824 $1500 €1203 Shepherd returning home (41x61cm-16x24in) s.d.1912. 19-Jun-4 Jackson's, Cedar Falls #57/R est:500-700

FENTANES, Carlos (20th C) ?
£1029 $1800 €1502 La sagrada familia (114x114cm-45x45in) s.d.MCMXCIII. 19-Dec-3 Sotheby's, New York #1217/R est:3000-4000

FENTON, Beatrice (1887-1983) American
Sculpture
£1576 $2900 €2301 Dancers (40cm-16in) i.d.1924 brown pat bronze st.f.Roman Bronze Works NY. 27-Jun-4 Freeman, Philadelphia #96/R est:2500-4000

FENTON, John Nathaniel (1912-1977) American
£299 $475 €437 Figure with birds (91x61cm-36x24in) s. painted c.1960 prov. 9-Mar-3 William Jenack, New York #99
£566 $900 €826 Motorcycle boys (102x127cm-40x50in) s. painted c.1960. 4-May-3 William Jenack, New York #169
£617 $1000 €901 Man with fir trimmed hat in a surreal landscape (56x46cm-22x18in) s. 2-Aug-3 Neal Auction Company, New Orleans #558/R est:750-1500
£741 $1200 €1082 Bearded man in a surreal landscape (56x46cm-22x18in) s. 2-Aug-3 Neal Auction Company, New Orleans #557/R est:750-1500

FENTON, Roger (1819-1869) British
Photographs
£2000 $3520 €2920 Tintern Abbey (19x21cm-7x8in) s.i. salt print. 19-May-4 Christie's, London #61/R est:3000-5000
£4800 $8448 €7008 Bolton woods (29x36cm-11x14in) num.H97 salt print prov. 19-May-4 Christie's, London #75/R est:1500-2000

FENYES, Adolphe (1867-1945) Hungarian
£1069 $1892 €1561 Field (16x22cm-6x9in) s. panel. 28-Apr-4 Kieselbach, Budapest #173/R (H.F 400000)
£1122 $1987 €1638 Fairy landscape (27x36cm-11x14in) s. 28-Apr-4 Kieselbach, Budapest #40/R (H.F 420000)
£1603 $2838 €2340 Boy (24x18cm-9x7in) s. canvas on cardboard. 28-Apr-4 Kieselbach, Budapest #149/R (H.F 600000)
£2088 $3612 €3048 Fairy Tale landscape with a river (50x70cm-20x28in) s. 12-Dec-3 Kieselbach, Budapest #55/R (H.F 800000)
£2271 $4020 €3316 Sunny autumn afternoon (25x35cm-10x14in) s. canvas on cardboard. 28-Apr-4 Kieselbach, Budapest #139/R (H.F 850000)
£4615 $7661 €6738 Sunny yard (51x47cm-20x19in) s. 4-Oct-3 Kieselbach, Budapest #200/R (H.F 1700000)
£5973 $9914 €8721 Fairy tale landscape (73x100cm-29x39in) s. 4-Oct-3 Kieselbach, Budapest #23/R (H.F 2200000)
£13361 $23649 €19507 Rocking the cradle (57x45cm-22x18in) s. canvas on cardboard. 28-Apr-4 Kieselbach, Budapest #170/R (H.F 5000000)
£24433 $40559 €35672 Sunlit street (66x81cm-26x32in) s.d.1904. 4-Oct-3 Kieselbach, Budapest #96/R (H.F 9000000)
£57420 $99337 €83833 Celebration day - In the room (90x68cm-35x27in) s.d.1909 cardboard. 12-Dec-3 Kieselbach, Budapest #156/R (H.F 22000000)

FEODOROV, Ivan (?) Russian
£2703 $4838 €4000 Girl reading a book (14x16cm-6x6in) s. 8-May-4 Bukowskis, Helsinki #426/R est:1500-2000

FEODOROVA, Maria Alekseevna (1859-1916) Russian
£878 $1572 €1300 The churchyard (51x40cm-20x16in) s. 8-May-4 Bukowskis, Helsinki #424/R
£1081 $1935 €1600 Calm summers day (27x19cm-11x7in) s. 8-May-4 Bukowskis, Helsinki #442/R est:800-1000
£1351 $2419 €2000 Bench in the park (47x40cm-19x16in) s. 8-May-4 Bukowskis, Helsinki #428/R est:800-1000
£1959 $3507 €2900 The pavilion (52x61cm-20x24in) s. 8-May-4 Bukowskis, Helsinki #423/R est:1300-1600

FERAT, Serge (1881-1958) Russian
£3901 $6514 €5500 Nature morte au vase de fleurs (81x60cm-32x24in) s. 19-Jun-3 Millon & Associes, Paris #246/R
£6164 $10479 €9000 Composition musicale (25x20cm-10x8in) s. panel. 9-Nov-3 Eric Pillon, Calais #252/R
£8000 $14560 €11680 Nature morte (43x50cm-17x20in) s. 4-Feb-4 Sotheby's, London #334/R est:10000-15000
Works on paper
£550 $952 €803 Vaches a la riviere (18x11cm-7x4in) s. gouache prov. 11-Dec-3 Christie's, Kensington #93/R
£1538 $2615 €2200 Maternite (21x13cm-8x5in) s. gouache prov. 23-Nov-3 Cornette de St.Cyr, Paris #113/R est:600-800
£3147 $5350 €4500 Le cirque (16x8cm-6x3in) s. gouache prov. 23-Nov-3 Cornette de St.Cyr, Paris #114/R est:600-800
£4027 $7208 €6000 Cirque (37x22cm-15x9in) s. gouache. 30-May-4 Eric Pillon, Calais #252/R

FERAU Y ALSINA, Enrique (1825-1887) Spanish
£4932 $8384 €7200 Landscape with buildings and figures (50x67cm-20x26in) s. 4-Nov-3 Ansorena, Madrid #360/R est:7200

FERAUD, Albert (1921-) French
Sculpture
£1081 $1902 €1600 Untitled (88x68x45cm-35x27x18in) s.d.1975-6 steel prov. 18-May-4 Tajan, Paris #109/R est:800-1000

FERBER, Herbert (1906-1991) American
Sculpture
£6135 $10000 €8957 Calligraphic Mercury II (129x111x41cm-51x44x16in) s.d.55 bronze wood base prov.exhib.lit. 23-Sep-3 Christie's, Rockefeller NY #19/R est:10000-15000

FERDINAND, Roy (1959-) American
Works on paper
£264 $475 €385 Pennyland (71x56cm-28x22in) ink col pencil posterboard. 24-Apr-4 Slotin Folk Art, Buford #674/R

FEREKIDIS, Nicholaos (1862-1929) Greek
£1600 $2800 €2336 Country side road (30x39cm-12x15in) s. hardboard. 16-Dec-3 Bonhams, New Bond Street #72/R est:1500-2000

FERENCZY, Karoly (1862-1917) Hungarian
£344 $554 €502 Gypsy camp (20x31cm-8x12in) s. panel. 25-Aug-3 Blomqvist, Lysaker #1068 (N.KR 4000)
£851 $1421 €1200 Playing in the cellar (38x33cm-15x13in) s. 14-Oct-3 Finarte Semenzato, Milan #34/R
£9086 $16081 €13266 Landscape in Nagybanya (42x48cm-17x19in) s. 28-Apr-4 Kieselbach, Budapest #109/R (H.F 3400000)
£62640 $108368 €91454 My studio in Nagybanya - House among trees (85x115cm-33x45in) s. 12-Dec-3 Kieselbach, Budapest #88/R (H.F 24000000)

FERENCZY, Valer (1885-1954) Hungarian
£699 $1168 €1000 Theatre (60x75cm-24x30in) 10-Oct-3 Stadion, Trieste #222

FEREY, Edouard (19/20th C) French
£850 $1573 €1241 Caravans in the snow (50x92cm-20x36in) s. 14-Jul-4 Sotheby's, Olympia #172/R

FEREY, Prosper (19th C) French
£2000 $3700 €2920 Rest for refreshments. Shepherd and his flock (60x73cm-24x29in) s. one d.1857 one indis.d. pair. 14-Jul-4 Sotheby's, Olympia #156/R est:1500-2000

FERFOGLIA, Pino (19/20th C) Italian
£455 $782 €650 Trieste, view of the canal (43x60cm-17x24in) s. canvas on cardboard. 3-Dec-3 Stadion, Trieste #1148/R

FERG, Franz de Paula (1689-1740) Austrian
£1207 $2160 €1762 Ambush by Italian ruins (24x31cm-9x12in) panel. 17-May-4 Beurret, Zurich #2/R est:3000-5000 (S.FR 2800)
£2500 $4500 €3650 Mountainous landscape with peasants travelling on a path (32x26cm-13x10in) s. copper. 23-Apr-4 Christie's, Kensington #160/R est:2000-3000
£3421 $6295 €5200 Bergers et troupeau (27x21cm-11x8in) s. copperr. 25-Jun-4 Piasa, Paris #88/R est:3000-4000
£7308 $12569 €10670 Figures resting by ruins in landscape (33x25cm-13x10in) copper. 3-Dec-3 AB Stockholms Auktionsverk #2658/R est:100000-150000 (S.KR 95000)
£7500 $13500 €10950 Landscapes with travellers (29x24cm-11x9in) one s. copper pair. 23-Apr-4 Christie's, Kensington #159/R est:5000-8000
£19000 $34200 €27740 Rhenish landscapes with figures at a quay, and travellers near a mill (81x69cm-32x27in) mono. pair prov. 22-Apr-4 Sotheby's, London #117/R est:12000-18000
£22000 $40260 €32120 Classical landscape with travellers. Classical landscape with ruined temple (26x36cm-10x14in) init. panel pair. 8-Jul-4 Sotheby's, London #340/R est:15000-20000

FERG, Franz de Paula (attrib) (1689-1740) Austrian
£2027 $3649 €2959 Landscape with figures (27x38cm-11x15in) panel. 26-Jan-4 Lilla Bukowskis, Stockholm #365 est:15000-20000 (S.KR 27000)
£8882 $16076 €13500 Vues de port mediterraneen (29x41cm-11x16in) pair. 19-Apr-4 Boscher, Cherbourg #762/R est:12000-15000

FERG, Franz de Paula (style) (1689-1740) Austrian

£8000	$14560	€12000	Elegant figures in a park. Figures playing with ball (20x27cm-8x11in) panel pair prov. 29-Jun-4 Sotheby's, Paris #35/R est:15000-20000

FERGNANI, Corrado (1910-1986) Italian

£1818	$3091	€2600	Landscape in Liguria (45x55cm-18x22in) 19-Nov-3 Cambi, Genoa #425/R est:2500-3000

FERGUSON, Andrew (1959-) Australian

£576	$1043	€841	Acrobats (61x61cm-24x24in) s. i.d.89 verso. 30-Mar-4 Lawson Menzies, Sydney #18 est:1000-1500 (A.D 1400)

FERGUSON, Henry Augustus (1842-1911) American

£3333	$6000	€4866	Hudson river landscape (41x66cm-16x26in) s. 24-Apr-4 Weschler, Washington #605/R est:3000-5000
£3495	$6500	€5103	After the rain - ships in the Venetian Lagoon (32x48cm-13x19in) s.i. board. 3-Mar-4 Christie's, Rockefeller NY #21/R est:3000-5000
£8025	$13000	€11636	Spring farming on the Hudson (38x69cm-15x27in) s. indis d. 8-Aug-3 Barridorf, Portland #145/R est:15000-20000

FERGUSON, Nancy Maybin (1872-1967) American

£1932	$3400	€2821	Fairmount Park, Philadelphia (30x41cm-12x16in) i. canvasboard. 21-May-4 Pook & Pook, Downington #376/R est:1200-1800
£1963	$3200	€2866	Excursion (30x41cm-12x16in) s. board. 19-Jul-3 Outer Cape Auctions, Provincetown #84/R
£6832	$11000	€9975	Road to the monument, provincetown, Mass (76x91cm-30x36in) s. verso. 20-Aug-3 James Julia, Fairfield #1398/R est:12500-15000

FERGUSON, Peter John (1956-) Australian

£350	$633	€511	Untitled (125x90cm-49x35in) s.i.verso. 30-Mar-4 Lawson Menzies, Sydney #29 est:1000-1500 (A.D 850)
£611	$1111	€892	War dance (109x137cm-43x54in) s.i.verso prov. 16-Jun-4 Deutscher-Menzies, Melbourne #534/R est:1000-1500 (A.D 1600)
£1215	$1955	€1774	Neighbourhood Party (111x188cm-44x74in) s.i.verso prov. 25-Aug-3 Sotheby's, Paddington #283/R est:2000-3000 (A.D 3000)
Works on paper			
£412	$745	€602	Builder's dream (42x63cm-17x25in) s.d.95 s.i.d.verso mixed media. 30-Mar-4 Lawson Menzies, Sydney #9 est:300-600 (A.D 1000)

FERGUSON, Shaun (20th C) British

£350	$655	€511	Cuenca, Spain (117x147cm-46x58in) s.verso prov. 25-Jul-4 Lots Road Auctions, London #352

FERGUSON, William (19/20th C) British

£340	$544	€496	Red roofs, Fife (34x26cm-13x10in) s.d.1920 canvasboard. 15-May-3 Bonhams, Edinburgh #343

FERGUSON, William Gowe (1632-1695) British

£2500	$4650	€3650	Gamebirds by a plinth, in a wooded landscape (127x102cm-50x40in) 4-Mar-4 Christie's, Kensington #397a/R est:3000-4000

FERGUSON, William James (fl.1849-1886) British

Works on paper			
£550	$1012	€803	Isolo pescatoria. Lago Orta (23x40cm-9x16in) s.d.1885 W/C pair. 29-Mar-4 Bonhams, Bath #22/R

FERGUSON, William James (attrib) (fl.1849-1886) British

£600	$1020	€876	Cottage scenery, ruins, cattle and figures (30x36cm-12x14in) s. i.verso. 19-Nov-3 Tennants, Leyburn #1117/R

FERGUSSON, John Duncan (1874-1961) British

£6000	$10860	€8760	Princes Street Gardens, Edinburgh (11x14cm-4x6in) bears i. board prov.exhib. 19-Apr-4 Sotheby's, London #75/R est:6000-8000
£7000	$10990	€10150	Princes Street gardens, Edinburgh (11x14cm-4x6in) bears i. board prov.exhib. 27-Aug-3 Sotheby's, London #1203/R est:5000-7000
£7200	$12240	€10512	Figures by a loch (11x14cm-4x6in) board. 30-Oct-3 Christie's, London #166/R est:3000-5000
£8000	$13600	€11680	Flowers from the roadside, Kelmdale (34x27cm-13x11in) s.d.1943 verso board. 30-Oct-3 Christie's, London #164/R est:8000-12000
£25000	$43000	€36500	Nude and Cliff (56x61cm-22x24in) s.verso prov.exhib.lit. 4-Dec-3 Bonhams, Edinburgh #47/R est:25000-30000
Works on paper			
£280	$512	€409	Head in profile (14x10cm-6x4in) conte. 8-Apr-4 Bonhams, Edinburgh #122/R
£380	$695	€555	The mother in law (20x12cm-8x5in) conte. 29-Jan-4 Bonhams, Edinburgh #339
£380	$695	€555	Top hat and cigar, Paris (15x11cm-6x4in) conte. 8-Apr-4 Bonhams, Edinburgh #127/R
£450	$824	€657	Corpulent man, Paris (15x11cm-6x4in) conte on card. 8-Apr-4 Bonhams, Edinburgh #125/R
£550	$1007	€803	Midinette in broad-brimmed hat, Paris (17x10cm-7x4in) conte. 8-Apr-4 Bonhams, Edinburgh #120/R
£700	$1099	€1015	Parisian smoking a pipe (18x11cm-7x4in) pencil prov.exhib. 27-Aug-3 Sotheby's, London #1211/R
£700	$1281	€1022	Fruit and flowers, Antibes (25x21cm-10x8in) i.d.Aug 58 conte. 8-Apr-4 Bonhams, Edinburgh #121/R
£720	$1318	€1051	Man with lunettes, Paris (15x9cm-6x4in) conte. 8-Apr-4 Bonhams, Edinburgh #119/R
£850	$1462	€1241	Head study in profile (21x12cm-8x5in) conte. 4-Dec-3 Bonhams, Edinburgh #41/R
£900	$1449	€1305	Woman in profile with a broad brimmed hat (12x20cm-5x8in) conte. 21-Aug-3 Bonhams, Edinburgh #1091/R
£1000	$1610	€1450	Woman's head in three quarter view (20x12cm-8x5in) conte. 21-Aug-3 Bonhams, Edinburgh #1085/R est:1000-1500
£1200	$2064	€1752	Feather Bonnet (21x12cm-8x5in) conte. 4-Dec-3 Bonhams, Edinburgh #39/R est:1200-1800
£1250	$2013	€1813	Feathered hat (20x12cm-8x5in) conte. 21-Aug-3 Bonhams, Edinburgh #1089/R est:1000-1500
£1350	$2322	€1971	Beaded necklace (21x12cm-8x5in) conte. 4-Dec-3 Bonhams, Edinburgh #42/R est:1200-1800
£1400	$2408	€2044	Fontal head study of a a girl in a floral bonnet (21x12cm-8x5in) conte. 4-Dec-3 Bonhams, Edinburgh #40/R est:1000-1500
£1450	$2335	€2103	Elegant woman in a hat and a man head (20x12cm-8x5in) conte executed c.1909. 21-Aug-3 Bonhams, Edinburgh #1083/R est:1200-1800
£1500	$2415	€2175	Woman in a large hat (20x12cm-8x5in) conte. 21-Aug-3 Bonhams, Edinburgh #1090/R est:800-1200
£1800	$2826	€2610	Portrait of Joan Wernfaur (22x15cm-9x6in) pencil prov. 27-Aug-3 Sotheby's, London #1215/R est:2000-3000
£1800	$3096	€2628	Rose bonnet (21x12cm-8x5in) conte. 4-Dec-3 Bonhams, Edinburgh #43/R est:1200-1800
£2000	$3140	€2900	Harbour, Royan. Beach at St. Palais. Still life with a statue and apples (12x20cm-5x8in) pencil set of three. 27-Aug-3 Sotheby's, London #1209/R est:1500-2000
£2200	$3542	€3190	Necklace (20x12cm-8x5in) conte. 21-Aug-3 Bonhams, Edinburgh #1087/R est:1200-1800
£2400	$4080	€3504	Sailing boat (17x11cm-7x4in) i.verso pencil W/C. 30-Oct-3 Christie's, London #167/R est:1000-1500
£2600	$4082	€3770	Woods, St Palais. Street singer, Paris. Young poet, Roffy (12x12cm-5x5in) pencil set of three different sizes. 27-Aug-3 Sotheby's, London #1205/R est:1000-1500
£2700	$4347	€3915	Elegant woman in profile (20x12cm-8x5in) conte. 21-Aug-3 Bonhams, Edinburgh #1086/R est:1200-1800
£2800	$4508	€4060	Hint of a smile (20x12cm-8x5in) conte. 21-Aug-3 Bonhams, Edinburgh #1088/R est:1000-1500
£2800	$4396	€4060	Street singer, Paris. Stood up, Paris. Violin section, Paris (20x12cm-8x5in) pencil set of three. 27-Aug-3 Sotheby's, London #1213/R est:1000-1500
£3000	$4710	€4350	Street scene, Royan. Parisian waiters, 1909. Going home, Paris 1909 (20x12cm-8x5in) pencil three. 27-Aug-3 Sotheby's, London #1207/R est:1500-2000
£3000	$4710	€4350	Woods, St. Palais. At the concert. Young poet Roffy, Paris (20x12cm-8x5in) pencil set of three. 27-Aug-3 Sotheby's, London #1210/R est:1000-1500
£3000	$4710	€4350	Rita at Thorenc. Guitar player, Paris. Member of the chorus, Paris (24x19cm-9x7in) pencil set of three different sizes. 27-Aug-3 Sotheby's, London #1212/R est:1000-1500
£3200	$5024	€4640	Peploe and his wife, Royan St. Palais. Happy couple, Paris. Street singer (12x20cm-5x8in) pencil set of three different sizes. 27-Aug-3 Sotheby's, London #1204/R est:1500-2000
£3200	$5792	€4672	Man walking against the wind. Fashionable lady (28x13cm-11x5in) W/C two. 19-Apr-4 Sotheby's, London #76/R est:1500-2000
£3400	$6188	€5100	Portrait of a lady, Margaret Morris the artist's wife (21x13cm-8x5in) chl exec.c.1910. 2-Jul-4 Bloomsbury, London #104/R est:1000-1500
£3500	$5495	€5075	Margaret Morris, the artist wife. Self portriat (20x12cm-8x5in) pencil two. 27-Aug-3 Sotheby's, London #1206/R est:1500-2000
£3500	$5950	€5110	Road, Pourville (27x33cm-11x13in) s.d.1926 verso W/C chl. 30-Oct-3 Christie's, London #168/R est:2000-3000
£4400	$8008	€6600	Portrait of a lady in a hat, Margaret Morris the artist's wife (21x13cm-8x5in) chl exec.c.1910. 2-Jul-4 Bloomsbury, London #105/R est:1000-1500
£7000	$12670	€10220	Meg, Cap d'Antibes. Sea and sands, Cap d'Antibes (17x12cm-7x5in) W/C two. 19-Apr-4 Sotheby's, London #77/R est:2000-3000
£7800	$12558	€11310	Study for magnolias (22x16cm-9x6in) pencil W/C gouache. 21-Aug-3 Bonhams, Edinburgh #1036/R est:3000-5000
£8500	$13345	€12325	Reclining female nude (23x32cm-9x13in) chl prov.exhib. 27-Aug-3 Sotheby's, London #1214/R est:2000-3000

FERMARIELLO, Sergio (1961-) Italian

Works on paper			
£450	$809	€657	Senza titolo (40x40cm-16x16in) s. verso mixed media panel exhib. 26-Apr-4 Bukowskis, Stockholm #626/R (S.KR 6200)

FERMER, Nicholas Wilhelm (20th C) ?

£492	$900	€718	Flowering grasses with mountains in the distance (41x56cm-16x22in) s. painted c.1930. 5-Jun-4 Treadway Gallery, Cincinnati #640/R

FERMEUS, Victor (1894-1963) Belgian

£464	$844	€700	Le potager en fleurs (40x49cm-16x19in) s.d.1928. 15-Jun-4 Vanderkindere, Brussels #96
£738	$1358	€1100	Moulin a Grimbergen (80x100cm-31x39in) 23-Mar-4 Galerie Moderne, Brussels #332/R

FERNANDES, Augustine (20th C) American?

£472	$850	€689	F67-39 (21x18cm-8x7in) s. 24-Apr-4 David Rago, Lambertville #115/R

FERNANDEZ CERSA, Arturo (1866-1937) Spanish

£461	$770	€650	Landscape (13x22cm-5x9in) s. panel. 23-Jun-3 Durán, Madrid #699/R
£567	$948	€800	Marina (28x50cm-11x20in) s. 23-Jun-3 Durán, Madrid #131/R
£638	$1066	€900	Landscape (28x50cm-11x20in) s. 23-Jun-3 Durán, Madrid #130/R
£709	$1184	€1000	Landscape (18x40cm-7x16in) s. panel. 23-Jun-3 Durán, Madrid #729/R est:400
£1250	$2263	€1900	Landscape with river (17x40cm-7x16in) s. panel. 14-Apr-4 Ansorena, Madrid #169/R est:1900

FERNANDEZ DE VILLASANTE, Julio Moises (1888-1968) Spanish

£1329	$2219	€1900	Still life with loaf of bread (51x59cm-20x23in) s.d.MCMLXVIII board. 30-Jun-3 Ansorena, Madrid #389/R
£3873	$6701	€5500	Charillo (97x82cm-38x32in) s.d.1934. 15-Dec-3 Ansorena, Madrid #340/R est:6000

FERNANDEZ HIDALGO, Eulalio (19/20th C) Spanish

£278	$453	€400	Cathedral interior (54x32cm-21x13in) s. 23-Sep-3 Durán, Madrid #12/R

FERNANDEZ LUQUE, Manuel (1919-) Spanish
£612 $1096 €900 End of life (54x64cm-21x25in) s.d.74. 22-Mar-4 Durán, Madrid #48/R

FERNANDEZ MURO, Jose Antonio (1920-) Spanish
Works on paper
£897 $1614 €1300 Dance (122x122cm-48x48in) s.d.1975 mixed media exhib. 26-Jan-4 Durán, Madrid #126/R

FERNANDEZ, Alexis (1969-) Venezuelan
£1272 $2125 €1857 Figures (110x78cm-43x31in) s. painted 1998. 19-Oct-3 Subastas Odalys, Caracas #141

FERNANDEZ, Augustin (1928-) Cuban
£340 $609 €500 Untitled (112x115cm-44x45in) s.d.63 prov. 21-Mar-4 Calmels Cohen, Paris #127/R
£1389 $2319 €2000 Untitled (76cm-30in circular) s.d. 24-Oct-3 Ketterer, Hamburg #342/R est:2500-3000

FERNANDEZ, Francisco (1897-?) Venezuelan
£475 $750 €694 Landscape (45x61cm-18x24in) s. 27-Apr-3 Subastas Odalys, Caracas #11
£476 $810 €695 Still life with pomegranates (23x30cm-9x12in) s. painted 1971. 23-Nov-3 Subastas Odalys, Caracas #47/R
£1016 $1625 €1483 Oripoto (54x65cm-21x26in) s. 21-Sep-3 Subastas Odalys, Caracas #11/R

FERNANDEZ, H (?) ?
£2100 $3570 €3066 Doubtful finish. Cicero. Doubtful lead. Pretty Polly (30x40cm-12x16in) one s. three init. two d.1905 set of four. 19-Nov-3 Sotheby's, Olympia #59/R est:1000-1500

FERNANDEZ, Soledad (1945-) Spanish
Works on paper
£1074 $2008 €1600 Him and her (60x30cm-24x12in) s. graphite. 24-Feb-4 Durán, Madrid #20/R est:1000

FERNANDEZ, Teresita (1968-) American
£17365 $29000 €25353 Double orange climber (107x234cm-42x92in) acrylic on plastic in two parts executed 2001 prov. 14-Nov-3 Phillips, New York #248/R est:20000-30000
Sculpture
£3593 $6000 €5246 Supernova 3 (28x116x116cm-11x46x46in) wood scrim mirror plexiglas executed 1999 prov. 14-Nov-3 Phillips, New York #251/R est:12000-18000

FERNANDEZ-MURO, Jose Antonio (1920-) Argentinian
Works on paper
£670 $1200 €978 Book X (93x73cm-37x29in) s.i.d.1966 mixed media prov. 6-May-4 Doyle, New York #127/R est:900-1200

FERNEKES, Max (jnr) (1905-1984) American
Works on paper
£254 $425 €371 Side street in Monterey , Mexico (23x28cm-9x11in) s.i.d.1934 W/C. 27-Oct-3 Schrager Galleries, Milwaukee #670/R

FERNELEY, Claude Lorraine (1822-1892) British
£900 $1449 €1314 Gun dogs and game in a woodland clearing (20x28cm-8x11in) s.d.1844 board. 13-Aug-3 Andrew Hartley, Ilkley #804
£1100 $2013 €1606 Horses in a wooded landscape (48x38cm-19x15in) s.d.1850. 8-Jul-4 Duke & Son, Dorchester #214/R est:500-1000
£1408 $2437 €2000 Bess and Polly in a stable (61x78cm-24x31in) s.i.d.1879. 10-Dec-3 Christie's, Amsterdam #877/R est:2000-3000
£3000 $5100 €4380 Bay hunter in the park of a country house (51x63cm-20x25in) s.i.d.62. 27-Nov-3 Christie's, Kensington #92/R est:3000-4000

FERNELEY, John (jnr) (1815-1862) British
£1163 $2000 €1698 Bay hunter in an extensive landscape (41x56cm-16x22in) indis sig. 5-Dec-3 Christie's, Rockefeller NY #25/R est:6000-8000
£1676 $3000 €2447 Bay with dog (50x60cm-20x24in) s.d.1857. 27-May-4 Sotheby's, New York #254/R est:6000-8000
£2500 $4575 €3650 Sergeant of the 1st or Royal Regiment of Dragoons and two others (39x52cm-15x20in) 28-Jan-4 Dreweatt Neate, Newbury #107/R est:3000-5000
£4000 $7360 €5840 Old Dick, a bay in a wooded landscape (46x61cm-18x24in) s.i.d.1840. 10-Jun-4 Christie's, Kensington #21/R est:4000-6000
£4118 $7000 €6012 Officer of the Dragoon Guards (30x38cm-12x15in) s.indis.d.185. 29-Oct-3 Christie's, Rockefeller NY #82/R est:10000-15000
£4469 $8000 €6525 Ion and Palmeria in landscape (53x84cm-21x33in) s.d.1844 prov. 27-May-4 Sotheby's, New York #252/R est:10000-15000
£9000 $15300 €13140 Bay hunter in a landscape with figures and horses by a path in the distance (71x92cm-28x36in) s.d.1835. 25-Nov-3 Christie's, London #95/R est:6000-8000

FERNELEY, John (snr) (1781-1860) British
£2200 $3938 €3212 Northumberland, portrait of a dark bay racehorse in a stable interior (44x58cm-17x23in) s.d. 16-Mar-4 Bonhams, Oxford #63/R est:2000-3000
£4469 $8000 €6525 Hunter in landscape (63x76cm-25x30in) 27-May-4 Sotheby's, New York #253/R est:10000-15000
£9000 $15300 €13140 Bay hunter in a loose box (83x105cm-33x41in) 27-Nov-3 Sotheby's, London #207/R est:10000-15000
£11628 $20000 €16977 Attila, winner of the 1842 Derby, in a stall (71x91cm-28x36in) s.i. painted 1842 prov.lit. 5-Dec-3 Christie's, Rockefeller NY #37/R est:18000-25000
£20000 $35200 €29200 Bay hunter in a extensive landscape with a lake beyond (72x104cm-28x41in) s. prov. 21-May-4 Christie's, London #49/R est:25000-35000
£40698 $70000 €59419 Belvoir crossing the Smite (61x122cm-24x48in) painted c.1823 prov. 5-Dec-3 Christie's, Rockefeller NY #27/R est:70000-100000
£90000 $153000 €131400 Two bay mares with a terrier by a tree in a landscape (127x102cm-50x40in) s.d.1842 prov. 25-Nov-3 Christie's, London #91/R est:70000-100000
£127907 $220000 €186744 Two hunters at grass (112x160cm-44x63in) s.i.d.1827 lit. 5-Dec-3 Christie's, Rockefeller NY #34/R est:250000-350000

FERNHOUT, Edgar (1912-1976) Dutch
£23333 $42933 €35000 Still life with pears (40x40cm-16x16in) init.d.32 s.i.d. verso prov.exhib.lit. 8-Jun-4 Sotheby's, Amsterdam #24/R est:20000-30000

FERNIER, Robert (1895-1977) French
£367 $613 €532 Maison derriere les arbres (25x31cm-10x12in) s.d. cardboard. 21-Jun-3 Galerie du Rhone, Sion #105/R (S.FR 800)

FERNSTROM, Linn (1974-) Swedish
Works on paper
£1051 $1893 €1534 Among people (29x41cm-11x16in) s.d.2002 verso pastel prov. 26-Apr-4 Bukowskis, Stockholm #497/R (S.KR 14500)

FERON, William (1858-1894) Swedish
£2439 $4366 €3561 Fishermen at sunset (76x114cm-30x45in) s.d.86. 25-May-4 Bukowskis, Stockholm #114/R est:30000-35000 (S.KR 33000)
£3800 $6840 €5548 Figures on a beach (23x34cm-9x13in) s. prov. 22-Apr-4 Lawrence, Crewkerne #898/R est:2000-3000
Works on paper
£321 $590 €482 The easel outside (29x22cm-11x9in) s. W/C prov. 14-Jun-4 Lilla Bukowskis, Stockholm #244 (S.KR 4400)

FERRAGUTI, Arnaldo (1862-1925) Italian
£2700 $4914 €3942 Children in a meadow (40x31cm-16x12in) s. 16-Jun-4 Bonhams, New Bond Street #77/R est:3000-5000
£17606 $29225 €25000 Povera Nini (73x125cm-29x49in) s. exhib.lit. 11-Jun-3 Christie's, Rome #277/R est:25000-30000
Works on paper
£274 $427 €400 Camelia (22x22cm-9x9in) s. mixed media cardboard. 8-Apr-3 Il Ponte, Milan #509
£548 $855 €800 Study of horse heads (27x36cm-11x14in) init.d.1917 mixed media. 8-Apr-3 Il Ponte, Milan #633
£680 $1218 €1000 Girl in profile (62x50cm-24x20in) s. pastel double-sided. 22-Mar-4 Sant Agostino, Torino #123/R
£685 $1068 €1000 Mowers (39x18cm-15x7in) init. mixed media. 8-Apr-3 Il Ponte, Milan #622
£833 $1417 €1200 Natin (36x47cm-14x19in) init.i.d.1917 mixed media. 29-Oct-3 Il Ponte, Milan #551
£1875 $3187 €2700 Portrait of lady (45x54cm-18x21in) mixed media. 29-Oct-3 Il Ponte, Milan #534/R

FERRAJ, Viktor (1968-) Albanian
£268 $497 €400 Nature archetypes (70x80cm-28x31in) s. s.i.d.2003 verso oil acrylic. 13-Mar-4 Meeting Art, Vercelli #344

FERRAN, Brian (1940-) British
£810 $1401 €1150 Calatin (29x29cm-11x11in) s.d.73 board prov. 10-Dec-3 Bonhams & James Adam, Dublin #84/R
£2027 $3831 €3000 Corleck Head VI (61x61cm-24x24in) s.d.1995 i.verso acrylic gold leaf exhib. 17-Feb-4 Whyte's, Dublin #32/R est:2000-3000
£2533 $4585 €3800 White Island (107x80cm-42x31in) s.i.stretcher. 31-Mar-4 James Adam, Dublin #100/R est:4000-6000
Works on paper
£775 $1340 €1100 Abstract landscape (27x37cm-11x15in) s.d.1969 mixed media. 10-Dec-3 Bonhams & James Adam, Dublin #167/R

FERRAND, Jacques Philippe (attrib) (1653-1732) French
Miniatures
£1800 $3312 €2628 Nobleman wearing a doublet with heavy gold embroidery (10cm-4in) i. oil on copper rectangular frame. 24-Jun-4 Bonhams, New Bond Street #30/R est:800-1200

FERRANDIZ Y BADENES, Bernardo (1835-1890) Spanish
Works on paper
£2349 $4205 €3500 Bandits (39x28cm-15x11in) s.d.1879 W/C. 25-May-4 Durán, Madrid #61/R est:600

FERRANT Y FISCHERMANS, Alejandro (1843-1917) Spanish
£903 $1472 €1300 Official visit (21x14cm-8x6in) s. s.i.d.1895 verso board. 23-Sep-3 Durán, Madrid #17/R
£987 $1816 €1500 Allegory of Art (41x58cm-16x23in) s. 22-Jun-4 Durán, Madrid #603/R est:1500

FERRANTE, Mario de (1898-1992) Italian
£215 $400 €314 Abstract composition (71x56cm-28x22in) s. painted c.1960. 7-Mar-4 Treadway Gallery, Cincinnati #749/R
£219 $400 €320 Abstraction (76x102cm-30x40in) s. painted c.1960. 5-Jun-4 Treadway Gallery, Cincinnati #769/R
£233 $400 €340 Abstract composition (61x51cm-24x20in) s. board painted c.1950. 7-Dec-3 Treadway Gallery, Cincinnati #719/R
£233 $400 €340 Abstract composition (61x51cm-24x20in) s. board painted c.1950. 7-Dec-3 Treadway Gallery, Cincinnati #721/R
£233 $400 €340 Abstracted beach scene (58x61cm-23x24in) s. board painted c.1950. 7-Dec-3 Treadway Gallery, Cincinnati #722/R
£233 $400 €340 Abstract shapes (58x61cm-23x24in) s. board painted c.1950. 7-Dec-3 Treadway Gallery, Cincinnati #724/R

£287 $525 €419 Abstract (58x48cm-23x19in) s. board. 5-Jun-4 Dan Ripley, Indianapolis #279
£296 $550 €432 Abstract composition (76x61cm-30x24in) s. painted c.1960. 7-Mar-4 Treadway Gallery, Cincinnati #738/R
£316 $500 €461 Abstract composition (71x56cm-28x22in) s. board. 7-Sep-3 Treadway Gallery, Cincinnati #701/R
£316 $500 €461 Abstract composition (71x56cm-28x22in) s. board. 7-Sep-3 Treadway Gallery, Cincinnati #739/R
£316 $500 €461 Abstract composition (71x56cm-28x22in) s. 7-Sep-3 Treadway Gallery, Cincinnati #740/R
£323 $600 €472 Abstract composition (76x61cm-30x24in) s. painted 1960. 7-Mar-4 Treadway Gallery, Cincinnati #741/R
£369 $650 €539 Abstract composition (76x61cm-30x24in) s. painted c.1960. 23-May-4 Treadway Gallery, Cincinnati #767/R
£430 $800 €628 Abstract composition (71x56cm-28x22in) s. painted c.1960. 7-Mar-4 Treadway Gallery, Cincinnati #751/R
£443 $700 €647 Abstract composition (71x56cm-28x22in) s. board. 7-Sep-3 Treadway Gallery, Cincinnati #689/R
£443 $700 €647 Abstract composition (71x56cm-28x22in) s. board. 7-Sep-3 Treadway Gallery, Cincinnati #730/R
£570 $900 €832 Abstract composition (56x71cm-22x28in) s. board. 7-Sep-3 Treadway Gallery, Cincinnati #756/R
£591 $1100 €863 Abstract composition (56x71cm-22x28in) s. painted c.1960. 7-Mar-4 Treadway Gallery, Cincinnati #742/R est:800-1200
£753 $1400 €1099 Abstract composition (61x76cm-24x30in) s. painted c.1960. 7-Mar-4 Treadway Gallery, Cincinnati #745/R est:1000-1500

FERRANTI, Carlo (19th C) Italian
£2700 $4995 €3942 Chess problem (45x61cm-18x24in) s. 14-Jul-4 Sotheby's, Olympia #207/R est:3000-5000
Works on paper
£320 $605 €467 Fisherman's wooing (53x35cm-21x14in) s.i. W/C. 19-Feb-4 Lyon & Turnbull, Edinburgh #11/R
£345 $638 €500 Jeunes bergers a la lanterne (36x25cm-14x10in) s. 19-Jan-4 Horta, Bruxelles #418
£429 $700 €626 Luscious fruits, outside of Naples (76x53cm-30x21in) init. i.verso W/C. 24-Sep-3 Doyle, New York #29
£598 $1100 €873 Bashful offer (53x74cm-21x29in) init.i. W/C. 9-Jun-4 Doyle, New York #3032

FERRARA, Daniel (1906-) Algerian
£314 $541 €450 Vue du port (60x65cm-24x26in) s. 3-Dec-3 Tajan, Paris #208
£314 $541 €450 L'amerio vespucci (54x72cm-21x28in) s. 3-Dec-3 Tajan, Paris #209

FERRARESE SCHOOL (15th C) Italian
£14765 $26430 €22000 Madonna and Child (52x40cm-20x16in) tempera board. 26-May-4 Porro, Milan #10/R est:25000-30000

FERRARESE SCHOOL (16th C) Italian
£7042 $12183 €10000 Saint Jerome in the desert (86x109cm-34x43in) board. 9-Dec-3 Pandolfini, Florence #31/R est:11000-15000
£24000 $43920 €35040 Christ crowned with thorns (42x27cm-17x11in) panel. 8-Jul-4 Sotheby's, London #303/R est:8000-12000

FERRARI, Adolfo de (1898-1978) Argentinian
£1639 $3000 €2393 Still life (50x39cm-20x15in) board. 1-Jun-4 Arroyo, Buenos Aires #13

FERRARI, Agostino (1938-) Italian
£533 $971 €800 Composition (94x63cm-37x25in) s. paper on canvas. 12-Jul-4 Il Ponte, Milan #990
£1333 $2453 €2000 Composition (100x80cm-39x31in) s.d.1991 acrylic sand. 12-Jun-4 Meeting Art, Vercelli #456/R est:750
£2000 $3680 €3000 Untitled (160x75cm-63x30in) s. acrylic sand. 12-Jun-4 Meeting Art, Vercelli #782/R est:2000
Works on paper
£282 $468 €400 Untitled (65x50cm-26x20in) s.verso mixed media board. 14-Jun-3 Meeting Art, Vercelli #279

FERRARI, Antoine (1910-1996) French
£638 $1129 €950 Le chene (65x54cm-26x21in) s. panel. 29-Apr-4 Claude Aguttes, Neuilly #91
£1879 $3326 €2800 Les amandiers (65x92cm-26x36in) s. panel. 29-Apr-4 Claude Aguttes, Neuilly #76/R est:500-600

FERRARI, Arturo (1861-1932) Italian
£780 $1303 €1100 Saint Anthony's Church, Milan (31x21cm-12x8in) s. board. 14-Oct-3 Finarte Semenzato, Milan #143/R
£2465 $4264 €3500 The Naviglio in Milan (25x39cm-10x15in) s. cardboard. 11-Dec-3 Christie's, Rome #188/R est:1300-1800
Works on paper
£280 $476 €400 Views of Milan (22x31cm-9x12in) s.i. pencil. 19-Nov-3 Finarte Semenzato, Milan #536/R
£16901 $29239 €24000 Milan disappearing (72x126cm-28x50in) s.d.1911 W/C card. 11-Dec-3 Christie's, Rome #187/R est:10000-15000

FERRARI, Berto (1887-1965) Italian
£417 $679 €600 Lights at sea (27x17cm-11x7in) card. 24-Sep-3 Cambi, Genoa #1025
£474 $849 €692 Marina a Nervi (30x40cm-12x16in) s. board. 12-May-4 Dobiaschofsky, Bern #3574 (S.FR 1100)
£474 $849 €692 Le scogliere del mare (29x39cm-11x15in) s. i. verso board. 12-May-4 Dobiaschofsky, Bern #3575 (S.FR 1100)
£704 $1218 €1000 Coast in Liguria (14x19cm-6x7in) s.d.1923 cardboard. 10-Dec-3 Finarte Semenzato, Rome #276/R
£762 $1219 €1105 Scogliere del mare (32x41cm-13x16in) s.d.1952 board. 15-May-3 Stuker, Bern #1182 (S.FR 1600)
£872 $1632 €1300 Spring in Cortina (30x40cm-12x16in) card. 26-Feb-4 Cambi, Genoa #426/R
£940 $1757 €1400 Moonlight (30x40cm-12x16in) board. 26-Feb-4 Cambi, Genoa #551/R
£1074 $2008 €1600 Landscape in Liguria (35x50cm-14x20in) cardboard on canvas. 26-Feb-4 Cambi, Genoa #427/R est:500-600
£2685 $5020 €4000 Orero church square (35x50cm-14x20in) board. 26-Feb-4 Cambi, Genoa #507/R
Works on paper
£565 $1034 €825 Coastal landscape (30x40cm-12x16in) s.d.1951 mixed media cardboard. 4-Jun-4 Zofingen, Switzerland #2452 (S.FR 1300)

FERRARI, Ettore (1849-1929) Italian
Works on paper
£979 $1635 €1400 Landscape near Lake Nemi (28x45cm-11x18in) init. W/C. 24-Jun-3 Finarte Semenzato, Rome #156

FERRARI, F (19th C) Italian
Sculpture
£24000 $42960 €36000 Allegory of Music (115x97x50cm-45x38x20in) s.d.1895 white marble. 17-May-4 Finarte Semenzato, Rome #190/R est:22000-25000

FERRARI, Gaudenzio (attrib) (1484-1546) Italian
Works on paper
£328 $600 €479 Head of a woman looking up (19x14cm-7x6in) col chk. 29-Jan-4 Swann Galleries, New York #14/R

FERRARI, Giovanni Andrea de (attrib) (1598-1669) Italian
£16312 $27241 €23000 Lot e le figlie (93x115cm-37x45in) 18-Jun-3 Christie's, Rome #450/R est:20000-30000
£20000 $36600 €29200 Banishment of Hagar (110x135cm-43x53in) 7-Jul-4 Bonhams, New Bond Street #6/R est:5000-8000

FERRARI, Giovanni Battista (1829-1906) Italian
£2448 $4088 €3500 Vue d'Isola Bella. s.d.1880 panel. 26-Jun-3 Artcurial Briest, Paris #543 est:1500-2000
Works on paper
£2419 $4500 €3532 Canale de New York (21x32cm-8x13in) s. gouache exhib. 5-Mar-4 Skinner, Boston #323/R est:3000-5000

FERRARI, Giuseppe (1840-1905) Italian
£1765 $3000 €2577 Domestic bliss (71x94cm-28x37in) s. canvas on panel. 19-Nov-3 Bonhams & Butterfields, San Francisco #43/R
Sculpture
£2800 $5124 €4200 Bull scene (38x49x21cm-15x19x8in) s. pat bronze. 3-Jun-4 E & Eve, Paris #55/R est:2800-3000

FERRARI, Gregorio de (1647-1726) Italian
Works on paper
£544 $974 €800 Un ange volant vu de dos (22x31cm-9x12in) i.verso black chk lit. 18-Mar-4 Christie's, Paris #221/R

FERRARI, Joseph (19th C) Italian
£1200 $2100 €1752 Figures conversing on a bridge, Cefalonia (24x31cm-9x12in) s.i.d.1851 board. 16-Dec-3 Bonhams, New Bond Street #83/R est:800-1200

FERRARI, Lorenzo de (1680-1744) Italian
Works on paper
£559 $951 €800 Young men (14x12cm-6x5in) pencil tempera prov. 19-Nov-3 Finarte Semenzato, Milan #494/R
£6500 $11895 €9490 An allegory of innocence holding a lamp and a lily (54x36cm-21x14in) black chk squared black chk. 6-Jul-4 Christie's, London #53/R est:5000-7000

FERRARI, Luca (studio) (1605-1654) Italian
£6711 $12349 €10000 Daughter of jephta (106x131cm-42x52in) prov. 24-Mar-4 Dorotheum, Vienna #42/R est:5000-7000

FERRARI, Maria Rosa de (1908-) South American
£397 $750 €580 Tiovivo (73x95cm-29x37in) s. prov. 22-Feb-4 Galeria y Remates, Montevideo #155

FERRARI, Teodoro Wolf (1876-1945) Italian
£1056 $1754 €1500 Countryside near Mount Grappa (40x50cm-16x20in) s. board. 11-Jun-3 Finarte Semenzato, Milan #517/R

FERRARI, Vincenzo (1941-) Italian
Sculpture
£1611 $2883 €2400 Useless (40x21cm-16x8in) s. glass marble bronze exec.c.1970. 25-May-4 Sotheby's, Milan #150/R est:300-400

FERRARIS, Arthur (1856-1936) Hungarian
£259 $463 €378 Portrait of an oriental wearing a turban (34x28cm-13x11in) s.i.d.1896. 12-May-4 Dobiaschofsky, Bern #487 (S.FR 600)

FERRATER FELIU, Antonio (1868-1942) Spanish
£986 $1706 €1400 Urban landscape with river (38x49cm-15x19in) s.d.1918 lit. 15-Dec-3 Ansorena, Madrid #283/R

FERRAZZI, Ferruccio (1891-1978) Italian
£5245 $8916 €7500 Self-portrait (29x22cm-11x9in) s.i.d.1925 board. 25-Nov-3 Sotheby's, Milan #102/R est:7000-9000
£13333 $24000 €20000 Storm in Aniene Valley (47x33cm-19x13in) s.d.1925 prov.exhib.lit. 22-Apr-4 Finarte Semenzato, Rome #265/R est:18000-20000
£25676 $45189 €38000 Spring night (162x201cm-64x79in) s.d.1936 exhib. 24-May-4 Christie's, Milan #158/R est:20000-30000
Works on paper
£986 $1725 €1400 Landscape (31x38cm-12x15in) s.d.1957 W/C. 16-Dec-3 Finarte Semenzato, Milan #109/R est:1500-1700

FERRAZZI, Luigi (19th C) Italian
£426 $711 €600 Ritratto de signora (50x36cm-20x14in) s.d.1887. 21-Jun-3 Stadion, Trieste #193/R

FERRE, Georges (19th C) French
Works on paper
£1268 $2193 €1800 Paysage d'ete (72x91cm-28x36in) s.d.1890 pastel. 12-Dec-3 Libert, Castor, Paris #24/R est:2000-2500

FERREIRA, Manuel (?) ?
£336 $601 €500 Landscape with bridge (40x50cm-16x20in) s.d.1952 board. 31-May-4 Cabral Moncada Leiloes, Lisbon #243
Works on paper
£249 $450 €364 Pescador Nazare (36x23cm-14x9in) W/C. 2-Apr-4 Douglas, South Deerfield #35
£249 $450 €364 Pescador Nazare (36x23cm-14x9in) W/C. 2-Apr-4 Douglas, South Deerfield #36

FERREN, John (1905-1970) American
£5429 $9500 €7926 Untitled (38x57cm-15x22in) s.d.33 prov. 19-Dec-3 Sotheby's, New York #1022/R est:6000-9000

FERREOL, Maurice (1906-1969) French
£1333 $2427 €2000 Oiseaux et nuages (116x82cm-46x32in) s.d.1964. 29-Jun-4 Chenu & Scrive, Lyon #84/R est:2000-2200

FERRER AMBLAR, Adolfo (1906-1993) Spanish
Works on paper
£306 $548 €450 Seated man (62x46cm-24x18in) s. chl dr exhib.lit. 22-Mar-4 Durán, Madrid #17/R
£374 $670 €550 Male nude (102x39cm-40x15in) s. pencil dr. 22-Mar-4 Durán, Madrid #19/R

FERRER CALATAYUD, Pedro (1860-1944) Spanish
£638 $1186 €950 Seascpe (37x53cm-15x21in) s. 2-Mar-4 Ansorena, Madrid #145/R

FERRER, Anne (20th C) French?
Sculpture
£1042 $1740 €1500 Noces de Vermeil (160x70x40cm-63x28x16in) textiles wire suspenders pen flannel prov.exhib. 21-Oct-3 Artcurial Briest, Paris #565/R est:2000-3000
£1319 $2203 €1900 Ambroisie (150x75x50cm-59x30x20in) textiles wire flannel braiding prov.exhib. 21-Oct-3 Artcurial Briest, Paris #566/R est:2000-3000

FERRER, Joaquin (1929-) Cuban
£322 $596 €480 Bleu clair (73x60cm-29x24in) s. s.d.1975. 13-Mar-4 De Vuyst, Lokeren #139
£470 $869 €700 Tentative de paysage, toujours et jamais (50x50cm-20x20in) s. s.i.d.1990. 13-Mar-4 De Vuyst, Lokeren #138
£604 $1117 €900 Ciel giratoire (88x72cm-35x28in) s. s.i.d.1991. 13-Mar-4 De Vuyst, Lokeren #137
£629 $1083 €900 L'homme sans terre (73x54cm-29x21in) s. s.i.d.1993 verso acrylic cardboard on panel prov.lit. 3-Dec-3 Tajan, Paris #472
£1000 $1800 €1500 Prestidigitateur de la pensee (116x89cm-46x35in) s. 24-Apr-4 Cornette de St.Cyr, Paris #520/R est:1500-2000
£1208 $2235 €1800 Sejour d'une reverie (89x116cm-35x46in) s. s.i.d.1990. 13-Mar-4 De Vuyst, Lokeren #136/R est:2000-3000
£1333 $2387 €2000 Le visiteur absent (116x89cm-46x35in) s. s.i.d.1983 verso. 15-May-4 De Vuyst, Lokeren #133/R est:2000-3000
£2000 $3580 €3000 La capitale du verrtige IV (130x130cm-51x51in) s. s.i.d.1988 verso. 15-May-4 De Vuyst, Lokeren #131/R est:3000-4000
Works on paper
£738 $1374 €1100 Paysage avec symbole de desirs (73x54cm-29x21in) s. mixed media cardboard prov.lit. 3-Mar-4 Artcurial Briest, Paris #369

FERRER, Jose (19/20th C) Spanish
£455 $759 €650 Fishing day (22x71cm-9x28in) s. 30-Jun-3 Ansorena, Madrid #252/R
£455 $759 €650 Beach scene (22x71cm-9x28in) s. 30-Jun-3 Ansorena, Madrid #251/R

FERRERE, Cecile (1847-?) French
£1818 $3091 €2600 La premiere lecon d'escrime (60x50cm-24x20in) s.d.1870 canvas laid down. 1-Dec-3 Palais de Beaux Arts, Brussels #353/R est:2500-3500
£5556 $10000 €8112 Flower seller (147x91cm-58x36in) s. 22-Apr-4 Christie's, Rockefeller NY #149/R est:12000-18000

FERRERO, Alberto (1883-1963) Italian
£1067 $1963 €1600 Snowfall in Sostagno (25x30cm-10x12in) cardboard. 10-Jun-4 Christie's, Rome #209/R est:1700-1900
£1200 $2208 €1800 Flowers pointing to the sky (48x59cm-19x23in) s. board. 10-Jun-4 Christie's, Rome #208/R est:1700-1900
£2133 $3925 €3200 Landscapes. s. triptych. 10-Jun-4 Christie's, Rome #210/R est:3200-3500
£2133 $3925 €3200 Roses ander the arcade (40x37cm-16x15in) s. board. 10-Jun-4 Christie's, Rome #207/R est:1700-1900

FERRERO, Attilio (20th C) Italian
£336 $594 €500 Shadows and lights at the farm (50x70cm-20x28in) s. 1-May-4 Meeting Art, Vercelli #193

FERRERO, Lionel (?) ?
£1267 $2305 €1900 Magnificat I (60x73cm-24x29in) s.d.04 s.i.verso. 5-Jul-4 Millon & Associes, Paris #300/R

FERRETTI, Gian Domenico (1692-1766) Italian
£4545 $8000 €6636 Masquerade ball (74x98cm-29x39in) 18-May-4 Bonhams & Butterfields, San Francisco #8/R est:4000-6000
£4698 $8644 €7000 Venus and Diana with putti (64x52cm-25x20in) 24-Mar-4 Dorotheum, Vienna #332/R est:7000-10000
£7000 $11900 €10220 Dwarves in a rocky landscape (88x72cm-35x28in) panel lit. 29-Oct-3 Christie's, London #82/R est:7000-10000
£22069 $36855 €32000 Still life with pans (15x25cm-6x10in) s.d.1713 verso prov.exhib.lit. 15-Nov-3 Porro, Milan #244/R est:25000

FERRETTINI ROSSOTTI, Emilia (1866-1951) Italian
£347 $590 €500 Waterfalls by Bognanca (44x29cm-17x11in) s.d.1908 board. 1-Nov-3 Meeting Art, Vercelli #263
£417 $708 €600 Landscape (31x44cm-12x17in) s.d.1916 board. 1-Nov-3 Meeting Art, Vercelli #26
£544 $974 €800 Hilly landscape (30x43cm-12x17in) s.d.1917. 22-Mar-4 Sant Agostino, Torino #181/R
£638 $1129 €950 Flowers (41x52cm-16x20in) s.d.1937 board. 1-May-4 Meeting Art, Vercelli #196
£671 $1188 €1000 Countryside in Piedmonte (21x46cm-8x18in) s. cardboard. 1-May-4 Meeting Art, Vercelli #23
£1007 $1782 €1500 Winter landscape (70x90cm-28x35in) s.d.1927 board. 1-May-4 Meeting Art, Vercelli #409 est:1500
£1064 $1777 €1500 Mountainous landscape (80x100cm-31x39in) s.d.1926 board. 20-Oct-3 Sant Agostino, Torino #102/R

FERREZ, Marc (1843-1923) American
Photographs
£2395 $4000 €3497 Charles F Hartt gathering soil samples in Recife (19x25cm-7x10in) albumen print lit. 17-Oct-3 Sotheby's, New York #109/R est:7000-10000

FERRI, Antonio (1938-) Spanish
£1067 $1931 €1600 Apollus celebration (195x195cm-77x77in) s. s.i.d.1991 verso. 30-Mar-4 Segre, Madrid #243/R est:1200

FERRI, Augusto (1829-1895) Italian
£617 $1048 €901 Evening bay at low tide (38x22cm-15x9in) s.d.95. 5-Nov-3 Dobiaschofsky, Bern #537/R (S.FR 1400)
£776 $1389 €1133 Still life with grapes (26x45cm-10x18in) s.d.93 board glass two. 12-May-4 Dobiaschofsky, Bern #488/R est:1400 (S.FR 1800)
£1277 $2132 €1800 Still life with plums and peaches (50x70cm-20x28in) s. 14-Oct-3 Finarte Semenzato, Milan #30/R

FERRI, Cesare (1864-1936) Italian
£1042 $1771 €1500 Rio Santa Maria, Venice (57x43cm-22x17in) s.i.d.1923. 1-Nov-3 Meeting Art, Vercelli #323/R est:1000

FERRI, Ciro (1634-1689) Italian
£9139 $16633 €13800 Judah and Tamar (93x101cm-37x40in) 16-Jun-4 Christie's, Rome #402/R est:15000-20000
£13475 $22504 €19000 Cleopatra (80x67cm-31x26in) 17-Jun-3 Finarte Semenzato, Milan #624/R est:15000-20000
Works on paper
£361 $650 €527 Study for a ceiling design at the Sala di Marte, Pitti Palace, Florence (14x28cm-6x11in) black chk. 21-Jan-4 Doyle, New York #39
£12222 $22000 €17844 Resurrection (31x20cm-12x8in) i. black chk pen brown ink wash prov.lit. 22-Jan-4 Christie's, Rockefeller NY #55/R est:20000-30000
£15000 $25950 €21900 Design for the high altarpiece of St Agnese, Rome (71x51cm-28x20in) i.verso pen brown ink wash W/C over black chk. 9-Dec-3 Bonhams, Knightsbridge #13/R est:3000-5000

FERRI, Ciro (attrib) (1634-1689) Italian
£2209 $3800 €3225 Christ and the woman of Samaria (48x36cm-19x14in) 6-Dec-3 Neal Auction Company, New Orleans #424/R est:5000-7000
Works on paper
£568 $1045 €829 Putto sitting in clouds (26x21cm-10x8in) i. i. verso ochre. 14-Jun-4 Philippe Schuler, Zurich #4416/R (S.FR 1300)

FERRI, Gesualdo Francesco (attrib) (1728-1788) Italian
Works on paper
£377 $600 €550 Allegory of the arts (17x23cm-7x9in) s.i.d.1757 sepia ink wash. 13-Sep-3 Weschler, Washington #701/R

FERRIER, Andre Gabriel (attrib) (19/20th C) French
Works on paper
£345 $572 €500 Portrait of young woman in Italian costume (25x19cm-10x7in) i. brush. 30-Sep-3 Dorotheum, Vienna #193/R

FERRIER, Arthur (20th C) British
£620 $1110 €905 Portrait of Christabel Leighton-Porter, the original model for Jane (90x75cm-35x30in) s. 17-May-4 David Duggleby, Scarborough #704/R

FERRIER, Dick (1929-) Canadian
£447 $800 €653 North of Calgary (101x152cm-40x60in) s. i.verso. 6-May-4 Heffel, Vancouver #54/R (C.D 1100)

FERRIER, Gabriel (attrib) (1847-1914) French
£280 $467 €400 Dans l'atelier (33x22cm-13x9in) 7-Oct-3 Livinec, Gaudcheau & Jezequel, Rennes #81

FERRIER, Henry (19th C) French
£313 $560 €457 Forest scene (76x53cm-30x21in) with sig. 19-Mar-4 Aspire, Cleveland #3

FERRIER, James (fl.1843-1883) British
Works on paper
£420 $785 €613 Loch scene (32x49cm-13x19in) s. W/C. 24-Feb-4 Bonhams, Knowle #35

FERRIERE, Francis (1752-1839) Swiss
Miniatures
£2000 $3600 €2920 Gentleman in a dark coat (8cm-3in) gold frame oval exhib. 22-Apr-4 Bonhams, New Bond Street #109/R est:1000-1500

FERRIERE, Francis (attrib) (1752-1839) Swiss
Miniatures
£1034 $1728 €1500 Gentleman (4cm-2in) oval. 12-Nov-3 Sotheby's, Milan #25/R est:800-1200

FERRIERES, Jacques Martin (1893-1972) French
£1630 $3000 €2380 Vase of roses (51x66cm-20x26in) s. 11-Jun-4 David Rago, Lambertville #292/R est:900-1200

FERRIS, Mary (20th C) Irish?
Sculpture
£1589 $2893 €2400 First past the post (24x35cm-9x14in) s. bronze. 15-Jun-4 James Adam, Dublin #198/R est:2000-3000

FERRIS, R D (19th C) American
£1018 $1700 €1486 Naragansett (36x61cm-14x24in) s. 20-Jun-3 Freeman, Philadelphia #232/R est:1500-2000
£1285 $2300 €1876 Indian Rock, Narragansett (35x61cm-14x24in) s. i.verso. 14-May-4 Skinner, Boston #122/R est:800-1200

FERRO, Cesare (1880-1934) Italian
Works on paper
£2245 $4018 €3300 Portrait (30x25cm-12x10in) s. pastel cardboard exec.1908 lit. 22-Mar-4 Sant Agostino, Torino #502/R est:2500-3500

FERRO, Guido (20th C) ?
£300 $567 €438 Gondolier on a Venetian backwater (58x117cm-23x46in) s.i. 19-Feb-4 Christie's, Kensington #175/R

FERRON, Marcelle (1924-2001) Canadian
£1644 $2845 €2400 Untitled (21x27cm-8x11in) s. painted 1952. 15-Dec-3 Iegor de Saint Hippolyte, Montreal #17 (C.D 3700)
Works on paper
£446 $768 €651 Untitled (62x49cm-24x19in) s.d.88 mixed media. 2-Dec-3 Joyner Waddington, Toronto #425 (C.D 1000)
£1613 $2968 €2355 Abstract composition (64x49cm-25x19in) s. mixed media board. 9-Jun-4 Walker's, Ottawa #165/R est:2000-3000 (C.D 4000)

FERRONI, Elena Tommasi (1962-) Italian
£625 $1100 €913 Still life with pumpkin (48x69cm-19x27in) s.d.1991 prov. 23-May-4 Hindman, Chicago #71/R

FERRONI, Gianfranco (1927-2001) Italian
£450 $725 €653 Bay of Naples (56x89cm-22x35in) s. 15-Aug-3 Keys, Aylsham #668/R
£1300 $2431 €1898 Extensive panorama of Bay of Naples with Vesuvius (58x89cm-23x35in) 24-Feb-4 Rogers Jones, Clwyd #153
£9155 $15197 €13000 Objects (74x61cm-29x24in) s.d.63 i.verso. 11-Jun-3 Finarte Semenzato, Milan #530/R est:18000
Works on paper
£507 $832 €700 Compositions (27x33cm-11x13in) s.d.1966 Chinese ink. 27-May-3 Il Ponte, Milan #413
£1000 $1840 €1500 Prisoner (36x39cm-14x15in) s.d.1966 pencil. 8-Jun-4 Finarte Semenzato, Milan #127/R est:1500-2000
£1133 $2085 €1700 Landscape souvenir (30x42cm-12x17in) s.d.1963 pencil. 8-Jun-4 Finarte Semenzato, Milan #126/R est:1500-2000
£1467 $2699 €2200 Landscape 65 (32x37cm-13x15in) d.1967 pencil card. 8-Jun-4 Finarte Semenzato, Milan #125/R est:1500-2000
£1600 $2944 €2400 Landscape in Quiesa (24x34cm-9x13in) s.i.d.62 mixed media card lit. 8-Jun-4 Finarte Semenzato, Milan #387/R est:2500-3000
£1600 $2944 €2400 Garden in Tradate (19x29cm-7x11in) s.d.1963 mixed media. 8-Jun-4 Finarte Semenzato, Milan #128/R est:1800-2000

FERRONI, Guido (1888-1979) Italian
£669 $1111 €950 Tuscan landscape (35x49cm-14x19in) s. cardboard. 13-Jun-3 Farsetti, Prato #420

FERRUZZA, F (20th C) American?
£490 $885 €715 Maine coastal scene (51x46cm-20x18in) s. 16-Apr-4 James Julia, Fairfield #624n/R est:1000-1500

FERTBAUER, Leopold (1802-1875) Austrian
Works on paper
£759 $1259 €1100 Portrait of young woman wearing white dress (16x12cm-6x5in) s. W/C ivory. 30-Sep-3 Dorotheum, Vienna #398/R

FERY, John (1859-1934) American/Hungarian
£2674 $5000 €3904 Glacier elk (30x46cm-12x18in) s. 24-Jul-4 Coeur d'Alene, Hayden #196/R est:3000-5000
£3956 $7200 €5776 Bellowing elk (152x102cm-60x40in) s. 19-Jun-4 Jackson's, Cedar Falls #5/R est:5500-7500
£4624 $8000 €6751 Lake Mary, Wasatch Mountains, Utah (61x102cm-24x40in) s.i.verso prov. 10-Dec-3 Bonhams & Butterfields, San Francisco #6110/R est:4000-6000
£5080 $9500 €7417 Winter in Minnesota (46x76cm-18x30in) s. 24-Jul-4 Coeur d'Alene, Hayden #221/R est:5000-10000
£8021 $15000 €11711 Jackson Lake, Wyoming (56x91cm-22x36in) s. 24-Jul-4 Coeur d'Alene, Hayden #273/R est:5000-10000
£8235 $14000 €12023 Lake Josephine and Grinnell Glacier, Glacier National Park (102x152cm-40x60in) s.i. prov. 22-Nov-3 Jackson's, Cedar Falls #71/R est:8000-12000

FESENMAIER, Helene (1937-) American
Works on paper
£351 $650 €512 Eloges V (32x28cm-13x11in) s.d.77 mixed media found objects collage board prov. 13-Jul-4 Christie's, Rockefeller NY #25/R

FESER, Albert (1901-1993) German
£355 $592 €500 Front gardens in Droysenstrasse (49x59cm-19x23in) s.d.85 i. verso board. 21-Jun-3 Hans Stahl, Hamburg #80
£355 $592 €500 Harbour with boats (23x33cm-9x13in) s. 16-Oct-3 Dorotheum, Salzburg #664/R
£461 $770 €650 Siethwende (28x38cm-11x15in) s.d.1981 i. verso board. 21-Jun-3 Hans Stahl, Hamburg #82/R
£674 $1125 €950 Street in Klein Flottbek (40x50cm-16x20in) s.d.1971 panel. 21-Jun-3 Hans Stahl, Hamburg #83
£699 $1203 €1000 View of Blankensee (34x44cm-13x17in) s.d.1967 cardboard. 6-Dec-3 Quittenbaum, Hamburg #129/R
£769 $1285 €1100 On the harbour wall (39x49cm-15x19in) s.d.1977 i. verso board. 11-Oct-3 Hans Stahl, Hamburg #101
£903 $1435 €1300 Canal in Hammerbrook (45x50cm-18x20in) s.d.1955 board. 13-Sep-3 Quittenbaum, Hamburg #124/R
£1274 $1962 €2000 Small harbour (30x38cm-12x15in) s.d.1966. 4-Sep-2 Schopman, Hamburg #248/R est:1700

FESSER-BORRHEE, Josephine (1819-1891) French
£3125 $5219 €4500 Moulin au clair de lune (26x42cm-10x17in) s.d.98 prov. 21-Oct-3 Sotheby's, Amsterdam #121/R est:3000-5000
£3333 $6000 €5000 Town by a river (27x42cm-11x17in) s.d.1887. 20-Apr-4 Sotheby's, Amsterdam #73/R est:2500-3500
£6667 $12000 €10000 Washerwoman by a watermill (26x42cm-10x17in) s.d.88. 20-Apr-4 Sotheby's, Amsterdam #82/R est:2500-3500

FESTA, Tano (1938-1988) Italian
£1172 $1958 €1700 Homage to colour (100x100cm-39x39in) s. acrylic painted 1985. 14-Nov-3 Farsetti, Prato #202/R est:1100-1400
£1216 $2141 €1800 Confetti (50x70cm-20x28in) s.d.1980 verso acrylic confetti. 22-May-4 Galleria Pananti, Florence #388/R est:1500-1800
£1389 $2194 €2000 After Michelangelo (100x70cm-39x28in) enamel. 6-Sep-3 Meeting Art, Vercelli #331 est:2000
£1611 $2980 €2400 Fo J Pollock (60x80cm-24x31in) s.i.verso acrylic. 13-Mar-4 Meeting Art, Vercelli #97 est:2000
£1667 $3067 €2500 Scarecrow (100x70cm-39x28in) s.d.1986 verso. 14-Jun-4 Sant Agostino, Torino #394/R est:2000-2500
£1667 $3067 €2500 Italian square (55x80cm-22x31in) s.i.d.1982 on stretcher acrylic. 8-Jun-4 Finarte Semenzato, Milan #302/R est:2500-2700
£1667 $3067 €2500 Landscape (70x60cm-28x24in) s.d.1973. 12-Jun-4 Meeting Art, Vercelli #345/R est:2500
£1701 $3095 €2500 From four rivers (70x100cm-28x39in) s. acrylic confetti painted 1986. 6-Feb-4 Galleria Rosenberg, Milan #124/R est:2500
£1745 $3228 €2600 After Michelangelo (60x50cm-24x20in) s.d.1978 verso acrylic. 13-Mar-4 Meeting Art, Vercelli #356 est:2000
£1769 $3166 €2600 Michelangelo (66x53cm-26x21in) s.d.78 verso enamel. 16-Mar-4 Finarte Semenzato, Milan #358/R est:2800
£1901 $3156 €2700 Mulini, anni 80 (60x100cm-24x39in) s.verso acrylic. 14-Jun-3 Meeting Art, Vercelli #266/R est:2500
£1958 $3329 €2800 Elsinore (80x59cm-31x23in) s.d.1976 verso acrylic. 24-Nov-3 Christie's, Milan #179/R est:2000-3000
£2042 $3390 €2900 Paesaggio (70x60cm-28x24in) s.d.1973 acrylic. 14-Jun-3 Meeting Art, Vercelli #98/R est:2500
£2069 $3310 €3000 Megaliti (80x110cm-31x43in) s.verso acrylic painted c.1980. 13-Mar-3 Galleria Pace, Milan #53/R est:3400-4400
£2177 $3897 €3200 Red diptych (60x51cm-24x20in) s.d.78 verso acrylic. 16-Mar-4 Finarte Semenzato, Milan #351/R est:3500

£2292	$3621	€3300	Balaklava (100x100cm-39x39in) acrylic painted 1986. 6-Sep-3 Meeting Art, Vercelli #690 est:3000
£2483	$3972	€3600	Clouds and window (80x60cm-31x24in) s.verso acrylic painted 1985/86. 13-Mar-3 Galleria Pace, Milan #52/R est:4000-5200
£2535	$4208	€3600	Untitled (70x30cm-28x12in) s.d.1984 verso acrylic four parts. 14-Jun-3 Meeting Art, Vercelli #92/R est:3000
£2535	$4208	€3600	After Michelangelo (60x80cm-24x31in) s.d.78 verso acrylic. 13-Jun-3 Farsetti, Prato #129/R
£2600	$4784	€3900	Untitled (70x50cm-28x20in) s.d.1976 acrylic. 10-Jun-4 Galleria Pace, Milan #129/R est:6000
£2617	$4842	€3900	Cardinal (100x80cm-39x31in) s.verso acrylic. 11-Mar-4 Galleria Pace, Milan #73/R est:4500-6000
£2617	$4685	€3900	Window (100x80cm-39x31in) s.verso enamel acrylic panel. 28-May-4 Farsetti, Prato #329/R est:3600-4000
£2657	$4517	€3800	Window (70x100cm-28x39in) s.verso acrylic. 18-Nov-3 Babuino, Rome #534/R est:2000-3000
£2676	$4683	€3800	Rebus (55x55cm-22x22in) s.i.d.1979 verso acrylic. 16-Dec-3 Finarte Semenzato, Milan #308/R est:3800-4200
£2759	$4607	€4000	Wardrobe and sky (70x100cm-28x39in) s.verso acrylic. 13-Nov-3 Finarte Semenzato, Rome #253/R est:3800-4500
£2759	$4414	€4000	Untitled (125x130cm-49x51in) s.verso acrylic painted 1980. 13-Mar-3 Galleria Pace, Milan #102/R est:4400-6000
£2817	$4676	€4000	Da Michelangelo (80x60cm-31x24in) s.d.1978 verso acrylic. 14-Jun-3 Meeting Art, Vercelli #585/R est:4000
£2819	$5046	€4200	Cardinal (90x70cm-35x28in) s.d.87 verso acrylic. 28-May-4 Farsetti, Prato #239/R est:3800-4200
£2933	$5397	€4400	After Michelangelo (79x60cm-31x24in) s.d.78 verso acrylic. 8-Jun-4 Finarte Semenzato, Milan #339/R est:4200-5000
£3020	$5406	€4500	After Michelangelo (80x60cm-31x24in) s.d.78 acrylic. 28-May-4 Farsetti, Prato #362/R est:4300-4800
£3043	$4991	€4200	Untitled (63x80cm-25x31in) s.d.1962 enamel pencil prov. 27-May-3 Sotheby's, Milan #209d/R est:4000-6000
£3103	$5183	€4500	After Michelangelo (120x100cm-47x39in) s.d.78 verso acrylic. 14-Nov-3 Farsetti, Prato #136/R est:4200-4700
£3103	$4966	€4500	After Michelangelo (80x60cm-31x24in) s.verso acrylic. 13-Mar-3 Galleria Pace, Milan #22/R est:5500-6500
£3103	$5183	€4500	Blind (122x65cm-48x26in) s.d.82 verso enamel panel. 13-Nov-3 Galleria Pace, Milan #71/R est:7000
£3172	$5076	€4600	After Michelangelo (50x70cm-20x28in) s.i.verso acrylic painted 1978. 13-Mar-3 Galleria Pace, Milan #150/R est:5200-7000
£3329	$5659	€4760	Eve (80x60cm-31x24in) s.d.1978 acrylic prov. 18-Nov-3 Babuino, Rome #533/R est:3000-4000
£3356	$6208	€5000	After Michelangelo (100x60cm-39x24in) s.i.verso acrylic painted 1975. 11-Mar-4 Galleria Pace, Milan #74/R est:5700-7000
£3472	$5486	€5000	Duke of Wellington (100x90cm-39x35in) painted 1986. 6-Sep-3 Meeting Art, Vercelli #590 est:5000
£3497	$5944	€5000	After Michelangelo (60x70cm-24x28in) s.d.76 acrylic on 2 canvases. 24-Nov-3 Christie's, Milan #181/R est:5000-7000
£3497	$5944	€5000	Original sin (100x100cm-39x39in) i.verso oil scarf chain. 18-Nov-3 Babuino, Rome #484/R est:3000-4000
£3537	$6332	€5200	After Michelangelo (101x60cm-40x24in) s.d.78 verso acrylic. 16-Mar-4 Finarte Semenzato, Milan #352/R est:5500
£3667	$6600	€5500	Elements for landscape (80x60cm-31x24in) s.verso enamel painted 1972 lit. 22-Apr-4 Finarte Semenzato, Rome #318/R est:5000-6000
£4000	$7360	€6000	After Michelangelo (140x40cm-55x16in) s.d.1978 acrylic. 10-Jun-4 Galleria Pace, Milan #128/R est:9000
£4392	$7730	€6500	Landscape (100x100cm-39x39in) s.d.69 s.i.d.verso acrylic enamel. 24-May-4 Christie's, Milan #188/R est:5000-7000
£4690	$7832	€6800	Blind (120x80cm-47x31in) s.d.1963 enamel panel. 13-Nov-3 Finarte Semenzato, Rome #354/R est:6800-7200
£5072	$8319	€7000	Don Quixote (165x125cm-65x49in) s.verso. 29-May-3 Galleria Pace, Milan #103/R est:12000
£5517	$8828	€8000	Don Quixote (160x130cm-63x51in) s.verso acrylic painted 1986. 13-Mar-3 Galleria Pace, Milan #100/R est:8500-12000
£7902	$13434	€11300	Cardinal (160x180cm-63x71in) s.i.d.1973 verso. 18-Nov-3 Babuino, Rome #485/R est:4000-6000
£10135	$17838	€15000	Michelangelo according to Tano Festa (81x65cm-32x26in) s.i.d.67 verso prov.exhib. 24-May-4 Christie's, Milan #176/R est:15000-20000
Works on paper			
£367	$675	€550	Robert de Niro (50x70cm-20x28in) s.i. pastel varnish. 12-Jun-4 Meeting Art, Vercelli #786/R
£979	$1664	€1400	Obelisk (68x99cm-27x39in) s.d.85 felt-tip pen prov. 25-Nov-3 Sotheby's, Milan #115/R
£2333	$4293	€3500	Outdoor (100x79cm-39x31in) s.i.d.71 verso mixed media on canvas. 8-Jun-4 Finarte Semenzato, Milan #413/R est:2000-2500
£2391	$3922	€3300	Room (70x100cm-28x39in) s.i.d.1962 mixed media. 30-May-3 Farsetti, Prato #75/R
£2448	$4161	€3500	Sky dimensions (70x100cm-28x39in) s.i.d.1965 mixed media prov. 20-Nov-3 Finarte Semenzato, Milan #220/R est:2500-3000
£3020	$5406	€4500	Window (69x90cm-27x35in) s.d.62 gouache pencil. 28-May-4 Farsetti, Prato #205/R est:3200-3700
£3087	$5526	€4600	Newsagent's (70x100cm-28x39in) s.i.d.1962 mixed media card. 28-May-4 Farsetti, Prato #138/R est:3200-3700
£4027	$7208	€6000	Monument 5 (100x70cm-39x28in) s.i.d.1962 pastel W/C oil prov. 25-May-4 Sotheby's, Milan #191/R est:2500-3000

FETI, Domenico (attrib) (1589-1624) Italian

£10738	$20081	€16000	Saint John at the source (40x34cm-16x13in) prov.exhib.lit. 25-Feb-4 Porro, Milan #20/R est:14000

FETT, William (1918-) American

Works on paper			
£235	$400	€343	Mexican landscape (56x74cm-22x29in) s.d.1965 W/C dr. 7-Nov-3 Selkirks, St. Louis #448

FETTERMAN, Alan (20th C) American

£867	$1500	€1266	Little lane, Carversville (46x51cm-18x20in) s. oil on linen. 10-Dec-3 Alderfer's, Hatfield #505/R est:1500-1800
£1006	$1600	€1469	Winter's Sun, Doylestown (38x46cm-15x18in) s. 10-Sep-3 Alderfer's, Hatfield #339/R est:800-1200

FETTING, Rainer (1949-) German

£457	$850	€667	Portrait of a woman (41x30cm-16x12in) s.verso painted c.1980. 7-Mar-4 Treadway Gallery, Cincinnati #723/R
£4577	$7919	€6500	Hommage a Van Gogh (75x107cm-30x42in) s.i.d.83 paper on canvas. 13-Dec-3 Lempertz, Koln #134/R est:4500
£4595	$8500	€6709	View from 23rd Street Loft (162x152cm-64x60in) s.i.d.86 verso prov. 13-Jul-4 Christie's, Rockefeller NY #71/R est:5000-7000
£5000	$9100	€7300	Andre (125x85cm-49x33in) s.i.d.88 verso prov. 4-Feb-4 Sotheby's, Olympia #87/R est:4000-6000
£5135	$9500	€7497	Empire State Man (122x91cm-48x36in) s.i.d.83 verso prov. 13-Jul-4 Christie's, Rockefeller NY #72/R est:4000-6000
£6000	$10920	€8760	Havellandschaft (79x100cm-31x39in) s.i.d.88 verso prov. 6-Feb-4 Sotheby's, London #254/R est:4000-6000
£9000	$16560	€13140	Van Gogh and lamp (255x198cm-100x78in) i.d.1983 verso acrylic prov. 24-Jun-4 Sotheby's, London #290/R est:8000-10000
£9500	$15865	€13870	Zitronen (160x230cm-63x91in) s.i.d.98 prov.exhib. 22-Oct-3 Christie's, London #92/R est:12000-15000
£9500	$17290	€13870	Man and Axe II (220x160cm-87x63in) s.i.d.1980 verso tempera cotton prov. 4-Feb-4 Sotheby's, Olympia #88/R est:6000-8000
£10490	$17832	€15000	North Sea (220x280cm-87x110in) s.i.d.90 verso. 27-Nov-3 Lempertz, Koln #118/R est:15000-20000
£10500	$19110	€15330	Des-masque (201x145cm-79x57in) s.i.d.85 acrylic prov. 6-Feb-4 Sotheby's, London #249/R est:8000-10000
£12000	$22080	€17520	Winterpier (264x213cm-104x84in) s.i.d.86 verso prov. 24-Jun-4 Sotheby's, London #289/R est:8000-10000
£14685	$24965	€21000	Field of rapeseed (250x230cm-98x91in) s.i.d.90 verso. 27-Nov-3 Lempertz, Koln #117/R est:20000-25000
£16667	$30500	€25000	Times Square (152x216cm-60x85in) s.i.d.91 verso jute prov.exhib. 4-Jun-4 Lempertz, Koln #132/R est:15000-20000
£19333	$35380	€29000	Self portrait with yellow hat II (150x140cm-59x55in) s.i.d.82 verso prov.lit. 4-Jun-4 Lempertz, Koln #131/R est:12000
£24476	$42098	€35000	Self at green table (175x120cm-69x47in) s.i.d.1980/83 verso acrylic oil sand prov. 5-Dec-3 Ketterer, Munich #174/R est:14000-18000
Works on paper			
£2797	$4755	€4000	Self polling (61x48cm-24x19in) s.i.d.85 W/C. 27-Nov-3 Lempertz, Koln #116/R est:3000-3500

FETZ, Leopold (1915-) Austrian

£979	$1684	€1400	Flowers (50x70cm-20x28in) s.i.d.85. 5-Dec-3 Michael Zeller, Lindau #869/R

FEUCHERE, Jean-Jacques (1807-1852) French

Sculpture			
£1125	$1800	€1643	Gutenberg and his printing press (43cm-17in) s. st.f.Delabroue bronze. 20-Sep-3 Jeffery Burchard, Florida #94/R
£4200	$7644	€6132	Satan (21cm-8in) dark brown pat bronze variegated green marble plinth prov.lit. 17-Jun-4 Christie's, London #60/R est:2000-3000
£5862	$9731	€8500	Amazone (44x43cm-17x17in) s.d.1843 pat bronze lit. 2-Oct-3 Sotheby's, Paris #15/R est:7500

FEUERBACH, Anselm (1829-1880) German

£2721	$4871	€4000	Mother with child (117x69cm-46x27in) lit. 17-Mar-4 Neumeister, Munich #453/R est:4000
£2759	$4607	€4000	Les naufrages (95x124cm-37x49in) exhib. 17-Nov-3 Tajan, Paris #64 est:4000-5000
£2778	$4528	€4000	Study of bearded man (45x35cm-18x14in) lit. 24-Sep-3 Neumeister, Munich #421/R est:2500
£5333	$9707	€8000	The death of Pietro Aretino (100x81cm-39x32in) painted 1853 prov. 3-Jul-4 Geble, Radolfzell #399/R est:8000
£6667	$12133	€10000	Young girls bathing (37x47cm-15x19in) mono. cardboard painted c.1856 lit. 3-Jul-4 Geble, Radolfzell #400/R est:8000
Works on paper			
£411	$699	€600	Prometheus fighting eagle (19x20cm-7x8in) mono. pen. 4-Nov-3 Hartung & Hartung, Munich #3037/R
£944	$1577	€1350	Park steps in Ginori Gardens, Verona (39x29cm-15x11in) i.d.Oct 22.64 wash chk. 10-Oct-3 Winterberg, Heidelberg #579/R

FEUERRING, Maximilian (1896-1985) Polish

£607	$978	€886	The Party (46x64cm-18x25in) s. card. 25-Aug-3 Sotheby's, Paddington #341/R (A.D 1500)

FEURE, Georges de (1868-1943) French

£5944	$10105	€8500	Bord de mer corse (65x81cm-26x32in) s. 27-Nov-3 Millon & Associes, Paris #153/R est:8000-10000
Prints			
£4000	$7360	€6000	Lithographes originales (59x43cm-23x17in) col lithograph exec. 1896. 11-Jun-4 Villa Grisebach, Berlin #1503/R est:2500-3500
Works on paper			
£2000	$3400	€2920	Orchidees (44x37cm-17x15in) gouache. 18-Nov-3 Sotheby's, London #397/R
£2700	$4590	€3942	Femmes amoureuses (35x25cm-14x10in) s. gouache. 18-Nov-3 Sotheby's, London #398/R
£3800	$6460	€5548	Nonnes et le diable (35x25cm-14x10in) s. gouache over pencil. 18-Nov-3 Sotheby's, London #395/R

FEU'U, Fatu (20th C) New Zealander

£355	$628	€518	Te Uaka Moana (121x79cm-48x31in) s.d.99 board. 28-Apr-4 Dunbar Sloane, Auckland #78 (NZ.D 1000)
£2762	$5027	€4033	To aspire (200x250cm-79x98in) painted c.1992. 29-Jun-4 Peter Webb, Auckland #19/R est:8000-12000 (NZ.D 7900)

FEUZ, Werner (1882-1956) Swiss

£435	$796	€635	Mountain village bathed in sunlight (64x75cm-25x30in) s. 4-Jun-4 Zofingen, Switzerland #2796/R (S.FR 1000)
Works on paper			
£226	$391	€330	Paysage alpin (43x34cm-17x13in) s.d.05 W/C. 12-Dec-3 Galerie du Rhone, Sion #489 (S.FR 500)

FEVEN, Eugen (19th C) ?
£412 $672 €602 Two southern women (24x16cm-9x6in) s. panel. 27-Sep-3 Rasmussen, Havnen #2225 (D.KR 4400)

FEVRET DE ST MEMIN, Charles (attrib) (1770-1852) American
Works on paper
£2235 $4000 €3263 Sailing Master Moses Rogers Smith, United States Navy (30x25cm-12x10in) i.d.1814 W/C prov. 18-Mar-4 Richard Opfer, Timonium #257/R est:4500-7500

FEYDEAU, Georges (1862-1921) French
Works on paper
£600 $1104 €900 La mer et la cote de Biarritz, avec des rochers et le phare (14x18cm-6x7in) s.i. black crayon. 9-Jun-4 Piasa, Paris #65

FEYEN, Eugène (1826-1895) French
£528 $877 €750 Roulottes de plage (30x23cm-12x9in) panel. 15-Jun-3 Teitgen, Nancy #48
£1944 $3306 €2800 Breton woman at spinning wheel (54x31cm-21x12in) s. panel. 28-Oct-3 Dorotheum, Vienna #50/R est:2800-3200
£2308 $3854 €3300 Femmes dans un bateau (17x23cm-7x9in) mono. panel. 12-Oct-3 Teitgen, Nancy #52
£2937 $4905 €4200 Ramasseuses de coquillages (24x30cm-9x12in) panel. 12-Oct-3 Teitgen, Nancy #53
£3026 $5478 €4600 Bretonne a la fenetre (11x8cm-4x3in) s. panel. 17-Apr-4 Livinec, Gaudcheau & Jezequel, Rennes #65
£3099 $5144 €4400 Pecheuse aux paniers (32x23cm-13x9in) panel. 15-Jun-3 Teitgen, Nancy #46
£3618 $6549 €5500 Paysannes cancalaises (16x22cm-6x9in) s. panel. 17-Apr-4 Livinec, Gaudcheau & Jezequel, Rennes #67/R
£3800 $6080 €5510 Morning banter at the market (19x23cm-7x9in) s. board. 18-Sep-3 Christie's, Kensington #14/R est:1200-1800
£4225 $7014 €6000 Interieur d'auberge (34x50cm-13x20in) 15-Jun-3 Teitgen, Nancy #49
£4934 $8931 €7500 Lavandieres au bord de riviere (16x22cm-6x9in) s. panel. 17-Apr-4 Livinec, Gaudcheau & Jezequel, Rennes #66
£4934 $8931 €7500 Lavandiere au bord de la riviere. panel. 17-Apr-4 Bretagne Encheres, St Malo #1 est:4500-5000
Works on paper
£270 $488 €410 Ramasseuse de coquillages a genoux (17x26cm-7x10in) s. crayon. 17-Apr-4 Livinec, Gaudcheau & Jezequel, Rennes #48
£270 $488 €410 Ramasseuse de coquillage un panier (15x16cm-6x6in) s. crayon. 17-Apr-4 Livinec, Gaudcheau & Jezequel, Rennes #52
£270 $488 €410 Jeune ramasseuse de coquillages (29x19cm-11x7in) s. crayon. 17-Apr-4 Livinec, Gaudcheau & Jezequel, Rennes #56
£283 $512 €430 Ramasseuse de coquillages (26x19cm-10x7in) s. crayon. 17-Apr-4 Livinec, Gaudcheau & Jezequel, Rennes #58
£294 $505 €420 Pecheuse en pied (30x19cm-12x7in) s. crayon. 7-Dec-3 Livinec, Gaudcheau & Jezequel, Rennes #53
£296 $536 €450 Femme assise assoupie (23x23cm-9x9in) s. crayon. 17-Apr-4 Livinec, Gaudcheau & Jezequel, Rennes #60
£309 $560 €470 Ramasseuse de coquillages baissee (26x19cm-10x7in) s. crayon. 17-Apr-4 Livinec, Gaudcheau & Jezequel, Rennes #38
£316 $572 €480 Femme assise (48x31cm-19x12in) s. crayon. 17-Apr-4 Livinec, Gaudcheau & Jezequel, Rennes #62
£350 $601 €500 Cuisson des crevettes (22x30cm-9x12in) s. wax crayon. 7-Dec-3 Livinec, Gaudcheau & Jezequel, Rennes #44/R
£447 $810 €680 Cancalaise ramassant coquillages (19x26cm-7x10in) s. crayon. 17-Apr-4 Livinec, Gaudcheau & Jezequel, Rennes #47
£605 $1096 €920 Ramasseuse de coquillages (46x30cm-18x12in) s. crayon. 17-Apr-4 Livinec, Gaudcheau & Jezequel, Rennes #63
£625 $1131 €950 Jeune fille regardant le ciel. graphite. 17-Apr-4 Bretagne Encheres, St Malo #59
£625 $1131 €950 Jeune fille assise (18x26cm-7x10in) s. crayon. 17-Apr-4 Livinec, Gaudcheau & Jezequel, Rennes #59
£650 $1170 €949 Study of young boy, nude, seated with his back to the artist (60x45cm-24x18in) s. chl dr. 21-Apr-4 Tennants, Leyburn #976
£769 $1323 €1100 Lavage des huitres (29x20cm-11x8in) s. ink. 7-Dec-3 Livinec, Gaudcheau & Jezequel, Rennes #43
£1053 $1905 €1600 Depart des ramasseuses de crevettes. graphite. 17-Apr-4 Bretagne Encheres, St Malo #64 est:800-1000
£1053 $1905 €1600 Depart des ramasseuses (19x32cm-7x13in) s. crayon. 17-Apr-4 Livinec, Gaudcheau & Jezequel, Rennes #64

FEYEN, Eugène (attrib) (1826-1895) French
£1034 $1893 €1500 Bretonne aux champs (31x47cm-12x19in) s. panel. 1-Feb-4 Teitgen, Nancy #10

FEYEN, Leon Arie (?) German?
£268 $494 €400 Dutch landscape in summer (18x24cm-7x9in) s. lit. panel. 25-Mar-4 Karlheinz Kaupp, Staufen #2431/R

FEYEN-PERRIN, François Nicolas Augustin (1826-1888) French
£922 $1567 €1346 Coastal landscape with two women seated on tree trunk (41x33cm-16x13in) s. 10-Nov-3 Rasmussen, Vejle #203/R (D.KR 10000)
£1268 $2193 €1800 Nu allonge au bord de la riviere (15x22cm-6x9in) s. panel. 14-Dec-3 Eric Pillon, Calais #25/R

FEYERABEND, Johann Rudolf (1779-1814) Swiss
Works on paper
£8389 $14849 €12500 Natures mortes (15x21cm-6x8in) gouache three. 28-Apr-4 Beaussant & Lefèvre, Paris #21/R est:3000-4000

FFOLKES, Michael (1925-1988) British
Works on paper
£280 $468 €409 Spring books (46x38cm-18x15in) s. red htd. 14-Oct-3 Bonhams, New Bond Street #251

FIALA, Kurt (1929-) Austrian
£367 $660 €550 Soul of Miljeva Fuchs (40x30cm-16x12in) s.d.63 panel. 21-Apr-4 Dorotheum, Vienna #172/R
£503 $931 €750 Cloud palace (55x100cm-22x39in) masonite. 9-Mar-4 Dorotheum, Vienna #141/R

FIALA, Vaclav (1896-1980) Czechoslovakian
£328 $545 €479 View from Fuji (39x50cm-15x20in) s. 4-Oct-3 Dorotheum, Prague #136/R est:15000-23000 (C.KR 15000)

FIAMMINGO, Giusto (17th C) Italian
£95070 $152113 €135000 Joseph imprisoned (171x146cm-67x57in) lit. 21-Sep-3 Finarte, Venice #30/R est:90000-120000

FIAMMINGO, Paolo (1540-1596) Flemish
£28082 $47740 €41000 Wooded river landscape with couple, chickens, and huntsmen (86x116cm-34x46in) 4-Nov-3 Sotheby's, Amsterdam #135/R est:20000-30000
Works on paper
£3973 $6753 €5800 Forge of Vulcan (15x21cm-6x8in) pen brown ink over black chk. 4-Nov-3 Sotheby's, Amsterdam #7/R est:6000-8000

FIAMMINGO, Paolo (attrib) (1540-1596) Flemish
£5400 $9342 €7884 Penitent Magdalene (100x92cm-39x36in) panel. 9-Dec-3 Sotheby's, Olympia #372/R est:4000-6000

FIASCHI, E (19th C) Italian
Sculpture
£2600 $4914 €3796 Sogno de amore (57x61x30cm-22x24x12in) s. alabaster. 17-Feb-4 Sotheby's, Olympia #41/R est:2500-3500

FIASCHI, P C E (19/20th C) Italian
Sculpture
£1667 $2717 €2400 Arabian woman (42cm-17in) s.i. brown pat.bronze alabaster. 25-Sep-3 Dr Fritz Nagel, Stuttgart #1582/R est:1600
£1765 $3000 €2577 Figures on camel (48x38x20cm-19x15x8in) s. bronze alabaster marble base. 9-Nov-3 Bonhams & Butterfields, Los Angeles #5152/R est:3000-4000
£2600 $4134 €3796 Sherazade (56cm-22in) i. painted alabaster pair. 9-Sep-3 Sotheby's, Olympia #374/R est:3000-5000
£2815 $4786 €4110 Standing, partially clothed woman with a Sphinx at her feet (29cm-11in) white marble sold with mottled white marble base. 21-Nov-3 Walker's, Ottawa #373/R est:5000-7000 (C.D 6250)

FIASELLA, Domenico (1589-1669) Italian
£4027 $7530 €6000 Nativity (150x120cm-59x47in) 26-Feb-4 Cambi, Genoa #114/R est:4000-5000
£25166 $45801 €38000 Sansone and Dalila (121x211cm-48x83in) 16-Jun-4 Christie's, Rome #482/R est:25000-30000

FICARA, Franz (1926-1994) Italian
£333 $613 €500 Men from the South (70x50cm-28x20in) s. s.d.1980 verso. 12-Jun-4 Meeting Art, Vercelli #576/R

FICH, Erik Carl Frederik (1816-1870) Danish
£1200 $2148 €1800 Storm over Idstedt (47x70cm-19x28in) s. lit. 14-May-4 Schloss Ahlden, Ahlden #2811/R est:1800

FICHEL, Benjamin Eugène (1826-1895) French
£2000 $3600 €3000 Choosing the right colour (25x19cm-10x7in) s.d.1854 panel. 21-Apr-4 Christie's, Amsterdam #55/R est:3000-5000
£2953 $5493 €4400 L'animateur d'antiques (21x16cm-8x6in) s.d.1860 panel. 8-Mar-4 Bernaerts, Antwerp #98/R est:1000-1500
£3600 $5976 €5256 Chess players (22x16cm-9x6in) s.d.1883 panel. 1-Oct-3 Sotheby's, Olympia #249/R est:2000-3000
£4819 $8000 €7036 In the Artist's studio (38x53cm-15x21in) s.d.1886. 4-Oct-3 Neal Auction Company, New Orleans #225/R est:7000-10000
£18824 $32000 €27483 Music concert (45x55cm-18x22in) s.d.1891 panel. 29-Oct-3 Christie's, Rockefeller NY #155/R est:12000-18000

FICHEL, Eugène (19th C) French
£1361 $2163 €2000 Interieur de collectionneur (32x24cm-13x9in) s. panel. 23-Mar-3 Mercier & Cie, Lille #266/R est:2000-2500

FICHET, Pierre (1927-) French
£500 $900 €750 Composition (100x81cm-39x32in) s. s.d.1989 verso prov. 25-Apr-4 Versailles Encheres #34
£600 $1080 €900 Composition (97x130cm-38x51in) s.d.1962 s.d.verso prov. 25-Apr-4 Versailles Encheres #61

FICKLIN, Herb (1911-1980) American
£359 $600 €524 Coastal sunset (51x76cm-20x30in) 18-Oct-3 David Dike, Dallas #302/R
£479 $800 €699 Grandad's wagon (51x76cm-20x30in) 18-Oct-3 David Dike, Dallas #307/R

FICO, Ettore (1917-) Italian
£552 $916 €800 Pomgranates (40x54cm-16x21in) s. cardboard painted 1965. 1-Oct-3 Della Rocca, Turin #50/R

£800 $1472 €1200 Garden (45x60cm-18x24in) s.board. 14-Jun-4 Sant Agostino, Torino #112/R

FIDAKIS, Panos (1956-2003) Greek
£2000 $3580 €2920 View of Piraeus (42x55cm-17x22in) s. 10-May-4 Sotheby's, Olympia #121/R est:2000-3000
£2800 $5012 €4088 View of Varkiza (45x56cm-18x22in) s. painted 1995. 11-May-4 Bonhams, New Bond Street #127/R est:2500-3500

FIDANZA, Francesco (1747-1819) Italian
£8725 $16054 €13000 Southern port with Grotto of Posilip near Naples (35x53cm-14x21in) 24-Mar-4 Dorotheum, Vienna #92/R est:10000-15000

FIDANZA, Francesco (attrib) (1747-1819) Italian
£1310 $2384 €1913 Evening coastal landscape (30x39cm-12x15in) panel. 16-Jun-4 Fischer, Luzern #1084/R est:3000-3500 (S.FR 3000)

FIDLER, Harry (1856-1935) British
£744 $1346 €1086 Untitled - summer pasture (28x58cm-11x23in) indis sig. prov. 18-Apr-4 Levis, Calgary #207/R est:1500-2000 (C.D 1800)
£950 $1739 €1387 Feeding the hens (23x30cm-9x12in) mono. 8-Jul-4 Duke & Son, Dorchester #265/R
£1000 $1790 €1460 Harvest time (55x67cm-22x26in) s. 28-May-4 Lyon & Turnbull, Edinburgh #5/R est:800-1200
£1250 $2088 €1825 Haymaking (25x29cm-10x11in) s. 11-Nov-3 Bonhams, Knightsbridge #86f/R est:700-1000
£1500 $2595 €2190 Impressionist scene with figures in garden (23x30cm-9x12in) 9-Dec-3 Louis Taylor, Stoke on Trent #1196
£1600 $2944 €2336 Summer evening (76x88cm-30x35in) s. i.verso. 8-Jun-4 Bonhams, Knightsbridge #278/R est:1800-2500
£2446 $4500 €3571 Lady in farm scape with cow. 11-Jun-4 Du Mouchelle, Detroit #2187/R est:5000-8000
£4000 $7040 €5840 Ploughing. Drawing the cart (20x26cm-8x10in) s.verso two. 19-May-4 Dreweatt Neate, Newbury #122/R est:1500-2000

FIDUS (1868-1948) German
Works on paper
£2013 $3604 €3000 Fulfilment (40x47cm-16x19in) s.d.1912 i. verso pencil chl W/C prov. 25-May-4 Dorotheum, Vienna #330/R est:3000-4000

FIECHTER, Arnold (1879-1943) German
£326 $597 €476 Fishermen on the lakeside (55x75cm-22x30in) 4-Jun-4 Zofingen, Switzerland #2798 (S.FR 750)

FIEDLER, Arnold (1900-) ?
£468 $767 €650 Soir d'ete (25x33cm-10x13in) s.i.d. col tempera Indian ink. 4-Jun-3 Ketterer, Hamburg #349/R
£504 $826 €700 Abstract composition (25x33cm-10x13in) s.d. mixed media col oil chk tempera. 4-Jun-3 Ketterer, Hamburg #350/R
£567 $1014 €850 Abstraction (72x65cm-28x26in) s. s.i. verso. 13-May-4 Neumeister, Munich #588/R
Works on paper
£486 $812 €700 Nocturno (24x31cm-9x12in) s.i.d. pastel chk tempera. 24-Oct-3 Ketterer, Hamburg #743/R

FIEDLER, Bernhard (1816-1904) German
£1056 $1827 €1500 Rowers in Triest Bay (30x51cm-12x20in) s.d.1850. 10-Dec-3 Dorotheum, Vienna #180/R est:1500-1800
£1477 $2717 €2200 Southern park landscape in moonlight (58x49cm-23x19in) s. panel. 24-Mar-4 Hugo Ruef, Munich #961/R est:2200
£2013 $3765 €3000 Valley crossing near Triest (43x63cm-17x25in) s.i.d.1852. 24-Feb-4 Dorotheum, Vienna #4/R est:2600-3000

FIEDLER, Franz (1885-1956) German
Photographs
£3667 $6747 €5500 Otto Dix (22x17cm-9x7in) s. i. verso lit.exhib. 10-Jun-4 Villa Grisebach, Berlin #1082/R est:1500-2000

FIEDLER, Herbert (1891-1962) Dutch
£278 $439 €400 Portrait of a woman against a purple background (27x24cm-11x9in) s.d.59 canvasboard. 2-Sep-3 Christie's, Amsterdam #448
£658 $1211 €1000 The flight to Egypt (35x26cm-14x10in) s.d.33 canvasboard. 22-Jun-4 Christie's, Amsterdam #543/R
£1156 $2105 €1700 Landschap met verdorde boom in Laren (40x60cm-16x24in) s.d.36 board prov. 3-Feb-4 Christie's, Amsterdam #486/R est:1000-1500
£1208 $2235 €1800 Clown (44x26cm-17x10in) s. board prov. 15-Mar-4 Sotheby's, Amsterdam #188/R est:1000-1500
£1224 $2229 €1800 De Kraamkamer - nursery (53x31cm-21x12in) painted c.1933 prov.exhib. 3-Feb-4 Christie's, Amsterdam #490 est:1200-1600
£1316 $2421 €2000 Two circus clowns (72x61cm-28x24in) s. cardboard. 22-Jun-4 Christie's, Amsterdam #547/R est:2500-3500
£1497 $2724 €2200 Christ and Barnabas (76x90cm-30x35in) s. board prov.exhib. 3-Feb-4 Christie's, Amsterdam #485/R est:2500-3500
£1944 $3072 €2800 Giving the eye (53x41cm-21x16in) s.d.18 exhib. 2-Sep-3 Christie's, Amsterdam #450 est:3000-5000
£1958 $3329 €2800 Still life with apples, vegetables and a bottle of wine (66x80cm-26x31in) s. cardboard. 25-Nov-3 Christie's, Amsterdam #22/R est:2500-3000
£2000 $3680 €3000 Clown musicians (81x65cm-32x26in) 9-Jun-4 Christie's, Amsterdam #75/R est:4000-6000
£2333 $4293 €3500 Clowns with musical instruments (124x62cm-49x24in) st.sig. board exhib. 9-Jun-4 Christie's, Amsterdam #76/R est:5000-7000
£2448 $4161 €3500 Clown with saxophone (88x68cm-35x27in) s.d.58 board exhib.lit. 25-Nov-3 Christie's, Amsterdam #23/R est:4500-5500
£3333 $5267 €4800 Laren in winter (64x81cm-25x32in) s.i.d.36. 2-Sep-3 Christie's, Amsterdam #446 est:3000-5000
£4196 $7133 €6000 Circusparade I (107x74cm-42x29in) s. burlap painted c.1940 exhib.lit. 25-Nov-3 Christie's, Amsterdam #20/R est:7000-9000
£7246 $11884 €10000 Cafe concert in Paris (115x63cm-45x25in) s.d.1913 verso exhib. 27-May-3 Sotheby's, Amsterdam #301/R est:3000-4000
Works on paper
£263 $484 €400 Kneeling female nude (36x24cm-14x9in) s.d.24 W/C pastel. 22-Jun-4 Christie's, Amsterdam #545/R
£1049 $1804 €1500 In front of the mirror (40x32cm-16x13in) s. gouache. 2-Dec-3 Sotheby's, Amsterdam #250/R est:1500-1800
£1111 $1756 €1600 Clown with a rooster (69x60cm-27x24in) s. gouache eexcuted c.1948 exhib. 2-Sep-3 Christie's, Amsterdam #445/R est:1800-2500

FIELD, E Loyal (1856-1914) American
£359 $600 €524 Sunset. s. 16-Nov-3 CRN Auctions, Cambridge #23
£1076 $1700 €1571 Tonalist landscape (30x38cm-12x15in) s. 7-Sep-3 Treadway Gallery, Cincinnati #665/R est:800-1200
£1266 $2000 €1848 Landscape with house in the distance (51x76cm-20x30in) s. 7-Sep-3 Treadway Gallery, Cincinnati #617/R est:2000-3000

FIELD, Erastus Salisbury (attrib) (1805-1900) American
£2910 $5500 €4249 Portrait of Sarah Bartholomew Atwater (76x61cm-30x24in) 17-Feb-4 John Moran, Pasadena #27/R est:5000-7000

FIELD, Erastus Salisbury (school) (1805-1900) American
£4641 $7750 €6776 Overview of Arcadia (86x109cm-34x43in) 16-Nov-3 CRN Auctions, Cambridge #63/R

FIELD, Robert (1948-) Canadian
Works on paper
£200 $366 €292 Jumping salmon (31x48cm-12x19in) s.d.2001 pastel. 1-Jun-4 Hodgins, Calgary #295/R (C.D 500)

FIELD, Tom (20th C) New Zealander
£417 $663 €609 Bumbolt 1 (120x80cm-47x31in) s. board. 9-Sep-3 Watson's, Christchurch #39 (NZ.D 1150)
£543 $880 €787 Bridge over Thomson's Creek (22x29cm-9x11in) s.d.1994 board. 31-Jul-3 International Art Centre, Auckland #99/R est:1400-1800 (NZ.D 1500)

FIELD, Walter (1837-1901) British
£6000 $10800 €8760 Men were deceivers ever (61x48cm-24x19in) s.d.1859. 21-Jan-4 Sotheby's, Olympia #283/R est:4000-6000
Works on paper
£480 $816 €701 Scene in the Thames Valley (23x50cm-9x20in) s.d.1885 W/C. 25-Nov-3 Bonhams, Knightsbridge #158/R

FIELDING, Anthony Vandyke Copley (1787-1855) British
£1678 $2853 €2400 Landscape in Sussex with cows and cowherd (20x28cm-8x11in) s.d.1850 panel. 20-Nov-3 Van Ham, Cologne #1567/R est:1800
£2000 $3580 €2920 Sunset, Sussex (20x28cm-8x11in) s. panel. 27-May-4 Christie's, Kensington #169/R est:2000-3000
Works on paper
£250 $418 €365 Saddleback and river Greta, view near Keswick (12x20cm-5x8in) init.d.1828 i.verso W/C over pencil scratching out. 14-Oct-3 Bearnes, Exeter #319/R
£300 $510 €438 Sea piece, a sailing boat and row boat at sea (7x12cm-3x5in) W/C. 31-Oct-3 Moore Allen & Innocent, Cirencester #491/R
£300 $549 €438 Cattle grazing in an open landscape, a harbour beyond (21x31cm-8x12in) s. brown wash pencil. 7-Apr-4 Woolley & Wallis, Salisbury #45/R
£333 $577 €486 Gap in the downs (39x53cm-15x21in) s.d.1847 W/C. 9-Dec-3 Pinneys, Montreal #66 (C.D 750)
£380 $684 €570 Country town with figures (33x28cm-13x11in) s.d.1825 W/C. 21-Jan-4 John Bellman, Billingshurst #1874/R
£500 $935 €750 Chepstow Castle (15x20cm-6x8in) s.d.1880 W/C. 21-Jul-4 John Nicholson, Haslemere #74
£600 $996 €876 Figures with a rowing boat in an extensive river landscape (41x61cm-16x24in) s. W/C. 3-Oct-3 Mallams, Oxford #109/R
£600 $1074 €876 Life boats approaching a ship wreck off the coast (12x18cm-5x7in) s. W/C. 17-Mar-4 Bonhams, Chester #383
£600 $1074 €876 Vale of Clwyd. Ruined abbey (18x26cm-7x10in) i.d.1833 verso W/C pair. 17-May-4 David Duggleby, Scarborough #674/R
£600 $1110 €876 Farmers and cattle in a landscape with cottage and windmill beyond (19x28cm-7x11in) W/C. 14-Jul-4 Sotheby's, Olympia #43/R
£720 $1296 €1051 Cattle grazing on the South Downs (15x22cm-6x9in) s.d.1841 W/C over pencil bodycol. 21-Jan-4 Sotheby's, Olympia #137/R
£750 $1343 €1095 Off Filey (20x30cm-8x12in) s.d.1847 pencil W/C scratching out. 26-May-4 Christie's, Kensington #467/R
£800 $1360 €1168 Off to the fishing grounds (18x27cm-7x11in) s. pencil W/C. 19-Nov-3 Christie's, Kensington #319/R
£800 $1328 €1168 Drover and cattle in a landscape with church in the distance (38x58cm-15x23in) mono. W/C. 3-Oct-3 Mallams, Oxford #108/R
£900 $1548 €1314 Sussex coast (16x25cm-6x10in) s. pencil W/C prov.exhib. 3-Dec-3 Christie's, Kensington #156/R
£950 $1615 €1387 Coniston beck (29x40cm-11x16in) W/C. 4-Nov-3 Bonhams, New Bond Street #69/R
£980 $1813 €1431 Scene on the downs near Goodwood, Sussex (15x22cm-6x9in) s. W/C. 10-Mar-4 Sotheby's, Olympia #17/R est:800-1200
£1000 $1870 €1460 View of Terin towards Pecugia, expansive landscape (2x33cm-1x13in) s. W/C prov. 26-Feb-4 Lane, Penzance #241 est:1000-1200
£1100 $1793 €1606 Stormy seascape with distant boats (36x43cm-14x17in) s. W/C. 27-Sep-3 Rogers Jones, Clwyd #112
£1304 $2100 €1904 Marine scene with island castles (18x36cm-7x14in) s. W/C. 20-Aug-3 James Julia, Fairfield #1032/R est:2000-3000
£1400 $2590 €2044 Classical landscape (20x29cm-8x11in) s.d.Nov 1809 W/C. 10-Mar-4 Sotheby's, Olympia #136/R est:600-800
£1700 $2890 €2482 Loch Lomond with Ben Lomond in the distance (15x22cm-6x9in) s.i.verso W/C prov. 4-Nov-3 Rowley Fine Art, Newmarket #362/R est:800-1200
£2180 $3750 €3183 Snowdon (18x25cm-7x10in) s. W/C scratching out prov. 7-Dec-3 Freeman, Philadelphia #38 est:1500-2500
£2400 $4392 €3504 Unloading the catch, Whitby (20x29cm-8x11in) s. pencil W/C gum arabic scratching out prov. 3-Jun-4 Christie's, London #141/R est:1500-2000

£2600 $4420 €3796 View of Bolton Abbey from the river, Wharfedale (51x89cm-20x35in) s.d.1849 W/C exhib. 4-Nov-3 Bonhams, New Bond Street #65/R est:3000-5000
£3200 $5728 €4672 Off Ramsgate at sunset (16x25cm-6x10in) s.d.1851 pencil W/C scratching out gum Arabic. 26-May-4 Christie's, Kensington #404/R est:1500-2000
£5782 $10350 €8500 Off the South coast (37x56cm-15x22in) s.d.1853 W/C gouache prov. 17-Mar-4 Maigret, Paris #7/R est:2000-3000
£6122 $10959 €9000 Glen Locks from loch Tay (49x64cm-19x25in) s. W/C htd gouache. 17-Mar-4 Maigret, Paris #9/R est:3000-4000
£9864 $17656 €14500 Scarborough Castle (39x60cm-15x24in) s.d.1854 W/C gouache prov. 17-Mar-4 Maigret, Paris #8/R est:3000-4000
£9864 $17656 €14500 Bolton Abbey, looking down Wharfdale (62x98cm-24x39in) s.d.1841 W/C. 17-Mar-4 Maigret, Paris #10/R est:4000-5000

FIELDING, Anthony Vandyke Copley (attrib) (1787-1855) British
Works on paper
£290 $531 €423 Shoreham Harbour (15x25cm-6x10in) W/C exhib. 28-Jul-4 Mallams, Oxford #89/R
£360 $659 €526 South Foreland (18x26cm-7x10in) with sig.d.1845 W/C scratching out. 8-Jul-4 Lawrence, Crewkerne #1505
£520 $900 €759 Highland castle across a loch with figures in the foreground (18x26cm-7x10in) d.1836 W/C. 10-Dec-3 Bonhams, Bury St Edmunds #461

FIELDING, Edward (fl.1877) British
£260 $486 €380 Lakeland Valley (22x56cm-9x22in) panel painted 1874. 25-Jul-4 Lots Road Auctions, London #364

FIELDING, Newton Limbird Smith (1799-1856) British
Works on paper
£260 $434 €380 Wild turkey (15x23cm-6x9in) W/C. 14-Oct-3 Bonhams, Knightsbridge #43/R
£709 $1149 €1000 Abreuvoir et canards (16x28cm-6x11in) s.d.1832 W/C varnish. 21-May-3 Daguerre, Paris #81
£709 $1149 €1000 Le repos merite du chasseur (15x22cm-6x9in) s.d.1826. 21-May-3 Daguerre, Paris #82
£900 $1530 €1314 Fisherman in a rowing boat at sea (12x22cm-5x9in) s. W/C over pencil htd bodycol prov. 27-Nov-3 Sotheby's, London #286/R
£922 $1494 €1300 Barque et bateau sur une mer agitee (12x22cm-5x9in) mono.d.1828 W/C varnish. 21-May-3 Daguerre, Paris #83
£1000 $1700 €1460 Ducks by a pool of water (16x25cm-6x10in) s. W/C over pencil htd bodycol prov. 27-Nov-3 Sotheby's, London #288/R est:1200-1800
£1400 $2380 €2044 Golden pheasant and moorhens (14x21cm-6x8in) s. W/C over pencil htd bodycol prov. 27-Nov-3 Sotheby's, London #287/R est:1200-1800
£2000 $3400 €2920 Hunter with his dogs (15x22cm-6x9in) s. W/C over pencil htd bodycol gum arabic prov. 27-Nov-3 Sotheby's, London #285/R est:800-1200

FIELDING, Thales (1793-1837) British
Works on paper
£260 $484 €380 Kilchurn Castle, Loch Awe (20x30cm-8x12in) pencil W/C scratching out. 4-Mar-4 Christie's, Kensington #109
£500 $910 €730 The Schooner Waterwitch off Hastings (13x20cm-5x8in) pencil W/C gum arabic. 1-Jul-4 Christie's, Kensington #306/R

FIELDING, Theodore Henry Adolphus (1781-1851) British
Works on paper
£650 $1105 €949 Shipping off the coast (13x19cm-5x7in) s. W/C over pencil htd bodycol prov. 27-Nov-3 Sotheby's, London #289/R
£922 $1494 €1300 Voiliers le long d'une falaise (13x19cm-5x7in) W/C grattage. 21-May-3 Daguerre, Paris #84/R

FIELDING, Thomas (?) British?
Works on paper
£350 $585 €508 Study of an old fisherman seated on a barrel (38x26cm-15x10in) pencil W/C htd white. 26-Jun-3 Mellors & Kirk, Nottingham #824

FIENE, Ernest (1894-1965) American/German
£311 $500 €454 Still life glass bowl with flowers (33x41cm-13x16in) s. 20-Aug-3 James Julia, Fairfield #1475/R est:1200-1800
£359 $600 €524 Western mountain landscape with deer (69x107cm-27x42in) s.d.1920. 19-Oct-3 Jeffery Burchard, Florida #78
£703 $1300 €1026 Sunset, Monhegan Island (18x46cm-7x18in) s. masonite. 15-Jul-4 Doyle, New York #30/R est:1500-2500
£1397 $2250 €2040 Newtown Church (61x51cm-24x20in) s. i. stretcher. 20-Aug-3 James Julia, Fairfield #1474/R est:2000-3000
£1955 $3500 €2854 Nocturne (18x38cm-7x15in) s. canvas on masonite. 26-May-4 Doyle, New York #153/R est:1500-2500
£2395 $4000 €3497 Before the act (72x71cm-28x28in) s. s.i.verso masonite. 7-Oct-3 Sotheby's, New York #205 est:3000-5000
Works on paper
£541 $1000 €790 High noon, Tryall, Jamaica. Coral Cove, Jamaica (38x58cm-15x23in) s.d.49 W/C double-sided. 15-Jul-4 Doyle, New York #31/R est:600-800

FIERAVINO, Francesco (17th C) Italian
£2448 $4210 €3500 Still life with pottery and rugs (64x78cm-25x31in) 2-Dec-3 Sotheby's, Milan #91/R est:3000-4000

FIERAVINO, Francesco (attrib) (17th C) Italian
£4437 $7764 €6300 Pieces d'orfevrerie disposees sur un tapis (75x99cm-30x39in) 19-Dec-3 Delvaux, Paris #85/R est:5000-7000

FIERAVINO, Francesco (style) (17th C) Italian
£11000 $20130 €16060 Still life with silver and gilt urns (116x165cm-46x65in) i.verso. 6-Jul-4 Sotheby's, Olympia #494/R est:8000-12000

FIERRO, Michelle (1967-) American
£706 $1200 €1031 Territory, territorial (137x122cm-54x48in) s.i.d.88 oil acrylic paper on canvas. 9-Nov-3 Bonhams & Butterfields, Los Angeles #4097/R est:3000-5000

FIERROS, Dionisio (1827-1894) Spanish
£2740 $4658 €4000 Shepherd (34x24cm-13x9in) s. board. 4-Nov-3 Ansorena, Madrid #54/R est:3200
Works on paper
£1250 $2300 €1900 Woman by the sea (39x30cm-15x12in) s. W/C. 22-Jun-4 Durán, Madrid #626/R est:1900
£1275 $2257 €1900 Children cuddling (37x22cm-15x9in) s. W/C. 27-Apr-4 Durán, Madrid #152/R est:1900

FIESSI, Angelo (1891-1979) Italian
£451 $767 €650 Landscape (20x27cm-8x11in) s. masonite. 1-Nov-3 Meeting Art, Vercelli #274

FIETZ, Gerhard (1910-1997) German
£420 $713 €600 Volcanic (28x28cm-11x11in) s.d.90 s.d.1990 verso panel. 29-Nov-3 Villa Grisebach, Berlin #769/R
£694 $1132 €1000 Composition (70x35cm-28x14in) s.d.1951 s.i. verso egg tempera. 27-Sep-3 Dr Fritz Nagel, Stuttgart #9533/R

FIEVRE, Yolande (1907-) French
Sculpture
£1734 $3000 €2532 Les Petit Sieges d'Ocean (64x8cm-25x3in) s.i.d.Juillet 1965 mixed media wood prov. 15-Dec-3 Hindman, Chicago #80/R est:6000-8000
£10690 $19776 €15500 Demons, no 49 (125x65x6cm-49x26x2in) s.d.janvier 1962 verso driftwood pebbles plexiglas box prov. 13-Feb-4 Charbonneaux, Paris #81/R est:10000-12000

FIFE, Ivy Grace (1905-1976) New Zealander
£509 $799 €743 Sunflower No 1 (72x46cm-28x18in) s. i.d.1960 verso exhib. 27-Aug-3 Dunbar Sloane, Wellington #126 (NZ.D 1400)

FIGARI, Andrea (1858-1945) Italian
£851 $1421 €1200 Landscape with stream (28x31cm-11x12in) board. 14-Oct-3 Finarte Semenzato, Milan #13
£1409 $2636 €2100 Rural houses (48x35cm-19x14in) board. 26-Feb-4 Cambi, Genoa #487/R est:1800-2000
£4267 $7765 €6400 Charrette (50x79cm-20x31in) s. 29-Jun-4 Gioffredo, Nice #3/R
£5333 $9813 €8000 Sea storm (140x180cm-55x71in) s. 10-Jun-4 Christie's, Rome #155/R est:8000-12000
£9333 $17173 €14000 Sea storm on the cliffs (140x180cm-55x71in) s. 10-Jun-4 Christie's, Rome #156/R est:8000-12000

FIGARI, Juan Carlos (1894-1927) South American
£2751 $5200 €4016 Green (40x50cm-16x20in) prov.lit. 22-Feb-4 Galeria y Remates, Montevideo #69/R est:6000-7000

FIGARI, Pedro (1861-1938) Uruguayan
£3267 $5750 €4770 Candombe (38x56cm-15x22in) s. masonite. 23-May-4 William Jenack, New York #292/R est:3000-5000
£3523 $6200 €5144 Cart (35x50cm-14x20in) s. cardboard prov.exhib.lit. 5-Jan-4 Galeria y Remates, Montevideo #66/R est:7000-10000
£4192 $7000 €6120 Indians (74x100cm-29x39in) exhib. 7-Oct-3 Galeria y Remates, Montevideo #25/R est:10000
£4706 $8000 €6871 Landscape (33x40cm-13x16in) s. 25-Nov-3 Galeria y Remates, Montevideo #153/R
£5294 $9000 €7729 Los pasteles (40x31cm-16x12in) i. i.verso board prov.exhib. 19-Nov-3 Sotheby's, New York #84/R est:12000-18000
£6176 $10500 €9017 Council (40x50cm-16x20in) s. cardboard. 25-Nov-3 Galeria y Remates, Montevideo #152/R
£6471 $11000 €9448 Candombe (16x25cm-6x10in) cardboard. 25-Nov-3 Galeria y Remates, Montevideo #151/R
£8163 $12980 €12000 Promenade en calenche (48x63cm-19x25in) s. panel. 23-Mar-3 Mercier & Cie, Lille #284/R est:12000-15000
£11364 $20000 €16591 Cowboy (40x50cm-16x20in) i.verso cardboard. 5-Jan-4 Galeria y Remates, Montevideo #65/R est:20000-25000
£11765 $20000 €17177 Un cuento (40x40cm-16x16in) s. board. 19-Nov-3 Sotheby's, New York #45/R est:22000-28000
£12667 $23307 €19000 La novia (32x49cm-13x19in) s.d.1933 cardboard prov. 8-Jun-4 Artcurial Briest, Paris #168/R est:20000-25000
£12805 $21000 €18695 Figure (40x33cm-16x13in) s. cardboard. 3-Jun-3 Galeria y Remates, Montevideo #88
£14130 $26000 €20630 Old times (35x55cm-14x22in) s. cardboard prov. 22-Jun-4 Galeria y Remates, Montevideo #50/R est:26000-29000
£14205 $25000 €20739 Visit (48x62cm-19x24in) s. i.verso cardboard lit. 5-Jan-4 Galeria y Remates, Montevideo #64/R est:27000-32000
£16471 $28000 €24048 El maturrango (32x49cm-13x19in) s.d.1935 board prov. 18-Nov-3 Christie's, Rockefeller NY #28/R est:20000-30000
£18667 $34347 €28000 Life (32x49cm-13x19in) cardboard painted 1933. 10-Jun-4 Christie's, Paris #17/R est:32000-48000
£19048 $36000 €27810 Trail (48x63cm-19x25in) s. cardboard. 22-Feb-4 Galeria y Remates, Montevideo #34/R est:40000-50000
£19333 $35380 €29000 Toros 4 (32x50cm-13x20in) mono. cardboard prov.exhib. 7-Jun-4 Artcurial Briest, Paris #43/R est:30000-40000
£20588 $35000 €30058 Candombe (33x40cm-13x16in) s. cardboard. 25-Nov-3 Galeria y Remates, Montevideo #150/R
£23529 $40000 €34352 Encuentro en el camino - Meeting on the path (40x60cm-16x24in) s. board painted c.1935 prov. 18-Nov-3 Christie's, Rockefeller NY #29/R est:35000-45000
£25967 $47000 €37912 Dusk in the farm (50x70cm-20x28in) cardboard. 30-Mar-4 Arroyo, Buenos Aires #82
£26667 $49067 €40000 Visits (48x61cm-19x24in) s. cardboard painted c.1935 lit. 10-Jun-4 Christie's, Paris #18/R est:40000-48000

Works on paper
£341 $600 €498 Deep (8x8cm-3x3in) pencil prov. 5-Jan-4 Galeria y Remates, Montevideo #5
£478 $750 €698 Candombe (14x16cm-6x6in) pencil dr. 1-Sep-3 Galeria y Remates, Montevideo #31

FIGEL, Albert (1889-1955) German
£387 $693 €550 Madonna with infant under a starlit sky (51x36cm-20x14in) s.d.23 panel lit. 8-Jan-4 Allgauer, Kempten #2380/R

FIGGE, Eddie (1904-2003) Swedish
£1624 $2761 €2371 Inescapable (44x45cm-17x18in) s.d.1961. 4-Nov-3 Bukowskis, Stockholm #581/R est:8000-10000 (S.KR 21500)
£3481 $6265 €5082 With emeralds II (140x71cm-55x28in) s.d.1961 verso exhib. 26-Apr-4 Bukowskis, Stockholm #524/R est:60000-70000 (S.KR 48000)
£7326 $12455 €10696 Deeply rooted red (80x110cm-31x43in) s.i.d.1955 verso exhib. 4-Nov-3 Bukowskis, Stockholm #547/R est:25000-30000 (S.KR 97000)
Works on paper
£264 $449 €385 Neil Armstrong, the step (49x38cm-19x15in) s.d.1995 mixed media. 4-Nov-3 Bukowskis, Stockholm #582/R (S.KR 3500)
£348 $627 €508 God of Rain I (19x23cm-7x9in) s.d.1965 W/C collage exhib. 26-Apr-4 Bukowskis, Stockholm #493/R (S.KR 4800)
£529 $899 €772 Farewell Voyger II (34x26cm-13x10in) s.d.1988 col crayon collage. 5-Nov-3 AB Stockholms Auktionsverk #1047/R (S.KR 7000)
£642 $1091 €937 Look for balance (46x38cm-18x15in) s.d.1992 col crayon. 5-Nov-3 AB Stockholms Auktionsverk #1048/R (S.KR 8500)
£2030 $3655 €2964 Passage (124x142cm-49x56in) s.d.1981 verso mixed media exhib. 26-Apr-4 Bukowskis, Stockholm #526/R est:35000-40000 (S.KR 28000)
£3626 $6526 €5294 Watch out (210x200cm-83x79in) s.d.1986 i.verso mixed media exhib. 26-Apr-4 Bukowskis, Stockholm #525/R est:50000-60000 (S.KR 50000)

FIGINO, Giovanni Ambrogio (1548-1608) Italian
Works on paper
£270 $484 €400 Figure studies (20x15cm-8x6in) pen pencil. 4-May-4 Hartung & Hartung, Munich #4031/R

FIGUEIREDO, Aurora (1891-?) Portuguese
£805 $1442 €1200 Landscape with field (36x45cm-14x18in) s. 31-May-4 Cabral Moncada Leiloes, Lisbon #93/R

FIGUEIREDO, Jose de (19th C) Portuguese
£940 $1682 €1400 Portrait of man with sword (73x59cm-29x23in) s. 31-May-4 Cabral Moncada Leiloes, Lisbon #81/R

FIGURA, Hans (1898-?) Austrian
Works on paper
£347 $566 €500 Snowy landscape (36x47cm-14x19in) s. mixed media. 23-Sep-3 Wiener Kunst Auktionen, Vienna #121/R

FIJALKOWSKI, Stanislaw (1922-) Polish
£2759 $4607 €4000 March 1999 (100x73cm-39x29in) s.i.d.99 verso. 16-Nov-3 Agra, Warsaw #50/R est:1000
£7586 $12669 €11000 Autumn in the forest (50x61cm-20x24in) s.d.1949 verso. 16-Nov-3 Agra, Warsaw #7/R est:2000

FILARSKI, D H W (1885-1964) Belgian
£1477 $2746 €2200 Gezicht op schin op geul (40x50cm-16x20in) s.d.46 verso. 4-Mar-4 Auction Maastricht #1000/R est:2000-3500

FILARSKI, Dirk Herman Willem (1885-1964) Belgian
£1000 $1830 €1500 Garden (32x47cm-13x19in) s.d.1948 panel. 7-Jun-4 Glerum, Amsterdam #107/R est:1400-1600
£1133 $2029 €1700 Nude sitting (65x48cm-26x19in) s. 11-May-4 Vendu Notarishuis, Rotterdam #231 est:1500-2000
£1958 $3329 €2800 Still life with sunflowers and a candlestick (80x64cm-31x25in) s.d.49. 25-Nov-3 Christie's, Amsterdam #18/R est:3000-5000
£1974 $3632 €3000 Passage de la Petite Boucherie (64x52cm-25x20in) s.d.30 i. verso. 28-Jun-4 Sotheby's, Amsterdam #169/R est:3000-5000
£2000 $3680 €3000 Stadsgezicht (65x81cm-26x32in) s.d.32. 8-Jun-4 Sotheby's, Amsterdam #171/R est:3000-5000
£2177 $3962 €3200 Mont Blanc (46x56cm-18x22in) s.d.1961. 3-Feb-4 Christie's, Amsterdam #450/R est:1500-2500
£2400 $4392 €3600 Fishing village in southern France (65x54cm-26x21in) s. 7-Jun-4 Glerum, Amsterdam #117/R est:2000-4000
£2430 $3961 €3500 Small bridge in a wooded landscape, Giethoorn (84x66cm-33x26in) s.d.1946. 29-Sep-3 Sotheby's, Amsterdam #208/R
£2917 $4608 €4200 View of Daroca, Spain (54x65cm-21x26in) s. i.d.1935 on stretcher. 2-Sep-3 Christie's, Amsterdam #380/R est:3000-5000
£3846 $6615 €5500 Bormes les mimosas (101x80cm-40x31in) s. i.verso. 2-Dec-3 Sotheby's, Amsterdam #235/R est:1800-2500
£5208 $8489 €7500 City behind the wall (80x100cm-31x39in) s. prov. 29-Sep-3 Sotheby's, Amsterdam #204/R
£6643 $11427 €9500 Gezicht op de Brug van Mostar (100x120cm-39x47in) s.d.1938 i.stretcher. 2-Dec-3 Sotheby's, Amsterdam #240/R est:4000-6000
Works on paper
£724 $1332 €1100 A plant (51x65cm-20x26in) s.d.18 W/C. 22-Jun-4 Christie's, Amsterdam #560/R
£816 $1486 €1200 Still life white flowers (49x38cm-19x15in) s.d.47 gouache prov. 3-Feb-4 Christie's, Amsterdam #499/R est:800-1200
£1156 $2105 €1700 Landscape near Menton, France (53x43cm-21x17in) s.d.51 gouache prov. 3-Feb-4 Christie's, Amsterdam #500 est:800-1200
£1250 $2037 €1800 Still life with a Japanese bowl and a sunflower (65x91cm-26x36in) s. W/C prov. 29-Sep-3 Sotheby's, Amsterdam #199/R

FILATOV, Alexei (1972-) Russian
£390 $651 €550 Girl with vase of flowers (40x50cm-16x20in) s. 20-Oct-3 Durán, Madrid #706/R
£400 $716 €584 Girl with a flower (61x27cm-24x11in) s. after John William Godward. 5-May-4 John Nicholson, Haslemere #22
£400 $716 €584 New ring (35x50cm-14x20in) s. after John William Godward. 5-May-4 John Nicholson, Haslemere #23
£436 $816 €650 Figures on classical balcony (41x33cm-16x13in) s.verso. 24-Feb-4 Durán, Madrid #724/R
£450 $734 €657 Girl with tambourine (53x33cm-21x13in) s. after John William Godward. 28-Sep-3 John Nicholson, Haslemere #39
£500 $815 €730 Favourite melody (50x40cm-20x16in) s. 28-Sep-3 John Nicholson, Haslemere #73
£575 $960 €840 Odalisque (41x33cm-16x13in) s. 13-Jul-3 John Nicholson, Haslemere #29/R
£650 $1086 €949 After the bathing (65x35cm-26x14in) s. 13-Jul-3 John Nicholson, Haslemere #152/R

FILCER, Louis (1927-1998) Mexican
Works on paper
£689 $1150 €999 Three people (35x47cm-14x19in) s. mixed media card. 24-Jun-3 Louis Morton, Mexico #354/R (M.P 12000)

FILDES, Sir Luke (1843-1927) British
£1500 $2685 €2190 Portrait of Sir George Sutton, former chairman of Henley's (132x99cm-52x39in) s. sold with engraving. 13-May-4 Rendalls, Ashburton #1856
£36000 $61200 €52560 Sisters, double portrait of Misses Renton (188x142cm-74x56in) s.d.1889 exhib. 19-Nov-3 Bonhams, New Bond Street #119/R est:12000-18000

FILIGER, Charles (1863-1928) French
Works on paper
£6000 $10919 €9000 Notation chromatique (24x28cm-9x11in) gouache crayon exec c.1903 prov. 30-Jun-4 Calmels Cohen, Paris #3/R est:8000-10000

FILIP, Demetrio (1921-) Argentinian
£769 $1400 €1123 Saint Mark's Square, Venice (16x21cm-6x8in) s. i.verso board. 5-Jul-4 Arroyo, Buenos Aires #40/R

FILIP, Konrad (1874-?) ?
£1074 $1976 €1600 Portrait of a Mullah (75x60cm-30x24in) i. 29-Mar-4 Dr Fritz Nagel, Stuttgart #7094/R est:700

FILIPKIEWICZ, Stefan (1879-1944) Polish
£2161 $3934 €3155 Landscape in the snow (70x81cm-28x32in) s.d.1917. 20-Jun-4 Agra, Warsaw #11/R (P.Z 15000)

FILIPOV, Konstantin Nikolaivich (1830-1878) Russian
£18000 $30600 €26280 Mounted Cossacks in the mountains (33x26cm-13x10in) s.d.1872. 19-Nov-3 Sotheby's, London #6/R est:12000-15000

FILIPPA, Corrado (1893-1974) Italian
£331 $550 €480 Landscape in autumn (50x70cm-20x28in) s. masonite. 1-Oct-3 Della Rocca, Turin #90/R

FILIPPELLI, Cafiero (1889-1973) Italian
£1295 $2124 €1800 Interior with figures (24x28cm-9x11in) s. masonite. 10-Jun-3 Pandolfini, Florence #216/R est:1800-2200
£1523 $2772 €2300 Wind (13x21cm-5x8in) s.d.1930 board. 21-Jun-4 Pandolfini, Florence #177/R est:1800-2000
£1583 $2596 €2200 On the quay (10x18cm-4x7in) s. board. 10-Jun-3 Pandolfini, Florence #230/R est:1400-1600
£1586 $2649 €2300 Seascape (21x29cm-8x11in) s. board. 14-Nov-3 Farsetti, Prato #569/R est:1900-2200
£1745 $3089 €2600 Interior with figures and dog (24x31cm-9x12in) s. board. 1-May-4 Meeting Art, Vercelli #334 est:2000
£1931 $3225 €2800 Coastal road (21x26cm-8x10in) s. board. 14-Nov-3 Farsetti, Prato #558/R est:2400-2800
£2800 $5152 €4200 Evening at home (37x50cm-15x20in) s. 11-Jun-4 Farsetti, Prato #557/R est:3000-4000
£4000 $7360 €6000 Ardenza with figures (25x35cm-10x14in) s. board prov. 8-Jun-4 Sotheby's, Milan #54/R est:6000-8000

FILIPPI, Camillo (studio) (1500-1574) Italian
£12081 $22228 €18000 Madonna and angels adoring the Infant (33x43cm-13x17in) i.verso board lit. 24-Mar-4 Finarte Semenzato, Rome #102/R est:18000-20000

FILIPPI, Fernando de (1940-) Italian
£690 $1103 €1000 Soaked with light (63x57cm-25x22in) acrylic. 13-Mar-3 Galleria Pace, Milan #36/R
Works on paper
£267 $491 €400 Life tree (73x51cm-29x20in) s. mixed media cardboard. 12-Jun-4 Meeting Art, Vercelli #2

FILIPPINI, Felice (1917-1988) Italian
Works on paper
£388 $694 €566 Woman in dress with feathers (49x70cm-19x28in) s. gouache. 12-May-4 Dobiaschofsky, Bern #489/R (S.FR 900)

FILIPPO, Leonida de (1969-) Italian
£3099 $5423 €4400 Gedankenfrei sein (160x120cm-63x47in) s.i.d.2003 verso enamel. 16-Dec-3 Finarte Semenzato, Milan #258/R est:2800-3200

FILKUKA, Anton (1888-1957) Austrian
£648 $1043 €946 Winter light - an Austrian village (102x129cm-40x51in) s. 13-Oct-3 Joel, Victoria #337 est:1500-2500 (A.D 1600)
£694 $1132 €1000 Alt Aussee (76x86cm-30x34in) s. 23-Sep-3 Wiener Kunst Auktionen, Vienna #33/R
£851 $1421 €1200 Early spring in the Salzkammergut (70x85cm-28x33in) s. canvas on board. 14-Oct-3 Dorotheum, Vienna #113/R
£1042 $1698 €1500 Bad Aussee (81x104cm-32x41in) s. 23-Sep-3 Wiener Kunst Auktionen, Vienna #34/R est:1500-3000

FILLA, Emil (1882-1953) Czechoslovakian
£11176 $19000 €16317 Nature morte (37x45cm-15x18in) s.d.28 prov. 9-Nov-3 Bonhams & Butterfields, Los Angeles #4016/R
£13000 $23920 €18980 Still life (37x45cm-15x18in) s.d.28 prov. 22-Jun-4 Sotheby's, London #184/R est:15000-20000
Sculpture
£2000 $3680 €3000 Weiblicher Akt (39cm-15in) i.d.35 bronze prov.exhib. 8-Jun-4 Sotheby's, Amsterdam #48/R est:3000-4000

FILLERUP, Mel (1924-) American
£359 $600 €521 Riders with pack horses crossing a river (38x76cm-15x30in) s.i.d.1983 board. 13-Jul-3 Butterfields, San Francisco #2028/R

FILLIA (1904-1936) Italian
£7383 $13215 €11000 Coeur poilu (69x50cm-27x20in) s. tempera card painted 1929 prov. 25-May-4 Sotheby's, Milan #231/R est:10000-15000
£26087 $42783 €36000 Plastic patterns in a nude (59x47cm-23x19in) s. s.i.on stretcher prov.exhib.lit. 27-May-3 Sotheby's, Milan #215/R est:25000-35000

FILLIARD, Ernest (1868-1933) French
Works on paper
£417 $696 €600 Le bassin a Rouen (27x39cm-11x15in) s.i. W/C. 23-Oct-3 Credit Municipal, Paris #104
£430 $731 €628 Still life with roses (12x15cm-5x6in) s. w/C. 28-Nov-3 Zofingen, Switzerland #2585 (S.FR 950)
£511 $853 €720 Still life with flowers in a bowl (6x8cm-2x3in) s. W/C. 20-Oct-3 Glerum, Amsterdam #130
£642 $1213 €950 Nature morte au vase de fleurs (36cm-14in circular) s. W/C. 21-Feb-4 Livinec, Gaudcheau & Jezequel, Rennes #108

FILLIOU, Robert (1926-1987) French
Sculpture
£7333 $13420 €11000 Green boxes (17x60cm-7x24in) s. verso panel three. 4-Jun-4 Lempertz, Koln #135/R est:5000

FILLOL GRANER, Antonio (1870-1930) Spanish
£1275 $2372 €1900 Children on the beach (12x28cm-5x11in) s. board. 2-Mar-4 Ansorena, Madrid #29/R est:1200

FILLON, Arthur (1900-1974) French
£709 $1184 €1000 Paris enneige (50x65cm-20x26in) s. 15-Oct-3 Claude Aguttes, Neuilly #40/R

FILMUS, Tully (1903-) American
£378 $700 €552 In the artist's studio (76x61cm-30x24in) s. 18-Jul-4 Bonhams & Butterfields, Los Angeles #7048/R
£391 $700 €571 Orthodox man with cane (43x25cm-17x10in) s. 7-May-4 Sloans & Kenyon, Bethesda #1217/R
£466 $750 €680 Seated figure - self portrait (30x23cm-12x9in) s. 22-Feb-3 Bunte, Elgin #1215
£1786 $3250 €2608 Young girl in a striped dress (51x86cm-20x34in) s. 29-Jun-4 Sotheby's, New York #278/R est:2500-3500
£3281 $5250 €4790 Gladys Filmus as a dancer (132x76cm-52x30in) s. 17-May-3 Bunte, Elgin #1210 est:2000-3000

FIMA (1916-) Russian
£882 $1500 €1288 Female nude with a blue chair (80x80cm-31x31in) s. prov. 1-Dec-3 Ben-Ami, Tel Aviv #4302/R est:2500-3000
£1807 $3000 €2638 Composition (64x92cm-25x36in) s. prov. 2-Oct-3 Christie's, Tel Aviv #89/R est:3000-5000

FIN, Jose (1916-1969) Spanish
£604 $1130 €900 Bull scene (60x73cm-24x29in) s. 24-Feb-4 Durán, Madrid #1164/R

FINA, A (?) ?
Sculpture
£6358 $11000 €9283 Torse d'adolescent (203cm-80in) i. bronze. 10-Dec-3 Alderfer's, Hatfield #233/R est:1500-2000

FINALY, O (19th C) Italian
£5000 $8600 €7300 Doge's Palace, Venice (38x76cm-15x30in) s. 4-Dec-3 Christie's, Kensington #63/R est:5000-7000

FINART, Noel Dieudonne (1797-1852) French
Works on paper
£500 $930 €730 Turkish cavalry in battle skirmish (29x47cm-11x19in) s.d.1861 pencil W/C. 4-Mar-4 Christie's, London #432/R

FINART, Noel Dieudonne (attrib) (1797-1852) French
£830 $1510 €1212 Young officer on horseback with a town in the distance (21x27cm-8x11in) d.1826. 16-Jun-4 Fischer, Luzern #2104/R (S.FR 1900)

FINCH, Alfred William (1854-1930) Belgian
£1074 $1976 €1600 Still life (40x50cm-16x20in) s.d.1922. 25-Mar-4 Hagelstam, Helsinki #985 est:1000
£2937 $4993 €4200 Red cliffs by the sea (31x40cm-12x16in) s. 29-Nov-3 Bukowskis, Helsinki #52/R est:2500-3000
£3133 $5609 €4700 Still life of pewter mug and bowl of apples (46x72cm-18x28in) s. exhib. 15-May-4 Hagelstam, Helsinki #164/R est:5000
Works on paper
£320 $589 €480 Sand dunes (31x38cm-12x15in) s.d.1915 W/C. 9-Jun-4 Bukowskis, Helsinki #387/R
£563 $901 €800 Urajarvi (29x35cm-11x14in) s. W/C. 18-Sep-3 Hagelstam, Helsinki #845

FINCH, Francis Oliver (1802-1862) British
Works on paper
£450 $824 €657 Elopement (38x56cm-15x22in) s. W/C. 27-Jan-4 Bonhams, Knightsbridge #46/R

FINCH, Roger (20th C) British
£300 $498 €438 Thames barge, Tuesday (40x51cm-16x20in) s.d.59 board. 1-Oct-3 Bonhams, Knightsbridge #130/R

FINCHER, John H (1941-) American
£447 $800 €653 Road to Mt. Ventoux. s.i. panel. 13-May-4 Dallas Auction Gallery, Dallas #186/R
£670 $1200 €978 Opera poplars. s. oil on paper. 13-May-4 Dallas Auction Gallery, Dallas #3/R est:600-1000
£782 $1400 €1142 Demons of memory. 13-May-4 Dallas Auction Gallery, Dallas #301/R est:1800-2200
£950 $1700 €1387 36 postcards. s. 13-May-4 Dallas Auction Gallery, Dallas #106/R est:1200-1500
£2235 $4000 €3263 F.C.G.V.B and R brush. s.i. set of six. 13-May-4 Dallas Auction Gallery, Dallas #156/R est:1500-2500

FINCK, Furman J (20th C) Australian?
Works on paper
£387 $700 €565 Pablo casals (76x61cm-30x24in) pencil. 16-Apr-4 American Auctioneer #124/R

FINCK, Hazel (1894-1977) American
£523 $900 €764 Still life with tulips and pears (51x62cm-20x24in) s. 2-Dec-3 Christie's, Rockefeller NY #103/R
£814 $1400 €1188 Essex boat works (51x61cm-20x24in) s. 2-Dec-3 Christie's, Rockefeller NY #106/R
£872 $1500 €1273 Old houses, Elizabeth (51x61cm-20x24in) s. 2-Dec-3 Christie's, Rockefeller NY #105/R est:1500-2500
£988 $1700 €1442 Boats (51x61cm-20x24in) s. 2-Dec-3 Christie's, Rockefeller NY #107/R est:1500-2500
£1047 $1800 €1529 Autumn landscape with houses (41x72cm-16x28in) s. 2-Dec-3 Christie's, Rockefeller NY #104/R est:1500-2500

FIND, Ludvig (1869-1945) Danish
£295 $501 €431 Flowers on window ledge (60x66cm-24x26in) s.d.21. 10-Nov-3 Rasmussen, Vejle #401/R (D.KR 3200)
£344 $558 €499 Interior scene with woman reading (70x51cm-28x20in) s. 4-Aug-3 Rasmussen, Vejle #87/R (D.KR 3600)

FIND, Ludvig (attrib) (1869-1945) Danish
£450 $733 €657 Portrait of girl with hat (41x33cm-16x13in) 27-Sep-3 Rasmussen, Havnen #2145/R (D.KR 4800)

FINDLAY, William (fl.1900-1930) British
£5200 $8164 €7540 Harbour at Honfleur (46x61cm-18x24in) s.d.1923. 27-Aug-3 Sotheby's, London #1079/R est:4000-6000
£6500 $12090 €9490 Portrait of a mother and her daughter on a sofa (142x102cm-56x40in) s.d.1908. 4-Mar-4 Christie's, Kensington #395/R est:6000-8000

FINDORFF, Dietrich (1722-1792) German
£16667 $30000 €24334 Exotic species of monkey from the private zoo of the Herzog (84x65cm-33x26in) 23-Jan-4 Christie's, Rockefeller NY #186/R est:25000-35000

FINE, Perle (1908-1988) American
£9341 $17000 €13638 Impact (86x172cm-34x68in) s.d.61 prov. 29-Jun-4 Sotheby's, New York #527/R est:2000-3000
Works on paper
£1618 $2800 €2362 Untitled (57x76cm-22x30in) s.d.57 gouache paper collage foil prov. 10-Dec-3 Phillips, New York #433/R est:500-700
£4118 $7000 €6012 Untitled (30x41cm-12x16in) gouache prov. 9-Nov-3 Wright, Chicago #251 est:3000-4000

FINELLI, Giuliano (after) (1601-1657) Italian
Sculpture
£10500 $17850 €15330 Young noblewoman (93cm-37in) marble lit. 28-Oct-3 Sotheby's, London #48/R est:3000-4000

FINES, Eugène Francois (1826-1882) French
£1225 $1984 €1776 Italian scene with monk praying for woman and children (56x69cm-22x27in) s. 4-Aug-3 Rasmussen, Vejle #370/R est:10000-12000 (D.KR 12800)
£1800 $3096 €2628 Family at prayer (55x69cm-22x27in) s. 4-Dec-3 Christie's, Kensington #111/R est:2000-3000

FINETTI, Gino Ritter von (1877-?) Italian
£340 $544 €493 Boxing ring (63x76cm-25x30in) s. 16-Sep-3 Bonhams, Knightsbridge #10/R
Works on paper
£972 $1585 €1400 Horse jumping (100x80cm-39x31in) s.d.22. 26-Sep-3 Bolland & Marotz, Bremen #647/R

FINEY, George Edmund (1895-1987) New Zealander
Works on paper
£520 $895 €759 Colour in music (45x33cm-18x13in) s. 3-Dec-3 Dunbar Sloane, Auckland #107 (NZ.D 1400)

FINGESTEN, Michel (1884-1943) German?
£364 $625 €520 Andaluisisch mountain village (53x41cm-21x16in) s. tempera. 5-Dec-3 Bolland & Marotz, Bremen #802
Works on paper
£280 $467 €400 Landscape with trees (42x54cm-17x21in) s. W/C gouache. 28-Jun-3 Bolland & Marotz, Bremen #830/R
£406 $690 €580 Ex Libris Sebastian Malz (62x41cm-24x16in) s.i. Indian ink pencil bodycol. 29-Nov-3 Bassenge, Berlin #6704
£455 $759 €650 In the wine bar (70x55cm-28x22in) s. chk W/C. 28-Jun-3 Bolland & Marotz, Bremen #831/R
£520 $931 €770 Harbour street in Almeria (49x104cm-19x41in) s.i. pastel gouache. 8-May-4 Hans Stahl, Toestorf #19/R
£805 $1482 €1200 Streets in Valencia (47x39cm-19x15in) s.i.d. gouache board two. 26-Mar-4 Ketterer, Hamburg #405/R

FINGLETON, Sean (20th C) Irish?
£513 $929 €770 Sea and island, Howth (49x59cm-19x23in) s. s.i.verso. 30-Mar-4 De Veres Art Auctions, Dublin #71b

FINI, Leonor (1908-1996) Italian
£2000 $3620 €2920 Portrait de femme (22x16cm-9x6in) indis.sig. painted c.1945. 1-Apr-4 Christie's, Kensington #61/R est:2500-3500
£2400 $4248 €3504 Jardin (22x62cm-9x24in) s. panel painted c.1954 prov.exhib. 27-Apr-4 Bonhams, Knightsbridge #199/R est:2000-3000
£2700 $4968 €3942 Colloque entre monos et una (34x26cm-13x10in) s. oil paper on canvas painted 1987. 24-Mar-4 Sotheby's, Olympia #157/R est:3000-4000
£12000 $22080 €17520 Composition (88x59cm-35x23in) panel prov. 23-Jun-4 Christie's, London #261/R est:12000-16000
£14667 $26693 €22000 Amazone (60x45cm-24x18in) s. prov. 29-Jun-4 Sotheby's, Paris #19/R est:20000-30000
£20667 $36993 €31000 Shadows (92x60cm-36x24in) s. 12-May-4 Stadion, Trieste #694/R est:18000-22000
£34965 $59441 €50000 La boite de Pandora (97x147cm-38x58in) s.d.1972 prov. 27-Nov-3 Millon & Associes, Paris #249/R est:20000-30000
£50000 $92000 €73000 Margot Fonteyn et son ami (55x46cm-22x18in) s. painted 1948 prov. 22-Jun-4 Sotheby's, London #192/R est:50000-70000
£54545 $92727 €78000 Les mutantes (95x147cm-37x58in) s. prov. 27-Nov-3 Millon & Associes, Paris #248/R est:20000-30000
Works on paper
£267 $491 €400 Fragment d'une scene de theatre antique (43x32cm-17x13in) s. gouache pastel. 11-Jun-4 Pierre Berge, Paris #152/R
£420 $701 €600 Figure (37x31cm-15x12in) s. 11-Oct-3 De Vuyst, Lokeren #148
£490 $817 €700 Four dancing figures (39x32cm-15x13in) s. pen ink. 11-Oct-3 De Vuyst, Lokeren #147
£490 $832 €700 Visage (42x35cm-17x14in) s. wash. 1-Dec-3 Palais de Beaux Arts, Brussels #351
£490 $832 €700 Women. Two figures (30x24cm-12x9in) init. Chinese ink paper on canvas two. 25-Nov-3 Sotheby's, Milan #71
£559 $951 €800 Hedresa (9x7cm-4x3in) s. ballpoint pen. 27-Nov-3 Millon & Associes, Paris #249a
£594 $993 €850 Woman-animal (26x17cm-10x7in) s. mixed media. 10-Oct-3 Stadion, Trieste #524/R
£671 $1248 €1000 Visages (31x22cm-12x9in) s. pen ink wash. 3-Mar-4 Tajan, Paris #134
£694 $1132 €1000 Face. s. W/C. 23-Sep-3 Galerie Moderne, Brussels #819/R
£699 $1203 €1000 Monsieur Venus special no.19 (34x26cm-13x10in) s. ink executed 1971. 2-Dec-3 Sotheby's, Amsterdam #210/R est:1000-1500
£734 $1320 €1100 Le Jardin du Luxembourg, le Mardi Gras (26x38cm-10x15in) gouache. 26-Apr-4 Tajan, Paris #81
£805 $1498 €1200 Madame Pigasse (47x29cm-19x11in) s.i. W/C wash gouache. 2-Mar-4 Artcurial Briest, Paris #74
£833 $1500 €1216 Two women, one reclining (18x29cm-7x11in) s. W/C cream wove paper. 22-Jan-4 Swann Galleries, New York #162 est:700-1000
£1000 $1840 €1500 Femme au manchon (49x19cm-19x7in) s. gouache W/C. 11-Jun-4 Pierre Berge, Paris #149/R est:800-1000
£1064 $1777 €1500 Femme dansant (46x30cm-18x12in) s. W/C. 15-Oct-3 Neret-Minet, Paris #12
£1333 $2400 €2000 Portrait of woman (70x50cm-28x20in) s. pastel W/C card prov. 22-Apr-4 Finarte Semenzato, Rome #89/R est:2500
£2055 $3493 €3000 Femme fleur (42x30cm-17x12in) s. W/C gouache sepia ink. 9-Nov-3 Eric Pillon, Calais #182/R
£2192 $3726 €3200 Femme en robe de soiree (36x27cm-14x11in) s. Chinese ink wash dr. 9-Nov-3 Eric Pillon, Calais #183/R

FINIGUERRA, Maso (attrib) (1426-1464) Italian
Works on paper
£2313 $4140 €3400 Saint Sebastien et Saint Roch (17x11cm-7x4in) i. pen brown ink wash two joined sheets. 18-Mar-4 Christie's, Paris #212/R est:2000-3000

FINK, Aaron (1955-) American
Sculpture
£250 $450 €365 Untitled (12x16cm-5x6in) s.d.1982 verso. 24-Apr-4 David Rago, Lambertville #303/R
Works on paper
£1294 $2200 €1889 Macintosh (56x76cm-22x30in) s.d.91 mixed media. 21-Nov-3 Skinner, Boston #594/R est:1000-1500

FINK, C (19th C) ?
£2200 $3960 €3212 Ginger cat sitting on a cushion under a Gothic inspired arch (36x46cm-14x18in) s.d.1868. 24-Apr-4 Tamlyn, Bridgwater #145/R

FINK, Don (1923-) American
£646 $1176 €950 Abstract (81x100cm-32x39in) s.d.1960 prov. 3-Feb-4 Segre, Madrid #323/R

FINK, Larry (1941-) American
Photographs
£1556 $2800 €2272 English speaking union, New York City (38x38cm-15x15in) i.d.1976 s.verso gelatin silver print prov.lit. 23-Apr-4 Phillips, New York #168/R est:2500-3500
£2275 $3800 €3322 Studio 54 (34x35cm-13x14in) s.i.d.1977 verso gelatin silver print prov.lit. 17-Oct-3 Phillips, New York #245/R est:3000-5000
£2874 $4800 €4196 Olsin graduation party (35x35cm-14x14in) s.i.d.1977 verso gelatin silver print board prov.lit. 17-Oct-3 Phillips, New York #176/R est:3000-5000
£3892 $6500 €5682 Pat Sabatina's 8th birthday party (38x38cm-15x15in) s.d.1977 verso silver print. 21-Oct-3 Swann Galleries, New York #313/R est:1200-1800

FINK, Tone (1944-) Austrian
£390 $651 €550 Untitled (29x20cm-11x8in) mono.d.88 mixed media collage. 14-Oct-3 Dorotheum, Vienna #265/R
£426 $711 €600 Untitled (50x40cm-20x16in) 14-Oct-3 Dorotheum, Vienna #267/R
Works on paper
£563 $986 €800 Untitled (99x70cm-39x28in) s.d.1980 mixed media board. 19-Dec-3 Dorotheum, Vienna #380/R

FINK, Waldemar (1893-1948) Swiss
£259 $463 €378 Mountain village in autumn (61x90cm-24x35in) s.d.1930. 13-May-4 Stuker, Bern #629 (S.FR 600)
£286 $457 €415 Autumn landscape with lakeside village (60x89cm-24x35in) s.d.1938 s.i.d.25.10.1938 verso. 15-May-3 Stuker, Bern #1185 (S.FR 600)
£431 $772 €629 Dusk (60x80cm-24x31in) s.d.1943 i. verso. 12-May-4 Dobiaschofsky, Bern #491/R (S.FR 1000)

FINLAY, Verner (20th C) ?
£400 $664 €584 Still life (61x71cm-24x28in) s. board. 1-Oct-3 John Ross, Belfast #194
£480 $797 €701 Still life (61x81cm-24x32in) s. board. 1-Oct-3 John Ross, Belfast #47

FINLAY, Virgil (1914-1971) American
£3293 $5500 €4808 Surrealistic scene with sculptures coming to life (30x23cm-12x9in) s. board. 15-Nov-3 Illustration House, New York #23/R est:7000-10000

FINN, Herbert John (1861-?) British
£300 $474 €438 Tenby, the West Town Gate (46x56cm-18x22in) s. 22-Jul-3 Peter Francis, Wales #3/R

FINNE, Ferdinand (1910-1999) Norwegian
£734 $1218 €1064 The red chair, New York 1965 (48x61cm-19x24in) s. 16-Jun-3 Blomqvist, Lysaker #1042/R (N.KR 8500)
£834 $1393 €1218 Flowers by the fjord (38x45cm-15x18in) s. 17-Nov-3 Blomqvist, Lysaker #1058 (N.KR 10000)

FINNE, Henrik (1898-1992) Norwegian
£563 $1030 €822 Still life of green jug (42x58cm-17x23in) s. 2-Feb-4 Blomqvist, Lysaker #1067/R (N.KR 7000)
£1841 $3296 €2688 Ship yard (55x70cm-22x28in) s.d.31. 22-Mar-4 Blomqvist, Oslo #405/R est:22000-24000 (N.KR 23000)

FINNEGA, T G G (?) Dutch?
£2767 $4953 €4040 Prince Hendrick passing through the Suez Canal (50x82cm-20x32in) s.i. 15-May-4 Christie's, Sydney #302/R est:3000-5000 (A.D 7000)

FINNEMORE, Joseph (1860-1939) British
Works on paper
£529 $946 €772 Cavalier (34x24cm-13x9in) s.d.93 W/C. 10-May-4 Joel, Victoria #431 est:640-740 (A.D 1300)

FINNIE, John (1829-1907) British
£320 $509 €464 Incoming tide (30x41cm-12x16in) s. board exhib. 11-Sep-3 Morphets, Harrogate #249
£1800 $3222 €2628 School Fever (41x28cm-16x11in) s.d.March 1863 board. 17-Mar-4 Bonhams, Chester #241/R est:1400-1800

FINSLER, Hans (1891-1972) Swiss?
Photographs
£2448 $4161 €3500 Untitled (14x22cm-6x9in) mono.i. verso silver gelatin. 27-Nov-3 Villa Grisebach, Berlin #1169/R est:2500-3000
£2609 $4278 €3600 The egg (35x27cm-14x11in) vintage silver gelatin lit. 30-May-3 Villa Grisebach, Berlin #1166/R est:1000-1200

FINSON, Louis (1580-1617) Flemish
£25000 $45750 €36500 Triumph of David over Goliath (113x82cm-44x32in) s. panel prov.lit. 7-Jul-4 Christie's, London #40/R est:30000-50000

FINSTER, Herbert (1930-) German
£345 $576 €500 Bather (26x34cm-10x13in) s.d.81 panel. 9-Jul-3 Hugo Ruef, Munich #340
£552 $921 €800 Hovering (24x30cm-9x12in) s.d.99 panel. 9-Jul-3 Hugo Ruef, Munich #339/R

FINSTER, Howard (1916-) American
£389 $700 €568 Antonia Pollaiolo (43x23cm-17x9in) painted cutout wood board. 24-Apr-4 Slotin Folk Art, Buford #308/R
£444 $800 €648 Elvis (71x25cm-28x10in) paint marker cutout wood prov. 24-Apr-4 Slotin Folk Art, Buford #311/R
£611 $1100 €892 Trumpeting angel (30x122cm-12x48in) paint marker cutout wooden board. 24-Apr-4 Slotin Folk Art, Buford #312/R est:500-1000
£722 $1300 €1054 Coke bottle (86x25cm-34x10in) paint marker cutout wooden board prov. 24-Apr-4 Slotin Folk Art, Buford #309/R est:1000-2000
£806 $1500 €1177 Outsider art, stylized skyline with palm trees (36x56cm-14x22in) s.d.March 19.90 board. 3-Mar-4 Alderfer's, Hatfield #360 est:300-500
£1167 $2100 €1704 God's people will soon be happy (41x51cm-16x20in) enamel on masonite. 24-Apr-4 Slotin Folk Art, Buford #297/R est:4000-6000
£1444 $2600 €2108 In the old city over the hills (36x43cm-14x17in) enamel on wood. 24-Apr-4 Slotin Folk Art, Buford #298/R est:3000-5000
£1497 $2500 €2186 Queen Victoria, number 1057 (130x48cm-51x19in) enamel board. 15-Nov-3 Slotin Folk Art, Buford #165/R est:3000-5000
£1946 $3250 €2841 Judgement of the killer (38x48cm-15x19in) panel. 15-Nov-3 Slotin Folk Art, Buford #167/R est:1000-3000
£1946 $3250 €2841 Elements, number 1248 (71x38cm-28x15in) board. 15-Nov-3 Slotin Folk Art, Buford #168/R est:1000-3000
£2096 $3500 €3060 Visions of other worlds, number 4385 (61x91cm-24x36in) acrylic board. 15-Nov-3 Slotin Folk Art, Buford #164/R est:3000-5000
£2754 $4600 €4021 A small corner of the world's last war (48x91cm-19x36in) household paint fibreboard. 15-Nov-3 Slotin Folk Art, Buford #163/R est:3000-5000
£3892 $6500 €5682 Jesus take a fig tree (41x33cm-16x13in) board prov. 15-Nov-3 Slotin Folk Art, Buford #166/R est:1000-3000
£8889 $16000 €12978 Angels of the sacred clouds (109x109cm-43x43in) d.1981 board prov. 24-Apr-4 Slotin Folk Art, Buford #296/R est:10000-15000
Sculpture
£556 $1000 €812 We could have been strong. painted wood glass plate nailed over image. 24-Apr-4 Slotin Folk Art, Buford #302/R est:2000-3000
£958 $1600 €1399 Blessed are the dead, number 2946 (33x18x8cm-13x7x3in) wood enamel mirror prov. 15-Nov-3 Slotin Folk Art, Buford #170/R est:1000-3000
£1250 $2250 €1825 Untitled (41x25x8cm-16x10x3in) 2 ply plexi box mirror backing. 24-Apr-4 Slotin Folk Art, Buford #303/R est:2000-3000
£1667 $3000 €2434 Little town of Love and Peace (43x33cm-17x13in) wood painted on mirror. 24-Apr-4 Slotin Folk Art, Buford #299/R est:3000-5000
£1796 $3000 €2622 Watch out for lambs with lion's paws (33x28x8cm-13x11x3in) enamel wood cutout prov. 15-Nov-3 Slotin Folk Art, Buford #171/R est:1000-3000
Works on paper
£403 $725 €588 Coke bottle (86cm-34in) marker wooden cutout board. 24-Apr-4 Slotin Folk Art, Buford #313/R
£472 $850 €689 Tinfoil art (36x15cm-14x6in) mixed media exhib. 24-Apr-4 Slotin Folk Art, Buford #306/R

FINSTERLIN, Hermann (1887-1973) German
£336 $594 €500 Easter lamb (70x80cm-28x31in) s.d. hessian. 30-Apr-4 Dr Fritz Nagel, Stuttgart #141/R

FINZI, Ennio (1931-) Italian
£448 $749 €650 Composition (70x100cm-28x39in) s. tempera paper. 13-Nov-3 Galleria Pace, Milan #25/R
£500 $920 €750 Untitled (70x100cm-28x39in) s.d.1987 tempera paper. 12-Jun-4 Meeting Art, Vercelli #802/R
£552 $883 €800 Untitled (70x50cm-28x20in) s. paper on canvas. 13-Mar-3 Galleria Pace, Milan #39/R
£567 $1043 €850 Untitled (50x70cm-20x28in) s. paper on canvas. 12-Jun-4 Meeting Art, Vercelli #32/R
£567 $1043 €850 Untitled (50x70cm-20x28in) s. cardboard. 12-Jun-4 Meeting Art, Vercelli #766/R
£580 $951 €800 Composition (30x30cm-12x12in) s. 29-May-3 Galleria Pace, Milan #81/R
£600 $1104 €900 Untitled (70x100cm-28x39in) s. tempera paper on canvas. 12-Jun-4 Meeting Art, Vercelli #680/R
£621 $993 €900 Sunset along the Brenta (60x80cm-24x31in) card painted 1998. 13-Mar-3 Galleria Pace, Milan #139/R
£638 $1180 €950 Untitled (30x30cm-12x12in) s. s.verso. 11-Mar-4 Galleria Pace, Milan #79/R
£667 $1227 €1000 Untitled (30x30cm-12x12in) s. 12-Jun-4 Meeting Art, Vercelli #797/R
£671 $1242 €1000 Untitled (30x30cm-12x12in) s. 13-Mar-4 Meeting Art, Vercelli #331
£671 $1242 €1000 Untitled (70x100cm-28x39in) s. acrylic paper. 11-Mar-4 Galleria Pace, Milan #7/R
£671 $1242 €1000 Untitled (30x30cm-12x12in) s. 11-Mar-4 Galleria Pace, Milan #124/R
£680 $1238 €1000 Untitled (70x100cm-28x39in) s. 6-Feb-4 Galleria Rosenberg, Milan #110/R
£761 $1248 €1050 Yellow (40x40cm-16x16in) s.d.1990 verso. 29-May-3 Galleria Pace, Milan #79/R
£797 $1307 €1100 Spacial concept (40x30cm-16x12in) s. hydropaint on canvas painted 1956. 30-May-3 Farsetti, Prato #26
£800 $1448 €1200 Untitled (70x100cm-28x39in) s. card on canvas. 2-Apr-4 Farsetti, Prato #133/R
£800 $1472 €1200 Composition (40x40cm-16x16in) s. 10-Jun-4 Galleria Pace, Milan #145/R
£828 $1324 €1200 Seducer (40x40cm-16x16in) s. s.d.2000 verso. 13-Mar-3 Galleria Pace, Milan #113/R
£828 $1382 €1200 Composition (30x30cm-12x12in) s. s.verso. 13-Nov-3 Galleria Pace, Milan #20/R
£1000 $1840 €1500 Fluorescent pink (70x50cm-28x20in) s. painted 1998. 12-Jun-4 Meeting Art, Vercelli #470/R est:1500
£1014 $1784 €1500 Colour trend in grey (40x40cm-16x16in) s. i.d.2000 verso. 22-May-4 Galleria Pananti, Florence #502/R est:400-500
£1081 $1903 €1600 Towards the blue (70x50cm-28x20in) 22-May-4 Galleria Pananti, Florence #485/R est:500-600
£1103 $1843 €1600 Red and green (50x40cm-20x16in) s.i.d.1953 tempera board. 13-Nov-3 Galleria Pace, Milan #116/R
£1141 $2111 €1700 Untitled (70x100cm-28x39in) s. cardboard. 11-Mar-4 Galleria Pace, Milan #67/R est:2200-2800
£1149 $2022 €1700 Colour trend (50x50cm-20x20in) s. painted 2000. 22-May-4 Galleria Pananti, Florence #499/R est:500-600
£1208 $2235 €1800 Untitled (70x100cm-28x39in) s. cardboard. 11-Mar-4 Galleria Pace, Milan #41/R est:2200-2800
£1216 $2141 €1800 Yellow trend (80x80cm-31x31in) s. painted 2001. 22-May-4 Galleria Pananti, Florence #484/R est:700-800
£1275 $2359 €1900 Colour sound in blue (50x50cm-20x20in) s. s.i.verso painted 1998. 13-Mar-4 Meeting Art, Vercelli #385 est:1500
£1400 $2576 €2100 Space light (55x55cm-22x22in) s.i.d.1991 verso. 12-Jun-4 Meeting Art, Vercelli #85/R est:1000
£1477 $2643 €2200 Untitled (65x65cm-26x26in) s.d.74 verso acrylic. 28-May-4 Farsetti, Prato #273/R est:2100-2400
£1622 $2854 €2400 Forthcoming (70x70cm-28x28in) s. 22-May-4 Galleria Pananti, Florence #487/R est:600-700
£1678 $3003 €2500 Colour pattern (70x100cm-28x39in) s. s.i.verso painted 1999. 30-May-4 Meeting Art, Vercelli #23 est:2500
£1757 $3092 €2600 Light segments (65x65cm-26x26in) s.d.1980 acrylic. 22-May-4 Galleria Pananti, Florence #494/R est:700-800
£1892 $3330 €2800 Light (100x100cm-39x39in) s.i.d.1998 verso. 22-May-4 Galleria Pananti, Florence #489/R est:1000-1100
£2027 $3568 €3000 Blue (60x80cm-24x31in) s. s.i.d.2001 verso. 22-May-4 Galleria Pananti, Florence #488/R est:700-800
£2432 $4281 €3600 Colour samples (100x100cm-39x39in) s.i.d.1999 verso. 22-May-4 Galleria Pananti, Florence #498/R est:1000-1100
£2432 $4281 €3600 Towards the black (100x100cm-39x39in) s.i.d.1990 verso. 22-May-4 Galleria Pananti, Florence #495/R est:1000-1100
£2635 $4638 €3900 Colour architecture (100x150cm-39x59in) s.i.d.1994 verso. 22-May-4 Galleria Pananti, Florence #500/R est:1200-1400
£3041 $5351 €4500 Colour trend in white (70x100cm-28x39in) s. s.i.d.1990 verso. 22-May-4 Galleria Pananti, Florence #503/R est:700-800
Works on paper
£369 $683 €550 Composition (100x70cm-39x28in) s. mixed media card on canvas. 13-Mar-4 Meeting Art, Vercelli #369
£403 $745 €600 Composition (70x100cm-28x39in) s. mixed media card on canvas. 13-Mar-4 Meeting Art, Vercelli #69

FIOL, Gabriel (1905-) Spanish
£709 $1149 €1000 Masia mallorquina (33x41cm-13x16in) s. panel. 20-May-3 Ansorena, Madrid #202/R

FIORE, Jacobello del (style) (1370-1439) Italian
£10738 $19758 €16000 Mystical marriage of St Cahterine (75x53cm-30x21in) oil tempera panel prov.panel prov. 24-Mar-4 Dorotheum, Vienna #48/R est:12000-16000

FIORESI, Garcia (1888-1968) Italian
£671 $1242 €1000 Wood (39x56cm-15x22in) s. tempera W/C card. 13-Mar-4 Meeting Art, Vercelli #432

FIORI, Ernesto di (attrib) (1884-1945) German
£11404 $19044 €16650 Still life of flowers (122x92cm-48x36in) prov. 15-Nov-3 Galerie Gloggner, Luzern #76/R est:6800-7500 (S.FR 26000)

FIORINI, Ilio (1912-) Italian
£280 $515 €420 Boats in the harbour (61x80cm-24x31in) s. board. 11-Jun-4 Farsetti, Prato #433

FIORITI, Bernardo (attrib) (1623-1673) Italian
Sculpture
£25000 $45000 €36500 Figures of putti (77cm-30in) s. marble pair lit. 22-Jan-4 Sotheby's, New York #164/R est:40000-60000

FIORONI, Giosetta (1932-) Italian
Works on paper
£436 $807 €650 Something. (25x18cm-10x7in) s.i.verso mixed media board lit. 13-Mar-4 Meeting Art, Vercelli #16a
£650 $1106 €930 Untitled (65x50cm-26x20in) s. collage mixed media. 18-Nov-3 Babuino, Rome #429/R
£839 $1427 €1200 Untitled (100x70cm-39x28in) s.d.1998 mixed media collage paper on canvas. 18-Nov-3 Babuino, Rome #290/R
£2800 $5040 €4200 Sixties girl (100x70cm-39x28in) s.i.d.1965 verso pencil paint on canvas. 22-Apr-4 Finarte Semenzato, Rome #201/R est:4000-4500

FIOT, Maximilien Louis (1886-1953) French
Sculpture
£1053 $1937 €1600 Deer (41cm-16in) s. brown pat. bronze incl. base. 22-Jun-4 Sotheby's, Amsterdam #96/R est:2000-3000
£1500 $2550 €2190 Standing greyhound (35x36cm-14x14in) s. brown-black pat bronze. 19-Nov-3 Sotheby's, Olympia #145/R est:1500-2500
£1888 $3210 €2700 Couple de pantheres (13x21x7cm-5x8x3in) s.st.f.Susse pat bronze. 25-Nov-3 Millon & Associes, Paris #21/R est:1500-2000

£2000	$3580	€3000	Le chevreuil (41cm-16in) s.st.f.Susse brown black pat bronze. 12-May-4 Coutau Begarie, Paris #247/R est:3000-3500
£2238	$3804	€3200	L'aigle aux ailes deployees perche sur un rocher (94cm-37in) s.st.f.Susse dark pat bronze. 21-Nov-3 Piasa, Paris #14 est:5000-6000
£4000	$7360	€6000	Couple de pantheres (42cm-17in) s. red brown pat bronze cire perdue st.f.Susse. 10-Jun-4 Camard, Paris #31/R est:4000-5000
£4800	$8640	€7008	Young stag with two hinds (38x62cm-15x24in) s.num.2 brown pat bronze st.f.Susse. 21-Apr-4 Sotheby's, London #96/R est:4000-6000
£6993	$11678	€10000	Tigre se lechant (30x50x15cm-12x20x6in) s. blk pat bronze. 24-Jun-3 Millon & Associes, Paris #21b/R

FIRFIRES, Nicholas S (1917-1990) American

£331	$600	€483	Heading for camp (43x58cm-17x23in) s.d.1965. 18-Apr-4 Bonhams & Butterfields, Los Angeles #7020
£870	$1400	€1270	Gathering them in (30x41cm-12x16in) 22-Aug-3 Altermann Galleries, Santa Fe #99

FIRLE, Walter (1859-1929) German

£855	$1453	€1248	Woman sewing (85x63cm-33x25in) s. 4-Nov-3 Stephan Welz, Johannesburg #582/R est:10000-15000 (SA.R 10000)
£1818	$3127	€2600	Three girls looking at a picture book together (67x50cm-26x20in) s. 3-Dec-3 Neumeister, Munich #565/R est:2000
£2308	$3969	€3300	Grandmother playing with her grandchildren in the living room (63x84cm-25x33in) s. panel. 3-Dec-3 Neumeister, Munich #564/R est:2000
£4362	$7809	€6500	The singing hour (112x162cm-44x64in) s. 27-May-4 Dorotheum, Vienna #97/R est:5000-6000

FIRMENICH, Josef (1821-1891) German

£1722	$3134	€2600	Island with architectural ruins (94x126cm-37x50in) s.d.1871. 19-Jun-4 Quittenbaum, Hamburg #17/R est:700

FIRMIN, Claude (1864-?) French

£932	$1500	€1361	Les colines de Toulon (33x36cm-13x14in) s.i. 14-Jan-4 Christie's, Rockefeller NY #36/R est:800-1200
£1700	$3213	€2482	Feeding time (39x55cm-15x22in) s.d.901. 19-Feb-4 Christie's, Kensington #341/R est:1000-1500
£2482	$4145	€3500	Panorama de Constantine (29x104cm-11x41in) s.d.1886 lit. 19-Oct-3 Rabourdin & Choppin de Janvry, Paris #61/R est:3500-4000

FIRTH, E W (19/20th C) British?

Works on paper

£1900	$3230	€2774	Inside the estuary at Dartmouth (34x69cm-13x27in) mono.d.1905 pencil W/C htd white. 19-Nov-3 Christie's, Kensington #339/R est:600-800

FIRTH, Jack (1917-) British

£250	$400	€365	Gamrie Bay and Silver Cloud (20x90cm-8x35in) s. 15-May-3 Bonhams, Edinburgh #389

FIRTH-SMITH, John (1943-) Australian

£2143	$3943	€3129	Tide (167x137cm-66x54in) s.i.d.1969 verso prov. 29-Mar-4 Goodman, Sydney #52/R est:4000-6000 (A.D 5250)
£5532	$9404	€8077	Land and Sea 3 (84x120cm-33x47in) s.d.98 verso linen exhib. 26-Nov-3 Deutscher-Menzies, Melbourne #7/R est:16000-20000 (A.D 13000)
£8471	$15671	€12368	Light no.3 (60x182cm-24x72in) s.i.d.87 verso oil on linen prov. 15-Mar-4 Sotheby's, Melbourne #38/R est:15000-25000 (A.D 20500)
£9016	$14246	€13163	Differences No 1 (180x120cm-71x47in) s.i.d.93 verso linen prov. 2-Sep-3 Deutscher-Menzies, Melbourne #102/R est:25000-35000 (A.D 22000)
£9091	$16818	€13273	Foreshore I (84x120cm-33x47in) s. i.d.98 verso prov. 10-Mar-4 Deutscher-Menzies, Melbourne #136/R est:24000-28000 (A.D 22000)
£9160	$16672	€13374	Waterfront No.3 (84x120cm-33x47in) s.d.1998 i.verso. 16-Jun-4 Deutscher-Menzies, Melbourne #110/R est:24000-28000 (A.D 24000)
£10569	$16593	€15325	Enter (121x121cm-48x48in) s.i.d.1985 verso linen prov. 26-Aug-3 Christie's, Sydney #16/R est:30000-40000 (A.D 26000)
£11064	$18809	€16153	Rhythms No.2 (91x274cm-36x108in) s.i.d.2002 linen prov. 25-Nov-3 Christie's, Melbourne #18/R est:30000-40000 (A.D 26000)
£14754	$23311	€21541	Chance (180x270cm-71x106in) s.i.d.1993 verso linen prov. 2-Sep-3 Deutscher-Menzies, Melbourne #60/R est:38000-55000 (A.D 36000)
£16260	$29106	€23740	Find (152x305cm-60x120in) s.d.86 verso linen canvas prov.exhib. 4-May-4 Sotheby's, Melbourne #17/R est:35000-40000 (A.D 40000)

Works on paper

£1107	$1793	€1616	Magpie geese at Red Lily Billabong No. 2 (56x76cm-22x30in) s.i.d.81 mixed media prov. 30-Jul-3 Goodman, Sydney #31/R (A.D 2700)
£1527	$2779	€2229	Anatomy of a fero cement hull (79x119cm-31x47in) s. i.d.76 verso mixed media. 16-Jun-4 Deutscher-Menzies, Melbourne #181/R est:4500-6500 (A.D 4000)
£1557	$2460	€2273	New York City (76x28cm-30x11in) s.i.d.82 W/C gouache pastel. 2-Sep-3 Deutscher-Menzies, Melbourne #254/R est:3200-3800 (A.D 3800)
£1721	$2789	€2513	Anatomy of a Ferro Cement hull (79x120cm-31x47in) s.i.d.76 mixed media. 30-Jul-3 Goodman, Sydney #10/R est:2500-3500 (A.D 4200)
£1860	$3440	€2716	Sayonara (64x95cm-25x37in) s.i.d.72 synthetic polymer prov. 10-Mar-4 Deutscher-Menzies, Melbourne #265/R est:5000-7000 (A.D 4500)

FISAREK, Alois (1906-1980) Czechoslovakian

£285	$472	€416	Ricky (27x34cm-11x13in) s.i.d.1952 verso board. 4-Oct-3 Dorotheum, Prague #127/R est:10000-15000 (C.KR 13000)

FISCHBACH, Johann (1797-1871) German

£277	$488	€410	View of Vienna from the Turkenschanz (12x24cm-5x9in) s. paper on board. 22-May-4 Lempertz, Koln #1517
£9091	$15455	€13000	Riverside town in the pre-Alps (45x55cm-18x22in) 24-Nov-3 Dorotheum, Vienna #23/R est:5000-7000

FISCHBECK, Ludwig (1866-1954) German

£292	$475	€420	Path through Hasbruch in autumn (65x110cm-26x43in) s. 26-Sep-3 Bolland & Marotz, Bremen #323
£331	$603	€500	Winter evening in Hasbruch (45x65cm-18x26in) s. 18-Jun-4 Bolland & Marotz, Bremen #345/R
£470	$864	€700	Early autumn in Hasbruch (55x95cm-22x37in) s. 26-Mar-4 Bolland & Marotz, Bremen #328/R
£568	$885	€840	Winter wood (65x45cm-26x18in) s. one of pair. 28-Mar-3 Behringer, Furth #1213/R

FISCHER, Abraham Samuel (1744-1809) Swiss

Works on paper

£2643	$4493	€3859	Vue des Bains de Loeche en Valais (54x46cm-21x18in) i. W/C. 7-Nov-3 Dobiaschofsky, Bern #29/R est:2800 (S.FR 6000)

FISCHER, Adolf (1856-1908) Austrian

£276	$505	€400	Brennerstrasse in the evening near KLausen (27x36cm-11x14in) s.i. verso panel. 27-Jan-4 Dorotheum, Vienna #25/R

FISCHER, Anton Otto (1882-1962) American

£469	$750	€685	Winter landscape with town in background behind a fence (30x43cm-12x17in) s.indis.d. 20-Sep-3 Pook & Pook, Downington #58
£588	$1000	€858	Ship run aground (41x61cm-16x24in) 21-Nov-3 Skinner, Boston #543/R est:1500-3000
£914	$1700	€1334	Untitled (61x91cm-24x36in) 6-Mar-4 Page, Batavia #196
£930	$1600	€1358	Sailing vessel with sharks in the water (51x76cm-20x30in) s.d.1923. 7-Dec-3 Treadway Gallery, Cincinnati #482/R est:2000-4000
£1117	$2000	€1631	Depth charge attack (81x66cm-32x26in) s. 15-May-4 Illustration House, New York #38/R est:2500-4000
£1400	$2380	€2044	Three masted man of war in full sail (66x91cm-26x36in) s.d.1940. 5-Nov-3 John Nicholson, Haslemere #652/R est:1000-1500
£1620	$2900	€2365	Coast guard cutter came like a ghost out of the fog (46x112cm-18x44in) s. 15-May-4 Illustration House, New York #37/R est:3000-5000
£1766	$3250	€2578	Men in lifeboat, sinking ship in background (56x102cm-22x40in) s.d.1949. 9-Jun-4 Alderfer's, Hatfield #402/R est:1500-2000
£1818	$3200	€2654	Landscape with river (51x71cm-20x28in) s. painted c.1950. 23-May-4 William Jenack, New York #183 est:1500-2500
£2983	$5250	€4355	Landscape with river (51x71cm-20x28in) s. painted c.1950. 23-May-4 William Jenack, New York #283 est:1500-2500

FISCHER, Anton Otto (attrib) (1882-1962) American

£246	$450	€359	Windjammer. bears sig.i. 5-Jun-4 Treadway Gallery, Cincinnati #575/R

FISCHER, August (1854-1921) Danish

£269	$484	€393	Street scene with young woman (52x46cm-20x18in) s.d.1919. 24-Apr-4 Rasmussen, Havnen #2124 (D.KR 3000)
£284	$508	€415	Tower by ruins (38x22cm-15x9in) 12-Jan-4 Rasmussen, Vejle #379/R (D.KR 3000)
£300	$516	€438	Farmyard with girl feeding ducks (45x33cm-18x13in) s.d.86. 2-Dec-3 Kunsthallen, Copenhagen #530 (D.KR 3200)
£395	$672	€577	Street scene in Rothenburg with figures (37x27cm-15x11in) s.i. 29-Nov-3 Rasmussen, Havnen #2011/R (D.KR 4200)
£403	$737	€588	View towards the old town gate, Nuremberg (27x21cm-11x8in) s. 9-Jun-4 Rasmussen, Copenhagen #1894/R (D.KR 4500)
£403	$737	€588	Girl with donkey (41x62cm-16x24in) s. 9-Jun-4 Rasmussen, Copenhagen #1925/R (D.KR 4500)
£407	$729	€594	From Horby ferry inn towards Holbaek (38x57cm-15x22in) s.d.82. 10-May-4 Rasmussen, Vejle #365/R (D.KR 4500)
£450	$733	€657	From Ribe Cathedral (37x26cm-15x10in) s.i.d.1917. 27-Sep-3 Rasmussen, Havnen #2135/R (D.KR 4800)
£492	$901	€718	Henckerstieg in Nuremberg (40x28cm-16x11in) s. 9-Jun-4 Rasmussen, Copenhagen #1892/R (D.KR 5500)
£609	$1048	€889	Farmyard with children, chickens and washing. s.d.1875. 3-Dec-3 Museumsbygningen, Copenhagen #127/R (D.KR 6500)
£699	$1097	€1021	Italian flower market with figures (23x32cm-9x13in) s.i.d.88 panel. 30-Aug-3 Rasmussen, Havnen #2124/R (D.KR 7500)
£894	$1519	€1305	View from Nuremberg with washerwomen (37x52cm-15x20in) s. 29-Nov-3 Rasmussen, Havnen #2010/R (D.KR 9500)
£1319	$2243	€1900	Kasemattentor in Nurnberg (48x37cm-19x15in) s.d.1913. 28-Oct-3 Dorotheum, Vienna #109/R est:1800-2200
£1343	$2457	€1961	Italian coastal town with beached boats on shore (54x92cm-21x36in) s. 7-Jun-4 Museumsbygningen, Copenhagen #134/R est:15000-20000 (D.KR 15000)
£1607	$2780	€2346	The market, Mercato Vecchio, Florence (49x39cm-19x15in) s.i.d.84. 9-Dec-3 Rasmussen, Copenhagen #1349/R est:10000-15000 (D.KR 17000)
£1831	$3039	€2600	Hamburg (43x56cm-17x22in) s. 16-Jun-3 Dorotheum, Vienna #182/R est:2200-2600
£1831	$3168	€2600	Part of Hamburg canal (41x52cm-16x20in) i.verso. 10-Dec-3 Dorotheum, Vienna #12/R est:2400-2800
£2437	$4557	€3558	Town scene with Borsen and figures walking (40x64cm-16x25in) s.d.1902. 25-Feb-4 Museumsbygningen, Copenhagen #113/R est:8000-10000 (D.KR 27000)
£4112	$6497	€5962	Summer's day at Silssoen, Switzerland (64x93cm-25x37in) s.i.d.89. 2-Sep-3 Rasmussen, Copenhagen #1526/R est:50000 (D.KR 44000)
£4726	$8176	€6900	View of Rome with the Tiber and the Vatican (48x82cm-19x32in) s.i.d.1895. 9-Dec-3 Rasmussen, Copenhagen #1240/R est:50000-75000 (D.KR 50000)
£7610	$13926	€11111	View of the Tiber towards St Peter's church (48x82cm-19x32in) s.i.d.1887. 9-Jun-4 Rasmussen, Copenhagen #1484/R est:30000-50000 (D.KR 85000)

FISCHER, Carl (1887-1962) Danish

£269	$491	€393	Interior scene with potted plants (66x71cm-26x28in) s. 9-Jun-4 Rasmussen, Copenhagen #2016 (D.KR 3000)
£300	$489	€438	Interior scene with man and woman (58x43cm-23x17in) s. 27-Sep-3 Rasmussen, Havnen #2052/R (D.KR 3200)
£356	$647	€534	Interior scene with figures partying (34x47cm-13x19in) s. panel. 19-Jun-4 Rasmussen, Havnen #2191/R (D.KR 4000)
£412	$672	€602	Interior scene with woman reading (56x42cm-22x17in) s. panel. 27-Sep-3 Rasmussen, Havnen #2050/R (D.KR 4400)
£492	$901	€718	Young woman seated wearing black hat and folded hands (44x35cm-17x14in) s. 9-Jun-4 Rasmussen, Copenhagen #2018/R (D.KR 5500)
£627	$1147	€915	Still life of fruit and potted plant (44x53cm-17x21in) s. 9-Jun-4 Rasmussen, Copenhagen #2021/R (D.KR 7000)
£629	$1170	€918	Couple at Langelinie, Flak fort in background (61x47cm-24x19in) s. 2-Mar-4 Rasmussen, Copenhagen #1387/R (D.KR 7000)
£716	$1311	€1045	Studies of women (29x23cm-11x9in) s. one oil one W/C two. 9-Jun-4 Rasmussen, Copenhagen #2014/R (D.KR 8000)
£806	$1474	€1177	Still life of fruit, hat and shoes (33x44cm-13x17in) s. 9-Jun-4 Rasmussen, Copenhagen #2022/R (D.KR 9000)

£985 $1802 €1438 Seated young woman sewing (43x36cm-17x14in) s.d.1923. 9-Jun-4 Rasmussen, Copenhagen #2013/R (D.KR 11000)
£985 $1802 €1438 Young woman wearing green hat (51x41cm-20x16in) s. 9-Jun-4 Rasmussen, Copenhagen #2020/R (D.KR 11000)
£1074 $1966 €1568 Young woman seated wearing black hat (56x39cm-22x15in) s. 9-Jun-4 Rasmussen, Copenhagen #2017/R est:10000 (D.KR 12000)
£1495 $2363 €2168 Interior scene with woman seated by chest of drawers (55x51cm-22x20in) s.d.20 exhib. 3-Sep-3 Museumsbygningen, Copenhagen #103/R est:12000-15000 (D.KR 16000)
Photographs
£313 $573 €457 Seated woman with red shawl (35x25cm-14x10in) s. 9-Jun-4 Rasmussen, Copenhagen #2019/R (D.KR 3500)

FISCHER, Carl H (1885-1955) Danish
£302 $550 €441 Floral still life (86x117cm-34x46in) s. 19-Jun-4 Jeffery Burchard, Florida #61

FISCHER, E (19th C) ?
£562 $917 €821 Scene from the French-German war in 1870 (94x137cm-37x54in) s. 27-Sep-3 Rasmussen, Havnen #2196/R (D.KR 6000)

FISCHER, Egon (1935-) Danish
Sculpture
£1444 $2700 €2108 I remember Constant (40x64x64cm-16x25x25in) painted iron exhib.prov. 25-Feb-4 Kunsthallen, Copenhagen #107/R est:10000 (D.KR 16000)

FISCHER, Ernst Albert (1853-1932) German
£455 $773 €650 Still life with tulips and Chinese porcelain (73x60cm-29x24in) s.d.1930. 20-Nov-3 Van Ham, Cologne #1569

FISCHER, Ernst Maria (1907-1939) German
£1000 $1820 €1500 Quarrel (50x70cm-20x28in) lit. 3-Jul-4 Badum, Bamberg #29/R est:3300

FISCHER, Fritz (1925-1986) Austrian
£268 $499 €400 Mountain lake on summer day (50x61cm-20x24in) s. board. 6-Mar-4 Arnold, Frankfurt #718/R

FISCHER, Heide (1942-) German
£479 $815 €700 Wild roses (100x120cm-39x47in) s. lit. 6-Nov-3 Allgauer, Kempten #3445/R

FISCHER, Heinrich (1820-1886) Swiss
£1342 $2510 €2000 Goats in the high mountains (27x37cm-11x15in) s. board. 24-Feb-4 Dorotheum, Vienna #114/R est:2200-2600

FISCHER, Holger (20th C) Danish
£284 $475 €415 Still life with roses (37x48cm-15x19in) s. 19-Oct-3 Bonhams & Butterfields, Los Angeles #7060
£600 $1080 €876 Still life with roses (71x51cm-28x20in) s. 21-Jan-4 Sotheby's, Olympia #498/R

FISCHER, Hugo (?) ?
Works on paper
£376 $700 €549 Dutch scene (43x76cm-17x30in) W/C. 6-Mar-4 Page, Batavia #106
£395 $700 €577 River landscape with cows watering beyond (30x22cm-12x9in) s. pencil W/C. 2-May-4 Bonhams & Butterfields, San Francisco #1112/R

FISCHER, Isaac (?-1705) German
£2802 $5015 €4091 Goddess Isis (150x86cm-59x34in) s.d.1700. 13-May-4 Stuker, Bern #128 est:6000-8000 (S.FR 6500)

FISCHER, Joel (1947-) American
Sculpture
£3514 $6500 €5130 Wanderer (122x101x66cm-48x40x26in) brown pat bronze Cast 1985 prov. 12-Feb-4 Sotheby's, New York #227/R est:2500-3500
£6486 $12000 €9470 Eggman (100x74x56cm-39x29x22in) green pat bronze edn 2/3 Cast 1987 prov. 12-Feb-4 Sotheby's, New York #223/R est:1200-1800
Works on paper
£1604 $2598 €2342 Untitled (194x118cm-76x46in) chl prov. 24-May-3 Burkhard, Luzern #125/R est:3000-4500 (S.FR 3400)

FISCHER, Johann (1919-) Austrian
Works on paper
£705 $1304 €1050 Washing (43x61cm-17x24in) mono.d.17-18-19 u 22 May 1989 pencil col pen. 9-Mar-4 Dorotheum, Vienna #176/R

FISCHER, Johann Martin (attrib) (1740-1820) Austrian
Sculpture
£4500 $8235 €6570 Reclining tiger (18x35cm-7x14in) s.d.1779 lead-tin alloy lit. 9-Jul-4 Sotheby's, London #88/R est:5000-7000

FISCHER, Johannes (1888-1955) Austrian
£764 $1245 €1100 French landscape (55x74cm-22x29in) s.d.34. 23-Sep-3 Wiener Kunst Auktionen, Vienna #53/R

FISCHER, Joseph (attrib) (1769-1822) Austrian
Works on paper
£276 $458 €400 Interior of church in Vienna (29x20cm-11x8in) s.d.1815 pen wash. 30-Sep-3 Dorotheum, Vienna #149

FISCHER, Lothar (1933-) German
Sculpture
£1181 $1972 €1700 Furniture facade with drawers (51x25x7cm-20x10x3in) s.d. verso clay iron plinth. 24-Oct-3 Ketterer, Hamburg #343/R est:1800-2000
£1342 $2470 €2000 Female torso (36x56x22cm-14x22x9in) s.d. plaster. 26-Mar-4 Ketterer, Hamburg #406/R est:2200-2500
£1538 $2615 €2200 Small kneeling figure (18x13x12cm-7x5x5in) s.d.79 brown black pat.bronze. 27-Nov-3 Lempertz, Koln #119/R est:1500-2000
£1800 $3312 €2628 Dreikantenstele III (122cm-48in) s.d.Jan 1976 terracotta prov.exhib. 24-Jun-4 Sotheby's, Olympia #555/R est:2000-3000
£2533 $4636 €3800 Kneeling female torso (62x34x38cm-24x13x15in) s.d.1985 clay. 4-Jun-4 Lempertz, Koln #136/R est:5000

FISCHER, Ludwig Hans (1848-1915) German
£335 $600 €489 Three-quarter length portrait of North African man wearing a fez (25x15cm-10x6in) s. 14-May-4 Eldred, East Dennis #757/R
£8000 $13360 €11680 Street market (36x58cm-14x23in) s. panel. 14-Oct-3 Sotheby's, London #71/R est:7000-9000
Works on paper
£470 $864 €700 Pestsaule on the Graben (14x9cm-6x4in) s. W/C. 26-Mar-4 Dorotheum, Vienna #265/R
£483 $801 €700 Oriental cafe (9x14cm-4x6in) mono. W/C. 30-Sep-3 Dorotheum, Vienna #270/R

FISCHER, Mark (20th C) American
£1800 $2880 €2610 Summer flowers in a basket (76x63cm-30x25in) 18-Sep-3 Christie's, Kensington #44/R est:1800-2200

FISCHER, Nathalia (19th C) Danish
£1402 $2215 €2033 View from Charlotte Amalie, Danish West Indies with ships and houses (56x97cm-22x38in) s.d.1885 exhib. 3-Sep-3 Museumsbygningen, Copenhagen #221/R est:12000-15000 (D.KR 15000)

FISCHER, Oskar (1892-1955) German
Works on paper
£2667 $4773 €4000 Illustration for poem (20x13cm-8x5in) s.i.d.1920 W/C Indian ink prov. 14-May-4 Ketterer, Munich #19/R est:1800-2400

FISCHER, Paul (1860-1934) Danish
£383 $620 €555 Figures on the way to church in winter (11x16cm-4x6in) grisaille. 4-Aug-3 Rasmussen, Vejle #482 (D.KR 4000)
£978 $1780 €1467 Portrait of the artist's wife Musse (33x25cm-13x10in) mono.d.1913. 19-Jun-4 Rasmussen, Havnen #2339/R (D.KR 11000)
£985 $1802 €1438 Portrait of Martin Daniel Muller (40x30cm-16x12in) s.i.d.1895 prov. 9-Jun-4 Rasmussen, Copenhagen #1988/R (D.KR 11000)
£1816 $3250 €2651 Harvesters (92x46cm-36x18in) s. prov. 6-May-4 Doyle, New York #68/R est:6000-8000
£1890 $3270 €2759 Norwegian landscape with yellow wooden houses by water (30x23cm-12x9in) s. 9-Dec-3 Rasmussen, Copenhagen #1588/R est:15000 (D.KR 20000)
£2062 $3546 €3011 View of Nyhavn (32x40cm-13x16in) s.d.Jan 1924. 2-Dec-3 Kunsthallen, Copenhagen #575/R est:20000 (D.KR 22000)
£2336 $3692 €3387 Street scene in Naples with shepherd and goats (50x57cm-20x22in) s.i.d.1922. 3-Sep-3 Museumsbygningen, Copenhagen #207/R est:40000-50000 (D.KR 25000)
£2464 $3943 €3597 Beach at Hornbaek with reclining female nude (29x39cm-11x15in) s. 22-Sep-3 Rasmussen, Vejle #39/R est:25000 (D.KR 26000)
£2809 $5027 €4101 Young lady wearing hat (42x28cm-17x11in) s.d.25.4.1933. 26-May-4 AB Stockholms Auktionsverk #2372/R est:40000-45000 (S.KR 38000)
£2956 $5292 €4316 The cycle trip - winter scene by the castle (28x22cm-11x9in) s. panel. 26-May-4 AB Stockholms Auktionsverk #2453/R est:35000-40000 (S.KR 40000)
£3145 $5849 €4592 Young harvester girl from Varmland in Sweden (26x32cm-10x13in) s.d.4.8.1901. 2-Mar-4 Rasmussen, Copenhagen #1304/R est:30000-40000 (D.KR 35000)
£3655 $5958 €5336 Winter's day in Bredgade (24x20cm-9x8in) s. panel. 27-Sep-3 Rasmussen, Havnen #2266/R est:15000-20000 (D.KR 39000)
£3970 $6868 €5796 Daisies in vase by green curtain (36x46cm-14x18in) s.d.4.8.1888. 9-Dec-3 Rasmussen, Copenhagen #1304/R est:25000-35000 (D.KR 42000)
£4029 $7372 €5882 Figures at Town Hall Square (25x20cm-10x8in) s. panel prov. 9-Jun-4 Rasmussen, Copenhagen #1932/R est:50000-60000 (D.KR 45000)
£4297 $7864 €6274 Snowy weather at Christiansborg with mother and child (20x25cm-8x10in) s. panel. 9-Jun-4 Rasmussen, Copenhagen #1465/R est:30000-50000 (D.KR 48000)
£4615 $7938 €6738 Italian street scene (51x58cm-20x23in) s.i.d.1922. 2-Dec-3 Bukowskis, Stockholm #258/R est:100000-120000 (S.KR 60000)
£4673 $7383 €6776 On the look out - Interior scene with young girl at window (41x32cm-16x13in) s. panel. 2-Sep-3 Rasmussen, Copenhagen #1517/R est:60000 (D.KR 50000)
£4769 $8203 €6963 Niels Juel's statue, Gammelholm (20x24cm-8x9in) s. panel. 2-Dec-3 Bukowskis, Stockholm #259/R est:40000-50000 (S.KR 62000)
£4924 $9011 €7189 Waiting for the visitors (43x58cm-17x23in) mono.d.1906 prov. 9-Jun-4 Rasmussen, Copenhagen #1456/R est:50000-75000 (D.KR 55000)
£5372 $9830 €7843 Foggy evening at Kongen's Nytorv (39x56cm-15x22in) s. prov. 9-Jun-4 Rasmussen, Copenhagen #1935/R est:50000 (D.KR 60000)
£5769 $9923 €8423 Town Hall Square, Copenhagen (20x25cm-8x10in) s. panel. 3-Dec-3 AB Stockholms Auktionsverk #2587/R est:100000-125000 (S.KR 75000)
£5866 $10970 €8564 Town Hall Tower seen from Vester Voldgade in winter (39x32cm-15x13in) s. 25-Feb-4 Museumsbygningen, Copenhagen #169/R est:60000-80000 (D.KR 65000)
£6144 $10629 €8970 Walking in King's Garden, autumn (32x38cm-13x15in) s. panel. 9-Dec-3 Rasmussen, Copenhagen #1302/R est:50000-60000 (D.KR 65000)
£6616 $11446 €9659 Female nude model with red flower in her hand in front of yellow curtain (128x73cm-50x29in) s.d.Marts 1889. 9-Dec-3 Rasmussen, Copenhagen #1305/R est:200000-250000 (D.KR 70000)
£6616 $11446 €9659 Princess Marie at Langelinie 1908 (28x22cm-11x9in) s. grisaille. 9-Dec-3 Rasmussen, Copenhagen #1312/R est:75000 (D.KR 70000)

£6714 $12287 €9802 Figures walking by the old Langelinie pavilion in summer (25x32cm-10x13in) s. 9-Jun-4 Rasmussen, Copenhagen #1601/R est:100000 (D.KR 75000)
£7089 $12264 €10350 A misunderstanding - boudoir-scene with young lady talking on the phone (34x26cm-13x10in) s. 9-Dec-3 Rasmussen, Copenhagen #1313/R est:75000 (D.KR 75000)
£7188 $13369 €10494 In a potato field near Stabaek Station near Oslo (66x119cm-26x47in) s.d.1887. 2-Mar-4 Rasmussen, Copenhagen #1275/R est:50000 (D.KR 80000)
£7583 $12133 €11071 Two young women on a jetty (33x49cm-13x19in) s. 22-Sep-3 Rasmussen, Vejle #18/R est:75000-100000 (D.KR 80000)
£8507 $14716 €12420 Model seated on bed in light of red table-lamp (34x42cm-13x17in) s. 9-Dec-3 Rasmussen, Copenhagen #1299/R est:75000-100000 (D.KR 90000)
£8507 $14716 €12420 Man dressed in black with hand-cart in front of bakery (25x20cm-10x8in) s. panel. 9-Dec-3 Rasmussen, Copenhagen #1306/R est:100000 (D.KR 90000)
£8985 $16712 €13118 Under the palm trees in San Remo (40x55cm-16x22in) s.i. 2-Mar-4 Rasmussen, Copenhagen #1287/R est:100000 (D.KR 100000)
£9848 $18021 €14378 Elegant ladies buying fish (33x39cm-13x15in) s. exhib.prov. 9-Jun-4 Rasmussen, Copenhagen #1600/R est:150000 (D.KR 110000)
£10000 $18000 €14600 Kongens Nytorv, Copenhagen (57x74cm-22x29in) s. 22-Apr-4 Christie's, Rockefeller NY #12/R est:25000-35000
£10138 $17235 €14801 Two friends wearing bathing costumes on beach (39x32cm-15x13in) s. 10-Nov-3 Rasmussen, Vejle #155/R est:60000-80000 (D.KR 110000)
£10556 $19000 €15412 Storkespringvand, Copenhagen (39x55cm-15x22in) s. 22-Apr-4 Christie's, Rockefeller NY #14/R est:25000-35000
£10588 $18000 €15458 Street scene in Copenhagen (49x56cm-19x22in) s. 28-Oct-3 Sotheby's, New York #83/R est:8000-12000
£10870 $18804 €15870 Winter's day at Queen Louise's Bridge (33x25cm-13x10in) s. 9-Dec-3 Rasmussen, Copenhagen #1297/R est:100000-125000 (D.KR 115000)
£11923 $20508 €17408 In the interval - Royal Opera, Copenhagen (27x33cm-11x13in) s. 3-Dec-3 AB Stockholms Auktionsverk #2577/R est:150000-200000 (S.KR 155000)
£13846 $23815 €20215 The bus stop (40x31cm-16x12in) s.d.1907 panel. 2-Dec-3 Bukowskis, Stockholm #254/R est:100000-125000 (S.KR 180000)
£14178 $24527 €20700 Many figures at Kongen's Nytorv (25x33cm-10x13in) s. panel. 9-Dec-3 Rasmussen, Copenhagen #1318/R est:75000-100000 (D.KR 150000)
£16068 $27798 €23459 Winter's day at Vesterbrogade with ladies chatting (74x57cm-29x22in) s. 9-Dec-3 Rasmussen, Copenhagen #1298/R est:200000 (D.KR 170000)
£17905 $32766 €26141 Three bathing girls by the sea (42x63cm-17x25in) s. 9-Jun-4 Rasmussen, Copenhagen #1504/R est:225000 (D.KR 200000)
£20591 $37681 €30063 Buying flowers at Hojbro Plads (38x32cm-15x13in) s. painted c.1920s. 9-Jun-4 Rasmussen, Copenhagen #1463/R est:200000 (D.KR 230000)
£20794 $35974 €30359 Winter's day at Osterbrogade with the artist's wife and daughter out shopping (39x57cm-15x22in) s.d.1912. 9-Dec-3 Rasmussen, Copenhagen #1307/R est:250000-350000 (D.KR 220000)
£21434 $38367 €31294 Evening street scene, Copenhagen (53x37cm-21x15in) s. 25-May-4 Bukowskis, Stockholm #314/R est:200000-225000 (S.KR 290000)
£21486 $39320 €31370 Young girl buying fish at Gammel Strand (57x74cm-22x29in) s. 9-Jun-4 Rasmussen, Copenhagen #1489/R est:300000 (D.KR 240000)
£25000 $45000 €36500 Vesterbrogade, Copenhagen (57x74cm-22x29in) s. 22-Apr-4 Christie's, Rockefeller NY #10/R est:30000-50000
£27103 $42822 €39299 Two young girls wearing summer dresses on the beach at Hornbaek (37x54cm-15x21in) s. 2-Sep-3 Rasmussen, Copenhagen #1515/R est:300000-350000 (D.KR 290000)
£30439 $55703 €44441 Evening street scene in lights from cars, Ostergade near Illum (51x37cm-20x15in) s. exhib.prov. 9-Jun-4 Rasmussen, Copenhagen #1517/R est:250000-350000 (D.KR 340000)
£31447 $58491 €45913 An elegant cyclist reading and young lady dressed in white in a hammock (59x48cm-23x19in) s. 2-Mar-4 Rasmussen, Copenhagen #1289/R est:300000-500000 (D.KR 350000)
£56711 $98110 €82798 By Peter Liep's house in Dyrehaven, girls at table (43x65cm-17x26in) s.d.1904. 9-Dec-3 Rasmussen, Copenhagen #1301/R est:700000-1000000 (D.KR 600000)
£89526 $163832 €130708 The artist's wife Musse and daughter Grethe passing girls on bikes, Copenhagen (76x58cm-30x23in) s. painted 1918 exhib.prov. 9-Jun-4 Rasmussen, Copenhagen #1477/R est:1200000 (D.KR 1000000)
£98832 $183827 €144295 Cyclists at Emilias Kilde - evening at Strandvejen (65x58cm-26x23in) s.d.1899. 2-Mar-4 Rasmussen, Copenhagen #1258/R est:1200000-1500000 (D.KR 1100000)

Works on paper

£449 $836 €656 Elegant lady with large fan (27x18cm-11x7in) mono. Indian ink. 2-Mar-4 Rasmussen, Copenhagen #1686/R (D.KR 5000)
£487 $813 €711 Man smoking pipe (26x19cm-10x7in) s.i.d.aug.91 W/C. 25-Oct-3 Rasmussen, Havnen #2096/R (D.KR 5200)
£674 $1253 €984 Carnival (32x47cm-13x19in) s.d.17 Febr. 94 pen W/C. 2-Mar-4 Rasmussen, Copenhagen #1693/R (D.KR 7500)
£898 $1671 €1311 Young elegant lady negotiating with street vendor (40x18cm-16x7in) s.d.97 crayon Indian ink. 2-Mar-4 Rasmussen, Copenhagen #1692/R (D.KR 10000)
£937 $1528 €1368 Portrait of young woman standing (28x19cm-11x7in) s. pencil W/C. 27-Sep-3 Rasmussen, Havnen #2259/R (D.KR 10000)
£945 $1635 €1380 The last train (19x24cm-7x9in) s. W/C. 9-Dec-3 Rasmussen, Copenhagen #1755/R (D.KR 10000)
£1134 $1962 €1656 The tower of Vor Frelser's church, old year going out, new year pushing in (24x17cm-9x7in) s. W/C. 9-Dec-3 Rasmussen, Copenhagen #1754/R est:12000-15000 (D.KR 12000)
£4706 $8000 €6871 Vista de Durango (25x42cm-10x17in) s.i. W/C on board prov. 19-Nov-3 Sotheby's, New York #77/R est:10000-15000
£5028 $9000 €7341 Tloexica, Oaxaca (21x34cm-8x13in) s.i. W/C. 26-May-4 Sotheby's, New York #73/R est:10000-15000

FISCHER, Paul (attrib) (1860-1934) Danish

£948 $1517 €1384 Street scene with women (53x45cm-21x18in) 22-Sep-3 Rasmussen, Vejle #26/R (D.KR 10000)

FISCHER, Siegfried (1899-?) Austrian

£333 $600 €500 Bottom of the sea (57x60cm-22x24in) mono. panel. 21-Apr-4 Dorotheum, Vienna #186/R

FISCHER, Vilhelm Theodor (1857-1928) Danish

£269 $484 €393 Hare eating from a branch (69x45cm-27x18in) s. 24-Apr-4 Rasmussen, Havnen #2154/R (D.KR 3000)
£448 $819 €654 Birds on the shore of Lammefjord in summer (48x76cm-19x30in) s.i.d.1916. 9-Jun-4 Rasmussen, Copenhagen #1984/R (D.KR 5000)
£455 $728 €664 Coastal landscape with birds at edge of water (44x63cm-17x25in) s.d.1918. 22-Sep-3 Rasmussen, Vejle #361/R (D.KR 4800)
£945 $1692 €1380 Landscape with storks by river (58x83cm-23x33in) s. 12-Jan-4 Rasmussen, Vejle #95/R (D.KR 10000)

FISCHER-HANSEN, Else (1905-) Danish

£379 $607 €550 Composition (165x43cm-65x17in) s.d.1957 verso. 17-Sep-3 Kunsthallen, Copenhagen #79 (D.KR 4000)

FISCHER-HANSEN, Judith (1952-) Danish

£394 $710 €575 Composition in colour (100x81cm-39x32in) init.d.88 verso. 24-Apr-4 Rasmussen, Havnen #4183 (D.KR 4400)

FISCHETTI, Fedele (1734-1789) Italian

£6207 $10303 €9000 Death of Alexander the Great (49x73cm-19x29in) 1-Oct-3 Dorotheum, Vienna #294/R est:12000-16000
£26000 $47580 €37960 Allegorical figures (59x98cm-23x39in) pair oval. 8-Jul-4 Sotheby's, London #160/R est:15000-20000

Works on paper

£592 $1089 €900 Magdalen with two angels (21x13cm-8x5in) pencil exhib. 22-Jun-4 Sotheby's, Milan #57/R
£1200 $2160 €1752 Visitation (47x37cm-19x15in) pen brown ink grey wash black chk oval. 20-Apr-4 Sotheby's, Olympia #100/R est:800-1200

FISCHHOF, Georg (1859-1914) Austrian

£302 $540 €441 Sorrento (20x31cm-8x12in) s. 12-May-4 Dobiaschofsky, Bern #493 (S.FR 700)
£336 $628 €500 Autumn landscape with woodland pond and boys fishing (42x69cm-17x27in) s. 27-Feb-4 Altus, Berlin #400/R
£350 $601 €500 Landscape with farm houses and cows (50x81cm-20x32in) s.d.97. 4-Dec-3 Dorotheum, Graz #9/R
£409 $733 €597 Nervi (20x31cm-8x12in) s. 12-May-4 Dobiaschofsky, Bern #492/R (S.FR 950)
£430 $788 €650 Southern landscape (70x55cm-28x22in) 8-Apr-4 Dorotheum, Vienna #254/R
£467 $854 €700 Evening time at the coast with fishing village (50x82cm-20x32in) s.d.1894 canvas on canvas. 5-Jun-4 Arnold, Frankfurt #574/R
£493 $908 €750 Venice (49x80cm-19x31in) s.d.99. 22-Jun-4 Wiener Kunst Auktionen, Vienna #190/R
£530 $964 €800 Dutch winter landscape (50x100cm-20x39in) s. 21-Jun-4 Dorotheum, Vienna #220/R
£795 $1446 €1200 Town view (69x55cm-27x22in) s. 21-Jun-4 Dorotheum, Vienna #269/R
£1258 $2290 €1900 Sailing ship in front of harbour town (69x105cm-27x41in) s. 21-Jun-4 Dorotheum, Vienna #312/R est:1300-1500
£1408 $2338 €2000 Summer landscape. Winter landscape (54x26cm-21x10in) s. two. 16-Jun-3 Dorotheum, Vienna #131/R est:1500-1700

FISCHL, Eric (1948-) American

£8649 $16000 €12628 Untitled (65x91cm-26x36in) s.d.96 prepared paper prov. 12-Feb-4 Sotheby's, New York #323/R est:12000-18000
£14970 $25000 €21856 Bathroom scene (187x194cm-74x76in) oil four sheets of glassine on board painted 1979-80 prov.exhib. 12-Nov-3 Christie's, Rockefeller NY #638/R est:20000-30000
£18436 $33000 €26917 Two nudes on green grass (71x89cm-28x35in) s.d.87 paper prov. 13-May-4 Sotheby's, New York #453/R est:22000-28000
£50279 $90000 €73407 Untitled (126x99cm-50x39in) s.d.86 paper prov.lit. 13-May-4 Sotheby's, New York #452/R est:40000-60000
£86667 $160333 €130000 Collector and family (272x190cm-107x75in) s.i.d.1991 verso prov. 18-Jul-4 Sotheby's, Paris #231/R est:70000-90000
£94972 $170000 €138659 Father and son sleeping (188x188cm-74x74in) s.i.d.80 verso prov.exhib.lit. 13-May-4 Phillips, New York #24/R est:200000-300000
£125749 $210000 €183594 Japanese bath (122x152cm-48x60in) s.d.1988 verso prov. 12-Nov-3 Sotheby's, New York #68/R est:180000-220000

Works on paper

£2246 $3750 €3279 Untitled (37x32cm-15x13in) s.d.94 W/C prov. 7-Oct-3 Sotheby's, New York #394 est:5000-7000

FISCHLI, Alfred (1921-) Swiss

£249 $423 €364 Winter landscape with two farmers (30x40cm-12x16in) mono.d.77 masonite. 1-Dec-3 Koller, Zurich #6508 (S.FR 550)
£543 $923 €793 Transport of wood in winter (54x49cm-21x19in) mono.d.77 masonite. 1-Dec-3 Koller, Zurich #6509 (S.FR 1200)

FISCHLI, Peter and WEISS, David (20th C) Swiss

£14525 $26000 €21207 Lugano at night (156x217cm-61x85in) c-print edition of six prov. 14-May-4 Phillips, New York #182/R est:10000-15000

Photographs

£2197 $3800 €3208 Pilze - Fungi (74x107cm-29x42in) s.d.1998 verso inkjet print on plexiglas one of 9 prov. 10-Dec-3 Phillips, New York #589/R est:3000-4000
£2400 $4008 €3504 Untitled, blumen (74x107cm-29x42in) inkjet print UV glass edition 9 of 9 prov. 22-Oct-3 Christie's, London #153/R est:2000-3000
£3468 $6000 €5063 Blumenphoto (74x107cm-29x42in) inkjet print one of 9 prov. 10-Dec-3 Phillips, New York #588/R est:2000-3000
£4022 $7200 €5872 Untitled (74x107cm-29x42in) s.d.98 num. of 9 verso inkjet print prov. 14-May-4 Phillips, New York #302/R est:5000-7000
£4190 $7500 €6117 Untitled (74x107cm-29x42in) s.d.98 num. of 9 verso inkjet print prov. 14-May-4 Phillips, New York #299/R est:5000-7000
£4192 $7000 €6120 Untitled (74x104cm-29x41in) s.verso c-print two prov. 13-Nov-3 Sotheby's, New York #480/R est:10000-15000
£8380 $15000 €12235 Uber dem abgrund (24x30cm-9x12in) s.i. num.3 verso black white photo prov. 14-May-4 Phillips, New York #197/R est:15000-20000
£11173 $20000 €16313 Untitled, Equilibrium series (36x47cm-14x19in) col photo edition of three prov.exhib. 14-May-4 Phillips, New York #194/R est:8000-12000
£11173 $20000 €16313 Untitled, Equilibrium series (47x36cm-19x14in) col photo edition of three prov.exhib. 14-May-4 Phillips, New York #195/R est:8000-12000

Sculpture
£22973 $42500 €33541 Kerze 1/4 (30x15cm-12x6in) s. rubber edn 1/5 Cast 1986-7 prov. 12-Feb-4 Sotheby's, New York #249/R est:2000-3000
£32934 $55000 €48084 Kanalarbeiter (17x46x26cm-7x18x10in) s.d.87 rubber prov. 13-Nov-3 Sotheby's, New York #142/R est:4000-6000
£34132 $57000 €49833 Krahe (27x41x14cm-11x16x6in) rubber executed 1986 prov.exhib.lit. 13-Nov-3 Phillips, New York #49/R est:35000-45000
£38000 $69920 €55480 Putzequipe - cleaning team. painted polyurethane variable dimensions executed 1985 exhib. 24-Jun-4 Christie's, London #51/R est:25000-35000
£65000 $119600 €94900 Untitled (178x94x94cm-70x37x37in) painted polyurethane executed c.1983 prov. 24-Jun-4 Christie's, London #2/R est:40000-60000
£78212 $140000 €114190 Plant. Square cushion. Diver (40x17x16cm-16x7x6in) rubber executed 1987 different sizes prov.exhib.lit. 13-May-4 Phillips, New York #65/R est:80000-120000

FISCHNALLER, Josef (1927-) Austrian?
£455 $773 €650 Brother and sister (62x80cm-24x31in) s.d.76. 27-Nov-3 Dorotheum, Linz #495

FISH, Anne Harriet (?-1964) British
Works on paper
£260 $434 €380 Two cats (23x29cm-9x11in) s. W/C brush black ink. 16-Oct-3 Christie's, Kensington #237/R
£720 $1310 €1051 St. Ives Harbour (25x36cm-10x14in) s. W/C mixed media. 15-Jun-4 David Lay, Penzance #236/R

FISH, George Drummond (1876-1938) Irish
Works on paper
£260 $484 €380 Sunset over loch (28x40cm-11x16in) s. W/C. 2-Mar-4 Bearnes, Exeter #336/R

FISH, George G (fl.1846-1880) American
Works on paper
£770 $1425 €1155 Still lifes of birds (48x38cm-19x15in) s. one d.1875 one d.1874 pastel pair prov. 14-Jul-4 American Auctioneer #490305/R

FISH, Janet (1938-) American
£5988 $10000 €8742 Green bananas (78x101cm-31x40in) s.d.69. 7-Oct-3 Sotheby's, New York #398 est:8000-10000

FISHER, Albert (20th C) American
£2941 $5500 €4294 Young woman being forcibly pulled into back of car (58x43cm-23x17in) s. painted c.1940. 26-Feb-4 Illustration House, New York #69

FISHER, Anna S (1873-1942) American
£313 $550 €457 Beached row boat (36x25cm-14x10in) prov. 18-May-4 Arthur James, Florida #236
£682 $1200 €996 Still life, flowers in a window (53x69cm-21x27in) prov. 18-May-4 Arthur James, Florida #235/R est:1000-1500
Works on paper
£398 $700 €581 April shower (38x51cm-15x20in) s. W/C exhib. 18-May-4 Arthur James, Florida #53

FISHER, Carl H (20th C) ?
£688 $1100 €1004 Still life with roses in a blue vase (89x79cm-35x31in) s. 21-Sep-3 Bonhams & Butterfields, San Francisco #2815/R est:600-800

FISHER, Charles (19/20th C) ?
Works on paper
£512 $850 €742 Coastal scene (13x41cm-5x16in) W/C. 14-Jun-3 Du Mouchelle, Detroit #1176/R

FISHER, D A (19th C) American
£1553 $2500 €2267 View of Peabody stream near Gorham, NH (64x89cm-25x35in) s.d.1889. 20-Aug-3 James Julia, Fairfield #90/R est:2750-3250

FISHER, Daniel (19th C) British
£222 $400 €324 Forest scene with large tree (58x48cm-23x19in) board. 25-Jan-4 Hindman, Chicago #1037/R

FISHER, Harrison (1875-1934) American
Works on paper
£326 $600 €476 Woman with big hat and terrier pet (25x23cm-10x9in) s.d.1911 pencil. 11-Jun-4 David Rago, Lambertville #344/R
£1397 $2500 €2040 Dutch girl (36x28cm-14x11in) s.d.1909 W/C gouache sketching board. 10-Jan-4 Auctions by the Bay, Alameda #572/R
£4972 $9000 €7259 Portrait of a lady and her suitor (61x48cm-24x19in) s.d.1909 W/C. 3-Apr-4 Neal Auction Company, New Orleans #670/R est:10000-15000

FISHER, Horace (1861-1928) British
£5000 $7950 €7250 Young girl carrying a water jug (77x51cm-30x20in) s. 9-Sep-3 Bonhams, Knightsbridge #167/R est:2500-3500
£5200 $9620 €7592 Pergola in autumn, Capri (70x191cm-28x75in) s. 13-Jan-4 Bonhams, Knightsbridge #272/R est:4000-6000

FISHER, Hugo Antoine (1854-1916) American
Works on paper
£405 $725 €591 Winter stroll in the woods (36x53cm-14x21in) s. W/C. 8-Jan-4 James Julia, Fairfield #802/R

FISHER, Hugo Melville (1876-1946) American
£1087 $2000 €1587 Sailing boats in an inlet (66x73cm-26x29in) s. prov. 8-Jun-4 Bonhams & Butterfields, San Francisco #4319/R est:3000-5000
£2160 $3500 €3132 Esopus Creek (65x107cm-26x42in) s. prov. 8-Aug-3 Barridorf, Portland #142/R est:4000-6000
Works on paper
£265 $475 €387 Cow standing at river's edge (41x81cm-16x32in) s. W/C. 29-May-4 Brunk, Ashville #470/R

FISHER, J (?) British
Miniatures
£1034 $1728 €1500 Victorian portrait of two sisters (16x12cm-6x5in) i. gouache ivory gold frame. 14-Nov-3 Lempertz, Koln #546/R est:1800

FISHER, Jonathan (?-1809) British
Works on paper
£9000 $16110 €13140 Views of Curraghmore House in 1768, Waterford (23x37cm-9x15in) i. pencil grey pale blue wash album sold with photo. 14-May-4 Christie's, London #100/R est:10000-15000

FISHER, Joshua (1859-?) British
Works on paper
£400 $668 €584 Poultry (36x25cm-14x10in) s. W/C. 17-Oct-3 Keys, Aylsham #496

FISHER, Major General Benjamin (1753-1814) British
Works on paper
£900 $1530 €1314 Elizabeth Castle, Jersey (30x47cm-12x19in) W/C two. 4-Nov-3 Bonhams, New Bond Street #17/R
£2000 $3400 €2920 Coastal town overlooked by a fort (32x48cm-13x19in) W/C sold with two others prov. 4-Nov-3 Bonhams, New Bond Street #16/R est:1500-2000

FISHER, Mrs Flavius J (19th C) American
£269 $450 €393 Still life (38x76cm-15x30in) s. 16-Nov-3 Simpson's, Houston #114/R
£276 $450 €403 Still life (38x76cm-15x30in) s. 28-Sep-3 Simpson's, Houston #92a/R

FISHER, R A (20th C) British
Works on paper
£1500 $2595 €2190 Churchill, Stalin, Roosevelt, De Gaulle and others, posing for a camera (19x28cm-7x11in) s.d.45 ink W/C sold with a press photo. 11-Dec-3 Sotheby's, London #19/R est:600-800

FISHER, Randi (1920-1997) Swedish
£676 $1251 €987 The joker (94x81cm-37x32in) s. exhib. 15-Mar-4 Rasmussen, Vejle #626/R (D.KR 7500)
£733 $1297 €1070 Window towards the harbour, Hallevikstrand (32x62cm-13x24in) s.d.57. 27-Apr-4 AB Stockholms Auktionsverk #822/R (S.KR 10000)
£870 $1566 €1270 The actress - Karin Kavli (63x40cm-25x16in) s.d.46 panel prov. 26-Apr-4 Bukowskis, Stockholm #230/R (S.KR 12000)
Works on paper
£364 $671 €546 Boat under bridge (48x75cm-19x30in) s.d.53 mixed media panel. 14-Jun-4 Lilla Bukowskis, Stockholm #298 (S.KR 5000)

FISHER, Rowland (1885-1969) British
£260 $416 €380 Three masted sailing vessel and tug (38x48cm-15x19in) s. 18-Sep-3 Mallams, Cheltenham #285/R
£320 $582 €467 Yarmouth trawlers returning with the catch (34x39cm-13x15in) s. 1-Jul-4 Mellors & Kirk, Nottingham #773
£360 $659 €526 Port Isaac, August (30x36cm-12x14in) s.i.verso. 7-Apr-4 Gardiner & Houlgate, Bath #313/R
£450 $815 €657 Gorleston Pier (15x20cm-6x8in) s.d.1965. 16-Apr-4 Keys, Aylsham #688

FISHER, Sandra (1947-) British
£360 $576 €526 Giovanna and Kitty (38x38cm-15x15in) s.d.1991. 19-May-3 Bruton Knowles, Cheltenham #210a

FISHER, Thomas (1782-1836) British
Works on paper
£550 $990 €803 Mrs Brown's School at Harrold, Bedfordshire (31x41cm-12x16in) i. W/C over pencil prov. 21-Jan-4 Sotheby's, Olympia #116/R

FISHER, William Mark (1841-1923) British/American
£300 $555 €438 Thatched cottage (23x33cm-9x13in) s. board. 10-Feb-4 David Lay, Penzance #148
£550 $919 €803 Cattle in a mountainous landscape (39x42cm-15x17in) oil paper on board. 16-Oct-3 Christie's, Kensington #380/R
£950 $1587 €1387 Kitchen garden, Widdington (46x61cm-18x24in) s. prov. 16-Oct-3 Christie's, Kensington #381/R
£1300 $2405 €1898 Mill stream (43x62cm-17x24in) s.d.96 prov. 10-Feb-4 Bonhams, Knightsbridge #267/R est:1500-2000
£1300 $2392 €1898 Cattle by a river (34x42cm-13x17in) s. 24-Mar-4 Hamptons Fine Art, Godalming #274

£1397 $2500 €2040 Gathering flowers (36x51cm-14x20in) s. prov. 6-May-4 Shannon's, Milford #232/R est:3000-5000
£1802 $3063 €2631 Surrey pastures (26x36cm-10x14in) i.verso panel prov. 21-Nov-3 Walker's, Ottawa #253/R est:900-1200 (C.D 4000)
£2000 $3340 €2920 Cattle watering in a river landscape (46x66cm-18x26in) s.indis.d.85. 13-Nov-3 Christie's, Kensington #169/R est:2000-3000
£2215 $3500 €3234 Farmyard (46x61cm-18x24in) s. 7-Sep-3 Treadway Gallery, Cincinnati #575/R est:2500-3500
Works on paper
£420 $777 €613 Continental Harbour scene (25x36cm-10x14in) s. W/C. 13-Feb-4 Sworder & Son, Bishops Stortford #65/R
£500 $850 €730 Overlooking the harbour (26x36cm-10x14in) s. pencil W/C exhib. 18-Nov-3 Bonhams, Leeds #79/R
£500 $850 €730 Bay, Antibes (25x35cm-10x14in) s. W/C htd white exhib. 18-Nov-3 Bonhams, Leeds #80/R
£550 $880 €803 Figure seated in a sun dappled glade, the sea beyond (23x33cm-9x13in) s. W/C panel. 16-Sep-3 Gorringes, Bexhill #1610
£600 $1020 €876 Woman seated beneath a tree, a coastal by beyond (25x35cm-10x14in) s. W/C. 4-Nov-3 Rowley Fine Art, Newmarket #374/R
£600 $1104 €876 Cattle grazing (23x33cm-9x13in) s. W/C. 23-Jun-4 Bonhams, Bury St Edmunds #304
£5500 $9845 €8030 Blacksmith (70x106cm-28x42in) s.d.76 W/C. 26-May-4 Sotheby's, Olympia #123/R est:6000-8000

FISHWICK, Clifford (1923-1997) British
£300 $480 €435 Ice flow (61x76cm-24x30in) studio st. 16-Sep-3 Bonhams, Knightsbridge #24/R
£500 $850 €730 Green coast (14x61cm-6x24in) s.d.58 board. 26-Nov-3 Sotheby's, Olympia #161/R
£600 $1080 €876 Woman and black cat (50x38cm-20x15in) s. board. 20-Jan-4 Bonhams, Knightsbridge #202/R
£850 $1420 €1241 Beach huts (15x61cm-6x24in) s.d.60 s.i.d.1960 verso board. 16-Oct-3 Christie's, Kensington #715/R
£1400 $2338 €2044 Still life Abstract (61x77cm-24x30in) s.d.56 board pair. 16-Oct-3 Christie's, Kensington #649 est:500-700
Sculpture
£1000 $1790 €1460 Totemic abstract (77x16cm-30x6in) init.d.59 wood sacking paint panel. 14-May-4 Christie's, Kensington #636/R est:500-800
Works on paper
£260 $416 €377 Influx (42x54cm-17x21in) s.d.1964 gouache W/C. 16-Sep-3 Bonhams, Knightsbridge #51
£260 $416 €377 Coastal plateau and mine (53x37cm-21x15in) s.d.63 gouache. 16-Sep-3 Bonhams, Knightsbridge #52
£800 $1272 €1168 Abstract composition (18x27cm-7x11in) s.d.1980 gouache ink sold with two others by the same hand. 10-Sep-3 Sotheby's, Olympia #303/R

FISK, Harry T (1887-1974) American
£403 $750 €588 Portrait of a black woman (41x30cm-16x12in) s. canvasboard painted c.1925. 7-Mar-4 Treadway Gallery, Cincinnati #672/R

FISK, William Henry (1827-1884) British
£671 $1248 €1000 Portrait of the Pre-Raphaelite Frederick George Stephens (77x64cm-30x25in) 6-Mar-4 Arnold, Frankfurt #721/R

FISSETTE, Leopold (1814-1889) German
£1500 $2730 €2250 Woman at arched window watering potted plants on window sill (30x23cm-12x9in) panel. 20-Jun-4 Wilkinson, Doncaster #339 est:1500-2000

FISSORE, Daniele (1947-) Italian
£268 $497 €400 Green (24x18cm-9x7in) s. 13-Mar-4 Meeting Art, Vercelli #182
£282 $468 €400 Mare e Green (18x24cm-7x9in) s. 14-Jun-3 Meeting Art, Vercelli #140
£289 $534 €430 Summer (35x30cm-14x12in) s.d.1977 acrylic canvas on board. 13-Mar-4 Meeting Art, Vercelli #149
£333 $613 €500 Sea and green (25x25cm-10x10in) s. 12-Jun-4 Meeting Art, Vercelli #162/R
£333 $613 €500 Sea and green (25x25cm-10x10in) s. 12-Jun-4 Meeting Art, Vercelli #539/R
£367 $675 €550 Sea and green (25x25cm-10x10in) s. 12-Jun-4 Meeting Art, Vercelli #659/R
£367 $675 €550 Sea and green (25x25cm-10x10in) s. 12-Jun-4 Meeting Art, Vercelli #910/R
£408 $731 €600 Green (17x40cm-7x16in) s. acrylic panel oval. 22-Mar-4 Sant Agostino, Torino #372/R
£420 $701 €600 Green (50x30cm-20x12in) s. acrylic painted 1994. 26-Jun-3 Sant Agostino, Torino #321/R
£528 $877 €750 Mare e Green (40x50cm-16x20in) s. 14-Jun-3 Meeting Art, Vercelli #458/R
£563 $935 €800 Mare e Green (40x50cm-16x20in) s. 14-Jun-3 Meeting Art, Vercelli #193/R
£570 $1055 €850 Green (40x50cm-16x20in) s. cardboard. 13-Mar-4 Meeting Art, Vercelli #469

FITLER, William Crothers (1857-1915) American
£1033 $1900 €1508 Winter landscape (36x53cm-14x21in) s. 23-Mar-4 Arthur James, Florida #156/R est:1500-2000
£1087 $2000 €1587 Houses by a river (35x51cm-14x20in) s. 27-Jun-4 Freeman, Philadelphia #82/R est:2000-3000
£1776 $3250 €2593 Meadow at dusk (30x41cm-12x16in) s. 5-Jun-4 Treadway Gallery, Cincinnati #655/R est:4000-6000
£2348 $4250 €3428 Close of day (30x41cm-12x16in) s. prov. 31-Mar-4 Sotheby's, New York #67/R est:2500-3500

FITTKE, Arturo (1873-1910) Spanish
£569 $945 €831 Boy portrait (34x25cm-13x10in) s. board. 4-Oct-3 Dorotheum, Prague #26/R est:20000-30000 (C.KR 26000)
£2448 $4210 €3500 Chatting in the kitchen (75x100cm-30x39in) s. 3-Dec-3 Stadion, Trieste #979/R est:3500-4500
£3497 $6014 €5000 Girl in red dress (50x40cm-20x16in) s. cardboard. 3-Dec-3 Stadion, Trieste #1177/R est:3500-4500

FITZGERALD, Edmond James (1912-1989) American
£472 $850 €689 Riverscape with ducks (30x41cm-12x16in) s. 23-Jan-4 Freeman, Philadelphia #188/R

FITZGERALD, Florence (?-1927) British
£8200 $13038 €11890 Extensive autumnal woodland scene, with children in the foreground (75x126cm-30x50in) s. 9-Sep-3 Bonhams, Knightsbridge #229/R est:2500-3500

FITZGERALD, Frederick R (19/20th C) British
Works on paper
£450 $806 €657 Sogne Fjord, Norway (25x36cm-10x14in) s. W/C. 13-May-4 Mitchells, Cockermouth #1046
£480 $888 €701 St Ives fishing boats putting to sea (28x46cm-11x18in) s. W/C. 9-Mar-4 Gorringes, Lewes #2303

FITZGERALD, James (1899-?) American
Works on paper
£8642 $14000 €12531 Dance of the dories (49x63cm-19x25in) s. W/C. 8-Aug-3 Barridorf, Portland #351/R est:12000-18000

FITZGERALD, John Austen (1832-1906) British
£81081 $150000 €118378 Five scenes taken from A Midsummer Night's Dream (23x81cm-9x32in) board five in one frame. 24-Jan-4 Jeffery Burchard, Florida #12/R est:6000-8000
Works on paper
£9000 $15300 €13140 Realms of fairydom (17x22cm-7x9in) s. W/C bodycol. 4-Nov-3 Bonhams, New Bond Street #93/R est:5000-8000
£60000 $102000 €87600 Fairies in the snow (56x77cm-22x30in) pencil W/C bodycol gum arabic scratching out exhib. 20-Nov-3 Christie's, London #151/R est:25000-35000

FITZGERALD, Lionel Lemoine (1890-1956) Canadian
£362 $605 €529 Untitled - tree study (22x29cm-9x11in) col pencil prov. 17-Nov-3 Hodgins, Calgary #284/R (C.D 800)
£6400 $11712 €9344 Still life with jug (27x20cm-11x8in) board painted c.1945 prov. 1-Jun-4 Joyner Waddington, Toronto #15/R est:3000-4000 (C.D 16000)
£6696 $11518 €9776 Landscape with setting sun (19x22cm-7x9in) init. 2-Dec-3 Joyner Waddington, Toronto #227/R est:2500-3000 (C.D 15000)
£13514 $22973 €19730 Prairie scene (25x30cm-10x12in) s.d.1921 i.d.verso canvas on board prov. 18-Nov-3 Sotheby's, Toronto #8/R est:7000-10000 (C.D 30000)
£15200 $27816 €22192 Prairies (29x36cm-11x14in) s.d.1929 prov. 1-Jun-4 Joyner Waddington, Toronto #81/R est:12000-18000 (C.D 38000)
£34553 $61850 €50447 Figure in the woods (91x61cm-36x24in) s.d.1920 lit. 27-May-4 Heffel, Vancouver #85/R est:25000-30000 (C.D 85000)
Works on paper
£289 $524 €422 Untitled - figure study (30x13cm-12x5in) init. graphite. 18-Apr-4 Levis, Calgary #451/R (C.D 700)
£315 $536 €460 Tulips (39x27cm-15x11in) init. ink prov. 23-Nov-3 Levis, Calgary #35/R (C.D 700)
£610 $1091 €891 Untitled abstract (18x23cm-7x9in) init. col pencil prov. 6-May-4 Heffel, Vancouver #55/R (C.D 1500)
£625 $1075 €913 Still life of flower (57x44cm-22x17in) wash prov. 2-Dec-3 Joyner Waddington, Toronto #285/R (C.D 1400)
£714 $1229 €1042 Cloud study (29x22cm-11x9in) init.d.July 11 35 pencil. 2-Dec-3 Joyner Waddington, Toronto #470 (C.D 1600)
£893 $1518 €1304 Abstract composition (14x22cm-6x9in) s. col pencil prov. 6-Nov-3 Heffel, Vancouver #42/R est:1500-2000 (C.D 2000)
£1727 $3092 €2521 Hill and trees (19x25cm-7x10in) s.1925 W/C prov.lit. 27-May-4 Heffel, Vancouver #101/R est:3000-4000 (C.D 4250)
£1915 $3255 €2796 Driftwood, Bowen Island, BC (57x43cm-22x17in) s.init.d.1942 col crayon prov.exhib. 27-Nov-3 Heffel, Vancouver #161/R est:2500-3500 (C.D 4250)
£2000 $3660 €2920 Farm scene (24x29cm-9x11in) W/C exec c.1930 prov. 1-Jun-4 Joyner Waddington, Toronto #188/R est:2000-2500 (C.D 5000)

FITZGERALD, Lloyd (1941-) Canadian
£1464 $2489 €2137 Apple in bloom (76x102cm-30x40in) s.d.1987 i.verso on stretcher prov. 18-Nov-3 Sotheby's, Toronto #157/R est:3500-4500 (C.D 3250)
£2703 $4595 €3946 Return of the hunters (39x43cm-15x17in) s.d.1991 s.i.d. verso on board prov. 18-Nov-3 Sotheby's, Toronto #97/R est:2000-2500 (C.D 6000)

FITZHARRIS, Mike (20th C) Irish
£513 $929 €770 Boat yard (20x33cm-8x13in) s.d.1990 oil graphite board. 30-Mar-4 De Veres Art Auctions, Dublin #169/R
£1216 $2299 €1800 Winter harbour (50x62cm-20x24in) s.d.1989 board. 17-Feb-4 Whyte's, Dublin #210/R est:1800-2200
£1316 $2421 €2000 Landscape (59x84cm-23x33in) s.d.98 board. 22-Jun-4 De Veres Art Auctions, Dublin #80/R est:2000-3000
£2013 $3564 €3000 View from Dollymount, Dublin (51x64cm-20x25in) s.d.1989 board. 27-Apr-4 Whyte's, Dublin #159/R est:2000-3000
£2292 $3598 €3300 Dublin Bay (61x86cm-24x34in) s.d.98 board. 26-Aug-3 James Adam, Dublin #220/R est:3500-4500
£3600 $6516 €5400 Shoreline (80x110cm-31x43in) s. board exhib. 31-Mar-4 James Adam, Dublin #71/R est:4000-6000

FITZI, Johann Ulrich (1798-1855) Swiss
Works on paper
£1514 $2528 €2195 Loft (26x45cm-10x18in) s. W/C. 23-Jun-3 Philippe Schuler, Zurich #3614 est:2000-2400 (S.FR 3300)
£9865 $16475 €14403 Trogen (26x45cm-10x18in) s.i.d.1851 W/C pen. 24-Oct-3 Hans Widmer, St Gallen #80/R est:12000-18000 (S.FR 22000)

FITZPATRICK, Arthur and KAUFMAN, van (20th C) American
Works on paper
£1198 $2000 €1749 Silver two-door Pontiac on oceanside highway (41x41cm-16x16in) init. gouache. 15-Nov-3 Illustration House, New York #92/R est:1800-2600

FITZPATRICK, Daniel Robert (1891-1969) American
Works on paper
£348 $650 €508 Fat Nazi vulture roosting in the snow (46x38cm-18x15in) s.d.1943 brush ink lithopencil. 26-Feb-4 Illustration House, New York #71

FITZPATRICK, Tony (1958-) American
Works on paper
£751 $1300 €1096 Mother of mother of birds (20x25cm-8x10in) col pencil slate exec.c.1999 prov. 10-Dec-3 Phillips, New York #508/R est:1500-2000

FIUME, Salvatore (1915-1997) Italian
£1479 $2588 €2100 Snail (20x14cm-8x6in) s. masonite. 17-Dec-3 Il Ponte, Milan #1094/R est:1200-1500
£1479 $2588 €2100 Lighthouse (20x13cm-8x5in) s. masonite. 17-Dec-3 Il Ponte, Milan #1096/R est:1200-1500
£1761 $3081 €2500 Snail strolling (17x25cm-7x10in) s. masonite. 17-Dec-3 Il Ponte, Milan #1095/R est:1800-2000
£2657 $4517 €3800 Dead Christ (25x36cm-10x14in) s.d.1956 masonite. 25-Nov-3 Sotheby's, Milan #27/R est:2500-3000
£3311 $6026 €5000 Landscape with cupola (39x59cm-15x23in) s. board. 17-Jun-4 Galleria Pananti, Florence #583/R est:5000-8000
£3667 $6747 €5500 Silence of the islands (36x54cm-14x21in) s. masonite painted 1960. 8-Jun-4 Finarte Semenzato, Milan #432/R est:5000-6000
£4027 $7450 €6000 Meeting (40x40cm-16x16in) s. on foil lit. 11-Mar-4 Galleria Pace, Milan #51/R est:6500-8500
£5245 $8916 €7500 Lovers in Andalucia (35x53cm-14x21in) s. masonite prov. 20-Nov-3 Finarte Semenzato, Milan #215/R est:7000-7500
£5667 $10200 €8500 Stone islands (40x60cm-16x24in) s. masonite painted 1963. 22-Apr-4 Finarte Semenzato, Rome #148/R est:7000-8000
£5705 $10211 €8500 Odalisk (72x54cm-28x21in) s. board. 25-May-4 Sotheby's, Milan #54/R est:10000
£5903 $10035 €8500 Island (64x73cm-25x29in) s. masonite prov. 28-Oct-3 Il Ponte, Milan #245/R
£6333 $11400 €9500 Battle amongst statue (54x36cm-21x14in) s. board painted 1960. 22-Apr-4 Finarte Semenzato, Rome #264/R est:9000-11000
£6711 $12013 €10000 Favourite (72x54cm-28x21in) s. masonite. 30-May-4 Meeting Art, Vercelli #59 est:10000
£8333 $15333 €12500 Statue island (50x81cm-20x32in) s. masonite painted 1963 prov. 8-Jun-4 Finarte Semenzato, Milan #347/R est:8000-10000
£9091 $15455 €13000 Stone island (74x102cm-29x40in) s. board. 25-Nov-3 Sotheby's, Milan #25/R est:10000-15000
£10067 $18020 €15000 Stone island (74x102cm-29x40in) s. paper on board. 25-May-4 Sotheby's, Milan #42/R est:6000
£11034 $17655 €16000 Model (54x72cm-21x28in) masonite painted 1994 lit. 13-Mar-3 Galleria Pace, Milan #133/R est:18000-23000
Sculpture
£2657 $4517 €3800 Woman, spring (91cm-36in) s. num.37/75 bronze. 26-Nov-3 Pandolfini, Florence #177/R est:4000-5000
Works on paper
£616 $1048 €900 Reclining woman (60x80cm-24x31in) s. mixed media. 7-Nov-3 Tuttarte, Modena #776
£867 $1595 €1300 Adam and Eve (49x35cm-19x14in) s. pen. 12-Jun-4 Meeting Art, Vercelli #901/R
£1733 $3189 €2600 Figure (30x20cm-12x8in) s. Chinese ink W/C. 10-Jun-4 Galleria Pace, Milan #26/R est:4000
£1793 $2869 €2600 Modella al balcone (52x42cm-20x17in) s. felt pen exec 1970 lit. 13-Mar-3 Galleria Pace, Milan #70/R est:3000-4000
£1931 $3090 €2800 Female nude (40x50cm-16x20in) s. felt pen brocade. 13-Mar-3 Galleria Pace, Milan #50/R est:3300-4500
£2238 $3804 €3200 Odalisk (66x48cm-26x19in) s. mixed media. 24-Nov-3 Christie's, Milan #104/R est:2000-3000

FIVIAN, Bendicht (1940-) Swiss
£362 $615 €529 Nature morte (35x30cm-14x12in) s.d.86 acrylic paper on canvas exhib. 22-Nov-3 Burkhard, Luzern #235/R (S.FR 800)
£736 $1317 €1075 Embrach (80x80cm-31x31in) s.d. i. verso acrylic. 22-Mar-4 Philippe Schuler, Zurich #4321 (S.FR 1700)
£866 $1550 €1264 Zimmermond (80x85cm-31x33in) s.d. verso acrylic. 22-Mar-4 Philippe Schuler, Zurich #4322 (S.FR 2000)

FIX-MASSEAU, Pierre-Felix (1869-1937) French
£4200 $7560 €6132 Still life (54x65cm-21x26in) s. 21-Jan-4 Sotheby's, Olympia #501/R est:2000-3000

FIZELLE, Rah (1891-1964) Australian
Works on paper
£405 $652 €591 Nude (53x30cm-21x12in) bears st.sig.verso pencil tissue paper prov.exhib. 25-Aug-3 Sotheby's, Paddington #391 (A.D 1000)
£420 $764 €613 Storm approaching Pittwater (30x41cm-12x16in) s. W/C. 16-Jun-4 Deutscher-Menzies, Melbourne #629/R est:500-800 (A.D 1100)
£483 $753 €700 Washing day (32x43cm-13x17in) s. W/C. 1-Aug-2 Joel, Victoria #187 est:1400-1600 (A.D 1400)
£702 $1300 €1025 Steam train, Milson's Point (30x41cm-12x16in) s. W/C. 10-Mar-4 Deutscher-Menzies, Melbourne #578/R est:1200-1800 (A.D 1700)

FJAESTAD, Gustaf (1868-1948) Swedish
£1458 $2682 €2187 Tufts of grass in waterway (33x42cm-13x17in) s. panel. 14-Jun-4 Lilla Bukowskis, Stockholm #413 est:25000-30000 (S.KR 20000)
£6061 $10848 €8849 Winter landscape (92x116cm-36x46in) s. panel. 25-May-4 Bukowskis, Stockholm #202/R est:80000-100000 (S.KR 82000)
£6308 $10849 €9210 Winter landscape in sunshine (95x100cm-37x39in) s.d.17. 2-Dec-3 Bukowskis, Stockholm #190a/R est:80000-100000 (S.KR 82000)
£7021 $12568 €10251 Hoare frost on frozen lake (83x106cm-33x42in) s.d.24. 25-May-4 Bukowskis, Stockholm #192/R est:130000-150000 (S.KR 95000)
£7761 $13891 €11331 Summer night by Racken (86x110cm-34x43in) s.d.06. 25-May-4 Bukowskis, Stockholm #99/R est:80000-100000 (S.KR 105000)
£11538 $19846 €16845 Winter landscape in evening glow (105x136cm-41x54in) s.d.12. 3-Dec-3 AB Stockholms Auktionsverk #2325/R est:150000-175000 (S.KR 150000)
£12934 $23152 €18884 Winter landscape with hoare frost, Varmland (151x184cm-59x72in) s.i.d.1911. 26-May-4 AB Stockholms Auktionsverk #2281/R est:175000-200000 (S.KR 175000)
£18477 $33075 €26976 Winter landscape with hoare frost and punt frozen on water (106x145cm-42x57in) s.d.19. 28-May-4 Uppsala Auktionskammare, Uppsala #185/R est:250000-300000 (S.KR 250000)
£20000 $34400 €29200 Winter landscape from Varmland (103x128cm-41x50in) s.d.32 panel. 3-Dec-3 AB Stockholms Auktionsverk #2248/R est:125000-150000 (S.KR 260000)
£23077 $39692 €33692 Hoare frost on frozen lake, Varmland. Sketch of Winter landscape (99x125cm-39x49in) s.i.d.23 double-sided. 2-Dec-3 Bukowskis, Stockholm #36/R est:175000-200000 (S.KR 300000)
Works on paper
£3538 $6086 €5165 Birch grove by the shore of lake (55x104cm-22x41in) s.d.99 wax crayon paper on canvas. 2-Dec-3 Bukowskis, Stockholm #34/R est:35000-40000 (S.KR 46000)

FJEDERHOLT, Preben (20th C) Danish
£564 $960 €823 Composition (73x89cm-29x35in) s.d.1992 verso. 26-Nov-3 Kunsthallen, Copenhagen #175 (D.KR 6000)

FJELL, Kai (1907-1989) Norwegian
£2447 $4380 €3573 Mother and child (33x24cm-13x9in) s.d.38 panel. 25-May-4 Grev Wedels Plass, Oslo #101/R est:30000-40000 (N.KR 30000)
£2602 $4787 €3799 Village street with two women (75x70cm-30x28in) s. 10-Jun-4 Grev Wedels Plass, Oslo #174/R est:20000-30000 (N.KR 32000)
£2882 $5159 €4208 Half-nude and head (26x46cm-10x18in) s.d.41. 22-Mar-4 Blomqvist, Oslo #602/R est:35000-45000 (N.KR 36000)
£5203 $9574 €7596 Pupil who has got detention (126x145cm-50x57in) s.d.36 exhib. 10-Jun-4 Grev Wedels Plass, Oslo #173/R est:40000-60000 (N.KR 64000)
£5636 $9412 €8229 Woman with medallion (35x27cm-14x11in) s.d.61 panel. 13-Oct-3 Blomqvist, Oslo #316/R est:40000-50000 (N.KR 66000)
£6362 $11388 €9289 Mother and child (33x24cm-13x9in) s.d.55 panel exhib. 25-May-4 Grev Wedels Plass, Oslo #103/R est:70000-90000 (N.KR 78000)
£36029 $64492 €52602 Two women (73x60cm-29x24in) s. lit. 22-Mar-4 Blomqvist, Oslo #607/R est:350000-450000 (N.KR 450000)
£40460 $69591 €59072 Young girl (110x120cm-43x47in) s. painted c.1948 exhib.lit. 8-Dec-3 Blomqvist, Oslo #486/R est:600000-700000 (N.KR 475000)
Prints
£1903 $3502 €2778 The bride (50x36cm-20x14in) init. col silkscreen. 29-Mar-4 Blomqvist, Lysaker #1069/R est:25000-30000 (N.KR 24000)
£2572 $4707 €3755 The bride (50x36cm-20x14in) s.num.9/275 col silkscreen. 2-Feb-4 Blomqvist, Lysaker #1069/R est:25000-30000 (N.KR 32000)
£3753 $6268 €5479 The blue jug (57x46cm-22x18in) s.num.76/100 col lithograph. 17-Nov-3 Blomqvist, Lysaker #1067/R est:25000-30000 (N.KR 45000)
Works on paper
£285 $525 €416 The god (13x17cm-5x7in) s. pencil. 29-Mar-4 Blomqvist, Lysaker #1063/R (N.KR 3600)
£644 $1127 €940 Beethoven (20x28cm-8x11in) s.i.indis.d.81 W/C. 16-Dec-3 Grev Wedels Plass, Oslo #24/R (N.KR 7500)
£993 $1649 €1440 Head of girl (20x28cm-8x11in) s. W/C. 16-Jun-3 Blomqvist, Lysaker #1044/R (N.KR 11500)
£1045 $1912 €1526 Lyarslott - man and woman in interior (36x44cm-14x17in) s.i.d.74 W/C Indian ink. 2-Feb-4 Blomqvist, Lysaker #1068/R est:15000-18000 (N.KR 13000)
£1121 $2006 €1637 Interior scene with seated woman (27x20cm-11x8in) s. mixed media. 22-Mar-4 Blomqvist, Oslo #672/R est:14000-18000 (N.KR 14000)
£2447 $4380 €3573 Female nude (62x46cm-24x18in) s. i.verso pastel. 25-May-4 Grev Wedels Plass, Oslo #102/R est:30000-40000 (N.KR 30000)

FLACHET, Maurice (1872-1964) Belgian
£1000 $1840 €1500 Boulevard parisien a la tombee du jour (60x90cm-24x35in) s. 14-Jun-4 Horta, Bruxelles #53 est:1000-1500

FLACK, Audrey (1931-) American
£5525 $10000 €8067 War protest march (53x79cm-21x31in) 16-Apr-4 American Auctioneer #129/R
£5525 $10000 €8067 Amanetti fountain (66x102cm-26x40in) 16-Apr-4 American Auctioneer #130/R

FLAD, Alois (19th C) German
Works on paper
£1000 $1820 €1500 Munich (22x29cm-9x11in) s.d.1862 W/C. 30-Jun-4 Neumeister, Munich #409/R

FLAGG, Charles Noel (1848-1916) American
£348 $550 €508 Portrait of H E Russell, with mutton chop sideburns (76x64cm-30x25in) s.d.1912 i.stretcher. 8-Sep-3 Winter Associates, Plainville #81
£364 $575 €531 Portrait of C B Erwin, in grey suit and black tie (74x61cm-29x24in) s.d.1912 i.stretcher. 8-Sep-3 Winter Associates, Plainville #171

FLAGG, H Peabody (1859-1937) American
£241 $425 €352 Landscape (20x25cm-8x10in) s. board. 18-May-4 Arthur James, Florida #125
£302 $556 €441 Road to Boulogne (27x34cm-11x13in) s. panel. 14-Jun-4 Waddingtons, Toronto #7/R (C.D 750)

FLAGG, James Montgomery (1877-1960) American
£720 $1325 €1051 Lady on a telephone (61x51cm-24x20in) s. 23-Mar-4 Rosebery Fine Art, London #896/R

Works on paper
£1198 $2000 €1749 Man carrying woman into room (69x38cm-27x15in) s. W/C en grisaille exec.c.1910. 15-Nov-3 Illustration House, New York #32/R est:1500-2400
£1508 $2700 €2202 Seated formal couple (56x56cm-22x22in) s. ink wash en grisaille. 15-May-4 Illustration House, New York #97/R est:1500-2400
£2374 $4250 €3466 Seated woman with tea cup (56x41cm-22x16in) s. W/C lit. 15-May-4 Illustration House, New York #89/R est:4000-7000
£3867 $7000 €5646 By the brook (38x56cm-15x22in) s.i.d.May 11 1930 W/C. 31-Mar-4 Sotheby's, New York #55/R est:5000-7000

FLAMENG, François (1856-1923) French
Works on paper
£1074 $1987 €1600 Portrait de Mademoiselle F a l'eventail (33x68cm-13x27in) s. gouache. 14-Mar-4 St-Germain-en-Laye Encheres #51/R est:1500-2000

FLAMM, Albert (1823-1906) German
£483 $893 €700 Shepherd with sheep by town in southern Italy (28x21cm-11x8in) s. panel. 14-Feb-4 Hans Stahl, Hamburg #23/R
£2013 $3705 €3000 Bay of Naples (28x45cm-11x18in) s. bears d.59 canvas on panel double-sided. 26-Mar-4 Ketterer, Hamburg #182/R est:2200-2500
£4196 $7133 €6000 Peasants and market women resting on Via Appia (76x112cm-30x44in) s. 20-Nov-3 Van Ham, Cologne #1571/R est:8000
£4667 $8493 €7000 Italian street (76x60cm-30x24in) s. 30-Jun-4 Neumeister, Munich #544/R est:4500
£26667 $48533 €40000 View towards Capri (107x148cm-42x58in) s. 1-Jul-4 Van Ham, Cologne #1341/R est:14000

FLANAGAN, Barry (1941-) British
Sculpture
£1800 $3276 €2628 Untitled (9x19cm-4x7in) init. plaster. 4-Feb-4 Sotheby's, Olympia #38/R est:2000-3000
£130000 $236600 €189800 Nijinski hares on globe form (164x51x53cm-65x20x21in) mono.num.5/8 brown pat. bronze two prov. 4-Feb-4 Christie's, London #44/R est:100000-150000
£140000 $257600 €204400 Drummer (244x173x91cm-96x68x36in) bronze executed 1989-90 prov. 23-Jun-4 Sotheby's, London #36/R est:180000-220000

FLANAGAN, Fergal (?) British?
£395 $726 €600 Connemara coast near Ballyconneely (34x44cm-13x17in) s.i.verso board. 22-Jun-4 De Veres Art Auctions, Dublin #206/R
£861 $1567 €1300 Connemara coastline, near Ballyconneely (46x60cm-18x24in) s. board. 15-Jun-4 James Adam, Dublin #148/R

FLANAGAN, Francis (fl.1897-1927) American
£941 $1600 €1374 Crushing surf, Maine view (76x102cm-30x40in) s. 21-Nov-3 Skinner, Boston #565/R est:1500-3000

FLANAGAN, John Richard (1895-1964) American
Sculpture
£7558 $13000 €11035 Mother and child (37cm-15in) beige stone wood base prov.lit. 3-Dec-3 Sotheby's, New York #94/R est:15000-20000

FLANAGAN, T P (1929-) British
Works on paper
£1189 $2021 €1700 In the Donegal hills (40x48cm-16x19in) s.d.84 W/C prov. 25-Nov-3 De Veres Art Auctions, Dublin #43/R est:1800-2200

FLANAGAN, Terence P (1929-) British
£1761 $3046 €2500 Landscape (36x38cm-14x15in) s. board. 10-Dec-3 Bonhams & James Adam, Dublin #125/R est:2000-3000
£2500 $4575 €3650 Beach, Donegal (76x76cm-30x30in) s. board. 2-Jun-4 John Ross, Belfast #111 est:1800-2000
£3092 $5689 €4700 Benbulben from the Catrans (59x73cm-23x29in) s. board prov. 22-Jun-4 De Veres Art Auctions, Dublin #19/R est:4000-6000
Works on paper
£450 $738 €657 Fermanagh Series I (28x40cm-11x16in) s. pastel. 4-Jun-3 John Ross, Belfast #174a
£855 $1574 €1300 Sea path, Lissadell (37x44cm-15x17in) s.d.71 col chk prov. 22-Jun-4 De Veres Art Auctions, Dublin #177
£1250 $2037 €1800 Tree and Hill (34x28cm-13x11in) s. W/C prov. 24-Sep-3 James Adam, Dublin #100/R est:1500-2500
£1818 $3091 €2600 In Fermanagh (41x51cm-16x20in) s.i. W/C prov. 18-Nov-3 Whyte's, Dublin #78/R est:2000-3000
£2500 $4650 €3650 Lisadell (56x76cm-22x30in) s.d.90 W/C. 3-Mar-4 John Ross, Belfast #157 est:1000-1500
£2533 $4585 €3800 Study in stillness (59x78cm-23x31in) s.d.73 W/C prov. 31-Mar-4 James Adam, Dublin #127/R
£2900 $5307 €4234 Rain clouds, Fermanagh (58x76cm-23x30in) s. W/C. 2-Jun-4 John Ross, Belfast #113/R est:2500-3000
£3087 $5464 €4600 Atlantic roar I (56x76cm-22x30in) s.d.1978 W/C prov. 27-Apr-4 Whyte's, Dublin #147/R est:3000-4000

FLANDIN, Eugène Napoleon (1803-1876) French
£22353 $38000 €32635 Gondolas on the Grand Canal in front of the Doge's Palace, Venice (51x82cm-20x32in) s.d.1836. 29-Oct-3 Christie's, Rockefeller NY #240/R est:25000-35000
Works on paper
£709 $1184 €1000 Ottoman fumant le chibouk (17x11cm-7x4in) W/C. 16-Jun-3 Gros & Delettrez, Paris #113/R

FLANDRIN, Jean Hippolyte (1809-1864) French
£704 $1218 €1000 Saint Francois guerissant un blesse (40x30cm-16x12in) paper on canvas. 10-Dec-3 Piasa, Paris #112
£5986 $10356 €8500 Head of a young man (32x29cm-13x11in) s. paper on canvas. 10-Dec-3 Piasa, Paris #111/R est:3000
Works on paper
£298 $542 €450 Le Christ benissant (28x21cm-11x8in) i. black crayon stump. 16-Jun-4 Piasa, Paris #180
£662 $1205 €1000 Moise devant le buisson ardent (30x17cm-12x7in) pen ink oil. 16-Jun-4 Piasa, Paris #176
£861 $1567 €1300 Le Christ couronnant la Vierge (38x49cm-15x19in) sanguine. 16-Jun-4 Piasa, Paris #175

FLANDRIN, Jean Hippolyte (attrib) (1809-1864) French
£350 $601 €500 Moise dans le desert (37x20cm-15x8in) 5-Dec-3 Gros & Delettrez, Paris #49

FLANDRIN, Jules (1871-1947) French
£1761 $3046 €2500 Le Stade du Palatin a Rome (35x80cm-14x31in) s. prov. 12-Dec-3 Piasa, Paris #87/R est:2500-3000
£2000 $3680 €3000 Retour des champs (54x81cm-21x32in) s.d.1902. 14-Jun-4 Tajan, Paris #26/R est:1500-2000
£2042 $3533 €2900 Bouquet au vase bleu (65x50cm-26x20in) s. 10-Dec-3 Rossini, Paris #73
£7801 $12638 €11000 La fontaine Saint Michel a Paris (97x146cm-38x57in) s. 23-May-3 Sotheby's, Paris #58/R est:3000-4000

FLANDRIN, Paul Jean (1811-1902) French
£1497 $2724 €2200 Paysage anime (21x29cm-8x11in) mono.d.1859 canvas on cardboard prov.exhib. 8-Feb-4 Anaf, Lyon #171/R est:1500-1800
£2933 $5309 €4400 Jardin (24x24cm-9x9in) s. paper on canvas round painted c.1870. 1-Apr-4 Credit Municipal, Paris #42 est:400-600
£3400 $6154 €5100 Fontainebleau, le Bas-Breau (36x54cm-14x21in) oil paper on canvas exhib. 30-Mar-4 Rossini, Paris #209/R est:4000-7000

FLANDRIN, René Auguste (1804-1842) French
Works on paper
£539 $863 €750 Portrait of a woman reading a book (17x12cm-7x5in) s.d.1832 W/C htd white gouache traces of blk crayon. 16-May-3 Tajan, Paris #115

FLANDRIN, René Auguste (attrib) (1804-1842) French
£600 $1086 €900 Cascade (34x22cm-13x9in) oil paper on canvas. 30-Mar-4 Rossini, Paris #979

FLANNAGAN, John B (1895-1942) American
Sculpture
£2994 $5000 €4371 Little head (14cm-6in) cast stone. 11-Nov-3 Christie's, Rockefeller NY #131/R est:3000-5000

FLANNERY, Vaughn (1898-1955) American
£2096 $3500 €3060 Swan Island, Maryland (76x102cm-30x40in) s. s.i.stretcher prov.exhib.lit. 7-Oct-3 Sotheby's, New York #235 est:1000-2000

FLANNIGAN, Lucy (c.1900-?) American
Works on paper
£531 $950 €775 Views of Capri (28x21cm-11x8in) one s. W/C paperboard pair. 14-May-4 Skinner, Boston #147/R

FLASHAR, Bruno (1887-1961) German
£451 $713 €650 Landscape near Kitzbuhl (50x69cm-20x27in) s.d.19. 5-Sep-3 Wendl, Rudolstadt #3354/R
£761 $1407 €1111 Vase of flowers (73x91cm-29x36in) 14-Mar-4 Agra, Warsaw #59/R (P.Z 5500)
£833 $1375 €1200 Reclining female nude (65x100cm-26x39in) s.d.27. 3-Jul-3 Neumeister, Munich #2830/R

FLASOW, Alexej Fedorowitsch (1952-) Russian?
£315 $541 €450 Still life (40x60cm-16x24in) s.d.1992 i.d.verso. 4-Dec-3 Van Ham, Cologne #141

FLASSCHOEN, Gustave (1868-1940) Belgian
£310 $559 €450 Fantasia (15x11cm-6x4in) s. cardboard. 20-Jan-4 Galerie Moderne, Brussels #263/R
£517 $931 €750 Campement berbere (14x27cm-6x11in) s. canvas laid down. 20-Jan-4 Galerie Moderne, Brussels #186/R
£590 $939 €850 Le moulin (43x49cm-17x19in) s. panel. 9-Sep-3 Palais de Beaux Arts, Brussels #236/R
£594 $993 €850 Voilier amarre devant le moulin (37x40cm-15x16in) s. panel. 13-Oct-3 Horta, Bruxelles #441
£775 $1340 €1100 Les pecheurs (29x40cm-11x16in) s. 9-Dec-3 Campo, Vlaamse Kaai #310
£2297 $4043 €3400 Fez-Maroc (73x63cm-29x25in) s. 24-May-4 Bernaerts, Antwerp #580/R est:2000-3000
£3000 $5460 €4500 Arabian cavalry scene (65x75cm-26x30in) 20-Jun-4 Wilkinson, Doncaster #322 est:4000-6000
£6419 $12132 €9500 Fantasia en Afrique du Nord (75x150cm-30x59in) s. 17-Feb-4 Vanderkindere, Brussels #46/R est:3750-6250
£20219 $37000 €29520 With the troop (81x100cm-32x39in) 1-Jun-4 Arroyo, Buenos Aires #21
Works on paper
£282 $521 €420 Cavalier (23x23cm-9x9in) s.d.1938 W/C. 15-Mar-4 Horta, Bruxelles #484
£369 $683 €550 Marchand de face (23x23cm-9x9in) s.d.1938 W/C. 15-Mar-4 Horta, Bruxelles #485

FLATHER, Donald M (1903-1990) Canadian
£1607 $2764 €2346 Autumn splendor (90x67cm-35x26in) s. board exhib. 2-Dec-3 Joyner Waddington, Toronto #310/R est:4000-5000 (C.D 3600)
£2027 $3446 €2959 Looking up Shuswap Lake from main road to Celista (25x34cm-10x13in) i.d.July 1940 verso board. 27-Nov-3 Heffel, Vancouver #168/R est:1500-2000 (C.D 4500)
£2232 $3795 €3259 Storm in the Rockies (55x82cm-22x32in) s. s.i.d.1943 verso. 6-Nov-3 Heffel, Vancouver #43/R est:5000-7000 (C.D 5000)
£4279 $7275 €6247 Bleached snags (61x83cm-24x33in) s. s.i.d.1958 verso board. 27-Nov-3 Heffel, Vancouver #164/R est:5000-7000 (C.D 9500)
£5804 $9982 €8474 October evening, Knouff Lake (60x90cm-24x35in) s. canvasboard exhib. 2-Dec-3 Joyner Waddington, Toronto #209/R est:4000-5000 (C.D 13000)

FLATMAN, Thomas (1635-1688) British
Miniatures
£2200 $3740 €3212 Gentleman wearing black cloak and grey cravat (6cm-2in) W/C oval. 18-Nov-3 Bonhams, New Bond Street #8/R est:1500-2500

FLATTERS, Richard (1822-1876) German
£1083 $2025 €1581 Interior scene with two women and cat (64x54cm-25x21in) s.d.1850. 25-Feb-4 Museumsbygningen, Copenhagen #139 est:10000-12000 (D.KR 12000)

FLAUBERT, Paul (1928-) French
£420 $701 €600 Verger au printemps (46x55cm-18x22in) s. 29-Jun-3 Eric Pillon, Calais #227/R

FLAVIN, Dan (1933-1996) American
Sculpture
£24000 $40080 €35040 Untitled, for Otto Freundlich (120x60x35cm-47x24x14in) blue and red fluorescent lights 1 from edition of 5 prov.exhib. 22-Oct-3 Christie's, London #70/R est:20000-30000
£47486 $85000 €69330 Untitled (123cm-48in) col flourescent light edition of 5 exhib. 12-May-4 Christie's, Rockefeller NY #414/R est:60000-80000
£65868 $110000 €96167 Untitled (122x122cm-48x48in) daylight cool white fluorescent light executed 1970 prov.exhib. 12-Nov-3 Sotheby's, New York #50/R est:100000-150000
£83799 $150000 €122347 Untitled - To Frank Stella (61x183cm-24x72in) pink yellow fluorescent light exec 1966 prov.exhib.lit. 12-May-4 Sotheby's, New York #50/R est:100000-150000
£83832 $140000 €122395 Untitled (18x244x13cm-7x96x5in) red yellow fluorescent light exec 1964 prov. 12-Nov-3 Christie's, Rockefeller NY #593/R est:100000-150000
£89385 $160000 €130502 Untitled (183x11x9cm-72x4x4in) col flourescent light edition of 3 prov.exhib. 12-May-4 Christie's, Rockefeller NY #413/R est:120000-180000
£100559 $180000 €146816 Untitled (244x244x25cm-96x96x10in) pink yellow fluorescent light exec 1987 edn 2/3 prov.exhib. 13-May-4 Sotheby's, New York #176/R est:80000-120000
£117318 $210000 €171284 Untitled - to Alex and Nikki (360cm-142in) red yellow pink green fluorescent lights executed 1987. 13-May-4 Phillips, New York #47/R est:120000-180000
£234637 $420000 €342570 Untitled (185x550x114cm-73x217x45in) fluorescent light tubes nine elements exec 1966 prov.exhib.lit. 11-May-4 Christie's, Rockefeller NY #53/R est:350000-550000
£335196 $600000 €489386 Alternate diagonals of March 2 1964 (366cm-144in) red gold fluorescent light edn 2/3 exec 1964 prov.exhib.lit. 11-May-4 Christie's, Rockefeller NY #36/R est:350000-450000

FLAVITSKY, Constantin Dmitrievitch (1830-1866) Russian
£1176 $1965 €1717 Study for the Princess Tarakanova (42x33cm-17x13in) s. lit. 17-Nov-3 Waddingtons, Toronto #292/R est:3000-5000 (C.D 2600)

FLAXMAN, John (1755-1826) British
Works on paper
£260 $471 €380 Classical figures (33x43cm-13x17in) pen ink. 16-Apr-4 Keys, Aylsham #328
£743 $1308 €1100 Four ladies, three standing and one seated (22x19cm-9x7in) i.d.June 10 1800 pen brown ink exhib.lit. 19-May-4 Sotheby's, Amsterdam #185/R
£1467 $2699 €2200 Fall from grace (13x20cm-5x8in) i. wash brush over pencil. 11-Jun-4 Hauswedell & Nolte, Hamburg #948/R est:1800

FLECK, Karl Anton (1928-1983) Austrian
Works on paper
£304 $535 €450 Evening music (23x30cm-9x12in) mono.d.1981 W/C. 19-May-4 Dorotheum, Klagenfurt #43/R
£400 $720 €600 Reclining female nude (44x61cm-17x24in) mono.d.1982 pencil board. 21-Apr-4 Dorotheum, Vienna #266/R
£805 $1490 €1200 Landscape (45x62cm-18x24in) mono.i.d.1981 pencil. 9-Mar-4 Dorotheum, Vienna #198/R
£845 $1479 €1200 Bucher Herzog (90x62cm-35x24in) mono.i.d.1977 pencil board. 19-Dec-3 Dorotheum, Vienna #300/R
£1208 $2235 €1800 Martin Luther Fleck as Junker Jorg (88x61cm-35x24in) mono.i.d.1973 mixed media board. 9-Mar-4 Dorotheum, Vienna #166/R est:1800-2600
£1477 $2732 €2200 Landscape (62x83cm-24x33in) mono.i.d.1981 pencil col pen. 9-Mar-4 Dorotheum, Vienna #196/R est:600-2200

FLECK, Ralph (1951-) German
£479 $766 €680 Petri fish (65x75cm-26x30in) s.d.83 i.d.1983 verso wrapping paper lit. 19-Sep-3 Karlheinz Kaupp, Staufen #2171/R
£704 $1127 €1000 Tree 5/XII (100x80cm-39x31in) s.i.d.86 verso lit. 19-Sep-3 Karlheinz Kaupp, Staufen #2188/R
£1364 $2345 €1950 Pond - Giverny 7/IV (201x249cm-79x98in) s.i.d. verso. 3-Dec-3 Hauswedell & Nolte, Hamburg #769/R est:1500
£2254 $3899 €3200 Tree, Italy (100x81cm-39x32in) s.i.d.88 verso. 13-Dec-3 Lempertz, Koln #135/R est:1500

FLEER, Fritz (1921-1997) German
Sculpture
£1119 $1924 €1600 Woman playing lute II (28x21x23cm-11x8x9in) mono.d.1973 bronze. 2-Dec-3 Hauswedell & Nolte, Hamburg #186/R
£1736 $2743 €2500 Female nude (43x63cm-17x25in) mono.i.d.1966 brown pat.bronze Cast.Schmack. 6-Sep-3 Schopman, Hamburg #357/R est:3000

FLEETWOOD-WALKER, Bernard (1893-1969) British
£625 $1119 €913 Study of a mother and child (58x48cm-23x19in) s. 6-May-4 Biddle & Webb, Birmingham #903
£2600 $4862 €3796 Repose (94x101cm-37x40in) s.d.1925 prov. 24-Feb-4 Bonhams, Knowle #123/R est:1500-2000

FLEISCHMANN, Adolf (1892-1969) German
£3147 $5413 €4500 Untitled (81x65cm-32x26in) s. prov.exhib. 5-Dec-3 Ketterer, Munich #153/R est:5000-7000
Works on paper
£2013 $3705 €3000 Cattle in stable (46x61cm-18x24in) s. W/C Indian ink. 26-Mar-4 Ketterer, Hamburg #410/R est:2800-3000

FLEMING, Alexander M (1878-1929) Canadian
£402 $747 €587 Grey day in midsummer (46x56cm-18x22in) 2-Mar-4 Ritchie, Toronto #40/R (C.D 1000)

FLEMING, Ian (1906-1994) British
£580 $1061 €847 Briar dykes (68x80cm-27x31in) s. board. 8-Apr-4 Bonhams, Edinburgh #3
£1000 $1770 €1460 Ben Lomond (51x61cm-20x24in) s. double-sided. 28-Apr-4 Halls, Shrewsbury #503/R est:800-1200
£2100 $3843 €3066 Shetland croft (90x70cm-35x28in) s. s.i.verso. 8-Apr-4 Bonhams, Edinburgh #21 est:600-800

FLEMING, John (attrib) (1792-1845) British
£8000 $13600 €11680 View of Alloa, with cows and figures in the foreground (69x122cm-27x48in) 25-Nov-3 Christie's, London #72/R est:8000-12000

FLEMING, Richard (20th C) Canadian
£317 $529 €463 Polar bears (50x60cm-20x24in) s. acrylic. 17-Nov-3 Hodgins, Calgary #127/R (C.D 700)

FLEMING, Rona (1901-1976) New Zealander
£364 $571 €531 Pororari Lagoon, west coast (41x55cm-16x22in) s. 27-Aug-3 Dunbar Sloane, Wellington #254 (NZ.D 1000)

FLEMISH SCHOOL, 15th C
£6897 $12414 €10000 Christ aux outrages (61x41cm-24x16in) panel. 20-Jan-4 Galerie Moderne, Brussels #151/R est:8000-12000
£9459 $16649 €14000 Still life with silver, box and money (53x69cm-21x27in) prov. 22-May-4 Lempertz, Koln #1161/R est:10000-12000

FLEMISH SCHOOL, 15th/16th C
£8389 $15436 €12500 Annunciation (27x34cm-11x13in) 29-Mar-4 Pandolfini, Florence #762/R est:8000

FLEMISH SCHOOL, 16th C
£5000 $9000 €7300 Penitent Saint Jerome (105x77cm-41x30in) panel. 22-Apr-4 Sotheby's, London #15/R est:6000-8000
£5634 $9014 €8000 Saul's fall (75x102cm-30x40in) board. 21-Sep-3 Finarte, Venice #25/R
£5846 $10055 €8535 Battle scene (64x129cm-25x51in) panel. 2-Dec-3 Bukowskis, Stockholm #330/R est:80000-100000 (S.KR 76000)
£6500 $11700 €9490 Portrait of a lady, holding a chain (108x79cm-43x31in) i.d.1566 panel. 22-Apr-4 Sotheby's, London #41/R est:8000-12000
£6993 $12028 €10000 Taking Christ off the cross (69x53cm-27x21in) panel. 3-Dec-3 Neumeister, Munich #460/R est:6000
£7200 $12456 €10512 Penitent Magdalene (80x68cm-31x27in) panel. 9-Dec-3 Sotheby's, Olympia #307/R est:6000-8000
£11333 $20740 €17000 Saint Hugh ad Saint Bruno (86x114cm-34x45in) board. 1-Jun-4 Sotheby's, Milan #70/R est:15000-20000
£13380 $23415 €19000 Marie Madeleine au pied de la Croix (76x74cm-30x29in) panel. 17-Dec-3 Piasa, Paris #6/R est:20000-30000
£16667 $30000 €24334 Annunciation (102x71cm-40x28in) prov.lit. 22-Jan-4 Sotheby's, New York #227/R est:20000-30000
£21477 $38013 €32000 Mythological scenes (42x59cm-17x23in) board. 2-May-4 Finarte, Venice #15/R est:28000-35000
£22000 $40260 €32120 Rebecca and Eliezer at the well (77x109cm-30x43in) panel painted c.1565 prov. 8-Jul-4 Sotheby's, London #248/R est:20000-30000
£52980 $96424 €80000 Andrea Doria with The Emperor and the Pope (131x200cm-52x79in) prov.exhib.lit. 16-Jun-4 Christie's, Rome #517/R est:80000-120000
Sculpture
£13793 $22897 €20000 Christ (122cm-48in) painted wood prov. 6-Oct-3 Amberes, Antwerp #525/R

FLEMISH SCHOOL, 16th/17th C
£11154 $19185 €16285 Mountain landscape with scene from The New Testament (33x43cm-13x17in) panel. 2-Dec-3 Bukowskis, Stockholm #352/R est:25000-30000 (S.KR 145000)

FLEMISH SCHOOL, 17th C
£5263 $9684 €8000 Arrival of a queen (117x169cm-46x67in) s.d.1600. 25-Jun-4 Piasa, Paris #3/R est:6000-8000
£5500 $10285 €8250 Portrait of woman (28x33cm-11x13in) panel. 21-Jul-4 John Nicholson, Haslemere #195/R est:3000-5000
£5822 $9897 €8500 Battle scene (45x66cm-18x26in) board. 9-Nov-3 Finarte, Venice #87/R est:9000-11000
£5890 $9189 €8600 Canaa's wedding (94x122cm-37x48in) board. 8-Apr-3 Il Ponte, Milan #118

£5903	$9740	€8500	Three county boys playing cards under tree (100x127cm-39x50in) 3-Jul-3 Van Ham, Cologne #974/R est:3000
£6000	$10380	€8760	Wooded landscape with travellers on a track by a lake (73x114cm-29x45in) panel painted c.1630. 12-Dec-3 Christie's, Kensington #69/R est:6000-8000
£6000	$10740	€8760	Portrait of Sir Henry Spellman wearing a lace cap (76x61cm-30x24in) 22-Mar-4 Bonhams & Brooks, Norfolk #317/R est:2000-3000
£6000	$10980	€8760	Extensive river landscape (73x103cm-29x41in) panel. 8-Jul-4 Sotheby's, London #234/R est:8000-12000
£6164	$10479	€9000	Apollus and the muses (32x41cm-13x16in) copper lit. 7-Nov-3 Farsetti, Prato #482/R est:6500-7500
£6250	$10438	€9000	Landscape with figures and cattle (118x119cm-46x47in) 23-Oct-3 Finarte Semenzato, Milan #334/R
£6419	$11490	€9500	Wreath of flowers centred by Madonna and Child (64x48cm-25x19in) panel. 9-May-4 Sotheby's, Amsterdam #119/R est:5000-8000
£6667	$12000	€9734	Pygmalion (147x160cm-58x63in) 23-Jan-4 Christie's, Rockefeller NY #184/R est:15000-20000
£6993	$12028	€10000	Apollon et les Muses (38x43cm-15x17in) copper. 8-Dec-3 Cornette de St.Cyr, Paris #49/R est:2000-3000
£7440	$12871	€10862	Allegory of reason overcoming desire with minerva and scholars expelling Venus and Cupid (40x32cm-16x13in) bears sig. 9-Dec-3 Sotheby's, Olympia #308b/R est:3000-4000
£7931	$13245	€11500	Sheep shearing (81x118cm-32x46in) prov. 15-Nov-3 Lempertz, Koln #1171/R est:10000-12000
£8451	$13606	€12000	Venere esce dal mare (62x82cm-24x32in) 8-May-3 Farsetti, Prato #791/R est:15000-18000
£8500	$15555	€12410	Annunciation (112x85cm-44x33in) panel. 6-Jul-4 Sotheby's, Olympia #423/R est:8000-12000
£8667	$15513	€13000	Christ shown to the people (59x84cm-23x33in) 17-May-4 Finarte Semenzato, Rome #38/R est:12000-15000
£8667	$15513	€13000	Animal fantastique (112x141cm-44x56in) 16-May-4 Joron-Derem, Paris #15/R est:15000-20000
£9500	$17100	€13870	Elegant crowd watching men wrestling in a landscape (24x34cm-9x13in) copper on panel. 22-Apr-4 Sotheby's, London #72/R est:6000-8000
£10067	$18725	€15000	Crossing of the Red Sea (118x168cm-46x66in) 2-Mar-4 Ansorena, Madrid #270/R est:10000
£10211	$17870	€14500	Basket with fish, vegetables and cat (76x99cm-30x39in) 17-Dec-3 Christie's, Rome #494/R est:15000-20000
£10345	$19034	€15104	Diana and Adonis (157x132cm-62x52in) 26-Mar-4 Koller, Zurich #3046/R est:12000-18000 (S.FR 24000)
£11149	$19622	€16500	Portrait of boy with dog (115x83cm-45x33in) panel. 22-May-4 Lempertz, Koln #1162/R est:4000
£12000	$21480	€18000	Preparation for the party (55x68cm-22x27in) 16-May-4 Joron-Derem, Paris #75/R est:10000-12000
£12333	$22447	€18500	Carnival ball (79x118cm-31x46in) i. 4-Jul-4 Finarte, Venice #31/R est:25000-35000
£13333	$24400	€20000	Rural scene (168x212cm-66x83in) 1-Jun-4 Sotheby's, Milan #136/R est:20000-30000
£14474	$26632	€22000	Three young princes (114x159cm-45x63in) 25-Jun-4 Piasa, Paris #2/R est:6000-8000
£15068	$25616	€22000	Portrait of a bearded man with a golden chain and sword (105x77cm-41x30in) i. 4-Nov-3 Sotheby's, Amsterdam #33/R est:10000-15000
£17450	$31235	€26000	Allegory of Autumn (42x43cm-17x17in) on slate. 26-May-4 Porro, Milan #1/R est:30000-40000
£20794	$35974	€30359	Lady arranging flowers in basket (126x97cm-50x38in) 9-Dec-3 Rasmussen, Copenhagen #1213/R est:250000 (D.KR 220000)
£21111	$38000	€30822	Anthropomorphic landscape (51x67cm-20x26in) pair prov. 23-Jan-4 Christie's, Rockefeller NY #159/R est:15000-20000
£22000	$39600	€32120	Moorish soldier, holding a flintlock musket and rest in, in a landscape (107x80cm-42x31in) prov. 21-Apr-4 Christie's, London #1/R est:7000-10000
£26389	$47500	€38528	Belshazzar;s feast (142x196cm-56x77in) panel. 22-Jan-4 Sotheby's, New York #228/R est:30000-40000
£38194	$63021	€55000	Building the Tower of Babel (74x95cm-29x37in) lit.prov. 3-Jul-3 Dr Fritz Nagel, Stuttgart #437/R est:12000
£48000	$87840	€70080	Opening of a ball in a palatial assembly room (89x128cm-35x50in) lit. 7-Jul-4 Christie's, London #27/R est:25000-35000
£60606	$108485	€88485	Still life with fruit, playing cards and musical instruments (53x115cm-21x45in) 22-Mar-4 Philippe Schuler, Zurich #4401/R est:10000-14000 (S.FR 140000)
£68966	$126897	€100690	Landscape with St Anthony (8x12cm-3x5in) i. copper. 26-Mar-4 Koller, Zurich #3040/R est:4000-6000 (S.FR 160000)

Miniatures

£9000	$15300	€13140	Noblewoman (5cm-2in) oil copper. 18-Nov-3 Bonhams, New Bond Street #14/R est:2000-3000

Works on paper

£6897	$12759	€10000	Paysage arbore (26x38cm-10x15in) pen wash htd col. 16-Feb-4 Horta, Bruxelles #132 est:1800-2200

FLEMISH SCHOOL, 17th/18th C

£8811	$14978	€12864	Susanna with the Elders (91x119cm-36x47in) 5-Nov-3 Dobiaschofsky, Bern #540/R est:1800 (S.FR 20000)
£12387	$22297	€18085	The Death of Virgin Mary (66x49cm-26x19in) canvas on panel. 26-Jan-4 Lilla Bukowskis, Stockholm #230 est:15000-18000 (S.KR 165000)
£14640	$26351	€21374	The Holy Family (120x103cm-47x41in) 26-Jan-4 Lilla Bukowskis, Stockholm #161 est:25000-30000 (S.KR 195000)

FLEMISH SCHOOL, 18th C

£5634	$9860	€8000	La noce villageoise (80x118cm-31x46in) 16-Dec-3 Artcurial Briest, Paris #214/R est:8000-10000
£6704	$12000	€9788	Figures ascending into clouds (427x274cm-168x108in) ceiling panel prov. 21-Mar-4 Hindman, Chicago #772/R est:3000-5000
£7200	$12240	€10512	Landscape with cavalry engagements (13x17cm-5x7in) mono.d.1660 panel pair. 30-Oct-3 Sotheby's, Olympia #128/R est:4000-6000
£8219	$13973	€12000	Singes jouant aux carted (15x38cm-6x15in) bears sig copper on panel. 6-Nov-3 Sotheby's, Paris #109/R est:1000-1500
£10870	$17609	€15762	At the fair (41x59cm-16x23in) oil on copper style of Jean Pillement. 31-Jul-3 International Art Centre, Auckland #58/R est:15000-25000 (NZ.D 30000)
£11806	$20069	€17000	Coppia di dipinti su pergamena raffiguranti paesaggi con figure (22x25cm-9x10in) 28-Oct-3 Della Rocca, Turin #300 est:14000-16000
£22222	$40000	€32444	Market stall with a young woman pointing to a hare and a peasant paying for a chicken (127x104cm-50x41in) prov. 23-Jan-4 Christie's, Rockefeller NY #70/R est:30000-50000

Sculpture

£8451	$14620	€12000	Bacchanal (51x83cm-20x33in) marble relief lit. 15-Dec-3 Sotheby's, Paris #2/R est:12000-18000

FLEMISH SCHOOL, 19th C

£8780	$15980	€12819	Madonna beneath a canopy holding the Christ child flanked by angels (313x233cm-123x92in) i. 8-Feb-4 Bonhams & Butterfields, Los Angeles #2312/R est:10000-15000
£21277	$35532	€30000	Jupiter et Mercure chez Philemon et Baucis (53x77cm-21x30in) after Jordaens. 23-Jun-3 Ribeyre & Baron, Paris #44/R est:1800-2300

FLEMISH-FRENCH SCHOOL, 18th C

£6207	$10303	€9000	Apotheosis of French monarchy (30x60cm-12x24in) panel. 1-Oct-3 Dorotheum, Vienna #127/R est:9000-14000

FLEMMING, Jean Robinson (1874-?) American

£274	$450	€400	Landscape with trees at water's edge (18x23cm-7x9in) s. fiberboard prov. 31-May-3 Brunk, Ashville #345/R

FLENSBURG, Anette Harboe (1961-) Danish

£516	$862	€753	Composition (50x120cm-20x47in) s.d.93 verso. 7-Oct-3 Rasmussen, Copenhagen #160/R (D.KR 5500)

FLERS, Camille (1802-1868) French

£933	$1680	€1400	Barque sur l'etang au crepuscule (19x24cm-7x9in) s. panel. 20-Apr-4 Chenu & Scrive, Lyon #88/R
£1380	$2304	€2000	Nature morte (82x101cm-32x40in) s.d.1862. 17-Nov-3 Tajan, Paris #96 est:2000-3000
£1600	$2896	€2400	Sous-bois a Fontainebleau (20x30cm-8x12in) s.d.1860 oil paper on canvas exhib.lit. 30-Mar-4 Rossini, Paris #227/R est:2500-3500
£1667	$3050	€2500	Vie champetre (41x60cm-16x24in) s. 6-Jun-4 Osenat, Fontainebleau #43/R est:4500-5000
£2267	$4148	€3400	Peche dans le bocage normand (47x68cm-19x27in) s.d.1857. 6-Jun-4 Osenat, Fontainebleau #42/R est:4000-4500
£2937	$5052	€4200	Paysage en Normandie (32x46cm-13x18in) s. 7-Dec-3 Osenat, Fontainebleau #107
£2994	$5000	€4371	End of the day (110x161cm-43x63in) s. 7-Oct-3 Sotheby's, New York #156 est:6000-8000

Works on paper

£467	$845	€700	Bords de Seine pres de Gaillon (14x22cm-6x9in) s.d.1836 W/C exhib.lit. 30-Mar-4 Rossini, Paris #229
£559	$962	€800	Bord de Seine a Samois (15x24cm-6x9in) s.d.1837 W/C. 7-Dec-3 Osenat, Fontainebleau #3/R
£814	$1385	€1188	Scene champetre (30x46cm-12x18in) s.d.1864 pastel. 28-Nov-3 Zofingen, Switzerland #2460 est:1800 (S.FR 1800)

FLERS, Camille (attrib) (1802-1868) French

£1333	$2413	€2000	Environs de Thiers (32x40cm-13x16in) painted c.1840 exhib. 30-Mar-4 Rossini, Paris #228/R est:2000-2500
£1399	$2406	€2000	La vie a la ferme (48x59cm-19x23in) painted c.1835-1840. 7-Dec-3 Osenat, Fontainebleau #44 est:2300-2500

FLETCHER, Aaron Dean (1817-1902) American

£4324	$8000	€6313	Portrait of a young boy holding a pocket watch (74x66cm-29x26in) painted c.1830 prov. 16-Jan-4 Sotheby's, New York #6/R est:9000-12000

FLETCHER, Aaron Dean (attrib) (1817-1902) American

£2358	$3750	€3443	Eleanor McLeary in a cap with pink bows (74x64cm-29x25in) s.i.d.Nov 28 1835. 10-Sep-3 Sotheby's, New York #331/R est:2500-3500

FLETCHER, Blythe (1890-1949) New Zealander

£372	$639	€543	Gathering firewood (54x78cm-21x31in) board. 7-Dec-3 International Art Centre, Auckland #304/R (NZ.D 1000)

Works on paper

£277	$496	€404	Old English Lane (25x17cm-10x7in) s. W/C. 11-May-4 Watson's, Christchurch #100/R (NZ.D 800)
£277	$496	€404	Clam gatherers (27x37cm-11x15in) s. W/C. 11-May-4 Watson's, Christchurch #113/R (NZ.D 800)
£286	$517	€418	Lake side evening. W/C. 4-Apr-4 International Art Centre, Auckland #201/R (NZ.D 800)
£421	$779	€615	Pastorl scene (36x48cm-14x19in) s.d.74 gouache. 9-Mar-4 Watson's, Christchurch #52 est:1400-2000 (NZ.D 1150)
£440	$813	€642	Street scene with cathedral (29x14cm-11x6in) s. W/C. 9-Mar-4 Watson's, Christchurch #43 est:1500-3000 (NZ.D 1200)
£507	$817	€740	Figure in moonlight (51x41cm-20x16in) s.d.1929 gouache. 12-Aug-3 Peter Webb, Auckland #158/R (NZ.D 1400)
£1062	$1965	€1551	Evening seascape with sunset (41x58cm-16x23in) s. gouache. 9-Mar-4 Watson's, Christchurch #34 est:3000-4000 (NZ.D 2900)

FLETCHER, Edwin (1857-1945) British

£700	$1169	€1022	Busy river (51x76cm-20x30in) s. 11-Nov-3 Bonhams, Knightsbridge #86a/R
£794	$1500	€1159	Shipping on the Thames, St Paul's Cathedral on the right (51x76cm-20x30in) s. 21-Feb-4 Brunk, Ashville #286/R est:800-1500
£900	$1530	€1314	Unloading on the river (13x11cm-5x4in) board. 19-Nov-3 Christie's, Kensington #594/R
£1250	$2075	€1825	The launching of the lifeboat (38x60cm-15x24in) s. 2-Oct-3 Lane, Penzance #339 est:1000-1200
£1400	$2506	€2044	Pool of London (51x76cm-20x30in) s. 26-May-4 Sotheby's, Olympia #67/R est:800-1200
£2000	$3660	€2920	HMS Victory at anchor in Portsmouth Harbour (50x76cm-20x30in) s. 7-Apr-4 Bonhams, Bury St Edmunds #471 est:1500-2000
£2400	$4368	€3504	Shipping on the Thames, London (38x58cm-15x23in) s. pair. 16-Jun-4 Andrew Hartley, Ilkley #1054/R est:500-800

Works on paper

£503	$900	€734	Marine, ship in storm and sailboats by the shore (28x46cm-11x18in) s. W/C two. 16-May-4 CRN Auctions, Cambridge #51/R

FLETCHER, Frances Ann (1846-1935) New Zealander
Works on paper

£1128	$1917	€1647	Maori wars - British redcoats facing Maoris with muskets. s. W/C. 26-Nov-3 Dunbar Sloane, Wellington #49/R est:3000-5000 (NZ.D 3000)

FLETCHER, Hugh (20th C) British

£2200	$3938	€3212	Swag of plums and other fruit. Swag of peaches and other fruit (104x25cm-41x10in) s. pair. 27-May-4 Christie's, Kensington #339/R est:300-500

FLETCHER, W (19th C) British?

£1000	$1700	€1460	Full length portrait of Helen Whitworth holding a doll in her arms (100x76cm-39x30in) s. i.verso. 27-Nov-3 Greenslade Hunt, Taunton #999/R est:1000-1500

FLETCHER, William (1924-1983) Australian

£496	$903	€724	Mulla mulla and other flowers (73x61cm-29x24in) s.d.70 board prov. 16-Jun-4 Deutscher-Menzies, Melbourne #329/R est:1500-2000 (A.D 1300)

FLETCHER, William Blandford (1858-1936) British

£4435	$7938	€6475	Street scene (51x40cm-20x16in) s. 26-May-4 AB Stockholms Auktionsverk #2458/R est:20000-25000 (S.KR 60000)

FLETSCHERO, Gaspard (attrib) (17th C) ?

£780	$1443	€1139	Portrait of Charles II (36x30cm-14x12in) i.on stretcher. 14-Jan-4 Brightwells, Leominster #930

FLEUR, Johan Willem (1888-1967) Dutch

£325	$553	€475	Amaryllis (78x58cm-31x23in) s.d.33. 5-Nov-3 Vendue Huis, Gravenhage #517/R
£406	$650	€593	Still life with chrysanthemums. s. 20-Sep-3 Harvey Clar, Oakland #1370b
£816	$1486	€1200	Still life with flowering cactus (60x50cm-24x20in) s. 3-Feb-4 Christie's, Amsterdam #503/R est:1400-1800

FLEURBAAY, Hendrik (1896-1975) Dutch

£307	$549	€460	Activity on the river (38x48cm-15x19in) s. 11-May-4 Vendu Notarishuis, Rotterdam #83

FLEURY, Auguste Antoine (?-1881) French

£2639	$4169	€3800	Private lesson (100x74cm-39x29in) s. lit. 19-Sep-3 Schloss Ahlden, Ahlden #1473/R est:3800

FLEURY, François-Antoine (1804-1858) French

£1788	$3272	€2700	Le pont de bois (27x41cm-11x16in) s. panel. 7-Apr-4 Doutrebente, Paris #37 est:1000-1500
£7667	$14030	€11500	Vie champetre (70x100cm-28x39in) s.d.1853. 6-Jun-4 Osenat, Fontainebleau #45/R est:12000-15000

FLEURY, François-Antoine (attrib) (1804-1858) French

£19000	$34390	€28500	Chateau de l'Isle d'Ischia (23x33cm-9x13in) cardboard exhib. 30-Mar-4 Rossini, Paris #264/R est:1800-2500

FLEURY, J Vivien de (19th C) British

£348	$650	€522	View of Mont St Michel, on the North Brittany coast of France (33x55cm-13x22in) s.d.1884 prov. 25-Jul-4 Bonhams & Butterfields, San Francisco #6029/R
£1800	$3186	€2628	Italianate landscape with figures on a path (43x70cm-17x28in) s.d.1863. 28-Apr-4 Peter Wilson, Nantwich #50 est:1500-2000

FLEURY, Jules Amedee Louis (1845-?) French

£750	$1403	€1125	Beach scene with figures besides rocks, other figures unloading boats (33x53cm-13x21in) s.indis.d. 22-Jul-4 Tennants, Leyburn #806

FLEURY, Leon (1804-1858) French

£3217	$5469	€4600	Scene de village (33x49cm-13x19in) s. 21-Nov-3 Coutau Begarie, Paris #134/R est:3000-4000

FLEURY, Marie Berthe (1857-1929) French

£3125	$5000	€4563	Two children, horse and rooster in barnyard (76x91cm-30x36in) s. 20-Sep-3 Sloans & Kenyon, Bethesda #1177/R est:5000-7000

FLEURY, Mme Fanny (1848-?) French

£455	$773	€650	Portrait de jeune femme (55x47cm-22x19in) s. 24-Nov-3 Boscher, Cherbourg #787b
£2238	$3804	€3200	Jeune femme assise au ruban bleu. Yvonne et Bobette (130x97cm-51x38in) pair. 24-Nov-3 Boscher, Cherbourg #787/R est:1000-1500
£2324	$4020	€3300	Femme et enfant (65x46cm-26x18in) s. 12-Dec-3 Piasa, Paris #63/R est:1500-2000

FLEURY, Sylvie (1961-) French
Photographs

£1389	$2500	€2028	Sex money compromise (155x120cm-61x47in) s.d.1993 verso chromogenic colour print on aluminum. 23-Apr-4 Phillips, New York #146/R est:4000-6000
£2682	$4800	€3916	Glam rocks, English Vogue, December 94 (173x119cm-68x47in) s.d.95 verso c-print aluminum prov. 14-May-4 Phillips, New York #163/R est:4000-6000
£9000	$15030	€13140	Harper's Bazaar (163x124cm-64x49in) s.d.94 verso c-print aluminium prov. 22-Oct-3 Christie's, London #146/R est:4000-6000

Sculpture

£4348	$8000	€6348	Gucci shoes (16x20x8cm-6x8x3in) s.num.8 chrome plated bronze prov. 10-Jun-4 Phillips, New York #466/R est:6000-8000
£4500	$8280	€6570	Pleasures (40x120x5cm-16x47x2in) red orange neon edition 1 of 25 prov.exhib. 24-Jun-4 Sotheby's, Olympia #642/R est:2500-3500
£6250	$11500	€9125	Eagle good year (22x58x58cm-9x23x23in) s.num.8 chromed bronze prov. 10-Jun-4 Phillips, New York #558/R est:6000-8000
£6287	$10500	€9179	Crash teat 3-31 (179x102x9cm-70x40x4in) s.d.01 verso acrylic steel in two parts prov. 14-Nov-3 Phillips, New York #286/R est:8000-12000
£6704	$12000	€9788	Gucci mules (11x8x24cm-4x3x9in) i.num. of eight chrome plated bronze two parts prov.exhib. 14-May-4 Phillips, New York #113 est:8000-12000
£7263	$13000	€10604	Eagle good year (22x58x58cm-9x23x23in) i.num. of eight chromed bronze prov.exhib. 14-May-4 Phillips, New York #116/R est:6000-8000
£7263	$13000	€10604	Pleasures (40x120x5cm-16x47x2in) neon light edition of 25 prov.exhib. 14-May-4 Phillips, New York #135/R est:12000-18000
£8696	$16000	€12696	Be amazing (68x290x5cm-27x114x2in) neon edition of three. 10-Jun-4 Phillips, New York #401/R est:10000-15000
£20134	$37047	€30000	Sac Louis Vuitton (34x46x20cm-13x18x8in) s. num.3/8 bronze silver Cast f.Venurie Arte exec 2000 prov. 29-Mar-4 Cornette de St.Cyr, Paris #94/R est:20000-25000

Works on paper

£1400	$2548	€2044	Fur painting (27x27cm-11x11in) s.d.95 stretcher synthetic fur prov. 4-Feb-4 Sotheby's, Olympia #249/R est:800-1200

FLEXOR, Samson (1907-1971) French

£4945	$9049	€7418	Untitled (96x130cm-38x51in) s.d.1966. 6-Jul-4 Bolsa de Arte, Rio de Janeiro #159/R (B.R 27000)

FLICKEL, Paul Franz (1852-1903) German

£350	$584	€500	Northern German landscape (31x27cm-12x11in) s. 28-Jun-3 Dannenberg, Berlin #682/R
£662	$1205	€1000	Village path in autumn sunshine (31x27cm-12x11in) s. 18-Jun-4 Bolland & Marotz, Bremen #613/R
£1500	$2400	€2190	Landscape with cattle grazing (71x102cm-28x40in) s.d.1903. 17-May-3 Bunte, Elgin #1259 est:2000-3000

FLIEGERBAUER, John (?) American

£278	$500	€406	Two pigeons (51x66cm-20x26in) acrylic. 24-Apr-4 Slotin Folk Art, Buford #259/R

FLIEHER, Karl (1881-1958) Austrian

£934	$1560	€1364	Aus durnstein wachau (28x36cm-11x14in) s.i. 14-Nov-3 Aspire, Cleveland #50

Works on paper

£540	$950	€788	Corte Madera landscape (36x46cm-14x18in) s.i.d.1937 mixed media board. 23-May-4 Bonhams & Butterfields, San Francisco #6615/R
£570	$1050	€850	Arnsdorf farmstead, Wachau (32x23cm-13x9in) s.i.d1919 W/C. 26-Mar-4 Dorotheum, Vienna #286/R
£660	$1050	€964	Altes Gobchen in Durnstein ob Danube Wachau (15x20cm-6x8in) W/C. 25-Feb-3 Bunch, West Chester #532/R
£778	$1300	€1136	Village at Wachau (33x25cm-13x10in) s.i. gouache sold with another by the same hand. 20-Jun-3 Freeman, Philadelphia #63/R
£1342	$2470	€2000	Garden in Weissenkirchen an der Donau, Wachau (33x24cm-13x9in) s.i. mixed media. 26-Mar-4 Dorotheum, Vienna #317/R est:1600-1800
£2069	$3434	€3000	Old village street in Weissenkirchen a d Donau, Wachau (25x34cm-10x13in) s.i. mixed media. 30-Sep-3 Dorotheum, Vienna #309/R est:1000-11200

FLIER, Jan (1878-1958) Dutch

£335	$600	€489	Still life with red box, apples, orange and knife (56x69cm-22x27in) s. 7-May-4 Sloans & Kenyon, Bethesda #1645/R

FLIGHT, Claude (1881-1955) British
Prints

£1800	$3330	€2628	Le Pont Voluntre, Cahors, Lot (21x27cm-8x11in) s.d.1925 num.2/50 linocut. 10-Mar-4 Sotheby's, Olympia #111/R est:2000-3000
£2600	$4420	€3796	Swing boats (22x28cm-9x11in) s. num.46/50 woodcut exec.1921. 1-Dec-3 Bonhams, New Bond Street #169/R est:1000-1500
£3200	$5440	€4672	Madonna and Child (20x19cm-8x7in) s.i. num.4/50 linocut. 1-Dec-3 Bonhams, New Bond Street #170/R est:1200-1800

Works on paper

£207	$374	€302	Untitled - mountain landscape (34x48cm-13x19in) s. W/C. 18-Apr-4 Levis, Calgary #208/R (C.D 500)
£280	$510	€409	Calm river (26x33cm-10x13in) s. W/C. 15-Jun-4 Bonhams, Knightsbridge #142
£291	$481	€422	Untitled, seascape (35x48cm-14x19in) s. W/C. 3-Jul-3 Heffel, Vancouver #39/R (C.D 650)

FLINCK, Govaert (1615-1660) Dutch

£28571	$45714	€41428	Man reading book and woman playing lute (87x107cm-34x42in) s. 15-May-3 Stuker, Bern #1192/R est:60000-80000 (S.FR 60000)

FLINT, Francis Russell (1915-1977) British
Works on paper

£280	$482	€409	Snow hills, north Devon (27x37cm-11x15in) s. W/C. 3-Dec-3 Christie's, Kensington #617
£300	$555	€438	Possibly South of France or Majorca, harbour side (69x48cm-27x19in) s.d.1957 W/C. 14-Feb-4 Hogben, Folkstone #116
£460	$727	€672	River landscape to a distant bridge (28x112cm-11x44in) s. i.verso W/C. 4-Apr-3 Biddle & Webb, Birmingham #85
£750	$1328	€1095	St. Paul's Bay, Malta (28x39cm-11x15in) s. W/C. 27-Apr-4 Bonhams, New Bond Street #76a/R

FLINT, Robert Purves (1883-1947) British
Works on paper

£480	$826	€701	Donkey man (21x37cm-8x15in) s.d.1923 pencil W/C prov.exhib. 3-Dec-3 Christie's, Kensington #217/R

FLINT, Sir William Russell (1880-1969) British

£400	$668	€584	Model and washing basket in a landscape (26x31cm-10x12in) s. 24-Jun-3 Bonhams, Chester #789
£960	$1747	€1402	Rocky Hill tops, Berthshire (24x36cm-9x14in) s. prov. 29-Jun-4 Bonhams, Knowle #35
£5000	$9300	€7300	Consuelito's pink comb (61x51cm-24x20in) s. prov. 4-Mar-4 Christie's, Kensington #200/R est:5000-7000
£10000	$18300	€14600	Carol Raye, Bernard Clifton and Gretchen Franklin in 'Dear Miss Phoebe' (51x76cm-20x30in) s. board prov.exhib. 2-Jun-4 Sotheby's, London #43/R est:10000-15000
£14500	$24650	€21170	Before the curtain rises (51x68cm-20x27in) s. s.i.d.1951 verso prov.exhib. 26-Nov-3 Sotheby's, Olympia #23/R est:8000-12000
Works on paper			
£380	$635	€555	Study of Pirates of Penzance (17x14cm-7x6in) pencil sold with two other by same hand. 16-Oct-3 Bonhams, Edinburgh #146
£380	$692	€555	Flamenco Dancers and Ballerina (28x42cm-11x17in) pencil. 1-Jul-4 Christie's, Kensington #22
£500	$860	€730	Pretty Gitana (26x17cm-10x7in) init.i. pencil brown chk W/C. 3-Dec-3 Christie's, Kensington #422/R
£550	$968	€803	Island of the Madonna (23x32cm-9x13in) s. W/C. 18-May-4 Bonhams, Knightsbridge #6/R
£600	$1032	€876	Study for Idlers, Senne. Study for the Shrimp Net (9x12cm-4x5in) init.i. pencil pair. 3-Dec-3 Christie's, Kensington #477
£650	$1086	€949	Preliminary title page design for Breakfast in Perigord (52x30cm-20x12in) s.i.d.April 1966 verso W/C. 16-Oct-3 Christie's, Kensington #253/R
£650	$1183	€949	Chartres (26x18cm-10x7in) s. i. W/C. 1-Jul-4 Christie's, Kensington #9/R
£800	$1488	€1168	Study for gypsy chorus, Granada (19x24cm-7x9in) i. pencil sold with two other by same hand. 4-Mar-4 Christie's, Kensington #201/R
£800	$1456	€1168	Loch Lomond from the golf course (23x33cm-9x13in) s. W/C scratching out. 1-Jul-4 Christie's, Kensington #443/R
£900	$1449	€1305	Snow, Gairloch (18x27cm-7x11in) s. W/C. 21-Aug-3 Bonhams, Edinburgh #1133/R
£900	$1530	€1314	Cherry seller (16x11cm-6x4in) s. chk prov. 26-Nov-3 Sotheby's, Olympia #22/R
£920	$1674	€1343	Waiting in the wings (23x16cm-9x6in) s.d.1904 gouache. 15-Jun-4 Bonhams, Knightsbridge #153/R
£1100	$1749	€1606	Bellringers, Eschebarria, Basque (18x15cm-7x6in) s. pencil. 10-Sep-3 Cheffins, Cambridge #486/R est:1000-1500
£1150	$1921	€1679	Landscape, Provencal mountains, winter (36x51cm-14x20in) s.i.verso W/C. 21-Oct-3 Peter Francis, Wales #43 est:1000-1500
£1198	$2000	€1749	Gondoliere (22x30cm-9x12in) s.d.1910 W/C gouache paper on board. 7-Oct-3 Sotheby's, New York #128 est:2500-3500
£1279	$2200	€1867	Untitled, landscape (23x3cm-9x1in) s. W/C. 7-Dec-3 Hindman, Chicago #821/R est:2500-3500
£1500	$2730	€2190	Fisherwomen, Etaples (24x35cm-9x14in) s.d.1906 W/C. 1-Jul-4 Christie's, Kensington #11/R est:1500-2000
£1528	$2750	€2231	Perseus and Danae - illustration (28x22cm-11x9in) s.d.1911 W/C. 21-Jan-4 Sotheby's, New York #216/R est:1500-2500
£1550	$2589	€2263	Betty Paul as Mistress Pepys in and so to bed (18x15cm-7x6in) s.i. s.i.verso conte chk. 14-Oct-3 David Lay, Penzance #293/R est:1000-1500
£1600	$2960	€2336	Near Loch Earn (23x33cm-9x13in) s. W/C. 10-Feb-4 David Lay, Penzance #584/R est:1000-1500
£1676	$3000	€2447	Untitled ocean view (23x30cm-9x12in) s. W/C prov. 21-Mar-4 Hindman, Chicago #849/R est:2000-3000
£1800	$3096	€2628	Spanish lady (29x20cm-11x8in) s. pencil. 2-Dec-3 Bonhams, New Bond Street #34/R est:1500-2000
£1900	$3458	€2774	Autumn on the Baise (16x24cm-6x9in) s. i.verso W/C. 15-Jun-4 Bonhams, Leeds #9/R est:800-1200
£2100	$3822	€3066	At the water's edge, Gareloch (24x34cm-9x13in) s. i.verso W/C prov. 15-Jun-4 Bonhams, Leeds #8/R est:1000-1500
£2206	$3750	€3221	Reclining female (18x29cm-7x11in) s. crayon prov. 21-Nov-3 Skinner, Boston #406/R est:1000-1500
£2326	$4000	€3396	Autumn at Morar (36x25cm-14x10in) s. W/C. 7-Dec-3 Hindman, Chicago #822/R est:3000-5000
£2600	$4420	€3796	Lochnagar from Deeside (24x33cm-9x13in) s. s.i.d.1927 verso W/C prov. 30-Oct-3 Christie's, London #201/R est:2000-3000
£2600	$4420	€3796	Standing nude (30x20cm-12x8in) s. blk crayon. 30-Oct-3 Christie's, London #181/R est:2000-3000
£2600	$4836	€3796	Julia (37x24cm-15x9in) s.i. red chk prov. 4-Mar-4 Christie's, Kensington #197/R est:2000-3000
£2759	$4607	€4028	Andalusian petticoat (34x21cm-13x8in) s.d.23.3.57 red chk. 20-Oct-3 Stephan Welz, Johannesburg #210/R est:8000-12000 (SA.R 32000)
£2778	$5000	€4056	Water nymph (49x30cm-19x12in) s.d.1903 W/C. 21-Jan-4 Sotheby's, New York #217/R est:6000-9000
£2800	$4760	€4088	Study of Audrey Fields, as Amanda (31x20cm-12x8in) s.i.d.1948 blue crayon. 20-Nov-3 Christie's, London #186/R est:3000-5000
£3000	$5160	€4380	Bend in the river (27x38cm-11x15in) s. W/C lit. 2-Dec-3 Bonhams, New Bond Street #27/R est:3000-5000
£3167	$5290	€4624	Then the King was sworn upon the four evangelists (28x21cm-11x8in) s.d.MCMX i.verso board prov. 17-Nov-3 Waddingtons, Toronto #77/R est:5000-7000 (C.D 7000)
£3400	$6324	€4964	Sonnet XLIX, Cecila reading (34x41cm-13x16in) s.i. red chk prov. 4-Mar-4 Christie's, Kensington #198/R est:2000-3000
£3500	$6020	€5110	Low tide, St Malo (33x53cm-13x21in) s. W/C prov.exhib. 3-Dec-3 Christie's, Kensington #616/R est:4000-6000
£3500	$5950	€5110	Hermione (24x40cm-9x16in) s. sanguine chk sepia crayon Italian paper exec c.1780 exhib. 20-Nov-3 Christie's, London #184/R est:2000-3000
£3500	$6265	€5110	Scantily dressed lady (30x43cm-12x17in) s. chk. 28-May-4 Tring Auctions, Tring #382/R est:1500-2000
£3800	$6460	€5548	Model for Goddesses (25x18cm-10x7in) s. col crayon. 30-Oct-3 Christie's, London #182/R est:2500-3500
£4000	$6800	€5840	Summer Haze (24x33cm-9x13in) s. s.i.d.1929 verso W/C prov. 30-Oct-3 Christie's, London #203/R est:3500-5000
£4000	$6800	€5840	Andromeda (35x24cm-14x9in) s.i. col crayon blue paper sketch verso. 30-Oct-3 Christie's, London #204/R est:2500-3500
£4200	$7140	€6132	Reclining nude (20x37cm-8x15in) s. brown crayon. 30-Oct-3 Christie's, London #185/R est:4000-6000
£4200	$7518	€6132	Lady walking along a beach with other figures and children playing with dunes (48x66cm-19x26in) s. W/C. 9-Jan-4 Dickins, Middle Claydon #16 est:4000-6000
£4294	$7686	€6269	Amazon with bow (23x16cm-9x6in) s. W/C. 31-May-4 Stephan Welz, Johannesburg #447/R est:20000-30000 (SA.R 52000)
£4800	$8160	€7008	Study of a semi nude model (16x30cm-6x12in) s. chk dr. 29-Oct-3 Bonhams, Chester #462/R est:700-1000
£4800	$8256	€7008	Lavinia (20x35cm-8x14in) s. col chk prov. 2-Dec-3 Bonhams, New Bond Street #33/R est:3000-5000
£5000	$9150	€7300	Old Channel Fortresses, Brittany (25x33cm-10x13in) s. W/C. 3-Jun-4 Christie's, London #209/R est:6000-8000
£5200	$8840	€7592	Study for Gypsy Scandal Market (23x36cm-9x14in) s. red crayon. 30-Oct-3 Christie's, London #184/R est:5000-8000
£6000	$10200	€8760	Pay l'Eveque on the River Lot, Perigord (48x66cm-19x26in) s. s.i.d.1965 verso W/C. 20-Nov-3 Christie's, London #174/R est:6000-8000
£6000	$10980	€8760	Haunt of the nymphs (42x54cm-17x21in) s. W/C prov. 3-Jun-4 Christie's, London #208/R est:6000-8000
£7500	$11925	€10950	Two ladies (27x40cm-11x16in) s.i. s.i.d.Nov 1952 verso col chk. 10-Sep-3 Sotheby's, Olympia #117/R est:3000-4000
£7500	$13650	€10950	St Malo (32x49cm-13x19in) s. W/C. 29-Jun-4 Anderson & Garland, Newcastle #266/R est:7000-11000
£8000	$13600	€11680	On the beach at Bamburgh, Northumberland (35x31cm-14x12in) s.i.d.1921 W/C bodycol. 30-Oct-3 Christie's, London #202/R est:7000-10000
£8500	$13345	€12325	Bathers picnic (44x37cm-17x15in) s. W/C. 27-Aug-3 Sotheby's, London #1069/R est:7000-10000
£8500	$15555	€12410	In sight of the Farnes (41x53cm-16x21in) s. s.i. backboard W/C prov. 3-Jun-4 Christie's, London #210/R est:10000-15000
£8721	$15000	€12733	Leading lady (30x38cm-12x15in) s. W/C. 7-Dec-3 Hindman, Chicago #819/R est:20000-30000
£8800	$16280	€12848	Nicolette (25x20cm-10x8in) s.d.1960 W/C. 10-Feb-4 David Lay, Penzance #526/R est:4000-6000
£9050	$15113	€13213	Campo S Simon Grando, Venice (49x67cm-19x26in) s. s.i.d.Sept.30 1963 W/C prov. 17-Nov-3 Waddingtons, Toronto #78/R est:25000-30000 (C.D 20000)
£10000	$17200	€14600	Blue salotto, Il salotto, Tuscany (37x55cm-15x22in) s. W/C prov. 2-Dec-3 Bonhams, New Bond Street #32/R est:12000-16000
£10000	$17000	€14600	Teresa, Yolanda and Anna-maria (30x59cm-12x23in) s. s.i.d.1966 backboard red chk prov. 20-Nov-3 Christie's, London #183/R est:4000-6000
£10000	$18500	€14600	Five studies in three chalks (37x55cm-15x22in) s. col crayon prov. 11-Feb-4 Sotheby's, Olympia #103/R est:6000-8000
£12000	$20640	€17520	On summer day (49x66cm-19x26in) s. W/C prov. 2-Dec-3 Bonhams, New Bond Street #30/R est:10000-15000
£12500	$21500	€18250	Twin towers, Shandon (38x51cm-15x20in) s. W/C prov. 2-Dec-3 Bonhams, New Bond Street #29/R est:12000-18000
£15500	$26660	€22630	Melinda posing in a Devon lindhay (36x53cm-14x21in) s. W/C prov. 2-Dec-3 Bonhams, New Bond Street #31/R est:12000-18000
£17000	$31620	€24820	Spanish windows (61x49cm-24x19in) s. W/C prov.exhib. 4-Mar-4 Christie's, Kensington #199/R est:15000-25000
£18198	$31301	€26569	Nomads at Aigueze, Ardeche, France (49x67cm-19x26in) s.i.verso W/C prov. 3-Dec-3 Stephan Welz, Johannesburg #12/R est:100000-150000 (SA.R 200000)
£18198	$31301	€26569	Listener, Cordes, Tarn, France, a XIII century corner (67x50cm-26x20in) s. s.i.d.May 1961 verso W/C prov. 3-Dec-3 Stephan Welz, Johannesburg #13/R est:100000-150000 (SA.R 200000)
£18786	$32500	€27428	And so she went with the wing roaring and yelling that it seemed all the water brent after her (28x22cm-11x9in) s.d.MC/MXI pencil gouache prov.exhib. 11-Dec-3 Sotheby's, New York #177/R est:18000-25000
£26000	$44200	€37960	White dress (35x56cm-14x22in) s. W/C. 30-Oct-3 Christie's, London #180/R est:20000-30000
£76000	$139080	€110960	Reclining nude (35x63cm-14x25in) s. W/C prov. 7-Apr-4 Woolley & Wallis, Salisbury #117/R est:12000-18000

FLIPART, Charles Joseph (attrib) (1721-1797) French

£2448	$4087	€3500	Lessive (46x38cm-18x15in) 30-Jun-3 Bailly Pommery, Paris #68/R est:3500

FLIS, Adam (19th C) ?

£360	$634	€526	The Alphonse Parran under steam (152x229cm-60x90in) s.d.1866. 24-May-4 Bonhams, Bath #436

FLIS, Giorgio (1941-) Italian

£333	$613	€500	Bird on the Nile (70x90cm-28x35in) s. oil enamel painted 2002 exhib.lit. 12-Jun-4 Meeting Art, Vercelli #433/R

FLOCH, Jean Claude (1954-) French

Works on paper			
£486	$802	€700	Untitled (33x62cm-13x24in) felt pen collage. 3-Jul-3 Christie's, Paris #54/R

FLOCH, Josef (1895-1977) American/Austrian

£875	$1400	€1278	Woman resting (46x36cm-18x14in) init.verso paper. 20-Sep-3 Bunte, Elgin #1231 est:400-600
£2484	$4000	€3627	Seated woman (117x91cm-46x36in) s. painted c.1973. 22-Feb-3 Bunte, Elgin #1202 est:2000-3000
£3727	$6000	€5441	Self portrait (107x71cm-42x28in) s. 22-Feb-3 Bunte, Elgin #1196 est:2000-3000
£3727	$6000	€5441	Woman watering flowers (64x53cm-25x21in) painted c.1960. 22-Feb-3 Bunte, Elgin #1197 est:1500-2500
£4651	$8000	€6790	Sisters (38x41cm-15x16in) s. 3-Dec-3 Doyle, New York #118/R est:6000-8000
£4969	$8000	€7255	Interior with sculpture (53x46cm-21x18in) s. 22-Feb-3 Bunte, Elgin #1198 est:1500-2500
£7453	$12000	€10881	Rocky landscape with boat (66x99cm-26x39in) s. painted c.1937. 22-Feb-3 Bunte, Elgin #1200 est:2000-3000
£8380	$15000	€12235	Three women in an interior (61x38cm-24x15in) s. 6-May-4 Doyle, New York #66/R est:8000-12000
£10180	$17000	€14863	Seated figure (94x65cm-37x26in) s. painted c.1936 exhib.lit. 7-Oct-3 Sotheby's, New York #216 est:10000-15000
£11250	$18000	€16425	Seated woman and screen (127x104cm-50x41in) s. 20-Sep-3 Bunte, Elgin #1220 est:4000-6000
£11801	$19000	€17229	Studio with sculpture and nude (119x107cm-47x42in) studio st. painted c.1966. 22-Feb-3 Bunte, Elgin #1195 est:3000-5000
£11801	$19000	€17229	Tapestry (91x74cm-36x29in) s. 22-Feb-3 Bunte, Elgin #1201 est:3000-5000
£13665	$22000	€19951	Construction near park (86x61cm-34x24in) s. painted c.1959. 22-Feb-3 Bunte, Elgin #1194 est:3000-5000
£14765	$26430	€22000	Fisherwoman from Collioure (52x43cm-20x17in) s.d.1926 lit. 27-May-4 Hassfurther, Vienna #44/R est:12000-15000
£16770	$27000	€24484	Terrace scene (97x130cm-38x51in) s. painted c.1937. 22-Feb-3 Bunte, Elgin #1199 est:3000-5000
£27778	$47222	€40000	Woman supporting head on hand (74x57cm-29x22in) s. prov.lit. 28-Oct-3 Wiener Kunst Auktionen, Vienna #69/R est:15000-50000

Works on paper			
£219	$350	€320	Nude with hand on hip (38x28cm-15x11in) init.verso dr. 20-Sep-3 Bunte, Elgin #1226
£234	$375	€342	Sketch for lithograph, self portrait (43x36cm-17x14in) init.i.verso dr. 20-Sep-3 Bunte, Elgin #1224
£234	$375	€342	Woman seated at table (48x36cm-19x14in) s. dr. 20-Sep-3 Bunte, Elgin #1235
£282	$450	€412	Interior with three figures (48x38cm-19x15in) init.verso dr. 20-Sep-3 Bunte, Elgin #1244
£297	$475	€434	Reclining nude (33x51cm-13x20in) init.verso dr. 20-Sep-3 Bunte, Elgin #1245
£336	$601	€500	Young woman sitting (44x29cm-17x11in) mono. brown chl wash. 27-May-4 Hassfurther, Vienna #47
£375	$600	€548	Reclining nude. Sketch of nude woman (36x48cm-14x19in) s. dr double-sided. 20-Sep-3 Bunte, Elgin #1228
£407	$650	€594	Winter scene with figures (20x20cm-8x8in) s.d.1915 dr. 20-Sep-3 Bunte, Elgin #1243
£493	$818	€700	Sketch (50x36cm-20x14in) col chk. 12-Jun-3 Dorotheum, Graz #135/R
£532	$850	€777	Seated nude (51x33cm-20x13in) init.verso dr. 20-Sep-3 Bunte, Elgin #1229
£1007	$1802	€1500	Visit (38x51cm-15x20in) s. mixed media. 27-May-4 Hassfurther, Vienna #48 est:1500-2000
£1074	$1922	€1600	Visit (25x40cm-10x16in) mono.d.1950 pastel. 27-May-4 Hassfurther, Vienna #46 est:1500-2000
£1105	$1900	€1613	Southern villa. Study of mountains (45x40cm-18x16in) s. W/C crayon gouache double-sided. 3-Dec-3 Doyle, New York #119/R est:1500-2500
£1745	$3123	€2600	View through a door (48x33cm-19x13in) s.d.1948 mixed media board lit. 27-May-4 Hassfurther, Vienna #45/R est:1500-2000

FLOCH, Lionel (1895-1972) French

£317	$555	€450	Barques au sec a Brehat (22x27cm-9x11in) s. panel. 21-Dec-3 Thierry & Lannon, Brest #314
£1408	$2465	€2000	Elegante dans un jardin fleuri (60x73cm-24x29in) s.d.1925. 21-Dec-3 Thierry & Lannon, Brest #315 est:1200-1500
£2333	$4317	€3500	Ramasseurs de goemon (53x72cm-21x28in) s. 14-Jul-4 Livinec, Gaudcheau & Jezequel, Rennes #168
£3179	$5944	€4800	Le pecheur au panier (100x80cm-39x31in) s. 24-Jul-4 Thierry & Lannon, Brest #242/R est:2500-3000

FLOCKENHAUS, Heinz (1856-1919) German

£1181	$1948	€1700	Winter evening with peasant women returning home. Summer stream (18x26cm-7x10in) s. panel two. 3-Jul-3 Van Ham, Cologne #1178/R est:2200
£1333	$2413	€2000	Stormy weather over northern Rhine landscape (26x43cm-10x17in) s.d.1881. 1-Apr-4 Van Ham, Cologne #1370/R est:2500

FLODIN, Hilda (1877-1958) Finnish

£387	$711	€580	The harbour (27x48cm-11x19in) s.d.36. 9-Jun-4 Bukowskis, Helsinki #389/R

FLODMAN, Carl (1863-1888) Swedish

£2077	$3572	€3032	Lake landscape (30x40cm-12x16in) s. 3-Dec-3 AB Stockholms Auktionsverk #2424/R est:12000-15000 (S.KR 27000)

FLOOD, Patricia Vaughan (1919-) Australian

Works on paper			
£331	$612	€483	Kingfishers (99x150cm-39x59in) s.d.1978 i.verso synthetic polymer. 15-Mar-4 Sotheby's, Melbourne #211 (A.D 800)

FLOQUET, Simon (attrib) (17th C) Flemish

£3378	$5946	€5000	David and Abigail (54x70cm-21x28in) copper. 24-May-4 Bernaerts, Antwerp #178/R est:6000-8000

FLORA, Paul (1922-) Austrian

Works on paper			
£387	$620	€550	The dwarf Diogenes (6x12cm-2x5in) s. Indian ink. 16-Sep-3 Dorotheum, Vienna #24/R
£390	$651	€550	Fasching (5x7cm-2x3in) s. Indian ink W/C. 16-Oct-3 Dorotheum, Salzburg #991/R
£390	$651	€550	Faschings figure (6x9cm-2x4in) s. Indian ink W/C. 16-Oct-3 Dorotheum, Salzburg #993/R
£483	$883	€700	Harlequin (12x16cm-5x6in) s.i. Indian ink col pen. 27-Jan-4 Dorotheum, Vienna #233/R
£638	$1066	€900	Night messenger (16x20cm-6x8in) s.i. Indian ink. 14-Oct-3 Dorotheum, Vienna #244/R
£664	$1129	€950	Old Austrian spy dressed as tree (37x52cm-15x20in) s.i. Indian ink. 19-Nov-3 Dorotheum, Klagenfurt #93
£822	$1397	€1200	Circus (50x40cm-20x16in) s. pen col pen. 5-Nov-3 Dorotheum, Vienna #77/R est:1800
£833	$1358	€1200	Square with people (48x62cm-19x24in) s. ink. 23-Sep-3 Wiener Kunst Auktionen, Vienna #160/R
£851	$1421	€1200	Serious order (30x28cm-12x11in) s.i. Indian ink. 16-Oct-3 Dorotheum, Salzburg #989/R
£851	$1421	€1200	Tyrolean riflemen (45x62cm-18x24in) s. Indian ink. 16-Oct-3 Dorotheum, Salzburg #990/R
£855	$1574	€1300	Today one more on splendid horses (28x38cm-11x15in) s.d.1983 ink col pencil. 22-Jun-4 Wiener Kunst Auktionen, Vienna #302/R
£1053	$1937	€1600	Marabu and military (28x38cm-11x15in) s.d.1984 ink col pencil. 22-Jun-4 Wiener Kunst Auktionen, Vienna #301/R est:1000
£1053	$1937	€1600	Large train station II (32x50cm-13x20in) s. ink. 22-Jun-4 Wiener Kunst Auktionen, Vienna #303/R est:1200
£1200	$2148	€1800	Flight pioneers over icebergs (34x50cm-13x20in) s.d.79 pen. 13-May-4 Dorotheum, Linz #605/R est:1400-1600
£1267	$2267	€1900	Soldiers (44x63cm-17x25in) s.d.64 Indian ink. 13-May-4 Dorotheum, Linz #604/R est:1400-1600
£1268	$2218	€1800	A fighter from Tyrol (46x56cm-18x22in) s. pen ink. 19-Dec-3 Dorotheum, Vienna #303/R est:1700-2200
£1702	$2843	€2400	Rifle club formation (55x74cm-22x29in) s. Indian ink W/C. 16-Oct-3 Dorotheum, Salzburg #994/R est:2000-2600

FLORENCE, Mary Sargant (1857-1954) British

£3000	$5400	€4380	Love's baubles (53x133cm-21x52in) s.d.92 canvas on board prov.exhib. 21-Jan-4 Sotheby's, Olympia #295/R est:3000-4000

FLORENTINE SCHOOL, Italian

£7400	$12580	€10804	Portrait of young lady (94x86cm-37x34in) 22-Nov-3 Bonhams, Chester #326 est:3000-5000

FLORENTINE SCHOOL (14th C) Italian

£29054	$52007	€43000	Holy Mary on throne (96x36cm-38x14in) panel prov. 8-May-4 Schloss Ahlden, Ahlden #1028/R est:6800

FLORENTINE SCHOOL (15th C) Italian

£11000	$19030	€16060	Presentation of Christ in the temple (24x29cm-9x11in) tempera pine panel gold ground. 11-Dec-3 Sotheby's, London #172/R est:3000-4000
£14000	$25200	€20440	Crucifixion (65x38cm-26x15in) tempera gold ground panel painted c.1400 prov. 22-Apr-4 Sotheby's, London #54/R est:15000-20000
£22800	$39444	€33288	Nativity (37x34cm-15x13in) bears d.MCCC/LXXXXVI panel. 9-Dec-3 Sotheby's, Olympia #366/R est:5000-7000
£28369	$47376	€40000	Crucifixion (54x51cm-21x20in) board. 15-Oct-3 Finarte Semenzato, Rome #144/R est:40000

FLORENTINE SCHOOL (16th C) Italian

£6000	$10980	€8760	Portrait of lady (107x84cm-42x33in) lit. 8-Jul-4 Sotheby's, London #195/R est:8000-12000
£10000	$17900	€15000	Holy Family with Saint John (111x89cm-44x35in) board. 17-May-4 Finarte Semenzato, Rome #97/R est:14000-16000
£12000	$21960	€18000	Judgement of souls (190x141cm-75x56in) 1-Jun-4 Sotheby's, Milan #78/R est:15000-20000
£14388	$23597	€20000	Madonna and Child and Saint John (81x63cm-32x25in) board prov. 4-Jun-3 Sotheby's, Milan #79/R est:12000-16000
£19444	$35000	€28388	Portrait of Pope Clement VII (66x51cm-26x20in) i. panel. 22-Jan-4 Sotheby's, New York #185/R est:35000-45000
Works on paper			
£5500	$10065	€8030	Seated woman with child (19x28cm-7x11in) red chk brown ink corners made up prov. 6-Jul-4 Christie's, London #16/R est:2500-3500

FLORENTINE SCHOOL (16th/17th C) Italian

£34899	$64215	€52000	St George (54x45cm-21x18in) prov. 25-Mar-4 Dr Fritz Nagel, Stuttgart #636/R est:5000

FLORENTINE SCHOOL (17th C) Italian

£7200	$12456	€10512	Rinaldo and Armida (117x76cm-46x30in) 9-Dec-3 Sotheby's, Olympia #391/R est:4000-6000
£8451	$13606	€12000	Maddona and child, Saint Francis and Holy Bishop (183x140cm-72x55in) 8-May-3 Farsetti, Prato #589/R est:10000-14000
£10000	$17900	€15000	Saint Benedict and two angels (95x133cm-37x52in) 12-May-4 Finarte Semenzato, Milan #75/R est:5000-7000
£12667	$23180	€19000	Still life with vase of flowers and putti, Florence beyond (147x118cm-58x46in) 1-Jun-4 Sotheby's, Milan #173/R est:12000-15000
£14085	$22676	€20000	Antonio di Neri Acciaiuoli, secondo Duca d'Atene, in costume moresco (152x114cm-60x45in) i. 8-May-3 Farsetti, Prato #785/R est:7000-8000
£14085	$22676	€20000	Antonio di Francesco Acciaiuoli, terzo Duca di Atene (153x114cm-60x45in) i. 8-May-3 Farsetti, Prato #786/R est:7000-8000
£17606	$28345	€25000	Neri di Francesco Acciaiuoli, quarto Duca d'Atene in costume oreintale (152x114cm-60x45in) i. 8-May-3 Farsetti, Prato #787/R est:7000-8000
£25694	$42910	€37000	Apollus (118x91cm-46x36in) 22-Oct-3 Finarte Semenzato, Milan #32/R
Sculpture			
£4491	$7500	€6557	Sleeping nymph (15cm-6in) pat bronze. 18-Oct-3 Sotheby's, New York #79/R est:6000-8000
£14000	$25200	€20440	Figure of a bagpiper (18cm-7in) gilt bronze marble socle after Giambologna lit. 21-Apr-4 Sotheby's, London #33/R est:15000-20000

FLORENTINE SCHOOL (18th C) Italian

£4564	$8397	€6800	Madonna and Child with Saint John (108x81cm-43x32in) 24-Mar-4 Finarte Semenzato, Rome #198/R est:4000
£25352	$40817	€36000	Ritratto di Cosimo I de Medici in costume da Granduca (134x98cm-53x39in) 8-May-3 Farsetti, Prato #764/R est:42000-52000

FLORENTINE SCHOOL (19th C) Italian

£5200	$8684	€7592	Madonna and Child and two saints (165x83cm-65x33in) oil gilt panel folding side panels. 7-Oct-3 Bonhams, Knightsbridge #360/R est:4000-6000
Sculpture			
£24324	$43541	€36000	Dogs (57x103x36cm-22x41x14in) marble pair. 9-May-4 Sotheby's, Amsterdam #837/R est:20000-30000

FLORES KAPEROTXIPI, Mauricio (1901-1997) Argentinian

£1831	$3168	€2600	Basque with red scarf (50x40cm-20x16in) s. s.i.verso. 15-Dec-3 Ansorena, Madrid #354/R est:2600
£1897	$3167	€2750	Two generations (33x41cm-13x16in) s. 17-Nov-3 Durán, Madrid #104/R est:2400
£1993	$3268	€2750	Rosquillas para los nietos (55x45cm-22x18in) s. board. 27-May-3 Durán, Madrid #113/R est:2000
£2041	$3653	€3000	Basque man with red scarf (50x40cm-20x16in) s. i.verso. 22-Mar-4 Durán, Madrid #189/R est:2400
£3061	$5480	€4500	Grandparents (50x61cm-20x24in) s. 22-Mar-4 Durán, Madrid #198/R est:3000

FLORES, Francisco (1919-1984) Mexican

£861	$1438	€1248	San Mateo bull (49x63cm-19x25in) s. 24-Jun-3 Louis Morton, Mexico #116/R est:20000-25000 (M.P 15000)

FLORES, Leonardo (attrib) (1650-1710) Peruvian
£8235 $14000 €12023 La Ascencion - The Ascension (239x150cm-94x59in) painted c.1700 prov. 18-Nov-3 Christie's, Rockefeller NY #76/R est:8000-10000

FLORES, Pedro (1897-1967) Spanish
£1497 $2500 €2186 Don Quichotte et Sancho (61x81cm-24x32in) s. 16-Nov-3 Simpson's, Houston #306/R
Works on paper
£1846 $3267 €2750 Calvary (32x26cm-13x10in) s.d.62 gouache. 27-Apr-4 Durán, Madrid #19/R est:750

FLOREZ (?) ?
£2270 $3790 €3200 Portrait d'Arabes (27x16cm-11x6in) s.d.1906 panel pair. 16-Jun-3 Gros & Delettrez, Paris #344/R est:3500-4000

FLORIAN, Maximilian (1901-1982) Austrian
£2778 $4528 €4000 Prostitute (40x30cm-16x12in) s.i.d.1933 board. 23-Sep-3 Wiener Kunst Auktionen, Vienna #102/R est:4000-7000

FLORIDO, Enrique (19th C) Spanish
£1690 $2924 €2400 Seascape (40x75cm-16x30in) s. 15-Dec-3 Ansorena, Madrid #289/R est:1200

FLORIS, Carmelo (1891-1960) Italian
£1118 $2058 €1700 Sardinian women (67x52cm-26x20in) s.d.1960. 23-Jun-4 Finarte Semenzato, Rome #106/R est:1500-1700

FLORIS, Frans (16/17th C) Flemish
£2979 $4974 €4200 Profeta (39x31cm-15x12in) panel prov. 18-Jun-3 Christie's, Rome #417/R est:3000-5000

FLORIS, Frans (attrib) (16/17th C) Flemish
£1467 $2655 €2200 Infant Jesus (52x42cm-20x17in) panel. 1-Apr-4 Van Ham, Cologne #1191/R est:1200

FLORIS, Frans (elder) (1516-1570) Flemish
£22222 $40000 €32444 Christ blessing the children (141x226cm-56x89in) 23-Jan-4 Christie's, Rockefeller NY #18/R est:50000-70000

FLORIS, Frans (elder-attrib) (1516-1570) Flemish
Works on paper
£529 $900 €772 Nymph seated in nitch with titon (18x13cm-7x5in) i. chk. 25-Nov-3 Christie's, Rockefeller NY #497/R

FLORIS, Marcel (1914-) French
£834 $1435 €1218 Untitled (92x82cm-36x32in) s. painted 1964. 7-Dec-3 Subastas Odalys, Caracas #55

FLORIT, Josep Lluis (1909-) Spanish
Works on paper
£297 $496 €425 By the sea (40x33cm-16x13in) s.d.36 W/C. 30-Jun-3 Ansorena, Madrid #10/R

FLOROT, Gustave (20th C) French
£431 $772 €629 Clown et femme (72x49cm-28x19in) s. board on panel. 12-May-4 Dobiaschofsky, Bern #496/R (S.FR 1000)

FLORSHEIM, Richard Aberle (1916-1979) American
£226 $400 €330 Bayou (30x23cm-12x9in) s. board. 1-May-4 Susanin's, Chicago #5065/R
£275 $475 €402 Marchers (10x30cm-4x12in) s. board prov. 13-Dec-3 Weschler, Washington #585
£282 $500 €412 Rain (30x46cm-12x18in) s. board. 1-May-4 Susanin's, Chicago #5059/R

FLOUQUET, Pierre Louis (attrib) (1900-1967) Belgian
£861 $1567 €1300 Le combat de coqs (71x96cm-28x38in) 15-Jun-4 Vanderkindere, Brussels #104

FLOUTIER, Louis (20th C) French
£366 $641 €520 Juan les Pins (16x22cm-6x9in) s. board. 21-Dec-3 Thierry & Lannon, Brest #316
£800 $1464 €1168 Street scene with figures (63x48cm-25x19in) s. 5-Jun-4 Windibank, Dorking #368/R
£1100 $1980 €1606 Hanging out the washing (53x73cm-21x29in) s. 20-Jan-4 Bonhams, Knightsbridge #14/R est:1200-1800
£1333 $2427 €2000 Saint-Etienne de Baigorry (40x32cm-16x13in) s.i. panel. 30-Jun-4 Delvaux, Paris #46 est:900-1400
£1400 $2548 €2100 Ferme au Pays Basque (40x32cm-16x13in) s. panel. 30-Jun-4 Delvaux, Paris #45 est:800-1200
£3000 $5460 €4500 Marine au soleil couchant (50x73cm-20x29in) s. 4-Jul-4 Eric Pillon, Calais #90/R
£3889 $6417 €5600 Scene de marche (44x54cm-17x21in) s. panel painted c.1930. 1-Jul-3 Lemoine & Ferrando, Paris #67/R est:1000-1200

FLOWER, Cedric (1920-) Australian
£255 $434 €372 Afternoon Ride (35x47cm-14x19in) s. composition board. 26-Nov-3 Deutscher-Menzies, Melbourne #248/R (A.D 600)
£450 $797 €657 Sydney Terraces (22x38cm-9x15in) s. board. 27-Apr-4 Bonhams, Knightsbridge #107/R
£531 $977 €775 Shamrock hotel (30x61cm-12x24in) s. board. 29-Mar-4 Goodman, Sydney #228/R (A.D 1300)

FLOWER, Charles Edwin (1871-?) British
£2448 $4161 €3500 Dusseldorf park hotel with Cornelius fountain (21x34cm-8x13in) s. tempera paper. 20-Nov-3 Van Ham, Cologne #1572/R est:3800
Works on paper
£460 $833 €672 Rural cottage with floral lined path (40x29cm-16x11in) s. W/C. 2-Apr-4 Moore Allen & Innocent, Cirencester #763/R

FLOWER, John (?-1861) British
Works on paper
£260 $465 €380 In the Newarke, Leicester (27x19cm-11x7in) s.i. pencil sepia. 16-Mar-4 Gildings, Market Harborough #409
£440 $788 €642 View of the Old Green Dragon Inn, Leicester Market place (27x36cm-11x14in) s. s.i.mount pencil sepia wash. 16-Mar-4 Gildings, Market Harborough #411/R
£460 $823 €672 In the Newarke, Leicester, Mr Henry House, Henry 7th's time (26x36cm-10x14in) s.i. pencil sepia wash. 16-Mar-4 Gildings, Market Harborough #413
£580 $1038 €847 The old west bridge Leicester (22x35cm-9x14in) s.i. pencil sepia wash. 16-Mar-4 Gildings, Market Harborough #407
£1000 $1790 €1460 View of the Old Green Dragon Inn, Leicester Market place (26x36cm-10x14in) s. pencil sepia wash. 16-Mar-4 Gildings, Market Harborough #412/R

FLOWERS, Alfred (19/20th C) ?
Works on paper
£500 $830 €730 Off St. Maws (26x40cm-10x16in) W/C. 1-Oct-3 Woolley & Wallis, Salisbury #155/R

FLOYD, Donald H (1892-1965) British
£320 $518 €467 Early autumn, Tintern Abbey (36x48cm-14x19in) s. s.i.verso. 7-Aug-3 Neales, Nottingham #493
£500 $835 €730 River Neavy, south Devon (41x61cm-16x24in) s. 15-Nov-3 Nigel Ward, Hereford #1450
Works on paper
£490 $877 €715 Tintern Abbey (51x610cm-20x240in) s.d. W/C. 8-May-4 British Auctioneer #1

FLUCK, Johann Peter (1902-1954) Swiss
£560 $1003 €818 Peasant couple in field (80x100cm-31x39in) s.d.53. 12-May-4 Dobiaschofsky, Bern #497/R (S.FR 1300)

FLUCK, Martin Peter (1935-) Swiss
Works on paper
£323 $579 €472 Coloured abstract composition (64x76cm-25x30in) s.d.67 W/C. 12-May-4 Dobiaschofsky, Bern #498/R (S.FR 750)

FLUER, Johann Limpert (?-c.1755) German
£3611 $6500 €5272 Roses, peonies and other flowers in a vase on a ledge (43x35cm-17x14in) 23-Jan-4 Christie's, Rockefeller NY #156/R est:6000-8000

FLUGGEN, Hans (1875-1942) German
£331 $603 €500 Portrait of an woman against an oriental coastline (37x30cm-15x12in) s.d.1925 panel. 18-Jun-4 Bolland & Marotz, Bremen #614/R

FLUGI VAN ASPERMONT, Carel Hendrik Christiaan (1869-1935) Dutch
£451 $736 €650 Bronze statue on a draped table (89x64cm-35x25in) s. 29-Sep-3 Sotheby's, Amsterdam #36/R

FLUMIANI, Ugo (1876-1938) Italian
£559 $962 €800 Fishing boat (18x25cm-7x10in) cardboard. 3-Dec-3 Stadion, Trieste #1153/R
£699 $1203 €1000 Landscape (19x27cm-7x11in) s. board. 3-Dec-3 Stadion, Trieste #1122/R
£1081 $2043 €1600 Seisera Valley, Tarvisio (46x38cm-18x15in) s. board. 20-Feb-4 Stadion, Trieste #811/R
£1189 $2045 €1700 Path to the valley (51x65cm-20x26in) s. 3-Dec-3 Stadion, Trieste #1037/R est:1600-2000
£1333 $2387 €2000 Boats at sea (56x42cm-22x17in) s. 12-May-4 Stadion, Trieste #673 est:2200-3300
£1538 $2646 €2200 San Giusto (41x31cm-16x12in) s. board. 3-Dec-3 Stadion, Trieste #1166/R est:1500-2000
£1844 $3079 €2600 Veduta di San Giusto (44x39cm-17x15in) s. plywood. 21-Jun-3 Stadion, Trieste #370/R est:2000-3000
£2098 $3608 €3000 Seascape with boats (29x40cm-11x16in) s. board. 3-Dec-3 Stadion, Trieste #1176/R est:1600-2000
£2133 $3819 €3200 Road to Opicina (66x50cm-26x20in) s. 12-May-4 Stadion, Trieste #814/R est:2200-3200
£2448 $4210 €3500 Seascape in Grado (44x61cm-17x24in) s. s.verso. 3-Dec-3 Stadion, Trieste #1096/R est:2500-3500
£3000 $5370 €4500 High sea (61x86cm-24x34in) s. 12-May-4 Stadion, Trieste #789/R est:4000-5000
£3404 $5685 €4800 Barche al largo (37x45cm-15x18in) s. plywood. 21-Jun-3 Stadion, Trieste #195/R est:3000-4000
£3636 $6073 €5200 View of Trieste from above (51x66cm-20x26in) s. 10-Oct-3 Stadion, Trieste #636/R est:4000-5000
£3846 $6615 €5500 Trieste from the sky (40x65cm-16x26in) s. board. 3-Dec-3 Stadion, Trieste #1040/R est:4000-5000
£6000 $9600 €8700 Sailing home (93x110cm-37x43in) s. 18-Sep-3 Christie's, Kensington #113/R est:6000-8000
£7343 $12629 €10500 View of Zoppe' di Cadore (110x150cm-43x59in) s. s.i.verso. 3-Dec-3 Stadion, Trieste #1002/R est:7000-9000

£8741 $15035 €12500 Windy day in the bay (85x112cm-33x44in) s. 3-Dec-3 Stadion, Trieste #985/R est:8000-12000

FLURER, Ignaz (attrib) (1686-1742) Austrian
£3356 $6174 €5000 Southern port with ships at anchor (52x70cm-20x28in) prov. 24-Mar-4 Dorotheum, Vienna #261/R est:3000-5000

FLURY, Burckhardt (1862-1928) Swiss
£739 $1353 €1079 Mother cat with kittens (33x31cm-13x12in) s. 4-Jun-4 Zofingen, Switzerland #2800/R (S.FR 1700)
£2685 $4805 €4000 Cat family (49x65cm-19x26in) s.d.1919. 27-May-4 Dorotheum, Vienna #207/R est:4000-4500
Works on paper
£560 $1003 €818 Three kittens (18x34cm-7x13in) s. pastel. 14-May-4 Dobiaschofsky, Bern #213/R (S.FR 1300)
£655 $1192 €956 Two kittens on the sofa (25x33cm-10x13in) s. pastel. 16-Jun-4 Fischer, Luzern #2762/R (S.FR 1500)
£676 $1162 €987 Family of cats (33x45cm-13x18in) s. pastel chk. 8-Dec-3 Philippe Schuler, Zurich #3191/R (S.FR 1500)

FLURY, Burckhardt (attrib) (1862-1928) Swiss
£1034 $1852 €1510 Three kittens playing (37x55cm-15x22in) i. 12-May-4 Dobiaschofsky, Bern #499/R est:1800 (S.FR 2400)

FLURY, Urs (1937-) Swiss
£818 $1358 €1186 Landscape with trees (95x90cm-37x35in) s.d.79 hessian. 13-Jun-3 Zofingen, Switzerland #2844 est:1800 (S.FR 1800)

FLY, Camillus S (1849-1901) American
Photographs
£3473 $5800 €5071 Council between General Crook and Geronimo (8x19cm-3x7in) albumen print. 21-Oct-3 Swann Galleries, New York #55/R est:6000-9000

FLYNN, Dianne (20th C) British?
Works on paper
£600 $1098 €876 Catching the ferry (27x37cm-11x15in) s. gouache board. 3-Jun-4 Lane, Penzance #299

FLYNN, Richard (20th C) British
Works on paper
£460 $731 €672 Figures taking refreshment at the snack bar, Grainger Market, Newcastle (38x42cm-15x17in) s. pastel. 18-Mar-3 Anderson & Garland, Newcastle #118/R

FOCARDI, Alberto (20th C) Italian
£500 $920 €750 Cliffs in Antignano (22x33cm-9x13in) s. board painted 1937. 11-Jun-4 Farsetti, Prato #441

FOCARDI, Piero (1889-1945) Italian
£5245 $9021 €7500 Chemin pres du lac (46x70cm-18x28in) s.d.1908. 5-Dec-3 Gros & Delettrez, Paris #61/R est:2500-3000

FOCARDI, Ruggero (1864-1934) Italian
£5282 $9137 €7500 Autumnal stroll (57x74cm-22x29in) s. 9-Dec-3 Pandolfini, Florence #262/R est:2500-3000

FOCHT, Frederic (1879-?) French
Sculpture
£18786 $32500 €27428 Man in flight (98x86x35cm-39x34x14in) with sig. bronze. 11-Dec-3 Sotheby's, New York #156/R est:15000-20000

FOCK, Hermanus (1766-1822) Dutch
Works on paper
£4392 $7730 €6500 Boy on a bridge over a stream (14x18cm-6x7in) black chk prov.exhib.lit. 19-May-4 Sotheby's, Amsterdam #275/R est:1400-1800

FOCKE, Wilhelm (1878-?) German
£364 $663 €550 Evening on the coast (17x28cm-7x11in) mono. canvas on board. 18-Jun-4 Bolland & Marotz, Bremen #347

FOGEL, Seymour (1911-1984) American
£1497 $2500 €2186 Red and black (76x91cm-30x36in) s.d.48 masonite prov. 26-Oct-3 Bonhams & Butterfields, San Francisco #6599/R
£1946 $3250 €2841 Untitled, no 2 (76x91cm-30x36in) s.d.48 masonite prov. 26-Oct-3 Bonhams & Butterfields, San Francisco #6595/R
£2096 $3500 €3060 Roundup (33x46cm-13x18in) oil paper. 18-Oct-3 David Dike, Dallas #123/R est:4000-6000
Works on paper
£2395 $4000 €3497 Desert landscape (53x74cm-21x29in) W/C. 18-Oct-3 David Dike, Dallas #225/R est:4000-6000

FOGG, Howard (1917-1996) American
Works on paper
£1934 $3500 €2824 Untitled - scene with trains (41x56cm-16x22in) W/C. 16-Apr-4 Du Mouchelle, Detroit #2069/R est:2500-4500

FOGG, Sarah Anne (attrib) (1829-1922) Australian
£2459 $3885 €3590 Quamby Bluff, near Hagley, Northern Tasmania (30x45cm-12x18in) W/C prov. 2-Sep-3 Deutscher-Menzies, Melbourne #207/R est:7000-10000 (A.D 6000)

FOGGIA, Mario Moretti (1882-1954) Italian
£782 $1400 €1142 Levar del sole dul monte rosa (33x41cm-13x16in) s. i.verso board. 20-Mar-4 Selkirks, St. Louis #521/R est:1000-1500
£1096 $1710 €1600 Thoghts (41x32cm-16x13in) s. board. 8-Apr-3 Il Ponte, Milan #532
£1371 $2523 €2002 Monte rosa (34x42cm-13x17in) s. panel. 14-Jun-4 Waddingtons, Toronto #328/R est:1800-2000 (C.D 3400)
£1552 $2778 €2266 Cresta Segantini (29x39cm-11x15in) s. panel. 12-May-4 Dobiaschofsky, Bern #817/R est:2800 (S.FR 3600)
£2483 $4445 €3700 Spanish moorish (57x40cm-22x16in) s. board prov. 25-May-4 Finarte Semenzato, Milan #107/R est:3000-3500
£2617 $4633 €3900 In the mountains (32x50cm-13x20in) s. board. 1-May-4 Meeting Art, Vercelli #69 est:3000
£2671 $4167 €3900 View of Pecetto (50x60cm-20x24in) s. board. 8-Apr-3 Il Ponte, Milan #559/R
£3667 $6747 €5500 Stream. s. i.d.1952 verso. 8-Jun-4 Sotheby's, Milan #48/R est:4000-6000

FOGGIE, David (1878-1948) British
Works on paper
£420 $794 €613 Girl by a stream (28x38cm-11x15in) s.d.46 W/C. 19-Feb-4 Lyon & Turnbull, Edinburgh #21
£500 $860 €730 Fisher family (25x35cm-10x14in) s.d.1919 W/C buff paper. 4-Dec-3 Bonhams, Edinburgh #88

FOGGINI, Giovanni Battista (attrib) (1652-1725) Italian
Sculpture
£531469 $914126 €760000 Group representing Apollo flaying Marsyas (55cm-22in) dark brown pat bronze base bronze prov.lit. 2-Dec-3 Christie's, Paris #80/R est:150000-250000

FOGTT, Andrzej (1950-) Polish
£298 $512 €435 Woman sitting on stool, smoking (38x55cm-15x22in) s.i.d.97. 4-Dec-3 Agra, Warsaw #17/R (P.Z 2000)
£306 $508 €447 The earth's cycle (86x129cm-34x51in) painted 1979. 2-Oct-3 Agra, Warsaw #45/R (P.Z 2000)
£508 $920 €742 Composition (70x60cm-28x24in) s.d.1997. 4-Apr-4 Agra, Warsaw #37/R (P.Z 3600)
£567 $1014 €828 Composition (50x60cm-20x24in) painted 2003. 6-May-4 Agra, Warsaw #34/R (P.Z 4000)
£688 $1142 €1004 Self-portrait (70x65cm-28x26in) painted 1997. 2-Oct-3 Agra, Warsaw #57/R (P.Z 4500)
£690 $1152 €1000 Trees of memory (130x150cm-51x59in) s. s.i.d.2003 verso. 16-Nov-3 Agra, Warsaw #88/R
£1793 $2994 €2600 Spring birds in a winter landscape (195x130cm-77x51in) s.d.1997 s.i.d.verso. 16-Nov-3 Agra, Warsaw #85/R est:2000
£1921 $3477 €2805 Composition (72x99cm-28x39in) s.d.2003. 4-Apr-4 Agra, Warsaw #93/R (P.Z 13600)
£2147 $3886 €3135 Composition (72x99cm-28x39in) s.d.2003. 4-Apr-4 Agra, Warsaw #49/R (P.Z 15200)

FOHN, Emanuel (1881-1966) German
£1135 $1895 €1600 Still life with grapes and peaches (26x46cm-10x18in) s. masonite. 14-Oct-3 Dorotheum, Vienna #158/R est:2000-2600
£1206 $2013 €1700 Still life with plums and peaches (22x32cm-9x13in) s. masonite. 14-Oct-3 Dorotheum, Vienna #160/R est:1700-2200
£1517 $2534 €2200 Harlequin puppet and rocking horses (54x46cm-21x18in) s. canvas on board lit. 10-Jul-3 Allgauer, Kempten #2483/R est:900

FOHN, Sofie (1899-1990) German
£267 $477 €400 Narcissi (31x23cm-12x9in) s. board. 13-May-4 Neumeister, Munich #350/R

FOHR, Karl Philipp (attrib) (1795-1818) German
£685 $1164 €1000 Deep valley (33x22cm-13x9in) 5-Nov-3 Hugo Ruef, Munich #967/R

FOISIL, Edith (20th C) French
£762 $1424 €1150 Voiles blanches, balade en solitaire (50x73cm-20x29in) s. 24-Jul-4 Thierry & Lannon, Brest #257/R

FOKKE, Simon (attrib) (1712-1784) Dutch
Works on paper
£377 $640 €550 Study of a standing man in a hat (21x12cm-8x5in) black chk. 4-Nov-3 Sotheby's, Amsterdam #139/R

FOLDI, Augusto (20th C) ?
£828 $1490 €1200 Fille (45x54cm-18x21in) s.d.2000 verso. 25-Jan-4 Cornette de St.Cyr, Paris #270

FOLEY, Henry (19th C) British
£260 $442 €380 River landscape with figures on a stone bridge, cottages nearby (25x35cm-10x14in) s. 19-Nov-3 Tennants, Leyburn #1103
£297 $550 €434 Landscape with waterfall and mill (91x71cm-36x28in) 13-Feb-4 Du Mouchelle, Detroit #2099/R

FOLEY, Herb (20th C) New Zealander
£942 $1526 €1366 Cares and birds (93x93cm-37x37in) s.d.2000 board. 31-Jul-3 International Art Centre, Auckland #98/R est:1500-2500 (NZ.D 2600)

FOLINSBEE, John F (1892-1972) American
£1159 $1900 €1681 Portrait of a young woman (61x51cm-24x20in) s. 4-Jun-3 Alderfer's, Hatfield #394/R est:2000-2500
£3632 $6500 €5303 At the docks (25x36cm-10x14in) s. canvasboard. 6-May-4 Shannon's, Milford #242/R est:3000-5000
£4469 $8000 €6525 Ocean spray (53x69cm-21x27in) s. 8-Jan-4 James Julia, Fairfield #573/R est:5000-7000
£4491 $7500 €6557 The Squall (41x46cm-16x18in) s. board. 23-Oct-3 Shannon's, Milford #70/R est:3000-5000
£5814 $10000 €8488 Island (51x76cm-20x30in) s. i.verso prov. 7-Dec-3 Freeman, Philadelphia #152 est:12000-18000
£5988 $10000 €8742 Village Street (20x25cm-8x10in) s. s.i.verso canvas on board. 23-Oct-3 Shannon's, Milford #63/R est:3000-5000
£8140 $14000 €11884 Jersey Marshes (41x51cm-16x20in) s. i.verso prov. 7-Dec-3 Freeman, Philadelphia #154 est:8000-12000
£9302 $16000 €13581 Beached boat on the Maine coastline (66x102cm-26x40in) prov. 7-Dec-3 Freeman, Philadelphia #151 est:15000-25000
£10326 $19000 €15076 Maine landscape (41x61cm-16x24in) i. verso. 27-Jun-4 Freeman, Philadelphia #213/R est:12000-18000

FOLKARD, R W (?) ?
£1100 $2024 €1606 Mariner, winner of the Swaffham Cup, 1934, in a landscape (59x72cm-23x28in) s.d.1834 prov.lit. 10-Jun-4 Christie's, Kensington #433/R est:1000-1500

FOLKERTS, Poppe (1875-1943) German
£1400 $2408 €2044 Rounding the Needles (52x62cm-20x24in) s. board. 2-Dec-3 Sotheby's, London #50/R est:600-900
£4615 $7708 €6600 The cutter, Fortuna off Norderney (53x72cm-21x28in) s. panel. 11-Oct-3 Hans Stahl, Hamburg #137/R est:5500
£7962 $12261 €12500 Norderney harbour (68x100cm-27x39in) s.d.1900. 4-Sep-2 Schopman, Hamburg #249/R est:7800
£13889 $22639 €20000 Schooner in full sail (123x176cm-48x69in) s.d.1924. 26-Sep-3 Bolland & Marotz, Bremen #529/R est:6000

FOLLAK, Alex (1915-) Russian
£414 $766 €600 Lakeside beer garden (60x80cm-24x31in) s. 12-Feb-4 Weidler, Nurnberg #315/R
£688 $1121 €990 Market in Munich (80x70cm-31x28in) s. 19-Jul-3 Berlinghof, Heidelberg #206
£903 $1472 €1300 Flower market (70x80cm-28x31in) s. 24-Sep-3 Neumeister, Munich #261/R
£1565 $2801 €2300 Snowy old town, Munich (70x60cm-28x24in) s. i.d.1937 verso. 20-Mar-4 Bergmann, Erlangen #1140 est:2300

FOLLI, Sebastiano (attrib) (1568-1621) Italian
Works on paper
£522 $955 €762 Religious dispute (14x18cm-6x7in) s. W/C sepia. 4-Jun-4 Zofingen, Switzerland #2342 (S.FR 1200)

FOLLINI, Carlo (1848-1938) Italian
£1197 $1987 €1700 La raccolta delle zucche. Paesaggio con figura (12x20cm-5x8in) s. panel two prov. 11-Jun-3 Christie's, Rome #123/R est:1800-2500
£1333 $2453 €2000 Venice (11x14cm-4x6in) s. cardboard. 8-Jun-4 Della Rocca, Turin #281/R est:1700-2200
£1644 $2795 €2400 Vue d'un village en montagne (27x44cm-11x17in) s. panel. 5-Nov-3 Rabourdin & Choppin de Janvry, Paris #31/R est:3000-3500
£2585 $4627 €3800 Pine grove in Forte dei Marmi (22x32cm-9x13in) s. board. 22-Mar-4 Sant Agostino, Torino #255/R est:4000
£2933 $5397 €4400 Beach in Versilia (24x35cm-9x14in) s.d.1904 cardboard. 14-Jun-4 Sant Agostino, Torino #291/R est:3500-4500
£3691 $6534 €5500 Sunset (26x44cm-10x17in) s. board painted 1910 lit. 1-May-4 Meeting Art, Vercelli #115 est:5000
£4000 $7360 €6000 Chanoux Street, Saint-Vincent (15x24cm-6x9in) s. board. 8-Jun-4 Della Rocca, Turin #267/R est:4500-6000
£4027 $7128 €6000 Reflections (27x44cm-11x17in) s. board. 1-May-4 Meeting Art, Vercelli #250 est:6000
£4545 $7591 €6500 Road in Susa Valley (26x44cm-10x17in) s.d.1914 board. 26-Jun-3 Sant Agostino, Torino #303/R est:4000-5000
£5034 $8909 €7500 Afternoon (26x44cm-10x17in) s.d.1910 boar lit. 1-May-4 Meeting Art, Vercelli #464 est:7000
£5556 $9444 €8000 Santa Margherita and Portofino (26x47cm-10x19in) s. board lit. 1-Nov-3 Meeting Art, Vercelli #237/R est:8000
£5705 $10097 €8500 Landscape with figures (44x27cm-17x11in) s. board painted 1895 lit. 1-May-4 Meeting Art, Vercelli #369 est:7000
£6383 $10660 €9000 Pasture (60x90cm-24x35in) s. 20-Oct-3 Sant Agostino, Torino #288/R est:12000
£6977 $12000 €10186 Afternoon walk along a country path (41x73cm-16x29in) s. 3-Dec-3 Doyle, New York #123/R est:6000-8000
£6993 $11678 €10000 Seascape (26x44cm-10x17in) s.d.1899 board. 26-Jun-3 Sant Agostino, Torino #304/R est:7000-9000
£7639 $12986 €11000 Piedmontese countryside (65x90cm-26x35in) s. lit. 1-Nov-3 Meeting Art, Vercelli #448/R est:10000
£8054 $15060 €12000 Seascape (24x39cm-9x15in) d.1930 prov.exhib. 25-Feb-4 Porro, Milan #30/R est:15000
£8844 $15830 €13000 Beach in Bordighera (60x90cm-24x35in) s. 22-Mar-4 Sant Agostino, Torino #237/R est:16000
£12081 $22591 €18000 Landscape (84x139cm-33x55in) d.1880-90 prov.lit. 25-Feb-4 Porro, Milan #24/R est:18000-22000
Works on paper
£671 $1188 €1000 Landscape (29x45cm-11x18in) chl exec.1885. 1-May-4 Meeting Art, Vercelli #124
£704 $1169 €1000 Landscape scene with figure (25x41cm-10x16in) s. W/C cardboard. 11-Jun-3 Christie's, Rome #181/R
£915 $1520 €1300 Country scene with peasant woman (23x32cm-9x13in) s. W/C cardboard. 11-Jun-3 Christie's, Rome #180/R
£1007 $1782 €1500 Landscape in Piedmonte (24x34cm-9x13in) s. W/C. 1-May-4 Meeting Art, Vercelli #47 est:1500
£1200 $2208 €1800 King Umberto I (28x38cm-11x15in) s.i.d.1879 W/C lit. 14-Jun-4 Sant Agostino, Torino #188/R est:1800-2200

FOLLIOTT, Anna (?) Irish?
Works on paper
£769 $1308 €1100 Garden at Lissadell (25x17cm-10x7in) W/C pair. 25-Nov-3 Hamilton Osborne King, Dublin #47/R

FOLLMER, Frank (20th C) American
Works on paper
£455 $841 €664 Naughty Disney characters on the garden path (30x46cm-12x18in) s. W/C. 10-Mar-4 Deutscher-Menzies, Melbourne #582/R est:1200-1500 (A.D 1100)
£537 $994 €784 Naughty Disney characters in the garden (30x46cm-12x18in) s. W/C. 10-Mar-4 Deutscher-Menzies, Melbourne #581/R est:1200-1500 (A.D 1300)

FOLMER, Georges (1895-1977) French
£1667 $3000 €2500 Composition geometrique (60x71cm-24x28in) s. prov. 24-Apr-4 Cornette de St.Cyr, Paris #360/R est:3000

FOLON, Jean Michel (1934-) Belgian
Sculpture
£4895 $8322 €7000 Oiseau et main (34cm-13in) num.4/4 bronze. 1-Dec-3 Palais de Beaux Arts, Brussels #162/R est:2250-3000
Works on paper
£599 $1000 €875 Viewer manhandled by aggressive television set (28x20cm-11x8in) s. W/C exec.c.1978. 15-Nov-3 Illustration House, New York #50/R
£789 $1453 €1200 Bicyclettes (23x25cm-9x10in) s. W/C. 24-Jun-4 Credit Municipal, Paris #27/R
£1549 $2680 €2200 Untitled (50x50cm-20x20in) W/C ink. 9-Dec-3 Artcurial Briest, Paris #533 est:1500-2000
£2657 $4517 €3800 L'Amerique (30x22cm-12x9in) s.i.d.1983 verso W/C gouache. 1-Dec-3 Palais de Beaux Arts, Brussels #163/R est:2000-3000

FOLOP (19/20th C) French?
£2340 $3909 €3300 Cavaliers (74x96cm-29x38in) s. 16-Jun-3 Gros & Delettrez, Paris #317/R est:2000-3000

FOLSOM, Fred Gorham III (1945-) American
£2235 $4000 €3263 Please stand by (152x114cm-60x45in) s.d.1988. 7-May-4 Sloans & Kenyon, Bethesda #1744/R est:1000-2000

FOLTA, L (?) ?
£1872 $3500 €2733 Sheep in a barn. Sheep with hen and chicks (53x41cm-21x16in) s. pair. 29-Feb-4 Grogan, Boston #39/R

FOLTYN, Frantisek (1891-1976) ?
£6993 $11888 €10000 Composition (81x60cm-32x24in) s.i.d.1930 s.verso prov. 23-Nov-3 Cornette de St.Cyr, Paris #116 est:2000-3000
Works on paper
£839 $1427 €1200 Composition (29x23cm-11x9in) s.d.1935 W/C prov. 23-Nov-3 Cornette de St.Cyr, Paris #118/R
£909 $1545 €1300 Composition (24x21cm-9x8in) s.i.d.17 juin 1973 W/C prov. 23-Nov-3 Cornette de St.Cyr, Paris #117/R

FOLTZ, Philipp von (1805-1877) German
£4545 $7727 €6500 Fisher woman on Italian coast (87x73cm-34x29in) s. 24-Nov-3 Dorotheum, Vienna #135/R est:3000-4000

FOLWELL, Samuel (attrib) (1765-1813) American
£2973 $5500 €4341 Mourning (44x60cm-17x24in) i. oil on sil embroidery prov.lit. 15-Jan-4 Sotheby's, New York #336/R est:1500-2500

FOMISON, Tony (1939-1990) New Zealander
£781 $1343 €1140 Untitled (43x28cm-17x11in) 3-Dec-3 Dunbar Sloane, Auckland #54/R (NZ.D 2100)
£3160 $5435 €4614 We are you (33x40cm-13x16in) s.i.d.1989 verso prov. 3-Dec-3 Dunbar Sloane, Auckland #51 est:10000-15000 (NZ.D 8500)
£3532 $6074 €5157 Time for an Ice-cream (35x45cm-14x18in) s.i.d.1989 verso prov. 3-Dec-3 Dunbar Sloane, Auckland #50 est:10000-15000 (NZ.D 9500)
£13011 $22379 €18996 Ophelia feeling triumphant (31x41cm-12x16in) s.i.d.1988 verso hessian board. 3-Dec-3 Dunbar Sloane, Auckland #68/R est:35000-45000 (NZ.D 35000)
£14498 $24937 €21167 Untitled no.75 (31x45cm-12x18in) s.d. 3-Dec-3 Dunbar Sloane, Auckland #53/R est:50000-60000 (NZ.D 39000)
£17537 $30340 €25604 In solitary (55x39cm-22x15in) s.i.d.3.2.73-13.4.73 jute canvas. 9-Dec-3 Peter Webb, Auckland #63/R est:50000-60000 (NZ.D 47000)
£23134 $40022 €33776 Circus hand remembers Taranaki (29x40cm-11x16in) s.i.d.1984 verso hessian board. 9-Dec-3 Peter Webb, Auckland #67/R est:45000-55000 (NZ.D 62000)
£24221 $43356 €35363 Someone's visit (91x64cm-36x25in) s.i.d.10.8.71 oil on hessian exhib. 12-May-4 Dunbar Sloane, Wellington #40/R est:70000-100000 (NZ.D 70000)
Works on paper
£5357 $9696 €7821 Tangi for Mururoa Atoll (30x50cm-12x20in) s.d.15.3.73-74 pencil. 30-Mar-4 Peter Webb, Auckland #43a/R est:12000-16000 (NZ.D 15000)

FOMSGAARD, Jes (20th C) Danish
Works on paper
£395 $672 €577 Building fragment (48x67cm-19x26in) s.i.d.1988 pencil W/C. 26-Nov-3 Kunsthallen, Copenhagen #68 (D.KR 4200)

FONDA, Enrico (1892-1929) Italian
£1678 $2887 €2400 San Giusto, Trieste (16x25cm-6x10in) s. cardboard. 3-Dec-3 Stadion, Trieste #1149/R est:700-1000
£2000 $3580 €3000 My chair (52x71cm-20x28in) s. cardboard. 12-May-4 Stadion, Trieste #715/R est:2500-3500

FONECHE, Andre (20th C) French
£594 $993 €850 Seascapes (14x22cm-6x9in) s. panel pair. 29-Jun-3 Eric Pillon, Calais #60/R

FONFRIA, Jose Manuel (?) Spanish
£940 $1757 €1400 Fishing vessel (73x100cm-29x39in) s.d.2003 s.i.d.verso. 24-Feb-4 Durán, Madrid #23/R

FONG GUA OF MACAO (attrib) (19th C) Chinese
£30000 $51600 €43800 Treaty ports, Hong Kong. Bombardment of the barrier ports (46x79cm-18x31in) pair. 2-Dec-3 Sotheby's, London #16/R est:10000-15000

FONG, Alex (20th C) Canadian
Works on paper
£600 $1098 €876 Irises beside a stream (55x145cm-22x57in) s. W/C. 1-Jun-4 Hodgins, Calgary #331/R (C.D 1500)

FONG, Flora (1949-) Cuban
£4706 $8000 €6871 La colada cotidiana - The daily laundry (116x89cm-46x35in) s.d.03 prov. 18-Nov-3 Christie's, Rockefeller NY #120/R est:10000-15000

FONG, Luise (1912-) New Zealander
£846 $1438 €1235 Feral (61x91cm-24x36in) s.d.1994 verso acrylic. 27-Nov-3 International Art Centre, Auckland #7/R (NZ.D 2250)
£1625 $2648 €2373 Yan-hua, flowers of smoke (60x44cm-24x17in) s.i.d.1993 verso board diptych. 23-Sep-3 Peter Webb, Auckland #6/R est:3500-5500 (NZ.D 4500)
£2076 $3384 €3031 Untitled (56x56cm-22x22in) s.i.d.1994 verso acrylic diptych. 23-Sep-3 Peter Webb, Auckland #7/R est:5000-7000 (NZ.D 5750)
£2857 $5171 €4171 Untitled II from the low tech series (120x80cm-47x31in) i. s.d.1995 verso acrylic on board. 30-Mar-4 Peter Webb, Auckland #17/R est:7000-12000 (NZ.D 8000)
£3717 $6394 €5427 Lantern (204x185cm-80x73in) s.i.d.1994 verso wood two panels. 3-Dec-3 Dunbar Sloane, Auckland #20/R est:15000-25000 (NZ.D 10000)

FONSECA, Caio (1958-) American
£10180 $17000 €14863 Untitled (69x91cm-27x36in) s.d.1999 verso prov. 12-Nov-3 Christie's, Rockefeller NY #591/R est:10000-15000
£18994 $34000 €27731 Pietrasanta painting, C97 41 (112x178cm-44x70in) s.verso acrylic prov. 12-May-4 Christie's, Rockefeller NY #475/R est:35000-45000

FONSECA, Carlos (20th C) Venezuelan?
£283 $520 €413 Untitled (101x76cm-40x30in) s. acrylic cardboard. 28-Mar-4 Subastas Odalys, Caracas #97/R

FONSECA, Gonzalo (1922-1997) Uruguayan
£1765 $3000 €2577 Landscape (40x50cm-16x20in) s.d.45 cardboard. 25-Nov-3 Galeria y Remates, Montevideo #62
£2670 $4700 €3898 Cart with figures (33x43cm-13x17in) s. cardboard. 5-Jan-4 Galeria y Remates, Montevideo #47/R est:4500-5500
£5096 $8000 €7440 Still life (44x35cm-17x14in) s. panel. 23-Nov-2 Subastas Odalys, Caracas #22/R
£5882 $10000 €8588 Steam boat (46x55cm-18x22in) s.d.48 cardboard. 25-Nov-3 Galeria y Remates, Montevideo #61/R
£6707 $11000 €9792 Landscape seen from Bovedas (50x60cm-20x24in) s.d.47. 3-Jun-3 Galeria y Remates, Montevideo #67
£16760 $30000 €24470 Composition with figures (75x105cm-30x41in) s.d.53 board on canvas prov.exhib. 26-May-4 Sotheby's, New York #15/R est:25000-35000
Works on paper
£235 $400 €343 Harbour (18x23cm-7x9in) ink. 25-Nov-3 Galeria y Remates, Montevideo #74
£305 $500 €445 Urban composition with tram (12x17cm-5x7in) ink pencil. 3-Jun-3 Galeria y Remates, Montevideo #34
£407 $680 €594 Urban composition (12x17cm-5x7in) pencil. 7-Oct-3 Galeria y Remates, Montevideo #18/R
£568 $1000 €829 Harbour (16x26cm-6x10in) ink pencil prov. 5-Jan-4 Galeria y Remates, Montevideo #109/R
£617 $1000 €895 Pastoral scene (18x27cm-7x11in) s. W/C Indian ink. 29-Jul-3 Galeria y Remates, Montevideo #111/R
£647 $1100 €945 Urban landscape (30x40cm-12x16in) d.1944 ink pencil. 25-Nov-3 Galeria y Remates, Montevideo #73
£938 $1650 €1369 Montevideo Bay (20x28cm-8x11in) ink W/C prov. 5-Jan-4 Galeria y Remates, Montevideo #110/R est:800-1000

FONT Y VIDAL, Juan (fl.1852-1874) Spanish
£3276 $5471 €4750 The Juanita Clar (60x87cm-24x34in) s.i.d.1876. 17-Nov-3 Durán, Madrid #206/R est:4000
£4861 $7924 €7000 Vessel Juanita Clar in Mahon harbour (41x69cm-16x27in) s. 23-Sep-3 Durán, Madrid #165/R est:6500
£5208 $8490 €7500 Royal Navy ship in Mahon harbour (44x65cm-17x26in) s.d.1874 canvas on board. 23-Sep-3 Durán, Madrid #164/R est:5500
£20833 $33958 €30000 Duke of Montpensier getting off steam boat in Minorca (39x61cm-15x24in) s.d.1852. 23-Sep-3 Durán, Madrid #166/R est:25000

FONT, Constantin (1890-1954) French
£333 $600 €500 Jeune fille aux nattes (66x50cm-26x20in) s.d.1921. 25-Apr-4 Daniel Herry, Beaune #103
£400 $720 €600 Paysage au bord de riviere (60x51cm-24x20in) d.1937. 25-Apr-4 Daniel Herry, Beaune #111
£1049 $1804 €1500 Vue du port de Rapallo (50x61cm-20x24in) s. 5-Dec-3 Gros & Delettrez, Paris #68 est:1500-2000

FONT, Jean la (19th C) ?
£282 $519 €420 Beached boats (16x22cm-6x9in) s. board. 27-Mar-4 Farsetti, Prato #305

FONT, Villar (?) Spanish
£532 $888 €750 Seascape (60x110cm-24x43in) s. 20-Oct-3 Durán, Madrid #1191/R

FONTAINE, Alexandre Victor (1815-) French
£9732 $17906 €14500 Rural dance (90x160cm-35x63in) s. 24-Mar-4 Finarte Semenzato, Rome #8/R est:15000-18000

FONTAINE, Pierre François L and PERCIER, Charles (attrib) (18th C) French
Works on paper
£573 $975 €820 Plan de la villa MonteDragone (33x32cm-13x13in) ink W/C black crayon. 24-Nov-3 E & Eve, Paris #122/R

FONTAINE, Thomas Sherwood la (1915-) British
£1900 $3078 €2774 Impromptu (85x131cm-33x52in) s. 27-Jan-3 Bristol Auction Rooms #491/R est:600-800
£2616 $4500 €3819 Harry Cooke Cushing, IV, Rome (71x91cm-28x36in) s.d.67 prov. 5-Dec-3 Christie's, Rockefeller NY #130/R est:6000-8000

FONTAINE, Victoria (20th C) Australian
Works on paper
£281 $469 €407 Summer hat (59x48cm-23x19in) s. pastel. 30-Jun-3 Australian Art Auctions, Sydney #164 (A.D 700)

FONTAINEBLEAU SCHOOL (16th C) French
£17606 $30458 €25000 Sleeping cupid surrounded by satyrs (65x94cm-26x37in) panel. 11-Dec-3 Dr Fritz Nagel, Stuttgart #467/R
Sculpture
£118919 $220000 €173622 Untitled. marble exec.c.1580. 18-Jan-4 Carlsen Gallery, Greenville #101/R
Works on paper
£17687 $31660 €26000 Une femme montrant a un homme cinq taureaux dans un paysage (18x23cm-7x9in) pen brown ink wash exec.c.1540 prov. 18-Mar-4 Christie's, Paris #115/R est:25000-35000

FONTAINEBLEAU SCHOOL (17th C) French
£5921 $10895 €9000 Bacchus et Ariane (75x117cm-30x46in) painted c.1600. 24-Jun-4 Tajan, Paris #48/R est:10000-12000
£14000 $25200 €20440 Idealised portrait of Diane de Poitiers as the Godess Diana (37x54cm-15x21in) panel painted c.1600 prov. 22-Apr-4 Sotheby's, London #13/R est:8000-12000
£21053 $38737 €32000 Sabina Poppaea (100x80cm-39x31in) i. painted c.1600. 23-Jun-4 Sotheby's, Paris #1/R est:10000-12000

FONTAINES, Andre des (1869-1910) French
£453 $780 €661 Paysage anime (42x61cm-17x24in) s. board. 3-Dec-3 Naón & Cia, Buenos Aires #36/R
£1000 $1670 €1450 Les Meules (35x24cm-14x9in) s. cardboard. 17-Nov-3 Delorme & Bocage, Paris #140/R
Works on paper
£345 $638 €500 Champ de ble (49x75cm-19x30in) s. pastel. 16-Feb-4 Giraudeau, Tours #36

FONTALLARD, Jean François Gerard (1877-1858) French
£1267 $2305 €1900 Portrait d'artiste barbu (45x29cm-18x11in) s. cardboard painted c.1880. 5-Jul-4 Neret-Minet, Paris #38 est:1500
Miniatures
£5800 $9860 €8468 Lady leaning on plinth (7cm-3in) s. gold frame oval. 18-Nov-3 Bonhams, New Bond Street #111/R est:800-1200

FONTANA, Daniele (1900-) German?
£347 $590 €500 Como Lake (34x49cm-13x19in) s. board. 1-Nov-3 Meeting Art, Vercelli #267
£2979 $4974 €4200 Saint Christopher's Church in Milan (110x100cm-43x39in) s. 14-Oct-3 Finarte Semenzato, Milan #53/R est:5000-6000

FONTANA, Ernesto (1837-1918) Italian
£2303 $4237 €3500 The awakening of the daughter of Jairis (80x116cm-31x46in) s. 22-Jun-4 Christie's, Amsterdam #56/R est:4000-6000

FONTANA, Ernesto (attrib) (1837-1918) Italian
£352 $599 €514 Peasant woman with sticks on path alongside wood (45x37cm-18x15in) i. 5-Nov-3 Dobiaschofsky, Bern #543 (S.FR 800)

FONTANA, Francesco (19th C) Italian
Works on paper
£324 $531 €450 Free (31x23cm-12x9in) s.d.1875 W/C. 10-Jun-3 Pandolfini, Florence #32

FONTANA, Lavinia (1552-1614) Italian
£5000 $9000 €7300 Madonna and Child with a Donor (23x17cm-9x7in) copper. 22-Jan-4 Sotheby's, New York #231/R est:8000-12000
£33520 $60000 €48939 Portrait of girl in pink embroidered dress (10cm-4in circular) metal. 27-May-4 Sotheby's, New York #101/R est:70000-90000
£98592 $157746 €140000 Saint Catherine's mystic marriage (26x20cm-10x8in) s. copper exhib.lit. 21-Sep-3 Finarte, Venice #50/R est:160000

FONTANA, Lavinia (attrib) (1552-1614) Italian

£10000	$17300	€14600	Portrait of a gentleman, three-quarter length, seated by an open window (126x96cm-50x38in) 11-Dec-3 Sotheby's, London #186/R est:10000-15000

FONTANA, Lavinia (circle) (1552-1614) Italian

£6000	$10380	€8760	Portrait of a lady (48x35cm-19x14in) panel. 12-Dec-3 Christie's, Kensington #205/R est:6000-8000

FONTANA, Lucio (1899-1968) Italian

£1583	$2596	€2200	Concetto spaziale (12x9cm-5x4in) s.d. biro perforation silver foil. 4-Jun-3 Ketterer, Hamburg #360/R est:2200-2400
£3566	$6063	€5100	White theatre (72x72cm-28x28in) s.i.verso cardboard. 20-Nov-3 Finarte Semenzato, Milan #36/R est:3800-4200
£9790	$16643	€14000	Sliding door (73x108cm-29x43in) painted glass. 24-Nov-3 Christie's, Milan #293/R est:4000-6000
£10140	$17238	€14500	Sliding door (77x108cm-30x43in) painted glass. 24-Nov-3 Christie's, Milan #292/R est:4000-6000
£28000	$51520	€40880	Concetto spaziale (49x64cm-19x25in) s.d.1956 verso oil col pencil paper on canvas prov.exhib.lit. 24-Jun-4 Sotheby's, London #230/R est:20000-30000
£42000	$70140	€61320	Spatial concept (49x35cm-19x14in) s.d.59 tempera ink pencil paper prov. 20-Oct-3 Sotheby's, London #10/R est:20000
£66434	$112937	€95000	Spatial concept (80x50cm-31x20in) s.d.53 verso prov.lit. 25-Nov-3 Sotheby's, Milan #232/R est:80000-120000
£83916	$142657	€120000	Spatial concept (65x54cm-26x21in) s. s.i.verso painted 1965 prov.lit. 25-Nov-3 Sotheby's, Milan #235/R est:120000-150000
£98187	$166918	€143353	Concetto Spaziale - cardazzo tondo memo (54x84cm-21x33in) s.indis.d. oil perforations lit. 5-Nov-3 AB Stockholms Auktionsverk #1114/R est:800000-1000000 (S.KR 1300000)
£102000	$170340	€148920	Concetto spaziale (80x60cm-31x24in) s.d.55 s.i.d.1955 verso oil glitter prov.exhib.lit. 21-Oct-3 Christie's, London #37/R est:90000-120000
£108000	$198720	€157680	Concetto spaziale (130x97cm-51x38in) s. s.i. verso painted 1962 prov.lit. 24-Jun-4 Sotheby's, London #227/R est:100000-150000
£140000	$233800	€204400	Concetto spaziale (100x81cm-39x32in) s. prov.exhib.lit. 21-Oct-3 Christie's, London #31/R est:140000-180000
£170000	$283900	€248200	Spatial concept (60x70cm-24x28in) s.d.55 s.d.verso oil glass pebbles prov.exhib.lit. 20-Oct-3 Sotheby's, London #17/R est:250000
£221175	$398115	€322916	Concetto Spazziale (50x79cm-20x31in) s. executed 1952 prov.lit. 26-Apr-4 Bukowskis, Stockholm #239/R est:1200000-1400000 (S.KR 3050000)
£248252	$422028	€355000	Spacial concept (79x59cm-31x23in) s.d.52 s.i.d.verso oil glass lit. 29-Nov-3 Farsetti, Prato #479/R est:28000-320000

Prints

£1829	$3000	€2670	Bianco (63x49cm-25x19in) s. num.4/50 embossed print prov. 28-May-3 Sotheby's, Amsterdam #22/R est:2000-3000
£2271	$4020	€3316	Concetto Spaziale (49x34cm-19x13in) s.num.74/80 col lithograph with perforations. 27-Apr-4 AB Stockholms Auktionsverk #1295/R est:10000-12000 (S.KR 31000)
£2292	$3827	€3300	Concetto spaziale (65x50cm-26x20in) s.num.28/30 lithograph lacerations. 25-Oct-3 Cornette de St.Cyr, Paris #201/R est:3500-4000
£2733	$4920	€4100	Untitled (64x48cm-25x19in) s. eau forte exec.1963 exhib. 22-Apr-4 Finarte Semenzato, Rome #203/R est:2500-3000
£2937	$4993	€4200	Spatial concept (70x50cm-28x20in) s. num.9/95 serigraph lit. 24-Nov-3 Christie's, Milan #3/R

Sculpture

£3357	$5706	€4800	Spatial concept (52x52cm-20x20in) s.d.52 verso glazed ceramic. 25-Nov-3 Sotheby's, Milan #121/R est:5000-7000
£4710	$7725	€6500	Head of boy (21x14x15cm-8x6x6in) terracotta exec.1929-30 lit. 27-May-3 Sotheby's, Milan #72/R est:9000
£4800	$8832	€7200	Little angel (12x21x14cm-5x8x6in) polychrome ceramic. 11-Jun-4 Farsetti, Prato #378/R est:5000-7000
£5072	$8319	€7000	Spatial concept (10x9x5cm-4x4x2in) init.num.89/90 bronze. 27-May-3 Sotheby's, Milan #71/R est:6000
£6993	$11888	€10000	Fight (41x41cm-16x16in) s.d.54 painted ceramic. 24-Nov-3 Christie's, Milan #294/R est:10000-15000
£7568	$14000	€11049	Tralicio de Vite (39x59cm-15x23in) sig. d.59 painted glazed ceramic. 12-Feb-4 Sotheby's, New York #92/R est:6000-8000
£8054	$14899	€12000	Profile (39x39cm-15x15in) s. ceramic. 13-Mar-4 Meeting Art, Vercelli #407 est:10000
£8333	$14167	€12000	Portrait of girl (17x11cm-7x4in) gilt terracotta exec.c.1930. 28-Oct-3 Il Ponte, Milan #258/R
£8725	$15617	€13000	Spatial concept (27cm-11in) s. num.495/500 polished brass exec.1967. 25-May-4 Sotheby's, Milan #190/R est:9000-12000
£9091	$15455	€13000	Spatial concept (27cm-11in) s. num.405/500 polished brass. 25-Nov-3 Sotheby's, Milan #161/R est:8000-10000
£9375	$15937	€13500	Cross (26x15cm-10x6in) init.verso col terracotta. 28-Oct-3 Il Ponte, Milan #257/R
£12245	$21918	€18000	Crucifixion (38x24x13cm-15x9x5in) init.d.53 ceramic. 16-Mar-4 Finarte Semenzato, Milan #415/R est:14000
£12462	$21186	€18195	Concetto Spaziale (26cm-10in) s.num.474/500 polished bronze two. 5-Nov-3 AB Stockholms Auktionsverk #1178/R est:100000-125000 (S.KR 165000)
£13000	$21710	€18980	Concetto Spaziale (32x43cm-13x17in) s. glazed ceramic exec 1955-60. 21-Oct-3 Sotheby's, London #377/R est:15000-20000
£13287	$22587	€19000	Spatial concept (28x40cm-11x16in) s. painted terracotta prov. 25-Nov-3 Sotheby's, Milan #239/R est:20000-25000
£13986	$23776	€20000	Nature (26x20x23cm-10x8x9in) s. num.46/500 polished bronze pair. 24-Nov-3 Christie's, Milan #239/R est:18000-24000
£13986	$23776	€20000	Washbasin (55x43x14cm-22x17x6in) s. ceramic. 24-Nov-3 Christie's, Milan #291/R est:7000-10000
£14765	$26430	€22000	Flowers (46x46cm-18x18in) s.d.49 verso polychrome ceramic two. 25-May-4 Sotheby's, Milan #185/R est:18000-20000
£15845	$26303	€22500	Spatial concept (26cm-10in) s.verso polished brass pair. 11-Jun-3 Finarte Semenzato, Milan #687/R est:26000
£16902	$29240	€24000	Spatial concept (26x20x20cm-10x8x8in) s. num.313/500 bronze pair prov. 9-Dec-3 Artcurial Briest, Paris #386/R est:20000-25000
£18919	$33297	€28000	Spatial concept - Nature (18x11cm-7x4in) init. terracotta pair exec.1959 prov.lit. 24-May-4 Christie's, Milan #261/R est:30000-40000
£19000	$31730	€27740	Seated woman (30x18x13cm-12x7x5in) init. underside glazed ceramic exec c.1955 prov. 21-Oct-3 Sotheby's, London #378/R est:8000-10000
£20290	$33275	€28000	Spatial concept (34x25cm-13x10in) s. painted terracotta exec.1960-61. 27-May-3 Sotheby's, Milan #281/R est:15000-20000
£21978	$38901	€32088	Concetto Spaziale (29x34cm-11x13in) s. ceramic multiple. 27-Apr-4 AB Stockholms Auktionsverk #1150/R est:30000-35000 (S.KR 300000)
£22000	$40040	€32120	Concetto spaziale (20x28x22cm-8x11x9in) s.num.250/500 polished bronze two parts prov. 6-Feb-4 Sotheby's, London #153/R est:10000-15000
£22464	$36841	€31000	Spatial concept (42x28cm-17x11in) s.d.50 ceramic. 30-May-3 Farsetti, Prato #511/R est:9500
£25676	$45189	€38000	Crucifix (36x19x12cm-14x7x5in) init. polychrome ceramic. 24-May-4 Christie's, Milan #322/R est:15000-20000
£26574	$45175	€38000	Spatial concept (20x28x22cm-8x11x9in) s. num.244/500 gilt bronze pair. 19-Nov-3 Tajan, Paris #56/R est:24000-28000
£26667	$48000	€40000	Spatial concept (29x36cm-11x14in) s.d.50 painted terracotta exhib. 22-Apr-4 Finarte Semenzato, Rome #349/R est:20000-22000
£27536	$45159	€38000	Christ (43x31x7cm-17x12x3in) s. terracott aenamel. 27-May-3 Sotheby's, Milan #261/R est:18000-25000
£28188	$50456	€42000	Christ (76x66cm-30x26in) painted terracotta prov. 25-May-4 Sotheby's, Milan #304/R est:40000-50000
£29371	$49930	€42000	Fireplace (111x142x16cm-44x56x6in) s. ceramic. 24-Nov-3 Christie's, Milan #290/R est:18000-24000
£32215	$57664	€48000	Deposition (59x70x10cm-23x28x4in) s.d.56 painted terracotta prov. 25-May-4 Sotheby's, Milan #301/R est:15000-20000
£62000	$103540	€90520	Concetto spaziale, natura (47x35x10cm-19x14x4in) init.num.2/2 gold brown pat bronze conceived 1959-1960 prov.lit. 21-Oct-3 Christie's, London #42/R est:50000-70000
£65000	$108550	€94900	La mujer del marinero (91x42x90cm-36x17x35in) terracotta prov.lit. 22-Oct-3 Christie's, London #47/R est:20000-30000
£70000	$128800	€102200	Concetto spaziale, ellisse (173x72cm-68x28in) s. verso lacquered wood panel exec 1967 prov.exhib.lit. 24-Jun-4 Sotheby's, London #232/R est:40000-60000
£100000	$167000	€146000	Spatial concept, nature (32x35x32cm-13x14x13in) init. num.2/2 bronze prov.exhib.lit. 20-Oct-3 Sotheby's, London #23/R est:150000
£172297	$303243	€255000	Warrior (118cm-46in) s.d.49 enamel on ceramic prov.lit. 24-May-4 Christie's, Milan #320/R est:100000-150000
£480000	$883200	€700800	Concetto spaziale, natura (60x75x67cm-24x30x26in) bronze executed 1959-60 prov.lit. 23-Jun-4 Sotheby's, London #23/R est:300000-400000
£510000	$928200	€744600	Concetto Spaziale, Natura (71x73cm-28x29in) terracotta exec 1959-60 prov.exhib.lit. 5-Feb-4 Sotheby's, London #14/R est:200000-250000

Works on paper

£1333	$2453	€2000	Study of seven female figures (29x23cm-11x9in) ink exhib.lit. 11-Jun-4 Farsetti, Prato #322/R est:2000-3000
£1342	$2403	€2000	Study for sculpture (20x21cm-8x8in) s.i.d.46 Chinese ink prov. 25-May-4 Sotheby's, Milan #101 est:2000
£1449	$2377	€2000	Figure and horse (22x26cm-9x10in) s. pencil Chinese ink pastel prov. 27-May-3 Sotheby's, Milan #68 est:1500
£1476	$2613	€2200	Sculpture spaziali (21x29cm-8x11in) s.i.d.49 ink. 28-Apr-4 Artcurial Briest, Paris #382 est:1600-1800
£1733	$3189	€2600	Female nude (22x28cm-9x11in) s.d.36 ink exhib.lit. 11-Jun-4 Farsetti, Prato #168/R est:2000-3000
£1748	$2972	€2500	Figure (33x22cm-13x9in) s. pen. 25-Nov-3 Sotheby's, Milan #35/R
£1748	$2972	€2500	Figure (33x22cm-13x9in) s. pen. 25-Nov-3 Sotheby's, Milan #91/R est:2500-3000
£1793	$2869	€2600	Spatial concept (35x25cm-14x10in) s.d.1957 blue pen. 13-Mar-3 Galleria Pace, Milan #95/R est:2600-3500
£1812	$3207	€2700	Progetto (28x22cm-11x9in) s.i.d.49 studio st. verso ink. 28-Apr-4 Artcurial Briest, Paris #383 est:1600-1800
£1818	$3091	€2600	Figure (33x22cm-13x9in) s. pen chl. 25-Nov-3 Sotheby's, Milan #92/R est:2300-2800
£1818	$3091	€2600	Figure (50x35cm-20x14in) s. Chinese ink exec.1960. 25-Nov-3 Sotheby's, Milan #89/R est:1500-2000
£1879	$3477	€2800	Portrait of lady (50x35cm-20x14in) s. pen exec.1955 lit. 11-Mar-4 Galleria Pace, Milan #90/R est:3500-4500
£1879	$3439	€2800	Untitled (27x21cm-11x8in) s.d.50 Indian ink. 7-Jul-4 Artcurial Briest, Paris #261 est:2000-2500
£2098	$3567	€3000	Concetto spaziale (47x31cm-19x12in) s. ball point pen prov. 25-Nov-3 Tajan, Paris #44/R est:2000-3000
£2100	$3864	€3066	Concetto spaziale (20x27cm-8x11in) s.d.46 pencil. 24-Jun-4 Sotheby's, Olympia #505/R est:2000-3000
£2148	$3844	€3200	Female nude (33x50cm-13x20in) s. Chinese ink exec.1960. 25-May-4 Sotheby's, Milan #6/R est:3000
£2238	$3804	€3200	Study (50x35cm-20x14in) Chinese ink prov. 24-Nov-3 Christie's, Milan #34/R est:2800-3500
£2238	$3804	€3200	Figure (50x35cm-20x14in) s. Chinese ink exec.1960. 25-Nov-3 Sotheby's, Milan #90/R est:2000-3000
£2536	$4159	€3500	Study for sculpture (28x22cm-11x9in) s. s.verso Chinese ink. 27-May-3 Sotheby's, Milan #160/R est:3000-4000
£2754	$4516	€3800	Cupboard door (47x74cm-19x29in) s. mixed media on glass exec.1952. 27-May-3 Sotheby's, Milan #69 est:2000-3000
£2867	$5275	€4300	Seated woman (50x33cm-20x13in) s. pen pastel paper on canvas exec.1951. 12-Jun-4 Meeting Art, Vercelli #82/R est:4000
£2867	$5275	€4300	Seated woman (50x33cm-20x13in) s. pen pastel paper on canvas exec.1951. 12-Jun-4 Meeting Art, Vercelli #848/R est:4000
£2899	$4754	€4000	Studies (22x28cm-9x11in) s. Chinese ink prov. 27-May-3 Sotheby's, Milan #158/R est:4000-5000
£2937	$4993	€4200	Reclining female nude (50x70cm-20x28in) s. Chinese ink W/C. 25-Nov-3 Sotheby's, Milan #34/R est:2500-3000
£2973	$5232	€4400	Nude (31x21cm-12x8in) s.d.1935 ink. 22-May-4 Galleria Pananti, Florence #306/R est:4000-4500
£3041	$5351	€4500	Untitled (23x17cm-9x7in) s.d.1963 s.i.verso ink sequin card. 24-May-4 Christie's, Milan #65/R est:5000-7000
£3315	$6000	€4840	Homage I (17x11cm-7x4in) ink. 30-Mar-4 Arroyo, Buenos Aires #47
£3333	$6133	€5000	Studies (32x25cm-13x10in) s.d.53 pen Chinese ink prov. 8-Jun-4 Finarte Semenzato, Milan #401/R est:5000-6000
£3623	$5942	€5000	Studies (28x22cm-11x9in) s.d.53 Chinese ink prov. 27-May-3 Sotheby's, Milan #159/R est:5000-6000
£4082	$7306	€6000	Nude (70x50cm-28x20in) s. Chinese ink silver exec.1960. 16-Mar-4 Finarte Semenzato, Milan #436/R est:5000
£5743	$10108	€8500	Spatial concept (70x70cm-28x28in) s.i.verso cardboard wood exec.1968. 24-May-4 Christie's, Milan #2/R est:6000-8000
£5944	$10105	€8500	Spatial concept (70x70cm-28x28in) s.i. collage cardboard. 24-Nov-3 Christie's, Milan #2/R
£5944	$10105	€8500	Spatial concepts (26x35cm-10x14in) s. pen holes chk prov. 25-Nov-3 Sotheby's, Milan #167 est:6000-8000
£6098	$10000	€8903	Concetto spaziale (41x36cm-16x14in) s. pencil prov. 28-May-3 Sotheby's, Amsterdam #19/R est:7000-9000
£6500	$11830	€9490	Concetto spaziale (47x33cm-19x13in) s. pencil prov. 6-Feb-4 Sotheby's, London #193/R est:4000-6000
£7971	$13072	€11000	Figure (42x36cm-17x14in) W/C graphite. 27-May-3 Sotheby's, Milan #265/R est:10000-15000
£9155	$15838	€13000	Concetto spaziale (32x46cm-13x18in) s. pencil perforations prov. 13-Dec-3 De Vuyst, Lokeren #500/R est:12000-15000
£10000	$18200	€14600	Concetto spaziale (50x59cm-20x23in) incised sig. incision paper on card exec 1964-66 prov. 5-Feb-4 Christie's, London #134/R est:8000-10000

£10490 $17832 €15000 Untitled (13x39cm-5x15in) s.d.58 ink aniline on canvas. 24-Nov-3 Christie's, Milan #188/R est:9000-12000
£10870 $17826 €15000 Spatial concept (62x47cm-24x19in) s. torn paper prov. 27-May-3 Sotheby's, Milan #205/R est:12000-15000
£12069 $20155 €17500 Spatial concept (46x59cm-18x23in) s.d.51 gouache. 14-Nov-3 Farsetti, Prato #303/R est:7500-8500
£13542 $21396 €19500 Spatial concept (58x45cm-23x18in) s. perforations grattage prov. 27-Apr-3 Versailles Encheres #58
£13793 $23034 €20000 Spacial concept (45x60cm-18x24in) s. graffiti holes prov. 13-Nov-3 Finarte Semenzato, Rome #224/R est:16000-18000
£13986 $23776 €20000 Spatial concept (58x45cm-23x18in) s. graffiti. 25-Nov-3 Sotheby's, Milan #214 est:20000-25000
£16667 $26333 €24000 Spatial concept (59x49cm-23x19in) paint holes exec.1951. 6-Sep-3 Meeting Art, Vercelli #619 est:20000
£17450 $31235 €26000 Spatial concept (46x58cm-18x23in) s. torn paper exec.1965-66 prov. 25-May-4 Sotheby's, Milan #159/R est:15000
£27517 $49255 €41000 Spatial (22x32cm-9x13in) s.d.60 pen Chinese ink holes two. 25-May-4 Sotheby's, Milan #181/R est:10000-15000
£28859 $51658 €43000 Spatial (22x32cm-9x13in) s.d.60 pen Chinese ink holes set of 3. 25-May-4 Sotheby's, Milan #100/R est:20000
£42177 $75497 €62000 Spatial concept (18x14cm-7x6in) s.i.d.1959 verso hydropaint. 16-Mar-4 Finarte Semenzato, Milan #421/R est:60000-65000
£46980 $84094 €70000 Spatial concept (70x85cm-28x33in) pastel on canvas exec.1956 prov.lit. 25-May-4 Sotheby's, Milan #276/R est:70000-90000
£47101 $77246 €65000 Spatial concept (81x65cm-32x26in) s. hydropaint on canvas prov.lit. 27-May-3 Sotheby's, Milan #283/R est:90000-120000
£48951 $83217 €70000 Spatial concept (50x40cm-20x16in) s.d.57 pastel on canvas prov. 24-Nov-3 Christie's, Milan #343/R est:50000-70000
£49275 $80812 €68000 Spatial concept (41x27cm-16x11in) s.i.verso hydropaint on canvas. 27-May-3 Sotheby's, Milan #262/R est:65000-80000
£50350 $85594 €72000 Spatial concept (100x70cm-39x28in) s.d.57 s.i.d.verso pastel collage on canvas prov.exhib.lit. 24-Nov-3 Christie's, Milan #317/R est:70000-100000
£60000 $109200 €87600 Concetto spaziale, attesa (27x22cm-11x9in) s.i.verso waterpaint canvas prov. 6-Feb-4 Sotheby's, London #154/R est:40000-60000
£60000 $110400 €87600 Concetto spaziale, attesa (27x24cm-11x9in) s.i. i.verso waterpaint on canvas executed 1964 prov.lit. 25-Jun-4 Christie's, London #155/R est:35000-45000
£61745 $110523 €92000 Spatial concept (33x24cm-13x9in) s.i. hydropaint on canvas prov. 25-May-4 Sotheby's, Milan #308/R est:50000-60000
£68027 $121769 €100000 Spatial concept (41x33cm-16x13in) s.i.verso hydropaint on canvas exec.1967 lit. 16-Mar-4 Finarte Semenzato, Milan #433/R est:110000
£83916 $142657 €120000 Spatial concept, waiting (35x27cm-14x11in) s. i.verso hydropaint on canvas prov. 25-Nov-3 Sotheby's, Milan #243/R est:60000-80000
£87413 $148601 €125000 Spacial concept (74x73cm-29x29in) waterpaint wood on canvas sold with pencil study exec.1964. 29-Nov-3 Farsetti, Prato #478/R est:120000-150000
£100000 $167000 €146000 Spatial concept (102x89cm-40x35in) s.i.verso waterpaint on canvas exec.1965 lit. 20-Oct-3 Sotheby's, London #42/R est:90000
£107639 $182986 €155000 Spatial concept (61x50cm-24x20in) s.i.verso hydropaint on canvas. 28-Oct-3 Il Ponte, Milan #254/R est:200000
£109756 $180000 €160244 Concetto spaziale attese (73x60cm-29x24in) s.i. verso waterpaint canvas prov.lit. 28-May-3 Sotheby's, Amsterdam #50/R est:200000-250000
£114094 $204228 €170000 Spatial concept (55x74cm-22x29in) s.i. hydropaint on canvas exec.1961 prov.exhib.lit. 25-May-4 Sotheby's, Milan #298/R est:150000-200000
£119565 $196087 €165000 Spatial concept (83x102cm-33x40in) s.i. hydropaint on canvas on panel lit. 27-May-3 Sotheby's, Milan #286/R est:140000-180000
£125000 $230000 €182500 Concetto spaziale, attese (60x49cm-24x19in) s.i. verso waterpaint canvas exec 1967 prov.lit. 24-Jun-4 Sotheby's, London #237/R est:80000-120000
£140000 $257600 €204400 Concetto spaziale, attese (81x100cm-32x39in) s.d.verso waterpaint on canvas executed 1962 prov.exhib.lit. 24-Jun-4 Christie's, London #10/R est:80000-120000
£146853 $249650 €210000 Spacial concept (57x81cm-22x32in) s.i.d.1958 pastel oil on canvas lit. 28-Nov-3 Farsetti, Prato #374/R est:210000-240000
£150838 $270000 €220223 Concetto Spaziale - attese (93x73cm-37x29in) s.i. verso waterpaint canvas exec 1965 prov.exhib.lit. 13-May-4 Sotheby's, New York #169/R est:250000-350000
£167785 $300336 €250000 Spatial concept (61x50cm-24x20in) s. i.verso hydropaint lit. 25-May-4 Sotheby's, Milan #270/R est:200000-250000
£170000 $309400 €248200 Concetto Spaziale, Teatrino (100x110cm-39x43in) s.i.verso waterpaint canvas lacquered wood prov.exhib.lit. 5-Feb-4 Sotheby's, London #8/R est:100000-150000
£171329 $291259 €245000 Spacial concept (55x46cm-22x18in) s.i.verso hydropaint on canvas exec.1964-65 exhib.lit. 28-Nov-3 Farsetti, Prato #365/R est:200000-230000
£173184 $310000 €252849 Concetto spazial (54x65cm-21x26in) s.i. verso silver paint col stones prov.exhib.lit. 13-May-4 Phillips, New York #37/R est:200000-300000
£187919 $336376 €280000 Spatial concept (65x46cm-26x18in) s. s.i.d.1960 verso prov.lit. 25-May-4 Sotheby's, Milan #314/R est:220000-280000
£190000 $349600 €277400 Concetto spaziale, teatrino (130x130cm-51x51in) s.verso waterpaint canvas on lacquered wood prov.exhib.lit. 23-Jun-4 Sotheby's, London #29/R est:120000-150000
£200000 $364000 €292000 Concetto Spaziale, Attesa (100x73cm-39x29in) s.i.verso waterpaint canvas exec 1964 prov.lit. 5-Feb-4 Sotheby's, London #7/R est:150000-200000
£220000 $400400 €321200 Concetto spaziale, attese (61x46cm-24x18in) s.i.verso executed 1961 prov.lit. 4-Feb-4 Christie's, London #8/R est:140000-180000
£220000 $404800 €321200 Concetto spaziale, attese (65x54cm-26x21in) s. i.verso waterpaint on canvas prov.lit. 23-Jun-4 Sotheby's, London #24/R est:155000-200000
£231544 $414463 €345000 Spatial concept (65x50cm-26x20in) s.i.verso hydropaint on canvas painted 1962 lit. 28-May-4 Farsetti, Prato #331/R est:340000-390000
£240000 $441600 €350400 Concetto spaziale, attese (92x73cm-36x29in) s.i. waterpaint on canvas prov. 23-Jun-4 Sotheby's, London #31/R est:250000-350000
£250000 $460000 €365000 Concetto spaziale, attesa (92x73cm-36x29in) s. i.verso waterpaint on canvas executed 1968 prov.exhib.lit. 24-Jun-4 Christie's, London #8/R est:250000-350000
£281879 $504564 €420000 Spatial concept (92x73cm-36x29in) s.i.verso hydropaint on canvas prov.lit. 25-May-4 Sotheby's, Milan #286/R est:300000-400000
£350000 $637000 €511000 Concetto spaziale, attese (100x81cm-39x32in) s.i.verso waterpaint on canvas executed 1966 prov.exhib.lit. 4-Feb-4 Christie's, London #11/R est:250000-350000
£430000 $782600 €627800 Concetto Spaziale, Attese (75x200cm-30x79in) s.i.verso waterpaint canvas exec 1964 prov.lit. 5-Feb-4 Sotheby's, London #6/R est:400000-600000
£440000 $809600 €642400 Concetto spaziale, attese (73x92cm-29x36in) s. i.verso waterpaint on canvas prov.lit. 23-Jun-4 Sotheby's, London #9/R est:280000-350000
£610000 $1110200 €890600 Concetto Spaziale, Attese (89x116cm-35x46in) s.i.verso waterpaint canvas exec 1962 prov.lit. 5-Feb-4 Sotheby's, London #5/R est:200000-400000

FONTANA, Lucio and COSTANTINI, Egidio (20th C) Italian

Sculpture
£9091 $15455 €13000 Panel (85x35x23cm-33x14x9in) s.i.d.1965 glass on metal. 25-Nov-3 Sotheby's, Milan #15/R est:3000-4000

FONTANA, Prospero (1512-1597) Italian

£85000 $155550 €124100 Holy Family with Saint John (79x65cm-31x26in) panel prov. 7-Jul-4 Sotheby's, London #44/R est:50000-70000
£123239 $204577 €175000 Adoration of the Magi. Adoration of the sheperds (52x24cm-20x9in) copper pair lit. 11-Jul-3 Finarte, Venice #550/R est:160000-170000

FONTANA, Prospero (attrib) (1512-1597) Italian

£26000 $47580 €37960 Holy Family with Saint John (15x11cm-6x4in) panel. 8-Jul-4 Sotheby's, London #149/R est:15000-20000

FONTANA, Prospero (circle) (1512-1597) Italian

£8000 $13840 €11680 Mystic marriage of Saint Catherine (58x46cm-23x18in) panel. 10-Dec-3 Bonhams, New Bond Street #62/R est:4000-6000

FONTANA, Roberto (1844-1907) Italian

£1027 $1603 €1500 Woman in profile (54x37cm-21x15in) s. 8-Apr-3 Il Ponte, Milan #589
£13000 $23660 €18980 Dante in the underworld (186x247cm-73x97in) s.d.1873. 16-Jun-4 Christie's, Kensington #114/R est:8000-12000

FONTANAROSA, Lucien (1912-1975) French

£940 $1748 €1400 Le vin de Loire (32x54cm-13x21in) s. 3-Mar-4 Ferri, Paris #329
£1806 $2943 €2600 Jeune fille a la lecture (100x82cm-39x32in) s. 26-Sep-3 Rabourdin & Choppin de Janvry, Paris #71 est:2600-2800
£1972 $3411 €2800 Plage animee (43x62cm-17x24in) 14-Dec-3 Eric Pillon, Calais #150/R
£3497 $6014 €5000 Jeune homme aux instruments de musique (63x115cm-25x45in) s. prov. 3-Dec-3 Oger, Dumont, Paris #13/R est:3800
£4362 $7721 €6500 Fille au rideau (50x100cm-20x39in) s. painted c.1964. 27-Apr-4 Artcurial Briest, Paris #197/R est:3000-3500
Works on paper
£2374 $3894 €3300 Ballerine (63x49cm-25x19in) s. pastel. 6-Jun-3 Chochon-Barre & Allardi, Paris #47/R est:3500-3800

FONTANESI, Antonio (1818-1882) Italian

£18000 $33120 €27000 Landscape in the Dauphine (28x39cm-11x15in) i. prov.exhib.lit. 10-Jun-4 Christie's, Rome #157/R est:20000-30000
£49296 $85282 €70000 At the source (50x68cm-20x27in) s.d.1860 exhib. 10-Dec-3 Sotheby's, Milan #65/R est:70000-90000
£114094 $213356 €170000 Evening (80x70cm-31x28in) s.d.1862 prov.exhib.lit. 25-Feb-4 Porro, Milan #31/R est:200000
Works on paper
£733 $1349 €1100 Landscape (19x22cm-7x9in) s. pencil. 14-Jun-4 Sant Agostino, Torino #189/R

FONTANESI, Antonio (attrib) (1818-1882) Italian

£2616 $4500 €3819 Cows grazing beside a stream (45x76cm-18x30in) i.on stretcher. 3-Dec-3 Doyle, New York #125/R est:4000-6000
£7042 $11690 €10000 Alberi sullo stagno (67x53cm-26x21in) s.d.62 oval. 11-Jun-3 Christie's, Rome #179/R est:2000-3000
Works on paper
£685 $1165 €980 Landscape (8x14cm-3x6in) i.verso W/C. 19-Nov-3 Finarte Semenzato, Milan #518/R

FONTANESI, Antonio (circle) (1818-1882) Italian

£7042 $11690 €10000 Melanconie autunnali (85x105cm-33x41in) prov. 11-Jun-3 Christie's, Rome #176/R est:2000-3000

FONTANI, Voltolino (1920-1976) Italian

£483 $806 €700 Bocca d'Arno (20x30cm-8x12in) s. s.i.verso board. 14-Nov-3 Farsetti, Prato #466

FONTEBASSO, Francesco (1709-1769) Italian

£95023 $152036 €138734 Triumph of Peace (450x360cm-177x142in) prov.lit. oval. 19-Sep-3 Koller, Zurich #3058/R est:120000-180000 (S.FR 210000)
Works on paper
£2041 $3653 €3000 La Lamentation avec Joseph d'Arimathaea (27x19cm-11x7in) pen brown ink. 18-Mar-4 Christie's, Paris #66/R est:3000-5000
£5556 $10000 €8112 Four gesturing hands (42x28cm-17x11in) black white chk. 22-Jan-4 Christie's, Rockefeller NY #74/R est:5000-7000

FONTEBASSO, Francesco (attrib) (1709-1769) Italian

£2623 $4250 €3830 David and Goliath (36x56cm-14x22in) prov. 3-Aug-3 North East Auctions, Portsmouth #1773 est:3000-5000
Works on paper
£884 $1583 €1300 L'hiver (25x19cm-10x7in) i. black pencil pen brown ink wash. 19-Mar-4 Piasa, Paris #47/R

FONTEBASSO, Francesco (circle) (1709-1769) Italian

£5960 $10907 €9000 Hommage a Venise (91x71cm-36x28in) 7-Apr-4 Libert, Castor, Paris #10/R est:1000-1500

FONTEIN, Adriana Sophia (1888-1965) Dutch

£822 $1397 €1200 Breakfast table (46x64cm-18x25in) s. 5-Nov-3 Vendue Huis, Gravenhage #220a

FONTENAY, Jean Baptiste Belin de (1653-1715) French

£9000 $15570 €13140 Peaches, grapes, plums with rose, carnations and other flowers in a basket in a landscape (73x109cm-29x43in) 10-Dec-3 Bonhams, New Bond Street #27/R est:6000-8000

FONTENAY, Jean Baptiste Belin de (attrib) (1653-1715) French
£8500 $15214 €12410 Still life of flowers (65x46cm-26x18in) 26-May-4 AB Stockholms Auktionsverk #2510/R est:40000-50000 (S.KR 115000)

FONTEYN, Georges (1903-1984) Belgian
£671 $1242 €1000 After the bath (180x99cm-71x39in) s.d.1930. 13-Mar-4 De Vuyst, Lokeren #141

FONTI, Michel (?) ?
Works on paper
£1007 $1782 €1500 Encensoir (130x81cm-51x32in) s. pastel paper on canvas. 30-Apr-4 Tajan, Paris #125 est:1500-2000

FONTIROSSI, Roberto (1940-) Italian
£704 $1169 €1000 L'abito da cerimonia (40x50cm-16x20in) s. s.i.verso canvasboard painted 2000. 14-Jun-3 Meeting Art, Vercelli #424/R
Works on paper
£336 $621 €500 Musician (30x20cm-12x8in) s. mixed media. 13-Mar-4 Meeting Art, Vercelli #437

FONVILLE, Horace-Antoine (1832-1910) French
£606 $1085 €885 Eglise de Montagnat pres des Bois de Rivoire (49x65cm-19x26in) s. i. verso panel. 22-Mar-4 Philippe Schuler, Zurich #4402/R (S.FR 1400)
£1879 $3458 €2800 Ferme aux environs de Bourge dans l'Ain (65x81cm-26x32in) s. i.verso. 28-Mar-4 Anaf, Lyon #130/R est:3500-4000

FONYI, Geza (1899-1971) Hungarian
£731 $1264 €1067 Girl with a bird (80x60cm-31x24in) s. 12-Dec-3 Kieselbach, Budapest #157/R (H.F 280000)

FOOT, Frederick (fl.1857-1867) British
£1000 $1670 €1460 On the River Dart (75x103cm-30x41in) s. 14-Oct-3 Bearnes, Exeter #369/R est:1000-1200

FOOTE, Hamish (20th C) New Zealander?
Works on paper
£542 $883 €791 View from the picnic ground (19x36cm-7x14in) s.i.d.1996 W/C. 23-Sep-3 Peter Webb, Auckland #103/R (NZ.D 1500)

FOOTE, Will Howe (1874-1965) American
£683 $1100 €997 Baboquivaris (30x41cm-12x16in) s.i. board. 20-Aug-3 James Julia, Fairfield #1228/R est:1800-2400
£1946 $3600 €2841 Early fall landscape (64x76cm-25x30in) 13-Feb-4 Du Mouchelle, Detroit #2011/R est:2500-4500
£4348 $7000 €6348 Hyrdangeas and sunlight 1913 (76x76cm-30x30in) s. 20-Aug-3 James Julia, Fairfield #1227/R est:15000-18000

FOPPIANI, Gustavo (1925-1986) Italian
£2685 $4805 €4000 Ancient town (35x58cm-14x23in) s.d.55 s.i.d.verso prov. 25-May-4 Sotheby's, Milan #77/R est:1000
£4267 $7680 €6400 Artificial satelliate over Volterra (83cm-33in circular) s.d.66 board prov. 22-Apr-4 Finarte Semenzato, Rome #351/R est:1600-2200

FORABOSCO, Gerolamo (1605-1679) Italian
£26000 $44980 €37960 Head of Apollo (43x36cm-17x14in) i.verso panel. 10-Dec-3 Christie's, London #108/R est:20000-30000

FORAIN, Jean Louis (1852-1931) French
£1600 $2960 €2336 Female nude (40x30cm-16x12in) s. 10-Mar-4 Sotheby's, Olympia #311/R est:1500-2000
£3000 $4770 €4350 Apres le spectacle (61x46cm-24x18in) init. painted 1910. 11-Sep-3 Christie's, Kensington #33/R est:3000-4000
£3000 $4770 €4350 Personnes en attente (46x55cm-18x22in) s. 11-Sep-3 Christie's, Kensington #34/R est:3000-4000
£5828 $10607 €8800 Au casino (56x61cm-22x24in) lit. 19-Jun-4 St-Germain-en-Laye Encheres #98/R est:9000
£9000 $16560 €13500 Personnages et danseuses dans les coulisses (92x74cm-36x29in) mono. painted c.1910. 10-Jun-4 Camard, Paris #64/R est:9000-12000
£9732 $17419 €14500 Femme elegante (36x28cm-14x11in) init. panel prov. 26-May-4 Christie's, Paris #6/R est:8000-12000
£10500 $19320 €15330 Derriere les coulisses (41x32cm-16x13in) s. panel prov. 24-Mar-4 Sotheby's, Olympia #54/R est:6000-8000
£12829 $23605 €19500 Danseuse au tambourin (73x60cm-29x24in) mono. 28-Jun-4 Joron-Derem, Paris #89/R est:25000-30000
£13333 $24000 €19466 A perpetuite (65x81cm-26x32in) s. painted c.1910 prov.exhib.lit. 22-Apr-4 Christie's, Rockefeller NY #158/R est:30000-40000
£41176 $70000 €60117 Danseuses au repos (60x73cm-24x29in) init. painted c.1905 prov.exhib. 5-Nov-3 Christie's, Rockefeller NY #208/R est:45000-65000
£264901 $482119 €400000 Les courses (65x92cm-26x36in) s. painted c.1885-1890 prov.exhib. 18-Jun-4 Piasa, Paris #8/R est:60000-80000
Works on paper
£296 $545 €450 La couturiere (25x18cm-10x7in) W/C. 23-Jun-4 Maigret, Paris #54/R
£352 $609 €500 Femme debout (25x13cm-10x5in) s. Chinese ink col crayon. 14-Dec-3 Eric Pillon, Calais #46/R
£379 $702 €550 La toilette (26x20cm-10x8in) s. black crayon. 11-Feb-4 Beaussant & Lefèvre, Paris #186
£387 $624 €550 Algarade (27x35cm-11x14in) crayon dr prov. 11-May-3 Versailles Encheres #112
£464 $848 €700 L'amateur de tableaux (53x41cm-21x16in) s. wash. 7-Apr-4 Piasa, Paris #23
£470 $879 €700 Sans titre (35x49cm-14x19in) s. pencil. 29-Feb-4 Versailles Encheres #133/R
£559 $1029 €850 Rencontre du cure et du notaire (33x42cm-13x17in) s. chl wash. 25-Jun-4 Millon & Associes, Paris #31
£563 $975 €800 Danseuse (35x24cm-14x9in) s. W/C. 14-Dec-3 Eric Pillon, Calais #47/R
£634 $1096 €900 Toi, dans la deche - Faut pas me raconter ca - ton notaire sort d'ici (35x26cm-14x10in) s.i. chl. 10-Dec-3 Piasa, Paris #145
£667 $1200 €974 L'ecole de michets (38x28cm-15x11in) ink. 24-Apr-4 Du Mouchelle, Detroit #3106/R est:1000-2000
£671 $1235 €1000 Scene de famille (31x45cm-12x18in) s. Indian ink. 24-Mar-4 Joron-Derem, Paris #58
£795 $1454 €1200 L'actrice en pleurs (34x24cm-13x9in) s.i. W/C wash. 7-Apr-4 Piasa, Paris #22
£795 $1400 €1161 Contens c'est un vache (36x27cm-14x11in) s.i. pen ink pencil crayon W/C. 18-May-4 Sotheby's, New York #124/R est:1500-2000
£819 $1466 €1196 In conversation (21x16cm-8x6in) s. Indian ink brush wash. 12-May-4 Dobiaschofsky, Bern #1594 est:600 (S.FR 1900)
£822 $1397 €1200 Scenes (35x27cm-14x11in) pen ink chl set of 3. 6-Nov-3 Tajan, Paris #233
£979 $1684 €1400 Portrait d'homme (25x17cm-10x7in) s. W/C. 3-Dec-3 Tajan, Paris #10 est:300-500
£1056 $1827 €1500 Danseuse en coulisse (36x25cm-14x10in) W/C prov. 12-Dec-3 Artus Associes, Paris #150
£1099 $2000 €1605 Une famille, etudes d'homme and une couple (30x51cm-12x20in) s. pencil ink three. 4-Feb-4 Christie's, Rockefeller NY #286/R est:2500-3500
£1126 $2049 €1700 Le temoin a la barre (29x39cm-11x15in) s. pen ink wash black crayon. 16-Jun-4 Piasa, Paris #194 est:950-1000
£1351 $2500 €1972 Horse and Jockey (38x46cm-15x18in) init. pencil W/C card sketches verso. 12-Feb-4 Sotheby's, New York #1/R est:2500-3500
£1359 $2500 €1984 Two ladies and gentleman in a top hat (28x20cm-11x8in) pencil. 10-Jun-4 Sotheby's, New York #261/R est:800-1200
£8803 $15230 €12500 Jeune danseuse (44x36cm-17x14in) s. pastel chl paper on canvas. 9-Dec-3 Artcurial Briest, Paris #75/R est:12000-15000
£22000 $40480 €32120 Nocturne (65x55cm-26x22in) s. pastel exec c.1890 prov. 24-Jun-4 Christie's, London #304/R est:20000-30000

FORAIN, Jean Louis (attrib) (1852-1931) French
£793 $1348 €1158 Szene a personnages (105x63cm-41x25in) 5-Nov-3 Dobiaschofsky, Bern #544/R (S.FR 1800)
£1400 $2590 €2044 Woman riding side-saddle (23x17cm-9x7in) board. 10-Mar-4 Sotheby's, Olympia #303/R est:150-2000

FORBAT, Alfred (1897-1972) European
Works on paper
£1119 $1924 €1600 Composition (22x26cm-9x10in) mono. pencil col pen exhib. 3-Dec-3 Hauswedell & Nolte, Hamburg #774/R est:1000

FORBES, Charles Stuart (1856-1926) American
£1064 $1777 €1500 Portraits of ladies (71x55cm-28x22in) one s. set of 3. 17-Jun-3 Finarte Semenzato, Milan #418

FORBES, Elizabeth Adela (1859-1912) British
Works on paper
£6200 $10292 €9052 Young girl with hands behind her back (43x26cm-17x10in) chl prov. 2-Oct-3 Lane, Penzance #250/R est:5000-6000

FORBES, Helen K (1891-1945) American
£215 $400 €314 Portrait of man (38x30cm-15x12in) i.verso board painted c.1940. 7-Mar-4 Treadway Gallery, Cincinnati #661/R
£594 $950 €867 Portrait of a woman in a blue hat (107x89cm-42x35in) s. board. 18-May-3 Auctions by the Bay, Alameda #1152/R
£2335 $4250 €3409 Death Valley II (91x81cm-36x32in) prov.exhib. 15-Jun-4 John Moran, Pasadena #161 est:1500-2500

FORBES, James G (1800-?) British
£2389 $4300 €3488 Cobbler's daughter (51x41cm-20x16in) s.d.1857. 21-Jan-4 Sotheby's, New York #225/R est:3000-4000

FORBES, John Colin (1846-1925) Canadian
£536 $895 €777 New York (33x46cm-13x18in) s. i.verso board. 17-Jun-3 Pinneys, Montreal #143 est:1200-1600 (C.D 1200)

FORBES, Leighton (?) British
Works on paper
£350 $634 €511 Poultry in a lane by cottages in summer (23x33cm-9x13in) s. W/C. 16-Apr-4 Keys, Aylsham #476

FORBES, Leyton (fl.1900-1925) British
Works on paper
£250 $448 €365 Cattle on a rural lane (24x35cm-9x14in) s. W/C. 25-May-4 Bonhams, Knightsbridge #34/R
£280 $468 €409 Midsummer glory (38x63cm-15x25in) s. W/C. 13-Nov-3 Bonhams, Edinburgh #322
£300 $510 €438 Cornish cottage near Helston. s. W/C. 28-Nov-3 Moore Allen & Innocent, Cirencester #715
£340 $622 €496 Feeding the chickens (28x45cm-11x18in) s. W/C. 27-Jan-4 Bonhams, Knightsbridge #6/R
£390 $632 €569 Old cottage at Strattford (13x23cm-5x9in) s. W/C. 31-Jul-3 Biddle & Webb, Birmingham #900
£660 $1181 €964 Country cottage with woman attending gardens. Country land with figures (15x22cm-6x9in) s. W/C pair. 17-Mar-4 Bonhams, Chester #326

FORBES, Robert (1948-) American
£588 $1000 €858 Paradox 2 (84x117cm-33x46in) s. painted 1974. 7-Nov-3 Selkirks, St. Louis #450/R

FORBES, Stanhope Alexander (1857-1947) British
£1500 $2595 €2190 Head and shoulder study of a man with red neckerchief (29x24cm-11x9in) 11-Dec-3 Lane, Penzance #342 est:1000-1200
£1700 $2839 €2482 Artist's nephew playing the piano (46x33cm-18x13in) s. i.d.1926 verso board. 14-Oct-3 David Lay, Penzance #427/R est:1500-2500
£2200 $3674 €3212 Portrait of a lady, seated, in a black dress (91x71cm-36x28in) s.d.1882. 13-Nov-3 Christie's, Kensington #40/R est:1500-2000
£2200 $3784 €3212 Cottage at Mousehole (33x28cm-13x11in) s.d.1902. 5-Dec-3 Keys, Aylsham #689 est:1000-1500
£3221 $5702 €4800 Self portrait of the artist as a young man (22x15cm-9x6in) s.d.1882 board. 27-Apr-4 Whyte's, Dublin #116/R est:2000-4000
£3400 $5678 €4964 Head of a girl, study of the fleet is Sighted (20x20cm-8x8in) 14-Oct-3 David Lay, Penzance #429/R est:2500-3500
£3750 $6900 €5700 Autumn landscape (30x38cm-12x15in) s. board. 22-Jun-4 De Veres Art Auctions, Dublin #109/R est:6000-9000
£5000 $9100 €7300 Angler (36x28cm-14x11in) s.d.1932 canvasboard. 21-Jun-4 Bonhams, Bath #465/R est:5000-8000
£5800 $9686 €8468 Mousehole Harbour (36x46cm-14x18in) prov. 14-Oct-3 David Lay, Penzance #599/R est:3000-4000
£7500 $13500 €10950 Rowing boat (51x61cm-20x24in) s.d.1904. 21-Jan-4 Sotheby's, Olympia #349/R est:4000-6000
£27000 $49140 €39420 Study for Homealong (86x71cm-34x28in) s. prov. 15-Jun-4 Bonhams, New Bond Street #9/R est:30000-50000
£36000 $61200 €52560 Lighting up (62x52cm-24x20in) s.d.1903. 21-Nov-3 Christie's, London #32/R est:15000-25000
£250000 $425000 €365000 Safe anchorage (117x153cm-46x60in) s.d.1909. 27-Nov-3 Sotheby's, London #31/R est:300000-500000
£300000 $549000 €438000 Convent (86x76cm-34x30in) s.i.d.1882 exhib.lit. 2-Jun-4 Sotheby's, London #6/R est:300000-400000

FORBES, Vivian (1891-1937) British
£260 $434 €380 Still life with gramophone record and needles on a white cloth table (23x36cm-9x14in) s.d.1931. 14-Oct-3 Canterbury Auctions, UK #104

FORCADE, Raoul (19th C) French
£587 $981 €840 Magrelia coasts (28x46cm-11x18in) s. 30-Jun-3 Ansorena, Madrid #246/R

FORCELLA, N (19th C) Italian
£1922 $3440 €2806 En Zouave (39x23cm-15x9in) s. 26-May-4 AB Stockholms Auktionsverk #2450/R est:18000-20000 (S.KR 26000)

FORCELLA, Nicola (19th C) Italian
£2953 $5434 €4400 Portrait d'un femme a l'anneau (51x34cm-20x13in) s. 24-Mar-4 Joron-Derem, Paris #230/R est:4500-5000

FORCHONDT, Gilliam (elder-attrib) (1608-1678) Belgian
£3000 $5400 €4380 David playing the harp before Saul (28x37cm-11x15in) init.d.1655 copper. 21-Apr-4 Bonhams, New Bond Street #5/R est:3000-5000
£7895 $14526 €12000 Eliezer and Rebecca (114x207cm-45x81in) 25-Jun-4 Piasa, Paris #81/R est:12000-15000

FORCONE, N (19th C) Italian
£1200 $2160 €1752 Peasant girl knitting by a market stall (25x39cm-10x15in) s. 21-Apr-4 Cheffins, Cambridge #503/R est:300-400

FORD, Elise (20th C) American
£359 $600 €524 Yellow and pink blooms in a vase (71x58cm-28x23in) s. 15-Nov-3 Sloans & Kenyon, Bethesda #118/R

FORD, Henry Chapman (1828-1894) American
£3409 $6000 €4977 Western landscape (36x48cm-14x19in) paper on canvas prov. 23-May-4 Hindman, Chicago #138/R est:6000-8000

FORD, Henry Justice (1860-1941) British
Works on paper
£2600 $4420 €3796 Escape (27x19cm-11x7in) mono. pencil pen blk ink grey wash scratching out. 20-Nov-3 Christie's, London #159/R est:2000-3000

FORD, John A (19th C) British
£1200 $2232 €1752 Sheep in a loch landscape (61x107cm-24x42in) s. 4-Mar-4 Christie's, Kensington #185/R est:600-900

FORD, Marcus (1914-) British
£340 $615 €496 Whitby (50x60cm-20x24in) s. 30-Mar-4 David Duggleby, Scarborough #146/R

FORD, Michael (?-1765) British
£2500 $4250 €3650 Portrait of the Rt. Hon Henry Singleton (124x99cm-49x39in) lit. 27-Nov-3 Sotheby's, London #139/R est:3000-5000

FORDHAM, Elwood James (1913-1981) American
£1156 $2000 €1688 Ranch in Calabasas (42x53cm-17x21in) s. 10-Dec-3 Bonhams & Butterfields, San Francisco #6293/R est:3000-5000

FOREAU, Claude (1903-) French
£1467 $2655 €2200 Marche en Poitou (170x151cm-67x59in) s. 4-Apr-4 Salle des ventes Pillet, Lyon la Foret #29/R est:1500-1800

FOREAU, Louis Henri (1866-1938) French
£800 $1440 €1168 Open landscape with figures on a country track (16x27cm-6x11in) init. panel. 21-Apr-4 Tennants, Leyburn #1146
£851 $1421 €1200 Le bassin dans un parc (60x81cm-24x32in) s. 19-Jun-3 Millon & Associes, Paris #193
£1064 $1777 €1500 Paysage anime au crepuscule (190x132cm-75x52in) s. 19-Oct-3 St-Germain-en-Laye Encheres #37/R est:1200-1500
£3000 $5490 €4500 Passage du bac. s. 6-Jun-4 Osenat, Fontainebleau #197/R est:4000-4500
Works on paper
£350 $601 €500 Berger et troupeau (29x39cm-11x15in) s. W/C. 7-Dec-3 Livinec, Gaudcheau & Jezequel, Rennes #14
£397 $727 €600 Le passage du bac (27x36cm-11x14in) s. W/C htd gouache. 7-Apr-4 Doutrebente, Paris #39
£567 $948 €800 Les bouquinistes sur les quais (27x37cm-11x15in) W/C. 19-Jun-3 Millon & Associes, Paris #197/R
£600 $1104 €900 Hiver, le kiosque (37x52cm-15x20in) s. W/C gouache prov. 9-Jun-4 Beaussant & Lefèvre, Paris #159
£795 $1446 €1200 Carriole sur chemin (40x50cm-16x20in) s. pastel paper on canvas. 19-Jun-4 St-Germain-en-Laye Encheres #188/R

FORES, Mary H (19th C) British
£380 $635 €555 Head study of young west country female (28x23cm-11x9in) s. painted c.1880. 16-Nov-3 Desmond Judd, Cranbrook #1033

FOREST, Henry J de (1860-1924) Canadian
£226 $378 €330 Untitled - river in BC (23x35cm-9x14in) s.d.1897. 17-Nov-3 Hodgins, Calgary #116/R (C.D 500)

FOREST, Pierre (1881-1971) French
£252 $400 €368 Moonlit rustic shoreway (58x97cm-23x38in) s. 12-Sep-3 Aspire, Cleveland #46

FOREST, Roy de (1930-) American
Works on paper
£7300 $13432 €10950 Teh Taylor brothers in the Great North Woods (168x183cm-66x72in) s.i.d.1973 verso mixed media canvas prov. 9-Jun-4 Artcurial Briest, Paris #411/R est:8000-12000

FORESTIER, Andre (20th C) Swiss
£229 $383 €332 Grimentz (38x46cm-15x18in) s.d. i.verso. 21-Jun-3 Galerie du Rhone, Sion #363/R (S.FR 500)

FORESTIER, Antonin Clair (1865-1912) French
Sculpture
£1103 $1843 €1600 Beatrix (84cm-33in) marble. 12-Nov-3 Chassaing Rivet, Toulouse #151

FORESTIER, Henri-Claude (1875-1922) Swiss
£302 $540 €441 Still life of flowers with chrysanthemums (61x50cm-24x20in) s. 13-May-4 Stuker, Bern #635 (S.FR 700)
£952 $1524 €1380 Still life of flowers (46x38cm-18x15in) s. two. 15-May-3 Stuker, Bern #1196 (S.FR 2000)

FORESTIER, Marius (fl.1906-1914) British
Works on paper
£360 $623 €526 Still life of tulips, carnations, peonies and other summer blossom in a basket (43x53cm-17x21in) s. W/C. 14-Dec-3 Desmond Judd, Cranbrook #1094

FORESTIER, René le (20th C) ?
£360 $590 €500 Le Port de Concarneau (16x21cm-6x8in) s. panel. 3-Jun-3 Livinec, Gaudcheau & Jezequel, Rennes #70

FORG, Gunther (1952-) German
£2793 $5000 €4078 Untitled (262x148cm-103x58in) s.d.20/11/89 acrylic Canson paper prov. 13-May-4 Sotheby's, New York #439/R est:8000-12000
£4507 $7797 €6400 Untitled (90x60cm-35x24in) s.d.91 verso lead. 13-Dec-3 Lempertz, Koln #136/R est:5000
£5000 $8350 €7300 Lund (70x45cm-28x18in) s.i.d.88 acrylic panel four prov. 22-Oct-3 Christie's, London #97/R est:7000-9000
£10596 $19391 €16000 Bleidbild (243x211cm-96x83in) acrylic panel triptych prov. 7-Apr-4 Piasa, Paris #246 est:8000-12000
Photographs
£3000 $5430 €4380 Ika (187x127cm-74x50in) black white photograph executed c.1986. 1-Apr-4 Christie's, Kensington #307/R est:3000-5000
£17000 $28390 €24820 Eur, Roma (282x131cm-111x52in) gelatin silver print prov. 22-Oct-3 Christie's, London #142/R est:5000-7000
Works on paper
£294 $505 €420 Untitled (23x32cm-9x13in) s.d. chk. 3-Dec-3 Hauswedell & Nolte, Hamburg #773/R
£465 $772 €660 Untitled (34x49cm-13x19in) s.d.1997 brush. 13-Jun-3 Hauswedell & Nolte, Hamburg #625/R
£629 $1083 €900 Untitled (13x9cm-5x4in) s. ballpoint pen pair executed 1995 prov. 2-Dec-3 Sotheby's, Amsterdam #339/R est:1000-1500
£1000 $1840 €1460 Patchwork (53x35cm-21x14in) s.d.94 gouache prov. 24-Jun-4 Sotheby's, Olympia #607/R est:1000-1500
£1408 $2465 €2000 Being 10 (36x48cm-14x19in) s.d.2001 W/C prov. 16-Dec-3 Segre, Madrid #200/R est:2500
£2098 $3567 €3000 Composition abstraite (55x38cm-22x15in) s.d.1992 gouache vellum prov. 25-Nov-3 Tajan, Paris #84/R est:2000-3000
£2797 $4811 €4000 Untitled (41x29cm-16x11in) s.d.96 mixed media oil gouache pencil. 4-Dec-3 Van Ham, Cologne #143/R est:4500
£7246 $11884 €10000 Untitled (56x38cm-22x15in) s.i.d.1991 gouache eight. 27-May-3 Sotheby's, Amsterdam #451/R est:10000-15000

FORGIOLI, Attilio (1933-) Italian

£420	$713	€600	June (50x60cm-20x24in) s.s.verso paintedc.1989. 24-Nov-3 Christie's, Milan #77
£704	$1169	€1000	Island (45x68cm-18x27in) s. s.i.d.1983 on stretcher. 11-Jun-3 Finarte Semenzato, Milan #547/R
£1200	$2160	€1800	Shoe (38x33cm-15x13in) s. 22-Apr-4 Finarte Semenzato, Rome #204/R est:1600-1800
£1300	$2392	€1950	Landscape (70x80cm-28x31in) s. 12-Jun-4 Meeting Art, Vercelli #854/R est:1500

FORMANI, G (19th C) Italian

Works on paper

£944	$1700	€1378	Ball masque in Venice (32x63cm-13x25in) s. W/C. 21-Jan-4 Sotheby's, New York #260/R est:800-1200

FORMICOLA, John (20th C) American

£1890	$3250	€2759	Young girl reading (157x218cm-62x86in) s.d.61 prov. 7-Dec-3 Freeman, Philadelphia #219 est:1000-1500

FORNARA, Carlo (1871-1968) Italian

£13423	$23758	€20000	Landscape (40x30cm-16x12in) s. i.verso cardboard exhib.lit. 1-May-4 Meeting Art, Vercelli #471 est:20000
£15385	$25692	€22000	Mountain flowers (76x63cm-30x25in) s. 24-Jun-3 Finarte Semenzato, Rome #198/R est:14000
£20000	$36400	€29200	Un village nella valle Vigezzo (38x29cm-15x11in) s. prov.lit. 16-Jun-4 Christie's, Kensington #91/R est:6000-8000

Works on paper

£17483	$29196	€25000	Spring night dream (47x48cm-19x19in) s. pas. card. 24-Jun-3 Finarte Semenzato, Rome #199/R est:28000-32000

FORNASETTI, Piero (20th C) ?

Prints

£6486	$12000	€9470	Libreria (199x200cm-78x79in) lithograph print four panel wood screen double-sided exec.1950. 9-Mar-4 Christie's, Rockefeller NY #473/R est:7000-9000

Sculpture

£4348	$8000	€6348	Folding screen (137x142x5cm-54x56x2in) hand painted transfer wood brass. 28-Mar-4 Wright, Chicago #121/R est:7000-9000

FORNER, Raquel (1902-1990) Argentinian

£2235	$4000	€3263	Astronaut (40x50cm-16x20in) s. s.i.verso. 4-May-4 Arroyo, Buenos Aires #19/R est:4000
£2568	$4700	€3749	Head of astronaut (30x40cm-12x16in) 1-Jun-4 Arroyo, Buenos Aires #93
£18579	$34000	€27125	Compromised (73x100cm-29x39in) 1-Jun-4 Arroyo, Buenos Aires #63

Works on paper

£3352	$6000	€4894	Fight (38x51cm-15x20in) s.d.1973 mixed media. 4-May-4 Arroyo, Buenos Aires #49/R est:3500

FORNEROD, Rodolphe (1877-1953) Swiss

£362	$605	€529	Still life (26x33cm-10x13in) s. 24-Jun-3 Germann, Zurich #79/R (S.FR 800)
£658	$1211	€1000	Portrait de jeune fille (65x54cm-26x21in) s. 25-Jun-4 Daguerre, Paris #145/R
£699	$1203	€1000	Nature morte au faisan. Nature morte aux pommes et aux poires (73x92cm-29x36in) s. cardboard double-sided. 2-Dec-3 Campo & Campo, Antwerp #143/R

FORNIER, Kitty (?-1908) French

£280	$467	€400	Model in the study (55x34cm-22x13in) s. panel. 27-Jun-3 Doutrebente, Paris #46
£839	$1401	€1200	Woman with shawl (29x21cm-11x8in) s. panel. 27-Jun-3 Doutrebente, Paris #47

FORNS BADA, Carlos (1956-) French

£2493	$4363	€3540	Garden in February (130x162cm-51x64in) s.d.1986 exhib.lit. 16-Dec-3 Segre, Madrid #188/R est:5500

FORNS Y ROMANS, Rafael (1868-1939) Spanish

£1268	$2218	€1800	Cathedral exit (37x48cm-15x19in) s. cardboard. 16-Dec-3 Durán, Madrid #86/R est:1400

FORREST, Archibald Stevenson (1869-1963) British

£550	$974	€803	Road in Mandeville, Jamaica (41x46cm-16x18in) s.i.d.July 24 1904 canvasboard. 29-Apr-4 Christie's, Kensington #160/R

FORREST, Captain J Haughton (1826-1925) Australian

£791	$1415	€1187	River at sunset (13x30cm-5x12in) s. board. 17-May-4 Sotheby's, Melbourne #577 (A.D 2000)
£824	$1400	€1203	French fishing boats offshore with Eddystone lighthouse in the foreground (46x76cm-18x30in) s.d.1884. 19-Nov-3 Bonhams & Butterfields, San Francisco #133/R
£1021	$1736	€1491	Night storm and sea (29x46cm-11x18in) s. board. 25-Nov-3 Christie's, Melbourne #313 (A.D 2400)
£1356	$2305	€1980	Highland scene (29x45cm-11x18in) s. bears i.verso board. 24-Nov-3 Sotheby's, Melbourne #150150 est:3000-5000 (A.D 3200)
£1702	$2894	€2485	Ben Cruachan, Scotland (29x45cm-11x18in) s. board. 25-Nov-3 Christie's, Melbourne #266 est:4000-6000 (A.D 4000)
£2553	$4340	€3727	Chepstowe Castle, England (29x44cm-11x17in) s. board. 25-Nov-3 Christie's, Melbourne #155/R est:6000-8000 (A.D 6000)
£3617	$6149	€5281	Mount Gould, Ducane Range, Tasmania (62x46cm-24x18in) s. i.verso. 26-Nov-3 Deutscher-Menzies, Melbourne #130/R est:10000-15000 (A.D 8500)
£3925	$6948	€5731	Riverside farm. On the Severn. Westmoreland. Ben Luack, Scotland (31x47cm-12x19in) s. i.verso board four prov. 3-May-4 Christie's, Melbourne #102/R est:10000-15000 (A.D 9500)
£4065	$7276	€5935	Ships in a storm (28x44cm-11x17in) s. board. 10-May-4 Joel, Victoria #339 est:10000-12000 (A.D 10000)
£5106	$8681	€7455	Cliffs, River Derwent (47x31cm-19x12in) s. i.verso. 26-Nov-3 Deutscher-Menzies, Melbourne #129/R est:8000-12000 (A.D 12000)
£10000	$16000	€14600	Legendary racing cutter, Arrow, flying the colours of the Royal Thames Yacht Club (46x76cm-18x30in) s. 16-Sep-3 Bonhams, New Bond Street #49/R est:10000-15000

FORREST, Charles Ramus (1787-1826) Canadian/British

Works on paper

£1200	$1956	€1752	Sacred tank and pagodas near Benares (23x33cm-9x13in) pencil W/C prov.exhib. two. 24-Sep-3 Christie's, London #47/R est:600-800

FORREST, Robert Smith (fl.1908-1934) British

£380	$699	€555	Portrait of a Viking warrior holding a staff (58x71cm-23x28in) s.d.09 W/C. 23-Mar-4 Rosebery Fine Art, London #804/R

FORREST, Thomas Theodosius (1728-1784) British

Works on paper

£260	$478	€380	Windsor Castle - a study (36x53cm-14x21in) pen ink grey wash. 14-Jun-4 Bonhams, Bath #9
£727	$1142	€1061	Pall Mall in the early 17th Century (21x33cm-8x13in) i.verso W/C. 27-Aug-3 Dunbar Sloane, Wellington #90/R (NZ.D 2000)

FORREST, Tony (1961-) British

£275	$501	€402	Study of a cheetah (38x74cm-15x29in) s. 4-Feb-4 John Nicholson, Haslemere #108/R

FORREST, William S (attrib) (fl.1840-1866) British

£1486	$2750	€2170	Hunting scenes (18x23cm-7x9in) init. panel four. 10-Feb-4 Doyle, New York #230/R est:3000-5000

FORRESTALL, Thomas de Vany (1936-) Canadian

£1339	$2277	€1955	Fallen tree cut up, startled bird (49x70cm-19x28in) s. s.i.d.1981 verso egg tempera board. 6-Nov-3 Heffel, Vancouver #44/R est:3000-4000 (C.D 3000)

Works on paper

£600	$1098	€876	Living room. The Commission - Kentucky Rifle (37x55cm-15x22in) both s. W/C two. 1-Jun-4 Joyner Waddington, Toronto #333/R (C.D 1500)

FORRESTER, Janet Nala (20th C) Australian?

£298	$540	€435	Sugarbag dreaming. acrylic. 1-Apr-4 Joel, Victoria #249 (A.D 725)

FORRESTER, John (1922-) New Zealander

£500	$815	€730	Abstract, Aldila Mark (99x56cm-39x22in) i.verso prov. 23-Sep-3 John Nicholson, Haslemere #168/R
£900	$1467	€1314	Abstract, Mark Black Two (91x74cm-36x29in) s.i.verso prov. 23-Sep-3 John Nicholson, Haslemere #167
£1700	$3043	€2482	Mark black two (91x73cm-36x29in) s.i.d.1961 verso. 14-May-4 Christie's, Kensington #641/R est:700-900
£2000	$3580	€2920	Aldila mark (91x81cm-36x32in) s.i.d.1962 verso. 14-May-4 Christie's, Kensington #642/R est:600-800

FORRESTER, Patricia Tobacco (20th C) American

Works on paper

£1589	$2750	€2320	Hand Hollow, Birches, Caterpillar Ridge (132x206cm-52x81in) s. W/C prov. 10-Dec-3 Bonhams & Butterfields, San Francisco #6133/R est:3000-5000

FORSBERG, Carl Johan (1868-1938) Swedish

Works on paper

£474	$758	€692	Mountain landscape, Italy (54x73cm-21x29in) s.i. W/C. 22-Sep-3 Rasmussen, Vejle #370/R (D.KR 5000)

FORSBERG, Jim (1919-) American

£491	$800	€717	No.23 floral impulse (76x56cm-30x22in) s. board. 19-Jul-3 Outer Cape Auctions, Provincetown #89

Works on paper

£307	$500	€448	Untitled (102x76cm-40x30in) s. collage. 19-Jul-3 Outer Cape Auctions, Provincetown #73

FORSBERG, Nils (elder) (1842-1934) Swedish

£240	$400	€350	Self portrait (46x36cm-18x14in) s.d.1923 panel. 7-Oct-3 Sotheby's, New York #120

FORSETH, Einar (1892-1988) Swedish

£730	$1189	€1066	Winter evening, Blaahammaren Sylarna (46x55cm-18x22in) s. verso panel. 29-Sep-3 Lilla Bukowskis, Stockholm #199 (S.KR 9500)

FORSLUND, Leonard (1959-) Swedish

Works on paper

£952	$1686	€1390	16 April 1974 (130x70cm-51x28in) s.d.1988 mixed media collage canvas exhib. 27-Apr-4 AB Stockholms Auktionsverk #957/R (S.KR 13000)

FORSSELL, Victor (1846-1931) Swedish

£923 $1588 €1348 Still life of fruit and bottle (35x34cm-14x13in) s.d.1897 panel. 3-Dec-3 AB Stockholms Auktionsverk #2271/R (S.KR 12000)
£2692 $4631 €3930 From the outskirts of Stockholm, Fjallgatan with man, horse and cart (20x27cm-8x11in) s. panel exhib. 2-Dec-3 Bukowskis, Stockholm #117/R est:25000-30000 (S.KR 35000)
£2846 $4895 €4155 Horse and carriage at Sodermalm, Stockholm (26x32cm-10x13in) s. panel. 3-Dec-3 AB Stockholms Auktionsverk #2280/R est:35000-40000 (S.KR 37000)

FORSSLUND, Jonas (1754-1809) Swedish

£846 $1455 €1235 Portrait of merchant Bolin's wife (74x59cm-29x23in) s.d.1804. 3-Dec-3 AB Stockholms Auktionsverk #2331/R (S.KR 11000)
£1846 $3175 €2695 Portrait of Baroness Catharina Margareta Cederhielm (135x110cm-53x43in) prov.lit. 3-Dec-3 AB Stockholms Auktionsverk #2458/R est:30000-40000 (S.KR 24000)

FORSTEN, Lennart (1817-1886) Finnish

£634 $1096 €900 Lake landscape (26x39cm-10x15in) s.d.1879. 13-Dec-3 Hagelstam, Helsinki #99/R
£2550 $4693 €3800 Stormy weather over Haminanlaks (70x96cm-28x38in) s.d.1875. 25-Mar-4 Hagelstam, Helsinki #978/R est:3000

FORSTER, C (?) ?

£1399 $2378 €2000 Jeune Orientale assise (66x55cm-26x22in) s. 27-Nov-3 Millon & Associes, Paris #145/R est:500-600

FORSTER, George (1817-1896) American

£14525 $26000 €21207 Still life with bird's nest, figs, peaches and grapes (43x53cm-17x21in) s. prov. 6-May-4 Shannon's, Milford #69/R est:25000-35000
£23256 $40000 €33954 Still life of fruit, nest of eggs and insects (44x37cm-17x15in) s.d.1862. 4-Dec-3 Christie's, Rockefeller NY #6/R

FORSTER, H (20th C) ?

Miniatures
£1840 $3000 €2686 Ladies on an exotic terrace (18x13cm-7x5in) s. velvet gilt metal frame easel backing rectangular. 19-Jul-3 Skinner, Boston #435 est:1500-2000

FORSTER, John Wycliffe Lowes (1850-1938) Canadian

£600 $1098 €876 Picking flowers (22x36cm-9x14in) canvas on board prov. 1-Jun-4 Joyner Waddington, Toronto #293/R (C.D 1500)

FORSTER, Thomas (18th C) British

Miniatures
£2800 $5040 €4088 Portrait of a bewiggered gentleman, reputed to be Richard Steele (10x8cm-4x3in) s.d.1700 oval. 21-Apr-4 Tennants, Leyburn #518/R est:800-1200

FORSYTH, Constance (1903-1987) American

Works on paper
£299 $500 €437 Mining town, Colorado (33x23cm-13x9in) W/C. 18-Oct-3 David Dike, Dallas #262/R
£719 $1200 €1050 West Texas, mesas and clouds (36x46cm-14x18in) W/C exec.c.1950. 18-Oct-3 David Dike, Dallas #331/R

FORSYTH, William (1854-1935) American

£887 $1650 €1295 WPA covered bridge (74x89cm-29x35in) s.d.1935 board. 6-Mar-4 Dan Ripley, Indianapolis #239
£3023 $5200 €4414 The Big Rock, Forsyth's front yard in Irvington, Indiana (46x56cm-18x22in) s. board. 6-Dec-3 Neal Auction Company, New Orleans #620/R est:4000-6000
£4070 $7000 €5942 Sunlight in the woods (46x61cm-18x24in) s. painted c.1900-1905 prov. 7-Dec-3 Freeman, Philadelphia #129 est:7000-10000
£4972 $9000 €7259 Evening light (36x51cm-14x20in) s.i.verso. 3-Apr-4 Neal Auction Company, New Orleans #428/R est:12000-18000
Works on paper
£232 $425 €339 Tree lined path (23x30cm-9x12in) s.i. charcoal executed 1890. 5-Jun-4 Treadway Gallery, Cincinnati #633/R
£1038 $1900 €1515 Rowboats at lake Winona Indina (41x53cm-16x21in) s.d.30 W/C. 5-Jun-4 Neal Auction Company, New Orleans #422/R est:2500-3500
£1374 $2500 €2006 Across the Whitewater River, Bookville, Indiana (33x51cm-13x20in) s. W/C pencil exec c.1899-1900 prov. 7-Feb-4 Neal Auction Company, New Orleans #451/R est:2500-4000

FORSYTHE, Victor Clyde (1885-1962) American

£313 $500 €457 Desert landscape with cactus (76x102cm-30x40in) i.verso board. 18-May-3 Auctions by the Bay, Alameda #1133/R
£604 $1100 €882 Landscape (30x41cm-12x16in) canvasboard. 15-Jun-4 John Moran, Pasadena #61a
£934 $1700 €1364 Landscape (61x76cm-24x30in) s. i. stretcher prov. 15-Jun-4 John Moran, Pasadena #79 est:2500-3500
£1786 $3250 €2608 Panoramic landscape (61x86cm-24x34in) s.d.1949 masonite. 15-Jun-4 John Moran, Pasadena #61 est:5000-7000

FORT, Jean Antoine Simeon (1793-1861) French

£1056 $1849 €1500 Paysage mediterraneen au soleil couchant (23x34cm-9x13in) s. 17-Dec-3 Piasa, Paris #99 est:1200-1500

FORT, Jean Antoine Simeon (attrib) (1793-1861) French

£371 $676 €542 Two horses in front of a stable (49x65cm-19x26in) s. 16-Jun-4 Fischer, Luzern #2109/R (S.FR 850)

FORT, Theodore (19th C) French

£559 $1029 €850 Chasse acourre (19x24cm-7x9in) s. 25-Jun-4 Millon & Associes, Paris #48
£1399 $2406 €2000 Chez le marechal-ferrant (35x65cm-14x26in) s. 7-Dec-3 Osenat, Fontainebleau #92 est:2500-2800

FORTE, Vicente (1912-1980) Argentinian

£2099 $3800 €3065 Composition (45x70cm-18x28in) 30-Mar-4 Arroyo, Buenos Aires #107
£2514 $4500 €3670 Composition with jug and fruit bowl (60x80cm-24x31in) s.i.d.51. 4-May-4 Arroyo, Buenos Aires #56/R est:3500
£2514 $4500 €3670 Composition (70x50cm-28x20in) s.d.58. 4-May-4 Arroyo, Buenos Aires #67/R est:2600
£2793 $5000 €4078 Composition with figures (70x100cm-28x39in) s.d.63 board. 4-May-4 Arroyo, Buenos Aires #18/R est:5000
£3388 $6200 €4946 Old instrument (65x95cm-26x37in) 1-Jun-4 Arroyo, Buenos Aires #17
£4144 $7500 €6050 Lamp with grapes (70x100cm-28x39in) 30-Mar-4 Arroyo, Buenos Aires #91
£4918 $9000 €7180 Bird and fruit (60x120cm-24x47in) 1-Jun-4 Arroyo, Buenos Aires #47

FORTESCUE, William B (1850-1924) British

£750 $1395 €1095 Extensive river landscape (37x61cm-15x24in) s. 4-Mar-4 Christie's, Kensington #470/R
£1500 $2790 €2190 Noonday shade (43x35cm-17x14in) indis.sig. exhib. 4-Mar-4 Christie's, Kensington #471/R est:1500-2000
£1646 $2700 €2387 Woman holding a book, and standing beside a lily in a garden (61x46cm-24x18in) s.d.1886. 31-May-3 Brunk, Ashville #580/R est:2000-4000
£4000 $7440 €5840 Fisherman's dwelling (46x36cm-18x14in) s. exhib. 4-Mar-4 Christie's, Kensington #469/R est:4000-6000
£9400 $15604 €13724 Mending nets, young woman in a Newlyn cottage doorway (29x21cm-11x8in) s. 2-Oct-3 Lane, Penzance #50/R est:8000-12000
Works on paper
£460 $764 €672 Boats at anchor in a west country harbour (22x27cm-9x11in) s. W/C. 2-Oct-3 Lane, Penzance #57

FORTESS, Karl Eugene (1907-1995) American

£250 $425 €365 Untitled, abstract (41x51cm-16x20in) s. paper. 9-Nov-3 Outer Cape Auctions, Provincetown #65/R
£599 $1000 €875 Modernist beach scene with markers and buoys (102x51cm-40x20in) s. exhib. 19-Oct-3 Jeffery Burchard, Florida #58

FORTEZA FORTEZA, Miguel (1881-?) Spanish

£352 $616 €500 Seascape (38x45cm-15x18in) s. 16-Dec-3 Durán, Madrid #646/R
£592 $1072 €900 Majorca coast (38x46cm-15x18in) s. 14-Apr-4 Ansorena, Madrid #27/R

FORTEZA, Nicolas (1918-) Spanish

£345 $621 €500 Seascape (25x30cm-10x12in) s. board. 26-Jan-4 Durán, Madrid #79/R
£345 $621 €500 Seascape (25x30cm-10x12in) s. board. 26-Jan-4 Durán, Madrid #80/R
£379 $683 €550 Laguila (18x24cm-7x9in) s. board. 26-Jan-4 Ansorena, Madrid #142/R

FORTI, Ettore (19th C) Italian

£23529 $40000 €34352 Carpet seller (60x74cm-24x29in) indis.s.i. st.sig. 29-Oct-3 Christie's, Rockefeller NY #212/R est:40000-60000
£26471 $45000 €38648 At the fruit sellers (49x77cm-19x30in) s.i. 29-Oct-3 Christie's, Rockefeller NY #210/R est:50000-70000
£26471 $45000 €38648 Afternoon at the jewelry shop (53x83cm-21x33in) s.i. 29-Oct-3 Christie's, Rockefeller NY #211/R est:50000-70000
£41667 $75000 €60834 Art lesson (49x77cm-19x30in) s.i. 23-Apr-4 Sotheby's, New York #88/R est:30000-40000

FORTI, Fermo (1839-1911) Italian

£3467 $6309 €5200 Playing with water (23x45cm-9x18in) s. 29-Jun-4 Pandolfini, Florence #39/R est:6000-8000
£5333 $9707 €8000 Joking model (36x52cm-14x20in) s. 29-Jun-4 Pandolfini, Florence #40/R est:9000-10000
£6400 $11648 €9600 Polenta (35x47cm-14x19in) s. 29-Jun-4 Pandolfini, Florence #41/R est:10000-12000
£8000 $14560 €12000 Back from Africa (62x86cm-24x34in) s. 29-Jun-4 Pandolfini, Florence #43/R est:12000-14000
£8333 $15167 €12500 Tantrums (57x81cm-22x32in) s.d.1892. 29-Jun-4 Pandolfini, Florence #42/R est:11000-13000
£11000 $20020 €16500 Message (50x76cm-20x30in) s. 29-Jun-4 Pandolfini, Florence #44/R est:12000-14000
£11000 $20020 €16500 Nosy (64x50cm-25x20in) s. 29-Jun-4 Pandolfini, Florence #45/R est:13000-15000
Sculpture
£1533 $2791 €2300 Saint Francis (49cm-19in) s. terracotta. 29-Jun-4 Pandolfini, Florence #192/R est:1200-1400

FORTIN, Marc-Aurele (1888-1970) Canadian

£880 $1610 €1285 Figure on a beach (16x14cm-6x6in) s.i. board prov. 1-Jun-4 Joyner Waddington, Toronto #414 est:1200-1500 (C.D 2200)
£1591 $2593 €2323 Stone bridge (30x35cm-12x14in) bears sig. 23-Sep-3 Ritchie, Toronto #80/R est:2000-3000 (C.D 3500)
£3200 $5856 €4672 Boats beneath a yellow sky (17x25cm-7x10in) board. 1-Jun-4 Joyner Waddington, Toronto #198/R est:4000-5000 (C.D 8000)
£3659 $6549 €5342 Village houses with figure (25x30cm-10x12in) s. panel prov.lit. 27-May-4 Heffel, Vancouver #56/R est:8000-10000 (C.D 9000)
£5691 $10187 €8309 Hochelaga, Vue Du Mont Royal (25x36cm-10x14in) s. card painted c.1927 prov. 31-May-4 Sotheby's, Toronto #122/R est:10000-15000 (C.D 14000)
£6306 $10721 €9207 Hochelaga (22x27cm-9x11in) s. canvas on board prov. 27-Nov-3 Heffel, Vancouver #106/R est:12000-16000 (C.D 14000)

£13600 $24888 €19856 Vieille maison (40x42cm-16x17in) s. painted c.1925 prov. 1-Jun-4 Joyner Waddington, Toronto #103/R est:25000-30000 (C.D 34000)
£15244 $27287 €22256 Wolf Street, Montreal (33x55cm-13x22in) board painted c.1918-1920 prov.lit. 27-May-4 Heffel, Vancouver #57/R est:25000-30000 (C.D 37500)
£18750 $34313 €27375 Maison en automne (57x71cm-22x28in) s. panel. 27-Jan-4 Iegor de Saint Hippolyte, Montreal #14 (C.D 45000)
£38000 $69540 €55480 Village road, Ste, Rose (59x61cm-23x24in) s. board painted. c.1930 prov. 1-Jun-4 Joyner Waddington, Toronto #89/R est:40000-60000 (C.D 95000)
£52000 $95160 €75920 Hiver Laurentien (85x70cm-33x28in) s. painted c.1925 prov.lit. 1-Jun-4 Joyner Waddington, Toronto #75/R est:80000-120000 (C.D 130000)
£54000 $98820 €78840 Vue de Montreal, the St Lawrence in winter (76x91cm-30x36in) s. painted c.1915 prov.exhib.lit. 1-Jun-4 Joyner Waddington, Toronto #65/R est:80000-120000 (C.D 135000)

Works on paper
£3120 $5710 €4555 En Gaspesie (50x37cm-20x15in) s. W/C col crayons exec c.1942. 1-Jun-4 Joyner Waddington, Toronto #144/R est:8000-10000 (C.D 7800)

FORTIN, P (?) ?
£1267 $2293 €1900 Pecheurs relevant leur filet (60x89cm-24x35in) s. 2-Apr-4 Rossini, Paris #58/R est:1000-1200

FORTIS CAMUSSI, Maria (1880-?) Italian
£952 $1705 €1400 Susa Valley (31x44cm-12x17in) s.i.d.1902 board. 22-Mar-4 Sant Agostino, Torino #41/R

FORTT, Frederick (19th C) British
£420 $794 €613 Temple of the Sybil of Vesta, Tivoli, Rome (61x46cm-24x18in) s.d.1893 i.on stretcher. 19-Feb-4 Christie's, Kensington #165/R

FORTUNATO, Franco (1946-) Italian
£500 $920 €750 Cardboard king (60x50cm-24x20in) s. s.i.d.1986 verso. 12-Jun-4 Meeting Art, Vercelli #177/R
£500 $920 €750 Island (30x30cm-12x12in) s. s.i.verso. 12-Jun-4 Meeting Art, Vercelli #912/R
£527 $969 €790 Re-discovered city (30x30cm-12x12in) s. 12-Jun-4 Meeting Art, Vercelli #168/R
£599 $994 €850 Casa della notte (50x60cm-20x24in) s. i.verso. 14-Jun-3 Meeting Art, Vercelli #717/R
£738 $1321 €1100 Island (50x60cm-20x24in) s. s.i.verso. 30-May-4 Meeting Art, Vercelli #64
£900 $1656 €1350 Wanderer (50x60cm-20x24in) s. s.i.verso. 12-Jun-4 Meeting Art, Vercelli #619/R

FORTUNE, Euphemia Charlton (1885-1969) American
£30347 $52500 €44307 Church interior (41x30cm-16x12in) i.d.1925 verso canvasboard. 10-Dec-3 Bonhams & Butterfields, San Francisco #6238/R est:40000-60000

FORTUNEY (1878-1950) French
Works on paper
£461 $847 €700 L'extase (49x31cm-19x12in) s.d.1923 pastel. 28-Jun-4 Joron-Derem, Paris #135/R

FORTUNEY, Louis (1878-1950) French
Works on paper
£323 $594 €472 Sunday on the Seine (52x34cm-20x13in) s. pastel. 14-Jun-4 Waddingtons, Toronto #261/R (C.D 800)
£592 $1089 €900 Actrice (50x32cm-20x13in) s. pastel. 25-Jun-4 Millon & Associes, Paris #134

FORTUNY Y CARBO, Mariano (1838-1874) Spanish
£680 $1217 €1000 Venise, Coin de Rue (17x13cm-7x5in) artist st.verso board. 17-Mar-4 Tajan, Paris #112
£1079 $1770 €1500 Ladies and gentlemen (19x30cm-7x12in) s.i.verso. 10-Jun-3 Pandolfini, Florence #138/R est:2000-2500
£2381 $4262 €3500 Immeuble detruit a Venise pendant la premiere Guerre Mondiale (62x32cm-24x13in) paper on wood. 17-Mar-4 Tajan, Paris #114/R est:3000-4000
£4333 $7887 €6500 Portrait of a monk in prayer (16x13cm-6x5in) st.sig. 1-Jul-4 Van Ham, Cologne #1342/R est:2500
£9155 $14648 €13000 Balcony (18x11cm-7x4in) i.verso board lit. 16-Sep-3 Segre, Madrid #38/R est:2700
£27632 $50842 €42000 Passer-by along a wall in a Roman park (13x19cm-5x7in) panel. 24-Jun-4 Christie's, Paris #144/R est:1000-1200

Works on paper
£396 $649 €550 Man in profile (9x5cm-4x2in) i. Chinese ink. 10-Jun-3 Pandolfini, Florence #137
£458 $801 €650 Oxen (24x15cm-9x6in) pencil dr. 16-Dec-3 Durán, Madrid #49
£563 $986 €800 Shepherd and oxen (24x15cm-9x6in) pencil dr. 16-Dec-3 Durán, Madrid #50/R
£13793 $24690 €20138 At the butchers (24x17cm-9x7in) s.d.74 W/C bodycol. 12-May-4 Dobiaschofsky, Bern #502/R est:9000 (S.FR 32000)

FORTUNY Y CARBO, Mariano (attrib) (1838-1874) Spanish
£4000 $7240 €6000 Moroccan traders (20x42cm-8x17in) s.d.1867 panel. 3-Apr-4 Hans Stahl, Hamburg #25/R est:5000

FORTUNY Y MADRAZO, Mariano (1871-1949) Spanish
£1361 $2435 €2000 Watching a work of art (30x20cm-12x8in) s. board. 22-Mar-4 Durán, Madrid #130/R est:1500
£1531 $2740 €2250 Mosquetaire (30x20cm-12x8in) s. board. 22-Mar-4 Durán, Madrid #129/R
£4577 $7599 €6500 Portrait of teenage boy (46x37cm-18x15in) s. 11-Jun-3 Christie's, Rome #183/R est:2000-3000
£8276 $13821 €12000 Village (30x55cm-12x22in) s. 14-Nov-3 Farsetti, Prato #546/R est:12000-15000

FORTUNY Y MADRAZO, Mariano (attrib) (1871-1949) Spanish
£596 $1085 €900 Street (62x49cm-24x19in) i. board. 17-Jun-4 Finarte Semenzato, Milan #349/R

FORTUNY, Francisco (20th C) Argentinian
Works on paper
£2346 $4200 €3425 Cowboy on horseback (24x17cm-9x7in) s. W/C. 4-May-4 Arroyo, Buenos Aires #92/R est:3800

FORTUYN O'BRIEN, Irene (1959-) ?
Sculpture
£1000 $1840 €1500 Eden - From the series House and Garden (78x65x36cm-31x26x14in) textile foamrubber metal frame exec c.1996 prov. 8-Jun-4 Sotheby's, Amsterdam #295/R est:2000-3000

FORUP, Carl Christian (1883-1939) Danish
£330 $600 €482 Small girl seated on chair by window (37x35cm-15x14in) s. 7-Feb-4 Rasmussen, Havnen #2294 (D.KR 3600)
£469 $764 €685 Small girl with apple (57x47cm-22x19in) s,. 27-Sep-3 Rasmussen, Havnen #2298 (D.KR 5000)
£513 $805 €749 Autumn scene with women (85x94cm-33x37in) s.d.19. 30-Aug-3 Rasmussen, Havnen #2144/R (D.KR 5500)

FOSBURGH, James (1910-1978) American
£500 $850 €730 Snowy owl (81x66cm-32x26in) init.d.1967 prov. 18-Nov-3 Doyle, New York #21

FOSCHI, Francesco (?-1780) Italian
£3667 $6563 €5500 Winter landscape with figures (34x45cm-13x18in) init. 12-May-4 Finarte Semenzato, Milan #82/R est:2000-3000
£11184 $20579 €17000 Winter landscape (43x60cm-17x24in) lit. 25-Jun-4 Piasa, Paris #40/R est:8000-12000
£24000 $41520 €35040 Mountainous winter landscape with peasants by a farmhouses (125x179cm-49x70in) prov. 10-Dec-3 Christie's, London #89/R est:12000-16000
£26000 $47580 €37960 Winter landscape (33x47cm-13x19in) s.i.d.1779 prov.lit. 8-Jul-4 Sotheby's, London #338/R est:14000-18000

FOSCHI, Francesco (attrib) (?-1780) Italian
£1982 $3370 €2894 Winter landscape (46x60cm-18x24in) 5-Nov-3 Dobiaschofsky, Bern #545/R est:5000 (S.FR 4500)
£10440 $18061 €15242 Waterside landscape in winter (34x48cm-13x19in) painted c.1760. 12-Dec-3 Kieselbach, Budapest #219/R (H.F 4000000)

FOSHKO, Josef (1891-1969) American
£299 $550 €437 Park scene, autumn (43x53cm-17x21in) s. canvas on masonite prov. 25-Jun-4 Freeman, Philadelphia #198/R

FOSNES, Sigurd (1877-1943) Norwegian
£278 $481 €406 Seascape with boats (44x60cm-17x24in) s. 13-Dec-3 Blomqvist, Lysaker #1095/R (N.KR 3200)
£313 $542 €457 Tjoeme (63x88cm-25x35in) s. 13-Dec-3 Blomqvist, Lysaker #1092 (N.KR 3600)
£365 $632 €533 Wooded landscape with children picking berries (74x91cm-29x36in) s. 13-Dec-3 Blomqvist, Lysaker #1096 (N.KR 4200)

FOSS, Harald (1843-1922) Danish
£325 $527 €471 Hilly landscape with girl watching sheep (44x74cm-17x29in) s. 4-Aug-3 Rasmussen, Vejle #262 (D.KR 3400)
£397 $711 €580 Landscape from Silkeborg (40x70cm-16x28in) s.d.1876. 12-Jan-4 Rasmussen, Vejle #68/R (D.KR 4200)
£677 $1266 €988 Mountain landscape, Northern Italy (34x60cm-13x24in) 25-Feb-4 Museumsbygningen, Copenhagen #144/R (D.KR 7500)
£1398 $2586 €2041 Coastal landscape from Mariager Fjord (58x89cm-23x35in) s.d.1868 exhib.prov. 15-Mar-4 Rasmussen, Vejle #17/R est:8000 (D.KR 15500)
£2435 $4504 €3555 Landscape from Buderupholmen (71x95cm-28x37in) s.d.april 1866 exhib.prov. 15-Mar-4 Rasmussen, Vejle #16/R est:15000 (D.KR 27000)

FOSS, Olivier (1920-) French/American
£275 $460 €399 Paris - Place du Tertre (38x55cm-15x22in) s. 23-Jun-3 Philippe Schuler, Zurich #8590 (S.FR 600)
£317 $510 €450 Montmartre (50x61cm-20x24in) s. 11-May-3 Versailles Encheres #113
£556 $1000 €812 Boatyard (58x74cm-23x29in) s. prov. 23-Jan-4 Freeman, Philadelphia #244/R

FOSSATI, Andrea (1844-?) Italian
£1467 $2640 €2200 Hero (98x56cm-39x22in) s. 24-Apr-4 Quittenbaum, Munich #706/R est:1200

FOSSATI, C (?) Italian?
£732 $1200 €1069 Rival suitors (56x69cm-22x27in) s. 4-Jun-3 Alderfer's, Hatfield #240

FOSSATI, Domenico (1743-1784) Italian
£32967 $60000 €48132 Stage set, figures in the courtyard of a fantastical Roman palace, with a fountain of Neptune (223x322cm-88x127in) s.o.d.MDCCLXXIII tempera prov. 17-Jun-4 Christie's, Rockefeller NY #28/R est:30000-40000

FOSSATI, E (?) Italian
£541 $968 €800 Italian village (20x31cm-8x12in) s. panel. 8-May-4 Bukowskis, Helsinki #387/R

FOSSATI, Emilio (20th C) Italian
£242 $450 €353 Portrait of elderly couple seated on bench (46x61cm-18x24in) s. 3-Mar-4 Alderfer's, Hatfield #315/R

FOSSI, Paolo (?) Italian
£7905 $14150 €11541 Portrait of Lord Frederic Leighton (77x64cm-30x25in) after Leighton prov. 15-May-4 Christie's, Sydney #54/R est:20000-30000 (A.D 20000)

FOSSOMBRONE, Andrea (1887-1963) Italian
Works on paper
£272 $487 €400 Knitting (24x19cm-9x7in) s.i. pastel. 22-Mar-4 Sant Agostino, Torino #141/R

FOSSOUX, Claude (1946-) French
£461 $847 €700 Cafe des Deux Magots a Paris (50x61cm-20x24in) s. 25-Jun-4 Daguerre, Paris #166
£1812 $3244 €2700 Jeune fille dans le champs fleuri (41x33cm-16x13in) s. 30-May-4 Eric Pillon, Calais #147/R

FOSTER, Agnes E (20th C) American
Works on paper
£193 $350 €282 Forested landscape (25x36cm-10x14in) W/C. 16-Apr-4 James Julia, Fairfield #852a/R

FOSTER, Arthur J (fl.1880-1904) British
£1100 $1980 €1606 Hazelbury, Somerset (41x51cm-16x20in) mono.d.1910 i.verso. 21-Jan-4 Sotheby's, Olympia #372/R est:800-1200
£3000 $5520 €4380 In the cornfields, Hazelbury, Somerset (38x48cm-15x19in) mono.d.1910 prov. 23-Jun-4 Cheffins, Cambridge #510/R est:3000-4000

FOSTER, B (?) ?
Works on paper
£460 $782 €672 Catching minnows (10x13cm-4x5in) bears sig W/C. 5-Nov-3 Brightwells, Leominster #999/R

FOSTER, Ben (1852-1926) American
£196 $350 €286 Early morning Mt Desert Island, Maine (107x150cm-42x59in) s. 8-Jan-4 James Julia, Fairfield #986/R
£530 $900 €774 Landscape (20x25cm-8x10in) bears sig i.verso panel prov. 21-Nov-3 Skinner, Boston #467/R est:700-900
£1040 $1800 €1518 Autumn landscape at sunset (28x22cm-11x9in) s. canvas on masonite. 13-Dec-3 Weschler, Washington #553 est:800-1200
£1553 $2500 €2267 Nighttime over New England (91x107cm-36x42in) s. 20-Aug-3 James Julia, Fairfield #1394/R est:3000-5000
£1582 $2500 €2310 Rural scene (36x46cm-14x18in) s. 7-Sep-3 Treadway Gallery, Cincinnati #635/R est:1000-1500
£2581 $4750 €3768 On the riverbank (76x91cm-30x36in) s. 27-Jun-4 Freeman, Philadelphia #105/R est:4000-6000
£3088 $5250 €4508 Landscape sunset with shallow river bed, trees and distant houses (64x76cm-25x30in) s. 8-Nov-3 Van Blarcom, South Natick #151/R est:1500-2500
£3409 $6000 €4977 Big spring (61x58cm-24x23in) s. prov. 3-Jan-4 Collins, Maine #31/R est:3000-5000
£4198 $6800 €6087 Coast of Maine (61x61cm-24x24in) s. prov. 8-Aug-3 Barridorf, Portland #353/R est:6000-9000

FOSTER, Bernard (?) ?
Works on paper
£480 $802 €701 The weald of Surrey (25x38cm-10x15in) s. W/C sold with another. 23-Oct-3 Honiton Galleries, Honiton #482/R

FOSTER, Deryck (1924-) British
£350 $627 €511 Yachts under spinnakers in the tidal gate off Hurst Castle (42x57cm-17x22in) s.d.71 board. 26-May-4 Christie's, Kensington #521/R
£650 $1105 €949 Gybing downwind (61x76cm-24x30in) s.d.50 board prov. 19-Nov-3 Christie's, Kensington #416/R

FOSTER, Gilbert (?) British
Works on paper
£350 $627 €511 Haymaking (26x37cm-10x15in) s. W/C. 26-May-4 Sotheby's, Olympia #89/R
£460 $846 €672 Village street with woman leaning over a cottage fence (25x35cm-10x14in) s. W/C. 10-Jun-4 Morphets, Harrogate #532/R
£460 $846 €672 Youth seated by a meandering stream, with grazing cattle (25x35cm-10x14in) s. W/C. 10-Jun-4 Morphets, Harrogate #533/R

FOSTER, Hal (1892-1982) American
Works on paper
£428 $800 €625 Prince Valiant on horseback returns to waiting maiden (28x20cm-11x8in) i. pen ink red ballpoint pen. 26-Feb-4 Illustration House, New York #72

FOSTER, Herbert Wilson (fl.1881-1917) British
Works on paper
£250 $448 €365 House at Welford-on-Avon, Warwickshire, with mother and children (19x28cm-7x11in) s.d.1914 verso W/C. 18-Mar-4 Neales, Nottingham #713
£500 $810 €725 Yeoman of the soil (36x25cm-14x10in) s.d.89 W/C. 30-Jul-3 Hamptons Fine Art, Godalming #44

FOSTER, John B (19/20th C) American
Works on paper
£279 $500 €469 Coastal scene (25x33cm-10x13in) s. W/C. 20-Mar-4 Pook & Pook, Downington #373/R
£529 $1000 €772 Seaside scene (23x33cm-9x13in) s. W/C exhib. 22-Feb-4 Skinner, Boston #373/R

FOSTER, Myles Birket (1825-1899) British
Works on paper
£300 $501 €438 Lion Inn (13x10cm-5x4in) bears mono. W/C. 17-Oct-3 Keys, Aylsham #481
£340 $541 €496 Hunt followers, busy summer scene (8x27cm-3x11in) mono. W/C. 9-Sep-3 Bamfords, Derby #1049
£450 $734 €657 Walking along a country lane, a parish church beyond (20x42cm-8x17in) mono. W/C. 24-Sep-3 Dreweatt Neate, Newbury #11
£480 $802 €701 By the meadow stream (20x28cm-8x11in) bears mono. W/C. 17-Oct-3 Keys, Aylsham #493
£540 $967 €788 Lion Inn, with figures and horses outside (13x10cm-5x4in) mono. W/C. 5-May-4 Goldings, Lincolnshire #499
£600 $1086 €876 The cliffs at Bonchurch (43x53cm-17x21in) mono. W/C. 15-Apr-4 Rendalls, Ashburton #1613
£600 $1092 €876 A shepherd with his flock beside a woodland pond (16x16cm-6x6in) mono. pencil W/C htd white. 1-Jul-4 Christie's, Kensington #244/R
£670 $1119 €978 Family by thatched cottage. Shrimpers on a beach (18x23cm-7x9in) bear mono. W/C pair. 17-Oct-3 Keys, Aylsham #492
£700 $1253 €1022 Mumbles Head, fisherman and girl on a cliff top path (15x36cm-6x14in) mono. W/C. 5-May-4 Goldings, Lincolnshire #498
£764 $1420 €1115 Young girl with parasol strolling in summer (32x18cm-13x7in) mono. W/C. 2-Mar-4 Rasmussen, Copenhagen #1687/R (D.KR 8500)
£1087 $2000 €1587 Figures by a thatched cottage (12x18cm-5x7in) mono. W/C. 27-Jun-4 Freeman, Philadelphia #55/R est:2000-3000
£1166 $1900 €1702 Store at Pevensey (16x23cm-6x9in) mono. W/C. 17-Jul-3 Naón & Cia, Buenos Aires #11/R
£1300 $2210 €1898 Estuary, Chichester (7x11cm-3x4in) W/C prov. 4-Nov-3 Bonhams, New Bond Street #126/R est:1500-2000
£1700 $2941 €2482 Scene in the highlands with a shepherd and flock passing two girls resting (23x38cm-9x15in) st.sig. W/C. 9-Dec-3 Anderson & Garland, Newcastle #329/R est:2500-3500
£1800 $3006 €2628 Cattle watering (13x20cm-5x8in) mono. W/C htd bodycol. 16-Oct-3 Lawrence, Crewkerne #643/R
£1900 $3230 €2774 St. Andrews Abbey (14x10cm-6x4in) mono. W/C htd bodycol prov. 27-Nov-3 Sotheby's, London #350/R est:1200-1800
£1900 $3515 €2774 Fishing village (13x9cm-5x4in) W/C prov. 9-Mar-4 Bonhams, New Bond Street #93/R est:2000-3000
£2300 $3956 €3358 Happy days (15x10cm-6x4in) s. W/C. 5-Dec-3 Chrystals Auctions, Isle of Man #263 est:300-500
£2300 $4301 €3358 Autumn leaves (23x19cm-9x7in) mono.i. W/C bodycol. 20-Jul-4 Sworder & Son, Bishops Stortford #732/R est:600-800
£2400 $4440 €3504 Quay at dusk (7x11cm-3x4in) mono. W/C. 9-Mar-4 Bonhams, New Bond Street #98/R est:2000-3000
£2500 $4150 €3650 Lemon gatherers, Lake Garda, Italy (16x12cm-6x5in) mono. W/C oval. 1-Oct-3 Sotheby's, Olympia #89/R est:2000-3000
£2700 $4968 €3942 Dover Castle with fishermen in the foreground paying out a net (11x13cm-4x5in) mono. W/C. 23-Mar-4 Anderson & Garland, Newcastle #308/R est:2000-3000
£2800 $5152 €4088 Herding the flock, Sussex (7x18cm-3x7in) mono. W/C. 8-Jun-4 Bonhams, New Bond Street #89/R est:2000-3000
£3000 $5010 €4380 Figures outside a house, France (14x9cm-6x4in) mono. pencil W/C. 16-Oct-3 Christie's, Kensington #95/R est:2000-3000
£3000 $5100 €4380 Fisherman's Island, Lake Maggiore (12x18cm-5x7in) mono. W/C bodycol prov. 27-Nov-3 Sotheby's, London #349/R est:2500-4500
£3000 $5520 €4380 Gibraltar (23x34cm-9x13in) bears studio st. W/C prov. 8-Jun-4 Bonhams, New Bond Street #88/R est:3000-5000
£3200 $5824 €4672 Lyme Regis (10x14cm-4x6in) mono. pencil W/C bodycol vignette. 1-Jul-4 Christie's, Kensington #255/R est:2000-3000
£3400 $6256 €4964 Cologne (11x16cm-4x6in) mono. W/C vignette. 24-Mar-4 Hamptons Fine Art, Godalming #236
£4000 $7280 €5840 Lyme Regis from the Cobb (10x14cm-4x6in) mono. pencil W/C vignette. 1-Jul-4 Christie's, Kensington #254/R est:2500-3500
£4200 $7770 €6132 Continental town (13x9cm-5x4in) mono. W/C prov. 9-Mar-4 Bonhams, New Bond Street #99/R est:1500-2000
£4200 $7644 €6132 Lancaster from the River Lune (10x14cm-4x6in) mono. pencil W/C bodycol. 1-Jul-4 Christie's, Kensington #257/R est:2500-3500
£4722 $8500 €6894 Cliffs near Shoreham (20x28cm-8x11in) mono.i. W/C gouache. 21-Jan-4 Sotheby's, New York #209/R est:8000-12000
£4942 $8500 €7215 In the garden (20x25cm-8x10in) mono. W/C prov. 7-Dec-3 Freeman, Philadelphia #43 est:5000-8000
£5000 $8500 €7300 Como (11x18cm-4x7in) mono. W/C bodycol prov. 27-Nov-3 Sotheby's, London #348/R est:4000-6000
£5000 $8500 €7300 King's College, Cambridge (10x14cm-4x6in) pencil W/C htd bodycol prov.lit. 20-Nov-3 Christie's, London #104/R est:6000-8000
£5200 $9620 €7592 Isola Pescatori, Lago Maggiore (15x22cm-6x9in) mono. W/C pencil. 9-Mar-4 Bonhams, New Bond Street #97/R est:3000-5000
£5500 $9185 €8030 Children with a donkey beside a duck pond (14x21cm-6x8in) mono. pencil W/C bodycol. 16-Oct-3 Christie's, Kensington #92/R est:1000-2000
£5500 $10010 €8030 Morecambe Sands (10x14cm-4x6in) mono. pencil W/C. 1-Jul-4 Christie's, Kensington #256/R est:2500-3500
£6000 $10920 €8760 The attention seekers (14x10cm-6x4in) mono. pencil W/C htd white prov. 1-Jul-4 Christie's, Kensington #250/R est:4000-6000
£6977 $12000 €10186 Children feeding ducks from a punt (15x20cm-6x8in) mono. W/C htd white prov. 7-Dec-3 Freeman, Philadelphia #44 est:4000-6000
£8000 $14800 €11680 Arbroath Abbey, Angus, Scotland (14x19cm-6x7in) mono. W/C. 9-Mar-4 Bonhams, New Bond Street #91/R est:7000-10000
£8000 $14560 €11680 Posy (17x13cm-7x5in) mono. W/C over bodycol. 1-Jul-4 Sotheby's, London #259/R est:7000-10000
£10000 $18400 €14600 Near Braemar (20x27cm-8x11in) mono. W/C. 23-Jun-4 Cheffins, Cambridge #451/R est:7000-10000
£10500 $17850 €15330 Pet kitten (13x18cm-5x7in) mono. W/C htd bodycol. 4-Nov-3 Bonhams, New Bond Street #124/R est:7000-10000
£10500 $17850 €15330 Thames at Abingdon (25x35cm-10x14in) mono. W/C. 4-Nov-3 Bonhams, New Bond Street #125/R est:10000-15000
£12500 $21250 €18250 Playful kitten (13x18cm-5x7in) mono. W/C htd bodycol. 4-Nov-3 Bonhams, New Bond Street #123/R est:8000-12000

£13000	$22360	€18980	Errant harvesters (14x18cm-6x7in) mono. pencil W/C bodycol. 3-Dec-3 Christie's, Kensington #60/R est:4000-6000
£13500	$24570	€19710	Tea time (20x27cm-8x11in) mono. W/C over traces pencil htd bodycol prov. 1-Jul-4 Sotheby's, London #258/R est:8000-12000
£17000	$28900	€24820	Cottage in Surrey (21x33cm-8x13in) mono. W/C bodycol. 4-Nov-3 Bonhams, New Bond Street #122/R est:12000-18000
£30612	$54796	€45000	Rhiems (78x67cm-31x26in) mono. W/C gouache prov.exhib.lit. 17-Mar-4 Maigret, Paris #13/R est:30000-40000

FOSTER, Walter and NOBLE, John Sargeant (19th C) British

£400	$720	€584	Hindhead, Surrey (29x44cm-11x17in) s. s.i.verso. 22-Apr-4 Mellors & Kirk, Nottingham #1060/R
£4000	$7360	€5840	Count out (41x66cm-16x26in) s.i.verso. 10-Jun-4 Christie's, Kensington #398/R est:4000-6000
£5233	$9000	€7640	Edge of the wood (76x61cm-30x24in) s.i. 5-Dec-3 Christie's, Rockefeller NY #92/R est:10000-15000

FOSTER, Will (1882-1953) American

£329	$550	€480	At the train station. Study of a lady (18x51cm-7x20in) init.d.27 en grisaille board double-sided. 20-Jun-3 Freeman, Philadelphia #249/R
£598	$1100	€873	After dinner conversation (66x91cm-26x36in) s. 27-Mar-4 New Orleans Auction, New Orleans #768/R est:1200-1800
£1324	$2250	€1933	Seated nude (81x64cm-32x25in) init. 18-Nov-3 John Moran, Pasadena #107 est:2500-3500

FOSTER, William (1853-1924) British

Works on paper

£700	$1169	€1022	Harvest time (28x36cm-11x14in) s. W/C. 14-Oct-3 Bonhams, Knightsbridge #176/R
£750	$1245	€1095	Hungry squirrels (28x23cm-11x9in) s.d.June 1875 W/C. 1-Oct-3 Sotheby's, Olympia #50/R
£1400	$2590	€2044	Orchard in springtime. Walk home through the woods (27x42cm-11x17in) s. W/C htd bodycol pair. 14-Jan-4 Lawrence, Crewkerne #1327/R est:1500-2000

FOSTER, William Gilbert (1855-1906) British

£300	$546	€438	Old Warwick (31x41cm-12x16in) 15-Jun-4 Rosebery Fine Art, London #584/R
£1450	$2683	€2117	Children in afield overlooking the sea (16x28cm-6x11in) s. 16-Feb-4 Bonhams, Bath #63 est:100-200
£1700	$2703	€2465	Lady Palmer's cottage Runswick Bay, children playing (22x45cm-9x18in) s. 9-Sep-3 David Duggleby, Scarborough #269/R est:500-800

Works on paper

£5100	$9231	€7446	Be the day weary, or be the day long, at last it ryngeth to evensong (54x89cm-21x35in) s.d.06 W/C exhib. 30-Mar-4 David Duggleby, Scarborough #160/R est:5000-7000

FOSTER, William Harden (1886-1941) American

£1258	$2000	€1837	Fishing (66x51cm-26x20in) s.d.1924. 12-Sep-3 Skinner, Boston #506a/R

FOTH, Joan B (1930-) American

Works on paper

£223	$400	€326	Spring storm over Chimayo Mountains. s. W/C. 13-May-4 Dallas Auction Gallery, Dallas #95/R
£429	$700	€626	Road to Los Alamos II (71x203cm-28x80in) s. W/C. 19-Jul-3 Susanin's, Chicago #5015

FOTHERGILL, Thomas (?) British

£1800	$3186	€2628	Family portrait of mother with young child, seated, holding flowers (142x112cm-56x44in) prov. 27-Apr-4 Henry Adams, Chichester #666/R est:2000-3000

FOTINSKY, Serge (1897-1971) Russian

£596	$1085	€900	Allee dans le parc (55x46cm-22x18in) s. 16-Jun-4 Claude Boisgirard, Paris #59
£1192	$2170	€1800	Bateaux de peche (38x45cm-15x18in) s. cardboard. 16-Jun-4 Claude Boisgirard, Paris #358 est:2000-2200
£2000	$3400	€3000	Still life (38x46cm-15x18in) s. board. 25-Nov-3 Christie's, London #217/R est:2500-3500
£2053	$3736	€3100	Bateaux au port (46x55cm-18x22in) s. 16-Jun-4 Claude Boisgirard, Paris #57 est:1200-1500
£2886	$5339	€4300	La chapelle au milieu des arbres (73x54cm-29x21in) s. 15-Mar-4 Claude Boisgirard, Paris #38/R est:2000-2500

Works on paper

£7947	$14464	€12000	Les grands boulevards (150x110cm-59x43in) s. gouache. 16-Jun-4 Claude Boisgirard, Paris #61/R est:5000-6000

FOTOPOULOS, Basilis (1934-) Greek

£600	$1074	€876	Untitled (160x139cm-63x55in) s. indis.d. oil paper collage. 10-May-4 Sotheby's, Olympia #98/R

Works on paper

£1900	$3401	€2774	Untitled (100x200cm-39x79in) s. indis.d. mixed media canvas. 10-May-4 Sotheby's, Olympia #96/R est:800-1200

FOUACE, Guillaume Romain (1827-1895) French

£1667	$3000	€2500	Still life with sugarpot and strawberries (35x54cm-14x21in) s. 26-Apr-4 Bernaerts, Antwerp #407/R est:2500-3000
£10490	$17832	€15000	Nature morte aux huitres et aux moules (58x73cm-23x29in) s.d.1892. 24-Nov-3 Boscher, Cherbourg #725b

FOUACE, Guillaume Romain (attrib) (1827-1895) French

Works on paper

£680	$1218	€1000	Peasant and girl resting in field (23x19cm-9x7in) s. chk. 18-Mar-4 Neumeister, Munich #2494

FOUBERT, Émile (1848-1911) French

£1342	$2497	€2000	Portrait du peintre Leon-Germaine Pelouse (90x110cm-35x43in) s.d.1891. 3-Mar-4 Ferri, Paris #379/R est:600-900
£3873	$6430	€5500	Bord de riviere (65x81cm-26x32in) s.d.1900. 15-Jun-3 Peron, Melun #211

FOUCART, A (?) ?

£1773	$2961	€2500	Caravane arrivant a la fontaine (28x46cm-11x18in) s. 19-Oct-3 Rabourdin & Choppin de Janvry, Paris #36/R est:2500-3000

FOUCHE, Nicolas (attrib) (1653-1733) French

£1151	$2118	€1750	Portrait d'homme (81x65cm-32x26in) 24-Jun-4 Credit Municipal, Paris #5/R
£6738	$11252	€9500	La Vierge a l'Enfant (81x65cm-32x26in) 17-Oct-3 Tajan, Paris #88/R est:7000-9000

FOUCOU, Jean Joseph (1739-1815) French

Sculpture

£15493	$26803	€22000	Pan (80cm-31in) s.d. marble lit. 15-Dec-3 Sotheby's, Paris #127/R est:18000-25000

FOUGERAT, Emmanuel (1869-1945) French

£620	$1110	€905	Female nude bathing (25x14cm-10x6in) s. board. 18-Mar-4 Christie's, Kensington #454/R

FOUGSTEDT, Arvid (1888-1949) Swedish

£659	$1167	€962	Interior scene with Erik reading (41x33cm-16x13in) s. 27-Apr-4 AB Stockholms Auktionsverk #686/R (S.KR 9000)

Works on paper

£4103	$7262	€5990	French cafe (37x45cm-15x18in) s.d.1928 W/C gouache exhib. 27-Apr-4 AB Stockholms Auktionsverk #685/R est:15000-20000 (S.KR 56000)

FOUILHOUZE, Felix (?-1885) French

£6000	$10020	€8760	View over Naples (54x84cm-21x33in) s.i.d.1862. 12-Nov-3 Sotheby's, Olympia #172/R est:6000-8000

FOUILLE, Georges (1909-1994) French

£1905	$3410	€2800	Trois mats en mer (44x54cm-17x21in) s. 21-Mar-4 Claude Boisgirard, Paris #123/R est:2600-3000

Works on paper

£559	$951	€800	Les trois mats (70x123cm-28x48in) s. gouache. 27-Nov-3 Millon & Associes, Paris #61

FOUJITA, Tsuguharu (1886-1968) French/Japanese

£1748	$2972	€2500	Two little dogs (33x50cm-13x20in) mono. panel lit. 1-Dec-3 Camard, Paris #63/R est:1500-2500
£5634	$9746	€8000	Construction (19x24cm-7x9in) s. panel. 12-Dec-3 Piasa, Paris #124/R est:6000-8000
£12752	$22826	€19000	Rue de la banlieue de Paris (33x41cm-13x16in) s. painted c.1917. 30-May-4 Eric Pillon, Calais #35/R
£19118	$32500	€27912	Poupee en blanc et rose (56x33cm-22x13in) s. painted 1920 prov.exhib.lit. 6-Nov-3 Sotheby's, New York #370/R est:35000-40000
£20588	$35000	€30058	Paysage de Cagnes (46x55cm-18x22in) s. painted c.1918 prov.lit. 6-Nov-3 Sotheby's, New York #331/R est:35000-45000
£25658	$47211	€39000	Mon interieur (45x55cm-18x22in) s.i. s.i.d.1922 verso lit. 23-Jun-4 Maigret, Paris #29/R est:20000-30000
£34118	$58000	€49812	Chat (24x33cm-9x13in) s.i.d.1929. 5-Nov-3 Christie's, Rockefeller NY #279/R est:20000-30000
£36290	$66774	€52983	Les fleurs (41x27cm-16x11in) s. tempera prov. 14-Jun-4 Waddingtons, Toronto #342/R est:50000-70000 (C.D 90000)
£54930	$95028	€78000	Les deux jeunes filles (53x72cm-21x28in) s.d.1926. 12-Dec-3 Piasa, Paris #23/R est:40000-50000
£57616	$105437	€87000	Nu a l'oreiller (41x33cm-16x13in) s. s.d.1927 verso. 7-Apr-4 Doutrebente, Paris #48/R est:60000-70000
£117647	$200000	€171765	Nu au bras leve (81x45cm-32x18in) s.d.1923 lit. 5-Nov-3 Christie's, Rockefeller NY #271/R est:200000-300000

Prints

£1879	$3514	€2800	Chat couche sur le dos (44x50cm-17x20in) bears sig eau forte aquatint one of 10. 1-Mar-4 Artcurial Briest, Paris #101 est:1000-1200
£2000	$3320	€2920	Deux enfants (52x42cm-20x17in) s.num.41/100 col etching aquatint roulette. 6-Oct-3 Sotheby's, London #82/R est:2500-3500
£2098	$3503	€3000	Nu couche au chat (34x44cm-13x17in) s. num.92/100 eau forte. 25-Jun-3 Blanchet, Paris #21/R
£2148	$3995	€3200	Boy (37x28cm-15x11in) s. num.27/100 col engraving. 2-Mar-4 Ansorena, Madrid #379/R est:2200
£2238	$3849	€3200	Nu debout, planche de l'album Femmes (73x51cm-29x20in) s.d.1930 num.61/100 etching col aquatint. 2-Dec-3 Christie's, Paris #435/R est:4000-6000
£2448	$4210	€3500	Femme nue couchee (38x56cm-15x22in) s.num.73/100 col etching. 3-Dec-3 Beaussant & Lefèvre, Paris #6/R est:2000-3000
£2500	$4150	€3650	Enfant endormi a la poupee (42x52cm-17x20in) s.num.v/x col etching aquatint roulette. 6-Oct-3 Sotheby's, London #83/R est:3000-4000
£2500	$4150	€3650	Nu etendu (50x67cm-20x26in) s.num.34/100 col etching aquatint exec.c.1929. 6-Oct-3 Sotheby's, London #84/R est:3000-4000
£2518	$4029	€3500	Les enfants (36x26cm-14x10in) col eau forte. 18-May-3 Salle des ventes Pillet, Lyon la Foret #66/R
£2518	$4029	€3500	Nu allonge (59x41cm-23x16in) eau forte. 18-May-3 Salle des ventes Pillet, Lyon la Foret #70/R
£2937	$5052	€4200	Nu allonge, planche de l'album Femmes (51x73cm-20x29in) s.d.1930 num.61/100 etching col aquatint. 2-Dec-3 Christie's, Paris #434/R est:4000-6000
£3121	$5211	€4400	Fillette a la fleur (36x28cm-14x11in) s.num.94/100 col etching aquatint. 20-Jun-3 Drouot Estimations, Paris #28/R est:4500-5000
£3147	$5413	€4500	Nu assis, planche de l'album Femmes (73x51cm-29x20in) s.d.1930 num.61/100 etching col aquatint. 2-Dec-3 Christie's, Paris #432/R est:4000-6000

£3309 $5295 €4600 Chat noir (35x28cm-14x11in) print. 18-May-3 Salle des ventes Pillet, Lyon la Foret #69/R
£3357 $5773 €4800 Nu etendu, planche de l'album Femmes (51x73cm-20x29in) s.d.1930 num.61/100 etching col aquatint. 2-Dec-3 Christie's, Paris #436/R est:4000-6000
£3439 $5743 €5021 Chatton (38x32cm-15x13in) s.num.22/100 col etching aquatint roulette. 16-Oct-3 Waddingtons, Toronto #173/R est:6000-8000 (C.D 7600)
£3813 $6101 €5300 Chat brun (37x28cm-15x11in) col eau forte aquatint. 18-May-3 Salle des ventes Pillet, Lyon la Foret #68/R
£3986 $7136 €5900 Chat assis (33x40cm-13x16in) s. num.86/100 eau forte aquatint. 5-May-4 Coutau Begarie, Paris #10/R est:1800-2300
£4054 $7257 €6000 Chat couche (33x40cm-13x16in) s. num.86/100 eau forte aquatint. 5-May-4 Coutau Begarie, Paris #11 est:1800-2300
£5245 $8916 €7500 Femme nue (38x59cm-15x23in) s. col etching aquatint. 26-Nov-3 Lempertz, Koln #672/R est:8000

Works on paper
£1250 $2088 €1800 Femme assise (29x24cm-11x9in) s.i. pen Indian ink. 25-Oct-3 Cornette de St.Cyr, Paris #506 est:1800-2000
£1400 $2576 €2100 Le chat (18x24cm-7x9in) s.i. blue ink. 11-Jun-4 Claude Aguttes, Neuilly #196/R est:1000-1200
£1528 $2551 €2200 Jeune levrier (52x40cm-20x16in) s. lead pencil drawing lit. 21-Oct-3 Artcurial Briest, Paris #67/R est:1500-2000
£1700 $3128 €2482 Le chat (25x20cm-10x8in) s.i.d.1.Jan.1931 pen ink. 24-Mar-4 Sotheby's, Olympia #30a/R est:1000-1500
£1854 $3393 €2800 Paysage de Paris (30x40cm-12x16in) W/C Japan paper exec 1951. 7-Apr-4 Piasa, Paris #169/R est:2500-3000
£1946 $3484 €2900 Portrait de femme (42x29cm-17x11in) s. graphite dr htd chk. 30-May-4 Eric Pillon, Calais #32/R
£2000 $3340 €2920 Study of feet (15x21cm-6x8in) s.d.1924 pen ink wash. 22-Oct-3 Sotheby's, Olympia #19/R est:2500-3500
£2258 $4200 €3297 Femme avec parasol (20x13cm-8x5in) s.d.1926 brush ink wash. 2-Mar-4 Swann Galleries, New York #192a/R est:6000-9000
£2377 $4089 €3400 Visage de femme (22x15cm-9x6in) s. ink. 3-Dec-3 Tajan, Paris #87/R est:1800-2000
£2431 $4059 €3500 Deux cocker spaniels (41x62cm-16x24in) s.i.d.22 Juillet 1960 chl drawing lit. 21-Oct-3 Artcurial Briest, Paris #66/R est:4000-6000
£2639 $4407 €3800 Profil de femme (24x14cm-9x6in) s. bears i. Indian ink prov. 21-Oct-3 Artcurial Briest, Paris #17/R est:4000-5000
£3333 $6133 €5000 Rose et libellule (31x45cm-12x18in) s. W/C ink exec. c.1958. 9-Jun-4 Oger, Dumont, Paris #55/R est:8000-10000
£4011 $7500 €5856 Enfant (39x30cm-15x12in) s. pencil. 25-Feb-4 Christie's, Rockefeller NY #51/R est:4000-6000
£4079 $7505 €6200 Petit chat endormi (13x18cm-5x7in) s. ink oval. 25-Jun-4 Millon & Associes, Paris #148/R est:2500-3000
£5556 $9278 €8000 Portrait de jeune femme (22x25cm-9x10in) s.d.1928 ink stumping lit. 21-Oct-3 Artcurial Briest, Paris #68/R est:6000-8000
£5960 $10907 €9000 Chiot se lechant (23x29cm-9x11in) s.d.1924 Indian ink drawing wash. 7-Apr-4 Piasa, Paris #168/R est:6000-8000
£6704 $12000 €9788 Mother and child in Mexico (39x27cm-15x11in) s.i.d.1933 W/C pen blk ink buff paper on board prov.lit. 5-May-4 Christie's, Rockefeller NY #154/R est:15000-20000
£7821 $14000 €11419 Jeune Mexicain (39x28cm-15x11in) s.d.1933 pen ink gouache prov. 6-May-4 Sotheby's, New York #469/R est:14000-18000
£8000 $13360 €11680 Portrait de jeune fille (25x19cm-10x7in) s.i. pen ink wash executed 1928. 21-Oct-3 Sotheby's, London #115/R est:6000-8000
£8000 $14320 €11680 Deux visages (32x25cm-13x10in) s.d.1926 ink prov. 6-May-4 Sotheby's, London #59/R est:8000-10000
£8108 $15000 €11838 Fillette (38x26cm-15x10in) s. India ink exec.1951. 11-Feb-4 Sotheby's, New York #56/R est:15000-20000
£8844 $15830 €13000 Jeune fille (25x19cm-10x7in) s. ink wash Japan paper. 19-Mar-4 Millon & Associes, Paris #103/R est:3000-4000
£9507 $15782 €13500 Le ramassage des foins, Bretagne (26x22cm-10x9in) s.i.d.1917 W/C ink pl. 10-Jun-3 Renaud, Paris #39/R est:10000-12000
£10056 $18000 €14682 Chien (29x19cm-11x7in) s.d.1932 gouache W/C pen India ink buff paper on board prov.lit. 5-May-4 Christie's, Rockefeller NY #151/R est:12000-16000
£11000 $19690 €16060 Chat et chaton (29x32cm-11x13in) s. col ink. 6-May-4 Sotheby's, London #60/R est:8000-12000
£11950 $19000 €17447 Jeune fille a l'oiseau (45x32cm-18x13in) s.d.1949 ink brush. 12-Sep-3 Skinner, Boston #328/R est:8000
£12324 $19842 €17500 Jeune fille a l'eventail (88x53cm-35x21in) s.d.1925 crayon dr lit. 22-Aug-3 Deauville, France #83/R est:30000-40000
£12333 $22693 €18500 Modele endormi (14x21cm-6x8in) s.i. ink wash lit. 9-Jun-4 Tajan, Paris #57/R est:12000-15000
£12570 $22500 €18352 Jeune fille a l'oiseau (45x32cm-18x13in) s.d.1949 pen ink. 6-May-4 Sotheby's, New York #454/R est:20000-25000
£12667 $23307 €19000 Priere (47x31cm-19x12in) s. mixed media. 11-Jun-4 Claude Aguttes, Neuilly #197/R est:15000-20000
£12752 $23718 €19000 Portrait de jeune fille (21x15cm-8x6in) s.i.d.1950 pen wash. 3-Mar-4 Fraysse & Associes, Paris #19/R est:9000-12000
£13333 $24533 €20000 Cariole et cycliste, POrte d'Orleans a Paris (21x29cm-8x11in) s.i. i.d.1917 verso W/C lit. 9-Jun-4 Tajan, Paris #53/R est:20000-25000
£15493 $26803 €22000 Fillette (29x20cm-11x8in) s. W/C. 12-Dec-3 Piasa, Paris #25/R est:18000-20000
£16667 $30667 €25000 Maternite (22x15cm-9x6in) s.d.1950 india ink prov. 11-Jun-4 Pierre Berge, Paris #233/R est:15000-20000
£19118 $32500 €27912 Nu (144x47cm-57x19in) s. pencil exec c.1930. 6-Nov-3 Sotheby's, New York #360/R est:40000-60000
£19412 $33000 €28342 Jeune fille aux raisins (33x24cm-13x9in) s. W/C prov. 5-Nov-3 Christie's, Rockefeller NY #115/R est:20000-30000
£19553 $35000 €28547 Sleeping cat (25x32cm-10x13in) s.d.1931 W/C chl pen ink. 5-May-4 Christie's, Rockefeller NY #153/R est:20000-25000
£30822 $48390 €45000 Couple allonge aux colombes (35x48cm-14x19in) s. W/C lit. 20-Apr-3 Deauville, France #124/R est:45000-55000
£32886 $61168 €49000 Maternite (29x23cm-11x9in) s.i.d.1951 pen wash W/C. 3-Mar-4 Fraysse & Associes, Paris #18/R est:15000-18000
£43421 $79895 €66000 Chute des Titans (92x147cm-36x58in) s.d.1928 wax crayons stumping out prov. 28-Jun-4 Joron-Derem, Paris #166/R est:30000-35000

FOULET, Louis (19/20th C) French
£744 $1264 €1086 Confidante (34x23cm-13x9in) s. board. 29-Oct-3 Lawson Menzies, Sydney #93/R est:2000-3000 (A.D 1800)

FOULKES, Lynn (1934-) American
£540 $950 €788 Untitled (10x10cm-4x4in) s.d.61 oil on paper prov. 23-May-4 Bonhams & Butterfields, Los Angeles #7086/R

FOUQUE, Charles (19th C) French
£1733 $3189 €2600 In the kitchen (55x45cm-22x18in) s. 10-Jun-4 Christie's, Rome #133/R est:2600-2900

FOUQUERAY, Charles (1872-1956) French
£306 $548 €450 Ocean Indien (15x24cm-6x9in) st.sig. panel. 21-Mar-4 St-Germain-en-Laye Encheres #120/R
£340 $609 €500 Marche oriental. st.sig.verso panel. 21-Mar-4 St-Germain-en-Laye Encheres #23
£340 $609 €500 Rues de Hanoi (19x24cm-7x9in) st.sig. panel. 21-Mar-4 St-Germain-en-Laye Encheres #126/R
£378 $677 €560 Troupeau de moutons (15x23cm-6x9in) s. i.verso panel. 10-May-4 Giraudeau, Tours #142
£490 $877 €720 Entree de la pagode a Pnom-Penh (24x19cm-9x7in) st.sig. panel. 21-Mar-4 St-Germain-en-Laye Encheres #127/R
£533 $965 €800 Vue de l'Erechteion. Vue de l'Andrinople (15x24cm-6x9in) s.i.d.1919 panel pair. 1-Apr-4 Credit Municipal, Paris #36
£567 $948 €800 Devant la mosquee (40x27cm-16x11in) s.i.d.1908 cardboard. 19-Oct-3 Rabourdin & Choppin de Janvry, Paris #85/R
£748 $1339 €1100 Grand bazar a Constantinople (24x18cm-9x7in) s.d.1919. 21-Mar-4 St-Germain-en-Laye Encheres #21/R
£1224 $2192 €1800 Marche a Beyrouth (14x18cm-6x7in) s.i. panel. 21-Mar-4 St-Germain-en-Laye Encheres #22/R est:500-600
£1500 $2775 €2190 Rowing ashore (116x90cm-46x35in) s. 10-Mar-4 Sotheby's, Olympia #304/R est:1000-1500

Works on paper
£576 $921 €800 Marins a la manoeuvre par gros temps (28x21cm-11x8in) s. W/C gouache. 18-May-3 Claude Boisgirard, Paris #158/R
£2109 $3775 €3100 Bain sacre a Madura (37x28cm-15x11in) s.i.d.1921 i.verso W/C. 21-Mar-4 St-Germain-en-Laye Encheres #119/R est:2000

FOUQUERAY, Charles (attrib) (1872-1956) French
Works on paper
£333 $597 €500 Portrait de jeune Tonkinois Meo Peu (59x39cm-23x15in) W/C. 16-May-4 Thierry & Lannon, Brest #243

FOUQUES, Robert Henry (1892-1956) French
£319 $542 €466 Douarnenez (26x34cm-10x13in) s. wood panel painted c.1940. 26-Nov-3 Deutscher-Menzies, Melbourne #291/R (A.D 750)
£425 $723 €621 Une Calanque a Carry-le-Rouet, Bouches-de-Rhone (33x46cm-13x18in) s. painted c.1920. 26-Nov-3 Deutscher-Menzies, Melbourne #290/R (A.D 1000)
£456 $808 €680 Plage de Luc-sur-Mer (16x21cm-6x8in) s. cardboard. 30-Apr-4 Tajan, Paris #222

FOUQUIER, F (18th C) Flemish
£6044 $11000 €8824 River landscape with figures on a path and village beyond (67x129cm-26x51in) s. prov. 17-Jun-4 Christie's, Rockefeller NY #58/R est:5000-7000

FOURES, Blas (20th C) Spanish
£828 $1490 €1200 Bathers (41x33cm-16x13in) s.d.85 s.i.d.verso. 26-Jan-4 Durán, Madrid #608/R

FOURIE, Audrey (20th C) South African
£264 $473 €385 Street scene with figures (84x69cm-33x27in) s.d.99. 31-May-4 Stephan Welz, Johannesburg #272 (SA.R 3200)

FOURMOIS, Theodore (1814-1871) Belgian
£667 $1200 €1000 Figures at the edge of the wood (17x23cm-7x9in) s. panel. 26-Apr-4 Bernaerts, Antwerp #112/R
£1192 $2170 €1800 Children on a wooden bridge (43x62cm-17x24in) s.indis.d. 21-Jun-4 Dorotheum, Vienna #77/R est:1800-2000

Works on paper
£1000 $1790 €1500 Landscape with cows and herdsman (33x48cm-13x19in) s. W/C. 15-May-4 De Vuyst, Lokeren #137/R est:1400-1700

FOURNIER, Alain (1931-1983) French
£317 $548 €450 Paris, amoureux sur les quais de la Seine (73x60cm-29x24in) s. 13-Dec-3 Touati, Paris #92

FOURNIER, Alexis Jean (1865-1948) American
£479 $800 €699 Castle on bluff (25x36cm-10x14in) s. board. 19-Oct-3 Susanin's, Chicago #6077/R
£568 $1000 €829 Rural landscape (30x41cm-12x16in) s. board. 28-May-4 Aspire, Cleveland #23/R est:1500-2000
£1463 $2400 €2121 Sheep in a landscape (8x12cm-3x5in) s. painted c.1900. 7-Jun-3 Treadway Gallery, Cincinnati #1440 est:2000-3000
£1829 $3000 €2652 Indiana farm (12x16cm-5x6in) s. painted c.1930. 7-Jun-3 Treadway Gallery, Cincinnati #1427 est:3000-4000
£2256 $3700 €3271 East Aurora landscape (13x16cm-5x6in) s.i. board painted c.1910. 7-Jun-3 Treadway Gallery, Cincinnati #1426 est:2000-3000
£6707 $11000 €9725 Harvest (46x61cm-18x24in) s. painted c.1906. 7-Jun-3 Treadway Gallery, Cincinnati #1403 est:6000-8000
£8537 $14000 €12379 Cattle in a landscape (46x61cm-18x24in) s. painted c.1906. 7-Jun-3 Treadway Gallery, Cincinnati #1402 est:6000-8000

FOURNIER, Hippolyte (fl.1881-1910) French
£1933 $3557 €2900 Le soir, Paris, modele nu assis (167x134cm-66x53in) s. prov. 11-Jun-4 Pierre Berge, Paris #198 est:3000-4000

FOURNIER, Louis Edouard Paul (1857-?) French
£3500 $6265 €5110 Au bord de Riviere (73x100cm-29x39in) s. 26-May-4 Sotheby's, Olympia #277/R est:4000-6000

FOURNIER, Marcel (1869-1917) French
£289 $531 €430 Southern landscape (70x50cm-28x20in) s. 27-Mar-4 L & B, Essen #109/R

FOURNIER, Paul (1939-) Canadian
£400 $732 €584 Improvisation, on Reddish Buff (21x91cm-8x36in) s.i.d.1980 verso acrylic. 3-Jun-4 Heffel, Vancouver #23/R (C.D 1000)

FOURNIER, Real (20th C) Canadian
£220 $403 €321 Linges au soleil (40x50cm-16x20in) s.i. board. 1-Jun-4 Hodgins, Calgary #406/R (C.D 550)

FOURNIER, Victor Alfred (1872-1924) French
£604 $1111 €900 Bretonne sur la plage (27x18cm-11x7in) s. panel exhib. 24-Mar-4 Joron-Derem, Paris #243
£865 $1367 €1350 Coin du marche a Concarneau (24x35cm-9x14in) i.verso panel prov. 12-Nov-2 Adjug'art, Brest #93
£1900 $3154 €2774 Concarneau (38x46cm-15x18in) s.i.d.1915. 1-Oct-3 Sotheby's, Olympia #274/R est:600-900

FOUS, Jean (1901-1971) French
£334 $600 €500 Le banquet republicain (21x26cm-8x10in) s. panel. 26-Apr-4 Tajan, Paris #345/R
£467 $835 €700 Place Furstenberg (32x23cm-13x9in) s. 16-May-4 other European Auctioneer #54
£800 $1384 €1168 Chasse a Courre, le retour (54x66cm-21x26in) s. s.i.verso sold with two more by the same artist. 11-Dec-3 Christie's, Kensington #178/R
Works on paper
£2098 $3608 €3000 Scenes de village (22x27cm-9x11in) s. gouache set of 6. 8-Dec-3 Christie's, Paris #74/R est:3000-4000

FOUSSIER, J V (?) British?
£1078 $2005 €1574 Vessels on the river, possibly Thames at Greenwich (31x40cm-12x16in) s. panel. 2-Mar-4 Rasmussen, Copenhagen #1404/R est:8000 (D.KR 12000)

FOVELINE, Alexandra Ivanovna (c.1850-?) Russian
£15000 $26850 €21900 Favourite pastimes (138x100cm-54x39in) s.d.1882 prov. 26-May-4 Sotheby's, London #18/R est:15000-20000

FOWERAKER, A M (1873-1942) British
£1000 $1700 €1460 Near Hanlyn Bay, a twilight scene with stone cottage and figure (28x23cm-11x9in) 30-Oct-3 Grant, Worcester #582/R est:300-500

FOWERAKER, A Moulton (1873-1942) British
£1200 $2004 €1752 Malaga (23x28cm-9x11in) 21-Oct-3 Gorringes, Lewes #2200/R
£1800 $3366 €2628 Sheep in a meadow before a church and distant town (23x32cm-9x13in) s. board. 26-Feb-4 Lane, Penzance #324 est:1800-2500
Works on paper
£320 $592 €467 Arab street at night (28x23cm-11x9in) s. W/C. 10-Feb-4 David Lay, Penzance #297
£360 $644 €526 Algiceras, Southern Spain (24x34cm-9x13in) s. W/C. 17-Mar-4 Bonhams, Chester #290
£360 $659 €526 Sunset, Albi, Tarn, France (23x28cm-9x11in) s.d.5/31 W/C. 8-Jul-4 Duke & Son, Dorchester #57/R
£480 $778 €701 In a Spanish town (27x36cm-11x14in) mono. W/C. 30-Jul-3 Hamptons Fine Art, Godalming #144
£500 $900 €730 Beach scene at low tide. Sunlight catching rocks on a beach (17x25cm-7x10in) s. pencil W/C pair prov. 21-Apr-4 Tennants, Leyburn #938
£520 $832 €759 Courtyard of Posada Malago (25x36cm-10x14in) s. W/C. 8-Jan-3 Biddle & Webb, Birmingham #809
£550 $1007 €803 Mother Ives Bay and the Merope Rocjs, Trevose, North Cornwall (28x23cm-11x9in) s.verso W/C. 8-Jul-4 Duke & Son, Dorchester #52
£600 $1002 €876 Figures in a street (27x22cm-11x9in) s. W/C. 14-Oct-3 Bonhams, Knightsbridge #25/R
£750 $1253 €1095 Pudding Back Lane (29x23cm-11x9in) s. i.verso W/C. 12-Nov-3 Sotheby's, Olympia #141/R
£800 $1464 €1168 Cornish coastal views (18x25cm-7x10in) s. W/C pair. 3-Jun-4 Lane, Penzance #286
£820 $1525 €1197 Little Petherick, North Cornwall (51x34cm-20x13in) s. i. verso W/C. 2-Mar-4 Bearnes, Exeter #329/R
£850 $1590 €1241 Figure on a Cornish moonlit beach (23x29cm-9x11in) s. 26-Feb-4 Lane, Penzance #328
£920 $1702 €1343 Italian town (23x28cm-9x11in) s. W/C. 10-Feb-4 David Lay, Penzance #295
£1100 $2024 €1606 On the outskirts of a Spanish village (23x26cm-9x10in) s. pencil W/C. 25-Mar-4 Christie's, Kensington #259/R est:500-700
£1100 $2024 €1606 Washing day, house in the woods (25x35cm-10x14in) s. W/C. 29-Mar-4 Bonhams, Bath #24/R est:600-800
£1150 $1840 €1679 Convent of Incamatia (25x33cm-10x13in) s. W/C. 8-Jan-3 Biddle & Webb, Birmingham #895
£1150 $2116 €1679 Moonlight - Santa Maria, Antequera (25x35cm-10x14in) s.i. W/C. 29-Mar-4 Bonhams, Bath #23/R est:600-800
£1300 $2236 €1898 Spanish riverside town by moonlight (35x53cm-14x21in) s. pencil W/C. 3-Dec-3 Christie's, Kensington #195/R est:700-900
£1380 $2277 €2015 Moonlit evening street scene with figures in a tree lined town square (23x28cm-9x11in) s. W/C. 3-Jul-3 Biddle & Webb, Birmingham #893

FOWLER, Daniel (1810-1894) British?
£930 $1692 €1358 Neapolitan Fisherman (37x25cm-15x10in) canvas on masonite prov. 5-Feb-4 Heffel, Vancouver #32/R est:1500-2000 (C.D 2250)
Works on paper
£200 $366 €292 In the mountains (18x27cm-7x11in) W/C. 1-Jun-4 Hodgins, Calgary #93/R (C.D 500)
£720 $1318 €1051 Country Road chat, Autumn (22x33cm-9x13in) s.d.1887 W/C. 1-Jun-4 Joyner Waddington, Toronto #13/R est:2000-3000 (C.D 1800)
£1696 $2918 €2476 Woodland wanderer (23x33cm-9x13in) s.d.75 W/C prov. 2-Dec-3 Joyner Waddington, Toronto #192/R est:2500-3000 (C.D 3800)

FOWLER, George (?) British
Works on paper
£380 $699 €555 Waves breaking on the shore (43x66cm-17x26in) s. W/C. 8-Jun-4 Gorringes, Lewes #2127

FOWLER, Robert (1853-1926) British
£274 $467 €400 Seascape (41x56cm-16x22in) s. 21-Nov-3 Walker's, Ottawa #245/R (C.D 610)
£920 $1647 €1343 Conway - early morning (61x111cm-24x44in) s. exhib. 17-Mar-4 Bonhams, Chester #250
£950 $1549 €1387 Extensive landscape with a figure and sheep (76x127cm-30x50in) s. 25-Sep-3 Mellors & Kirk, Nottingham #765/R
£5000 $8950 €7300 Gypsy encampment (102x165cm-40x65in) s. 7-May-4 Chrystals Auctions, Isle of Man #233 est:3000-4000
£10000 $17900 €14600 Artists (122x92cm-48x36in) mono.d.1884 exhib. 27-May-4 Christie's, Kensington #314/R est:10000-15000
Works on paper
£5929 $10613 €8656 Moonbeam (64x31cm-25x12in) s. W/C prov. 15-May-4 Christie's, Sydney #258/R est:10000-20000 (A.D 15000)

FOWLER, William (19th C) British
£419 $700 €612 Still life of woodcocks (20x30cm-8x12in) s.d.1828 panel. 16-Nov-3 William Jenack, New York #410
£3000 $5010 €4380 Portrait of Lieutenant General Robert Ballard Long, wearing uniform of Hussars (74x61cm-29x24in) i.verso. 14-Oct-3 Sotheby's, London #494 est:1000-1500

FOWLES, Arthur W (c.1815-1878) British
£4000 $6800 €5840 Latona and Florinda (61x107cm-24x42in) s.d.1881. 19-Nov-3 Christie's, Kensington #404/R

FOX, Charles James (1860-?) British
£520 $962 €759 In the Dales (53x74cm-21x29in) s.i. 14-Jan-4 Brightwells, Leominster #785/R

FOX, E M (19th C) British
£1600 $2656 €2336 Longhorn cow in an open field (61x75cm-24x30in) init.d.1840 prov. 1-Oct-3 Woolley & Wallis, Salisbury #324/R est:800-1200

FOX, E P (1865-1915) Australian
£2033 $3638 €2968 Temple of love (42x28cm-17x11in) 10-May-4 Joel, Victoria #305 est:3000-5000 (A.D 5000)

FOX, Edwin M (19th C) British
£3172 $5869 €4600 Cheval (63x76cm-25x30in) s.d.1846. 13-Jan-4 Vanderkindere, Brussels #175/R est:2000-3000
£3600 $6372 €5256 Prize shorthorn in a field (51x61cm-20x24in) s.d.1854. 27-Apr-4 Bonhams, Knowle #78 est:2000-3000
£3700 $6549 €5402 Portrait of a gentleman on a dark bay hunter after a day's coursing (60x76cm-24x30in) s.d.1847. 27-Apr-4 Bonhams, Knowle #88/R est:2000-3000

FOX, Emanuel Phillips (1865-1915) Australian
£5691 $8935 €8252 Wheat stacks, Giverny (32x46cm-13x18in) prov. 27-Aug-3 Christie's, Sydney #551/R est:18000-25000 (A.D 14000)
£7025 $12434 €10257 Place de la Concorde (25x34cm-10x13in) s. board prov. 3-May-4 Christie's, Melbourne #65/R est:10000-15000 (A.D 17000)
£8943 $14041 €12967 French fishing boats (34x44cm-13x17in) s. prov.exhib. 26-Aug-3 Christie's, Sydney #42/R est:22000-28000 (A.D 22000)
£10744 $19017 €15686 Village of Les Andelys (37x44cm-15x17in) s. prov. 3-May-4 Christie's, Melbourne #52/R est:25000-35000 (A.D 26000)
£20661 $36570 €30165 On a French beach (26x34cm-10x13in) board prov. 3-May-4 Christie's, Melbourne #114/R est:18000-25000 (A.D 50000)
Works on paper
£687 $1250 €1003 Portrait of Sir Harry Brookes Allen (60x44cm-24x17in) s.i. chl. 16-Jun-4 Deutscher-Menzies, Melbourne #390/R est:2000-3000 (A.D 1800)

FOX, Ethel Carrick (1872-1952) Australian
£1224 $2253 €1787 White lillies (55x37cm-22x15in) s. 29-Mar-4 Goodman, Sydney #143/R est:3000-5000 (A.D 3000)
£6504 $10211 €9431 Children playing in a park (16x22cm-6x9in) s. canvasboard prov. 26-Aug-3 Christie's, Sydney #43/R est:12000-18000 (A.D 16000)
£9746 $16568 €14229 Luxembourg gardens (27x35cm-11x14in) wood panel prov. 24-Nov-3 Sotheby's, Melbourne #5/R est:28000-35000 (A.D 23000)

FOX, George (19th C) British
£500 $865 €730 Lunch in a tavern (29x39cm-11x15in) s. 12-Dec-3 Bracketts, Tunbridge Wells #872/R
£520 $853 €759 Points of law, interior library scene with three gentlemen seated (29x23cm-11x9in) s. i.verso board. 3-Jun-3 Fellows & Sons, Birmingham #13/R
£1400 $2324 €2044 English gossip. French intrigue. (10x14cm-4x6in) one canvas one board two. 1-Oct-3 George Kidner, Lymington #173/R est:1500-2500

FOX, Henry Charles (1860-1929) British
£1200 $2220 €1752 Street, Hayes (36x25cm-14x10in) s.i.d.1886 board. 11-Mar-4 Christie's, Kensington #82/R est:1200-1800
Works on paper
£260 $476 €380 Sailing barge on the river, possibly at Richmond (33x47cm-13x19in) s.d.1899 W/C. 6-Apr-4 Bristol Auction Rooms #403/R
£300 $519 €438 Cattle in a lane (52x35cm-20x14in) s.d.1901 W/C. 9-Dec-3 Bearnes, Exeter #791

£340 $622 €496 Country lane with farmer droving cattle (25x35cm-10x14in) s.d.1924 W/C. 6-Apr-4 Bonhams, Chester #913
£350 $644 €511 Cattle on the banks of a river, autumn (41x72cm-16x28in) s.d.1900 pencil W/C bodycol. 25-Mar-4 Christie's, Kensington #162
£360 $666 €526 Cattle watering and grazing beside a river, church beyond (36x51cm-14x20in) s.d.1903 W/C bodycol. 11-Mar-4 Duke & Son, Dorchester #107/R
£380 $699 €555 Herding sheep (35x53cm-14x21in) s. W/C bodycol. 22-Jun-4 Bonhams, Knightsbridge #73/R
£400 $708 €584 Shepperton on Thames (36x51cm-14x20in) s.d.1902 W/C. 29-Apr-4 Gorringes, Lewes #2545
£400 $728 €584 Cattle returning home on a wintry day (36x53cm-14x21in) s.d.1920 W/C. 15-Jun-4 Bonhams, Oxford #29/R
£450 $725 €653 Country lane with cattle and drover (36x53cm-14x21in) s.d.1905 W/C. 13-Aug-3 Andrew Hartley, Ilkley #728/R
£450 $720 €657 Sunny pastoral (36x53cm-14x21in) s.d.1922 i.verso W/C. 16-Sep-3 Capes Dunn, Manchester #824/R
£450 $819 €657 The faggot gatherers (52x34cm-20x13in) s. pencil W/C bodycol. 1-Jul-4 Christie's, Kensington #236/R
£450 $824 €675 Bridge at Sonning (32x50cm-13x20in) s.d.1893 W/C. 27-Jul-4 Henry Adams, Chichester #402
£460 $856 €672 Cattle and drover on country lane (53x35cm-21x14in) s.d.1915 W/C. 2-Mar-4 Bearnes, Exeter #391/R
£480 $763 €701 Hay wagon drawn by two horses in a rural setting (36x54cm-14x21in) s.d.1910 W/C. 30-Apr-3 Peter Wilson, Nantwich #90
£500 $850 €730 Cattle watering in the Thames with punt and church beyond (37x53cm-15x21in) s.d.1919 W/C. 1-Dec-3 Bonhams, Bath #61/R
£500 $910 €730 The plough team watering at the ford (53x36cm-21x14in) s.d.1906 pencil W/C htd white. 1-Jul-4 Christie's, Kensington #238/R
£520 $832 €759 Wooded landscapes with horses at a stream and milkmaid and cows (36x53cm-14x21in) s.d.1906 W/C pair. 16-Sep-3 Capes Dunn, Manchester #822/R
£550 $1007 €803 On the banks of the Avon (36x54cm-14x21in) s. W/C. 27-Jan-4 Bonhams, Knightsbridge #50/R
£560 $1030 €818 Drover with cattle in a wooded lane (10x14cm-4x6in) s.d.1924 W/C. 11-Jun-4 Keys, Aylsham #421/R
£565 $1039 €825 Near Saxmundum, Suffolk (36x51cm-14x20in) s.d.1905 W/C. 14-Jun-4 Waddingtons, Toronto #75/R est:800-1200 (C.D 1400)
£600 $1080 €876 Wooded landscape with cattle grazing beside a pond (35x53cm-14x21in) s.d.1922 pencil W/C htd white. 21-Apr-4 Tennants, Leyburn #1033
£600 $1110 €876 Shepherdess and sheep on a tree lined lane. Girl drover with cattle on a lane (36x53cm-14x21in) s.d.1918 W/C pair. 9-Mar-4 Capes Dunn, Manchester #601/R
£600 $1110 €900 Fording the stream. s.d.1905 W/C bodycol. 14-Jul-4 John Bellman, Billingshurst #1717/R
£620 $1054 €905 Hackness, Yorkshire. Ferry cottage, Burpham (37x26cm-15x10in) s.d.1922 pencil W/C pair. 19-Nov-3 Tennants, Leyburn #978
£650 $1027 €949 Summer river landscape with cattle watering (38x56cm-15x22in) s.d.1907 W/C. 23-Jul-3 Hampton & Littlewood, Exeter #418/R
£650 $1196 €949 Returning to the farm. Off to the fields (36x51cm-14x20in) s.d.99 pencil W/C. 25-Mar-4 Christie's, Kensington #145/R
£680 $1129 €993 River landscape with figures overlooking a bridge (33x51cm-13x20in) s.d.1902 W/C. 3-Oct-3 Mallams, Oxford #80
£700 $1274 €1022 Watering the horses (35x56cm-14x22in) s.d.1906 pencil W/C bodycol. 1-Jul-4 Christie's, Kensington #104
£800 $1480 €1168 Drover with cattle by a ford (33x48cm-13x19in) s.d.1905 W/C. 13-Feb-4 Keys, Aylsham #495/R
£800 $1456 €1168 Cattle crossing a ford at Fordingbridge, Hampshire (27x37cm-11x15in) s.d.1922 pencil W/C htd white. 1-Jul-4 Christie's, Kensington #237/R
£820 $1419 €1197 Cattle watering at a ford on an autumn day (36x54cm-14x21in) s.d.1909 W/C sold with companion piece pair. 9-Dec-3 Bonhams, Oxford #75/R
£850 $1539 €1241 Figures, horse and hay cart before country cottages in summer (25x38cm-10x15in) s.d.1899 W/C. 16-Apr-4 Keys, Aylsham #474/R
£900 $1503 €1314 Shepherd with his flock on a farm track (36x51cm-14x20in) s.d.1920 W/C. 12-Nov-3 Halls, Shrewsbury #250/R
£950 $1587 €1387 Shepherd and sheep (38x51cm-15x20in) s.d.1892 W/C. 17-Oct-3 Keys, Aylsham #507
£1000 $1720 €1460 Driving cattle on a wet day (37x45cm-15x18in) s.d.1907 pencil W/C htd white. 4-Dec-3 Mellors & Kirk, Nottingham #867 est:1000-1500
£1000 $1870 €1460 Pastoral scene with shepherd and sheep. Farmyard with man watering horses (55x37cm-22x15in) s.d.25 pencil W/C htd white pair. 22-Jul-4 Tennants, Leyburn #741 est:800-1000
£1128 $1917 €1647 Country scenes (38x56cm-15x22in) s.d.1910 W/C pair. 27-Nov-3 International Art Centre, Auckland #193 est:1800-2600 (NZ.D 3000)
£1200 $2244 €1800 Shepherd driving a flock of sheep along a country lane (55x76cm-22x30in) s.d.1917 W/C bodycol. 26-Jul-4 Bonhams, Bath #20/R est:700-900
£1350 $2484 €1971 Watering place. Cattle on a track (38x56cm-15x22in) s.d.1909 W/C pair. 24-Mar-4 Hamptons Fine Art, Godalming #234/R
£1500 $2505 €2190 Frosty morning, landscape with cattle (62x98cm-24x39in) s. W/C htd white. 8-Oct-3 Rupert Toovey, Partridge Green #105/R est:700-1000

FOX, John R (1927-) Canadian
£203 $364 €296 Bridget in the park (25x17cm-10x7in) s. i.verso panel prov. 6-May-4 Heffel, Vancouver #56/R (C.D 500)
Works on paper
£282 $519 €412 Mother and child (47x39cm-19x15in) s. i.verso mixed media prov. 9-Jun-4 Walker's, Ottawa #153/R (C.D 700)

FOX, John Shirley (1860-?) British
£978 $1800 €1428 English Barbizon landscape (41x51cm-16x20in) s. 26-Jun-4 Susanin's, Chicago #6073/R est:1500-2600
£4500 $7515 €6570 Lilac time (91x61cm-36x24in) s.d.96. 13-Nov-3 Christie's, Kensington #273/R est:5000-7000

FOX, Kathleen (1880-1963) British
£1678 $2853 €2400 Snowdrops (36x45cm-14x18in) s. prov. 25-Nov-3 De Veres Art Auctions, Dublin #100b/R est:2000-3000
£1958 $3329 €2800 Morning in the Claddagh, Galway (28x37cm-11x15in) s.i. s.verso board. 25-Nov-3 De Veres Art Auctions, Dublin #1001 est:1500-2000

FOX, Liam (20th C) Irish?
Works on paper
£347 $624 €520 Reclining nude (59x55cm-23x22in) s.d.99 pencil. 20-Apr-4 James Adam, Dublin #157/R

FOX, Lorraine (1925-1976) American
Works on paper
£447 $800 €653 Teens at carnival in gymnasium (48x38cm-19x15in) s. gouache. 15-May-4 Illustration House, New York #83/R

FOX, Rowland William (19/20th C) British
£300 $555 €438 Figures on a riverbank with cottage beyond (30x43cm-12x17in) s.d.1896 panel. 13-Feb-4 Halls, Shrewsbury #720

FOXHILL, George (1921-) Australian
£617 $1117 €901 Obedience (181x246cm-71x97in) init. i.d.1989 verso. 30-Mar-4 Lawson Menzies, Sydney #59 est:2000-3000 (A.D 1500)

FOY, Frances (1890-1963) American
Works on paper
£237 $425 €346 Still life with lilacs and tulips (66x84cm-26x33in) s.d.1937 W/C. 8-May-4 Susanin's, Chicago #6051/R
£363 $650 €530 Still life with zinnias and gladiolas (56x71cm-22x28in) s. W/C. 8-May-4 Susanin's, Chicago #6052/R
£1156 $2000 €1688 Floral still life (32x30cm-13x12in) s.d.1930 W/C prov. 10-Dec-3 Bonhams & Butterfields, San Francisco #6060/R est:3000-5000

FOY, Henry (?) Irish?
£280 $512 €409 In the Derryvaghs, Donegal (36x51cm-14x20in) s.i.verso board. 8-Jul-4 Duke & Son, Dorchester #257/R
£500 $925 €730 Twelve pins beyond Costolloe, Connemara (41x61cm-16x24in) s. prov. 11-Mar-4 Duke & Son, Dorchester #222

FRACANZANO, Francesco (attrib) (1612-1656) Italian
£7761 $13891 €11331 Josef and infant Christ (92x67cm-36x26in) 25-May-4 Bukowskis, Stockholm #429/R est:100000-125000 (S.KR 105000)

FRACANZANO, Francesco (circle) (1612-1656) Italian
£6627 $11000 €9675 Head of a bearded man, possibly Saint Peter (79x69cm-31x27in) 30-Sep-3 Christie's, Rockefeller NY #37/R est:4000-6000

FRADEL, Henri Joseph (1778-1865) French
£2381 $4262 €3500 Moliere and servant (65x54cm-26x21in) s. board. 22-Mar-4 Durán, Madrid #112/R est:3500

FRADET-MOUNIER, Stephane (1951-) French
Sculpture
£1119 $1902 €1600 Les 4 points cardinaux (80x80cm-31x31in) s. rusty metal orange anti-rusting paint. 28-Nov-3 Blanchet, Paris #247/R est:1500-1800

FRAENKEL, Theodore Oscar (1857-1924) American
Works on paper
£1657 $3000 €2419 New Basin Canal, New Orleans (33x25cm-13x10in) s. W/C. 3-Apr-4 Neal Auction Company, New Orleans #446/R est:1500-2500

FRAENKEL, Walter (1879-?) German
£271 $462 €396 Angels making music (80x61cm-31x24in) mono.d.1920 i. verso board. 19-Nov-3 Fischer, Luzern #2095/R (S.FR 600)

FRAGIACOMO, Pietro (1856-1922) Italian
£915 $1584 €1300 Pond in the park (14x19cm-6x7in) s. cardboard exhib. 9-Dec-3 Finarte Semenzato, Milan #40/R est:1300-1500
£1678 $2970 €2500 Landscape (11x20cm-4x8in) s. cardboard. 1-May-4 Meeting Art, Vercelli #97 est:2500
£1986 $3316 €2800 Boat in the lagoon (10x17cm-4x7in) s. board. 14-Oct-3 Finarte Semenzato, Milan #16/R est:4000
£3380 $5848 €4800 Lagoon in Venice (33x39cm-13x15in) s. cardboard. 11-Dec-3 Christie's, Rome #154/R est:3000-4000
£3521 $5845 €5000 Barche in laguna (30x45cm-12x18in) s. 11-Jun-3 Christie's, Rome #152/R est:6000-8000
£6667 $12267 €10000 Boats in the Lagoon (21x39cm-8x15in) s. 10-Jun-4 Christie's, Rome #123/R est:6000-9000
£28188 $52711 €42000 Venice (49x97cm-19x38in) s. i.verso board prov.lit. 25-Feb-4 Porro, Milan #15/R est:42000
£35507 $58232 €49000 Venice (65x103cm-26x41in) s. 27-May-3 Finarte Semenzato, Milan #86/R est:45000-55000

FRAGIACOMO, Pietro (attrib) (1856-1922) Italian
£5634 $9352 €8000 Venezia dalla Laguna (52x90cm-20x35in) s. 11-Jun-3 Christie's, Rome #175/R est:1200-1800

FRAGONARD, Alexandre Evariste (1780-1850) French
Works on paper
£704 $1218 €1000 Scene de genre (15x11cm-6x4in) s. W/C gouache. 10-Dec-3 Piasa, Paris #88/R
£1701 $3044 €2500 Christophe Colomb presentant a Ferdinand et Isabelle ses trouvailles (17x25cm-7x10in) s. pen brown ink wash htd gouache black pencil. 19-Mar-4 Piasa, Paris #123/R est:3000-4000
£22222 $37111 €32000 Homere contant l'Odyssee aux bergers (53x86cm-21x34in) s.d.1823 Chinese ink wash dr. 25-Oct-3 Dianous, Marseille #421

FRAGONARD, Jean Honore (1732-1806) French
£17105 $31474 €26000 Cuisine des saltimbanques (27x34cm-11x13in) prov.exhib.lit. 24-Jun-4 Christie's, Paris #129/R est:20000-30000
£21053 $38737 €32000 Etude d'amours (46x27cm-18x11in) oval. 23-Jun-4 Sotheby's, Paris #31/R est:30000-40000
£82759 $137379 €120000 Jupiter et Callisto (46x55cm-18x22in) prov.lit. 30-Sep-3 Christie's, Paris #18/R est:100000-150000
£502793 $900000 €734078 Watering place (51x63cm-20x25in) prov.exhib.lit. 27-May-4 Sotheby's, New York #39/R est:1000000-1500000
Prints
£2800 $5096 €4088 L'armoire (42x51cm-17x20in) etching. 1-Jul-4 Sotheby's, London #44/R est:3000-4000
Works on paper
£1256 $2249 €1834 Landscapes with trees and figures (30x23cm-12x9in) red chk pair. 25-May-4 Bukowskis, Stockholm #548/R est:15000-20000 (S.KR 17000)
£10959 $18630 €16000 Promenade dans un parc italien (17x23cm-7x9in) wash over crayon prov.exhib. 6-Nov-3 Tajan, Paris #63/R
£110345 $183172 €160000 Songe de Plutarque (35x49cm-14x19in) i. chk brush ink wash prov.exhib.lit. 30-Sep-3 Christie's, Paris #19/R est:200000-300000

FRAGONARD, Jean Honore (attrib) (1732-1806) French
Sculpture
£12057 $19532 €17000 Enfant anatomise (100x41x38cm-39x16x15in) col wax window rosewood veneer exhib.lit. 21-May-3 Artcurial Briest, Paris #254/R est:12000-15000
Works on paper
£1014 $1724 €1450 Bishop praying (47x34cm-19x13in) ochre. 27-Nov-3 Bassenge, Berlin #5424
£1200 $2196 €1752 Seated girl, leaning with folded arms on a sketch book, grazing up at the female bust on mantelpiece (29x23cm-11x9in) red chk over black chk framing lines. 7-Jul-4 Bonhams, Knightsbridge #65/R est:1500-2000

FRAGONARD, Jean Honore (circle) (1732-1806) French
£7947 $14543 €12000 Representation d'un ballet dans un parc (44x71cm-17x28in) painted c.1760. 7-Apr-4 Libert, Castor, Paris #40/R est:8000-12000

FRAGONARD, Jean Honore and GERARD, Marguerite (18th C) French
£197370 $363161 €300000 Contrat (48x56cm-19x22in) prov.lit. 24-Jun-4 Tajan, Paris #60/R est:80000-100000

FRAHM, Art (1907-1981) American
£3691 $6607 €5500 By the traffic light (81x61cm-32x24in) s. painted c.1950-1960 lit. 27-May-4 Sotheby's, Paris #114/R est:1000-1500

FRAHM, Hans (?) German
£420 $722 €600 Zugspitze in spring (82x120cm-32x47in) s. 4-Dec-3 Schopman, Hamburg #670/R
£596 $1091 €900 Beer garden (22x40cm-9x16in) s. 8-Apr-4 Dorotheum, Vienna #253/R

FRAHM-PAULI, Wilhelm (1879-?) German
£315 $526 €450 Moor canal with boat near Worspswede (68x80cm-27x31in) s.d.37. 28-Jun-3 Bolland & Marotz, Bremen #766a/R
£570 $1010 €850 Still life of fruit (60x85cm-24x33in) s.d.97. 28-Apr-4 Schopman, Hamburg #613/R

FRAICHOT, Claude Joseph (1732-1803) French
£2759 $4579 €4000 Still life with vegetables and jar (65x81cm 26x32in) prov. 1-Oct-3 Dorotheum, Vienna #183/R est:3000-4500
£11620 $19289 €16500 Nature morte aux brioches, framboises et bouteille de vin (55x69cm-22x27in) 10-Jun-3 Renaud, Paris #6/R est:2000-3000

FRAIKIN, Charles Auguste (1817-1893) Belgian
Sculpture
£6000 $10800 €8760 Bust of the water fairy (62cm-24in) white marble socle lit. 21-Apr-4 Sotheby's, London #115/R est:6000-8000

FRAILE, Alfonso (1930-1988) Spanish
£2414 $4031 €3500 Garden (50x55cm-20x22in) s. exhib. 17-Nov-3 Durán, Madrid #102/R est:2500
£7586 $12669 €11000 In the kitchen (81x100cm-32x39in) s. 17-Nov-3 Durán, Madrid #228/R est:11000
£9859 $17254 €14000 Figures (150x130cm-59x51in) s.d.1981 mixed media paper on board prov. 16-Dec-3 Segre, Madrid #152/R est:6000
£10145 $16638 €14000 En la cocina (81x100cm-32x39in) s. 27-May-3 Durán, Madrid #282/R est:11000
Works on paper
£280 $510 €420 Felicitacion (20x15cm-8x6in) s.d.1967 W/C col pencil ball point pen. 29-Jun-4 Segre, Madrid #162/R
£500 $910 €750 Untitled (20x15cm-8x6in) s. ink wash col wax crayons paper on card. 29-Jun-4 Segre, Madrid #161/R

FRAME, Robert Aaron (1924-1999) American
£1243 $2250 €1815 Sunset beach (46x61cm-18x24in) s. prov. 18-Apr-4 Bonhams & Butterfields, Los Angeles #7094 est:700-900
£5367 $9500 €7836 Nude by the window (144x162cm-57x64in) s. s.i.verso prov. 28-Apr-4 Christie's, Los Angeles #74/R est:3000-5000

FRAME, Statira E (1870-1935) Canadian
£569 $1019 €831 Indian woman sitting on a log (22x30cm-9x12in) init. i.verso prov.lit. 27-May-4 Heffel, Vancouver #64/R (C.D 1400)
£813 $1455 €1187 Summer cottage (33x40cm-13x16in) s. i.verso board prov. 27-May-4 Heffel, Vancouver #148/R est:1200-1600 (C.D 2000)

FRAMPTON, Edward Reginald (1872-1923) British
£45000 $76500 €65700 Angel of the sea (122x69cm-48x27in) s.d.1906 prov.exhib.lit. 26-Nov-3 Christie's, London #20/R est:50000-70000

FRAMPTON, Sir George James (1860-1928) British
Sculpture
£28000 $50400 €40880 Peter Pan (52cm-20in) init.i.d.1915 brown green pat bronze marble base prov.lit. 21-Apr-4 Sotheby's, London #143/R est:30000-50000
£30000 $51600 €43800 Peter Pan (52cm-20in) mono.i.d.1919 dark pat bronze incl. marble base. 4-Dec-3 Mellors & Kirk, Nottingham #1032/R

FRAN-BARO (1926-2000) French
£280 $476 €400 Nature morte aux pommes (45x53cm-18x21in) 30-Nov-3 Teitgen, Nancy #72
£350 $594 €500 Promenade au Luxembourg (20x25cm-8x10in) 30-Nov-3 Teitgen, Nancy #73
£1373 $2376 €1950 Peniches (60x73cm-24x29in) s. 14-Dec-3 Eric Pillon, Calais #216/R
£2181 $4079 €3250 Grand-Prix a DEauville (65x93cm-26x37in) s. s.i.verso. 24-Feb-4 Durán, Madrid #225/R est:1200

FRANC, François (1926-) French
£420 $701 €600 Pont de Sully (60x90cm-24x35in) s. 25-Jun-3 Blanchet, Paris #89

FRANC, Pierre (20th C) French
£464 $844 €700 Nature morte aux fleurs et aux fruits (60x60cm-24x24in) s.i.d.1932. 20-Jun-4 Imberdis, Pont Audemer #45a

FRANCAIS, Anne (1909-1995) French
£1310 $2188 €1900 Loire (60x73cm-24x29in) s. 11-Nov-3 Lesieur & Le Bars, Le Havre #33
£1793 $2994 €2600 Miroir du bois dore (110x76cm-43x30in) s. 11-Nov-3 Lesieur & Le Bars, Le Havre #32
£2013 $3745 €3000 Bain de soleil (60x91cm-24x36in) s. 7-Mar-4 Lesieur & Le Bars, Le Havre #45/R
£3448 $5759 €5000 Douarnenez (130x98cm-51x39in) s. exhib. 11-Nov-3 Lesieur & Le Bars, Le Havre #31

FRANCAIS, François Louis (1814-1897) French
£959 $1630 €1400 Bord de riviere (39x59cm-15x23in) s.d.1880. 6-Nov-3 Sotheby's, Paris #124/R est:800-1200
£1449 $2377 €2000 Vallee de l'Eaugronne a Plombieres (27x44cm-11x17in) s.d.1894. 11-May-3 Osenat, Fontainebleau #143 est:3000-3500
£1467 $2655 €2200 Baigneuses en sous-bois (33x24cm-13x9in) s. panel. 30-Mar-4 Rossini, Paris #292/R est:2200-3000
£2414 $4031 €3500 Retour du troupeau, le soir (26x35cm-10x14in) s. panel prov. 17-Nov-3 Tajan, Paris #47/R est:3500-4000
£2667 $4853 €4000 Washerwoman at the edge of a forest stream (58x70cm-23x28in) s.d.1857. 1-Jul-4 Van Ham, Cologne #1343/R est:3000
£2797 $4811 €4000 Interieur de foret (39x56cm-15x22in) s. panel painted c.1850. 7-Dec-3 Osenat, Fontainebleau #116 est:5000-6000
£3667 $6637 €5500 Vallee de Rossillon (61x46cm-24x18in) s.i.d.1873 exhib.lit. 30-Mar-4 Rossini, Paris #291/R est:5000-8000
£19444 $31694 €28000 Paysage hivernal (101x135cm-40x53in) s. 26-Sep-3 Rabourdin & Choppin de Janvry, Paris #49/R est:4000-4500
Works on paper
£933 $1689 €1400 Autoportrait (58x47cm-23x19in) pastel lit. 30-Mar-4 Rossini, Paris #294/R

FRANCALANCIA, Riccardo (1886-1965) Italian
£1580 $2687 €2260 Landscape with valley (25x33cm-10x13in) s.d.1921. 18-Nov-3 Babuino, Rome #368/R
£6081 $10703 €9000 Street in Wales I (42x34cm-17x13in) s.d.1928 board exhib.lit. 24-May-4 Christie's, Milan #220/R est:10000-15000
£11511 $18878 €16000 Villages. Landscape (67x82cm-26x32in) s.d.27 pair. 10-Jun-3 Pandolfini, Florence #302/R est:16000-18000

FRANCE, Ada (19/20th C) ?
£250 $400 €365 Still life of fruit, nuts and claret jug (51x76cm-20x30in) s.d.1906. 18-Sep-3 Goldings, Lincolnshire #774/R
£360 $659 €526 Still life of fruit, flowers and a ewer on a table (48x74cm-19x29in) s.d.1903. 6-Jul-4 Bonhams, Knightsbridge #75/R
£425 $680 €621 Still life study of fruit, roses and wine jug (51x76cm-20x30in) 18-Sep-3 Goldings, Lincolnshire #752/R
£550 $1018 €803 Still life with pinks and red roses in a wicker basket. Still life with flower around a vase (32x94cm-13x37in) s.d.1905 one s.d.1901 pair. 15-Jan-4 Christie's, Kensington #1043/R

FRANCE, Anatole (1844-1924) French
Works on paper
£467 $859 €700 Mon coeur est a toi (8x12cm-3x5in) pen. 9-Jun-4 Piasa, Paris #69

FRANCE, Felix (1844-1903) French?
£1565 $2801 €2300 Nature morte au violon (59x81cm-23x32in) s. 21-Mar-4 Muizon & Le Coent, Paris #33/R

FRANCE, Patricia (1911-1995) New Zealander
£426 $753 €622 Still life for Nikki (39x30cm-15x12in) s. board. 28-Apr-4 Dunbar Sloane, Auckland #79/R (NZ.D 1200)
£433 $774 €632 Still life of flowers in vase (54x43cm-21x17in) s. board. 12-May-4 Dunbar Sloane, Wellington #116/R est:1500-3000 (NZ.D 1250)
Works on paper
£714 $1314 €1042 Girl in a field. s.d.1977 gouache prov. 25-Mar-4 International Art Centre, Auckland #134/R (NZ.D 2000)
£1306 $2259 €1907 Figures in landscape III (39x45cm-15x18in) s. gouache board. 9-Dec-3 Peter Webb, Auckland #17/R est:2500-3500 (NZ.D 3500)

FRANCES, Fernanda (19th C) Spanish
£285 $505 €425 Still life with lobster (57x70cm-22x28in) s.d.1879. 27-Apr-4 Durán, Madrid #1208/R

FRANCES, Juana (1926-) Spanish
£1200 $2172 €1800 Comet (73x95cm-29x37in) s.d.1985 acrylic paper exhib.lit. 30-Mar-4 Segre, Madrid #183/R est:1200

FRANCESCA, Piero della (after) (?-1492) Italian
£8000 $13600 €11680 Duchess of Urbino. Duke of Urbino (49x34cm-19x13in) s.verso oil on ceramic pair. 31-Oct-3 Christie's, Kensington #115/R est:5000-7000

FRANCESCHI, Louis Julien (1825-1893) French
Sculpture
£1268 $2104 €1800 Seated nude, flanked by a couple of pigeons (63cm-25in) s. brown pat. bronze. 11-Jun-3 Sotheby's, Amsterdam #294/R est:2000-3000

FRANCESCHI, Mariano de (1849-1896) Italian
£650 $1164 €949 Fountain of the Academy - Rome (49x64cm-19x25in) s. 10-May-4 Joel, Victoria #247/R est:1000-2000 (A.D 1600)

FRANCESCHINI, Baldassare (1611-1689) Italian
£320000 $553600 €467200 Diana and Callisto (200x258cm-79x102in) prov.lit. 11-Dec-3 Sotheby's, London #19/R est:150000-200000
Works on paper
£430 $783 €650 Madonna visited by two angels (18x22cm-7x9in) sanguine. 18-Jun-4 Bolland & Marotz, Bremen #452
£546 $1000 €797 Adoration of the Shepherds (19x27cm-7x11in) i. pencil black chk card stock. 29-Jan-4 Swann Galleries, New York #61/R
£1892 $3500 €2762 Seated woman with three small children asleep on her lap (79x112cm-31x44in) s. red chk htd white. 16-Jan-4 Aspire, Cleveland #98/R est:6000-8000
£22000 $40260 €32120 Young musician playing the violin (17x16cm-7x6in) bears attrib red chk prov. 8-Jul-4 Sotheby's, London #52/R est:12000-15000

FRANCESCHINI, Baldassare (attrib) (1611-1689) Italian
Works on paper
£380 $700 €555 St Anthony (18x10cm-7x4in) conte crayon. 26-Jun-4 Selkirks, St. Louis #442/R

FRANCESCHINI, Baldassare (studio) (1611-1689) Italian
£11034 $18317 €16000 Christ with Crown of Thorns (72x58cm-28x23in) prov. 1-Oct-3 Dorotheum, Vienna #14/R est:6000-9000

FRANCESCHINI, Edoardo (1928-) Italian
£268 $497 €400 Composition (60x50cm-24x20in) s.s.d.1991 verso. 13-Mar-4 Meeting Art, Vercelli #291
£436 $807 €650 Composition (90x90cm-35x35in) s.d.1960 mixed media cardboard. 13-Mar-4 Meeting Art, Vercelli #12
£458 $801 €650 Study for man (100x80cm-39x31in) s.d.1965. 17-Dec-3 Il Ponte, Milan #872
£533 $981 €800 Composition (70x60cm-28x24in) s.d.1979 verso. 10-Jun-4 Galleria Pace, Milan #38/R
£1267 $2331 €1900 Untitled (130x162cm-51x64in) s.d.1961. 12-Jun-4 Meeting Art, Vercelli #856/R est:1500

FRANCESCHINI, Marco Antonio (1648-1729) Italian
£26000 $44980 €37960 Holy Family with Saint Anne (69x55cm-27x22in) 10-Dec-3 Christie's, London #102/R est:20000-30000
Works on paper
£3741 $6697 €5500 Thetis confiant le jeune Achille au centaure Chiron (34x41cm-13x16in) pen brown ink brown wash htd white. 18-Mar-4 Christie's, Paris #63/R est:3000-5000

FRANCESCO, Benjamino de (?-1869) Italian
£563 $975 €800 Petrarca's house (22x21cm-9x8in) s.d.1839 paper. 10-Dec-3 Sotheby's, Milan #155 est:800-1200

FRANCESE, Franco (1920-1996) Italian
£3000 $5400 €4500 Love night (67x70cm-26x28in) s. s.i.d.1959 verso canvas on board. 22-Apr-4 Finarte Semenzato, Rome #206/R est:3500-3800
Works on paper
£342 $582 €500 Untitled (22x25cm-9x10in) s. chl. 7-Nov-3 Galleria Rosenberg, Milan #26/R
£933 $1717 €1400 Girl with cow (53x43cm-21x17in) s.d.1953 chl. 8-Jun-4 Finarte Semenzato, Milan #129/R est:300-400

FRANCHERE, Joseph-Charles (1866-1921) Canadian
£313 $538 €457 Pond (11x20cm-4x8in) s. panel. 2-Dec-3 Joyner Waddington, Toronto #499 (C.D 700)
£407 $639 €594 Autumn scene (11x20cm-4x8in) s. board. 26-Aug-3 Iegor de Saint Hippolyte, Montreal #80 (C.D 900)
£1210 $2226 €1767 Afternoon glow, Laurentians (22x33cm-9x13in) s. panel. 9-Jun-4 Walker's, Ottawa #2/R est:1500-2000 (C.D 3000)
£4241 $7295 €6192 Lady with parasol (40x55cm-16x22in) s. 2-Dec-3 Joyner Waddington, Toronto #203/R est:8000-10000 (C.D 9500)

FRANCHI, Alberto Zeballos (19/20th C) Italian
£900 $1503 €1314 Aztec ceremony (64x122cm-25x48in) s. 14-Oct-3 Sotheby's, London #230/R

FRANCHI, Antonio (1634-1709) Italian
£15000 $27450 €21900 Allegory of Music, Saint Cecilia (87x67cm-34x26in) oval prov. 8-Jul-4 Sotheby's, London #159/R est:15000-20000

FRANCHI, Antonio (attrib) (1634-1709) Italian
£7263 $13000 €10604 Flora. Ceres (73x61cm-29x24in) pair prov. 27-May-4 Sotheby's, New York #82/R est:10000-15000
£7394 $12940 €10500 Portrait of lady in black. i.verso. 17-Dec-3 Christie's, Rome #472/R est:7000-10000

FRANCHINA, Nino (1912-1988) Italian
Sculpture
£1379 $2303 €2000 Red wing (47cm-19in) metal wood enamel one of 4 prov. 13-Nov-3 Finarte Semenzato, Rome #277/R est:1800-2200
Works on paper
£326 $535 €450 Untitled (50x35cm-20x14in) s.d.62 felt-tip pen prov. 27-May-3 Sotheby's, Milan #167/R

FRANCIA, Alexandre T (1820-1884) French
£1258 $2290 €1900 Le depart des pecheurs (21x30cm-8x12in) mono. panel. 15-Jun-4 Vanderkindere, Brussels #154 est:2000-3000
£2740 $4658 €4000 Vue des environs de Venise (41x64cm-16x25in) s. 6-Nov-3 Sotheby's, Paris #121/R est:2000-3000
Works on paper
£1200 $2148 €1752 City ablaze (44x68cm-17x27in) s. pencil W/C scratching out. 26-May-4 Christie's, Kensington #413/R est:1200-1800

FRANCIA, Camillo (1955-) Italian
£282 $468 €400 Giusto equilibrio (50x50cm-20x20in) s. s.i.d.2002. 14-Jun-3 Meeting Art, Vercelli #549
£317 $526 €450 Risaia (50x50cm-20x20in) s.i.d.2001 enamel oil wood. 14-Jun-3 Meeting Art, Vercelli #347
£317 $526 €450 Bambino (50x50cm-20x20in) s. s.d.2001 verso. 14-Jun-3 Meeting Art, Vercelli #587
£333 $613 €500 Angel (80x45cm-31x18in) s.d.2003 tempera terracotta board lit. 12-Jun-4 Meeting Art, Vercelli #65
£347 $638 €520 Lady (50x50cm-20x20in) s. s.i.d.2000 verso lit. 12-Jun-4 Meeting Art, Vercelli #47
£352 $585 €500 Simbiosi (55x32cm-22x13in) s.i.d.2000 verso oil assembly panel. 14-Jun-3 Meeting Art, Vercelli #24/R
£369 $683 €550 Portrait (45x55cm-18x22in) s. s.i.d.2001 verso. 13-Mar-4 Meeting Art, Vercelli #51
£400 $736 €600 Strength of faith (100x100cm-39x39in) s. s.i.d.2000 verso. 12-Jun-4 Meeting Art, Vercelli #41/R
£467 $859 €700 Flowers (70x40cm-28x16in) s. s.i.d.2000 verso. 12-Jun-4 Meeting Art, Vercelli #420
£604 $1117 €900 Migrations (80x80cm-31x31in) s. painted 2001 lit. 13-Mar-4 Meeting Art, Vercelli #387
£667 $1227 €1000 Angel (100x100cm-39x39in) s. painted 2001 lit. 12-Jun-4 Meeting Art, Vercelli #502/R
£805 $1442 €1200 Night in Jerusalem (100x100cm-39x39in) s.i.d.200 verso lit. 30-May-4 Meeting Art, Vercelli #11
£1000 $1840 €1500 Sunny landscape (100x150cm-39x59in) s.i.d.2002 verso exhib.lit. 12-Jun-4 Meeting Art, Vercelli #859/R est:1500
£1007 $1862 €1500 Right balance (150x100cm-59x39in) s.i.d.2001 verso lit. 13-Mar-4 Meeting Art, Vercelli #115 est:1500

FRANCIA, Francesco di Marco (1450-1517) Italian
£307042 $509690 €436000 Saint Francis receiving the stigmatae (29x55cm-11x22in) board lit. 11-Jun-3 Semenzato, Florence #22/R est:450000-500000

FRANCIA, Francesco di Marco (school) (1450-1517) Italian
£6294 $10825 €9000 Madonna and Child (62x47cm-24x19in) board. 2-Dec-3 Sotheby's, Milan #74/R est:8000-12000

FRANCIA, François Louis Thomas (1772-1839) French
Works on paper
£946 $1665 €1400 Mountain gorge, with mine buildings (19x14cm-7x6in) bears i.verso W/C prov. 19-May-4 Sotheby's, Amsterdam #367/R
£1200 $2220 €1752 Continental town (17x23cm-7x9in) s.indis.i.d.1814 W/C. 9-Mar-4 Bonhams, New Bond Street #44/R est:1500-2000

FRANCIA, Giacomo (1486-1557) Italian
£6500 $11700 €9490 Mystic marriage of Saint Catherine (76x62cm-30x24in) panel. 23-Apr-4 Christie's, Kensington #203/R est:5000-7000

FRANCIS, Dorothea (?) ?
£421 $767 €615 White House. board. 1-Jul-4 Joel, Victoria #344 (A.D 1100)

FRANCIS, George (18th C) American?

Works on paper

£679	$1100	€991	Portrait of Mr William Syndercombe. Portrait of Mrs Syndercombe (15cm-6in) i.verso ink wash pair oval. 3-Aug-3 North East Auctions, Portsmouth #1850/R

FRANCIS, Ivor Pengelly (1906-1993) Australian

£1029	$1862	€1502	Balanced king size (76x61cm-30x24in) s.d.66 s.i.verso. 31-Mar-4 Goodman, Sydney #427/R (A.D 2500)

FRANCIS, John (1780-1861) British

Sculpture

£2410	$4000	€3519	Veiled lady (74x53x25cm-29x21x10in) s.d.1839 verso marble. 4-Oct-3 Neal Auction Company, New Orleans #316/R est:3000-5000

FRANCIS, John F (1808-1886) American

£824	$1500	€1203	Still life with fruit and sweets (61x46cm-24x18in) 19-Jun-4 Jackson's, Cedar Falls #15/R est:3000-5000
£2844	$4750	€4152	Apples, oranges and grapes (15x23cm-6x9in) s.d.1869 panel prov. 23-Oct-3 Shannon's, Milford #170/R est:3000-5000
£18466	$32500	€26960	Still life fruit and wine glass (38x48cm-15x19in) s.d.1856 prov.exhib.lit. 19-May-4 Sotheby's, New York #75/R est:3000-50000

FRANCIS, Linda (20th C) American

£278	$500	€406	Untitled (58x60cm-23x24in) 24-Apr-4 David Rago, Lambertville #125/R

Works on paper

£264	$475	€385	Untitled (33x60cm-13x24in) s.d.1978 pastel pencil. 24-Apr-4 David Rago, Lambertville #121/R

FRANCIS, Margaret (1909-1987) Australian

Works on paper

£451	$712	€658	Children in the street (50x35cm-20x14in) s. gouache. 2-Sep-3 Deutscher-Menzies, Melbourne #371/R (A.D 1100)

FRANCIS, Mark (1962-) British

£400	$740	€584	Abstract landscape (48x48cm-19x19in) canvas on board. 13-Jul-4 Bonhams, Knightsbridge #62/R
£509	$850	€743	Untitled (776x776cm-306x306in) monotype oil based ink. 16-Nov-3 Bonhams & Butterfields, Los Angeles #7098/R
£5000	$9200	€7500	Oscillate - Study (92x92cm-36x36in) s.i.d.1997 verso prov. 8-Jun-4 Artcurial Briest, Paris #286/R est:5000-7000
£5028	$9000	€7341	Positive, clones (244x213cm-96x84in) s.i.d.94 verso prov. 14-May-4 Phillips, New York #327/R est:10000-15000
£5500	$10010	€8030	Compression no 4 (99x91cm-39x36in) s.i.d.1994 stretcher prov. 6-Feb-4 Sotheby's, London #266/R est:5000-7000
£6486	$12000	€9470	Study for Cluster (91x76cm-36x30in) s.d.94 i.verso prov. 12-Feb-4 Sotheby's, New York #341/R est:4000-6000
£7000	$12880	€10220	Compression No. 7 (108x88cm-43x35in) s.i.d.94 verso prov. 24-Jun-4 Sotheby's, London #297/R est:5000-7000
£7500	$12525	€10950	Untitled (177x152cm-70x60in) painted c.1995 prov. 21-Oct-3 Sotheby's, London #448/R est:7000-9000
£8000	$14320	€11680	Abacus (213x183cm-84x72in) s.i.d.1997 verso. 13-May-4 Sotheby's, London #75/R est:8000-12000
£9000	$16560	€13140	Growth (152x122cm-60x48in) s.i.d.95 verso prov.exhib. 25-Jun-4 Christie's, London #228/R est:8000-12000
£9000	$16380	€13140	Grid, TW VB IY plus B (213x213cm-84x84in) s.d.1997 verso pr. 21-Jun-4 Bonhams, New Bond Street #167/R est:10000-15000
£17000	$30770	€24820	Untitled (213x183cm-84x72in) s.d.1996 verso prov. 1-Apr-4 Christie's, Kensington #322/R est:10000-15000
£18000	$30060	€26280	Surface, hyphae (213x183cm-84x72in) s.i.d.98 verso prov. 22-Oct-3 Christie's, London #133/R est:10000-15000

FRANCIS, Michael (20th C) American

£251	$450	€366	Key Bridge overcast (30x41cm-12x16in) s. s.i.verso panel prov. 20-Mar-4 Sloans & Kenyon, Bethesda #349/R

FRANCIS, Mike (1938-) British

£650	$1164	€949	Morning Tease (122x122cm-48x48in) s. acrylic board. 16-Mar-4 Bonhams, Knightsbridge #55/R
£700	$1253	€1022	And all things nice (122x91cm-48x36in) s. acrylic board painted 1980. 16-Mar-4 Bonhams, Knightsbridge #56/R

FRANCIS, Ron (20th C) Australian?

£1570	$2669	€2292	Blind leading the blind (106x121cm-42x48in) s.verso painted c.1985. 29-Oct-3 Lawson Menzies, Sydney #138/R est:1000-2000 (A.D 3800)

FRANCIS, Sam (1923-1994) American

£1748	$3182	€2552	Untitled (48x39cm-19x15in) i.d.1980 acrylic on paper prov. 29-Jun-4 Peter Webb, Auckland #107/R est:4500-7500 (NZ.D 5000)
£2096	$3500	€3060	Untitled - SF80-1125 (34x26cm-13x10in) s.i.d.1980 acrylic on paper prov. 14-Nov-3 Phillips, New York #318/R est:4000-6000
£3784	$7000	€5525	Untitled (45x30cm-18x12in) s.d.80 verso acrylic paper. 12-Feb-4 Sotheby's, New York #285/R est:3000-4000
£4500	$7155	€6525	Untitled (32x37cm-13x15in) s.d.81 acrylic on paper. 11-Sep-3 Christie's, Kensington #252/R est:4000-6000
£4514	$7448	€6500	Composition bleue (48x31cm-19x12in) s.verso acrylic painted c.1960 prov. 2-Jul-3 Cornette de St.Cyr, Paris #95/R est:6000-8000
£4514	$7538	€6500	Composition rouge (43x32cm-17x13in) s.d.1960 verso acrylic. 25-Oct-3 Cornette de St.Cyr, Paris #683/R est:7000-8000
£4800	$7632	€6960	Untitled (34x28cm-13x11in) st.sig. acrylic on paper painted c.1990-92. 11-Sep-3 Christie's, Kensington #253/R est:4000-6000
£5000	$8350	€7300	Untitled (45x31cm-18x12in) s.d.1989 verso acrylic paper. 21-Oct-3 Sotheby's, London #347/R est:7000-10000
£5500	$9185	€8030	Untitled, SF75-1131 (35x43cm-14x17in) s.verso acrylic paper painted c.1975-78 prov. 22-Oct-3 Christie's, London #60/R est:5000-7000
£5500	$9185	€8030	Untitled, SF75-1130 (39x48cm-15x19in) st.verso acrylic paper painted c.1975 prov. 22-Oct-3 Christie's, London #61/R est:6000-8000
£6500	$11830	€9490	Untitled (45x30cm-18x12in) s.d.1990 verso oil acrylic paper prov. 4-Feb-4 Sotheby's, Olympia #86/R est:5000-7000
£7642	$13908	€11157	Eight (46x31cm-18x12in) s.d.1986 verso acrylic. 17-Jun-4 Kornfeld, Bern #365/R est:12500 (S.FR 17500)
£8054	$14416	€12000	Untitled (60x45cm-24x18in) s.i. verso acrylic paper. 25-May-4 Dorotheum, Vienna #94/R est:12000-16000
£8500	$14195	€12410	Flash point (82x58cm-32x23in) s.d.1975 verso acrylic paper prov.exhib. 21-Oct-3 Sotheby's, London #341/R est:8000-12000
£8800	$14696	€12848	Untitled (41x33cm-16x13in) s.d.1967 verso acrylic on paper. 22-Oct-3 Bonhams, New Bond Street #81/R est:9000-12000
£9000	$16560	€13140	Untitled - SF86-101 (38x76cm-15x30in) acrylic on paper painted 1986. 25-Jun-4 Christie's, London #193/R est:8000-12000
£9581	$16000	€13988	Untitled (107x71cm-42x28in) s.d.1967 verso acrylic prov. 12-Nov-3 Christie's, Rockefeller NY #358/R est:12000-18000
£9722	$16042	€14000	SF 85/24 (78x40cm-31x16in) acrylic prov. 2-Jul-3 Cornette de St.Cyr, Paris #93/R est:15000-20000
£10000	$18200	€14600	Untitled (48x73cm-19x29in) acrylic exhib. 6-Feb-4 Sotheby's, London #234/R est:6000-8000
£10169	$18000	€14847	Venice (105x86cm-41x34in) s.i.d.1990 verso prov. 2-May-4 Bonhams & Butterfields, Los Angeles #3065/R est:15000-20000
£10860	$18462	€15856	Untitled (33x22cm-13x9in) s.d.1989 verso acrylic paper prov. 22-Nov-3 Burkhard, Luzern #140/R est:18000-22000 (S.FR 24000)
£14724	$24000	€21497	Untitled (77x61cm-30x24in) acrylic canvas on matboard prov.exhib. 23-Sep-3 Christie's, Rockefeller NY #117/R est:20000-30000
£16760	$30000	€24470	Untitled (69x103cm-27x41in) s.d.1968 verso acrylic paper prov.exhib. 13-May-4 Sotheby's, New York #250/R est:20000-30000
£16760	$30000	€24470	Untitled (73x61cm-29x24in) s.d.1972 verso acrylic prov. 14-May-4 Phillips, New York #266/R est:30000-40000
£17483	$30070	€25000	Untitled (75x56cm-30x22in) s.i.d.1972 verso acrylic paper prov. 2-Dec-3 Calmels Cohen, Paris #75/R est:25000-30000
£18182	$31273	€26000	Composition (55x76cm-22x30in) s.d.1976 verso acrylic W/C paper prov. 4-Dec-3 Van Ham, Cologne #145/R est:32000
£19444	$31694	€28000	Untitled (73x60cm-29x24in) s.d.1972 acrylic. 27-Sep-3 Dr Fritz Nagel, Stuttgart #9525/R est:35000
£20958	$35000	€30599	Untitled (75x105cm-30x41in) s.d.1978 verso acrylic paper prov.exhib. 13-Nov-3 Sotheby's, New York #262/R est:35000-45000
£21472	$35000	€31349	Untitled, bright ring no 1 (220x350cm-87x138in) acrylic. 23-Sep-3 Christie's, Rockefeller NY #118/R est:10000-60000
£22455	$37500	€32784	Untitled (52x106cm-20x42in) s. acrylic paper on foamcore prov.exhib. 13-Nov-3 Sotheby's, New York #301/R est:25000-35000
£23464	$42000	€34257	2 Pri - Rain (57x76cm-22x30in) s.i.d.1964 verso oil gouache paper prov. 12-May-4 Christie's, Rockefeller NY #147/R est:30000-40000
£24000	$43680	€35040	Los Angeles (33x24cm-13x9in) s.i.d.1963 verso acrylic paper prov. 6-Feb-4 Sotheby's, London #143/R est:16000-20000
£29940	$50000	€43712	Yellow (70x104cm-28x41in) oil gouache paper painted 1964 prov.exhib. 12-Nov-3 Christie's, Rockefeller NY #320/R est:60000-80000
£32314	$58812	€47178	Yellow stream (185x92cm-73x36in) s.d.16/7/1990 acrylic paper. 18-Jun-4 Kornfeld, Bern #40/R est:70000 (S.FR 74000)
£35928	$60000	€52455	Untitled (93x182cm-37x72in) st.sig. acrylic rice paper painted 1977 prov.exhib. 12-Nov-3 Christie's, Rockefeller NY #415/R est:35000-45000
£47486	$85000	€69330	Composition (91x102cm-36x40in) s.d.48 prov.exhib. 12-May-4 Christie's, Rockefeller NY #122/R est:50000-70000
£47486	$85000	€69330	Untitled (120x90cm-47x35in) s.d.1988 verso acrylic prov.exhib. 13-May-4 Sotheby's, New York #251/R est:40000-60000
£48035	$88384	€70131	Untitled (93x181cm-37x71in) s. verso acrylic ricepaper prov.exhib. 8-Jun-4 Germann, Zurich #89/R est:100000-130000 (S.FR 110000)
£55000	$91850	€80300	Fragrant breath, SFP80-43 (242x150cm-95x59in) s.d.1980 verso acrylic prov.exhib. 22-Oct-3 Christie's, London #66/R est:40000-60000
£56886	$95000	€83054	Untitled (183x92cm-72x36in) s.d.1984 verso acrylic exhib.lit. 12-Nov-3 Christie's, Rockefeller NY #425/R est:60000-80000
£69832	$125000	€101955	Untitled (153x183cm-60x72in) s.d.1973 verso acrylic prov. 12-May-4 Christie's, Rockefeller NY #159/R est:70000-90000
£74000	$134680	€108040	Untitled (60x100cm-24x39in) s.verso acrylic paper prov. 6-Feb-4 Sotheby's, London #145/R est:40000-60000
£85000	$156400	€124100	Dark blue (65x54cm-26x21in) s.d.54 verso prov.exhib. 23-Jun-4 Sotheby's, London #25/R est:120000-150000
£418994	$750000	€611731	White (246x150cm-97x59in) painted 1952 prov.exhib. 11-May-4 Christie's, Rockefeller NY #24/R est:400000-600000

Prints

£1657	$3000	€2419	From the Pasadena Box (60x40cm-24x16in) s.num.8/100 col lithograph. 19-Apr-4 Bonhams & Butterfields, San Francisco #255/R est:2000-3000
£1765	$3000	€2577	Ting (59x75cm-23x30in) s. col screenprint. 31-Oct-3 Sotheby's, New York #537/R
£1882	$3200	€2748	Untitled (48x71cm-19x28in) s. num.24/75 etching aquatint. 7-Nov-3 Selkirks, St. Louis #451/R est:3000-4000
£1902	$3500	€2777	Untitled (72x101cm-28x40in) s. col lithograph. 8-Jun-4 Auctions by the Bay, Alameda #1136/R
£1977	$3500	€2886	Untitled (66x91cm-26x36in) s.num.28/40 col lithograph. 28-Apr-4 Christie's, Rockefeller NY #271/R est:5000-7000
£2000	$3660	€3000	Blue dip (61x47cm-24x19in) s.i. col lithograph. 4-Jun-4 Lempertz, Koln #140/R est:3200
£2000	$3680	€3000	Another disappearance (57x76cm-22x30in) s. col lithograph. 11-Jun-4 Hauswedell & Nolte, Hamburg #1258/R est:3000
£2028	$3448	€2900	Heart stone (63x90cm-25x35in) s. col lithograph. 29-Nov-3 Villa Grisebach, Berlin #773/R est:1500-2000
£2054	$3800	€2999	Trietto 3 (70x99cm-28x39in) s.num.57/66 col aquatint. 12-Feb-4 Christie's, Rockefeller NY #67/R est:2500-3500
£2059	$3500	€3006	Trietto 3 (68x98cm-27x39in) s. col aquatint. 31-Oct-3 Sotheby's, New York #540/R
£2341	$3980	€3418	Freshet - composition (97x74cm-38x29in) s.num.32/100 col silkscreen lit. 4-Nov-3 Bukowskis, Stockholm #370/R est:20000-25000 (S.KR 31000)
£2348	$4250	€3428	Ting (60x75cm-24x30in) s.num.44/75 col silkscreen. 19-Apr-4 Bonhams & Butterfields, San Francisco #256/R est:2500-3500
£2365	$4234	€3500	Bright jade ghost V (64x90cm-25x35in) s. num.6/6 col lithograph exec.1963. 4-May-4 Calmels Cohen, Paris #110/R est:3500-4000
£2432	$4500	€3551	Trietto 4 (97x120cm-38x47in) s.num.33/66 col aquatint. 12-Feb-4 Christie's, Rockefeller NY #68/R est:3500-4500
£2500	$4575	€3650	Doubled cross (69x105cm-27x41in) s.num.28/30 col lithograph. 3-Jun-4 Christie's, Kensington #347/R est:2500-3000
£2982	$4979	€4324	Firework. s.i. col lithograph. 19-Jun-3 Kornfeld, Bern #393 est:7500 (S.FR 6500)
£3057	$5563	€4463	Chinese balloons. s.i. col lithograph. 17-Jun-4 Kornfeld, Bern #367 est:7500 (S.FR 7000)
£3057	$5563	€4463	Heart stone. s.i. col lithograph. 17-Jun-4 Kornfeld, Bern #368/R est:7500 (S.FR 7000)

£3500 $6370 €5110 Untitled (61x46cm-24x18in) s.num.17/20 col aquatint. 1-Jul-4 Sotheby's, London #330/R est:3500-4000
£3578 $5975 €5188 Black circle (45x60cm-18x24in) s.i. col lithograph. 19-Jun-3 Kornfeld, Bern #394 est:5000 (S.FR 7800)
£3761 $6282 €5453 Pasadena box. s.i. col lithograph. 19-Jun-3 Kornfeld, Bern #395 est:5000 (S.FR 8200)
£4520 $8000 €6599 Foot print (63x90cm-25x35in) s. num.20/55 col lithograph. 30-Apr-4 Sotheby's, New York #327/R est:5000-6000
£5085 $9000 €7424 Untitled (152x107cm-60x42in) i. monotype oil paint. 30-Apr-4 Sotheby's, New York #330/R est:10000-15000
£5294 $9000 €7729 King corpse (106x149cm-42x59in) s. col screenprint. 31-Oct-3 Sotheby's, New York #538/R
£5588 $9500 €8158 Untitled (213x153cm-84x60in) s. num.20/56 col screenprint exec.1986. 4-Nov-3 Christie's, Rockefeller NY #236/R est:10000-15000
£5588 $9500 €8158 Untitled (65x75cm-26x30in) s. monotype oil pigment exec.1982. 4-Nov-3 Christie's, Rockefeller NY #234/R est:12000-18000
£6114 $11127 €8926 The upper yellow. s.i. col lithograph. 17-Jun-4 Kornfeld, Bern #366/R est:10000 (S.FR 14000)
£6215 $11000 €9074 Ammonite (57x57cm-22x22in) s.i.verso col pigment monotype. 28-Apr-4 Christie's, Rockefeller NY #273/R est:8000-12000
£6215 $11000 €9074 Untitled (198x102cm-78x40in) s.i.verso col pigment monotype. 28-Apr-4 Christie's, Rockefeller NY #275/R est:10000-11000
£10169 $18000 €14847 Pasadena box, Pasadena, California (43x43cm-17x17in) s.num. col lithograph set of eight box. 28-Apr-4 Christie's, Rockefeller NY #272/R est:18000-22000
£10734 $19000 €15672 Untitled (107x192cm-42x76in) s.i.verso col pigment oil monotype. 28-Apr-4 Christie's, Rockefeller NY #274/R est:15000-18000
£11864 $21000 €17321 Untitled (212x151cm-83x59in) s. num.46/56 col screenprint. 30-Apr-4 Sotheby's, New York #329/R est:10000-15000
£14124 $25000 €20621 Untitled (199x76cm-78x30in) s. col monotype. 30-Apr-4 Sotheby's, New York #328/R est:20000-30000
£15284 $27817 €22315 The white line (85x63cm-33x25in) s. col lithograph. 18-Jun-4 Kornfeld, Bern #41/R est:40000 (S.FR 35000)
Works on paper
£1923 $3500 €2808 Untitled (63x48cm-25x19in) chl executed c.1959 prov. 29-Jun-4 Sotheby's, New York #466/R est:5000-7000
£2577 $4200 €3762 Untitled (48x31cm-19x12in) s. ink exec.c.1950-53 prov.exhib. 23-Sep-3 Christie's, Rockefeller NY #17/R est:6000-8000
£2797 $4755 €4000 Composition (51x40cm-20x16in) mixed media. 25-Nov-3 Tajan, Paris #45/R est:8000-10000
£2903 $5342 €4238 Composition (49x64cm-19x25in) gouache. 14-Jun-4 Waddingtons, Toronto #19/R est:8000-12000 (C.D 7200)
£3057 $5563 €4463 Tokyo 1974 (35x28cm-14x11in) s.i.d.1974 verso bodycol. 17-Jun-4 Kornfeld, Bern #363 est:10000 (S.FR 7000)
£3293 $5500 €4808 Untitled, from Pasadena box no 77 (9x9cm-4x4in) s.verso gouache exec.c.1964 prov. 7-Oct-3 Sotheby's, New York #400 est:6000-8000
£3600 $6624 €5400 SF74-780 (22x20cm-9x8in) s. gouache. 11-Jun-4 Farsetti, Prato #179/R est:5000-6000
£3846 $7000 €5615 Sketch (33x53cm-13x21in) s.i.d.1965 verso gouache prov. 29-Jun-4 Sotheby's, New York #471/R est:7000-9000
£6419 $11298 €9500 Papillons bleus (14x10cm-6x4in) s. verso W/C prov. 18-May-4 Tajan, Paris #70/R est:9500-11000
£6422 $10725 €9312 Red and blue (20x30cm-8x12in) s.d.1961 verso bodycol W/C. 19-Jun-3 Kornfeld, Bern #385/R est:10000 (S.FR 14000)
£7343 $12483 €10500 Composition (38x57cm-15x22in) mixed media. 25-Nov-3 Tajan, Paris #46/R est:10000-12000
£7931 $13482 €11579 Untitled (44x33cm-17x13in) s.d.1960 gouache. 5-Nov-3 AB Stockholms Auktionsverk #1170/R est:100000-125000 (S.KR 105000)
£9441 $15766 €13500 Composition (48x31cm-19x12in) studio st. W/C prov. 29-Jun-3 Versailles Encheres #86/R
£10429 $17000 €15226 Untitled (54x43cm-21x17in) s.d.1953 Dec verso ink W/C prov.exhib.lit. 23-Sep-3 Christie's, Rockefeller NY #14/R est:10000-15000
£10667 $19627 €16000 SFM 78-028 (68x78cm-27x31in) s.i.verso oil powdered pigment ink exec 1978 lit. 8-Jun-4 Sotheby's, Amsterdam #129/R est:12000-15000
£14085 $23521 €20564 Composition (36x23cm-14x9in) s.i.d.1959 verso gouache oil prov. 7-Oct-3 Rasmussen, Copenhagen #95/R est:75000-100000 (D.KR 150000)
£16667 $30667 €25000 Untitled (30x14cm-12x6in) s.i.d. verso W/C tempera. 11-Jun-4 Hauswedell & Nolte, Hamburg #1255/R est:18000
£16760 $30000 €24470 Untitled (27x35cm-11x14in) s. gouache exec 1960 prov. 12-May-4 Christie's, Rockefeller NY #146/R est:30000-40000
£19553 $35000 €28547 Untitled - Tokyo (69x101cm-27x40in) s.d.1973 verso gouache acrylic prov. 12-May-4 Christie's, Rockefeller NY #212/R est:25000-35000
£21834 $39738 €31878 Blue in black (41x45cm-16x18in) s.i.d.1950 verso W/C. 18-Jun-4 Kornfeld, Bern #38/R est:27500 (S.FR 50000)
£30667 $56427 €46000 Flash (46x46cm-18x18in) s.i.d. verso W/C tempera. 11-Jun-4 Hauswedell & Nolte, Hamburg #1256/R est:30000
£58952 $107293 €86070 Blue balls (92x46cm-36x18in) s.i.d.1963 W/C. 18-Jun-4 Kornfeld, Bern #39/R est:60000 (S.FR 135000)

FRANCIS, Thomas E (fl.1899-1912) British
£640 $1146 €934 Thames at Goring. Kingston Blount, Oxfordshire (39x59cm-15x23in) s. pair. 16-Mar-4 Bonhams, Oxford #57
Works on paper
£181 $334 €264 Romorantin, France (32x47cm-13x19in) s. i.verso W/C. 14-Jun-4 Waddingtons, Toronto #60/R (C.D 450)
£300 $501 €438 Britwell Salome (28x38cm-11x15in) s. W/C. 17-Oct-3 Keys, Aylsham #445

FRANCISCO, Carlos Villaluz (1913-1968) Philippino
Works on paper
£5208 $8698 €7604 Planting (29x26cm-11x10in) s.d.1954 W/C. 12-Oct-3 Sotheby's, Singapore #71/R est:15000-20000 (S.D 15000)
£6884 $10670 €10051 Wedding (23x75cm-9x30in) W/C board. 6-Oct-2 Sotheby's, Singapore #91/R est:8000-12000 (S.D 19000)

FRANCISCO, J Bond (1863-1931) American
£308 $550 €450 Western landscape (25x36cm-10x14in) s.d.02 board. 8-Jan-4 James Julia, Fairfield #1011/R
£2174 $4000 €3174 Sunlit trees in a mountain landscape (41x51cm-16x20in) s. prov. 27-Jun-4 Freeman, Philadelphia #89/R est:2500-4000
£5026 $9500 €7338 View of San Francisco harbour (56x66cm-22x26in) s. exhib. 17-Feb-4 John Moran, Pasadena #36/R est:9000-12000

FRANCISCO, Pietro de (19th C) Italian
£2685 $4805 €4000 Landscape in Vezelay (38x46cm-15x18in) s. i.verso. 25-May-4 Finarte Semenzato, Milan #108/R est:2500-3000
£25175 $43301 €36000 Paris, la grand roue (125x125cm-49x49in) s.i.d.1932. 3-Dec-3 Oger, Dumont, Paris #14/R est:15000-20000

FRANCK, Albert Jacques (1899-1973) Canadian
£407 $639 €594 Rue enneige (30x40cm-12x16in) s. canvas on board. 26-Aug-3 Iegor de Saint Hippolyte, Montreal #81 (C.D 900)
£640 $1171 €934 Montmartre courtyard (50x40cm-20x16in) s.d.64 board prov. 1-Jun-4 Joyner Waddington, Toronto #337/R (C.D 1600)
£1600 $2928 €2336 Half House (29x25cm-11x10in) s.d.60 board. 1-Jun-4 Joyner Waddington, Toronto #276/R est:5000-7000 (C.D 4000)
£2300 $4209 €3358 Richmond street, West (30x25cm-12x10in) s.d.71 board prov. 1-Jun-4 Joyner Waddington, Toronto #212/R est:3500-4500 (C.D 5750)
£2846 $5093 €4155 Backyard on Belmont Street (25x40cm-10x16in) s.d.69 i.verso prov. 31-May-4 Sotheby's, Toronto #127/R est:4000-6000 (C.D 7000)
Prints
£625 $1075 €913 Two works depicting backyards in winter (34x44cm-13x17in) both s. first d.51 monotype second W/C. 2-Dec-3 Joyner Waddington, Toronto #403 (C.D 1400)
Works on paper
£560 $1025 €818 Houses on Hazelton Avenue (12x15cm-5x6in) s. ink wash htd white. 1-Jun-4 Joyner Waddington, Toronto #354/R (C.D 1400)
£580 $998 €847 Two works depicting street scenes (15x12cm-6x5in) both s. second i.indis.d. W/C ink two. 2-Dec-3 Joyner Waddington, Toronto #402 (C.D 1300)
£714 $1229 €1042 Yellow chair, Montreal (30x25cm-12x10in) W/C ink exec 1960 lit. 2-Dec-3 Joyner Waddington, Toronto #242/R (C.D 1600)
£800 $1464 €1168 Behind Henry street (13x14cm-5x6in) s.d.64 W/C prov. 1-Jun-4 Joyner Waddington, Toronto #432 est:1200-1500 (C.D 2000)
£920 $1684 €1343 Backyard on Bleeker Street (17x13cm-7x5in) s.d.66 W/C. 1-Jun-4 Joyner Waddington, Toronto #301/R est:1800-2200 (C.D 2300)
£1040 $1903 €1518 Behind Ross Street (17x13cm-7x5in) s.d.66 W/C prov. 1-Jun-4 Joyner Waddington, Toronto #306/R est:1800-2200 (C.D 2600)
£1563 $2656 €2282 Lowther Avenue, Toronto (51x60cm-20x24in) s. W/C gouache ink prov. 6-Nov-3 Heffel, Vancouver #47/R est:4000-5000 (C.D 3500)

FRANCK, L (1944-) French
£1034 $1728 €1500 Femme au travail dans la riviere (32x43cm-13x17in) s. panel. 17-Nov-3 Bernaerts, Antwerp #290 est:1500-2000

FRANCK, Philipp (1860-1944) German
£720 $1325 €1051 Parkland - a misty autumn day (71x96cm-28x38in) s. canvas laid down prov. 14-Jun-4 Bonhams, Bath #115
£12587 $21399 €18000 Boots on the Havel in Potsdam (90x115cm-35x45in) s.d.1936. 29-Nov-3 Villa Grisebach, Berlin #128/R est:18000-24000

FRANCKE-NAUTSCHUTZ, Rudolf (1860-?) German
Sculpture
£1469 $2452 €2100 Figure. s. marble alabaster lit. 27-Jun-3 Auktionhaus Georg Rehm, Augsburg #6170/R est:120

FRANCKEN (studio) (16/17th C) Flemish
£7285 $13623 €11000 Le repas chez Simon le Pharisien (35x26cm-14x10in) copper. 20-Jul-4 Gioffredo, Nice #45

FRANCKEN, Ambrosius I (1544-1618) Flemish
£6897 $12414 €10000 Canan wedding (34x43cm-13x17in) copper prov. 26-Jan-4 Ansorena, Madrid #56/R est:10000

FRANCKEN, Ambrosius II (attrib) (?-1632) Flemish
£3819 $6226 €5500 Crucifixion (72x90cm-28x35in) copper one of pair. 25-Sep-3 Dr Fritz Nagel, Stuttgart #1234/R est:9800
£3819 $6226 €5500 Taunting Christ (72x90cm-28x35in) copper one of pair. 25-Sep-3 Dr Fritz Nagel, Stuttgart #1234a/R est:9800

FRANCKEN, F II (1581-1642) Flemish
£16000 $27200 €23360 Martyrdom of Saint Ursula (41x53cm-16x21in) s.d.1621 copper. 29-Oct-3 Christie's, London #3/R est:10000-15000

FRANCKEN, Frans (circle) (16/17th C) Flemish
£6383 $10660 €9000 La distribution des pains (24x18cm-9x7in) copper. 17-Oct-3 Tajan, Paris #72/R est:6000-8000

FRANCKEN, Frans I (attrib) (1542-1616) Flemish
£5174 $9261 €7554 Ecce homo (21x16cm-8x6in) i.verso slate prov. 26-May-4 AB Stockholms Auktionsverk #2497/R est:60000-80000 (S.KR 70000)

FRANCKEN, Frans II (1581-1642) Flemish
£8846 $15215 €12915 Israelis leaving Egypt. The dance around the Golden Calf (39x50cm-15x20in) copper pair prov. 2-Dec-3 Bukowskis, Stockholm #340/R est:100000-150000 (S.KR 115000)
£12766 $20681 €18000 David triumphant. Esther and Asuero (58x78cm-23x31in) one s. copper pair. 20-May-3 Ansorena, Madrid #88/R est:24000
£13000 $22490 €18980 Way to Calvary (45x63cm-18x25in) indis sig. panel prov. 10-Dec-3 Christie's, London #6/R est:12000-16000
£13000 $23790 €18980 Pieta' surrounded by the Evangelists and scenes from the Old Testamen t (50x37cm-20x15in) panel. 8-Jul-4 Sotheby's, London #249/R est:8000-12000
£13103 $21752 €19000 Moses at the Red Sea (51x41cm-20x16in) copper lit. 30-Sep-3 Ansorena, Madrid #58/R est:16000
£13423 $24966 €20000 Salomon's judgement (40x57cm-16x22in) board. 2-Mar-4 Ansorena, Madrid #271/R est:16000
£24138 $40069 €35000 Charity (115x112cm-45x44in) lit. 30-Sep-3 Ansorena, Madrid #44/R est:35000
£36111 $65000 €52722 Nimrod supervising the construction of the Tower of Babel (57x44cm-22x17in) copper prov. 23-Jan-4 Christie's, Rockefeller NY #20/R est:30000-50000

£54000 $98280 €81000 Battle scene (202x285cm-80x112in) 5-Jul-4 Marc Kohn, Paris #12/R est:80000-100000
£161184 $296579 €245000 Two collectors having lunch in an art gallery (57x87cm-22x34in) panel prov.lit. 25-Jun-4 Piasa, Paris #6/R est:80000-120000
Sculpture
£75000 $129750 €109500 Interior scenes (82x89x41cm-32x35x16in) painted ebony cabinet prov. 10-Dec-3 Christie's, London #1/R est:20000-30000

FRANCKEN, Frans II (after) (1581-1642) Flemish
£5986 $9577 €8500 The tale of the vineyard (28x38cm-11x15in) copper. 19-Sep-3 Finarte, Venice #228/R est:7000-9000

FRANCKEN, Frans II (attrib) (1581-1642) Flemish
£1478 $2646 €2158 Stigmatism of Saint Francis (22x17cm-9x7in) panel prov. 28-May-4 Uppsala Auktionskammare, Uppsala #34/R est:30000-40000 (S.KR 20000)
£2083 $3437 €3000 St Veronica offering Christ a cloth (51x66cm-20x26in) i. copper panel. 3-Jul-3 Dr Fritz Nagel, Stuttgart #443/R est:5000

FRANCKEN, Frans II (circle) (1581-1642) Flemish
£8500 $15300 €12410 Story of the Golden Calf (59x77cm-23x30in) copper prov. 21-Apr-4 Christie's, London #15/R est:7000-10000

FRANCKEN, Frans II (studio) (1581-1642) Flemish
£4930 $8528 €7000 Adoration of the Kings (30x24cm-12x9in) copper. 13-Dec-3 Lempertz, Koln #17/R est:8000
£7200 $12456 €10512 Feast of Herod. panel. 9-Dec-3 Sotheby's, Olympia #308a/R est:3000-4000
£15000 $27000 €21900 Lot and his daughters (67x85cm-26x33in) copper. 23-Jan-4 Christie's, Rockefeller NY #162/R est:15000-20000

FRANCKEN, Frans II and GOVAERTS, Abraham (17th C) Flemish
£20000 $34600 €29200 Allegory of the four seasons (53x74cm-21x29in) with sig panel prov. 10-Dec-3 Christie's, London #7/R est:20000-30000

FRANCKEN, Frans II and MOMPER, Philips de (17th C) Flemish
£23490 $43691 €35000 Biblical scene (112x165cm-44x65in) 2-Mar-4 Ansorena, Madrid #280/R est:35000

FRANCKEN, Frans II and NEEFFS, Pieter (elder) (17th C) Flemish
£10563 $17535 €15000 Scene d'interieur d'eglise anime de personnages (41x59cm-16x23in) s. panel. 13-Jun-3 Renaud, Paris #16/R est:8000-12000

FRANCKEN, Frans III (1607-1667) Flemish
£8392 $14434 €12000 Scenes from the Life of Abraham (12x29cm-5x11in) copper eight. 3-Dec-3 Palais de Beaux Arts, Brussels #1263/R est:7500-10000

FRANCKEN, Frans and MOMPER, Joos de (circle) (16/17th C) Flemish
£8000 $13600 €11680 River landscape with Saint Philip baptising the Moor (113x151cm-44x59in) 30-Oct-3 Sotheby's, Olympia #36/R est:8000-10000

FRANCKEN, Hieronymus (16/17th C) Flemish
£2993 $5448 €4400 L'adoration des bergers (55x44cm-22x17in) panel. 8-Feb-4 Anaf, Lyon #173/R est:4500-5000

FRANCKEN, Hieronymus I (1540-1610) Flemish
£2676 $4630 €3800 Dice players (26x19cm-10x7in) mono. copper. 15-Dec-3 Ansorena, Madrid #114/R est:3000

FRANCKEN, Hieronymus II (1578-1623) Flemish
£4828 $8690 €7000 Peter's denial (40x53cm-16x21in) board. 26-Jan-4 Ansorena, Madrid #61a/R est:7000
£5517 $9159 €8000 Jesus before Pilate (56x72cm-22x28in) copper. 30-Sep-3 Ansorena, Madrid #61/R est:8000
£12000 $21480 €18000 Poor mans' meal, loaf of bread, porridge, buns and a herring on a table (36x46cm-14x18in) indis.mono.d.1599 panel prov.exhib.lit. 17-May-4 Christie's, Amsterdam #72/R est:18000-22000

FRANCKEN, Hieronymus II (attrib) (1578-1623) Flemish
£2465 $4313 €3500 Salomon's judgement (48x75cm-19x30in) board. 17-Dec-3 Christie's, Rome #311/R est:2500-3500

FRANCKEN, Jan Baptist (attrib) (1599-1653) Flemish
£923 $1588 €1348 Scene from Golgatha (16x14cm-6x6in) copper. 2-Dec-3 Bukowskis, Stockholm #338/R (S.KR 12000)

FRANCO Y CORDERO, Jose (19th C) Spanish
£1087 $1783 €1500 Landscape (40x75cm-16x30in) s. 27-May-3 Durán, Madrid #106/R est:1200
£1549 $2680 €2200 Landscape with houses and river (40x79cm-16x31in) s. 15-Dec-3 Ansorena, Madrid #297/R est:2000
£1724 $3103 €2500 Landscape with house (60x101cm-24x40in) s. 26-Jan-4 Ansorena, Madrid #178/R est:2300
£2069 $3434 €3000 Plucking turkey (30x56cm-12x22in) s. 30-Sep-3 Ansorena, Madrid #98/R est:3000
£2069 $3455 €3000 Landscape (44x62cm-17x24in) s. board. 11-Nov-3 Castellana, Madrid #123/R est:2250
£2536 $4159 €3500 Orillas del Manzanares (58x100cm-23x39in) s.d.1884. 27-May-3 Durán, Madrid #267/R est:1800
£2685 $4805 €4000 Near Somosierra (54x82cm-21x32in) s. 25-May-4 Durán, Madrid #206/R est:2500
£2877 $4890 €4200 Landscape with white house (81x49cm-32x19in) s.d.1903. 4-Nov-3 Ansorena, Madrid #49/R est:4200
£3194 $5431 €4600 Landscape with houses (40x65cm-16x26in) s. 28-Oct-3 Segre, Madrid #93/R est:5400
£5594 $9343 €8000 Landscape with houses (48x78cm-19x31in) s. 30-Jun-3 Ansorena, Madrid #343/R est:7200

FRANCO Y SALINAS, Luis (1850-1899) Spanish
£290 $475 €400 Portrait of the mother of the painter Dna (17x14cm-7x6in) s. i.verso panel. 27-May-3 Durán, Madrid #44/R

FRANCO, Giovanni Battista (c.1498-1580) Italian
Prints
£3497 $5944 €5000 Adoration of the shepherds (38x52cm-15x20in) etching engraving. 27-Nov-3 Bassenge, Berlin #5161/R est:7500
Works on paper
£8163 $14612 €12000 La fuite de Clelie (18x24cm-7x9in) pen brown ink wash prov.lit. 18-Mar-4 Christie's, Paris #1/R est:5000-7000

FRANCO, Siron (1947-) Brazilian
£4706 $8000 €6871 Ocasal - da serie a festa (91x81cm-36x32in) s. s.i.d.1982 verso prov. 19-Nov-3 Sotheby's, New York #159/R est:10000-15000
£9158 $16758 €13737 Untitled (156x137cm-61x54in) s.d.1980 i.verso. 6-Jul-4 Bolsa de Arte, Rio de Janeiro #174/R (B.R 50000)
£15018 $26582 €22527 Horror stories (200x180cm-79x71in) s.d.1975. 27-Apr-4 Bolsa de Arte, Rio de Janeiro #82/R (B.R 82000)

FRANCO-FLEMISH SCHOOL, 17th C
£5369 $9879 €8000 Diana and Callisto (147x200cm-58x79in) prov. 24-Mar-4 Dorotheum, Vienna #283/R est:8000-12000

FRANCO-FLEMISH SCHOOL, 18th C
£5500 $9900 €8030 Allegory of spring (22x29cm-9x11in) copper. 20-Apr-4 Sotheby's, Olympia #309/R est:2000-3000

FRANCOIS, Ange (1800-?) Flemish
£748 $1362 €1100 Seascape (35x65cm-14x26in) s. 3-Feb-4 Segre, Madrid #112/R
£859 $1400 €1254 Street vendors (28x23cm-11x9in) panel. 24-Sep-3 Doyle, New York #32
£19580 $33287 €28000 Cleopatre et Antoine (113x145cm-44x57in) s. 1-Dec-3 Millon & Associes, Paris #77/R est:25000-30000

FRANCOIS, Georges (1880-1968) French
£1915 $3198 €2700 Rue Fort Carre, Alger (46x32cm-18x13in) s. lit. 16-Jun-3 Gros & Delettrez, Paris #485/R est:2500-3000
Works on paper
£333 $613 €500 Etude dans un Souk, Maroc (11x51cm-4x20in) s.i. W/C pierre noire gouache. 14-Jun-4 Gros & Delettrez, Paris #269
£333 $613 €500 Projet d'affiche pour l'Exposition coloniale de 1931 (65x50cm-26x20in) s. gouache. 14-Jun-4 Gros & Delettrez, Paris #540/R
£426 $711 €600 Projet d'affiche pour l'exposition coloniale de 1931 (65x50cm-26x20in) s. gouache. 16-Jun-3 Gros & Delettrez, Paris #79/R

FRANCOIS, Guy (1580-1650) French
£2000 $3680 €3000 Madeleine (50x47cm-20x19in) 11-Jun-4 Maigret, Paris #46/R est:3000-4000

FRANCOIS, Joseph Charles (1851-1940) Belgian
£270 $511 €400 Le retour au village (21x29cm-8x11in) s. panel. 17-Feb-4 Vanderkindere, Brussels #108
£340 $569 €480 Les hauts de l'Ambleve (80x140cm-31x55in) s.d.14. 15-Oct-3 Hotel des Ventes Mosan, Brussels #236
£528 $924 €750 Paysage des Fagnes avant l'orage (55x75cm-22x30in) s. 16-Dec-3 Galerie Moderne, Brussels #629
£541 $968 €800 Fagoteuse au bord du ruisseau (60x76cm-24x30in) s. 10-May-4 Horta, Bruxelles #28
£563 $975 €800 Bateau de peche en mer (45x63cm-18x25in) s. 9-Dec-3 Campo, Vlaamse Kaai #313
£563 $975 €800 L'etang dans le bois (55x65cm-22x26in) s. 9-Dec-3 Campo, Vlaamse Kaai #315
£596 $1085 €900 La ferme (65x80cm-26x31in) s. 16-Jun-4 Hotel des Ventes Mosan, Brussels #145
£608 $1149 €900 Le repas des chiens de chasse (62x50cm-24x20in) s. 17-Feb-4 Vanderkindere, Brussels #99
£642 $1213 €950 Cour de ferme animee (40x50cm-16x20in) s.d.92. 17-Feb-4 Vanderkindere, Brussels #51
£642 $1149 €950 Les travaux avant l'hiver (45x65cm-18x26in) s. 10-May-4 Horta, Bruxelles #27
£795 $1446 €1200 Riviere dans le bois (70x100cm-28x39in) s. 16-Jun-4 Hotel des Ventes Mosan, Brussels #180/R
£1014 $1784 €1500 Village in the Ardennes in spring (65x80cm-26x31in) s. 24-May-4 Bernaerts, Antwerp #638/R est:1500-1750

FRANCOIS, Michel (1956-) Belgian
Photographs
£2235 $4000 €3263 Neon brise (120x180cm-47x71in) s.num. of five verso c-print prov. 14-May-4 Phillips, New York #329/R est:4000-6000

FRANCOIS, Pierre Joseph C (attrib) (1759-1851) Flemish
£1867 $3341 €2800 La Richesse aveugle l'amour (31x25cm-12x10in) indis.sig. panel. 17-May-4 Christie's, Amsterdam #102/R est:1200-1600

FRANCOIS, Simon (1606-1671) French

£800	$1384	€1168	Portrait of a gentleman (8x6cm-3x2in) mono. copper oval. 12-Dec-3 Christie's, Kensington #180/R

FRANCOVILLA (20th C) Italian

£1000	$1800	€1500	Female nude study (68x48cm-27x19in) s.d.81. 20-Apr-4 James Adam, Dublin #105/R est:500-800

FRANCUCCI, Innocenzo (1494-1550) Italian

£1399	$2378	€2000	Circumcision (12x31cm-5x12in) pradella panel. 26-Nov-3 James Adam, Dublin #4/R est:2000-3000

FRANDSEN, Erik A (1957-) Danish

£677	$1266	€988	Eye-fucking (100x70cm-39x28in) s.d.96 paper exhib. 25-Feb-4 Kunsthallen, Copenhagen #13 (D.KR 7500)
£1625	$3038	€2373	Camel milking machine (185x135cm-73x53in) init.d.83 verso. 25-Feb-4 Kunsthallen, Copenhagen #159/R est:20000 (D.KR 18000)
£2795	$5171	€4081	Composition with figure (165x130cm-65x51in) s.indist.i.d.85 verso. 15-Mar-4 Rasmussen, Vejle #539/R est:20000 (D.KR 31000)

FRANDZEN, Eugene M (1893-1972) American

£2060	$3750	€3008	Approaching storm, Laguna Canyon (56x76cm-22x30in) i.indis.d.1937 verso prov. 15-Jun-4 John Moran, Pasadena #54 est:2500-3500

FRANG, Felix (1862-1932) Finnish

£872	$1605	€1300	Lake landscape (30x32cm-12x13in) s.d.1914. 25-Mar-4 Hagelstam, Helsinki #956

FRANG, Felix (attrib) (1862-1932) Finnish

£872	$1605	€1300	Landscape (31x48cm-12x19in) init.d.1901. 25-Mar-4 Hagelstam, Helsinki #1037

FRANG, Thomas (1889-1968) Norwegian

£254	$467	€371	Landscape from Tjome (50x61cm-20x24in) s. 29-Mar-4 Blomqvist, Lysaker #1070/R (N.KR 3200)
£777	$1290	€1127	Entrance to Oslo, view from Ekeberg (101x120cm-40x47in) s. 16-Jun-3 Blomqvist, Lysaker #1312 (N.KR 9000)

FRANGI, Giovanni (1959-) Italian

£2000	$3600	€3000	Island (60x80cm-24x31in) s. acrylic cardboard on canvas. 22-Apr-4 Finarte Semenzato, Rome #179/R est:3000-3500
£3020	$5406	€4500	Night scene. s. painted 1992. 28-May-4 Farsetti, Prato #209/R est:3200-3600
£3217	$5469	€4600	Samos (46x55cm-18x22in) s.i.verso. 28-Nov-3 Farsetti, Prato #115/R est:3600-4600
£3333	$6133	€5000	Sunset (74x84cm-29x33in) s.i.d.1991 verso. 12-Jun-4 Meeting Art, Vercelli #588/R est:5000
£3592	$5962	€5100	Acquatico (70x90cm-28x35in) s.i. 14-Jun-3 Meeting Art, Vercelli #348
£3623	$5942	€5000	Canal in Lomabardy (46x81cm-18x32in) s.i.verso painted 1999. 30-May-3 Farsetti, Prato #235/R
£4000	$7360	€6000	Untitled (140x100cm-55x39in) s. paper on canvas. 12-Jun-4 Meeting Art, Vercelli #247/R est:3000
£4196	$7133	€6000	Capri (73x92cm-29x36in) s.i.verso. 28-Nov-3 Farsetti, Prato #308/R est:4200-5200
£5986	$9937	€8500	Notte-Notte (140x100cm-55x39in) s. s.i.d.1999 board on canvas. 14-Jun-3 Meeting Art, Vercelli #245/R est:5000
£6040	$11174	€9000	Pink harbour (70x90cm-28x35in) s.i.verso painted 1999. 13-Mar-4 Meeting Art, Vercelli #120 est:5000
£6690	$11708	€9500	Milan (100x120cm-39x47in) s.i.d.1987 verso. 16-Dec-3 Finarte Semenzato, Milan #239/R est:6800-7200
£8725	$15617	€13000	Point of view (200x150cm-79x59in) s.i.d.2001. 30-May-4 Meeting Art, Vercelli #61 est:10000
Works on paper			
£946	$1665	€1400	Figure (31x25cm-12x10in) s. mixed media. 19-May-4 Il Ponte, Milan #1014a est:1200-1400
£1067	$1920	€1600	Landscape (42x54cm-17x21in) s. mixed media. 22-Apr-4 Finarte Semenzato, Rome #119/R est:1500-1700
£2042	$3390	€2900	Falc (70x100cm-28x39in) s. pastel paper on panel exec 1988. 14-Jun-3 Meeting Art, Vercelli #596/R est:2000

FRANGIAMORE, Salvatore (1853-1915) Italian

£2209	$3800	€3225	Eavesdropping (50x59cm-20x23in) s.i. 2-Dec-3 Christie's, Rockefeller NY #59/R est:3000-5000
£3662	$6335	€5200	Chess game (48x62cm-19x24in) s.d.1912. 11-Dec-3 Christie's, Rome #121/R est:5500-7000

FRANK WILL (1900-1951) French

£1107	$2071	€1650	Louvier (27x35cm-11x14in) s.i. 29-Feb-4 Versailles Encheres #134/R est:1200-1500
£1118	$2058	€1700	Cathedrale vue du Fleuve (22x33cm-9x13in) s. 28-Jun-4 Joron-Derem, Paris #173/R est:1000-1200
£1172	$2110	€1700	Montmartre (32x41cm-13x16in) s. 26-Jan-4 Gros & Delettrez, Paris #25 est:800-1200
£1776	$3215	€2700	Marche de la Rue des Abbesses (47x55cm-19x22in) s. 19-Apr-4 Boscher, Cherbourg #817/R est:3000
£1818	$3128	€2600	Paris (61x81cm-24x32in) s. 3-Dec-3 Tajan, Paris #327/R est:1500-2000
£1933	$3557	€2900	Vue de Rouen (65x93cm-26x37in) s.i. 14-Jun-4 Tajan, Paris #75/R est:3000-5000
£2384	$4339	€3600	Le marche a Honfleur (63x76cm-25x30in) s.i. 17-Jun-4 Marie & Robert, Paris #66 est:3500-3800
£2448	$4210	€3500	Pont Neuf in the snow (38x55cm-15x22in) s.i. 5-Dec-3 Maigret, Paris #80/R est:2200-2500
Works on paper			
£394	$657	€565	Paris, Notre Dame (23x31cm-9x12in) s.i. W/C chl. 21-Oct-3 Artcurial Briest, Paris #63
£414	$687	€600	Rue de Montmartre (30x21cm-12x8in) s. W/C. 5-Oct-3 Lombrail & Teucquam, Paris #186
£420	$713	€600	Pointu dans un calanque (23x15cm-9x6in) s. W/C. 20-Nov-3 Gioffredo, Nice #8/R
£559	$962	€800	Cathedrale (61x75cm-24x30in) s.i. W/C crayon. 7-Dec-3 Livinec, Gaudcheau & Jezequel, Rennes #18
£629	$1070	€900	Le pont Marie, Paris (22x31cm-9x12in) s.i. W/C. 18-Nov-3 Pierre Berge, Paris #72
£638	$1129	€950	Port de Dunkerque (48x61cm-19x24in) s.i. W/C traces crayon. 27-Apr-4 Artcurial Briest, Paris #26
£640	$1100	€934	Outdoor market, Pont Audemer (46x56cm-18x22in) s.i. s.i.d.7.7.36 verso W/C chl. 3-Dec-3 Doyle, New York #132/R est:2000-3000
£704	$1218	€1000	Paris, Pont Neuf (23x32cm-9x13in) s.i. W/C. 12-Dec-3 Piasa, Paris #61/R
£828	$1531	€1200	Paris, le Pont Neuf (23x34cm-9x13in) s.i. W/C. 13-Feb-4 Rossini, Paris #24/R
£855	$1574	€1300	Untitled (32x44cm-13x17in) s.i. crayon W/C. 25-Jun-4 Millon & Associes, Paris #174/R
£872	$1623	€1300	Treport (40x55cm-16x22in) s. W/C. 3-Mar-4 Tajan, Paris #44/R est:1500-1800
£951	$1645	€1350	Transport du charbon dans le port du Havre (43x61cm-17x24in) s.i. W/C traces blk crayon. 10-Dec-3 Piasa, Paris #151
£966	$1786	€1400	Paris, quay de Bercy (23x34cm-9x13in) s.i. W/C. 13-Feb-4 Rossini, Paris #18/R
£972	$1624	€1400	Grand voiliers, port de Fecamps (23x34cm-9x13in) s.i. W/C. 26-Oct-3 Feletin, Province #114
£1042	$1698	€1500	Le Treport (26x20cm-10x8in) s.i. W/C. 26-Sep-3 Rabourdin & Choppin de Janvry, Paris #20/R est:1200-1500
£1049	$1783	€1500	Vue de la Seine a Thomery (45x54cm-18x21in) s.i. W/C. 21-Nov-3 Coutau Begarie, Paris #54/R est:2000
£1105	$1900	€1613	La Consiergerie, Paris. Notre Dame (22x28cm-9x11in) s.i. i.verso W/C chl two. 3-Dec-3 Doyle, New York #131/R est:2000-3000
£1118	$2058	€1700	La Rochelle (44x59cm-17x23in) s.i. chl W/C. 25-Jun-4 Millon & Associes, Paris #173 est:1000-1200
£1126	$2060	€1700	Regate a Barfleur (39x58cm-15x23in) s. W/C. 9-Apr-4 Claude Aguttes, Neuilly #17 est:1500-1800
£1127	$1972	€1600	Place de la Concorde (33x51cm-13x20in) s.i. W/C. 19-Dec-3 Delvaux, Paris #23/R est:1600-2200
£1233	$2096	€1800	Paris, Notre-Dame (23x30cm-9x12in) s. W/C. 9-Nov-3 Eric Pillon, Calais #214/R
£1241	$2234	€1800	Eglise de Moret (54x41cm-21x16in) s.i. W/C. 26-Jan-4 Gros & Delettrez, Paris #23/R est:1000-1500
£1241	$2234	€1800	Paris, le Sacre-Coeur (45x32cm-18x13in) s.i. W/C. 26-Jan-4 Gros & Delettrez, Paris #24 est:450-600
£1316	$2421	€2000	Place du Tertre (52x44cm-20x17in) s.i. W/C chl prov. 25-Jun-4 Millon & Associes, Paris #172 est:1000-1200
£1379	$2552	€2000	Vue de la Seine avec Notre Dame (45x60cm-18x24in) s.i. W/C. 19-Jan-4 Horta, Bruxelles #92 est:2000-2500
£1389	$2320	€2000	Paris, Notre Dame (44x54cm-17x21in) s.i. W/C crayon. 21-Oct-3 Artcurial Briest, Paris #62/R est:1800-2200
£1467	$2699	€2200	Rouen (37x54cm-15x21in) s.i. W/C lead pencil. 9-Jun-4 Le Roux & Morel, Paris #22/R est:2100-2300
£1479	$2558	€2100	Louviers (32x45cm-13x18in) s. W/C gouache. 14-Dec-3 Eric Pillon, Calais #169/R
£1497	$2679	€2200	Paris, bord de Seine (44x53cm-17x21in) s.i. W/C. 19-Mar-4 Oger, Dumont, Paris #24 est:1200-1500
£1589	$2909	€2400	Rue de l'Abreuvoir a Montmartre (53x44cm-21x17in) s.i. W/C blk crayon. 7-Apr-4 Piasa, Paris #107 est:2500-3000
£1600	$2912	€2400	View of Antibes (45x54cm-18x21in) s.i. W/C. 4-Jul-4 Eric Pillon, Calais #192/R
£1701	$3044	€2500	Paris, la Bourse (43x54cm-17x21in) s.i. W/C pencil. 19-Mar-4 Ribeyre & Baron, Paris #71/R est:1000-1500
£1712	$2911	€2500	Vue de la POrte Saint-Denis (45x53cm-18x21in) s. W/C over crayon. 6-Nov-3 Tajan, Paris #231/R
£2042	$3533	€2900	Paris, la Seine et la Cite (41x51cm-16x20in) s. W/C. 14-Dec-3 Eric Pillon, Calais #160/R
£2042	$3533	€2900	Paris, les bouquinistes (32x45cm-13x18in) s. W/C gouache. 14-Dec-3 Eric Pillon, Calais #167/R
£2055	$3493	€3000	Port de Honfleur (45x62cm-18x24in) s.i.d.1920 W/C. 9-Nov-3 Eric Pillon, Calais #216/R
£2113	$3655	€3000	Paris, Notre-Dame (50x63cm-20x25in) s.d.1926 W/C. 14-Dec-3 Eric Pillon, Calais #166/R
£2183	$3777	€3100	Bateaux a l'entree du port de Concarneau (45x58cm-18x23in) s. W/C gouache. 14-Dec-3 Eric Pillon, Calais #159/R
£2734	$4483	€3800	Le port de Fecamp (54x45cm-21x18in) s. W/C. 6-Jun-3 Chochon-Barre & Allardi, Paris #50/R est:3900-4000
£2877	$4516	€4200	Le Havre, cargo a quai (45x64cm-18x25in) s. W/C gouache. 20-Apr-3 Deauville, France #29 est:4000-5000
£3000	$5400	€4500	Paris, la Seine a Notre-Dame (36x53cm-14x21in) s.i. W/C. 26-Apr-4 Tajan, Paris #17/R est:4500-5000
£3028	$5239	€4300	Paris, les bouquinistes (45x58cm-18x23in) s. W/C gouache. 14-Dec-3 Eric Pillon, Calais #158/R
£4667	$8400	€7000	Paris, la Seine au pont Louis-Philippe (60x90cm-24x35in) s. W/C. 26-Apr-4 Tajan, Paris #16/R est:6500-7000

FRANK, Dale (1958-) Australian

£7660	$13021	€11184	Rufus Sewell (200x200cm-79x79in) init.d.2000 acrylic varnish linen prov. 25-Nov-3 Christie's, Melbourne #24/R est:18000-25000 (A.D 18000)
Works on paper			
£3053	$5557	€4457	Tyson stable III 2000 (140x120cm-55x47in) s.d.2000 synthetic polymer varnish on linen prov. 16-Jun-4 Deutscher-Menzies, Melbourne #5/R est:7500-9500 (A.D 8000)

FRANK, Franz (1897-1986) German

£1389	$2264	€2000	Summer day on the Baltic (61x82cm-24x32in) mono.d.1970. 27-Sep-3 Dr Fritz Nagel, Stuttgart #947/R est:3000
£1477	$2717	€2200	Still life in wood (75x90cm-30x35in) mono. 27-Mar-4 Geble, Radolfzell #721/R est:1200
Works on paper			
£268	$475	€400	Window ledge (51x46cm-20x18in) mono.d. W/C chl col chk board. 30-Apr-4 Dr Fritz Nagel, Stuttgart #145/R

FRANK, Franz Friedrich (1627-1687) German
£9211 $16947 €14000 Bullfight on Venetian square (330x78cm-130x31in) mono.d.1657. 24-Jun-4 Dr Fritz Nagel, Stuttgart #658/R est:9500

FRANK, Friedrich (1871-1945) Austrian
Works on paper
£671 $1235 €1000 Brindisi from the sea (30x40cm-12x16in) s. i. W/C paper on canvas. 26-Mar-4 Dorotheum, Vienna #243/R
£805 $1442 €1200 Heiligenkreuzer Courtyard (14x12cm-6x5in) s. gouache. 27-May-4 Hassfurther, Vienna #49/R
£872 $1605 €1300 Konigsee (11x9cm-4x4in) s.i. W/C. 26-Mar-4 Dorotheum, Vienna #233/R
£1141 $2099 €1700 Mountain road in Upper Inn valley (48x64cm-19x25in) s.i. WC. 26-Mar-4 Dorotheum, Vienna #232/R est:3000-3500
£1208 $2223 €1800 Alexandria seen from the sea (49x75cm-19x30in) s.i. W/C paper on canvas. 26-Mar-4 Dorotheum, Vienna #220/R est:200-2500
£1208 $2223 €1800 Ships off Trieste (61x85cm-24x33in) s. W/C paper on canvas. 26-Mar-4 Dorotheum, Vienna #221/R est:2400-2800
£1208 $2223 €1800 Venice seen from the sea (46x61cm-18x24in) s.i. W/C paper on canvas. 26-Mar-4 Dorotheum, Vienna #222/R est:2400-2800
£1641 $2725 €2396 Vienna Karntnerstrasse (23x31cm-9x12in) s.i. /WC. 4-Oct-3 Dorotheum, Prague #256/R est:70000-100000 (C.KR 75000)
£2300 $4117 €3358 Wien - Hoher Market (23x31cm-9x12in) s.i. W/C. 17-Mar-4 Bonhams, Chester #293 est:900-1200

FRANK, Frigyes (1890-1976) Hungarian
£1148 $1987 €1676 Still life of flowers (72x57cm-28x22in) s. 12-Dec-3 Kieselbach, Budapest #154/R (H.F 440000)
£1195 $1983 €1745 Kitchen still life (50x70cm-20x28in) s. 4-Oct-3 Kieselbach, Budapest #63 (H.F 440000)
£1305 $2258 €1905 Still life with Margaret flowers (70x60cm-28x24in) s. 12-Dec-3 Kieselbach, Budapest #195/R (H.F 500000)
£1976 $3577 €2885 Winding street (50x60cm-20x24in) s. 16-Apr-4 Mu Terem Galeria, Budapest #119/R (H.F 750000)
£3915 $6773 €5716 Stormy Lake Balaton (62x80cm-24x31in) s. fibreboard. 12-Dec-3 Kieselbach, Budapest #138/R (H.F 1500000)
£11000 $20020 €16060 Vase of flowers (80x65cm-31x26in) s.d.936 prov. 15-Jun-4 Sotheby's, London #71/R est:8000-12000
Works on paper
£1069 $1892 €1561 Houses (43x61cm-17x24in) s. pastel. 28-Apr-4 Kieselbach, Budapest #13/R (H.F 400000)

FRANK, Hans (1884-1948) Austrian
£1267 $2280 €1900 Landscape (29x35cm-11x14in) s. s.i. verso board. 21-Apr-4 Dorotheum, Vienna #90/R est:1600-2200
Works on paper
£352 $616 €500 Dachstein group of mountains viewed from the south (30x44cm-12x17in) s.i.d.42 verso W/C. 19-Dec-3 Dorotheum, Vienna #86/R
£382 $623 €550 Swans in park (23x32cm-9x13in) s.d.25 pastel. 25-Sep-3 Dorotheum, Graz #82

FRANK, Josef (1873-1967) Austrian
£645 $1187 €942 Art connoisseur. Gentlemen playing chess (29x19cm-11x7in) s. panel pair. 14-Jun-4 Waddingtons, Toronto #325/R est:1500-2500 (C.D 1600)
£887 $1632 €1295 Flirtation. In the boudoir (30x23cm-12x9in) s. s.i.verso pair. 14-Jun-4 Waddingtons, Toronto #326/R est:1500-2500 (C.D 2200)
£903 $1490 €1300 Before the departure of the post coach (28x42cm-11x17in) s.i.d.1920 panel. 3-Jul-3 Neumeister, Munich #2831/R
£1987 $3616 €3000 Antiques dealer (33x48cm-13x19in) s.d.1926 i.verso. 18-Jun-4 Bolland & Marotz, Bremen #615/R est:4600
£2215 $4075 €3300 Looking for antiques (24x32cm-9x13in) s.d.1924 panel. 26-Mar-4 Bolland & Marotz, Bremen #514/R est:3400

FRANK, Joseph Egon (19/20th C) German
£1549 $2680 €2200 Print collectors (41x26cm-16x10in) s. panel. 10-Dec-3 Christie's, Amsterdam #667/R est:1000-1500

FRANK, Louis (19th C) Australian
£1611 $2996 €2400 Goldminers' quarters (58x84cm-23x33in) s.i.d.1858. 6-Mar-4 Arnold, Frankfurt #722/R est:1000

FRANK, Lucien (1857-1920) Belgian
£387 $670 €550 L'etang (29x36cm-11x14in) s. 9-Dec-3 Vanderkindere, Brussels #123/R
£524 $876 €750 View of Oudenburg (24x16cm-9x6in) s. panel. 11-Oct-3 De Vuyst, Lokeren #149
£556 $928 €800 Marine (14x20cm-6x8in) s. panel. 21-Oct-3 Campo, Vlaamse Kaai #435a
£789 $1429 €1200 Pecheur en barque pres du moulin (24x15cm-9x6in) s. panel. 19-Apr-4 Horta, Bruxelles #41
£933 $1671 €1400 Le crepuscule (16x24cm-6x9in) s. panel. 15-May-4 De Vuyst, Lokeren #138/R
£1192 $2170 €1800 Village au canal (16x26cm-6x10in) s. panel. 15-Jun-4 Vanderkindere, Brussels #22 est:800-1200
£1342 $2470 €2000 Canal a Papendeek (16x24cm-6x9in) s. panel. 23-Mar-4 Galerie Moderne, Brussels #319/R est:600-800
£2069 $3828 €3000 Boulevard Parisien anime (32x24cm-13x9in) s. cardboard panel. 13-Jan-4 Vanderkindere, Brussels #36 est:2000-3000
Works on paper
£4196 $7133 €6000 Journee de neige a Bruxelles (70x90cm-28x35in) s. pastel. 1-Dec-3 Palais de Beaux Arts, Brussels #255/R est:2000-3000

FRANK, Magda (20th C) Argentinian
Sculpture
£3846 $7000 €5615 Figures (39cm-15in) init. pat bronze. 29-Jun-4 Arroyo, Buenos Aires #41/R est:3000
£6044 $11000 €8824 Union (28cm-11in) init. pat bronze. 29-Jun-4 Arroyo, Buenos Aires #33/R est:5000

FRANK, Mary (1933-) American
Works on paper
£1081 $2000 €1578 Untitled (60x44cm-24x17in) s.d.1965 pencil ink wash. 13-Jul-4 Christie's, Rockefeller NY #21/R est:500-800

FRANK, Robert (1924-) American/Swiss
Photographs
£1796 $3000 €2622 Black Foot, Idaho (19x27cm-7x11in) s.i.d.1955 gelatin silver print. 20-Oct-3 Christie's, Rockefeller NY #114/R est:4000-6000
£1916 $3200 €2797 Railroad station, Memphis (22x32cm-9x13in) with sig.d.1955 verso silver print. 21-Oct-3 Swann Galleries, New York #218/R est:5000-7000
£1916 $3200 €2797 Allen Ginsberg (20x28cm-8x11in) s.i.verso gelatin silver print exec.c.1959 prov. 20-Oct-3 Christie's, Rockefeller NY #204/R est:4000-6000
£1916 $3200 €2797 Backyard, Venice West, California (21x30cm-8x12in) s.d.1955-56 i.verso gelatin silver print lit. 20-Oct-3 Christie's, Rockefeller NY #220/R est:3000-5000
£2096 $3500 €3060 Cowboy and girl (21x33cm-8x13in) s. i.verso photo exec.c.1955 printed c.1960 prov. 17-Oct-3 Sotheby's, New York #262/R est:4000-6000
£2275 $3800 €3322 Road to La Paz (21x33cm-8x13in) s.i.d.1948 gelatin silver print prov.lit. 17-Oct-3 Phillips, New York #258/R est:4000-6000
£2395 $4000 €3497 White Tower on 14th Street, NYC (22x34cm-9x13in) s.i.d.1949 photo printed later. 17-Oct-3 Sotheby's, New York #263/R est:5000-7000
£2646 $5000 €3863 NYC, 1954 (29x20cm-11x8in) s.i.d. gelatin silver print. 17-Feb-4 Christie's, Rockefeller NY #213/R est:4000-6000
£2712 $4800 €3960 Tennessee -Chattanooga main street, 1956 (23x34cm-9x13in) s.i.d.1956 gelatin silver print. 27-Apr-4 Christie's, Rockefeller NY #155/R est:6000-8000
£2800 $4928 €4088 NYC, 1947 (35x28cm-14x11in) s.d.1979 black white photo print. 18-May-4 Bonhams, New Bond Street #393/R est:3000-4500
£2857 $5400 €4171 Madison Square Garden (22x32cm-9x13in) s.i. verso silver print. 17-Feb-4 Swann Galleries, New York #84/R est:6000-9000
£3107 $5500 €4536 London, 1951 (22x34cm-9x13in) s.i.d.1951 gelatin silver print prov.lit. 27-Apr-4 Christie's, Rockefeller NY #153/R est:5000-7000
£3175 $6000 €4636 4th of July, Coney Island (18x26cm-7x10in) s.i.d. silver print. 17-Feb-4 Swann Galleries, New York #85/R est:6000-9000
£4167 $7500 €6084 Metropolitan life insurance building, New York City (32x22cm-13x9in) s.i.d.1955 gelatin silver print lit. 23-Apr-4 Phillips, New York #86/R est:9000-12000
£4491 $7500 €6557 Daytona Florida (19x29cm-7x11in) with sig.i.d.1962 silver print. 21-Oct-3 Swann Galleries, New York #219/R est:10000-15000
£4790 $8000 €6993 Rodeo, Detroit (23x34cm-9x13in) s.i.d.1955 gelatin silver print printed later lit. 20-Oct-3 Christie's, Rockefeller NY #115/R est:9000-12000
£5090 $8500 €7431 Peru (31x46cm-12x18in) s.i.d.1948 gelatin silver print printed c.1970 exhib.lit. 20-Oct-3 Christie's, Rockefeller NY #116/R est:7000-9000
£5090 $8500 €7431 Belle Isle, Detroit (16x24cm-6x9in) s.i.d. gelatin silver print exec.1955 printed c.1970 lit. 20-Oct-3 Christie's, Rockefeller NY #225/R est:5000-7000
£5389 $9000 €7868 Hoover Dam (46x61cm-18x24in) s.i.d.1956 photo printed later. 17-Oct-3 Sotheby's, New York #261/R est:10000-15000
£5650 $10000 €8249 London, 1951 (23x35cm-9x14in) s.i.d.1951 gelatin silver print lit. 27-Apr-4 Christie's, Rockefeller NY #151/R est:12000-18000
£5689 $9500 €8306 Cape Cod, the day the Daily News cam out (32x21cm-13x8in) s.i.d.1963 gelatin silver print. 20-Oct-3 Christie's, Rockefeller NY #113/R est:9000-12000
£6215 $11000 €9074 Detroit, Mich (22x33cm-9x13in) i.d.1955 verso photo prov. 27-Apr-4 Sotheby's, New York #8/R est:7000-10000
£6886 $11500 €10054 Italian women in Venice (17x23cm-7x9in) st.sig.i.verso gelatin silver print exec.1949 prov.lit. 17-Oct-3 Phillips, New York #120/R est:8000-12000
£7485 $12500 €10928 London (22x34cm-9x13in) s.i.d.1951 gelatin silver print lit. 17-Oct-3 Phillips, New York #104/R est:10000-15000
£8475 $15000 €12374 NYC, 1948 (34x19cm-13x7in) s.i.d.verso gelatin silver print. 27-Apr-4 Christie's, Rockefeller NY #152/R est:15000-20000
£9040 $16000 €13198 On the road (22x32cm-9x13in) s.i.d.1955 photo printed later prov. 27-Apr-4 Sotheby's, New York #9/R est:7000-10000
£10180 $17000 €14863 Denver, Richard and Pat Nixon (26x34cm-10x13in) s.i.d.1962 gelatin silver print prov.lit. 17-Oct-3 Phillips, New York #41/R est:20000-30000
£11976 $20000 €17485 Covered car, Long Beach, CA (22x34cm-9x13in) s. gelatin silver print exec.1955-56 printed later lit. 20-Oct-3 Christie's, Rockefeller NY #221/R est:10000-15000
£14371 $24000 €20982 Fourth of July, Jay, NY (31x20cm-12x8in) s.i. gelatin silver print exec.1955 printed c.1970 lit. 20-Oct-3 Christie's, Rockefeller NY #112/R est:12000-18000
£15819 $28000 €23096 Indianapolis (22x31cm-9x12in) i.verso photo prov.lit. 27-Apr-4 Sotheby's, New York #10/R est:15000-25000
£16766 $28000 €24478 London (32x21cm-13x8in) i.d.1951-52 verso gelatin silver print board prov.lit. 17-Oct-3 Phillips, New York #38/R est:18000-22000
£16949 $30000 €24746 Hollywood premiere (32x21cm-13x8in) s.i.d.1956 i.verso photo prov. 27-Apr-4 Sotheby's, New York #6/R est:8000-12000
£19162 $32000 €27977 Charleston, South Carolina (21x32cm-8x13in) s.d.1956 gelatin silver print prov.lit. 17-Oct-3 Phillips, New York #242/R est:30000-50000
£20958 $35000 €30599 City fathers, Hoboken, New Jersey (22x29cm-9x11in) s. i.d.1955 verso gelatin silver print prov.exhib.lit. 17-Oct-3 Phillips, New York #40/R est:40000-60000
£23952 $40000 €34970 Tulip/Paris (33x20cm-13x8in) s. num.5 and 5-9-80 verso photo prov.lit. 17-Oct-3 Sotheby's, New York #256/R est:30000-50000
£23952 $40000 €34970 Pablo (20x35cm-8x14in) s.i.d.1953 gelatin silver print. 17-Oct-3 Phillips, New York #72/R est:20000-30000
£25150 $42000 €36719 Charleston (31x46cm-12x18in) s.i.d.1955 photo printed later prov. 17-Oct-3 Sotheby's, New York #260/R est:40000-60000
£25150 $42000 €36719 Political rally, Chicago (33x22cm-13x9in) s.i.d.1956 gelatin silver print prov.lit. 17-Oct-3 Phillips, New York #39/R est:40000-60000
£36723 $65000 €53616 Covered car, Long Beach, California (17x25cm-7x10in) s.i.d.1955-56 photo printed later prov.lit. 27-Apr-4 Sotheby's, New York #5/R est:15000-25000
£62147 $110000 €90735 Chicago (40x26cm-16x10in) s.i.d.1956 verso photo printed later prov.lit. 27-Apr-4 Sotheby's, New York #7/R est:20000-30000

FRANK, Sepp (1889-1970) German
£414 $691 €600 Coastal landscape (11x11cm-4x4in) s.d.1932 plywood. 13-Nov-3 Neumeister, Munich #323/R

FRANK-KRAUSS, Robert (1893-1950) German
£333 $600 €500 Tailor threading needle (21x16cm-8x6in) s. panel lit. 22-Apr-4 Allgauer, Kempten #3527/R
£479 $815 €700 Old flautist (24x19cm-9x7in) s. panel. 5-Nov-3 Hugo Ruef, Munich #969
£493 $853 €700 Young girl in national costume (25x20cm-10x8in) s. cardboard. 10-Dec-3 Hugo Ruef, Munich #2408/R

FRANK-KRAUSS, Robert (attrib) (1893-1950) German

£417	$679	€600	Small town at night (78x105cm-31x41in) i. verso panel. 25-Sep-3 Neumeister, Munich #2763
£470	$874	€700	Group of men making music in the street at night (78x105cm-31x41in) panel. 5-Mar-4 Wendl, Rudolstadt #3642/R

FRANKE, Albert (1860-1924) German

£7031	$11742	€10265	Street scene in Tunisie (32x44cm-13x17in) s.d.86 board. 19-Oct-3 Agra, Warsaw #6/R est:43000 (P.Z 45000)

FRANKE, Hanny (1890-1973) German

£338	$605	€500	Taunus landscape in autumn (21x31cm-8x12in) s.d.24 board. 6-May-4 Michael Zeller, Lindau #661/R
£350	$594	€500	Birch tree in early spring (36x25cm-14x10in) s.d.1954 board. 22-Nov-3 Arnold, Frankfurt #504/R
£400	$732	€600	Elder-blossom (36x28cm-14x11in) s. board. 5-Jun-4 Arnold, Frankfurt #576/R
£500	$915	€750	White thorn blossom (38x28cm-15x11in) board. 5-Jun-4 Arnold, Frankfurt #577/R
£521	$823	€750	River Nidda in summer (30x387cm-12x152in) s.d.1957. 6-Sep-3 Arnold, Frankfurt #553/R
£533	$976	€800	View from Westerbach (38x27cm-15x11in) s.d.1966 board. 5-Jun-4 Arnold, Frankfurt #578/R
£559	$951	€800	Still life with grapes and apples (22x31cm-9x12in) s.d.1935 board. 22-Nov-3 Arnold, Frankfurt #508/R
£839	$1427	€1200	Summer in the Taunus (61x80cm-24x31in) s.d.1934. 22-Nov-3 Arnold, Frankfurt #507/R est:800
£867	$1586	€1300	Blossoming forest meadow (34x27cm-13x11in) s.d.1948 board. 5-Jun-4 Arnold, Frankfurt #575/R
£1049	$1783	€1500	View over Taunus to Feldberg (60x80cm-24x31in) s. 22-Nov-3 Arnold, Frankfurt #509/R est:1200

FRANKE, Hans (20th C) German

£426	$689	€600	Black Forest landscape in October (40x50cm-16x20in) s. i. verso. 23-May-3 Karlheinz Kaupp, Staufen #1833
£567	$919	€800	Nidda at Ulmenruck (41x51cm-16x20in) s. i. verso. 23-May-3 Karlheinz Kaupp, Staufen #1742

FRANKE, Ronald (20th C) German

£347	$580	€500	Hamburg harbour, landing stage (40x49cm-16x19in) s. 24-Oct-3 Ketterer, Hamburg #9/R

FRANKEL-HARRIS, Marcia (20th C) American

Works on paper

£191	$350	€287	Shell life with fluted clams (76x102cm-30x40in) col pencil pastel. 10-Jul-4 Hindman, Chicago #152/R

FRANKEN, Johannes Petrus Josephus (1896-1977) Dutch

£526	$968	€800	Still life with a Chinese lantern in a ginger jar (59x42cm-23x17in) s.d. canvas on board. 22-Jun-4 Christie's, Amsterdam #493/R

FRANKEN, Paul von (1818-1884) German

£20946	$36865	€31000	Caucasus landscape (36x24cm-14x9in) one s.d.83 panel two. 22-May-4 Lempertz, Koln #1518/R est:8000
£27517	$50631	€41000	Caucasian landscape with mountain village and figures (66x82cm-26x32in) s.d.1866. 27-Mar-4 Dannenberg, Berlin #556/R est:3000
£30000	$53700	€43800	Caucasian scene (97x156cm-38x61in) s. 26-May-4 Sotheby's, London #80/R est:30000-40000
£36667	$66367	€55000	Kura shore in evening with Tiflis (84x116cm-33x46in) s.d.1865. 1-Apr-4 Van Ham, Cologne #1372/R est:6000
£40000	$68000	€58400	Travellers resting by the Lake, Georgia (64x82cm-25x32in) s.d.1854. 19-Nov-3 Sotheby's, London #28/R est:20000-30000
£55000	$93500	€80300	View of Tiflis (72x102cm-28x40in) s.d.1866. 19-Nov-3 Sotheby's, London #26/R est:50000-70000

FRANKEN, Rob (1914-) ?

Works on paper

£308	$524	€450	Chrysanthemum (37x47cm-15x19in) s. pastel. 5-Nov-3 Vendue Huis, Gravenhage #217/R

FRANKENBERGER, Johann (1807-1874) German

£729	$1159	€1050	Portrait de gentilhomme. Portrait de dame de qualite (68x55cm-27x22in) s.d.1839 pair. 9-Sep-3 Vanderkindere, Brussels #117

FRANKENTHAL SCHOOL (17th C) German

£8380	$15000	€12235	Saint John the Baptist preaching (35x47cm-14x19in) copper. 27-May-4 Sotheby's, New York #85/R est:20000-30000

FRANKENTHALER, Helen (1928-) American

£3571	$6500	€5214	Untitled 8 (34x25cm-13x10in) s.d.67 acrylic on card prov. 29-Jun-4 Sotheby's, New York #478/R est:5000-7000
£5689	$9500	€8306	Holiday (61x46cm-24x18in) s.d.75 acrylic canvasboard prov. 13-Nov-3 Sotheby's, New York #169/R est:12000-18000
£35928	$60000	€52455	Summer frame (31x79cm-12x31in) s.i.d.1-64 i.stretcher acrylic prov. 13-Nov-3 Sotheby's, New York #168/R est:25000-35000
£35928	$60000	€52455	Lozenge (262x237cm-103x93in) s.d.69 acrylic prov.lit. 13-Nov-3 Sotheby's, New York #181/R est:60000-80000
£67039	$120000	€97877	Big dipper (208x131cm-82x52in) s. s.i.d.85 verso acrylic prov.exhib. 13-May-4 Sotheby's, New York #197/R est:60000-80000
£77844	$130000	€113652	Giant Step (236x406cm-93x160in) s.d.1975 verso acrylic prov.exhib. 12-Nov-3 Christie's, Rockefeller NY #356/R est:80000-120000
£119760	$200000	€174850	Courtyard of El Greco's House (116x154cm-46x61in) painted 1959 prov.exhib.lit. 12-Nov-3 Christie's, Rockefeller NY #318/R est:200000-300000
£269461	$450000	€393413	Mountain Storm (183x122cm-72x48in) s.d.1955 prov.exhib. 11-Nov-3 Christie's, Rockefeller NY #26/R est:300000-400000

Prints

£1613	$3000	€2355	Bronze smoke (79x57cm-31x22in) s.d.1978 num.9/38 col lithograph. 2-Mar-4 Swann Galleries, New York #194/R est:2000-3000
£2246	$3750	€3279	Bay area wednesday VII (64x74cm-25x29in) s.d.1982 col monotype. 11-Nov-3 Doyle, New York #251/R est:4000-6000
£2260	$4000	€3300	Radius (72x72cm-28x28in) s.d.1992-93 col woodcut. 30-Apr-4 Sotheby's, New York #334/R est:4000-6000
£2310	$4250	€3373	Solar imp (102x76cm-40x30in) silk screen. 28-Mar-4 Wright, Chicago #572/R est:2500-3000
£2331	$3800	€3403	First Stone (56x76cm-22x30in) s.d.1961 num.7/12 col lithograph on Arches. 24-Sep-3 Christie's, Rockefeller NY #238/R est:3500-4500
£2647	$4500	€3865	All about blue (123x73cm-48x29in) s. col lithograph woodcut. 31-Oct-3 Sotheby's, New York #546/R
£2703	$5000	€3946	Eve (112x76cm-44x30in) s.num.43/108 col screenprint. 12-Feb-4 Christie's, Rockefeller NY #70/R est:3000-4000
£2794	$4750	€4079	Corot's mark (51x63cm-20x25in) s. col aquatint etching lithograph. 31-Oct-3 Sotheby's, New York #544/R
£2825	$5000	€4125	Tiger's eye (48x56cm-19x22in) s.d.1987 num.2/56 col aquatint etching. 30-Apr-4 Sotheby's, New York #333/R est:3000-4000
£2941	$5000	€4294	Tribal sign (61x46cm-24x18in) s.d.1987 col lithograph. 31-Oct-3 Sotheby's, New York #543/R
£3297	$6000	€4814	Triptych (310x71cm-122x28in) color lithograph. 19-Jun-4 Du Mouchelle, Detroit #3072/R est:6000-8000
£3514	$6500	€5130	Grey fireworks (66x117cm-26x46in) s.num.94/108 col screenprint. 12-Feb-4 Christie's, Rockefeller NY #72/R est:2500-3500
£3955	$7000	€5774	All about blue (122x74cm-48x29in) s.d.1994 num.37/38 col lithograph woodcut. 30-Apr-4 Sotheby's, New York #335/R est:4000-5000
£4706	$8000	€6871	Deep sun (77x102cm-30x40in) s. col intaglio. 31-Oct-3 Sotheby's, New York #542/R
£5882	$10000	€8588	Tales of Genji II (119x106cm-47x42in) s. col woodcut. 31-Oct-3 Sotheby's, New York #551/R
£7059	$12000	€10306	Tales of Genji VI (119x107cm-47x42in) s. col woodcut pochoir. 31-Oct-3 Sotheby's, New York #554/R
£9040	$16000	€13198	Spring run XV (102x80cm-40x31in) s. i.d.4/10/96 verso col monotype print. 30-Apr-4 Sotheby's, New York #336/R est:10000-15000
£9040	$16000	€13198	Tales of Genji IV (119x107cm-47x42in) s. num.8/30 col woodcut. 30-Apr-4 Sotheby's, New York #338/R est:8000-12000
£12429	$22000	€18146	East and beyond (80x54cm-31x21in) s.d.1973 num.3/18 col woodcut. 30-Apr-4 Sotheby's, New York #332/R est:15000-20000
£13235	$22500	€19323	Tales of Genji III (119x106cm-47x42in) s. col woodcut pochoir. 31-Oct-3 Sotheby's, New York #552/R
£14124	$25000	€20621	Tales of Genji V (107x119cm-42x47in) s. num.2/36 col woodcut. 30-Apr-4 Sotheby's, New York #339/R est:24000-30000
£16176	$27500	€23617	Tales of Genji I (107x119cm-42x47in) s. col woodcut. 31-Oct-3 Sotheby's, New York #550/R
£16176	$27500	€23617	Tales of Genji V (107x119cm-42x47in) s. col woodcut. 31-Oct-3 Sotheby's, New York #553/R
£28249	$50000	€41244	Madame Butterfly (105x202cm-41x80in) s.i.d.2000 col woodcut. 30-Apr-4 Sotheby's, New York #341/R est:45000-55000
£32353	$55000	€47235	Madame Butterfly (105x202cm-41x80in) s. col woodcut. 31-Oct-3 Sotheby's, New York #557/R

FRANKFORT, Ed (1864-1920) Dutch

£2500	$4600	€3800	Peeling potatoes in Nieuwe Kerkstraat, Amsterdam (35x48cm-14x19in) s. prov. 22-Jun-4 Christie's, Amsterdam #92/R est:2000-3000

FRANKFURT SCHOOL (18th C) German

£11111	$18111	€16000	Scenes from soldiers life (53x65cm-21x26in) pair. 25-Sep-3 Dr Fritz Nagel, Stuttgart #1273/R est:22000

FRANKL, Franz (1881-1940) German

£267	$485	€400	Landscape with mill (41x58cm-16x23in) s. panel. 1-Jul-4 Van Ham, Cologne #1345
£443	$691	€700	Mill near Gauting (45x55cm-18x22in) s. 18-Oct-2 Von Zezschwitz, Munich #60/R
£605	$1047	€883	Landscape with pond and church in background (71x100cm-28x39in) s.d.1922. 14-Dec-3 Agra, Warsaw #43/R (P.Z 4000)

FRANKL, Gerhart (1901-1965) Austrian

£15972	$27153	€23000	Still life with herring, chicken and grapes (42x61cm-17x24in) lit. 28-Oct-3 Wiener Kunst Auktionen, Vienna #74/R est:17000-35000

FRANKLIN, John (20th C) American

£450	$752	€657	Rome (25x38cm-10x15in) mono.i.d.May 22 1841 oil paper. 13-Nov-3 Christie's, Kensington #341

FRANKO, Gregory Henry (1966-) Canadian

£226	$378	€330	K.L study (15x13cm-6x5in) s.i.d.2002 panel. 17-Nov-3 Hodgins, Calgary #330/R (C.D 500)

FRANKS, Leon (20th C) American

£1081	$2000	€1578	Basket of melons (122x81cm-48x32in) s.i. 14-Jan-4 Dallas Auction Gallery, Dallas #517/R est:800-1200

FRANQUELIN, Jean Augustin (attrib) (1798-1839) French

£2222	$4000	€3244	Une Malice (33x28cm-13x11in) 24-Apr-4 Skinner, Boston #230 est:5000-7000

FRANQUINET, Eugene Pierre (1875-1940) American

£824	$1500	€1203	Chickens by back porch. Mother and child on a porch (20x25cm-8x10in) init. masonite two. 15-Jun-4 John Moran, Pasadena #100 est:2000-3000

FRANS, Paul (1958-) French

£270	$484	€400	Rencontre (34x71cm-13x28in) 10-May-4 Amberes, Antwerp #265
£270	$484	€400	Repos (48x59cm-19x23in) 10-May-4 Amberes, Antwerp #266

£408 $743 €600 Les cabines de plage (49x71cm-19x28in) 9-Feb-4 Amberes, Antwerp #260
£1141 $2019 €1700 Trouville-sur-Mer (60x60cm-24x24in) s. 27-Apr-4 Campo & Campo, Antwerp #92/R est:1200-1600

FRANSIOLI, Thomas Adrian (1906-) American
£435 $800 €635 Still life with moon (43x38cm-17x15in) s.d.1960. 11-Jun-4 David Rago, Lambertville #229/R

FRANSSEN, Leonardus Martinus Hubertus (1905-1990) Dutch
£490 $842 €700 Still life with apples and black bottle (65x90cm-26x35in) s. 3-Dec-3 Auction Maastricht #968/R
£872 $1623 €1300 French riviera (50x80cm-20x31in) s. board. 4-Mar-4 Auction Maastricht #1092/R est:250-400
£1259 $2165 €1800 Still life of flowers (80x60cm-31x24in) s. 4-Dec-3 Vendue Huis, Gravenhage #1019
£1259 $2165 €1800 Still life with flowers (80x60cm-31x24in) s. board. 3-Dec-3 Auction Maastricht #1019/R est:1500-2000

FRANSSEN, Leonardus Martinus Hubertus (attrib) (1905-1990) Dutch
£490 $842 €700 Still life with apples and black bottle (65x90cm-26x35in) s. 4-Dec-3 Vendue Huis, Gravenhage #968

FRANTA, Hans (1893-?) Austrian
£350 $594 €500 Winter landscape (38x33cm-15x13in) s. board. 27-Nov-3 Dorotheum, Linz #496/R
£352 $616 €500 Water, clouds (50x59cm-20x23in) s.d. masonite. 19-Dec-3 Dorotheum, Vienna #251/R
£420 $713 €600 Ukraine (52x42cm-20x17in) s.i.verso panel. 27-Nov-3 Dorotheum, Linz #497/R
Works on paper
£233 $420 €350 Untitled (105x74cm-41x29in) s. mixed media. 26-Apr-4 Tajan, Paris #251

FRANTZ, Marshall (1890-?) American
£578 $1000 €844 Illustration, interior scene with two women (53x81cm-21x32in) s. monochromatic. 10-Dec-3 Alderfer's, Hatfield #397 est:300-400
Works on paper
£267 $500 €390 Man bending down to speak to young woman and her puppy (38x38cm-15x15in) s. gouache. 26-Feb-4 Illustration House, New York #73

FRANTZ, Thomas (18th C) German
Works on paper
£559 $962 €800 Still life with flowers (24x18cm-9x7in) one s.i.d.1783 mixed media one paper on board pair. 6-Dec-3 Quittenbaum, Hamburg #7/R

FRANZ, Ettore Roesler (1845-1907) Italian
Works on paper
£1250 $1988 €1825 Villa Adriana (53x30cm-21x12in) s. W/C. 12-Sep-3 Gardiner & Houlgate, Bath #55/R est:500-800
£1700 $3043 €2482 Flight of stone steps, Villa d'Este (76x30cm-30x12in) s.i. W/C. 4-May-4 Gorringes, Bexhill #1363/R est:300-500
£1800 $2988 €2628 Remains on the Villa di Cassio, Tivoli (51x64cm-20x25in) s.i. 30-Sep-3 Andrew Smith, Winchester #113/R est:2000-3000
£1831 $3039 €2600 Bufali a Maccarese. Barca a Sorrento (14x25cm-6x10in) both s.i. W/C cardboard two. 11-Jun-3 Christie's, Rome #271/R est:2800-3200
£3700 $6290 €5402 Coloseum (34x23cm-13x9in) s. W/C over pencil. 1-Dec-3 Bonhams, Bath #77/R est:1000-1500
£3892 $6500 €5682 Landscape with pond (51x102cm-20x40in) s.d.1903 W/C board. 7-Oct-3 Sotheby's, New York #131 est:8000-12000

FRANZEN, John E (1942-) Swedish
Works on paper
£435 $783 €635 Untitled (12x12cm-5x5in) init.d.1984 W/C. 26-Apr-4 Bukowskis, Stockholm #571/R (S.KR 6000)
£586 $1037 €856 Angel in the room (25x25cm-10x10in) s.i.d.1976-77 mixed media. 27-Apr-4 AB Stockholms Auktionsverk #1040/R (S.KR 8000)

FRAPPA, Jose (1854-1904) French
£2000 $3600 €2920 Surprised (61x45cm-24x18in) s. panel. 21-Jan-4 Sotheby's, Olympia #444/R est:2000-3000
£5556 $10000 €8112 L'intrus (66x76cm-26x30in) s. panel. 22-Apr-4 Christie's, Rockefeller NY #151/R est:12000-18000

FRAPPA, Jose (attrib) (1854-1904) French
£254 $475 €371 Monsignor's breakfast (24x18cm-9x7in) bears sig. panel. 29-Feb-4 Bonhams & Butterfields, San Francisco #4513

FRARY, Michael (1918-) American
Works on paper
£269 $450 €393 Galveston beach (53x74cm-21x29in) W/C. 18-Oct-3 David Dike, Dallas #128/R
£269 $450 €393 Edge falls (74x53cm-29x21in) W/C. 18-Oct-3 David Dike, Dallas #132/R
£329 $550 €480 Untitled (74x53cm-29x21in) W/C. 18-Oct-3 David Dike, Dallas #133/R
£359 $600 €524 Sea Wolf, Galveston (53x74cm-21x29in) W/C. 18-Oct-3 David Dike, Dallas #130/R
£509 $850 €743 Regatta (53x74cm-21x29in) W/C. 18-Oct-3 David Dike, Dallas #127/R
£659 $1100 €962 Untitled (74x53cm-29x21in) W/C. 18-Oct-3 David Dike, Dallas #131/R

FRASCHETTI, Giuseppe (?) Italian
£1079 $1770 €1500 Bridge in Ema (55x69cm-22x27in) s. s.i.verso board. 10-Jun-3 Pandolfini, Florence #223/R est:1000-1200

FRASER, Alexander (jnr) (1828-1899) British
£600 $1116 €876 Sketch in Stoke Park (23x36cm-9x14in) s.i.verso board. 4-Mar-4 Christie's, Kensington #102/R
£1072 $1823 €1565 West Highland sea loch (51x91cm-20x36in) s. 21-Nov-3 Walker's, Ottawa #241/R est:2500-3500 (C.D 2380)
£1150 $1852 €1668 Strome, Perthshire (26x39cm-10x15in) s. panel. 21-Aug-3 Bonhams, Edinburgh #1223 est:1200-1500
£1250 $2288 €1825 The yellow room at Barncluith (20x30cm-8x12in) s.i.verso panel. 7-Apr-4 Woolley & Wallis, Salisbury #334/R est:250-350
£1400 $2198 €2030 Cattle at a ford (35x51cm-14x20in) s. prov. 27-Aug-3 Sotheby's, London #927/R est:1500-2000
£1500 $2355 €2175 Searching for coppers (25x20cm-10x8in) s. board prov. 27-Aug-3 Sotheby's, London #944/R est:1500-2000
£1700 $3213 €2482 Prince Charlie's bedroom, Holyrood (34x50cm-13x20in) s. s.i.verso panel. 19-Feb-4 Lyon & Turnbull, Edinburgh #148 est:500-800
£2000 $3140 €2900 Queen Mary's well, Barncluith (33x50cm-13x20in) s. i.verso panel prov. 27-Aug-3 Sotheby's, London #935/R est:2000-3000
£2027 $3446 €2959 Fishing at Puneugh Point, Dairy, Ayshire (30x47cm-12x19in) s.i. prov. 21-Nov-3 Walker's, Ottawa #240/R est:1500-2500 (C.D 4500)
Works on paper
£780 $1256 €1131 Roslin Chapel (25x22cm-10x9in) s. W/C. 21-Aug-3 Bonhams, Edinburgh #1118/R

FRASER, Alexander (jnr-attrib) (1828-1899) British
£300 $537 €438 Loch landscape with figures in rowing boat (34x44cm-13x17in) panel. 17-Mar-4 Bonhams, Chester #371

FRASER, Alexander (snr) (1786-1865) British
£343 $631 €501 Cobbler's fine vintage (25x36cm-10x14in) s. 14-Jun-4 Waddingtons, Toronto #185/R (C.D 850)
£610 $1091 €891 Interior of a mill in the Hebrides (70x96cm-28x38in) s. i.verso panel exhib. 4-May-4 Ritchie, Toronto #38/R est:3000-5000 (C.D 1500)
£1500 $2760 €2190 Children at the village pump (46x36cm-18x14in) s.d.1829. 12-Jun-4 Finan Watkins & Co, Mere #48/R
£1800 $3366 €2700 Robinson Crusoe (30x40cm-12x16in) s. board. 26-Jul-4 Bonhams, Bath #87/R est:800-1200

FRASER, Donald Hamilton (1929-) British
£600 $1092 €876 Landscape (18x18cm-7x7in) s. paper on board painted c.1960. 1-Jul-4 Christie's, Kensington #343/R
£650 $1183 €949 Night Landscape (22x16cm-9x6in) s. paper on board. 1-Jul-4 Christie's, Kensington #342/R
£650 $1183 €949 Sunset mountains (18x19cm-7x7in) s. paper on board painted c.1960. 1-Jul-4 Christie's, Kensington #341/R
£1200 $2004 €1752 Church (15x12cm-6x5in) s. oil on paper. 21-Oct-3 Bonhams, Knightsbridge #23/R est:800-1200
£1200 $2064 €1752 Fish (30x38cm-12x15in) s. oil collage paper. 2-Dec-3 Bonhams, New Bond Street #167/R est:800-1200
£1648 $3000 €2406 Suffolk landscape (71x91cm-28x36in) s. painted 1968 prov.exhib. 29-Jun-4 Sotheby's, New York #517/R est:5000-7000
£1800 $3060 €2628 Landscape study (13x19cm-5x7in) s. paper painted 1981 prov. 26-Nov-3 Sotheby's, Olympia #167/R est:1800-2500
£1800 $3276 €2628 Landscape composition (48x34cm-19x13in) paper. 1-Jul-4 Christie's, Kensington #346/R est:2000-3000
£1892 $3500 €2762 Lagoon (71x91cm-28x36in) s. painted 1967 prov. 15-Jul-4 Sotheby's, New York #96/R est:2000-3000
£1900 $3515 €2774 Boatyard (48x31cm-19x12in) init. board. 11-Feb-4 Sotheby's, Olympia #300/R est:2000-3000
£2400 $4320 €3600 Figure in interior (34x44cm-13x17in) s. board. 20-Apr-4 James Adam, Dublin #64/R est:800-1200
£2600 $4342 €3796 Kilchurn Castle (47x34cm-19x13in) s. oil on paper. 21-Oct-3 Bonhams, Knightsbridge #20/R est:1000-1500
£5800 $10556 €8468 Study for beach and breakwater (46x35cm-18x14in) s. painted 1959 exhib. 1-Jul-4 Christie's, Kensington #340/R est:2000-3000
£7000 $12670 €10220 Blue and orange still life (91x122cm-36x48in) s. prov. 19-Apr-4 Sotheby's, London #152/R est:7000-10000
£11000 $20020 €16060 Evening landscape (91x71cm-36x28in) s. i.d.1957 stretcher prov. 1-Jul-4 Christie's, Kensington #344/R est:5000-7000
Works on paper
£700 $1288 €1022 Pas-de-Deux- pink tunic (71x41cm-28x16in) s.i.verso mixed media. 23-Mar-4 Rosebery Fine Art, London #858/R

FRASER, Florence (fl.1880-1910) British
£550 $1012 €803 Chestnut hunter in a landscape (46x62cm-18x24in) s. 23-Jun-4 Cheffins, Cambridge #535/R

FRASER, J (?) ?
£720 $1246 €1051 Seascape with waves breaking below a heavy sky. s. 9-Dec-3 Lawrences, Bletchingley #1642

FRASER, James Baillie (1783-1856) British
Prints
£25000 $40750 €36500 Views in the Himala Mountains. hand-coloured aquatint title sold with 20 aquatint plates. 24-Sep-3 Christie's, London #63/R est:20000-30000

FRASER, James Earle (1876-1953) American
Sculpture
£2235 $4000 €3263 Roosevelt Bas-Relief (30x23cm-12x9in) bas-relief bronze iron. 15-May-4 Altermann Galleries, Santa Fe #72/R

FRASER, James Earle (after) (1876-1953) American
Sculpture
£5525 $10000 €8067 End of the trail (88cm-35in) i. brown pat bronze st.f.Kunst prov.exhib. 31-Mar-4 Sotheby's, New York #166/R est:2000-3000

FRASER, John (20th C) ?
£300 $567 €438 Island of Palma (24x34cm-9x13in) s. i.verso board. 18-Feb-4 Peter Wilson, Nantwich #8

FRASER, John (1858-1927) British
£500 $920 €730 Island of Palma (24x34cm-9x13in) indis sig. 8-Jun-4 Bonhams, Knightsbridge #168/R

FRASER, John Arthur (1839-1898) Canadian/British
Works on paper
£387 $630 €565 Stone bridge (35x48cm-14x19in) s. W/C. 23-Sep-3 Ritchie, Toronto #59/R (C.D 850)
£495 $842 €723 In the Pass of Brauder (34x48cm-13x19in) s. W/C paperboard. 23-Nov-3 Levis, Calgary #39/R (C.D 1100)

FRASER, Malcolm (?) British
£1018 $1700 €1486 Organ-grinder's monkey scares dog to amusement of master and children (48x33cm-19x13in) s. board on masonite painted c.1910. 15-Nov-3 Illustration House, New York #97/R est:1500-2400

FRASER, Peter Gordon (1808-1888) Australian
Works on paper
£2000 $3640 €2920 Browns river Tasmania (23x34cm-9x13in) s.i. pencil W/C scratching out htd white. 5-Feb-4 Mellors & Kirk, Nottingham #508/R est:1000-1500
£2400 $4368 €3504 Kangaroos in Hutton Park, Tasmania (23x34cm-9x13in) s.i.d.1844 pencil W/C scratching out. 5-Feb-4 Mellors & Kirk, Nottingham #509/R est:1000-1500

FRASER, Robert Winchester (1848-1906) British
Works on paper
£340 $537 €493 Quiet meadow pool (24x44cm-9x17in) s. W/C over pencil bodycol. 24-Jul-3 Lawrence, Crewkerne #856/R
£350 $581 €511 Thames Ditton (21x33cm-8x13in) s.i.d.95 W/C. 1-Oct-3 Sotheby's, Olympia #96/R
£450 $833 €657 Chertsea (19x37cm-7x15in) s.d.90 W/C. 11-Feb-4 Cheffins, Cambridge #396
£480 $883 €701 Hastings (16x35cm-6x14in) s.i.d.86 W/C. 23-Jun-4 Bonhams, Bury St Edmunds #352
£480 $874 €701 On the Eley (24x54cm-9x21in) s.i.d.91 pencil W/C htd white. 1-Jul-4 Mellors & Kirk, Nottingham #760/R
£620 $1135 €905 Hartford, hunts (43x71cm-17x28in) s.i.d.95 W/C. 7-Apr-4 Bonhams, Bury St Edmunds #404/R
£650 $1125 €949 At Brandon - Norfolk (17x37cm-7x15in) s.i. W/C sold with companion pair. 10-Dec-3 Bonhams, Bury St Edmunds #483/R

FRASER, Robert Winter (1872-1930) British
Works on paper
£250 $465 €365 Landscape with a lake and rushes, cottage and church beyond (18x38cm-7x15in) s. W/C. 4-Mar-4 Bonhams, Cornwall #242
£260 $450 €380 Panoramic landscape scene. s. W/C. 13-Dec-3 Hogben, Folkstone #179
£550 $946 €803 Fenland river landscapes (13x28cm-5x11in) s.d.83 W/C pair. 5-Dec-3 Keys, Aylsham #532/R

FRASER, Thomas Douglas (1883-1955) American
£387 $700 €565 Grand Canyon, Arizone (25x30cm-10x12in) s.i. 3-Apr-4 Harvey Clar, Oakland #1242

FRATER, William (1890-1974) Australian/British
£272 $498 €408 Landscape with trees. board. 3-Jun-4 Joel, Victoria #126/R (A.D 700)
£311 $570 €467 Lorne. canvas on board. 3-Jun-4 Joel, Victoria #278 (A.D 800)
£779 $1230 €1137 Seated nude (81x66cm-32x26in) s.d.1974 verso board. 2-Sep-3 Deutscher-Menzies, Melbourne #319/R est:1500-2500 (A.D 1900)
£1527 $2779 €2229 Street scene (44x55cm-17x22in) s. canvas on board exhib. 16-Jun-4 Deutscher-Menzies, Melbourne #221/R est:4000-6000 (A.D 4000)
Works on paper
£319 $542 €466 Bush Sentinal (53x35cm-21x14in) s.d.1968 W/C. 26-Nov-3 Deutscher-Menzies, Melbourne #257/R (A.D 750)

FRATIN, Christopher (1800-1864) French
Sculpture
£1000 $1700 €1460 Retriever with pheasant (23x37cm-9x15in) s. pat bronze. 28-Oct-3 Sotheby's, London #161/R
£1056 $1827 €1500 Cachet a l'ours sur un tronc d'arbre (10cm-4in) brown pat bronze. 14-Dec-3 St-Germain-en-Laye Encheres #87/R est:1500-1800
£1206 $2013 €1700 Le singe chiffonnier (24x16x16cm-9x6x6in) s. brown pat bronze. 12-Oct-3 St-Germain-en-Laye Encheres #20/R est:1500
£1389 $2194 €2000 Les ours acrobates (11cm-4in) s. brown pat bronze. 25-Apr-3 Etude de Provence, Marseille #130 est:2000-2500
£1408 $2437 €2000 L'ours et a l'ourson jouant (10cm-4in) s. brown pat bronze Cast Daubree. 14-Dec-3 St-Germain-en-Laye Encheres #86 est:2000-2500
£1477 $2377 €2200 Cachet a l'ours juche (10cm-4in) s. red brown pat bronze. 23-Feb-3 St-Germain-en-Laye Encheres #7/R est:2000-2200
£1500 $2505 €2190 Lion taking a boar (76cm-30in) s. bronze exec.c.1840-1860. 16-Nov-3 Desmond Judd, Cranbrook #534
£2200 $4158 €3212 Horse protecting its foal from a dog. s. brown pat bronze marble base. 17-Feb-4 Sotheby's, Olympia #27/R est:1500-2000
£4196 $7133 €6000 Singerie (52cm-20in) s. pat bronze. 21-Nov-3 Lombrail & Teucquam, Paris #80/R est:1500-2000
£5298 $8636 €8000 Chasse au sanglier. s. dark pat bronze. 1-Feb-3 Dubee & Berron, Vernou en Sologne #94

FRAU, Jose (1898-1976) Spanish
£517 $957 €750 Untitled (60x47cm-24x19in) s. on crystal. 14-Jan-4 Castellana, Madrid #64/R
£1241 $2234 €1800 Landscapes (36x50cm-14x20in) s.d.1913 pair. 26-Jan-4 Ansorena, Madrid #171/R est:1500
£2695 $4501 €3800 Landscape (49x70cm-19x28in) s. panel. 23-Jun-3 Durán, Madrid #170/R est:3800
£4255 $6894 €6000 Landscape (90x116cm-35x46in) s. 20-May-3 Ansorena, Madrid #167/R est:4800

FRAUSTADT, Friedrich Auguste (1821-?) German
£909 $1600 €1364 Scene of a man, woman and child in a doorway (81x66cm-32x26in) s. panel. 21-May-4 North East Auctions, Portsmouth #287
£7587 $12670 €11000 Danse Orientale dans un palais de la Rome Antique (106x185cm-42x73in) s. panel. 17-Nov-3 Tajan, Paris #82/R est:12000-15000

FRAZER, Neil (?) Australian?
£1038 $1858 €1515 Untitled (160x220cm-63x87in) s.d.1987 verso. 11-May-4 Watson's, Christchurch #65/R est:10000-12000 (NZ.D 3000)

FRAZER, William Miller (1864-1961) British
£250 $458 €365 Portrait of Mrs Grace McNichol (20x15cm-8x6in) i.d.1886 board. 28-Jul-4 Mallams, Oxford #374/R
£280 $468 €409 Remilton cottages, near Newburgh, Clatchard Crag in the distance (31x46cm-12x18in) 19-Jun-3 Bonhams, Edinburgh #326
£480 $802 €701 Woodland lane (33x23cm-13x9in) s. 14-Oct-3 David Lay, Penzance #200
£500 $795 €730 River landscape (23x28cm-9x11in) s. board sketch prov. 1-May-3 John Nicholson, Haslemere #754
£720 $1202 €1051 Mallard landing in reeds. 19-Jun-3 Bonhams, Edinburgh #338
£760 $1338 €1110 Cattle. Farm carts (19x28cm-7x11in) board pair. 18-May-4 Woolley & Wallis, Salisbury #188/R
£1000 $1830 €1460 Landscape with sheep (62x74cm-24x29in) s.d.1901. 7-Jul-4 George Kidner, Lymington #154/R est:1000-1500
£1450 $2335 €2103 At Machrihanish (20x34cm-8x13in) s. i.verso canvasboard. 21-Aug-3 Bonhams, Edinburgh #1015/R est:400-600
£1500 $2355 €2175 Farmyard (41x51cm-16x20in) s. 27-Aug-3 Sotheby's, London #1133/R est:1500-2000
£1500 $2805 €2190 Crofters cottages in a landscape (7x10cm-3x4in) s. canvasboard. 25-Feb-4 Mallams, Oxford #185/R est:1000-1500
£1700 $3043 €2482 Horse and cart on Blackwaterfoot beach, Arran (25x35cm-10x14in) s. board. 26-May-4 Sotheby's, Olympia #231/R est:2000-3000
£1750 $3255 €2555 Near St. Andrews, Fife (28x36cm-11x14in) s. canvasboard. 4-Mar-4 Christie's, Kensington #104/R est:1000-1500
£2300 $3611 €3335 Loch Torridon, showing the buttress of Liatach and Ben Alligin in the background (64x92cm-25x36in) s.d.09. 27-Aug-3 Sotheby's, London #1112/R est:2500-3000
£2300 $3611 €3335 Boy with a barrow (18x61cm-7x24in) s.d.1889 i.on stretcher. 27-Aug-3 Sotheby's, London #1142/R est:1500-2000
£2692 $4631 €3930 Woman on the green (76x50cm-30x20in) s.d.1890. 3-Dec-3 AB Stockholms Auktionsverk #2617/R est:18000-20000 (S.KR 35000)
£3000 $4710 €4350 Duddington Mill. Village of Duddinton, Northamptonshire (25x35cm-10x14in) s. canvasboard pair. 27-Aug-3 Sotheby's, London #1128/R est:3000-5000
£3000 $5430 €4380 Herding the sheep (41x61cm-16x24in) s. 19-Apr-4 Sotheby's, London #106/R est:3000-4000
£3800 $6574 €5548 Wooded river landscape with punt (61x51cm-24x20in) s. 11-Dec-3 Lyon & Turnbull, Edinburgh #7/R est:2000-3000
£3800 $6574 €5548 Harvest landscape, summer skies (51x75cm-20x30in) s. 11-Dec-3 Lyon & Turnbull, Edinburgh #66/R est:3000-4000
£6000 $11220 €8760 Summer river landscape with young boy fishing from a punt (76x63cm-30x25in) s. prov. 22-Jul-4 Tennants, Leyburn #856/R est:6000-8000

FRAZIER, John Robinson (1889-1966) American
£350 $550 €511 Still life (51x61cm-20x24in) 20-Apr-3 Outer Cape Auctions, Provincetown #90/R

FRAZIER, Kenneth (1867-1949) American
£378 $700 €567 Woman in a blue dress. s. 14-Jul-4 Dallas Auction Gallery, Dallas #372/R

FRAZIER, Luke (20th C) American
£2514 $4500 €3670 Working the chute (51x61cm-20x24in) board. 15-May-4 Altermann Galleries, Santa Fe #164/R
£12032 $22500 €17567 Sanctuary (76x122cm-30x48in) s. board. 24-Jul-4 Coeur d'Alene, Hayden #21/R est:12000-18000

FRECH, August (1875-1945) Austrian
£336 $594 €500 Tyrolean farmers with their cows in an extensive landscape (78x90cm-31x35in) s.d.1945 lit. 30-Apr-4 Auktionhaus Georg Rehm, Augsburg #8023

FRECHON, Charles (1856-1929) French
£12000 $21601 €18000 Orchidees en fleurs dans le jardin d'une maison de campagne (44x56cm-17x22in) s. 26-Apr-4 Tajan, Paris #120/R est:8000-10000
£22001 $39601 €33000 Travailleur des rues dans la froidure de l'hiver (43x55cm-17x22in) s. 26-Apr-4 Tajan, Paris #119/R est:8000-10000

FRECKELTON, Sondra (20th C) American
Works on paper
£608 $1100 €888 Ten and king (18x25cm-7x10in) W/C. 16-Apr-4 American Auctioneer #140/R

FREDDIE, Wilhelm (1909-1995) Danish

£1344 $2191 €1962 Surrealistic composition (35x27cm-14x11in) s.d.juli 1946. 29-Sep-3 Lilla Bukowskis, Stockholm #368 est:8000-10000 (S.KR 17500)
£1976 $3358 €2885 La cuisiniere (110x65cm-43x26in) s.d.63-64 i.verso oil assemblage exhib. 26-Nov-3 Kunsthallen, Copenhagen #126/R est:30000 (D.KR 21000)
£3286 $5488 €4798 Deserted valley - convalescence - Surrealistic landscape (46x38cm-18x15in) s.d.Nov.44 masonite exhib.lit. 7-Oct-3 Rasmussen, Copenhagen #120/R est:40000 (D.KR 35000)
£3430 $6310 €5008 Femme se repose - Surrealistic figure composition (33x41cm-13x16in) s.d.juli 1946 exhib. 29-Mar-4 Rasmussen, Copenhagen #164/R est:30000 (D.KR 38000)
£3756 $6272 €5484 Figure composition with head (40x37cm-16x15in) s.d.33. 7-Oct-3 Rasmussen, Copenhagen #83/R est:60000 (D.KR 40000)
£4796 $8586 €7002 Scandal in the social life - the kitchen (97x130cm-38x51in) s.d.66 s.d.1966 verso exhib. 10-May-4 Rasmussen, Vejle #709/R est:50000-75000 (D.KR 53000)
£5235 $9632 €7643 Bathers (35x26cm-14x10in) s.d.Juni 1947 exhib.prov. 29-Mar-4 Rasmussen, Copenhagen #153/R est:30000-40000 (D.KR 58000)
£7671 $14116 €11200 Forward and backward (114x163cm-45x64in) s.d.80 s.d.1980 verso exhib. 29-Mar-4 Rasmussen, Copenhagen #157/R est:100000 (D.KR 85000)
£13270 $21232 €19242 Je vais certainement avoir une meilleure chemise (100x80cm-39x31in) s.d.1937 i.verso exhib.lit. 17-Sep-3 Kunsthallen, Copenhagen #12/R est:125000 (D.KR 140000)

Sculpture
£1083 $2025 €1581 Seated lady (54x35cm-21x14in) s.d.63 assemblage. 25-Feb-4 Kunsthallen, Copenhagen #85/R est:15000 (D.KR 12000)

Works on paper
£340 $609 €496 Erotic composition (21x16cm-8x6in) s.d.80 col pencil. 12-Jan-4 Rasmussen, Vejle #671/R (D.KR 3600)
£451 $844 €658 Reclining model (23x33cm-9x13in) s.d.81 W/C. 25-Feb-4 Kunsthallen, Copenhagen #3 (D.KR 5000)
£496 $928 €724 Wilhelm Freddie - Drawing, Collages and Graphic (70x49cm-28x19in) W/C crayon collage. 25-Feb-4 Kunsthallen, Copenhagen #168/R (D.KR 5500)
£948 $1517 €1375 Model (65x48cm-26x19in) s.d.81 pastel exhib. 17-Sep-3 Kunsthallen, Copenhagen #75/R (D.KR 10000)

FREDERIC, Léon (1856-1940) Belgian

£276 $508 €420 Etude d'Italie (15x18cm-6x7in) d.1879 exhib. 22-Jun-4 Palais de Beaux Arts, Brussels #243
£350 $584 €500 Rayon de soleil en mer du Nord (35x60cm-14x24in) s. canvas on panel. 13-Oct-3 Horta, Bruxelles #126
£382 $638 €550 Kanaal te Heyst (30x44cm-12x17in) s. panel. 21-Oct-3 Campo, Vlaamse Kaai #825
£433 $797 €650 Canal a Heist sur Mer (28x43cm-11x17in) s. canvas on panel. 14-Jun-4 Horta, Bruxelles #284
£694 $1160 €1000 Tournesols (29x45cm-11x18in) s.d.1905. 21-Oct-3 Galerie Moderne, Brussels #226/R
£839 $1443 €1200 Paysage vallone (34x44cm-13x17in) s. i.verso canvas on board. 2-Dec-3 Sotheby's, Amsterdam #245/R est:1200-1500
£839 $1443 €1200 Interieur ensoleille (54x47cm-21x19in) s.d.1886. 8-Dec-3 Horta, Bruxelles #28
£966 $1786 €1400 Village in summer (36x56cm-14x22in) s.d.1902 panel. 19-Jan-4 Horta, Bruxelles #318
£979 $1635 €1400 Chemin de campagne (27x43cm-11x17in) s. panel. 13-Oct-3 Horta, Bruxelles #124
£1611 $2851 €2400 Vieillard fumant sa pipe au coin de feu (80x65cm-31x26in) s.d.1896 exhib. 27-Apr-4 Campo & Campo, Antwerp #93/R est:2500-3500
£2238 $3737 €3200 La Trinite (30x60cm-12x24in) s.d.1882 panel. 13-Oct-3 Horta, Bruxelles #125 est:600-800
£3846 $6538 €5500 La Chaussee de'Alsemberg. La rue de Turquie sous la neige (20x45cm-8x18in) s.d.1883 canvas on panel. 1-Dec-3 Palais de Beaux Arts, Brussels #68/R est:1200-1800

Works on paper
£600 $1086 €900 Les tonneaux (38x44cm-15x17in) s. chl. 30-Mar-4 Palais de Beaux Arts, Brussels #587
£1467 $2655 €2200 Baigneuse (100x118cm-39x46in) s. pastel. 30-Mar-4 Campo, Vlaamse Kaai #69 est:2500-3500

FREDERICK, Frank Forest (1866-?) American

£242 $450 €353 West Chop, Vineyard Haven (22x30cm-9x12in) s. board. 5-Mar-4 Skinner, Boston #582/R

FREDERICK, Linden (1953-) American

£7647 $13000 €11165 Adobe (109x109cm-43x43in) s. oil linen prov. 1-Nov-3 Santa Fe Art, Santa Fe #243/R est:15000-18000

FREDERICK, Rod (20th C) American

£2500 $4500 €3650 Down to Winter Rang, Big Horn Sheep (86x142cm-34x56in) s.d.86 exhib. 26-Jan-4 Schrager Galleries, Milwaukee #1317
£2754 $4600 €4021 Rainforest rendezvous (43x97cm-17x38in) s. 11-Oct-3 Nadeau, Windsor #145/R est:6000-9000

FREDERICK, William (?) ?

£281 $458 €410 Portrait of woman with bonnet (93x71cm-37x28in) s. 27-Sep-3 Rasmussen, Havnen #2081 (D.KR 3000)

FREDERICKS, Ernest (1877-1927) American

£250 $400 €365 Winter landscape (41x51cm-16x20in) s. painted c.1930's. 20-Sep-3 Bunte, Elgin #1437
£254 $425 €368 Autumn landscape (41x51cm-16x20in) s. 28-Jun-3 Susanin's, Chicago #5062
£264 $475 €385 Landscape (61x86cm-24x34in) s. 24-Jan-4 Susanin's, Chicago #5043/R
£277 $440 €402 Winter scene of trees, and distant house (69x56cm-27x22in) s. 12-Sep-3 Aspire, Cleveland #45
£313 $500 €457 Landscape with trees and stream (61x76cm-24x30in) s. 17-May-3 Bunte, Elgin #1283
£328 $600 €479 Ozarks (71x97cm-28x38in) s. painted c.1920. 5-Jun-4 Treadway Gallery, Cincinnati #609/R
£410 $750 €599 Mother and child on a path (61x76cm-24x30in) s. painted c.1920. 5-Jun-4 Treadway Gallery, Cincinnati #658/R
£419 $750 €612 Summer river landscape (71x97cm-28x38in) s. 15-May-4 Jeffery Burchard, Florida #139
£447 $800 €653 Autumnal river landscape (61x91cm-24x36in) s. 15-May-4 Jeffery Burchard, Florida #140
£479 $800 €699 Landscape with brook (61x91cm-24x36in) s. 20-Jun-3 Freeman, Philadelphia #124/R
£898 $1500 €1311 Landscape with stream (71x97cm-28x38in) s. 20-Jun-3 Freeman, Philadelphia #215/R est:2000-3000

FREDERICKS, Marshall Maynard (1908-1998) American

Sculpture
£8982 $15000 €13114 Mother bear and cub (41cm-16in) bronze. 17-Oct-3 Du Mouchelle, Detroit #2082/R est:18000-20000

FREDOU, Jean Martial (attrib) (1711-1795) French

Works on paper
£986 $1706 €1400 Portrait de femme (40x33cm-16x13in) pierre noire sanguine chk. 10-Dec-3 Maigret, Paris #1/R

FREDRIKS, Johannes Hendrik (1751-1822) Dutch

£9400 $15322 €13724 Still life with a lavish of display of various fruits and flowers on marble ledge (77x60cm-30x24in) 28-Sep-3 Wilkinson, Doncaster #285/R
£38462 $70000 €56155 Irises, peonies, roses and other flowers surrounding a terracotta urn, with bird's nest (58x46cm-23x18in) s.d.1774 panel prov. 17-Jun-4 Christie's, Rockefeller NY #25/R est:80000-120000

FREDRIKSSON, Carl Einar (1887-1951) Swedish

£437 $805 €656 View of Town Hall, Stockholm (85x66cm-33x26in) s.d.1922. 14-Jun-4 Lilla Bukowskis, Stockholm #227 (S.KR 6000)

FREDRIKSSON, Stig (1929-) Finnish

£361 $604 €527 Nude lovers (131x162cm-52x64in) s. panel. 20-Oct-3 Blomqvist, Lysaker #1091 (N.KR 4200)
£811 $1451 €1200 Lovers (130x162cm-51x64in) S.D.64 BOARD. 8-May-4 Bukowskis, Helsinki #274/R

FREED, Leonard (20th C) American

Photographs
£1778 $3200 €2596 Man taken into custody in a police car (30x20cm-12x8in) s.verso gelatin silver print. 24-Apr-4 Phillips, New York #99/R est:2000-3000
£17778 $32000 €25956 Black white America, maquette (28x54cm-11x21in) album 119 gelatin silver print. 24-Apr-4 Phillips, New York #73/R est:40000-60000

FREEDLY, George (20th C) American

£520 $900 €759 Autumn landscape with two figures (48x66cm-19x26in) s.i. 10-Dec-3 Alderfer's, Hatfield #370/R est:1000-1500

FREEDMAN, Barnett (1901-1958) British

£440 $801 €642 Corfe Castle. s.d.29. 3-Feb-4 Sworder & Son, Bishops Stortford #257/R
£800 $1480 €1168 Corfe Castle (51x71cm-20x28in) s.d.29. 11-Feb-4 Sotheby's, Olympia #167/R
£1800 $3096 €2628 Buckinghamshire (23x62cm-9x24in) s.indis.d. prov. 3-Dec-3 Christie's, Kensington #463/R est:1000-1500

FREEDMAN, Maurice (1904-) American

£615 $1100 €898 Pennsylvania farm (48x97cm-19x38in) s. prov. 16-May-4 Wright, Chicago #157/R

FREEMAN, Dick (1932-1991) Canadian

£541 $919 €790 Just walking in the rain (46x61cm-18x24in) s. i.verso hardboard prov. 23-Nov-3 Levis, Calgary #40/R (C.D 1200)
£1810 $3023 €2643 Round up (60x90cm-24x35in) s.i.d.1976 board. 17-Nov-3 Hodgins, Calgary #196/R est:2750-3250 (C.D 4000)

FREEMAN, Don (1908-1978) American

Works on paper
£321 $500 €469 Opening night high times (53x74cm-21x29in) s.d.1959 W/C. 12-Apr-3 Auctions by the Bay, Alameda #319/R

FREEMAN, James (1828-1858) British

£1156 $2000 €1688 Horse in landscape (64x79cm-25x31in) s.d.1838. 13-Dec-3 Charlton Hall, Columbia #357/R

FREEMAN, Kathryn (1956-) American

£442 $800 €663 Long mornings (38x56cm-15x22in) 16-Apr-4 American Auctioneer #141/R
£1105 $2000 €1658 Dream of jealousy (76x142cm-30x56in) 16-Apr-4 American Auctioneer #142/R est:4000-6000

FREEMAN, Mary Winefride (attrib) (fl.1886-1904) British

Works on paper
£380 $654 €555 Two ladies fishing from a punt (43x30cm-17x12in) W/C. 5-Dec-3 Chrystals Auctions, Isle of Man #291

FREEMAN, William Philip Barnes (1813-1897) British
£280 $501 €409 Costessey Ford (23cm-9in circular) init.d.79 board. 25-May-4 Sworder & Son, Bishops Stortford #389/R
£300 $501 €438 Norfolk river landscape (25x33cm-10x13in) 17-Oct-3 Keys, Aylsham #687
Works on paper
£300 $501 €438 Fishermen with boats (25x36cm-10x14in) init.indis.d. pastel. 17-Oct-3 Keys, Aylsham #646

FREER, Frederick W (1849-1908) American
£472 $750 €689 Portrait of a woman (61x46cm-24x18in) s.d.1901. 14-Sep-3 Susanin's, Chicago #6052/R

FREER, Henry Branston (fl.1870-1900) British
Works on paper
£260 $458 €380 Schooner picking up pilot (23x36cm-9x14in) s. W/C. 31-Dec-3 Lambrays, Wadebridge #641
£300 $537 €438 Running home on the tide (15x23cm-6x9in) s. W/C. 26-May-4 Christie's, Kensington #431/R
£300 $537 €438 Running into the estuary (13x26cm-5x10in) s. W/C. 26-May-4 Christie's, Kensington #450/R
£400 $704 €584 Shipping on the river Medway (23x33cm-9x13in) s. W/C. 31-Dec-3 Lambrays, Wadebridge #640
£460 $796 €672 Figures in a Victorian boatyard. W/C. 14-Dec-3 Desmond Judd, Cranbrook #1151
£550 $1012 €803 Messina (21x33cm-8x13in) s.i. W/C. 23-Mar-4 Bonhams, Knightsbridge #71/R
£900 $1656 €1314 An estuary scene, HMS Victory to the fore (42x66cm-17x26in) s. W/C. 23-Jun-4 Bonhams, Bury St Edmunds #324/R

FREESE, F (20th C) ?
Sculpture
£1397 $2500 €2040 Nude maiden seated on rocks (46cm-18in) s. brown pat. bronze. 20-Mar-4 Selkirks, St. Louis #559/R est:1000-1200

FREESE, N (fl.1794-1814) British
Miniatures
£1100 $2024 €1606 Gentleman wearing a blue coat (7cm-3in) gold frame. 24-Jun-4 Bonhams, New Bond Street #101/R est:700-900
£2400 $4320 €3504 Lady wearing a white dress with lace cap to the sleeve (7cm-3in) gold frame oval exhib.lit. 22-Apr-4 Bonhams, New Bond Street #144/R est:1500-2500

FREEZOR, George Augustus (fl.1861-1879) British
£660 $1201 €964 Taking grandmother's hand (20x25cm-8x10in) s.indis.d. 3-Feb-4 Sworder & Son, Bishops Stortford #299/R

FREGIER, F (20th C) ?
£1408 $2437 €2000 Ruelle couverte a Marrakech (40x30cm-16x12in) s. panel. 15-Dec-3 Gros & Delettrez, Paris #519/R est:1500-2000

FREHNER, Johannes (20th C) Swiss
Works on paper
£259 $463 €378 Farmstead (31x40cm-12x16in) W/C bodycol prov. 12-May-4 Dobiaschofsky, Bern #527/R (S.FR 600)

FREI, Emil (1882-1955) Swiss
£286 $475 €415 Girl's portrait (38x29cm-15x11in) s.d.1914 prov. 13-Jun-3 Zofingen, Switzerland #2845 (S.FR 630)

FREILICHER, Jane (1924-) American
£3297 $6000 €4814 Cabana days (102x76cm-40x30in) painted 1958 prov. 29-Jun-4 Sotheby's, New York #468/R est:10000-15000
Works on paper
£2000 $3500 €2920 Study for autumnal landscape (65x50cm-26x20in) s. pastel prov. 19-Dec-3 Sotheby's, New York #1028/R est:4000-6000

FREIMAN, Lillian (1908-1986) Canadian
£317 $529 €463 Symphony orchestra (19x28cm-7x11in) oil pastel. 17-Nov-3 Hodgins, Calgary #293/R (C.D 700)
Works on paper
£200 $366 €292 Portrait of a woman (29x24cm-11x9in) s. col chks wash. 1-Jun-4 Joyner Waddington, Toronto #462 (C.D 500)
£357 $614 €521 Orchestra (31x53cm-12x21in) s. col pencil htd white. 2-Dec-3 Joyner Waddington, Toronto #328/R (C.D 800)

FREINIK, William (1905-) American/German
£1266 $2000 €1848 Painting number 43 (122x112cm-48x44in) s.i.verso masonite. 7-Sep-3 Treadway Gallery, Cincinnati #691/R est:2500-4500

FREIRE, Maria (20th C) South American?
Works on paper
£293 $480 €428 Abstract (41x31cm-16x12in) s.d.1953 ink. 3-Jun-3 Galeria y Remates, Montevideo #12

FREIST, Greta (1904-1993) Austrian
Works on paper
£1000 $1790 €1500 Birds in tree (46x38cm-18x15in) s.d. W/C. 13-May-4 Neumeister, Munich #351/R est:1000-1200

FREITAG, Clemens (1883-?) German
£1133 $2051 €1700 Two hunting dogs stalking pheasant (87x120cm-34x47in) s. 1-Apr-4 Van Ham, Cologne #1383/R est:1800
£1273 $2240 €1859 Landscape with river (60x50cm-24x20in) s. 23-May-4 Agra, Warsaw #24/R (P.Z 9000)

FREITAG, Conrad (?-1894) American
£1899 $3000 €2773 Ship Norway passing Sandy Hook (64x94cm-25x37in) s. 25-Jul-3 Eldred, East Dennis #291a/R est:5000-10000

FREIXANES, Jose (1953-) Spanish
£764 $1299 €1100 Bois Maio (60x52cm-24x20in) s.i.d.1987 oil acrylic board. 28-Oct-3 Segre, Madrid #270/R
£1127 $1972 €1600 Map of lost continents (140x200cm-55x79in) s.d.1990 verso exhib. 16-Dec-3 Durán, Madrid #183/R est:1500
£1733 $3155 €2600 Figura adoecida (100x81cm-39x32in) s. s.i.d.1986 verso oil fabric. 29-Jun-4 Segre, Madrid #144/R est:1500

FREIXAS CORTES, Jordi (1917-1984) Spanish
£374 $595 €550 Fishing boats (55x74cm-22x29in) s. 21-Mar-3 Bailly Pommery, Paris #130

FRELAUT, Jean (1879-1954) French?
£400 $716 €600 Slec (50x40cm-20x16in) s.d.1925 panel. 16-May-4 Renault-Aubry, Pontivy #448
Works on paper
£467 $835 €700 Chapelle de Saint-Philibert (15x25cm-6x10in) s.d.1935 gouache. 16-May-4 Renault-Aubry, Pontivy #447

FREMAUX, Auguste (?) French?
£360 $601 €526 Jeune fille de Paris (36x28cm-14x11in) 21-Oct-3 Gorringes, Lewes #2086

FREMIET, E (1824-1910) French
Sculpture
£879 $1600 €1319 Joan of Arc (71cm-28in) bronze. 16-Jun-4 Wolf's, New York #486573/R est:3000-5000
£882 $1500 €1288 Cavalier Romain (41cm-16in) dark brown pat. bronze. 22-Nov-3 Jackson's, Cedar Falls #191/R est:1750-2500
£1806 $3015 €2600 Du Guesclin (75x39x10cm-30x15x4in) s.st.f. brown pat bronze. 23-Oct-3 Credit Municipal, Paris #125/R est:1500-2000

FREMIET, Emmanuel (1824-1910) French
Sculpture
£941 $1600 €1374 Le chef Gaulois (38cm-15in) brown pat. bronze. 22-Nov-3 Jackson's, Cedar Falls #198/R est:1500-3000
£978 $1750 €1428 Minerva, patron of Athens on her chariot pulled by three horses (53x53cm-21x21in) s. gilt bronze st.f. F Barbedienne. 16-May-4 CRN Auctions, Cambridge #31/R
£1020 $1622 €1500 Attelage (25x32cm-10x13in) s. plaster. 23-Mar-3 Salle des ventes Pillet, Lyon la Foret #160
£1027 $1747 €1500 Cachet grenouille (11cm-4in) s. num.344 pat bronze lit. 6-Nov-3 Sotheby's, Paris #146/R est:1000-1200
£1126 $2049 €1700 Port Marly (27cm-11in) s. plaster. 16-Jun-4 Beaussant & Lefèvre, Paris #140/R est:600-800
£1242 $1999 €1850 Elephanteau entrave (17cm-7in) s. green pat bronze. 23-Feb-3 St-Germain-en-Laye Encheres #27/R est:1800-2000
£1382 $2542 €2100 Chiens bassets, Ravageot et Ravageode (18cm-7in) s. bronze marble base exec. 1853. 25-Jun-4 Daguerre, Paris #264/R est:1200-1800
£1400 $2380 €2044 Seated daschunds, one peering at a snail (15cm-6in) s. bronze oval base. 25-Nov-3 Bonhams, Knowle #419 est:400-500
£1400 $2576 €2100 Louis d'Orleans (47cm-19in) s. brown pat. bronze exec. 1870 Cast Barbedienne lit. 10-Jun-4 Camard, Paris #8/R est:2000-2500
£1538 $2615 €2200 Cavalier en costume de la Renaissance (45cm-18in) medaille pat bronze Cast F. Barbedienne. 27-Nov-3 Millon & Associes, Paris #93/R est:2000-2500
£1538 $2646 €2200 Groupe de deux chiots assis (14x17x14cm-6x7x6in) s.num.278 pat bronze. 3-Dec-3 Palais de Beaux Arts, Brussels #862/R est:1500-2000
£1588 $2700 €2318 Saint Michael Terrassant le dragon (64cm-25in) brown pat. bronze. 22-Nov-3 Jackson's, Cedar Falls #194/R est:2000-3000
£1631 $2724 €2300 Ravageot-ravageole (16x18cm-6x7in) s. brown pat bronze. 12-Oct-3 St-Germain-en-Laye Encheres #39/R est:2000
£1657 $3000 €2419 Roman Charioteer with two rearing horses (51x38x25cm-20x15x10in) bears sig brown pat. bronze marble base. 3-Apr-4 Neal Auction Company, New Orleans #35/R est:3000-5000
£1706 $2900 €2491 Louis XIII enfant, sortie de manege (46cm-18in) dark brown pat. bronze st.f.F.Barbedienne. 22-Nov-3 Jackson's, Cedar Falls #212/R est:3500-5500
£1724 $2879 €2500 Bertrand Duguesclin (66x47cm-26x19in) s. pat bronze. 11-Jul-3 Rabourdin & Choppin de Janvry, Paris #153/R
£1733 $3155 €2600 Conducteur de char romain (40x35cm-16x14in) s. pat bronze. 29-Jun-4 Gioffredo, Nice #79/R
£1800 $3330 €2628 Credo (41cm-16in) dark brown pat bronze circular red marble base. 13-Jul-4 Sotheby's, Olympia #255/R est:2000-3000
£1860 $3200 €2716 Ape holding a woman with arrow in his shoulder and rock in his hand (46cm-18in) s. brown pat bronze. 6-Dec-3 Selkirks, St. Louis #695 est:800-1200
£2000 $3400 €2920 Ravageot et Ravageole (19cm-7in) s. pat bronze. 28-Oct-3 Sotheby's, London #140/R
£2000 $3400 €2920 Louis D'Orleans (64cm-25in) brown pat. bronze. 22-Nov-3 Jackson's, Cedar Falls #193/R est:2000-3000
£2200 $3740 €3212 Chef arabe a cheval (33x23cm-13x9in) s. pat bronze lit. 28-Oct-3 Sotheby's, London #104/R
£2200 $3740 €3212 Sapeur (28cm-11in) s.st.f.Barbedienne pat bronze marble base lit. 28-Oct-3 Sotheby's, London #186/R
£2500 $4500 €3650 St Michel (59cm-23in) s.num.521 gilt bronze marble base. 21-Apr-4 Sotheby's, London #52/R est:3000-5000

£2588 $4400 €3778 Coucher Romaine (41cm-16in) brown pat. bronze. 22-Nov-3 Jackson's, Cedar Falls #197/R est:4500-6500
£2603 $4425 €3800 Louis XIII enfant a cheval (46cm-18in) brown pat bronze Cast Barbedienne. 7-Nov-3 Coutau Begarie, Paris #141 est:4000-5000
£2605 $4480 €3803 Couple de chiens attaches. bronze. 3-Dec-3 Naón & Cia, Buenos Aires #594
£2800 $4760 €4088 Saint Michel (59cm-23in) s. pat bronze lit. 28-Oct-3 Sotheby's, London #171/R
£3352 $6000 €4894 Soldiers on horseback (43cm-17in) s. brown pat bronze pair. 20-Mar-4 Freeman, Philadelphia #590/R est:6000-8000
£3741 $5949 €5500 Grand Conde (55x39cm-22x15in) s. pat bronze marble base. 23-Mar-3 Salle des ventes Pillet, Lyon la Foret #158
£4000 $6800 €5840 Duguesclin (65x38cm-26x15in) s. pat bronze lit. 28-Oct-3 Sotheby's, London #106/R
£4200 $7644 €6132 St Michael and the dragon (59cm-23in) s.d.1876 num.202 gilt pat bronze red marble base. 15-Jun-4 Sotheby's, Olympia #64/R est:2000-3000
£4333 $7843 €6500 Louis X III enfant a cheval (34x27cm-13x11in) s.base brown pat bronze Cast Barbedienne. 2-Apr-4 Coutau Begarie, Paris #206 est:6500-7500
£5235 $9632 €7800 Pelicans (23cm-9in) s. pat bronze pair sold with pencil dr. 23-Mar-4 Piasa, Paris #5/R
£6000 $10980 €8760 Saint George et le dragon (54cm-21in) s. num.270 gilt bronze lit. 9-Jul-4 Sotheby's, London #137/R est:6000-8000
£25000 $45000 €36500 Cat feeding her kittens (25x62cm-10x24in) s.d.1849 white marble prov.exhib.lit. 21-Apr-4 Sotheby's, London #81/R est:25000-30000

FREMLIN, Carol (20th C) ?
£401 $750 €585 Still life (132x102cm-52x40in) s. prov. 29-Feb-4 Bonhams & Butterfields, San Francisco #4592

FREMONT, L Charles (19th C) French
Sculpture
£1701 $2704 €2500 Elephant (34x46cm-13x18in) s.i. plaster prov. 23-Mar-3 Salle des ventes Pillet, Lyon la Foret #161 est:350-450

FREMY, Jacques Noel Marie (1782-1867) French
£24000 $39840 €35040 Entry into Paris of the Comte D'Artois (90x71cm-35x28in) exhib.lit. 30-Sep-3 Sotheby's, London #270/R est:12000-18000

FRENCH SCHOOL
£3557 $6368 €5193 Woman with shaved head (60x45cm-24x18in) init.d.1852 prov. 15-May-4 Christie's, Sydney #431/R est:2000-3000 (A.D 9000)
Sculpture
£6711 $12013 €10000 Horse (66x51x20cm-26x20x8in) bronze marble base. 27-May-4 Semenzato, Florence #126/R est:12000
£10277 $18395 €15004 Bust of Diana (75cm-30in) marble prov. 15-May-4 Christie's, Sydney #511/R est:10000-15000 (A.D 26000)
£16197 $28021 €23000 Saturne enlevant Cybele (210x116x110cm-83x46x43in) lead. 10-Dec-3 Ferri, Paris #206/R est:20000-25000
Works on paper
£6757 $11892 €10000 Etude de nu. dr. 18-May-4 Galerie Moderne, Brussels #81

FRENCH SCHOOL, 15th C
Sculpture
£4200 $7140 €6132 Anna Selbdritt (86cm-34in) wood. 28-Oct-3 Sotheby's, London #8/R

FRENCH SCHOOL, 16th C
Sculpture
£12245 $19469 €18000 Madonna and Child (134cm-53in) polychrome wood. 23-Mar-3 Salle des ventes Pillet, Lyon la Foret #172 est:10000

FRENCH SCHOOL, 17th C
£5500 $9515 €8030 Gypsy encampment (104x147cm-41x58in) i. 10-Dec-3 Bonhams, New Bond Street #101/R est:5000-7000
£5517 $9214 €8000 Portrait presume d'Anne d'Autriche (110x140cm-43x55in) 16-Nov-3 Muizon & Le Coent, Paris #13/R
£6210 $10185 €8570 Portrait of the Princess of Orleans (112x90cm-44x35in) 1-Jun-3 Babuino, Rome #70/R est:4000-6000
£6623 $12119 €10000 Portrait de Philippe II, roi d'Espagne (116x90cm-46x35in) 7-Apr-4 Libert, Castor, Paris #31/R est:8000-10000
£6667 $12200 €10000 Henry and Charles Beaubrun painting (145x180cm-57x71in) 1-Jun-4 Sotheby's, Milan #80/R est:10000-15000
£6711 $12349 €10000 Portrait of lady (80x63cm-31x25in) 24-Mar-4 Finarte Semenzato, Rome #92/R est:8500
£9000 $14310 €13140 Extensive wooded landscape with mythological figures (124x175cm-49x69in) 12-Sep-3 Gardiner & Houlgate, Bath #235/R est:800-1500
£9000 $16560 €13500 Procession de la ligue (128x188cm-50x74in) i. 14-Jun-4 Cornette de St.Cyr, Paris #32/R est:10000-15000
£12000 $20760 €17520 Still life with onions, peas and other vegetables in a wicker basket on a ledge (55x77cm-22x30in) panel prov. 11-Dec-3 Sotheby's, London #110/R est:15000-20000
£12081 $21624 €18000 Still life with asparagus, artichokes, cherries. strawberries and pewter jug (47x54cm-19x21in) prov.lit. 26-May-4 Porro, Milan #4/R est:25000-30000
£15600 $26988 €22776 Portrait of a lady wearing a red and gold embroidered dress and headdress (26x21cm-10x8in) panel. 9-Dec-3 Sotheby's, Olympia #324/R est:4000-6000
£40000 $69200 €58400 Procession with pages holding torches before two knights (162x71cm-64x28in) 11-Dec-3 Sotheby's, London #9/R est:40000-60000
£40141 $69444 €57000 L'enlevement d'Europe (63x48cm-25x19in) panel. 10-Dec-3 Maigret, Paris #43/R est:12000-15000
Sculpture
£5000 $9200 €7300 Emperor on horseback (39cm-15in) green brown pat bronze ebonised wood base. 10-Jun-4 Christie's, London #153/R est:6000-9000
£11500 $19895 €16790 Rearing bull (14cm-6in) gilt bronze green marble base. 12-Dec-3 Sotheby's, London #209/R est:3000-5000
£18367 $29204 €27000 Femme (104cm-41in) marble. 23-Mar-3 Salle des ventes Pillet, Lyon la Foret #204
£23810 $37857 €35000 Vieillard barbu (96cm-38in) marble. 23-Mar-3 Salle des ventes Pillet, Lyon la Foret #203 est:6000
£26761 $46831 €38000 Samson et les Philistins (33cm-13in) brown pat bronze wood socle lit. 19-Dec-3 Delvaux, Paris #214/R est:15000-25000
Miniatures
£5200 $8840 €7592 Nobleman (5cm-2in circular) enamel gilt frame prov.exhib. 18-Nov-3 Bonhams, New Bond Street #38/R est:1500-2500
Works on paper
£8356 $14205 €12200 Moine capucin (19x14cm-7x6in) i. pen ink. 5-Nov-3 Beaussant & Lefèvre, Paris #8/R

FRENCH SCHOOL, 17th/18th C
£6294 $10699 €9000 Louis XIV sur le champ de bataille (77x110cm-30x43in) 18-Nov-3 Vanderkindere, Brussels #86/R est:3750-5000
£8000 $14560 €12000 View of a cove near Naples (37x50cm-15x20in) i. panel. 3-Jul-4 Geble, Radolfzell #378/R
Sculpture
£30000 $51900 €43800 Bust repesenting the seasons (45cm-18in) carved marble set of four prov. 11-Dec-3 Christie's, London #131/R est:10000-15000
£48000 $88320 €70080 Venus de Medici (69cm-27in) brown pat bronze lacquered brass in-laid ormolu base lit. 10-Jun-4 Christie's, London #145/R est:50000-80000
£83333 $149167 €125000 Four Seasons (310cm-122in) stone set of 4. 16-May-4 Joron-Derem, Paris #161/R est:120000-150000

FRENCH SCHOOL, 18th C
£1778 $3200 €2596 Portrait of M Barnave. Portrait of M Mounier (34x29cm-13x11in) oval pair. 23-Jan-4 Christie's, Rockefeller NY #76/R est:4000-6000
£4722 $8500 €6894 Portrait of an old man sitting in an interior (60x50cm-24x20in) prov. 23-Jan-4 Christie's, Rockefeller NY #109/R est:2000-3000
£5000 $8500 €7300 Roses, tulips and other flowers in a gilt vase on a stone ledge with a parrot (58x77cm-23x30in) 29-Oct-3 Bonhams, New Bond Street #110/R est:5000-7000
£5000 $9000 €7300 Portrait of an artist at his easel (122x97cm-48x38in) prov. 23-Jan-4 Christie's, Rockefeller NY #102/R est:5000-7000
£5000 $9000 €7300 Portrait of a lady with roses (65x49cm-26x19in) 22-Apr-4 Sotheby's, London #112/R est:6000-8000
£5090 $8500 €7431 Portrait of a dog seated on a pillow (50x60cm-20x24in) 7-Oct-3 Sotheby's, New York #34/R est:6000-8000
£5333 $9547 €8000 Portrait of lady as Diana (143x113cm-56x44in) 17-May-4 Finarte Semenzato, Rome #111/R est:7000-9000
£5500 $9900 €8030 Still life of peaches, grapes pears and other fruits with a dog (63x82cm-25x32in) 20-Apr-4 Sotheby's, Olympia #366/R est:5000-7000
£5556 $10000 €8112 Joseph recognized by his brothers (49x57cm-19x22in) 22-Jan-4 Sotheby's, New York #246/R est:12000-15000
£5671 $9811 €8280 Portrait of an elegant noble gentleman (120x95cm-47x37in) 9-Dec-3 Rasmussen, Copenhagen #1606/R est:40000-50000 (D.KR 60000)
£5944 $9927 €8500 Moise sauve des eaux (88x109cm-35x43in) 26-Jun-3 Artcurial Briest, Paris #492 est:6000-8000
£5986 $10356 €8500 Herminie chez les bergers (38x46cm-15x18in) 10-Dec-3 Beaussant & Lefèvre, Paris #45/R est:10000-12000
£6667 $12133 €10000 Portrait of a lady (127x102cm-50x40in) prov. 1-Jul-4 Van Ham, Cologne #1107/R est:13000
£6806 $11569 €9800 Apollo incorona la musa della musica. Allegoria della Pittura (35x41cm-14x16in) pair. 28-Oct-3 Della Rocca, Turin #279/R est:6000-8000
£7077 $12172 €10332 Scene from the Antique history with Grachus' sons (65x98cm-26x39in) 2-Dec-3 Bukowskis, Stockholm #428/R est:30000-40000 (S.KR 92000)
£8065 $15000 €11775 Floral still lifes in high relief urns (64x48cm-25x19in) pair. 5-Mar-4 Skinner, Boston #212/R est:4000-6000
£8150 $13855 €11899 Idyllic landscape (36x44cm-14x17in) 5-Nov-3 Dobiaschofsky, Bern #551/R est:2200 (S.FR 18500)
£8200 $15006 €11972 Pan and Syrinx (213x335cm-84x132in) 6-Jul-4 Bonhams, Knightsbridge #259a/R est:6000-8000
£8500 $15300 €12410 Sacrifice to Venus. Sacrifice to Cupid (93x68cm-37x27in) i.verso oval pair. 22-Apr-4 Sotheby's, London #116/R est:8000-12000
£8667 $15513 €13000 Vase of flowers (71x58cm-28x23in) 17-May-4 Finarte Semenzato, Rome #102/R est:16000-18000
£9271 $16874 €14000 Still life of figs and redcurrents (13x17cm-5x7in) canvas on panel. 15-Jun-4 Artcurial Briest, Paris #232/R est:2000-2500
£10490 $19091 €15315 Athalia repulsed by Joad (133x178cm-52x70in) prov. 29-Jun-4 Peter Webb, Auckland #97/R est:35000-55000 (NZ.D 30000)
£10563 $18275 €15000 Still life with oysters and pot (69x72cm-27x28in) 15-Dec-3 Bailly Pommery, Paris #56/R est:15000-18000
£10764 $18299 €15500 Seascapes (180x115cm-71x45in) pair. 29-Oct-3 Il Ponte, Milan #568/R
£11620 $20335 €16500 Chiens a l'arret (91x116cm-36x46in) pair. 19-Dec-3 Pierre Berge, Paris #83/R est:8000-10000
£11644 $19795 €17000 Ouverture du bal (87x126cm-34x50in) 10-Nov-3 Horta, Bruxelles #86
£13000 $22490 €18980 Portrait of a blackamoor, head and shoulders (65x52cm-26x20in) prov.exhib. 11-Dec-3 Sotheby's, London #218/R est:8000-12000
£19005 $32308 €27747 View out of cave of waterfall with figures (89x131cm-35x52in) 19-Nov-3 Fischer, Luzern #1056/R est:8000-12000 (S.FR 42000)
£20000 $34600 €29200 Day nursery. Night nursery (75x109cm-30x43in) with sig.d.1731 pair. 10-Dec-3 Christie's, London #69/R est:30000-50000
£22000 $40260 €32120 Portrait of blackmoor (65x52cm-26x20in) prov.lit. 8-Jul-4 Sotheby's, London #334/R est:8000-12000
£84507 $147887 €120000 Vue imaginaire de la basilique St Marc, du Palais des Doges et la Piazetta (110x192cm-43x76in) s.d.1788 prov. 16-Dec-3 Artcurial Briest, Paris #221/R est:80000-100000

Sculpture
£6000 $11160 €8760 Pacing horse wearing a tassled saddle cloth (32cm-13in) black brown pat bronze marble base. 4-Mar-4 Christie's, London #331/R est:4000-6000
£10000 $18400 €14600 Swan in a startled pose with spreaded wings (19cm-7in) ormolu. 10-Jun-4 Christie's, London #36/R est:5000-10000
£10564 $17536 €15000 Une dame de qualite (92x65cm-36x26in) plaster marble base prov. 12-Jun-3 Tajan, Paris #110/R est:15000-20000
£10839 $18427 €15500 Saturne tenant sa faux prenant la vie d'une jeune femme Alanguie (32x29x19cm-13x11x7in) 1-Dec-3 Millon & Associes, Paris #248/R est:15000
£28169 $48732 €40000 Leda et le cygne (79cm-31in) marble lit. 15-Dec-3 Sotheby's, Paris #27/R est:60000-80000
£29371 $50517 €42000 Male and female dancers (44cm-17in) i. brown red pat bronze prov.lit. pair. 2-Dec-3 Christie's, Paris #185/R est:23000-30000
£33333 $61333 €50000 Elephant (29x41x18cm-11x16x7in) brown pat. bronze incl. wood base lit. 11-Jun-4 Maigret, Paris #178/R est:16000-20000

£34000 $58820 €49640 Portrait of infant boy and girl (51x53cm-20x21in) i. marble reliefs. 11-Dec-3 Christie's, London #75/R est:15000-25000

Miniatures

£5000 $9000 €7300 Joseph-Hyacinthe-Francois de Paule de Rigaud, Comte de Rigaud (6cm-2in) ruby diamond silver frame oval exhib. 22-Apr-4 Bonhams, New Bond Street #79 est:6000-8000

Works on paper

£10884 $19483 €16000 Projet de chateau (47x36cm-19x14in) i.verso pen W/C. 19-Mar-4 Beaussant & Lefèvre, Paris #28/R est:2500-3000

FRENCH SCHOOL, 18th/19th C

Sculpture

£32000 $58880 €46720 Two Amoretti fighting over a flaming heart on the ground (58cm-23in) marble base. 10-Jun-4 Christie's, London #77/R est:20000-30000

FRENCH SCHOOL, 19th C

£800 $1328 €1168 Statue di Cesere, Villa Borghese (63x44cm-25x17in) init.i.d.1899 verso panel. 1-Oct-3 Sotheby's, Olympia #270/R
£3333 $6000 €4866 Allegory of architecture (46x168cm-18x66in) 22-Jan-4 Sotheby's, New York #202/R est:6000-8000
£4294 $7000 €6269 Very young girl with terrier in her lap and pug looking on. painted c.1880. 27-Sep-3 Thomaston Place, Thomaston #225
£4722 $8500 €6894 Portrait of a lady, said to be Louise Catherine Eleonore Denuelle de la Plaigne, seated with her son (161x134cm-63x53in) i. prov.exhib.lit. 23-Jan-4 Christie's, Rockefeller NY #113/R est:8000-12000
£4800 $8160 €7008 Study of a white geranium (37x28cm-15x11in) 30-Oct-3 Sotheby's, Olympia #177/R est:3000-4000
£5500 $9130 €8030 Portrait of a young couple (47x47cm-19x19in) round. 30-Sep-3 Sotheby's, London #275/R est:6000-8000
£6014 $10043 €8600 Course a l'hippodrome (40x81cm-16x32in) bears mono.d.1826. 27-Jun-3 Millon & Associes, Paris #51/R est:5000-7000
£6376 $11732 €9500 Vue de Paris (114x278cm-45x109in) 26-Mar-4 Piasa, Paris #73/R est:6000-8000
£6500 $11050 €9490 Portrait of the Duke of Duros, in military uniform (72x61cm-28x24in) i. oval. 19-Nov-3 Tennants, Leyburn #1163a/R est:2500-3500
£6500 $11700 €9490 Nude warrior (97x135cm-38x53in) painted c.1800. 23-Apr-4 Christie's, Kensington #196/R est:5000-8000
£6579 $12105 €10000 Portrait presume de Sebastien Bourdon (52x45cm-20x18in) prov. 24-Jun-4 Christie's, Paris #122/R est:5000-7000
£11000 $19030 €16060 River landscape with soldiers. Wooded landscape with woman on a horse (97x134cm-38x53in) painted c.1800 pair. 12-Dec-3 Christie's, Kensington #166/R
£11301 $19212 €16500 Roman scenes (193x128cm-76x50in) pair. 6-Nov-3 Sotheby's, Paris #118/R est:4000-6000
£12057 $20135 €17000 Recolte de canne a sucre. Le port (111x305cm-44x120in) pair. 16-Jun-3 Gros & Delettrez, Paris #119/R est:15000-20000
£13966 $25000 €20390 Two artists sketching among Roman ruins (49x68cm-19x27in) painted c.1840. 27-May-4 Sotheby's, New York #78/R est:5000-7000
£16197 $28345 €23000 Bouquet (246x168cm-97x66in) 19-Dec-3 Pierre Berge, Paris #89/R est:20000-50000
£18027 $32269 €26500 La Galerie d'Apollon au Louvre (150x180cm-59x71in) indis.sig.Poilliez d.1850. 19-Mar-4 Oger, Dumont, Paris #32/R est:6000-7000
£25504 $46672 €38000 Allegory. Mythological scenes. panel set of 5. 7-Jul-4 Tajan, Paris #93

Photographs

£4756 $7942 €6800 Femme creole. daguerrotype. 10-Oct-3 Tajan, Paris #34/R
£19581 $32700 €28000 Homme au chevet d'un homme mort. daguerrotype exec.1850 exhib. 10-Oct-3 Tajan, Paris #21/R

Sculpture

£1882 $3200 €2748 Tartare Mandchou (53cm-21in) i. pat bronze. 25-Nov-3 Christie's, Rockefeller NY #440/R est:1500-2000
£2235 $3800 €3263 Lady (74cm-29in) indis.sig. pat bronze. 28-Oct-3 Christie's, Rockefeller NY #108/R
£4500 $7650 €6570 Hercules slaying the Cretan bull (56x64cm-22x25in) bronze lit. 28-Oct-3 Sotheby's, London #69/R
£4698 $8315 €7000 Venus de Milo (85cm-33in) st.f.Barbedienne pat bronze. 29-Apr-4 Sotheby's, Paris #60/R est:6000-8000
£5298 $9695 €8000 Young lady with a bird (75cm-30in) bronze. 6-Apr-4 Sotheby's, Amsterdam #294/R est:8000-12000
£5578 $8869 €8200 Lavandiere (91x70cm-36x28in) terracotta. 23-Mar-3 Salle des ventes Pillet, Lyon la Foret #250
£6711 $11879 €10000 Apollon (60cm-24in) pat bronze. 29-Apr-4 Sotheby's, Paris #100/R est:4000-5000
£8000 $14400 €11680 Halberdier with sword and spearhead (245cm-96in) gilt brown pat bronze velvet wood box. 21-Apr-4 Sotheby's, London #53/R est:8000-10000
£11176 $19000 €16317 Sphinxes (70x81x35cm-28x32x14in) i. terracotta pair. 25-Nov-3 Christie's, Rockefeller NY #52/R est:4000-6000
£11972 $20711 €17000 Enfant pleurant (37cm-15in) bronze marble socle lit. 15-Dec-3 Sotheby's, Paris #85/R est:15000-20000
£20000 $33400 €29200 Equestrian figure of Louis XIV (212x78x44cm-83x31x17in) bronze pedestal. 14-Oct-3 Sotheby's, Olympia #37/R est:20000-30000
£20958 $35000 €30599 Indians (112cm-44in) painted wood pair. 18-Oct-3 Sotheby's, New York #41/R est:7000-9000
£65772 $121020 €98000 Figures (221x39x39cm-87x15x15in) bronze wooden base Cast Thomire pair lit. 27-Mar-4 Farsetti, Prato #258/R est:105000

Miniatures

£6500 $11050 €9490 Princess Catherine of Wurttemberg (22cm-9in) painted c.1810. 18-Nov-3 Bonhams, New Bond Street #99/R est:1500-2500

Works on paper

£5000 $8350 €7300 View of a town, central America (45x85cm-18x33in) i. W/C over pencil htd bodycol. 14-Oct-3 Sotheby's, London #223/R est:5000-7000
£26241 $43823 €37000 Interior scenes (63x143cm-25x56in) s.d.1878 W/C panel. 15-Oct-3 Finarte Semenzato, Rome #137/R est:25000

FRENCH SCHOOL, 20th C

Sculpture

£5594 $9510 €8000 Buste de femme (30x15x8cm-12x6x3in) stone exec.c.1930. 26-Nov-3 Christie's, Paris #6/R est:5000-7000
£8392 $14266 €12000 Aloes (500cm-197in) forged iron exec.c.1940-1950. 24-Nov-3 Tajan, Paris #137/R est:12000-15000
£8824 $15000 €12883 Agrarian fi (53x104x51cm-21x41x20in) i. pat bronze lit. 28-Oct-3 Christie's, Rockefeller NY #68/R

FRENCH, Annie (1872-1965) British

Works on paper

£1300 $2431 €1950 Portrait of a lady with flowers (15x18cm-6x7in) ink W/C. 20-Jul-4 Peter Francis, Wales #61/R est:400-600
£1500 $2715 €2190 Elf dance. Lady in floral cape. Church yard. Blue turban (7x13cm-3x5in) pen ink set of four different sizes. 19-Apr-4 Sotheby's, London #54/R est:1500-2000
£2500 $4625 €3650 Othelia in the lake (25x20cm-10x8in) init. W/C ink. 9-Mar-4 Peter Francis, Wales #37/R est:600-800
£3000 $5550 €4380 Flora (23x18cm-9x7in) s. W/C. 10-Feb-4 David Lay, Penzance #583/R est:3000-3500
£3200 $5984 €4800 Portrait of a lady in floral gown in front of a stylised rose hedge (23x15cm-9x6in) s. ink W/C. 20-Jul-4 Peter Francis, Wales #62/R est:1000-1500
£3800 $5966 €5510 Flowers for mother (10x13cm-4x5in) pen ink W/C. 27-Aug-3 Sotheby's, London #1064/R est:1500-2000
£4400 $7920 €6424 Queen and her attendants (16x48cm-6x19in) W/C htd bodycol. 21-Apr-4 Lyon & Turnbull, Edinburgh #246/R est:3000-4000
£4800 $8880 €7008 Fairy Queen picking flowers (25x38cm-10x15in) s. W/C ink. 9-Mar-4 Peter Francis, Wales #38/R est:1000-1500
£7000 $12670 €10220 Peacock and the roses (22x20cm-9x8in) s. W/C pen. 19-Apr-4 Sotheby's, London #52/R est:5000-7000

FRENCH, Daniel Chester (1850-1931) American

Sculpture

£4813 $9000 €7027 Lincoln (23cm-9in) bronze Cast Roman Bronze. 25-Feb-4 Dallas Auction Gallery, Dallas #128/R

FRENCH, Jared (1905-1987) American

Works on paper

£2429 $4250 €3546 Syzygy (67x100cm-26x39in) s. pencil crayon ink prov. 19-Dec-3 Sotheby's, New York #1044/R est:2000-3000

FRENCH, Leonard (1928-) Australian

£1617 $2700 €2361 Untitled (55x122cm-22x48in) s.d.54 enamel paint masonite. 7-Oct-3 Sotheby's, New York #354 est:2000-3000
£2834 $4563 €4138 Warrior (136x121cm-54x48in) s.d.63 i.on stretcher oil paper on board. 13-Oct-3 Joel, Victoria #297 est:7000-9000 (A.D 7000)
£5725 $10420 €8359 Night landscape - moonflowers (81x91cm-32x36in) s. gold leaf enamel hessian on board. 16-Jun-4 Deutscher-Menzies, Melbourne #81/R est:22000-28000 (A.D 15000)
£6504 $10211 €9431 Sun study (48x41cm-19x16in) enamel board. 26-Aug-3 Christie's, Sydney #348/R est:7000-10000 (A.D 16000)
£6504 $11642 €9496 Copernicus (135x120cm-53x47in) s. enamel hessian on composition board prov. 4-May-4 Sotheby's, Melbourne #273/R est:15000-20000 (A.D 16000)
£10569 $16593 €15325 Man in the garden (120x121cm-47x48in) s.i. enamel hessian board prov. 26-Aug-3 Christie's, Sydney #8/R est:18000-22000 (A.D 26000)
£11915 $20255 €17396 Duet (137x222cm-54x87in) s. enamel gold leaf hessian on board prov. 26-Nov-3 Deutscher-Menzies, Melbourne #11/R est:32000-38000 (A.D 28000)
£21721 $35189 €31713 The Tower (229x122cm-90x48in) s.d.61 enamel gold leaf hessian on board prov.exhib.lit. 30-Jul-3 Goodman, Sydney #50/R est:35000-45000 (A.D 53000)
£35124 $64979 €51281 Storm (152x183cm-60x72in) s. i.verso enamel gold leaf hessian on hardboard painted 1987-89. 15-Mar-4 Sotheby's, Melbourne #44/R est:25000-35000 (A.D 85000)

Works on paper

£348 $550 €508 Dragon fly (33x29cm-13x11in) s. s. verso W/C ink gouache paper on board. 2-Sep-3 Deutscher-Menzies, Melbourne #317/R (A.D 850)
£545 $997 €818 The Islands. mixed media. 3-Jun-4 Joel, Victoria #209 (A.D 1400)
£726 $1213 €1089 Ship (28x37cm-11x15in) s.i.d.67 pencil. 27-Oct-3 Goodman, Sydney #64/R (A.D 1750)
£854 $1528 €1247 Passing Parade (33x28cm-13x11in) s. mixed media paper on board. 10-May-4 Joel, Victoria #220 est:1000-2000 (A.D 2100)
£934 $1559 €1401 Study for First Chant I (39x29cm-15x11in) s.verso mixed media board. 27-Oct-3 Goodman, Sydney #74/R (A.D 2250)
£1220 $2183 €1781 Untitled (17x16cm-7x6in) init. mixed media paper on board. 4-May-4 Sotheby's, Melbourne #280a est:500-600 (A.D 3000)
£1322 $2340 €1930 Sketch for 5th day II (28x22cm-11x9in) ink W/C. 3-May-4 Christie's, Melbourne #335/R est:1500-2500 (A.D 3200)

FRENCH, Michael (1951-) Canadian

Works on paper

£335 $576 €489 Existing by the lake (33x49cm-13x19in) s.i.d.1983 W/C prov. 2-Dec-3 Joyner Waddington, Toronto #430 (C.D 750)

FRENCH, Percy (1854-1920) Irish

Works on paper

£700 $1127 €1015 Irish lakeland landscape (18x23cm-7x9in) s.d.1907 W/C. 15-Aug-3 Keys, Aylsham #522/R
£700 $1281 €1022 St. Moritz (16x12cm-6x5in) W/C. 2-Jun-4 John Ross, Belfast #107a
£1050 $1691 €1523 Misty Irish moorland landscape (15x33cm-6x13in) s. W/C. 15-Aug-3 Keys, Aylsham #524/R est:300-400
£1319 $2151 €1900 Landscape after rain (12x21cm-5x8in) s.d.1903 i.verso W/C. 24-Sep-3 James Adam, Dublin #138/R est:2000-3000
£1350 $2511 €1971 Donkey and cart (10x15cm-4x6in) mono. W/C. 3-Mar-4 John Ross, Belfast #250
£1500 $2685 €2190 Road along the shore (12x17cm-5x7in) s. W/C prov. 14-May-4 Christie's, Kensington #339/R est:1500-2000
£1600 $2880 €2336 Sutton, County Dublin (13x25cm-5x10in) s.i.d.1904 W/C. 21-Apr-4 Tennants, Leyburn #1040/R est:1000-1500

£1736	$2830	€2500	Lakeshore scene (10x16cm-4x6in) s. W/C. 24-Sep-3 James Adam, Dublin #4/R est:2000-3000
£1800	$3294	€2628	River and bogland, Connemara (19x24cm-7x9in) s. W/C. 2-Jun-4 John Ross, Belfast #65 est:1800-2000
£1818	$3091	€2600	Ballyvaughan Bay (16x24cm-6x9in) s.i.d.1911 W/C. 25-Nov-3 De Veres Art Auctions, Dublin #12/R est:2500-3500
£1879	$3326	€2800	Seascape (17x24cm-7x9in) s. W/C. 27-Apr-4 Whyte's, Dublin #213/R est:2000-3000
£2000	$3600	€2920	Sunset over the lake (24x35cm-9x14in) s.d.1907 W/C. 22-Apr-4 Mellors & Kirk, Nottingham #1010/R est:500-600
£2035	$3500	€2971	Sunrise on a bog (16x24cm-6x9in) s.d.1907 W/C paper on board. 3-Dec-3 Doyle, New York #127/R est:2500-3500
£2133	$3861	€3200	Howth (13x24cm-5x9in) s.i.d.1900 W/C. 31-Mar-4 James Adam, Dublin #14/R est:2000-3000
£2148	$3801	€3200	Bog lake with sun breaking through clouds (18x25cm-7x10in) s. W/C. 27-Apr-4 Whyte's, Dublin #47/R est:3000-4000
£2394	$3831	€3400	Bog landscape (19x27cm-7x11in) s. W/C. 16-Sep-3 Whyte's, Dublin #165/R est:2000-3000
£2400	$4320	€3504	Storm over the lake (16x24cm-6x9in) s.d.1907 W/C. 22-Apr-4 Mellors & Kirk, Nottingham #1012/R est:500-700
£2639	$4301	€3800	Bogland Scene (23x29cm-9x11in) s. W/C. 24-Sep-3 James Adam, Dublin #14/R est:3500-5000
£2639	$4301	€3800	Sailing boat off shore (16x24cm-6x9in) init.d.1919 W/C. 24-Sep-3 James Adam, Dublin #31/R est:3000-5000
£2676	$4282	€3800	Bogland stream (17x25cm-7x10in) s. W/C prov. 16-Sep-3 Whyte's, Dublin #14/R est:3000-4000
£2676	$4630	€3800	Estuary scene at dusk (16x25cm-6x10in) s. W/C. 10-Dec-3 Bonhams & James Adam, Dublin #49/R est:1500-2500
£2800	$4564	€4088	Sunset over a boggy landscape with two trees in the foreground (18x27cm-7x11in) s. W/C. 25-Sep-3 Clevedon Sale Rooms #164 est:1200-1600
£2800	$5040	€4088	Trees in an Irish landscape (17x25cm-7x10in) s. W/C htd white. 22-Apr-4 Mellors & Kirk, Nottingham #1011/R est:500-600
£2917	$4754	€4200	Castle by a lake (24x34cm-9x13in) init. W/C. 24-Sep-3 James Adam, Dublin #26/R est:4000-6000
£2958	$5117	€4200	River through forest and mountain landscape (6x22cm-2x9in) s. W/C prov. 10-Dec-3 Bonhams & James Adam, Dublin #55/R est:2000-3000
£3000	$5160	€4380	Boglands, Connemara (15x20cm-6x8in) s.d.1908 W/C. 3-Dec-3 John Ross, Belfast #76 est:2000-2500
£3000	$5370	€4380	Shoreline, early morning (13x18cm-5x7in) s. W/C. 14-May-4 Christie's, Kensington #337/R est:2000-3000
£3000	$5370	€4380	Marshland (16x23cm-6x9in) s.d.1906 W/C. 14-May-4 Christie's, Kensington #338/R est:1500-2000
£3099	$5361	€4400	River through the bog (18x23cm-7x9in) s. W/C. 10-Dec-3 Bonhams & James Adam, Dublin #47/R est:2000-3000
£3100	$5673	€4526	Boats in sail (28x21cm-11x8in) mono.d.1891 W/C. 2-Jun-4 John Ross, Belfast #111a est:1850-2250
£3200	$5760	€4672	Sailing boats at sunset (16x24cm-6x9in) s. W/C htd white. 22-Apr-4 Mellors & Kirk, Nottingham #1013/R est:500-600
£3239	$5604	€4600	Casey's cottage, Co Donegal (24x34cm-9x13in) W/C. 10-Dec-3 Bonhams & James Adam, Dublin #48/R est:4500-6000
£3287	$5587	€4700	Bogland scene. sailing boat (17x24cm-7x9in) s. W/C double-sided. 25-Nov-3 De Veres Art Auctions, Dublin #74/R est:2500-3500
£3300	$6138	€4818	Cottage and turf stacks, Connemara (17x25cm-7x10in) s. W/C. 3-Mar-4 John Ross, Belfast #145 est:3000-4000
£3500	$6265	€5110	Stormy landscape (16x23cm-6x9in) s.d.1906 W/C. 14-May-4 Christie's, Kensington #341/R est:1500-2000
£3662	$6335	€5200	Hyde Park (25x29cm-10x11in) s.i. W/C. 10-Dec-3 Bonhams & James Adam, Dublin #53/R est:3000-5000
£3750	$6900	€5700	Dublin Bay, Sutton, County Dublin (13x25cm-5x10in) s.i.d.1904 W/C. 22-Jun-4 De Veres Art Auctions, Dublin #110/R est:4000-6000
£4000	$7160	€5840	Sunburst (13x18cm-5x7in) s. W/C. 14-May-4 Christie's, Kensington #340/R est:2000-3000
£4161	$7448	€6200	Lough at dawn (17x27cm-7x11in) s.d.1918 W/C. 26-May-4 James Adam, Dublin #38/R est:2000-3000
£4200	$7518	€6132	Bog stream (15x26cm-6x10in) s.d.1900 W/C. 13-May-4 Sotheby's, London #12/R est:2000-3000
£4336	$7371	€6200	Sailing boats in a calm sea (24x31cm-9x12in) init.d.09 W/C. 25-Nov-3 De Veres Art Auctions, Dublin #17/R est:2500-3500
£4400	$7920	€6424	Irish landscape (24x35cm-9x14in) s.d.1908 W/C. 22-Apr-4 Mellors & Kirk, Nottingham #1009/R est:600-800
£4600	$8510	€6716	Girld and ducks beside a lough (15x25cm-6x10in) s.d.13 W/C. 9-Mar-4 Gorringes, Lewes #2211 est:800-1200
£4698	$8409	€7000	Bogland scene (21x33cm-8x13in) s.d.1897 W/C prov. 26-May-4 James Adam, Dublin #37/R est:3000-5000
£4698	$8409	€7000	Bog landscape (17x25cm-7x10in) s.d.1907 W/C. 26-May-4 James Adam, Dublin #44/R est:3000-5000
£5200	$9516	€7592	Road by the tuf stacks, Connemara (17x35cm-7x14in) s. W/C. 2-Jun-4 John Ross, Belfast #141 est:2500-3000
£5369	$9611	€8000	Coastal scene with girl and ducks on shore (17x25cm-7x10in) s.d.1913 W/C. 26-May-4 James Adam, Dublin #35/R est:8000-10000
£6200	$10354	€9052	Moorland landscapes (15x23cm-6x9in) s.d.1908-09 W/C pair. 17-Oct-3 Keys, Aylsham #487/R
£6338	$10965	€9000	Donegal bog, sunset (27x38cm-11x15in) s. W/C. 10-Dec-3 Bonhams & James Adam, Dublin #46/R est:4500-6000
£8200	$14678	€11972	Irish bog at sunset. River estuary with a mountain range in the distance (18x25cm-7x10in) s.d.1906 W/C pair prov. 14-May-4 Christie's, London #207/R est:4000-6000
£10067	$18020	€15000	River fall. Moonlight on the water. Geese on a country track (13x18cm-5x7in) s. W/C three framed as one. 26-May-4 James Adam, Dublin #33/R est:4000-6000

FRENCH, Percy (attrib) (1854-1920) Irish

Works on paper

£1818	$3091	€2600	Bog landscape at sunset with cottages (14x32cm-6x13in) i.verso W/C. 25-Nov-3 Hamilton Osborne King, Dublin #40/R

FRENCZ, Lajos (?) Hungarian?

£2378	$3971	€3400	Female nude (95x150cm-37x59in) 10-Oct-3 Stadion, Trieste #81/R est:2500-3500

FRENEL (20th C) French

£717	$1198	€1047	Southern city (50x100cm-20x39in) s. composition. 24-Oct-3 Hans Widmer, St Gallen #11117/R est:1800-4000 (S.FR 1600)

FRENKEL, Itzhak (1900-1981) Israeli

£341	$620	€512	Portrait of a Rabbi (23x19cm-9x7in) s. canvas on cardboard. 1-Jul-4 Ben-Ami, Tel Aviv #4949/R
£347	$650	€507	Portrait of a Jewish Rabbi (27x22cm-11x9in) s. painted c.1950. 1-Mar-4 Ben-Ami, Tel Aviv #4333/R
£412	$700	€602	Jewish wedding (22x27cm-9x11in) s. painted c.1950. 1-Dec-3 Ben-Ami, Tel Aviv #4332/R
£984	$1800	€1437	Zaffed, view through the trees (46x55cm-18x22in) s. painted c.1950. 1-Feb-4 Ben-Ami, Tel Aviv #4642/R est:2400-3000
£1925	$3600	€2811	Sunset in Safed (49x57cm-19x22in) s. painted c.1948 lit. 1-Mar-4 Ben-Ami, Tel Aviv #4674/R est:4000-6000

Works on paper

£202	$370	€295	Street in Tel Aviv (20x28cm-8x11in) i. pastel exec.c.1930 prov. 1-Feb-4 Ben-Ami, Tel Aviv #4542/R
£202	$370	€295	Commercial Center in Tel Aviv (18x26cm-7x10in) s.i. pastel exec.c.1930 prov. 1-Feb-4 Ben-Ami, Tel Aviv #4527/R
£213	$390	€311	Central station in Tel Aviv (20x28cm-8x11in) s.i. pastel exec.c.1930 prov. 1-Feb-4 Ben-Ami, Tel Aviv #4530/R
£219	$400	€320	Neighbourhood in Tel Aviv (20x28cm-8x11in) s.i. pastel exec.c.1930 prov. 1-Feb-4 Ben-Ami, Tel Aviv #4547/R
£219	$400	€320	Figures and cars in a street of Tel Aviv (20x28cm-8x11in) s. pastel exec.c.1930 prov. 1-Feb-4 Ben-Ami, Tel Aviv #4543/R
£219	$400	€320	Yehuda Halevy Street in Tel Aviv (23x31cm-9x12in) s.i. pastel exec.c.1930 prov. 1-Feb-4 Ben-Ami, Tel Aviv #4521/R
£220	$400	€330	Tel-Aviv harbour (20x28cm-8x11in) s.i. exec.c.1930 prov. 1-Jul-4 Ben-Ami, Tel Aviv #4974/R
£220	$400	€330	Landscape of Tel-Aviv (21x31cm-8x12in) s. pastel exec.c.1930 prov. 1-Jul-4 Ben-Ami, Tel Aviv #4975/R
£220	$400	€330	Markolet street in Tel-Aviv (23x28cm-9x11in) s.i. pastel exec.c.1930 prov. 1-Jul-4 Ben-Ami, Tel Aviv #4976/R
£224	$410	€327	Zoo in Tel Aviv (19x29cm-7x11in) s.i. pastel exec.c.1930 prov. 1-Feb-4 Ben-Ami, Tel Aviv #4540/R
£230	$420	€336	Riding horses on the beach in Tel Aviv (18x26cm-7x10in) s. pastel exec.c.1930 prov. 1-Feb-4 Ben-Ami, Tel Aviv #4550/R
£230	$420	€336	Gordon Street in Tel Aviv (19x29cm-7x11in) s.i. pastel exec.c.1930 prov. 1-Feb-4 Ben-Ami, Tel Aviv #4549/R
£230	$420	€336	Street in Tel Aviv (20x28cm-8x11in) s.i. pastel exec.c.1930 prov. 1-Feb-4 Ben-Ami, Tel Aviv #4539/R
£230	$420	€336	Massada Street in Tel Aviv (20x28cm-8x11in) s.i. pastel exec.c.1930 prov. 1-Feb-4 Ben-Ami, Tel Aviv #4537/R
£230	$420	€336	Immigrants' house in Tel Aviv (20x28cm-8x11in) s.i. pastel exec.c.1930 prov. 1-Feb-4 Ben-Ami, Tel Aviv #4533/R
£246	$450	€359	Landscape of Tel Aviv with trees (23x31cm-9x12in) s. pastel exec.c.1930 prov. 1-Feb-4 Ben-Ami, Tel Aviv #4558/R
£246	$450	€359	Tel Aviv harbour (23x28cm-9x11in) s.i. pastel exec.c.1930 prov. 1-Feb-4 Ben-Ami, Tel Aviv #4556/R
£246	$450	€359	Tel Aviv harbour (19x29cm-7x11in) s.i. pastel exec.c.1930 prov. 1-Feb-4 Ben-Ami, Tel Aviv #4555/R
£246	$450	€359	Tel Aviv harbour (20x28cm-8x11in) s.i. pastel exec.c.1930 prov. 1-Feb-4 Ben-Ami, Tel Aviv #4554/R
£246	$450	€359	Ben Yehuda Street in Tel Aviv (20x28cm-8x11in) s.i. pastel exec.c.1930 prov. 1-Feb-4 Ben-Ami, Tel Aviv #4552/R
£246	$450	€359	Wooden huts in Tel Aviv (26x36cm-10x14in) s.i. pastel exec.c.1930 prov. 1-Feb-4 Ben-Ami, Tel Aviv #4546/R
£246	$450	€359	Bethlehem Street in Tel Aviv (23x28cm-9x11in) s.i. pastel exec.c.1930 prov. 1-Feb-4 Ben-Ami, Tel Aviv #4525/R
£246	$450	€359	Rothschild Boulevard in Tel Aviv (28x23cm-11x9in) s.i. pastel exec.c.1930 prov. 1-Feb-4 Ben-Ami, Tel Aviv #4518/R
£262	$480	€383	Trumpeldor street and the old cemetery in Tel Aviv (23x31cm-9x12in) s.i. pastel exec.c.1930 prov. 1-Feb-4 Ben-Ami, Tel Aviv #4559/R
£262	$480	€383	Yirmiyahu Street in Tel Aviv (23x28cm-9x11in) s.i. pastel exec.c.1930 prov. 1-Feb-4 Ben-Ami, Tel Aviv #4551/R
£262	$480	€383	Landscape with trees and houses (23x31cm-9x12in) s. pastel exec.c.1930 prov. 1-Feb-4 Ben-Ami, Tel Aviv #4548/R
£262	$480	€383	Figures in a street, Tel Aviv (28x23cm-11x9in) s.i. pastel exec.c.1930 prov. 1-Feb-4 Ben-Ami, Tel Aviv #4535/R
£262	$480	€383	Markolet Street in Tel Aviv (23x28cm-9x11in) s.i. pastel exec.c.1930 prov. 1-Feb-4 Ben-Ami, Tel Aviv #4532/R
£273	$500	€399	New Central Market in Tel Aviv (23x31cm-9x12in) s.i. pastel exec.c.1930 prov. 1-Feb-4 Ben-Ami, Tel Aviv #4528/R
£278	$510	€406	Mugraby Theater in Tel Aviv (23x28cm-9x11in) s.i. pastel exec.c.1930 prov. 1-Feb-4 Ben-Ami, Tel Aviv #4523/R
£278	$510	€406	Yehuda Hanasi Street in Neve Shalom in Tel Aviv (23x28cm-9x11in) s.i. pastel exec.c.1930 prov. 1-Feb-4 Ben-Ami, Tel Aviv #4517/R
£295	$540	€431	Landscape of Tel Aviv (21x31cm-8x12in) s. pastel exec.c.1930 prov. 1-Feb-4 Ben-Ami, Tel Aviv #4557/R
£306	$560	€447	Figures and cars by Mugraby Theater in Tel Aviv (23x28cm-9x11in) s.i. pastel exec.c.1930 prov. 1-Feb-4 Ben-Ami, Tel Aviv #4524/R
£306	$560	€447	Allenby Street in Tel Aviv (23x28cm-9x11in) s.i. pastel exec.c.1930 prov. 1-Feb-4 Ben-Ami, Tel Aviv #4519/R
£339	$620	€495	Hashuk, the market, street in Tel Aviv (23x28cm-9x11in) s.i. pastel exec.c.1930 prov. 1-Feb-4 Ben-Ami, Tel Aviv #4529/R
£393	$720	€574	Tel Aviv by night (18x26cm-7x10in) s. pastel exec.c.1930 prov. 1-Feb-4 Ben-Ami, Tel Aviv #4544/R
£410	$750	€599	Yarkon Street in Tel Aviv (23x31cm-9x12in) s.i. pastel exec.c.1930 prov. 1-Feb-4 Ben-Ami, Tel Aviv #4553/R

FRENNET, Lucien (1838-?) Belgian

£3793	$7017	€5500	L'eglise Saint Nicolas a Amsterdam avec remorqueur an avant-plan (73x92cm-29x36in) s. 16-Feb-4 Horta, Bruxelles #93/R est:6000-8000

FRENO, Virgilio (1891-1928) Italian

£748	$1339	€1100	Aprica (45x64cm-18x25in) s. 16-Mar-4 Finarte Semenzato, Milan #132/R

FRENZ, Rudolph R (20th C) Russian

£467	$850	€682	Battle scene along the river (76x132cm-30x52in) i.verso. 7-Feb-4 Sloans & Kenyon, Bethesda #1265/R

FRENZEL, Oskar (1855-?) German

£3333	$6000	€5000	Milkmaid (80x101cm-31x40in) s.i.d.1892. 21-Apr-4 Christie's, Amsterdam #20/R est:4000-6000

FRERE, Charles Theodore (1814-1888) French

£2318	$4219	€3500	Sur les bords du Nil (15x33cm-6x13in) s.d. 18-Jun-4 Piasa, Paris #78/R est:3000-4000
£2800	$5180	€4088	Evening on the Nile (23x35cm-9x14in) s. s.i.d.1877 verso board. 14-Jul-4 Sotheby's, Olympia #175/R est:4000-6000
£3800	$6346	€5548	Embarkation by the Nile (19x30cm-7x12in) s. panel prov. 14-Oct-3 Sotheby's, London #75/R est:4000-6000
£4000	$7320	€6000	Buffles au bord du Nil (23x33cm-9x13in) s. panel. 3-Jun-4 Tajan, Paris #268/R est:6000-8000
£4000	$7320	€6000	Vue de Boulak pres du Caire (23x31cm-9x12in) s. panel. 3-Jun-4 Tajan, Paris #271/R est:6000-8000
£4091	$6791	€5932	Le soir sur les bords du Nil (21x37cm-8x15in) s. i. verso panel. 13-Jun-3 Zofingen, Switzerland #2359/R est:8500 (S.FR 9000)
£4898	$8767	€7200	Femme arabe en voyage a Gerouth (25x41cm-10x16in) s. i.verso panel prov.lit. 21-Mar-4 St-Germain-en-Laye Encheres #41/R est:7500-8000
£5334	$9761	€8000	Une rue au Caire (35x26cm-14x10in) s. i.verso panel. 3-Jun-4 Tajan, Paris #267/R est:8000-10000
£5430	$9231	€7928	On the banks of the Nile (37x64cm-15x25in) s. 1-Dec-3 Koller, Zurich #6454/R est:6000-9000 (S.FR 12000)
£5500	$9185	€8030	Evening on the Nile (21x32cm-8x13in) s. panel. 14-Oct-3 Sotheby's, London #64/R est:6000-8000
£7021	$11726	€9900	Halte au bord du Nil (35x55cm-14x22in) s. cardboard. 20-Jun-3 Drouot Estimations, Paris #35/R est:10000-12000
£7334	$13421	€11000	Effet du soir, rives du Nil (21x37cm-8x15in) s. i.verso panel. 3-Jun-4 Tajan, Paris #244/R est:8000-10000
£7692	$13231	€11230	Bedouins pres d'un point d'eau (40x61cm-16x24in) s. 3-Dec-3 AB Stockholms Auktionsverk #2560/R est:50000-60000 (S.KR 100000)
£8000	$14640	€12000	Le Caire (38x68cm-15x27in) s.i.d.1853. 3-Jun-4 Tajan, Paris #243/R est:12000-14000
£9220	$15397	€13000	L'entree de la caravane dans les rues du Caire (34x53cm-13x21in) panel. 16-Jun-3 Gros & Delettrez, Paris #374/R est:10000-15000
£10638	$17766	€15000	Scene de marche au Caire (63x41cm-25x16in) s.i. 19-Oct-3 Rabourdin & Choppin de Janvry, Paris #72/R est:15000-20000
£15603	$26057	€22000	Caravane au Moyen-Orient (39x61cm-15x24in) 16-Jun-3 Gros & Delettrez, Paris #355/R est:20000-23000
Works on paper			
£316	$581	€480	Reunion de personnages dans un kiosk au bord du Nil (13x19cm-5x7in) s. wash prov. 25-Jun-4 Daguerre, Paris #97
£954	$1755	€1450	La pryamide et sphinx (47x68cm-19x27in) s. crayon. 25-Jun-4 Daguerre, Paris #98
£1007	$1682	€1450	Porteuses d'eau au coucher de soleil pres des pyramides (12x17cm-5x7in) s. W/C. 25-Oct-3 Binoche, Orleans #40
£1645	$3026	€2500	L'arrivee de la caravanne (33x49cm-13x19in) s. chl stump. 23-Jun-4 Maigret, Paris #9/R est:1000-1200

FRERE, Charles Theodore (attrib) (1814-1888) French

£2667	$4907	€4000	Une rue du Caire au crepuscule (18x25cm-7x10in) i.d.1861 verso panel. 14-Jun-4 Gros & Delettrez, Paris #575/R est:3000-4000
£2685	$4966	€4000	Beni Souef, Haute Egypte (21x35cm-8x14in) i.verso panel. 15-Mar-4 Gros & Delettrez, Paris #71/R est:2500-3000
£2800	$5152	€4200	Fontaine dans une rue du aire (18x26cm-7x10in) i.d.1861 verso panel. 14-Jun-4 Gros & Delettrez, Paris #576/R est:3000-4000
Works on paper			
£655	$1192	€956	Dark skinned slave with her children (56x32cm-22x13in) mono. gouache. 16-Jun-4 Fischer, Luzern #2576/R (S.FR 1500)

FRERE, Edouard (1819-1886) French

£2500	$4625	€3650	The alms (52x73cm-20x29in) s.d.1861. 14-Jul-4 Sotheby's, Olympia #179/R est:2500-3500
£3664	$6558	€5349	Interior with girl and small children (41x33cm-16x13in) s. panel. 17-May-4 Beurret, Zurich #22/R est:8000-12000 (S.FR 8500)
£15000	$25500	€21900	First steps in life (63x76cm-25x30in) s.d.1867 panel. 19-Nov-3 Bonhams, New Bond Street #128/R est:15000-20000

FRERE, Jean Jules (1851-1906) French

Sculpture			
£765	$1300	€1117	Seated maiden with distaff (79cm-31in) s. brown pat. bronze bronze. 21-Nov-3 Skinner, Boston #239/R est:2000-4000

FRERE, Samuel (19/20th C) French

£528	$914	€750	Vue du Cap Hernu (60x73cm-24x29in) s. 9-Dec-3 Vanderkindere, Brussels #120
£690	$1262	€1000	Pavillon et ponton au bord d'un etang (38x55cm-15x22in) s. 28-Jan-4 Libert, Castor, Paris #28

FRERICHS, William C A (1829-1905) American

£5247	$8500	€7608	Toula waterfalls (79x117cm-31x46in) s. board. 8-Aug-3 Barridorf, Portland #224/R est:9000-12000

FRESCO, Abraham (1903-1942) Dutch

£382	$623	€550	Roses in a ginger jar and a fan (31x36cm-12x14in) s. 29-Sep-3 Sotheby's, Amsterdam #179/R

FRESENIUS, Hermann Julius Richard (1844-1903) German

£403	$749	€600	Landscape with lake after storm (15x22cm-6x9in) board. 6-Mar-4 Arnold, Frankfurt #724/R

FRESIA, Vito (1963-) Italian

£268	$497	€400	It might be evening (120x70cm-47x28in) s. acrylic painted 2003. 13-Mar-4 Meeting Art, Vercelli #534

FRESNAYE, Roger de la (1885-1925) French

£3691	$6792	€5500	Paysage aux deux ponts (33x41cm-13x16in) s.d.1907 prov.lit. 24-Mar-4 Joron-Derem, Paris #60/R est:12000-15000
£6577	$12168	€9800	Le Vaincu (26x20cm-10x8in) s.d.23 chl estompe prov.lit. 15-Mar-4 Blanchet, Paris #116/R est:8000-10000
£36364	$62545	€52000	La bouilloire (52x77cm-20x30in) s. board on canvas painted c.1911 prov.exhib.lit. 5-Dec-3 Gros & Delettrez, Paris #87/R est:50000-70000
Sculpture			
£7333	$13493	€11000	Eve (30x44x20cm-12x17x8in) s. num.5/10 brown pat. bronze cire perdue Cast Valsuani prov.lit. 8-Jun-4 Artcurial Briest, Paris #151/R est:8000-10000
£52447	$90209	€75000	Grand nu (117cm-46in) s. num.2/6 pat bronze Cast Rudier exec.1911 prov.exhib.lit. 8-Dec-3 Artcurial Briest, Paris #17/R est:80000-100000
Works on paper			
£403	$749	€600	Chef de musique au bonnet de police (26x18cm-10x7in) blk crayon drawing stumping out exec c.1917-1918 prov.exhib.lit. 3-Mar-4 Tajan, Paris #60
£839	$1427	€1200	Personnages cubistes (33x26cm-13x10in) st.sig. pen exec.c.1912-1913 prov. 23-Nov-3 Cornette de St.Cyr, Paris #87
£1358	$2471	€2050	Pastorale (20x14cm-8x6in) india ink prov. 18-Jun-4 Piasa, Paris #124 est:1500-2000

FRESSINAT, Jules de (1820-?) French

£791	$1298	€1100	Portrait of man (80x63cm-31x25in) 5-Jun-3 Adma, Formigine #259

FREUD, Lucian (1922-) British/German

£1500000	$2760000	€2190000	Painter, redheaded man no.II (91x71cm-36x28in) painted 1962 prov.exhib. 23-Jun-4 Sotheby's, London #6/R est:1500000-2000000
£1850000	$3367000	€2701000	Factory in North London (71x71cm-28x28in) painted 1972 prov.exhib.lit. 4-Feb-4 Christie's, London #9/R est:800000-1200000
Prints			
£2941	$5000	€4294	Two men in a studio (40x36cm-16x14in) init. etching exec.1989. 4-Nov-3 Christie's, Rockefeller NY #237/R est:6000-8000
£4118	$7000	€6012	Head and shoulders (24x29cm-9x11in) init. etching. 31-Oct-3 Sotheby's, New York #558/R
£4800	$7968	€7008	Egyptian book (30x3cm-12x1in) init.num.33/40 etching sold with a book. 6-Oct-3 Sotheby's, London #134/R est:4000-6000
£4802	$8500	€7011	David Dawson (52x43cm-20x17in) init.num.25/46 etching. 30-Apr-4 Sotheby's, New York #342/R est:10000-15000
£5000	$8300	€7300	Portrait head (76x57cm-30x22in) init.num.40/45 etching. 6-Oct-3 Sotheby's, London #133/R est:6000-8000
£7500	$13650	€10950	Head and shoulders (24x29cm-9x11in) s.num.1/20 etching. 21-Jun-4 Bonhams, New Bond Street #141/R est:8000-12000
£14000	$24080	€20440	Large head (69x54cm-27x21in) init.i.num.2/2 etching. 2-Dec-3 Christie's, London #146/R est:12000-18000
£15217	$28000	€22217	Garden in winter (77x60cm-30x24in) s.nun.46 verso etching prov. 10-Jun-4 Phillips, New York #405/R est:10000-15000
£16000	$29120	€24000	Head and shoulders of a girl (69x54cm-27x21in) init.num.29/50 etching. 2-Jul-4 Bloomsbury, London #107/R est:14000-16000
Works on paper			
£11000	$20240	€16060	Untitled (24x33cm-9x13in) ink exec 1983 prov. 24-Jun-4 Sotheby's, London #241/R est:10000-15000
£53892	$90000	€78682	Self portrait (34x24cm-13x9in) chl pastel executed 1980 prov. 12-Nov-3 Sotheby's, New York #12/R est:80000-120000

FREUDENBERGER, Sigmund (1745-1801) Swiss

Prints			
£2371	$4244	€3462	Depart du soldat suisse. Retour du soldat suisse dans le pays (22x26cm-9x10in) col etching two. 13-May-4 Stuker, Bern #9267/R est:2000-3000 (S.FR 5500)
Works on paper			
£280	$502	€409	Girl in traditional costume (21x19cm-8x7in) s. pencil. 13-May-4 Stuker, Bern #9269/R (S.FR 650)
£388	$694	€566	Woman and maid in boudoir (19x14cm-7x6in) Indian ink wash on pencil. 13-May-4 Stuker, Bern #9159/R (S.FR 900)
£1034	$1852	€1510	Untitled (11x16cm-4x6in) Indian ink pen brush four. 13-May-4 Stuker, Bern #9266/R est:2500-3500 (S.FR 2400)
£3165	$5286	€4589	Les premiers pas (43x32cm-17x13in) s. crayon ink W/C prov. 21-Jun-3 Galerie du Rhone, Sion #442/R est:8000-10000 (S.FR 6900)
£3211	$5362	€4656	La visite (43x32cm-17x13in) s. crayon ink W/C prov. 21-Jun-3 Galerie du Rhone, Sion #441/R est:8000-10000 (S.FR 7000)

FREUDENTHAL, Peter (1938-) Swedish

£435	$783	€653	Happenings in Chicago (65x130cm-26x51in) s.d.1999-98 verso acrylic. 25-Apr-4 Goteborg Auktionsverk, Sweden #305/R (S.KR 6000)

FREUDWEILER, Heinrich (1755-1795) Swiss

£6040	$11114	€9000	Portrait of Johann Georg Sulzer with grandson Carl Anton Graff (23x20cm-9x8in) panel prov.lit. 24-Mar-4 Dorotheum, Vienna #271/R est:9000-12000

FREUND, Fritz (1859-1942) German

£1200	$2184	€1800	Lady dressed in finery playing a mandolin (32x25cm-13x10in) s. panel. 20-Jun-4 Wilkinson, Doncaster #331 est:1500-2000
£1636	$2716	€2372	Sunny track (115x97cm-45x38in) s.i. 13-Jun-3 Zofingen, Switzerland #2448/R est:4500 (S.FR 3600)

FREUND, Gisele (1908-2000) French

Photographs			
£2098	$3566	€3000	Frida Kahlo with her doctor, Mexico (28x25cm-11x10in) i. verso silver gelatin lit.exhib. 27-Nov-3 Villa Grisebach, Berlin #1177/R est:1500-2000

FREUND, Harry Louis (1905-1979) American

£376	$700	€549	Midwestern street scene (25x20cm-10x8in) s. board painted c.1940. 7-Mar-4 Treadway Gallery, Cincinnati #603/R
£578	$1000	€844	Stafford's store (51x61cm-20x24in) s. masonite. 13-Dec-3 Weschler, Washington #575

FREUNDLICH, Otto (1878-1943) German

Works on paper

£489	$842	€700	Etude pour arbre (16x12cm-6x5in) mono. graphite dr prov.lit. 8-Dec-3 Artcurial Briest, Paris #55/R
£629	$1083	€900	Etude pour arbre (14x11cm-6x4in) mono. graphite dr prov.lit. 8-Dec-3 Artcurial Briest, Paris #56/R
£1208	$2223	€1800	Composition (23x15cm-9x6in) mono. Indian ink. 26-Mar-4 Ketterer, Hamburg #415/R est:1800-2400
£3758	$6915	€5600	Composition in black and white (30x21cm-12x8in) mono. Indian ink. 26-Mar-4 Ketterer, Hamburg #414/R est:3000-3500
£9091	$15636	€13000	Gelb baum (31x23cm-12x9in) mono. gouache exec.1933 prov.lit. 8-Dec-3 Artcurial Briest, Paris #50/R est:15000-20000
£9441	$16238	€13500	Blau baum (31x20cm-12x8in) s.d.33 gouache prov.lit. 8-Dec-3 Artcurial Briest, Paris #49/R est:15000-20000
£9790	$16839	€14000	Rote baum (31x20cm-12x8in) s.i.d.1933 gouache prov.lit. 8-Dec-3 Artcurial Briest, Paris #48/R est:15000-20000
£23000	$38410	€33580	Composition abstraite (47x35cm-19x14in) init. gouache on board prov. 21-Oct-3 Sotheby's, London #72/R est:12000-15000
£32868	$56532	€47000	Rote baum (40x75cm-16x30in) mono. s.i.d.1933 verso gouache prov.lit. 8-Dec-3 Artcurial Briest, Paris #52/R est:50000-70000

FREXAS, Lola (?) Argentinian?

Works on paper

£447	$800	€653	Saint Felicita (54x71cm-21x28in) W/C. 11-May-4 Arroyo, Buenos Aires #42
£559	$1000	€816	Paraguay (60x43cm-24x17in) W/C. 11-May-4 Arroyo, Buenos Aires #41

FREY, Albert (1870-1948) Swiss

£356	$581	€520	Wooded landscape (37x46cm-15x18in) s. 27-Sep-3 Rasmussen, Havnen #2034 (D.KR 3800)

FREY, Alice (1895-1981) Belgian

£270	$476	€400	Three angels (24x19cm-9x7in) s. panel. 24-May-4 Bernaerts, Antwerp #707
£500	$895	€750	Jeune fille aux fleurs (50x40cm-20x16in) s. panel. 11-May-4 Vanderkindere, Brussels #55
£1268	$2193	€1800	Girl with blue stockings (62x50cm-24x20in) s. exhib. 13-Dec-3 De Vuyst, Lokeren #154/R est:1500-2000
£1958	$3270	€2800	A l'opera (70x63cm-28x25in) s.d.1935 s.i.verso exhib. 11-Oct-3 De Vuyst, Lokeren #151/R est:3000-3500
£2797	$4755	€4000	Enfants et chien sur la plage (62x73cm-24x29in) s. 1-Dec-3 Palais de Beaux Arts, Brussels #69/R est:2000-3000

FREY, Eugène (1864-1930) French

£1033	$1891	€1550	Jardin rustique (46x65cm-18x26in) s. 6-Jun-4 Osenat, Fontainebleau #88

FREY, Frederike (fl.1869-1883) Swiss

£616	$1048	€900	Still life of flowers and fruit (54x39cm-21x15in) mono. canvas on panel lit. 6-Nov-3 Allgauer, Kempten #3416/R
£1528	$2551	€2200	Still life (44x36cm-17x14in) mono. lit. 25-Oct-3 Bergmann, Erlangen #916/R est:1900
£1921	$3497	€2805	Still life with autumn fruit (60x50cm-24x20in) s.d.1863. 16-Jun-4 Fischer, Luzern #1127/R est:3000-4000 (S.FR 4400)

FREY, Jane (20th C) American

£492	$900	€718	Still life part 12 (76x102cm-30x40in) 10-Jul-4 Hindman, Chicago #156/R est:300-500

FREY, Johann Jakob (1813-1865) Swiss

£2937	$4993	€4200	Paysage rocheux (35x52cm-14x20in) paper on canvas exhib. 26-Nov-3 Daguerre, Paris #74 est:3000-3500
£4148	$7633	€6056	Shepherd with flock resting by stream (62x73cm-24x29in) s.d. 14-Jun-4 Philippe Schuler, Zurich #4206/R est:3000-5000 (S.FR 9500)
£10204	$18265	€15000	Bay of Naples (42x60cm-17x24in) s.i.d.1842. 17-Mar-4 Neumeister, Munich #457a/R est:10000
£11000	$18920	€16060	Mountainous landscape (101x138cm-40x54in) s.d.1859. 3-Dec-3 Christie's, London #98/R est:12000-16000
Works on paper			
£289	$531	€430	Souvenir du Vesuve (22x38cm-9x15in) crayon exhib. 26-Mar-4 Daguerre, Paris #66

FREY, Johann Jakob (attrib) (1813-1865) Swiss

£544	$974	€800	Swiss landscape (21x29cm-8x11in) paper on canvas. 19-Mar-4 Beaussant & Lefèvre, Paris #83/R
£563	$1025	€850	Paysage suisse (21x29cm-8x11in) paper. 16-Jun-4 Beaussant & Lefèvre, Paris #69
£1351	$2324	€1972	Southern landscape with bathing beauties (31x25cm-12x10in) panel. 8-Dec-3 Philippe Schuler, Zurich #3327/R est:2500-3000 (S.FR 3000)

FREY, Johann Wilhelm (1830-1909) Austrian

Works on paper

£345	$572	€500	Griechengasse (28x20cm-11x8in) s. W/C. 30-Sep-3 Dorotheum, Vienna #321/R
£414	$687	€600	Ratzenstadl (20x27cm-8x11in) s. W/C. 30-Sep-3 Dorotheum, Vienna #324/R
£448	$744	€650	Square (20x26cm-8x10in) s. Indian ink W/C. 30-Sep-3 Dorotheum, Vienna #310/R
£483	$801	€700	Saltzgriess in Vienna (22x28cm-9x11in) s.i. W/C paper on board. 30-Sep-3 Dorotheum, Vienna #299/R
£483	$801	€700	Trebitsch silk factory (34x43cm-13x17in) s.d.1902 w/C. 30-Sep-3 Dorotheum, Vienna #320/R

FREY, Joseph F (1892-1977) American

£450	$850	€657	High Sierras landscape (61x76cm-24x30in) s. prov. 17-Feb-4 John Moran, Pasadena #178/R
£1176	$2000	€1717	La Quinta, the cove (25x36cm-10x14in) s. i.verso canvasboard. 18-Nov-3 John Moran, Pasadena #11a est:1000-1500
£1389	$2250	€2028	Blooming desert landscape (51x41cm-20x16in) s. 9-Aug-3 Auctions by the Bay, Alameda #1475/R
£2206	$3750	€3221	California mountains (51x61cm-20x24in) s. i.verso. 18-Nov-3 John Moran, Pasadena #41 est:2000-3000

FREY, Louis (19th C) German

£268	$475	€400	Hunting party in a landscape (20x40cm-8x16in) s. panel. 30-Apr-4 Auktionhaus Georg Rehm, Augsburg #8025
£352	$630	€500	Landscape, near the Ammersee (15x30cm-6x12in) s. panel lit. 8-Jan-4 Allgauer, Kempten #2384
£414	$691	€600	Allgau lake landscape (19x25cm-7x10in) s. panel lit. 10-Jul-3 Allgauer, Kempten #2489/R
£467	$840	€700	Landscape near Kempten (22x40cm-9x16in) s. panel lit. 22-Apr-4 Allgauer, Kempten #3531/R

FREY, Max (1874-?) German

£828	$1531	€1200	Papagena (70x70cm-28x28in) i. verso panel. 14-Feb-4 Hans Stahl, Hamburg #25/R

FREY, Oskar (1883-1966) German

£264	$449	€385	Colourful parrot on perch with grapes (63x42cm-25x17in) s. 5-Nov-3 Dobiaschofsky, Bern #573/R (S.FR 600)

FREY, Samuel (1785-1836) Swiss

Works on paper

£262	$482	€383	Campagna landscape (46x61cm-18x24in) pencil htd white. 14-Jun-4 Philippe Schuler, Zurich #6038n (S.FR 600)

FREY, Wilhelm (1826-1911) German

£340	$609	€500	Mountain landscape 'The Blue Mountain' (46x39cm-18x15in) d.94 board lit. 20-Mar-4 Bergmann, Erlangen #1167

FREY-MOOCK, Adolf (1881-1954) German

£342	$582	€500	Crossing (24x34cm-9x13in) s. panel. 5-Nov-3 Hugo Ruef, Munich #970
£345	$617	€504	Pan and nymph (59x50cm-23x20in) s. 12-May-4 Dobiaschofsky, Bern #530/R (S.FR 800)
£352	$630	€500	Christ with Mary (51x41cm-20x16in) s. lit. 8-Jan-4 Allgauer, Kempten #2387/R
£403	$741	€600	Bacchanten (34x34cm-13x13in) s. board. 24-Mar-4 Hugo Ruef, Munich #964/R
£436	$803	€650	Mythological scene. 26-Mar-4 Karrenbauer, Konstanz #1717/R est:250
£545	$905	€790	Satyr orgy (34x49cm-13x19in) s. board. 13-Jun-3 Zofingen, Switzerland #2847/R (S.FR 1200)
£667	$1213	€1000	The departure of Orpheus (38x54cm-15x21in) s. board. 1-Jul-4 Van Ham, Cologne #1353
£1027	$1747	€1500	Portrait of a woman holding dish (45x35cm-18x14in) s. panel lit. 6-Nov-3 Allgauer, Kempten #3420/R est:1300
£1049	$1804	€1500	Meditation (84x67cm-33x26in) s. i.verso. 3-Dec-3 Neumeister, Munich #569/R est:1500
£1224	$2192	€1800	Nymph and Satyr (33x45cm-13x18in) s. panel. 17-Mar-4 Neumeister, Munich #458/R est:1600
£1762	$2996	€2573	Orpheus - Eurydike (137x105cm-54x41in) s. i. verso panel. 7-Nov-3 Dobiaschofsky, Bern #182/R est:5500 (S.FR 4000)
£4362	$7809	€6500	In thought (65x80cm-26x31in) s. panel. 25-May-4 Dorotheum, Vienna #150/R est:5000-7000

FREY-MOOCK, Adolf (attrib) (1881-1954) German

Works on paper

£616	$1048	€900	Susanna bathing (26x23cm-10x9in) mixed media. 5-Nov-3 Hugo Ruef, Munich #1214

FREYBERG, Conrad (1842-?) German

£7042	$12183	€10000	Elegant ladies on horseback (126x107cm-50x42in) s.d.1871. 10-Dec-3 Christie's, Amsterdam #820/R est:8000-12000

FREYBURG, Frank P (1862-?) British

£793	$1300	€1150	Landscape with sheep grazing (76x122cm-30x48in) s.d.1905 prov. 31-May-3 Brunk, Ashville #20/R est:400-800

FREYMUTH, Alphons (1940-) Dutch

£1333	$2453	€2000	Untitled (140x120cm-55x47in) s.d.71 verso acrylic. 9-Jun-4 Christie's, Amsterdam #192/R est:2000-3000

FREYTAG, Heinrich (1876-1951) German

£440	$796	€660	Sister of the artist reading (80x60cm-31x24in) s.i. 2-Apr-4 Winterberg, Heidelberg #973/R
£729	$1189	€1050	View of Stein near Konigsbach (71x100cm-28x39in) s.i.d.1908. 24-Sep-3 Neumeister, Munich #423/R

FREYTAG, Otto (20th C) German?

£633	$1134	€950	Still life (45x64cm-18x25in) s. panel. 15-May-4 Van Ham, Cologne #592

FREYTAG-LORINGHOVEN, Mathilde von (1860-1932) German/Danish

£403	$749	€600	Woodland scene (154x112cm-61x44in) s. i.verso. 5-Mar-4 Wendl, Rudolstadt #3647/R

FRIAS Y ESCALANTI, Juan Antonio de (attrib) (1630-1670) Spanish
£7383 $13585 €11000 Saint Joseph et l'Enfant Jesus (193x141cm-76x56in) 24-Mar-4 Tajan, Paris #22/R est:12000-15000
Works on paper
£364 $663 €550 Saint Francois tenant un crane dans sa main (19x11cm-7x4in) black crayon sold with dr by Spanish School prov. 16-Jun-4 Piasa, Paris #36

FRIAS, Onofre (1953-) Venezuelan
Works on paper
£310 $480 €453 Soul flowers (120x130cm-47x51in) s. mixed media on canvas. 29-Sep-2 Subastas Odalys, Caracas #21
£310 $480 €453 Soul uncertainties (120x130cm-47x51in) s. mixed media on canvas. 29-Sep-2 Subastas Odalys, Caracas #56/R

FRIBERG, Roj (1934-) Swedish
£3021 $5136 €4411 Facade (109x127cm-43x50in) s.d.89 wax crayon panel lit. 4-Nov-3 Bukowskis, Stockholm #608/R est:25000-30000 (S.KR 40000)
Works on paper
£529 $899 €772 Lofoten (90x110cm-35x43in) init.d.92 pencil. 5-Nov-3 AB Stockholms Auktionsverk #1056/R (S.KR 7000)
£793 $1348 €1158 From here to eternity (109x139cm-43x55in) init.d.81 pencil. 4-Nov-3 Bukowskis, Stockholm #621/R (S.KR 10500)
£1020 $1733 €1489 In the jungle (102x123cm-40x48in) init.d.87 mixed media cardboard. 4-Nov-3 Bukowskis, Stockholm #619/R (S.KR 13500)
£2683 $4830 €3917 Untitled (121x140cm-48x55in) init.d.88 wax crayon panel lit. 26-Apr-4 Bukowskis, Stockholm #487/R est:25000-30000 (S.KR 37000)

FRIBOULET, Jef (1919-2003) French
£350 $601 €500 La sieste (30x38cm-12x15in) s. oil paper. 7-Dec-3 Lesieur & Le Bars, Le Havre #216
£455 $773 €650 Femme en bleu (65x46cm-26x18in) s. 28-Nov-3 Drouot Estimations, Paris #225
£470 $874 €700 La lampe a petrole (24x82cm-9x32in) s.d.59 cardboard. 7-Mar-4 Lesieur & Le Bars, Le Havre #56
£490 $832 €700 Nature morte aux raisisns (64x53cm-25x21in) s. i.verso painted 1976. 28-Nov-3 Drouot Estimations, Paris #224
£753 $1183 €1100 Glaneuses (70x35cm-28x14in) s.d.1960. 20-Apr-3 Deauville, France #116
£805 $1498 €1200 Ciel d'orage (65x81cm-26x32in) s. 7-Mar-4 Lesieur & Le Bars, Le Havre #55
£872 $1623 €1300 Couple de pecheurs (46x55cm-18x22in) s. 7-Mar-4 Lesieur & Le Bars, Le Havre #51
£872 $1623 €1300 La femme en bleu (65x46cm-26x18in) s. 7-Mar-4 Lesieur & Le Bars, Le Havre #58
£897 $1497 €1300 Chantier sur le port (50x73cm-20x29in) s. 11-Nov-3 Lesieur & Le Bars, Le Havre #45
£940 $1748 €1400 La romanciere (40x33cm-16x13in) s. 7-Mar-4 Lesieur & Le Bars, Le Havre #54
£966 $1612 €1400 Chantier naval (22x48cm-9x19in) s. 11-Nov-3 Lesieur & Le Bars, Le Havre #44
£1000 $1800 €1500 Les bains le Havre (54x80cm-21x31in) d.1954. 25-Apr-4 Daniel Herry, Beaune #109
£1007 $1872 €1500 Nature morte aux mais (60x73cm-24x29in) s. 7-Mar-4 Lesieur & Le Bars, Le Havre #50/R
£1103 $1843 €1600 Etretat (27x35cm-11x14in) s. d.1946 verso. 11-Nov-3 Lesieur & Le Bars, Le Havre #39
£1103 $1843 €1600 Enfant dans l'escalier (55x38cm-22x15in) s. 11-Nov-3 Lesieur & Le Bars, Le Havre #41
£1103 $1843 €1600 Nature morte au violon (73x92cm-29x36in) s. 11-Nov-3 Lesieur & Le Bars, Le Havre #54
£1172 $1958 €1700 Faisan (100x50cm-39x20in) s. 11-Nov-3 Lesieur & Le Bars, Le Havre #52
£1241 $2073 €1800 Goudes (50x61cm-20x24in) s. 11-Nov-3 Lesieur & Le Bars, Le Havre #51
£1241 $2073 €1800 Buffet de la gare (81x65cm-32x26in) s. 11-Nov-3 Lesieur & Le Bars, Le Havre #48
£1241 $2073 €1800 Fecamp (65x81cm-26x32in) s. 11-Nov-3 Lesieur & Le Bars, Le Havre #50
£1241 $2073 €1800 Chantier naval (65x100cm-26x39in) s. 11-Nov-3 Lesieur & Le Bars, Le Havre #53
£1241 $2073 €1800 Desolation (73x54cm-29x21in) s. 11-Nov-3 Lesieur & Le Bars, Le Havre #55
£1310 $2188 €1900 Etretat (27x35cm-11x14in) s. d.1946 verso. 11-Nov-3 Lesieur & Le Bars, Le Havre #38
£1310 $2188 €1900 Poisson (50x100cm-20x39in) s. 11-Nov-3 Lesieur & Le Bars, Le Havre #40
£1379 $2303 €2000 Aveugle (65x46cm-26x18in) s.d.54. 11-Nov-3 Lesieur & Le Bars, Le Havre #46
£1379 $2303 €2000 Scene de cafe (65x54cm-26x21in) s. 11-Nov-3 Lesieur & Le Bars, Le Havre #47
£1409 $2621 €2100 La ramasseur de galets (73x92cm-29x36in) s. 7-Mar-4 Lesieur & Le Bars, Le Havre #53
£1862 $3110 €2700 Mere et enfants (55x38cm-22x15in) s.d.58. 11-Nov-3 Lesieur & Le Bars, Le Havre #37
£2000 $3340 €2900 Bains sur la plage du Havre (54x81cm-21x32in) s.d.54. 11-Nov-3 Lesieur & Le Bars, Le Havre #49
£2069 $3455 €3000 Muleta (54x72cm-21x28in) s.d.58. 11-Nov-3 Lesieur & Le Bars, Le Havre #36
£2207 $3686 €3200 Barques a Yport (80x116cm-31x46in) s.d.58. 11-Nov-3 Lesieur & Le Bars, Le Havre #43
£2639 $4301 €3800 Paysage de marais (53x65cm-21x26in) s.d.62. 21-Jul-3 Lesieur & Le Bars, Le Havre #24
£2690 $4492 €3900 Hiver (73x92cm-29x36in) s. 11-Nov-3 Lesieur & Le Bars, Le Havre #35
£3103 $5183 €4500 Famille (60x73cm-24x29in) s. 11-Nov-3 Lesieur & Le Bars, Le Havre #42
£3379 $5643 €4900 Barques a Yport (54x81cm-21x32in) s. 11-Nov-3 Lesieur & Le Bars, Le Havre #34
Sculpture
£1678 $3121 €2500 Les deux amis. d.1999 num.3/8 gilt pat bronze. 7-Mar-4 Lesieur & Le Bars, Le Havre #207/R
Works on paper
£671 $1248 €1000 Femmes au bain (38x46cm-15x18in) s. mixed media. 7-Mar-4 Livinec, Gaudcheau & Jezequel, Rennes #82

FRICERO, Joseph (1807-1870) French
Works on paper
£700 $1274 €1050 Paillon et le vieux Nice (26x36cm-10x14in) W/C. 29-Jun-4 Gioffredo, Nice #326

FRICH, Joachim (1810-1858) Norwegian
£922 $1567 €1346 Mountain landscape in evening (22x27cm-9x11in) i.verso. 10-Nov-3 Rasmussen, Vejle #357/R (D.KR 10000)

FRICH, Joachim (attrib) (1810-1858) Norwegian
£961 $1720 €1403 Vestlands fjord landscape with church (24x30cm-9x12in) panel. 22-Mar-4 Blomqvist, Oslo #318/R (N.KR 12000)
£1201 $2150 €1753 Landscape from Mieldalen in Hauge at sunset (24x31cm-9x12in) panel. 22-Mar-4 Blomqvist, Oslo #317/R est:18000-20000 (N.KR 15000)

FRICK, Ferdinand (19th C) German
Sculpture
£1173 $2100 €1713 Male cryer (61cm-24in) s. brown pat bronze. 20-Mar-4 Freeman, Philadelphia #733/R est:1000-1500

FRICK, Guido (1947-) German
£268 $494 €400 Hegau landscape in summer (68x78cm-27x31in) s. panel lit. 26-Mar-4 Karrenbauer, Konstanz #1719
£302 $556 €450 Seerhein (80x70cm-31x28in) panel. 26-Mar-4 Karrenbauer, Konstanz #1718

FRICK, Paul de (1864-1935) French
£490 $817 €700 Cour de ferme (40x53cm-16x21in) 12-Oct-3 Teitgen, Nancy #25
£1972 $3411 €2800 Life in the lagoon (90x145cm-35x57in) s.d.99. 11-Dec-3 Christie's, Rome #82/R est:3000-3500
£2000 $3680 €3000 Femme jouant avec ses petits chatons (46x55cm-18x22in) s.d.96. 9-Jun-4 Beaussant & Lefèvre, Paris #158/R est:1200-1500

FRICKE, August (1829-1894) German
£1141 $2099 €1700 Regatta on the Weser (51x80cm-20x31in) s. 26-Mar-4 Bolland & Marotz, Bremen #330/R est:1100

FRICKE, Heinrich (attrib) (1860-1917) German
Works on paper
£490 $842 €700 Paradise (73x120cm-29x47in) s. mixed media. 3-Dec-3 Neumeister, Munich #390/R

FRID, Ludvig (1855-1909) Swedish
£5923 $10188 €8648 The fall of man - Adam and Eve in Paradise (220x155cm-87x61in) s. exhib.lit. 3-Dec-3 AB Stockholms Auktionsverk #2509/R est:50000-60000 (S.KR 77000)

FRIDELL, Axel (1894-1935) Swedish
£806 $1315 €1177 Early spring, church hill at Falun (23x31cm-9x12in) s.d.13 panel. 29-Sep-3 Lilla Bukowskis, Stockholm #227 (S.KR 10500)
Prints
£3776 $6420 €5513 Mr Simmons reading a newspaper (30x24cm-12x9in) s.i. drypoint. 4-Nov-3 Bukowskis, Stockholm #372/R est:50000-60000 (S.KR 50000)
£4351 $7832 €6352 Mr Simmons - the newspaper reader (30x24cm-12x9in) s.i. drypoint lit. 26-Apr-4 Bukowskis, Stockholm #353/R est:50000-70000 (S.KR 60000)
£4846 $8335 €7075 Mr Simmons reading the paper (30x24cm-12x9in) s.i. drypoint prov.lit. 7-Dec-3 Uppsala Auktionskammare, Uppsala #300/R est:40000-50000 (S.KR 63000)
Works on paper
£2077 $3572 €3032 Out walking (23x32cm-9x13in) s. W/C. 2-Dec-3 Bukowskis, Stockholm #44a/R est:12000-15000 (S.KR 27000)

FRIDO, Maurice (1926-) French
£262 $482 €383 Over the rooftops (65x92cm-26x36in) s.d. 14-Jun-4 Philippe Schuler, Zurich #5719 (S.FR 600)

FRIE, Peter (1947-) Swedish
£1305 $2350 €1905 Landscape (14x20cm-6x8in) s. paper. 26-Apr-4 Bukowskis, Stockholm #501/R est:10000-15000 (S.KR 18000)
£1905 $3371 €2781 Sunny landscape (33x35cm-13x14in) s.d.1997 verso panel lit. 27-Apr-4 AB Stockholms Auktionsverk #1908/R est:15000-18000 (S.KR 26000)
£2271 $4020 €3316 Blue landscape (100x110cm-39x43in) s. 27-Apr-4 AB Stockholms Auktionsverk #939/R est:20000-25000 (S.KR 31000)
£4786 $8615 €6988 Untitled (66x93cm-26x37in) s.i. d.93/94 verso canvas on panel. 26-Apr-4 Bukowskis, Stockholm #463/R est:45000-50000 (S.KR 66000)
£5568 $9855 €8129 Landscape - from Norwegian landscapes (101x101cm-40x40in) s.d.98 verso panel prov.lit. 27-Apr-4 AB Stockholms Auktionsverk #979/R est:40000-50000 (S.KR 76000)
£6420 $10914 €9373 Untitled (153x98cm-60x39in) s.d.99 verso panel lit. 4-Nov-3 Bukowskis, Stockholm #592/R est:60000-80000 (S.KR 85000)
£9063 $15408 €13232 Slappeterp - Painting No.1 (180x120cm-71x47in) s.d.95 verso canvas and panel exhib.lit. 5-Nov-3 AB Stockholms Auktionsverk #995/R est:70000-80000 (S.KR 120000)
Works on paper
£2030 $3655 €2964 Landscape (10x15cm-4x6in) s. s.d.95 verso mixed media prov. 26-Apr-4 Bukowskis, Stockholm #500/R est:15000-18000 (S.KR 28000)

£2115	$3595	€3088	Landscape (15x10cm-6x4in) s. s.d.1998 verso mixed media exhib. 5-Nov-3 AB Stockholms Auktionsverk #989/R est:12000-15000 (S.KR 28000)

FRIEBERGER, Padhi (1929-) Austrian

Sculpture

£2797	$4755	€4000	The love of women of objects (112x80x42cm-44x31x17in) s. plastic metal collage. 26-Nov-3 Dorotheum, Vienna #305/R est:5000-7000

FRIED, Heinrich Jakob (1802-1870) German

£2953	$5434	€4400	Crowd beside ruined cloisters of Limburg (42x36cm-17x14in) s. 25-Mar-4 Dr Fritz Nagel, Stuttgart #709/R est:2800

FRIED, Pal (1893-1976) Hungarian/American

£396	$674	€578	Daisy (60x72cm-24x28in) s. i. verso. 5-Nov-3 Dobiaschofsky, Bern #3418/R (S.FR 900)
£462	$850	€675	Ballerinas (69x97cm-27x38in) s. 9-Jun-4 Doyle, New York #3036
£465	$800	€679	Portrait of a ballerina (41x56cm-16x22in) s. board. 6-Dec-3 Pook & Pook, Downington #536
£500	$925	€730	Young ballerina (76x56cm-30x22in) s. 15-Jan-4 Christie's, Kensington #847
£549	$1000	€824	Young ballet dancer sitting by a mirror (74x58cm-29x23in) s. 16-Jun-4 Wolf's, New York #486564/R
£683	$1100	€997	Ballerina (79x61cm-31x24in) 15-Aug-3 Du Mouchelle, Detroit #2013/R
£696	$1100	€1016	Two women in dresses, hats and veils (71x58cm-28x23in) s. i.verso. 6-Sep-3 Brunk, Ashville #364
£699	$1300	€1021	Three ballerinas (76x61cm-30x24in) s. 6-Mar-4 North East Auctions, Portsmouth #1198/R
£749	$1400	€1094	Mona (76x61cm-30x24in) s. i.verso. 25-Feb-4 Doyle, New York #77/R
£793	$1300	€1158	Trotters (61x76cm-24x30in) s. 1-Jun-3 William Jenack, New York #272a
£824	$1500	€1236	Ballet dancer (74x58cm-29x23in) s.i. 16-Jun-4 Wolf's, New York #487285/R est:3000-5000
£838	$1500	€1223	Maxine, Cafe Madrigal (61x76cm-24x30in) s. i.verso. 8-Jan-4 Doyle, New York #23/R est:1000-1500
£963	$1800	€1406	Francine (61x76cm-24x30in) s. i.verso. 25-Feb-4 Doyle, New York #71/R est:1500-2500
£1007	$1872	€1500	Dancer (80x60cm-31x24in) s. 4-Mar-4 Auction Maastricht #1124/R est:450-700
£1016	$1900	€1483	Woman in red, Paris (61x76cm-24x30in) s. 25-Feb-4 Doyle, New York #79/R est:1500-2500
£1018	$1700	€1486	Portrait of a woman (61x76cm-24x30in) s. 16-Nov-3 Bonhams & Butterfields, Los Angeles #7030/R est:1000-1500
£1070	$2000	€1562	Carmen (61x76cm-24x30in) s. i.verso. 25-Feb-4 Doyle, New York #68/R est:1500-2500
£1161	$1938	€1695	Audrey (61x76cm-24x30in) s. 17-Jun-3 Maynards, Vancouver #307 est:2500-3500 (C.D 2600)
£1163	$1850	€1686	Nude of Nina (76x61cm-30x24in) s. 12-Sep-3 Aspire, Cleveland #55 est:1500-2500
£1167	$2100	€1704	Surfeited (61x76cm-24x30in) s. i.verso. 23-Jan-4 Freeman, Philadelphia #175/R est:700-1000
£1173	$2100	€1713	The ballerinas (76x61cm-30x24in) s. 11-Jan-4 William Jenack, New York #177 est:1500-2000
£1176	$2200	€1717	Red tights (76x61cm-30x24in) s. i.verso. 25-Feb-4 Doyle, New York #65/R est:1500-2500
£1183	$2200	€1727	Portrait of Blanche (61x76cm-24x30in) s. i.verso. 6-Mar-4 North East Auctions, Portsmouth #1214/R est:1000-2000
£1183	$2200	€1727	Coming down the stretch (61x76cm-24x30in) s. 6-Mar-4 North East Auctions, Portsmouth #1216/R est:1000-2000
£1203	$2250	€1756	Winter in Paris (76x61cm-30x24in) s. 25-Feb-4 Doyle, New York #61/R est:1500-2500
£1203	$2250	€1756	Annabella, woman in green (61x76cm-24x30in) s. i.verso. 25-Feb-4 Doyle, New York #81/R est:1500-2500
£1222	$2200	€1784	Black female nude (76x61cm-30x24in) s. 23-Jan-4 Freeman, Philadelphia #221/R est:700-1000
£1250	$2000	€1825	Ballerina (61x76cm-24x30in) s. 19-Sep-3 Freeman, Philadelphia #137/R est:500-800
£1290	$2400	€1883	Portrait of Carmeu (61x76cm-24x30in) s. 6-Mar-4 North East Auctions, Portsmouth #1215/R
£1337	$2300	€1952	La senorita (76x61cm-30x24in) s. painted c.1950. 7-Dec-3 Treadway Gallery, Cincinnati #693/R est:2000-3000
£1392	$2200	€2032	Cafe des Lilla's (76x61cm-30x24in) s. 7-Sep-3 Treadway Gallery, Cincinnati #608/R est:2000-3000
£1444	$2600	€2108	Female nude stretching (76x61cm-30x24in) s. 23-Jan-4 Freeman, Philadelphia #199/R est:700-1000
£1463	$2400	€2136	Two Parisians (71x58cm-28x23in) s.i. 1-Jun-3 William Jenack, New York #212 est:2500-4000
£1500	$2400	€2190	Parisian flower market (61x76cm-24x30in) s. 21-Sep-3 William Jenack, New York #87 est:1500-2500
£1611	$2900	€2352	Girl on chair (76x61cm-30x24in) s. 23-Jan-4 Freeman, Philadelphia #93/R est:700-1000
£1738	$3250	€2537	Ballerina (127x76cm-50x30in) s. 25-Feb-4 Doyle, New York #60/R est:1500-2500
£1860	$3366	€2716	Maxine (61x76cm-24x30in) s. prov. 18-Apr-4 Levis, Calgary #209/R est:2500-3500 (C.D 4500)
£1988	$3200	€2902	Annabella (61x76cm-24x30in) s. 14-Jan-4 Christie's, Rockefeller NY #35/R est:2500-3500
£1989	$3500	€2904	Reclining nude (61x76cm-24x30in) s. 21-May-4 North East Auctions, Portsmouth #988/R est:1000-2000
£2045	$3600	€2986	Madeleine, portrait of a nude woman (76x61cm-30x24in) s. 21-May-4 North East Auctions, Portsmouth #987/R
£2177	$4006	€3178	Maxine (61x76cm-24x30in) s. i.verso. 14-Jun-4 Waddingtons, Toronto #313/R est:1800-2200 (C.D 5400)
£3091	$5750	€4513	Portrait of a nude (76x61cm-30x24in) s. 6-Mar-4 North East Auctions, Portsmouth #1199/R est:1000-2000
£3165	$5000	€4621	Nanette, Moulin Rouge (61x76cm-24x30in) s. 6-Apr-3 William Jenack, New York #298 est:3000-5000
£3472	$5486	€5000	Midday sleep (70x119cm-28x47in) s. lit. 19-Sep-3 Schloss Ahlden, Ahlden #1652/R est:1800

Works on paper

£506	$800	€739	Semi nude woman using her compact mirror (23x38cm-9x15in) s. pastel. 6-Apr-3 William Jenack, New York #220
£543	$907	€793	Nude from the back (24x24cm-9x9in) s. pastel. 17-Nov-3 Waddingtons, Toronto #251/R (C.D 1200)
£664	$1109	€950	Female nude (70x50cm-28x20in) pastel. 10-Oct-3 Stadion, Trieste #167/R
£989	$1800	€1444	Reclining nude (51x46cm-20x18in) s. pastel. 15-Jun-4 John Moran, Pasadena #192 est:1000-2000
£1023	$1800	€1494	Nude woman with downcast eyes (69x48cm-27x19in) s. pastel. 21-May-4 North East Auctions, Portsmouth #989/R est:1000-2000

FRIED, Theodore (fl.1925-1928) Hungarian

£468	$750	€683	Turku Trajan memoriam. Reading, girl of the golden west. s. double-sided. 17-May-3 Bunte, Elgin #1276
£469	$750	€685	The champ (53x53cm-21x21in) s.d.1942 s.i.d. verso canvas on board. 20-Sep-3 Bunte, Elgin #1203
£491	$800	€717	No.12 newspaper (48x33cm-19x13in) s.verso board. 19-Jul-3 Outer Cape Auctions, Provincetown #80/R

FRIEDEBERG, Pedro (1937-) Italian

Sculpture

£811	$1500	€1184	Untitled (69cm-27in) painted wood. 17-Jan-4 Susanin's, Chicago #124/R est:400-600

FRIEDENBERG, Wilhelm (1845-1911) German

£699	$1189	€1000	Young girl tying flower garland (39x32cm-15x13in) s.d.1881. 20-Nov-3 Van Ham, Cologne #1586/R
£972	$1604	€1400	Brother and sister (13x10cm-5x4in) s.d.75 W/C bodycol over pencil. 3-Jul-3 Dr Fritz Nagel, Stuttgart #490/R

FRIEDENSON, Arthur (1872-1955) British

£360	$659	€526	Poole Harbour (33x41cm-13x16in) panel. 7-Apr-4 Woolley & Wallis, Salisbury #233/R
£380	$695	€555	Simon Bromet painting (21x27cm-8x11in) panel. 7-Apr-4 Woolley & Wallis, Salisbury #232/R
£420	$769	€613	Yarmouth, Isle of Wight (21x27cm-8x11in) i.d.1949 verso panel. 7-Apr-4 Woolley & Wallis, Salisbury #231/R
£500	$895	€730	Breezy day, Poole harbour (20x27cm-8x11in) s. s.i.verso panel. 18-Mar-4 Christie's, Kensington #693/R
£500	$915	€730	Extensive view of Poole Harbour (30x40cm-12x16in) panel. 7-Apr-4 Woolley & Wallis, Salisbury #238/R
£550	$1007	€803	Dorset landscape (33x41cm-13x16in) panel. 7-Apr-4 Woolley & Wallis, Salisbury #236/R
£600	$1098	€876	Corfe Castle common (21x27cm-8x11in) init. i.verso panel. 7-Apr-4 Woolley & Wallis, Salisbury #246/R
£660	$1188	€964	Road to Steeperton Tor, Belstone, Dartmoor (32x40cm-13x16in) s.d.1926 i.verso board. 22-Apr-4 Lawrence, Crewkerne #944
£750	$1373	€1095	Cowshed, Newfoundland, Dorset (21x27cm-8x11in) panel. 7-Apr-4 Woolley & Wallis, Salisbury #237/R
£800	$1464	€1168	Wareham meadows (30x40cm-12x16in) s.d.1922 board. 7-Apr-4 Woolley & Wallis, Salisbury #245/R
£800	$1456	€1168	River scene with fishermen (53x74cm-21x29in) s. 16-Jun-4 Andrew Hartley, Ilkley #1121/R
£850	$1556	€1241	Cloud study (21x27cm-8x11in) one s.i.verso two init. panel three. 7-Apr-4 Woolley & Wallis, Salisbury #242/R
£950	$1739	€1387	Cloud study (21x27cm-8x11in) one i.d.1913 verso panel one init. board two. 7-Apr-4 Woolley & Wallis, Salisbury #243/R
£1000	$1830	€1460	Study of a Dartmoor road (17x26cm-7x10in) one s.i.verso board one board one init. sold with W/C four. 7-Apr-4 Woolley & Wallis, Salisbury #241/R est:120-180
£1000	$1830	€1460	Cloud study. Stormy evening from Eastmoor (22x27cm-9x11in) init i.verso board i.verso panel two. 7-Apr-4 Woolley & Wallis, Salisbury #244/R est:100-150
£1300	$2379	€1898	Redcliffe, Wareham (26x35cm-10x14in) s.i.d.1909 verso board. 7-Apr-4 Woolley & Wallis, Salisbury #234/R est:300-400
£1300	$2379	€1898	Sky study, Wareham. Study (21x27cm-8x11in) init. i.verso panel one init. i.d.1920 verso two. 7-Apr-4 Woolley & Wallis, Salisbury #247/R
£1300	$2379	€1898	River Frome (33x41cm-13x16in) panel. 7-Apr-4 Woolley & Wallis, Salisbury #248/R est:150-250
£1400	$2562	€2044	Study of sunset clouds. Cloud study (21x27cm-8x11in) one s.i.verso panel two. 7-Apr-4 Woolley & Wallis, Salisbury #249/R est:100-150
£1500	$2685	€2190	Gravel pit, Isle of Purbeck (28x39cm-11x15in) s. indis d.1938 board. 16-Mar-4 Bonhams, Leeds #657/R est:1500-2000
£1500	$2745	€2190	Runswick sketch, daffodils (26x35cm-10x14in) s.i.verso. 7-Apr-4 Woolley & Wallis, Salisbury #239/R est:150-250
£1600	$2720	€2336	Wareham church and village (31x41cm-12x16in) s.d.1912 panel. 19-Nov-3 Tennants, Leyburn #1055/R est:800-1200
£2000	$3660	€2920	Thruxton, Hampshire (26x35cm-10x14in) s.i.verso board. 7-Apr-4 Woolley & Wallis, Salisbury #235/R est:250-350
£2000	$3660	€2920	Sky study, Wareham. Newfoundland Bridge, Wareham (20x26cm-8x10in) one init. i.verso panel one i.verso two. 7-Apr-4 Woolley & Wallis, Salisbury #250/R est:120-180
£2600	$4758	€3796	Winter sketch, Wensleydale, Yorkshire (21x27cm-8x11in) board. 7-Apr-4 Woolley & Wallis, Salisbury #240/R est:150-250
£2900	$4930	€4234	River landscape (31x39cm-12x15in) s. board. 18-Nov-3 Bonhams, Leeds #259/R est:2000-3000

FRIEDERICI, Walter (1874-?) German

£839	$1443	€1200	Dresden, Kronentor in the snow (53x37cm-21x15in) s. board. 4-Dec-3 Schopman, Hamburg #613/R

FRIEDL, Peter (20th C) ?

Sculpture

£7042	$12324	€10000	Things to come. Neon. 18-Dec-3 Cornette de St.Cyr, Paris #52/R est:10000-15000

FRIEDLANDER, Alfred (1860-1927) Austrian

£658	$1119	€961	Campaign (38x50cm-15x20in) s. canvas on canvas. 29-Nov-3 Dorotheum, Prague #37/R (C.KR 30000)
£724	$1231	€1057	Busy field camp (60x90cm-24x35in) s. 28-Nov-3 Zofingen, Switzerland #2594/R (S.FR 1600)
£764	$1299	€1100	Resting in front of tavern (24x36cm-9x14in) s. panel. 28-Oct-3 Dorotheum, Vienna #277/R

£1078 $1929 €1574 Lively military camp on beach (60x90cm-24x35in) s. 13-May-4 Stuker, Bern #141/R est:3000-3500 (S.FR 2500)

FRIEDLANDER, Augustus Maurice (1856-1897) American/German
£6250 $11000 €9125 Street Musician (36x23cm-14x9in) s.i. panel painted c.1880-90. 18-May-4 Christie's, Rockefeller NY #65/R est:12000-18000

FRIEDLANDER, Camilla (1856-1928) Austrian
£856 $1600 €1250 Still life with Japanese vase, Persian ewer, ivory fan and other objects (18x23cm-7x9in) s. panel prov. 25-Feb-4 Doyle, New York #99/R est:3000-5000
£1469 $2452 €2100 Oriental still life with pistol (17x23cm-7x9in) s. panel one of pair. 9-Oct-3 Michael Zeller, Lindau #566/R est:1200
£1469 $2452 €2100 Oriental still life with Japanese teapot, sheet music and shell (17x23cm-7x9in) s. panel one of pair. 9-Oct-3 Michael Zeller, Lindau #567/R est:1200
£1958 $3329 €2800 Autumn still life with fruit, dead birds, bottle and glass (26x16cm-10x6in) s. panel. 24-Nov-3 Dorotheum, Vienna #125/R est:2400-3000
£2144 $3966 €3130 Still life with vase on a table top (16x23cm-6x9in) 14-Mar-4 Agra, Warsaw #21/R (P.Z 15500)
£4539 $7852 €6627 Still life with vase, flowers, shells, newspaper (17x23cm-7x9in) s. panel painted before 1901. 14-Dec-3 Agra, Warsaw #67/R est:15000 (P.Z 30000)

FRIEDLANDER, Friedrich (1825-1901) Austrian
£270 $484 €400 Seated veteran with pipe and glass tankard (18x13cm-7x5in) s. panel. 6-May-4 Michael Zeller, Lindau #665/R
£839 $1443 €1200 The sculpture collector (21x15cm-8x6in) s.d.879 panel. 3-Dec-3 Neumeister, Munich #570/R
£1965 $3576 €2869 In the local inn (29x21cm-11x8in) s. panel prov. 16-Jun-4 Fischer, Luzern #1215/R est:5000-7000 (S.FR 4500)
£4977 $8462 €7266 Celebrating the new wine (69x57cm-27x22in) s.d.1863. 19-Nov-3 Fischer, Luzern #1195/R est:12000-15000 (S.FR 11000)

FRIEDLANDER, Hedwig (1863-1916) Austrian
£1132 $1800 €1653 Interior scene of a mother bathing her children (48x38cm-19x15in) s. 13-Sep-3 Selkirks, St. Louis #483/R est:3500-4500

FRIEDLANDER, Isac (1890-1968) American
Works on paper
£217 $400 €317 Village with steeple (36x48cm-14x19in) s.d.1948 W/C. 10-Jun-4 Swann Galleries, New York #87/R

FRIEDLANDER, Johnny (1912-1992) French
£4225 $7014 €6000 Paysage 7.1982 (81x100cm-32x39in) s.d.1982 i. verso. 13-Jun-3 Hauswedell & Nolte, Hamburg #635/R est:8000
Works on paper
£769 $1323 €1100 Seated female nude (24x16cm-9x6in) s.d. W/C pencil. 3-Dec-3 Hauswedell & Nolte, Hamburg #777/R

FRIEDLANDER, Julius (1810-1861) Danish
£375 $645 €548 The vain girl (53x44cm-21x17in) panel prov. 2-Dec-3 Kunsthallen, Copenhagen #531 (D.KR 4000)
£467 $738 €677 The wounded soldier (24x28cm-9x11in) prov. 2-Sep-3 Rasmussen, Copenhagen #1777/R (D.KR 5000)
£567 $981 €828 Winter's day with couple walking on path (26x30cm-10x12in) init. 9-Dec-3 Rasmussen, Copenhagen #1559/R (D.KR 6000)
£1493 $2673 €2180 Fisherboy from Aalsgaard who has been collecting worms (52x41cm-20x16in) init.d.1859 exhib. 10-May-4 Rasmussen, Vejle #349/R est:10000-15000 (D.KR 16500)
£1522 $2785 €2222 Interior scene with the artist's daughter Thea and two women (50x38cm-20x15in) 7-Jun-4 Museumsbygningen, Copenhagen #26/R est:15000-20000 (D.KR 17000)
£1797 $3342 €2624 Figures by fishing village on the coast of North Sjaelland (66x95cm-26x37in) 2-Mar-4 Rasmussen, Copenhagen #1403/R est:25000-30000 (D.KR 20000)
£2617 $4135 €3795 The young hornblower saying Goodbye to his family (62x73cm-24x29in) init.d.25/3 1850. 2-Sep-3 Rasmussen, Copenhagen #1501/R est:30000 (D.KR 28000)
£5819 $10649 €8496 The mouse hunt - family and their cat hunting mouse in cottage (63x80cm-25x31in) init.d.1852 exhib.prov. 9-Jun-4 Rasmussen, Copenhagen #1737/R est:50000-60000 (D.KR 65000)

FRIEDLANDER, Lee (1934-) American
Photographs
£2059 $3500 €3006 Self portrait, route 9w, New York (18x28cm-7x11in) gelatin silver print prov.exhib. 9-Nov-3 Wright, Chicago #481 est:4000-6000
£2395 $4000 €3497 George Washington Bridge (19x28cm-7x11in) s.i.d.1973 verso silver print. 21-Oct-3 Swann Galleries, New York #306/R est:3000-5000
£2515 $4200 €3672 Hillcrest, New York (19x28cm-7x11in) s. gelatin silver print lit. 16-Oct-3 Phillips, New York #193/R est:5000-7000
£2994 $5000 €4371 Untitled (14x21cm-6x8in) s. gelatin silver print. 16-Oct-3 Phillips, New York #198/R
£11976 $20000 €17485 Philadelphia (14x21cm-6x8in) s. gelatin silver print set of 2 lit. 16-Oct-3 Phillips, New York #185/R est:8000-12000
£12575 $21000 €18360 Wilmington, Delaware (18x15cm-7x6in) s. gelatin silver print on board lit. 16-Oct-3 Phillips, New York #197/R est:8000-12000

FRIEDLANDER, Nadia (1911-) ?
£420 $743 €613 Net (56x39cm-22x15in) board. 27-Apr-4 Bonhams, Knightsbridge #313/R

FRIEDLIN-BINAEPFEL, Monique (1923-) French
£278 $506 €420 Still life with summer flowers and a lemon on a window still (64x50cm-25x20in) s. 17-Jun-4 Frank Peege, Freiburg #1198/R
£278 $506 €420 Female rider on a prancing horse with a flute player (46x60cm-18x24in) s. 17-Jun-4 Frank Peege, Freiburg #1199/R
£400 $724 €600 Still life with flowers (55x64cm-22x25in) s. 1-Apr-4 Frank Peege, Freiburg #1162/R

FRIEDLINGER, Jeno (?) Hungarian
£432 $708 €600 Sitting room (60x79cm-24x31in) s. 10-Jun-3 Pandolfini, Florence #280

FRIEDMAN, Arnold (1879-1946) American
£6044 $11000 €8824 Flushing meadow no.2 (38x38cm-15x15in) s. i.verso board painted 1944 prov.exhib. 29-Jun-4 Sotheby's, New York #317/R est:7000-10000
£12637 $23000 €18450 Untitled - leaf abstraction (41x53cm-16x21in) s. painted 1923 prov. 29-Jun-4 Sotheby's, New York #318/R est:10000-15000
£13966 $25000 €20390 Floral still life on a table (51x61cm-20x24in) s. 26-May-4 Doyle, New York #162/R est:30000-50000
Works on paper
£640 $1100 €934 Flowers in a vase (30x23cm-12x9in) s. pastel. 7-Dec-3 Grogan, Boston #81/R
£1648 $3000 €2406 Boy with a blue cap (62x51cm-24x20in) d. prov. 29-Jun-4 Sotheby's, New York #322/R est:4000-6000

FRIEDMAN, Martin (1896-?) American/Hungarian
£227 $400 €331 Dancers (51x36cm-20x14in) s. board painted c.1950. 23-May-4 Treadway Gallery, Cincinnati #681/R

FRIEDMAN, Tom (1965-) American
£2514 $4500 €3670 Untitled, stacked cups (102x8cm-40x3in) s.num. of 95 acrylic 75 hand painted Styrofoam cups glue prov. 14-May-4 Phillips, New York #361/R est:4000-6000
£26000 $47840 €37960 Untitled. acrylic styrofoam pellets dimension variable prov. 25-Jun-4 Christie's, London #276/R est:22000-28000
Photographs
£25449 $42500 €37156 Untitled (86x60cm-34x24in) s.num.7/7 verso black white photo board prov. 13-Nov-3 Sotheby's, New York #413/R est:30000-40000
Prints
£2000 $3660 €2920 Untitled (34x85cm-13x33in) inkjet print edition of 100. 3-Jun-4 Christie's, Kensington #348/R est:2000-3000
£2395 $4000 €3497 Untitled (54x105cm-21x41in) s.num.100 verso inkjet print executed 2000 prov. 14-Nov-3 Phillips, New York #282/R est:5000-7000
£3529 $6000 €5152 Untitled (33x83cm-13x33in) s. col inkjet. 31-Oct-3 Sotheby's, New York #560/R
£3824 $6500 €5583 Untitled (55x105cm-22x41in) s.verso inkjet print. 4-Nov-3 Christie's, Rockefeller NY #238/R est:5000-7000
Sculpture
£2515 $4200 €3672 Untitled - stacked cups (102x8x8cm-40x3x3in) s.num.95 acrylic styrofoam cups glue executed 2000 prov.exhib. 14-Nov-3 Phillips, New York #301/R est:3000-5000
Works on paper
£20958 $35000 €30599 Down (181x23cm-71x9in) s.verso press-on lettering prov.exhib.lit. 13-Nov-3 Sotheby's, New York #463/R est:40000-60000

FRIEDRICH, A L (20th C) American
£581 $1000 €848 Portrait of a woman (36x28cm-14x11in) board painted c.1920. 7-Dec-3 Treadway Gallery, Cincinnati #592/R

FRIEDRICH, Adolf (1821-1889) ?
Works on paper
£278 $453 €400 Horses in a stable (35x47cm-14x19in) s.d.1872 W/C. 29-Sep-3 Sotheby's, Amsterdam #145

FRIEDRICH, Caroline (1828-1914) German
£1200 $2220 €1800 Still life with globe and books on a desk (25x30cm-10x12in) s. panel. 14-Jul-4 Sotheby's, Olympia #218/R est:800-1200

FRIEDRICH, Caspar David (1774-1840) German
£920000 $1674400 €1343200 A Nordic landscape, spring (35x49cm-14x19in) painted c.1825. 15-Jun-4 Sotheby's, London #26/R est:400000-600000
Works on paper
£54667 $100587 €82000 Two sailboats at sea (26x20cm-10x8in) India ink wash sepia prov.exhib.lit. 11-Jun-4 Villa Grisebach, Berlin #1/R est:40000-60000

FRIEDRICH, Gustav-Adolf (1824-1889) German
£395 $726 €600 The approaching storm (33x41cm-13x16in) mono.d.1870. 22-Jun-4 Christie's, Amsterdam #53/R
£537 $988 €800 Dresden on winter evening (10x20cm-4x8in) s. i. verso board. 26-Mar-4 Bolland & Marotz, Bremen #519/R
£1812 $3334 €2700 Sachsen Switzerland (22x30cm-9x12in) i. verso board prov. 26-Mar-4 Bolland & Marotz, Bremen #518/R est:1300

FRIEDRICH, Harald (1858-1933) German
£800 $1456 €1200 Writing table in corner of old room. s. canvas on board. 30-Jun-4 Neumeister, Munich #548
£933 $1671 €1400 The letter (70x89cm-28x35in) s. i. verso lit. 14-May-4 Schloss Ahlden, Ahlden #2816/R

FRIEDRICH, M G (?) ?
£903 $1508 €1300 Yacht (60x92cm-24x36in) s. 26-Oct-3 Lesieur & Le Bars, Le Havre #101

FRIEDRICH, Waldemar (1846-1910) German
£2657 $4571 €3800 Middle Ages mounted hunt (110x175cm-43x69in) s.d.69 sold with sketch. 3-Dec-3 Neumeister, Munich #806/R est:2000

FRIEDRICHS, Fritz (1882-?) German

£432	$800	€631	Reclining figure (30x36cm-12x14in) s. verso. 18-Jan-4 Bonhams & Butterfields, Los Angeles #7025/R
£1748	$3007	€2500	Still life (43x37cm-17x15in) s.d.16. 4-Dec-3 Schopman, Hamburg #727/R est:2500
£2069	$3828	€3000	Garden of Lazareth (24x32cm-9x13in) s. one of pair. 14-Feb-4 Hans Stahl, Hamburg #141/R est:4500

FRIEDRICHSEN, Ernestine (1824-1892) German

£2128	$3447	€3000	Interior with grandmother and children (56x50cm-22x20in) s.d.1864 lit. 23-May-3 Karlheinz Kaupp, Staufen #1767/R est:2500

FRIEND, Donald Stuart Leslie (1915-1989) Australian

£840	$1528	€1226	Parrot in the interior (20x25cm-8x10in) s. oil gouache on board. 16-Jun-4 Deutscher-Menzies, Melbourne #374/R est:2800-3800 (A.D 2200)
£1220	$2183	€1781	Bridge and river scene (49x59cm-19x23in) s. artist board. 4-May-4 Sotheby's, Melbourne #317 est:3000-5000 (A.D 3000)
£3306	$5851	€4827	Still life (24x30cm-9x12in) glass painted c.1939 prov. 3-May-4 Christie's, Melbourne #107/R est:10000-15000 (A.D 8000)
£4752	$8079	€6938	Bali boy (24x18cm-9x7in) s. board painted c.1975. 29-Oct-3 Lawson Menzies, Sydney #10/R est:12000-18000 (A.D 11500)
£6098	$9573	€8842	Tea for the master (27x38cm-11x15in) s. oil gold leaf board prov. 26-Aug-3 Christie's, Sydney #72/R est:15000-25000 (A.D 15000)
£6568	$11165	€9589	Portrait of a boy (30x23cm-12x9in) s.d.47 wood panel prov. 24-Nov-3 Sotheby's, Melbourne #3/R est:15000-20000 (A.D 15500)
£8511	$14468	€12426	Dog fight (37x44cm-15x17in) s.d.1954 i.verso prov. 25-Nov-3 Christie's, Melbourne #19/R est:20000-30000 (A.D 20000)
£9091	$16818	€13273	Girl amongst the leaves and flowers, Bali (63x47cm-25x19in) s. i.verso oil gouache ink. 10-Mar-4 Deutscher-Menzies, Melbourne #180/R est:9000-12000 (A.D 22000)
£15267	$27786	€22290	Girl, London (51x60cm-20x24in) s.d.50 prov. 16-Jun-4 Deutscher-Menzies, Melbourne #80/R est:35000-45000 (A.D 40000)
£20325	$31911	€29471	Cairns harbour (37x50cm-15x20in) s.d.42 board prov.exhib.lit. 26-Aug-3 Christie's, Sydney #85/R est:45000-65000 (A.D 50000)
£28455	$44675	€41761	Motley jacket, Ischia (58x48cm-23x19in) s.d.50 s.i.d. Jan 1950 verso prov. 26-Aug-3 Christie's, Sydney #73/R est:40000-50000 (A.D 70000)

Works on paper

£276	$430	€400	Quinalow, Queensland (38x50cm-15x20in) s.i. pen ink. 1-Aug-2 Joel, Victoria #165 (A.D 800)
£405	$652	€591	Nude (55x40cm-22x16in) s. ink wash. 25-Aug-3 Sotheby's, Paddington #402 (A.D 1000)
£496	$917	€724	Retun (28x20cm-11x8in) s.i. gouache pen board. 10-Mar-4 Deutscher-Menzies, Melbourne #513/R est:1500-2500 (A.D 1200)
£527	$986	€791	Double bay (47x35cm-19x14in) i. gouache. 20-Jul-4 Goodman, Sydney #125/R (A.D 1350)
£620	$1147	€905	Boy, Bali (34x25cm-13x10in) s.i. pastel gouache pen ink. 10-Mar-4 Deutscher-Menzies, Melbourne #501/R est:1800-2500 (A.D 1500)
£720	$1225	€1051	Skyros (49x32cm-19x13in) s.i. W/C prov. 24-Nov-3 Sotheby's, Melbourne #186 (A.D 1700)
£785	$1389	€1146	Houses at Freshwater (27x35cm-11x14in) s. ink W/C. 3-May-4 Christie's, Melbourne #299/R est:1500-2500 (A.D 1900)
£950	$1672	€1387	Ship in a bottle (30x48cm-12x19in) s.d.1949 ink wash prov. 18-May-4 Woolley & Wallis, Salisbury #293/R
£1016	$1819	€1483	Rocky landscape (32x47cm-13x19in) s.i. gouache ink. 10-May-4 Joel, Victoria #402 est:2500-3500 (A.D 2500)
£1065	$1683	€1555	Bali (32x42cm-13x17in) s.i. W/C pen. 2-Sep-3 Deutscher-Menzies, Melbourne #278/R est:3000-5000 (A.D 2600)
£1157	$1967	€1689	Couple (33x48cm-13x19in) s. gouache ink. 29-Oct-3 Lawson Menzies, Sydney #155/R est:2500-4500 (A.D 2800)
£1300	$2288	€1898	Interior with artist (31x47cm-12x19in) W/C prov. 18-May-4 Woolley & Wallis, Salisbury #282/R est:1000-1500
£1576	$2710	€2301	Double Bay. s.i. mixed media. 7-Dec-3 Joel, Victoria #159/R est:3000-4000 (A.D 3750)
£1721	$2719	€2513	Maria (33x49cm-13x19in) s.i. W/C pen prov. 2-Sep-3 Deutscher-Menzies, Melbourne #200/R est:4000-6000 (A.D 4200)
£1800	$3168	€2628	Blue Anchor, Aldgate (30x47cm-12x19in) s.i. ink mixed media. 18-May-4 Woolley & Wallis, Salisbury #295/R est:1200 1800
£1862	$2998	€2719	Two boys (77x56cm-30x22in) s. ink W/C card exec 1963 prov. 25-Aug-3 Sotheby's, Paddington #369/R est:3000-6000 (A.D 4600)
£1983	$3511	€2895	Head studies, Bali (31x47cm-12x19in) s.i. W/C ink prov. 3-May-4 Christie's, Melbourne #352/R est:4000-6000 (A.D 4800)
£2672	$4863	€3901	Boy with frill neck lizard (52x44cm-20x17in) s.d.45 W/C ink wash. 16-Jun-4 Deutscher-Menzies, Melbourne #176/R est:8000-12000 (A.D 7000)
£2734	$5113	€4101	Boy with an Icon Venezia (46x30cm-18x12in) s. ink wash crayon. 20-Jul-4 Goodman, Sydney #31/R est:5000-7000 (A.D 7000)
£2754	$4682	€4021	Fisherman, Portofino, Italy (47x30cm-19x12in) s.i.d.49 ink W/C prov. 24-Nov-3 Sotheby's, Melbourne #112/R est:4000-6000 (A.D 6500)
£2846	$4467	€4127	Beach boys (75x64cm-30x25in) s. W/C gouache ink prov. 26-Aug-3 Christie's, Sydney #74/R est:7000-10000 (A.D 7000)
£2846	$5093	€4155	Celebrated Mango trick (34x49cm-13x19in) s. indis.d. i. in gouache paper on board prov. 4-May-4 Sotheby's, Melbourne #306/R est:7000-10000 (A.D 7000)
£2959	$5445	€4320	Porta San Fernando, Florence (30x47cm-12x19in) s.i. W/C mixed media prov. 29-Mar-4 Goodman, Sydney #149/R est:6000-8000 (A.D 7250)
£3049	$4786	€4421	Bali boys (77x55cm-30x22in) s.i. W/C gouache ink exec.c.1970 prov. 26-Aug-3 Christie's, Sydney #87/R est:7000-10000 (A.D 7500)
£3053	$5557	€4457	Two boys reclining (43x69cm-17x27in) s. W/C gouache pen ink. 16-Jun-4 Deutscher-Menzies, Melbourne #321/R est:5000-7500 (A.D 8000)
£3067	$5000	€4478	Two youths and satyr (74x61cm-29x24in) s.i. ink W/C wash. 27-Sep-3 Charlton Hall, Columbia #110/R est:4000-7000
£3252	$5106	€4715	Studio interior, Bali (56x76cm-22x30in) s.i. W/C gouache prov.exhib.lit. 26-Aug-3 Christie's, Sydney #78/R est:7000-12000 (A.D 8000)
£3390	$5763	€4949	Paris (46x35cm-18x14in) s.i.d.71 mixed media paper on board. 24-Nov-3 Sotheby's, Melbourne #153/R est:6000-9000 (A.D 8000)
£4049	$6518	€5912	Boy with pigeons (61x47cm-24x19in) s.i. W/C ink gold leaf artist card. 25-Aug-3 Sotheby's, Paddington #346/R est:10000-15000 (A.D 10000)
£4131	$7023	€6031	Guitar player (34x26cm-13x10in) s.d.Oct 41 ink ink wash. 24-Nov-3 Sotheby's, Melbourne #154/R est:2000-3000 (A.D 9750)
£4472	$8004	€6529	Harlequins (66x51cm-26x20in) s.d.46 mixed media paper on board prov.exhib. 4-May-4 Sotheby's, Melbourne #171/R est:10000-15000 (A.D 11000)
£5556	$9278	€8112	Friendship (76x56cm-30x22in) s. mixed media. 12-Oct-3 Sotheby's, Singapore #19/R est:6000-9000 (S.D 16000)
£14225	$25605	€20769	Ketjak (149x109cm-59x43in) s.i. W/C. 25-Apr-4 Christie's, Hong Kong #506/R est:160000-250000 (HK.D 200000)

FRIEND, Washington F (1820-1886) British

Works on paper

£600	$1020	€876	Hudson River from Fort Putnam, New York (24x32cm-9x13in) s. i.verso W/C bodycol. 4-Nov-3 Bonhams, New Bond Street #144
£2200	$3586	€3212	Quebec from Point Levi (35x55cm-14x22in) s. pencil W/C oval. 24-Sep-3 Christie's, London #92/R est:1000-1500

FRIER, Harry (c.1849-1919) British

Works on paper

£620	$1054	€905	Minehead, North Hill and the harbour from the east (26x52cm-10x20in) s.d.1900 W/C. 27-Nov-3 Greenslade Hunt, Taunton #971/R
£900	$1530	€1314	Winter scene, the leper hospital, Tauton (13x18cm-5x7in) mono. W/C. 27-Nov-3 Greenslade Hunt, Taunton #969
£1050	$1754	€1533	Taunton, extensive view from Cotlake hill (35x53cm-14x21in) W/C. 26-Jun-3 Greenslade Hunt, Taunton #482/R est:350-450

FRIER, Jessie (fl.1880-1912) British

Works on paper

£700	$1288	€1022	Fisherman's home, Largo (34x53cm-13x21in) s. W/C. 25-Mar-4 Bonhams, Edinburgh #317/R

FRIERS, Julian (1956-) British

£600	$984	€876	Crows (35x45cm-14x18in) s. board. 4-Jun-3 John Ross, Belfast #43
£2200	$4092	€3212	Ducks (50x71cm-20x28in) s. board. 3-Mar-4 John Ross, Belfast #68 est:2250-2500

Works on paper

£420	$781	€613	Woodcock (28x35cm-11x14in) s. W/C. 3-Mar-4 John Ross, Belfast #134
£450	$738	€657	Falcon (35x25cm-14x10in) s.d.1977 W/C. 4-Jun-3 John Ross, Belfast #89
£600	$996	€876	Pheasants (20x30cm-8x12in) s. W/C. 1-Oct-3 John Ross, Belfast #99

FRIES, Bernhard (1820-1879) German

£1702	$2689	€2400	Italian mountain landscape with two figures by stream (44x60cm-17x24in) s. panel. 25-Jul-3 Altus, Berlin #551/R est:1800
£2292	$3735	€3300	Italian coast landscape in evening (142x209cm-56x82in) s. 25-Sep-3 Dr Fritz Nagel, Stuttgart #1301/R est:900
£2961	$5447	€4500	Southern Italian coastline in morning light (97x130cm-38x51in) s. 24-Jun-4 Dr Fritz Nagel, Stuttgart #707/R est:2700

FRIES, Charles Arthur (1854-1940) American

£870	$1600	€1270	Trail of the lonesome pine (30x46cm-12x18in) s. i.verso prov. 27-Jun-4 Bonhams & Butterfields, San Francisco #3825/R est:2500-3500
£899	$1700	€1313	Landscape - Mts from Mason Valley (25x36cm-10x14in) i.d.1934 verso prov. 17-Feb-4 John Moran, Pasadena #13/R est:2000-3000
£3495	$6500	€5103	Hills near San Diego Gorge (38x51cm-15x20in) s. i.verso canvasboard. 6-Mar-4 Harvey Clar, Oakland #1584
£3529	$6000	€5152	Old river bed (46x61cm-18x24in) s. i.verso prov. 18-Nov-3 John Moran, Pasadena #16 est:4000-6000
£4762	$9000	€6953	Evening light on Morongo Mts at Palm Springs (61x76cm-24x30in) s. i. verso canvasboard. 17-Feb-4 John Moran, Pasadena #111a/R est:6000-9000

FRIES, Ernst (1801-1833) German

£14085	$24366	€20000	Landscape near Massa (23x17cm-9x7in) panel. 13-Dec-3 Lempertz, Koln #18/R est:10000

FRIES, Hans (c.1460-1518) Swiss

£25000	$46000	€38000	Holy Family (26x18cm-10x7in) panel prov.lit. 24-Jun-4 Christie's, Paris #39/R est:8000-12000

FRIES, Pia (1955-) Swiss

£2000	$3660	€3000	Peder (65x80cm-26x31in) s.i.d.1999 verso panel. 4-Jun-4 Lempertz, Koln #141/R est:3000

FRIES, Wilhelm (1819-1878) German

£699	$1203	€1000	Lower alpine landscape in Bavaria with view of the high mountains (36x42cm-14x17in) s.d.1845 prov. 5-Dec-3 Ketterer, Munich #9/R
£2215	$4075	€3300	Tree lined stream in valley (47x62cm-19x24in) s.d.1874. 25-Mar-4 Dr Fritz Nagel, Stuttgart #711/R est:1400

FRIES, Willy (1881-1965) Swiss

£1293	$2315	€1888	Reverence with flowers (40x54cm-16x21in) mono. s.i.d.1972 verso panel lit. 14-May-4 Dobiaschofsky, Bern #215/R est:3800 (S.FR 3000)

FRIESEKE, Frederick Carl (1874-1939) American

£3727	$6000	€5441	Beach study (51x61cm-20x24in) s. 20-Aug-3 James Julia, Fairfield #1345a/R est:10000-20000
£73864	$130000	€107841	Luxembourg Gardens (66x81cm-26x32in) s.d.1901 prov. 19-May-4 Sotheby's, New York #28/R est:40000-60000
£186047	$320000	€271629	Woman seated in park with basket (73x92cm-29x36in) s.d.1921 prov. 4-Dec-3 Christie's, Rockefeller NY #61/R est:300000-500000

FRIESZ, Émile Othon (1879-1949) French

£1056	$1827	€1500	Portrait d'homme barbu a la pipe (30x24cm-12x9in) board. 14-Dec-3 St-Germain-en-Laye Encheres #72/R est:1500
£1333	$2453	€2000	Ville au crepuscule (24x74cm-9x29in) s. panel painted c.1901-1902. 11-Jun-4 Pierre Berge, Paris #218/R est:2000-2500
£1400	$2562	€2100	Village with church (46x38cm-18x15in) bears sig. board prov. 5-Jun-4 Lempertz, Koln #722/R est:2000
£1573	$2675	€2250	Bretagne (50x41cm-20x16in) s.i. painted c.1893-1896 exhib. 18-Nov-3 Pierre Berge, Paris #93/R est:3000-4500

£1608 $2734 €2300 View between two palm trees of bathing beach (40x50cm-16x20in) s. panel. 21-Nov-3 Reiss & Sohn, Konigstein #12/R est:2000
£2098 $3566 €3000 Jeune femme assise (92x73cm-36x29in) s.d.1942. 28-Nov-3 Blanchet, Paris #114/R est:3000-4000
£2254 $3899 €3200 Anemones au gobelet blanc (41x33cm-16x13in) s. 10-Dec-3 Rossini, Paris #74/R
£2448 $4161 €3500 Groupe de personnages dans un paysage du midi (39x49cm-15x19in) st.sig. 18-Nov-3 Pierre Berge, Paris #65/R est:3400-3600
£2649 $4954 €4000 Cote rocheuse (39x47cm-15x19in) mono. panel. 24-Jul-4 Thierry & Lannon, Brest #208 est:4000-6000
£2657 $4571 €3800 Paysage de Rocca spartera, Italie (54x65cm-21x26in) s.i.d.1920 prov.lit. 3-Dec-3 Fraysse & Associes, Paris #106/R est:4000-6000
£2980 $5454 €4500 Landscape (46x38cm-18x15in) s.d.40. 7-Apr-4 Piasa, Paris #80/R est:3000-4000
£3020 $5618 €4500 La bastide au soleil (65x54cm-26x21in) s.d.24. 2-Mar-4 Artcurial Briest, Paris #128 est:3500-4000
£3077 $5231 €4400 Park (46x38cm-18x15in) s. 28-Nov-3 Drouot Estimations, Paris #167/R est:3500-4000
£3125 $5219 €4500 Saint-Malo, le Grand Bee (65x82cm-26x32in) s. s.i.d.1937 verso. 21-Oct-3 Artcurial Briest, Paris #182/R est:5000-6000
£3476 $6500 €5075 Estuaire de Honfleur (37x46cm-15x18in) init.i.d.48 verso. 25-Feb-4 Christie's, Rockefeller NY #26/R est:6000-8000
£3514 $6500 €5130 Dragon dans les fleurs (38x46cm-15x18in) s. prov. 11-Feb-4 Sotheby's, New York #28/R est:8000-12000
£3521 $6092 €5000 La fontaine du jardin (81x65cm-32x26in) s. painted c.1922. 10-Dec-3 Remi Ader, Paris #58/R est:5000-7000
£3521 $6092 €5000 La fontaine du jardin (81x65cm-32x26in) s. painted c.1922 lit. 10-Dec-3 Neret-Minet, Paris #58/R est:5000-7000
£3759 $6277 €5300 Femme endormie (54x65cm-21x26in) s.d.1927. 15-Oct-3 Neret-Minet, Paris #21
£3873 $6701 €5500 Bouquet de fleurs (65x81cm-26x32in) s. 9-Dec-3 Chambelland & Giafferi, Paris #50/R est:10000-12000
£3946 $7063 €5800 Port de Toulon (38x46cm-15x18in) s. 19-Mar-4 Millon & Associes, Paris #107/R est:3000-4000
£4027 $7369 €6000 Repos du guerrier (46x61cm-18x24in) s. prov.exhib. 7-Jul-4 Artcurial Briest, Paris #83/R est:4000-6000
£4225 $7014 €6000 Paysage aux cypres (46x55cm-18x22in) s. 11-Jun-3 Delorme & Bocage, Paris #60/R est:6000-8000
£4225 $7310 €6000 Baigneuses (92x73cm-36x29in) s.d.1922 exhib. 10-Dec-3 Neret-Minet, Paris #52 est:6000-8000
£4225 $7310 €6000 Baigneuses (92x73cm-36x29in) s.d.1922 exhib. 10-Dec-3 Remi Ader, Paris #52 est:6000-8000
£4324 $8000 €6313 Nature morte avec statuette de porcelaine (54x65cm-21x26in) s. prov. 11-Feb-4 Sotheby's, New York #31/R est:10000-15000
£5467 $9785 €8200 St-Malo (65x81cm-26x32in) s.d.34. 16-May-4 Thierry & Lannon, Brest #141/R est:9000-10000
£5594 $9510 €8000 Honfleur, l'avant port (65x81cm-26x32in) s. s.d.1938 verso. 28-Nov-3 Blanchet, Paris #109/R est:6000-8000
£5903 $9858 €8500 Nature morte a la cafetiere (60x73cm-24x29in) s. painted c.1950 exhib.lit. 21-Oct-3 Artcurial Briest, Paris #183/R est:8000-9000
£5986 $9697 €8500 Peches et raisins sur une table (60x73cm-24x29in) s.d.1929 prov. 5-Aug-3 Tajan, Paris #5/R est:9000-12000
£6164 $10479 €9000 Port (54x65cm-21x26in) s.d.1947. 9-Nov-3 Eric Pillon, Calais #124/R
£6486 $12000 €9470 Port de La Rochelle (65x81cm-26x32in) s. 11-Feb-4 Sotheby's, New York #25/R est:15000-20000
£6667 $12267 €10000 Honfleur (54x65cm-21x26in) s. prov. 14-Jun-4 Tajan, Paris #52/R est:10000-12000
£6711 $12013 €10000 Bassin du port (65x81cm-26x32in) s. 30-May-4 Eric Pillon, Calais #38/R
£7042 $12183 €10000 Pommier en fleurs (65x81cm-26x32in) s. exhib. 12-Dec-3 Piasa, Paris #117/R est:12000-18000
£7333 $13493 €11000 Baigneuses dans un paysage (65x81cm-26x32in) s.d.1943 verso prov.lit. 8-Jun-4 Artcurial Briest, Paris #159/R est:7000-9000
£8000 $14480 €11680 Le Jura (65x53cm-26x21in) s. 1-Apr-4 Christie's, Kensington #25/R est:3000-4000
£8219 $13973 €12000 Paysage de Provence (65x54cm-26x21in) s.d.1930. 9-Nov-3 Eric Pillon, Calais #130/R
£8451 $14620 €12000 Baigneuses (60x73cm-24x29in) s.d.23 i.d.verso. 10-Dec-3 Claude Boisgirard, Paris #38/R est:12000-15000
£9130 $16709 €13330 Village (65x82cm-26x32in) s. 4-Jun-4 Zofingen, Switzerland #2456/R est:20000 (S.FR 21000)
£10500 $19110 €15330 Le port de Toulon (65x82cm-26x32in) s. painted c.1925 prov. 4-Feb-4 Sotheby's, London #324/R est:8000-12000
£10884 $19483 €16000 Port de Fecamp (66x82cm-26x32in) s. 19-Mar-4 Millon & Associes, Paris #108/R est:7000-8000
£11173 $20000 €16313 Labour (45x50cm-18x20in) s. s.i.verso prov.exhib.lit. 6-May-4 Sotheby's, New York #438/R est:25000-35000
£12000 $21840 €17520 La haute ecole du cirque medrano (65x81cm-26x32in) s.d.1909 s.i.d.stretcher prov. 4-Feb-4 Sotheby's, London #237/R est:15000-20000
£12000 $22080 €17520 La fenetre sur le port de Toulon (81x65cm-32x26in) s.d.27 prov. 23-Jun-4 Christie's, London #187/R est:15000-20000
£13000 $23920 €18980 Le port de La Rochelle (51x72cm-20x28in) s.d.48 init.i.d. stretcher prov. 23-Jun-4 Christie's, London #142/R est:10000-15000
£13333 $24533 €20000 Paysage de la Creuse (62x81cm-24x32in) s.indis.d. painted c.1903. 9-Jun-4 Le Roux & Morel, Paris #29/R est:6000-8000
£22346 $40000 €32625 Untitled (15x22cm-6x9in) st.sig. panel prov. 6-May-4 Sotheby's, New York #286/R est:12000-18000
£28000 $51520 €40880 Baigneuses (82x67cm-32x26in) s.d.09 exhib.lit. 23-Jun-4 Christie's, London #178/R est:25000-35000
£32000 $58240 €46720 Anvers (38x46cm-15x18in) s. painted c.1906 prov.exhib.lit. 3-Feb-4 Christie's, London #185/R est:25000-35000
£42000 $77280 €63000 Port d'Anvers (33x41cm-13x16in) s. 9-Jun-4 Le Roux & Morel, Paris #30/R est:20000-25000

Works on paper
£282 $487 €400 Nu assis (50x61cm-20x24in) s. sanguine. 10-Dec-3 Millon & Associes, Paris #33/R
£336 $628 €500 Nu debout (43x27cm-17x11in) s. chl prov. 29-Feb-4 Versailles Encheres #135/R
£470 $874 €700 Vendeur de cidre a Falaise (15x20cm-6x8in) s.i.d.93 ink W/C. 7-Mar-4 Lesieur & Le Bars, Le Havre #60
£490 $832 €700 Entree du Port de Honfleur (33x50cm-13x20in) st.sig. pencil. 29-Nov-3 Villa Grisebach, Berlin #546/R
£833 $1317 €1200 Leda and the swan (32x51cm-13x20in) s. W/C lit. 19-Sep-3 Schloss Ahlden, Ahlden #1653/R
£894 $1600 €1305 Vase of flowers (33x25cm-13x10in) s. W/C gouache. 11-Jan-4 William Jenack, New York #110 est:2000-3000
£979 $1664 €1400 Etude de nu assis (44x32cm-17x13in) s. chl sanguine. 20-Nov-3 Gioffredo, Nice #12/R
£1042 $1740 €1500 Nu allonge (19x27cm-7x11in) s. chl red chk exec. c.1930. 21-Oct-3 Christie's, Paris #64/R est:200-300
£1333 $2453 €2000 Detente a la campagne (23x19cm-9x7in) s. gouache W/C. 9-Jun-4 Oger, Dumont, Paris #56/R est:2200-3000
£2797 $4811 €4000 Forest and hill landscape (37x51cm-15x20in) s. W/C pencil. 2-Dec-3 Sotheby's, Amsterdam #83/R est:4000-6000
£5594 $9622 €8000 Provencal landscape (36x25cm-14x10in) st.sig. W/C. 2-Dec-3 Hauswedell & Nolte, Hamburg #187/R est:4000
£5986 $10356 €8500 Paris, Notre-Dame (49x64cm-19x25in) s. W/C prov. 10-Dec-3 Claude Boisgirard, Paris #11/R est:3000-4000

FRIESZ, Emile Othon (attrib) (1879-1949) French
£330 $562 €482 Ferme bretonne (24x32cm-9x13in) i. board. 5-Nov-3 Dobiaschofsky, Bern #575/R (S.FR 750)
£514 $873 €750 Le port de la Rochelle au clair de lune (50x98cm-20x39in) s. panel. 8-Nov-3 Gerard, Besancon #68

FRIFARARE, Arne (1956-) Swedish
Works on paper
£586 $1037 €856 Seeking contact (60x60cm-24x24in) s. mixed media panel. 27-Apr-4 AB Stockholms Auktionsverk #1047/R (S.KR 8000)

FRIGERIO, Raffaele (19th C) Italian
£426 $750 €622 Italian fishermen (41x29cm-16x11in) pair. 23-May-4 Bonhams & Butterfields, Los Angeles #7061/R
£780 $1232 €1139 Lighting grandfather's pipe (28x38cm-11x15in) s. painted c.1880. 27-Apr-3 Desmond Judd, Cranbrook #1066

FRIIO, Rino (20th C) Canadian
£498 $831 €727 Umbrellas James Joyce (56x48cm-22x19in) s.i.d.2002. 17-Nov-3 Hodgins, Calgary #203/R est:700-900 (C.D 1100)
£680 $1244 €993 Streetscape (90x60cm-35x24in) s.d.2002. 1-Jun-4 Hodgins, Calgary #191/R (C.D 1700)

FRIIS, Eleonora (?) Danish
£1533 $2836 €2238 Still life of roses and branches of oak on tree trunk (53x66cm-21x26in) indis.init. i.verso. 15-Mar-4 Rasmussen, Vejle #198/R est:20000 (D.KR 17000)

FRIIS, Erling (1913-) Danish
£395 $672 €577 Seascape with Ceres off Kronborg (50x70cm-20x28in) s.d.1935. 29-Nov-3 Rasmussen, Havnen #2347/R (D.KR 4200)

FRIIS, Hans Gabriel (1838-1892) Danish
£332 $531 €485 Woodland with bridge (28x41cm-11x16in) s.d.1885. 22-Sep-3 Rasmussen, Vejle #348/R (D.KR 3500)
£422 $725 €616 Woodland road with beechtrees, spring (33x52cm-13x20in) s.d.1889. 3-Dec-3 Museumsbygningen, Copenhagen #221 (D.KR 4500)
£556 $1000 €812 View of rooftops in Rome (19x36cm-7x14in) i. verso paper on canvas. 24-Apr-4 Rasmussen, Havnen #2049 (D.KR 6200)
£561 $886 €813 Fjord landscape, sunset (37x53cm-15x21in) mono.d.1863. 2-Sep-3 Rasmussen, Copenhagen #1894 (D.KR 6000)
£719 $1337 €1050 Horse and cart by farmhouse in a Danish summer landscape (40x63cm-16x25in) s.d.1863. 2-Mar-4 Rasmussen, Copenhagen #1380/R (D.KR 8000)
£5957 $11139 €8697 Landscape from Kjaerstrup, morning fog, late summer (108x160cm-43x63in) s.d.1871. 25-Feb-4 Museumsbygningen, Copenhagen #190/R est:15000-25000 (D.KR 66000)

FRILLI, Antonio (19/20th C) Italian
Sculpture
£8000 $13600 €11680 Native American girl in boat (52x78cm-20x31in) s.i. marble. 28-Oct-3 Sotheby's, London #191/R

FRILLI, Gallerio (20th C) Italian
Sculpture
£1316 $2421 €2000 Young female nude with wrap (74cm-29in) s. alabaster. 24-Jun-4 Credit Municipal, Paris #74/R est:550-650

FRINK, Elizabeth (1930-1993) British
£440 $801 €642 Portrait of a woman (46x66cm-18x26in) s.d.8/48. 30-Jun-4 Neal & Fletcher, Woodbridge #266

Prints
£2200 $3872 €3212 Wild boar (77x59cm-30x23in) s. lithograph exec. 1967. 18-May-4 Woolley & Wallis, Salisbury #47/R est:1000-1500
£2200 $4026 €3212 Horse and rider V (58x78cm-23x31in) s.num.62/70 col lithograph. 3-Jun-4 Christie's, Kensington #358/R est:1400-1600

Sculpture
£3488 $6000 €5092 Portrait of head of Benjamin Bernstein (41cm-16in) s. num.2 dark brown pat bronze incl blk slate base prov. 7-Dec-3 Freeman, Philadelphia #47 est:2000-3000
£4500 $7155 €6570 Phoenix (28cm-11in) s.num.8/10 bronze. 10-Sep-3 Sotheby's, Olympia #345/R est:4000-6000
£6800 $11696 €9928 Maquette for the Alcock and Brown Memorial (40cm-16in) Clay wood. 2-Dec-3 Bonhams, New Bond Street #181/R est:800-1200
£7000 $12040 €10220 Bird (51cm-20in) s. num 4/7 black pat bronze. 2-Dec-3 Bonhams, New Bond Street #178/R est:5000-7000
£7500 $12900 €10950 New bird II (39cm-15in) s. num 5/6 brown pat bronze. 2-Dec-3 Bonhams, New Bond Street #177/R est:5000-7000
£10000 $18300 €14600 Small bird I (30cm-12in) s. num.9/9 pat bronze lit. 2-Jun-4 Sotheby's, London #136/R est:6000-8000
£12000 $20640 €17520 Harbinger bird IV (19cm-7in) s. num 9/9 bronze brown pat. 2-Dec-3 Bonhams, New Bond Street #176/R est:10000-15000
£13000 $22100 €18980 Running man II (36cm-14in) s. num.7/8 light brown pat. bronze conceived 1976 lit. 21-Nov-3 Christie's, London #163/R est:8000-12000

£13000	$22360	€18980	New bird I (56cm-22in) s.num 5/6 brown pat bronze lit. 2-Dec-3 Bonhams, New Bond Street #190/R est:10000-15000
£17000	$31110	€24820	Bird (40cm-16in) s. pat bronze lit. 2-Jun-4 Sotheby's, London #137/R est:10000-15000
£28000	$49280	€40880	Childhood (29cm-11in) s. num.40/50 bronze lit. 18-May-4 Woolley & Wallis, Salisbury #383/R est:12000-15000
£38000	$69540	€55480	Man running II (38cm-15in) s. num.8/8 pat bronze lit. 2-Jun-4 Sotheby's, London #139/R est:8000-12000
£44000	$74800	€64240	Goggled head II - teeth (61cm-24in) s.num.4/6 brown pat. bronze polished glasses conceived 1969 lit. 21-Nov-3 Christie's, London #164/R est:30000-50000
£48000	$87840	€70080	Sentinel (129cm-51in) s. num.1/4 pat bronze prov.lit. 2-Jun-4 Sotheby's, London #135/R est:15000-20000
£55000	$93500	€80300	Standing dog (112cm-44in) s.num.3/8 brown pat. bronze, conceived 1980. 21-Nov-3 Christie's, London #178/R est:40000-60000
£55000	$94600	€80300	Horse and rider (34cm-13in) s. num.A/C mid-brown pat bronze exec 1974 prov.lit. 3-Dec-3 Sotheby's, London #97/R est:25000-35000
£60000	$102000	€87600	Eagle (44x117cm-17x46in) s.num.4/5 grey green pat. bronze conceived 1962 prov.lit. 21-Nov-3 Christie's, London #165/R est:50000-80000
£70000	$128100	€102200	Lying down horse (18x38cm-7x15in) s. num.3/9 pat bronze prov.lit. 2-Jun-4 Sotheby's, London #138/R est:20000-30000
£75000	$137250	€109500	Rolling over horse (35cm-14in) s.num.2/9 brown pat. bronze lit. 4-Jun-4 Christie's, London #151/R est:30000-50000
£90000	$164700	€131400	In memoriam I (127cm-50in) s.num.A/C green grey pat bronze prov.lit. 4-Jun-4 Christie's, London #150/R est:80000-120000
£92000	$158240	€134320	Easter Head I (49cm-19in) s.num.2/6 col pat bronze exec 1989 prov.exhib.lit. 3-Dec-3 Sotheby's, London #98/R est:30000-40000
£110000	$187000	€160600	In memoriam II (127cm-50in) s.num.A/C green pat. bronze conceived 1981 prov.lit. 21-Nov-3 Christie's, London #177/R est:80000-120000

Works on paper

£1000	$1630	€1450	Eagle, Corbez (65x49cm-26x19in) s.i.d.65 W/C exhib. 23-Sep-3 Bonhams, Leeds #89/R est:1000-1500
£1100	$1936	€1606	Cat. Study of a male nude (76x46cm-30x18in) s.d.55 pen ink W/C double-sided. 19-May-4 Sotheby's, Olympia #262/R est:1000-1500
£1500	$2685	€2190	Eagle (65x49cm-26x19in) s.i.d.65 W/C. 14-May-4 Christie's, Kensington #576/R est:1500-2000
£1648	$3000	€2406	Study of a horse (77x57cm-30x22in) s.i.d.80 pencil prov. 29-Jun-4 Sotheby's, New York #543/R est:2500-3500
£1700	$2839	€2482	Kestrel (58x78cm-23x31in) s.d.67 W/C wash. 21-Oct-3 Bonhams, Knightsbridge #9/R est:1200-1800
£1800	$3276	€2628	Bird (72x54cm-28x21in) s.d.67 W/C chl. 1-Jul-4 Christie's, Kensington #265/R est:2000-3000
£2600	$4576	€3796	Couple dancing. Female nude (56x38cm-22x15in) s.d.55 pen ink W/C double-sided. 19-May-4 Sotheby's, Olympia #261/R est:1000-1500
£2900	$5104	€4234	Horse's head (63x48cm-25x19in) s.d.88 chl gouache. 18-May-4 Woolley & Wallis, Salisbury #49/R est:2000-2500
£3297	$6000	€4814	Boar (77x58cm-30x23in) s.d.67 W/C gouache. 29-Jun-4 Sotheby's, New York #542/R est:5000-7000
£3800	$6346	€5548	Seabird (58x79cm-23x31in) s.d.67 W/C. 14-Oct-3 Sotheby's, London #537/R est:3000-5000
£4200	$7434	€6132	Horse and rider (55x74cm-22x29in) s.d.67 pencil wash. 28-Apr-4 George Kidner, Lymington #204/R est:4000-6000
£4800	$8016	€7008	Sea eagle (65x50cm-26x20in) s. W/C. 14-Oct-3 Sotheby's, London #539/R est:3000-5000
£8200	$14678	€11972	Swan (67x100cm-26x39in) s.d.85 pencil. 16-Mar-4 Bonhams, New Bond Street #95/R est:3000-5000
£11000	$18700	€16060	Horse (70x99cm-28x39in) s.d.84 pencil lit. 21-Nov-3 Christie's, London #154/R est:5000-8000
£11000	$18920	€16060	Seated nude (99x71cm-39x28in) s.d.90 W/C gouache blk chk. 3-Dec-3 Sotheby's, London #100/R est:4000-6000
£13000	$23660	€18980	Horse (56x78cm-22x31in) s.d.77 pencil W/C prov. 15-Jun-4 Bonhams, New Bond Street #116/R est:4000-6000

FRIPP, Alfred Downing (1822-1895) British

£2400	$4440	€3504	Hallowed relic (33x48cm-13x19in) s.d.1847. 14-Jan-4 Lawrence, Crewkerne #1409/R est:800-1200

Works on paper

£2400	$4080	€3504	Pompeii, Italy (344x240cm-135x94in) s.i. pencil W/C. 20-Nov-3 Christie's, London #123/R est:2000-3000

FRIPP, George Arthur (1813-1896) British

Works on paper

£320	$573	€467	Wading across a river (24x34cm-9x13in) W/C. 25-May-4 Bonhams, Knightsbridge #246a
£450	$828	€657	Figures on a rural track (22x28cm-9x11in) s.d.1836 W/C. 22-Jun-4 Bonhams, Knightsbridge #168c/R
£550	$919	€803	View through a wooded landscape (15x23cm-6x9in) s.d.1836 pencil W/C exhib. 16-Oct-3 Christie's, Kensington #106/R
£550	$1018	€803	Cattle grazing by Streatley on Thames (10x18cm-4x7in) s. W/C. 10-Mar-4 Sotheby's, Olympia #64/R
£800	$1456	€1168	Clouds descending over the valley (34x48cm-13x19in) s.i.d.1857 pencil W/C scratching out prov. 1-Jul-4 Christie's, Kensington #125
£1400	$2380	€2044	Woman and her donkey resting in an extensive landscape (29x49cm-11x19in) s. W/C prov. 4-Nov-3 Bonhams, New Bond Street #89/R est:1200-1800
£1450	$2552	€2117	View at Dilsa (35x52cm-14x20in) pencil W/C from a sketch by R Peyton. 19-May-4 Dreweatt Neate, Newbury #5/R est:1800-2200
£1500	$2805	€2250	Fishing for salmon under the Three Sisters, Glencoe (29x49cm-11x19in) s. W/C pencil. 26-Jul-4 Bonhams, Bath #4/R est:1000-1500
£2143	$3879	€3129	Dorset landscape (35x63cm-14x25in) s. W/C. 30-Mar-4 Peter Webb, Auckland #124/R est:6000-8000 (NZ.D 6000)
£2200	$3674	€3212	View of a lock (35x50cm-14x20in) s.d.1848 W/C. 14-Oct-3 Bonhams, Knightsbridge #162/R est:1000-1500
£2200	$3740	€3212	On the banks of Loch Tay (32x49cm-13x19in) s.i. W/C prov. 4-Nov-3 Bonhams, New Bond Street #87/R est:1500-2000
£2200	$3740	€3212	On the river Dee (34x60cm-13x24in) W/C prov. 4-Nov-3 Bonhams, New Bond Street #88/R est:1500-2000
£2300	$4232	€3358	Eel traps on the Thames (25x35cm-10x14in) s. W/C prov. 8-Jun-4 Bonhams, New Bond Street #55/R est:1500-2000
£2400	$4416	€3504	Haymaking at Sonning (21x34cm-8x13in) s.i.d.1866 W/C prov. 8-Jun-4 Bonhams, New Bond Street #56/R est:1000-1500
£2600	$4758	€3796	Nant Ffancon, North Wales - Sunrise (35x50cm-14x20in) s. pencil W/C bodycol scratching out prov.exhib.lit. 3-Jun-4 Christie's, London #17/R est:3000-5000
£2800	$4760	€4088	View of Finchale Priory on the River Wear (35x51cm-14x20in) pencil W/C gum arabic htd bodycol scratching prov. 20-Nov-3 Christie's, London #86/R est:2000-3000
£4500	$8100	€6570	Loch Awe with Kilchurn Castle (33x59cm-13x23in) s.d.1853 pencil W/C prov. 21-Apr-4 Tennants, Leyburn #925/R est:1500-2000

FRIPP, Innes (fl.1893-1904) British

Works on paper

£450	$819	€657	Rocky coastal scene (53x76cm-21x30in) s.d.1921. 16-Jun-4 John Nicholson, Haslemere #641

FRIS, Jan (1627-1672) Dutch

£17000	$31110	€24820	Vanitas still life (138x115cm-54x45in) s.d.1670 prov.lit. 7-Jul-4 Christie's, London #48/R est:20000-30000

FRISCH, Johann Christoph (1738-1815) German

£500	$850	€730	Horse and cart leaving a busy town via a stone bridge (50x75cm-20x30in) intaglio sig. 1-Dec-3 Bonhams, Bath #98

FRISCHE, Heinrich Ludwig (1831-1901) German

£979	$1664	€1400	Deer at dawn (53x79cm-21x31in) s. 20-Nov-3 Van Ham, Cologne #1588/R est:1400
£5245	$8916	€7500	Near Cuxhafen in the evening (69x107cm-27x42in) s. 20-Nov-3 Van Ham, Cologne #1587/R est:4000

FRISHMUTH, Harriet Whitney (1880-1980) American

Sculpture

£3798	$6800	€5545	Nude dancer, The Star (51cm-20in) s.d.1918 green pat bronze. 8-Jan-4 James Julia, Fairfield #711/R est:2000-4000
£5435	$10000	€7935	Desha (36cm-14in) s.d.1927 brown pat. bronze st.f. Gorham prov. 8-Jun-4 Bonhams & Butterfields, San Francisco #4046/R est:10000-15000
£5793	$9500	€8400	Crest of the wave (56cm-22in) s.d.1925 green brown pat bronze marble base st.f.Gorham Co. prov. 31-May-3 Brunk, Ashville #430/R est:3000-6000
£7182	$13000	€10486	Desha (34cm-13in) s.d.1927 green brown pat bronze marble base st.f.Gorham. 31-Mar-4 Sotheby's, New York #114/R est:10000-15000
£7735	$14000	€11293	Star (49cm-19in) s.d.1918 num.153 red brown pat bronze st.f.Gorham. 31-Mar-4 Sotheby's, New York #115/R est:8000-12000
£7784	$13000	€11365	The star (49cm-19in) s.d.1918 num.229 brown pat bronze st.f.Gorham lit. 9-Oct-3 Christie's, Rockefeller NY #27/R est:10000-15000
£8840	$16000	€12906	Pushing man and pushing woman (20cm-8in) s.d.1912 red brown pat bronze bookends pair st.f.Gorham. 31-Mar-4 Sotheby's, New York #123/R est:7000-10000
£9091	$16000	€13273	Vine (30cm-12in) i.d.1921 st.f.Gorham Co green pat bronze inc. blk marble bas lit. 18-May-4 Christie's, Rockefeller NY #86/R est:20000-30000
£9140	$17000	€13344	Crest of the wave (53cm-21in) s.d.1925 bronze black plinth base st.f.Gorham. 5-Mar-4 Skinner, Boston #396/R est:6000-8000
£9392	$17000	€13712	Allegra (30cm-12in) s. blue green pat bronze marble base st.f.Roman Bronze prov. 31-Mar-4 Sotheby's, New York #120/R est:8000-12000
£10180	$17000	€14863	The vine (30cm-12in) s.d.1921 brown pat bronze black marble base st.f.Gorham lit. 9-Oct-3 Christie's, Rockefeller NY #64/R est:15000-25000
£11364	$20000	€16591	Crest of the wave (53cm-21in) i.d.1925 brown green pat bronze blk marble past prov. 19-May-4 Sotheby's, New York #139/R est:20000-30000
£11602	$21000	€16939	Extase (49cm-19in) s.d.1920 red verdigris pat bronze st.f.Gorham prov. 31-Mar-4 Sotheby's, New York #122/R est:12000-18000
£11724	$19579	€17000	Crest of the wave (148cm-58in) i. polychrome pat bronze. 13-Nov-3 Neumeister, Munich #185/R est:22000-25000
£13174	$22000	€19234	Crest of the wave (55cm-22in) s.d.1925 green brown pat bronze black marble base lit. 9-Oct-3 Christie's, Rockefeller NY #28/R est:12000-18000
£13174	$22000	€19234	Desha (37cm-15in) s.d.1927 green brown pat bronze black marble base st.f.Gorham lit. 9-Oct-3 Christie's, Rockefeller NY #38/R est:10000-15000
£13529	$23000	€19752	Crest of the wave (51cm-20in) s.d.1925 brown pat. bronze marble plinth prov. 21-Nov-3 Skinner, Boston #402/R est:15000-25000
£14365	$26000	€20973	Slavonic dancer (32cm-13in) s.d.1921 red brown pat bronze marble base st.f.Roman Bronze prov. 31-Mar-4 Sotheby's, New York #124/R est:7000-10000
£14371	$24000	€20982	Laughing waters (42cm-17in) s.d.1929 green brown pat bronze black marble base st.f.Gorham lit. 9-Oct-3 Christie's, Rockefeller NY #26/R est:10000-15000
£15341	$27000	€22398	Play Days (56cm-22in) green brown pat bronze. 3-Jan-4 Brunk, Ashville #655/R est:12000-18000
£15625	$27500	€22813	Laughing waters (41cm-16in) i.d.1929 blue green pat bronze blk marble base prov. 19-May-4 Sotheby's, New York #149/R est:15000-25000
£18466	$32500	€26960	Thread of life (30cm-12in) i. yellow green pat bronze Cast Gorham Co prov. 19-May-4 Sotheby's, New York #148/R est:15000-25000
£19337	$35000	€28232	Rhapsody (30cm-12in) s.d.1925 gree pat bronze marble base st.f.Gorham. 31-Mar-4 Sotheby's, New York #121/R est:12000-18000
£19886	$35000	€29034	Figure of a young girl (41cm-16in) i.d.1929 golden brown pat bronze blk marble base prov. 19-May-4 Sotheby's, New York #162/R est:15000-25000
£21307	$37500	€31108	Playdays - A fountain (56cm-22in) i.d.1925 green pat bronze Cast Gorham Co. 19-May-4 Sotheby's, New York #137/R est:20000-30000
£21307	$37500	€31108	Little Goddess of Happiness (33cm-13in) i.d.1926 golden brown pat bronze blk marble base prov. 19-May-4 Sotheby's, New York #138/R est:20000-30000
£25132	$47500	€36693	Pas de deux (69cm-27in) s.d.1921 bronze marble socle prov. 17-Feb-4 John Moran, Pasadena #28/R est:20000-30000
£26989	$47500	€39404	Dancers (41x69cm-16x27in) i.d.1921 dark brown pat bronze blk marble base prov. 19-May-4 Sotheby's, New York #160/R est:20000-30000
£28743	$48000	€41965	Dream days (46cm-18in) s.d.1939 green brown pat black marble base st.f.Roman Bronze prov. 9-Oct-3 Christie's, Rockefeller NY #65/R est:25000-35000
£30233	$52000	€44140	Fantaisie (26cm-10in) i.d.1922 pat bronze lit. 4-Dec-3 Christie's, Rockefeller NY #84/R est:20000-30000
£71856	$120000	€104910	Crest of the wave (168cm-66in) bronze fountain. 14-Nov-3 Du Mouchelle, Detroit #2022/R est:60000-80000
£73864	$130000	€107841	Playdays - a fountain (132cm-52in) i.d.1925 base weathered green pat bronze. 19-May-4 Sotheby's, New York #150/R est:60000-90000
£87209	$150000	€127325	Joy of the waters (160cm-63in) i.d.1917 pat bronze prov.lit. 4-Dec-3 Christie's, Rockefeller NY #59/R est:120000-180000

FRISK, Guy (1934-) Finnish

£450	$836	€670	Geometric still life (60x72cm-24x28in) s.d.67. 7-Mar-4 Bukowskis, Helsinki #321/R

FRISON, Jehan (1882-1961) Belgian

£263	$476	€400	La cote Belge vue du large (40x55cm-16x22in) s. 19-Apr-4 Horta, Bruxelles #385
£299	$500	€437	Still life, Faience jug filled with flowers (51x61cm-20x24in) s. 14-Nov-3 Aspire, Cleveland #51

£342	$582	€500	Nature morte aux poissons (50x60cm-20x24in) s.d.1960. 10-Nov-3 Horta, Bruxelles #498
£578	$1052	€850	Le tarte aux prunes (58x69cm-23x27in) s.d.1942 mono.i.verso canvasboard. 3-Feb-4 Christie's, Amsterdam #471/R
£638	$1066	€900	Nature morte sur Samovar et aux fleurs (50x60cm-20x24in) s. 17-Jun-3 Galerie Moderne, Brussels #180/R
£979	$1635	€1400	L'equipement du peintre (60x69cm-24x27in) s.d.1942. 7-Oct-3 Palais de Beaux Arts, Brussels #561/R
£1600	$2864	€2400	Still life (60x70cm-24x28in) s.d.1942 canvas on board. 15-May-4 De Vuyst, Lokeren #139/R est:2800-3300

FRISSEN, Willy (?) ?

£336	$601	€500	Seascape (60x50cm-24x20in) s. 25-May-4 Durán, Madrid #671/R

FRISTON, William (19th C) British

£680	$1258	€993	View from Hapmstead looking towards Harrow on the Hill (20x25cm-8x10in) s.d.1883. 9-Mar-4 Gorringes, Lewes #2293

FRISTROM, Claus Eduard (1864-1942) Swedish

£2347	$3825	€3427	Wellington Harbour (22x32cm-9x13in) s. board. 23-Sep-3 Peter Webb, Auckland #26/R est:9000-12000 (NZ.D 6500)

FRISTROM, Oscar (1856-1918) Swedish/Australian

£846	$1581	€1235	Catchpenny (29x20cm-11x8in) s.i.d.1910 canvasboard. 24-Feb-4 Peter Webb, Auckland #171/R (NZ.D 2300)

FRISTRUP, Niels (1837-1909) Danish

£2804	$4430	€4066	Landscape from Strandmolle river with water lilies and reeds (66x80cm-26x31in) 2-Sep-3 Rasmussen, Copenhagen #1607/R est:30000 (D.KR 30000)
£4500	$7200	€6525	San Giorgio Maggiore seen from the Piazzetta, Venice (106x79cm-42x31in) s.d.1878. 18-Sep-3 Christie's, Kensington #73/R est:5000-7000

FRITH, Francis (1822-1898) American?

Photographs

£26000	$45760	€37960	Egypt. album prints album lit. 19-May-4 Christie's, London #108/R est:25000-35000

FRITH, William Powell (1819-1909) British

£1000	$1840	€1500	Evening disturbance (45x35cm-18x14in) s. panel. 11-Jun-4 Hauswedell & Nolte, Hamburg #1021/R est:2500
£1400	$2212	€2030	Dolly Varden (18x13cm-7x5in) s. panel. 4-Sep-3 Christie's, Kensington #243/R est:800-1200
£1900	$3496	€2774	Honeywood introducing the bailiffs as his friend (17x24cm-7x9in) s.d.1850 board. 8-Jun-4 Holloways, Banbury #264/R est:2000-3000
£3200	$5056	€4640	Scene from Le Bourgeois Gentihomme (23x30cm-9x12in) s.d.1862. 4-Sep-3 Christie's, Kensington #242/R est:3000-5000
£12000	$21840	€17520	Crossing sweeper (43x36cm-17x14in) s.d.1893 prov. 16-Jun-4 Bonhams, New Bond Street #35/R est:15000-20000
£13500	$24570	€19710	Green parrot (61x51cm-24x20in) init. prov. 16-Jun-4 Bonhams, New Bond Street #36/R est:10000-15000
£35000	$64400	€51100	Hope (84x76cm-33x30in) s. prov.exhib.lit. 11-Jun-4 Christie's, London #184/R est:35000-45000

FRITH, William Powell (attrib) (1819-1909) British

£850	$1590	€1275	Girl with flowers (25x20cm-10x8in) panel. 26-Jul-4 Bonhams, Bath #74/R
£4000	$7400	€5840	Portrait of a lady (26x20cm-10x8in) board. 10-Mar-4 Sotheby's, Olympia #181/R est:800-1200

FRITZ, Andreas (1828-1906) Danish

£777	$1244	€1134	View towards Aarhus from Moesgaard (89x83cm-35x33in) s.d.1905. 22-Sep-3 Rasmussen, Vejle #333/R (D.KR 8200)
£2120	$3604	€3095	The garden of Hvirring Vicarage with the artist's sister sewing (55x75cm-22x30in) s.d.1867. 10-Nov-3 Rasmussen, Vejle #122/R est:6000-8000 (D.KR 23000)

FRITZ, Max (1849-?) German

Works on paper

£322	$547	€460	Different views (52x41cm-20x16in) s.i.d.1893 W/C collage of paintings. 28-Nov-3 Wendl, Rudolstadt #3968/R

FRITZ, Max (attrib) (1849-?) German

£361	$600	€527	Farmyard (46x56cm-18x22in) init.d.93 verso. 4-Oct-3 Skinner, Boston #359/R

FRITZEL, Wilhelm (1870-1943) German

£333	$603	€500	Lower Rhine landscape in late summer (50x60cm-20x24in) s. 1-Apr-4 Van Ham, Cologne #1386
£400	$728	€600	Summer day, view of a village (51x60cm-20x24in) s. 1-Jul-4 Van Ham, Cologne #1355
£833	$1392	€1200	Cows in extensive country landscape with stream (53x74cm-21x29in) s. lit. 25-Oct-3 Bergmann, Erlangen #940/R
£972	$1604	€1400	Hay harvest in extensive landscape (61x80cm-24x31in) s. 3-Jul-3 Van Ham, Cologne #1195

FRITZSCHE, Marcus (19th C) German

Sculpture

£1611	$2964	€2400	Dancing Bacchus (76cm-30in) s. dark pat.bronze Cast.Oscar Gladenbeck and Co, Friedrichshagen. 25-Mar-4 Dr Fritz Nagel, Stuttgart #948/R est:1500

FRITZVOLD, Reidar (1920-1998) Norwegian

£258	$451	€377	Jetty (38x46cm-15x18in) s.d.52 s.i.d.verso panel. 16-Dec-3 Grev Wedels Plass, Oslo #156 (N.KR 3000)
£313	$542	€457	Light in forest (41x33cm-16x13in) s. panel. 13-Dec-3 Blomqvist, Lysaker #1101 (N.KR 3600)
£464	$811	€677	Autumn morning by Bossvatn, Bykle in Setesdal (46x53cm-18x21in) s.d.64 s.i.d.verso panel. 16-Dec-3 Grev Wedels Plass, Oslo #155/R (N.KR 5400)
£563	$1030	€822	The bridge across Fjelldalsbekken (46x38cm-18x15in) s. panel. 2-Feb-4 Blomqvist, Lysaker #1071 (N.KR 7000)
£601	$1052	€877	In the birch forest (81x63cm-32x25in) s. s.i.d.66 verso. 16-Dec-3 Grev Wedels Plass, Oslo #157/R (N.KR 7000)
£698	$1118	€1012	Winter's day (73x92cm-29x36in) s. 22-Sep-3 Blomqvist, Lysaker #1063/R (N.KR 8200)
£714	$1313	€1042	Winter in Bykleheiene, Setesdal (81x100cm-32x39in) s. 29-Mar-4 Blomqvist, Lysaker #1074/R (N.KR 9000)
£1334	$2229	€1948	Near Valle, Setesdal (75x101cm-30x40in) s. panel. 17-Nov-3 Blomqvist, Lysaker #1074/R est:12000-15000 (N.KR 16000)

FRIZE, Bernard (1949-) French

£4076	$7500	€5951	Lucky XVI (41x62cm-16x24in) s.i.d.2000 verso acrylic resin prov. 10-Jun-4 Phillips, New York #459/R est:3000-4000
£11173	$20000	€16313	Normale (162x130cm-64x51in) i.d.1998 verso acrylic resin prov.lit. 14-May-4 Phillips, New York #129/R est:6000-8000
£14130	$26000	€20630	Oreiller III, pillow III (237x237cm-93x93in) acrylic resin ink mother of pearl prov. 10-Jun-4 Phillips, New York #411/R est:10000-15000
£21229	$38000	€30994	Darche (162x148cm-64x58in) s.i.d.2003 overlap acrylic resin prov. 14-May-4 Phillips, New York #131/R est:6000-8000

Works on paper

£914	$1527	€1315	Exploits Martiaux (55x76cm-22x30in) s.i.d.1982 W/C mixed media. 21-Oct-3 Artcurial Briest, Paris #567/R est:1000-1200
£5328	$8418	€7779	Untitled, Detail No 1 (160x140cm-63x55in) i. verso synthetic polymer prov. 2-Sep-3 Deutscher-Menzies, Melbourne #114/R est:15000-20000 (A.D 13000)

FRIZZELL, Dick (1943-) New Zealander

£521	$828	€761	No. bigger than a shoebox (11x15cm-4x6in) s.i.d.21/11/93. 1-May-3 Dunbar Sloane, Wellington #132 est:1100-1800 (NZ.D 1500)
£1159	$1971	€1692	Still life with ukulele and pineapple juice (22x24cm-9x9in) s.i.d.8/9/78. 4-Nov-3 Peter Webb, Auckland #181/R est:2000-3000 (NZ.D 3200)
£2054	$3779	€2999	Crying boy, Bruce Wayne as a child (49x39cm-19x15in) s.d.1977 enamel board. 25-Mar-4 International Art Centre, Auckland #35/R est:4000-6000 (NZ.D 5750)
£2054	$3779	€2999	Murdered partnts (49x39cm-19x15in) s.d.1977 enamel board. 25-Mar-4 International Art Centre, Auckland #36/R est:4000-6000 (NZ.D 5750)
£2143	$3943	€3129	Guardian Angel of angry lions (33x32cm-13x13in) s.d.1979 board prov. 25-Mar-4 International Art Centre, Auckland #32/R est:5000-7000 (NZ.D 6000)
£2500	$4525	€3650	Autumn trees, Hastings (43x50cm-17x20in) s.d.30.6.87 board. 30-Mar-4 Peter Webb, Auckland #16/R est:7000-9000 (NZ.D 7000)
£2766	$4896	€4038	My brother Bill (75x56cm-30x22in) s.d.13.9.84 oil paper. 28-Apr-4 Dunbar Sloane, Auckland #47/R est:5000-8000 (NZ.D 7800)
£4286	$7757	€6258	Detail from fresh is best (43x39cm-17x15in) s.i.d.12/9/81 enamel on board prov. 30-Mar-4 Peter Webb, Auckland #55/R est:12000-18000 (NZ.D 12000)
£4666	$8352	€6812	Here I don't thank Beckmann so much as just use him! (67x58cm-26x23in) s.i. enamel on board prov. 12-May-4 Dunbar Sloane, Wellington #31/R est:15000-25000 (NZ.D 13480)
£5000	$9050	€7300	Shinto urns (50x60cm-20x24in) s.i.d.20/6/90. 30-Mar-4 Peter Webb, Auckland #54/R est:14000-18000 (NZ.D 14000)
£5536	$10020	€8083	Still life with jug, green pepper, parsley and tomato (34x39cm-13x15in) s.i.d.28.9.83 prov. 30-Mar-4 Peter Webb, Auckland #31/R est:9000-12000 (NZ.D 15500)
£5714	$10514	€8342	Pukeko's by a pond. s.i.d.1990 prov. 25-Mar-4 International Art Centre, Auckland #17/R est:15000-20000 (NZ.D 16000)
£6134	$10550	€8956	Screen stars (62x77cm-24x30in) s.i.d.76 prov. 3-Dec-3 Dunbar Sloane, Auckland #22/R est:10000-15000 (NZ.D 16500)
£7857	$14457	€11471	Street sleeping men (103x118cm-41x46in) s.d.6/11/1979 board prov. 25-Mar-4 International Art Centre, Auckland #37/R est:20000-30000 (NZ.D 22000)
£10638	$18830	€15531	Who will save her (50x50cm-20x20in) s.d.20/2/2001 triptych. 28-Apr-4 Dunbar Sloane, Auckland #22/R est:20000-30000 (NZ.D 30000)
£14894	$26362	€21745	Female phantom (151x181cm-59x71in) s.i.d.9/5/99. 28-Apr-4 Dunbar Sloane, Auckland #28/R est:30000-40000 (NZ.D 42000)

FRIZZELL, Otis (20th C) New Zealander

£519	$929	€758	Hannya 2 (240x120cm-94x47in) s.d.2000 spray enamel on board. 11-May-4 Peter Webb, Auckland #165/R est:2000-3000 (NZ.D 1500)

FROBERG, Maja (1866-1962) Swedish

£613	$1098	€895	Northern landscape with cabins in evening sunshine (65x202cm-26x80in) s. 28-May-4 Uppsala Auktionskammare, Uppsala #218/R (S.KR 8300)

FRODMAN-CLUZEL, Boris (1878-?) Swedish/Russian

Sculpture

£1931	$3534	€2800	Danseuse (16cm-6in) green pat bronze. 31-Jan-4 Gerard, Besancon #244
£2692	$4631	€3930	Girl dancing (41cm-16in) s.i.d.1912 bronze incl. stone socle. 3-Dec-3 AB Stockholms Auktionsverk #2646/R est:6000-8000 (S.KR 35000)
£3310	$6058	€4800	Danseuse (14cm-6in) green pat bronze. 31-Jan-4 Gerard, Besancon #243

FRODMAN-CLUZEL, Boris (attrib) (1878-?) Swedish/Russian

Sculpture

£3615	$6218	€5278	Seated girl with guitar (38cm-15in) init.d.00 dark pat.bronze Cast Hebrand cire perdue. 3-Dec-3 AB Stockholms Auktionsverk #2644/R est:12000-15000 (S.KR 47000)

FROGNER, Dag (1929-) Norwegian

£339	$587	€495	Summer (100x80cm-39x31in) s. 13-Dec-3 Blomqvist, Lysaker #1103/R (N.KR 3900)

FROHLICH, Bernard (1823-1885) Austrian

£567	$1031	€850	Fishermen sorting their nets (29x37cm-11x15in) s. 1-Jul-4 Van Ham, Cologne #1356

FROHLICH, Fritz (1910-) Austrian
£4333 $7757 €6500 Composition (110x100cm-43x39in) s.d.1978 i. stretcher. 13-May-4 Dorotheum, Linz #523/R est:9000-11000
Works on paper
£414 $757 €600 Untitled (31x29cm-12x11in) s.d.82 mixed media. 27-Jan-4 Dorotheum, Vienna #231/R

FROHLICH, Leopold (1873-1946) Austrian
£497 $909 €750 Leda et le cygne (50x40cm-20x16in) s. 7-Apr-4 Piasa, Paris #55

FROHLICH, Otto (1869-?) German
£694 $1132 €1000 Temptation of the hermits (140x170cm-55x67in) mono. 26-Sep-3 Bolland & Marotz, Bremen #534/R

FROHNER, Adolf (1934-) German
£6294 $10699 €9000 The Three Graces (99x80cm-39x31in) s. prov. 26-Nov-3 Dorotheum, Vienna #319/R est:9000-12000
Works on paper
£1103 $2019 €1600 Untitled (100x70cm-39x28in) s.d.72 graphite prov. 27-Jan-4 Dorotheum, Vienna #199/R est:1800-2600
£17361 $29514 €25000 Crucifixion (200x300cm-79x118in) s.d.77 mixed media canvas exhib.lit. 28-Oct-3 Wiener Kunst Auktionen, Vienna #264/R est:25000-40000

FROIDEVAUX, Roger Paul (1918-1998) Swiss
£362 $626 €529 Village mediterraneen (38x46cm-15x18in) s.indis.d. 12-Dec-3 Galerie du Rhone, Sion #491 (S.FR 800)

FROLICH, Lorenz (1820-1908) Danish
£269 $491 €393 Mythological scene with angels making music (13x24cm-5x9in) 7-Jun-4 Museumsbygningen, Copenhagen #93/R (D.KR 3000)
£269 $491 €393 Portrait of young woman with brown hair (64x55cm-25x22in) 7-Jun-4 Museumsbygningen, Copenhagen #94 (D.KR 3000)
£299 $473 €434 View across meadows (14x22cm-6x9in) init.i. i.d.1837 verso cardboard. 3-Sep-3 Museumsbygningen, Copenhagen #266 (D.KR 3200)
£299 $473 €434 Coastal meadow at Oresund (17x23cm-7x9in) i.d.1837 verso cardboard. 3-Sep-3 Museumsbygningen, Copenhagen #270 (D.KR 3200)
£299 $473 €434 Nude man seated on stone, woman standing (17x12cm-7x5in) cardboard. 3-Sep-3 Museumsbygningen, Copenhagen #276 (D.KR 3200)
£337 $563 €492 Wooded landscape with deer and kid (34x25cm-13x10in) s.d.1860. 25-Oct-3 Rasmussen, Havnen #2013 (D.KR 3600)
£358 $655 €523 Self-portrait - en face (22x18cm-9x7in) 7-Jun-4 Museumsbygningen, Copenhagen #78 (D.KR 4000)
£358 $655 €523 Self-portrait - en face (22x19cm-9x7in) 7-Jun-4 Museumsbygningen, Copenhagen #92 (D.KR 4000)
£374 $591 €542 Plants in flower bed (14x21cm-6x8in) i.d.1837 verso cardboard. 3-Sep-3 Museumsbygningen, Copenhagen #272 (D.KR 4000)
£374 $591 €542 Cliffs (21x25cm-8x10in) i.d.12 July 45 cardboard. 3-Sep-3 Museumsbygningen, Copenhagen #280 (D.KR 4000)
£374 $591 €542 Portrait of small girl (27x25cm-11x10in) i.verso. 3-Sep-3 Museumsbygningen, Copenhagen #287/R (D.KR 4000)
£394 $721 €575 Ruth and Boas (18x24cm-7x9in) study. 7-Jun-4 Museumsbygningen, Copenhagen #76 (D.KR 4400)
£403 $737 €588 Woman and baby having a rest during the harvest (15x26cm-6x10in) 7-Jun-4 Museumsbygningen, Copenhagen #70/R (D.KR 4500)
£421 $664 €610 Large tree (26x17cm-10x7in) i.d.1837 verso cardboard. 3-Sep-3 Museumsbygningen, Copenhagen #277/R (D.KR 4500)
£467 $738 €677 Autumn study of young woman, France. 3-Sep-3 Museumsbygningen, Copenhagen #257 (D.KR 5000)
£467 $738 €677 Seated blond boy. Studies of cows, horses and figures (20x26cm-8x10in) double-sided. 3-Sep-3 Museumsbygningen, Copenhagen #263 (D.KR 5000)
£467 $738 €677 Coastal meadow at Oresund with rider (15x22cm 6x9in) i.d.1837 verso cardboard. 3-Sep-3 Museumsbygningen, Copenhagen #267 (D.KR 5000)
£467 $738 €677 Woodland meadow with red evening sky (13x21cm-5x8in) i.d.1837 cardboard. 3-Sep-3 Museumsbygningen, Copenhagen #271/R (D.KR 5000)
£533 $842 €773 Winter landscape with fox attacking stag (10x13cm-4x5in) paper on canvas. 3-Sep-3 Museumsbygningen, Copenhagen #273/R (D.KR 5700)
£537 $983 €784 Portrait of Italian boy (41x29cm-16x11in) study. 7-Jun-4 Museumsbygningen, Copenhagen #71/R (D.KR 6000)
£537 $983 €784 Coastal landscape, Oresund (21x28cm-8x11in) 7-Jun-4 Museumsbygningen, Copenhagen #79/R (D.KR 6000)
£561 $886 €813 Self-portrait (38x33cm-15x13in) exec.c.1860. 3-Sep-3 Museumsbygningen, Copenhagen #254/R (D.KR 6000)
£561 $886 €813 Mythological scene with children dancing and young man with dog (27x47cm-11x19in) 3-Sep-3 Museumsbygningen, Copenhagen #301/R (D.KR 6000)
£579 $916 €840 Estuary, Oresund (13x22cm-5x9in) i.d.37 verso cardboard. 3-Sep-3 Museumsbygningen, Copenhagen #275/R (D.KR 6200)
£607 $960 €880 Plants in woodland (14x17cm-6x7in) indis.s.d.38 cardboard. 3-Sep-3 Museumsbygningen, Copenhagen #274 (D.KR 6500)
£627 $1147 €915 Meadow landscape (20x28cm-8x11in) 7-Jun-4 Museumsbygningen, Copenhagen #77/R (D.KR 7000)
£673 $1063 €976 A tree (21x9cm-8x4in) i.d.1837 verso cardboard. 3-Sep-3 Museumsbygningen, Copenhagen #278/R (D.KR 7200)
£716 $1311 €1045 Summer landscape with road (26x34cm-10x13in) 7-Jun-4 Museumsbygningen, Copenhagen #72 (D.KR 8000)
£748 $1181 €1085 Plants and grasses with stone in woodland (15x17cm-6x7in) i.d.37 cardboard. 3-Sep-3 Museumsbygningen, Copenhagen #288 (D.KR 8000)
£841 $1329 €1219 Empire interior with chair covered in blanket (19x19cm-7x7in) cardboard. 3-Sep-3 Museumsbygningen, Copenhagen #283/R (D.KR 9000)
£935 $1477 €1356 Waterway with reeds (27x34cm-11x13in) cardboard. 3-Sep-3 Museumsbygningen, Copenhagen #269 (D.KR 10000)
£985 $1802 €1438 Wolf sleeping (16x29cm-6x11in) mono.i. study. 7-Jun-4 Museumsbygningen, Copenhagen #87/R (D.KR 11000)
£985 $1802 €1438 Gifion - study with two bulls (36x56cm-14x22in) painted c.1880. 7-Jun-4 Museumsbygningen, Copenhagen #88/R (D.KR 11000)
£1028 $1624 €1491 Italian village with brown and white building in landscape (28x40cm-11x16in) init. 3-Sep-3 Museumsbygningen, Copenhagen #286/R (D.KR 11000)
£1028 $1624 €1491 Figure of a blond faun inside large plant, alsation dog by root of plant (36x27cm-14x11in) paper. 3-Sep-3 Museumsbygningen, Copenhagen #304/R (D.KR 11000)
£1121 $1772 €1625 Beech trees in spring (28x31cm-11x12in) i.d.37 verso cardboard. 3-Sep-3 Museumsbygningen, Copenhagen #268 est:2000 (D.KR 12000)
£1121 $1772 €1625 French autumn scene with harvesters resting (21x27cm-8x11in) 3-Sep-3 Museumsbygningen, Copenhagen #285/R est:10000-12000 (D.KR 12000)
£1121 $1772 €1625 Still life of carrots, leeks and cabbage on kitchen floor, rat in background (28x36cm-11x14in) s.d.1877. 3-Sep-3 Museumsbygningen, Copenhagen #293/R est:10000-15000 (D.KR 12000)
£1215 $1920 €1762 Large tree (26x20cm-10x8in) i.d.1837 verso. 3-Sep-3 Museumsbygningen, Copenhagen #279/R est:8000-10000 (D.KR 13000)
£1253 $2294 €1829 Two goats (22x23cm-9x9in) 7-Jun-4 Museumsbygningen, Copenhagen #89/R est:18000 (D.KR 14000)
£1402 $2215 €2033 Hilly coastal landscape with girl walking, France (30x45cm-12x18in) 3-Sep-3 Museumsbygningen, Copenhagen #284/R est:10000-12000 (D.KR 15000)
£1432 $2621 €2091 L fontaine de Jouvance (23x40cm-9x16in) 7-Jun-4 Museumsbygningen, Copenhagen #90/R est:20000-25000 (D.KR 16000)
£1449 $2289 €2101 Portrait of young Italian girl with head dress (29x22cm-11x9in) cardboard. 3-Sep-3 Museumsbygningen, Copenhagen #290/R est:5000 (D.KR 15500)
£1589 $2510 €2304 Italian peasants on country road (48x37cm-19x15in) painted c.1850. 3-Sep-3 Museumsbygningen, Copenhagen #296/R est:15000-20000 (D.KR 17000)
£1791 $3277 €2615 From Marina Piccola, Capri (27x40cm-11x16in) mono.d.48. 7-Jun-4 Museumsbygningen, Copenhagen #100/R est:15000 (D.KR 20000)
£2059 $3768 €3006 Italian boy sleeping (45x55cm-18x22in) study. 7-Jun-4 Museumsbygningen, Copenhagen #69/R est:6000-8000 (D.KR 23000)
£2149 $3932 €3138 Group portrait of Lorenz Frolich, his wife and baby daughter (100x81cm-39x32in) mono.i.d.1860. 7-Jun-4 Museumsbygningen, Copenhagen #85/R est:20000-30000 (D.KR 24000)
£2430 $3839 €3524 Self-portrait (46x34cm-18x13in) cardboard painted c.1860. 3-Sep-3 Museumsbygningen, Copenhagen #295/R est:6000-8000 (D.KR 26000)
£3271 $5168 €4743 Portrait of the artist's second wife Benedicte Frolich (60x44cm-24x17in) painted c.1878. 3-Sep-3 Museumsbygningen, Copenhagen #292/R est:40000-60000 (D.KR 35000)
£5192 $9502 €7580 Wild plants and trees by water (18x24cm-7x9in) mono.d.31 juli 1844. 7-Jun-4 Museumsbygningen, Copenhagen #75/R est:6000 (D.KR 58000)
£6446 $11796 €9411 Studies of a model, heads of men, clouds and figures. Reclining model (92x73cm-36x29in) double-sided. 7-Jun-4 Museumsbygningen, Copenhagen #84/R est:20000-30000 (D.KR 72000)
Works on paper
£280 $443 €406 French suburban garden (27x23cm-11x9in) i.verso W/C. 3-Sep-3 Museumsbygningen, Copenhagen #256 (D.KR 3000)
£561 $886 €813 Small boy marching with dog by his side (12x11cm-5x4in) W/C pen sketch of two children verso. 3-Sep-3 Museumsbygningen, Copenhagen #302/R (D.KR 6000)

FROLICH, Lorenz (attrib) (1820-1908) Danish
£361 $667 €527 Adam and Eve (83x60cm-33x24in) 15-Mar-4 Rasmussen, Vejle #223/R (D.KR 4000)

FROLICHER, Otto (1840-1890) Swiss
£325 $581 €475 Landscape study with cornfield (34x45cm-13x18in) mono. canvas on board. 22-Mar-4 Philippe Schuler, Zurich #4324 (S.FR 750)
£702 $1172 €1025 Landscape with girl resting by stream (26x22cm-10x9in) mono. prov. 15-Nov-3 Galerie Gloggner, Luzern #50/R (S.FR 1600)
£1256 $2097 €1834 Path through forest clearing (45x60cm-18x24in) mono. 24-Oct-3 Hans Widmer, St Gallen #131/R est:1400-3200 (S.FR 2800)
£1293 $2315 €1888 Small landscape (20x35cm-8x14in) mono. board. 17-May-4 Beurret, Zurich #26/R est:2000-3000 (S.FR 3000)
£1316 $2197 €1921 Landscape near Solothurn (38x63cm-15x25in) prov. 15-Nov-3 Galerie Gloggner, Luzern #51/R est:3800-4500 (S.FR 3000)
£1638 $2932 €2391 Rocky landscape (47x56cm-19x22in) mono. board exhib. 17-May-4 Beurret, Zurich #23/R est:2500-3500 (S.FR 3800)
£1724 $3086 €2517 Mountain river (70x105cm-28x41in) s. 14-May-4 Dobiaschofsky, Bern #10/R est:7000 (S.FR 4000)
£1724 $3086 €2517 Birch trees near Solothurn (45x58cm-18x23in) mono. board. 14-May-4 Dobiaschofsky, Bern #30/R est:6000 (S.FR 4000)
£1724 $3086 €2517 Woodland (33x47cm-13x19in) i. paper on board lit. 17-May-4 Beurret, Zurich #27/R est:3000-4000 (S.FR 4000)
£1940 $3472 €2832 Willow tree trunk (36x24cm-14x9in) mono. canvas on board lit. 17-May-4 Beurret, Zurich #24/R est:2500-3000 (S.FR 4500)
£1940 $3472 €2832 Hillock in field (30x45cm-12x18in) mono. board lit. 17-May-4 Beurret, Zurich #28/R est:3000-4000 (S.FR 4500)
£2036 $3258 €2973 Storm gathering over wooded landscape (64x53cm-25x21in) s. 16-Sep-3 Philippe Schuler, Zurich #3234/R est:4000-6000 (S.FR 4500)
£2069 $3703 €3021 Aare landscape with poplars (29x46cm-11x18in) s. board. 17-May-4 Beurret, Zurich #25/R est:3000-4000 (S.FR 4800)
£3534 $6327 €5160 Landscape with shepherdess (75x100cm-30x39in) s.d.1878. 14-May-4 Dobiaschofsky, Bern #32/R est:7000 (S.FR 8200)
£19397 $34720 €28320 Gathering storm (73x104cm-29x41in) s. prov.lit. 17-May-4 Beurret, Zurich #29/R est:20000-30000 (S.FR 45000)

FROLOV, Youri (1925-) Russian
£280 $510 €409 Portrait of a fisherman (35x24cm-14x9in) s. board painted 1960. 20-Jun-4 Lots Road Auctions, London #375/R
£300 $546 €438 In the artist's studio (49x70cm-19x28in) s. board painted 1974. 20-Jun-4 Lots Road Auctions, London #367/R
£350 $637 €511 On the beach (40x50cm-16x20in) s. board painted c.1960. 20-Jun-4 Lots Road Auctions, London #360/R
£350 $637 €511 Model (50x70cm-20x28in) s. board painted 1964. 20-Jun-4 Lots Road Auctions, London #366/R
£450 $819 €657 Green Dress (48x37cm-19x15in) s. board painted 1950. 20-Jun-4 Lots Road Auctions, London #358/R

FROMANGER, Gerard (1939-) French
£4730 $8324 €7000 Orange (200x250cm-79x98in) s.i.d.1989 verso acrylic prov.exhib. 18-May-4 Tajan, Paris #123/R est:8000-10000

FROMENT-MEURICE (19/20th C) French
Sculpture
£165517 $276414 €240000 Baccant (100x39cm-39x15in) s.d.1851 ivory silver bronze prov. 15-Nov-3 Porro, Milan #169/R est:200000
£168966 $282172 €245000 Venus (100x39cm-39x15in) s.d.1851 ivory silver bronze marble base prov. 15-Nov-3 Porro, Milan #170/R est:200000

FROMENTIN, Eugène (1820-1876) French

£805 $1490 €1200 En priere (29x11cm-11x4in) mono. canvas on panel. 15-Mar-4 Horta, Bruxelles #412
£5245 $9021 €7500 Vue de Donzere (14x32cm-6x13in) s.i.d.1866 oil paper on panel. 3-Dec-3 Oger, Dumont, Paris #84/R est:3000
£5263 $9684 €8000 Depart pour la chasse (37x30cm-15x12in) s. panel. 22-Jun-4 Ribeyre & Baron, Paris #37/R est:10000-12000
£6250 $10000 €9125 Warriors on horseback (38x43cm-15x17in) s. prov. 20-Sep-3 Sloans & Kenyon, Bethesda #1181/R est:12000-15000
£14118 $24000 €20612 Halte de muletiers, Algerie (46x55cm-18x22in) s.d.68 panel prov.exhib.lit. 29-Oct-3 Christie's, Rockefeller NY #166/R est:12000-18000
£14894 $24872 €21000 Campement dans le desert (48x95cm-19x37in) s. 16-Jun-3 Gros & Delettrez, Paris #404/R est:12000-20000
£16667 $30501 €25000 Cavaliers au bord d'une mare (40x31cm-16x12in) s.d.73 panel. 3-Jun-4 Tajan, Paris #259/R est:30000-40000
Works on paper
£800 $1472 €1200 Cavalier et son faucon (4x14cm-2x6in) crayon. 14-Jun-4 Gros & Delettrez, Paris #41/R
£2007 $3472 €2850 Le bivouac a In-Ousera (26x43cm-10x17in) st.i.d.27 mai chl estompe. 12-Dec-3 Renaud, Paris #73 est:2000
£2113 $3655 €3000 Le bivouac du Rocher de Sel (26x42cm-10x17in) studio st.i.d.29 mai chl estompe. 12-Dec-3 Renaud, Paris #72/R est:3000
£3472 $5660 €5000 Depart pour la chasse au faucon (44x36cm-17x14in) W/C. 26-Sep-3 Millon & Associes, Paris #60

FROMENTIN, Eugène (attrib) (1820-1876) French

Works on paper
£699 $1189 €1000 Cavalier arabe (20x26cm-8x10in) bears sig. pen Indian ink gouache. 26-Nov-3 Daguerre, Paris #51

FROMKES, Maurice (1872-?) American

£1506 $2500 €2199 Young girl with doll (61x46cm-24x18in) s.d.17. 4-Oct-3 Neal Auction Company, New Orleans #575/R est:3000-5000
£2805 $4600 €4067 Portrait of a young girl in an elaborate Oriental style background (69x56cm-27x22in) s. prov. 31-May-3 Brunk, Ashville #539/R est:1500-2500

FROMMEL, Carl Ludwig (1789-1863) German

£995 $1593 €1453 Landscape with seated monk and view of monastery (35x28cm-14x11in) s.d.1833 panel. 16-Sep-3 Philippe Schuler, Zurich #3329/R est:2000-2500 (S.FR 2200)
Works on paper
£811 $1427 €1200 Villa Sommariva on Lake Como (28x38cm-11x15in) s.d.9 Sept/1846 pencil wash htd white board. 22-May-4 Lempertz, Koln #1412/R
£1419 $2497 €2100 Como (28x38cm-11x15in) s.d.11/Sept 1846 pencil htd white board. 22-May-4 Lempertz, Koln #1411/R est:1300

FROMUTH, Charles Henry (1861-1937) American

Works on paper
£629 $1176 €950 Depart des sardinieres, Concarneau (23x31cm-9x12in) s. chl. 24-Jul-4 Thierry & Lannon, Brest #39
£1017 $1800 €1485 Sailboats at rest (36x30cm-14x12in) s.d.1906 pastel. 2-May-4 Grogan, Boston #81/R
£4085 $7148 €5800 Voiles (73x45cm-29x18in) s. pastel. 21-Dec-3 Thierry & Lannon, Brest #87/R est:6000-8000

FROND, Victor (19th C) ?

Prints
£1923 $3404 €2885 Panorama of Rio de Janeiro (41x49cm-16x19in) lithograph W/C. 27-Apr-4 Bolsa de Arte, Rio de Janeiro #1/R (B.R 10500)
£1923 $3404 €2885 Panorama of Sacco do Alferes (34x49cm-13x19in) lithograph W/C. 27-Apr-4 Bolsa de Arte, Rio de Janeiro #4/R (B.R 10500)
£2015 $3566 €3023 Panorama of Rio de Janeiro, bay entrance (40x48cm-16x19in) lithograph W/C. 27-Apr-4 Bolsa de Arte, Rio de Janeiro #2/R (B.R 11000)

FRONIUS, Hans (1903-1988) Austrian

£10067 $18020 €15000 Toledo (51x70cm-20x28in) s.d.78 s.i.d. stretcher prov. 25-May-4 Dorotheum, Vienna #260/R est:14000-20000
£10738 $19007 €16000 St Denis (60x54cm-24x21in) mono.d. s.i.d.1982 verso panel. 28-Apr-4 Wiener Kunst Auktionen, Vienna #201/R est:10000-18000
Works on paper
£336 $601 €500 Winter landscape (38x52cm-15x20in) s.d.55 chl. 27-May-4 Dorotheum, Graz #141/R
£352 $616 €500 River in winter (39x49cm-15x19in) s.d.73 black chk. 19-Dec-3 Dorotheum, Vienna #302/R
£390 $651 €550 Portrait of Gerhard Hauptmann (42x30cm-17x12in) s.d.72 chl. 16-Oct-3 Dorotheum, Salzburg #1044/R
£493 $863 €700 ETA Hoffmann (26x19cm-10x7in) s.i.d.76 pencil pen brush ink. 19-Dec-3 Dorotheum, Vienna #301/R
£629 $1070 €900 Hugo Wolf (29x20cm-11x8in) s.i. ink. 27-Nov-3 Dorotheum, Linz #634/R

FRONTH, Per (1963-) Norwegian

£1301 $2380 €1899 Landscape from Olavsundet, Ny Hellesund - study I (58x75cm-23x30in) s.i. verso. 7-Jun-4 Blomqvist, Oslo #456/R est:13000-15000 (N.KR 16000)
Works on paper
£1382 $2529 €2018 SALT - genome III -study I (53x76cm-21x30in) s.i. verso mixed media. 7-Jun-4 Blomqvist, Oslo #472/R est:16000-18000 (N.KR 17000)

FROOMAN, Richard (1930-) American

£1371 $2400 €2002 Dave Brubeck Quartet (164x109cm-65x43in) s. painted Feb 1965. 17-Dec-3 Christie's, Rockefeller NY #96/R est:2000-3000
£2400 $4200 €3504 Duke Ellington (109x81cm-43x32in) s. painted 1965. 17-Dec-3 Christie's, Rockefeller NY #97/R est:2500-3500

FROSCHL, Carl (1848-1934) Austrian

Works on paper
£628 $1125 €930 Portrait of Crown Princess Stephanie von Habsburg (71x52cm-28x20in) s. pastel. 6-May-4 Michael Zeller, Lindau #666/R

FROSCHL, Daniel (attrib) (1563-1613) German

Works on paper
£1701 $3044 €2500 Le Jugement de Paris (20x30cm-8x12in) pen grey ink wash htd white. 18-Mar-4 Christie's, Paris #190/R est:2500-3500

FROST, Anthony (1951-) British

£650 $1203 €949 Shown mercy (69x58cm-27x23in) i.verso. 10-Feb-4 David Lay, Penzance #464

FROST, Arthur Burdett (1851-1928) American

Works on paper
£645 $1200 €942 Cape Breton folk (37x29cm-15x11in) s.d.1885 i.verso gouache grisaille. 5-Mar-4 Skinner, Boston #305/R
£838 $1500 €1223 All paint and no engine (20x15cm-8x6in) s.d.1913 pen ink W/C. 15-May-4 Illustration House, New York #55/R est:900-1200
£3073 $5500 €4487 Posing a young subject for photograph (15x10cm-6x4in) s. pen ink three book illustration. 15-May-4 Illustration House, New York #147/R est:1500-2000
£11976 $20000 €17485 Successful bearhunters with quarry (36x41cm-14x16in) s. W/C lit. 15-Nov-3 Illustration House, New York #11/R est:22000-28000

FROST, Cyril James (18/19th C) British

£290 $531 €423 Country scene with trees and a farmstead (53x66cm-21x26in) s.d.1949. 28-Jul-4 Mallams, Oxford #423

FROST, Denis (?) Irish?

£789 $1453 €1200 Portrait of George Bernard Shaw (14x11cm-6x4in) s. board. 22-Jun-4 De Veres Art Auctions, Dublin #261

FROST, Francis Shedd (1825-1902) American

£8824 $15000 €12883 Mt. Chocorua, New Hampshire (30x50cm-12x20in) s.d.1856. 21-Nov-3 Skinner, Boston #270/R est:800-1200

FROST, John (1890-1937) American

£9497 $17000 €13866 Tranquil reflections (48x58cm-19x23in) s.d.35 d.March 29 1935 verso board prov. 6-May-4 Shannon's, Milford #45/R est:4000-6000
£47418 $80610 €69230 Buckboard and two horses beneath trees against lavender mountains, and sunset (61x71cm-24x28in) s. 21-Nov-3 Eldred, East Dennis #829/R est:8000-10000
£160428 $300000 €234225 Live oaks (81x102cm-32x40in) s.d.1921 prov. 24-Jul-4 Coeur d'Alene, Hayden #75/R est:125000-175000

FROST, Sergius (1900-1994) Danish

£1308 $2249 €1910 The training ship Danmark near Kronborg Palace (70x100cm-28x39in) s.d.1936. 3-Dec-3 AB Stockholms Auktionsverk #2581/R est:10000-12000 (S.KR 17000)

FROST, Terry (1915-2003) British

£800 $1480 €1168 Untitled (13x16cm-5x6in) s. d.93 card. 13-Jul-4 Bonhams, Knightsbridge #63/R
£950 $1758 €1387 Red black (44x33cm-17x13in) s.d.96 oil monotype. 11-Mar-4 Christie's, Kensington #381/R
£1000 $1660 €1460 Abstract (38x55cm-15x22in) s.i. oil pastel. 2-Oct-3 Lane, Penzance #180/R est:500-800
£1600 $2672 €2336 Abstract of coloured circles (39x29cm-15x11in) s.d.87 i.verso. 27-Jun-3 Bigwood, Stratford on Avon #305 est:550-750
£1900 $3173 €2774 Squeeze, red black and white (9x20cm-4x8in) s.i. verso acrylic paper. 16-Oct-3 Christie's, Kensington #713/R est:500-700
£1900 $3401 €2774 Blue, black and purple collage (56x56cm-22x22in) s.d.2001 verso. 14-May-4 Christie's, Kensington #638/R est:2000-3000
£1950 $3374 €2847 Olympic rings in red white and black (22x44cm-9x17in) s.d.1996 acrylic paper. 11-Dec-3 Lane, Penzance #332 est:2000-2500
£2000 $3440 €2920 Spiral (63x63cm-25x25in) s.d.96 overlap. 3-Dec-3 Christie's, Kensington #786/R est:2000-3000
£2200 $3938 €3212 Purple and blue collage (56x56cm-22x22in) s.d.2001 verso. 14-May-4 Christie's, Kensington #640/R est:2000-3000
£2800 $4928 €4088 Blue moon (40x29cm-16x11in) s.d.98 acrylic canvas collage. 19-May-4 Sotheby's, Olympia #286/R est:2500-3500
£3000 $5280 €4380 Still life with flowers (37x33cm-15x13in) init.d.44 s.i.d.verso board. 19-May-4 Sotheby's, Olympia #217/R est:1000-1500
£3000 $5280 €4380 Blue collage (46x46cm-18x18in) s.i.d.2001 overlap s.verso oil canvas collage. 19-May-4 Sotheby's, Olympia #325/R est:3000-5000
£3000 $5460 €4380 Suspended collage (50x40cm-20x16in) s.i.d.May 1967 verso oil collage prov.exhib. 15-Jun-4 Bonhams, New Bond Street #89/R est:3500-4500
£3200 $5504 €4672 Ochre and black collage (56x56cm-22x22in) s.i.overlap s.d.2001 verso oil collage. 3-Dec-3 Christie's, Kensington #788/R est:2000-3000
£3200 $5920 €4672 Squeeze blue (12x40cm-5x16in) s. s.i.d.99 verso acrylic collage. 11-Feb-4 Sotheby's, Olympia #287/R est:2000-3000
£3300 $5907 €4818 Red Movement (24x52cm-9x20in) s.d.99 acrylic collage board. 16-Mar-4 Bonhams, Knightsbridge #67/R est:2000-3000
£3800 $6042 €5548 Five spirals (51x75cm-20x30in) s. acrylic. 10-Sep-3 Sotheby's, Olympia #337/R est:3000-5000
£4000 $7040 €5840 Hearts (26x19cm-10x7in) s.d. canvas collage on painted board. 19-May-4 Sotheby's, Olympia #308/R est:4000-6000
£5200 $9308 €7592 Purple and gold Sun (63x43cm-25x17in) s.d.99 acrylic collage. 16-Mar-4 Bonhams, Knightsbridge #68 est:4000-6000
£7000 $12530 €10220 Sun up (59x59cm-23x23in) prov. 16-Mar-4 Bonhams, New Bond Street #84/R est:4000-6000
£11000 $18920 €16060 Blue sunset (26x36cm-10x14in) board prov. 3-Dec-3 Sotheby's, London #94/R est:3000-5000
£12500 $21250 €18250 Blue and red - harbour (61x76cm-24x30in) s.i.d.54-55 canvasboard prov.exhib. 21-Nov-3 Christie's, London #187/R est:10000-15000
£12500 $22875 €18250 Red midland (183x183cm-72x72in) s. i.d.65 verso. 4-Jun-4 Christie's, London #129/R est:10000-15000

£21000	$37590	€30660	Yellow winter lemon (95x46cm-37x18in) s.i.d.59 verso board. 16-Mar-4 Bonhams, New Bond Street #80/R est:4000-6000
£25000	$45500	€36500	Blue and white figure (106x73cm-42x29in) s.i.d.59 verso oil chl prov.lit. 15-Jun-4 Bonhams, New Bond Street #88/R est:25000-30000
Prints			
£4800	$8736	€7008	Force nine (122x244cm-48x96in) col monotype. 1-Jul-4 Sotheby's, London #331/R est:3000-5000
Works on paper			
£380	$711	€555	Boats before cottages (19x13cm-7x5in) s. pencil exec.c.1949. 26-Feb-4 Lane, Penzance #12
£420	$764	€613	Laced ovals (15x13cm-6x5in) mixed media. 15-Jun-4 David Lay, Penzance #410
£450	$833	€657	Sun and sea (28x26cm-11x10in) s.i.d.1994 col crayon felt tip pen. 11-Mar-4 Christie's, Kensington #383/R
£500	$910	€730	Untitled (8x20cm-3x8in) collage. 15-Jun-4 David Lay, Penzance #411
£700	$1309	€1022	Half study of female nude (15x20cm-6x8in) s. pencil. 26-Feb-4 Lane, Penzance #58
£900	$1683	€1314	Seated female nude (33x20cm-13x8in) s. pencil. 26-Feb-4 Lane, Penzance #57
£1100	$2035	€1606	Leaves in red, blue and yellow (11x145cm-4x57in) gouache sold with two other by same hand three. 13-Jul-4 Bonhams, Knightsbridge #64/R
£1400	$2380	€2044	Abstract in red, white and black (24x34cm-9x13in) d.July 56 pencil W/C. 18-Nov-3 Bonhams, Knightsbridge #80/R est:800-1200
£1450	$2625	€2117	Upstaged III (28x38cm-11x15in) s.d.87 W/C. 16-Apr-4 Keys, Aylsham #533 est:1200-1500
£1700	$2771	€2465	Red, black and white rhythm (26x26cm-10x10in) s.d.95 collage on board exhib. 23-Sep-3 Bonhams, Leeds #126 est:500-700
£1700	$3094	€2482	Challenger (47x76cm-19x30in) s.d.90 pencil W/C. 1-Jul-4 Christie's, Kensington #403/R est:1000-1500
£1800	$3222	€2628	Red and blue collage (70x48cm-28x19in) s.i.d.98 verso gouache collage. 14-May-4 Christie's, Kensington #639/R est:1500-2000
£2000	$3700	€2920	Untitled (41x51cm-16x20in) s.d.65 W/C acrylic. 11-Mar-4 Christie's, Kensington #382/R est:1200-1800
£2000	$3700	€2920	Lemon and black (42x59cm-17x23in) s.d.77 pencil W/C. 11-Mar-4 Christie's, Kensington #384/R est:1000-1500
£2200	$4004	€3212	Bikini study (60x47cm-24x19in) gouache chl collage exec. c.1964 prov. 15-Jun-4 Bonhams, New Bond Street #90/R est:2500-3500
£2720	$4923	€3971	July sun (48x70cm-19x28in) s.d.1984 i.verso W/C collage prov. 1-Apr-4 Heffel, Vancouver #34/R est:7000-9000 (C.D 6500)
£2929	$5301	€4276	Purple for summer (55x76cm-22x30in) s. i.d.1984 verso mixed media collage prov. 1-Apr-4 Heffel, Vancouver #35/R est:7000-9000 (C.D 7000)
£3347	$6059	€4887	II blue, sun moon series, Cyprus, autumn (78x57cm-31x22in) s.i.d.1978 verso mixed media prov. 1-Apr-4 Heffel, Vancouver #33/R est:7000-9000 (C.D 8000)
£3400	$5406	€4964	Black sun (16x40cm-6x16in) s.d.00 mixed media. 10-Sep-3 Sotheby's, Olympia #338/R est:1500-2000
£3600	$6552	€5256	Suspended forms (54x77cm-21x30in) gouache collage. 1-Jul-4 Christie's, Kensington #402/R est:1500-2000
£3600	$6552	€5256	Suspended forms on black (43x58cm-17x23in) s.i.d.1970 verso W/C bodycol collage. 1-Jul-4 Christie's, Kensington #404/R est:1500-2000
£3800	$6688	€5548	Untitled (76x53cm-30x21in) s.i. collage acrylic over lithograph. 19-May-4 Sotheby's, Olympia #285/R est:2000-3000
£4000	$6800	€5840	Red and black for Newlyn (60x44cm-24x17in) s.i.d.98 mixed media collage. 26-Nov-3 Sotheby's, Olympia #166/R est:2000-3000
£4000	$7280	€5840	Lemon glow (51x62cm-20x24in) d.1990 verso gouache collage. 1-Jul-4 Christie's, Kensington #405/R est:1000-1500
£5500	$10175	€8030	Green chord (30x57cm-12x22in) s.i.d.98 verso mixed media collage. 11-Feb-4 Sotheby's, Olympia #286/R est:3000-5000
£6800	$12172	€9928	Long bow (24x76cm-9x30in) s.d.97 verso gouache collage. 16-Mar-4 Bonhams, New Bond Street #83/R est:3000-5000

FROST, William Edward (1810-1877) British

£1600	$2864	€2336	Disarming cupid (9cm-4in circular) i. board prov. 27-May-4 Christie's, Kensington #327/R est:800-1200
£2000	$3440	€2920	Nude lady reclined on a river bank (43x58cm-17x23in) 5-Dec-3 Keys, Aylsham #613/R est:2500-3000
£6000	$10740	€8760	Sea nymph (91x56cm-36x22in) arched top. 27-May-4 Christie's, Kensington #326/R est:5000-8000

FROSTERUS-SALTIN, Alexandra (1837-1916) Finnish

£1733	$3103	€2600	Young lady (40x33cm-16x13in) 15-May-4 Hagelstam, Helsinki #102/R est:700

FROSTERUS-SEGERSTRALE, Hanna (1867-1946) Finnish

Works on paper			
£1088	$1981	€1600	Lady sewing (31x29cm-12x11in) s.d.1903 mixed media. 8-Feb-4 Bukowskis, Helsinki #347/R est:400

FROY, Martin (1926-) British

£550	$880	€803	Standing cubist figure (121x60cm-48x24in) board exhib. 16-Sep-3 Bonhams, Knightsbridge #56/R

FRUEAUF, Rueland (elder-circle) (1440-1507) German

£8000	$14400	€11680	Agony in the garden (38x52cm-15x20in) panel prov.lit. 22-Apr-4 Sotheby's, London #10/R est:8000-12000

FRUGE, Nestor (20th C) American

Works on paper			
£552	$1000	€806	St. Louis Cathedral (38x28cm-15x11in) s. W/C pair. 3-Apr-4 Neal Auction Company, New Orleans #908 est:500-700

FRUH, Eugen (1914-1975) Swiss

Works on paper			
£533	$965	€800	City in winter (61x46cm-24x18in) s. pastel board. 1-Apr-4 Van Ham, Cologne #1387/R

FRUHMANN, Johann (1928-1985) Austrian

£9396	$16631	€14000	Untitled (150x130cm-59x51in) s.d. verso bears i. verso dispersion. 28-Apr-4 Wiener Kunst Auktionen, Vienna #230/R est:14000-18000

FRUHMESSER, Joseph (20th C) German?

£324	$550	€473	German village scene (58x89cm-23x35in) 21-Nov-3 Shelley, Hendersonville #711/R

FRUHTRUNK, Gunther (1923-1983) German

£7383	$13215	€11000	Red and green energy (80x80cm-31x31in) s.i.d.1971 verso acrylic prov. 25-May-4 Sotheby's, Milan #166/R est:3000-4000
£8451	$14620	€12000	Cadenza (71x100cm-28x39in) s.i.d.1982 verso acrylic. 13-Dec-3 Lempertz, Koln #137/R est:8000-10000

FRUMERIE, Agnes de (1869-1937) Swedish

Sculpture			
£1900	$3230	€2774	Female figure (54cm-21in) s. bronze. 2-Nov-3 Lots Road Auctions, London #370 est:600-900

FRUWIRTH, Carl (1810-1878) Austrian

£1552	$2778	€2266	Waiting for the return home (70x88cm-28x35in) s. panel. 13-May-4 Stuker, Bern #143/R est:3000-5000 (S.FR 3600)

FRY, Anthony (1927-) British

Works on paper			
£580	$945	€847	Young girl standing before a kitchen table (41x35cm-16x14in) s. W/C. 24-Sep-3 Dreweatt Neate, Newbury #47/R

FRY, John Hemming (1861-1946) American

£1347	$2250	€1967	Road to the farm (48x64cm-19x25in) s. canvas on masonite. 23-Oct-3 Shannon's, Milford #222/R est:1500-2500

FRY, R Douglas (1872-1911) British

£450	$828	€657	Dachshund in an interior (27x36cm-11x14in) s.d.1891. 10-Jun-4 Christie's, Kensington #429/R
£820	$1419	€1197	Janita - Portrait of a dachsund (25x40cm-10x16in) s.d.1891 sold with companion piece pair. 9-Dec-3 Bonhams, Oxford #95

FRY, Roger (1866-1934) British

£1400	$2464	€2044	French landscape (33x40cm-13x16in) board. 19-May-4 Sotheby's, Olympia #127/R est:1000-1500
£2200	$4070	€3212	Blue pool (72x60cm-28x24in) s. 11-Mar-4 Christie's, Kensington #84/R est:3000-5000
£3200	$5984	€4672	St. Paul's from the Thames (48x59cm-19x23in) s. 21-Jul-4 Bonhams, New Bond Street #174/R est:4000-6000
£6600	$10428	€9570	Still life of bottle, cup and bowl of fruit on a tray (41x31cm-16x12in) prov. 24-Jul-3 Lawrence, Crewkerne #972/R est:2500-3500
Works on paper			
£620	$1110	€905	Roqueburne Alpes (30x20cm-12x8in) pencil W/C. 7-May-4 Mallams, Oxford #161

FRY, Roger (attrib) (1866-1934) British

£1650	$2954	€2409	Continental landscape (30x41cm-12x16in) board. 7-May-4 Mallams, Oxford #335

FRYDENSBERG, Carl (1872-1944) Danish

£312	$558	€456	Portrait of H C Andersen's Muse - Ingeborg Vogt (52x46cm-20x18in) mono.d.29. 12-Jan-4 Rasmussen, Vejle #289/R (D.KR 3300)

FRYDMAN, Maurice (1928-) French

£483	$893	€700	Nu couche dans l'herbe (60x81cm-24x32in) s. panel. 13-Jan-4 Vanderkindere, Brussels #58
£493	$893	€750	Couple (60x60cm-24x24in) s. panel. 19-Apr-4 Horta, Bruxelles #22

FRYDMAN, Monique (20th C) ?

£6333	$11527	€9500	Ivresse de Noe (180x193cm-71x76in) s.i.d.78 acrylic collage. 29-Jun-4 Cornette de St.Cyr, Paris #143/R est:2000-3000

FRYE, Thomas (1710-1762) British

£2600	$4836	€3796	Portrait of Benjamin Day (127x102cm-50x40in) s.d.1753. 4-Mar-4 Christie's, Kensington #339/R est:800-1200
£5800	$10382	€8468	Portrait of Henry Hansons (91x71cm-36x28in) i.verso. 27-May-4 Christie's, Kensington #44/R est:2500-3500
Prints			
£3400	$6256	€4964	Self portrait (50x35cm-20x14in) mezzotint. 28-Jun-4 Bonhams, New Bond Street #36/R est:1000-1500

FRYER, George (1746-1776) Italian

£480	$816	€701	On the French coast (46x77cm-18x30in) s.d.1881. 29-Oct-3 Bonhams, Chester #490a

FRYER, George G (fl.1882) British

£400	$740	€584	Fishing boats on calm seas off the coast at sunset (28x50cm-11x20in) s. 9-Mar-4 Bonhams, Knightsbridge #223/R
£700	$1260	€1022	Coastal scene with figures sorting the days catch (30x50cm-12x20in) s. 21-Apr-4 Tennants, Leyburn #1096

FU BAOSHI (1904-1965) Chinese

Works on paper			
£20077	$33529	€29312	Two ladies (133x67cm-52x26in) i.d.1983 ink col hanging scroll prov. 27-Oct-3 Sotheby's, Hong Kong #286/R est:200000-250000 (HK.D 260000)
£42674	$76814	€62304	Elegant conversation in a mountain pavilion (67x45cm-26x18in) s.i.d.1946 ink col hanging scroll prov.exhib.lit. 26-Apr-4 Sotheby's, Hong Kong #590/R est:600000-800000 (HK.D 600000)
£50193	$83822	€73282	Waterfall in a pine forest (102x29cm-40x11in) s.i.d.1943 ink col hanging scroll. 26-Oct-3 Christie's, Hong Kong #329/R est:200000-250000 (HK.D 650000)
£52510	$87691	€76665	Greeting a friend on the bridge (109x30cm-43x12in) s.i. ink col. 27-Oct-3 Sotheby's, Hong Kong #336/R est:500000-700000 (HK.D 680000)
£73359	$122510	€107104	Drunken monk (31x37cm-12x15in) s.i.d.1945 ink col hanging scroll. 27-Oct-3 Sotheby's, Hong Kong #283/R est:300000-400000 (HK.D 950000)
£77220	$128958	€112741	Lady under a tree (105x41cm-41x16in) s.i.d.1944 ink col scroll. 26-Oct-3 Christie's, Hong Kong #330/R est:1000000-1200000 (HK.D 1000000)
£128023	$230441	€186914	Strolling in spring (133x41cm-52x16in) s.d.1945 ink col exhib. 26-Apr-4 Sotheby's, Hong Kong #648/R est:600000-800000 (HK.D 1800000)
£384068	$691323	€560739	Seven sages (113x67cm-44x26in) s.i.d.1946 ink col hanging scroll prov.exhib.lit. 26-Apr-4 Sotheby's, Hong Kong #584/R est:3500000-5000000 (HK.D 5400000)
£401544	$670579	€586254	Bidding farewell to Shitao (84x58cm-33x23in) s.i.d.1942 ink col hanging scroll exhib. 27-Oct-3 Sotheby's, Hong Kong #262/R est:2000000-3000000 (HK.D 5200000)

FU BAOSHI (attrib) (1904-1965) Chinese

Works on paper			
£743	$1308	€1100	Landscape with scholar (65x29cm-26x11in) s.d.1960 Indian ink col hanging scroll. 21-May-4 Dr Fritz Nagel, Stuttgart #1093/R

FU YAN (19/20th C) Chinese

Works on paper			
£939	$1700	€1371	Landscape with waterfall (196x94cm-77x37in) s.d.1904 ink wash silk. 6-Apr-4 Bonhams & Butterfields, San Francisco #6205/R est:300-500

FUCHS, Bernard (1932-) American

£2793	$5000	€4078	Launch leaving anchored sailing ship (97x56cm-38x22in) init. 15-May-4 Illustration House, New York #43/R est:6000-8000
£5988	$10000	€8742	Statue of Liberty with tall ships passing (102x76cm-40x30in) s. 15-Nov-3 Illustration House, New York #87/R est:7000-10000
Works on paper			
£3911	$7000	€5710	There's nothing like a new car to enjoy a site-seeing tour (33x66cm-13x26in) s. gouache. 15-May-4 Illustration House, New York #45/R est:3000-5000

FUCHS, Daniele (1931-) French

£276	$508	€420	Pension pour petits animaux (81x100cm-32x39in) s. 22-Jun-4 Palais de Beaux Arts, Brussels #244

FUCHS, Emile (1866-1929) Austrian

£363	$650	€530	Head of a woman (61x49cm-24x19in) s.d.1916 panel prov. 14-May-4 Skinner, Boston #326/R
£765	$1300	€1117	Head of a woman (61x50cm-24x20in) panel prov. 21-Nov-3 Skinner, Boston #363/R est:1000-2000
£786	$1250	€1148	Portrait of young woman (77x61cm-30x24in) prov. 12-Sep-3 Skinner, Boston #322/R
£881	$1400	€1286	Portrait of Miss Clements (127x102cm-50x40in) prov. 12-Sep-3 Skinner, Boston #323/R
£1341	$2400	€1958	Interior with two figures, genre scene at a piano (76x62cm-30x24in) panel prov. 14-May-4 Skinner, Boston #331/R est:2500-3500
£1384	$2200	€2021	Portrait of Mrs Nolan (59x40cm-23x16in) s.d.1916 prov. 12-Sep-3 Skinner, Boston #321/R
£2151	$4000	€3140	Portrait of a man (51x30cm-20x12in) s.i.d.1915 panel prov. 5-Mar-4 Skinner, Boston #352/R est:700-900
£2353	$4000	€3435	Standing nudes (190x61cm-75x24in) pair prov. 21-Nov-3 Skinner, Boston #400/R est:1500-3000
£4706	$8000	€6871	Portrait of Forbes Robertson (100x74cm-39x29in) s. prov. 21-Nov-3 Skinner, Boston #365/R est:3000-6000

FUCHS, Ernst (1930-2000) Austrian

£278	$500	€406	Wildflowers (61x51cm-24x20in) s. i.verso board. 26-Jan-4 Schrager Galleries, Milwaukee #1420
£2349	$4299	€3500	Portrait d'un roi (17x9cm-7x4in) s.d.1961 panel. 7-Jul-4 Artcurial Briest, Paris #153 est:2000-2500
£10345	$18931	€15000	Fantasy flowers (60x80cm-24x31in) s.d.1992. 27-Jan-4 Dorotheum, Vienna #259/R est:15000-20000
£11888	$20210	€17000	White negro woman (78x55cm-31x22in) s.d.Juli/August 1968 oil tempera prov. 26-Nov-3 Dorotheum, Vienna #241/R est:16000-22000
Sculpture			
£1000	$1800	€1500	Achilles (13cm-5in) s. dark pat.bronze marble sockle Cast.Venturi-Arte. 21-Apr-4 Dorotheum, Vienna #216/R est:1800-2400
£1119	$1924	€1600	Sphinx (19x35x16cm-7x14x6in) i. num.298/1000 brown pat bronze marble base st.f. Venturi Arte. 4-Dec-3 Van Ham, Cologne #156/R est:1600
£1197	$2071	€1700	Reclining Sphinx (12cm-5in) num.202/299 silver. 10-Dec-3 Hugo Ruef, Munich #2779/R est:1500
£1678	$2887	€2400	Sphinx (12x22cm-5x9in) i. num.187/299 silver marble base exec. 1994 st.f.Sussen. 4-Dec-3 Van Ham, Cologne #155/R est:2200
Works on paper			
£533	$981	€800	Girl's head (30x24cm-12x9in) s.d.72 pencil. 9-Jun-4 Dorotheum, Vienna #108/R
£1467	$2640	€2200	Standing female nude (54x36cm-21x14in) s.d.1961 ochre. 21-Apr-4 Dorotheum, Vienna #177/R est:1200-1800
£2381	$4262	€3476	Woman in Turkish dress (73x46cm-29x18in) s. i. verso pastel chk W/C lit.prov. 22-Mar-4 Philippe Schuler, Zurich #4017/R est:4000-5300 (S.FR 5500)
£4895	$8322	€7000	Death tree (34x20cm-13x8in) W/C. 26-Nov-3 Dorotheum, Vienna #280/R est:3000-5000

FUCHS, Georg Mathias (1719-1797) Austrian

£3581	$6553	€5228	Portrait of baron Reinhard Iselin (78x62cm-31x24in) s.d.1766 lit. 7-Jun-4 Museumsbygningen, Copenhagen #114/R est:30000-40000 (D.KR 40000)

FUCHS, Heinz (1886-?) German

£490	$832	€700	Alpine landscape with lake (26x35cm-10x14in) s. s.d.57 verso. 29-Nov-3 Villa Grisebach, Berlin #777/R

FUCHS, Jacques (1922-1980) Swiss

£308	$524	€450	Algerie (22x41cm-9x16in) s.d.68 i. stretcher. 5-Nov-3 Dobiaschofsky, Bern #577/R (S.FR 700)
£374	$637	€546	Canal St Martin (73x92cm-29x36in) s. i. verso i. stretcher. 5-Nov-3 Dobiaschofsky, Bern #576/R (S.FR 850)

FUCHS, Karl (1836-1886) German

£805	$1506	€1200	Rubain castle near Merano with figures (12x18cm-5x7in) s. i. verso board. 24-Feb-4 Dorotheum, Vienna #54/R

FUCHS, Karl (1872-1968) German

£724	$1332	€1100	View over St Dionys on a spring day (80x60cm-31x24in) s. 25-Jun-4 Michael Zeller, Lindau #631/R

FUCHS, Robert (1896-1981) Austrian

£517	$947	€750	Dream from the Far East (100x70cm-39x28in) s. 27-Jan-4 Dorotheum, Vienna #83/R
£1844	$3079	€2600	Paradise (94x110cm-37x43in) s.d.1952. 14-Oct-3 Dorotheum, Vienna #174/R est:3200-4000

FUCHS, Therese (1849-?) German

£348	$549	€490	Norwegian fjord landscape (52x78cm-20x31in) s. i. verso. 22-Jul-3 Sigalas, Stuttgart #355/R
£497	$904	€750	Extensive Norwegian fjord landscape (70x125cm-28x49in) s.d.1889. 19-Jun-4 Bergmann, Erlangen #820
Works on paper			
£800	$1448	€1200	Winter sun setting over snowy woodland stream (80x120cm-31x47in) s. 1-Apr-4 Van Ham, Cologne #1388

FUCHSEL, Hermann (1833-1915) American

£2232	$3839	€3259	Extensive river landscape with figure nearing chalet (38x74cm-15x29in) s.d.1864 masonite. 2-Dec-3 Ritchie, Toronto #81/R est:6000-8000 (C.D 5000)
£2746	$4750	€4009	Two travellers beneath snowcapped mountains (30x51cm-12x20in) s.i. painted 1874 prov. 10-Dec-3 Bonhams & Butterfields, San Francisco #6002/R est:4000-6000

FUCHSEL, Hermann (attrib) (1833-1915) American

£11413	$21000	€17120	View of Storm King Mountain and Constitution Island with River Hudson (56x112cm-22x44in) 23-Mar-4 American Auctioneer #453755/R

FUEGER, Friedrich Heinrich (1751-1818) German

£300	$501	€438	Whom shall I release unto you? (7x11cm-3x4in) s.i.verso oil on tine. 21-Oct-3 Bruton Knowles, Cheltenham #479
£580	$969	€847	Wild boar hunt (9x13cm-4x5in) s.i.verso oil on tin. 21-Oct-3 Bruton Knowles, Cheltenham #478
Miniatures			
£19000	$32870	€27740	Young lady (7cm-3in) gilt-metal frame oval prov.exhib. 9-Dec-3 Christie's, London #36/R est:10000-15000

FUEGER, Friedrich Heinrich (attrib) (1751-1818) German

Miniatures			
£1208	$2138	€1800	Field Marshall Erzherzog Karl (7cm-3in circular) W/C ivory. 29-Apr-4 Dorotheum, Vienna #39/R est:1200-1800
Works on paper			
£345	$572	€500	Mythological scene (33x22cm-13x9in) pen over chk. 30-Sep-3 Dorotheum, Vienna #13
£414	$687	€600	Classical warrior (33x22cm-13x9in) pen over chk. 30-Sep-3 Dorotheum, Vienna #132/R

FUENTE, Luis de la (19th C) Spanish

£9868	$17862	€15000	Interior scene (52x37cm-20x15in) s.i.d.1896. 14-Apr-4 Ansorena, Madrid #159/R est:15000

FUENTES ALGORA, Fernando (20th C) Spanish

£428	$787	€650	Falls (81x100cm-32x39in) s. i.verso. 22-Jun-4 Durán, Madrid #95/R

FUENTETAJA, Jose Luis (1951-) Spanish

£345	$576	€500	Houses (46x64cm-18x25in) s.d.68 card. 11-Nov-3 Castellana, Madrid #131/R

FUERTES, Louis Agassiz (1874-1927) American

Works on paper			
£938	$1500	€1369	Bird study of great tits (25x23cm-10x9in) s.i. W/C. 20-Sep-3 Pook & Pook, Downington #533 est:1800-2200
£2286	$3750	€3315	Wren (28x23cm-11x9in) s. W/C gouache. 2-Jun-3 Grogan, Boston #621/R
£3774	$6000	€5510	Pestrels in flight (38x50cm-15x20in) s. W/C paper on board. 12-Sep-3 Skinner, Boston #531/R est:5000

FUEURRING, Maximilian (1896-1985) Australian
£607 $978 €886 Children's Birthday Party (47x67cm-19x26in) s. card. 25-Aug-3 Sotheby's, Paddington #432 (A.D 1500)

FUGE, William Haydon (?) British?
£1600 $2928 €2336 Gentleman writing letters in an interior (28x41cm-11x16in) i.verso. 8-Jul-4 Duke & Son, Dorchester #270/R est:500-1000

FUGEL, Gebhard (1863-1939) German
£634 $1014 €900 Peasants resting (45x67cm-18x26in) s. 18-Sep-3 Rieber, Stuttgart #1015/R

FUGERE, Henry (1872-?) French
Sculpture
£2400 $4296 €3504 Salome (38cm-15in) s.num.7235 gilt cold pat bronze ivory. 13-May-4 Christie's, Kensington #407/R est:2000-3000

FUHR, Franz Xaver (1898-1973) German
£1408 $2437 €2000 Village street (30x41cm-12x16in) s. 13-Dec-3 Lempertz, Koln #139/R est:2000
Works on paper
£791 $1298 €1100 Ghost (36x52cm-14x20in) s. bodycol on W/C. 4-Jun-3 Ketterer, Hamburg #374/R

FUHRER, Kai (?) ?
£281 $469 €410 Concrete composition (100x100cm-39x39in) 25-Oct-3 Rasmussen, Havnen #4145 (D.KR 3000)

FUHRER, Ottmar von (1900-1967) American/Austrian
Works on paper
£299 $550 €437 Clarion River, Cooksburg PA (53x74cm-21x29in) s. gouache. 26-Jun-4 Sloans & Kenyon, Bethesda #1023/R

FUHRICH, Josef von (1800-1876) Austrian
Works on paper
£336 $617 €500 Mary crossing the mountains (26x35cm-10x14in) pencil pen squared paper double-sided. 26-Mar-4 Dorotheum, Vienna #90/R

FUHRKEN, Fritz (1894-1943) German
Works on paper
£1867 $3341 €2800 Composition (32x25cm-13x10in) s.d. W/C over pencil prov. 14-May-4 Ketterer, Munich #20/R est:1200-1500

FUHRMANN, Arend (1918-1984) Swiss?
£370 $700 €540 Abstract composition (80x80cm-31x31in) init. 22-Feb-4 Bonhams & Butterfields, Los Angeles #7047
£1081 $1859 €1578 Untitled (94x94cm-37x37in) mono. 8-Dec-3 Philippe Schuler, Zurich #3445 (S.FR 2400)
£1900 $3231 €2774 Horizontal and vertical rhythms (80x80cm-31x31in) s. painted 1975. 22-Nov-3 Burkhard, Luzern #128/R est:3000-4000 (S.FR 4200)

FUKS, Alexander (1863-?) Russian
£2400 $4368 €3504 An audience in the parlour (59x76cm-23x30in) s. 16-Jun-4 Christie's, Kensington #168/R est:2500-3500

FUKUI, Nobu (1942-) American
£405 $750 €591 Number III (122x122cm-48x48in) s.d.1971 verso acrylic. 17-Jan-4 Susanin's, Chicago #83/R

FUKUI, Ryonosuke (1924-1986) Japanese
£900 $1530 €1314 Kneeling nude (65x53cm-26x21in) s. oil on paper. 4-Nov-3 Bonhams, New Bond Street #11/R
£1890 $3250 €2759 Profile of a woman (53x33cm-21x13in) s. 3-Dec-3 Doyle, New York #65/R est:4000-6000
Works on paper
£739 $1300 €1079 Still life (36x20cm-14x8in) s. gouache casein. 22-May-4 Selkirks, St. Louis #781/R
£795 $1400 €1161 Still life of fruit (20x36cm-8x14in) s. gouache casein. 22-May-4 Selkirks, St. Louis #780/R

FULCHER, Nora (fl.1898) British
Works on paper
£223 $400 €326 Portrait of Mrs Lyon Campbell (74x56cm-29x22in) s. W/C. 10-Jan-4 Auctions by the Bay, Alameda #546/R

FULLARTON, James (1946-) British
£520 $957 €759 Harvest landscape (46x86cm-18x34in) s. 10-Jun-4 Lyon & Turnbull, Edinburgh #4
£1500 $2595 €2190 Braes, Saltcoats (61x66cm-24x26in) s. 11-Dec-3 Lyon & Turnbull, Edinburgh #42/R est:800-1200

FULLBROOK, Samuel Sydney (1922-) Australian
£7660 $13021 €11184 Woman in desert (90x49cm-35x19in) init. i.verso exhib.prov. 25-Nov-3 Christie's, Melbourne #41/R est:18000-25000 (A.D 18000)
£10213 $17362 €14911 Clown (51x40cm-20x16in) init. prov. 26-Nov-3 Deutscher-Menzies, Melbourne #84/R est:18000-24000 (A.D 24000)
£10687 $19450 €15603 Flowers (46x51cm-18x20in) init. 16-Jun-4 Deutscher-Menzies, Melbourne #164/R est:18000-24000 (A.D 28000)
£19672 $31082 €28721 Flower piece No 1 (106x96cm-42x38in) init. prov.exhib. 2-Sep-3 Deutscher-Menzies, Melbourne #94/R est:38000-50000 (A.D 48000)
Works on paper
£372 $688 €543 Dudley Flats (33x42cm-13x17in) s.d.47 W/C prov.exhib. 15-Mar-4 Sotheby's, Melbourne #226/R est:600-800 (A.D 900)
£573 $1042 €837 Untitled (26x33cm-10x13in) pastel prov. 16-Jun-4 Deutscher-Menzies, Melbourne #521/R est:1200-1800 (A.D 1500)
£1859 $3291 €2714 Foster mother (30x23cm-12x9in) init. pastel prov. 3-May-4 Christie's, Melbourne #303/R est:5000-7000 (A.D 4500)

FULLER, Arthur Davenport (1889-1967) American
Works on paper
£387 $700 €565 Yellowlegs in decent (61x46cm-24x18in) s. W/C. 16-Apr-4 James Julia, Fairfield #770/R

FULLER, Augustus (1812-1873) American
Miniatures
£2206 $3750 €3221 Portrait of a boy (5x5cm-2x2in) s.verso black embossed leather case prov. 1-Nov-3 Skinner, Boston #2/R est:400-600

FULLER, Augustus (attrib) (1812-1873) American
Miniatures
£2500 $4250 €3650 Portrait of a boy (8x5cm-3x2in) embossed brown leather case prov. 1-Nov-3 Skinner, Boston #3/R est:400-600

FULLER, Edmund G (19/20th C) British
£650 $1203 €949 Seascape (56x61cm-22x24in) s. 10-Feb-4 David Lay, Penzance #301
Works on paper
£250 $418 €365 Fishing boats (20x28cm-8x11in) s. W/C. 17-Oct-3 Keys, Aylsham #490/R
£480 $763 €701 Two fishermen caulking a boat on the Cornish coast (35x45cm-14x18in) s. pencil W/C. 30-Apr-3 Peter Wilson, Nantwich #94/R

FULLER, Florence (fl.1897-1904) British
£5957 $10128 €8697 Swan River, Perth (25x45cm-10x18in) s. s.i.verso painted c.1904 prov. 26-Nov-3 Deutscher-Menzies, Melbourne #127/R est:15000-18000 (A.D 14000)

FULLER, George (1822-1884) American
£483 $850 €705 Arethusia at the fountain (25x18cm-10x7in) init. canvas on board prov. 3-Jan-4 Collins, Maine #55/R
£511 $900 €746 Landscape with figures (51x36cm-20x14in) init. prov.exhib. 3-Jan-4 Collins, Maine #53/R
£824 $1400 €1203 Ideal head (29x22cm-11x9in) indis int. panel. 30-Oct-3 Phillips, New York #6/R est:1000-1500
£852 $1500 €1244 Dancing before the shrine (69x56cm-27x22in) s. prov.exhib. 3-Jan-4 Collins, Maine #54/R est:1200-1600
£1591 $2800 €2323 Wash day (36x51cm-14x20in) s. prov. 3-Jan-4 Collins, Maine #52/R est:1000-1500
£1695 $3000 €2475 The sprite (50x41cm-20x16in) s. painted c.1880 prov.exhib.lit. 28-Apr-4 Christie's, Los Angeles #64/R est:4000-6000
£2614 $4600 €3816 Connecticut Valley (38x69cm-15x27in) prov.exhib. 3-Jan-4 Collins, Maine #56/R est:2000-3000

FULLER, Leonard John (1891-1973) British
£350 $648 €511 Cliff top (25x36cm-10x14in) s. i.verso. 10-Feb-4 David Lay, Penzance #299/R
£1000 $1820 €1460 At his studio, St. Ives (61x71cm-24x28in) s. i.verso. 15-Jun-4 David Lay, Penzance #372/R est:800-1200

FULLER, Martin (1943-) British
£400 $720 €584 Declining Nude (28x40cm-11x16in) panel prov. 20-Jan-4 Bonhams, Knightsbridge #241/R

FULLER, Warwick (1948-) Australian
£1660 $2772 €2490 Midday sun (92x122cm-36x48in) s. board. 27-Oct-3 Goodman, Sydney #218/R est:3000-4000 (A.D 4000)

FULLERTON, Henry (19th C) American
Miniatures
£1023 $1800 €1494 Portrait of George Washington (5cm-2in) s. pen ink. 22-May-4 Pook & Pook, Downington #604/R est:600-900

FULLEYLOVE, J (1845-1908) British
Works on paper
£540 $934 €788 Great Court, Trinity College, Cambridge (23x15cm-9x6in) s.d.1889 sold with a companion. 9-Dec-3 Louis Taylor, Stoke on Trent #1203

FULLEYLOVE, John (1845-1908) British
£520 $842 €754 Manorban Castle, near Tenby (33x51cm-13x20in) s.d.1888 i.verso wood panel. 25-May-3 Desmond Judd, Cranbrook #1054
Works on paper
£420 $697 €613 Paris (13x18cm-5x7in) s.i.d.1893 W/C. 1-Oct-3 Sotheby's, Olympia #162/R
£650 $1118 €949 Theatre of Herodes Atticus, Athens (17x15cm-7x6in) s. pencil W/C. 3-Dec-3 Christie's, Kensington #34/R

£750 $1290 €1095 In the chamber of the White Tower, Tower of London (33x42cm-13x17in) s. pencil W/C. 3-Dec-3 Christie's, Kensington #85/R
£920 $1647 €1343 Roma (23x51cm-9x20in) s.i.d.1875 W/C. 6-Jan-4 Gildings, Market Harborough #391/R
£1200 $2064 €1752 Minaret, Cairo (24x16cm-9x6in) s. pencil W/C. 3-Dec-3 Christie's, Kensington #36/R est:500-700
£1300 $2405 €1898 Entrance gate, john's (17x12cm-7x5in) s.d.1889 W/C exhib. 14-Jul-4 Sotheby's, Olympia #93/R est:800-1200
£1600 $2912 €2336 Hampton Court Palace from the Long Water (32x49cm-13x19in) s.d.1885 pencil W/C. 1-Jul-4 Christie's, Kensington #127/R est:1000-2000
£2400 $4392 €3504 Virgin's fountain, Nazareth (26x36cm-10x14in) s.i.d.1901 pencil W/C htd bodycol exhib.lit. 3-Jun-4 Christie's, London #160/R est:1200-1800

FULLWOOD, Albert Henry (1863-1930) British
£553 $940 €807 Landscape (23x34cm-9x13in) init. board. 25-Nov-3 Christie's, Melbourne #316 (A.D 1300)
£732 $1149 €1061 Seascape with shipping (43x100cm-17x39in) s. 26-Aug-3 Christie's, Sydney #379 est:2000-4000 (A.D 1800)
£810 $1304 €1183 Landscape at dusk (14x18cm-6x7in) canvas on board prov. 25-Aug-3 Sotheby's, Paddington #472 (A.D 2000)
£823 $1490 €1202 Harbour scene (44x102cm-17x40in) s. 31-Mar-4 Goodman, Sydney #337/R (A.D 2000)
£1064 $1808 €1553 Portrait of Robert Bonar, Metallurgist (61x51cm-24x20in) s.i.d.1926 verso. 26-Nov-3 Deutscher-Menzies, Melbourne #269/R (A.D 2500)
£2979 $5064 €4349 Droving, Ballarat 1891 (14x23cm-6x9in) init.d.91 board prov. 25-Nov-3 Christie's, Melbourne #286 est:4000-6000 (A.D 7000)
£9717 $15644 €14187 View from Balmoral (25x33cm-10x13in) s. indis.d. wood panel prov. 25-Aug-3 Sotheby's, Paddington #156/R est:18000-22000 (A.D 24000)
Works on paper
£386 $691 €564 Saint Paul's London (72x52cm-28x20in) s. gouache. 10-May-4 Joel, Victoria #253 est:1000-2000 (A.D 950)
£480 $859 €701 London street scene at night (30x20cm-12x8in) s. W/C. 13-May-4 Mitchells, Cockermouth #1040/R
£763 $1297 €1114 Kendals Punt, Narara Creek (32x46cm-13x18in) s.i. W/C artist's card. 24-Nov-3 Sotheby's, Melbourne #158/R (A.D 1800)
£1037 $1732 €1556 My old house, Kent Street, Sydney (23x18cm-9x7in) s.i. W/C pencil exec. 1835. 27-Oct-3 Goodman, Sydney #120/R (A.D 2500)

FULLWOOD, C (fl.1888-1889) British
£1757 $3145 €2600 Blacksmith at work (80x67cm-31x26in) s. 6-May-4 Michael Zeller, Lindau #669/R est:2400

FULLWOOD, John (1854-1931) British
Works on paper
£447 $800 €653 Summer landscape (36x53cm-14x21in) s. W/C. 20-Mar-4 Rachel Davis, Shaker Heights #394/R

FULOP, Antal Andor (1908-) Hungarian
£1096 $1896 €1600 Still life of oranges and magnolia (44x50cm-17x20in) s.d.1938. 12-Dec-3 Kieselbach, Budapest #100/R (H.F 420000)

FULOP, Karoly (1893-1963) American
Works on paper
£568 $1000 €829 Procession (46x36cm-18x14in) s. mixed media prov. 23-May-4 Bonhams & Butterfields, Los Angeles #7029a/R

FULTON, David (1848-1930) British
£420 $773 €613 Daydreams (23x33cm-9x13in) s.d.1877 s.i.d.1877 verso. 10-Jun-4 Lyon & Turnbull, Edinburgh #23
£1400 $2506 €2044 Autumn, west highlands (46x41cm-18x16in) s. 26-May-4 Sotheby's, Olympia #249/R est:1500-2000
£2700 $4941 €3942 Herd laddie (75x90cm-30x35in) s. 8-Apr-4 Bonhams, Edinburgh #167/R est:2000-3000
£6000 $10860 €8760 Blustery seas (51x76cm-20x30in) s.d.1887 s.verso. 19-Apr-4 Sotheby's, London #97/R est:3000-5000
Works on paper
£360 $659 €526 Elderly bonneted lady seated reading a letter in her kitchen (36x28cm-14x11in) s. W/C. 27-Jan-4 Rogers Jones, Clwyd #100/R
£700 $1253 €1022 Coastal scenes with figures. s. W/C pair. 7-May-4 Chrystals Auctions, Isle of Man #230

FULTON, Hamish (1946-) British
£3500 $6370 €5110 Counting 48/49 Dots. s. acrylic board pencil acrylic paper two parts exec 1993. 4-Feb-4 Sotheby's, Olympia #17/R est:3000-4000
Photographs
£3380 $5848 €4800 Juniper (144x118cm-57x46in) s.d.1986 verso black/white photograph prov. 9-Dec-3 Artcurial Briest, Paris #439/R est:4000-5000
£3800 $6992 €5548 Sunrise, places seen and visited (77x242cm-30x95in) black white photo board prov. 24-Jun-4 Sotheby's, Olympia #466/R est:4000-6000
£4014 $7025 €5700 Untitled (28x18cm-11x7in) photograph pair. 16-Dec-3 Finarte Semenzato, Milan #280/R est:6200
Works on paper
£1297 $2400 €1894 Counting 1604 Dots (125x125cm-49x49in) s.d.1996 one gouache other gouache pencil two prov. 13-Jul-4 Christie's, Rockefeller NY #81/R est:1500-2000

FULTON, Samuel (1855-1941) British
£649 $1200 €948 Portrait of a German shepherd (43x36cm-17x14in) s. 10-Feb-4 Doyle, New York #151/R
£1300 $2379 €1898 Portrait of a foxhound (63x76cm-25x30in) s. 28-Jul-4 Bonhams, Knightsbridge #183/R est:1200-1800
£2000 $3400 €2920 Netherby II, K.C.S.B, a dandie dinmont (51x61cm-20x24in) s.i. 27-Nov-3 Christie's, Kensington #291/R est:2000-3000
£2900 $5191 €4234 Fox Terrier in a kennel (45x35cm-18x14in) s. exhib. 26-May-4 Sotheby's, Olympia #217/R est:2000-3000
£3500 $6335 €5110 On alert (51x41cm-20x16in) s. prov. 19-Apr-4 Sotheby's, London #7/R est:3000-4000
£4324 $8000 €6313 Two cairn terriers (43x51cm-17x20in) s. 10-Feb-4 Doyle, New York #266/R est:7000-9000
£5000 $7850 €7250 Wistfull, a west highland terrier (46x36cm-18x14in) s. 27-Aug-3 Sotheby's, London #1013/R est:2000-3000
£6500 $10205 €9425 Best friends (51x61cm-20x24in) s. 27-Aug-3 Sotheby's, London #1012/R est:3000-5000
£8140 $14000 €11884 West highland terrier (36x25cm-14x10in) s. canvas on board. 5-Dec-3 Christie's, Rockefeller NY #44/R est:6000-8000

FULWIDER, Edwin (1913-) American
£414 $750 €604 Prairie town with two churches (41x102cm-16x40in) 16-Apr-4 American Auctioneer #143/R
£442 $800 €645 Train (41x81cm-16x32in) 16-Apr-4 American Auctioneer #145/R
£884 $1600 €1291 Two men near railroad tracks (25x38cm-10x15in) oil linen. 16-Apr-4 American Auctioneer #144/R est:1000-1500
Works on paper
£670 $1200 €978 Along the tracks (51x71cm-20x28in) s. W/C. 16-May-4 Wright, Chicago #164/R

FUMAGALLI, Celestino (1864-1941) Italian
£1418 $2369 €2000 Fruit (69x39cm-27x15in) s. pair. 14-Oct-3 Finarte Semenzato, Milan #55/R est:1600-1800

FUMERON, Rene (1921-) French
Works on paper
£268 $494 €400 Les Filets (140x109cm-55x43in) gouache canvas. 24-Mar-4 Joron-Derem, Paris #215/R
£791 $1298 €1100 Allegorie (125x149cm-49x59in) gouache panel. 3-Jun-3 Livinec, Gaudcheau & Jezequel, Rennes #98/R

FUMPSTON, Rodney (1947-) New Zealander
Works on paper
£326 $525 €476 Abstract landscape (68x98cm-27x39in) s.d.1988 pastel. 12-Aug-3 Peter Webb, Auckland #68 (NZ.D 900)

FUNCH, Hermann (1841-1919) Danish
£375 $611 €548 Pair of ducks by lake, fox in background (68x92cm-27x36in) s. 28-Sep-3 Hindemae, Ullerslev #31/R (D.KR 4000)
£383 $620 €555 Cock pheasant on woodland path (64x79cm-25x31in) s.d.88. 4-Aug-3 Rasmussen, Vejle #103/R (D.KR 4000)
£427 $682 €623 Landscape with swallows on branch (33x24cm-13x9in) s. 22-Sep-3 Rasmussen, Vejle #114/R (D.KR 4500)

FUNI, Achille (1890-1972) Italian
£23239 $40669 €33000 Study of nude (86x71cm-34x28in) s.d.1928 exhib.lit. 16-Dec-3 Finarte Semenzato, Milan #346/R est:30000-35000
Works on paper
£1538 $2569 €2200 Still life of fruit (39x52cm-15x20in) s. mixed media cardboard. 26-Jun-3 Sant Agostino, Torino #197/R est:2500
£3472 $5486 €5000 MYthological figure (160x115cm-63x45in) chk tempera paper on canvas. 6-Sep-3 Meeting Art, Vercelli #498 est:5000
£13103 $21883 €19000 Young shepherd (162x126cm-64x50in) s.d.1937. 17-Nov-3 Sant Agostino, Torino #242/R est:20000-25000

FUNK, Adolf (1903-1996) Swiss
Works on paper
£271 $462 €396 Ruisseau No 8 (108x78cm-43x31in) s.d.1969 s.i. verso mixed media. 25-Nov-3 Germann, Zurich #785 (S.FR 600)

FUNK, Emil (fl.1854-1864) German
£1100 $1903 €1606 Continental figures in conversation. 9-Dec-3 Lawrences, Bletchingley #1734

FUNK, Hans (elder-attrib) (c.1470-1539) Swiss
Works on paper
£1014 $1784 €1500 Allegory of envy (12x7cm-5x3in) bears d.1537 pen wash paper on copperplate prov. 22-May-4 Lempertz, Koln #1270/R est:1500

FUNKE, Anton (1869-1955) Dutch
£411 $699 €600 Still life with melon, currants and grapes (41x56cm-16x22in) s. 5-Nov-3 Vendue Huis, Gravenhage #285
£548 $932 €800 Still life with strawberry and grapes (42x57cm-17x22in) s. 5-Nov-3 Vendue Huis, Gravenhage #286/R

FUNKE, Bernd (1912-) German
£280 $517 €409 Still life of flowers in vase (60x50cm-24x20in) s. panel. 15-Mar-4 Rasmussen, Vejle #201/R (D.KR 3100)

FUNKE, Franciscus Wilhelmus Aloysius (1908-1993) Dutch
£227 $400 €331 Still life with roses in a blue vase (46x30cm-18x12in) s. 22-May-4 Harvey Clar, Oakland #2191

FUNKE, Jaromir (1896-1945) Czechoslovakian
Photographs
£1808 $3200 €2640 Cycle, composition IV (12x17cm-5x7in) s.i.d.1927-29 verso gelatin silver print lit. 27-Apr-4 Christie's, Rockefeller NY #66/R est:4000-6000

£2096 $3500 €3060 Nude (18x22cm-7x9in) i. gelatin silver print lit. 16-Oct-3 Phillips, New York #13/R est:4000-6000
£2156 $3600 €3148 Street scene, Prague (28x23cm-11x9in) with sig silver print. 21-Oct-3 Swann Galleries, New York #107/R est:2000-3000
£6587 $11000 €9617 Untitled, neon advertising signs (13x10cm-5x4in) s.verso gelatin silver print prov.lit. 20-Oct-3 Christie's, Rockefeller NY #81/R est:7000-9000

FUNNO, Michele (19th C) ?
Works on paper
£1412 $2400 €2062 British Levant Packet, James Lingham, Commander in Naples Bay, Feb 1838 (46x69cm-18x27in) s. W/C. 31-Oct-3 North East Auctions, Portsmouth #1709

FUNNO, Michele (attrib) (19th C) ?
Works on paper
£850 $1522 €1241 The brig Brothers of Poole under full sail off Naples (44x66cm-17x26in) i.d.1838 bodycol. 26-May-4 Christie's, Kensington #442/R

FURBECK, Allen (20th C) American
£273 $500 €410 Tulip poplars - Ashland Nature Center (81x102cm-32x40in) oil on linen. 10-Jul-4 Hindman, Chicago #158/R

FURET, François (1842-1919) Swiss
£323 $579 €472 Landscape near Aeschi (14x22cm-6x9in) s. i. verso board prov. 12-May-4 Dobiaschofsky, Bern #535/R (S.FR 750)
£390 $651 €566 Village sous la neige (18x27cm-7x11in) s. cardboard. 21-Jun-3 Galerie du Rhone, Sion #366 (S.FR 850)
£409 $733 €597 Woodland stream (41x33cm-16x13in) s. 12-May-4 Dobiaschofsky, Bern #536/R (S.FR 950)
£901 $1550 €1315 Allegorical representation of spring (60x41cm-24x16in) s. 8-Dec-3 Philippe Schuler, Zurich #3328/R (S.FR 2000)

FURINI, Francesco (1604-1646) Italian
£10791 $17698 €15000 Allegory of Vanity (68x55cm-27x22in) 4-Jun-3 Sotheby's, Milan #92/R est:10000-15000
Works on paper
£2600 $4498 €3796 Two studies of a left hand holding a cloth (22x17cm-9x7in) i. red chk prov. 12-Dec-3 Christie's, Kensington #338/R est:1000-2000

FURINI, Francesco (attrib) (1604-1646) Italian
£988 $1788 €1442 Flora, portrait of a woman with a floral crown (92x74cm-36x29in) 30-Mar-4 Christie's, Melbourne #385/R est:2000-3000 (A.D 2400)
Works on paper
£500 $900 €730 Study of a pair of crossed legs (23x8cm-9x3in) bears i.mount red chk sold with another by Italian School 17th C. 20-Apr-4 Sotheby's, Olympia #9/R

FURINI, Francesco (style) (1604-1646) Italian
£8101 $14500 €11827 Portrait of Diana (61x76cm-24x30in) 11-May-4 Roland's, New York #473265/R

FURIO, Ernesto (1902-1995) Spanish
Works on paper
£436 $811 €650 Boat. Portrait of man (22x30cm-9x12in) s. W/C double-sided. 2-Mar-4 Ansorena, Madrid #357/R

FURLONGER, Joseph (1952-) Australian
£851 $1447 €1242 Bathers (39x101cm-15x40in) init.d.88 prov. 25-Nov-3 Christie's, Melbourne #139/R (A.D 2000)
Works on paper
£729 $1173 €1064 Deposition (119x152cm-47x60in) init.d.89 gouache W/C pastel prov. 25-Aug-3 Sotheby's, Paddington #300/R (A.D 1800)

FURNESS, Robin (1933-) British
£250 $425 €365 Brough Castle, evening light (17x24cm-7x9in) init. canvasboard. 19-Nov-3 Tennants, Leyburn #1266/R

FURSE, Charles Wellington (1868-1904) British
£550 $990 €803 Foal and groom (31x46cm-12x18in) s. sold with Memoir of Charles Wellington Furse. 21-Jan-4 Sotheby's, Olympia #324/R
£10000 $18400 €14600 Portrait of the artist's wife, late Dame Katherine Furse (66x51cm-26x20in) init.i. 11-Jun-4 Christie's, London #190/R est:10000-15000

FURSMAN, Frederick Frary (1874-1943) American
£1377 $2300 €2010 Mother and children gathering mussels at sea shore (56x48cm-22x19in) i.verso. 27-Oct-3 Schrager Galleries, Milwaukee #1433/R
£2036 $3400 €2973 Mother and daughter at sea shore (58x48cm-23x19in) s. i.verso. 27-Oct-3 Schrager Galleries, Milwaukee #1428/R

FURST, Edmund (1874-?) German
£521 $849 €750 Cloudy seaside (28x51cm-11x20in) s. 27-Sep-3 Dannenberg, Berlin #541/R
£867 $1551 €1300 Nude outdoors (49x49cm-19x19in) s. board. 15-May-4 Van Ham, Cologne #602/R

FURST, Geo (1888-?) German
£300 $537 €438 Trading vessels at sea (68x98cm-27x39in) s.i. 26-May-4 Christie's, Kensington #669/R

FURTWANGLER, Albert (1902-1984) German
£355 $574 €500 Still life of fruit including grapes, peaches, apples (69x99cm-27x39in) s.d.1927. 23-May-3 Karlheinz Kaupp, Staufen #2003

FURUHJELM, Dagmar (1868-?) Finnish
Works on paper
£1127 $1803 €1600 Girl with child (57x38cm-22x15in) s.d.1894 pastel. 21-Sep-3 Bukowskis, Helsinki #339/R est:1000

FURY (20th C) ?
£537 $1004 €800 Polyptique rouge (100x125cm-39x49in) s.i.d.1990 verso acrylic two parts. 29-Feb-4 Versailles Encheres #236

FUSARO, Jean (1925-) French
£1469 $2452 €2100 Voiles sur l'etang (16x27cm-6x11in) s. s.i.d.1969 verso. 25-Jun-3 Blanchet, Paris #104
£1724 $3086 €2517 Parisian street in winter (27x41cm-11x16in) s. 12-May-4 Dobiaschofsky, Bern #537/R est:4600 (S.FR 4000)
£2789 $4993 €4100 Le port (34x48cm-13x19in) s. peinture. 20-Mar-4 Binoche, Orleans #35 est:1500-2000
£2887 $4995 €4100 Les vendanges (60x73cm-24x29in) s. 9-Dec-3 Chambelland & Giafferi, Paris #51/R est:1200-1500
Works on paper
£738 $1366 €1100 Promeneurs sur la plage (32x50cm-13x20in) s. pastel. 15-Mar-4 Blanchet, Paris #141/R
£933 $1680 €1400 Falaise par gros temps (32x48cm-13x19in) s. pastel. 20-Apr-4 Chenu & Scrive, Lyon #88a/R

FUSCO, Mario (1934-1988) Italian
£667 $1227 €1000 Composition (60x80cm-24x31in) s.d.1962 s.d.verso. 8-Jun-4 Finarte Semenzato, Milan #130/R

FUSCO, Paul (1930-) American
Photographs
£8333 $15000 €12166 RFK funeral train (218x36cm-86x14in) s.i.d.1968 album 53 chromogenic colour prints. 24-Apr-4 Phillips, New York #92/R est:10000-15000

FUSI, Walter (1924-) Italian
£333 $613 €500 Brunello (65x80cm-26x31in) s.i.d.1986 verso mixed media on canvas. 12-Jun-4 Meeting Art, Vercelli #428/R
Works on paper
£336 $621 €500 Composition (50x70cm-20x28in) s.verso mixed media cardboard on canvas. 13-Mar-4 Meeting Art, Vercelli #325
£400 $736 €600 Composition (50x70cm-20x28in) s. s.verso mixed media cardboard on canvas. 12-Jun-4 Meeting Art, Vercelli #31/R
£500 $920 €750 Algund (81x100cm-32x39in) s.d.1985 mixed media on canvas. 12-Jun-4 Meeting Art, Vercelli #792/R

FUSS, Adam (1961-) American
Photographs
£1389 $2500 €2028 Untitled (25x20cm-10x8in) s.i.d.1988 verso cibachrome photogram mounted on plexiglass prov. 23-Apr-4 Phillips, New York #223/R est:2500-3500
£1916 $3200 €2797 Untitled, balloon (61x50cm-24x20in) cibachrome photogram exec.1989 prov.lit. 17-Oct-3 Phillips, New York #276/R est:3000-4000
£2222 $4000 €3244 Untitled (120x89cm-47x35in) s.d.1999 gelatin silver print print photogram. 23-Apr-4 Phillips, New York #224/R est:8000-12000
£2874 $4800 €4196 Untitled, from the Pinhole View series (59x49cm-23x19in) s.d.1986 num.2/10 gelatin silver print prov. 20-Oct-3 Christie's, Rockefeller NY #237/R est:5000-7000
£2889 $5200 €4218 Untitled (61x51cm-24x20in) s.d.1996 cibachrome photogram prov.lit. 23-Apr-4 Phillips, New York #221/R est:5000-7000
£3114 $5200 €4546 Untitled, blue spiral (62x51cm-24x20in) cibachrome photogram exec.1990 prov.lit. 17-Oct-3 Phillips, New York #277/R est:4000-6000
£3222 $5800 €4704 Untitled (61x51cm-24x20in) s.d.1996 cibachrome photogram. 23-Apr-4 Phillips, New York #220/R est:5000-7000
£3444 $6200 €5028 Untitled (59x49cm-23x19in) s.d.1991 cibachrome mounted on plexiglass prov. 23-Apr-4 Phillips, New York #222/R est:6000-9000
£3611 $6500 €5272 Untitled (36x28cm-14x11in) s.d.1994 num.284.9 verso cibachrome photogram prov. 23-Apr-4 Phillips, New York #59/R est:5000-7000
£3704 $7000 €5408 Untitledfrom the series My Ghost (60x50cm-24x20in) num.551 gelatin silver print. 17-Feb-4 Christie's, Rockefeller NY #283/R est:8000-10000
£5090 $8500 €7431 Untitled, flower (35x27cm-14x11in) s.d.1993 verso cibachrome photogram prov. 17-Oct-3 Phillips, New York #20/R est:5000-7000
£5389 $9000 €7868 Untitled, pink spiral (163x125cm-64x49in) cibachrome photogram exec.1992 prov.lit. 17-Oct-3 Phillips, New York #19/R est:15000-20000
£6780 $12000 €9899 Untitled - pansies (36x28cm-14x11in) s.d.1991 dye destruction print prov. 27-Apr-4 Christie's, Rockefeller NY #197/R est:7000-9000
£7910 $14000 €11549 Untitled - sunflower (36x28cm-14x11in) s.d.1998 verso dye destruction print prov. 27-Apr-4 Christie's, Rockefeller NY #196/R est:7000-9000
£9000 $16380 €13140 Untitled, from my ghost (60x50cm-24x20in) silver print photogram prov. 6-Feb-4 Sotheby's, London #269/R est:4000-6000
£10734 $19000 €15672 Untitled, yellow bird (36x28cm-14x11in) s.d.1994 num.262.6 verso cibachrome photogram prov.lit. 27-Apr-4 Sotheby's, New York #39/R est:4000-6000
£11111 $20000 €16222 Untitled (102x76cm-40x30in) cibachrome photogram prov. 23-Apr-4 Phillips, New York #60/R est:20000-30000
£12222 $22000 €17844 Untitled (215x142cm-85x56in) gelatin silver print photogram on muslin prov. 23-Apr-4 Phillips, New York #58/R est:20000-30000
£13174 $22000 €19234 From the series my ghost (136x107cm-54x42in) gelatin silver print executed 1995 prov. 14-Nov-3 Phillips, New York #210/R est:20000-30000
£15569 $26000 €22731 Sunflower series (127x102cm-50x40in) s.d.1993 verso cibachrome photogram on plexiglass prov. 12-Nov-3 Christie's, Rockefeller NY #549/R est:20000-30000
£22754 $38000 €33221 Untitled, from the series My Ghost (159x103cm-63x41in) gelatin silver photogram prov. 20-Oct-3 Christie's, Rockefeller NY #239/R est:20000-30000

FUSSLI, Heinrich (younger) (1755-1829) Swiss
£1119 $1902 €1600 Bridge over river with horses (21x35cm-8x14in) s.i. W/C over pencil paper on board. 21-Nov-3 Reiss & Sohn, Konigstein #77/R est:1200

FUSSLI, Johann Heinrich (1741-1825) Swiss
Works on paper
£4600 $8418 €6716 Cardinal Pandulph granting King John absolution (14x8cm-6x3in) i.verso black chk pen ink wash. 6-Jul-4 Christie's, London #188/R est:6000-8000
£8500 $15555 €12410 Callipyga - Mrs Fuseli with her skirts lifted to her waist (16x9cm-6x4in) i. brown ink prov.exhib.lit. 3-Jun-4 Christie's, London #79/R est:6000-8000
£26000 $47580 €37960 Female nude lying backwards on a bed - Study for the Nightmare (7x12cm-3x5in) bears i. blk chk prov.exhib.lit. 8-Jul-4 Sotheby's, London #149/R est:14000-18000

FUSSLI, Johann Heinrich (attrib) (1741-1825) Swiss
Works on paper
£903 $1472 €1300 Return of the prodigal son (29x18cm-11x7in) W/C htd white. 25-Sep-3 Dr Fritz Nagel, Stuttgart #1315/R

FUSSLI, Wilhelm Heinrich (1830-1916) Swiss
£2207 $3686 €3200 Portrait of six year old Baroness Natalie von Uexkull (53x45cm-21x18in) s.d.1858 oval. 15-Nov-3 Lempertz, Koln #1605/R est:4000

FUSSMANN, Klaus (1938-) German
£1250 $2088 €1800 Baltic (15x22cm-6x9in) s.d. tempera. 24-Oct-3 Ketterer, Hamburg #351/R est:1800-2000
£2098 $3566 €3000 Clouds (95x110cm-37x43in) s.i.d.Juni 79 verso. 29-Nov-3 Villa Grisebach, Berlin #373/R est:3000-4000
£3000 $5370 €4500 Still life with jug (48x47cm-19x19in) s.d. prov. 14-May-4 Ketterer, Munich #270/R est:4500-5500
Works on paper
£364 $607 €520 Clouds and sea - Norway (14x21cm-6x8in) mono.i. bears d.73 W/C. 11-Oct-3 Hans Stahl, Hamburg #179
£559 $934 €800 Pansies (11x15cm-4x6in) mono. bears d.95 gouache mixed media. 11-Oct-3 Hans Stahl, Hamburg #180/R
£769 $1323 €1100 Rapeseed field (15x22cm-6x9in) d. gouache. 3-Dec-3 Hauswedell & Nolte, Hamburg #784/R
£800 $1440 €1200 Still life of flowers (30x39cm-12x15in) s.i.d.6 III 79 W/C board. 24-Apr-4 Dr Lehr, Berlin #120/R
£800 $1472 €1200 Still life of flowers (29x41cm-11x16in) s.d. W/C tempera. 11-Jun-4 Hauswedell & Nolte, Hamburg #1267/R
£828 $1382 €1200 Chrysanthemum (11x19cm-4x7in) s. W/C gouache. 13-Nov-3 Neumeister, Munich #535/R
£833 $1392 €1200 View of Goran Anger (29x41cm-11x16in) mono.i.d.1.1.85 W/C. 24-Oct-3 Ketterer, Hamburg #350/R
£839 $1427 €1200 Yellow pansies (15x22cm-6x9in) s.d.7.8.82. 29-Nov-3 Bassenge, Berlin #6711/R
£867 $1586 €1300 Untitled - Baltic (14x22cm-6x9in) bears i. s.d.96 verso gouache sand. 4-Jun-4 Lempertz, Koln #144/R
£1000 $1790 €1500 Landscape near Gelting (15x22cm-6x9in) s. pastel. 13-May-4 Neumeister, Munich #614/R est:1000-1500
£1067 $1963 €1600 Florence (17x25cm-7x10in) s.i.d.98 W/C pencil. 11-Jun-4 Villa Grisebach, Berlin #1612/R est:500-700
£1189 $1985 €1700 Flowers (24x31cm-9x12in) mono.d.93 gouache mixed media. 11-Oct-3 Hans Stahl, Hamburg #181/R est:1700
£1333 $2453 €2000 Face at window (72x71cm-28x28in) W/C. 11-Jun-4 Hauswedell & Nolte, Hamburg #1268/R est:1500
£1379 $2303 €2000 Landscape near Gelting (42x56cm-17x22in) s. pastel. 13-Nov-3 Neumeister, Munich #533/R est:3000-3500
£1467 $2625 €2200 Field of oilseed rape (15x22cm-6x9in) s.d. pastel. 13-May-4 Neumeister, Munich #613/R est:2000-2500
£1573 $2675 €2250 Wheat field with trees (42x56cm-17x22in) s.d.97 pastel chk. 27-Nov-3 Lempertz, Koln #134/R est:3000
£1600 $2944 €2400 Still life with flowers (29x40cm-11x16in) s.i.d.93 W/C gouache. 11-Jun-4 Villa Grisebach, Berlin #1614/R est:800-1200
£1933 $3461 €2900 Asters and dahlias (30x40cm-12x16in) s.d. pastel. 13-May-4 Neumeister, Munich #612/R est:2800-3000
£2000 $3580 €3000 Asters (42x55cm-17x22in) s.d. pastel board. 13-May-4 Neumeister, Munich #610/R est:3500-3800
£2000 $3680 €3000 Two bouquets of flowers (56x41cm-22x16in) s.d.89 gouache. 11-Jun-4 Villa Grisebach, Berlin #1611/R est:1000-1500
£2098 $3566 €3000 Roses (29x38cm-11x15in) mono.d.6.8.84 i.d. verso gouache. 27-Nov-3 Lempertz, Koln #131/R est:3000
£2098 $3566 €3000 Flowers (47x58cm-19x23in) s.d.94 W/C. 27-Nov-3 Lempertz, Koln #133/R est:4000-5000
£2113 $3507 €3000 Portrait B (71x70cm-28x28in) s.i.d.1982 W/C. 13-Jun-3 Hauswedell & Nolte, Hamburg #640/R est:4000
£2133 $3840 €3200 January gold (62x70cm-24x28in) s.i.d.1.4.1974. 24-Apr-4 Dr Lehr, Berlin #119/R est:4000
£2133 $3819 €3200 Hyacinths (41x55cm-16x22in) s.d. pastel. 13-May-4 Neumeister, Munich #611/R est:3500-3800
£2158 $3540 €3000 Landscape near Gelting (64x76cm-25x30in) s.i.d. W/C. 4-Jun-3 Ketterer, Hamburg #375/R est:3000-4000
£2200 $4026 €3300 Untitled - white dahlias (29x39cm-11x15in) mono.d.1.8.84 gouache W/C. 4-Jun-4 Lempertz, Koln #142/R est:2500
£2267 $4171 €3400 Still life with pink and yellow flowers (41x56cm-16x22in) s.i.d.91 pastel. 11-Jun-4 Villa Grisebach, Berlin #1610/R est:1000-1500
£2448 $4210 €3500 Landscape near Gelting (64x76cm-25x30in) s.d.79 W/C opaque white prov. 5-Dec-3 Ketterer, Munich #180/R est:3500-4500
£2667 $4773 €4000 Landscape near Gelting (42x56cm-17x22in) s.i. s.d.9.99 verso gouache pastel prov. 14-May-4 Ketterer, Munich #269/R est:3500-4500
£2667 $4880 €4000 Untitled - garden in Gelting (64x76cm-25x30in) s.i.d.94 W/C. 4-Jun-4 Lempertz, Koln #143/R est:4000
£2797 $4811 €4000 Marguerites (28x39cm-11x15in) s.d.01 W/C opaque white. 5-Dec-3 Ketterer, Munich #178/R est:4800-5500
£2800 $5152 €4200 Poppies (20x28cm-8x11in) s.d.98 W/C lacquer. 11-Jun-4 Villa Grisebach, Berlin #1613/R est:800-1200
£2897 $4837 €4200 Roses in bloom (32x49cm-13x19in) s.d.2002 W/C gouache. 13-Nov-3 Neumeister, Munich #534/R est:4000-4200
£4333 $7973 €6500 Still life with flowers (40x48cm-16x19in) s.i.d.1998 W/C cardboard. 11-Jun-4 Villa Grisebach, Berlin #1609/R est:1000-1500

FUSTER INSA, Rafael (1934-) Spanish
£526 $968 €800 Landscape in Alicante (65x80cm-26x31in) s. s.i.d.1992 verso. 22-Jun-4 Durán, Madrid #90/R

FUSTER, Juan (attrib) (1870-1934) Spanish
£1233 $2096 €1800 Woman from Valldemosa (99x80cm-39x31in) s. 4-Nov-3 Ansorena, Madrid #67/R est:1600

FYFE, S H (19th C) British
£2154 $3596 €3145 Ship's portrait of Alexandra II off Gibraltar. 25-Oct-3 Rasmussen, Havnen #2604/R est:20000-25000 (D.KR 23000)

FYT, Jan (1609-1661) Flemish
£6711 $12483 €10000 Still life with dead game (93x75cm-37x30in) 2-Mar-4 Ansorena, Madrid #291/R est:7000
£9655 $16028 €14000 Dead game and cat (93x75cm-37x30in) bears sig. 30-Sep-3 Ansorena, Madrid #28/R est:13000
£12081 $21624 €18000 Deux chiens surveillant du gibier (80x121cm-31x48in) prov. 25-May-4 Palais de Beaux Arts, Brussels #74/R est:20000-30000
£47222 $85000 €68944 Peacock in a landscape with roosters, turkeys, ducks and a heron (119x173cm-47x68in) 22-Jan-4 Sotheby's, New York #192/R est:30000-40000
Works on paper
£1329 $2259 €1900 Greyhound (11x18cm-4x7in) brush wash. 27-Nov-3 Bassenge, Berlin #5204/R est:1800

FYT, Jan (attrib) (17th C) Flemish
Works on paper
£710 $1300 €1037 Studies of birds (42x28cm-17x11in) black chk. 29-Jan-4 Swann Galleries, New York #170/R

GAAG, Lotti van der (1923-1999) Dutch
£651 $1106 €950 Four figures (50x70cm-20x28in) s.d.1996. 5-Nov-3 Vendue Huis, Gravenhage #499/R
Sculpture
£3667 $6747 €5500 Gatepaan (44cm-17in) s.d.58 num.3/7 grey pat bronze stone base conceived 1958 lit. 9-Jun-4 Christie's, Amsterdam #261/R est:1500-2000

GAAL, Ferenc (1891-1956) Hungarian
£1449 $2623 €2116 In the harbour (60x80cm-24x31in) s. 16-Apr-4 Mu Terem Galeria, Budapest #17/R (H.F 550000)

GAAL, Ignacz (1820-1880) Austrian
Works on paper
£1419 $2497 €2100 Still life of fruit with silver pheasant (80x64cm-31x25in) s. gouache paper on canvas. 22-May-4 Lempertz, Koln #1413/R est:2000

GAAL, Pieter (1785-1819) Dutch
£3000 $5370 €4500 Italianate river landscape with shepherd and cattle (25x36cm-10x14in) indis.sig.verso panel. 17-May-4 Christie's, Amsterdam #114/R est:5000-7000

GAASENDAM, Flip (20th C) ?
£479 $815 €700 Still life (29x38cm-11x15in) s.d.1991 panel. 5-Nov-3 Vendue Huis, Gravenhage #293

GABAIN, Ethel (1883-1950) British
£600 $1092 €876 Zinnias (26x36cm-10x14in) s. canvas on board prov.exhib. 1-Jul-4 Christie's, Kensington #130/R

GABALI, Alfred (c.1870-1940) German
£237 $375 €346 Flying Cloud under fall sail (91x61cm-36x24in) s. 25-Jul-3 Eldred, East Dennis #202/R

GABANI, Giuseppe (1849-1899) Italian
£3200 $5728 €4672 Arab marketplace (37x54cm-15x21in) s. panel. 26-May-4 Sotheby's, Olympia #307/R est:3000-5000
£8333 $15000 €12166 Snake charmer (29x47cm-11x19in) s.i. panel prov. 22-Apr-4 Christie's, Rockefeller NY #213/R est:20000-30000
Works on paper
£616 $1108 €899 Monk reading (52x35cm-20x14in) s. W/C. 26-Jan-4 Lilla Bukowskis, Stockholm #507 (S.KR 8200)
£1035 $1852 €1511 Street scene with musicians (52x35cm-20x14in) s.i. W/C. 25-May-4 Bukowskis, Stockholm #351/R (S.KR 14000)

GABARRON, Cristobal (1945-) Spanish
£3542 $6021 €5100 Composition (116x89cm-46x35in) s.d.1985 s.i.verso. 28-Oct-3 Segre, Madrid #200/R est:5100

GABBASOVA, Elena (?) Finnish?
£638 $1173 €950 Bullfinches (36x27cm-14x11in) s. 25-Mar-4 Hagelstam, Helsinki #1072

GABE, Nicolas Edward (1814-1865) French
£419 $711 €612 The mouse trap (32x41cm-13x16in) s. 5-Nov-3 Dobiaschofsky, Bern #580/R (S.FR 950)
£1600 $2768 €2336 Fete Champetre - two ladies and a young boy picnicking by a stream (52x62cm-20x24in) 9-Dec-3 Bonhams, Oxford #87/R est:2000-3000
£1645 $3026 €2500 Diligence lancee au galop (48x59cm-19x23in) s.d.1840. 25-Jun-4 Piasa, Paris #137/R est:3000-4000
£2254 $3651 €3200 Voiliers rentrant au port (41x57cm-16x22in) s. 11-Aug-3 Boscher, Cherbourg #734 est:3000-4000

GABINO, Amadeo (1922-) Spanish
Works on paper
£709 $1149 €1000 Untitled (68x49cm-27x19in) s.d.1978 collage. 20-May-3 Ansorena, Madrid #348/R

GABLE, John (1944-) American
Works on paper
£250 $425 €365 Porch (45x71cm-18x28in) s. W/C. 21-Nov-3 Skinner, Boston #476/R

GABLER, Hans (1908-1977) German
£420 $701 €600 Wasserburg on Bodensee (88x110cm-35x43in) s. board. 9-Oct-3 Michael Zeller, Lindau #570/R

GABO, Naum (1890-1977) American/Russian
Sculpture
£8000 $14720 €12000 Construction with alabaster carving (21x16x4cm-8x6x2in) bronze. 10-Jun-4 Hauswedell & Nolte, Hamburg #219/R est:7000

GABONESE SCHOOL (19th C) African
Sculpture
£231788 $424172 €350000 Personnage masculin en position assise (47cm-19in) wood brown pat prov. 7-Apr-4 Fraysse & Associes, Paris #50/R est:120000-180000

GABOR, Jeno (1893-1971) Hungarian
£695 $1230 €1015 Bricklayer (140x119cm-55x47in) s. tempera paper. 28-Apr-4 Kieselbach, Budapest #117/R (H.F 260000)
£2503 $4530 €3654 Woman with violin (83x63cm-33x25in) s. tempera on paper. 16-Apr-4 Mu Terem Galeria, Budapest #158/R (H.F 950000)
£3474 $6149 €5072 Side show (90x69cm-35x27in) s.d.1933. 28-Apr-4 Kieselbach, Budapest #118/R (H.F 1300000)
£6786 $11740 €9908 Still life with mandolin (71x50cm-28x20in) s.d.1933. 12-Dec-3 Kieselbach, Budapest #115/R (H.F 2600000)
£9620 $17027 €14045 Vaudeville (93x92cm-37x36in) s.d.1925. 28-Apr-4 Kieselbach, Budapest #165/R (H.F 3600000)
£57420 $99337 €83833 Port - Le Havre (77x88cm-30x35in) s.d.1927. 12-Dec-3 Kieselbach, Budapest #27/R (H.F 22000000)

GABOR, Vida (?) ?
£5333 $9600 €8000 Cordial greeting (49x40cm-19x16in) s. plywood. 21-Apr-4 Christie's, Amsterdam #47/R est:4000-6000
£5333 $9600 €8000 Artistic licence (50x40cm-20x16in) s. plywood. 21-Apr-4 Christie's, Amsterdam #48/R est:4000-6000

GABRIEL, François (?-1993) French
£500 $800 €730 Floral still life (51x41cm-20x16in) s. panel. 21-Sep-3 Grogan, Boston #20/R
£661 $1124 €965 Still life with flowers (49x38cm-19x15in) s. board. 29-Oct-3 Lawson Menzies, Sydney #262/R est:2000-3000 (A.D 1600)

GABRIEL, Justin J (1838-?) French
£700 $1169 €1022 Cattle with windmills in a landscape (79x138cm-31x54in) s. 22-Oct-3 Cheffins, Cambridge #538

GABRIEL, Michael (?) Irish?
Sculpture
£1711 $3147 €2600 Group of crows (36cm-14in) s. bronze incl. marble base unique. 22-Jun-4 De Veres Art Auctions, Dublin #52/R est:1500-2500

GABRIEL, Paul Joseph Constantin (1828-1903) Dutch
£1450 $2610 €2117 Canal landscape (32x56cm-13x22in) s.d.79 canvas on panel. 21-Jan-4 Sotheby's, Olympia #421/R est:500-800
£1653 $2992 €2413 Untitled - skating scene (13x20cm-5x8in) s. panel. 18-Apr-4 Levis, Calgary #210/R est:3500-4500 (C.D 4000)
£2222 $3511 €3200 Observing the chickens (23x31cm-9x12in) s.d.93 canvas on panel. 2-Sep-3 Christie's, Amsterdam #203 est:2000-3000
£2800 $5040 €4200 Landscape with a white bridge (19x29cm-7x11in) s. canvas on panel prov. 21-Apr-4 Christie's, Amsterdam #87/R est:3000-5000
£3819 $6493 €5500 Polder landscape (28x44cm-11x17in) s. prov. 28-Oct-3 Christie's, Amsterdam #117/R est:3000-5000
£6944 $11597 €10000 Windmill in a polder landscape (16x26cm-6x10in) s.i. panel. 21-Oct-3 Sotheby's, Amsterdam #173/R est:3000-5000
£10044 $18480 €14664 Dutch polder landscape (63x97cm-25x38in) s. 14-Jun-4 Philippe Schuler, Zurich #4280/R est:10000-14000 (S.FR 23000)
£11111 $18889 €16000 Carriage approaching a drawbridge (60x102cm-24x40in) s. 28-Oct-3 Christie's, Amsterdam #118/R est:12000-16000
£17361 $28993 €25000 Windmills in a polder landscape (30x46cm-12x18in) s. 21-Oct-3 Sotheby's, Amsterdam #170/R est:7000-9000
Works on paper
£268 $499 €400 Windmill in landscape (32x48cm-13x19in) s. pastel. 4-Mar-4 Auction Maastricht #1140/R
£394 $670 €575 View of polder with mill, bridge and farm (9x24cm-4x9in) W/C three in one frame. 5-Nov-3 Vendue Huis, Gravenhage #101
£1944 $3247 €2800 Polder landscape (26x41cm-10x16in) s. W/C prov. 21-Oct-3 Sotheby's, Amsterdam #90/R est:3000-4000
£4000 $7200 €6000 Windmill near Abcoude (35x62cm-14x24in) s. W/C. 20-Apr-4 Sotheby's, Amsterdam #102/R est:7000-9000

GABRIEL, Paul Joseph Constantin (attrib) (1828-1903) Dutch
£260 $476 €380 Windmill in a landscape (18x23cm-7x9in) board. 27-Jan-4 Gorringes, Lewes #1644

GABRIEL, Paul Joseph Constantin and HAAS, Johannes Hubertus (19th C) Dutch
£5556 $9444 €8000 Cows in a summer meadow (66x101cm-26x40in) s. both artists prov.exhib.lit. 28-Oct-3 Christie's, Amsterdam #124/R est:7000-9000

GABRIEL-FOURNIER (1893-1963) French
£1400 $2562 €2044 Remorse of Judas (101x130cm-40x51in) 6-Apr-4 Bonhams, Knightsbridge #110/R est:1500-2000

GABRINI, Pietro (1865-1926) Italian
£4225 $7310 €6000 Chapel in the Lagoon (137x100cm-54x39in) s. 10-Dec-3 Sotheby's, Milan #28/R est:6000-8000
£10556 $19000 €15412 Royal visit (84x149cm-33x59in) s.i.d.1882. 23-Apr-4 Sotheby's, New York #194/R est:25000-35000
£16901 $29239 €24000 Auction in Rome (64x108cm-25x43in) s. 9-Dec-3 Pandolfini, Florence #78/R est:18000-25000
Works on paper
£378 $650 €552 Courting scene (36x25cm-14x10in) s.i. W/C. 7-Dec-3 Freeman, Philadelphia #25
£550 $1018 €803 Man walking his dog in the Roman countryside, St Peters in the distance (42x31cm-17x12in) s.d.1897 W/C. 9-Mar-4 Bonhams, New Bond Street #6/R
£867 $1551 €1300 Soldier (42x27cm-17x11in) s. W/C. 17-May-4 Finarte Semenzato, Rome #8/R
£867 $1586 €1300 Garde de palais (52x35cm-20x14in) s. W/C gouache. 3-Jun-4 Tajan, Paris #247/R est:1500-2000
£7182 $13000 €10486 Exotic beauty (61x46cm-24x18in) s.i. W/C pair. 30-Mar-4 Christie's, Rockefeller NY #66/R est:10000-15000

GABRON, Guilliam (1619-1678) Belgian
£8276 $13738 €12000 Still life with ham and bread on pewter plate (49x40cm-19x16in) panel lit. 1-Oct-3 Dorotheum, Vienna #117/R est:15000-18000

GAC, Jean le (c.1936-) French
Photographs
£4667 $8400 €7000 Delassement du peintre parisien (150x212cm-59x83in) s.d.1984 photograph dr prov. 25-Apr-4 Versailles Encheres #215/R est:6000-8000
Works on paper
£1990 $3662 €2985 Biographie avec masque Bakongo (58x102cm-23x40in) s.d.88 mixed media collage black white photograph prov. 9-Jun-4 Artcurial Briest, Paris #528a/R est:3000-3500

GACHET, Jules (1859-1914) Swiss
£1222 $2114 €1784 Matin bleu aux Grangettes (52x80cm-20x31in) s. prov. 12-Dec-3 Galerie du Rhone, Sion #650/R est:3500-4500 (S.FR 2700)

GACHET, Mario (1879- 1981) Italian
£336 $594 €500 Mount Blanc (35x45cm-14x18in) s. s.i.verso cardboard. 1-May-4 Meeting Art, Vercelli #314
£336 $594 €500 Sunset (35x45cm-14x18in) s. s.i.verso cardboard. 1-May-4 Meeting Art, Vercelli #304
£336 $594 €500 Landscape in Cesana (35x44cm-14x17in) s. cardboard. 1-May-4 Meeting Art, Vercelli #473
£347 $590 €500 Autumn (44x35cm-17x14in) s. cardboard. 1-Nov-3 Meeting Art, Vercelli #58
£369 $653 €550 Cogne (35x45cm-14x18in) s. i.verso cardboard. 1-May-4 Meeting Art, Vercelli #456
£382 $649 €550 Still life of flowers (35x45cm-14x18in) s. s.verso cardboard. 1-Nov-3 Meeting Art, Vercelli #276
£467 $859 €700 Landscape covered in snow (34x45cm-13x18in) s. cardboard. 14-Jun-4 Sant Agostino, Torino #206/R
£496 $829 €700 Soana Valley (33x43cm-13x17in) s. i.verso board. 20-Oct-3 Sant Agostino, Torino #155/R
£521 $885 €750 Andora (35x45cm-14x18in) s. cardboard. 1-Nov-3 Meeting Art, Vercelli #414
£638 $1066 €900 Piedmontese countryside (45x65cm-18x26in) s. cardboard. 20-Oct-3 Sant Agostino, Torino #105/R
£638 $1066 €900 Old farms in Brusson (35x44cm-14x17in) s.d.1921 cardboard. 20-Oct-3 Sant Agostino, Torino #108/R
£940 $1663 €1400 Landscape in Piedmonte (34x45cm-13x18in) s. board. 1-May-4 Meeting Art, Vercelli #353
£1389 $2361 €2000 Pasture (60x80cm-24x31in) s. 1-Nov-3 Meeting Art, Vercelli #177/R est:2000

GADAN, Antoine (1854-1934) French
£933 $1717 €1400 Crepuscule sur le Sud Algerien (20x35cm-8x14in) s. 14-Jun-4 Gros & Delettrez, Paris #518
£2676 $4630 €3800 Lavandieres (33x61cm-13x24in) s. 15-Dec-3 Gros & Delettrez, Paris #375/R est:3500-4000
£3169 $5482 €4500 Moisson, Algerie (55x100cm-22x39in) s. 15-Dec-3 Gros & Delettrez, Paris #371/R est:4500-6000
£3289 $6053 €5000 Gardeuse de moutons (55x98cm-22x39in) s. 25-Jun-4 Millon & Associes, Paris #85/R est:7000-8000
£6690 $11574 €9500 Ouider (100x150cm-39x59in) s.i.d.18868. 15-Dec-3 Gros & Delettrez, Paris #474/R est:8000-10000

GADANYI, Jeno (1896-1960) Hungarian
£855 $1514 €1248 Still life with a blue vase (51x35cm-20x14in) s.d.1924 canvas on cardboard. 28-Apr-4 Kieselbach, Budapest #18/R (H.F 320000)
£4176 $7225 €6097 Woman with a cockerel (98x73cm-39x29in) s.d.1951. 12-Dec-3 Kieselbach, Budapest #199/R (H.F 1600000)
Works on paper
£744 $1264 €1086 Models (53x37cm-21x15in) W/C chl. 29-Oct-3 Lawson Menzies, Sydney #252/R est:2000-3000 (A.D 1800)

GADD, Arthur (20th C) British
£260 $413 €380 The shape of destiny, Hawker Hurricane and Hawker Henly prototypes (58x89cm-23x35in) 24-Feb-4 Clarke Gammon, Guildford #14

GADD, Gerald V (?) British
Works on paper
£340 $609 €496 Farm near Trefonen (41x58cm-16x23in) s. W/C. 6-Jan-4 Gildings, Market Harborough #388

GADDI, Angelo di Taddeo (attrib) (c.1345-1396) Italian
£8889 $16000 €12978 Presentation of Christ in the temple (27x33cm-11x13in) gold ground tempera on prov. 22-Jan-4 Sotheby's, New York #223/R est:12000-16000

GADEA, Patricia (1960-) Spanish
£272 $495 €400 Untitled (59x42cm-23x17in) s.d.1984 acrylic collage prov. 3-Feb-4 Segre, Madrid #265/R
£1020 $1857 €1500 Miss World (180x160cm-71x63in) s.d.1984 acrylic prov. 3-Feb-4 Segre, Madrid #264/R
Works on paper
£272 $495 €400 Untitled (59x42cm-23x17in) s.d.1984 gouache card prov. 3-Feb-4 Segre, Madrid #266/R

GADEGAARD, Paul (1920-1996) Danish
£1127 $1882 €1645 Concrete composition (23x28cm-9x11in) s.d.53. 7-Oct-3 Rasmussen, Copenhagen #291/R est:6000-8000 (D.KR 12000)
£1221 $2038 €1783 Concrete composition (23x28cm-9x11in) s.d.53. 7-Oct-3 Rasmussen, Copenhagen #287/R est:6000-8000 (D.KR 13000)
£2085 $3336 €3023 Composition (60x73cm-24x29in) s.d.1955 verso. 17-Sep-3 Kunsthallen, Copenhagen #16/R est:14000 (D.KR 22000)
£2688 $4839 €3924 Concrete composition (135x153cm-53x60in) prov. 24-Apr-4 Rasmussen, Havnen #4277/R est:30000-50000 (D.KR 30000)

GADEYNE, Jules (1857-1936) Belgian?
£671 $1242 €1000 Fishing boats (16x30cm-6x12in) s. panel two. 13-Mar-4 De Vuyst, Lokeren #143

GAEL, Barent (c.1620-1703) Dutch
£2207 $3686 €3200 Travellers in front of the public house (13x19cm-5x7in) s. panel. 11-Nov-3 Vendu Notarishuis, Rotterdam #145/R est:1500-2000
£2378 $4042 €3400 Riders talking with woman and child seated nearby (39x55cm-15x22in) s. panel. 20-Nov-3 Dorotheum, Salzburg #96/R est:4400-6500
£2447 $4087 €3500 Travellers resting near an inn (60x52cm-24x20in) s. 30-Jun-3 Sotheby's, Amsterdam #32/R
£2778 $4389 €4000 Travellers resting at the edge of a wood (36x30cm-14x12in) indis sig. panel. 2-Sep-3 Christie's, Amsterdam #41/R est:3000-5000
£3200 $5856 €4672 Cavaliers resting before an inn (39x55cm-15x22in) s. panel prov. 6-Jul-4 Sotheby's, Olympia #468/R est:3000-5000
£3425 $5822 €5000 Horsemen resting before houses (32x38cm-13x15in) s. 4-Nov-3 Sotheby's, Amsterdam #51/R est:5000-7000
£3800 $6840 €5548 Wooded landscape with hawking party (26x29cm-10x11in) s. panel. 23-Apr-4 Christie's, Kensington #99/R est:2000-3000
£4500 $7650 €6570 Peasants and horsemen in a village street (31x43cm-12x17in) init. panel. 29-Oct-3 Bonhams, New Bond Street #53/R est:2000-3000
£4500 $8235 €6570 Peasants brawling outside a village tavern (48x61cm-19x24in) 7-Jul-4 Bonhams, New Bond Street #131/R est:5000-8000
£4600 $8280 €6716 Landscape with peasant selling chickens outside a cottage (22x19cm-9x7in) s. prov. 20-Apr-4 Sotheby's, Olympia #269/R est:2000-3000
£5333 $9547 €8000 Village landscape with travellers on the street by a vegetable seller (48x62cm-19x24in) s. 17-May-4 Christie's, Amsterdam #27/R est:8000-12000
£8276 $14897 €12000 Riders by farm (32x38cm-13x15in) s. 26-Jan-4 Ansorena, Madrid #59/R est:12000
£11000 $20130 €16060 Hunting party fording a stream. Horsemen and peasants outside an inn (31x35cm-12x14in) s. canvas on panel pair. 7-Jul-4 Bonhams, New Bond Street #15/R est:10000-15000
£12000 $21960 €17520 Village with peasants at a chicken market. Village with peasants at a pig market (30x36cm-12x14in) s. panel pair. 7-Jul-4 Bonhams, New Bond Street #132/R est:6000-8000

GAEL, Barent (attrib) (c.1620-1703) Dutch
£1655 $2764 €2400 Market with figures and riders on horseback (38x53cm-15x21in) panel. 11-Nov-3 Vendu Notarishuis, Rotterdam #141 est:1000-1500

GAELEN, Alexander van (attrib) (1670-1728) Dutch
£4000 $7280 €5840 William III's procession to the Houses of Parliament (56x88cm-22x35in) prov. 1-Jul-4 Sotheby's, London #151/R est:5000-7000

GAERTNER, Carl (1898-1952) American
£299 $500 €437 Mining landscape (53x71cm-21x28in) s.d.1948 oil on paper. 14-Nov-3 Aspire, Cleveland #72
£1732 $3100 €2529 Lewis Hollow (56x74cm-22x29in) s.d.1945 panel exhib. 7-May-4 Sloans & Kenyon, Bethesda #1724/R est:6000-8000
£2096 $3500 €3060 Covert's old pasture (55x75cm-22x30in) s.d.1947 tempera masonite prov.exhib.lit. 7-Oct-3 Sotheby's, New York #225 est:2000-3000
Works on paper
£324 $600 €473 Winter country landscape with houses (38x53cm-15x21in) s.d.1953 gouache. 24-Jan-4 Jeffery Burchard, Florida #18a/R
£528 $950 €771 The suburb (38x53cm-15x21in) i.d.1946 verso gouache. 26-Apr-4 Winter Associates, Plainville #167/R est:1000-1500

GAGARIN (?) ?
£1648 $2918 €2472 View of Serra dos Orgaos (100x200cm-39x79in) s. 27-Apr-4 Bolsa de Arte, Rio de Janeiro #16/R (B.R 9000)

GAGE, George W (1887-1957) American
£1557 $2600 €2273 Couple looking across vast African expanse (76x51cm-30x20in) s. painted c.1920. 15-Nov-3 Illustration House, New York #115/R est:3000-4000

GAGEN, Robert Ford (1847-1926) Canadian
£579 $1053 €845 Pastoral landscape (38x53cm-15x21in) s.d.1898 prov. 5-Feb-4 Heffel, Vancouver #33/R (C.D 1400)
£1000 $1830 €1460 Don river scene (37x52cm-15x20in) s.d.189 prov. 1-Jun-4 Joyner Waddington, Toronto #237/R est:2500-3000 (C.D 2500)
Works on paper
£181 $336 €264 Brook (25x35cm-10x14in) s.d.06 W/C. 2-Mar-4 Ritchie, Toronto #55/R (C.D 450)
£280 $529 €409 Venice (25x25cm-10x10in) s.d.1868 W/C. 23-Feb-4 David Duggleby, Scarborough #619/R
£294 $491 €429 Incoming fog (24x34cm-9x13in) s.i. W/C. 17-Nov-3 Hodgins, Calgary #264/R (C.D 650)
£335 $576 €489 Dorys (20x29cm-8x11in) s.i. W/C. 2-Dec-3 Joyner Waddington, Toronto #365/R (C.D 750)
£800 $1464 €1168 Cascading stream, Rockies (32x434cm-13x171in) s.d.1908 W/C. 1-Jun-4 Joyner Waddington, Toronto #6/R est:2000-3000 (C.D 2000)

GAGLIARDI, Giovanni (fl.1860-1908) Italian
£1690 $2721 €2400 Saint Agnese (80x71cm-31x28in) 8-May-3 Farsetti, Prato #258/R est:2000-2500

GAGLIARDINI, Julien Gustave (1846-1927) French
£345 $572 €500 Retour des pecheurs (21x29cm-8x11in) s. cardboard. 1-Oct-3 Millon & Associes, Paris #53
£789 $1453 €1200 Bateau a voile (37x54cm-15x21in) s. 22-Jun-4 Chassaing Rivet, Toulouse #291
£1000 $1790 €1500 Paysage et maisons (38x55cm-15x22in) s. 15-May-4 other European Auctioneer #65
£1067 $1963 €1600 Bord de mer (27x40cm-11x16in) s. panel. 11-Jun-4 Claude Aguttes, Neuilly #180/R est:2000-2500
£1325 $2411 €2000 Paysage de dunes aux moulins (54x38cm-21x15in) s. 16-Jun-4 Renaud, Paris #25 est:2000-2500
£1918 $3260 €2800 Ruelle de village en Provence (73x54cm-29x21in) s.d.1908. 9-Nov-3 Eric Pillon, Calais #112/R
£1933 $3557 €2900 Chevriere sur les bords d'un rivage mediterraneen (96x141cm-38x56in) s. 14-Jun-4 Tajan, Paris #13 est:2000-3000
£2333 $4293 €3500 Mistral sur l'Etang de Berre (54x73cm-21x29in) s. 11-Jun-4 Claude Aguttes, Neuilly #178/R est:4000-6000

GAGLIOLO, Sergio (1934-) Italian
£629 $1051 €900 Two riverbanks (60x50cm-24x20in) s. i.verso. 26-Jun-3 Sant Agostino, Torino #215/R

GAGNEREAUX, Benigne (1756-1795) French
Works on paper
£319 $533 €450 Italianate landscape (21x30cm-8x12in) ink wash. 14-Oct-3 Finarte Semenzato, Rome #234/R
£1176 $2000 €1717 Classical figures at an anvil (33x47cm-13x19in) s.i. pen ink sepia wash htd white pair. 19-Nov-3 Bonhams & Butterfields, San Francisco #7/R

GAGNEREAUX, Jean Baptiste Claude Benigne (1765-1846) French
Works on paper
£612 $1096 €900 Portrait de femme portant un mantille. Portrait d'homme portant un jabot (61x45cm-24x18in) s.d.1807 pastel pair. 18-Mar-4 Christie's, Paris #261/R

GAGNON, Clarence A (1881-1942) Canadian
£1600 $2928 €2336 Forest trail (14x22cm-6x9in) s.d.1906 board. 1-Jun-4 Joyner Waddington, Toronto #178/R est:5000-7000 (C.D 4000)
£1818 $2964 €2654 Quebec farmstead (16x23cm-6x9in) s. panel. 23-Sep-3 Ritchie, Toronto #78/R est:2000-2500 (C.D 4000)
£2928 $4977 €4275 Engadine, Suisse (15x23cm-6x9in) panel prov. 21-Nov-3 Walker's, Ottawa #81/R est:7000-9000 (C.D 6500)
£3378 $5743 €4932 Ranafjord, Norway (11x18cm-4x7in) panel prov. 21-Nov-3 Walker's, Ottawa #80/R est:7000-8000 (C.D 7500)
£3500 $5845 €5110 Jour de boucherie (11x17cm-4x7in) s.verso panel. 14-Oct-3 Sotheby's, London #204/R est:1000-1500
£3600 $6588 €5256 Dans les Alpes (15x22cm-6x9in) panel painted 1927 prov. 1-Jun-4 Joyner Waddington, Toronto #226/R est:12000-15000 (C.D 9000)
£4241 $7295 €6192 Estuaire de la riviere du Gouffre, Baie St Paul (12x17cm-5x7in) board painted 1939. 2-Dec-3 Joyner Waddington, Toronto #57/R est:8000-10000 (C.D 9500)
£5417 $9913 €7909 Etude Baie St-Paul (19x27cm-7x11in) panel painted c.1923. 27-Jan-4 Iegor de Saint Hippolyte, Montreal #15 (C.D 13000)
£6000 $10980 €8760 Rang de la Gondrouenie, Baie St Paul (11x17cm-4x7in) panel painted 1939. 1-Jun-4 Joyner Waddington, Toronto #63/R est:12000-15000 (C.D 15000)
£243902 $436585 €356097 Landscape at Baie St. Paul (51x66cm-20x26in) s.i. prov.exhib.lit. 31-May-4 Sotheby's, Toronto #81/R est:500000-700000 (C.D 600000)
Prints
£8800 $16104 €12848 Le Lac, Seminaire St Sulpice, Montreal (19x24cm-7x9in) studio st. etching exec 1909-1917 prov.lit. 1-Jun-4 Joyner Waddington, Toronto #148/R est:2500-3000 (C.D 22000)
Works on paper
£360 $659 €526 Glacier study (8x7cm-3x3in) studio st. col crayons. 1-Jun-4 Joyner Waddington, Toronto #282/R (C.D 900)
£600 $1002 €876 Moulin a St. Briac (13x20cm-5x8in) i. pencil. 14-Oct-3 Sotheby's, London #212/R
£600 $1002 €876 Town in France (19x24cm-7x9in) pencil. 14-Oct-3 Sotheby's, London #215/R
£800 $1336 €1168 View of Quebec City (13x20cm-5x8in) i. pencil. 14-Oct-3 Sotheby's, London #206/R
£1400 $2338 €2044 French towns (20x27cm-8x11in) two i. brown wash over pencil five. 14-Oct-3 Sotheby's, London #213/R est:600-800

£1900 $3173 €2774 Riviere du Gouffre (14x20cm-6x8in) s. gouache prov. 14-Oct-3 Sotheby's, London #205/R est:800-1200
£1900 $3173 €2774 Bend of a river (15x23cm-6x9in) s. gouache pencil. 14-Oct-3 Sotheby's, London #208/R est:400-600
£4600 $7682 €6716 Untitled (25x20cm-10x8in) folio of ten drawings and W/C. 14-Oct-3 Sotheby's, London #209/R est:1000-1500
£11607 $19964 €16946 Sunday Mass (17x12cm-7x5in) init. gouache. 2-Dec-3 Joyner Waddington, Toronto #38/R est:10000-15000 (C.D 26000)

GAGO PASCUAL, Elena (1938-) Spanish
£379 $683 €550 Boats (30x21cm-12x8in) s. board. 26-Jan-4 Durán, Madrid #1239/R

GAHAGAN, Lawrence (18/19th C) British
Sculpture
£1358 $2200 €1983 George III (28cm-11in) indis.i.base bronze prov. 3-Aug-3 North East Auctions, Portsmouth #1666/R

GAHMAN, Floyd (1894-1979) American
£302 $550 €453 Winter landscape (43x53cm-17x21in) s. board. 20-Jun-4 Charlton Hall, Columbia #699/R

GAI QI (1773-1828) Chinese
Works on paper
£890 $1514 €1300 Beautiful woman in garden (84x34cm-33x13in) s.i. seals Indian ink col. 7-Nov-3 Dr Fritz Nagel, Stuttgart #861/R
£2134 $3841 €3116 Flowers (20x26cm-8x10in) s.i. ink col leaves six album. 25-Apr-4 Christie's, Hong Kong #438/R est:30000-40000 (HK.D 30000)
£2276 $4097 €3323 Flowers (31x105cm-12x41in) s.i.d.1823 ink col scroll silk. 25-Apr-4 Christie's, Hong Kong #408/R est:10000-15000 (HK.D 32000)

GAIDAN, Louis (1847-1925) French
£2449 $3894 €3600 Ruines romaines (50x73cm-20x29in) s. panel. 21-Mar-3 Bailly Pommery, Paris #124
£13000 $23920 €18980 Au bord de la riviere (50x38cm-20x15in) s. 22-Jun-4 Sotheby's, London #127/R est:8000-12000
£16760 $30000 €24470 Cap brun (54x73cm-21x29in) s. prov. 6-May-4 Sotheby's, New York #257/R est:18000-25000
£20000 $36400 €30000 Cap brun (54x73cm-21x29in) s. prov. 29-Jun-4 Sotheby's, Paris #15/R est:10000-15000
£27000 $49140 €39420 Sous les pins a carqueiranne (110x150cm-43x59in) s. prov. 4-Feb-4 Sotheby's, London #210/R est:30000-40000

GAIGHER, Horazio (1870-1938) ?
£1806 $2979 €2600 Bacchantal women (50x60cm-20x24in) bears s. board. 2-Jul-3 Neumeister, Munich #642/R est:1500
£2292 $3781 €3300 Female model in drawing class (43x52cm-17x20in) i. panel. 2-Jul-3 Neumeister, Munich #643 est:1000

GAIGNOUX, Yves (?) French
£369 $687 €550 Tempete au Havre (33x46cm-13x18in) s. panel. 7-Mar-4 Lesieur & Le Bars, Le Havre #167

GAIL, Wilhelm (1804-1890) German
£1259 $2140 €1800 Bull fighters waiting for the bullfight (51x61cm-20x24in) s.d.1870. 28-Nov-3 Wendl, Rudolstadt #3971/R est:1800
£3400 $6222 €5100 Harvest (33x41cm-13x16in) s. panel pair. 6-Jun-4 Osenat, Fontainebleau #111/R est:4200-4500

GAILLARD-DESCHAMPS, Alexandre (c.1903-1984) French
£1067 $1909 €1600 Jour de marche a Quimperle (33x41cm-13x16in) s. panel. 16-May-4 Thierry & Lannon, Brest #316/R est:800-900

GAILLARDOT, Pierre (1910-2002) French
£662 $1205 €1000 Vue de quai (73x92cm-29x36in) s. 18-Jun-4 Piasa, Paris #172/R
£662 $1205 €1000 Les voiliers (54x65cm-21x26in) s. 18-Jun-4 Piasa, Paris #173
£1096 $1721 €1600 Clairefontaine (27x41cm-11x16in) s.d.1971. 20-Apr-3 Deauville, France #156 est:3000-4000
Works on paper
£306 $548 €450 Chevaux au paddock (24x32cm-9x13in) s. W/C. 21-Mar-4 Muizon & Le Coent, Paris #38
£417 $654 €600 Course (25x49cm-10x19in) s. W/C. 29-Aug-3 Deauville, France #180
£479 $753 €700 Planches a Deauville (42x62cm-17x24in) s. W/C. 20-Apr-3 Deauville, France #26
£542 $850 €780 Course (35x51cm-14x20in) s. W/C. 29-Aug-3 Deauville, France #170
£563 $883 €810 Etudes de chevaux (42x62cm-17x24in) s. W/C. 29-Aug-3 Deauville, France #183
£903 $1417 €1300 Chevaux montes a Deauville (45x60cm-18x24in) s. W/C. 29-Aug-3 Deauville, France #181
£951 $1494 €1370 Etudes de chevaux (50x66cm-20x26in) s. W/C. 29-Aug-3 Deauville, France #171/R
£1284 $2426 €1900 Course de sulky (47x64cm-19x25in) s. W/C. 21-Feb-4 Livinec, Gaudcheau & Jezequel, Rennes #110

GAILLIARD, Franz (1861-1932) Belgian
£811 $1532 €1200 Portrait en pied de Cyril van Overberg (170x125cm-67x49in) s. 17-Feb-4 Vanderkindere, Brussels #50
£980 $1852 €1450 Bord de mer (39x59cm-15x23in) s. 17-Feb-4 Vanderkindere, Brussels #38
£2703 $5108 €4000 L'incendie de Louvain (125x175cm-49x69in) s.d.1914. 17-Feb-4 Vanderkindere, Brussels #70 est:2000-3000
£6757 $12770 €10000 Paysage anime a Delphes Grece (99x77cm-39x30in) s. 17-Feb-4 Vanderkindere, Brussels #27 est:2500-4000
£7971 $13072 €11000 Plage (38x57cm-15x22in) s. s.i.verso canvas on board prov. 27-May-3 Sotheby's, Amsterdam #309/R est:12000-15000
£12838 $24264 €19000 Femmes donnant a manger aux pigeons Place Saint Marc a Venise (170x125cm-67x49in) s. 17-Feb-4 Vanderkindere, Brussels #85/R est:15000-25000
£13851 $26179 €20500 L'Acropole a Athenes (170x125cm-67x49in) s. 17-Feb-4 Vanderkindere, Brussels #16/R est:7500-12500
£23333 $42000 €34066 Sidewalk cafe (65x51cm-26x20in) s.d.1884. 22-Apr-4 Christie's, Rockefeller NY #181/R est:50000-70000
Works on paper
£490 $832 €700 La renommee. s. ink W/C. 18-Nov-3 Galerie Moderne, Brussels #594/R

GAILLIARD, Jean Jacques (1890-1976) Belgian
£533 $955 €800 Summer landscape (40x55cm-16x22in) s. canvas on panel. 15-May-4 De Vuyst, Lokeren #140
£594 $1022 €850 Entrainement pour le championnat du sommeil (57x36cm-22x14in) s. panel. 8-Dec-3 Horta, Bruxelles #117
£800 $1464 €1200 Chemin au bord de l'etang (64x43cm-25x17in) s. panel. 7-Jun-4 Palais de Beaux Arts, Brussels #259/R
£903 $1435 €1300 Jeune femme nue (40x20cm-16x8in) s.d.1949 panel. 15-Sep-3 Horta, Bruxelles #90
£909 $1545 €1300 Ostende, apres le beau temps vient la pluie (26x33cm-10x13in) s. s.i.verso board. 25-Nov-3 Christie's, Amsterdam #240a/R
£967 $1730 €1450 Je suis dans les vagues (45x60cm-18x24in) s. i.verso panel. 11-May-4 Vanderkindere, Brussels #121
£1172 $2169 €1700 Deux peintres dans les dunes (34x46cm-13x18in) s. panel. 16-Feb-4 Horta, Bruxelles #159 est:1800-2000
£1224 $2192 €1800 Nuit et jour sur le tombeau de la Malibran (35x48cm-14x19in) s. panel. 16-Mar-4 Vanderkindere, Brussels #180 est:1250-1750
£1319 $2150 €1900 View of Lake Lugano (68x40cm-27x16in) s. panel. 29-Sep-3 Sotheby's, Amsterdam #338/R
£2349 $4158 €3500 Le portrait de ma mere (51x35cm-20x14in) s. cardboard. 27-Apr-4 Campo, Vlaamse Kaai #422/R est:4000-5000
£2819 $5215 €4200 Entree du paradis (60x40cm-24x16in) s. painted c.1945. 15-Mar-4 Horta, Bruxelles #181/R est:3500-5000
£3836 $6521 €5600 Casino d'Ixelles (46x65cm-18x26in) s. panel. 10-Nov-3 Horta, Bruxelles #129/R
£5208 $8281 €7500 Ensor a Tervuren (37x47cm-15x19in) s. s.i.verso panel. 15-Sep-3 Horta, Bruxelles #89/R est:5500-7500
Works on paper
£276 $508 €420 Place Royale a Bruxelles (31x50cm-12x20in) s.d.1956. 22-Jun-4 Palais de Beaux Arts, Brussels #245
£280 $507 €420 Fussen (35x26cm-14x10in) s. india ink W/C. 30-Mar-4 Palais de Beaux Arts, Brussels #592
£320 $579 €480 Musee d'Ensor (26x35cm-10x14in) s.d.1961 india ink htd W/C. 30-Mar-4 Palais de Beaux Arts, Brussels #590
£805 $1490 €1200 Le temple de Paestum en Sicile (35x47cm-14x19in) s.d.3 juin 1969 W/C. 15-Mar-4 Horta, Bruxelles #182
£850 $1522 €1250 Maison Van Bellinghem-Tomberg (50x38cm-20x15in) s.i.verso W/C. 16-Mar-4 Vanderkindere, Brussels #173

GAIMARI, Enrique (20th C) Argentinian?
Sculpture
£1099 $2000 €1605 Couple (27cm-11in) s.d.65 wood. 29-Jun-4 Arroyo, Buenos Aires #31/R est:2000
£1099 $2000 €1605 Nude (30cm-12in) s.d.79 wood. 29-Jun-4 Arroyo, Buenos Aires #37/R est:1800
£3279 $6000 €4787 Tranformation (68cm-27in) wood. 1-Jun-4 Arroyo, Buenos Aires #34

GAINSBOROUGH, Thomas (1727-1788) British
£1650000 $2805000 €2409000 Portrait of Richard Tickell, wearing a brown coat (74x62cm-29x24in) 27-Nov-3 Sotheby's, London #8/R est:400000-600000
Works on paper
£1048 $1750 €1530 Sketch of the family Ponsonby (20x25cm-8x10in) i.verso dr. 16-Nov-3 Simpson's, Houston #68/R
£5000 $9150 €7300 Wooded landscape with figures, donkeys and buildings (16x20cm-6x8in) pencil prov.lit. 3-Jun-4 Christie's, London #64/R est:6000-8000
£7000 $12810 €10220 Wooded landscape with herdsmen, cows, river and church tower (16x20cm-6x8in) pencil prov.lit. 3-Jun-4 Christie's, London #63/R est:8000-12000
£8200 $14924 €11972 Mountainous landscape with cart and figures (25x35cm-10x14in) blk chk stump white chk buff laid paper prov.lit. 1-Jul-4 Sotheby's, London #173/R est:6000-8000
£9000 $15300 €13140 Figures and cattle in a wooded landscape (27x35cm-11x14in) i. pencil grey wash white chk. 20-Nov-3 Christie's, London #3/R est:6000-7000
£9884 $17000 €14431 Covered wagon with horses and rider before a church (25x36cm-10x14in) black chk htd white. 7-Dec-3 Hindman, Chicago #710/R est:20000-40000
£11500 $19550 €16790 Portrait of Anne Lynch as a child (12x10cm-5x4in) i. pencil on vellum oval prov. 27-Nov-3 Sotheby's, London #213/R est:12000-15000
£12000 $20400 €17520 Faggot gatherer (19x15cm-7x6in) pencil prov.lit. 20-Nov-3 Christie's, London #55/R est:7000-10000
£35000 $64050 €51100 Wooded landscape with sheep grazing by a winding track (28x38cm-11x15in) i. blk chk stump W/C htd touches white prov.lit. 3-Jun-4 Christie's, London #62/R est:40000-60000
£40000 $68000 €58400 Wooded landscape with riders, sheep and pool (27x36cm-11x14in) black chk stump. 27-Nov-3 Sotheby's, London #2/R est:40000-60000

GAINSBOROUGH, Thomas (attrib) (1727-1788) British
£2963 $4800 €4296 Figures outside a cottage. Untitled (30x24cm-12x9in) s. board double-sided. 8-Aug-3 Barridorf, Portland #85/R est:3000-5000
£21978 $40000 €32088 Portrait of Rev Humphry Gainsborough in a black coat (76x63cm-30x25in) 17-Jun-4 Christie's, Rockefeller NY #51/R est:30000-50000

GAINSBOROUGH, Thomas (circle) (1727-1788) British
£10056 $18000 €14682 Cottage door (148x122cm-58x48in) 27-May-4 Sotheby's, New York #258/R est:7000-10000

GAINSBOROUGH, Thomas (style) (1727-1788) British
£5800 $10266 €8468 Portrait of Charlotte Louisa Paterson, seated in a woodland setting (120x90cm-47x35in) 27-Apr-4 Henry Adams, Chichester #672/R est:2000-3000

GAISSER, Jakob Emmanuel (1825-1899) German
£660 $1042 €950 The ambush (52x43cm-20x17in) s. 5-Sep-3 Wendl, Rudolstadt #3363/R
£1800 $3330 €2628 Toasting a new song (38x28cm-15x11in) s. panel. 9-Mar-4 Bonhams, Knightsbridge #189/R est:1500-2000
£2414 $4031 €3500 La promenade du gentilhomme (112x87cm-44x34in) s. 17-Nov-3 Tajan, Paris #143/R est:4000-5000
£2416 $4277 €3600 Surprise home coming (65x90cm-26x35in) s. d.1876 verso. 28-Apr-4 Schopman, Hamburg #472/R est:2800
£3082 $4839 €4500 Card game (34x44cm-13x17in) s. panel. 20-Apr-3 Deauville, France #59/R est:4000-4500
£5245 $9021 €7500 Celebration in castle room (60x79cm-24x31in) s. panel. 5-Dec-3 Bolland & Marotz, Bremen #550/R est:7900

GAISSER, Max (1857-1922) German
£1176 $2175 €1717 Gentleman looking out the window (20x15cm-8x6in) 14-Mar-4 Agra, Warsaw #7/R (P.Z 8500)
£1189 $2045 €1700 Old man counting money (15x18cm-6x7in) s. panel. 3-Dec-3 Neumeister, Munich #571/R est:1500
£1765 $3000 €2577 Composer in his loft (40x50cm-16x20in) s. panel. 21-Nov-3 Skinner, Boston #232/R est:3000-5000
£1831 $3168 €2600 Notary (18x14cm-7x6in) s. panel. 13-Dec-3 Lempertz, Koln #19/R est:2000
£20000 $36800 €29200 In the goldsmith's house (101x121cm-40x48in) s. prov. 25-Mar-4 Christie's, Kensington #203/R est:12000-18000

GAISSNER, Jeanne (?) French?
£1400 $2562 €2100 Coin de jardin, les rosiers rouge et jaune (134x89cm-53x35in) s.d.90. 6-Jun-4 Anaf, Lyon #387 est:3000-4000

GAITIS, Yannis (1923-1984) Greek
£2400 $4296 €3504 Composition (33x46cm-13x18in) s. 11-May-4 Bonhams, New Bond Street #105/R est:2000-3000
£4000 $7000 €5840 Composition (49x64cm-19x25in) s.d.4.12.54 tempera card. 16-Dec-3 Bonhams, New Bond Street #135/R est:2000-3000
£4000 $7160 €5840 Untitled (46x38cm-18x15in) s. 10-May-4 Sotheby's, Olympia #40/R est:4000-6000
£5500 $9845 €8030 Abstract composition (46x61cm-18x24in) s. lit. 10-May-4 Sotheby's, Olympia #39/R est:3000-4000
£9500 $17005 €13870 Angel (146x114cm-57x45in) s. prov.lit. 11-May-4 Bonhams, New Bond Street #114/R est:8000-12000
£15000 $26250 €21900 Blue composition (116x80cm-46x31in) s.d.62. 16-Dec-3 Bonhams, New Bond Street #131/R est:8000-12000
Sculpture
£14667 $26987 €22000 Men in black and white (103cm-41in) painted wooden sculpture exec c.1970. 9-Jun-4 Artcurial Briest, Paris #509/R est:8000-10000
Works on paper
£2000 $3580 €2920 Le cock (45x33cm-18x13in) s.d.52 gouache. 11-May-4 Bonhams, New Bond Street #118/R est:2000-3000

GAKUTEI, Yashima (c.1786-1868) Japanese
Prints
£13000 $23920 €18980 Portraits of six generals (21x18cm-8x7in) s. print six exec. early 1820's lit. 8-Jun-4 Sotheby's, London #474/R est:4500-6500

GAL, Menchu (1923-) Spanish
£2014 $3323 €2900 Vase with mimosas (37x27cm-15x11in) s. board. 2-Jul-3 Ansorena, Madrid #848/R
£2324 $4020 €3300 Balcony (23x29cm-9x11in) s. board. 15-Dec-3 Ansorena, Madrid #948/R est:2500
£9396 $16819 €14000 Hendaya beach (28x70cm-11x28in) s. board. 25-May-4 Durán, Madrid #142/R est:8000
£11806 $18771 €17000 Landscape with Salamanca in the background (47x46cm-19x18in) s. panel. 29-Apr-3 Durán, Madrid #153/R est:17000
£13423 $24027 €20000 Landscape in Baztan (50x61cm-20x24in) s. board. 25-May-4 Durán, Madrid #141/R est:10000
£17450 $32456 €26000 Landscape (54x66cm-21x26in) s. 2-Mar-4 Ansorena, Madrid #858/R est:10000
£20690 $37241 €30000 Village in Catalunia (81x103cm-32x41in) s. s.i.d.1957 verso. 26-Jan-4 Durán, Madrid #209/R est:12000
Works on paper
£4362 $8158 €6500 Parasols (30x42cm-12x17in) s. W/C lit. 24-Feb-4 Durán, Madrid #213/R est:6000
£4362 $8158 €6500 Ondarraitz Cape (34x49cm-13x19in) s. W/C lit. 24-Feb-4 Durán, Madrid #235/R est:6000

GALAN, Julio (1958-) Mexican
£13408 $24000 €19576 Collage (190x130cm-75x51in) s.d.1998 oil collage mixed media prov. 26-May-4 Sotheby's, New York #170/R est:25000-35000

GALAND, Léon (1872-1960) French
£552 $1021 €800 Communiantes en Provence (35x27cm-14x11in) s.d.1914. 16-Feb-4 Giraudeau, Tours #72
£667 $1227 €1000 Jeune femme au bord d'un lac (60x70cm-24x28in) s. panel. 14-Jun-4 Horta, Bruxelles #457

GALANIS, Demetrius (1882-1966) French
£50000 $85000 €73000 Cabaret scene (67x59cm-26x23in) s.d.1910 paper on panel prov. 18-Nov-3 Sotheby's, London #37/R est:30000-50000
£100000 $175000 €146000 La danseuse, portrait de mademoiselle Schwartz de l'Opera (151x110cm-59x43in) s.d.1920 exhib.lit. 16-Dec-3 Bonhams, New Bond Street #49/R est:120000-180000
Works on paper
£1600 $2864 €2336 The hare (19x23cm-7x9in) s. ink. 11-May-4 Bonhams, New Bond Street #97/R est:1200-1800
£1800 $3150 €2628 Boy on a chair (50x40cm-20x16in) s.i. pastel. 16-Dec-3 Bonhams, New Bond Street #88/R est:1800-2200
£2800 $5012 €4088 Easter Procession (37x27cm-15x11in) s. gouache. 10-May-4 Sotheby's, Olympia #2/R est:3000-4000

GALANTE, Francesco (1884-1972) Italian
£845 $1403 €1200 Veduta costiera con bagnanti (25x35cm-10x14in) canvasboard. 11-Jun-3 Christie's, Rome #71/R

GALANTE, Nicola (1883-1969) Italian
£1733 $3189 €2600 Nella (39x27cm-15x11in) s.d.1962. 14-Jun-4 Sant Agostino, Torino #346/R est:2500-3000
£5517 $9214 €8000 Alpine lake (40x55cm-16x22in) s.d.1961. 17-Nov-3 Sant Agostino, Torino #209/R est:8000-10000
Works on paper
£1172 $1958 €1700 Sailing boats on the lake (38x48cm-15x19in) pastel. 17-Nov-3 Sant Agostino, Torino #202/R est:2200

GALANTI, Mario (1923-) Italian
£521 $885 €750 Fishermen at sunset (70x100cm-28x39in) s. 1-Nov-3 Meeting Art, Vercelli #412

GALARNEAU, Leopold (fl.1882-1896) Canadian
£335 $576 €489 Adonis (21x25cm-8x10in) s.d.1887-1900 mono.i.verso prov. 2-Dec-3 Ritchie, Toronto #103/R (C.D 750)
£580 $998 €847 Two equestrian portraits, Martydom. Dauntless (38x51cm-15x20in) s.d.1894 pair. 2-Dec-3 Ritchie, Toronto #104/R (C.D 1300)

GALBRUND, Alphonse (1810-1885) French
Works on paper
£1000 $1850 €1460 Portrait of a young lady (53x31cm-21x12in) s.d.1876 pastel. 9-Mar-4 Bonhams, New Bond Street #9/R est:1000-1500

GALBUSERA, Giovacchino (1871-1944) Italian
£866 $1550 €1264 Shore with reeds and waterlilies (19x42cm-7x17in) s. panel. 22-Mar-4 Philippe Schuler, Zurich #4405/R (S.FR 2000)
£1034 $1852 €1510 Mountain lake in the Alps (25x35cm-10x14in) s. panel. 14-May-4 Dobiaschofsky, Bern #67/R est:1800 (S.FR 2400)
£1086 $1846 €1586 Cows on alpine pasture with view of Lake Lugano (25x34cm-10x13in) s. i. verso panel. 19-Nov-3 Fischer, Luzern #2104/R est:1800-2200 (S.FR 2400)
£1087 $1989 €1587 Still life with plums (40x63cm-16x25in) s. 4-Jun-4 Zofingen, Switzerland #2802/R est:3000 (S.FR 2500)
£1629 $2769 €2378 Moesolasee (23x33cm-9x13in) s. panel. 19-Nov-3 Fischer, Luzern #1277/R est:3000-4000 (S.FR 3600)
£1810 $3241 €2643 Still life with pears and black grapes (28x57cm-11x22in) s. 14-May-4 Dobiaschofsky, Bern #66/R est:3000 (S.FR 4200)
£1940 $3472 €2832 Woman walking in Tessin Alps (31x52cm-12x20in) s. 14-May-4 Dobiaschofsky, Bern #65/R est:5500 (S.FR 4500)
£2353 $4000 €3435 Lugano (41x52cm-16x20in) s. 19-Nov-3 Fischer, Luzern #1276/R est:2500-3500 (S.FR 5200)
£5727 $9736 €8361 Flower children (151x96cm-59x38in) s. 7-Nov-3 Dobiaschofsky, Bern #183/R est:18000 (S.FR 13000)

GALDAMEZ, Fabian (20th C) Argentinian?
Sculpture
£2077 $3800 €3032 Homage to Stonehenge (55cm-22in) stone. 1-Jun-4 Arroyo, Buenos Aires #33
£2186 $4000 €3192 Woman riding (34cm-13in) granite. 1-Jun-4 Arroyo, Buenos Aires #36

GALE, Denise (20th C) American
£256 $450 €374 Untitled, abstract expressionist composition (183x198cm-72x78in) acrylic. 22-May-4 Selkirks, St. Louis #558/R

GALE, Martin (1949-) British
£4430 $7840 €6600 Weekend (41x51cm-16x20in) s. 27-Apr-4 Whyte's, Dublin #62/R est:3000-4000
Works on paper
£1268 $2028 €1800 Field day no 2 (30x30cm-12x12in) s.d.2003 i.verso W/C prov. 16-Sep-3 Whyte's, Dublin #141/R est:1500-2000
£3380 $5408 €4800 Red ribbon. Way out east (30x48cm-12x19in) s.d.1989 W/C pair exhib. 16-Sep-3 Whyte's, Dublin #140/R est:3500-4500

GALE, William (1823-1909) British
£700 $1169 €1022 King Charles I in the Bodleian Library (61x46cm-24x18in) mono. panel. 13-Nov-3 Christie's, Kensington #280/R
£3200 $5216 €4672 Autumn (30x41cm-12x16in) mono. panel. 23-Sep-3 John Nicholson, Haslemere #233/R est:1000-2000

GALEA, Jean Francois (1944-) French
Sculpture
£1056 $1827 €1500 Trois tetes de taureaux camarguais (24x43cm-9x17in) s. num.1/8 pat bronze Cast Barthelemy. 14-Dec-3 Eric Pillon, Calais #256/R

GALEA, Luigi M (1847-1917) Maltese

£500	$850	€730	Luzzu in the Grand Harbour, Valletta (27x18cm-11x7in) s. board. 4-Nov-3 Bonhams, New Bond Street #108
£900	$1638	€1314	Grand Harbour, Valetta, Malta (22x55cm-9x22in) s. board. 16-Jun-4 Christie's, Kensington #136/R
£1000	$1580	€1450	Views of the Grand Harbour, Valletta, Malta (7x16cm-3x6in) s. card pair. 24-Jul-3 Lawrence, Crewkerne #933/R est:700-1000
£1300	$2210	€1898	St. Pauls Bay, Malta (18x43cm-7x17in) s. board. 4-Nov-3 Bonhams, New Bond Street #113/R est:1200-1800
£1400	$2380	€2044	Medina, Malta (18x43cm-7x17in) s. board. 4-Nov-3 Bonhams, New Bond Street #116/R est:1200-1800
£1500	$2550	€2190	At prayer (44x71cm-17x28in) s.d.1914 board. 4-Nov-3 Bonhams, New Bond Street #109/R est:1400-1800
£1500	$2685	€2190	Crowded small craft running out of Grand Harbour, Valetta by moonlight (21x55cm-8x22in) s. board. 26-May-4 Christie's, Kensington #668/R est:1500-2000
£1700	$2890	€2482	Grand Harbour at dawn. At dusk (15x34cm-6x13in) s. board pair. 4-Nov-3 Bonhams, New Bond Street #115/R est:1500-2000
£1800	$3060	€2628	Warships steaming out of the Grand Harbour, Valletta, Malta (28x80cm-11x31in) s. board. 4-Nov-3 Bonhams, New Bond Street #110/R est:2000-3000
£1800	$3060	€2628	Evening, the Grand Harbour, Valletta, Malta (28x80cm-11x31in) s. board. 4-Nov-3 Bonhams, New Bond Street #111/R est:2000-3000
£1800	$3060	€2628	Early morning, Marsamaxett Harbour, Valletta, Malta (28x80cm-11x31in) s.d.1915 board. 4-Nov-3 Bonhams, New Bond Street #112/R est:2000-3000
£2100	$3885	€3066	Valetta harbour (23x53cm-9x21in) s. board. 9-Mar-4 Gorringes, Lewes #2255 est:1500-2000
£2300	$4071	€3358	Off Fort St. Elmo, Malta (18x42cm-7x17in) bears sig.d.1859 board. 27-Apr-4 Bonhams, New Bond Street #82/R est:2000-3000
£2400	$4368	€3504	Valletta Harbour at sunset (20x52cm-8x20in) i.verso panel. 16-Jun-4 Christie's, Kensington #135/R est:2000-3000
£2600	$4602	€3796	Fort St. Angelo from Valletta, Malta (29x19cm-11x7in) s. board. 27-Apr-4 Bonhams, New Bond Street #73/R est:1500-2000
£3000	$4800	€4350	Shipping in calm waters, and in a stiff breeze, in the Grand Harbour (15x35cm-6x14in) s. board pair. 18-Sep-3 Christie's, Kensington #134/R est:3000-5000
£3500	$6440	€5110	View of Valletta, Malta (9x17cm-4x7in) s. board four. 25-Mar-4 Christie's, Kensington #144/R est:4000-6000
£3800	$6726	€5548	Fort St. Elmo from the sea, Malta (28x74cm-11x29in) s.d.1891 board. 27-Apr-4 Bonhams, New Bond Street #75/R est:3000-5000
£5800	$10266	€8468	Three cities from Valletta, Malta (28x74cm-11x29in) s. board. 27-Apr-4 Bonhams, New Bond Street #76/R est:2000-3000

GALEA, Luigi M (attrib) (1847-1917) Maltese

Works on paper

£2000	$3740	€3000	Malta harbour (18x25cm-7x10in) W/C pair oval. 21-Jul-4 John Nicholson, Haslemere #90
£2200	$4114	€3300	Malta harbour (13x33cm-5x13in) W/C pair. 21-Jul-4 John Nicholson, Haslemere #91 est:1500-2500

GALEANO, Raimondo (1948-) Italian

£333	$613	€500	Philosopher (140x100cm-55x39in) s.verso concrete. 12-Jun-4 Meeting Art, Vercelli #457/R

GALEK, Stanislaw (1876-1961) Polish

£274	$498	€400	Mountainous landscape with lake (30x40cm-12x16in) s. paper board. 20-Jun-4 Agra, Warsaw #12/R (P.Z 1900)
£346	$629	€505	Snow scene with timber house (27x36cm-11x14in) s. paper board. 20-Jun-4 Agra, Warsaw #13/R (P.Z 2400)

GALEMA, Arjen (1886-1974) Dutch

£671	$1242	€1000	Aanleg bataviastraat 1925 (67x99cm-26x39in) 15-Mar-4 Sotheby's, Amsterdam #154/R est:1000-1500

GALEOTA-RUSSO, Leopoldo (1868-1938) Italian

£432	$700	€631	Portrait of a lady (117x97cm-46x38in) s. 2-Aug-3 Neal Auction Company, New Orleans #89/R
£1127	$1949	€1600	Market in the square (30x40cm-12x16in) s. panel. 11-Dec-3 Christie's, Rome #31 est:1800-2200

GALEOTTI, Sebastiano (1676-1746) Italian

Works on paper

£541	$951	€800	Allegory of noble virtue (28x17cm-11x7in) i. pen wash htd white prov. 22-May-4 Lempertz, Koln #1271/R
£671	$1235	€1000	Adoration of the Three Kings (31x22cm-12x9in) bears sig.d.1748 wash pen. 26-Mar-4 Dorotheum, Vienna #38/R

GALERNE, Prosper (1836-?) French

£580	$951	€800	Bord de l'Essonne, La Ferte. s.d.1902. 11-May-3 Osenat, Fontainebleau #222

GALGIANI, Oscar (1903-1994) American

£2601	$4500	€3797	Old Woollen Mills, Stockton, California (41x56cm-16x22in) s.d.39. 10-Dec-3 Bonhams & Butterfields, San Francisco #6294/R est:3000-5000

GALICIA, Jose Luis (1930-) Spanish

£669	$1070	€950	Abstract (130x195cm-51x77in) s.d.1965. 16-Sep-3 Segre, Madrid #242/R

GALIEN-LALOUE (1854-1941) French

£2867	$4931	€4100	Bateau a quai. Bateaux a la manoeuvre (33x24cm-13x9in) s. panel sold with lot 237. 7-Dec-3 Lesieur & Le Bars, Le Havre #236

Works on paper

£5986	$10356	€8500	Les Grands Boulevards par un soir d'hiver (17x30cm-7x12in) s. gouache. 12-Dec-3 Renaud, Paris #149/R est:7500

GALIEN-LALOUE, E (1854-1941) French

£1233	$2097	€1800	Evening landscape with pond (43x64cm-17x25in) s. 5-Nov-3 Dobiaschofsky, Bern #582/R est:2300 (S.FR 2800)

GALIEN-LALOUE, Eugène (1854-1941) French

£576	$944	€800	La Stele (14x23cm-6x9in) s. panel painted c.1880 prov. 6-Jun-3 Chochon-Barre & Allardi, Paris #53
£662	$1205	€1000	Romantic river landscape (32x24cm-13x9in) s. 19-Jun-4 Bergmann, Erlangen #804
£738	$1381	€1100	Paysage anime (22x15cm-9x6in) s. panel. 29-Feb-4 Versailles Encheres #136/R est:1000-1200
£1050	$1911	€1575	Sailing boat in the harbour (22x16cm-9x6in) s. with pseudonym panel lit. 1-Jul-4 Van Ham, Cologne #1358/R est:1500
£1056	$1849	€1500	Le petit pont pres de Joigny (15x20cm-6x8in) s.pseudonym L. Dupuy panel. 17-Dec-3 Rabourdin & Choppin de Janvry, Paris #49/R est:1500-1700
£1056	$1849	€1500	Fermiere devant un petit village autour de Barbizon (15x20cm-6x8in) s.pseudonym L Dupuy panel. 17-Dec-3 Rabourdin & Choppin de Janvry, Paris #50/R est:1500-1700
£1447	$2663	€2200	Paysanne dans un chemin. Paysanne se rendant au village (16x22cm-6x9in) s. panel pair. 22-Jun-4 Calmels Cohen, Paris #44/R est:2000-3000
£1608	$2766	€2300	Chemin au bord de la riviere (41x33cm-16x13in) s.d.1911 i.d.verso. 5-Dec-3 Chochon-Barre & Allardi, Paris #95 est:2000-2500
£1628	$2800	€2377	Distant figure in a wooded landscape (15x23cm-6x9in) s. panel. 6-Dec-3 Neal Auction Company, New Orleans #109/R est:2500-3500
£1655	$3029	€2400	Au mouillage, le campement (17x36cm-7x14in) s. panel. 31-Jan-4 Neret-Minet, Paris #133/R est:1200-1500
£1799	$2950	€2500	Paysage a l'etang (26x33cm-10x13in) panel prov. 6-Jun-3 Chochon-Barre & Allardi, Paris #51/R est:2500-2800
£2035	$3500	€2971	Country cottages by a stream (18x36cm-7x14in) s. panel. 3-Dec-3 Doyle, New York #137/R est:3000-5000
£2041	$3653	€3000	Bateau a quai (41x60cm-16x24in) s. 19-Mar-4 Millon & Associes, Paris #58 est:3000-4000
£2105	$3874	€3200	Surle chemin de la ferme (33x46cm-13x18in) s. 25-Jun-4 Millon & Associes, Paris #158/R est:2000-3000
£2113	$3655	€3000	Canards au bord de l'eau (43x65cm-17x26in) s. 12-Dec-3 Piasa, Paris #53/R est:3000-4000
£2431	$3962	€3500	Village d'Ile-de-France (48x66cm-19x26in) s. 26-Sep-3 Rabourdin & Choppin de Janvry, Paris #52/R est:4000-5000
£3000	$5430	€4500	Deux moutons (21x40cm-8x16in) s. panel. 5-Apr-4 Deburaux, Boulogne #111/R est:2500-3000
£3007	$5172	€4300	Bateaux dans le port de Martigues (48x65cm-19x26in) s. 5-Dec-3 Chochon-Barre & Allardi, Paris #94/R est:3800-4000
£3333	$5467	€4600	Les canards au bord de la riviere (43x65cm-17x26in) s. 11-May-3 Osenat, Fontainebleau #154/R est:5500-6000
£3409	$6000	€4977	Boats at dusk (33x23cm-13x9in) s. panel. 22-May-4 New Orleans Auction, New Orleans #129/R est:6000-9000
£3977	$7000	€5806	Rural landscape (46x38cm-18x15in) s. 22-May-4 New Orleans Auction, New Orleans #126/R est:7000-10000
£4225	$7563	€6000	Rue de Paris (20x28cm-8x11in) s. panel. 11-Jan-4 Rouillac, Vendome #344
£6294	$10825	€9000	La vie au village (46x65cm-18x26in) s. 7-Dec-3 Osenat, Fontainebleau #213 est:10000-12000
£6507	$11062	€9500	Cour de ferme (47x55cm-19x22in) s. 5-Nov-3 Rabourdin & Choppin de Janvry, Paris #32/R est:4500-5000
£7292	$11448	€10500	Spring in Paris - elegant figures on Quai de la Megisserie (26x35cm-10x14in) s. tempera gouache board. 30-Aug-3 Hans Stahl, Toestorf #36/R est:4800
£8000	$14720	€12000	Le port de peche (48x65cm-19x26in) s. 11-Jun-4 Pierre Berge, Paris #219/R est:15000-20000
£16667	$27167	€24000	Busy boulevard with Place de la Bastille (21x34cm-8x13in) s. gouache. 25-Sep-3 Dr Fritz Nagel, Stuttgart #1350/R est:26000
£23000	$41860	€33580	Le Pont Neuf a Paris (40x65cm-16x26in) s. 15-Jun-4 Sotheby's, London #176/R est:15000-20000

Works on paper

£1690	$2924	€2400	L'Arc de Triomphe du Caroussel (19x31cm-7x12in) s. gouache varnish. 10-Dec-3 Rossini, Paris #9/R
£3594	$6685	€5247	Figures on the streets in Paris, winter (19x30cm-7x12in) s. gouache. 2-Mar-4 Rasmussen, Copenhagen #1510/R est:30000 (D.KR 40000)
£5882	$10000	€8588	Place Clichy (19x31cm-7x12in) s. W/C gouache. 29-Oct-3 Christie's, Rockefeller NY #186/R est:12000-18000
£6294	$10825	€9000	La sortie des communiantes (31x18cm-12x7in) s. gouache. 5-Dec-3 Chochon-Barre & Allardi, Paris #96/R est:9000-10000
£6552	$10941	€9500	La Madeleine (27x22cm-11x9in) s. gouache. 17-Nov-3 Delorme & Bocage, Paris #118/R est:10000-12000
£6711	$11879	€10000	Grands Boulevards a Paris (19x31cm-7x12in) s. gouache prov. 30-Apr-4 Tajan, Paris #165/R est:10000-12000
£7200	$13248	€10512	La Madeleine, Paris (23x32cm-9x13in) s. gouache. 23-Mar-4 Bonhams, New Bond Street #111/R est:6000-8000
£7686	$12835	€11222	Place de la Bastille (21x33cm-8x13in) s. gouache W/C. 13-Oct-3 Blomqvist, Oslo #355/R est:50000-60000 (N.KR 90000)
£7778	$14000	€11356	Flower market by the Madeleine, Paris (20x32cm-8x13in) s. pencil W/C gouache. 22-Apr-4 Christie's, Rockefeller NY #189/R est:12000-16000
£8392	$14266	€12000	Tramways (20x31cm-8x12in) s. gouache lit. 28-Nov-3 Drouot Estimations, Paris #135/R est:5000-7000
£8487	$15191	€12391	Quai du Louvre (20x34cm-8x13in) s. mixed media. 22-Mar-4 Blomqvist, Oslo #365/R est:40000-50000 (N.KR 106000)
£8639	$15465	€12700	Grands boulevards (19x23cm-7x9in) s. gouache. 19-Mar-4 Millon & Associes, Paris #57/R est:4000-6000
£10000	$16700	€14500	La Place de la Republique (25x33cm-10x13in) s. gouache. 17-Nov-3 Delorme & Bocage, Paris #119/R est:12000-15000
£10000	$18000	€14600	La Madeleine (27x22cm-11x9in) s. gouache. 23-Apr-4 Sotheby's, New York #128/R est:12000-15000
£10000	$18000	€14600	Place de la Republique (25x33cm-10x13in) s. gouache. 23-Apr-4 Sotheby's, New York #132/R est:18000-25000
£10000	$18200	€14600	Nortre Dame, Paris (19x31cm-7x12in) s. gouache. 16-Jun-4 Bonhams, New Bond Street #102/R est:7000-10000
£10345	$18931	€15000	Les grands boulevards pres de l'Etoile (19x31cm-7x12in) s. gouache. 1-Feb-4 Robin & Fattori, Granville #6
£10556	$19000	€15412	L'Arche de la Porte St Denis (20x33cm-8x13in) s. pencil W/C gouache. 22-Apr-4 Christie's, Rockefeller NY #193/R est:12000-16000
£10556	$19000	€15412	Un boulevard, le soir, Paris (19x30cm-7x12in) s. pencil W/C gouache card. 22-Apr-4 Christie's, Rockefeller NY #194/R est:12000-16000
£10588	$18000	€15458	Grands boulevards a Paris (18x30cm-7x12in) s. gouache. 28-Oct-3 Sotheby's, New York #176/R est:12000-15000
£11111	$20000	€16222	La Madeleine en hiver (22x39cm-9x15in) s. gouache. 23-Apr-4 Sotheby's, New York #133/R est:20000-30000
£11500	$19550	€16790	La porte Saint-Martin (18x31cm-7x12in) s. gouache. 19-Nov-3 Bonhams, New Bond Street #132/R est:6000-8000

£11538	$19846	€16845	Les grands Boulevards (21x33cm-8x13in) s. gouache. 2-Dec-3 Bukowskis, Stockholm #285/R est:40000-60000 (S.KR 150000)
£12000	$21840	€17520	La Porte Saint-Denis (19x31cm-7x12in) s. W/C pencil. 15-Jun-4 Sotheby's, London #216/R est:6000-8000
£12222	$22000	€17844	Place de la Republique en hiver, Paris (20x33cm-8x13in) s. pencil W/C gouache. 22-Apr-4 Christie's, Rockefeller NY #191/R est:10000-15000
£13333	$24267	€20000	Paris, soir d'hiver (20x33cm-8x13in) s. gouache. 30-Jun-4 Delvaux, Paris #21/R est:10000-12000
£13380	$23415	€19000	La Place de la Republique (18x31cm-7x12in) s. gouache. 16-Dec-3 Claude Aguttes, Neuilly #101/R est:10000-12000
£14041	$23870	€20500	Paris, Place de la Bastille sous la neige (26x44cm-10x17in) s. gouache W/C. 9-Nov-3 Eric Pillon, Calais #1/R
£14444	$26000	€21088	Place d'Anvers, Paris (20x33cm-8x13in) s. pencil W/C gouache. 22-Apr-4 Christie's, Rockefeller NY #196/R est:15000-20000
£14444	$26000	€21088	Place de la Bastille (25x44cm-10x17in) s. gouache. 23-Apr-4 Sotheby's, New York #134/R est:20000-30000
£14752	$24635	€20800	Les bouquinistes sur le quai de la tournelle (26x45cm-10x18in) s. W/C gouache. 19-Jun-3 Millon & Associes, Paris #47/R est:20000-25000
£15068	$25616	€22000	Paris, marchande de fleurs, Boulevard de la Bastille (26x45cm-10x18in) s. W/C gouache. 9-Nov-3 Eric Pillon, Calais #2/R
£16000	$29120	€23360	L'Arc de Triomohe, Paris (33x46cm-13x18in) s. gouache. 16-Jun-4 Bonhams, New Bond Street #101/R est:10000-15000
£20423	$33901	€29000	Boulevard enneige (32x45cm-13x18in) s. gouache htd W/C. 15-Jun-3 Peron, Melun #63
£28017	$51552	€40905	Paris, street scene (42x72cm-17x28in) s. gouache. 26-Mar-4 Koller, Zurich #513/R est:35000-55000 (S.FR 65000)
£51064	$85277	€72000	La porte Saint-Denis sous la neige. Le marche aux fleurs (37x44cm-15x17in) s. W/C gouache pair. 20-Jun-3 Drouot Estimations, Paris #196/R est:22000-25000

GALINDO, Carlos (20th C) Venezuelan?

£235	$405	€343	Untitled (56x71cm-22x28in) s. painted 1980. 7-Dec-3 Subastas Odalys, Caracas #120

GALINDO, Jorge (1965-) Spanish

£563	$986	€800	Untitled (45x33cm-18x13in) s.d.1992 acrylic W/C paper prov. 16-Dec-3 Segre, Madrid #177/R
£1399	$2336	€2000	Untitled (100x81cm-39x32in) s.d.1992 hessian. 24-Jun-3 Segre, Madrid #145/R est:2500
£2133	$3861	€3200	Sort of red II (160x130cm-63x51in) s.i.d.1991-92. 30-Mar-4 Segre, Madrid #157/R est:3000

GALIZIA, Fede (1578-1630) Italian

£67114	$120134	€100000	Metal bowl with peaches and flowers (31x43cm-12x17in) board prov.exhib.lit. 26-May-4 Porro, Milan #36/R est:120000-150000
£97241	$162393	€141000	Fruit bowl with grapes, plums and pears (22x35cm-9x14in) board prov.lit. 15-Nov-3 Porro, Milan #222/R est:125000

GALIZZI, Luigi (1841-1902) Italian

£3310	$5792	€4700	Portrait of Bettina carsana at the piano (103x77cm-41x30in) 17-Dec-3 Il Ponte, Milan #665/R est:4000-5000

GALL, François (1912-1987) French

£263	$484	€400	Jeune femme en buste (81x60cm-32x24in) s.d.1937. 22-Jun-4 Chassaing Rivet, Toulouse #292
£729	$1203	€1050	Scene de port a Honfleur (22x27cm-9x11in) s. 3-Jul-3 Claude Aguttes, Neuilly #90
£800	$1408	€1168	Townscape with mountains beyond (46x62cm-18x24in) s. 18-May-4 Bonhams, Knightsbridge #85/R
£838	$1400	€1223	La Seine a Paris, le Pont du Louvre (22x27cm-9x11in) s.i. 7-Oct-3 Sotheby's, New York #310
£1056	$1827	€1500	Jeune femme a la coiffeuse (27x22cm-11x9in) s.i. 10-Dec-3 Rossini, Paris #75/R
£1100	$1903	€1606	Bouquet de fleurs (27x22cm-11x9in) s. prov. 11-Dec-3 Christie's, Kensington #109/R est:800-1200
£1200	$2196	€1800	Aux courses (22x27cm-9x11in) s. panel. 7-Jun-4 Palais de Beaux Arts, Brussels #336/R est:1800-2200
£1293	$2197	€1888	Apres la course (22x27cm-9x11in) s. prov. 21-Nov-3 Walker's, Ottawa #226/R est:3500-4000 (C.D 2870)
£1308	$2250	€1910	Woman in red, Paris (61x46cm-24x18in) s. i.indis d. 3-Dec-3 Doyle, New York #146/R est:4000-6000
£1313	$2350	€1917	Final touches (25x20cm-10x8in) s. sold with a gift card. 8-Jan-4 James Julia, Fairfield #497/R est:3000-5000
£1333	$2307	€1946	In the Park (22x26cm-9x10in) s.i. board. 9-Dec-3 Pinneys, Montreal #41 est:3500-4500 (C.D 3000)
£1448	$2418	€2114	La coiffeuse (27x22cm-11x9in) s. i.verso prov. 17-Nov-3 Waddingtons, Toronto #206/R est:3000-5000 (C.D 3200)
£1453	$2600	€2121	Paris street scene (30x46cm-12x18in) s. board. 16-May-4 CRN Auctions, Cambridge #22/R
£1538	$2723	€2245	Dans le Parc (26x34cm-10x13in) s.i.d.1969 panel. 27-Apr-4 AB Stockholms Auktionsverk #1222/R est:15000-20000 (S.KR 21000)
£1600	$2768	€2336	Jeune fille assise dans un champ (19x24cm-7x9in) s. prov. 11-Dec-3 Christie's, Kensington #108/R est:1000-1500
£1600	$2768	€2336	Aperitif (22x27cm-9x11in) s.i. prov. 11-Dec-3 Christie's, Kensington #110/R est:1200-1800
£1604	$3000	€2342	Plage (22x27cm-9x11in) s. 25-Feb-4 Christie's, Rockefeller NY #30/R est:3500-4500
£1702	$2843	€2400	Baigneurs sur la plage de Deauville (22x27cm-9x11in) s. 20-Jun-3 Drouot Estimations, Paris #100 est:900-1000
£2036	$3400	€2973	Devant le miroir (45x33cm-18x13in) s. 17-Nov-3 Waddingtons, Toronto #209/R est:4500-6000 (C.D 4500)
£2246	$3750	€3279	Bouquet champetre (61x50cm-24x20in) s. prov. 7-Oct-3 Sotheby's, New York #312 est:4000-6000
£2262	$3778	€3303	Jeune fille devant le miroir (50x61cm-20x24in) s.i. 24-Jun-3 Germann, Zurich #80/R est:4000-6000 (S.FR 5000)
£2271	$4020	€3316	Low tide in the fishing harbour (50x73cm-20x29in) s. 27-Apr-4 AB Stockholms Auktionsverk #1221/R est:15000-18000 (S.KR 31000)
£2454	$4000	€3583	La plage, Arcachon (22x27cm-9x11in) s. painted c.1955-57 prov. 25-Sep-3 Christie's, Rockefeller NY #543/R est:2500-3500
£2473	$4500	€3611	La plage a Trouville (27x46cm-11x18in) s.i. prov. 29-Jun-4 Sotheby's, New York #373/R est:6000-8000
£2500	$4250	€3650	Port of Hornfleur (63x79cm-25x31in) s.i. prov. 9-Nov-3 Bonhams & Butterfields, Los Angeles #4001/R
£2510	$4544	€3665	Still life with flowers (59x48cm-23x19in) s. 1-Apr-4 Heffel, Vancouver #37/R est:7000-9000 (C.D 6000)
£2534	$4232	€3700	Trouville (49x61cm-19x24in) s. i. stretcher. 17-Nov-3 Waddingtons, Toronto #210/R est:6000-8000 (C.D 5600)
£2667	$4800	€4000	Promeneurs dans un parc a l'automne (70x80cm-28x31in) s.d.27 lit. 26-Apr-4 Tajan, Paris #168/R est:2000-3000
£2761	$4500	€4031	Le 14 juillet a Saint-Germain des Pres, Paris (22x27cm-9x11in) s.i. masonite painted c.1952 lit. 25-Sep-3 Christie's, Rockefeller NY #544/R est:3000-5000
£2784	$4927	€4065	Sur les quais de la Seine (54x73cm-21x29in) s.i.d.46. 27-Apr-4 AB Stockholms Auktionsverk #1227/R est:35000-40000 (S.KR 38000)
£2794	$4750	€4079	Girl seated at table (81x64cm-32x25in) s. prov. 9-Nov-3 Bonhams & Butterfields, Los Angeles #4007/R
£2797	$4755	€4000	Portrait of the artist's wife Eugenie (27x22cm-11x9in) s.i. board painted c.1950 prov. 25-Nov-3 Christie's, Amsterdam #38/R est:2000-3000
£2802	$5015	€4091	Jeune femme au cafe (27x22cm-11x9in) s. 12-May-4 Dobiaschofsky, Bern #538/R est:7500 (S.FR 6500)
£2844	$4750	€4152	Before the race (24x33cm-9x13in) s. 7-Oct-3 Sotheby's, New York #308 est:3000-4000
£2910	$5500	€4249	Pink dress (51x61cm-20x24in) s. 22-Feb-4 Bonhams & Butterfields, Los Angeles #7043 est:2500-3500
£3333	$6000	€4866	Young girl on a river bank (20x25cm-8x10in) s. prov. 20-Apr-4 Arthur James, Florida #47/R est:5000-7000
£3374	$5500	€4926	Nature morte avec deux vase (46x38cm-18x15in) board. 25-Sep-3 Christie's, Rockefeller NY #606/R est:5000-7000
£3593	$6000	€5246	Girl seated at a table (27x22cm-11x9in) s. 7-Oct-3 Sotheby's, New York #307 est:3000-4000
£3691	$6607	€5500	Bateaux amarres a Honfleur (54x64cm-21x25in) s. 26-May-4 Christie's, Paris #1/R est:2000-3000
£4082	$7306	€6000	Terrasse a Montmartre (54x65cm-21x26in) s.i. 19-Mar-4 Millon & Associes, Paris #117/R est:4000
£4294	$7000	€6269	Danseuse au repos (40x33cm-16x13in) s.i. painted c.1952-53 lit. 25-Sep-3 Christie's, Rockefeller NY #514/R est:7000-9000
£4525	$7828	€6607	Promenade a Montmartre (50x61cm-20x24in) s.i. prov. 12-Dec-3 Galerie du Rhone, Sion #188/R est:10000-15000 (S.FR 10000)
£4601	$7500	€6717	Jardin des Tuileries, Paris (49x73cm-19x29in) s.i. painted c.1939-40. 25-Sep-3 Christie's, Rockefeller NY #548/R est:5000-7000
£4830	$8500	€7052	Beach scenes at Wimereux (23x28cm-9x11in) one s. one s.i. pair. 21-May-4 North East Auctions, Portsmouth #1512/R est:3000-5000
£5652	$10343	€8252	Les quais de Seine en automne (50x61cm-20x24in) s. prov. 5-Jun-4 Galerie du Rhone, Sion #568/R est:10000-15000 (S.FR 13000)
£6376	$11413	€9500	Eugenie a Argenteuil (50x61cm-20x24in) s.i. 26-May-4 Christie's, Paris #18/R est:6000-8000
£6447	$11411	€9413	Les petits rats (26x21cm-10x8in) s.i. 27-Apr-4 AB Stockholms Auktionsverk #1226/R est:20000-25000 (S.KR 88000)
£7263	$13000	€10604	A la terasse du cafe (61x46cm-24x18in) s. s.i.verso painted c.1970 prov. 6-May-4 Sotheby's, New York #450/R est:8000-12000
£7326	$12967	€10696	Jeune femme au chapeau (27x22cm-11x9in) s.i. 27-Apr-4 AB Stockholms Auktionsverk #1225/R est:20000-25000 (S.KR 100000)
£7487	$14000	€10931	Scene de plage (33x55cm-13x22in) s. 25-Feb-4 Christie's, Rockefeller NY #25/R est:6000-8000
£8556	$16000	€12492	Danseuse au repos (27x22cm-11x9in) s. prov. 25-Feb-4 Christie's, Rockefeller NY #46/R est:3000-5000
£9626	$18000	€14054	Eugenie au bord de la riviere (22x27cm-9x11in) s. 25-Feb-4 Christie's, Rockefeller NY #29/R est:4000-6000
Works on paper			
£266	$480	€400	Femme nue assise de dos (30x22cm-12x9in) s.i.d.1938 W/C lit. 26-Apr-4 Tajan, Paris #106b
£1100	$1837	€1606	Marie-Lize a Montparnasse. Eugene ajustant son bas (30x21cm-12x8in) both s. chl col chks cardboard 2nd oil chl cardboard pair. 22-Oct-3 Sotheby's, Olympia #195/R est:600-800

GALLAGHER, Ellen (1967-) American

£15951	$26000	€23288	Shiner (61x61cm-24x24in) s.d.1993 verso oil pencil collage prov.exhib. 23-Sep-3 Christie's, Rockefeller NY #76/R est:15000-20000

GALLAGHER, Mary (1952-) British

£380	$635	€555	Sunset sea (40x58cm-16x23in) s. 16-Oct-3 Lyon & Turnbull, Edinburgh #117
£380	$654	€555	Beach scene (46x61cm-18x24in) board. 6-Dec-3 Shapes, Edinburgh #478
£400	$744	€584	Striped roses (53x39cm-21x15in) s. board. 6-Mar-4 Shapes, Edinburgh #456
£850	$1420	€1241	Old crofter (52x58cm-20x23in) s. 16-Oct-3 Bonhams, Edinburgh #25

GALLAGHER, Michael (1945-) American

£467	$850	€682	Saxifraga stolonifera (107x127cm-42x50in) s.i.d.80 overlap acrylic prov. 29-Jun-4 Sotheby's, New York #544/R

GALLAGHER, Sears (1869-1955) American

Works on paper			
£621	$1000	€907	French or Dutch street scene (23x15cm-9x6in) s. W/C. 20-Aug-3 James Julia, Fairfield #1755/R
£645	$1200	€942	On the river (37x50cm-15x20in) s. W/C paper on board. 5-Mar-4 Skinner, Boston #443/R
£1229	$2200	€1794	Summer clouds, Gloucester (33x48cm-13x19in) s. i.verso W/C. 8-Jan-4 James Julia, Fairfield #877/R est:1500-1800

GALLAIT, Louis (1810-1887) Belgian

£400	$724	€600	L'adoration des bergers (38x28cm-15x11in) after Ribera. 30-Mar-4 Rossini, Paris #800
£528	$914	€750	Adversity (34x19cm-13x7in) s.i.d.1883 panel. 13-Dec-3 De Vuyst, Lokeren #157
£1267	$2293	€1900	L'Assomption, eglise de Sainte Marie Glorieuse des Moines, Venise (88x50cm-35x20in) after le Titieny. 30-Mar-4 Rossini, Paris #801/R est:800-1200
£1991	$3565	€2907	Young woman from Rome (115x76cm-45x30in) s.i. prov. 22-Mar-4 Philippe Schuler, Zurich #4406/R est:4000-6000 (S.FR 4600)
Works on paper			
£396	$633	€550	Portrait of Charlotte, sister of the artist (25x19cm-10x7in) mono.d. studio st. blk crayon. 16-May-3 Tajan, Paris #117
£500	$900	€730	Vue d'Innsbruck (30x43cm-12x17in) i. W/C ink gouache over pencil prov.exhib. 21-Jan-4 Sotheby's, New York #203/R est:800-1200

£567 $948 €800 Funerailles (47x37cm-19x15in) s.d.1835 W/C. 15-Oct-3 Hotel des Ventes Mosan, Brussels #110

GALLAND, Pierre Victor (1822-1892) French
£260 $434 €380 Sleeping cupid (20x38cm-8x15in) oil on paper arched top. 11-Nov-3 Bonhams, Knightsbridge #29

GALLARD, Michel de (1921-) French
£336 $625 €500 Paysage aux arbres et toits rouges (61x38cm-24x15in) s.d.58 panel. 2-Mar-4 Artcurial Briest, Paris #272
£436 $811 €650 Maison au bord de l'etang (46x27cm-18x11in) s.d.54 panel. 2-Mar-4 Artcurial Briest, Paris #273
£624 $1117 €930 Port de Vanves (54x65cm-21x26in) s.i.d.53. 27-May-4 Christie's, Paris #125/R
£867 $1577 €1300 Village sous la neige (41x33cm-16x13in) s. 4-Jul-4 Eric Pillon, Calais #281/R
£1399 $2336 €2000 Paysage (65x92cm-26x36in) s.d.61. 25-Jun-3 Blanchet, Paris #105/R
£1730 $3200 €2526 Rooftops (89x116cm-35x46in) s. prov. 13-Jul-4 Christie's, Rockefeller NY #185/R est:2000-3000
£1745 $3123 €2600 Passage Dantzig, Paris (65x81cm-26x32in) s.d.56 s.i.verso masonite. 27-May-4 Christie's, Paris #127/R est:1000-1200
£1748 $2920 €2500 Vase de tournesols (116x89cm-46x35in) s. 13-Oct-3 Pierre Berge, Paris #28/R est:2500-3000

GALLARD-LEPINAY, Paul Charles Emmanuel (1842-1885) French
£966 $1612 €1400 Sailing ship, steamer and fishing boats outside harbour entrance (27x46cm-11x18in) s. lit. 10-Jul-3 Allgauer, Kempten #2500/R
£4054 $7662 €6000 Trois mats a l'entree du port (46x74cm-18x29in) s. 21-Feb-4 Livinec, Gaudcheau & Jezequel, Rennes #113
£4296 $6916 €6100 Port de La Rochelle (38x55cm-15x22in) s. 22-Aug-3 Deauville, France #36/R
£5517 $10097 €8000 Marine (46x74cm-18x29in) s. peinture. 1-Feb-4 Robin & Fattori, Granville #8

GALLARDO, Gustavo (1891-1971) Spanish
£485 $824 €708 Field workers harvesting corn (4x41cm-2x16in) s. 5-Nov-3 Dobiaschofsky, Bern #587/R (S.FR 1100)
£753 $1281 €1100 Celebration in Andalucia (35x51cm-14x20in) s. 4-Nov-3 Ansorena, Madrid #343/R
£1007 $1782 €1500 Water carrier in Seville (34x47cm-13x19in) s. 27-Apr-4 Durán, Madrid #177/R est:1400
£1172 $2110 €1700 Watercarrier in Seville (35x48cm-14x19in) s. 26-Jan-4 Ansorena, Madrid #248/R est:1700

GALLARDO, Luis (19/20th C) Spanish
£382 $607 €550 Emboscada (47x37cm-19x15in) s.d.1891. 29-Apr-3 Durán, Madrid #755/R

GALLARO, M de (20th C) ?
£1325 $2477 €2000 Maison. 20-Jul-4 other European Auctioneer #118

GALLATIN, Albert E (1881-1952) American
£11765 $20000 €17177 Abstract composition (41x30cm-16x12in) s.d.1940 verso board prov. 9-Nov-3 Wright, Chicago #230 est:10000-15000

GALLE, Pierre Vincent (1883-1960) French
£567 $1043 €850 Portrait de Madame Lassus, Salon des Artistes Francais (81x98cm-32x39in) s.d.1932. 8-Jun-4 Livinec, Gaudcheau & Jezequel, Rennes #96/R

GALLEGO, Alonso (16th C) Spanish
£9444 $17000 €13788 Lamentation (128x116cm-50x46in) panel prov. 23-Jan-4 Christie's, Rockefeller NY #187/R est:15000-20000

GALLEGOS Y ARNOSA, Jose (1859-1917) Spanish
£11921 $21695 €18000 Trop charge (35x21cm-14x8in) s. panel. 18-Jun-4 Piasa, Paris #12/R est:9000-12000
£13793 $23034 €20000 Seville Cathedral (25x18cm-10x7in) s.d.1897 board. 17-Nov-3 Durán, Madrid #218/R est:20000
£21277 $35532 €30000 Las noticias (25x34cm-10x13in) s. panel. 23-Jun-3 Durán, Madrid #233/R est:25000
Works on paper
£1215 $1920 €1762 Flute player (20x14cm-8x6in) s.d.85 W/C. 2-Sep-3 Rasmussen, Copenhagen #1707/R est:4000 (D.KR 13000)

GALLELLI, Massimiliano (1863-1956) Italian
£658 $1211 €1000 Portrait of man (105x80cm-41x31in) s. 23-Jun-4 Finarte Semenzato, Rome #77

GALLEN-KALLELA, Akseli Valdemar (1865-1931) Finnish
£8392 $14266 €12000 Hoar-frost on trees, frosty night (19x17cm-7x7in) s.d.1899 board. 29-Nov-3 Bukowskis, Helsinki #322/R est:12000-15000
£9667 $17303 €14500 Old-fashioned old man (55x42cm-22x17in) s. canvas on board exhib. 15-May-4 Hagelstam, Helsinki #113/R est:18000
£9790 $16643 €14000 Seascape with lighthouse (15x54cm-6x21in) s.d.84 panel. 29-Nov-3 Bukowskis, Helsinki #40/R est:14000-16000
£10490 $17832 €15000 Moonlight in June (48x33cm-19x13in) s.d.1915 oil tempera paper on board. 29-Nov-3 Bukowskis, Helsinki #66/R est:15000-18000
£10490 $17832 €15000 Boat on beach (29x31cm-11x12in) s.i.d.1905 canvas on board exhib. 29-Nov-3 Bukowskis, Helsinki #124/R est:15000-20000
£17483 $29720 €25000 Landscape view with Tyrvaa Church (23x36cm-9x14in) s.d.1883 board exhib. 29-Nov-3 Bukowskis, Helsinki #68/R est:30000-40000
£18000 $32760 €26280 Sunset (43x29cm-17x11in) s.d.1902 canvas on board prov.exhib. 15-Jun-4 Sotheby's, London #316/R est:10000-15000
£27703 $49588 €41000 Sunlit pine tree (19x13cm-7x5in) s.i.d.1898 board. 8-May-4 Bukowskis, Helsinki #205/R est:15000-20000
£32168 $54685 €46000 Woodland tarn (23x36cm-9x14in) s.d.Aug.83 board. 29-Nov-3 Bukowskis, Helsinki #62/R est:30000-40000
Works on paper
£1141 $2122 €1700 Woman from Lapland (53x44cm-21x17in) s.d.1927 mixed media. 7-Mar-4 Bukowskis, Helsinki #322/R est:2000
£4196 $7133 €6000 Imatra in electric light (41x32cm-16x13in) Indian ink wash gouache lit. 29-Nov-3 Bukowskis, Helsinki #220/R est:6000-8000
£28378 $50797 €42000 Female nude rowing (72x71cm-28x28in) s.d.1909 pastel. 8-May-4 Bukowskis, Helsinki #94/R est:25000-35000

GALLERY, Dennis (20th C) British
£300 $549 €438 Bartin's Day (30x40cm-12x16in) s. board. 2-Jun-4 John Ross, Belfast #205

GALLET, Jean Baptiste (1820-1848) French
£11842 $21789 €18000 Branches en fleurs (96x71cm-38x28in) s.d.1845. 23-Jun-4 Sotheby's, Paris #72/R est:10000-15000

GALLET, Judd (20th C) ?
£363 $650 €530 Beach scene with woman and children (58x89cm-23x35in) s. 8-May-4 Susanin's, Chicago #6125/R

GALLET, Louis (1873-?) French
Sculpture
£1958 $3270 €2800 Ludwig v Beethoven (54cm-21in) s. marble. 27-Jun-3 Altus, Berlin #1824/R est:3500

GALLI, G (?) Italian
£898 $1652 €1311 Watching the marionettes (29x40cm-11x16in) s. exhib. 29-Mar-4 Goodman, Sydney #136/R (A.D 2200)

GALLI, Giuseppe (1866-1953) Italian
Works on paper
£255 $456 €380 Vase of flowers (30x21cm-12x8in) s.d.46 W/C card. 25-May-4 Finarte Semenzato, Milan #7
£336 $601 €500 Ponte Vecchio, Florence (34x50cm-13x20in) s.d.1930 W/C. 25-May-4 Finarte Semenzato, Milan #152/R

GALLI, Luigi (1820-1906) Italian
£326 $535 €450 Lion and lioness (17x28cm-7x11in) s.i. cardboard. 27-May-3 Il Ponte, Milan #734
£1986 $3316 €2800 Diana bathing (56x30cm-22x12in) s. board lit. 14-Oct-3 Finarte Semenzato, Milan #105/R est:3000

GALLI, Riccardo (1869-1944) Italian
£1014 $1784 €1500 Farmhouses in Macugnaga (25x35cm-10x14in) s. i.verso board. 19-May-4 Il Ponte, Milan #591 est:1600-1700
£1342 $2376 €2000 Red kimono (66x60cm-26x24in) s. s.i.verso. 1-May-4 Meeting Art, Vercelli #330 est:2000
£1544 $2763 €2300 Old fishing boat on Lake Como (50x75cm-20x30in) s. lit. 25-May-4 Finarte Semenzato, Milan #99/R est:2000-2500
£1892 $3330 €2800 Nude at stream (60x50cm-24x20in) s. 19-May-4 Il Ponte, Milan #643 est:2200-2300
£2254 $3899 €3200 Strolling with geese (47x32cm-19x13in) s.i. cardboard on canvas. 10-Dec-3 Sotheby's, Milan #55/R est:2500-3500
£3108 $5470 €4600 View of Alagna (61x77cm-24x30in) s.i. 19-May-4 Il Ponte, Milan #596 est:3200-3400

GALLI, Stefano (1950-) Italian
£333 $613 €500 Moving (60x60cm-24x24in) s. acrylic painted 2002. 12-Jun-4 Meeting Art, Vercelli #167/R
£333 $613 €500 Carpet seller (50x50cm-20x20in) s. acrylic. 12-Jun-4 Meeting Art, Vercelli #313/R
£333 $613 €500 Last show (60x60cm-24x24in) s. acrylic painted 2001. 12-Jun-4 Meeting Art, Vercelli #660/R
£333 $613 €500 Secretary (60x60cm-24x24in) s. s.i.d.2002 verso acrylic lit. 12-Jun-4 Meeting Art, Vercelli #907/R
£352 $585 €500 Cameretta (25x30cm-10x12in) s. s.i.d.2001 verso acrylic. 14-Jun-3 Meeting Art, Vercelli #413
£470 $869 €700 Mobile cafe (50x50cm-20x20in) s. s.i.d.1998 verso acrylic. 13-Mar-4 Meeting Art, Vercelli #157
£533 $981 €800 Landscape in Novara (50x50cm-20x20in) s. s.i.d.2002 verso lit. 12-Jun-4 Meeting Art, Vercelli #540/R
£667 $1227 €1000 Tragedy (50x50cm-20x20in) s. s.i.d.2002 verso. 12-Jun-4 Meeting Art, Vercelli #163/R

GALLIANI, Omar (1954-) Italian
£1304 $2139 €1800 The shipwrecked eyebrows (30x35cm-12x14in) s.d.83 verso. 30-May-3 Farsetti, Prato #118/R
£1538 $2615 €2200 Virago (50x50cm-20x20in) s.i.d.1986 verso. 26-Nov-3 Pandolfini, Florence #183/R est:2500-2600
£2400 $4416 €3600 Diamond (50x50cm-20x20in) s.i.verso pastel board exec.2001. 12-Jun-4 Meeting Art, Vercelli #968/R est:3000
£2667 $4827 €4000 In your heart (88x78cm-35x31in) s.i.d.1990. 2-Apr-4 Farsetti, Prato #360/R est:4000-4500
£2917 $4608 €4200 If you do not open your eyes (60x60cm-24x24in) graphite pastel board. 6-Sep-3 Meeting Art, Vercelli #360 est:3000
Works on paper
£671 $1242 €1000 Untitled (51x70cm-20x28in) s.d.1987 sanguine. 13-Mar-4 Meeting Art, Vercelli #192
£1141 $2111 €1700 Drawing (70x100cm-28x39in) s.i.d.1997 verso graphite. 13-Mar-4 Meeting Art, Vercelli #265 est:1500
£1333 $2453 €2000 Untitled (70x100cm-28x39in) s. mixed media card exec.1983. 12-Jun-4 Meeting Art, Vercelli #603/R est:2000

£2416 $4470 €3600 At sea (50x50cm-20x20in) s.i.verso mixed media board exec.1999. 13-Mar-4 Meeting Art, Vercelli #245 est:3000
£2817 $4676 €4000 Stremiz (50x150cm-20x59in) s.i.d.1994 graffiti canvas. 14-Jun-3 Meeting Art, Vercelli #562/R est:4000
£3289 $5887 €4900 Drawing (50x50cm-20x20in) s.i.d.1992 verso pencil board. 28-May-4 Farsetti, Prato #237/R est:2300-2700
£3356 $6007 €5000 Interior (50x50cm-20x20in) s.i. mixed media board. 30-May-4 Meeting Art, Vercelli #78 est:2500
£4027 $7450 €6000 Miriam's house (57x187cm-22x74in) s.i.d.1998 graphite board lit. 13-Mar-4 Meeting Art, Vercelli #547 est:5000

GALLIANO, Daniele (1961-) Italian
£2013 $3604 €3000 Stalin (100x70cm-39x28in) s.i.d.92 verso acrylic. 25-May-4 Sotheby's, Milan #220/R est:3000-4000
£3380 $5611 €4800 Untitled (70x100cm-28x39in) s.d.1993 verso. 14-Jun-3 Meeting Art, Vercelli #366/R est:4000

GALLIANO, John (20th C) Italian?
Works on paper
£4636 $8483 €7000 Portrait de femme (64x44cm-25x17in) s.d.16 mars 2004 mixed media htd paint. 7-Apr-4 Tajan, Paris #20 est:10000-10500

GALLIANY, Eugene (attrib) (?) ?
£927 $1697 €1400 Automne, soleil couchant sur la Marne (38x46cm-15x18in) init. 7-Apr-4 Doutrebente, Paris #41/R
£1192 $2181 €1800 Canards a la riviere (38x46cm-15x18in) init. 7-Apr-4 Doutrebente, Paris #40/R est:1500-2000

GALLIARI, Fabrizio (attrib) (1709-1790) Italian
Works on paper
£612 $1096 €900 Un mausolee vu d'une colonnade, une ville dans le fond (22x31cm-9x12in) pen brown ink grey wash. 18-Mar-4 Christie's, Paris #228/R

GALLIBERT, Genevieve (1888-?) French
£300 $501 €438 Villa amongst olive trees in the south of France (65x56cm-26x22in) s.i.d.48. 8-Oct-3 Christie's, Kensington #773

GALLINA, Lodovico (1752-1787) Italian
Works on paper
£370 $676 €540 The Holy Family (42x23cm-17x9in) i. chl ink. 4-Jun-4 Zofingen, Switzerland #2344 (S.FR 850)

GALLIOT, F P Louis (19th C) French
Sculpture
£2069 $3786 €3000 Grenadier au repost sur son fusil. Canonnier Agenouille (112x33cm-44x13in) s.d.1834 polychrome walnut panel pair. 31-Jan-4 Osenat, Fontainebleau #593

GALLIZIO, Pinot (1902-1964) Italian
£10690 $17852 €15500 Untitled (100x150cm-39x59in) s.d.1959. 17-Nov-3 Sant Agostino, Torino #295/R est:16000-20000

GALLO, Beppe (1942-) Italian
£267 $491 €400 Big vineyard (50x40cm-20x16in) s. painted 1997 lit. 12-Jun-4 Meeting Art, Vercelli #518
£302 $559 €450 Evening lights at Murazzi (30x30cm-12x12in) s. s.i.verso. 13-Mar-4 Meeting Art, Vercelli #260
£352 $585 €500 Filari e Colline (50x70cm-20x28in) s. s.i.d.2001 verso. 14-Jun-3 Meeting Art, Vercelli #228/R
£355 $592 €500 Langa (50x60cm-20x24in) s. 20-Oct-3 Sant Agostino, Torino #133/R
£403 $745 €600 Flowers in bloom in Fenillaz (50x50cm-20x20in) s. painted 2000. 13-Mar-4 Meeting Art, Vercelli #186
£528 $877 €750 Langa - Terra da vino (80x80cm-31x31in) s. s.i.d.1999 verso. 14-Jun-3 Meeting Art, Vercelli #438/R
£570 $1055 €850 Portofino (80x70cm-31x28in) s. 13-Mar-4 Meeting Art, Vercelli #235
£800 $1472 €1200 Langa (90x100cm-35x39in) s. s.i.d.1997 verso lit. 12-Jun-4 Meeting Art, Vercelli #970/R
£833 $1533 €1250 Langa, Italy (60x70cm-24x28in) s. s.i.d.1983 verso lit. 12-Jun-4 Meeting Art, Vercelli #673/R
£900 $1656 €1350 Last light in the Langhe (70x60cm-28x24in) s. s.i.d.1985 verso lit. 12-Jun-4 Meeting Art, Vercelli #343/R

GALLO, Frank (1933-) American
Sculpture
£1176 $2000 €1717 Quiet nude (79x69cm-31x27in) s.d.1966 epoxy resin mahogany. 9-Nov-3 Wright, Chicago #454 est:3000-5000
£2473 $4500 €3611 Quiet nude (81cm-32in) s.d.66 polychromed epoxy resin revolving wooden base prov.exhib.lit. 29-Jun-4 Sotheby's, New York #470/R est:2500-3500

GALLO, Giovanni (20th C) Italian
Works on paper
£650 $1196 €949 Pompeiian fresco depicting putti driving chariots drawn by stags (16x56cm-6x22in) s.i.d.1894 bodycol. 25-Mar-4 Christie's, Kensington #69

GALLO, Giuseppe (1954-) Italian
£270 $500 €394 Untitled (47x37cm-19x15in) s.i.d.1989 verso paper prov. 12-Feb-4 Sotheby's, New York #226/R
£541 $1000 €790 Untitled (47x36cm-19x14in) s.d.1989 verso oil W/C prov. 13-Jul-4 Christie's, Rockefeller NY #138/R
£1408 $2465 €2000 Unity (47x36cm-19x14in) s.d.1987 verso paper prov. 16-Dec-3 Finarte Semenzato, Milan #270/R est:1800-2200
£10000 $18200 €14600 Meta-Meta (156x152cm-61x60in) s.i.d.1987 verso wood. 4-Feb-4 Sotheby's, Olympia #205/R est:1500-2000

GALLOCHE, Louis (1670-1761) French
£5333 $9653 €8000 Diane et Acteon (47x64cm-19x25in) 4-Apr-4 St-Germain-en-Laye Encheres #3/R est:7000-8000

GALLOCHE, Louis (attrib) (1670-1761) French
£833 $1492 €1250 Alexandre et Dyogene (55x64cm-22x25in) 16-May-4 other European Auctioneer #19
£4000 $6920 €5840 Evilmerodach delivering Jehoiachin (96x124cm-38x49in) 10-Dec-3 Bonhams, New Bond Street #10/R est:4000-6000
£4027 $7410 €6000 Scene biblique (55x65cm-22x26in) 24-Mar-4 Tajan, Paris #113/R est:6000-8000

GALLON, Robert (1845-1925) British
£260 $434 €380 Evening on the Lledr valley, north Wales. 21-Oct-3 Gorringes, Lewes #2050
£750 $1275 €1095 On the Lledr (51x76cm-20x30in) s. 20-Nov-3 Gorringes, Worthing #699
£2330 $3658 €3402 Evening by the river, landscape with figures and boats by house (62x92cm-24x36in) s. 30-Aug-3 Rasmussen, Havnen #2251/R est:3000-5000 (D.KR 25000)
£2600 $4342 €3796 On Derwentwater (51x76cm-20x30in) s. 13-Nov-3 Christie's, Kensington #209/R est:1000-1500
£2800 $4424 €4060 Tranquil river, summer (61x102cm-24x40in) s. 4-Sep-3 Christie's, Kensington #139/R est:3000-5000
£3500 $5845 €5110 Evening glow (51x76cm-20x30in) s. 13-Nov-3 Christie's, Kensington #210/R est:1000-1500
£4200 $7014 €6132 At the waters edge (46x81cm-18x32in) s. 13-Nov-3 Christie's, Kensington #211/R est:1000-1500
£4250 $7608 €6205 English landscapes (30x43cm-12x17in) s. pair prov. 5-May-4 John Nicholson, Haslemere #540/R est:2500-4000
£4800 $8832 €7008 Cattle watering in a Highland landscape (61x102cm-24x40in) s. 23-Mar-4 Bonhams, New Bond Street #121/R est:3000-5000
£5000 $9250 €7300 River landscape beneath a sunset sky, with figures on a rustic bridge (46x81cm-18x32in) s. 14-Jan-4 Brightwells, Leominster #920/R est:5500-7000
£6000 $10020 €8760 On the canal (76x51cm-30x20in) s. 13-Nov-3 Christie's, Kensington #212/R est:1000-1500

GALLOP, Herbert Reginald (1890-1958) Australian
£810 $1304 €1183 Still life with pink flowers in a blue vase (44x36cm-17x14in) s. canvasboard. 13-Oct-3 Joel, Victoria #342 est:2000-3000 (A.D 2000)

GALLOTTI, Alessandro (1879-1961) Italian
£1733 $3189 €2600 View of Rovetta (60x40cm-24x16in) s. 8-Jun-4 Sotheby's, Milan #64/R est:1000-2000
£1867 $3435 €2800 Harvest time (49x35cm-19x14in) s. board. 8-Jun-4 Sotheby's, Milan #65/R est:1000-2000

GALLOTTI, Alessandro (attrib) (1879-1961) Italian
£1000 $1840 €1500 Market (34x48cm-13x19in) s. cardboard. 11-Jun-4 Farsetti, Prato #492 est:1400-1700

GALOFRE Y GIMENEZ, Baldomero (1849-1902) Spanish
£5500 $9350 €8030 Una feria andaluza (20x32cm-8x13in) s. panel exhib.lit. 19-Nov-3 Bonhams, New Bond Street #97/R est:6000-8000
£7059 $12000 €10306 Hombres a Caballo (20x35cm-8x14in) s. board. 29-Oct-3 Christie's, Rockefeller NY #197/R est:15000-20000
£7931 $13245 €11500 Spanish gypsy gathering (22x39cm-9x15in) s.d.94 panel. 9-Jul-3 Hugo Ruef, Munich #90/R est:5000
£8054 $15060 €12000 Campment (20x31cm-8x12in) s. board. 24-Feb-4 Durán, Madrid #244/R est:12000
£17000 $28900 €24820 Country fair (43x67cm-17x26in) s.d.1891 panel. 18-Nov-3 Sotheby's, London #200/R
Works on paper
£759 $1267 €1100 Tarragona church (35x27cm-14x11in) s. W/C. 17-Nov-3 Durán, Madrid #113/R
£775 $1340 €1100 Landscape in Catalunia (19x28cm-7x11in) s. W/C. 15-Dec-3 Ansorena, Madrid #155/R
£800 $1456 €1200 Preja de majos a caballo (16x12cm-6x5in) s. ink gouache. 29-Jun-4 Segre, Madrid #69/R
£1135 $1895 €1600 Peasants (26x20cm-10x8in) s. wash. 20-Oct-3 Durán, Madrid #194/R

GALOYER, Francois (1944-) French
Sculpture
£1127 $1949 €1600 Rouge-gorge sur une branche epineuse (15x12cm-6x5in) s.num.6/8 red green brown pat bronze socle st.f.C.A.I. 13-Dec-3 Martinot & Savignat, Pontoise #97/R est:1600-1700
£1170 $1896 €1650 Mesange huppee (14x9cm-6x4in) s.num.EAIII/IV col pat bronze green base st.f.CAI. 24-May-3 Martinot & Savignat, Pontoise #119/R est:1400-1500
£1831 $3168 €2600 Aegothele (29x28cm-11x11in) s.num.5/8 green brown pat bronze st.f.Paumelle. 13-Dec-3 Martinot & Savignat, Pontoise #98 est:2600-2800
£1950 $3160 €2750 Grand duc (38cm-15in) s.num.7/8 green brown pat bronze st.f.CAI. 24-May-3 Martinot & Savignat, Pontoise #120/R est:3000-3200

GALSCHIOT, Jens (1954-) Danish
Sculpture
£1217 $2252 €1777 Female fragment (127cm-50in) s.d.2004 num.7 bronze on wood stand. 15-Mar-4 Rasmussen, Vejle #692/R est:15000-20000 (D.KR 13500)
£1353 $2502 €1975 Bess - female figure (66cm-26in) s.d.2002 num.8/8 copper on stone base. 15-Mar-4 Rasmussen, Vejle #690/R est:15000 (D.KR 15000)
£3246 $6005 €4739 Berliner boy (118cm-46in) copper. 15-Mar-4 Rasmussen, Vejle #693/R est:50000 (D.KR 36000)

GALT, Charles Franklin (1884-?) American
£269 $500 €393 Autumn landscape (25x30cm-10x12in) s. board painted c.1930. 7-Mar-4 Treadway Gallery, Cincinnati #618/R
£8671 $15000 €12660 Gypsy (224x113cm-88x44in) s.d.1914 verso prov.exhib. 10-Dec-3 Bonhams & Butterfields, San Francisco #6007/R est:5000-7000

GALTSYAN, Simon (1914-2000) ?
£550 $974 €803 Mount Ararat (48x65cm-19x26in) s.d.1971. 29-Apr-4 Christie's, Kensington #180/R

GALVANI, A P (1804-1885) Italian?
£1781 $3027 €2600 Accordion player (57x43cm-22x17in) s. 5-Nov-3 Vendue Huis, Gravenhage #98/R est:2800-3200

GALVANO, Albino (1907-1991) Italian
£352 $585 €500 Composition (79x79cm-31x31in) s.d.1974 verso. 14-Jun-3 Meeting Art, Vercelli #39/R
£352 $585 €500 Composition (48x40cm-19x16in) s. mixed media paper on canvas. 14-Jun-3 Meeting Art, Vercelli #49/R
£369 $683 €550 Nude and flowers (67x49cm-26x19in) s. cardboard. 13-Mar-4 Meeting Art, Vercelli #99
£423 $701 €600 Anello di moebius (90x80cm-35x31in) s.d.1972. 14-Jun-3 Meeting Art, Vercelli #286/R
£467 $859 €700 Nude (60x50cm-24x20in) s.d.1941 verso. 12-Jun-4 Meeting Art, Vercelli #181/R
£500 $920 €750 Figures (66x49cm-26x19in) s. cardboard. 12-Jun-4 Meeting Art, Vercelli #922/R
£503 $931 €750 Still life (65x46cm-26x18in) s. cardboard. 13-Mar-4 Meeting Art, Vercelli #430
£503 $931 €750 Masks (70x50cm-28x20in) s. cardboard. 13-Mar-4 Meeting Art, Vercelli #453

GALVEZ, Laila (20th C) South American
£433 $780 €632 Stroll (107x67cm-42x26in) s. acrylic oil painted 2004. 25-Apr-4 Subastas Odalys, Caracas #19/R

GALWEY Y GARCIA, Enrique (1864-1931) Spanish
£570 $1010 €850 Landscape (18x34cm-7x13in) s. 27-Apr-4 Durán, Madrid #159/R
£872 $1632 €1300 Landscape (35x25cm-14x10in) s. 24-Feb-4 Durán, Madrid #180/R

GAMAGE, Parker (20th C) American
£335 $600 €489 Autumn forest (41x51cm-16x20in) s.i. s.verso board. 8-Jan-4 James Julia, Fairfield #853/R
£447 $800 €653 Near Long Cove, Maine, Chamberlain (41x51cm-16x20in) s. s.i.verso board. 8-Jan-4 James Julia, Fairfield #854/R

GAMARRA, Jose (1934-) Uruguayan
£24818 $42190 €36234 No smoking (130x160cm-51x63in) s.verso painted 1997. 23-Nov-3 Subastas Odalys, Caracas #57/R est:40000

GAMBA, Giovan Battista (1846-?) Italian
Sculpture
£8389 $13507 €12500 L'odalisque allongee, grande taille (64x37x29cm-25x15x11in) s. Carrare marble black beige marble socle. 23-Feb-3 St-Germain-en-Laye Encheres #93/R est:12000

GAMBARA, Lattanzio (1530-1574) Italian
£67606 $116958 €96000 Deposition (102x82cm-40x32in) board. 14-Dec-3 Finarte, Venice #144/R est:80000-90000
Works on paper
£9500 $17385 €13870 Design for a fresco with many figures. Four figure studies (25x37cm-10x15in) pen brown ink over blk chk double-sided prov. 8-Jul-4 Sotheby's, London #36/R est:8000-12000

GAMBARELLI, Crescenzio (attrib) (16th C) Italian
£625 $1044 €900 Portrait of priest (102x80cm-40x31in) 23-Oct-3 Finarte Semenzato, Milan #336

GAMBARINI, Giuseppe (1680-1725) Italian
£8000 $14640 €11680 Two women embroidering with a gentleman looking on (55x42cm-22x17in) canvas on board prov. 7-Jul-4 Bonhams, New Bond Street #39/R est:7000-10000
Works on paper
£5500 $10065 €8030 Peasants dancing in a landscape surrounded by musicians (21x28cm-8x11in) i. black chk pen ink wash prov. 6-Jul-4 Christie's, London #68/R est:3000-5000

GAMBARINI, Giuseppe (attrib) (1680-1725) Italian
£3333 $6000 €4866 Lady at her toilet (32x27cm-13x11in) mono.i. copper prov. 22-Jan-4 Sotheby's, New York #141/R est:8000-12000

GAMBIER, Michel (20th C) French
£1620 $2802 €2300 Toromagie (90x90cm-35x35in) s. 9-Dec-3 Chambelland & Giafferi, Paris #53/R est:2500-3000
Works on paper
£352 $609 €500 L'ingenue (65x50cm-26x20in) s. sanguine. 9-Dec-3 Chambelland & Giafferi, Paris #52/R

GAMBINO, Duilio (1937-) Italian
£272 $487 €400 Bond's style 3 (100x70cm-39x28in) s.i.d.1965 verso oil collage. 22-Mar-4 Sant Agostino, Torino #395/R

GAMBLE, John M (1863-1957) American
£3571 $6500 €5214 Eucalyptus landscape (15x23cm-6x9in) s. panel prov. 15-Jun-4 John Moran, Pasadena #10 est:6000-8000
£10326 $19000 €15076 Poppies and yellow lupine, Point Lobos (12x20cm-5x8in) s. i.verso board prov. 8-Jun-4 Bonhams & Butterfields, San Francisco #4302/R est:10000-15000
£19118 $32500 €27912 Poppies and lupine, Santa Paula (30x46cm-12x18in) s. i.verso prov. 18-Nov-3 John Moran, Pasadena #31 est:30000-50000
£20588 $35000 €30058 Zion Canyon, Utah (51x66cm-20x26in) s.i. s.i.verso. 29-Oct-3 Christie's, Los Angeles #20/R est:20000-30000
£25000 $46000 €36500 Wild flowers along a Santa Barbara path (45x61cm-18x24in) s.i. prov. 8-Jun-4 Bonhams & Butterfields, San Francisco #4318/R est:30000-50000
£36723 $65000 €53616 Wild buckwheat (50x76cm-20x30in) s. s.i.verso prov. 28-Apr-4 Christie's, Los Angeles #20/R est:80000-120000
£36723 $65000 €53616 Poppy field (76x101cm-30x40in) s. prov.exhib. 28-Apr-4 Christie's, Los Angeles #77/R est:80000-120000

GAMBOGI, Émile (19th C) French
£403 $737 €588 Italian wearing colourful dress (65x40cm-26x16in) s. 9-Jun-4 Rasmussen, Copenhagen #1930/R (D.KR 4500)
£828 $1382 €1200 Portrait d'homme (124x92cm-49x36in) s.d.1859. 12-Nov-3 Chassaing Rivet, Toulouse #196
£1862 $3110 €2700 Portrait de jeune fille (129x96cm-51x38in) s. 12-Nov-3 Chassaing Rivet, Toulouse #195
£2345 $3916 €3400 Portrait de deux jeunes femmes (155x124cm-61x49in) s. 12-Nov-3 Chassaing Rivet, Toulouse #197

GAMBOGI, G (19th C) Italian
Sculpture
£983 $1700 €1435 Young woman wearing flowered dress and scarf (33cm-13in) s. white marble. 10-Dec-3 Alderfer's, Hatfield #230/R est:2500-3500
£1049 $1752 €1500 Girls reading (58cm-23in) s. alabaster. 7-Oct-3 Sotheby's, Amsterdam #238/R est:1800-2200

GAMBOGI, Raffaello (1874-1943) Italian
£733 $1313 €1100 Sunset (48x68cm-19x27in) s. board. 12-May-4 Stadion, Trieste #667/R

GAMELIN, Jacques (1738-1803) French
Prints
£2098 $3566 €3000 Orate ne intretis in tentationem (35x24cm-14x9in) etching. 27-Nov-3 Bassenge, Berlin #5187/R est:3500

GAMELIN, Jacques (attrib) (1738-1803) French
Works on paper
£1389 $2208 €2000 La muerte de Pirro, Rey de Epiro (42x56cm-17x22in) W/C. 29-Apr-3 Durán, Madrid #122/R est:1800

GAMERITH, Walter (1903-1949) Austrian
£775 $1356 €1100 Female nude, sitting (124x70cm-49x28in) 19-Dec-3 Dorotheum, Vienna #19/R

GAMLEY, Andrew (?-1949) British
£270 $497 €394 In harbour (31x36cm-12x14in) s. 25-Mar-4 Bonhams, Edinburgh #377
Works on paper
£300 $552 €438 House on the rock (28x38cm-11x15in) s. W/C. 10-Jun-4 Lyon & Turnbull, Edinburgh #109

GAMMELGAARD, Albert (1897-1963) Danish
£344 $558 €499 Interior scene with woman (100x80cm-39x31in) s.d.48 exhib. 4-Aug-3 Rasmussen, Vejle #629/R (D.KR 3600)

GAMMELL, Robert Hale Ives (1893-1981) American
£398 $700 €581 Fallen tree (38x28cm-15x11in) s. board painted c.1900. 23-May-4 Treadway Gallery, Cincinnati #613/R
Works on paper
£339 $600 €495 Jane. Man with pitchfork (66x48cm-26x19in) s.d.1938 pastel two. 2-May-4 Grogan, Boston #95/R
£378 $650 €552 Frolic in the park (38x28cm-15x11in) s.i.d.1919 ink gouache. 7-Dec-3 Grogan, Boston #70/R

GAMMON, Reg (1894-1997) British
£280 $510 €409 Cottage gossip in Ireland (38x49cm-15x19in) s. board. 21-Jun-4 Bonhams, Bath #449
£320 $589 €467 Feeding time (27x37cm-11x15in) s. oil on card. 29-Mar-4 Bonhams, Bath #47/R
£350 $595 €511 Girl with red hair (39x27cm-15x11in) s. board. 1-Dec-3 Bonhams, Bath #45/R
£420 $752 €613 Red Jacket (35x44cm-14x17in) s. i.d.1978 verso board. 17-Mar-4 Bonhams, Chester #299
£420 $773 €613 Near Nefyn, Wales (25x44cm-10x17in) s. i.verso board. 29-Mar-4 Bonhams, Bath #46/R
£450 $842 €675 Woman and fishing boat on a beach (46x61cm-18x24in) s. board. 22-Jul-4 Gorringes, Lewes #1981/R
£460 $837 €672 Still life of violin, jug and pears (45x56cm-18x22in) s. oil sand on board. 21-Jun-4 Bonhams, Bath #446
£460 $837 €672 Woman and donkey outside a croft (30x40cm-12x16in) s. board. 21-Jun-4 Bonhams, Bath #447
£500 $910 €730 Hopeful on the stocks, Balimore, Co. Cork (42x53cm-17x21in) s. board. 21-Jun-4 Bonhams, Bath #450

£540 $983 €788 Woman in a red jacket (60x74cm-24x29in) s. board. 15-Jun-4 Bonhams, Knightsbridge #23/R
£560 $1019 €818 Worker in the field (62x72cm-24x28in) s. board. 15-Jun-4 Bonhams, Knightsbridge #20/R
£620 $1054 €905 Girl with a calf (55x75cm-22x30in) s. 1-Dec-3 Bonhams, Bath #43
£650 $1105 €949 Three friends in Confluent (56x66cm-22x26in) s. board. 1-Dec-3 Bonhams, Bath #44
£780 $1435 €1139 Cafe Switzerland (40x54cm-16x21in) s. board. 29-Mar-4 Bonhams, Bath #45/R
£800 $1440 €1168 Potato Pickers (51x61cm-20x24in) s. board. 20-Jan-4 Bonhams, Knightsbridge #245/R
£900 $1638 €1314 Market scene (53x72cm-21x28in) s. board. 15-Jun-4 Bonhams, Knightsbridge #22/R
£2000 $3640 €2920 Dublin corner shop (60x70cm-24x28in) s. board. 15-Jun-4 Bonhams, Knightsbridge #19/R est:1000-1500
Works on paper
£280 $476 €409 Bee hives (27x37cm-11x15in) s.d.42 W/C over pencil double-sided. 1-Dec-3 Bonhams, Bath #46/R

GAMP, Botho von (1894-1977) German
£1645 $3026 €2500 Colourful bouquet of flowers in a blue vase (60x50cm-24x20in) s. 25-Jun-4 Michael Zeller, Lindau #554/R est:2500

GAMPERT, Otto (1842-1924) Swiss
£216 $387 €315 Guarda (28x41cm-11x16in) s. board. 22-Mar-4 Philippe Schuler, Zurich #6012 (S.FR 500)
£346 $620 €505 Narrow pass (29x45cm-11x18in) mono. i. verso canvas on board. 22-Mar-4 Philippe Schuler, Zurich #4329 (S.FR 800)
£459 $766 €666 Green river delta (48x70cm-19x28in) s. 23-Jun-3 Philippe Schuler, Zurich #3390 (S.FR 1000)
£503 $941 €750 Mountain farmstead (48x66cm-19x26in) s. 24-Feb-4 Dorotheum, Vienna #35/R

GANAMBARR, Larrtjanga (1932-) Australian
Works on paper
£16260 $25691 €23577 Balirlira and the Macassans (155x61cm-61x24in) earth pigments eucalyptus bark exec.c.1958 prov. 28-Jul-3 Sotheby's, Paddington #84/R est:25000-35000 (A.D 40000)

GANDARA, Antonio de la (1862-1917) French
£449 $836 €656 Louvre Pavilion (25x19cm-10x7in) 2-Mar-4 Rasmussen, Copenhagen #1475/R (D.KR 5000)
£2059 $3500 €3006 Portrait of lady in a black satin dress with her son (190x140cm-75x55in) s. 19-Nov-3 Bonhams & Butterfields, San Francisco #98/R

GANDEZ, A (?) ?
Sculpture
£798 $1300 €1165 Young boy (65x25x25cm-26x10x10in) s. marble. 28-Sep-3 Bonhams & Butterfields, Los Angeles #7555 est:1500-2000

GANDIA, Vicente (1935-) Mexican
£8380 $15000 €12235 Still life with table and flowers (100x120cm-39x47in) s. painted c.1985 prov. 26-May-4 Sotheby's, New York #149/R est:15000-20000

GANDINI, Bernardino (attrib) (1587-1651) Italian
£3125 $5219 €4500 Angel concert in honour of the Trinity (28x19cm-11x7in) pen wash exhib. 24-Oct-3 Ketterer, Hamburg #65/R est:4500-5000

GANDOLFI, Gaetano (1734-1802) Italian
Works on paper
£1967 $3600 €2872 Studies of six grotesque heads (26x19cm-10x7in) pen brown ink wash. 29-Jan-4 Swann Galleries, New York #134/R est:2000-3000
£3611 $6500 €5272 Judith and Esther, with other figures on a cloud (42x32cm-17x13in) black white chk prov.lit. 22-Jan-4 Christie's, Rockefeller NY #66/R est:8000-12000
£5556 $10000 €8112 Study of five heads (23x17cm-9x7in) bears sig pen brown ink. 21-Jan-4 Sotheby's, New York #91/R est:6000-8000

GANDOLFI, Gaetano (attrib) (1734-1802) Italian
Works on paper
£1517 $2715 €2230 Tete de petite fille (34x27cm-13x11in) i.verso sanguine double-sided. 22-Mar-4 Digard, Paris #20/R est:800-1000

GANDOLFI, Mauro (1764-1834) Italian
Works on paper
£533 $981 €800 Portrait de femme (17x14cm-7x6in) i.d.1808 crayon. 9-Jun-4 Oger, Dumont, Paris #26
£6000 $10980 €8760 Sheet of studies of heads (19x28cm-7x11in) pen brown ink. 8-Jul-4 Sotheby's, London #106/R est:6000-8000

GANDOLFI, Mauro (attrib) (1764-1834) Italian
£5634 $9859 €8000 Portrait de jeune garcon avec poule (50x39cm-20x15in) 17-Dec-3 Piasa, Paris #64/R est:8000-10000
£6579 $12105 €10000 Madonna and Child (67x51cm-26x20in) 25-Jun-4 Piasa, Paris #66/R est:5000-6000

GANDOLFI, Ubaldo (1728-1781) Italian
£52349 $97893 €78000 Holy Family (89x70cm-35x28in) 25-Feb-4 Porro, Milan #80/R est:42000
£80000 $138400 €116800 Sybil (85x63cm-33x25in) init. prov.lit. 10-Dec-3 Christie's, London #112/R est:60000-80000
Works on paper
£294 $500 €429 Standing nymphs and satyrs (20x22cm-8x9in) chk. 25-Nov-3 Christie's, Rockefeller NY #499/R
£658 $1210 €1000 Moise sauve des eaux (21x30cm-8x12in) pen ink wash. 22-Jun-4 Calmels Cohen, Paris #16/R
£984 $1800 €1437 St Michael casting Satan into Hell (24x18cm-9x7in) pen brown ink wash red chk. 29-Jan-4 Swann Galleries, New York #130/R est:1500-2500
£1600 $2928 €2336 Flying putto among stars (19x15cm-7x6in) pen ink wash. 6-Jul-4 Christie's, London #93/R est:1000-1500
£4167 $7500 €6084 Diana and Callisto (15x20cm-6x8in) black lead pen brown ink wash. 22-Jan-4 Christie's, Rockefeller NY #64/R est:4000-6000
£4396 $8000 €6418 Christ and the woman taken in adultery (33x41cm-13x16in) red chk. 29-Jun-4 Sotheby's, New York #2/R est:4000-6000
£12222 $22000 €17844 Christ on the way to Calvary (28x19cm-11x7in) i. black chk pen brown ink grey wash prov.lit. 22-Jan-4 Christie's, Rockefeller NY #65/R est:15000-20000

GANDOLFI, Ubaldo (attrib) (1728-1781) Italian
Works on paper
£944 $1700 €1378 Male nude (28x41cm-11x16in) red chk prov. 21-Jan-4 Doyle, New York #26 est:1000-1500

GANDOLFI, Ubaldo (circle) (1728-1781) Italian
£12500 $22875 €18250 Christ and the woman taken in adultery (43x58cm-17x23in) prov.exhib.lit. 9-Jul-4 Christie's, Kensington #183/R est:4000-6000

GANDOLFINO D'ASTI (style) (16th C) Italian
£7798 $13023 €11307 Wedding of Mary. Death of Mary (29x32cm-11x13in) panel pair. 23-Jun-3 Philippe Schuler, Zurich #3520/R est:3500-4000 (S.FR 17000)

GANDON, Adolphe (1828-1889) French
£958 $1600 €1399 Pause of the family cart (39x51cm-15x20in) s. board. 7-Oct-3 Sotheby's, New York #87/R est:2000-3000

GANDY, Joseph Michael (1771-1843) British
Works on paper
£18000 $30600 €26280 Album of landscapes and studies from nature including views of Dorking (12x21cm-5x8in) most i.d. 15 July 1820-5 July 1826 pencil W/C 97 prov. 20-Nov-3 Christie's, London #7/R est:1500-2000

GANDY, William (1660-1729) British
£8000 $14720 €11680 Portrait of a young boy in a blue coat with a red cloak, holding a parakeet (76x63cm-30x25in) 11-Jun-4 Christie's, London #4/R est:10000-15000

GANGOLF, Paul (1879-1945) German
Works on paper
£667 $1227 €1000 Bordighera (20x26cm-8x10in) s.i.d.25 W/C pencil. 12-Jun-4 Villa Grisebach, Berlin #549/R
£1067 $1963 €1600 Ascona (16x12cm-6x5in) W/C collage paper on board. 12-Jun-4 Villa Grisebach, Berlin #548/R est:800-1000

GANGUTIA, Clara (1952-) Spanish?
£2254 $3899 €3200 Rainbow (31x50cm-12x20in) 15-Dec-3 Ansorena, Madrid #952/R est:3000

GANKU, Kishi (1756-1838) Japanese
Works on paper
£822 $1397 €1200 Hawk (139x77cm-55x30in) s. Indian ink col hanging scroll. 8-Nov-3 Dr Fritz Nagel, Stuttgart #1855/R

GANLY, Rose Brigid (1934-) Irish?
£2113 $3655 €3000 Roses in the President's Cup (50x60cm-20x24in) init. exhib. 10-Dec-3 Bonhams & James Adam, Dublin #142/R est:3000-5000
Works on paper
£267 $483 €400 Copper Beach, Corrig Avenue (28x37cm-11x15in) init. pastel. 31-Mar-4 James Adam, Dublin #151/R
£629 $1070 €900 White monastery, Skopilos (25x38cm-10x15in) i.d.1964 verso gouache chl prov.exhib. 18-Nov-3 Whyte's, Dublin #28/R

GANNAM, John (1907-1965) American
Works on paper
£1786 $3250 €2608 Broadway at 72nd Street (21x30cm-8x12in) s. gouache. 29-Jun-4 Sotheby's, New York #286/R est:1500-2000
£1946 $3250 €2841 After the recital, woman signing autographs (38x51cm-15x20in) s.indis.d.1936 W/C. 15-Nov-3 Illustration House, New York #128/R est:3000-4000
£2545 $4250 €3716 Crowd leaving church on Christmas Eve (38x58cm-15x23in) s. W/C gouache. 15-Nov-3 Illustration House, New York #127/R est:3000-4000
£2844 $4750 €4152 Young woman pauses from book to admire photograph on nightstand (51x41cm-20x16in) s. W/C gouache. 15-Nov-3 Illustration House, New York #126/R est:4000-6000
£4595 $8500 €6709 Van Hueme and Baume (37x45cm-15x18in) s. gouache pencil prov. 11-Mar-4 Christie's, Rockefeller NY #46/R est:4000-6000

GANNE, Yves (1931-) French
£280 $484 €409 Tournesolles et figues (100x81cm-39x32in) s.d.1955 s.i.d.55 verso prov. 10-Dec-3 Bonhams, Bury St Edmunds #551/R

GANREI, Kishi (1816-1883) Japanese
Works on paper
£5435 $10000 €7935 Manpuku - ten thousand felicties (156x82cm-61x32in) s.d.1864 col ink hanging scroll. 23-Mar-4 Christie's, Rockefeller NY #127/R est:12000-18000

GANS, Paula (1883-1941) Czechoslovakian
£2199 $3672 €3100 Reclining female nude (49x60cm-19x24in) lit. 21-Jun-3 Hans Stahl, Hamburg #84/R est:1700

GANSO, Emil (1895-1941) American
£521 $850 €761 Sunbath (53x43cm-21x17in) s. board. 17-Jul-3 Doyle, New York #30/R
£6818 $12000 €9954 Bather (54x36cm-21x14in) s. board. 18-May-4 Sotheby's, New York #95/R est:3000-5000
Works on paper
£462 $850 €675 Reclining nude from behind. Reclining nude with raised legs (43x56cm-17x22in) s. exec. c.1930. 10-Jun-4 Swann Galleries, New York #88/R

GANTAI, Kishi (1785-1865) Japanese
Works on paper
£850 $1420 €1241 Tiger (110x42cm-43x17in) s. ink col silk. 12-Nov-3 Christie's, London #5/R

GANTNER, Bernard (1928-) French
£347 $580 €500 Bouquet de fleurs (34x30cm-13x12in) s. 21-Oct-3 Artcurial Briest, Paris #357
£700 $1211 €1022 Village en Alsace (48x63cm-19x25in) s.d.68 s.verso i.d.1968 stretcher. 11-Dec-3 Christie's, Kensington #209/R
Works on paper
£300 $543 €450 Leman au lever du Soleil (42x49cm-17x19in) s.d.78 W/C. 1-Apr-4 Credit Municipal, Paris #80
£333 $603 €500 Les etangs du Genedrey (24x35cm-9x14in) s.d.78 W/C. 1-Apr-4 Credit Municipal, Paris #78
£367 $664 €550 Amsterdam (42x64cm-17x25in) s.d.78 W/C. 1-Apr-4 Credit Municipal, Paris #79
£467 $845 €700 L'etang (40x48cm-16x19in) s.d.81 W/C ink. 1-Apr-4 Credit Municipal, Paris #20

GANTZ, Ann Cushing (1935-) American
£299 $500 €437 Weavers (64x41cm-25x16in) masonite. 18-Oct-3 David Dike, Dallas #95/R
£299 $500 €437 Picasso (36x25cm-14x10in) 18-Oct-3 David Dike, Dallas #244/R
£599 $1000 €875 Frank and Jesse James (28x36cm-11x14in) 18-Oct-3 David Dike, Dallas #108/R
£719 $1200 €1050 Remington skies (76x64cm-30x25in) 18-Oct-3 David Dike, Dallas #287/R
£778 $1300 €1136 Caddo lake (91x46cm-36x18in) 18-Oct-3 David Dike, Dallas #243/R

GANTZ, John (18/19th C) British
Works on paper
£3500 $5705 €5110 Resting palanquin-bearers, near the Guindy Palace (28x53cm-11x21in) i.d.1826 pencil W/C. 24-Sep-3 Christie's, London #81/R est:4000-6000

GANTZ, Justinian (1802-1862) British
Works on paper
£1500 $2445 €2190 Figures drawing water from a Tank. Oxen cart by a river (27x37cm-11x15in) pencil pen ink W/C pair. 24-Sep-3 Christie's, London #250/R est:1500-2000

GANZ, Edwin (1871-1948) Swiss
£1517 $2731 €2200 Les chevaux de trait (55x70cm-22x28in) d.1907. 20-Jan-4 Galerie Moderne, Brussels #309/R est:700-1000

GANZ, Henry F W (19/20th C) British
£300 $552 €438 Venetian fishing boats at quay side (46x56cm-18x22in) 8-Jun-4 Peter Francis, Wales #21/R

GANZ, Valerie (1936-) British
£1700 $3094 €2482 Swansea docks (80x136cm-31x54in) s.d.75. 21-Jun-4 Bonhams, Bath #325/R est:1200-1800
£3500 $5950 €5110 Break at the coal face (80x100cm-31x39in) s. 18-Nov-3 Sotheby's, Olympia #214/R est:2000-3000
Works on paper
£2550 $4335 €3723 End of the day at Tower Colliery (38x57cm-15x22in) s. pastel chl W/C. 18-Nov-3 Sotheby's, Olympia #215/R est:1000-1500

GAO JIANFU (1879-1951) Chinese
Works on paper
£7824 $14083 €11423 Birds by the reed (82x36cm-32x14in) s.i.d.1908 ink col silk hanging scroll. 26-Apr-4 Sotheby's, Hong Kong #561/R est:50000-70000 (HK.D 110000)
£8000 $14720 €11680 Monkey on hilltop (27x17cm-11x7in) i. ink col. 9-Jun-4 Sotheby's, London #120/R est:8000-12000
£12802 $23044 €18691 Night journey (134x58cm-53x23in) s.d.1908 ink col hanging scroll. 26-Apr-4 Sotheby's, Hong Kong #559/R est:60000-80000 (HK.D 180000)
£14672 $24502 €21421 Pine branches (112x50cm-44x20in) s.i.d.1928 ink col hanging scroll prov.exhib. 27-Oct-3 Sotheby's, Hong Kong #277/R est:200000-300000 (HK.D 190000)

GAO JIANSENG (1894-1916) Chinese
Works on paper
£64011 $115220 €93456 Midnight hunter (133x63cm-52x25in) s.d.1914 ink col lit. 26-Apr-4 Sotheby's, Hong Kong #560/R est:200000-300000 (HK.D 900000)

GAO QIFENG (1889-1933) Chinese
Works on paper
£1307 $2366 €1908 Lotus after the rain. s.i. ink rice paper. 3-Apr-4 Glerum, Singapore #85/R est:6000-8000 (S.D 4000)
£19203 $34566 €28036 Woodpeckers (132x46cm-52x18in) s.i. ink col hanging scroll. 26-Apr-4 Sotheby's, Hong Kong #563/R est:280000-350000 (HK.D 270000)
£29344 $49004 €42842 Owl (120x39cm-47x15in) artist seal ink col hanging scroll exhib. 27-Oct-3 Sotheby's, Hong Kong #255/R est:250000-300000 (HK.D 380000)
£30888 $51583 €45096 Sketches of monkey (19x13cm-7x5in) s. ink 76 leaves album. 27-Oct-3 Sotheby's, Hong Kong #253/R est:80000-120000 (HK.D 400000)
£54054 $90270 €78919 Return of spring (156x49cm-61x19in) artist seal ink col hanging scroll exhib. 27-Oct-3 Sotheby's, Hong Kong #254/R est:450000-550000 (HK.D 700000)
£56899 $102418 €83073 Ape. Carp (20cm-8in circular) s.i. one d.1915 ink silk hanging scroll pair exhib.lit. 26-Apr-4 Sotheby's, Hong Kong #570/R est:180000-220000 (HK.D 800000)
£248933 $448080 €363442 Landscape (25x35cm-10x14in) s.i. one d.1967 ink col eight on four mounts prov.exhib.lit. 26-Apr-4 Sotheby's, Hong Kong #564/R est:900000-1200000 (HK.D 3500000)

GAO QIPEI (1660-1734) Chinese
Works on paper
£5405 $9027 €7891 Winter landscape (197x53cm-78x21in) i. ink on silk. 26-Oct-3 Christie's, Hong Kong #453/R (HK.D 70000)
£12091 $21764 €17653 Gazing at a waterfall (174x77cm-69x30in) s.i. ink col hanging scroll. 25-Apr-4 Christie's, Hong Kong #420/R est:95000-120000 (HK.D 170000)

GAO QIPEI (attrib) (1660-1734) Chinese
Works on paper
£1257 $2250 €1835 Duck flying over reeds (201x99cm-79x39in) with sig. ink. 10-May-4 Bonhams & Butterfields, San Francisco #4382/R est:1000-1500

GARABEDIAN, Charles (20th C) ?
£329 $550 €480 Column study (37x55cm-15x22in) s.d.1981 acrylic graphite. 19-Oct-3 Bonhams & Butterfields, Los Angeles #7092

GARABITO, Ricardo (1930-) Argentinian
£1547 $2800 €2259 Family (67x80cm-26x31in) board. 30-Mar-4 Arroyo, Buenos Aires #19

GARARRADJ, Sam (20th C) Australian
Works on paper
£325 $514 €475 Mother and baby dugong (33x71cm-13x28in) i.verso earth pigments eucalyptus bark prov. 28-Jul-3 Sotheby's, Paddington #534 (A.D 800)

GARAT, Francis (19th C) French
Works on paper
£290 $531 €423 Place de la Concorde (25x36cm-10x14in) s. W/C pencil. 28-Jul-4 Mallams, Oxford #142
£467 $854 €700 Elegantes a Place de la Concorde (33x46cm-13x18in) W/C. 3-Jun-4 E & Eve, Paris #21/R
£600 $1032 €876 La Cathedrale de Notre Dame, Paris (21x24cm-8x9in) s. pencil W/C pair. 3-Dec-3 Christie's, Kensington #92/R
£685 $1164 €1000 Lancement de montgolfiere (23x29cm-9x11in) s. W/C over crayon. 6-Nov-3 Tajan, Paris #242

GARATE Y CLAVERO, Juan Jose (1870-1939) Spanish
£308 $514 €440 View of barn (30x20cm-12x8in) cardboard. 30-Jun-3 Ansorena, Madrid #279/R
£870 $1600 €1270 The coquette (23x15cm-9x6in) s. panel. 25-Jun-4 Freeman, Philadelphia #143/R est:800-1200
£1293 $2314 €1900 Bay (70x100cm-28x39in) s. 22-Mar-4 Durán, Madrid #147/R est:1500
£4500 $7200 €6525 Enel souk (58x79cm-23x31in) s. 18-Sep-3 Christie's, Kensington #201/R est:5000-7000
Works on paper
£671 $1201 €1000 Piedralaves (33x45cm-13x18in) s. W/C. 25-May-4 Durán, Madrid #674/R

GARAU, Salvatore (1953-) Italian
£1477 $2643 €2200 Sculpture and bugs (165x130cm-65x51in) s.i.d.1992 verso acrylic graphite resin exhib.lit. 28-May-4 Farsetti, Prato #112/R est:2100-2400
£8667 $15947 €13000 Seated on dawn (100x90cm-39x35in) s.i.d.2003 verso acrylic. 8-Jun-4 Finarte Semenzato, Milan #466/R est:6000-7000

GARAVAGLIA, Ercole (19th C) Italian
£661 $1123 €965 Mountain landscape (25x25cm-10x10in) s.i.d.1918. 5-Nov-3 Dobiaschofsky, Bern #588/R (S.FR 1500)

GARAY Y AREVALO, Manuel (19th C) Spanish
£2013 $3765 €3000 Flirting (35x27cm-14x11in) s. board. 24-Feb-4 Durán, Madrid #229/R est:2750

GARAY, Akos (1866-?) Hungarian
£545 $856 €796 Two horses in snow landscape (39x48cm-15x19in) s. board. 27-Aug-3 Dunbar Sloane, Wellington #98/R (NZ.D 1500)

GARBELL, Alexandre (1903-1970) Latvian

£236	$431	€350	Scene de plage (25x45cm-10x18in) s. 7-Jul-4 Artcurial Briest, Paris #103
£333	$597	€500	Landscape with golden trees (33x55cm-13x22in) s. d.1950 verso. 17-May-4 Chayette & Cheval, Paris #120
£400	$716	€600	Procida (34x51cm-13x20in) i.d.1965 verso. 17-May-4 Chayette & Cheval, Paris #128
£400	$716	€600	Cannes in the evening (60x38cm-24x15in) i.d.1949. 17-May-4 Chayette & Cheval, Paris #116
£433	$776	€650	Figures (46x61cm-18x24in) i. 17-May-4 Chayette & Cheval, Paris #124
£467	$835	€700	Cliffs seen frm the beach (61x38cm-24x15in) s. i.d.1947 verso. 17-May-4 Chayette & Cheval, Paris #117
£483	$869	€700	Halles (75x85cm-30x33in) s.d.1957. 25-Jan-4 Chayette & Cheval, Paris #153
£483	$869	€700	Paysage au pont (60x92cm-24x36in) s. painted c.1952. 25-Jan-4 Chayette & Cheval, Paris #154
£500	$895	€750	Beach at dusk (33x55cm-13x22in) 17-May-4 Chayette & Cheval, Paris #126/R
£538	$968	€780	Les chaises longues sur le pont d'un bateau (46x33cm-18x13in) painted 1955. 25-Jan-4 Chayette & Cheval, Paris #151/R
£600	$1074	€900	Figures in Algiers harbour (55x46cm-22x18in) s.i.d. 17-May-4 Chayette & Cheval, Paris #119
£634	$1096	€900	Beach scene (53x66cm-21x26in) s.d.1947. 15-Dec-3 Bailly Pommery, Paris #129/R
£634	$1142	€920	Paysage de Pricida (50x100cm-20x39in) painted c.1960. 25-Jan-4 Chayette & Cheval, Paris #155
£733	$1313	€1100	Abstract (100x81cm-39x32in) s.d.1955. 17-May-4 Chayette & Cheval, Paris #122
£867	$1551	€1300	Seated woman (65x50cm-26x20in) i.d.1944 verso. 17-May-4 Chayette & Cheval, Paris #115/R
£872	$1623	€1300	Untitled (99x86cm-39x34in) s.d.1961. 3-Mar-4 Tajan, Paris #219/R est:1500-2000

GARBER, Daniel (1880-1958) American

£1808	$2875	€2640	Wood (61x52cm-24x20in) s. 29-Apr-3 Louis Morton, Mexico #105/R est:70000 (M.P 30000)
£41765	$71000	€60977	Milford Road (35x41cm-14x16in) s. s.i.verso board prov. 21-Nov-3 Skinner, Boston #464/R est:10000-15000
£581395	$1000000	€848837	Byram Hills, springtime (107x127cm-42x50in) s. painted 1937 prov. 3-Dec-3 Sotheby's, New York #33/R est:400000-600000

GARBIERI, Lorenzo (1580-1654) Italian

£1655	$2748	€2400	Jacob in rock cave (72x60cm-28x24in) 1-Oct-3 Dorotheum, Vienna #301/R est:3000-5000

GARBO, Raffaellino del (c.1476-1524) Italian

£61453	$110000	€89721	Madonna and Child with Saint John the Baptist (91cm-36in) panel prov.lit. 27-May-4 Sotheby's, New York #5/R est:80000-120000

GARBOLINO RU, Gabriele (1974-) Italian

Sculpture

£2098	$3503	€3000	Athlete resting (62x53x30cm-24x21x12in) s.d.2000 bronze. 26-Jun-3 Sant Agostino, Torino #274/R est:3000-4000

GARCES, Juan (1935-) Spanish

£278	$458	€400	Figure (55x46cm-22x18in) s. s.verso. 2-Jul-3 Ansorena, Madrid #898/R
£521	$859	€750	Portrait of young woman with hat (55x46cm-22x18in) s. board. 2-Jul-3 Ansorena, Madrid #905/R

GARCIA BARRENA, Carmelo (1926-) Spanish

£1172	$2110	€1700	Carnival (65x54cm-26x21in) s. lit. 26-Jan-4 Durán, Madrid #112/R est:1500

GARCIA CAMPOS, Luis (1928-) Spanish

£352	$616	€500	Bulls in the village (46x55cm-18x22in) 16-Dec-3 Segre, Madrid #297/R

Works on paper

£296	$518	€420	Impression (49x60cm-19x24in) s.i. gouache. 16-Dec-3 Segre, Madrid #294/R
£350	$584	€500	Torada (42x61cm-17x24in) s. gouache. 24-Jun-3 Segre, Madrid #287/R

GARCIA ELVIRA, Santiso (1883-1961) Spanish

£4336	$7241	€6200	Peasant woman (93x65cm-37x26in) s. 30-Jun-3 Ansorena, Madrid #337/R est:6200

GARCIA ERGUIN, Ignacio (1934-) Spanish

£293	$534	€440	Calle (29x23cm-11x9in) s.d.1974 panel. 29-Jun-4 Segre, Madrid #309/R
£458	$801	€650	Village (30x42cm-12x17in) s.d.1963 cardboard. 16-Dec-3 Segre, Madrid #268/R
£1056	$1849	€1500	Carmen (50x61cm-20x24in) s.d.1992 s.i.d.verso. 16-Dec-3 Segre, Madrid #263/R

GARCIA LLORT, Jose Maria (1921-2003) Spanish

£676	$1189	€1000	Corrupia (33x46cm-13x18in) s.i. s.d.1986 verso. 18-May-4 Segre, Madrid #265/R

Works on paper

£301	$503	€425	Hello (33x41cm-13x16in) s.d.53 mixed media lit. 20-Oct-3 Durán, Madrid #35/R

GARCIA MARTINEZ, Emilio (1875-1950) Spanish

£391	$716	€571	Landscape with church and group of houses (38x46cm-15x18in) s.i.d.1948. 4-Jun-4 Zofingen, Switzerland #2458 (S.FR 900)
£565	$1034	€825	Summer landscape (69x81cm-27x32in) s.i.d.1942. 4-Jun-4 Zofingen, Switzerland #2459 (S.FR 1300)

GARCIA MONZON, Ana Maria (1937-) Spanish

£390	$632	€550	Still life (60x91cm-24x36in) s. 20-May-3 Ansorena, Madrid #73/R

GARCIA MORALES (20th C) ?

£1985	$3375	€2898	Flowers (50x82cm-20x32in) s. 23-Nov-3 Subastas Odalys, Caracas #171 est:5000

GARCIA OCHOA, Luis (1920-) Spanish

£671	$1188	€1000	Face of woman (22x27cm-9x11in) s. board. 27-Apr-4 Durán, Madrid #71/R
£903	$1490	€1300	Figure (22x27cm-9x11in) s. board. 2-Jul-3 Ansorena, Madrid #888/R

Works on paper

£276	$497	€400	Study for Lecochandegui (35x25cm-14x10in) ink dr. 26-Jan-4 Ansorena, Madrid #343/R
£439	$773	€650	Rural landscape (21x31cm-8x12in) s.i. W/C exec.c.1950. 18-May-4 Segre, Madrid #111/R
£1400	$2534	€2100	Landscape (49x64cm-19x25in) s. W/C painted c.1950. 30-Mar-4 Segre, Madrid #258/R est:1950
£1748	$2920	€2500	Landscape (50x71cm-20x28in) s. W/C. 30-Jun-3 Ansorena, Madrid #19/R

GARCIA REINO, Oscar (1910-1993) Uruguayan

£366	$600	€534	Young profile (50x34cm-20x13in) s. cardboard. 3-Jun-3 Galeria y Remates, Montevideo #50
£435	$800	€635	Boats (60x73cm-24x29in) s. acrylic. 22-Jun-4 Galeria y Remates, Montevideo #174/R
£529	$900	€772	Abstract (60x76cm-24x30in) s. cardboard. 25-Nov-3 Galeria y Remates, Montevideo #88
£838	$1400	€1223	Young woman (62x49cm-24x19in) s. acrylic. 7-Oct-3 Galeria y Remates, Montevideo #71/R
£1176	$2000	€1717	Composition (75x93cm-30x37in) s. 25-Nov-3 Galeria y Remates, Montevideo #87/R
£1534	$2700	€2240	Composition (97x162cm-38x64in) s. 5-Jan-4 Galeria y Remates, Montevideo #15/R est:3200-3700

GARCIA Y HISPALETO, Manuel (1836-1898) Spanish

£21739	$37609	€31739	The toreadors entrance to town (78x90cm-31x35in) s.d.1864. 9-Dec-3 Rasmussen, Copenhagen #1230/R est:30000-50000 (D.KR 230000)
£28523	$51057	€42500	In the square (67x89cm-26x35in) s.d.1864. 25-May-4 Durán, Madrid #205/R est:42500

GARCIA Y HISPALETO, Rafael (1833-1854) Spanish

£408	$743	€600	Self-portrait (22x17cm-9x7in) s.i.d.1850 board oval. 3-Feb-4 Segre, Madrid #31/R
£603	$1007	€850	Visita del doctor (36x26cm-14x10in) s. 23-Jun-3 Durán, Madrid #86/R

GARCIA Y MENCIA, Antonio (1853-1915) Spanish

Works on paper

£1103	$1986	€1600	Gypsy woman (33x29cm-13x11in) s. W/C. 26-Jan-4 Durán, Madrid #122/R est:1500

GARCIA Y MENENDEZ (19th C) Spanish

£400	$736	€584	Spanish fairground with bull fighter (13x23cm-5x9in) s. panel. 8-Jun-4 Gorringes, Lewes #2078
£1769	$3166	€2600	Young oriental party (15x30cm-6x12in) s. panel. 20-Mar-4 Bergmann, Erlangen #1111 est:2600

GARCIA Y RAMOS, Jose (1852-1912) Spanish

£3401	$6190	€5000	Exit of the bride and groom (33x16cm-13x6in) s. board. 3-Feb-4 Segre, Madrid #117/R est:4500
£4500	$8190	€6570	Garden in Granada (26x17cm-10x7in) s.i. panel prov. 16-Jun-4 Bonhams, New Bond Street #84/R est:5000-8000

Works on paper

£1711	$3096	€2600	Music time (10x15cm-4x6in) s. W/C. 14-Apr-4 Ansorena, Madrid #60c/R est:2600
£1711	$3096	€2600	Dancing time (10x15cm-4x6in) s. W/C. 14-Apr-4 Ansorena, Madrid #60d/R est:2600

GARCIA Y RODRIGUEZ, Manuel (1863-1925) Spanish

£2535	$4056	€3600	River landscape (14x16cm-6x6in) s.d.1898 canvas on cardboard. 16-Sep-3 Segre, Madrid #37/R
£5102	$9286	€7500	Landscape with shepherd (38x26cm-15x10in) s.d.1896. 3-Feb-4 Segre, Madrid #61/R est:6000
£10000	$18000	€14600	Spanish courtyard (50x72cm-20x28in) s.i.d.1919. 22-Apr-4 Christie's, Rockefeller NY #221/R est:20000-30000
£10000	$18500	€14600	Garden in Seville (46x26cm-18x10in) s.i.d.96. 14-Jul-4 Sotheby's, Olympia #245/R est:6000-9000
£11765	$20000	€17177	Patio con Nonos (37x59cm-15x23in) s.d.1906. 29-Oct-3 Christie's, Rockefeller NY #198/R est:15000-20000
£15000	$25500	€21900	Courtyard with sundial (27x35cm-11x14in) s.i.d.1919 panel. 18-Nov-3 Sotheby's, London #253/R
£18000	$30600	€26280	Ladies in courtyard (71x56cm-28x22in) s.i.d.1922. 18-Nov-3 Sotheby's, London #203/R
£18824	$32000	€27483	Patio Sevillano (71x86cm-28x34in) s.d.1925. 29-Oct-3 Christie's, Rockefeller NY #194/R est:25000-35000
£22000	$37400	€32120	Fountain (42x56cm-17x22in) s.i. 18-Nov-3 Sotheby's, London #254/R

£25000 $42500 €36500 View of the Giralda, Seville (40x32cm-16x13in) s.i.d.1905 panel prov. 18-Nov-3 Sotheby's, London #204/R
£29000 $49300 €42340 Sevillian courtyard (43x55cm-17x22in) s.i.d.1922. 18-Nov-3 Sotheby's, London #205/R
£48951 $81748 €70000 Damas con mantilla en los Jardines del Alcazar (59x70cm-23x28in) s. 24-Jun-3 Segre, Madrid #91/R est:27000
Works on paper
£940 $1748 €1400 Washerwomen (11x16cm-4x6in) s.d.1913 W/C. 2-Mar-4 Ansorena, Madrid #354/R
£1319 $2151 €1900 Granada street (20x12cm-8x5in) s.d.98 W/C. 23-Sep-3 Durán, Madrid #118/R est:1900
£1319 $2151 €1900 Toledo street (21x13cm-8x5in) s.i. W/C. 23-Sep-3 Durán, Madrid #119/R
£1348 $2183 €1900 Street of Toledo (22x19cm-9x7in) s. gouache. 20-May-3 Ansorena, Madrid #998/R est:1900
£1418 $2298 €2000 Steet of Granada (22x19cm-9x7in) s.d.98 gouache. 20-May-3 Ansorena, Madrid #999/R est:1900

GARCIA YORK, Roberto (20th C) ?
£490 $832 €700 Habitacle d'Antigone (91x148cm-36x58in) s. 20-Nov-3 Claude Aguttes, Neuilly #199

GARCIA, Carlo (19/20th C) Spanish?
£1167 $2100 €1704 Fruit carrier of St Mark's (36x61cm-14x24in) s. 24-Apr-4 Weschler, Washington #581/R est:1000-1500

GARCIA, Carlos (1954-) Puerto Rican
£4667 $8587 €7000 Still life (76x101cm-30x40in) s.d.2002 verso acrylic prov. 10-Jun-4 Christie's, Paris #74/R est:8000-11000

GARCIA, Horacio G (20th C) American
£1622 $3000 €2368 Windjammer in the Tradewinds (51x76cm-20x30in) s.d.932. 10-Feb-4 Christie's, Rockefeller NY #247/R est:4000-6000

GARCIA, Joe (20th C) American
Works on paper
£599 $1000 €875 Quails (74x53cm-29x21in) s.d. W/C. 11-Oct-3 Nadeau, Windsor #140/R

GARCIA, Jose Maria (19th C) Mexican?
£2734 $5002 €3992 Portrait of Don Jose Ignacio de Basadre (61x47cm-24x19in) 27-Jan-4 Louis Morton, Mexico #290/R est:25000-30000 (M.P 55000)

GARCIA, Juan Gil (1879-1931) Cuban
£348 $550 €508 Avocados and grapes (28x30cm-11x12in) s. 6-Sep-3 Brunk, Ashville #73

GARCIA, Victor Manuel (20th C) South American
£1935 $3000 €2825 Untitled (57x47cm-22x19in) s. 3-Nov-2 Subastas Odalys, Caracas #12/R est:4000

GARCIA-ROSSI, Horacio (1929-) Argentinian
£264 $449 €385 P.OB (30x30cm-12x12in) acrylic prov. 5-Nov-3 Dobiaschofsky, Bern #590/R (S.FR 600)
£286 $487 €418 P.021 (20x20cm-8x8in) acrylic prov. 5-Nov-3 Dobiaschofsky, Bern #591/R (S.FR 650)
£286 $487 €418 P.20 (20x20cm-8x8in) acrylic prov. 5-Nov-3 Dobiaschofsky, Bern #592/R (S.FR 650)
£308 $524 €450 P.015 (25x25cm-10x10in) s.d.75 acrylic prov. 5-Nov-3 Dobiaschofsky, Bern #589/R (S.FR 700)
£748 $1339 €1100 Space (50x50cm-20x20in) s.d.73 tempera board prov. 16-Mar-4 Finarte Semenzato, Milan #229/R
Works on paper
£268 $499 €400 Composition (13x13cm-5x5in) s.d.1977 gouache. 3-Mar-4 Tajan, Paris #224

GARCIA-SEVILLA, Ferran (1949-) Spanish
£1343 $2376 €2000 Colas (73x53cm-29x21in) s. verso board prov. 28-Apr-4 Artcurial Briest, Paris #301 est:1500-2000
£4362 $7721 €6500 Cien No. 14 (162x130cm-64x51in) s. verso painted 1987 prov. 28-Apr-4 Artcurial Briest, Paris #302/R est:4000-6000
Works on paper
£1469 $2452 €2100 Flechas (72x50cm-28x20in) s. gouache. 24-Jun-3 Segre, Madrid #137/R est:2100
£2128 $3553 €3000 Untitled (81x116cm-32x46in) sand pigment glue canvas. 14-Oct-3 Dorotheum, Vienna #272/R est:2800-4000

GARDAIR, Christian (1938-) French
£237 $425 €346 Air de Seine (99x81cm-39x32in) s.d.1987 s.i.verso prov. 20-Mar-4 Sloans & Kenyon, Bethesda #353/R

GARDANNE, Auguste (19th C) French
£839 $1401 €1200 Clairon. Batterie (24x19cm-9x7in) s. pair. 29-Jun-3 St-Germain-en-Laye Encheres #5/R

GARDELL-ERICSON, Anna (1853-1939) Swedish
Works on paper
£489 $788 €714 Saltsjobaden (34x50cm-13x20in) s. W/C. 25-Aug-3 Lilla Bukowskis, Stockholm #758 (S.KR 6400)
£887 $1588 €1295 Woman rowing across the bay (31x47cm-12x19in) s. W/C. 28-May-4 Uppsala Auktionskammare, Uppsala #151/R (S.KR 12000)
£1015 $1827 €1523 Coastal landscape from Kooen (30x44cm-12x17in) s.i. W/C htd white. 25-Apr-4 Goteborg Auktionsverk, Sweden #224/R (S.KR 14000)
£1146 $2051 €1673 Moonlight over Marstrand (32x49cm-13x19in) s. W/C. 26-May-4 AB Stockholms Auktionsverk #2118/R est:20000-25000 (S.KR 15500)
£1256 $2249 €1834 Evening landscape (48x38cm-19x15in) s.d.1893 gouache. 28-May-4 Uppsala Auktionskammare, Uppsala #150/R est:12000-15000 (S.KR 17000)
£1692 $2911 €2470 The Skansen Lion, Gothenburg (47x64cm-19x25in) s. W/C. 2-Dec-3 Bukowskis, Stockholm #32/R est:30000-35000 (S.KR 22000)
£1848 $3307 €2698 St. Hansgatan in Visby (35x50cm-14x20in) s.i. W/C. 28-May-4 Uppsala Auktionskammare, Uppsala #147/R est:12000-15000 (S.KR 25000)
£1923 $3308 €2808 Coastal landscape with moonlight (45cm-18in circular) s.d.1887 W/C htd white. 3-Dec-3 AB Stockholms Auktionsverk #2443/R est:25000-30000 (S.KR 25000)
£2231 $3837 €3257 The vegetable garden, Visby (36x53cm-14x21in) s. W/C. 2-Dec-3 Bukowskis, Stockholm #33/R est:35000-40000 (S.KR 29000)
£2956 $5292 €4316 Young lady out walking (53x36cm-21x14in) s. W/C. 26-May-4 AB Stockholms Auktionsverk #2089/R est:20000-25000 (S.KR 40000)

GARDELLE, Robert (1682-1766) Swiss
£1357 $2308 €1981 Portrait of Maria Catharina Effinger von Wildegg-von Diessbach (92x73cm-36x29in) s. verso. 19-Nov-3 Fischer, Luzern #2105/R est:1500-1800 (S.FR 3000)

GARDELLE, Theodore (1722-1761) Swiss
Miniatures
£1700 $2890 €2482 Lady wearing blue sleevless dress (5cm-2in) enamel gilt frame oval prov. 18-Nov-3 Bonhams, New Bond Street #42/R est:1000-1500

GARDEN, William Fraser (1856-1921) British
Works on paper
£310 $527 €453 Landscape with cottages by weir on a river (29x23cm-11x9in) s.d.1894 W/C. 4-Nov-3 Bristol Auction Rooms #507
£750 $1275 €1095 Two children fishing in a river (19x27cm-7x11in) s.d.1888 W/C. 4-Nov-3 Holloways, Banbury #500/R
£900 $1503 €1314 Rustic dwellings (28x37cm-11x15in) s.d.1882 W/C bodycol. 16-Oct-3 Christie's, Kensington #52/R
£1200 $2208 €1752 Peaceful stretch of the river (15x28cm-6x11in) s.d.94 pencil W/C. 25-Mar-4 Christie's, Kensington #180/R est:1200-1800
£1500 $2730 €2190 River Ouse, Bedfordshire (19x28cm-7x11in) s. pen grey ink W/C over pencil htd white. 1-Jul-4 Sotheby's, London #242/R est:2000-3000

GARDET, Georges (1863-1939) French
Sculpture
£872 $1544 €1300 Ours assis (17cm-7in) s.st.f.Siot num.V792 pat bronze. 30-Apr-4 Tajan, Paris #39 est:700
£1131 $1923 €1651 Hunting dog (58cm-23in) i. brown pat.bronze. 19-Nov-3 Fischer, Luzern #1450/R est:2500-3000 (S.FR 2500)
£1200 $2184 €1800 Combat de tigres (58cm-23in) s. pat bronze. 30-Jun-4 Delvaux, Paris #68/R est:1800-2500
£1500 $2835 €2190 Pointer (26x55cm-10x22in) s.num.5879 brown pat bronze. 17-Feb-4 Sotheby's, Olympia #38/R est:1000-1500
£1600 $2896 €2400 Le combat des cerfs (36x26cm-14x10in) s.st.f.Barbedienne green pat bronze incl. red marble base. 31-Mar-4 Sotheby's, Paris #282/R est:2100-3000
£1724 $2879 €2500 Levriere Afghan et Levrette (28x20x45cm-11x8x18in) s. brown pat bronze. 17-Nov-3 Tajan, Paris #174 est:1200-1500
£2800 $4676 €4088 Pointer (28x55cm-11x22in) s. mid brown pat. bronze marble base. 14-Oct-3 Sotheby's, Olympia #57/R est:2000-2500
£7500 $13725 €10950 Standing antelope (91x70cm-36x28in) s.st.f.Valsuani pat bronze. 9-Jul-4 Sotheby's, London #125/R est:4000-6000
£12000 $22080 €18000 Tigresse et ses petits (50cm-20in) marble onyx bronze pate de verre. 11-Jun-4 Claude Aguttes, Neuilly #83/R est:15000-20000

GARDETTE, Sylvia (20th C) French
£251 $450 €366 The tasting (102x81cm-40x32in) s. i.verso. 20-Mar-4 Sloans & Kenyon, Bethesda #345/R
£261 $475 €381 Harmonie des choses (39x32cm-15x13in) s. 7-Feb-4 Sloans & Kenyon, Bethesda #311/R

GARDIER, Raoul du (1871-1952) French
£600 $1086 €900 Vue de Paris (30x40cm-12x16in) init. panel. 5-Apr-4 Marie & Robert, Paris #36
£3222 $5992 €4800 La mer au vent au sud de la crete (65x81cm-26x32in) s. 2-Mar-4 Artcurial Briest, Paris #219 est:2000-3000

GARDINER, Alfred Clive (1891-1960) British
£250 $450 €365 Leda and the Swan (20x18cm-8x7in) board prov. 20-Apr-4 Canterbury Auctions, UK #131

GARDINER, Anna (fl.1900-1920) British
£202 $371 €295 Still life fruit and flowers on a table top (79x64cm-31x25in) s.d.1921 canvas on board. 14-Jun-4 Waddingtons, Toronto #112/R (C.D 500)
£300 $528 €438 Dionne I (32x26cm-13x10in) 18-May-4 Bonhams, Knightsbridge #121/R

GARDINER, Stanley (1888-1952) British
£400 $740 €584 Lamorna woods (36x46cm-14x18in) s. board. 10-Feb-4 David Lay, Penzance #477
£500 $935 €730 Summer avenue (45x50cm-18x20in) s. board. 22-Jul-4 Bonhams, Edinburgh #303
£500 $935 €750 Logan Rock (38x46cm-15x18in) s. board. 22-Jul-4 Gorringes, Lewes #1968/R
£520 $962 €759 Lamorna stream (51x61cm-20x24in) s. board. 10-Feb-4 David Lay, Penzance #440
£520 $972 €759 Figures seated before corn barges Lamorna cove (30x37cm-12x15in) s. 26-Feb-4 Lane, Penzance #83
£1100 $1826 €1606 Lamorna valley (33x39cm-13x15in) s. board. 2-Oct-3 Lane, Penzance #160/R est:500-600
£1650 $2739 €2409 Still life, glass vase of mixed flowers on a window ledge (61x51cm-24x20in) s.d.47. 10-Jun-3 Canterbury Auctions, UK #103/R est:500-700

£3000 $5610 €4380 Lamorna, vase of flowers before an open window. s.d.1947. 26-Feb-4 Lane, Penzance #95/R est:3000-4000
Works on paper
£260 $432 €380 Trees above Lamorna (38x50cm-15x20in) s. W/C. 2-Oct-3 Lane, Penzance #101

GARDNER, Alexander (1821-1882) American
Photographs
£39521 $66000 €57701 Gardner's photographic sketch book of the war. i.d. albumen photos 100 two volumes multiple artists. 17-Oct-3 Sotheby's, New York #108/R est:60000-80000

GARDNER, Daniel (1750-1805) British
Works on paper
£400 $668 €584 Portrait of a mother and child (47x37cm-19x15in) pencil W/C bodycol chk prov. 16-Oct-3 Christie's, Kensington #1/R
£1000 $1670 €1460 Portrait of Philadelphia de Lancy (98x70cm-39x28in) bodycol. 16-Oct-3 Christie's, Kensington #3/R est:1000-2000
£2200 $3938 €3212 Portrait of Admiral Sir William Sidney Smith KCB and Vice Admiral Thomas Pringle (24x22cm-9x9in) W/C bodycol oval pair. 26-May-4 Christie's, Kensington #369/R est:800-1200
£3800 $6992 €5548 Portrait of Elizabeth Farren, later Countess of Derby, seated at an organ (84x55cm-33x22in) gouache prov.lit. 26-Mar-4 Sotheby's, London #12/R est:3000-5000

GARDNER, Daniel (attrib) (1750-1805) British
£662 $1212 €1000 Portrait d'Elizabeth Stevenson, contess of Mexborough (23x17cm-9x7in) copper oval. 7-Apr-4 Libert, Castor, Paris #25/R
£1600 $2960 €2336 Portrait of Elisabeth Stevenson, Countess of Mexborough (23x18cm-9x7in) copper oval prov. 14-Jul-4 Sotheby's, Olympia #13/R est:800-1200

GARDNER, Derek George Montague (1914-) British
£3200 $6048 €4672 Emigrant Ship, Morayshire (25x41cm-10x16in) s. board. 17-Feb-4 Bonhams, New Bond Street #25/R est:1000-1500

GARDNER, Edwin C (fl.1880-1888) British
Works on paper
£300 $546 €438 Study of a mongrel (16x10cm-6x4in) s.d.92 W/C. 5-Feb-4 Amersham Auction Rooms, UK #234/R

GARDNER, Frederick (?) British
£850 $1573 €1241 Coming across the trenches (76x51cm-30x20in) s. 11-Mar-4 Duke & Son, Dorchester #171/R
£900 $1665 €1314 Keeping a look out (74x46cm-29x18in) 11-Mar-4 Duke & Son, Dorchester #172/R

GARDNER, Rev J (?) British
Works on paper
£380 $692 €555 Between Deptford and Greenwich (28x42cm-11x17in) pencil W/C. 1-Jul-4 Mellors & Kirk, Nottingham #710/R

GARDNER, Sidney (19/20th C) British
£280 $484 €409 Windermere from Brant Fell (40x61cm-16x24in) s. i.stretcher. 10-Dec-3 Bonhams, Bury St Edmunds #591
£360 $648 €526 A June morning, Windermere (63x84cm-25x33in) s. 20-Apr-4 Bonhams, Ipswich #191

GARDNER, Tim (1973-) American?
Works on paper
£6704 $12000 €9788 Untitled, Utah (64x58cm-25x23in) s.d.99 W/C prov. 14-May-4 Phillips, New York #337/R est:3000-4000

GARDNER, William Biscombe (c.1847-1919) British
£7500 $13800 €10950 Packing the golden hops (81x137cm-32x54in) s.d.1913 s.i.verso prov.exhib. 11-Jun-4 Christie's, London #170/R est:8000-12000
Works on paper
£600 $978 €870 View over a wooded landscape (18x26cm-7x10in) s. W/C. 23-Sep-3 Bonhams, Knightsbridge #162/R
£1400 $2548 €2044 Donkeys resting in the sun (20x14cm-8x6in) s. pencil W/C. 1-Jul-4 Christie's, Kensington #218/R est:800-1200

GARDUNO, Flor (1957-) South American
Photographs
£4706 $8000 €6871 Arbol de la vida I. La mujer. Woman making corncakes (21x25cm-8x10in) two s. gelatin silver print set of three. 19-Nov-3 Sotheby's, New York #150/R est:10000-15000

GARDY, Claude (1949-) French
£1034 $1914 €1500 Grands Boulevards (22x27cm-9x11in) s. panel. 16-Feb-4 Giraudeau, Tours #73

GAREIS, Fritz (elder) (1845-1903) Austrian
£1987 $3636 €3000 Broken sledge (100x73cm-39x29in) s.d.81. 8-Apr-4 Dorotheum, Vienna #64/R est:2500-3000

GAREL, Philippe (1945-) French
Works on paper
£345 $576 €500 Portrait en buste (60x44cm-24x17in) s.d.1984 mixed media exhib. 17-Nov-3 Sant Agostino, Torino #93/R
£350 $584 €500 Portrait (29x19cm-11x7in) s.d. mixed media. 29-Jun-3 Versailles Encheres #236

GARET, Jedd (1955-) American
£541 $1000 €790 Life on Earth (213x267cm-84x105in) s.i.d.1985 verso prov. 13-Jul-4 Christie's, Rockefeller NY #157/R

GARF, Salomon (1879-1943) Dutch
£362 $655 €550 Still life with fruit (37x48cm-15x19in) s. 19-Apr-4 Glerum, Amsterdam #279/R
Works on paper
£278 $453 €400 Rabbi at prayer (41x31cm-16x12in) s. chl chk. 29-Sep-3 Sotheby's, Amsterdam #57/R
£12057 $20135 €17000 At the dressing table (70x53cm-28x21in) s. pastel. 20-Oct-3 Glerum, Amsterdam #96/R est:500-700

GARFINKIEL, David (1902-1970) Polish
£738 $1374 €1100 14 juillet a Montmartre (81x65cm-32x26in) s. 2-Mar-4 Artcurial Briest, Paris #170

GARGALLO, Pablo (1881-1934) Spanish
Sculpture
£16176 $27500 €23617 Porteuse d'eau (44cm-17in) s.d.1925 brown pat. bronze prov. 9-Nov-3 Bonhams & Butterfields, Los Angeles #4012/R

GARGIULIO, Domenico (1612-1679) Italian
Works on paper
£492 $900 €718 Studies of grotesque heads and figures (18x14cm-7x6in) pen brown ink. 29-Jan-4 Swann Galleries, New York #63/R

GARGIULIO, Domenico (attrib) (1612-1679) Italian
£25000 $42500 €36500 Adoration of the shepherds (100x128cm-39x50in) 30-Oct-3 Sotheby's, Olympia #118/R est:4000-6000

GARIANI, Garibaldi (1862-1930) Italian
£2083 $3542 €3000 Old Garibaldi soldier (65x86cm-26x34in) s. 1-Nov-3 Meeting Art, Vercelli #178/R est:3000

GARIAZZO, Piero Antonio (1879-1963) Italian
£263 $476 €400 Portrait et buste (80x70cm-31x28in) s. panel. 19-Apr-4 Horta, Bruxelles #183
£400 $736 €600 Stream (56x65cm-22x26in) s.d.1934 board. 14-Jun-4 Sant Agostino, Torino #200/R
£522 $950 €762 Tuscany summer landscape (23x28cm-9x11in) s.d.1937 board. 19-Jun-4 Jackson's, Cedar Falls #62/R
£674 $1125 €950 Shepherdess (47x38cm-19x15in) s.d.1956 i.verso card. 20-Oct-3 Sant Agostino, Torino #152/R
£680 $1218 €1000 Stream (70x120cm-28x47in) init.d.1963. 22-Mar-4 Sant Agostino, Torino #542/R
£690 $1262 €1000 Musicians in southern Tyrolean costume (101x70cm-40x28in) s.d.1922. 27-Jan-4 Dorotheum, Vienna #29/R
£966 $1612 €1400 Decking (50x70cm-20x28in) s.d.1954 board. 17-Nov-3 Sant Agostino, Torino #129/R
£1046 $1893 €1527 Three Balinese maidens (64x60cm-25x24in) s.d.1959 panel. 4-Apr-4 Sotheby's, Singapore #15/R est:2000-3000 (S.D 3200)

GARIBALDI, Joseph (1863-?) French
£2715 $4697 €3964 Paysage mediterraneen (73x59cm-29x23in) s. prov. 12-Dec-3 Galerie du Rhone, Sion #191/R (S.FR 6000)
£7240 $12525 €10570 Femme au puits (97x130cm-38x51in) s. prov. 12-Dec-3 Galerie du Rhone, Sion #189/R est:9000-12000 (S.FR 16000)
£14118 $24000 €20612 Vue de la Cathedrale d'Auxerre (118x161cm-46x63in) s. prov. 28-Oct-3 Sotheby's, New York #113/R est:30000-40000

GARIN, Louis (1888-1959) French
£671 $1248 €1000 L'oree du village (50x73cm-20x29in) s. 7-Mar-4 Livinec, Gaudcheau & Jezequel, Rennes #78
£2000 $3580 €3000 Procession a Houat (73x92cm-29x36in) s.d.1920. 16-May-4 Renault-Aubry, Pontivy #451

GARINEI, Michele (1871-1960) Italian
£335 $600 €489 Man in green cap (30x20cm-12x8in) s. 20-Mar-4 Selkirks, St. Louis #518
£397 $723 €600 Fonteboni (9x15cm-4x6in) s. i.verso board. 21-Jun-4 Pandolfini, Florence #131/R
£430 $783 €650 Bobolino (12x21cm-5x8in) s. i.verso board. 21-Jun-4 Pandolfini, Florence #129/R
£600 $1086 €900 Luna Square (16x24cm-6x9in) s. board. 2-Apr-4 Farsetti, Prato #557/R
£1871 $3068 €2600 Strozzi Street. Sant'Andrea Square. Amieri Square. (16x24cm-6x9in) s. board. 10-Jun-3 Pandolfini, Florence #120/R est:1800-2000

GARINO, Angelo (1860-?) Italian
£1593 $2597 €2326 Coastal landscape from St Jean a Bautien (73x92cm-29x36in) s.d.1899. 27-Sep-3 Rasmussen, Havnen #2202/R est:10000-15000 (D.KR 17000)
£1667 $2717 €2400 Femmes au marche (50x65cm-20x26in) s. 18-Jul-3 Feletin, Province #304

GARINO, Piero (1922-) Italian
£333 $613 €500 Still life (50x70cm-20x28in) s.d.1969 verso. 14-Jun-4 Sant Agostino, Torino #172/R
£340 $609 €500 Landscape (50x70cm-20x28in) s. masonite painted 1970. 22-Mar-4 Sant Agostino, Torino #368/R
£340 $609 €500 Landscape (50x70cm-20x28in) s.d.1971 acrylic. 22-Mar-4 Sant Agostino, Torino #367/R
£340 $609 €500 Clown (80x60cm-31x24in) s.d.1970. 22-Mar-4 Sant Agostino, Torino #385/R
£367 $675 €550 Grey landscape (55x80cm-22x31in) s.d.1965 board. 14-Jun-4 Sant Agostino, Torino #171/R
£408 $731 €600 Altar (100x60cm-39x24in) s.d.1959 exhib. 22-Mar-4 Sant Agostino, Torino #386/R

GARLAND, Charles Trevor (1851-1906) British
£1100 $2079 €1606 Mending nets (61x51cm-24x20in) mono. 19-Feb-4 Christie's, Kensington #97/R est:800-1200

GARLAND, George (20th C) American
Works on paper
£361 $650 €527 O Mara's Municipal Tavern (36x48cm-14x19in) s. gouache. 23-Jan-4 Freeman, Philadelphia #81/R
£528 $950 €771 He gotta keep Eve laughing (30x41cm-12x16in) s. W/C prov. 23-Jan-4 Freeman, Philadelphia #36/R

GARLAND, Henry (fl.1854-1900) British
£1050 $1932 €1533 On the beach (29x45cm-11x18in) s. board. 8-Jun-4 Bonhams, Knightsbridge #144/R est:300-500
£1750 $3238 €2555 On their way South (30x44cm-12x17in) s. indis.d. 88 s.i. verso. 14-Jul-4 Bonhams, Chester #439/R est:800-1200
£3500 $5950 €5110 Highlanders resting (36x53cm-14x21in) s.d.1898 s.i.d.1898 verso. 30-Oct-3 Christie's, London #81/R est:2500-3500
£7500 $13500 €10950 Keeping the herd at bay (36x68cm-14x27in) s.d.1881. 21-Apr-4 Christie's, Kensington #58/R est:7000-10000

GARLAND, Leon (1896-1941) American
£753 $1400 €1099 Mexican landscape (46x56cm-18x22in) s. painted c.1930. 7-Mar-4 Treadway Gallery, Cincinnati #657/R est:1000-1500

GARLAND, Valentine Thomas (1868-1914) British
£884 $1600 €1291 By the hearth (30x20cm-12x8in) s. board. 30-Mar-4 Bonhams & Butterfields, San Francisco #105/R est:1500-2200

GARLING, Frederick (1806-1873) Australian
Works on paper
£3000 $5310 €4380 Barque Ann bound for Calcutta, Off Millers Point, Sydney 19 August 1845 (30x43cm-12x17in) W/C scratching out. 27-Apr-4 Bonhams, New Bond Street #5/R est:3000-5000

GARM, C V (20th C) Danish
£361 $675 €527 Hilly coastal landscape from Mors (70x80cm-28x31in) s.d.1925. 25-Feb-4 Museumsbygningen, Copenhagen #8 (D.KR 4000)

GARMAN, Ed (20th C) American
£539 $900 €787 Variation of a structure no 24, geometric abstraction (91x58cm-36x23in) s.i.verso masonite. 25-Oct-3 David Rago, Lambertville #160

GARMS, Coenraad Matthias (1863-1944) Belgian?
£805 $1490 €1200 Winter landscape (60x49cm-24x19in) s. 15-Mar-4 Sotheby's, Amsterdam #219/R est:1000-1500

GARNEAU, Hector de Saint Denys (1912-1943) Canadian?
£533 $923 €778 Paysage a Sainte Catherine de Fosambault, Quebec (27x19cm-11x7in) board prov. 9-Dec-3 Pinneys, Montreal #162 (C.D 1200)

GARNEFF, Konstantin (1894-1966) ?
£303 $507 €440 Dancer from Pompeii (145x102cm-57x40in) mono.d.56 i. verso lit. 12-Jul-3 Bergmann, Erlangen #706/R

GARNELO Y ALDA, Jose (1866-1945) Spanish
£423 $731 €600 River (21x29cm-8x11in) s. cardboard. 15-Dec-3 Ansorena, Madrid #268/R

GARNER, E M (1881-?) British
£1200 $1884 €1740 Crescent bathed in morning sunlight (46x57cm-18x22in) s. 28-Aug-3 Christie's, Kensington #307/R est:400-600

GARNER, Lionel (1931-) French
£337 $550 €492 Le Pont Neuf (38x56cm-15x22in) s. 24-Sep-3 Doyle, New York #34
£353 $600 €515 Le chateau de Chambord (38x58cm-15x23in) s. 5-Nov-3 Doyle, New York #28/R

GARNER, Phillipa (20th C) Irish?
£573 $975 €820 Interior with table (59x51cm-23x20in) s.d.87. 25-Nov-3 De Veres Art Auctions, Dublin #208/R

GARNERAY, Ambroise Louis (1783-1857) French
£4306 $7190 €6200 Tempete (38x46cm-15x18in) s. 21-Oct-3 Fraysse & Associes, Paris #12/R
Works on paper
£811 $1532 €1200 Depart pour la peche (14x18cm-6x7in) s. W/C. 21-Feb-4 Livinec, Gaudcheau & Jezequel, Rennes #84

GARNERAY, Ambroise Louis (attrib) (1783-1857) French
Works on paper
£476 $852 €700 Vue de la Porte Royale dns le Port du Havre (21x29cm-8x11in) W/C traces black crayon pen black ink. 17-Mar-4 Tajan, Paris #102/R
£816 $1461 €1200 Paire de Marines (13x19cm-5x7in) mono. pen brown ink grey wash pair. 17-Mar-4 Tajan, Paris #103/R

GARNERAY, Jean François (1755-1837) French
£15385 $26154 €22000 Visit of the Grand Dauphin, sun of Louis XIV (113x147cm-44x58in) s. 24-Nov-3 Dorotheum, Vienna #58/R est:20000-25000

GARNEREY, Hippolyte Jean-Baptiste (1787-1858) French
£1500 $2685 €2190 Continental street scene with many figures (20x15cm-8x6in) s. panel. 5-May-4 John Nicholson, Haslemere #524/R est:1500-2500
Works on paper
£890 $1513 €1300 Vue de ville normande (15x11cm-6x4in) s. W/C gouache over crayon. 6-Nov-3 Tajan, Paris #105
£1277 $2068 €1800 Bateaux sur un canal traversant une ville (12x18cm-5x7in) s. W/C gouache varnish. 21-May-3 Daguerre, Paris #86 est:1500

GARNIER, François (attrib) (17th C) French
£42763 $78684 €65000 Still life with cherries (48x60cm-19x24in) panel. 25-Jun-4 Piasa, Paris #44/R est:50000-60000

GARNIER, H (?) ?
£833 $1500 €1216 Venetian view (36x58cm-14x23in) s. 23-Jan-4 Freeman, Philadelphia #142/R est:500-800

GARNIER, Henri (19/20th C) French
£1600 $2960 €2336 Rome from the Tiber. Town and river landscape (18x30cm-7x12in) s. panel pair. 11-Mar-4 Ewbank, Send #451/R est:800-1200

GARNIER, Jules Arsene (1847-1889) French
£738 $1307 €1100 Bal champetre (47x35cm-19x14in) 28-Apr-4 Schopman, Hamburg #473/R
£1006 $1800 €1688 Pierrot with flagon (25x15cm-10x6in) board. 20-Mar-4 Pook & Pook, Downington #380/R est:1200-1800
£2533 $4636 €3800 Rencontre (41x28cm-16x11in) 6-Jun-4 Osenat, Fontainebleau #231/R est:4000-4500
£2667 $4773 €4000 Girl chatting to two travelling monks (21x33cm-8x13in) s. panel. 15-May-4 Hagelstam, Helsinki #46/R est:4000

GARNIER, Michel (18th C) French
£59441 $102238 €85000 Jeune femme eplorее lisant une lettre, ou l'Attente (46x55cm-18x22in) s.d.1793 prov.lit. 2-Dec-3 Christie's, Paris #722/R est:50000-70000

GARNIER, Pierre (1847-1937) French
£1000 $1800 €1500 Bouquet d'hortensias (63x80cm-25x31in) s.d.1917. 20-Apr-4 Chenu & Scrive, Lyon #94/R est:1500-1800
£2340 $3909 €3300 Vase de roses et violettes sur entablement (81x64cm-32x25in) s. 19-Oct-3 Anaf, Lyon #140 est:3000-4000
£4500 $8325 €6570 Still life with roses (81x65cm-32x26in) s. 10-Mar-4 Sotheby's, Olympia #294/R est:3000-4000

GAROUSTE, Gerard (1946-) French
£11972 $20951 €17000 Untitled (201x181cm-79x71in) exhib.lit. 18-Dec-3 Cornette de St.Cyr, Paris #148/R est:20000-25000
£41259 $68902 €59000 L'homme a la veste verte, autoportrait (230x200cm-91x79in) s.d.1984 prov.lit. 11-Oct-3 Cornette de St.Cyr, Paris #128/R est:45000-55000
Sculpture
£4167 $6959 €6000 Minemosye (55x21x14cm-22x8x6in) s.i.num.1/8 bronze. 21-Oct-3 Artcurial Briest, Paris #618/R est:5000-7000
Works on paper
£828 $1382 €1200 Bomarzo (56x49cm-22x19in) s. mixed media card. 13-Nov-3 Finarte Semenzato, Rome #114 est:1300-1500
£3333 $6067 €5000 Untitled (65x50cm-26x20in) s. gouache diptych prov. 2-Jul-4 Binoche, Paris #8/R est:6000-7000

GARRALDA, Elias (1926-) Spanish
£1268 $2218 €1800 Cerdana (49x60cm-19x24in) s. s.i.verso. 16-Dec-3 Durán, Madrid #121/R est:1800

GARRARD, George (1760-1826) British
£7000 $12740 €10220 Chestnut in a landscape (63x73cm-25x29in) s.d.1788. 21-Jun-4 Christie's, London #182/R est:7000-10000

GARRARD, Peter John (1929-) British
£250 $400 €365 San Gimignano, early morning (44x59cm-17x23in) init. 17-Sep-3 Bonhams, Brooks & Langlois, Jersey #69/R
£800 $1456 €1168 Forsaken garden, Cadques (76x102cm-30x40in) init. 15-Jun-4 Bonhams, Knightsbridge #230/R

GARRAUD, Léon (1877-1961) French

£733	$1320	€1100	Bord de Rhone a Lyon (24x38cm-9x15in) s. panel painted c.1905. 20-Apr-4 Chenu & Scrive, Lyon #85a/R

GARRETT, Carlton E (1900-?) American

Sculpture			
£1444	$2600	€2108	Five figures around a table (25x33x25cm-10x13x10in) carved pained wood prov. 24-Apr-4 Slotin Folk Art, Buford #355/R est:1000-3000

GARRETT, Edmund (1853-1929) American

£579	$950	€840	Path of the Marina Grande, Capri (64x46cm-25x18in) s. i.verso board. 2-Jun-3 Grogan, Boston #651/R
£621	$1100	€907	Young girl in a cottage garden (20x24cm-8x9in) s. 2-May-4 Bonhams & Butterfields, San Francisco #1162/R
£1582	$2800	€2310	Boats in a harbour (41x51cm-16x20in) s. board. 2-May-4 Bonhams & Butterfields, San Francisco #1080/R est:1500-2000

GARRETT, Thomas Balfour (1879-1952) Australian

£327	$545	€474	Pittwater scene (21x25cm-8x10in) s. card. 13-Jul-3 James Lawson, Sydney #481 est:1800-2400 (A.D 800)
Works on paper			
£325	$582	€475	Cottage (33x26cm-13x10in) s. W/C htd gum arabic. 10-May-4 Joel, Victoria #301 (A.D 800)
£804	$1479	€1174	Waterfall (22x14cm-9x6in) s. W/C. 25-Mar-4 International Art Centre, Auckland #168/R (NZ.D 2250)
£813	$1455	€1187	Artist's easel (27x34cm-11x13in) s. W/C. 10-May-4 Joel, Victoria #471 est:2000-2500 (A.D 2000)
£1301	$2328	€1899	Stone Bridge (24x30cm-9x12in) s. mixed media. 10-May-4 Joel, Victoria #277/R est:2500-3500 (A.D 3200)

GARRIDO ROMANOS, Francisco Javier (1970-) Spanish

£268	$502	€400	Opera scene (46x55cm-18x22in) s. board. 24-Feb-4 Durán, Madrid #25/R

GARRIDO, Eduardo Léon (1856-1949) Spanish

£1374	$2500	€2006	Portrait of a young woman (56x46cm-22x18in) s. 29-Jun-4 Sotheby's, New York #106/R est:5000-7000
£3200	$5760	€4672	Walk in the country (19x24cm-7x9in) s. panel. 21-Jan-4 Sotheby's, Olympia #510/R est:3000-5000
£3200	$5920	€4672	Lady in front of a mirror (94x75cm-37x30in) s. 14-Jul-4 Sotheby's, Olympia #270/R est:1000-1500
£11765	$20000	€17177	Mujeres (55x45cm-22x18in) s. board. 29-Oct-3 Christie's, Rockefeller NY #202/R est:25000-35000
£17483	$29196	€25000	Ladies in concert (62x76cm-24x30in) s. board. 30-Jun-3 Ansorena, Madrid #344/R est:25000
£20833	$37500	€30416	Ball (80x100cm-31x39in) s. 23-Apr-4 Sotheby's, New York #116/R est:35000-45000
£21812	$39044	€32500	Reception (53x65cm-21x26in) s. board. 25-May-4 Durán, Madrid #195/R est:25000
£25175	$42042	€36000	Bal (80x100cm-31x39in) s. panel. 29-Jun-3 Eric Pillon, Calais #19/R
£56738	$94752	€80000	El Galan del sarao (80x100cm-31x39in) s. panel. 23-Jun-3 Durán, Madrid #235/R est:55000

GARRIDO, Leandro Ramon (1868-1909) Spanish

£4200	$7644	€6132	Le soir (119x146cm-47x57in) s.d.94. 16-Jun-4 Bonhams, New Bond Street #86/R est:4000-6000

GARRIDO, Louis Edouard (1893-1982) French

£937	$1491	€1350	Moissons (49x64cm-19x25in) s. panel. 9-Sep-3 Vanderkindere, Brussels #64
£2535	$4107	€3600	Port de Courseulles (60x81cm-24x32in) s. isorel. 11-Aug-3 Boscher, Cherbourg #712/R est:2500-3000

GARRONE, Romolo (1891-1959) Italian

£336	$594	€500	Mountains (21x33cm-8x13in) s. board. 1-May-4 Meeting Art, Vercelli #261
£369	$653	€550	Mountainous landscape (35x49cm-14x19in) s. board. 1-May-4 Meeting Art, Vercelli #349
£408	$731	€600	Donkey in Entraque (69x38cm-27x15in) s.d.1955. 22-Mar-4 Sant Agostino, Torino #192/R
£442	$791	€650	The Teleccio (34x44cm-13x17in) s.i.d.1940 card. 22-Mar-4 Sant Agostino, Torino #168/R

GARROS, Catherine (1954-) French

£805	$1442	€1200	Joueurs de petanque (54x65cm-21x26in) s. 30-May-4 Eric Pillon, Calais #136/R

GARROUSTE, Henri (1890-?) French

£369	$661	€550	Sous bois (22x27cm-9x11in) s. 25-May-4 Chambelland & Giafferi, Paris #33/R

GARRY, Charley (1891-) French

£867	$1595	€1300	La Congolaise (61x50cm-24x20in) s.d.1922 cardboard. 9-Jun-4 Beaussant & Lefèvre, Paris #155/R

GARSCHAGEN, Willy (19th C) German

£1512	$2707	€2208	Madonna in der Rosenlaube (46x37cm-18x15in) after Stefan Lochner. 12-Jan-4 Rasmussen, Vejle #212/R est:15000 (D.KR 16000)

GARSIDE, Oswald (1879-1942) British

Works on paper			
£202	$371	€295	Thames barge at Barnes (42x51cm-17x20in) s. i.verso W/C. 14-Jun-4 Waddingtons, Toronto #84/R (C.D 500)
£250	$430	€365	Neath the shade of the whispering trees (30x38cm-12x15in) s.d.05 s.i.d.1905 verso pencil W/C. 3-Dec-3 Christie's, Kensington #234/R
£260	$465	€380	Autumnal scene with woman on a path (23x20cm-9x8in) s. W/C. 17-Mar-4 Bonhams, Chester #238
£280	$501	€409	Shepherdess with her flock (26x47cm-10x19in) s. W/C. 17-Mar-4 Bonhams, Chester #246
£320	$573	€467	Old Whitby (74x39cm-29x15in) s. W/C. 17-Mar-4 Bonhams, Chester #243
£350	$602	€511	Idle gossip (30x45cm-12x18in) s. pencil W/C. 3-Dec-3 Christie's, Kensington #235/R
£350	$602	€511	Young boy seated beside a stream (27x40cm-11x16in) s. pencil W/C. 3-Dec-3 Christie's, Kensington #237/R
£400	$680	€584	Mount Bay (19x26cm-7x10in) W/C linen. 6-Nov-3 Ambrose, Loughton #66
£600	$1032	€876	Goatherder in a wooded landscape (39x56cm-15x22in) s. pencil W/C. 3-Dec-3 Christie's, Kensington #236/R
£600	$1032	€876	Ackles lane (29x26cm-11x10in) s.i.d.1925 pencil W/C bodycol. 3-Dec-3 Christie's, Kensington #238/R
£740	$1258	€1080	Winter landscape with figures, horse and cart (35x53cm-14x21in) s. W/C. 29-Oct-3 Bonhams, Chester #330
£800	$1336	€1168	Twilight on the shore (48x58cm-19x23in) s. W/C. 8-Oct-3 Andrew Hartley, Ilkley #1027/R

GARSIDE, Thomas H (1906-1980) Canadian

£300	$549	€438	Rockport Harbour (30x40cm-12x16in) prov. 1-Jun-4 Joyner Waddington, Toronto #456 (C.D 750)

GARSTIN, Alethea (1894-1978) British

£1500	$2685	€2190	Morning ride (25x30cm-10x12in) board prov. 28-May-4 Lyon & Turnbull, Edinburgh #69/R est:1500-2000
Works on paper			
£986	$1577	€1400	Pastoral scene with cattle before a church. Cattle grazing (28x38cm-11x15in) s. W/C pair. 16-Sep-3 Whyte's, Dublin #15/R

GARSTIN, Norman (1847-1926) British/Irish

£700	$1169	€1022	Garden steps (27x21cm-11x8in) s.i. board. 12-Nov-3 Sotheby's, Olympia #140/R
£1900	$3401	€2774	Norah Bolitho (69x51cm-27x20in) i.stretcher verso. 11-May-4 Bonhams, Knightsbridge #113/R est:600-800
£5400	$9666	€7884	Fashionable Parisian stood on a doorstep (53x35cm-21x14in) s.i.d.1883. 16-Mar-4 Bonhams, Leeds #633/R est:800-1200
£8054	$14416	€12000	Young lady descending steps from a doorway (54x35cm-21x14in) s.i. 26-May-4 James Adam, Dublin #21/R est:12000-15000
£11678	$19853	€16700	Among the pots (27x20cm-11x8in) s. panel prov. 25-Nov-3 De Veres Art Auctions, Dublin #36/R est:10000-15000
£23000	$42320	€33580	The red houses (60x48cm-24x19in) 27-Mar-4 Thos Mawer, Lincoln #201/R est:200-400
Works on paper			
£550	$919	€803	Hayle estuary, Cornwall (24x28cm-9x11in) s. W/C. 16-Oct-3 Christie's, Kensington #284/R
£720	$1332	€1051	St. Mary's church, Penzance (18x13cm-7x5in) s. W/C. 10-Feb-4 David Lay, Penzance #204/R
£1972	$3155	€2800	Young boy standing at the water's edge (24x18cm-9x7in) s. W/C. 16-Sep-3 Whyte's, Dublin #13/R est:1800-2200
£2083	$3396	€3000	The Market, Caudebec (17x12cm-7x5in) s.i.verso W/C. 24-Sep-3 James Adam, Dublin #3/R est:1500-2000

GARTEN, Otto (1902-1960) German

£451	$713	€650	Town landscape in winter (75x101cm-30x40in) s.d.36. 5-Sep-3 Wendl, Rudolstadt #3364/R

GARTHE, William Edward de (1907-1983) Canadian

£315	$500	€460	Winter at Peggy's Cove (41x51cm-16x20in) s. s.i.verso canvas on board. 12-Sep-3 Skinner, Boston #454/R
£1240	$2256	€1810	Fishing in a storm sea (38x76cm-15x30in) s. 5-Feb-4 Heffel, Vancouver #23/R est:1500-2000 (C.D 3000)

GARTMEIER, Hans (1910-1986) Swiss

£317	$538	€463	View from the Emme of Schloss Burgdorf (59x68cm-23x27in) s.d.38 board. 18-Nov-3 Hans Widmer, St Gallen #1053/R (S.FR 700)
£409	$733	€597	Woman peeling potatoes (12x9cm-5x4in) s. pavatex. 13-May-4 Stuker, Bern #648 (S.FR 950)
£431	$772	€629	Arab on white horse in the Levade (60x60cm-24x24in) s. panel. 12-May-4 Dobiaschofsky, Bern #542/R (S.FR 1000)
£437	$795	€638	Elderly peasants sharpening tools (32x24cm-13x9in) s. panel. 16-Jun-4 Fischer, Luzern #2132 (S.FR 1000)
£441	$749	€644	Portrait of old bearded man in pipe (28x21cm-11x8in) s. panel. 7-Nov-3 Dobiaschofsky, Bern #215/R (S.FR 1000)
£583	$974	€851	Spring near Kaltacker, Wil (70x100cm-28x39in) s.d.1938 i. stretcher. 24-Oct-3 Hans Widmer, St Gallen #141/R (S.FR 1300)
£611	$1125	€892	Potato harvest (50x61cm-20x24in) s. masonite. 14-Jun-4 Philippe Schuler, Zurich #4207/R (S.FR 1400)
£661	$1123	€965	Emmental peasant (49x38cm-19x15in) s. panel. 7-Nov-3 Dobiaschofsky, Bern #213/R (S.FR 1500)
£881	$1498	€1286	Peasant with horse drawn plough (48x69cm-19x27in) s. panel. 7-Nov-3 Dobiaschofsky, Bern #214/R (S.FR 2000)

GARTNER, Adolf (1889-1937) Czechoslovakian

Works on paper			
£2079	$3452	€3035	Girl in landscape (64x76cm-25x30in) chl. 4-Oct-3 Dorotheum, Prague #289/R est:80000-150000 (C.KR 95000)

GARTNER, Fritz (1882-?) German

£400	$728	€600	Obersee (134x68cm-53x27in) mono.d.58 i.verso panel triptych. 1-Jul-4 Neumeister, Munich #2684

GARTNER, Heinrich (1828-1909) German
£2066 $3844 €3016 View of the Bay of Naples with figures working on beach (20x34cm-8x13in) s. 2-Mar-4 Rasmussen, Copenhagen #1615/R est:25000 (D.KR 23000)
Works on paper
£5240 $9537 €7650 Roman landscape with ruins and fruit seller in foreground (38x49cm-15x19in) mono.i.d.1863 W/C prov.exhib. 17-Jun-4 Kornfeld, Bern #17/R est:15000 (S.FR 12000)

GARUTTI, Alberto (1948-) Italian
Works on paper
£1761 $3081 €2500 Untitled (80x100cm-31x39in) i.d.91 mixed media on canvas prov. 16-Dec-3 Finarte Semenzato, Milan #248/R est:3200

GARUZIO, Gian Piero (20th C) South African
£314 $562 €458 Boys fishing on the Natal coast (44x59cm-17x23in) s. canvas on board. 31-May-4 Stephan Welz, Johannesburg #245 (SA.R 3800)

GARVEY, Brian (20th C) Irish?
£486 $763 €700 Quarry, Co. Carlow (25x30cm-10x12in) s.verso. 26-Aug-3 James Adam, Dublin #153/R

GARVEY, Edmund (fl.1767-1813) British
£4000 $6680 €5840 Figures in the grounds of Hestercombe, Somerset (79x119cm-31x47in) 13-Nov-3 Christie's, Kensington #65/R est:5000-8000

GARVEY, Edmund (attrib) (fl.1767-1813) British
£5000 $9200 €7300 View of Royal Crescent, Bath, a couple walking in the foreground (46x58cm-18x23in) 26-Mar-4 Sotheby's, London #55/R est:6000-8000

GARVIE, T Bowman (1859-1944) British
£2800 $4760 €4088 Cottage interior with young girl by a fire, and cat on a stool (46x41cm-18x16in) s. prov. 19-Nov-3 Tennants, Leyburn #1235/R est:1500-2000

GARVIN, Barbara (1936-) American
£1863 $3000 €2720 Quiet time (46x61cm-18x24in) 22-Aug-3 Altermann Galleries, Santa Fe #62

GARZANTI, Wilfredo (20th C) Italian
Sculpture
£2098 $3566 €3000 Garzanti moved to Florence more than 35 years ago (35cm-14in) s. bronze. 25-Nov-3 De Veres Art Auctions, Dublin #134/R est:3000-4000

GARZI, Luigi (attrib) (1638-1721) Italian
£2752 $5146 €4100 L'ange gardien (67x50cm-26x20in) 29-Feb-4 Osenat, Fontainebleau #215
£5319 $8883 €7500 Angelica e Medoro (65x50cm-26x20in) 18-Jun-3 Christie's, Rome #416/R est:4000-6000

GARZOLINI, Giuseppe (1850-1938) Italian
£233 $418 €350 Along the river (12x21cm-5x8in) s. cardboard. 12-May-4 Stadion, Trieste #709
£467 $835 €700 Farm interior (26x36cm-10x14in) s. 12-May-4 Stadion, Trieste #684/R
£567 $1014 €850 Self-portrait (45x35cm-18x14in) s.verso. 12-May-4 Stadion, Trieste #619
£664 $1109 €950 Still life with fish and fruit (42x122cm-17x48in) s. 10-Oct-3 Stadion, Trieste #553/R
£1049 $1804 €1500 Seascape (40x55cm-16x22in) s. 3-Dec-3 Stadion, Trieste #974/R est:800-1200

GASCAR, Henri (1635-1701) French
£5000 $9300 €7300 Portrait of Hortense Mancini, Duchess of Mazarin, seated in a landscape (96x121cm-38x48in) s.i.d.1680. 4-Mar-4 Christie's, Kensington #293/R est:3000-5000
£26000 $47320 €37960 Portrait of Barbara Villiers, Countess of Castlemaine and her daughter (97x125cm-38x49in) oval. 1-Jul-4 Sotheby's, London #111/R est:10000-15000

GASCAR, Henri (attrib) (1635-1701) French
£5500 $9350 €8030 Portrait of William Douglas, 1st duke of Queensberry (122x98cm-48x39in) prov. 27-Nov-3 Sotheby's, London #125/R est:4000-6000

GASCOIGNE, Rosalie (1917-1999) New Zealander
£20325 $36382 €29675 Strictly ballroom (81x71cm-32x28in) s.d.1996 i.verso painted sawn wood board prov.exhib.lit. 4-May-4 Sotheby's, Melbourne #9/R est:50000-70000 (A.D 50000)
£30738 $48565 €44877 Apricot letters (112x80cm-44x31in) s.d.1990 verso panel prov.exhib. 2-Sep-3 Deutscher-Menzies, Melbourne #27/R est:65000-85000 (A.D 75000)
Sculpture
£3947 $6355 €5763 Black birds (13x64x14cm-5x25x6in) init.d.76 verso mixed media construction prov.exhib. 25-Aug-3 Sotheby's, Paddington #265/R est:5000-7000 (A.D 9750)
£10744 $19876 €15686 Tesserae (43x37cm-17x15in) s.i.d.1990 wood assemblage prov. 10-Mar-4 Deutscher-Menzies, Melbourne #86/R est:30000-40000 (A.D 26000)
£28926 $53512 €42232 Dandelion (99x91cm-39x36in) s.d.1990 i.verso swan retro-reflective road sing exhib. 15-Mar-4 Sotheby's, Melbourne #19/R est:50000-80000 (A.D 70000)
Works on paper
£2834 $4563 €4138 Two lovely blue eyes (51x35cm-20x14in) mixed media construction prov.exhib. 25-Aug-3 Sotheby's, Paddington #255/R est:1000-2000 (A.D 7000)
£15385 $24769 €22462 Turn of the tide (61x47cm-24x19in) s.d.1983 i.verso prov.exhib.lit. 25-Aug-3 Sotheby's, Paddington #120/R est:35000-45000 (A.D 38000)
£36260 $65992 €52940 Summer stack (91x68cm-36x27in) s. i.d.1990 verso sawn soft drink crayon on board exhib. 16-Jun-4 Deutscher-Menzies, Melbourne #56/R est:90000-120000 (A.D 95000)

GASCON DE GOTOR, Anselmo (1865-1927) Spanish
Works on paper
£313 $509 €450 Carnival (23x16cm-9x6in) s.d.1900 pen dr. 23-Sep-3 Durán, Madrid #1275/R

GASH, Walter Bonner (1869-1928) British
£850 $1564 €1241 Girl in a white dress (76x63cm-30x25in) s. 29-Mar-4 Bonhams, Bath #40/R
£1700 $2839 €2482 At the seaside (23x28cm-9x11in) s. 16-Oct-3 Christie's, Kensington #308/R est:1000-1500

GASIOROWSKI, Gerard (1930-1986) French
£3169 $5483 €4500 Quatre pots (78x63cm-31x25in) s.d.1973 acrylic prov. 9-Dec-3 Artcurial Briest, Paris #428/R est:2500-3000

GASKELL, Anna (20th C) American?
Photographs
£1788 $3200 €2610 Untitled, num 41 hide (48x59cm-19x23in) s.d.1998 num. of three verso c-print aluminum prov.exhib. 14-May-4 Phillips, New York #323/R est:4000-6000
£3073 $5500 €4487 Untitled num 50 (127x152cm-50x60in) s.d.1999 num. of three verso c-print prov.exhib.lit. 14-May-4 Phillips, New York #165/R est:8000-12000
£8383 $14000 €12239 Untitled no. 56 (127x152cm-50x60in) colour coupler print on plexiglass exec 1999 prov.exhib. 12-Nov-3 Christie's, Rockefeller NY #540/R est:18000-22000
£21229 $38000 €30994 Untitled, Wonder series (74x89cm-29x35in) s.d.1997 num.2/5 verso col coupler print plexiglas prov. 12-May-4 Christie's, Rockefeller NY #458a/R est:12000-18000

GASKIN, Arthur Joseph (1862-1928) British
£360 $612 €526 At Southwold, Suffolk (13x18cm-5x7in) init. tempera prov. 4-Nov-3 Bonhams, New Bond Street #121
£500 $920 €730 Portrait of Joscelyn Verney Gaskin. The nursery fire (51x44cm-20x17in) one bears i.d.1925 verso one s.i.verso tempera pair. 8-Jun-4 Bonhams, New Bond Street #66/R
£1800 $3060 €2628 Illustration to Grimm's fairy tales (10x10cm-4x4in) d.1927 i.verso tempera sold with three others by same hand. 4-Nov-3 Bonhams, New Bond Street #116/R est:2000-3000
£2800 $4760 €4088 Portrait of Joscelyne Verney Gaskin, aged 12 years (36x28cm-14x11in) s.i.verso prov. 4-Nov-3 Bonhams, New Bond Street #120/R est:2000-3000
Works on paper
£1000 $1700 €1460 Portrait of Joseph Southall (22x16cm-9x6in) col chks prov. 4-Nov-3 Bonhams, New Bond Street #115a est:800-1200
£4800 $8160 €7008 Blue feather (21x13cm-8x5in) init.i. W/C sold with 16 drawings by same hand. 4-Nov-3 Bonhams, New Bond Street #114/R est:3000-5000

GASPARD, Léon (1882-1964) French
£1455 $2750 €2124 Team No 5 Russia (13x18cm-5x7in) panel prov. 17-Feb-4 John Moran, Pasadena #123b/R est:3000-4000
£2674 $5000 €3904 Wagon team, Russia (20x25cm-8x10in) s. board prov. 24-Jul-4 Coeur d'Alene, Hayden #229/R est:4000-6000
£2907 $5000 €4244 Perched eagle (50x75cm-20x30in) i.verso canvasboard. 3-Dec-3 Doyle, New York #251/R est:8000-12000
£3073 $5500 €4487 Mongolian horsemen (28x18cm-11x7in) s.i.d.1921 oil W/C prov. 6-May-4 Shannon's, Milford #202/R est:6000-8000
£5587 $10000 €8157 Sleighs in winter, Russia (25x36cm-10x14in) board. 15-May-4 Altermann Galleries, Santa Fe #69/R
£6417 $12000 €9369 Birch trees (51x38cm-20x15in) board prov. 24-Jul-4 Coeur d'Alene, Hayden #227/R est:8000-12000
£6952 $13000 €10150 Indian in grey with green scarf (25x23cm-10x9in) s.d.1919 canvas on board prov. 24-Jul-4 Coeur d'Alene, Hayden #228/R est:8000-12000
£7263 $13000 €10604 War Red Cross (33x25cm-13x10in) 15-May-4 Altermann Galleries, Santa Fe #67/R
£24709 $42500 €36075 La Russie blanche (27x41cm-11x16in) s.i.d.1911 canvas on board prov. 3-Dec-3 Sotheby's, New York #164/R est:35000-45000
Works on paper
£604 $1100 €882 Portrait of a lady with sketches (51x41cm-20x16in) s.i. pastel prov. 19-Jun-4 Harvey Clar, Oakland #2203
£2941 $5500 €4294 North African bazaar (38x25cm-15x10in) s. W/C prov. 24-Jul-4 Coeur d'Alene, Hayden #225/R est:4000-6000
£4469 $8000 €6525 Russian forest scene with horsemen (33x25cm-13x10in) W/C paper on board. 15-May-4 Altermann Galleries, Santa Fe #68/R
£5080 $9500 €7417 Woman of Moscow (61x46cm-24x18in) s. pastel prov. 24-Jul-4 Coeur d'Alene, Hayden #226/R est:10000-15000
£31792 $55000 €46416 Flight Vitebsk (51x51cm-20x20in) s.d.1940 mixed media board prov.lit. 10-Dec-3 Bonhams & Butterfields, San Francisco #6112/R est:80000-100000

GASPARI, Luciano (1913-) Italian
£490 $832 €700 Study for fabric (58x63cm-23x25in) s. tempera paper. 26-Nov-3 Pandolfini, Florence #516/R
£909 $1545 €1300 Drawing for fabric (58x61cm-23x24in) s. tempera paper. 26-Nov-3 Pandolfini, Florence #510

GASPARO, Oronzo Vito (1903-1969) American/Italian
Works on paper
£978 $1800 €1428 David Smith's first sculpture exhibition (41x33cm-16x13in) i. W/C brush ink exec. c.1938. 10-Jun-4 Swann Galleries, New York #89/R est:1500-2500

GASPAROLI, Mary (?) ?
£800 $1448 €1200 Jonchees de fleurs (53x67cm-21x26in) s. pair. 2-Apr-4 Rossini, Paris #62

GASPARS, Jean Baptist (attrib) (fl.1641-1692) ?
£380 $597 €551 Portrait of a gentleman wearing a brown coat (36x32cm-14x13in) 28-Aug-3 Christie's, Kensington #46

GASSER, Henry (1909-1981) American
£2072 $3750 €3025 Harbour vista (41x51cm-16x20in) s. i.d.verso board. 2-Apr-4 Freeman, Philadelphia #140 est:200-300
Works on paper
£245 $450 €358 Back Rock Road (23x30cm-9x12in) s. W/C. 10-Jun-4 Swann Galleries, New York #90/R
£297 $550 €434 Baiting the nets (38x56cm-15x22in) s. W/C over pencil. 15-Jul-4 Doyle, New York #36/R
£297 $550 €434 Montmartre - Place du Tertre (38x56cm-15x22in) s.i. W/C paper on board. 15-Jul-4 Doyle, New York #39/R
£486 $900 €710 Eddie Mack's cocktail lounge, New Orleans (38x56cm-15x22in) s.i. W/C gouache pen ink. 15-Jul-4 Doyle, New York #37/R
£516 $950 €753 Sketch for city landscape (25x36cm-10x14in) s. W/C sketch verso. 10-Jun-4 Swann Galleries, New York #91/R
£591 $1100 €863 Street corner. Venetian canal (19x24cm-7x9in) s. W/C two. 5-Mar-4 Skinner, Boston #509/R
£920 $1500 €1343 Beached boat (36x53cm-14x21in) s. W/C. 19-Jul-3 Outer Cape Auctions, Provincetown #107/R
£968 $1800 €1413 Dry dock (36x53cm-14x21in) s. W/C gouache. 5-Mar-4 Skinner, Boston #542/R est:800-1200
£1117 $2000 €1631 Fishing shacks (48x61cm-19x24in) s. W/C pencil paper on board prov. 26-May-4 Doyle, New York #143/R est:2500-3500
£1236 $2250 €1805 Canal in Venice (57x77cm-22x30in) s.i. gouache. 29-Jun-4 Sotheby's, New York #276/R est:3000-5000
£1766 $3250 €2578 Getting Salvation (20x25cm-8x10in) s. W/C. 11-Jun-4 David Rago, Lambertville #269/R est:400-600
£1955 $3500 €2854 Main Street, winter (48x61cm-19x24in) s. W/C prov. 26-May-4 Doyle, New York #144/R est:2500-3500
£2941 $5000 €4294 The underpass (20x29cm-8x11in) s. i.verso W/C prov. 18-Nov-3 John Moran, Pasadena #126 est:2500-3500
£3488 $6000 €5092 Backyard in Newark (48x61cm-19x24in) s. W/C paper on board. 3-Dec-3 Doyle, New York #294/R est:3000-5000

GASSER, Henry (attrib) (1909-1981) American
£2016 $3750 €2943 To Eric McLean with my best wishes (56x69cm-22x27in) oil on paper. 6-Mar-4 Page, Batavia #141

GASSIES, Jean Baptiste Georges (1829-1919) French
Works on paper
£559 $962 €800 Birches en foret de Fontainebleau (26x42cm-10x17in) s.d.1904 W/C. 7-Dec-3 Osenat, Fontainebleau #26

GASSLANDER, Karl (?) American?
£500 $800 €730 Flying bread (56x51cm-22x20in) 17-May-3 Bunte, Elgin #1344

GASSNER, George (1811-1861) American
£43750 $70000 €63875 Massachusetts full-length portraits of young girl and young boy (89x71cm-35x28in) i. pair prov. 20-Sep-3 Pook & Pook, Downington #175/R est:25000-35000

GASSNER, George (attrib) (1811-1861) American
£16250 $26000 €23725 Massachusetts half-length portrait of Mr and Mrs Colbey (71x89cm-28x35in) prov. 20-Sep-3 Pook & Pook, Downington #174/R est:5000-6000

GASTALDI, Andrea (1826-1889) Italian
£805 $1426 €1200 Isaac's sacrifice (28x22cm-11x9in) cardboard. 1-May-4 Meeting Art, Vercelli #264

GASTE, Constant Georges (1869-1910) French
£2128 $3553 €3000 Jeune berbere (40x29cm-16x11in) s.i.d.sept.1893 panel. 16-Jun-3 Gros & Delettrez, Paris #343/R est:3200-3500
£2333 $4293 €3500 Ali Ben Mohamed de Tangier (24x14cm-9x6in) mono.i.d.1905 panel. 14-Jun-4 Gros & Delettrez, Paris #581/R est:3000-4000

GASTEIGER, Anna Sophie (1878-1954) German
£633 $1165 €950 Still life with vase of poppies (53x71cm-21x28in) s. board. 11-Jun-4 Wendl, Rudolstadt #4034/R
£1733 $3189 €2600 Blue grapes and roses (65x80cm-26x31in) s. cardboard i.verso. 11-Jun-4 Wendl, Rudolstadt #4033/R est:650
£2333 $4177 €3500 Autumn flowers with fruit basket (71x52cm-28x20in) s. s.i. verso board. 13-May-4 Neumeister, Munich #353/R est:3500-3800

GASTEIGER, Jacob (1953-) Austrian
£800 $1464 €1200 Untitled (33x78cm-13x31in) s.d.1990. 4-Jun-4 Lempertz, Koln #147/R
£940 $1738 €1400 Untitled (62x55cm-24x22in) s.d.2000 verso. 9-Mar-4 Dorotheum, Vienna #251/R

GASTEMANS, Émile (1883-1956) Belgian
£284 $474 €400 Three women (31x21cm-12x8in) mono. painted c.1919. 20-Oct-3 Bernaerts, Antwerp #279/R
£1141 $2019 €1700 Trois espagnoles et leur enfant (81x100cm-32x39in) s. 27-Apr-4 Campo & Campo, Antwerp #97/R est:1800-2000
£1745 $3089 €2600 Figures devant une porte dans un paysage espagnol (70x80cm-28x31in) s. 27-Apr-4 Campo & Campo, Antwerp #98/R est:2000-3000
£1944 $3092 €2800 Binnenhuis te San Lorenzo (100x120cm-39x47in) s. painted c.1935 prov. 15-Sep-3 Bernaerts, Antwerp #743/R est:3000-4000
£2837 $4738 €4000 Interior in Sevilla with figures (10x103cm-4x41in) s. 20-Oct-3 Bernaerts, Antwerp #169a est:3500-4500
Works on paper
£738 $1307 €1100 Portrait of woman, child and dog (90x80cm-35x31in) mono. chl painted c.1920. 27-Apr-4 Campo & Campo, Antwerp #96/R

GASTINA, F (20th C) ?
£600 $996 €876 Sculpture study (41x34cm-16x13in) s.d.98. 30-Sep-3 Sotheby's, London #256/R

GASTINEAU, Henry (1791-1876) British
Works on paper
£1100 $1870 €1606 Park near Middleham Castle in Yorkshire, King Henry VI, part III (26x38cm-10x15in) s.d.1840 W/C. 18-Nov-3 Bonhams, Leeds #42 est:600-800

GASTINI, Marco (1938-) Italian
Works on paper
£680 $1218 €1000 X (75x80cm-30x31in) s.i.d.1977 verso collage board. 22-Mar-4 Sant Agostino, Torino #393/R
£708 $1146 €1034 Untitled (70x100cm-28x39in) s.d.80 mixed media tempera collage. 24-May-3 Burkhard, Luzern #123/R (S.FR 1500)
£2439 $4000 €3561 Seven lines plus 1 (56x104cm-22x41in) s.verso gouache pencil prov. 28-May-3 Sotheby's, Amsterdam #15/R est:4000-6000

GASTO, Pedro (1908-1997) Spanish
£1644 $2795 €2400 Actor (47x39cm-19x15in) s.i.verso. 4-Nov-3 Ansorena, Madrid #901/R est:2400

GASTON, Johnny (20th C) ?
£479 $800 €699 Paris street scene (51x61cm-20x24in) 14-Nov-3 Du Mouchelle, Detroit #2287/R

GAT, Eliahu (1919-1987) Israeli
£588 $1100 €858 Reclining female nude (51x73cm-20x29in) s. 1-Mar-4 Ben-Ami, Tel Aviv #4702/R

GATCH, Lee (1902-1968) American
£2581 $4750 €3768 Tawny garden (20x38cm-8x15in) s.d.61 i. verso oil canvas collage panel prov.exhib. 27-Jun-4 Freeman, Philadelphia #140/R est:1500-2500
£2624 $4750 €3831 Summer solstice (18x73cm-7x29in) s. studio st.i.verso oil black ink canvasboard prov. 31-Mar-4 Sotheby's, New York #156/R est:3000-5000
£3529 $6000 €5152 Under the street lamp (40x51cm-16x20in) s. 30-Oct-3 Phillips, New York #95/R est:6000-8000
£3533 $6500 €5158 Lamb (17x82cm-7x32in) s. canvas on panel prov. 27-Jun-4 Freeman, Philadelphia #146/R est:2000-3000
£5233 $9000 €7640 Amphora (86x66cm-34x26in) s.d.62 oil collage mixed media board prov.exhib. 7-Dec-3 Freeman, Philadelphia #144 est:1500-2500
£14674 $27000 €21424 Study in white (51x36cm-20x14in) painted 1925-6 prov.exhib. 27-Jun-4 Freeman, Philadelphia #144/R est:1500-2500
Works on paper
£3226 $6000 €4710 Fetish gate (132x74cm-52x29in) s.d.64 s.i.verso mixed media natural stone on panel prov. 3-Mar-4 Christie's, Rockefeller NY #56/R est:2000-3000
£4696 $8500 €6856 Untitled (92x127cm-36x50in) s. collage oil canvas. 31-Mar-4 Sotheby's, New York #146/R est:4000-5000

GATEHOUSE, Charles E (1866-1952) British
£780 $1217 €1139 Mustard, portrait of a chestnut hunter in a yard (41x51cm-16x20in) s.i.d.1928. 28-Mar-3 Greenslade Hunt, Taunton #508/R
£950 $1748 €1387 Castle. Kissing time (41x51cm-16x20in) s.d.1924 pair. 10-Jun-4 Christie's, Kensington #69/R

GATHERER, Stuart Luke (?) British?
£2300 $4163 €3358 The ancestral letter (152x152cm-60x60in) s.d.95 verso. 3-Apr-4 Shapes, Edinburgh #407 est:1500-2000

GATT, Ferdinand (1847-1909) Austrian
Works on paper
£1745 $3211 €2600 Brenner mountain valley (48x69cm-19x27in) s. W/C. 26-Mar-4 Dorotheum, Vienna #307/R est:1600-2000

GATTA, Anacleto Nino della (1868-) Italian
Works on paper
£247 $427 €350 Narrow street (37x24cm-15x9in) Chinese ink. 9-Dec-3 Pandolfini, Florence #163

GATTA, Saverio della (?-1829) Italian
Works on paper
£1316 $2421 €2000 Procida (20x26cm-8x10in) s.d.1794 pen ink W/C. 22-Jun-4 Sotheby's, Milan #191 est:2000-3000
£1400 $2212 €2044 Sepolcro di Virgilio (29x33cm-11x13in) s.d.1790 brown wash sold with a companion. 23-Jul-3 Hampton & Littlewood, Exeter #378/R est:300-500
£2113 $3655 €3000 Femmes des faubourgs de Mahon (20x15cm-8x6in) both s. i.verso gouache pair. 10-Dec-3 Piasa, Paris #16/R est:3000
£3333 $6000 €4866 Overgrown tomb in a rocky landscape, with figures (24x38cm-9x15in) s.d.1791 bodycol. 22-Jan-4 Christie's, Rockefeller NY #224/R est:6000-8000
£3472 $5660 €5000 Veduta di Persano (34x55cm-13x22in) s.d.1813 gouache. 25-Sep-3 Dr Fritz Nagel, Stuttgart #1145/R est:5000
£3521 $6092 €5000 Costumes (29x41cm-11x16in) W/C pair. 10-Dec-3 Finarte Semenzato, Rome #148/R est:7000-8000
£3846 $6615 €5500 Having dinner (20x14cm-8x6in) s.d.1799 gouache two. 7-Dec-3 Sotheby's, Amsterdam #571/R

£4444 $8000 €6488 Man serving pasta by a house. Grain seller by city walls (21x27cm-8x11in) s.d.1812 pen brown ink W/C pair. 22-Jan-4 Christie's, Rockefeller NY #77/R est:5000-7000
£4469 $8000 €6525 Peasant family on a horse. Woman and child winding yarn (21x16cm-8x6in) one indis.sig. one i. gouache pair. 27-May-4 Sotheby's, New York #45a/R est:8000-12000

GATTA, Saverio della (attrib) (?-1829) Italian
Works on paper
£1000 $1800 €1460 Two natural hot baths at Piscarelli. Tomb of Cicero on the Via Appia (23x70cm-9x28in) bodycol pair. 22-Jan-4 Christie's, Rockefeller NY #245/R est:2000-4000

GATTEAUX, Jacques Edouard (1788-1881) French
Sculpture
£3691 $6534 €5500 Minerve (74cm-29in) s.d.1843 pat bronze. 29-Apr-4 Sotheby's, Paris #205/R est:5500

GATTI, Annibale (1828-1909) Italian
Works on paper
£1467 $2699 €2200 Beach on the Sorrento coast. Galln t scene on the beach (27x33cm-11x13in) gouache oval pair. 10-Jun-4 Christie's, Rome #41/R est:2300-2800

GATTI, Bernardino (1495-1575) Italian
Works on paper
£22000 $36520 €32120 Study of the Virgin Mother and Child (28x20cm-11x8in) i.verso sepia chk. 3-Oct-3 Mallams, Oxford #79/R
£26667 $48000 €38934 Madonna and Child with the Infant Baptist, with subsidiary studies (29x21cm-11x8in) red chk prov. 22-Jan-4 Christie's, Rockefeller NY #23/R est:40000-60000

GATTI, C (?) Italian?
Works on paper
£837 $1515 €1222 Extensive view, Bay of Naples (34x45cm-13x18in) s. gouache prov. 1-Apr-4 Heffel, Vancouver #39/R est:850-1000 (C.D 2000)

GATTIKER, Hermann (1865-1950) Swiss
£294 $500 €429 Salavers ruins near Grusch (24x28cm-9x11in) s.i.d.1920 verso board. 18-Nov-3 Hans Widmer, St Gallen #1056 (S.FR 650)
£306 $562 €447 Trees at foot of mountain (35x66cm-14x26in) s.d. 14-Jun-4 Philippe Schuler, Zurich #5720 (S.FR 700)
£452 $724 €660 Coastal landscape (32x45cm-13x18in) 16-Sep-3 Philippe Schuler, Zurich #5612 (S.FR 1000)

GATTO, Victor Joseph (1893-1965) American
£389 $650 €568 Black-eyed Susan (20x25cm-8x10in) 15-Nov-3 Slotin Folk Art, Buford #390/R
£750 $1200 €1095 Wild horses at night (56x84cm-22x33in) s. painted c.1942. 17-May-3 Bunte, Elgin #1290 est:400-600
£811 $1500 €1184 In the jungle (41x51cm-16x20in) one s. canvasboard pair. 15-Jul-4 Sotheby's, New York #51/R est:2500-3500
£1027 $1900 €1499 Tigers and water buffalo. Tigers in the jungle (56x76cm-22x30in) each s. canvasboard pair. 15-Jul-4 Sotheby's, New York #49/R est:3000-4000
£1351 $2500 €1972 Field of flowers (64x76cm-25x30in) s. canvasboard. 15-Jul-4 Sotheby's, New York #50/R est:1500-2500
£5000 $8500 €7300 Rockefeller Plaza (56x76cm-22x30in) s. i.verso canvasboard. 18-Nov-3 Doyle, New York #22/R est:8000-10000

GAUCI, A M (19/20th C) ?
£1600 $2976 €2336 Princess, prize bull in a landscape (53x68cm-21x27in) s.d.1865 prov. 4-Mar-4 Christie's, Kensington #537/R est:600-800

GAUCI, E S (19/20th C) British
£1200 $2232 €1752 Tarquin, a prize bull in a paddock (51x68cm-20x27in) s.d.1888 prov. 4-Mar-4 Christie's, Kensington #545/R est:600-800

GAUD, Jules (1848-1912) Swiss
£647 $1157 €945 Lake in evening (44x82cm-17x32in) s. 12-May-4 Dobiaschofsky, Bern #544/R est:1900 (S.FR 1500)
£1810 $3077 €2643 Summer lake landscape with fisherman (27x40cm-11x16in) s. 19-Nov-3 Fischer, Luzern #1249/R est:4000-6000 (S.FR 4000)

GAUD, Léon (1844-1908) Swiss
£260 $465 €380 Village on summer's day (29x41cm-11x16in) s. 22-Mar-4 Philippe Schuler, Zurich #6013 (S.FR 600)

GAUDAIRE-THOR, Jean (1947-) French
£972 $1536 €1400 Sanam (81x100cm-32x39in) s.i.d.1997 verso lit. 27-Apr-3 Versailles Encheres #152

GAUDEFROY, Alphonse (1845-1936) French
£680 $1218 €1000 Scene de taverne (54x65cm-21x26in) s.d.94. 22-Mar-4 Digard, Paris #96/R
£12941 $22000 €18894 De retour de la chasse (114x157cm-45x62in) s.d.89. 29-Oct-3 Christie's, Rockefeller NY #103/R est:25000-35000

GAUDENZI, Pietro (1880-1955) Italian
£1678 $3087 €2500 Three graces (60x30cm-24x12in) s. board. 24-Mar-4 Il Ponte, Milan #552/R est:3000

GAUDEZ, Adrien Étienne (1845-1902) French
Sculpture
£490 $817 €700 Le Faucheur (30x11cm-12x4in) s. brown pat bronze. 11-Oct-3 De Vuyst, Lokeren #156
£1064 $1777 €1500 Le devoir (77cm-30in) s. brown pat bronze. 17-Jun-3 Galerie Moderne, Brussels #1504 est:1500-2000
£1104 $1800 €1612 Gypsy maiden modelled in diaphanous dress wearing a bracelet (86cm-34in) s. brown green pat bronze ovoid base. 19-Jul-3 Skinner, Boston #343 est:2000-3000
£1154 $2031 €1650 Le devoir (76cm-30in) s. brown pat bronze. 4-Jan-4 Rouillac, Vendome #10
£1250 $1975 €1825 Lulli, young street musician. s. bronze. 7-Sep-3 Desmond Judd, Cranbrook #109
£1622 $3000 €2433 Girl with a posy (58cm-23in) s. brown pat. bronze. 17-Jul-4 Skinner, Boston #771/R est:4000-6000
£1702 $2843 €2400 Chatelaine jouant du Luth (72cm-28in) s. green pat bronze socle. 17-Jun-3 Galerie Moderne, Brussels #1521 est:3000-4000
£2500 $4550 €3650 La fortune recompense le travail (58cm-23in) s. green brown pat bronze. 15-Jun-4 Sotheby's, Olympia #105/R est:2500-3500
£3056 $5500 €4462 Chevalier and serving girl (81cm-32in) incised sig. bronze. 24-Apr-4 Skinner, Boston #232/R est:5000-7000
£5000 $8500 €7300 Ecole d'honneur (82cm-32in) s. bronze marble base lit. 28-Oct-3 Sotheby's, London #94/R

GAUDFROY, F (1885-1964) Belgian
£1946 $3620 €2900 Spanish beauty with toreador (95x80cm-37x31in) s.d.1941. 4-Mar-4 Auction Maastricht #1006/R est:2000-3000

GAUDFROY, Fernand (1885-1964) Belgian
£331 $612 €480 Jeune femme nue dans une barque (40x31cm-16x12in) s.d.1955 panel. 16-Feb-4 Horta, Bruxelles #484

GAUDIER-BRZESKA, Henri (1891-1915) French
Sculpture
£41000 $75030 €59860 Maternity (27cm-11in) pat bronze exhib. 2-Jun-4 Sotheby's, London #50/R est:12000-18000
Works on paper
£633 $1140 €950 Homme debout (37x22cm-15x9in) ink prov. 24-Apr-4 Cornette de St.Cyr, Paris #338
£700 $1169 €1022 Macaw (37x24cm-15x9in) init. pencil. 16-Oct-3 Christie's, Kensington #294/R
£980 $1617 €1431 Vulture. Peacock (20x13cm-8x5in) s. chl double-sided. 1-Jul-3 Tayler & Fletcher, Cheltenham #5
£1400 $2548 €2044 Two deer grazing (25x39cm-10x15in) s.d.13 pen brown ink. 1-Jul-4 Christie's, Kensington #69/R est:1000-1500
£1446 $2676 €2111 Standing male nude (37x23cm-15x9in) s. ink prov. 10-Mar-4 Deutscher-Menzies, Melbourne #229/R est:4500-6500 (A.D 3500)
£1500 $2730 €2190 Walking deer (20x33cm-8x13in) pen blk ink. 1-Jul-4 Christie's, Kensington #70/R est:800-1200
£3600 $5724 €5256 Portrait of Ossip Zadkine (64x51cm-25x20in) pastel W/C prov. 10-Sep-3 Sotheby's, Olympia #140/R est:3000-5000
£4000 $7320 €5840 Two dancing figures (19x13cm-7x5in) ink dr prov. 8-Apr-4 Christie's, London #760/R est:1500-2500
£36000 $65880 €52560 Ezra Pound (38x26cm-15x10in) brush ink dr. 8-Apr-4 Christie's, London #758/R est:15000-20000

GAUDILLIERE, Roland (20th C) French
Works on paper
£318 $579 €480 Botte de paille (27x35cm-11x14in) s. mixed media masonite. 19-Jun-4 Gerard, Besancon #67
£384 $699 €580 Petit ecolier (27x35cm-11x14in) s. mixed media masonite. 19-Jun-4 Gerard, Besancon #68

GAUDINA, Carlo (1878-1937) Italian
£3356 $5940 €5000 Hunting (120x183cm-47x72in) s.d.1937. 1-May-4 Meeting Art, Vercelli #278 est:5000
Works on paper
£1141 $2019 €1700 Portrait of two boys (54x45cm-21x18in) s. pastel exec.1910. 1-May-4 Meeting Art, Vercelli #153 est:1500

GAUDISSARD, Émile (1872-?) French
£2267 $4171 €3400 Cap Cavallo, Bougie (54x65cm-21x26in) s.i.d.08. 14-Jun-4 Gros & Delettrez, Paris #541/R est:3000-4000

GAUDRY-ALLARD, Julie (attrib) (20th C) French
Works on paper
£493 $853 €700 Young woman in green skirt (68x54cm-27x21in) s. pastel. 10-Dec-3 Hugo Ruef, Munich #2549

GAUERMANN, Friedrich (1807-1862) Austrian
£1722 $3134 €2600 Studies of clouds (15x25cm-6x10in) oil paper on board one double-sided two. 21-Jun-4 Dorotheum, Vienna #186/R est:2600-3000
£2098 $3566 €3000 Plant (8x12cm-3x5in) study pencil sketch verso. 24-Nov-3 Dorotheum, Vienna #27/R est:3000-3500
£3020 $5648 €4500 Sunlit path. Clouds in sky (16x23cm-6x9in) two. 24-Feb-4 Dorotheum, Vienna #172/R est:2400-3000
£11333 $20287 €17000 Mountain thunder storm (36x44cm-14x17in) 14-May-4 Behringer, Furth #1770/R est:17000
£26846 $48054 €40000 Hunting party in a rocky ravine with Gutenstein mountain in the background (73x54cm-29x21in) s.d.1831 panel. 27-May-4 Dorotheum, Vienna #40/R est:40000-50000
£104895 $178322 €150000 Boy with two horses (71x95cm-28x37in) s.d.1832. 24-Nov-3 Dorotheum, Vienna #29/R est:100000-130000

Works on paper
£448 $744 €650 Boy lying on ground in wood (15x20cm-6x8in) i. pencil. 30-Sep-3 Dorotheum, Vienna #170/R
£694 $1132 €1000 Tree by water (34x25cm-13x10in) i.d.25 July 1833 pencil wash. 26-Sep-3 Venator & Hansten, Koln #830
£833 $1375 €1200 Mountain landscape with Watzmann (27x21cm-11x8in) s.d.849 W/C over pencil. 2-Jul-3 Neumeister, Munich #454/R
£872 $1605 €1300 Couple on horse (28x35cm-11x14in) pen brush. 26-Mar-4 Dorotheum, Vienna #77/R
£897 $1488 €1300 Salzburg (26x36cm-10x14in) i.d.1833 pencil study verso. 30-Sep-3 Dorotheum, Vienna #153/R

GAUERMANN, Friedrich (attrib) (1807-1862) Austrian
£5369 $9611 €8000 Study of a rock (26x33cm-10x13in) mono. board. 27-May-4 Dorotheum, Vienna #143/R est:5000-6000
Works on paper
£417 $679 €600 Descent from the alpine pastures (24x34cm-9x13in) i. pen Indian ink brush htd white pencil sketch verso. 26-Sep-3 Venator & Hansten, Koln #834/R
£671 $1235 €1000 Stag and wolf (25x46cm-10x18in) i. verso pencil. 26-Mar-4 Dorotheum, Vienna #79/R

GAUERMANN, Jakob (1773-1843) German
£11111 $18333 €16000 Extensive landscape with Altaussee (46x66cm-18x26in) i.d. stretcher. 3-Jul-3 Dr Fritz Nagel, Stuttgart #487/R est:6000
£11111 $18333 €16000 Extensive landscape with Illtal (46x66cm-18x26in) s. i. stretcher. 3-Jul-3 Dr Fritz Nagel, Stuttgart #488/R est:6000
Works on paper
£274 $466 €400 Italian river landscape (23x30cm-9x12in) chl. 4-Nov-3 Hartung & Hartung, Munich #3043
£621 $1030 €900 Lower alpine landscape with peasant woman (22x31cm-9x12in) s. W/C. 30-Sep-3 Dorotheum, Vienna #249/R

GAUFFRIAUX, Emile (1877-1957) French
£387 $678 €550 Golfe du Morbihan pres Noyalo (33x41cm-13x16in) mono. panel. 21-Dec-3 Thierry & Lannon, Brest #318
£397 $743 €600 Bretonne sur le halage (50x61cm-20x24in) s. 24-Jul-4 Thierry & Lannon, Brest #168

GAUGUIN, Jean René (1881-1961) Danish
Sculpture
£1625 $2989 €2373 Two figures (31cm-12in) mono. pat.bronze two. 29-Mar-4 Rasmussen, Copenhagen #34/R est:20000 (D.KR 18000)

GAUGUIN, Paul (1848-1903) French
£134078 $240000 €195754 Seine a Rouen (46x65cm-18x26in) painted 1884 prov.exhib.lit. 5-May-4 Christie's, Rockefeller NY #211/R est:250000-350000
£140000 $233800 €204400 La petite laveuse (32x45cm-13x18in) s. executed 1887 prov.exhib. 22-Oct-3 Bonhams, New Bond Street #25/R est:200000-300000
£180505 $332130 €263537 Cerises et carafon - still life of cherries and wine decanter (33x54cm-13x21in) i.stretcher painted c.1874-1878 prov.exhib.lit. 29-Mar-4 Rasmussen, Copenhagen #141/R est:2000000-2500000 (D.KR 2000000)
£705882 $1200000 €1030588 Rochers sur la Cote Bretonne (60x93cm-24x37in) s.d.88 prov.exhib.lit. 5-Nov-3 Sotheby's, New York #7/R est:1500000-2000000
Prints
£2374 $4250 €3466 Auti te pape (21x36cm-8x14in) i.num.53 woodcut chine volant printed 1921. 4-May-4 Doyle, New York #169/R est:3000-5000
£2752 $4870 €4100 Portrait de Stephane Mallarme. eau forte aquatint exec.1891. 29-Apr-4 Piasa, Paris #189/R est:1500-2000
£2824 $4800 €4123 Manao Tupapau (27x42cm-11x17in) i. woodcut. 4-Nov-3 Christie's, Rockefeller NY #95/R est:3500-4500
£2824 $4800 €4123 Nave nave fenua (41x26cm-16x10in) s. woodcut. 4-Nov-3 Christie's, Rockefeller NY #94/R est:3000-4000
£3500 $5950 €5110 Noa noa (35x20cm-14x8in) i. woodcut. 30-Oct-3 Christie's, Kensington #268/R est:3000-4000
£3521 $6092 €5000 Titre pour Le Sourire (14x22cm-6x9in) num. wood engraving edition of 30. 11-Dec-3 Piasa, Paris #43
£3911 $7000 €5710 Noa noa (35x20cm-14x8in) s. woodcut. 6-May-4 Swann Galleries, New York #288/R est:5000-8000
£4000 $7280 €5840 Nave nave fenua (35x20cm-14x8in) s.num.21 woodcut. 30-Jun-4 Christie's, London #205/R est:2500-3500
£4706 $8000 €6871 Te Po and Mano (27x42cm-11x17in) i. woodcut pair. 31-Oct-3 Sotheby's, New York #268
£5245 $9021 €7500 Title for 'Le sourire' (11x18cm-4x7in) mono.i. wooduct. 2-Dec-3 Hauswedell & Nolte, Hamburg #1891/R est:10000
£7671 $14116 €11200 Soyez amoureuses, vous serez heureuses (16x27cm-6x11in) mono.num.18 woodcut prov.lit. 29-Mar-4 Rasmussen, Copenhagen #144/R est:100000 (D.KR 85000)
£35211 $60915 €50000 Portrait de Stephane Mallarme (18x14cm-7x6in) init. etching drypoint aquatint burin. 11-Dec-3 Piasa, Paris #38/R
Sculpture
£1469 $2526 €2100 La petite Parisienne (27x6x7cm-11x2x3in) s. bronze. 2-Dec-3 Hauswedell & Nolte, Hamburg #189/R est:1500
£32168 $54685 €46000 Untitled (12x9cm-5x4in) mono. coconut brown green polychrome htd gold prov.lit. 27-Nov-3 Millon & Associes, Paris #103/R est:32000-38000
£50000 $85000 €73000 Masque d'une femme (40cm-16in) plaster with tan glaze prov.lit. 6-Nov-3 Sotheby's, New York #123a/R est:40000-60000
Works on paper
£5500 $10120 €8030 Personnage lisant et etude de main (25x20cm-10x8in) chl exec.c.1880 prov. 22-Jun-4 Sotheby's, London #424/R est:5000-7000
£11892 $22000 €17362 Femme cousant (27x20cm-11x8in) chl chk prov. 11-Feb-4 Sotheby's, New York #5/R est:12000-18000
£17124 $29110 €25000 Bretonne de profil (31x22cm-12x9in) i.verso crayon W/C prov.lit. 6-Nov-3 Tajan, Paris #187/R
£36471 $62000 €53248 Vallee Bretonne (26x17cm-10x7in) st.init. W/C over blk chk paper on paper prov.exhib. 5-Nov-3 Christie's, Rockefeller NY #110/R est:60000-80000
£42000 $77280 €61320 Tete de fille des Iles Marquises (14x11cm-6x4in) brush wash ink double-sided exec c.1902 prov.exhib.lit. 24-Jun-4 Christie's, London #322/R est:40000-60000
£50000 $92000 €73000 Paysage de campagne (17x26cm-7x10in) s. gouache W/C pencil card exec c.1879 prov.lit. 24-Jun-4 Christie's, London #314/R est:25000-35000
£52941 $90000 €77294 Deux Tahitiennes (20x19cm-8x7in) W/C brush blk ink Japan paper laid at edges board prov.exhib. 5-Nov-3 Christie's, Rockefeller NY #107/R est:100000-150000
£110000 $202400 €160600 Nature morte au compotier (16x25cm-6x10in) s.d.1880 W/C gouache on silk prov.exhib. 22-Jun-4 Christie's, London #4/R est:120000-180000
£150000 $273000 €219000 Vue de la plage de bellangenay (31x43cm-12x17in) pastel on board painted 1889 prov.lit. 4-Feb-4 Sotheby's, London #216/R est:150000-200000
£302817 $529930 €430000 Deux tetes de Bretonnes (30x42cm-12x17in) s. pastel. 21-Dec-3 Thierry & Lannon, Brest #88/R
£352941 $600000 €515294 Eve Bretonne II (56x26cm-22x10in) s. pastel chk paper on canvas executed 1889 prov.exhib.lit. 4-Nov-3 Christie's, Rockefeller NY #14/R est:400000-600000

GAUGUIN, Paul (after) (1848-1903) French
Sculpture
£13408 $24000 €19576 Luxure (69cm-27in) init. num.2/12 brown pat bronze st.f.Valsuani prov.lit. 5-May-4 Christie's, Rockefeller NY #268/R est:30000-40000

GAUGUIN, Paul René (1911-1979) Norwegian
Works on paper
£800 $1384 €1168 Composition (55x57cm-22x22in) s. collage metal lithograph. 13-Dec-3 Blomqvist, Lysaker #1105/R (N.KR 9200)

GAUL, Arrah Lee (20th C) American
£217 $375 €317 Cheig-Mai, Thailand (30x23cm-12x9in) s. canvasboard. 10-Dec-3 Alderfer's, Hatfield #447/R
£403 $750 €588 Evening, Bay of Fundi (20x30cm-8x12in) s. canvasboard. 3-Mar-4 Alderfer's, Hatfield #402
£625 $1100 €913 Peter and Paul's Cathedral Philadelphia, streetscape (76x64cm-30x25in) s. 21-May-4 Pook & Pook, Downington #193/R est:1000-1500
£860 $1600 €1256 Portrait of a tree in blues (51x41cm-20x16in) s. canvasboard. 3-Mar-4 Alderfer's, Hatfield #401/R est:1000-1500
£2023 $3500 €2954 Still life of magnolias (76x64cm-30x25in) s. 10-Dec-3 Alderfer's, Hatfield #446/R est:1200-1500
£3892 $6500 €5682 Along the St Lawrence River, Harbour-Baie, St Pauls, Canada (64x76cm-25x30in) s. i.verso. 23-Oct-3 Shannon's, Milford #87/R est:5000-7000

GAUL, August (1869-1921) German
Sculpture
£933 $1717 €1400 Ostrich standing (6cm-2in) s.verso yellow brown pat bronze sold with marble base one of 15. 12-Jun-4 Villa Grisebach, Berlin #551/R est:1500-2000
£1049 $1783 €1500 Lioness (4x15x7cm-2x6x3in) s. dark brown pat.bronze Cast.Noack Berlin marble socle. 29-Nov-3 Bassenge, Berlin #6712/R est:3000
£1389 $2292 €2000 Lioness (29x51cm-11x20in) i. mid brown pat.bronze. 3-Jul-3 Van Ham, Cologne #912 est:3500
£1538 $2646 €2200 Owlett (7x3x5cm-3x1x2in) bronze. 2-Dec-3 Hauswedell & Nolte, Hamburg #194/R est:1000
£1667 $3050 €2500 Standing bear (5x2cm-2x1in) s. dark brown pat.bronze marble soclee prov. 5-Jun-4 Lempertz, Koln #725a/R est:3000
£2098 $3503 €3000 Fighting bison (14x36x7cm-6x14x3in) s. black gold pat.bronze Cast.H.Noack Berlin. 28-Jun-3 Dannenberg, Berlin #263/R est:3000
£2207 $3686 €3200 Fish otter (13x6x7cm-5x2x3in) s. black light green pat bronze Cast Noack. 13-Nov-3 Neumeister, Munich #327/R est:2500-2800
£2550 $4693 €3800 Cat arching back. i. brown pat.bronze marble socle Cast.Noack Berlin. 26-Mar-4 Bolland & Marotz, Bremen #731/R est:3300
£3333 $6133 €5000 Deer (32cm-13in) s.st.f. Noack brown pat. bronze exec. 1919 one of ten. 12-Jun-4 Villa Grisebach, Berlin #110/R est:3000-4000
£3533 $6325 €5300 Ram (30x35x7cm-12x14x3in) s. dark brown pat.bronze marble socle. 15-May-4 Bassenge, Berlin #6829/R est:3500
£4011 $7500 €5856 Three geese (13x28x9cm-5x11x4in) s.st.f.Friedenau d.1901 pat bronze lit. 25-Feb-4 Christie's, Rockefeller NY #39/R est:4000-6000

GAUL, Gilbert (1855-1919) American
£2139 $4000 €3123 Dead buffalo (30x46cm-12x18in) s. en grisaille prov. 24-Jul-4 Coeur d'Alene, Hayden #262/R est:3000-5000
£7263 $13000 €10604 Break from battle (41x30cm-16x12in) s. 14-May-4 Skinner, Boston #113/R est:15000-25000
£12032 $22500 €17567 Indian alone (91x69cm-36x27in) s. 24-Jul-4 Coeur d'Alene, Hayden #200/R est:20000-30000
Works on paper
£588 $1000 €858 Figural studies of soldiers (48x17cm-19x7in) s. gouache pair. 21-Nov-3 Skinner, Boston #327/R est:800-1200

GAUL, Gustave (1836-1888) Austrian
Works on paper
£1958 $3250 €2859 European Court Scenes (20x38cm-8x15in) s. one d.1880 W/C gouache six. 4-Oct-3 Neal Auction Company, New Orleans #46/R est:1500-2500

GAUL, Winfred (1928-) German
£2667 $4907 €4000 O.T. (40x50cm-16x20in) s. s.i.d.17-4-58. 11-Jun-4 Hauswedell & Nolte, Hamburg #625/R est:4000
£3333 $6100 €5000 Untitled (64x96cm-25x38in) s.d.55/56 s.i. verso oil collage newspaper masonite. 4-Jun-4 Lempertz, Koln #148/R est:5000-5500
£6993 $11888 €10000 Argueing with Mr Pythagoras (180x180cm-71x71in) s.i.d.85 verso acrylic. 27-Nov-3 Lempertz, Koln #136/R est:12000
£8000 $14320 €12000 Composition (179x130cm-70x51in) s.d.57 d.Dez.55-apr.57 verso panel lit. 15-May-4 Van Ham, Cologne #603/R est:12000

GAULD, David (1865-1936) British
£1600 $2672 €2336 Watermill under the snow (40x51cm-16x20in) s. 16-Oct-3 Lyon & Turnbull, Edinburgh #78 est:400-600
£2000 $3140 €2900 Cows in a meadow (61x91cm-24x36in) s. 27-Aug-3 Sotheby's, London #1111/R est:2000-3000
£2800 $4396 €4060 Resting calf (30x46cm-12x18in) s. 27-Aug-3 Sotheby's, London #1087/R est:2000-3000
£2900 $4988 €4234 Two calves lying by a fence (40x60cm-16x24in) s. 4-Dec-3 Bonhams, Edinburgh #9 est:2000-3000

£3800 $6156 €5548 French country house beside a river (61x76cm-24x30in) s. 2-Aug-3 Shapes, Edinburgh #304 est:2000-3000
£4200 $6594 €6090 Two calves in a stable (61x76cm-24x30in) s. prov. 27-Aug-3 Sotheby's, London #1131/R est:3000-4000
£4600 $7406 €6670 Calves in a byre (50x75cm-20x30in) s. 21-Aug-3 Bonhams, Edinburgh #1213/R est:3000-5000
£6500 $10465 €9425 Normandy farm (70x91cm-28x36in) s. 21-Aug-3 Bonhams, Edinburgh #1063/R est:4000-6000
£6500 $10205 €9425 Young trio (71x91cm-28x36in) s. prov. 27-Aug-3 Sotheby's, London #1114/R est:4000-6000
£6500 $11765 €9490 Monteuil sur mer, pas de Calais (61x76cm-24x30in) s. 19-Apr-4 Sotheby's, London #105/R est:7000-10000
£8500 $15215 €12410 Calves by a water-butt (63x75cm-25x30in) s. 28-May-4 Lyon & Turnbull, Edinburgh #85/R est:4000-6000
Works on paper
£1300 $2041 €1885 Calves resting by the sea (35x45cm-14x18in) s. W/C prov. 27-Aug-3 Sotheby's, London #1090/R est:1000-1500

GAULEY, Steven (1953-) Canadian
£189 $350 €276 Wired cloud (94x102cm-37x40in) s.d.1983 verso acrylic. 16-Jan-4 Aspire, Cleveland #81/R

GAULIS, Fernand (1860-1924) Swiss
£283 $517 €413 Arbres au bord du lac (36x46cm-14x18in) s. 4-Jun-4 Zofingen, Switzerland #2805 (S.FR 650)
Works on paper
£390 $651 €566 Phare a Menton (25x34cm-10x13in) s. pastel. 21-Jun-3 Galerie du Rhone, Sion #367 (S.FR 850)

GAULLI, Giovanni Battista (1639-1709) Italian
£11111 $20000 €16222 Portrait of Clement X (86x74cm-34x29in) 23-Jan-4 Christie's, Rockefeller NY #203/R est:25000-35000
£15556 $28000 €22712 Apostle Saint Thomas (74x61cm-29x24in) 23-Jan-4 Christie's, Rockefeller NY #192/R est:10000-15000
£53333 $96533 €80000 Strength and Charity (65x60cm-26x24in) lit. 30-Mar-4 Babuino, Rome #68/R est:30000-40000
£60000 $109800 €87600 Continence of Scipio (33x44cm-13x17in) canvas on panel prov. 7-Jul-4 Sotheby's, London #48/R est:30000-50000
Works on paper
£3889 $7000 €5678 Caricature of a man with long moustache in a hat and cloak (27x20cm-11x8in) i.d.15 Aprile 1666 pen brown ink. 22-Jan-4 Christie's, Rockefeller NY #52/R est:3000-5000
£10197 $18763 €15500 Drawing for map (23x18cm-9x7in) pen ink W/C over pencil. 22-Jun-4 Sotheby's, Milan #25/R est:12000-15000
£18056 $32500 €26362 Angel seated in the clouds playing a harp (28x23cm-11x9in) pen brown ink wash over black chk. 21-Jan-4 Sotheby's, New York #15/R est:12000-18000

GAULLI, Giovanni Battista (circle) (1639-1709) Italian
£19000 $34200 €27740 Portrait of a Cardinal, seated (133x97cm-52x38in) i. 23-Apr-4 Christie's, Kensington #245/R est:6000-8000

GAULT DE SAINT-GERMAIN, Pierre-Marie (1754-1842) French
Works on paper
£2667 $4827 €4000 Portrait de jeune garcon. Portrait de fillette (55x46cm-22x18in) s.d.1786 pastel paper on canvas oval pair prov.exhib.lit. 2-Apr-4 Rossini, Paris #10/R est:4000-5000

GAULT, George (20th C) Irish?
£500 $835 €730 Figures by a cottage with mountains beyond (38x51cm-15x20in) s. 8-Oct-3 Andrew Hartley, Ilkley #1133
£628 $1136 €917 The Rosses, County Donegal (50x76cm-20x30in) s. i.verso board prov. 1-Apr-4 Heffel, Vancouver #40/R (C.D 1500)

GAUNT, W Norman (1918-) British
£250 $468 €365 Two figures on horseback beside a tree in a sunlit landscape (56x76cm-22x30in) s. canvasboard. 22-Jul-4 Tennants, Leyburn #919/R
£250 $468 €365 Cattle in a sunlit marsh with trees nearby (51x76cm-20x30in) s. 22-Jul-4 Tennants, Leyburn #923
£300 $561 €438 Woodland in springtime with artist's children picking flowers (183x91cm-72x36in) s. 22-Jul-4 Tennants, Leyburn #916
£320 $589 €467 Middleham horses on the gallop (34x45cm-13x18in) s. 26-Jun-4 British Auctioneer #158/R
£400 $748 €584 Figure exercising a white horse along a path (61x76cm-24x30in) s. canvasboard. 22-Jul-4 Tennants, Leyburn #921
£450 $828 €657 Meet (51x61cm-20x24in) s. board. 10-Jun-4 Christie's, Kensington #189/R
£450 $842 €657 Figure seated on a white horse with open moorland nearby (61x91cm-24x36in) s. canvasboard. 22-Jul-4 Tennants, Leyburn #922
£500 $935 €730 Beach scene with two small boys making sandcastles (51x61cm-20x24in) s. canvasboard. 22-Jul-4 Tennants, Leyburn #917
£600 $1122 €876 Cockle gathering (61x121cm-24x48in) s. canvasboard. 22-Jul-4 Tennants, Leyburn #918
£800 $1440 €1168 The finish, racehorses with jockeys. Racehorses and jockeys at start (61x121cm-24x48in) s. canvasboard two. 21-Apr-4 Tennants, Leyburn #1254/R
£850 $1445 €1241 Beach scenes (38x53cm-15x21in) s. one canvasboard three. 19-Nov-3 Tennants, Leyburn #1261/R
£1000 $1800 €1460 Figures with horses and carts on quayside. Boats on a river. Fishing boats and figures on beach (51x61cm-20x24in) two s. board canvas board three. 21-Apr-4 Tennants, Leyburn #1250 est:300-500
£1100 $1870 €1606 Feeding the poultry. Watching from the deck chair (61x50cm-24x20in) s. canvasboard pair. 19-Nov-3 Tennants, Leyburn #1281 est:150-250
£1300 $2210 €1898 Beach scenes (61x76cm-24x30in) s. two canvasboard three. 19-Nov-3 Tennants, Leyburn #1259
£1300 $2210 €1898 Beach scene (61x76cm-24x30in) canvasboard sold with two W/C's by the same hand. 19-Nov-3 Tennants, Leyburn #1260/R est:300-400
£1700 $3060 €2482 Children on donkeys on beach. Two small girls on donkeys. Donkeys on the sands (50x61cm-20x24in) two s. one i.verso canvasboard three. 21-Apr-4 Tennants, Leyburn #1249/R est:500-600
£2200 $3740 €3212 Hunting scenes (51x76cm-20x30in) s. three. 19-Nov-3 Tennants, Leyburn #1279 est:300-500
Works on paper
£260 $476 €380 Pause for breath, chatting huntsman (36x47cm-14x19in) s. W/C. 3-Jun-4 Lane, Penzance #144
£300 $561 €438 Beach scene with figures with a Punch and Judy show (32x49cm-13x19in) s. pencil W/C htd white. 22-Jul-4 Tennants, Leyburn #698
£400 $748 €584 Coastal scene with figures (51x63cm-20x25in) s. pencil W/C gouache htd white. 22-Jul-4 Tennants, Leyburn #700
£420 $701 €613 Horses at Appleby Fair (33x46cm-13x18in) s. W/C. 8-Oct-3 Andrew Hartley, Ilkley #1074

GAUPP, Gustav Adolf (1844-1918) German
£4333 $7800 €6500 Girl by fence (121x84cm-48x33in) s.d.1905. 26-Apr-4 Rieber, Stuttgart #1271/R est:2500

GAUQUIE, Henri (1858-1927) French
Sculpture
£1273 $2113 €1846 Nil virtuti invium (60cm-24in) s.i. bronze. 13-Jun-3 Zofingen, Switzerland #2269/R est:3500 (S.FR 2800)

GAUSACHS, Jose (1891-?) Spanish
£563 $975 €800 Autumn landscape (46x55cm-18x22in) s. 15-Dec-3 Ansorena, Madrid #278/R

GAUSE, Wilhelm (1853-1916) German
Works on paper
£470 $832 €700 Erzherzogin Elisabeth with other figures (75x50cm-30x20in) s. mixed media paper on board. 29-Apr-4 Dorotheum, Vienna #176

GAUSH, Alexander Fedorovich (1873-1947) Russian
£8446 $15118 €12500 Church in Moscow (67x58cm-26x23in) s.d.99. 8-May-4 Bukowskis, Helsinki #429/R est:2000-4000

GAUSSEN, Adolphe-Louis (1871-1954) French
£957 $1599 €1350 Anes dans un cour au Maroc (33x40cm-13x16in) s. 19-Jun-3 Millon & Associes, Paris #148/R
£1200 $1908 €1740 Passe des Iles d'Hyeres (16x22cm-6x9in) s. panel. 11-Sep-3 Christie's, Kensington #45/R est:500-800
£2014 $3363 €2900 Bord de mer (27x41cm-11x16in) s. 25-Oct-3 Dianous, Marseille #395
£2465 $4313 €3500 Voiliers au large des calanques (50x65cm-20x26in) s. 16-Dec-3 Claude Aguttes, Neuilly #6/R est:3000-4000
£3800 $6954 €5548 Les quais (46x55cm-18x22in) s. 8-Apr-4 Christie's, Kensington #184/R est:800-1200

GAUSSEN, Alfred (19th C) French
£1342 $2470 €2000 Cabanon en Provence (33x46cm-13x18in) s.d.92. 29-Mar-4 Rieunier, Paris #53/R est:1500-2000

GAUSSON, Leo (1860-1944) French
£1500 $2760 €2190 La ferme (33x46cm-13x18in) st.sig. 24-Mar-4 Sotheby's, Olympia #72/R est:1500-2000
£5000 $9200 €7300 Route traversant le village de Thorigny, pres de lagny (38x46cm-15x18in) s.d.1888 lit. 24-Mar-4 Sotheby's, Olympia #91/R est:5000-7000
£6500 $10855 €9490 Meules (33x46cm-13x18in) st.sig. 22-Oct-3 Sotheby's, Olympia #23/R est:4000-5000
Works on paper
£1788 $3272 €2700 Sentier de campagne (21x34cm-8x13in) s.d.1889 col crayons pastel. 7-Apr-4 Piasa, Paris #98/R est:1000-1500

GAUT, Joseph (19th C) New Zealander?
£893 $1616 €1304 Waikato River (49x75cm-19x30in) s.d.1888 s.i.verso. 30-Mar-4 Peter Webb, Auckland #167/R est:2500-3500 (NZ.D 2500)

GAUTHERIN (19/20th C) French
Sculpture
£2980 $5573 €4500 Premier amour (85cm-33in) pat bronze Cast Thiebaut. 25-Jul-4 Versailles Encheres #141 est:5000-5500

GAUTHERIN, J (19/20th C) French
Sculpture
£1500 $2595 €2190 Draped girl with her hair tied back with flowers, holding nest of fledglings (48cm-19in) s. num.8750 bronze bears st.Paris A.B. 10-Dec-3 Bonhams, Bury St Edmunds #610 est:800-1200

GAUTHERIN, Jean (1840-1890) French
Sculpture
£1374 $2500 €2006 Head of Jesus (32cm-13in) s.i. red brown pat bronze. 7-Feb-4 Sloans & Kenyon, Bethesda #1208/R est:1000-1500

GAUTHIER, A (19/20th C) French?
£797 $1299 €1164 Stream running through landscape with boy fishing (130x89cm-51x35in) s.d.85. 28-Sep-3 Hindemae, Ullerslev #65/R (D.KR 8500)

GAUTHIER, Joachim (1897-1988) Canadian
£313 $538 €457 Surf - Lake Superior (30x37cm-12x15in) s. board prov. 2-Dec-3 Joyner Waddington, Toronto #440 (C.D 700)
£383 $705 €559 Wild cherry in blossom (25x30cm-10x12in) s. s.i.verso board prov. 9-Jun-4 Walker's, Ottawa #75/R (C.D 950)
£680 $1244 €993 Polish boys, Whitney, Ontario (25x30cm-10x12in) s. board painted 1946 prov. 1-Jun-4 Joyner Waddington, Toronto #486 (C.D 1700)
£720 $1318 €1051 Credit River - Springtime (30x37cm-12x15in) s. board. 1-Jun-4 Joyner Waddington, Toronto #460 est:800-1200 (C.D 1800)
£763 $1419 €1114 Alogonquin park (50x61cm-20x24in) s. i.verso masonite prov. 2-Mar-4 Ritchie, Toronto #123/R est:1000-1500 (C.D 1900)
£1365 $2540 €1993 Lake Louise (51x61cm-20x24in) s. i.verso masonite. 2-Mar-4 Ritchie, Toronto #124/R est:3000-4000 (C.D 3400)
Works on paper
£536 $921 €783 Lake reflections. Hills and water (26x35cm-10x14in) both s. second d.48 W/C two. 2-Dec-3 Joyner Waddington, Toronto #422 (C.D 1200)

GAUTHIER, Oscar (1921-) French
£315 $535 €450 Composition (27x23cm-11x9in) s. 20-Nov-3 Claude Aguttes, Neuilly #141/R
£1549 $2680 €2200 Composition (92x73cm-36x29in) s. prov. 14-Dec-3 Versailles Encheres #40/R est:2000-2500
£2394 $4142 €3400 Composition (116x89cm-46x35in) s. prov. 14-Dec-3 Versailles Encheres #39/R est:2500-3000
£4400 $8008 €6600 Composition (92x60cm-36x24in) s. s.verso. 29-Jun-4 Cornette de St.Cyr, Paris #31/R est:4000
Works on paper
£1056 $1827 €1500 Composition (27x29cm-11x11in) s.d.1948 gouache prov. 14-Dec-3 Versailles Encheres #56/R est:1000-1200

GAUTIER, Albert (?-1938) French
£1316 $2382 €2000 Vue de Constantinople (23x33cm-9x13in) diptych. 19-Apr-4 Horta, Bruxelles #91 est:2000-3000

GAUTIER, Armand Desire (1825-1899) French
£814 $1303 €1188 Still life with flowers in Chinese vase (38x26cm-15x10in) s. 16-Sep-3 Philippe Schuler, Zurich #3330/R est:2000-2500 (S.FR 1800)
£1138 $1900 €1661 Nuns (33x23cm-13x9in) s. panel prov. 7-Oct-3 Sotheby's, New York #160 est:2000-3000

GAUTIER, Jacques (1831-?) French
Sculpture
£3800 $6840 €5548 Mephistopheles (87cm-34in) s. two-tone brown pat bronze. 21-Apr-4 Sotheby's, London #151/R est:3000-5000
£9486 $16980 €13850 Mephistopheles (89cm-35in) s. deep brown pat bronze cast 1855 prov.lit. 15-May-4 Christie's, Sydney #631/R est:6000-8000 (A.D 24000)

GAUTIER, Jean Rodolphe (1764-1820) Swiss
Miniatures
£3800 $6802 €5548 Girl, in a white dress, brown plaited hair (6cm-2in) s. enamel on copper. 25-May-4 Christie's, London #37/R est:1800-2800

GAUTIER, Pierre Jules Theophile (1811-1872) French
Works on paper
£1067 $1963 €1600 Jolie tete d'Italienne (19x14cm-7x6in) d.1847 wash htd gouache exhib. 9-Jun-4 Piasa, Paris #79/R est:1500-2000

GAUTIER, Pierre Jules Theophile (attrib) (1811-1872) French
Works on paper
£400 $736 €600 Baigneuse a moitie denudee, assise sur un fauteuil (34x16cm-13x6in) pastel. 9-Jun-4 Piasa, Paris #80

GAUTSCHI, Joseph (1900-1977) Swiss
£249 $431 €364 Vue de Sion a travers les arbres (47x66cm-19x26in) s.d.40. 12-Dec-3 Galerie du Rhone, Sion #494 (S.FR 550)
£633 $1096 €924 Ruelle du vieux Sion (50x40cm-20x16in) s. 12-Dec-3 Galerie du Rhone, Sion #492 (S.FR 1400)
£1267 $2192 €1850 Vue de Valere (55x71cm-22x28in) s. cardboard. 12-Dec-3 Galerie du Rhone, Sion #493/R est:2000-2500 (S.FR 2800)

GAUZY, Jeanne L (1886-1968) French
£378 $631 €540 Portrait of young woman (41x31cm-16x12in) s. board. 30-Jun-3 Ansorena, Madrid #303/R
£420 $701 €600 Landscape (54x65cm-21x26in) s. 30-Jun-3 Ansorena, Madrid #263/R

GAVA, Cristy (1916-1985) Uruguayan
£455 $800 €664 Piriapolis (42x59cm-17x23in) s.d.45 cardboard. 5-Jan-4 Galeria y Remates, Montevideo #108
£463 $750 €671 Faces (34x47cm-13x19in) s.d.1977 board. 29-Jul-3 Galeria y Remates, Montevideo #82/R
£854 $1400 €1247 Composition in primary colours (48x59cm-19x23in) cardboard painted c.1952 prov. 3-Jun-3 Galeria y Remates, Montevideo #79
Works on paper
£1359 $2500 €1984 Bathers (68x90cm-27x35in) s.d.1967 mixed media. 22-Jun-4 Galeria y Remates, Montevideo #115/R est:3000-4000

GAVA, Pedro (1918-) ?
£272 $500 €397 Composition (50x40cm-20x16in) init.d.54. 22-Jun-4 Galeria y Remates, Montevideo #117/R

GAVAGNIN, Natale (1851-?) Italian
£957 $1550 €1388 Entrance to an Italian town (21x53cm-8x21in) s. 4-Aug-3 Rasmussen, Vejle #367/R (D.KR 10000)

GAVARDIE, Jean de (1909-1961) French
£775 $1340 €1100 Nature morte au compotier sur une nappe rouge (65x54cm-26x21in) painted c.1935/1940. 13-Dec-3 Martinot & Savignat, Pontoise #31/R

GAVARNI, Paul (1804-1866) French
Works on paper
£272 $487 €400 Pour Lors, un soir, talma me dit - Cora (28x20cm-11x8in) s.i. W/C pen brown ink htd white gouache. 17-Mar-4 Tajan, Paris #123
£340 $609 €500 Bardon de la courtille (29x20cm-11x8in) s.i. W/C gouache pen red ink. 17-Mar-4 Tajan, Paris #124
£500 $905 €750 Paysagiste a l'Hotel des Haricots (21x15cm-8x6in) s.i. pen brown ink wash lit. 30-Mar-4 Rossini, Paris #803/R

GAVIN, Robert (1827-1883) British
£2800 $5152 €4088 Girl from New Orleans (67x47cm-26x19in) 25-Mar-4 Bonhams, Edinburgh #370/R est:700-1000

GAVRIELATOS, Panagis (1915-) Greek
£3000 $5250 €4380 Greek market (70x60cm-28x24in) s. 16-Dec-3 Bonhams, New Bond Street #81/R est:2000-3000

GAVRILOV, V N (1923-1970) Russian
£556 $1000 €812 Portrait of an old woman (61x41cm-24x16in) oil on cardboard. 24-Apr-4 Shishkin Gallery, Moscow #56/R est:3000-4000

GAW, William Alexander (1891-1973) American
Works on paper
£273 $500 €399 Bay (23x38cm-9x15in) s.i. W/C executed c.1930. 5-Jun-4 Treadway Gallery, Cincinnati #621/R

GAWDIE, Sir John Bart (1639-1709) British
£2000 $3580 €2920 Self portrait, wearing a lace jabot and black cloak and wig (76x63cm-30x25in) i.verso. 22-Mar-4 Bonhams & Brooks, Norfolk #195/R est:1500-2500

GAWELL, Oskar (1888-1955) Austrian
Works on paper
£800 $1440 €1200 Lotus flower - head (61x44cm-24x17in) W/C board double-sided. 21-Apr-4 Dorotheum, Vienna #82/R

GAWLIK, Waclaw (1958-) Polish
£636 $1150 €954 Untitled (131x121cm-52x48in) s.d.1992. 4-Apr-4 Agra, Warsaw #40/R (P.Z 4500)

GAY, August (1890-1949) American
£4348 $8000 €6348 Entrance to a garden (22x27cm-9x11in) s. paper on board prov. 8-Jun-4 Bonhams & Butterfields, San Francisco #4310/R est:10000-15000
£17341 $30000 €25318 Figures wading in the surf with boats in distance. A landscape study (25x34cm-10x13in) s.i.verso double-sided prov. 10-Dec-3 Bonhams & Butterfields, San Francisco #6259/R est:15000-20000
£21739 $40000 €31739 Monterey landscape with buildings (40x50cm-16x20in) prov.exhib. 8-Jun-4 Bonhams & Butterfields, San Francisco #4309/R est:40000-60000

GAY, Edward (1837-1928) American
£898 $1500 €1311 Marsh at sunset (28x38cm-11x15in) s. canvas on board. 18-Jun-3 Doyle, New York #29/R est:1000-1500
£1882 $3500 €2748 Twilight shore (38x64cm-15x25in) s. board. 6-Mar-4 North East Auctions, Portsmouth #225/R
£1923 $3500 €2808 Landscape (46x38cm-18x15in) s. 29-Jun-4 Sotheby's, New York #225/R est:3000-5000
£3315 $6000 €4840 Spring landscape with blooming orchard and herd of sheep (51x69cm-20x27in) s. 3-Apr-4 Nadeau, Windsor #245 est:4000-7000
£4118 $7000 €6012 When the day is done (51x68cm-20x27in) s. painted c.1900-10. 30-Oct-3 Phillips, New York #57/R est:8000-12000
£4469 $8000 €6525 Autumn landscape (23x46cm-9x18in) s.d.79 panel. 6-May-4 Shannon's, Milford #42/R est:8000-12000

GAY, George Howell (1858-1931) American
£222 $350 €324 Three masted ship at sea (64x76cm-25x30in) s. 25-Jul-3 Eldred, East Dennis #197/R
£261 $450 €381 Going home (46x36cm-18x14in) s.d.29. 6-Dec-3 Neal Auction Company, New Orleans #347
£528 $850 €771 Boat in full sail on ocean (76x64cm-30x25in) s. painted c.1910. 22-Feb-3 Bunte, Elgin #1239
Works on paper
£202 $375 €295 Autumn river with birches (24x49cm-9x19in) s. W/C gouache. 5-Mar-4 Skinner, Boston #289/R
£220 $350 €321 Quiet river (57x38cm-22x15in) s. W/C. 12-Sep-3 Skinner, Boston #268/R
£220 $400 €321 Autumn stream landscape (71x38cm-28x15in) s. W/C. 1-Jul-4 Dan Ripley, Indianapolis #105
£315 $500 €460 Open seas (60x91cm-24x36in) s. W/C. 12-Sep-3 Skinner, Boston #292/R
£323 $600 €472 Coastal view (39x65cm-15x26in) s. W/C gouache. 5-Mar-4 Skinner, Boston #314/R
£335 $550 €486 Coastal scene (25x51cm-10x20in) s. W/C exec.c.1900. 7-Jun-3 Treadway Gallery, Cincinnati #1343

£353 $650 €515 Wintry country road (48x38cm-19x15in) s.d.1924 W/C gouache. 27-Mar-4 New Orleans Auction, New Orleans #598
£357 $650 €521 Early spring (33x79cm-13x31in) s. W/C. 19-Jun-4 Jackson's, Cedar Falls #190/R
£414 $750 €604 Rocky coast, sunset (25x46cm-10x18in) s. W/C. 16-Apr-4 James Julia, Fairfield #915/R
£447 $800 €653 Near Indian Head, Narragansett pier, Rhode Island (24x49cm-9x19in) s. W/C paperboard prov. 14-May-4 Skinner, Boston #119/R
£541 $1000 €790 Late autumn (30x56cm-12x22in) s. W/C paper on board. 10-Mar-4 Doyle, New York #21/R
£552 $950 €806 Winter stream (38x74cm-15x29in) s. W/C exec.c.1890. 7-Dec-3 Treadway Gallery, Cincinnati #477/R

GAY, Nikolai Nikolajewitsch (circle) (1831-1894) Russian
£8939 $16000 €13051 Lazarus in the house of a rich man (139x183cm-55x72in) indis sig. 6-May-4 Doyle, New York #60/R est:5000-7000

GAY, Walter (1856-1937) American
£1006 $1600 €1469 Classical figure (62x51cm-24x20in) s. 12-Sep-3 Skinner, Boston #360/R
£11377 $19000 €16610 Yellow room (56x71cm-22x28in) s. 18-Oct-3 Sotheby's, New York #214/R est:20000-30000
£29940 $50000 €43712 Drawing room, Paris (81x99cm-32x39in) s. prov.exhib. 18-Oct-3 Sotheby's, New York #213/R est:30000-50000
Works on paper
£250 $400 €365 Woman reading (23x18cm-9x7in) s. W/C. 21-Sep-3 Grogan, Boston #62/R
£6000 $10980 €9000 White symphony (52x43cm-20x17in) s. W/C gouache exhib. 3-Jun-4 E & Eve, Paris #22/R est:4000-5000
£7784 $13000 €11365 The screen, dining room, le Brean (28x39cm-11x15in) s.i. W/C chl prov. 7-Oct-3 Sotheby's, New York #191 est:7000-9000
£11429 $20000 €16686 The dejeuner (55x46cm-22x18in) s. W/C chl board. 19-Dec-3 Sotheby's, New York #1073/R est:6000-8000

GAY, Winkworth Allen (1821-1910) American
£765 $1300 €1117 Geese swimming in a cove (30x20cm-12x8in) s. board. 31-Oct-3 North East Auctions, Portsmouth #1732
£1359 $2500 €1984 Temple in Okura (28x41cm-11x16in) s.i. prov.exhib. 8-Jun-4 Bonhams & Butterfields, San Francisco #4032/R est:2500-3500
£1582 $2800 €2310 Windmill and canal in Holland (61x46cm-24x18in) s.d.1875. 2-May-4 Grogan, Boston #66/R
£4054 $7500 €5919 Glades, Cohasset (20x30cm-8x12in) s. i.verso board prov. 11-Mar-4 Christie's, Rockefeller NY #19/R est:4000-6000

GAYA, Ramon (1910-) Spanish
Works on paper
£839 $1401 €1200 The painter in the wood (23x31cm-9x12in) s.d.1939 ink. 24-Jun-3 Segre, Madrid #111/R
£1268 $2218 €1800 Boats at sea (24x34cm-9x13in) s.d.1959 ink wash. 16-Dec-3 Segre, Madrid #118/R est:1500

GAYRAL, Jean Philippe (1872-?) French
£410 $750 €599 Still life with kettle and fruit (36x23cm-14x9in) s.verso. 31-Jul-4 Sloans & Kenyon, Bethesda #1225/R

GAYRARD, Joseph Raymond Paul (1807-1855) French
Sculpture
£4828 $8834 €7000 Cheval de l'Empereur Napoleon III enharnachement de parade (58x68cm-23x27in) s. dark pat bronze. 31-Jan-4 Osenat, Fontainebleau #596

GAYS, Eugenio (1861-1938) Italian
£382 $649 €550 Stairs (29x17cm-11x7in) s. board. 1-Nov-3 Meeting Art, Vercelli #377

GAZE, Harold (20th C) American
Works on paper
£3757 $6500 €5485 Plucking a quill and teasing a crocodile (27x20cm-11x8in) s.d.1918 pencil ink W/C prov. 10-Dec-3 Bonhams & Butterfields, San Francisco #6053/R est:3000-5000
£9249 $16000 €13504 Dream. Fairy sleeping. Fairy searching (38x25cm-15x10in) all s.indis.d. pencil in, W/C paper on board three prov. 10-Dec-3 Bonhams & Butterfields, San Francisco #6052/R est:7000-10000

GAZZARDI, Giusseppi (1845-1914) Italian?
£1023 $1800 €1494 Children with a donkey (38x46cm-15x18in) s. 3-Jan-4 Cobbs, Peterborough #54/R

GAZZERA, Romano (1908-1985) Italian
£340 $609 €500 Riders fighting (8x10cm-3x4in) s. board. 22-Mar-4 Sant Agostino, Torino #361/R
£867 $1595 €1300 General Alessandro La Marmora (45x35cm-18x14in) s. s.i.d.1979 verso. 12-Jun-4 Meeting Art, Vercelli #977/R
£915 $1602 €1300 Wild flowers (35x45cm-14x18in) s. prov. 17-Dec-3 Il Ponte, Milan #1160 est:1500-1800
£1793 $2994 €2600 Arpino Knight (45x35cm-18x14in) s. s.i.d.1978 verso masonite. 17-Nov-3 Sant Agostino, Torino #110/R est:2500
£2083 $3542 €3000 Mythological landscape (90x70cm-35x28in) s. prov. 28-Oct-3 Il Ponte, Milan #240/R
£2098 $3503 €3000 Confidences under the geraniums (40x30cm-16x12in) s. s.i.d.1984 verso masonite. 26-Jun-3 Sant Agostino, Torino #293/R est:2000-2500
£2177 $3897 €3200 Red anemones (37x56cm-15x22in) s. board. 22-Mar-4 Sant Agostino, Torino #547/R est:4000
£4558 $8159 €6700 Tropical plant (90x70cm-35x28in) s. exhib. 22-Mar-4 Sant Agostino, Torino #534/R est:8000

GAZZERI, E (19/20th C) Italian
Sculpture
£8743 $16000 €12765 Female figures (168x168cm-66x66in) i. white metal marble pedestal two different sizes. 3-Jun-4 Christie's, Rockefeller NY #916/R est:4000-6000

GAZZONE, Enzo (1894-1970) Italian
£1111 $1889 €1600 Rice harvest (37x47cm-15x19in) s. i.verso board. 1-Nov-3 Meeting Art, Vercelli #278 est:500

GDANIETZ, Wilhelm (1893-1962) German
£433 $776 €650 Musician (81x71cm-32x28in) s. lit. 14-May-4 Schloss Ahlden, Ahlden #2867/R
£486 $768 €700 Reading the news (80x70cm-31x28in) s. 2-Sep-3 Christie's, Amsterdam #232

GEACH, Portia (1873-1959) Australian
Works on paper
£820 $1295 €1197 Spring banishing winter (30x66cm-12x26in) s. W/C collage prov. 2-Sep-3 Deutscher-Menzies, Melbourne #111/R est:3000-4000 (A.D 2000)

GEAR, Mabel (1900-) British
Works on paper
£250 $468 €365 Collie dog with sheep and lambs in the foreground, shepherd nearby (17x28cm-7x11in) s. pencil W/C htd white. 22-Jul-4 Tennants, Leyburn #688
£550 $891 €798 Two terriers. Head of a dog (18x23cm-7x9in) s. pencil W/C two. 30-Jul-3 Hamptons Fine Art, Godalming #68
£1027 $1900 €1499 Portrait of a bulldog (25x15cm-10x6in) s. W/C htd white paper on board prov. 10-Feb-4 Doyle, New York #133/R est:800-1200

GEAR, William (1915-1997) British
£1000 $1670 €1460 Abstract (61x71cm-24x28in) s.d.57. 16-Oct-3 Christie's, Kensington #689/R est:1500-2000
£2400 $4440 €3504 Two trunks (53x33cm-21x13in) s. s.i.d.53 verso. 11-Mar-4 Christie's, Kensington #368/R est:2500-3500
£4500 $8190 €6570 Gray unit (33x41cm-13x16in) s.d.55 s.i.d. verso. 1-Jul-4 Christie's, Kensington #390/R est:1800-2500
£10000 $18100 €14600 Sculpture project (81x121cm-32x48in) 19-Apr-4 Sotheby's, London #155/R est:5000-7000
Works on paper
£300 $555 €438 Still life on table top (26x25cm-10x10in) pencil gouache W/C. 11-Feb-4 Sotheby's, Olympia #260/R
£330 $604 €482 Female nude leaning forwards, full length (32x16cm-13x6in) pen ink. 5-Jun-4 Shapes, Edinburgh #492
£780 $1381 €1139 Study of a seated figure. s.d.24 W/C bodycol. 1-May-4 Shapes, Edinburgh #449
£900 $1431 €1314 Standing nude (46x28cm-18x11in) s.d.37 W/C gouache. 10-Sep-3 Sotheby's, Olympia #286/R
£1100 $2035 €1606 Trujillo (28x39cm-11x15in) s.i.d.89 W/C bodycol. 11-Mar-4 Christie's, Kensington #369/R est:700-1000
£1400 $2380 €2044 People walking (42x57cm-17x22in) s.d.48 W/C gouache prov. 26-Nov-3 Sotheby's, Olympia #180/R
£1600 $2928 €2336 Blue and yellow abstract (40x56cm-16x22in) s.d.74 W/C. 8-Apr-4 Bonhams, Edinburgh #15/R est:1000-1500
£1800 $3276 €2628 Black on Red no 2 (33x44cm-13x17in) s.d.49 brush blk ink bodycol prov. 1-Jul-4 Christie's, Kensington #388/R est:1000-1500
£2000 $3660 €2920 Abstract in green, red and blue (52x68cm-20x27in) s.d.1961 W/C. 8-Apr-4 Bonhams, Edinburgh #14/R est:1500-2000
£2400 $4440 €3504 Figure dancing (49x28cm-19x11in) s.d.47 chl W/C bodycol. 11-Mar-4 Christie's, Kensington #194/R est:700-1000

GEARHART, Frances Hammell (1869-1958) American
Prints
£1919 $3300 €2802 Incoming fog (25x28cm-10x11in) s.i. woodcut. 6-Dec-3 Skinner, Boston #228 est:1000-1500

GEARY, Kevin (1952-) Irish?
£1879 $3326 €2800 Summer day on San Francisco Bay (91x122cm-36x48in) s.i.verso acrylic exhib. 27-Apr-4 Whyte's, Dublin #177/R est:2000-3000

GEBAUER, Paul Ernst (1782-1865) German
£7432 $13304 €11000 Self portrait. Portrait of wife (52x44cm-20x17in) prov.lit. pair. 8-May-4 Schloss Ahlden, Ahlden #690/R est:12500

GEBER, Roma (?) Argentinian
£1341 $2400 €1958 Aspiring to a great cathedral (70x50cm-28x20in) board. 11-May-4 Arroyo, Buenos Aires #44

GEBHARD, Albert (1869-1937) Finnish
£1119 $1902 €1600 Washing day (40x65cm-16x26in) s. 29-Nov-3 Bukowskis, Helsinki #147/R est:2000-3000
£1600 $2864 €2400 Summer in the skerries (46x55cm-18x22in) s. 15-May-4 Hagelstam, Helsinki #169/R est:2500
Works on paper
£1831 $3168 €2600 Before the rowing trip (45x54cm-18x21in) s.d.1902 W/C paper on canvas. 13-Dec-3 Hagelstam, Helsinki #101/R est:1000

GEBHARD, August (1880-?) German
£2333 $4200 €3500 Black Forest valley (73x58cm-29x23in) s. 26-Apr-4 Rieber, Stuttgart #1215/R est:3400

GEBHARD, Johannes (1894-1976) Finnish
£699 $1189 €1000 Sunny woodland glade in winter (66x47cm-26x19in) s. 29-Nov-3 Bukowskis, Helsinki #25e/R
£805 $1498 €1200 Coastal breakers (50x65cm-20x26in) s. 7-Mar-4 Bukowskis, Helsinki #326/R

GEBHARDT, Alexander (?) German?
£590 $962 €850 High mountain farmstead (60x80cm-24x31in) s.i. 25-Sep-3 Neumeister, Munich #2768/R

GEBHARDT, Eduard K F von (1838-1925) German
£278 $458 €400 Portrait of old woman wearing white hat (24x20cm-9x8in) s. panel. 3-Jul-3 Dr Fritz Nagel, Stuttgart #494/R
£278 $458 €400 Christ wearing crown of thorns (40x31cm-16x12in) s. canvas on panel. 3-Jul-3 Van Ham, Cologne #1592
£280 $467 €400 Portrait study of peasant in red waistcoat (24x18cm-9x7in) s. panel. 27-Jun-3 Altus, Berlin #608/R
£289 $531 €430 Christ carrying cross (54x45cm-21x18in) s. panel. 27-Mar-4 L & B, Essen #117/R
£436 $803 €650 And they removed his clothes (31x25cm-12x10in) s. panel. 27-Mar-4 L & B, Essen #118/R
£436 $803 €650 Crucified Christ (75x60cm-30x24in) s. panel. 27-Mar-4 L & B, Essen #119/R
£638 $1034 €900 Portrait of Dutch patrician (39x31cm-15x12in) s.d.1910 board lit. 23-May-3 Karlheinz Kaupp, Staufen #1759/R
£638 $1173 €950 Portrait of man in Renaissance dress (96x73cm-38x29in) s.d.1916. 26-Mar-4 Bolland & Marotz, Bremen #522/R
£959 $1630 €1400 Old gentleman with document. Gentleman in fur coat (92x72cm-36x28in) one s.d.1917 one s.d.1916 two. 5-Nov-3 Vendue Huis, Gravenhage #244a

GEBHARDT, Karl (1860-1917) German
£614 $1100 €896 Voir Benezit (48x33cm-19x13in) s. panel. 21-Mar-4 Bonhams & Butterfields, Los Angeles #7344/R est:800-1200

GEBHARDT, Ludwig (1830-1908) German
£625 $1044 €900 In the wood (38x51cm-15x20in) s. 24-Oct-3 Ketterer, Hamburg #168/R
£1156 $2070 €1700 Harlaching near Munich. Lakeside garden in Lindau (16x28cm-6x11in) mono. panel pair. 17-Mar-4 Neumeister, Munich #459/R est:1400

GEBHARDT, Wolfgang Magnus (fl.1730-1750) German
£2300 $4209 €3358 Figures in an Italianate landscape with classical ruins (36x46cm-14x18in) s. 28-Jan-4 Mallams, Oxford #504/R est:2000-3000

GEBLER, Otto Friedrich (1838-1917) German
£236 $425 €345 Sailing ship (25x51cm-10x20in) s. 24-Jan-4 Susanin's, Chicago #5067/R
£382 $630 €550 Ram's head (24x19cm-9x7in) s. canvas on board. 2-Jul-3 Neumeister, Munich #646
£1081 $1935 €1600 Hunting dog with dead fox (44cm-17in circular) s. panel. 8-May-4 Dawo, Saarbrucken #127/R est:650
£2953 $5522 €4400 Sheep with lambs in stable (24x29cm-9x11in) s. panel. 28-Feb-4 Bolland & Marotz, Bremen #291/R est:2200
£5556 $9056 €8000 Hunting dogs with dead fox (76x102cm-30x40in) s.i. 24-Sep-3 Neumeister, Munich #424/R est:8000

GECELLI, Johannes (1925-) German
£986 $1706 €1400 Road through houses (60x45cm-24x18in) s.d.69 verso s.i.d. stretcher acrylic linen. 13-Dec-3 Lempertz, Koln #140/R

GECHTER, Jean François Theodore (1796-1844) French
Sculpture
£1399 $2336 €2000 Mort de Tancrede (46cm-18in) s.i. pat bronze. 7-Oct-3 Sotheby's, Amsterdam #253 est:2000-3000
£1600 $2992 €2400 Arab stallion (33x36cm-13x14in) s.d.1841 pat bronze sold with base. 21-Jul-4 John Nicholson, Haslemere #850/R est:2000
£2941 $5000 €4294 Death of Harold (22cm-9in) s.d.1842 pat bronze. 28-Oct-3 Christie's, Rockefeller NY #124/R
£4000 $7200 €5840 Joan of Arc defeating the English (69x48cm-27x19in) s. brown pat bronze. 21-Apr-4 Sotheby's, London #60/R est:4000-6000
£4056 $6895 €5800 Combat (35x39x21cm-14x15x8in) s. pat bronze. 28-Nov-3 Drouot Estimations, Paris #157 est:3000-4500

GECHTOFF, Leonid (1883-1941) American
£269 $450 €393 Street in Cairo (51x61cm-20x24in) s.d.39 s.i.d.verso board. 20-Jun-3 Freeman, Philadelphia #185/R
£449 $750 €656 Cairo street scene (64x76cm-25x30in) s.d.39. 20-Jun-3 Freeman, Philadelphia #241/R
£462 $850 €675 Trees in autumn (74x74cm-29x29in) s. board. 25-Jun-4 Freeman, Philadelphia #338/R
£525 $950 €767 Tree in a landscape (76x102cm-30x40in) s. board. 2-Apr-4 Freeman, Philadelphia #202
£539 $900 €787 Winter (61x76cm-24x30in) s.d.39 s.i.d.verso. 20-Jun-3 Freeman, Philadelphia #127/R

GEDDES, Andrew (1783-1844) British
£980 $1578 €1421 Portrait of Mrs Copeland in mob cap (75x62cm-30x24in) 21-Aug-3 Bonhams, Edinburgh #1020

GEDDES, Margaret (1914-) British
£320 $534 €467 Target (100x100cm-39x39in) s.verso. 21-Oct-3 Bonhams, Knightsbridge #129

GEDDES, William (1841-1884) British
£650 $1105 €949 Study of a young boy beside a wooden table cutting turnip (28x21cm-11x8in) mono.indis.d.1875 board. 19-Nov-3 Tennants, Leyburn #1252

GEDLEK, Ludwig (1847-1904) Austrian
£1007 $1852 €1500 Three saddled horses with armed Cossacks lying on grass (24x29cm-9x11in) s. lit. panel. 25-Mar-4 Karlheinz Kaupp, Staufen #2443/R est:1500
£1812 $3334 €2700 Horse cart with peasants and dogs by farmstead (36x57cm-14x22in) s.i. panel. 26-Mar-4 Ketterer, Hamburg #185/R est:3000-3500
£2841 $5000 €4148 Cossack figures gathered by a wall (21x32cm-8x13in) s.i. panel. 18-May-4 Bonhams & Butterfields, San Francisco #109/R est:3000-5000
£2978 $4646 €4348 Soldiers on horseback (32x26cm-13x10in) s. panel painted c.1890. 30-Mar-3 Agra, Warsaw #17/R est:19000 (P.Z 19000)
£4196 $7217 €6000 Cossacks with Turkish prisoners walking home (32x63cm-13x25in) s.i. 3-Dec-3 Neumeister, Munich #575/R est:6000
£4500 $8325 €6570 Cossacks (58x100cm-23x39in) s.i. 10-Mar-4 Sotheby's, Olympia #271/R est:3000-5000
£4688 $7828 €6844 Taking a break (78x63cm-31x25in) s. painted c.1890. 19-Oct-3 Agra, Warsaw #13/R est:30000 (P.Z 30000)
£7837 $12226 €11442 Departure of the hunt (36x58cm-14x23in) s. panel painted c.1890. 30-Mar-3 Agra, Warsaw #8/R est:45000 (P.Z 50000)

GEDOVIUS, German (1867-1937) Mexican
£8430 $14331 €12308 Landscape with river (86x108cm-34x43in) s. 30-Oct-3 Louis Morton, Mexico #83/R est:170000-180000 (M.P 160000)

GEE, David (?) British?
£630 $1147 €920 Interior of St Michael's Church, Coventry (65x76cm-26x30in) s.d.1861. 29-Jun-4 Bonhams, Knowle #77

GEEL, Joost van (attrib) (1631-1698) Dutch
Works on paper
£1027 $1747 €1500 Mountainous landscape (15x15cm-6x6in) pen brown grey ink wash prov. 4-Nov-3 Sotheby's, Amsterdam #29/R est:2000-3000

GEER, Gerard de (19th C) ?
£1147 $1846 €1675 Vessel in stormy seas (44x59cm-17x23in) s.d.1826. 25-Aug-3 Lilla Bukowskis, Stockholm #297 est:8000-10000 (S.KR 15000)

GEER, Livingston (20th C) American
£385 $700 €562 Figures strolling by a river in autumn (25x30cm-10x12in) s.d.1899. 7-Feb-4 Sloans & Kenyon, Bethesda #901/R

GEERARDS, Jasper (17th C) Dutch
£28000 $51240 €40880 Lemons, oyster, grapes on a silver plate with shells on a velvet box (52x66cm-20x26in) indis sig. panel prov.exhib. 7-Jul-4 Bonhams, New Bond Street #84/R est:15000-20000

GEERINCK, Cesar (1862-1919) Belgian
£552 $921 €800 Scene orientaliste avec dromadaire et figures (73x52cm-29x20in) s.d.1887. 17-Nov-3 Bernaerts, Antwerp #16/R

GEERT, Edith (1908-) ?
£313 $497 €450 Still life (68x97cm-27x38in) s. 29-Apr-3 Durán, Madrid #69/R

GEERTS, François (fl.1850-1884) Belgian
£331 $603 €500 Paysage aux vaches et moulin au pres de l'eau (52x82cm-20x32in) s. 21-Jun-4 Bernaerts, Antwerp #172
£333 $603 €500 Dame Armenienne (67x56cm-26x22in) s.d.1900. 30-Mar-4 Campo & Campo, Antwerp #119

GEERTSEN, Ib (1919-) Danish
£526 $853 €763 Composition (65x50cm-26x20in) s.d.1959 verso. 4-Aug-3 Rasmussen, Vejle #541/R (D.KR 5500)
£604 $1100 €906 Concrete composition (81x65cm-32x26in) s.d.23 aug - 18 jan 1958 verso. 19-Jun-4 Rasmussen, Havnen #4086/R (D.KR 6800)

GEEST, Chris van (1942-) Dutch
£3986 $6536 €5500 Castle garden in Florence (76x94cm-30x37in) s.d.1999. 27-May-3 Sotheby's, Amsterdam #354/R est:5500-7000

GEEST, Julien Franciscus de (?-1699) Flemish
£1205 $2000 €1759 Vanitas portrait of a gentleman (43x36cm-17x14in) s.i.d.1662 panel prov. 30-Sep-3 Christie's, Rockefeller NY #403/R est:4000-6000

GEEST, Wybrand-Simonsz de (elder-attrib) (1592-1659) Dutch
£2534 $4054 €3700 Portrait of young boy, probably Philip Ferdinand van der Veecken (42x33cm-17x13in) i.d.1611 panel. 19-Sep-3 Koller, Zurich #3039/R est:6000-9000 (S.FR 5600)

GEEST, Wybrand-Simonsz de (elder-circle) (1592-1659) Dutch
£6500 $11245 €9490 Portrait of a young girl holding a tethered goat (90x100cm-35x39in) 12-Dec-3 Christie's, Kensington #15/R est:4000-6000

GEETS, Willem (1838-1919) Belgian
£694 $1104 €1000 Le tir a l'arbalete a Anvers (38x56cm-15x22in) s. panel. 15-Sep-3 Horta, Bruxelles #222
£2819 $5158 €4200 La demande en mariage (27x36cm-11x14in) s. panel. 8-Jul-4 Campo, Vlaamse Kaai #116/R est:3000-4000

Works on paper

£559	$951	€800	La carte geografique (34x23cm-13x9in) s. W/C. 1-Dec-3 Palais de Beaux Arts, Brussels #256/R
£633	$1140	€950	Interior with mandoline player and young woman. Boy at the water pump (75x29cm-30x11in) s. W/C double-sided. 26-Apr-4 Bernaerts, Antwerp #24/R
£867	$1560	€1300	Interior with woman in anticipation. s.d.1891 W/C. 26-Apr-4 Bernaerts, Antwerp #23/R

GEEX DELAVALLEE (17th C) Belgian

£3521	$6162	€5000	Minerve et les muses sur le Mont Helicon (56x72cm-22x28in) copper. 18-Dec-3 Tajan, Paris #106/R est:3000-4000

GEFFCKEN, Walter (1872-1950) German

£267	$480	€400	Cavalier in front of mirror (31x25cm-12x10in) s. bears d. board. 21-Apr-4 Neumeister, Munich #2644/R
£1111	$1811	€1600	Figures round table in rococo salon (58x76cm-23x30in) s. board. 24-Sep-3 Neumeister, Munich #425/R est:2400

GEGERFELT, Wilhelm von (1844-1920) Swedish

£344	$554	€502	Landscape, Dalarna (17x28cm-7x11in) s. panel. 25-Aug-3 Lilla Bukowskis, Stockholm #127 (S.KR 4500)
£471	$815	€688	Breakers (47x64cm-19x25in) s. 15-Dec-3 Lilla Bukowskis, Stockholm #93 (S.KR 6000)
£541	$1001	€790	Landscape with farm (37x54cm-15x21in) s. 15-Mar-4 Rasmussen, Vejle #300/R (D.KR 6000)
£739	$1323	€1079	Venetian street scene (68x42cm-27x17in) s. 28-May-4 Uppsala Auktionskammare, Uppsala #203/R (S.KR 10000)
£1014	$1824	€1480	Fyris river in winter (56x85cm-22x33in) s.d.86. 26-Jan-4 Lilla Bukowskis, Stockholm #482 (S.KR 13500)
£1077	$1852	€1572	Canal in Brugghe (46x36cm-18x14in) i.verso. 2-Dec-3 Bukowskis, Stockholm #192/R (S.KR 14000)
£1130	$2079	€1695	Fishermen, Torekow (23x36cm-9x14in) st.sig. verso panel. 14-Jun-4 Lilla Bukowskis, Stockholm #509 est:8000-10000 (S.KR 15500)
£1300	$2093	€1898	Landscape from Hallands weather island (39x50cm-15x20in) s. 25-Aug-3 Lilla Bukowskis, Stockholm #861 est:12000-15000 (S.KR 17000)
£1462	$2514	€2135	Winter landscape with skaters (97x60cm-38x24in) s.d.80. 2-Dec-3 Bukowskis, Stockholm #140/R est:25000-30000 (S.KR 19000)
£1491	$2400	€2177	Venetian scene (45x65cm-18x26in) s. 25-Aug-3 Lilla Bukowskis, Stockholm #455 est:25000 (S.KR 19500)
£1531	$2816	€2297	View in Italy (64x90cm-25x35in) s. 14-Jun-4 Lilla Bukowskis, Stockholm #301 est:30000-35000 (S.KR 21000)
£1552	$2778	€2266	Coastal landscape with fisherwomen on jetty in evening (68x76cm-27x30in) s/. 26-May-4 AB Stockholms Auktionsverk #2144/R est:15000-18000 (S.KR 21000)
£1552	$2778	€2266	Boats in the lagoon (56x46cm-22x18in) s. panel. 25-May-4 Bukowskis, Stockholm #237/R est:30000-35000 (S.KR 21000)
£1603	$2950	€2405	Coastal landscape with sailing boats (50x76cm-20x30in) s. 14-Jun-4 Lilla Bukowskis, Stockholm #755 est:40000-50000 (S.KR 22000)
£1923	$3308	€2808	Moonlight over windmill in winter landscape (100x75cm-39x30in) s. 3-Dec-3 AB Stockholms Auktionsverk #2360/R est:12000-15000 (S.KR 25000)
£1996	$3572	€2914	Bay with boats (36x46cm-14x18in) s. exhib. 25-May-4 Bukowskis, Stockholm #163/R est:30000-35000 (S.KR 27000)
£2069	$3704	€3021	Quay in Venice (56x45cm-22x18in) s. panel. 25-May-4 Bukowskis, Stockholm #208/R est:30000-35000 (S.KR 28000)
£2956	$5292	€4316	Feeding the pigeons (30x19cm-12x7in) s. panel painted 1882 exhib.prov. 25-May-4 Bukowskis, Stockholm #195/R est:30000-40000 (S.KR 40000)
£3046	$5482	€4569	Terrace view with figures, Italy (100x80cm-39x31in) s. 25-Apr-4 Goteborg Auktionsverk, Sweden #200/R est:35000 (S.KR 42000)
£3178	$5689	€4640	Sunshine on the jetty in the Mediterranean (60x95cm-24x37in) s. 25-May-4 Bukowskis, Stockholm #206/R est:50000-60000 (S.KR 43000)
£3326	$5953	€4856	Venetian quay in evening (54x81cm-21x32in) s. 26-May-4 AB Stockholms Auktionsverk #2192/R est:35000-40000 (S.KR 45000)
£3385	$5822	€4942	Three master by Venetian quay (29x54cm-11x21in) s.d.83. 3-Dec-3 AB Stockholms Auktionsverk #2486/R est:20000-25000 (S.KR 44000)
£3692	$6351	€5390	Quay in Venice (39x67cm-15x26in) s. 3-Dec-3 AB Stockholms Auktionsverk #2418/R est:30000-40000 (S.KR 48000)
£3695	$6615	€5395	Shore scene with fishing boats, Venice (52x40cm-20x16in) s. panel. 26-May-4 AB Stockholms Auktionsverk #2193/R est:35000-40000 (S.KR 50000)
£3846	$6615	€5615	Figures on a Venetian quay (60x100cm-24x39in) s.d.80. 2-Dec-3 Bukowskis, Stockholm #95/R est:50000-70000 (S.KR 50000)
£3991	$7144	€5827	Street scene, Venice (38x36cm-15x14in) s. 26-May-4 AB Stockholms Auktionsverk #2139/R est:40000-50000 (S.KR 54000)
£4923	$8468	€7188	The lagoon, Venice (52x44cm-20x17in) s.d.81. 2-Dec-3 Bukowskis, Stockholm #97/R est:40000-50000 (S.KR 64000)
£5231	$8997	€7637	Positano (81x126cm-32x50in) s. 2-Dec-3 Bukowskis, Stockholm #96/R est:40000-50000 (S.KR 68000)
£5322	$9525	€7770	Harbour in the Mediterranean (115x70cm-45x28in) s. 25-May-4 Bukowskis, Stockholm #39/R est:70000-80000 (S.KR 72000)
£12934	$23152	€18884	Rain clouds over Paris (56x42cm-22x17in) s. panel. 25-May-4 Bukowskis, Stockholm #41/R est:75000-100000 (S.KR 175000)

Works on paper

£754	$1305	€1101	View St Mark's Square, Venice (40x28cm-16x11in) s. W/C. 15-Dec-3 Lilla Bukowskis, Stockholm #712 (S.KR 9600)
£769	$1323	€1123	View from Venice (46x63cm-18x25in) s. 7-Dec-3 Uppsala Auktionskammare, Uppsala #157/R (S.KR 10000)
£933	$1502	€1362	Venetian view (52x35cm-20x14in) s. W/C. 25-Aug-3 Lilla Bukowskis, Stockholm #141 (S.KR 12200)

GEHR, Ferdinand (1896-1996) Swiss

£1448	$2462	€2114	Head of Christ (65x54cm-26x21in) s. tempera. 18-Nov-3 Hans Widmer, St Gallen #1057 est:1200-3800 (S.FR 3200)
£34081	$56915	€49758	Yarrow and phlox (60x75cm-24x30in) s.d.50 tempera. 24-Oct-3 Hans Widmer, St Gallen #40/R est:14000-20000 (S.FR 76000)

Works on paper

£452	$769	€660	Jerusalem (35x40cm-14x16in) W/C lit. 18-Nov-3 Hans Widmer, St Gallen #1058 (S.FR 1000)
£1164	$2083	€1699	Adoration of the three kings (8x14cm-3x6in) s. W/C on chl four. 14-May-4 Dobiaschofsky, Bern #284/R est:4500 (S.FR 2700)
£1293	$2315	€1888	Holy figure (21x16cm-8x6in) s. W/C. 13-May-4 Stuker, Bern #145/R est:3000-3500 (S.FR 3000)
£1435	$2396	€2095	Ried landscape in St Galler, Rhine valley (25x36cm-10x14in) s.d.53 W/C over chl. 24-Oct-3 Hans Widmer, St Gallen #137/R est:2800-4800 (S.FR 3200)
£1480	$2471	€2161	Rhine valley landscape (14x20cm-6x8in) s.d.42 W/C. 24-Oct-3 Hans Widmer, St Gallen #41/R est:3500-5500 (S.FR 3300)
£11211	$18722	€16368	Dahlias (50x66cm-20x26in) s.d.73 W/C. 24-Oct-3 Hans Widmer, St Gallen #8/R est:12000-18000 (S.FR 25000)
£12556	$20969	€18332	Peonies and roses (66x51cm-26x20in) s.d.86 W/C over chl. 24-Oct-3 Hans Widmer, St Gallen #3/R est:9000-14000 (S.FR 28000)

GEHRI, Franz (1882-1960) Swiss

£252	$456	€368	Lake surrounded by mountains (60x77cm-24x30in) s. 30-Mar-4 Stephan Welz, Johannesburg #418 est:3000-4000 (SA.R 3000)

GEHRIG, Jakob (1846-1922) German

£550	$1018	€803	Trading vessels on the Lagoon, Venice (14x18cm-6x7in) s. board pair. 15-Jan-4 Christie's, Kensington #966/R

GEHRTS, Johannes (1855-?) German

Works on paper

£385	$662	€550	Wild boar (28x42cm-11x17in) s.d.14 gouache. 4-Dec-3 Schopman, Hamburg #673/R

GEIAI (15th C) Japanese

Works on paper

£135870	$250000	€198370	Small birds and herons in a lotus pond (111x50cm-44x20in) ink hanging scrolls pair prov.exhib. 23-Mar-4 Christie's, Rockefeller NY #94/R est:80000-100000

GEIGER, Caspar Augustin (1847-1924) German

£594	$1010	€850	Arab man holding a child (100x83cm-39x33in) s. i.verso. 28-Nov-3 Wendl, Rudolstadt #3973/R

GEIGER, Ernst (1876-1965) Swiss

£28017	$50151	€40905	Bielersee (45x55cm-18x22in) s. 14-May-4 Dobiaschofsky, Bern #181/R est:14000 (S.FR 65000)

GEIGER, Richard (1870-1945) Austrian

£322	$593	€480	Tavern (75x99cm-30x39in) s. 26-Mar-4 Altus, Berlin #594/R
£382	$603	€550	Female nude reclining on the sofa with a parrot (60x80cm-24x31in) s. 5-Sep-3 Wendl, Rudolstadt #3367/R
£383	$697	€559	Young musician in a cafe (79x61cm-31x24in) s. 15-Jun-4 Ritchie, Toronto #2214 (C.D 950)
£450	$828	€657	Attractive gaze (74x100cm-29x39in) s. 23-Mar-4 Rosebery Fine Art, London #925
£550	$935	€803	Reclining beauty (60x79cm-24x31in) s. 6-Nov-3 Christie's, Kensington #751/R
£600	$1002	€876	Perfect reflection (76x99cm-30x39in) s. 8-Oct-3 Christie's, Kensington #924/R
£612	$1096	€900	La gitane (80x60cm-31x24in) s. 17-Mar-4 Hotel des Ventes Mosan, Brussels #118
£650	$1203	€949	Tryat at the ball (79x60cm-31x24in) s. 15-Jan-4 Christie's, Kensington #848/R
£1192	$2181	€1800	Nymphe and Satyr (67x87cm-26x34in) s. canvas on panel. 8-Apr-4 Dorotheum, Vienna #249/R est:1800-2000

Works on paper

£282	$451	€400	Columbine and admirer (45x54cm-18x21in) s. gouache. 18-Sep-3 Rieber, Stuttgart #1193/R
£331	$603	€500	Viennese scene with a theatre scene (44x54cm-17x21in) s. W/C. 19-Jun-4 Bergmann, Erlangen #832
£448	$744	€650	Man wearing cap with red haired woman (65x51cm-26x20in) s. W/C. 30-Sep-3 Dorotheum, Vienna #371/R

GEIGER, Rupprecht (1908-) German

£1338	$2315	€1900	Square in red (50x66cm-30x26in) s.i.d.l/89 verso oil chk. 13-Dec-3 Lempertz, Koln #313/R est:1000
£2333	$4293	€3500	Square in red - chalk (50x66cm-20x26in) s.i.d.1/89 verso acrylic paper. 11-Jun-4 Hauswedell & Nolte, Hamburg #1274/R est:3500
£8000	$14720	€12000	Composition (85x80cm-33x31in) s.i.verso acrylic exec. 1991. 12-Jun-4 Villa Grisebach, Berlin #409/R est:12000-18000
£8099	$14011	€11500	535/68 (95x80cm-37x31in) s.stretcher acrylic. 13-Dec-3 Lempertz, Koln #312/R est:10000
£12587	$21650	€18000	E 102 (65x75cm-26x30in) s.i.verso s.i.d.1950 on stretcher egg tempera prov.exhib. 5-Dec-3 Ketterer, Munich #154/R est:14000-18000
£14085	$24366	€20000	E I (72x98cm-28x39in) s.i.d.1955 stretcher lit. 13-Dec-3 Lempertz, Koln #141/R est:15000-18000
£15385	$26462	€22000	E 140 (50x84cm-20x33in) s.i.d.1950 on stretcher egg tempera prov. 5-Dec-3 Ketterer, Munich #156/R est:15000-20000
£16000	$28640	€24000	444/66 (92x81cm-36x32in) s. verso prov.exhib. 14-May-4 Ketterer, Munich #264/R est:20000-25000
£16667	$30667	€25000	469/67 (90x80cm-35x31in) canvas on panel. 11-Jun-4 Hauswedell & Nolte, Hamburg #1273/R est:28000
£20000	$35800	€30000	372/62 (50x95cm-20x37in) s. verso i. stretcher exhib.lit. 15-May-4 Van Ham, Cologne #609/R est:30000
£32168	$55329	€46000	Picture 1 (115x120cm-45x47in) s.d.1959 verso i.d.1959 on stretcher egg tempera prov. 5-Dec-3 Ketterer, Munich #160/R est:28000-35000

GEILLE DE SAINT LEGER, Léon (1864-?) French

£308	$524	€450	L'Amiraute a Alger (27x19cm-11x7in) s. panel. 8-Nov-3 Gerard, Besancon #72
£1277	$2132	€1800	Caravane (38x61cm-15x24in) s. 19-Oct-3 Rabourdin & Choppin de Janvry, Paris #37 est:2000-2200
£1467	$2699	€2200	Koubba de Sidi Mohamed Ben Medjoube (46x33cm-18x13in) s. 14-Jun-4 Gros & Delettrez, Paris #395/R est:2500-3500
£1560	$2606	€2200	Halte de caravane (33x46cm-13x18in) s. 19-Oct-3 Rabourdin & Choppin de Janvry, Paris #35/R est:2800-3200

GEIPEL, Hans (1927-) Austrian
Sculpture
£1000 $1790 €1500 Kinetic object (20x35x35cm-8x14x14in) painted wood other materials. 15-May-4 Van Ham, Cologne #611/R est:1500

GEIRNAERT, Jozef (1791-1859) Belgian
£2333 $4200 €3500 Blowing bubbles (44x36cm-17x14in) s.d.1842 panel. 20-Apr-4 Sotheby's, Amsterdam #89/R est:2500-3500

GEISELER, Hermann (1903-) German
£552 $921 €800 Slovenian landscape (75x106cm-30x42in) s. 13-Nov-3 Neumeister, Munich #332/R

GEISER, Bernard F (1877-1965) American
£391 $700 €571 Hermit (122x71cm-48x28in) s.d.Oct 1961 masonite. 16-Mar-4 Matthew's, Oregon #96/R

GEISER, Karl (1898-1957) Swiss
Sculpture
£3587 $5848 €5237 Study for 'David' (85cm-33in) i. pat.bronze Cast.M Pastor/Geneve lit. 29-Sep-3 Christie's, Zurich #100/R est:8000-12000 (S.FR 8000)
£3712 $6644 €5420 Woman with scarf (55cm-22in) s.d.1933 st.f.M Pastori bronze lit. 26-May-4 Sotheby's, Zurich #50/R est:8000-12000 (S.FR 8500)
Works on paper
£216 $387 €315 Seated woman (26x21cm-10x8in) pen. 22-Mar-4 Philippe Schuler, Zurich #4168 (S.FR 500)

GEISLER, G G (18th C) German?
£1007 $1852 €1500 Portraits of elegant man and woman (38x30cm-15x12in) one s.d.1781 pair. 26-Mar-4 Auktionhaus Georg Rehm, Augsburg #8035/R est:2100

GEISMAYR, Christian (1977-) Austrian
£1067 $1920 €1600 Water tap (150x130cm-59x51in) s.d.1990 verso. 21-Apr-4 Dorotheum, Vienna #329/R est:1100-1800

GEISS, Otto (20th C) German?
£604 $1111 €900 Woman in fur coat (12x10cm-5x4in) s.d.1981 board. 26-Mar-4 Auktionhaus Georg Rehm, Augsburg #8039/R
£604 $1069 €900 Surrealist garden landscape (24x33cm-9x13in) s.d.1997 acrylic. 30-Apr-4 Auktionhaus Georg Rehm, Augsburg #7651/R
£872 $1605 €1300 Still life with mussels (30x40cm-12x16in) s.d.1978. 26-Mar-4 Auktionhaus Georg Rehm, Augsburg #8043/R
£1007 $1852 €1500 Surreal portrait of a woman with mask and flower (16x13cm-6x5in) s.d.1981 panel. 26-Mar-4 Auktionhaus Georg Rehm, Augsburg #8036/R est:700
Works on paper
£671 $1188 €1000 Lion and a young woman (40x29cm-16x11in) s.d.1998 W/C. 30-Apr-4 Auktionhaus Georg Rehm, Augsburg #7650/R

GEISSER, Johann Josef (1824-1894) Swiss
£603 $1080 €880 Sunny shore of Lake Geneva (36x55cm-14x22in) s. 12-May-4 Dobiaschofsky, Bern #545/R (S.FR 1400)
£913 $1671 €1333 In the Alps (33x46cm-13x18in) s. 4-Jun-4 Zofingen, Switzerland #2345/R (S.FR 2100)
£1429 $2286 €2072 Boy's portrait (135x94cm-53x37in) s.d.1853 canvas on pavatex. 15-May-3 Stuker, Bern #1246 est:4000-4500 (S.FR 3000)
£1638 $2932 €2391 Alpine pasture (28x41cm-11x16in) s. panel. 14-May-4 Dobiaschofsky, Bern #1/R est:1800 (S.FR 3800)
£2412 $4029 €3522 Rimpfischorn, Strahlhorn, Adlerhorn, Zermatt (80x120cm-31x47in) s. 16-Nov-3 Koller, Geneva #1255/R est:3000-5000 (S.FR 5500)

GEISSLER, Christian Gottfried Heinrich (1770-1844) German
Works on paper
£432 $691 €600 Caravane en Asie du nord (25x20cm-10x8in) s. pen blk ink grey wash. 16-May-3 Tajan, Paris #122

GEISSLER, Paul (1881-1965) German
£769 $1285 €1100 Snowy wood by the Eibsee (90x61cm-35x24in) s.i. s.i.d. verso. 10-Oct-3 Winterberg, Heidelberg #1294/R

GEIST, Karl Ritter von (attrib) (fl.1885-1900) Austrian
£1106 $1913 €1570 Idyllic scene with old town houses by river (41x52cm-16x20in) s.d.1885 panel. 11-Dec-3 Dr Fritz Nagel, Stuttgart #520/R est:2200

GEITLINGER, Ernst (1895-1972) German
£2400 $4416 €3600 Green marks (130x89cm-51x35in) s.d. verso i. stretcher. 11-Jun-4 Hauswedell & Nolte, Hamburg #1275/R est:4000
£12667 $22673 €19000 New York (80x60cm-31x24in) mono.d. prov. 14-May-4 Ketterer, Munich #23/R est:5000-7000
£16667 $29833 €25000 Variety show (61x80cm-24x31in) prov. 14-May-4 Ketterer, Munich #22/R est:5000-7000

GELANZE, Giuseppe (1876-?) Italian
£393 $715 €574 Young woman wearing a headscarf (29x18cm-11x7in) s. 16-Jun-4 Fischer, Luzern #2136/R (S.FR 900)

GELB, Jan (1906-1978) American
£234 $375 €342 Song to earth (122x81cm-48x32in) s. 20-Sep-3 Bunte, Elgin #1262

GELDER, Aert de (1645-1727) Dutch
£24795 $42896 €36201 Kisfiu porteja (57x47cm-22x19in) 12-Dec-3 Kieselbach, Budapest #204/R (H.F 9500000)

GELDER, Rebecca (1891-1945) Dutch
Works on paper
£903 $1508 €1300 Girl with flowers (51x42cm-20x17in) s.d. gouache over pencil board. 25-Oct-3 Dr Lehr, Berlin #498/R

GELDEREN, Simon van (1905-1986) Belgian
£426 $711 €600 Nature morte a la volaille (50x40cm-20x16in) s. 17-Jun-3 Vanderkindere, Brussels #33

GELDORP, Gortzius (1553-1618) Flemish
£13514 $23784 €20000 Portrait of a lady, aged 28 wearing a black and white dress (52x43cm-20x17in) i.d.1597 prov. 18-May-4 Sotheby's, Amsterdam #62/R est:5000-7000

GELDORP, Gortzius (attrib) (1553-1618) Flemish
£728 $1326 €1100 Virgin Annunciate (33x25cm-13x10in) panel prov. 16-Jun-4 Dorotheum, Vienna #100/R
£800 $1432 €1200 Portrait of a nobleman, aged 50, in a black costume (59x45cm-23x18in) i.d.1608 panel prov. 17-May-4 Christie's, Amsterdam #19/R
£1000 $1700 €1460 Madonna in prayer (51x42cm-20x17in) panel. 30-Oct-3 Sotheby's, Olympia #51/R est:1500-2000
£1831 $3168 €2600 Portrait of a girl (67x51cm-26x20in) i. panel. 11-Dec-3 Dr Fritz Nagel, Stuttgart #470/R est:1800
£4080 $7058 €5957 Portrait of a gentleman, aged 29 wearing a black jacket (60x50cm-24x20in) i. panel. 9-Dec-3 Sotheby's, Olympia #327/R est:3000-4000
£5705 $10497 €8500 Portraits of Heinrich Krufft and Maria Krufft (99x72cm-39x28in) d.1604 panel pair. 25-Mar-4 Dr Fritz Nagel, Stuttgart #596/R est:9000

GELEEDTS, Flore (19th C) Belgian
£3000 $5460 €4380 Roses cascading from a china vase into a bowl on a draped table (91x68cm-36x27in) s. 16-Jun-4 Christie's, Kensington #54/R est:2000-3000

GELENG, Otto (19th C) German
£380 $597 €551 On the Amalfi Coast (27x48cm-11x19in) s. board. 28-Aug-3 Christie's, Kensington #232/R
£1192 $2181 €1800 Farmstead above amphitheatre at Taormina (40x64cm-16x25in) s. 8-Apr-4 Dorotheum, Vienna #53/R est:2600-3000

GELHAY, Edouard (1856-?) French
£5000 $9200 €7300 French town scene (64x79cm-25x31in) s. 28-Mar-4 Carlsen Gallery, Greenville #141/R

GELIBERT, Gaston (1850-1931) French
Works on paper
£537 $999 €800 Faisans et lapins (41x33cm-16x13in) s. W/C. 3-Mar-4 Ferri, Paris #146/R

GELIBERT, Jules-Bertrand (1834-1916) French
£2886 $5368 €4300 Deux chiens (48x65cm-19x26in) s.d.aout 1886. 3-Mar-4 Ferri, Paris #145/R est:4000-5000
Works on paper
£490 $842 €700 Loutre et truite (26x36cm-10x14in) W/C. 3-Dec-3 Coutau Begarie, Paris #67/R
£552 $921 €800 Chiens de chasse au repos (22x29cm-9x11in) s.d.1864 W/C. 12-Nov-3 Chassaing Rivet, Toulouse #56
£2431 $3962 €3500 Griffons vendeens gardant le sanglier (43x32cm-17x13in) ink dr. 29-Sep-3 Coutau Begarie, Paris #240/R

GELISSEN, Maximilien Lambert (1786-1867) Belgian
£1611 $2980 €2400 Extensive wooded landscape with horseman, maid and other travelers on a path (65x84cm-26x33in) s.d.1823 panel. 15-Mar-4 Sotheby's, Amsterdam #4/R est:1500-2000

GELLEE, Claude (c.1600-1682) French
£211111 $380000 €308222 Dance of the Seasons (28x35cm-11x14in) copper exhib.lit. 22-Jan-4 Sotheby's, New York #80/R est:150000-200000
Works on paper
£55000 $100650 €80300 Sheet of studies of deer (20x20cm-8x8in) s.i. point of the brush brown ink grey wash prov.lit. 8-Jul-4 Sotheby's, London #64/R est:20000-25000

GELLEE, Claude (after) (c.1600-1682) French
£8160 $14117 €11914 Landscape with Juno putting 10 under the care of Argus (60x76cm-24x30in) 9-Dec-3 Sotheby's, Olympia #428/R est:4000-6000

GELLEE, Claude (attrib) (c.1600-1682) French
£1745 $3211 €2600 La fuite en Egypte (29x39cm-11x15in) octogonal panel. 24-Mar-4 Tajan, Paris #120 est:1500-2000
Works on paper
£2238 $3849 €3200 Troupeau de boeufs et veau (11x16cm-4x6in) pen ink. 5-Dec-3 Gros & Delettrez, Paris #6/R est:3000-4000

GELLEE, Claude (style) (c.1600-1682) French
£8500 $14705 €12410 Arcadian landscape with the marriage of Isaac and Rebekah (99x162cm-39x64in) 10-Dec-3 Bonhams, New Bond Street #66/R est:4000-6000

£17905 $32766 €26141 Pastoral landscape with Apollo and Daphne (135x190cm-53x75in) 9-Jun-4 Rasmussen, Copenhagen #1559/R est:60000-80000 (D.KR 200000)
£21053 $38737 €32000 Landscape with nymphs (155x198cm-61x78in) 25-Jun-4 Piasa, Paris #39/R est:10000-15000

GELLER, Barry (20th C) American
£2171 $3800 €3170 Illustration to Ian Fleming's Octopussy (77x86cm-30x34in) s. exec March 1966. 17-Dec-3 Christie's, Rockefeller NY #72/R est:3000-4000

GELLER, Johann Nepomuk (1860-1954) Austrian
£1042 $1771 €1500 Inner courtyard in Wachau (30x20cm-12x8in) s. canvas on board. 28-Oct-3 Dorotheum, Vienna #234/R est:1800-2400
£3691 $6607 €5500 Garden and church in Weissenkirchen (38x29cm-15x11in) s. board. 27-May-4 Hassfurther, Vienna #50/R est:4000-6000
£6711 $12013 €10000 Sunday in the Prater (57x88cm-22x35in) s. 27-May-4 Dorotheum, Vienna #36/R est:15000-18000

GELLER, Peter (1862-1933) Russian
£3514 $6289 €5200 In the garden (38x46cm-15x18in) s. 8-May-4 Bukowskis, Helsinki #412/R est:5000-6000

GELMUYDEN, R E (19/20th C) Dutch
Works on paper
£898 $1500 €1311 Harvesting cockles (49x69cm-19x27in) s. pencil W/C. 26-Oct-3 Bonhams & Butterfields, San Francisco #6466/R

GELTMAN, Lillian (1903-?) American
£324 $550 €473 Untitled, self portrait in studio (53x43cm-21x17in) s. 9-Nov-3 Outer Cape Auctions, Provincetown #30/R

GELY, Gabriel (1924-) Canadian?
£242 $445 €353 Allalou back from seal hunt, Clyde River (50x71cm-20x28in) s. i.d.74 verso. 9-Jun-4 Walker's, Ottawa #213/R (C.D 600)

GEMELLI, Ivo (1897-1964) Italian
£319 $533 €450 Snowfall (50x70cm-20x28in) s.d.1959 cardboard. 20-Oct-3 Sant Agostino, Torino #129/R
£374 $670 €550 Flirting (49x69cm-19x27in) s. board. 22-Mar-4 Sant Agostino, Torino #164/R
£390 $651 €550 Revigliasco (70x50cm-28x20in) s.i.d.1946 cardboard. 20-Oct-3 Sant Agostino, Torino #141/R

GEMITO (19/20th C) Italian
Sculpture
£2766 $4619 €3900 Marchand d'eau. s. brown pat bronze. 17-Jun-3 Vanderkindere, Brussels #453 est:1000-1500

GEMITO, Vincenzo (1852-1929) Italian
Sculpture
£1259 $2140 €1800 Petit pecheur (20cm-8in) s. brown pat bronze. 1-Dec-3 Camard, Paris #15 est:1200-1500
£1408 $2437 €2000 Head of Medusa (13x13x13cm-5x5x5in) s.st.f.Gemito pat bronze. 11-Dec-3 Christie's, Rome #110 est:1200-1500
£1467 $2655 €2200 Boy (33cm-13in) s.st.f.Gemito bronze. 30-Mar-4 Babuino, Rome #303/R est:3000
£1500 $2685 €2190 Water seller (56cm-22in) bronze. 25-May-4 Sotheby's, Billingshurst #382/R est:1500-2500
£3500 $6300 €5110 Water vendor (56cm-22in) s.i.num.142 brown pat bronze lit. 21-Apr-4 Sotheby's, London #123/R est:3000-5000
£7333 $13493 €11000 Water carrier (77cm-30in) s. bronze. 8-Jun-4 Sotheby's, Milan #162/R est:8000-12000
£8000 $14400 €11680 Narcissus (63cm-25in) num.55 brown pat bronze st.f. Gemito Napoli lit. 21-Apr-4 Sotheby's, London #103/R est:4000-6000
£12676 $21930 €18000 Bust of Anna Gemito (50cm-20in) s. wax. 11-Dec-3 Christie's, Rome #109/R est:8000-12000
Works on paper
£621 $1037 €900 Mastro Ciccio (5x4cm-2x2in) s. pencil. 13-Nov-3 Galleria Pace, Milan #2/R
£704 $1169 €1000 Portrait of Pia (50x39cm-20x15in) s.i.d.1925 mixed media cardboard. 11-Jun-3 Christie's, Rome #97/R
£1056 $1754 €1500 La figlia Giuseppina (50x37cm-20x15in) s. pencil cardboard. 11-Jun-3 Christie's, Rome #174/R est:1500-2500
£1103 $1843 €1600 Countess B Ruspoli (25x18cm-10x7in) pencil. 13-Nov-3 Galleria Pace, Milan #1/R est:2400
£1103 $1843 €1600 Face of woman (25x18cm-10x7in) s. pencil. 13-Nov-3 Galleria Pace, Milan #3/R est:1900-2400
£3067 $5643 €4600 Hostess (59x44cm-23x17in) s.i.d.1891 mixed media exhib.lit. 10-Jun-4 Christie's, Rome #58/R est:2500-3500
£4930 $8528 €7000 Woman with white shawl (70x99cm-28x39in) s.d.1921 mixed media card. 10-Dec-3 Finarte Semenzato, Rome #196/R est:7000-8000

GEMITO, Vincenzo (attrib) (1852-1929) Italian
Sculpture
£1064 $1723 €1500 Little angler (42cm-17in) bronze. 22-May-3 Finarte Semenzato, Rome #13 est:1200

GEMM, Walter (1898-?) German
£556 $878 €800 Country landscape with hills in distance (60x80cm-24x31in) s.d.56 i.verso. 5-Sep-3 Wendl, Rudolstadt #3368/R

GEMPT, Bernard de (attrib) (1826-1879) Dutch
£1268 $2193 €1800 Three hunting dogs with dead birds (76x63cm-30x25in) s. 11-Dec-3 Dr Fritz Nagel, Stuttgart #517/R est:2400

GEN-PAUL (1895-1975) French
£216 $400 €315 Head of a clown (55x33cm-22x13in) s.i. verso. 13-Jul-4 Christie's, Rockefeller NY #188/R
£757 $1400 €1105 Bouquet of flowers (40x26cm-16x10in) s. masonite. 12-Feb-4 Sotheby's, New York #59/R est:2000-3000
£1060 $1928 €1600 Bouquet de fleurs (41x27cm-16x11in) s. isorel. 18-Jun-4 Piasa, Paris #144 est:1300-1500
£1189 $1985 €1700 Vase d'anemones (55x33cm-22x13in) s. masonite. 25-Jun-3 Blanchet, Paris #71/R
£1399 $2406 €2000 Marseille, le Chateau d'If (50x65cm-20x26in) s.i. ink crayolor gouache paper on canvas. 3-Dec-3 Tajan, Paris #385/R est:3000-4000
£1418 $2369 €2000 Portrait d'homme (46x27cm-18x11in) s. 20-Jun-3 Drouot Estimations, Paris #43 est:2800-3000
£1500 $2400 €2190 Tanarif sur mer (46x65cm-18x26in) s.i. oil gouache ink chl card. 18-Sep-3 Swann Galleries, New York #482/R est:1800-2200
£1748 $2920 €2500 Cavalier a l'habit brun (41x27cm-16x11in) s. masonite. 25-Jun-3 Blanchet, Paris #74/R
£1879 $3364 €2800 Vase de fleurs (41x27cm-16x11in) s. panel. 30-May-4 Eric Pillon, Calais #209/R
£1892 $3576 €2800 Bouquet de fleurs (54x33cm-21x13in) s. panel. 21-Feb-4 Cornette de St.Cyr, Paris #204/R est:3000-4000
£1986 $3316 €2800 Portrait de Primo (55x33cm-22x13in) s.d.1960 s.d.verso panel. 15-Oct-3 Neret-Minet, Paris #24
£2028 $3387 €2900 Cavalier a l'habit rouge (55x33cm-22x13in) s. masonite. 25-Jun-3 Blanchet, Paris #73/R
£2238 $3849 €3200 Le moulin de la galette (65x81cm-26x32in) s. painted c.1950. 2-Dec-3 Calmels Cohen, Paris #41/R est:10000-12000
£2518 $4330 €3600 Le violoncelliste (41x27cm-16x11in) s. isorel. 3-Dec-3 Tajan, Paris #384/R est:3000-4000
£2603 $4425 €3800 Trois cavaliers (50x65cm-20x26in) s. panel. 9-Nov-3 Eric Pillon, Calais #189/R
£2817 $4535 €4000 Clown (33x24cm-13x9in) s. panel lit. 11-May-3 Versailles Encheres #117/R
£3179 $5817 €4800 Seine au Louvre (50x61cm-20x24in) s. 7-Apr-4 Piasa, Paris #84/R est:5000-6000
£3404 $5685 €4800 Portrait d'homme (65x54cm-26x21in) s. painted c.1926. 20-Jun-3 Drouot Estimations, Paris #44 est:4800-5000
£3557 $6581 €5300 Violoncelliste (41x27cm-16x11in) s. panel. 14-Mar-4 Eric Pillon, Calais #196/R
£3691 $6533 €5500 Cavaliers (50x65cm-20x26in) s. 27-Apr-4 Artcurial Briest, Paris #229/R est:5000-7000
£4225 $6803 €6000 Clown (55x33cm-22x13in) s. s.i.d.1944 verso panel. 22-Aug-3 Deauville, France #109/R est:6000-8000
£5000 $9100 €7500 Paris, la Seine (50x61cm-20x24in) s.d.1921. 4-Jul-4 Eric Pillon, Calais #116/R
£6711 $12013 €10000 Clown blanc (92x61cm-36x24in) s. 30-May-4 Eric Pillon, Calais #196/R
£7042 $12324 €10000 Le violoniste (92x60cm-36x24in) s. 16-Dec-3 Claude Aguttes, Neuilly #14/R est:12000-15000
£8392 $14014 €12000 Le violoniste (92x59cm-36x23in) s. painted c.1928 lit. 30-Jun-3 Artcurial Briest, Paris #740/R est:10000-15000
£8392 $14014 €12000 Portrait du peintre Creixams (92x64cm-36x25in) s.i.d.1929 i.d.22 mars 1929 verso lit. 30-Jun-3 Artcurial Briest, Paris #747/R est:12000-15000
£11888 $19853 €17000 Les cyclistes devant l'eglise (50x60cm-20x24in) s. painted c.1924-25 lit. 30-Jun-3 Artcurial Briest, Paris #746/R est:16000-22000
£14000 $25620 €21000 Dinard (73x92cm-29x36in) s. painted c.1924 prov. 6-Jun-4 Anaf, Lyon #465/R est:23000-25000
£16784 $28029 €24000 La cafetiere jaune ou l'heure douce (65x81cm-26x32in) s. prov.lit. 30-Jun-3 Artcurial Briest, Paris #738/R est:20000-22000
£18543 $33934 €28000 Terrasse de Cafe (65x81cm-26x32in) s. i.verso. 7-Apr-4 Piasa, Paris #88/R est:22000-25000
£20980 $35036 €30000 Clowns musiciens (62x65cm-24x26in) s. painted c.1926. 30-Jun-3 Artcurial Briest, Paris #739/R est:30000-35000
Works on paper
£245 $421 €350 Joueurs de polo (41x65cm-16x26in) s. ink. 3-Dec-3 Tajan, Paris #114
£268 $499 €400 Portrait de femme (47x30cm-19x12in) s. ink wash. 2-Mar-4 Artcurial Briest, Paris #90
£268 $497 €400 Portrait d'homme (27x21cm-11x8in) s.d.1940 sepia ink dr. 14-Mar-4 Eric Pillon, Calais #242/R
£302 $540 €441 Crucifix (47x34cm-19x13in) s. Indian ink. 13-May-4 Stuker, Bern #148 (S.FR 700)
£331 $606 €500 Molard a Geneve (25x29cm-10x11in) s.i.d.53 col crayons. 7-Apr-4 Piasa, Paris #89
£397 $723 €600 Etude preparatoire pour mort a credit de Celine (24x14cm-9x6in) s. ink wash. 18-Jun-4 Piasa, Paris #145
£433 $780 €650 Notre-Dame (49x69cm-19x27in) ink. 24-Apr-4 Cornette de St.Cyr, Paris #364
£461 $770 €650 D'apres Goya (21x27cm-8x11in) s.i. Indian ink W/C. 19-Oct-3 Charbonneaux, Paris #107/R
£486 $812 €700 Portrait de Mr Chatte (26x20cm-10x8in) mono.i.d.14 ballpoint pen htd col crayon. 23-Oct-3 Credit Municipal, Paris #53
£517 $926 €755 Three horses with riders (29x38cm-11x15in) s. 13-May-4 Stuker, Bern #147/R (S.FR 1200)
£526 $968 €800 Caleche (27x39cm-11x15in) s.i. wax crayon. 24-Jun-4 Credit Municipal, Paris #43
£533 $960 €800 Accordeoniste (30x21cm-12x8in) s. pastel. 24-Apr-4 Cornette de St.Cyr, Paris #363
£534 $960 €800 Femme assise (60x40cm-24x16in) s. crayon. 26-Apr-4 Tajan, Paris #68
£534 $960 €800 Bouquet de fleurs (40x25cm-16x10in) s. pastel. 26-Apr-4 Tajan, Paris #69
£552 $993 €800 Clown du cirque Medrano (39x30cm-15x12in) s. wax crayon exec c.1926. 25-Jan-4 Chayette & Cheval, Paris #269
£556 $906 €800 Portrait d'Attilio (27x21cm-11x8in) i. ink dr. 29-Sep-3 Charbonneaux, Paris #222
£556 $1000 €812 Flutist (28x20cm-11x8in) pastel. 24-Apr-4 Du Mouchelle, Detroit #3116/R est:1000-2000
£556 $1000 €812 Violinists (30x20cm-12x8in) pastel. 24-Apr-4 Du Mouchelle, Detroit #3117/R est:1000-2000
£567 $948 €800 Avant la course (20x26cm-8x10in) s. gouache. 12-Oct-3 St-Germain-en-Laye Encheres #189/R
£573 $974 €837 Busy boulevard in Paris (26x33cm-10x13in) s. mixed media. 5-Nov-3 Dobiaschofsky, Bern #594/R (S.FR 1300)
£600 $1074 €900 Courses (50x65cm-20x26in) s. W/C exec.c.1970. 17-May-4 Chayette & Cheval, Paris #200

£600 $1104 €900 Le contrebassiste (28x20cm-11x8in) s. crayolor prov. 14-Jun-4 Tajan, Paris #145/R
£604 $1124 €900 Montmartre (27x38cm-11x15in) s. chl pastel. 3-Mar-4 Tajan, Paris #103/R
£616 $1048 €900 Cavaliers (21x29cm-8x11in) col crayon dr. 9-Nov-3 Eric Pillon, Calais #191/R
£685 $1075 €1000 Saxophoniste (56x41cm-22x16in) s. ink pastel. 20-Apr-3 Deauville, France #35
£734 $1320 €1100 Le clown accordeoniste (41x28cm-16x11in) s. chl pastel. 26-Apr-4 Tajan, Paris #67 est:1200-1500
£764 $1245 €1100 Clown musicien (41x26cm-16x10in) s. crayolor. 29-Sep-3 Charbonneaux, Paris #223
£764 $1276 €1100 Bain de soleil (26x27cm-10x11in) s.i.d.56 graphite col crayon ink. 23-Oct-3 Credit Municipal, Paris #54
£780 $1420 €1139 Horses and figures (48x64cm-19x25in) s. gouache. 15-Jun-4 Bonhams, Knightsbridge #18/R
£822 $1397 €1200 Caleche (21x29cm-8x11in) s. col crayon dr. 9-Nov-3 Eric Pillon, Calais #190/R
£839 $1443 €1200 Le petit port (32x42cm-13x17in) s. W/C Indian ink. 3-Dec-3 Tajan, Paris #104
£909 $1563 €1300 Aux courses (36x46cm-14x18in) s. W/C ink. 3-Dec-3 Tajan, Paris #106 est:600-800
£909 $1563 €1300 Django reinhardt (48x44cm-19x17in) s.i. pastel. 3-Dec-3 Tajan, Paris #108 est:600-800
£909 $1545 €1300 La Tour Eiffel (48x63cm-19x25in) s. gouache. 28-Nov-3 Blanchet, Paris #119/R est:2500-3000
£919 $1700 €1342 La porte St Denis (47x62cm-19x24in) i. gouache. 18-Jul-4 Bonhams & Butterfields, Los Angeles #7061/R est:1000-1500
£940 $1757 €1400 Jardins bosquets (50x65cm-20x26in) s.i. gouache prov. 29-Feb-4 Versailles Encheres #138/R est:1200-1500
£979 $1684 €1400 Aux courses (41x54cm-16x21in) s. pastel. 3-Dec-3 Tajan, Paris #112 est:500-700
£979 $1684 €1400 Serenade des clowns (65x50cm-26x20in) s. W/C. 3-Dec-3 Tajan, Paris #117 est:600-800
£1026 $1868 €1550 Les Sulkys (49x62cm-19x24in) s. gouache. 15-Jun-4 Blanchet, Paris #203/R est:1200-1500
£1047 $1800 €1529 Horse drawn carriage by the sea (50x65cm-20x26in) s.i. i.verso gouache. 3-Dec-3 Doyle, New York #141/R est:3000-5000
£1119 $1924 €1600 Montmartre (28x39cm-11x15in) s. pastel. 3-Dec-3 Tajan, Paris #105 est:300-500
£1119 $1924 €1600 Django reinhardt (43x41cm-17x16in) s.i.d.1950 pastel. 3-Dec-3 Tajan, Paris #107 est:600-800
£1141 $2123 €1700 Collioure (30x38cm-12x15in) s. pastel. 3-Mar-4 Tajan, Paris #105 est:1200-1500
£1189 $2045 €1700 Courses de haies (65x50cm-26x20in) s. W/C. 3-Dec-3 Tajan, Paris #118 est:600-800
£1208 $2235 €1800 Port (48x63cm-19x25in) s. W/C gouache Chinese ink. 14-Mar-4 Eric Pillon, Calais #220/R
£1216 $2250 €1775 Horseback riders in Central Park (50x60cm-20x24in) s.i. gouache. 12-Feb-4 Sotheby's, New York #72/R est:1500-2500
£1259 $2165 €1800 Joueurs de polo (65x50cm-26x20in) s. W/C. 3-Dec-3 Tajan, Paris #120 est:600-800
£1259 $2140 €1800 Les courses (49x64cm-19x25in) s. gouache. 27-Nov-3 Millon & Associes, Paris #78/R est:2500-3000
£1268 $2193 €1800 Le champ de courses (49x63cm-19x25in) s. W/C htd gouache. 10-Dec-3 Millon & Associes, Paris #123 est:2000-3000
£1399 $2406 €2000 Montmartre (49x64cm-19x25in) s. ink gouache. 3-Dec-3 Tajan, Paris #115 est:600-800
£1408 $2437 €2000 Le steamer (49x64cm-19x25in) s. W/C gouache. 9-Dec-3 Chambelland & Giafferi, Paris #55/R est:2000-2500
£1477 $2732 €2200 Passage de la haie (35x45cm-14x18in) s. gouache wax crayon. 14-Mar-4 Eric Pillon, Calais #223/R
£1538 $2646 €2200 Le clown saxo et le clown accordeoniste (46x31cm-18x12in) s. gouache pair. 3-Dec-3 Tajan, Paris #103 est:1000-1200
£1538 $2646 €2200 Saint Jean de Luz (41x55cm-16x22in) s. pastel. 3-Dec-3 Tajan, Paris #109 est:500-700
£1538 $2646 €2200 Saint Jean de Luz (41x55cm-16x22in) s.i. pastel. 3-Dec-3 Tajan, Paris #110 est:500-700
£1538 $2646 €2200 Marie Pierre (64x50cm-25x20in) s.i.d.1968 pastel. 3-Dec-3 Tajan, Paris #116 est:500-700
£1538 $2646 €2200 Aux courses (65x50cm-26x20in) s. W/C. 3-Dec-3 Tajan, Paris #119 est:600-800
£1600 $2880 €2400 La Seine et Notre-Dame (48x63cm-19x25in) s. W/C ink. 26-Apr-4 Tajan, Paris #70/R est:2000-2500
£1620 $2802 €2300 Tierce gagnant (47x62cm-19x24in) s. W/C gouache. 14-Dec-3 Eric Pillon, Calais #280/R
£1655 $2714 €2300 Les cavaliers. gouache. 6-Jun-3 Chochon-Barre & Allardi, Paris #53a
£1678 $2887 €2400 Montmartre (41x55cm-16x22in) s. pastel. 3-Dec-3 Tajan, Paris #111 est:500-700
£1678 $3104 €2500 Musicien (45x32cm-18x13in) s. W/C gouache. 14-Mar-4 Eric Pillon, Calais #225/R
£1712 $2911 €2500 Deux enfants (55x44cm-22x17in) s.d.1935 W/C. 9-Nov-3 Eric Pillon, Calais #187/R
£1733 $3189 €2600 Les cavaliers (49x65cm-19x26in) s. gouache prov. 14-Jun-4 Tajan, Paris #144/R est:600-800
£1734 $3120 €2600 Joueurs de polo (48x60cm-19x24in) s. W/C ink gouache. 26-Apr-4 Tajan, Paris #66/R est:2000-2500
£1745 $3088 €2600 Trois chevaux a l'obstacle (49x64cm-19x25in) s. gouache. 27-Apr-4 Artcurial Briest, Paris #231/R est:2000-2500
£1818 $3036 €2600 Pont-Neuf, Paris (48x63cm-19x25in) gouache. 12-Oct-3 Teitgen, Nancy #59
£1854 $3393 €2800 Rue Norvins a Montmartre (35x28cm-14x11in) s. W/C. 7-Apr-4 Piasa, Paris #86/R est:1600-2000
£1879 $3477 €2800 Cyclistes (48x63cm-19x25in) s. gouache W/C. 14-Mar-4 Eric Pillon, Calais #221/R
£1944 $3169 €2800 Le train en gare (48x63cm-19x25in) s. gouache. 21-Jul-3 Lesieur & Le Bars, Le Havre #27
£2013 $3705 €3000 Clowns musiciens (63x48cm-25x19in) s. gouache. 29-Mar-4 Rieunier, Paris #58/R est:1800-2000
£2083 $3479 €3000 Corrida (48x73cm-19x29in) s.i.d.70 gouache. 21-Oct-3 Artcurial Briest, Paris #65/R est:2600-3000
£2113 $3655 €3000 Musiciens (62x48cm-24x19in) s. gouache. 13-Dec-3 Martinot & Savignat, Pontoise #248/R
£2483 $4594 €3700 Django Reinhardt (45x43cm-18x17in) s.i.d.1950 pastel. 14-Mar-4 St-Germain-en-Laye Encheres #167/R est:2500
£2584 $4806 €3850 La course de chevaux (48x62cm-19x24in) s. gouache. 7-Mar-4 Lesieur & Le Bars, Le Havre #61
£2684 $4993 €4000 Trio de musiciens (49x64cm-19x25in) s. gouache. 2-Mar-4 Artcurial Briest, Paris #89/R est:1800-2000
£2819 $5243 €4200 Terrasse a Montmartre (48x36cm-19x14in) s. gouache. 3-Mar-4 Tajan, Paris #104 est:2500-3000
£3020 $5587 €4500 Musiciens (65x49cm-26x19in) s.d.1929 mixed media paper on canvas. 14-Mar-4 Eric Pillon, Calais #200/R
£3194 $5207 €4600 Notre Dame, Paris (60x48cm-24x19in) s. gouache. 18-Jul-3 Feletin, Province #96
£3521 $5669 €5000 Chateau d'If (50x65cm-20x26in) s.i.d.1926 gouache panel. 22-Aug-3 Deauville, France #19/R est:6000-8000
£4225 $6803 €6000 Paddock (48x62cm-19x24in) s.i. W/C. 22-Aug-3 Deauville, France #16 est:5000-7000
£5479 $8603 €8000 Promenade en caleche (50x60cm-20x24in) s.i. gouache. 20-Apr-3 Deauville, France #33/R est:6000-7000
£8099 $13039 €11500 Partie de cartes (48x62cm-19x24in) s. W/C. 22-Aug-3 Deauville, France #17/R est:6000-8000

GENAILLE, Felix François Barthelemy (1826-1885) French
Works on paper
£360 $576 €500 Portrait, thought to be Ernestine Huber (42x28cm-17x11in) s.d. W/C pastel. 16-May-3 Tajan, Paris #123

GENBERG, Anton (1862-1939) Swedish
£370 $661 €540 Farm by waterway (51x74cm-20x29in) s.i.d.1933. 28-May-4 Uppsala Auktionskammare, Uppsala #335 (S.KR 5000)
£631 $1135 €921 Winter landscape (43x43cm-17x17in) s.d.1918 canvas on panel. 26-Jan-4 Lilla Bukowskis, Stockholm #490 (S.KR 8400)
£665 $1191 €971 Landscape from Palhajaner (70x100cm-28x39in) s. 26-May-4 AB Stockholms Auktionsverk #2280/R (S.KR 9000)
£692 $1274 €1038 View of Venice (54x36cm-21x14in) s.i.d.94. 14-Jun-4 Lilla Bukowskis, Stockholm #373 (S.KR 9500)
£734 $1182 €1072 Winter landscape (55x75cm-22x30in) s. 25-Aug-3 Lilla Bukowskis, Stockholm #702 (S.KR 9600)
£769 $1323 €1123 Summer landscape with trees and waterway (57x72cm-22x28in) s. 3-Dec-3 AB Stockholms Auktionsverk #2534/R (S.KR 10000)
£879 $1416 €1283 Landscape from Aare (50x63cm-20x25in) s.i.d.86. 25-Aug-3 Lilla Bukowskis, Stockholm #440 (S.KR 11500)
£899 $1465 €1313 Winter idyll (60x80cm-24x31in) s.d.92. 29-Sep-3 Lilla Bukowskis, Stockholm #334 (S.KR 11700)
£903 $1563 €1318 The surface of the water (65x90cm-26x35in) s. 15-Dec-3 Lilla Bukowskis, Stockholm #403 (S.KR 11500)
£923 $1588 €1348 Cliffs in sunshine, Haro (111x151cm-44x59in) s. 3-Dec-3 AB Stockholms Auktionsverk #2247/R (S.KR 12000)
£1057 $1945 €1586 View from Aareskutan towards Duved (55x75cm-22x30in) s.d.98. 14-Jun-4 Lilla Bukowskis, Stockholm #448 (S.KR 14500)
£1154 $1985 €1685 Mountain landscape with buildings, summer in Aare (49x63cm-19x25in) s.i.d.86. 3-Dec-3 AB Stockholms Auktionsverk #2373/R est:15000-20000 (S.KR 15000)
£2000 $3440 €2920 Girl in green summer landscape, Avesta (73x100cm-29x39in) s.i.d.1911. 3-Dec-3 AB Stockholms Auktionsverk #2410/R est:35000-40000 (S.KR 26000)
£2077 $3572 €3032 Winter landscape, Aare (75x100cm-30x39in) s.i.d.1915. 2-Dec-3 Bukowskis, Stockholm #110/R est:15000-18000 (S.KR 27000)
£2151 $3505 €3140 Aare barge (70x90cm-28x35in) s. 29-Sep-3 Lilla Bukowskis, Stockholm #509 est:15000-20000 (S.KR 28000)
£3846 $6615 €5615 Winter sun, Aareskutan (73x103cm-29x41in) s.d.1932. 2-Dec-3 Bukowskis, Stockholm #179b/R est:25000-30000 (S.KR 50000)

GENDALL, John (1790-1865) British
Works on paper
£800 $1376 €1168 Louvre from the Hotel de la Monnaie (24x36cm-9x14in) pencil W/C. 3-Dec-3 Christie's, Kensington #91/R

GENDALL, John (attrib) (1790-1865) British
Works on paper
£451 $736 €650 Deutsche Eck near Koblenz (16x23cm-6x9in) W/C gouache over pencil. 26-Sep-3 Venator & Hansten, Koln #838

GENDRON, Ernest August (1817-1881) French
£1348 $2507 €1968 The last journey - girl being taken to her last resting place in a gondola (84x147cm-33x58in) s. 2-Mar-4 Rasmussen, Copenhagen #1440/R est:30000-50000 (D.KR 15000)

GENDRON, Pierre (1934-) Canadian
£605 $1113 €883 Study in light (73x61cm-29x24in) s.d.September 59 s.i.d.verso. 9-Jun-4 Walker's, Ottawa #173/R est:600-900 (C.D 1500)
£2600 $4758 €3796 Turangalila (150x100cm-59x39in) s.d.1992 acrylic. 1-Jun-4 Joyner Waddington, Toronto #190/R est:5000-7000 (C.D 6500)

GENEAU, Alain (1935-) French
£382 $650 €558 Le choix (38x46cm-15x18in) s. 5-Nov-3 Doyle, New York #29/R
£412 $700 €602 Belle a la poire (38x46cm-15x18in) s. 5-Nov-3 Doyle, New York #30/R
£491 $800 €717 Les fleurs de la Salzach (46x56cm-18x22in) s.i. on stretcher. 24-Sep-3 Doyle, New York #35

GENEGEN, Jos van (1857-1936) Belgian
£403 $737 €600 Bord de riviere (45x70cm-18x28in) s. 8-Jul-4 Campo, Vlaamse Kaai #269
£423 $731 €600 Hiver apres-midi (35x54cm-14x21in) s. 9-Dec-3 Campo, Vlaamse Kaai #454
£738 $1373 €1100 Landscape with shepherd at sunset. Farmer's wife near water (21x27cm-8x11in) s. pair. 8-Mar-4 Bernaerts, Antwerp #68

GENELLI, Bonaventura (1798-1868) German
Works on paper
£2000 $3580 €3000 Figure study (20x25cm-8x10in) pencil two. 13-May-4 Bassenge, Berlin #5554/R est:1500

GENERAL IDEA (20th C) Canadian
£382 $710 €558 Untitled (34x25cm-13x10in) s. painted masonite. 2-Mar-4 Ritchie, Toronto #32/R (C.D 950)
Photographs
£2432 $4354 €3600 P as for poodle (75x63cm-30x25in) s.i.d.83 verso col photo prov. 8-May-4 Lempertz, Koln #99/R est:3000
Works on paper
£2252 $3829 €3288 Untitled, yellow man (35x26cm-14x10in) init.d.85 mixed media. 18-Nov-3 Sotheby's, Toronto #133/R est:3000-5000 (C.D 5000)

GENERALIC, Milan (1941-) Yugoslavian
£261 $477 €381 Mother and boy in a park landscape (15x39cm-6x15in) s.d.1982. 4-Jun-4 Zofingen, Switzerland #2460 (S.FR 600)
£267 $491 €400 Spring (45x56cm-18x22in) s.d.1976 behind glass. 9-Jun-4 Dorotheum, Salzburg #765/R

GENESEN, Ana van (?) ?
£329 $605 €500 Voiliers en Mer de Nord (70x60cm-28x24in) s. 22-Jun-4 Palais de Beaux Arts, Brussels #322

GENESEN, Frans van (1887-1945) Dutch
£331 $603 €500 Country lane with two cottages (50x45cm-20x18in) s. 21-Jun-4 Bernaerts, Antwerp #87/R
£480 $754 €696 Fishing vessels in calm waters at dusk (71x90cm-28x35in) s. 28-Aug-3 Christie's, Kensington #210/R
£567 $1014 €850 Forest scene (80x110cm-31x43in) s. 15-May-4 De Vuyst, Lokeren #349

GENET, Paulette (c.1890-?) French
£567 $1031 €850 Scenes de fenaison (50x64cm-20x25in) cardboard double-sided. 29-Jun-4 Chenu & Scrive, Lyon #94

GENGA, Girolamo (1476-1551) Italian
Works on paper
£9500 $17385 €13870 Madonna and Child seated on a throne (26x19cm-10x7in) i. red chk. 6-Jul-4 Christie's, London #2/R est:10000-15000

GENICOT, Robert Albert (1890-1981) French
£671 $1242 €1000 Village d'Agazarai, Maroc (16x24cm-6x9in) s. panel. 15-Mar-4 Gros & Delettrez, Paris #36/R
£1342 $2483 €2000 Jeune femme Marocaine et son enfant (35x21cm-14x8in) s.d.1927 panel. 15-Mar-4 Gros & Delettrez, Paris #224/R est:2000-2500
£1879 $3477 €2800 Femme nue a la tasse de the (92x73cm-36x29in) s. 15-Mar-4 Blanchet, Paris #74 est:2500-3000

GENILLION, Jean Baptiste François (1750-1829) French
£995 $1722 €1453 Paysage fluvial anime (32x45cm-13x18in) panel prov. 12-Dec-3 Galerie du Rhone, Sion #166/R (S.FR 2200)

GENILLION, Jean Baptiste François (attrib) (1750-1829) French
£296 $512 €420 La halte des bergers pres de la riviere (20x26cm-8x10in) bears sig. panel. 10-Dec-3 Remi Ader, Paris #68
£296 $512 €420 La halte des bergers pres de la riviere (20x26cm-8x10in) bears sig. panel. 10-Dec-3 Neret-Minet, Paris #68

GENIN, Lucien (1894-1958) French
£470 $874 €700 Rue de Paris (41x27cm-16x11in) s. 3-Mar-4 Tajan, Paris #100
£780 $1303 €1100 Vase de fleurs (24x16cm-9x6in) s. 15-Oct-3 Rabourdin & Choppin de Janvry, Paris #3
£1476 $2746 €2200 Neige, Moulin de la Galette (22x16cm-9x6in) s. s.i.verso. 3-Mar-4 Tajan, Paris #99/R est:400-500
£2000 $3340 €2920 Paris, le Pont Marie (50x65cm-20x26in) s. prov. 22-Oct-3 Sotheby's, Olympia #115/R est:2000-3000
£2192 $3726 €3200 Paris, Arc de Triomphe (50x61cm-20x24in) s. 9-Nov-3 Eric Pillon, Calais #143/R
£2222 $3711 €3200 Le port de Marseille (32x42cm-13x17in) s.i. 23-Oct-3 Credit Municipal, Paris #96/R est:1800-2200
£2416 $4470 €3600 Paris, quai aux fleurs (33x41cm-13x16in) s. 14-Mar-4 Eric Pillon, Calais #134/R
£3759 $6277 €5300 La place Pigalle (60x73cm-24x29in) s. 20-Jun-3 Drouot Estimations, Paris #167 est:4000-4500
£4564 $8489 €6800 Pecheurs sur les quais de la Seine (60x73cm-24x29in) s. 3-Mar-4 Tajan, Paris #98/R est:3000-4000
Works on paper
£336 $621 €500 Passerelle (13x19cm-5x7in) s. gouache W/C. 14-Mar-4 Eric Pillon, Calais #136/R
£400 $740 €580 Place animee de Montmartre (21x28cm-8x11in) s. gouache. 16-Feb-4 Giraudeau, Tours #21
£420 $722 €600 Rue animee a Paris (40x30cm-16x12in) s. W/C. 3-Dec-3 Tajan, Paris #123
£464 $844 €700 Paris, sur les Grands Boulevards (52x42cm-20x17in) s. W/C gouache. 18-Jun-4 Piasa, Paris #109
£489 $842 €700 Pont sur la Seine a Paris (21x27cm-8x11in) s. gouache pair. 3-Dec-3 Tajan, Paris #124
£503 $921 €750 Paris, Place de l'Opera (46x56cm-18x22in) s. gouache. 7-Jul-4 Artcurial Briest, Paris #160
£528 $914 €750 Moulin a Montmartre (22x28cm-9x11in) s. gouache. 12-Dec-3 Piasa, Paris #143/R
£570 $1055 €850 Paris, Theatre de l'Atelier (21x27cm-8x11in) s. gouache. 14-Mar-4 Eric Pillon, Calais #165/R
£604 $1117 €900 Au Vieux Chene (26x20cm-10x8in) s. gouache W/C chl. 14-Mar-4 Eric Pillon, Calais #164/R
£638 $1180 €950 Paris, la Seine et le Pont-Neuf (16x22cm-6x9in) s. gouache W/C. 14-Mar-4 Eric Pillon, Calais #135/R
£800 $1440 €1200 Rouen, bateaux a quai (38x46cm-15x18in) s.i. gouache. 26-Apr-4 Tajan, Paris #34
£800 $1440 €1200 Rouen, le pont Corneille (38x45cm-15x18in) s.i. gouache. 26-Apr-4 Tajan, Paris #35
£839 $1401 €1200 Place de l'opera (23x31cm-9x12in) s. gouache. 25-Jun-3 Digard, Paris #76/R
£855 $1574 €1300 Moulin Rouge (23x25cm-9x10in) s. W/C. 24-Jun-4 Credit Municipal, Paris #28
£1127 $1949 €1600 Paris, Place du Tertre (23x31cm-9x12in) s. gouache. 14-Dec-3 Eric Pillon, Calais #170/R
£1208 $2235 €1800 Place du Tertre (33x42cm-13x17in) s. gouache paper on canvas. 14-Mar-4 Eric Pillon, Calais #163/R
£1409 $2437 €2000 Attente (35x46cm-14x18in) s. W/C Chinese ink. 9-Dec-3 Artcurial Briest, Paris #264/R est:2000-3000

GENIN, Robert (1884-1939) French
£1250 $2088 €1800 Young woman with coffee cup (110x77cm-43x30in) s. linen. 25-Oct-3 Dr Lehr, Berlin #146/R est:2400
Works on paper
£979 $1664 €1400 Nude seated in summer meadow (50x35cm-20x14in) s.d.1921 pastel. 22-Nov-3 Arnold, Frankfurt #521/R est:300
£979 $1664 €1400 Portrait of Balinese woman with small monkey (52x38cm-20x15in) s. pastel. 22-Nov-3 Arnold, Frankfurt #523/R est:300
£1119 $1902 €1600 Balinese woman (54x35cm-21x14in) s. pastel. 22-Nov-3 Arnold, Frankfurt #522/R est:300

GENIS, René (1922-2004) French
£1000 $1820 €1500 Trois pots (50x61cm-20x24in) s. 4-Jul-4 Eric Pillon, Calais #285/R
£1905 $3410 €2800 Les filets a Patmos (61x61cm-24x24in) s. 20-Mar-4 Binoche, Orleans #37 est:2200-3000

GENISSON, Georges Paul (1835-1896) Belgian
£1711 $3147 €2600 View of town in mountainous landscape (61x49cm-24x19in) s.d.68. 22-Jun-4 Palais de Beaux Arts, Brussels #246/R est:3000-4000

GENISSON, Jules Victor (1805-1860) Belgian
£460 $814 €672 Cathedral interior (29x32cm-11x13in) s.d.1849 panel. 27-Apr-4 Bonhams, Knowle #97

GENN, Robert (1936-) Canadian
£224 $370 €325 Of Beaverpond (25x30cm-10x12in) s. s.i.d.1972 verso canvasboard. 3-Jul-3 Heffel, Vancouver #10/R (C.D 500)
£227 $414 €331 Pattern in blue and grey (28x36cm-11x14in) s. s.i.verso acrylic. 5-Feb-4 Heffel, Vancouver #35/R (C.D 550)
£227 $411 €331 Village above Lillooet, BC (41x30cm-16x12in) s. s.i. hard board prov. 18-Apr-4 Levis, Calgary #456/R (C.D 550)
£236 $402 €345 Murchison West, Queen Charlotte Islands (20x25cm-8x10in) s. s.i.d.1977 verso board prov. 23-Nov-3 Levis, Calgary #462/R (C.D 525)
£268 $455 €391 Green drum (41x51cm-16x20in) s. s.i.d.1971 verso canvasboard prov. 6-Nov-3 Heffel, Vancouver #52/R (C.D 600)
£269 $444 €390 Summer flowers at Campbell river (30x36cm-12x14in) s. s.i.d.August 22 1972 verso canvasboard. 3-Jul-3 Heffel, Vancouver #11/R (C.D 600)
£310 $564 €453 Streamlet at Goldstream, Vancouver Island (28x36cm-11x14in) s. s.i.verso acrylic. 5-Feb-4 Heffel, Vancouver #36/R (C.D 750)
£317 $529 €463 June at Finlayson (40x50cm-16x20in) s.i.d.1972 prov. 17-Nov-3 Hodgins, Calgary #160/R (C.D 700)
£320 $586 €467 Silent arrival (50x61cm-20x24in) s. s.i.d.1970 verso board prov. 3-Jun-4 Heffel, Vancouver #26/R (C.D 800)
£331 $602 €483 Little Joe Lake, October, Algonquin Park, Ontario (28x36cm-11x14in) s. s.i.verso prov. 5-Feb-4 Heffel, Vancouver #34/R (C.D 800)
£372 $677 €543 Wood Pattern, Cowichan River (30x41cm-12x16in) s. s.i.verso acrylic. 5-Feb-4 Heffel, Vancouver #37/R (C.D 900)
£407 $728 €594 High Falls, Whistler (40x50cm-16x20in) s. s.i.verso prov. 6-May-4 Heffel, Vancouver #58/R (C.D 1000)
£413 $748 €603 Sky pattern with four (28x36cm-11x14in) s. s.i.verso. 18-Apr-4 Levis, Calgary #455/R est:700-900 (C.D 1000)
£600 $1098 €876 December pattern with warm (40x50cm-16x20in) s.i. acrylic. 1-Jun-4 Hodgins, Calgary #61/R (C.D 1500)
£760 $1391 €1110 High exaltation (40x50cm-16x20in) s.i. 1-Jun-4 Hodgins, Calgary #257/R (C.D 1900)
£1000 $1830 €1460 Gulf Offskip (61x76cm-24x30in) s. s.i.verso acrylic. 3-Jun-4 Heffel, Vancouver #25/R est:2500-3500 (C.D 2500)
£1200 $2196 €1752 Caribou Lake (61x76cm-24x30in) s. s.i.verso acrylic. 3-Jun-4 Heffel, Vancouver #24/R est:2500-3500 (C.D 3000)
£1280 $2342 €1869 In an Abbey Garden, Brittany (75x85cm-30x33in) s. 1-Jun-4 Joyner Waddington, Toronto #281/R est:2000-2500 (C.D 3200)
Works on paper
£633 $995 €918 Flight of ibis. Pelicans (61x76cm-24x30in) s. s.i.d.1973 verso two. 30-Aug-3 Heffel, Vancouver #11 est:1500-2000 (C.D 1400)

GENNAI, Guido (1895-?) Italian
Works on paper
£290 $475 €400 Arch in San Gimignano (51x38cm-20x15in) s. W/C. 27-May-3 Finarte Semenzato, Milan #152/R

GENNARELLI, Amedeo (20th C) Italian
Sculpture
£1734 $3000 €2532 Nymph with two dogs (33x79cm-13x31in) s. green gold pat bronze. 13-Dec-3 Sloans & Kenyon, Bethesda #769/R est:3000-5000

GENNARI, Bartolomeo (1594-1661) Italian
£5755 $9439 €8000 Saint Catherine (247x173cm-97x68in) s.d.1631. 4-Jun-3 Sotheby's, Milan #23/R est:8000-12000

GENNARI, Bartolomeo (attrib) (1594-1661) Italian
£40000 $69200 €58400 Flora (144x98cm-57x39in) prov. 10-Dec-3 Christie's, London #103/R est:15000-20000

GENNARI, Benedetto (16/17th C) Italian
Works on paper
£437 $800 €638 Kneeling female Saint in prayer (29x21cm-11x8in) red chk card stock. 29-Jan-4 Swann Galleries, New York #77/R

GENNARI, Benedetto (younger) (1633-1715) Italian
£77778 $140000 €113556 Cleopatra (124x105cm-49x41in) prov. 22-Jan-4 Sotheby's, New York #50/R est:80000-120000

GENNARI, Cesare (attrib) (1637-1688) Italian
£4200 $7560 €6132 Penitent Magdalen (119x99cm-47x39in) prov. 21-Apr-4 Bonhams, New Bond Street #59/R est:2000-3000
£6376 $11732 €9500 Venus et l'Amour (118x151cm-46x59in) 26-Mar-4 Pierre Berge, Paris #20/R est:10000-12000

GENNARI, Cesare (circle) (1637-1688) Italian
£4261 $7500 €6221 Holy Family (65x84cm-26x33in) prov. 18-May-4 Bonhams & Butterfields, San Francisco #7/R est:3000-5000

GENNAY, A (?) ?
Sculpture
£1189 $2045 €1700 Jeune femme avec coquille et poissons (37cm-15in) alabaster. 3-Dec-3 Palais de Beaux Arts, Brussels #866 est:1750-2500

GENOD, Michel Philebert (1795-1862) French
£5282 $9137 €7500 Le serment du jeune combattant (32x40cm-13x16in) s. lit. 10-Dec-3 Ferri, Paris #47/R est:2000-3000

GENOD, Michel Philebert (attrib) (1795-1862) French
£851 $1421 €1200 Scene d'interieur avec une fenetre ouverte (44x34cm-17x13in) 17-Oct-3 Tajan, Paris #113

GENOELS, Abraham (1640-1723) Flemish
Works on paper
£303 $548 €460 Paysage (22x16cm-9x6in) dr. 19-Apr-4 Horta, Bruxelles #499/R

GENOESE SCHOOL (17th C) Italian
£7746 $12472 €11000 Nettuno affiancato da Tritoni e Nereidi (46x133cm-18x52in) 8-May-3 Farsetti, Prato #502/R est:14000-16000
£10333 $19013 €15500 Retour de Bacchus (120x205cm-47x81in) 8-Jun-4 Livinec, Gaudcheau & Jezequel, Rennes #168/R
£10667 $19093 €16000 Allegory of Spring. Allegory of Autumn (83x121cm-33x48in) pair exhib.lit. 17-May-4 Finarte Semenzato, Rome #93/R est:20000-22000

GENOESE SCHOOL (18th C) Italian
Sculpture
£40000 $72800 €60000 Allegory of Africa. Allegory of Asia (166x66cm-65x26in) white marble pair lit. 29-Jun-4 Sotheby's, Paris #83/R est:70000-100000

GENOUD, Nanette (1907-1987) Swiss
£308 $524 €450 Southern harbour city (28x40cm-11x16in) s. mixed media. 5-Nov-3 Dobiaschofsky, Bern #597/R (S.FR 700)
£611 $1113 €892 Landscape near Carona (54x73cm-21x29in) s.d. 17-Jun-4 Kornfeld, Bern #374 (S.FR 1400)

GENOVES LLANSOL, Jose (c.1850-?) Spanish
£1348 $2183 €1900 Bodegon de caza. Bodegon con perdices (60x41cm-24x16in) s. pair. 20-May-3 Segre, Madrid #41/R est:1100

GENOVES, Juan (1930-) Spanish
£3514 $6500 €5130 Testimonio Grafico - Photographic Evidence (150x200cm-59x79in) s.i.d.1973 verso acrylic prov. 13-Jul-4 Christie's, Rockefeller NY #76/R est:8000-12000
£3691 $6903 €5500 Two figures (100x81cm-39x32in) s.d.59 oil sand prov. 24-Feb-4 Durán, Madrid #231/R est:3000
£4167 $6792 €6000 Two figures (100x81cm-39x32in) s.d.59 oil sand prov. 23-Sep-3 Durán, Madrid #220/R est:5000
£4167 $7083 €6000 Maternity (99x85cm-39x33in) s.d.1961. 28-Oct-3 Segre, Madrid #152/R est:7000
£5369 $10040 €8000 Figures (150x210cm-59x83in) s.d.71 verso. 24-Feb-4 Durán, Madrid #238/R est:7000
£10563 $18275 €15000 Untitled (150x210cm-59x83in) s.d.71 verso. 15-Dec-3 Ansorena, Madrid #977/R est:15000
Works on paper
£2326 $4000 €3396 Maternidad (91x79cm-36x31in) s.d.60 mixed media prov.exhib. 7-Dec-3 Freeman, Philadelphia #70 est:2000-3000

GENT, Arjan van (1970-) Dutch
£937 $1481 €1350 Passage (65x65cm-26x26in) s.d.1999 canvas on panel. 26-Apr-3 Auction Maastricht #47/R
Works on paper
£315 $541 €450 After you've gone (22x19cm-9x7in) s.d.2001 W/C. 8-Dec-3 Glerum, Amsterdam #432/R
£420 $722 €600 Alone together (21x21cm-8x8in) s.d.2001 W/C lit. 8-Dec-3 Glerum, Amsterdam #423/R

GENTA, Albert (1901-1989) French
£225 $375 €329 Figures on the lakeside (65x81cm-26x32in) s.d.1970. 19-Oct-3 Bonhams & Butterfields, Los Angeles #7043
£382 $638 €550 Nu de dos (55x73cm-22x29in) s. 21-Oct-3 Galerie Moderne, Brussels #325/R

GENTENAAR, Pat (1949-) Dutch?
Works on paper
£278 $439 €400 Solitary Koi (112x78cm-44x31in) s. pigments paper pulp. 26-Apr-3 Auction Maastricht #48/R

GENTH, Lillian (1876-1953) American
£346 $550 €505 Spanish woman wearing yellow flounced dress and red shawl (41x30cm-16x12in) s.verso canvasboard. 10-Sep-3 Alderfer's, Hatfield #365
£543 $1000 €793 Impressionist representation of water flowing under arch from rock formation (41x51cm-16x20in) s. canvasboard. 9-Jun-4 Alderfer's, Hatfield #403 est:1000-1500
£898 $1500 €1311 Prayers in the great mosque of Sidi Okba (74x61cm-29x24in) s. i.d.1902 stretcher. 18-Jun-3 Doyle, New York #30/R est:1500-2000
£1572 $2500 €2295 Paupuan Wedding (74x89cm-29x35in) s. 10-Sep-3 Alderfer's, Hatfield #364 est:2000-3000
£8696 $16000 €12696 Whisperings of June (99x76cm-39x30in) s. prov. 8-Jun-4 Bonhams & Butterfields, San Francisco #4059/R est:10000-15000

GENTILESCHI, Orazio (circle) (1562-1647) Italian
£5319 $8883 €7500 Riposo durante la fuga in Egitto (115x170cm-45x67in) 17-Jun-3 Finarte Semenzato, Milan #659/R est:8000-12000

GENTILINI, Franco (1909-1981) Italian
£7292 $12396 €10500 Little mermaid (35x25cm-14x10in) s. prov.lit. 28-Oct-3 Il Ponte, Milan #250/R
£10738 $19973 €16000 Portrait of young woman (37x25cm-15x10in) s.d.1973 oil card on canvas. 4-Mar-4 Babuino, Rome #118 est:6000-8000
£15862 $26490 €23000 Saint Basil's (36x26cm-14x10in) s.d.68 oil sand canvas on cardboard lit. 13-Nov-3 Finarte Semenzato, Rome #398/R est:20000-24000
£17241 $28793 €25000 Table with objects (100x70cm-39x28in) s.d.1957 verso oil collage exhib.lit. 14-Nov-3 Farsetti, Prato #291/R est:6500-8500
£18500 $30895 €27010 Stazione Roma Nord (79x57cm-31x22in) s.d.48 exhib. 22-Oct-3 Bonhams, New Bond Street #32/R est:10000-15000
£36364 $61818 €52000 Banquet (101x149cm-40x59in) s. oil sand prov.exhib.lit. 24-Nov-3 Christie's, Milan #245/R est:60000-80000
£44966 $83638 €67000 Composition with figures (135x103cm-53x41in) painted 1935 lit. 4-Mar-4 Babuino, Rome #418 est:10000-15000
£45775 $75986 €65000 Ricordo di Amalfi (65x50cm-26x20in) s.d.1954 sanded canvas exhib.lit. 14-Jun-3 Meeting Art, Vercelli #250/R
Works on paper
£448 $749 €650 Capri (23x31cm-9x12in) s.d.62 pencil dr. 14-Nov-3 Farsetti, Prato #300/R
£470 $874 €700 Two figures (20x29cm-8x11in) s. ink. 4-Mar-4 Babuino, Rome #16
£570 $1061 €850 View from the terrace (22x31cm-9x12in) s.d.1963 chl card. 4-Mar-4 Babuino, Rome #81
£738 $1366 €1100 Figure (30x22cm-12x9in) s. Chinese ink. 11-Mar-4 Galleria Pace, Milan #6/R
£966 $1545 €1400 Female nude (29x39cm-11x15in) s. pen drawing exec 1970. 13-Mar-3 Galleria Pace, Milan #121/R est:1700-2200
£1103 $1843 €1600 Cat and fish (43x36cm-17x14in) s.d.1957 pastel card. 13-Nov-3 Finarte Semenzato, Rome #167/R est:1500-1800
£1517 $2534 €2200 Houses in New York (34x24cm-13x9in) s. pencil paper on canvas. 13-Nov-3 Finarte Semenzato, Rome #152/R est:1400-1600
£2098 $3566 €3000 Cathedral (41x29cm-16x11in) s.d.74 Chinese ink tempera prov. 25-Nov-3 Sotheby's, Milan #79/R est:1500-2000
£2200 $3960 €3300 Banquet (33x43cm-13x17in) s. mixed media exec.1963 exhib. 22-Apr-4 Finarte Semenzato, Rome #356/R est:3500-4000
£2413 $4101 €3450 Lonely woman (23x33cm-9x13in) s. sanguine paper on canvas prov. 18-Nov-3 Babuino, Rome #414/R est:1600-1800
£4895 $8322 €7000 Woman (38x27cm-15x11in) s.d.79 sanguine W/C tempera. 26-Nov-3 Pandolfini, Florence #92/R est:8000-9000
£5245 $8916 €7500 Roses (32x28cm-13x11in) s. mixed media sand on canvas prov. 25-Nov-3 Sotheby's, Milan #39/R est:7000-9000
£8784 $15459 €13000 Four apples (40x35cm-16x14in) s.d.1970 fresco on canvas. 22-May-4 Galleria Pananti, Florence #521/R est:12000-14000

GENTILS, Vic (1919-1997) Belgian
Sculpture
£1733 $3172 €2600 Assemblage (52cm-20in) s.d.1962 wood ivory bronze pieces of piano. 7-Jun-4 Palais de Beaux Arts, Brussels #177/R est:2000-3000
£1867 $3416 €2800 Paysage 7 (50x36cm-20x14in) s.d.1970 wood. 7-Jun-4 Palais de Beaux Arts, Brussels #178/R est:2000-3000
£2133 $3904 €3200 Composition (115x40cm-45x16in) s.d.60 verso wood paint. 7-Jun-4 Palais de Beaux Arts, Brussels #363/R est:2000-3000
£2667 $4773 €4000 Untitled (142x45cm-56x18in) s.verso burnt wood piano keys on burnt piano panel exhib.lit. 15-May-4 De Vuyst, Lokeren #588/R est:4000-5000
£3451 $5970 €4900 Yvonne (41x32cm-16x13in) s. wood polycrome exhib.lit. 13-Dec-3 De Vuyst, Lokeren #512/R est:5000-6000
£4333 $7757 €6500 Gold black (103x104cm-41x41in) s.i.d.1963 verso wood exhib.lit. 15-May-4 De Vuyst, Lokeren #490/R est:5500-6500
£4333 $7757 €6500 Ne pas toucher, dangereux (40x76cm-16x30in) s.i.d.1986 wood lit. 15-May-4 De Vuyst, Lokeren #498/R est:6500-7500
£6667 $12200 €10000 Big landscape (115x80x82cm-45x31x32in) s.d.4/70 wood. 7-Jun-4 Palais de Beaux Arts, Brussels #364/R est:10000-15000

GENTINETTA, Anita (1938-) Swiss
Works on paper
£390 $697 €569 Flowers (63x47cm-25x19in) s. W/C. 22-Mar-4 Philippe Schuler, Zurich #4169 (S.FR 900)

GENTLING, Scott (1942-) American
Works on paper
£1048 $1750 €1530 Duck and knapsack (33x23cm-13x9in) gouache. 18-Oct-3 David Dike, Dallas #259/R est:2000-3000

GENTZ, Karl Wilhelm (1822-1890) German
£4054 $7135 €6000 Market scene in north Africa or Arabia (18x26cm-7x10in) mono.d.72 s. verso prov. 22-May-4 Lempertz, Koln #1520/R est:6000

GENUCCHI, Carlo Luigi Giovanni (1904-1979) Belgian
Sculpture
£1630 $2771 €2380 Madonna with child (44cm-17in) s. olive green pat.plaster wooden socle. 5-Nov-3 Dobiaschofsky, Bern #2447/R est:450 (S.FR 3700)

GENUTAT, Fritz (1876-?) German
£336 $561 €480 Heidelberg with castle (63x106cm-25x42in) s.d. 27-Jun-3 Altus, Berlin #645/R

GENZKEN, Isa (1948-) German?
Photographs
£2098 $3566 €3000 Ear (174x117cm-69x46in) s.d.1980 col photo. 27-Nov-3 Lempertz, Koln #141/R est:2000-3000
Sculpture
£14333 $26230 €21500 Small pavillion (143x39x39cm-56x15x15in) cement glaze. 4-Jun-4 Lempertz, Koln #151/R est:14000
Works on paper
£533 $976 €800 Untitled (30x21cm-12x8in) s.d.1987 pencil Indian ink brush spary. 4-Jun-4 Lempertz, Koln #152/R

GEO-FOURRIER, Georges (1898-1966) French
Works on paper
£303 $548 €460 Joueur de biniou (12x12cm-5x5in) studio st. dr. pochoir. 17-Apr-4 Livinec, Gaudcheau & Jezequel, Rennes #104
£397 $743 €600 Porz Carn, St Guenole, la maison du pecheur (27x35cm-11x14in) mono. ink crayon. 24-Jul-4 Thierry & Lannon, Brest #315
£500 $895 €750 Femme d'Ouessant (26x34cm-10x13in) d.33 mixed media. 16-May-4 Thierry & Lannon, Brest #249
£526 $953 €800 Chaumiere bretonne (27x35cm-11x14in) mono. W/C gouache. 17-Apr-4 Livinec, Gaudcheau & Jezequel, Rennes #108
£775 $1356 €1100 Guerrier marocain (34x26cm-13x10in) studio st. gouache ink. 21-Dec-3 Thierry & Lannon, Brest #91
£795 $1486 €1200 Tronoen (26x34cm-10x13in) s.d.34 gouache ink. 24-Jul-4 Thierry & Lannon, Brest #100/R
£1127 $1972 €1600 Courtisane de Marrakech (19x24cm-7x9in) studio st. pastel ink. 21-Dec-3 Thierry & Lannon, Brest #90/R est:1000-1200
£1197 $2095 €1700 St Pierre Penmarch (26x34cm-10x13in) s.d.1951 gouache ink. 21-Dec-3 Thierry & Lannon, Brest #252/R est:1200-1500
£1776 $3215 €2700 Bigoudene (35x23cm-14x9in) mono. gouache. 17-Apr-4 Livinec, Gaudcheau & Jezequel, Rennes #110
£1776 $3215 €2700 Bigoudene devant la Tout Carree a Saint-Guneole. gouache. 17-Apr-4 Bretagne Encheres, St Malo #109 est:1200-1500
£2914 $5449 €4400 Costume de fete (37x24cm-15x9in) mono.i. gouache. 24-Jul-4 Thierry & Lannon, Brest #99/R est:1500-2000
£3377 $6316 €5100 Couple et enfant de Plougastel devant la mer (26x37cm-10x15in) s.d.1932 W/C gouache. 24-Jul-4 Thierry & Lannon, Brest #98/R est:1500-2000

GEO-REMY, Virginie (19th C) French?
£750 $1388 €1095 Dutch fishergirls (74x61cm-29x24in) s.indis.i.d.1884. 13-Jan-4 Bonhams, Knightsbridge #86/R

GEOFFRAY, Stephane (1830-1881) French
Photographs
£4546 $7591 €6500 Chambre photographique dans la cour du couvent des Cordeliers a Charlieu (22x23cm-9x9in) photograph exec.c.1850 prov. 10-Oct-3 Tajan, Paris #136/R est:7000-8000

GEOFFROY, Geo (attrib) (?) French?
£915 $1602 €1300 Les enfants (40x25cm-16x10in) bears sig. 19-Dec-3 Delvaux, Paris #11

GEOFFROY, Henry Jules Jean (1853-1924) French
£333 $613 €500 Chats (17x27cm-7x11in) s. 9-Jun-4 Le Roux & Morel, Paris #70
£664 $1143 €950 Vue d'un salon (22x16cm-9x6in) s. panel. 5-Dec-3 Maigret, Paris #85
£664 $1143 €950 Vue d'une salle a manger (22x16cm-9x6in) s. panel. 5-Dec-3 Maigret, Paris #86
£4832 $8650 €7200 La partie d'echecs (53x43cm-21x17in) s.d.1897 panel. 25-May-4 Chambelland & Giafferi, Paris #81/R est:3000-4000
£22000 $37840 €32120 Theorie des petites filles a la procession de la fete dieu (201x150cm-79x59in) s.d.1906. 3-Dec-3 Christie's, London #58/R est:20000-30000
Works on paper
£520 $931 €780 Un futur Avocat (28x21cm-11x8in) s. pen. 16-May-4 Feletin, Province #142
£1600 $2960 €2336 Difficult exercise (56x46cm-22x18in) s. pastel. 14-Jul-4 Sotheby's, Olympia #162/R est:500-700

GEOGHEGAN, Trevor (1946-) Irish
£604 $1081 €900 Winter scene (66x76cm-26x30in) s. i.d. 1991 verso acrylic. 31-May-4 Hamilton Osborne King, Dublin #118/R
£1745 $3123 €2600 River backwater at Cappoquin (60x60cm-24x24in) s. board. 26-May-4 James Adam, Dublin #84/R est:2500-3500

GEORG, Erling (1956-) Norwegian
£400 $692 €584 Pair of birds (50x70cm-20x28in) s. panel. 13-Dec-3 Blomqvist, Lysaker #1108/R (N.KR 4600)
£406 $674 €589 Magpie (70x50cm-28x20in) s. 16-Jun-3 Blomqvist, Lysaker #1052/R (N.KR 4700)

GEORGAS, Michalis (1947-) Greek
£3000 $5370 €4380 View of the harbour of Piraeus (59x124cm-23x49in) s. panel. 11-May-4 Bonhams, New Bond Street #100/R est:3000-5000

GEORGE, Adrian (1944-) British
£400 $720 €584 Le Matelot (87x65cm-34x26in) s.d.1987. 20-Jan-4 Bonhams, Knightsbridge #228
£550 $990 €803 Atelier de Paris (98x72cm-39x28in) s.d.1987 prov. 20-Jan-4 Bonhams, Knightsbridge #265/R
Works on paper
£260 $468 €380 Classical study (42x30cm-17x12in) s. pencil prov. 20-Jan-4 Bonhams, Knightsbridge #227

GEORGE, Ernest (1839-1922) British
Works on paper
£320 $534 €467 View of the Sphinx (35x25cm-14x10in) s. W/C. 14-Oct-3 Bonhams, Knightsbridge #121
£380 $608 €555 Igtham Moat. s.d.1870 W/C. 17-Sep-3 Bonhams, Brooks & Langlois, Jersey #101/R
£400 $668 €584 San Remo (42x29cm-17x11in) s.i. W/C. 14-Oct-3 Bonhams, Knightsbridge #65/R
£750 $1358 €1095 Cathedral and town, Chatres, France (42x29cm-17x11in) s.d.1875 W/C. 1-Apr-4 Martel Maides, Guernsey #266/R

GEORGE, Herbert (19th C) British?
Works on paper
£300 $498 €438 Walled garden with floral border (35x26cm-14x10in) s. W/C. 6-Oct-3 David Duggleby, Scarborough #236/R

GEORGE-JULLIARD, Jean Philippe (1818-1888) Swiss
£329 $549 €480 Vue de Vevey (27x36cm-11x14in) panel. 16-Nov-3 Koller, Geneva #1223 (S.FR 750)
£362 $615 €529 Villa garden (31x40cm-12x16in) s. panel. 19-Nov-3 Fischer, Luzern #2108/R (S.FR 800)
£388 $694 €566 Pond and trees in hilly landscape (16x30cm-6x12in) s. paper on board. 12-May-4 Dobiaschofsky, Bern #547/R (S.FR 900)
£433 $775 €632 Cascade de Pissevache a Vernayaz (57x47cm-22x19in) s. i. verso. 22-Mar-4 Philippe Schuler, Zurich #4330/R (S.FR 1000)
£1140 $1904 €1664 Paysage dans la valle du Linth (46x65cm-18x26in) s. 16-Nov-3 Koller, Geneva #1224/R est:1800-2500 (S.FR 2600)
£1429 $2286 €2072 Chateau de Vufflens (48x66cm-19x26in) s. i. verso. 15-May-3 Stuker, Bern #1251/R est:3000-4000 (S.FR 3000)
£2805 $4769 €4095 Environs de Vevey - Lac Leman (32x47cm-13x19in) s. 19-Nov-3 Fischer, Luzern #1238/R est:3500-5000 (S.FR 6200)

GEORGES, Charles E (19/20th C) British
Works on paper
£360 $587 €522 Blossom time (38x27cm-15x11in) W/C. 23-Sep-3 Bonhams, Knightsbridge #17/R

GEORGES, Claude (1929-1988) French
£347 $549 €500 Composition (65x81cm-26x32in) s.d.1970. 27-Apr-3 Versailles Encheres #11
£347 $580 €500 Passage au rouge (54x73cm-21x29in) s.d.1968. 25-Oct-3 Cornette de St.Cyr, Paris #685/R

GEORGES, Jean Louis (1860-1894) French
£1176 $2000 €1717 Apples and pears (32x40cm-13x16in) s.d.92 board pair. 19-Nov-3 Fischer, Luzern #2107/R est:100-1200 (S.FR 2600)

GEORGET, Elisa Antoinette (19th C) French
£319 $533 €450 Vase de fleurs blanches (82x57cm-32x22in) s. 21-Jun-3 Peron, Melun #69

GEORGI, Edwin (1896-1964) American
Works on paper
£1198 $2000 €1749 The offender (43x41cm-17x16in) gouache col pencil. 15-Nov-3 Illustration House, New York #137/R est:1800-2400

GEORGI, Friedrich Otto (1819-1874) German
£5862 $9790 €8500 Spinx avenue, Luxor (188x163cm-74x64in) s.d.1871 lit. 12-Jul-3 Bergmann, Erlangen #649/R est:9800
£13889 $25000 €20278 Caravan at the oasis (95x143cm-37x56in) s.d.1865. 23-Apr-4 Sotheby's, New York #185/R est:20000-30000

GEORGI, Traugott (1783-1838) German
£1589 $2893 €2400 The young chimney sweep (43x36cm-17x14in) s. 18-Jun-4 Bolland & Marotz, Bremen #619/R est:3300

GEORGI, Walter (1871-1924) German

£2800	$5012	€4200	Young woman with a peony (80x65cm-31x26in) s.d.08 lit. 14-May-4 Von Zezschwitz, Munich #284/R est:3000

GEORGIADIS, Margarita (1969-) Australian

£810	$1304	€1183	Requiem for a sentinel (122x122cm-48x48in) s.d.2000 verso composition board prov. 25-Aug-3 Sotheby's, Paddington #305 (A.D 2000)

GEORGIADIS, Nicholas (20th C) Continental

£2000	$3580	€2920	Abstract composition (102x81cm-40x32in) board prov. 10-May-4 Sotheby's, Olympia #73/R est:2000-3000

Works on paper

£1200	$2148	€1752	Abstract composition (55x76cm-22x30in) s.i.d.54 gouache prov. 10-May-4 Sotheby's, Olympia #69/R est:1000-1500

GEORGIOU, Kostis (1956-) Greek

£4800	$8592	€7008	Kosmikon (100x100cm-39x39in) s. 11-May-4 Bonhams, New Bond Street #131/R est:2000-3000

GEORGIUS, R (19th C) ?

£3846	$6538	€5500	Dogs by kennel (87x105cm-34x41in) s. 20-Nov-3 Van Ham, Cologne #1594/R est:7200

GEOROY (1906-1983) Belgian

£367	$660	€550	Landschap Reims (100x120cm-39x47in) i.d.1963 verso. 26-Apr-4 Bernaerts, Antwerp #586/R

GEPPERT, Eugène (1890-1979) Polish

£625	$1044	€913	In the park (26x33cm-10x13in) s.d.1929 cardboard. 19-Oct-3 Agra, Warsaw #67/R (P.Z 4000)
£1706	$2730	€2491	Horses and women (97x131cm-38x52in) s. 22-Sep-3 Rasmussen, Vejle #570/R est:20000-30000 (D.KR 18000)

GERALIS, Apostolos (1886-1983) Greek

£3000	$5250	€4380	Tree (32x39cm-13x15in) s. panel. 16-Dec-3 Bonhams, New Bond Street #65/R est:3000-4000
£4800	$8592	€7008	Girl at the fountain (46x33cm-18x13in) s.d.1951 board. 10-May-4 Sotheby's, Olympia #7/R est:3000-5000
£6000	$10500	€8760	Girl sewing (80x60cm-31x24in) s.d.1938 prov. 16-Dec-3 Bonhams, New Bond Street #40/R est:6000-8000
£6000	$10740	€8760	Woman leaning over a balcony (54x37cm-21x15in) s. board prov. 11-May-4 Bonhams, New Bond Street #55/R est:4000-6000
£7000	$11900	€10220	Smoking the hookah (40x32cm-16x13in) s.d.1917 panel. 18-Nov-3 Sotheby's, London #84/R est:2000-3000
£8000	$13600	€11680	Woman praying (61x51cm-24x20in) s.d.1918. 18-Nov-3 Sotheby's, London #18/R est:3000-5000
£32000	$54400	€46720	Love letter (91x68cm-36x27in) s. prov. 18-Nov-3 Sotheby's, London #17/R est:15000-20000

GERALIS, Loucas (1875-1958) Greek

£1400	$2506	€2044	Still life of roses (46x36cm-18x14in) s. board. 10-May-4 Sotheby's, Olympia #160/R est:1200-1800
£2400	$4200	€3504	Chrysanthemums (75x42cm-30x17in) s. prov. 16-Dec-3 Bonhams, New Bond Street #33/R est:1200-1800
£3400	$6086	€4964	Fishermen off the coast (66x85cm-26x33in) s. 11-May-4 Bonhams, New Bond Street #50/R est:3000-4000
£7000	$11900	€10220	Celebration under trees (31x40cm-12x16in) s. board. 18-Nov-3 Sotheby's, London #83/R est:4000-6000

GERANZANI, Cornelio (1880-1955) Italian

£1611	$3012	€2400	Sirens (14x20cm-6x8in) pair. 26-Feb-4 Cambi, Genoa #521/R est:2000-2500

GERARD, Baron François (1770-1837) French

£5495	$10000	€8023	Corinne at Miseno (123x123cm-48x48in) with sig.d.1796 prov.exhib. 4-Feb-4 Christie's, Rockefeller NY #36/R est:2000-3000
£14901	$27119	€22500	Trois ages de la vie (28x35cm-11x14in) panel. 15-Jun-4 Claude Aguttes, Neuilly #53/R est:20000-22000
£98684	$181579	€150000	Portrait de Maximilien-Sebastien Foy (229x141cm-90x56in) prov.exhib.lit. 24-Jun-4 Christie's, Paris #98/R est:150000-200000

GERARD, Baron François (after) (1770-1837) French

£5517	$9214	€8000	Madame de Stael (24cm-9in) panel. 12-Nov-3 Sotheby's, Milan #50/R est:2200-2800

GERARD, Baron François (attrib) (1770-1837) French

£16231	$30027	€23697	Young woman with white veil holding her sleeping baby (78cm-31in circular) exhib. 15-Mar-4 Rasmussen, Vejle #46/R est:60000-80000 (D.KR 180000)

GERARD, Baron François (circle) (1770-1837) French

£6207	$10303	€9000	Alleged portrait of Maria Walesca Countess of Ornano (66x54cm-26x21in) prov. 1-Oct-3 Dorotheum, Vienna #260/R est:9000-12000

GERARD, Baron François (style) (1770-1837) French

£6111	$11000	€8922	Three ages of man (91x117cm-36x46in) 21-Jan-4 Doyle, New York #62/R est:6000-8000
£10284	$17174	€14500	Belisaire (91x72cm-36x28in) 23-Jun-3 Ribeyre & Baron, Paris #36/R est:2000-3000

GERARD, Emile (?) ?

£199	$375	€291	Inside the artist studio (89x71cm-35x28in) s. 22-Feb-4 Bonhams & Butterfields, Los Angeles #7054
£239	$450	€349	Seated figure (91x76cm-36x30in) s. 22-Feb-4 Bonhams & Butterfields, Los Angeles #7055
£251	$475	€366	Dedoublement, cubistic woman (91x60cm-36x24in) s. 22-Feb-4 Bonhams & Butterfields, Los Angeles #7052
£317	$600	€463	Accordion player (91x76cm-36x30in) s. 22-Feb-4 Bonhams & Butterfields, Los Angeles #7056

GERARD, Henry (1860-1925) French

£378	$684	€552	Figures outside a Mosque (25x34cm-10x13in) s. panel. 30-Mar-4 Stephan Welz, Johannesburg #163 est:2000-4000 (SA.R 4500)
£1761	$3046	€2500	Vues de Venise (35x27cm-14x11in) s. panel two. 14-Dec-3 Rabourdin & Choppin de Janvry, Paris #34/R est:2500-3000
£3521	$6092	€5000	La lagune de Venise (48x72cm-19x28in) s. panel. 14-Dec-3 Rabourdin & Choppin de Janvry, Paris #36/R est:5000-6000

GERARD, John (1900-1965) Belgian

£473	$847	€700	Bruxelles sous la neige (30x40cm-12x16in) s. i.verso. 10-May-4 Horta, Bruxelles #491

GERARD, Lucien (1852-1935) Belgian

£387	$678	€550	Femme au chat dans un interieur (35x23cm-14x9in) 16-Dec-3 Galerie Moderne, Brussels #749/R
£594	$1010	€850	La colporteur (45x60cm-18x24in) s. panel. 1-Dec-3 Palais de Beaux Arts, Brussels #258/R

GERARD, Marguerite (1761-1837) French

£15789	$29053	€24000	Visit (40x32cm-16x13in) prov.exhib.lit. 24-Jun-4 Christie's, Paris #117/R est:15000-20000
£100000	$180000	€146000	Piano lesson (46x38cm-18x15in) s.indis.d prov.exhib.lit. 22-Jan-4 Sotheby's, New York #94/R est:150000-200000

GERARD, Michel (20th C) French

£329	$549	€480	Village street (54x73cm-21x29in) s.d.64. 7-Oct-3 Rasmussen, Copenhagen #190 (D.KR 3500)

GERARD, Pascal (1941-) French

£426	$711	€600	Paris, vue de Sacre-Coeur (54x65cm-21x26in) s. 12-Oct-3 St-Germain-en-Laye Encheres #214

GERARD, Robert Ulderic (1920-2000) Belgian

£1316	$2382	€2000	La maison d'Alfred Bastien au Rouge-cloitre (84x120cm-33x47in) s. 19-Apr-4 Horta, Bruxelles #309 est:300-500

GERARD, Simonin (?) Belgian

£1074	$1987	€1600	Le chien complice (50x40cm-20x16in) s. 15-Mar-4 Horta, Bruxelles #274 est:800-1000

GERARD, Theodore (1829-1895) Belgian

£350	$584	€500	Head of a woman (23x16cm-9x6in) s. panel. 11-Oct-3 De Vuyst, Lokeren #159
£658	$1211	€1000	Peasant woman and cow on a path (36x49cm-14x19in) s. 28-Jun-4 Sotheby's, Amsterdam #45/R est:1000-1500
£1761	$2800	€2571	Repose (50x38cm-20x15in) s. 13-Sep-3 Weschler, Washington #679/R est:4000-6000
£2667	$4800	€4000	Writing to a loved one (42x30cm-17x12in) s.d.82. 21-Apr-4 Christie's, Amsterdam #186/R est:4000-6000
£4637	$8532	€6770	Pet canary (52x45cm-20x18in) s.d.70. 14-Jun-4 Waddingtons, Toronto #44/R est:10000-15000 (C.D 11500)
£6207	$11483	€9000	Lecture de la lettre sous surveillance (75x59cm-30x23in) s. 19-Jan-4 Horta, Bruxelles #180/R est:10000-15000
£6897	$12759	€10000	Chante petit oiseau (41x31cm-16x12in) s.d.1881. 16-Feb-4 Horta, Bruxelles #171 est:12000-15000
£7383	$13510	€11000	Scene de famille (48x70cm-19x28in) s. 8-Jul-4 Campo, Vlaamse Kaai #128/R est:5000-6000

GERARDI, Alberto (1889-1965) Italian

Works on paper

£552	$921	€800	Crow (33x28cm-13x11in) graphite paper on card. 13-Nov-3 Finarte Semenzato, Rome #387

GERARDTS, Lambert (19th C) Dutch

£475	$850	€694	Barnyard scenes with chickens (36x30cm-14x12in) s. pair. 21-Mar-4 Jeffery Burchard, Florida #41/R

GERASCH, August (1822-1894) Austrian

£300	$480	€438	Boy flying a kite by a pond (32x26cm-13x10in) s. panel. 16-Sep-3 Rosebery Fine Art, London #603/R
£528	$877	€750	Hunting (49x63cm-19x25in) s. 12-Jun-3 Dorotheum, Graz #12
£1020	$1827	€1500	Young love in evening mountain landscape (52x41cm-20x16in) s.d.1877 panel lit. 20-Mar-4 Bergmann, Erlangen #1085 est:1500
£1745	$3123	€2600	Cows and goats on the alpine meadow (45x57cm-18x22in) s. panel. 27-May-4 Dorotheum, Vienna #74/R est:2600-3000

GERASCH, Franz (1822-1908) Austrian

Works on paper

£403	$741	€600	Behind the Karlskirche (18x22cm-7x9in) s. W/C. 26-Mar-4 Dorotheum, Vienna #263/R
£604	$1111	€900	Old Burgtheater in Vienna (19x23cm-7x9in) s. mixed media bone. 26-Mar-4 Dorotheum, Vienna #266/R

GERASIMOV, Andrei (20th C) Russian
£241 $450 €352 Cutting in the winter forest (69x41cm-27x16in) s. 29-Feb-4 Bonhams & Butterfields, San Francisco #4584
£299 $550 €437 Summer landscape with distant house and geese on a pond (48x64cm-19x25in) s. s.i.verso. 29-Mar-4 O'Gallerie, Oregon #749/R

GERASIMOV, Sergei Vassilievich (1885-1964) Russian
£571 $1050 €834 Morning in the park (67x89cm-26x35in) 27-Mar-4 Shishkin Gallery, Moscow #69/R
£2267 $4103 €3400 Autumn birch wood (48x69cm-19x27in) s.d. board. 1-Apr-4 Van Ham, Cologne #1393/R est:1200
£3352 $6000 €4894 Summer day (27x36cm-11x14in) canvas on cardboard painted 1950's. 29-May-4 Shishkin Gallery, Moscow #35/R est:3000-4000
£5163 $9500 €7538 Landscape with a man (27x48cm-11x19in) cardboard painted 1950's. 27-Mar-4 Shishkin Gallery, Moscow #70/R est:1500-1800

GERBAUD, Abel (1888-1954) French
£537 $993 €800 Entree du port de Honfleur (33x41cm-13x16in) s. 14-Mar-4 Eric Pillon, Calais #184/R
£2800 $5040 €4088 Still life with flowers and fruit on a table (100x81cm-39x32in) s. 20-Jan-4 Bonhams, Knightsbridge #264/R est:2000-3000

GERBER, Eg (19th C) ?
£302 $565 €450 La pause du mousquetaire (48x38cm-19x15in) s. 29-Feb-4 Osenat, Fontainebleau #217

GERBER, Theo (1928-) Swiss
£2041 $3653 €3000 Untitled (100x65cm-39x26in) s.d.69 prov. 21-Mar-4 Calmels Cohen, Paris #128/R est:500-700

GERBIG, Alexander (?) Dutch?
£313 $494 €450 Sunlit pine wood (91x61cm-36x24in) s. 6-Sep-3 Arnold, Frankfurt #561/R
£556 $878 €800 Peasant workers (80x80cm-31x31in) s. 6-Sep-3 Arnold, Frankfurt #562/R

GERBINO, Rosario Urbino (1900-1972) American
£405 $700 €591 Fishing harbour at sunrise (61x76cm-24x30in) s. 13-Dec-3 Weschler, Washington #606
£434 $750 €634 Apple tree (41x51cm-16x20in) s. canvasboard. 13-Dec-3 Weschler, Washington #604

GERCHE, Geoff la (1940-) Australian
£1564 $2830 €2283 Betinas 1976-1977 (122x122cm-48x48in) exhib. 30-Mar-4 Lawson Menzies, Sydney #124/R est:2500-3500 (A.D 3800)

GERCHMAN, Rubens (1942-) Brazilian
£10588 $18000 €15458 Pele (148x148cm-58x58in) s.i.d.1997 verso acrylic exhib. 19-Nov-3 Sotheby's, New York #53/R est:20000-30000

GERE, Charles M (attrib) (1869-1957) British
£938 $1500 €1369 London docks (61x86cm-24x34in) mono. 20-Sep-3 Sloans & Kenyon, Bethesda #143/R est:1750-2250

GERELL, Greta (1898-1982) Swedish
£370 $661 €540 Farmer ploughing the field (60x73cm-24x29in) s.i.d.1939. 28-May-4 Uppsala Auktionskammare, Uppsala #199/R (S.KR 5000)
£518 $897 €756 White facades (34x33cm-13x13in) s. panel. 15-Dec-3 Lilla Bukowskis, Stockholm #636 (S.KR 6600)
£654 $1125 €955 Red buildings (21x27cm-8x11in) s. panel prov. 2-Dec-3 Bukowskis, Stockholm #14/R (S.KR 8500)
£692 $1191 €1010 Wooden but with green apples (23x37cm-9x15in) s.d.66 cardboard prov. 2-Dec-3 Bukowskis, Stockholm #12/R (S.KR 9000)
£1000 $1720 €1460 Waiting (46x56cm-18x22in) s. prov. 2-Dec-3 Bukowskis, Stockholm #13/R (S.KR 13000)
£1700 $3043 €2482 Les Tuileries, Paris (38x46cm-15x18in) s.d.34. 26-May-4 AB Stockholms Auktionsverk #2196/R est:6000-8000 (S.KR 23000)
£2077 $3572 €3032 Girl with still life (35x27cm-14x11in) s.d.38 panel. 3-Dec-3 AB Stockholms Auktionsverk #2235/R est:8000-10000 (S.KR 27000)

GERGELY, Imre (1868-1914) Hungarian
£906 $1676 €1350 Gathering flowerrs on the terrace (60x80cm-24x31in) s. 15-Mar-4 Sotheby's, Amsterdam #162/R est:800-1200

GERHARD, Hubert (after) (1540-1620) Flemish
Sculpture
£13000 $23920 €18980 Figure of Venus holding a conch shell (77cm-30in) brown pat bronze base ebony wood plinth lit. 10-Jun-4 Christie's, London #95/R est:8000-12000

GERHARDINGER, Constantin (1888-1970) German
£282 $493 €400 Cheimsee (30x47cm-12x19in) s. board. 19-Dec-3 Dorotheum, Vienna #128/R
£1879 $3495 €2800 Rainy market (35x50cm-14x20in) s.d.Okt 1919. 6-Mar-4 Arnold, Frankfurt #730/R est:600
£2215 $4119 €3300 Market day in autumn (35x49cm-14x19in) s. board. 6-Mar-4 Arnold, Frankfurt #729/R est:600
£3357 $5773 €4800 Still life with violets (60x89cm-24x35in) s. 5-Dec-3 Michael Zeller, Lindau #625/R est:2000
£3448 $5759 €5000 Nude female sitting with black stockings (35x50cm-14x20in) i.d.20 board prov. 13-Nov-3 Neumeister, Munich #333/R est:5000-6000

GERHARDT, Aloys (1837-1889) Hungarian
£790 $1431 €1153 In the garden (25x18cm-10x7in) 16-Apr-4 Mu Terem Galeria, Budapest #99/R (H.F 300000)

GERHARDT, C (19th C) ?
Works on paper
£979 $1684 €1400 Kairouan (36x25cm-14x10in) s.i.d.1849 W/C. 8-Dec-3 Tajan, Paris #291/R est:1500-1600

GERICAULT, Theodore (1791-1824) French
£2800 $5152 €4200 Horses going to fair (25x35cm-10x14in) lithograph exec.1821. 10-Jun-4 Piasa, Paris #93/R
£6993 $12028 €10000 Le grenadier blesse (85x96cm-33x38in) 2-Dec-3 Sotheby's, Paris #69/R est:10000-15000
£977654 $1750000 €1427375 Cheval de Napoleon (37x46cm-15x18in) painted c.1813 prov.exhib.lit. 5-May-4 Sotheby's, New York #2/R est:500000-700000
Prints
£4000 $7360 €6000 Horses exercising (29x41cm-11x16in) lithograph exec.1821. 10-Jun-4 Piasa, Paris #94/R
£4533 $8341 €6800 Chariot charge de soldats blesses (28x29cm-11x11in) lithograph exec.1818. 10-Jun-4 Piasa, Paris #91/R
£13559 $24000 €19796 Boxeurs (35x41cm-14x16in) lithograph prov. 28-Apr-4 Christie's, Rockefeller NY #49/R est:25000-35000
Works on paper
£3333 $6000 €4866 Carthorse eating from a nosebag (21x28cm-8x11in) i. black chk. 22-Jan-4 Christie's, Rockefeller NY #137/R est:7000-10000
£5000 $9000 €7300 Nude turned to the left, seated on a bench (16x11cm-6x4in) i. black chk pen brown ink prov.lit. 22-Jan-4 Christie's, Rockefeller NY #135/R est:7000-10000
£8333 $15000 €12166 Postal conductor attending to two saddled horses in front of a station (21x28cm-8x11in) i. black lead. 22-Jan-4 Christie's, Rockefeller NY #136/R est:15000-20000
£10000 $18200 €15000 Different scenes (21x29cm-8x11in) pen ink wash htd oil double-sided prov.lit. 30-Jun-4 Delvaux, Paris #120/R est:15000
£14789 $24549 €21000 Un cavalier attaque par une lionne (20x27cm-8x11in) black crayon. 13-Jun-3 Ferri, Paris #38 est:15000-20000
£34965 $59441 €50000 Marine coitiere (12x18cm-5x7in) W/C grattages. 26-Nov-3 Daguerre, Paris #47/R est:45000-60000
£61453 $110000 €89721 Officier de chevalerie a cheval (17x13cm-7x5in) W/C over pencil exec.c.1822 prov.exhib. 5-May-4 Sotheby's, New York #15/R est:125000-175000

GERICAULT, Theodore (attrib) (1791-1824) French
Works on paper
£1692 $2911 €2470 Horses with drivers (29x24cm-11x9in) Indian ink wash htd white. 2-Dec-3 Bukowskis, Stockholm #441/R est:10000-12000 (S.KR 22000)
£2133 $3883 €3200 Tete de jeune fille (18x12cm-7x5in) crayon prov.exhib. 30-Jun-4 Delvaux, Paris #123/R est:3000-4000

GERING, Andreas (1892-1957) German
£1067 $1920 €1600 Reclining female nude (50x65cm-20x26in) board lit. 22-Apr-4 Allgauer, Kempten #3550/R est:1400

GERLE, Aron (1860-1930) Swedish
£1256 $2249 €1834 Outside the bookshop (86x59cm-34x23in) s. panel. 25-May-4 Bukowskis, Stockholm #20/R est:15000-20000 (S.KR 17000)

GERLO, Urbain (1897-?) Belgian
£280 $481 €400 Het gespan in de avondschemer (50x70cm-20x28in) s. 2-Dec-3 Campo & Campo, Antwerp #153
£280 $481 €400 Vaches dans la prairie ensoleillee (50x70cm-20x28in) s. 2-Dec-3 Campo & Campo, Antwerp #154

GERLOVIN, Rimma and Valeriy (20th C) American?
Photographs
£1796 $3000 €2622 Birth of Aphrodite (78x88cm-31x35in) s.i.d.1992 num.6/10 chromogenic print. 17-Oct-3 Sotheby's, New York #279/R est:5000-7000
£2646 $5000 €3863 Vintage (96x100cm-38x39in) i.d.1990 num.6/25 color coupler print. 17-Feb-4 Christie's, Rockefeller NY #176/R est:5000-7000

GERMAIN, Jacques (1915-2001) French
£333 $613 €500 Composition (36x29cm-14x11in) mono. canvas on cardboard painted c.1980. 11-Jun-4 Pierre Berge, Paris #41
£336 $628 €500 Composition (29x46cm-11x18in) s.d.1976 verso. 29-Feb-4 Versailles Encheres #237
£336 $628 €500 Composition (17x38cm-7x15in) mono.d.21 IX 76 verso. 29-Feb-4 Versailles Encheres #239
£570 $1067 €850 Composition (33x40cm-13x16in) s.d.1965. 29-Feb-4 Versailles Encheres #238/R
£604 $1124 €900 Composition 245 (60x40cm-24x16in) s.d.70 s.d.7 XI 70 verso prov. 3-Mar-4 Artcurial Briest, Paris #378
£604 $1124 €900 Composition 124 (66x46cm-26x18in) mono.d.7 IX 70 prov. 3-Mar-4 Artcurial Briest, Paris #379
£671 $1248 €1000 Composition 112 (50x60cm-20x24in) s.d.48 oil paper on cardboard prov. 3-Mar-4 Artcurial Briest, Paris #370/R
£671 $1248 €1000 Composition 184 (50x61cm-20x24in) mono. s.d.60 verso prov. 3-Mar-4 Artcurial Briest, Paris #374
£671 $1248 €1000 Composition 68 (46x55cm-18x22in) s.d.63 verso prov. 3-Mar-4 Artcurial Briest, Paris #377
£671 $1248 €1000 Composition 379 (41x33cm-16x13in) st.mono. prov. 3-Mar-4 Artcurial Briest, Paris #384
£700 $1260 €1050 Composition (37x45cm-15x18in) st.mono. paper on canvas. 24-Apr-4 Cornette de St.Cyr, Paris #530
£738 $1374 €1100 Composition 61 (65x54cm-26x21in) st.mono. prov. 3-Mar-4 Artcurial Briest, Paris #373
£738 $1374 €1100 Composition 79 (73x60cm-29x24in) s.d.69.70 verso prov. 3-Mar-4 Artcurial Briest, Paris #375
£738 $1374 €1100 Composition 240 (34x45cm-13x18in) mono. s.d.60-70 verso prov. 3-Mar-4 Artcurial Briest, Paris #382
£805 $1498 €1200 Mouchetee composition (73x54cm-29x21in) s.d.68 s.i.d.1 II 68 verso prov. 3-Mar-4 Artcurial Briest, Paris #372

£872	$1623	€1300	Composition 503 (41x88cm-16x35in) mono.d.66 prov. 3-Mar-4 Artcurial Briest, Paris #381 est:500-600
£940	$1748	€1400	Composition 443 (30x67cm-12x26in) mono.d.15 XI 69 prov. 3-Mar-4 Artcurial Briest, Paris #380 est:350-400
£940	$1719	€1400	Untitled (27x19cm-11x7in) js.d.59. 7-Jul-4 Artcurial Briest, Paris #265 est:600-800
£1007	$1873	€1500	Composition 186 (64x49cm-25x19in) s.d.89 prov. 3-Mar-4 Artcurial Briest, Paris #371 est:700-800
£1007	$1873	€1500	Composition 174 (65x54cm-26x21in) s. s.d.63 verso prov. 3-Mar-4 Artcurial Briest, Paris #376 est:400-500
£1007	$1873	€1500	Composition 239 (40x47cm-16x19in) mono.d.66 verso prov. 3-Mar-4 Artcurial Briest, Paris #383 est:300-400
£1007	$1873	€1500	Composition 88 (42x88cm-17x35in) s.verso prov. 3-Mar-4 Artcurial Briest, Paris #406 est:400-500
£1074	$1997	€1600	Composition 30 (110x100cm-43x39in) st.mono. prov. 3-Mar-4 Artcurial Briest, Paris #390 est:800-1200
£1074	$1997	€1600	Composition 94 (65x81cm-26x32in) mono.d.9.12.67 prov. 3-Mar-4 Artcurial Briest, Paris #398 est:600-800
£1074	$1997	€1600	Compositions. oil paper and canvas painted c.1980-90 prov. 3-Mar-4 Artcurial Briest, Paris #439 est:400-500
£1119	$1902	€1600	Composition bleue (116x73cm-46x29in) mono.d.1-VIII-1982. 28-Nov-3 Blanchet, Paris #233/R est:900-1000
£1141	$2123	€1700	Composition 403 (27x42cm-11x17in) s.d.62 oil paper on canvas prov. 3-Mar-4 Artcurial Briest, Paris #385 est:200-300
£1141	$2123	€1700	Composition (42x88cm-17x35in) mono.d.65 prov. 3-Mar-4 Artcurial Briest, Paris #410 est:400-500
£1141	$2088	€1700	Untitled (27x22cm-11x9in) mono. prov. 7-Jul-4 Artcurial Briest, Paris #263 est:400-500
£1208	$2247	€1800	Composition 97 (60x92cm-24x36in) mono.d.7.10.67 prov. 3-Mar-4 Artcurial Briest, Paris #397 est:600-800
£1343	$2376	€2000	Composition (55x36cm-22x14in) mono. s.verso. 28-Apr-4 Artcurial Briest, Paris #254/R est:1500-1800
£1343	$2497	€2000	Composition 153 (65x81cm-26x32in) s.d.70 s.d.28 XII 69 verso prov. 3-Mar-4 Artcurial Briest, Paris #399 est:550-600
£1343	$2497	€2000	Composition 73 (87x52cm-34x20in) s.d.67 s.d.18 XI 67 verso prov. 3-Mar-4 Artcurial Briest, Paris #403 est:600-800
£1343	$2497	€2000	Composition (81x65cm-32x26in) mono.d.26 VIII 68 prov. 3-Mar-4 Artcurial Briest, Paris #407 est:600-800
£1409	$2622	€2100	Composition 168 (60x92cm-24x36in) st.mono. prov. 3-Mar-4 Artcurial Briest, Paris #402 est:600-800
£1476	$2746	€2200	Composition 295 (92x73cm-36x29in) s.d.69 prov. 3-Mar-4 Artcurial Briest, Paris #409 est:800-1000
£1476	$2746	€2200	Composition 459 (61x50cm-24x20in) mono.d.49 isorel prov. 3-Mar-4 Artcurial Briest, Paris #414 est:300-400
£1477	$2702	€2200	Composition (86x81cm-34x32in) s.d.75. 7-Jul-4 Artcurial Briest, Paris #262/R est:1500-2000
£1544	$2872	€2300	Composition 169 (92x60cm-36x24in) mono. prov. 3-Mar-4 Artcurial Briest, Paris #412 est:600-800
£1549	$2680	€2200	Composition (33x54cm-13x21in) s.i.d.1966. 14-Dec-3 Versailles Encheres #44/R est:600-800
£1831	$3168	€2600	Composition (73x100cm-29x39in) s. s.d.28 VIII 71 verso prov. 14-Dec-3 Versailles Encheres #45/R est:3000-3500
£1879	$3495	€2800	Composition 35 (97x130cm-38x51in) s.d.88 s.d.2.VIII.88 verso prov. 3-Mar-4 Artcurial Briest, Paris #388/R est:1500-1800
£1879	$3495	€2800	Composition 11 (89x116cm-35x46in) s.d.76 s.d.30 V 76 verso prov. 3-Mar-4 Artcurial Briest, Paris #400 est:800-1000
£1879	$3495	€2800	Composition 144 (81x65cm-32x26in) st.mono. prov. 3-Mar-4 Artcurial Briest, Paris #404 est:600-800
£1879	$3495	€2800	Composition 298 (92x73cm-36x29in) st.mono. painted c.1950 prov. 3-Mar-4 Artcurial Briest, Paris #405 est:1000-1200
£2013	$3745	€3000	Composition 32 (120x120cm-47x47in) s.d.82 s.d.25 XI 82 verso prov. 3-Mar-4 Artcurial Briest, Paris #392 est:1000-1200
£2013	$3745	€3000	Composition 34 (89x116cm-35x46in) s.d.79 s.d.30 III 79 verso prov. 3-Mar-4 Artcurial Briest, Paris #401 est:800-1000
£2013	$3745	€3000	Composition 355 (73x92cm-29x36in) s.d.1966 prov. 3-Mar-4 Artcurial Briest, Paris #408 est:800-1000
£2013	$3745	€3000	Composition 354 (91x73cm-36x29in) s.d.64 prov. 3-Mar-4 Artcurial Briest, Paris #413/R est:800-1000
£2349	$4370	€3500	Composition (130x130cm-51x51in) s. s.d.30 IV 83 verso prov. 3-Mar-4 Artcurial Briest, Paris #394 est:1200-1500
£2349	$4370	€3500	Composition 356 (81x65cm-32x26in) s.d.63 prov. 3-Mar-4 Artcurial Briest, Paris #411/R est:800-1000
£2416	$4494	€3600	Composition (130x97cm-51x38in) s.d.63 prov. 3-Mar-4 Artcurial Briest, Paris #389 est:1200-1500
£2684	$4993	€4000	Composition 901 (146x114cm-57x45in) st.mono. prov. 3-Mar-4 Artcurial Briest, Paris #395 est:1200-1500
£3020	$5618	€4500	Composition 20 (97x130cm-38x51in) st.mono. prov. 3-Mar-4 Artcurial Briest, Paris #387 est:1200-1500
£3021	$5528	€4500	Untitled (92x65cm-36x26in) js.d.62. 7-Jul-4 Artcurial Briest, Paris #264 est:1800-2200
£4027	$7490	€6000	Composition (89x116cm-35x46in) s.d.56 prov. 3-Mar-4 Artcurial Briest, Paris #386/R est:1800-2200
£4698	$8738	€7000	Composition 281 (195x130cm-77x51in) s.d.90 prov. 3-Mar-4 Artcurial Briest, Paris #415 est:3000-3500
£4832	$8988	€7200	Composition 269 (114x148cm-45x58in) st.mono. prov. 3-Mar-4 Artcurial Briest, Paris #393 est:1200-1500
£5369	$9987	€8000	Noue bleue (130x162cm-51x64in) s.d.60 prov. 3-Mar-4 Artcurial Briest, Paris #416/R est:3000-3500
£6376	$11860	€9500	Composition 38 (146x114cm-57x45in) s.d.87 s.d.30 VII 87 verso prov. 3-Mar-4 Artcurial Briest, Paris #396 est:1200-1500
£6376	$11860	€9500	Composition 48 (161x130cm-63x51in) s.d.68 s.d.20 XI 68 verso prov. 3-Mar-4 Artcurial Briest, Paris #417/R est:1800-2200
£7718	$14356	€11500	Composition 52 (146x114cm-57x45in) s.d.90 mono.d.10 VIII 90 verso prov. 3-Mar-4 Artcurial Briest, Paris #391/R est:2000-3000
Works on paper			
£267	$480	€400	Composition (32x38cm-13x15in) st.mono. gouache. 24-Apr-4 Cornette de St.Cyr, Paris #529/R
£267	$485	€400	Composition (64x49cm-25x19in) s.d.1978 gouache prov. 2-Jul-4 Binoche, Paris #17
£333	$600	€500	Composition (26x45cm-10x18in) st.mono. W/C gouache. 24-Apr-4 Cornette de St.Cyr, Paris #526/R
£470	$874	€700	Composition (13x13cm-5x5in) mono.d.Decembre 1930 gouache prov. 3-Mar-4 Artcurial Briest, Paris #427
£533	$960	€800	Composition (28x46cm-11x18in) mono.d.1986 mixed media. 24-Apr-4 Cornette de St.Cyr, Paris #527/R
£671	$1188	€1000	Composition (76x56cm-30x22in) s.d.1975 gouache. 28-Apr-4 Charbonneaux, Paris #159/R
£940	$1719	€1400	Composition (82x49cm-32x19in) s.d.87 gouache. 7-Jul-4 Artcurial Briest, Paris #265b est:300-500

GERMAIN, Jean Pierre (?) French

£302	$562	€450	Vue panoramique de la plage du Havre (50x65cm-20x26in) s. 7-Mar-4 Lesieur & Le Bars, Le Havre #150

GERMAIN, Jean-Baptiste (1841-1910) French

Sculpture			
£1333	$2427	€2000	Allegorie du printemps (85cm-33in) s. bronze incl socle st.f.E Colin Paris. 29-Jun-4 Gioffredo, Nice #82
£1343	$2457	€1961	Standing figure (80cm-31in) s. pat.bronze. 2-Jun-4 Rasmussen, Copenhagen #1304/R est:15000 (D.KR 15000)
£4930	$8627	€7000	Le printemps d'amour (78cm-31in) brown pat bronze. 17-Dec-3 Rabourdin & Choppin de Janvry, Paris #214/R est:9000-10000

GERMAIN-THILL, Alphonse Leon Antoine (1873-1925) French

£1584	$2740	€2313	El Golea (61x114cm-24x45in) s.i.d.1899. 12-Dec-3 Galerie du Rhone, Sion #151/R est:4000-6000 (S.FR 3500)

GERMAN SCHOOL, 15th C

£12676	$20282	€18000	Jesus in the temple (53x51cm-21x20in) board. 21-Sep-3 Finarte, Venice #48/R
£28169	$46761	€40000	La cene (75x85cm-30x33in) panel. 11-Jun-3 Delorme & Bocage, Paris #7/R est:40000-50000
Works on paper			
£9797	$17243	€14500	Lamentation of Christ (18x14cm-7x6in) chk pen htd grey double-sided prov. 22-May-4 Lempertz, Koln #1233/R est:12000-15000

GERMAN SCHOOL, 15th/16th C

Sculpture			
£8334	$13584	€12000	Saint George and the dragon (71x77x47cm-28x30x19in) painted wood. 24-Sep-3 Tajan, Paris #134/R

GERMAN SCHOOL, 16th C

£4362	$8158	€6500	Portrait of man (64x50cm-25x20in) i. board. 28-Feb-4 Finarte, Venice #204/R est:5000-6000
£5244	$8758	€7500	Christ and his disciples (43x124cm-17x49in) panel. 30-Jun-3 Sotheby's, Amsterdam #62/R
£5369	$9987	€8000	Burial of the Virgin (153x100cm-60x39in) board painted c.1520. 2-Mar-4 Ansorena, Madrid #268/R est:8000
£5674	$9475	€8000	Salomon (72x53cm-28x21in) indis.mono. panel. 17-Jun-3 Galerie Moderne, Brussels #251/R est:4000-6000
£8000	$14640	€11680	Flight into Egypt (41x53cm-16x21in) panel prov. 8-Jul-4 Sotheby's, London #241/R est:6000-8000
£8503	$13520	€12500	Saint-Ambroise et Saint Etienne (126x52cm-50x20in) panel. 23-Mar-3 Salle des ventes Pillet, Lyon la Foret #15
£10859	$18026	€15854	Marthe of Bethany (94x28cm-37x11in) panel painted c.1500. 4-Oct-3 Kieselbach, Budapest #102/R (H.F 4000000)
£11667	$19483	€16800	Annunciation angel (158x80cm-62x31in) panel. 21-Oct-3 Fraysse & Associes, Paris #4b
Sculpture			
£7639	$12146	€11000	Mary Magdalen. Madonna and Child (30cm-12in) painted wood two. 9-Sep-3 Vanderkindere, Brussels #168/R
£13605	$21633	€20000	Saint George (131cm-52in) wood. 23-Mar-3 Salle des ventes Pillet, Lyon la Foret #187

GERMAN SCHOOL, 17th C

£7000	$12530	€10500	Genre scene (75x96cm-30x38in) panel. 16-May-4 Joron-Derem, Paris #32/R est:15000-20000
£12500	$23000	€19000	Still life of fruit (53x79cm-21x31in) 25-Jun-4 Piasa, Paris #17/R est:18000-22000
£30216	$49554	€42000	L'adoration des bergers (44x59cm-17x23in) panel. 6-Jun-3 Maigret, Paris #88/R est:2500-3500
Sculpture			
£5282	$9137	€7500	Christ au liens (24cm-9in) wood lit. 15-Dec-3 Sotheby's, Paris #1/R est:8000-10000

GERMAN SCHOOL, 18th C

£2715	$4507	€3964	Birds in landscape (45x34cm-18x13in) 4-Oct-3 Kieselbach, Budapest #44/R (H.F 1000000)
£5333	$9547	€8000	Wedding ceremony (34x24cm-13x9in) panel. 16-May-4 Joron-Derem, Paris #101/R est:8000-10000
£5879	$10406	€8583	Riverside scene (49x57cm-19x22in) 28-Apr-4 Kieselbach, Budapest #143/R (H.F 2200000)
£6000	$10200	€8760	Portrait of Prince Franz Xavier of Saxony (65x54cm-26x21in) 30-Oct-3 Sotheby's, Olympia #150/R est:3000-5000
£6944	$10972	€10000	Landscape with river and figures (74x107cm-29x42in) 6-Sep-3 Arnold, Frankfurt #679/R est:4800
£10211	$16338	€14500	St Anthony of Padua (99x74cm-39x29in) 19-Sep-3 Karlheinz Kaupp, Staufen #1899/R est:1000
£12000	$20040	€17520	Troopers f the Scots Greys with allied troops during the seven year war, taking refreshments (99x125cm-39x49in) 14-Oct-3 Sotheby's, London #458/R est:12000-18000
£14000	$25200	€20440	Stag hunt. End of a stag hunt (33x43cm-13x17in) pair. 23-Apr-4 Christie's, Kensington #151/R est:4000-6000
Works on paper			
£10000	$18500	€14600	Flowers (35x21cm-14x8in) W/C twenty-nine album. 15-Jul-4 Bonhams, New Bond Street #33/R est:10000-15000

GERMAN SCHOOL, 19th C

£5000	$8150	€7300	Challenge (68x113cm-27x44in) mono.i.d.1849. 25-Sep-3 Mellors & Kirk, Nottingham #770/R est:5000-7000
£5240	$9537	€7650	Riverside town (42x58cm-17x23in) indis.s. 16-Jun-4 Fischer, Luzern #1243/R est:12000-15000 (S.FR 12000)

£8451 $14028 €12000 Paysage a la cascade et au monastere (225x158cm-89x62in) painted c.1820. 10-Jun-3 Renaud, Paris #15/R est:4000-6000
£12048 $20000 €17590 Lush wooded landscape with distant deer (152x224cm-60x88in) s. 4-Oct-3 Neal Auction Company, New Orleans #205/R est:10000-15000
Sculpture
£8784 $15459 €13000 Triumph of Bacchus (14x33cm-6x13in) ivory relief. 18-May-4 Sotheby's, Milan #67/R est:4000-7000
Works on paper
£8889 $16000 €12978 Portrait of a man (43x30cm-17x12in) black white chk. 22-Jan-4 Christie's, Rockefeller NY #158/R est:4000-6000
£9500 $17385 €13870 View of an Alpine village with figures, a lady in the foreground (42x53cm-17x21in) mono.d.1808 blk chk brown grey wash htd white. 8-Jul-4 Sotheby's, London #135/R est:8000-12000

GERMAN, Christopher S (19th C) American
Photographs
£3593 $6000 €5246 Portrait of Lincoln (20x15cm-8x6in) i.verso varnished salt print oval. 17-Oct-3 Sotheby's, New York #106/R est:6000-9000

GERMAN, Louis (20th C) French?
£500 $850 €730 Cannes harbour (28x41cm-11x16in) s. s.i.verso board. 19-Nov-3 Christie's, Kensington #552/R

GERMAN-FLEMISH SCHOOL, 16th C
£6800 $12171 €9928 Via Dolorosa (140x174cm-55x69in) panel prov. 25-May-4 Bukowskis, Stockholm #420/R est:100000-125000 (S.KR 92000)

GERMANA, Mimmo (1944-1992) Italian
£1408 $2338 €2000 Untitled (50x50cm-20x20in) s.d.1991. 11-Jun-3 Finarte Semenzato, Milan #667/R
£1479 $2455 €2100 Untitled (50x50cm-20x20in) s.d.1991. 11-Jun-3 Finarte Semenzato, Milan #666/R
£1549 $2572 €2200 Black house (61x100cm-24x39in) s.i.d.1982-3 board diptych. 11-Jun-3 Finarte Semenzato, Milan #721/R
£1736 $2743 €2500 Untitled (80x60cm-31x24in) painted 1990. 6-Sep-3 Meeting Art, Vercelli #554 est:2500
£2414 $3862 €3500 Untitled (90x70cm-35x28in) s.verso painted 1990. 13-Mar-3 Galleria Pace, Milan #118/R est:3300-4300
£2465 $4092 €3500 Untitled (54x49cm-21x19in) s.d.1981 verso. 11-Jun-3 Finarte Semenzato, Milan #583/R
£2667 $4907 €4000 Untitled (120x100cm-47x39in) s.d.1990. 12-Jun-4 Meeting Art, Vercelli #864/R est:4000
£2886 $5166 €4300 Portrait (121x100cm-48x39in) s.d.1990 verso acrylic. 28-May-4 Farsetti, Prato #139/R est:3600-4200
£4138 $6621 €6000 Ombra nell (89x116cm-35x46in) s.i.d.1988 verso. 13-Mar-3 Galleria Pace, Milan #154/R est:5500-7000
Works on paper
£676 $1189 €1000 Maternity (70x49cm-28x19in) s.d.1988 gouache pastel pencil. 24-May-4 Christie's, Milan #25

GERMASCHEFF, Michail (1868-1930) Russian
£5500 $9350 €8030 Indian summer (54x65cm-21x26in) s. 19-Nov-3 Sotheby's, London #97/R est:3000-4000
£7000 $11900 €10220 Last Rays (55x46cm-22x18in) s. 19-Nov-3 Sotheby's, London #95/R est:5000-7000
£10000 $17000 €14600 Still waters (46x55cm-18x22in) s. 19-Nov-3 Sotheby's, London #91/R est:4000-6000

GERMELA, Raimund (1868-1945) Hungarian
£1006 $1600 €1469 Festival in Vienna (74x86cm-29x34in) s.i.verso. 25-Feb-3 Bunch, West Chester #487a/R
Works on paper
£347 $566 €500 Spanish dancer (58x44cm-23x17in) s.i.d.1900 mixed media. 23-Sep-3 Wiener Kunst Auktionen, Vienna #47/R

GERMENIS, Vasilis (1896-1966) Greek
£1900 $3401 €2774 Ploughing (34x49cm-13x19in) s. board. 10-May-4 Sotheby's, Olympia #171/R est:1200-1800
£2600 $4654 €3796 Countrymen on donkeys crossing a river (50x70cm-20x28in) s. cardboard. 11-May-4 Bonhams, New Bond Street #68/R est:2500-3500
£5200 $9100 €7592 Windmill in Myconos (47x56cm-19x22in) s. prov. 16-Dec-3 Bonhams, New Bond Street #14/R est:5000-7000
£6500 $11375 €9490 Port entrance (66x101cm-26x40in) s. 16-Dec-3 Bonhams, New Bond Street #50/R est:5000-7000
£6500 $11635 €9490 Fresh breeze (60x80cm-24x31in) s.d.1938. 10-May-4 Sotheby's, Olympia #11/R est:5000-7000
£13000 $22100 €18980 Packing mules at Santorini (56x76cm-22x30in) s. canvasboard prov. 18-Nov-3 Sotheby's, London #82/R est:8000-12000

GERNES, Poul (1925-1996) Danish
£1040 $1861 €1518 Square composition (91x91cm-36x36in) s. verso. 12-Jan-4 Rasmussen, Vejle #620/R (D.KR 11000)
£1087 $1946 €1587 Square composition (91x91cm-36x36in) s. verso. 12-Jan-4 Rasmussen, Vejle #618/R (D.KR 11500)

GERNEZ, Paul Elie (1888-1948) French
£719 $1129 €1050 Nu allonge (9x17cm-4x7in) cardboard. 20-Apr-3 Deauville, France #107
£839 $1443 €1200 Honfleur, estuaire (32x48cm-13x19in) s. W/C chl. 8-Dec-3 Christie's, Paris #63/R
£1333 $2387 €2000 Bouquet de marguerites et de tulipes (36x28cm-14x11in) 16-May-4 Osenat, Fontainebleau #82/R est:2000-3000
£2282 $4221 €3400 Quatre baigneuses (35x42cm-14x17in) s.d.1918. 14-Mar-4 St-Germain-en-Laye Encheres #119/R est:3500-4000
£3356 $6007 €5000 Bouquet au pot vert (46x38cm-18x15in) s. painted c.1930 prov. 26-May-4 Christie's, Paris #55/R est:3000-5000
£4792 $8002 €6900 Paysage vue de l'atelier (65x81cm-26x32in) s.d.1918 canvas on panel. 23-Oct-3 Credit Municipal, Paris #99/R est:2500-3000
£5369 $9987 €8000 Semi de fleurs et coquillages (86x95cm-34x37in) s. panel prov. 7-Mar-4 Lesieur & Le Bars, Le Havre #62/R
£5705 $10211 €8500 Personnages au bord de la mer (40x61cm-16x24in) s.exhib. 27-May-4 Christie's, Paris #109/R est:7000-9000
Works on paper
£667 $1213 €1000 Paysage pres des Martigues (21x30cm-8x12in) s. pastel. 4-Jul-4 Eric Pillon, Calais #89/R
£900 $1548 €1314 Deauville, la plage (29x45cm-11x18in) s. pencil W/C prov. 7-Dec-3 Lots Road Auctions, London #350
£1056 $1827 €1500 Nu allonge de dos (35x52cm-14x20in) s. W/C dr. 9-Dec-3 Chambelland & Giafferi, Paris #58/R est:2000-2500
£1103 $1832 €1600 Allegorie de la mer (24x29cm-9x11in) s. W/C gouache. 30-Sep-3 Blanchet, Paris #272/R est:1800-2000
£1523 $2772 €2300 Cote Normande (31x47cm-12x19in) s. W/C prov. 15-Jun-4 Blanchet, Paris #150/R est:1000-1200
£1597 $2667 €2300 Saint-Claude (54x65cm-21x26in) st.sig. 23-Oct-3 Credit Municipal, Paris #92 est:1200-1500
£2349 $4370 €3500 Le port de Honfleur (36x53cm-14x21in) s.d.30 W/C pencil. 2-Mar-4 Artcurial Briest, Paris #43/R est:3000-4000
£2517 $4580 €3800 Port (48x63cm-19x25in) s.d.20 pastel. 18-Jun-4 Piasa, Paris #126/R est:2000-3000
£3448 $5759 €5000 Deux femmes a l'ouvrage (45x55cm-18x22in) s.d.28 pastel. 16-Nov-3 Muizon & Le Coent, Paris #43/R
£6053 $11137 €9200 Nature morte aux cartes (48x63cm-19x25in) s.d.1920 wax pastel prov. 28-Jun-4 Joron-Derem, Paris #159/R est:4000-5000

GERNLER, Karl Heinrich (1811-1880) Swiss
£705 $1198 €1029 Schloss Tarasp in Bundnerland (31x46cm-12x18in) s.i.d.1877 verso. 5-Nov-3 Dobiaschofsky, Bern #599/R (S.FR 1600)

GEROME, François (20th C) French?
£444 $800 €648 Luxembourg Park (61x76cm-24x30in) s.i. 20-Jan-4 Arthur James, Florida #153
£649 $1200 €948 La Notre Dame, Paris (58x74cm-23x29in) s.i. 13-Mar-4 DeFina, Austinburg #787/R
£1183 $2200 €1727 Champs Elysees (61x76cm-24x30in) s. painted c.1950. 7-Mar-4 Treadway Gallery, Cincinnati #534/R est:2500-3000

GEROME, J L (1824-1904) French
Sculpture
£1557 $2600 €2273 Woman with hoop (23cm-9in) s. bronze marble base. 19-Oct-3 Susanin's, Chicago #6005/R est:1000-1500

GEROME, Jean Léon (1824-1904) French
£5000 $9100 €7300 Tete de cheval en profil (23x31cm-9x12in) canvas on paper prov. 15-Jun-4 Sotheby's, London #106/R est:5000-7000
£7500 $13800 €10950 Porte (32x23cm-13x9in) 25-Mar-4 Christie's, Kensington #215/R est:3000-5000
£7500 $13650 €10950 Village dans une vallee (23x31cm-9x12in) prov. 15-Jun-4 Sotheby's, London #102/R est:7000-10000
£13000 $23660 €18980 L'ane egyptien (23x31cm-9x12in) canvas on paper painted c.1868 prov. 15-Jun-4 Sotheby's, London #107/R est:8000-12000
£16000 $29120 €23360 Campement pres de Constantinople (23x31cm-9x12in) prov. 15-Jun-4 Sotheby's, London #101/R est:12000-18000
£18000 $32760 €26280 Halte dans le desert (23x31cm-9x12in) prov. 15-Jun-4 Sotheby's, London #100/R est:7000-10000
£18000 $32760 €26280 Les montagnes au bord d'un wadi (23x31cm-9x12in) prov. 15-Jun-4 Sotheby's, London #104/R est:8000-12000
£19000 $34580 €27740 Route de Sinai (23x31cm-9x12in) s.i.verso prov. 15-Jun-4 Sotheby's, London #103/R est:8000-12000
£19000 $34580 €27740 Wadi (25x33cm-10x13in) prov. 15-Jun-4 Sotheby's, London #105/R est:7000-10000
£30000 $50100 €43800 Caravane dans le desert (14x63cm-6x25in) s. panel painted c.1860 prov.exhib. 14-Oct-3 Sotheby's, London #70/R est:30000-40000
£161972 $283451 €230000 Garcon et son ane (57x47cm-22x19in) s. prov. 16-Dec-3 Claude Aguttes, Neuilly #57/R est:250000-300000
£1700000 $3094000 €2482000 La grande piscine a Brusa (70x100cm-28x39in) s. painted 1885 prov.exhib.lit. 15-Jun-4 Sotheby's, London #112/R est:900000-1200000
Sculpture
£1655 $2764 €2400 Femme nue a la quenouille a l'enfant (34cm-13in) st.f.Siot gilt pat bronze. 17-Nov-3 Tajan, Paris #23/R est:1500-2000
£2964 $5306 €4327 Gladiator (39cm-15in) s. bronze granite pedestal prov. 15-May-4 Christie's, Sydney #177/R est:2500-3500 (A.D 7500)
£3360 $6014 €4906 Gladiator (39cm-15in) s. bronze granite pedestal prov. 15-May-4 Christie's, Sydney #176/R est:2500-3500 (A.D 8500)
£3497 $5944 €5000 La toilette (30cm-12in) s. num.P.119 gold bronze. 28-Nov-3 Doutrebente, Paris #50/R est:3000
£3824 $6500 €5583 Cesar franchissant le Rubicon (38cm-15in) s.i. pat bronze. 28-Oct-3 Christie's, Rockefeller NY #54/R
£4348 $7783 €6348 Dancer with a hoop (24cm-9in) painted marble onyx base prov. 15-May-4 Christie's, Sydney #370/R est:8000-12000 (A.D 11000)
£4500 $8100 €6570 The pursuit (25x18cm-10x7in) s.num.1758 brown green pat bronze st.f.Siot-Decauville lit. 21-Apr-4 Sotheby's, London #82/R est:5000-7000
£5000 $8650 €7300 Bacchante with a child (58cm-23in) s.num.C738 gilt brown pat bronze st.f.Siot-Decauville lit. 12-Dec-3 Sotheby's, London #251/R est:5000-7000
£6526 $11550 €9720 Bacchante et enfant a la quenouille (59cm-23in) s.st.f.Siot pat bronze prov. 30-Apr-4 Tajan, Paris #49/R est:5000-7000
£9000 $16380 €13140 Danseuse a la pomme (52cm-20in) s.num.G174 gilt bronze st.f.Siot Paris prov.lit. 17-Jun-4 Christie's, London #54/R est:10000-15000
£10500 $19110 €15330 Bacchante a la grappe (58cm-23in) s. gilt bronze st.f.Siot-Decauville prov.lit. 17-Jun-4 Christie's, London #53/R est:10000-15000
£27778 $50000 €40556 Nu se devoilant (99cm-39in) s. white marble prov.lit. 22-Apr-4 Christie's, Rockefeller NY #134/R est:60000-80000
Works on paper
£616 $1048 €900 Etude pour vente d'esclaves (34x22cm-13x9in) s.i. crayon. 6-Nov-3 Tajan, Paris #222
£7222 $13000 €10544 Study for le bain des femmes (29x22cm-11x9in) s.i. graphite exhib.lit. 23-Apr-4 Sotheby's, New York #46/R est:10000-15000

GEROS, Dimitris (1948-) Greek
£4500 $8055 €6570 Boat and cat (50x35cm-20x14in) s. 10-May-4 Sotheby's, Olympia #84/R est:2000-3000

GERRARD, Roy (20th C) British
Works on paper
£350 $644 €511 Battle (25x46cm-10x18in) s. W/C. 24-Jun-4 Locke & England, Leamington Spa #140/R

GERRITS, Gerrit Jacobus (1893-1965) Dutch
£336 $561 €480 Untitled (45x30cm-18x12in) s.d.61 paper. 30-Jun-3 Sotheby's, Amsterdam #167
Works on paper
£526 $968 €800 Composition (40x28cm-16x11in) init.d.46 gouache pastel. 22-Jun-4 Christie's, Amsterdam #372/R

GERRITSEN, Wim (1929-) Dutch
Works on paper
£294 $499 €420 Composition (27x36cm-11x14in) s.d.59 Indian ink. 24-Nov-3 Glerum, Amsterdam #230/R
£664 $1129 €950 Read hop (52x73cm-20x29in) s.d.57 gouache. 24-Nov-3 Glerum, Amsterdam #247/R
£699 $1189 €1000 Composition (53x74cm-21x29in) s.d.55 gouache. 24-Nov-3 Glerum, Amsterdam #244/R
£769 $1308 €1100 Composition (74x53cm-29x21in) s.d.56 gouache. 24-Nov-3 Glerum, Amsterdam #242/R
£1538 $2615 €2200 Figure with large ear (74x53cm-29x21in) s.d.54 gouache. 24-Nov-3 Glerum, Amsterdam #240/R est:1000-2000

GERRITSZ, Hessel (1581-1632) Dutch
Prints
£2797 $4755 €4000 Outdoor party (12x17cm-5x7in) etching. 27-Nov-3 Bassenge, Berlin #5205/R est:2000

GERRY, Samuel Lancaster (1813-1891) American
£667 $1200 €974 Mother and child in an Alpine landscape (47x32cm-19x13in) s. 24-Apr-4 Weschler, Washington #627/R est:2500-3500
£2335 $3900 €3409 Forest landscape with cows in stream (51x76cm-20x30in) s. 16-Nov-3 CRN Auctions, Cambridge #13/R
£2582 $4750 €3770 Pastoral landscape with cows by the riverside (30x51cm-12x20in) s. 26-Jun-4 Sloans & Kenyon, Bethesda #1101/R est:4000-6000

GERSHT, Ori (1967-) Israeli
Photographs
£2793 $5000 €4078 Sarajevo (127x122cm-50x48in) c-print edition 3 of 5. 18-Mar-4 Sotheby's, New York #82/R est:5000-7000

GERSHUNI, Moshe (1936-) Israeli
£4469 $8000 €6525 Untitled (89x73cm-35x29in) s.d.1996 verso exhib. 18-Mar-4 Sotheby's, New York #73/R est:6000-8000
Works on paper
£5028 $9000 €7341 Where are you now (70x99cm-28x39in) i. mixed media card exec.c.1980. 18-Mar-4 Sotheby's, New York #54/R est:8000-10000

GERSON, Hans (1882-?) German
£329 $605 €500 Vue de village (54x73cm-21x29in) s. 28-Jun-4 Joron-Derem, Paris #103

GERSON, Wojciech (1831-1901) Polish
£1567 $2445 €2288 Smoking fire in a landscape (18x32cm-7x13in) s. 30-Mar-3 Agra, Warsaw #32/R est:7000-10000 (P.Z 10000)

GERSTENBRAND, Alfred (1891-1977) Austrian
Works on paper
£1208 $2223 €1800 At the race track (45x67cm-18x26in) s. col chk W/C. 26-Mar-4 Dorotheum, Vienna #333/R est:1200-1500

GERT, Edith (1906-) Danish
£380 $700 €555 Parlor scene with woman seated doing needlework (66x76cm-26x30in) s. 29-Mar-4 O'Gallerie, Oregon #748/R

GERTLER, Mark (1891-1939) British
£18000 $32940 €26280 Still life with dahlias and chrysanthemums (47x28cm-19x11in) board painted c.1925 prov. 4-Jun-4 Christie's, London #24/R est:8000-12000
Works on paper
£310 $518 €453 Reclining female nude (28x33cm-11x13in) pencil dr. 17-Oct-3 Keys, Aylsham #551
£550 $946 €803 Portrait of girl (36x26cm-14x10in) pencil prov. 3-Dec-3 Cheffins, Cambridge #602/R
£600 $1092 €876 Standing female nude with raised arms (28x18cm-11x7in) s. pencil. 16-Jun-4 Andrew Hartley, Ilkley #990/R
£620 $1091 €905 Standing female nude, rear view (22x39cm-9x15in) s. pencil sketch. 18-May-4 Fellows & Sons, Birmingham #299/R
£900 $1593 €1314 Female nude (37x28cm-15x11in) s. pencil. 28-Apr-4 George Kidner, Lymington #190/R
£1500 $2580 €2190 Dorset garden (36x28cm-14x11in) W/C prov. 3-Dec-3 Cheffins, Cambridge #589/R est:300-400
£2100 $3843 €3066 Head of a girl (27x22cm-11x9in) s. chl. 7-Apr-4 Woolley & Wallis, Salisbury #114/R est:800-1200
£2400 $4008 €3504 Head of a girl (30x20cm-12x8in) s.d.1932 chl. 14-Oct-3 David Lay, Penzance #180/R est:1200-1800

GERTLER, Tibor (1902-?) Hungarian
Works on paper
£769 $1308 €1100 Nu debout (31x20cm-12x8in) st. pencil. 27-Nov-3 Calmels Cohen, Paris #39/R

GERTNER, Johan Vilhelm (1818-1871) Danish
£10743 $19660 €15685 After the fall of man - Adam and Eve outside Garden of Eden (122x95cm-48x37in) 9-Jun-4 Rasmussen, Copenhagen #1413/R est:40000-50000 (D.KR 120000)

GERTSCH, Franz (1930-) Swiss
£2826 $5172 €4126 Friends (103x115cm-41x45in) s. 7-Jun-4 Christie's, Zurich #130/R est:6000-8000 (S.FR 6500)
Prints
£10839 $18427 €15500 Water (85x102cm-33x40in) s. verso wood engraving. 29-Nov-3 Villa Grisebach, Berlin #396/R est:7000-9000

GERUZEZ, Victor (1840-1906) French
Works on paper
£822 $1397 €1200 Promenade en caleche (15x26cm-6x10in) s.d. W/C pen ink sold with other 3 dr. 6-Nov-3 Tajan, Paris #232

GERVAIS, Eugène (19th C) French
Works on paper
£333 $557 €480 Untitled. W/C. 27-Oct-3 Giraudeau, Tours #11

GERVAIS, Lise (1933-1998) Canadian
£250 $408 €365 Bijoux marins (46x61cm-18x24in) s.d.62oil on paper prov. 23-Sep-3 Ritchie, Toronto #182 (C.D 550)
£268 $447 €389 Sans titre (46x36cm-18x14in) s. board. 17-Jun-3 Pinneys, Montreal #149 (C.D 600)
£2400 $4392 €3504 D'Azure et de nuit (150x150cm-59x59in) painted 1969. 1-Jun-4 Joyner Waddington, Toronto #85/R est:10000-12000 (C.D 6000)
£3252 $5821 €4748 Untitled abstract composition (72x81cm-28x32in) s.d.1974 prov. 31-May-4 Sotheby's, Toronto #115/R est:5000-7000 (C.D 8000)
£3829 $6509 €5590 Untitled 7 (91x91cm-36x36in) s.d.65 prov. 18-Nov-3 Sotheby's, Toronto #30/R est:5000-7000 (C.D 8500)
£6098 $10915 €8903 Untitled (183x61cm-72x24in) s.d.79 prov. 31-May-4 Sotheby's, Toronto #98/R est:10000-12000 (C.D 15000)
£6757 $11486 €9865 Les iles sous le vent (97x88cm-38x35in) s.d.61 exhib.prov. 18-Nov-3 Sotheby's, Toronto #29/R est:7000-9000 (C.D 15000)
£8036 $13821 €11733 Empire de sources diaprees (180x150cm-71x59in) painted 1972 prov.lit. 2-Dec-3 Joyner Waddington, Toronto #115/R est:10000-12000 (C.D 18000)

GERVAIS, Paul Jean (1859-1936) French
Works on paper
£300 $537 €450 Scene de parc (59x71cm-23x28in) s. gouache. 12-May-4 Brissoneau, France #69

GERVASONI, Federica Giuliano (1838-1915) Italian
£2349 $4393 €3500 Beach with figures (40x60cm-16x24in) 26-Feb-4 Cambi, Genoa #573/R est:500-600

GERVEX, Henri (1852-1929) French
£267 $485 €400 Untitled (17x10cm-7x4in) s. panel. 30-Jun-4 Delvaux, Paris #22
£3355 $6174 €5100 Bord de plage a Trouville (21x33cm-8x13in) s. panel. 25-Jun-4 Millon & Associes, Paris #87/R est:2500-3000
£4082 $7306 €6000 Femme se degantant (35x26cm-14x10in) mono. panel. 19-Mar-4 Millon & Associes, Paris #70/R est:7000-8000
£4333 $7973 €6500 La cabane sur la plage de Trouville (16x21cm-6x8in) s. cardboard. 11-Jun-4 Pierre Berge, Paris #226/R est:4000-6000
£8333 $15000 €12166 Roulee par la vague (27x49cm-11x19in) s. 23-Apr-4 Sotheby's, New York #205/R est:15000-20000
£250000 $430000 €365000 Retour de bal (151x201cm-59x79in) s.d.1879 prov.exhib.lit. 3-Dec-3 Christie's, London #32/R est:100000-150000

GERVILLE, A de (19th C) French
£1408 $2437 €2000 Le marche aux fleurs a Rouen (62x73cm-24x29in) s. 13-Dec-3 Martinot & Savignat, Pontoise #224 est:2000-2500
£1549 $2680 €2200 Le marche a Rouen (54x73cm-21x29in) s. 13-Dec-3 Martinot & Savignat, Pontoise #223/R est:2000-2500

GERZSO, Gunther (1915-2000) Mexican
£22059 $37500 €32206 Paisaje (37x81cm-15x32in) s.d.91 prov.exhib.lit. 19-Nov-3 Sotheby's, New York #16/R est:45000-55000
£22353 $38000 €32635 Figura (45x36cm-18x14in) s.d.57 oil on masonite prov. 18-Nov-3 Christie's, Rockefeller NY #24/R est:40000-60000
£36313 $65000 €53017 Green landscape I (60x81cm-24x32in) s.d.69 s.d.verso masonite. 26-May-4 Sotheby's, New York #12/R est:50000-60000
Works on paper
£3022 $5500 €4412 Proyecto (19x28cm-7x11in) s.d.72 ink. 29-Jun-4 Sotheby's, New York #417/R est:6000-7000

GESELSCHAP, Eduard (1814-1878) Dutch
£1733 $3137 €2600 Mother and child (21x17cm-8x7in) s.d.1859 panel. 1-Apr-4 Van Ham, Cologne #1394/R est:2600

£2313 $3678 €3400 Le matin de Saint-Nicolas (48x56cm-19x22in) s. 23-Mar-3 Mercier & Cie, Lille #204/R est:4000-5000
£8511 $14213 €12000 Sister and brother (43x33cm-17x13in) s.d.1855. 21-Jun-3 Hans Stahl, Hamburg #22/R est:12000

GESMAR, Charles (1900-1928) ?
Works on paper
£379 $630 €550 Danseuse aux etoiles (30x23cm-12x9in) s. pen ink. 6-Oct-3 Blanchet, Paris #268/R

GESSA Y ARIAS, Sebastian (1840-1920) Spanish
£922 $1540 €1300 Still life with lobster (26x17cm-10x7in) s.d.86 panel. 23-Jun-3 Durán, Madrid #75/R
£2174 $3565 €3000 Still life with fruit (51x61cm-20x24in) s. 27-May-3 Durán, Madrid #250/R est:3000
£2819 $5243 €4200 Fruit (39x23cm-15x9in) s. 2-Mar-4 Ansorena, Madrid #11/R est:1200

GESSI, Francesco (1588-1649) Italian
£3500 $6055 €5110 Madonna and Child (73x95cm-29x37in) feigned oval. 12-Dec-3 Christie's, Kensington #184/R est:6000-8000

GESSNER, Alberto (19/20th C) German
£270 $430 €392 Dock scene with houses (20x28cm-8x11in) s. canvasboard. 12-Sep-3 Aspire, Cleveland #69

GESSNER, Conrad (1764-1826) Swiss
Works on paper
£407 $692 €594 Goatherd by woodland stream (28x40cm-11x16in) s. i. verso sepia bodycol. 28-Nov-3 Zofingen, Switzerland #2462 (S.FR 900)

GESSNER, Richard (1894-1988) German
£764 $1260 €1100 Landscape near Reil an der Mosel (87x100cm-34x39in) s.d.31. 3-Jul-3 Van Ham, Cologne #1201/R
Works on paper
£451 $745 €650 Rhine shore in Dusseldorf (44x55cm-17x22in) s.d.26 pastel. 3-Jul-3 Van Ham, Cologne #1202/R

GESSNER, Robert S (1908-1982) Swiss
£679 $1133 €991 Gorges (14x50cm-6x20in) s.i.d.1973 verso board. 24-Jun-3 Germann, Zurich #102 (S.FR 1500)
£679 $1133 €991 Untitled (50x55cm-20x22in) s.d.1958 verso pavatex. 24-Jun-3 Germann, Zurich #105/R (S.FR 1500)
£860 $1436 €1256 Memorial to Thomas Moore Street London (43x31cm-17x12in) s.i.d.1948 oil chk paper on board. 24-Jun-3 Germann, Zurich #104 (S.FR 1900)
Works on paper
£407 $692 €594 Music by night (24x19cm-9x7in) s.i.d.1953 W/C Indian ink. 25-Nov-3 Germann, Zurich #105/R (S.FR 900)
£679 $1154 €991 Pharos (39x57cm-15x22in) s.i.d.1958 gouache Indian ink. 25-Nov-3 Germann, Zurich #106/R est:1800-2300 (S.FR 1500)

GESSNER, Salomon (1730-1788) Swiss
Works on paper
£3493 $6253 €5100 Arcadian landscape (25x35cm-10x14in) s.d.1783 gouache. 26-May-4 Sotheby's, Zurich #1/R est:8000-12000 (S.FR 8000)
£5046 $8427 €7317 Sleeping nymph by waterfall with herd of sheep (34x28cm-13x11in) s.d.1781 gouache prov.lit.exhib. 23-Jun-3 Philippe Schuler, Zurich #3893/R est:8000-9000 (S.FR 11000)

GESSNER, Salomon (attrib) (1730-1788) Swiss
£352 $563 €500 Alpine landscape with waterfall by farmstead (43x52cm-17x20in) panel lit. 19-Sep-3 Karlheinz Kaupp, Staufen #1890/R
£388 $694 €566 Self portrait (66x52cm-26x20in) i. stretcher. 12-May-4 Dobiaschofsky, Bern #549/R (S.FR 900)

GESTA, Louis Victor (1828-?) French
£1413 $2600 €2063 Still life with daisies, poppies and mums (53x36cm-21x14in) s. panel. 27-Mar-4 New Orleans Auction, New Orleans #602/R est:3000-5000

GESTEL, Leo (1881-1941) Dutch
£3497 $6014 €5000 Nacht (52x64cm-20x25in) s.i.d.08 prov. 2-Dec-3 Sotheby's, Amsterdam #249/R est:8000-12000
£12000 $22080 €18000 Schovenladen (34x48cm-13x19in) s.d.08 s.i. stretcher prov. 9-Jun-4 Christie's, Amsterdam #198/R est:18000-22000
£41958 $72168 €60000 Het land van montfoort (51x85cm-20x33in) s.d.09 s.i.stretcher prov. 2-Dec-3 Sotheby's, Amsterdam #9/R est:60000-90000
£43478 $71304 €60000 Landscape near Montfoort (45x57cm-18x22in) s.d.09 s.i. on stretcher prov.exhib. 27-May-3 Sotheby's, Amsterdam #312/R est:40000-60000
Works on paper
£349 $642 €520 Swiss mountain landscape (23x32cm-9x13in) studio st. black chk. 29-Mar-4 Glerum, Amsterdam #88
£461 $847 €700 Mountain village (45x60cm-18x24in) s.i.d.1924 black chk. 22-Jun-4 Christie's, Amsterdam #451/R
£467 $854 €700 German mountain landscape (49x65cm-19x26in) s.d.1923 black chk. 7-Jun-4 Glerum, Amsterdam #123/R
£625 $1150 €950 Portrait of a woman (33x25cm-13x10in) s.d.30 pastel. 22-Jun-4 Christie's, Amsterdam #473/R
£658 $1211 €1000 The chair-bottomer (21x16cm-8x6in) mono.i.d.02 pencil W/C gouache prov. 22-Jun-4 Christie's, Amsterdam #533/R
£658 $1211 €1000 Portrait of a man (20x17cm-8x7in) s. blk chk sold with work by Lucebert two. 28-Jun-4 Sotheby's, Amsterdam #247/R
£680 $1238 €1000 View of Positano (28x19cm-11x7in) s. black chk pastel two. 3-Feb-4 Christie's, Amsterdam #445 est:1000-1500
£699 $1189 €1000 Farmers at work (35x48cm-14x19in) s.d.25 blk chk prov. 25-Nov-3 Christie's, Amsterdam #6/R
£789 $1453 €1200 A farm in winter (50x63cm-20x25in) s.d.37 black chk. 22-Jun-4 Christie's, Amsterdam #537/R
£855 $1574 €1300 Beach scene (28x36cm-11x14in) i. d.1941 verso pastel. 28-Jun-4 Sotheby's, Amsterdam #246/R
£874 $1460 €1250 Portrait of a little girl (59x45cm-23x18in) s.d.1920 i.verso black chk prov. 30-Jun-3 Sotheby's, Amsterdam #403/R
£903 $1426 €1300 Cows in the orchard (42x58cm-17x23in) s. W/C black chk. 2-Sep-3 Christie's, Amsterdam #384/R est:1000-1500
£921 $1695 €1400 Doing needle work (22x14cm-9x6in) s.i.d.02 pencil W/C gouache htd white prov. 22-Jun-4 Christie's, Amsterdam #532/R
£1088 $1981 €1600 Schwarzwald (64x50cm-25x20in) s.d.1923 chl. 3-Feb-4 Christie's, Amsterdam #501 est:700-900
£1316 $2421 €2000 Doing the laundry (44x30cm-17x12in) s. black chk pastel. 22-Jun-4 Christie's, Amsterdam #433/R est:2000-3000
£1319 $2085 €1900 Horses (24x31cm-9x12in) studio st. pastel pencil crayons. 2-Sep-3 Christie's, Amsterdam #399 est:1000-1500
£1333 $2453 €2000 Belgische vluchtelingen nachtelijk kamp (40x54cm-16x21in) s.i.d.1914 pencil blk chk W/C exhib. 9-Jun-4 Christie's, Amsterdam #63/R est:3000-5000
£1361 $2435 €2000 Belgian refugees 1914 (46x62cm-18x24in) chl. 17-Mar-4 De Zwann, Amsterdam #4640/R est:2000-4000
£1467 $2699 €2200 Bavarian village (65x50cm-26x20in) s.i. blk chk W/C. 9-Jun-4 Christie's, Amsterdam #11/R est:2500-3500
£2000 $3680 €3000 Reclining nude (46x63cm-18x25in) s.d.33 blk red white chk prov. 8-Jun-4 Sotheby's, Amsterdam #203/R est:3000-4000
£3846 $6538 €5500 Sailing boats in a canal (31x49cm-12x19in) studio st. gouache. 25-Nov-3 Christie's, Amsterdam #28/R est:5000-7000
£4545 $7727 €6500 Reclining nude with white horses (49x59cm-19x23in) studio st. gouache. 25-Nov-3 Christie's, Amsterdam #161/R est:6000-8000
£4800 $8832 €7200 De Beemster (49x64cm-19x25in) s.i.d.1921 W/C prov. 8-Jun-4 Sotheby's, Amsterdam #3/R est:8000-12000
£5000 $9000 €7500 Still life with flowers (47x36cm-19x14in) s.d.1912 W/C exhib. 26-Apr-4 Bernaerts, Antwerp #539/R est:3500-4000
£5594 $9622 €8000 Bloemstilleven (74x52cm-29x20in) s.d.17 W/C. 2-Dec-3 Sotheby's, Amsterdam #14/R est:8000-12000
£6250 $11500 €9500 Figuren met Paard (36x44cm-14x17in) s.d.28 pastel. 28-Jun-4 Sotheby's, Amsterdam #242/R est:1500-2000
£6643 $11294 €9500 Still life with tulips and daffodils in a vase (74x54cm-29x21in) s.d.18 W/C blk chk. 25-Nov-3 Christie's, Amsterdam #17/R est:6000-8000
£7692 $13077 €11000 Seated elegant lady (28x20cm-11x8in) s. blk chk pencil gouache W/C. 25-Nov-3 Christie's, Amsterdam #158/R est:7000-9000
£8392 $14434 €12000 Piet Boendermaker (77x69cm-30x27in) s.d.1 Aug 1917 verso W/C black chk prov.lit. 2-Dec-3 Sotheby's, Amsterdam #24/R est:10000-15000
£13986 $23776 €20000 Milking time in the Beemster (66x89cm-26x35in) s.i.d.1922 W/C. 25-Nov-3 Christie's, Amsterdam #162/R est:10000-15000
£14667 $26987 €22000 Rollerskating (39x51cm-15x20in) s. blk chk pastel exec. c.1908-1910. 9-Jun-4 Christie's, Amsterdam #194/R est:20000-30000
£21739 $35652 €30000 Girl friends (56x75cm-22x30in) s.d.1927 s.i.d.1927 verso pastel prov.lit. 27-May-3 Sotheby's, Amsterdam #314/R est:20000-30000
£93333 $171733 €140000 Chatting ladies (102x130cm-40x51in) s.d.1912 pastel prov. 8-Jun-4 Sotheby's, Amsterdam #5/R est:70000-90000

GETAZ, Jean Louis (1931-) Swiss
£345 $617 €504 Village in winter with horse drawn sledge (70x89cm-28x35in) s. 12-May-4 Dobiaschofsky, Bern #550/R (S.FR 800)

GETHIN, Percy (19th C) Irish?
Works on paper
£420 $713 €600 Continental village with canal bridge (21x25cm-8x10in) pencil exhib. 25-Nov-3 Hamilton Osborne King, Dublin #46/R

GETZ, Arthur (1913-1996) American
Works on paper
£2994 $5000 €4371 Movie theatre lobby scene, usherette watching film (58x43cm-23x17in) s. casein prov. 15-Nov-3 Illustration House, New York #107/R est:6000-8000

GETZELMANN, C (19th C) European
£3100 $5673 €4526 Horse ferry (68x106cm-27x42in) s. indis d. 7-Apr-4 Bonhams, Bury St Edmunds #462/R est:1200-1800

GEUDENS, Albert (?) Belgian
£289 $533 €440 Interieur de beguinage (65x54cm-26x21in) s. 22-Jun-4 Palais de Beaux Arts, Brussels #247
£360 $637 €526 Still life of chrysanthemums in Satsuma vase (89x71cm-35x28in) s. 29-Apr-4 Gorringes, Lewes #2470
£400 $720 €600 Still life with chrysantemums in pewter vase (60x70cm-24x28in) s. 26-Apr-4 Bernaerts, Antwerp #408/R
£500 $895 €750 Woman at the window (80x70cm-31x28in) s.d.1946. 15-May-4 De Vuyst, Lokeren #144
£500 $900 €750 Interieur rustique anime (70x80cm-28x31in) s. 20-Apr-4 Galerie Moderne, Brussels #251/R
£503 $931 €750 Alter-boys (100x80cm-39x31in) s. 13-Mar-4 De Vuyst, Lokeren #149
£1333 $2387 €2000 The disguiser (100x63cm-39x25in) s. 15-May-4 De Vuyst, Lokeren #143 est:750-1000

GEVA, Tzibi (1951-) Israeli?
£10056 $18000 €14682 Starry night (213x193cm-84x76in) s.d.89 verso s.i.d.1989 stretcher diptych. 18-Mar-4 Sotheby's, New York #66/R est:18000-24000

GEVERS, Emma (19th C) British?
£280 $476 €409 Still life with blue and white vase of roses and other flowers (51x41cm-20x16in) s.d.1896. 29-Nov-3 Canterbury Auctions, UK #589

GEYER, Alexius (1816-1883) German

£431	$772	€629	Goatherd by lake in the mountains (41x57cm-16x22in) s. 12-May-4 Dobiaschofsky, Bern #551/R (S.FR 1000)

GEYER, Fritz (1875-1947) German

£350	$648	€511	Figures in North European street, Cathedral beyond (79x69cm-31x27in) s. 15-Jan-4 Christie's, Kensington #978/R
£979	$1635	€1400	Oriental scene (53x79cm-21x31in) s. 24-Jun-3 Finarte Semenzato, Rome #83

GEYER, Georg (1823-1912) Austrian

£280	$476	€400	Mountain stream (47x38cm-19x15in) s.d.1883. 22-Nov-3 Arnold, Frankfurt #524/R
£350	$594	€500	Summer valley with watermill (47x38cm-19x15in) s.d.1883. 22-Nov-3 Arnold, Frankfurt #525/R
£369	$679	€550	Watermill in mountains (54x42cm-21x17in) s.d.1878 paper on canvas. 27-Mar-4 L & B, Essen #121/R
£667	$1200	€1000	Cairo (43x32cm-17x13in) s.d.1871. 26-Apr-4 Rieber, Stuttgart #1221/R
£861	$1575	€1300	Trees (56x43cm-22x17in) s.d.879. 8-Apr-4 Dorotheum, Vienna #128/R
£867	$1569	€1300	Stream through mountain woodlands (52x42cm-20x17in) s.d.878 lit. 3-Apr-4 Hans Stahl, Hamburg #28/R
£1745	$3263	€2600	Alpine landscape (31x41cm-12x16in) s.d.853 i. verso board. 24-Feb-4 Dorotheum, Vienna #170/R est:1500-1800

GEYER, Herman (19th C) American

£2890	$5000	€4219	Man fishing (76x102cm-30x40in) s.i. 10-Dec-3 Alderfer's, Hatfield #325/R est:4000-6000

GEYER, Max (1904-1958) Czechoslovakian

Works on paper

£667	$1193	€1000	Light path (37x27cm-15x11in) s. W/C bodycol prov. 14-May-4 Ketterer, Munich #24/R
£1533	$2745	€2300	Trees in mountain landscape (46x31cm-18x12in) W/C double-sided prov. 14-May-4 Ketterer, Munich #25/R est:150-2500

GEYGER, Ernst Moritz (1861-1941) German

Sculpture

£1689	$3074	€2550	Archer (61cm-24in) s. black brown pat.bronze Cast.C.F.Otto Muller Karlsruhe. 19-Jun-4 Dannenberg, Berlin #186/R est:400

GEYLING, Carl (1814-1880) Austrian

£4196	$7133	€6000	Hallstatter See (69x55cm-27x22in) s. 24-Nov-3 Dorotheum, Vienna #169/R est:6000-8000
£4895	$8322	€7000	Hohen Salzburg seen from the foot of the Kreutzberg (41x49cm-16x19in) s.i.d.1840 verso board. 24-Nov-3 Dorotheum, Vienna #3/R est:7000-8000

GEYP, Adriaan Marinus (1855-1926) Dutch

£420	$713	€600	Farmer's wife and child walking home (71x50cm-28x20in) s. 29-Nov-3 Sigalas, Stuttgart #275/R
£700	$1323	€1022	Skaters and sledgers in a frozen winter landscape (66x53cm-26x21in) s. 19-Feb-4 Christie's, Kensington #163
£1042	$1646	€1500	Little saleswoman (53x43cm-21x17in) s.d.1902. 2-Sep-3 Christie's, Amsterdam #196/R est:1200-1600
£1701	$3095	€2500	Seasons, forest path in summer and autumn (50x40cm-20x16in) s. pair. 3-Feb-4 Christie's, Amsterdam #278/R est:2500-3500

GEZA, Veros (1897-?) Hungarian

£3480	$6159	€5220	Vase of flowers (100x73cm-39x29in) painted 1897. 27-Apr-4 Bolsa de Arte, Rio de Janeiro #36/R (B.R 19000)

GFELLER, Rolf (1926-) Swiss

£341	$566	€494	Female nude on blue cloth (34x32cm-13x13in) s.d.1996 dispersion panel. 13-Jun-3 Zofingen, Switzerland #2852/R (S.FR 750)

GFELLER, Werner (1895-1985) Swiss?

£431	$772	€629	Yellow meadow flowers (29x21cm-11x8in) mono. board. 12-May-4 Dobiaschofsky, Bern #552/R (S.FR 1000)
£560	$1003	€818	Bielersee shore (24x36cm-9x14in) i. verso canvas on panel. 14-May-4 Dobiaschofsky, Bern #118/R (S.FR 1300)
£733	$1312	€1070	Still life with geranium (30x35cm-12x14in) panel. 14-May-4 Dobiaschofsky, Bern #117/R est:1800 (S.FR 1700)
£991	$1775	€1447	Emmental (33x48cm-13x19in) mono. s.i. verso panel. 14-May-4 Dobiaschofsky, Bern #138/R est:2600 (S.FR 2300)

GHAFARI, Abul Hasan (18th C) Persian

Works on paper

£30000	$53100	€43800	Karim Khan Zand with his horse and groom (20x29cm-8x11in) i. gouache htd gold. 27-Apr-4 Christie's, London #81/R est:8000-12000

GHEDUZZI, Augusto (1883-1969) Italian

£2800	$5152	€4200	Vase of flowers (116x179cm-46x70in) s. 8-Jun-4 Della Rocca, Turin #214/R est:2800-3200

GHEDUZZI, Cesare (1894-1944) Italian

£1007	$1782	€1500	Figure in landscape (30x40cm-12x16in) s. board. 1-May-4 Meeting Art, Vercelli #100 est:1500
£1111	$1889	€1600	Back from pasture (44x29cm-17x11in) s. board. 1-Nov-3 Meeting Art, Vercelli #77/R est:1000
£1181	$2007	€1700	Along the Liguria coast (30x40cm-12x16in) s. board. 1-Nov-3 Meeting Art, Vercelli #218/R est:1000
£1192	$2170	€1800	Coast in Liguria (30x44cm-12x17in) s. board. 17-Jun-4 Finarte Semenzato, Milan #313/R est:1200-1400
£1208	$2138	€1800	Cottages in Macugnaga (27x44cm-11x17in) s. board. 1-May-4 Meeting Art, Vercelli #416 est:1500
£1361	$2435	€2000	Venice (29x37cm-11x15in) s. board. 22-Mar-4 Sant Agostino, Torino #269/R est:2500
£1800	$3258	€2700	Shepherdess in the field (50x70cm-20x28in) s. 30-Mar-4 Babuino, Rome #392/R est:1200
£1946	$3445	€2900	Composition with flowers (32x45cm-13x18in) s. s.i.verso cardboard. 1-May-4 Meeting Art, Vercelli #327 est:1500
£2657	$4571	€3800	Seascape with boats (60x90cm-24x35in) s. 3-Dec-3 Stadion, Trieste #1010/R est:2500-3500
£2721	$4871	€4000	Rural landscape (70x100cm-28x39in) s. 22-Mar-4 Sant Agostino, Torino #248/R est:4500
£2781	$5062	€4200	San Michele, Pagana (30x44cm-12x17in) s. board. 17-Jun-4 Finarte Semenzato, Milan #314/R est:1500-1700
£3356	$5940	€5000	Countryside in Piedmonte (70x100cm-28x39in) s. 1-May-4 Meeting Art, Vercelli #489 est:5000
£3472	$5903	€5000	Seascape in BOrdighera (70x100cm-28x39in) s. 1-Nov-3 Meeting Art, Vercelli #447/R est:5000
£3662	$6335	€5200	Farm on the lake (70x100cm-28x39in) s. 9-Dec-3 Finarte Semenzato, Milan #53/R est:4000-5000
£4317	$7079	€6000	Mount Cervino (45x120cm-18x47in) board. 5-Jun-3 Adma, Formigine #476 est:5500-6000

GHEDUZZI, Giuseppe (1889-1957) Italian

£559	$934	€800	Landscape with peasant woman (15x15cm-6x6in) s. 26-Jun-3 Sant Agostino, Torino #54/R
£565	$1039	€825	Pressi di carignano (30x46cm-12x18in) s. s.i.verso panel. 14-Jun-4 Waddingtons, Toronto #327/R est:1000-1500 (C.D 1400)
£1042	$1771	€1500	Fishing (15x19cm-6x7in) s. board. 1-Nov-3 Meeting Art, Vercelli #68/R est:1500
£1087	$1783	€1500	Landscape with figure (39x31cm-15x12in) s. cardboard on canvas. 29-May-3 Galleria Pace, Milan #90/R
£1342	$2376	€2000	San Maurizio's Church (33x44cm-13x17in) s. i.verso board. 1-May-4 Meeting Art, Vercelli #48 est:2000
£1611	$2851	€2400	Cottages in Valtournanche (27x32cm-11x13in) s. board. 1-May-4 Meeting Art, Vercelli #437 est:2000
£1678	$2970	€2500	Landscape in Piedmonte (32x45cm-13x18in) s. board. 1-May-4 Meeting Art, Vercelli #352 est:2500
£1812	$3207	€2700	Snowfall (35x24cm-14x9in) s. board. 1-May-4 Meeting Art, Vercelli #442 est:2500
£2000	$3680	€3000	Rural scene (31x43cm-12x17in) s. board prov. 14-Jun-4 Sant Agostino, Torino #281/R est:3000-4000
£2200	$4048	€3212	Veduta di Valtournanche nel mese di Guigno (32x45cm-13x18in) indis.sig. s.i.verso panel. 23-Mar-4 Bonhams, New Bond Street #82/R est:1000-15000
£2378	$3971	€3400	Sheep (40x60cm-16x24in) s. board. 26-Jun-3 Sant Agostino, Torino #42/R
£3819	$6493	€5500	Still life (60x90cm-24x35in) s.d.1938. 1-Nov-3 Meeting Art, Vercelli #337/R
£3819	$6493	€5500	Still life (60x90cm-24x35in) s.d.1939. 1-Nov-3 Meeting Art, Vercelli #338/R est:5000
£3889	$6611	€5600	Cottages in Macugnaga (33x45cm-13x18in) s. i.verso board. 1-Nov-3 Meeting Art, Vercelli #432/R est:4000
£5556	$9444	€8000	Farms in Macugnaga (50x65cm-20x26in) s. i.verso board. 1-Nov-3 Meeting Art, Vercelli #236/R est:8000

GHEDUZZI, Mario (1891-1970) Italian

£272	$487	€400	Landscape with herd in Leyni (18x23cm-7x9in) s. s.i.verso cardboard. 22-Mar-4 Sant Agostino, Torino #200/R
£500	$920	€750	By Rivara, pasture (24x30cm-9x12in) s. s.i.verso board. 14-Jun-4 Sant Agostino, Torino #125/R
£1042	$1771	€1500	Countryside near Vercelli (40x50cm-16x20in) s. s.i.verso board. 1-Nov-3 Meeting Art, Vercelli #311/R est:1500
£1067	$1963	€1600	Still life (36x51cm-14x20in) board. 8-Jun-4 Della Rocca, Turin #332/R est:500-900

GHEDUZZI, Ugo (1853-1925) Italian

£667	$1193	€1000	Landscape with waterfall (36x53cm-14x21in) s. 13-May-4 Babuino, Rome #223
£2308	$3854	€3300	Rural scene (37x59cm-15x23in) s. board. 26-Jun-3 Sant Agostino, Torino #47/R est:4000
£2465	$4264	€3500	Back from the Alps (31x46cm-12x18in) s. cardboard exhib. 10-Dec-3 Sotheby's, Milan #45/R est:3500-4500
£5369	$9503	€8000	Alpine view (87x149cm-34x59in) s. lit. 1-May-4 Meeting Art, Vercelli #108 est:8000

GHEDUZZI, Ugo (attrib) (1853-1925) Italian

£1067	$1909	€1600	River landscape with angler and mountains beyond (97x138cm-38x54in) s. 13-May-4 Babuino, Rome #272/R est:800-1000

GHEE, Robert Edgar Taylor (1872-1951) Australian

£569	$1019	€831	Camp Juoliet, Ballarat (15x22cm-6x9in) painted 1914 board. 10-May-4 Joel, Victoria #224 est:1000-1500 (A.D 1400)

GHEERAERTS, Marcus (younger-circle) (1561-1635) British

£14000	$25760	€20440	Portrait of a lady, a member of the Spiering family of Baden and Bavaria (196x102cm-77x40in) i. 26-Mar-4 Sotheby's, London #5/R est:5000-7000
£20000	$33200	€29200	Portrait of a lady, wearing white embroidered dress with flowers and figures (112x89cm-44x35in) panel prov. 30-Sep-3 Sotheby's, London #36/R est:15000-20000

GHEERAERTS, Marcus (younger-style) (1561-1635) Belgian

£18000	$33120	€26280	Portrait of Sir John Needham, in armour with a grey doublet and hose (209x109cm-82x43in) prov. 11-Jun-4 Christie's, London #1/R est:20000-30000

GHELARDUCCI, Giulio (1883-1970) Italian

£360	$590	€500	Madonna del Sasso (31x44cm-12x17in) s. s.i.d.1944 board. 10-Jun-3 Pandolfini, Florence #279/R

GHELLI, Giuliano (1944-) Italian
£298 $542 €450 Poet's journey (40x50cm-16x20in) s. painted 1994. 17-Jun-4 Galleria Pananti, Florence #533/R
£414 $691 €600 That night (70x100cm-28x39in) s.d.94 acrylic oil board. 14-Nov-3 Farsetti, Prato #431

GHENT SCHOOL (15th C) Flemish
£229730 $404324 €340000 The Annuniciation (107x70cm-42x28in) panel triptych prov.lit. 22-May-4 Lempertz, Koln #1052/R est:200000-300000

GHENT SCHOOL (16th C) Flemish
£8219 $13973 €12000 Holy Family with Saint Joachim and Saint Anne (43x29cm-17x11in) panel. 5-Nov-3 Christie's, Amsterdam #31/R est:12000-16000

GHENT, Peter (1856-1911) British
£450 $752 €657 Fisherman on a river (30x50cm-12x20in) s. 23-Oct-3 Bonhams, Edinburgh #322
Works on paper
£250 $443 €365 River scene, Wales (36x56cm-14x22in) s. 30-Apr-4 Dee Atkinson & Harrison, Driffield #794
£260 $424 €380 North Wales lake scene (25x36cm-10x14in) s. W/C exhib. 27-Sep-3 Rogers Jones, Clwyd #64
£600 $1074 €876 River landscape with figures resting on a bank (39x69cm-15x27in) s. W/C. 17-Mar-4 Bonhams, Chester #236

GHERARDI, Antonio (1644-1702) Italian
£3521 $6162 €5000 Sainte Praxede (80x64cm-31x25in) 19-Dec-3 Pierre Berge, Paris #69/R est:5200-5500
£21333 $39040 €32000 Dalila and Sansone (97x135cm-38x53in) 1-Jun-4 Sotheby's, Milan #156/R est:25000-30000

GHERARDI, Giuseppe (19th C) Italian
£16500 $29700 €24090 Piazza della Signoria, Florence (40x57cm-16x22in) s. 21-Jan-4 Sotheby's, Olympia #395/R est:8000-12000
Works on paper
£719 $1180 €1000 View of Florence from Boboli (12x19cm-5x7in) s. W/C. 10-Jun-3 Pandolfini, Florence #1/R

GHERARDINI, Alessandro (attrib) (1655-1723) Italian
Works on paper
£600 $1080 €876 Three figures (21x20cm-8x8in) pen brown ink wash. 20-Apr-4 Sotheby's, Olympia #40/R

GHERSI PARUZZA, Felice (fl.1870-1875) Italian
£367 $675 €550 Reflections (32x48cm-13x19in) s. board exhib. 14-Jun-4 Sant Agostino, Torino #127/R

GHEYN, Jacob de (younger) (1565-1629) Dutch
Works on paper
£60000 $109800 €87600 Head of a bearded man wearing a cap (9x8cm-4x3in) pen ink wash pencil framing lines. 6-Jul-4 Christie's, London #167/R est:8000-12000
£106164 $180479 €155000 River view with fisherman hauling in a net (14x23cm-6x9in) bears i.mount pen brown ink. 4-Nov-3 Sotheby's, Amsterdam #31/R est:50000-70000
£465753 $791781 €680000 Studies of heads, arms, hands and youth seen from behind (30x19cm-12x7in) bears i. pen brown ink over black chk prov. 4-Nov-3 Sotheby's, Amsterdam #27/R est:180000-240000

GHEYN, Jacob de III (attrib) (c.1596-1644) Dutch
Works on paper
£1351 $2378 €2000 Study of a cow, part of a cow's head, and a child in a basket (13x21cm-5x8in) bears i.indis. pen brown ink black chk prov.lit. 19-May-4 Sotheby's, Amsterdam #45/R est:3000-4000

GHEYNST, Berroni van der (1876-1946) Belgian
£510 $913 €750 Promenade sur le brise-lames (14x23cm-6x9in) s. cardboard. 16-Mar-4 Vanderkindere, Brussels #166

GHEZZI, Pier Leone (1674-1755) Italian
Works on paper
£3521 $6162 €5000 Un homme tenant un masque et neuf caricatures de prelats (19x19cm-7x7in) i. red chk pen brown ink col wash prov. 17-Dec-3 Christie's, Paris #18/R est:6000-8000
£6667 $12000 €9734 Double caricature of Ghezzi and the engraver Osterreich (34x22cm-13x9in) i. pen brown ink prov.exhib. 21-Jan-4 Sotheby's, New York #97/R est:6000-8000

GHEZZO, Antonio (1915-) Italian
£336 $594 €500 Venice (39x50cm-15x20in) s. masonite. 1-May-4 Meeting Art, Vercelli #72

GHIGLIA, Oscar (1876-1945) Italian
£12676 $21930 €18000 Still life with trout (35x40cm-14x16in) s. prov. 11-Dec-3 Christie's, Rome #150/R est:20000-30000
£13245 $24106 €20000 Portrait of Giuseppe Prezzolini (94x66cm-37x26in) lit. 21-Jun-4 Pandolfini, Florence #162/R est:15000-20000
£16197 $28021 €23000 Wife resting (32x33cm-13x13in) s. cardboard. 11-Dec-3 Christie's, Rome #166/R est:18000-25000
£52113 $90155 €74000 Cherries (34x43cm-13x17in) s. cardboard. 10-Dec-3 Sotheby's, Milan #80/R est:30000-40000
£54667 $100587 €82000 Still life with apples (38x45cm-15x18in) i.d.1918 verso prov.lit. 8-Jun-4 Sotheby's, Milan #103/R est:40000-60000
£56338 $97465 €80000 Still life with flower and oranges (55x65cm-22x26in) prov. 11-Dec-3 Christie's, Rome #149/R est:30000-40000

GHIGLIA, Paulo (1905-1979) Italian
£497 $844 €710 Listening to the radio (25x26cm-10x10in) board. 1-Dec-3 Babuino, Rome #506/R
£621 $1037 €900 Little tables (35x30cm-14x12in) s. 14-Nov-3 Farsetti, Prato #427
£671 $1201 €1000 Vineyard (83x65cm-33x26in) s.d.45 cardboard. 25-May-4 Finarte Semenzato, Milan #64/R
£872 $1562 €1300 Wood (83x59cm-33x23in) s.d.45 cardboard. 25-May-4 Finarte Semenzato, Milan #68/R
£927 $1687 €1400 Peasant woman (70x50cm-28x20in) s. s.d.1979 verso. 17-Jun-4 Galleria Pananti, Florence #515/R
£933 $1671 €1400 Letting go (36x33cm-14x13in) s. s.verso cardboard. 12-May-4 Stadion, Trieste #838/R
£979 $1635 €1400 Maternity (100x80cm-39x31in) s. 24-Jun-3 Finarte Semenzato, Rome #103/R
£1583 $2596 €2200 Garden (70x100cm-28x39in) s. 10-Jun-3 Pandolfini, Florence #398/R est:1300-1400
£1854 $3375 €2800 Peasant woman (100x70cm-39x28in) s. 17-Jun-4 Galleria Pananti, Florence #518/R est:2200
£1972 $3411 €2800 Lady in interior (60x50cm-24x20in) s. 11-Dec-3 Christie's, Rome #51/R est:3000
£2013 $3604 €3000 Seated girl (80x50cm-31x20in) 25-May-4 Finarte Semenzato, Milan #111/R est:3000-3200
£12072 $19799 €16660 Protest (220x451cm-87x178in) 1-Jun-3 Babuino, Rome #380/R est:6000-8000

GHIGLIA, Valentino (1903-1960) Italian
£400 $736 €600 Landscape (38x60cm-15x24in) s. board. 11-Jun-4 Farsetti, Prato #401/R
£629 $1145 €950 View of the Maremma (34x41cm-13x16in) s. board. 17-Jun-4 Galleria Pananti, Florence #498/R
£690 $1152 €1000 Bather (44x23cm-17x9in) cardboard. 14-Nov-3 Farsetti, Prato #502

GHIGLIERI, Lorenzo E (1931-) American
Sculpture
£2095 $3750 €3059 Grand Endeavor, three men of Lewis and Clark expedition (58cm-23in) i. bronze. 20-Mar-4 Selkirks, St. Louis #561 est:1800-2400
£3086 $5000 €4506 First jump (56x71x25cm-22x28x10in) s.d.1999 num.25/135 bronze. 2-Aug-3 Neal Auction Company, New Orleans #401/R est:5000-7000

GHIGLION-GREEN, Maurice (1913-) French
£362 $666 €550 View of park (46x61cm-18x24in) s. 22-Jun-4 Palais de Beaux Arts, Brussels #248
£1119 $1924 €1600 Paris, la Vigne de Montmarte sous la neige (35x27cm-14x11in) s. 3-Dec-3 Tajan, Paris #192/R est:1200-1500

GHIKA, Nicolas (1906-1994) Greek
£13000 $22100 €18980 Garden (41x35cm-16x14in) s.d.62 prov. 18-Nov-3 Sotheby's, London #106/R est:8000-12000
£13000 $22100 €18980 Garden (38x33cm-15x13in) s.d.62 prov. 18-Nov-3 Sotheby's, London #105/R est:8000-12000
£13000 $23270 €18980 Landscape (43x53cm-17x21in) s.d.88. 10-May-4 Sotheby's, Olympia #55/R est:10000-15000
£15000 $25500 €21900 Chairs and tables by the sea (21x27cm-8x11in) s.d.48 prov.exhib. 18-Nov-3 Sotheby's, London #33/R est:15000-20000
£16000 $28640 €23360 Portrait of Lady Menuhin (100x71cm-39x28in) s.d.75 s.verso. 11-May-4 Sotheby's, Olympia #558/R est:2000-3000
£19000 $32300 €27740 Garden (76x35cm-30x14in) s.d.68. 18-Nov-3 Sotheby's, London #32/R est:8000-12000
£46000 $82340 €67160 Long walls (55x32cm-22x13in) s.d.56 board prov.exhib.lit. 10-May-4 Sotheby's, Olympia #42/R est:20000-30000
£60000 $102000 €87600 Caterpillar (73x92cm-29x36in) s.d.39 prov.exhib.lit. 18-Nov-3 Sotheby's, London #44/R est:60000-100000
£65000 $110500 €94900 Interior with still life (59x70cm-23x28in) s.d.35 panel prov.lit. 18-Nov-3 Sotheby's, London #36/R est:40000-60000
Sculpture
£1000 $1750 €1460 Tanagrea (25cm-10in) i.num.13/90 green pat bronze. 16-Dec-3 Bonhams, New Bond Street #97/R est:1000-1500
£4000 $7160 €5840 Garden work (41x55cm-16x22in) s.d.1934 s.i.num.3/12 verso plaster relief. 10-May-4 Sotheby's, Olympia #51/R est:4000-6000
£4000 $7160 €5840 The Game (38x55cm-15x22in) s. i.num.3/12 verso plaster relief. 10-May-4 Sotheby's, Olympia #52/R est:4000-6000
Works on paper
£350 $627 €511 Portrait of Lady Menuhin (57x38cm-22x15in) s.i.d.18 March 1975 pencil. 11-May-4 Sotheby's, Olympia #554/R
£400 $716 €584 Portrait of Yehudi Menuhin (35x27cm-14x11in) s.i.d.19 March 75 col crayon. 11-May-4 Sotheby's, Olympia #555/R
£900 $1611 €1314 Figures (23x17cm-9x7in) s.d.63 col pencil. 10-May-4 Sotheby's, Olympia #112/R
£1500 $2625 €2190 Stone wall and plants, Hydra (52x35cm-20x14in) s.d.53 ink pencil exhib. 16-Dec-3 Bonhams, New Bond Street #128/R est:1500-2000
£2200 $3938 €3212 Potted plant (23x23cm-9x9in) s.d.58 ink gouache. 11-May-4 Bonhams, New Bond Street #107/R est:1500-2000
£2600 $4654 €3796 Portrait of Lady Menuhin (55x34cm-22x13in) i. W/C pencil. 11-May-4 Sotheby's, Olympia #556/R est:800-1200
£6500 $11635 €9490 Village in Mani (19x26cm-7x10in) s.i.d.70 pencil ink wash. 10-May-4 Sotheby's, Olympia #116/R est:2000-3000

GHILCHIK, David L (1892-?) Rumanian
£820 $1443 €1197 Venice Scene (60x91cm-24x36in) s. 18-May-4 Bonhams, Knightsbridge #185/R

GHINIS, Alkis (1933-) Greek
£3000 $5370 €4380 The choreographer Agapi Evangelidi (80x60cm-31x24in) s.d.73 lit. 11-May-4 Bonhams, New Bond Street #116/R est:3000-5000

GHIRARDELLI, Alida (1881-1909) American
£3261 $6000 €4892 French family in winter attire (125x60cm-49x24in) init. prov. 8-Jun-4 Bonhams & Butterfields, San Francisco #4221/R est:3000-5000

GHIRARDINI, Stefano (attrib) (1696-1756) Italian
£5500 $9350 €8030 Allegory of autumn (47x74cm-19x29in) 29-Oct-3 Bonhams, New Bond Street #1/R est:2000-3000

GHIRINGHELLI, Virginio (1898-1964) Italian
£734 $1226 €1064 Les ecueils - Riva Trigoso (65x79cm-26x31in) s.d.928. 23-Jun-3 Philippe Schuler, Zurich #3562 (S.FR 1600)

GHIRLANDAIO, Domenico (1449-1494) Italian
£55000 $100650 €80300 Two angel in adoration (87x49cm-34x19in) fresco prov. 7-Jul-4 Christie's, London #4/R est:15000-25000

GHIRLANDAIO, Ridolfo (1483-1561) Italian
£14286 $22857 €20715 Man's portrait (49x35cm-19x14in) panel. 15-May-3 Stuker, Bern #1253/R est:35000-45000 (S.FR 30000)

GHIRRI, Luigi (1943-1992) Italian
Photographs
£1942 $3108 €2700 Beyond the stream (37x46cm-15x18in) s. i.verso col print exec.1984. 19-May-3 Sotheby's, Milan #75/R est:2800-3200

GHISI, Giorgio (16th C) Italian
Prints
£2200 $3938 €3300 Dream of Raphael - Allegory of Life (37x53cm-15x21in) copperplate. 14-May-4 Bassenge, Berlin #5864/R est:2400
£12587 $21399 €18000 Dream of Raphael - allegory of life (38x54cm-15x21in) engraving. 27-Nov-3 Bassenge, Berlin #5163/R est:25000

GHISI, Teodore (attrib) (1536-1601) Italian
£10067 $18523 €15000 Saint Messalina (130x105cm-51x41in) lit. 24-Mar-4 Finarte Semenzato, Rome #100/R est:18500

GHISLANDI, Vittore (1655-1743) Italian
£27972 $48112 €40000 Portrait of Giovanni Dannielli di Guidizzolo (106x75cm-42x30in) 2-Dec-3 Sotheby's, Milan #107/R est:40000-60000
£44295 $82832 €66000 Portrait of boy blowing bubbles (75x61cm-30x24in) prov. 25-Feb-4 Porro, Milan #21/R est:33000
£219079 $403105 €333000 Portrait of young man (60x49cm-24x19in) lit. 25-Jun-4 Piasa, Paris #37/R est:120000-150000

GHISLANDI, Vittore (attrib) (1655-1743) Italian
£8000 $14560 €12000 Portrait of a young boy (65x60cm-26x24in) 1-Jul-4 Van Ham, Cologne #1109/R est:15000

GHISLANDI, Vittore (studio) (1655-1743) Italian
£5369 $9879 €8000 Portrait of young nobleman (89x63cm-35x25in) 24-Mar-4 Dorotheum, Vienna #8/R est:8000-12000

GHISOLFI, Enrico (1837-1918) Italian
£2721 $4871 €4000 Coazze (33x51cm-13x20in) s. board. 22-Mar-4 Sant Agostino, Torino #258/R est:4000-5000

GHISOLFI, Giovanni (1632-1683) Italian
£22000 $38060 €32120 Capriccio view of the Molo from the Piazzetta looking South (115x146cm-45x57in) prov. 11-Dec-3 Sotheby's, London #41/R est:30000-50000

GHISOLFI, Giovanni (attrib) (1632-1683) Italian
£4231 $7277 €6177 Figures with ruins in landscape (62x72cm-24x28in) 3-Dec-3 AB Stockholms Auktionsverk #2707/R est:50000-60000 (S.KR 55000)
£7333 $13127 €11000 Capriccio with ruins (91x126cm-36x50in) 17-May-4 Finarte Semenzato, Rome #116/R est:12000-14000

GHISOLFI, Giovanni (circle) (1632-1683) Italian
£6500 $11895 €9490 Capriccio of Roman ruins (74x99cm-29x39in) 9-Jul-4 Christie's, Kensington #199/R est:4000-6000
£11268 $19493 €16000 Classical view with fountain. Classical view with soldier (74x97cm-29x38in) pair. 14-Dec-3 Finarte, Venice #54/R est:14000-16000

GHISOLFI, Giovanni (style) (1632-1683) Italian
£5500 $9900 €8030 Figures amongst Roman ruins (113x78cm-44x31in) 21-Apr-4 Bonhams, New Bond Street #13/R est:6000-8000
£12667 $22927 €19000 Sacrifice to Hercules (74x102cm-29x40in) lit.prov. 1-Apr-4 Van Ham, Cologne #1199/R est:15000

GHITI, Pompeo (1631-1703) Italian
Works on paper
£791 $1266 €1100 Holy scene (25x38cm-10x15in) pen W/C. 14-May-3 Finarte Semenzato, Milan #496/R est:1000-1500

GHIVARELLO, Benedetto (1882-1955) Italian
£268 $475 €400 Rural road (10x14cm-4x6in) init. cardboard. 1-May-4 Meeting Art, Vercelli #3
£336 $594 €500 Courtyard (24x33cm-9x13in) s.d.1939 cardboard. 1-May-4 Meeting Art, Vercelli #138
£436 $772 €650 Landscape at sunset (24x32cm-9x13in) s.d.1945 cardboard. 1-May-4 Meeting Art, Vercelli #399
£467 $859 €700 Landscape with figure (27x36cm-11x14in) s.d.1948 board. 14-Jun-4 Sant Agostino, Torino #130/R
£467 $859 €700 Hilly landscape (23x33cm-9x13in) s. cardboard. 14-Jun-4 Sant Agostino, Torino #131/R
£486 $826 €700 Reflections (22x25cm-9x10in) s.d.1913 cardboard. 1-Nov-3 Meeting Art, Vercelli #282
£748 $1339 €1100 Winter landscape (33x40cm-13x16in) s.d.1946 card. 22-Mar-4 Sant Agostino, Torino #172/R

GHIZZARDI, Pietro (1906-1986) Italian
Works on paper
£369 $683 €550 Figures. Lady (79x55cm-31x22in) s.d.1960 mixed media card double-sided exec.1960. 13-Mar-4 Meeting Art, Vercelli #433

GHOBERT, Bernard (20th C) ?
Works on paper
£455 $759 €650 Interior (39x49cm-15x19in) s.d.65 col dr. 11-Oct-3 De Vuyst, Lokeren #162
£544 $974 €800 Fenetre sur cour (39x50cm-15x20in) s.d.71 col crayon. 16-Mar-4 Vanderkindere, Brussels #365

GIACHI, E (19th C) Italian
£2514 $4500 €3670 Tea time (51x35cm-20x14in) s.i. 14-May-4 Skinner, Boston #54/R est:6000-8000

GIACHINO, Bice (20th C) Italian
£340 $609 €500 Pansies (34x50cm-13x20in) s.d.1930. 22-Mar-4 Sant Agostino, Torino #4/R

GIACHINO, Marcello (1877-1929) Italian
£230 $425 €336 Vase of flowers (51x38cm-20x15in) s.i. panel. 14-Jan-4 Dallas Auction Gallery, Dallas #420b
£436 $772 €650 Vase of flowers (50x38cm-20x15in) s. on glass. 1-May-4 Meeting Art, Vercelli #382
£738 $1307 €1100 Still life with mushrooms (45x70cm-18x28in) s. 1-May-4 Meeting Art, Vercelli #74
£805 $1426 €1200 Still life with grapes (45x70cm-18x28in) s. 1-May-4 Meeting Art, Vercelli #73

GIACOMELLI, Hector (1822-1904) French
£461 $847 €700 Moineaux pres d'arbuste fleuri (100x60cm-39x24in) s. 22-Jun-4 Palais de Beaux Arts, Brussels #250
£972 $1546 €1400 Moineaux pres d'un arbuste fleuri (100x60cm-39x24in) s. 9-Sep-3 Palais de Beaux Arts, Brussels #237

GIACOMELLI, Mario (1925-2000) Italian
Photographs
£1871 $2993 €2600 Landscape (34x22cm-13x9in) s. silver gelatin print exec.1955. 19-May-3 Sotheby's, Milan #62/R est:2500-3000
£8383 $14000 €12239 Mario Giacomelli, la gente (39x30cm-15x12in) s.i.d.1981 gelatin silver print 18 folio clamshell box. 20-Oct-3 Christie's, Rockefeller NY #173/R est:9000-12000

GIACOMELLI, Vincenzo (1841-1890) Italian
£1056 $1900 €1542 Fruit seller (51x41cm-20x16in) s.d.1877. 24-Apr-4 Weschler, Washington #578/R est:1500-2500

GIACOMETTI, Alberto (1901-1966) Swiss
£32609 $59674 €47609 Orchids in a blue vase (27x21cm-11x8in) mono. s.d.1932 verso prov.lit. 7-Jun-4 Christie's, Zurich #80/R est:80000-120000 (S.FR 75000)
£295652 $541044 €431652 My garden (73x103cm-29x41in) s.d.1914 i.verso prov.lit. 7-Jun-4 Christie's, Zurich #81/R est:280000-350000 (S.FR 680000)
Prints
£1765 $3000 €2577 Objets mobiles et muets (33x50cm-13x20in) s.i. lithograph exec.1931. 31-Oct-3 Sotheby's, New York #269/R
£1765 $3000 €2577 Dans le miroir (68x50cm-27x20in) s.num.61/75 lithograph. 6-Nov-3 Swann Galleries, New York #545/R est:3000-5000
£1882 $3200 €2748 Rue d'Alesia (74x54cm-29x21in) s. col lithograph exec.1954. 4-Nov-3 Christie's, Rockefeller NY #97/R est:4000-6000
£2054 $3800 €2999 Man standing (25x10cm-10x4in) s. lithograph edition of 100. 12-Feb-4 Christie's, Rockefeller NY #309/R est:2000-3000
£2366 $4400 €3454 Rue d'Alesia (65x54cm-26x21in) s.num.173/200 col lithograph. 2-Mar-4 Swann Galleries, New York #205/R est:3000-5000
£2477 $4137 €3592 Bouquet II. s.i. etching. 19-Jun-3 Kornfeld, Bern #421 est:5000 (S.FR 5400)
£2500 $4250 €3650 Rue d'Alesia (74x53cm-29x21in) s. col lithograph exec.1954. 31-Oct-3 Sotheby's, New York #272/R
£2647 $4500 €3865 Sculptures (54x35cm-21x14in) s. lithograph exec.1954. 31-Oct-3 Sotheby's, New York #270
£2667 $4907 €4000 Female Bust II (32x20cm-13x8in) s. lithograph exec. 1960 one of 150. 11-Jun-4 Villa Grisebach, Berlin #1583/R est:3000-4000
£2882 $5245 €4208 Portrait Michel Leiris. s. etching. 17-Jun-4 Kornfeld, Bern #380 est:3000 (S.FR 6600)
£3107 $5500 €4536 Buste II (31x20cm-12x8in) s.num.28/150 lithograph. 28-Apr-4 Christie's, Rockefeller NY #50/R est:4000-6000
£3200 $5824 €4672 Nu aux fleurs (37x28cm-15x11in) s.num.50/90 lithograph. 1-Jul-4 Sotheby's, London #178/R est:2500-3000
£3390 $6000 €4949 Studio II (36x52cm-14x20in) s.num.21/30 lithograph. 30-Apr-4 Sotheby's, New York #94 est:2000-3000

£3611 $6031 €5200 La suspension. s.num.E 50/75 lithograph. 23-Oct-3 Credit Municipal, Paris #50/R est:3000-4000
£3763 $7000 €5494 Chien et chat (65x50cm-26x20in) s.i. lithograph. 2-Mar-4 Swann Galleries, New York #206/R est:3000-5000
£4000 $6880 €5840 L'atelier (48x39cm-19x15in) s.num.49/125 lithograph. 2-Dec-3 Christie's, London #144/R est:3000-5000
£4336 $7457 €6200 Au cafe (35x49cm-14x19in) s. lithograph. 2-Dec-3 Hauswedell & Nolte, Hamburg #201/R est:5000
£4358 $7278 €6319 Chaises et gueridon. s.i. lithograph. 19-Jun-3 Kornfeld, Bern #420 est:10000 (S.FR 9500)
£4587 $7661 €6651 L'atelier. s.i. lithograph. 19-Jun-3 Kornfeld, Bern #418 est:6000 (S.FR 10000)
£4762 $8667 €7000 Nu assis (15x8cm-6x3in) s. num.49/50 eau forte. 3-Feb-4 Segre, Madrid #283/R est:7000
£4762 $8667 €7000 Sculptures dans l'atelier (15x10cm-6x4in) s. num.42/100 eau forte. 3-Feb-4 Segre, Madrid #282/R est:7000
£4817 $8044 €6985 Montagnes a Maloja - la Margna. s.i. lithograph. 19-Jun-3 Kornfeld, Bern #419/R est:10000 (S.FR 10500)
£5245 $8916 €7500 Tetes et tabouret (54x33cm-21x13in) s. lithograph. 29-Nov-3 Villa Grisebach, Berlin #302/R est:7000-9000
£5389 $9000 €7868 Bust of a man (58x46cm-23x18in) s.num.9/75 lithograph. 11-Nov-3 Doyle, New York #255/R est:7000-9000
£5588 $9500 €8158 Bust (50x65cm-20x26in) s. num.26/30 lithograph. 4-Nov-3 Christie's, Rockefeller NY #96/R est:4000-6000
£6769 $12319 €9883 L'atelier. s.i. lithograph. 17-Jun-4 Kornfeld, Bern #378/R est:10000 (S.FR 15500)
£6993 $11888 €10000 Homme debout et soleil (36x47cm-14x19in) s. lithograph prov. 29-Nov-3 Villa Grisebach, Berlin #303/R est:6000-8000
£7333 $13273 €11000 Objets mobiles et muets (33x50cm-13x20in) s. num.7/30 lithograph exec 1931. 1-Apr-4 Credit Municipal, Paris #18/R est:3000-4000
£9170 $16690 €13388 Petit nu debout - trois figurines. s.i.d.1959 etching two. 17-Jun-4 Kornfeld, Bern #379/R est:10000 (S.FR 21000)

Sculpture
£6500 $11765 €9490 Tete de femme (4cm-2in) gold pat bronze cast c.1935 sold with base prov. 1-Apr-4 Christie's, Kensington #86/R est:5000-7000
£6957 $12730 €10157 Tete de Silvio (5cm-2in) plaster prov. 7-Jun-4 Christie's, Zurich #132/R est:10000-15000 (S.FR 16000)
£9565 $17504 €13965 Tete d'Annetta (7cm-3in) plaster prov. 7-Jun-4 Christie's, Zurich #134/R est:10000-15000 (S.FR 22000)
£19005 $32878 €27747 Tete de Rita (10cm-4in) s.d.1936 verso plaster prov.lit. 9-Dec-3 Sotheby's, Zurich #122/R est:15000-20000 (S.FR 42000)
£21834 $39738 €31878 Tete de Rita (23cm-9in) s.st.f. Susse num.6/8 bronze exec. 1937-38 prov.exhib. 18-Jun-4 Kornfeld, Bern #48/R est:40000 (S.FR 50000)
£22346 $40000 €32625 Tete de Rita (24cm-9in) i.sig. num.2/8 st.f.Susse green brown pat bronze prov. 6-May-4 Sotheby's, New York #403/R est:20000-25000
£26000 $43420 €37960 Tete de Meduse (24cm-9in) gilded plaster prov.lit. 21-Oct-3 Sotheby's, London #78/R est:10000-15000
£40789 $75053 €62000 Untitled. s. pat bronze lit. 24-Jun-4 Credit Municipal, Paris #81/R est:30000-40000
£42000 $76440 €61320 Fauteuil aux pommeaux de canne (79cm-31in) bronze conceived c.1963 prov.lit. 4-Feb-4 Sotheby's, London #293/R est:18000-25000
£44693 $80000 €65252 Tete de femme - Flora Mayo (30cm-12in) i.sig. num.4/8 st.f.Susse brown pat bronze prov.ex. 6-May-4 Sotheby's, New York #402/R est:70000-90000
£280000 $509600 €408800 Tete sans crane (43cm-17in) s.st.f.Susse num.5/6 bronze prov.lit. 21-Jun-4 Sotheby's, London #53/R est:250000-350000
£1235294 $2100000 €1803529 Buste de Diego (22cm-9in) s.i. num 3/6 brown gold pat bronze prov.lit. 4-Nov-3 Christie's, Rockefeller NY #43/R est:600000-800000
£1700000 $3094000 €2482000 Femme debout (118cm-46in) st.f.Susse i. num.2/6 bronze prov.lit. 3-Feb-4 Sotheby's, London #39/R est:1500000-2000000
£1700000 $3128000 €2482000 Femme de Venise VII (118cm-46in) s.st.f.Susse num.00/6 brown pat bronze prov.lit. 22-Jun-4 Christie's, London #31/R est:1200000-1800000
£5058824 $8600000 €7385883 Grande femme debout IV (270cm-106in) i.num.5/6 dark brown pat. bronze st.f.Susse conceived 1960 prov. 5-Nov-3 Sotheby's, New York #28/R est:8000000-10000000

Works on paper
£1079 $1770 €1500 Standing female nude (18x6cm-7x2in) pencil. 4-Jun-3 Ketterer, Hamburg #389/R est:1500-2500
£1659 $3020 €2422 Le chat (21x13cm-8x5in) pencil. 17-Jun-4 Kornfeld, Bern #377 est:2000 (S.FR 3800)
£2800 $5152 €4088 Femme sur un tabouret (37x25cm-15x10in) pencil prov. 24-Mar-4 Sotheby's, Olympia #176/R est:4000-6000
£3147 $5413 €4500 Houses in Stampa (15x11cm-6x4in) ink. 2-Dec-3 Hauswedell & Nolte, Hamburg #299/R est:4500
£3250 $5200 €4745 Portrait of Iliazd (43x29cm-17x11in) pen violet ink. 18-Sep-3 Swann Galleries, New York #256/R est:5000-8000
£3394 $5667 €4955 Portrait studies of Maurice Lefevre-Foinet (21x16cm-8x6in) biro on newspaper prov.exhib. 24-Jun-3 Germann, Zurich #45/R est:4000-7000 (S.FR 7500)
£5652 $10343 €8252 Portrait of a man (13x6cm-5x2in) s. pencil prov. 7-Jun-4 Christie's, Zurich #133/R est:10000-12000 (S.FR 13000)
£7200 $13248 €10512 Le chat sous la table (33x24cm-13x9in) s. pencil double-sided. 24-Mar-4 Sotheby's, Olympia #171/R est:3000-4000
£8000 $14720 €12000 Portrait de femme (35x27cm-14x11in) crayon dr prov.exhib.lit. 9-Jun-4 Tajan, Paris #39/R est:12000-15000
£8500 $15470 €12410 Trois femmes nues debout (22x9cm-9x4in) blue ballpoint pen exec.c.1960 prov. 4-Feb-4 Sotheby's, London #534/R est:6000-8000
£30000 $54600 €43800 Head of Diego (35x27cm-14x11in) s.d.1950 col crayon pencil double-sided prov. 5-Feb-4 Christie's, London #429/R est:18000-24000
£30568 $55633 €44629 In the room next to the kitchen in the house of Giacometti in Stampa (64x49cm-25x19in) s.d.1957 pencil. 18-Jun-4 Kornfeld, Bern #49/R est:80000 (S.FR 70000)
£55944 $96224 €80000 Nu debout (65x19cm-26x7in) s. ball point pen dr prov.exhib. 8-Dec-3 Artcurial Briest, Paris #16/R est:30000-40000
£58000 $105560 €84680 Atelier (50x32cm-20x13in) s.d.1957 pencil lit. 4-Feb-4 Sotheby's, London #457/R est:50000-70000

GIACOMETTI, Alberto and Diego (20th C) Swiss

Sculpture
£9000 $16560 €13140 Lampe a tete de femme (44cm-17in) brown green pat bronze conceived c.1936 prov. 23-Jun-4 Christie's, London #215/R est:10000-15000
£10000 $17000 €14600 Lampe trepied a etoile (41cm-16in) i. green pat bronze conceived 1935-37 lit. 6-Nov-3 Sotheby's, New York #241/R est:20000-30000
£20000 $36800 €29200 Vase (42x37cm-17x15in) plaster white paint conceived c.1936 prov.lit. 23-Jun-4 Christie's, London #204/R est:20000-25000
£24667 $44893 €37000 Etoile (150cm-59in) s. pat bronze prov.lit. 29-Jun-4 Cornette de St.Cyr, Paris #6/R est:30000-40000
£24706 $42000 €36071 Lampe trepied a l'etoile (41cm-16in) brown gold pat bronze lamp prov.lit. 5-Nov-3 Christie's, Rockefeller NY #316/R est:25000-35000
£28000 $50960 €40880 Lampe tete de femme (51cm-20in) indis i. bronze prov.lit. 4-Feb-4 Sotheby's, London #296/R est:10000-15000
£28235 $48000 €41223 Lampe trepied a l'etoile (41cm-16in) brown green pat bronze prov.lit. 5-Nov-3 Christie's, Rockefeller NY #319/R est:25000-35000
£29371 $49930 €42000 Etoile (150cm-59in) s. pat bronze. 26-Nov-3 Christie's, Paris #51/R est:15000-20000
£29412 $50000 €42942 Lampe trepied a l'etoile (40cm-16in) st. blk pat bronze prov.lit. 5-Nov-3 Christie's, Rockefeller NY #320/R est:25000-35000
£30000 $55200 €43800 Lampadaire a tete de femme (157cm-62in) black pat bronze conceived 1935-37 prov.lit. 23-Jun-4 Christie's, London #214/R est:30000-40000
£30726 $55000 €44860 Lampe a tete de femme (51cm-20in) indis.s. brown pat bronze conceived c.1937 prov.lit. 5-May-4 Christie's, Rockefeller NY #323/R est:60000-80000
£32000 $58240 €46720 Lampadaire a l'etoile (150cm-59in) i. bronze prov.lit. 4-Feb-4 Sotheby's, London #297/R est:15000-20000
£32402 $58000 €47307 Lampe a tete de femme (51cm-20in) indis.s. base brown pat bronze conceived c.1937 prov.lit. 5-May-4 Christie's, Rockefeller NY #322/R est:60000-80000
£38000 $69160 €55480 Lampadaire tete de femme (154cm-61in) bronze prov.lit. 4-Feb-4 Sotheby's, London #292/R est:15000-20000
£39106 $70000 €57095 Lampadaire a tete de femme (155cm-61in) brown green pat bronze conceived c.1936 prov.lit. 5-May-4 Christie's, Rockefeller NY #320/R est:70000-90000
£39106 $70000 €57095 Lampadaire a tete de femme (155cm-61in) green brown pat bronze conceived c.1936 prov.lit. 5-May-4 Christie's, Rockefeller NY #321/R est:70000-90000
£46099 $76986 €65000 Lampadaire de parquet tete de femme (155cm-61in) brown pat bronze antique green. 17-Jun-3 Camard, Paris #189/R est:60000-80000
£50000 $85000 €73000 Lampadaire a l'etoile (148cm-58in) brown green pat bronze lamp prov.lit. 5-Nov-3 Christie's, Rockefeller NY #318/R est:70000-90000
£51748 $87972 €74000 Etoile (150cm-59in) s. pat bronze. 26-Nov-3 Christie's, Paris #52/R est:15000-20000
£55882 $95000 €81588 Lampadaire a l'etoile (153cm-60in) brown green pat bronze lamp prov.lit. 5-Nov-3 Christie's, Rockefeller NY #317/R est:70000-90000
£105882 $180000 €154588 Lampadaire surrealiste (150cm-59in) green brown pat bronze lamp prov.lit. 5-Nov-3 Christie's, Rockefeller NY #314/R est:80000-120000

GIACOMETTI, Augusto (1877-1947) Swiss

£72398 $125249 €105701 Poppies I (69x67cm-27x26in) mono. s.i.d.1943 prov.lit. 9-Dec-3 Sotheby's, Zurich #105/R est:160000-220000 (S.FR 160000)
£73991 $120605 €108027 Carnations in glass vase (27x21cm-11x8in) mono. s.d.1932 verso prov.lit. 29-Sep-3 Christie's, Zurich #82/R est:130000-150000 (S.FR 165000)
£157205 $286114 €229519 Narcissus (69x200cm-27x79in) s. tempera fresco panel painted 1905 prov.exhib.lit. 18-Jun-4 Kornfeld, Bern #46/R est:450000 (S.FR 360000)
£305677 $556332 €446288 Autumn (69x97cm-27x38in) s.d.1911 s.i.verso prov.exhib.lit. 18-Jun-4 Kornfeld, Bern #45/R est:600000 (S.FR 700000)
£489083 $890131 €714061 Garden in Stampa (65x92cm-26x36in) s. s.i.d.1912 verso prov.exhib.lit. 18-Jun-4 Kornfeld, Bern #44/R est:600000 (S.FR 1120000)

Works on paper
£734 $1226 €1064 Portrait of child, Spillman (20x24cm-8x9in) mono.d.1929 col chks. 19-Jun-3 Kornfeld, Bern #434 est:2000 (S.FR 1600)
£2252 $3874 €3288 Madonna with child (62x47cm-24x19in) Indian ink pencil W/C prov. 2-Dec-3 Koller, Zurich #3031/R est:3000-4000 (S.FR 5000)
£2466 $4020 €3600 Abstract in green and yellow (10x10cm-4x4in) pastel prov.lit. 29-Sep-3 Christie's, Zurich #80/R est:6000-8000 (S.FR 5500)
£2466 $4020 €3600 Abstract in yellow and blue (9x9cm-4x4in) pastel prov.lit. 29-Sep-3 Christie's, Zurich #81/R est:6000-8000 (S.FR 5500)
£2800 $5152 €4088 Portrait de Marie Laure de Noailles (15x28cm-6x11in) i. pen ink. 24-Mar-4 Sotheby's, Olympia #173/R est:2000-3000
£3049 $4970 €4452 Pumpkin (50x32cm-20x13in) W/C prov. 29-Sep-3 Christie's, Zurich #88/R est:6500-8500 (S.FR 6800)
£3363 $5482 €4910 Abstracts in black and violet and black, yellow and grey (10x20cm-4x8in) pastel two on one sheet prov.lit. 29-Sep-3 Christie's, Zurich #79/R est:8000-10000 (S.FR 7500)
£3587 $5848 €5237 Two abstracts in green, blue and yellow (10x20cm-4x8in) pastel two on one sheet prov.lit. 29-Sep-3 Christie's, Zurich #83/R est:8000-10000 (S.FR 8000)
£6726 $10964 €9820 Abstract, colour study with nine areas (12x12cm-5x5in) pastel. 29-Sep-3 Christie's, Zurich #84/R est:8000-10000 (S.FR 15000)
£7424 $13511 €10839 Small bookshop (24x31cm-9x12in) mono. pastel prov. 16-Jun-4 Fischer, Luzern #1322/R est:22000-28000 (S.FR 17000)
£19565 $35804 €28565 The gate (24x32cm-9x13in) mono. s.i.d.1933 verso pastel paper on board prov.lit. 7-Jun-4 Christie's, Zurich #79/R est:20000-30000 (S.FR 45000)
£32895 $60526 €48027 View of Stampa (31x37cm-12x15in) s. W/C prov. 23-Jun-4 Koller, Zurich #3045/R est:30000-50000 (S.FR 75000)

GIACOMETTI, Diego (1902-1985) Swiss

Sculpture
£1700 $3128 €2482 Tete de levrette (5cm-2in) brown pat. bronze prov. 23-Jun-4 Christie's, London #205/R est:2000-3000
£1872 $3500 €2733 Renard de Stampa (3x15cm-1x6in) st.mono. pat bronze prov. 25-Feb-4 Christie's, Rockefeller NY #132/R est:4000-6000
£1892 $3500 €2762 Chien (14cm-6in) brown pat bronze prov.lit. 12-Feb-4 Sotheby's, New York #49/R est:2000-3000
£2059 $3500 €3006 Oisau fixe (10x15cm-4x6in) st.mono green pat bronze prov. 5-Nov-3 Christie's, Rockefeller NY #338/R est:4000-6000
£2500 $4600 €3650 Tete de levrette (18cm-7in) st.mono. green pat bronze prov. 23-Jun-4 Christie's, London #199/R est:3000-5000
£2500 $4600 €3650 Poignees de portes (18cm-7in) brown pat. bronze two prov. 23-Jun-4 Christie's, London #207/R est:3000-4000
£2567 $4800 €3748 Marlene Dietrich (12cm-5in) st.mono. pat bronze prov. two pairs. 25-Feb-4 Christie's, Rockefeller NY #130/R est:1800-2200
£2647 $4500 €3865 Coupelle a la chauve-souris (8x30cm-3x12in) st.sig.base green brown pat bronze prov. 5-Nov-3 Christie's, Rockefeller NY #339/R est:5000-7000
£2674 $5000 €3904 Panthere (6x10cm-2x4in) st.mono. pat bronze prov. 25-Feb-4 Christie's, Rockefeller NY #131/R est:2800-3500
£3147 $5350 €4595 L'autruche (49cm-19in) i. brown green pat bronze ostrich egg prov.lit. 1-Dec-3 Ben-Ami, Tel Aviv #4334/R est:6000-8000
£3529 $6000 €5152 Paire de portes anciennes avec pommeaux, parures et feuillages (175x81cm-69x32in) st.mono. green pat bronze wooden doors prov. 5-Nov-3 Christie's, Rockefeller NY #342/R est:10000-15000
£4118 $7000 €6012 Coupe a la souris (2x19cm-1x7in) st.base green pat bronze prov. 5-Nov-3 Christie's, Rockefeller NY #337/R est:8000-12000
£5882 $10000 €8588 Petit oiseau volant a la coupe (8x17cm-3x7in) st.base brown pat bronze prov. 5-Nov-3 Christie's, Rockefeller NY #335/R est:10000-15000
£8235 $14000 €12023 Porte-plume aux feuilles et hibou (30cm-12in) s.base green pat bronze prov. 5-Nov-3 Christie's, Rockefeller NY #333/R est:16000-18000

£8939	$16000	€13051	Oiseau fixe (8x14cm-3x6in) mono. base brown pat bronze prov. 5-May-4 Christie's, Rockefeller NY #332/R est:4000-6000
£10588	$18000	€15458	Etude cheval, modele ancien a la tete baissee (9cm-4in) st.mono brown pat bronze designed c.1974 prov.lit. S5 999 30 999333 R 16000 18000 14000 0. 5-Nov-3 Christie's, Rockefeller NY #332/R est:12000-14000
£11765	$20000	€17177	Porte manteau au feuillage (60cm-24in) s.base green pat bronze prov. 5-Nov-3 Christie's, Rockefeller NY #329/R est:12000-16000
£12000	$22080	€17520	Porte-manteau aux feuilles (60cm-24in) st.mono green pat bronze prov. 23-Jun-4 Christie's, London #211/R est:12000-14000
£13000	$23920	€18980	Basset sur petite terrasse (13cm-5in) st.mono. green pat bronze prov. 23-Jun-4 Christie's, London #218/R est:10000-12000
£13514	$25000	€19730	Coupe a l'oiseau (7x6cm-3x2in) st.sig. brown pat bronze prov. 11-Feb-4 Sotheby's, New York #50/R est:12000-18000
£14118	$24000	€20612	Coupelle-cendrier a l'oiseau, modele pour cigarette (24cm-9in) st.mono green pat bronze designed c.1966 prov. 5-Nov-3 Christie's, Rockefeller NY #331/R est:18000-22000
£14667	$26987	€22000	Autruche (49cm-19in) s. brown pat. bronze htd gold green lit. 10-Jun-4 Camard, Paris #154/R est:25000-30000
£17982	$33088	€26254	Chat maitre d'hotel; version holding a bowl (19x8cm-7x3in) s. dark brown pat bronze prov.lit. 23-Jun-4 Koller, Zurich #3039/R est:30000-40000 (S.FR 41000)
£18456	$34513	€27500	Loup (10x35x5cm-4x14x2in) s.i. gilt pat bronze sold with base Cast Susse prov.lit. 29-Feb-4 Versailles Encheres #142/R est:5000-6000
£20588	$35000	€30058	Coupelle-centrier a l'oiseau, modele pour cigare (25cm-10in) st. green pat bronze designed c.1966 prov. 5-Nov-3 Christie's, Rockefeller NY #328/R est:18000-22000
£22000	$40480	€32120	Paire de chenets aux etoiles (26x26x22cm-10x10x9in) st.sig. gold pat bronze prov. 23-Jun-4 Christie's, London #201/R est:18000-24000
£29412	$50000	€42942	Table-Berceau, premiere version (41x137x39cm-16x54x15in) brown red green pat bronze conceived c.1963 prov.lit. 6-Nov-3 Sotheby's, New York #240/R est:60000-80000
£30496	$50929	€43000	Lampe de table au hibou (50cm-20in) s. brown pat bronze prov.lit. 17-Jun-3 Camard, Paris #188/R est:40000-50000
£30726	$55000	€44860	Chair (95cm-37in) green brown pat bronze iron htd red designed c.1962 prov.lit. 5-May-4 Christie's, Rockefeller NY #316/R est:35000-45000
£30726	$55000	€44860	Chair (95cm-37in) brown green pat bronze htd red designed c.1962 prov.lit. 5-May-4 Christie's, Rockefeller NY #317/R est:35000-45000
£30726	$55000	€44860	Couple (34cm-13in) s. blk pat bronze incl base designed c.1957 prov.lit. 5-May-4 Christie's, Rockefeller NY #319/R est:20000-30000
£31765	$54000	€46377	Paysage au cheval et au palmier (31cm-12in) st. green pat bronze designed c.1967 prov. 5-Nov-3 Christie's, Rockefeller NY #330/R est:40000-60000
£32000	$58880	€46720	Plafonnier (23cm-9in) green brown pat bronze exec. c.1965-1970 prov.lit. 23-Jun-4 Christie's, London #197/R est:30000-50000
£32123	$57500	€46900	Ostrich (50cm-20in) green pat bronze prov.lit. 6-May-4 Sotheby's, New York #333/R est:35000-45000
£32353	$55000	€47235	Fauteuil aux pommeaux de canne (82cm-32in) gold blk pat bronze leather seat chair prov.lit. 5-Nov-3 Christie's, Rockefeller NY #315/R est:40000-60000
£32353	$55000	€47235	Table-Berceau, premiere version (38x135x46cm-15x53x18in) i. brown red green pat bronze conceived c.1963 prov.lit. 6-Nov-3 Sotheby's, New York #239/R est:60000-80000
£32887	$61169	€49000	Lampadaire, modele a la feuille (148cm-58in) gilt pat bronze exec.c.1935-1937 prov.lit. 2-Mar-4 Artcurial Briest, Paris #149/R est:50000-70000
£33520	$60000	€48939	Lampe a quatre feuilles (61cm-24in) green brown pat bronze conceived c.1959 prov.lit. 5-May-4 Christie's, Rockefeller NY #318/R est:50000-70000
£33520	$60000	€48939	Table-berceau, second version (36x116x42cm-14x46x17in) green pat bronze conceived c.1970 prov.lit. 6-May-4 Sotheby's, New York #332/R est:50000-70000
£33558	$60068	€50000	Les dompteuses (36cm-14in) s. brown green pat bronze iron andirons prov.lit. 27-May-4 Tajan, Paris #129/R est:55000-60000
£35000	$64400	€51100	Petit paysage, la promenade des amis (49cm-19in) st.mono. green pat bronze prov. 23-Jun-4 Christie's, London #198/R est:25000-35000
£35294	$60000	€51529	Table basse trapezoidale, modele aux hiboux et aux grenouilles (42x57x34cm-17x22x13in) st. green brown pat bronze glass top prov.lit. 5-Nov-3 Christie's, Rockefeller NY #311/R est:70000-90000
£35294	$60000	€51529	Table basse trapezoidale, model aux cerfs et aux chiens (43x57x49cm-17x22x19in) st. green brown pat bronze glass top prov.lit. 5-Nov-3 Christie's, Rockefeller NY #312/R est:70000-90000
£35294	$60000	€51529	Basset sur terrasse (30cm-12in) s.base brown pat bronze prov. 5-Nov-3 Christie's, Rockefeller NY #336/R est:8000-12000
£38235	$65000	€55823	Table feuilles, modele bas aux grenouilles (57x58x48cm-22x23x19in) st.mono green pat bronze glass top prov.lit. 5-Nov-3 Christie's, Rockefeller NY #334/R est:70000-90000
£40000	$72800	€58400	Table carcasse, modele bas a double plateau (43x126x82cm-17x50x32in) dark green pat bronze glass top conceived c.1970 prov.lit. 3-Feb-4 Christie's, London #202/R est:40000-60000
£42000	$77280	€61320	Table treteau a motifs de bambou. st.sig. green pat bronze glass top conceived c. 1979 prov.lit. 23-Jun-4 Christie's, London #210/R est:25000-35000
£44000	$80080	€64240	Fauteuil aux pommeaux de canne (79cm-31in) bronze conceived c.1963 prov.lit. 4-Feb-4 Sotheby's, London #295/R est:18000-25000
£44118	$75000	€64412	Table berceau, premiere version (39x137x41cm-15x54x16in) green pat bronze glass top prov.lit. 5-Nov-3 Christie's, Rockefeller NY #310/R est:60000-80000
£48000	$87360	€70080	Fauteuil aux pommeaux de canne (79cm-31in) bronze conceived c.1963 prov.lit. 4-Feb-4 Sotheby's, London #294/R est:18000-25000
£50000	$91000	€73000	Table basse (41cm-16in) bronze conceived c.1957 prov.lit. 4-Feb-4 Sotheby's, London #300/R est:30000-40000
£52000	$94640	€75920	Table berceau, premiere version (137cm-54in) bronze glass table top conceived c.1963 prov.lit. 4-Feb-4 Sotheby's, London #298/R est:35000-45000
£55882	$95000	€81588	Gueridon-racines avec hibou (40cm-16in) blk pat bronze glass top cast 1967 prov.lit. 5-Nov-3 Christie's, Rockefeller NY #309/R est:50000-70000
£58659	$105000	€85642	Gueridon-arbre, version a l'oiseau prenant son envol (70cm-28in) st.sig. brown green pat bronze glass top prov.lit. 5-May-4 Christie's, Rockefeller NY #329/R est:80000-120000
£60000	$110400	€87600	La table carcasse, version a la chauve-souris (44x128x86cm-17x50x34in) st.sig. green brown pat bronze conceived c.1979 prov.lit. 23-Jun-4 Christie's, London #219/R est:40000-60000
£69832	$125000	€101955	Deux lampes au chien et au fauchon (32cm-13in) brown green pat bronze lamps conceived c.1965 two prov.lit. 5-May-4 Christie's, Rockefeller NY #314/R est:60000-80000
£72000	$132480	€105120	Table feuille aux oiseaux et tortues (47x58x58cm-19x23x23in) st.mono. green pat bronze glass top conceived c.1980 prov.lit. 23-Jun-4 Christie's, London #200/R est:40000-60000
£75000	$138000	€109500	Table basse, modele aux boutons (60x81x61cm-24x32x24in) brown pat. bronze conceived c.1960 prov.lit. 23-Jun-4 Christie's, London #220/R est:40000-60000
£78000	$141960	€113880	Table basse trapezoidale (42cm-17in) bronze glass top conceived c.1969 prov.lit. 4-Feb-4 Sotheby's, London #291/R est:40000-60000
£88000	$160160	€128480	Lampes au chien et au fauchon (33cm-13in) bronze two conceived c.1965 prov.lit. 4-Feb-4 Sotheby's, London #299/R est:30000-40000
£95000	$174800	€138700	Grand paysage, la promenade des amis (150cm-59in) st.sig. green pat bronze prov. 23-Jun-4 Christie's, London #203/R est:80000-120000
£105882	$180000	€154588	Miroir aux feuilles et a la souris (90x60cm-35x24in) mono. green pat bronze prov. 5-Nov-3 Christie's, Rockefeller NY #343/R est:25000-35000
£165000	$303600	€240900	Miroir aux feuilles et a la souris (87x60x2cm-34x24x1in) st.mono. green pat bronze conceived c.1982 prov. 23-Jun-4 Christie's, London #206/R est:60000-80000
£270000	$496800	€394200	Bibliotheques aux Victoires de Samothrace (315x111x37cm-124x44x15in) green pat bronze wooden shelves two exec.1961 prov.lit. 23-Jun-4 Christie's, London #221/R est:140000-180000

GIACOMETTI, Giovanni (1868-1934) Swiss

£11659	$19004	€17022	Bathers in mountain stream near Daganece (41x35cm-16x14in) mono s.i. verso board prov.exhib.lit. 29-Sep-3 Christie's, Zurich #94/R est:30000-50000 (S.FR 26000)
£15766	$27117	€23018	Christmas (60x70cm-24x28in) painted 1888/90 prov. 8-Dec-3 Philippe Schuler, Zurich #3331/R est:35000-40000 (S.FR 35000)
£15837	$27398	€23122	Interior of a kitchen (40x32cm-16x13in) prov.exhib.lit. 9-Dec-3 Sotheby's, Zurich #73/R est:35000-45000 (S.FR 35000)
£30435	$55696	€44435	Precipice with larches on lake shore (55x45cm-22x18in) mono. s.i.verso. 7-Jun-4 Christie's, Zurich #69/R est:80000-120000 (S.FR 70000)
£34935	$63581	€51005	Mountain landscape (61x50cm-24x20in) mono. s.i.d.1915 verso prov.exhib.lit. 18-Jun-4 Kornfeld, Bern #43/R est:90000 (S.FR 80000)
£39179	$67780	€57201	Winter garden (73x89cm-29x35in) mono.d.1909 prov.exhib. 9-Dec-3 Peter Webb, Auckland #94/R est:100000-150000 (NZ.D 105000)
£65502	$119214	€95633	Mattino d'estate (51x55cm-20x22in) mono. i.verso painted 1924 prov.exhib.lit. 16-Jun-4 Fischer, Luzern #1320/R est:150000-180000 (S.FR 150000)
£87336	$158952	€127511	Pomo fiorito (50x40cm-20x16in) painted c.1921 lit. 16-Jun-4 Fischer, Luzern #1319/R est:90000-120000 (S.FR 200000)
£108696	$198913	€158696	Giardino nella neve - garden in snow (75x90cm-30x35in) mono.d.1909 prov.exhib.lit. 7-Jun-4 Christie's, Zurich #74/R est:150000-180000 (S.FR 250000)
£113122	$195701	€165158	Autumn landscape in the Engadine (37x48cm-15x19in) mono. s.i.d.1930 verso. 9-Dec-3 Sotheby's, Zurich #76/R est:200000-250000 (S.FR 250000)
£113537	$203231	€165764	Winter landscape (50x62cm-20x24in) mono. s.i.d.1927 verso prov.lit. 26-May-4 Sotheby's, Zurich #85/R est:220000-260000 (S.FR 260000)
Prints			
£2800	$5012	€4200	Fanciulli nel lago - Alberto and Diego in Silsersee (26x23cm-10x9in) s. col woodcut. 13-May-4 Neumeister, Munich #356/R est:4000-4500
£2928	$5036	€4275	Il ponte al sole (15x15cm-6x6in) s. woodcut. 2-Dec-3 Koller, Zurich #3333/R est:700-1000 (S.FR 6500)
Works on paper			
£2523	$4213	€3658	Fruit tree in Stampa (23x29cm-9x11in) W/C over pencil. 19-Jun-3 Kornfeld, Bern #439 est:5000 (S.FR 5500)
£4817	$8044	€6985	Spoleto (26x36cm-10x14in) mono.i.d.25 Apr 1931 W/C over pencil. 19-Jun-3 Kornfeld, Bern #440/R est:12500 (S.FR 10500)
£5046	$8427	€7317	Annetta (25x20cm-10x8in) s. Indian ink. 19-Jun-3 Kornfeld, Bern #437 est:12500 (S.FR 11000)
£6114	$10943	€8926	View of Capolago (22x29cm-9x11in) pencil W/C prov. 26-May-4 Sotheby's, Zurich #76/R est:10000-15000 (S.FR 14000)
£7333	$13127	€11000	Mountain landscape with lake (23x29cm-9x11in) mono.d. W/C on chk prov. 14-May-4 Ketterer, Munich #129/R est:9000-12000
£8969	$14619	€13095	Bathers with sailing ships (23x30cm-9x12in) mono.d.1925 w/C. 29-Sep-3 Christie's, Zurich #42/R est:10000-15000 (S.FR 20000)
£9174	$15321	€13302	Annetta in bed (29x46cm-11x18in) W/C over pencil. 19-Jun-3 Kornfeld, Bern #436 est:12500 (S.FR 20000)
£9417	$15350	€13749	Capolago with Piz Salacina (22x29cm-9x11in) mono. W/C over pencil. 29-Sep-3 Christie's, Zurich #47/R est:20000-25000 (S.FR 21000)
£10762	$17543	€15713	Chapel in wood (22x29cm-9x11in) mono. w/C. 29-Sep-3 Christie's, Zurich #46/R est:25000-30000 (S.FR 24000)
£11354	$20664	€16577	Gravedona III Lago di Como (23x29cm-9x11in) mono. i. verso W/C. 17-Jun-4 Kornfeld, Bern #384/R est:17500 (S.FR 26000)
£13100	$23450	€19126	Albigna-Bondasca (36x50cm-14x20in) s.i.d.1917 pencil. 26-May-4 Sotheby's, Zurich #86/R est:4000-6000 (S.FR 30000)

GIACOMOTTI, Felix Henri (1828-1909) French/Italian

£1564	$2800	€2283	The masker (72x58cm-28x23in) s. oval prov. 14-May-4 Skinner, Boston #318/R est:3000-4000

GIALLINA (1857-1939) Greek

Works on paper			
£2700	$4914	€3942	Corfu (31x49cm-12x19in) s. pencil W/C htd white. 5-Feb-4 Mellors & Kirk, Nottingham #474 est:300-400
£3947	$7263	€6000	Busy Greek port with figures and boats (38x56cm-15x22in) s. 22-Jun-4 Mealy's, Castlecomer #150/R est:3000-4000

GIALLINA, Angelos (1857-1939) Greek

Works on paper			
£1500	$2550	€2190	Street market (32x15cm-13x6in) s. W/C htd bodycol. 18-Nov-3 Sotheby's, London #125/R est:500-700
£1500	$2685	€2190	Trees by the coast, a view of Corfu town beyond (26x13cm-10x5in) s. W/C. 11-May-4 Bonhams, New Bond Street #9/R est:600-900
£1800	$3060	€2628	Fishermen in a boat mending nets (24x42cm-9x17in) s. W/C over pencil. 25-Nov-3 Bonhams, Knowle #163 est:500-800
£2000	$3340	€2920	Figure in landscape with mountain background (41x23cm-16x9in) s.d.94 W/C. 17-Oct-3 Keys, Aylsham #498/R
£2400	$4080	€3504	Citadel, Corfu (16x31cm-6x12in) s.d.94 W/C. 18-Nov-3 Sotheby's, London #122/R est:2000-3000
£3000	$5370	€4380	Girl in a landscape (40x22cm-16x9in) s.d.94 W/C. 10-May-4 Sotheby's, Olympia #20/R est:2000-3000
£3400	$6222	€4964	Corfu coastline (38x74cm-15x29in) s. 27-Jan-4 Gorringes, Lewes #1536/R est:1000-1500
£3400	$6256	€4964	Greek island coastal view seen through flowering trees (13x9cm-5x4in) s. W/C. 11-Jun-4 Keys, Aylsham #406/R est:1000-1500

£3571 $6500 €5214 Old porta reale, Corfu (75x41cm-30x16in) s. W/C paper on board. 29-Jun-4 Sotheby's, New York #109/R est:3000-5000
£3800 $6954 €5548 Fishing boat off the coast of Corfu (38x71cm-15x28in) s. 27-Jan-4 Gorringes, Lewes #1537 est:1000-1500
£4000 $7320 €5840 View of the coast of Corfu (38x71cm-15x28in) s. 27-Jan-4 Gorringes, Lewes #1535/R est:1000-1500
£4800 $8592 €7008 Church in an extensive landscape (37x69cm-15x27in) s. W/C. 10-May-4 Sotheby's, Olympia #19/R est:4000-6000
£5000 $8950 €7300 View of the Acropolis (33x48cm-13x19in) s. W/C. 11-May-4 Bonhams, New Bond Street #1/R est:5000-7000
£5200 $9308 €7592 Mending the nets (25x42cm-10x17in) s. W/C. 10-May-4 Sotheby's, Olympia #22/R est:3000-5000
£5500 $9845 €8030 Guarding the flock (39x70cm-15x28in) s. W/C. 10-May-4 Sotheby's, Olympia #17/R est:2500-3500
£6000 $10500 €8760 Islands of Pontikonissi and Vlacherna, Corfu (38x72cm-15x28in) s. W/C. 16-Dec-3 Bonhams, New Bond Street #16/R est:4000-6000
£7000 $12250 €10220 View of Corfu (40x72cm-16x28in) s.d.1899 W/C. 16-Dec-3 Bonhams, New Bond Street #35/R est:7000-9000
£8000 $14320 €11680 Mouse Island (39x70cm-15x28in) s. W/C prov. 10-May-4 Sotheby's, Olympia #18/R est:8000-12000
£8500 $14450 €12410 Sailing in calm waters (41x87cm-16x34in) s. W/C. 18-Nov-3 Sotheby's, London #126/R est:4000-6000
£8500 $15215 €12410 Mouse Island (39x71cm-15x28in) s. W/C. 10-May-4 Sotheby's, Olympia #21/R est:4000-6000
£12000 $20400 €17520 Parthenon (54x91cm-21x36in) s.d.97 W/C prov. 18-Nov-3 Sotheby's, London #69/R est:12000-18000

GIALLINA, Angelos (attrib) (1857-1939) Greek
Works on paper
£1650 $3020 €2409 Two figures seated in a boat (21x12cm-8x5in) s. 5-Jun-4 Windibank, Dorking #326 est:120-180

GIAMBATTISTA, Noli (18th C) Italian
Prints
£2177 $3962 €3200 Plan monumental de la Ville de Rome (168x205cm-66x81in) engraving copper. 8-Feb-4 Anaf, Lyon #5/R est:1500-1800

GIAMBIAGI, Carlos (?) Argentinian?
£503 $900 €734 Impression of wood (25x19cm-10x7in) cardboard. 11-May-4 Arroyo, Buenos Aires #45
£659 $1200 €962 Landscape (28x36cm-11x14in) s. cardboard. 5-Jul-4 Arroyo, Buenos Aires #50/R
£1397 $2500 €2040 Landscape with mission village (25x33cm-10x13in) cardboard. 11-May-4 Arroyo, Buenos Aires #46
Works on paper
£670 $1200 €978 Landscape (48x37cm-19x15in) mixed media cardboard. 11-May-4 Arroyo, Buenos Aires #47

GIAMBOLOGNA (c.1529-1608) Italian
Sculpture
£500000 $915000 €730000 Christ (38x32cm-15x13in) gilt bronze exec. with A Susini prov. 9-Jul-4 Sotheby's, London #71/R est:500000-700000

GIAMBOLOGNA (after) (c.1529-1608) Italian
Sculpture
£5294 $9000 €7729 Rape of Sabine (33cm-13in) ivory sold with base. 28-Oct-3 Christie's, Rockefeller NY #4/R
£6500 $10790 €9490 Mercury (100cm-39in) i. num.108 dk brown pat bronze blk marble base Cast Barbedienne. 30-Sep-3 Sotheby's, London #121/R est:3000-5000
£8000 $13840 €11680 Pacing horse with plaited tail (37cm-15in) gilt bronze wood marble base lit. 12-Dec-3 Sotheby's, London #210/R est:7000-9000
£9000 $15570 €13140 Bust of Giambologna (20cm-8in) dark brown pat. bronze lit. 11-Dec-3 Christie's, London #48/R est:6000-9000
£11000 $19030 €16060 Rape of a Sabine woman (66cm-26in) dark brown pat. lit. 11-Dec-3 Christie's, London #73/R est:10000-15000
£13000 $23920 €18980 Executioner holding a sword and a head (46cm-18in) brown pat bronze plinth green marble base lit. 10-Jun-4 Christie's, London #94/R est:4000-6000
£78947 $145263 €120000 Cheval au pas (36cm-14in) pat bronze sold with base prov.lit. 23-Jun-4 Sotheby's, Paris #35/R est:120000-150000
£266667 $485333 €400000 Rapt of Dejanire (44x30cm-17x12in) pat bronze sold with bronze after F Girardon prov.lit. 29-Jun-4 Sotheby's, Paris #67/R est:300000-400000

GIAMBOLOGNA (attrib) (c.1529-1608) Italian
Works on paper
£2953 $5463 €4400 Taking a prisoner (42x28cm-17x11in) i. wash Indian ink. 12-Mar-4 Zadick, Uberlingen #5076/R est:250

GIAMBOLOGNA (style) (c.1529-1608) Italian
Sculpture
£4696 $8500 €6856 Figure of a birdcatcher (31cm-12in) bronze. 16-Apr-4 Sotheby's, New York #10/R est:7000-10000
£50000 $83500 €72000 Hercule domptant le centaure (41x30x23cm-16x12x9in) brown pat bronze. 22-Oct-3 Ribeyre & Baron, Paris #180/R est:37000-45000

GIAMPEDI, Giuseppe (18th C) Italian
£11111 $18889 €16000 Roman antiques (42x54cm-17x21in) s.i. tempera paper on canvas set of 6 prov. 28-Oct-3 Il Ponte, Milan #317/R

GIANGRANDE, Alicia (20th C) Argentinian?
£1639 $3000 €2393 Untitled (99x50cm-39x20in) mixed media on panel. 1-Jun-4 Arroyo, Buenos Aires #44

GIANI, Felice (1760-1823) Italian
Works on paper
£1000 $1800 €1500 Study (22x17cm-9x7in) pen W/C double-sided. 21-Apr-4 Finarte Semenzato, Milan #549/R est:600-900
£2133 $3840 €3200 Virginia. Orazio Coclite (22x23cm-9x9in) pen W/C two. 21-Apr-4 Finarte Semenzato, Milan #548/R est:2000-3000
£3667 $6563 €5500 Burial of Christ (37x48cm-15x19in) bears i. pen over pencil wash. 13-May-4 Bassenge, Berlin #5391/R est:1500

GIANI, Felice (attrib) (1760-1823) Italian
£748 $1339 €1100 Un jeune homme entoure d'un couple de vieillards (33x49cm-13x19in) oil paper. 18-Mar-4 Christie's, Paris #238/R
Works on paper
£870 $1426 €1200 More than once her eyes. (29x37cm-11x15in) i.verso pencil W/C prov. 29-May-3 Galleria Pace, Milan #96/R

GIANI, Felice (circle) (1760-1823) Italian
£8000 $14640 €11680 Moses transforming his rod into a snake (52x73cm-20x29in) 9-Jul-4 Christie's, Kensington #188/R est:5000-8000

GIANI, Giovanni (1866-1937) Italian
£690 $1145 €1000 Landscape (24x31cm-9x12in) s.d.932 board. 1-Oct-3 Della Rocca, Turin #312/R
£775 $1340 €1100 Courtyard (27x17cm-11x7in) s. cardboard. 10-Dec-3 Sotheby's, Milan #40/R
£7500 $12000 €10875 Midday, Valletta harbour, Malta. Evening, Valletta harbour (15x40cm-6x16in) one s.d.1889 board oval pair prov. 18-Sep-3 Christie's, Kensington #133/R est:8000-12000
£10345 $17172 €15000 Painter's study (151x201cm-59x79in) s.d.87. 1-Oct-3 Della Rocca, Turin #37/R est:20000
Works on paper
£5493 $9503 €7800 Face of woman (51cm-20in circular) s.d.1911 pastel paper on canvas. 10-Dec-3 Sotheby's, Milan #117/R est:6000-8000

GIANI, Vincenzo (1831-1900) Italian
Sculpture
£13475 $22504 €19000 Education of the soul (116cm-46in) s. marble lit. 17-Jun-3 Finarte Semenzato, Milan #273/R est:18000

GIANLISI, Antonio (younger) (1677-1727) Italian
£16448 $30264 €25000 Still life with biscuits and vase of flowers (118x115cm-46x45in) prov. 24-Jun-4 Tajan, Paris #41/R est:25000-30000

GIANNACCINI, Ilio (1897-1968) Italian
£202 $371 €295 Spanish dancer (61x51cm-24x20in) s. 14-Jun-4 Waddingtons, Toronto #323/R (C.D 500)
£503 $891 €750 Peasant woman (70x50cm-28x20in) s.i. 1-May-4 Meeting Art, Vercelli #288
£514 $873 €750 The Sarno near Naples. s. board. 7-Nov-3 Farsetti, Prato #42

GIANNATTASIO, Ugo (1888-1958) Italian
£664 $1109 €950 Untitled (44x54cm-17x21in) s.verso. 26-Jun-3 Sant Agostino, Torino #231/R

GIANNETTI, Raffaele (1832-1916) Italian
£4607 $7463 €6495 Masked ball (123x160cm-48x63in) 21-May-3 Babuino, Rome #207/R est:4000

GIANNI, G (19th C) Italian
£1400 $2408 €2044 Neapolitan vessel at sunset (15x22cm-6x9in) s.d.1886 board. 4-Dec-3 Christie's, Kensington #66/R est:1500-2000
£3974 $7232 €6000 Naples harbour steam ships (54x102cm-21x40in) s.d.1865. 16-Jun-4 Hugo Ruef, Munich #964/R est:5000

GIANNI, Gerolamo (1837-1887) Italian
£2800 $4760 €4088 St. Angelo and barges. St. Angelo at night (14x35cm-6x14in) s.d.1876 board pair. 4-Nov-3 Bonhams, New Bond Street #120/R est:2000-3000
£3000 $5460 €4380 Ferry rowing from Valetta (20x30cm-8x12in) s.d.1878 board. 15-Jun-4 David Lay, Penzance #297/R est:800-1400
£3175 $6000 €4636 Malta landscape (23x68cm-9x27in) s.d.1876. 22-Feb-4 Galeria y Remates, Montevideo #163/R est:15000
£3800 $6992 €5548 Arabs on a backwater, with lighthouse and shipping beyond (32x66cm-13x26in) s.d.1883. 23-Jun-4 Bonhams, Bury St Edmunds #381/R est:2500-4000
£4000 $6680 €5840 Gozo boat leaving the harbour, Valetta (50x33cm-20x13in) s.d.1881 prov. 14-Oct-3 Sotheby's, London #31/R est:2500-3500
£13000 $23010 €18980 Vessels off Fort St. Elmo, Valletta, Malta (14x40cm-6x16in) s.d.1878. 27-Apr-4 Bonhams, New Bond Street #78/R est:10000-15000

GIANNI, Gian (19th C) Italian
£610 $1092 €891 Bay of Naples showing Vesuvius (37x72cm-15x28in) s.d.1871 canvas on board. 10-May-4 Joel, Victoria #201 est:1500-2500 (A.D 1500)
£1600 $2672 €2336 Valletta harbour (22x54cm-9x21in) s.d.1881 board. 12-Nov-3 Sotheby's, Olympia #186/R est:600-800
£2000 $3580 €2920 Yacht in Valletta harbour (24x70cm-9x28in) s.d.1889. 26-May-4 Sotheby's, Olympia #180/R est:2000-3000

GIANNI, M (19th C) Italian
Works on paper
£1379 $2290 €2000 Naples, coastline and Vesuvius (32x59cm-13x23in) s. gouache. 30-Sep-3 Dorotheum, Vienna #273/R est:1800-2000

GIANNI, Maria (19th C) Italian
Works on paper
£400 $728 €584 Bay of Naples (30x48cm-12x19in) s. bodycol. 15-Jun-4 David Lay, Penzance #564

GIANNI, Umberto (19/20th C) Italian
£750 $1245 €1095 Neapolitan waterfront with boats and figures (38x48cm-15x19in) s.d.1918. 30-Sep-3 Rogers Jones, Clwyd #126
£850 $1411 €1241 Grand Canal, Venice scene with figures and gondolas (38x48cm-15x19in) s. 30-Sep-3 Rogers Jones, Clwyd #125/R

GIANNI, Y (19/20th C) Italian
Works on paper
£400 $732 €584 Coastal scene with figures and boats (18x42cm-7x17in) s. gouache. 7-Apr-4 Woolley & Wallis, Salisbury #137/R
£850 $1420 €1241 Mount Versuvius (30x48cm-12x19in) s. W/C two. 20-Jun-3 Chrystals Auctions, Isle of Man #277

GIANOLI, Louis (1868-1957) Swiss
£229 $383 €332 Bouquet de roses (27x35cm-11x14in) s. i.verso. 21-Jun-3 Galerie du Rhone, Sion #370 (S.FR 500)

GIANPIETRINO (attrib) (1493-1540) Italian
£36667 $66367 €55000 Madonna and Child (31x44cm-12x17in) panel. 4-Apr-4 St-Germain-en-Laye Encheres #4/R est:35000-40000

GIANQUINTO, Alberto (1929-2002) Italian
£1119 $1924 €1600 Sunflower (75x35cm-30x14in) s.i.d.1964. 3-Dec-3 Stadion, Trieste #1060/R est:700-1000
£2069 $3455 €3000 Naxos (100x45cm-39x18in) s.i.d.1972 verso. 17-Nov-3 Sant Agostino, Torino #144/R est:1500-2000
£2381 $4262 €3500 Sky (100x90cm-39x35in) s. s.d.1995 verso. 22-Mar-4 Sant Agostino, Torino #555/R est:3500
£4600 $8280 €6900 Landscape seen from the window (90x116cm-35x46in) s.indis.d. 22-Apr-4 Finarte Semenzato, Rome #365/R est:3500-4000

GIANVENUTI, Alessandro (1974-) Italian
Works on paper
£1793 $2994 €2600 Aquatic dream (180x120cm-71x47in) s.i.d.2000 verso emulsion on canvas exhib.lit. 13-Nov-3 Finarte Semenzato, Rome #480/R est:3500-3800

GIAQUINTO, Corrado (c.1690-1765) Italian
£9868 $18158 €15000 Saint Joseph's dream (93x79cm-37x31in) 24-Jun-4 Christie's, Paris #79/R est:20000-30000
£18792 $34577 €28000 Madonna and Child with Saints (132x99cm-52x39in) 29-Mar-4 Pandolfini, Florence #788/R est:35000

GIAQUINTO, Corrado (attrib) (c.1690-1765) Italian
£11667 $21000 €17034 Martyrdom of Saint Lawrence (150x127cm-59x50in) oval. 22-Jan-4 Sotheby's, New York #199/R est:20000-30000

GIAQUINTO, Corrado (studio) (c.1690-1765) Italian
£5396 $8849 €7500 Moses receiving the law borads (53x75cm-21x30in) 4-Jun-3 Sotheby's, Milan #62/R est:8000-12000

GIARDELLI, Arthur (1911-) British
Works on paper
£420 $722 €613 Carew Castle (38x56cm-15x22in) mono. 2-Dec-3 Peter Francis, Wales #63

GIARDELLO, Giuseppe (19th C) Italian
£2000 $3640 €3000 Portrait of a Neapolitan fisherman smoking a pipe (61x42cm-24x17in) s. 1-Jul-4 Van Ham, Cologne #1361/R est:1900

GIARDIELLO, C (?) Italian
£1622 $2854 €2400 Bay in Campania, Italy (26x52cm-10x20in) s. 19-May-4 Il Ponte, Milan #694 est:700-750

GIARDIELLO, G (?) Italian
£4500 $8325 €6570 Italian coastal village (65x100cm-26x39in) s. 14-Jul-4 Sotheby's, Olympia #227/R est:3000-5000

GIARDIELLO, Giuseppe (19/20th C) Italian
£680 $1136 €993 Feeding the hens (44x30cm-17x12in) s. 16-Oct-3 Lyon & Turnbull, Edinburgh #25
£770 $1378 €1124 Neapolitan girl feeding the chickens (44x30cm-17x12in) s. 18-Mar-4 Christie's, Kensington #614/R
£979 $1635 €1400 Green composition (69x50cm-27x20in) s. 11-Oct-3 De Vuyst, Lokeren #163
£1129 $2100 €1648 On the street, evening (35x50cm-14x20in) s. 5-Mar-4 Skinner, Boston #584/R est:1000-1500
£1293 $2379 €1888 Fishermen on Naples coast (17x30cm-7x12in) s. panel. 26-Mar-4 Koller, Zurich #3106/R est:2500-3500 (S.FR 3000)
£1300 $2041 €1885 Fishing sorting their nets on the Neapolitan coast (25x40cm-10x16in) s. 28-Aug-3 Christie's, Kensington #242/R est:500-700
£1422 $2617 €2076 Fishing off Capri (17x30cm-7x12in) s. panel. 26-Mar-4 Koller, Zurich #3105/R est:2500-3500 (S.FR 3300)
£1517 $2807 €2200 Fishing off Capri in the evening (25x40cm-10x16in) s. 14-Feb-4 Hans Stahl, Hamburg #28/R est:2500
£3986 $6657 €5700 Fishermen on the beach (69x119cm-27x47in) s. canvas on cardboard. 24-Jun-3 Finarte Semenzato, Rome #118/R

GIARDINO, Pasquale (1961-) Australian
£1065 $1683 €1555 Women grooming their hair (74x54cm-29x21in) s.d.95 pastel gouache. 2-Sep-3 Deutscher-Menzies, Melbourne #273/R est:1500-2000 (A.D 2600)
£1362 $2356 €1989 Apparition (149x130cm-59x51in) s.d.93. 10-Dec-3 Shapiro, Sydney #43b/R est:3000-5000 (A.D 3200)
£1532 $2650 €2237 Untitled, landscape (81x102cm-32x40in) s. 10-Dec-3 Shapiro, Sydney #46/R est:2500-3500 (A.D 3600)
£1646 $2979 €2403 Fountain tar painters 1985 (177x202cm-70x80in) s. 30-Mar-4 Lawson Menzies, Sydney #169/R est:2500-3000 (A.D 4000)
£1781 $2868 €2600 Untitled (137x147cm-54x58in) painted 1986 prov. 25-Aug-3 Sotheby's, Paddington #284/R est:2000-3000 (A.D 4400)
£2066 $3822 €3016 Red harem (182x182cm-72x72in) s. 10-Mar-4 Deutscher-Menzies, Melbourne #211/R est:6000-8000 (A.D 5000)
£2254 $3562 €3291 Nude and Richmond cityscape (87x107cm-34x42in) s.d.95. 2-Sep-3 Deutscher-Menzies, Melbourne #274/R est:4500-6000 (A.D 5500)
£3306 $5620 €4827 Vacant faces on the street no.2 (91x122cm-36x48in) s.i.verso. 29-Oct-3 Lawson Menzies, Sydney #140/R est:5000-8000 (A.D 8000)
Works on paper
£534 $973 €780 Nude (75x58cm-30x23in) s. W/C pastel chl. 16-Jun-4 Deutscher-Menzies, Melbourne #533/R est:1800-2500 (A.D 1400)
£681 $1157 €994 Beast and Bird (70x50cm-28x20in) s. pastel. 26-Nov-3 Deutscher-Menzies, Melbourne #262/R (A.D 1600)
£1106 $1881 €1615 Reclining nude and cat (49x67cm-19x26in) s. gouache pastel ink. 26-Nov-3 Deutscher-Menzies, Melbourne #163/R est:1800-2400 (A.D 2600)
£2043 $3472 €2983 Standing nude (167x51cm-66x20in) s. synthetic polymer paint canvas exec 1997. 26-Nov-3 Deutscher-Menzies, Melbourne #261/R est:3000-5000 (A.D 4800)

GIAUME, Charles (1925-) French
£267 $485 €400 Periscope sur diable (50x65cm-20x26in) s.d.64. 29-Jun-4 Chenu & Scrive, Lyon #97/R

GIAUQUE, Fernand (1895-1973) Swiss
£302 $540 €441 Lac de Morat - Salavaux (30x38cm-12x15in) s.d.45. 12-May-4 Dobiaschofsky, Bern #554/R (S.FR 700)
£304 $557 €444 Still life with poppies (50x40cm-20x16in) s.i.verso prov. 4-Jun-4 Zofingen, Switzerland #2810 (S.FR 700)
£636 $1056 €922 Summer by lake (30x39cm-12x15in) s.d.1945 board. 13-Jun-3 Zofingen, Switzerland #2853/R (S.FR 1400)
£1810 $3077 €2643 Summer's day (100x72cm-39x28in) s.d.50. 19-Nov-3 Fischer, Luzern #1114/R est:3000-4000 (S.FR 4000)

GIBB, H W Phelan (1870-1948) British
£330 $525 €482 Woman in a summer dress standing at the bank of a wooded river (39x49cm-15x19in) s. 18-Mar-3 Anderson & Garland, Newcastle #430
£3000 $5280 €4380 Two nudes in landscape (158x89cm-62x35in) s. 19-May-4 Sotheby's, Olympia #143/R est:3000-5000

GIBB, J H (19th C) British
£1958 $3329 €2800 Northumbrian coast, Dunstambro Castle in the distance (58x77cm-23x30in) s.i.d.1872 verso. 26-Nov-3 James Adam, Dublin #56/R est:3000-4000

GIBB, John (1831-1909) New Zealander
£3610 $5884 €5271 Harbour scene with figures and cattle - possibly Kaikoura Harbour (34x54cm-13x21in) s.d.1890. 23-Sep-3 Peter Webb, Auckland #106/R est:10000-15000 (NZ.D 10000)
£5254 $8458 €7671 Mitre Peak (36x56cm-14x22in) s.d.1890 s.verso. 20-Aug-3 Dunbar Sloane, Auckland #57/R est:16000-20000 (NZ.D 14500)

GIBB, William Menzies (1859-1931) New Zealander
£286 $526 €418 Water of the Leith, Dunedin (34x52cm-13x20in) s.d.1888. 25-Mar-4 International Art Centre, Auckland #157 (NZ.D 800)

GIBBERD, Eric Waters (1897-1972) American
£357 $650 €521 Adobes in a mountain landscape (30x41cm-12x16in) s. masonite prov.exhib. 15-Jun-4 John Moran, Pasadena #186

GIBBON, J (19/20th C) British
£600 $1020 €876 River landscape with cattle watering, and drover on a bridge nearby (76x127cm-30x50in) s. 19-Nov-3 Tennants, Leyburn #1066

GIBBONS, Ruth (?) ?
£607 $1100 €886 Kerry blue terrier, Aquire Extrella (30x41cm-12x16in) s. 30-Mar-4 Bonhams & Butterfields, San Francisco #133/R
£828 $1500 €1209 Kerry blue terrier, Champion Acquire Best Blue (30x41cm-12x16in) s. sold with original Kennel Club Champion certificate. 30-Mar-4 Bonhams & Butterfields, San Francisco #132/R est:1200-1800

GIBBS, Anthony (1951-) British
£700 $1281 €1022 Lioness and her cubs (51x76cm-20x30in) s.d.74. 7-Apr-4 Woolley & Wallis, Salisbury #279/R

GIBBS, Isaac (19th C) German?
Works on paper
£400 $664 €584 Elderly man wearing a tricorne hat, seated reading a book (33x25cm-13x10in) s.d.1887 i.verso. 4-Oct-3 Finan Watkins & Co, Mere #138

GIBBS, Len (1929-) Canadian
£1033 $1870 €1508 Country girl (36x67cm-14x26in) s. s.i.d.1971 acrylic hard board prov. 18-Apr-4 Levis, Calgary #32/R est:2500-3000 (C.D 2500)

£1040 $1903 €1518 Steeds (40x60cm-16x24in) s.i.d.1979 acrylic board. 1-Jun-4 Hodgins, Calgary #361/R est:2500-3000 (C.D 2600)
Works on paper
£248 $449 €362 Gathering eggs (27x34cm-11x13in) s.d.1978 mixed media. 18-Apr-4 Levis, Calgary #32a/R (C.D 600)

GIBBS, Thomas Binney (1870-?) British
£250 $418 €365 Portrait of a lady, thought to be the daughter of Samuel Greenwood (61x51cm-24x20in) s. 8-Oct-3 Christie's, Kensington #688/R

GIBERT, A (19th C) French
£707 $1300 €1032 Portrait of French officer (97x76cm-38x30in) s.d.1861. 27-Jun-4 Hindman, Chicago #866/R est:300-500

GIBERT, E (?) ?
Sculpture
£2432 $4500 €3551 Archer (74x78x15cm-29x31x6in) i. bronze marble. 11-Mar-4 Sotheby's, New York #121/R est:5000-7000

GIBERT, Lucien (1904-1988) French
Sculpture
£1549 $2680 €2200 Buste feminin (44cm-17in) s. brown pat bronze. 10-Dec-3 Millon & Associes, Paris #130/R est:1800-2200
£2483 $4395 €3700 Femme et enfant (33x24x13cm-13x9x5in) s. pat bronze marble socle. 27-Apr-4 Claude Aguttes, Neuilly #31/R est:2000-2500
£3028 $5239 €4300 Vacances (65cm-26in) s.num.1/8 brown pat bronze sold with socle Cast Coubertin. 10-Dec-3 Millon & Associes, Paris #130a est:3500-4000
Works on paper
£604 $1069 €900 Femme nue de face (60x48cm-24x19in) st.sig. crayon. 27-Apr-4 Claude Aguttes, Neuilly #33/R

GIBINSKI, Stanislaw (1882-1971) Polish
Works on paper
£707 $1245 €1032 Landscape covered in snow with children playing (69x100cm-27x39in) s. W/C. 23-May-4 Agra, Warsaw #47/R (P.Z 5000)

GIBNEY, Arthur (20th C) Irish
Works on paper
£556 $906 €800 Study of Patrick Kavanagh (55x38cm-22x15in) s.i. W/C. 23-Sep-3 De Veres Art Auctions, Dublin #203
£868 $1415 €1250 Roman studies (84x141cm-33x56in) s.d.1963 ink col pencils. 24-Sep-3 James Adam, Dublin #65/R est:1000-2000

GIBSON, Bessie (1868-1961) Australian
£2273 $4205 €3319 High tide (38x46cm-15x18in) s.acrylic panel double-sided prov. 10-Mar-4 Deutscher-Menzies, Melbourne #68/R est:4000-6000 (A.D 5500)
£2341 $3979 €3418 Small boats (35x26cm-14x10in) s. i.verso wood panel painted c.1908. 26-Nov-3 Deutscher-Menzies, Melbourne #279/R est:3000-5000 (A.D 5500)

GIBSON, Charles Dana (1867-1944) American
£719 $1200 €1050 Countryside (48x58cm-19x23in) s.i. 19-Jun-3 Shelley, Hendersonville #1214
Works on paper
£284 $475 €415 Portrait of a young man. s. pencil chk. 15-Nov-3 Harvey Clar, Oakland #1329
£1676 $3000 €2447 Couple conversing (33x46cm-13x18in) s. pen ink. 15-May-4 Illustration House, New York #98/R est.3500-5000
£2096 $3500 €3060 Two men with cigars talking (48x36cm-19x14in) s. pen ink exec.c.1910. 15-Nov-3 Illustration House, New York #31/R est:3000-4000
£3593 $6000 €5246 Social nuisances, for a man to face the music of afternoon tea (41x69cm-16x27in) s. pen ink. 15-Nov-3 Illustration House, New York #30/R est:4000-6000

GIBSON, Charles Dana (attrib) (1867-1944) American
Works on paper
£489 $900 €714 Card players (30x46cm-12x18in) pen ink. 10-Jun-4 Swann Galleries, New York #94/R

GIBSON, David (fl.1790-1808) British
Miniatures
£1000 $1700 €1460 Probably husband and wife (6cm-2in) s.d.1796 double-sided gold frame oval. 18-Nov-3 Bonhams, New Bond Street #84/R est:600-800

GIBSON, David (1939-) American
Photographs
£2246 $3750 €3279 Storm light passage, Canyon de Chelley, National Monument, Arizona (48x150cm-19x59in) num.235 edition 2/12 selenium toned gelatin silver print. 18-Oct-3 David Dike, Dallas #21/R est:7000-10000

GIBSON, George (1904-2001) American/British
Works on paper
£1695 $3000 €2475 Caribbean fishermen (38x57cm-15x22in) s. W/C graphite. 28-Apr-4 Christie's, Los Angeles #50/R est:2500-3500

GIBSON, James (20th C) American
£269 $450 €393 Highwaymen Florida landscape (56x74cm-22x29in) s. board. 19-Oct-3 Jeffery Burchard, Florida #112a
£447 $800 €653 Florida highwaymen coastal scene (56x97cm-22x38in) s. board. 21-Mar-4 Jeffery Burchard, Florida #84a/R

GIBSON, James Brown (attrib) (1880-?) British
£580 $986 €847 Moredun landscape (70x90cm-28x35in) s. 10-Nov-3 Thomson Roddick & Medcalf, Edinburgh #264

GIBSON, John (20th C) American?
£1405 $2600 €2051 Pile of Magenta and white balls (114x79cm-45x31in) s.d.12/89 verso prov. 13-Jul-4 Christie's, Rockefeller NY #168/R est:800-1200

GIBSON, John (1790-1866) British
Sculpture
£13000 $23790 €18980 Bust of nymph (44cm-17in) s. white marble. 9-Jul-4 Sotheby's, London #102/R est:8000-12000
£78000 $132600 €113880 Sleeping shepherd boy (116cm-46in) s. marble prov.lit. 28-Oct-3 Sotheby's, London #91/R est:50000-70000

GIBSON, Maurice (20th C) Australian?
£453 $819 €661 Untitled (153x90cm-60x35in) s.verso acrylic. 30-Mar-4 Lawson Menzies, Sydney #269/R est:1000-1500 (A.D 1100)

GIBSON, Richard (1615-1690) British
Miniatures
£1000 $1840 €1460 Gentleman, called James Graham, 5th Earl of Montrose (7cm-3in) W/C on vellum gilt mounted rec. papier-mache frame. 24-Jun-4 Bonhams, New Bond Street #38/R est:1000-1500
£3500 $5950 €5110 Gentleman (6cm-2in) W/C oval. 18-Nov-3 Bonhams, New Bond Street #17/R est:3500-4500

GIBSON, Sybil (1908-1995) American
£278 $500 €406 Woman in pink (84x46cm-33x18in) oil on paper. 24-Apr-4 Slotin Folk Art, Buford #472/R
£299 $500 €437 Three faces (56x46cm-22x18in) tempera paper prov. 15-Nov-3 Slotin Folk Art, Buford #221/R
£417 $750 €609 Three faces (69x53cm-27x21in) tempera on paper grocery bag. 24-Apr-4 Slotin Folk Art, Buford #470/R
£444 $800 €648 She was also there (69x56cm-27x22in) tempera on newspaper. 24-Apr-4 Slotin Folk Art, Buford #471/R
£479 $800 €699 Six yellow flowers in a blue vase (46x36cm-18x14in) tempera paper prov. 15-Nov-3 Slotin Folk Art, Buford #219/R
£500 $900 €730 Three faces (97x48cm-38x19in) tempera on paper grocery bag. 24-Apr-4 Slotin Folk Art, Buford #467/R
£722 $1300 €1054 Man with green tie (94x61cm-37x24in) tempera on paper bag. 24-Apr-4 Slotin Folk Art, Buford #468/R est:1000-3000
£1078 $1800 €1574 Five purple flowers in an orange vase (51x41cm-20x16in) s. tempera paper double-sided prov. 15-Nov-3 Slotin Folk Art, Buford #220/R est:1000-1500
Works on paper
£240 $400 €350 Pink flower vase (48x38cm-19x15in) W/C paper bag. 15-Nov-3 Slotin Folk Art, Buford #222/R
£240 $400 €350 Abstract (43x36cm-17x14in) W/C paper bag. 15-Nov-3 Slotin Folk Art, Buford #223/R

GIBSON, Thomas (1680-1751) British
£1700 $3060 €2482 Portrait of Frances Wynn (72x58cm-28x23in) s.d.1744 painted oval prov.lit. 22-Apr-4 Lawrence, Crewkerne #877/R est:1500-2000

GIBSON, Thomas (attrib) (1680-1751) British
£1816 $3250 €2651 Portrait of Miss Kitty Owen (76x64cm-30x25in) i. 20-Mar-4 Sloans & Kenyon, Bethesda #1182/R est:4000-6000

GIBSON, W A (1866-1931) British
£921 $1695 €1400 View in a dock yard (24x32cm-9x13in) panel. 22-Jun-4 Mealy's, Castlecomer #320/R est:1200-1800

GIBSON, William Alfred (1866-1931) British
£340 $568 €496 Sheep by a barn (10x15cm-4x6in) s. panel. 16-Oct-3 Bonhams, Edinburgh #165
£1200 $2232 €1752 Returning the flock (24x28cm-9x11in) s. 4-Mar-4 Christie's, Kensington #144/R est:800-1200
£1600 $2880 €2400 Return of the fihing boats (27x35cm-11x14in) s. canvass on panel prov.exhib. 20-Apr-4 Sotheby's, Amsterdam #139/R est:2000-3000
£2000 $3520 €2920 Port in Holland (39x49cm-15x19in) s. 19-May-4 Dreweatt Neate, Newbury #55/R est:1800-2000
£3800 $6308 €5548 Stream through the trees (64x76cm-25x30in) s. prov. 1-Oct-3 Sotheby's, Olympia #147/R est:1500-2500

GIDDY, Mary Ann (18/19th C) British
£800 $1432 €1168 Portrait of Davies Giddy (76x63cm-30x25in) i.d.1806 i.verso. 22-Mar-4 Bonhams & Brooks, Norfolk #331/R

GIDE, François Theophile Etienne (1822-1890) French
£7200 $13320 €10512 Recitation (74x60cm-29x24in) s. 10-Mar-4 Sotheby's, Olympia #284/R est:4000-6000
Works on paper
£699 $1203 €1000 Paysages de bords d'eau (24x46cm-9x18in) s. W/C pair. 7-Dec-3 Osenat, Fontainebleau #34

GIEBERICH, Oscar H (1886-?) American
£244 $400 €354 Still life with game (56x76cm-22x30in) s. painted c.1943. 7-Jun-3 Treadway Gallery, Cincinnati #1398

GIEGERICH, Jill (1952-) American
Sculpture
£1081 $2000 €1578 Untitled - large stacked cubes (315x84x10cm-124x33x4in) s.i.d.1984 ink collage paper on masonite prov.exhib. 12-Feb-4 Sotheby's, New York #302/R est:2500-3500

GIEL, Frans van (1892-1975) Belgian
£338 $595 €500 Still life with fruit on pewter plate, Delft jug and Chianti bottle (62x57cm-24x22in) s. panel. 24-May-4 Bernaerts, Antwerp #710/R
£567 $948 €800 Still life with sunflowers and apples (89x70cm-35x28in) s. 20-Oct-3 Bernaerts, Antwerp #263
£709 $1184 €1000 Landscape in the Kempen (90x110cm-35x43in) s. 20-Oct-3 Bernaerts, Antwerp #48/R
£800 $1440 €1200 Three nudes (110x80cm-43x31in) s. 26-Apr-4 Bernaerts, Antwerp #431/R

GIEROWSKI, Stefan (1925-) Polish
Works on paper
£333 $532 €486 Untitled (103x73cm-41x29in) W/C. 17-Sep-3 Agra, Warsaw #8/R (P.Z 2100)

GIERS, Walter (1937-) German
Sculpture
£2083 $3396 €3000 Light game (50x75x12cm-20x30x5in) s.i.d.1972 verso electronics bulbs panel plexiglas. 27-Sep-3 Dr Fritz Nagel, Stuttgart #9530/R est:3500

GIERSING, Harald (1881-1927) Danish
£293 $533 €428 Portrait of young woman (36x36cm-14x14in) i.verso canvas on panel. 7-Feb-4 Rasmussen, Havnen #4024 (D.KR 3200)
£1895 $3544 €2767 Seated girl (53x50cm-21x20in) mono. plywood. 25-Feb-4 Kunsthallen, Copenhagen #243/R est:25000 (D.KR 21000)
£2392 $3876 €3468 Portrait of young woman (64x55cm-25x22in) mono. 4-Aug-3 Rasmussen, Vejle #550/R est:30000 (D.KR 25000)
£2708 $5063 €3954 Reclining model with fan (66x85cm-26x33in) i.verso painted c.1915 exhib.lit. 25-Feb-4 Kunsthallen, Copenhagen #231/R est:40000 (D.KR 30000)

GIERYMSKI, Aleksander (1850-1901) Polish
£280 $515 €409 Country scene with woodsmen (29x55cm-11x22in) init.d.1897. 10-Jun-4 Lyon & Turnbull, Edinburgh #86
£8389 $15436 €12500 Winter town (28x40cm-11x16in) s. panel lit. 25-Mar-4 Karlheinz Kaupp, Staufen #2454/R est:8500

GIERYMSKI, Maksymilian (1846-1874) Polish
£2000 $3680 €3000 Chasseurs et officier a cheval sous l'empire (15x20cm-6x8in) s. panel. 14-Jun-4 Tajan, Paris #12 est:400-600
£45386 $78517 €66264 Austrian cavalry men (31x43cm-12x17in) s. painted 1869 exhib. 14-Dec-3 Agra, Warsaw #15/R est:260000 (P.Z 300000)

GIES, Emil (1872-?) German
£533 $976 €800 Small artist with palette (92x73cm-36x29in) s. 5-Jun-4 Arnold, Frankfurt #582/R

GIES, Joseph W (1860-1935) American
£405 $700 €591 Port scene (18x30cm-7x12in) board. 12-Dec-3 Du Mouchelle, Detroit #1241/R
£447 $800 €653 Goose girl (46x30cm-18x12in) s.d.1900. 16-May-4 CRN Auctions, Cambridge #29/R

GIES, Ludwig (1887-1966) German
Sculpture
£2000 $3660 €3000 Mother and child (30x7cm-12x3in) mid brown pat.bronze exhib.lit. 5-Jun-4 Lempertz, Koln #728/R est:3000
£2800 $5124 €4200 Eva (40cm-16in) mono. wood exhib.lit. 5-Jun-4 Lempertz, Koln #729/R est:3000
£3133 $5734 €4700 Figure in mourning (54cm-21in) wood exhib.lit. 5-Jun-4 Lempertz, Koln #730/R est:3000

GIESE, Max Eduard (1867-1916) German
£1103 $2041 €1600 Extensive Dachau landscape with hay harvesting in distance (50x74cm-20x29in) s. tempera gouache. 14-Feb-4 Hans Stahl, Hamburg #29/R est:450

GIESEL, Hermann (1847-1906) Rumanian
£4082 $7306 €6000 Hunting party (82x60cm-32x24in) s. panel lit. 20-Mar-4 Bergmann, Erlangen #1093 est:4200-6000

GIESKER, Karl Heinrich (1913-2000) Swiss
£349 $615 €510 Still life with flowers in blue vase (50x40cm-20x16in) s.d.41 prov. 22-May-4 Galerie Gloggner, Luzern #44/R (S.FR 800)

GIESSEL, Franz (1902-) Austrian
£486 $871 €720 Still life with flowers (68x114cm-27x45in) s. 6-May-4 Michael Zeller, Lindau #675/R
£500 $895 €750 Still life of flowers and fruit (58x78cm-23x31in) s. board. 13-May-4 Dorotheum, Linz #508/R
£503 $926 €750 From an inn (57x78cm-22x31in) s. 25-Mar-4 Hagelstam, Helsinki #999
£570 $1050 €850 Figures at an inn (57x78cm-22x31in) s. 25-Mar-4 Hagelstam, Helsinki #1000
£738 $1358 €1100 Card players (46x62cm-18x24in) s. 25-Mar-4 Hagelstam, Helsinki #998

GIESSEL, W (19th C) German
£486 $777 €705 Baroque interior from an inn (52x42cm-20x17in) s. 22-Sep-3 Blomqvist, Lysaker #1068 (N.KR 5700)

GIESSEL, Wilhelm (19th C) German
£594 $1010 €850 Pipe smoking men in tavern (64x92cm-25x36in) s. 20-Nov-3 Van Ham, Cologne #1595
£1325 $2424 €2000 Men in tavern (64x92cm-25x36in) s. 8-Apr-4 Dorotheum, Vienna #28/R est:1700-1900

GIESSEL, Wilhelm F (1869-1938) Austrian
£839 $1401 €1200 Village musician practising the flute (20x15cm-8x6in) s. panel. 9-Oct-3 Michael Zeller, Lindau #575/R

GIETL, Josua von (1847-1922) German
£414 $691 €600 Pre-alpine landscape (23x35cm-9x14in) s. paper. 9-Jul-3 Hugo Ruef, Munich #94
£1197 $2071 €1700 Farm buildings by a stream (90x70cm-35x28in) canvas on canvas. 10-Dec-3 Hugo Ruef, Munich #2415/R est:1200
£1736 $2760 €2500 Hay harvest (46x33cm-18x13in) s. 13-Sep-3 Quittenbaum, Hamburg #18/R est:2200

GIEZENDANNER, Babeli (1831-1905) German
Works on paper
£8520 $14229 €12439 Fruit market, Herisau (22x26cm-9x10in) pen W/C. 24-Oct-3 Hans Widmer, St Gallen #111/R est:12000-18000 (S.FR 19000)

GIFFINGER, Rudolf (19th C) ?
£1341 $2400 €1958 Moonlit harbour twilight fishing scene (41x53cm-16x21in) s. 7-May-4 Sloans & Kenyon, Bethesda #1653/R est:2000-4000

GIFFORD, C (?) ?
£1439 $2360 €2000 Landscape with hounds (120x127cm-47x50in) s.d.88. 10-Jun-3 Pandolfini, Florence #63/R est:2000-2200

GIFFORD, Charles H (1839-1904) American
£1117 $2000 €1631 Coastal view (10x23cm-4x9in) s. canvasboard. 14-May-4 Skinner, Boston #90/R est:1200-1500
£4192 $7000 €6120 Maine coastal landscape (43x66cm-17x26in) s.d.1869. 16-Nov-3 CRN Auctions, Cambridge #20/R
£4420 $8000 €6453 Ship at sea (16x25cm-6x10in) s. 31-Mar-4 Sotheby's, New York #68/R est:3000-5000
£5091 $8500 €7433 New Bedford fisherman (18x25cm-7x10in) s.d.86 canvas on board prov. 23-Oct-3 Shannon's, Milford #241/R est:6000-8000
£10180 $17000 €14863 Off the Maine coast (43x66cm-17x26in) s.d.1869 prov. 23-Oct-3 Shannon's, Milford #140/R est:15000-25000
£13174 $22000 €19234 Luminous coast (23x36cm-9x14in) s.d.80 prov. 23-Oct-3 Shannon's, Milford #108/R est:12000-18000
£21605 $35000 €31327 Sunset (24x36cm-9x14in) s.d.99. 8-Aug-3 Barridorf, Portland #138/R est:15000-25000

GIFFORD, J (19th C) British
£2617 $4868 €3900 Hunting dogs (91x71cm-36x28in) s. 4-Mar-4 Auction Maastricht #1020/R est:3000-5000

GIFFORD, John (19th C) British
£1000 $1730 €1460 Day's Bag (28x38cm-11x15in) 11-Dec-3 Neales, Nottingham #606/R est:600-800
£1319 $2400 €1926 Spaniels putting up bird (30x41cm-12x16in) s. 19-Jun-4 Charlton Hall, Columbia #378/R est:1000-1500
£1484 $2700 €2167 Spaniels after the hunt (30x41cm-12x16in) s. 19-Jun-4 Charlton Hall, Columbia #377/R est:1000-1500
£4800 $8592 €7008 Retrievers in a highland landscape (59x89cm-23x35in) s. 26-May-4 Outhwaite & Litherland, Liverpool #311/R
£5135 $9500 €7497 Setters at day's end (61x91cm-24x36in) s. 10-Feb-4 Doyle, New York #235/R est:5000-7000
£9302 $16000 €13581 English and Gordon setter with the day's bog on a moor (61x91cm-24x36in) s. 5-Dec-3 Christie's, Rockefeller NY #86/R est:10000-15000

GIFFORD, R Swain (1840-1905) American
£3412 $5800 €4982 Seashore scene (64x102cm-25x40in) s. 29-Nov-3 Carlsen Gallery, Greenville #461/R

GIFFORD, Sanford Robinson (1823-1880) American
£6211 $10000 €9068 Early fall in the White Mountains (10x15cm-4x6in) s. canvas on board. 20-Aug-3 James Julia, Fairfield #1307/R est:10000-15000
£10366 $17000 €15031 Italian coastal scene (23x36cm-9x14in) s.d.72 prov. 31-May-3 Brunk, Ashville #331/R est:10000-20000
£73864 $130000 €107841 Near Manchester, Massachusetts (27x47cm-11x19in) painted 1865 prov.lit. 18-May-4 Christie's, Rockefeller NY #13/R est:150000-250000
£181818 $320000 €265454 Galleries of the Stelvio, Lake Como (64x51cm-25x20in) s.d.1871 s.i.verso prov.exhib.lit. 19-May-4 Sotheby's, New York #78/R est:150000-250000

GIGANTE, Achille (1823-1846) Italian
Works on paper
£2800 $4816 €4088 Un porto nel Baia di Napoli. Un castello (25x45cm-10x18in) s. one d.21 Novembre 1843 one d.1842 pencil pair. 4-Dec-3 Christie's, Kensington #67/R est:2000-3000

GIGANTE, Ercole (1815-1860) Italian
£2267 $4103 €3400 Villa in Marechiaro (10x15cm-4x6in) board lit. 30-Mar-4 Babuino, Rome #318/R est:2500
Works on paper
£800 $1456 €1168 Italian coastal town (8x12cm-3x5in) s. gouache. 5-Feb-4 Mellors & Kirk, Nottingham #501/R
£850 $1547 €1241 The Isle of Ischia (20x28cm-8x11in) s.i.d.1838 pencil htd white three. 1-Jul-4 Christie's, Kensington #371

GIGANTE, G (19th C) Italian
£3642 $6629 €5500 A well on the coast road (33x45cm-13x18in) s. 21-Jun-4 Dorotheum, Vienna #16/R est:3000-3400

GIGANTE, Giacinto (1806-1876) Italian
£3401 $6088 €5000 View of POzzuoli (17x16cm-7x6in) paper. 22-Mar-4 Sant Agostino, Torino #239/R est:6000
Works on paper
£2300 $4255 €3358 Musical serenade on a terrace overlooking the bay of Naples (23x34cm-9x13in) s. indis.i. d.1846 W/C. 14-Jul-4 Bonhams, Chester #402 est:500-700
£3034 $5068 €4400 Southern landscapes (16x22cm-6x9in) s.mono.i. W/C pencil three. 15-Nov-3 Lempertz, Koln #1482/R est:900
£4577 $7919 €6500 Rural church (15x23cm-6x9in) s. W/C card prov.exhib.lit. 11-Dec-3 Christie's, Rome #175/R est:6500-8000
£8500 $15470 €12410 Bay of Naples (21x35cm-8x14in) s.i.d.1838 pencil W/C blk ink htd white. 17-Jun-4 Christie's, London #90/R est:7000-10000
£9091 $15455 €13000 Gulf of Naples and Posillipo (35x28cm-14x11in) s.d.1835 W/C. 27-Nov-3 Bassenge, Berlin #5581/R est:12000
£28000 $51520 €42000 Naples quay (24x38cm-9x15in) s.i.d.1842 W/C paper on card prov.exhib.lit. 8-Jun-4 Sotheby's, Milan #37/R est:30000-40000

GIGANTE, Giacinto (attrib) (1806-1876) Italian
£5800 $10440 €8468 Naples, view of the harbour with Vesuvius beyond (14x20cm-6x8in) s. indis d. panel. 20-Apr-4 Sotheby's, Olympia #400/R est:3000-4000

GIGER, Hans-Rudolf (1940-) Swiss
Sculpture
£4730 $8135 €6906 Baby alien (31cm-12in) mono. num.3/5 brown green pat bronze. 8-Dec-3 Philippe Schuler, Zurich #3252/R est:13000-15000 (S.FR 10500)

GIGLI, Ormond (1925-) American?
Photographs
£2260 $4000 €3300 Girls in the window (60x61cm-24x24in) s.d.1960 num.15/25 color coupler print. 27-Apr-4 Christie's, Rockefeller NY #320/R est:5000-7000
£3234 $5400 €4722 Fashion study - models in windows (50x51cm-20x20in) with sig.d.1960 verso chromogenic print. 21-Oct-3 Swann Galleries, New York #265/R est:5000-7000

GIGLI, Roberto (19/20th C) Italian
Works on paper
£475 $750 €694 View of Rome with Castel Sant Angelo on Tiber river (38x53cm-15x21in) s. W/C on card. 6-Sep-3 Brunk, Ashville #856
£726 $1300 €1060 Arch of Constantine, Rome (38x55cm-15x22in) s.i. W/C. 14-May-4 Skinner, Boston #26/R est:1000-1500
£1173 $2100 €1713 View of Roman ruins (38x55cm-15x22in) s.i. W/C. 14-May-4 Skinner, Boston #28/R est:1000-1500

GIGLI, Romeo (20th C) Italian
Works on paper
£2465 $4264 €3500 Rome, the Forum and Titus' Arch (77x57cm-30x22in) s.i. W/C card. 11-Dec-3 Christie's, Rome #44/R est:3300-3800

GIGNOUS, Eugenio (1850-1906) Italian
£2349 $4205 €3500 Landscape with hens (24x38cm-9x15in) s. 25-May-4 Finarte Semenzato, Milan #89/R est:3500-4000
£3667 $6747 €5500 Landscape at dusk (32x43cm-13x17in) s.d.73 tempera paper. 8-Jun-4 Sotheby's, Milan #40/R est:1000-2000
£6884 $11290 €9500 Mountainous landscape with lake (50x26cm-20x10in) s. 27-May-3 Finarte Semenzato, Milan #54/R est:11000
Works on paper
£1181 $1924 €1700 Canal landscape (40x24cm-16x9in) s.d.1872 W/C. 25-Sep-3 Dr Fritz Nagel, Stuttgart #1147/R est:1750
£3819 $6226 €5500 Women gathering wood in autumnal mountain landscape (33x25cm-13x10in) s.d.73 W/C. 25-Sep-3 Dr Fritz Nagel, Stuttgart #1146/R est:1750

GIGNOUS, Lorenzo (1862-c.1954) Italian
£313 $531 €450 Seascape (9x8cm-4x3in) s. cardboard. 1-Nov-3 Meeting Art, Vercelli #9
£369 $653 €550 Countryside with figures (16x22cm-6x9in) s. oil tempera card. 1-May-4 Meeting Art, Vercelli #33
£521 $885 €750 Mountainous landscape (25x34cm-10x13in) s. cardboard on canvas on board. 1-Nov-3 Meeting Art, Vercelli #73/R
£667 $1227 €1000 Peasnats in the fields (18x25cm-7x10in) s. cardboard. 8-Jun-4 Sotheby's, Milan #52/R
£940 $1748 €1400 Flowers (81x45cm-32x18in) s.indis.d. 2-Mar-4 Ansorena, Madrid #2/R
£940 $1748 €1400 Flowers (80x45cm-31x18in) s.d.89. 2-Mar-4 Ansorena, Madrid #1/R
£1418 $2369 €2000 Winter landscape with figures (46x67cm-18x26in) s. 14-Oct-3 Finarte Semenzato, Milan #93
£1972 $3411 €2800 Landscapes (33x24cm-13x9in) s. cardboard set of 3. 10-Dec-3 Sotheby's, Milan #54/R est:1500-2500
£2500 $4250 €3600 View of Pallanza (45x74cm-18x29in) s. exhib.lit. 1-Nov-3 Meeting Art, Vercelli #434/R est:3000
£2933 $5339 €4400 Fishermen's island (56x100cm-22x39in) s.indis.d. 12-Jul-4 Il Ponte, Milan #514 est:5000-5500

GIGNOUX, François Regis (1816-1882) American/French
£3469 $6210 €5100 Chutes du Niagara (25x53cm-10x21in) s. lit. 21-Mar-4 St-Germain-en-Laye Encheres #5/R est:6000-7000

GIGOUX, Jean (1806-1894) French
Works on paper
£867 $1569 €1300 Portrait d'Honore de Balzac. s.i.14 avril 1822 W/C gouache. 30-Mar-4 Rossini, Paris #808

GIHON, Albert Dakin (1866-?) American
£719 $1200 €1050 Along a canal (81x53cm-32x21in) canvas on board. 18-Jun-3 Doyle, New York #31/R

GIHON, Clarence M (1871-1929) American
£580 $969 €841 View of the farm house in summer (26x34cm-10x13in) s. painted c.1940 prov. 17-Jun-3 Pinneys, Montreal #36 est:1400-1800 (C.D 1300)

GIL GALLANGO, Felipe (1838-1938) Spanish
£1241 $2061 €1800 Landscape in Guillena (48x82cm-19x32in) s.i. 30-Sep-3 Ansorena, Madrid #113/R est:1700

GIL SALA, Ignacio (1912-) Spanish
£1846 $3267 €2750 Women in courtyard (36x46cm-14x18in) s. 27-Apr-4 Durán, Madrid #51/R est:1200
£2355 $3862 €3250 Hacia El Rocio (38x46cm-15x18in) s. 27-May-3 Durán, Madrid #180/R est:2000
£3691 $6607 €5500 Choir boys (59x73cm-23x29in) s. 25-May-4 Durán, Madrid #194/R est:5500

GIL, A B (16th C) Spanish
£1033 $1829 €1508 Cavaliers (32x22cm-13x9in) s.d.81 panel. 3-May-4 Lawson Menzies, Sydney #402 est:2500-3500 (A.D 2500)

GIL, Ignacio (1913-) Spanish
£4106 $7473 €6200 Ibiza (81x100cm-32x39in) s. 15-Jun-4 Rossini, Paris #174/R est:4000-6000

GIL, Javier (20th C) Spanish?
Works on paper
£690 $1152 €1000 Cibeles Square (70x100cm-28x39in) s.d.2002 dr. 11-Nov-3 Castellana, Madrid #75/R
£690 $1152 €1000 Giralda (100x70cm-39x28in) s.d.2002 dr. 11-Nov-3 Castellana, Madrid #74/R

GILADI, Aharon (1907-1993) Israeli
£304 $557 €444 Family with baby (46x38cm-18x15in) s.i. 4-Jun-4 Zofingen, Switzerland #2462 (S.FR 700)

GILARDI, Pier Celestino (1837-1905) Italian
£1118 $1900 €1632 Preparing the meal (51x34cm-20x13in) s.d.1889. 21-Nov-3 Skinner, Boston #234/R est:800-1200
£1135 $1895 €1600 View of village (18x11cm-7x4in) s. board. 20-Oct-3 Sant Agostino, Torino #272/R est:1200
Sculpture
£1149 $2022 €1700 Pope Pius IX. s.i.d.1870 ivory. 19-May-4 Il Ponte, Milan #561/R est:1600-1700

GILARDI, Piero (1942-) Italian
£1040 $1924 €1550 View of Alcala' (60x40cm-24x16in) s.d.1962. 13-Mar-4 Meeting Art, Vercelli #200 est:750
Sculpture
£1133 $2085 €1700 Roses on the beach (50x50cm-20x20in) s.i.d.2002 painted polyurethane. 12-Jun-4 Meeting Art, Vercelli #384/R est:1000
£1293 $2314 €1900 Mallende (59x60x20cm-23x24x8in) s.i.d.1995 foam. 22-Mar-4 Sant Agostino, Torino #454/R est:2000
£1611 $2980 €2400 Shell (50x50cm-20x20in) s.i.d.1990 verso polyurethane. 13-Mar-4 Meeting Art, Vercelli #67 est:1000
£2174 $3565 €3000 Seagull (80x120x27cm-31x47x11in) s.i.d.86 verso painted polytherene. 30-May-3 Farsetti, Prato #30/R
£2416 $4325 €3600 Vineyard (70x100cm-28x39in) s.i.d.2002 verso polyurethan. 30-May-4 Meeting Art, Vercelli #24 est:3000
£2685 $4805 €4000 Stream bank (50x50cm-20x20in) s. i.d.85 verso painted foam prov. 25-May-4 Sotheby's, Milan #196/R est:3500
£2685 $4805 €4000 Coconuts. s.i.d.2003 painted polyurethane. 28-May-4 Farsetti, Prato #295/R est:3400-4400
£3133 $5765 €4700 Citrus in Greece (100x100cm-39x39in) s.i.d.1992 verso painted polyurethane. 12-Jun-4 Meeting Art, Vercelli #508/R est:3000
£3221 $5960 €4800 Grapes and sweetcorn (100x100cm-39x39in) s.i.d.1992 verso polyurethane. 13-Mar-4 Meeting Art, Vercelli #405 est:4000

Works on paper

£367	$675	€550	Leaves (20x14cm-8x6in) painted foam. 8-Jun-4 Finarte Semenzato, Milan #137
£676	$1189	€1000	Poppies (25x25cm-10x10in) s.i.d.90 verso foam. 24-May-4 Christie's, Milan #17

GILBAULT, Aglae (19th C) French

£705	$1198	€1029	Still life with peaches and roses on leaf (32x46cm-13x18in) s. 5-Nov-3 Dobiaschofsky, Bern #603/R (S.FR 1600)

GILBERT (?) ?

£392	$666	€560	La ramassage du varech (22x41cm-9x16in) s. panel. 24-Nov-3 Boscher, Cherbourg #852
£497	$800	€721	Alpine landscape with river and boats (71x104cm-28x41in) s. 17-Aug-3 Jeffery Burchard, Florida #50

GILBERT and GEORGE (20th C) British

Photographs

£40000	$72800	€58400	Cheeky boy (60x50cm-24x20in) s.i.d.1980 black white photo four parts prov.exhib.lit. 6-Feb-4 Sotheby's, London #126/R est:40000-60000
£52000	$86840	€75920	Swaying (38x31cm-15x12in) blk white photographs exec 1972 three prov.lit. 21-Oct-3 Sotheby's, London #331/R est:35000-45000
£65000	$119600	€94900	British Lion (241x201cm-95x79in) s.i.d.1980 hand-dyed gelatin silver print 16 parts prov.exhib. 24-Jun-4 Sotheby's, London #116/R est:50000-70000
£69832	$125000	€101955	Patriots (181x301cm-71x119in) s.i.d.1980 black white photo 18 album prov.exhib.lit. 14-May-4 Phillips, New York #245/R est:90000-120000
£122905	$220000	€179441	Basket (181x151cm-71x59in) s.i.d.1978 coloured gelatin silver print 9 parts prov.exhib.lit. 13-May-4 Sotheby's, New York #381/R est:180000-220000
£134078	$240000	€195754	The Penis (241x201cm-95x79in) s.i.d.1978 blk and white photograph 16 parts prov.exhib.lit. 12-May-4 Sotheby's, New York #59/R est:200000-300000
£145000	$263900	€211700	Bad thoughts No.5 (122x102cm-48x40in) s.i.d.1975 hand-dyed gelatin silver print four prov.exhib.lit. 5-Feb-4 Sotheby's, London #3/R est:100000-150000

Prints

£11972	$19873	€17000	People World (241x175cm-95x69in) s.i.d.1989 postcard on board. 13-Jun-3 Hauswedell & Nolte, Hamburg #641/R est:20000

Sculpture

£4722	$8500	€6894	The challenge (37x50cm-15x20in) s.i.d.1981 post-card exhib. 24-Apr-4 David Rago, Lambertville #323/R est:6000-8000

Works on paper

£5000	$9100	€7300	Nature queen (135x99cm-53x39in) s.i.d.1981 postcard collage board prov. 21-Jun-4 Bonhams, New Bond Street #118/R est:4000-6000
£5500	$9185	€8030	Queen Elizabeth II (112x82cm-44x32in) s.i.d.1980 collage postcards on paper prov. 22-Oct-3 Christie's, London #158/R est:6000-8000
£5988	$10000	€8742	Courtship (112x81cm-44x32in) s.i.d.1981 postcard collage board prov. 13-Nov-3 Sotheby's, New York #534/R est:10000-15000
£6000	$10920	€8760	Budgeriguards (107x103cm-42x41in) s.i.d.1981 postcard collage board prov.exhib. 21-Jun-4 Bonhams, New Bond Street #119/R est:4000-6000
£7000	$12740	€10220	Postcard sculpture, summer (113x79cm-44x31in) s.i.d.1974 postcard collage felt-tip pen card prov.exhib. 6-Feb-4 Sotheby's, London #132/R est:7000-10000
£7000	$12880	€10220	Marching cross (124x103cm-49x41in) s.i.d.1981 postcard collage felt tip pen card prov. 24-Jun-4 Sotheby's, Olympia #459/R est:7000-9000
£7500	$13800	€10950	Piccadilly day in and day out (109x125cm-43x49in) s.i.d.1981 felt-tip pen postcard collage card prov.exhib. 24-Jun-4 Sotheby's, London #306/R est:6000-8000
£9000	$16380	€13140	Queen's birthday (84x140cm-33x55in) s.i.d.1981 felt tip pen postcard collage card prov.exhib. 6-Feb-4 Sotheby's, London #105/R est:6000-8000
£15642	$28000	€22837	Polish cross - from the post-card sculpture series (112x81cm-44x32in) s.i.d.1981 post-card collage felt pen on board prov.lit. 13-May-4 Sotheby's, New York #421/R est:8000-12000
£16000	$29440	€23360	Sunset window (241x182cm-95x72in) s.i.d.1989 felt-tip pen postcard collage card prov.exhib. 24-Jun-4 Sotheby's, London #305/R est:8000-12000

GILBERT, A (19/20th C) ?

£1900	$3154	€2774	Sunrise on a river landscape (84x135cm-33x53in) s.d.1854. 30-Sep-3 Andrew Smith, Winchester #132/R est:2500-3500

GILBERT, Albert (fl.1880-1920) British

£247	$450	€361	Rothesay from Barone Hill (25x41cm-10x16in) s.i.verso. 19-Jun-4 Jackson's, Cedar Falls #281/R

GILBERT, Alfred (1854-1934) British

Sculpture

£1800	$3276	€2628	Offering to Hymen (28cm-11in) brown pat bronze. 15-Jun-4 Sotheby's, Olympia #132/R est:2000-3000
£2400	$4416	€3504	An offering to Hymen (29cm-11in) brown pat. bronze wooded plinth prov.lit. 11-Jun-4 Christie's, London #75/R est:2000-3000
£3600	$6624	€5256	George Frederic Watts (17cm-7in) s.d.1890 brown pat. bronze wooden plinth prov.lit. 11-Jun-4 Christie's, London #89/R est:2000-3000
£24000	$44160	€35040	Eros (60cm-24in) black pat. bronze prov.exhib.lit. 11-Jun-4 Christie's, London #91/R est:25000-35000
£26000	$44980	€37960	Perseus arming (41cm-16in) brown pat bronze wood base exhib.lit. 12-Dec-3 Sotheby's, London #236/R est:15000-20000

GILBERT, Andre (20th C) ?

Sculpture

£1850	$3275	€2701	Two girls playing ring a ring a roses (42cm-17in) s. bronze marble base exec.c.1920. 27-Apr-4 Bonhams, Chester #89/R est:1200-1800
£4000	$7320	€5840	Harlequinade with roses (46cm-18in) s. bronze ivory. 3-Jun-4 Sotheby's, Olympia #241/R est:3000-4000

GILBERT, Arthur (1819-1895) British

£850	$1581	€1241	Sunset over the loch (23x36cm-9x14in) i. 4-Mar-4 Christie's, Kensington #57/R
£856	$1567	€1284	Landscape. d.1853. 3-Jun-4 Joel, Victoria #198 (A.D 2200)
£903	$1472	€1300	Highland cattle in a mountain landscape (19x26cm-7x10in) 23-Sep-3 De Veres Art Auctions, Dublin #205/R
£1500	$2775	€2190	Moonrise, near Oxted, Surrey (24x44cm-9x17in) i.verso panel. 10-Feb-4 Bonhams, Knightsbridge #100/R est:1500-2000
£1700	$2771	€2482	The road up Snowdon. Loch Maree (15x23cm-6x9in) s.i.verso board pair. 25-Sep-3 Gorringes, Worthing #673/R est:400-600
£4000	$6400	€5840	Guernsey coastal scene (20x25cm-8x10in) board. 17-Sep-3 Bonhams, Brooks & Langlois, Jersey #56/R est:2500-3000
£4800	$8928	€7008	Road to Snowdon, North Wales. Loch Mree, Scotland (16x23cm-6x9in) s. indis d.1889 i.verso board pair. 4-Mar-4 Christie's, Kensington #58/R est:2000-3000

GILBERT, Arthur (attrib) (1819-1895) British

£900	$1494	€1314	Highland cattle by moonlight (20x30cm-8x12in) inis.s. i.stretcher. 1-Oct-3 Sotheby's, Olympia #61/R

GILBERT, Arthur Hill (1894-1970) American

£1236	$2250	€1805	Carmel Valley landscape (23x30cm-9x12in) s. i.verso canvasboard. 15-Jun-4 John Moran, Pasadena #91 est:2000-3000
£1317	$2200	€1923	Summer hills, Monterey California (25x30cm-10x12in) s. board prov. 29-Jun-3 William Jenack, New York #98 est:1000-1500
£1377	$2300	€2010	Carmel Valley, Monterey, CA (23x30cm-9x12in) s.i. canvasboard prov. 29-Jun-3 William Jenack, New York #264 est:1000-1500
£2989	$5500	€4364	Green hills at the seaside (30x40cm-12x16in) s. canvasboard prov. 8-Jun-4 Bonhams & Butterfields, San Francisco #4240/R est:3000-5000
£4790	$8000	€6993	Haystacks, Monterey, CA (64x76cm-25x30in) s. prov. 29-Jun-3 William Jenack, New York #147 est:10000-15000
£4913	$8500	€7173	View along 17 Mile Drive (63x76cm-25x30in) s.i. 10-Dec-3 Bonhams & Butterfields, San Francisco #6195/R est:5000-7000
£4945	$9000	€7220	Rocky cypress coastal scene (71x76cm-28x30in) s. 15-Jun-4 John Moran, Pasadena #55 est:7000-9000
£10405	$18000	€15191	Path though the trees (61x76cm-24x30in) s. 10-Dec-3 Bonhams & Butterfields, San Francisco #6243/R est:12000-16000

GILBERT, Henry (19th C) British

Works on paper

£380	$604	€555	Portrait of John Sear, wearing velvet jacket (32x24cm-13x9in) s.d.1847 W/C. 9-Sep-3 Bamfords, Derby #1106/R

GILBERT, Horace W (1855-?) British

£1500	$2370	€2175	Quarry, Warlingham, Surrey (46x61cm-18x24in) s.d.1892. 4-Sep-3 Christie's, Kensington #127 est:700-1200

Works on paper

£900	$1548	€1314	Eagle's throne (86x56cm-34x22in) s.d.1878 W/C. 3-Dec-3 Bonhams, Knightsbridge #26/R

GILBERT, Joseph Francis (1792-1855) British

£503	$926	€750	Romantic lake landscape with house and fishing boats (69x105cm-27x41in) s. 26-Mar-4 Altus, Berlin #502/R

GILBERT, Kate (1843-?) British

£3000	$5400	€4380	Noon in the Essex marches. Thames below Sonning (12x23cm-5x9in) s.indis.d. board pair. 21-Jan-4 Sotheby's, Olympia #329/R est:800-1200

GILBERT, L (19/20th C) ?

£950	$1748	€1387	Cavalier's pet (41x51cm-16x20in) s.d.1883 after Sir Edwin Landseer. 10-Jun-4 Christie's, Kensington #444/R

GILBERT, R (19/20th C) British

£994	$1600	€1451	Stag hunt (33x41cm-13x16in) s. 14-Jan-4 Christie's, Rockefeller NY #60/R est:1000-1500

GILBERT, Sir John (1817-1897) British

Works on paper

£260	$468	€380	Portrait of a gentleman (44x34cm-17x13in) init.d.1869 W/C. 21-Jan-4 Sotheby's, Olympia #189/R
£450	$774	€657	Cardinal Pandolphus at the ex-communication of King John (25x41cm-10x16in) s.d.1864 pencil W/C bodycol. 3-Dec-3 Christie's, Kensington #67/R
£450	$765	€657	Sketch of a portion of Rufford Abbey with Lord Saville and a monk (18x26cm-7x10in) W/C. 25-Nov-3 Bonhams, Knightsbridge #168/R
£520	$931	€759	Mary Queen of Scots (28x34cm-11x13in) W/C. 17-Mar-4 Bonhams, Chester #346
£850	$1573	€1241	Archbishop of York, Lords Hastings, Mowbray and Bardolph, Act 1 (31x46cm-12x18in) mono.d.1866 W/C bodycol. 9-Mar-4 Bonhams, Knightsbridge #74/R
£1800	$2988	€2628	Bearing the colours (47x35cm-19x14in) s.d.1865 W/C. 1-Oct-3 Sotheby's, Olympia #168/R est:1000-1500
£3000	$5010	€4380	Rhine wine (89x69cm-35x27in) s.d.1887 pencil W/C bodycol. 16-Oct-3 Christie's, Kensington #83/R est:3000-5000
£3600	$6624	€5256	Portrait of a gentleman in middle Eastern dress (73x50cm-29x20in) s. col chk arched top. 26-Mar-4 Sotheby's, London #139/R est:2000-3000
£6250	$11688	€9375	Miss Flute introduces the wards in Jarndyce to the Lord Chancellor (69x91cm-27x36in) s.d.1860 W/C. 21-Jul-4 John Nicholson, Haslemere #71/R est:3000-5000

GILBERT, Sir John (attrib) (1817-1897) British

£355	$628	€518	Portrait of musketeer (40x29cm-16x11in) init. 28-Apr-4 Dunbar Sloane, Auckland #53/R (NZ.D 1000)

GILBERT, Stephen (1910-) British

£987	$1816	€1500	Abstract composition. Composition (45x32cm-18x13in) s.d.51 verso double-sided. 28-Jun-4 Sotheby's, Amsterdam #237/R est:1500-1800

Works on paper

£256	$409	€371	Composition (68x51cm-27x20in) s. W/C. 22-Sep-3 Blomqvist, Lysaker #1069 (N.KR 3000)

£941 $1599 €1374 Composition (34x25cm-13x10in) init.d.50 W/C. 26-Nov-3 Kunsthallen, Copenhagen #63/R (D.KR 10000)

GILBERT, Thomas (19th C) British
£994 $1800 €1451 Circus is here again (81x61cm-32x24in) with sig.d.1891. 3-Apr-4 South Bay, Long Island #161

GILBERT, Victor (1847-1933) French
£493 $882 €700 Scene de port (14x10cm-6x4in) s. panel. 11-Jan-4 Rouillac, Vendome #346
£1600 $2896 €2400 Scene parisienne (30x38cm-12x15in) s. 5-Apr-4 Marie & Robert, Paris #37 est:1500-2000
£1958 $3329 €2800 Femme dans un interieur (36x49cm-14x19in) s. cardboard. 28-Nov-3 Drouot Estimations, Paris #148 est:3000-4000
£3892 $6500 €5682 Recitation (46x38cm-18x15in) s. 7-Oct-3 Sotheby's, New York #90 est:2000-3000
£4121 $7500 €6017 At the market (46x38cm-18x15in) s. 29-Jun-4 Sotheby's, New York #93/R est:7000-10000
£4121 $7500 €6017 Naughty brother (38x46cm-15x18in) s. 29-Jun-4 Sotheby's, New York #96/R est:4000-6000
£5220 $9500 €7621 Best friends (46x38cm-18x15in) s. 29-Jun-4 Sotheby's, New York #91/R est:8000-12000
£5689 $9500 €8306 Buying cherries (38x46cm-15x18in) s. 7-Oct-3 Sotheby's, New York #89 est:4000-6000
£5988 $10000 €8742 Lunch time in the park (38x46cm-15x18in) s. 7-Oct-3 Sotheby's, New York #88/R est:5000-7000
£6268 $10404 €8900 Petites filles jouant a la marchande (38x46cm-15x18in) s. 15-Jun-3 Peron, Melun #89
£7483 $11898 €11000 Le jeu de la marelle (27x35cm-11x14in) s. panel. 23-Mar-3 Mercier & Cie, Lille #238/R est:8000-10000
£8000 $13760 €11680 Early start (80x120cm-31x47in) s.d.1883. 4-Dec-3 Christie's, Kensington #5/R est:7000-10000
£9500 $17480 €13870 Birthday party preparations (55x46cm-22x18in) s. 25-Mar-4 Christie's, Kensington #36/R est:10000-12000
£10000 $18400 €14600 At the fruit stall (38x46cm-15x18in) s. panel. 23-Mar-4 Bonhams, New Bond Street #104/R est:10000-15000
£12000 $20640 €17520 Young friends (46x37cm-18x15in) s. panel. 4-Dec-3 Christie's, Kensington #121/R est:12000-16000
£18056 $32500 €26362 La marchande de fleurs (65x54cm-26x21in) s. 23-Apr-4 Sotheby's, New York #111/R est:35000-45000
£35294 $60000 €51529 La cueillette de fleurs (54x46cm-21x18in) s. 29-Oct-3 Christie's, Rockefeller NY #151/R est:40000-60000
£48235 $82000 €70423 La marchande de fleurs (38x46cm-15x18in) s.d.1878. 29-Oct-3 Christie's, Rockefeller NY #122/R est:40000-60000
£51765 $88000 €75577 Un marche parisien (46x61cm-18x24in) s.d.1878 panel. 29-Oct-3 Christie's, Rockefeller NY #146/R est:40000-60000
Works on paper
£1200 $2160 €1752 Flower seller (28x21cm-11x8in) s. W/C. 21-Jan-4 Sotheby's, Olympia #506/R est:1200-1800
£2550 $4693 €3800 L'heure du gouter (30x39cm-12x15in) s. W/C htd gouache. 28-Mar-4 Anaf, Lyon #132/R est:4500-5500
£2762 $4750 €4033 Flower girl (20x30cm-8x12in) s. gouache. 7-Dec-3 Freeman, Philadelphia #26 est:4000-6000
£15882 $27000 €23188 Flower Market (71x52cm-28x20in) s. gouache W/C. 28-Oct-3 Sotheby's, New York #7/R est:30000-40000

GILBERT-ROLFE, Jeremy (1945-) American
£294 $500 €429 Vermeer (86x86cm-34x34in) init.i.d.91 verso oil on linen. 9-Nov-3 Bonhams & Butterfields, Los Angeles #4081/R
£441 $750 €644 Glance (71x71cm-28x28in) init.i.d.1991 oil on linen. 9-Nov-3 Bonhams & Butterfields, Los Angeles #4082/R
Works on paper
£236 $425 €345 Fifth study for warfare and pleasure (22x30cm-9x12in) init.i.d.1976 graphite gouache. 24-Apr-4 David Rago, Lambertville #68/R

GILBOA, Nahum (1917-) Bulgarian
£608 $1100 €888 A family scene (38x47cm-15x19in) s. painted 1970's. 1-Apr-4 Ben-Ami, Tel Aviv #4719/R

GILCHREST, Joan (1918-) British
£260 $432 €380 Study of mushrooms (20x24cm-8x9in) init. board. 2-Oct-3 Lane, Penzance #3
£400 $740 €584 Cornish cottages (25x36cm-10x14in) s.d.1968 i.verso board. 10-Feb-4 David Lay, Penzance #366
£650 $1203 €949 Church in a landscape (13x18cm-5x7in) init. board. 10-Feb-4 David Lay, Penzance #315
£720 $1332 €1051 St. Ives (13x18cm-5x7in) init. board. 10-Feb-4 David Lay, Penzance #313
£750 $1388 €1095 Grey sky (13x18cm-5x7in) init. board. 10-Feb-4 David Lay, Penzance #312
£820 $1492 €1197 Chapel by the sea (13x13cm-5x5in) i.verso board. 15-Jun-4 David Lay, Penzance #111
£880 $1628 €1285 Two black boats (13x18cm-5x7in) init. board. 10-Feb-4 David Lay, Penzance #314/R
£1300 $2366 €1898 Peace and quiet at Old Hill Cottage (20x20cm-8x8in) init. board. 15-Jun-4 David Lay, Penzance #397/R est:650-750
£1500 $2490 €2190 Arum lilies before the studio window (43x31cm-17x12in) init. board. 2-Oct-3 Lane, Penzance #70/R est:2000-3000
£1900 $3458 €2774 Black hens (25x36cm-10x14in) board. 15-Jun-4 David Lay, Penzance #576/R est:2000-2500
£2100 $3486 €3066 Watching the fishing fleet from a field of anemones (40x58cm-16x23in) init. board. 2-Oct-3 Lane, Penzance #15/R est:2500-2800
£3500 $6405 €5110 Rough seas Mousehole (55x43cm-22x17in) init. board prov.exhib. 3-Jun-4 Lane, Penzance #225/R est:2500-3000
£4000 $7320 €5840 Winter in St Buryan (75x90cm-30x35in) mono. board. 3-Jun-4 Lane, Penzance #5/R est:4000-5000

GILCHRIST, Philip Thomson (1865-1956) British
£300 $549 €438 Training Brig getting under weigh (39x24cm-15x9in) s.d.1903 s.i. verso. 8-Jul-4 Lawrence, Crewkerne #1654/R
£440 $774 €642 Cattle on headland (51x69cm-20x27in) s. 19-May-4 James Thompson, Kirby Lonsdale #173
£490 $862 €715 Boats at Corfu (48x32cm-19x13in) s. 19-May-4 James Thompson, Kirby Lonsdale #123
£530 $933 €774 Moonlit scene, Sunderland Point (31x41cm-12x16in) s. board. 19-May-4 James Thompson, Kirby Lonsdale #98
£580 $1021 €847 Lune Estuary with sailing boat (29x39cm-11x15in) init. panel. 19-May-4 James Thompson, Kirby Lonsdale #95
£840 $1478 €1226 Calm coastal scene with sailing boat (27x36cm-11x14in) board. 19-May-4 James Thompson, Kirby Lonsdale #97
£950 $1701 €1387 Rainbow over Niagara Falls (37x29cm-15x11in) s.d.1893 board. 27-May-4 Christie's, Kensington #246/R
£1200 $2112 €1752 Latent Power, Valetta Harbour (90x60cm-35x24in) s.d.1902. 19-May-4 James Thompson, Kirby Lonsdale #99
£6400 $11264 €9344 Valetta Harbour, Malta with warships (62x91cm-24x36in) 19-May-4 James Thompson, Kirby Lonsdale #100

GILDOR, Jacob (1948-) Israeli
£395 $700 €577 Midnight cafe (53x46cm-21x18in) s. 1-May-4 Harvey Clar, Oakland #1228
£413 $748 €620 Red sun (19x25cm-7x10in) s.i. tempera pencil. 2-Apr-4 Winterberg, Heidelberg #1020/R

GILE, Selden Connor (1877-1947) American
£2890 $5000 €4219 Marin Landscape (29x37cm-11x15in) s.d.1912 prov. 10-Dec-3 Bonhams & Butterfields, San Francisco #6366/R est:5000-7000
£5202 $9000 €7595 Old Medau Place, Oakland (41x51cm-16x20in) board prov. 10-Dec-3 Bonhams & Butterfields, San Francisco #6265/R est:10000-15000
£6250 $11500 €9125 Stevenson House, Monterey, California (14x23cm-6x9in) panel prov. 8-Jun-4 Bonhams & Butterfields, San Francisco #4311/R est:8000-12000
£7881 $14500 €11506 Cows at the trough, Marin County, California (30x40cm-12x16in) painted c.1926 prov. 8-Jun-4 Bonhams & Butterfields, San Francisco #4308/R est:15000-20000
£9341 $17000 €13638 Boat house and boats (20x25cm-8x10in) s.i.d.32 verso panel. 15-Jun-4 John Moran, Pasadena #15 est:7000-9000
£20231 $35000 €29537 San Rafael Avenue, Tiburon (40x51cm-16x20in) painted c.1935 board prov.exhib. 10-Dec-3 Bonhams & Butterfields, San Francisco #6261/R est:35000-45000
£28902 $50000 €42197 Iris and fruit. Sun-washed homes on a hill (38x46cm-15x18in) s.d.34 masonite double-sided prov. 10-Dec-3 Bonhams & Butterfields, San Francisco #6258/R est:30000-50000
£59783 $110000 €87283 Italian fishermen in Belvedere Cove (38x45cm-15x18in) painted c.1927 prov. 8-Jun-4 Bonhams & Butterfields, San Francisco #4307/R est:70000-90000

GILE, Selden Connor (attrib) (1877-1947) American
£419 $700 €612 Lake Geneva (46x33cm-18x13in) board. 14-Nov-3 Aspire, Cleveland #49

GILES, Carl (1916-1995) British
Works on paper
£750 $1328 €1095 Save em a lot of embarrassment if we pranged em before they reach London Docks (30x48cm-12x19in) s. ink W/C. 29-Apr-4 Gorringes, Lewes #2309

GILES, Catherina Dawson (1878-1955) British
Works on paper
£330 $551 €482 Catherine Giles and Jessica Dismorr at Cassis (24x34cm-9x13in) s.i. W/C pencil. 16-Oct-3 Lawrence, Crewkerne #666

GILES, Geoffrey Douglas (1857-1941) British
£524 $892 €750 Study of Cloister, winner of the Grand National 1893 (22x30cm-9x12in) mono.d.1896 i.verso. 18-Nov-3 Mealy's, Castlecomer #1034/R
£1410 $2496 €2059 Watering at the old mill (86x112cm-34x44in) s. 29-Apr-4 Christie's, Kensington #119/R est:1500-2000
£1707 $3175 €2492 Portrait of brown horses in stable (50x61cm-20x24in) s.d.1901 pair. 2-Mar-4 Rasmussen, Copenhagen #1579/R est:10000 (D.KR 19000)

GILES, Horace P (fl.c.1906) American
£552 $1000 €806 Sun through fall wooded landscape (20x25cm-8x10in) s. board. 16-Apr-4 James Julia, Fairfield #879/R est:1250-1750

GILES, James William (1801-1870) British
£800 $1488 €1168 Figures on a rocky beach (25x30cm-10x12in) s. pair. 4-Mar-4 Christie's, Kensington #67/R
£4500 $7245 €6525 Averian and Lucerne Lakes, Bay of Baiae (49x75cm-19x30in) s.d.1826. 21-Aug-3 Bonhams, Edinburgh #1123/R est:5000-8000
£4500 $7650 €6570 Aqua Claudia, near Tivoli (30x76cm-12x30in) s.d.1856 panel prov.exhib. 30-Oct-3 Christie's, London #71/R est:3000-5000
Works on paper
£750 $1253 €1095 Glen (34x49cm-13x19in) s.d.1847 W/C htd white sold with three similar. 16-Oct-3 Bonhams, Edinburgh #142

GILES, Tony (1925-1994) British
£270 $500 €394 Boats (51x66cm-20x26in) s. board. 10-Feb-4 David Lay, Penzance #159
£300 $555 €438 Harbour (51x66cm-20x26in) s. board. 10-Feb-4 David Lay, Penzance #127
£300 $555 €438 Cornish buildings (51x66cm-20x26in) s. 10-Feb-4 David Lay, Penzance #160
£350 $585 €511 Landscape with mines (71x91cm-28x36in) s.i.verso. 14-Oct-3 David Lay, Penzance #555
£380 $635 €555 Polperro (56x99cm-22x39in) s. board. 14-Oct-3 David Lay, Penzance #563
£420 $701 €613 Landscape banns (76x102cm-30x40in) s. board. 14-Oct-3 David Lay, Penzance #562

GILHOFER, Johann (20th C) Austrian
Works on paper
£1611 $2964 €2400 Sunshine on farmstead on the Hochschwab (22x30cm-9x12in) s.i.d.1924 verso W/C. 26-Mar-4 Dorotheum, Vienna #315/R est:1200-1400

GILI Y ROIG, Baldomero (1837-1926) Spanish
£327 $594 €480 Young woman in profile (28x22cm-11x9in) s.d.1907. 3-Feb-4 Segre, Madrid #121/R
£629 $1051 €900 Portrait of a young woman (27x31cm-11x12in) s. canvas on board. 24-Jun-3 Segre, Madrid #86/R

GILIBERTO, Tony (20th C) American
£328 $600 €479 Untitled (168x137cm-66x54in) acrylic. 10-Jul-4 Hindman, Chicago #174/R

GILIEN, Ted (1915-1967) American
£815 $1500 €1223 Macibean archer (150x89cm-59x35in) s.d.57 s.i.verso masonite prov. 8-Jun-4 Auctions by the Bay, Alameda #1137/R

GILIOLI, Émile (1911-1977) French
£266 $480 €400 Untitled (48x35cm-19x14in) s.i.d.1951 chl. 26-Apr-4 Tajan, Paris #210
Sculpture
£1127 $1949 €1600 La Tour de David (66x11cm-26x4in) s.num.3/6 gilt bronze. 12-Dec-3 Renaud, Paris #164/R est:1500
£1370 $2329 €2000 Composition (26x30cm-10x12in) pat bronze. 10-Nov-3 Horta, Bruxelles #160
£1667 $3000 €2500 Bas-relief (80x64cm-31x25in) s.d.1960 plaster. 24-Apr-4 Cornette de St.Cyr, Paris #551 est:1500-2000
£1701 $3044 €2500 Christ en croix (55x53cm-22x21in) s. num.2/5 base pat bronze. 19-Mar-4 Millon & Associes, Paris #199/R est:1500-2000
£2245 $4018 €3300 Untitled (36cm-14in) s. bears no.3 bronze. 19-Mar-4 Millon & Associes, Paris #200/R est:1000-1200
£2533 $4636 €3800 Puissance de la vie (44cm-17in) num.2/6 polished bronze blk marble base. 7-Jun-4 Palais de Beaux Arts, Brussels #337/R est:3000-4000
£3667 $6747 €5500 La droite du Seigneur est coupante comme un glaive (55cm-22in) s. num.3/3 polished bronze blk marble base st.f. Susse. 10-Jun-4 Camard, Paris #177/R est:6000-8000
£3733 $6720 €5600 Basilic (56cm-22in) s. num.3/8 pat bronze exec.1957. 24-Apr-4 Cornette de St.Cyr, Paris #552 est:4000-5000
£4795 $8151 €7000 Homme et femme (43x60cm-17x24in) s. num.1/6 pat bronze Cast Susse. 10-Nov-3 Horta, Bruxelles #159
£4861 $7681 €7000 Coq (46x36x15cm-18x14x6in) s. num.2/5 polished bronze. 27-Apr-3 Versailles Encheres #100
£5333 $9600 €8000 Dormeuse (38x60x40cm-15x24x16in) s. num.3/6 polished bronze Cast Susse exec.1962 prov.exhib. 25-Apr-4 Versailles Encheres #214 est:8000-10000
£7895 $14526 €12000 Paquier (70x52x42cm-28x20x17in) s. num.3/3 polished bronze prov.exhib.lit. 27-Jun-4 Versailles Encheres #146/R est:12000-15000
Works on paper
£369 $690 €550 Visage (64x49cm-25x19in) s. wax crayon. 29-Feb-4 Versailles Encheres #241/R
£470 $832 €700 Visage (33x25cm-13x10in) s.d.61 felt pen ink. 27-Apr-4 Artcurial Briest, Paris #98
£493 $853 €700 Composition (66x52cm-26x20in) st.sig. chl dr exec.c.1950-1955. 14-Dec-3 Versailles Encheres #3
£604 $1124 €900 Composition (46x31cm-18x12in) s.d.1972 gouache. 3-Mar-4 Tajan, Paris #223
£903 $1507 €1300 Composition (64x49cm-25x19in) s. gouache. 21-Oct-3 Artcurial Briest, Paris #408 est:800-1000

GILL, Charles (1871-1918) Canadian
£412 $750 €618 Portrait of a young woman in a white dress (38x43cm-15x17in) 16-Jun-4 Wolf's, New York #486551/R

GILL, DeLancey (1859-1940) American
£540 $950 €788 Impresionist field scene (36x28cm-14x11in) s.d.1919 board. 1-Jan-4 Quinn's, Falls Church #185/R
Works on paper
£652 $1200 €952 Untitled - Adobe (71x48cm-28x19in) W/C. 24-Jun-4 Sotheby's, New York #168/R

GILL, Edmund (1820-1894) British
£280 $512 €409 A land storm (79x91cm-31x36in) i.verso. 7-Apr-4 Woolley & Wallis, Salisbury #323/R
£600 $1098 €876 Figures by a waterfall (23x18cm-9x7in) s.d.1868 panel. 3-Jun-4 Lane, Penzance #272
£2150 $3655 €3139 Waterfall, Com Camlan (38x52cm-15x20in) s. board. 26-Nov-3 Hamptons Fine Art, Godalming #164/R est:2000-3000
£2500 $4675 €3750 Fall of the River Cain, North Wales (85x64cm-33x25in) s.d.1869 s.i.d.verso prov. 22-Jul-4 Tennants, Leyburn #845/R est:2500-3000

GILL, Eric (1882-1940) British
Sculpture
£3200 $5920 €4672 Madonna and Child (19cm-7in) init.num.65 painted plaster exec.c.1913 lit. 11-Feb-4 Sotheby's, Olympia #115/R est:1500-2000
Works on paper
£300 $510 €438 Portrait of D.R. (13x8cm-5x3in) init.i. pencil. 26-Nov-3 Sotheby's, Olympia #12/R
£2200 $3784 €3212 Preliminary study for The Tumbler (46x31cm-18x12in) pencil blue crayon. 3-Dec-3 Christie's, Kensington #424/R est:1500-2000
£8500 $15725 €12410 Nativity - who were the first to cry nowell? animals all, as it befell (37x41cm-15x16in) init. pen ink prov.lit. 10-Mar-4 Cheffins, Cambridge #52/R est:1500-2500

GILL, Frederick (20th C) American
£278 $500 €406 Abstract in jazz (76x51cm-30x20in) s. masonite. 23-Jan-4 Freeman, Philadelphia #107/R
£598 $1100 €873 Portrait of boy reading Mickey Mouse book (71x56cm-28x22in) s.d.36. 9-Jun-4 Alderfer's, Hatfield #470/R est:1200-1800

GILL, Naylor (1873-c.1945) Australian
£328 $531 €479 Settler (53x75cm-21x30in) s.d.97 board. 30-Jul-3 Goodman, Sydney #117/R (A.D 800)

GILL, S T (1818-1880) Australian
Works on paper
£1012 $1630 €1478 Cattle in the moonlight (13x22cm-5x9in) init. W/C. 13-Oct-3 Joel, Victoria #394/R est:2500-3500 (A.D 2500)
£1106 $1881 €1615 Grass Tree (16x24cm-6x9in) init.i. sepia ink wash prov. 26-Nov-3 Deutscher-Menzies, Melbourne #197/R est:3500-5000 (A.D 2600)
£1362 $2315 €1989 Waterfall with Aborigines (12x20cm-5x8in) init. W/C prov. 26-Nov-3 Deutscher-Menzies, Melbourne #195/R est:4000-6000 (A.D 3200)
£1362 $2315 €1989 Aborigines in a Northern Landscape, South Australia (15x31cm-6x12in) init. sepia ink wash prov. 26-Nov-3 Deutscher-Menzies, Melbourne #196/R est:4000-6000 (A.D 3200)
£4580 $8336 €6687 Hill River, South Australia (30x53cm-12x21in) init. W/C prov. 16-Jun-4 Deutscher-Menzies, Melbourne #121/R est:8000-12000 (A.D 12000)
£14504 $26397 €21176 Diggings in the Mount Alexander district of Victoria (24x35cm-9x14in) init.d.74 W/C prov. 16-Jun-4 Deutscher-Menzies, Melbourne #120/R est:25000-35000 (A.D 38000)
£20992 $38206 €30648 Rush to Ballarat Goldfields in 1854 (24x36cm-9x14in) init. W/C pencil. 16-Jun-4 Deutscher-Menzies, Melbourne #73/R est:35000-45000 (A.D 55000)

GILL, Samuel Thomas (1818-1880) Australian
Works on paper
£5508 $9364 €8042 Battery Point (15x26cm-6x10in) W/C. 24-Nov-3 Sotheby's, Melbourne #226/R est:7000-10000 (A.D 13000)
£8600 $15566 €12556 Gum trees, natives opposum hunting, SA (43x33cm-17x13in) W/C sold with another possibly by the same hand. 15-Apr-4 Hobbs Parker, Ashford #711

GILL, William (19th C) British
£903 $1426 €1300 Playing hunt for the slipper in class (24x32cm-9x13in) s. indis d. oil paper on cardboard. 2-Sep-3 Christie's, Amsterdam #182 est:700-900

GILL, William F (?) American?
£438 $700 €639 Two-masted American sailing ship (30x46cm-12x18in) s. 20-Sep-3 Nadeau, Windsor #16/R

GILL, William W (19th C) British
£400 $724 €584 Colwith Fall (23x18cm-9x7in) i.verso. 16-Apr-4 Keys, Aylsham #783
£500 $905 €730 Hay mill near Ludlow (18x15cm-7x6in) s. 16-Apr-4 Keys, Aylsham #785/R
£550 $995 €803 Hermitage Fall, Dunkeld (23x18cm-9x7in) 16-Apr-4 Keys, Aylsham #784

GILLARD, William (1812-?) British
£757 $1400 €1105 Home through the field (61x51cm-24x20in) i.verso. 13-Feb-4 David Rago, Lambertville #32/R est:800-1200

GILLARDUZZI, Luigi Alois (1822-?) Italian
£1633 $2971 €2400 Portrait of Empress Maria Theresa (196x108cm-77x43in) s.d.1852. 3-Feb-4 Christie's, Amsterdam #100/R est:2000-3000

GILLBERG, Jacob Axel (1769-1845) Swedish
Miniatures
£2000 $3440 €2920 Crown prince Karl Johan XIV (6x5cm-2x2in) s.d.1811 gouache. 2-Dec-3 Bukowskis, Stockholm #443/R est:8000-10000 (S.KR 26000)

GILLE, Christian Friedrich (1805-1899) German
£3712 $6755 €5420 Stormy breakers between rocks (22x30cm-9x12in) cardboard prov. 17-Jun-4 Kornfeld, Bern #18/R est:3000 (S.FR 8500)

GILLE, Christian Friedrich (attrib) (1805-1899) German
£800 $1448 €1200 Small village near Dresden (27x37cm-11x15in) i. verso board. 2-Apr-4 Winterberg, Heidelberg #418/R

GILLE, Jocelyn (20th C) French
Works on paper
£576 $921 €800 Le paquebot a quai au Havre (39x59cm-15x23in) s. gouache. 18-May-3 Claude Boisgirard, Paris #35
£909 $1545 €1300 La Normandie en pleine mer (40x60cm-16x24in) s. gouache exec. 1935. 23-Nov-3 Claude Boisgirard, Paris #50/R

GILLEMANS, Jan Pauwel (17th C) Flemish
£7000 $11410 €10220 Still life depicting a lavish array of fruit on a draped marble platform with parrot (35x56cm-14x22in) s. 28-Sep-3 Wilkinson, Doncaster #287/R

GILLEMANS, Jan Pauwel (elder) (1618-1675) Flemish
£7000 $12110 €10220 Still life of swags of fruit adorning a stone fountain (55x40cm-22x16in) canvas on panel. 11-Dec-3 Sotheby's, London #165/R est:6000-8000

£12324 $21320 €17500 Fruit (46x61cm-18x24in) 13-Dec-3 Lempertz, Koln #20/R est:15000
£26389 $47500 €38528 Still life of peaches, grapes, peeled lemon an oyster and wine on a draped table (48x63cm-19x25in) i. panel prov. 22-Jan-4 Sotheby's, New York #133/R est:15000-20000

GILLEMANS, Jan Pauwel (elder-attrib) (1618-1675) Flemish
£4200 $7140 €6132 Still life of fruit and flowers (53x64cm-21x25in) 30-Oct-3 Sotheby's, Olympia #7/R est:4000-6000

GILLEMANS, Jan Pauwel (younger) (1651-1704) Flemish
£6993 $11888 €10000 Nature morte de fruits et agrumes sur fond de paysage (47x56cm-19x22in) 1-Dec-3 Millon & Associes, Paris #28/R est:4000-6000
£12081 $22470 €18000 Fruit garland in a garden (65x81cm-26x32in) s.d.1691. 2-Mar-4 Ansorena, Madrid #285/R est:18000

GILLEMANS, Jan Pauwel (younger-attrib) (1651-1704) Flemish
£2917 $4754 €4200 Still life of melons, grapes, peaches and other fruits (63x81cm-25x32in) 25-Sep-3 Dr Fritz Nagel, Stuttgart #1260/R est:7500

GILLEN, Arthur (20th C) American
£232 $425 €339 Wisconsin farm (76x71cm-30x28in) s. d.1924 verso board. 5-Jun-4 Treadway Gallery, Cincinnati #669/R

GILLES, Barthel (1891-1977) German
£1399 $2336 €2000 Faithful Hussar (40x30cm-16x12in) i. verso. 27-Jun-3 Auktionhaus Georg Rehm, Augsburg #8058/R est:2400
£10490 $17832 €15000 Nude girl in hilly landscape (40x29cm-16x11in) s. egg tempera panel. 26-Nov-3 Lempertz, Koln #681/R est:16000

GILLES, Franco (?) ?
Sculpture
£1053 $1905 €1600 Sculpture. wood. 17-Apr-4 Deburaux, Boulogne #147

GILLES, Werner (1894-1961) German
£3333 $5967 €5000 Ischia landscape (60x73cm-24x29in) s. prov. 14-May-4 Ketterer, Munich #207/R est:5000-7000
Works on paper
£350 $584 €500 Appearance of an angel (27x38cm-11x15in) i. verso Indian ink brush pastel chk pencil. 10-Oct-3 Winterberg, Heidelberg #1302
£385 $642 €550 Interior with female figures in classical dress. i. verso Indian ink brush pastel chk pencil. 10-Oct-3 Winterberg, Heidelberg #1303/R
£469 $806 €670 Boats on St Angelo beach (31x43cm-12x17in) pen. 2-Dec-3 Hauswedell & Nolte, Hamburg #203/R
£533 $955 €800 Olmitello grotto I (32x45cm-13x18in) s.d. pencil. 15-May-4 Bassenge, Berlin #6835
£833 $1392 €1200 Boy with apple (52x23cm-20x9in) s.d. W/C sketch verso. 24-Oct-3 Ketterer, Hamburg #354/R
£933 $1671 €1400 Phantasie (22x31cm-9x12in) s.d. W/C. 15-May-4 Bassenge, Berlin #6834/R
£1250 $1975 €1800 Peasant woman under pine trees before fortress (32x47cm-13x19in) s. W/C lit. 19-Sep-3 Schloss Ahlden, Ahlden #1672/R est:1800
£1408 $2437 €2000 Harbour scene - Porto d'Ischia (21x32cm-8x13in) s.i.d.10.6.55 W/C prov. 13-Dec-3 Lempertz, Koln #314/R est:2500
£1538 $2615 €2200 Monte Epomeo, Ischia (23x32cm-9x13in) s.d.58 W/C. 29-Nov-3 Bassenge, Berlin #6720/R est:2400
£1867 $3416 €2800 Landscape - Ischia (47x67cm-19x26in) s.d.1936 W/C prov. 5-Jun-4 Lempertz, Koln #735/R est:3000
£2098 $3566 €3000 Ischia landscape (45x56cm-18x22in) s. bodycol. 29-Nov-3 Villa Grisebach, Berlin #278/R est:3000-4000
£2098 $3608 €3000 Twilight (32x43cm-13x17in) s.d.1960 i.verso W/C prov. 5-Dec-3 Ketterer, Munich #115/R est:3000-4000
£3000 $5520 €4500 Composition (23x19cm-9x7in) s.d.1920 W/C ink blue-grey paper. 12-Jun-4 Villa Grisebach, Berlin #718/R est:2500-3000
£4545 $7727 €6500 Blue mountains (33x44cm-13x17in) i. verso gouache double-sided prov. 26-Nov-3 Lempertz, Koln #686/R est:7000-8000
£5944 $10105 €8500 Mythological scene (48x62cm-19x24in) i. i. verso W/C gouache. 29-Nov-3 Villa Grisebach, Berlin #279/R est:8000-10000

GILLESPIE, George K (1924-1996) British
£800 $1488 €1168 Foreshore, Co. Antrim (30x50cm-12x20in) s. board. 3-Mar-4 John Ross, Belfast #3
£805 $1442 €1200 Winter in the park (33x44cm-13x17in) s. 31-May-4 Hamilton Osborne King, Dublin #132/R
£850 $1556 €1241 Cornfield, Castlefin, Donegal (23x30cm-9x12in) s. board. 2-Jun-4 John Ross, Belfast #37
£1000 $1810 €1500 Innisfallen Island (25x20cm-10x8in) s.i.verso board. 31-Mar-4 James Adam, Dublin #49/R est:1800-2000
£1100 $1804 €1606 Glendun River (35x45cm-14x18in) s. board. 4-Jun-3 John Ross, Belfast #26
£1100 $1892 €1606 Scrabo from Ballybarnes (30x40cm-12x16in) s. board. 3-Dec-3 John Ross, Belfast #7 est:1200-1400
£1200 $1992 €1752 Connemara (14x20cm-6x8in) s. board. 1-Oct-3 John Ross, Belfast #112b
£1250 $2050 €1825 County Down landscape (45x55cm-18x22in) s. 4-Jun-3 John Ross, Belfast #128
£1400 $2324 €2044 Scrabo from Mahee Island, Co. Down (50x61cm-20x24in) s. 1-Oct-3 John Ross, Belfast #186 est:1500-1800
£1469 $2497 €2100 West of Ireland landscape (41x51cm-16x20in) s. 18-Nov-3 Mealy's, Castlecomer #1399/R est:2500-3200
£1600 $2976 €2336 On the Lagan near Hillsborough, Co. Down (45x61cm-18x24in) s. 3-Mar-4 John Ross, Belfast #124 est:1800-2000
£1700 $2788 €2482 Reflections (45x61cm-18x24in) s. 4-Jun-3 John Ross, Belfast #127b
£1800 $2988 €2628 Donegal farmstead (30x40cm-12x16in) s. board. 1-Oct-3 John Ross, Belfast #111 est:1200-1400
£1958 $3329 €2800 Coastal landscape (39x57cm-15x22in) s. 25-Nov-3 De Veres Art Auctions, Dublin #3/R est:3000-4000
£1974 $3632 €3000 On the Lagan River, near Hillsborough (39x50cm-15x20in) s. 22-Jun-4 De Veres Art Auctions, Dublin #5/R est:3000-5000
£2282 $4085 €3400 Donegal coast near Dunfanaghy (25x30cm-10x12in) s. board. 26-May-4 James Adam, Dublin #152/R est:1500-2500
£2300 $3956 €3358 Sailing Belfast Lough (61x91cm-24x36in) s. 3-Dec-3 John Ross, Belfast #46 est:2000-2500
£2349 $4205 €3500 On the road to Achill Island (53x73cm-21x29in) s. board. 31-May-4 Hamilton Osborne King, Dublin #121/R est:3000-5000
£2800 $5068 €4200 River Finn, Co Donegal (34x45cm-13x18in) s.i. s.verso. 30-Mar-4 De Veres Art Auctions, Dublin #94/R est:2000-3000
£2819 $5046 €4200 River landscape (59x89cm-23x35in) s. 31-May-4 Hamilton Osborne King, Dublin #120/R est:4000-6000
£2900 $4814 €4234 Sorting the nets, Killary, Co. Galway (61x91cm-24x36in) s. 1-Oct-3 John Ross, Belfast #213 est:2500-3000
£2953 $5227 €4400 Lackagh Bridge, Donegal (46x61cm-18x24in) s. prov.exhib. 27-Apr-4 Whyte's, Dublin #236/R est:4000-6000
£2973 $5619 €4400 Children at the beach (30x41cm-12x16in) s. 17-Feb-4 Whyte's, Dublin #168/R est:2000-3000
£3099 $4958 €4400 Reflections (46x61cm-18x24in) s. 16-Sep-3 Whyte's, Dublin #213/R est:4000-6000
£3108 $5874 €4600 Gypsy caravan near Dunlewy, County Donegal (46x61cm-18x24in) s. 17-Feb-4 Whyte's, Dublin #135/R est:4000-6000
£3108 $5874 €4600 Dunlewey, County Donegal (46x61cm-18x24in) s. i.verso. 17-Feb-4 Whyte's, Dublin #136/R est:4000-5000
£3472 $5660 €5000 Shimna River in the Mournes, Co. Down (61x91cm-24x36in) s. i.verso. 24-Sep-3 James Adam, Dublin #78/R est:5000-8000
£3873 $6197 €5500 Glen Head, Glencolumbcille, County Donegal (51x76cm-20x30in) s. i.verso prov. 16-Sep-3 Whyte's, Dublin #149/R est:5000-7000
£4014 $6423 €5700 Children on the beach (61x91cm-24x36in) s. prov. 16-Sep-3 Whyte's, Dublin #147/R est:5000-7000
£4362 $7721 €6500 Mournebeg River, near Killeter, County Tyrone (51x76cm-20x30in) s. i.verso. 27-Apr-4 Whyte's, Dublin #208/R est:6000-8000
£4615 $7846 €6600 Murlough Bay, County Antrim (51x76cm-20x30in) s. 18-Nov-3 Whyte's, Dublin #40/R est:6000-8000
£5175 $8797 €7400 Sorting the nets, Killary, County Galway (61x91cm-24x36in) s. i.verso. 18-Nov-3 Whyte's, Dublin #39/R est:6000-8000
£6711 $11879 €10000 Woman and child feeding chickens (51x76cm-20x30in) s. 27-Apr-4 Whyte's, Dublin #199/R est:6000-8000
£7770 $14686 €11500 Summer beach scene (76x102cm-30x40in) s. board. 17-Feb-4 Whyte's, Dublin #133/R est:8000-10000

GILLESPIE, J H (fl.c.1820-1838) British
£2716 $4400 €3965 Portraits of New Hampshire family members (41x33cm-16x13in) oval six framed together. 1-Aug-3 North East Auctions, Portsmouth #971/R est:2000-3000

GILLESPIE, Rowan (1953-) Irish?
Sculpture
£2113 $3655 €3000 Sitting man (30cm-12in) s.d.78 num.2/9 silver aluminium. 10-Dec-3 Bonhams & James Adam, Dublin #138/R est:3000-4000
£2254 $3899 €3200 Evolution (25x25cm-10x10in) aluminium silver copper perspex. 10-Dec-3 Bonhams & James Adam, Dublin #137/R est:3000-4000
£2368 $4358 €3600 Man holding a bunch of flowers (39cm-15in) s.d.1986 bronze marble base. 22-Jun-4 De Veres Art Auctions, Dublin #145/R est:2500-3500
£6000 $10740 €8760 The egg (34cm-13in) s.num.6/9 brown pat bronze base conceived 1977 exhib. 14-May-4 Christie's, Kensington #446/R est:1200-1500

GILLET, Edward Frank (1874-1927) British
Works on paper
£880 $1496 €1285 Lemon, blue sleeves (46x45cm-18x18in) init. chl W/C bodycol exhib. 19-Nov-3 Sotheby's, Olympia #113/R

GILLET, Roger Edgar (1924-2003) French
£357 $608 €521 Figure composition (65x54cm-26x21in) prov. 29-Nov-3 Rasmussen, Havnen #4272 (D.KR 3800)
£541 $968 €800 Personnage avec chapeau (33x19cm-13x7in) s.d.61. 4-May-4 Calmels Cohen, Paris #162
£676 $1209 €1000 Personnage (65x50cm-26x20in) s.d.50. 4-May-4 Calmels Cohen, Paris #167/R
£1127 $1949 €1600 Composition (41x33cm-16x13in) s.d.1958 oil paper on canvas prov. 14-Dec-3 Versailles Encheres #74/R est:800-1000
£1972 $3411 €2800 Composition (97x146cm-38x57in) s.d.1960 prov.exhib. 9-Dec-3 Artcurial Briest, Paris #493/R est:2000-2500

GILLETTE, Lester A (1855-?) American
£228 $425 €333 Among the hills (46x61cm-18x24in) s. i.verso board painted c.1920. 7-Mar-4 Treadway Gallery, Cincinnati #557/R

GILLI, Claude (1938-) French
£2324 $4020 €3300 Brigitte Bardot la nuit (120x182cm-47x72in) s.i.d.1965-1999 verso. 14-Dec-3 Rabourdin & Choppin de Janvry, Paris #66/R est:3000-4000
Sculpture
£3497 $6014 €5000 Nature morte (92x141cm-36x56in) s. s.d.X.62 verso painted wood pieces. 4-Dec-3 Piasa, Paris #16/R est:2000-3000
£3916 $6657 €5600 Trois pots de peinture se deversant. bears sig.num.1/8 and 5/8 gilt pat bronze st.f.Anpire 3 parts. 20-Nov-3 Gioffredo, Nice #30
£14333 $26087 €21500 Souvenirs (120x60x25cm-47x24x10in) s. painted wood collage photograph prov.exhib. 29-Jun-4 Cornette de St.Cyr, Paris #69/R est:22000-25000
Works on paper
£347 $549 €500 Coulees (41x31cm-16x12in) s. s.verso collage painted cardboard on panel. 27-Apr-3 Versailles Encheres #83
£350 $584 €500 Peinture en danger (42x31cm-17x12in) s.i.d.2002 verso assemblage collage panel. 29-Jun-3 Versailles Encheres #190
£353 $636 €530 Traces d'escargots dans l'herbe (64x45cm-25x18in) s.d.1978 graphite collage collage decoupage. 24-Apr-4 Cornette de St.Cyr, Paris #553/R
£937 $1481 €1350 Untitled (29x20cm-11x8in) s.d.1963 collage. 27-Apr-3 Versailles Encheres #81
£1554 $2937 €2300 Nine escargots (85x64cm-33x25in) s.d.1976 s.i.d.verso W/C resin coquilles d'escargots. 21-Feb-4 Cornette de St.Cyr, Paris #295 est:2500-3000

GILLIAM, Sam (1933-) American

£1563 $2500 €2282 Monument to Walter Hopps (224x389cm-88x153in) acrylic. 20-Sep-3 Sloans & Kenyon, Bethesda #1000/R est:2000-3000
£2813 $4500 €4107 Lady day II (279x406cm-110x160in) s.i.d.July 21 1971 verso acrylic. 20-Sep-3 Sloans & Kenyon, Bethesda #1001/R est:8000-10000
£2890 $5000 €4219 Rainfall (155x305cm-61x120in) prov. 15-Dec-3 Hindman, Chicago #106/R est:7000-9000
£4688 $7500 €6844 Warmth a lightness, glow and then (241x599cm-95x236in) s.d.68 verso acrylic. 20-Sep-3 Sloans & Kenyon, Bethesda #999/R est:4000-6000

GILLIARD, Valentine (19/20th C) Swiss

£407 $692 €594 Village street (55x38cm-22x15in) s. 19-Nov-3 Fischer, Luzern #2110/R (S.FR 900)

GILLIES, Margaret (1803-1887) British

£1000 $1790 €1460 Portrait of Mrs Charles Walpole, wearing a pink gown (20x17cm-8x7in) panel oval. 22-Mar-4 Bonhams & Brooks, Norfolk #264/R est:500-700
Works on paper
£310 $580 €453 Young girl of Arran (41x28cm-16x11in) s.i.d.1863 W/C over pencil. 24-Feb-4 Bonhams, Knowle #18

GILLIES, Sir William George (1898-1973) British

£1800 $2898 €2610 Pentlands (30x53cm-12x21in) s. exhib. 21-Aug-3 Bonhams, Edinburgh #1043/R est:2000-3000
£2200 $3938 €3212 Cornfields, temple (33x41cm-13x16in) s. 28-May-4 Lyon & Turnbull, Edinburgh #37 est:1500-2000
£3000 $5190 €4380 Limekilns (36x51cm-14x20in) s.d.1946 board prov.exhib. 11-Dec-3 Lyon & Turnbull, Edinburgh #78/R est:3000-4000
£3400 $5780 €4964 Still life with jugs (66x109cm-26x43in) prov. 30-Oct-3 Christie's, London #194/R est:2000-3000
£4200 $7812 €6132 Trees at Arniston (43x60cm-17x24in) s. board. 4-Mar-4 Christie's, Kensington #214/R est:4000-6000
£4500 $7650 €6570 Apples (34x44cm-13x17in) s. 30-Oct-3 Christie's, London #193/R est:3000-5000
£4600 $8464 €6716 Garden under snow (81x99cm-32x39in) s. prov. 24-Jun-4 Scarborough Perry Fine Arts, Hove #753
£5000 $8050 €7250 Mixed bouquet in a bowl (68x81cm-27x32in) s. 21-Aug-3 Bonhams, Edinburgh #1147/R est:6000-8000
£5500 $8855 €7975 Rainbow (60x64cm-24x25in) s. s.i.verso. 21-Aug-3 Bonhams, Edinburgh #1115/R est:8000-12000
£5500 $10230 €8030 Gattonside (41x66cm-16x26in) s.d.49 board prov. 4-Mar-4 Christie's, Kensington #212/R est:6000-8000
£9800 $15778 €14210 Tarbert (62x75cm-24x30in) s.d.1939 double-sided. 21-Aug-3 Bonhams, Edinburgh #1044/R est:6000-8000
Works on paper
£280 $515 €409 The ravine, Heriot Water (25x35cm-10x14in) s. pencil. 10-Jun-4 Lyon & Turnbull, Edinburgh #108
£440 $801 €642 Willow Brae woods (20x24cm-8x9in) s. pencil sketch. 3-Jul-4 Shapes, Edinburgh #431/R
£550 $886 €798 Cottage and trees, Fearnon (31x24cm-12x9in) s.i. pen ink. 21-Aug-3 Bonhams, Edinburgh #1171
£600 $1020 €876 Old Lime Kiln (33x47cm-13x19in) s.d.1956 W/C bodycol. 30-Oct-3 Christie's, London #196/R
£700 $1204 €1022 Heathery Ha, Haddington (16x27cm-6x11in) s.d.1916 W/C. 4-Dec-3 Bonhams, Edinburgh #1
£980 $1578 €1421 Temple (23x31cm-9x12in) s. W/C. 21-Aug-3 Bonhams, Edinburgh #1030
£1500 $2550 €2190 Arniston Park, Lothian (33x51cm-13x20in) s. pencil W/C. 30-Oct-3 Christie's, London #195/R est:1500-2000
£1600 $2976 €2336 St Monans (14x16cm-6x6in) s. W/C. 6-Mar-4 Shapes, Edinburgh #418/R est:700-1000
£1800 $3060 €2628 Lyne (25x35cm-10x14in) s.d.58 pencil W/C bodycol. 30-Oct-3 Christie's, London #190/R est:1500-2500
£2300 $3703 €3335 Hill Farm, autumn (39x57cm-15x22in) s.d.1953 W/C prov. 21-Aug-3 Bonhams, Edinburgh #1170/R est:1500-2000
£2500 $4575 €3650 Evening, the pentland from temple (23x33cm-9x13in) s. ink W/C. 8-Apr-4 Bonhams, Edinburgh #190/R est:1200-1800
£3400 $5780 €4964 Landscape with red sun (38x56cm-15x22in) s.d.1953 crayon W/C. 30-Oct-3 Christie's, London #192/R est:1500-2500
£3700 $6771 €5402 Flowerpiece (40x55cm-16x22in) s. W/C. 8-Apr-4 Bonhams, Edinburgh #146/R est:2500-4000
£3900 $7137 €5694 Borthwick Farm (28x45cm-11x18in) s. ink W/C. 8-Apr-4 Bonhams, Edinburgh #189/R est:2000-3000
£4000 $6280 €5800 Village church (25x40cm-10x16in) s. W/C pen ink. 27-Aug-3 Sotheby's, London #1145/R est:1500-2000
£5000 $9050 €7300 Country path, Saltoun (25x34cm-10x13in) s. i.verso pen ink wash. 19-Apr-4 Sotheby's, London #148/R est:1500-2000
£7200 $13176 €10512 St. Monans (24x31cm-9x12in) s.d.49 ink W/C. 8-Apr-4 Bonhams, Edinburgh #148/R est:3000-5000

GILLIG, Jacob (1636-1701) Dutch

£6897 $11517 €10000 Still life of fish (51x67cm-20x26in) s.d.1685. 15-Nov-3 Lempertz, Koln #1051/R est:12000

GILLIG, Jacob (attrib) (1636-1701) Dutch

£1183 $2117 €1727 Still life of fish (44x32cm-17x13in) panel. 28-May-4 Uppsala Auktionskammare, Uppsala #10/R est:20000-25000 (S.KR 16000)

GILLILAND, Hector Beaumont (1911-) Australian

£2642 $4730 €3857 Backyard - Lemon (50x38cm-20x15in) s.d.1959 s.i.d.verso board. 4-May-4 Sotheby's, Melbourne #144 est:2000-3000 (A.D 6500)

GILLOT, Claude (1673-1722) French

Works on paper
£5634 $9859 €8000 Les deux sources. Le renard et le chat (8x10cm-3x4in) red chk sanguine wash pair prov. 17-Dec-3 Christie's, Paris #42/R est:10000-15000

GILLOT, Eugène Louis (1868-1925) French

£590 $986 €850 Arbres au jardin du Luxembourg (27x35cm-11x14in) s. board. 21-Oct-3 Artcurial Briest, Paris #147
£1389 $2320 €2000 Peniches a quai (38x54cm-15x21in) s. board. 21-Oct-3 Artcurial Briest, Paris #150/R est:1800-2200
£1757 $3145 €2600 On the Canal du Midi (41x52cm-16x20in) s. board lit. 8-May-4 Schloss Ahlden, Ahlden #826/R est:2400
£2431 $4059 €3500 La salute a Venise (38x62cm-15x24in) s. peinture a l'essence board. 21-Oct-3 Artcurial Briest, Paris #149/R est:2200-2500
£2448 $4210 €3500 Paris, soiree de gala lors de la visite du roi George V d'Angleterre (69x120cm-27x47in) s.i.d.21 avril 1914. 3-Dec-3 Beaussant & Lefèvre, Paris #37/R est:2000-2500
£3611 $6030 €5200 Trafalgar Square (35x27cm-14x11in) s. board lit. 21-Oct-3 Artcurial Briest, Paris #137/R est:1500-2000
£4167 $6959 €6000 Vitrine de mode (46x38cm-18x15in) s. board. 21-Oct-3 Artcurial Briest, Paris #136/R est:2000-3000
£4861 $8118 €7000 Londres, coucher de soleil (65x81cm-26x32in) s. 21-Oct-3 Artcurial Briest, Paris #138/R est:3500-4000
£6944 $11597 €10000 Port de Rouen (117x162cm-46x64in) s. lit. 21-Oct-3 Artcurial Briest, Paris #153/R est:4500-6000
£7639 $12758 €11000 Depart pour la chasse a Saint-Lazare (51x92cm-20x36in) s. 21-Oct-3 Artcurial Briest, Paris #141/R est:3500-4000
Works on paper
£347 $580 €500 Les Meules (53x35cm-21x14in) s. pastel board on panel. 21-Oct-3 Artcurial Briest, Paris #154
£625 $1044 €900 Pecheur dans sa barque (26x33cm-10x13in) s. W/C gouache. 21-Oct-3 Artcurial Briest, Paris #148/R
£694 $1159 €1000 Usine rouge sur la Seine (38x44cm-15x17in) gouache W/C crayon. 21-Oct-3 Artcurial Briest, Paris #139/R
£694 $1159 €1000 Music Hall (25x33cm-10x13in) s. gouache board. 21-Oct-3 Artcurial Briest, Paris #151/R
£2431 $4059 €3500 L'Hydravion (33x58cm-13x23in) s. W/C gouache crayon. 21-Oct-3 Artcurial Briest, Paris #144/R est:1300-1500

GILLOT, Francoise (1921-) French

Works on paper
£4667 $8587 €7000 Pablo Picasso (65x50cm-26x20in) s.d.1944 col crayon wax crayon. 14-Jun-4 Tajan, Paris #158 est:1000-1200

GILLRAY, James (1757-1815) British

Prints
£2100 $3507 €3066 L'assemblee nationale (31x45cm-12x18in) hand col etching. 14-Oct-3 Bonhams, New Bond Street #151/R est:1000-1500
£2200 $3674 €3212 Temperance enjoying a frugal meal (37x29cm-15x11in) etching. 14-Oct-3 Bonhams, New Bond Street #68/R est:1500-2000
£2200 $3674 €3212 Hand writing upon the wall (24x35cm-9x14in) col etching. 14-Oct-3 Bonhams, New Bond Street #145 est:700-900
£2200 $3674 €3212 Very slippy weather (25x20cm-10x8in) hand col etching. 14-Oct-3 Bonhams, New Bond Street #177/R est:1000-1500
£2400 $4008 €3504 Voluptuary under the horrors of digestion (37x29cm-15x11in) etching. 14-Oct-3 Bonhams, New Bond Street #67/R est:1500-2000
£2600 $4342 €3796 Zenith of French glory (35x24cm-14x9in) etching. 14-Oct-3 Bonhams, New Bond Street #71/R est:1000-1500
£2700 $4509 €3942 Grand Coronation of Napoleon the 1st Emperor of France (24x77cm-9x30in) hand col etching. 14-Oct-3 Bonhams, New Bond Street #159/R est:1500-2000
£3400 $5678 €4964 Light expelling darkness (34x44cm-13x17in) etching. 14-Oct-3 Bonhams, New Bond Street #79/R est:1200-1800
£4000 $6680 €5840 John Bull taking a luncheon (24x35cm-9x14in) etching. 14-Oct-3 Bonhams, New Bond Street #101/R est:4000-6000
£10500 $17535 €15330 Plumb pudding in danger (26x36cm-10x14in) etching. 14-Oct-3 Bonhams, New Bond Street #155/R est:4000-6000
Works on paper
£6500 $11050 €9490 Spanish patriots attacking the French banditti - loyal Britons lending a lift (29x47cm-11x19in) indis.i. i.verso pen brown red wash htd.bodycol prov.exhib.lit. 20-Nov-3 Christie's, London #13/R est:7000-10000

GILMAN, Harold (1876-1919) British

£410 $652 €599 Portrait of woman (27x19cm-11x7in) s. 29-Apr-3 Louis Morton, Mexico #152/R (M.P 6800)
£2600 $4758 €3796 Flower beds (25x36cm-10x14in) s. panel prov. 4-Jun-4 Christie's, London #12/R est:3000-5000
£7000 $12950 €10220 Breton girl (91x61cm-36x24in) s. prov. 11-Feb-4 Sotheby's, Olympia #116/R est:5000-7000
£27000 $46440 €39420 Studio interior with oil lamp (32x27cm-13x11in) s. 3-Dec-3 Sotheby's, London #9/R est:18000-25000
£36000 $65880 €52560 Blue dress, Sylvia Gilman (68x46cm-27x18in) painted c.1917 prov.exhib. 4-Jun-4 Christie's, London #18/R est:30000-50000
£120000 $219600 €175200 Portrait of a woman (38x32cm-15x13in) s. i.verso board painted c.1911-13 prov. 4-Jun-4 Christie's, London #17/R est:30000-50000

GILMAN, Peter (20th C) British

£340 $568 €496 Greenwich Reach, September evening (39x51cm-15x20in) s. i.verso. 7-Oct-3 Bonhams, Knightsbridge #59/R

GILMOUR, G F (?) ?

£280 $510 €409 Old Home, Lambeth. s. 18-Jun-4 Moore Allen & Innocent, Cirencester #1030

GILMOUR, Guy (1955-) Australian

£426 $723 €622 Study for Philodendron (35x45cm-14x18in) s. acrylic paper prov. 25-Nov-3 Christie's, Melbourne #294/R (A.D 1000)
£596 $1013 €870 Town (36x59cm-14x23in) s. prov. 25-Nov-3 Christie's, Melbourne #229/R (A.D 1400)

GILMOUR, James (19/20th C) Irish?
Works on paper
£300 $567 €438 Harbour scene (43x28cm-17x11in) s.d.1908 W/C. 19-Feb-4 Rendalls, Ashburton #1576

GILOT, Françoise (1921-1986) French
£1457 $2652 €2200 Etude de portrait de Chantal (65x54cm-26x21in) s.d.59. 18-Jun-4 Piasa, Paris #197 est:1000-1200
£2813 $4500 €4107 Rivages (74x91cm-29x36in) 20-Sep-3 Bunte, Elgin #1272 est:1000-1500

GILPIN, Laura (1891-1979) American
Photographs
£1808 $3200 €2640 Prelude (15x21cm-6x8in) i.d.1917 verso platinum print lit. 27-Apr-4 Christie's, Rockefeller NY #236/R est:4000-6000
£1808 $3200 €2640 Corn grinding song, Mesa Verde National Park (24x19cm-9x7in) s.i.d.1925 platinum print. 27-Apr-4 Christie's, Rockefeller NY #311/R est:4000-6000
£4192 $7000 €6120 Temple, Bryce Canyon (19x24cm-7x9in) s.d.1930 waxed platinum print. 20-Oct-3 Christie's, Rockefeller NY #258/R est:8000-10000
£4237 $7500 €6186 Square Tower house, Mesa Verde National Park (24x19cm-9x7in) platinum print executed 1925. 27-Apr-4 Christie's, Rockefeller NY #310/R est:6000-8000
£10000 $18000 €14600 Bryce canyon no.2 (25x20cm-10x8in) s.d.1930 platinum print. 22-Apr-4 Phillips, New York #49/R est:15000-20000
£10180 $17000 €14863 Colarado sand dunes (19x24cm-7x9in) s.i.d.1931 platinum print lit. 20-Oct-3 Christie's, Rockefeller NY #257/R est:10000-15000

GILPIN, Rev William (1724-1804) British
Works on paper
£850 $1573 €1241 Essay in the picturesque. Lake landscape studies (27x36cm-11x14in) col wash ink pencil pair. 14-Jan-4 Lawrence, Crewkerne #1308

GILPIN, Sawrey (1733-1807) British
£5814 $10000 €8488 Bay horse in a wooded landscape (62x76cm-24x30in) s.d.1795. 5-Dec-3 Christie's, Rockefeller NY #26/R est:12000-18000
Works on paper
£360 $634 €526 Young bull (12x16cm-5x6in) pencil wash. 18-May-4 Woolley & Wallis, Salisbury #218/R
£1050 $1848 €1533 Galloway Scotch cow near calving (23x35cm-9x14in) i.d.1788 pencil wash sold with another by James Ward attrib two. 18-May-4 Woolley & Wallis, Salisbury #220/R est:300-500

GILROY, Jack (?) British
£280 $468 €409 Portrait of Sir Melford Stevenson (76x64cm-30x25in) s. 21-Oct-3 Bonhams, Knightsbridge #120

GILROY, John Thomas Young (1898-1985) British
£820 $1492 €1197 Trawler on the North Sea (49x74cm-19x29in) s. 15-Jun-4 Bonhams, Leeds #117/R
Works on paper
£260 $478 €380 Full-length study of a female dancer (35x20cm-14x8in) s. pencil. 23-Mar-4 Anderson & Garland, Newcastle #200

GILROY, John William (1868-1944) British
£283 $456 €413 Cavalier (40x25cm-16x10in) s. board. 13-Oct-3 Joel, Victoria #380 (A.D 700)
£2400 $4416 €3504 Fishing port on the North Yorkshire coast (34x44cm-13x17in) s. 23-Mar-4 Anderson & Garland, Newcastle #414/R est:1000-1800
Works on paper
£300 $489 €438 Runswick Bay (37x25cm-15x10in) s. W/C. 23-Sep-3 Anderson & Garland, Newcastle #214/R
£500 $815 €730 Steam freighter unloading at Newcastle Quay (26x38cm-10x15in) s.indis.d. W/C. 23-Sep-3 Anderson & Garland, Newcastle #216
£500 $850 €730 Along side the quay, Whitby (26x36cm-10x14in) s.i. W/C. 4-Nov-3 Bristol Auction Rooms #557/R

GILSON, Henri (19th C) French
Works on paper
£1135 $1895 €1600 Dignitaires turcs (60x42cm-24x17in) s. wax crayon dr pair. 19-Oct-3 Rabourdin & Choppin de Janvry, Paris #98/R est:1200-1500

GILSOUL, Victor (1867-1939) Belgian
£267 $477 €400 Paysage industriel au clair de lune (28x53cm-11x21in) s.i. cardboard. 11-May-4 Vanderkindere, Brussels #12
£340 $609 €500 Paysage a l'etang (26x36cm-10x14in) s. panel. 16-Mar-4 Vanderkindere, Brussels #12
£414 $766 €600 Au bord du chemin (43x60cm-17x24in) s. i.verso. 19-Jan-4 Horta, Bruxelles #485
£442 $791 €650 Ciel d'avril dans la vallee de la Lame (51x80cm-20x31in) s.i. 16-Mar-4 Vanderkindere, Brussels #102
£521 $828 €750 Le Croisic en 1916 (55x38cm-22x15in) s. panel. 15-Sep-3 Horta, Bruxelles #253
£533 $981 €800 Pont a triple arcade (33x41cm-13x16in) s. panel. 14-Jun-4 Horta, Bruxelles #395
£567 $1014 €850 Interieur (55x65cm-22x26in) s. 11-May-4 Vanderkindere, Brussels #23
£570 $1055 €850 Autumn scene (55x70cm-22x28in) s. 13-Mar-4 De Vuyst, Lokeren #152
£704 $1218 €1000 Vue d'Overijse (55x70cm-22x28in) s.d.1908. 9-Dec-3 Vanderkindere, Brussels #69
£733 $1342 €1100 La place de Furnes (55x70cm-22x28in) s. 7-Jun-4 Palais de Beaux Arts, Brussels #86
£738 $1366 €1100 Cour de ferme (38x47cm-15x19in) s. 15-Mar-4 Horta, Bruxelles #71
£764 $1276 €1100 Route du Littoral (33x41cm-13x16in) s. panel. 21-Oct-3 Galerie Moderne, Brussels #269/R
£805 $1490 €1200 Le depart de la Vedette, Holland (35x54cm-14x21in) s. panel. 13-Mar-4 De Vuyst, Lokeren #151/R
£828 $1382 €1200 Houses by summer stream with cows (27x31cm-11x12in) s. panel lit. 10-Jul-3 Allgauer, Kempten #2510/R
£839 $1427 €1200 L'atelier du peintre. s. 18-Nov-3 Vanderkindere, Brussels #208
£851 $1421 €1200 View of Newport (36x47cm-14x19in) s. 14-Oct-3 Vanderkindere, Brussels #13
£1125 $1800 €1643 Sunset over pond and chateau (51x79cm-20x31in) s. 20-Sep-3 Sloans & Kenyon, Bethesda #1175/R est:1750-2250
£1189 $1985 €1700 Oudergem pond (35x54cm-14x21in) s.d.1901 panel. 11-Oct-3 De Vuyst, Lokeren #164/R est:1250-1500
£1268 $2193 €1800 Landscape with mill (35x55cm-14x22in) s. 13-Dec-3 De Vuyst, Lokeren #162 est:1900-2200
£2535 $4386 €3600 Brugge canal (70x55cm-28x22in) s.i.d.09. 13-Dec-3 De Vuyst, Lokeren #544/R est:3000-4000

GILSOUL-HOPPE, Ketty (1868-1939) Belgian
£333 $600 €500 Still life with earthenware liter jug, white roses, fan and Japanese print (63x53cm-25x21in) s. oil paper. 26-Apr-4 Bernaerts, Antwerp #252/R
Works on paper
£385 $654 €550 Entree de maison (26x20cm-10x8in) s. W/C. 1-Dec-3 Palais de Beaux Arts, Brussels #67
£430 $783 €650 Le beguinage (45x70cm-18x28in) s. W/C gouache. 15-Jun-4 Galerie Moderne, Brussels #351
£704 $1232 €1000 Ruelle anime a Bruges. s. W/C. 16-Dec-3 Galerie Moderne, Brussels #711/R
£804 $1367 €1150 Bouquet de fleurs dans un vase (54x37cm-21x15in) s. W/C pair. 18-Nov-3 Vanderkindere, Brussels #192

GILST, Aanout van (1898-1981) Dutch
£503 $936 €750 Grote kerk, main church in Dordrecht seen from the water (60x80cm-24x31in) s. 4-Mar-4 Auction Maastricht #1076/R

GIMBEL, Tobias (18th C) German
£352 $599 €514 Rocky landscape with peasant and donkey (33x41cm-13x16in) s.d.1780. 5-Nov-3 Dobiaschofsky, Bern #606/R (S.FR 800)
£573 $974 €837 Unexpected alms (33x41cm-13x16in) s. bears d. panel. 5-Nov-3 Dobiaschofsky, Bern #605/R (S.FR 1300)

GIMBLETT, Max (20th C) New Zealander
£236 $425 €345 Two (20x20cm-8x8in) s.i.d.1978/79 verso. 24-Apr-4 David Rago, Lambertville #152/R
£333 $600 €486 Chinese lush and green (70x50cm-28x20in) s.i.d.1976-77 verso acrylic. 24-Apr-4 David Rago, Lambertville #150/R
£1940 $3357 €2832 Untitled (58x76cm-23x30in) s.d.1988/89 platinum leaf acrylic polymer paper. 9-Dec-3 Peter Webb, Auckland #140/R est:3500-4500 (NZ.D 5200)
£2797 $5091 €4084 Fate the mirror group (81x51cm-32x20in) s.i.d.1983-89 prov. 29-Jun-4 Peter Webb, Auckland #153/R est:8000-10000 (NZ.D 8000)
£3393 $6141 €4954 Weather (88x152cm-35x60in) i. s.d.1995 verso acrylic polymer metallic pigments copper linen. 30-Mar-4 Peter Webb, Auckland #141/R est:10000-15000 (NZ.D 9500)
Works on paper
£1866 $3228 €2724 Pearls of the Pacific (76x106cm-30x42in) s.d.1988/89 mixed media. 9-Dec-3 Peter Webb, Auckland #139/R est:4000-6000 (NZ.D 5000)

GIMENO Y ARASA, Francisco (1858-1927) Spanish
£9155 $15838 €13000 Celebrating, bull scene (48x36cm-19x14in) s. 15-Dec-3 Ansorena, Madrid #44/R est:10500
Works on paper
£486 $826 €700 Study of man (57x40cm-22x16in) s. chl dr. 28-Oct-3 Segre, Madrid #351/R
£625 $1063 €900 Nude (60x42cm-24x17in) s. chl dr. 28-Oct-3 Segre, Madrid #352/R

GIMENO, Andres (1879-1927) Spanish
£2067 $3699 €3100 Lady on the Boulevards (33x24cm-13x9in) s. panel painted 1905. 17-May-4 Chayette & Cheval, Paris #171/R est:3800-4500

GIMIGNANI, Giacinto (1611-1681) Italian
£13000 $23400 €18980 Venus and Cupid with putti (44x31cm-17x12in) 21-Apr-4 Christie's, London #72/R est:8000-12000

GIMIGNANI, Giacinto (attrib) (1611-1681) Italian
Works on paper
£3200 $5760 €4672 Hercules in the garden of the Hesperides, daughters of the evening (21x28cm-8x11in) pen brown ink wash. 20-Apr-4 Sotheby's, Olympia #19/R est:2000-3000

GIMMI, Wilhelm (1886-1965) Swiss
£699 $1286 €1021 Dans la vigne, Lavaux (37x46cm-15x18in) s.d.1943 prov. 8-Jun-4 Germann, Zurich #797 (S.FR 1600)
£766 $1317 €1118 Nu assis aux pantoufles rouges (46x38cm-18x15in) s. painted 1960. 8-Dec-3 Philippe Schuler, Zurich #3334 (S.FR 1700)
£814 $1409 €1188 Paysage alpin (29x40cm-11x16in) s. 12-Dec-3 Galerie du Rhone, Sion #501 (S.FR 1800)
£862 $1543 €1259 Nu allonge (21x27cm-8x11in) s. panel prov. 13-May-4 Pierre Berge, Paris #26/R est:3000-4000 (S.FR 2000)
£873 $1607 €1275 Painter and model (56x46cm-22x18in) s. 8-Jun-4 Germann, Zurich #796 (S.FR 2000)
£1256 $2097 €1834 Don Quichotte et Panso (55x46cm-22x18in) s.d.59 i. stretcher lit. 24-Oct-3 Hans Widmer, St Gallen #121/R est:1700-3500 (S.FR 2800)

£1273 $2113 €1846 L'espagnole (35x27cm-14x11in) s. lit. 13-Jun-3 Zofingen, Switzerland #2855 est:3500 (S.FR 2800)
£1410 $2396 €2059 Chevaux de vendanges (53x65cm-21x26in) s.d.44 prov.lit. 7-Nov-3 Dobiaschofsky, Bern #114/R est:6000 (S.FR 3200)
£1629 $2720 €2378 Femme assise (46x38cm-18x15in) s.d.1955 lit. 24-Jun-3 Germann, Zurich #163/R est:3000-4000 (S.FR 3600)
£1747 $3214 €2551 Demi-nu de face (73x60cm-29x24in) s.d. lit.prov. 14-Jun-4 Philippe Schuler, Zurich #4209/R est:5000-8000 (S.FR 4000)
£1900 $3041 €2774 Street scene in Paris (27x35cm-11x14in) s. d.1947 verso. 16-Sep-3 Philippe Schuler, Zurich #3236/R est:3000-5000 (S.FR 4200)
£1982 $3370 €2894 Nu assis (55x46cm-22x18in) s. prov.lit. 7-Nov-3 Dobiaschofsky, Bern #118/R est:7000 (S.FR 4500)
£2172 $3475 €3171 Drinker and girl (65x54cm-26x21in) s. prov. 16-Sep-3 Philippe Schuler, Zurich #3235/R est:6000-8000 (S.FR 4800)
£2174 $3978 €3174 Bateau du Leman (60x73cm-24x29in) s.d.60 prov.exhib.lit. 7-Jun-4 Christie's, Zurich #112/R est:6000-8000 (S.FR 5000)
£4484 $7309 €6547 La lavandiere, quai d'Anjou (100x81cm-39x32in) s.d.57/58 exhib.lit. 29-Sep-3 Christie's, Zurich #93/R est:12000-15000 (S.FR 10000)
£4817 $8044 €6985 James Joyce et Madame Bloom (46x38cm-18x15in) 19-Jun-3 Kornfeld, Bern #441/R est:10000 (S.FR 10500)
£6114 $10943 €8926 Paysage de Cahors (54x65cm-21x26in) s.i.d.1926 prov.exhib.lit. 26-May-4 Sotheby's, Zurich #36/R est:10000-15000 (S.FR 14000)
£10480 $18760 €15301 Eglise Saint-Gervais, Paris (92x73cm-36x29in) s.d.1925 prov.exhib.lit. 26-May-4 Sotheby's, Zurich #48/R est:24000-28000 (S.FR 24000)

Works on paper

£294 $491 €429 Still life with woman (94x66cm-37x26in) chl. 24-Jun-3 Germann, Zurich #966 (S.FR 650)
£590 $986 €850 Femmes a leurs toilettes (45x61cm-18x24in) s. gouache. 21-Oct-3 Artcurial Briest, Paris #61/R
£773 $1283 €1121 James Joyce (33x26cm-13x10in) s.i.d.1961 W/C. 13-Jun-3 Zofingen, Switzerland #2858 est:2000 (S.FR 1700)

GINDERTAEL, Roger van (1899-1982) Belgian

£664 $1129 €950 Nature morte cubiste (64x48cm-25x19in) oil paper prov. 1-Dec-3 Palais de Beaux Arts, Brussels #138/R
£2013 $3564 €3000 Buste de femme nu (73x60cm-29x24in) s. 27-Apr-4 Campo & Campo, Antwerp #104/R est:3000-4000
£6711 $11879 €10000 Nu dans un interieur (92x73cm-36x29in) s. 27-Apr-4 Campo & Campo, Antwerp #103/R est:9000-11000

GINE, Alexander Vasilievitsch (1830-1880) Russian

£9412 $16000 €13742 Lake scene at sunset with a summer palace on the shore and figures in a dinghy (30x39cm-12x15in) bears sig. 19-Nov-3 Bonhams & Butterfields, San Francisco #90/R

GINE, Alexander Vasilievitsch (attrib) (1830-1880) Russian

£3693 $6500 €5392 Moonlit scene with a Russian church by a lake (29x39cm-11x15in) bears sig. 18-May-4 Bonhams & Butterfields, San Francisco #87a/R est:4000-6000

GINER BUENO, Luis (1935-) Spanish

£382 $649 €550 Factory (46x55cm-18x22in) s. 28-Oct-3 Segre, Madrid #359/R
£704 $1232 €1000 Fishermen on the beach (46x65cm-18x26in) s. 16-Dec-3 Durán, Madrid #614/R
£1333 $2427 €2000 Vuelta de la pesca (55x65cm-22x26in) s. 29-Jun-4 Segre, Madrid #92/R est:2000

GINER, Johann (elder) (1756-1833) Austrian

Sculpture

£1517 $2519 €2200 Baroque horse (24cm-9in) wood glass. 30-Sep-3 Dorotheum, Vienna #64/R est:1200-1300

GINER, Vicente (?) Spanish

£369 $687 €550 Waiting for the fishermen (73x54cm-29x21in) s. s.i.verso. 2-Mar-4 Ansorena, Madrid #205/R

GINGELEN, Jacques van (1801-?) Flemish

£533 $971 €800 Figures at the water's edge in the morning mist (27x38cm-11x15in) s. 1-Jul-4 Van Ham, Cologne #1364

GINN, Jennifer (?) British?

Works on paper

£420 $722 €613 The ballerina (66x50cm-26x20in) s.d.91 pastel. 3-Dec-3 John Ross, Belfast #193

GINNEKEN, Matthieu van (1811-1888) Dutch

£1233 $2096 €1800 Poultry (37x50cm-15x20in) s.d.1869 panel. 5-Nov-3 Vendue Huis, Gravenhage #82/R est:2500-3000

GINNER, Charles (1878-1952) British

Works on paper

£3000 $5460 €4380 Batheaston, Somerset (40x28cm-16x11in) s. pen blk ink W/C bodycol exec 1926 exhib. 1-Jul-4 Christie's, Kensington #80/R est:3000-5000

GINNETT, Louis (1875-1946) British

£600 $1080 €876 Model (75x55cm-30x22in) s.d.1910. 22-Apr-4 Mellors & Kirk, Nottingham #1058/R
£2500 $4650 €3650 Love (63x53cm-25x21in) s.d.1900 i.verso. 4-Mar-4 Christie's, Kensington #638/R est:2000-3000

GINNPIELLA, C (?) ?

£1000 $1790 €1500 Musical troupe near a rocky coast with view of a volcano (46x85cm-18x33in) 11-May-4 Vendu Notarishuis, Rotterdam #156/R est:1500-2000

GINOVSZKY, Joseph (1800-1857) Austrian

£3356 $5940 €5000 Kaiser Franz I von Osterreich (44x34cm-17x13in) s.d.1836 verso board. 29-Apr-4 Dorotheum, Vienna #27/R est:2500-4000

GINSBERG, Allen (1926-1997) American

Photographs

£2515 $4200 €3672 Jack Kerouac with a railroad brakeman's rule book in pocket (40x27cm-16x11in) with sig.i.d.1953 verso silver print. 21-Oct-3 Swann Galleries, New York #230/R est:3000-5000

GINZBURG, Yankel (1945-) American

£231 $400 €337 The cry (30x23cm-12x9in) s. prov. 13-Dec-3 Weschler, Washington #567
£260 $450 €380 Gem (36x46cm-14x18in) s.d.1975 prov. 13-Dec-3 Weschler, Washington #596
£318 $550 €464 Renaissance (61x91cm-24x36in) s. prov. 13-Dec-3 Weschler, Washington #594
£405 $700 €591 Dreams of transformation (52x61cm-20x24in) s.d.1973 prov. 13-Dec-3 Weschler, Washington #595

GIOBBI, Edward (1926-) American

Works on paper

£444 $800 €648 Untitled, rainy street scene (53x66cm-21x26in) s.d.51 W/C prov. 25-Jan-4 Hindman, Chicago #1093/R

GIOJA, Theresia von (19th C) Austrian

£5000 $9200 €7300 Duel after the masked ball (96x115cm-38x45in) s.d.1871 verso. 25-Mar-4 Christie's, Kensington #192/R est:2000-3000

GIOLFINO, Niccolo II (style) (1476-1555) Italian

£21538 $37046 €31445 Mythological scene with Epimendes sleeping (95x131cm-37x52in) 2-Dec-3 Bukowskis, Stockholm #328/R est:80000-100000 (S.KR 280000)

GIOLI, Francesco (1849-1922) Italian

£1127 $1870 €1600 Casale nel verde (37x30cm-15x12in) s. canvas on board. 11-Jun-3 Christie's, Rome #64 est:1500-2000
£1127 $1949 €1600 Self-portrait (49x39cm-19x15in) s.i.d.83. 10-Dec-3 Sotheby's, Milan #140/R est:1500-2500
£2000 $3680 €3000 Tuscan landscape (31x44cm-12x17in) s. 8-Jun-4 Sotheby's, Milan #53/R est:3000-5000
£2254 $3899 €3200 Livorno (11x18cm-4x7in) s. i.verso board. 9-Dec-3 Pandolfini, Florence #250 est:2100-2300
£2349 $4205 €3500 Maternity joys (35x21cm-14x8in) s. board. 25-May-4 Finarte Semenzato, Milan #65/R est:2500-3000
£4638 $7606 €6400 Chatting in the garden (39x30cm-15x12in) s.d.92 cardboard. 27-May-3 Finarte Semenzato, Milan #47/R est:5000-6000

Works on paper

£467 $845 €700 Motherly joys (31x24cm-12x9in) s. pencil dr. 2-Apr-4 Farsetti, Prato #569/R

GIOLI, Francesco (attrib) (1849-1922) Italian

£420 $722 €600 Bell tower and olive trees (39x19cm-15x7in) s. cardboard. 3-Dec-3 Stadion, Trieste #1058
£560 $1003 €818 The wine's good! (67x32cm-26x13in) i.d.75. 12-May-4 Dobiaschofsky, Bern #557/R (S.FR 1300)

GIOLI, Luigi (1854-1947) Italian

£1126 $2049 €1700 Trees (34x46cm-13x18in) s. board. 21-Jun-4 Pandolfini, Florence #169 est:1700-1800
£1268 $2193 €1800 Horse (33x40cm-13x16in) s. 11-Dec-3 Christie's, Rome #68 est:1800-2500
£2734 $4483 €3800 View of church (30x43cm-12x17in) s. canvas on card. 10-Jun-3 Pandolfini, Florence #128/R est:4000-4500
£7042 $12183 €10000 Countryside at sunset (52x48cm-20x19in) s.d.92. 11-Dec-3 Christie's, Rome #171/R est:6000-9000
£8621 $14397 €12500 Soldiers on horseback (19x34cm-7x13in) s. 14-Nov-3 Farsetti, Prato #537/R est:11000-13000

GIOLITO, Beppe (?) Italian

£336 $594 €500 Composition with flowers on table (70x100cm-28x39in) s. 1-May-4 Meeting Art, Vercelli #345

GIORDA, Patrice (1952-) French

£417 $696 €600 L'Histoire de la Croix l'aide (130x97cm-51x38in) s.i.d.89 verso acrylic. 21-Oct-3 Artcurial Briest, Paris #629
£867 $1595 €1300 La promenade numero VI, les feux de bois (160x200cm-63x79in) s.i.d.1986 verso acrylic. 11-Jun-4 Pierre Berge, Paris #69
£933 $1717 €1400 Les terrasses numero 4 (180x164cm-71x65in) s.i.d.1984 verso prov. 11-Jun-4 Pierre Berge, Paris #71
£1250 $2088 €1800 Promenade No. 3 (162x200cm-64x79in) s.i.d.1986 verso acrylic prov. 21-Oct-3 Artcurial Briest, Paris #628/R est:1500-2000
£1467 $2640 €2200 Saturne (165x183cm-65x72in) s.d.1986 verso prov. 25-Apr-4 Versailles Encheres #228 est:2000-2500
£1760 $3046 €2500 Corpus Christi VIII (130x196cm-51x77in) s.i.d.1988 verso prov.lit. 9-Dec-3 Artcurial Briest, Paris #552/R est:3000-4000

GIORDANI, Italo (19/20th C) Italian

£369 $661 €550 Bord de lac au Nord de l'Italie (60x80cm-24x31in) s. 25-May-4 Palais de Beaux Arts, Brussels #369/R
£470 $841 €700 Gondole a Venise (60x79cm-24x31in) s. 25-May-4 Palais de Beaux Arts, Brussels #368/R

£638 $1180 €950 Gondolier a Venise (79x58cm-31x23in) s. panel. 14-Mar-4 St-Germain-en-Laye Encheres #108/R

GIORDANO, Edoardo (1904-1974) Italian
Works on paper
£2657 $4517 €3800 Composition (70x50cm-28x20in) s.d.1952 mixed media paper on masonite prov.exhib. 24-Nov-3 Christie's, Milan #258/R est:1300-1800

GIORDANO, Felice (1880-1964) Italian
£467 $859 €700 Green gate (60x43cm-24x17in) s. 10-Jun-4 Christie's, Rome #14a
£528 $914 €750 Landscape (34x43cm-13x17in) s. canvas on board. 10-Dec-3 Finarte Semenzato, Rome #277
£775 $1340 €1100 Landscape with stream (19x23cm-7x9in) s. board. 9-Dec-3 Finarte Semenzato, Milan #14/R est:1000-1200
£870 $1426 €1200 Landscape of stream and figures (19x23cm-7x9in) s. board. 27-May-3 Finarte Semenzato, Milan #29/R
£1000 $1840 €1500 Holy Rosary (43x35cm-17x14in) s. 10-Jun-4 Christie's, Rome #76a est:500-700
£1319 $2151 €1900 Cliff (89x70cm-35x28in) s. 23-Sep-3 Durán, Madrid #55/R
£1399 $2336 €2000 Beached boats (70x85cm-28x33in) s. 26-Jun-3 Sant Agostino, Torino #86/R est:2000
£1408 $2437 €2000 Fireworks in Capri (35x50cm-14x20in) s. 9-Dec-3 Finarte Semenzato, Milan #21/R est:2300
£1910 $3113 €2750 Italian port (80x120cm-31x47in) s. 23-Sep-3 Durán, Madrid #54/R
£2133 $3925 €3200 Market scene in Trieste (27x38cm-11x15in) s. board. 8-Jun-4 Sotheby's, Milan #70/R est:1300-1500
£2361 $4014 €3400 Beached boats (70x85cm-28x33in) s. canvas on cardboard. 1-Nov-3 Meeting Art, Vercelli #426/R est:2500
£2371 $4244 €3462 Riva degli Schiavoni (30x59cm-12x23in) s.d.1928 i. stretcher. 12-May-4 Dobiaschofsky, Bern #558/R est:4000 (S.FR 5500)
£2567 $4750 €3748 Marina Piccoroa, Capri (80x121cm-31x48in) s. 18-Jan-4 Bonhams & Butterfields, Los Angeles #7032/R est:2500-3500
£2617 $4633 €3900 NIght scene in Capri (70x90cm-28x35in) s. 1-May-4 Meeting Art, Vercelli #218 est:3000
£2685 $4752 €4000 Back from fishing (74x101cm-29x40in) s. 1-May-4 Meeting Art, Vercelli #433 est:4000
£3169 $5482 €4500 Little harbour, Capri (32x47cm-13x19in) s. 10-Dec-3 Sotheby's, Milan #3/R est:4500-5500
£3867 $7115 €5800 Life on the coast (50x70cm-20x28in) s. 10-Jun-4 Christie's, Rome #108/R est:1800-2200
£4058 $6655 €5600 Terrace in Capri (48x58cm-19x23in) s.d.1938. 27-May-3 Finarte Semenzato, Milan #30/R est:2000-2500

GIORDANO, Luca (1632-1705) Italian
£18000 $32940 €27000 Lazarus resurrection (65x54cm-26x21in) board lit. 1-Jun-4 Sotheby's, Milan #154/R est:30000-40000
£22368 $41158 €34000 Saint Michael and the rebellious angels (76x62cm-30x24in) painted with studio exhib. 24-Jun-4 Christie's, Paris #81/R est:6000-8000
£36111 $65000 €52722 Venus and Mars (63x77cm-25x30in) prov. 22-Jan-4 Sotheby's, New York #77/R est:30000-40000
£38000 $65740 €55480 Diana and Niobe (150x200cm-59x79in) 11-Dec-3 Sotheby's, London #26/R est:30000-50000
£40000 $72000 €58400 Diana and Actaeon (101x128cm-40x50in) prov. 22-Apr-4 Sotheby's, London #64/R est:15000-20000
Prints
£1788 $3200 €2610 Elijah's sacrifice (38x51cm-15x20in) etching. 6-May-4 Swann Galleries, New York #89/R est:2500-3500
Works on paper
£1316 $2421 €2000 Resting during the Flight to Egypt (13x17cm-5x7in) pen ink W/C lit. 22-Jun-4 Sotheby's, Milan #63/R est:2000-2500
£1645 $3026 €2500 Resting during the Flight to Egypt (12x16cm-5x6in) pen ink W/C over pencil exhib. 22-Jun-4 Sotheby's, Milan #60/R est:2500-3000
£3022 $4835 €4200 Muse. Study for mythological scene (11x19cm-4x7in) pen ink W/C two. 14-May-3 Finarte Semenzato, Milan #497/R est:3000-4000
£3289 $6053 €5000 Hercules and Onphales (14x18cm-6x7in) sanguine exhib. 22-Jun-4 Sotheby's, Milan #22/R est:4500-5000
£5132 $9442 €7800 Study of Hercules (39x25cm-15x10in) sanguine W/C. 22-Jun-4 Sotheby's, Milan #21/R est:4000-6000

GIORDANO, Luca (attrib) (1632-1705) Italian
£16556 $30132 €25000 Cain and Abel (193x145cm-76x57in) 16-Jun-4 Christie's, Rome #488/R est:25000-35000
£20979 $35664 €30000 Judgement of Paris with Mercury and Cupid (216x305cm-85x120in) prov.lit. 25-Nov-3 Hamilton Osborne King, Dublin #283/R est:50000-80000
£20979 $35664 €30000 Pan and Syrinx (216x305cm-85x120in) prov.lit. 25-Nov-3 Hamilton Osborne King, Dublin #284 est:50000-80000
Works on paper
£397 $723 €600 Salomon's judgement (22x32cm-9x13in) sanguine. 16-Jun-4 Christie's, Rome #456a

GIORDANO, Luca (circle) (1632-1705) Italian
£5479 $9315 €8000 Coronation of the Virgin (47x30cm-19x12in) 4-Nov-3 Ansorena, Madrid #35/R est:8000
£6000 $10380 €8760 Two putti (88x98cm-35x39in) 9-Dec-3 Sotheby's, Olympia #394/R est:5000-7000
£6028 $10067 €8500 L'adoration des Mages (117x87cm-46x34in) 17-Oct-3 Tajan, Paris #1/R est:4000-6000
£6690 $11574 €9500 Deer hunt - Diana and Actaeon (102x128cm-40x50in) 13-Dec-3 Hagelstam, Helsinki #29/R est:10000
£13793 $24690 €20138 St Peter (71x60cm-28x24in) 12-May-4 Dobiaschofsky, Bern #559/R est:16000 (S.FR 32000)
£25000 $43000 €36500 Neptune (74x95cm-29x37in) prov. 2-Dec-3 Bukowskis, Stockholm #349/R est:50000-60000 (S.KR 325000)

GIORDANO, Luca (school) (1632-1705) Italian
£10638 $17766 €15000 Salomon worshippingthe idols (179x256cm-70x101in) 14-Oct-3 Finarte Semenzato, Rome #294/R est:15000-18000

GIORDANO, Luca (style) (1632-1705) Italian
£6000 $10800 €8760 Christ and Saint Veronica on the road to Calvary (97x135cm-38x53in) 20-Apr-4 Sotheby's, Olympia #315/R est:6000-8000
£7231 $12437 €10557 Venus and Vulcanus (120x185cm-47x73in) 2-Dec-3 Bukowskis, Stockholm #347/R est:60000-80000 (S.KR 94000)

GIORGETTI, Angelo (1899-1952) Swiss
£262 $477 €383 Still life with vegetables (22x32cm-9x13in) s. masonite. 16-Jun-4 Fischer, Luzern #2142/R (S.FR 600)
£349 $636 €510 At the beach (19x23cm-7x9in) s. panel. 16-Jun-4 Fischer, Luzern #2143/R (S.FR 800)

GIORGI, Bruno (c.1905-?) Brazilian
Sculpture
£4487 $7942 €6731 Flame (26cm-10in) white marble. 27-Apr-4 Bolsa de Arte, Rio de Janeiro #89/R (B.R 24500)
£6777 $11995 €10166 Woman standing in the moonlight (45cm-18in) marble. 27-Apr-4 Bolsa de Arte, Rio de Janeiro #46/R (B.R 37000)
Works on paper
£366 $670 €549 Study for a sculpture (21x29cm-8x11in) s. mixed media. 6-Jul-4 Bolsa de Arte, Rio de Janeiro #22/R (B.R 2000)

GIORNI ZORN SAVIOLI, Lionello (1910-) Italian
Works on paper
£1067 $1909 €1600 Women at well (70x100cm-28x39in) s.i.d.1931 verso mixed media on canvas. 12-May-4 Stadion, Trieste #831/R est:600-800

GIOVACCHINI, Ulderico (1890-?) Italian
£652 $1070 €900 Alpine church (36x26cm-14x10in) s. i.verso board. 27-May-3 Il Ponte, Milan #804

GIOVANNI DEL BIONDO (fl.1356-1398) Italian
£13000 $22100 €18980 Madonna and Child with Saint Bartholomew, Saint with a book and six Angles (78x44cm-31x17in) gold ground panel. 29-Oct-3 Christie's, London #75/R est:6000-8000
£63758 $114128 €95000 Saint Maurice (145x42cm-57x17in) tempera gold board arched top. 27-May-4 Semenzato, Florence #195/R est:100000-150000

GIOVANNI DI ILARIO DA PARMA (15th C) Italian
£13121 $21255 €18500 Saint Agapius and martyrs (158x154cm-62x61in) d.1496 tempera. 21-May-3 Babuino, Rome #1/R est:10000-12000

GIOVANNI DI NICCOLA DA PISA (fl.1326-1358) Italian
£70000 $121100 €102200 Madonna and Child (62x39cm-24x15in) gold ground panel pointed top prov.lit. 10-Dec-3 Christie's, London #78/R est:60000-80000

GIOVANNI DI TANO FEI (15th C) Italian
£58219 $98973 €85000 Madonna and Child enthroned (68x40cm-27x16in) tempera gold panel lit. 9-Nov-3 Finarte, Venice #155a/R est:180000-200000

GIOVANNI, Luigi di (1856-1938) Italian
Works on paper
£1119 $1869 €1600 Yellow scarf (60x46cm-24x18in) s.i. pastel card. 26-Jun-3 Sant Agostino, Torino #25/R est:1400

GIOVANNI, Matteo di (16th C) Italian
£56338 $93521 €80000 Madonna and Child (58x42cm-23x17in) gold tempera panel. 11-Jun-3 Semenzato, Florence #171/R est:95000-105000

GIPE, Lawrence (1962-) American?
£1757 $3250 €2565 Study for Sentimental paintings for Blaise Cendrars (96x119cm-38x47in) vellum exec 1991 prov. 12-Feb-4 Sotheby's, New York #346/R est:2000-3000

GIPPIUS, N A (1905-1995) Russian
£389 $700 €568 Girl in lilac (55x37cm-22x15in) 24-Apr-4 Shishkin Gallery, Moscow #26/R
£1222 $2200 €1784 Swimming women at the green background (50x39cm-20x15in) canvas on cardboard. 24-Apr-4 Shishkin Gallery, Moscow #27/R est:2000-3000
£1222 $2200 €1784 From the Altai series (45x55cm-18x22in) 24-Apr-4 Shishkin Gallery, Moscow #28/R est:2000-2500

GIR, Charles-Felix (1883-1941) French
Sculpture
£1099 $2000 €1605 Cantine des Polus (20x84x23cm-8x33x9in) cast sig. d.1917 base pat bronze f.Alexin Budier. 7-Feb-4 Neal Auction Company, New Orleans #401/R est:2500-3500

GIRALT, Juan (1940-) Spanish
£704 $1127 €1000 Head with helmet (92x73cm-36x29in) s.d.1975 i.verso prov. 16-Sep-3 Segre, Madrid #150/R

GIRAN-MAX, Léon (1867-1927) French
£762 $1386 €1150 Meules (54x81cm-21x32in) s. 19-Jun-4 St-Germain-en-Laye Encheres #170/R
£839 $1552 €1250 Dejeuner a la guinguette (82x101cm-32x40in) s.d.1918 i.verso. 14-Mar-4 St-Germain-en-Laye Encheres #63/R

£10265	$18785	€15500	Saint-Briac, elegante a la Pointe du Crosnier (54x81cm-21x32in) s. lit. 7-Apr-4 Piasa, Paris #26/R est:8000-10000

GIRARD, Andre (1901-1968) French

£436	$811	€650	Le quai des Esclavons a Venise (300x210cm-118x83in) 3-Mar-4 Ferri, Paris #76/R

GIRARD, Karine Firmin (1965-) French

£355	$574	€500	Paseo por la playa (27x34cm-11x13in) s. panel. 20-May-3 Ansorena, Madrid #13/R
£355	$574	€500	Young woman on the beach (45x54cm-18x21in) s. panel. 20-May-3 Ansorena, Madrid #120/R
£733	$1335	€1100	Quai de Saone (49x60cm-19x24in) 29-Jun-4 Chenu & Scrive, Lyon #98/R
£1107	$2049	€1650	Plage animee (60x72cm-24x28in) s. panel. 14-Mar-4 Eric Pillon, Calais #258/R

GIRARD, Marie Firmin (1838-1921) French

£1400	$2478	€2044	Young girl on a coastal path (60x42cm-24x17in) studio st. 29-Apr-4 Christie's, Kensington #137/R est:1500-2000
£12778	$23000	€18656	Notre Dame de Paris et marchande de fleurs (54x73cm-21x29in) s. 23-Apr-4 Sotheby's, New York #138/R est:20000-30000
£13448	$22459	€19500	Quai de Notre-Dame (51x70cm-20x28in) s. 12-Nov-3 Chassaing Rivet, Toulouse #200
£72222	$130000	€105444	Flower seller on the Pont Royal with the Louvre beyond, Paris (72x96cm-28x38in) s.d.1872 lit. 22-Apr-4 Christie's, Rockefeller NY #148/R est:50000-70000

GIRARD, Marie Firmin (attrib) (1838-1921) French

£1181	$1924	€1700	Young woman by pool (30x21cm-12x8in) i. panel. 25-Sep-3 Neumeister, Munich #2773/R est:1500

GIRARD, Paul Albert (1839-1920) French

£1512	$2600	€2208	Racetrack scenes (41x25cm-16x10in) s. pair. 6-Dec-3 Neal Auction Company, New Orleans #232 est:700-900
£3200	$5824	€4672	Deer in a river landscape (92x116cm-36x46in) s. 16-Jun-4 Christie's, Kensington #14/R est:3000-5000

GIRARDET, Edouard-Henri (1819-1880) Swiss

£3448	$6172	€5034	Storm gathering in the mountains (135x64cm-53x25in) 17-May-4 Beurret, Zurich #9/R est:7000-9000 (S.FR 8000)

GIRARDET, Eugène Alexis (1853-1907) French

£986	$1706	€1400	Malle-POste (11x26cm-4x10in) s. panel. 15-Dec-3 Gros & Delettrez, Paris #328
£1348	$2250	€1900	Homme avec son ane (26x21cm-10x8in) s. panel. 15-Oct-3 Claude Aguttes, Neuilly #55 est:1200-1800
£1718	$2921	€2508	Interior with young woman in traditional costume (46x32cm-18x13in) s. 5-Nov-3 Dobiaschofsky, Bern #607/R est:6000 (S.FR 3900)
£1761	$3081	€2500	L'ombrelle (35x27cm-14x11in) s. 21-Dec-3 Thierry & Lannon, Brest #a3
£2955	$4905	€4285	L'attente au client (40x26cm-16x10in) i. verso panel. prov. 13-Jun-3 Zofingen, Switzerland #2450/R est:8000 (S.FR 6500)
£3200	$5856	€4800	Le passage du pont. Fileuses at tailleur a Bou-Saada (26x41cm-10x16in) s. one i.d.1894 pair. 3-Jun-4 Tajan, Paris #250/R est:4500-6000
£7500	$12525	€10950	Sorti de la mosque d'el assar, Cairo (40x27cm-16x11in) s. board prov.exhib. 14-Oct-3 Sotheby's, London #90/R est:6000-8000
£7801	$12638	€11000	Bateaux au bord de l'eau (38x67cm-15x26in) s. 23-May-3 Sotheby's, Paris #26/R est:7000-9000
£8000	$13760	€11680	Desert caravan, Algeria (30x69cm-12x27in) s.i. 3-Dec-3 Christie's, London #87/R est:8000-12000
£8000	$14640	€12000	Tanger (71x55cm-28x22in) s.d.1878. 3-Jun-4 Tajan, Paris #249/R est:9000-12000
£9929	$16582	€14000	Les joueurs d'echecs (22x33cm-9x13in) s.d.1880. 16-Jun-3 Gros & Delettrez, Paris #463/R est:6000-9000
£12000	$21840	€17520	Pres du puits (64x100cm-25x39in) s. prov. 15-Jun-4 Sotheby's, London #120/R est:6000-8000

GIRARDET, F (20th C) French

Sculpture

£1989	$3500	€2904	Joan of Arc (89cm-35in) s. brown pat. bronze. 18-May-4 Arthur James, Florida #107 est:3500-4500

GIRARDET, Jules (1856-1946) French/Swiss

£6667	$12200	€10000	La partie des boules devant l'auberge (60x74cm-24x29in) s. 6-Jun-4 Anaf, Lyon #389/R est:10000-12000

Works on paper

£1156	$1839	€1700	La partie gagnee (45x60cm-18x24in) s. indis.d. W/C. 23-Mar-3 Mercier & Cie, Lille #225 est:1500-2000

GIRARDET, Karl (1813-1871) Swiss

£819	$1466	€1196	Landscape with fortress (16x26cm-6x10in) mono. 14-May-4 Dobiaschofsky, Bern #4/R est:2500 (S.FR 1900)
£1584	$2692	€2313	Peasant children (34x43cm-13x17in) mono. 28-Nov-3 Zofingen, Switzerland #2463/R est:4000 (S.FR 3500)
£1810	$3077	€2643	Farmsteads by pond with geese (33x55cm-13x22in) s. 19-Nov-3 Fischer, Luzern #1241/R est:4000-6000 (S.FR 4000)
£2619	$4190	€3798	Jean Paul et Biquette (27x45cm-11x18in) s. 15-May-3 Stuker, Bern #1257/R est:6000-8000 (S.FR 5500)
£2802	$5015	€4091	Souvenir d'Anet (38x46cm-15x18in) s.d. 17-May-4 Beurret, Zurich #7/R est:4000-6000 (S.FR 6500)
£3000	$5490	€4380	Lake scene with figures ploughing, at rest and a shepherd (53x86cm-21x34in) s. 27-Jan-4 Gorringes, Lewes #1509/R est:3200-3600
£3233	$5787	€4720	Boy by boat (9x22cm-4x9in) mono. paper on board. 17-May-4 Beurret, Zurich #10/R est:3000-4000 (S.FR 7500)
£3333	$5333	€4833	Une prise a Sorento (42x32cm-17x13in) s.d.1842. 15-May-3 Stuker, Bern #1256/R est:8000-12000 (S.FR 7000)
£5587	$10000	€8157	Washer women by a riverbank (53x91cm-21x36in) s. 6-May-4 Shannon's, Milford #145/R est:10000-15000
£11312	$19570	€16516	Paysage en ete avec pecheurs (48x64cm-19x25in) s. 9-Dec-3 Sotheby's, Zurich #16/R est:25000-30000 (S.FR 25000)
£11638	$20832	€16991	Examining a female slave (60x40cm-24x16in) s.d.1843. 17-May-4 Beurret, Zurich #8/R est:25000-35000 (S.FR 27000)

GIRARDET, Karl (attrib) (1813-1871) Swiss

£529	$899	€772	Lake in summer (24x33cm-9x13in) panel. 7-Nov-3 Dobiaschofsky, Bern #3/R (S.FR 1200)
£18100	$30769	€26426	Cattle watering (33x46cm-13x18in) s.d.1859. 19-Nov-3 Fischer, Luzern #1240/R est:4000-6000 (S.FR 40000)

GIRARDET, Léon (1857-1895) French

£1761	$2923	€2500	Jeune fille au papillon (48x31cm-19x12in) s. 15-Jun-3 Peron, Melun #102
£5634	$9746	€8000	Halte aux environs de Biskra (38x55cm-15x22in) s.i.d.1880. 15-Dec-3 Gros & Delettrez, Paris #116/R est:5500-7000

GIRARDET, Leopold Henri (1848-1904) Swiss

£563	$1007	€822	Fruit seller in Biskra (23x19cm-9x7in) s.i.d. canvas on board. 22-Mar-4 Philippe Schuler, Zurich #4331 (S.FR 1300)
£704	$1261	€1000	Dutch lady seated by a window binding a bunch of flowers (59x36cm-23x14in) s. board lit. 8-Jan-4 Allgauer, Kempten #2395/R

GIRARDIN, Frank J (1856-1945) American

£301	$550	€439	Malibu (23x30cm-9x12in) init.i.verso. 5-Jun-4 Treadway Gallery, Cincinnati #619/R
£794	$1500	€1159	California coastal (23x36cm-9x14in) Board. 17-Feb-4 John Moran, Pasadena #190/R est:800-1200
£815	$1500	€1190	Haystacks (50x76cm-20x30in) s. 8-Jun-4 Bonhams & Butterfields, San Francisco #4051/R est:3000-5000

GIRARDON, François (after) (1628-1715) French

Sculpture

£18000	$33120	€26280	Louis XIV on horseback (198cm-78in) i.d.1740 brown pat bronze plinth wood pedestal. 10-Jun-4 Christie's, London #146/R est:18000-25000

GIRARDOT, Ernest Gustave (fl.1860-1893) British

£9940	$16500	€14512	Young Master (155x112cm-61x44in) 4-Oct-3 Neal Auction Company, New Orleans #224/R est:7500-10000

GIRARDOT, Louis Auguste (1858-1933) French

£2993	$5358	€4400	Marche, lumiere rose a Tanger (14x23cm-6x9in) s.i.d.1894 canvas on panel. 21-Mar-4 St-Germain-en-Laye Encheres #33/R est:4000

GIRAULT DE PRANGEY, Joseph Philibert (19th C) French

Photographs

£2200	$3872	€3212	Baalbec, Grande Cour Frontons et chapiteau (9x7cm-4x3in) daguerreotype. 18-May-4 Christie's, London #48/R est:2500-3500
£2200	$3872	€3212	Alexandrie, mosquee au nord est (9x8cm-4x3in) daguerreotype. 18-May-4 Christie's, London #73/R est:2000-2500
£2600	$4576	€3796	Djebel Selseleh, Temple chapiteau (9x8cm-4x3in) daguerreotype. 18-May-4 Christie's, London #45/R est:3000-5000
£2600	$4576	€3796	Medinet abou Grande Temple, Cour (9x8cm-4x3in) daguerreotype. 18-May-4 Christie's, London #37/R est:1800-2400
£2800	$4928	€4088	Constantinople, Bosphore, Sud, Skengel Keni (8x9cm-3x4in) daguerreotype. 18-May-4 Christie's, London #1/R est:2500-3500
£3000	$5280	€4380	Jerusalem Grande Mosquee prise de S Meryem (9x8cm-4x3in) daguerreotype. 18-May-4 Christie's, London #17/R est:3000-5000
£3000	$5280	€4380	Athenes, Monument de Philopapus (9x8cm-4x3in) daguerreotype. 18-May-4 Christie's, London #30/R est:1800-2400
£3200	$5632	€4672	Alexandrie datiers (8x9cm-3x4in) daguerreotype. 18-May-4 Christie's, London #15/R est:3000-5000
£3200	$5632	€4672	Jaffa, fontaine (9x12cm-4x5in) daguerreotype. 18-May-4 Christie's, London #25/R est:4000-6000
£3200	$5632	€4672	Baalbec Petit Temple, exterieur plafond (12x9cm-5x4in) daguerreotype. 18-May-4 Christie's, London #50/R est:4000-6000
£3200	$5632	€4672	Baalbec, Petit Temple, exterieur frize entablement (9x12cm-4x5in) daguerreotype. 18-May-4 Christie's, London #51/R est:4000-6000
£3500	$6160	€5110	Alexandrie, cafe (8x9cm-3x4in) daguerreotype. 18-May-4 Christie's, London #26/R est:4000-6000
£3800	$6688	€5548	Constantinople, Bosphore Nord, Village Sud (8x9cm-3x4in) daguerreotype. 18-May-4 Christie's, London #2/R est:3000-5000
£3800	$6688	€5548	Kaire, Gama Amr fenetre (9x8cm-4x3in) daguerreotype. 18-May-4 Christie's, London #43/R est:2500-3500
£4000	$7040	€5840	Kaire,Tombeau Siffi Neficeh (9x8cm-4x3in) daguerreotype. 18-May-4 Christie's, London #23/R est:2500-3500
£4000	$7040	€5840	Kaire, Tombeau Sud (9x8cm-4x3in) daguerreotype. 18-May-4 Christie's, London #24/R est:2500-3500
£4000	$7040	€5840	Baalbec, petit temple interieur chapiteau (9x8cm-4x3in) daguerreotype. 18-May-4 Christie's, London #47/R est:2500-3500
£4200	$7392	€6132	Ile pres Phile Temple (8x9cm-3x4in) daguerreotype. 18-May-4 Christie's, London #38/R est:2000-3000
£4200	$7392	€6132	Karnac, Temple (8x9cm-3x4in) daguerreotype. 18-May-4 Christie's, London #39/R est:3000-5000
£4200	$7392	€6132	Brousse, Yechil Djami, porte (9x8cm-4x3in) daguerreotype. 18-May-4 Christie's, London #55/R est:4000-6000
£4500	$7920	€6570	Villa Adriana paysage - Pins (9x8cm-4x3in) daguerreotype. 18-May-4 Christie's, London #7/R est:2500-3500
£4800	$8448	€7008	Toscanella Eglise S Pietro chapiteau interieur (9x8cm-4x3in) daguerreotype. 18-May-4 Christie's, London #44/R est:2000-3000
£5000	$8800	€7300	Baalbec, Petit Temple, exterieur angle sud ouest (8x9cm-3x4in) daguerreotype. 18-May-4 Christie's, London #67/R est:2500-3500
£6000	$10560	€8760	Scutari, fontaine (9x8cm-4x3in) daguerreotype. 18-May-4 Christie's, London #57/R est:3000-5000
£6200	$10912	€9052	Toscanella, Eglise S Pietro facade (8x9cm-3x4in) daguerreotype. 18-May-4 Christie's, London #22/R est:2500-3500
£6500	$11440	€9490	Aphrodisias, Konac (8x9cm-3x4in) daguerreotype. 18-May-4 Christie's, London #27/R est:3000-5000

£6500 $11440 €9490 Constantinople, petite fontaine, pres du Serail (9x8cm-4x3in) daguerreotype. 18-May-4 Christie's, London #56/R est:3000-5000
£6500 $11440 €9490 Assuouan, Nubiens (9x8cm-4x3in) daguerreotype. 18-May-4 Christie's, London #86/R est:8000-10000
£7000 $12320 €10220 Alexandrie, Mosquee El Euenaoui (8x9cm-3x4in) daguerreotype. 18-May-4 Christie's, London #16/R est:3000-5000
£7500 $13200 €10950 Assouan, Palmiers Dattiers (9x8cm-4x3in) daguerreotype. 18-May-4 Christie's, London #5/R est:4000-6000
£7500 $13200 €10950 Kaire Chamelier (12x9cm-5x4in) daguerreotype. 18-May-4 Christie's, London #88/R est:9000-12000
£8000 $14080 €11680 Kaire, Kouttab Kaidbey rue (9x8cm-4x3in) daguerreotype. 18-May-4 Christie's, London #83/R est:2500-3500
£9000 $15840 €13140 Edfou, Temple chapiteau (8x9cm-3x4in) daguerreotype. 18-May-4 Christie's, London #46/R est:3000-5000
£10000 $17600 €14600 Phile Temple decouvert et Palmiers datiers (8x9cm-3x4in) daguerreotype. 18-May-4 Christie's, London #11/R est:3000-5000
£11000 $19360 €16060 Kaire, Gama Amr, minaret publie (16x9cm-6x4in) daguerreotype. 18-May-4 Christie's, London #75/R est:12000-18000
£11000 $19360 €16060 Jerusalem, El aksa (9x8cm-4x3in) daguerreotype. 18-May-4 Christie's, London #81/R est:3000-5000
£13000 $22880 €18980 Kaire, Mouristan, detail (19x12cm-7x5in) daguerreotype. 18-May-4 Christie's, London #54/R est:15000-20000
£14000 $24640 €20440 Buyukdere, Platanes de Godefroid de Bouillon (8x9cm-3x4in) daguerreotype. 18-May-4 Christie's, London #6/R est:3000-5000
£15000 $26400 €21900 Untitled, Fontaine des Quatre Fleuves, Square Louvois Paris (12x9cm-5x4in) daguerreotype exec.c.1841. 18-May-4 Christie's, London #65/R est:8000-10000
£15000 $26400 €21900 Kaire, pres S Kerabat (19x12cm-7x5in) daguerreotype. 18-May-4 Christie's, London #85/R est:15000-20000
£15000 $26400 €21900 Kaire, Bedouine de Ghiseh (12x9cm-5x4in) daguerreotype. 18-May-4 Christie's, London #89/R est:9000-12000
£16000 $28160 €23360 Damas, Grande Mosquee prise du Khan d'effad Pacha (9x24cm-4x9in) panoramic daguerreotype. 18-May-4 Christie's, London #14/R est:20000-30000
£16000 $28160 €23360 Athenes Tour des Vents (12x19cm-5x7in) daguerreotype. 18-May-4 Christie's, London #18/R est:20000-25000
£16000 $28160 €23360 Kaire, Gama Emir Yakhour, minaret (24x9cm-9x4in) panoramic daguerreotype. 18-May-4 Christie's, London #77/R est:20000-30000
£16000 $28160 €23360 Untitled, Damascus Gate, Jerusalem, detail (24x9cm-9x4in) panoramic daguerreotype. 18-May-4 Christie's, London #79/R est:20000-30000
£16000 $28160 €23360 Kaire, Ayoucha, figure entiere (12x9cm-5x4in) daguerreotype. 18-May-4 Christie's, London #87/R est:10000-15000
£17000 $29920 €24820 Untitled, the Nile and temples, Philae (12x19cm-5x7in) daguerreotype. 18-May-4 Christie's, London #12/R est:18000-22000
£19000 $33440 €27740 Kaire, Mouristan (24x9cm-9x4in) daguerreotype lit. 18-May-4 Christie's, London #76/R est:20000-30000
£24000 $42240 €35040 Rome, Graecostator et col de (9x24cm-4x9in) daguerreotype lit. 18-May-4 Christie's, London #34/R est:30000-50000
£24000 $42240 €35040 Jeronda, temple - colonnes (19x12cm-7x5in) daguerreotype. 18-May-4 Christie's, London #70/R est:30000-40000
£25000 $44000 €36500 Athenes, Tour des Vents (12x19cm-5x7in) daguerreotype lit. 18-May-4 Christie's, London #19/R est:30000-50000
£32000 $56320 €46720 Tivoli, Villa Adriana (9x24cm-4x9in) panoramic daguerreotype. 18-May-4 Christie's, London #8/R est:30000-50000
£40000 $70400 €58400 Villa (24x19cm-9x7in) init.i. daguerreotype. 18-May-4 Christie's, London #10/R est:50000-70000
£42000 $73920 €61320 Jerusalem, piscine probatique (19x12cm-7x5in) daguerreotype. 18-May-4 Christie's, London #28/R est:15000-20000
£42000 $73920 €61320 Genes, Cathedrale, detail du portail (24x9cm-9x4in) panoramic daguerreotype lit. 18-May-4 Christie's, London #66/R est:30000-50000
£75000 $132000 €109500 Athenes, Propylees, pris de l'interieur (19x24cm-7x9in) daguerreotype lit. 18-May-4 Christie's, London #35/R est:90000-120000

GIRDLESTONE, Lucy (19/20th C) British
£450 $792 €657 Potting plants (51x76cm-20x30in) s. 19-May-4 Dreweatt Neate, Newbury #77/R

GIRIEUD, Pierre (1876-1940) French
£1007 $1873 €1500 Paysage de Sainte Maxime (80x65cm-31x26in) s.d.1920 oil paper on canvas. 2-Mar-4 Artcurial Briest, Paris #141 est:2000-3000
£3681 $6147 €5300 Noli me Tangere (65x81cm-26x32in) s.d.1914 i.verso exhib. 21-Oct-3 Artcurial Briest, Paris #189/R est:5000-6000
£8389 $15017 €12500 Nu debout de dos, sur fond rouge (104x74cm-41x29in) s.d.1911 board. 25-May-4 Karl & Faber, Munich #290/R est:8000
£11074 $19822 €16500 Nu debout de dos, sur fond jaune (105x75cm-41x30in) s.d.1909 board. 25-May-4 Karl & Faber, Munich #289/R est:12000-14000

GIRIN, David Eugène (1848-1917) French
£268 $475 €400 Fillette (35x28cm-14x11in) s. 30-Apr-4 Tajan, Paris #184
£650 $1190 €949 Cello player (41x32cm-16x13in) s. 8-Apr-4 Christie's, Kensington #68/R
£933 $1680 €1400 Paysage de la Dombes avec bergere et troupeau (40x33cm-16x13in) s. cardboard. 20-Apr-4 Chenu & Scrive, Lyon #90/R
£952 $1733 €1400 Berger et ses moutons (56x47cm-22x19in) s. 8-Feb-4 Anaf, Lyon #191/R
£1200 $2208 €1800 A la fontaine (31x54cm-12x21in) s. panel. 9-Jun-4 Beaussant & Lefèvre, Paris #160/R est:600-800
£4615 $7846 €6600 Barques de peche au mouillage dans le Golfe de Saint Tropez (87x114cm-34x45in) s. 30-Nov-3 Anaf, Lyon #37/R est:6000-7000

GIRKE, Raimund (1930-) German
£1000 $1790 €1500 Untitled (30x40cm-12x16in) 15-May-4 Van Ham, Cologne #617/R est:1700
£1267 $2318 €1900 Untitled (50x40cm-20x16in) s.i.d.Marz 81 verso. 4-Jun-4 Lempertz, Koln #156/R est:2500
£1538 $2615 €2200 Untitled - structural picture (26x33cm-10x13in) s.d.62 verso varnish tempera board. 27-Nov-3 Lempertz, Koln #146/R est:2000
£2000 $3680 €3000 Untitled (100x70cm-39x28in) s.i.d.84 board. 12-Jun-4 Villa Grisebach, Berlin #720/R est:2000-2500
£4930 $8183 €7000 Staccato - rot (120x100cm-47x39in) s.i.d.1993 verso. 13-Jun-3 Hauswedell & Nolte, Hamburg #642/R est:4500
£6000 $10980 €9000 Untitled (100x120cm-39x47in) s.i.d.88 verso. 4-Jun-4 Lempertz, Koln #157/R est:8000-9000
£8667 $15947 €13000 Rhythm (100x125cm-39x49in) s. stretcher resin. 11-Jun-4 Hauswedell & Nolte, Hamburg #1276/R est:10000
Works on paper
£433 $776 €650 Untitled (24x30cm-9x12in) pencil. 15-May-4 Van Ham, Cologne #618/R
£452 $756 €660 Untitled (30x25cm-12x10in) s.i.d.1972 verso pencil tempera. 24-Jun-3 Germann, Zurich #5/R (S.FR 1000)
£1667 $3067 €2500 Untitled (62x88cm-24x35in) s.d.72 gouache over pencil. 12-Jun-4 Villa Grisebach, Berlin #719/R est:2500-3000
£4667 $8587 €7000 Untitled (27x67cm-11x26in) s.d. verso mixed media. 11-Jun-4 Hauswedell & Nolte, Hamburg #1277/R est:3000

GIROD-LAMBERT, Claude François (fl.1771-1815) French
Works on paper
£993 $1658 €1400 Enlevement des Sabines. pierre noire pen ink Chinese ink wash htd white after Poussin. 15-Oct-3 Sotheby's, Paris #132/R

GIRODET DE ROUCY TRIOSON, Anne Louis (1767-1824) French
Works on paper
£288 $460 €400 Young female nude in a rocking chair (25x19cm-10x7in) blk crayon. 16-May-3 Tajan, Paris #53
£13000 $23790 €18980 Death of Hannibal (22x29cm-9x11in) i. black chk wash htd white prov.lit. 6-Jul-4 Christie's, London #196/R est:5000-7000

GIRODET DE ROUCY TRIOSON, Anne Louis (attrib) (1767-1824) French
£1751 $2977 €2556 Portrait of woman (75x60cm-30x24in) oval. 10-Nov-3 Rasmussen, Vejle #369/R est:10000 (D.KR 19000)
Works on paper
£1773 $2872 €2500 Autoportrait presume (14x13cm-6x5in) black crayon estompe. 21-May-3 Daguerre, Paris #94/R est:2500
£28571 $51143 €42000 Belisaire. Oedipe conduit par sa fille (26cm-10in circular) mono.d.1814 black crayon htd gouache pair. 22-Mar-4 Digard, Paris #57/R est:15000-20000

GIRON, Charles (1850-1914) Swiss
£495 $852 €723 Narcisse (61x50cm-24x20in) i.verso painted 1912. 8-Dec-3 Philippe Schuler, Zurich #5921 (S.FR 1100)
£3500 $6440 €5110 Debonair swordsman (176x90cm-69x35in) s.i.d.1878. 25-Mar-4 Christie's, Kensington #190/R est:3500-4500

GIRON, Robert (20th C) Belgian
£1958 $3368 €2800 La conversation (68x78cm-27x31in) s.d.1925 canvas on panel. 8-Dec-3 Horta, Bruxelles #460 est:700-900

GIRONA, Julio (1914-) Cuban
£800 $1432 €1200 White forms (128x125cm-50x49in) s. prov. 15-May-4 Van Ham, Cologne #619/R

GIRONCOLI, Bruno (1936-) Austrian
Works on paper
£3472 $5903 €5000 Two heads (47x67cm-19x26in) s.i. mixed media. 28-Oct-3 Wiener Kunst Auktionen, Vienna #260/R est:5000-7000
£4545 $7727 €6500 Shoulder kiss, shoulder bite (90x62cm-35x24in) i. one graphite one mixed media pair. 28-Nov-3 Wiener Kunst Auktionen, Vienna #652/R est:8000-10000
£4698 $8409 €7000 Design Nr 13 (88x62cm-35x24in) gouache pen Indian ink metal. 25-May-4 Dorotheum, Vienna #65/R est:7000-9000
£5944 $10105 €8500 Decreptitude (62x90cm-24x35in) pen Indian ink goauche metal board. 26-Nov-3 Dorotheum, Vienna #219/R est:9000-11000
£13423 $23758 €20000 Untitled (200x152cm-79x60in) s. mixed media. 28-Apr-4 Wiener Kunst Auktionen, Vienna #266/R est:14000-23000

GIRONELLA, Alberto (1929-1999) Mexican
Works on paper
£527 $896 €769 Rubens (25x33cm-10x13in) s.d.1971 pastel. 30-Oct-3 Louis Morton, Mexico #138/R (M.P 10000)

GIROTTO, Napoleon (19/20th C) Italian
Works on paper
£233 $400 €340 Fish seller (33x23cm-13x9in) s.d.1900 W/C. 7-Dec-3 Grogan, Boston #16/R

GIROUD, Paul (?) French
£1304 $2387 €1904 La promenade (50x70cm-20x28in) s.i. 4-Jun-4 Zofingen, Switzerland #2463/R est:1500 (S.FR 3000)

GIROUX, Alfred (?) Belgian?
£276 $510 €400 Paysage du midi ensoleille (60x8cm-24x3in) mono. 16-Feb-4 Horta, Bruxelles #277

GIROUX, Andre (1801-1879) French
£692 $1191 €1010 Les braconniers (64x52cm-25x20in) i.d.1837 verso. 3-Dec-3 AB Stockholms Auktionsverk #2623/R (S.KR 9000)
£1800 $3258 €2700 Chataignier foudroye (46x37cm-18x15in) exhib.lit. 30-Mar-4 Rossini, Paris #111/R est:600-1000
£2533 $4636 €3800 Nid de l'aigle a Fontainebleau (37x46cm-15x18in) 6-Jun-4 Osenat, Fontainebleau #30/R est:3000-3500

GIROUX, Andre (attrib) (1801-1879) French
£6000 $10860 €9000 Monastere de Grotta-Ferrata, au sud de Rome (24x44cm-9x17in) 30-Mar-4 Rossini, Paris #110/R est:1200-1800

GIROUX, Ernest (1851-?) Italian/French
£778 $1323 €1136 Portrait d'une dame en robe blanche (80x52cm-31x20in) s. 28-Nov-3 Zofingen, Switzerland #2464/R est:3000 (S.FR 1720)

GIROUX, Henri (1951-) Canadian
£339 $567 €495 After school (40x50cm-16x20in) s.i. 17-Nov-3 Hodgins, Calgary #266/R (C.D 750)

GIRSCHER, Bernhard Moritz (1822-1870) German
£1259 $2140 €1800 Little castle by lake (53x72cm-21x28in) s.d.1866. 20-Nov-3 Van Ham, Cologne #1596/R est:2000

GIRTIN, Thomas (1775-1802) British
Works on paper
£400 $688 €584 River scene (8x18cm-3x7in) W/C prov. 5-Dec-3 Keys, Aylsham #418/R
£1200 $2148 €1752 View in Northumberland (7x11cm-3x4in) W/C over pencil prov. 26-May-4 Sotheby's, Olympia #41/R est:1200-1800
£2000 $3400 €2920 Figures on a street in Dover (25x41cm-10x16in) pencil. 27-Nov-3 Sotheby's, London #240/R est:2500-3500
£4000 $6800 €5840 Southampton (13x18cm-5x7in) pencil W/C prov. 20-Nov-3 Christie's, London #83/R est:3000-5000
£5200 $9464 €7592 Trees on a riverbank (9x15cm-4x6in) W/C over pencil prov. 1-Jul-4 Sotheby's, London #177/R est:3000-4000
£10000 $18400 €14600 Pegwell Bay near Ramsgate (10x16cm-4x6in) s.i.verso W/C over pencil. 26-Mar-4 Sotheby's, London #105/R est:8000-12000

GIRTIN, Thomas (attrib) (1775-1802) British
Works on paper
£1533 $2775 €2300 Vue 'dune cathedrale (24x30cm-9x12in) W/C pen brown ink exhib. 30-Mar-4 Rossini, Paris #19/R est:2000-2500

GISBERT, Antonio (1835-1901) Spanish
£5319 $8883 €7500 Carlo V in Yuste Monastery (83x65cm-33x26in) s. 20-Oct-3 Durán, Madrid #112/R

GISCHIA, Léon (1903-1991) French
£851 $1421 €1200 Nature morte au bouquet de fleurs (32x18cm-13x7in) s.d.42 cardboard. 15-Oct-3 Claude Aguttes, Neuilly #4
£1007 $1862 €1500 Black shawl (55x38cm-22x15in) s. s.i.d.1971 verso. 13-Mar-4 Meeting Art, Vercelli #108 est:1500
£1007 $1802 €1500 Shapes (50x73cm-20x29in) s.d.73 i.d.verso prov. 25-May-4 Sotheby's, Milan #93/R est:2000
£1206 $2013 €1700 Nature morte au pot de gres (38x55cm-15x22in) s.d.38. 15-Oct-3 Claude Aguttes, Neuilly #6 est:1200-1800
£1631 $2724 €2300 Nature morte a la cafetiere rouge (46x38cm-18x15in) s.d.38. 15-Oct-3 Claude Aguttes, Neuilly #5 est:1200-1800
£2098 $3503 €3000 Composition (81x60cm-32x24in) s. 29-Jun-3 Versailles Encheres #26/R
£2517 $4280 €3600 Mingled trees (99x73cm-39x29in) s. painted 1967 exhib.lit. 28-Nov-3 Farsetti, Prato #214/R est:3600-4200
Works on paper
£503 $941 €750 Composition (63x47cm-25x19in) s.d.1953 gouache. 29-Feb-4 Versailles Encheres #144/R

GISCLARD, Stephane (20th C) French
£1972 $3411 €2800 Escale II (114x146cm-45x57in) s. 9-Dec-3 Chambelland & Giafferi, Paris #59 est:3000-3500

GISEL, A (19th C) ?
£1224 $1947 €1800 Gros horloge a Rouen (116x89cm-46x35in) s. 23-Mar-3 Salle des ventes Pillet, Lyon la Foret #7 est:800-1000

GISELA, Josef (1851-1899) Austrian
£2155 $3858 €3146 Love letter (32x24cm-13x9in) s. panel. 12-May-4 Dobiaschofsky, Bern #560/R est:7500 (S.FR 5000)
£16783 $28531 €24000 Needlework (37x30cm-15x12in) s. panel. 24-Nov-3 Dorotheum, Vienna #126/R est:11000-15000

GISIKO-SPARCK, Ida (1859-1940) Swedish
£786 $1359 €1148 Morning glow on the jetty (42x64cm-17x25in) s. panel. 15-Dec-3 Lilla Bukowskis, Stockholm #477 (S.KR 10000)
£2143 $3837 €3129 Harbour view with Stockholm's Palace in background (21x35cm-8x14in) s.d.91. 26-May-4 AB Stockholms Auktionsverk #2151/R est:8000-10000 (S.KR 29000)

GISLANDER, William (1890-1937) Swedish
£467 $738 €677 Swans off the coast in snowy weather, Faroe Islands (105x130cm-41x51in) s. 2-Sep-3 Rasmussen, Copenhagen #1635/R (D.KR 5000)

GISMONDI, Lia (20th C) Argentinian
£495 $900 €723 Hill top (32x45cm-13x18in) s. board. 5-Jul-4 Arroyo, Buenos Aires #36/R

GISSING, Roland (1895-1967) Canadian
£201 $373 €293 Ghost river valley. s. 2-Mar-4 Ritchie, Toronto #115a (C.D 500)
£331 $598 €483 Grey day in the mountains (30x38cm-12x15in) s. oil paper board prov. 18-Apr-4 Levis, Calgary #35/R (C.D 800)
£409 $667 €597 Cloud shadows (35x46cm-14x18in) s. s.i.d.1962 verso board prov. 23-Sep-3 Ritchie, Toronto #122/R est:1000-1500 (C.D 900)
£413 $748 €603 Sunset - Kootenay River (30x41cm-12x16in) s. oil paper board prov. 18-Apr-4 Levis, Calgary #34/R est:1000-12000 (C.D 1000)
£446 $759 €651 Kootenay Lake near Proctor BC (30x41cm-12x16in) s. s.i.d.1955 verso board prov. 6-Nov-3 Heffel, Vancouver #55/R (C.D 1000)
£446 $759 €651 River bank (30x41cm-12x16in) s. s.i. verso board prov. 6-Nov-3 Heffel, Vancouver #56/R (C.D 1000)
£479 $767 €699 Golden September (56x76cm-22x30in) s. 16-Sep-3 Maynards, Vancouver #393 est:1500-2000 (C.D 1050)
£536 $911 €783 Hill near De Winton, Alberta (41x51cm-16x20in) s. i.verso board prov. 6-Nov-3 Heffel, Vancouver #54/R (C.D 1200)
£578 $959 €844 St Mary's lake (26x34cm-10x13in) s. oil paperboard. 5-Oct-3 Levis, Calgary #33/R (C.D 1300)
£579 $1047 €845 Untitled - fall colours, Kananskis (36x50cm-14x20in) s. oil paper board prov. 18-Apr-4 Levis, Calgary #33/R est:1400-1800 (C.D 1400)
£600 $1098 €876 Ghost Lake (30x50cm-12x20in) s. board. 1-Jun-4 Hodgins, Calgary #335/R (C.D 1500)
£640 $1171 €934 Autumn sunset (40x50cm-16x20in) s.i. prov. 1-Jun-4 Hodgins, Calgary #23/R (C.D 1600)
£840 $1537 €1226 Cloud shadows (35x45cm-14x18in) s.i.d.1962 board. 1-Jun-4 Hodgins, Calgary #88/R est:1750-2250 (C.D 2100)
£915 $1665 €1336 Mount Eisenhower, Alberta (41x51cm-16x20in) s. prov. 1-Jul-4 Heffel, Vancouver #15/R est:1500-2000 (C.D 2250)
£995 $1662 €1453 Lake Minnewanka (38x51cm-15x20in) s.i. panel. 17-Nov-3 Hodgins, Calgary #343/R est:1800-2400 (C.D 2200)
£1176 $1965 €1717 Winter Ghost River (45x60cm-18x24in) s.i. prov. 17-Nov-3 Hodgins, Calgary #135/R est:3000-3500 (C.D 2600)
£1176 $1965 €1717 Autumn Ghost River (60x75cm-24x30in) s.i. 17-Nov-3 Hodgins, Calgary #375/R est:2750-3250 (C.D 2600)
£1222 $2004 €1784 Early spring (56x76cm-22x30in) s. 28-May-3 Maynards, Vancouver #18/R est:2000-3000 (C.D 2750)
£1448 $2418 €2114 Harvest in the foothills (60x75cm-24x30in) s.i. 17-Nov-3 Hodgins, Calgary #280/R est:3000-3500 (C.D 3200)
£1471 $2456 €2148 Bow River near Banff (60x75cm-24x30in) s.i. 17-Nov-3 Hodgins, Calgary #55/R est:3000-3500 (C.D 3250)
£1500 $2745 €2190 Harvest in Bow Valley (55x75cm-22x30in) s.i.d.1953. 1-Jun-4 Hodgins, Calgary #148/R est:3000-3500 (C.D 3750)
£1524 $2774 €2225 Sunset at Sawback Range (51x61cm-20x24in) s. prov. 1-Jul-4 Heffel, Vancouver #16/R est:2500-3500 (C.D 3750)
£1532 $2604 €2237 Mount Selkirk and Vermillion River (56x76cm-22x30in) s. s.i.verso prov. 23-Nov-3 Levis, Calgary #43/R est:2500-3500 (C.D 3400)
£1577 $2680 €2302 Ghost river (69x89cm-27x35in) s. prov. 23-Nov-3 Levis, Calgary #42a/R est:3500-4500 (C.D 3500)
£1577 $2680 €2302 Ghost River (69x89cm-27x35in) s. prov. 23-Nov-3 Levis, Calgary #42a/R est:3500-4500 (C.D 3500)
£1600 $2928 €2336 Kananaskis River (50x60cm-20x24in) s.i. 1-Jun-4 Hodgins, Calgary #398/R est:2250-2750 (C.D 4000)
£1810 $3023 €2643 Evening drilling, Leduc, Alberta (70x100cm-28x39in) s. 17-Nov-3 Hodgins, Calgary #403/R est:3000-3500 (C.D 4000)
Works on paper
£289 $524 €422 Untitled - Ghost lake (22x29cm-9x11in) s. pastel prov. 18-Apr-4 Levis, Calgary #36/R (C.D 700)
£1267 $2116 €1850 Untitled - Indian mother on horseback (26x31cm-10x12in) s.d.1926 W/C. 17-Nov-3 Hodgins, Calgary #75/R est:2000-2500 (C.D 2800)

GISSON, Andre (1928-2003) American
£373 $600 €541 Girl in a museum (23x30cm-9x12in) s. 24-Aug-3 Bonhams & Butterfields, Los Angeles #7030
£404 $650 €586 Lisa (30x41cm-12x16in) s. 24-Aug-3 Bonhams & Butterfields, Los Angeles #7031
£491 $850 €717 Woman in a red hat in a garden (61x30cm-24x12in) s. 13-Dec-3 Sloans & Kenyon, Bethesda #781/R
£520 $900 €759 Mother and child in a garden (61x30cm-24x12in) s. 13-Dec-3 Sloans & Kenyon, Bethesda #782/R
£543 $1000 €793 Seaside bathers (18x23cm-7x9in) s. 26-Jun-4 Susanin's, Chicago #6110/R est:800-1200
£588 $982 €858 Busy street scene (61x30cm-24x12in) s. 17-Nov-3 Waddingtons, Toronto #7/R (C.D 1300)
£598 $1100 €873 Woman seated in garden (18x23cm-7x9in) s. 26-Jun-4 Susanin's, Chicago #6109/R est:800-1200
£629 $1000 €918 Lily pond (23x30cm-9x12in) s. 10-Sep-3 Sotheby's, New York #170/R
£633 $1058 €924 Children by a lake (61x30cm-24x12in) s. 17-Nov-3 Waddingtons, Toronto #6/R (C.D 1400)
£652 $1200 €952 Woman seated on grass by a wall (18x23cm-7x9in) s. 26-Jun-4 Susanin's, Chicago #6108/R est:800-1200
£750 $1343 €1095 Vase of flowers (30x23cm-12x9in) s. prov. 26-May-4 Sotheby's, Olympia #311/R
£853 $1500 €1245 Paris street scene with Notre Dame (30x61cm-12x24in) s. 23-May-4 Hindman, Chicago #67/R est:1500-2500
£860 $1600 €1256 Floral still life (51x40cm-20x16in) s. 5-Mar-4 Skinner, Boston #393/R est:1000-1500
£898 $1500 €1311 Still life with flowers (41x30cm-16x12in) s. sold with another by same hand. 16-Nov-3 Bonhams & Butterfields, Los Angeles #7034/R est:3000-5000
£1051 $1650 €1534 Paris street scene (41x51cm-16x20in) 1-Sep-3 William A Smith, Plainfield #2/R
£1136 $2000 €1659 Arc de Triomphe, Paris (30x61cm-12x24in) s. 23-May-4 Hindman, Chicago #66/R est:1500-2500
£1136 $2000 €1659 Park landscape (51x41cm-20x16in) s. 23-May-4 Hindman, Chicago #69/R est:2000-4000
£1163 $2000 €1698 Figures in dappled sunlight (61x91cm-24x36in) s. 7-Dec-3 Freeman, Philadelphia #139 est:2000-3000
£1250 $2200 €1825 Floral still life (61x51cm-24x20in) s. 23-May-4 Hindman, Chicago #68/R est:2000-4000
£1301 $2250 €1899 Girl and statue in courtyard setting (61x91cm-24x36in) s. 10-Dec-3 Alderfer's, Hatfield #304 est:2000-3000
£1351 $2500 €1972 Carousel (64x92cm-25x36in) s. 12-Feb-4 Sotheby's, New York #56/R est:4000-6000
£1366 $2500 €2049 Landscapes (23x30cm-9x12in) pair. 9-Jul-4 Du Mouchelle, Detroit #1017/R est:1500-2500
£1478 $2750 €2158 Impressionist urban landscape with many figures (41x51cm-16x20in) s. 3-Mar-4 Alderfer's, Hatfield #333/R est:1200-1800
£1478 $2750 €2158 Impressionist urban landscape with monument in background (41x51cm-16x20in) s. i.verso. 3-Mar-4 Alderfer's, Hatfield #334/R est:1200-1800
£1505 $2650 €2197 Urban landscape (61x76cm-24x30in) s. 28-May-4 Aspire, Cleveland #39/R est:2000-3000
£1553 $2500 €2252 Cloudy beach (61x91cm-24x36in) s. 24-Aug-3 Bonhams & Butterfields, Los Angeles #7032 est:2000-4000
£1595 $2600 €2329 Paris street scene (61x30cm-24x12in) s. pair. 24-Sep-3 Doyle, New York #37 est:2000-3000

£1635	$2600	€2387	Landscape with figures (41x51cm-16x20in) s. 9-Sep-3 Arthur James, Florida #101
£1676	$3000	€2447	Parisian street scene (33x89cm-13x35in) s. 8-May-4 Susanin's, Chicago #6139/R est:1500-2000
£1750	$2800	€2555	At the fountain (102x76cm-40x30in) s. 19-Sep-3 Freeman, Philadelphia #203/R est:2000-3000
£1766	$3250	€2578	Spring landscape with dominant central trees in riverside field (41x51cm-16x20in) s. 9-Jun-4 Alderfer's, Hatfield #404/R est:2500-3000
£1766	$3250	€2578	Flower market, Notre-Dame (51x61cm-20x24in) s. 25-Jun-4 Freeman, Philadelphia #167/R est:1500-2500
£1875	$3000	€2738	Ocean beach scene (61x91cm-24x36in) 19-Sep-3 Du Mouchelle, Detroit #2002/R est:4000-6000
£2335	$4250	€3409	Children on the river bank (62x91cm-24x36in) s. 29-Jun-4 Sotheby's, New York #375/R est:4000-6000
£2454	$4000	€3583	Nude (41x51cm-16x20in) s. 28-Sep-3 Simpson's, Houston #330/R
£3593	$6000	€5246	At the beach (23x30cm-9x12in) s. 16-Nov-3 Simpson's, Houston #257/R
£3988	$6500	€5822	Walking in a field (61x91cm-24x36in) s. 28-Sep-3 Simpson's, Houston #340/R
£4545	$8500	€6636	Champs-Elysees (61x91cm-24x36in) s. 25-Feb-4 Christie's, Rockefeller NY #33/R est:4000-6000

GITTLESON, Albert Abram (fl.1911-1940) British

£340	$551	€493	Still life of French roses in a vase (61x51cm-24x20in) s.d.1929. 26-Jan-3 Desmond Judd, Cranbrook #826

GITZ-JOHANSEN, Aage (1897-1977) Danish

£709	$1269	€1035	Small flock of looms on iceberg, Greenland (91x136cm-36x54in) init. 12-Jan-4 Rasmussen, Vejle #560/R (D.KR 7500)

GIUDICE, Marcello lo (1955-) Italian

£1622	$2854	€2400	Paradise in red (51x40cm-20x16in) s.i.d.98 verso oil pigment prov. 24-May-4 Christie's, Milan #106/R est:1500-2000

GIUDICI, Reinaldo (1853-1921) Argentinian

£2186	$4000	€3192	Dusk on the lake (27x62cm-11x24in) 1-Jun-4 Arroyo, Buenos Aires #41
£3631	$6500	€5301	On the mountains (67x41cm-26x16in) s.d.1903. 4-May-4 Arroyo, Buenos Aires #24/R est:4800

GIUFFRIDA, Nino (1924-) Italian

£267	$477	€400	Animation sur la plage de Deauville (33x41cm-13x16in) s.i.d.1980 verso. 16-May-4 Thierry & Lannon, Brest #322

GIULI, Franco (1934-) Italian

£867	$1560	€1300	Untitled (50x50cm-20x20in) s. s.verso acrylic painted 1972 exhib. 22-Apr-4 Finarte Semenzato, Rome #314/R est:1200-1400

GIULIANI, Giovanni (1893-1965) Italian

£423	$701	€600	Raining on the vegetable garden (70x50cm-28x20in) s.d.1968 verso prov. 11-Jun-3 Finarte Semenzato, Milan #560/R

GIULIANI, Giulio (?) Italian

Works on paper

£493	$853	€700	Interior of the Bargello (45x70cm-18x28in) s. W/C. 9-Dec-3 Pandolfini, Florence #41/R

GIULIANI, Maria Letizia (1908-1985) Italian

Works on paper

£1135	$1838	€1600	Male nude on pedestal. Man bust (73x50cm-29x20in) graphite pastel two. 22-May-3 Finarte Semenzato, Rome #105

GIULIANO, Bartolomeo (1829-1909) Italian

£4203	$6893	€5800	Back from the wood (41x29cm-16x11in) s.d.1882. 27-May-3 Il Ponte, Milan #936/R
£4965	$8291	€7000	Venetian impression (45x55cm-18x22in) s. 20-Oct-3 Sant Agostino, Torino #303/R est:9000
£36667	$67467	€55000	Post Prandium (113x166cm-44x65in) s.d.1898 exhib.lit. 10-Jun-4 Christie's, Rome #202/R est:60000-70000

GIULIO DA MILANO (20th C) Italian

£382	$603	€550	Odalisk (20x17cm-8x7in) board. 6-Sep-3 Meeting Art, Vercelli #643
£667	$1227	€1000	Pink vase with lemons (34x56cm-13x22in) s d.1970 verso tempera paper on canvas. 12-Jun-4 Meeting Art, Vercelli #983/R
£1133	$2085	€1700	Before San Rocco (34x42cm-13x17in) s. s.i.verso. 14-Jun-4 Sant Agostino, Torino #340/R est:1600-2000
£1200	$2208	€1800	Undergrowth (50x40cm-20x16in) s. s.on stretcher. 14-Jun-4 Sant Agostino, Torino #337/R est:2500-3000
£1538	$2569	€2200	Odalisk (60x100cm-24x39in) s. tempera paper on canvas. 26-Jun-3 Sant Agostino, Torino #157/R est:2500-3000
£1667	$3067	€2500	After the bath (60x30cm-24x12in) painted c.1930. 14-Jun-4 Sant Agostino, Torino #351/R est:2500-3000
£3401	$6088	€5000	Odalisk (34x42cm-13x17in) s.d.1945. 22-Mar-4 Sant Agostino, Torino #462/R est:3500-4500
£7143	$12786	€10500	Portrait of Tamiri at the bar (80x50cm-31x20in) s.d.1935. 22-Mar-4 Sant Agostino, Torino #527/R est:7000-9000

Works on paper

£359	$599	€520	Seated model (28x16cm-11x6in) s. W/C exec.1940. 17-Nov-3 Sant Agostino, Torino #84/R

GIUNNI, Piero (1912-2001) Italian

£302	$559	€450	Autumn (25x40cm-10x16in) s.d.1982. 13-Mar-4 Meeting Art, Vercelli #198
£309	$571	€460	Clean winter colour (25x40cm-10x16in) s.d.1981. 13-Mar-4 Meeting Art, Vercelli #429
£775	$1286	€1100	Still life with soup bowl and vase of flowers (50x50cm-20x20in) s.d.48 s.verso. 11-Jun-3 Finarte Semenzato, Milan #510
£1007	$1862	€1500	Dove (70x100cm-28x39in) s.d.1964. 13-Mar-4 Meeting Art, Vercelli #103 est:1500

GIUNTI, Umberto (attrib) (?) Italian?

£719	$1200	€1050	Portrait of a gentleman in a red hat (58x43cm-23x17in) panel. 7-Oct-3 Sotheby's, New York #49/R

GIUNTOTARDI, Philippe (1768-1831) Italian

Works on paper

£800	$1384	€1168	Pastoral river landscape (16x23cm-6x9in) gouache sold with a companion. 9-Dec-3 Bonhams, Knightsbridge #6/R
£6145	$11000	€8972	View of Tivoli waterfalls (63x86cm-25x34in) W/C paper on board. 27-May-4 Sotheby's, New York #97/R est:10000-15000

GIUSTI, Guglielmo (1824-1916) Italian

Works on paper

£3100	$5270	€4526	View of Naples with figures in foreground (27x40cm-11x16in) s. gouache pair. 27-Nov-3 Clevedon Sale Rooms #136/R est:600-900

GIUSTO, Faust (1867-1941) Italian

£1956	$3500	€2856	Bay of Biscaya, Naples (41x58cm-16x23in) s. prov. 14-May-4 Skinner, Boston #138/R est:1800-2200

GJEDSTED, Rolf (1947-) Danish

£300	$502	€438	Anima - thoughts at night (80x100cm-31x39in) s. i.d.2000 verso. 7-Oct-3 Rasmussen, Copenhagen #209 (D.KR 3200)
£376	$627	€549	Solei ivre (120x100cm-47x39in) s. s.d.97 verso. 7-Oct-3 Rasmussen, Copenhagen #159 (D.KR 4000)
£542	$996	€791	Future love (100x140cm-39x55in) s. d.1999 verso cardboard on canvas. 29-Mar-4 Rasmussen, Copenhagen #402/R (D.KR 6000)

GJEMRE, Per (1864-1928) Norwegian

£365	$671	€533	Outhouse at Jaeren (31x43cm-12x17in) s. panel. 29-Mar-4 Blomqvist, Lysaker #1082/R (N.KR 4600)

GJERDEVIK, Niels Erik (1962-) Norwegian

£380	$680	€555	Composition with speedboat and palms (80x100cm-31x39in) s.i.d.93. 10-May-4 Rasmussen, Vejle #773/R (D.KR 4200)

Works on paper

£394	$659	€575	Composition with house and cranium (75x64cm-30x25in) s.d.82-85/86 W/C gouache plastic masonite paper. 7-Oct-3 Rasmussen, Copenhagen #290 (D.KR 4200)

GJOSTOL, Anne Lise (20th C) Norwegian

£259	$430	€376	Oscarshall (30x40cm-12x16in) s. 16-Jun-3 Blomqvist, Lysaker #1055 (N.KR 3000)

GLAAB, Karl Heinz (1896-?) German

£317	$507	€450	Portrait of Angela with teddy bear (107x88cm-42x35in) s.d.1928. 18-Sep-3 Rieber, Stuttgart #918

GLACKENS, William (1870-1938) American

£3293	$5500	€4808	Banana and nuts (20x28cm-8x11in) prov. 9-Oct-3 Christie's, Rockefeller NY #60/R est:7000-9000
£6587	$11000	€9617	Nymph series (30x41cm-12x16in) canvasboard prov. 9-Oct-3 Christie's, Rockefeller NY #62/R est:10000-15000
£10811	$20000	€15784	Tree trunk (30x41cm-12x16in) canvasboard prov. 11-Mar-4 Christie's, Rockefeller NY #50/R est:20000-30000
£13174	$22000	€19234	Window at 110, rue de Bac (41x33cm-16x13in) canvasboard prov. 9-Oct-3 Christie's, Rockefeller NY #58/R est:25000-35000
£15625	$27500	€22813	Still life with apples (25x30cm-10x12in) board prov. 19-May-4 Sotheby's, New York #119/R est:20000-30000
£16216	$30000	€23675	The tent, Conway (30x41cm-12x16in) canvas on board prov. 11-Mar-4 Christie's, Rockefeller NY #49/R est:30000-50000
£22093	$38000	€32256	Black and white cow (51x61cm-20x24in) painted c.1920 prov. 4-Dec-3 Christie's, Rockefeller NY #82/R est:40000-60000
£25150	$42000	€36719	Still life with vase of flowers (42x29cm-17x11in) init. canvas on board prov. 9-Oct-3 Christie's, Rockefeller NY #66/R est:30000-50000
£34884	$60000	€50931	Nude sitting on bed (46x39cm-18x15in) prov.exhib. 4-Dec-3 Christie's, Rockefeller NY #89/R est:25000-35000
£49419	$85000	€72152	Jonquils, tulips and roses (61x46cm-24x18in) s. s.i.on stretcher painted 1930 prov. 3-Dec-3 Sotheby's, New York #45/R est:30000-50000
£72626	$130000	€106034	Boats and car track (46x61cm-18x24in) painted c.1915 prov. 26-May-4 Doyle, New York #91/R est:80000-120000
£110465	$190000	€161279	East Point, Gloucester (51x65cm-20x26in) painted 1919 prov. 3-Dec-3 Sotheby's, New York #46/R est:125000-175000
£181818	$320000	€265454	Swing (66x81cm-26x32in) painted 1913 prov.exhib.lit. 18-May-4 Christie's, Rockefeller NY #81/R est:250000-350000

Works on paper

£378	$650	€552	Atlantic City (30x51cm-12x20in) pen ink pencil prov. 3-Dec-3 Doyle, New York #303/R
£1105	$1900	€1613	Seated woman (20x15cm-8x6in) s. chl wash htd white prov. paper on board. 3-Dec-3 Doyle, New York #304/R est:1000-1500
£1105	$1900	€1613	Study for Fryeburg Fair II (25x41cm-10x16in) chl prov. 7-Dec-3 Freeman, Philadelphia #169 est:1000-1500
£3213	$5750	€4691	One rowboat (23x28cm-9x11in) s. W/C. 8-Jan-4 James Julia, Fairfield #515/R est:4000-6000
£3919	$7250	€5879	The ultimatum (13x18cm-5x7in) pencil W/C prov. 14-Jul-4 American Auctioneer #490223/R est:5000-7000
£4696	$8500	€6856	Park at Gracie Square (34x46cm-13x18in) pastel chl prov. 31-Mar-4 Sotheby's, New York #6/R est:10000-15000

£10811 $20000 €15784 Carriage scene (24x15cm-9x6in) s. W/C ink pencil. 11-Mar-4 Christie's, Rockefeller NY #44/R est:15000-25000

GLADE, Hildegard (1885-?) German

£733 $1335 €1100 Still life with peaches (37x50cm-15x20in) s. panel. 1-Jul-4 Van Ham, Cologne #1365

GLADWELL, Rodney (1934-) British

£432 $800 €631 New York (69x104cm-27x41in) s.i.d.69 board. 10-Mar-4 Doyle, New York #72/R

GLAIZE, Auguste Barthelemy (1807-1893) French

£3267 $5945 €4900 Scene orientale (70x100cm-28x39in) s.d.1870. 5-Jul-4 Le Mouel, Paris #5/R est:6000-8000

GLAIZE, Pierre Paul Léon (1842-1932) French

£684 $1141 €999 Woodland slope with woman seated (74x94cm-29x37in) s.d.91. 25-Oct-3 Rasmussen, Havnen #2222/R (D.KR 7300)

GLANSDORFF (1877-1964) Belgian

£574 $1028 €850 Vase fleuri sur fond de papier peint (80x60cm-31x24in) s. 10-May-4 Horta, Bruxelles #358

GLANSDORFF, Hubert (1877-1964) Belgian

£428 $787 €650 Bouquet champetre (60x80cm-24x31in) s.d.27. 22-Jun-4 Palais de Beaux Arts, Brussels #252

£528 $914 €750 Vase de fleurs (50x60cm-20x24in) s.indis.d.1934. 9-Dec-3 Vanderkindere, Brussels #80

£789 $1453 €1200 Vase de fleurs (80x100cm-31x39in) s. 22-Jun-4 Palais de Beaux Arts, Brussels #251

£867 $1551 €1300 Jeune femme devant le miroir (80x60cm-31x24in) s. 11-May-4 Vanderkindere, Brussels #11

£1224 $2192 €1800 Bouquet de fleurs rouges (78x108cm-31x43in) s.d.44. 16-Mar-4 Vanderkindere, Brussels #553 est:1250-1750

£1250 $1987 €1800 Vases fleuri de dahlias (80x100cm-31x39in) s.d.39. 15-Sep-3 Horta, Bruxelles #198 est:1200-1800

£6122 $10959 €9000 Vase de fleurs (100x120cm-39x47in) s.d.47. 16-Mar-4 Vanderkindere, Brussels #557/R est:2000-3000

GLANVILLE, Christopher (1948-) British

£440 $774 €642 Studio Light III (39x29cm-15x11in) s.d.1995 board. 18-May-4 Woolley & Wallis, Salisbury #13/R

GLAOUI, Hassan el (1924-) Moroccan

Works on paper

£458 $792 €650 Sortie du Pacha (30x23cm-12x9in) s. W/C. 15-Dec-3 Gros & Delettrez, Paris #443

£7746 $13401 €11000 Chevaux arabes (75x106cm-30x42in) s. mixed media panel. 15-Dec-3 Gros & Delettrez, Paris #475/R est:5000-6000

GLARNER, Fritz (1899-1972) American/Swiss

£560 $1003 €818 Christ with dove (150x150cm-59x59in) s. tempera. 12-May-4 Dobiaschofsky, Bern #562/R (S.FR 1300)

£113772 $190000 €166107 Study for Tondo no 54 (37x37cm-15x15in) s.i.d.1960 verso masonite round prov. 11-Nov-3 Christie's, Rockefeller NY #18/R est:70000-90000

Works on paper

£3670 $6128 €5322 Tondo (33x26cm-13x10in) pencil. 19-Jun-3 Kornfeld, Bern #441a est:10000 (S.FR 8000)

GLASCO, Joseph (1925-) American

£270 $500 €405 Delos I (61x76cm-24x30in) s.d.62 prov. 14-Jul-4 American Auctioneer #490251/R

GLASIER, Florence E (fl.1866-1879) British

£722 $1177 €1054 Portrait of Mary of Manbeck (35x30cm-14x12in) init.d.1879. 23-Sep-3 Peter Webb, Auckland #154/R (NZ.D 2000)

GLASS, Hamilton (19/20th C) British

£600 $1134 €876 On the Tay, evening (40x60cm-16x24in) s. 19-Feb-4 Lyon & Turnbull, Edinburgh #130

Works on paper

£250 $408 €365 Dutch river landscape with sailing barges landing near a windmill (25x35cm-10x14in) s. W/C. 23-Sep-3 Anderson & Garland, Newcastle #273

£260 $478 €380 At the entrance to the harbour (29x39cm-11x15in) s. W/C. 10-Jun-4 Lyon & Turnbull, Edinburgh #87

£280 $448 €409 Buckhaven. s. W/C. 18-Sep-3 Bonhams, Edinburgh #370

£340 $622 €496 River landscape (30x45cm-12x18in) s. W/C. 27-Jan-4 Bonhams, Knightsbridge #204/R

GLASS, J Hamilton (19/20th C) British

Works on paper

£380 $680 €555 Bend in the river (33x48cm-13x19in) s. W/C. 13-May-4 Mitchells, Cockermouth #1083

£500 $930 €730 East coast fishing village (36x48cm-14x19in) s. W/C. 4-Mar-4 Mitchells, Cockermouth #770

GLASS, James Hamilton (1820-1885) British

Works on paper

£300 $549 €438 Dutch Landscape with windmills on a canal (24x33cm-9x13in) s. W/C. 31-Jan-4 Shapes, Edinburgh #372

GLASS, John Hamilton (fl.1890-1925) British

£433 $801 €632 Sunny afternoon St Monans (35x52cm-14x20in) s.i. 15-Mar-4 Rasmussen, Vejle #188/R (D.KR 4800)

£820 $1369 €1197 Drover (45x60cm-18x24in) s. 13-Nov-3 Bonhams, Edinburgh #371

Works on paper

£260 $447 €380 Old mill (31x46cm-12x18in) s. W/C. 6-Dec-3 Shapes, Edinburgh #421

£260 $458 €380 Evening at Pittenweem, Fifeshire (34x24cm-13x9in) s. bears i. verso W/C htd white. 18-May-4 Fellows & Sons, Birmingham #114/R

£260 $458 €380 End of the town, Buckhaven (34x24cm-13x9in) s. bears i. verso W/C htd white. 18-May-4 Fellows & Sons, Birmingham #115/R

£260 $458 €380 At Buckhaven, Fifeshire (34x24cm-13x9in) s. bears i. verso W/C htd white. 18-May-4 Fellows & Sons, Birmingham #117/R

£290 $499 €423 East coast village with fishing boats (31x46cm-12x18in) s. W/C. 6-Dec-3 Shapes, Edinburgh #420

£300 $549 €438 Evening Cockenzie (22x35cm-9x14in) s. W/C. 31-Jan-4 Shapes, Edinburgh #373

£340 $568 €496 Dutch coastal landscape with fishing boats (26x36cm-10x14in) s. W/C. 11-Oct-3 Shapes, Edinburgh #321

£350 $585 €511 Dutch landscape with figures by a canal and windmill (26x36cm-10x14in) s. W/C. 11-Oct-3 Shapes, Edinburgh #320

£500 $900 €730 Old mill on the Whiteadder (34x48cm-13x19in) s. pencil W/C htd white. 21-Apr-4 Tennants, Leyburn #1035

GLASS, John W (?-1885) British

£500 $850 €730 Two long-haired terriers in an interior with a chair and a picture (29x35cm-11x14in) indis.s.d.1885. 26-Nov-3 Mervyn Carey, Tenterden #168

GLASS, Margaret (1950-) British

Works on paper

£280 $518 €409 Early spring near Reedham (28x36cm-11x14in) s.d.93 pastel. 13-Feb-4 Keys, Aylsham #958

£310 $518 €453 Fishing boats (30x38cm-12x15in) s.d.94 pastel. 17-Oct-3 Keys, Aylsham #667

£360 $652 €526 Morston Creek (25x36cm-10x14in) init.d.91 pastel. 16-Apr-4 Keys, Aylsham #607a

GLASS, Sarah Kramer (1885-?) American

£278 $450 €406 View of Gloucester (25x20cm-10x8in) s. board. 2-Aug-3 Neal Auction Company, New Orleans #194

GLASS, William Mervyn (1885-1965) British

£500 $880 €730 White Sands, Iona (41x51cm-16x20in) 20-May-4 Bonhams, Edinburgh #302

£1400 $2338 €2044 Iona (37x45cm-15x18in) init. board. 23-Oct-3 Bonhams, Edinburgh #310 est:1000-1500

GLATTE, Adolf (1866-1920) German

£915 $1584 €1300 Farmyard in an extensive landscape (70x99cm-28x39in) s.d.1897. 10-Dec-3 Christie's, Amsterdam #166/R

£1364 $2400 €1991 Landscape with river (79x99cm-31x39in) s. i.v. 21-May-4 Pook & Pook, Downington #191/R est:1000-1500

GLATTER, Armin (1861-?) Hungarian

£382 $607 €550 Reclining figure (49x79cm-19x31in) s. 13-Sep-3 Quittenbaum, Hamburg #49/R

£470 $864 €700 Nude (56x41cm-22x16in) s. 25-Mar-4 Hagelstam, Helsinki #1009

£1049 $1752 €1500 Reading (70x50cm-28x20in) 10-Oct-3 Stadion, Trieste #178/R est:500-700

GLATTFELDER, Hansjorg (1939-) Swiss

£1509 $2445 €2203 Eclipse permutation (67x96cm-26x38in) s.i.d.1991 verso acrylic canvas on panel. 24-May-3 Burkhard, Luzern #163/R est:3000-3500 (S.FR 3200)

£1991 $3385 €2907 Yellow on 9 horizontals (75x112cm-30x44in) s.i.d.1992 verso acrylic canvas on panel. 25-Nov-3 Germann, Zurich #149/R est:4000-6000 (S.FR 4400)

£12217 $20769 €17837 Red and blue passageway (66x107cm-26x42in) s.i.d.1987 verso acrylic canvas on board prov. 22-Nov-3 Burkhard, Luzern #172/R est:2000-3500 (S.FR 27000)

Sculpture

£1719 $2923 €2510 Pyramid relief (91x91x10cm-36x36x4in) s.i.d.1973 verso polystrene. 22-Nov-3 Burkhard, Luzern #169/R est:3000-4000 (S.FR 3800)

£2051 $3631 €2994 PYR 319 (100x90cm-39x35in) st.sig. s.d.1972 verso polystyrol relief exhib.prov. 27-Apr-4 AB Stockholms Auktionsverk #1198/R est:30000-35000 (S.KR 28000)

£2941 $5000 €4294 Pyramid relief (70x210x10cm-28x83x4in) s.i.d.1976 verso polystyrene. 22-Nov-3 Burkhard, Luzern #170/R est:4000-5000 (S.FR 6500)

GLATZ, Oszkar (1872-1958) Hungarian

£641 $1135 €936 Girl with a green pitcher (38x30cm-15x12in) s. 28-Apr-4 Kieselbach, Budapest #95/R (H.F 240000)

£1283 $2270 €1873 Boy with a doll (66x50cm-26x20in) s.d.1926. 28-Apr-4 Kieselbach, Budapest #69/R (H.F 480000)

£1470 $2601 €2146 Boat on the lake (73x89cm-29x35in) s. 28-Apr-4 Kieselbach, Budapest #33/R (H.F 550000)

£1900 $3155 €2774 Girl with a doll (62x46cm-24x18in) s.d.1941. 4-Oct-3 Kieselbach, Budapest #37/R (H.F 700000)

£2308 $3831 €3370 Sunlit park (74x91cm-29x36in) s.d.1911. 4-Oct-3 Kieselbach, Budapest #47/R (H.F 850000)

£2635 $4769 €3847 Small girl with mirror (62x46cm-24x18in) s. 16-Apr-4 Mu Terem Galeria, Budapest #159/R (H.F 1000000)

£2672 $4730 €3901 Sisters (70x53cm-28x21in) s.d.1933. 28-Apr-4 Kieselbach, Budapest #96/R (H.F 1000000)

£2939 $5203 €4291 Girl in green head scarf (60x45cm-24x18in) s.d.1945. 28-Apr-4 Kieselbach, Budapest #70/R (H.F 1100000)

£5973 $9914 €8721 Lady feeding horses (90x115cm-35x45in) s. 4-Oct-3 Kieselbach, Budapest #91/R (H.F 2200000)

GLAUBACHER, Franz (1896-1974) Yugoslavian
£1067 $1909 €1600 River landscape (41x51cm-16x20in) s.d.28. 13-May-4 Dorotheum, Linz #495/R est:200-2500

GLAUBER, Johannes (1646-1726) Dutch
£5208 $8854 €7500 Celebrating Diana (73x61cm-29x24in) 29-Oct-3 Il Ponte, Milan #749/R
£10211 $17870 €14500 River landscape with peasants. River landscape with bridge (123x145cm-48x57in) init. pair. 17-Dec-3 Christie's, Rome #408/R est:5000-6000

GLAUBER, Johannes (attrib) (1646-1726) Dutch
£900 $1467 €1314 Classical landscape with a figure by a rock (36x44cm-14x17in) copper. 26-Sep-3 Christie's, Kensington #218/R
£2587 $4630 €3777 Mercurius leading a party carrying offerings (55x44cm-22x17in) 26-May-4 AB Stockholms Auktionsverk #2591/R est:35000-40000 (S.KR 35000)
£8054 $14819 €12000 Arcadian landscape with Leda and the swan (98x135cm-39x53in) prov. 24-Mar-4 Dorotheum, Vienna #184/R est:16000-20000

GLAZEBROOK, Hugh de (1855-1937) British
£500 $860 €730 Portrait of a young girl (89x147cm-35x58in) s.d.1896. 3-Dec-3 Neal & Fletcher, Woodbridge #335
£2500 $4475 €3650 Portrait study of a young girl seated in an armchair (146x91cm-57x36in) s.d.1896. 28-May-4 Lyon & Turnbull, Edinburgh #42/R est:800-1200

GLAZIER, Vicki (1966-) Australian
£1619 $2607 €2364 Letter from Sydney (121x121cm-48x48in) s. 25-Aug-3 Sotheby's, Paddington #271/R est:4000-6000 (A.D 4000)

GLAZUNOV, Ilya (1930-) Russian
Works on paper
£441 $750 €644 Suzdal by the lake (64x79cm-25x31in) s. pastel. 22-Nov-3 Jackson's, Cedar Falls #39/R

GLEASON, Joe Duncan (1881-1959) American
£2116 $4000 €3089 Mountain sentinels, crestline, San Bernardino mountains (41x51cm-16x20in) s. 17-Feb-4 John Moran, Pasadena #60/R est:4000-6000

GLEESON, Gerald (1915-1986) American
Works on paper
£604 $1100 €882 Bay area cityscape (41x61cm-16x24in) s.d.51 W/C. 15-Jun-4 John Moran, Pasadena #138

GLEESON, James Timothy (1915-) Australian
£847 $1441 €1237 Fisherman (19x12cm-7x5in) s. bears i.verso board. 24-Nov-3 Sotheby's, Melbourne #217 est:2000-4000 (A.D 2000)
£1106 $1881 €1615 Hercules 1 (12x14cm-5x6in) s. board. 26-Nov-3 Deutscher-Menzies, Melbourne #145/R est:2000-3000 (A.D 2600)
£1215 $1955 €1774 Man and the sea (19x14cm-7x6in) s. board prov. 25-Aug-3 Sotheby's, Paddington #275/R est:3000-5000 (A.D 3000)
£1293 $2017 €1875 Fantasy (14x12cm-6x5in) s. board. 1-Aug-2 Joel, Victoria #355 est:3000-5000 (A.D 3750)
£1406 $2630 €2109 Untitled (14x12cm-6x5in) board. 21-Jul-4 Shapiro, Sydney #158 est:2500-3500 (A.D 3600)
£1452 $2425 €2178 Man in surreal landscape (15x12cm-6x5in) s. board. 27-Oct-3 Goodman, Sydney #23/R est:4000-5000 (A.D 3500)
£1527 $2779 €2229 Male figure in a psychoscape (20x15cm-8x6in) s. board. 16-Jun-4 Deutscher-Menzies, Melbourne #130/R est:4000-6000 (A.D 4000)
£1545 $2425 €2240 Polyphemus (14x11cm-6x4in) s. s.i.verso board. 26-Aug-3 Christie's, Sydney #260 est:2500-3500 (A.D 3800)
£1556 $2599 €2334 Surreal landscape (15x12cm-6x5in) s. board. 27-Oct-3 Goodman, Sydney #21/R est:4000-5000 (A.D 3750)
£1577 $2633 €2366 Allegory (10x13cm-4x5in) s. board. 27-Oct-3 Goodman, Sydney #56/R est:3000-5000 (A.D 3800)
£1603 $2918 €2340 Apollo at the gates (10x10cm-4x4in) s. i.verso board. 16-Jun-4 Deutscher-Menzies, Melbourne #522/R est:2500-3500 (A.D 4200)
£1626 $2553 €2358 Figures in pyschoscape (15x12cm-6x5in) s. board prov. 26-Aug-3 Christie's, Sydney #345/R est:4000-5000 (A.D 4000)
£1736 $2950 €2535 Figure in a psychoscape (15x12cm-6x5in) s. board. 29-Oct-3 Lawson Menzies, Sydney #156/R est:2000-3000 (A.D 4200)
£1736 $2950 €2535 Cretan bull 1965 (10x15cm-4x6in) board exhib. 29-Oct-3 Lawson Menzies, Sydney #157/R est:2000-3000 (A.D 4200)
£1953 $3652 €2930 Surrealscape (27x16cm-11x6in) s. board. 20-Jul-4 Goodman, Sydney #106/R est:5000-7000 (A.D 5000)
£2033 $3191 €2948 Rumour of Hercules (20x25cm-8x10in) s. i.verso board. 26-Aug-3 Christie's, Sydney #75/R est:5000-9000 (A.D 5000)
£2119 $3602 €3094 Man in psychoscape (15x12cm-6x5in) s. composition board. 24-Nov-3 Sotheby's, Melbourne #135/R est:5000-8000 (A.D 5000)
£2254 $3562 €3291 Variation on the Titan theme (20x14cm-8x6in) s. board. 2-Sep-3 Deutscher-Menzies, Melbourne #197/R est:4000-6000 (A.D 5500)
£2331 $3962 €3403 Man in psychoscape (15x12cm-6x5in) s. composition board. 24-Nov-3 Sotheby's, Melbourne #137/R est:3000-5000 (A.D 5500)
£9091 $16818 €13273 Patmos revisited (133x178cm-52x70in) s.d.89 i.verso prov.exhib. 15-Mar-4 Sotheby's, Melbourne #50/R est:20000-30000 (A.D 22000)
£10638 $18404 €15531 Genesis no 2 (172x235cm-68x93in) s.d.91 i.verso. 10-Dec-3 Shapiro, Sydney #41/R est:25000-35000 (A.D 25000)
£11570 $21405 €16892 Apotheosis of Heracles (122x91cm-48x36in) s.d.67 i.stretcher verso. 10-Mar-4 Deutscher-Menzies, Melbourne #207/R est:20000-25000 (A.D 28000)
£12977 $23618 €18946 Totems in Arcadia (51x40cm-20x16in) s.d.81 board. 16-Jun-4 Deutscher-Menzies, Melbourne #63/R est:20000-30000 (A.D 34000)
£16194 $26073 €23643 Unauthorised storm at Port headland (167x143cm-66x56in) s.d.92 i.verso prov.exhib. 25-Aug-3 Sotheby's, Paddington #160/R est:22000-28000 (A.D 40000)
£24390 $38293 €35366 Preparations at Patmos (181x323cm-71x127in) s.d.86 s.i.stretcher prov.exhib.lit. 26-Aug-3 Christie's, Sydney #77/R est:60000-90000 (A.D 60000)
Works on paper
£356 $637 €520 Untitled (75x57cm-30x22in) s.d.76 ink collage. 15-May-4 Christie's, Sydney #174 (A.D 900)
£947 $1713 €1383 Untitled (50x37cm-20x15in) s.d.23.12.83 chl prov. 30-Mar-4 Lawson Menzies, Sydney #368/R est:2500-3500 (A.D 2300)

GLEESON, Terry (20th C) Australian?
£286 $449 €418 Solitude (43x54cm-17x21in) s. 24-Nov-2 Goodman, Sydney #85/R (A.D 800)
£1286 $2019 €1878 Gums near barn, Murray River (69x90cm-27x35in) s. 24-Nov-2 Goodman, Sydney #36/R est:1000-2000 (A.D 3600)

GLEESON, William James (1927-) Australian
£976 $1532 €1415 East Essex landscape (124x183cm-49x72in) s. s.i.d.1908 verso prov.exhib. 27-Aug-3 Christie's, Sydney #748 est:700-1000 (A.D 2400)

GLEGHORN, Thomas (1925-) Australian
£456 $762 €684 Abstract harbour (92x76cm-36x30in) s.d.58 board. 27-Oct-3 Goodman, Sydney #81/R (A.D 1100)
£1277 $2209 €1864 Mount Vesuvius (103x73cm-41x29in) s.d.62 oil paper. 10-Dec-3 Shapiro, Sydney #95 est:3000-5000 (A.D 3000)
£1983 $3669 €2895 Net menders (121x90cm-48x35in) s.d.XII.56 board prov. 15-Mar-4 Sotheby's, Melbourne #101/R est:2500-3500 (A.D 4800)

GLEHN, Jane de (1873-1961) British
£4000 $7400 €5840 White villa (46x51cm-18x20in) s.d.1934 board exhib. 11-Mar-4 Christie's, Kensington #68/R est:4000-6000

GLEHN, Wilfred Gabriel de (1870-1951) British
£3352 $6000 €4894 Strolling down a park lane (17x22cm-7x9in) 6-May-4 Shannon's, Milford #103/R est:6000-8000
£4500 $7740 €6570 Portrait of Annie Whitworth (95x75cm-37x30in) s.d.1936. 3-Dec-3 Christie's, Kensington #405 est:5000-8000
£8800 $16016 €12848 Reclining female nude (56x71cm-22x28in) s. i.verso prov. 15-Jun-4 Bonhams, New Bond Street #33/R est:7000-10000
£11000 $20020 €16060 The Ford, Stratford Tony (76x91cm-30x36in) s. 15-Jun-4 Bonhams, New Bond Street #34/R est:8000-12000
Works on paper
£500 $925 €730 Rural landscape (25x35cm-10x14in) s. pencil W/C bodycol. 11-Mar-4 Christie's, Kensington #69
£1900 $3515 €2774 St Tropez (40x50cm-16x20in) s. pencil W/C gouache. 11-Feb-4 Sotheby's, Olympia #111/R est:800-1200

GLEICH, H (19/20th C) ?
£293 $533 €428 Horses in hilly landscape. Profile portrait (77x88cm-30x35in) s. double-sided. 7-Feb-4 Rasmussen, Havnen #2031 (D.KR 3200)

GLEICH, John (1879-?) German
£333 $610 €500 Wood collecting vehicle in snowy forest edge (90x120cm-35x47in) s. canvas on canvas. 5-Jun-4 Arnold, Frankfurt #583/R
£940 $1729 €1400 View through city gate of white houses and figures (33x26cm-13x10in) s. 25-Mar-4 Karlheinz Kaupp, Staufen #2460/R
£1074 $1976 €1600 Standing female nude with brown hair (52x32cm-20x13in) s. 25-Mar-4 Karlheinz Kaupp, Staufen #2459/R est:1500
£1135 $1838 €1600 Herders with goats (34x36cm-13x14in) s. 23-May-3 Karlheinz Kaupp, Staufen #1964/R est:600
£2336 $3692 €3387 Young exotic model (70x100cm-28x39in) s. 2-Sep-3 Rasmussen, Copenhagen #1973/R est:25000-30000 (D.KR 25000)
£2721 $4871 €4000 Fideles et vaches sacrees a Puri (63x50cm-25x20in) s. 21-Mar-4 St-Germain-en-Laye Encheres #122/R est:4000
£2721 $4871 €4000 Femmes au sari dans l'ancienne cite (63x50cm-25x20in) s. 21-Mar-4 St-Germain-en-Laye Encheres #123/R est:4000
£4490 $8037 €6600 Temple au bord du Gange (81x100cm-32x39in) s. lit. 21-Mar-4 St-Germain-en-Laye Encheres #121/R est:6000
Works on paper
£276 $458 €400 Horse drawn coach outside Indian temple (19x25cm-7x10in) s. W/C. 30-Sep-3 Dorotheum, Vienna #374/R

GLEICH, Rosalie (19th C) German
£633 $1165 €950 Village scene with farmhouse and geese (43x80cm-17x31in) s. i.verso painted c.1870. 11-Jun-4 Wendl, Rudolstadt #4047/R

GLEICHMANN, Otto (1887-1963) German
Works on paper
£833 $1392 €1200 Two figures (44x31cm-17x12in) s.d. s.i.d. verso gouache pen. 24-Oct-3 Ketterer, Hamburg #356/R

GLEITSMANN, Raphael (1910-) American
£4595 $8500 €6709 View of Akron (69x99cm-27x39in) s. panel. 13-Mar-4 DeFina, Austinburg #910/R est:7000-10000

GLEIZES, Albert (1881-1953) French
£2411 $4027 €3400 Nature morte (24x31cm-9x12in) s. panel. 17-Jun-3 Galerie Moderne, Brussels #188/R est:5000-8000
£6294 $10699 €9000 Composition abstraite (25x23cm-10x9in) s.d.1947 cardboard prov.lit. 23-Nov-3 Cornette de St.Cyr, Paris #127/R est:2000-3000
£7733 $14075 €11600 Composition (24x22cm-9x9in) s.d.1947 panel. 4-Jul-4 Eric Pillon, Calais #295/R
£20001 $36801 €30000 Composition cubiste (64x54cm-25x21in) prov.exhib.lit. 9-Jun-4 Tajan, Paris #21/R est:35000-40000
£22000 $40480 €32120 Composition (73x60cm-29x24in) s.d.46. 23-Jun-4 Christie's, London #242/R est:22000-28000
£24476 $41608 €35000 Composition cubiste (65x54cm-26x21in) painted c.1921 prov.exhib. 23-Nov-3 Cornette de St.Cyr, Paris #126/R est:10000-12000
£27941 $47500 €40794 Vue de Budapest (86x96cm-34x38in) s.d.1904. 6-Nov-3 Sotheby's, New York #177/R est:25000-35000

£28000	$51520	€40880	Study for the portrait of Jacques Nayral (65x54cm-26x21in) s.d.11 prov.exhib.lit. 22-Jun-4 Sotheby's, London #294/R est:10000-15000
£75000	$138000	€109500	Paysage au Moulin a Vent (56x39cm-22x15in) s.d.13 s.i.d.verso prov.exhib. 22-Jun-4 Sotheby's, London #176/R est:60000-80000
Prints			
£2153	$3595	€3100	Composition (40x31cm-16x12in) s.d.1920 pochoir. 25-Oct-3 Cornette de St.Cyr, Paris #513/R est:3000-4000
£4106	$7473	€6200	La gare de Moscou (37x28cm-15x11in) s.d.20 pochoir gouache. 15-Jun-4 Blanchet, Paris #189/R est:3000-4000
Works on paper			
£385	$654	€550	Paysage a l'arbre et aux maisons (22x15cm-9x6in) mono.i.d.1909 graphite W/C prov. 23-Nov-3 Cornette de St.Cyr, Paris #122/R
£524	$892	€750	Composition (11x22cm-4x9in) mono. Indian ink wash exec.c.1940 prov. 23-Nov-3 Cornette de St.Cyr, Paris #124
£532	$888	€750	Nu sur un divan (17x24cm-7x9in) s.d.40 W/C gouache graphite lit. 20-Jun-3 Drouot Estimations, Paris #130
£532	$888	€750	L'eglise et la synagogue (26x20cm-10x8in) mono.i. ink wash paper on cardboard exec.c.1949 lit. 20-Jun-3 Drouot Estimations, Paris #133/R
£604	$1117	€900	Descente de croix (30x35cm-12x14in) studio st.i. pochoir gouache. 15-Mar-4 Blanchet, Paris #119
£629	$1083	€900	Autoportrait (19x13cm-7x5in) s.d.44 ink. 3-Dec-3 Tajan, Paris #66
£638	$1066	€900	Christ en gloire (25x11cm-10x4in) s.i. ink paper on cardboard exec.c.1949 exhib.lit. 20-Jun-3 Drouot Estimations, Paris #134
£674	$1125	€950	Imagination (13x10cm-5x4in) i. ink wash paper on cardboard exec.c.1949 lit. 20-Jun-3 Drouot Estimations, Paris #131
£816	$1362	€1150	L'Ange et la Bete (16x13cm-6x5in) s.i. ink wash paper on cardboard exec.c.1949 lit. 20-Jun-3 Drouot Estimations, Paris #132/R
£851	$1421	€1200	Composition (16x18cm-6x7in) s.d.43 gouache graphite cardboard lit. 20-Jun-3 Drouot Estimations, Paris #140
£993	$1658	€1400	Evangiles (32x25cm-13x10in) s.i.d.40 col crayons exhib.lit. 20-Jun-3 Drouot Estimations, Paris #138
£1000	$1590	€1450	Village Francais (30x23cm-12x9in) s.i.d.1916 chl brush ink col crayon. 11-Sep-3 Christie's, Kensington #88/R est:1000-1500
£1184	$2179	€1800	La couture au parc (21x26cm-8x10in) s.d.1907 gouache chl. 28-Jun-4 Rossini, Paris #85/R est:1800-2000
£1241	$2073	€1750	Descente de croix (21x28cm-8x11in) graphite cardboard exec.c.1928-29 exhib.lit. 20-Jun-3 Drouot Estimations, Paris #128 est:1500-1800
£1310	$2359	€1900	Femme et enfant (40x26cm-16x10in) s. pochoir at the gouache painted c.1926-29 lit. 25-Jan-4 Chayette & Cheval, Paris #268 est:2000-2500
£1458	$2435	€2100	Pascal, l'ange et la bete (17x14cm-7x6in) s.i. ink tracing paper on board. 21-Oct-3 Artcurial Briest, Paris #107/R est:2300-2500
£1538	$2615	€2200	Le peintre et ses modeles (15x11cm-6x4in) s. gouache exec.c.1913 prov. 23-Nov-3 Cornette de St.Cyr, Paris #128 est:600-800
£1678	$2853	€2400	Gitanes (15x14cm-6x6in) s.i. graphite prov. 23-Nov-3 Cornette de St.Cyr, Paris #121/R
£1944	$3247	€2800	Portrait de jeune fille (24x19cm-9x7in) s.d.50 W/C ink lit. 21-Oct-3 Artcurial Briest, Paris #106/R est:2800-3500
£1972	$3411	€2800	Composition (30x22cm-12x9in) s.d.50 W/C ink lit. 9-Dec-3 Chambelland & Giafferi, Paris #68/R est:3000-4000
£2042	$3533	€2900	Barcelone (27x20cm-11x8in) s.d.16 chl crayon ink prov.exhib.lit. 9-Dec-3 Chambelland & Giafferi, Paris #63/R est:2500-3000
£2042	$3533	€2900	Danse (30x19cm-12x7in) s.d.50 W/C ink lit. 9-Dec-3 Chambelland & Giafferi, Paris #66/R est:3000-4000
£2113	$3655	€3000	Centre noir (19x24cm-7x9in) s.d.1925 crayon wash dr exhib.lit. 9-Dec-3 Artcurial Briest, Paris #238/R est:3000-4000
£2113	$3655	€3000	Composition (30x20cm-12x8in) s.d.50 ink W/C lit. 9-Dec-3 Chambelland & Giafferi, Paris #67/R est:3000-4000
£2289	$3960	€3250	Composition (30x19cm-12x7in) s.d.50 ink W/C lit. 9-Dec-3 Chambelland & Giafferi, Paris #64/R est:3500-4500
£2378	$4042	€3400	Autoportrait (13x11cm-5x4in) s.d.1927 gouache prov. 23-Nov-3 Cornette de St.Cyr, Paris #123/R est:200-300
£2465	$4264	€3500	Composition (28x23cm-11x9in) s.d.50 ink W/C lit. 9-Dec-3 Chambelland & Giafferi, Paris #65/R est:3500-4500
£3334	$6134	€5000	Composition cubiste (26x18cm-10x7in) s.d.48 gouache paper on cardboard prov.lit. 8-Jun-4 Artcurial Briest, Paris #79/R est:6000-8000
£3521	$6092	€5000	Sur le roof du Bankers Club Eqyuitable Building (28x21cm-11x8in) s.i.d.1916 crayon Chinese ink wash dr cardboard prov.lit. 9-Dec-3 Artcurial Briest, Paris #234/R est:5000-7000
£4000	$7360	€6000	Village aux Cypres (26x19cm-10x7in) s.d.14 ink. 14-Jun-4 Tajan, Paris #59/R est:4000-5000
£4196	$7133	€6000	Composition cubiste (15x7cm-6x3in) s.d.1924 gouache prov. 23-Nov-3 Cornette de St.Cyr, Paris #120/R est:800-1000
£4930	$8528	€7000	Paysage (27x19cm-11x7in) s.d.1915 pen Chinese ink exhib.lit. 9-Dec-3 Artcurial Briest, Paris #237/R est:8000-12000
£5369	$9987	€8000	Composition (19x14cm-7x6in) s. gouache exec.c.1922-1927 lit. 2-Mar-4 Artcurial Briest, Paris #66/R est:7000-8000
£5986	$10356	€8500	Paysage cubiste (19x21cm-7x8in) s.i.d.14 Chinese ink htd gouache dr lit. 9-Dec-3 Artcurial Briest, Paris #233/R est:6000-8000
£7986	$13337	€11500	Femme au livre (32x24cm-13x9in) s. gouache. 23-Oct-3 Credit Municipal, Paris #85/R est:12000-15000
£8000	$14720	€11680	Catalane (20x17cm-8x7in) pen ink gouache pencil. 22-Jun-4 Sotheby's, London #475/R est:6000-8000
£9155	$15838	€13000	Paysage (15x19cm-6x7in) s.d.1911 ink crayon dr prov.lit. 9-Dec-3 Artcurial Briest, Paris #232/R est:4000-6000
£16000	$26720	€23360	Danseuse espagnole (40x27cm-16x11in) s. gouache brush ink executed 1916 prov. 21-Oct-3 Sotheby's, London #50/R est:8000-12000
£18156	$32500	€26508	Scene de village (26x20cm-10x8in) W/C pencil executed c.1914. 6-May-4 Doyle, New York #128 est:2000-3000
£21000	$38010	€30660	Tete d'homme (23x25cm-9x10in) s.d.1913 gouache. 1-Apr-4 Christie's, Kensington #51/R est:8000-12000
£26761	$46296	€38000	Untitled (92x73cm-36x29in) peinture a l'essence prov.lit. 9-Dec-3 Artcurial Briest, Paris #239/R est:28000-35000
£27000	$49680	€39420	Portrait de Georges Valmier (19x17cm-7x7in) s.i.d.1915 pencil W/C gouache pen ink prov.exhib. 22-Jun-4 Sotheby's, London #476/R est:12000-15000

GLENAVY, Lady Beatrice (1883-1970) British

£5263	$9684	€8000	The love seat (41x41cm-16x16in) mono. canvasboard. 22-Jun-4 De Veres Art Auctions, Dublin #66/R est:8000-12000

GLENDENING, A A (19th C) British

£400	$744	€584	Woodland landscape with waterfall, view of aire force in Ullswater (43x33cm-17x13in) mono. 3-Mar-4 Brightwells, Leominster #944

GLENDENING, Alfred (19th C) British

Works on paper			
£1568	$2900	€2289	Haymakers (51x74cm-20x29in) mono.d.1905 W/C board. 13-Mar-4 DeFina, Austinburg #797/R est:1500-2500
£4054	$7500	€5919	On the Thames (76x56cm-30x22in) W/C. 13-Feb-4 Du Mouchelle, Detroit #2176/R est:1500-1800

GLENDENING, Alfred Augustus (19th C) British

£588	$982	€858	Early morning on the coast near Brighton (20x38cm-8x15in) init.d.1868. 17-Nov-3 Hodgins, Calgary #42/R est:2000-3000 (C.D 1300)
£2500	$3950	€3625	Thames at sunset (25x43cm-10x17in) s.d.69. 4-Sep-3 Christie's, Kensington #129/R est:3000-5000
£2800	$5096	€4088	Shepherd and flock by the shore of a loch (29x49cm-11x19in) init. 15-Jun-4 Bonhams, Oxford #86 est:800-1200
£2800	$5180	€4200	Mountainous landscape with angler approaching a waterfall (39x29cm-15x11in) s.d.96. 14-Jul-4 Rupert Toovey, Partridge Green #50/R est:2500-3500
£3800	$6460	€5548	Moel Siabod, near Capel Curig, North Wales (31x51cm-12x20in) s. i.on stretcher. 25-Nov-3 Christie's, London #109/R est:2000-3000
£4000	$7360	€5840	Driving sheep, Alfriston, Sussex (46x81cm-18x32in) s.d.96. 23-Mar-4 Bonhams, New Bond Street #122/R est:4000-6000
£4000	$7160	€5840	Man and his dog resting beside the road with cows and pond (28x53cm-11x21in) s. prov. 5-May-4 John Nicholson, Haslemere #541/R est:4000-5000
£5000	$9150	€7300	On the river (29x49cm-11x19in) init.d.90. 6-Apr-4 Bonhams, Knightsbridge #183/R est:800-1200
£10000	$16500	€14600	Country harvest scene, figures and a dog walking (58x89cm-23x35in) mono.d.72. 1-Jul-3 Tayler & Fletcher, Cheltenham #6

GLENDENING, Alfred Augustus (attrib) (19th C) British

£1000	$1850	€1460	Eton College (46x46cm-18x18in) with sig. 14-Jul-4 Christie's, Kensington #824/R est:1200-1800
£1200	$2064	€1752	River scene with fishermen (33x53cm-13x21in) mono.d.1864. 3-Dec-3 Andrew Hartley, Ilkley #1192 est:800-1200

GLENDENING, Alfred Augustus (jnr) (1861-1907) British

£1150	$1909	€1679	Two swans on a lake (7x11cm-3x4in) d.d.1885. 2-Oct-3 Ewbank, Send #883/R est:800-1200
£2600	$4732	€3796	River in Snowdonia (41x68cm-16x27in) init.d.91. 21-Jun-4 Bonhams, Bath #314/R est:2500-3500
£3024	$5565	€4415	Watering the horses (61x91cm-24x36in) s.d.1875. 9-Jun-4 Walker's, Ottawa #333/R est:8000-10000 (C.D 7500)
£4396	$8000	€6418	Griesdale, near Patterdale (46x58cm-18x23in) s.d.96 prov. 29-Jun-4 Sotheby's, New York #148/R est:8000-12000
£5800	$10730	€8468	Ferryman (30x55cm-12x22in) s. 10-Mar-4 Sotheby's, Olympia #205/R est:3000-5000
£7500	$13425	€10950	Dove (90x59cm-35x23in) init.d.1895. 26-May-4 Sotheby's, Olympia #147/R est:3000-5000
Works on paper			
£340	$588	€496	Cattle watering in a wooded river landscape (46x74cm-18x29in) mono.d.88 W/C htd white. 12-Dec-3 Halls, Shrewsbury #515
£1200	$2040	€1752	By the river (49x32cm-19x13in) s.d.1895 W/C. 18-Nov-3 Bonhams, Leeds #33 est:1200-1600
£2400	$4128	€3504	Far away thoughts (30x39cm-12x15in) mono.d.1895 pencil W/C htd white. 4-Dec-3 Mellors & Kirk, Nottingham #842/R est:2500-3000

GLENDENING, Alfred Augustus (snr) (?-c.1910) British

£4804	$8599	€7014	At the garden door (35x27cm-14x11in) init.d.1882. 26-May-4 AB Stockholms Auktionsverk #2446/R est:70000-80000 (S.KR 65000)
£5800	$9860	€8468	Mill near Southend, Essex (30x51cm-12x20in) s. 25-Nov-3 Christie's, London #114/R est:2500-3500

GLENNIE, Arthur (attrib) (1803-1890) British

Works on paper			
£993	$1808	€1500	Rome vue du Pincio (57x24cm-22x9in) W/C htd black crayon. 16-Jun-4 Renaud, Paris #7/R est:1200-1500

GLERFOSS, Hans Jakup (1937-) Danish

£632	$1162	€923	Landscape, Klaksvig (94x115cm-37x45in) s. 29-Mar-4 Rasmussen, Copenhagen #279/R (D.KR 7000)

GLEYRE, Charles (1806-1874) Swiss

£20979	$35035	€30000	Young woman riding goat led by satyr (46cm-18in circular) mono. tondo. 28-Jun-3 Bolland & Marotz, Bremen #652/R est:4000
£176724	$316336	€258017	La Nymphe Echo (130x97cm-51x38in) prov.lit. 17-May-4 Beurret, Zurich #11/R est:40000-60000 (S.FR 410000)
Works on paper			
£2886	$5310	€4300	Portrait de l'architecte Vincent Boulle (27x21cm-11x8in) s.i.d.1832 i.verso graphite. 29-Mar-4 Rieunier, Paris #5/R est:3000-4000

GLEYRE, Charles (attrib) (1806-1874) Swiss

£1800	$3096	€2628	Flora and Zepherus (34x26cm-13x10in) canvas on board. 4-Dec-3 Christie's, Kensington #159/R est:1800-2200

GLIKSBERG, Haim (1904-1970) Israeli

£1989	$3500	€2904	Still life with flowers (46x38cm-18x15in) s. painted c.1940. 1-Jan-4 Ben-Ami, Tel Aviv #4399/R est:4000-5000

GLINDONI, Henry Gillard (1852-1913) British

£700	$1232	€1022	Vertuoso (33x27cm-13x11in) s. board. 19-May-4 Christie's, Kensington #585
Works on paper			
£1100	$1804	€1606	Portrait of dancing girl in a pink dress. Musician playing the violin (26x38cm-10x15in) s.d.1886 one indis.i.verso W/C pair. 3-Jun-3 Fellows & Sons, Birmingham #177/R est:800-1200

GLINN, Burt (1925-) American?
Photographs
£1778 $3200 €2596 Elizabeth Taylor on the set of suddenly, Last Summer, 1959 (24x36cm-9x14in) i.verso gelatin silver print. 24-Apr-4 Phillips, New York #47/R est:4000-6000
£1778 $3200 €2596 Nikita Khrushchev in front of the Lincoln Memorial (25x17cm-10x7in) i.verso gelatin silver print. 24-Apr-4 Phillips, New York #60/R est:2000-3000

GLINTENKAMP, Hendrik (1887-1946) American
£5090 $8500 €7431 Rooftops, Hoboken (66x81cm-26x32in) s. prov. 9-Oct-3 Christie's, Rockefeller NY #45/R est:7000-10000
Works on paper
£924 $1700 €1349 Love's young dream (28x38cm-11x15in) s. s.i.d.1913 verso W/C prov. 25-Jun-4 Freeman, Philadelphia #106/R est:800-1200

GLINZ, Theo (1890-1962) Swiss
£673 $1123 €983 Garend near Wiggen Castle (48x52cm-19x20in) s.d.26 s.i.d.1926 verso. 24-Oct-3 Hans Widmer, St Gallen #122/R est:1200-2500 (S.FR 1500)
£1166 $1947 €1702 Old Bad Horn (37x64cm-15x25in) s. s.i.d. verso panel. 24-Oct-3 Hans Widmer, St Gallen #135/R est:2200-3800 (S.FR 2600)
£1435 $2396 €2095 Bodensee landscape near the Rhine (54x70cm-21x28in) s.d.1918. 24-Oct-3 Hans Widmer, St Gallen #133/R est:1500-3200 (S.FR 3200)

GLOCKNER, Hermann (1889-1987) German
£533 $976 €800 Profile (15x10cm-6x4in) mono.d.3.6.57 verso oil scratching. 4-Jun-4 Lempertz, Koln #159/R
£600 $1080 €900 White on red (21x15cm-8x6in) tempera. 24-Apr-4 Dr Lehr, Berlin #128/R
£694 $1160 €1000 Untitled - abstract composition (15x10cm-6x4in) s.i.d. verso casein tempera postcard. 25-Oct-3 Dr Lehr, Berlin #153/R
£4400 $7920 €6600 Composition with red brown (48x65cm-19x26in) s.i.d. verso tempera paper. 24-Apr-4 Dr Lehr, Berlin #126/R est:4500
£5594 $9510 €8000 White curves on dark background (35x25cm-14x10in) i. verso latex chk varnish board prov. 27-Nov-3 Lempertz, Koln #148/R est:7500
£8000 $14400 €12000 Composition (23x18cm-9x7in) mono. tempera board double-sided. 24-Apr-4 Dr Lehr, Berlin #125/R est:11000
£9028 $15076 €13000 Coloured circle in silver (35x25cm-14x10in) i.d.1951 verso oil silver varnish board. 25-Oct-3 Dr Lehr, Berlin #148/R est:8000
Works on paper
£417 $696 €600 Untitled (130x145cm-51x57in) gouache newspaper. 25-Oct-3 Dr Lehr, Berlin #149/R
£800 $1440 €1200 Composition (43x61cm-17x24in) mono.i.d.28.7/83 chk. 24-Apr-4 Dr Lehr, Berlin #129/R
£1389 $2319 €2000 Flourishes (50x70cm-20x28in) mono.i.d.23/8/83 verso wax over pencil. 25-Oct-3 Dr Lehr, Berlin #154/R est:1500
£1538 $2615 €2200 Untitled (56x43cm-22x17in) s.i.d.1971 verso gouache. 27-Nov-3 Lempertz, Koln #149/R est:750
£1678 $2853 €2400 Peaks on violet (50x72cm-20x28in) s.i.d.1976 verso gouache. 27-Nov-3 Lempertz, Koln #150/R est:2500

GLOERSEN, Jakob (1852-1912) Norwegian
£1900 $3154 €2755 Farm by river (75x100cm-30x39in) s. 16-Jun-3 Blomqvist, Lysaker #1056/R est:18000-22000 (N.KR 22000)
£5873 $10512 €8575 Winter landscape with fox (72x90cm-28x35in) s.d.79 lit. 25-May-4 Grev Wedels Plass, Oslo #1/R est:60000-80000 (N.KR 72000)

GLORIA, Daniel (1908-1989) French
Works on paper
£467 $849 €700 Composition (23x10cm-9x4in) s. gouache. 29-Jun-4 Chenu & Scrive, Lyon #100/R

GLORIANI, A (?) Italian
£1232 $2020 €1700 Idyll in the park (130x86cm-51x34in) s.d.99. 27-May-3 Il Ponte, Milan #747 est:700-800

GLORION, Rene (?) French?
Works on paper
£408 $731 €600 Velsheda (60x80cm-24x31in) s. W/C. 21-Mar-4 Claude Boisgirard, Paris #115/R
£442 $791 €650 Pen Duick I (80x100cm-31x39in) s. W/C gouache. 21-Mar-4 Claude Boisgirard, Paris #116/R

GLOSSOP, Allerley (1870-1955) South African
£299 $509 €437 Mountainous landscape with cattle grazing (44x74cm-17x29in) s. canvas on board. 4-Nov-3 Stephan Welz, Johannesburg #606 est:2500-3500 (SA.R 3500)
£347 $621 €507 Extensive landscape with trees (32x40cm-13x16in) init. 31-May-4 Stephan Welz, Johannesburg #188 (SA.R 4200)
£550 $974 €803 Heartsease Farm, Drakensberg (25x35cm-10x14in) s. i.verso board. 27-Apr-4 Bonhams, New Bond Street #91
£560 $936 €818 Autumn sunset, New Forest (19x24cm-7x9in) init. s.i.d.1928 verso. 20-Oct-3 Stephan Welz, Johannesburg #524 est:700-1000 (SA.R 6500)

GLOUTCHENKO, Nicholai Petrovitch (1902-1977) Russian
£2649 $4821 €4000 Danseuse (81x60cm-32x24in) s. 16-Jun-4 Claude Boisgirard, Paris #63/R est:4000-5000
£3046 $5544 €4600 Paysage (60x80cm-24x31in) s. 16-Jun-4 Claude Boisgirard, Paris #64/R est:1500-1800
£7500 $13425 €10950 Nude with chrysanthemums (72x60cm-28x24in) s.d.1933. 26-May-4 Sotheby's, Olympia #494/R est:3000-5000

GLOVER, Ablade (1934-) British/Ghanean
£417 $750 €609 Sleeping village (76x152cm-30x60in) s. acrylic. 24-Apr-4 Weschler, Washington #555/R
£700 $1169 €1022 Never again (102x100cm-40x39in) 21-Oct-3 Bonhams, Knightsbridge #139/R

GLOVER, John (1767-1849) British
£6198 $11467 €9049 Stone bridge, Loxton, Norfolk (40x56cm-16x22in) prov.exhib. 10-Mar-4 Deutscher-Menzies, Melbourne #199/R est:16000-20000 (A.D 15000)
£14634 $26195 €21366 Byland Abbey (77x114cm-30x45in) 4-May-4 Sotheby's, Melbourne #79/R est:40000-60000 (A.D 36000)
Works on paper
£293 $531 €440 Cottages at Howth, Co Dublin (21x28cm-8x11in) s.i.verso W/C exhib. 30-Mar-4 De Veres Art Auctions, Dublin #243
£500 $915 €730 Elterwater and Skiddaw in the lake District (8x13cm-3x5in) i. ink wash pair. 7-Apr-4 Gardiner & Houlgate, Bath #155/R
£720 $1202 €1051 Milking time (46x65cm-18x26in) W/C. 12-Nov-3 Sotheby's, Olympia #5/R
£1000 $1800 €1460 Two views in the Lake District (9x16cm-4x6in) W/C pair exhib. 21-Jan-4 Sotheby's, Olympia #121/R est:1000-1500
£1600 $2960 €2336 Cattle at twilight (76x114cm-30x45in) W/C. 9-Mar-4 Bonhams, Knightsbridge #76/R est:700-900
£1780 $3151 €2599 Donkeys and a horseman in an extensive wooded landscape (28x48cm-11x19in) W/C. 28-Apr-4 Halls, Shrewsbury #478/R est:1000-1500
£1908 $3473 €2786 Landscape (29x42cm-11x17in) W/C. 16-Jun-4 Deutscher-Menzies, Melbourne #555/R est:1500-2500 (A.D 5000)
£2400 $4368 €3504 Cattle watering at dusk (43x67cm-17x26in) W/C over pencil. 1-Jul-4 Sotheby's, London #175/R est:2000-3000
£3306 $5851 €4827 Cattle in a lakeland landscape (23x33cm-9x13in) W/C prov.exhib. 3-May-4 Christie's, Melbourne #56/R est:8000-10000 (A.D 8000)
£4000 $7320 €5840 Figures in an extensive landscape with a church in the distance (26x41cm-10x16in) W/C gouache. 7-Apr-4 Woolley & Wallis, Salisbury #101/R est:2000-3000
£4049 $6518 €5912 Cattle watering in a wooded river in a classical landscape (52x68cm-20x27in) W/C prov. 25-Aug-3 Sotheby's, Paddington #424/R est:10000-15000 (A.D 10000)
£4959 $9174 €7240 Ullswater from Gowbarrow Park (42x60cm-17x24in) i.verso W/C executed c.1805 prov.exhib. 10-Mar-4 Deutscher-Menzies, Melbourne #200/R est:11000-14000 (A.D 12000)

GLOVER, John (attrib) (1767-1849) British
£7438 $13760 €10859 Lakes District landscape (51x71cm-20x28in) 10-Mar-4 Deutscher-Menzies, Melbourne #161/R est:20000-30000 (A.D 18000)
£16194 $26073 €23643 Villagers by a river (72x112cm-28x44in) prov. 25-Aug-3 Sotheby's, Paddington #140/R est:40000-60000 (A.D 40000)
Works on paper
£680 $1136 €993 End of the vale of Llannost, north Wales (40x59cm-16x23in) W/C. 20-Oct-3 Bonhams, Bath #187

GLOVER, Sybil Mullen (fl.1940s) British
Works on paper
£320 $586 €467 On the pier (14x27cm-6x11in) s. W/C. 7-Apr-4 Woolley & Wallis, Salisbury #135/R

GLOVER, William (c.1791-?) British
Works on paper
£540 $956 €788 Ullswater (27x40cm-11x16in) s.d.1818 i.verso W/C over pencil. 27-Apr-4 Bonhams, Knowle #60

GLOVER, William (fl.1875-1903) British
Works on paper
£600 $1062 €876 Cattle resting by a pond, with York Minster beyond (53x74cm-21x29in) W/C. 1-May-4 Hamptons Fine Art, Godalming #30

GLUCK, Anselm (1950-) Austrian
£867 $1551 €1300 Composition (40x60cm-16x24in) s.i.d.98 verso acrylic. 13-May-4 Dorotheum, Linz #517/R
£1733 $3103 €2600 Composition (50x150cm-20x59in) s.i.d.2002 verso acrylic. 13-May-4 Dorotheum, Linz #518/R est:3600-4400

GLUCKERT, Johannes (1868-?) German
£347 $549 €500 Spring flowers by buildings and stream (40x60cm-16x24in) s.i.d.1906. 6-Sep-3 Arnold, Frankfurt #563
£366 $586 €520 Skaters in Holland (33x56cm-13x22in) s. 18-Sep-3 Rieber, Stuttgart #1319/R
£599 $958 €850 Street in Cronberg/T (35x26cm-14x10in) s.d.1918. 18-Sep-3 Rieber, Stuttgart #1335/R
£750 $1380 €1095 Cattle watering at a river (41x71cm-16x28in) s. 24-Mar-4 Hamptons Fine Art, Godalming #305/R

GLUCKMANN, Grigory (1898-1973) American/Russian
£1020 $1846 €1550 Bal (57x40cm-22x16in) s.i.d.1925. 19-Apr-4 Boscher, Cherbourg #807/R
£1536 $2750 €2243 Mother and child (44x34cm-17x13in) s. panel. 21-Mar-4 Bonhams & Butterfields, Los Angeles #7333/R est:2000-3000
£2890 $5000 €4219 Montmartre (38x28cm-15x11in) s. panel prov. 9-Dec-3 Arthur James, Florida #109
£4762 $9000 €6953 Teendage dancer (53x43cm-21x17in) i. verso panel exhib.prov. 17-Feb-4 John Moran, Pasadena #41/R est:8000-10000
£5034 $8910 €7500 Nu a la fourrure (27x35cm-11x14in) s.i.d.1931 panel. 27-Apr-4 Artcurial Briest, Paris #148 est:2000-3000
£12000 $20400 €17520 In the bathhouse (39x29cm-15x11in) s. panel. 19-Nov-3 Sotheby's, London #77/R est:8000-12000
Works on paper
£363 $650 €530 Santa Anita (36x51cm-14x20in) s. mixed media. 21-Mar-4 Bonhams & Butterfields, Los Angeles #7336/R

GLUD, W P (1872-1946) Danish
£404 $650 €590 Woman and child in garden (102x132cm-40x52in) 15-Aug-3 Douglas, South Deerfield #3

GLUD, Wilfred Peter (1872-1946) Danish
£404 $752 €590 Girl playing with her dog (50x44cm-20x17in) s. 2-Mar-4 Rasmussen, Copenhagen #1575/R (D.KR 4500)

GLUSING, Martin Franz (1885-1956) German
£317 $538 €463 Hamburg harbour (39x48cm-15x19in) s. 19-Nov-3 Fischer, Luzern #2113/R (S.FR 700)
£430 $783 €650 Full sail (70x100cm-28x39in) s. i.verso. 19-Jun-4 Hans Stahl, Hamburg #133/R
£489 $900 €714 Ship in high seas (71x99cm-28x39in) s. 25-Mar-4 Doyle, New York #20/R
£610 $1122 €915 Two master in wind (80x120cm-31x47in) s. 14-Jun-4 Blomqvist, Lysaker #1109/R (N.KR 7500)
£1328 $2218 €1939 Sailing vessel at sunset (81x120cm-32x47in) s. painted c.1920. 19-Oct-3 Agra, Warsaw #41/R est:8000 (P.Z 8500)

GLYDE, Henry George (1906-1998) Canadian
£1126 $1914 €1644 Ruins at Bank Head (41x51cm-16x20in) s. s.i.d.1970 canvasboard prov. 23-Nov-3 Levis, Calgary #45/R est:2000-2500 (C.D 2500)
£1160 $2123 €1694 BC shore (25x30cm-10x12in) board painted c.1953. 1-Jun-4 Hodgins, Calgary #279/R est:2000-2500 (C.D 2900)
£1524 $2728 €2225 Edge of town, Southern Alberta (40x50cm-16x20in) s. i.d.1975 verso prov. 27-May-4 Heffel, Vancouver #121/R est:1800-2200 (C.D 3750)
£1756 $3196 €2564 Near Canmore, Alberta (25x30cm-10x12in) s. s.i.d.1973 board. 5-Feb-4 Heffel, Vancouver #38/R est:700-900 (C.D 4250)
£1847 $3140 €2697 Dancers (41x33cm-16x13in) board prov. 23-Nov-3 Levis, Calgary #44/R est:3500-4500 (C.D 4100)
£1915 $3255 €2796 Off Pender Island (33x40cm-13x16in) s.d.1964 s.i.d.verso board. 27-Nov-3 Heffel, Vancouver #91/R est:1200-1600 (C.D 4250)
£2477 $4212 €3616 Jasper Louise Highway, High Country, Alberta (40x50cm-16x20in) s. i.d.1979 verso. 27-Nov-3 Heffel, Vancouver #169/R est:1200-1600 (C.D 5500)
£3455 $6185 €5044 Crosswalk, Victoria, BC (76x101cm-30x40in) s. s.d.1982 verso. 27-May-4 Heffel, Vancouver #134/R est:2000-3000 (C.D 8500)
Works on paper
£249 $416 €364 Sawback Range no.2 (45x59cm-18x23in) s. chl prov. 17-Nov-3 Hodgins, Calgary #133/R (C.D 550)
£320 $586 €467 Sunshine, near Banff (28x37cm-11x15in) s.d.1981 W/C. 1-Jun-4 Hodgins, Calgary #166/R (C.D 800)
£633 $1058 €924 Tree rhythm, Pender Island (58x76cm-23x30in) s. W/C ink prov. 17-Nov-3 Hodgins, Calgary #286/R est:1200-1800 (C.D 1400)

GLYKAS, Aristidis (1870-1940) Greek
Works on paper
£5000 $8950 €7300 Ship - Kapodistria (40x58cm-16x23in) s.i.d.1914 gouache. 10-May-4 Sotheby's, Olympia #145/R est:1000-1500

GLYNN, Gerard (?) British?
£350 $602 €511 Summer light, South William Street, Dublin (40x30cm-16x12in) s.d.03 board. 3-Dec-3 John Ross, Belfast #165
£460 $856 €672 Crown bar, Belfast (45x35cm-18x14in) s.d.03 board. 3-Mar-4 John Ross, Belfast #171

GNIEWEK, Robert (1951-) American
£414 $750 €604 Late night meal (71x102cm-28x40in) acrylic. 16-Apr-4 American Auctioneer #160/R
£18792 $33638 €28000 Ginza Line (96x167cm-38x66in) s. painted 1988 prov. 27-May-4 Sotheby's, Paris #261/R est:8000-12000

GNOLI, Domenico (1933-1970) Italian
£30000 $50100 €43800 Empty closet no. 2 (100x75cm-39x30in) s.d.60 oil sand prov. 21-Oct-3 Sotheby's, London #381/R est:20000-30000
£360000 $601200 €525600 White bed (140x201cm-55x79in) s.i.d.1968 verso acrylic sand prov.exhib.lit. 21-Oct-3 Christie's, London #45/R est:200000-300000
Works on paper
£3147 $5350 €4500 Masks (70x50cm-28x20in) ink card prov.lit. 24-Nov-3 Christie's, Milan #122/R est:3000-4000
£3243 $5708 €4800 View of street with boxes and wheelbarrow (70x50cm-28x20in) s.d.60 ink prov. 24-May-4 Christie's, Milan #33/R est:4000-6000
£3261 $5348 €4500 Empty wine shop (70x50cm-28x20in) Chinese ink card prov. 27-May-3 Sotheby's, Milan #74/R est:6000

GOBAILLE, Jean (?) French?
£1633 $3005 €2450 Marche, Place des Lices (45x61cm-18x24in) s. panel. 8-Jun-4 Livinec, Gaudcheau & Jezequel, Rennes #95/R

GOBAU, Anton (1616-1698) Belgian
£4667 $8447 €7000 Stopping at the inn with players. Resting after the hunt (48x37cm-19x15in) pair lit. 30-Mar-4 Babuino, Rome #72/R est:5000-7000

GOBAUT, Gaspard (1814-1882) French
Works on paper
£400 $724 €600 Paysage de montagne anime (24x34cm-9x13in) s. W/C. 5-Apr-4 Deburaux, Boulogne #59

GOBAUT, Gaspard (attrib) (1814-1882) French
Works on paper
£288 $460 €400 Colonne de l'armee passant a cote de la citadelle de Strasbourg (22x35cm-9x14in) W/C traces of blk crayon. 16-May-3 Tajan, Paris #124

GOBELL, Gerrit Hendrik (1786-1833) Dutch
£1958 $3368 €2800 Dutch dune landscape with horse and cart and children playing (41x55cm-16x22in) s. canvas on canvas. 5-Dec-3 Bolland & Marotz, Bremen #556/R est:2400

GOBER, Robert (1954-) American
£7186 $12000 €10492 Untitled (22x14cm-9x6in) s.d.1996 verso acrylic printed paper prov. 13-Nov-3 Sotheby's, New York #447/R est:10000-15000
£67039 $120000 €97877 Cat litter (48x25cm-19x10in) s.d.1990 verso oil graphite plaster prov.exhib. 12-May-4 Christie's, Rockefeller NY #365/R est:60000-80000
Photographs
£30726 $55000 €44860 Untitled (20x25cm-8x10in) s.d.86 num.AP verso gelatin silver print prov.exhib. 12-May-4 Christie's, Rockefeller NY #366/R est:35000-45000
Prints
£1351 $2500 €1972 Untitled (45x35cm-18x14in) s.d.1991 num.2/6 photolithograph. 12-Feb-4 Sotheby's, New York #245/R est:1800-2200
£6780 $12000 €9899 Hanging man, sleeping man (892x75cm-351x30in) screenprint on wallpaper. 30-Apr-4 Sotheby's, New York #343/R est:12000-15000
£9497 $17000 €13866 Newspaper, love triangle (13x38cm-5x15in) s.d.1993 num.4/10 photolithography twine prov.exhib. 12-May-4 Christie's, Rockefeller NY #367/R est:15000-20000
£20950 $37500 €30587 Untitled (81x109cm-32x43in) iris print on starched cotton fabric exec 1995 1 edn 5 prov. 13-May-4 Sotheby's, New York #412/R est:10000-15000
Sculpture
£11976 $20000 €17485 Newspaper (10x38x41cm-4x15x16in) s.d.93 num.10/10 photolithography paper twine prov. 13-Nov-3 Sotheby's, New York #514/R est:20000-30000
£26946 $45000 €39341 Rat bait (23x16x5cm-9x6x2in) s.i.d.1992 num.9 of 10 verso plaster casein ink prov.exhib. 13-Nov-3 Sotheby's, New York #484/R est:45000-55000
£44311 $74000 €64694 Untitled (3x12x3cm-1x5x1in) s.d.1993 pigmented beeswax W/C on vellum prov.exhib.lit. 13-Nov-3 Phillips, New York #1/R est:40000-60000
£89820 $150000 €131137 Two breasts (21x18x10cm-8x7x4in) wax pigment prov. 13-Nov-3 Sotheby's, New York #448a/R est:12000-140000
Works on paper
£11377 $19000 €16610 Untitled, RG 34D (35x28cm-14x11in) s.d.1985 verso pencil prov. 13-Nov-3 Sotheby's, New York #446/R est:15000-20000

GOBERT, Henri Toussaint (19th C) French
£800 $1472 €1200 Paysage aux fermiers (16x21cm-6x8in) s.d.1825. 11-Jun-4 Maigret, Paris #88

GOBERT, Pierre (1662-1744) French
£6338 $10965 €9000 Vertumnus and Pomona (91x75cm-36x30in) 11-Dec-3 Dr Fritz Nagel, Stuttgart #503/R est:9000
£14444 $26000 €21088 Portrait of Mademoiselle de Blois as Galatea Triumphant (166x140cm-65x55in) prov. 23-Jan-4 Christie's, Rockefeller NY #11/R est:10000-15000
£38462 $66154 €56155 Portrait d'une jeune princesse accompagnee de son chien et de son singe (100x80cm-39x31in) 3-Dec-3 AB Stockholms Auktionsverk #2696/R est:300000-350000 (S.KR 500000)

GOBERT, Pierre (attrib) (1662-1744) French
£2198 $4000 €3209 Portrait of a young gentleman, three-quarter length, in armour and red mantle (69x55cm-27x22in) prov. 4-Feb-4 Christie's, Rockefeller NY #99/R est:3000-5000
£4161 $7448 €6200 Portrait presume de Elisabeth Alexandrine de Bourbon-Conde (74x59cm-29x23in) oval. 26-May-4 Blanchet, Paris #166/R est:4500-5000
£11842 $21790 €18000 Portrait de jeune femme assise (91x72cm-36x28in) 24-Jun-4 Tajan, Paris #51/R est:10000-15000

GOBILLARD, Paule (1869-1946) French
£233 $425 €350 Nature morte au fleurs et bijoux (27x35cm-11x14in) 30-Jun-4 Calmels Cohen, Paris #132
£233 $425 €350 Les toits (33x41cm-13x16in) st.sig. 30-Jun-4 Calmels Cohen, Paris #139
£266 $485 €400 Nature morte aux fleurs et a la nappe fleurie (41x33cm-16x13in) i. verso. 30-Jun-4 Calmels Cohen, Paris #138
£266 $485 €400 Still life of flowers (41x33cm-16x13in) s. i.verso. 30-Jun-4 Calmels Cohen, Paris #162
£266 $485 €400 Nature morte aux capucines et aux poires (33x41cm-13x16in) st.sig. board. 30-Jun-4 Calmels Cohen, Paris #170
£366 $667 €550 Portrait of Claudie Naive (55x46cm-22x18in) st.sig.i. verso. 30-Jun-4 Calmels Cohen, Paris #158/R
£366 $667 €550 Nature morte aux fleurs at aux pivoines (33x46cm-13x18in) st.sig. i. verso. 30-Jun-4 Calmels Cohen, Paris #169
£399 $727 €600 Belle vue (33x24cm-13x9in) mono. i. verso. 30-Jun-4 Calmels Cohen, Paris #106
£399 $727 €600 Bassin au Mesnil (33x41cm-13x16in) s. 30-Jun-4 Calmels Cohen, Paris #168
£399 $727 €600 Nature morte au vase et au masque (52x45cm-20x18in) st.sig. 30-Jun-4 Calmels Cohen, Paris #184/R
£399 $727 €600 Fleurs de printemps (33x41cm-13x16in) st.sig. i. verso. 30-Jun-4 Calmels Cohen, Paris #191
£399 $727 €600 Bouquet of roses (41x33cm-16x13in) s. i. verso. 30-Jun-4 Calmels Cohen, Paris #192
£466 $849 €700 Roses. L'Orateur en rouge (45x37cm-18x15in) st.sig. verso two. 30-Jun-4 Calmels Cohen, Paris #109
£466 $849 €700 Still life with a basket and apples (34x41cm-13x16in) st.sig. 30-Jun-4 Calmels Cohen, Paris #165
£500 $910 €750 Scene d'interieur au Fautueil (65x36cm-26x14in) st.sig. 30-Jun-4 Calmels Cohen, Paris #149
£533 $970 €800 Flowers and porcelain (46x28cm-18x11in) st.sig. 30-Jun-4 Calmels Cohen, Paris #93
£533 $970 €800 Paysage. La vierge aux fleurs (27x35cm-11x14in) st.sig. two. 30-Jun-4 Calmels Cohen, Paris #145
£533 $970 €800 Nature morte aux fleurs. L'acacia (41x33cm-16x13in) s. i. verso two. 30-Jun-4 Calmels Cohen, Paris #202
£599 $1091 €900 Fleurs chez elles (39x49cm-15x19in) st.sig.i. verso. 30-Jun-4 Calmels Cohen, Paris #97
£599 $1091 €900 Portrait de Madeleine Valery. Kikou Yamata au salon d'autumne (21x30cm-8x12in) st.sig. canvas on board pair. 30-Jun-4 Calmels Cohen, Paris #161/R

£599 $1091 €900 Chant. Paule Valery devant une fenetre (32x35cm-13x14in) mono. canvas on board. 30-Jun-4 Calmels Cohen, Paris #177/R
£599 $1091 €900 Nature morte aux vases de porcelaine (53x39cm-21x15in) st.sig. 30-Jun-4 Calmels Cohen, Paris #185/R
£667 $1213 €1000 Portrait oriental (51x43cm-20x17in) s.d.38. 30-Jun-4 Calmels Cohen, Paris #112/R est:1500-2500
£667 $1213 €1000 Vue de bord de mer, Dinard (38x46cm-15x18in) s. 30-Jun-4 Calmels Cohen, Paris #122/R
£733 $1334 €1100 Voilier dans la Rade (32x44cm-13x17in) s. 30-Jun-4 Calmels Cohen, Paris #94
£733 $1334 €1100 Nature morte aux pommes et au pichet de faience bleu blanc (41x33cm-16x13in) st.sig. 30-Jun-4 Calmels Cohen, Paris #99
£733 $1334 €1100 Vase of flowers (55x46cm-22x18in) s. isorel. 30-Jun-4 Calmels Cohen, Paris #117/R
£733 $1334 €1100 Still life with a basket of flowers (35x46cm-14x18in) st.sig. 30-Jun-4 Calmels Cohen, Paris #152/R
£733 $1334 €1100 Bassin du Mesnil (55x46cm-22x18in) s. 30-Jun-4 Calmels Cohen, Paris #204/R
£799 $1455 €1200 Still life of a vase of roses (46x38cm-18x15in) s. 30-Jun-4 Calmels Cohen, Paris #104/R
£799 $1455 €1200 Still life with violin (41x49cm-16x19in) st.sig. 30-Jun-4 Calmels Cohen, Paris #190/R
£933 $1698 €1400 Nature morte aux fleurs et aux groseilles (46x38cm-18x15in) s. 30-Jun-4 Calmels Cohen, Paris #142/R est:1200-1500
£933 $1698 €1400 Lecon de musique. Chef d'Orchestre. Esposition Manet (29x31cm-11x12in) all mono. one i.verso two board one isorel three. 30-Jun-4 Calmels Cohen, Paris #157 est:1000-1200
£933 $1698 €1400 Conference de Paul Valery. Lecture Oreintale. Chat Noir (28x38cm-11x15in) st.sig. i. verso three one double-sided. 30-Jun-4 Calmels Cohen, Paris #188/R est:800-1000
£999 $1819 €1500 Bord de mer au clocher (55x46cm-22x18in) s. i.verso. 30-Jun-4 Calmels Cohen, Paris #135/R est:800-1200
£1067 $1941 €1600 Elegantes a la plage (25x31cm-10x12in) st.sig.i. verso. 30-Jun-4 Calmels Cohen, Paris #107 est:200-400
£1133 $2062 €1700 Garden (46x55cm-18x22in) st.sig. 30-Jun-4 Calmels Cohen, Paris #127/R est:1000-1500
£1267 $2305 €1900 Fleurs tendres (46x48cm-18x19in) s. 30-Jun-4 Calmels Cohen, Paris #215/R est:1000-1500
£1333 $2426 €2000 Nature morte aux coings (38x61cm-15x24in) st.sig. 30-Jun-4 Calmels Cohen, Paris #96/R est:1500-2000
£1333 $2426 €2000 Lac Noir (78x49cm-31x19in) i. st.sig.verso. 30-Jun-4 Calmels Cohen, Paris #179/R est:1800-2300
£1333 $2426 €2000 Nature morte aux prunes et a la jatte (28x38cm-11x15in) s. 30-Jun-4 Calmels Cohen, Paris #198/R est:1000-1500
£1333 $2426 €2000 Nature morte aux pivoines (46x38cm-18x15in) st.sig. 30-Jun-4 Calmels Cohen, Paris #217/R est:1500-2000
£1467 $2669 €2200 Still life of bouquet of flowers (53x78cm-21x31in) st.sig. 30-Jun-4 Calmels Cohen, Paris #108 est:2000-2500
£1597 $2635 €2300 Nature morte aux fruits (38x61cm-15x24in) 3-Jul-3 Claude Aguttes, Neuilly #96 est:1500-1800
£1667 $3033 €2500 Scene de famille au bord de la mer (27x41cm-11x16in) st.sig. 30-Jun-4 Calmels Cohen, Paris #95/R est:500-1000
£1667 $3033 €2500 Still life of a vase of flowers (45x55cm-18x22in) st.sig. 30-Jun-4 Calmels Cohen, Paris #101/R est:2500-3000
£1733 $3154 €2600 Intimite fleurie (46x55cm-18x22in) s. i. verso. 30-Jun-4 Calmels Cohen, Paris #200/R est:2500-3000
£1867 $3397 €2800 Perron (64x53cm-25x21in) st.sig. 30-Jun-4 Calmels Cohen, Paris #173/R est:2000-3000
£1987 $3616 €3000 Panier de roses (33x41cm-13x16in) s. 18-Jun-4 Piasa, Paris #92/R est:3000-4000
£2000 $3639 €3000 Mesnil (38x46cm-15x18in) st.sig.i. verso. 30-Jun-4 Calmels Cohen, Paris #143/R est:800-1200
£2000 $3639 €3000 Still life with a blue vase (68x57cm-27x22in) s. 30-Jun-4 Calmels Cohen, Paris #155/R est:2000-2500
£2067 $3761 €3100 Still life with fuschias (33x40cm-13x16in) st.sig. verso. 30-Jun-4 Calmels Cohen, Paris #213/R est:1000-1500
£2133 $3882 €3200 Nature morte aux peches et au raisin (32x40cm-13x16in) st.sig. 30-Jun-4 Calmels Cohen, Paris #123/R est:800-1200
£2133 $3882 €3200 Maison fleurie (61x50cm-24x20in) st.sig. 30-Jun-4 Calmels Cohen, Paris #210/R est:2500-3000
£2267 $4125 €3400 Sous bois (51x39cm-20x15in) s. 30-Jun-4 Calmels Cohen, Paris #219/R est:1000-1500
£2333 $4246 €3500 Portraits d'elegantes (73x92cm-29x36in) st.sig. 30-Jun-4 Calmels Cohen, Paris #92/R est:2000-3000
£2533 $4610 €3800 Paysage aux Pins (56x54cm-22x21in) s. 30-Jun-4 Calmels Cohen, Paris #144/R est:2500-3000
£2533 $4610 €3800 Paysage. Le jardin public. Nature morte aux prunes (36x25cm-14x10in) st.sig. one panel two board three. 30-Jun-4 Calmels Cohen, Paris #175 est:500-1000
£3333 $6066 €5000 Maternite (73x60cm-29x24in) st.sig. 30-Jun-4 Calmels Cohen, Paris #90/R est:3500-4000
£3867 $7037 €5800 Petite danseuse de Degas (65x55cm-26x22in) s. i.verso. 30-Jun-4 Calmels Cohen, Paris #137/R est:3500-4000
£4667 $8493 €7000 Lecture dans un sous bois (55x46cm-22x18in) s. 30-Jun-4 Calmels Cohen, Paris #193/R est:1800-2200
£8000 $14559 €12000 Elegante au chapeau (72x66cm-28x26in) s. 30-Jun-4 Calmels Cohen, Paris #100/R est:3500-4000
£8000 $14559 €12000 Mere et enfant, la lecon (65x54cm-26x21in) st.sig. 30-Jun-4 Calmels Cohen, Paris #102/R est:3000-3500
£8000 $14559 €12000 Lecon (80x71cm-31x28in) st.sig. 30-Jun-4 Calmels Cohen, Paris #113/R est:1500-2000

Works on paper

£266 $485 €400 Vue de Louvre des Jardins des Tuileries (24x31cm-9x12in) mono. st.sig. verso pastel. 30-Jun-4 Calmels Cohen, Paris #212/R
£366 $667 €550 Bord de mer a Guethary (24x33cm-9x13in) mono. pastel. 30-Jun-4 Calmels Cohen, Paris #115
£466 $849 €700 Printemps, pommier en fleurs. La Regate (22x31cm-9x12in) mono. i.verso pastel two. 30-Jun-4 Calmels Cohen, Paris #134
£533 $970 €800 Homme de profil dans un interieur (57x46cm-22x18in) st.sig. pastel. 30-Jun-4 Calmels Cohen, Paris #167
£795 $1400 €1161 Still life with bouquet of flowers (36x30cm-14x12in) s. pastel. 23-May-4 Hindman, Chicago #53/R est:3000-5000

GOBL, Camilla (1871-1965) Austrian

£423 $739 €600 Basket with asters (70x98cm-28x39in) s. 19-Dec-3 Dorotheum, Vienna #127/R
£600 $1080 €900 Still life with pine twigs, cones and mushrooms (63x100cm-25x39in) s. 21-Apr-4 Dorotheum, Vienna #145/R
£1034 $1893 €1500 Flowers (100x70cm-39x28in) s. 27-Jan-4 Dorotheum, Vienna #37/R est:2000-3000
£1135 $1895 €1600 Autumnal still life (82x110cm-32x43in) s. 14-Oct-3 Dorotheum, Vienna #29/R est:1200-2000

GOBL, Carl (1866-1936) German

£503 $926 €750 Roses (60x45cm-24x18in) s. board. 24-Mar-4 Hugo Ruef, Munich #970

GOBLE, Warwick (?-1943) British

Works on paper

£1700 $3043 €2482 Green willow. Japanese fairy tale (24x34cm-9x13in) s. pen ink W/C pair. 25-May-4 Sworder & Son, Bishops Stortford #411/R est:400-600
£6000 $10380 €8760 Saved, sea sprites steadying a cot in which a baby sleeps soundly (23x24cm-9x9in) s. ink W/C. 11-Dec-3 Sotheby's, London #217/R est:4000-6000

GOBO, Georges (20th C) French

£1042 $1740 €1500 Les lavandieres a Douardenez (55x46cm-22x18in) s. prov. 23-Oct-3 Credit Municipal, Paris #69 est:500-600
£1690 $2958 €2400 Thoniers sous violes a Douarnenez (65x53cm-26x21in) s. 21-Dec-3 Thierry & Lannon, Brest #165/R est:2500-3000

GODARD (19/20th C) French

Sculpture

£5078 $9496 €7617 Bubble dance (51cm-20in) st.sig. pat bronze prov. 25-Jul-4 Lawson Menzies, Sydney #152/R est:12000-15000 (A.D 13000)

GODARD, Armand (19th C) French

£2684 $4993 €4000 Paysage avec batiments (59x92cm-23x36in) s.d.1837. 8-Mar-4 Artcurial Briest, Paris #24/R est:2000-2500

Sculpture

£5800 $10556 €8700 Charme de l'Orient (49cm-19in) s. brown red silver golden pat bronze ivory onyx base lit. 29-Jun-4 Millon & Associes, Paris #12/R est:4000-5000

GODARD, Gabriel (1933-) ?

£432 $800 €631 Les enfants du port (81x99cm-32x39in) s. acrylic. 13-Mar-4 Susanin's, Chicago #6006/R

GODARD, Lise (19th C) ?

Works on paper

£993 $1808 €1500 Bouquet de fleurs (63x52cm-25x20in) s. W/C. 20-Jun-4 Versailles Encheres #62/R est:800-1200

GODARD, Pierre (1909-) French

Sculpture

£1184 $2143 €1800 Athlete au repos (45x83x28cm-18x33x11in) s. stone. 16-Apr-4 Pierre Berge, Paris #4/R
£1579 $2858 €2400 Femme nue allongee (22x42x17cm-9x17x7in) pat bronze. 16-Apr-4 Pierre Berge, Paris #6/R
£1974 $3572 €3000 Naissance d'Eve (75x61x59cm-30x24x23in) s. pat bronze exhib. 16-Apr-4 Pierre Berge, Paris #2/R
£2039 $3691 €3100 Torse de femme (113x41x34cm-44x16x13in) s. stone exhib. 16-Apr-4 Pierre Berge, Paris #5/R
£2500 $4525 €3800 Femme nue allongee (52x27x17cm-20x11x7in) s.d.1946 marble. 16-Apr-4 Pierre Berge, Paris #8/R

GODARD, Rene (1886-?) French

Works on paper

£400 $724 €600 Georges Clemenceau (32x44cm-13x17in) s.d.1929 graphite dr. 1-Apr-4 Piasa, Paris #381
£2133 $3861 €3200 Georges Clemenceau (33x36cm-13x14in) i. graphite stump dr. 1-Apr-4 Piasa, Paris #380/R est:400-500

GODCHAUX (?) ?

£1618 $2750 €2362 Mediterranean coastal landscape with dinghies and figures in the foreground (38x60cm-15x24in) s. indis d.89. 19-Nov-3 Bonhams & Butterfields, San Francisco #104/R
£1844 $3079 €2600 Les martigues (65x92cm-26x36in) s. 19-Oct-3 Anaf, Lyon #163 est:2500-3000

GODCHAUX, Alfred (1835 1895) French

£473 $847 €700 Cabane de forestier au bord de la riviere (37x61cm-15x24in) s. 10-May-4 Horta, Bruxelles #408
£700 $1190 €1022 At a bridge in a mountainous landscape. Figure in an alpine landscape (32x55cm-13x22in) s. pair. 6-Nov-3 Christie's, Kensington #782/R
£1014 $1814 €1500 Barques de peche amarrees (38x61cm-15x24in) s. 10-May-4 Horta, Bruxelles #407 est:1200-1500
£1600 $2912 €2400 Rescate en la playa (41x65cm-16x26in) s. 29-Jun-4 Segre, Madrid #80/R est:2400
£2431 $4132 €3500 Moonlit night in the harbour (43x65cm-17x26in) s. 28-Oct-3 Segre, Madrid #87/R est:2000

GODCHAUX, Emil (1860-?) Austrian?

£867 $1595 €1300 Paysages de montagne (54x73cm-21x29in) s. pair. 8-Jun-4 Livinec, Gaudcheau & Jezequel, Rennes #138
£950 $1700 €1387 Still life with astors (61x86cm-24x34in) s. 7-May-4 Sloans & Kenyon, Bethesda #1703/R est:1500-2000
£1056 $1827 €1500 Nature morte aux fruits (55x64cm-22x25in) s. 9-Dec-3 Chambelland & Giafferi, Paris #62/R est:1000-1500

£1408	$2437	€2000	Bouquet de dahlias (73x100cm-29x39in) s. 9-Dec-3 Chambelland & Giafferi, Paris #61/R est:3000-3500

GODCHAUX, Roger (1878-1958) French

£2072	$3750	€3025	Lilacs (48x64cm-19x25in) s. 3-Apr-4 Neal Auction Company, New Orleans #364/R est:5000-7000

Sculpture

£1257	$2300	€1835	Two panthers (25x48cm-10x19in) bronze i.f.Suisse. 31-Jan-4 South Bay, Long Island #81a
£2447	$3964	€3450	Lionne marchant (13x20x7cm-5x8x3in) s.i. green pat bronze exec.c.1940. 24-May-3 Martinot & Savignat, Pontoise #111/R est:3500-4000
£13830	$22404	€19500	Deux lionceaux jouant (32x89x25cm-13x35x10in) s.d.1928 num.4/6 green pat bronze st.f.Susse. 24-May-3 Martinot & Savignat, Pontoise #110/R est:20000-22000

GODDARD, J Bedloe (fl.1880-1894) British

£420	$764	€613	Landscape country lane with shepherd and sheep and houses to background (36x53cm-14x21in) s. 30-Jun-4 Neal & Fletcher, Woodbridge #278

GODDARD, Walter W (?) ?

£428	$800	€642	View of a calm river on a cloudy day (23x30cm-9x12in) s. sold with a companion prov. 25-Jul-4 Bonhams & Butterfields, San Francisco #6037/R

GODDERIS, Jack (1916-1971) Belgian

£397	$723	€600	Scene de cafe (80x98cm-31x39in) s. 21-Jun-4 Bernaerts, Antwerp #286
£417	$654	€600	Nature morte (60x80cm-24x31in) s. 26-Aug-3 Galerie Moderne, Brussels #361
£417	$696	€600	Night (70x85cm-28x33in) s. 21-Oct-3 Campo & Campo, Antwerp #130

GODDING, Emiel Hendrik Karel (1841-1898) Belgian

£1141	$2122	€1700	Love letter (96x69cm-38x27in) s.d.82. 8-Mar-4 Bernaerts, Antwerp #268/R est:2000-2500

GODEBSKI, Cyprian (1835-1909) French

Sculpture

£6365	$11202	€9293	Couple (91cm-36in) pat bronze. 23-May-4 Agra, Warsaw #11/R (P.Z 45000)

GODEL, Carl (1870-1948) Austrian

£1549	$2711	€2200	Perchtoldsdorf with church and military tower (60x80cm-24x31in) s.d.1944. 19-Dec-3 Dorotheum, Vienna #129/R est:1900-2600

GODET, Henri (1863-1937) French

Sculpture

£10556	$19000	€15412	Le ravissement de Psyche (80cm-31in) i. brown pat. bronze. 23-Apr-4 Sotheby's, New York #42/R est:10000-15000

GODFRINON, Ernest (1878-1927) Belgian

£738	$1373	€1100	Dutch city view with bridge (60x80cm-24x31in) s. 8-Mar-4 Bernaerts, Antwerp #604/R

GODIE, Lee (20th C) American

£359	$600	€524	Big read bird (79x64cm-31x25in) paint ink window-shade prov. 15-Nov-3 Slotin Folk Art, Buford #257/R
£1078	$1800	€1574	Young red head on green (51x38cm-20x15in) paint ink window-shade prov. 15-Nov-3 Slotin Folk Art, Buford #258/R est:500-1000

Works on paper

£240	$400	€350	Chicago we own it (79x56cm-31x22in) ink pen window-shade prov. 15-Nov-3 Slotin Folk Art, Buford #261/R
£299	$500	€437	Jean in late 1980's (69x51cm-27x20in) ink paint window-shade prov. 15-Nov-3 Slotin Folk Art, Buford #260/R
£419	$700	€612	Woman with leaves on her dress (91x46cm-36x18in) pencil paint window-shade prov. 15-Nov-3 Slotin Folk Art, Buford #259/R
£472	$850	€689	Woman's profile (71x56cm-28x22in) ink marker on window shade double-sided. 24-Apr-4 Slotin Folk Art, Buford #435/R
£833	$1500	€1216	Happy Easter (71x28cm-28x11in) ink paint. 24-Apr-4 Slotin Folk Art, Buford #434/R est:1000-2000

GODLEVSKY, Ivan (1908-1998) Russian

£690	$1152	€1000	Village au bord de mer (47x65cm-19x26in) s.d.1971. 17-Nov-3 Claude Boisgirard, Paris #30/R
£993	$1808	€1500	Petit port (48x65cm-19x26in) 16-Jun-4 Claude Boisgirard, Paris #65 est:1500-2000
£1391	$2531	€2100	Descente vers la mer (60x73cm-24x29in) cardboard. 16-Jun-4 Claude Boisgirard, Paris #67 est:2000-2500
£1544	$2856	€2300	Les rochers rouges (47x65cm-19x26in) studio st. 15-Mar-4 Claude Boisgirard, Paris #41 est:400-600
£2416	$4470	€3600	Les arbres rouges (93x68cm-37x27in) 15-Mar-4 Claude Boisgirard, Paris #44 est:500-700
£2416	$4470	€3600	Une rue a Bakhtchisarai (70x92cm-28x36in) studio st. 15-Mar-4 Claude Boisgirard, Paris #43/R est:600-800
£2649	$4821	€4000	Au bord de la riviere Volkova (87x114cm-34x45in) s.d.1970 verso. 16-Jun-4 Claude Boisgirard, Paris #66/R est:4000-6000
£2941	$5500	€4294	Tchekhov's Bay at night (70x93cm-28x37in) painted 1979 prov.lit. 25-Feb-4 Christie's, Rockefeller NY #63/R est:6000-8000
£3758	$6953	€5600	Une matinee sur la riviere Pskov (68x93cm-27x37in) s.d.1958. 15-Mar-4 Claude Boisgirard, Paris #42 est:600-800
£4545	$8500	€6636	Surroundings of Bakhchisarai (69x83cm-27x33in) s. board on canvas painted 1966 prov.lit. 25-Feb-4 Christie's, Rockefeller NY #76/R est:6000-8000
£6952	$13000	€10150	Bay of Tchekhov (110x90cm-43x35in) s. prov.lit. 25-Feb-4 Christie's, Rockefeller NY #62/R est:7000-9000
£6952	$13000	€10150	Fisherman's boat (60x80cm-24x31in) s. painted 1982 prov.lit. 25-Feb-4 Christie's, Rockefeller NY #78/R est:5000-7000

GODWARD, John William (1858-1922) British

£29412	$50000	€42942	Siesta (30x35cm-12x14in) s.d.1895 lit. 29-Oct-3 Christie's, Rockefeller NY #59/R est:60000-80000
£45000	$81900	€65700	Pompeian bath (57x26cm-22x10in) s.d.1890 prov.exhib.lit. 1-Jul-4 Sotheby's, London #333/R est:40000-60000
£66000	$121440	€96360	Knuckle bones (35x65cm-14x26in) s.d.1890 prov.lit. 11-Jun-4 Christie's, London #162/R est:30000-50000
£77778	$140000	€113556	Pompeian lady (93x46cm-37x18in) s.d.1916 s.i.d.verso. 23-Apr-4 Sotheby's, New York #59/R est:100000-150000
£88000	$161920	€128480	Atalanta (29x45cm-11x18in) s.d.1908 prov. 26-Mar-4 Sotheby's, London #68/R est:50000-80000
£450000	$828000	€657000	Pompeian garden (61x76cm-24x30in) s.d.1904 prov.lit. 9-Jun-4 Christie's, London #15/R est:200000-300000

GODWIN, Karl (1893-?) American

£1018	$1700	€1486	Older pipe smoking man telling story to young boy (64x76cm-25x30in) s. painted c.1930. 15-Nov-3 Illustration House, New York #161/R est:2500-3500

GODWIN, Ted (1933-) Canadian

£1518	$2611	€2216	Late Spring - Dog Pound 2 (97x157cm-38x62in) s.i.d.1982 verso. 2-Dec-3 Joyner Waddington, Toronto #497 est:2500-3000 (C.D 3400)

GOEBEL, Carl (1824-1899) Austrian

£828	$1374	€1200	Mountain fortress (54x40cm-21x16in) s. W/C. 30-Sep-3 Dorotheum, Vienna #253/R

Works on paper

£2394	$3831	€3400	Young angler (41x58cm-16x23in) s. W/C. 18-Sep-3 Rieber, Stuttgart #860/R est:1980
£3500	$5950	€5110	Pilgrimage to the Kiev-Pecherskaya Lavra (22x33cm-9x13in) s. W/C over pencil. 19-Nov-3 Sotheby's, London #4/R est:2000-3000

GOEBEL, Karl (1866-?) German

£1719	$2923	€2510	Girl in traditional costume carrying basket (100x75cm-39x30in) s.i. 19-Nov-3 Fischer, Luzern #1155/R est:4000-4500 (S.FR 3800)

GOEBEL, Karl Peter (1793-1823) Austrian

£927	$1687	€1400	Portrait of a young woman with a landscape in background (67x67cm-26x26in) s. 18-Jun-4 Bolland & Marotz, Bremen #621/R

GOEBEL, Rod (1946-1993) American

£932	$1500	€1351	Penitente Morada at Valdez, NM (11x17cm-4x7in) board. 22-Aug-3 Altermann Galleries, Santa Fe #147
£932	$1500	€1351	Sunset on Monument Valley (25x36cm-10x14in) board. 22-Aug-3 Altermann Galleries, Santa Fe #175
£932	$1500	€1351	Taos adobes (30x41cm-12x16in) 22-Aug-3 Altermann Galleries, Santa Fe #176
£1176	$2000	€1717	Mountain landscape at dusk (41x51cm-16x20in) s. 22-Nov-3 Jackson's, Cedar Falls #78/R est:4000-6000
£1176	$2000	€1717	Autumn reflections (71x51cm-28x20in) 1-Nov-3 Altermann Galleries, Santa Fe #187
£2235	$4000	€3263	Winter light in Sacred Zuni Mountain (91x122cm-36x48in) 15-May-4 Altermann Galleries, Santa Fe #140/R
£2446	$4500	€3571	Desert landscape (101x152cm-40x60in) s. 8-Jun-4 Bonhams & Butterfields, San Francisco #4140/R est:3000-5000
£5028	$9000	€7341	Morning in the orchard (76x91cm-30x36in) 15-May-4 Altermann Galleries, Santa Fe #177/R

GOEDE, Kees de (1954-) Dutch

£8000	$14720	€12000	Innerworld, outerworld III (180x165cm-71x65in) acrylic chl silk on canvas painted c.1987-1988 exhib. 9-Jun-4 Christie's, Amsterdam #377/R est:7000-9000

GOEDHART, Jan Andreas (1919-1991) Dutch

Works on paper

£483	$806	€700	View of the quay (35x48cm-14x19in) s. W/C. 11-Nov-3 Vendu Notarishuis, Rotterdam #56

GOEDHART, Jan Catharinus Adriaan (1893-1975) Dutch

£1467	$2655	€2200	Still life with chrysanthemums and autumn leaves in vase (105x76cm-41x30in) s. 1-Apr-4 Van Ham, Cologne #1395/R est:1400

GOEDING, Andreas (c.1570-1625) German

Works on paper

£517	$864	€750	David with the head of Goliath (17x12cm-7x5in) s.d.1618 brush wash prov. 15-Nov-3 Lempertz, Koln #1322

GOEDVRIEND, Theodor Franciscus (1879-1969) Dutch

£521	$849	€750	Still life of mushrooms (58x78cm-23x31in) s. 29-Sep-3 Sotheby's, Amsterdam #277/R
£590	$962	€850	Still life of mushrooms (65x85cm-26x33in) s. 29-Sep-3 Sotheby's, Amsterdam #306
£759	$1267	€1100	Still life with mushrooms (63x73cm-25x29in) s. board. 11-Nov-3 Vendu Notarishuis, Rotterdam #85/R

GOEJE, Pieter de (1779-1859) Dutch

£2603	$4425	€3800	Landscape with herdsmen and cattle (60x75cm-24x30in) s.d.1853. 5-Nov-3 Vendue Huis, Gravenhage #45/R est:4000-6000

GOENAGA, Juan Luis (1950-) Spanish

£510	$929	€750	Untitled (80x64cm-31x25in) s. 3-Feb-4 Segre, Madrid #246/R

GOENEUTTE, Norbert (1854-1894) French
£880 $1408 €1285 Fisher girls on the shore (38x46cm-15x18in) s. 16-Sep-3 Bonhams, Knowle #101
£2098 $3566 €3000 Jeune elegante au chapeau (41x32cm-16x13in) 18-Nov-3 Sotheby's, Paris #12/R est:3000-4000
£2397 $4075 €3500 Marchande de paniers (31x41cm-12x16in) s.d.1880 panel. 6-Nov-3 Sotheby's, Paris #133/R est:3000-4000
£2907 $5000 €4244 Femme au balcon (31x41cm-12x16in) s.d.1880 panel. 2-Dec-3 Christie's, Rockefeller NY #30/R est:3000-5000
£4043 $7520 €5903 Parisian town scenes (32x22cm-13x9in) one s. panel pair. 2-Mar-4 Rasmussen, Copenhagen #1507/R est:35000 (D.KR 45000)
£19000 $32300 €27740 Peintre au bord de riviere (46x55cm-18x22in) s. panel. 18-Nov-3 Sotheby's, London #317/R
£30000 $51000 €43800 Galants, Dordrecht (46x56cm-18x22in) s.d.1887 prov. 18-Nov-3 Sotheby's, London #316/R

GOEPFERT, Hermann (1926-1982) German
£403 $713 €600 Construction positive (200x110cm-79x43in) s. d.1979 verso. 27-Apr-4 Campo & Campo, Antwerp #106
£436 $772 €650 Cruciforme (140x160cm-55x63in) s. d.1979. 27-Apr-4 Campo & Campo, Antwerp #107
£3497 $5944 €5000 W 41-60 (65x65cm-26x26in) s. verso prov. 27-Nov-3 Lempertz, Koln #151/R est:2000
Sculpture
£1958 $3329 €2800 Reflector No 6 (101x93x6cm-40x37x2in) s. verso aluminium. 29-Nov-3 Arnold, Frankfurt #223/R est:600

GOEREE, Jan (1670-1731) Dutch
Works on paper
£383 $700 €559 David receiving the Five Holy Breads and the Sword of Goliath (32x20cm-13x8in) i. pen gray ink wash. 29-Jan-4 Swann Galleries, New York #183/R
£2055 $3493 €3000 Allegory of the decline of classical civilization (33x22cm-13x9in) pen brown ink grey wash over red chk. 4-Nov-3 Sotheby's, Amsterdam #132/R est:1000-1500

GOERG, Edouard (1893-1969) French
£1020 $1827 €1500 Le manteau de fourrure (55x32cm-22x13in) s. i.d.1955 verso. 19-Mar-4 Ribeyre & Baron, Paris #94/R est:1500-2000
£1192 $2170 €1800 Artistes (55x46cm-22x18in) s. i.verso. 18-Jun-4 Piasa, Paris #220 est:1200-1800
£1268 $2193 €1800 La baigneuse rose au bouquet rose (41x33cm-16x13in) s.d.47 s.i.verso prov. 12-Dec-3 Piasa, Paris #208 est:1200-1500
£1343 $2497 €2000 Trois silhouettes de femme (81x54cm-32x21in) s. 3-Mar-4 Tajan, Paris #116/R est:2400-3000
£1678 $3003 €2500 Fenetre sur la riviere (61x46cm-24x18in) s. s.i.d.53 verso. 27-May-4 Christie's, Paris #122/R est:3000-4000
£1761 $3046 €2500 La cueillette des dahlias (55x46cm-22x18in) s. s.i.d.Aout-Sept 1955 verso prov. 13-Dec-3 Touati, Paris #122/R est:3500
£1879 $3364 €2800 Ecaillere et fleuriste (65x54cm-26x21in) s. s.i.d.1955 verso. 27-May-4 Christie's, Paris #123/R est:4000-6000
£2067 $3741 €3100 Deux femmes dans les fleurs (38x46cm-15x18in) s.d.47. 1-Apr-4 Credit Municipal, Paris #69 est:1000-1200
£3103 $5183 €4500 La veuve (90x72cm-35x28in) s. i.verso. 16-Nov-3 Muizon & Le Coent, Paris #68/R
£3241 $5932 €4700 Des femmes et des fleurs (65x54cm-26x21in) s. 1-Feb-4 Feletin, Province #87
£3521 $6162 €5000 Nu au bouquet de fleurs (55x46cm-22x18in) s. prov. 16-Dec-3 Claude Aguttes, Neuilly #18/R est:6000-8000
Works on paper
£315 $526 €450 French Cancan (36x26cm-14x10in) s. pen Chinese ink wash. 25-Jun-3 Blanchet, Paris #24
£467 $845 €700 Dessin surrealiste (25x32cm-10x13in) graphite. 5-Apr-4 Marie & Robert, Paris #112
£480 $869 €720 Dessin surrealiste (25x32cm-10x13in) ink. 5-Apr-4 Marie & Robert, Paris #113
£667 $1207 €1000 Le chateau sombre (50x32cm-20x13in) s.d.36 pen. 5-Apr-4 Marie & Robert, Paris #111

GOERITZ, Mathias (1915-1990) Mexican/German
Sculpture
£1054 $1791 €1539 Christ of Auschwitz (52x15x4cm-20x6x2in) bronze. 30-Oct-3 Louis Morton, Mexico #116/R est:25000-30000 (M.P 20000)
£3161 $5374 €4615 Butcher (73x53x28cm-29x21x11in) wood lit. 30-Oct-3 Louis Morton, Mexico #97/R est:65000-70000 (M.P 60000)
Works on paper
£790 $1344 €1153 Animal (27x47cm-11x19in) s. gouache. 30-Oct-3 Louis Morton, Mexico #127/R est:17000-19000 (M.P 15000)

GOERSCHNER, Ted (1935-) American
£328 $600 €479 Senator's daughter (56x71cm-22x28in) s.d.1988 masonite. 5-Jun-4 Neal Auction Company, New Orleans #431

GOERSS, Rainer (1960-) German
Works on paper
£403 $741 €600 Untitled (78x55cm-31x22in) s.d. gouache Indian in col chks. 26-Mar-4 Ketterer, Hamburg #879/R

GOERTZ, Augustus (1948-) American
£694 $1200 €1013 Untitled (165x234cm-65x92in) acrylic prov. 15-Dec-3 Hindman, Chicago #117/R

GOES, Hugo van der (style) (1420-1482) Flemish
£6944 $11319 €10000 Mourning of Christ (43x31cm-17x12in) mono. panel prov.lit. 19-Jul-3 Berlinghof, Heidelberg #212 est:20000
£38000 $69540 €55480 Lamentation (76x75cm-30x30in) panel prov.exhib. 8-Jul-4 Sotheby's, London #108/R est:25000-35000
£47887 $83803 €68000 Annonciation (56x40cm-22x16in) panel exhib. 17-Dec-3 Piasa, Paris #4/R est:15000-20000

GOESCH, Paul (1885-1940) German
Works on paper
£333 $597 €500 Christ on cross (25x21cm-10x8in) mono. W/C on pen board. 15-May-4 Bassenge, Berlin #6837
£350 $594 €500 Black landscape with Mary and child (25x35cm-10x14in) i. verso W/C over pen board. 29-Nov-3 Bassenge, Berlin #6723/R
£433 $776 €650 Christ entering Jerusalem (15x19cm-6x7in) mono. pencil col pen. 15-May-4 Bassenge, Berlin #6838

GOESER, August (1858-?) American
£683 $1100 €997 At Gloucester, Mass on Sunday afternoon (23x30cm-9x12in) s. board. 20-Aug-3 James Julia, Fairfield #1661/R

GOETHALS, Charles (1854-1886) Belgian
£709 $1184 €1000 Portrait de femme, Mariucce, Capri (80x62cm-31x24in) s. 17-Jun-3 Vanderkindere, Brussels #141

GOETHALS, Theophile (1870-1949) Dutch?
£2055 $3493 €3000 Small dyke (78x139cm-31x55in) s.d.90. 5-Nov-3 Vendue Huis, Gravenhage #178/R est:2000-3000

GOETHE, Johann Wolfgang von (1749-1832) German
Works on paper
£4161 $7448 €6200 Italian landscape with city wall (21x31cm-8x12in) pen wash. 25-May-4 Karl & Faber, Munich #28/R est:5000

GOETING, Jan (1918-1984) Dutch
£455 $782 €650 Roses (100x80cm-39x31in) s.d.71. 8-Dec-3 Glerum, Amsterdam #339/R

GOETING-STULTIENS, Catherina (1912-1987) Dutch
£699 $1203 €1000 Still life (65x90cm-26x35in) s.d.55. 8-Dec-3 Glerum, Amsterdam #256/R

GOETSCH, Gustave (1877-1969) American
£516 $950 €753 Artist at work (30x25cm-12x10in) s. masonite. 26-Jun-4 Selkirks, St. Louis #137/R
£1630 $3000 €2380 New York harbour (84x89cm-33x35in) s.d.1934 board. 26-Jun-4 Selkirks, St. Louis #138/R est:3000-5000

GOETZ, Ferdinand (1955-) Austrian
£1049 $1783 €1500 Untitled (205x135cm-81x53in) s.d.1987 verso oil mixed media. 28-Nov-3 Wiener Kunst Auktionen, Vienna #710/R est:1500-2500

GOETZ, Gottfried Bernhard (1708-1774) German
Works on paper
£414 $691 €600 Drawing of a man (8x5cm-3x2in) s. W/C over pencil prov. sketch verso. 15-Nov-3 Lempertz, Koln #1327/R

GOETZ, Henri (1909-1989) French
£235 $437 €350 Composition (32x33cm-13x13in) s. oil pastel. 3-Mar-4 Artcurial Briest, Paris #448
£237 $425 €346 Fishing boats in the canal (56x71cm-22x28in) s.d.53. 11-Jan-4 William Jenack, New York #16
£333 $600 €500 Composition (30x35cm-12x14in) s. panel prov. 24-Apr-4 Cornette de St.Cyr, Paris #557
£659 $1167 €962 Le Muy Incendie (54x64cm-21x25in) s.d.62 prov. 27-Apr-4 AB Stockholms Auktionsverk #1204/R (S.KR 9000)
£1034 $1717 €1500 La guerre des mondes (54x65cm-21x26in) s. i.d.1983 stretcher. 5-Oct-3 Lombrail & Teucquam, Paris #365
£1745 $3211 €2600 Composition (65x81cm-26x32in) s. painted 1985. 24-Mar-4 Joron-Derem, Paris #193/R est:4000-5000
£1748 $2972 €2500 Composition aux formes flottantes (73x60cm-29x24in) s. 21-Nov-3 Lombrail & Teucquam, Paris #163/R est:2300-2800
£2098 $3608 €3000 Sans titre (60x72cm-24x28in) s.d.56 prov. 4-Dec-3 Piasa, Paris #62/R est:4000-6000
£2482 $4145 €3500 Sainte-Genevieve-des-bois (63x79cm-25x31in) s. i.verso. 19-Oct-3 Charbonneaux, Paris #134/R est:4500
£3020 $5618 €4500 Composition (145x114cm-57x45in) s. painted c.1988. 3-Mar-4 Artcurial Briest, Paris #449/R est:4000-5000
Works on paper
£300 $546 €450 Untitled (15x11cm-6x4in) s.d.37 ink. 30-Jun-4 Calmels Cohen, Paris #87/R
£403 $749 €600 Composition (35x46cm-14x18in) s. pastel. 3-Mar-4 Artcurial Briest, Paris #444
£559 $951 €800 Composition (50x65cm-20x26in) s. pastel paper on canvas. 20-Nov-3 Claude Aguttes, Neuilly #144/R
£563 $1030 €850 Karnak (38x54cm-15x21in) s. i.d.1964 verso pastel prov. 9-Apr-4 Bailly Pommery, Paris #92
£694 $1159 €1000 Sans titre (49x64cm-19x25in) s. pastel. 21-Oct-3 Artcurial Briest, Paris #653 est:1000-1200
£739 $1279 €1050 Composition (49x39cm-19x15in) s. crayon prov. 14-Dec-3 Versailles Encheres #19
£772 $1436 €1150 Composition (23x32cm-9x13in) s. ink. 3-Mar-4 Artcurial Briest, Paris #442
£805 $1482 €1200 Composition surrealiste (31x24cm-12x9in) s. wax crayon exec 1947 lit. 24-Mar-4 Joron-Derem, Paris #86
£940 $1729 €1400 Camille Renault (61x50cm-24x20in) s.d.1954 pastel paper on canvas prov.lit. 24-Mar-4 Joron-Derem, Paris #194

£1418 $2369 €2000 Composition (34x50cm-13x20in) s. pastel exhib. 19-Oct-3 Charbonneaux, Paris #114/R est:2000
£1867 $3360 €2800 Composition surrealiste (21x29cm-8x11in) s.d.1941 gouache oil. 24-Apr-4 Cornette de St.Cyr, Paris #556/R est:4000
£2000 $3680 €3000 Formes flottantes (81x100cm-32x39in) s. pastel. 13-Jun-4 Lombrail & Teucquam, Paris #127/R
£2394 $4142 €3400 Composition (12x21cm-5x8in) s. W/C prov.lit. 14-Dec-3 Versailles Encheres #48/R est:4000-4500
£2448 $4087 €3500 Composition (45x41cm-18x16in) s. pastel prov.lit. 29-Jun-3 Versailles Encheres #29/R

GOEYE, Michel de (1900-1958) Belgian
£869 $1608 €1260 Les bouquinistes. Le guide. Le caricaturiste (36x44cm-14x17in) s. canvas on cardboard three. 16-Feb-4 Horta, Bruxelles #254

GOEZU, Andre (1939-) Belgian
£289 $533 €440 Nuages d'aout (55x46cm-22x18in) s. 22-Jun-4 Palais de Beaux Arts, Brussels #253

GOFF, Frederick E J (1855-1931) British
£5000 $8000 €7300 Westminster. Blackfriar's bridge (21x30cm-8x12in) s.i. pair. 16-Sep-3 Bonhams, New Bond Street #48/R est:5000-7000
Works on paper
£460 $856 €672 Church in river landscape (47x67cm-19x26in) s.d.1895 W/C. 2-Mar-4 Bearnes, Exeter #341/R
£600 $1002 €876 Canterbury Cathedral (51x71cm-20x28in) s.i. pencil W/C. 16-Oct-3 Christie's, Kensington #44/R
£600 $1104 €876 Westminster (11x14cm-4x6in) s.i. W/C. 8-Jun-4 Bonhams, New Bond Street #92/R
£1000 $1600 €1460 St Pauls from the river (14x11cm-6x4in) s.indis.i. W/C. 16-Sep-3 Bonhams, New Bond Street #66/R est:1000-1500
£1000 $1790 €1460 Westminster (11x15cm-4x6in) s.i. pencil W/C bodycol exhib. 26-May-4 Christie's, Kensington #453/R est:1000-1500
£1000 $1790 €1460 Houses of Parliament, Westminster (11x15cm-4x6in) s.i. pencil W/C bodycol exhib. 26-May-4 Christie's, Kensington #455/R est:1000-1500
£1400 $2576 €2044 St Pauls from Bankside (14x11cm-6x4in) s.i. W/C. 8-Jun-4 Bonhams, New Bond Street #93/R est:1200-2000
£1600 $2672 €2336 London Bridge (11x15cm-4x6in) s.i. pencil W/C. 16-Oct-3 Christie's, Kensington #154/R est:600-800
£1600 $2752 €2336 Blackfriars bridge (11x14cm-4x6in) s.i. pencil W/C. 3-Dec-3 Christie's, Kensington #95/R est:400-600
£1700 $3060 €2482 London Bridge (11x15cm-4x6in) s.i. pencil W/C htd white. 21-Apr-4 Tennants, Leyburn #949/R est:600-800
£2000 $3400 €2920 Strand on the green. Broadway Wharf. Shiplake Mill (15x35cm-6x14in) s. W/C together in one frame. 28-Oct-3 Henry Adams, Chichester #389/R est:1000-1500
£2600 $4810 €3796 St Paul's from Bankside (17x12cm-7x5in) s.i. W/C. 9-Mar-4 Bonhams, New Bond Street #127/R est:1000-1500
£3400 $6426 €4964 London Bridge. Off Greenwich (11x15cm-4x6in) s. W/C pair. 18-Feb-4 John Bellman, Billingshurst #1845/R est:800-1200

GOFF, Lloyd Lozes (1917-1982) American
£299 $500 €437 Fuente de Venus Alameda Central, Mexico (41x51cm-16x20in) board. 18-Oct-3 David Dike, Dallas #257/R
£539 $900 €787 Acapulco beach (43x69cm-17x27in) board. 18-Oct-3 David Dike, Dallas #222/R
£1497 $2500 €2186 New Mexico landscape (36x51cm-14x20in) oil paper. 18-Oct-3 David Dike, Dallas #199/R est:3000-4000

GOFF, Robert Charles (1837-1922) British
Works on paper
£280 $476 €409 Monte Ceceri, Fiesole (19x26cm-7x10in) s.d.1902 W/C. 4-Nov-3 Rowley Fine Art, Newmarket #364
£450 $765 €657 Grand Canal, Venice (20x26cm-8x10in) s.d.1908 W/C prov. 4-Nov-3 Rowley Fine Art, Newmarket #363/R

GOFFINON, Aristide (1881-1952) Belgian
£909 $1545 €1300 Bouquet d'oeillets dans un vase (50x60cm-20x24in) s. 1-Dec-3 Palais de Beaux Arts, Brussels #260/R

GOGARTEN, Heinrich (1850-1911) German
£4861 $7681 €7000 Evening view of Naples with Vesuvius (68x106cm-27x42in) s.d.1879. 6-Sep-3 Arnold, Frankfurt #565/R est:3000

GOGARTEN, Heinrich (attrib) (1850-1911) German
£331 $603 €500 Winter landscape with ice skaters (14x17cm-6x7in) panel. 16-Jun-4 Hugo Ruef, Munich #965

GOGGER, Franz (1882-1973) Austrian
£278 $453 €400 River landscape (30x41cm-12x16in) mono.d.23 board. 25-Sep-3 Dorotheum, Graz #16

GOGH, Vincent van (1853-1890) Dutch
£2294118 $3900000 €3349412 Nature morte, branche d'amandier (24x19cm-9x7in) s. painted February-March 1888 prov.exhib.lit. 4-Nov-3 Christie's, Rockefeller NY #6/R est:3000000-4000000
£4600000 $8372000 €6716000 Deux crabes (47x61cm-19x24in) painted 1888-89 prov.exhib.lit. 21-Jun-4 Sotheby's, London #5/R est:1200000-1500000
£6176471 $10500000 €9017648 L'allee des alyscamps (92x73cm-36x29in) pained October-November 1888 prov.exhib.lit. 4-Nov-3 Christie's, Rockefeller NY #25/R est:12000000-18000000
Prints
£32000 $58880 €48000 Portrait du Docteur Gachet - L'homme a la pipe (18x15cm-7x6in) etching. 10-Jun-4 Hauswedell & Nolte, Hamburg #223/R est:40000
£220000 $378400 €321200 Travail des champs, burning weeds (15x27cm-6x11in) pen col ink transfer lithograph prov. 4-Dec-3 Sotheby's, London #151/R est:80000-120000
Works on paper
£76923 $132308 €110000 Field of stubble with a thunderstorm overhead (46x49cm-18x19in) pencil black chk wash htd white executed 1881 prov.lit. 2-Dec-3 Sotheby's, Amsterdam #81/R est:120000-150000
£90000 $163800 €131400 Peatery in Drenthe (41x54cm-16x21in) W/C exec.1883 prov.lit. 4-Feb-4 Sotheby's, London #417/R est:70000-90000
£117647 $200000 €171765 Pecheur (47x25cm-19x10in) pencil exec 1883 prov.lit. 6-Nov-3 Sotheby's, New York #130/R est:200000-300000
£360000 $662400 €525600 Paysanne glanant (53x42cm-21x17in) s. chk wash htd white exec.1885 prov.exhib.lit. 22-Jun-4 Christie's, London #3/R est:200000-300000
£4352941 $7400000 €6355294 Le pont de Langlois a Arles (30x30cm-12x12in) s.i. W/C gouache chk pen ink over pencil prov.exhib.lit. 4-Nov-3 Christie's, Rockefeller NY #21/R est:6000000-8000000
£5411765 $9200000 €7901177 La moisson en Provence (50x61cm-20x24in) s.i. W/C chl reed quill pen ink paper on millboard prov.exhib.lit. 5-Nov-3 Sotheby's, New York #6/R est:7000000-9000000

GOGO, Felix (19/20th C) Belgian
Works on paper
£455 $759 €650 Woman viewed from the back (37x30cm-15x12in) s. chl. 11-Oct-3 De Vuyst, Lokeren #167

GOGOIS, Pierre (1935-) French
£775 $1340 €1100 Vue de l'Alfama, Lisbonne (60x70cm-24x28in) s. 10-Dec-3 Remi Ader, Paris #44
£775 $1340 €1100 Vue de l'Alfama, Lisbonne (60x70cm-24x28in) s. 10-Dec-3 Neret-Minet, Paris #44

GOGOS, Basil (20th C) American
Works on paper
£856 $1600 €1250 American soldiers capturing Germans in snowy townscape (53x41cm-21x16in) s. casein exec.c.1960. 26-Feb-4 Illustration House, New York #81 est:1200-1600

GOGOS, Nicholaos (1898-1974) Greek
£600 $1074 €876 L'arc de triomphe (38x46cm-15x18in) s. 11-May-4 Bonhams, New Bond Street #63/R

GOHLER, Hermann (1874-?) German
£387 $620 €550 Summer flowers in vase (42x42cm-17x17in) s. board. 18-Sep-3 Rieber, Stuttgart #1238
£1329 $2219 €1900 Wasserburg on Bodensee (96x103cm-38x41in) s.i. 27-Jun-3 Michael Zeller, Lindau #527/R est:1900
£2238 $3804 €3200 Nude (100x75cm-39x30in) s. 20-Nov-3 Dorotheum, Salzburg #204/R est:3000-4000

GOHSTEIN, M (20th C) Russian
£259 $463 €378 Clenched hand (17x23cm-7x9in) s.d.8/V 31 panel. 28-May-4 Uppsala Auktionskammare, Uppsala #276 (S.KR 3500)

GOINGS, Ralph (1928-) American
£8725 $15617 €13000 Red counter still life (36x30cm-14x12in) s.d.89 i.d.verso acrylic crayon cardboard lit. 27-May-4 Sotheby's, Paris #255/R est:4000-6000
£80537 $144161 €120000 Still life with mustard (101x101cm-40x40in) s.d.93 s.d.verso prov. 27-May-4 Sotheby's, Paris #256/R est:30000-40000

GOITINO, Yuyo (1935-) Uruguayan
£276 $461 €400 Untitled (15x30cm-6x12in) s. 11-Nov-3 Castellana, Madrid #202/R
£276 $461 €400 Composition (20x24cm-8x9in) s. board. 11-Nov-3 Castellana, Madrid #27/R
£276 $461 €400 Composition (21x24cm-8x9in) s. board. 11-Nov-3 Castellana, Madrid #6/R
£276 $461 €400 Untitled (20x24cm-8x9in) s. board. 11-Nov-3 Castellana, Madrid #42/R
£276 $461 €400 Untitled (15x28cm-6x11in) s. 11-Nov-3 Castellana, Madrid #187/R
£276 $461 €400 Untitled (20x27cm-8x11in) s. board. 11-Nov-3 Castellana, Madrid #188/R
£276 $461 €400 Untitled (20x24cm-8x9in) s. board. 11-Nov-3 Castellana, Madrid #234/R
£414 $691 €600 Untitled (26x40cm-10x16in) s. 11-Nov-3 Castellana, Madrid #189/R
£414 $691 €600 Untitled (24x39cm-9x15in) s. 11-Nov-3 Castellana, Madrid #205/R
£414 $691 €600 Untitled (30x32cm-12x13in) s. board. 11-Nov-3 Castellana, Madrid #203/R
£448 $749 €650 Untitled (29x44cm-11x17in) s. 11-Nov-3 Castellana, Madrid #214/R
£448 $749 €650 Untitled (30x42cm-12x17in) s. 11-Nov-3 Castellana, Madrid #206/R
£448 $749 €650 Untitled (29x40cm-11x16in) s. 11-Nov-3 Castellana, Madrid #231/R
£448 $749 €650 Untitled (30x40cm-12x16in) s. 11-Nov-3 Castellana, Madrid #232/R

GOLA, Emilio (1852-1923) Italian
Works on paper
£3261 $5348 €4500 Villa amongst trees (51x61cm-20x24in) s. pastel. 27-May-3 Finarte Semenzato, Milan #55/R est:5500
£3404 $5685 €4800 Portrait of Mrs Carminati (96x76cm-38x30in) s.d.1912 pastel paper on canvas. 14-Oct-3 Finarte Semenzato, Milan #130/R

GOLADANTIJO, Nicolaus de (?) ?
£369 $683 €550 Christ on the cross (37x31cm-15x12in) s. board. 10-Mar-4 James Adam, Dublin #43

GOLDBERG, Eric (1890-1969) Canadian
£586 $995 €856 The ballet performance (53x63cm-21x25in) s. board prov. 21-Nov-3 Walker's, Ottawa #106/R (C.D 1300)
£691 $1237 €1009 The circus (66x53cm-26x21in) s. i.verso board prov. 27-May-4 Heffel, Vancouver #202 (C.D 1700)
£766 $1302 €1118 Village by the beach (51x69cm-20x27in) s. prov. 23-Nov-3 Levis, Calgary #46/R (C.D 1700)
Works on paper
£676 $1149 €987 Girl knitting (40x30cm-16x12in) s. mixed media board prov. 27-Nov-3 Heffel, Vancouver #55/R (C.D 1500)

GOLDBERG, Fred (1889-1973) American
£247 $450 €371 Seascape with rocky cliffs (81x91cm-32x36in) s. 19-Jun-4 Harvey Clar, Oakland #2381

GOLDBERG, Glenn (20th C) American
Works on paper
£324 $550 €473 Abstract composition (91x56cm-36x22in) init.d.1989 mixed media collage. 21-Nov-3 Swann Galleries, New York #59/R

GOLDBERG, Gustav (1874-?) German
£1119 $1902 €1600 Konigssee (60x75cm-24x30in) s.d.1877. 20-Nov-3 Weidler, Nurnberg #324/R est:1800

GOLDBERG, Gustav Adolf (1848-1911) German
£503 $926 €750 Portrait of young woman wearing hat with feathers (25x21cm-10x8in) s. 24-Mar-4 Hugo Ruef, Munich #971/R

GOLDBERG, Michael (1924-) American
£667 $1200 €974 James P Johnson I. Utitled (36x36cm-14x14in) one s.i.d.1978 verso one s.d.1974-75 verso one s.d.1975 verso 3. 24-Apr-4 David Rago, Lambertville #337/R
£722 $1300 €1054 Untitled (24x27cm-9x11in) s. one d.1983 one d.1986 verso pair. 24-Apr-4 David Rago, Lambertville #315/R
£6522 $12000 €9522 Abstract (124x150cm-49x59in) s. verso. 27-Jun-4 Freeman, Philadelphia #149/R est:5000-8000
Works on paper
£472 $850 €689 Untitled (22x17cm-9x7in) s.d.1968 gouache chl. 24-Apr-4 David Rago, Lambertville #32/R
£528 $950 €771 Jacques Callot. Untitled (29x27cm-11x11in) s.d.1984 one chl gouache one chl acrylic pair. 24-Apr-4 David Rago, Lambertville #546/R
£889 $1600 €1298 Untitled Albert facade (29x27cm-11x11in) s.d.1984 pastel s.d.1975-77 W/C s.d.1979 chl s.d.1989 pastel four. 24-Apr-4 David Rago, Lambertville #142/R est:800-1200
£1111 $2000 €1622 Untitled (72x72cm-28x28in) s.d.1974 verso bronze powders clear alkid canvas prov. 24-Apr-4 David Rago, Lambertville #412/R est:2000-4000
£1500 $2700 €2190 Untitled (14x14cm-6x6in) two s.d.1984 one s.d.1972 bronze powder paint three. 24-Apr-4 David Rago, Lambertville #455/R est:600-900
£3611 $6500 €5272 Untitled (108x36cm-43x14in) s.d.1972 bronze powders alkin canvas. 24-Apr-4 David Rago, Lambertville #530/R est:2000-3000
£8333 $15000 €12166 Untitled (72x72cm-28x28in) s.d.1974 verso bronze powders alkin canvas. 24-Apr-4 David Rago, Lambertville #189/R est:2000-4000

GOLDBERG, Rube (1883-1970) American
Sculpture
£2072 $3750 €3025 Cheering at the prize fight (25x46x22cm-10x18x9in) s. brown pat bronze. 31-Mar-4 Sotheby's, New York #173/R est:2000-3000
Works on paper
£241 $450 €352 Man interrupted at bedtime prayers (18x15cm-7x6in) s. pen ink. 26-Feb-4 Illustration House, New York #82

GOLDBERGER, Siegfried (1954-) Austrian
Works on paper
£267 $491 €400 Astronomical labyrinth (52x46cm-20x18in) s. W/C mixed media. 9-Jun-4 Dorotheum, Salzburg #763/R
£284 $474 €400 Rofenhofe (40x41cm-16x16in) s. W/C Indian ink. 16-Oct-3 Dorotheum, Salzburg #884/R

GOLDEN, Daniel van (1936-) Dutch
£80000 $147200 €120000 Schilderij (70x70cm-28x28in) s. verso board painted 1964 prov. 8-Jun-4 Sotheby's, Amsterdam #145/R est:20000-25000

GOLDEN, Rolland (1931-) American
Works on paper
£432 $700 €631 Civil War series (53x74cm-21x29in) s.d.1970 W/C. 2-Aug-3 Neal Auction Company, New Orleans #556

GOLDIE, Charles Alphonse (19/20th C) British
Works on paper
£339 $566 €495 The fisherman (33x24cm-13x9in) s. W/C prov. 17-Nov-3 Waddingtons, Toronto #59/R (C.D 750)

GOLDIE, Charles Frederick (1870-1947) New Zealander
£28671 $52182 €41860 No Koora te cigaretti, portrait Te Heu Heu of the Arawa Tribe (24x19cm-9x7in) s.d.1915. 29-Jun-4 Peter Webb, Auckland #59/R est:90000-120000 (NZ.D 82000)
£59441 $108182 €86784 Weariness of the aged - Kapi Kapi an Arawa chieftainess aged 102 years (25x20cm-10x8in) s.d.1918 prov. 29-Jun-4 Peter Webb, Auckland #32/R est:100000-150000 (NZ.D 170000)
Works on paper
£700 $1281 €1022 An old salt (33x24cm-13x9in) s. W/C. 3-Jun-4 Lane, Penzance #280/R

GOLDIE, Geoffrey (20th C) ?
Works on paper
£344 $554 €502 Man (121x52cm-48x20in) s.d.1999 synthetic polymer paint board. 25-Aug-3 Sotheby's, Paddington #393 (A.D 850)
£424 $720 €619 Male nude (101x76cm-40x30in) s.d.2003 s.i.d.verso synthetic polymer paint canvas. 24-Nov-3 Sotheby's, Melbourne #235/R (A.D 1000)

GOLDIN, Nan (1953-) American
Photographs
£2036 $3400 €2973 Siobhan with cat, New York (39x59cm-15x23in) with sig.i.d.1993 num.25/25 cibachrome print. 21-Oct-3 Swann Galleries, New York #341/R est:3500-4500
£2096 $3500 €3060 Siobhan in the house, nude, Provincetown (61x51cm-24x20in) s.i. num.25 cibachrome prov.lit. 14-Nov-3 Phillips, New York #263/R est:6000-8000
£2153 $3595 €3100 Joana with cigaret at chateauneuf de Gadagne (38x29cm-15x11in) s.i.d.may 2000 num.23/40 col photo. 25-Oct-3 Cornette de St.Cyr, Paris #687/R est:3500-4000
£2646 $5000 €3863 Siobhan in the shower, NYC (98x65cm-39x26in) s.i.d.1991 dye destruction print. 17-Feb-4 Christie's, Rockefeller NY #274/R est:3000-5000
£2800 $4760 €4088 Jimmy Paulette after the parade (48x59cm-19x23in) s.verso cibachrome print. 18-Nov-3 Christie's, Kensington #235/R est:1000-1200
£2905 $5113 €4300 Anto in the red room, Brighton, England (50x34cm-20x13in) s.i.d.1979 verso col photograph prov.lit. 18-May-4 Tajan, Paris #179/R est:2000-3000
£2930 $5187 €4278 Pavel laughing on the beach, Positano, Italy (69x101cm-27x40in) s.i.num.A.P.1 cibachrome lit. 27-Apr-4 AB Stockholms Auktionsverk #966/R est:40000-50000 (S.KR 40000)
£2994 $5000 €4371 Self-portrait, Berlin (28x36cm-11x14in) s.verso cibachrome print exec.1984. 17-Oct-3 Phillips, New York #97/R est:6000-8000
£2994 $5000 €4371 Bruce in his car, NYC (66x99cm-26x39in) s.i.d.1981 num.17/25 verso cibachrome print prov.lit. 17-Oct-3 Phillips, New York #250/R est:7000-9000
£3041 $5351 €4500 Suzanne on her bed, New York City (50x60cm-20x24in) s. num.7/25 verso col photograph exec 1983 prov.exhib.lit. 18-May-4 Tajan, Paris #178/R est:4000-5000
£3200 $5792 €4672 Simon in the snow at dawn, Christmas, Umea (102x69cm-40x27in) s.i.d.1997 num.7/15 cibachrome. 1-Apr-4 Christie's, Kensington #313/R est:2500-3500
£3800 $6346 €5548 Pawel on the beach laughing, Positano (76x102cm-30x40in) s.i.d.1996 num.8/15 verso cibachrome prov. 22-Oct-3 Christie's, London #145/R est:4000-6000
£4000 $7360 €6000 Brian in the hotel room, Merida, Mexico (37x57cm-15x22in) s. num.7/25 verso cibachrome prov.lit. 9-Jun-4 Artcurial Briest, Paris #566/R est:6000-8000
£4192 $7000 €6120 Hafen bar, Berlin (76x102cm-30x40in) s.i.d.1991 cibachrome prov.exhib.lit. 14-Nov-3 Phillips, New York #265/R est:6000-8000
£5307 $9500 €7748 Fatima candles, portugal (64x95cm-25x37in) s.i.d.1988 versoc-print prov.lit. 14-May-4 Phillips, New York #321/R est:6000-8000
£5500 $10120 €8030 Suzanne in yellow hotel room. Hotel Seville, Merida Mexico (72x104cm-28x41in) i.d.1981 num.9/25 two cibachrome print. 25-Jun-4 Christie's, London #239/R est:5500-7000
£5665 $9630 €8271 Pavel laughing on the beach, Positano, Italy (76x102cm-30x40in) s.d.1996 num.4/15 cibachrome prov.exhib.lit. 5-Nov-3 AB Stockholms Auktionsverk #1036/R est:30000-40000 (S.KR 75000)
£5988 $10000 €8742 Yogo in the club mirror, Bangkok (70x101cm-28x40in) s.i.num.d.1992 verso silver dye bleach print prov.exhib.lit. 12-Nov-3 Christie's, Rockefeller NY #544/R est:12000-18000
£5988 $10000 €8742 Jimmy Paulette on David's bike, NYC (38x58cm-15x23in) s.i.d.1991 num.7 verso cibachrome print one of 25 lit. 17-Oct-3 Phillips, New York #108/R est:10000-15000
£7000 $12740 €10220 Guy at Wigstock (100x68cm-39x27in) cibachrome print edition 5 of 25 lit. 6-Feb-4 Sotheby's, London #277/R est:7000-10000
£7500 $13650 €10950 French Family before the bath (59x102cm-23x40in) cibachrome prints three exec 2000 prov.lit. 5-Feb-4 Christie's, London #233/R est:8000-12000
£8000 $14720 €11680 Yogo and C putting on make-up, second tip, Bangkok (66x97cm-26x38in) s.i.d.1992 num.3/15 verso cibachrome print prov. 24-Jun-4 Sotheby's, London #318/R est:8000-12000
£8000 $14720 €12000 Morning light, hotel village, Hambourg (69x100cm-27x39in) s.i.d.1992 num.3/25 verso cibachrome print prov.lit. 8-Jun-4 Artcurial Briest, Paris #299/R est:8000-10000
£8389 $15436 €12500 Toon so and Yogo on stage at Second Tip Bar, Bangkok (68x100cm-27x39in) s.i.d.1992 num.5/25 verso col photograph. 29-Mar-4 Cornette de St.Cyr, Paris #102/R est:12000-15000
£8982 $15000 €13114 Kim in her dressing room at Le Carousel, Paris (101x68cm-40x27in) i.num.d.1991 silver dye bleach process print prov.lit. 12-Nov-3 Christie's, Rockefeller NY #543/R est:12000-18000
£9000 $15030 €13140 Self portrait on the bridge at Golden river, Silver Hill Hospital (76x102cm-30x40in) s.i.d.1998 num.13/15 verso cibachrome prov. 22-Oct-3 Christie's, London #114/R est:4000-6000
£9497 $17000 €13866 Kathe in the tub (51x61cm-20x24in) s.i.d.1984 num.5/25 verso cibachrome print prov.exhib.lit. 13-May-4 Sotheby's, New York #365/R est:8000-12000
£10615 $19000 €15498 Breakfast in bed, torre di bellosguardo, Florence (70x102cm-28x40in) s.i.d.1996 num.12/15 verso cibachrome print on foamcore prov. 13-May-4 Sotheby's, New York #393/R est:8000-12000

GOLDING, John (1929-) British
£2432 $4500 €3551 J.I - Odyssey (172x248cm-68x98in) s.i.d.88 verso acrylic mixed media cotton duck prov.exhib. 12-Feb-4 Sotheby's, New York #313/R est:4000-6000
Works on paper
£350 $585 €511 Drawing L (64x94cm-25x37in) s.d.74 col chk prov. 16-Oct-3 Christie's, Kensington #641

GOLDING, Tomás (1909-) Venezuelan
£316 $500 €461 Landscape (50x39cm-20x15in) s. 27-Apr-3 Subastas Odalys, Caracas #12

£316 $500 €461 Landscape (29x39cm-11x15in) s. 27-Apr-3 Subastas Odalys, Caracas #71
£317 $530 €463 Landscape (29x65cm-11x26in) s. panel painted 1967. 13-Jul-3 Subastas Odalys, Caracas #12
£336 $625 €491 Landscape (51x64cm-20x25in) s. masonite. 14-Mar-4 Subastas Odalys, Caracas #2/R
£346 $595 €505 Untitled (31x36cm-12x14in) s. masonite painted 1953. 7-Dec-3 Subastas Odalys, Caracas #86/R
£363 $625 €530 Andes (40x50cm-16x20in) s. painted 1978. 7-Dec-3 Subastas Odalys, Caracas #97/R
£469 $750 €685 Untitled (50x40cm-20x16in) s. painted 1973. 21-Sep-3 Subastas Odalys, Caracas #53
£503 $935 €734 Burning (35x47cm-14x19in) s. painted 1971. 14-Mar-4 Subastas Odalys, Caracas #117
£559 $1040 €816 Landscape (56x76cm-22x30in) s. painted 1976. 14-Mar-4 Subastas Odalys, Caracas #10/R
£559 $1040 €816 Seascape (76x76cm-30x30in) s. painted 1971. 14-Mar-4 Subastas Odalys, Caracas #27/R
£565 $1040 €825 Catia La Mar (26x30cm-10x12in) s. masonite painted 1942. 28-Mar-4 Subastas Odalys, Caracas #16/R
£654 $1125 €955 Park in Tunjas (58x76cm-23x30in) s. masonite painted 1973. 7-Dec-3 Subastas Odalys, Caracas #107/R
£686 $1125 €1002 Flowers (76x61cm-30x24in) s. 1-Jun-3 Subastas Odalys, Caracas #30
£749 $1250 €1094 Wood (40x50cm-16x20in) s. painted 1975. 19-Oct-3 Subastas Odalys, Caracas #127/R
£749 $1250 €1094 Bucare (34x25cm-13x10in) s. painted 1930. 13-Jul-3 Subastas Odalys, Caracas #62
£774 $1200 €1130 Flowers (76x56cm-30x22in) s. painted 1973. 3-Nov-2 Subastas Odalys, Caracas #53
£774 $1200 €1130 Untitled (56x46cm-22x18in) s. cardboard. 3-Nov-2 Subastas Odalys, Caracas #110/R
£886 $1400 €1294 Flowers (77x66cm-30x26in) s. painted 1970. 1-Dec-2 Subastas Odalys, Caracas #70
£949 $1500 €1386 Seascape (31x40cm-12x16in) s. painted 1954. 1-Dec-2 Subastas Odalys, Caracas #27/R
£1029 $1690 €1502 Landscape (56x67cm-22x26in) s. 1-Jun-3 Subastas Odalys, Caracas #63
£1065 $1980 €1555 Flowers (51x40cm-20x16in) s. painted 1973. 14-Mar-4 Subastas Odalys, Caracas #78/R
£1088 $1980 €1632 Burning (50x65cm-20x26in) s. painted 1963. 21-Jun-4 Subastas Odalys, Caracas #93/R
£1123 $1875 €1640 Landscape (77x66cm-30x26in) s. painted 1965. 19-Oct-3 Subastas Odalys, Caracas #145/R
£1143 $1875 €1669 Landscape (75x65cm-30x26in) s. painted 1961. 1-Jun-3 Subastas Odalys, Caracas #45
£1250 $2000 €1825 Flowers (67x56cm-26x22in) s. panel painted 1965. 21-Sep-3 Subastas Odalys, Caracas #10/R
£1266 $2000 €1848 Landscape (59x74cm-23x29in) s. painted 1945. 1-Dec-2 Subastas Odalys, Caracas #100/R
£1317 $2450 €1923 Banana plantation (74x65cm-29x26in) s. painted 1960. 14-Mar-4 Subastas Odalys, Caracas #31/R
£1355 $2100 €1978 Landscape (77x66cm-30x26in) s. painted 1965. 3-Nov-2 Subastas Odalys, Caracas #100/R
£1457 $2710 €2127 May flower (76x66cm-30x26in) s. painted 1967. 14-Mar-4 Subastas Odalys, Caracas #16
£1519 $2400 €2218 Landscape (43x49cm-17x19in) s. masonite painted 1937. 1-Dec-2 Subastas Odalys, Caracas #40/R
£1533 $2560 €2238 Rain (76x66cm-30x26in) s. painted 1966. 13-Jul-3 Subastas Odalys, Caracas #96/R
£1592 $2865 €2324 Banana plantation (77x66cm-30x26in) s. painted 1970. 25-Apr-4 Subastas Odalys, Caracas #45/R
£1646 $2600 €2403 Burning (67x77cm-26x30in) s. painted 1974. 1-Dec-2 Subastas Odalys, Caracas #97/R
£1659 $3020 €2489 Seascape (50x60cm-20x24in) s. painted 1953. 21-Jun-4 Subastas Odalys, Caracas #59
£1683 $2810 €2457 White chrysanthemums (76x66cm-30x26in) s. painted 1968. 13-Jul-3 Subastas Odalys, Caracas #60/R
£1778 $2845 €2596 White chrysanthemums (76x66cm-30x26in) s. painted 1968. 21-Sep-3 Subastas Odalys, Caracas #73/R
£1935 $3000 €2825 Landscape (64x74cm-25x29in) s. painted 1945. 3-Nov-2 Subastas Odalys, Caracas #44/R
£1945 $3540 €2918 Landscape (76x67cm-30x26in) s. painted 1968. 21-Jun-4 Subastas Odalys, Caracas #13/R
£1946 $3250 €2841 Burning (66x76cm-26x30in) s. painted 1970. 13-Jul-3 Subastas Odalys, Caracas #108/R
£1991 $3185 €2907 Burning (66x76cm-26x30in) s. painted 1970. 21-Sep-3 Subastas Odalys, Caracas #92/R
£2096 $3500 €3060 White tree (76x66cm-30x26in) s. painted 1966. 13-Jul-3 Subastas Odalys, Caracas #33/R
£2132 $3560 €3113 Yellow roses (75x65cm-30x26in) s. painted 1967. 13-Jul-3 Subastas Odalys, Caracas #48/R
£2279 $3875 €3327 Apamate (75x66cm-30x26in) s. painted 1969. 23-Nov-3 Subastas Odalys, Caracas #65/R
£3871 $6580 €5652 Landscape (45x51cm-18x20in) s. masonite painted 1937. 23-Nov-3 Subastas Odalys, Caracas #45/R est:4000

Works on paper
£374 $625 €546 Vase of flowers (59x45cm-23x18in) s. pastel exec.1964. 13-Jul-3 Subastas Odalys, Caracas #103

GOLDMAN, Lester (20th C) American
£492 $900 €718 Chuck and Joanna (81x97cm-32x38in) 10-Jul-4 Hindman, Chicago #180/R est:500-700

GOLDMAN, Robert (1955-) German?
£511 $900 €746 Sunset on Sabino Wash (30x41cm-12x16in) s. painted c.1999. 23-May-4 Treadway Gallery, Cincinnati #599/R
£625 $1100 €913 Across the canyon, Mission Hills (51x61cm-20x24in) s.d.2000. 23-May-4 Treadway Gallery, Cincinnati #600/R

GOLDSCHEIDER, Friedrich (1845-1897) Austrian/French
Sculpture
£2158 $3453 €3000 Oriental figures (46cm-18in) i.verso terracotta pair. 18-May-3 Salle des ventes Pillet, Lyon la Foret #124/R
£2587 $4399 €3700 Dancer (114cm-45in) s. painted terracotta. 19-Nov-3 Cambi, Genoa #116/R est:3500-4000
£2685 $4966 €4000 Jeune femme au papillon (68x43cm-27x17in) s.num. polychrome terracotta exec.c.1889 lit. 15-Mar-4 Gros & Delettrez, Paris #190/R est:4000-6000
£4667 $8540 €7000 Couple d'orientaux (65cm-26in) polychrome terracotta lit. 3-Jun-4 Tajan, Paris #251/R est:6000-10000

GOLDSCHMIDT, David (1896-?) Swiss
£281 $504 €410 Nude reading (46x38cm-18x15in) s. masonite. 22-Mar-4 Philippe Schuler, Zurich #6146 (S.FR 650)

GOLDSCHMIDT, Henrique (1867-1952) ?
Works on paper
£275 $486 €413 Coastal landscape (16x24cm-6x9in) s. W/C. 27-Apr-4 Bolsa de Arte, Rio de Janeiro #7/R (B.R 1500)

GOLDSCHMIDT, Hilde (1897-1980) Austrian?
Works on paper
£282 $493 €400 Young girl (44x34cm-17x13in) mono. i.verso W/C. 19-Dec-3 Dorotheum, Vienna #166/R
£537 $993 €800 Sheep (22x31cm-9x12in) s.d.Okt 1920 mixed media board. 9-Mar-4 Dorotheum, Vienna #21/R

GOLDSMITH, Sybil (20th C) American
£369 $650 €539 Monomy (61x91cm-24x36in) s. 23-May-4 Hindman, Chicago #996/R

GOLDSMITH, Walter (fl.1880-1898) British
£1604 $3000 €2342 Windsor (61x91cm-24x36in) s. 24-Feb-4 Arthur James, Florida #313
Works on paper
£800 $1336 €1168 Goring. Streatley (36x75cm-14x30in) s.i.d.1901 W/C pair. 21-Oct-3 Sworder & Son, Bishops Stortford #302/R
£1600 $2560 €2336 Autumn landscape with sheep. Landscape with boat and weir (50x70cm-20x28in) s.d.1888 W/C pair. 19-May-3 Bruton Knowles, Cheltenham #171/R est:800-1200

GOLDSTEIN, Jack (1946-2003) Canadian
£633 $1000 €924 Untitled (91x244cm-36x96in) acrylic. 7-Sep-3 Treadway Gallery, Cincinnati #758/R est:4000-6000
£1329 $2100 €1940 Untitled (91x244cm-36x96in) acrylic. 7-Sep-3 Treadway Gallery, Cincinnati #759/R est:4000-6000
£1582 $2500 €2310 Untitled (213x183cm-84x72in) acrylic. 7-Sep-3 Treadway Gallery, Cincinnati #757/R est:4000-6000

GOLDSTEIN, Johann Theodor (1798-c.1871) German
£604 $1105 €900 Nightime eruption of Vesuvius (50x77cm-20x30in) s.d.1872 lit. 8-Jul-4 Allgauer, Kempten #2100/R

GOLDSTEIN, Louise Marks (1899-?) American
£359 $600 €524 Floral still life (64x76cm-25x30in) 18-Oct-3 David Dike, Dallas #87/R

GOLDSWORTHY, Andy (1956-) British
Photographs
£2778 $5000 €4056 Clay holes, October-November (40x40cm-16x16in) s.d.1992 cibachrome prints mounted on board smaller text photo. 23-Apr-4 Phillips, New York #246/R est:7000-10000
£3200 $5440 €4672 Snow stack, North Pole (102x76cm-40x30in) cibachrome print. 18-Nov-3 Christie's, Kensington #238/R est:4000-6000
£4000 $7280 €5840 Iris blade (75x75cm-30x30in) cibachrome print prov. 21-Jun-4 Bonhams, New Bond Street #117/R est:4000-6000
£5000 $8350 €7300 Blocks of snow, carved and stacked (124x124cm-49x49in) cibachrome print exec 1989 prov.lit. 21-Oct-3 Sotheby's, London #449/R est:5000-7000

GOLDTHWAIT, Harold (19th C) British
£280 $501 €409 View near Arundel, Sussex (23x36cm-9x14in) panel. 7-May-4 Mallams, Oxford #349/R
£403 $742 €588 Cottage by the marshes, Sussex (41x61cm-16x24in) s. i.verso. 14-Jun-4 Waddingtons, Toronto #131/R est:1000-1500 (C.D 1000)

GOLDTHWAITE, Anne (1875-1944) American
£598 $1100 €873 Two women and baby (48x41cm-19x16in) s. 10-Jun-4 Swann Galleries, New York #95/R
£1413 $2600 €2063 Seated nude (53x46cm-21x18in) s. 10-Jun-4 Swann Galleries, New York #96/R est:1000-1500

GOLFINOS, Georgios (1948-) Greek
Works on paper
£3000 $5370 €4380 Anudsia (104x78cm-41x31in) s.i.d.1990 verso mixed media collage board. 10-May-4 Sotheby's, Olympia #48/R est:2000-3000

GOLINKIN, Joseph Webster (1896-1977) American
Works on paper
£216 $400 €315 Trotting horse race (46x58cm-18x23in) s. W/C. 19-Jan-4 Winter Associates, Plainville #125/R

GOLIWAS, Ruth (20th C) American
£865 $1600 €1298 Shrimp boats (91x122cm-36x48in) s. 17-Jul-4 New Orleans Auction, New Orleans #872/R est:2000-4000

GOLLER, Bruno (1901-) German
£2273 $4000 €3319 Portrait of a woman (102x51cm-40x20in) s. 23-May-4 Hindman, Chicago #953/R est:8000-12000

GOLLINGS, William Elling (1878-1932) American
£11765 $20000 €17177 On the drive (25x61cm-10x24in) s.d.1904 prov.lit. 1-Nov-3 Santa Fe Art, Santa Fe #128/R est:30000-40000
£14706 $27500 €21471 Hunter (28x18cm-11x7in) s.d.1917 canvas on board prov. 24-Jul-4 Coeur d'Alene, Hayden #125/R est:20000-30000
£17380 $32500 €25375 Crow camp by moonlight (18x25cm-7x10in) s.d.1923 canvasboard prov. 24-Jul-4 Coeur d'Alene, Hayden #20/R est:15000-25000
£24064 $45000 €35133 Horses grazing in the snow (18x25cm-7x10in) s.d.1923 board prov. 24-Jul-4 Coeur d'Alene, Hayden #123/R est:20000-30000
£32086 $60000 €46846 Indian walking through the snow (25x18cm-10x7in) s.d.1923 canvasboard prov. 24-Jul-4 Coeur d'Alene, Hayden #124/R est:15000-25000
Works on paper
£12032 $22500 €17567 Watching the herd (30x23cm-12x9in) s.d.1910 W/C. 24-Jul-4 Coeur d'Alene, Hayden #126/R est:8000-12000

GOLOVIN, Aleksandr (1863-1930) Russian
Works on paper
£500 $800 €730 Stage costume design Harlequin (23x15cm-9x6in) W/C exec.c.1920. 21-Sep-3 William Jenack, New York #68
£1900 $3401 €2774 Costume design for Lermonotov's Masquerda (35x30cm-14x12in) s. W/C gouache. 26-May-4 Sotheby's, Olympia #405/R est:800-1200
£2200 $3938 €3212 Elegant lady in masquerade costume (33x28cm-13x11in) init.i. pen gouache. 26-May-4 Sotheby's, Olympia #413/R est:800-1200

GOLOVIN, Aleksandr (attrib) (1863-1930) Russian
Works on paper
£223 $400 €326 Castle (20x18cm-8x7in) W/C gouache. 11-Jan-4 William Jenack, New York #144

GOLTZIUS, Hendrik (1558-1616) Dutch
Prints
£2667 $4773 €4000 Midas judgement (42x67cm-17x26in) copperplate. 13-May-4 Bassenge, Berlin #5164/R est:4000
£11765 $20000 €17177 Great standard-bearer (28x19cm-11x7in) init. engraving. 31-Oct-3 Sotheby's, New York #146/R

GOLUB, Leon Albert (1922-) American
£1111 $2000 €1622 Untitled, penis. Untitled, penis. Untitled, head (2x7cm-1x3in) s. cut canvas three. 24-Apr-4 David Rago, Lambertville #453/R est:1000-2000
£2778 $5000 €4056 Untitled (15x13cm-6x5in) s. s.i.d.1984 verso. 24-Apr-4 David Rago, Lambertville #221/R est:2000-4000
£3514 $6500 €5130 Head VII (51x36cm-20x14in) s.i.d.1959 verso. 12-Feb-4 Sotheby's, New York #130/R est:4000-6000
£3800 $6992 €5548 New limb (107x91cm-42x36in) s.i. s.i.d.Dec. 1985 verso acrylic prov. 24-Jun-4 Sotheby's, Olympia #605/R est:3000-5000
£5278 $9500 €7706 Anchovie man (36x24cm-14x9in) s. prov. 24-Apr-4 David Rago, Lambertville #61/R est:2000-3000
£10556 $19000 €15412 Head XIV (24x19cm-9x7in) s. s.i.d.1962 verso prov. 24-Apr-4 David Rago, Lambertville #532/R est:4000-6000
Works on paper
£3056 $5500 €4462 City image (20x30cm-8x12in) mixed media masonite prov. 24-Apr-4 David Rago, Lambertville #328/R est:2000-3000

GOLZE, M (20th C) ?
Sculpture
£1400 $2380 €2044 Figure of a maiden (38cm-15in) s. bronze alabaster red marble pedestal. 25-Nov-3 Sotheby's, Olympia #49/R est:1500-2000

GOMAR Y GOMAR, Antonio (1853-1911) Spanish
£1449 $2377 €2000 Village street (47x32cm-19x13in) s. 27-May-3 Durán, Madrid #133/R est:2000

GOMBAR, Andras (?) French
£317 $529 €463 Brass and copper bowls with glass jars on a table (61x91cm-24x36in) s. 17-Nov-3 Waddingtons, Toronto #181/R (C.D 700)
£400 $748 €600 Still life of red pigment in a glass jar, a ladle and other receptacles (30x40cm-12x16in) s. board. 26-Jul-4 Bonhams, Bath #40/R

GOMES, Andre (20th C) ?
Works on paper
£340 $609 €500 Untitled (45x54cm-18x21in) collage. 21-Mar-4 Calmels Cohen, Paris #86

GOMEZ CORNET, Ramon (1898-1964) Argentinian
£4420 $8000 €6453 Flowers (33x23cm-13x9in) cardboard. 30-Mar-4 Arroyo, Buenos Aires #78

GOMEZ GIL, Lola (1895-?) Spanish
£580 $951 €800 Marine scene (74x92cm-29x36in) s. 27-May-3 Durán, Madrid #49/R

GOMEZ MAYORGA, Guillermo (1887-1962) Mexican
£2083 $3437 €3000 Figures outside Mexican church. Procession (23x35cm-9x14in) s. canvs on panel two. 2-Jul-3 Neumeister, Munich #647/R est:2200
£2296 $3835 €3329 Buscando cahmba en Xochimilco (120x180cm-47x71in) s. masonite. 24-Jun-3 Louis Morton, Mexico #127/R est:45000-100000 (M.P 40000)

GOMEZ PERALES, Jose Luis (1923-) Spanish
£405 $714 €600 8813 (24x24cm-9x9in) s.i.d.1988 verso acrylic board prov. 18-May-4 Segre, Madrid #218/R
£1127 $1972 €1600 Composition on three floors (52x51cm-20x20in) s.i.d.1983 panel on board prov. 16-Dec-3 Segre, Madrid #201/R est:1000

GOMEZ Y GIL, Guillermo (1862-1942) Spanish
£423 $739 €600 Seascape (17x21cm-7x8in) s. cardboard. 16-Dec-3 Segre, Madrid #81/R
£1862 $3091 €2700 Seascape (50x60cm-20x24in) s. 30-Sep-3 Ansorena, Madrid #109/R est:2300
£8553 $15737 €13000 Reflections (75x90cm-30x35in) s. i.verso. 22-Jun-4 Durán, Madrid #213/R est:4500

GOMEZ Y NIEDERLEYTNER, German (19th C) Spanish
£1135 $1895 €1600 Seascapes (31x50cm-12x20in) one s.d.80 pair. 20-Oct-3 Durán, Madrid #78/R est:1600

GOMEZ Y PLASENT, Vicente (19/20th C) Spanish
£986 $1706 €1400 Woman with flowers (55x40cm-22x16in) s. 15-Dec-3 Ansorena, Madrid #355/R

GOMEZ, E (20th C) Spanish
£1111 $1811 €1600 Soldiers on horseback (40x22cm-16x9in) s. 23-Sep-3 Durán, Madrid #590/R est:600
£1111 $1811 €1600 Soldiers in formation (40x22cm-16x9in) s. 23-Sep-3 Durán, Madrid #591/R est:600

GOMEZ, Gabriel (19th C) Spanish
£3000 $5520 €4380 Preparation for the fiesta (26x34cm-10x13in) s.i. panel. 25-Mar-4 Christie's, Kensington #151/R est:4000-6000

GOMEZ, Manuel Vicente (20th C) Venezuelan?
£275 $460 €402 Landscape (73x85cm-29x33in) s. painted 1970. 19-Oct-3 Subastas Odalys, Caracas #129

GOMEZ, Marco Antonio (1910-1972) American/Mexican
£559 $1000 €816 Rendez'vous (61x76cm-24x30in) s. s.i.verso. 8-Jan-4 James Julia, Fairfield #693/R

GOMEZ, Sebastian (attrib) (1646-1682) Spanish
£2752 $5118 €4100 Immaculate Conception (83x64cm-33x25in) 2-Mar-4 Ansorena, Madrid #256/R est:2500

GOMEZ-PABLOS, Mercedes (20th C) Spanish
Works on paper
£278 $453 €400 Composition (72x115cm-28x45in) s. s.verso collage. 23-Sep-3 Durán, Madrid #15/R

GOMIDE, Antonio Goncalves (attrib) (1895-1967) Brazilian
Works on paper
£3663 $6484 €5495 Children playing (24x35cm-9x14in) s. gouache. 27-Apr-4 Bolsa de Arte, Rio de Janeiro #55/R (B.R 20000)

GOMILA, Juan (1942-) Spanish
Works on paper
£1014 $1784 €1500 Figure (31x22cm-12x9in) s. gouache. 18-May-4 Segre, Madrid #261/R est:1500

GOMOT, S (19/20th C) French
£2200 $4070 €3212 Boats at St Malo (28x55cm-11x22in) s.i. pair. 14-Jul-4 Sotheby's, Olympia #278/R est:1800-2500

GOMZE, Paul (1870-1949) Belgian
£461 $834 €700 Jeune femme nue se mirant (50x34cm-20x13in) s. panel. 19-Apr-4 Horta, Bruxelles #461

GONCOURT, Jules de (1830-1870) French
Works on paper
£933 $1717 €1400 Paysage avec moulin vert (8x14cm-3x6in) s. W/C exhib. 9-Jun-4 Piasa, Paris #85/R
£1067 $1963 €1600 Paysage industriel (10x16cm-4x6in) s. W/C exhib. 9-Jun-4 Piasa, Paris #84/R est:1000-1200

GONDOUIN, Emmanuel (1883-1934) French
£2013 $3242 €3000 Deux zebres. s.d.28 oil brush couteau grattage exhib. 23-Feb-3 St-Germain-en-Laye Encheres #132/R est:2500-3000
£2113 $3655 €3000 Vase de fleurs (51x40cm-20x16in) s.d.1911. 9-Dec-3 Artcurial Briest, Paris #256/R est:3000-4000
£3490 $5619 €5200 La danseuse rouge et bleue. s. oil brush couteau grattage exhib. 23-Feb-3 St-Germain-en-Laye Encheres #129/R est:5000-6000
£7343 $12483 €10500 Portrait de Van Dongen (81x66cm-32x26in) s.d.1917 prov. 23-Nov-3 Cornette de St.Cyr, Paris #129/R est:300-400

Works on paper
£667 $1200 €1000 Nature morte au bouquet (47x28cm-19x11in) s.d.1924 gouache. 24-Apr-4 Cornette de St.Cyr, Paris #365/R

GONDRY, Jules (1860-1921) French
£769 $1323 €1123 Cockerel (54x40cm-21x16in) s.d.82. 7-Dec-3 Uppsala Auktionskammare, Uppsala #85/R (S.KR 10000)

GONG XIAN (1599-1689) Chinese
Works on paper
£12802 $23044 €18691 Dwelling in the mountains (218x98cm-86x39in) s.i. ink hanging scroll. 25-Apr-4 Christie's, Hong Kong #359/R est:200000-300000 (HK.D 180000)

GONGELAS, T (19th C) French
£1100 $1980 €1606 Au secret bien garde - two young ladies at a table (54x45cm-21x18in) s. 20-Apr-4 Hutchinson, Boroughbridge #319/R est:1000-1500

GONI SUAREZ, Lorenzo (1911-1992) Spanish
Works on paper
£263 $484 €400 Discrete charm of strip-tease (35x25cm-14x10in) s. dr. 22-Jun-4 Durán, Madrid #28
£317 $507 €450 Woman with roses (25x35cm-10x14in) s. W/C ink cardboard. 16-Sep-3 Segre, Madrid #302/R

GONIN, Francesco (1808-1889) Italian
Works on paper
£319 $533 €450 Rose scent (26x19cm-10x7in) s. W/C. 20-Oct-3 Sant Agostino, Torino #249/R

GONIN, Jacques Ferdinand (1883-?) French
£389 $650 €568 Portrait of an elegant lady (51x41cm-20x16in) s. 16-Nov-3 Bonhams & Butterfields, Los Angeles #7011/R
£400 $728 €600 Elegante dans le parc (51x40cm-20x16in) s. 4-Jul-4 Eric Pillon, Calais #216/R

GONNE, Friedrich (?) ?
£867 $1551 €1300 Two women in peasant kitchen (35x30cm-14x12in) s. i. stretcher. 13-May-4 Bassenge, Berlin #5555/R
£1944 $3169 €2800 Portrait of young Italian girl (102x85cm-40x33in) s.d.1863. 25-Sep-3 Dr Fritz Nagel, Stuttgart #1309/R est:2200

GONNER, Rudolf (1872-1926) German
£1184 $2179 €1800 View of Triest Harbour (60x80cm-24x31in) s.d.23. 22-Jun-4 Wiener Kunst Auktionen, Vienna #58/R est:1800

GONON, Eugène (1814-1892) French
Sculpture
£3500 $6405 €5110 Janissaire (51cm-20in) s.d.1863 pat bronze. 9-Jul-4 Sotheby's, London #133/R est:3000-5000

GONSCHIOR, Kuno (1935-) German
£4437 $7675 €6300 Green (100x80cm-39x31in) s.i.d.1994 verso lit. 13-Dec-3 Lempertz, Koln #142/R est:3000

GONTARD, Moris (1940-) French
£604 $1069 €900 Icons XV (42x40cm-17x16in) s. acrylic paper. 30-Apr-4 Auktionhaus Georg Rehm, Augsburg #7591
£694 $1097 €1000 Quelques objets insolites dans ce doux paysage (110x115cm-43x45in) s.d.1989 s.i.on stretcher acrylic painted wood prov. 27-Apr-3 Versailles Encheres #155
£868 $1372 €1250 Un froid inexplicable s'etait glisse (97x130cm-38x51in) s.d.1989 s.i.on stretcher acrylic prov. 27-Apr-3 Versailles Encheres #157

GONTCHAROVA, Natalia (1881-1962) Russian
£2657 $4517 €3800 Paysage rayonniste (22x15cm-9x6in) s.d.1956 verso oil gouache cardboard prov.exhib. 23-Nov-3 Cornette de St.Cyr, Paris #134 est:500-600
£2703 $4838 €4000 Fox (41x50cm-16x20in) s. mono.i. verso panel lit. 8-May-4 Schloss Ahlden, Ahlden #836/R est:3800
£5742 $9934 €8383 Composition (25x15cm-10x6in) s. tempera paper. 12-Dec-3 Kieselbach, Budapest #28/R (H.F 2200000)
£8333 $15000 €12166 Le bouquet (16x22cm-6x9in) s. i.verso board prov. 23-Apr-4 Sotheby's, New York #48/R est:15000-20000
£13333 $24000 €19466 Vase de roses (35x24cm-14x9in) s. 23-Apr-4 Sotheby's, New York #49/R est:25000-35000
£16000 $28800 €24000 Still life with laburnum (100x76cm-39x30in) 24-Apr-4 Dr Lehr, Berlin #133/R est:20000
£20000 $36800 €30000 Bouquet de fleurs (46x38cm-18x15in) s. painted c.1912. 8-Jun-4 Artcurial Briest, Paris #179/R est:20000-30000
£27703 $48757 €41000 Vase de fleurs (53x41cm-21x16in) s. 19-May-4 Camard, Paris #104/R est:30000-40000
£32000 $54400 €46720 Female Portrait (60x46cm-24x18in) s. 19-Nov-3 Sotheby's, London #217/R est:30000-40000
£90000 $153000 €131400 Espagnole (81x45cm-32x18in) s. s.i.stretcher prov. 19-Nov-3 Sotheby's, London #176/R est:80000-120000
£120000 $204000 €175200 Espagnole with pink magnolia (68x49cm-27x19in) s.i. prov. 19-Nov-3 Sotheby's, London #175/R est:50000-70000
Works on paper
£379 $630 €550 Loups (28x23cm-11x9in) ink. 6-Oct-3 Blanchet, Paris #226
£379 $630 €550 Coq (17x23cm-7x9in) crayon. 6-Oct-3 Blanchet, Paris #236
£414 $687 €600 Loups (28x23cm-11x9in) ink. 6-Oct-3 Blanchet, Paris #234/R
£414 $687 €600 Paon et loup (28x23cm-11x9in) ink. 6-Oct-3 Blanchet, Paris #229
£621 $1030 €900 Colombe (23x28cm-9x11in) ink felt-tip pen gouache. 6-Oct-3 Blanchet, Paris #227
£629 $1083 €900 Projet de costume (23x15cm-9x6in) mono. graphite. 2-Dec-3 Calmels Cohen, Paris #1/R
£690 $1145 €1000 Esquisse aux pans (28x23cm-11x9in) ink gouache. 6-Oct-3 Blanchet, Paris #233
£897 $1488 €1300 Maquette (30x22cm-12x9in) ink. 6-Oct-3 Blanchet, Paris #237/R
£1049 $1783 €1500 L'Africain au masque (20x15cm-8x6in) init. Indian ink prov. 23-Nov-3 Cornette de St.Cyr, Paris #133/R est:100-120
£1119 $1902 €1600 Apotre (34x26cm-13x10in) i.verso crayon prov. 23-Nov-3 Cornette de St.Cyr, Paris #132/R est:180-200
£1126 $2049 €1700 Portrait de femme (36x24cm-14x9in) s.i.d.1918 crayon. 18-Jun-4 Charbonneaux, Paris #88 est:700-800
£1457 $2652 €2200 Composition constructiviste (26x20cm-10x8in) s. crayon. 18-Jun-4 Charbonneaux, Paris #89/R est:1000-1200
£1549 $2680 €2200 Bord de mer a la Faviere (62x47cm-24x19in) W/C prov. 9-Dec-3 Artcurial Briest, Paris #242/R est:2000-3000
£1549 $2680 €2200 Paysage a la Faviere (47x62cm-19x24in) W/C prov. 9-Dec-3 Artcurial Briest, Paris #241 est:2000-3000
£1549 $2680 €2200 Vase de fleurs devant la mer (62x47cm-24x19in) W/C prov. 9-Dec-3 Artcurial Briest, Paris #243 est:2000-3000
£1623 $2953 €2450 La princesse, projet pour le Theatre Antoine (47x31cm-19x12in) s. i.verso india ink graphite W/C. 16-Jun-4 Claude Boisgirard, Paris #68/R est:2500-3000
£1689 $2973 €2500 Projet de costume (36x25cm-14x10in) s. W/C. 19-May-4 Camard, Paris #78/R est:4000-5000
£1793 $2994 €2600 Costume for 'Bolero' (37x27cm-15x11in) s. i.verso Chinese ink. 13-Nov-3 Finarte Semenzato, Rome #162/R est:1500-2000
£1900 $3439 €2774 Nymphe des bois (42x27cm-17x11in) s. pencil. 1-Apr-4 Christie's, Kensington #62/R est:1000-1500
£1972 $3411 €2800 Bord de mer a la Faviere (47x62cm-19x24in) W/C prov. 9-Dec-3 Artcurial Briest, Paris #244 est:2500-3500
£2067 $3761 €3100 Paysage (24x15cm-9x6in) s. W/C gouache exec c.1930. 5-Jul-4 Le Mouel, Paris #37/R est:3000-4000
£2083 $3479 €3000 Portrait of Serge Diaghilev (50x32cm-20x13in) mono. bodycol. 25-Oct-3 Dr Lehr, Berlin #155/R est:2000
£2222 $4000 €3244 Landscapes (25x20cm-10x8in) s. ink pair. 23-Apr-4 Sotheby's, New York #116/R est:5000-7000
£2676 $4630 €3800 Bord de mer a la Faviere (62x47cm-24x19in) W/C prov. 9-Dec-3 Artcurial Briest, Paris #240/R est:4000-6000
£2703 $4757 €4000 Projet de costume (55x43cm-22x17in) i.verso chl dr. 19-May-4 Camard, Paris #69/R est:4000
£3000 $5370 €4380 Forest (33x26cm-13x10in) mono. pastel. 26-May-4 Sotheby's, Olympia #499/R est:3000-5000
£3514 $6184 €5200 Reine des cygnes (57x44cm-22x17in) s. W/C. 19-May-4 Camard, Paris #67 est:4000-5000
£3716 $6541 €5500 Projet de costume (55x43cm-22x17in) i.verso chl dr. 19-May-4 Camard, Paris #70/R est:3000-4000
£4054 $7135 €6000 Projet de costume (56x43cm-22x17in) s. i.verso chl dr. 19-May-4 Camard, Paris #68/R est:3000-4000
£4730 $8324 €7000 Projet de costume (56x43cm-22x17in) i.verso chl dr. 19-May-4 Camard, Paris #71/R est:3000-4000
£4895 $8322 €7000 Composition cubiste (46x28cm-18x11in) s. graphite exec.c.1912 prov. 23-Nov-3 Cornette de St.Cyr, Paris #130/R est:400-500
£4895 $8322 €7000 Personnage (36x28cm-14x11in) s. graphite exec.c.1912 prov. 23-Nov-3 Cornette de St.Cyr, Paris #131/R est:600-800
£5000 $8950 €7300 Costume design for Les Noces (47x30cm-19x12in) s. gouache over pencil prov.exhib. 26-May-4 Sotheby's, London #219/R est:5000-7000
£5068 $8919 €7500 Projet de costume (31x44cm-12x17in) mono. W/C gouache. 19-May-4 Camard, Paris #79/R est:4000-5000
£5933 $10917 €8900 Danseuse aux boules articulees (86x67cm-34x26in) mono. gouache india ink prov. 11-Jun-4 Pierre Berge, Paris #173 est:1400-1600
£6643 $11294 €9500 Espagnole (51x27cm-20x11in) s.i. graphite prov. 23-Nov-3 Cornette de St.Cyr, Paris #135 est:500-600
£8000 $14320 €11680 Spanish dancer (33x24cm-13x9in) init. W/C pencil. 26-May-4 Sotheby's, London #221/R est:8000-12000
£9444 $17000 €13788 Flamenco dancer (73x51cm-29x20in) s.i.d.1916 pencil. 23-Apr-4 Sotheby's, New York #117/R est:10000-15000
£12324 $19965 €17500 La peri (40x140cm-16x55in) s. i.verso W/C ink gouache five panels prov. 5-Aug-3 Tajan, Paris #22/R est:20000-25000
£32000 $58240 €46720 La danse, rayonnisme (29x21cm-11x8in) init. col crayon painted c.1913 prov. 21-Jun-4 Bonhams, New Bond Street #21/R est:30000-40000
£38000 $69920 €55480 Rayonnisme (43x31cm-17x12in) s.i.d.1916 gouache W/C prov.exhib. 24-Jun-4 Christie's, London #370/R est:12000-15000

GONTHIER, Jean Pierre (1956-) Belgian
£302 $556 €450 Le masque (195x178cm-77x70in) s. 28-Mar-4 MonsAntic, Maisieres #391

GONTHIER, Marc (1895-1954) Swiss
£281 $477 €410 Still life with tulips (62x51cm-24x20in) s. board. 28-Nov-3 Zofingen, Switzerland #2998 (S.FR 620)

GONTIER, C (19th C) French
£2000 $3320 €2920 Still life, with peonies, plants and other flowers, and fruit on a ledge (74x91cm-29x36in) s. prov. 10-Jun-3 Canterbury Auctions, UK #105/R est:2000-2500
£2600 $4342 €3796 Still life of peonies, geranium and other plants and flowers (74x91cm-29x36in) s. prov. 14-Oct-3 Canterbury Auctions, UK #114/R est:1250-1600

GONTIER, Clement (19th C) French
£1183 $2117 €1727 Still lifes of flowers (35x27cm-14x11in) s. pair. 26-May-4 AB Stockholms Auktionsverk #2402/R est:15000-18000 (S.KR 16000)

GONTIER, Pierre Camille (1840-?) French
£1250 $2000 €1825 Cavaliers (61x28cm-24x11in) s.i. pair. 17-May-3 Bunte, Elgin #1234 est:2000-3000

GONZAGA, Giovanfrancesco (1921-) Italian
£500 $920 €750 Spahi (40x30cm-16x12in) s.i. s.i.verso mixed media paper on canvas. 12-Jun-4 Meeting Art, Vercelli #541/R

£769	$1323	€1100	Arabian horse (25x35cm-10x14in) s.i. 3-Dec-3 Stadion, Trieste #995/R
£867	$1551	€1300	Mushrooms (21x31cm-8x12in) s. s.i.d.1951 verso board. 12-May-4 Stadion, Trieste #719/R
£915	$1520	€1300	L'ussaro sulla neve (35x25cm-14x10in) s. s.i.verso. 14-Jun-3 Meeting Art, Vercelli #198/R
£966	$1545	€1400	Horse in water (30x24cm-12x9in) s. s.i.verso. 13-Mar-3 Galleria Pace, Milan #31/R est:1600-2000
£1000	$1840	€1500	Warrior (35x25cm-14x10in) s. 12-Jun-4 Meeting Art, Vercelli #997/R est:1500
£1056	$1754	€1500	Fruitti sulla spiaggia (30x40cm-12x16in) s. s.i.d.1991 verso. 14-Jun-3 Meeting Art, Vercelli #422/R est:1000
£1172	$1876	€1700	L (35x25cm-14x10in) s. s.i.verso. 13-Mar-3 Galleria Pace, Milan #126/R est:2000-2600
£1259	$2165	€1800	Horse with saddle (24x30cm-9x12in) s. s.i.d.1978 verso. 3-Dec-3 Stadion, Trieste #996/R est:1000-1500
£1319	$2085	€1900	Mushrooms in the under-growth (40x50cm-16x20in) painted 1990. 6-Sep-3 Meeting Art, Vercelli #696 est:1500
£1333	$2453	€2000	Green peppers (35x50cm-14x20in) s. painted 1945. 12-Jun-4 Meeting Art, Vercelli #617/R est:1500
£1477	$2732	€2200	Mushrooms and under-growth (40x50cm-16x20in) s. s.i.d.1965 verso. 13-Mar-4 Meeting Art, Vercelli #473 est:2000
£1517	$2428	€2200	Saddle seller (55x40cm-22x16in) s. 13-Mar-3 Galleria Pace, Milan #146/R est:2200-2800
£1528	$2414	€2200	Mythological horse amongst waves (40x50cm-16x20in) painted 1992. 6-Sep-3 Meeting Art, Vercelli #680 est:2000
£1533	$2821	€2300	Savoy Knight (50x40cm-20x16in) s. painted 1991. 12-Jun-4 Meeting Art, Vercelli #359/R est:1500
£1544	$2856	€2300	Rider (50x40cm-20x16in) s.s.i.verso. 13-Mar-4 Meeting Art, Vercelli #255
£1667	$2633	€2400	Tuscan cowboy in the snow (60x50cm-24x20in) 6-Sep-3 Meeting Art, Vercelli #449 est:2000
£1733	$3189	€2600	Tuscan cowboy (50x40cm-20x16in) s. painted 1975. 12-Jun-4 Meeting Art, Vercelli #259/R est:1500
£1733	$3189	€2600	The Finzi-Contini's garden (50x60cm-20x24in) s. s.i.d.1995v. 12-Jun-4 Meeting Art, Vercelli #740/R est:2000
£1793	$2869	€2600	Tuscan cowboy (70x50cm-28x20in) s. s.i.d.1994 verso. 13-Mar-3 Galleria Pace, Milan #141/R est:3000-4000
£1875	$2963	€2700	Tuscan cowboy on seashore (70x50cm-28x20in) 6-Sep-3 Meeting Art, Vercelli #477 est:2500
£2098	$3608	€3000	Fruit in landscape (40x50cm-16x20in) s. s.i.d.1990 verso. 3-Dec-3 Stadion, Trieste #994/R est:3000-4000
£2148	$3973	€3200	Tuscan cowboy in the snow (60x50cm-24x20in) s. s.i.verso. 13-Mar-4 Meeting Art, Vercelli #488 est:2000
£2200	$4048	€3300	Tuscan cowboy (70x50cm-28x20in) s. 12-Jun-4 Meeting Art, Vercelli #631/R est:2500
£2324	$3858	€3300	Corsieri nel bosco (50x70cm-20x28in) s. s.i.verso. 14-Jun-3 Meeting Art, Vercelli #714/R est:2500
£2416	$4470	€3600	Black stallion (40x50cm-16x20in) s. s.i.d.1989 verso. 13-Mar-4 Meeting Art, Vercelli #536 est:1500
£2685	$4805	€4000	Column Verziere Vecchio (60x50cm-24x20in) s.d.1945. 30-May-4 Meeting Art, Vercelli #71 est:4000
£2752	$5091	€4100	Two stags (50x70cm-20x28in) s. s.i.verso. 13-Mar-4 Meeting Art, Vercelli #543 est:2500
£2800	$5152	€4200	Horse (50x60cm-20x24in) s. painted 1952. 12-Jun-4 Meeting Art, Vercelli #971/R est:2500
£5224	$8881	€7625	Carabiniere (70x90cm-28x35in) s. 7-Nov-3 Galleria Rosenberg, Milan #39/R est:7000
£5224	$8881	€7625	Olive grove (70x90cm-28x35in) s. painted 1981. 7-Nov-3 Galleria Rosenberg, Milan #125/R est:7000
Works on paper			
£500	$920	€750	Tuscan cowboys (35x50cm-14x20in) s. mixed media card. 12-Jun-4 Meeting Art, Vercelli #154/R

GONZALES COLLADO, Antonio (1930-) Spanish

£533	$955	€800	Ballerinas (41x33cm-16x13in) s. 15-May-4 De Vuyst, Lokeren #146

GONZALES, Eva (1849-1883) French

Works on paper			
£710	$1300	€1037	Actress with mask (30x22cm-12x9in) init. brush black ink wash black chk. 29-Jan-4 Swann Galleries, New York #275/R

GONZALES, Roberta (1909-1976) French

£280	$476	€400	Nu a la draperie rose (32x15cm-13x6in) s.i.d.1950 verso panel prov. 23-Nov-3 Cornette de St.Cyr, Paris #511/R
Works on paper			
£638	$1034	€900	Jeune fille en jaune (43x34cm-17x13in) s.d.1964 pastel chl sketch. 20-May-3 Segre, Madrid #119/R

GONZALES, Xavier (1898-1993) American

£202	$375	€295	Royal ship on the Nile, Old Kingdom (67x114cm-26x45in) board prov.lit. 5-Mar-4 Skinner, Boston #338/R
£538	$1000	€785	Old Kingdom of Heb-Sed (68x60cm-27x24in) init. board prov.lit. 5-Mar-4 Skinner, Boston #341/R
£591	$1100	€863	Old Kingdom entertainment scene (60x71cm-24x28in) s. board prov.lit. 5-Mar-4 Skinner, Boston #340/R
£914	$1700	€1334	Burial ceremonies of King Unas, Saqqara, 5th Dynasty (90x76cm-35x30in) i.verso board prov.lit. 5-Mar-4 Skinner, Boston #342/R est:300-500
£2994	$5000	€4371	West Texas (30x23cm-12x9in) board. 18-Oct-3 David Dike, Dallas #194/R est:2500-3500

GONZALEZ ARENAL, Vidal (1857-1925) Spanish

£41781	$71027	€61000	Council meeting (90x150cm-35x59in) s. lit. 4-Nov-3 Ansorena, Madrid #143/R est:47000

GONZALEZ ARES, Antonio (1930-) Spanish

£517	$931	€750	Woman with flamenco dress (92x73cm-36x29in) s. 26-Jan-4 Ansorena, Madrid #82/R
£552	$993	€800	Young women with fruit (73x67cm-29x26in) s. 26-Jan-4 Ansorena, Madrid #264/R
£759	$1366	€1100	Womna with shawl (90x73cm-35x29in) s. 26-Jan-4 Ansorena, Madrid #81/R

GONZALEZ BOGEN, Carlos (20th C) South American

£1366	$2185	€1994	Self-portrait (65x50cm-26x20in) s. acrylic panel painted 1980. 21-Sep-3 Subastas Odalys, Caracas #68
£1806	$2800	€2637	Sp. with hat (65x55cm-26x22in) s. painted 1983. 29-Sep-2 Subastas Odalys, Caracas #36/R
£9191	$15625	€13419	Angostura Speech (110x200cm-43x79in) s. painted 1986. 23-Nov-3 Subastas Odalys, Caracas #43/R
Sculpture			
£4594	$7810	€6707	Dynamic (145x77x70cm-57x30x28in) wood exec.c.1950. 23-Nov-3 Subastas Odalys, Caracas #75/R

GONZALEZ BRAVO, Justo (1944-) Spanish

£1181	$1924	€1700	Untitled (54x65cm-21x26in) s. s.d.2002 verso exhib. 27-Sep-3 Dr Fritz Nagel, Stuttgart #9526/R est:1350

GONZALEZ CARBONELL, Rosendo (1910-) Spanish

£1053	$1905	€1600	Woman with lamp (73x60cm-29x24in) s. 14-Apr-4 Ansorena, Madrid #171/R est:1600

GONZALEZ DE ALEDO, Guillermo (1923-) Spanish

Works on paper			
£268	$475	€400	Boat (74x100cm-29x39in) s. W/C. 27-Apr-4 Durán, Madrid #666/R

GONZALEZ FERNANDEZ, Roberto (1948-) Spanish

£1408	$2437	€2000	Roofs (36x24cm-14x9in) s. board. 15-Dec-3 Ansorena, Madrid #944/R est:2000
£6333	$11653	€9500	Untitled (100x80cm-39x31in) s.d.2003 acrylic prov. 10-Jun-4 Christie's, Paris #73/R est:9500-12000

GONZALEZ GONZALEZ, Pedro (1927-) Spanish

£1944	$3208	€2800	Figure (102x86cm-40x34in) s.d.71. 2-Jul-3 Ansorena, Madrid #900/R est:400

GONZALEZ MARCOS, Angel (1900-1977) Spanish

£310	$518	€450	Catching a bull (72x100cm-28x39in) s. s.i.verso. 17-Nov-3 Durán, Madrid #1282/R
£426	$689	€600	Al quite con el palo dentro (50x65cm-20x26in) s. s.i.verso. 20-May-3 Ansorena, Madrid #15/R
£461	$747	€650	Batacazo en la puerta (50x65cm-20x26in) s. s.i.verso. 20-May-3 Ansorena, Madrid #16/R
£461	$747	€650	Saliendo de chiqueros (71x53cm-28x21in) s. 20-May-3 Ansorena, Madrid #17/R
£503	$901	€750	Bull (74x101cm-29x40in) s. 25-May-4 Durán, Madrid #641/R
£503	$901	€750	Cowboy (74x101cm-29x40in) s. s.i.d.1967 verso. 25-May-4 Durán, Madrid #640/R
£915	$1584	€1300	Bull ring (71x101cm-28x40in) s. 15-Dec-3 Ansorena, Madrid #358/R
£922	$1494	€1300	El ultimo tercio (73x101cm-29x40in) s. s.i.d.1975 verso. 20-May-3 Ansorena, Madrid #18/R
£922	$1494	€1300	Las doce (73x100cm-29x39in) s. s.i.d.1975 verso. 20-May-3 Ansorena, Madrid #19/R
£922	$1494	€1300	El arrastre (73x100cm-29x39in) s. s.i.d.1975 verso. 20-May-3 Ansorena, Madrid #20/R
£922	$1494	€1300	Segundo tercio (73x102cm-29x40in) s. s.i.verso. 20-May-3 Ansorena, Madrid #21/R
£922	$1494	€1300	El ultimo tercio (73x101cm-29x40in) s. s.i.d.1975 verso. 20-May-3 Ansorena, Madrid #22/R
£1972	$3451	€2800	Joselito el Gallo (82x100cm-32x39in) s. s.i.d.1942 verso. 16-Dec-3 Segre, Madrid #296/R est:2800
Works on paper			
£280	$467	€400	Bulls (48x62cm-19x24in) s. gouache. 30-Jun-3 Ansorena, Madrid #117/R

GONZALEZ PRIETO, Fermin (1900-1987) Spanish

£586	$979	€850	Landscape (29x39cm-11x15in) s. board. 17-Nov-3 Durán, Madrid #614/R
£1034	$1862	€1500	San Cugat del Valles, Barcelona (41x50cm-16x20in) s. board. 26-Jan-4 Durán, Madrid #667/R est:900

GONZALEZ VELAZQUEZ, Antonio (1723-1793) Spanish

£21053	$38105	€32000	Ascension (90x45cm-35x18in) 14-Apr-4 Ansorena, Madrid #133/R est:30000

GONZALEZ VELAZQUEZ, Zacarias (1763-1834) Spanish

£6081	$10703	€9000	Portrait of Sir Juan Palarea El Medico (45x35cm-18x14in) 18-May-4 Segre, Madrid #81/R est:7000
£8553	$15480	€13000	Portrait of lady (65x50cm-26x20in) 14-Apr-4 Ansorena, Madrid #141/R est:12000
£11842	$21434	€18000	Saint Francis and a leper (29x37cm-11x15in) 14-Apr-4 Ansorena, Madrid #137/R est:18000

GONZALEZ VELAZQUEZ, Zacarias (circle) (1763-1834) Spanish

£5000	$8500	€7300	Saint Francis receiving the host. Lamentation (66x48cm-26x19in) pair. 30-Oct-3 Sotheby's, Olympia #147/R est:5000-7000

GONZALEZ Y BOLIVAR, Pedro (19/20th C) Spanish

£517	$931	€750	View of Venice (61x40cm-24x16in) s.d.1912. 26-Jan-4 Ansorena, Madrid #154/R

GONZALEZ, Bartolome (style) (1564-1627) Spanish
£62000 $105400 €90520 Portrait of a lady wearing elaborately embroidered red dress, holding a handkerchief (117x94cm-46x37in) i. prov. 30-Oct-3 Sotheby's, Olympia #98/R est:7000-10000

GONZALEZ, Curro (1960-) Spanish
Works on paper
£845 $1479 €1200 General view (39x120cm-15x47in) s.d.1990 d.verso ink wash mixed media prov. 16-Dec-3 Segre, Madrid #188a/R

GONZALEZ, Juan Antonio (1842-1914) Spanish
£6000 $11040 €8760 Recital (35x48cm-14x19in) s.i.d.1875. 25-Mar-4 Christie's, Kensington #154/R est:5000-7000
Works on paper
£655 $1094 €950 Letter (44x28cm-17x11in) s. gouache. 17-Nov-3 Durán, Madrid #220/R
£655 $1094 €950 Reading (44x28cm-17x11in) s. W/C. 17-Nov-3 Durán, Madrid #221/R

GONZALEZ, Julio (1876-1942) Spanish
Sculpture
£60000 $110400 €87600 Petite Venus (20cm-8in) s. nim.0/6 brown pat. bronze conceived c.1936-1937 prov.lit. 23-Jun-4 Christie's, London #235/R est:70000-100000
£72626 $130000 €106034 Petite sculpture d'espace abstraite (11cm-4in) iron iron wire exec c.1933-34 prov.lit. 6-May-4 Sotheby's, New York #302/R est:120000-180000
£235294 $400000 €343529 Tete couchee abstraite (13cm-5in) s.d.1930 brown pat. bronze prov.exhib.lit. 4-Nov-3 Christie's, Rockefeller NY #33/R est:200000-400000
£310000 $564200 €452600 Teted dite le pompier (17cm-7in) white metal executed c.1933 prov.exhib.lit. 3-Feb-4 Sotheby's, London #60/R est:200000-300000
Works on paper
£2500 $4325 €3650 Tete de Montserrat (22x16cm-9x6in) init.d.1927 pencil. 11-Dec-3 Christie's, Kensington #77/R est:3000-4000
£4000 $7280 €5840 Vierge blue et ocre (20x16cm-8x6in) init.d.41 W/C pen ink over pencil prov.lit. 4-Feb-4 Sotheby's, London #462/R est:4000-6000
£5000 $9100 €7300 Deux femmes debout (16x11cm-6x4in) i.d.1930 verso W/C pencil ink prov.exhib.lit. 4-Feb-4 Sotheby's, London #461/R est:5000-7000
£5102 $9286 €7500 Paysanne (15x11cm-6x4in) pen ink pencil dr double-sided exhib.lit. 3-Feb-4 Segre, Madrid #367/R est:7500
£7500 $12000 €10950 Study for Cactus Man. Study for sculpture (32x24cm-13x9in) init.d.1938 col pencil ink double-sided. 18-Sep-3 Swann Galleries, New York #259/R est:7000-10000
£8939 $16000 €13051 Tete cubiste (22x10cm-9x4in) init.d.1936-5 pen India ink col wax crayons over pencil prov.lit. 5-May-4 Christie's, Rockefeller NY #131/R est:15000-20000
£10000 $18400 €15000 Etude pour l'homme cactus (25x17cm-10x7in) mono.d.1939 Indian ink wash. 10-Jun-4 Hauswedell & Nolte, Hamburg #225/R est:8000
£10615 $19000 €15498 Abstract (31x19cm-12x7in) init.d.1936 col wax crayons pen India ink over pencil prov.lit. 5-May-4 Christie's, Rockefeller NY #130/R est:18000-22000
£11000 $20020 €16060 Maternite (24x14cm-9x6in) pastel black crayon exec.1906 prov.lit. 4-Feb-4 Sotheby's, London #418/R est:8000-12000
£11333 $20853 €17000 Monsieur Cactus - Homme cactus I (26x13cm-10x5in) mono.d.1939 col chk Indian ink pencil. 10-Jun-4 Hauswedell & Nolte, Hamburg #224/R est:10000
£13000 $23660 €18980 La peur (24x14cm-9x6in) init.d.40 pen brush ink over pencil prov.exhib.lit. 4-Feb-4 Sotheby's, London #469/R est:9000-12000

GONZALEZ, Lorenzo (20th C) Spanish
£8276 $14897 €12000 In the study (162x130cm-64x51in) s.d.1990. 26-Jan-4 Ansorena, Madrid #900/R est:12000

GONZALEZ, Marcel (20th C) French
£493 $863 €700 Partie de cartes (30x21cm-12x8in) s.d.89. 21-Dec-3 Thierry & Lannon, Brest #386

GONZALEZ, Pedro Angel (1901-1981) Venezuelan
£759 $1200 €1108 Flower, jug and crystals (34x41cm-13x16in) s. painted 1976. 1-Dec-2 Subastas Odalys, Caracas #33
£898 $1500 €1311 Green window (36x27cm-14x11in) s. painted 1962. 13-Jul-3 Subastas Odalys, Caracas #18/R
£1431 $2605 €2147 Trees (46x55cm-18x22in) s. painted 1981. 21-Jun-4 Subastas Odalys, Caracas #28/R
£2183 $4060 €3187 Trees and fields (55x65cm-22x26in) s. painted 1967. 14-Mar-4 Subastas Odalys, Caracas #69/R
£2958 $4940 €4319 Peak at dusk (54x64cm-21x25in) s. painted 1976. 13-Jul-3 Subastas Odalys, Caracas #110/R
£3354 $5300 €4897 Avila (80x100cm-31x39in) s. 1-Dec-2 Subastas Odalys, Caracas #54/R
£3407 $5690 €4974 La Guaira (81x65cm-32x26in) s. painted 1975. 13-Jul-3 Subastas Odalys, Caracas #104/R
£3602 $6195 €5259 Landscape in Urbina (46x55cm-18x22in) S. P. 1970. 7-Dec-3 Subastas Odalys, Caracas #54/R est:8000
£4186 $6990 €6112 Path (54x65cm-21x26in) s. painted 1976. 13-Jul-3 Subastas Odalys, Caracas #39/R est:6000
£7644 $12995 €11160 Peak and town (54x65cm-21x26in) s. painted 1972. 23-Nov-3 Subastas Odalys, Caracas #63/R est:12000
£8903 $14245 €12998 Landscape (66x81cm-26x32in) s. painted 1965. 21-Sep-3 Subastas Odalys, Caracas #65/R
Works on paper
£269 $450 €393 Seascape (27x27cm-11x11in) s. mixed media exec.1953. 13-Jul-3 Subastas Odalys, Caracas #32/R

GONZALEZ, Rafael Ramón (1894-1975) Portuguese
£331 $530 €483 Lake (30x36cm-12x14in) s. 21-Sep-3 Subastas Odalys, Caracas #88
£332 $530 €485 Landscape (56x67cm-22x26in) s. 16-Mar-3 Subastas Odalys, Caracas #93
£469 $750 €685 Maria Lionza (100x81cm-39x32in) s. 16-Mar-3 Subastas Odalys, Caracas #94/R
£1614 $2970 €2356 Village (55x75cm-22x30in) s. painted 1967. 28-Mar-4 Subastas Odalys, Caracas #87/R

GONZALEZ, Ricardo (20th C) Venezuelan?
£323 $555 €472 Still life (101x180cm-40x71in) s. painted 2002. 7-Dec-3 Subastas Odalys, Caracas #114/R
£371 $675 €557 Still life (102x180cm-40x71in) s. acrylic painted 2002. 21-Jun-4 Subastas Odalys, Caracas #44

GONZALEZ, Roberto (20th C) Argentinian
£670 $1200 €978 Two figures (37x35cm-15x14in) cardboard. 11-May-4 Arroyo, Buenos Aires #48
£1547 $2800 €2259 Composition with figure (72x84cm-28x33in) board. 30-Mar-4 Arroyo, Buenos Aires #29

GONZALEZ, Zacarias (1923-2003) Spanish
£1200 $2172 €1800 Musician with clarinet (28x20cm-11x8in) s. board. 30-Mar-4 Segre, Madrid #118/R est:1200
£1342 $2497 €2000 Still life with tins (48x70cm-19x28in) s. board. 2-Mar-4 Ansorena, Madrid #866/R est:2000
Works on paper
£297 $523 €440 Abstract (26x34cm-10x13in) s. ink collage. 18-May-4 Segre, Madrid #123/R

GONZALEZ-TORRES, Felix (1957-1996) Cuban
Prints
£2994 $5000 €4371 Untitled - for parkett (317x691cm-125x272in) silkscreen printed billboard appleton stock in eight parts. 14-Nov-3 Phillips, New York #292/R est:6000-8000
£6587 $11000 €9617 Untitled (28x36cm-11x14in) photostat edition 1 of 2 prov. 13-Nov-3 Sotheby's, New York #194/R est:8000-12000
£10056 $18000 €14682 Untitled (27x33cm-11x13in) s.i.d.1987 verso photostat prov.exhib.lit. 12-May-4 Christie's, Rockefeller NY #363/R est:9000-12000
£10056 $18000 €14682 Untitled (21x26cm-8x10in) s.d.1987 verso photostat paperboard prov.lit. 14-May-4 Phillips, New York #170/R est:9000-12000
Works on paper
£36313 $65000 €53017 Untitled, t-cell count (49x40cm-19x16in) s.i.d.1990 verso graphite col pencil gouache prov.exhib.lit. 12-May-4 Christie's, Rockefeller NY #362/R est:40000-60000

GONZALO, Alberto (1954-) Spanish
£313 $516 €450 Storage place (100x81cm-39x32in) s.i.d.1989 verso. 2-Jul-3 Ansorena, Madrid #903/R

GONZALVO Y PEREZ, Pablo (1830-1896) Spanish
Works on paper
£738 $1321 €1100 Church interior (40x23cm-16x9in) s. W/C. 25-May-4 Durán, Madrid #184/R

GOOD, Bernard Stafford (1893-?) American
£275 $500 €402 Pirates loot (51x36cm-20x14in) init. board. 7-Feb-4 Sloans & Kenyon, Bethesda #1290/R
£549 $1000 €802 Two men cutting down a tree. Hunter in red jacket (51x33cm-20x13in) init. one d.39 one board one W/C pair. 7-Feb-4 Sloans & Kenyon, Bethesda #1289/R

GOOD, John Willis (1845-1879) British
Sculpture
£3250 $5915 €4745 Horse and jockey. s. bronze. 16-Jun-4 John Nicholson, Haslemere #268/R est:3500-4000
£4000 $7560 €5840 A hunter with the saddle hung with a fox's mask (36cm-14in) s. pat bronze. 23-Feb-4 David Duggleby, Scarborough #856/R est:1500-2000
£4000 $7320 €5840 Calling hounds out of cover (29x26cm-11x10in) s. plaster pair prov.exhib.lit. 9-Jul-4 Sotheby's, London #129/R est:4000-6000
£4200 $7686 €6132 Huntsman with hounds (31x27cm-12x11in) s.d.1875 pat bronze. 9-Jul-4 Sotheby's, London #128/R est:4000-6000
£5800 $9860 €8468 Calling hounds out of cover. Huntsman (28x25cm-11x10in) s.st.f.Elkington pat bronze lit. 28-Oct-3 Sotheby's, London #110/R

GOODACRE, Glenna (20th C) American
Sculpture
£932 $1500 €1351 Prudence (28cm-11in) bronze edition of 25. 22-Aug-3 Altermann Galleries, Santa Fe #188
£1647 $2800 €2405 Proud brave (33cm-13in) bronze. 1-Nov-3 Altermann Galleries, Santa Fe #141
£11765 $20000 €17177 Bather (122x112x51cm-48x44x20in) s.d.1989 num.1/15 bronze prov. 1-Nov-3 Santa Fe Art, Santa Fe #187/R est:30000-40000

GOODALL, Edward (1795-1870) British
Works on paper
£227 $370 €331 View from Malahat Mountain highway, Vancouver Island, BC (45x29cm-18x11in) s.i.d.1940 s.i.verso W/C. 23-Sep-3 Ritchie, Toronto #146/R (C.D 500)
£331 $598 €483 View from Malahatm mountain highway, Vancouver Island, B.C (43x27cm-17x11in) s.d.1940 d.verso W/C. 18-Apr-4 Levis, Calgary #38/R (C.D 800)

GOODALL, Edward Alfred (1819-1908) British
Works on paper
£280 $476 €409 Interior of a cafe in Brittany with domino players (24x34cm-9x13in) indis.sig.d.1834 W/C. 25-Nov-3 Martel Maides, Guernsey #215
£420 $769 €613 Walled mosque in the desert (16x52cm-6x20in) W/C pencil. 8-Jul-4 Lawrence, Crewkerne #1523
£650 $1164 €949 The islands of Murano, Burano and the Campo Santo, Venice (15x29cm-6x11in) s. W/C. 25-May-4 Bonhams, Knightsbridge #163/R

£950 $1634 €1387 Public gardens, Gibraltar (33x49cm-13x19in) s.i. pencil W/C. 3-Dec-3 Christie's, Kensington #103/R
£1200 $2040 €1752 Venetian canal scene (14x24cm-6x9in) s.d.1885 pencil W/C. 19-Nov-3 Tennants, Leyburn #896 est:300-400
£1800 $3312 €2628 In the souk, Tangier (34x47cm-13x19in) s.i.d.1880 W/C. 8-Jun-4 Bonhams, New Bond Street #57/R est:800-1200
£3600 $6480 €5256 Venice, the Grand Canal with gondolas and fishing boats in foreground (32x53cm-13x21in) s.i. pencil W/C. 21-Apr-4 Tennants, Leyburn #951/R est:1500-2000

GOODALL, Frederick (1822-1904) British
£400 $680 €584 Distraction from chores (25x32cm-10x13in) s.d.1845 panel. 6-Nov-3 Christie's, Kensington #756/R
£475 $850 €694 Pyramids of Ghizah (25x61cm-10x24in) mono. board. 21-Mar-4 Hindman, Chicago #778/R est:1000-2000
£900 $1422 €1305 In the grounds of the ruined abbey (27x37cm-11x15in) s. indis d. panel. 4-Sep-3 Christie's, Kensington #162
£1000 $1800 €1460 Shepherds at Gizeh (38x92cm-15x36in) mono.d.1895. 21-Jan-4 Sotheby's, Olympia #377/R est:1000-1500
£1100 $1837 €1606 Flight into Egypt (42x62cm-17x24in) mono.d.1884-97. 12-Nov-3 Sotheby's, Olympia #103/R est:1000-1500
£2000 $3680 €2920 Brickmakers in Egypt (38x92cm-15x36in) mono.d.1884 prov. 11-Jun-4 Christie's, London #152/R est:2500-3500
£2500 $3950 €3625 Of such the Kingdom of Heaven (38x23cm-15x9in) oil on paper. 4-Sep-3 Christie's, Kensington #232/R est:800-1200
£2890 $5000 €4219 Evening meal (38x91cm-15x36in) mono.d.1884 i.verso prov. 13-Dec-3 Weschler, Washington #534 est:2000-4000
£3000 $5370 €4380 Resting from the days journey (35x53cm-14x21in) mono.i.d.1870 prov. 26-May-4 Sotheby's, Olympia #135/R est:3000-5000
£3474 $6218 €5072 On the water of the Nile (39x93cm-15x37in) mono. prov. 26-May-4 AB Stockholms Auktionsverk #2447/R est:30000-35000 (S.KR 47000)
£4500 $8280 €6570 Arabian desert scene with figures and camels by an oasis (20x49cm-8x19in) s.d.1901. 11-Jun-4 Keys, Aylsham #663/R est:5000-7000
£6630 $12000 €9680 Journey in Egypt the Nile Pyramid (41x61cm-16x24in) 16-Apr-4 Du Mouchelle, Detroit #2046/R est:18000-22000
£10000 $17000 €14600 Hagar and Ishmael, she departed, and wandered in the wilderness of Beer-Sheba (118x90cm-46x35in) prov.exhib.lit. 25-Nov-3 Christie's, London #164/R est:10000-15000

Works on paper
£280 $501 €409 Head and shoulders portrait of an Arab (35x29cm-14x11in) init. 17-Mar-4 Anthemion, Cardiff #417
£300 $501 €438 Yg Italian girl (48x33cm-19x13in) s. W/C. 17-Oct-3 Keys, Aylsham #514
£350 $655 €511 Desert scene (41x71cm-16x28in) mono. W/C. 23-Jul-4 Tring Auctions, Tring #269/R
£2587 $4630 €3777 View of Istanbul (59x72cm-23x28in) mono. W/C gouache. 26-May-4 AB Stockholms Auktionsverk #2487/R est:20000-25000 (S.KR 35000)
£2601 $4500 €3797 Returning from the well (74x54cm-29x21in) mono.d.1867 W/C htd varnish. 11-Dec-3 Sotheby's, New York #95/R est:5000-7000
£3537 $6332 €5200 Water for the camp (35x60cm-14x24in) mono.d.1878 W/C. 17-Mar-4 Maigret, Paris #3/R est:1500-2000
£7500 $13650 €10950 Street Musician (74x96cm-29x38in) s.d.1864 W/C htd white. 17-Jun-4 Christie's, London #119/R est:8000-12000

GOODALL, Frederick (attrib) (1822-1904) British
£620 $1135 €905 Marsh cart (30x41cm-12x16in) 7-Apr-4 Bonhams, Bury St Edmunds #472

GOODALL, George William (19/20th C) British
£444 $800 €648 View of an English village with strolling figures (41x61cm-16x24in) s. 24-Apr-4 Weschler, Washington #549/R

GOODALL, John Edward (fl.1877-1891) British
Works on paper
£1600 $2896 €2400 Crossing the Great Sahara (56x77cm-22x30in) i. i. verso W/C board lit. 3-Apr-4 Badum, Bamberg #68/R est:2000

GOODALL, John Strickland (1908-1996) British
Works on paper
£250 $430 €365 On the tideway (15x20cm-6x8in) s. W/C. 5-Dec-3 Keys, Aylsham #408
£270 $451 €394 Sudden shower (12x14cm-5x6in) s. W/C bodycol over pencil. 20-Oct-3 Bonhams, Bath #48
£480 $758 €696 Late for luncheon (26x36cm-10x14in) s. pencil W/C. 2-Sep-3 Bonhams, Oxford #54
£480 $778 €696 Proposal (16x20cm-6x8in) s. W/C. 30-Jul-3 Hamptons Fine Art, Godalming #80
£480 $816 €701 Market day (15x20cm-6x8in) s. W/C over pencil. 26-Nov-3 Hamptons Fine Art, Godalming #41
£500 $910 €730 East wind (15x18cm-6x7in) s. W/C bodycol. 15-Jun-4 David Lay, Penzance #454
£550 $935 €803 Andorra (37x50cm-15x20in) s. W/C bodycol. 1-Dec-3 Bonhams, Bath #29/R
£600 $1092 €876 Family on a beach (13x18cm-5x7in) s. W/C bodycol. 15-Jun-4 David Lay, Penzance #455/R

GOODALL, Walter (1830-1889) British
£1000 $1700 €1460 Come to me Peter (60x50cm-24x20in) s.d.1863/69. 1-Dec-3 Bonhams, Bath #135/R est:1000-1500
Works on paper
£280 $524 €420 Children fishing beside a canal (28x41cm-11x16in) s.d.1877 W/C. 22-Jul-4 Gorringes, Lewes #2033
£1400 $2338 €2044 Gleaners (27x39cm-11x15in) s.d.1863 W/C. 9-Jul-3 Peter Wilson, Nantwich #69

GOODAY, Leslie (20th C) British
£300 $501 €438 Concept 31, pears (25x25cm-10x10in) s. acrylic collage board. 16-Oct-3 Christie's, Kensington #365/R
£320 $550 €467 Concept 34 (20x74cm-8x29in) s. acrylic board. 3-Dec-3 Christie's, Kensington #535

GOODCHILD, George (20th C) American
£298 $542 €450 Canal a Bruges (80x89cm-31x35in) s. 15-Jun-4 Galerie Moderne, Brussels #202

GOODELL, Ira Chaffee (1800-1875) American
£6111 $11000 €8922 Portraits of Nathan and Freelove Drury (64x53cm-25x21in) s. oil linen wood panel. 20-Apr-4 Bunch, West Chester #400/R est:10000-13000

GOODERSON, Thomas Youngman (19th C) ?
£480 $898 €701 Portrait of a gentleman, in a black suit and white shirt (129x101cm-51x40in) s. after F Grant. 24-Feb-4 Bonhams, Knowle #68

GOODIN, Walter (1907-1992) British
£260 $468 €380 Bempton Cliffs from Little Thornwick Bay (49x75cm-19x30in) s. board. 20-Apr-4 Bonhams, Leeds #340
£380 $646 €555 Prancing horse (58x43cm-23x17in) s. hardboard painted c.1950. 21-Nov-3 Dee Atkinson & Harrison, Driffield #711
£680 $1156 €993 Thornwick Bay Flamborough (60x75cm-24x30in) s. board. 1-Dec-3 David Duggleby, Scarborough #339
£820 $1394 €1197 South landing Flamborough with fishing cobles on the slope (60x75cm-24x30in) s. board. 1-Dec-3 David Duggleby, Scarborough #337/R
£1050 $1880 €1533 Flamborough (70x90cm-28x35in) board. 17-May-4 David Duggleby, Scarborough #720/R est:800-1000
£1350 $2390 €1971 Fishing boats on the shore, North landing, Flamborough (53x74cm-21x29in) s. board. 30-Apr-4 Dee Atkinson & Harrison, Driffield #770/R est:800-1200
£3000 $5400 €4380 Nine horses in a parkland setting with hills beyond (110x310cm-43x122in) s.d.1967 board. 21-Apr-4 Tennants, Leyburn #1181/R est:1500-2000

GOODMAN, Catherine (1961-) British
£1000 $1850 €1460 View from the attic, St Mary of Angels (116x101cm-46x40in) s. prov.exhib. 11-Feb-4 Cheffins, Cambridge #462 est:800-1200

GOODMAN, George (19th C) British
£3600 $6696 €5256 Primulas, pansies, apple blossom, butterflies and a bird's nest with eggs on a mossy bank (30x41cm-12x16in) s. painted oval. 4-Mar-4 Christie's, Kensington #667/R est:3000-5000

GOODMAN, Mark (1931-) American
£629 $1070 €900 Jeunes maries III (55x46cm-22x18in) s. 27-Nov-3 Calmels Cohen, Paris #135/R

GOODMAN, Maude (1860-1938) British
Works on paper
£1200 $2148 €1752 When the heart is young (23x28cm-9x11in) s.d.87 W/C. 5-May-4 John Nicholson, Haslemere #385/R est:500-1000

GOODMAN, Rob (20th C) British
£320 $592 €467 Landscape with gentleman fishing by a canal (44x60cm-17x24in) s. 13-Jan-4 Bonhams, Oxford #270

GOODMAN, Robert Gwelo (1871-1939) South African
£289 $517 €422 La Lavandam (39x53cm-15x21in) i. verso board. 31-May-4 Stephan Welz, Johannesburg #125 (SA.R 3500)
£3419 $5812 €4992 Table Mountain, view from Wynberg (49x59cm-19x23in) s. 4-Nov-3 Stephan Welz, Johannesburg #608/R est:30000-40000 (SA.R 40000)
£5172 $8638 €7551 Mountainous landscape (75x101cm-30x40in) s. 20-Oct-3 Stephan Welz, Johannesburg #307/R est:28000-36000 (SA.R 60000)
Works on paper
£330 $591 €482 Landscape with trees and a river (35x47cm-14x19in) init. pastel. 31-May-4 Stephan Welz, Johannesburg #196 (SA.R 4000)
£437 $791 €638 Extensive Western Cape landscape (36x52cm-14x20in) init. pencil W/C. 30-Mar-4 Stephan Welz, Johannesburg #451 est:3500-5000 (SA.R 5200)
£908 $1626 €1326 Cape mountain landscape (35x45cm-14x18in) init. pastel. 31-May-4 Stephan Welz, Johannesburg #498/R (SA.R 11000)
£940 $1598 €1372 Old cape homestead (29x35cm-11x14in) init. pastel. 4-Nov-3 Stephan Welz, Johannesburg #681/R est:8000-12000 (SA.R 11000)
£1404 $2513 €2050 Venice (35x47cm-14x19in) s. pastel. 31-May-4 Stephan Welz, Johannesburg #550 est:10000-15000 (SA.R 17000)
£2064 $3695 €3013 River winding through the hills (49x63cm-19x25in) s. pastel. 31-May-4 Stephan Welz, Johannesburg #487/R est:25000-35000 (SA.R 25000)
£2241 $3743 €3272 River winding through the hills (49x63cm-19x25in) s. pastel. 20-Oct-3 Stephan Welz, Johannesburg #259/R est:9000-12000 (SA.R 26000)
£5345 $8926 €7804 Stellenrust (56x68cm-22x27in) s. pastel. 20-Oct-3 Stephan Welz, Johannesburg #273/R est:35000-45000 (SA.R 62000)

GOODMAN, Sidney (1936-) American
Works on paper
£326 $600 €476 On the wall (30x53cm-12x21in) s.d.1962 gouache wash pen ink. 10-Jun-4 Swann Galleries, New York #98/R
£353 $650 €515 Figurine composition (18x30cm-7x12in) s.d.66 black ink wash htd white. 25-Jun-4 Freeman, Philadelphia #62/R
£652 $1200 €952 Mapleshade Incinerator (64x102cm-25x40in) s.d.1967 chl exhib. 10-Jun-4 Swann Galleries, New York #99/R
£707 $1300 €1032 Living room (58x61cm-23x24in) s.d.1972 chl. 10-Jun-4 Swann Galleries, New York #100/R
£870 $1600 €1270 The orphan (58x43cm-23x17in) s.d.1961 W/C wash pen ink exhib. 10-Jun-4 Swann Galleries, New York #97/R est:1000-1500
£1622 $3000 €2368 Laocoon and Nun (73x117cm-29x46in) s.d.83-84 graphite stick pencil 2 joined sheets prov. 12-Feb-4 Sotheby's, New York #290/R est:4000-6000
£3591 $6500 €5243 Crowd at Tisbury Fair (30x48cm-12x19in) pencil. 16-Apr-4 American Auctioneer #162/R est:500-750

GOODNIGHT, Veryl (1947-) American

Sculpture

£1863	$3000	€2701	Light in the west (43cm-17in) bronze edition 9/30. 22-Aug-3 Altermann Galleries, Santa Fe #43
£3416	$5500	€4953	Painted horse, mare and foal (38x51cm-15x20in) bronze. 22-Aug-3 Altermann Galleries, Santa Fe #33

GOODNOUGH, Robert (1917-) American

£237	$425	€346	Small boat trip (8x18cm-3x7in) prov. 16-May-4 Wright, Chicago #365/R
£266	$425	€388	Bright colours on pale green (122x147cm-48x58in) s.i.d.1976 verso acrylic. 20-Sep-3 Bunte, Elgin #385d
£307	$550	€448	Colours on yellow gold (102x137cm-40x54in) s.i.d.1973 oil acrylic prov. 16-May-4 Wright, Chicago #299/R
£500	$800	€730	Abstract in yellow (81x112cm-32x44in) s.verso painted c.1968. 17-May-3 Bunte, Elgin #1312
£597	$950	€872	Color mass on blue (117x152cm-46x60in) s.verso acrylic. 14-Sep-3 Susanin's, Chicago #6018/R
£625	$1000	€913	Colours on pale green pink (91x122cm-36x48in) s.d.1976 acrylic oil. 20-Sep-3 Bunte, Elgin #1295
£633	$1000	€924	Yellow on yellow (81x112cm-32x44in) s.i.d.1970 verso acrylic. 7-Sep-3 Treadway Gallery, Cincinnati #767/R
£667	$1200	€974	White on white (20x20cm-8x8in) s.i.d.1977 verso acrylic oil. 24-Apr-4 David Rago, Lambertville #164/R
£811	$1500	€1184	Color, Gray, Color (106x137cm-42x54in) s.d.1981 i.verso oil acrylic prov. 12-Feb-4 Sotheby's, New York #154/R est:2000-3000
£1081	$2000	€1578	Figures (91x91cm-36x36in) s. s.i. verso. 13-Jul-4 Christie's, Rockefeller NY #65/R est:3000-5000
£1117	$2000	€1631	Brown shapes II (157x157cm-62x62in) s.i.d.1968 acrylic oil linen prov. 16-May-4 Wright, Chicago #300/R est:3000-4000
£1205	$2000	€1759	Variations N (198x183cm-78x72in) s. s.i.verso painted c.1969-70. 4-Oct-3 Neal Auction Company, New Orleans #1135/R est:2000-4000
£1351	$2500	€1972	Colours with yellow (92x96cm-36x38in) s.d.1972 i.verso acrylic oil over pencil. 12-Feb-4 Sotheby's, New York #155/R est:2500-3500
£1374	$2500	€2006	Figure group (21x25cm-8x10in) s.d.57. 29-Jun-4 Sotheby's, New York #424/R est:1500-2000
£1506	$2500	€2199	Composition with coloured shapes (122x183cm-48x72in) s.d. 4-Oct-3 Neal Auction Company, New Orleans #1136/R est:2500-3500
£2027	$3750	€2959	Abduction XX. Happy boat in triangle (20x26cm-8x10in) first s.i.d.1963 wood second s.i.d.65 canvas two. 12-Feb-4 Sotheby's, New York #147/R est:2000-3000
£2410	$4000	€3519	Black and white petals (183x183cm-72x72in) s. painted c.1969-70. 4-Oct-3 Neal Auction Company, New Orleans #1134/R est:4000-6000
£2545	$4250	€3716	Circle III (150cm-59in circular) s. s.i.d.1962 verso prov.exhib. 7-Oct-3 Sotheby's, New York #351 est:1500-2500

Works on paper

£707	$1300	€1032	Red boat (25x33cm-10x13in) s.d.1964 collage board exhib. 10-Jun-4 Swann Galleries, New York #101/R

GOODRICH, J B (19th C) British

£280	$476	€409	Rider watering his horse (40x60cm-16x24in) s. 30-Nov-3 Lots Road Auctions, London #351

GOODRIDGE, Eliza (attrib) (1798-1882) American

Works on paper

£4321	$7000	€6309	Round Hill, Northampton, Massachusetts (23x30cm-9x12in) W/C. 3-Aug-3 North East Auctions, Portsmouth #2108/R

GOODSIR, Agnes (1865-1939) Australian

£1021	$1736	€1491	Hydrangeas (55x46cm-22x18in) s. exhib. 26-Nov-3 Deutscher-Menzies, Melbourne #126/R est:2000-3000 (A.D 2400)
£1191	$2026	€1739	Flowers and green beads (55x46cm-22x18in) s. 26-Nov-3 Deutscher-Menzies, Melbourne #39/R est:3000-4000 (A.D 2800)

GOODWIN, Albert (1845-1932) British

£1810	$3023	€2643	On the coast of North Devon (43x61cm-17x24in) s.i.d.1912 init. verso board prov. 17-Nov-3 Waddingtons, Toronto #122/R est:4000-6000 (C.D 4000)
£2500	$4675	€3750	The Lifeboat, from the old chain pier, Brighton (43x48cm-17x19in) s.i. board. 22-Jul-4 Gorringes, Lewes #2016/R est:2500-3000
£4500	$8280	€6570	Sunset (45x51cm-18x20in) s.d.95 board. 23-Mar-4 Bonhams, New Bond Street #80/R est:2000-3000
£12000	$20400	€17520	Ali Baba and the forty thieves (78x102cm-31x40in) i. 27-Nov-3 Sotheby's, London #418/R est:12000-18000

Works on paper

£345	$576	€500	Amalfi (17x24cm-7x9in) s.i. gouache. 17-Nov-3 Tajan, Paris #7/R
£360	$659	€526	Woodland viaduct (13x16cm-5x6in) s. W/C. 6-Jul-4 Bearnes, Exeter #435/R
£420	$769	€613	Gathering for battle (35x53cm-14x21in) s.i.d.1915/16 W/C. 6-Apr-4 Bonhams, Chester #901
£450	$747	€657	Wild night at sea (20x25cm-8x10in) s.i. W/C ink. 1-Oct-3 Sotheby's, Olympia #158/R
£460	$814	€672	South Foreland (18x28cm-7x11in) mono.d.1888 W/C. 29-Apr-4 Gorringes, Lewes #2361
£620	$1029	€905	Altdorf, view of valley with figure herding goats (15x23cm-6x9in) mono.i.d.March 87 W/C prov. 10-Jun-3 Canterbury Auctions, UK #133/R
£700	$1120	€1022	Continental street scene showing figures collecting water beneath arches (13x23cm-5x9in) mono.d.1886. 16-Sep-3 Gorringes, Bexhill #1557/R
£800	$1448	€1168	Fenland scene (39x47cm-15x19in) s. pastel. 30-Mar-4 David Duggleby, Scarborough #11/R
£1000	$1700	€1460	Aylesford on the Medway (17x25cm-7x10in) s.i. W/C pen ink. 4-Nov-3 Bonhams, New Bond Street #134/R est:1000-1500
£1500	$2595	€2190	Sion, Valley of the Rhone, a rainy townscape with umbrellas (23x37cm-9x15in) mono.i. indis.d. W/C pen ink. 9-Dec-3 Bonhams, Oxford #40/R est:1500-1800
£1600	$2928	€2336	Salisbury (18x24cm-7x9in) s.i. W/C htd white. 7-Apr-4 Woolley & Wallis, Salisbury #165/R est:800-1200
£2000	$3680	€2920	Oberhofen, Lake Thun (26x38cm-10x15in) s.i.d.1909 pencil W/C brown ink bodycol prov. 25-Mar-4 Christie's, Kensington #99/R est:1000-1500
£2200	$4114	€3212	Winchester Cathedral (23x28cm-9x11in) s.i.d.1900 W/C pen ink. 26-Feb-4 Mallams, Cheltenham #253/R est:1200-1600
£2400	$4440	€3504	Loncoln Cathedral (25x37cm-10x15in) s.i. W/C prov. 14-Jul-4 Sotheby's, Olympia #94/R est:1000-1500
£2700	$4968	€3942	Old Hastings, stormbound (25x35cm-10x14in) i. W/C bodycol. 8-Jun-4 Bonhams, New Bond Street #133/R est:2500-3500
£2800	$4816	€4088	In the Guistini Garden, Verona, sunset (22x29cm-9x11in) s.i.d.1902 black ink W/C. 3-Dec-3 Christie's, Kensington #104/R est:1800-2500
£3500	$6405	€5110	Venice in grey weather (16x25cm-6x10in) mono.i. pencil W/C htd bodycol prov. 3-Jun-4 Christie's, London #158/R est:2000-3000
£4200	$7770	€6132	Atrani near Amalfi (25x35cm-10x14in) s.i.d.1901 W/C pen ink prov. 9-Mar-4 Bonhams, New Bond Street #115/R est:2000-3000
£4200	$7686	€6132	Rialto, Venice (16x21cm-6x8in) mono.i. pencil blk ink W/C htd bodycol scratching out. 3-Jun-4 Christie's, London #157/R est:2000-3000
£4400	$8140	€6424	St Mary Radcliffe, Bristol (21x27cm-8x11in) s.i.d.1926 W/C pen ink. 9-Mar-4 Bonhams, New Bond Street #114/R est:2500-3000
£11000	$20130	€16060	October (49x79cm-19x31in) s.i.d.70 W/C htd bodycol scratching out prov. 3-Jun-4 Christie's, London #1/R est:8000-12000

GOODWIN, Albert (attrib) (1845-1932) British

Works on paper

£300	$555	€438	The South Foreland (17x28cm-7x11in) mono.d.88 W/C. 11-Feb-4 Cheffins, Cambridge #399

GOODWIN, Arthur C (1866-1929) American

£1765	$3000	€2577	Early snow (85x91cm-33x36in) s. 21-Nov-3 Skinner, Boston #501/R est:6000-8000
£1912	$3250	€2792	October, view towards Boston (63x76cm-25x30in) s. 21-Nov-3 Skinner, Boston #489/R est:5000-7000
£2162	$4000	€3157	Spuyten Duvyil, New York (63x76cm-25x30in) s. 11-Mar-4 Christie's, Rockefeller NY #51/R est:6000-8000
£3533	$6500	€5158	Tea Wharf in Boston Harbour (55x68cm-22x27in) s. oil pencil prov. 8-Jun-4 Bonhams & Butterfields, San Francisco #4049/R est:8000-12000
£4670	$8500	€6818	Tremont Street Mall (49x61cm-19x24in) s. s.i.stretcher. 29-Jun-4 Sotheby's, New York #206/R est:7000-10000
£4706	$8000	€6871	In the rain, Tremont Street, Boston (61x84cm-24x33in) s.d.09. 21-Nov-3 Skinner, Boston #587/R est:8000-12000
£4938	$8000	€7160	Park Street Church, Boston (51x66cm-20x26in) s. 8-Aug-3 Barridorf, Portland #107/R est:12000-18000
£4945	$9000	€7220	Snowy day in Boston (51x66cm-20x26in) s. canvas on board. 29-Jun-4 Sotheby's, New York #207/R est:5000-7000
£5090	$8500	€7431	Palisades from Riverdale (51x62cm-20x24in) s. prov. 9-Oct-3 Christie's, Rockefeller NY #44/R est:6000-8000
£9497	$17000	€13866	Fifth Avenue, New York (56x69cm-22x27in) s. prov. 6-May-4 Shannon's, Milford #58/R est:15000-25000

Works on paper

£335	$600	€489	New England landscape (30x41cm-12x16in) s. pastel. 8-May-4 Susanin's, Chicago #6064/R
£419	$750	€612	New England landscape (46x58cm-18x23in) s. 8-Jan-4 James Julia, Fairfield #728/R
£459	$850	€670	Dockside reflections (28x36cm-11x14in) s. i.verso pastel on board. 15-Jul-4 Doyle, New York #40/R
£538	$1000	€785	Dedham woods (46x63cm-18x25in) s. pastel linenboard. 5-Mar-4 Skinner, Boston #469/R
£1304	$2400	€1904	Tree by the lake shore (53x43cm-21x17in) s. pastel. 26-Jun-4 Sloans & Kenyon, Bethesda #1093/R est:1000-1500

GOODWIN, Betty (1923-) Canadian

Works on paper

£1932	$3149	€2821	Unemployed (35x61cm-14x24in) s.d.49 chl wash prov. 23-Sep-3 Ritchie, Toronto #168/R est:3000-4000 (C.D 4250)
£2768	$4761	€4041	Pieces of Time VII (41x27cm-16x11in) s.d.96 mixed media mylar prov.lit. 2-Dec-3 Joyner Waddington, Toronto #86/R est:3000-4000 (C.D 6200)
£3795	$6527	€5541	Beyond Chaos No.9 (54x39cm-21x15in) s.d.98 mixed media. 2-Dec-3 Joyner Waddington, Toronto #230/R est:4000-6000 (C.D 8500)

GOODWIN, Edwin Weyburn (1800-?) American

£1069	$1700	€1561	Portrait of Rachel Smith (76x61cm-30x24in) i. s.i.d.1834 verso. 10-Sep-3 Sotheby's, New York #374/R est:1500-2000

GOODWIN, Francis (1784-1835) British

Works on paper

£320	$576	€467	View of a half timbered lodge at entrance to country house (33x51cm-13x20in) W/C. 20-Apr-4 Canterbury Auctions, UK #192/R

GOODWIN, Harry (?-1925) British

Works on paper

£290	$458	€421	Sheep grazing in a river landscape (25x34cm-10x13in) mono.d.1910 W/C. 2-Sep-3 Bonhams, Oxford #44
£400	$716	€584	Grasmere lake and village (30x50cm-12x20in) mono.d.1917 W/C. 17-Mar-4 Bonhams, Chester #308

GOODWIN, Karl (20th C) American

£1087	$2000	€1587	Briton peasant knitting (61x51cm-24x20in) canvas on panel exhib. 25-Jun-4 Freeman, Philadelphia #265/R est:600-1000

GOODWIN, Phillip R (1882-1935) American

£4813	$9000	€7027	Fall landscape. Winter landscape (28x36cm-11x14in) s. pair prov. 24-Jul-4 Coeur d'Alene, Hayden #84/R est:6000-9000
£16043	$30000	€23423	Pack train (64x91cm-25x36in) prov. 24-Jul-4 Coeur d'Alene, Hayden #210/R est:8000-12000

Works on paper

£2406	$4500	€3513	Bear. Hunting bear. Golden opportunity (13x18cm-5x7in) init.d W/C set of three prov. 24-Jul-4 Coeur d'Alene, Hayden #213/R est:3000-5000
£2540	$4750	€3708	Two riders. Horse and cart. Man getting rifle. Man and green canoe (13x18cm-5x7in) s. mixed media set of four prov.lit. 24-Jul-4 Coeur d'Alene, Hayden #81/R est:5000-8000

£2941 $5500 €4294 Studies of hunting scenes (18x13cm-7x5in) s. mixed media set of five prov.lit. 24-Jul-4 Coeur d'Alene, Hayden #80/R est:5000-8000
£2941 $5500 €4294 Landscape. Indian. Deer (13x8cm-5x3in) s. one s.d.1897 mixed media set of three prov. 24-Jul-4 Coeur d'Alene, Hayden #215/R est:5000-8000
£4011 $7500 €5856 Studies of loggers (8x13cm-3x5in) s. mixed media set of five prov.lit. 24-Jul-4 Coeur d'Alene, Hayden #77/R est:5000-8000
£4278 $8000 €6246 Going good. Two men in a canoe (13x20cm-5x8in) s. W/C pair prov. 24-Jul-4 Coeur d'Alene, Hayden #85/R est:3000-5000
£4813 $9000 €7027 Glacier park bears (25x33cm-10x13in) s. W/C prov.lit. 24-Jul-4 Coeur d'Alene, Hayden #82/R est:5000-8000
£9091 $17000 €13273 Moose. Trapper's cabin (20x25cm-8x10in) s. pen ink pair prov.lit. 24-Jul-4 Coeur d'Alene, Hayden #282/R est:3000-5000

GOODWIN, Richard Labarre (1840-1910) American
£2038 $3750 €2975 Hanging rabbit (86x43cm-34x17in) s.d.1889 prov. 27-Jun-4 Freeman, Philadelphia #85/R est:4000-6000

GOODWIN, Sidney (1867-1944) British
Works on paper
£250 $418 €365 Plough team (25x36cm-10x14in) s.d.1909 W/C over pencil. 20-Oct-3 Bonhams, Bath #107
£310 $518 €453 Mouth of the Thames (15x33cm-6x13in) s. W/C. 17-Oct-3 Keys, Aylsham #418
£400 $728 €584 Loading the cart (30x49cm-12x19in) s.d.95 pencil W/C. 1-Jul-4 Christie's, Kensington #121/R
£660 $1234 €964 Westminster from the Thames (25x36cm-10x14in) s.d.1913 W/C. 26-Feb-4 Mallams, Cheltenham #220/R
£800 $1456 €1168 End of the day (36x54cm-14x21in) pencil W/C htd white. 1-Jul-4 Mellors & Kirk, Nottingham #680/R
£1000 $1570 €1450 Unloading boats, Southampton quay (38x25cm-15x10in) indis.sig. W/C exec.c.1880-1890. 15-Dec-2 Desmond Judd, Cranbrook #882

GOOL, Jan van (1685-1763) Dutch
£1250 $1975 €1800 Pastoral landscape with cattle and goats by a fence (27x35cm-11x14in) indis sig.d. prov. 2-Sep-3 Christie's, Amsterdam #94/R est:1800-2200
£2205 $3528 €3219 River landscape with shepherds and cattle (31x43cm-12x17in) panel. 19-Sep-3 Koller, Zurich #3064/R est:6000-8000 (S.FR 4875)
£4790 $8000 €6993 Extensive landscape with shepherds, sheep, goats and cows (41x62cm-16x24in) s. panel. 7-Oct-3 Sotheby's, New York #45/R est:8000-10000

GOOL, Jan van (attrib) (1685-1763) Dutch
£2128 $3362 €3000 Landscape with cattle and herder (31x36cm-12x14in) two. 25-Jul-3 Altus, Berlin #549/R est:2800

GOOSEN, Frits J (1943-) Dutch
£350 $641 €511 Barges on the river (18x24cm-7x9in) s. i.stretcher. 8-Apr-4 Christie's, Kensington #103/R
£979 $1684 €1400 Moored boats in a polder landscape (60x90cm-24x35in) s. 7-Dec-3 Sotheby's, Amsterdam #680
£1399 $2406 €2000 Cows in a polder landscape (60x90cm-24x35in) s. 7-Dec-3 Sotheby's, Amsterdam #653/R

GOOZEE, Dan (1943-) American
£223 $400 €326 Portrait of a seated lady (61x51cm-24x20in) s. masonite. 20-Mar-4 Selkirks, St. Louis #156

GOPAS, Rudolph (1913-1982) New Zealander
£2482 $4592 €3624 Still life (75x60cm-30x24in) board. 13-Jul-4 Watson's, Christchurch #65/R est:12000-18000 (NZ.D 7000)
Works on paper
£313 $497 €457 Brick kiln, Central Otago (38x51cm-15x20in) W/C prov. 1-May-3 Dunbar Sloane, Wellington #86 (NZ.D 900)
£554 $991 €809 Pahiatua (37x50cm-15x20in) s.i.d.1949 W/C. 12-May-4 Dunbar Sloane, Wellington #54 est:1500-3000 (NZ.D 1600)
£634 $1027 €919 Portrait of a lady (41x30cm-16x12in) s.d.1953 W/C. 31-Jul-3 International Art Centre, Auckland #125/R est:2200-2800 (NZ.D 1750)
£1007 $1743 €1470 Road through a rural landscape (38x49cm-15x19in) s. W/C. 9-Dec-3 Peter Webb, Auckland #181/R (NZ.D 2700)
£1049 $1909 €1532 Portrait of Jonathan Hulme (37x24cm-15x9in) W/C executed c.1954. 29-Jun-4 Peter Webb, Auckland #195/R est:3000-5000 (NZ.D 3000)
£1119 $1937 €1634 Portrait of Bob Rasa (37x30cm-15x12in) W/C. 9-Dec-3 Peter Webb, Auckland #182/R est:2500-3500 (NZ.D 3000)
£1455 $2284 €2110 Boats in harbour (20x30cm-8x12in) s.d.1959 W/C ink. 27-Aug-3 Dunbar Sloane, Wellington #3/R est:2500-4000 (NZ.D 4000)

GORANSON, Paul Alexander (1911-) Canadian
Prints
£1794 $2960 €2619 Purse seiners (20x37cm-8x15in) s.i. etching edition 32/60. 3-Jul-3 Heffel, Vancouver #12/R est:1500-2000 (C.D 4000)

GORANSSON, Ake (1902-1942) Swedish
£1378 $2480 €2012 Composition (15x14cm-6x6in) st.sig. panel. 26-Apr-4 Bukowskis, Stockholm #44/R est:25000-30000 (S.KR 19000)
£4079 $6934 €5955 Still life (39x34cm-15x13in) st.sig. cardboard. 4-Nov-3 Bukowskis, Stockholm #67/R est:60000-80000 (S.KR 54000)
£4230 $7190 €6176 Portrait of man in purple and brown (30x23cm-12x9in) s. paper on panel painted c.1941-42 exhib.lit. 4-Nov-3 Bukowskis, Stockholm #58/R est:60000-80000 (S.KR 56000)
£4532 $7704 €6617 The boat in the skerries (22x28cm-9x11in) st.sig. i.verso canvas on panel painted c.1930-32 exhib.lit. 4-Nov-3 Bukowskis, Stockholm #63/R est:60000-80000 (S.KR 60000)
£7553 $12840 €11027 The organist. Still life of pipe and carafe (33x26cm-13x10in) st.sig. painted c.1933-37 double-sided prov.exhib.lit. 4-Nov-3 Bukowskis, Stockholm #64/R est:60000-80000 (S.KR 100000)
£8308 $14124 €12130 The artist's mother resting (28x39cm-11x15in) st.sig. i.verso canvas on panel painted c.1932-33 prov.exhib. 4-Nov-3 Bukowskis, Stockholm #66/R est:100000-125000 (S.KR 110000)
£9441 $16050 €13784 The brook in Landala. Still life (50x42cm-20x17in) s.d.1934 double-sided prov.exhib.lit. 4-Nov-3 Bukowskis, Stockholm #72/R est:125000-150000 (S.KR 125000)
£10574 $17976 €15438 On the kitchen sofa (27x34cm-11x13in) st.sig. painted c.1932/35 exhib.lit. 5-Nov-3 AB Stockholms Auktionsverk #896/R est:140000-160000 (S.KR 140000)
£12328 $22190 €18492 Inga seated on the red sofa (53x40cm-21x16in) st.sig. painted c.1933-37 prov.exhib.lit. 25-Apr-4 Goteborg Auktionsverk, Sweden #363/R est:100000 (S.KR 170000)
£16239 $27606 €23709 Interior scene with the artist's mother wearing yellow top (29x39cm-11x15in) with sig. i.verso canvas on panel painted 1930-32 prov.exhib.lit. 4-Nov-3 Bukowskis, Stockholm #59/R est:120000-140000 (S.KR 215000)
£16994 $28890 €24811 The boy and the frog in the red-brown room (50x40cm-20x16in) st.sig. i.verso canvas on panel painted 1928-30 prov.exhib.lit. 4-Nov-3 Bukowskis, Stockholm #61/R est:150000-175000 (S.KR 225000)
£20393 $34668 €29774 Gothenburg street scene with horse and wagon (46x55cm-18x22in) st.sig. i. painted c.1932-35 exhib.lit. 4-Nov-3 Bukowskis, Stockholm #60/R est:200000-250000 (S.KR 270000)
Works on paper
£347 $591 €507 Head, pier (28x20cm-11x8in) chk sketch from sketchbook. 4-Nov-3 Bukowskis, Stockholm #69/R (S.KR 4600)
£438 $745 €639 Yellow and red (28x20cm-11x8in) chk sketch from sketchbook. 4-Nov-3 Bukowskis, Stockholm #68/R (S.KR 5800)

GORBATOFF, Konstantin (1876-1945) Russian
£16000 $27200 €24000 View of Capri (24x34cm-9x13in) s. panel. 25-Nov-3 Christie's, London #168/R est:5000-7000
£32000 $57280 €46720 View of Amalfi (50x60cm-20x24in) s.verso. 26-May-4 Sotheby's, London #190/R est:18000-25000
£37838 $66595 €56000 In Venice (65x81cm-26x32in) s. prov. 22-May-4 Lempertz, Koln #1521/R est:4000
£38000 $68020 €55480 Cioggia (50x60cm-20x24in) s.verso prov. 26-May-4 Sotheby's, London #189/R est:18000-25000
£72222 $130000 €105444 Bouquets on the ledge, Paris (74x96cm-29x38in) s.d.1923 prov. 23-Apr-4 Sotheby's, New York #44/R est:60000-80000
£78000 $132600 €117000 Winter landscape (90x75cm-35x30in) s. 25-Nov-3 Christie's, London #131/R est:35000-45000
£80000 $143200 €116800 Salzburg (80x110cm-31x43in) s.d.1940 i.verso. 26-May-4 Sotheby's, London #195/R est:30000-40000
£95000 $170050 €138700 Venice (65x81cm-26x32in) s. i.verso. 26-May-4 Sotheby's, London #191/R est:40000-60000
Works on paper
£1458 $2377 €2100 Fishing village in Capri (28x37cm-11x15in) s.d.1927 W/C chl. 27-Sep-3 Dannenberg, Berlin #547/R est:1000
£1493 $2434 €2150 Capri (28x37cm-11x15in) s.i.d.1927 W/C chl. 27-Sep-3 Dannenberg, Berlin #546/R est:1000
£7500 $13425 €10950 Venetian waterscape (32x40cm-13x16in) s.i.d.1925 W/C. 26-May-4 Sotheby's, Olympia #427/R est:4000-6000
£9122 $16054 €13500 In St Petersburg (43x54cm-17x21in) s.d.1916 s.d. verso gouache prov. 22-May-4 Lempertz, Koln #1415/R est:2000
£10000 $17000 €14600 View of Capri (35x46cm-14x18in) s. W/C gouache over pencil. 19-Nov-3 Sotheby's, London #131/R est:7000-9000
£10000 $17000 €15000 Capture of Berlin (35x48cm-14x19in) s.d.1945 pencil W/C bodycol paper on card. 25-Nov-3 Christie's, London #199/R est:10000-15000
£10000 $17000 €15000 Capture of Berlin (34x47cm-13x19in) s.d.1945 pencil W/C bodycol paper on card. 25-Nov-3 Christie's, London #198/R est:10000-15000
£14000 $25060 €20440 Flowers in a vase (65x50cm-26x20in) s.d.1944 gouache. 26-May-4 Sotheby's, London #194/R est:6000-8000

GORBATOFF, Konstantin (attrib) (1876-1945) Russian
£778 $1300 €1136 Landscape with house (20x28cm-8x11in) s. cardboard. 21-Oct-3 Christie's, Rockefeller NY #108
£15789 $29053 €24000 Pecheurs (50x65cm-20x26in) s.d.1955 prov. 28-Jun-4 Joron-Derem, Paris #124 est:800-1000
Works on paper
£2586 $4629 €3776 Winter landscape near Pskov (32x40cm-13x16in) i.d.1919 gouache. 12-May-4 Dobiaschofsky, Bern #569/R est:7500 (S.FR 6000)

GORDER, Luther Emerson van (1861-1931) American
Works on paper
£1796 $3000 €2622 The autumn of life (66x48cm-26x19in) W/C exec. 1894. 17-Oct-3 Du Mouchelle, Detroit #1019/R est:800-1200

GORDIGIANI, Edoardo (1866-1961) Italian
£503 $891 €750 Vase of flowers (55x39cm-22x15in) s. board. 1-May-4 Meeting Art, Vercelli #321
£537 $950 €800 Hay harvest (30x40cm-12x16in) s. board. 1-May-4 Meeting Art, Vercelli #485
£563 $975 €800 Sunset (20x28cm-8x11in) s. board prov. 9-Dec-3 Pandolfini, Florence #360/R
£638 $1141 €950 Blond river (27x36cm-11x14in) s. painted 1941. 25-May-4 Finarte Semenzato, Milan #13/R
£775 $1340 €1100 View of square with tower (40x30cm-16x12in) s.d.20 board. 9-Dec-3 Pandolfini, Florence #363/R
£1377 $2258 €1900 Alpine landscape with figures (36x54cm-14x21in) s. board. 29-May-3 Galleria Pace, Milan #87/R est:2800
£1761 $3046 €2500 Self-portrait with boy (130x75cm-51x30in) s.d.53. 9-Dec-3 Pandolfini, Florence #366/R est:2500-2800
£2318 $4219 €3500 Odalisque (115x83cm-45x33in) s. prov. 21-Jun-4 Pandolfini, Florence #160/R est:3600-3800

GORDIGIANI, Michele (1835-1909) Italian
£600 $1074 €876 Leda and the swan (47x30cm-19x12in) s. 11-May-4 Bonhams, Knightsbridge #91/R

£6471 $11000 €9448 Daughter of the Piatti family of Florence (42x33cm-17x13in) 29-Oct-3 Christie's, Rockefeller NY #225/R est:10000-15000
Works on paper
£1049 $1752 €1500 Portrait of young woman (59x39cm-23x15in) s. col pastel. 10-Oct-3 Stadion, Trieste #811/R est:900-1200

GORDILLO, Gun (20th C) ?
Sculpture
£2164 $3678 €3159 Light sculpture (90x145cm-35x57in) s.d.90 lead painted wood neon lights. 26-Nov-3 Kunsthallen, Copenhagen #101/R est:30000 (D.KR 23000)

GORDILLO, Luis (1939-) Spanish
£2254 $3944 €3200 Untitled (57x16cm-22x6in) s.d.1984 acrylic col wax crayon paper prov. 16-Dec-3 Segre, Madrid #150/R est:2500
£16901 $29577 €24000 Woman with telephone (100x83cm-39x33in) s.i.d.1971 prov. 16-Dec-3 Segre, Madrid #153/R est:16000
£20833 $35417 €30000 Flying (180x117cm-71x46in) s.d.1972 acrylic exhib.lit. 28-Oct-3 Segre, Madrid #159/R est:45000
Works on paper
£455 $759 €650 Untitled (18x26cm-7x10in) d.25-Julio-1959 gouache blue pen. 24-Jun-3 Segre, Madrid #123/R
£490 $817 €700 Untitled (26x18cm-10x7in) d.30-Jul-1959 W/C gouache pen. 24-Jun-3 Segre, Madrid #122/R
£524 $876 €750 Untitled (32x22cm-13x9in) d.2-Jun-59 gouache Indian ink col pen. 24-Jun-3 Segre, Madrid #121/R
£541 $968 €800 Untitled (24x22cm-9x9in) s.d.96 crayon W/C. 4-May-4 Calmels Cohen, Paris #243
£559 $934 €800 Untitled (31x22cm-12x9in) d.2-Julio-1959 ink wash. 24-Jun-3 Segre, Madrid #1116/R
£2432 $4281 €3600 Untitled (50x70cm-20x28in) s.d.1986 gouache acrylic ink pencil prov. 18-May-4 Segre, Madrid #219/R est:3600

GORDINE, Dora (1906-1991) British
Sculpture
£2200 $3960 €3212 Standing female dancer (68cm-27in) s.num.3/6 green pat bronze incl wooden base. 20-Jan-4 Bonhams, Knightsbridge #289/R est:1500-2500
£3600 $6336 €5256 Dreamer (53cm-21in) incised sig num.4/6 bronze. 19-May-4 Sotheby's, Olympia #163/R est:4000-6000

GORDON, Arthur (19th C) British
£340 $585 €496 Portrait of a dog, Staffordshire bull terrier (38x30cm-15x12in) s.d.09. 2-Dec-3 Canterbury Auctions, UK #156
£640 $1101 €934 Portrait of a dog, Staffordshire bull terrier puppy (38x30cm-15x12in) s.d.09. 2-Dec-3 Canterbury Auctions, UK #157/R
£3100 $5487 €4526 Sculling on the Thames at Twickenham (76x120cm-30x47in) s.d.1891. 27-Apr-4 Henry Adams, Chichester #708/R est:3000-5000
Works on paper
£280 $504 €409 Small craft on the Thames at Twickenham (33x48cm-13x19in) s. W/C. 25-Jan-4 Desmond Judd, Cranbrook #1059

GORDON, Douglas (1966-) British
Photographs
£5090 $8500 €7431 Croque mort (98x140cm-39x55in) s.verso digital c-print executed 2000 prov.exhib.lit. 14-Nov-3 Phillips, New York #114/R est:10000-15000
£10000 $18400 €14600 Don't think about it. DVD with Beta SP master tape. 25-Jun-4 Christie's, London #270/R est:12000-18000
Sculpture
£10056 $18000 €14682 Kissing with scopolamine. 35mm slide projection edition of 10 prov.exhib.lit. 14-May-4 Phillips, New York #178/R est:20000-30000

GORDON, Hilda May (1874-1972) British
£272 $487 €400 Temple dance (45x54cm-18x21in) s. 16-Mar-4 Christie's, Amsterdam #73

GORDON, Hortense Mattice (1889-1961) Canadian
£342 $635 €499 On the valley road (25x35cm-10x14in) s. panel. 2-Mar-4 Ritchie, Toronto #75/R (C.D 850)

GORDON, Sir John Watson (1788-1864) British
£2410 $4000 €3519 Portrait of a lady, said to be Mrs Hamilton Dundas (76x63cm-30x25in) prov. 30-Sep-3 Christie's, Rockefeller NY #343/R est:6000-8000

GORDON, Sir John Watson (attrib) (1788-1864) British
£1105 $2000 €1613 Portrait of a young gentleman (130x99cm-51x39in) 3-Apr-4 Neal Auction Company, New Orleans #141/R est:3000-5000

GORDON, Steven (1951-) American
£191 $350 €279 Two on our side (10x10cm-4x4in) 10-Jul-4 Hindman, Chicago #182/R

GORDON, Ted (1924-) American
Works on paper
£264 $475 €385 Black cat (28x36cm-11x14in) ink cardstock prov. 24-Apr-4 Slotin Folk Art, Buford #474/R
£269 $450 €393 Man's face on orange (28x20cm-11x8in) marker pen prov. 15-Nov-3 Slotin Folk Art, Buford #283/R
£329 $550 €480 Red man's face (43x33cm-17x13in) ink marker prov. 15-Nov-3 Slotin Folk Art, Buford #282/R
£444 $800 €648 Red mule (28x38cm-11x15in) ink marker. 24-Apr-4 Slotin Folk Art, Buford #473/R
£500 $900 €730 Man with cane (38x30cm-15x12in) ink marker. 24-Apr-4 Slotin Folk Art, Buford #475/R

GORDY, Robert (20th C) American
£1294 $2200 €1889 Oasis no.3 (107x89cm-42x35in) s.i.on stretcher acrylic. 22-Nov-3 New Orleans Auction, New Orleans #1263/R est:2500-4000
£4294 $7000 €6226 Reclining female nudes with fruit and pickles (122x145cm-48x57in) inid.d. 19-Jul-3 New Orleans Auction, New Orleans #991/R est:4000-7000
Works on paper
£872 $1500 €1273 Study for bright night no 2 (74x53cm-29x21in) s.d.77 W/C ink marker prov. 7-Dec-3 Freeman, Philadelphia #100 est:1500-2500

GORDYN, Hermanus Gerardus (1932-) Dutch
£2933 $5368 €4400 Passer-by (122x80cm-48x31in) s.d.1967. 7-Jun-4 Glerum, Amsterdam #339/R est:3000-4000

GORE, A (19th C) French
Sculpture
£1585 $2900 €2378 Bust of a lady (38x36cm-15x14in) marble bronze. 9-Jul-4 Du Mouchelle, Detroit #1079/R est:500-800

GORE, Elizabeth Crampton (20th C) Irish
£417 $654 €600 View across Dublin Bay (50x39cm-20x15in) s.d.1989 i.verso. 26-Aug-3 James Adam, Dublin #16/R

GORE, Frederick (1913-) British
£1600 $2816 €2336 Provencal Bouquet (61x46cm-24x18in) s.i.d.2001 stretcher. 18-May-4 Bonhams, Knightsbridge #96/R est:1000-1500
£2000 $3520 €2920 Still life Bonnieux, Vaucluse (66x76cm-26x30in) s.i.d.stretcher. 18-May-4 Bonhams, Knightsbridge #59/R est:1000-1500
£2400 $3816 €3504 Pistachio trees, Aegine (61x79cm-24x31in) s.d.88. 1-May-3 John Nicholson, Haslemere #704/R est:2000-3000
£2800 $4676 €4088 Sunflowers, St Remy de Provence (71x91cm-28x36in) s.i.d.1979 overlap. 16-Oct-3 Christie's, Kensington #463/R est:3000-5000
£3800 $6346 €5548 Les Opies. Acipilles at Eyguieres (63x81cm-25x32in) s. s.i.d.1976 overlap. 16-Oct-3 Christie's, Kensington #462/R est:3000-5000
£4200 $7770 €6132 Field of petunias, Romanil (71x91cm-28x36in) s. s.i. 11-Mar-4 Christie's, Kensington #285/R est:3000-5000
£4500 $7650 €6570 Isles of Greece (51x75cm-20x30in) prov. 26-Nov-3 Sotheby's, Olympia #102/R est:2500-3500
£4800 $8880 €7008 Early corn, Clements Reach, Meopham (76x101cm-30x40in) s. s.i.on stretcher painted 1976. 11-Mar-4 Christie's, Kensington #289/R est:2500-3500
£6000 $9540 €8760 Still life (81x71cm-32x28in) s. 10-Sep-3 Sotheby's, Olympia #259/R est:6000-8000
£8200 $14924 €11972 Charlotte Street (64x76cm-25x30in) s.d.46. 15-Jun-4 Bonhams, New Bond Street #48/R est:2500-3500
£12500 $22000 €18250 Mausanne (59x71cm-23x28in) s. i.d.1938 stretcher prov. 19-May-4 Sotheby's, Olympia #209/R est:5000-7000
Works on paper
£1300 $2405 €1898 Wildflowers along a roadside hedge (60x46cm-24x18in) s.d.98 pencil W/C. 11-Mar-4 Christie's, Kensington #287/R est:600-800

GORE, Spencer (1878-1914) British
£5500 $10065 €8030 House behind trees (36x25cm-14x10in) painted c.1910-11 prov. 4-Jun-4 Christie's, London #15/R est:4000-6000
£60000 $102000 €87600 Alhambra ballet (38x32cm-15x13in) studio st. board painted c.1910-11 prov.exhib. 21-Nov-3 Christie's, London #84/R est:40000-60000
£62000 $105400 €90520 Tennis in Mornington Crescent Gardens (41x51cm-16x20in) i.d.1909 prov.exhib. 21-Nov-3 Christie's, London #85/R est:50000-70000

GORE, William Crampton (1871-1946) Irish
£1300 $2236 €1898 Calais, France (48x64cm-19x25in) s.d.1925. 2-Dec-3 Gorringes, Lewes #2282/R est:1200-1500
£3147 $5350 €4500 Christmas rose (76x64cm-30x25in) s.d.1928. 25-Nov-3 De Veres Art Auctions, Dublin #152/R est:5000-7000

GORE, William Henry (fl.1880-1916) British
Works on paper
£1200 $2184 €1752 Calm and beautiful the moon arose (25x19cm-10x7in) s. W/C. 29-Jun-4 Anderson & Garland, Newcastle #240 est:200-300

GORE-BOOTH, Colum Robert (1913-1959) British
Works on paper
£350 $594 €500 River landscape (39x56cm-15x22in) W/C. 25-Nov-3 Hamilton Osborne King, Dublin #43/R

GORE-BOOTH, Constance (1868-1927) British
Works on paper
£1049 $1783 €1500 Countess Markievicz, Portrait of Mable Gore-Booth (57x44cm-22x17in) chl htd white. 25-Nov-3 Hamilton Osborne King, Dublin #118/R
£2238 $3804 €3200 Study of Sarah Purser (55x43cm-22x17in) i. chl. 25-Nov-3 Hamilton Osborne King, Dublin #119/R

GORE-BOOTH, Mable (1874-?) British
£420 $713 €600 Study of Constance Markievicz's poodle in the galley at Lissadell (23x11cm-9x4in) mono. 25-Nov-3 Hamilton Osborne King, Dublin #148/R

GOREY, Edward (1929-) American
Works on paper
£814 $1400 €1188 Happy ending - Larry and Freddie (11x14cm-4x6in) s. pen ink prov. 3-Dec-3 Doyle, New York #35 est:800-1200
£1617 $2700 €2361 Three sneers for the invasion of American football (18x13cm-7x5in) s. pen ink W/C. 15-Nov-3 Illustration House, New York #49/R est:2500-3500
£2907 $5000 €4244 Three attempts at murder (9x12cm-4x5in) s. pen ink set of three prov. 3-Dec-3 Doyle, New York #34/R est:2000-3000

GORGE, Paul Eugène (1856-1941) Belgian
£282 $487 €400 Pres de la ferme (28x37cm-11x15in) s. 9-Dec-3 Campo, Vlaamse Kaai #321
£541 $1000 €790 Landscape with castle (33x48cm-13x19in) s.d.1896. 13-Mar-4 Susanin's, Chicago #6077/R

GORGON, Vincenz (1891-1961) Austrian
£344 $550 €502 Procession through town square (99x68cm-39x27in) s.d.1918. 21-Sep-3 Bonhams & Butterfields, San Francisco #2814/R
Works on paper
£336 $617 €500 Kahlenberg village with Donau (18x18cm-7x7in) s. gouache. 26-Mar-4 Dorotheum, Vienna #290/R

GORGY, Soloman (?) ?
£300 $549 €438 Interior scene with lady and cat on a sofa (41x30cm-16x12in) s. board. 7-Apr-4 Andrew Hartley, Ilkley #1101

GORI, Affortunato (19/20th C) Italian
Sculpture
£1100 $1870 €1606 Figure in bare feet (34cm-13in) i. gilt bronze ivory. 25-Nov-3 Sotheby's, Olympia #135/R est:1200-1800

GORI, Caterina (18th C) Italian?
£16438 $27945 €24000 Still life of flowers. Still life of flowers and butterflies (34x25cm-13x10in) tempera vellum pair. 7-Nov-3 Farsetti, Prato #500/R est:15000-18000

GORI, G (20th C) French
Sculpture
£1126 $2049 €1700 Elegante au levrier (33x58cm-13x23in) ivory pat bronze onyx base. 19-Jun-4 St-Germain-en-Laye Encheres #83/R est:500

GORI, Georges (20th C) French
Sculpture
£2933 $5397 €4400 Salome (46cm-18in) s. ivory bronze marble base. 8-Jun-4 Livinec, Gaudcheau & Jezequel, Rennes #179/R

GORI, Gino Paolo (1911-1991) Italian
£352 $609 €500 Santa Maria Square (66x50cm-26x20in) s.i.d.1945 verso card. 9-Dec-3 Pandolfini, Florence #93/R
£388 $671 €550 Signoria Square, Florence (59x30cm-23x12in) s.i.verso card. 9-Dec-3 Pandolfini, Florence #101

GORI, Giorgio (1910-) French
£371 $675 €557 Valerie (90x71cm-35x28in) s. cardboard painted 1965. 21-Jun-4 Subastas Odalys, Caracas #76/R
£449 $750 €656 Paper boats (40x50cm-16x20in) s. painted 1960. 19-Oct-3 Subastas Odalys, Caracas #101
£544 $935 €794 Untitled (60x40cm-24x16in) s. masonite painted 1961. 7-Dec-3 Subastas Odalys, Caracas #32/R
Sculpture
£1209 $1935 €1765 Seated woman (40x25x27cm-16x10x11in) s.verso num.P/A285 bronze. 21-Sep-3 Subastas Odalys, Caracas #54/R
£1363 $2345 €1990 Dancer (45x12x12cm-18x5x5in) s. num.3/249 bronze. 7-Dec-3 Subastas Odalys, Caracas #23/R est:2200
£1613 $3000 €2355 Seated woman (27x31x26cm-11x12x10in) s.verso bronze. 14-Mar-4 Subastas Odalys, Caracas #28/R est:6000
£1840 $3385 €2760 Seated woman (14x24x26cm-6x9x10in) s. num.9/249 pat bronze. 27-Jun-4 Subastas Odalys, Caracas #57/R est:2500
£2162 $3935 €3243 Seated woman combing her hair (41x25x30cm-16x10x12in) s. num.1/7 pat bronze. 21-Jun-4 Subastas Odalys, Caracas #96 est:5000
£2686 $4835 €3922 Bust (42x20x12cm-17x8x5in) s. bronze. 25-Apr-4 Subastas Odalys, Caracas #35/R est:6000
£2778 $5000 €4056 Seated woman (36x28x30cm-14x11x12in) s.verso bronze. 25-Apr-4 Subastas Odalys, Caracas #56
£5162 $8775 €7537 Woman resting (18x46x16cm-7x18x6in) s. bronze. 23-Nov-3 Subastas Odalys, Caracas #131/R est:5000
£7941 $13500 €11594 Figure (40x110x33cm-16x43x13in) s. bronze. 23-Nov-3 Subastas Odalys, Caracas #86/R est:15000
Works on paper
£231 $425 €347 Crystallised flowers (60x79cm-24x31in) s. mixed media panel exec.1966. 27-Jun-4 Subastas Odalys, Caracas #116/R
£727 $1250 €1061 Ril (130x150cm-51x59in) s. mixed media panel exec.1963. 7-Dec-3 Subastas Odalys, Caracas #41/R

GORIELOFF, Gavril N (attrib) (19/20th C) Russian
£699 $1189 €1000 At the market place (41x60cm-16x24in) s. 29-Nov-3 Bukowskis, Helsinki #426/R

GORIN, Jean (1899-1981) French
£4909 $8346 €7167 Composition Spatio - temporelle (50x50cm-20x20in) s.d.1971 verso vinyl wood prov.lit. 5-Nov-3 AB Stockholms Auktionsverk #1108/R est:30000-40000 (S.KR 65000)
£10067 $18020 €15000 Composition 17 (66x55cm-26x22in) s.i.d.1961 verso board prov. 25-May-4 Sotheby's, Milan #168/R est:6000
£15000 $27450 €22500 Relief No 6 (84x110cm-33x43in) s.i.d.1960 panel prov.exhib. 5-Jun-4 Lempertz, Koln #740/R est:15000-20000
Works on paper
£1319 $2334 €1926 Composition plastique No.17 (31x31cm-12x12in) s.d.1964 gouache exhib. 27-Apr-4 AB Stockholms Auktionsverk #1199/R est:20000-25000 (S.KR 18000)

GORIOUNOVA, Lioudmila (?) Russian
£272 $495 €400 Muguets et papillon. s. 8-Feb-4 Lesieur & Le Bars, Le Havre #138

GORIUSHKIN-SOROKOVPUDOV, Ivan (1873-1954) Russian
£10769 $18523 €15723 Portrait of lady wearing red skirt (96x129cm-38x51in) s.d.1901. 7-Dec-3 Uppsala Auktionskammare, Uppsala #143/R est:30000-40000 (S.KR 140000)

GORKA, Paul (20th C) American
£256 $450 €374 Winter scene (25x41cm-10x16in) s. painted c.1951. 3-Jan-4 Outer Cape Auctions, Provincetown #123/R
£329 $550 €480 Nasturtiums and barn swallows (97x61cm-38x24in) s. 20-Jun-3 Freeman, Philadelphia #234/R
£778 $1300 €1136 Playground (36x188cm-14x74in) s. 20-Jun-3 Freeman, Philadelphia #238/R

GORKY, Arshile (1904-1948) American
£56886 $95000 €83054 Study for Agony (14x36cm-6x14in) s. painted 1947 prov.lit. 12-Nov-3 Christie's, Rockefeller NY #310/R est:40000-60000
Works on paper
£21229 $38000 €30994 Study for painting (25x38cm-10x15in) ink exec c.1932 prov.exhib. 12-May-4 Christie's, Rockefeller NY #101/R est:30000-40000
£22754 $38000 €33221 Study for Aviation Murals (43x56cm-17x22in) graphite drawn c.1935-1936 prov.exhib. 12-Nov-3 Christie's, Rockefeller NY #312/R est:40000-60000

GORLOV, Nikolai Nikolaievitch (1917-1987) Russian
£397 $723 €600 Moscow (160x133cm-63x52in) s.i.d.1985 verso. 19-Jun-4 Dannenberg, Berlin #563/R

GORMAN, Des (?) ?
£650 $1086 €949 The custodian (150x150cm-59x59in) s.verso. 11-Oct-3 Shapes, Edinburgh #325

GORMAN, Greg (20th C) American?
Photographs
£2029 $3328 €2800 Brigitte Nielsen (76x61cm-30x24in) silver gelatin. 30-May-3 Villa Grisebach, Berlin #1180/R est:1500-1800
£3704 $7000 €5408 Janice Dickinson (38x48cm-15x19in) s.i.d.1988 num.2.25 gelatin silver print. 17-Feb-4 Christie's, Rockefeller NY #228/R est:2000-3000

GORMAN, Richard (1946-) Irish
£2098 $3566 €3000 Three nudes (86x86cm-34x34in) s.i.d.1981 verso. 18-Nov-3 Whyte's, Dublin #81/R est:4000-6000

GORMAN, Richard Borthwick (1933-) Canadian
£1273 $2075 €1859 Inside (61x76cm-24x30in) s.d.62 prov. 23-Sep-3 Ritchie, Toronto #194/R est:1000-1500 (C.D 2800)
£5804 $9982 €8474 Sanctuary (210x192cm-83x76in) s.d.60 oil lucite lit. 2-Dec-3 Joyner Waddington, Toronto #112/R est:8000-12000 (C.D 13000)

GORMLEY, Anthony (1950-) British
Sculpture
£15000 $25050 €21900 Lost dog IV (44x50x24cm-17x20x9in) forged ball bearings series 4 of 5 prov. 22-Oct-3 Christie's, London #121/R est:15000-20000
£49102 $82000 €71689 Total stranger (193x56x30cm-76x22x12in) init.i.d.1996 num. cast iron prov.exhib.lit. 13-Nov-3 Phillips, New York #44/R est:60000-80000
£61453 $110000 €89721 Drawn apart III (154x133x187cm-61x52x74in) cast iron executed 2000. 13-May-4 Phillips, New York #58/R est:80000-120000
£80000 $145600 €116800 Quantum cloud XIV (250x163x160cm-98x64x63in) stainless steel prov. 21-Jun-4 Bonhams, New Bond Street #148/R est:80000-120000
Works on paper
£867 $1500 €1266 Untitled (41x61cm-16x24in) gouache prov. 10-Dec-3 Phillips, New York #562/R est:3000-4000
£2800 $5096 €4088 Untitled (84x59cm-33x23in) s.d.82 verso pencil gouache. 21-Jun-4 Bonhams, New Bond Street #160/R est:2000-3000
£3500 $6370 €5110 Linger, loiter, turn, touch (29x41cm-11x16in) s.i.d.96 verso coffee sugar prov. 4-Feb-4 Sotheby's, Olympia #39/R est:3500-4000
£4000 $7280 €5840 Untitled (90x64cm-35x25in) s.d.82 verso gouache. 21-Jun-4 Bonhams, New Bond Street #162/R est:2000-3000
£4500 $8190 €6570 Untitled (60x86cm-24x34in) s.d.85 verso gouache. 21-Jun-4 Bonhams, New Bond Street #161/R est:2000-3000

GORNEMANN, Alejandro (1964-) Spanish
£408 $743 €600 Untitled (187x215cm-74x85in) s.d.1986 exhib.lit. 3-Feb-4 Segre, Madrid #206/R

GOROG, Rudi (1930-) Hungarian
£503 $936 €750 Saint Lucy's sister. Homer's daughters (100x65cm-39x26in) s. acrylic two. 4-Mar-4 Babuino, Rome #517
£604 $1123 €900 Sunday afternoon. Unknown saint (70x100cm-28x39in) s. oil acrylic two. 4-Mar-4 Babuino, Rome #504

GOROVSKY, Apolinary (1833-1900) Russian
£2098 $3566 €3000 Boats on the shore (28x38cm-11x15in) s.d.1890. 29-Nov-3 Bukowskis, Helsinki #407/R est:1000-1200

GORP, Henri Nicolas van (1756-1819) French
£1000 $1790 €1500 Portrait de jeune femme (12x10cm-5x4in) 11-May-4 Christie's, Paris #194/R est:800-1200

GORP, Henri Nicolas van (attrib) (1756-1819) French
£1552 $2778 €2266 Seated young woman (31x25cm-12x10in) 26-May-4 AB Stockholms Auktionsverk #2572/R est:30000-40000 (S.KR 21000)
£4444 $8000 €6488 Lady playing virginals (45x36cm-18x14in) prov. 22-Jan-4 Sotheby's, New York #103/R est:8000-12000

GORPENKO, A A (1918-1980) Russian
£707 $1300 €1032 In the port, Murmansk (40x59cm-16x23in) painted 1952. 27-Mar-4 Shishkin Gallery, Moscow #32/R
£707 $1300 €1032 On the open seas (54x68cm-21x27in) painted 1952. 27-Mar-4 Shishkin Gallery, Moscow #33/R

GORRA, Giulio (1832-1884) Italian
£6803 $12177 €10000 Carnival in the garden (90x128cm-35x50in) prov. 22-Mar-4 Sant Agostino, Torino #223/R est:2500

GORRIARENA, Carlos (20th C) Argentinian
£7821 $14000 €11419 Bevelled (135x180cm-53x71in) s.d.93 s.i.d.verso acrylic. 4-May-4 Arroyo, Buenos Aires #77/R est:13000
£15642 $28000 €22837 On the right, far away (175x175cm-69x69in) s.d.86 s.i.d.verso acrylic. 4-May-4 Arroyo, Buenos Aires #76/R est:20000

GORRITI, Gilles (1939-) French
£1014 $1693 €1450 Interieur rouge (73x60cm-29x24in) s. prov. 7-Oct-3 Livinec, Gaudcheau & Jezequel, Rennes #150
£1902 $3500 €2777 La croisette de St Maxime (53x64cm-21x25in) s. s.i.verso. 9-Jun-4 Doyle, New York #3039 est:1000-1500

GORROCHATEGUI, Claudio (1917-1991) Argentinian
£659 $1200 €962 Bar (21x30cm-8x12in) s. i.verso board. 5-Jul-4 Arroyo, Buenos Aires #34/R

GORSON, Aaron Henry (1872-1933) American
£3412 $5800 €4982 Along the river, dusk (41x56cm-16x22in) s. prov. 30-Oct-3 Phillips, New York #73/R est:6000-8000
£4261 $7500 €6221 Industrial landscape (79x66cm-31x26in) 21-May-4 Pook & Pook, Downington #305/R est:5000-7000
£4261 $7500 €6221 Industrial landscape (36x51cm-14x20in) s. 21-May-4 Pook & Pook, Downington #308/R est:3000-4000
£6250 $11000 €9125 Industrial landscape (41x51cm-16x20in) s. 21-May-4 Pook & Pook, Downington #307/R est:5000-7000
£15569 $26000 €22731 Pittsburgh at night (91x107cm-36x42in) s. prov. 9-Oct-3 Christie's, Rockefeller NY #49/R est:20000-30000
£15909 $28000 €23227 Industrial landscape (74x112cm-29x44in) s. 21-May-4 Pook & Pook, Downington #306/R est:10000-15000

GORTER, Arnold Marc (1866-1933) Dutch
£625 $1000 €913 Forest scene (64x43cm-25x17in) s. 20-Sep-3 New Orleans Auction, New Orleans #483/R
£1241 $2073 €1800 View of Vordense brook (55x44cm-22x17in) s. 11-Nov-3 Vendu Notarishuis, Rotterdam #18/R est:2000-2500
£1300 $2405 €1898 Autumnal river landscape (43x32cm-17x13in) s. 13-Jan-4 Bonhams, Knightsbridge #89/R est:1000-1500
£1344 $2406 €1962 Cows in a landscape (60x75cm-24x30in) indis.s. 15-May-4 Christie's, Sydney #481/R est:3000-5000 (A.D 3400)
£1532 $2819 €2237 Autumn time (38x51cm-15x20in) s. prov. 14-Jun-4 Waddingtons, Toronto #245/R est:3500-4000 (C.D 3800)
£1579 $2905 €2400 View of the Vordense Beek (40x50cm-16x20in) s. 28-Jun-4 Sotheby's, Amsterdam #78/R est:2500-3500
£1786 $3071 €2608 Autumn in the glade (38x51cm-15x20in) s. 2-Dec-3 Ritchie, Toronto #123/R est:4000-6000 (C.D 4000)
£1802 $3063 €2631 Cattle in a sunny pasture (46x56cm-18x22in) s. prov. 21-Nov-3 Walker's, Ottawa #210/R est:5000-6000 (C.D 4000)
£1810 $3023 €2643 Golden autumn (46x56cm-18x22in) s. 17-Nov-3 Waddingtons, Toronto #164/R est:4000-4500 (C.D 4000)
£1905 $3467 €2800 Autumn (51x71cm-20x28in) s. 3-Feb-4 Christie's, Amsterdam #199/R est:2500-3500
£2600 $4758 €3796 Harmelen, a milkmaid and cows by a river (41x55cm-16x22in) s. 7-Apr-4 Woolley & Wallis, Salisbury #188/R est:800-1200
£3293 $5500 €4808 Landscape (76x102cm-30x40in) 14-Nov-3 Du Mouchelle, Detroit #2010/R
£3472 $5799 €5000 An autumn landscape (76x102cm-30x40in) s. 21-Oct-3 Sotheby's, Amsterdam #143/R est:6000-8000
£4000 $7200 €6000 Claire de lune (100x135cm-39x53in) s. prov.exhib. 21-Apr-4 Christie's, Amsterdam #150/R est:7000-9000
£5208 $8698 €7500 Sheep in a sunny autumn landscape (44x58cm-17x23in) s. 21-Oct-3 Sotheby's, Amsterdam #109/R est:4000-6000
£9028 $15347 €13000 Homewood bound in winter (100x136cm-39x54in) s. 28-Oct-3 Christie's, Amsterdam #145/R est:10000-15000
Works on paper
£503 $926 €750 Trees on the Vordense brook (46x32cm-18x13in) s. W/C. 29-Mar-4 Glerum, Amsterdam #173
£833 $1358 €1200 Landscape (53x79cm-21x31in) s. W/C. 29-Sep-3 Sotheby's, Amsterdam #128

GORUS, Pieter (1881-1941) Belgian
£2467 $4415 €3700 Summer landscape with pond (99x121cm-39x48in) s. 15-May-4 De Vuyst, Lokeren #558/R est:3000-4000
£2817 $4873 €4000 Scheldt dike and the church of Vlassenbrouck under snow (81x95cm-32x37in) s. 13-Dec-3 De Vuyst, Lokeren #165/R est:3500-4500
£3867 $6960 €5800 River Schelde (150x190cm-59x75in) s.d.1926. 26-Apr-4 Bernaerts, Antwerp #307/R est:5000-7500
£6690 $11574 €9500 Fun in the snow near a mill (80x100cm-31x39in) s. 13-Dec-3 De Vuyst, Lokeren #457/R est:9000-12000
Works on paper
£839 $1401 €1200 Summer landscape (46x40cm-18x16in) s. 11-Oct-3 De Vuyst, Lokeren #168

GORUS, Stephan (1913-) Belgian
£537 $993 €800 City square (150x120cm-59x47in) s. 13-Mar-4 De Vuyst, Lokeren #156
£633 $1165 €950 Vue de ville (115x145cm-45x57in) s. 14-Jun-4 Horta, Bruxelles #31

GORY, Affortunato (fl.1895-1925) Italian
Sculpture
£1389 $2208 €2000 Buste de soubrette (56cm-22in) s. gilt bronze marble. 15-Sep-3 Horta, Bruxelles #315 est:650-750
£2483 $4395 €3700 Couple de venitiens (53x44x18cm-21x17x7in) s.i. pat bronze marble base. 27-Apr-4 Claude Aguttes, Neuilly #15/R est:4000-4200
£11000 $18370 €16060 Dancer (73cm-29in) marble and gilt bronze. 14-Oct-3 Sotheby's, Olympia #34/R est:8000-12000

GORY, Affortunato (after) (fl.1895-1925) Italian
Sculpture
£7000 $12810 €10500 Guerrier au repos (58cm-23in) i. gold pat bronze marble lit. 3-Jun-4 Tajan, Paris #256/R est:8000-10000

GOS, Albert (1852-1942) Swiss
£286 $457 €415 Mountain hut (15x17cm-6x7in) panel. 15-May-3 Stuker, Bern #1261 (S.FR 600)
£302 $540 €441 Matterhorn in evening light (17x21cm-7x8in) s. board. 12-May-4 Dobiaschofsky, Bern #570 (S.FR 700)
£315 $542 €460 View of the Matterhorn (24x22cm-9x9in) mono. 8-Dec-3 Philippe Schuler, Zurich #5922 (S.FR 700)
£344 $575 €499 Crepuscule a Clarens, la Roche aux mouettes (18x23cm-7x9in) s. 21-Jun-3 Galerie du Rhone, Sion #376 (S.FR 750)
£433 $775 €632 Winter landscape (27x22cm-11x9in) s. 22-Mar-4 Philippe Schuler, Zurich #6016 (S.FR 1000)
£463 $786 €676 La chaine du Grand-Muveran vu du nord de Chesieres (28x40cm-11x16in) s. 5-Nov-3 Dobiaschofsky, Bern #3441 (S.FR 1050)
£519 $930 €758 Rock study (35x27cm-14x11in) s. panel. 22-Mar-4 Philippe Schuler, Zurich #4333 (S.FR 1200)
£529 $899 €772 Mountain hut with Matterhorn beyond (20x16cm-8x6in) s. canvas on panel. 5-Nov-3 Dobiaschofsky, Bern #3439 (S.FR 1200)
£603 $1080 €880 Matterhorn (32x23cm-13x9in) s. panel. 12-May-4 Dobiaschofsky, Bern #571 (S.FR 1400)
£617 $1048 €901 Barques a Montreux (59x70cm-23x28in) s. i. verso exhib. 7-Nov-3 Dobiaschofsky, Bern #37/R (S.FR 1400)
£619 $990 €898 Lake and mountains (74x60cm-29x24in) s. 15-May-3 Stuker, Bern #1260/R (S.FR 1300)
£1009 $1685 €1463 Ancienne chapelle de Zinal au claire de lune (35x24cm-14x9in) s. s.i.verso painted c.1915. 21-Jun-3 Galerie du Rhone, Sion #377/R est:1500-2000 (S.FR 2200)
£1101 $1839 €1596 Castor et Pollux, lever de soleil (46x66cm-18x26in) s. init.verso. 21-Jun-3 Galerie du Rhone, Sion #471/R est:2500-3500 (S.FR 2400)
£1810 $3077 €2643 Mountain peak at dusk (55x46cm-22x18in) s. 19-Nov-3 Fischer, Luzern #1237/R est:3000-4000 (S.FR 4000)
£2719 $4541 €3970 Le Cervin (75x62cm-30x24in) s. 16-Nov-3 Koller, Geneva #1215/R est:2200-3200 (S.FR 6200)
£4977 $8611 €7266 Cervin en automne (129x102cm-51x40in) s. 12-Dec-3 Galerie du Rhone, Sion #652/R est:10000-15000 (S.FR 11000)
£6897 $12345 €10070 Matterhorn (127x92cm-50x36in) s. i. verso. 14-May-4 Dobiaschofsky, Bern #102/R est:20000 (S.FR 16000)
£7860 $14070 €11476 Matterhorn (82x68cm-32x27in) s. 26-May-4 Sotheby's, Zurich #39/R est:5000-8000 (S.FR 18000)

GOS, François (1880-1975) Swiss
£229 $383 €332 Valere (28x35cm-11x14in) s. 21-Jun-3 Galerie du Rhone, Sion #380/R (S.FR 500)
£286 $457 €415 Dents du Midi (31x47cm-12x19in) s. 15-May-3 Stuker, Bern #1262 (S.FR 600)
£302 $540 €441 L'Aiguille Verte - Col des Montets (39x32cm-15x13in) s. canvas on board. 12-May-4 Dobiaschofsky, Bern #3622/R (S.FR 700)
£323 $579 €472 Aurore (25x33cm-10x13in) s. panel. 12-May-4 Dobiaschofsky, Bern #572 (S.FR 750)
£339 $587 €495 Lac des Chavonnes (33x41cm-13x16in) s. 12-Dec-3 Galerie du Rhone, Sion #502 (S.FR 750)
£371 $676 €542 Farmhouse in an autumnal landscape (37x44cm-15x17in) s. masonite. 16-Jun-4 Fischer, Luzern #2147/R (S.FR 850)
£571 $914 €828 The Weisshorn (39x3cm-15x1in) s. board. 15-May-3 Stuker, Bern #1263 (S.FR 1200)
£596 $996 €864 Paysage de montagne (26x32cm-10x13in) s. pavatex. 21-Jun-3 Galerie du Rhone, Sion #379 est:1500-2000 (S.FR 1300)
£733 $1312 €1070 Riffelhorn et Cervin (45x60cm-18x24in) s. 12-May-4 Dobiaschofsky, Bern #573/R est:1400 (S.FR 1700)
£1733 $3120 €2600 Figure (100x70cm-39x28in) s. 26-Apr-4 Bernaerts, Antwerp #532/R est:500-750
Works on paper
£344 $575 €499 Gletsch (46x31cm-18x12in) s.i.d. gouache. 21-Jun-3 Galerie du Rhone, Sion #381/R (S.FR 750)

GOSCHL, Roland (1932-) Austrian
£5594 $9510 €8000 Untitled (200x131cm-79x52in) panel. 28-Nov-3 Wiener Kunst Auktionen, Vienna #638/R est:8000-12000

GOSEDA, Horyu (1827-1892) Japanese
£2098 $3608 €3000 Shakyamuni meditating in a cave sitting on a bed of leaves (72x52cm-28x20in) s. 5-Dec-3 Lempertz, Koln #807/R est:3500

GOSLING, William (1824-1883) British
£1500 $2760 €2190 Pony before a cottage (47x63cm-19x25in) s. s.i.verso. 10-Jun-4 Christie's, Kensington #94/R est:1500-2000
Works on paper
£750 $1290 €1095 Anglers by a weir (25x47cm-10x19in) s. pencil W/C. 3-Dec-3 Christie's, Kensington #130/R

GOSNET FRASSETTO, Michele (20th C) French?
£2685 $4752 €4000 Brume portuaire (130x89cm-51x35in) s. 29-Apr-4 Claude Aguttes, Neuilly #265 est:4000-4200

GOSSAERT, Jan (circle) (1478-1533) Flemish
£8500 $15300 €12410 Salvator Mundi (12x8cm-5x3in) i. panel arched top. 23-Apr-4 Christie's, Kensington #7/R est:2000-3000

GOSSE, Nicolas (1787-1878) French
£4667 $8447 €7000 Portrait de jeune femme lisant (116x89cm-46x35in) s.d.1836 prov. 31-Mar-4 Sotheby's, Paris #86/R est:5000-7000

GOSSE, Sylvia (1881-1968) British
Works on paper
£300 $510 €438 Sp. (38x28cm-15x11in) pencil chl. 26-Nov-3 Sotheby's, Olympia #13/R
£340 $609 €496 Street scene possibly Chelsea (48x41cm-19x16in) s. gouache. 7-May-4 Mallams, Oxford #245

GOSSELIN, Colonel Joshua (1739-1813) British
Works on paper
£782 $1400 €1142 Forts Royal and Edward in the Island of Martinque (20x36cm-8x14in) init.d.1800 ink grey wash. 18-Mar-4 Richard Opfer, Timonium #145/R

GOSWIN, Gerard (attrib) (?-1691) Flemish
£6711 $12349 €10000 Nature morte au vase de fleurs sur en entablement (54x71cm-21x28in) 24-Mar-4 Tajan, Paris #103/R est:12000-15000

GOTAAS, Gerhard (?) Norwegian?
£313 $542 €457 Evening (58x96cm-23x38in) s. 13-Dec-3 Blomqvist, Lysaker #1109 (N.KR 3600)

GOTCH, Bernard Cecil (1876-1940) British
Works on paper
£300 $498 €438 View of Worcester Street and college, Oxford (23x36cm-9x14in) s. W/C. 3-Oct-3 Mallams, Oxford #116/R

GOTCH, Thomas Cooper (1854-1931) British
£2600 $4420 €3796 Study of lilies (46x30cm-18x12in) s. 26-Nov-3 Sotheby's, Olympia #36/R est:800-1200
Works on paper
£1100 $1837 €1606 French crabbers in Newlyn harbour (10x18cm-4x7in) s. i.verso W/C. 14-Oct-3 David Lay, Penzance #581 est:600-800
£1350 $2498 €1971 Midday, Perranporth (13x20cm-5x8in) s. W/C. 10-Feb-4 David Lay, Penzance #452/R est:500-600

GOTH, Imre (1893-1982) Hungarian
£632 $1132 €923 Portrait of a woman, the artist's muse three-quarter (39x31cm-15x12in) wood panel prov. 15-May-4 Christie's, Sydney #134/R est:2000-3000 (A.D 1600)
£5929 $10613 €8656 Portrait of a woman, the artist's muse (35x27cm-14x11in) mono.d.1932 panel prov. 15-May-4 Christie's, Sydney #133/R est:3000-5000 (A.D 15000)

GOTH, Moricz (1873-1944) Hungarian
£347 $565 €500 View of farms near Heeze (50x60cm-20x24in) s. 29-Sep-3 Sotheby's, Amsterdam #267
£825 $1319 €1205 African woman with her child, three women in background (73x60cm-29x24in) s. exhib. 22-Sep-3 Rasmussen, Vejle #571/R (D.KR 8700)
£2466 $4192 €3600 Woman reading on the terrace (59x49cm-23x19in) s. 5-Nov-3 Vendue Huis, Gravenhage #508/R est:800-1000

GOTH, Sarika (1900-) Hungarian
£500 $915 €750 Still life with birds and flowers (42x50cm-17x20in) s.d.1979. 7-Jun-4 Glerum, Amsterdam #41/R
£872 $1614 €1300 Flowers still life (24x18cm-9x7in) s.d.1919 panel. 15-Mar-4 Sotheby's, Amsterdam #197/R est:750-900

GOTHBER, Leona (?) American
£223 $400 €326 City street scene (33x43cm-13x17in) s. 13-May-4 Dallas Auction Gallery, Dallas #124/R

GOTHLIN, Hans (1949-) Swedish
£340 $578 €496 For no one (43x43cm-17x17in) s.d.2000 oil acrylicglass. 5-Nov-3 AB Stockholms Auktionsverk #954/R (S.KR 4500)

GOTKO, Jacques (19/20th C) ?
£1192 $2170 €1800 Personnages au bord de riviere (60x73cm-24x29in) s.d.1928. 16-Jun-4 Claude Boisgirard, Paris #69/R est:2000-2500

GOTSCH, Friedrich Karl (1900-1984) Danish
£2667 $4773 €4000 Hochdorf house (76x61cm-30x24in) s.mono.i.d.9.9.67. 15-May-4 Van Ham, Cologne #623/R est:4500
£8451 $14620 €12000 Girl (76x64cm-30x25in) mono. s.i.d.1929-54 verso prov.exhib. 9-Dec-3 Artcurial Briest, Paris #269/R est:12000-15000
£10000 $18400 €15000 Two trees in front of houses (56x60cm-22x24in) mono. s.i.d.31 verso prov.exhib.lit. 11-Jun-4 Villa Grisebach, Berlin #1572/R est:9000-12000
£10072 $16518 €14000 Dyck on St Peter (51x79cm-20x31in) mono.d. prov. 4-Jun-3 Ketterer, Hamburg #393/R est:13000-15000
Works on paper
£1133 $2085 €1700 Horses in Friesian landscape (50x68cm-20x27in) s.mono.i.d.1951 W/C. 9-Jun-4 Dorotheum, Salzburg #788/R est:3000-4000
£1319 $2203 €1900 Tree and house (53x76cm-21x30in) s.mono.i.d. W/C gouache double-sided. 24-Oct-3 Ketterer, Hamburg #357/R est:1900-2200

GOTT, Hans (1883-?) German
£268 $494 €400 Young woman with sewing (54x41cm-21x16in) s. board. 24-Mar-4 Hugo Ruef, Munich #1225/R
£268 $494 €400 Nude girl in garden (50x37cm-20x15in) s. board. 24-Mar-4 Hugo Ruef, Munich #1226/R

GOTT, Joseph (1785-1860) British
Sculpture
£4054 $7500 €5919 Spaniel and kitten with a basket of fruit (33x69x30cm-13x27x12in) marble. 14-Jan-4 Dallas Auction Gallery, Dallas #85/R est:800-1600
£12752 $22826 €19000 Hound (80cm-31in) s. white marble. 27-May-4 Semenzato, Florence #142/R est:18000-25000

GOTTFREDSON, Floyd (1907-) American
Works on paper
£5090 $8500 €7431 Tanglefoot the horse attends to Pluto (15x66cm-6x26in) s. pen ink. 15-Nov-3 Illustration House, New York #63/R est:2000-3000

GOTTLIEB, Adolph (1903-1974) American
£18405 $30000 €26871 Table (63x73cm-25x29in) s.i.d.1956 verso prov. 23-Sep-3 Christie's, Rockefeller NY #11/R est:15000-20000
£32402 $58000 €47307 Centipede (51x61cm-20x24in) i.d.1955 verso masonite. 12-May-4 Christie's, Rockefeller NY #154/R est:35000-45000
£35928 $60000 €52455 Looming no 2 (122x152cm-48x60in) s.i.d.1969 verso acrylic alkyd resin prov.exhib. 13-Nov-3 Sotheby's, New York #190/R est:70000-90000
£50279 $90000 €73407 Above and below no 2 (61x76cm-24x30in) s.i.d.1965 verso prov. 12-May-4 Christie's, Rockefeller NY #155/R est:70000-90000
£83832 $140000 €122395 Orange on Red (76x61cm-30x24in) s.i.d.1965 verso prov. 12-Nov-3 Christie's, Rockefeller NY #301/R est:60000-80000
£156425 $280000 €228381 Rising (175x102cm-69x40in) s. i.d.1958 verso prov.exhib. 13-May-4 Sotheby's, New York #109/R est:150000-200000
£209581 $350000 €305988 Waterscape (92x123cm-36x48in) s. s.i.d.1952 verso prov.exhib.lit. 12-Nov-3 Christie's, Rockefeller NY #317/R est:150000-200000
£233533 $390000 €340958 Red and green (229x185cm-90x73in) s.i.d.1966 oil linen prov.exhib. 13-Nov-3 Sotheby's, New York #183/R est:350000-450000
Works on paper
£4895 $8420 €7000 Composition (22x30cm-9x12in) s.i.d. Indian ink brush. 3-Dec-3 Hauswedell & Nolte, Hamburg #786/R est:10000
£9890 $18000 €14439 Nights of the fishermen (39x29cm-15x11in) s.d.46 gouache prov. 29-Jun-4 Sotheby's, New York #450/R est:8000-12000
£17178 $28000 €25080 Burst (76x56cm-30x22in) indis.sig. ink gouache pencil board exec.c.1958-59 exhib. 23-Sep-3 Christie's, Rockefeller NY #20/R est:10000-15000
£41899 $75000 €61173 Mood Indigo (65x49cm-26x19in) s.d.1946 s.i.d.verso gouache W/C graphite prov. 12-May-4 Christie's, Rockefeller NY #102/R est:40000-60000

GOTTLIEB, Harry (1895-?) American
£447 $800 €653 Still life, Woodstock (41x51cm-16x20in) s. prov. 4-May-4 Ritchie, Toronto #55/R est:1000-1500 (C.D 1100)
£5814 $10000 €8488 Roundhouse (76x102cm-30x40in) s.d.27 i.on stretcher. 3-Dec-3 Doyle, New York #292/R est:3000-5000
Works on paper
£326 $600 €476 New York snow scene (48x23cm-19x9in) s. brush ink chl exec. c.1935. 10-Jun-4 Swann Galleries, New York #103/R
£380 $700 €555 Patchin Place (33x28cm-13x11in) s.d.1921 pencil card. 10-Jun-4 Swann Galleries, New York #102/R
£640 $1100 €934 Mining (36x43cm-14x17in) s.d.1938 W/C ink. 7-Dec-3 Treadway Gallery, Cincinnati #670/R

GOTTLIEB, Leopold (1883-1934) Polish
Works on paper
£950 $1682 €1387 Washing of the fish (19x21cm-7x8in) s.d.1920 W/C. 27-Apr-4 Bonhams, Knightsbridge #232/R

GOTTLIEB, Moritz (1856-1879) Polish
£15837 $26448 €23122 Rabbi holding a Torah scroll (68x54cm-27x21in) s. 17-Nov-3 Waddingtons, Toronto #284/R est:4000-6000 (C.D 35000)

GOTTSCHALK, Albert (1866-1906) Danish
£563 $941 €822 Study of head (45x41cm-18x16in) canvas on plywood prov.exhib.lit. 7-Oct-3 Rasmussen, Copenhagen #326/R (D.KR 6000)
£945 $1635 €1380 Summer landscape with houses (36x49cm-14x19in) mono. s.d.97 verso. 9-Dec-3 Rasmussen, Copenhagen #1695/R (D.KR 10000)

GOTTSCHO, Samuel (1875-1971) American
Photographs
£2156 $3600 €3148 Late afternoon silhouette from the Bolivar Monument, Central Park (18x25cm-7x10in) i. silver print. 21-Oct-3 Swann Galleries, New York #142/R est:2500-3500

GOTZ, J (?) German?
Sculpture
£1538 $2615 €2200 Roman soldier (44cm-17in) i. bronze. 20-Nov-3 Van Ham, Cologne #126/R est:600

GOTZ, Johannes (1865-?) German
Sculpture
£1646 $2567 €2600 Boy balancing on ball (49x51cm-19x20in) s.i. black brown pat.bronze. 18-Oct-2 Von Zezschwitz, Munich #5a/R est:3200

GOTZ, Karl Otto (1914-) German
£5333 $9760 €8000 Untitled (30x40cm-12x16in) s. s.d.26.1.1954 verso tempera. 4-Jun-4 Lempertz, Koln #161/R est:8000
Works on paper
£1467 $2625 €2200 Composition (20x14cm-8x6in) s. s.i.d. verso gouache. 13-May-4 Neumeister, Munich #624/R est:1800-2000
£1667 $3067 €2500 Untitled (42x62cm-17x24in) s. W/C. 12-Jun-4 Villa Grisebach, Berlin #722/R est:2500-3000
£1867 $3435 €2800 Untitled (42x62cm-17x24in) s. W/C. 12-Jun-4 Villa Grisebach, Berlin #721/R est:2500-3000
£2098 $3566 €3000 Untitled (37x54cm-15x21in) gouache prov. 27-Nov-3 Lempertz, Koln #152/R est:3000
£2098 $3566 €3000 Untitled (29x42cm-11x17in) s. s.d.17.5.1956 verso Indian ink. 27-Nov-3 Lempertz, Koln #153/R est:4000
£2657 $4517 €3800 Untitled (64x50cm-25x20in) s. i. verso gouache board prov. 27-Nov-3 Lempertz, Koln #154/R est:5000
£2667 $4907 €4000 Scene V (43x60cm-17x24in) s.d.47 s.i.d.verso gouache. 12-Jun-4 Villa Grisebach, Berlin #338/R est:6000-8000
£2667 $4907 €4000 Scene VI (43x58cm-17x23in) s.d.47 s.i.d.verso gouache. 12-Jun-4 Villa Grisebach, Berlin #339/R est:6000-8000
£2727 $4636 €3900 Composition (50x65cm-20x26in) s. gouache board prov. 29-Nov-3 Villa Grisebach, Berlin #340/R est:500-7000
£12587 $21650 €18000 Composition (120x100cm-47x39in) s. s.i.d. verso gouache paste prov.exhib. 5-Dec-3 Ketterer, Munich #311/R est:15000-20000
£14667 $26253 €22000 Blob (150x120cm-59x47in) s. s.i.d. verso gouache paste prov. 14-May-4 Ketterer, Munich #253/R est:22000-25000
£14685 $25259 €21000 Untitled (70x55cm-28x22in) s. s.d.18.2.1954 verso gouache paste. 5-Dec-3 Ketterer, Munich #314/R est:18000-24000

GOTZE, Josef (1887-?) German
£462 $772 €670 Afternoon walk (40x29cm-16x11in) s. i. verso canvas on board. 15-Nov-3 Von Zezschwitz, Munich #98/R

GOTZE, L (19th C) German
£3800 $7030 €5700 Butterfly (111x60cm-44x24in) s.d.84. 14-Jul-4 Sotheby's, Olympia #150/R est:2000-3000

GOTZELMANN, Edward (1830-1903) Austrian
£975 $1658 €1424 Farmyard scene with cottage, drover, cattle, horses and fowl (50x80cm-20x31in) s. 27-Nov-3 Clevedon Sale Rooms #178
£1325 $2411 €2000 Riding party on the way for a drink (25x47cm-10x19in) s. panel. 21-Jun-4 Dorotheum, Vienna #218/R est:2000-2500

GOTZENBERGER, Jakob (1800-1866) German
£2262 $3620 €3303 Self portrait with family (97x74cm-38x29in) prov. 16-Sep-3 Philippe Schuler, Zurich #3331/R est:6000-8000 (S.FR 5000)

GOTZINGER, Hans (1867-1941) Austrian
£1342 $2510 €2000 Portrait of girl with dog (110x47cm-43x19in) s.d.1895 arched top. 24-Feb-4 Dorotheum, Vienna #209/R est:2500-2800

GOTZL, Willi (1907-1978) Austrian
£541 $951 €800 Ossiach (48x63cm-19x25in) s.d.1971 board. 19-May-4 Dorotheum, Klagenfurt #6/R

GOTZLOFF, Carl (1799-1866) German
£6000 $10200 €8760 Palermo from Belmonte (46x65cm-18x26in) indis.sig. 18-Nov-3 Sotheby's, London #327/R
£7000 $11900 €10220 Piedimonte d'Alife (54x77cm-21x30in) s.verso. 18-Nov-3 Sotheby's, London #326/R
£9333 $16800 €14000 Am Golf von Sorrent (41x66cm-16x26in) s.d.1832 prov. 21-Apr-4 Christie's, Amsterdam #169/R est:8000-12000
Works on paper
£1538 $2615 €2200 Couple de bergers et leur troupeau au bord de l'eau (17x28cm-7x11in) s.d.1828 crayon W/C. 18-Nov-3 Vanderkindere, Brussels #221/R est:2000-3000

GOTZLOFF, Carl (attrib) (1799-1866) German
£12676 $21930 €18000 Castel dell'Ovo. Fishermen on the beach (50x63cm-20x25in) pair. 10-Dec-3 Finarte Semenzato, Rome #223/R est:22000-25000

GOUBAU, Antoni (1616-1698) Dutch
£7778 $14000 €11356 Travelers resting by a house, with architectural ruins beyond (57x43cm-22x17in) init. panel prov. 22-Jan-4 Sotheby's, New York #251/R est:15000-20000
£11111 $20000 €16222 Landscape with figures (76x129cm-30x51in) i.d.1667 prov. 22-Jan-4 Sotheby's, New York #132/R est:10000-15000
£42763 $78684 €65000 Marche pres de port (182x246cm-72x97in) s.d.1670 prov. 24-Jun-4 Christie's, Paris #22/R est:30000-50000
£45390 $75801 €64000 Les vendanges dans la campagne aux environs de Tivoli (168x244cm-66x96in) s.d.1656 prov. 19-Oct-3 Anaf, Lyon #164/R est:35000-40000

GOUBAU, Antoni (attrib) (1616-1698) Dutch
£2533 $4535 €3800 Peasants at inn (74x55cm-29x22in) oval. 17-May-4 Finarte Semenzato, Rome #54 est:3500-4500

GOUBERT, Lucien Georges (1887-1964) French
£317 $513 €450 Vase of flowers (46x33cm-18x13in) s. 11-Aug-3 Boscher, Cherbourg #740
£317 $513 €450 Vase of flowers (50x61cm-20x24in) s.i.d.1939. 11-Aug-3 Boscher, Cherbourg #743
£323 $579 €472 Fishing boat in storm (70x100cm-28x39in) s. 13-May-4 Stuker, Bern #159 (S.FR 750)
£352 $570 €500 Bord de mer dans la Hague (38x61cm-15x24in) s. 11-Aug-3 Boscher, Cherbourg #741
£458 $742 €650 Maquereaux (38x61cm-15x24in) s. 11-Aug-3 Boscher, Cherbourg #745
£592 $1072 €900 Nature morte aux oignons et a la casserole de cuivre (43x54cm-17x21in) s. canvas on cardboard. 19-Apr-4 Boscher, Cherbourg #845
Works on paper
£423 $685 €600 Le nez de Jobourg (30x49cm-12x19in) s. crayon W/C. 11-Aug-3 Boscher, Cherbourg #744

GOUBIE, Jean Richard (1842-1899) French
£1796 $3000 €2622 Huntsman (27x35cm-11x14in) s.d.1880 panel. 7-Oct-3 Sotheby's, New York #162 est:3000-5000
£3239 $5215 €4600 Depart de la chasse a courre (24x32cm-9x13in) s. paper on canvas. 22-Aug-3 Deauville, France #38/R est:4000-5000
£6667 $12000 €9734 Looking out to sea (38x46cm-15x18in) s. prov. 22-Apr-4 Christie's, Rockefeller NY #185/R est:12000-16000
£56604 $90000 €82642 Before the hunt (68x100cm-27x39in) s.d.1888. 12-Sep-3 Skinner, Boston #226/R est:18000
Works on paper
£865 $1600 €1263 Equestrian studies (15x23cm-6x9in) s.d.1884 pencil col pencil. 10-Feb-4 Doyle, New York #226/R est:1000-1500

GOUBITZ, Alida (1904-) Dutch
£2378 $4090 €3400 Branches at sunset (31x34cm-12x13in) init.d.33 prov. 2-Dec-3 Sotheby's, Amsterdam #267/R est:2000-3000

GOUD, Laxma (1940-) Indian
Works on paper
£5163 $9500 €7538 Untitled (27x37cm-11x15in) s.d.1974 Aug 29th inside cover pen ink W/C twenty-two album. 24-Mar-4 Sotheby's, New York #184/R est:5000-7000

GOUDIE, Alexander (1933-) British
£1800 $3114 €2628 Crystal lamp (91x91cm-36x36in) s. 11-Dec-3 Lyon & Turnbull, Edinburgh #43/R est:1500-2000
£2500 $4250 €3650 Self Portrait with a palette (96x91cm-38x36in) s. painting of young lady verso prov. 30-Oct-3 Christie's, London #216/R est:3000-5000
£4000 $6800 €5840 Still life with clock and flowers (86x61cm-34x24in) s. 30-Oct-3 Christie's, London #212/R est:4000-6000
£5000 $8500 €7300 Portrait of the artist's daughter, Gwen, as a harlequin (152x91cm-60x36in) s. painted 1970. 30-Oct-3 Christie's, London #217/R est:6000-10000
£10000 $15700 €14500 Tam O'Shanter (131x183cm-52x72in) s. board. 27-Aug-3 Sotheby's, London #1168/R est:10000-15000

GOUDRIAAN, Johanna (1913-) Dutch
£274 $466 €400 Rocky coast (75x100cm-30x39in) s.verso. 5-Nov-3 Vendue Huis, Gravenhage #415/R
£274 $466 €400 Olive grove (65x96cm-26x38in) s. 5-Nov-3 Vendue Huis, Gravenhage #416/R

GOUGH, Robert Alan (20th C) American?
£268 $475 €391 March line (30x41cm-12x16in) s. acrylic. 1-May-4 Susanin's, Chicago #5055/R

GOULBORN, Cecilia (19/20th C) British
Works on paper
£650 $1105 €949 Salmon caught by L J Richardson-Gardner (38x111cm-15x44in) s.i. W/C bodycol. 27-Nov-3 Christie's, Kensington #254/R

GOULD, Alexander Carruthers (1870-1948) British
£260 $481 €380 Figures by a farm gate (22x34cm-9x13in) s. panel. 16-Feb-4 Bonhams, Bath #67
£360 $623 €526 Porlock Exmoor, a sunlit village scene with figures and flowers (25x33cm-10x13in) s. artist board. 11-Dec-3 Neales, Nottingham #601/R
£580 $963 €847 Minehead at low tide (24x35cm-9x14in) s. 1-Oct-3 Woolley & Wallis, Salisbury #275/R
£620 $1116 €905 Shadow'd Coves on a sunny shore from North Devon coast (39x59cm-15x23in) s.d.1922 i.overlap. 22-Apr-4 Lawrence, Crewkerne #943

GOULD, Elizabeth (1804-1841) British
Works on paper
£580 $969 €847 Singing parrots (30x22cm-12x9in) s.i.verso W/C. 14-Oct-3 Bonhams, Knightsbridge #66/R

GOULD, John (1804-1881) British
Prints
£2058 $3724 €3005 Gang-gang cockatoo, callocephalon galeatum. hand col lithograph exec.c.1840-1869. 30-Mar-4 Christie's, Melbourne #301/R est:3500-4000 (A.D 5000)
£2222 $4022 €3244 Crested cockatoo, cacatua galertia. hand col lithograph exec.c.1840-1869. 30-Mar-4 Christie's, Melbourne #327/R est:6000-9000 (A.D 5400)
£2263 $4096 €3304 Western black cockatoo, calyptorhynchus naso. hand col lithograph exec.c.1840-1869. 30-Mar-4 Christie's, Melbourne #311/R est:3000-3500 (A.D 5500)
£2263 $4096 €3304 Leach's cockatoo, calyptorhynchus leachii. hand col lithograph exec.c.1840-1869. 30-Mar-4 Christie's, Melbourne #320/R est:2000-4000 (A.D 5500)
£3086 $5586 €4506 Great-billed black cockatoo, calypthorhynchus macrohynchus. hand col lithograph exec.c.1840-1869. 30-Mar-4 Christie's, Melbourne #347/R est:5000-6000 (A.D 7500)
£3292 $5959 €4806 Funereal cockatoo, calyptorhynchus funereus. hand col lithograph exec.c.1840-1869. 30-Mar-4 Christie's, Melbourne #354 est:1500-2500 (A.D 8000)
£3704 $6704 €5408 Splendid parrakeet, platycercus splendidus. hand col lithograph exec.c.1840-1869. 30-Mar-4 Christie's, Melbourne #304/R est:5000-7000 (A.D 9000)
£4527 $8193 €6609 Banksian cockatoo, calptorhynchus banksii. hand col lithograph exec.c.1840-1869. 30-Mar-4 Christie's, Melbourne #337/R est:5000-8000 (A.D 11000)
£4527 $8193 €6609 Leadbeater's cockatoo, cacatua leadbeaterii. hand col lithograph exec.c.1840-1869. 30-Mar-4 Christie's, Melbourne #353/R est:5000-8000 (A.D 11000)
Works on paper
£6173 $11173 €9013 Galahs (51x35cm-20x14in) W/C. 30-Mar-4 Christie's, Melbourne #356/R est:15000-20000 (A.D 15000)

GOULD, John (20th C) American
£778 $1300 €1136 Moodna Creek, Washingtonville, NY (76x122cm-30x48in) s.d.1968 masonite. 19-Oct-3 William Jenack, New York #139

GOULD, John Howard (1929-) Canadian
Works on paper
£732 $1310 €1069 Deposed king (119x63cm-47x25in) s. collage mixed media board exec. 1978 prov. 27-May-4 Heffel, Vancouver #213/R est:2000-2500 (C.D 1800)
£840 $1538 €1219 Seated actor (95x60cm-37x24in) s. chk pastel. 1-Jun-4 Joyner Waddington, Toronto #174/R est:1200-1500 (C.D 2100)

GOULD, Rosa (20th C) New Zealander
£326 $554 €476 Portrait of Ena Te Papatahi (39x30cm-15x12in) s. oil on card after C F Goldie. 4-Nov-3 Peter Webb, Auckland #175 (NZ.D 900)

GOULDING, Tim (1945-) Irish
£660 $1075 €950 Lagoon, Venice (61x61cm-24x24in) s.d.1966 verso acrylic. 23-Sep-3 De Veres Art Auctions, Dublin #142
£733 $1327 €1100 Ragwort (66x14cm-26x6in) init.d.72 acrylic wood prov. 31-Mar-4 James Adam, Dublin #123/R
Works on paper
£946 $1788 €1400 Silver birch (51x41cm-20x16in) s.d.1987 i.verso mixed media. 17-Feb-4 Whyte's, Dublin #23/R est:1500-2000

GOULDING, Tim and KINGERLEE, John (20th C) Irish
£789 $1453 €1200 Untitled (62x43cm-24x17in) mono.d.89 board. 22-Jun-4 De Veres Art Auctions, Dublin #187/R

GOULET, Lorrie (20th C) French
Sculpture
£932 $1500 €1361 Partially robed woman (23x15x71cm-9x6x28in) s.verso exec. c.1960 stone. 22-Feb-3 Bunte, Elgin #1150j est:1800-2200

GOULET, Yann Renard (1914-1999) Irish/French
Sculpture
£1141 $2042 €1700 Group of workmen in procession (38x68cm-15x27in) s. bronze relief. 26-May-4 James Adam, Dublin #160/R est:1800-2200

GOULINAT, Jean Gabriel (1883-1972) French
£528 $877 €750 Portrait d'un avocat (116x81cm-46x32in) s.i. 15-Jun-3 Muizon & Le Coent, Paris #50
£845 $1596 €1250 Le Fort National, baie de Saint Malo (38x46cm-15x18in) s. panel. 21-Feb-4 Livinec, Gaudcheau & Jezequel, Rennes #104

GOUNAROPOULOS, Georges (1889-1977) Greek
£2000 $3500 €2920 Dreamscape (30x54cm-12x21in) s. oil pencil varnish hardboard prov. 16-Dec-3 Bonhams, New Bond Street #62/R est:2000-3000
£2000 $3500 €2920 Portrait of a man (33x28cm-13x11in) s. cardboard. 16-Dec-3 Bonhams, New Bond Street #90/R est:2000-3000
£4000 $7000 €5840 Flowers (80x55cm-31x22in) s. panel prov. 16-Dec-3 Bonhams, New Bond Street #61/R est:4000-6000
£8000 $13600 €11680 Houses in dream landscape (60x73cm-24x29in) s. 18-Nov-3 Sotheby's, London #138/R est:8000-12000
£15000 $26250 €21900 Pierrot et poupees (60x81cm-24x32in) s. 16-Dec-3 Bonhams, New Bond Street #87/R est:15000-20000
£18000 $30600 €26280 Easter procession (43x55cm-17x22in) s. board prov. 18-Nov-3 Sotheby's, London #129/R est:8000-12000
£20000 $34000 €29200 Dreamscape (81x121cm-32x48in) s.d.65 board prov. 18-Nov-3 Sotheby's, London #147/R est:20000-30000
Works on paper
£800 $1432 €1168 Head of a young boy (34x24cm-13x9in) init. pastel crayon. 11-May-4 Bonhams, New Bond Street #46/R

GOUNOT, A (19/20th C) French
Works on paper
£1400 $2240 €2044 Preparing for the games at the Colosseum, Rome (101x147cm-40x58in) s.d.1905 W/C gouache. 18-Sep-3 Christie's, Kensington #108/R est:1200-1500

GOUPIL, Ernest (?-1841) French
Works on paper
£5500 $8524 €8030 Les corvettes L'astrolabe et Zelee amarrees dans les glaces (46x56cm-18x22in) s.i.d.1838 pencil. 25-Sep-2 Christie's, London #28/R est:5000-7000
£5800 $8990 €8468 Les corvettes L'astrolabe et la Zelee dans les glaces (46x56cm-18x22in) s.i.d.1838 pencil. 25-Sep-2 Christie's, London #27/R est:5000-7000

GOUPIL, Jules Adolphe (1839-1883) French
£1800 $3312 €2628 Girl with red ribbon (32x24cm-13x9in) s. panel. 23-Mar-4 Bonhams, New Bond Street #107/R est:2000-3000

GOURDAULT, Pierre (1880-1915) French
£1818 $3036 €2600 La riviere de l'Aven (46x55cm-18x22in) s. 29-Jun-3 Eric Pillon, Calais #148/R

GOURDON, René (1855-?) French
£333 $603 €500 Marine Orientaliste (16x22cm-6x9in) s. panel. 4-Apr-4 Salle des ventes Pillet, Lyon la Foret #35
£400 $720 €600 Sous-bois anime (38x46cm-15x18in) s. 20-Apr-4 Chenu & Scrive, Lyon #98a/R

GOURDON, Robert (1820-?) French
£470 $800 €686 Landscape with woman (82x65cm-32x26in) i. 29-Nov-3 Rasmussen, Havnen #2240/R (D.KR 5000)

GOURGUE, E J (1930-) Haitian
£3267 $5847 €4900 Le sacrifice (61x51cm-24x20in) s. 17-May-4 Rogeon, Paris #90/R

GOURGUE, Enguerrand-Jean (1930-) Haitian
£838 $1400 €1223 Mother and child (102x61cm-40x24in) s. masonite. 20-Jun-3 Freeman, Philadelphia #109/R

GOUSSEV, Vladimir (1957-) Russian
£250 $448 €365 Young girl with ducks and ducklings (35x27cm-14x11in) s. 5-May-4 John Nicholson, Haslemere #248
£272 $495 €400 Apres le travail. s. 8-Feb-4 Lesieur & Le Bars, Le Havre #88
£300 $525 €438 My playful kitten (33x24cm-13x9in) s. 17-Dec-3 John Nicholson, Haslemere #58/R
£300 $525 €438 Winter Day (41x33cm-16x13in) s. 17-Dec-3 John Nicholson, Haslemere #112/R
£300 $501 €438 Young mistress of the farm (35x27cm-14x11in) s. 13-Jul-3 John Nicholson, Haslemere #83/R
£300 $561 €450 Drinking milk (27x32cm-11x13in) s. 21-Jul-4 John Nicholson, Haslemere #413
£350 $613 €511 March in the country (40x50cm-16x20in) s. 17-Dec-3 John Nicholson, Haslemere #171/R
£399 $654 €550 Paseo por los Jardines de Luxemburgo (35x50cm-14x20in) s. 27-May-3 Durán, Madrid #769/R
£400 $716 €584 Etude of a girl in a pink dress (50x40cm-20x16in) s. 5-May-4 John Nicholson, Haslemere #66
£400 $748 €600 In the living room (38x55cm-15x22in) s. 21-Jul-4 John Nicholson, Haslemere #327/R
£450 $752 €657 Pullets (41x33cm-16x13in) s. 13-Jul-3 John Nicholson, Haslemere #84/R
£500 $815 €730 Girl on the Farm (27x46cm-11x18in) s. 28-Sep-3 John Nicholson, Haslemere #6/R
£500 $835 €730 At the farm (40x50cm-16x20in) s. 13-Jul-3 John Nicholson, Haslemere #192
£544 $974 €800 Beach scene (46x38cm-18x15in) s. 22-Mar-4 Durán, Madrid #691/R
£550 $897 €803 Catherine (46x38cm-18x15in) s. 28-Sep-3 John Nicholson, Haslemere #170/R
£550 $963 €803 Girl with umbrella (50x40cm-20x16in) s. 17-Dec-3 John Nicholson, Haslemere #190
£556 $906 €800 Young women on the lake (73x60cm-29x24in) s. 16-Jul-3 Durán, Madrid #642/R
£600 $1002 €876 An afternoon tea (46x55cm-18x22in) s. 13-Jul-3 John Nicholson, Haslemere #166
£625 $1150 €950 Blooming garden (50x40cm-20x16in) s. 22-Jun-4 Durán, Madrid #699/R
£650 $1138 €949 Laundresses (55x46cm-22x18in) s. 17-Dec-3 John Nicholson, Haslemere #26/R
£650 $1161 €949 In the park (35x50cm-14x20in) s. 5-May-4 John Nicholson, Haslemere #67
£660 $1075 €950 Lake (54x81cm-21x32in) s. 23-Sep-3 Durán, Madrid #663/R
£660 $1075 €950 Sunflowers (50x40cm-20x16in) s. 23-Sep-3 Durán, Madrid #662/R
£700 $1253 €1022 Snowman (40x50cm-16x20in) s. 5-May-4 John Nicholson, Haslemere #16/R
£800 $1432 €1168 On the square (54x65cm-21x26in) s. 5-May-4 John Nicholson, Haslemere #84/R
£900 $1503 €1314 Evening ramble (61x46cm-24x18in) s. 13-Jul-3 John Nicholson, Haslemere #81/R
£900 $1575 €1314 Stroll on the bicycle (55x46cm-22x18in) s. 17-Dec-3 John Nicholson, Haslemere #111
£903 $1472 €1300 El rosal trepador (50x35cm-20x14in) s. 16-Jul-3 Durán, Madrid #643/R
£1000 $1750 €1460 Sitting on the beach (46x61cm-18x24in) s. 17-Dec-3 John Nicholson, Haslemere #79/R est:1250-1500
£1200 $2004 €1752 By the river (50x40cm-20x16in) s. 13-Jul-3 John Nicholson, Haslemere #14/R
£1250 $2088 €1825 In father's study (46x38cm-18x15in) s. 13-Jul-3 John Nicholson, Haslemere #13/R

£1250 $2088 €1825 At the stroll (50x40cm-20x16in) s. 13-Jul-3 John Nicholson, Haslemere #189/R
£1550 $2589 €2263 On the shore of the lake (46x65cm-18x26in) s. 13-Jul-3 John Nicholson, Haslemere #85/R
£1800 $3006 €2628 Flower girls (61x50cm-24x20in) s. 13-Jul-3 John Nicholson, Haslemere #188/R

GOUTSKEVITCH, Eugene (1876-1956) French?
£486 $763 €700 Riviere des tribunes a Auteuil (53x64cm-21x25in) mono. masonite. 29-Aug-3 Deauville, France #149

GOUWE, Adriaan Herman (1875-1965) Dutch
£336 $624 €500 African head Tahiti (36x20cm-14x8in) s. 4-Mar-4 Auction Maastricht #1119/R
£769 $1284 €1100 A plough team (48x97cm-19x38in) s. 30-Jun-3 Sotheby's, Amsterdam #345/R
£2081 $3870 €3100 Camel caravan (48x88cm-19x35in) s. 4-Mar-4 Auction Maastricht #1042/R est:3000-5000
£5333 $9760 €8000 Landscape with corn stacks in the evening sun (26x58cm-10x23in) s.d.1917. 7-Jun-4 Glerum, Amsterdam #80/R est:5000-6000
Works on paper
£369 $687 €550 Farmer plowing with horse (60x85cm-24x33in) s.d.1917 pastel. 4-Mar-4 Auction Maastricht #1148/R
£503 $936 €750 Woman with goat (35x30cm-14x12in) s. pastel. 4-Mar-4 Auction Maastricht #1149/R

GOUWELOOS, Charles (1867-?) Belgian
£349 $643 €510 Summer landscape with cows grazing (25x32cm-10x13in) s. canvas on board. 14-Jun-4 Philippe Schuler, Zurich #5847 (S.FR 800)

GOUWELOOS, Jean (1868-1943) Belgian
£414 $766 €600 Elegante souriant (75x62cm-30x24in) 19-Jan-4 Horta, Bruxelles #367
£592 $1072 €900 Barques au bord de la riviere (37x87cm-15x34in) s. 19-Apr-4 Horta, Bruxelles #200
£1034 $1914 €1500 Jeune femme nue se mirant (50x30cm-20x12in) s. 19-Jan-4 Horta, Bruxelles #366 est:1200-1500
£1467 $2625 €2200 Nude in the artist's studio (35x16cm-14x6in) s. 15-May-4 De Vuyst, Lokeren #147/R est:2200-2800
£1538 $2615 €2200 L'entree au lit (34x27cm-13x11in) s. cardboard on panel. 18-Nov-3 Vanderkindere, Brussels #193 est:700-900
£1678 $3104 €2500 La toilette (40x29cm-16x11in) s. panel. 13-Mar-4 De Vuyst, Lokeren #157/R est:2500-2800
£2676 $4630 €3800 Nude in front of a mirror (72x60cm-28x24in) s. 13-Dec-3 De Vuyst, Lokeren #549/R est:3500-4500
£5800 $9976 €8468 Dreaming (65x49cm-26x19in) s. painted c.1920. 3-Dec-3 Christie's, London #18/R est:5000-7000

GOVAERTS, Abraham (1589-1626) Flemish
£20690 $38276 €30000 Landscape with peasants (34x64cm-13x25in) panel. 16-Feb-4 Giraudeau, Tours #45

GOVARDHAN (attrib) (17th C) Indian
Works on paper
£140000 $247800 €204400 Nariman kills the son of the Khaqan of Chin (34x22cm-13x9in) i. gouache htd gold text exec.c.1610 prov. 28-Apr-4 Sotheby's, London #57/R est:80000-100000

GOW, Andrew Carrick (1848-1920) British
£6471 $11000 €9448 News from the front (76x63cm-30x25in) s.d.1877 prov.exhib. 29-Oct-3 Christie's, Rockefeller NY #84/R est:12000-18000
£44444 $80000 €64888 Washington's farewell to the army (94x183cm-37x72in) s.d.1902 exhib. 22-Apr-4 Christie's, Rockefeller NY #80/R est:80000-120000
Works on paper
£2200 $3586 €3212 Monk's blessing (22x16cm-9x6in) s.d.1872 W/C htd white. 25-Sep-3 Mellors & Kirk, Nottingham #718/R est:1500-2000

GOW, Mary L (1851-1929) British
Works on paper
£583 $1073 €875 Autumn landscape (17x25cm-7x10in) s.d.1885 W/C grisaille. 14-Jun-4 Lilla Bukowskis, Stockholm #691 (S.KR 8000)

GOWA, Henry H (1902-1990) German
£278 $464 €400 Landscape with red (73x60cm-29x24in) s.d.1968. 24-Oct-3 Ketterer, Hamburg #774/R
£403 $741 €600 La masion rose (25x31cm-10x12in) s.d. oil sold with another. 26-Mar-4 Ketterer, Hamburg #886/R
£417 $696 €600 La maison rose (25x31cm-10x12in) s.d. 24-Oct-3 Ketterer, Hamburg #773/R

GOWANS, George Russell (1843-1924) British
Works on paper
£250 $430 €365 Loading the hay wagon (25x30cm-10x12in) s. W/C. 3-Dec-3 Christie's, Kensington #199
£380 $665 €555 Meadow, Prestonkirk (23x27cm-9x11in) s. W/C. 18-Dec-3 Bonhams, Edinburgh #322

GOWANS, Peter (19th C) American
£874 $1600 €1276 Autumnal landscape (33x51cm-13x20in) s.d.87. 5-Jun-4 Neal Auction Company, New Orleans #423/R est:800-1200

GOWER, Elizabeth Ann (1952-) Australian
Works on paper
£310 $573 €453 Beyond the everyday (66x66cm-26x26in) s.d.1990 synthetic polymer prov. 15-Mar-4 Sotheby's, Melbourne #216 (A.D 750)

GOWIN, Emmet (1941-) American
Photographs
£1852 $3500 €2704 Effluent holding pond, Chemopetrol Mines, Bohemia (24x20cm-9x8in) s.i.d.1992 gelatin silver print. 17-Feb-4 Christie's, Rockefeller NY #253/R est:2500-3500
£1852 $3500 €2704 Snow over a marginal field, near Liberal, Kansas (24x24cm-9x9in) s.i.d.1996 gelatin silver print. 17-Feb-4 Christie's, Rockefeller NY #252/R est:2000-3000
£2011 $3800 €2936 Agricultural pivet, San Luis Valley near the Great sand dune, Colorado (24x24cm-9x9in) s.i.d.1991 gelatin silver print. 17-Feb-4 Christie's, Rockefeller NY #251/R est:2000-3000
£2395 $4000 €3497 Edith, Danville, Virginia (15x15cm-6x6in) s.i.d.1971/1975 num.2 verso gelatin silver print prov. 20-Oct-3 Christie's, Rockefeller NY #42/R est:3000-5000
£2695 $4500 €3935 Edith and Renee, Danville, VA (14x18cm-6x7in) s.i.d.1970 gelatin silver print. 20-Oct-3 Christie's, Rockefeller NY #200/R est:3000-5000
£4491 $7500 €6557 Nancy, Danville, Virginia (13x16cm-5x6in) gelatin silver print exec.1969 lit. 17-Oct-3 Phillips, New York #64/R est:3000-5000

GOWING, Lawrence (1918-1991) British
£950 $1511 €1387 Parabolic perspective (122x142cm-48x56in) board. 10-Sep-3 Sotheby's, Olympia #324/R
£10000 $17000 €14600 Self portrait in Oakleigh Avenue (22x28cm-9x11in) s.i. verso canvasboard painted 1936 prov.exhib. 21-Nov-3 Christie's, London #78/R est:5000-8000

GOWLAND MORENO, Luis (1902-1971) Argentinian
£3352 $6000 €4894 South (55x68cm-22x27in) s.d.48 cardboard. 4-May-4 Arroyo, Buenos Aires #7/R est:3500

GOYA Y LUCIENTES, Francisco Jose de (1746-1828) Spanish
£1796 $3000 €2622 Portrait of the Marquesa de Villa Franca (46x56cm-18x22in) 16-Nov-3 Simpson's, Houston #223
Prints
£1724 $2879 €2500 Les caprices (21x14cm-8x5in) etching engraving aquatint. 9-Jul-3 Tajan, Paris #71 est:1500
£2267 $4057 €3400 Shouldn't the scholar know better? (21x15cm-8x6in) etching aquatint. 13-May-4 Bassenge, Berlin #5395/R est:1800
£2569 $4290 €3725 Maja - La Maya tournee a droite. etching scratching. 19-Jun-3 Kornfeld, Bern #442 est:4000 (S.FR 5600)
£2657 $4438 €3800 War disasters (25x35cm-10x13in) eau forte aquatint. 30-Jun-3 Ansorena, Madrid #104/R
£4200 $7644 €6132 Los proverbios (31x43cm-12x17in) etchings aquatint complete set folio prov. 1-Jul-4 Sotheby's, London #52 est:3000-5000
£5459 $9934 €7970 Fiero monstro!. i. etching copperplate drypoint. 17-Jun-4 Kornfeld, Bern #393/R est:10000 (S.FR 12500)
£8000 $13760 €11680 Bien tirada esta (22x15cm-9x6in) i. etching aquatint. 4-Dec-3 Sotheby's, London #31/R est:12000-15000
£8000 $13760 €11680 Asi sucedio (15x20cm-6x8in) num.38 etching aquatint. 4-Dec-3 Sotheby's, London #33/R est:15000-20000
£12000 $21840 €17520 Los proverbios (31x43cm-12x17in) etchings aquatint complete set folio prov. 1-Jul-4 Sotheby's, London #51/R est:6000-8000
£14410 $26227 €21039 On account of a knife (18x23cm-7x9in) line etching drypoint exec. 1808-1814 prov. 18-Jun-4 Kornfeld, Bern #51/R est:40000 (S.FR 33000)
£17467 $31790 €25502 That's tough (15x20cm-6x8in) line etching aquatint drypoint exec. 1808-1814 prov. 18-Jun-4 Kornfeld, Bern #50/R est:40000 (S.FR 40000)
£18000 $30960 €26280 Sera la mismo (14x21cm-6x8in) num.25 etching aquatint. 4-Dec-3 Sotheby's, London #32/R est:15000-20000
£20588 $35000 €30058 Bull scene (32x45cm-13x18in) etching aquatint set of 33. 4-Nov-3 Christie's, Rockefeller NY #100/R est:20000-30000
£25000 $43000 €36500 Tampoco (15x20cm-6x8in) num.39 etching aquatint. 4-Dec-3 Sotheby's, London #34/R est:15000-20000
Works on paper
£528 $950 €771 Study of fantastic creatures (11x9cm-4x4in) graphite paper laid down. 24-Apr-4 Weschler, Washington #576/R

GOYA Y LUCIENTES, Francisco Jose de (circle) (1746-1828) Spanish
£6704 $12000 €9788 Portrait of lady (84x62cm-33x24in) prov.lit. 27-May-4 Sotheby's, New York #84/R est:10000-15000
£8392 $14434 €12000 Portrait of Isabel Parreno Arce, Marquesa of Llano (87x69cm-34x27in) oval prov. 2-Dec-3 Christie's, Paris #142/R est:4000-6000
£141333 $255813 €212000 Portrait presume de Jose Romero (59x45cm-23x18in) 31-Mar-4 Sotheby's, Paris #75/R est:10000-15000

GOYA Y LUCIENTES, Francisco Jose de (style) (1746-1828) Spanish
£8099 $14011 €11500 Portrait of Sebastian Martinez (105x81cm-41x32in) i. 11-Dec-3 Binoche, Paris #24/R est:8000-10000

GOYEN, Jan van (1596-1656) Dutch
£41379 $68690 €60000 Wooded landscape with view of Haarlem (57x74cm-22x29in) mono.d.164 panel lit. 1-Oct-3 Dorotheum, Vienna #93/R est:80000-120000
£54000 $93420 €78840 River landscape with fishermen and small vessels (57x83cm-22x33in) init.d.1650 prov.lit. 11-Dec-3 Sotheby's, London #65/R est:60000-80000
£65000 $118950 €94900 River landscape with travelers and elegant figures near a village (76x111cm-30x44in) s.d.1624 panel prov.lit. 7-Jul-4 Christie's, London #53/R est:60000-80000
£77778 $140000 €113556 River landscape with fishermen in a boat before a village jetty (39x60cm-15x24in) init.d.1643 panel prov.exhib.lit. 23-Jan-4 Christie's, Rockefeller NY #27/R est:80000-120000
£130000 $237900 €189800 View of Gorinchem with shipping on the Rhine in the foreground (68x95cm-27x37in) mono.d.1650 panel prov.lit. 7-Jul-4 Christie's, London #44/R est:80000-120000
£135000 $233550 €197100 Winter landscape with skaters on a frozen river, village and windmill beyond (37cm-15in circular) panel prov.lit. 10-Dec-3 Bonhams, New Bond Street #52/R est:250000-350000

£800000 $1384000 €1168000 Estuary scene with small vessels in light airs, distant view of Woudrichem (52x73cm-20x29in) mono. oak panel prov.lit. 11-Dec-3 Sotheby's, London #67/R est:400000-600000

Works on paper

£367 $660 €550 Boat with angler (19x15cm-7x6in) pen ink. 21-Apr-4 Finarte Semenzato, Milan #541/R
£3500 $6405 €5110 Castle of Rupelmonde seen from across the river (11x20cm-4x8in) indis i. black chk wash prov. 6-Jul-4 Christie's, London #175/R est:3000-5000
£7000 $12810 €10220 River landscape with fishermen in their boats and a herdsman with his flock (12x20cm-5x8in) mono.d.1653 blk chk grey wash prov. 8-Jul-4 Sotheby's, London #86/R est:6000-8000
£10959 $18630 €16000 Figures seated among dunes, tower and ships drawn up on the beach beyond (12x17cm-5x7in) mono. black chk pen ink framing lines. 5-Nov-3 Christie's, Amsterdam #117/R est:6000-8000
£12914 $23503 €19500 Patineurs et traineau d'approvisionnement sur un cours d'eau gele en hiver (17x29cm-7x11in) mono.d.1626 wash black crayon. 16-Jun-4 Piasa, Paris #61/R est:20000-25000
£13514 $23784 €20000 Landscape with a chapel on a hill (8x15cm-3x6in) bears i.verso pen brown ink prov.exhib.lit. 19-May-4 Sotheby's, Amsterdam #57/R est:8000-12000
£19178 $32603 €28000 River landscape with fishermen in their boats (11x20cm-4x8in) mono.d.1653 black chk grey wash. 4-Nov-3 Sotheby's, Amsterdam #58/R est:15000-20000

GOYEN, Jan van (attrib) (1596-1656) Dutch

£909 $1600 €1327 Landscape (20x19cm-8x7in) panel. 19-May-4 Doyle, New York #6049/R est:3000-5000

Works on paper

£1172 $1958 €1700 Seascape (23x34cm-9x13in) Indian ink brush prov. 15-Nov-3 Lempertz, Koln #1326/R est:2000

GOYEN, Jan van (style) (1596-1656) Dutch

£9500 $17385 €13870 River landscape with figures (66x102cm-26x40in) s. panel prov. 8-Jul-4 Sotheby's, London #293/R est:6000-8000

GOZZARD, J W (19th C) British

£320 $598 €467 Thatched cottages and figures returning home at dusk (23x43cm-9x17in) s.verso. 24-Feb-4 Rogers Jones, Clwyd #160/R
£500 $800 €725 Homeward (24x19cm-9x7in) s. 17-Sep-3 James Thompson, Kirby Lonsdale #179

GOZZARD, J Walter (1888-1950) British

£500 $850 €730 Fond farewell (51x76cm-20x30in) s. 6-Nov-3 Christie's, Kensington #768/R
£748 $1181 €1085 The last steps of day (76x51cm-30x20in) s. 2-Sep-3 Rasmussen, Copenhagen #1681/R (D.KR 8000)
£850 $1590 €1241 Street scene with figures returning from the market (39x59cm-15x23in) s. board prov. 22-Jul-4 Tennants, Leyburn #854
£3200 $5888 €4672 Traveller on a grey horse with woman selling vegetables. Returning from the market (38x59cm-15x23in) s. pair prov. 23-Jun-4 Cheffins, Cambridge #520/R est:2000-3000

GOZZOLI, Benozzo (1420-1497) Italian

£18534 $34103 €27060 St Lucia (53x26cm-21x10in) tempera panel prov. 26-Mar-4 Koller, Zurich #3006/R est:4000-70000 (S.FR 43000)

GRAAFF, Jacoba A de (attrib) (1857-1940) Dutch

£420 $722 €600 Sheep in the shed (40x57cm-16x22in) s. 4-Dec-3 Vendue Huis, Gravenhage #1030

GRAAFLAND, R A A J (1875-1940) Dutch

£1399 $2336 €2000 Portrait of Mrs Graafland (34x28cm-13x11in) 10-Oct-3 Auction Maastricht #872/R est:2200-2500
£1399 $2336 €2000 Portrait of Mrs Graafland (34x28cm-13x11in) 10-Oct-3 Vendue Huis, Gravenhage #872
£1538 $2569 €2200 Sp. (40x34cm-16x13in) s.d.36. 10-Oct-3 Auction Maastricht #822/R
£1538 $2569 €2200 Self portrait (40x34cm-16x13in) s.d.26 nov.'36. 10-Oct-3 Vendue Huis, Gravenhage #822
£2215 $4119 €3300 Lady in mirror with fan (40x40cm-16x16in) s. 4-Mar-4 Auction Maastricht #1003/R est:1500-2500
£2448 $4087 €3500 Woman with hat, veil and fur collar (40x30cm-16x12in) s.d.1934. 10-Oct-3 Auction Maastricht #874/R est:3500-4000
£2448 $4087 €3500 Woman with hat with veil and fur collar (40x30cm-16x12in) s.d.1934. 10-Oct-3 Vendue Huis, Gravenhage #874
£3087 $5742 €4600 Female nude (50x27cm-20x11in) s. 4-Mar-4 Auction Maastricht #1118/R est:2000-3000
£3862 $6179 €5600 Mrs Graafland on the St Pietersberg (94x52cm-37x20in) s.d.1909. 12-Mar-3 Auction Maastricht #1014 est:6000-8000
£8389 $15604 €12500 Oriental scene (90x125cm-35x49in) s.d. 4-Mar-4 Auction Maastricht #1008/R est:15000-20000

GRAAFLAND, Robert Archibald Antonius Joan (1875-1940) Dutch

Works on paper

£292 $476 €420 Study of an elegant lady (27x18cm-11x7in) s. col chk. 29-Sep-3 Sotheby's, Amsterdam #112

GRAAT, Barend (attrib) (1628-1709) Flemish

£1278 $2250 €1866 Leaving for the hunt (25x33cm-10x13in) panel. 19-May-4 Doyle, New York #6045/R est:4000-6000

GRAB, Walter (1927-1989) Swiss

£253 $431 €369 Trampoline (60x72cm-24x28in) s.d.85 i. verso board. 18-Nov-3 Hans Widmer, St Gallen #1070 (S.FR 560)
£317 $529 €463 Hidden things (46x65cm-18x26in) s.d.1951 i.d. verso. 24-Jun-3 Germann, Zurich #968 (S.FR 700)
£317 $538 €463 Duality (61x50cm-24x20in) s.d.1954 pavatex exhib. 25-Nov-3 Germann, Zurich #793 (S.FR 700)
£390 $697 €569 No man's land (65x81cm-26x32in) s.d. i. verso masonite. 22-Mar-4 Philippe Schuler, Zurich #6018 (S.FR 900)
£452 $769 €660 In the morning (46x66cm-18x26in) s.d.1958 panel exhib. 25-Nov-3 Germann, Zurich #792 (S.FR 1000)
£476 $852 €695 Home of a precious stone (65x81cm-26x32in) s.d. i. verso masonite. 22-Mar-4 Philippe Schuler, Zurich #6017 (S.FR 1100)
£786 $1446 €1148 My space (41x28cm-16x11in) s.d.1966 board prov. 8-Jun-4 Germann, Zurich #798 (S.FR 1800)
£1584 $2740 €2313 Web (54x46cm-21x18in) s.d.1958 tempera masonite exhib. 9-Dec-3 Sotheby's, Zurich #129/R est:800-1200 (S.FR 3500)

GRABACH, John R (1886-1981) American

£276 $500 €403 Italian gentleman (41x30cm-16x12in) plywood. 16-Apr-4 American Auctioneer #166/R
£276 $500 €403 Who cares (41x30cm-16x12in) board. 16-Apr-4 American Auctioneer #167/R
£299 $550 €437 Sacred Heart Cathedral, Newark, New Jersey (28x38cm-11x15in) s. canvas on panel. 25-Jun-4 Freeman, Philadelphia #311/R
£304 $550 €444 Good wine (41x30cm-16x12in) plywood. 16-Apr-4 American Auctioneer #165/R
£615 $1100 €898 Friends (61x61cm-24x24in) s. i.verso panel. 26-May-4 Doyle, New York #113/R
£761 $1400 €1111 Autumn (30x41cm-12x16in) s. canvas on panel. 25-Jun-4 Freeman, Philadelphia #309/R est:1000-1500
£1006 $1800 €1469 Garden walk (30x41cm-12x16in) s. board. 8-Jan-4 James Julia, Fairfield #1039/R est:1000-1500
£1087 $2000 €1587 Trout fishing (30x41cm-12x16in) s. linen on panel. 25-Jun-4 Freeman, Philadelphia #307/R est:1500-2500
£10811 $20000 €15784 Balcony (30x41cm-12x16in) s. panel. 11-Mar-4 Christie's, Rockefeller NY #64/R est:5000-7000

Works on paper

£331 $600 €483 Tug boat (56x69cm-22x27in) W/C. 16-Apr-4 American Auctioneer #168/R

GRABAR, Igor (1872-1960) Russian

£32000 $54400 €48000 Still life with apples, jugs and plates (52x37cm-20x15in) s. 25-Nov-3 Christie's, London #219/R est:5000-7000

GRABAR, Igor (attrib) (1872-1960) Russian

£523 $900 €764 Winter landscape (41x41cm-16x16in) cardboard. 7-Dec-3 William Jenack, New York #257
£18056 $32500 €26362 Riding through the village (39x55cm-15x22in) s.d.1905 board. 23-Apr-4 Sotheby's, New York #25a/R est:10000-15000

GRABAU, Christian Johann (1810-1874) German

£850 $1445 €1241 Attentive audience at dusk (67x86cm-26x34in) s. indis d. canvas on board. 6-Nov-3 Christie's, Kensington #810/R

GRABER, Margit (1895-1993) Hungarian

£2108 $3815 €3078 Vintage (45x34cm-18x13in) s. oil on card. 16-Apr-4 Mu Terem Galeria, Budapest #178/R (H.F 800000)

GRABER, Otto (1885-1952) German

£352 $609 €500 Still life with tomatoes (40x55cm-16x22in) s. 12-Dec-3 Berlinghof, Heidelberg #1044/R
£493 $853 €700 Still life with apples (51x47cm-20x19in) s. panel. 12-Dec-3 Berlinghof, Heidelberg #1045/R

GRABMAYER, Franz (1927-) German

£1748 $2972 €2500 Tree (65x81cm-26x32in) s.d.1965 verso jute. 28-Nov-3 Wiener Kunst Auktionen, Vienna #603/R est:2500-3500
£2105 $3874 €3200 Houses (80x100cm-31x39in) s.d.1966 verso. 22-Jun-4 Wiener Kunst Auktionen, Vienna #327/R est:3000
£3356 $5940 €5000 Sandpit (83x100cm-33x39in) s.d.1983 verso. 28-Apr-4 Wiener Kunst Auktionen, Vienna #211/R est:4500-6000
£5034 $8909 €7500 Untitled (102x140cm-40x55in) s.d.1989 verso. 28-Apr-4 Wiener Kunst Auktionen, Vienna #221/R est:7000-9000

Works on paper

£3020 $5346 €4500 Untitled (78x60cm-31x24in) s.d.1989 verso jute. 28-Apr-4 Wiener Kunst Auktionen, Vienna #209/R est:4000-6000

GRABNER, E Ferdinand (1913-1980) Austrian?

Works on paper

£1748 $2972 €2500 Machine (46x57cm-18x22in) s.d.79 mixed media. 28-Nov-3 Wiener Kunst Auktionen, Vienna #499/R est:1500-3000
£1958 $3329 €2800 Aeroplanes (42x59cm-17x23in) s.d.69 mixed media. 28-Nov-3 Wiener Kunst Auktionen, Vienna #498/R est:1500-3000

GRABNER, Hans (20th C) Austrian?

£3819 $6226 €5500 Factory (50x65cm-20x26in) s.d.79. 23-Sep-3 Wiener Kunst Auktionen, Vienna #108/R est:1000-2000

GRABON, Eugen (?) Swiss?

£1086 $1846 €1586 Still life (27x36cm-11x14in) s. panel. 1-Dec-3 Koller, Zurich #6538/R est:2500-3500 (S.FR 2400)

GRABONE, Arnold (1896-1981) German

£272 $487 €400 Farmstead in high mountains (60x80cm-24x31in) s. 18-Mar-4 Neumeister, Munich #2632

£278 $453 €400 Autumn day on Taubenseeweg in the Ramsau (60x80cm-24x31in) s. i. verso. 25-Sep-3 Neumeister, Munich #2732/R
£298 $542 €450 View over the Konigssee (80x70cm-31x28in) s. 16-Jun-4 Hugo Ruef, Munich #967
£308 $524 €450 Wayside cross in the high mountains (55x65cm-22x26in) s. 5-Nov-3 Hugo Ruef, Munich #985
£317 $567 €450 Fishing boats in a harbour (70x80cm-28x31in) s. lit. 8-Jan-4 Allgauer, Kempten #2332/R
£333 $603 €500 Storm on the Kaiser mountain (50x60cm-20x24in) s. 3-Apr-4 Badum, Bamberg #267/R
£333 $597 €500 Landscape near Lake Riesser (79x68cm-31x27in) s. i.verso. 14-May-4 Behringer, Furth #1517
£336 $577 €480 High mountain chapel (72x100cm-28x39in) s. 4-Dec-3 Neumeister, Munich #2692/R
£345 $631 €500 Mountain landscape (60x70cm-24x28in) s. 27-Jan-4 Dorotheum, Vienna #79/R
£347 $566 €500 Moor landscape (90x76cm-35x30in) s. 25-Sep-3 Neumeister, Munich #2731
£362 $666 €550 On the shore of Lake Maggiore (60x80cm-24x31in) s. i.verso. 26-Jun-4 Karrenbauer, Konstanz #1724
£396 $725 €590 Sunset landscape with lake (61x76cm-24x30in) s.d.68 i.verso stretcher. 9-Jul-4 Dawo, Saarbrucken #78/R
£403 $673 €580 La Moletta - Dolmites (80x120cm-31x47in) s. i.d.1966 verso. 22-Oct-3 Neumeister, Munich #664/R
£403 $741 €600 Leutstettner Moos (80x70cm-31x28in) i. 29-Mar-4 Dr Fritz Nagel, Stuttgart #7078/R
£414 $757 €600 Wilder Kaiser mountain (70x101cm-28x40in) s. 27-Jan-4 Dorotheum, Vienna #73/R
£420 $722 €600 Mountain chapel (75x64cm-30x25in) s. i. verso. 4-Dec-3 Neumeister, Munich #2693
£426 $711 €600 On the alpine pasture (60x80cm-24x31in) s. 16-Oct-3 Dorotheum, Salzburg #648/R
£442 $805 €650 Mountain lake (100x90cm-39x35in) s. 4-Feb-4 Neumeister, Munich #655
£447 $746 €630 Roadside cross in the mountains (78x68cm-31x27in) s. 17-Oct-3 Behringer, Furth #1527/R
£473 $847 €700 Donkeys drinking (68x57cm-27x22in) s. 6-May-4 Michael Zeller, Lindau #572/R
£605 $1047 €883 Autumn landscape (90x76cm-35x30in) painted after 1945. 14-Dec-3 Agra, Warsaw #40/R (P.Z 4000)
£625 $1044 €913 Mountainous landscape (70x80cm-28x31in) s. 19-Oct-3 Agra, Warsaw #64/R (P.Z 4000)
£1445 $2398 €2110 Boats on the ocean (50x60cm-20x24in) s. painted c.1945. 15-Jun-3 Agra, Warsaw #28/R est:4000 (P.Z 9000)

GRABWINKLER, Paul (1880-1946) Austrian
Works on paper
£1200 $2160 €1800 Portrait of young girl wearing blue hat (30x27cm-12x11in) s. mixed media. 21-Apr-4 Dorotheum, Vienna #60/R est:500-800

GRACE, A F (1844-1903) British
£475 $808 €694 Amberley, village scene with farmer and his dog, horses and cart (62x91cm-24x36in) s.i. 27-Nov-3 Morphets, Harrogate #424

GRACE, A L (19th C) British
£1800 $3222 €2628 Chelsea pensioners band practice (61x91cm-24x36in) s. 18-Mar-4 Christie's, Kensington #455/R est:2000-3000

GRACE, Alfred Fitzwalter (1844-1903) British
£270 $500 €394 Meeting a friend on the way home (53x36cm-21x14in) s. canvas on board. 14-Jul-4 Christie's, Kensington #908
£650 $1190 €949 Meeting a friend on the way home (36x53cm-14x21in) s. canvas on board. 8-Apr-4 Christie's, Kensington #82/R
Works on paper
£950 $1777 €1387 October evening (50x86cm-20x34in) s. W/C. 21-Jul-4 Lyon & Turnbull, Edinburgh #134

GRACE, James Edward (1851-1908) British
£351 $597 €527 Sunny cornfield (34x51cm-13x20in) s. board. 28-Oct-3 Goodman, Sydney #463/R (A.D 850)
£1100 $1738 €1595 Still pool, in the vale of the Ledr, North Wales (39x64cm-15x25in) s.d.1870 i.verso. 4-Sep-3 Christie's, Kensington #182/R est:600-800
Works on paper
£580 $1044 €847 Farmyard (35x52cm-14x20in) s.d.1880 W/C. 21-Jan-4 Sotheby's, Olympia #246/R

GRACEY, Theodore J (1895-1959) British
£500 $930 €730 Cottages, Donegal (45x61cm-18x24in) s. 3-Mar-4 John Ross, Belfast #218
£1879 $3326 €2800 Morning, Lough Conn (51x61cm-20x24in) s. prov. 27-Apr-4 Whyte's, Dublin #20/R est:3000-4000
Works on paper
£400 $640 €580 Irish landscape (33x48cm-13x19in) s. W/C. 16-Sep-3 Bonhams, Knightsbridge #256
£480 $826 €701 Figures on beach (26x36cm-10x14in) s. W/C pair. 3-Dec-3 Cheffins, Cambridge #592
£1208 $2162 €1800 Near Ballintoy, Coastal Antrim. Evening Lough Neagh (26x36cm-10x14in) s.i.verso W/C two. 26-May-4 James Adam, Dublin #128/R est:800-1200
£1338 $2141 €1900 Cushendun, County Antrim (55x75cm-22x30in) s. W/C prov. 16-Sep-3 Whyte's, Dublin #157/R est:1800-2200

GRACHEV (19th C) Russian
Sculpture
£3000 $5100 €4380 Rider (42cm-17in) s.st.f.Woerffel d.1877 pat bronze. 20-Nov-3 Sotheby's, Olympia #191/R est:3000-4000

GRACIA, Casimiro (20th C) Spanish
£403 $749 €600 Landscape in Valencia (27x37cm-11x15in) s.d.51 s.d.verso. 2-Mar-4 Ansorena, Madrid #163/R

GRACIA, Manuel de (1937-) Spanish
£470 $879 €700 Dusk (22x27cm-9x11in) s. s.i.verso board. 24-Feb-4 Durán, Madrid #596/R
£580 $951 €800 Crepusculo (22x27cm-9x11in) s. s.i.verso panel. 27-May-3 Durán, Madrid #700/R
£1275 $2385 €1900 Dusk on the stream (65x81cm-26x32in) s. s.i.d.1975 verso. 24-Feb-4 Durán, Madrid #191/R est:1900
£2013 $3745 €3000 Dusk in Urigoiti (60x73cm-24x29in) s. s.i.verso. 2-Mar-4 Ansorena, Madrid #105/R est:3000

GRADA, Raffaele de (1885-1957) Italian
£346 $620 €505 Birch trees on shore (22x30cm-9x12in) s. canvas on board. 22-Mar-4 Philippe Schuler, Zurich #6148 (S.FR 800)
£1042 $1646 €1500 Girl from San Gimignano (56x35cm-22x14in) tempera paper. 6-Sep-3 Meeting Art, Vercelli #398 est:1500
£1538 $2462 €2245 Thaw (39x49cm-15x19in) s. board prov. 16-Sep-3 Philippe Schuler, Zurich #3358/R est:1000-1500 (S.FR 3400)
£2291 $3894 €3345 Summer village (37x56cm-15x22in) s. 5-Nov-3 Dobiaschofsky, Bern #611/R est:4000 (S.FR 5200)
£2685 $4805 €4000 Landscape with the river Sihl, Switzerland (38x48cm-15x19in) s. cardboard. 30-May-4 Meeting Art, Vercelli #92 est:4000
£2899 $4754 €4000 Darsena di Viareggio (55x70cm-22x28in) s. 31-May-3 Farsetti, Prato #619/R est:2000-3000
£3478 $5704 €4800 Case sul fiume (50x38cm-20x15in) s. 31-May-3 Farsetti, Prato #620/R est:4000-5000
£4225 $7014 €6000 View of village on the hill (101x94cm-40x37in) s.d.1913. 11-Jun-3 Finarte Semenzato, Milan #699/R
£4698 $8691 €7000 Pasture (66x96cm-26x38in) s. painted 1914. 13-Mar-4 Meeting Art, Vercelli #553 est:6000
£4828 $8062 €7000 Tuscan landscape with haystacks (50x60cm-20x24in) s. 17-Nov-3 Sant Agostino, Torino #238/R est:6000-8000
£4895 $8322 €7000 Tuscan countryside (60x75cm-24x30in) s.d.1942. 20-Nov-3 Finarte Semenzato, Milan #157/R est:7000-8000
£5333 $9600 €8000 Harbour in Veneto (70x90cm-28x35in) s. 22-Apr-4 Finarte Semenzato, Rome #247/R est:8000-8500
£5442 $9741 €8000 San Gimignano (60x75cm-24x30in) s.d.1943. 22-Mar-4 Sant Agostino, Torino #526/R est:7000-9000
£5634 $9352 €8000 Dintorni di Serravezza (59x68cm-23x27in) s.d.1946. 14-Jun-3 Meeting Art, Vercelli #708/R est:6000
Works on paper
£2826 $4635 €3900 Fishing spot on the Cinquale (34x49cm-13x19in) s. W/C paper on canvas. 29-May-3 Galleria Pace, Milan #145/R est:5500
£2897 $4634 €4200 Olive grove in Querceta (39x49cm-15x19in) s. W/C. 13-Mar-3 Galleria Pace, Milan #48/R est:4500-6000

GRADL, Hermann (1883-1964) German
£315 $535 €450 Landscape (48x58cm-19x23in) i.d. verso panel. 20-Nov-3 Weidler, Nurnberg #7000
£315 $535 €450 Country view (37x30cm-15x12in) s. i. verso. 20-Nov-3 Weidler, Nurnberg #7013/R
£400 $716 €600 Hilly landscape (57x73cm-22x29in) s. i.verso board. 14-May-4 Behringer, Furth #1692
£556 $883 €800 Frank landscape (23x29cm-9x11in) s. board. 11-Sep-3 Weidler, Nurnberg #7001/R
£633 $1140 €950 Lovers uncovered (32x26cm-13x10in) s. board. 22-Apr-4 Weidler, Nurnberg #7066/R
£867 $1577 €1300 Woodland scene in Bayern with houses (18x23cm-7x9in) s. s.i.verso board. 1-Jul-4 Weidler, Nurnberg #7000/R
£967 $1730 €1450 Landscape near Chiemgau (31x38cm-12x15in) s. i.verso board. 14-May-4 Behringer, Furth #1562/R
£979 $1635 €1400 Rhine near Godesberg (48x59cm-19x23in) s. i. verso panel. 26-Jun-3 Weidler, Nurnberg #7004/R
£1111 $1767 €1600 St Quirin in Bavarian wood (24x31cm-9x12in) s. i.d.1932 verso board. 11-Sep-3 Weidler, Nurnberg #7046/R est:1800
£1259 $2140 €1800 Landscape (49x58cm-19x23in) s. i. verso board. 20-Nov-3 Weidler, Nurnberg #7230/R est:2000
£1361 $2435 €2000 Neunburg (32x38cm-13x15in) s. i. verso panel. 17-Mar-4 Neumeister, Munich #460/R est:1000
£1399 $2378 €2000 Hottingen near Weissenburg (30x36cm-12x14in) s. s.i. verso panel. 20-Nov-3 Weidler, Nurnberg #7012/R est:2000
£1469 $2526 €2100 Spruce trees (37x31cm-15x12in) s. cardboard. 5-Dec-3 Weidler, Nurnberg #9021/R est:2200
£1875 $2981 €2700 Cows watering with figures (48x59cm-19x23in) s. i. verso board. 11-Sep-3 Weidler, Nurnberg #7000/R est:3000
£2292 $3644 €3300 Extensive landscape with figures (68x88cm-27x35in) s. 11-Sep-3 Weidler, Nurnberg #7003/R est:2500
Works on paper
£367 $667 €550 View of Altmannhausen (37x30cm-15x12in) s.d.1943 W/C ink pencil. 1-Jul-4 Weidler, Nurnberg #7040
£420 $701 €600 Peasant ploughing (22x29cm-9x11in) s. mixed media on etching board. 26-Jun-3 Weidler, Nurnberg #7005/R

GRADT, Johan H (c.1770-?) Danish
£342 $553 €499 Village scene (37x48cm-15x19in) s.d.1853. 9-Aug-3 Hindemae, Ullerslev #84/R (D.KR 3600)
£342 $553 €499 Village scene with figures (37x48cm-15x19in) s.d.1853. 9-Aug-3 Hindemae, Ullerslev #87/R (D.KR 3600)

GRADY, Napoleone (1860-1949) Italian
£563 $935 €800 Ritratto di donna (55x35cm-22x14in) 11-Jun-3 Christie's, Rome #50

GRAEB, Karl Georg Anton (1816-1884) German
Works on paper
£1834 $3338 €2678 Marketplace in Piazenza (34x44cm-13x17in) s. W/C. 16-Jun-4 Fischer, Luzern #2578/R est:2500-2800 (S.FR 4200)

£4585 $8345 €6694 Interior of Saint Severin Church with view of Severin Altar (29x39cm-11x15in) s.i.d.1855 W/C over pencil. 17-Jun-4 Kornfeld, Bern #19/R est:12500 (S.FR 10500)

GRAEF, Gustav (1821-1895) German
Works on paper
£486 $792 €700 Fortress and village above pond (23x43cm-9x17in) s.d.77 W/C. 26-Sep-3 Bolland & Marotz, Bremen #538/R

GRAEFLE, Albert (1807-1889) German
£274 $466 €400 Boy's portrait (37x31cm-15x12in) s.d.1860. 5-Nov-3 Hugo Ruef, Munich #986

GRAEME, Colin (fl.1858-1910) British
£720 $1332 €1051 Fly and Maysie. s.d.verso. 11-Mar-4 John Ross, Belfast #800
£800 $1360 €1168 White race horse and chestnut race horse at their stable doors (25x20cm-10x8in) s.d.1901 pair. 25-Nov-3 Bonhams, Knowle #250
£1000 $1570 €1460 Gun dog with hare in a moorland landscape (17x24cm-7x9in) 31-Aug-3 Paul Beighton, Rotherham #492 est:800-1000
£1200 $2184 €1752 Portrait of a border collie, Rover (56x76cm-22x30in) s.i.d.96. 15-Jun-4 Canterbury Auctions, UK #103/R est:1200-1500
£1200 $2244 €1752 Hunter standing in a loose box, with horse blanket and water bucket (46x61cm-18x24in) s.i.d.98. 22-Jul-4 Tennants, Leyburn #861/R est:1200-1800
£1350 $2295 €1971 Head study of a English setter. Head study of a pointer (25x20cm-10x8in) s. one d.1904 pair. 18-Nov-3 Bonhams, Leeds #253/R est:600-800
£1550 $2635 €2263 Head study of a setter. Head study of a sporting dog (31x25cm-12x10in) s. pair. 18-Nov-3 Bonhams, Leeds #254/R est:600-800
£1600 $2576 €2320 Winner of Mayor's Cup for the beat beast in show, Wisbech (38x48cm-15x19in) s.d.86. 15-Aug-3 Keys, Aylsham #678/R est:800-1200
£1657 $3000 €2419 Hunting companions (30x25cm-12x10in) s. 30-Mar-4 Bonhams & Butterfields, San Francisco #91/R est:2200-3300
£1900 $3287 €2774 Portraits of spaniels (19x14cm-7x6in) s.d.1902 board pair. 9-Dec-3 Rosebery Fine Art, London #599/R est:300-400
£2000 $3680 €2920 Gey at a stable door. Chestnut at a stable door (25x20cm-10x8in) s.d.1901 pair. 10-Jun-4 Christie's, Kensington #66/R est:2000-3000
£2027 $3750 €2959 Setter and pointer on point (41x61cm-16x24in) s.d.1901. 10-Feb-4 Doyle, New York #194/R est:300-5000
£2200 $3454 €3212 Two gun dogs on the moors (11x16cm-4x6in) 31-Aug-3 Paul Beighton, Rotherham #481 est:1800-2400
£2300 $4117 €3358 Hounds at the mouth (57x43cm-22x17in) s. indis d. 16-Mar-4 Bonhams, Leeds #632/R est:700-1000
£2400 $4488 €3600 Portrait of a Collie (56x76cm-22x30in) s.i.d.96. 21-Jul-4 John Nicholson, Haslemere #193/R est:3000-5000
£2641 $4938 €3856 Hunter and dogs (55x40cm-22x16in) s.d.97. 24-Feb-4 Louis Morton, Mexico #24/R est:35000-45000 (M.P 54000)
£2800 $4396 €4088 Grouse resting in a heather. Cock pheasant in a winter wooded landscape (11x9cm-4x4in) pair. 31-Aug-3 Paul Beighton, Rotherham #504 est:1600-2400
£3000 $4800 €4380 Gundogs (11x9cm-4x4in) pair. 16-Sep-3 Lawrences, Bletchingley #1943/R est:3000-4000
£3000 $5580 €4380 Setter in a moorland landscape (51x69cm-20x27in) s. 4-Mar-4 Christie's, Kensington #36/R est:4000-6000
£3100 $4867 €4526 Gun dogs in a highland landscape (21x29cm-8x11in) 31-Aug-3 Paul Beighton, Rotherham #490 est:2000-3000
£3100 $4867 €4526 Gun dog in a highland landscape (20x26cm-8x10in) 31-Aug-3 Paul Beighton, Rotherham #505 est:2400-2800
£3200 $5824 €4800 Horse and dog in front of a stable in the Scottish highlands (50x69cm-20x27in) s.d.97. 1-Jul-4 Van Ham, Cologne #1368/R est:1500
£3700 $5920 €5402 Setter and a pointer searching for a grouse (51x76cm-20x30in) s.d.1899. 17-Sep-3 Brightwells, Leominster #857/R est:1000-1500
£4000 $6800 €5840 Highland cattle, with a setter and grouse on the moor (84x110cm-33x43in) s.d.87. 30-Oct-3 Christie's, London #80/R est:4000-6000
£5500 $10285 €8030 English setter on a grouse moor (51x69cm-20x27in) s.d.1904. 22-Jul-4 Tennants, Leyburn #860/R est:4000-5000
£7600 $12160 €11096 Three setters with shot pheasant and gun (51x76cm-20x30in) s. 17-Sep-3 Brightwells, Leominster #856/R est:1000-1500

GRAESER, Camille (1892-1980) Swiss
£676 $1162 €987 Translocation C (30x30cm-12x12in) acrylic pavatex. 2-Dec-3 Koller, Zurich #3337 (S.FR 1500)
£766 $1317 €1118 Composition (31x31cm-12x12in) acrylic pavatex. 2-Dec-3 Koller, Zurich #3336 est:1700-2500 (S.FR 1700)
£873 $1607 €1275 Complementary tension fields (31x31cm-12x12in) s. acrylic pavatex lit. 8-Jun-4 Germann, Zurich #425/R (S.FR 2000)
£2838 $5223 €4143 Dislocation (25x24cm-10x9in) s.d.28/1/71 tempera board prov. 8-Jun-4 Germann, Zurich #47/R est:5000-7000 (S.FR 6500)
£4803 $8838 €7012 Shove against shove (10x170cm-4x67in) s.d.1972 verso panel prov.exhib.lit. 8-Jun-4 Germann, Zurich #46/R est:13000-18000 (S.FR 11000)

GRAF, Carl C (1892-1947) American
£3297 $6000 €4814 Woodcutters with team of horses in Brown County landscape (56x71cm-22x28in) s. canvas on board. 7-Feb-4 Dan Ripley, Indianapolis #1

GRAF, Emil (1901-1980) Swiss
£950 $1615 €1387 Peasant with two horses (28x36cm-11x14in) s.d.1963 board. 18-Nov-3 Hans Widmer, St Gallen #1241 est:2000-3000 (S.FR 2100)

GRAF, Emil Friedrich (1845-1924) Swiss
£371 $683 €542 Still life with grapes and peaches (49x67cm-19x26in) s. 14-Jun-4 Philippe Schuler, Zurich #4211 (S.FR 850)

GRAF, Ernst (1909-1988) Swiss
Works on paper
£543 $923 €793 Untersee in winter (28x51cm-11x20in) s.d.Nov. 1963 W/C. 18-Nov-3 Hans Widmer, St Gallen #1071 (S.FR 1200)

GRAF, Gerhard (1883-1960) German
£403 $741 €600 Breslau market place in the evening (67x80cm-26x31in) s. 26-Mar-4 Bolland & Marotz, Bremen #626
£420 $701 €600 Hamburg harbour (70x100cm-28x39in) s. 28-Jun-3 Dannenberg, Berlin #687/R
£490 $832 €700 Old city with memorial (112x97cm-44x38in) s. 22-Nov-3 Arnold, Frankfurt #527/R
£625 $1019 €900 Lubeck harbour (70x60cm-28x24in) s. 26-Sep-3 Bolland & Marotz, Bremen #650/R
£629 $1083 €900 The marketplace in the rain, Rostock (80x68cm-31x27in) s. 4-Dec-3 Van Ham, Cologne #172/R
£1202 $2116 €1755 Cityscape (67x80cm-26x31in) s. 23-May-4 Agra, Warsaw #26/R (P.Z 8500)

GRAF, Hermann (1873-?) German
£615 $1058 €898 Interior scene with woman by mirror (70x59cm-28x23in) s. panel. 7-Dec-3 Uppsala Auktionskammare, Uppsala #159/R (S.KR 8000)

GRAF, Ludwig Ferdinand (1868-1932) Austrian
£11111 $18889 €16000 Valley in the Upper Steir (72x91cm-28x36in) s.d.19 s.i. verso board exhib.lit. 28-Oct-3 Wiener Kunst Auktionen, Vienna #67/R est:13000-25000
Works on paper
£1611 $2964 €2400 Trompe l'oeil (50x74cm-20x29in) s.d.1916 mixed media. 26-Mar-4 Dorotheum, Vienna #164/R est:1600-1800

GRAF, Paul (c.1856-1903) Swedish
£292 $503 €426 Girl and old woman in village (51x68cm-20x27in) s.i.d.1902. 7-Dec-3 Uppsala Auktionskammare, Uppsala #160/R (S.KR 3800)
£484 $789 €707 Outside Leksands Church (69x83cm-27x33in) s.i.d.99. 29-Sep-3 Lilla Bukowskis, Stockholm #130 (S.KR 6300)
£813 $1455 €1187 Boys fishing (35x45cm-14x18in) s.d.1902. 25-May-4 Bukowskis, Stockholm #331/R (S.KR 11000)

GRAF, Philip (1874-?) German
£694 $1160 €1000 Spring awakening in Chiemgau (75x86cm-30x34in) s.i. i. verso. 24-Oct-3 Ketterer, Hamburg #67/R

GRAF, Urs (1936-) Swiss
£431 $772 €629 Farmstead in fields in evening (46x61cm-18x24in) s. 12-May-4 Dobiaschofsky, Bern #575/R (S.FR 1000)

GRAFF, Anton (1736-1813) German/Swiss
£5381 $8771 €7856 Portrait of Julius Christian von Schauroth (68x57cm-27x22in) oval prov.lit. 29-Sep-3 Christie's, Zurich #3/R est:10000-15000 (S.FR 12000)
£6000 $10200 €8760 Portrait of Eva Charlotte Friederike, Grafin von Einsiedel in a blue silkj dress trimmed with fur (63x50cm-25x20in) 29-Oct-3 Christie's, London #50/R est:6000-8000
£8333 $13583 €12000 Ernst Haubold von Miltitz (64x57cm-25x22in) i. verso. 25-Sep-3 Dr Fritz Nagel, Stuttgart #1290/R est:22000
£8597 $13756 €12552 Portrait of Gertrud Elisabeth Mara (57x44cm-22x17in) prov.lit. 19-Sep-3 Koller, Zurich #3079a/R est:8000-12000 (S.FR 19000)
£9910 $17045 €14469 Elisabetha Graff and her daughter Caroline (132x95cm-52x37in) oval prov.exhib.lit. 8-Dec-3 Philippe Schuler, Zurich #3335/R est:25000-30000 (S.FR 22000)
£11207 $20621 €16362 Portrait of Dr Johann Michael Eltz (78x61cm-31x24in) prov.lit. 26-Mar-4 Koller, Zurich #3083a/R est:25000-30000 (S.FR 26000)

GRAFF, Anton (style) (1736-1813) German/Swiss
£9000 $14940 €13140 Portrait of a young lady in a red dress and holding a dog (74x62cm-29x24in) 30-Sep-3 Sotheby's, London #164/R est:6000-8000

GRAFF, George Adam (1900-1977) Dutch
Sculpture
£1325 $2411 €2000 Veil-tailed fish (22x34cm-9x13in) wood relief. 15-Jun-4 Christie's, Amsterdam #340/R est:2000-3000
£2098 $3566 €3000 Figure of a parakeet (24cm-9in) ivory circular wood base. 18-Nov-3 Christie's, Amsterdam #324/R est:3000-5000
£2937 $4993 €4200 Figure of a sitting monkey (20cm-8in) mono.d.1921 oak square base. 18-Nov-3 Christie's, Amsterdam #323/R est:2500-3500
£11189 $19021 €16000 Owl (26cm-10in) mono. wood base. 18-Nov-3 Christie's, Amsterdam #327/R est:4000-6000
£13986 $23776 €20000 Figure of a monkey (52cm-20in) stone oval base. 18-Nov-3 Christie's, Amsterdam #326/R est:7000-9000

GRAFF, Johann (1838-1917) German
Works on paper
£822 $1397 €1200 Self portrait (19x14cm-7x6in) s.d.90 board. 4-Nov-3 Hartung & Hartung, Munich #3046

GRAFFENRIED, Adolf von (1801-1859) Swiss?
Works on paper
£396 $674 €578 Campo dei SS Giovanni e Paolo in Venice (23x34cm-9x13in) s. bears i. pen W/C. 5-Nov-3 Dobiaschofsky, Bern #612/R (S.FR 900)

GRAFTON, Robert W (1876-1936) American
£2762 $4750 €4033 Study of reflections (51x41cm-20x16in) s.i.d.1917 verso canvas on board. 7-Dec-3 Treadway Gallery, Cincinnati #505/R est:3000-5000
£3279 $6000 €4787 French quarter courtyard (28x38cm-11x15in) canvasboard. 5-Jun-4 Neal Auction Company, New Orleans #364/R est:7000-10000
£3846 $7000 €5615 Courtyard with Hollyhocks (127x99cm-50x39in) s.d.1925. 7-Feb-4 Neal Auction Company, New Orleans #490/R est:8000-10000
£10759 $17000 €15708 Woman descending a stairway, New Orleans (71x51cm-28x20in) s.d.1917 canvas on board. 7-Sep-3 Treadway Gallery, Cincinnati #594/R est:8000-10000

GRAGNOLI-ARONA, Nino (19/20th C) Italian
£333 $597 €500 Chrysanthemums (72x53cm-28x21in) s. cardboard. 12-May-4 Stadion, Trieste #722
£333 $597 €500 Mimosas (71x51cm-28x20in) s. cardboard. 12-May-4 Stadion, Trieste #791/R

GRAHAM, Allen (1943-) American
£279 $500 €407 Untitled. oil gouache stick pigment triptych. 13-May-4 Dallas Auction Gallery, Dallas #302/R

GRAHAM, Anne Marie (1925-) Australian
£581 $970 €872 Old fountain in Baynac (37x54cm-15x21in) s.d.87. 27-Oct-3 Goodman, Sydney #207/R (A.D 1400)

GRAHAM, Carol (1951-) British
£300 $498 €438 Summer shoes (50x50cm-20x20in) s. board. 1-Oct-3 John Ross, Belfast #72

GRAHAM, Charles S (1852-1911) American
Works on paper
£898 $1500 €1311 Portrait of the artist (41x33cm-16x13in) canvas on board sold with sketchbook and 2 W/C's by the same hand. 18-Jun-3 Doyle, New York #35/R est:1000-1500

GRAHAM, Dan (1942-) American
Photographs
£3333 $6000 €4866 Warehouse in Neo-Colonial style, Westfield, NJ (27x20cm-11x8in) s.i.d.1978 type C print pair. 24-Apr-4 David Rago, Lambertville #378/R est:4000-8000
£6145 $11000 €8972 Jersey City, New Jersey, row houses (26x30cm-10x12in) s.i.d.1966 c-print on paperboard prov. 14-May-4 Phillips, New York #280/R est:3000-4000
£6145 $11000 €8972 Jersey City, New Jersey (26x30cm-10x12in) s.i.d.1966 c-print on paperboard prov. 14-May-4 Phillips, New York #281/R est:3000-4000
Sculpture
£10000 $18400 €14600 Empty shoji screen pergola - two way mirror container (184x122x86cm-72x48x34in) two way mirror wood aluminium gravel executed 1991 prov.lit. 25-Jun-4 Christie's, London #273/R est:10000-15000
Works on paper
£845 $1462 €1200 Untitled (30x20cm-12x8in) s.d.1982 ink ballpoint pen. 9-Dec-3 Artcurial Briest, Paris #164

GRAHAM, David (1926-) British
£450 $833 €657 Barges before Tower Bridge at dusk (71x91cm-28x36in) s. 15-Jan-4 Christie's, Kensington #915/R
£550 $919 €803 Passenger ferry docking at Gravesend (61x51cm-24x20in) s. 7-Oct-3 Bonhams, Knightsbridge #47/R

GRAHAM, Dougal (20th C) ?
£1757 $3092 €2600 Study 847 (70x100cm-28x39in) s.i.d.2003 verso diptych prov. 24-May-4 Christie's, Milan #60/R est:2500-3000
£1818 $3091 €2600 Can't stop thinking of you (95x70cm-37x28in) s.i.d.2001 verso prov. 24-Nov-3 Christie's, Milan #63/R est:2500-3000

GRAHAM, George (1881-1949) British
£450 $725 €653 Continental river estuary view with boats and figures by building (28x38cm-11x15in) s. 15-Aug-3 Keys, Aylsham #716
£550 $963 €803 Wooden winter river scene (28x33cm-11x13in) s. 18-Dec-3 John Nicholson, Haslemere #1163
Works on paper
£280 $504 €409 Haymaking (28x36cm-11x14in) s.d.1914 W/C prov. 20-Apr-4 Canterbury Auctions, UK #168/R
£420 $756 €613 Continental landscape with milkmaid and a cow on a country lane (25x35cm-10x14in) s.d.1914 pencil W/C htd white. 21-Apr-4 Tennants, Leyburn #1021
£460 $828 €672 Amiens, street scene with figures fishing beside a stream (59x48cm-23x19in) s.i.d.1915 pencil W/C htd white. 21-Apr-4 Tennants, Leyburn #1022

GRAHAM, James Lillie (1873-1965) Canadian
£383 $705 €559 Stable interior (33x40cm-13x16in) s. i. stretcher prov. 9-Jun-4 Walker's, Ottawa #120/R (C.D 950)

GRAHAM, John (20th C) Australian?
£309 $559 €451 Call to prayer (90x122cm-35x48in) s. 30-Mar-4 Lawson Menzies, Sydney #36/R (A.D 750)
£391 $708 €571 Mona had the highway blues. init. init.i.d.1991 verso. 30-Mar-4 Lawson Menzies, Sydney #35/R est:500-700 (A.D 950)

GRAHAM, John D (c.1881-1961) American/Russian
£1156 $2000 €1688 Fountain, New York (38x55cm-15x22in) s.verso prov. 10-Dec-3 Phillips, New York #439/R
Works on paper
£11377 $19000 €16610 Untitled (29x18cm-11x7in) ink oil wash exec.c.1950 prov. 13-Nov-3 Sotheby's, New York #156/R est:18000-25000
£13473 $22500 €19671 Donna Maria (58x38cm-23x15in) carbon transfer exec.c.1950 prov.exhib. 13-Nov-3 Sotheby's, New York #158/R est:12000-18000
£14970 $25000 €21856 Soldier in dress uniform (60x47cm-24x19in) pencil tracing paper exec.c.1950 prov.exhib. 13-Nov-3 Sotheby's, New York #155/R est:25000-35000

GRAHAM, Kathleen Margaret D (1913-) Canadian
£301 $560 €439 Grey on grey (30x45cm-12x18in) s.d.1981 s.i.d.verso acrylic paper. 4-Mar-4 Heffel, Vancouver #18/R (C.D 750)
Works on paper
£446 $768 €651 Beginning with red (55x76cm-22x30in) s.d.83 mixed media. 2-Dec-3 Joyner Waddington, Toronto #508 (C.D 1000)

GRAHAM, Olive (20th C) American
£615 $1100 €898 Portrait of two cats, one sitting on a book called Happiness (25x30cm-10x12in) s. 20-Mar-4 Pook & Pook, Downington #311

GRAHAM, Paul (1956-) British
Photographs
£3000 $5010 €4380 Girl with white face, Tokyo (104x78cm-41x31in) colour photograph exec 1992 prov.lit. 21-Oct-3 Sotheby's, London #326/R est:3000-4000

GRAHAM, Peter (1836-1921) British
£370 $673 €540 Stormy coast (89x67cm-35x26in) s. 4-Jul-4 Lots Road Auctions, London #350a
£1500 $2550 €2190 Cradle of the seabird (92x67cm-36x26in) s.d.1883. 1-Dec-3 Bonhams, Bath #119/R est:1000-1500
£2400 $3768 €3480 Cross roads (56x76cm-22x30in) s.d.1875. 27-Aug-3 Sotheby's, London #953/R est:2000-3000
£4800 $8016 €7008 River landscape in the highlands (168x122cm-66x48in) s. 21-Oct-3 Bruton Knowles, Cheltenham #448/R est:1000-1500
£16000 $27200 €23360 Lonely sea cliffs where the gannet finds a home (127x183cm-50x72in) s.d.1903 prov.exhib. 30-Oct-3 Christie's, London #103/R est:5000-8000
Works on paper
£300 $510 €438 Gulls on rocks (52x70cm-20x28in) s.d.1880 W/C bodycol. 10-Nov-3 Thomson Roddick & Medcalf, Edinburgh #233

GRAHAM, Peter (1959-) British
£260 $421 €380 English roses (88x114cm-35x45in) s. 27-Jan-3 Bristol Auction Rooms #463
£430 $697 €628 Magical table (92x81cm-36x32in) s. 27-Jan-3 Bristol Auction Rooms #464
£500 $810 €730 Star fruit (93x81cm-37x32in) s. 27-Jan-3 Bristol Auction Rooms #465
£540 $875 €788 Japanese print with flowers (59x74cm-23x29in) s.d.98. 27-Jan-3 Bristol Auction Rooms #467
£600 $1002 €876 Japanese print with flowers (61x73cm-24x29in) s.d.94 prov. 16-Oct-3 Christie's, Kensington #371/R

GRAHAM, Robert (1938-) American
Sculpture
£1412 $2500 €2062 Moca torso (28cm-11in) pat bronze. 2-May-4 Bonhams & Butterfields, Los Angeles #3061/R est:2500-3500
£1892 $3500 €2762 MOCA Torso (29cm-11in) s. pat bronze edition of 3500. 12-Feb-4 Christie's, Rockefeller NY #78/R est:2500-3500
£2747 $5000 €4011 Lisa Ann mask (39cm-15in) brown pat. bronze golf leaf. 29-Jun-4 Sotheby's, New York #600/R est:6000-8000
£3846 $7000 €5615 Column (29x7x7cm-11x3x3in) bronze gilded lit. 29-Jun-4 Sotheby's, New York #599/R est:10000-15000
£4396 $8000 €6418 Kentucky Derby (183x78x65cm-72x31x26in) init.num.2/15 brown pat. bronze relief two pieces. 29-Jun-4 Sotheby's, New York #523/R est:6000-8000
£6522 $12000 €9522 Bedroom fantasies (67x47x27cm-26x19x11in) wax mixed media perspex box prov. 10-Jun-4 Phillips, New York #453/R est:6000-8000
£6593 $12000 €9626 Female torso (142cm-56in) brown pat. bronze concrete column prov. 29-Jun-4 Sotheby's, New York #528/R est:8000-12000
£8242 $15000 €12033 Olympic plaque (79x54x9cm-31x21x4in) brown pat. bronze. 29-Jun-4 Sotheby's, New York #602/R est:10000-15000

GRAHAM, Robert Alexander (1873-1946) American
£2457 $4250 €3587 Harlem River in the snow (41x51cm-16x20in) s.d.1920 prov. 10-Dec-3 Bonhams & Butterfields, San Francisco #6034/R est:4000-6000
£3545 $6700 €5176 Seated girl painting at an easel in an interior (30x41cm-12x16in) s.d.1911. 21-Feb-4 Brunk, Ashville #303/R est:5000-10000

GRAHAM, Robert Macdonald (1919-) American
£269 $500 €393 Woman on a porch (46x61cm-18x24in) s.d.1959 board. 7-Mar-4 Treadway Gallery, Cincinnati #646/R
£2131 $3750 €3111 Still life (64x48cm-25x19in) s.d.1942 oil tempera board. 23-May-4 Treadway Gallery, Cincinnati #737/R est:3000-5000

GRAHAM, Stanley (19/20th C) British
£331 $592 €483 Mountain landscape with Highland cattle in lake (51x76cm-20x30in) s. i.verso. 12-Jan-4 Rasmussen, Vejle #444/R (D.KR 3500)
£344 $550 €502 Slopes of Ben Nevis NB (51x76cm-20x30in) s. i.verso. 20-Sep-3 Jeffery Burchard, Florida #192a/R

GRAHAM, William (1841-1910) American
£1061 $1900 €1549 Venice street scene (43x69cm-17x27in) s.d.1885. 16-May-4 CRN Auctions, Cambridge #9/R

GRAHAME, Pierre (1938-1996) Belgian
£272 $487 €400 L'Ourthe a Fairon (59x79cm-23x31in) s.d.68 i.verso panel. 17-Mar-4 Hotel des Ventes Mosan, Brussels #161
£1127 $1949 €1600 L'Arlequin (162x100cm-64x39in) s. 10-Dec-3 Hotel des Ventes Mosan, Brussels #282 est:1800-2200
£1156 $2070 €1700 La colombe (80x70cm-31x28in) s.d.87. 17-Mar-4 Hotel des Ventes Mosan, Brussels #162 est:600-800
£1408 $2437 €2000 La Perle (65x54cm-26x21in) s. 10-Dec-3 Hotel des Ventes Mosan, Brussels #283 est:700-900

GRAHL, August (attrib) (1791-1868) German
Miniatures
£1034 $1728 €1500 Lady (13cm-5in) exec.c.1840. 12-Nov-3 Sotheby's, Milan #62/R est:1000-1500

GRAHN, Hjalmar (1882-1949) Swedish
£393 $679 €574 The castle in evening light (33x39cm-13x15in) s. panel exhib. 15-Dec-3 Lilla Bukowskis, Stockholm #43/R (S.KR 5000)

GRAILLON, Cesar (1831-?) French
Sculpture
£2857 $4543 €4200 Scene d'interieur (46x33cm-18x13in) s.d.1880 terracotta relief. 23-Mar-3 Salle des ventes Pillet, Lyon la Foret #247 est:1800

GRAILLY, Victor de (1804-1889) French
£2704 $4922 €4000 Paysage pastoral (55x47cm-22x19in) oval. 21-Jun-4 Tajan, Paris #112/R est:3000-4000
£6452 $12000 €9420 Passamaquoddy Bay, Maine (46x58cm-18x23in) 6-Mar-4 North East Auctions, Portsmouth #551/R est:8000-10000

GRAILLY, Victor de (attrib) (1804-1889) French
£4830 $8500 €7052 View of Mount Vernon with figures, and a sailboat (41x53cm-16x21in) 22-May-4 Pook & Pook, Downington #597/R est:4000-6000
£5682 $10000 €8296 View of Washington's tomb, with Mt. Vernon (41x53cm-16x21in) 22-May-4 Pook & Pook, Downington #598/R est:4000-6000

GRAILLY, Victor de (style) (1804-1889) French
£5108 $9500 €7458 View of Mount Vernon (41x53cm-16x21in) 6-Mar-4 North East Auctions, Portsmouth #415/R est:3000-5000

GRAIN, F (19th C) French?
Sculpture
£1429 $2271 €2100 La baigneuse (85cm-33in) s. brown pat bronze. 23-Mar-3 Mercier & Cie, Lille #76/R est:1500-2500

GRAMATKY, Hardie (1907-1979) American
Works on paper
£2249 $4250 €3284 At the lumber mill (28x43cm-11x17in) s. W/C gouache prov. 17-Feb-4 John Moran, Pasadena #84/R est:3000-4000

GRAMATZKI, Eve (1935-) German
Works on paper
£347 $580 €500 Sans titre (73x103cm-29x41in) W/C cardboard prov. 25-Oct-3 Cornette de St.Cyr, Paris #413
£451 $754 €650 Sans titre (82x100cm-32x39in) s.d.1988 graphite W/C cardboard prov. 25-Oct-3 Cornette de St.Cyr, Paris #411
£455 $759 €650 Composition (120x60cm-47x24in) ink W/C col crayon exec.1999 prov. 29-Jun-3 Versailles Encheres #210
£764 $1276 €1100 Sans titre, ref 275 (120x200cm-47x79in) s.d.1990 W/C crayon chk prov. 25-Oct-3 Cornette de St.Cyr, Paris #412
£874 $1460 €1250 Untitled (66x194cm-26x76in) s.d.1990 mixed media prov. 29-Jun-3 Versailles Encheres #211

GRAMM, T K (?) American?
£1387 $2400 €2025 Winter scene of Darby Paoli Rd in Ardmore (99x86cm-39x34in) 12-Dec-3 York Town, York #1036 est:2400

GRAMMATICA, Antiveduto (1571-1626) Italian
£66667 $111333 €94000 Il trionfo di Davide (134x191cm-53x75in) 18-Jun-3 Christie's, Rome #420/R est:10000-15000

GRAMMATICA, Antiveduto (attrib) (1571-1626) Italian
£4930 $8528 €7000 Salvator Mundi (78x64cm-31x25in) 9-Dec-3 Pandolfini, Florence #32/R est:8000-12000

GRAMMER, George (1898-1982) American
Works on paper
£269 $450 €393 Backstage (25x36cm-10x14in) mixed media. 18-Oct-3 David Dike, Dallas #146/R
£509 $850 €743 Rooftops over San Miguel (25x36cm-10x14in) W/C. 18-Oct-3 David Dike, Dallas #145/R

GRAN, Halfdan (1869-1930) Norwegian
£278 $481 €406 Woodcocks (40x59cm-16x23in) s. 13-Dec-3 Blomqvist, Lysaker #1113 (N.KR 3200)
£499 $834 €729 Capercaillies mating game (69x98cm-27x39in) s. 20-Oct-3 Blomqvist, Lysaker #1099/R (N.KR 5800)

GRANA, Gabriel (1965-) American
£239 $375 €349 Provincetown, east end view (41x51cm-16x20in) s. 20-Apr-3 Outer Cape Auctions, Provincetown #30/R

GRANATA, L (19/20th C) French
£1197 $2071 €1700 Baigneuse sur la cote algerienne (38x85cm-15x33in) s. 15-Dec-3 Gros & Delettrez, Paris #383/R est:1800-2000

GRANATA, Louis (19/20th C) French
£1277 $2132 €1800 Lavandieres au bord de l'Oued (56x132cm-22x52in) s. panel. 19-Oct-3 Rabourdin & Choppin de Janvry, Paris #76/R est:2000-2500

GRANCHI-TAYLOR, Achille (1857-1921) French
£2781 $5201 €4200 La priere du soir (38x53cm-15x21in) s.i. 24-Jul-4 Thierry & Lannon, Brest #169/R est:4000-5000
Works on paper
£1589 $2972 €2400 Le mousse. s.i. pen wash. 24-Jul-4 Thierry & Lannon, Brest #40 est:600-800
£1831 $3204 €2600 Jeune fille croquant une pomme (36x25cm-14x10in) d.97 W/C chl. 21-Dec-3 Thierry & Lannon, Brest #55 est:1000-1200

GRANCHI-TAYLOR, Achille (attrib) (1857-1921) French
Works on paper
£493 $863 €700 Jeune Bretonne epluchant des legumes (52x40cm-20x16in) chl. 21-Dec-3 Thierry & Lannon, Brest #110

GRAND, Cnne le (fl.c.1800) French
Miniatures
£1200 $2208 €1752 Mother and son, in a wooded landscape (8cm-3in) s. wood frame exhib.lit. 24-Jun-4 Bonhams, New Bond Street #78/R est:1200-1800

GRAND-CARTERET, Jean Albert (1903-) French
Works on paper
£397 $727 €600 Modele, dos au miroir (47x41cm-19x16in) s.d.27 or 21 pastel. 7-Apr-4 Piasa, Paris #252
£537 $950 €800 Portrait de femme (61x50cm-24x20in) s. d.36 pastel. 27-Apr-4 Claude Aguttes, Neuilly #7/R

GRANDE, Giovanni (1887-1937) Italian
£680 $1218 €1000 Girl in pink (45x35cm-18x14in) board. 22-Mar-4 Sant Agostino, Torino #195/R
£816 $1461 €1200 Interior (38x38cm-15x15in) s. board. 22-Mar-4 Sant Agostino, Torino #205/R
£1400 $2576 €2100 Reading. Nun (46x37cm-18x15in) board double-sided prov. 14-Jun-4 Sant Agostino, Torino #421/R est:1500-2000

GRANDE, Severin (1869-1934) Norwegian
£293 $489 €428 Flowers in vase (42x28cm-17x11in) s. panel. 20-Oct-3 Blomqvist, Lysaker #1104/R (N.KR 3400)
£317 $584 €463 View towards Trefoldinghets church in winter (29x34cm-11x13in) s. 29-Mar-4 Blomqvist, Lysaker #1083/R (N.KR 4000)
£365 $671 €533 The bathing hut (30x36cm-12x14in) s. 29-Mar-4 Blomqvist, Lysaker #1084/R (N.KR 4600)
£688 $1150 €1004 Family by water (59x70cm-23x28in) s. 20-Oct-3 Blomqvist, Lysaker #1102/R (N.KR 8000)
£826 $1429 €1206 Girl with needlework (76x67cm-30x26in) s. 13-Dec-3 Blomqvist, Lysaker #1115/R (N.KR 9500)
£858 $1502 €1253 Woman and child on bare rock-face (60x66cm-24x26in) s/d/28. 16-Dec-3 Grev Wedels Plass, Oslo #159/R (N.KR 10000)
£861 $1437 €1257 Still life of grapes in fruit bowl (56x64cm-22x25in) s. 20-Oct-3 Blomqvist, Lysaker #1103/R (N.KR 10000)
£976 $1795 €1425 Interior scene with girl reading by lamp light (55x45cm-22x18in) s. 10-Jun-4 Grev Wedels Plass, Oslo #177/R (N.KR 12000)
£2135 $3565 €3117 Interior scene with woman reading (76x69cm-30x27in) s. 13-Oct-3 Blomqvist, Oslo #287/R est:30000-40000 (N.KR 25000)
£15854 $29012 €23147 Kristiania (97x131cm-38x52in) s.d.04. 7-Jun-4 Blomqvist, Oslo #363/R est:60000-80000 (N.KR 195000)

GRANDEE, Joe (1929-1976) American
£519 $950 €758 Ready for anything (61x46cm-24x18in) mono.d.1973 masonite. 5-Jun-4 Neal Auction Company, New Orleans #433/R
Works on paper
£435 $700 €631 Buffalo hunt (48x36cm-19x14in) W/C. 22-Aug-3 Altermann Galleries, Santa Fe #73

GRANDGERARD, Lucien Henri (1880-1965) French
£320 $582 €480 River landscape with a village church in the background (25x35cm-10x14in) s. paper on board. 1-Jul-4 Van Ham, Cologne #1369
Works on paper
£280 $518 €409 Portrait of a lady, with a cat (29x19cm-11x7in) s. ink. 9-Mar-4 Bonhams, Knightsbridge #47/R

GRANDI, Giuseppe (1843-1897) Italian
Sculpture
£2254 $3899 €3200 Beccaria (52cm-20in) s.i. bronze. 10-Dec-3 Sotheby's, Milan #150/R est:2000-3000

GRANDI, Italo de (1912-1988) Swiss
£407 $705 €594 Blue jug and prunes (27x41cm-11x16in) s. i.verso panel prov. 12-Dec-3 Galerie du Rhone, Sion #503 (S.FR 900)
£543 $939 €793 Figs and grapes (33x46cm-13x18in) s. s.i.verso canvas on panel prov. 12-Dec-3 Galerie du Rhone, Sion #504 (S.FR 1200)

GRANDI, Mario Dario (1918-1971) Argentinian
£1381 $2500 €2016 Fan (75x53cm-30x21in) pastel. 30-Mar-4 Arroyo, Buenos Aires #27

Works on paper
£1657 $3000 €2419 Intimacy (57x38cm-22x15in) pastel. 30-Mar-4 Arroyo, Buenos Aires #4

GRANDIN, Eugène (1833-1919) French
£2007 $3632 €3050 Cargo Javita navigant par mer formee (26x16cm-10x6in) s.i.d.1884 W/C. 17-Apr-4 Deburaux, Boulogne #215
£2039 $3691 €3100 Yacht mixte Jupiter navigant au moteur (26x16cm-10x6in) s.i.d.1884 W/C. 17-Apr-4 Deburaux, Boulogne #211
Works on paper
£417 $696 €600 S.S.Brantwood (30x46cm-12x18in) s.i.d.1897 W/C. 26-Oct-3 Lesieur & Le Bars, Le Havre #172
£671 $1248 €1000 Voiliers (11x14cm-4x6in) s. W/C pair. 7-Mar-4 Lesieur & Le Bars, Le Havre #177
£671 $1248 €1000 Bateau pilote (19x31cm-7x12in) W/C. 7-Mar-4 Lesieur & Le Bars, Le Havre #19a
£1023 $1800 €1494 Ship portraits (10x15cm-4x6in) s.i. graphite W/C two. 22-May-4 Pook & Pook, Downington #757/R est:500-800

GRANDIO, Constantino (1923-1977) Spanish
£1056 $1827 €1500 Portrait of man (41x32cm-16x13in) s.d.1916. 15-Dec-3 Ansorena, Madrid #363/R
£6040 $10812 €9000 Seascape (62x100cm-24x39in) s. painted 1973 exhib. 25-May-4 Durán, Madrid #148/R est:9000

GRANDJEAN, Jean (1755-1781) French
Works on paper
£1507 $2562 €2200 Arcadian landscape with figures resting near a classical tomb (14x11cm-6x4in) s.d.1777 verso pen black ink brown wash. 4-Nov-3 Sotheby's, Amsterdam #114/R est:1000-1500

GRANDKOVSKY, Nikolai Karlovich (1864-1907) Russian
£22000 $39380 €32120 Evening concert at the village (73x112cm-29x44in) s. 26-May-4 Sotheby's, London #89/R est:15000-20000

GRANDMAISON, Nickola de (1892-1978) Canadian/Russian
£237 $425 €346 Portrait of an outdoorsman (61x46cm-24x18in) s.d.1930. 7-May-4 Sloans & Kenyon, Bethesda #1164/R
£679 $1133 €991 Foothills nocturne (40x50cm-16x20in) s.i. 17-Nov-3 Hodgins, Calgary #315/R est:1000-1400 (C.D 1500)
£1351 $2297 €1972 Strong Bear (35x27cm-14x11in) s. i.verso on canvas on board painted c.1935 prov. 27-Nov-3 Heffel, Vancouver #134/R est:3500-4500 (C.D 3000)
Works on paper
£440 $805 €642 Portrait of Rennie (44x34cm-17x13in) s. pastel prov. 1-Jun-4 Hodgins, Calgary #351/R (C.D 1100)
£1810 $3023 €2643 Young Indian boy (26x22cm-10x9in) s. pastel. 17-Nov-3 Hodgins, Calgary #48/R est:5000-7000 (C.D 4000)
£2489 $4156 €3634 Papoose (24x19cm-9x7in) s. pastel. 17-Nov-3 Hodgins, Calgary #74/R est:5000-7000 (C.D 5500)
£2789 $5049 €4072 Untitled - papoose (23x20cm-9x8in) s. pastel. 18-Apr-4 Levis, Calgary #28/R est:6000-8000 (C.D 6750)
£5856 $9955 €8550 Papoose (37x29cm-15x11in) s. pastel prov. 27-Nov-3 Heffel, Vancouver #133/R est:10000-12000 (C.D 13000)
£6250 $10625 €9125 Young Indian girl (41x30cm-16x12in) s. pastel prov. 6-Nov-3 Heffel, Vancouver #57/R est:8000-10000 (C.D 14000)
£6400 $11712 €9344 Portrait of an Indian brave (64x47cm-25x19in) s. pastel. 1-Jun-4 Joyner Waddington, Toronto #158/R est:8000-12000 (C.D 16000)
£8800 $16104 €12848 Black white man, Siksa Pikwan, Blood Indian, Standoff, Alberta (71x56cm-28x22in) s. pastel lit. 1-Jun-4 Joyner Waddington, Toronto #59/R est:10000-12000 (C.D 22000)

GRANDMAISON, Oreste de (1932-1985) Canadian
£248 $449 €362 Autumn forest (41x50cm-16x20in) s. hard board prov. 18-Apr-4 Levis, Calgary #28a/R (C.D 600)
£362 $605 €529 Untitled - active skies over the mountains (30x40cm-12x16in) s. board prov. 17-Nov-3 Hodgins, Calgary #190/R (C.D 800)
£450 $766 €657 Spring colour, Osoyoos Lake, Southern BC (36x46cm-14x18in) s.i.verso prov. 23-Nov-3 Levis, Calgary #28/R (C.D 1000)
£520 $952 €759 Barn in the poplars (35x45cm-14x18in) s.i. board. 1-Jun-4 Hodgins, Calgary #434/R (C.D 1300)
£541 $919 €790 February sunset near Priddis (36x46cm-14x18in) s. s.i.verso board prov. 23-Nov-3 Levis, Calgary #26/R (C.D 1200)
£541 $919 €790 Foothill sunset (36x46cm-14x18in) s. s.i.verso. 23-Nov-3 Levis, Calgary #27/R (C.D 1200)
£640 $1171 €934 The dock in late afternoon (40x50cm-16x20in) s.i.d.1980 board. 1-Jun-4 Hodgins, Calgary #321/R (C.D 1600)
£679 $1133 €991 Spring colour (35x45cm-14x18in) s.i. board. 17-Nov-3 Hodgins, Calgary #353/R est:1500-2000 (C.D 1500)
£680 $1244 €993 Gate by the old oak, Sidney, BC (35x45cm-14x18in) s.i. board. 1-Jun-4 Hodgins, Calgary #38/R (C.D 1700)
£720 $1318 €1051 Okanagan lights (28x35cm-11x14in) s.i. board. 1-Jun-4 Hodgins, Calgary #336/R (C.D 1800)
£724 $1209 €1057 Untitled - winter trees (30x40cm-12x16in) s.d. board. 17-Nov-3 Hodgins, Calgary #165/R est:1000-1400 (C.D 1600)
£760 $1391 €1110 Hillscape in spring (35x45cm-14x18in) s.i. board. 1-Jun-4 Hodgins, Calgary #63/R (C.D 1900)
£811 $1378 €1184 Derelict gill netter (61x81cm-24x32in) s. s.i.verso prov. 23-Nov-3 Levis, Calgary #25/R est:2000-2500 (C.D 1800)
£840 $1537 €1226 October sunset, BC (40x50cm-16x20in) s.i. board. 1-Jun-4 Hodgins, Calgary #87/R est:1750-2250 (C.D 2100)
£905 $1511 €1321 Misty morning (45x60cm-18x24in) s.i. board. 17-Nov-3 Hodgins, Calgary #47/R est:2000-2500 (C.D 2000)
£905 $1511 €1321 Evening solitude (35x45cm-14x18in) s.i. board. 17-Nov-3 Hodgins, Calgary #142/R est:1500-2000 (C.D 2000)
£1131 $1889 €1651 Fall blizzard, Southern Alberta (55x75cm-22x30in) s.i. 17-Nov-3 Hodgins, Calgary #348/R est:2500-3000 (C.D 2500)
Works on paper
£200 $366 €292 Horses in the trees (14x19cm-6x7in) mixed media board. 1-Jun-4 Hodgins, Calgary #403/R (C.D 500)

GRANDT, Didier (20th C) French
£294 $499 €420 Vieux Paris (50x60cm-20x24in) s.d.1962. 29-Nov-3 Arnold, Frankfurt #228

GRANDVILLE, Jean Ignace (1803-1847) French
Works on paper
£340 $609 €500 La fileuse et la cuisiniere (11x9cm-4x4in) i. pen brown ink. 19-Mar-4 Piasa, Paris #162/R
£816 $1461 €1200 Je ne sais pas ce que j'ai mais c'te soif la n'est pas naturelle (15x20cm-6x8in) s.i. pen brown ink. 18-Mar-4 Christie's, Paris #293/R
£1700 $3111 €2482 Greyhound in bonnet and shawl (26x15cm-10x6in) pen ink W/C black chl. 7-Jul-4 Bonhams, Knightsbridge #50/R est:1500-2000
£1800 $3294 €2628 An ass holding books under his arm (24x16cm-9x6in) pen ink W/C. 7-Jul-4 Bonhams, Knightsbridge #49/R est:1500-2000

GRANELL, Eugenio F (1912-2001) Spanish
£6944 $11319 €10000 Night bird (66x48cm-26x19in) prov. 23-Sep-3 Durán, Madrid #240/R est:10000
£11565 $20701 €17000 Women playing devils (51x66cm-20x26in) s.d.45. 22-Mar-4 Durán, Madrid #227/R est:10000
Works on paper
£408 $743 €600 Figure (24x18cm-9x7in) s.d.1983 ink dr. 3-Feb-4 Segre, Madrid #180/R
£533 $971 €800 Personaje y elefante (16x23cm-6x9in) s.d.1974 W/C ink. 29-Jun-4 Segre, Madrid #122/R
£633 $1153 €950 Untitled (23x31cm-9x12in) s.d.1975 W/C ink. 29-Jun-4 Segre, Madrid #121/R
£655 $1179 €950 Figures (24x19cm-9x7in) s.d.1956 ink W/C. 26-Jan-4 Ansorena, Madrid #919/R
£1088 $1948 €1600 Untitled (28x44cm-11x17in) s.d.1963 ink. 21-Mar-4 Calmels Cohen, Paris #74 est:600-800
£1284 $2259 €1900 Accusation (24x31cm-9x12in) s.d.1975 W/C ink. 18-May-4 Segre, Madrid #121/R est:1200
£1373 $2403 €1950 An order is an order (31x24cm-12x9in) s.d.1974 i.verso ink W/C. 16-Dec-3 Segre, Madrid #116/R est:1450
£1408 $2437 €2000 Lecture (35x25cm-14x10in) s.d.1975 W/C. 15-Dec-3 Ansorena, Madrid #985/R
£1493 $2538 €2150 Royal confident (31x24cm-12x9in) s.d.1978 W/C ink. 28-Oct-3 Segre, Madrid #216/R est:1450

GRANER Y ARRUFI, Luis (1863-1929) Spanish
£1000 $1600 €1460 Moonlit coastal scene, Brazil (48x72cm-19x28in) 16-Sep-3 Rosebery Fine Art, London #539 est:1000-1500
£2446 $4500 €3571 Sunset on the shore (43x61cm-17x24in) s.d.1925 board on masonite. 9-Jun-4 Doyle, New York #3041 est:3000-5000
£8392 $14014 €12000 Coastal landscape (65x82cm-26x32in) s. 30-Jun-3 Ansorena, Madrid #360/R

GRANER, E (1865-1943) Austrian
Works on paper
£2467 $4440 €3700 Monuments in Vienna (34x23cm-13x9in) s.d.22 W/C two. 21-Apr-4 Neumeister, Munich #2499/R est:700

GRANER, Ernst (1865-1943) Austrian
£1611 $3012 €2400 Girls tying onions in Chioggia (39x56cm-15x22in) s.d.94 i. verso board. 24-Feb-4 Dorotheum, Vienna #48/R est:2400-2600
Works on paper
£537 $988 €800 Village on Kahlenberg (22x28cm-9x11in) s. W/C. 26-Mar-4 Dorotheum, Vienna #258/R
£600 $1092 €900 St Anna's Portal in Vienna (49x34cm-19x13in) s.d.1911 W/C study verso. 3-Jul-4 Badum, Bamberg #81/R
£872 $1605 €1300 Building (18x19cm-7x7in) s.d.17 W/C. 26-Mar-4 Dorotheum, Vienna #251/R
£1109 $1984 €1619 Beethovenplatz, Vienna (40x52cm-16x20in) s.d.14 W/C. 26-May-4 AB Stockholms Auktionsverk #2467/R est:8000-10000 (S.KR 15000)
£1200 $1896 €1740 Busy street in Venice (24x33cm-9x13in) s.d.1908 W/C. 2-Sep-3 Bonhams, Oxford #31 est:400-600
£1316 $2421 €2000 Summer house (22x31cm-9x12in) s.d.22 W/C. 22-Jun-4 Wiener Kunst Auktionen, Vienna #183/R est:2000
£1342 $2470 €2000 Karlskirche in Vienna in winter (54x41cm-21x16in) s.d.28 W/C. 24-Mar-4 Hugo Ruef, Munich #1178 est:1700
£1379 $2290 €2000 Schulhof (28x26cm-11x10in) s. W/C paper on board. 30-Sep-3 Dorotheum, Vienna #298/R est:3000-3500
£2685 $4940 €4000 Vienna market (24x33cm-9x13in) s.d.1908 W/C paper on board. 26-Mar-4 Dorotheum, Vienna #246/R est:5000-6000
£2685 $4940 €4000 Doorway in Singerstrasse (43x30cm-17x12in) s. W/C. 26-Mar-4 Dorotheum, Vienna #257/R est:8000-10000
£4895 $8322 €7000 Stephansplatz (76x57cm-30x22in) s.d.16 W/C. 28-Nov-3 Wiener Kunst Auktionen, Vienna #450/R est:5000-10000

GRANET, François Marius (1775-1849) French
£1648 $3000 €2406 Cloister with a gardener wheeling a barrow (73x59cm-29x23in) prov. 29-Jun-4 Sotheby's, New York #62/R est:4000-6000
Works on paper
£276 $461 €400 Monastery or castle interior (13x12cm-5x5in) s. pen W/C prov. 15-Nov-3 Lempertz, Koln #1484/R
£1342 $2497 €2000 Moines sous une voute, priant devant une statue (12x15cm-5x6in) grey wash. 7-Mar-4 Livinec, Gaudcheau & Jezequel, Rennes #45
£2028 $3488 €2900 Vues d'Italie. wash over crayon 5 in one frame. 8-Dec-3 Claude Aguttes, Neuilly #9/R est:2000-3000
£2168 $3729 €3100 Vues d'Italie. wash over crayon 5 in one frame. 8-Dec-3 Claude Aguttes, Neuilly #8/R est:2000-3000
£2181 $4057 €3250 Moines en priere dans une chapelle voutee (13x17cm-5x7in) s. brown wash W/C. 7-Mar-4 Livinec, Gaudcheau & Jezequel, Rennes #44

£3061 $5480 €4500 Les souterrains d'un palais Romain. Une vue de l'eglise de San Stefano (12x10cm-5x4in) s. one d.1805 one d.1804 graphite pen black ink brown wash pair. 18-Mar-4 Christie's, Paris #268/R est:1500-2000

GRANET, François Marius (attrib) (1775-1849) French
£2800 $5068 €4200 Moine ecrivant devant une fenetre (37x29cm-15x11in) 30-Mar-4 Rossini, Paris #69/R est:2000-3000

GRANFELT, Erik (1919-1990) Finnish
£333 $557 €480 Town (73x76cm-29x30in) s. 23-Oct-3 Hagelstam, Helsinki #902
£986 $1706 €1400 Dinner time (82x130cm-32x51in) s. 13-Dec-3 Hagelstam, Helsinki #163/R
£1419 $2540 €2100 Magpies (43x60cm-17x24in) s.d.1893. 8-May-4 Bukowskis, Helsinki #36/R est:2500-2800

GRANGER-VEYRON (20th C) French?
Works on paper
£734 $1226 €1050 Le cirque Amar (105x73cm-41x29in) s. chl chk. 24-Jun-3 Millon & Associes, Paris #7a

GRANGES, David des (1611-1675) British
Miniatures
£7200 $13248 €10512 King Charles II of England, wearing the blue sash of the Garter (7cm-3in) W/C on vellum rectangular wood frame prov. 24-Jun-4 Bonhams, New Bond Street #42/R est:8000-12000
£16000 $28800 €23360 King Charles II of England, wearing armour (6cm-2in) i. vellum card oval sharkskin case exec.c.1653 prov.exhib.lit. 22-Apr-4 Bonhams, New Bond Street #10/R est:12000-18000

GRANINGER, Leopold (19/20th C) Austrian
Works on paper
£380 $699 €555 Springtime in the Austrian Alps (37x51cm-15x20in) s. W/C bodycol. 25-Mar-4 Christie's, Kensington #87

GRANJEAN, Marie (19/20th C) French
£1207 $2184 €1762 Still life with hens (91x130cm-36x51in) s. 31-Mar-4 Zurichsee Auktionen, Erlenbach #8/R est:3000-4000 (S.FR 2800)

GRANOVSKI, Sam (19/20th C) Russian
Works on paper
£331 $603 €500 Female nude (30x24cm-12x9in) s. pastel. 15-Jun-4 Rossini, Paris #81
£470 $874 €700 Les puces (38x50cm-15x20in) s.d.1935 gouache. 2-Mar-4 Artcurial Briest, Paris #172

GRANSOW, Helmut (1921-) Canadian
£680 $1244 €993 Lake Memphramagog, Eastern Townships, hot summer day (55x71cm-22x28in) s. s.i.d.1982 verso prov. 3-Jun-4 Heffel, Vancouver #28/R (C.D 1700)

GRANT, Alice (fl.1881-1907) British
£460 $846 €672 What is it (60x48cm-24x19in) s.i. verso. 14-Jun-4 Bonhams, Bath #156
£500 $850 €730 Still life of fruit and leaves (25x30cm-10x12in) s.d.1888 board. 30-Oct-3 Duke & Son, Dorchester #266/R

GRANT, Alistair (1925-) British
£500 $910 €730 Arras (25x35cm-10x14in) s. s.i. verso. 1-Jul-4 Christie's, Kensington #398/R
£700 $1274 €1022 Le touquet - 6am (71x91cm-28x36in) s. s.i. verso. 1-Jul-4 Christie's, Kensington #400/R
£900 $1638 €1314 Le touquet noon (122x91cm-48x36in) s.i. verso painted 1990. 1-Jul-4 Christie's, Kensington #399/R
£900 $1638 €1314 Happy day (46x61cm-18x24in) s.i. verso. 1-Jul-4 Christie's, Kensington #401/R

GRANT, Blanche (1874-1948) American
£2794 $4750 €4079 Isabel, Taos Indian girl (41x30cm-16x12in) s.d.1936 s.i.d.verso canvas on board prov. 1-Nov-3 Santa Fe Art, Santa Fe #161/R est:8000-10000
£2794 $4750 €4079 Indian eyes, Taos (36x28cm-14x11in) s. s.i.d.1937 verso masonite panel prov. 1-Nov-3 Santa Fe Art, Santa Fe #162/R est:8000-10000

GRANT, Carleton (fl.1885-1899) British
Works on paper
£280 $501 €409 Moonlight on a lake (21x34cm-8x13in) s.d.1898 W/C. 25-May-4 Bonhams, Knightsbridge #27/R
£360 $666 €526 Shore scene with fisherman caulking his boat (17x34cm-7x13in) s. W/C. 14-Jul-4 Bonhams, Chester #344
£660 $1181 €964 Figures with donkey and cart on a Welsh country road (33x48cm-13x19in) s.d.1890 W/C. 17-Mar-4 Bonhams, Chester #228/R
£1100 $1969 €1606 Coastal cottage (45x72cm-18x28in) s.d.1888 W/C htd white. 25-May-4 Bonhams, Knightsbridge #295/R est:700-900

GRANT, Charles Henry (1866-1939) American
£247 $400 €361 Waves on coast (30x36cm-12x14in) s. 31-Jul-3 Eldred, East Dennis #472/R

GRANT, Donald (1930-) British
£1900 $3420 €2774 Wapiti (59x90cm-23x35in) s. 20-Apr-4 Hutchinson, Boroughbridge #327/R
£2600 $4680 €3796 Tiger amidst grasses (64x89cm-25x35in) s. 20-Apr-4 Hutchinson, Boroughbridge #326/R est:2000-3000

GRANT, Duncan (1885-1978) British
£750 $1320 €1095 Portrait of a model. Standing nude (51x40cm-20x16in) two prov. 19-May-4 Sotheby's, Olympia #161/R
£900 $1584 €1314 Male nude (56x35cm-22x14in) init. oil chl paper on board prov. 19-May-4 Sotheby's, Olympia #162/R
£950 $1672 €1387 Portrait of David Pape (68x61cm-27x24in) prov. 19-May-4 Sotheby's, Olympia #157/R
£1300 $2288 €1898 Portrait of Richard Shone seated (58x42cm-23x17in) oil paper on board prov. 19-May-4 Sotheby's, Olympia #154/R est:800-1200
£1400 $2464 €2044 Two girls seated. Seated woman (46x35cm-18x14in) board two prov. 19-May-4 Sotheby's, Olympia #151/R est:800-1200
£1400 $2464 €2044 Portrait of Nerissa of Fanny Garnett, dressed as Rembrandt. Nerissa and Fanny Garnett (56x38cm-22x15in) s. oil paper on board two. 19-May-4 Sotheby's, Olympia #152/R est:800-1200
£1400 $2464 €2044 Portrait of Peter Morris (51x40cm-20x16in) board two. 19-May-4 Sotheby's, Olympia #160/R est:1500-2000
£1500 $2775 €2190 Rigoletto (29x23cm-11x9in) painted c.1925 p. 11-Mar-4 Christie's, Kensington #4/R est:1500-2000
£1500 $2640 €2190 Portrait of George Bergen (40x33cm-16x13in) board two prov. 19-May-4 Sotheby's, Olympia #153/R est:500-700
£1600 $2816 €2336 Portrait of Quentin Bell (46x38cm-18x15in) prov. 19-May-4 Sotheby's, Olympia #156/R est:600-800
£1700 $2992 €2482 Portrait of Pierre (46x35cm-18x14in) sold with another by same hand prov. 19-May-4 Sotheby's, Olympia #155/R est:600-800
£1724 $3086 €2517 Seated female nude (82x64cm-32x25in) paper lit. 12-May-4 Dobiaschofsky, Bern #576/R est:6000 (S.FR 4000)
£1800 $3006 €2628 Still life of books, ceramics and wine bottle (60x50cm-24x20in) s. 16-Oct-3 Lawrence, Crewkerne #753/R
£2200 $4004 €3212 Vanessa Bell's monkey (33x24cm-13x9in) s. board. 1-Jul-4 Christie's, Kensington #143/R est:1000-1500
£2400 $4296 €3504 Venice (55x38cm-22x15in) s.i.d.48 board. 16-Mar-4 Bonhams, New Bond Street #39/R est:2500-3500
£2500 $4300 €3650 Guidecca, Venice (53x37cm-21x15in) s.d.75. 3-Dec-3 Christie's, Kensington #485/R est:3000-5000
£2600 $4472 €3796 After chardin (26x32cm-10x13in) s.d.63 board exhib. 2-Dec-3 Bonhams, New Bond Street #52/R est:1500-2000
£2800 $4928 €4088 Lindy painting in the studio at Charleston (76x56cm-30x22in) board painted c.1969 prov. 19-May-4 Sotheby's, Olympia #150/R est:800-1200
£3000 $5490 €4380 Woman in blue (83x89cm-33x35in) painted c.1925-27. 4-Jun-4 Christie's, London #20/R est:4000-6000
£3200 $5824 €4672 Sussex farm (40x51cm-16x20in) s.d.26 prov. 15-Jun-4 Bonhams, New Bond Street #28/R est:3000-4000
£3500 $5530 €5075 Figures at the waterfront, looking across to St Mark's, Venice (56x99cm-22x39in) s.d.51 prov. 24-Jul-3 Lawrence, Crewkerne #976/R est:2500-3500
£4200 $7224 €6132 Still life with dahlias in a glass (23x30cm-9x12in) init.indis.d. exhib. 3-Dec-3 Christie's, Kensington #520/R est:2500-3500
£5000 $9150 €7300 Still life of flowers in a carafe (51x41cm-20x16in) s.i. canvasboard painted c.1926-28. 4-Jun-4 Christie's, London #23/R est:6000-8000
£5800 $9976 €8468 Still life on a painted table (46x38cm-18x15in) s. canvas on board. 3-Dec-3 Christie's, Kensington #522/R est:5000-7000
£6000 $10920 €8760 Duncan's folly, Charleston (56x46cm-22x18in) init.d.42 i.verso prov. 15-Jun-4 Bonhams, New Bond Street #27/R est:7000-9000
£6200 $11098 €9052 Lamps (51x77cm-20x30in) s.i.overlap. 16-Mar-4 Bonhams, New Bond Street #38/R est:3000-5000
£6500 $11050 €9490 Vieux port, Marseilles (38x46cm-15x18in) painted c.1929. 21-Nov-3 Christie's, London #147/R est:7000-10000
£7000 $12040 €10220 Still life with bottle and mandolin (46x35cm-18x14in) s. s.i.d.1940 verso. 3-Dec-3 Sotheby's, London #38/R est:7000-10000
£7500 $12750 €10950 Portrait of a seated girl (62x37cm-24x15in) init. board painted c.1908 prov.exhib. 21-Nov-3 Christie's, London #74/R est:4000-6000
£7500 $13650 €10950 Venice (55x102cm-22x40in) s.d.51. 15-Jun-4 Bonhams, New Bond Street #26/R est:8000-12000
£10000 $18300 €14600 Angelica painting (77x51cm-30x20in) s. board painted c.1950-55 prov.exhib. 4-Jun-4 Christie's, London #19/R est:7000-10000
£11000 $19360 €16060 Charleston (51x61cm-20x24in) s.d.1954 prov. 19-May-4 Dreweatt Neate, Newbury #90/R est:8000-10000
£12000 $20400 €17520 Tulips (61x30cm-24x12in) s. painted c.1932. 21-Nov-3 Christie's, London #141/R est:6000-8000
£15000 $26400 €21900 Green jug and brush pot (36x25cm-14x10in) prov.lit. 19-May-4 Dreweatt Neate, Newbury #91/R est:1500-2000
£17000 $29240 €24820 Ballet decoration (81x56cm-32x22in) s. board painted c.1929-30 prov.exhib. 3-Dec-3 Sotheby's, London #8/R est:12000-18000
£90000 $154800 €131400 Still life with flowers below a mantelpiece (76x61cm-30x24in) prov. 3-Dec-3 Sotheby's, London #6/R est:30000-50000
Works on paper
£500 $835 €730 Seated male nude (17x9cm-7x4in) W/C pen col ink. 16-Oct-3 Christie's, Kensington #344/R
£600 $1002 €876 Lovers in a hammock (13x18cm-5x7in) pencil W/C. 16-Oct-3 Christie's, Kensington #342/R
£600 $1002 €876 Chicken. Turkey (18x14cm-7x6in) mono. pencil pastel pair. 21-Oct-3 Bonhams, Knightsbridge #27/R
£600 $1032 €876 Two standing male nudes (25x35cm-10x14in) pencil. 3-Dec-3 Christie's, Kensington #438/R
£650 $1177 €949 Reclining nude (43x48cm-17x19in) black chalk prov. 16-Apr-4 Keys, Aylsham #512/R
£700 $1169 €1022 Lovers entangled (22x30cm-9x12in) W/C felt tip pen double-sided. 16-Oct-3 Christie's, Kensington #340/R
£700 $1169 €1022 Lovers entwined (19x20cm-7x8in) init. chl W/C. 16-Oct-3 Christie's, Kensington #345/R
£700 $1204 €1022 Red pillow (18x25cm-7x10in) pencil pen black ink W/C. 3-Dec-3 Christie's, Kensington #441/R
£750 $1253 €1095 Rural church (24x34cm-9x13in) s.i.d.1940 pencil W/C. 16-Oct-3 Christie's, Kensington #416/R
£750 $1275 €1095 Costume design for ballet (43x28cm-17x11in) s. pen ink gouache. 19-Nov-3 Tennants, Leyburn #926
£800 $1376 €1168 Head and torso study (11x6cm-4x2in) pencil. 3-Dec-3 Christie's, Kensington #440/R
£850 $1420 €1241 Acrobats (39x27cm-15x11in) init. chl W/C. 16-Oct-3 Christie's, Kensington #341/R
£850 $1462 €1241 Madonna and Child (37x29cm-15x11in) W/C oil. 3-Dec-3 Christie's, Kensington #434/R

£1000	$1670	€1460	Red rug (22x30cm-9x12in) pencil pastel. 16-Oct-3 Christie's, Kensington #343/R est:1000-1500
£1100	$1837	€1606	Cheerful weather for the wedding (18x12cm-7x5in) init.i.d.1972 pencil bodycol. 16-Oct-3 Christie's, Kensington #347/R est:500-800
£1300	$2327	€1898	Interior, flowers on a mantlepiece, 46 Gordon Square (55x44cm-22x17in) s.d.1913 pencil W/C. 14-May-4 Christie's, Kensington #507/R est:1500-2000
£1500	$2505	€2190	Red underpants (50x17cm-20x7in) pencil W/C bodycol col ink. 16-Oct-3 Christie's, Kensington #346/R est:1500-2000
£1600	$2672	€2336	Lovers (26x25cm-10x10in) init. pencil W/C bodycol col ink. 16-Oct-3 Christie's, Kensington #353/R est:1200-1800
£1800	$3006	€2628	Two male lovers (49x37cm-19x15in) pencil W/C. 16-Oct-3 Christie's, Kensington #339/R est:1500-2000
£2200	$3498	€3212	Farmyard birds (34x24cm-13x9in) mono. W/C three. 10-Sep-3 Sotheby's, Olympia #135/R est:600-800
£2600	$4472	€3796	Three sailors (34x23cm-13x9in) pencil biro gouache. 3-Dec-3 Christie's, Kensington #435/R est:1500-2500
£4500	$7650	€6570	Portrait of David Garnett (38x63cm-15x25in) s.d.1915 pencil pastel. 21-Nov-3 Christie's, London #146/R est:5000-7000

GRANT, Dwinell (1912-) American

Works on paper			
£543	$950	€793	Contrathemis (22x28cm-9x11in) mono.d.41 col pencil graphite prov. 19-Dec-3 Sotheby's, New York #1021/R

GRANT, Frederick M (1886-1959) American

£1413	$2600	€2063	Landscape (41x30cm-16x12in) s. prov. 27-Jun-4 Hindman, Chicago #891/R est:1500-2000
£1429	$2500	€2086	An autumnal gathering (76x76cm-30x30in) s. 19-Dec-3 Sotheby's, New York #1125/R est:3000-5000
£1875	$3000	€2738	Floral scene (76x81cm-30x32in) 19-Sep-3 Du Mouchelle, Detroit #2112/R est:3000-5000
£6329	$10000	€9240	Gypsy camp (127x127cm-50x50in) s. prov. 7-Sep-3 Treadway Gallery, Cincinnati #656/R est:9000-12000
Works on paper			
£511	$950	€746	Park view, autumn (9x10cm-4x4in) init. gouache. 5-Mar-4 Skinner, Boston #475/R

GRANT, Frederick M (attrib) (1886-1959) American

Works on paper			
£206	$350	€301	Figures on a city street with fall foliage (10x10cm-4x4in) mono. gouache. 21-Nov-3 Eldred, East Dennis #259d/R

GRANT, Gordon (1875-1962) American

£663	$1200	€968	Lakeside beach with bathers (30x41cm-12x16in) s. board. 16-Apr-4 James Julia, Fairfield #833/R est:1250-1750
£1118	$1900	€1632	Figures, Skiff and house on the shore (30x41cm-12x16in) s. board. 21-Nov-3 Eldred, East Dennis #889/R est:1200-1400
£2180	$3750	€3183	Ship builders (30x40cm-12x16in) s. i.verso canvasboard. 3-Dec-3 Doyle, New York #210/R est:2000-3000
£2732	$5000	€3989	Westward Ho (61x76cm-24x30in) s. i.verso prov. 29-Jul-4 Christie's, Rockefeller NY #288/R est:5000-7000
Works on paper			
£245	$450	€358	Rocky shore (33x53cm-13x21in) s. W/C. 10-Jun-4 Swann Galleries, New York #104/R
£326	$600	€476	Hauled out (25x33cm-10x13in) s.i. pencil. 10-Jun-4 Swann Galleries, New York #105/R
£378	$700	€552	Moran tug - Welfare Island and the 59th Street Bridge (36x30cm-14x12in) s. i.d.1950 verso W/C over pencil. 15-Jul-4 Doyle, New York #42/R
£514	$950	€750	Untitled, harbour scene (36x53cm-14x21in) s. W/C. 17-Jul-4 Outer Cape Auctions, Provincetown #58/R
£568	$1050	€829	Sailboats (48x33cm-19x13in) s. W/C. 15-Feb-4 Outer Cape Auctions, Provincetown #58/R
£1166	$1900	€1702	Back harbour (36x56cm-14x22in) s. W/C executed c.1945. 19-Jul-3 Outer Cape Auctions, Provincetown #78/R
£1500	$2400	€2190	Sailing vessel. s. W/C. 20-Sep-3 Nadeau, Windsor #119/R
£1676	$3000	€2447	Fishermen at the docks (36x51cm-14x20in) s. W/C prov. 6-May-4 Shannon's, Milford #163/R est:2500-3500
£2180	$3750	€3183	Afternoon shadows (40x55cm-16x22in) s. W/C over pencil prov. 3-Dec-3 Doyle, New York #209/R est:3000-4000

GRANT, Gordon (attrib) (1875-1962) American

£353	$600	€515	Rocky shore scene (30x41cm-12x16in) board. 21-Nov-3 Eldred, East Dennis #888/R

GRANT, Henry (fl.1872-1888) British

£380	$695	€555	Red squirrel (23cm-9in circular) s.d.1872. 7-Apr-4 Woolley & Wallis, Salisbury #290/R

GRANT, Ian (1947-) Australian?

£1220	$1915	€1781	Flight of birds (169x181cm-67x71in) init.d.77 s.i.d.April-May 1977 verso acrylic prov. 26-Aug-3 Christie's, Sydney #377 est:1000-2000 (A.D 3000)

GRANT, Ian Macdonald (1904-1993) British

£280	$448	€409	Tapping No 1 furnace (43x53cm-17x21in) s. painted 1952 exhib. 16-Sep-3 Rosebery Fine Art, London #429/R
£320	$512	€467	Two nudes in a landscape (35x38cm-14x15in) pastel acrylic board prov. 16-Sep-3 Bonhams, Knightsbridge #214
£350	$613	€511	Self portrait, seated before a canvas, holding a palette (76x61cm-30x24in) s.d.1974 exhib. 16-Dec-3 Capes Dunn, Manchester #708/R
£400	$748	€584	Self portrait (15x11cm-6x4in) panel. 25-Feb-4 Mallams, Oxford #146
£420	$781	€613	Nudes in a landscape (35x38cm-14x15in) board prov. 4-Mar-4 Christie's, Kensington #206/R

GRANT, J Jeffrey (1883-1960) American

£426	$750	€622	Street scene (36x41cm-14x16in) s. canvas on board painted c.1930. 23-May-4 Treadway Gallery, Cincinnati #569/R
£633	$1000	€924	Fishermen (36x41cm-14x16in) s. board. 7-Sep-3 Treadway Gallery, Cincinnati #628/R
£1163	$2000	€1698	Illinois farm (36x41cm-14x16in) s. i.verso canvas on board painted c.1930. 7-Dec-3 Treadway Gallery, Cincinnati #557/R est:2000-3000
£1505	$2800	€2197	Rainy Sunday (76x51cm-30x20in) s. painted c.1925. 7-Mar-4 Treadway Gallery, Cincinnati #570/R est:3000-5000

GRANT, James (fl.1885-1890) British

£3800	$6460	€5548	Extensive view of Edinburgh, from the Castle (113x167cm-44x66in) s.d.1885. 30-Oct-3 Christie's, London #17/R est:3000-5000

GRANT, James (1924-) American

Works on paper			
£281	$523	€420	Composition (21x28cm-8x11in) s. mixed media collage canvas on card. 4-Mar-4 Babuino, Rome #508

GRANT, James Ardern (1885-1973) British

£982	$1600	€1434	Portrait of a young woman (91x71cm-36x28in) s. board. 27-Sep-3 Charlton Hall, Columbia #672/R est:300-800

GRANT, Keith (1930-) British

£2400	$4296	€3504	Mountain coast (91x273cm-36x107in) triptych prov. 14-May-4 Christie's, Kensington #626/R est:2000-3000
Works on paper			
£300	$555	€438	Portrait of Emma (30x30cm-12x12in) s. chl. 10-Mar-4 Cheffins, Cambridge #70/R
£550	$985	€803	Sunset Gruinard Bay (53x79cm-21x31in) s.i.d.71 prov. 14-May-4 Christie's, Kensington #627/R

GRANT, Kenneth (20th C) British

£650	$1125	€949	The Royal yacht Brittannia, racing off Cowes (48x76cm-19x30in) s. 11-Dec-3 Ewbank, Send #404/R

GRANT, Sir Francis (1810-1878) British

£5000	$9000	€7300	Portrait of Matthew Piers Boulton (127x102cm-50x40in) 22-Apr-4 Christie's, Rockefeller NY #84/R est:10000-15000
£11000	$18700	€16060	Portrait of Margaret Henry, standing beside a table with her hat on it (91x57cm-36x22in) prov. 27-Nov-3 Sotheby's, London #171/R est:10000-15000
£30000	$54300	€43800	Knitting a stocking (101x124cm-40x49in) prov.exhib.lit. 19-Apr-4 Sotheby's, London #9/R est:30000-40000
Works on paper			
£600	$966	€870	Golfer (17x11cm-7x4in) pen ink. 21-Aug-3 Bonhams, Edinburgh #1019/R

GRANT, Thomas (19th C) British

£780	$1443	€1139	Bird of prey with its kill in a landscape (64x76cm-25x30in) s. indis d. 10-Feb-4 David Lay, Penzance #572
£1900	$3363	€2774	Hawk with his pray (63x76cm-25x30in) s.i. 29-Apr-4 Christie's, Kensington #31/R est:1000-2000

GRANT, Zdenek (20th C) American

£314	$500	€458	Landscape (61x76cm-24x30in) s. prov. 9-Sep-3 Arthur James, Florida #352

GRARD, Georges (1901-1984) Belgian

Sculpture			
£1208	$2235	€1800	Reclining woman (11x22cm-4x9in) s. terracotta lit. 13-Mar-4 De Vuyst, Lokeren #159 est:1700-1800
£25333	$46360	€38000	Le printemps a la couronne (128x79x100cm-50x31x39in) num.7/9 pat bronze. 7-Jun-4 Palais de Beaux Arts, Brussels #62/R est:30000-40000
Works on paper			
£800	$1432	€1200	Nude sitting. Reclining nude. Nude standing (52x39cm-20x15in) s. pen ink three. 15-May-4 De Vuyst, Lokeren #148

GRASDORP, Willem (1678-1723) Dutch

£15000	$27000	€21900	Plum, grapes on the vine and medlars on a ledge with peaches, snail in the foreground (40x33cm-16x13in) s. prov. 21-Apr-4 Christie's, London #43/R est:15000-20000

GRASHOF, Otto (1812-1876) German

£1333	$2427	€2000	Portrait of Deacon Simon Petrowitsch (26x23cm-10x9in) s.d.1842 lit. 1-Jul-4 Van Ham, Cologne #1371/R est:1800
£7000	$11900	€10220	Tsarevich Alexander's Bearhunt on the outskirts of Moscow (109x148cm-43x58in) s.i.d.1843. 19-Nov-3 Sotheby's, London #14/R est:6000-8000
£9000	$16380	€13500	Cossacks on horseback (146x103cm-57x41in) s.d.1840. 1-Jul-4 Van Ham, Cologne #1370/R est:10000

GRASS, Gunter (1927-) German

Works on paper			
£292	$487	€420	Untitled - figure with mirror in hand (29x21cm-11x8in) s.d. Indian ink brush. 25-Oct-3 Dr Lehr, Berlin #162/R
£517	$926	€755	Mushrooms in surreal landscape (18x24cm-7x9in) s.d.7.97 W/c. 12-May-4 Dobiaschofsky, Bern #1647 (S.FR 1200)
£764	$1177	€1200	Bird's nest (45x63cm-18x25in) s.d.61. 4-Sep-2 Schopman, Hamburg #198/R
£933	$1717	€1400	Monstre marin (32x47cm-13x19in) s.d.21/10/74 black crayon. 9-Jun-4 Piasa, Paris #91/R

GRASS-MICK, Augustin (1873-1963) French
Works on paper
£270 $494 €394 L'Ecole Militaire apres la pluie (20x33cm-8x13in) init.d.08 W/C gouache. 28-Jul-4 Mallams, Oxford #143

GRASSE, Wolfgang (1930-) Australian
Works on paper
£288 $521 €420 Australian made 1967 (47x35cm-19x14in) s. synthetic polymer on board. 30-Mar-4 Lawson Menzies, Sydney #242 (A.D 700)

GRASSEL, Franz (1861-1948) German
£2759 $5048 €4000 Poultry yard (22x33cm-9x13in) s.d.1943 panel. 30-Jan-4 Altus, Berlin #589/R est:280
£4718 $7549 €6700 Six ducks in water (23x37cm-9x15in) s. panel lit. 19-Sep-3 Karlheinz Kaupp, Staufen #2040/R est:3000
£6164 $10479 €9000 White ducks by pond (63x100cm-25x39in) s.d.1927. 8-Nov-3 Hans Stahl, Toestorf #7/R est:9000

GRASSERE, Gerard Joseph (1915-1993) Dutch
£340 $619 €500 Untitled (90x90cm-35x35in) s.d.71 s.verso oil burlap on canvas. 3-Feb-4 Christie's, Amsterdam #532
£476 $867 €700 At the exhibition (30x30cm-12x12in) s.d.75 board. 3-Feb-4 Christie's, Amsterdam #527/R
£476 $867 €700 Woman and flowers (40x29cm-16x11in) s. board. 3-Feb-4 Christie's, Amsterdam #529
£537 $999 €800 Cosmic experience (116x81cm-46x32in) s.d.87 verso. 4-Mar-4 Auction Maastricht #1084/R
£567 $1037 €850 Evening landscape (39x48cm-15x19in) s. panel. 7-Jun-4 Glerum, Amsterdam #246/R
£612 $1114 €900 Composition (50x60cm-20x24in) s.d.52 i.d.verso board. 3-Feb-4 Christie's, Amsterdam #528/R
£1224 $2229 €1800 Geluiden uit de Efteling (55x55cm-22x22in) s.d.57 s.d.verso. 3-Feb-4 Christie's, Amsterdam #533/R est:1200-1600
Works on paper
£272 $495 €400 Kunstmarkt te Utrecht (40x65cm-16x26in) s. W/C executed c.1964. 3-Feb-4 Christie's, Amsterdam #535
£333 $610 €500 Sinking sun (16x49cm-6x19in) s.d.66 mixed media. 7-Jun-4 Glerum, Amsterdam #283/R
£544 $990 €800 Mechanische compositie (48x62cm-19x24in) s.d.50 gouache. 3-Feb-4 Christie's, Amsterdam #531

GRASSET, Eugène (1841-1917) Swiss
£578 $1035 €850 L'actrice et l'admirateur (40x30cm-16x12in) mono. board. 19-Mar-4 Millon & Associes, Paris #55/R

GRASSI, Alfonso (1919-) Italian
£1544 $2871 €2300 Amalfi (34x28cm-13x11in) s. i.verso board prov. 4-Mar-4 Babuino, Rome #166

GRASSI, Giuseppe Serafino (1863-1904) Italian
Works on paper
£1724 $2862 €2500 Portrait of young lady (62x46cm-24x18in) s.d.95 pastel. 1-Oct-3 Della Rocca, Turin #98/R est:2000-2200

GRASSI, Nicola (1662-1748) Italian
£22000 $38060 €32120 Madonna and Child (49x40cm-19x16in) 11-Dec-3 Sotheby's, London #197/R est:5000-7000

GRASSIN, Alexandre Marie (20th C) French
£1509 $2400 €2203 On the banks of the Aven (50x61cm-20x24in) s.d.1919 prov. 12-Sep-3 Skinner, Boston #471/R

GRASSIS, Giuseppe (1870-1949) Italian
£1745 $3123 €2600 Lake landscape with shepherds (59x103cm-23x41in) s. 25-May-4 Finarte Semenzato, Milan #34/R est:3000-3500
£1946 $3445 €2900 Working by the cottages (50x60cm-20x24in) s. 1-May-4 Meeting Art, Vercelli #52 est:2500

GRASSO, Alfio (1945-) Italian
£369 $683 €550 Girls on the quay (60x80cm-24x31in) s. i.verso. 13-Mar-4 Meeting Art, Vercelli #540

GRATCHEFF (?) Russian
Sculpture
£2028 $3448 €2900 Sleigh ride (28cm-11in) s, bronze. 29-Nov-3 Bukowskis, Helsinki #422/R est:300-500

GRATCHEFF, Alexei Petrovitch (1780-1850) Russian
Sculpture
£1141 $1837 €1700 La defense du cosaque (22cm-9in) s.st.f. brown pat bronze. 23-Feb-3 St-Germain-en-Laye Encheres #18/R est:1500-1800

GRATCHEFF, Georgi (1860-1893) Russian
Sculpture
£2400 $4344 €3600 Troika (20x32cm-8x13in) i. cyrillic bronze. 1-Apr-4 Van Ham, Cologne #1127/R est:1400

GRATCHEV, Vassily (1831-1905) Russian
Sculpture
£1400 $2422 €2044 Soldier's farewell (23cm-9in) s. bronze. 9-Dec-3 Clarke Gammon, Guildford #566/R est:500-800

GRATE, Eric (1896-1983) Swedish
Sculpture
£2611 $4699 €3812 The wanderer (27cm-11in) init.num.H.C XXXI brown pat.bronze cire perdue Cast Bergman. 26-Apr-4 Bukowskis, Stockholm #268/R est:20000-25000 (S.KR 36000)
£3663 $6484 €5348 Navigare (58cm-23in) s.num.1/4 pat.bronze socle Cast Bergman cire perdue exhib.lit. 27-Apr-4 AB Stockholms Auktionsverk #776/R est:60000-80000 (S.KR 50000)
£20770 $35310 €30324 Wind turn (211cm-83in) hammered copper executed 1967 exhib.prov. 4-Nov-3 Bukowskis, Stockholm #72a/R est:200000-250000 (S.KR 275000)

GRATH, Anton (1881-?) Austrian
Sculpture
£1477 $2717 €2200 Diana (60cm-24in) s.i. bronze. 25-Mar-4 Dr Fritz Nagel, Stuttgart #941/R est:3200

GRATHWOL, Ray Anthony (1900-1992) American
£205 $380 €299 Harbour scene with ships, seagulls and clapboard boathouses (58x89cm-23x35in) s. board. 16-Jan-4 Aspire, Cleveland #49/R
£265 $475 €387 Fall scene on a lake with figures (81x109cm-32x43in) i. masonite. 19-Mar-4 Aspire, Cleveland #83
£302 $480 €438 Arrival at Plymouth Rock (79x109cm-31x43in) s. board. 12-Sep-3 Aspire, Cleveland #109
£540 $950 €788 Steamship on Lake Erie by harbor (61x91cm-24x36in) s. 28-May-4 Aspire, Cleveland #58/R est:800-1000

GRAU I FIGUERAS, Alejandro de (1834-1896) Spanish
Works on paper
£409 $733 €597 Portrait of Spaniard (55x33cm-22x13in) s.d.1872 pastel. 12-May-4 Dobiaschofsky, Bern #577/R (S.FR 950)

GRAU SANTOS, Julian (1937-) Spanish
£940 $1757 €1400 Study for poster (100x70cm-39x28in) s. 24-Feb-4 Durán, Madrid #27/R
£1027 $1747 €1500 Garden (40x32cm-16x13in) s. 4-Nov-3 Ansorena, Madrid #362/R est:1500
£1164 $1979 €1700 Landscape with almond trees (37x45cm-15x18in) s.d.1975. 4-Nov-3 Ansorena, Madrid #347/R est:1500
£1370 $2329 €2000 The Duero (50x61cm-20x24in) s.d.1982 sid.verso. 4-Nov-3 Ansorena, Madrid #72/R est:2000
£1549 $2479 €2200 Blooming (33x24cm-13x9in) s. s.i.verso prov. 16-Sep-3 Segre, Madrid #164/R
£1667 $2833 €2400 Pear tree and daffodils (35x27cm-14x11in) s.d.2002 s.i.d.verso. 28-Oct-3 Segre, Madrid #148/R est:2200
£2105 $3811 €3200 Portrait of young woman (56x46cm-22x18in) s. s.i.verso. 14-Apr-4 Ansorena, Madrid #286/R est:1500
£2306 $4036 €3275 Roses branch in the garden (41x33cm-16x13in) s. s.i.d.2003 verso. 16-Dec-3 Segre, Madrid #260/R est:3275
£2917 $4813 €4200 Houses in Huecar (54x65cm-21x26in) s. s.i.verso. 2-Jul-3 Ansorena, Madrid #866/R
£3077 $5138 €4400 Vases of flowers with musical instruments (45x55cm-18x22in) s. 30-Jun-3 Ansorena, Madrid #386/R est:4000
£3261 $5348 €4500 Trilla en Ribatejada, Cuenca (65x82cm-26x32in) s. s.i.d:1974 verso. 27-May-3 Durán, Madrid #162/R est:4500
£3310 $5959 €4800 View from the terrace (130x97cm-51x38in) s. 26-Jan-4 Ansorena, Madrid #177/R est:2000
£3380 $5408 €4800 Pear tree in bloom (41x33cm-16x13in) s. s.i.verso painted 2002 prov. 16-Sep-3 Segre, Madrid #159/R est:3300
£4255 $6894 €6000 Still life with flowers (81x100cm-32x39in) s. 20-May-3 Ansorena, Madrid #79/R est:5500
£6021 $10537 €8550 Anemones and fan (54x65cm-21x26in) s. s.i.d.1995 verso. 16-Dec-3 Segre, Madrid #266/R est:8550
Works on paper
£652 $1070 €900 Catalan village (50x70cm-20x28in) s. W/C. 27-May-3 Durán, Madrid #66/R
£816 $1486 €1200 Easter week (98x67cm-39x26in) s.i.d.1964 gouache. 3-Feb-4 Segre, Madrid #139/R

GRAU, Gustave (1873-1919) French
£3333 $6133 €5000 L'heure du bain (130x170cm-51x67in) s.d.1911. 9-Jun-4 Beaussant & Lefèvre, Paris #161/R est:6000-7000

GRAU, Xavier (20th C) French?
£4422 $8048 €6500 Untitled (146x114cm-57x45in) s.d.1988 verso prov.exhib. 3-Feb-4 Segre, Madrid #370/R est:5800

GRAU-SALA (1911-1975) Spanish
Works on paper
£870 $1591 €1270 Paysage, marin au couchant (46x61cm-18x24in) s. gouache pastel exhib. 5-Jun-4 Galerie du Rhone, Sion #331/R (S.FR 2000)

GRAU-SALA, Emile (1911-1975) Spanish
£1453 $2600 €2121 Arrangement with bag of oranges (36x66cm-14x26in) s.d.66. 11-Jan-4 William Jenack, New York #49 est:1500-2000
£2081 $3870 €3100 Two women (61x24cm-24x9in) s. cardboard. 2-Mar-4 Ansorena, Madrid #104/R est:2900

£3165	$5000	€4621	Woman seated at table birdcage in background (41x51cm-16x20in) s. 6-Sep-3 Brunk, Ashville #341
£3901	$6319	€5500	Young girl surrounded with flowers (12x34cm-5x13in) s. board. 20-May-3 Ansorena, Madrid #83/R est:4000
£5031	$8000	€7345	Interior with figure and flowers (41x51cm-16x20in) s.d.72. 4-May-3 William Jenack, New York #369 est:2000-3000
£5946	$11000	€8681	Mother and child (33x23cm-13x9in) s. 13-Mar-4 Susanin's, Chicago #6122/R est:2000-4000
£5946	$11000	€8681	Brook (28x36cm-11x14in) s. 13-Mar-4 Susanin's, Chicago #6127/R est:800-1200
£7027	$13000	€10259	The feeding (30x25cm-12x10in) s. board. 13-Mar-4 Susanin's, Chicago #6131/R est:1000-1500
£8054	$14416	€12000	Les Tuileries (55x33cm-22x13in) s.d.41. 25-May-4 Durán, Madrid #197/R est:9000
£9800	$16366	€14308	Trouville (33x55cm-13x22in) s. painted August 1953. 22-Oct-3 Sotheby's, Olympia #36/R est:7000-9000
£11111	$18111	€16000	Honfleur harbour (38x46cm-15x18in) s. s.d.1965 verso. 23-Sep-3 Durán, Madrid #210/R est:12000
£11184	$20579	€17000	Hippodrome (46x55cm-18x22in) s. s.d.1973 verso. 22-Jun-4 Durán, Madrid #194/R est:15000
£11268	$19493	€16000	La lecture, femme au canape (38x46cm-15x18in) s. i.d.1950 verso panel. 12-Dec-3 Piasa, Paris #101/R est:10000-15000
£12000	$20040	€17520	Interieur (46x55cm-18x22in) s. s.i.d.73 verso. 21-Oct-3 Sotheby's, London #156/R est:12000-15000
£12081	$22349	€18000	Paris, Bois de Boulogne, enfant au bord de lac (64x80cm-25x31in) s. panels. 14-Mar-4 Eric Pillon, Calais #190/R
£12270	$20000	€17914	Dancers (51x66cm-20x26in) s.i.d.1955 pastel board. 28-Sep-3 Simpson's, Houston #360/R
£12766	$20681	€18000	Meeting on the terrace (55x46cm-22x18in) s. 20-May-3 Ansorena, Madrid #160/R est:18000
£12925	$23136	€19000	Untitled (48x55cm-19x22in) s. s.i.d.57 verso panel. 19-Mar-4 Millon & Associes, Paris #101b
£13287	$22189	€19000	Greenhouse (50x61cm-20x24in) s. cardboard. 30-Jun-3 Ansorena, Madrid #356/R
£13380	$23148	€19000	Girl at window (46x38cm-18x15in) s.d.1972. 15-Dec-3 Ansorena, Madrid #40/R est:19000
£13736	$25000	€20055	La marchande de fleurs (54x65cm-21x26in) s. s.i.d.67 verso prov. 29-Jun-4 Sotheby's, New York #372/R est:20000-30000
£15337	$25000	€22392	Aquarium (66x81cm-26x32in) s.i.d.1955 verso. 28-Sep-3 Simpson's, Houston #370/R
£15988	$27500	€23342	Spanish woman holding a fan seated before a window (60x73cm-24x29in) s. s.d.1971 verso. 3-Dec-3 Doyle, New York #156/R est:10000-15000
£16000	$29440	€23360	Bailarinas (82x63cm-32x25in) s. prov. 22-Jun-4 Sotheby's, London #253/R est:20000-30000
£16043	$30000	€23423	Interior (55x46cm-22x18in) s. s.i.verso. 25-Feb-4 Christie's, Rockefeller NY #61/R est:20000-30000
£16260	$29106	€23740	Girl on balcony (54x39cm-21x15in) s. s.d.sept.1936 panel. 28-May-4 Uppsala Auktionskammare, Uppsala #278/R est:120000-150000 (S.KR 220000)
£16438	$27945	€24000	Coastal view (54x65cm-21x26in) s. s.d.1970. 4-Nov-3 Ansorena, Madrid #357/R est:24000
£18121	$33705	€27000	Playing cards (54x65cm-21x26in) s. s.i.d.1967 verso. 2-Mar-4 Ansorena, Madrid #55/R est:27000
£18462	$31754	€26955	Two girls playing an instrument (59x72cm-23x28in) s. d.1964 verso. 7-Dec-3 Uppsala Auktionskammare, Uppsala #239/R est:120000-150000 (S.KR 240000)
£18881	$31531	€27000	Paddock (54x72cm-21x28in) s. 29-Jun-3 Eric Pillon, Calais #154/R
£18919	$35000	€27622	Interieur au bouquet (66x81cm-26x32in) s. s.i.d.1969 verso prov. 11-Feb-4 Sotheby's, New York #79/R est:20000-30000
£19553	$35000	€28547	Marchande de fleurs (80x100cm-31x39in) s. s.i.d.1971 verso. 6-May-4 Sotheby's, New York #471/R est:25000-35000
£19718	$34113	€28000	Horse race (73x50cm-29x20in) s. s.i.d.1958 verso masonite. 11-Dec-3 Binoche, Paris #8/R est:20000-30000
£20423	$35331	€29000	Mediterranean interior (38x46cm-15x18in) s. s.i.d.1964 verso. 15-Dec-3 Ansorena, Madrid #317/R est:21000
£20950	$37500	€30587	Interieur Andalou (65x81cm-26x32in) s. i.d.1966 verso. 6-May-4 Doyle, New York #72/R est:20000-30000
£20950	$37500	€30587	Femme au divan (38x46cm-15x18in) s. s.i.d.1950 verso board. 6-May-4 Sotheby's, New York #285/R est:28000-35000
£22109	$39575	€32500	Playing the mandolin (61x73cm-24x29in) s. 22-Mar-4 Durán, Madrid #240/R est:32500
£24648	$43134	€35000	Fishtank (65x81cm-26x32in) s. s.i.d.1955 verso. 16-Dec-3 Durán, Madrid #207/R est:32500
£25510	$45663	€37500	Red interior (120x120cm-47x47in) s. 22-Mar-4 Durán, Madrid #239/R est:36000

Prints

£8966	$14883	€13000	Orchestra (26x17cm-10x7in) s. num.6/280 engraving. 1-Oct-3 Ansorena, Madrid #459 est:130

Works on paper

£350	$594	€500	Visage de petite fille (20x16cm-8x6in) s.d.69 crayon dr. 21-Nov-3 Coutau Begarie, Paris #49
£448	$807	€650	Fete foraine de Paris (22x22cm-9x9in) s.d.60 W/C. 26-Jan-4 Durán, Madrid #11/R
£514	$873	€750	Fetes foraines de Paris (22x22cm-9x9in) s.d. W/C. 4-Nov-3 Ansorena, Madrid #161/R
£559	$1012	€850	Sowing by the window (21x15cm-8x6in) s. ink dr. 14-Apr-4 Ansorena, Madrid #395/R
£591	$1058	€863	Lady wearing hat and crinoline (37x30cm-15x12in) s. W/C. 28-May-4 Uppsala Auktionskammare, Uppsala #285/R (S.KR 8000)
£616	$1048	€900	Boats and women (32x48cm-13x19in) gouache. 4-Nov-3 Ansorena, Madrid #286/R
£655	$1088	€950	Woman sewing by window (21x19cm-8x7in) s. ink dr. 1-Oct-3 Ansorena, Madrid #477/R
£753	$1281	€1100	Landscape (25x33cm-10x13in) wax crayon. 4-Nov-3 Ansorena, Madrid #188/R
£1056	$1690	€1500	Street with passers-by (17x14cm-7x6in) s. W/C. 16-Sep-3 Segre, Madrid #108/R
£1064	$1723	€1500	Winter (32x25cm-13x10in) s. W/C. 20-May-3 Ansorena, Madrid #965/R est:1300
£1118	$2024	€1700	Lady with hat (45x36cm-18x14in) s. chl col dr. 14-Apr-4 Ansorena, Madrid #396/R est:900
£1338	$2342	€1900	Opera (32x25cm-13x10in) s.d.44 wash. 16-Dec-3 Durán, Madrid #104/R
£1399	$2406	€2000	L'attelage (20x26cm-8x10in) s. pastel W/C. 3-Dec-3 Tajan, Paris #139 est:200-300
£1400	$2506	€2100	Jeune fille au balcon (24x20cm-9x8in) W/C ball point pen. 16-May-4 Osenat, Fontainebleau #25/R est:1500-2000
£1549	$2680	€2200	Manege (20x17cm-8x7in) s.i.d.1938 col crayon dr. 14-Dec-3 Eric Pillon, Calais #250/R
£1761	$3081	€2500	Girl (19x12cm-7x5in) s.d.62 W/C. 16-Dec-3 Durán, Madrid #108/R est:1400
£1867	$3341	€2800	La lecture (30x22cm-12x9in) W/C. 16-May-4 Osenat, Fontainebleau #24/R est:1200-1500
£1972	$3175	€2800	Artistes a Place du Tertre (41x23cm-16x9in) s.d.1941. 22-Aug-3 Deauville, France #8 est:3000-4000
£2416	$4470	€3600	Jeune fille a sa coiffure (31x24cm-12x9in) s. W/C gouache. 14-Mar-4 Eric Pillon, Calais #208/R
£2450	$4484	€3700	Bouquet of flowers in front of a window (64x48cm-25x19in) s.d.36 gouache. 7-Apr-4 Piasa, Paris #182/R est:2000-3000
£2994	$5000	€4371	El matador (18x23cm-7x9in) s. W/C. 16-Nov-3 Simpson's, Houston #350a/R
£3357	$5706	€4800	Barques de peche (37x44cm-15x17in) s. gouache. 28-Nov-3 Drouot Estimations, Paris #178 est:1200-1500
£3537	$6332	€5200	Clown et ecuyere (32x25cm-13x10in) s.d.60 W/C ink. 19-Mar-4 Millon & Associes, Paris #101 est:1200-1500
£4027	$7128	€6000	From the balcony (51x38cm-20x15in) s. W/C. 27-Apr-4 Durán, Madrid #97/R est:6000
£6000	$10320	€8760	Plage de Deauville (49x64cm-19x25in) s.d.63 pastel. 7-Dec-3 Uppsala Auktionskammare, Uppsala #240/R est:40000-50000 (S.KR 78000)
£6738	$10915	€9500	Cafe de Paris (40x42cm-16x17in) s. mixed media. 20-May-3 Ansorena, Madrid #152/R est:9500
£6846	$12664	€10200	Coulisses du cirque (37x45cm-15x18in) s.d.1964 pastel gouache. 14-Mar-4 Eric Pillon, Calais #188/R
£7343	$12262	€10500	Tables fleuries et paniers de fruits (48x62cm-19x24in) s. W/C. 29-Jun-3 Eric Pillon, Calais #152/R
£7383	$13658	€11000	Deauville, regates devant la plage (47x63cm-19x25in) s. pastel gouache. 14-Mar-4 Eric Pillon, Calais #191/R
£8054	$14255	€12000	Dress maker (48x62cm-19x24in) s.d.1960 dr en grisaille. 27-Apr-4 Durán, Madrid #184/R est:12000
£8190	$14659	€11957	Young woman in salon (55x38cm-22x15in) s. col chk. 12-May-4 Dobiaschofsky, Bern #578/R est:8000 (S.FR 19000)
£8824	$15000	€12883	Figures in a park (65x81cm-26x32in) s. pastel. 9-Nov-3 Bonhams & Butterfields, Los Angeles #4004/R
£10490	$17517	€15000	Marche aux fleurs (59x72cm-23x28in) s. pastel. 29-Jun-3 Eric Pillon, Calais #157/R

GRAU-SALA, Emile (attrib) (1911-1975) Spanish

£824	$1500	€1203	Young girl and dog (51x61cm-20x24in) 8-Feb-4 William Jenack, New York #241 est:1500

GRAUBNER, Gotthard (1930-) German

£15385	$26154	€22000	Untitled - cushion picture (140x140cm-55x55in) s.i.d.1986 verso oil canvas on material. 27-Nov-3 Lempertz, Koln #156/R est:20000-24000

Works on paper

£298	$542	€450	Untitled (15x14cm-6x6in) s.d.1960 verso W/C. 18-Jun-4 Bolland & Marotz, Bremen #880
£839	$1443	€1200	Sponge gouache (33x29cm-13x11in) s.d. W/C pencil. 3-Dec-3 Hauswedell & Nolte, Hamburg #788/R
£903	$1508	€1300	Untitled (24x46cm-9x18in) s.d. gouache prov.exhib. 24-Oct-3 Ketterer, Hamburg #358/R
£16760	$30000	€24470	Torso (100x100cm-39x39in) s.i.d.1967-1968 verso nylon foam latex pillows canvas prov.exhib. 14-May-4 Phillips, New York #260/R est:30000-40000

GRAUER, Sherry (1939-) Canadian

£1205	$2241	€1759	BC telephone (144x122cm-57x48in) s.i.d.62 verso acrylic. 2-Mar-4 Ritchie, Toronto #199/R est:600-800 (C.D 3000)

GRAUMANN, Julius (1878-1945) German

£1799	$2950	€2500	Alexanderplatz, Berlin (46x57cm-18x22in) s.d. i. stretcher. 4-Jun-3 Ketterer, Hamburg #400/R est:2500-3000

GRAUPNER, Annemarie (1920-) Swiss

£271	$462	€396	Five to twelve (33x15cm-13x6in) s. i. verso behind glass. 28-Nov-3 Zofingen, Switzerland #3000 (S.FR 600)
£452	$769	€660	The approach (33x23cm-13x9in) s. i. verso behind glass. 28-Nov-3 Zofingen, Switzerland #2999 (S.FR 1000)

GRAUX, A (19th C) ?

£2254	$3899	€3200	Fruits and roses on a ledge (62x75cm-24x30in) s. 10-Dec-3 Christie's, Amsterdam #690/R est:2000-3000

GRAVE, Josua de (17/18th C) Dutch

£5500	$9900	€8030	Elegant figures walking in the garden of a palace (63x76cm-25x30in) s.d.1684 prov. 23-Apr-4 Christie's, Kensington #83/R est:6000-8000

Works on paper

£1301	$2212	€1900	Classical garden with arcades, statues and fountain (21x16cm-8x6in) pen brown ink grey wash. 4-Nov-3 Sotheby's, Amsterdam #121/R est:2000-3000
£3973	$6753	€5800	View of the St Jacobskerk and the Gasthuis, Maastricht (18x23cm-7x9in) s. i.verso pen brown ink col wash. 4-Nov-3 Sotheby's, Amsterdam #67/R est:7000-9000

GRAVELY, Percy (fl.1886-1904) British

£750	$1365	€1095	Castanet and Duchess, equestrian portraits (38x48cm-15x19in) s.d.1894 pair. 3-Feb-4 Gorringes, Bexhill #1037/R

GRAVES, Abbott Fuller (1859-1936) American

£1816	$3250	€2651	Pink rose (56x35cm-22x14in) s. 14-May-4 Skinner, Boston #332/R est:4000-6000
£1955	$3500	€2854	French landscape (15x28cm-6x11in) s. panel. 8-Jan-4 James Julia, Fairfield #743/R est:2500-3000
£2235	$4000	€3263	River landscape (23x33cm-9x13in) s. panel prov. 26-May-4 Doyle, New York #49/R est:5000-7000
£2733	$4400	€3990	Fishing in France (13x25cm-5x10in) s. 20-Aug-3 James Julia, Fairfield #1346/R est:4000-6000
£3704	$6000	€5371	Still life (46x23cm-18x9in) s. 8-Aug-3 Barridorf, Portland #115/R est:6000-8000
£17500	$28000	€25550	Seaside cottage with flowering path (36x51cm-14x20in) s.i. 21-Sep-3 Grogan, Boston #59/R

£39773 $70000 €58069 Garden landscape with white clad lady amongst peonies and irises. s. 1-Jan-4 Nadeau, Windsor #150/R est:30000-50000
Works on paper
£1339 $2304 €1955 Garden gate (35x25cm-14x10in) s. col chk pastel prov. 2-Dec-3 Ritchie, Toronto #88/R est:1500-2000 (C.D 3000)
£1648 $3000 €2406 In the garden (51x36cm-20x14in) s. i.verso gouache on board. 29-Jun-4 Sotheby's, New York #204/R est:5000-7000

GRAVES, François (1934-) French
£282 $456 €400 Plage (17x51cm-7x20in) s. panel. 11-Aug-3 Boscher, Cherbourg #841
£336 $594 €500 L Havre l'hiver (33x41cm-13x16in) s. 28-Apr-4 Charbonneaux, Paris #168

GRAVES, Henry Richard (fl.1846-1881) British
£8000 $14560 €11680 Portrait of Colonel Robert Myddelton Biddulph, M.P (140x99cm-55x39in) init.d.1869 prov.lit. 21-Jun-4 Christie's, London #135/R est:6000-9000

GRAVES, Michael (1934-) American
£1242 $2000 €1813 Rockport Beach (25x36cm-10x14in) s. 20-Aug-3 James Julia, Fairfield #1302/R est:1200-1800

GRAVES, Morris (1910-2001) American
£13081 $22500 €19098 Dream vision lion (76x117cm-30x46in) s. painted 1952-54 prov. 3-Dec-3 Sotheby's, New York #90/R est:15000-25000
Works on paper
£1850 $3200 €2701 Bird (46x61cm-18x24in) s. W/C red chk exhib. 15-Dec-3 Hindman, Chicago #14/R est:4000-6000
£10180 $17000 €14863 Altar (24x32cm-9x13in) s.i.d.51 wash pastel prov. 11-Nov-3 Christie's, Rockefeller NY #138/R est:6000-8000
£14371 $24000 €20982 Message (60x75cm-24x30in) gouache W/C executed c.1940. 11-Nov-3 Christie's, Rockefeller NY #136/R est:12000-18000
£17964 $30000 €26227 Letter to Dorothy Miller (67x74cm-26x29in) i.d.42 gouache W/C prov.exhib.lit. 11-Nov-3 Christie's, Rockefeller NY #137/R est:10000-15000
£71856 $120000 €104910 Bird singing in the moonlight (67x74cm-26x29in) s.i. gouache W/C prov.exhib.lit. 11-Nov-3 Christie's, Rockefeller NY #135/R est:20000-30000

GRAVES, Nancy (1940-1995) American
Sculpture
£7362 $12000 €10749 Discoid (96x96x107cm-38x38x42in) polychrome pat bronze. 23-Sep-3 Christie's, Rockefeller NY #179/R est:7000-9000

GRAVINA, Antonio (1934-) Italian?
£305 $550 €445 Primavera (49x59cm-19x23in) s. i.verso. 25-Apr-4 Bonhams & Butterfields, San Francisco #5495/R

GRAY, Douglas Stannus (1890-1959) British
£400 $636 €584 Portrait of a seated gentleman (38x32cm-15x13in) board exhib. 10-Sep-3 Sotheby's, Olympia #264/R

GRAY, Eileen and SOUGAWARA, Seizo (20th C) British/Japanese
Works on paper
£265734 $457063 €380000 La foret enchantee dit aussi Le magicien de la nuit (65x81cm-26x32in) s.verso lacquer exhib.lit. 3-Dec-3 Beaussant & Lefèvre, Paris #85/R est:50000-60000

GRAY, Eileen and SOUGAWARA, Seizo (attrib) (20th C) British/Japanese
Sculpture
£70629 $121483 €101000 Tete de femme coiffee d'un foulard (45x41x95cm-18x16x37in) s.i.verso wood black lacquer htd silver leaf exec.c.1912. 3-Dec-3 Beaussant & Lefèvre, Paris #86/R est:40000-50000

GRAY, Gustave le (1820-1882) French
Photographs
£4167 $7500 €6084 Zouaves, the haircut (32x37cm-13x15in) s. albumen print lit. 22-Apr-4 Phillips, New York #29/R est:8000-12000
£8333 $15000 €12166 Les invalides, Paris (51x40cm-20x16in) num.23369 albumen print. 22-Apr-4 Phillips, New York #140/R est:20000-30000
£11232 $18420 €15500 Flotte francaise en rade de Cherbourg (31x40cm-12x16in) photo. 27-May-3 Beaussant & Lefèvre, Paris #114/R est:10000-15000
£11333 $20853 €17000 Palais Royal de Palerme (35x25cm-14x10in) albumen print. 7-Jun-4 Tajan, Paris #93/R est:10000-12000
£16000 $28160 €23360 Souvenirs du Camp de Chalons (54x67cm-21x26in) albumen prints album lit. 19-May-4 Christie's, London #29/R est:18000-20000
£30667 $56428 €46000 Rue de Tolede a Palerme (24x40cm-9x16in) albumen print. 7-Jun-4 Tajan, Paris #92/R est:15000-20000
£40845 $70662 €58000 Effet de soleil, Ocean 23 (32x42cm-13x17in) i. photograph exec.1856 exhib.lit. 10-Dec-3 Artcurial Briest, Paris #5/R est:15000-20000

GRAY, Gustave le and MESTRAL, Olivier (19th C) French
Photographs
£16667 $30000 €24334 Le cloitre de la cathedrale Notre Dame, le puy en Auvergne (29x38cm-11x15in) salt print prov.lit. 22-Apr-4 Phillips, New York #14/R est:40000-60000

GRAY, Henry Percy (1869-1952) American
Works on paper
£3179 $5500 €4641 Rocky Coastline (25x35cm-10x14in) s. W/C prov. 10-Dec-3 Bonhams & Butterfields, San Francisco #6162/R est:7000-10000
£6824 $12215 €9963 Poppies and lupines (15x20cm-6x8in) s. W/C paperboard. 16-Mar-4 Matthew's, Oregon #88/R est:4000-6000
£7065 $13000 €10315 Eucalyptus at Moss Landing, Monterey County, California (27x34cm-11x13in) s. pencil W/C paper on board prov. 8-Jun-4 Bonhams & Butterfields, San Francisco #4231/R est:10000-15000
£7910 $14000 €11549 Monterey surf (35x51cm-14x20in) s.indis.d. W/C paper on board prov. 28-Apr-4 Christie's, Los Angeles #55/R est:12000-18000
£8380 $15000 €12570 Autumn landscape (41x53cm-16x21in) s. W/C. 16-May-4 Abell, Los Angeles #107/R
£8696 $16000 €12696 Landscape with live oaks (26x35cm-10x14in) s. pencil W/C prov. 8-Jun-4 Bonhams & Butterfields, San Francisco #4194/R est:15000-20000
£9143 $16000 €13349 Eucalyptus trees (37x48cm-15x19in) s.d.1926 W/C board. 19-Dec-3 Sotheby's, New York #1127/R est:5000-7000
£10734 $19000 €15672 Cliffs and cove (40x50cm-16x20in) s. W/C paper on board prov. 28-Apr-4 Christie's, Los Angeles #33/R est:15000-25000
£10983 $19000 €16035 Thunderhead over a country road (49x36cm-19x14in) s. W/C pencil paper board prov. 10-Dec-3 Bonhams & Butterfields, San Francisco #6164/R est:10000-15000
£11585 $19000 €16914 Wooded landscape with eucalyptus trees and fence (41x51cm-16x20in) s.d.1922 W/C pasteboard prov. 31-May-3 Brunk, Ashville #522/R est:4000-8000
£12429 $22000 €18146 The old oak (40x52cm-16x20in) s.d.1929 W/C paper on board prov. 28-Apr-4 Christie's, Los Angeles #12/R est:20000-30000
£13006 $22500 €18989 After the rain, Marin Hills (25x36cm-10x14in) s.d.1926 W/C paper board prov. 10-Dec-3 Bonhams & Butterfields, San Francisco #6165/R est:15000-20000
£14689 $26000 €21446 Carmel Valley (41x50cm-16x20in) s. i.verso W/C paper on board prov. 28-Apr-4 Christie's, Los Angeles #56/R est:20000-30000
£15714 $27500 €22942 Field of bluebonnets (35x50cm-14x20in) s.d.1926 W/C board. 19-Dec-3 Sotheby's, New York #1128/R est:5000-7000
£15819 $28000 €23096 Monterey cypress (40x50cm-16x20in) s. W/C prov.exhib. 28-Apr-4 Christie's, Los Angeles #35/R est:20000-30000
£19841 $37500 €28968 Oak glade with poppies and lupine (38x48cm-15x19in) s. W/C prov. 17-Feb-4 John Moran, Pasadena #79/R est:20000-30000
£21196 $39000 €30946 Wildflowers and eucalyptus near the shore (40x50cm-16x20in) s. pencil W/C prov. 8-Jun-4 Bonhams & Butterfields, San Francisco #4193/R est:40000-60000
£23529 $40000 €34352 Spring landscape with eucalyptus (38x55cm-15x22in) s.d.1925 W/C paper on board. 29-Oct-3 Christie's, Los Angeles #17/R est:25000-35000
£23729 $42000 €34644 Flower field, Carmel Valley (40x50cm-16x20in) s. W/C paper on board prov. 28-Apr-4 Christie's, Los Angeles #19/R est:25000-35000

GRAY, Jack L (1927-1981) American
£546 $1000 €797 Top sail schooner (2x30cm-1x12in) s. panel. 29-Jul-4 Christie's, Rockefeller NY #274/R est:2000-3000
£10056 $18000 €14682 Lone fisherman (66x102cm-26x40in) s.d.68. 26-May-4 Doyle, New York #115/R est:20000-30000
£12575 $21000 €18360 Lobstermen (61x86cm-24x34in) s. prov. 23-Oct-3 Shannon's, Milford #56/R est:10000-15000

GRAY, James (?-1947) British
Works on paper
£300 $552 €438 Honeysuckle (34x52cm-13x20in) s. W/C. 10-Jun-4 Lyon & Turnbull, Edinburgh #118
£375 $638 €548 Still life, bowl or roses (33x48cm-13x19in) s. W/C prov. 5-Nov-3 John Nicholson, Haslemere #568

GRAY, Jessie D (fl.1881-1893) British
£700 $1323 €1022 Orchard in bloom (35x58cm-14x23in) s.d.1881. 19-Feb-4 Lyon & Turnbull, Edinburgh #23

GRAY, John (?-1957) British
£299 $500 €437 Portrait of a brown and white setter (41x51cm-16x20in) s. 15-Nov-3 Sloans & Kenyon, Bethesda #125/R

GRAY, John Warrener (1824-1912) Canadian
Works on paper
£215 $335 €312 Chateauguay Lake, Quebec (30x44cm-12x17in) s.i. W/C. 26-Mar-3 Walker's, Ottawa #474/R (C.D 500)

GRAY, Kate (fl.1870-1987) British
£460 $810 €672 Little girl and a dog with an infant in a cradle (34x49cm-13x19in) s. paper on panel. 18-May-4 Rosebery Fine Art, London #799
£1050 $1922 €1533 Children in an interior playing with a cat (50x60cm-20x24in) s. 28-Jul-4 Hampton & Littlewood, Exeter #618a/R est:850-900
£1870 $2936 €2730 Untitled, girl with mirror (77x64cm-30x25in) s. 1-Sep-3 Shapiro, Sydney #341/R est:4000-6000 (A.D 4600)

GRAY, Leonard (20th C) British
Works on paper
£280 $468 €409 Murtlemill and farm in the snow (35x48cm-14x19in) s. W/C. 16-Oct-3 Lyon & Turnbull, Edinburgh #5

GRAY, Mary (20th C) American
£1648 $2900 €2406 Interior (41x30cm-16x12in) s. board painted c.1930. 23-May-4 Treadway Gallery, Cincinnati #608/R est:2000-2500

GRAY, Reginald (1930-) British
£400 $668 €584 Portrait of Juliette Binoche (22x16cm-9x6in) s. board. 21-Oct-3 Bonhams, Knightsbridge #157/R

GRAY, Victor (20th C) ?
£937 $1566 €1350 The journey VI (180x180cm-71x71in) s.i.d.1991 verso acrylic prov. 25-Oct-3 Cornette de St.Cyr, Paris #414/R

GRAY, W H (jnr) (19th C) British
Works on paper
£750 $1245 €1095 Isle of Wight, coastal landscapes (5x13cm-2x5in) s.d.1874 W/C pair. 2-Oct-3 Ewbank, Send #876

GRAY, William (19th C) British
Works on paper
£270 $486 €394 Dyffryn Mymbyr and the Snowdon Horseshoe (18x25cm-7x10in) W/C. 24-Apr-4 Rogers Jones, Clwyd #99

GRAZIA, Ted de (1909-) American
£514 $950 €750 Portrait of mother and her children (41x30cm-16x12in) s. board. 14-Jan-4 Dallas Auction Gallery, Dallas #163/R
£865 $1600 €1263 Portrait of a girl (46x36cm-18x14in) s. 14-Jan-4 Dallas Auction Gallery, Dallas #164/R est:1000-2000

GRAZIANI, Alfio Paolo (1900-?) Italian
£743 $1308 €1100 Flowers (60x80cm-24x31in) s. 19-May-4 Il Ponte, Milan #820 est:400
£1126 $2049 €1700 Vase with poppies (70x100cm-28x39in) s. 18-Jun-4 Stadion, Trieste #215b
£1250 $2300 €1900 Still life of fruit (70x100cm-28x39in) s. 23-Jun-4 Finarte Semenzato, Rome #95/R est:2000-2200

GRAZIANI, Ercole (younger-attrib) (1688-1765) Italian
£1343 $2470 €2000 Paysage boise avec cavaliers (34x99cm-13x39in) pair. 24-Mar-4 Tajan, Paris #10 est:2000-3000

GRAZIANI, Francesco (17th C) Italian
£2303 $4237 €3500 Rural landscapes with ruins, villages and anglers (62x111cm-24x44in) pair lit. 22-Jun-4 Babuino, Rome #64/R est:3000-4000

GRAZIANI, Francesco (attrib) (17th C) Italian
£4138 $6869 €6000 Cavalry engagement between Christians and Turks (22x32cm-9x13in) prov. 1-Oct-3 Dorotheum, Vienna #36/R est:6000-9000
£16216 $28541 €24000 Battle scenes (23x64cm-9x25in) pair. 18-May-4 Sotheby's, Milan #454/R est:8000-12000

GRAZIANI, Francesco (style) (17th C) Italian
£12676 $20408 €18000 Battle with cavalry (72x120cm-28x47in) 8-May-3 Farsetti, Prato #607/R est:22000-25000

GRAZIANI, Pierre (18th C) Italian
£347 $580 €500 Composition (73x92cm-29x36in) s. 21-Oct-3 Artcurial Briest, Paris #654

GRAZIOSI, Giuseppe (1879-1942) Italian
£5705 $10668 €8500 The Forum (38x53cm-15x21in) board. 25-Feb-4 Porro, Milan #40/R est:5000-6000
£7383 $13805 €11000 Campidoglio (38x53cm-15x21in) board. 25-Feb-4 Porro, Milan #39/R est:6000
£14094 $26356 €21000 Spinner (69x92cm-27x36in) s. exhib. 25-Feb-4 Porro, Milan #42/R est:5000-6000
Sculpture
£1379 $2303 €2000 Allegory of Agriculture (44x55cm-17x22in) s. bronze relief. 15-Nov-3 Porro, Milan #129/R est:2000
£1799 $2950 €2500 Housewife (18x22cm-7x9in) bronze. 5-Jun-3 Adma, Formigine #477 est:2500-2700
£1942 $3186 €2700 Turkeys (19x27cm-7x11in) bronze. 5-Jun-3 Adma, Formigine #465 est:2700-2800
£5282 $9137 €7500 Peasant sharpening his axe (30x40cm-12x16in) s. bronze. 10-Dec-3 Finarte Semenzato, Rome #199/R est:800-1200
Works on paper
£3034 $5068 €4400 View of Piazza Maggiore, Modena (55x30cm-22x12in) s. pastel. 15-Nov-3 Porro, Milan #132/R est:2000
£3448 $5759 €5000 Rural views (35x32cm-14x13in) pencil dr set of 6. 15-Nov-3 Porro, Milan #134

GRAZZINI, Renzo (1912-1989) Italian
£288 $472 €400 Still life with vases (50x70cm-20x28in) s. board. 10-Jun-3 Pandolfini, Florence #395/R
£364 $663 €550 House on the river (50x70cm-20x28in) 17-Jun-4 Galleria Pananti, Florence #207/R
£364 $663 €550 Figures (60x80cm-24x31in) s. 17-Jun-4 Galleria Pananti, Florence #258/R

GREACEN, Edmund William (1877-1949) American
£958 $1600 €1399 Winter landscape at sunset (25x36cm-10x14in) s.d.39 canvasboard. 16-Nov-3 William Jenack, New York #422
£1676 $3000 €2447 Southport Harbour (41x30cm-16x12in) bears sig. canvasboard prov. 6-May-4 Shannon's, Milford #254/R est:3000-5000
£3039 $5500 €4437 Gardener's cottages and the meadow, Zealandia (33x20cm-13x8in) s. canvas on board painted c.1928 pair prov. 31-Mar-4 Sotheby's, New York #111/R est:2500-3500
£10465 $18000 €15279 Old post office building, New York City (55x60cm-22x24in) s.d.1916 prov.exhib. 3-Dec-3 Doyle, New York #262/R est:10000-15000
£21802 $37500 €31831 Girl with umbrella in the garden, Giverny (72x60cm-28x24in) painted 1908. 3-Dec-3 Sotheby's, New York #2/R est:40000-60000

GREACEN, Nan (1909-) American
Works on paper
£820 $1500 €1197 Roses on the fence (20x64cm-8x25in) s. W/C. 5-Jun-4 Neal Auction Company, New Orleans #821/R est:1000-1500

GREASON, William (1884-?) American
£405 $700 €591 Landscape (79x107cm-31x42in) 12-Dec-3 Du Mouchelle, Detroit #1235/R
£867 $1500 €1266 Landscape (76x102cm-30x40in) 12-Dec-3 Du Mouchelle, Detroit #1236/R

GREAVES, Derrick (1927-) British
£3000 $5370 €4380 Pinks (141x102cm-56x40in) s.i.d.1981/2 verso oil gouache collage laid down on canvas. 16-Mar-4 Bonhams, New Bond Street #109/R est:3000-4000
Works on paper
£300 $552 €438 Sketch of a girl with earrings - head and shoulder (17x18cm-7x7in) s. pencil htd white. 14-Jun-4 Bonhams, Bath #53
£333 $600 €500 Winter drawing, bottle (68x100cm-27x39in) s.d.70 mixed media prov. 20-Apr-4 James Adam, Dublin #179/R
£360 $572 €526 Summer garden (32x27cm-13x11in) s.d.61 W/C gouache exhib. 10-Sep-3 Sotheby's, Olympia #334/R
£3000 $5160 €4380 Skull (91x105cm-36x41in) s.i.overlap mixed media canvas prov. 3-Dec-3 Sotheby's, London #96/R est:3000-5000

GREAVES, Henry and Walter (19/20th C) British
Works on paper
£1700 $2941 €2482 Church Street, Old Chelsea, carnival procession with figures in costume (60x48cm-24x19in) s.d.1860 W/C. 9-Dec-3 Bonhams, Oxford #36/R est:600-800

GREAVES, Walter (1846-1930) British
£900 $1503 €1314 Promenade (60x40cm-24x16in) s. 21-Oct-3 Bonhams, Knightsbridge #41/R
£1500 $2700 €2190 River at night (41x61cm-16x24in) s. 20-Jan-4 Bonhams, Knightsbridge #189/R est:1000-1500
£4500 $7650 €6570 Portrait of Henry Greaves, the artist brother (76x63cm-30x25in) s. painted c.1874 prov. 21-Nov-3 Christie's, London #125/R est:5000-8000
£4600 $7820 €6716 Chelsea wharf on the Thames with figures, horses and carriages (35x44cm-14x17in) 19-Nov-3 Tennants, Leyburn #1300/R est:3000-4000
Prints
£1000 $1670 €1460 Portrait of Whistler (49x35cm-19x14in) 21-Oct-3 Bonhams, Knightsbridge #44/R est:2000-3000
Works on paper
£280 $515 €409 Street leading to a harbour (19x18cm-7x7in) init. pencil W/C. 23-Mar-4 Rosebery Fine Art, London #791
£300 $477 €438 Lady seated wearing a blue dress (25x20cm-10x8in) s. col chk. 9-Sep-3 Gorringes, Lewes #2015
£450 $797 €657 Chelsea Old Swan Tavern and part of the old Chain Pier (35x25cm-14x10in) s. W/C crayon. 27-Apr-4 Henry Adams, Chichester #590/R
£600 $1080 €876 Battersea Reach (25x38cm-10x15in) W/C. 20-Jan-4 Bonhams, Knightsbridge #186/R
£600 $1110 €876 Thames coffee house, Cheyne Walk (19x25cm-7x10in) s. pen brush ink prov. 11-Mar-4 Christie's, Kensington #59/R
£700 $1295 €1022 Swan Tavern, Battersea (20x28cm-8x11in) s.i. pen ink prov.exhib. 11-Mar-4 Christie's, Kensington #63/R

GREAVES, William (1852-1938) British
£270 $440 €394 Richmond, summer evening (50x76cm-20x30in) s. board. 23-Sep-3 Anderson & Garland, Newcastle #314
£300 $489 €438 Pink and white roses in a vase (21x29cm-8x11in) s. board. 23-Sep-3 Anderson & Garland, Newcastle #317
£300 $516 €438 Riverside cottages (36x25cm-14x10in) s.d.1880. 2-Dec-3 Gorringes, Lewes #2464
£380 $619 €555 Springtime at Woodhall Bridge near East Keswick (24x34cm-9x13in) s. i.verso board. 23-Sep-3 Anderson & Garland, Newcastle #315
£400 $680 €584 Two figures boating down the river (34x24cm-13x9in) s. board. 18-Nov-3 Bonhams, Leeds #213
£420 $777 €613 Moorland pool, Perthshire (49x74cm-19x29in) s. i.stretcher. 9-Mar-4 Bonhams, Knightsbridge #247/R
£750 $1388 €1095 Farmer with rake and three sheep on a woodland path (40x60cm-16x24in) s.d.88. 16-Feb-4 Bonhams, Bath #58
£950 $1720 €1387 Summer river landscape with figures (43x61cm-17x24in) s.d.1921. 16-Apr-4 Keys, Aylsham #709/R
£1000 $1590 €1450 On the Westmoreland river scene with farmhouse (45x60cm-18x24in) s.i.verso. 9-Sep-3 David Duggleby, Scarborough #314 est:1000-1500
£1050 $1659 €1533 Children picking flowers in a meadow (38x46cm-15x18in) s. 24-Jul-3 Mallams, Cheltenham #319/R est:100-200

GREBBER, Pieter de (1600-c.1655) Dutch
£5800 $10614 €8468 Young boy drinking from a glass held by a woman, an allegory (91x71cm-36x28in) prov. 7-Jul-4 Bonhams, New Bond Street #18/R est:7000-10000

GREBBER, Pieter de (circle) (1600-c.1655) Dutch
£8054 $14819 €12000 Head of an evangelist (43x34cm-17x13in) prov. 24-Mar-4 Dorotheum, Vienna #116/R est:8000-12000

GREBE, Fritz (1850-1925) German
£306 $504 €440 Sailing boats of the coast (31x29cm-12x11in) s. paper on board. 3-Jul-3 Van Ham, Cologne #1207
£336 $594 €500 Shepherd and his flock in an extensive landscape (30x40cm-12x16in) s. lit. 30-Apr-4 Auktionhaus Georg Rehm, Augsburg #8036/R
£348 $637 €508 Snowy woodland scene (53x40cm-21x16in) s. cardboard. 4-Jun-4 Zofingen, Switzerland #2465 (S.FR 800)
£448 $819 €654 Rowing boat on a Norwegian fjord (25x35cm-10x14in) s. 9-Jun-4 Rasmussen, Copenhagen #1777/R (D.KR 5000)
£594 $1010 €850 Norwegian fjord (60x80cm-24x31in) s. board. 20-Nov-3 Van Ham, Cologne #1599/R
£10280 $16243 €14906 Steam ship and rowing boat on a Norwegian fjord (87x130cm-34x51in) s. exhib. 2-Sep-3 Rasmussen, Copenhagen #1528/R est:125000 (D.KR 110000)

GRECO, Alberto (1931-1965) ?
Works on paper
£503 $901 €750 Composition (29x21cm-11x8in) s. mixed media. 25-May-4 Durán, Madrid #634/R
£669 $1157 €950 Figures (29x21cm-11x8in) s.d.59 ink W/C. 15-Dec-3 Ansorena, Madrid #1019/R

GRECO, El (style) (1541-1614) Spanish
£10000 $18300 €14600 Saint Francis standing in meditation (105x87cm-41x34in) prov.exhib.lit. 6-Jul-4 Sotheby's, Olympia #418/R est:6000-8000

GRECO, Emilio (1913-1995) Italian
£671 $1100 €980 Floral still life (66x56cm-26x22in) s. panel. 2-Jun-3 Grogan, Boston #646/R
£1892 $3500 €2762 Head of a young lady (59x50cm-23x20in) s.d.61 prov. 12-Feb-4 Sotheby's, New York #66/R est:3000-5000
Sculpture
£3209 $6000 €4685 Dancer (34cm-13in) s.d.1955 pat bronze prov. 25-Feb-4 Christie's, Rockefeller NY #65/R est:6000-8000
£3497 $5839 €5000 Figure for study of monument (57x40x25cm-22x16x10in) s. bronze exec.1967 lit. 26-Jun-3 Sant Agostino, Torino #275/R est:5000-6000
£6135 $10000 €8957 Piccola bagnante (58cm-23in) s.d.1958 black pat bronze prov. 25-Sep-3 Christie's, Rockefeller NY #622/R est:12000-16000
£8000 $14400 €12000 Seated woman (83x40cm-33x16in) s. terracotta exec.1949 lit. 22-Apr-4 Finarte Semenzato, Rome #340/R est:12000-15000
£9396 $16819 €14000 Meditation (58cm-23in) s. bronze exec.1985. 29-May-4 Farsetti, Prato #458/R est:14000-18000
£13000 $23920 €18980 Piccola bagnante (57cm-22in) s.d.1958 brown pat. bronze prov. 23-Jun-4 Christie's, London #240/R est:8000-12000
£15000 $25050 €21900 Piccola bagnante (61cm-24in) i.d.1961 num.6 bronze prov. 21-Oct-3 Sotheby's, London #104/R est:15000-20000
£15894 $28927 €24000 Girl (53x35x21cm-21x14x8in) s.d.1959 bronze. 17-Jun-4 Galleria Pananti, Florence #619/R est:30000-33000
£17877 $32000 €26100 Pattinatrice II (140cm-55in) s.d.1959 base blk pat bronze prov.lit. 5-May-4 Christie's, Rockefeller NY #327/R est:40000-60000
£28000 $51520 €40880 Piccola bagnante discobola (58cm-23in) i. bronze cast c.1955 edn of 3 prov.lit. 22-Jun-4 Sotheby's, London #283/R est:15000-20000
Works on paper
£567 $1043 €850 Figures (70x52cm-28x20in) s.i.d.1977 Chinese ink card. 12-Jun-4 Meeting Art, Vercelli #579/R
£800 $1472 €1200 Nude (45x30cm-18x12in) s.d.1943 Chinese ink. 8-Jun-4 Finarte Semenzato, Milan #140/R
£1000 $1730 €1460 Testa di donna (50x36cm-20x14in) s.i.d.1954 s.i.verso pen black ink prov. 11-Dec-3 Christie's, Kensington #168/R est:1000-1500
£1067 $1920 €1600 Face (70x50cm-28x20in) s. Chinese ink exec.1965. 22-Apr-4 Finarte Semenzato, Rome #136/R est:1200-1500
£1379 $2303 €2000 Model (70x50cm-28x20in) s. Chinese ink exec.1966. 13-Nov-3 Finarte Semenzato, Rome #135/R est:1800-2400
£2536 $4159 €3500 Nude. Portrait of man (45x30cm-18x12in) s. Chinese ink exhib. two sold with chl by Francesco Messina. 27-May-3 Sotheby's, Milan #75 est:2200-2500

GRECO, Emilio (?) Spanish?
£302 $550 €441 Floral still life (91x122cm-36x48in) s. 19-Jun-4 Jackson's, Cedar Falls #262/R

GRECO, Ferdinand (1939-) Italian
£278 $500 €406 Reperto (104x88cm-41x35in) s.verso oil resin mixed media pvc prov. 25-Apr-4 Bonhams & Butterfields, San Francisco #5621/R

GRECO, Frank (20th C) American
£4545 $8000 €6636 Geometric dimension (86x107cm-34x42in) s.d.1944. 23-May-4 Treadway Gallery, Cincinnati #720/R est:7000-9000

GRECO, Gennaro (1663-1714) Italian
£3974 $7232 €6000 Arcade with figures (29x23cm-11x9in) painted with Ascanio Luciani. 16-Jun-4 Christie's, Rome #332/R est:6000-8000
£7500 $12750 €10950 Capriccio of architectural ruins with figures by a fountain, Dutch frigate and other shipping (37cm-15in circular) panel. 29-Oct-3 Christie's, London #66/R est:6000-8000

GRECO, Gennaro (attrib) (1663-1714) Italian
£2113 $3697 €3000 Promeneurs pres de ruines antiques (73x97cm-29x38in) 18-Dec-3 Tajan, Paris #66/R est:3000-4000
£2517 $4580 €3800 Classical landscape with statues (73x111cm-29x44in) 16-Jun-4 Christie's, Rome #325/R est:4000-5000
£3521 $6162 €5000 Classical ruins (73x98cm-29x39in) 17-Dec-3 Christie's, Rome #379/R est:5000-8000
£4225 $7394 €6000 Biblical scene (75x96cm-30x38in) 17-Dec-3 Christie's, Rome #378/R est:6000-9000

GRECO, Gennaro (style) (1663-1714) Italian
£7000 $11900 €10220 Mediterranean harbour with shipping and figures on a quay by a ruined classical temple (92x132cm-36x52in) 31-Oct-3 Christie's, Kensington #161/R est:7000-10000

GRECO, Robert (1923-1965) American
£282 $450 €412 Anatomical figure (91x46cm-36x18in) s. s.i.d.1950-51 verso. 20-Sep-3 Bunte, Elgin #295

GRECOLINI, Giovanni Antonio (1675-1725) Italian
Works on paper
£10383 $19000 €15159 Designs for processional coach for the Prince of Lichtenstein (22x16cm-9x6in) pen ink wash red chk exec.c.1690 pair. 29-Jan-4 Swann Galleries, New York #97/R est:3000-5000

GREEFF, Peter (1865-c.1916) German
£306 $504 €440 Peasant woman with grazing cattle and poultry (37x56cm-15x22in) s. 3-Jul-3 Van Ham, Cologne #1208

GREEK SCHOOL, 19th C
Sculpture
£6376 $11413 €9500 Untitled (158cm-62in) marble. 25-May-4 Palais de Beaux Arts, Brussels #108/R est:10000-15000

GREEN, Alan (1932-) British
£1600 $2944 €2400 Small blue (80x80cm-31x31in) s.i.d. silk. 11-Jun-4 Hauswedell & Nolte, Hamburg #1281/R est:2600
£4532 $7704 €6617 Two reds divided by pink (70x70cm-28x28in) s.d.91 verso prov. 5-Nov-3 AB Stockholms Auktionsverk #1172/R est:60000-80000 (S.KR 60000)
£8308 $14124 €12130 Black rectangle above white (95x95cm-37x37in) s.d.91 verso prov. 5-Nov-3 AB Stockholms Auktionsverk #1168/R est:60000-80000 (S.KR 110000)
Works on paper
£378 $642 €552 Drawing No.187 (45x45cm-18x18in) s.d.1978 mixed media prov. 5-Nov-3 AB Stockholms Auktionsverk #1164/R (S.KR 5000)
£476 $843 €695 Drawing No.286 (49x44cm-19x17in) s.d.88 mixed media prov. 27-Apr-4 AB Stockholms Auktionsverk #927/R (S.KR 6500)

GREEN, B F (fl.1857) British
£1500 $2700 €2190 Snake charmer (73x61cm-29x24in) s.i.d.1857 stretcher. 21-Jan-4 Sotheby's, Olympia #77/R est:2000-3000

GREEN, Charles (1840-1898) British
Works on paper
£400 $668 €584 Lord Nelson and Lady Hamilton in a parkland (28x23cm-11x9in) s. W/C. 8-Oct-3 Andrew Hartley, Ilkley #1058
£800 $1472 €1168 Gordon Riots (19x37cm-7x15in) init.d.1896 W/C htd bodycol. 8-Jun-4 Holloways, Banbury #233/R
£1500 $2745 €2190 Bruges. View of Stokesay Castle, Shropshire (17x33cm-7x13in) init.i. pencil W/C htd touches bodycol two prov. 3-Jun-4 Christie's, London #30/R est:2000-3000
£6000 $11040 €8760 News from the war (33x47cm-13x19in) s.d.1867 pencil W/C bodycol. 25-Mar-4 Christie's, Kensington #238/R est:4000-6000
£10000 $16300 €14600 Dancing girls and Musicians, Coromandel, Madras (51x41cm-20x16in) s.i. pencil pen blk ink W/C exhib. 24-Sep-3 Christie's, London #37/R est:4000-6000

GREEN, Charles Lewis (1844-1915) American
£756 $1300 €1104 Buggy on a country road (25x20cm-10x8in) s. board. 7-Dec-3 Grogan, Boston #59/R
£1198 $2000 €1749 Boston harbour (20x30cm-8x12in) s. 16-Nov-3 CRN Auctions, Cambridge #29/R

GREEN, David (1854-1917) British
Works on paper
£297 $512 €434 Bit of old Plymouth (24x34cm-9x13in) s. W/C. 3-Dec-3 Dunbar Sloane, Auckland #98 (NZ.D 800)

GREEN, Denise (1946-) American
£370 $670 €540 Pompeian interior (154x154cm-61x61in) s. i.d.1976 verso acrylic masking tape on canvas. 30-Mar-4 Lawson Menzies, Sydney #87/R est:1000-1500 (A.D 900)
£391 $708 €571 Blue tree (122x122cm-48x48in) s. i.d.1976 verso. 30-Mar-4 Lawson Menzies, Sydney #88/R est:1000-1500 (A.D 950)
£638 $1085 €931 Suseneo (79x79cm-31x31in) s.i.d.1985 verso oil paintstick exhib.prov. 25-Nov-3 Christie's, Melbourne #161/R (A.D 1500)

GREEN, Donald H (20th C) Australian
£389 $712 €584 Storks. 3-Jun-4 Joel, Victoria #365 (A.D 1000)

GREEN, Elizabeth Shippen (1871-1954) American
Works on paper
£3293 $5500 €4808 I was alone in a palace of leaves (58x38cm-23x15in) s. chl wash. 15-Nov-3 Illustration House, New York #70/R est:5000-7000

GREEN, Frank Russell (1856-1940) British
£532 $850 €777 Civil war soldiers on horseback (46x76cm-18x30in) s.d.1878. 21-Sep-3 Grogan, Boston #44/R
£1317 $2200 €1923 Still life with mandolin and fruit (36x51cm-14x20in) s.d.1882. 19-Oct-3 Susanin's, Chicago #6047/R est:1000-2000

GREEN, Harriet (1751-?) British
Works on paper
£380 $711 €555 Bassenthwaite Water with distant mountains beyond, including Helvellyn (20x30cm-8x12in) pencil W/C prov. 22-Jul-4 Tennants, Leyburn #635

GREEN, James (1771-1834) British
Works on paper
£1950 $3627 €2847 Portrait of four children in summer house (60x47cm-24x19in) s.d.1830 W/C over pencil. 2-Mar-4 Bearnes, Exeter #363/R est:800-1200

GREEN, Margaret (20th C) British
£250 $455 €365 Bamburgh Castle - Farne Islands (16x34cm-6x13in) canvas on board. 1-Jul-4 Christie's, Kensington #283/R
£360 $673 €526 Interior at Elm Park Gardens (51x61cm-20x24in) init. i.verso. 24-Feb-4 Bonhams, Knowle #137

GREEN, R (19th C) ?
£1250 $2200 €1825 October crescent (46x41cm-18x16in) mono. s.d.1923 verso board. 23-May-4 Treadway Gallery, Cincinnati #495/R est:2500-3000

GREEN, Reginald (?) British
£560 $1014 €818 Washer woman near an old water mill (43x33cm-17x13in) s. i.verso. 16-Apr-4 Keys, Aylsham #717/R

GREEN, Richard Crafton (19th C) British
£540 $902 €788 Portrait of a young girl (51x41cm-20x16in) init. 19-Oct-3 Desmond Judd, Cranbrook #1057

GREEN, Roland (1896-1972) British
£550 $990 €803 Pheasants in a wood (40x50cm-16x20in) s. board. 22-Apr-4 Mellors & Kirk, Nottingham #1062
£650 $1086 €949 Study from Gatton Park, mallard in flight (36x53cm-14x21in) s.i. 18-Jun-3 John Nicholson, Haslemere #668/R
£1600 $2720 €2336 Golden eagles (51x61cm-20x24in) s. exhib. 19-Nov-3 Tennants, Leyburn #1187/R est:1000-1500
Works on paper
£260 $468 €380 Mountainous landscape with grouse (29x44cm-11x17in) s. W/C. 22-Apr-4 Charles Ross, Woburn #251
£280 $507 €409 Mallard rising (25x33cm-10x13in) s. W/C. 16-Apr-4 Keys, Aylsham #633/R
£300 $543 €438 Broadland landscape with heron in the foreground (25x36cm-10x14in) s. W/C. 16-Apr-4 Keys, Aylsham #635
£380 $688 €555 Plovers at Blakeney, Norfolk (30x44cm-12x17in) s. W/C. 30-Mar-4 David Duggleby, Scarborough #167/R
£420 $769 €613 Mallards in flight (37x27cm-15x11in) s. W/C pencil. 7-Apr-4 Woolley & Wallis, Salisbury #93/R
£460 $768 €672 Mallard (43x28cm-17x11in) s. W/C. 17-Oct-3 Keys, Aylsham #541
£520 $894 €759 Male and two female pheasants in a woodland clearing (25x33cm-10x13in) s. W/C. 5-Dec-3 Keys, Aylsham #527/R
£581 $1000 €848 Canvasbacks. Green-winged teal. s. pencil W/C htd white pair. 5-Dec-3 Christie's, Rockefeller NY #95/R est:2000-3000
£650 $1086 €949 Mute swans in flight (38x53cm-15x21in) s. W/C prov. 18-Jun-3 John Nicholson, Haslemere #667/R
£900 $1503 €1314 Winter, widgeon and lapwings (36x53cm-14x21in) s. W/C prov. 18-Jun-3 John Nicholson, Haslemere #666/R
£1750 $3238 €2555 Mallard rising and alighting in summer. Winter (43x28cm-17x11in) s. W/C pair. 13-Feb-4 Keys, Aylsham #625/R est:900-1200

GREEN, William (1760-1823) British
Works on paper
£300 $474 €435 Stonethwaite bridge in Borrowdale (13x19cm-5x7in) s.d.1809 i.verso W/C pencil. 24-Jul-3 Lawrence, Crewkerne #830
£450 $842 €657 Grange in Borrowdale (21x31cm-8x12in) pencil W/C. 22-Jul-4 Tennants, Leyburn #637

GREENAWAY, Kate (1846-1901) British
Works on paper
£250 $460 €365 Young girl (6x5cm-2x2in) init.d.1884 pencil. 22-Jun-4 Bonhams, Knightsbridge #173/R
£280 $482 €409 Botanical studies. Decorative designs (33x48cm-13x19in) one init. pencil W/C two on one sheet. 3-Dec-3 Christie's, Kensington #267
£380 $699 €555 Girl with fan (10x6cm-4x2in) pencil. 23-Mar-4 Bonhams, Knightsbridge #34/R
£500 $910 €730 Portrait of Eddie (24x21cm-9x8in) i.verso pencil W/C. 1-Jul-4 Christie's, Kensington #569/R
£7000 $12810 €10220 Study of a young girl in a garden, a border of nasturtiums beyond (43x33cm-17x13in) pencil W/C htd white prov. 3-Jun-4 Christie's, London #181/R est:7000-10000

GREENAWAY, Roy (1891-1972) ?
£381 $629 €552 Untitled, fishing boats (41x51cm-16x20in) i.verso canvasboard prov. 3-Jul-3 Heffel, Vancouver #13/R (C.D 850)

GREENBANK, Arthur (fl.1880-1902) British
£250 $430 €365 Three quarter length portrait of lady. board. 3-Dec-3 Brightwells, Leominster #1266
Works on paper
£460 $754 €672 Seated portrait of young fashionable lady (21x33cm-8x13in) s. i.verso W/C. 3-Jun-3 Fellows & Sons, Birmingham #179/R

GREENBLAT, Rodney Alan (1960-) American
Sculpture
£1514 $2800 €2210 Harp Chair (65cm-26in) acrylic mixed media wood chair exec 1985 prov. 13-Jul-4 Christie's, Rockefeller NY #139/R est:1000-1500
Works on paper
£649 $1200 €948 Robot in a box (46x46cm-18x18in) int.i.d.1985 chl prov. 13-Jul-4 Christie's, Rockefeller NY #60/R

GREENE, Albert van Nesse (1887-1971) American
£414 $750 €604 Boats in harbour (13x20cm-5x8in) s. board. 2-Apr-4 Freeman, Philadelphia #169
£435 $800 €635 Winter landscape (20x25cm-8x10in) s. board. 25-Jun-4 Freeman, Philadelphia #183/R
£1630 $3000 €2380 Snowfall at Yellow Springs (35x43cm-14x17in) board prov. 27-Jun-4 Freeman, Philadelphia #189/R est:3000-5000
£2310 $4250 €3373 Canal Scene (35x41cm-14x16in) s. board prov. 27-Jun-4 Freeman, Philadelphia #171/R est:3000-5000
Works on paper
£259 $425 €376 Along the river (23x30cm-9x12in) s. pastel. 4-Jun-3 Alderfer's, Hatfield #347/R
£289 $500 €422 Along the river (23x30cm-9x12in) s. pastel. 10-Dec-3 Alderfer's, Hatfield #486

GREENE, Anne Alison (1878-1954) Australian
£1405 $2599 €2051 Still life with lemons (53x76cm-21x30in) s. board prov. 10-Mar-4 Deutscher-Menzies, Melbourne #59/R est:2000-3000 (A.D 3400)

GREENE, Bruce (1953-) American
£3416 $5500 €4953 Thick as pea soup (22x26cm-9x10in) 22-Aug-3 Altermann Galleries, Santa Fe #134
£6704 $12000 €9788 Jingling the JA horses (66x71cm-26x28in) 15-May-4 Altermann Galleries, Santa Fe #98/R

GREENE, Evan (1910-) Canadian?
£446 $759 €651 Bedside conversation (71x91cm-28x36in) s.verso on stretcher. 6-Nov-3 Heffel, Vancouver #58/R (C.D 1000)

GREENE, Homer (20th C) American
Sculpture
£1018 $1700 €1486 Winged man (112x76cm-44x30in) paint wood prov. 15-Nov-3 Slotin Folk Art, Buford #457/R est:500-800

GREENE, J Barry (1895-1966) American
£299 $500 €437 Tyringham valley (61x76cm-24x30in) s. 20-Jun-3 Freeman, Philadelphia #154/R
£2301 $3750 €3359 Granainas, a gypsy song (130x97cm-51x38in) s.d.1933 i. on stretcher. 24-Sep-3 Doyle, New York #39 est:2000-3000

GREENE, John Beasley (19th C) American
Photographs
£2910 $5500 €4249 Town of Constantine, Algeria (24x30cm-9x12in) num.29 salted paper print. 17-Feb-4 Christie's, Rockefeller NY #27/R est:4000-6000
£12698 $24000 €18539 Untitled (30x25cm-12x10in) num.21 salted paper print. 17-Feb-4 Christie's, Rockefeller NY #25/R est:3000-5000

GREENFIELD, Giles (1963-) British
Works on paper
£4000 $6880 €5840 Back cover design of Harry Potter and the Goblet of Fire (33x23cm-13x9in) s.d.2000 pencil lit. 3-Dec-3 Christie's, Kensington #341/R est:4000-6000

GREENHALGH, Thomas (19th C) British
£250 $463 €365 Duck pond (35x53cm-14x21in) mono. 10-Feb-4 Bonhams, Knightsbridge #1
£900 $1413 €1305 Flower sellers in a Continental square (127x61cm-50x24in) s. 28-Aug-3 Christie's, Kensington #347/R

GREENHAM, Peter (1909-1992) British
£960 $1690 €1402 Llangranog 3 (17x30cm-7x12in) init. board prov. 18-May-4 Woolley & Wallis, Salisbury #56/R
£2400 $4224 €3504 The sculptor's studio (51x40cm-20x16in) init. 18-May-4 Woolley & Wallis, Salisbury #5/R est:1000-1500
£2400 $4224 €3504 Girl seated at a table (46x35cm-18x14in) init. 18-May-4 Woolley & Wallis, Salisbury #6/R est:1000-1500

GREENHAM, Robert Duckworth (1906-1975) British
£1000 $1820 €1460 Suburban snow (44x55cm-17x22in) s.d.45 s.i.d.verso. 3-Feb-4 Sworder & Son, Bishops Stortford #268/R est:1000-1200
£2600 $4732 €3796 Paddington Station (24x31cm-9x12in) init.d.46 board. 3-Feb-4 Sworder & Son, Bishops Stortford #267/R est:800-1000

GREENHILL, Harold (1914-) Australian
£496 $917 €724 Luxembourg Gardens, Paris (32x43cm-13x17in) s.d.51 board. 10-Mar-4 Deutscher-Menzies, Melbourne #472/R est:1000-1500 (A.D 1200)

GREENHILL, John (1649-1676) British
£2200 $4048 €3212 Portrait of a gentleman in a brown cloak, in a sculpted cartouche (76x63cm-30x25in) 11-Jun-4 Christie's, London #9/R est:2500-4000

GREENHILL, John (attrib) (1649-1676) British
£5500 $9130 €8030 Portrait of Sir Matthew Dudley of Clapton three quarter length with blue cloak (123x100cm-48x39in) i. 30-Sep-3 Sotheby's, London #13/R est:6000-8000

GREENLEAF, Jacob I (1837-?) American
£279 $450 €407 March day (23x30cm-9x12in) s. board. 20-Aug-3 James Julia, Fairfield #1722/R

GREENLEES, James (fl.1860-1903) British
£1700 $3111 €2482 Glengoil (75x101cm-30x40in) s.d.1886 s.i.verso. 8-Apr-4 Bonhams, Edinburgh #101/R est:2000-3000

£2000 $3140 €2900 Inverloch Castle, Inverness-shire (61x91cm-24x36in) s. 27-Aug-3 Sotheby's, London #915/R est:1800-2500

GREENSHIELDS, Tom (20th C) British?
Sculpture
£1100 $1837 €1606 Mother and child (32cm-13in) num.93/100 sold with certificate. 21-Oct-3 Gildings, Market Harborough #346/R est:300-500

GREENWOOD, Ethan Allen (1779-1856) American
£3416 $5500 €4987 Portrait of a woman in blue dress (66x51cm-26x20in) s.d.1812. 20-Aug-3 James Julia, Fairfield #115/R est:8000-10000

GREENWOOD, John (1959-) British
Works on paper
£360 $644 €526 World without texture (33x25cm-13x10in) s. conte. 16-Mar-4 Bonhams, Knightsbridge #71/R

GREENWOOD, Joseph H (1857-1927) American
£370 $600 €540 Marshy landscape (15x25cm-6x10in) s. board. 31-Jul-3 Eldred, East Dennis #844/R
£617 $1000 €901 Landscape with sheep (13x20cm-5x8in) s. panel. 31-Jul-3 Eldred, East Dennis #843/R
£1176 $2000 €1717 Snowy winter landscape with brook (61x76cm-24x30in) s. 21-Nov-3 Eldred, East Dennis #985/R est:2000-3000

GREENWOOD, Orlando (1892-1989) British
£519 $950 €758 Country road (66x76cm-26x30in) painted c.1930. 5-Jun-4 Treadway Gallery, Cincinnati #744/R
£700 $1274 €1022 Boudoir Cap (56x46cm-22x18in) s.d.1928. 1-Jul-4 Christie's, Kensington #48/R
£1800 $3096 €2628 Provencal landscape (63x76cm-25x30in) prov. 3-Dec-3 Christie's, Kensington #470/R est:1000-1500

GREENWOOD, Parker (fl.1880-c.1904) British
£600 $1002 €876 View from Seaforth towards New Brighton (55x90cm-22x35in) s.d.1891. 9-Jul-3 Peter Wilson, Nantwich #34
£1023 $1800 €1494 View of the Ocean (56x91cm-22x36in) s.d.1884 i. verso prov. 23-May-4 Hindman, Chicago #41/R est:2000-4000

GREER, A D (1904-1998) American
£486 $900 €710 Still life with flower (51x41cm-20x16in) s. 14-Jan-4 Dallas Auction Gallery, Dallas #463/R
£872 $1500 €1273 Floral still life (64x76cm-25x30in) s. 6-Dec-3 Neal Auction Company, New Orleans #626/R est:3000-5000
£882 $1500 €1288 Asters (30x36cm-12x14in) s. i.verso prov. 18-Nov-3 John Moran, Pasadena #121 est:2000-3000
£1027 $1900 €1499 Floral still life. s. board. 14-Jul-4 Dallas Auction Gallery, Dallas #355/R est:2000-3000
£1198 $2000 €1749 Fire of autumn (61x91cm-24x36in) s.d.85. 18-Jun-3 Doyle, New York #36/R est:2000-3000
£1421 $2600 €2132 Up the Rio Grand (61x76cm-24x30in) prov. 7-Jun-4 Everard, Savannah #476392/R est:3000-5000
£1486 $2750 €2170 Bouquet of roses (76x102cm-30x40in) s. 14-Jan-4 Dallas Auction Gallery, Dallas #404 est:2000-4000
£1622 $3000 €2368 Landscape of countryside (81x109cm-32x43in) s. 14-Jan-4 Dallas Auction Gallery, Dallas #97/R est:3000-5000
£1622 $3000 €2368 Landscape of night river scene (61x91cm-24x36in) s. 14-Jan-4 Dallas Auction Gallery, Dallas #150/R est:1500-2500
£1892 $3500 €2762 Landscape, pool (61x91cm-24x36in) s.i. 14-Jan-4 Dallas Auction Gallery, Dallas #98b est:3000-5000
£4054 $7500 €5919 Mountain solitude (76x102cm-30x40in) s. 14-Jan-4 Dallas Auction Gallery, Dallas #76/R est:6000-8000

GREER, Aubrey Dale (1904-1998) American
£778 $1300 €1136 Still life with vivid red roses beside blue vase against pale green back ground (76x102cm-30x40in) s. prov. 14-Jul-3 O'Gallerie, Oregon #828 est:1500-2000
£920 $1500 €1343 Sunset (23x33cm-9x13in) s.d.1963. 28-Sep-3 Simpson's, Houston #377/R

GREER, John (19/20th C) American
£652 $1200 €952 New York parade (36x30cm-14x12in) s.i. prov. 25-Jun-4 Freeman, Philadelphia #179/R

GREF, Franz Heinrich (1872-1957) German
£336 $594 €500 Still life of flowers (51x43cm-20x17in) s.d. 30-Apr-4 Dr Fritz Nagel, Stuttgart #163/R
£382 $623 €550 Girl with hen and cockerel (80x80cm-31x31in) s.d.1920 tempera. 27-Sep-3 Dr Fritz Nagel, Stuttgart #9158/R
£403 $713 €600 Herders with cows by pond (50x55cm-20x22in) s.d. s.d. verso. 30-Apr-4 Dr Fritz Nagel, Stuttgart #164/R

GREFERATH, Johannes (1872-1946) German
£533 $955 €800 Bullfight (62x78cm-24x31in) s. 15-May-4 Van Ham, Cologne #624/R

GREGAN, Kerry (1950-) Australian
£248 $459 €362 Doral Hill (121x121cm-48x48in) s.d.98 i.verso prov. 15-Mar-4 Sotheby's, Melbourne #224 (A.D 600)

GREGERSEN, Emil (1921-1993) Danish
£271 $486 €396 Still life of objects on table (22x26cm-9x10in) exhib. 10-May-4 Rasmussen, Vejle #628/R (D.KR 3000)
£379 $709 €553 Composition (40x48cm-16x19in) s. panel. 25-Feb-4 Kunsthallen, Copenhagen #22 (D.KR 4200)
£578 $1052 €867 Coffee maker (81x65cm-32x26in) s. exhib. 19-Jun-4 Rasmussen, Havnen #4184/R (D.KR 6500)

GREGERSEN, Julius (1860-1953) German
£345 $576 €500 The freighter, Fritz von Stolpmunde off the coast (52x74cm-20x29in) s.d.1904. 9-Jul-3 Hugo Ruef, Munich #98
£1450 $2611 €2175 Ship's portrait of Gerda of Goteborg (55x75cm-22x30in) s.i.d.13/8 1910. 25-Apr-4 Goteborg Auktionsverk, Sweden #689/R est:20000 (S.KR 20000)

GREGOIR, Henry (1818-1853) Belgian
£336 $614 €500 Portrait d'un ecrivain (38x30cm-15x12in) s.d.1943 panel. 8-Jul-4 Campo, Vlaamse Kaai #132

GREGOIRE (19th C) French
£2721 $4871 €4000 Vente publique sur la Place de Burcht (47x61cm-19x24in) panel. 22-Mar-4 Amberes, Antwerp #206
Sculpture
£1150 $1817 €1679 Bust of a young woman her hair dressed with poppies, flowers and wheat (46cm-18in) brown pat bronze scotia base. 27-Apr-3 Wilkinson, Doncaster #5/R

GREGOIRE, Albert A (1882-?) Belgian
£467 $835 €700 Quai industriel anime (78x113cm-31x44in) s.d.1941. 11-May-4 Vanderkindere, Brussels #132

GREGOIRE, Gaspard (1751-1846) French
Miniatures
£1667 $3033 €2500 Dauphin Louis XVII enfant (6cm-2in circular) on silk. 30-Jun-4 Pierre Berge, Paris #124/R est:400-600

GREGOIRE, Jean (1913-) Canadian
£260 $447 €380 Winter in Ile d'Orleans (34x45cm-13x18in) 3-Dec-3 Cheffins, Cambridge #640

GREGOIRE, Jean-Louis (1840-1890) French
Sculpture
£1400 $2576 €2044 Fisher girl (48cm-19in) s. brown pat. bronze st.f.Susse. 12-Jun-4 Finan Watkins & Co, Mere #20/R
£5882 $10000 €8588 Three running putti (58cm-23in) s. marble. 28-Oct-3 Christie's, Rockefeller NY #51/R

GREGOIRE, Paul (19/20th C) French
Works on paper
£340 $609 €500 Le jeune pecheur (19x24cm-7x9in) s. W/C. 22-Mar-4 E & Eve, Paris #40

GREGOR-GRIESHABER, Riccarda (20th C) German?
£625 $1019 €900 Garden (117x88cm-46x35in) mono. masonite. 27-Sep-3 Dr Fritz Nagel, Stuttgart #9160/R

GREGORI, Gino (1906-1973) Italian
£3768 $6180 €5200 Agreements (73x91cm-29x36in) s.d.55 s.i.d.verso exhib. sold with oil by Domenico Spinosa. 27-May-3 Sotheby's, Milan #76 est:400-600

GREGORIO, Francesco de (1862-?) Italian
£702 $1172 €1025 Wine tasting (39x26cm-15x10in) s.i. prov. 15-Nov-3 Galerie Gloggner, Luzern #27/R (S.FR 1600)

GREGORIO, Giuseppe de (1920-) Italian
£389 $650 €568 Cold light, luce frecca (100x80cm-39x31in) s.i.d.63 verso. 7-Oct-3 Sotheby's, New York #318
£570 $1055 €850 Composition (50x70cm-20x28in) s. masonite. 13-Mar-4 Meeting Art, Vercelli #298

GREGORIO, Marco de (1829-1876) Italian
£471 $815 €688 A man of the church (27x18cm-11x7in) s.d.1872 panel. 15-Dec-3 Lilla Bukowskis, Stockholm #302 (S.KR 6000)

GREGORITSCH, Anton (1868-1923) Austrian
£1049 $1783 €1500 Study from 7 hills (24x37cm-9x15in) board. 19-Nov-3 Dorotheum, Klagenfurt #13/R est:1500

GREGORIUS, Albertus Jacob Frans (1774-1853) Belgian
£1560 $2699 €2278 Portrait of Louis Charles D'Orleans (65x54cm-26x21in) i.verso. 9-Dec-3 Sotheby's, Olympia #413/R est:800-1200

GREGORY, Arthur V (1867-1957) Australian
£1226 $2231 €1790 Ozone. oil W/C. 1-Jul-4 Joel, Victoria #393/R est:1200-1500 (A.D 3200)
Works on paper
£250 $455 €365 The Dutch barque Anna in coastal waters (40x59cm-16x23in) s.d.02 pencil W/C bodycol. 1-Jul-4 Christie's, Kensington #327/R
£621 $968 €900 Kobenhavn, under full sail (53x83cm-21x33in) s.d.1927 W/C. 1-Aug-2 Joel, Victoria #341 est:2500-3500 (A.D 1800)
£851 $1447 €1242 The St Vincent off the Semaphore (43x67cm-17x26in) s.i.d.18 W/C prov. 25-Nov-3 Christie's, Melbourne #307 (A.D 2000)
£1123 $1820 €1628 Barque. Brigantine (41x61cm-16x24in) s. W/C pair. 31-Jul-3 International Art Centre, Auckland #147/R est:2500-3500 (NZ.D 3100)

£1277 $2170 €1864 Start of Tea Race, 1872 - Cutty Sark and Thermopylae (59x84cm-23x33in) s.i.d.1932 W/C prov. 25-Nov-3 Christie's, Melbourne #310 est:3000-5000 (A.D 3000)
£1551 $2854 €2264 Sydney Belle (41x60cm-16x24in) s.d.97 W/C gouache. 29-Mar-4 Goodman, Sydney #200/R est:2500-3500 (A.D 3800)

GREGORY, Charles (1810-1896) British
£900 $1701 €1314 Frigate lying off the covered slips at Devonport (30x46cm-12x18in) s.indis.d. 17-Feb-4 Bonhams, New Bond Street #71/R

GREGORY, Charles (1850-1920) British
Works on paper
£500 $810 €730 In the fields (35x53cm-14x21in) s. W/C. 30-Jul-3 Hamptons Fine Art, Godalming #71/R
£1000 $1700 €1460 Wooded river landscape with cottage and farmer and boy in a punt (34x52cm-13x20in) s. W/C. 29-Oct-3 Bonhams, Chester #391 est:1200-1600
£1000 $1820 €1500 Washerwoman on the Italian coast (33x53cm-13x21in) s. pencil W/C bodycol scratching out. 1-Jul-4 Christie's, Kensington #307/R est:400-600

GREGORY, Dorothy Lake (1893-?) American
£249 $450 €364 Untitled (25x20cm-10x8in) s. board. 3-Apr-4 Outer Cape Auctions, Provincetown #36/R
£459 $850 €670 Still life (36x53cm-14x21in) s. board. 17-Jul-4 Outer Cape Auctions, Provincetown #82/R
Works on paper
£257 $475 €375 Fisherman (20x28cm-8x11in) s. W/C. 17-Jul-4 Outer Cape Auctions, Provincetown #48a/R
£271 $425 €396 House (13x18cm-5x7in) s. pencil. 20-Apr-3 Outer Cape Auctions, Provincetown #99/R

GREGORY, G (19th C) British
Works on paper
£1200 $2040 €1752 Full-rigged ship Hurricane at sea (41x69cm-16x27in) s.i. pencil W/C htd white. 19-Nov-3 Christie's, Kensington #374/R

GREGORY, George (1849-1938) British
£420 $714 €613 Sailing off Yarmouth, Isle of Wight (15x30cm-6x12in) s.d.1920 board. 1-Dec-3 Bonhams, Bath #130/R
£600 $954 €876 Coastal shipping. Views of sailing boats (15x30cm-6x12in) s.d.29 board pair. 9-Sep-3 Rowley Fine Art, Newmarket #444/R
£1000 $1840 €1460 Shipping in choppy seas. Off the coast at sunset (14x22cm-6x9in) s. board pair. 8-Jun-4 Bonhams, Knightsbridge #328/R est:500-700
£1200 $2148 €1752 Barge setting sail on the Medina River (32x49cm-13x19in) s.d.1882. 26-May-4 Christie's, Kensington #701/R est:1000-1500
£1400 $2590 €2044 Hulk and other shipping in harbour (33x51cm-13x20in) s.d.1898. 9-Mar-4 Gorringes, Lewes #2012 est:500-700
£1550 $2635 €2263 Rouen France (75x125cm-30x49in) s.d.1882. 19-Nov-3 James Thompson, Kirby Lonsdale #160a
£15000 $27600 €21900 HMS Victory, 100 guns, in Portsmouth Harbour, with HMS, the Duke of Wellington (54x99cm-21x39in) s. prov. 23-Jun-4 Cheffins, Cambridge #484/R est:14000-18000
Works on paper
£280 $518 €409 Channel fort (23x36cm-9x14in) s.d.1915 W/C. 13-Feb-4 Keys, Aylsham #441
£520 $863 €759 Royal Yacht Squadron, Cowes (20x30cm-8x12in) s.d.1904 W/C. 1-Oct-3 Bonhams, Knightsbridge #72/R
£600 $1104 €876 Wreck at low tide off the Isle of Wight. Fisherfolk on the shore (7x10cm-3x4in) s.d.1900 W/C pair. 25-Mar-4 Christie's, Kensington #257/R

GREIFFENHAGEN, Maurice (1862-1931) British
£6000 $10200 €8760 Mermaid (119x113cm-47x44in) s.d.1928 oil gold leaf. 4-Nov-3 Dreweatt Neate, Newbury #127/R est:300-500
Works on paper
£280 $512 €409 Brittany wedding dance (39x17cm-15x7in) s. pencil card. 28-Jan-4 Dreweatt Neate, Newbury #5/R

GREIG, Donald (1916-) British
£380 $692 €555 Green hill above the quays, Salcombe (55x90cm-22x35in) s. canvasboard. 21-Jun-4 Bonhams, Bath #445

GREIG, J Alexander (attrib) (19th C) British?
£532 $888 €750 Landscape (34x52cm-13x20in) s.d.1844 verso. 14-Oct-3 Finarte Semenzato, Milan #85

GREIL, Alois (1841-1902) Austrian
Works on paper
£2517 $4280 €3600 Military policeman (23x15cm-9x6in) s.d.1895 W/C. 24-Nov-3 Dorotheum, Vienna #214/R est:3000-3500

GREINER, Anton (1914-) German
£304 $544 €450 Christ on the Cross (51x40cm-20x16in) s.d.1989 panel lit. 8-May-4 Sebok, Bamberg #1675/R

GREINER, Otto (1869-1916) German
Works on paper
£333 $597 €500 Standing female nude (59x40cm-23x16in) chk. 13-May-4 Bassenge, Berlin #5561
£567 $1020 €850 Dancing female nude (27x28cm-11x11in) mono. Indian ink. 24-Apr-4 Reiss & Sohn, Konigstein #5489/R

GREIS, Otto (1913-2001) German
£563 $975 €800 Untitled (19x24cm-7x9in) s.d.66 masonite prov. 13-Dec-3 Lempertz, Koln #315
£1408 $2437 €2000 Variation No 4 (35x27cm-14x11in) s.d.61 i. verso tempera exhib. 13-Dec-3 Lempertz, Koln #144/R
Works on paper
£979 $1664 €1400 Composition - red and black (21x13cm-8x5in) s.d.6.2.58 gouache Indian ink prov. 27-Nov-3 Lempertz, Koln #160
£2000 $3680 €3000 Fugue lumineuse (100x95cm-39x37in) s.d. s.i.d. verso mixed media canvas. 11-Jun-4 Hauswedell & Nolte, Hamburg #1282/R est:4000
£2937 $4993 €4200 Composition - red, blue and black (67x52cm-26x20in) s. gouache pigments board prov. 27-Nov-3 Lempertz, Koln #158/R est:3000

GREIVE, Johan Conrad (jnr) (1837-1891) Dutch
£1447 $2620 €2200 Fisherman drying his net, a town in the background (24x37cm-9x15in) s. canvas on panel. 19-Apr-4 Glerum, Amsterdam #10/R est:2200-2400
£2639 $4486 €3800 Repairing the boat by the IJ, Amsterdam (24x35cm-9x14in) s. panel. 28-Oct-3 Christie's, Amsterdam #10/R est:4000-6000
£7639 $12757 €11000 Bomschuiten on the beach (56x85cm-22x33in) s. 21-Oct-3 Sotheby's, Amsterdam #207/R est:10000-15000

GRELA, Juan (1914-) Argentinian
£1341 $2400 €1958 Figure in grey (66x41cm-26x16in) s.d.1961. 4-May-4 Arroyo, Buenos Aires #57/R est:2400
£1923 $3500 €2808 Composition with figure (55x45cm-22x18in) s.d.1965. 29-Jun-4 Arroyo, Buenos Aires #13 est:2500
£2747 $5000 €4011 Tree (180x59cm-71x23in) s.d.1964 verso. 29-Jun-4 Arroyo, Buenos Aires #18/R est:5000
Works on paper
£1436 $2600 €2097 Fighter (45x30cm-18x12in) W/C. 30-Mar-4 Arroyo, Buenos Aires #10

GRELLE, Martin (1954-) American
£2000 $3400 €2920 When cold winds blow (46x61cm-18x24in) acrylic on linen. 1-Nov-3 Altermann Galleries, Santa Fe #136
£4118 $7000 €6012 West Texas weathered (46x36cm-18x14in) 1-Nov-3 Altermann Galleries, Santa Fe #133
£4190 $7500 €6117 Texas bonnets (23x30cm-9x12in) 15-May-4 Altermann Galleries, Santa Fe #113/R
£6145 $11000 €8972 Twilight dancer (69x48cm-27x19in) acrylic paper. 15-May-4 Altermann Galleries, Santa Fe #105/R
£32086 $60000 €46846 On a winter trail-crow (91x122cm-36x48in) s. oil on linen. 24-Jul-4 Coeur d'Alene, Hayden #132/R est:25000-35000

GREMBER, Norbert (1922-) Austrian
£267 $491 €400 View of old church of Tisis from studio (55x86cm-22x34in) mono. 9-Jun-4 Dorotheum, Salzburg #644/R
Works on paper
£533 $981 €800 Old church in Tisis (48x35cm-19x14in) s. mixed media. 9-Jun-4 Dorotheum, Salzburg #840/R

GREMKE, Henry Dietrick (1860-1939) American
£2023 $3500 €2954 Autumnal still life with melons and grapes (58x99cm-23x39in) s. prov. 10-Dec-3 Bonhams & Butterfields, San Francisco #6268/R est:4000-6000

GRENIER, Henri (20th C) French
Works on paper
£297 $475 €434 Paris street scene (56x74cm-22x29in) s. gouache. 20-Sep-3 Sloans & Kenyon, Bethesda #108/R
£352 $616 €500 Rue Royale, Paris (69x98cm-27x39in) s. gouache. 16-Dec-3 Durán, Madrid #574/R
£423 $739 €600 View of Paris (68x98cm-27x39in) s.i. gouache. 16-Dec-3 Durán, Madrid #573/R
£552 $916 €800 Rue Val de Grace, Paris (26x20cm-10x8in) s.i. gouache. 30-Sep-3 Ansorena, Madrid #10/R
£552 $916 €800 Rue Bertier, Paris (26x20cm-10x8in) s. gouache. 30-Sep-3 Ansorena, Madrid #9/R
£629 $1051 €900 View of Paris (42x49cm-17x19in) s. gouache. 30-Jun-3 Ansorena, Madrid #111/R
£699 $1168 €1000 Street in Paris (42x49cm-17x19in) s. gouache. 30-Jun-3 Ansorena, Madrid #112/R

GRENNESS, Johannes (1875-1963) Danish
£843 $1375 €1231 Small girl picking flowers (44x53cm-17x21in) s. 27-Sep-3 Rasmussen, Havnen #2011/R (D.KR 9000)

GRENO, Josefa (1850-1902) Portuguese
Works on paper
£2081 $3724 €3100 Still life with grapes (45x60cm-18x24in) s.d.1890 pastel. 31-May-4 Cabral Moncada Leiloes, Lisbon #400/R est:2000-3000

GRENON, Leo (?) French
Works on paper
£276 $458 €400 Soir a Concarneau (61x79cm-24x31in) s.i. W/C. 1-Oct-3 Millon & Associes, Paris #220

GREPPI, Antonio (19th C) Italian
£4667 $8587 €7000 Boats in Venice (52x35cm-20x14in) s. 10-Jun-4 Christie's, Rome #120/R est:7000-7500

GRES, Serge Czerefkow (1899-1970) French
£805 $1442 €1200 Portrait de Tahitienne (46x37cm-18x15in) s.i.d.39. 25-May-4 Chambelland & Giafferi, Paris #101/R

GRESELY, Gabriel (1712-1756) French
£5594 $9622 €8000 Achille reconnu parmi les filles de Lycomede (81x107cm-32x42in) s. 8-Dec-3 Claude Aguttes, Neuilly #37/R est:8000-10000

GRESLEY, Cuthbert (1876-1963) British
Works on paper
£370 $588 €540 Still life of roses in a bowl (34x45cm-13x18in) W/C. 9-Sep-3 Bamfords, Derby #1098/R
£700 $1099 €1022 Faggot gathering, on a Derbyshire lane, summer landscape (20x28cm-8x11in) s. W/C. 16-Apr-3 Bamfords, Derby #577/R

GRESLEY, Frank (1855-1936) British
£250 $433 €365 Woodland Nook, summer scene with stream (58x43cm-23x17in) s.i. 11-Dec-3 Neales, Nottingham #628/R
£600 $1098 €876 Weirpool with mill beyond (23x38cm-9x15in) s. 7-Apr-4 Gardiner & Houlgate, Bath #89/R
£770 $1286 €1124 In Bolton Woods, Yorks (33cm-13in circular) s. 20-Jun-3 Chrystals Auctions, Isle of Man #178/R
Works on paper
£323 $594 €472 Woman and child in a garden (29x48cm-11x19in) s. W/C. 14-Jun-4 Waddingtons, Toronto #69/R (C.D 800)
£460 $828 €672 Beside the Trent (21x43cm-8x17in) s. pencil W/C htd white. 22-Apr-4 Mellors & Kirk, Nottingham #983
£580 $963 €847 Steam coaster, Cromarty Firth (43x69cm-17x27in) s. W/C bodycol htd white. 2-Oct-3 Neales, Nottingham #689
£720 $1145 €1051 Fisherman on a bridge (29x20cm-11x8in) s.d.1891 W/C. 9-Sep-3 Bamfords, Derby #1104
£850 $1530 €1241 Children playing by a Derbyshire river (18x26cm-7x10in) s. pencil W/C htd white. 22-Apr-4 Mellors & Kirk, Nottingham #984
£900 $1431 €1314 Little hollow, with thatched cottage and figures walking (29x20cm-11x8in) s.d.1891 W/C. 9-Sep-3 Bamfords, Derby #1105/R
£900 $1674 €1314 Sale Abbey, figures with geese before a country house (18x26cm-7x10in) s. W/C. 2-Mar-4 Bamfords, Derby #412/R
£900 $1674 €1314 Fly fishing on the River Dove (31x51cm-12x20in) s.d. W/C. 2-Mar-4 Bamfords, Derby #426
£1000 $1730 €1460 Trent at Swarkestone, Derbyshire, with cattle and figure on riverside path (28x58cm-11x23in) s. W/C htd white. 11-Dec-3 Neales, Nottingham #554 est:500-600
£1050 $1953 €1533 Llanberis Pass, North Wales (38x55cm-15x22in) s. i.verso W/C. 2-Mar-4 Bamfords, Derby #417 est:500-700
£1250 $2325 €1825 Thatched cottage (20x33cm-8x13in) s.d.86 W/C. 2-Mar-4 Bamfords, Derby #413/R est:500-700
£1900 $3420 €2774 Picking flowers in a meadow beside the Tent. Children playing on a path, Swarkestone Church beyond (18x27cm-7x11in) s. pencil W/C htd white. 22-Apr-4 Mellors & Kirk, Nottingham #1016/R est:1000-1400
£2000 $3400 €2920 Mill on the Trent (39x59cm-15x23in) s. W/C over pencil sold with a companion. 1-Dec-3 Bonhams, Bath #75/R est:1500-2000

GRESLEY, Harold (1892-1967) British
Works on paper
£310 $493 €453 Feeding the ducks, Dovedale (19x27cm-7x11in) s.d.1913 W/C. 9-Sep-3 Bamfords, Derby #1099/R
£340 $534 €496 Derbyshire farm, summer river landscape with cattle and geese (18x27cm-7x11in) s.d.1925 W/C. 10-Dec-2 Bamfords, Derby #735a
£360 $648 €526 Eilean Donan Castle, Kyle of Lochalsh (38x55cm-15x22in) s. W/C. 21-Apr-4 Cheffins, Cambridge #446/R
£540 $848 €788 Gypsy caravan, near Derby (25x35cm-10x14in) s.d.1924 W/C. 10-Dec-2 Bamfords, Derby #738
£550 $935 €803 Coastal landscape (37x56cm-15x22in) s. W/C. 26-Nov-3 Hamptons Fine Art, Godalming #45
£600 $942 €876 Lion Rock, Dovedale, figure walking along a riverside path (30x22cm-12x9in) s. W/C. 10-Dec-2 Bamfords, Derby #733
£700 $1253 €1022 Walking along the bank (27x39cm-11x15in) s. W/C. 25-May-4 Bonhams, Knightsbridge #286/R
£750 $1343 €1095 The river Dove, Dovedale (27x39cm-11x15in) s. W/C. 25-May-4 Bonhams, Knightsbridge #289/R
£880 $1382 €1285 Snowy morning, village scene with cottages and figures (25x35cm-10x14in) s.d.1924 W/C. 10-Dec-2 Bamfords, Derby #739
£1500 $2700 €2190 Feeding the hens (27x37cm-11x15in) s. W/C htd white. 22-Apr-4 Mellors & Kirk, Nottingham #982/R est:500-600
£1550 $2883 €2263 Robin Hood's Bay, North Yorkshire (37x54cm-15x21in) s. W/C. 2-Mar-4 Bearnes, Exeter #331/R est:500-700
£1650 $2624 €2409 Church Lane, Swarkstone (27x38cm-11x15in) s. i.verso W/C. 9-Sep-3 Bamfords, Derby #1100/R
£1750 $2783 €2555 Trent at Swarkestone bridge, Derbyshire (27x37cm-11x15in) s.i. W/C. 9-Sep-3 Bamfords, Derby #1102/R
£2500 $3975 €3650 Jamine cottage, Chellaston, Derbyshire (28x37cm-11x15in) s.i.d.1958 W/C. 9-Sep-3 Bamfords, Derby #1103/R
£2700 $4293 €3942 Cathedral of the peak, Tideswell, North Derbyshire (38x54cm-15x21in) s.i. W/C. 9-Sep-3 Bamfords, Derby #1101/R est:600-1000

GRESLEY, J S (1829-1908) British
Works on paper
£520 $936 €759 Study of Bolton Abbey, with cattle watering in the foreground (25x38cm-10x15in) s.d.1883 W/C. 22-Apr-4 Mallams, Cheltenham #259/R

GRESLEY, James S (1829-1908) British
£550 $985 €803 Tintern Abbey (32x48cm-13x19in) s.d.1896. 26-May-4 Sotheby's, Olympia #90/R
£560 $879 €818 Rocky torrent, summer hilly landscape (40x59cm-16x23in) s. 16-Apr-3 Bamfords, Derby #653/R
£600 $954 €876 Fishing by the falls (49x81cm-19x32in) s. 9-Sep-3 Bamfords, Derby #1156/R
Works on paper
£260 $476 €380 Derbyshire river landscape (25x42cm-10x17in) s. W/C. 7-Apr-4 Dreweatt Neate, Newbury #86
£380 $631 €555 Derbyshire farm (30x46cm-12x18in) s. W/C bodycol htd white. 2-Oct-3 Neales, Nottingham #701/R
£420 $769 €613 Derbyshire river landscape with parish church (25x42cm-10x17in) s. W/C. 7-Apr-4 Dreweatt Neate, Newbury #87
£580 $1079 €847 Woodland stream, with stone bridge (16x23cm-6x9in) s. W/C. 2-Mar-4 Bamfords, Derby #410/R
£600 $1080 €876 Bolton Abbey on the river Wharfe. Cottage amongst trees (18cm-7in circular) s. W/C two one frame. 21-Apr-4 Tennants, Leyburn #1052
£800 $1360 €1168 Figures beside a waterfall (37cm-15in circular) s.d.1899 W/C. 1-Dec-3 Bonhams, Bath #76/R
£820 $1287 €1197 Bolton Abbey, with fisherman (35x52cm-14x20in) s. W/C. 10-Dec-2 Bamfords, Derby #735
£900 $1548 €1314 Cattle watering (25x33cm-10x13in) s.d.1901 W/C. 3-Dec-3 Andrew Hartley, Ilkley #1125
£2600 $4680 €3796 Cottage gate (33x24cm-13x9in) s.d.1864 pencil W/C htd white. 22-Apr-4 Mellors & Kirk, Nottingham #1043 est:2000-2500
£3000 $5400 €4380 Thatching the cottage (29x23cm-11x9in) s.d.1867 pencil W/C htd white. 22-Apr-4 Mellors & Kirk, Nottingham #1035/R est:1200-1600

GRESSE, John Alexander (1741-1794) British
Works on paper
£550 $1007 €803 House by the river Alde (25x36cm-10x14in) s.d.1781 i.verso pencil pen ink W/C prov. 27-Jan-4 Holloways, Banbury #328/R

GRETHE, Carlos (1864-1913) German
£700 $1260 €1050 Windmill (30x21cm-12x8in) mono. board. 26-Apr-4 Rieber, Stuttgart #849/R
£1081 $1686 €1600 Harbour scene - unloading the catch (80x57cm-31x22in) s. 28-Mar-3 Altus, Berlin #615/R est:1200

GRETZNER, Harold (1902-1977) American
Works on paper
£722 $1300 €1054 Homes by a pond (55x73cm-22x29in) s.i. W/C. 25-Apr-4 Bonhams & Butterfields, San Francisco #5544/R est:800-1200
£898 $1500 €1311 Chinatown, San Francisco (52x72cm-20x28in) s. pencil W/C. 26-Oct-3 Bonhams & Butterfields, San Francisco #6530/R

GREUZE, Jean-Baptiste (1725-1805) French
£6338 $10141 €9000 Danae (71x59cm-28x23in) exhib. 21-Sep-3 Finarte, Venice #2/R
£16667 $30000 €24334 Portrait of a young woman, said to be the artist's daughter (63x53cm-25x21in) oval prov.exhib. 22-Jan-4 Sotheby's, New York #213/R est:40000-60000
£19000 $34770 €27740 Portrait of gentleman (41x33cm-16x13in) i. panel prov.exhib.lit. 8-Jul-4 Sotheby's, London #173/R est:10000-15000
£60526 $111368 €92000 Jeune fille en priere (40x32cm-16x13in) s.d.1779 panel prov.exhib.lit. 24-Jun-4 Christie's, Paris #130/R est:10000-20000
£72222 $130000 €105444 Young girl with a dog on her lap (45x38cm-18x15in) prov.lit. 23-Jan-4 Christie's, Rockefeller NY #72/R est:150000-200000
£83799 $150000 €122347 Young girl with spaniel (46x38cm-18x15in) prov.lit. 27-May-4 Sotheby's, New York #100/R est:150000-200000
£111111 $200000 €162222 La jeune fille a la colombe - young girl holding a dove (64x53cm-25x21in) panel prov.lit. 23-Jan-4 Christie's, Rockefeller NY #68/R est:150000-200000
Works on paper
£6761 $11696 €9600 Amour triomphante (43x34cm-17x13in) i. sanguine stump. 15-Dec-3 Bailly Pommery, Paris #26/R est:10000-12000
£16667 $30000 €24334 Nude woman standing by an urn (18x31cm-7x12in) red chk prov. 22-Jan-4 Christie's, Rockefeller NY #103/R est:40000-50000
£27972 $48112 €40000 Lecture de la Bible (23x31cm-9x12in) i. blk chk brown ink pen brown grey wash prov.lit. 2-Dec-3 Christie's, Paris #513/R est:40000-60000
£38000 $69540 €55480 Head of a startled boy (42x32cm-17x13in) red chk. 8-Jul-4 Sotheby's, London #126/R est:40000-60000
£48611 $87500 €70972 Head of a girl (37x29cm-15x11in) red black chk stumping prov. 21-Jan-4 Sotheby's, New York #94/R est:40000-60000
£59441 $99266 €85000 La malediction paternelle, le fils ingrat (43x33cm-17x13in) i. sanguine. 27-Jun-3 Millon & Associes, Paris #31/R est:20000

GREUZE, Jean-Baptiste (after) (1725-1805) French
£5120 $8500 €7475 Innocence (112x86cm-44x34in) i.d.1882. 4-Oct-3 Neal Auction Company, New Orleans #384/R est:6000-8000

GREUZE, Jean-Baptiste (attrib) (1725-1805) French
£1014 $1724 €1450 Portrait de la jeune soubrette (47x38cm-19x15in) 18-Nov-3 Vanderkindere, Brussels #189
£1933 $3519 €2900 Half portrait of a young girl (46x36cm-18x14in) panel prov. 3-Jul-4 Geble, Radolfzell #402/R est:2500
£2069 $3434 €3000 Interior with family (38x39cm-15x15in) canvas on board. 6-Oct-3 Bloss, Merzhausen #1199/R est:350
Works on paper
£2183 $3974 €3187 Antique scene (34x41cm-13x16in) ink prov. 16-Jun-4 Fischer, Luzern #2523 est:400-500 (S.FR 5000)

GREUZE, Jean-Baptiste (circle) (1725-1805) French
£4828 $8062 €7000 Femme allaitant son enfant (83x71cm-33x28in) 17-Nov-3 Delorme & Bocage, Paris #86/R est:5000-8000

GREVEDON, Pierre-Louis (1776-1860) French
Miniatures
£2200 $3960 €3212 Officer, possibly of the de Lasalle family (9cm-4in) s. gilt mount rec. wood frame oval prov.exhib.lit. 22-Apr-4 Bonhams, New Bond Street #154/R est:2500-3500
£2200 $3960 €3212 Officer, of the de Lasalle family (10cm-4in) s.d.1818 gilt mount wood frame oval prov.exhib.lit. 22-Apr-4 Bonhams, New Bond Street #155/R est:800-1200

GREVENBROECK, Alessandro (18th C) Italian
£4800 $8304 €7008 Mediterranean harbour scene (23x46cm-9x18in) 9-Dec-3 Sotheby's, Olympia #361/R est:3000-4000

GREVENBROECK, Orazio (17/18th C) Dutch
£1690 $2924 €2400 Summer and winter landscapes (28x46cm-11x18in) panel. 11-Dec-3 Dr Fritz Nagel, Stuttgart #466/R est:4800
£1745 $3211 €2600 Summer and winter landscapes (28x46cm-11x18in) panel pair. 25-Mar-4 Dr Fritz Nagel, Stuttgart #651/R est:2400

GREVENBROECK, Orazio (attrib) (17/18th C) Dutch
£2800 $4760 €4088 Provisioning a galleon in inlet. Bringing the cargo ashore (6x15cm-2x6in) panel pair. 19-Nov-3 Christie's, Kensington #437/R est:3000-5000
£4930 $8627 €7000 Depart du navire (34x44cm-13x17in) 19-Dec-3 Pierre Berge, Paris #38/R est:6000-8000
£8889 $16000 €12978 Harbour scene with ships by a tower. Harbour scene with ships by a fortification (19x24cm-7x9in) copper on panel pair. 22-Jan-4 Sotheby's, New York #183/R est:10000-15000

GREY, Alfred (1845-1926) British
£960 $1536 €1402 Cattle resting in a landscape (18x28cm-7x11in) s. painted c.1880-1900. 21-Sep-3 Desmond Judd, Cranbrook #1022
£1111 $1811 €1600 Emmigrants farewell (29x24cm-11x9in) s. board. 24-Sep-3 James Adam, Dublin #12/R est:200-400
£1972 $3155 €2800 View from Shanganagh, County Dublin (36x51cm-14x20in) s. prov. 16-Sep-3 Whyte's, Dublin #178/R est:1500-2000
£2098 $3566 €3000 Dairy herd on path with thatched roofed homestead beyond (64x51cm-25x20in) s. 18-Nov-3 Whyte's, Dublin #115/R est:3000-5000
Works on paper
£570 $1021 €850 Fallen deer (30x34cm-12x13in) s. W/C. 26-May-4 James Adam, Dublin #184/R

GREY, James (19th C) British
£933 $1689 €1400 Haystacks and geese (40x60cm-16x24in) s. 31-Mar-4 James Adam, Dublin #161/R

GREY, Marcus (20th C) British
Works on paper
£300 $540 €438 Brindavan Scene (28x38cm-11x15in) gouache. 20-Jan-4 Bonhams, Knightsbridge #242/R

GREY, Roger de (1918-) British
£500 $925 €730 Landscape (25x36cm-10x14in) 13-Feb-4 Sworder & Son, Bishops Stortford #82/R
£900 $1665 €1314 La Tremblade (160x100cm-63x39in) init. s.i.stretcher. 11-Feb-4 Sotheby's, Olympia #198/R est:1000-1500
£2500 $4400 €3650 Open window (127x91cm-50x36in) s. prov. 19-May-4 Sotheby's, Olympia #194/R est:800-1200

GREY, William (19th C) British
Works on paper
£275 $448 €402 Snowdon from the Nant Nantle Valley with figures on a track (20x28cm-8x11in) s.i.d.1853 W/C. 27-Sep-3 Rogers Jones, Clwyd #65

GREY-SMITH, Guy (1916-1981) Australian
£3306 $6116 €4827 Verandah (41x52cm-16x20in) s.d.50. 10-Mar-4 Deutscher-Menzies, Melbourne #171/R est:10000-15000 (A.D 8000)
£4508 $7123 €6582 Northern banksia (52x41cm-20x16in) s.d.50 i. stretcher prov. 2-Sep-3 Deutscher-Menzies, Melbourne #152/R est:12000-18000 (A.D 11000)
£5738 $9066 €8377 Cityscape (97x72cm-38x28in) s.d.57 canvas board prov. 2-Sep-3 Deutscher-Menzies, Melbourne #99/R est:15000-20000 (A.D 14000)
£7660 $13021 €11184 Saw Millers (91x122cm-36x48in) s.d.74 s.i.d.verso composition board. 26-Nov-3 Deutscher-Menzies, Melbourne #83/R est:20000-25000 (A.D 18000)

GRIBAUDO, Ezio (1929-) Italian
Works on paper
£336 $621 €500 Metallogrifo (70x51cm-28x20in) polymer exec.1971. 13-Mar-4 Meeting Art, Vercelli #91

GRIBBLE, Bernard Finegan (1873-1962) British
£340 $629 €496 The Cheshire, full steam in the Mersey (24x36cm-9x14in) s. 13-Jan-4 Bonhams, Knightsbridge #40/R
£850 $1352 €1233 Whitby from the sea (41x30cm-16x12in) s. panel. 9-Sep-3 David Duggleby, Scarborough #385
£1400 $2590 €2044 Falmouth Bay (40x30cm-16x12in) s. board. 14-Jul-4 Sotheby's, Olympia #135/R est:800-1200
£1500 $2400 €2190 Confronting the villagers (61x91cm-24x36in) s. 21-Sep-3 William Jenack, New York #334 est:3000-5000
£1600 $2992 €2336 Poole harbour (61x81cm-24x32in) s. board. 24-Feb-4 Bonhams, Knowle #67/R est:1500-2000
£3000 $5460 €4380 St Marks Square, Venice (86x112cm-34x44in) s. 3-Feb-4 Sworder & Son, Bishops Stortford #292/R est:3000-5000
Works on paper
£300 $549 €438 Bound for home (19x29cm-7x11in) s. W/C htd white. 27-Jan-4 Bonhams, Knightsbridge #336/R
£541 $1000 €790 Armoured cruiser leaving Portsmouth with a Royal Naval two-decker (46x65cm-18x26in) s.indis.d. pencil W/C. 10-Feb-4 Christie's, Rockefeller NY #130/R

GRIBENNIKOV, Vasiliy Nicholayevich (1951-) Russian
£353 $650 €515 Pastoral landscape with milk cows and stream (36x48cm-14x19in) s.d.2003. 29-Mar-4 O'Gallerie, Oregon #129/R
£353 $650 €515 Morning landscape with two fishermen and dog. s. 29-Mar-4 O'Gallerie, Oregon #697/R

GRIBENNIKOV, Vladimir (1946-) Russian
£317 $555 €450 Dusk in Paris (24x18cm-9x7in) s. 16-Dec-3 Durán, Madrid #729/R
£317 $555 €450 Paris at night (30x40cm-12x16in) s. 16-Dec-3 Durán, Madrid #728/R
£426 $711 €600 The Seine (30x40cm-12x16in) s. 20-Oct-3 Durán, Madrid #707/R
£567 $948 €800 Summer (40x50cm-16x20in) s. 20-Oct-3 Durán, Madrid #709/R

GRICE, Jeremy le (1936-) British
£500 $900 €730 Rounding the buoy, Fowey Regatta (46x54cm-18x21in) s.i.d.98 verso board. 20-Jan-4 Bonhams, Knightsbridge #235/R

GRICE, Winifred Sarah (1913-) British
£480 $878 €701 Workhorse and cart with man and dog caught in a rain shower (36x46cm-14x18in) s. board. 7-Apr-4 Andrew Hartley, Ilkley #1091

GRIDNEV, Anatoliy (1946-) Russian
£250 $418 €365 Evening at the Building Comedie-Francaise (18x24cm-7x9in) s. cardboard. 13-Jul-3 John Nicholson, Haslemere #10
£275 $459 €402 Flower market near the Church of Magdalene, Paris (18x24cm-7x9in) s. 13-Jul-3 John Nicholson, Haslemere #35/R

GRIEBEN, Eduard (1813-1870) German
£1330 $2381 €1942 Landscape with farm (72x90cm-28x35in) mono. 28-May-4 Uppsala Auktionskammare, Uppsala #38/R est:18000-20000 (S.KR 18000)

GRIEKEN, Jef van (1950-) Belgian
£671 $1188 €1000 Paysage aux rochers (160x120cm-63x47in) s. 27-Apr-4 Campo & Campo, Antwerp #241/R
£972 $1624 €1400 Bois de Charmois (140x200cm-55x79in) s.d.1986. 21-Oct-3 Campo & Campo, Antwerp #321/R
Works on paper
£338 $585 €480 Rue l'epic, Paris (49x36cm-19x14in) s.i. pastel. 13-Dec-3 De Vuyst, Lokeren #342
£350 $584 €500 Igrape Manaus IV (94x74cm-37x29in) s. dr. 11-Oct-3 De Vuyst, Lokeren #366

GRIEPENKERL, Christian (attrib) (1839-1916) German
£1007 $1883 €1500 Bear protecting foundling (70x120cm-28x47in) 24-Feb-4 Dorotheum, Vienna #273/R est:2200-2500

GRIERSON, Charles MacIver (1864-1939) British
Works on paper
£300 $546 €438 The cabbage patch man (13x8cm-5x3in) s. bears d. pastel. 5-Feb-4 Amersham Auction Rooms, UK #230

GRIERSON, Mary (20th C) British
Works on paper
£420 $739 €613 Phalaenopsis Amabilis (41x30cm-16x12in) s. W/C pen ink. 18-May-4 Woolley & Wallis, Salisbury #198/R

GRIESEL, Hennie (20th C) ?
£403 $737 €588 Untitled (60x75cm-24x30in) 6-Jul-4 Dales, Durban #7 (SA.R 4500)

GRIESHABER, Helmut A P (1909-1981) German
Prints
£2292 $3735 €3300 Fertility (45x64cm-18x25in) s.d.1947 woodcut. 27-Sep-3 Dr Fritz Nagel, Stuttgart #9543/R est:6000
£2349 $4158 €3500 Couple (81x59cm-32x23in) s.d. woodcut sepia red black. 30-Apr-4 Dr Fritz Nagel, Stuttgart #805/R est:4500
£2416 $4277 €3600 Quartering of Jerg Ratgebs 1526 (118x170cm-46x67in) s. woodcut. 30-Apr-4 Dr Fritz Nagel, Stuttgart #793/R est:2500
£2416 $4277 €3600 Tilman Riemenschneider (181x100cm-71x39in) s. woodcut board. 30-Apr-4 Dr Fritz Nagel, Stuttgart #796/R est:2500
£3472 $5660 €5000 Dance (111x100cm-44x39in) s.i. woodcut. 27-Sep-3 Dr Fritz Nagel, Stuttgart #9536/R est:7500
£4514 $7358 €6500 Storm tide (86x61cm-34x24in) s.i. col woodcut. 27-Sep-3 Dr Fritz Nagel, Stuttgart #9535/R est:3000
£5594 $9622 €8000 Rocket man (120x68cm-47x27in) s. col woodcut. 2-Dec-3 Hauswedell & Nolte, Hamburg #217/R est:10000
£6993 $12028 €10000 Dancing Africans (120x89cm-47x35in) s. col woodcut. 2-Dec-3 Hauswedell & Nolte, Hamburg #216/R est:12000
£8392 $14434 €12000 Dancing arabs (120x105cm-47x41in) s. col woodcut. 2-Dec-3 Hauswedell & Nolte, Hamburg #218/R est:14000
Works on paper
£321 $536 €465 Fisherwoman (20x29cm-8x11in) s. W/C on letter. 19-Jun-3 Kornfeld, Bern #447 (S.FR 700)
£604 $1069 €900 Herdsman (39x26cm-15x10in) s.i.d.25/VIII/67 W/C. 30-Apr-4 Dr Fritz Nagel, Stuttgart #798/R
£1007 $1782 €1500 Untitled (30x21cm-12x8in) i.d. WC. 30-Apr-4 Dr Fritz Nagel, Stuttgart #797/R est:2100
£1049 $1783 €1500 Cher ami Stephan Hermlin (40x31cm-16x12in) s.i.d.1/V/79 brush over woodcut. 29-Nov-3 Bassenge, Berlin #6726/R est:2200
£1806 $2943 €2600 Figure composition (86x61cm-34x24in) s. pencil. 27-Sep-3 Dr Fritz Nagel, Stuttgart #9537/R est:3000
£2013 $3705 €3000 Harpyie (50x65cm-20x26in) s. W/C. 26-Mar-4 Ketterer, Hamburg #432/R est:3500-4500

£2550 $4693 €3800 Homage (50x37cm-20x15in) s.i. gouache oil wax chk carpenter's pencil. 26-Mar-4 Ketterer, Hamburg #431/R est:3800-4500

GRIEVE, Alan Robert Colquhoun (1910-1970) Australian
£411 $645 €600 Sentinel gum (43x53cm-17x21in) s. canvasboard. 24-Nov-2 Goodman, Sydney #81/R est:600-900 (A.D 1150)
£432 $782 €631 View from North Head (38x30cm-15x12in) s. canvasboard. 31-Mar-4 Goodman, Sydney #411 (A.D 1050)

GRIEVE, Robert Henderson (1924-) Australian
Works on paper
£264 $414 €383 Samurai's dream (43x57cm-17x22in) s.d.8/2/92 W/C gouache crayon prov. 27-Aug-3 Christie's, Sydney #707 (A.D 650)
£687 $1250 €1003 Untitled (111x130cm-44x51in) s. gouache synthetic polymer. 16-Jun-4 Deutscher-Menzies, Melbourne #363/R est:2000-3000 (A.D 1800)

GRIEVE, Walter Graham (1872-1937) British
£400 $668 €584 Pittenweem (30x40cm-12x16in) s. board. 23-Oct-3 Bonhams, Edinburgh #304
£452 $756 €660 Nanny (34x45cm-13x18in) 17-Nov-3 Waddingtons, Toronto #148/R (C.D 1000)
£3500 $6545 €5110 Still life of a lustre vase of marigolds (23x19cm-9x7in) s. 25-Feb-4 Mallams, Oxford #166 est:3500-4500

GRIFFA, Giorgio (1936-) Italian
Works on paper
£549 $900 €802 Strisce orrizontale policromi (70x100cm-28x39in) s.i.d. verso gouache prov. 28-May-3 Sotheby's, Amsterdam #172/R
£667 $1227 €1000 Untitled (44x31cm-17x12in) s.d.1985 verso mixed media on canvas. 12-Jun-4 Meeting Art, Vercelli #71
£671 $1100 €980 Strisce orizzontal in 2 tonalita blu (68x183cm-27x72in) s.i. verso gouache canvas prov. 28-May-3 Sotheby's, Amsterdam #65/R
£3221 $5766 €4800 Untitled (118x139cm-46x55in) ink. exec.1971 prov. 25-May-4 Sotheby's, Milan #162/R est:3500

GRIFFEL, Lois (?) American
Works on paper
£250 $425 €365 Spring lane (30x41cm-12x16in) s. chl pastel. 9-Nov-3 Outer Cape Auctions, Provincetown #19/R

GRIFFIER, Jan (elder) (1652-1718) Dutch
£12000 $20760 €17520 Leda and the swan (50x75cm-20x30in) s. 11-Dec-3 Sotheby's, London #219/R est:12000-18000
Works on paper
£642 $1130 €950 Ruins of a castle (10x16cm-4x6in) red chk col wash prov. 19-May-4 Sotheby's, Amsterdam #85/R

GRIFFIER, Jan (elder-style) (1652-1718) Dutch
£4667 $8493 €7000 Paysage de la Vallee du Rhin (31x39cm-12x15in) panel prov. 29-Jun-4 Sotheby's, Paris #26/R est:6000-8000

GRIFFIER, Robert (attrib) (1688-1750) British
£3357 $5706 €4800 Ideal Rhine landscape with figures (24x33cm-9x13in) panel. 20-Nov-3 Van Ham, Cologne #1342/R est:6000

GRIFFIN, Ambrose Sylvester (1912-) Australian
£292 $534 €438 Horses and haystacks. canvas on board. 3-Jun-4 Joel, Victoria #265 (A.D 750)
£506 $926 €759 View of Kallista. board. 3-Jun-4 Joel, Victoria #359 (A.D 1300)

GRIFFIN, Keith Alastair (1927-) British
£260 $481 €380 Torrens laying to (49x69cm-19x27in) s. 14-Jul-4 Bonhams, Chester #495

GRIFFIN, Miss J L (19th C) British
£1600 $2944 €2336 Cloisters (76x107cm-30x42in) s.d.1887 prov. 11-Jun-4 Christie's, London #165/R est:1500-2000

GRIFFIN, T B (19th C) American
£994 $1800 €1451 Mountain landscape with waterfall and river rapids (76x64cm-30x25in) s. 3-Apr-4 Nadeau, Windsor #94 est:2000-3000
£1602 $2900 €2339 Mountain landscape with stream and rapids (51x41cm-20x16in) s. 3-Apr-4 Nadeau, Windsor #103 est:1500-1800

GRIFFIN, Thomas Bailey (1858-1918) American
£806 $1500 €1177 Passing storm (40x60cm-16x24in) s. i. stretcher. 5-Mar-4 Skinner, Boston #292/R est:700-900
£856 $1600 €1250 Landscapes (41x53cm-16x21in) s. pair. 29-Feb-4 Grogan, Boston #62/R
£960 $1747 €1402 River landscape (39x49cm-15x19in) 19-Jun-4 Lacy Scott, Bury St.Edmunds #402/R
£1061 $1900 €1549 Birches by a stream (46x8cm-18x3in) s. 26-May-4 Doyle, New York #28/R est:2000-3000
£1125 $1800 €1643 Summer on the meadows (41x61cm-16x24in) s.i. 21-Sep-3 William Jenack, New York #208 est:1500-2500

GRIFFIN, Vaughan Murray (1903-1992) Australian
£810 $1304 €1183 River (44x53cm-17x21in) s. board. 13-Oct-3 Joel, Victoria #319 est:2000-3000 (A.D 2000)

GRIFFIN, Walter (1861-1935) American
£1553 $2500 €2267 French pastoral (30x23cm-12x9in) s. 20-Aug-3 James Julia, Fairfield #1529/R est:1500-2500
£1863 $3000 €2720 Under the bridge, Venice (33x41cm-13x16in) s. s.i.d.1913 verso prov. 20-Aug-3 James Julia, Fairfield #1528/R est:3000-5000
£4032 $7500 €5887 View of a village, France (23x33cm-9x13in) s.indis.i. d.1898. 3-Mar-4 Christie's, Rockefeller NY #42/R est:2500-3500
Works on paper
£462 $800 €675 Harbour in Brittany (28x34cm-11x13in) s. s.i.verso pastel. 13-Dec-3 Weschler, Washington #556
£530 $964 €800 Sortie d'eglise (39x29cm-15x11in) s. pastel. 16-Jun-4 Renaud, Paris #35
£898 $1500 €1311 Oaks (30x41cm-12x16in) s. pastel pencil. 19-Oct-3 Susanin's, Chicago #6039/R est:1500-2000

GRIFFIN, William (19th C) British
£2500 $4475 €3650 The snow Mary running past an offshore island under full sail (47x72cm-19x28in) s.d.1848 panel. 26-May-4 Christie's, Kensington #604/R est:3000-5000
£3500 $6265 €5110 Whaling ships Jane and Harmony off the port of Hull (51x80cm-20x31in) s.indis.d.1853 panel. 26-May-4 Christie's, Kensington #603/R est:3000-5000
£8000 $13600 €11680 Merchant shipping and Mediterranean pinke in close quarters off Gibraltar (60x105cm-24x41in) s.i.d.1845. 19-Nov-3 Christie's, Kensington #469/R est:8000-12000

GRIFFING, Robert (20th C) American
£8556 $16000 €12492 Lead scout (36x28cm-14x11in) s. 24-Jul-4 Coeur d'Alene, Hayden #207/R est:8000-12000
£26738 $50000 €39037 He befriended me greatly (91x127cm-36x50in) s. exhib.lit. 24-Jul-4 Coeur d'Alene, Hayden #128/R est:75000-125000

GRIFFITH, Grace Allison (1885-1955) American
Works on paper
£449 $750 €656 View of Hawaii (30x37cm-12x15in) s. W/C. 26-Oct-3 Bonhams & Butterfields, San Francisco #6513/R

GRIFFITH, Louis Oscar (1875-1956) American
Works on paper
£305 $500 €442 Summer sky (11x14cm-4x6in) s. W/C exec.c.1920. 7-Jun-3 Treadway Gallery, Cincinnati #1412

GRIFFITH, Marie Osthaus (20th C) American/German
£633 $1000 €924 Still life with grapes (30x30cm-12x12in) s. pair. 7-Sep-3 Treadway Gallery, Cincinnati #577/R

GRIFFITH, Moses (1747-1819) British
Works on paper
£360 $612 €526 Conway (17x11cm-7x4in) s.i. W/C. 18-Nov-3 Sotheby's, Olympia #177/R
£1000 $1700 €1460 Erddig (26x42cm-10x17in) pen ink W/C exhib. 18-Nov-3 Sotheby's, Olympia #181/R est:1000-1500

GRIFFITH, William Alexander (1866-1940) American
£1902 $3500 €2777 Tilled rows with golden hills beyond (50x61cm-20x24in) painted 1936 prov. 8-Jun-4 Bonhams & Butterfields, San Francisco #4246/R est:3000-5000

GRIFFITHS, David (1939-) British
£1800 $2934 €2628 Half-length portrait of the artist Sir Kyffin Williams (53x43cm-21x17in) s. 27-Sep-3 Rogers Jones, Clwyd #93/R

GRIFFITHS, Harley Cameron (1908-1981) Australian
£458 $834 €669 Flowers in a glass vase (44x34cm-17x13in) s.d.46. 16-Jun-4 Deutscher-Menzies, Melbourne #559/R est:1000-2000 (A.D 1200)

GRIFFITHS, James (1825-1896) Canadian
Works on paper
£234 $375 €342 Easy going (15x28cm-6x11in) s. W/C. 20-Sep-3 Bunte, Elgin #1464f
£250 $400 €365 Nearing the line (18x28cm-7x11in) s.d.1984 W/C. 20-Sep-3 Bunte, Elgin #1464
£266 $425 €388 Favourable winds (30x46cm-12x18in) s.d.1983 W/C. 20-Sep-3 Bunte, Elgin #1464a
£266 $425 €388 Making more sail (25x38cm-10x15in) s. W/C. 20-Sep-3 Bunte, Elgin #1464j
£266 $425 €388 Into the evening (25x38cm-10x15in) s.d.1982 W/C. 20-Sep-3 Bunte, Elgin #1464l
£281 $523 €410 Roses (23x16cm-9x6in) s. W/C. 2-Mar-4 Ritchie, Toronto #66/R (C.D 700)
£297 $475 €434 In light airs (25x38cm-10x15in) s.d.1983 W/C. 20-Sep-3 Bunte, Elgin #1464h
£375 $600 €548 Home before evening (25x38cm-10x15in) s.d.1981 W/C. 20-Sep-3 Bunte, Elgin #1464b
£375 $600 €548 Before the wind (30x46cm-12x18in) s.d.1983 W/C. 20-Sep-3 Bunte, Elgin #1464c
£407 $650 €594 Bound for the Horn (30x48cm-12x19in) s.d.1982 W/C. 20-Sep-3 Bunte, Elgin #1464k
£500 $800 €730 Every sea a race (30x46cm-12x18in) s.d.1983 W/C. 20-Sep-3 Bunte, Elgin #1464d
£500 $800 €730 On company business (46x66cm-18x26in) s.d.1980 W/C. 20-Sep-3 Bunte, Elgin #1464g
£800 $1464 €1168 Roses and morning glory (18x23cm-7x9in) mono. W/C. 1-Jun-4 Joyner Waddington, Toronto #396/R est:1500-1800 (C.D 2000)

£1120 $2050 €1635 Climbing morning glory (37x29cm-15x11in) s. W/C. 1-Jun-4 Joyner Waddington, Toronto #229/R est:3000-3500 (C.D 2800)

GRIFFITHS, Philip Jones (1936-) British
Photographs
£4833 $8700 €7056 Wounded civilian, Quang Ngai, Vietnam (35x23cm-14x9in) gelatin silver print. 24-Apr-4 Phillips, New York #97/R est:8000-12000

GRIGGS, Frederick Landseer Maur (1876-1932) British
Prints
£2200 $4048 €3212 Fen Monastery (20x24cm-8x9in) s. etching. 28-Jun-4 Bonhams, New Bond Street #151/R est:300-500
£2700 $4968 €3942 The Almonry (24x17cm-9x7in) init. etching. 23-Mar-4 Rosebery Fine Art, London #960 est:250-300

GRIGGS, Samuel W (1827-1898) American
£2112 $3400 €3084 Grouse in landscape (38x33cm-15x13in) s. 20-Aug-3 James Julia, Fairfield #1765/R est:1000-1500

GRIGORESCO, Nicolas (1838-1907) Rumanian
£6061 $10848 €8849 Summer landscape with peasant and ox plough (24x45cm-9x18in) s. panel. 22-Mar-4 Philippe Schuler, Zurich #4409/R est:3000-4000 (S.FR 14000)

GRIGORIEV, Boris (1886-1939) Russian
£45000 $80550 €65700 Flowers in the yard (74x61cm-29x24in) s. 26-May-4 Sotheby's, London #155/R est:30000-40000
£50000 $85000 €73000 Still life with poppies (60x72cm-24x28in) s. 19-Nov-3 Sotheby's, London #211/R est:25000-35000
£52778 $95000 €77056 Vibrant landscape (65x92cm-26x36in) s. 23-Apr-4 Sotheby's, New York #81/R est:70000-90000
£65000 $116350 €94900 Provincial French street (60x73cm-24x29in) s. 26-May-4 Sotheby's, London #154/R est:20000-30000
Works on paper
£1553 $2500 €2267 Beach scene (30x41cm-12x16in) s. pencil oil W/C. 20-Aug-3 James Julia, Fairfield #1066/R est:1750-2250
£3500 $5950 €5110 Black girl by the tree (33x49cm-13x19in) s. gouache. 19-Nov-3 Sotheby's, London #210/R est:4000-6000
£4000 $6800 €5840 West Indian Street Scene (36x49cm-14x19in) s. gouache. 19-Nov-3 Sotheby's, London #208/R est:4000-6000
£4000 $6800 €5840 House on stilts, West India (37x50cm-15x20in) s. gouache. 19-Nov-3 Sotheby's, London #209/R est:4000-6000
£4167 $7500 €6084 Chilean landscape (34x50cm-13x20in) s. i.verso pencil W/C gouache. 23-Apr-4 Sotheby's, New York #78/R est:6000-8000
£6000 $10200 €9000 Old houses in Quimper, Brittany (45x32cm-18x13in) s.d.924 pencil W/C gouache. 25-Nov-3 Christie's, London #200/R est:6000-8000
£7222 $13000 €10544 Blue Bay, Brazil (39x53cm-15x21in) s. pencil W/C gouache. 23-Apr-4 Sotheby's, New York #79/R est:6000-8000
£7692 $12000 € Le matin (28x42cm-11x17in) s.i. gouache prov.lit. 11-Apr-3 Christie's, Rockefeller NY #44/R est:12000-18000

GRIJN, Eric van der (20th C) Irish?
£733 $1327 €1100 Geese at Tsjernobyl (50x70cm-20x28in) s.d.1986 prov. 30-Mar-4 De Veres Art Auctions, Dublin #109e/R
£1579 $2905 €2400 Geese at Tsjernobyl (50x70cm-20x28in) s.i.d.1987 prov. 22-Jun-4 De Veres Art Auctions, Dublin #38/R est:1000-1500

GRILL, Oswald (1878-1969) Austrian
£528 $924 €750 Winter landscape (49x64cm-19x25in) s. 19-Dec-3 Dorotheum, Vienna #97/R
£2778 $4528 €4000 Attersee (80x96cm-31x38in) s. 23-Sep-3 Wiener Kunst Auktionen, Vienna #123/R est:2000-4000

GRILLO, John (1917-) American
£1477 $2600 €2156 Yellow abstraction (361x277cm-142x109in) 22-May-4 Selkirks, St. Louis #565/R est:3000-4000

GRILO, Sarah (1921-) Argentinian
£1285 $2300 €1876 Verde brillante (127x140cm-50x55in) s. s.d.1962 verso prov. 20-Mar-4 Sloans & Kenyon, Bethesda #1162/R est:1000-1500

GRIM, Maurice (1890-1968) French
£489 $842 €700 La vallee (38x56cm-15x22in) s. 3-Dec-3 Tajan, Paris #239/R
£567 $1020 €850 Paysage (33x41cm-13x16in) s. panel. 26-Apr-4 Tajan, Paris #362/R

GRIMALDI, Giovanni Francesco (1606-1680) Italian
Works on paper
£952 $1705 €1400 Deux figures au bord d'une fleuve, une montagne a l'arriere plan (10x13cm-4x5in) pen brown ink double-sided. 18-Mar-4 Christie's, Paris #223/R
£1088 $1948 €1600 Une etude de fontaine avec un cheval (18x12cm-7x5in) pen brown ink prov. 18-Mar-4 Christie's, Paris #224/R est:1200-1800

GRIMALDI, Giovanni Francesco (attrib) (1606-1680) Italian
Works on paper
£700 $1211 €1022 River landscape with boats seen in the distance (21x30cm-8x12in) i. pen brown ink. 12-Dec-3 Christie's, Kensington #357

GRIMALDI, Giovanni Francesco (style) (1606-1680) Italian
Works on paper
£290 $484 €420 Landscape with bridge and ruined walls (25x20cm-10x8in) pen prov. 15-Nov-3 Lempertz, Koln #1328

GRIMALDI, Mario (1927-1997) American
£227 $400 €331 Surrealist depiction of a man and a horse (119x119cm-47x47in) s. 22-May-4 Selkirks, St. Louis #566

GRIMALDI, Paolo (20th C) Italian
£267 $491 €400 Destroyed myth (25x50cm-10x20in) s.d.1992 s.i.d.verso tempera oil board. 12-Jun-4 Meeting Art, Vercelli #74

GRIMALDI, William (1751-1830) British
Miniatures
£7800 $13260 €11388 Sp. (12cm-5in) i. prov.exhib.lit. 18-Nov-3 Bonhams, New Bond Street #134/R est:3000-5000
£14000 $25200 €20440 Mrs Sophia Hawkins Whitshed, nee Bentinck with her son James (4cm-2in) s.d.1798 s.i.verso ormolu frame oval exhib. 22-Apr-4 Bonhams, New Bond Street #114/R est:6000-8000

GRIMANI, Guido (1871-1933) Italian
£1259 $2165 €1800 Pond in Comeno (26x35cm-10x14in) s. s.i.d.1926 verso board. 3-Dec-3 Stadion, Trieste #1123/R est:1500-2000
£1600 $2864 €2400 Coast (24x34cm-9x13in) s. cardboard. 12-May-4 Stadion, Trieste #679/R est:1500-2000

GRIMAUX, Louis (1811-1879) French
£1625 $2600 €2373 Portrait of a man (74x58cm-29x23in) after Rembrandt. 20-Sep-3 Bunte, Elgin #1402 est:3000-5000

GRIMELUND, Johannes Martin (1842-1917) Norwegian
£311 $516 €451 Norwegian fjord landscape (31x41cm-12x16in) s. panel. 16-Jun-3 Blomqvist, Lysaker #1315 (N.KR 3600)
£417 $722 €609 Woman on woodland path (35x24cm-14x9in) s. 13-Dec-3 Blomqvist, Lysaker #1117 (N.KR 4800)
£523 $956 €764 Canal landscape with church (38x55cm-15x22in) s. 2-Feb-4 Blomqvist, Lysaker #1076/R (N.KR 6500)
£793 $1459 €1158 Cheese farm (34x46cm-13x18in) s. 29-Mar-4 Blomqvist, Lysaker #1088/R (N.KR 10000)
£1030 $1803 €1504 Harbour scene from Antwerp (50x39cm-20x15in) s.i.d.1885. 16-Dec-3 Grev Wedels Plass, Oslo #161/R est:12000-15000 (N.KR 12000)
£1107 $1905 €1616 Soleil couchant, Bretagne (33x46cm-13x18in) s.d.1910 i.stretcher. 8-Dec-3 Blomqvist, Oslo #403/R est:15000-18000 (N.KR 13000)
£1220 $2232 €1781 Late summer in Ny-Hellesund (46x38cm-18x15in) s.d.5-9-90. 7-Jun-4 Blomqvist, Oslo #285/R est:20000-30000 (N.KR 15000)
£1223 $2190 €1786 View of Dordrecht, Holland (38x55cm-15x22in) s.d.1897 i.stretcher. 25-May-4 Grev Wedels Plass, Oslo #12/R est:15000-20000 (N.KR 15000)
£1397 $2500 €2040 Harbour scene with sailing ships and row boats landing (43x58cm-17x23in) s.d.1910. 21-Mar-4 Jeffery Burchard, Florida #12/R
£2402 $4299 €3507 Landscape with man and horse (66x85cm-26x33in) s.d.1875. 22-Mar-4 Blomqvist, Oslo #327/R est:35000-45000 (N.KR 30000)

GRIMM, Arthur (1883-1948) German
£2133 $3861 €3200 Schloss Neuweier near Baden-Baden (70x85cm-28x33in) s.d. 2-Apr-4 Winterberg, Heidelberg #1048/R est:4500

GRIMM, Ludwig Emil (1790-1863) German
Works on paper
£655 $1192 €956 Holy Elizabeth carrying her son humbly to church (21x26cm-8x10in) i. pencil prov. 17-Jun-4 Kornfeld, Bern #20/R (S.FR 1500)
£12000 $21960 €17520 Rugged moonlit landscape with a woman seated by gnarled tree roots (35x50cm-14x20in) pen point of the brush brown ink over blk chk blue paper prov. 8-Jul-4 Sotheby's, London #160/R est:2500-3500

GRIMM, Paul (1892-1974) American
£383 $700 €559 Eucalyptus trees in California landscape (30x48cm-12x19in) s. 10-Apr-4 Auctions by the Bay, Alameda #1567/R
£815 $1500 €1190 Front yard of San Gorgonia (41x51cm-16x20in) s. i.verso panel. 29-Mar-4 O'Gallerie, Oregon #712/R est:1500-2000
£1018 $1700 €1486 Sierra activity (41x51cm-16x20in) s. s.i.d.1964 verso canvasboard. 26-Oct-3 Bonhams & Butterfields, San Francisco #6527/R
£1156 $2000 €1688 Desert landscape (66x81cm-26x32in) s. 13-Dec-3 Charlton Hall, Columbia #578/R est:2000-3000
£1176 $2000 €1717 Desert contrasts (64x102cm-25x40in) s. i.verso. 18-Nov-3 John Moran, Pasadena #188 est:2000-3000
£1374 $2500 €2006 Autumn day (30x41cm-12x16in) s. i.verso canvasboard prov. 15-Jun-4 John Moran, Pasadena #177a est:2000-2500
£1445 $2500 €2110 Summer at the foot of the high Sierras. (46x61cm-18x24in) s. i.verso canvasboard prov. 10-Dec-3 Bonhams & Butterfields, San Francisco #6308/R est:3000-5000
£1587 $3000 €2317 Where silence reigns (41x76cm-16x30in) s. i. verso prov. 17-Feb-4 John Moran, Pasadena #194/R est:1500-2500
£1618 $2750 €2362 Eucalyptus banning (30x41cm-12x16in) s. i.d.42 verso. 18-Nov-3 John Moran, Pasadena #14 est:2000-3000
£1946 $3250 €2841 Desert jewels (66x102cm-26x40in) s. 27-Oct-3 O'Gallerie, Oregon #755/R est:2000-3000
£1984 $3750 €2897 Landscape - morning on the hillside (38x30cm-15x12in) s. canvasboard. 17-Feb-4 John Moran, Pasadena #62/R est:2500-3500
£2059 $3500 €3006 Where desert and mountains meet (41x51cm-16x20in) i.verso masonite painted c.1930. 18-Nov-3 John Moran, Pasadena #177 est:2000-3000
£2116 $4000 €3089 Sierra autumn (71x91cm-28x36in) s. i. verso prov. 17-Feb-4 John Moran, Pasadena #140/R est:2500-3500
£2418 $4400 €3530 Delightful region (76x61cm-30x24in) s. i.verso. 19-Jun-4 Jackson's, Cedar Falls #11/R est:2000-3000
£2890 $5000 €4219 Old San Jacinto (61x81cm-24x32in) s. i.verso masonite prov. 10-Dec-3 Bonhams & Butterfields, San Francisco #6331/R est:4000-6000
£3022 $5500 €4412 High Sierras landscape (30x41cm-12x16in) s. i.verso board prov. 15-Jun-4 John Moran, Pasadena #177 est:2500-3500

£3179 $5500 €4641 Desert river bed (51x61cm-20x24in) s. i.verso masonite prov. 10-Dec-3 Bonhams & Butterfields, San Francisco #6330/R est:4000-6000
£3439 $6500 €5021 Landscape - Country Road (61x51cm-24x20in) s. i.d.1950 verso canvasboard prov. 17-Feb-4 John Moran, Pasadena #61/R est:3000-5000
£3846 $7000 €5615 California vista (76x61cm-30x24in) s. i.d.1945 verso prov. 15-Jun-4 John Moran, Pasadena #118 est:4000-6000

GRIMM, Samuel Hieronymus (1733-1794) Swiss
Works on paper
£700 $1190 €1022 Village scenes (27x34cm-11x13in) s.d.1770 W/C over pen ink pair. 25-Nov-3 Bonhams, Knightsbridge #160/R

GRIMM, Samuel Hieronymus (attrib) (1733-1794) Swiss
Works on paper
£320 $534 €467 Parish church of St Paul's, Hammersmith (22x31cm-9x12in) pencil pen black ink W/C. 16-Oct-3 Christie's, Kensington #63

GRIMM, Walter O (1894-1919) American/German
Works on paper
£336 $561 €480 Self portrait (14x9cm-6x4in) s.d. pencil col pen card. 10-Oct-3 Winterberg, Heidelberg #1333/R

GRIMMER, Abel (1573-1619) Flemish
£18792 $34577 €28000 Winter landscape with woodcutters (35cm-14in circular) panel tondo. 24-Mar-4 Dorotheum, Vienna #177/R est:25000-30000

GRIMMER, Abel (circle) (1573-1619) Flemish
£18056 $29431 €26000 Landscape with harbour and flight of Mary (53x87cm-21x34in) panel. 25-Sep-3 Dr Fritz Nagel, Stuttgart #1228/R est:4800

GRIMMER, Jacob (1526-1589) Flemish
£29730 $52324 €44000 Extensive landscape with harvest (74x107cm-29x42in) panel prov. 22-May-4 Lempertz, Koln #1057/R est:50000-70000
£70000 $121100 €102200 Summer, landscape with peasants, cattle and sheep. Winter, a village scene (40x61cm-16x24in) panel pair. 10-Dec-3 Christie's, London #2/R est:60000-80000
Works on paper
£9444 $17000 €13788 Landscape with a village and church beyond. Ruined courtyard (14x20cm-6x8in) black chk pen brown ink col wash double-sided prov. 22-Jan-4 Christie's, Rockefeller NY #115/R est:15000-20000

GRIMMER, Jacob (attrib) (1526-1589) Flemish
£34000 $62220 €49640 Winter landscape with figures skating (31x47cm-12x19in) s. panel. 8-Jul-4 Sotheby's, London #231/R est:20000-30000

GRIMMER, Jacob (circle) (1526-1589) Flemish
£6250 $9875 €9000 Extensive wooded landscape with huntsmen, peasant and cattle in the distance (29x41cm-11x16in) panel exhib. 2-Sep-3 Christie's, Amsterdam #26/R est:3500-5500

GRIMMER, Jacob (school) (1526-1589) Flemish
£8054 $14416 €12000 Paysage d'hiver avec le massacre des innocents (72x105cm-28x41in) panel. 25-May-4 Palais de Beaux Arts, Brussels #538/R est:13500-17000

GRIMOU, Alexis (1680-1740) French
£23026 $42368 €35000 Portrait d'homme au chapeau a la plume (66x54cm-26x21in) prov. 23-Jun-4 Sotheby's, Paris #17/R est:40000-60000

GRIMSDALE, Murray (20th C) New Zealander
£321 $582 €469 Portrait of Tony Fomison (18x11cm-7x4in) s.d.1978 enamel on board prov. 30-Mar-4 Peter Webb, Auckland #30/R (NZ.D 900)

GRIMSHAW, Atkinson (1836-1893) British
£14000 $23800 €20440 Sunday night, Knostrup Cut, Leeds (20x30cm-8x12in) s.d.93 s.i.d.verso. 25-Nov-3 Christie's, London #176/R est:6000-8000
£19000 $32300 €27740 St. Cecilia (30x20cm-12x8in) s.d.1852 boardprov.exhib. 25-Nov-3 Christie's, London #145/R est:15000-20000
£26000 $47840 €37960 Colwith Force (35x44cm-14x17in) s.d.1869 card. 9-Jun-4 Christie's, London #37/R est:20000-30000
£29000 $49300 €42340 Whitby (21x41cm-8x16in) s. oil on card. 27-Nov-3 Sotheby's, London #319/R est:18000-25000
£35000 $63700 €51100 Broomielaw, Glasgow (30x46cm-12x18in) s. prov. 16-Jun-4 Bonhams, New Bond Street #71/R est:40000-60000
£40000 $73600 €58400 In the winter's twilight glow (31x45cm-12x18in) s. s.i.verso prov.exhib.lit. 23-Mar-4 Bonhams, New Bond Street #78/R est:20000-30000
£40000 $72800 €58400 Twilight, the vegetable garden (39x55cm-15x22in) s.d.1869 card on canvas lit. 1-Jul-4 Sotheby's, London #308/R est:40000-60000
£47222 $85000 €68944 Broomielaw, Glasgow (30x46cm-12x18in) s. s.i.d.1889 verso. 23-Apr-4 Sotheby's, New York #66/R est:70000-90000
£50000 $85000 €73000 Lovers at the gate (36x47cm-14x19in) s.d.1881 board on panel prov. 27-Nov-3 Sotheby's, London #321/R est:50000-70000
£53954 $96578 €78773 Palace park scene (77x63cm-30x25in) s.d.1881. 25-May-4 Bukowskis, Stockholm #354a/R est:200000-250000 (S.KR 730000)
£58000 $106720 €84680 Landscape in the lake District (38x51cm-15x20in) s.i.d.1863 board arched top. 26-Mar-4 Sotheby's, London #62/R est:40000-60000
£60000 $110400 €87600 Golden idyll (31x46cm-12x18in) s. i.verso. 23-Mar-4 Bonhams, New Bond Street #77/R est:30000-50000
£60000 $109200 €87600 Forge Valley near Scarborough (51x38cm-20x15in) s.i.d.1880 board prov. 1-Jul-4 Sotheby's, London #307/R est:40000-60000
£72000 $132480 €105120 Arriving at the hall (21x44cm-8x17in) s.d.1878 oil on card. 11-Jun-4 Christie's, London #140/R est:30000-50000
£75000 $127500 €109500 Evening on the Strand looking towards St. Mary's London (31x46cm-12x18in) s. panel prov. 27-Nov-3 Sotheby's, London #322/R est:70000-100000
£90000 $153000 €131400 Golden Idyll (31x46cm-12x18in) s. s.i.verso prov. 25-Nov-3 Christie's, London #173/R est:60000-80000
£105000 $178500 €153300 Boar Lane, Leeds, by lamplight (49x77cm-19x30in) s.d.1881 s.i.verso prov.exhib.lit. 19-Nov-3 Bonhams, New Bond Street #118/R est:70000-100000
£105882 $180000 €154588 Cheshire road by moonlight (51x76cm-20x30in) s.i.d.1883 verso. 28-Oct-3 Sotheby's, New York #75/R est:200000-300000
£120000 $220800 €175200 Fish landing, Whitby (61x92cm-24x36in) s. s.i.verso. 11-Jun-4 Christie's, London #141/R est:80000-120000
£130000 $221000 €189800 Thames below bridge (51x77cm-20x30in) s.d.1884 s.i.d.verso prov. 25-Nov-3 Christie's, London #172/R est:100000-150000
£135000 $229500 €197100 November (46x35cm-18x14in) s. s.i.d.1881 verso board. 27-Nov-3 Sotheby's, London #320/R est:50000-70000
£161111 $290000 €235222 Old Chelsea (76x64cm-30x25in) s. s.i.verso prov. 23-Apr-4 Sotheby's, New York #64/R est:250000-350000
£170000 $312800 €248200 Study of beeches (43x55cm-17x22in) s.d.1872 s.i.d.verso card prov.exhib. 9-Jun-4 Christie's, London #36/R est:150000-250000
£176471 $300000 €257648 Late October (51x76cm-20x30in) s.d.1882 s.i.verso. 28-Oct-3 Sotheby's, New York #76/R est:180000-220000
£180000 $306000 €262800 Whitby by moonlight (51x76cm-20x30in) s.d.1872 prov. 27-Nov-3 Sotheby's, London #323/R est:120000-180000
£190000 $349600 €277400 Reekie, Glasgow (61x93cm-24x37in) s. s.i.verso prov. 9-Jun-4 Christie's, London #39/R est:150000-250000
£205556 $370000 €300112 Autumn gold (76x63cm-30x25in) s. s.i.verso prov. 23-Apr-4 Sotheby's, New York #63/R est:250000-350000
£240000 $441600 €350400 Autumn (61x92cm-24x36in) s.d.1871 prov.exhib. 9-Jun-4 Christie's, London #35/R est:250000-350000

GRIMSHAW, Louis (1870-1943) British
£51000 $93840 €74460 Royal mile, Edinburgh, the approach to Holyrood Palace (31x42cm-12x17in) s.d.5/95 board. 11-Jun-4 Christie's, London #142/R est:10000-15000

GRIMSHAW, Marc (20th C) British
Works on paper
£300 $480 €438 Northern terraced street scene (41x48cm-16x19in) s. pastel. 16-Sep-3 Capes Dunn, Manchester #724
£320 $512 €467 Coalman (33x30cm-13x12in) s. 16-Sep-3 Capes Dunn, Manchester #704
£400 $640 €584 Ice-cream van (33x46cm-13x18in) s. pastel. 16-Sep-3 Capes Dunn, Manchester #703/R

GRINDELL, R (19th C) Australian
Works on paper
£2439 $4366 €3561 Colonial family portrait (43x54cm-17x21in) s. W/C prov. 4-May-4 Sotheby's, Melbourne #156/R est:3000-5000 (A.D 6000)

GRINEAU, Bryan de (1882-1957) French
Works on paper
£480 $874 €701 Stalinist edifice (47x36cm-19x14in) s.i. black chk. 15-Jun-4 Rosebery Fine Art, London #682/R

GRIOT, Francois Marie (1951-) French
Works on paper
£364 $681 €550 Le grand If rouge (54x81cm-21x32in) s. W/C canvas. 24-Jul-4 Thierry & Lannon, Brest #264/R

GRIPENHOLM, Ulf (1943-) Swedish
£1095 $1862 €1599 Lovers (15x21cm-6x8in) s.d.1984 tempera paper lit. 4-Nov-3 Bukowskis, Stockholm #576/R (S.KR 14500)

GRIPS, Charles Joseph (1825-1920) Belgian
£2368 $4358 €3600 Woman in an interior (28x20cm-11x8in) s.d.1866 panel. 28-Jun-4 Sotheby's, Amsterdam #5/R est:3000-5000
£9783 $18000 €14283 Baby sleeping in the crib (43x33cm-17x13in) s. panel. 26-Jun-4 Susanin's, Chicago #6086/R est:6000-8000

GRIS, Juan (1887-1927) Spanish
£180000 $327600 €262800 La liseuse (80x65cm-31x26in) s.d.26 prov.exhib.lit. 3-Feb-4 Christie's, London #240/R est:180000-240000
£220175 $405123 €321456 Bouteille et poires (35x27cm-14x11in) s. painted 1920 prov.exhib.lit. 23-Jun-4 Koller, Zurich #3040/R est:500000-800000 (S.FR 502000)
£402235 $720000 €587263 Bouteille, pipe et cartes a jouer (55x38cm-22x15in) s.d.19 prov.exhib.lit. 6-May-4 Sotheby's, New York #111/R est:400000-600000
£3687151 $6600000 €5383240 Console de marbre (61x50cm-24x20in) oil collage mirrored glass on canvas painted 1914 prov.exhib.lit. 6-May-4 Sotheby's, New York #114/R est:4500000-6500000
Prints
£1765 $3000 €2577 Nature morte (17x25cm-7x10in) col pochoir. 6-Nov-3 Swann Galleries, New York #546/R est:4000-6000
Works on paper
£2156 $3600 €3148 Au cafe. Female nude (43x34cm-17x13in) s. ink W/C over pencil double-sided prov. 7-Oct-3 Sotheby's, New York #257 est:6000-8000
£3988 $6500 €5822 Compotier aux deux pommes (21x27cm-8x11in) pencil prov.lit. 25-Sep-3 Christie's, Rockefeller NY #616/R est:6000-8000
£6000 $10980 €9000 Cafetiere (48x32cm-19x13in) chl prov.exhib.lit. 7-Jun-4 Artcurial Briest, Paris #6/R est:14000-18000
£7333 $13420 €11000 Cuilliere (11x17cm-4x7in) crayon dr prov.exhib.lit. 7-Jun-4 Artcurial Briest, Paris #1/R est:8000-12000
£10000 $18301 €15000 Lampe a petrole (48x32cm-19x13in) chl prov.exhib.lit. 7-Jun-4 Artcurial Briest, Paris #4/R est:20000-30000
£10667 $19520 €16000 Serment (20x13cm-8x5in) s.i. chi dr htd gouache prov.lit. 7-Jun-4 Artcurial Briest, Paris #15/R est:8000-12000
£10811 $19351 €16000 Chez Maxim (38x28cm-15x11in) s. col pen ink prov.lit. 8-May-4 Schloss Ahlden, Ahlden #812/R est:16000

£11333	$20740	€17000	Alcofibras et la demoiselle (32x23cm-13x9in) i. crayon Chinese ink dr prov.exhib.lit. 7-Jun-4 Artcurial Briest, Paris #13/R est:20000-30000
£13333	$24400	€20000	Portrait de Josette Gris (22x18cm-9x7in) crayon dr prov.exhib.lit. 7-Jun-4 Artcurial Briest, Paris #12/R est:20000-30000
£13333	$24399	€20	Guitariste (22x16cm-9x6in) crayon dr prov.exhib.lit. 7-Jun-4 Artcurial Briest, Paris #16/R est:20000-30000
£22000	$40260	€33000	Femme assise (48x32cm-19x13in) s.i.d.1910 chl prov.exhib.lit. 7-Jun-4 Artcurial Briest, Paris #9/R est:20000-30000
£27333	$50020	€41000	Vaporisateur (48x32cm-19x13in) chl prov.exhib.lit. 7-Jun-4 Artcurial Briest, Paris #7/R est:70000-90000
£30000	$54901	€45000	Nature morte au gobelet (48x32cm-19x13in) chl prov.exhib.lit. 7-Jun-4 Artcurial Briest, Paris #11/R est:60000-80000
£68000	$123760	€99280	Still life (39x28cm-15x11in) s.d.1916 pencil prov. 5-Feb-4 Christie's, London #354/R est:20000-30000

GRISENKO, Nikolas (1856-1900) Russian

£9000	$16560	€13500	Voiliers a quai a Saint-Valery-en-Caux (45x31cm-18x12in) s.d.1892 panel. 9-Jun-4 Beaussant & Lefèvre, Paris #163/R est:2000-3000
£14000	$23800	€20440	Harbour scene in France (74x49cm-29x19in) s. 19-Nov-3 Sotheby's, London #52/R est:6000-8000
£80000	$143200	€116800	Naval parade in the Baltic (142x221cm-56x87in) s. 26-May-4 Sotheby's, London #70/R est:30000-40000
Works on paper			
£3500	$6265	€5110	River Volga (8x20cm-3x8in) three int. i. W/C group of five. 26-May-4 Sotheby's, London #51/R est:4000-6000

GRISET, Ernest (1844-1907) French

Works on paper			
£26000	$45760	€37960	Boar, rabbit and wild fowl hunting. Salmon fishing in Scotland and fox hunting (24x34cm-9x13in) s. pencil blk ink W/C htd bodycol two albums 35 subjects. 21-May-4 Christie's, London #64/R est:6000-8000

GRISON, François Adolphe (1845-1914) French

£837	$1423	€1222	Proud musketeer (68x47cm-27x19in) s. 28-Nov-3 Zofingen, Switzerland #2598/R est:4000 (S.FR 1850)
£3964	$7095	€5787	Collector in an interior (69x90cm-27x35in) s. prov. 31-May-4 Stephan Welz, Johannesburg #461/R est:20000-30000 (SA.R 48000)

GRISOT, Pierre (1911-1995) French

£264	$475	€385	Pink dress (53x43cm-21x17in) s. 23-Jan-4 Freeman, Philadelphia #222/R
£400	$668	€584	Portrait of a young woman in yellow (35x27cm-14x11in) s. 21-Oct-3 Bonhams, Knightsbridge #123
£417	$750	€609	Susy at the races (46x53cm-18x21in) s. 23-Jan-4 Freeman, Philadelphia #104/R
£530	$970	€800	Still life with fruit (65x81cm-26x32in) s.d.70. 7-Apr-4 Piasa, Paris #248
£694	$1160	€1000	Young Parisian woman in park (34x27cm-13x11in) s. panel lit. 25-Oct-3 Bergmann, Erlangen #973/R
£700	$1190	€1022	Portrait of a lady on the banks of the river Seine (25x20cm-10x8in) s. board. 26-Nov-3 Peter Wilson, Nantwich #82/R
£724	$1209	€1057	Sophie (45x38cm-18x15in) s. i. verso. 17-Nov-3 Waddingtons, Toronto #203/R (C.D 1600)
£729	$1218	€1050	Young Parisian woman by Seine (34x27cm-13x11in) s. panel lit. 25-Oct-3 Bergmann, Erlangen #972/R
£828	$1515	€1250	Fillette blonde assise (24x19cm-9x7in) bears traces sig. panel. 7-Apr-4 Piasa, Paris #247
£897	$1641	€1300	Les petites ballerines (27x22cm-11x9in) s. panel. 1-Feb-4 Feletin, Province #74/R
£952	$1705	€1400	Jeune fille peignant (35x27cm-14x11in) s. isorel panel. 19-Mar-4 Millon & Associes, Paris #102
£1035	$1728	€1480	Jeune fille en robe jaune (27x22cm-11x9in) s. panel. 29-Jun-3 Feletin, Province #86/R
£1056	$1827	€1500	Dans les rues de Paris (46x38cm-18x15in) s. 12-Dec-3 Piasa, Paris #166 est:1000-1500
£1096	$1863	€1600	Jeune fille dans le parc (46x38cm-18x15in) s. 9-Nov-3 Eric Pillon, Calais #222/R
£1343	$2457	€1961	Parisienne au bois (61x50cm-24x20in) s. 9-Jun-4 Rasmussen, Copenhagen #1602/R est:15000 (D.KR 15000)
£1507	$2562	€2200	Jeune fille au champ des courses (55x46cm-22x18in) s. 9-Nov-3 Eric Pillon, Calais #220/R
£1517	$2807	€2200	Jeune fille nue de profil (85x73cm-33x29in) s. 16-Feb-4 Horta, Bruxelles #420 est:1000-1500
£1575	$2678	€2300	Nu a l'ombrelle (56x46cm-22x18in) s. 9-Nov-3 Eric Pillon, Calais #219/R
£1620	$2835	€2300	Jeune elegante a l'ombrelle jaune (27x22cm-11x9in) s. 21-Dec-3 Thierry & Lannon, Brest #321 est:1500-1800
£1888	$3153	€2700	Premiers beaux jours (54x46cm-21x18in) s. 29-Jun-3 Feletin, Province #90
£1944	$3247	€2800	Femme lisant (55x46cm-22x18in) s. 26-Oct-3 Feletin, Province #88

GRITSAI, A I (1914-1996) Russian

£1630	$3000	€2380	Blossoming willow (61x49cm-24x19in) cardboard painted 1963. 27-Mar-4 Shishkin Gallery, Moscow #74/R est:6000-7000
£4783	$8800	€6983	Bridge, evening at the Msta River (39x49cm-15x19in) cardboard painted 1973. 27-Mar-4 Shishkin Gallery, Moscow #75/R est:3000-4000

GRITTEN, Henry C (1818-1873) British

£1069	$1945	€1561	Landscape (26x38cm-10x15in) s. board. 16-Jun-4 Deutscher-Menzies, Melbourne #556/R est:1500-2000 (A.D 2800)

GRITTI, Calisto (1937-) Italian

£345	$576	€500	Integration (100x100cm-39x39in) s.d.1972 i.verso exhib. 17-Nov-3 Sant Agostino, Torino #51/R

GRIVEAU, Lucien (1858-?) Italian

£563	$935	€800	Gardienne de moutons (23x45cm-9x18in) s. 15-Jun-3 Peron, Melun #241

GRIZNOV, Vasily Vasilievich (?-1909) Russian

Works on paper			
£3500	$5950	€5110	Interior of the Church of Saint Nicholas (32x28cm-13x11in) s. W/C htd gold paint. 19-Nov-3 Sotheby's, London #13/R est:1200-1800

GROB, Konrad (1828-1904) Swiss

£1293	$2315	€1888	Gathering wood (72x91cm-28x36in) s. 12-May-4 Dobiaschofsky, Bern #579/R est:6000 (S.FR 3000)
£16667	$30000	€24334	Visit of the pet monkey (61x76cm-24x30in) s.i.d.1872. 23-Apr-4 Sotheby's, New York #166/R est:15000-20000

GROB, Paul (1942-) Swiss

£1403	$2385	€2048	Harem under surveillance (90x90cm-35x35in) s.d.i. acrylic masonite. 28-Nov-3 Zofingen, Switzerland #3001/R est:3500 (S.FR 3100)

GROBE, German (1857-1938) German

£556	$917	€800	Fishing boats off stormy coast (34x48cm-13x19in) s. canvas on panel. 3-Jul-3 Van Ham, Cologne #1209 est:1210
£590	$974	€850	Leisure time (41x50cm-16x20in) s. 3-Jul-3 Van Ham, Cologne #1595
£694	$1146	€1000	Fishing boats setting out (50x60cm-20x24in) s. 3-Jul-3 Van Ham, Cologne #1211
£811	$1451	€1200	Young Dutch girl looking at sea (35x46cm-14x18in) s. lit. 8-May-4 Dawo, Saarbrucken #48/R
£909	$1545	€1300	Dutch coast (69x101cm-27x40in) s. 20-Nov-3 Van Ham, Cologne #1601/R est:1800
£979	$1635	€1400	Dutch fishing boats returning home (60x50cm-24x20in) s. 28-Jun-3 Dannenberg, Berlin #688/R
£1319	$2177	€1900	Unloading the boats (29x30cm-11x12in) s. panel. 3-Jul-3 Van Ham, Cologne #1210 est:450
£1389	$2208	€2000	Two boats at sunset (50x60cm-20x24in) s. 13-Sep-3 Quittenbaum, Hamburg #19/R est:3000
£1507	$2562	€2200	Katwijk church (27x17cm-11x7in) s.d.1905. 5-Nov-3 Vendue Huis, Gravenhage #357/R est:2200-2600
£1842	$3334	€2800	Fishing boats at the coast (31x47cm-12x19in) s.d.1897 panel. 19-Apr-4 Glerum, Amsterdam #177/R est:1500-2000
£3586	$5989	€5200	Return from fishing (92x63cm-36x25in) s.d.1913. 15-Nov-3 Lempertz, Koln #1607/R est:4000

GROBON, Eugène (1820-1878) French

£2500	$4600	€3800	Peches et raisins (26x35cm-10x14in) s. panel. 23-Jun-4 Sotheby's, Paris #88/R est:4000-5000

GROBON, François Frederic (1815-1901) French

£709	$1184	€1000	La vache au pre (46x60cm-18x24in) s. 19-Oct-3 Anaf, Lyon #165

GROBON, Jean Michel (1770-1853) French

£4367	$7641	€6200	Le passage du Gue (41x49cm-16x19in) s. 18-Dec-3 Tajan, Paris #130/R est:4000-6000

GROCHOWIAK, Thomas (1914-) German

Works on paper			
£1000	$1790	€1500	Pressing for contact (72x101cm-28x40in) s.d.59 Indian ink board exhib.lit. 15-May-4 Van Ham, Cologne #628/R est:800

GROEBER, Hermann (1865-1935) German

£845	$1513	€1200	Blond girl holding flowers (36x27cm-14x11in) s. canvas on panel lit. 8-Jan-4 Allgauer, Kempten #2397/R
£991	$1705	€1447	Shore landscape with boats and children playing (32x48cm-13x19in) s. canvas on board. 8-Dec-3 Philippe Schuler, Zurich #3409 (S.FR 2200)

GROEN, Hendrik Pieter (1886-1964) Dutch

£276	$461	€400	Still life with roses and a ginger pot (49x59cm-19x23in) s. 11-Nov-3 Vendu Notarishuis, Rotterdam #118
£646	$1176	€950	Flowering plants on a table (75x100cm-30x39in) s. 3-Feb-4 Christie's, Amsterdam #269

GROENEVELD, C (19th C) Dutch?

£7800	$13728	€11388	Apple peeling (76x61cm-30x24in) s. 19-May-4 Christie's, Kensington #682/R est:2500-3500

GROENEWEGEN, Adrianus Johannes (1874-1963) Dutch

£467	$845	€700	Vaches le long du fosse (27x35cm-11x14in) s. panel. 30-Mar-4 Campo, Vlaamse Kaai #76
£467	$845	€700	Vaches broutant dans la prairie (26x35cm-10x14in) s. 30-Mar-4 Campo, Vlaamse Kaai #77
£526	$968	€800	Cows in a landscape (24x32cm-9x13in) s. 28-Jun-4 Sotheby's, Amsterdam #69/R
£855	$1574	€1300	Summer landscape with grazing cows nearby a farmhouse (18x31cm-7x12in) s. canvas on panel. 28-Jun-4 Sotheby's, Amsterdam #56/R
£938	$1500	€1369	End of day (30x41cm-12x16in) s. 17-May-3 Bunte, Elgin #1219 est:1800-2200
£1224	$2229	€1800	Guiding the flock (24x30cm-9x12in) s. panel prov. 3-Feb-4 Christie's, Amsterdam #195/R est:2000-3000
£2857	$5200	€4200	Dutch pasture, live stock by a farm (25x36cm-10x14in) s. prov. 3-Feb-4 Christie's, Amsterdam #197/R est:3000-4000
Works on paper			
£510	$929	€750	Peeling the potatoes (26x22cm-10x9in) s. pencil chk W/C htd white cardboard. 3-Feb-4 Christie's, Amsterdam #285
£533	$955	€800	Landscape with grazing cows (29x39cm-11x15in) s. W/C. 11-May-4 Vendu Notarishuis, Rotterdam #258

£750	$1403	€1125	Woman with shepherd dog (20x30cm-8x12in) s. W/C. 21-Jul-4 John Nicholson, Haslemere #73
£800	$1432	€1200	Calf and sheep near polder ditch (24x34cm-9x13in) s. W/C. 11-May-4 Vendu Notarishuis, Rotterdam #252
£1074	$1987	€1600	Ploughing the fields (33x51cm-13x20in) s. W/C. 15-Mar-4 Sotheby's, Amsterdam #166/R est:1000-1500
£1208	$2235	€1800	Woman on a path in a landscape (33x44cm-13x17in) s. W/C. 15-Mar-4 Sotheby's, Amsterdam #89/R est:1800-2300
£3000	$5400	€4500	Watering cows by a river (49x70cm-19x28in) s. pencil W/C bodycol. 21-Apr-4 Christie's, Amsterdam #165/R est:5000-7000

GROENEWEGEN, Gerrit (1754-1826) Dutch

Works on paper

£3041	$5351	€4500	River landscape with sailing vessels (23x35cm-9x14in) pen brown ink grey wash black chk prov.lit. 19-May-4 Sotheby's, Amsterdam #70/R est:2000-3000

GROENEWEGEN, Pieter Anthonisz van (?-1658) Dutch

£4027	$7409	€6000	Mountainous landscape with round tower and travellers (81x118cm-32x46in) panel. 24-Mar-4 Dorotheum, Vienna #388/R est:6000-9000
£17333	$31373	€26000	Ideal Italian landscape with ruins (49x72cm-19x28in) mono.d.1639 panel. 1-Apr-4 Van Ham, Cologne #1200/R est:15000

GROESBECK, Dan Sayre (1878-1950) American

£4046	$7000	€5907	Javanese dancers (96x107cm-38x42in) s. 10-Dec-3 Bonhams & Butterfields, San Francisco #6286/R est:3000-5000

GROGAN, Matt (20th C) Irish?

£1000	$1800	€1500	Still life with mackrel and clams (49x41cm-19x16in) s. board. 20-Apr-4 James Adam, Dublin #102/R est:1500-2000

GROHMANN, Reinhold (1877-1915) German

£299	$487	€430	Freight barges on Berlin canal (70x93cm-28x37in) s.d.1911. 27-Sep-3 Dannenberg, Berlin #548/R

GROISEILLIEZ, Marcelin de (1837-1880) French

£333	$600	€486	Sun dappled wooded landscape (24x33cm-9x13in) prov. 24-Apr-4 Weschler, Washington #556/R

GROLL, Albert Lorey (1866-1952) American

£406	$650	€593	Figure in a landscape at dusk (30x41cm-12x16in) s. prov. 19-Sep-3 Freeman, Philadelphia #159/R
£588	$1000	€858	Abandoned ship (10x15cm-4x6in) s. panel prov. 1-Nov-3 Santa Fe Art, Santa Fe #191/R
£1070	$2000	€1562	Laguna (15x20cm-6x8in) s. board prov. 24-Jul-4 Coeur d'Alene, Hayden #250/R est:1000-2000
£1242	$2000	€1801	Laguna cliffs (46x61cm-18x24in) 22-Aug-3 Altermann Galleries, Santa Fe #174

GROLL, Henriette (20th C) French?

£709	$1184	€1000	Nature morte (65x81cm-26x32in) s. 19-Oct-3 Charbonneaux, Paris #157/R
£748	$1339	€1100	Femme a la guitare (81x67cm-32x26in) s.d.57. 19-Mar-4 Ribeyre & Baron, Paris #88

GROLLERON, Paul Louis Narcisse (1848-1901) French

£2747	$5000	€4011	Preparing for battle (31x39cm-12x15in) s. panel. 29-Jun-4 Sotheby's, New York #82/R est:5000-7000
£7059	$12000	€10306	Fallen comrade (92x65cm-36x26in) s. 29-Oct-3 Christie's, Rockefeller NY #157/R est:12000-18000

GROLLERON, Paul Louis Narcisse (attrib) (1848-1901) French

£4545	$8000	€6636	Untitled (86x157cm-34x62in) s. after Jean Louis Ernest Meissongier prov. 23-May-4 Hindman, Chicago #29/R est:8000-12000

GROM-ROTTMAYER, Hermann (1877-1953) Austrian

£1351	$2419	€2000	Masked ball (112x82cm-44x32in) s. lit. 8-May-4 Schloss Ahlden, Ahlden #807/R est:1800

GROMAIRE, Marcel (1892-1971) French

£3000	$5520	€4500	La vieille (100x81cm-39x32in) s.d.1920 prov.exhib.lit. 8-Jun-4 Artcurial Briest, Paris #176/R est:4000-5000
£3610	$6643	€5271	Bouquet d'arbres (46x55cm-18x22in) s.d.22 s.i.d.1922 verso prov. 29-Mar-4 Rasmussen, Copenhagen #185/R est:50000-75000 (D.KR 40000)
£3776	$6420	€5513	Le grand peuplier (46x55cm-18x22in) s.d.1921 i.verso prov. 4-Nov-3 Bukowskis, Stockholm #264/R est:50000-60000 (S.KR 50000)
£4514	$7539	€6500	Chateau dans les Sapins (41x32cm-16x13in) s.d.1934 s.i.d.verso panel lit. 21-Oct-3 Artcurial Briest, Paris #217/R est:6000-8000
£13986	$23776	€20000	Trois clochers (80x100cm-31x39in) 27-Nov-3 Calmels Cohen, Paris #46/R est:20000-22500
£32000	$58240	€46720	La Seine traverse Paris (81x100cm-32x39in) s. s.i.d.1936 verso prov.lit. 4-Feb-4 Sotheby's, London #325/R est:35000-45000

Works on paper

£282	$487	€400	Femme nue debout de dos (30x23cm-12x9in) s.d.1923 ink. 12-Dec-3 Piasa, Paris #178
£375	$600	€548	Le diner (26x30cm-10x12in) s.d.1926 pen black ink. 18-Sep-3 Swann Galleries, New York #262/R
£387	$670	€550	Nu (23x31cm-9x12in) s.d.1961 ink. 13-Dec-3 Touati, Paris #123/R
£469	$750	€685	Nue assise (32x25cm-13x10in) s.d.1950 pen ink. 18-Sep-3 Swann Galleries, New York #263/R
£533	$960	€800	Nature morte (25x18cm-10x7in) d.1924 ink. 24-Apr-4 Cornette de St.Cyr, Paris #369
£556	$928	€800	Ville fortifiee (25x33cm-10x13in) s.d.1948 ink drawing. 21-Oct-3 Artcurial Briest, Paris #92
£828	$1507	€1250	Nu debout (33x25cm-13x10in) s.d.1958 Chinese ink dr. 19-Jun-4 St-Germain-en-Laye Encheres #208/R
£829	$1500	€1210	Femme nue allongee (29x47cm-11x19in) ink. 30-Mar-4 Arroyo, Buenos Aires #48
£1000	$1820	€1500	Nu en buste (32x25cm-13x10in) s. Chinese ink dr. 4-Jul-4 Eric Pillon, Calais #266/R
£1000	$1820	€1500	Nu debout (32x25cm-13x10in) s. Chinese ink dr. 4-Jul-4 Eric Pillon, Calais #265/R
£1208	$2223	€1800	Seated female nude (32x23cm-13x9in) studio st. ink. 24-Mar-4 Joron-Derem, Paris #42 est:2200-2500
£1275	$2385	€1900	Nu (33x25cm-13x10in) s.d.1955 ink. 29-Feb-4 Versailles Encheres #146/R est:1800-2000
£1275	$2346	€1900	Female nude (32x24cm-13x9in) studio st. ink. 24-Mar-4 Joron-Derem, Paris #41/R est:2200-2500
£1310	$2384	€1913	Female nude (34x25cm-13x10in) s.d.1952 Indian ink. 17-Jun-4 Kornfeld, Bern #394 est:3000 (S.FR 3000)
£1325	$2411	€2000	Paysage (23x31cm-9x12in) ink wash. 18-Jun-4 Piasa, Paris #138b est:2000-3000
£1361	$2435	€2000	Paysage a l'eglise (20x22cm-8x9in) s.d.1943 verso W/C Indian ink. 22-Mar-4 Digard, Paris #106/R est:2800-3200
£1479	$2558	€2100	Femme allongee (25x33cm-10x13in) s.d.1951 ink. 11-Dec-3 Binoche, Paris #1 est:1200-1600
£1528	$2551	€2200	Nu au fauteuil (32x23cm-13x9in) s.d.1960 Indian ink. 21-Oct-3 Artcurial Briest, Paris #95/R est:1800-2200
£1544	$2856	€2300	Nu assis (32x24cm-13x9in) s. pen Indian ink. 15-Mar-4 Blanchet, Paris #93/R est:2000-2500
£1600	$2880	€2400	Marine (31x48cm-12x19in) s.d.1966 W/C pen. 26-Apr-4 Tajan, Paris #79/R est:1800-2000
£1736	$2899	€2500	Nu de profil (38x28cm-15x11in) s.d.1967 ink drawing prov. 21-Oct-3 Artcurial Briest, Paris #19 est:2500-3000
£1760	$3046	€2500	Etude de nu (25x33cm-10x13in) s.d.1957 Chinese ink dr. 9-Dec-3 Artcurial Briest, Paris #206 est:1500-2000
£1767	$3180	€2650	Nu assis (33x25cm-13x10in) s. Chinese ink. 24-Apr-4 Cornette de St.Cyr, Paris #368 est:3000
£1824	$3266	€2700	Vue de chateau (24x31cm-9x12in) s.d.1943 ink W/C. 4-May-4 Calmels Cohen, Paris #137/R est:3000-4000
£2013	$3745	€3000	Etude pour la toilette (26x16cm-10x6in) st.sig. india ink exec. 1924 prov.lit. 3-Mar-4 Ferri, Paris #24/R est:3000-3200
£2081	$3683	€3100	Nu debout (30x23cm-12x9in) s.d.1925 Indian ink htd W/C. 27-Apr-4 Artcurial Briest, Paris #50/R est:3000-4000
£2113	$3655	€3000	Nu allonge (25x33cm-10x13in) s. Chinese ink dr. 9-Dec-3 Artcurial Briest, Paris #208/R est:1500-2000
£2331	$3800	€3403	Chariot flamand (33x43cm-13x17in) s.d.46 i.d.1946 verso W/C brush pen black ink prov. 25-Sep-3 Christie's, Rockefeller NY #637/R est:1800-2500
£2353	$4000	€3435	La danse (43x32cm-17x13in) s.d.1955 ink W/C prov. 9-Nov-3 Bonhams & Butterfields, Los Angeles #4026/R
£2465	$4265	€3500	Etude de nu (33x26cm-13x10in) s.d.1959 Chinese ink dr. 9-Dec-3 Artcurial Briest, Paris #205/R est:3000-4000
£3125	$5219	€4500	Potier (43x32cm-17x13in) s.d.1948 W/C ink. 21-Oct-3 Artcurial Briest, Paris #94/R est:3000-4000
£3154	$5646	€4700	Cariole (31x41cm-12x16in) s. W/C gouache. 30-May-4 Eric Pillon, Calais #225/R
£3356	$5940	€5000	Attente (32x44cm-13x17in) s.d.1950 W/C Indian ink prov.exhib. 27-Apr-4 Artcurial Briest, Paris #44/R est:5000-7000
£3691	$6533	€5500	Marche (32x43cm-13x17in) s.d.1956 W/C Indian ink. 27-Apr-4 Artcurial Briest, Paris #43/R est:6000-8000
£4028	$6726	€5800	Femme en deshabille (31x43cm-12x17in) s.d.1948 W/C ink. 21-Oct-3 Artcurial Briest, Paris #93/R est:4000-5000
£4362	$7809	€6500	Couple valsant (42x32cm-17x13in) s.d.1955 W/C. 30-May-4 Eric Pillon, Calais #259/R

GRONBECH, Niels (1907-1991) Danish

£496	$928	€724	Interior scene with young girl reading newspaper (130x122cm-51x48in) s.d.1941 exhib. 25-Feb-4 Kunsthallen, Copenhagen #216 (D.KR 5500)

GRONCKEL, Vital Jean de (1820-1890) Belgian

£1500	$2505	€2190	Romantic encounter on the coast (67x50cm-26x20in) s. 8-Oct-3 Christie's, Kensington #811/R est:800-1200

GRONHOLM, Paul (1907-1992) Finnish

£382	$638	€550	Interior (33x41cm-13x16in) s. 23-Oct-3 Hagelstam, Helsinki #853

GRONINGEN, Gerhard (16th C) Flemish

Works on paper

£7500	$13725	€11250	Fall of Jericho (19x29cm-7x11in) i. black chk pen ink wash htd white framing lines prov. 6-Jul-4 Christie's, London #157/R est:3000-5000

GRONLAND, Nelius (1859-?) French

£2685	$4805	€4000	Rome, Roman Forum (46x58cm-18x23in) s.d.1901. 27-May-4 Dorotheum, Vienna #64/R est:4500-6500

GRONLAND, Nelius (attrib) (1859-?) French

£1111	$1833	€1600	Fishing boat off San Vigilio on Lake Garda (64x48cm-25x19in) i. 2-Jul-3 Neumeister, Munich #648/R

GRONMYRA, Oscar (1874-1911) Norwegian

£647	$1184	€945	Driving timber in snow storm (40x65cm-16x26in) s. panel. 2-Feb-4 Blomqvist, Lysaker #1078/R (N.KR 8050)

GRONNEBERG, Hulda (1844-1924) Norwegian

£254	$467	€371	Smallholding (26x36cm-10x14in) s. panel. 29-Mar-4 Blomqvist, Lysaker #1090/R (N.KR 3200)
£1016	$1860	€1483	Landscape from Tyrifjord (38x57cm-15x22in) s.d.97 i.stretcher. 7-Jun-4 Blomqvist, Oslo #314/R (N.KR 12500)
£1057	$1934	€1543	View from Langesund (24x43cm-9x17in) s. i.verso panel. 7-Jun-4 Blomqvist, Oslo #257/R est:15000-18000 (N.KR 13000)
£4800	$8736	€7008	Grossehesselohe (79x94cm-31x37in) s.indis.d.1888 prov. 15-Jun-4 Sotheby's, London #363/R est:5000-7000

Works on paper
£267 $446 €390 View towards Oslofjord (34x22cm-13x9in) s. W/C. 17-Nov-3 Blomqvist, Lysaker #1087 (N.KR 3200)

GRONVOLD, Marcus (1845-1929) Norwegian
£325 $598 €475 Man with hat and wine-glass (28x24cm-11x9in) s.d.6/11 1920. 10-Jun-4 Grev Wedels Plass, Oslo #178/R (N.KR 4000)
£14011 $25080 €20456 Peasants moving day (111x180cm-44x71in) s. i.stretcher lit. 22-Mar-4 Blomqvist, Oslo #359b/R est:120000-150000 (N.KR 175000)
Works on paper
£380 $631 €551 Woman by old gate, possibly in Jarlsberg (25x21cm-10x8in) pen wash. 16-Jun-3 Blomqvist, Lysaker #1063/R (N.KR 4400)

GROOM, Jon (1953-) German?
Works on paper
£302 $514 €441 Untitled II (46x34cm-18x13in) s.d.1990 verso mixed media panel. 5-Nov-3 AB Stockholms Auktionsverk #956/R (S.KR 4000)

GROOME, William H C (fl.1881-1914) British
£5200 $8684 €7592 The best of friends must part (76x102cm-30x40in) s. 12-Nov-3 Sotheby's, Olympia #106/R est:3000-5000

GROOMS, Red (1937-) American
Sculpture
£1892 $3500 €2762 Times Square (69x54x21cm-27x21x8in) s.d.1995 num.3/75 cut out col lithograph plexiglas case. 12-Feb-4 Christie's, Rockefeller NY #81/R est:3000-5000
£2059 $3500 €3006 Charlie Chaplin (58x47x29cm-23x19x11in) s. col lithograph plexiglas. 31-Oct-3 Sotheby's, New York #504/R
£2206 $3750 €3221 Times Square (69x54x21cm-27x21x8in) s. col lithograph plexiglas. 31-Oct-3 Sotheby's, New York #565/R
£2353 $4000 €3435 Fats domino (44x52x44cm-17x20x17in) s. col lithograph plexiglas. 31-Oct-3 Sotheby's, New York #563/R
£2401 $4250 €3505 South sea sonata (52x55x28cm-20x22x11in) s.d.1992 col lithograph in plexiglas box. 30-Apr-4 Sotheby's, New York #344/R est:4000-6000
Works on paper
£3533 $6500 €5158 Billy Blitzer (74x53cm-29x21in) s.d.1978 W/C gouache. 10-Jun-4 Swann Galleries, New York #107/R est:4000-6000

GROOT, Gerardus Hendrikus de (1878-1947) Dutch
£489 $817 €700 Flower still life (56x40cm-22x16in) s. 30-Jun-3 Sotheby's, Amsterdam #187

GROOT, Jan Ernst de (1807-1872) Dutch
£671 $1242 €1000 Tavern interior with figures smoking (22x30cm-9x12in) s.d.1856 panel. 15-Mar-4 Sotheby's, Amsterdam #65/R est:800-1200

GROOT, Jan de (1650-1727) Dutch
Works on paper
£1200 $2076 €1752 Peasants dancing at a village feast (14x19cm-6x7in) i.verso black lead pen brown ink. 12-Dec-3 Christie's, Kensington #524/R est:700-1000

GROOT, Johannes de (attrib) (c.1688-?) Dutch
Works on paper
£333 $607 €500 Group of peasants relaxing over a meal (15x20cm-6x8in) ink. 1-Jul-4 Van Ham, Cologne #1111

GROOT, Joseph de (1828-1899) Dutch
£2100 $3423 €3066 Interior, mother seated in armchair with two children, maid and dog (38x48cm-15x19in) s.d.1838 panel. 23-Sep-3 John Nicholson, Haslemere #265/R est:2000-3000

GROOT, Maurits de (1880-1934) Dutch
£902 $1471 €1300 Chicken examination (33x41cm-13x16in) s. wood. 29-Sep-3 Sotheby's, Amsterdam #56/R
£1538 $2569 €2200 Dutch Rabbis studying the thora (70x90cm-28x35in) s. 30-Jun-3 Sotheby's, Amsterdam #158/R

GROOTE, A de (19/20th C) ?
£1700 $3145 €2482 Figures skating on a frozen river by a windmill (50x64cm-20x25in) s. panel. 14-Jan-4 Lawrence, Crewkerne #1399/R est:1200-1800
£4500 $8280 €6570 View on a canal near Gouda (61x91cm-24x36in) s. panel. 25-Mar-4 Christie's, Kensington #161/R est:5000-7000

GROOTECLAES, Hubert Louis Andre (1927-1994) Belgian
£704 $1218 €1000 La foule (85x116cm-33x46in) s. acrylic. 10-Dec-3 Hotel des Ventes Mosan, Brussels #272

GROOTH, Johann Niklaus (1723-1797) German
£2672 $4784 €3901 Portrait of Beatus Sigismund Ougspurger (87x70cm-34x28in) s.d.1764 verso. 13-May-4 Stuker, Bern #160/R est:4000-6000 (S.FR 6200)

GROOTVELT, J H van (1808-1855) Dutch
£1081 $1935 €1600 Enfants a la lumiere (29x24cm-11x9in) panel. 10-May-4 Amberes, Antwerp #334

GROOTVELT, Jan Hendrik van (1808-1855) Dutch
£1633 $2971 €2400 Bellen blazertje, playing children (23x18cm-9x7in) init.d.1845 panel. 3-Feb-4 Christie's, Amsterdam #50/R est:2500-3500

GROPIUS, Walter (1883-1969) American?
Works on paper
£254 $425 €371 Architectural sketch. pencil tracing vellum. 25-Oct-3 David Rago, Lambertville #1131

GROPPER, William (1897-1977) American
£652 $1200 €952 Clown (53x46cm-21x18in) s.i. 10-Jun-4 Swann Galleries, New York #108/R
£939 $1700 €1371 Little girl (30x25cm-12x10in) s. masonite. 31-Mar-4 Sotheby's, New York #153/R est:1200-1600
£5294 $9000 €7729 Committee chairman (51x61cm-20x24in) s. 9-Nov-3 Wright, Chicago #353 est:10000-15000
£9302 $16000 €13581 Senator (71x91cm-28x36in) s. canvas on masonite prov. 3-Dec-3 Sotheby's, New York #80/R est:15000-25000
£12973 $24000 €18941 Foreign delegates ordering a meal (29x43cm-11x17in) s. painted c.1946. 11-Mar-4 Christie's, Rockefeller NY #77/R est:10000-15000
Works on paper
£222 $400 €324 Fiddler (38x25cm-15x10in) s. W/C prov. 20-Jan-4 Arthur James, Florida #15
£1381 $2500 €2016 Politican (25x25cm-10x10in) s. gouache. 31-Mar-4 Sotheby's, New York #142 est:1500-2000

GROS, Achille (19th C) French
£7616 $13937 €11500 Paysage du Jura (220x160cm-87x63in) s.d.1892. 9-Apr-4 Claude Aguttes, Neuilly #27/R est:5000-7000

GROS, Antoine Jean (1771-1835) French
Works on paper
£600 $1038 €876 Mercury with Herse and her sisters (25x34cm-10x13in) col chk stumped prov. 12-Dec-3 Christie's, Kensington #484/R

GROS, Antoine Jean (style) (1771-1835) French
£5333 $9653 €8000 Tete du cheval de Murat (130x97cm-51x38in) exhib. 30-Mar-4 Rossini, Paris #52/R est:3000-4000

GROS, L (?) French?
£2041 $3714 €3000 Le harem (80x134cm-31x53in) s. 8-Feb-4 Anaf, Lyon #193/R est:3000-4000

GROS, Lucien Alphonse (1845-1913) French
Works on paper
£381 $700 €556 Garconnet portant une trompette (104x66cm-41x26in) s.d.1919 pastel. 25-Jun-4 Freeman, Philadelphia #109/R

GROSE, Daniel C (1838-1890) American
£305 $500 €442 Fisherman by a cascading brook (30x23cm-12x9in) s.indis.d.18. 2-Jun-3 Grogan, Boston #662/R
£313 $584 €470 Coastal scene with Aboriginals and grounded vessel (20x44cm-8x17in) s. board. 20-Jul-4 Goodman, Sydney #127/R (A.D 800)
£412 $750 €602 Autumn, Hudson river valley (30x20cm-12x8in) s.d.87. 19-Jun-4 Jackson's, Cedar Falls #17/R
£472 $850 €689 Fall river landscape (20x30cm-8x12in) s. prov.lit. 24-Apr-4 Weschler, Washington #592/R
£489 $900 €714 Landscape (20x30cm-8x12in) s.d.1867. 25-Jun-4 Freeman, Philadelphia #278/R est:500-800

GROSJEAN, Henry (1864-1948) French
£265 $475 €387 Caligny et la Bresse, fin d'automne (20x33cm-8x13in) s. 8-Jan-4 Doyle, New York #25/R

GROSPERIN, Claude (1936-1977) French
£586 $1084 €850 A l'oree du bois (81x100cm-32x39in) s. 11-Feb-4 Beaussant & Lefèvre, Paris #193/R

GROSPIETSCH, Florian (1789-1830) German
Works on paper
£433 $780 €650 Untitled (35x55cm-14x22in) s.d.1814 W/C. 22-Apr-4 Weidler, Nurnberg #303/R

GROSS, Anthony (1905-1984) British
£700 $1295 €1022 Church window (66x55cm-26x22in) init.d.70 board. 11-Mar-4 Christie's, Kensington #106/R
£850 $1462 €1241 Girl in blue checked dress, Algeria (41x30cm-16x12in) init.d.27 canvasboard prov.exhib. 3-Dec-3 Christie's, Kensington #401/R
£1600 $2864 €2336 Yellow Landscape (65x92cm-26x36in) s.d.56. 16-Mar-4 Bonhams, Knightsbridge #72/R est:600-800
£1800 $3330 €2628 French street (33x41cm-13x16in) s. canvasboard. 11-Mar-4 Christie's, Kensington #104/R est:1000-1500
Works on paper
£400 $740 €584 Promenade (48x30cm-19x12in) s.d.1932 pencil W/C bodycol. 11-Mar-4 Christie's, Kensington #130
£1150 $1909 €1679 River Lot in winter (38x56cm-15x22in) s. pen ink wash. 3-Oct-3 Mallams, Oxford #123/R est:300-500
£1250 $2288 €1825 Tow-Path, Putney (36x53cm-14x21in) s. ink W/C. 27-Jan-4 Gorringes, Lewes #1716 est:400-600

GROSS, Chaim (1904-1991) American
£294 $500 €429 Coney Island (30x41cm-12x16in) s. 9-Nov-3 Outer Cape Auctions, Provincetown #53/R
Sculpture
£1519 $2750 €2218 Seated mother holding a child (27cm-11in) s.d.39 green pat bronze st.f.Bedi-Makky. 31-Mar-4 Sotheby's, New York #20/R est:1000-2000
£1648 $3000 €2406 Performer (37cm-15in) s. wood. 29-Jun-4 Sotheby's, New York #274/R est:2500-3500
£1744 $3000 €2546 Little Babbet (29cm-11in) i.d.1947 wood. 2-Dec-3 Christie's, Rockefeller NY #94/R est:2000-4000
£1934 $3500 €2824 Seven mystic birds (101cm-40in) green pat bronze pair prov.exhib. 31-Mar-4 Sotheby's, New York #163/R est:6000-8000
£2286 $4000 €3338 Abstract figure (91cm-36in) i.d.40 mahogany prov. 19-Dec-3 Sotheby's, New York #1150/R est:1200-1800
£2395 $4000 €3497 Girl on wheel (33cm-13in) s.i. num.1 brown pat bronze prov. 23-Oct-3 Shannon's, Milford #102/R est:5000-7000
£3043 $5600 €4443 The artist's wife (30x20cm-12x8in) s.d.1954 wood relief. 10-Jun-4 Swann Galleries, New York #109/R est:4000-6000
£3867 $7000 €5646 Nude woman balancing a child (74cm-29in) s.num.1/6 verso green black pat bronze. 31-Mar-4 Sotheby's, New York #18/R est:4000-6000
£8721 $15000 €12733 Mother bird, fountain of a swan and three cygnets (193cm-76in) i. weathered brown pat. bronze prov.exhib.lit. 3-Dec-3 Sotheby's, New York #93/R est:20000-30000
Works on paper
£264 $475 €385 Two Rabbis (18x39cm-7x15in) s. ink W/C prov. 24-Apr-4 Weschler, Washington #636/R

GROSS, Einar (1895-?) Danish
£250 $450 €365 Fishing boats in a harbour (66x96cm-26x38in) s. 25-Apr-4 Bonhams & Butterfields, San Francisco #5485/R
£1946 $3250 €2841 Evening sail (69x94cm-27x37in) 14-Nov-3 Du Mouchelle, Detroit #2274/R est:3000-4000

GROSS, Erin (19/20th C) Danish
£782 $1400 €1142 Village landscape scene (66x61cm-26x24in) 14-May-4 Du Mouchelle, Detroit #2382/R est:1500-1800

GROSS, Frank (1908-1963) New Zealander
£1071 $1971 €1564 Wind and cloud (44x51cm-17x20in) board prov. 25-Mar-4 International Art Centre, Auckland #65/R est:3000-4500 (NZ.D 3000)
£1222 $2077 €1784 Lake house, Roturua (51x53cm-20x21in) s. board. 27-Nov-3 International Art Centre, Auckland #118/R est:4000-6000 (NZ.D 3250)
Works on paper
£393 $711 €574 North Island landscape (28x35cm-11x14in) s.d.1945 mixed media. 4-Apr-4 International Art Centre, Auckland #283/R (NZ.D 1100)

GROSS, Frantisek (1909-1985) Czechoslovakian
£2742 $4826 €4113 Gardens near Bertramka (38x52cm-15x20in) s.d.45. 22-May-4 Dorotheum, Prague #167/R est:100000-150000 (C.KR 130000)
Works on paper
£295 $520 €443 Factory (25x33cm-10x13in) mixed media. 22-May-4 Dorotheum, Prague #274 est:10000-15000 (C.KR 14000)

GROSS, George (20th C) American
£695 $1300 €1015 Standing Mexican rifleman (36x23cm-14x9in) s. board painted c.1970. 26-Feb-4 Illustration House, New York #83

GROSS, Michael (1920-) Israeli
£8380 $15000 €12235 Contrabass (199x131cm-78x52in) s. 18-Mar-4 Sotheby's, New York #43/R est:15000-20000
Works on paper
£330 $600 €495 Abstract composition (68x49cm-27x19in) s. W/C pencil. 1-Jul-4 Ben-Ami, Tel Aviv #4927/R

GROSS, Oskar (1871-?) American
£732 $1200 €1061 Spring blossoms (36x53cm-14x21in) s.d. 7-Jun-3 Treadway Gallery, Cincinnati #1363

GROSS, Otto (1898-1970) German
£336 $617 €500 Swabian landscape (45x60cm-18x24in) s.d. canvas on panel. 26-Mar-4 Ketterer, Hamburg #241/R

GROSS, Peter Alfred (1849-1914) American
£326 $600 €476 Landscape with village, figure on roadway (28x43cm-11x17in) s.d.1864 panel. 9-Jun-4 Alderfer's, Hatfield #375

GROSSBACH, Peter (1934-1988) German
Sculpture
£1189 $2045 €1700 Female Negro bust (31x25x14cm-12x10x6in) mono. brown pat bronze. 4-Dec-3 Van Ham, Cologne #179/R est:1900

GROSSBARD, Yehushua (1902-1992) Israeli
£882 $1500 €1288 Urban landscape (90x67cm-35x26in) s. board. 1-Dec-3 Ben-Ami, Tel Aviv #4348/R est:2000-3000

GROSSBERG, Carl (1894-1940) German
Works on paper
£1111 $1856 €1600 Bridge over the River Main linking Sommerhausen to Winterhausen (29x36cm-11x14in) s.mono.d.4.5.22 W/C Indian ink brush. 25-Oct-3 Dr Lehr, Berlin #169/R est:3000
£1200 $2148 €1800 Composition (30x35cm-12x14in) mono.i.d. pencil. 14-May-4 Ketterer, Munich #26/R est:2000-2500
£2533 $4535 €3800 Street in southern Germany (42x60cm-17x24in) s.d. W/C Indian ink over pencil prov. 14-May-4 Ketterer, Munich #27/R est:2000-3000
£3490 $6247 €5200 Stralsund (24x31cm-9x12in) mono.i.d.1920 W/C Indian ink. 25-May-4 Karl & Faber, Munich #303/R est:6800

GROSSEN, Maurice (20th C) ?
£271 $431 €396 View of fort (62x81cm-24x32in) s.d.1959. 29-Apr-3 Louis Morton, Mexico #157/R (M.P 4500)

GROSSER, Maurice (20th C) ?
£276 $500 €403 Greek theater at Isthmea (51x74cm-20x29in) 16-Apr-4 American Auctioneer #177/R
£552 $1000 €806 Spring farm, Tangier (36x58cm-14x23in) 16-Apr-4 American Auctioneer #178/R

GROSSI, Giannino (1889-1969) Italian
£326 $535 €450 Orta Lake (24x30cm-9x12in) s. i.d.1921 verso board. 27-May-3 Il Ponte, Milan #920
£2013 $3604 €3000 Arosio (55x69cm-22x27in) s.d.1938. 25-May-4 Finarte Semenzato, Milan #76/R est:2000-2300

GROSSI, Proferio (1923-2000) Italian
£274 $466 €400 Composition (50x70cm-20x28in) s. board. 7-Nov-3 Galleria Rosenberg, Milan #14/R
£671 $1242 €1000 Still life (50x70cm-20x28in) s.d.1990 masonite. 13-Mar-4 Meeting Art, Vercelli #444a
Works on paper
£510 $929 €750 Astoria (80x130cm-31x51in) s. mixed media board exec.1984 prov. 6-Feb-4 Galleria Rosenberg, Milan #22/R

GROSSMAN, Nancy (1940-) American
Sculpture
£3179 $5500 €4641 Head (41cm-16in) i. leather over wood prov. 15-Dec-3 Hindman, Chicago #54/R est:7000-10000
£3846 $7000 €5615 Swamp girl (115x133cm-45x52in) s.d.65 stretcher assemblage of found objects in leather metal. 29-Jun-4 Sotheby's, New York #430/R est:10000-15000
£7784 $13000 €11365 Head sculpture (41cm-16in) leather wood hardware lacquer prov.exhib.lit. 13-Nov-3 Sotheby's, New York #526/R est:7000-8000

GROSSMAN, Sid (1913-1955) American
Photographs
£1796 $3000 €2622 Harlem, New York (26x35cm-10x14in) i.verso gelatin silver print lit. 16-Oct-3 Phillips, New York #109/R est:3000-5000

GROSSMANN, Ludwig (1894-1960) German
£514 $873 €750 Still life of flowers (49x36cm-19x14in) s. board. 5-Nov-3 Hugo Ruef, Munich #993

GROSSMANN, Rudolf (1882-1941) German
Works on paper
£233 $429 €350 Group at the table (15x10cm-6x4in) s. W/C pen ink chk. 12-Jun-4 Villa Grisebach, Berlin #553/R

GROSSO, Alfonso (1893-1983) Spanish
£1879 $3495 €2800 Portrait of lady (78x58cm-31x23in) s. 2-Mar-4 Ansorena, Madrid #120/R est:1300
£2000 $3620 €3000 Portrait of woman (59x46cm-23x18in) s. 30-Mar-4 Segre, Madrid #91/R est:3500
£2899 $4754 €4000 Convent interior (54x41cm-21x16in) s. panel. 27-May-3 Durán, Madrid #145/R est:2250
£2899 $4754 €4000 Woman (100x80cm-39x31in) s. 27-May-3 Durán, Madrid #161/R est:4000
£4200 $6972 €6132 Courtyard in Ecija (100x105cm-39x41in) s.i. lit. 1-Oct-3 Sotheby's, Olympia #299/R est:2000-3000
£4452 $7568 €6500 Sevillan patio (83x62cm-33x24in) s. 4-Nov-3 Ansorena, Madrid #351/R est:6000

GROSSO, Giacomo (1860-1938) Italian
£6376 $11732 €9500 Female nude (82x64cm-32x25in) s. 24-Mar-4 Il Ponte, Milan #587/R est:8000-9000
£8451 $14028 €12000 Sulla terrazza (38x50cm-15x20in) s.d.91 panel. 11-Jun-3 Christie's, Rome #275/R est:10000-15000

GROSSO, Giuseppe (1925-) Italian
£408 $731 €600 Porta Nuova STation in Turin (59x80cm-23x31in) s.i.d.1954. 22-Mar-4 Sant Agostino, Torino #356/R

GROSTAD, Erlend (1923-) Norwegian
£539 $992 €787 Landscape from Tveiten in Seljord, summer 1980 (71x90cm-28x35in) s. 29-Mar-4 Blomqvist, Lysaker #1092/R (N.KR 6800)

GROSTAD, Terje (1925-) Norwegian
£952 $1751 €1390 The lighthouse (130x100cm-51x39in) s. 29-Mar-4 Blomqvist, Lysaker #1093/R est:15000-18000 (N.KR 12000)

GROSVENOR, Robert (1937-) American

£3333	$6000	€4866	Untitled (25x29cm-10x11in) s.d.1969 enamel graphite collage. 24-Apr-4 David Rago, Lambertville #542/R est:300-600

Works on paper

£556	$1000	€812	Untitled (7x10cm-3x4in) s.d.1981 graphite col pencil. 24-Apr-4 David Rago, Lambertville #339/R
£556	$1000	€812	Untitled (8x10cm-3x4in) s.d.1980 graphite crayon. 24-Apr-4 David Rago, Lambertville #480/R
£833	$1500	€1216	Untitled (7x10cm-3x4in) s.d.1980 graphite col pencil. 24-Apr-4 David Rago, Lambertville #173/R est:150-300
£2361	$4250	€3447	4 Sonsbeek Park, Arnem, Holland (23x31cm-9x12in) s.d.1974 ink collage graph paper. 24-Apr-4 David Rago, Lambertville #107/R est:600-1200

GROSZ, A (19/20th C) Austrian?

£1528	$2597	€2200	Village scribe (26x30cm-10x12in) s.d.897 panel. 28-Oct-3 Dorotheum, Vienna #16/R est:1800-2000

GROSZ, George (1893-1959) American/German

£1111	$1856	€1600	Street cafe (10x16cm-4x6in) i.d.18.06.12 st.sig. 25-Oct-3 Dr Lehr, Berlin #170/R est:1800
£4027	$7208	€6000	Woman (65x44cm-26x17in) s. tempera W/C paper painted 1940. 25-May-4 Sotheby's, Milan #128/R est:8000
£4076	$7500	€5951	Female nude (76x38cm-30x15in) s. paper on linen. 10-Jun-4 Swann Galleries, New York #113/R est:3000-5000
£5143	$9000	€7509	Seated nude (59x39cm-23x15in) s. paper on board. 19-Dec-3 Sotheby's, New York #1052/R est:8000-10000
£10497	$19000	€15326	After a swim, Wellfleet (51x70cm-20x28in) s. exhib. 31-Mar-4 Sotheby's, New York #144/R est:15000-25000
£12834	$24000	€18738	Nude in blue (41x61cm-16x24in) s. s.verso painted 1945 prov. 25-Feb-4 Christie's, Rockefeller NY #109/R est:18000-25000
£13043	$21391	€18000	Three women (45x56cm-18x22in) board painted 1939-1945 exhib. 27-May-3 Sotheby's, Amsterdam #336/R est:15000-20000
£14706	$25000	€21471	On the Beach (57x40cm-22x16in) s.d.1941 oil W/C prov.exhib. 6-Nov-3 Sotheby's, New York #226/R est:30000-40000
£30000	$54900	€45000	Still life with jug, lamp, puppet (63x50cm-25x20in) s.d.27 prov. 5-Jun-4 Lempertz, Koln #751/R est:5000-70000

Prints

£3200	$5888	€4800	Night cafe scene (43x56cm-17x22in) s. i.verso lithograph exec. 1918 one of 40. 11-Jun-4 Villa Grisebach, Berlin #1563/R est:500-700

Works on paper

£267	$491	€400	Woman with crutches (21x12cm-8x5in) s. pencil prov. 12-Jun-4 Villa Grisebach, Berlin #555/R
£503	$926	€750	Le tournage (27x20cm-11x8in) s. ink. 23-Mar-4 Galerie Moderne, Brussels #306/R
£724	$1209	€1050	Bedroom (14x19cm-6x7in) blue ink. 13-Nov-3 Neumeister, Munich #335/R
£733	$1349	€1100	Etudes de groupes de marins discutant, marchant, allumant un cigarette (15x21cm-6x8in) s.i.d.1919 crayon. 9-Jun-4 Piasa, Paris #92
£738	$1358	€1100	Figure studies (9x12cm-4x5in) d. pencil prov. 26-Mar-4 Ketterer, Hamburg #439/R
£800	$1472	€1200	Reclining female nude (21x28cm-8x11in) s. pencil. 8-Jun-4 Finarte Semenzato, Milan #141/R
£800	$1472	€1200	Harbour scene (23x31cm-9x12in) pencil. 12-Jun-4 Villa Grisebach, Berlin #556/R
£909	$1545	€1300	Pornographic scene (50x39cm-20x15in) Indian ink over pencil. 29-Nov-3 Villa Grisebach, Berlin #553/R est:1500-2000
£1000	$1840	€1500	Female nude standing (28x22cm-11x9in) black chk. 12-Jun-4 Villa Grisebach, Berlin #554/R est:1500-2000
£1087	$2000	€1587	Tree study (33x41cm-13x16in) s. pen ink W/C exec. c.1940. 10-Jun-4 Swann Galleries, New York #112/R est:2000-3000
£1154	$2100	€1685	Seated nude (28x23cm-11x9in) s. graphite prov. 19-Jun-4 Rachel Davis, Shaker Heights #152 est:1200-1800
£1304	$2400	€1904	Three figures, Marseilles (33x43cm-13x17in) s.i.d.1927 brush india ink. 10-Jun-4 Swann Galleries, New York #111/R est:3000-5000
£1333	$2400	€2000	Cafe Josty in Berlin (12x18cm-5x7in) i.d.27.10.12 st.sig. pencil. 24-Apr-4 Dr Lehr, Berlin #136/R est:1800
£1374	$2500	€2006	Untitled (13x13cm-5x5in) s.d.1916 W/C ink. 19-Jun-4 Rachel Davis, Shaker Heights #151 est:1800-2400
£1399	$2406	€2000	She's playing at being a dog (22x17cm-9x7in) s.i. Indian ink col pen. 2-Dec-3 Hauswedell & Nolte, Hamburg #237/R est:2500
£1400	$2338	€2044	Two nudes. Seated nude (21x33cm-8x13in) both s.d.12 st.verso pencil two. 22-Oct-3 Sotheby's, Olympia #135/R est:1000-1500
£1400	$2576	€2100	Reclining female nude (41x60cm-16x24in) s. pencil. 8-Jun-4 Finarte Semenzato, Milan #142/R est:2000-2500
£1467	$2700	€2142	Wounded veteran (15x10cm-6x4in) s. i.verso pencil exec. c.1918. 10-Jun-4 Swann Galleries, New York #110/R est:2000-3000
£1867	$3341	€2800	Portrait of Max Hermann-Neisse (31x25cm-12x10in) s.d. Indian ink W/C prov. 14-May-4 Ketterer, Munich #197/R est:2800-3800
£2000	$3180	€2900	Cape Cod (15x21cm-6x8in) s.i.d.39 W/C gouache exhib. 11-Sep-3 Christie's, Kensington #87/R est:2500-3000
£2013	$3604	€3000	Music Hall, New York (24x18cm-9x7in) s. pencil prov. 25-May-4 Dorotheum, Vienna #28/R est:2000-2500
£2133	$3925	€3200	Town square with horse drawn carriage and tram (28x22cm-11x9in) st.sig. i.verso chk exec. 1915. 11-Jun-4 Villa Grisebach, Berlin #1554/R est:2500-3500
£2158	$3540	€3000	Lady Hamilton (44x34cm-17x13in) s. Indian ink pen brush. 4-Jun-3 Ketterer, Hamburg #421/R est:5000-7000
£2174	$3565	€3000	Standing nude (57x39cm-22x15in) s. W/C black col chk exhib. 27-May-3 Sotheby's, Amsterdam #502/R est:3000-4000
£2333	$4293	€3500	Cape Cod (42x32cm-17x13in) s.i.d.1939 W/C. 10-Jun-4 Hauswedell & Nolte, Hamburg #252/R est:3000
£2333	$4293	€3500	Passer-bys (60x46cm-24x18in) ink i.verso exec. c.1930. 11-Jun-4 Villa Grisebach, Berlin #1559/R est:3000-4000
£2464	$4041	€3400	Nude (43x27cm-17x11in) s. chl. 27-May-3 Sotheby's, Milan #78/R est:4000
£2667	$4907	€4000	Nude (50x39cm-20x15in) s. gouache. 8-Jun-4 Finarte Semenzato, Milan #336/R est:3000-3500
£3287	$5587	€4700	Female nude (62x41cm-24x16in) s.d.1927 pencil W/C. 20-Nov-3 Finarte Semenzato, Milan #61/R est:4800-5200
£3315	$6000	€4840	Central Park (51x36cm-20x14in) s.d.34 W/C ink. 31-Mar-4 Sotheby's, New York #137/R est:6000-8000
£3497	$5944	€5000	Retired (62x50cm-24x20in) s.d.1920 pen brush. 29-Nov-3 Bassenge, Berlin #6731 est:6000
£3846	$6538	€5500	Nude (32x26cm-13x10in) d.16 wax crayon W/C prov. 24-Nov-3 Christie's, Milan #118/R est:5000-7000
£4333	$7973	€6500	Max Schmeling (54x35cm-21x14in) st.sig. i.d.1936 verso ink. 12-Jun-4 Villa Grisebach, Berlin #285/R est:7000-9000
£4698	$8409	€7000	Dr BIllig von Hulsenbeck (49x28cm-19x11in) s.i. Chinese ink exhib.lit. 29-May-4 Farsetti, Prato #411/R est:5000-6500
£4895	$8420	€7000	Standing female nude (60x31cm-24x12in) s. W/C chk. 2-Dec-3 Hauswedell & Nolte, Hamburg #243/R est:10000
£5000	$8350	€7300	Stunck in der strasse - Trouble in the street (28x22cm-11x9in) s.d.1971 s.i.d.verso pen ink prov. 21-Oct-3 Sotheby's, London #108/R est:6000-8000
£5102	$9133	€7500	Female nude (63x47cm-25x19in) st.sig. mixed media exec.1940. 16-Mar-4 Finarte Semenzato, Milan #326/R est:7500
£7647	$13000	€11165	Upheaval (23x18cm-9x7in) s.d.1917 pen India ink prov.exhib. 6-Nov-3 Sotheby's, New York #229/R est:15000-20000
£8380	$15000	€12235	Metzgerwagen (52x69cm-20x27in) s. W/C exec c.1930-1931 prov. 5-May-4 Christie's, Rockefeller NY #134/R est:15000-20000
£9730	$18000	€14206	Seduction (59x46cm-23x18in) s.i. brush ink prov. 11-Feb-4 Sotheby's, New York #41/R est:12000-18000
£9790	$16839	€14000	Concours de tir (23x34cm-9x13in) W/C pencil. 2-Dec-3 Hauswedell & Nolte, Hamburg #242/R est:18000
£11000	$20240	€16500	Christ on the cross being taunted (64x52cm-25x20in) s. W/C ink card sketch verso exec. c.1926-27 prov.lit. 12-Jun-4 Villa Grisebach, Berlin #246/R est:8000-10000
£14706	$25000	€21471	Drinkers (33x22cm-13x9in) s. pen India ink exec c.1915 prov.exhib. 6-Nov-3 Sotheby's, New York #219/R est:30000-40000
£15363	$27500	€22430	Baltic sea beach Prerow (48x66cm-19x26in) s.i. W/C exec 1931 prov. 6-May-4 Sotheby's, New York #325/R est:25000-35000
£20000	$36800	€29200	Gold diggers' bar (30x23cm-12x9in) s. s.i.d.1917 verso pen ink. 22-Jun-4 Sotheby's, London #501/R est:8000-12000
£22000	$40480	€32120	Visitors, Cassis-sur-Mer. Promenade Cafe (48x62cm-19x24in) pen ink W/C double-sided exec.1927 prov.exhib. 22-Jun-4 Sotheby's, London #505/R est:25000-35000
£25503	$45651	€38000	German men (51x36cm-20x14in) s.i.d.1917 Oktober Indian ink pencil exhib. 25-May-4 Dorotheum, Vienna #19/R est:38000-40000

GROTH, Jan (20th C) Danish

£1173	$2194	€1713	Composition (116x73cm-46x29in) s.d.1962 prov. 25-Feb-4 Kunsthallen, Copenhagen #141/R est:10000 (D.KR 13000)

Works on paper

£289	$540	€422	Composition (41x57cm-16x22in) s.d.69 chl. 25-Feb-4 Kunsthallen, Copenhagen #33 (D.KR 3200)
£415	$776	€606	Composition (44x60cm-17x24in) s.d.68 chl. 25-Feb-4 Kunsthallen, Copenhagen #32 (D.KR 4600)

GROTH, Vilhelm (1842-1899) Danish

£305	$548	€445	Wooded landscape with man walking (37x42cm-15x17in) s.d.1849. 24-Apr-4 Rasmussen, Havnen #2229 (D.KR 3400)
£473	$818	€691	Spring day in the woods (70x58cm-28x23in) s.d.1891. 9-Dec-3 Rasmussen, Copenhagen #1548 (D.KR 5000)
£549	$1000	€802	Evening by lake, young woman looking for her lover (32x36cm-13x14in) 7-Feb-4 Rasmussen, Havnen #2036 (D.KR 6000)
£724	$1296	€1057	Young woman standing by rowing boat at river (31x35cm-12x14in) 10-May-4 Rasmussen, Vejle #84/R (D.KR 8000)
£2392	$3876	€3468	In the evening at heath marshes near Skagen (84x127cm-33x50in) s.d.1882 exhib.prov. 4-Aug-3 Rasmussen, Vejle #15/R est:20000 (D.KR 25000)

GROTHE-NEUMANN, Brigitte (?) British?

Works on paper

£280	$459	€409	Sources (50x45cm-20x18in) s. W/C on silk. 4-Jun-3 John Ross, Belfast #232

GROUMELLEC, Loic le (1958-) French

£600	$1080	€900	Megalithe (35x35cm-14x14in) s.i.d. oil varnish painted 1980 prov.exhib. 26-Apr-4 Tajan, Paris #256/R
£1197	$2071	€1700	Megalithe (108x75cm-43x30in) peinture paper prov. 14-Dec-3 Versailles Encheres #218/R est:1500-2000
£1469	$2452	€2100	Megalithe (20x20cm-8x8in) s.i.d.1992 verso lacquer canvas on panel. 11-Oct-3 Cornette de St.Cyr, Paris #136/R est:2200-2500
£1469	$2452	€2100	Croix (20x20cm-8x8in) s.i.d.1992 verso lacquer canvas on panel prov. 11-Oct-3 Cornette de St.Cyr, Paris #137/R est:2200-2500
£1678	$3088	€2500	Chapelle (50x40cm-20x16in) s.i.d.1991 verso lacquer prov. 29-Mar-4 Cornette de St.Cyr, Paris #89/R est:3000-5000
£1733	$3189	€2600	Paysage imaginaire (150x100cm-59x39in) s.i.d.nov 1985 verso prov. 11-Jun-4 Pierre Berge, Paris #72/R est:1500-2500

GROUSINSKY, Peter (1837-1892) Russian

£6471	$11000	€9448	In the snow storm (31x44cm-12x17in) s.d.1884. 19-Nov-3 Bonhams & Butterfields, San Francisco #92/R

GROUX, Charles de (1825-1870) Belgian

Works on paper

£372	$654	€550	The daily bread (31x24cm-12x9in) s. 24-May-4 Bernaerts, Antwerp #379/R

GROUX, Henry de (1867-1930) Belgian

Works on paper

£467	$854	€700	Faust et Marguerite (62x46cm-24x18in) s. chl. 7-Jun-4 Palais de Beaux Arts, Brussels #243
£500	$920	€750	Dante au turban de profil (63x47cm-25x19in) s.i. pastel. 14-Jun-4 Horta, Bruxelles #144
£559	$951	€800	Orphee charmant les monstres (35x41cm-14x16in) s. pastel exec.c.1900 exhib. 1-Dec-3 Palais de Beaux Arts, Brussels #236/R
£2500	$4525	€3800	Le charnier (102x74cm-40x29in) s.d.94 pastel. 19-Apr-4 Horta, Bruxelles #107/R est:3500-5000

GROUX, Victor de (1895-1973) Belgian

£382 $607 €550 Les marais (60x80cm-24x31in) s. sold with documents. 15-Sep-3 Horta, Bruxelles #298

£405 $766 €600 La kermesse a Bruges (100x80cm-39x31in) s. 17-Feb-4 Vanderkindere, Brussels #543

£496 $829 €700 Verger en fleurs (60x80cm-24x31in) s. 14-Oct-3 Vanderkindere, Brussels #62

GROVE, Maria (19th C) Scandinavian

£535 $1000 €781 Woman pouring wine from pitcher to carafe, with other figures. s. 28-Feb-4 Thomaston Place, Thomaston #65/R

£1028 $1624 €1491 Still life of flowers in bowl (40x45cm-16x18in) s. 3-Sep-3 Museumsbygningen, Copenhagen #203/R (D.KR 11000)

GROVE, Nordahl (1822-1885) Danish

£271 $486 €396 Coastal landscape, Humlebaek (34x51cm-13x20in) s.i.d.1870. 10-May-4 Rasmussen, Vejle #126/R (D.KR 3000)

£667 $1234 €974 Sunset over landscape with stag (33x51cm-13x20in) s.d.1870. 15-Mar-4 Rasmussen, Vejle #448/R (D.KR 7400)

£1944 $3072 €2800 Early morning in winter (66x99cm-26x39in) s.d.1881. 2-Sep-3 Christie's, Amsterdam #166/R est:2500-3500

£2222 $3622 €3200 Danish coast (44x65cm-17x26in) s.d.75. 26-Sep-3 Bolland & Marotz, Bremen #539/R est:3000

GROVER, Oliver Dennett (1861-1927) American

£793 $1300 €1150 Midwestern landscape (18x24cm-7x9in) painted c.1914. 7-Jun-3 Treadway Gallery, Cincinnati #1425

£1648 $3000 €2406 Grinnell Mountain Lake McDermott, Montana (76x61cm-30x24in) s.d.1924. 19-Jun-4 Jackson's, Cedar Falls #2/R est:2000-3000

GROVES, Mary (fl.1884-1904) British

£320 $525 €467 Heathland flowers, distant hills (46x76cm-18x30in) s. 29-May-3 Neales, Nottingham #803/R

£450 $792 €657 Landscape with poppies, a parish church beyond (40x56cm-16x22in) 19-May-4 Dreweatt Neate, Newbury #118

£600 $1056 €876 Three kittens playing (36x46cm-14x18in) s. 19-May-4 Dreweatt Neate, Newbury #46

GROVES, Naomi Jackson (1910-2001) Canadian

£300 $469 €435 Greenland Harbour (53x66cm-21x26in) init.i. prov. 26-Mar-3 Walker's, Ottawa #440/R (C.D 700)

£360 $613 €526 Falls on the Magpie River near Michipicoleu Mission, Lake Superior (34x47cm-13x19in) s. s.d.August 1975 verso board prov. 27-Nov-3 Heffel, Vancouver #63 (C.D 800)

£383 $651 €559 Elgin Road, Quebec (22x24cm-9x9in) s. i.d.August 9, 1931 verso panel prov. 27-Nov-3 Heffel, Vancouver #84/R (C.D 850)

GROVES, Robert E (?-1944) British

Works on paper

£2100 $3507 €3066 Sennen fishing lugger (38x53cm-15x21in) s.i.d.1901 gouache. 14-Oct-3 David Lay, Penzance #309/R est:500-800

GROVES, Tiffany (1975-) British

£450 $806 €657 Rune (60x60cm-24x24in) s.i.d.2001 verso acrylic. 14-May-4 Christie's, Kensington #637/R

GRUAU, René (1910-) French?

£805 $1482 €1200 Elegante accoudee (39x33cm-15x13in) s. 24-Mar-4 Joron-Derem, Paris #77/R

GRUBACS, Carlo (19th C) Italian

£12931 $23793 €18879 St Marks' Square, Venice (21x27cm-8x11in) s.d.1845. 26-Mar-4 Koller, Zurich #3116/R est:17000-22000 (S.FR 30000)

£13158 $24211 €20000 View of Saint Mark's, Venice (23x32cm-9x13in) s. 24-Jun-4 Tajan, Paris #45/R est:20000-30000

£14765 $26430 €22000 Vie of the Rialto Bridge in Venice (20x27cm-8x11in) s. 27-May-4 Dorotheum, Vienna #195/R est:3000-3600

£16500 $28380 €24090 Riva degli Schiavoni. Gondolas on the lagoon in front of St Mark's Square (20x28cm-8x11in) s. pair. 3-Dec-3 Christie's, London #81/R est:10000-15000

£17000 $29240 €24820 St Marks's Square. St Mark's Square with Doge's Palace (20x28cm-8x11in) indis.sig. pair. 3-Dec-3 Christie's, London #80/R est:10000-15000

£17000 $31280 €24820 Figures in the Piazzetta with Santa Maria della Salute beyond (61x82cm-24x32in) s. 23-Mar-4 Bonhams, New Bond Street #89/R est:6000-8000

£21127 $36549 €30000 Grand Canal (44x65cm-17x26in) 14-Dec-3 Finarte, Venice #50/R est:35000-45000

£24138 $40310 €35000 Night view of the Piazzetta (21x31cm-8x12in) s. 12-Nov-3 Sotheby's, Milan #135/R est:10000-15000

Works on paper

£2055 $3493 €3000 View of Palazzo Ducale, Venice (11x15cm-4x6in) W/C gouache. 6-Nov-3 Tajan, Paris #150/R

GRUBACS, Carlo (attrib) (19th C) Italian

£11333 $20513 €17000 Vue de Rome et procession sur le pont du chateau Saint-Ange (45x60cm-18x24in) 30-Mar-4 Millon & Associes, Paris #37/R est:8000-12000

GRUBACS, Giovanni (1829-1919) Italian

£3026 $5568 €4600 Venice (25x13cm-10x5in) s. panel. 22-Jun-4 Chassaing Rivet, Toulouse #295

£4008 $7095 €5852 Venice, St Marc Square (24x13cm-9x5in) s. panel. 28-Apr-4 Kieselbach, Budapest #128/R (H.F 1500000)

GRUBACS, Giovanni (attrib) (1829-1919) Italian

£4577 $7919 €6500 Floods at the Piazza San Marco, Venice (54x73cm-21x29in) 10-Dec-3 Christie's, Amsterdam #673/R est:5000-7000

GRUBAS, Marco (1839-1910) Italian

£634 $1096 €900 Moonlight in Venice with view of SM della Salute (27x14cm-11x6in) s. panel. 10-Dec-3 Dorotheum, Vienna #174/R

£1600 $2912 €2336 The Doge's Palace and the Piazzetta, San Giorgio Maggiore beyond (13x25cm-5x10in) s. paper sold with photogravure. 1-Jul-4 Christie's, Kensington #361/R est:600-800

GRUBE, Louis (1812-1902) American

Works on paper

£556 $1000 €812 Mountain lake (30x56cm-12x22in) s. pastel. 23-Jan-4 Freeman, Philadelphia #19/R

GRUBER, Francis (1912-1948) French

£3610 $6643 €5271 Beach scene with lovers (51x40cm-20x16in) s.d.1931 prov. 29-Mar-4 Rasmussen, Copenhagen #200/R est:40000-60000 (D.KR 40000)

£11189 $19245 €16000 Judith (92x73cm-36x29in) s.d.1946 exhib. 8-Dec-3 Christie's, Paris #72/R est:7500-10000

£12238 $21049 €17500 Peti nu assis au tricot rouge (54x46cm-21x18in) s.d.1944. 8-Dec-3 Christie's, Paris #71/R est:4500-6000

Works on paper

£671 $1201 €1000 Modele (61x47cm-24x19in) s. graphite dr. 30-May-4 Eric Pillon, Calais #244/R

£694 $1146 €1000 Deux femmes allongees (45x60cm-18x24in) s.d.1942 dr. 3-Jul-3 Claude Aguttes, Neuilly #97a

£1958 $3368 €2800 Femme nue (64x50cm-25x20in) s.d.1946 graphite. 8-Dec-3 Christie's, Paris #68/R est:1800-2400

£2550 $4565 €3800 Nu sur canape (48x61cm-19x24in) s.d.1945 dr lit. 30-May-4 Eric Pillon, Calais #245/R

£3087 $5526 €4600 Nu (63x48cm-25x19in) s.d.1946 graphite dr. 30-May-4 Eric Pillon, Calais #243/R

GRUBER, Franz Xaver (1801-1862) Austrian

£2416 $4518 €3600 Sterzing, southern Tyrol (47x35cm-19x14in) i.d.1847 s. verso canvas on board. 24-Feb-4 Dorotheum, Vienna #243/R est:2000-2200

GRUBER, Hannes (1928-) Swiss

£452 $724 €660 Still life with oranges, coffee jug and lamp (81x100cm-32x39in) s.d.1969. 16-Sep-3 Philippe Schuler, Zurich #3238 (S.FR 1000)

£1900 $3231 €2774 Zurichsee (94x110cm-37x43in) s.d.1972 s.i.d. verso. 25-Nov-3 Germann, Zurich #120/R est:3000-5000 (S.FR 4200)

Works on paper

£543 $923 €793 Red landscape (56x78cm-22x31in) s.d.66 gouache. 18-Nov-3 Hans Widmer, St Gallen #1072 (S.FR 1200)

GRUBER, J (19/20th C) ?

£3800 $7182 €5548 After the Sunday service (100x73cm-39x29in) s. 19-Feb-4 Christie's, Kensington #75/R est:2000-3000

GRUBER-GLEICHENBERG, Franz (1886-1940) Austrian

£1477 $2643 €2200 Schwarzau in the mountains (49x61cm-19x24in) s. 27-May-4 Dorotheum, Graz #20/R est:2200

£1745 $3123 €2600 Still life with open book, wine glass and carafe (48x64cm-19x25in) s. 27-May-4 Dorotheum, Graz #19/R est:1800

GRUBICY DE DRAGON, Vittore (1851-1920) Italian

£5634 $9352 €8000 Anversa 85 (22x32cm-9x13in) s.d.85 canvas on board. 11-Jun-3 Christie's, Rome #163/R est:8000-12000

Works on paper

£496 $829 €700 Miazzina, Lake Maggiore (20x32cm-8x13in) s.d.1896 chl lead. 14-Oct-3 Finarte Semenzato, Milan #152/R

£1712 $2671 €2500 Landscape with stream (30x23cm-12x9in) i.d.85 pastel dr. 8-Apr-3 Il Ponte, Milan #576

GRUBISSA, Guglielmo (1908-1983) Italian

£559 $962 €800 View of sistiana (46x56cm-18x22in) s. board. 3-Dec-3 Stadion, Trieste #1072/R

GRUEBER, Frederich (17th C) Dutch

£6338 $10965 €9000 Vanite: les cinq sens (82x95cm-32x37in) s.d.52. 10-Dec-3 Beaussant & Lefèvre, Paris #17/R est:10000-12000

GRUGER, Frederic Roderigo (1871-1953) American

Works on paper

£374 $700 €546 Men in wind powered train car defending themselves against horse riders (23x56cm-9x22in) s. Wolff pencil wash gouache en grisaille. 26-Feb-4 Illustration House, New York #85

£1198 $2000 €1749 Confrontation around campfire. Stranded Couple. Venerated couple (28x41cm-11x16in) Wolff carbon pencil wash three lit. 15-Nov-3 Illustration House, New York #79/R est:2500-4000

GRUN, Jules Alexandre (1868-1934) French

£822 $1397 €1200 Still life of flowers (53x45cm-21x18in) s. 5-Nov-3 Vendue Huis, Gravenhage #282

GRUN, Maurice (1869-1947) French

£500	$905	€750	Rue enneigee (54x65cm-21x26in) s. 5-Apr-4 Deburaux, Boulogne #94/R
£986	$1725	€1400	Bretonne sur le chemin pres des chaumieres (33x44cm-13x17in) s. 21-Dec-3 Thierry & Lannon, Brest #167/R
£1049	$1783	€1500	Route de village effet de nuit (55x65cm-22x26in) s. 27-Nov-3 Millon & Associes, Paris #194/R est:1200-1500
£2185	$4087	€3300	Place animee a Concarneau, le cafe Guillou (24x33cm-9x13in) s. board. 24-Jul-4 Thierry & Lannon, Brest #172/R est:3000-3500

GRUND, Johann (1808-1887) Austrian

£1400	$2576	€2044	Young girl seated holding a daisy with floral garland in foreground (20x15cm-8x6in) s. 11-Jun-4 Keys, Aylsham #671/R est:500-700

GRUND, Norbert Joseph Carl (1717-1767) Czechoslovakian

£4225	$7310	€6000	Park landscape with a young woman sitting at a well (23x18cm-9x7in) zinc sheet. 10-Dec-3 Hugo Ruef, Munich #2370/R est:6000

GRUND, Norbert Joseph Carl (attrib) (1717-1767) Czechoslovakian

£1621	$2707	€2350	Paysages de riviere animes de paysans (41x56cm-16x22in) pair. 14-Nov-3 Drouot Estimations, Paris #16 est:2000-3000

GRUNDELL, Marta (?) Swedish

£471	$815	€688	Red amaryllis (92x73cm-36x29in) s. 15-Dec-3 Lilla Bukowskis, Stockholm #198 (S.KR 6000)

GRUNDIG, Hans (1901-1958) German

£1333	$2387	€2000	Landscape (61x71cm-24x28in) s.d.26. 15-May-4 Van Ham, Cologne #631 est:600
Works on paper			
£1007	$1852	€1500	Girl with dog (40x49cm-16x19in) s.d. W/C. 26-Mar-4 Ketterer, Hamburg #440/R est:1000-1500

GRUNDTVIG, Axel Valdemar (1867-1911) Danish

£366	$667	€534	Three-master in rough seas (81x121cm-32x48in) s.d.Juli 1889. 7-Feb-4 Rasmussen, Havnen #2060/R (D.KR 4000)
£756	$1308	€1104	Sailing vessel off the coast, sun breaking through clouds (51x77cm-20x30in) s.d.1892. 9-Dec-3 Rasmussen, Copenhagen #1480/R (D.KR 8000)

GRUNENWALD, Agnes (19th C) German

£4243	$7468	€6195	Asleep (77x54cm-30x21in) s. 23-May-4 Agra, Warsaw #13/R (P.Z 30000)

GRUNER, Elioth (1882-1939) Australian

£2075	$3465	€3113	Blue mountains (30x24cm-12x9in) s.d.1926 board. 27-Oct-3 Goodman, Sydney #115/R est:4000-6000 (A.D 5000)
£2893	$5351	€4224	Capri (45x38cm-18x15in) s. board painted c.1924 prov. 10-Mar-4 Deutscher-Menzies, Melbourne #58/R est:8000-12000 (A.D 7000)
£4065	$7276	€5935	Skillion, Terrigal N S W (28x39cm-11x15in) s.d.1929 board prov.exhib. 10-May-4 Joel, Victoria #221/R est:10000-15000 (A.D 10000)
£5061	$8148	€7389	Blue hills (39x44cm-15x17in) s. 13-Oct-3 Joel, Victoria #266/R est:15000-20000 (A.D 12500)
£6122	$11265	€8938	Robertson landscape (22x33cm-9x13in) s. canvas on board prov. 29-Mar-4 Goodman, Sydney #112/R est:15000-20000 (A.D 15000)
£6324	$11320	€9486	Harbour scene (20x21cm-8x8in) s.d.1918 canvas on board. 17-May-4 Sotheby's, Melbourne #590/R est:10000-15000 (A.D 16000)
£6800	$11968	€9928	Morning mist (34x44cm-13x17in) s.d.1921 canvas on board. 19-May-4 Sotheby's, Olympia #130/R est:3000-5000
£10270	$17150	€15405	The yellow wallflower (26x35cm-10x14in) s.i. board. 27-Oct-3 Goodman, Sydney #117/R est:25000-35000 (A.D 24750)
£11064	$18809	€16153	Sydney Harbour (48x58cm-19x23in) s.d.1929 exhib.prov. 25-Nov-3 Christie's, Melbourne #29/R est:25000-35000 (A.D 26000)
£12195	$19146	€16178	Steamers on Sydney harbour (14x34cm-6x13in) s.d.1913 board prov. 26-Aug-3 Christie's, Sydney #7/R est:30000-50000 (A.D 30000)
£16327	$30041	€23837	Study for On the Murrumbidgee (51x61cm-20x24in) s.d.1929 prov.exhib. 29-Mar-4 Goodman, Sydney #97/R est:40000-60000 (A.D 40000)
£16598	$27718	€24897	Blossom (43x55cm-17x22in) s.d.1916 canvas on board. 27-Oct-3 Goodman, Sydney #119/R est:40000-60000 (A.D 40000)
£17557	$31954	€25633	Tamarama, Bondi (68x81cm-27x32in) s. prov.exhib. 16-Jun-4 Deutscher-Menzies, Melbourne #69/R est:50000-70000 (A.D 46000)
£18776	$34547	€27413	Sheep country (38x46cm-15x18in) s.d.1931 canvas on board prov.exhib.lit. 29-Mar-4 Goodman, Sydney #109/R est:30000-40000 (A.D 46000)
£22857	$42057	€33371	Tamarama, Bondi (42x52cm-17x20in) s. painted c.1933 prov.exhib.lit. 29-Mar-4 Goodman, Sydney #114/R est:30000-40000 (A.D 56000)
£23470	$43184	€34266	Spring in the orchard (38x46cm-15x18in) s. canvas on board painted c.1932 prov.lit. 29-Mar-4 Goodman, Sydney #102/R est:35000-50000 (A.D 57500)
£23673	$43559	€34563	Nambucca bar (51x61cm-20x24in) s.d.1933 prov.exhib.lit. 29-Mar-4 Goodman, Sydney #105/R est:40000-60000 (A.D 58000)

GRUNEWALD, Isaac (1889-1946) Swedish

£2190	$3724	€3197	Woman seated on the sofa in the garden (54x65cm-21x26in) s. panel. 4-Nov-3 Bukowskis, Stockholm #13/R est:40000-45000 (S.KR 29000)
£2828	$4892	€4129	Red amaryllis (34x25cm-13x10in) s. panel. 15-Dec-3 Lilla Bukowskis, Stockholm #263 est:20000-25000 (S.KR 36000)
£2870	$4879	€4190	Northern landscape with rapids, Abiska (54x65cm-21x26in) s. 5-Nov-3 AB Stockholms Auktionsverk #848/R est:40000-50000 (S.KR 38000)
£3004	$5316	€4386	Still life of ruffled argaric and flowers (55x46cm-22x18in) s. panel. 27-Apr-4 AB Stockholms Auktionsverk #640/R est:35000-40000 (S.KR 41000)
£3336	$6004	€4871	Still life of lilies (46x38cm-18x15in) s. panel. 26-Apr-4 Bukowskis, Stockholm #24/R est:25000-30000 (S.KR 46000)
£3474	$5906	€5072	Amaryllis in vase (61x50cm-24x20in) s. panel. 4-Nov-3 Bukowskis, Stockholm #91/R est:30000-40000 (S.KR 46000)
£3663	$6484	€5348	Le belle Polonaise (46x38cm-18x15in) panel exhib. 27-Apr-4 AB Stockholms Auktionsverk #737/R est:75000-100000 (S.KR 50000)
£4308	$7409	€6290	Still life of flowers in vases (92x73cm-36x29in) s. 7-Dec-3 Uppsala Auktionskammare, Uppsala #222/R est:60000-80000 (S.KR 56000)
£4396	$7780	€6418	Interior scene with model (45x55cm-18x22in) s. panel. 27-Apr-4 AB Stockholms Auktionsverk #731/R est:45000-50000 (S.KR 60000)
£5136	$8731	€7499	Still life of asters and amaryllis (65x93cm-26x37in) s. 4-Nov-3 Bukowskis, Stockholm #155/R est:70000-80000 (S.KR 68000)
£5275	$9336	€7702	Girl with coffee tray in garden (38x46cm-15x18in) s. panel. 27-Apr-4 AB Stockholms Auktionsverk #878/R est:40000-45000 (S.KR 72000)
£5861	$10374	€8557	Still life of amaryllis (65x46cm-26x18in) s. 27-Apr-4 AB Stockholms Auktionsverk #643/R est:100000-125000 (S.KR 80000)
£6091	$10964	€8893	Time for a read (62x80cm-24x31in) s. 26-Apr-4 Bukowskis, Stockholm #104/R est:30000-35000 (S.KR 84000)
£6227	$11022	€9091	Lovely flowers (84x60cm-33x24in) s. i.d.1939 verso panel. 27-Apr-4 AB Stockholms Auktionsverk #807/R est:100000-125000 (S.KR 85000)
£6420	$10914	€9373	The yellow chair (45x37cm-18x15in) s.d.12. 5-Nov-3 AB Stockholms Auktionsverk #667/R est:80000-100000 (S.KR 85000)
£7252	$13053	€10588	Still life of amaryllis and carnations (74x60cm-29x24in) s. 26-Apr-4 Bukowskis, Stockholm #5/R est:100000-125000 (S.KR 100000)
£7614	$13706	€11116	Common hepatica hill at Saltsjobaden (82x66cm-32x26in) s. panel. 26-Apr-4 Bukowskis, Stockholm #125/R est:60000-70000 (S.KR 105000)
£7692	$13615	€11230	Dubonnet (53x64cm-21x25in) s. 27-Apr-4 AB Stockholms Auktionsverk #859/R est:100000-150000 (S.KR 105000)
£7977	$14358	€11646	Woman dressed in green - Mrs Streletskie (102x84cm-40x33in) painted 1928. 26-Apr-4 Bukowskis, Stockholm #172/R est:125000-150000 (S.KR 110000)
£9025	$16606	€13177	Odalisque - reclining female nude (54x65cm-21x26in) s. prov. 29-Mar-4 Rasmussen, Copenhagen #147/R est:100000-150000 (D.KR 100000)
£9819	$16692	€14336	Still life of flowers (46x38cm-18x15in) s. panel. 5-Nov-3 AB Stockholms Auktionsverk #768/R est:75000-100000 (S.KR 130000)
£9819	$16692	€14336	Still life of tulips (73x60cm-29x24in) s. 4-Nov-3 Bukowskis, Stockholm #92/R est:70000-80000 (S.KR 130000)
£10574	$17976	€15438	Plagen Cadiz (59x72cm-23x28in) s.d.33 exhib. 5-Nov-3 AB Stockholms Auktionsverk #668/R est:150000-175000 (S.KR 140000)
£10574	$17976	€15438	Old houses by the harbour, Cassis (54x65cm-21x26in) s.d.1911 exhib. 5-Nov-3 AB Stockholms Auktionsverk #892/R est:175000-200000 (S.KR 140000)
£11707	$19902	€17092	Still life of flowers (100x81cm-39x32in) s. 5-Nov-3 AB Stockholms Auktionsverk #649/R est:100000-125000 (S.KR 155000)
£13218	$22470	€19298	Still life of amaryllis (82x65cm-32x26in) s. panel. 4-Nov-3 Bukowskis, Stockholm #14a/R est:125000-150000 (S.KR 175000)
£23474	$39202	€34272	Garden scene with hammock, Saltsjobaden in summer (100x81cm-39x32in) s. prov. 7-Oct-3 Rasmussen, Copenhagen #144/R est:250000-300000 (D.KR 250000)
£27556	$49601	€40232	Ise Morssing wearing flowery hat (42x26cm-17x10in) s.d.10 panel lit. 26-Apr-4 Bukowskis, Stockholm #57/R est:200000-250000 (S.KR 380000)
£32967	$58352	€48132	The weeping willow, Fonteny-aus-Roses (65x54cm-26x21in) s. painted 1920 exhib.lit. 27-Apr-4 AB Stockholms Auktionsverk #735/R est:350000-400000 (S.KR 450000)
£46154	$81692	€67385	Still life of flowers (65x81cm-26x32in) s. 27-Apr-4 AB Stockholms Auktionsverk #750/R est:200000-225000 (S.KR 630000)
£73260	$129670	€106960	Susanna in the tent (80x64cm-31x25in) s. painted 1918 exhib.prov. 27-Apr-4 AB Stockholms Auktionsverk #692/R est:1200000-1500000 (S.KR 1000000)
£135531	$239890	€197875	Lady seated on red armchair (130x85cm-51x33in) s.d.17 exhib.lit. 27-Apr-4 AB Stockholms Auktionsverk #808/R est:1000000-1200000 (S.KR 1850000)
Works on paper			
£459	$739	€670	Girl standing (35x22cm-14x9in) s. chl. 25-Aug-3 Lilla Bukowskis, Stockholm #14 (S.KR 6000)
£689	$1240	€1006	The small model (38x29cm-15x11in) s. chl. 26-Apr-4 Bukowskis, Stockholm #174/R (S.KR 9500)
£691	$1243	€1009	Still life of flowers (49x34cm-19x13in) s. W/C. 26-Jan-4 Lilla Bukowskis, Stockholm #268 (S.KR 9200)
£692	$1191	€1010	Female nude (28x23cm-11x9in) s. W/C. 7-Dec-3 Uppsala Auktionskammare, Uppsala #233/R (S.KR 9000)
£943	$1697	€1377	Odalisque (24x32cm-9x13in) s. mixed media. 26-Apr-4 Bukowskis, Stockholm #59/R (S.KR 13000)
£1026	$1815	€1498	Landscape from the South of France (22x30cm-9x12in) s.i. W/C. 27-Apr-4 AB Stockholms Auktionsverk #815/R est:10000-12000 (S.KR 14000)
£1171	$1990	€1710	Seated model (26x32cm-10x13in) s.d.41 Indian ink W/C. 4-Nov-3 Bukowskis, Stockholm #172/R est:8000-10000 (S.KR 15500)
£1172	$2075	€1711	Trees going blue (35x25cm-14x10in) s.i. W/C. 27-Apr-4 AB Stockholms Auktionsverk #641/R est:18000-20000 (S.KR 16000)
£1197	$2154	€1796	From Assisi, the beach (24x34cm-9x13in) s. i.d.1934 verso W/C htd white. 25-Apr-4 Goteborg Auktionsverk, Sweden #418/R est:15000 (S.KR 16500)
£1360	$2311	€1986	Flowers (34x26cm-13x10in) s. W/C. 5-Nov-3 AB Stockholms Auktionsverk #734/R est:12000-15000 (S.KR 18000)
£1511	$2568	€2206	Sigrid reading (35x26cm-14x10in) s. chk. 4-Nov-3 Bukowskis, Stockholm #90/R est:20000-25000 (S.KR 20000)
£1586	$2696	€2316	Exotic bird (26x19cm-10x7in) s.d.28 chk. 4-Nov-3 Bukowskis, Stockholm #171/R est:12000-15000 (S.KR 21000)
£1662	$2825	€2427	In the garden (34x24cm-13x9in) s. W/C. 5-Nov-3 AB Stockholms Auktionsverk #655/R est:25000-30000 (S.KR 22000)
£1835	$2954	€2679	Still life of flowers (65x50cm-26x20in) s. pastel. 25-Aug-3 Lilla Bukowskis, Stockholm #660 est:12000-15000 (S.KR 24000)
£2051	$3631	€2994	The nuns at rue Notre Dame Des Champs (32x24cm-13x9in) s. W/C lit. 27-Apr-4 AB Stockholms Auktionsverk #688/R est:15000-20000 (S.KR 28000)
£2143	$3837	€3129	Nude couple by the shore (26x34cm-10x13in) s. mixed media. 28-May-4 Uppsala Auktionskammare, Uppsala #284/R est:10000-12000 (S.KR 29000)
£2248	$4046	€3282	The terrace, Saltsjobaden (27x34cm-11x13in) s. W/C. 26-Apr-4 Bukowskis, Stockholm #173/R est:15000-20000 (S.KR 31000)
£2870	$4879	€4190	The French steam boat (25x34cm-10x13in) s. W/C. 4-Nov-3 Bukowskis, Stockholm #12/R est:30000-35000 (S.KR 38000)
£2930	$5187	€4278	White sails - view of the old town, Stockholm (35x25cm-14x10in) s. W/C pencil. 27-Apr-4 AB Stockholms Auktionsverk #805/R est:40000-50000 (S.KR 40000)
£4396	$7780	€6418	Landscape from Provence (46x61cm-18x24in) s. W/C. 27-Apr-4 AB Stockholms Auktionsverk #715/R est:25000-30000 (S.KR 60000)
£5128	$9077	€7487	On the beach (48x64cm-19x25in) s. mixed media lit. 27-Apr-4 AB Stockholms Auktionsverk #663/R est:25000-30000 (S.KR 70000)

GRUNEWALD, Ivan (1911-1996) Swedish

£680	$1156	€993	The wreck (137x195cm-54x77in) s.d.1950. 5-Nov-3 AB Stockholms Auktionsverk #805/R (S.KR 9000)

GRUNFELD, Thomas (1956-) German

Sculpture			
£1573	$2675	€2250	Hau den Lukas (50x26x40cm-20x10x16in) st.sig.d.89 mirror leather metal wood lit. 27-Nov-3 Lempertz, Koln #161/R est:3000

GRUNLER, Ehregott (1797-1881) German

£805	$1426	€1200	Portrait of Joh Friedr Genthe (76x62cm-30x24in) i. stretcher. 28-Apr-4 Schopman, Hamburg #475/R

GRUNSWEIGH, Nathan (1880-c.1970) Polish

£298	$542	€450	Rue a Paris (33x41cm-13x16in) s. 15-Jun-4 Rossini, Paris #97
£331	$603	€500	Parc ombrage (38x46cm-15x18in) s. panel. 15-Jun-4 Rossini, Paris #95
£380	$673	€555	Still life with grinder (41x54cm-16x21in) s. 27-Apr-4 Bonhams, Knightsbridge #109/R
£596	$1085	€900	Couple conversant (41x33cm-16x13in) s. 15-Jun-4 Rossini, Paris #94
£738	$1374	€1100	Scene de village (38x46cm-15x18in) s.d.1929. 2-Mar-4 Artcurial Briest, Paris #173
£795	$1446	€1200	Place bordee d'arbres (46x61cm-18x24in) s. 15-Jun-4 Rossini, Paris #96/R
£795	$1446	€1200	Rue a la maison blanche (46x55cm-18x22in) s. 15-Jun-4 Rossini, Paris #93/R
£1126	$2049	€1700	Hotel du Sans-Souci (60x73cm-24x29in) s. 15-Jun-4 Rossini, Paris #92/R est:1500-2000
£1174	$2173	€1750	Hotel de l'Union (65x81cm-26x32in) s. 15-Mar-4 Claude Boisgirard, Paris #47/R est:2000-2500
£1241	$2073	€1800	Les roulottes (38x55cm-15x22in) s. cardboard. 17-Nov-3 Claude Boisgirard, Paris #33/R est:1800-2000
£1457	$2652	€2200	Maison dans un parc (60x45cm-24x18in) s. 16-Jun-4 Claude Boisgirard, Paris #70/R est:2000-2500
£1586	$2649	€2300	Rue de banlieue (41x65cm-16x26in) s. 17-Nov-3 Claude Boisgirard, Paris #31 est:1800-2000

GRUNWALD, Bela Ivanyi (1867-1940) Hungarian

£252	$400	€368	Duck pond (59x80cm-23x31in) s. 12-Sep-3 Skinner, Boston #396/R
£292	$464	€420	Still life (65x49cm-26x19in) s. 13-Sep-3 Quittenbaum, Hamburg #69/R
£869	$1442	€1269	Nude by a fountain (45x25cm-18x10in) s. cardboard. 4-Oct-3 Kieselbach, Budapest #84/R (H.F 320000)
£1126	$2015	€1644	Village landscape with windmill and figures (59x80cm-23x31in) s. 22-Mar-4 Philippe Schuler, Zurich #4446/R est:2000-2500 (S.FR 2600)
£1229	$2176	€1794	Mill amongst trees (60x80cm-24x31in) s. 28-Apr-4 Kieselbach, Budapest #41/R (H.F 460000)
£1305	$2258	€1905	Street in Balatonlelle (50x70cm-20x28in) s. painted c.1930. 12-Dec-3 Kieselbach, Budapest #54/R (H.F 500000)
£1493	$2479	€2180	Bathers (50x66cm-20x26in) s. 4-Oct-3 Kieselbach, Budapest #116/R (H.F 550000)
£1500	$2775	€2190	Nude in a landscape (72x100cm-28x39in) s. board. 10-Feb-4 Bonhams, Knightsbridge #179/R est:1500-2000
£1871	$3311	€2732	Girls in a field (70x60cm-28x24in) s. cardboard painted early 1910's. 28-Apr-4 Kieselbach, Budapest #174/R (H.F 700000)
£1900	$3155	€2774	Gils by waterside (80x60cm-31x24in) s. 4-Oct-3 Kieselbach, Budapest #99/R (H.F 700000)
£2610	$4515	€3811	Sunset by the Lake Balaton at Badacsony (60x80cm-24x31in) s. 12-Dec-3 Kieselbach, Budapest #119/R (H.F 1000000)
£2672	$4730	€3901	Nude with a red mantle (51x41cm-20x16in) s. cardboard. 28-Apr-4 Kieselbach, Budapest #39/R (H.F 1000000)
£4344	$7211	€6342	Still life of flowers (60x80cm-24x31in) s. 4-Oct-3 Kieselbach, Budapest #17/R (H.F 1600000)
£4810	$8514	€7023	Riverside (45x47cm-18x19in) s. painted c.1909. 28-Apr-4 Kieselbach, Budapest #148/R (H.F 1800000)
£5879	$10406	€8583	Still life of flowers (80x60cm-31x24in) s.d.1935. 28-Apr-4 Kieselbach, Budapest #101/R (H.F 2200000)
£13361	$23649	€19507	Spring, dressed woman in flowery garden (70x59cm-28x23in) s. 28-Apr-4 Kieselbach, Budapest #84/R (H.F 5000000)
£16289	$27040	€23782	Watering (100x100cm-39x39in) s. painted c.1902. 4-Oct-3 Kieselbach, Budapest #73/R (H.F 6000000)
£16289	$27040	€23782	Winter garden in Nagybanya (75x99cm-30x39in) s. painted c.1900. 4-Oct-3 Kieselbach, Budapest #127/R (H.F 6000000)

GRUNWALD, Carl (1907-1968) German

£278	$439	€400	River on summer's day (23x33cm-9x13in) mono.d.1964 board. 6-Sep-3 Arnold, Frankfurt #567/R
£469	$806	€670	Arcadian landscape (32x40cm-13x16in) s.d.1964 board. 2-Dec-3 Hauswedell & Nolte, Hamburg #245/R

GRUNZWEIG, Bedrich (20th C) ?

Photographs

£1808	$3200	€2640	Between heaven and earth, U.N building, 1950 (40x39cm-16x15in) s.i.d. gelatin silver print. 27-Apr-4 Christie's, Rockefeller NY #208/R est:2500-3500
£2100	$3570	€3066	TWA, Kennedy Airport NYC, ramp to planes (25x21cm-10x8in) s.i.d.1965 verso silver print. 19-Nov-3 Sotheby's, Olympia #69/R est:800-1200

GRUPPE, Charles Paul (1860-1940) American

£378	$700	€552	Landscape with windmill (30x41cm-12x16in) s. 15-Feb-4 Outer Cape Auctions, Provincetown #81/R
£447	$800	€653	Evening landscape (30x41cm-12x16in) s. 11-Jan-4 William Jenack, New York #8
£538	$1000	€785	Untitled (23x28cm-9x11in) board. 6-Mar-4 Page, Batavia #29
£559	$1000	€816	An old friend of mine (41x51cm-16x20in) 8-Jan-4 James Julia, Fairfield #708/R
£765	$1300	€1117	Mother and child in an exterior scene (56x46cm-22x18in) s. prov. 18-Nov-3 John Moran, Pasadena #79
£860	$1600	€1256	Untitled (30x46cm-12x18in) board. 6-Mar-4 Page, Batavia #131
£1576	$2475	€2301	Resting (46x36cm-18x14in) s. 1-Sep-3 William A Smith, Plainfield #7/R
£1882	$3200	€2748	Bass Rocks (76x101cm-30x40in) s. i.verso. 21-Nov-3 Skinner, Boston #557/R est:3000-5000
£1923	$3500	€2808	Fishing boat moored in low tide surf (30x41cm-12x16in) s. board prov. 15-Jun-4 John Moran, Pasadena #68b est:2500-3500
£1955	$3500	€2854	Gray sailing days (30x41cm-12x16in) s. 8-Jan-4 James Julia, Fairfield #707/R est:2500-3500
£2013	$3725	€3000	Woodcutters at work (56x76cm-22x30in) s. 15-Mar-4 Sotheby's, Amsterdam #104/R est:1500-2500
£2095	$3750	€3059	Autumn hilltop at Lyme, Connecticut (46x61cm-18x24in) s. s.i.verso. 6-May-4 Shannon's, Milford #9/R est:4000-6000
£2235	$4000	€3263	Landscape (81x130cm-32x51in) board. 14-May-4 Du Mouchelle, Detroit #2006/R est:5000-7000
£2415	$4250	€3526	Country landscape with stream and dam (51x61cm-20x24in) s. 1-Jan-4 Nadeau, Windsor #176/R est:2000-2500
£2614	$4600	€3816	November afternoon (61x51cm-24x20in) s. 3-Jan-4 Collins, Maine #10/R est:2500-3500
£2614	$4600	€3816	And all hands were lost at sea (76x61cm-30x24in) s.d.1890. 3-Jan-4 Collins, Maine #11/R est:2000-3000
£2695	$4500	€3935	Cows watering in a stream (64x76cm-25x30in) s. prov. 23-Oct-3 Shannon's, Milford #235/R est:4000-6000
£2699	$4400	€3941	Brook Catskills (76x102cm-30x40in) 28-Sep-3 Carlsen Gallery, Greenville #600/R
£2841	$5000	€4148	Along the canal (36x51cm-14x20in) s. 3-Jan-4 Collins, Maine #5/R est:3000-4000
£3352	$6000	€4894	Gloucester wharf (41x30cm-16x12in) 8-Jan-4 James Julia, Fairfield #706/R est:4000-6000
£3409	$6000	€4977	Youngsters on the beach (51x61cm-20x24in) s. 3-Jan-4 Collins, Maine #12/R est:2500-3500
£3481	$5500	€5082	Old waterwheel, Conesus Creek, Conesus Lake, Livingstone Co, NY (97x132cm-38x52in) s. painted c.1906 prov. 6-Apr-3 William Jenack, New York #123 est:6000-8000
£3593	$6000	€5246	Connecticut Winter landscape (71x91cm-28x36in) s. masonite prov. 23-Oct-3 Shannon's, Milford #177/R est:6000-8000
£4969	$8000	€7255	Gloucester harbour (20x25cm-8x10in) s. board. 20-Aug-3 James Julia, Fairfield #1296/R est:5000-7000

Works on paper

£272	$500	€397	Fishing boats (23x46cm-9x18in) s.d.90 W/C. 25-Jun-4 Freeman, Philadelphia #248/R
£435	$700	€635	Behind the dunes (28x38cm-11x15in) s. W/C. 20-Aug-3 James Julia, Fairfield #1298/R est:1200-1800
£483	$850	€705	Dutch landscape (18x25cm-7x10in) s. W/C. 3-Jan-4 Collins, Maine #8/R
£652	$1050	€952	Dutch landscape (30x46cm-12x18in) s. W/C. 20-Aug-3 James Julia, Fairfield #1297/R
£1932	$3400	€2821	Edge of canal at Voorburg (25x30cm-10x12in) s. W/C. 3-Jan-4 Collins, Maine #9/R est:800-1200
£2151	$4000	€3140	Dutch seascape (36x53cm-14x21in) W/C. 6-Mar-4 Page, Batavia #129
£2500	$4400	€3650	Peasant woman (38x53cm-15x21in) s. W/C. 3-Jan-4 Collins, Maine #6/R est:2500-4500

GRUPPE, Emile A (1896-1978) American

£621	$1100	€907	Study number two, Bass Rocks (36x46cm-14x18in) s. 1-May-4 Thomaston Place, Thomaston #104/R
£838	$1350	€1223	New England church (41x33cm-16x13in) s. 20-Aug-3 James Julia, Fairfield #1264/R est:1000-1500
£1105	$2000	€1613	Winter landscape (33x33cm-13x13in) s. board. 16-Apr-4 James Julia, Fairfield #531/R est:3000-5000
£1136	$2000	€1659	White house and trees (20x25cm-8x10in) s.d.1919 board. 3-Jan-4 Collins, Maine #2/R est:1200-1600
£1455	$2750	€2124	Wooded river landscape (30x41cm-12x16in) s. board prov. 17-Feb-4 John Moran, Pasadena #29/R est:2000-3000
£1508	$2700	€2202	Men in rowboats with tugboat (71x76cm-28x30in) s. 7-May-4 Sloans & Kenyon, Bethesda #1725/R est:4000-6000
£1518	$2611	€2216	Bass rocks (46x51cm-18x20in) s. i. on stretcher. 2-Dec-3 Ritchie, Toronto #91/R est:3000-4000 (C.D 3400)
£1537	$2750	€2244	At the wharf, Gloucester (30x38cm-12x15in) 8-Jan-4 James Julia, Fairfield #478/R est:1500-2500
£1647	$2800	€2405	Mrs Lorenzo (61x51cm-24x20in) s. 21-Nov-3 Skinner, Boston #536/R est:800-1200
£1705	$3000	€2489	Frozen stream (46x51cm-18x20in) s. i.verso. 23-May-4 Hindman, Chicago #151/R est:4000-6000
£1776	$3250	€2593	Gloucester fishing trawler (41x61cm-16x24in) s. canvasboard. 7-Jun-4 O'Gallerie, Oregon #778/R est:4000-6000
£2027	$3750	€2959	Docks with fishing boats (51x61cm-20x24in) s. board. 13-Feb-4 David Rago, Lambertville #9/R est:3000-4000
£2235	$4000	€3263	Snow banked stream (20x25cm-8x10in) s. board. 8-Jan-4 James Julia, Fairfield #476/R est:2500-3500
£2446	$4500	€3571	Evening light, Bass Rocks (50x61cm-20x24in) s. i.verso prov. 8-Jun-4 Bonhams & Butterfields, San Francisco #4093/R est:4000-6000
£2484	$4000	€3627	Bathers on rocky shore (61x51cm-24x20in) 20-Aug-3 James Julia, Fairfield #1261/R est:6000-8000
£2793	$5000	€4078	Early morning (51x46cm-20x18in) i.verso. 8-Jan-4 James Julia, Fairfield #477/R est:3000-5000
£2941	$5000	€4294	On the wharf, north shore scene (41x51cm-16x20in) s. 21-Nov-3 Skinner, Boston #554/R est:5000-7000
£3073	$5500	€4487	Study of a lobsterman (41x51cm-16x20in) i.verso board. 8-Jan-4 James Julia, Fairfield #475/R est:4000-6000
£3073	$5500	€4487	Foggy morning (20x24cm-8x9in) s. s.i.verso. 6-May-4 Shannon's, Milford #136/R est:5000-7000
£3106	$5000	€4535	Moonlight, Salt Island (46x76cm-18x30in) s. 20-Aug-3 James Julia, Fairfield #1262/R est:6000-8000
£3143	$5500	€4589	Fog, Gloucester (51x61cm-20x24in) s. prov. 19-Dec-3 Sotheby's, New York #1122/R est:6000-9000
£3213	$5750	€4691	Rock at Bass Rocks (41x51cm-16x20in) s. s.i.d.1960 verso board. 8-Jan-4 James Julia, Fairfield #473/R est:6000-8000
£3226	$6000	€4710	Places Michel Paris, Salmagundi Club (20x25cm-8x10in) board. 6-Mar-4 Page, Batavia #31
£3261	$6000	€4761	Boat docked at a small village (30x40cm-12x16in) s. board prov. 8-Jun-4 Bonhams & Butterfields, San Francisco #4094/R est:4000-6000
£3352	$6000	€4894	First light Gloucester harbour (51x46cm-20x18in) s. s.i.verso board. 8-Jan-4 James Julia, Fairfield #474/R est:4000-6000
£3352	$6000	€4894	Harbour scene (51x61cm-20x24in) s. 6-May-4 Shannon's, Milford #74/R est:5000-7000
£3488	$6000	€5092	Langford Terrace, Florida (41x51cm-16x20in) s. i.verso canvasboard. 7-Dec-3 Freeman, Philadelphia #135 est:4000-6000
£3593	$6000	€5246	Gloucester Docks (41x51cm-16x20in) s. prov. 23-Oct-3 Shannon's, Milford #42/R est:5000-7000
£3704	$6000	€5371	Winter, Gloucester (61x76cm-24x30in) s.i. 8-Aug-3 Barridorf, Portland #251/R est:7000-9000
£3882	$6250	€5668	March thaw or Melting snow (51x64cm-20x25in) 20-Aug-3 James Julia, Fairfield #1258/R est:12000-16000
£3882	$6250	€5668	Swordfisherman (61x51cm-24x20in) s. i. stretcher. 20-Aug-3 James Julia, Fairfield #1260/R est:8000-10000
£3892	$6500	€5682	At the Dock Gloucester (51x46cm-20x18in) s. prov. 23-Oct-3 Shannon's, Milford #1/R est:4000-6000
£3911	$7000	€5710	Gray day Gloucester (61x51cm-24x20in) s. i.verso prov. 6-May-4 Shannon's, Milford #2 est:6000-8000

£4037	$6500	€5894	Autumn (76x91cm-30x36in) s. 20-Aug-3 James Julia, Fairfield #1263/R est:5000-7000
£4204	$6600	€6138	Birches in autumn (61x51cm-24x20in) s. 1-Sep-3 William A Smith, Plainfield #4/R
£4348	$7000	€6348	Gloucester morning 1960 (61x51cm-24x20in) s. s.i. stretcher. 20-Aug-3 James Julia, Fairfield #1259/R est:8000-10000
£4412	$7500	€6442	New England cottage (50x60cm-20x24in) s. i.verso prov. 21-Nov-3 Skinner, Boston #570/R est:3000-5000
£4491	$7500	€6557	Wisteria on my studio door (64x76cm-25x30in) s. i.stretcher. 16-Nov-3 CRN Auctions, Cambridge #15/R
£4651	$8000	€6790	Florida coastal scene (76x91cm-30x36in) s. painted c.1950. 7-Dec-3 Treadway Gallery, Cincinnati #561/R est:6000-8000
£4651	$8000	€6790	Fish House, Florida (51x61cm-20x24in) s. s.i.stretcher. 7-Dec-3 Freeman, Philadelphia #134 est:5000-8000
£4790	$8000	€6993	Winding stream (76x91cm-30x36in) s. i.verso prov. 23-Oct-3 Shannon's, Milford #233/R est:8000-12000
£4888	$8750	€7136	Docked fishing boats, Rockport (64x76cm-25x30in) s. 16-May-4 CRN Auctions, Cambridge #13/R
£4891	$9000	€7141	Birches (76x91cm-30x36in) s. i. stretcher prov.exhib. 8-Jun-4 Bonhams & Butterfields, San Francisco #4099/R est:8000-12000
£5031	$8000	€7345	Harbour view (51x61cm-20x24in) s. 12-Sep-3 Skinner, Boston #503/R
£5114	$9000	€7466	Mending the nets, Gloucester (51x61cm-20x24in) s. 3-Jan-4 Collins, Maine #1/R est:4000-6000
£5294	$9000	€7729	Foggy morning, Gloucester (53x61cm-21x24in) s.d.1961. 29-Nov-3 Carlsen Gallery, Greenville #171/R
£5523	$9500	€8064	Fall birches (91x74cm-36x29in) s. painted c.1950. 7-Dec-3 Treadway Gallery, Cincinnati #565/R est:15000-20000
£5679	$9200	€8235	Regina Maris and the Westward at Gloucester (76x63cm-30x25in) s. i.verso. 8-Aug-3 Barridorf, Portland #80/R est:9000-12000
£5682	$10000	€8296	Gloucester Harbour morning (81x102cm-32x40in) s. prov. 18-May-4 Arthur James, Florida #122 est:7000-10000
£5682	$10000	€8296	Fog in Gloucester (64x76cm-25x30in) s. 3-Jan-4 Collins, Maine #4/R est:4000-6000
£5793	$9500	€8400	Gloucester harbour (51x46cm-20x18in) s. painted c.1928. 7-Jun-3 Treadway Gallery, Cincinnati #1364 est:6000-8000
£6471	$11000	€9448	Low tide, Gloucester (76x63cm-30x25in) s. i.verso prov. 21-Nov-3 Skinner, Boston #573/R est:3000-5000
£6704	$12000	€9788	River view, winter (63x77cm-25x30in) s. 14-May-4 Skinner, Boston #227/R est:8000-12000
£7386	$13000	€10784	Gloucester harbour (61x51cm-24x20in) s. 3-Jan-4 Collins, Maine #3/R est:3500-5000
£8152	$15000	€11902	The dock at low tide (50x40cm-20x16in) s. prov. 8-Jun-4 Bonhams & Butterfields, San Francisco #4091/R est:5000-7000
£9259	$15000	€13426	Gloucester morning (76x91cm-30x36in) s. 8-Aug-3 Barridorf, Portland #79/R est:15000-25000
£9877	$16000	€14322	Gloucester fog (91x76cm-36x30in) s. s.on stretcher prov. 8-Aug-3 Barridorf, Portland #352/R est:12000-18000

GRUPPE, Karl Heinrich (1893-1982) American

Sculpture

£2348	$4250	€3428	Kneeling women on pillows (20cm-8in) s.d.1918 green brown pat bronze bookends pair st.f.Roman Bronze. 31-Mar-4 Sotheby's, New York #119/R est:2000-3000

GRUPPE, Robert C (20th C) American

£1686	$2900	€2462	Gloucester harbour scene (61x74cm-24x29in) s. painted c.2000. 7-Dec-3 Treadway Gallery, Cincinnati #630/R est:2000-3000

GRUS, Jaroslav (1891-1981) Czechoslovakian

£1317	$2239	€1923	Behind a village (80x99cm-31x39in) s.d.1937 exhib. 29-Nov-3 Dorotheum, Prague #84/R est:60000-90000 (C.KR 60000)
£2085	$3545	€3044	Still life with bouquet and fruits (80x99cm-31x39in) s.d.1942. 29-Nov-3 Dorotheum, Prague #83/R est:60000-90000 (C.KR 95000)

GRUST, Theodor (1859-1909) German

£538	$926	€785	Monk carrying mug and bread (53x41cm-21x16in) s. panel. 7-Dec-3 Uppsala Auktionskammare, Uppsala #109 (S.KR 7000)

GRUTTEFIEN, Elisabeth (19th C) German

£1617	$3008	€2361	Large stone on beach, midnight sun (99x151cm-39x59in) s. 2-Mar-4 Rasmussen, Copenhagen #1352/R est:8000 (D.KR 18000)

GRUTZKE, Johannes (1937-) German

£4878	$8000	€7122	Uner junge ist weider daheim (120x130cm-47x51in) mono. s.i.d.1967 verso prov.exhib.lit. 28-May-3 Sotheby's, Amsterdam #180/R est:8000-12000

Works on paper

£600	$1098	€900	Portrait of Ulrich Tukur (40x30cm-16x12in) s.d.0.10.84 pencil. 4-Jun-4 Lempertz, Koln #172/R
£972	$1624	€1400	Reclining figure wearing red blouse (84x121cm-33x48in) s.d. chk board. 24-Oct-3 Ketterer, Hamburg #365/R
£1250	$2088	€1800	Self portrait (52x49cm-20x19in) pastel chk. 24-Oct-3 Ketterer, Hamburg #366/R est:2000-3000
£1573	$2675	€2250	Untitled - self portrait (113x98cm-44x39in) s.d.29.3.89 pastel chk tempera board. 27-Nov-3 Lempertz, Koln #162/R est:3000
£2000	$3680	€3000	Two men (126x99cm-50x39in) s.d.1984 pastel. 12-Jun-4 Villa Grisebach, Berlin #425/R est:3000-4000
£2158	$3540	€3000	Self portrait (100x56cm-39x22in) mono.i.d. col chk. 4-Jun-3 Ketterer, Hamburg #423/R est:3000-5000

GRUTZNER, Eduard von (1846-1925) German

£290	$536	€420	Monk with wine (23x16cm-9x6in) bears sig. panel. 14-Feb-4 Hans Stahl, Hamburg #30/R
£469	$750	€685	Gossip. s. paper on canvas. 20-Sep-3 Harvey Clar, Oakland #1262
£1406	$2250	€2053	Quiet meal. s. paper on canvas. 20-Sep-3 Harvey Clar, Oakland #1261
£1724	$2879	€2500	Monk drinking (51x41cm-20x16in) s.d.12 panel lit. 12-Jul-3 Bergmann, Erlangen #623/R est:2500
£2098	$3608	€3000	Portrait of Falstaff (17x12cm-7x5in) s.d.1918 panel. 3-Dec-3 Neumeister, Munich #581/R est:2500
£2183	$4017	€3187	Monk with tankard (17x13cm-7x5in) s.d.889 panel. 14-Jun-4 Philippe Schuler, Zurich #4288/R est:6000-8000 (S.FR 5000)
£4895	$8420	€7000	Portrait of Falstaff (20x15cm-8x6in) s.d.1898 panel. 3-Dec-3 Neumeister, Munich #580/R est:7000
£5022	$9240	€7332	Wine tasting in monastery cellar (35x27cm-14x11in) s.d.83 panel lit.prov. 14-Jun-4 Philippe Schuler, Zurich #4287/R est:15000-20000 (S.FR 11500)
£5459	$10044	€7970	Falstaff with petwter tankard (33x24cm-13x9in) s.d.05 panel. 14-Jun-4 Philippe Schuler, Zurich #4289/R est:10000-14000 (S.FR 12500)
£5634	$9014	€8000	Patron of the arts (35x43cm-14x17in) s. panel lit. 19-Sep-3 Karlheinz Kaupp, Staufen #2038/R est:8000
£5743	$10280	€8500	Midday snooze (27x22cm-11x9in) s. panel lit. 8-May-4 Schloss Ahlden, Ahlden #741/R est:8500
£6667	$12133	€10000	A pinch of snuff (33x25cm-13x10in) s.d.05 panel. 1-Jul-4 Van Ham, Cologne #1378/R est:10000
£6897	$12690	€10070	Rogue (16x12cm-6x5in) s.d.26.2.95 panel lit. 26-Mar-4 Koller, Zurich #3110/R est:20000-25000 (S.FR 16000)
£6944	$11319	€10000	Falstaff with wine jug and beaker (32x25cm-13x10in) s.d.11.03 panel lit. 24-Sep-3 Neumeister, Munich #430/R est:8000
£9028	$14896	€13000	Monk enjoying cigar after eating (50x40cm-20x16in) s.d.1904 lit. 2-Jul-3 Neumeister, Munich #651/R est:15000
£9412	$16000	€13742	Evening meal (42x36cm-17x14in) s.d.98 prov. 29-Oct-3 Christie's, Rockefeller NY #42/R est:18000-25000
£10204	$18265	€15000	Brother cellarmaster (48x40cm-19x16in) s.i.d.1901. 17-Mar-4 Neumeister, Munich #462/R est:15000
£17606	$30458	€25000	Clear gold (33x27cm-13x11in) s.i.d.1917 panel. 10-Dec-3 Hugo Ruef, Munich #2421/R est:25000
£21528	$35090	€31000	Wine testing (87x70cm-34x28in) s.d.1885 lit. 24-Sep-3 Neumeister, Munich #429/R est:40000

Works on paper

£338	$541	€480	Spitzweg sitting at easel (25x18cm-10x7in) s.d.89 pencil lit. 19-Sep-3 Karlheinz Kaupp, Staufen #2057/R

GRUTZNER, Eduard von (attrib) (1846-1925) German

£431	$742	€629	Four monks at a merry gathering (46x58cm-18x23in) s. 2-Dec-3 Kunsthallen, Copenhagen #532 (D.KR 4600)
£1421	$2600	€2075	Luck divine (69x51cm-27x20in) indis sig. 5-Jun-4 Treadway Gallery, Cincinnati #541/R est:3000-5000

GRUYTER, Jacob Willem (1856-1908) Dutch

£437	$800	€638	Fishing boats at sea (30x47cm-12x19in) s.d.1872. 10-Jul-4 Auctions by the Bay, Alameda #428/R
£625	$1000	€913	Two sailing ships at sea (46x76cm-18x30in) s. panel prov. 20-Sep-3 Bunte, Elgin #1425

GRUYTER, R de (1612-1670) Dutch

£4000	$6800	€5840	Interior of a cathedral, Groote Kerke, Rotterdam with figures and animals (69x69cm-27x27in) s.d.1651 panel. 5-Nov-3 John Nicholson, Haslemere #646/R est:3000-5000

GRUYTER, Willem (19th C) Dutch

£3147	$5255	€4500	Ships off coast (40x50cm-16x20in) s. 28-Jun-3 Bolland & Marotz, Bremen #655/R est:3200
£7692	$13231	€11000	Evening at Weser estuary with fishing boat (91x133cm-36x52in) s.d.1873. 5-Dec-3 Bolland & Marotz, Bremen #558/R est:9000

GRUZALSKI, James A (20th C) American

Sculpture

£1027	$1900	€1499	General George Custer (51cm-20in) bronze. 14-Jan-4 Dallas Auction Gallery, Dallas #91 est:3000-5000

GRYEFF, Adriaen de (1670-1715) Flemish

£679	$1154	€991	Herder with goats (24x29cm-9x11in) mono. 19-Nov-3 Fischer, Luzern #2116/R (S.FR 1500)
£1342	$2470	€2000	Huntsman with bag and hounds (29x41cm-11x16in) s. panel. 24-Mar-4 Dorotheum, Vienna #411/R est:2500-3500
£2100	$3864	€3066	Spaniels in a landscape (38x56cm-15x22in) 23-Jun-4 Bonhams, Bury St Edmunds #393/R est:1200-1800
£2500	$4600	€3800	Hunter and dogs by dead game (15x17cm-6x7in) s. panel. 25-Jun-4 Piasa, Paris #90/R est:4000-6000
£3077	$5292	€4492	Nature morte au chiens et gibiers (34x48cm-13x19in) panel. 3-Dec-3 AB Stockholms Auktionsverk #2666/R est:50000-60000 (S.KR 40000)
£3103	$5183	€4500	Hunting still life with dead birds before landscape (35x45cm-14x18in) prov. 15-Nov-3 Lempertz, Koln #1058/R est:4000
£6993	$11888	€10000	Canard, aigle et paon pres du rivage (21x29cm-8x11in) s. panel. 24-Nov-3 E & Eve, Paris #155/R est:8000-10000
£42553	$68936	€60000	El descanso del cazador (161x230cm-63x91in) 20-May-3 Ansorena, Madrid #95/R est:60000

GRYEFF, Adriaen de (attrib) (1670-1715) Flemish

£437	$795	€638	Hunters and dogs with their kill (20x26cm-8x10in) indis.s. canvas on panel. 16-Jun-4 Fischer, Luzern #2148 (S.FR 1000)
£1748	$3007	€2500	Chien la tete dresse pres d'un trophee. Chien observant des oiseaux (14x18cm-6x7in) panel two. 8-Dec-3 Rossini, Paris #48/R est:2500-3000
£3548	$6350	€5180	Hunting still life with dog and cat (65x46cm-26x18in) pair. 25-May-4 Bukowskis, Stockholm #484/R est:60000-80000 (S.KR 48000)
£3800	$6840	€5548	Wooded landscape with huntsman resting his dogs (20x26cm-8x10in) panel. 23-Apr-4 Christie's, Kensington #100/R est:2500-3500

GRYEFF, Adriaen de (circle) (1670-1715) Flemish

£22905	$41000	€33441	Hounds with catch (99x135cm-39x53in) 8-Jan-4 James Julia, Fairfield #173/R est:5000-10000

GRYSPOS, Nikitas (1873-1975) Greek

£1800	$3222	€2628	A pensive man (46x36cm-18x14in) s. 11-May-4 Bonhams, New Bond Street #66/R est:1200-1500

£2000 $3500 €2920 Farmhouse. Cows grazing. Sweet treat. Greek Easter (30x32cm-12x13in) s. two hardboard one cardboard one panel four. 16-Dec-3 Bonhams, New Bond Street #69/R est:2000-2800

GRZIMEK, Waldemar (1918-1984) Polish
Sculpture
£1467 $2699 €2200 Crouching (23cm-9in) s.verso st.f.Noack brown pat bronze. 12-Jun-4 Villa Grisebach, Berlin #729/R est:2500-3000
£2667 $4907 €4000 Dreaming woman (88cm-35in) mono.st.f. Barth gold brown pat. bronze exec. 1972 one of six. 12-Jun-4 Villa Grisebach, Berlin #345/R est:3000-5000

GRZYB, Ryszard (1956-) Polish
£521 $896 €761 To be or not to be (100x89cm-39x35in) s.i.d.1988 verso. 4-Dec-3 Agra, Warsaw #8/R (P.Z 3500)

GSCHOSMANN, Ludwig (c.1901-1988) German
£302 $562 €450 The old harbour in Nice (60x70cm-24x28in) s. i.verso. 5-Mar-4 Wendl, Rudolstadt #3668/R
£345 $638 €500 Venice (50x90cm-20x35in) s. 12-Feb-4 Weidler, Nurnberg #6563
£385 $654 €550 Porte Venere (61x70cm-24x28in) s. 22-Nov-3 Arnold, Frankfurt #531/R
£458 $819 €650 Sailing boat drawn up on the shore of Starnberger lake (60x70cm-24x28in) s. lit. 8-Jan-4 Allgauer, Kempten #2399/R
£521 $828 €750 Party in ballroom (69x78cm-27x31in) s. 11-Sep-3 Weidler, Nurnberg #6501/R
£690 $1152 €1000 Worthersee (80x100cm-31x39in) s. i. verso. 9-Jul-3 Hugo Ruef, Munich #100
£724 $1340 €1050 Woodcutters with Tegernsee beyond (80x100cm-31x39in) s. 12-Feb-4 Weidler, Nurnberg #6500/R
£728 $1326 €1100 Autumn landscape with numerous hunting riders (60x50cm-24x20in) indis.s. 19-Jun-4 Bergmann, Erlangen #860
£805 $1506 €1200 Harbour in Nice (60x50cm-24x20in) s. bears d. i. verso. 28-Feb-4 Bolland & Marotz, Bremen #304/R

GU FANG (17/18th C) Chinese
Works on paper
£19915 $35846 €29076 Landscape in snow (50x38cm-20x15in) s.i. hanging scroll ink colour silk. 26-Apr-4 Christie's, Hong Kong #961/R est:60000-80000 (HK.D 280000)

GU YUAN (17th C) Chinese
Works on paper
£1991 $3585 €2907 Figures, birds and flowers (22x33cm-9x13in) s.i.d. ink col leaves ten album. 25-Apr-4 Christie's, Hong Kong #423/R est:40000-50000 (HK.D 28000)

GUACCIMANNI, Vittorio (1859-1938) Italian
Works on paper
£480 $883 €715 Seated drummer in uniform (45x34cm-18x13in) s.i. W/C over pencil. 25-Mar-4 Dr Fritz Nagel, Stuttgart #512/R
£567 $1020 €850 Arabian fighter (44x25cm-17x10in) s.i. W/C lit. 22-Apr-4 Allgauer, Kempten #3394/R
£634 $1096 €900 Peasant girl (42x30cm-17x12in) s. pastel. 9-Dec-3 Pandolfini, Florence #232/R

GUALA, Pier Francesco (attrib) (1698-1757) Italian
£3448 $5724 €5000 Death of St Joseph (73x61cm-29x24in) prov. 1-Oct-3 Dorotheum, Vienna #291/R est:5000-7000

GUAN LIANG (1899-1985) Chinese
£7112 $12802 €10384 Scenery at the factory (36x28cm-14x11in) s. oil paperboard painted c.1950. 25-Apr-4 Christie's, Hong Kong #713/R est:70000-90000 (HK.D 100000)
£15444 $25792 €22548 Spring in Jiannan (60x75cm-24x30in) s.d.1982. 27-Oct-3 Sotheby's, Hong Kong #362/R est:200000-300000 (HK.D 200000)
£17070 $30725 €24922 View from the seashore (49x39cm-19x15in) s.i. painted c.1950 prov.exhib. 25-Apr-4 Christie's, Hong Kong #712/R est:120000-150000 (HK.D 240000)
£23166 $38687 €33822 Harbour of Shanghai (63x39cm-25x15in) s. painted c.1960 prov.exhib. 26-Oct-3 Christie's, Hong Kong #117/R est:350000-450000 (HK.D 300000)
£23166 $38687 €33822 Flower and fruit (63x39cm-25x15in) s. painted c.1980 prov.exhib. 26-Oct-3 Christie's, Hong Kong #118/R est:300000-350000 (HK.D 300000)
Works on paper
£10039 $16764 €14657 Drunken empress (178x96cm-70x38in) s.i. ink executed c.1980 exhib. 26-Oct-3 Christie's, Hong Kong #119/R est:60000-80000 (HK.D 130000)

GUAN SI (fl.c.1590-1630) Chinese
Works on paper
£6564 $10961 €9583 Fishing in autumn (159x46cm-63x18in) s.i. ink col on silk. 26-Oct-3 Christie's, Hong Kong #476/R (HK.D 85000)

GUANSE, Antonio (1926-) Spanish
£290 $481 €420 Crowd (46x38cm-18x15in) s.i.d.1974 verso. 1-Oct-3 Ansorena, Madrid #638/R
£395 $726 €600 Rencontre sur le bord de la mer (46x38cm-18x15in) s.i.d.74 verso. 22-Jun-4 Durán, Madrid #54/R
£556 $906 €800 Voyage immobile (65x54cm-26x21in) s.d.75. 23-Sep-3 Durán, Madrid #120/R
£582 $990 €850 Orage (65x81cm-26x32in) s.d.77. 4-Nov-3 Ansorena, Madrid #951/R
£599 $958 €850 Atelier III (65x54cm-26x21in) s.d.1975 i.verso. 16-Sep-3 Segre, Madrid #163/R
£662 $1192 €960 Conversation at the mirror (61x50cm-24x20in) s.d.75. 26-Jan-4 Durán, Madrid #73/R
£669 $1171 €950 Concierge (81x65cm-32x26in) s.d.77 i.verso exhib. 16-Dec-3 Durán, Madrid #91/R
£816 $1321 €1150 Studio of the painter (92x73cm-36x29in) s.d.1977 s.i.d.verso. 20-May-3 Ansorena, Madrid #343/R
£906 $1685 €1350 Bruns et bleus (100x81cm-39x32in) s.d.75. 2-Mar-4 Ansorena, Madrid #829/R
£951 $1645 €1350 Absences (100x81cm-39x32in) s.d.74. 15-Dec-3 Ansorena, Madrid #1033/R
£966 $1603 €1400 Tummy (81x65cm-32x26in) s.d.90 s.d.verso. 1-Oct-3 Ansorena, Madrid #539/R
£1118 $2024 €1700 Vons connaisser sarajosse (65x81cm-26x32in) s.d.75 s.i.d.verso. 14-Apr-4 Ansorena, Madrid #298/R est:900
Works on paper
£282 $493 €400 Collioure (35x50cm-14x20in) s.d.70 mixed media. 16-Dec-3 Durán, Madrid #47/R

GUARANA, Jacopo (1720-1808) Italian
£105556 $190000 €154112 Hercules and Omphale. Paris and Helen of Troy (126x420cm-50x165in) pair. 22-Jan-4 Sotheby's, New York #200/R est:15000-20000

GUARANA, Jacopo (attrib) (1720-1808) Italian
£18667 $34160 €28000 Moses fund in the river (81x108cm-32x43in) 1-Jun-4 Sotheby's, Milan #105/R est:18000-22000

GUARDABASSI, Guerrino (1841-?) Italian
£300 $498 €438 Portrait of an Italian peasant girl (20x15cm-8x6in) s.verso. 3-Oct-3 Mallams, Oxford #195
£559 $934 €800 Peasant woman in the Roman countryside (27x17cm-11x7in) s. board. 24-Jun-3 Finarte Semenzato, Rome #58/R
£3020 $5406 €4500 Southern coastal landscape (44x72cm-17x28in) s.d.1896. 27-May-4 Dorotheum, Vienna #67/R est:4000-4500
Works on paper
£520 $962 €759 Italian peasant boy before a country landscape. Peasant girl (49x32cm-19x13in) both s. W/C pair. 14-Jul-4 Bonhams, Chester #399

GUARDASSONI, Alessandro (1819-1888) Italian
£780 $1303 €1100 Mystical scene (37x26cm-15x10in) 20-Oct-3 Sant Agostino, Torino #37/R
£780 $1303 €1100 Saint Cecily and angels (39x30cm-15x12in) 20-Oct-3 Sant Agostino, Torino #38/R

GUARDI (after) (18/19th C) Italian
£10000 $18300 €15000 Still life of flowers in a basket with parrot (37x45cm-15x18in) 1-Jun-4 Sotheby's, Milan #183/R est:15000-20000

GUARDI (style) (18/19th C) Italian
£6349 $12000 €9270 Landscape with ruins, figures, boats and horses, possibly Bay of Naples (89x140cm-35x55in) 21-Feb-4 Jeffery Burchard, Florida #50/R

GUARDI, F (1712-1793) Italian
£1500 $2760 €2190 Venetian archway with figures, lagoon beyond (42x32cm-17x13in) panel. 26-Mar-4 ELR Auctions, Sheffield #336 est:600-800

GUARDI, Francesco (1712-1793) Italian
£30000 $51900 €43800 Pastoral landscape with peasants hoeing and a washerwomen before trees (21x27cm-8x11in) prov. 11-Dec-3 Sotheby's, London #235/R est:20000-30000
£46897 $78317 €68000 Venetian capriccio (25x21cm-10x8in) board prov.lit. 12-Nov-3 Sotheby's, Milan #129/R est:40000-60000
£50000 $86500 €73000 Architectural capriccio with figures in front of a ruined arch, with other ruins beyond (40x29cm-16x11in) prov. 10-Dec-3 Christie's, London #54/R est:100000-150000
£65517 $108759 €95000 Venetian capriccio (21x30cm-8x12in) 30-Sep-3 Ansorena, Madrid #46/R est:95000
£80000 $146400 €116800 Venetian capriccio with figures by the Lagoon (16x23cm-6x9in) panel prov.exhib.lit. 7-Jul-4 Sotheby's, London #58/R est:50000-70000
£83916 $140140 €120000 Venetian capriccio (21x30cm-8x12in) lit. 30-Jun-3 Ansorena, Madrid #175/R est:120000
£94444 $170000 €137888 View of San Michele Island. View of San Giorgio Island (11x18cm-4x7in) canvas on panel pair prov. 22-Jan-4 Sotheby's, New York #99/R est:140000-160000
£95000 $173850 €138700 Venetian capriccio of the Lagoon with figures and ruined arch (16x23cm-6x9in) panel prov.exhib.lit. 7-Jul-4 Sotheby's, London #57/R est:50000-70000
£110000 $190300 €160600 Architectural capriccio with elegant figures and a classical arch (40x29cm-16x11in) prov.exhib.lit. 10-Dec-3 Christie's, London #53/R est:100000-150000
£276316 $508421 €420000 View of the Grand Canal (34x53cm-13x21in) prov.exhib.lit. 25-Jun-4 Piasa, Paris #38/R est:300000-400000
Works on paper
£267 $483 €400 Riva Schiavan (16x29cm-6x11in) mixed media. 30-Mar-4 Campo & Campo, Antwerp #128
£3537 $6332 €5200 Des figures avec un palais dans le fond (15x9cm-6x4in) i. pen brown ink prov.lit. 18-Mar-4 Christie's, Paris #44/R est:5000-7000
£5500 $10065 €8030 Capriccio with a ruined arch and a figure (10x14cm-4x6in) i. verso pen brown ink wash. 8-Jul-4 Sotheby's, London #115/R est:6000-8000
£7639 $12451 €11000 Architectural capriccio with ruins (21x30cm-8x12in) pen brush. 24-Sep-3 Neumeister, Munich #246/R est:9500
£8333 $15000 €12166 Pieta (46x32cm-18x13in) pen ink wash htd white over black chk prov.exhib.lit. 21-Jan-4 Sotheby's, New York #100/R est:18000-22000
£15000 $27450 €21900 Christ and the Centurion (50x37cm-20x15in) red chk pen ink corners made up prov.exhib.lit. 6-Jul-4 Christie's, London #82/R est:8000-12000
£45000 $82350 €65700 Church of Santa Maria della Salute and the Dogana from the Grand Canal, Venice (28x44cm-11x17in) black chk pen ink wash prov. 6-Jul-4 Christie's, London #85/R est:40000-60000
£70000 $128100 €102200 View of the Borgo di Valsugana looking east (40x59cm-16x23in) i. i.verso black chk pen ink wash prov.lit. 6-Jul-4 Christie's, London #84/R est:60000-80000
£75000 $137250 €109500 Piazzetta and the Dog's Palace, Venice (47x80cm-19x31in) i. black chk pen ink wash exhib. 6-Jul-4 Christie's, London #87/R est:60000-80000

£85000 $155550 €124100 Bacino with S. Giorgio Maggiore and Santa Maria della Salute, Venice (47x80cm-19x31in) i. black chk pen ink wash. 6-Jul-4 Christie's, London #87a/R est:60000-80000
£200000 $366000 €292000 Scuola di San Marco, Venice, with the temporary platform erected for the Benediction (25x29cm-10x11in) black chk pen ink wash prov.exhib.lit. 6-Jul-4 Christie's, London #83/R est:100000-150000

GUARDI, Francesco (attrib) (1712-1793) Italian
£6623 $12053 €10000 Architectural ruins and Capriccio (38x58cm-15x23in) 18-Jun-4 Bolland & Marotz, Bremen #500/R est:15000
£16484 $30000 €24067 Architectural capriccio with Roman ruins. Another Capriccio (15x12cm-6x5in) panel prov.exhib.lit. pair. 4-Feb-4 Christie's, Rockefeller NY #83/R est:2000-3000
£194444 $350000 €283888 Venice, view of the Piazzetta (79x115cm-31x45in) prov. 22-Jan-4 Sotheby's, New York #71/R est:80000-120000

GUARDI, Francesco (circle) (1712-1793) Italian
£5000 $8500 €7300 Grand Canal, looking towards the Rialto Bridge, Venice (18x31cm-7x12in) 31-Oct-3 Christie's, Kensington #164/R est:8000-12000
£5369 $9879 €8000 Fire in the Oil Depository of San Marcuola in Venice (24x21cm-9x8in) 24-Mar-4 Dorotheum, Vienna #22/R est:10000-15000
£6000 $10200 €8760 Still lifes with various flowers in a landscape (51x64cm-20x25in) pair. 30-Oct-3 Sotheby's, Olympia #137/R est:6000-8000

GUARDI, Francesco (style) (1712-1793) Italian
£5991 $9765 €8747 San Giorgio Maggiore, Venice (28x32cm-11x13in) 29-Sep-3 Lilla Bukowskis, Stockholm #284 est:12000-15000 (S.KR 78000)
£6000 $10980 €8760 Capriccio scene with figures before a palazzo (70x118cm-28x46in) 6-Jul-4 Sotheby's, Olympia #604/R est:6000-8000
£7000 $12600 €10220 S Francesco della Vigna (47x70cm-19x28in) 21-Apr-4 Christie's, Kensington #306/R est:8000-12000
£10000 $18300 €14600 Venetian courtyard (38x32cm-15x13in) prov. 9-Jul-4 Christie's, Kensington #200/R est:3000-5000
£11500 $21045 €16790 Venetian scenes (34x54cm-13x21in) pair prov. 9-Jul-4 Christie's, Kensington #203/R est:8000-12000
Works on paper
£417 $688 €600 Venetian capriccio (16x23cm-6x9in) pen wash. 3-Jul-3 Dr Fritz Nagel, Stuttgart #373/R
£500 $825 €720 Venetian capriccio (16x23cm-6x9in) pen wash. 3-Jul-3 Dr Fritz Nagel, Stuttgart #372

GUARDI, Francesco and Giacomo (18th C) Italian
Works on paper
£8500 $15555 €12410 San Giorgio Maggiore, Venice, seen from the Bacino (28x43cm-11x17in) i. black chk pen ink wash prov. 6-Jul-4 Christie's, London #86/R est:6000-8000

GUARDI, Giacomo (1764-1835) Italian
£22069 $36855 €32000 Views of Venice (14x25cm-6x10in) s.i.verso tempera paper pair. 12-Nov-3 Sotheby's, Milan #130/R est:25000-35000
£119718 $207113 €170000 Vue de La Salute (18x32cm-7x13in) panel. 11-Dec-3 Binoche, Paris #26/R est:20000-30000
Works on paper
£1667 $3000 €2434 Port of Malamoco (11x16cm-4x6in) s.i.verso W/C bodycol. 22-Jan-4 Christie's, Rockefeller NY #246/R est:1000-1500
£1905 $3410 €2800 Une vue d'un canal a Venise (10x17cm-4x7in) gouache. 18-Mar-4 Christie's, Paris #42/R est:1200-1800
£2041 $3653 €3000 Une cour avec des figures, une portique au premier plan (52x35cm-20x14in) pen brown ink grey wash prov. 18-Mar-4 Christie's, Paris #45/R est:3000-5000
£2400 $4296 €3504 Veduta della Piaza di San Marco (14x24cm-6x9in) s.i.verso gouache. 11-May-4 Sotheby's, Olympia #616/R est:3000-5000
£2400 $4296 €3504 Veduta della Riva de Schiavoni (14x25cm-6x10in) s.i.verso gouache. 11-May-4 Sotheby's, Olympia #617/R est:3000-5000
£3514 $6184 €5200 View of S Nicolo del Lido, Venice (11x18cm-4x7in) init.i.verso pen brown ink grey wash exhib. 19-May-4 Sotheby's, Amsterdam #170/R est:2000-3000
£4800 $8304 €7008 View of the canal by Ca'Foscari, Venice (11x18cm-4x7in) s. i.verso bodycol. 12-Dec-3 Christie's, Kensington #402/R est:1000-1500
£7500 $12975 €10950 Views in Venice (11x18cm-4x7in) s.i. i.verso bodycol pair. 12-Dec-3 Christie's, Kensington #400/R est:2000-3000
£10000 $17300 €14600 Venetian canal scenes (11x18cm-4x7in) bodycol pair. 12-Dec-3 Christie's, Kensington #401/R est:1500-2000
£12664 $23048 €18489 Veduta della Chiesa si San Marco (21x32cm-8x13in) s.verso gouache prov. 16-Jun-4 Fischer, Luzern #1077/R est:8000-12000 (S.FR 29000)
£13100 $23843 €19126 Veduta del ponte di Rialto (21x32cm-8x13in) s.verso gouache prov. 16-Jun-4 Fischer, Luzern #1076/R est:8000-12000 (S.FR 30000)
£15721 $28611 €22953 Veduta si San Giorgio Maggiore e Duana di Oranjeto (21x32cm-8x13in) s.verso gouache prov. 16-Jun-4 Fischer, Luzern #1078/R est:8000-12000 (S.FR 36000)
£20833 $34792 €30000 Paysages d'Italie (46x79cm-18x31in) brown wash pen brown ink pair exhib. 22-Oct-3 Ribeyre & Baron, Paris #7/R est:20000-25000

GUARDI, Giacomo (attrib) (1764-1835) Italian
Works on paper
£1913 $3500 €2793 River landscape with figures (29x41cm-11x16in) pen ink wash prov. 3-Jun-4 Christie's, Rockefeller NY #1192/R est:300-500

GUARDI, Giovanni Antonio (1698-1760) Italian
Works on paper
£13000 $23790 €18980 Supper at Emmaus (31x25cm-12x10in) pen brown ink wash over blk chk prov.exhib.lit. 8-Jul-4 Sotheby's, London #104/R est:10000-15000

GUARIENTI, Carlo (1923-) Italian
Works on paper
£897 $1497 €1300 Controversial rebus (76x59cm-30x23in) s. mixed media collage canvas on board. 14-Nov-3 Farsetti, Prato #272

GUARINO DA SOLOFRA, Francesco (circle) (1611-1654) Italian
£14615 $25138 €21338 Judith (136x105cm-54x41in) 2-Dec-3 Bukowskis, Stockholm #334/R est:50000-60000 (S.KR 190000)

GUARLOTTI, Giovanni (1869-1954) Italian
£533 $981 €800 Pasture in the mountains (23x32cm-9x13in) s. cardboard. 14-Jun-4 Sant Agostino, Torino #207/R
£1300 $2392 €1950 Harvest (29x40cm-11x16in) s.d.1927 cardboard. 8-Jun-4 Della Rocca, Turin #213/R est:1800-2200

GUARLOTTI, Innocente (1870-1939) Italian
£1049 $1752 €1500 Peasant meal (35x50cm-14x20in) s. board. 26-Jun-3 Sant Agostino, Torino #41/R est:2000

GUARNIERI, Luciano (1930-) Italian
£775 $1340 €1100 Countryside with figures (50x65cm-20x26in) s.d.1958 board. 9-Dec-3 Pandolfini, Florence #387/R

GUASTAVINO, Arturo (1897-1978) Argentinian
£344 $550 €502 Flores en gris - spring bouquet (74x56cm-29x22in) s.d.1962 board. 20-Sep-3 Sloans & Kenyon, Bethesda #1038/R
£3571 $6500 €5214 Composition (90x78cm-35x31in) s. 29-Jun-4 Arroyo, Buenos Aires #65/R est:3000

GUATELLI, Rolando (1920-1976) Swiss
£286 $487 €418 Still life with apples, jug and knife on white cloth (50x70cm-20x28in) s. 5-Nov-3 Dobiaschofsky, Bern #3448 (S.FR 650)

GUAY, Gabriel (1848-?) French
£340 $626 €496 Standing female nude in an interior (99x64cm-39x25in) s. 23-Mar-4 Rosebery Fine Art, London #770

GUAYASAMIN, Oswaldo (1919-1999) Ecuadorian
£1714 $3000 €2502 Portrait of a lady (56x46cm-22x18in) s. acrylic. 19-Dec-3 Sotheby's, New York #1170/R est:5000-7000
£8824 $15000 €12883 Ciudad de quito (49x70cm-19x28in) s. oil board prov. 19-Nov-3 Sotheby's, New York #94/R est:12000-18000
£13158 $23816 €20000 Face (98x48cm-39x19in) s. painted 1980. 14-Apr-4 Ansorena, Madrid #277/R est:16000
£14706 $25000 €21471 Esperanza - de la serie edad de la ternura (60x60cm-24x24in) s. painted 1997 prov. 19-Nov-3 Sotheby's, New York #162/R est:25000-35000
£15068 $25616 €22000 Pain (97x53cm-38x21in) s. 4-Nov-3 Ansorena, Madrid #926/R est:18000
£15789 $28579 €24000 Vase of flowers (102x68cm-40x27in) s. painted 1980. 14-Apr-4 Ansorena, Madrid #273/R est:18000
£17647 $30000 €25765 Cabeza de mujer - de la serie indio (105x70cm-41x28in) s. painted 1954 prov.lit. 19-Nov-3 Sotheby's, New York #122/R est:25000-30000
£20000 $36000 €29000 Face (60x79cm-24x31in) s. painted 1980. 26-Jan-4 Ansorena, Madrid #894/R est:29000
£20134 $37450 €30000 Untitled (70x110cm-28x43in) s. painted 1980. 2-Mar-4 Ansorena, Madrid #848/R est:29000
£20588 $35000 €30058 El prisionero - de la serie huacaynan, tema indio (91x65cm-36x26in) s. painted 1949 prov.lit. 19-Nov-3 Sotheby's, New York #46/R est:40000-60000
£23973 $40753 €35000 Face (70x70cm-28x28in) s. 4-Nov-3 Ansorena, Madrid #918/R est:29000
£27933 $50000 €40782 Head of boy (70x70cm-28x28in) s. prov.lit. 26-May-4 Sotheby's, New York #162/R est:30000-40000
Works on paper
£1197 $2095 €1700 Face of woman (28x22cm-11x9in) s. wash ink. 16-Dec-3 Segre, Madrid #141/R est:1500

GUAZZO, Andreina Crepet (1909-) Italian
£326 $535 €450 San Antonio di Ranversa, Val di Susa (37x52cm-15x20in) indis.sig. board. 27-May-3 Finarte Semenzato, Milan #129/R

GUBA, Rudolf (1884-1950) German
£486 $812 €700 Northern German moor landscape (69x80cm-27x31in) s. prov. 24-Oct-3 Ketterer, Hamburg #173/R

GUBBELS, Klaas (1934-) Dutch
£658 $1211 €1000 Untitled (40x50cm-16x20in) init.d.64 burlap. 22-Jun-4 Christie's, Amsterdam #335/R
£694 $1132 €1000 Flower still life (40x30cm-16x12in) s. 29-Sep-3 Sotheby's, Amsterdam #213/R
£800 $1472 €1200 Pink table (40x30cm-16x12in) s.d.74. 9-Jun-4 Christie's, Amsterdam #342/R
£1399 $2378 €2000 Untitled (34x45cm-13x18in) s.d.64 board prov. 25-Nov-3 Christie's, Amsterdam #92/R est:1200-1600
£1748 $2972 €2500 Untitled (50x60cm-20x24in) s.d.96. 25-Nov-3 Christie's, Amsterdam #90/R est:2500-3500
£3200 $5888 €4800 The couple (100x69cm-39x27in) painted c.1958-60. 9-Jun-4 Christie's, Amsterdam #340/R est:4000-6000
£5000 $9200 €7500 Tafel met kan en trechter (65x50cm-26x20in) s. 9-Jun-4 Christie's, Amsterdam #345/R est:6000-8000
£5333 $9813 €8000 Jan Hein (100x80cm-39x31in) s.d.66 exhib.lit. 9-Jun-4 Christie's, Amsterdam #344/R est:7000-9000

GUBERNATIS, Giovanni Battista de (1774-1837) Italian
Works on paper
£1469 $2452 €2100 Lake landscape with figure (42x58cm-17x23in) W/C. 26-Jun-3 Sant Agostino, Torino #35/R est:2500

GUBERT-HELFRICH, Manlio (20th C) Italian
£1223 $2250 €1786 Aveugle. Floral still life (56x71cm-22x28in) s.d.52 two. 10-Jun-4 Sotheby's, New York #633/R est:500-700

GUBLER, Ernst (1895-1958) Swiss
£452 $769 €660 Interior with family (62x51cm-24x20in) tempera board. 19-Nov-3 Fischer, Luzern #2117/R (S.FR 1000)

GUBLER, Max (1898-1973) Swiss
£385 $642 €562 Flowers (48x33cm-19x13in) st.mono. oil chk. 24-Jun-3 Germann, Zurich #970 (S.FR 850)
£5286 $8987 €7718 Landscape with rider (77x78cm-30x31in) sketch verso lit. 7-Nov-3 Dobiaschofsky, Bern #188/R est:13000 (S.FR 12000)
£6193 $10342 €8980 Vase on chair (81x60cm-32x24in) s.d. lit.prov. 23-Jun-3 Philippe Schuler, Zurich #3393/R est:15000-20000 (S.FR 13500)
£7727 $12827 €11204 View (50x61cm-20x24in) 13-Jun-3 Zofingen, Switzerland #2865/R est:9500 (S.FR 17000)
£8145 $13846 €11892 Landscape, Surbtal, Unterengstringen (51x61cm-20x24in) painted c.1947 exhib. 22-Nov-3 Burkhard, Luzern #63/R est:18000-24000 (S.FR 18000)
£9170 $16690 €13388 Seated woman in a white dress (107x84cm-42x33in) painted 1929 prov.exhib. 18-Jun-4 Kornfeld, Bern #52/R est:25000 (S.FR 21000)
£11765 $20353 €17177 Limmat landscape in winter (114x146cm-45x57in) studio.st. exhib.lit. 9-Dec-3 Sotheby's, Zurich #98/R est:25000-30000 (S.FR 26000)
£15766 $27117 €23018 Scicilian musicians (180x141cm-71x56in) s.d.30 prov.exhib.lit. 2-Dec-3 Koller, Zurich #3037/R est:25000-40000 (S.FR 35000)
Works on paper
£682 $1132 €989 Landscape (36x46cm-14x18in) st.mono. chl col chk. 13-Jun-3 Zofingen, Switzerland #2864 est:2000 (S.FR 1500)
£1397 $2501 €2040 The old man and the sea (48x33cm-19x13in) s.d.1954 chk exhib. 26-May-4 Sotheby's, Zurich #144/R est:3000-5000 (S.FR 3200)
£2828 $4808 €4129 Standing nude with stick (65x54cm-26x21in) lit. 18-Nov-3 Hans Widmer, St Gallen #1073 est:6000-12000 (S.FR 6250)

GUBNER SIMONIS, Emma Vasilevna (1862-?) Russian
£29231 $50277 €42677 The 10 year old martyr St Akilina preaching to heathens (120x154cm-47x61in) s. prov. 7-Dec-3 Uppsala Auktionskammare, Uppsala #146/R est:80000-100000 (S.KR 380000)

GUCCIONE, Piero (1925-) Italian
£3161 $5373 €4520 Ofenafet and the lamb (70x60cm-28x24in) s.d.1961 lit. 18-Nov-3 Babuino, Rome #140 est:2000-3000
£4545 $7727 €6500 Seascape (50x40cm-20x16in) s. s.verso. 24-Nov-3 Christie's, Milan #198/R est:7000-10000
Works on paper
£909 $1545 €1300 Nude (36x33cm-14x13in) s.i.d.1971 W/C card exhib. 18-Nov-3 Babuino, Rome #375/R
£1310 $2188 €1900 Notes from New York (22x15cm-9x6in) one s. pastel pair. 13-Nov-3 Finarte Semenzato, Rome #150/R est:1400-1600
£1408 $2465 €2000 Study of portrait (34x35cm-13x14in) s.i.d.968 pencil pastel. 16-Dec-3 Finarte Semenzato, Milan #105/R est:1400-1700
£2077 $3531 €2970 Dawn on the city (27x42cm-11x17in) pencil. 18-Nov-3 Babuino, Rome #62/R est:2000-3000
£7692 $13077 €11000 Field (100x35cm-39x14in) mixed media lit. 20-Nov-3 Finarte Semenzato, Milan #225/R est:7000-8000
£10270 $19000 €14994 Interno dell studio con rittrato d'ignoto de timoteo viti (192x70cm-76x28in) s. i.verso pastel collage paper exec 1984-85 prov. 12-Feb-4 Sotheby's, New York #325/R est:2000-3000

GUCHT, Jose van (1913-1980) Belgian
£1337 $2500 €1952 Harbour scene (51x74cm-20x29in) s. 29-Feb-4 Grogan, Boston #13/R

GUDABI, Willie (1916-1996) Australian
Works on paper
£1875 $3506 €2813 Untitled (123x113cm-48x44in) synthetic polymer canvas exec. c.1994 prov. 21-Jul-4 Shapiro, Sydney #125/R est:5000-7000 (A.D 4800)
£2114 $3340 €3065 Handing down the law (186x64cm-73x25in) s. synthetic polymer paint canvas prov. 28-Jul-3 Sotheby's, Paddington #420/R est:5000-7000 (A.D 5200)

GUDDEN, Rudolf (1863-1935) German
£276 $450 €403 The Sacco, in Tanger (56x66cm-22x26in) i. on stretcher. 24-Sep-3 Doyle, New York #40
£367 $671 €550 Farmer with horse and cart (60x75cm-24x30in) s. i.verso. 5-Jun-4 Arnold, Frankfurt #587/R
£467 $854 €700 Portrait of Anna Caspari, nee Lambertz, concert singer (145x98cm-57x39in) s. 5-Jun-4 Arnold, Frankfurt #586/R
£1690 $2704 €2400 Woman at window (102x178cm-40x70in) mono. panel. 18-Sep-3 Rieber, Stuttgart #927/R est:1980

GUDE, Hans Fredrik (1825-1903) Norwegian
£1448 $2419 €2100 Norwegian fjord landscape (27x47cm-11x19in) board. 15-Nov-3 Lempertz, Koln #1608/R est:2000
£6000 $10320 €8760 Man and woman resting at edge of wood. s.d.1861 exhib. 3-Dec-3 AB Stockholms Auktionsverk #2562/R est:80000-100000 (S.KR 78000)
£6672 $11343 €9741 Fishermen in boats by rocky coast (31x26cm-12x10in) s.d.1866. 19-Nov-3 Grev Wedels Plass, Oslo #25/R est:80000-100000 (N.KR 78000)
£8392 $14434 €12000 Lauterbach beach, Rugen (33x45cm-13x18in) s.d.1897. 2-Dec-3 Hauswedell & Nolte, Hamburg #248/R est:14000
£9788 $17520 €14290 Woman and man resting by woodland path (41x34cm-16x13in) s.d.1861. 25-May-4 Grev Wedels Plass, Oslo #28/R est:150000-200000 (N.KR 120000)
£10221 $17581 €14923 Jetty, Drobak (48x42cm-19x17in) init.d.1875 exhib. 8-Dec-3 Blomqvist, Oslo #464/R est:180000-200000 (N.KR 120000)
£30000 $54600 €43800 Sailing off the Norwegian coast (36x50cm-14x20in) s.d.1880 prov. 15-Jun-4 Sotheby's, London #309/R est:30000-50000
£92000 $158240 €134320 Morning by the coast (150x254cm-59x100in) s.d.1898 lit. 3-Dec-3 Christie's, London #84/R est:50000-80000
£162254 $270965 €236891 Landscape with cattle and waterfall (99x88cm-39x35in) s.d.1852 prov.lit. 13-Oct-3 Blomqvist, Oslo #278/R est:1200000-1500000 (N.KR 1900000)
£166099 $285690 €242505 Seaward approach to Christiania fjorden (86x135cm-34x53in) s.d.1872 exhib.lit. 8-Dec-3 Blomqvist, Oslo #443/R est:1600000-1900000 (N.KR 1950000)
Works on paper
£1220 $2232 €1781 Two women in park (38x59cm-15x23in) s.i.d.Sept 86 mixed media. 7-Jun-4 Blomqvist, Oslo #396/R est:18000-20000 (N.KR 15000)
£1304 $2257 €1904 From Chiemsee (29x40cm-11x16in) mono. i.verso W/C. 13-Dec-3 Blomqvist, Lysaker #1123/R est:35000-45000 (N.KR 15000)
£1550 $2774 €2263 The old Tingplass, Rygge (15x23cm-6x9in) i.d.29 Aug 92 pencil pen W/C paper on panel. 25-May-4 Grev Wedels Plass, Oslo #23/R est:15000-20000 (N.KR 19000)
£1631 $2920 €2381 Landscape from Dyre near Moss (15x23cm-6x9in) init.i.d.4 Oct 92 pencil W/C. 25-May-4 Grev Wedels Plass, Oslo #22/R est:15000-20000 (N.KR 20000)
£2044 $3516 €2984 Fisherman with salmon coup (16x24cm-6x9in) mono.d.1857 W/C. 8-Dec-3 Blomqvist, Oslo #477/R est:20000-25000 (N.KR 24000)
£9223 $15402 €13466 Landscape from Aasterudtjernet, Ringerike (44x71cm-17x28in) s.d.1889 W/C gouache lit. 13-Oct-3 Blomqvist, Oslo #350/R est:40000-50000 (N.KR 108000)

GUDE, Nils (1859-1908) Norwegian
£1110 $1854 €1621 A rest during gardening (30x24cm-12x9in) s/d/1895. 13-Oct-3 Blomqvist, Oslo #251/R est:7000-9000 (N.KR 13000)

GUDGEON, Ralston (1910-1984) British
Works on paper
£216 $400 €315 Arabic horseback rider (36x51cm-14x20in) s. W/C. 13-Mar-4 Susanin's, Chicago #6159/R
£260 $411 €380 Pair of magpies on branches (50x60cm-20x24in) s. gouache. 6-Sep-3 Shapes, Edinburgh #322
£260 $434 €380 Cockfight. W/C. 19-Jun-3 Bonhams, Edinburgh #315
£280 $512 €409 Two mallards wading (48x56cm-19x22in) s. W/C bodycol. 7-Apr-4 Woolley & Wallis, Salisbury #89/R
£300 $567 €438 Lapwing (45x31cm-18x12in) W/C. 17-Feb-4 Patersons, Paisley #244
£310 $518 €453 Kingfishers. W/C. 19-Jun-3 Bonhams, Edinburgh #316
£350 $585 €511 Partridge - Winter Covey (50x63cm-20x25in) s. W/C. 16-Oct-3 Lyon & Turnbull, Edinburgh #144
£400 $636 €584 Lapwings (40x53cm-16x21in) s. W/C gouache. 10-Sep-3 Sotheby's, Olympia #194/R
£440 $717 €642 Barnyard brawl (49x62cm-19x24in) s. pencil W/C htd bodycol. 25-Sep-3 Mellors & Kirk, Nottingham #717/R
£550 $995 €803 Lapwings (36x62cm-14x24in) s. W/C. 31-Mar-4 Bonhams, Knightsbridge #15/R

GUDIN (?) French
£920 $1665 €1343 Shipping in the Bay of Naples (44x60cm-17x24in) 2-Apr-4 Bracketts, Tunbridge Wells #485/R

GUDIN, Henriette (1825-?) French
£1200 $2160 €1800 Marine with four yachts before the coast of Brittany (14x21cm-6x8in) s. panel. 26-Apr-4 Bernaerts, Antwerp #102/R est:1000-1250
£1329 $2285 €1900 Voilier pres d'une cote rocheuse (14x20cm-6x8in) s. panel. 5-Dec-3 Maigret, Paris #69 est:1200-1600
£1467 $2640 €2200 Fishing boats in a bay (15x23cm-6x9in) s. panel. 20-Apr-4 Sotheby's, Amsterdam #87/R est:2000-3000
£1867 $3360 €2800 Fishermen by the shore at sunset (16x25cm-6x10in) s. panel. 20-Apr-4 Sotheby's, Amsterdam #76/R est:2000-3000
£1931 $3572 €2800 Pecheurs au coucher du soleil (14x21cm-6x8in) s. panel. 16-Feb-4 Horta, Bruxelles #419 est:1200-1800
£2303 $4237 €3500 Retour de peche (14x20cm-6x8in) s. panel. 23-Jun-4 Maigret, Paris #73 est:1200-1500
£2358 $3750 €3443 Coastal scenes (15x23cm-6x9in) s. panel pair. 13-Sep-3 Selkirks, St. Louis #484/R est:3000-4000
£2483 $4569 €3700 Bateaux en mer, la nuit (13x20cm-5x8in) s. panel. 29-Mar-4 Rieunier, Paris #18/R est:2000-3000
£2550 $4693 €3800 Barques a maree basse (13x20cm-5x8in) s. panel. 29-Mar-4 Rieunier, Paris #19/R est:2000-3000
£2550 $4667 €3800 Coastal scene on the north French coast (32x49cm-13x19in) s. 9-Jul-4 Dawo, Saarbrucken #17/R est:2400
£3204 $5319 €4550 Voiliers au clair de lune (14x21cm-6x8in) s. panel. 15-Jun-3 Peron, Melun #111

GUDIN, Theodore (1802-1880) French
£972 $1546 €1400 Bateaux de peche au soleil couchant (14x20cm-6x8in) s. panel. 9-Sep-3 Palais de Beaux Arts, Brussels #239
£1400 $2534 €2100 L'ame abandonnant la terre (13x20cm-5x8in) s.i.d.19 mai 1860 verso panel lit. 30-Mar-4 Rossini, Paris #203/R est:1200-1800
£1597 $2524 €2300 Maree basse (40x58cm-16x23in) panel. 25-Apr-3 Etude de Provence, Marseille #167 est:2000-2500
£1806 $2979 €2600 Genua harbour (39x55cm-15x22in) s. 3-Jul-3 Van Ham, Cologne #121/R est:3000
£1933 $3499 €2900 Barques de peche au large aec des recifs (25x35cm-10x14in) s.d.Avril 1838. 30-Mar-4 Rossini, Paris #204/R est:1500-2500
£2083 $3437 €3000 Shipwreck off rocky coast (71x144cm-28x57in) s.d.1841. 3-Jul-3 Van Ham, Cologne #1213/R est:7500
£2133 $3861 €3200 Maree basse (28x40cm-11x16in) s.i.d.1859. 2-Apr-4 Rossini, Paris #53/R est:2000-2500
£2733 $5002 €4100 Cote italienne (31x47cm-12x19in) s.d.1863 panel. 6-Jun-4 Osenat, Fontainebleau #190 est:5500-6000
£3800 $7030 €5700 Prise de vaisseau Le Glacester par le Duguay-Trouin en 1667 (40x56cm-16x22in) s.d.1839 i.verso stretcher. 14-Jul-4 Livinec, Gaudcheau & Jezequel, Rennes #148
£10000 $17000 €14600 Shipwreck (70x142cm-28x56in) s.i.d.1841. 19-Nov-3 Sotheby's, London #47/R est:10000-15000
Works on paper
£366 $641 €520 Bord de mer anime (8x26cm-3x10in) s.d.76 wash htd gouache. 21-Dec-3 Thierry & Lannon, Brest #435
£433 $780 €650 After the shipwreck (27x39cm-11x15in) s. W/C. 26-Apr-4 Bernaerts, Antwerp #100/R
£769 $1285 €1100 Barque de peche au lever de lune (18x29cm-7x11in) s.i.d.1849 wash gouache. 13-Oct-3 Horta, Bruxelles #517

£867 $1569 €1300 Voiliers et vapeur par mer agitee (16x25cm-6x10in) s.d.1827 W/C sold with another by L Francia. 30-Mar-4 Rossini, Paris #990

GUDIOL, Montserrat (1933-) Spanish
£823 $1300 €1202 Tres Muchachas. s. board. 26-Jul-3 Harvey Clar, Oakland #1194
£1266 $2000 €1848 Stand nude. s. board. 26-Jul-3 Harvey Clar, Oakland #1191
£5085 $9000 €7424 La finestra (79x63cm-31x25in) s. board prov. 2-May-4 Bonhams & Butterfields, Los Angeles #3057/R est:2000-4000
Works on paper
£952 $1733 €1400 Lilac nude (64x50cm-25x20in) s. W/C. 3-Feb-4 Segre, Madrid #330/R

GUDMUNDSEN-HOLMGREEN, Johan (1858-1912) Danish
£629 $1170 €918 Woman reading newspaper (45x37cm-18x15in) s.d.1886. 2-Mar-4 Rasmussen, Copenhagen #1591/R (D.KR 7000)

GUDMUNDSSON, Kristjan (1942-) Icelandic
Works on paper
£440 $778 €642 Drawing (68x13cm-27x5in) init.d.87 pencil cardboard. 27-Apr-4 AB Stockholms Auktionsverk #1087/R (S.KR 6000)

GUDMUNDSSON, Sigurdur (1942-) Icelandic
Sculpture
£1267 $2331 €1900 Stella Maris (37x40x19cm-15x16x7in) s.i.d.87 concrete multiple paper iron wood perspex one of 20 lit. 9-Jun-4 Christie's, Amsterdam #368a/R est:1000-1500

GUDNASON, Svavar (1909-1988) Icelandic
£6573 $10977 €9597 Figure composition (100x90cm-39x35in) s.d.49. 7-Oct-3 Rasmussen, Copenhagen #44/R est:75000 (D.KR 70000)
Works on paper
£361 $664 €527 Composition (27x36cm-11x14in) s.d.45 verso W/C prov. 29-Mar-4 Rasmussen, Copenhagen #273/R (D.KR 4000)

GUE, Julien Michel (1789-1843) French
£1409 $2465 €2000 Jeune femme, enfant et chien, a la riviere (46x38cm-18x15in) s. 16-Dec-3 Artcurial Briest, Paris #245/R est:1000-1200

GUEBHARD, W H (19th C) ?
Photographs
£13287 $22189 €19000 Chutes de la pIque (25x35cm-10x14in) s.d.1854 salt print. 10-Oct-3 Beaussant & Lefèvre, Paris #70/R est:20000-30000

GUEDEZ, Jose (1968-) Venezuelan
£253 $400 €369 Cloaks (103x184cm-41x72in) s. painted 2001. 1-Dec-2 Subastas Odalys, Caracas #3
£285 $450 €416 Playing (100x130cm-39x51in) s. painted 2002. 1-Dec-2 Subastas Odalys, Caracas #83
£296 $545 €444 Blue space (100x120cm-39x47in) s. acrylic painted 1999. 27-Jun-4 Subastas Odalys, Caracas #1/R
£297 $460 €434 Game III (129x98cm-51x39in) s. painted 1988. 3-Nov-2 Subastas Odalys, Caracas #75
£418 $660 €610 Space (100x130cm-39x51in) s. painted 1998. 1-Dec-2 Subastas Odalys, Caracas #16/R
£1029 $1750 €1502 Untitled (205x92cm-81x36in) s. painted 2002. 23-Nov-3 Subastas Odalys, Caracas #31/R
£1121 $1905 €1637 Untitled (205x92cm-81x36in) s. painted 2002. 23-Nov-3 Subastas Odalys, Caracas #17/R
Works on paper
£272 $495 €408 Playing (98x129cm-39x51in) s. mixed media on canvas exec.1998. 21-Jun-4 Subastas Odalys, Caracas #103

GUELDRY, Charles Albert (1884-1973) French
£855 $1574 €1300 Peniches a quai (34x27cm-13x11in) s. 28-Jun-4 Joron-Derem, Paris #132/R

GUENOT, Auguste (1882-?) French
Sculpture
£3500 $6545 €5110 Nude girl (62cm-24in) indis.sig. pat bronze rosewood pedestal exec.c.1925. 24-Feb-4 Sotheby's, Olympia #255/R est:3500-4500

GUERARD, Amedee (1824-1908) French
£1267 $2318 €1900 Heureuse famille (46x38cm-18x15in) s. 6-Jun-4 Rouillac, Vendome #7

GUERARD, Bernard von (1780-1836) German
£450 $824 €657 Portrait of a young gentleman, possibly Mr R Strange (12x9cm-5x4in) i.verso panel. 6-Apr-4 Bonhams, Knightsbridge #164/R
£1711 $3096 €2600 Portrait of Josepha Gueard, nee Schultz of Lichtenthal, wife of the artist (23x16cm-9x6in) s. i.verso panel oval. 19-Apr-4 Glerum, Amsterdam #27/R est:800-1000
Miniatures
£5200 $8840 €7592 Maria Isabella of Spain (6cm-2in) oval. 18-Nov-3 Bonhams, New Bond Street #107/R est:600-800

GUERARD, Eugène von (1811-1901) Austrian
£20325 $36382 €29675 View of Naples and surrounding country from the foot of the crater-Vesuvius (48x72cm-19x28in) s.d.83 s.i.verso prov.exhib.lit. 4-May-4 Sotheby's, Melbourne #38/R est:50000-70000 (A.D 50000)

GUERARD, Henri Charles (1846-1897) French
£2333 $4270 €3500 Marche a Sainte-Catherine a Honfleur (88x63cm-35x25in) s. 6-Jun-4 Osenat, Fontainebleau #191/R est:4000-5000

GUERCHET-JEANNIN, Anne-Marie (20th C) French
£280 $476 €400 Une main qui s'aile (53x42cm-21x17in) s. acrylic chl. 29-Nov-3 Neret-Minet, Paris #77/R

GUERCHET-JEANNIN, Pierre (20th C) French
£280 $476 €400 Gehry Bale 2 (46x46cm-18x18in) s. acrylic paper. 29-Nov-3 Neret-Minet, Paris #90/R
£315 $535 €450 La maison Gehry (40x30cm-16x12in) s. acrylic paper. 29-Nov-3 Neret-Minet, Paris #24/R

GUERCI, Raymond (fl.1876) French
£302 $541 €450 Still life (39x50cm-15x20in) s.d.1876. 26-May-4 Blanchet, Paris #194

GUERCINO (1591-1666) Italian
Works on paper
£6500 $11700 €9490 Saint John the Baptist (27x21cm-11x8in) pen brown ink wash prov. 20-Apr-4 Sotheby's, Olympia #15/R est:5000-7000
£61972 $108451 €88000 Deux baigneuses pres d'un sarcophage Romain, une troisieme nageant (16x25cm-6x10in) i. black chk pen brown ink wash prov. 17-Dec-3 Christie's, Paris #6/R est:80000-120000

GUERCINO, Giovanni Francesco (1591-1666) Italian
£380000 $695400 €554800 Portrait of Francesco Righetti (83x67cm-33x26in) prov.exhib.lit. 7-Jul-4 Sotheby's, London #47/R est:350000-450000
£496454 $829078 €700000 Sibilla (68x79cm-27x31in) prov.lit. 18-Jun-3 Christie's, Rome #463/R
Works on paper
£2400 $4392 €3504 Seated Sybil looking up to the left (15x17cm-6x7in) pen ink wash. 6-Jul-4 Christie's, London #45/R est:1000-1500
£6111 $11000 €8922 Landscape with a natural bridge (27x43cm-11x17in) pen brown ink prov.exhib. 21-Jan-4 Sotheby's, New York #86/R est:12000-15000
£7000 $12810 €10220 Young man (18x15cm-7x6in) black red white chk prov. 6-Jul-4 Christie's, London #43/R est:7000-10000
£7778 $14000 €11356 Landscape with ruined fort on a hill. Putto and Pope Gregory XV Ludovisi (16x29cm-6x11in) i. pen brown ink double-sided. 22-Jan-4 Christie's, Rockefeller NY #40a/R est:3000-5000
£7778 $14000 €11356 Christ Child, seated and looking left (18x14cm-7x6in) red chk. 21-Jan-4 Sotheby's, New York #85/R est:10000-15000
£8000 $14640 €11680 Two bearded men, looking down (19x22cm-7x9in) red chk prov. 6-Jul-4 Christie's, London #44/R est:3000-5000
£10204 $18265 €15000 Marie-Madelaine se lavant les mains a une source (18x29cm-7x11in) pen brown ink prov. 18-Mar-4 Christie's, Paris #57/R est:6000-8000
£10556 $19000 €15412 Caricature of a man in a pointed hat (22x16cm-9x6in) i. pen ink prov.exhib. 21-Jan-4 Sotheby's, New York #83/R est:25000-35000
£14000 $25620 €20440 Head of girl, seen from behind, looking up to the right (23x17cm-9x7in) blk chk htd white blue paper prov.exhib.lit. 8-Jul-4 Sotheby's, London #59/R est:14000-16000
£14444 $26000 €21088 Man in a hat looking to the left (16x12cm-6x5in) pen brown ink prov. 22-Jan-4 Christie's, Rockefeller NY #38/R est:10000-15000
£15000 $25950 €21900 Seated Oriental, male figure and a youth (19x23cm-7x9in) pen brown ink prov. 9-Dec-3 Bonhams, Knightsbridge #69/R est:15000-20000
£15000 $27450 €21900 Return of the Prodigal Son. Clouds (26x21cm-10x8in) pen ink double-sided prov. 7-Jul-4 Bonhams, Knightsbridge #60/R est:15000-20000
£17124 $29110 €25000 Sybill seated (26x19cm-10x7in) pen ink prov. 6-Nov-3 Tajan, Paris #14/R
£26667 $48000 €38934 Cleopatra bitten by the asp (22x20cm-9x8in) red chk prov.exhib.lit. 22-Jan-4 Christie's, Rockefeller NY #37/R est:30000-50000
£44444 $80000 €64888 St John the Baptist, holding a bowl (24x20cm-9x8in) red chk prov.exhib.lit. 22-Jan-4 Christie's, Rockefeller NY #36/R est:40000-60000
£48611 $87500 €70972 Scenes of St. Roch taken to prison (20x28cm-8x11in) pen ink double-sided exhib.lit. 21-Jan-4 Sotheby's, New York #79/R est:35000-45000

GUERCINO, Giovanni Francesco (attrib) (1591-1666) Italian
£46154 $79385 €67385 The Penitent Magdalene. St John the Baptist (97x78cm-38x31in) 2-Dec-3 Bukowskis, Stockholm #360/R est:150000-200000 (S.KR 600000)
£46154 $79385 €67385 An Apostle. 2-Dec-3 Bukowskis, Stockholm #361/R est:600000-800000 (S.KR 600000)
Works on paper
£1200 $2076 €1752 Facial studies (12x29cm-5x11in) pen brown ink. 9-Dec-3 Bonhams, Knightsbridge #66/R est:1200-1600

GUERCINO, Giovanni Francesco (circle) (1591-1666) Italian
£10791 $17698 €15000 Saint Catherine of Cortona (63x51cm-25x20in) 4-Jun-3 Sotheby's, Milan #116/R est:5000-7000

GUERCINO, Giovanni Francesco (school) (1591-1666) Italian
£18667 $33413 €28000 Semyramidis hearing about Babylon's revolution (125x174cm-49x69in) lit. 17-May-4 Finarte Semenzato, Rome #121/R est:35000-40000

GUERCINO, Giovanni Francesco (style) (1591-1666) Italian
£6291 $11450 €9500 Christ and the woman of Samaria at the well (114x151cm-45x59in) 16-Jun-4 Dorotheum, Vienna #227/R est:1800-3000

GUERET, Pierre Martin (1907-1966) French
£280 $496 €409 River in summer (64x49cm-25x19in) 27-Apr-4 Bonhams, Knightsbridge #85/R

GUERIN, Armand (1913-1983) French
£300 $540 €450 Paris, la conciergerie (27x35cm-11x14in) s. panel. 26-Apr-4 Tajan, Paris #316/R
£367 $660 €550 Les berges de la Seine (60x73cm-24x29in) s. panel. 26-Apr-4 Tajan, Paris #317
£367 $660 €550 La tour Eifel (60x73cm-24x29in) s. panel. 26-Apr-4 Tajan, Paris #319
£367 $660 €550 Defense d'afficher (60x73cm-24x29in) s. panel. 26-Apr-4 Tajan, Paris #322
£400 $720 €600 La peniche sur la Seine (59x71cm-23x28in) s. panel. 26-Apr-4 Tajan, Paris #318
£400 $720 €600 Le pont aerien (65x81cm-26x32in) s. panel. 26-Apr-4 Tajan, Paris #320
£400 $720 €600 Le bus dans la rue (60x72cm-24x28in) s. panel. 26-Apr-4 Tajan, Paris #321
£400 $720 €600 Rue sous la neige (60x73cm-24x29in) s. panel. 26-Apr-4 Tajan, Paris #325
£400 $720 €600 Charrette dans une rue enneigee (59x74cm-23x29in) s. panel. 26-Apr-4 Tajan, Paris #326

GUERIN, Charles (1875-1939) French
£714 $1300 €1042 Le peintre (99x104cm-39x41in) s.stretcher. 19-Jun-4 Jeffery Burchard, Florida #22
£795 $1454 €1200 Jeune femme a la mantille (65x54cm-26x21in) mono. prov. 7-Apr-4 Piasa, Paris #42
£2013 $3725 €3000 Portrait d'homme (100x65cm-39x26in) s.d.1899. 15-Mar-4 Claude Boisgirard, Paris #48 est:3500-4000
£2262 $3846 €3303 Woodcutters on forest path (78x62cm-31x24in) s. 19-Nov-3 Fischer, Luzern #1098/R est:5500-6500 (S.FR 5000)
£3333 $6133 €5000 Cafe scene (65x81cm-26x32in) s. 8-Jun-4 Sotheby's, Amsterdam #202/R est:6000-8000
£3940 $6540 €5752 Garden party (46x55cm-18x22in) mono. 4-Oct-3 Dorotheum, Prague #117/R est:180000-300000 (C.KR 180000)
£7383 $13658 €11000 Le manchon (73x60cm-29x24in) s. 15-Mar-4 Claude Boisgirard, Paris #49/R est:12000-15000

GUERIN, Ernest (1887-1952) French
£367 $678 €550 Les toits de Rennes (21x12cm-8x5in) s. cardboard. 14-Jul-4 Livinec, Gaudcheau & Jezequel, Rennes #220
Works on paper
£265 $495 €400 Le ruisseau (33x21cm-13x8in) s. W/C exec. c.1905. 24-Jul-4 Thierry & Lannon, Brest #60
£267 $477 €400 Retable gothique (35x29cm-14x11in) s. W/C. 16-May-4 Thierry & Lannon, Brest #248
£268 $502 €400 Paysage de foret (23x31cm-9x12in) s. W/C. 24-Feb-4 Thierry & Lannon, Brest #173
£403 $753 €600 Paysage au Ruisseau (26x33cm-10x13in) s. W/C. 24-Feb-4 Thierry & Lannon, Brest #174
£567 $1014 €850 Riviere en sous-bois (46x29cm-18x11in) s. W/C exec. c.1905. 16-May-4 Thierry & Lannon, Brest #246
£933 $1671 €1400 Bretonnes pres de la chapelle (15x8cm-6x3in) s. W/C. 16-May-4 Thierry & Lannon, Brest #244y/R
£1181 $1865 €1700 Village en Bretagne (18x24cm-7x9in) s.i. W/C. 6-Sep-3 Arnold, Frankfurt #569/R
£1208 $2223 €1800 Chaumes d'automne Bretagne (19x23cm-7x9in) s.i. W/C lit. 25-Mar-4 Karlheinz Kaupp, Staufen #2468/R est:150
£1267 $2267 €1900 Village de pecheurs en Bretagne (15x22cm-6x9in) s. W/C. 16-May-4 Thierry & Lannon, Brest #52/R est:1800-2000
£1399 $2336 €2000 Bretagne, maisons pres du rivage (18x23cm-7x9in) s. W/C. 29-Jun-3 Eric Pillon, Calais #144a/R
£1469 $2452 €2100 Bretonnes et fillettes (18x23cm-7x9in) s. W/C gouache. 29-Jun-3 Eric Pillon, Calais #145/R
£1667 $2633 €2400 Village - Brittany (27x35cm-11x14in) s.i. W/C. 6-Sep-3 Arnold, Frankfurt #568/R est:600
£1667 $3067 €2500 Loctudy, Bretagne (37x45cm-15x18in) s.i. W/C. 8-Jun-4 Livinec, Gaudcheau & Jezequel, Rennes #89/R
£1727 $2832 €2400 Le Menez Hom, bloavez (44x60cm-17x24in) s.i.d.1918 W/C. 3-Jun-3 Livinec, Gaudcheau & Jezequel, Rennes #61/R
£1761 $3081 €2500 Le pardon de Saint Tremeur (26x34cm-10x13in) s. W/C. 21-Dec-3 Thierry & Lannon, Brest #51/R est:2500-2800
£1761 $3081 €2500 Village breton (18x23cm-7x9in) s. W/C. 21-Dec-3 Thierry & Lannon, Brest #54/R est:2300-2500
£1831 $3204 €2600 Pelerins de Bretagne (36x52cm-14x20in) s.d.1913 W/C. 21-Dec-3 Thierry & Lannon, Brest #230 est:2500-3000
£1967 $3520 €2950 Chez les pecheurs bretons (15x22cm-6x9in) s. W/C. 16-May-4 Thierry & Lannon, Brest #51/R est:1500-2000
£1972 $3451 €2800 Village en Bretagne (17x23cm-7x9in) s.i. W/C. 21-Dec-3 Thierry & Lannon, Brest #52 est:2000-2200
£2113 $3697 €3000 Vers le pardon de Penmarc'h - Bretagne (35x45cm-14x18in) s.i. W/C. 21-Dec-3 Thierry & Lannon, Brest #50/R est:2500-3000
£2183 $3820 €3100 St Malo, la regate (25x33cm-10x13in) s.i. W/C. 21-Dec-3 Thierry & Lannon, Brest #229 est:3000-4000
£2467 $4415 €3700 Retour de peche, Bretagne, pres de la chaumiere (27x34cm-11x13in) s.i. W/C. 16-May-4 Thierry & Lannon, Brest #53/R est:3500-4000
£2533 $4535 €3800 Notre-Dame de Joie, Bretagne (37x46cm-15x18in) W/C. 16-May-4 Renault-Aubry, Pontivy #455
£3169 $5546 €4500 Rencontre sur la dune a Penmarch (26x34cm-10x13in) s.i. W/C. 21-Dec-3 Thierry & Lannon, Brest #226/R est:2300-2800
£3380 $5915 €4800 Dolmen pres de Plouharmel, Carnac (26x34cm-10x13in) s.i. W/C. 21-Dec-3 Thierry & Lannon, Brest #228/R est:1800-2200
£5282 $8768 €7500 Retour du Pardon de Tronoen, Bretagne (53x118cm-21x46in) s.i. W/C gouache triptych. 10-Jun-3 Adjug'art, Brest #85

GUERIN, François (?-1791) French
£34965 $58392 €50000 Allegory of Painting and Architecture (55x65cm-22x26in) pair prov. 30-Jun-3 Ansorena, Madrid #176/R
Miniatures
£1931 $3225 €2800 Young man with long hair and flat cap (8x6cm-3x2in) s. copper oval. 9-Jul-3 Hugo Ruef, Munich #812/R est:400

GUERIN, Gilles (attrib) (c.1609-1678) French
Sculpture
£29578 $51761 €42000 Trois amours symbolisant le couronnement de l'amour (20x32cm-8x13in) bas relief pat bronze pair. 16-Dec-3 Artcurial Briest, Paris #266/R est:8000-12000

GUERIN, Jean Urbain (1760-1836) French
Miniatures
£1400 $2380 €2044 Gentleman (5cm-2in) s.verso oval. 18-Nov-3 Bonhams, New Bond Street #71/R est:1000-1500
£2200 $3960 €3212 Gentleman in a brown coat (6cm-2in) s. ormolu frame oval exhib. 22-Apr-4 Bonhams, New Bond Street #108/R est:1200-1800
£2483 $4569 €3700 General portant uniforme et redingote gris-anthracite (5x4cm-2x2in) s. oval lit. 26-Mar-4 Pierre Berge, Paris #93/R est:2000-3000

GUERIN, John (1920-) American
£726 $1300 €1060 Stream. s. 13-May-4 Dallas Auction Gallery, Dallas #271/R est:1500-2500

GUERIN, Jules (1866-1946) American
£692 $1100 €1010 Aquaduct, night (76x53cm-30x21in) s.i. 4-May-3 William Jenack, New York #241
£2195 $3600 €3183 Market place, Siena. Porto Romano, Siena (30x25cm-12x10in) s. i.verso pair prov. 31-May-3 Brunk, Ashville #372/R est:1500-2500
£2545 $4250 €3716 The aqueduct, night (76x56cm-30x22in) s. 15-Nov-3 Illustration House, New York #86/R est:4000-6000
Works on paper
£333 $600 €486 View of St Mark's Square from the Grand Canal (16x22cm-6x9in) s. W/C gouache. 24-Apr-4 Weschler, Washington #587/R
£2545 $4250 €3716 Farmer with herd of goats (61x51cm-24x20in) s. W/C gouache. 15-Nov-3 Illustration House, New York #84/R est:2000-3000

GUERIN, Marie (19th C) French
Works on paper
£852 $1500 €1244 La nuit (104x74cm-41x29in) s. pastel. 18-May-4 Bonhams & Butterfields, San Francisco #130/R est:3000-5000

GUERIN, Maximin (19th C) French
£887 $1480 €1250 Bouquet de fleurs et fruits sur entablement (65x82cm-26x32in) s.d.1851. 17-Oct-3 Renaud, Paris #35

GUERMACHEV, Mikhail Mikhailovich (1867-1930) Russian
£650 $1086 €949 Winter landscapes (53x66cm-21x26in) s. pair. 20-Jun-3 Chrystals Auctions, Isle of Man #233
£2300 $4209 €3358 Winter sun on snow covered landscape (46x55cm-18x22in) 9-Jul-4 Dreweatt Neate, Newbury #424/R est:500-700
£2400 $4392 €3504 Woodland winter scene (46x55cm-18x22in) 9-Jul-4 Dreweatt Neate, Newbury #425/R est:500-700
£3600 $6444 €5256 Landscape in snow (46x54cm-18x21in) s. 26-May-4 Sotheby's, Olympia #392/R est:4000-6000
£4200 $7518 €6132 Winter sunshine (46x55cm-18x22in) s. prov. 26-May-4 Sotheby's, London #93/R est:4000-6000
£5500 $9845 €8030 Snow scene (33x41cm-13x16in) s. 26-May-4 Sotheby's, Olympia #393/R est:4000-6000
£6000 $10740 €8760 Winter landscapes (46x55cm-18x22in) s. pair. 26-May-4 Sotheby's, London #107/R est:6000-8000
£7000 $12530 €10220 Path through the wood (53x46cm-21x18in) s. prov. 26-May-4 Sotheby's, London #94/R est:4000-6000

GUERNIER, Charles (1820-1881) French
£800 $1464 €1200 Maree basse a Saint-Malo (39x21cm-15x8in) s.d.79 panel. 6-Jun-4 Osenat, Fontainebleau #196

GUERNIER, Louis du I (1614-1659) French
Miniatures
£2400 $4080 €3504 Marguerite Louise d'Orleans (3cm-1in) enamel on gold oval. 18-Nov-3 Bonhams, New Bond Street #31/R est:1500-2500

GUERRA, Achille (1832-1903) Italian
£1000 $1800 €1500 Girl selling flowers (32x17cm-13x7in) s. panel lit. 22-Apr-4 Allgauer, Kempten #3554/R est:1400

GUERRA, Evaristo (1942-) Spanish?
£753 $1281 €1100 Apple trees (50x65cm-20x26in) s. 4-Nov-3 Ansorena, Madrid #952/R
£986 $1706 €1400 Village at night (55x78cm-22x31in) s. 15-Dec-3 Ansorena, Madrid #439/R est:1000
£1053 $1937 €1600 Three chimneys (53x73cm-21x29in) s.d.72 s.i.d.verso. 22-Jun-4 Durán, Madrid #32/R est:1000
£1250 $2063 €1800 Palm trees (65x81cm-26x32in) s.d.73 s.i.d.verso. 2-Jul-3 Ansorena, Madrid #912/R
£1517 $2519 €2200 Orange tree (81x65cm-32x26in) s.d.73 i.d.verso. 1-Oct-3 Ansorena, Madrid #600/R est:1200
£1690 $2704 €2400 Pepin's fields (73x92cm-29x36in) s.d.1974 prov. 16-Sep-3 Segre, Madrid #118/R est:1500
£1702 $2757 €2400 Barrio de San Sebastian (65x81cm-26x32in) s.d.63 s.i.d.verso. 20-May-3 Ansorena, Madrid #306/R est:1200
£1806 $2979 €2600 Chimney (81x65cm-32x26in) s.d.73 id.verso. 2-Jul-3 Ansorena, Madrid #939/R
£2553 $4136 €3600 Scare crow (85x11cm-33x4in) s. 20-May-3 Ansorena, Madrid #305/R est:2200

GUERRA, Giovanni (1544-1618) Italian

Works on paper

£728	$1326	€1100	Scene d'histoire romaine (14x18cm-6x7in) i. pen ink wash. 16-Jun-4 Piasa, Paris #4/R

GUERRANT, Roger (1930-1977) French

£552	$921	€800	Cycliste (65x81cm-26x32in) s. masonite. 11-Nov-3 Lesieur & Le Bars, Le Havre #59
£586	$979	€850	Arbres blancs au Havre (73x59cm-29x23in) s. 11-Nov-3 Lesieur & Le Bars, Le Havre #58

GUERRERO GALVAN, Jesus (1910-1973) Mexican

£772	$1405	€1158	Chair and window (163x194cm-64x76in) s. painted 1993. 21-Jun-4 Subastas Odalys, Caracas #86/R
£12849	$23000	€18760	Mother and child (65x80cm-26x31in) s.d.1948. 26-May-4 Sotheby's, New York #187/R est:25000-35000
£20588	$35000	€30058	Mujer con hojas (100x80cm-39x31in) s.d.1963 prov. 19-Nov-3 Sotheby's, New York #115/R est:20000-30000
£35294	$60000	€51529	La concepcion (71x63cm-28x25in) s.d.1939 prov.exhib.lit. 19-Nov-3 Sotheby's, New York #21/R est:60000-80000

Works on paper

£211	$358	€308	Boy with watermelons (44x60cm-17x24in) s.d.1972 col pencil. 30-Oct-3 Louis Morton, Mexico #153 (M.P 4000)

GUERRERO MALAGON, Cecilio (1909-1996) Spanish

£690	$1241	€1000	Peasants (16x29cm-6x11in) s. board. 26-Jan-4 Ansorena, Madrid #254/R
£828	$1490	€1200	View of Toledo (15x23cm-6x9in) s. board. 26-Jan-4 Ansorena, Madrid #169/R
£828	$1490	€1200	Nude at night (32x40cm-13x16in) canvas on board. 26-Jan-4 Ansorena, Madrid #250/R

GUERRERO, Jose (1914-1992) Spanish

£14966	$27238	€22000	Balance (91x76cm-36x30in) s.i.d.1974 prov. 3-Feb-4 Segre, Madrid #327/R est:18000
£26057	$45078	€37000	Saeta (162x97cm-64x38in) s. s.i.d.1969 verso prov. 9-Dec-3 Artcurial Briest, Paris #408/R est:12000-15000

Works on paper

£444	$800	€648	La catedral Zacatecas. Calle de las Arcos (34x22cm-13x9in) one s.i. one s.i.d.52 W/C two. 25-Apr-4 Bonhams & Butterfields, San Francisco #5597/R
£569	$950	€831	Untitled (16x12cm-6x5in) s. s.verso W/C prov. 11-Nov-3 Christie's, Rockefeller NY #139/R
£2041	$3714	€3000	Untitled (16x12cm-6x5in) s. W/C prov.exhib.lit. 3-Feb-4 Segre, Madrid #200/R est:2200
£5915	$10352	€8400	Untitled (63x48cm-25x19in) s. gouache prov. 16-Dec-3 Segre, Madrid #159/R est:7900
£6690	$11708	€9500	Untitled (63x47cm-25x19in) s.d.1977 gouache paper on board. 16-Dec-3 Segre, Madrid #131/R est:7000
£6993	$11678	€10000	Cerillas (64x49cm-25x19in) s. gouache exec c.1970-1974. 24-Jun-3 Segre, Madrid #120/R est:9500
£7746	$13556	€11000	Untitled (63x48cm-25x19in) s. gouache paper on board. 16-Dec-3 Segre, Madrid #133/R est:9000

GUERRESCHI, Giuseppe (1929-1985) Italian

£950	$1700	€1387	Abstract (33x53cm-13x21in) s. acrylic board. 8-May-4 Susanin's, Chicago #6093/R est:200-400
£2567	$4800	€3748	Bike rider (119x79cm-47x31in) s.d.954 i.d.verso. 25-Feb-4 Christie's, Rockefeller NY #108/R est:2500-3500

GUERRIER, Jean Pierre (1936-) Belgian

£265	$482	€400	Les moissonneurs (61x65cm-24x26in) s. i.d.1970 verso cardboard. 16-Jun-4 Hotel des Ventes Mosan, Brussels #272

GUERRIER, Raymond (1920-) French

£490	$832	€700	Paysage (166x263cm-65x104in) s. 20-Nov-3 Claude Aguttes, Neuilly #135/R
£699	$1189	€1000	Village road (114x146cm-45x57in) s. 1-Dec-3 Camard, Paris #107/R
£738	$1374	€1100	Phare (81x77cm-32x30in) s. prov. 3-Mar-4 Tajan, Paris #179
£804	$1367	€1150	Still life with oranges and herrings (100x81cm-39x32in) s. 1-Dec-3 Camard, Paris #104/R
£839	$1401	€1200	Composition (80x116cm-31x46in) s. 13-Oct-3 Pierre Berge, Paris #31/R
£1958	$3329	€2800	Still life with sunflowers and aubergines (100x65cm-39x26in) s. 1-Dec-3 Camard, Paris #105 est:900-1200
£2517	$4280	€3600	Barques sur la greve (114x163cm-45x64in) s. 1-Dec-3 Camard, Paris #106/R est:900-1200
£2900	$5336	€4234	Fleurs no.3 (65x54cm-26x21in) s. i.stretcher prov. 24-Mar-4 Sotheby's, Olympia #123/R est:800-1200

GUERRIERI, Giovanni Francesco (1589-1655) Italian

£241379	$403103	€350000	Hercules and Onfale (151x206cm-59x81in) prov.exhib.lit. 15-Nov-3 Porro, Milan #252/R est:165000

GUERY, Armand (1850-1912) French

£899	$1700	€1313	Sheep in field with haystacks, distant village and farm buildings (20x28cm-8x11in) s.i.d.4 September 1909 board. 21-Feb-4 Brunk, Ashville #54/R est:1000-2000
£1846	$3175	€2695	Troupeau dans la bruyere (45x60cm-18x24in) s.d.1908. 3-Dec-3 AB Stockholms Auktionsverk #2547/R est:15000-20000 (S.KR 24000)
£2600	$4472	€3796	Chez le Maraicher a Aumenaucourt (46x61cm-18x24in) s.d.1893. 4-Dec-3 Christie's, Kensington #1/R est:1500-2500

GUETIN, Victor Oscar (1873-1916) French

£294	$500	€429	Young woman with guitar (62x50cm-24x20in) s. 19-Nov-3 Fischer, Luzern #2118/R (S.FR 650)

GUEVARA MORENO, Luis (1926-) Spanish

£255	$470	€372	Music class (33x24cm-13x9in) s. 28-Mar-4 Subastas Odalys, Caracas #61
£255	$470	€383	U. (24x33cm-9x13in) s. 27-Jun-4 Subastas Odalys, Caracas #17/R
£283	$520	€425	Lois, naked (40x50cm-16x20in) s. painted 1973. 27-Jun-4 Subastas Odalys, Caracas #177
£343	$625	€515	Fliers (34x42cm-13x17in) s. painted 1971. 21-Jun-4 Subastas Odalys, Caracas #138
£476	$885	€695	Two women (33x41cm-13x16in) s. 14-Mar-4 Subastas Odalys, Caracas #19/R
£759	$1200	€1108	Circus tricks (81x100cm-32x39in) s. painted 1980. 1-Dec-2 Subastas Odalys, Caracas #44/R
£771	$1310	€1126	Arlequin (45x38cm-18x15in) s. painted 1960. 23-Nov-3 Subastas Odalys, Caracas #72/R

Works on paper

£714	$1300	€1071	Untitled (65x50cm-26x20in) s. mixed media card exec.1954. 21-Jun-4 Subastas Odalys, Caracas #57/R

GUFFENS, Godfried (1823-1901) Belgian

£15000	$27300	€21900	Der Mater Pausias und das Blumenmadchen Glykere (98x89cm-39x35in) s.d.1868. 17-Jun-4 Christie's, London #13/R est:15000-20000

GUGEL, Karl Adolf (1820-1885) German

£1361	$2476	€2000	Mother's kiss (114x93cm-45x37in) init.i.d.1871. 3-Feb-4 Christie's, Amsterdam #97/R est:2000-3000
£4800	$7968	€7008	Street musicians (117x94cm-46x37in) s. 1-Oct-3 Sotheby's, Olympia #209/R est:3000-4000

GUGGENBICHLER, Johann Meinrad (1649-1723) Austrian

Sculpture

£1342	$2470	€2000	Angel's head (28x37cm-11x15in) wood. 24-Mar-4 Hugo Ruef, Munich #1636/R est:1500
£10738	$19758	€16000	Angel (60cm-24in) painted gilded wood. 25-Mar-4 Dorotheum, Vienna #35/R est:2000-25000

GUGLIELMI, Gennaro (1804-?) Italian

£3691	$6607	€5500	Large, decorative still life of flowers (98x69cm-39x27in) s.d.1873. 27-May-4 Dorotheum, Vienna #222/R est:5500-6000

GUGLIELMI, O Louis (1906-1956) American

£2236	$3600	€3265	Objects and images (58x76cm-23x30in) cardboard. 24-Aug-3 William Jenack, New York #51 est:500-800

GUGLIELMI, Paolo (19th C) Italian

Works on paper

£420	$713	€600	Olympus (27x48cm-11x19in) pencil. 19-Nov-3 Finarte Semenzato, Milan #516/R

GUIAUD, Jacques (1811-1876) French

Works on paper

£767	$1395	€1150	Village mediterraneen (15x23cm-6x9in) s. W/C. 4-Jul-4 Eric Pillon, Calais #19/R

GUIBERNAU, J M (20th C) South American

£820	$1550	€1197	Dice players (90x80cm-35x31in) s. panel. 22-Feb-4 Galeria y Remates, Montevideo #75/R est:1800-2500

GUIBERT, Ignacio (1916-1992) Spanish

£897	$1497	€1300	Still life with flowers (100x81cm-39x32in) s. 17-Nov-3 Durán, Madrid #87/R

GUIDA, John (1897-1965) Italian

Works on paper

£1258	$2290	€1900	Study of dresses. s.d.21 mixed media. 21-Jun-4 Pandolfini, Florence #231/R est:1800-2000
£1589	$2893	€2400	Study of costumes. s.d. mixed media. 21-Jun-4 Pandolfini, Florence #232 est:1800-2000

GUIDI, Guido (1901-1998) Italian

£268	$475	€400	Washerwomen (50x70cm-20x28in) s. board. 1-May-4 Meeting Art, Vercelli #217

GUIDI, Ugo (?) Italian

£347	$566	€500	Nude (45x60cm-18x24in) 24-Sep-3 Cambi, Genoa #1621

GUIDI, Virgilio (1892-1984) Italian

£667	$1227	€1000	Against (23x31cm-9x12in) tempera W/C. 12-Jun-4 Meeting Art, Vercelli #129a
£800	$1440	€1200	Meeting (24x18cm-9x7in) s. s.verso. 22-Apr-4 Finarte Semenzato, Rome #185
£1127	$1870	€1600	Saint Mark's (25x30cm-10x12in) s. 11-Jun-3 Finarte Semenzato, Milan #508/R est:1500
£1133	$2085	€1700	Trees (24x18cm-9x7in) s. s.i.d.1973 verso. 8-Jun-4 Finarte Semenzato, Milan #147/R est:1500-2000
£1408	$2338	€2000	Hea (40x30cm-16x12in) 11-Jun-3 Finarte Semenzato, Milan #534/R

£1408	$2465	€2000	Cosmic architecture (20x35cm-8x14in) s. cardboard on canvas lit. 17-Dec-3 Il Ponte, Milan #1116/R est:2500-3000
£1467	$2699	€2200	Head (40x30cm-16x12in) s. painted 1974. 8-Jun-4 Finarte Semenzato, Milan #307/R est:2000-3000
£1549	$2572	€2200	Saint Mark's Bay (30x40cm-12x16in) s. 11-Jun-3 Finarte Semenzato, Milan #723/R
£1620	$2835	€2300	Venice (30x40cm-12x16in) s. prov. 17-Dec-3 Il Ponte, Milan #1118/R est:2000-2200
£1739	$2852	€2400	Face (30x40cm-12x16in) s. s.d.1959 verso. 29-May-3 Galleria Pace, Milan #47/R est:3500
£1800	$3312	€2700	Saint Mark's, Venice (20x30cm-8x12in) s.i.verso prov. 8-Jun-4 Finarte Semenzato, Milan #430/R est:2500-3000
£1802	$3100	€2631	Port scene (53x61cm-21x24in) s. 7-Dec-3 William Jenack, New York #292 est:2000-3000
£1892	$3330	€2800	San Giorgio, Venice (30x40cm-12x16in) s. s.i.verso. 22-May-4 Galleria Pananti, Florence #445/R est:2500-3000
£1931	$3225	€2800	Saint George (30x40cm-12x16in) s. 14-Nov-3 Farsetti, Prato #341/R est:1900-2200
£1972	$3273	€2800	Saint George Island (40x50cm-16x20in) s. 11-Jun-3 Finarte Semenzato, Milan #709/R
£1972	$3451	€2800	Figure (30x40cm-12x16in) i.verso prov. 16-Dec-3 Finarte Semenzato, Milan #340/R est:1800-2200
£2000	$3680	€3000	Saint Mark, Venice (30x40cm-12x16in) s. s.i.verso painted 1978. 10-Jun-4 Galleria Pace, Milan #160/R est:4000
£2029	$3328	€2800	Venice (40x50cm-16x20in) s. s.verso. 29-May-3 Galleria Pace, Milan #72/R est:3500
£2042	$3390	€2900	Saint Mark's Bay (40x50cm-16x20in) s. s.i.verso. 11-Jun-3 Finarte Semenzato, Milan #712/R
£2055	$3493	€3000	Head in green background (30x40cm-12x16in) s. i.verso. 7-Nov-3 Tuttarte, Modena #777 est:3500-4000
£2113	$3507	€3000	Meeting (40x30cm-16x12in) s. i.d.1973 verso. 13-Jun-3 Farsetti, Prato #378/R
£2349	$4322	€3500	Stormy sky (50x60cm-20x24in) s. s.d.1960 verso. 28-Mar-4 Finarte, Venice #6/R est:2000-2200
£2349	$4322	€3500	Trees (40x30cm-16x12in) s. s.i.d.1973. 28-Mar-4 Finarte, Venice #20/R est:1800-2000
£2349	$4322	€3500	Red heads (50x40cm-20x16in) s. s.i.d.1971 verso prov.exhib. 28-Mar-4 Finarte, Venice #22/R est:2200-2400
£2414	$4031	€3500	Still life with pheasant and cup (34x48cm-13x19in) s. cardboard. 13-Nov-3 Finarte Semenzato, Rome #409/R est:3500-4500
£2448	$4161	€3500	Saint George (40x50cm-16x20in) s. 20-Nov-3 Finarte Semenzato, Milan #203/R est:2200-2800
£2465	$4092	€3500	Meeting (60x50cm-24x20in) s. s.i.d. 1968 verso. 11-Jun-3 Finarte Semenzato, Milan #707/R
£2517	$4280	€3600	Saint Mark's Bay (40x50cm-16x20in) s. s.i.verso. 20-Nov-3 Finarte Semenzato, Milan #90/R est:2500-3000
£2580	$4387	€3690	Green head (50x40cm-20x16in) s. s.i.verso prov. 18-Nov-3 Babuino, Rome #487/R est:1000-1500
£2600	$4706	€3900	Meeting (40x50cm-16x20in) s. painted 1969. 2-Apr-4 Farsetti, Prato #299/R est:2400-2700
£2685	$4940	€4000	Meeting (50x40cm-20x16in) s. s.i.d.1973 verso prov.exhib. 28-Mar-4 Finarte, Venice #4/R est:2400-2600
£2685	$4940	€4000	Human architecture (40x50cm-16x20in) s. s.i.d.1957 verso canvas on cardboard exhib. 28-Mar-4 Finarte, Venice #26/R est:2200-2400
£2759	$4607	€4000	San Giorgio (40x50cm-16x20in) s.verso. 13-Nov-3 Finarte Semenzato, Rome #305 est:2000-2500
£2797	$4755	€4000	Head of woman (39x29cm-15x11in) s. 24-Nov-3 Christie's, Milan #66/R est:5000-7000
£2819	$5187	€4200	Constellation (50x60cm-20x24in) s. s.verso lit. 28-Mar-4 Finarte, Venice #7/R est:2300-2500
£2819	$5187	€4200	Trees (50x40cm-20x16in) s.s id.1974 verso exhib. 28-Mar-4 Finarte, Venice #14/R est:2000-2200
£2819	$5187	€4200	Dreamy (40x50cm-16x20in) s. s.verso exhib. 28-Mar-4 Finarte, Venice #30/R est:2000-2200
£3020	$5557	€4500	Meeting (60x50cm-24x20in) s. s.i.d.1969 verso. 28-Mar-4 Finarte, Venice #5/R est:2600-2800
£3020	$5557	€4500	Meeting (40x30cm-16x12in) s. s.i.d.1972 verso exhib. 28-Mar-4 Finarte, Venice #10/R est:2200-2400
£3020	$5557	€4500	Figure in space (40x50cm-16x20in) s.s.verso prov. 28-Mar-4 Finarte, Venice #18/R est:2200-2400
£3020	$5557	€4500	Head (50x40cm-20x16in) s. s.i.d.1970 verso prov. 28-Mar-4 Finarte, Venice #23/R est:2200-2400
£3020	$5557	€4500	Green head (50x40cm-20x16in) s. s.i.verso exhib.lit. 28-Mar-4 Finarte, Venice #28/R
£3221	$5928	€4800	Big heads (50x40cm-20x16in) s. s.i.d.1969 verso prov. 28-Mar-4 Finarte, Venice #11/R est:2700-3000
£3221	$5928	€4800	Saint Mark's (40x50cm-16x20in) s. s.i.d.1975 verso. 28-Mar-4 Finarte, Venice #24/R est:2000-2200
£3333	$6133	€5000	Trees (100x61cm-39x24in) i.verso lit. 8-Jun-4 Finarte Semenzato, Milan #427/R est:5000-6000
£3356	$6174	€5000	Big heads (60x50cm-24x20in) s. s.i.d.1969 verso prov. 28-Mar-4 Finarte, Venice #2/R est:2700-2900
£3356	$6174	€5000	Spatial seascape (50x60cm-20x24in) s. s.i.d.1979 verso. 28-Mar-4 Finarte, Venice #9/R est:2200-2400
£3356	$6174	€5000	La Dogana, Venice (35x50cm-14x20in) s. s.i.d.1967 prov. 28-Mar-4 Finarte, Venice #8/R est:2000-2200
£3356	$6174	€5000	San Giorgio (40x50cm-16x20in) s. s.i.d.1981. 28-Mar-4 Finarte, Venice #16/R est:2000-2200
£3356	$6174	€5000	Figures in space (68x88cm-27x35in) s. s.i.d.1955 prov.exhib.lit. 28-Mar-4 Finarte, Venice #19/R est:5000-5200
£3490	$6421	€5200	Big heads (60x50cm-24x20in) s. s.i.d.1970 verso. 28-Mar-4 Finarte, Venice #3/R est:2700-2900
£3662	$6408	€5200	Saint Mark's (50x60cm-20x24in) s. s.i.d.1981 verso prov. 16-Dec-3 Finarte Semenzato, Milan #342/R est:2300-2700
£3667	$6747	€5500	Head (40x30cm-16x12in) s. 8-Jun-4 Finarte Semenzato, Milan #308/R est:3000-4000
£3667	$6747	€5500	Saint Mark's, Venice (50x60cm-20x24in) i.verso painted 1972. 8-Jun-4 Finarte Semenzato, Milan #438/R est:4000-5000
£3691	$6792	€5500	Big heads (50x40cm-20x16in) s. s.i.d.1969 prov. 28-Mar-4 Finarte, Venice #29/R est:2400-2600
£3819	$6035	€5500	Head (60x50cm-24x20in) 6-Sep-3 Meeting Art, Vercelli #452 est:5000
£4027	$7409	€6000	Tragic masks (50x70cm-20x28in) s. s.i.d.1979 verso lit. 28-Mar-4 Finarte, Venice #13/R est:3000-3200
£4058	$6655	€5600	San Giorgio (50x60cm-20x24in) s. s.i.verso. 31-May-3 Farsetti, Prato #750/R est:4000-4500
£4698	$8644	€7000	Saint Mark's (50x60cm-20x24in) s. s.i.d.1974 verso prov. 28-Mar-4 Finarte, Venice #17/R est:2200-2400
£4698	$8644	€7000	Present condition (61x75cm-24x30in) s. s.verso prov.exhib.lit. 28-Mar-4 Finarte, Venice #27/R est:3000-3200
£4895	$8322	€7000	Dread (70x90cm-28x35in) s.s.d.955 prov. 25-Nov-3 Sotheby's, Milan #33/R est:4000-6000
£5369	$9879	€8000	Saint Mark's (50x70cm-20x28in) s. s.i.d.1983 verso. 28-Mar-4 Finarte, Venice #21/R est:3800-4000
£5493	$8789	€7800	Baroness (49x39cm-19x15in) s. s.d.1971 verso. 19-Sep-3 Finarte, Venice #465/R est:7000
£5705	$10497	€8500	Trees (90x70cm-35x28in) s. s.i.d.1976 verso lit. 28-Mar-4 Finarte, Venice #15/R est:3400-3600
£6040	$11114	€9000	Riots (71x89cm-28x35in) s. s.i.d.63 exhib.lit. 28-Mar-4 Finarte, Venice #31/R est:4800-5000
£6376	$11732	€9500	San Giorgio (45x60cm-18x24in) s. s.i.d.1976 verso. 28-Mar-4 Finarte, Venice #25/R est:4000-4200
£6757	$11892	€10000	Flowers (60x50cm-24x20in) s. 22-May-4 Galleria Pananti, Florence #512/R est:10000-12000
£6897	$11517	€10000	Figures in space (50x70cm-20x28in) s. painted 1956. 17-Nov-3 Sant Agostino, Torino #262/R est:10000-12000
£7042	$11690	€10000	Bacino di San Marco, Venezia (70x90cm-28x35in) s. s.i.verso painted 1977-1979. 14-Jun-3 Meeting Art, Vercelli #246/R est:10000
£8333	$15333	€12500	Saint Giorgio Islnd, Venice (50x80cm-20x31in) s. s.i.verso. 8-Jun-4 Finarte Semenzato, Milan #386/R est:12500-14000
£8392	$14266	€12000	Seascape in San Giorgio (45x65cm-18x26in) s. lit. 29-Nov-3 Farsetti, Prato #437/R est:6000-8000
£8696	$14261	€12000	Marina (60x115cm-24x45in) s. exhib. 31-May-3 Farsetti, Prato #749/R est:4200-5200
£9859	$16366	€14000	Bridge of the Accademia (50x60cm-20x24in) s. lit. 11-Jun-3 Finarte Semenzato, Milan #645/R
£10667	$19093	€16000	Venice (50x60cm-20x24in) s. board prov.exhib. 12-May-4 Stadion, Trieste #723/R est:5000-6000
£11538	$19615	€16500	Bridge of the Accademia (50x60cm-20x24in) cardboard prov.lit. 20-Nov-3 Finarte Semenzato, Milan #151/R est:12000-14000
£20979	$35664	€30000	Woman with black shawl (130x100cm-51x39in) s. prov.exhib.lit. 24-Nov-3 Christie's, Milan #246/R est:30000-40000
£25175	$42797	€36000	Venice (59x50cm-23x20in) s. painted 1927-28. 25-Nov-3 Sotheby's, Milan #187/R est:15000-20000
£33566	$57063	€48000	Landscape in Veneto (67x57cm-26x22in) s. board exhib.lit. 29-Nov-3 Farsetti, Prato #491/R est:45000-55000
Works on paper			
£345	$576	€500	Saint George Island (24x34cm-9x13in) s. W/C paper on canvas. 14-Nov-3 Farsetti, Prato #46
£483	$806	€700	Face (48x39cm-19x15in) s. W/C. 14-Nov-3 Farsetti, Prato #236
£690	$1152	€1000	Thoughtful girl (24x15cm-9x6in) s. Chinese ink W/C. 13-Nov-3 Finarte Semenzato, Rome #134/R
£733	$1349	€1100	Little head (24x16cm-9x6in) s.i. W/C. 8-Jun-4 Finarte Semenzato, Milan #145/R
£738	$1366	€1100	Face (46x35cm-18x14in) s. W/C card. 11-Mar-4 Galleria Pace, Milan #120/R
£915	$1520	€1300	Volto (33x23cm-13x9in) s. felt-pen cardboard exec 1974. 14-Jun-3 Meeting Art, Vercelli #681/R
£1007	$1852	€1500	Saint Mark's (39x47cm-15x19in) s. pencil W/C card. 28-Mar-4 Finarte, Venice #1/R est:1000-1200
£1007	$1852	€1500	Trees (52x38cm-20x15in) s. W/C pencil card. 28-Mar-4 Finarte, Venice #33/R est:1000-1200
£1074	$1976	€1600	Meeting (48x34cm-19x13in) s. W/C pencil. 28-Mar-4 Finarte, Venice #34/R est:1000-1200
£1141	$2099	€1700	Human architecture (31x46cm-12x18in) s.d.60 W/C paper on canvas. 28-Mar-4 Finarte, Venice #32/R est:1000-1200
£1477	$2717	€2200	Big head (33x24cm-13x9in) s. W/C prov. 28-Mar-4 Finarte, Venice #35/R est:1200-1400
£1611	$2964	€2400	Figures (48x67cm-19x26in) s. W/C card on canvas prov. 28-Mar-4 Finarte, Venice #12/R est:1800-2000

GUIDOBONO, Domenico (1670-1746) Italian

£59310	$99048	€86000	Still life with bird (67x88cm-26x35in) lit. 15-Nov-3 Porro, Milan #215/R est:75000

GUIDOTTI, Guiseppe (1929-) Italian

£486	$871	€720	Rhythmic composition with organic forms (80x60cm-31x24in) s.d.77 tempera. 8-May-4 Dawo, Saarbrucken #179/R
Sculpture			
£1892	$3386	€2800	Organic forms (92cm-36in) tin wood lit. 8-May-4 Dawo, Saarbrucken #169/R est:2800

GUIDROZ, Emile Sandroz (1906-) American

£299	$500	€437	Abstract (61x51cm-24x20in) 18-Oct-3 David Dike, Dallas #104/R
£749	$1250	€1094	Fredricka (51x41cm-20x16in) 18-Oct-3 David Dike, Dallas #197/R
£778	$1300	€1136	Christmas kittens (66x53cm-26x21in) 18-Oct-3 David Dike, Dallas #148/R

GUIETTE, Jules (1852-1901) Belgian

£1000	$1590	€1450	View of a city, believed to be Dunkirk (39x62cm-15x24in) s. 9-Sep-3 Bonhams, Knightsbridge #273/R est:800-1200

GUIETTE, René (1893-1976) Belgian

£336	$594	€500	Figure (50x40cm-20x16in) s.d.1949. 27-Apr-4 Campo & Campo, Antwerp #110
£486	$768	€700	Fleur miroir (50x40cm-20x16in) s.i.d.4/9/54 oil paper on canvas. 2-Sep-3 Christie's, Amsterdam #476
£699	$1189	€1000	Cinq oiseaux (40x50cm-16x20in) paper lit. 1-Dec-3 Amberes, Antwerp #308/R
£1678	$2853	€2400	La maison de l'artiste a Saint-Tropez (72x54cm-28x21in) s. 1-Dec-3 Palais de Beaux Arts, Brussels #165 est:2000-3000
£2685	$4966	€4000	Landscape (50x60cm-20x24in) s. lit. 13-Mar-4 De Vuyst, Lokeren #466/R est:4400-5000
£7333	$13493	€11000	Bateaux (73x91cm-29x36in) s.d.27 prov.lit. 8-Jun-4 Sotheby's, Amsterdam #15/R est:8000-12000
Works on paper			
£350	$584	€500	Untitled (36x25cm-14x10in) s. mixed media lit. 11-Oct-3 De Vuyst, Lokeren #171

£362 $666 €550 Untitled (56x44cm-22x17in) s.d.58 sand mixed media paper on canvas. 22-Jun-4 Christie's, Amsterdam #326/R
£503 $891 €750 Composition (30x40cm-12x16in) s.d.1960 mixed media. 27-Apr-4 Campo & Campo, Antwerp #112
£526 $968 €800 Caillou des miracles (55x44cm-22x17in) s.d.58 sand mixed media paper on board. 22-Jun-4 Christie's, Amsterdam #351/R
£612 $1096 €900 Untitled (55x43cm-22x17in) mixed media prov. 21-Mar-4 Calmels Cohen, Paris #131/R est:500-700
£629 $1070 €900 Composition Zen (72x45cm-28x18in) s.d.27/8/63 mixed media. 1-Dec-3 Palais de Beaux Arts, Brussels #166/R
£667 $1193 €1000 Papillon blanc (36x49cm-14x19in) s.d.XXX6 gouache. 11-May-4 Vanderkindere, Brussels #79
£839 $1427 €1200 La grande ville (50x35cm-20x14in) gouache lit. 1-Dec-3 Amberes, Antwerp #312
£897 $1659 €1300 Composition au voilier (55x45cm-22x18in) s. gouache. 16-Feb-4 Horta, Bruxelles #322
£1189 $2021 €1700 Cafetiere et pommes sur une table (38x54cm-15x21in) s.d.23 janvier 1946 gouache. 1-Dec-3 Palais de Beaux Arts, Brussels #159/R est:1000-1500

GUIGNARD, Alexandre Gaston (1848-1922) French
£362 $615 €529 End of the deer hunt (32x36cm-13x14in) s. 19-Nov-3 Fischer, Luzern #2120/R (S.FR 800)
£414 $691 €600 Etretat (49x70cm-19x28in) s. panel. 11-Nov-3 Lesieur & Le Bars, Le Havre #56

GUIGNARD, Jean Samson (1811-1897) Swiss
£229 $383 €332 A Sion, rue du Vieux-College (21x16cm-8x6in) i.verso. 21-Jun-3 Galerie du Rhone, Sion #291/R (S.FR 500)

GUIGNARD, Roland (1917-) Swiss
£295 $490 €428 Rouette (27x35cm-11x14in) s. 13-Jun-3 Zofingen, Switzerland #2869 (S.FR 650)
£682 $1132 €989 Composition (50x72cm-20x28in) s. masonite. 13-Jun-3 Zofingen, Switzerland #2868/R est:2000 (S.FR 1500)

GUIGNET, Jean Adrien (1816-1854) French
£1007 $1883 €1500 Lost after the battle (54x35cm-21x14in) board. 26-Feb-4 Cambi, Genoa #480/R est:400-500

GUIGNET, Jean Adrien (attrib) (1816-1854) French
£932 $1650 €1361 Landscape with artist sketching other figures. Drunken soldiers (30x51cm-12x20in) pair. 2-May-4 Bonhams & Butterfields, San Francisco #1023/R est:1000-1500

GUIGON, Charles-Louis (1807-1882) Swiss
£524 $838 €760 Bex (38x54cm-15x21in) board. 15-May-3 Stuker, Bern #1273/R (S.FR 1100)
Works on paper
£348 $637 €508 Le meage Saint Gervais (25x33cm-10x13in) s.i. W/C. 4-Jun-4 Zofingen, Switzerland #2346 (S.FR 800)

GUIGOU, Paul (1834-1871) French
£2667 $4853 €4000 Washerwomen at the edge of a mountain lake (29x42cm-11x17in) s. canvas on board. 1-Jul-4 Van Ham, Cologne #1380/R est:4200
£7383 $13584 €11000 Bords de la durance (23x40cm-9x16in) s.d.1856 canvas on panel. 29-Mar-4 Rieunier, Paris #39/R est:6000-7000
£9868 $18158 €15000 Coucher de soleil en Provence (29x46cm-11x18in) s.d.66 lit. 23-Jun-4 Sotheby's, Paris #83/R est:15000-20000
£36842 $67789 €56000 Pont du Gard (27x40cm-11x16in) s. prov.exhib.lit. 24-Jun-4 Christie's, Paris #153/R est:6000-8000
£40000 $73600 €58400 Route au bord de la Mediterranee, pres de Marseille (64x117cm-25x46in) s.d.66 prov.lit. 23-Jun-4 Christie's, London #104/R est:40000-60000
£77181 $136611 €115000 Silhouettes au pied de la montagne Sainte-Victoire (55x80cm-22x31in) s. prov.exhib.lit. 30-Apr-4 Tajan, Paris #157/R est:60000-80000

GUIGUET, François Joseph (1860-1937) French
£533 $960 €800 Portrait de la soeur du peintre (28x33cm-11x13in) canvas on panel. 20-Apr-4 Chenu & Scrive, Lyon #100/R
£833 $1500 €1250 Autoportrait au chevalet (27x22cm-11x9in) 20-Apr-4 Chenu & Scrive, Lyon #99/R
Works on paper
£306 $548 €450 Etude de jeune femme accoudee. Etude de femme (33x25cm-13x10in) s.d.1919 black crayon sanguine double-sided. 17-Mar-4 Maigret, Paris #96/R
£510 $913 €750 Etude de petite fille (33x25cm-13x10in) s.d.15 juin 1912 black crayon sanguine htd white. 17-Mar-4 Maigret, Paris #95/R
£533 $960 €800 Marie lisant (31x24cm-12x9in) chl. 20-Apr-4 Chenu & Scrive, Lyon #100a/R

GUIJARRO, Antonio (1923-) Spanish
£704 $1232 €1000 Boys (60x73cm-24x29in) s.d.1974. 16-Dec-3 Segre, Madrid #262/R
£833 $1500 €1216 Blue still life (41x43cm-16x17in) 24-Apr-4 Du Mouchelle, Detroit #3127/R est:1000-1500
£833 $1500 €1216 Blue still life (41x43cm-16x17in) 24-Apr-4 Du Mouchelle, Detroit #3129/R est:1000-1500
£1056 $1900 €1542 Water front (64x81cm-25x32in) 24-Apr-4 Du Mouchelle, Detroit #3130/R est:1000-1800
£1250 $2250 €1825 Red nude (64x81cm-25x32in) 24-Apr-4 Du Mouchelle, Detroit #3131/R est:800-1200
£1250 $2250 €1825 Mujer (99x117cm-39x46in) 24-Apr-4 Du Mouchelle, Detroit #3133/R est:2000-3000
£1250 $2250 €1825 Floral still life (66x81cm-26x32in) 24-Apr-4 Du Mouchelle, Detroit #3128/R est:1000-1500
£1250 $2250 €1825 Pajarro (79x99cm-31x39in) 24-Apr-4 Du Mouchelle, Detroit #3134/R est:1500-2500
£1630 $2674 €2250 Bedes (50x61cm-20x24in) s. i.verso. 27-May-3 Durán, Madrid #81/R est:1800
£1667 $3000 €2434 Bodegan (97x147cm-38x58in) 24-Apr-4 Du Mouchelle, Detroit #3132/R est:2000-3000
£1702 $2757 €2400 Pajaro de los montes de la tierra mia (46x61cm-18x24in) s. s.i.verso. 20-May-3 Ansorena, Madrid #331/R est:2400
Works on paper
£423 $739 €600 Lovers (23x35cm-9x14in) s. gouache prov. 16-Dec-3 Segre, Madrid #222/R

GUILBERT, A (?) Italian
£1233 $2096 €1800 Personnages au bord de la riviere (38x55cm-15x22in) 9-Nov-3 Versailles Encheres #18/R est:2000-2500

GUILBERT, Andre (19th C) French
£360 $620 €526 Landscape with lake and boats (38x54cm-15x21in) s. 8-Dec-3 Philippe Schuler, Zurich #5850 (S.FR 800)
£830 $1510 €1212 River landscape (38x55cm-15x22in) s. 16-Jun-4 Fischer, Luzern #2150/R (S.FR 1900)

GUILBERT, Maurice (1876-1933) Belgian
£2667 $4907 €4000 Veere (34x39cm-13x15in) s.i.d.20 paper. 8-Jun-4 Sotheby's, Amsterdam #207/R est:3500-4500

GUILBERT, Narcisse (1878-1942) French
£596 $1085 €900 Tilloloy, route de Lille (24x35cm-9x14in) 20-Jun-4 Imberdis, Pont Audemer #29
£700 $1267 €1050 Effet de neige, foret de Roumare (33x41cm-13x16in) s. 4-Apr-4 Salle des ventes Pillet, Lyon la Foret #32/R
£1900 $3439 €2850 Cours la Reine, matin d'automne (22x27cm-9x11in) s. cardboard. 4-Apr-4 Salle des ventes Pillet, Lyon la Foret #33/R est:600-800

GUILBERT, Octave (20th C) French
£423 $739 €600 Place de la Concorde (34x46cm-13x18in) s. s.i.verso. 19-Dec-3 Delvaux, Paris #59

GUILLAIN, Marthe (1890-1974) Belgian
£759 $1403 €1100 L'enfant et la poupee devant une fenetre (72x60cm-28x24in) s. 16-Feb-4 Horta, Bruxelles #29
£2657 $4438 €3800 La lecture (97x140cm-38x55in) s. 11-Oct-3 De Vuyst, Lokeren #173/R est:1500-2500

GUILLAUME, Albert (1873-1942) French
£16667 $30000 €24334 Blackjack players (27x35cm-11x14in) s. oil pencil artist board prov. 22-Apr-4 Christie's, Rockefeller NY #167/R est:10000-15000
Works on paper
£387 $643 €550 Soiree galante (31x24cm-12x9in) s. W/C. 15-Jun-3 Peron, Melun #161

GUILLAUME, Émile (1867-1942) French
Sculpture
£1600 $2896 €2400 Delivrance (155cm-61in) s. bronze. 30-Mar-4 Campo & Campo, Antwerp #129/R est:2000-4000

GUILLAUME, Jean (20th C) French
Works on paper
£1724 $2879 €2500 Port de Sauzon a Belle-Ile-en-Mer (28x64cm-11x25in) pastel. 11-Jul-3 Rabourdin & Choppin de Janvry, Paris #23/R est:2800-3000

GUILLAUMET, Gustave (1840-1887) French
£367 $660 €550 Portrait de femme (45x37cm-18x15in) s. 20-Apr-4 Galerie Moderne, Brussels #279
£3067 $5643 €4600 Priere dans le desert (41x72cm-16x28in) s.d.1872. 9-Jun-4 Oger, Dumont, Paris #88/R est:3500-4000
£26056 $45077 €37000 Halte, Algerie (54x65cm-21x26in) s. lit. 15-Dec-3 Gros & Delettrez, Paris #134/R est:30000-40000
Works on paper
£282 $487 €400 Etude d'arabe tenant un baton (34x25cm-13x10in) studio st. blk crayon white gouache. 10-Dec-3 Piasa, Paris #77
£4422 $7915 €6500 Casbah a l'aube (30x43cm-12x17in) s. pastel dr. 21-Mar-4 St-Germain-en-Laye Encheres #35/R est:6000

GUILLAUMET, Gustave (attrib) (1840-1887) French
£3167 $5385 €4624 Arcadian landscapes (26x67cm-10x26in) mono.d.1861 pair prov. 19-Nov-3 Fischer, Luzern #1074/R est:6000-7000 (S.FR 7000)

GUILLAUMIN, Armand (1841-1927) French
£772 $1382 €1150 Paysage a la riviere (27x34cm-11x13in) s. i.verso panel. 25-May-4 Chambelland & Giafferi, Paris #31/R
£3473 $5799 €5000 Paysage de la Creuse (9x13cm-4x5in) s.i.verso postcard lit. 21-Oct-3 Artcurial Briest, Paris #165/R est:4000-5000
£3473 $5799 €5000 Barrage de Genetin (9x13cm-4x5in) s.i.verso postcard lit. 21-Oct-3 Artcurial Briest, Paris #166/R est:4000-5000
£3533 $6501 €5300 Cote d'Agay (24x33cm-9x13in) s. 11-Jun-4 Pierre Berge, Paris #263/R est:6000-8000
£7947 $14464 €12000 Bords de la Marne en hiver (30x50cm-12x20in) s. painted c.1892. 18-Jun-4 Piasa, Paris #18/R est:12000-15000
£9500 $15865 €13870 Les ruines de chateau de crozant (46x65cm-18x26in) s. painted August 1913 prov.lit. 21-Oct-3 Sotheby's, London #25/R est:8000-12000
£9500 $17290 €13870 Nature morte au vase de fleurs (65x54cm-26x21in) s. painted c.1900 prov.lit. 4-Feb-4 Sotheby's, London #203/R est:10000-15000
£12000 $22080 €17520 Matin d'automne a la campagne (38x46cm-15x18in) s. prov.exhib. 23-Jun-4 Christie's, London #135/R est:12000-14000
£13000 $23920 €18980 Paysage de la Creuse (50x61cm-20x24in) s. painted c.1910 prov. 22-Jun-4 Sotheby's, London #226/R est:15000-20000

£13423 $23758 €20000 Crozant - La Roche de l'Echo (54x65cm-21x26in) s. prov.lit. 27-Apr-4 Artcurial Briest, Paris #170/R est:20000-25000
£14000 $23380 €20440 Damiette, ile de France (41x58cm-16x23in) s. painted c.1885 prov. 21-Oct-3 Sotheby's, London #5/R est:15000-20000
£14255 $23094 €20100 Paysage Mediterraneen (44x59cm-17x23in) s. 24-May-3 Martinot & Savignat, Pontoise #162/R est:6000-7000
£16107 $28832 €24000 Paysage boise (65x81cm-26x32in) s. 25-May-4 Chambelland & Giafferi, Paris #48/R est:12000-15000
£18000 $30060 €26280 Paysage de la creuse (60x73cm-24x29in) s. painted c.1903 prov.lit. 21-Oct-3 Sotheby's, London #135/R est:20000-30000
£18667 $34347 €28000 Les Brejots, premiers jours de mai (59x81cm-23x32in) s. i.d.1917 verso. 11-Jun-4 Claude Aguttes, Neuilly #189/R est:30000-40000
£19014 $30613 €27000 Barrage de Genetin (63x90cm-25x35in) s. lit. 22-Aug-3 Deauville, France #61/R est:30000-40000
£20588 $35000 €30058 Paysage a l'arbre (54x65cm-21x26in) s. painted c.1905. 6-Nov-3 Sotheby's, New York #146/R est:30000-40000
£21229 $38000 €30994 Moulin Brigand et les ruin du chateau de Crozant (54x73cm-21x29in) s. prov. 5-May-4 Christie's, Rockefeller NY #241/R est:35000-45000
£21831 $37768 €31000 Printemos a Damiette (41x58cm-16x23in) s. lit. 14-Dec-3 Eric Pillon, Calais #72/R
£22000 $40480 €32120 Paysage de la Creuse (60x72cm-24x28in) s. prov. 22-Jun-4 Sotheby's, London #227/R est:15000-20000
£23529 $40000 €34352 La cote de l'Esterel (49x70cm-19x28in) s. prov. 5-Nov-3 Christie's, Rockefeller NY #210/R est:30000-40000
£25352 $43859 €36000 Les rochers a Aguay (60x73cm-24x29in) s. 14-Dec-3 Rabourdin & Choppin de Janvry, Paris #39/R est:40000-45000
£26000 $47840 €37960 Moulins a vent sur le Canal en Hollande (38x46cm-15x18in) s. painted c.1904 prov.lit. 22-Jun-4 Sotheby's, London #102/R est:25000-35000
£26667 $47733 €40000 Roches rouges a Trayas (60x72cm-24x28in) s. i.d.1913 verso prov. 17-May-4 Chayette & Cheval, Paris #182/R est:20000-25000
£27972 $46713 €40000 Bords de riviere (60x73cm-24x29in) s. painted c.1895 lit. 25-Jun-3 Blanchet, Paris #29/R est:60000
£42000 $77280 €61320 La Seine a Samois (69x80cm-27x31in) s. painted c.1900. 23-Jun-4 Christie's, London #144/R est:28000-35000
£42657 $72517 €61000 Promeneuse en campagne (65x81cm-26x32in) s. 21-Nov-3 Lombrail & Teucquam, Paris #115/R est:60000-70000
£49162 $88000 €71777 Paysage de L'ile de France (61x101cm-24x40in) s. painted c.1875 prov. 5-May-4 Christie's, Rockefeller NY #226/R est:60000-80000
Works on paper
£464 $844 €700 Personnages et cheval sur les bords de la Seine (30x47cm-12x19in) s. chl. 16-Jun-4 Piasa, Paris #207
£1093 $2000 €1596 Portrait of a young girl (42x28cm-17x11in) col chk. 29-Jan-4 Swann Galleries, New York #274/R est:800-1200
£1127 $1949 €1600 Peniche sur la Seine (17x17cm-7x7in) s. pastel. 9-Dec-3 Chambelland & Giafferi, Paris #70/R est:1500-2000
£2933 $5339 €4400 Moulin (44x57cm-17x22in) s. pastel. 4-Jul-4 Eric Pillon, Calais #103/R
£20979 $35664 €30000 Paysage (60x47cm-24x19in) s. pastel chk prov. 26-Nov-3 Dorotheum, Vienna #27/R est:16000-22000
£38000 $69160 €55480 Still life with fruits (9x25cm-4x10in) s. pastel exec c.1900 prov.exhib. 5-Feb-4 Christie's, London #314/R est:12000-18000

GUILLE, Captain J D (20th C) British
£1400 $2422 €2044 County Galway Hounds on Rye Hill (50x60cm-20x24in) s. canvas on board. 9-Dec-3 Bonhams, Oxford #94/R est:300-500

GUILLEMARD, Dominique (20th C) ?
£1049 $1804 €1500 Violoncelliste partait en vacances le lendemain (97x130cm-38x51in) s. i.on stretcher prov. 2-Dec-3 Sotheby's, Amsterdam #224/R est:1500-2000

GUILLEMET, Jean Baptiste Antoine (1843-1918) French
£1594 $2614 €2200 Moulin de Crabec (22x32cm-9x13in) s. panel. 11-May-3 Osenat, Fontainebleau #223/R est:2500-3000
£2013 $3705 €3000 Promenade de sous-bois (41x33cm-16x13in) s. 29-Mar-4 Lombrail & Teucquam, Paris #52/R
£2029 $3328 €2800 Sur le chemin (24x35cm-9x14in) s. panel. 11-May-3 Osenat, Fontainebleau #224/R est:3000-3500
£2238 $3804 €3200 Morsalines (27x35cm-11x14in) s. 24-Nov-3 Boscher, Cherbourg #710/R est:3000-4000
£2431 $4132 €3500 Landscape in Moret-sur-Loing (39x56cm-15x22in) s.d.76 prov. 28-Oct-3 Christie's, Amsterdam #115/R est:3000-5000
£2700 $4860 €3942 River bank (46x55cm-18x22in) s.i.d.1884. 21-Jan-4 Sotheby's, Olympia #469/R est:2000-3000
£2733 $5002 €4100 Paris, le Quai de Bercy (17x27cm-7x11in) s. panel exhib. 6-Jun-4 Anaf, Lyon #100/R est:2000-2500
£2797 $4811 €4000 Paysage, la prairie en fleurs (24x35cm-9x14in) s. 7-Dec-3 Osenat, Fontainebleau #203 est:3800-4000
£3497 $6014 €5000 La grande allee (56x39cm-22x15in) s.d.75. 7-Dec-3 Osenat, Fontainebleau #204 est:3500-4000
£3944 $6823 €5600 Promeneuses sur la plage (27x35cm-11x14in) s.i. 14-Dec-3 St-Germain-en-Laye Encheres #43/R est:2000-2500
£4027 $7490 €6000 Rivage de Normandie (54x73cm-21x29in) s. 3-Mar-4 Tajan, Paris #51/R est:5000-7000
£4296 $7432 €6100 A maree basse (38x55cm-15x22in) s. 9-Dec-3 Chambelland & Giafferi, Paris #56/R est:5000-6000
£4957 $8873 €7237 Normandy coast (38x55cm-15x22in) s.i.d.84. 12-May-4 Dobiaschofsky, Bern #587/R est:5500 (S.FR 11500)
£5603 $10030 €8180 Coast in summer (38x55cm-15x22in) s. 12-May-4 Dobiaschofsky, Bern #586/R est:6500 (S.FR 13000)
£8392 $14266 €12000 Le moulin (24x32cm-9x13in) s.i. panel. 24-Nov-3 Boscher, Cherbourg #711b est:4500-5000
£10490 $17832 €15000 La Hougue vue de la baie de Morsalines (38x55cm-15x22in) s. 24-Nov-3 Boscher, Cherbourg #711/R est:6000-7000
£23000 $41630 €33580 Pont Marie, Paris (89x131cm-35x52in) s.d.1902. 1-Apr-4 Christie's, Kensington #28/R est:3000-5000
Works on paper
£347 $627 €520 Le chaos de Villers, Calvados (20x31cm-8x12in) mono. pierre noire. 30-Mar-4 Rossini, Paris #992

GUILLEMIN, Alexandre Marie (1817-1880) French
£2667 $4827 €4000 Barque sur le sable (18x26cm-7x10in) s. cardboard. 30-Mar-4 Rossini, Paris #263/R est:1000-5000

GUILLEMIN, E C H (1841-1907) French
Sculpture
£2390 $3800 €3489 Arabic beauty. s. bronze. 14-Sep-3 Susanin's, Chicago #6041/R est:3000-5000

GUILLEMIN, Émile Coriolan Hippolyte (1841-1907) French
Sculpture
£904 $1600 €1320 Arab with rifle (56x71cm-22x28in) s.st.f. bronze. 2-May-4 William Jenack, New York #269 est:1000-1500
£1000 $1850 €1460 Bust of an Algerian Woman (39cm-15in) gilt bronze red green cold-paint red veined marble socle. 13-Jul-4 Sotheby's, Olympia #232/R est:1000-1500
£15294 $26000 €22329 Young Kurdish woman (79cm-31in) s. bronze. 28-Oct-3 Christie's, Rockefeller NY #137/R

GUILLEMINET, Claude (1821-1860) French
£667 $1220 €1000 Coq, poules et canards (9x12cm-4x5in) s. panel. 6-Jun-4 Osenat, Fontainebleau #222
£1867 $3416 €2800 Basse cour (24x18cm-9x7in) s. panel pair. 6-Jun-4 Anaf, Lyon #101/R est:2000-2800

GUILLEN, Heliodoro (1864-1940) Spanish
£634 $1096 €900 Beach (25x36cm-10x14in) s. board. 15-Dec-3 Ansorena, Madrid #272/R
£1510 $2703 €2250 Village (37x27cm-15x11in) s. board. 25-May-4 Durán, Madrid #649/R est:600

GUILLERMET, Jean Pierre (1921-) French
£441 $749 €644 Summer afternoon in Paris (50x65cm-20x26in) s.d.66. 5-Nov-3 Dobiaschofsky, Bern #616/R (S.FR 1000)

GUILLERMO, Juan (1916-1968) Spanish
£1176 $2000 €1717 Barca abandonada (55x81cm-22x32in) s. i.verso prov. 9-Nov-3 Bonhams & Butterfields, Los Angeles #4003/R
£1176 $2000 €1717 Bodegola de la ventana (74x91cm-29x36in) s.i.verso prov. 9-Nov-3 Bonhams & Butterfields, Los Angeles #4017/R
£10563 $18275 €15000 Eating (84x100cm-33x39in) s.d.56. 15-Dec-3 Ansorena, Madrid #976/R est:15000

GUILLERY, Franz (1863-1933) German
£1467 $2655 €2200 Le long du canal, la tombee de la nuit (81x110cm-32x43in) s. 30-Mar-4 Campo, Vlaamse Kaai #78
£1600 $2880 €2400 Fishing boats off San Giorgio Maggiore (60x80cm-24x31in) s. 21-Apr-4 Dorotheum, Vienna #2/R est:2200-2500

GUILLERY, Theodor (1900-1976) German
£308 $524 €450 Still life - autumn flowers in glass vase (57x57cm-22x22in) s. panel lit. 6-Nov-3 Allgauer, Kempten #3435/R
£400 $640 €580 Sunflowers (67x61cm-26x24in) s. 16-Sep-3 Bonhams, Knightsbridge #63/R

GUILLIBAUD, Jean François (1718-1799) Swiss
Works on paper
£5000 $9150 €7300 Portrait of a young man holding a musical score (40x35cm-16x14in) i. pastel oval. 6-Jul-4 Christie's, London #132/R est:5000-7000

GUILLOD, Thomas Walker (fl.1839-1860) British
£1500 $2730 €2190 Kitchen utensils and game (25x35cm-10x14in) s.d.1849 panel pair. 16-Jun-4 Christie's, Kensington #61/R est:1500-2000

GUILLONNET, Octave Denis Victor (1872-1967) French
£331 $606 €500 La danse du tambourine (18x12cm-7x5in) s. 9-Apr-4 Claude Aguttes, Neuilly #63
£338 $639 €500 Portrait d'une dame de qualite (121x98cm-48x39in) s. oval. 17-Feb-4 Vanderkindere, Brussels #470
£699 $1189 €1000 Muse et Inspiration (33x46cm-13x18in) s. panel. 28-Nov-3 Drouot Estimations, Paris #166
£903 $1653 €1310 Venise, carnaval Place Saint-Marc (46x38cm-18x15in) s. 31-Jan-4 Gerard, Besancon #47
£1342 $2470 €2000 Etude pour Le Mariage Arabe (41x31cm-16x12in) s.i. panel prov. 24-Mar-4 Binoche, Paris #77 est:2000-3000
£3000 $5460 €4380 Les baigneuses (60x74cm-24x29in) s.d.25. 16-Jun-4 Christie's, Kensington #32/R est:2000-3000
£12000 $21840 €17520 Siesta in the shade (38x46cm-15x18in) s. 16-Jun-4 Christie's, Kensington #34/R est:6000-8000
£12000 $22200 €17520 Le jardin fleuri (81x65cm-32x26in) init. 14-Jul-4 Sotheby's, Olympia #283/R est:4000-6000
£13772 $23000 €20107 Garden party (121x121cm-48x48in) s.d.1920. 7-Oct-3 Sotheby's, New York #151 est:15000-20000
Works on paper
£924 $1700 €1349 Theatrical scene with three actors (48x71cm-19x28in) s.i. pastel. 23-Mar-4 Arthur James, Florida #91/R est:1000-1500

GUILLOT, Ann (1875-?) American
£359 $600 €524 Still life (41x30cm-16x12in) 18-Oct-3 David Dike, Dallas #178/R

GUILLOU, Alfred (1844-1926) French
£855 $1574 €1300 Mer d'huile a COncarneau (33x46cm-13x18in) s. 25-Jun-4 Millon & Associes, Paris #129/R
£1067 $1909 €1600 Les deux pecheurs (20x16cm-8x6in) s. cardboard. 16-May-4 Thierry & Lannon, Brest #321/R est:1000-1200
£1620 $2835 €2300 Benediction donnee aux marins (46x33cm-18x13in) s. 21-Dec-3 Thierry & Lannon, Brest #322 est:1500-2000

£4636 $8669 €7000 Baie de Concarneau (33x46cm-13x18in) s. 24-Jul-4 Thierry & Lannon, Brest #177/R est:3800-4000

GUILLOU, Jeannine (1909-1946) French
£604 $1117 €900 Paris vue de l'atelier (46x38cm-18x15in) s. 14-Mar-4 Eric Pillon, Calais #228/R

GUILLOUX, Albert Gaston (1871-1952) French
£364 $607 €520 Bouquet de roses (65x92cm-26x36in) s.d.1946. 7-Oct-3 Livinec, Gaudcheau & Jezequel, Rennes #133
£5102 $9133 €7500 Paysage de bords de riviere au soleil couchant (32x45cm-13x18in) s.d.1892. 19-Mar-4 Millon & Associes, Paris #87b est:2000-3000

GUILLOUX, Charles Victor (1866-1946) French
£1736 $2951 €2500 Coucher du soleil a Herblay (33x54cm-13x21in) s.i.d.1902 stretcher. 28-Oct-3 Dorotheum, Vienna #1/R est:3600-4000
£3662 $6335 €5200 Paris, Notre-Dame et la Seine au crepuscule (33x46cm-13x18in) s. i.verso stretcher. 12-Dec-3 Piasa, Paris #150/R est:2000-2500
Works on paper
£282 $487 €400 Rivage et arbres a contre-jour (14x18cm-6x7in) st. W/C. 10-Dec-3 Rossini, Paris #15

GUIMARAES, Jose de (1939-) Portuguese
£7047 $13037 €10500 Homage to Rubens (54x36cm-21x14in) s. 13-Mar-4 De Vuyst, Lokeren #575/R est:3500-4500

GUIMARD, Hector (1867-1942) French
Sculpture
£17450 $30886 €26000 Untitled (90x160cm-35x63in) mono. iron. 27-Apr-4 Claude Aguttes, Neuilly #230/R est:18000-20000

GUINAN, Robert (20th C) American?
Works on paper
£1757 $3320 €2600 Late hours (74x59cm-29x23in) s.d.1991 col crayon prov. 21-Feb-4 Cornette de St.Cyr, Paris #300/R est:600-800

GUINAND, René (1892-1984) Swiss
£292 $488 €426 Bateaux au bord du lac (50x61cm-20x24in) s. 16-Nov-3 Koller, Geneva #1237/R (S.FR 665)
£330 $562 €482 Tables et chevalets (65x81cm-26x32in) s. i.d.1980 verso. 5-Nov-3 Dobiaschofsky, Bern #3450/R (S.FR 750)

GUINART-CANDELICH, Francisco (1888-?) Spanish
£851 $1379 €1200 Flowers (61x74cm-24x29in) s. s.d.1947 verso. 20-May-3 Ansorena, Madrid #66/R
£1310 $2188 €1900 Harbour, Majorca (60x74cm-24x29in) s.d.36 s.i.d.verso. 17-Nov-3 Durán, Madrid #190/R est:1900
£1447 $2620 €2200 Palafrugell beach (60x75cm-24x30in) 14-Apr-4 Ansorena, Madrid #45/R est:2200
£1479 $2558 €2100 Patio (100x121cm-39x48in) s. s.d.1938 verso. 15-Dec-3 Ansorena, Madrid #299/R est:2100
£3080 $5051 €4250 Patio florido (100x121cm-39x48in) s.d.1938. 27-May-3 Durán, Madrid #239/R est:3750

GUINDANI, Giuseppe (1886-1946) Italian
£436 $772 €650 Landscape (24x30cm-9x12in) s. 1-May-4 Meeting Art, Vercelli #151

GUINDON, Andre-Marius (1830-1919) French
£423 $756 €600 Portrait de Mme Ernest Chupin a la harpe (150x100cm-59x39in) s.d.1897. 11-Jan-4 Rouillac, Vendome #349

GUINEA, Anselmo de (1855-1906) French
£5282 $9137 €7500 Roman woman (57x41cm-22x16in) s.i. s.i.verso. 15-Dec-3 Ansorena, Madrid #332/R est:6500

GUINEGAULT, Georges P (1893-?) French
£1197 $1939 €1700 Port of Cherbourg (54x73cm-21x29in) s. 11-Aug-3 Boscher, Cherbourg #836/R est:500-600
Works on paper
£364 $681 €550 Le port de Pontivy (47x56cm-19x22in) s. W/C gouache. 24-Jul-4 Thierry & Lannon, Brest #322
£397 $743 €600 Port Maria a Quiberon (47x56cm-19x22in) s. W/C gouache. 24-Jul-4 Thierry & Lannon, Brest #321

GUINIER, Henri Jules (1867-1927) French
Works on paper
£662 $1238 €1000 Concarneau (24x33cm-9x13in) st.sig. pastel. 24-Jul-4 Thierry & Lannon, Brest #101/R

GUINLE, Jorge (1947-1987) Brazilian
£5861 $10725 €8792 The master of flies (130x130cm-51x51in) s.i.verso. 6-Jul-4 Bolsa de Arte, Rio de Janeiro #171/R (B.R 32000)

GUINNESS, Elizabeth S (fl.1873-1900) British
Works on paper
£1200 $2208 €1752 Doll's tea party (45x34cm-18x13in) s.d.1878 pencil W/C bodycol. 25-Mar-4 Christie's, Kensington #232/R est:300-500

GUINNESS, Evelyn (fl.1890-1906) Irish
Works on paper
£439 $830 €650 Farm road (30x46cm-12x18in) mono. W/C exhib. 17-Feb-4 Whyte's, Dublin #140/R

GUINNESS, May (1863-1955) British
£3200 $5344 €4672 Still life with green bottle (63x51cm-25x20in) 16-Oct-3 Christie's, Kensington #481/R est:2000-4000
Works on paper
£490 $832 €700 At table (21x26cm-8x10in) pastel. 25-Nov-3 De Veres Art Auctions, Dublin #11/R

GUINNESS, May (attrib) (1863-1955) British
Works on paper
£250 $460 €365 Figures with horses and cart in a country lane by river (10x13cm-4x5in) bears sig W/C. 11-Jun-4 Keys, Aylsham #267

GUINO, Richard (1890-1973) French
Sculpture
£1126 $2060 €1700 Leda (46x37x16cm-18x15x6in) s. terracotta prov.lit. 7-Apr-4 Maigret, Paris #177/R est:1000-1500
£1192 $2170 €1800 Femme au paon (42cm-17in) s. terracotta exec.1940's. 18-Jun-4 Charbonneaux, Paris #200/R est:2000-2500
£1325 $2424 €2000 Tete aux capucines (30cm-12in) st.f.Susse num.5/25 pat bronze prov.lit. 7-Apr-4 Maigret, Paris #176/R est:2300-3000
£1600 $2944 €2400 Nymphe sortant des flots (102cm-40in) s. num.2 brown pat. bronze. 14-Jun-4 Horta, Bruxelles #117 est:2000-3000
£4539 $8353 €6900 Leda (50x31x48cm-20x12x19in) s. pat bronze Cast Taube. 24-Jun-4 Credit Municipal, Paris #70 est:7000-8000
Works on paper
£298 $542 €450 Faunesse et sirene (21x26cm-8x10in) graphite. 18-Jun-4 Charbonneaux, Paris #94
£331 $606 €500 Musicienne (21x21cm-8x8in) studio st. crayon ink. 7-Apr-4 Maigret, Paris #4
£331 $603 €500 Femme accroupie (30x23cm-12x9in) s. i.verso chl. 18-Jun-4 Charbonneaux, Paris #93
£364 $663 €550 Femme assise a la draperie (35x26cm-14x10in) s. i.verso crayon. 18-Jun-4 Charbonneaux, Paris #92
£464 $844 €700 Couple a l'enfant (24x23cm-9x9in) s. i.verso sanguine chk. 18-Jun-4 Charbonneaux, Paris #91/R

GUINO, Richard and RENOIR, Pierre Auguste (20th C) French
Sculpture
£17606 $30810 €25000 Maternite (54cm-21in) s.num.HC 5/6 bronze Cast Valsuani prov.lit. 16-Dec-3 Claude Aguttes, Neuilly #20/R est:28000-32000
£26000 $47840 €37960 Petite Venus au socle (81cm-32in) s.st.f. Valsuani num.III/IV brown pat. bronze one of 12. 23-Jun-4 Christie's, London #113/R est:30000-40000
£223464 $400000 €326257 Grande laveuse (129cm-51in) s.st.f.Susse d.1917 num.HC1/2 green brown pat bronze prov.lit. 6-May-4 Sotheby's, New York #128/R est:250000-350000

GUINOVART, Jose (1927-) Spanish
£694 $1146 €1000 Untitled (21x16cm-8x6in) s. 2-Jul-3 Ansorena, Madrid #941/R
£5903 $10035 €8500 Triangle (124x100cm-49x39in) s.d.1985 oil wood assemblage prov.exhib. 28-Oct-3 Segre, Madrid #153/R est:8000
Works on paper
£304 $535 €450 Composition (25x32cm-10x13in) s.d.1978 gouache ink. 18-May-4 Segre, Madrid #129/R
£574 $1011 €850 Composition 2 (25x32cm-10x13in) s.d.1978 gouache wash ink. 18-May-4 Segre, Madrid #264/R
£699 $1168 €1000 Faz (69x49cm-27x19in) s.i.d.1965 gouache pastel ink. 24-Jun-3 Segre, Madrid #117/R
£1974 $3632 €3000 Beheaded P (63x49cm-25x19in) s.d.71 s.i.d.verso mixed media on canvas. 22-Jun-4 Durán, Madrid #132/R est:1200

GUION, Molly (1910-) American
£30726 $55000 €44860 Portrait of drummer of the 7th/9th Battalion, the Royal Scots (183x122cm-72x48in) prov.lit. 27-May-4 Sotheby's, New York #305/R est:8000-12000

GUIRALDES, Alberto (1897-1961) Argentinian
Works on paper
£989 $1800 €1444 Putting the saddle on (31x24cm-12x9in) s. W/C. 5-Jul-4 Arroyo, Buenos Aires #27/R est:900

GUIRAMAND, Paul (1926-) French
£800 $1440 €1168 Cavalier dans le foret (92x65cm-36x26in) s. 20-Jan-4 Bonhams, Knightsbridge #261/R
£1222 $2200 €1784 Girl with flowers (81x99cm-32x39in) s. prov. 20-Jan-4 Arthur James, Florida #47
£1418 $2369 €2000 Chevaux et lad a l'ecurie (65x92cm-26x36in) s. 15-Oct-3 Rabourdin & Choppin de Janvry, Paris #33/R est:2000-2500
£1567 $2883 €2350 Still life of a vase of flowers (81x100cm-32x39in) s. 9-Jun-4 Le Roux & Morel, Paris #71 est:1200-1500
£2267 $4171 €3400 Les chevaux (46x55cm-18x22in) s. 11-Jun-4 Hauswedell & Nolte, Hamburg #1288/R est:3000
Works on paper
£310 $515 €450 Les passants sous la pluie pres de Notre Dame (55x42cm-22x17in) s. pastel. 30-Sep-3 Blanchet, Paris #276

GUIRAND DE SCEVOLA (1871-1950) French
£389 $724 €580 Autoportrait au pinceau (92x73cm-36x29in) 3-Mar-4 Ferri, Paris #174
£738 $1373 €1100 Le modele dans l'atelier (27x22cm-11x9in) s. panel. 3-Mar-4 Ferri, Paris #302
£1074 $1997 €1600 Bouquet de roses (36x46cm-14x18in) s. cardboard. 3-Mar-4 Ferri, Paris #298/R est:500-700
£1342 $2497 €2000 Nu a l'alcove (55x36cm-22x14in) s. panel. 3-Mar-4 Ferri, Paris #296 est:400-500

GUIRAND DE SCEVOLA, Lucien (1871-1950) French
£400 $716 €600 Versailles (24x33cm-9x13in) s. 11-May-4 Christie's, Paris #212/R
£420 $713 €600 Still life with porcelain figures and roses in glass vase (15x62cm-6x24in) s. 20-Nov-3 Van Ham, Cologne #1607
£490 $832 €700 Table on the veranda (24x33cm-9x13in) s. board. 1-Dec-3 Camard, Paris #27
£952 $1705 €1400 Vase de roses blanches sur un entablement (46x55cm-18x22in) s. cardboard. 21-Mar-4 Muizon & Le Coent, Paris #51/R
£1958 $3368 €2800 Portrait de Mme Therese Blanchard de la Comedie Francaise (210x154cm-83x61in) s. i.verso. 5-Dec-3 Gros & Delettrez, Paris #98/R est:3000-4000
Works on paper
£267 $480 €400 Les deux amies (26x20cm-10x8in) s. pastel. 20-Apr-4 Chenu & Scrive, Lyon #102/R
£320 $589 €480 Nu assis de dos (24x30cm-9x12in) s. pastel. 9-Jun-4 Beaussant & Lefèvre, Paris #217
£352 $609 €500 Au boudoir (20x19cm-8x7in) pastel. 10-Dec-3 Hotel des Ventes Mosan, Brussels #263
£780 $1303 €1100 Portrait de jeune femme (70x90cm-28x35in) s.d.1900 W/C. 19-Oct-3 Anaf, Lyon #168
£1409 $2593 €2100 Fleurs au vase bleu (81x170cm-32x67in) s. pastel. 28-Mar-4 Anaf, Lyon #137/R est:1200-1600
£1457 $2652 €2200 Buste de fillette (53x44cm-21x17in) s.i.d.Paques 1906 pastel canvas. 15-Jun-4 Blanchet, Paris #124 est:500-600

GUIRAUD-RIVIERE, Maurice (1881-?) French
Sculpture
£1816 $3250 €2651 Danseuse a la boule (61cm-24in) s. silver pat bronze marble base. 20-Mar-4 Freeman, Philadelphia #918/R est:3000-5000
£1816 $3250 €2651 Stella (58cm-23in) s. silver pat bronze marble base. 20-Mar-4 Freeman, Philadelphia #919/R est:3000-5000
£1892 $3386 €2800 Femme nue assise (40x49x29cm-16x19x11in) s. pat bronze prov. 5-May-4 Claude Boisgirard, Paris #37/R est:1500-2000
£3434 $6250 €5014 Dancing woman (51cm-20in) s. gilt bronze ivory. 8-Feb-4 William Jenack, New York #150 est:6250
£17297 $32000 €25254 Untitled (89cm-35in) s. parcel gilt ivory pat bronze exec.c.1930. 9-Mar-4 Christie's, Rockefeller NY #311/R est:15000-20000
£17341 $30000 €25318 Three athletes (43x81x23cm-17x32x9in) with sig. bronze prov. 11-Dec-3 Sotheby's, New York #157/R est:6000-8000

GUISE, Konstantin (1811-1858) Swiss
£560 $1003 €818 St Theodor Church in Basel (28x23cm-11x9in) s. canvas on pavatex. 13-May-4 Stuker, Bern #162/R (S.FR 1300)

GUITELZON, Rebeca (20th C) Argentinian?
Works on paper
£874 $1600 €1276 Summer evening (64x63cm-25x25in) mixed media. 1-Jun-4 Arroyo, Buenos Aires #4

GUITET, James (1925-) French
£533 $960 €800 20.F.3.73 (60x73cm-24x29in) s.d.1973 s.i.d.verso prov. 25-Apr-4 Versailles Encheres #30
£533 $960 €800 50.P.10.70 (116x81cm-46x32in) s.d.1970 prov. 25-Apr-4 Versailles Encheres #52
£600 $1080 €900 57.305.MA (50x100cm-20x39in) s.d.1957 s.i.verso oil mixed media panel prov. 25-Apr-4 Versailles Encheres #20
£789 $1453 €1200 Composition (73x22cm-29x9in) s.d.1955 isorel. 28-Jun-4 Joron-Derem, Paris #223/R
£800 $1440 €1200 40M.60.9 (100x65cm-39x26in) s.d.1960 s.i.d.verso prov. 25-Apr-4 Versailles Encheres #28
£807 $1452 €1210 Composition (100x73cm-39x29in) s.d.1970 s.i.d.verso prov. 25-Apr-4 Versailles Encheres #27
£2308 $3854 €3300 Composition (65x265cm-26x104in) i.verso panel triptych prov.lit. 29-Jun-3 Versailles Encheres #1/R

GULACSY, Lajos (1882-1932) Hungarian
£3529 $5859 €5152 Park with a lonely cottage (24x35cm-9x14in) s. cardboard. 4-Oct-3 Kieselbach, Budapest #183/R (H.F 1300000)
£3529 $5859 €5152 Female head (11x8cm-4x3in) cardboard. 4-Oct-3 Kieselbach, Budapest #199/R (H.F 1300000)
£8874 $15352 €12956 Strange room (34x40cm-13x16in) s. 12-Dec-3 Kieselbach, Budapest #207/R (H.F 3400000)
£14355 $24834 €20958 Woman in rose-arbor (60x46cm-24x18in) s. canvas on cardboard. 12-Dec-3 Kieselbach, Budapest #93/R (H.F 5500000)
£18706 $33109 €27311 Miraculous landscape (37x45cm-15x18in) s.d.1906 cardboard. 28-Apr-4 Kieselbach, Budapest #199/R (H.F 7000000)
£57965 $104916 €84629 Dewfall (43x54cm-17x21in) s. panel. 16-Apr-4 Mu Terem Galeria, Budapest #192/R (H.F 22000000)
Works on paper
£1122 $1987 €1638 Sailing boat (12x8cm-5x3in) s. mixed media. 28-Apr-4 Kieselbach, Budapest #191/R (H.F 420000)
£1229 $2176 €1794 Scene (14x16cm-6x6in) s. indian ink col pencil. 28-Apr-4 Kieselbach, Budapest #26/R (H.F 460000)
£2240 $4054 €3270 Woman nude (30x19cm-12x7in) s. pencil. 16-Apr-4 Mu Terem Galeria, Budapest #112/R (H.F 850000)

GULBRANSSON, Olaf (1873-1958) Norwegian
£344 $575 €502 The boat Rap (27x40cm-11x16in) s. panel. 20-Oct-3 Blomqvist, Lysaker #1107 (N.KR 4000)
£375 $600 €544 Texas of Kristiania (13cm-5in circular) s. panel. 22-Sep-3 Blomqvist, Lysaker #1077/R (N.KR 4400)
£428 $788 €625 Ceres - Norway (18x33cm-7x13in) s. panel. 29-Mar-4 Blomqvist, Lysaker #1097/R (N.KR 5400)
£530 $964 €800 Three rich town citizens (28x25cm-11x10in) s. 16-Jun-4 Hugo Ruef, Munich #1157
Works on paper
£460 $846 €672 Ship's portrait Margarethe (17x22cm-7x9in) s. gouache. 29-Mar-4 Blomqvist, Lysaker #1098/R (N.KR 5800)
£483 $806 €700 Josef Augsberger (17x13cm-7x5in) s.i. Indian ink. 9-Jul-3 Hugo Ruef, Munich #275/R
£690 $1152 €1000 Gallantry medal (33x24cm-13x9in) s.i. pen sepia board. 13-Nov-3 Neumeister, Munich #336/R
£1096 $1863 €1600 Caricature of French ambassador in Munich (23x21cm-9x8in) s. Indian ink over pencil. 4-Nov-3 Hartung & Hartung, Munich #1507/R est:1400
£2055 $3493 €3000 Heinrich von Zugel (29x23cm-11x9in) s.d.41 Indian ink brush pen over pencil. 4-Nov-3 Hartung & Hartung, Munich #1508/R est:1400

GULBRANSSON, Olaf (attrib) (1873-1958) Norwegian
£1800 $3330 €2628 Figures on horseback (135x135cm-53x53in) 14-Jul-4 Christie's, Kensington #1254/R est:2000-3000

GULDBRANDSEN, Olof (?) Norwegian
£285 $521 €416 Ship's portrait Standard (27x40cm-11x16in) s.i.d.1913 panel. 7-Jun-4 Blomqvist, Oslo #254/R (N.KR 3500)
£569 $1041 €831 Bergensfjord - ship's portrait (30x49cm-12x19in) s.d.1918. 7-Jun-4 Blomqvist, Oslo #224/R (N.KR 7000)

GULIK, Franciscus Lodewijk van (1841-1899) Dutch
£469 $750 €685 Ice skaters. s. panel. 20-Sep-3 Harvey Clar, Oakland #1235

GULLICHSEN, Alvar (1961-) Finnish
£1626 $2911 €2374 Plum! (120x150cm-47x59in) s.d.1997 verso. 28-May-4 Uppsala Auktionskammare, Uppsala #353/R est:10000-12000 (S.KR 22000)

GULLVAG, Hakon (1959-) Norwegian
£1502 $2629 €2193 Figure (46x38cm-18x15in) s. s.d.97 verso. 16-Dec-3 Grev Wedels Plass, Oslo #162/R est:10000-15000 (N.KR 17500)
£1549 $2587 €2262 Reading (37x55cm-15x22in) s. panel. 20-Oct-3 Blomqvist, Lysaker #1108 est:12000-15000 (N.KR 18000)
£2129 $3663 €3108 Dog sitting (74x60cm-29x24in) s. cardboard. 8-Dec-3 Blomqvist, Oslo #571/R est:12000-15000 (N.KR 25000)
£3169 $5293 €4627 Back of chair (70x60cm-28x24in) s. 17-Nov-3 Blomqvist, Lysaker #1091/R est:20000-25000 (N.KR 38000)
£5854 $10712 €8547 The pram (116x130cm-46x51in) s.d.1999-2000. 7-Jun-4 Blomqvist, Oslo #459/R est:45000-55000 (N.KR 72000)
£9821 $16401 €14339 The big day (189x190cm-74x75in) s.d.01-03. 13-Oct-3 Blomqvist, Oslo #334/R est:100000-120000 (N.KR 115000)

GULLY, John (1819-1888) New Zealander
Works on paper
£2799 $5178 €4087 Artist party on the tree line (44x68cm-17x27in) s.d.1881 W/C. 9-Mar-4 Watson's, Christchurch #58 est:12000-20000 (NZ.D 7640)
£5208 $8281 €7604 Mill buildings, Matai River, Nelson (30x49cm-12x19in) s.d.1866 W/C. 1-May-3 Dunbar Sloane, Wellington #42/R est:13000-18000 (NZ.D 15000)
£6391 $10865 €9331 Pipiriki Maori settlement, Wanganui river (30x38cm-12x15in) s.d.1875 W/C. 27-Nov-3 International Art Centre, Auckland #110/R est:15000-20000 (NZ.D 17000)
£7233 $11500 €10560 Mountain lake (56x91cm-22x36in) s.d.1885 W/C. 13-Sep-3 Selkirks, St. Louis #485/R est:6000-9000

GULSTON, Alan Stepney (1844-1919) British
Works on paper
£260 $447 €380 Mountain torrent (74x53cm-29x21in) s.d.1888 prov. 2-Dec-3 Peter Francis, Wales #58/R
£400 $688 €584 Woodland torrent (51x71cm-20x28in) s.d.1888 prov. 2-Dec-3 Peter Francis, Wales #57/R

GULWA (1915-) Australian
Sculpture
£2033 $3211 €2968 Maningrida superintendent, Mr Ted Harvey (50cm-20in) hardwood exec.c.1963 prov. 28-Jul-3 Sotheby's, Paddington #315/R est:2500-3500 (A.D 5000)

GUMERY, Adolphe (1861-1943) French
£3378 $6047 €5000 Leda et le cygne (100x81cm-39x32in) s.d.1900. 7-May-4 Millon & Associes, Paris #65 est:4500-6000

GUNARSA, Nyoman (1944-) Indonesian
£1307 $2366 €1908 Dua penari (70x70cm-28x28in) s.d.97. 4-Apr-4 Sotheby's, Singapore #157/R est:4000-6000 (S.D 4000)
£2581 $4129 €3768 Wayang (70x70cm-28x28in) s.d.90. 18-May-3 Sotheby's, Singapore #153/R est:6000-8000 (S.D 7200)
£3472 $5799 €5069 Dancers (145x145cm-57x57in) s.d.88. 12-Oct-3 Sotheby's, Singapore #163/R est:8000-15000 (S.D 10000)
£4348 $6739 €6348 Dancer (135x93cm-53x37in) s.d.1974. 6-Oct-2 Sotheby's, Singapore #139/R est:12000-15000 (S.D 12000)
£5161 $8258 €7535 Barong (93x143cm-37x56in) s.d.71. 18-May-3 Sotheby's, Singapore #152/R est:12000-15000 (S.D 14400)

GUNAWAN, Hendra (1918-1983) Indonesian
£6209 $11239 €9065 Street scene (48x48cm-19x19in) panel exhib.lit. 4-Apr-4 Sotheby's, Singapore #134/R est:9000-15000 (S.D 19000)

£12681 $19656 €18514 Self portrait (55x46cm-22x18in) s.d.1968. 6-Oct-2 Sotheby's, Singapore #119/R est:25000-30000 (S.D 35000)
£22876 $41405 €33399 Pemandangan samudera selatan (70x146cm-28x57in) s.i.d.1974. 4-Apr-4 Sotheby's, Singapore #131/R est:35000-55000 (S.D 70000)
£27778 $50278 €40556 Menangkap Ikan (96x134cm-38x53in) s.d.76. 3-Apr-4 Glerum, Singapore #36/R est:75000-90000 (S.D 85000)
£31884 $49420 €46551 Banana seller (70x145cm-28x57in) s.d.75. 6-Oct-2 Sotheby's, Singapore #148/R est:60000-80000 (S.D 88000)
£34722 $57986 €50694 Wayang (127x139cm-50x55in) s. 12-Oct-3 Sotheby's, Singapore #132/R est:100000-150000 (S.D 100000)
£35948 $65065 €52484 Kuda lumping (95x135cm-37x53in) s.d.1970. 4-Apr-4 Sotheby's, Singapore #135/R est:60000-80000 (S.D 110000)
£38194 $63785 €55763 Washing hair (140x70cm-55x28in) s.d.14-12-1981 i.verso. 12-Oct-3 Sotheby's, Singapore #118/R est:60000-80000 (S.D 110000)
£39216 $70980 €57255 Two women by the beach (93x135cm-37x53in) s. 4-Apr-4 Sotheby's, Singapore #132/R est:80000-100000 (S.D 120000)
£44015 $73506 €64262 Kuda lumping (130x190cm-51x75in) s. prov. 26-Oct-3 Christie's, Hong Kong #93/R est:380000-500000 (HK.D 570000)
£45139 $75382 €65903 Fish seller (141x80cm-56x31in) s.d.80. 12-Oct-3 Sotheby's, Singapore #120/R est:60000-80000 (S.D 130000)
£46230 $83215 €67496 Penjual pepaya - papaya vendor (135x94cm-53x37in) s. 25-Apr-4 Christie's, Hong Kong #588/R est:240000-400000 (HK.D 650000)
£47312 $75699 €69076 Mother and child (142x61cm-56x24in) s.d.80 prov. 18-May-3 Sotheby's, Singapore #133/R est:50000-70000 (S.D 132000)
£52083 $86979 €76041 Mencari Kutu (96x135cm-38x53in) s. i.verso. 12-Oct-3 Sotheby's, Singapore #119/R est:120000-150000 (S.D 150000)
£54054 $90270 €78919 Vegetable vendor (92x135cm-36x53in) s. 26-Oct-3 Christie's, Hong Kong #94/R est:220000-300000 (HK.D 700000)
£55556 $92778 €81112 Sea Odyssey (140x180cm-55x71in) s. 12-Oct-3 Sotheby's, Singapore #121/R est:120000-150000 (S.D 160000)
£55556 $100556 €81112 Papaya seller (95x144cm-37x57in) s. 4-Apr-4 Sotheby's, Singapore #137/R est:68000-88000 (S.D 170000)
£59028 $98576 €86181 Majestic Tree (197x89cm-78x35in) s.d.74. 12-Oct-3 Sotheby's, Singapore #124/R est:150000-200000 (S.D 170000)
£63406 $98279 €92573 Picking lice (95x160cm-37x63in) prov. 6-Oct-2 Sotheby's, Singapore #141/R est:120000-150000 (S.D 175000)
£64516 $103226 €94193 Landscape with buffaloes (102x153cm-40x60in) s. 18-May-3 Sotheby's, Singapore #144/R est:100000-150000 (S.D 180000)
£65217 $101087 €95217 Chicken vendors (140x194cm-55x76in) s.i. prov. 6-Oct-2 Sotheby's, Singapore #149/R est:150000-180000 (S.D 180000)
£71124 $128023 €103841 Women with fish (149x84cm-59x33in) s.d.75. 25-Apr-4 Christie's, Hong Kong #585/R est:400000-600000 (HK.D 1000000)
£71895 $130131 €104967 Muara, river delta (86x150cm-34x59in) s.d.76. 3-Apr-4 Glerum, Singapore #76/R est:200000-300000 (S.D 220000)
£78236 $140825 €114225 Batik vendor (132x88cm-52x35in) s. 25-Apr-4 Christie's, Hong Kong #587/R est:400000-600000 (HK.D 1100000)
£86022 $137634 €125592 Father playing with his children (95x150cm-37x59in) s.i.d.80 lit. 18-May-3 Sotheby's, Singapore #145/R est:120000-180000 (S.D 240000)
£128023 $230441 €186914 Panen padi - rice harvest (150x200cm-59x79in) s.i.d.76 prov. 25-Apr-4 Christie's, Hong Kong #586/R est:500000-700000 (HK.D 1800000)
£150579 $251467 €219845 Flower vendors (140x140cm-55x55in) s.d.73. 26-Oct-3 Christie's, Hong Kong #92/R est:600000-800000 (HK.D 1950000)
£156863 $283922 €229020 Mandi di pancuran (140x200cm-55x79in) s.d.79. 4-Apr-4 Sotheby's, Singapore #138/R est:120000-180000 (S.D 480000)

GUNAWAN, Hendra (attrib) (1918-1983) Indonesian
Works on paper
£3707 $6190 €5412 Market scene (48x57cm-19x22in) glass paint. 26-Oct-3 Christie's, Hong Kong #69/R est:22000-32000 (HK.D 48000)

GUNDELACH, Matthaeus (circle) (1566-1653) German
Works on paper
£7566 $13921 €11500 Satyr with nymph (16x21cm-6x8in) pen wash htd white paper on board. 24-Jun-4 Dr Fritz Nagel, Stuttgart #518/R est:400

GUNDERSEN, Gunnar S (1921-1983) Norwegian
£1206 $2207 €1761 Portrait of woman (54x45cm-21x18in) s. 2-Feb-4 Blomqvist, Lysaker #1084/R est:20000-25000 (N.KR 15000)
Works on paper
£241 $441 €352 Composition (41x30cm-16x12in) mixed media. 2-Feb-4 Blomqvist, Lysaker #1086 (N.KR 3000)
£317 $529 €463 Landscape (16x24cm-6x9in) s. W/C. 17-Nov-3 Blomqvist, Lysaker #1098 (N.KR 3800)
£322 $588 €470 Composition (43x64cm-17x25in) s. mixed media. 2-Feb-4 Blomqvist, Lysaker #1085 (N.KR 4000)
£709 $1184 €1035 Composition (44x38cm-17x15in) s. pastel. 17-Nov-3 Blomqvist, Lysaker #1095 (N.KR 8500)

GUNDERSEN, Helene (1858-1934) Norwegian
£1045 $1912 €1526 Interior from Bergsmarka (58x76cm-23x30in) painted c.1902-1910 lit. 2-Feb-4 Blomqvist, Lysaker #1088/R est:8000-10000 (N.KR 13000)
£1549 $2494 €2262 Interior from Maihaugen (65x56cm-26x22in) s. 25-Aug-3 Blomqvist, Lysaker #1100/R est:20000-25000 (N.KR 18000)

GUNDLACH, F C (1926-) German
Photographs
£2029 $3328 €2800 Apres ski on the Avus, Model Staebe-seger, Berlin (30x38cm-12x15in) s.i.d. verso lit. silver gelatin. 30-May-3 Villa Grisebach, Berlin #1184/R est:1500-1800

GUNDLACH, Henry (1884-1965) German
£417 $679 €600 Waves on Sylt beach (79x120cm-31x47in) s.d.36. 26-Sep-3 Bolland & Marotz, Bremen #653/R
£520 $931 €770 Thatched cottage on Warft Neukirchen (40x60cm-16x24in) s. board. 8-May-4 Hans Stahl, Toestorf #59/R

GUNN, Herbert James (1893-1964) British
£6000 $10320 €8760 Reclining nude (44x34cm-17x13in) 2-Dec-3 Bonhams, New Bond Street #8/R est:5000-7000
£16000 $27520 €23360 From a window on Quao d'Orleans (46x36cm-18x14in) s.i.d.May 31 1960 verso canvasboard. 2-Dec-3 Bonhams, New Bond Street #7/R est:8000-12000
£55000 $94600 €80300 July by the sea (61x45cm-24x18in) s. prov. 3-Dec-3 Sotheby's, London #16/R est:50000-70000
Works on paper
£420 $701 €613 View of Hyde Park, London (33x24cm-13x9in) pencil pen black ink W/C. 16-Oct-3 Christie's, Kensington #197

GUNNE, Carl (1893-1979) Scandinavian
£544 $979 €816 Sailing in summer (50x67cm-20x26in) s. 25-Apr-4 Goteborg Auktionsverk, Sweden #395/R (S.KR 7500)

GUNNING, Simon (20th C) American/Australian
£8287 $15000 €12099 Sundown at Schiros (168x244cm-66x96in) s.d.86/8. 3-Apr-4 Neal Auction Company, New Orleans #454/R est:15000-25000

GUNSAM, Karl Joseph (1900-1972) Austrian
£694 $1132 €1000 Grinzing (60x45cm-24x18in) s. mixed media board. 23-Sep-3 Wiener Kunst Auktionen, Vienna #60/R
£1748 $2972 €2500 Village in East Tyrol (67x53cm-26x21in) s.d.66 panel. 28-Nov-3 Wiener Kunst Auktionen, Vienna #481/R est:3000-6000
£3000 $5400 €4500 Grunau in Almtal (61x74cm-24x29in) s.d.1966. 21-Apr-4 Dorotheum, Vienna #189/R est:5000-7000
Works on paper
£570 $1055 €850 Houses by water (43x58cm-17x23in) s. WC gouache. 9-Mar-4 Dorotheum, Vienna #114/R

GUNSCHMANN, Karl (1895-1984) German
£769 $1308 €1100 Still life with tulips in blue white vase (83x66cm-33x26in) mono.d.1932 board. 29-Nov-3 Arnold, Frankfurt #248/R

GUNTEN, Roger von (1933-) Swiss
£790 $1344 €1153 Lagoon (37x23cm-15x9in) s.d.1974 acrylic paper. 30-Oct-3 Louis Morton, Mexico #126 est:17000-19000 (M.P 15000)

GUNTER, Hans Hermann (20th C) German
£465 $838 €679 Allegorical scene with musical genius and Beethoven's death mask (80x70cm-31x28in) s. oval. 26-Jan-4 Lilla Bukowskis, Stockholm #620 (S.KR 6200)

GUNTERMANN, Wilhelm (1887-?) German
£320 $579 €480 Self portrait (32x30cm-13x12in) s.d. panel. 2-Apr-4 Winterberg, Heidelberg #1062/R
£1200 $2172 €1800 Hollerbach (70x80cm-28x31in) s.d. double-sided. 2-Apr-4 Winterberg, Heidelberg #1063/R est:1800

GUNTHER, Erwin (1864-1927) German
£633 $1153 €950 Fishing boats returning home in twilight (65x101cm-26x40in) s. 1-Jul-4 Van Ham, Cologne #1379
£750 $1290 €1095 Moored vessels, Whitby harbour, towards St Mary's (43x30cm-17x12in) s. panel. 4-Dec-3 Richardson & Smith, Whitby #428/R
£940 $1729 €1400 Sea with angler on jetty (66x100cm-26x39in) lit. 25-Mar-4 Karlheinz Kaupp, Staufen #2470/R
£1020 $1857 €1500 Fisherboote vor der englischen kanalkuste (80x120cm-31x47in) s.i.d.07. 3-Feb-4 Christie's, Amsterdam #237/R est:1500-2000
£1100 $2013 €1606 On the Atlantic coast (80x121cm-31x48in) s.d.19. 8-Apr-4 Christie's, Kensington #157 est:800-1200
£1457 $2652 €2200 Fishing boat on the canal coast (80x120cm-31x47in) s.d.16. 21-Jun-4 Dorotheum, Vienna #292/R est:2600-3000
£1611 $2996 €2400 Fishing boat in rough seas (132x185cm-52x73in) s.i.d.1901. 6-Mar-4 Arnold, Frankfurt #735/R est:1600
£2396 $4074 €3498 Seascape with sailing ship and steamer at pier (58x81cm-23x32in) s. 10-Nov-3 Rasmussen, Vejle #290/R est:20000-25000 (D.KR 26000)
Works on paper
£933 $1671 €1400 Boats on beach (26x35cm-10x14in) s.i. gouache lit. 14-May-4 Schloss Ahlden, Ahlden #2834/R

GUNTHER, F (19th C) German
£1750 $3220 €2555 Figures in a tavern (26x33cm-10x13in) s.i. panel. 23-Mar-4 Bonhams, New Bond Street #19/R est:3000-5000

GUNTHER, Frank (20th C) American
£284 $500 €415 Hotel Lounge (66x81cm-26x32in) s. acrylic painted 1977. 23-May-4 Hindman, Chicago #1004/R

GUNTHER, Ignaz (1725-1775) German
Sculpture
£13333 $24267 €20000 Winged head of cherub (30cm-12in) wood s. 30-Jun-4 Neumeister, Munich #273/R est:18000

GUNTHER, Ignaz (circle) (1725-1775) German
Sculpture
£5000 $9100 €7500 Winged head of cherub (23cm-9in) wood lit. 30-Jun-4 Neumeister, Munich #274/R est:15000

GUNTHER, Peter Georg (fl.1820-1830) Danish
Works on paper
£520 $899 €759 Porte Orientale de la Summa Musijd a Delhi (31x43cm-12x17in) s.d.1824 W/C pen. 9-Dec-3 Rasmussen, Copenhagen #1737/R (D.KR 5500)

£895 $1638 €1307 Landscape with river and waterfall with two shepherds resting (40x48cm-16x19in) s.d.1823 pastel after Jens Juel. 9-Jun-4 Rasmussen, Copenhagen #1567/R (D.KR 10000)

GUNTHER-NAUMBURG, Otto (1856-1941) German
£347 $580 €500 Summer mountain landscape (74x107cm-29x42in) s. lit. 25-Oct-3 Bergmann, Erlangen #921/R
£795 $1446 €1200 Ruins in a landscape (70x96cm-28x38in) s. 18-Jun-4 Bolland & Marotz, Bremen #627/R
£1314 $2431 €1918 River landscape (75x107cm-30x42in) 14-Mar-4 Agra, Warsaw #27/R (P.Z 9500)
Works on paper
£355 $574 €500 Rothenburg ob de Tauber (32x48cm-13x19in) s. W/C. 23-May-3 Paul Kieffer, Pforzhiem #4846

GUO CHUANZHANG (1912-) Chinese
Works on paper
£1554 $2735 €2300 Mountain landscape with walker by water (101x32cm-40x13in) s.i. seals hanging scroll. 21-May-4 Dr Fritz Nagel, Stuttgart #1212/R est:300

GUO HANSHEN (1947-) Chinese
£2500 $4475 €3650 Tibet (139x64cm-55x25in) s. acrylic on paper hanging scroll. 6-May-4 Sotheby's, London #193/R est:2500-3500
Works on paper
£3000 $5370 €4380 Space (241x118cm-95x46in) i. ink acrylic hanging scroll. 6-May-4 Sotheby's, London #184/R est:3000-4000
£4000 $7160 €5840 Universal wisdom of Buddha (179x94cm-70x37in) ink acrylic. 6-May-4 Sotheby's, London #186/R est:4000-6000

GUO JIN (1964-) Chinese
£4000 $7360 €6000 Happy children (184x145cm-72x57in) s.d.1997 s.i.d. verso. 8-Jun-4 Sotheby's, Amsterdam #156/R est:6000-8000
£5690 $10242 €8307 Faces no 3, 6, 7, 9 (50x50cm-20x20in) s.d.2002. 25-Apr-4 Christie's, Hong Kong #742/R est:80000-120000 (HK.D 80000)

GUO WEI (1960-) Chinese
£2471 $4127 €3608 One way ticket (97x69cm-38x27in) s.d.2001 exhib.lit. 26-Oct-3 Christie's, Hong Kong #104/R est:32000-42000 (HK.D 32000)
£3201 $5761 €4673 Untitled (45x60cm-18x24in) s. oil paper three pieces. 25-Apr-4 Christie's, Hong Kong #770/R est:45000-55000 (HK.D 45000)

GUPPY, James (20th C) Australian
£620 $1054 €930 Memento Mori (60x60cm-24x24in) s. acrylic. 28-Oct-3 Goodman, Sydney #385/R (A.D 1500)

GURDON, Nora (1881-1974) Australian
£364 $587 €531 Hot evening (24x34cm-9x13in) s. board. 13-Oct-3 Joel, Victoria #421 (A.D 900)
£455 $841 €664 Winter day at Hurstbridge (35x23cm-14x9in) s. i.verso canvas on board prov. 10-Mar-4 Deutscher-Menzies, Melbourne #525/R est:800-1000 (A.D 1100)
£661 $1223 €965 At Kalorama (26x35cm-10x14in) s. panel. 10-Mar-4 Deutscher-Menzies, Melbourne #524/R est:1200-1500 (A.D 1600)
£820 $1295 €1197 Mistic Lake, Dandenongs (46x56cm-18x22in) 2-Sep-3 Deutscher-Menzies, Melbourne #350/R est:1500-2500 (A.D 2000)
£1157 $2140 €1689 Spring morning, Kalorama (41x53cm-16x21in) s. prov. 10-Mar-4 Deutscher-Menzies, Melbourne #523/R est:2000-3000 (A.D 2800)

GUREWICZ, Moses (1907-1944) Polish
£2933 $5309 €4400 Brother and sister reading (63x80cm-25x31in) s. 1-Apr-4 Van Ham, Cologne #1398/R est:3800

GURHOLT, Crispin (1965-) Norwegian
£852 $1465 €1244 Untitled (200x215cm-79x85in) s.verso exhib.lit. 8-Dec-3 Blomqvist, Oslo #583/R (N.KR 10000)

GURLITT, Louis (1812-1897) German
£645 $1078 €942 Study of goats in pine forest (26x30cm-10x12in) s.verso panel. 20-Oct-3 Blomqvist, Lysaker #1110 (N.KR 7500)
£1399 $2378 €2000 Italian coast near Sorrento at dusk (35x25cm-14x10in) s.d.1887. 20-Nov-3 Van Ham, Cologne #1608/R est:2000
£3514 $6289 €5200 Italian coastal in evening (25x35cm-10x14in) s.d.1887. 8-May-4 Hans Stahl, Toestorf #21/R est:4800
£5103 $8523 €7400 Testorf estate in east Holstein (63x90cm-25x35in) s.d.77 prov.lit. 15-Nov-3 Lempertz, Koln #1611/R est:3500
£16068 $27798 €23459 Coastal landscape from the Bay of Palermo, Sicily (27x43cm-11x17in) s.d.1846. 9-Dec-3 Rasmussen, Copenhagen #1244/R est:200000 (D.KR 170000)

GURNEY, James (1958-) American
£1557 $2600 €2273 Santa Claus (102x61cm-40x24in) s. 11-Oct-3 Nadeau, Windsor #212/R est:10000-15000

GURR, Lena (1897-?) American
£235 $425 €343 Self portrait (46x51cm-18x20in) s. oil on linen. 3-Apr-4 Outer Cape Auctions, Provincetown #85/R
£460 $750 €672 Floral still life (41x51cm-16x20in) s. board. 19-Jul-3 Outer Cape Auctions, Provincetown #91/R

GURREY, Hartley F (1907-1986) American
Works on paper
£363 $650 €530 Palm Springs, California landscape (53x74cm-21x29in) s. W/C. 16-Mar-4 Matthew's, Oregon #74/R

GURSCHNER, Gustav (1873-1971) Austrian
Sculpture
£2000 $3340 €2920 Figure (20cm-8in) s. pat bronze. 15-Oct-3 Christie's, Kensington #292/R
£2000 $3660 €2920 Draped nude (37cm-15in) bronze black marble pedestal. 3-Jun-4 Sotheby's, Olympia #113/R est:1500-2000

GURSCHNER, Herbert (1901-1975) Austrian
£490 $842 €700 Hilly landscape with farmhouse (14x9cm-6x4in) s. board. 4-Dec-3 Dorotheum, Graz #11/R
£524 $902 €750 Winter landscape with village church (12x7cm-5x3in) s. board. 4-Dec-3 Dorotheum, Graz #12/R
Works on paper
£470 $869 €700 Menton (32x25cm-13x10in) s.d.33 mixed media. 9-Mar-4 Dorotheum, Vienna #45/R

GURSKY, Andreas (1955-) German
£2083 $3542 €3000 Krefeld (33x26cm-13x10in) s.i.d.11/90 verso col Kodacolor lit. 31-Oct-3 Lempertz, Koln #378/R est:4000
£4335 $7500 €6329 Centre Georges Pompidou (54x70cm-21x28in) s.d.95 verso num.25 c-print one of 60 prov. 10-Dec-3 Phillips, New York #573/R est:4000-6000
£35000 $58450 €51100 Gelsenkirchen (131x167cm-52x66in) cibachrome print exec 1991 4 of edn of 5 prov.lit. 21-Oct-3 Sotheby's, London #318/R est:40000-60000
Photographs
£2297 $4112 €3400 Duisburg II (25x34cm-10x13in) s.i.d. verso col photo. 8-May-4 Lempertz, Koln #109/R est:2500
£2695 $4500 €3935 Ruhrspaziergang (103x181cm-41x71in) chromogenic col print. 16-Oct-3 Phillips, New York #66/R est:8000-12000
£3497 $5945 €5000 Madrid (33x26cm-13x10in) s.d.num.EA 1/3 verso col photo prov. 25-Nov-3 Tajan, Paris #85/R est:4000-6000
£3892 $6500 €5682 Acker Krefeld (201x291cm-79x115in) s.i.d.verso num.5/12 chromogenic col print. 16-Oct-3 Phillips, New York #67/R est:10000-15000
£3911 $7000 €5710 Centres Georges Pompidou (54x70cm-21x28in) s.d.10/95 num. of XXV verso c-print prov.lit. 14-May-4 Phillips, New York #309/R est:10000-15000
£4000 $7240 €5840 Centre Pompidou (54x70cm-21x28in) s.d.4.95 num.22/60 verso c-print. 1-Apr-4 Christie's, Kensington #330/R est:3000-5000
£4348 $7130 €6000 Klausenpass (30x39cm-12x15in) s.i.d. verso col photo lit. 30-May-3 Villa Grisebach, Berlin #1187/R est:4000-6000
£4500 $8280 €6570 Ohne titel (38x29cm-15x11in) s.i.d.1988 i.num.30/30 verso col photo. 24-Jun-4 Sotheby's, Olympia #440/R est:3000-4000
£4790 $8000 €6993 Salerno 1990 (34x44cm-13x17in) s.i.d.1990 cibachrome mounted on plexiglas prov.exhib.lit. 14-Nov-3 Phillips, New York #191/R est:8000-10000
£5587 $10000 €8157 Ruhrspaziergang (28x34cm-11x13in) col coupler print edition 4 of 10 prov. 12-May-4 Christie's, Rockefeller NY #441/R est:15000-20000
£5797 $9507 €8000 Rhine, Dusseldorf (29x37cm-11x15in) col photo. 30-May-3 Villa Grisebach, Berlin #1188/R est:4000-6000
£6587 $11000 €9617 Centre pompidou (52x38cm-20x15in) s.d.10/95 num.48/60 verso c-print prov.lit. 13-Nov-3 Sotheby's, New York #508/R est:10000-15000
£6886 $11500 €10054 Stadion, Krefeld (72x86cm-28x34in) s. colour photograph executed 1989 prov. 14-Nov-3 Phillips, New York #200/R est:8000-12000
£22455 $37500 €32784 Meerbusch, Krefeld (76x96cm-30x38in) c-print edition 2 of 12 prov. 13-Nov-3 Sotheby's, New York #502/R est:20000-30000
£27933 $50000 €40782 Untitled, II (180x216cm-71x85in) s.i.num. of six verso c-print prov.exhib.lit. 14-May-4 Phillips, New York #196/R est:50000-70000
£32934 $55000 €48084 Steiff, Hochstadt (137x242cm-54x95in) s.i.d.90 verso c-print artist's proof. 13-Nov-3 Sotheby's, New York #505/R est:70000-90000
£34637 $62000 €50570 Untitled, VII (186x224cm-73x88in) c-print plexiglas prov.exhib.lit. 14-May-4 Phillips, New York #190/R est:60000-80000
£35928 $60000 €52455 Hong Kong, Grand Hyatt Park (220x170cm-87x67in) c-print executed 1994 prov.exhib. 14-Nov-3 Phillips, New York #189/R est:60000-80000
£41916 $70000 €61197 Zurich V (131x154cm-52x61in) s.num.4/5 d.12/99 verso colour coupler prints diptych prov. 12-Nov-3 Christie's, Rockefeller NY #576/R est:80000-120000
£83799 $150000 €122347 Ayamonte (174x251cm-69x99in) s.i.d.97 num.5/6 colour coupler print prov.exhib.lit. 11-May-4 Christie's, Rockefeller NY #2/R est:150000-200000
£100000 $184000 €146000 May Day III (186x226cm-73x89in) s.i.d.98 3/6 color coupler print prov.lit. 24-Jun-4 Christie's, London #47/R est:100000-150000
£131285 $235000 €191676 Times Square (187x250cm-74x98in) s.i.d.97 num.6 c-print prov.exhib.lit. 13-May-4 Phillips, New York #62/R est:150000-200000
£155689 $260000 €227306 Prada II (166x316cm-65x124in) s.i.num.3/6 d.97 verso colour coupler print prov.exhib. 11-Nov-3 Christie's, Rockefeller NY #4/R est:200000-300000
£167665 $280000 €244791 Atlanta (186x256cm-73x101in) s.i.d.96 num.6 chromogenic color print prov.exhib.lit. 13-Nov-3 Phillips, New York #54/R est:180000-250000
£201117 $360000 €293631 Engadin (186x291cm-73x115in) s.i.d.1995 c-print prov.exhib.lit. 13-May-4 Phillips, New York #7/R est:200000-300000
£223464 $400000 €326257 Turner collection (236x176cm-93x69in) s.i.d.95 num.2/6 verso cibachrome print prov.exhib. 12-May-4 Sotheby's, New York #56/R est:150000-200000
£251497 $420000 €367186 Chicago, board of trade (186x242cm-73x95in) cibachrome print executed 1997 prov.lit. 12-Nov-3 Sotheby's, New York #34/R est:250000-350000

GURUWIRRI, Mithinari (1929-1976) Australian
Works on paper
£1406 $2630 €2109 Galpu yams at Caledon Bay (91x56cm-36x22in) earth pigments eucalyptus bark prov. 26-Jul-4 Sotheby's, Melbourne #232/R est:3500-4500 (A.D 3600)

GURVICH, Jose (1927-1974) Lithuanian
£412 $700 €602 Young woman (60x41cm-24x16in) 20-Nov-3 Galeria y Remates, Montevideo #209/R
£1059 $1800 €1546 Harbour (23x33cm-9x13in) cardboard. 25-Nov-3 Galeria y Remates, Montevideo #60/R
£1220 $2000 €1781 Abstract form in various colours (23x19cm-9x7in) s.d.60 panel. 3-Jun-3 Galeria y Remates, Montevideo #66
£1481 $2400 €2147 Hillside lunch (23x32cm-9x13in) s.d.60 board. 29-Jul-3 Galeria y Remates, Montevideo #74/R est:2700-3500
£1916 $3200 €2797 Still life (39x54cm-15x21in) s.d.53 cardboard. 7-Oct-3 Galeria y Remates, Montevideo #50/R
£2118 $3600 €3092 Card player (40x30cm-16x12in) s. cardboard. 25-Nov-3 Galeria y Remates, Montevideo #59/R
£2443 $4300 €3567 Still life (28x42cm-11x17in) cardboard. 5-Jan-4 Galeria y Remates, Montevideo #50/R est:4500-5500

£3409 $6000 €4977 Composition (26x36cm-10x14in) d.60 cardboard. 5-Jan-4 Galeria y Remates, Montevideo #48/R est:5000-6000
£4333 $7973 €6500 Still life (43x54cm-17x21in) s.d.52 cardboard. 10-Jun-4 Christie's, Paris #48/R est:5500-7500
£4469 $8000 €6525 Couple at table (41x45cm-16x18in) s.d.1950. 4-May-4 Arroyo, Buenos Aires #74/R est:3800
£5000 $8500 €7300 Bar Cafe (50x59cm-20x23in) s.d.1953 cardboard. 25-Nov-3 Galeria y Remates, Montevideo #57/R
£5587 $10000 €8157 Kibutz (27x43cm-11x17in) d.1957 board. 26-May-4 Sotheby's, New York #103/R est:10000-15000
£6707 $11000 €9792 Composition in black and white (50x63cm-20x25in) cardboard on canvas. 3-Jun-3 Galeria y Remates, Montevideo #64
Works on paper
£269 $450 €393 Still life (8x11cm-3x4in) s.d.1961 ink W/C. 7-Oct-3 Galeria y Remates, Montevideo #12
£333 $540 €483 The first reading (17x11cm-7x4in) s.d.1954 ink W/C prov. 29-Jul-3 Galeria y Remates, Montevideo #113
£4412 $7500 €6442 New York (30x44cm-12x17in) s.d.1971 W/C pencil. 25-Nov-3 Galeria y Remates, Montevideo #58/R

GUSH, William (attrib) (fl.1833-1874) British
£1500 $2685 €2190 Portrait of a lady in a white dress with a pink shawl and sash (76x63cm-30x25in) mono. 27-May-4 Christie's, Kensington #79/R est:1500-2000

GUSMAROLI, Riccardo (1963-) Italian
£2098 $3566 €3000 Sorrento coast and Capri (81x115cm-32x45in) s.d.2003 paper boat. 24-Nov-3 Christie's, Milan #62/R est:2200-2800

GUSSONI, Vittorio (1893-1968) Italian
£369 $653 €550 Landscape (17x24cm-7x9in) s. i.verso board. 1-May-4 Meeting Art, Vercelli #127
£1408 $2437 €2000 Maternity (50x43cm-20x17in) s. board. 9-Dec-3 Finarte Semenzato, Milan #106/R est:2000-2200
£1449 $2377 €2000 Portrait of woman at bar (60x50cm-24x20in) s. 27-May-3 Il Ponte, Milan #525/R
£1667 $2733 €2300 Lady in red dress (50x40cm-20x16in) s. card. 27-May-3 Il Ponte, Milan #535/R
£1831 $3168 €2600 Fruit and flowers on table (60x73cm-24x29in) s. 9-Dec-3 Finarte Semenzato, Milan #29/R est:2800
£1884 $3090 €2600 Portrait of woman at theatre (60x50cm-24x20in) s. 27-May-3 Il Ponte, Milan #523/R
£2215 $3964 €3300 Still life on the table (40x50cm-16x20in) s. 30-May-4 Meeting Art, Vercelli #84 est:3000

GUSSOW, Bernard (1881-1957) American
£241 $425 €352 Church at night (58x48cm-23x19in) s. 1-Jan-4 Quinn's, Falls Church #293/R
£434 $750 €634 Bordentown, NJ (51x104cm-20x41in) s. i.verso board. 10-Dec-3 Alderfer's, Hatfield #506
Works on paper
£870 $1600 €1270 Union Square at night (58x46cm-23x18in) s. col pastel. 10-Jun-4 Swann Galleries, New York #114/R est:1500-2500

GUSSOW, Ulrich (20th C) German?
£559 $951 €800 Female nude holding a fruit platter (66x56cm-26x22in) s.d.33-39. 28-Nov-3 Wendl, Rudolstadt #3983/R

GUSTAVSON, Henry (1864-?) American
£741 $1400 €1082 Landscape eucalyptus and flowerfield (46x61cm-18x24in) s. board prov. 17-Feb-4 John Moran, Pasadena #151/R est:2000-3000

GUSTAVSON, Herman (19/20th C) American
£278 $500 €406 California hills (68x55cm-27x22in) s. 25-Apr-4 Bonhams & Butterfields, San Francisco #5510/R
£361 $650 €527 Path through the oaks (45x61cm-18x24in) s. 25-Apr-4 Bonhams & Butterfields, San Francisco #5511/R

GUSTON, Philip (1913-1980) American
£178771 $320000 €261006 Scale (193x190cm-76x75in) s. s.i.d.1961 verso prov.exhib. 12-May-4 Christie's, Rockefeller NY #130/R est:150000-200000
£256983 $460000 €375195 Painting on floor (153x133cm-60x52in) s. s.i.d.1978 verso prov. 12-May-4 Christie's, Rockefeller NY #180/R est:200000-300000
£586592 $1050000 €856424 Waking up (170x328cm-67x129in) s. s.i.d.1975 verso prov.exhib. 11-May-4 Christie's, Rockefeller NY #19/R est:1000000-1500000
£754190 $1350000 €1101117 Untitled (81x91cm-32x36in) s. painted 1952 prov.exhib. 12-May-4 Sotheby's, New York #23/R est:400000-800000
Prints
£2260 $4000 €3300 Rug (50x74cm-20x29in) s.i.d.1981 num.38/50 lithograph. 28-Apr-4 Christie's, Rockefeller NY #285/R est:3000-4000
£2542 $4500 €3711 Elements (83x108cm-33x43in) s.i.d.1980 num.38/50 lithograph. 28-Apr-4 Christie's, Rockefeller NY #280/R est:4000-6000
£2712 $4800 €3960 Car (51x76cm-20x30in) s.i.d.1980 num.38/50 lithograph. 28-Apr-4 Christie's, Rockefeller NY #284/R est:2500-3500
£2712 $4800 €3960 Shoes (51x76cm-20x30in) s.i.d.1981 num.18/50 lithograph. 28-Apr-4 Christie's, Rockefeller NY #291/R est:2000-3000
£3672 $6500 €5361 Summer (51x76cm-20x30in) s.i.d.1980 num.38/50 lithograph. 28-Apr-4 Christie's, Rockefeller NY #283/R est:2500-3500
£3672 $6500 €5361 Door (51x76cm-20x30in) s.i.d.1981 num.18/50 lithograph. 28-Apr-4 Christie's, Rockefeller NY #292/R est:3000-4000
£3955 $7000 €5774 Room (83x108cm-33x43in) s.i.d.1980 num.38/50 lithograph. 28-Apr-4 Christie's, Rockefeller NY #279/R est:4000-6000
£3955 $7000 €5774 Curtain (78x103cm-31x41in) s.i.d.1980 num.18/50 lithograph. 28-Apr-4 Christie's, Rockefeller NY #287/R est:4000-6000
£4237 $7500 €6186 Studio corner (81x108cm-32x43in) s.i.d.1981 num.18/50 lithograph. 28-Apr-4 Christie's, Rockefeller NY #289/R est:4000-6000
£4520 $8000 €6599 Coat (81x108cm-32x43in) s.i.d.1980 num.38/50 lithograph. 28-Apr-4 Christie's, Rockefeller NY #282/R est:4000-6000
£5085 $9000 €7424 Sea (78x103cm-31x41in) s.i.d.1980 num.38/50 lithograph. 28-Apr-4 Christie's, Rockefeller NY #278/R est:4000-6000
£6215 $11000 €9074 East side (83x108cm-33x43in) s.i.d.1980 num.38/50 lithograph. 28-Apr-4 Christie's, Rockefeller NY #281/R est:4000-6000
Works on paper
£973 $1800 €1421 Summer. s.verso pencil dr. 18-Jan-4 Carlsen Gallery, Greenville #495/R
£3800 $6992 €5548 22 February (48x64cm-19x25in) s.i. pen ink exec.c.1976-78 prov. 24-Jun-4 Sotheby's, Olympia #477/R est:2000-3000
£44910 $75000 €65569 Untitled (46x61cm-18x24in) s.d.68 chl prov. 12-Nov-3 Christie's, Rockefeller NY #324/R est:60000-80000
£47904 $80000 €69940 Untitled (46x61cm-18x24in) s.d.68 chl prov.exhib. 12-Nov-3 Christie's, Rockefeller NY #325/R est:50000-70000
£125749 $210000 €183594 Drawing (45x60cm-18x24in) s. brush ink prov.exhib. 11-Nov-3 Christie's, Rockefeller NY #12/R est:80000-120000

GUTAHAZA, Gyula Nemeth (19th C) Hungarian
£324 $600 €473 Still life with grapes (23x30cm-9x12in) s. board. 13-Mar-4 Susanin's, Chicago #6199/R

GUTEKUNST, Johann Georg Adam Gottlob (attrib) (1801-1858) German
£5208 $8490 €7500 Fortune telling in Betzingen (52x59cm-20x23in) mono.d.1848 verso. 25-Sep-3 Dr Fritz Nagel, Stuttgart #1351/R est:6800

GUTERSLOH, Albert Paris (1887-1973) Austrian
Works on paper
£1119 $1902 €1600 Funeral wake for mother and wife (11x10cm-4x4in) s.i.d.71 mixed media. 26-Nov-3 Dorotheum, Vienna #238/R est:1800-2400
£2222 $3622 €3200 Egon Schiele (45x29cm-18x11in) mono. s.i.verso pencil. 23-Sep-3 Wiener Kunst Auktionen, Vienna #76/R est:1500-3000
£3007 $5112 €4300 First letter (17x15cm-7x6in) s.i.d.1925 mixed media. 25-Nov-3 Hassfurther, Vienna #34/R est:3800-4200

GUTFREUND, Otto (1889-1927) Czechoslovakian
Sculpture
£2195 $3731 €3205 Toilette (44cm-17in) pat plaster. 29-Nov-3 Dorotheum, Prague #217/R est:100000-150000 (C.KR 100000)
Works on paper
£340 $588 €496 Cubist still life of glass and spoon (29x39cm-11x15in) pencil. 9-Dec-3 Rosebery Fine Art, London #648/R

GUTHERZ, Carl (1844-1907) American/Swiss
£279 $500 €407 Portrait of a lady (69x56cm-27x22in) s.d.1899. 8-May-4 Susanin's, Chicago #6044/R
£391 $700 €571 Portrait of a man (69x56cm-27x22in) s.d.1899. 8-May-4 Susanin's, Chicago #6043/R

GUTHRIE, James (1859-1930) British
£582 $913 €844 Farmhouse, possibly European (17x24cm-7x9in) i.verso. 27-Aug-3 Dunbar Sloane, Wellington #94 (NZ.D 1600)
£820 $1337 €1197 Portrait of a young woman wearing a red ribbon in her hair (50x40cm-20x16in) s.d.1926 canvasboard. 24-Sep-3 Dreweatt Neate, Newbury #192

GUTHRIE, William (19th C) British
£460 $782 €672 Wooded landscape with mountains (60x90cm-24x35in) s. 10-Nov-3 Thomson Roddick & Medcalf, Edinburgh #263/R

GUTIERREZ DE LA VEGA, Jose (?-1865) Spanish
£9362 $15166 €13200 Virgin with baby (100x71cm-39x28in) s.d.1857. 20-May-3 Ansorena, Madrid #86/R est:13200

GUTIERREZ MONTIEL, Juan (1934-) Spanish
£1931 $3476 €2800 Before going out (118x162cm-46x64in) s. s.i.verso. 26-Jan-4 Ansorena, Madrid #913/R est:1800
Works on paper
£254 $450 €371 Family group of man, woman and child (74x94cm-29x37in) s. mixed media exec.c.1970. 1-May-4 Thomaston Place, Thomaston #888/R

GUTIERREZ NAVAS, Concha Maria (1926-) Spanish
£274 $466 €400 Jesus and the Apostles (100x80cm-39x31in) s. 4-Nov-3 Ansorena, Madrid #874/R

GUTIERREZ SOLANA, Jose (1886-1945) Spanish
Works on paper
£5034 $9362 €7500 Looking at the procession (16x25cm-6x10in) s. chl dr. 2-Mar-4 Ansorena, Madrid #324/R est:1800

GUTIERREZ, Ernesto (1873-1934) Spanish
£870 $1426 €1200 Rio de Cuenca (60x48cm-24x19in) s.d.1927. 27-May-3 Durán, Madrid #135/R
£1172 $1958 €1700 View of Madrid from Toledo bridge (27x19cm-11x7in) s.d.1899 board. 17-Nov-3 Durán, Madrid #72/R est:700
£1377 $2258 €1900 Landscape of Cuenca (60x48cm-24x19in) s.d.1927. 27-May-3 Durán, Madrid #134/R est:1200
£2280 $4014 €3375 Scene in Granada (18x40cm-7x16in) s.i. 18-May-4 Segre, Madrid #87/R est:4000

GUTIERREZ, Ramon (20th C) Spanish
£263 $476 €400 Playing the cello (46x55cm-18x22in) s.d.02 s.i.verso. 14-Apr-4 Ansorena, Madrid #99/R

GUTMAN, Nachum (1898-1978) Israeli

£6928	$11500	€10115	Fishermen (41x47cm-16x19in) s. board on board prov.exhib. 2-Oct-3 Christie's, Tel Aviv #61/R est:12000-16000
£7831	$13000	€11433	Mending the nets (38x46cm-15x18in) s. prov. 2-Oct-3 Christie's, Tel Aviv #68/R est:12000-16000
£12088	$22000	€18132	Figures in an alley in Zaffed (35x28cm-14x11in) s. 1-Jul-4 Ben-Ami, Tel Aviv #4924/R est:25000-30000
£18033	$33000	€26328	Jaffa port (38x46cm-15x18in) s. painted c.1930. 1-Feb-4 Ben-Ami, Tel Aviv #4633/R est:35000-45000
£23743	$42500	€34665	Carriage ride by the Jaffa port (53x73cm-21x29in) s. painted c.1960. 18-Mar-4 Sotheby's, New York #6/R est:40000-60000

Works on paper

£221	$400	€323	Man writing (21x16cm-8x6in) s. pencil. 1-Apr-4 Ben-Ami, Tel Aviv #4736/R
£784	$1404	€1145	Figures in a park (33x46cm-13x18in) s. W/C. 31-May-4 Stephan Welz, Johannesburg #88 (SA.R 9500)
£1593	$2900	€2390	Riders by the trees (28x37cm-11x15in) s. W/C exec.c.1940 prov.exhib. 1-Jul-4 Ben-Ami, Tel Aviv #4996/R est:3000-4000
£3073	$5500	€4487	At the beach (23x29cm-9x11in) s.d.68 W/C pencil. 18-Mar-4 Sotheby's, New York #2/R est:3000-4000
£3536	$6400	€5163	Boats and fishermen (23x29cm-9x11in) s. W/C exec. c.1950. 1-Apr-4 Ben-Ami, Tel Aviv #4763/R est:4000-6000
£3898	$6900	€5691	Police building in Jaffa (36x55cm-14x22in) s. W/C executed c.1920 prov. 1-May-4 Ben-Ami, Tel Aviv #4830/R est:7000-9000
£4518	$7500	€6596	Behind the curtain (50x34cm-20x13in) s.d.60 gouache W/C wax crayons brush India ink. 2-Oct-3 Christie's, Tel Aviv #58/R est:8000-12000
£7229	$12000	€10554	Succoth in Safed (52x68cm-20x27in) s. W/C over pencil prov. 2-Oct-3 Christie's, Tel Aviv #9/R est:7000-9000
£7263	$13000	€10604	Jaffa port (47x68cm-19x27in) s.d.52 W/C prov. 18-Mar-4 Sotheby's, New York #1/R est:8000-12000

GUTMANN, Bernhard (1869-1936) American

£1196	$2200	€1746	Nude in blue interior (46x38cm-18x15in) s.d.1912. 11-Jun-4 David Rago, Lambertville #334/R est:1500-2000

GUTMANN, John (1904-) American

Photographs

£5085	$9000	€7424	Dream of uprising (17x23cm-7x9in) photo prov. 28-Apr-4 Sotheby's, New York #118/R est:5000-8000

GUTMANN, Viktor (1887-1963) Italian

£284	$474	€400	View south towards Salzburg (36x49cm-14x19in) s. 16-Oct-3 Dorotheum, Salzburg #629/R

GUTSCHMIDT, Richard (1861-?) German

£414	$691	€600	Teufelssee (63x80cm-25x31in) s. 15-Nov-3 Von Zezschwitz, Munich #40/R

GUTTENBRUNN, Ludwig (18th C) German

£3000	$5100	€4380	Portrait of a lady as Hebe (26x20cm-10x8in) s.d.1788 panel. 31-Oct-3 Christie's, Kensington #81/R est:3000-5000

GUTTUSO, Renato (1912-1987) Italian

£2797	$4755	€4000	Untitled (59x31cm-23x12in) s. 24-Nov-3 Christie's, Milan #198/R est:4000-6000
£3623	$5942	€5000	Portrait of Jean Paul Sartre (55x65cm-22x26in) s.d.78 s.i. verso. 27-May-3 Il Ponte, Milan #408 est:5000-6000
£4667	$8353	€7000	Workman smiling (65x54cm-26x21in) s. painted 1962 prov.lit. 12-May-4 Stadion, Trieste #690/R est:16000-20000
£5333	$9813	€8000	Woman ironing (98x66cm-39x26in) s.d.1974 tempera paper. 8-Jun-4 Finarte Semenzato, Milan #373/R est:5000-6000
£5594	$9510	€8000	Model (45x63cm-18x25in) s.d.67 tempera oil paper on canvas prov.lit. 24-Nov-3 Christie's, Milan #271/R est:10000-15000
£6667	$11933	€10000	Figure (73x60cm-29x24in) s. s.d.62 verso prov. 12-May-4 Stadion, Trieste #724/R est:16000-20000
£6757	$11892	€10000	Mountain (52x102cm-20x40in) s. paper on canvas. 24-May-4 Christie's, Milan #167/R est:7000-10000
£7333	$13127	€11000	Portrait of girl (66x54cm-26x21in) s. prov. 12-May-4 Stadion, Trieste #689/R est:16000-20000
£10345	$17276	€15000	Cart on Milicia road (40x47cm-16x19in) s.d.1929 board exhib. lit. 13-Nov-3 Finarte Semenzato, Rome #405/R est:14000-16000
£11034	$18428	€16000	Sicilian peasant on horseback (79x65cm-31x26in) s. paper on canvas prov.lit. 13-Nov-3 Finarte Semenzato, Rome #447/R est:18000-20000
£11189	$18685	€16000	Still life (54x64cm-21x25in) s.s.d.verso prov.lit. 26-Jun-3 Sant Agostino, Torino #256/R est:14000-18000
£12587	$21399	€18000	Portrait of woman (100x81cm-39x32in) s.s.verso prov.lit. 24-Nov-3 Christie's, Milan #250/R est:20000-30000
£13793	$23034	€20000	Seated woman (64x56cm-25x22in) s. s.d.1961 verso. 17-Nov-3 Sant Agostino, Torino #268/R est:20000-25000
£14000	$25200	€21000	Steel factory in Piombino (104x58cm-41x23in) s. paper on canvas prov. 22-Apr-4 Finarte Semenzato, Rome #308/R est:20000-22000
£14667	$26400	€22000	Sulphur mine workers (52x28cm-20x11in) s.d.48 s.d.verso prov.exhib.lit. 22-Apr-4 Finarte Semenzato, Rome #370/R est:18000-20000
£16084	$27343	€23000	The Crocchio bending (55x75cm-22x30in) s. i.d.1937 verso board lit. 29-Nov-3 Farsetti, Prato #528/R est:15000
£18881	$32098	€27000	Nude (103x145cm-41x57in) s.d.1958 exhib.lit. 29-Nov-3 Farsetti, Prato #529/R est:15000
£20290	$33275	€28000	Vase with fruit and candle holder (51x33cm-20x13in) s. board lit. 27-May-3 Sotheby's, Milan #241/R est:22000-28000
£20979	$35664	€30000	Massacre (44x60cm-17x24in) s.d.41 prov.exhib. 24-Nov-3 Christie's, Milan #325/R est:30000-40000
£22378	$38042	€32000	Children on the beach (45x55cm-18x22in) d.55 verso lit. 26-Nov-3 Pandolfini, Florence #94/R est:32000-35000
£22378	$38042	€32000	Women making tomato paste (48x60cm-19x24in) s. s.d.1948 verso. 25-Nov-3 Sotheby's, Milan #203/R est:25000-30000
£24161	$43248	€36000	Roofs in Palermo (81x70cm-32x28in) s. painted 1976 exhib.lit. 29-May-4 Farsetti, Prato #469/R est:35000-45000
£24832	$46188	€37000	Still life with bottles and cigars (74x92cm-29x36in) s. s.verso painted 1961 prov.lit. 4-Mar-4 Babuino, Rome #494 est:20000-25000
£25503	$45651	€38000	Woman sitting by the sea (100x100cm-39x39in) s.d.50 s.d.verso lit. 29-May-4 Farsetti, Prato #472/R est:35000-50000
£26087	$42783	€36000	Spiaggia (50x75cm-20x30in) s. s.d.1950 verso lit. 31-May-3 Farsetti, Prato #689/R est:30000-40000
£26667	$48000	€40000	Window overseeing green (79x64cm-31x25in) s.d.46 s.d.verso. 22-Apr-4 Finarte Semenzato, Rome #369/R est:32000-35000
£30872	$55262	€46000	Hamburg (73x60cm-29x24in) s.d.68 s.i.d.verso lit. 29-May-4 Farsetti, Prato #475/R est:40000-55000
£33566	$57063	€48000	Still life (65x50cm-26x20in) s. prov.lit. 24-Nov-3 Christie's, Milan #326/R est:20000-30000
£43478	$71304	€60000	Peasant (95x40cm-37x16in) s.d.1935 board. 29-May-3 Galleria Pace, Milan #136/R est:90000
£50000	$88000	€74000	Scilla (84x78cm-33x31in) s.d.50 s.i.d.verso lit. 24-May-4 Christie's, Milan #330/R est:50000-70000
£67114	$120134	€100000	Roofs in Alcamo (130x153cm-51x60in) s. oil pencil paper on canvas prov.exhib.lit. 25-May-4 Sotheby's, Milan #259/R est:90000-120000
£97315	$174195	€145000	Spaghetti eater (87x80cm-34x31in) s. s.i.d.1956 verso exhib.lit. 29-May-4 Farsetti, Prato #482/R est:60000-70000

Works on paper

£333	$613	€500	Profile (30x21cm-12x8in) s. Chinese ink. 8-Jun-4 Finarte Semenzato, Milan #151/R
£503	$936	€750	Female nude (49x29cm-19x11in) s.d.1947 Chinese ink card. 4-Mar-4 Babuino, Rome #371
£521	$823	€750	Study (22x18cm-9x7in) pencil. 6-Sep-3 Meeting Art, Vercelli #409
£533	$981	€800	Cat (12x15cm-5x6in) s. Chinese ink felt-tip pen dr. 11-Jun-4 Farsetti, Prato #105
£671	$1248	€1000	Mimi, the artist's wife (44x29cm-17x11in) s. ink card. 4-Mar-4 Babuino, Rome #369
£867	$1595	€1300	Female nude (20x26cm-8x10in) s.d.56 Chinese ink. 8-Jun-4 Finarte Semenzato, Milan #156/R
£972	$1789	€1460	Woman (22x30cm-9x12in) s. ink prov. 14-Jun-4 Porro, Milan #19/R
£1000	$1840	€1500	Female nude (22x32cm-9x13in) s.d.1941 Chinese ink. 8-Jun-4 Finarte Semenzato, Milan #155/R est:1500-2000
£1067	$1963	€1600	Female nudes (39x13cm-15x5in) s. ink pair. 8-Jun-4 Finarte Semenzato, Milan #150/R est:1200-1400
£1074	$1997	€1600	Lady on deckchair (36x52cm-14x20in) s.d.1957 Chinese ink pencil. 4-Mar-4 Babuino, Rome #62
£1133	$2085	€1700	Study of nude (41x30cm-16x12in) s. Chinese ink exec.1938. 8-Jun-4 Finarte Semenzato, Milan #149/R est:1500-2000
£1133	$2085	€1700	Three doves (29x38cm-11x15in) s.i.d.1980 felt-tip pen. 10-Jun-4 Galleria Pace, Milan #124/R est:2500
£1267	$2280	€1900	Study of hands (28x22cm-11x9in) s. Chinese ink. 22-Apr-4 Finarte Semenzato, Rome #207/R est:1800-2400
£1267	$2331	€1900	Study (27x21cm-11x8in) s.d.1940 ink. 8-Jun-4 Finarte Semenzato, Milan #153/R est:2000-2500
£1293	$2314	€1900	Fmale face (44x31cm-17x12in) s.d.1968 Chinese ink dr. 22-Mar-4 Sant Agostino, Torino #413/R est:2200
£1443	$2669	€2150	Dance (27x21cm-11x8in) s.d.1949 Chinese ink W/C paper on board. 13-Mar-4 Meeting Art, Vercelli #154 est:1000
£1467	$2699	€2200	Peasant woman (50x35cm-20x14in) s. pencil Chinese ink. 12-Jun-4 Meeting Art, Vercelli #582/R est:750
£1586	$2649	€2300	Model (54x43cm-21x17in) s. Chinese ink W/C. 13-Nov-3 Finarte Semenzato, Rome #126 est:1400-1800
£1722	$3134	€2600	Virgin (50x36cm-20x14in) s.d.77 mixed media paper on canvas. 21-Jun-4 Pandolfini, Florence #337/R est:1600-1800
£1748	$2972	€2500	Reclining female nude (50x70cm-20x28in) s. Chinese ink paper on canvas prov. 25-Nov-3 Sotheby's, Milan #36/R est:2200-2800
£1748	$2920	€2500	Nude (26x30cm-10x12in) s. Chinese ink W/C. 26-Jun-3 Sant Agostino, Torino #177/R est:2500-3000
£1837	$3288	€2700	Composition (27x22cm-11x9in) s. Chinese ink W/C exec.1947 exhib. 22-Mar-4 Sant Agostino, Torino #414/R est:2200
£1862	$3110	€2700	Figure (50x36cm-20x14in) s. Chinese ink. 13-Nov-3 Finarte Semenzato, Rome #125 est:2500-3000
£1916	$3257	€2740	Standing nude (51x20cm-20x8in) s. Chinese ink prov. 18-Nov-3 Babuino, Rome #226/R est:800-1000
£1933	$3480	€2900	Footballers (67x63cm-26x25in) s. mixed media exec.1983 prov.exhib. 22-Apr-4 Finarte Semenzato, Rome #134/R est:2800-3500
£1933	$3480	€2900	Maternity (43x32cm-17x13in) s.verso Chinese ink oval. 22-Apr-4 Finarte Semenzato, Rome #208/R est:2800-3500
£2042	$3390	€2900	Screaming woman (49x72cm-19x28in) s. Chinese ink dr card. 13-Jun-3 Farsetti, Prato #71/R
£2133	$3840	€3200	Labourers (32x45cm-13x18in) s. ink exec.1949 lit. 22-Apr-4 Finarte Semenzato, Rome #209 est:2000-2500
£2333	$4293	€3500	Woman resting (50x70cm-20x28in) s. pencil. 8-Jun-4 Finarte Semenzato, Milan #374/R est:2500-3000
£2413	$4101	€3450	Couples (40x59cm-16x23in) s.d.1969 Chinese ink prov. 18-Nov-3 Babuino, Rome #455/R est:1400-1800
£2657	$4517	€3800	Devils' battle (50x36cm-20x14in) s. Chinese ink gouache. 24-Nov-3 Christie's, Milan #22/R est:1500-2000
£2685	$4993	€4000	Cubist portrait (33x22cm-13x9in) s.d.1946 Chinese ink W/C. 4-Mar-4 Babuino, Rome #103 est:1200-1800
£2727	$4691	€3900	Les furies (72x50cm-28x20in) s.d.1960 gouache W/C ink cardboard. 3-Dec-3 Tajan, Paris #446 est:4000-5000
£2727	$4691	€3900	Le combat (67x49cm-26x19in) s.d.1969 W/C ink. 3-Dec-3 Tajan, Paris #447 est:4000-5000
£2759	$4607	€4000	Figure running. Girl with mini-skirt (16x30cm-6x12in) s. Chinese ink two. 13-Nov-3 Finarte Semenzato, Rome #170/R est:2000-3000
£2819	$5215	€4200	Anglers (31x20cm-12x8in) s. Chinese ink. 11-Mar-4 Galleria Pace, Milan #88/R est:5000-7000
£2838	$4995	€4200	Trees (32x24cm-13x9in) s. W/C chl exec.1967-68. 24-May-4 Christie's, Milan #125/R est:2500-3000
£3221	$5766	€4800	Dance (35x50cm-14x20in) s.i.d.49 W/C Chinese ink card. 25-May-4 Sotheby's, Milan #16/R est:4000
£3333	$6133	€5000	Female nudes (56x37cm-22x15in) s.d.1963 gouache paper on canvas. 8-Jun-4 Finarte Semenzato, Milan #439/R est:5000-6000
£3333	$6133	€5000	Woman (68x47cm-27x19in) s. W/C gouache. 8-Jun-4 Finarte Semenzato, Milan #440/R est:5000-6000
£3819	$6035	€5500	Two women reclining and heads (50x70cm-20x28in) mixed media card. 6-Sep-3 Meeting Art, Vercelli #653 est:5000
£3846	$6538	€5500	Figures (52x46cm-20x18in) s.i. W/C Chinese ink pencil. 25-Nov-3 Sotheby's, Milan #40/R est:3500-4500
£3873	$6430	€5500	Untitled (41x59cm-16x23in) s. Indian ink tempera acrylic paper on canvas. 14-Jun-3 Meeting Art, Vercelli #186/R est:5000
£3919	$6897	€5800	Portrait of woman with stockings (50x36cm-20x14in) s. Chinese ink W/C paper on canvas exec.1970-71. 24-May-4 Christie's, Milan #24/R est:3000-4000
£3944	$6546	€5600	Medusa (52x36cm-20x14in) s. mixed media paper on canvas executed 1972. 14-Jun-3 Meeting Art, Vercelli #141/R

£4514 $7132 €6500 La Scala, Milan (50x70cm-20x28in) gouache collage exec.1978. 6-Sep-3 Meeting Art, Vercelli #713 est:6000
£4698 $8409 €7000 Dance (35x48cm-14x19in) s.i.d.1949 Chinese ink W/C. 25-May-4 Sotheby's, Milan #17/R est:4000
£5594 $9510 €8000 Portrait of Marta Marzotto (58x69cm-23x27in) s. Chinese ink W/C acrylic card on canvas. 24-Nov-3 Christie's, Milan #130/R est:6000-8000
£7931 $13245 €11500 Summer in Anacapri (51x68cm-20x27in) s.i.d.1953 mixed media paper on canvas. 17-Nov-3 Sant Agostino, Torino #194/R est:10000-12000

GUY, Jean Baptiste Louis (1824-1888) Italian
£780 $1303 €1100 Landscape with bull and cows (78x120cm-31x47in) s.d.1879 board. 14-Oct-3 Finarte Semenzato, Milan #59/R

GUY, Louis (1824-1886) French
£1915 $3198 €2700 Fantasia (29x38cm-11x15in) s.d.1885 panel. 19-Oct-3 Anaf, Lyon #169/R est:3000-4000

GUY, Seymour (1824-1910) American
£13580 $22000 €19691 School troubles (47x39cm-19x15in) s. 8-Aug-3 Barridorf, Portland #350/R est:12000-15000
£34884 $60000 €50931 Unconscious of danger (51x41cm-20x16in) mono.i.d.1865. 4-Dec-3 Christie's, Rockefeller NY #25/R
Works on paper
£615 $1100 €898 Fairies in the wood (20cm-8in circular) s. W/C. 16-May-4 CRN Auctions, Cambridge #30/R

GUYARD, Eugene (1901-1970) French
£276 $505 €400 La rafle (38x46cm-15x18in) s. 2-Feb-4 Millon & Associes, Paris #101
£276 $505 €400 Legumes de jardin (50x61cm-20x24in) s. isorel. 2-Feb-4 Millon & Associes, Paris #109
£276 $505 €400 Reflets (105x87cm-41x34in) s. exhib. 2-Feb-4 Millon & Associes, Paris #112
£400 $732 €580 Pirogue Africaine (123x61cm-48x24in) s. 2-Feb-4 Millon & Associes, Paris #113
£448 $820 €650 Jeux d'enfants (50x65cm-20x26in) s. 2-Feb-4 Millon & Associes, Paris #110/R
£552 $1010 €800 Le mineur (57x49cm-22x19in) s. 2-Feb-4 Millon & Associes, Paris #104
£828 $1514 €1200 Les clochards (93x74cm-37x29in) s. 2-Feb-4 Millon & Associes, Paris #111/R

GUYATT, Richard (1914-) British
Works on paper
£6000 $9540 €8760 Racing motorists prefer shell (51x96cm-20x38in) pastel gouache collage exhib.lit. 10-Sep-3 Sotheby's, Olympia #82/R est:800-1200

GUYEN KHANG (1912-1987) Vietnamese
Works on paper
£1300 $2171 €1898 Seated lady holding hat (51x48cm-20x19in) s. W/C on silk. 14-Nov-3 Christie's, Kensington #279/R est:800-1200

GUYMALA, Namerredje (1926-1978) Australian
Works on paper
£2642 $4175 €3857 Ngalyod and Ngalkunburriyaymi (84x52cm-33x20in) earth pigments eucalyptus bark exec.c.1972 prov.exhib.lit. 28-Jul-3 Sotheby's, Paddington #248/R est:4000-6000 (A.D 6500)

GUYOMARD, Gerard (1936-) French
£1007 $1782 €1500 Paul McCartney (73x54cm-29x21in) s.d.9 78 acrylic. 28-Apr-4 Artcurial Briest, Paris #405/R est:1500-2000
£1361 $2435 €2000 Samedi matin, quelque part a Versailles (162x130cm-64x51in) s.d.83. 19-Mar-4 Millon & Associes, Paris #183/R est:2000-3000
£2222 $3712 €3200 Rock no.30 (162x130cm-64x51in) s. acrylic collage. 21-Oct-3 Artcurial Briest, Paris #560/R est:2000-2500
£2533 $4661 €3800 Tournis (151x108cm-59x43in) s.d.1979 s.i.d. verso. 9-Jun-4 Artcurial Briest, Paris #510/R est:4500-5000
£2778 $4583 €4000 La strategie de l'atelier no 58 (97x130cm-38x51in) s.i.d.1989 acrylic. 2-Jul-3 Cornette de St.Cyr, Paris #131/R est:4000-5000
Works on paper
£2684 $4751 €4000 Lunettes (130x195cm-51x77in) mixed media canvas exec 1992 exhib. 28-Apr-4 Artcurial Briest, Paris #406/R est:4000-5000

GUYON, Maximilienne (1868-1903) French
Works on paper
£331 $603 €500 Beggar (41x25cm-16x10in) s. W/C. 21-Jun-4 Pandolfini, Florence #236/R

GUYOT, Georges Lucien (1885-1973) French
£769 $1308 €1100 Le geai ou nature morte au gibier (72x54cm-28x21in) s. isorel panel. 27-Nov-3 Millon & Associes, Paris #211
£1208 $2247 €1800 Cage a oiseau et vase chinois (60x73cm-24x29in) s. 2-Mar-4 Artcurial Briest, Paris #223 est:2000-2500
£2113 $3507 €3000 A la croisee des chemins, le Calvaire (59x78cm-23x31in) s.d.1925. 11-Jun-3 Delorme & Bocage, Paris #56/R est:3000-3500
£3636 $6182 €5200 Ours polaire (54x74cm-21x29in) s. 1-Dec-3 Camard, Paris #57/R est:4000-4500
Sculpture
£1133 $2085 €1700 Couple (16x21cm-6x8in) s. black pat bronze. 10-Jun-4 Camard, Paris #121/R est:1500-2000
£3691 $5943 €5500 Lion furieux (22cm-9in) s. brown pat bronze Cast Susse. 23-Feb-3 St-Germain-en-Laye Encheres #114/R est:5000-5500
£5822 $9897 €8500 Lion assis (24x31cm-9x12in) s. brown pat bronze. 5-Nov-3 Rabourdin & Choppin de Janvry, Paris #12/R est:6000-7500
£6993 $12028 €10000 Lionne aux aguets (31x58cm-12x23in) s.st.f.Susse brown pat bronze. 3-Dec-3 Tajan, Paris #297/R est:3000-3800
£8054 $12966 €12000 Panthere se lechant (33cm-13in) s.num.4/12 brown pat bronze. 23-Feb-3 St-Germain-en-Laye Encheres #102/R est:10000-12000
£8451 $14789 €12000 Panthere noire (34x34x12cm-13x13x5in) s. pat bronze prov.lit. 18-Dec-3 Tajan, Paris #23/R est:9000-10000
£9091 $15455 €13000 Panthere (34x50cm-13x20in) st.f.Susse pat bronze lit. 18-Nov-3 Sotheby's, Paris #122/R est:6000-8000
£9200 $16652 €13800 Panthere humant (34x50x13cm-13x20x5in) s.st.f.Susse pat bronze. 1-Apr-4 Millon & Associes, Paris #11/R est:7000-8000
Works on paper
£300 $540 €450 Etude de felins (19x24cm-7x9in) s. black crayon prov. 26-Apr-4 Tajan, Paris #10/R
£479 $815 €700 Ours brun (12x23cm-5x9in) s.i. sepia wash. 5-Nov-3 Rabourdin & Choppin de Janvry, Paris #1
£548 $932 €800 Maisons au bord e l'etang (25x33cm-10x13in) s.i.d.1950 W/C. 5-Nov-3 Rabourdin & Choppin de Janvry, Paris #10
£685 $1164 €1000 Cheval a la barriere (21x23cm-8x9in) s. Indian ink W/C. 5-Nov-3 Rabourdin & Choppin de Janvry, Paris #11
£753 $1281 €1100 Etude de lions (19x24cm-7x9in) s. wax crayon. 5-Nov-3 Rabourdin & Choppin de Janvry, Paris #8
£822 $1397 €1200 Nu debout (66x33cm-26x13in) s. pastel wax crayon. 5-Nov-3 Rabourdin & Choppin de Janvry, Paris #9
£1370 $2329 €2000 Lion et lionne assoupis (15x23cm-6x9in) s. s.i.d.59 verso Indian ink W/C. 5-Nov-3 Rabourdin & Choppin de Janvry, Paris #2/R est:1500-1800
£1370 $2329 €2000 Tete de fauve (17x16cm-7x6in) col crayon ink. 5-Nov-3 Rabourdin & Choppin de Janvry, Paris #5 est:1500-1800
£1521 $2585 €2220 Lion et son lionceau (14x26cm-6x10in) s. Indian ink. 5-Nov-3 Rabourdin & Choppin de Janvry, Paris #3/R est:1500-1800
£2397 $4075 €3500 Lionne au repos (17x25cm-7x10in) s. wash Indian ink. 5-Nov-3 Rabourdin & Choppin de Janvry, Paris #6 est:1500-1800
£2397 $4075 €3500 Lion et lionne endormis (17x26cm-7x10in) s. Indian ink W/C. 5-Nov-3 Rabourdin & Choppin de Janvry, Paris #7/R est:1500-1800
£2958 $5117 €4200 Panthere assise (39x48cm-15x19in) s. dr. 10-Dec-3 Ferri, Paris #48/R est:4000-5000
£5177 $8387 €7300 Panthere noire couchee (52x72cm-20x28in) s. chl white vellum exec.c.1930. 24-May-3 Martinot & Savignat, Pontoise #24/R est:5000-6000
£6507 $11062 €9500 Ours brun (47x64cm-19x25in) s. wax crayon. 5-Nov-3 Rabourdin & Choppin de Janvry, Paris #4 est:1500-1800

GUYS, Constantin (1802-1892) French
Works on paper
£282 $487 €400 Couple (21x17cm-8x7in) ink W/C. 9-Dec-3 Chambelland & Giafferi, Paris #71/R
£400 $716 €584 La caleche (22x31cm-9x12in) pencil pen ink W/C prov.exhib. 26-May-4 Sotheby's, Olympia #339/R
£455 $800 €664 Figures at the theater (18x15cm-7x6in) W/C. 23-May-4 William Jenack, New York #245
£503 $936 €750 Conversation (15x19cm-6x7in) ink ink wash graphite prov. 2-Mar-4 Artcurial Briest, Paris #12
£612 $1096 €900 Jeune homme se promenant a cheval (14x21cm-6x8in) pen brown ink grey wash. 17-Mar-4 Tajan, Paris #129
£704 $1218 €1000 Femme portant un fichu (29x16cm-11x6in) brush brown wash. 10-Dec-3 Piasa, Paris #92
£705 $1198 €1029 Caleche (16x22cm-6x9in) Indian ink wash W/C prov. 5-Nov-3 Dobiaschofsky, Bern #1128/R (S.FR 1600)
£778 $1400 €1136 Soldier and his girl (18x14cm-7x6in) black chk brown ink wash prov.exhib. 21-Jan-4 Sotheby's, New York #202/R est:1000-1500
£783 $1432 €1143 La voiture elegante (15x24cm-6x9in) ink wash prov. 4-Jun-4 Zofingen, Switzerland #2347/R (S.FR 1800)
£816 $1461 €1200 Jeune femme en robe de bal (32x20cm-13x8in) pen brown ink col wash black pencil. 19-Mar-4 Piasa, Paris #169
£816 $1461 €1200 Femme en noir vue en pied (35x21cm-14x8in) W/C traces black crayon. 17-Mar-4 Tajan, Paris #128
£837 $1423 €1222 Cavaliers (20x25cm-8x10in) Indian ink brush wash W/C prov. 5-Nov-3 Dobiaschofsky, Bern #1127/R (S.FR 1900)
£933 $1717 €1400 Femme a l'eventail (26x20cm-10x8in) ink wash htd W/C. 9-Jun-4 Beaussant & Lefèvre, Paris #164/R
£953 $1705 €1400 Promenade de deux femmes en caleche (17x26cm-7x10in) pen brown ink grey wash. 17-Mar-4 Tajan, Paris #130 est:1000
£957 $1599 €1350 Scene galante sous le Second Empire (19x28cm-7x11in) W/C ink wash. 20-Jun-3 Drouot Estimations, Paris #49
£1056 $1827 €1500 Elegantes a leur fenetre en Crimee (20x30cm-8x12in) pen brown ink grey wash. 10-Dec-3 Piasa, Paris #91/R est:1200-1500
£1141 $2122 €1700 Deux coquins et une elegante (21x15cm-8x6in) pen ink wash. 8-Mar-4 Artcurial Briest, Paris #15/R est:800-1200
£1300 $2340 €1898 Le Daumont Imperial au bois (12x27cm-5x11in) pen brown ink W/C exhib. 20-Apr-4 Sotheby's, Olympia #185/R est:800-1200
£1469 $2497 €2100 La caleche (22x28cm-9x11in) s. ink wash. 20-Nov-3 Claude Aguttes, Neuilly #277 est:1800-2000
£1743 $2911 €2527 Two Neapolitan girls before doorway (22x17cm-9x7in) W/C over ink. 19-Jun-3 Kornfeld, Bern #454 est:3000 (S.FR 3800)
£1761 $3046 €2500 Jeune femme (17x12cm-7x5in) W/C wash prov.exhib. 12-Dec-3 Piasa, Paris #83 est:1800-2000
£2177 $3897 €3200 Personnages dans un loge (24x34cm-9x13in) pen brown ink violet wash. 19-Mar-4 Piasa, Paris #153/R est:1800
£3562 $6055 €5200 Attelage (25x33cm-10x13in) pen ink W/C wash. 6-Nov-3 Sotheby's, Paris #141/R est:1000-1500

GUYS, Constantin (attrib) (1802-1892) French
Works on paper
£350 $585 €511 Party in the wood (34x25cm-13x10in) pencil chl W/C. 8-Oct-3 Christie's, Kensington #1084

GUZMAN, Juan Bautista de (19th C) Spanish
£1418 $2369 €2000 Riders (33x26cm-13x10in) s. cardboard. 20-Oct-3 Durán, Madrid #191/R
£1600 $2896 €2400 Lady with shawl (98x34cm-39x13in) s.d.1896 canvas on cardboard. 30-Mar-4 Segre, Madrid #85/R est:2400
£1773 $2961 €2500 Un poco alegres (25x35cm-10x14in) s. canvas on panel. 23-Jun-3 Durán, Madrid #151/R est:2000

GUZMAN, Manuel Rodriguez de (1818-1867) Spanish
£3014 $5034 €4250 Aquelarre (46x58cm-18x23in) s.d.1856. 23-Jun-3 Durán, Madrid #193/R est:3500

GUZZARDI, Giuseppe (?-1914) Italian
£1397 $2500 €2040 Street scene with children and donkey (48x41cm-19x16in) s.d.1872. 16-May-4 CRN Auctions, Cambridge #41/R

GUZZARDI, Rudolph (1903-1962) Italian/American
£1108 $1750 €1618 West Texas farm scene (20x25cm-8x10in) s.d.1930. 27-Jul-3 Simpson's, Houston #367

GUZZI, Beppe (1902-1982) Italian
£467 $859 €700 Vase of flowers (67x48cm-26x19in) s. s.i.verso. 10-Jun-4 Christie's, Rome #15
£1241 $2073 €1800 Road to the castle (100x70cm-39x28in) s.d.1959. 17-Nov-3 Sant Agostino, Torino #127/R est:1500-2000

GUZZI, Pier Enrico (20th C) Italian
£2331 $3800 €3403 Man and his soul (52x75cm-20x30in) s. board prov. 25-Sep-3 Christie's, Rockefeller NY #626/R est:2000-3000

GWATHMEY, Robert (1903-1988) American
Prints
£1882 $3200 €2748 Hitchhiker (43x33cm-17x13in) s.i. col screenprint. 6-Nov-3 Swann Galleries, New York #547/R est:3000-5000

GWOZDECKI, Gustav (1880-1935) Polish
£1395 $2400 €2037 Still life with statue (76x64cm-30x25in) s. 6-Dec-3 South Bay, Long Island #200/R
£1570 $2700 €2292 Modernist landscape (51x61cm-20x24in) s.verso. 6-Dec-3 South Bay, Long Island #199/R
£2035 $3500 €2971 Still life with pottery vessels on a table (64x76cm-25x30in) init. 6-Dec-3 South Bay, Long Island #200a/R

GWYNNE-JONES, Allan (1892-1982) British
£340 $636 €510 Polly Cox, a portrait (35x30cm-14x12in) init. board. 26-Jul-4 Bonhams, Bath #33/R
£400 $748 €600 River landscape with cattle and rickyard (50x60cm-20x24in) 26-Jul-4 Bonhams, Bath #34/R
£700 $1295 €1022 Bathers with greyhound (13x25cm-5x10in) init. i.verso board. 11-Mar-4 Christie's, Kensington #78/R
£800 $1480 €1168 Pansies (27x18cm-11x7in) init. oil paper on board exhib. 11-Mar-4 Christie's, Kensington #133/R
£1150 $1817 €1668 Still life of pansies (27x18cm-11x7in) init. board. 2-Sep-3 Bristol Auction Rooms #596/R est:600-800
£5200 $9152 €7592 Poppies and marguerites (48x38cm-19x15in) prov. 18-May-4 Woolley & Wallis, Salisbury #53/R est:4000-6000
Works on paper
£420 $739 €613 Sketch of a cow. pencil wash prov. 18-May-4 Woolley & Wallis, Salisbury #204/R
£550 $1018 €803 Cottages at twilight, Donegal (27x37cm-11x15in) s.d.1914 pencil W/C pen i k prov. 11-Mar-4 Christie's, Kensington #79/R

GYBORSON, Indiana (20th C) American
£2374 $4250 €3466 Woman in an interior (41x30cm-16x12in) s. panel. 6-May-4 Shannon's, Milford #62/R est:4000-6000
£3867 $7000 €5646 Pierette in the studio, Frivolitas (36x28cm-14x11in) s. board. 31-Mar-4 Sotheby's, New York #58/R est:6000-9000

GYENES, Gitta (1888-1960) Hungarian
£1976 $3577 €2885 Dream (73x60cm-29x24in) s. oil on wood. 16-Apr-4 Mu Terem Galeria, Budapest #72/R (H.F 750000)
£4344 $7211 €6342 Garden suburb with a tram (53x64cm-21x25in) painted c.1910. 4-Oct-3 Kieselbach, Budapest #19/R (H.F 1600000)
£5742 $9934 €8383 Lying nude (64x90cm-25x35in) s.d.1929. 12-Dec-3 Kieselbach, Budapest #45/R (H.F 2200000)

GYLLENHAMMAR, Gully (1878-?) Swedish?
£765 $1408 €1148 Absinthe drinkers (100x81cm-39x32in) s.d.1912. 14-Jun-4 Lilla Bukowskis, Stockholm #237 (S.KR 10500)

GYNGELL, Albert (fl.1873-1892) British
£420 $689 €613 River landscape (41x61cm-16x24in) s. 6-Jun-3 Biddle & Webb, Birmingham #226

GYSBRECHTS, Cornelis Norbertus (17th C) Flemish
£91391 $166331 €138000 Trompe-l'oeil au mur d'atelier et toile (148x110cm-58x43in) s. lit. 15-Jun-4 Claude Aguttes, Neuilly #42/R est:70000-80000

GYSBRECHTS, Franciscus (17th C) Dutch
£16000 $29280 €23360 Still life with musical instruments (97x118cm-38x46in) 8-Jul-4 Sotheby's, London #283/R est:15000-20000
£17361 $28993 €25000 Trompe l'oeil with wardrobe (100x120cm-39x47in) s.indis.d. exhib. 22-Oct-3 Finarte Semenzato, Milan #45/R

GYSELAER, Philip (17th C) Flemish
£11000 $19030 €16060 Joseph interpreting Pharoah's dreams (33x51cm-13x20in) s.d.1643 panel. 11-Dec-3 Sotheby's, London #138/R est:7000-10000

GYSELINCKX, Joseph (1845-?) Belgian
£966 $1786 €1400 La famille au jeu (45x54cm-18x21in) s. 16-Feb-4 Horta, Bruxelles #294
£2747 $5000 €4011 In Defense (38x30cm-15x12in) s.d.1879 i.verso panel. 7-Feb-4 Neal Auction Company, New Orleans #423/R est:3000-6000
£6333 $11463 €9500 La toilette des enfants (59x45cm-23x18in) s.d.1868 i.verso. 30-Mar-4 Palais de Beaux Arts, Brussels #601/R est:10000-12000

GYSELS, Pieter (1621-1690) Flemish
£16783 $28531 €24000 Landscape with a group of travellers resting (40x49cm-16x19in) s. lit. 28-Nov-3 Schloss Ahlden, Ahlden #1376/R est:24000
£44000 $80520 €64240 Village scene with figures dancing and merrymaking (17x23cm-7x9in) s. copper prov. 7-Jul-4 Sotheby's, London #2/R est:20000-30000
£45000 $82350 €65700 Village scene with figures shooting the popingay (13x17cm-5x7in) copper prov. 7-Jul-4 Sotheby's, London #1/R est:20000-30000
£90000 $164700 €131400 Late summer landscape with peasants harvesting corn (39x51cm-15x20in) copper prov.exhib.lit. 7-Jul-4 Sotheby's, London #3/R est:40000-60000
Works on paper
£3425 $5822 €5000 Studies of peasants, horses and carts (26x42cm-10x17in) pen brown ink grey wash. 4-Nov-3 Sotheby's, Amsterdam #32/R est:6000-8000

GYSELS, Pieter (attrib) (1621-1690) Flemish
£11724 $19462 €17000 Flemish village road with figures and card (24x17cm-9x7in) W/C parchment on panel prov. 1-Oct-3 Dorotheum, Vienna #137/R est:17000-22000
£30000 $54900 €43800 River landscape with watermill (18x22cm-7x9in) panel prov. 8-Jul-4 Sotheby's, London #100/R est:15000-20000

GYSIS, Nicolas (1842-1901) Greek
£1589 $2893 €2400 Oriental warrior (43x27cm-17x11in) s. board. 19-Jun-4 Bergmann, Erlangen #782 est:1500
£3333 $5433 €4800 Oriental man with stick and sabre (43x27cm-17x11in) s. board. 24-Sep-3 Neumeister, Munich #433/R est:4500
£4861 $8021 €7000 Cupid and the female artist (17x11cm-7x4in) mono. bears sig. canvas on panel. 2-Jul-3 Neumeister, Munich #653/R est:3000
£8000 $14320 €11680 House interior in Oberaudorf (26x34cm-10x13in) s.i.d.85 canvas on cardboard. 11-May-4 Bonhams, New Bond Street #30/R est:8000-12000
£38000 $64600 €55480 Portrait of old man drinking (30x24cm-12x9in) s. indis.sig.verso prov. 18-Nov-3 Sotheby's, London #11/R est:8000-12000
£80000 $140000 €116800 Zeybek (45x32cm-18x13in) init. prov. 16-Dec-3 Bonhams, New Bond Street #27/R est:80000-120000
Works on paper
£5000 $8950 €7300 The Apotheosis of Bavaria (43x31cm-17x12in) s.i. chl sanguine chk double-sided. 11-May-4 Bonhams, New Bond Street #7/R est:5000-7000
£17000 $29750 €24820 Drunken maenad (52x38cm-20x15in) s. pastel prov. 16-Dec-3 Bonhams, New Bond Street #9/R est:10000-15000

GYSIS, Nicolas (attrib) (1842-1901) Greek
£2553 $4136 €3600 Portrait d'homme (56x46cm-22x18in) bears mono. 21-May-3 Daguerre, Paris #64 est:500-800

GYSLING, Albert (1862-?) Swiss
£259 $463 €378 Jungfrau with Unspunnen ruins (31x46cm-12x18in) s. canvas on panel. 12-May-4 Dobiaschofsky, Bern #3631 (S.FR 600)

GYSMANS, Hendrik (16/17th C) Dutch
Works on paper
£3767 $6404 €5500 Path running through a wooded landscape (27x42cm-11x17in) pen brown ink grey wash. 4-Nov-3 Sotheby's, Amsterdam #22/R est:4000-6000

H S (?) ?
£900 $1629 €1314 Portrait of Primo, a hunter in a landscape (46x61cm-18x24in) mono.i.d.1834. 31-Mar-4 Brightwells, Leominster #865/R
£1400 $2338 €2044 Still life of fruit (30x25cm-12x10in) 21-Oct-3 Gorringes, Lewes #2197/R

H W (?) ?
Works on paper
£276 $497 €400 Le depart des cavaliers (21x30cm-8x12in) mono. W/C. 20-Jan-4 Galerie Moderne, Brussels #160

HAAG, Carl (1820-1915) German
£3800 $6992 €5548 New arrival (26x26cm-10x10in) s. panel. 25-Mar-4 Christie's, Kensington #72/R est:3000-5000
Works on paper
£380 $695 €555 Rosary (34x23cm-13x9in) s.d.1857 W/C. 27-Jan-4 Bonhams, Knightsbridge #16/R
£400 $716 €600 Study of fallen tree (15x21cm-6x8in) s. pencil. 13-May-4 Bassenge, Berlin #5564
£600 $1080 €876 Persian Hadji (34x24cm-13x9in) s. i.verso W/C. 21-Jan-4 Sotheby's, Olympia #450/R
£952 $1705 €1400 A Syrian monk (29x20cm-11x8in) s.d.1872 W/C. 17-Mar-4 Maigret, Paris #11/R
£1400 $2324 €2044 Ancient vestibule beneath temple area, Jerusalem. Subterranean doorway beneath temple area Jerusale (35x24cm-14x9in) both s.i.d.1859 W/C two. 1-Oct-3 Sotheby's, Olympia #240/R est:1500-2000
£2200 $3652 €3212 Zebeck (48x33cm-19x13in) s.i.d.October 1858 W/C. 1-Oct-3 Sotheby's, Olympia #242/R est:1000-1500
£2793 $5000 €4078 An Ashkenazi at his prayers (35x25cm-14x10in) s.i.d.31.8.1859 W/C gouache. 18-Mar-4 Sotheby's, New York #247/R est:5000-7000
£4500 $8055 €6570 The Acropolis of Athens as seen from the Prison of Socrates (29x60cm-11x24in) s.i.d.1858 W/C. 28-May-4 Lyon & Turnbull, Edinburgh #55/R est:3000-5000

HAAG, Hans (1841-1919) Austrian
£1629 $2704 €2378 Visitation in the farm (26x47cm-10x19in) s. panel. 4-Oct-3 Kieselbach, Budapest #118/R (H.F 600000)
£3258 $5408 €4757 Group of horsemen (42x64cm-17x25in) s. 4-Oct-3 Kieselbach, Budapest #180/R (H.F 1200000)

HAAG, Jean Paul (19th C) French
£1667 $3000 €2500 Playful moment (24x18cm-9x7in) s.d.73 panel. 21-Apr-4 Christie's, Amsterdam #56/R est:2000-3000
£1816 $3250 €2651 Young boy with his toy cannon (25x18cm-10x7in) s. panel prov. 14-May-4 Skinner, Boston #45/R est:2500-5500
£2600 $4732 €3796 Helping hand (32x23cm-13x9in) s. panel. 16-Jun-4 Christie's, Kensington #161/R est:3000-5000

HAAGENSEN, Anne Mette (1953-) Danish
£287 $465 €416 Composition with figures (190x160cm-75x63in) s.verso. 4-Aug-3 Rasmussen, Vejle #680/R (D.KR 3000)

HAALAND, Lars Laurits (1855-1938) Norwegian
£1711 $2908 €2498 Sailing boat in harbour (18x23cm-7x9in) s.d.87. 19-Nov-3 Grev Wedels Plass, Oslo #8/R est:25000 (N.KR 20000)
£2496 $4168 €3644 Full-rigged vessel and breakers (40x80cm-16x31in) s. 20-Oct-3 Blomqvist, Lysaker #1112/R est:25000-30000 (N.KR 29000)
£3402 $6226 €4967 Seascape with sailing boats off coastal cliffs (38x55cm-15x22in) s.d.1901. 9-Jun-4 Rasmussen, Copenhagen #1819/R est:40000 (D.KR 38000)
£3416 $5705 €4987 Evening in the skerries (38x54cm-15x21in) s.d.1924 i.verso. 13-Oct-3 Blomqvist, Oslo #279/R est:20000-30000 (N.KR 40000)
£3701 $5958 €5403 Storm by the coast (145x195cm-57x77in) s. 25-Aug-3 Blomqvist, Lysaker #1101/R est:35000 (N.KR 43000)
£5220 $9344 €7621 Pilot boat by the coast (55x80cm-22x31in) s.d.1901. 25-May-4 Grev Wedels Plass, Oslo #6/R est:50000-70000 (N.KR 64000)
£5295 $8842 €7731 With rowing boats in the outport (43x58cm-17x23in) s.d.86. 13-Oct-3 Blomqvist, Oslo #276/R est:25000-35000 (N.KR 62000)
£5537 $9523 €8084 Seascape with vessel in rough seas (45x70cm-18x28in) s.d.1901. 8-Dec-3 Blomqvist, Oslo #411/R est:70000-90000 (N.KR 65000)
£6000 $9600 €8700 Near the coast in rough seas (68x108cm-27x43in) s.d.97. 18-Sep-3 Christie's, Kensington #116/R est:3000-5000
£7240 $12453 €10570 Foaming sea (160x100cm-63x39in) s.d.1910. 8-Dec-3 Blomqvist, Oslo #425/R est:120000-150000 (N.KR 85000)

HAALKE, Hjalmar (1894-1964) Norwegian
£557 $963 €813 Landscape (37x47cm-15x19in) s. 13-Dec-3 Blomqvist, Lysaker #1130 (N.KR 6400)
£1348 $2332 €1968 Avenue in autumn colours (54x65cm-21x26in) s. 13-Dec-3 Blomqvist, Lysaker #1129 est:10000-12000 (N.KR 15500)

HAAN, Jurjen de (1936-) Dutch
£350 $601 €500 The trolley (100x70cm-39x28in) s.d.91. 8-Dec-3 Glerum, Amsterdam #405/R
£524 $902 €750 Fish (120x90cm-47x35in) s.d.2001 lit. 8-Dec-3 Glerum, Amsterdam #425/R
£559 $962 €800 Composition (116x68cm-46x27in) s.d.86. 8-Dec-3 Glerum, Amsterdam #411/R
£694 $1097 €1000 Dissolute (200x50cm-79x20in) s.d.2001. 26-Apr-3 Auction Maastricht #147/R
£1042 $1646 €1500 Bogey (150x100cm-59x39in) s.d.2002. 26-Apr-3 Auction Maastricht #55/R
£1096 $1863 €1600 Evolution (140x160cm-55x63in) s.d.96. 5-Nov-3 Vendue Huis, Gravenhage #524a est:1000-1500
£1118 $2058 €1700 Untitled (225x148cm-89x58in) s.d.95 paper. 22-Jun-4 Christie's, Amsterdam #377/R est:1000-1500
Works on paper
£350 $601 €500 Alain Delon (77x50cm-30x20in) s.d.66 gouache chk. 8-Dec-3 Glerum, Amsterdam #265/R

HAAN, Stephen de (?) ?
£550 $1018 €803 Skaters at a Dutch riverside hamlet in winter (61x92cm-24x36in) s. 15-Jan-4 Christie's, Kensington #821/R

HAAN, Willem Jacob de (1913-1967) Dutch
Works on paper
£789 $1453 €1200 Untitled (45x60cm-18x24in) s. mixed media. 28-Jun-4 Sotheby's, Amsterdam #274/R

HAANEN, Adriana (1814-1895) Dutch
£3497 $5944 €5000 Still life with grapes, pumpkin and peach (18x14cm-7x6in) s. panel. 24-Nov-3 Dorotheum, Vienna #188/R est:2000-2400
£3500 $6020 €5110 Roses in a glass vase on a ledge (26x24cm-10x9in) init.d.1849 panel exhib. 4-Dec-3 Christie's, Kensington #86/R est:3000-5000

HAANEN, Cecil van (1844-1914) Dutch
£1000 $1840 €1460 Beatific beauty (68x56cm-27x22in) i.verso. 25-Mar-4 Christie's, Kensington #125/R est:1500-2000
£1233 $2220 €1850 Portrait of Spanish woman (36x28cm-14x11in) s. 26-Apr-4 Rieber, Stuttgart #1234/R est:1800
£22378 $38042 €32000 Venetian women before ball (91x126cm-36x50in) st.sig. 24-Nov-3 Dorotheum, Vienna #1/R est:12000-14000
£105000 $191100 €153300 Pearl stringers (65x94cm-26x37in) s.i.d.876 exhib.lit. 17-Jun-4 Christie's, London #16/R est:60000-80000

HAANEN, Georg Gillis van (1807-1876) Dutch
£3819 $6225 €5500 Figures in a church (49x39cm-19x15in) s.d.1833 panel. 29-Sep-3 Sotheby's, Amsterdam #39/R

HAANEN, Remi van (1812-1894) Dutch
£855 $1574 €1300 Huntsman in a winter landscape (32x24cm-13x9in) s. 22-Jun-4 Christie's, Amsterdam #50/R est:700-900
£1316 $2421 €2000 Dutch river lit by evening sun (21x30cm-8x12in) mono.d.56 panel. 24-Jun-4 Dr Fritz Nagel, Stuttgart #714/R est:2000
£1806 $2979 €2600 On the ice - skaters on frozen canal in Holland (23x28cm-9x11in) s.d.45 panel. 3-Jul-3 Van Ham, Cologne #1217/R est:1800
£2013 $3604 €3000 Wood gatherers in winter forest (17x14cm-7x6in) mono.d.43 paper on board. 27-May-4 Dorotheum, Vienna #19/R est:3000-4000
£2585 $4627 €3800 Cattle watering (104x73cm-41x29in) 22-Mar-4 Sant Agostino, Torino #272/R est:2500
£9091 $15455 €13000 Winter pleasures (23x28cm-9x11in) s.d.45 panel. 24-Nov-3 Dorotheum, Vienna #78/R est:5000-7000
Works on paper
£621 $1030 €900 Cloudy landscape (25x25cm-10x10in) mono. grisaille. 30-Sep-3 Dorotheum, Vienna #269/R

HAAPANEN, John Nichols (1891-?) American
£192 $350 €280 Sunset on the Coast of Maine (41x51cm-16x20in) s. board. 7-Feb-4 Neal Auction Company, New Orleans #517
£335 $600 €489 Rocky shore (58x51cm-23x20in) 7-May-4 Douglas, South Deerfield #32
£546 $1000 €797 Winter in Maine (51x41cm-20x16in) s.d.1931 board. 5-Jun-4 Treadway Gallery, Cincinnati #623/R est:1500-2500

HAARD, Pieter de (1914-) Dutch
Works on paper
£489 $817 €700 Composition (44x33cm-17x13in) s.d. pastel. 30-Jun-3 Sotheby's, Amsterdam #197

HAARDT, Georges van (1907-) Polish
Works on paper
£448 $829 €650 Composition (74x73cm-29x29in) s.d.1962 pastel. 13-Feb-4 Charbonneaux, Paris #52/R

HAAREM, Remy van (?) ?
£3497 $5839 €5000 Winter landscapes (20x27cm-8x11in) i. two. 11-Oct-3 Dr Fritz Nagel, Leipzig #3921/R est:4000

HAAREN, Dirk Johannes van (1878-1953) Dutch
£367 $667 €550 Schelde near Amsterdam (30x41cm-12x16in) s. 30-Jun-4 Vendue Huis, Gravenhage #513/R

HAARLEM SCHOOL (17th C) Dutch
£5405 $9514 €8000 Young boy with his hand in his hair (50x38cm-20x15in) mono. panel. 18-May-4 Sotheby's, Amsterdam #28/R est:4000-6000
£7534 $12808 €11000 Still life with vegetables, baskets, wheelbarrow, rake and spade (38x30cm-15x12in) painted c.1650 panel prov.exhib. 4-Nov-3 Sotheby's, Amsterdam #23/R est:10000-15000
Works on paper
£5278 $9500 €7706 Seated man wearing a hat holding a roemer (42x28cm-17x11in) black white chk. 22-Jan-4 Christie's, Rockefeller NY #128/R est:3000-5000

HAARTMAN, Axel (1877-1969) Finnish
£395 $718 €580 Autumn (28x45cm-11x18in) s.i. board. 8-Feb-4 Bukowskis, Helsinki #354/R
£408 $743 €600 Coastal landscape from Kimito (55x46cm-22x18in) s.i.d.1945. 8-Feb-4 Bukowskis, Helsinki #353/R
£423 $676 €600 Flowers (33x30cm-13x12in) s. 18-Sep-3 Hagelstam, Helsinki #770/R
£634 $1014 €900 In the park (22x28cm-9x11in) s.d.1914. 18-Sep-3 Hagelstam, Helsinki #769
£816 $1486 €1200 Apple tree in blossom in the artist's garden (37x36cm-15x14in) s.i.d.1939. 8-Feb-4 Bukowskis, Helsinki #352/R

HAAS, Aad de (1920-1972) Dutch
£1048 $1929 €1530 Circuspaard (18x13cm-7x5in) board scratching out prov.exhib. 14-Jun-4 Waddingtons, Toronto #219/R est:8000-12000 (C.D 2600)

HAAS, Frans de (1934-) Dutch
£274 $466 €400 Cat in an Italian landscape (40x60cm-16x24in) s.d.75. 5-Nov-3 Vendue Huis, Gravenhage #419/R
£294 $491 €420 Cornwall memory (49x61cm-19x24in) s.d.74 i.verso board. 30-Jun-3 Sotheby's, Amsterdam #487

HAAS, Gustav (1889-1953) German
£244 $400 €354 Two trees in a landscape with distant hills (66x86cm-26x34in) s. prov. 31-May-3 Brunk, Ashville #148/R

HAAS, Johannes Hubertus Leonardus de (1832-1908) Flemish
£855 $1574 €1300 Cow in a field (35x26cm-14x10in) s. panel lit. 26-Jun-4 Karrenbauer, Konstanz #1728/R
£1451 $2496 €2118 Flemish pasturage (46x63cm-18x25in) s. panel prov. 2-Dec-3 Ritchie, Toronto #122/R est:5000-8000 (C.D 3250)
£3333 $5667 €4800 Cows on a waterside (69x125cm-27x49in) s. 28-Oct-3 Christie's, Amsterdam #125/R est:4000-6000
£3537 $6332 €5200 Cows in the meadow (31x47cm-12x19in) panel. 17-Mar-4 De Zwann, Amsterdam #4567/R est:3000-5000
£5333 $9600 €8000 Cattle in a meadow (80x125cm-31x49in) s. prov. 21-Apr-4 Christie's, Amsterdam #98/R est:8000-12000
£6897 $11517 €10000 Gathering storm (91x160cm-36x63in) s. panel prov. 15-Nov-3 Lempertz, Koln #1613/R est:4000-6000

HAAS, Mauritz F H de (1832-1895) Dutch
£3143 $5500 €4589 On the beach (35x56cm-14x22in) s. canvas on board. 19-Dec-3 Sotheby's, New York #1080/R est:4000-6000
£3395 $5500 €4923 September storm (56x91cm-22x36in) i. 8-Aug-3 Barridorf, Portland #149/R est:6000-9000
£5389 $9000 €7868 Ships off the coast (33x23cm-13x9in) s. prov. 23-Oct-3 Shannon's, Milford #109/R est:9000-12000
£6704 $12000 €9788 Rocky coast (14x22cm-6x9in) estate st. 6-May-4 Shannon's, Milford #116/R est:15000-20000
£7186 $12000 €10492 Stormy seas (69x117cm-27x46in) s.d.1872. 23-Oct-3 Shannon's, Milford #126/R est:10000-15000
£11765 $20000 €17177 Sunset, New York (61x86cm-24x34in) s.d.1881 prov. 30-Oct-3 Phillips, New York #51/R est:25000-35000
£14970 $25000 €21856 Afternoon sail (36x58cm-14x23in) prov. 23-Oct-3 Shannon's, Milford #88/R est:20000-30000
£16760 $30000 €24470 Gray day at Marblehead (19x30cm-7x12in) s. prov. 6-May-4 Shannon's, Milford #98/R est:30000-50000

HAAS, Michel (1934-) ?
Works on paper
£600 $1080 €900 One and another (133x120cm-52x47in) s. mixed media. 24-Apr-4 Cornette de St.Cyr, Paris #564/R

HAAS, Richard John (1936-) American
£5000 $8500 €7300 View corner Fifth Avenue and 55 Street 1977 (251x193cm-99x76in) oil acrylic canvas wood molding prov.exhib. 9-Nov-3 Wright, Chicago #473 est:5000-7000
Works on paper
£359 $650 €524 Brooklyn Tower (79x56cm-31x22in) W/C board. 16-Apr-4 American Auctioneer #180/R
£588 $1000 €858 94 Nassau Street, 1975 (80x50cm-31x20in) s. pencil marker pen prov. 9-Nov-3 Bonhams & Butterfields, Los Angeles #4055/R est:2000-3000

HAAS, William F de (1830-1880) Dutch
£18466 $32500 €26960 Along the shore, Fire Island, New York (51x91cm-20x36in) s.d.77 prov. 19-May-4 Sotheby's, New York #59/R est:20000-30000

HAAS-GERBER, Gretel (1903-?) German
£552 $916 €800 View from Haus Zahringerstr (35x53cm-14x21in) s.d.1960 panel. 6-Oct-3 Bloss, Merzhausen #1200/R

HAASE, Karl (?-1877) Italian
£1467 $2640 €2200 Italian riverside town (20x31cm-8x12in) s. 24-Apr-4 Reiss & Sohn, Konigstein #5342/R est:800

HAASE, Ove (1894-1989) Danish
£683 $1107 €997 Bouquet of flowers in vase on ledge (50x45cm-20x18in) exhib.prov. 9-Aug-3 Hindemae, Ullerslev #21/R (D.KR 7200)

HAASE-ILSENBURG, Hermann (1879-1960) German
Sculpture
£1007 $1872 €1500 Amazone on horseback (64cm-25in) i. dark pat.bronze. 8-Mar-4 Dorotheum, Vienna #177/R est:1800-2000
£1074 $1976 €1600 Farewell (64cm-25in) bronze. 26-Mar-4 Bolland & Marotz, Bremen #733/R est:1800

HAASE-WERKENTHIN, Julie (fl.1907-1913) German?
£966 $1612 €1400 Portrait of a lady (75x55cm-30x22in) s.d.1923 canvas on canvas. 13-Nov-3 Neumeister, Munich #337/R

HABBAH (1928-) French
Sculpture
£1453 $2600 €2121 Chain. prov. 16-May-4 Wright, Chicago #477/R est:1000-1500

HABBE, Nicolai (1827-1889) Danish
£632 $1181 €923 Portrait of a Roman lady (73x58cm-29x23in) mono. s.i.stretcher. 25-Feb-4 Kunsthallen, Copenhagen #552/R (D.KR 7000)
£1418 $2453 €2070 Christening in the country side (93x93cm-37x37in) s. exhib. 9-Dec-3 Rasmussen, Copenhagen #1393/R est:20000-30000 (D.KR 15000)
£1797 $3342 €2624 Autumn scene with harvesters loading hay on horse-wagon (65x84cm-26x33in) s.d.1852 prov. 2-Mar-4 Rasmussen, Copenhagen #1295/R est:20000-25000 (D.KR 20000)

HABENSCHADEN, Sebastian (1813-1868) German
£1549 $2680 €2200 Cows and goats on rivershore (49x65cm-19x26in) s. 11-Dec-3 Dr Fritz Nagel, Stuttgart #521/R est:2800

HABERJAHN, Ferdinand (19/20th C) ?
£280 $467 €400 Paysage de montagne enneige (37x25cm-15x10in) mono.d.1910 panel. 25-Jun-3 Blanchet, Paris #16

HABERJAHN, Gabriel (1890-1956) Swiss
£396 $674 €578 La riviere (50x50cm-20x20in) s. i. verso. 5-Nov-3 Dobiaschofsky, Bern #619/R (S.FR 900)
£396 $674 €578 River in winter (35x43cm-14x17in) s. board. 5-Nov-3 Dobiaschofsky, Bern #620 (S.FR 900)

HABERLE, John (1856-1933) American
£133721 $230000 €195233 Music (66x81cm-26x32in) s. prov.exhib. 4-Dec-3 Christie's, Rockefeller NY #54/R est:200000-300000

HABERMANN, Hugo von (1849-1929) German
£293 $525 €440 Corpse by sea at night (14x21cm-6x8in) s. board. 13-May-4 Neumeister, Munich #360/R
£733 $1342 €1100 Young Munich nude (75x46cm-30x18in) s. 5-Jun-4 Arnold, Frankfurt #590/R

HABERT, Alfred Louis (1824-1893) French
£2400 $4080 €3504 Interior, before dinner, with figures by the dining room door (53x64cm-21x25in) s. 5-Nov-3 John Nicholson, Haslemere #591/R est:2500-3000

HABERT, Eugène (?-1916) French
£379 $694 €550 Paysage d'ete aux trois nymphes (73x60cm-29x24in) s. 28-Jan-4 Libert, Castor, Paris #297
£1074 $1966 €1568 Allegorical scene of summer (125x50cm-49x20in) s. shaped top. 9-Jun-4 Rasmussen, Copenhagen #1999/R est:12000 (D.KR 12000)

HABL, Willy (1888-1964) German
£336 $594 €500 Cherry blossom in Holstein village (61x52cm-24x20in) s.d.34. 28-Apr-4 Schopman, Hamburg #616/R
Works on paper
£1583 $2532 €2200 Paysans (39x53cm-15x21in) mono.d.1911 col crayons. 16-May-3 Tajan, Paris #202 est:600
£2446 $3913 €3400 Two peasants (41x48cm-16x19in) mono.i.d.1911 col crayons. 16-May-3 Tajan, Paris #203 est:500

HACKAERT, Jan (1629-1699) Dutch
£2207 $3686 €3200 Sous-bois anime d'un homme a cheval (117x98cm-46x39in) 17-Nov-3 Bernaerts, Antwerp #298 est:3000-4000
£9000 $15570 €13140 Wooded river landscape with fishermen and a man with a donkey (68x57cm-27x22in) s. prov.exhib. 11-Dec-3 Sotheby's, London #102/R est:12000-18000

HACKAERT, Jan (attrib) (1629-1699) Dutch
£2953 $5404 €4400 Personnages dans un sous-bois (92x115cm-36x45in) 8-Jul-4 Campo, Vlaamse Kaai #134/R est:3500-4500

HACKELBERG, Wilhelm (1904-1985) German
Works on paper
£667 $1193 €1000 Cows (25x32cm-10x13in) s.d. chl wash prov. 14-May-4 Ketterer, Munich #30/R

HACKER, Arthur (1858-1919) British
£550 $1007 €803 Tangiers (25x34cm-10x13in) board. 6-Jun-4 Lots Road Auctions, London #339
£700 $1281 €1022 Bedtime (46x56cm-18x22in) s.d.1885. 6-Jul-4 Bonhams, Knightsbridge #79/R
£3600 $6012 €5256 Study of sweet peas (31x41cm-12x16in) s.d.1906 board. 12-Nov-3 Sotheby's, Olympia #142/R est:1000-1500
£3600 $6660 €5256 Portrait of the artist sister, Adeline (112x76cm-44x30in) s.d.1908 prov. 14-Jan-4 Lawrence, Crewkerne #1425/R est:2000-3000
£22000 $40480 €32120 Woodcutter and his daughter (103x128cm-41x50in) s.d.1892. 11-Jun-4 Christie's, London #114/R est:20000-30000
Works on paper
£750 $1380 €1095 Young Nelson (34x24cm-13x9in) s.d.1887 W/C. 8-Jun-4 Bonhams, New Bond Street #51/R

HACKER, Horst (1842-1906) German
£497 $904 €750 Boats on Lake Garda (57x78cm-22x31in) s.d.1898. 21-Jun-4 Dorotheum, Vienna #202/R
£530 $981 €790 Reichenau (46x77cm-18x30in) s.i. exhib. lit. 12-Mar-4 Zadick, Uberlingen #4053
£537 $983 €800 Stream with ducks in early autumn (85x124cm-33x49in) s.d.1906. 9-Jul-4 Dawo, Saarbrucken #47/R
£1275 $2372 €1900 Rocky coastline with a villa perched on the rocks (83x122cm-33x48in) s.d.1896 canvas on panel. 5-Mar-4 Wendl, Rudolstadt #3673/R est:950

HACKER, Horst (attrib) (1842-1906) German
£1184 $2179 €1800 Gosau Lake with Dachstein (59x85cm-23x33in) s.i. 22-Jun-4 Wiener Kunst Auktionen, Vienna #52/R est:1800

HACKER-TURAN, Maria (1886-?) Hungarian
£629 $1083 €900 Factory under snow (81x81cm-32x32in) s.d.1914. 3-Dec-3 Stadion, Trieste #1048/R

HACKERT, Carl Ludwig (1740-1800) German
Works on paper
£582 $990 €850 Pont. Tour (7x12cm-3x5in) W/C over engraving pair. 5-Nov-3 Christie's, Paris #827/R
£887 $1588 €1295 A aqua lagna fur la Canaigliano (36x46cm-14x18in) s. 28-May-4 Uppsala Auktionskammare, Uppsala #114/R (S.KR 12000)

HACKERT, Carl Ludwig (attrib) (1740-1800) German
£10563 $18275 €15000 Landscape with figures and herd (130x195cm-51x77in) 10-Dec-3 Beaussant & Lefèvre, Paris #48/R est:17000-20000
Prints
£2851 $4761 €4162 Vue de Geneve et du Montblack (40x62cm-16x24in) col engraving exec.c.1780. 16-Nov-3 Koller, Geneva #404/R est:2500-3500 (S.FR 6500)

HACKERT, J P (1737-1807) German

£4895 $8420 €7000 Landscape with rocks and lake (35x50cm-14x20in) i.d.1762. 3-Dec-3 Neumeister, Munich #469/R est:8000

HACKERT, Jacob Philippe (1737-1807) German

£8451 $14620 €12000 Villa Albani in Rome (56x68cm-22x27in) 13-Dec-3 Lempertz, Koln #23/R est:8000
£15000 $27450 €21900 View of the Villa Albani, Rome from the Patrizi Villa, with peasants, an elegant couple in foregroun (56x68cm-22x27in) prov. 7-Jul-4 Christie's, London #64/R est:15000-20000
£26000 $44980 €37960 Figures beside a waterfall in a ravine below a rock bridge (42x31cm-17x12in) s.d.1805 copper. 11-Dec-3 Sotheby's, London #40/R est:25000-35000
£61111 $110000 €89222 Hare in a forest (63x50cm-25x20in) bears sig. 23-Jan-4 Christie's, Rockefeller NY #185/R est:15000-20000
£99548 $159276 €145340 Maiori Grotto on the coast of Amalfi, Naples (63x88cm-25x35in) s.i.d.1770 prov.lit. 19-Sep-3 Koller, Zurich #3062/R est:220000-280000 (S.FR 220000)
£135747 $217195 €198191 River landscape with figures (40x31cm-16x12in) s.d.1767 copper prov. pair. 19-Sep-3 Koller, Zurich #3059/R est:250000-350000 (S.FR 300000)
Works on paper
£492 $900 €718 Italianate landscape with shepherd crossing a bridge (16x22cm-6x9in) pen black ink gray wash. 29-Jan-4 Swann Galleries, New York #305/R
£2318 $4219 €3500 Etudes d'arbres (51x38cm-20x15in) i. pen ink wash black crayon two. 16-Jun-4 Piasa, Paris #142/R est:3500-5000
£2778 $5000 €4056 Watermill at Ivry with fishermen on a boat in the foreground (20x28cm-8x11in) s.d.1767 bodycol prov.lit. 22-Jan-4 Christie's, Rockefeller NY #235/R est:4000-6000
£6500 $11635 €9490 Le temple de la Sibille a Tivoli (25x35cm-10x14in) s.i.d.1770 gouache. 28-May-4 Lyon & Turnbull, Edinburgh #18/R est:2000-3000
£6993 $11678 €10000 Albanian lake (67x50cm-26x20in) wash pen with pencil. 10-Oct-3 Winterberg, Heidelberg #454/R est:8400
£12329 $20959 €18000 Coastal landscapes, possibly French, with figures and boats (16x21cm-6x8in) s.d.1768 gouache vellum pair. 4-Nov-3 Sotheby's, Amsterdam #108/R est:8000-12000
£19444 $35000 €28388 View of a rocky area around lake Fucino (70x50cm-28x20in) s.i.d.1798 pen ink wash over black chk. 21-Jan-4 Sotheby's, New York #120/R est:35000-45000

HACKERT, Jacob Philippe (attrib) (1737-1807) German

Works on paper
£3611 $6500 €5272 Goat eating by the Colosseum, Rome. Stage eating, a lake beyond (12x16cm-5x6in) bodycol pair. 22-Jan-4 Christie's, Rockefeller NY #204/R est:3000-5000
£8000 $14640 €11680 Distant view of Naples from the south. Bay of Naples. Extensive mountainous landscape (59x84cm-23x33in) s. bodycol set of four. 6-Jul-4 Christie's, London #190/R est:4000-6000

HACKERT, Jacob Philippe (circle) (1737-1807) German

£11348 $18951 €16000 Paysage de riviere anime de bergers et pecheurs (211x168cm-83x66in) painted c.1770. 17-Oct-3 Tajan, Paris #41/R est:18000-20000

HACKERT, Jacob Philippe (style) (1737-1807) German

£30201 $55570 €45000 Hunters resting by river (70x90cm-28x35in) i. 25-Mar-4 Dr Fritz Nagel, Stuttgart #688/R est:1600

HACKERT, Johann Gottlieb (1744-1773) German

Works on paper
£4967 $9040 €7500 Fishermen in Naples Bay (34x46cm-13x18in) s.d.1772 pen ink W/C. 16-Jun-4 Christie's, Rome #447/R est:6000-8000
£6000 $10740 €8760 La temple de la Minerva Medica a Roma (25x35cm-10x14in) s.i.d.1770 gouache. 28-May-4 Lyon & Turnbull, Edinburgh #19/R

HACKERT, Johann Gottlieb (attrib) (1744-1773) German

£1208 $2223 €1800 Paysage a la cascade et a l'arc en ciel (91x66cm-36x26in) 26-Mar-4 Pierre Berge, Paris #5 est:2000-3000

HACKERT, Philippe (attrib) (?-1768) German

£1119 $1902 €1600 Landscape with stream and memorial (29x38cm-11x15in) 22-Nov-3 Arnold, Frankfurt #534/R est:2000

HACKINBURGER, Delores (20th C) American

£222 $400 €324 Stone houses and cows (33x58cm-13x23in) acrylic canvasboard. 24-Apr-4 Slotin Folk Art, Buford #261/R
£333 $600 €486 Barn raising (38x69cm-15x27in) acrylic. 24-Apr-4 Slotin Folk Art, Buford #260/R

HACKING, Frederick Sidney (1873-?) British

£500 $835 €730 Woodland stream (51x61cm-20x24in) 21-Oct-3 Gorringes, Lewes #2142

HACKMAN, Frederick James (fl.1908) British

£320 $550 €467 Rother, Rye (41x58cm-16x23in) s.d.1955. 2-Dec-3 Gorringes, Lewes #2421

HADDON, David W (fl.1884-1914) British

£280 $454 €406 Study of fisherman (58x41cm-23x16in) s. 7-Aug-3 Amersham Auction Rooms, UK #260
£300 $510 €438 Portrait of a fisherman standing on a quayside (52x34cm-20x13in) s. board. 27-Nov-3 Clevedon Sale Rooms #168
£300 $561 €438 Country girl in a bonnet (28x23cm-11x9in) s. board. 26-Feb-4 Lane, Penzance #188
£350 $655 €525 The coast guard (34x24cm-13x9in) s. board. 22-Jul-4 Dominic Winter, Swindon #141/R
£380 $597 €555 Coastal walk, girl with basket (44x29cm-17x11in) s. board. 16-Apr-3 Bamfords, Derby #626/R
£395 $726 €600 Little Red Riding Hood picking flowers on a woodland path (60x45cm-24x18in) s. 22-Jun-4 Mealy's, Castlecomer #364/R
£540 $999 €788 Portrait of a gypsy girl (28x20cm-11x8in) s.d.1890. 13-Feb-4 Keys, Aylsham #688
£559 $1000 €816 Portrait of a man selling items in a market (74x48cm-29x19in) s. 13-May-4 Dallas Auction Gallery, Dallas #304/R est:800-1200
£800 $1376 €1168 Old fisherman holding a basket of fish (56x38cm-22x15in) s. 5-Dec-3 Keys, Aylsham #619/R
£856 $1600 €1250 Interior scene (41x61cm-16x24in) s. pair. 24-Feb-4 Arthur James, Florida #310
£1050 $1680 €1533 Oysters Sir ? (53x35cm-21x14in) s.d.1886. 16-Sep-3 Bonhams, Knowle #105 est:500-800

HADDON, David W (attrib) (fl.1884-1914) British

£604 $1100 €906 Haywain (66x51cm-26x20in) indis sig. 19-Jun-4 Harvey Clar, Oakland #2415

HADDON, Joyce C (20th C) British

£270 $483 €394 After toil (23x28cm-9x11in) board. 7-May-4 Mallams, Oxford #306

HADDON, Trevor (1864-1941) British

£403 $749 €600 Shepherd with flock and girl (111x131cm-44x52in) s. 6-Mar-4 Arnold, Frankfurt #736/R
£636 $1100 €929 Figures feeding birds in a Spanish courtyard (51x76cm-20x30in) s. 13-Dec-3 Weschler, Washington #533
£700 $1169 €1022 Torre del Oro the Guadalquivir River, Seville (25x36cm-10x14in) s. board. 11-Nov-3 Bonhams, Knightsbridge #77/R
£750 $1395 €1095 Continental landscape with two women beside a classical well (62x40cm-24x16in) s. 4-Mar-4 Clevedon Sale Rooms #175
£933 $1689 €1400 View of Roman castles with cart and travellers (49x75cm-19x30in) s. canvas on board. 30-Mar-4 Babuino, Rome #409
£1250 $2313 €1825 Young women by a well (76x63cm-30x25in) s. 10-Feb-4 Bonhams, Knightsbridge #165/R est:1000-1500
£1519 $2750 €2218 Italian market (41cm-16in) s. 14-Apr-4 Dallas Auction Gallery, Dallas #272/R est:1800-2200
£1800 $3096 €2628 Venetian water carriers (53x76cm-21x30in) s. 5-Dec-3 Chrystals Auctions, Isle of Man #238 est:1800-2400
£1800 $3222 €2628 First sing of spring (71x91cm-28x36in) s. 27-May-4 Christie's, Kensington #291/R est:1200-1800
£2000 $3680 €2920 Traders in a middle eastern market place (43x33cm-17x13in) s. 14-Jun-4 Louis Taylor, Stoke on Trent #1256
£3500 $5670 €5075 Spring time (61x91cm-24x36in) s. 30-Jul-3 Hamptons Fine Art, Godalming #289 est:4000-6000
Works on paper
£430 $778 €628 Venetian canal scene with figures in gondolas (48x36cm-19x14in) s. W/C. 1-Apr-4 Biddle & Webb, Birmingham #902
£900 $1548 €1314 Mediterranean street scene (63x40cm-25x16in) s. W/C. 7-Dec-3 Lots Road Auctions, London #344

HADENGUE, Louis Michel (19th C) French

£1020 $1897 €1520 Le banquet (32x40cm-13x16in) s. 7-Mar-4 Lesieur & Le Bars, Le Havre #63
£1267 $2318 €1900 Fete foraine (27x41cm-11x16in) s. panel. 6-Jun-4 Osenat, Fontainebleau #236/R est:2000-2500
£4138 $6911 €6000 La fete foraine (107x135cm-42x53in) s.d. 17-Nov-3 Tajan, Paris #144/R est:6000-8000

HADJADJ, Bruno (1960-) French

Sculpture
£1119 $1902 €1600 Infante Margarita (72x30x25cm-28x12x10in) s.num.6/8 resin. 27-Nov-3 Calmels Cohen, Paris #107/R est:1500-1800

HADJIMICHAIL, Theofilos (1871-1933) Greek

£15000 $26850 €21900 The residence of Athanasios Kotonos in Varyia, Lesvos (37x30cm-15x12in) s.i.d.1932 prov.exhib. 11-May-4 Bonhams, New Bond Street #77/R est:6000-8000
£48000 $85920 €70080 Erotokritos and Aretousa (75x47cm-30x19in) s.i.d.1933 prov.exhib. 11-May-4 Bonhams, New Bond Street #86/R est:30000-40000

HADZI, Dimitri (1921-) American

Sculpture
£2200 $3938 €3212 Untitled (68cm-27in) bronze incl marble base exec c.1970. 16-Mar-4 Bonhams, Knightsbridge #73 est:500-700
£9189 $17000 €13416 Sheild 4 (185cm-73in) num.1/IV green pat bronze exec 1959-61 prov.exhib. 12-Feb-4 Sotheby's, New York #200/R est:3500-5500

HAECKE, Joseph (1811-?) German

£1067 $1952 €1600 Wallfahrts grotto in front of silhouette of town (105x90cm-41x35in) s.d.1845. 5-Jun-4 Arnold, Frankfurt #591/R est:1000

HAEFFLINGER, R (?) Canadian?

£223 $373 €323 Coast near Cap Ferrat (33x41cm-13x16in) s.d.49 prov. 17-Jun-3 Pinneys, Montreal #182 (C.D 500)

HAEFLIGER, Leopold (1929-1989) Swiss

£294 $500 €429 Portrait of Anna Hafliger (31x25cm-12x10in) s.d.1983. 28-Nov-3 Zofingen, Switzerland #3012 (S.FR 650)
£317 $538 €463 Winter landscape (17x50cm-7x20in) 28-Nov-3 Zofingen, Switzerland #3010 (S.FR 700)
£328 $576 €479 Autumn landscape (40x50cm-16x20in) s.d.72 prov. 22-May-4 Galerie Gloggner, Luzern #45 (S.FR 750)
£393 $692 €574 Chez Martha (40x32cm-16x13in) s.d.51 board prov. 22-May-4 Galerie Gloggner, Luzern #48 (S.FR 900)
£395 $659 €577 Girl in landscape (123x59cm-48x23in) panel prov. 15-Nov-3 Galerie Gloggner, Luzern #63 (S.FR 900)
£437 $769 €638 Winter landscape (20x24cm-8x9in) s.d.73 board prov. 22-May-4 Galerie Gloggner, Luzern #46 (S.FR 1000)

£482 $806 €704 Brown and Mackie (31x29cm-12x11in) s.i.d.82 W/C over Indian ink prov.lit. 15-Nov-3 Galerie Gloggner, Luzern #62/R (S.FR 1100)
£568 $1033 €829 Road towards the village (45x57cm-18x22in) s.d.68. 16-Jun-4 Fischer, Luzern #2152/R (S.FR 1300)
£606 $1085 €885 Night-time beach (51x60cm-20x24in) s.d. masonite. 22-Mar-4 Philippe Schuler, Zurich #4334 (S.FR 1400)
£633 $1077 €924 Trout (47x65cm-19x26in) mono.d.1962 panel. 28-Nov-3 Zofingen, Switzerland #3011 (S.FR 1400)
£679 $1154 €991 Winter landscape with houses (36x45cm-14x18in) s.d.63 panel. 19-Nov-3 Fischer, Luzern #2122/R (S.FR 1500)
£699 $1230 €1021 Winter landscape with trees (44x48cm-17x19in) s.d.81 prov. 22-May-4 Galerie Gloggner, Luzern #50 est:1400-1600 (S.FR 1600)
£702 $1172 €1025 Still life with shrimps (30x40cm-12x16in) s.d.80 prov. 15-Nov-3 Galerie Gloggner, Luzern #60 (S.FR 1600)
£702 $1172 €1025 My friend Hanns E Jager as Puntila (183x106cm-72x42in) s.i.d.78 panel prov. 15-Nov-3 Galerie Gloggner, Luzern #65/R (S.FR 1600)
£742 $1351 €1083 Winter landscape (32x72cm-13x28in) s.d.68. 16-Jun-4 Fischer, Luzern #2153/R (S.FR 1700)
£917 $1614 €1339 Harlequin (41x27cm-16x11in) s.d.69 panel prov. 22-May-4 Galerie Gloggner, Luzern #53 est:2000-2200 (S.FR 2100)
£965 $1611 €1409 Bielimann (51x38cm-20x15in) s.d.67 i. stretcher prov. 15-Nov-3 Galerie Gloggner, Luzern #59 est:1800-2500 (S.FR 2200)
£995 $1692 €1453 Trout (63x77cm-25x30in) s.d.58. 19-Nov-3 Fischer, Luzern #1304/R (S.FR 2200)
£1140 $1904 €1664 Fastnacht figures (67x62cm-26x24in) s.d.88 prov. 15-Nov-3 Galerie Gloggner, Luzern #64/R est:2500-2800 (S.FR 2600)
£1391 $2546 €2031 Villa Contone (64x120cm-25x47in) s.i.d.1956 verso panel. 4-Jun-4 Zofingen, Switzerland #2832/R est:3500 (S.FR 3200)
£1659 $3020 €2422 Harlequin with mandolin (151x45cm-59x18in) s.d.55 panel. 16-Jun-4 Fischer, Luzern #1339/R est:300-4000 (S.FR 3800)
£2353 $4000 €3435 Karneval activity in the streets (65x82cm-26x32in) s.d.78. 19-Nov-3 Fischer, Luzern #1302/R est:3000-4000 (S.FR 5200)
£2632 $4395 €3843 Caddy with golf bag (75x46cm-30x18in) s.d.80 prov.lit. 15-Nov-3 Galerie Gloggner, Luzern #57/R est:7000-8500 (S.FR 6000)
£2941 $5000 €4294 Karneval in the snow (80x100cm-31x39in) s.d.88. 19-Nov-3 Fischer, Luzern #1305/R est:3500-4500 (S.FR 6500)
£4825 $8057 €7045 Horse drawn hearse with priest (44x66cm-17x26in) s.d.80 prov.lit. 15-Nov-3 Galerie Gloggner, Luzern #58/R est:5800-6500 (S.FR 11000)
Works on paper
£262 $461 €383 Circus horses (49x69cm-19x27in) s.d.60 pastel chk prov. 22-May-4 Galerie Gloggner, Luzern #51 (S.FR 600)

HAEFLIGER, Paul (1914-1982) Australian/German
£369 $598 €539 Reclining girls (38x46cm-15x18in) init.d.67 i.d.verso prov. 30-Jul-3 Goodman, Sydney #45/R (A.D 900)
£496 $917 €724 Paddington (30x40cm-12x16in) init. board painted c.1940 prov. 10-Mar-4 Deutscher-Menzies, Melbourne #506/R est:1400-1800 (A.D 1200)
£612 $1127 €894 Girl resting II (45x55cm-18x22in) init.d.67 s.i.d.verso. 29-Mar-4 Goodman, Sydney #8/R (A.D 1500)
£615 $996 €898 Siesta (46x38cm-18x15in) init.d.67 i.d.verso prov. 30-Jul-3 Goodman, Sydney #44/R (A.D 1500)
£857 $1577 €1251 Seated girls (54x65cm-21x26in) init.d.67 s.i.d.verso. 29-Mar-4 Goodman, Sydney #160/R (A.D 2100)
£1021 $1878 €1491 Reclining nude (91x122cm-36x48in) s.d.71 i.verso masonite. 29-Mar-4 Goodman, Sydney #159/R (A.D 2500)
£1551 $2854 €2264 Figure study (91x122cm-36x48in) s.d.71 masonite. 29-Mar-4 Goodman, Sydney #9/R est:3000-4000 (A.D 3800)
£2131 $3452 €3111 Abstract figures (91x122cm-36x48in) s.d.71 board prov. 30-Jul-3 Goodman, Sydney #48/R est:1500-2500 (A.D 5200)
£3484 $5643 €5087 Aeroplane (97x146cm-38x57in) s.d.65 i.d.verso prov. 30-Jul-3 Goodman, Sydney #46/R est:4000-6000 (A.D 8500)

HAEHNEL, Ernst Julius (1811-1891) German
Sculpture
£1100 $1870 €1606 Striding lion (20x34cm-8x13in) s. pat bronze. 28-Oct-3 Sotheby's, London #166/R

HAEN, Abraham de (17/18th C) Dutch
Works on paper
£878 $1546 €1300 View of Castle Hardenbroek (21x29cm-8x11in) pen grey black ink wash prov. 19-May-4 Sotheby's, Amsterdam #248/R

HAEN, Abraham de II (1707-1748) Dutch
Works on paper
£3514 $6184 €5200 View of S-Hertogenbosch (9x19cm-4x7in) i. pen brown ink wash black chk. 19-May-4 Sotheby's, Amsterdam #55/R est:1200-1500

HAENEL, Eduard G (19/20th C) ?
£329 $550 €480 Untitled, winter landscape (69x99cm-27x39in) d.1910. 14-Nov-3 Du Mouchelle, Detroit #140/R

HAENSBERGEN, Jan van (1642-1705) Dutch
£4444 $8000 €6488 Nymphs and satyrs in a grotto (27cm-11in circular) panel. 23-Jan-4 Christie's, Rockefeller NY #165/R est:10000-15000

HAENSBERGEN, Jan van (attrib) (1642-1705) Dutch
£1900 $3420 €2774 Young Christ and Saint Joseph walking in a landscape (17x13cm-7x5in) panel. 20-Apr-4 Sotheby's, Olympia #275/R est:2000-3000

HAER, Adolf de (1892-1945) German
£2899 $4754 €4000 Winter scene, Hoorn (67x45cm-26x18in) s. panel. 27-May-3 Sotheby's, Amsterdam #306/R est:4000-6000
£4000 $7360 €6000 In front of the mirror (135x97cm-53x38in) s.d.27 exhib. 12-Jun-4 Villa Grisebach, Berlin #253/R est:6000-8000

HAERENS, L (?) Belgian
Sculpture
£1854 $3393 €2800 Playing cat (26cm-10in) s. dark brown pat. bronze. 6-Apr-4 Sotheby's, Amsterdam #231/R est:1000-1500

HAERNING, August (1874-1961) Danish
£356 $647 €534 Summer landscape from Aalsgaarde (43x68cm-17x27in) s.d.1934 exhib. 19-Jun-4 Rasmussen, Havnen #2152/R (D.KR 4000)
£739 $1300 €1079 Country landscape (46x69cm-18x27in) s. prov. 23-May-4 Hindman, Chicago #78/R est:800-1200
£922 $1567 €1346 Edge of wood (86x111cm-34x44in) s.d.1904 i.verso exhib. 10-Nov-3 Rasmussen, Vejle #94/R (D.KR 10000)
£1075 $1935 €1570 View of Fredensborg Castle (45x70cm-18x28in) s.d.1929. 24-Apr-4 Rasmussen, Havnen #2072/R est:3000-5000 (D.KR 12000)
£1343 $2457 €1961 Summer landscape with boys bathing in river (64x92cm-25x36in) s. 9-Jun-4 Rasmussen, Copenhagen #1585/R est:12000 (D.KR 15000)

HAES, Carlos de (1829-1898) Spanish
£2621 $4350 €3800 Egyptian landscape (21x37cm-8x15in) s. cardboard. 30-Sep-3 Ansorena, Madrid #73/R est:3600
£3793 $6297 €5500 Wooded landscape (20x27cm-8x11in) s. cardboard. 30-Sep-3 Ansorena, Madrid #72/R est:3600
£4934 $9079 €7500 Beached boat (24x34cm-9x13in) s. board. 22-Jun-4 Durán, Madrid #126/R est:5000
£5369 $10040 €8000 Choppy sea (23x37cm-9x15in) s. cardboard. 24-Feb-4 Durán, Madrid #216/R est:8000
£8511 $14213 €12000 Picos de Europa (33x53cm-13x21in) s.i. 20-Oct-3 Durán, Madrid #224/R
£10563 $18275 €15000 Landscape with river (46x71cm-18x28in) s. 15-Dec-3 Ansorena, Madrid #316/R est:15000
Works on paper
£350 $584 €500 Paisaje rocoso (23x31cm-9x12in) s.d. crayon htd.white. 24-Jun-3 Segre, Madrid #10/R
£387 $620 €550 Tree (23x30cm-9x12in) s.d.1857 pencil dr. 16-Sep-3 Segre, Madrid #1/R
£725 $1188 €1000 Landsacpe of Torremolinos (20x26cm-8x10in) s.d.1858 drawing. 27-May-3 Durán, Madrid #40/R
£797 $1307 €1100 Landscape of Cabeza Mediana, El Paular (24x30cm-9x12in) s. i.d.1858 verso drawing. 27-May-3 Durán, Madrid #39/R est:550

HAESE, Gunter (1924-) German
Sculpture
£3000 $5490 €4500 Nanda (20cm-8in) wire. 4-Jun-4 Lempertz, Koln #173/R est:4200
£4698 $8644 €7000 Untitled (17x19x18cm-7x7x7in) phosphorous brass wire plexiglas socle. 26-Mar-4 Ketterer, Hamburg #442/R est:7000-9000

HAESEKER, Alexandra (20th C) Canadian
£1016 $1819 €1483 Red, white and blue (161x203cm-63x80in) s.d.1979 i.verso. 6-May-4 Heffel, Vancouver #61/R est:2000-3000 (C.D 2500)
Works on paper
£383 $651 €559 Last light (53x72cm-21x28in) s.d.1983 s.i.d.1983 verso W/C prov. 23-Nov-3 Levis, Calgary #305/R (C.D 850)

HAESELICH, Johann Georg (1806-1894) German
£699 $1189 €1000 Woodland (31x40cm-12x16in) s. 20-Nov-3 Dorotheum, Salzburg #185/R
£1197 $2071 €1700 Pre-alpine landscape with peasants, cattle and other animals (68x96cm-27x38in) s. 12-Dec-3 Altus, Berlin #549/R est:1500
£3472 $5799 €5000 Farmstead by lake (41x58cm-16x23in) s. 24-Oct-3 Ketterer, Hamburg #69/R est:5200-5500

HAFENEDER, Siegfried (1936-) German
£301 $512 €440 Old Munich (26x48cm-10x19in) s.i. panel lit. 6-Nov-3 Allgauer, Kempten #3436/R

HAFFENRICHTER, Hans (20th C) German?
£699 $1203 €1000 Composition with meteor structure (43x61cm-17x24in) s. tempera exhib. 2-Dec-3 Hauswedell & Nolte, Hamburg #251/R

HAFFNER, Felix (1818-1875) French
£2000 $3620 €3000 Le ramassage du Tabac (162x114cm-64x45in) s. lit. 30-Mar-4 Rossini, Paris #812/R est:3000-5000

HAFFNER, Léon (1881-1972) French
Works on paper
£267 $485 €400 Yawl au pres bon plein (44x32cm-17x13in) s.i. gouache pochoir. 3-Jul-4 Neret-Minet, Paris #186/R
£276 $505 €400 Monotype en regate (44x32cm-17x13in) s. gouache pochoir. 31-Jan-4 Neret-Minet, Paris #165/R
£280 $510 €420 Trois mats carre devant un phare (38x78cm-15x31in) s. gouache pochoir. 3-Jul-4 Neret-Minet, Paris #181
£294 $499 €420 Le croiseur Dunkerque (43x80cm-17x31in) s. pochoir. 23-Nov-3 Claude Boisgirard, Paris #153
£300 $555 €450 Trois-mats (39x64cm-15x25in) s. gouache pochoir. 14-Jul-4 Livinec, Gaudcheau & Jezequel, Rennes #70
£300 $546 €450 Caravelle (37x73cm-15x29in) s. gouache pochoir. 3-Jul-4 Neret-Minet, Paris #183
£313 $516 €450 Yawl tribord amure (37x47cm-15x19in) s. gouache. 5-Jul-3 Neret-Minet, Paris #141
£313 $516 €450 Goelette (37x47cm-15x19in) s. gouache. 5-Jul-3 Neret-Minet, Paris #140
£345 $631 €500 Le combat de la Belle Poule en 1778 (22x28cm-9x11in) s. gouache pochoir. 31-Jan-4 Neret-Minet, Paris #143/R
£379 $694 €550 Grand yacht vu par tribord (39x79cm-15x31in) s. gouache pochoir. 31-Jan-4 Neret-Minet, Paris #162/R

£417 $688 €600 Cotre (42x31cm-17x12in) s. gouache. 5-Jul-3 Neret-Minet, Paris #145
£451 $745 €650 Goelette (42x31cm-17x12in) s. gouache. 5-Jul-3 Neret-Minet, Paris #146/R
£486 $802 €700 Classe J (76x39cm-30x15in) s. gouache. 5-Jul-3 Neret-Minet, Paris #143
£528 $856 €750 Trois mats carre par trois quart avant (73x57cm-29x22in) s. gouache pochoir. 11-Aug-3 Boscher, Cherbourg #702
£533 $971 €800 Yachts en regate (80x40cm-31x16in) s. gouache pochoir. 3-Jul-4 Neret-Minet, Paris #177/R
£612 $978 €850 Trois-mats sous voile par le travers (40x80cm-16x31in) s. gouache pochoir. 18-May-3 Claude Boisgirard, Paris #154
£612 $1096 €900 Yacht sous voiles vue par babord (28x63cm-11x25in) s. gouache pochoir. 21-Mar-4 Claude Boisgirard, Paris #125
£625 $1131 €950 Regate au passage de la bouee (39x77cm-15x30in) s. gouache pochoir. 17-Apr-4 Deburaux, Boulogne #208
£667 $1213 €1000 Deux yachts en regate (40x80cm-16x31in) s. gouache pochoir. 3-Jul-4 Neret-Minet, Paris #163/R
£667 $1213 €1000 Yacht gree en ketch vu par tribord (40x80cm-16x31in) s. gouache pochoir. 3-Jul-4 Neret-Minet, Paris #164/R
£680 $1218 €1000 Trois mats sous voiles vue par le travers (40x80cm-16x31in) s. gouache pochoir. 21-Mar-4 Claude Boisgirard, Paris #124/R
£690 $1152 €1000 Voilier borde (43x31cm-17x12in) s. pochoir. 11-Nov-3 Lesieur & Le Bars, Le Havre #61
£764 $1276 €1100 Yacht (40x80cm-16x31in) s. gouache. 26-Oct-3 Lesieur & Le Bars, Le Havre #195
£828 $1382 €1200 Regate par gros temps (38x76cm-15x30in) s. gouache. 11-Nov-3 Lesieur & Le Bars, Le Havre #60
£833 $1375 €1200 Goelette (76x39cm-30x15in) s. gouache. 5-Jul-3 Neret-Minet, Paris #142
£833 $1392 €1200 Trois-mats (40x80cm-16x31in) s. gouache. 26-Oct-3 Lesieur & Le Bars, Le Havre #199
£897 $1497 €1300 Voiliers en regate (42x31cm-17x12in) s. pochoir. 11-Nov-3 Lesieur & Le Bars, Le Havre #62
£937 $1547 €1350 Brick (40x80cm-16x31in) s. gouache. 5-Jul-3 Neret-Minet, Paris #121
£1042 $1740 €1500 Regate (43x31cm-17x12in) s. gouache. 26-Oct-3 Lesieur & Le Bars, Le Havre #112
£1111 $1856 €1600 Yachts (43x31cm-17x12in) s. gouache pair. 26-Oct-3 Lesieur & Le Bars, Le Havre #98

HAFFTEN, Karl von (1834-1884) German
£944 $1605 €1350 Le naufrage (92x141cm-36x56in) s. 18-Nov-3 Vanderkindere, Brussels #58
£1722 $3151 €2600 Storm gathering over castle on English coast (90x135cm-35x53in) s. 7-Apr-4 Dorotheum, Salzburg #114/R est:2200-3000

HAFFTER, Martha (1873-1951) Swiss
£302 $540 €441 Two girls by wall (36x45cm-14x18in) s. board. 12-May-4 Dobiaschofsky, Bern #3632/R (S.FR 700)
£362 $615 €529 Female nude (46x20cm-18x8in) s. i. verso canvas on pavatex. 18-Nov-3 Hans Widmer, St Gallen #1075 (S.FR 800)

HAFIF, Marcia (1929-) American
Works on paper
£1611 $2900 €2352 Untitled (25x40cm-10x16in) graphite. 24-Apr-4 David Rago, Lambertville #171/R est:200-400

HAFNER, Carl (1814-1873) German
£400 $716 €600 Evening on the Kochelsee (20x26cm-8x10in) s. canvas on board lit. 14-May-4 Schloss Ahlden, Ahlden #2782/R

HAFNER, Charles Andrew (1888-?) American
£798 $1300 €1165 Still life with delphiniums and shell (91x81cm-36x32in) s.d.1937. 17-Jul-3 Doyle, New York #32/R
Sculpture
£17442 $30000 €25465 Peter Pan (147cm-58in) s.d.1928 green pat. bronze. 3-Dec-3 Doyle, New York #236/R est:20000-30000

HAFNER, Rudolf (1893-1951) Austrian
£1020 $1827 €1500 Munich - Karlsplatz with Karlstor (52x39cm-20x15in) s.d.922 canvas on board. 17-Mar-4 Neumeister, Munich #466/R est:1800

HAFSTROM, Gillis (1841-1909) Swedish
£385 $662 €562 Lake landscape with washerwoman (38x46cm-15x18in) s. 3-Dec-3 AB Stockholms Auktionsverk #2311/R (S.KR 5000)

HAFSTROM, Jan (1937-) Swedish
£317 $539 €463 Memory terrain (27x42cm-11x17in) s.d.1980 verso acrylic paper. 4-Nov-3 Bukowskis, Stockholm #622/R (S.KR 4200)
£378 $642 €552 Untitled (48x39cm-19x15in) s.d.1976 paper prov. 4-Nov-3 Bukowskis, Stockholm #583/R (S.KR 5000)
£440 $778 €642 Academia (38x28cm-15x11in) s.d.1990 oil collage exhib.prov. 27-Apr-4 AB Stockholms Auktionsverk #1095/R (S.KR 6000)
£23443 $41495 €34227 Cloud of unknowing (195x200cm-77x79in) s.d.1979 verso acrylic prov.exhib.lit. 27-Apr-4 AB Stockholms Auktionsverk #1036/R est:125000-150000 (S.KR 320000)
Sculpture
£3021 $5136 €4411 Fifth station (116x86x12cm-46x34x5in) s.d.1989 verso oil wood construction exhib.lit. 5-Nov-3 AB Stockholms Auktionsverk #987/R est:35000-40000 (S.KR 40000)
Works on paper
£403 $713 €588 Untitled (22x85cm-9x33in) s.d.1991 verso mixed media panel. 27-Apr-4 AB Stockholms Auktionsverk #942/R (S.KR 5500)
£544 $979 €794 Untitled (41x57cm-16x22in) s.d.1981 verso mixed media. 26-Apr-4 Bukowskis, Stockholm #519/R (S.KR 7500)
£1233 $2219 €1800 Untitled (45x60cm-18x24in) s.d.1979 mixed media. 26-Apr-4 Bukowskis, Stockholm #531/R est:10000-12000 (S.KR 17000)
£6798 $11556 €9925 Untitled (100x100cm-39x39in) s.d.1982-86 verso mixed media assemblage canvas on panel prov.lit. 4-Nov-3 Bukowskis, Stockholm #587/R est:50000-60000 (S.KR 90000)

HAGAMAN, James H (1866-?) American
£231 $400 €337 Pastoral landscape with shepherd and flock (36x51cm-14x20in) s. 13-Dec-3 Weschler, Washington #542

HAGARTY, Clara (1871-1958) Canadian
£1406 $2614 €2053 Green and gold (41x35cm-16x14in) s. canvasboard prov.exhib. 2-Mar-4 Ritchie, Toronto #72/R est:1000-1500 (C.D 3500)

HAGARTY, Mary S (fl.1885-1938) British
Works on paper
£290 $522 €435 Autumn landscape with lake (60x90cm-24x35in) indis sig. W/C. 25-Apr-4 Goteborg Auktionsverk, Sweden #208/R (S.KR 4000)
£350 $567 €511 River side pastures (24x34cm-9x13in) s. W/C. 30-Jul-3 Hamptons Fine Art, Godalming #127
£450 $752 €657 Elegant walled garden in full bloom, thought to be Arley Hall (27x38cm-11x15in) init. W/C. 9-Jul-3 Peter Wilson, Nantwich #72

HAGARTY, Parker (1859-1934) British
£350 $655 €511 Young girl fishing beside a ford in a summer landscape (35x53cm-14x21in) s. 22-Jul-4 Tennants, Leyburn #853
£420 $701 €613 River landscape, possibly the vale of Glamorgan (35x48cm-14x19in) s. 7-Oct-3 Bonhams, Knightsbridge #111/R
£460 $768 €672 Maggie (51x41cm-20x16in) 21-Oct-3 Gorringes, Lewes #2136
£500 $785 €725 Sheep grazing in English summer landscape (28x36cm-11x14in) s. wood panel. 15-Dec-2 Desmond Judd, Cranbrook #845
£680 $1136 €993 Old house, upon on Severn (23x33cm-9x13in) mono.d.1884. 12-Nov-3 Halls, Shrewsbury #316/R

HAGBORG, August (1852-1925) Swedish
£768 $1252 €1121 Mussel gatherer (60x40cm-24x16in) st.sig. 29-Sep-3 Lilla Bukowskis, Stockholm #667 (S.KR 10000)
£783 $1410 €1175 Jean - boy in sailor's uniform (56x41cm-22x16in) i.verso. 25-Apr-4 Goteborg Auktionsverk, Sweden #170/R (S.KR 10800)
£788 $1419 €1150 Coastal landscape with boats and figures (26x40cm-10x16in) st.sig. panel. 26-Jan-4 Lilla Bukowskis, Stockholm #720 (S.KR 10500)
£923 $1588 €1348 Lake landscape with pine trees in evening sunshine (72x92cm-28x36in) s. 3-Dec-3 AB Stockholms Auktionsverk #2472/R (S.KR 12000)
£1077 $1852 €1572 Fishergirl with basket on the jetty (95x68cm-37x27in) s. 7-Dec-3 Uppsala Auktionskammare, Uppsala #134/R (S.KR 14000)
£2513 $4498 €3669 On the beach in Brittany (92x73cm-36x29in) s. 25-May-4 Bukowskis, Stockholm #122/R est:30000-40000 (S.KR 34000)
£2587 $4630 €3777 Gustaf I charging Peder Sunnanvader in the Cathedral in Westeraas (78x97cm-31x38in) s.i.d.1875. 26-May-4 AB Stockholms Auktionsverk #2316/R est:20000-25000 (S.KR 35000)
£2882 $5160 €4208 The country girl (60x40cm-24x16in) s.i.d.1878. 25-May-4 Bukowskis, Stockholm #123/R est:30000-35000 (S.KR 39000)
£3622 $6483 €5288 Oyster gatherer (73x53cm-29x21in) s. 26-May-4 AB Stockholms Auktionsverk #2122/R est:40000-50000 (S.KR 49000)
£3695 $6615 €5395 Girl carrying sheaf of corn (75x55cm-30x22in) s. 26-May-4 AB Stockholms Auktionsverk #2356/R est:60000-80000 (S.KR 50000)
£3769 $6483 €5503 Waiting on the beach (81x65cm-32x26in) s. 2-Dec-3 Bukowskis, Stockholm #175/R est:30000-35000 (S.KR 49000)
£5000 $8600 €7300 Mussel gatherer and fisherman (80x100cm-31x39in) s. 7-Dec-3 Uppsala Auktionskammare, Uppsala #120/R est:40000-50000 (S.KR 65000)
£5077 $8732 €7412 Stone quarry (98x132cm-39x52in) s. 2-Dec-3 Bukowskis, Stockholm #86/R est:50000-60000 (S.KR 66000)
£5385 $9262 €7862 Fisherman and oyster-gatherer on beach (60x81cm-24x32in) s. 3-Dec-3 AB Stockholms Auktionsverk #2385/R est:75000-100000 (S.KR 70000)
£5556 $10000 €8112 La plage (81x100cm-32x39in) s. 23-Apr-4 Sotheby's, New York #170/R est:15000-20000
£8500 $15214 €12410 Oyster gatherer (121x77cm-48x30in) s. 26-May-4 AB Stockholms Auktionsverk #2140/R est:60000-80000 (S.KR 115000)
£14782 $26460 €21582 Two fishergirls looking at their catch (73x100cm-29x39in) s. 25-May-4 Bukowskis, Stockholm #125/R est:100000-125000 (S.KR 200000)
£25868 $46305 €37767 Washerwomen (76x97cm-30x38in) s. painted c.1880. 26-May-4 AB Stockholms Auktionsverk #2272/R est:400000-500000 (S.KR 350000)

HAGEDORN, Friedrich (1814-1889) German
Works on paper
£2200 $3586 €3212 Landscape in the environs of Rio de Janeiro (36x57cm-14x22in) s. bodycol. 24-Sep-3 Christie's, London #125/R est:800-1200
£2717 $5000 €3967 View of Rio de Janeiro (35x53cm-14x21in) s. W/C gouache. 8-Jun-4 Auctions by the Bay, Alameda #1011/R

HAGEDORN, Karl (1889-1969) British
£600 $972 €870 St Paul's from Southward Bridge (66x81cm-26x32in) s.d.1936. 26-Jan-3 Desmond Judd, Cranbrook #844
Works on paper
£250 $440 €365 Sails of a Thames barge (33x49cm-13x19in) s. W/C. 18-May-4 Fellows & Sons, Birmingham #193/R

HAGEDORN-OLSEN, Thorvald (1902-1996) Danish
£301 $512 €439 Landscape from Roskilde fjord (54x65cm-21x26in) s. 29-Nov-3 Rasmussen, Havnen #4074/R (D.KR 3200)
£332 $597 €485 Autumn landscape (53x74cm-21x29in) s.d.47. 24-Apr-4 Rasmussen, Havnen #4130 (D.KR 3700)
£343 $631 €501 Winter landscape with fields (46x55cm-18x22in) s. 29-Mar-4 Rasmussen, Copenhagen #563 (D.KR 3800)

£358 $645 €523 Summer landscape with cattle (61x73cm-24x29in) s. 24-Apr-4 Rasmussen, Havnen #4128/R (D.KR 4000)
£379 $607 €550 Summer's day by the fjord (52x69cm-20x27in) s. 17-Sep-3 Kunsthallen, Copenhagen #254 (D.KR 4000)
£493 $887 €720 Sunshine over the fjord (54x69cm-21x27in) s.d.43. 24-Apr-4 Rasmussen, Havnen #4129 (D.KR 5500)
£521 $834 €755 View of the harbour, Roskilde Fjord (52x84cm-20x33in) s.d.39. 17-Sep-3 Kunsthallen, Copenhagen #253 (D.KR 5500)
£711 $1294 €1067 Potting on plants, spring (100x122cm-39x48in) s.d.1939 exhib. 19-Jun-4 Rasmussen, Havnen #4152/R (D.KR 8000)

HAGEL, Frank (1933-) American
£1719 $2750 €2510 Northern Blackfeet meet the Hairy Faces (104x74cm-41x29in) s. masonite. 22-Sep-3 O'Gallerie, Oregon #781/R est:3000-4000
Works on paper
£233 $400 €340 Watching the herd (28x30cm-11x12in) s.d.1956 W/C. 6-Dec-3 Selkirks, St. Louis #189

HAGELSTEIN, Paul (1825-1868) German
£1667 $2717 €2400 Young boy with hamster (117x78cm-46x31in) s. 24-Sep-3 Neumeister, Munich #434/R est:1200

HAGEMAN, Victor (1868-1938) Belgian
£728 $1326 €1100 Lieuse de gerbes (100x100cm-39x39in) s. 15-Jun-4 Galerie Moderne, Brussels #178

HAGEMANN, Albinia (1824-1897) Danish
£2695 $5013 €3935 Interior scene with mother and daughter looking in book (43x31cm-17x12in) s.d.1848. 2-Mar-4 Rasmussen, Copenhagen #1276/R est:20000-25000 (D.KR 30000)

HAGEMANN, Godefroy de (1820-1877) French
£1687 $2800 €2463 River landscape (65x100cm-26x39in) s. 30-Sep-3 Christie's, Rockefeller NY #444/R est:7000-9000
£2550 $4693 €3800 Dans les souks (74x61cm-29x24in) s.d.1869 panel. 26-Mar-4 Neret-Minet, Paris #8/R est:4000-5000

HAGEMANN, Louis (19th C) German
£506 $790 €800 The Isar near Bad Tolz (36x57cm-14x22in) s. board. 18-Oct-2 Von Zezschwitz, Munich #15/R

HAGEMANN, Oskar H (1888-1984) German
£317 $507 €450 Flowers in white porcelain vase (60x50cm-24x20in) s.d.1949. 18-Sep-3 Rieber, Stuttgart #1310

HAGEMANS, Maurice (1852-1917) Belgian
£490 $817 €700 Lever de soleil sur l'etang (17x36cm-7x14in) s. 13-Oct-3 Horta, Bruxelles #281
£738 $1366 €1100 Fagoteurs dans les dunes (29x49cm-11x19in) s. 15-Mar-4 Horta, Bruxelles #369
£1007 $1862 €1500 Calfatage de la barque de peche (40x70cm-16x28in) s. 15-Mar-4 Horta, Bruxelles #368 est:1800-2200
£1088 $1948 €1600 La Meuse a Dinant (49x60cm-19x24in) s. canvas on panel. 17-Mar-4 Hotel des Ventes Mosan, Brussels #87 est:2000-2500
£1333 $2440 €2000 Paysage avec vaches a l'abreuvoir (30x65cm-12x26in) s. 7-Jun-4 Palais de Beaux Arts, Brussels #65/R est:2000-3000
£1528 $2429 €2200 Vaches au pre (30x50cm-12x20in) s. 9-Sep-3 Vanderkindere, Brussels #105
£1958 $3329 €2800 Pecheur au bord de l'etang (30x55cm-12x22in) s. 1-Dec-3 Palais de Beaux Arts, Brussels #72/R est:1200-1500
Works on paper
£280 $507 €420 Pecheur au bord de l'etang (23x31cm-9x12in) s. W/C gouache. 30-Mar-4 Palais de Beaux Arts, Brussels #602
£300 $540 €450 Vaches dans le pre (25x35cm-10x14in) s. W/C. 20-Apr-4 Galerie Moderne, Brussels #235/R
£347 $566 €500 Vaches. s. W/C gouache. 23-Sep-3 Galerie Moderne, Brussels #615/R
£387 $678 €550 Paysage avec personnage. s. W/C. 16-Dec-3 Galerie Moderne, Brussels #563/R
£400 $736 €600 Vaches au coucher du soleil (21x32cm-8x13in) s. mixed media. 14-Jun-4 Horta, Bruxelles #28
£414 $766 €600 Fagoteuses (27x21cm-11x8in) s.d.84 W/C. 19-Jan-4 Horta, Bruxelles #211
£541 $968 €800 La conduite de la chevre (34x28cm-13x11in) s. W/C. 10-May-4 Horta, Bruxelles #413
£559 $934 €800 Le pecheur (24x40cm-9x16in) s. W/C. 11-Oct-3 De Vuyst, Lokeren #174
£590 $939 €850 Charrette attelee a un ane (35x50cm-14x20in) s. W/C. 15-Sep-3 Horta, Bruxelles #152
£603 $1007 €850 Vaches au pre (21x34cm-8x13in) s. W/C. 17-Jun-3 Vanderkindere, Brussels #87/R
£655 $1212 €950 Pecheur au lever du soleil (60x45cm-24x18in) s. W/C. 16-Feb-4 Horta, Bruxelles #26
£667 $1193 €1000 Cows by the bank of the river (28x37cm-11x15in) s. gouache. 15-May-4 De Vuyst, Lokeren #152/R
£667 $1193 €1000 Fermiere poussant sa brouette (55x78cm-22x31in) s. W/C. 11-May-4 Vanderkindere, Brussels #115
£694 $1160 €1000 La laboureur (26x55cm-10x22in) s. mixed media. 21-Oct-3 Campo, Vlaamse Kaai #443
£709 $1184 €1000 Fermiere et son troupeau (16x26cm-6x10in) s. W/C. 14-Oct-3 Vanderkindere, Brussels #103
£867 $1595 €1300 La conduite du troupeau (32x82cm-13x32in) s. 14-Jun-4 Horta, Bruxelles #27
£909 $1564 €1300 Trois-mats a quai a Anvers (46x30cm-18x12in) s. W/C. 8-Dec-3 Horta, Bruxelles #53
£979 $1664 €1400 Personnages dans une barque (24x55cm-9x22in) s. W/C gouache. 1-Dec-3 Palais de Beaux Arts, Brussels #71
£1064 $1777 €1500 Un berger et son troupeau (45x85cm-18x33in) s. mixed media canvas on panel. 15-Oct-3 Hotel des Ventes Mosan, Brussels #126 est:1800-2200
£1689 $3193 €2500 Fermiere et ses cochons en foret (90x58cm-35x23in) s. W/C. 17-Feb-4 Vanderkindere, Brussels #40 est:1750-2500
£4196 $7133 €6000 Aux enfants assistes (47x56cm-19x22in) s. W/C. 1-Dec-3 Palais de Beaux Arts, Brussels #70/R est:2000-3000

HAGEMANS, Paul (1884-1959) Belgian
£294 $490 €420 Nature morte aux faiences (30x40cm-12x16in) s. panel. 13-Oct-3 Horta, Bruxelles #282
£331 $603 €500 Les anciens (25x33cm-10x13in) s. panel. 15-Jun-4 Galerie Moderne, Brussels #176/R
£400 $716 €600 Au bord de l'eau (20x32cm-8x13in) s. panel. 11-May-4 Vanderkindere, Brussels #578
£400 $736 €600 A l'oree du bois (37x40cm-15x16in) s. panel. 14-Jun-4 Horta, Bruxelles #29
£436 $803 €650 Personnages dans un sous-bois (40x45cm-16x18in) s. 23-Mar-4 Galerie Moderne, Brussels #323/R
£537 $993 €800 Sous-bois anime (50x60cm-20x24in) s. 15-Mar-4 Horta, Bruxelles #370
£604 $1117 €900 Au bord de l'etang (37x40cm-15x16in) s. panel. 15-Mar-4 Horta, Bruxelles #372
£676 $1209 €1000 Estacade dans un paysage fluvial (49x59cm-19x23in) cardboard. 10-May-4 Amberes, Antwerp #131
£799 $1270 €1150 Pont aux canards (68x89cm-27x35in) s. panel. 9-Sep-3 Vanderkindere, Brussels #120
£940 $1729 €1400 Fleurs blanches (70x70cm-28x28in) s. 23-Mar-4 Galerie Moderne, Brussels #194/R
£1049 $1783 €1500 Retour au passe (93x89cm-37x35in) s. panel. 18-Nov-3 Vanderkindere, Brussels #231 est:1000-1500
£1447 $2663 €2200 Jour de fete (60x70cm-24x28in) s. panel. 22-Jun-4 Palais de Beaux Arts, Brussels #257/R est:2250-3500
£1711 $3147 €2600 Traversee de la riviere (80x100cm-31x39in) s. panel. 22-Jun-4 Palais de Beaux Arts, Brussels #258/R est:3000-3500
£1745 $3228 €2600 Pleasure beach (18x31cm-7x12in) s. W/C gouache. 13-Mar-4 De Vuyst, Lokeren #164/R est:3000-3300
£2759 $5103 €4000 Vase fleuri des roses sur fond d'estampe japonaise (60x60cm-24x24in) s. 19-Jan-4 Horta, Bruxelles #210/R est:3000-3500
£3448 $6379 €5000 Pecheur au lever de brume (70x90cm-28x35in) s. panel. 16-Feb-4 Horta, Bruxelles #129 est:6000-8000

HAGEMEISTER, Karl (1848-1933) German
£2797 $4755 €4000 Lake with waterlilies and trees on shore (72x117cm-28x46in) s. 26-Nov-3 Lempertz, Koln #694/R est:5000-6000
£2958 $5117 €4200 Sunlit water landscape (49x69cm-19x27in) s. board. 13-Dec-3 Lempertz, Koln #218/R est:3000
£4667 $8587 €7000 Breakers (77x128cm-30x50in) s. 12-Jun-4 Villa Grisebach, Berlin #113/R est:7000-9000
£6690 $11574 €9500 Waterlilies (52x76cm-20x30in) s. 13-Dec-3 Lempertz, Koln #219/R est:3000
£8054 $14819 €12000 Lake of water lilies (117x70cm-46x28in) s. prov. 26-Mar-4 Ketterer, Hamburg #443/R est:9000-11000
Works on paper
£1748 $2920 €2500 Reeds at river's edge at dusk (50x75cm-20x30in) s. pastel. 28-Jun-3 Dannenberg, Berlin #690/R est:2500
£2119 $3857 €3200 Reeds with waterlilies (50x59cm-20x23in) s. pastel. 19-Jun-4 Dannenberg, Berlin #566/R est:2000
£2797 $4755 €4000 Mark lake (70x100cm-28x39in) s. pastel. 29-Nov-3 Villa Grisebach, Berlin #125/R est:3500-4500
£3758 $6652 €5600 Stream in late autumn (76x108cm-30x43in) s. pastel. 28-Apr-4 Schopman, Hamburg #476/R est:5800

HAGEMEYER, Johan (1884-1962) American/Dutch
Photographs
£3107 $5500 €4536 Castles of today, San Francisco, 1930 (10x8cm-4x3in) s.d.1930 gelatin silver print prov.lit. 27-Apr-4 Christie's, Rockefeller NY #258/R est:7000-9000

HAGEN, Anny R (fl.1938-1940) British
£300 $510 €438 Still life with apples (24x35cm-9x14in) s. board. 27-Nov-3 Greenslade Hunt, Taunton #1027

HAGEN, Eduard von (1834-1909) German
£216 $400 €324 Cavalier with a pipe (20x15cm-8x6in) s. panel. 17-Jul-4 Skinner, Boston #159/R

HAGEN, Else (1914-) Norwegian
£1450 $2611 €2117 The pearl gate (87x71cm-34x28in) s. panel. 26-Apr-4 Bukowskis, Stockholm #254/R est:20000-22000 (S.KR 20000)
£2795 $4751 €4081 From Marseilles (75x91cm-30x36in) s. 4-Nov-3 Bukowskis, Stockholm #197a/R est:20000-22000 (S.KR 37000)

HAGEN, Johann van der (1676-1745) Dutch
£2000 $3400 €2920 English men-o'war (51x76cm-20x30in) 19-Nov-3 Christie's, Kensington #439/R

HAGEN, Johann van der (attrib) (1676-1745) Dutch
£1100 $1892 €1606 British man-o-war in heavy seas (63x61cm-25x24in) prov. 2-Dec-3 Sotheby's, London #2/R est:1000-1500

HAGEN, Peter (?) German
£283 $481 €405 Moorland with houses (40x50cm-16x20in) s. 20-Nov-3 Weidler, Nurnberg #6536

HAGEN, Robert (?) ?
£313 $584 €470 Making contact. 23-Jul-4 Lawson Menzies, Sydney #2047 (A.D 800)

HAGEN, Theodor (1842-1919) German
£369 $687 €550 On the edge of the forest (17x22cm-7x9in) s. board. 5-Mar-4 Wendl, Rudolstadt #3676/R
£467 $859 €700 Extensive landscape (32x44cm-13x17in) s. 11-Jun-4 Wendl, Rudolstadt #4054/R
£600 $1086 €900 Stormy weather over the dunes (30x38cm-12x15in) s. board. 1-Apr-4 Van Ham, Cologne #1402/R
£1275 $2372 €1900 Country scene in Oberweimar (33x46cm-13x18in) s. 5-Mar-4 Wendl, Rudolstadt #3675/R est:1900
£1678 $2853 €2400 Countryside in summer (67x110cm-26x43in) s. 22-Nov-3 Arnold, Frankfurt #535/R est:1500

HAGEN, Walter (1910-) Swiss
£431 $772 €629 Spring (60x81cm-24x32in) s. i. stretcher. 12-May-4 Dobiaschofsky, Bern #589/R (S.FR 1000)

HAGEN, William van der (?-1745) British
£248276 $459310 €360000 Corke Harbour (48x91cm-19x36in) s.d.1738. 11-Feb-4 Woodwards, Cork #21/R

HAGEN, William van der (circle) (?-1745) British
£6000 $10740 €8760 Landing of William III at Carrickfergus, 14 June 1690 with Men-o'-war in port (36x46cm-14x18in) prov. 14-May-4 Christie's, London #69/R est:3000-5000

HAGENAUER (20th C) Austrian
Sculpture
£1000 $1670 €1460 Figure (30cm-12in) st.f. brass. 13-Nov-3 Christie's, Kensington #311/R est:1000-1200
£1000 $1700 €1460 Female archer (28cm-11in) silvered bronze. 25-Nov-3 Sotheby's, Olympia #142/R est:1000-1200
£1078 $1800 €1574 Exotic rooster (28x20cm-11x8in) st. wood bronze. 25-Oct-3 David Rago, Lambertville #154 est:1000-1500
£1100 $1870 €1606 Nude on a gondolier (22x44cm-9x17in) nickel plated. 25-Nov-3 Sotheby's, Olympia #144/R est:1200-1800
£1300 $2171 €1898 African woman (26cm-10in) st.f. copper brass. 13-Nov-3 Christie's, Kensington #308/R est:600-900
£1500 $2550 €2190 Horse (27x33cm-11x13in) nickel plated. 25-Nov-3 Sotheby's, Olympia #145/R est:800-1200
£1900 $3173 €2774 Mask (26cm-10in) st.f. metal. 13-Nov-3 Christie's, Kensington #307/R est:800-1200
£2600 $4134 €3796 African lady in a boat (38cm-15in) st.f.WHW pat bronze. 9-Sep-3 Sotheby's, Olympia #382/R est:1000-1500
£2695 $4500 €3935 Woman's head with stylised features and locks of hair (53x43cm-21x17in) s. polished chrome base. 25-Oct-3 David Rago, Lambertville #149 est:2500-3500
£3593 $6000 €5246 Man's head with stylized features and locks of hair (53x43cm-21x17in) s. polished crhome base. 25-Oct-3 David Rago, Lambertville #150 est:2500-3500
£6200 $10354 €9052 Figure (54cm-21in) st.f.WHW brass wood. 13-Nov-3 Christie's, Kensington #312/R est:3000-4000
£9581 $16000 €13988 Waiter carrying a tray (165x53x53cm-65x21x21in) s. brass. 25-Oct-3 David Rago, Lambertville #156 est:20000-25000

HAGENAUER (studio) (20th C) Austrian
Sculpture
£3468 $6000 €5063 Woman and greyhound (24x27x9cm-9x11x4in) nickel plated metal wood. 11-Dec-3 Sotheby's, New York #56/R est:2500-3500
£14451 $25000 €21098 Three piece band (44cm-17in) brass plated metal. 11-Dec-3 Sotheby's, New York #57/R est:7000-10000
£24566 $42500 €35866 Butler (183x56x52cm-72x22x20in) stainless steel copper prov. 11-Dec-3 Sotheby's, New York #58/R est:10000-15000
£52023 $90000 €75954 Four piece band (185cm-73in) num.1077 polished aluminum prov. 11-Dec-3 Sotheby's, New York #59/R est:40000-60000

HAGENAUER, Franz (1906-1986) Austrian
Sculpture
£1007 $1872 €1500 Donkey (15cm-6in) brass. 8-Mar-4 Dorotheum, Vienna #217/R est:1800-2200
£1074 $1922 €1600 Donkey (16cm-6in) sheet brass. 26-May-4 Dorotheum, Vienna #340/R est:1200-1500
£1119 $1902 €1600 Antilope (20cm-8in) i. brass. 27-Nov-3 Wiener Kunst Auktionen, Vienna #26/R est:1600-2300
£1342 $2403 €2000 Ram (15cm-6in) brass prov. 26-May-4 Dorotheum, Vienna #342/R est:2000-2500
£1818 $3091 €2600 Ice skater (30cm-12in) s.i. sheet brass. 25-Nov-3 Dorotheum, Vienna #379/R est:1600-2200
£2013 $3604 €3000 Tennis players, male and female (33cm-13in) sheet brass two. 26-May-4 Dorotheum, Vienna #341/R est:3500-4500
£2238 $3804 €3200 Ram (18cm-7in) i. brass. 27-Nov-3 Wiener Kunst Auktionen, Vienna #27/R est:1800-2500
£3147 $5350 €4500 Skier (32cm-13in) i. brass. 27-Nov-3 Wiener Kunst Auktionen, Vienna #28/R est:1800-3000
£5000 $8950 €7300 Bust of a woman (32cm-13in) s. nickelled metal. 13-May-4 Christie's, Kensington #376/R est:5000-7000
£10500 $19635 €15330 Stylised nude (101cm-40in) s. hammered brass exec.c.1930. 24-Feb-4 Sotheby's, Olympia #274/R est:5000-7000

HAGENAUER, Johann Baptist (1732-1819) Austrian
Sculpture
£21622 $38054 €32000 Christ and column. pat bronze lit. 18-May-4 Sotheby's, Milan #438/R est:7000-10000

HAGENAUER, Karl (1898-1956) Austrian
Sculpture
£1042 $1656 €1500 Kneeling figure (23cm-9in) i. brass. 15-Sep-3 Dorotheum, Vienna #219/R est:1600-2000
£1141 $2042 €1700 Jumping horse (17cm-7in) brass. 26-May-4 Dorotheum, Vienna #338/R est:1200-1500
£1189 $2021 €1700 Boar (8x12cm-3x5in) i. brass. 25-Nov-3 Dorotheum, Vienna #376/R est:1100-1500
£1259 $2140 €1800 Bird (21cm-8in) i. brass. 25-Nov-3 Dorotheum, Vienna #378/R est:1200-1500
£1477 $2746 €2200 Classical figure (65cm-26in) pat.brass stone socle prov. 8-Mar-4 Dorotheum, Vienna #39/R est:2200-3000
£2416 $4325 €3600 Greyhound (25cm-10in) brass. 26-May-4 Dorotheum, Vienna #339/R est:1800-2200

HAGER, Albert (1857-1940) Belgian
Sculpture
£1931 $3572 €2800 Lionne et lionceau (28x74x23cm-11x29x9in) s.d.1923 pat bronze st.f.Petermann a Saint Gilles exec 1923. 19-Jan-4 Horta, Bruxelles #85/R est:3000-4000
£3733 $6832 €5600 Lionne et lionceau (27x73x22cm-11x29x9in) s. d.1923 pat bronze Cast Petermann. 7-Jun-4 Palais de Beaux Arts, Brussels #67/R est:2500-3500

HAGER, C (19/20thC) German
£824 $1500 €1203 Back from the pasture (99x74cm-39x29in) s. 19-Jun-4 Jackson's, Cedar Falls #56/R est:800-1200

HAGERBAUMER, David (1921-) American
£1279 $2200 €1867 Autumnal landscape with woodcock (56x76cm-22x30in) s. i.verso. 6-Dec-3 Pook & Pook, Downington #104 est:800-1200
Works on paper
£1078 $1800 €1574 In flight and wild turkeys (34x46cm-13x18in) s. one d.1962 one d.1964 gouache black ink pair. 7-Oct-3 Sotheby's, New York #200 est:3000-5000

HAGERUP, Nels (1864-1922) American
£412 $700 €602 The wave (12x20cm-5x8in) s. canvas on paperboard. 20-Nov-3 Auctions by the Bay, Alameda #1096/R
£444 $800 €648 Waves on the shore (47x64cm-19x25in) s. 25-Apr-4 Bonhams & Butterfields, San Francisco #5512/R
£475 $850 €694 West coast sunset (30x61cm-12x24in) s. 16-Mar-4 Matthew's, Oregon #94/R
£509 $850 €743 Washington seascape (30x41cm-12x16in) s. 26-Oct-3 Bonhams & Butterfields, San Francisco #6489/R
£659 $1100 €962 View of the ocean from the sand dunes (31x61cm-12x24in) s. 26-Oct-3 Bonhams & Butterfields, San Francisco #6488/R
£714 $1300 €1042 Seascape (25x56cm-10x22in) s. 7-Feb-4 Harvey Clar, Oakland #1495
£914 $1700 €1334 Coastal scene (51x76cm-20x30in) s. 7-Mar-4 Treadway Gallery, Cincinnati #523/R est:1000-1500
£924 $1700 €1349 Sailing ship in stormy seas (46x76cm-18x30in) s. 29-Mar-4 O'Gallerie, Oregon #820/R est:2000-3000
£1398 $2250 €2041 Squalls near the Golden Gate, a steamboat with sails in a stormy sea (46x76cm-18x30in) s. 20-Jan-3 O'Gallerie, Oregon #806/R est:2000-3000
£1436 $2600 €2097 Moonlight over San Francisco Harbour (61x91cm-24x36in) s. 16-Apr-4 James Julia, Fairfield #735/R est:3000-5000
£1511 $2750 €2206 Sunset coastal scene (36x61cm-14x24in) s. 15-Jun-4 John Moran, Pasadena #93 est:1500-2500

HAGG, Herman (1884-1966) Swedish
£538 $926 €785 Skeppsbron, Stockholm (39x55cm-15x22in) s.d.1964. 7-Dec-3 Uppsala Auktionskammare, Uppsala #197 (S.KR 7000)
£917 $1477 €1339 Seascape (126x99cm-50x39in) s.d.1923. 25-Aug-3 Lilla Bukowskis, Stockholm #76 (S.KR 12000)
£1296 $2242 €1892 Seascape (126x99cm-50x39in) s.d.1923. 15-Dec-3 Lilla Bukowskis, Stockholm #26 est:15000-18000 (S.KR 16500)
Works on paper
£590 $933 €850 Oriental street scene (53x41cm-21x16in) s.d.1896 W/C. 19-Sep-3 Schloss Ahlden, Ahlden #1536/R

HAGG, Jacob (1839-1931) Swedish
£3548 $6350 €5180 Stathoga Manor in summer sunshine (65x100cm-26x39in) s.d.1892. 25-May-4 Bukowskis, Stockholm #121/R est:50000-60000 (S.KR 48000)
£37694 $67472 €55033 The corvette Freja under sail off Karlso (108x168cm-43x66in) s.d.1917 lit. 25-May-4 Bukowskis, Stockholm #160/R est:200000-250000 (S.KR 510000)

HAGGAR, Reginald (1905-1988) British
Works on paper
£400 $732 €584 Demolition, Old Bottle Oven, Lockett's Lane, Longton (55x37cm-22x15in) s.d.1968 W/C. 6-Jul-4 Peter Wilson, Nantwich #97/R

HAGGER, Brian (1935-) British
£275 $448 €402 Coachmakers Arms, Trafalgar Street, Brighton (51x61cm-20x24in) s.d.1974 prov. 23-Sep-3 John Nicholson, Haslemere #136

HAGHE, Louis (1806-1885) Belgian
£1477 $2761 €2200 Cathedral service (62x53cm-24x21in) s. panel. 24-Feb-4 Dorotheum, Vienna #154/R est:3000-3200
Works on paper
£850 $1471 €1241 Hall of Bassola, Ducal Palace, Venice (40x57cm-16x22in) s.d.1880 pen ink W/C bodycol. 11-Dec-3 Lyon & Turnbull, Edinburgh #32/R
£1800 $3276 €2628 The Return, period scene (61x91cm-24x36in) s.d.1867. 16-Jun-4 John Nicholson, Haslemere #651/R est:2000-3000

HAGIN, Nancy (1940-) American
£994 $1800 €1451 Glass garden (91x76cm-36x30in) acrylic. 16-Apr-4 American Auctioneer #184/R est:1400-1800

HAGN, Alfred (1882-1958) Norwegian
£1107 $1772 €1605 Fjord landscape with birch trees (60x65cm-24x26in) s. 22-Sep-3 Blomqvist, Lysaker #1083 est:4000-6000 (N.KR 13000)

HAGN, Ludwig von (1819-1898) German
£350 $601 €500 Jesuit library (26x36cm-10x14in) i. verso panel. 5-Dec-3 Michael Zeller, Lindau #628/R

HAGN, Ludwig von (attrib) (1819-1898) German
£521 $859 €750 Study of pipe smoker reading (32x18cm-13x7in) board. 3-Jul-3 Van Ham, Cologne #1596

HAGUE, Joshua Anderson (1850-1916) British
Works on paper
£1600 $2720 €2336 January at the marl (89x68cm-35x27in) s. W/C. 29-Oct-3 Bonhams, Chester #323 est:1500-2000

HAGUE, Raoul (1905-) American
Sculpture
£1757 $3250 €2565 Phoenicia (120x61cm-47x24in) white wood exec 1959-60 prov.exhib. 12-Feb-4 Sotheby's, New York #188/R est:1500-2000

HAHN, Emanuel (1881-1926) Canadian
Sculpture
£1875 $3225 €2738 Head of a boy (31cm-12in) s.d.1918 bronze. 2-Dec-3 Joyner Waddington, Toronto #294/R est:3000-4000 (C.D 4200)
£2928 $4977 €4275 Child with butterfly (41cm-16in) s.i.d.45 pat bronze prov. 18-Nov-3 Sotheby's, Toronto #146/R est:5000-7000 (C.D 6500)
£4065 $7276 €5935 Offering of art (63cm-25in) s.d.24 bronze prov.exhib. 31-May-4 Sotheby's, Toronto #119/R est:10000-15000 (C.D 10000)

HAHN, Friedemann (1949-) German
Works on paper
£483 $806 €700 Portrait of a head, possibly Lincoln (60x46cm-24x18in) s.d.1984 mixed media. 13-Nov-3 Neumeister, Munich #549/R est:1000-1100
£500 $905 €750 Variations on self portrait of Vincent van Gogh (32x24cm-13x9in) W/C pencil lit. 1-Apr-4 Frank Peege, Freiburg #1287/R

HAHN, Karl (20th C) German?
£372 $654 €550 Architect (95x130cm-37x51in) s.d.30. 21-May-4 Mehlis, Plauen #15112/R

HAHN, Karl Wilhelm (1829-1887) German
£405 $632 €600 Elbe (84x90cm-33x35in) s. canvas on panel. 31-Mar-3 Bloss, Merzhausen #1554/R
£1069 $1700 €1561 Children in the forest (48x74cm-19x29in) s. i.verso. 14-Sep-3 Susanin's, Chicago #6114/R est:2000-4000
£1359 $2500 €2039 Peasant children (66x51cm-26x20in) s. prov.exhib. 8-Jun-4 Bonhams & Butterfields, San Francisco #4168/R est:5000-7000
£6452 $12000 €9420 Snowy day, sledging on the Boston Common (43x67cm-17x26in) s.d.1877 prov. 5-Mar-4 Skinner, Boston #307/R est:10000-20000
£30978 $57000 €46467 Gathering sedge (109x175cm-43x69in) s.i.d.1880 prov. 8-Jun-4 Bonhams & Butterfields, San Francisco #4169/R est:50000-70000

HAHN, Sylvia (20th C) Canadian?
£893 $1536 €1304 Little girl asleep (42x50cm-17x20in) painted c.1938 prov. 2-Dec-3 Joyner Waddington, Toronto #160/R est:2500-3500 (C.D 2000)

HAHN, William (1840-1890) American?
£1892 $3500 €2762 Turkey (102x61cm-40x24in) s.d.1889. 15-Jul-4 Sotheby's, New York #35/R est:2500-3500

HAHNEL, E J (19th C) French
Sculpture
£938 $1500 €1369 Classical nude with cherub on pedestal (53cm-21in) d.1877 bronze. 17-May-3 Bunte, Elgin #1098 est:1000-1500

HAID, Fritz (1904-) German
£336 $561 €480 Rosental messenger (41x30cm-16x12in) s. after Carl Spitzweg. 9-Oct-3 Michael Zeller, Lindau #581

HAID, Georg (1861-1935) German?
£1049 $1752 €1500 Sailing yacht in a storm (47x57cm-19x22in) s.d.1924 i. verso panel. 9-Oct-3 Michael Zeller, Lindau #583/R est:800

HAID, Johann Lorenz (1702-1750) German
Works on paper
£437 $795 €638 Male nude (43x58cm-17x23in) s.i.d.1721 red chk htd white. 16-Jun-4 Fischer, Luzern #2524/R (S.FR 1000)

HAIER, F (19th C) ?
£1325 $2200 €1921 Untitled. 14-Jun-3 Fallon, Copake #93/R

HAIER, Joseph (1816-1891) Austrian
£450 $824 €657 Mother's petition (103x74cm-41x29in) 8-Apr-4 Christie's, Kensington #91
£583 $1073 €875 Interior scene with figures and cat (50x57cm-20x22in) s. 14-Jun-4 Lilla Bukowskis, Stockholm #522 (S.KR 8000)
£764 $1299 €1100 In school (70x57cm-28x22in) s.d.1882. 28-Oct-3 Dorotheum, Vienna #31/R
£3039 $5500 €4437 Feeding time (74x53cm-29x21in) s. 3-Apr-4 Neal Auction Company, New Orleans #311/R est:6000-8000

HAIER, Joseph (attrib) (1816-1891) Austrian
£363 $650 €530 Interior scene with family seated at a table (74x99cm-29x39in) s. 29-May-4 Brunk, Ashville #162/R

HAIG, Axel Herman (1835-1921) Swedish
£1231 $2117 €1797 Santa Maria della Salute at sunset, Venice (62x47cm-24x19in) s.i. 3-Dec-3 AB Stockholms Auktionsverk #2359/R est:10000-12000 (S.KR 16000)
Works on paper
£480 $754 €696 Cairo, Egypt (36x25cm-14x10in) mono.d.1890 pencil W/C bodycol htd white. 28-Aug-3 Christie's, Kensington #412/R

HAIG, Earl (20th C) British
£329 $550 €480 White feathers 1 (36x41cm-14x16in) board exhib. 20-Jun-3 Freeman, Philadelphia #152/R
£500 $920 €730 River in autumn (70x91cm-28x36in) s. 10-Jun-4 Lyon & Turnbull, Edinburgh #10
Works on paper
£280 $442 €406 Moss (33x48cm-13x19in) s. W/C over pencil. 3-Sep-3 Bonhams, Bury St Edmunds #379

HAIG, Earl George Douglas (1918-) British
£450 $833 €657 White fathers I (35x41cm-14x16in) board. 11-Mar-4 Christie's, Kensington #347
£800 $1496 €1200 Garland Nightclub, Bembridge (61x75cm-24x30in) s. canvasboard. 22-Jul-4 Tennants, Leyburn #912
Works on paper
£320 $586 €467 River landscape (26x37cm-10x15in) s. pen ink W/C. 7-Apr-4 Bonhams, Bury St Edmunds #384
£360 $659 €526 Dryburgh Lane (23x30cm-9x12in) pen ink bodycol prov. 7-Apr-4 Bonhams, Bury St Edmunds #383

HAIGH, Alfred Grenfell (1870-1963) British
£450 $765 €657 Study of the stallion, Chivalrous, in a loose box (41x51cm-16x20in) s.i.d.1922. 19-Nov-3 Tennants, Leyburn #1185
£450 $828 €657 Dark brown hunter in a loose box (36x46cm-14x18in) s.d.1892. 10-Jun-4 Christie's, Kensington #75/R
£900 $1656 €1314 Chivalrous, bay pony in a stable (41x51cm-16x20in) s.i.d.1922. 10-Jun-4 Christie's, Kensington #181/R
£1100 $2013 €1606 Racehorse Mum with Fred Hassall up (51x61cm-20x24in) s.i. 6-Jul-4 Bonhams, Knightsbridge #233/R est:1200-1800
£1500 $2505 €2190 Portrait of English bull terrier, Houghton Adonis (30x41cm-12x16in) s.d.1905. 14-Oct-3 Canterbury Auctions, UK #98/R est:200-300
£4651 $8000 €6790 Mackintosh, a bay colt with Sam Loates up, at Newmarket (63x85cm-25x33in) s.d.1901 prov.lit. 5-Dec-3 Christie's, Rockefeller NY #17/R est:8000-12000
£9500 $17385 €13870 Magic, chestnut racehorse with groom and jockey (61x82cm-24x32in) s.i.d.1918. 7-Apr-4 Bonhams, Bury St Edmunds #468/R est:1500-2000

HAIGH, Peter (1914-1994) British
£600 $996 €876 Abstract (76x50cm-30x20in) s.i.verso. 2-Oct-3 Lane, Penzance #175/R

HAIGHT, Mary Trivette (20th C) American
£2210 $4000 €3227 Eagle with American flag (132x257cm-52x101in) s. 3-Apr-4 South Bay, Long Island #99

HAILSTONE, Bernard (1910-1987) British
£260 $416 €380 Smouldering ruins in the city (92x70cm-36x28in) s. exhib. 16-Sep-3 Bonhams, Knightsbridge #92

HAINARD-ROTEN, Germaine (1902-1990) German
£431 $772 €629 Park landscape with figures (39x51cm-15x20in) s.d.42. 13-May-4 Stuker, Bern #165/R (S.FR 1000)

HAINES, Frederick Stanley (1879-1960) Canadian
£520 $952 €759 Mt Stephen (25x30cm-10x12in) s.i. board. 1-Jun-4 Hodgins, Calgary #103/R (C.D 1300)
£670 $1152 €978 Sheep grazing in the shade of the trees (60x50cm-24x20in) s. board. 2-Dec-3 Joyner Waddington, Toronto #109/R (C.D 1500)
£714 $1229 €1042 Barn and fallow fields (40x50cm-16x20in) s. canvasboard. 2-Dec-3 Joyner Waddington, Toronto #125/R (C.D 1600)
£800 $1464 €1168 Cattle grazing (50x65cm-20x26in) s. board. 1-Jun-4 Joyner Waddington, Toronto #166/R est:2500-3000 (C.D 2000)
£1071 $1843 €1564 On the Moisy River (40x50cm-16x20in) s. board. 2-Dec-3 Joyner Waddington, Toronto #183/R est:1500-1800 (C.D 2400)
£1118 $2001 €1632 Winter stream (40x50cm-16x20in) s. board prov. 27-May-4 Heffel, Vancouver #25/R est:1500-2000 (C.D 2750)
£1118 $2001 €1632 The waterhole (30x36cm-12x14in) s. i.verso board prov. 6-May-4 Heffel, Vancouver #62/R est:1500-1800 (C.D 2750)

HAINES, Richard (1906-1984) American
£4396 $8000 €6418 Woman in an interior (76x66cm-30x26in) s. i.verso prov. 15-Jun-4 John Moran, Pasadena #150a est:4000-6000

HAINES, William Henry (1812-1884) British
£760 $1186 €1102 No 2, the burgomaster in his study (33x28cm-13x11in) s.indis.d.1856 wood panel. 22-Sep-2 Desmond Judd, Cranbrook #805
£2000 $3580 €2920 Gondolas on the Grand Canal at sunset (61x9cm-24x4in) s.d.1865. 27-May-4 Christie's, Kensington #255/R est:2000-3000

HAINS, Raymond (1926-) French
Sculpture
£2013 $3564 €3000 Seita (32x41cm-13x16in) s.d.2000 verso wood paper glass resin. 28-Apr-4 Artcurial Briest, Paris #357/R est:3000-3500
£8500 $15470 €12410 Seita (99x80x16cm-39x31x6in) s.d.1970 acrylic sandpaper board formica prov.lit. 30-Jun-4 Christie's, Kensington #150/R est:7000-10000
Works on paper
£800 $1472 €1200 Matches (50x35cm-20x14in) s. collage paper on board. 11-Jun-4 Farsetti, Prato #154/R
£2622 $4300 €3828 Untitled (30x37cm-12x15in) s.d.1964 verso aluminium and paper collage prov.exhib. 28-May-3 Sotheby's, Amsterdam #99/R est:4000-6000
£4200 $7644 €6132 Composition (50x49cm-20x19in) s.d.1961 decollage on metal. 4-Feb-4 Sotheby's, Olympia #157/R est:4000-6000
£4600 $8372 €6716 Untitled (62x80cm-24x31in) s.d.1976 verso decollage aluminium prov. 6-Feb-4 Sotheby's, London #216/R est:4000-6000
£11000 $20240 €16060 Untitled (64x101cm-25x40in) s.d.1965 decollage galvanised sheet metal prov. 24-Jun-4 Sotheby's, London #163/R est:8000-12000
£18056 $29792 €26000 Coucou bazar (97x97cm-38x38in) s.i.d.1973 verso torn poster on canvas. 2-Jul-3 Cornette de St.Cyr, Paris #62/R est:25000-30000

HAIR, Thomas Harrison (?) British
£1050 $1932 €1533 At Winlaton Mill (43x60cm-17x24in) s.i.verso. 23-Mar-4 Anderson & Garland, Newcastle #421/R est:600-900

HAIR, Thomas Henry (1810-1882) British
£440 $700 €642 Two small girls and their dog in a cornfield at harvest time with sun setting (62x82cm-24x32in) 18-Mar-3 Anderson & Garland, Newcastle #519/R
Works on paper
£280 $482 €409 Figures by a medieval gateway in a town (25x37cm-10x15in) s.d.1868 W/C over pencil. 2-Dec-3 Sworder & Son, Bishops Stortford #536/R
£1500 $2490 €2190 View of Hexham. Summer evening (38x57cm-15x22in) both s. d.1868 d.1869 W/C two. 1-Oct-3 Sotheby's, Olympia #74/R est:1500-2500

HAITE, George Charles (1855-1924) British
£580 $1044 €847 Fishing boats at dusk (28x41cm-11x16in) s. i.verso canvas on board. 24-Jan-4 British Auctioneer #263/R
Works on paper
£323 $594 €472 English garden (53x43cm-21x17in) s. W/C prov. 14-Jun-4 Waddingtons, Toronto #70/R (C.D 800)
£735 $1375 €1073 Figures before a castle (38x52cm-15x20in) s. W/C. 24-Feb-4 Peter Webb, Auckland #174/R (NZ.D 2000)

HAIVAOJA, Heikki (1929-) Finnish
Sculpture
£2098 $3566 €3000 The crack (113cm-44in) bronze. 29-Nov-3 Bukowskis, Helsinki #236/R est:3000-4000

HAIZMANN, Richard (1895-1963) German
Sculpture
£2667 $4800 €4000 Hen (32x12x23cm-13x5x9in) mono. bronze. 24-Apr-4 Dr Lehr, Berlin #140/R est:4000

HAJDU, Étienne (1907-1996) French
Sculpture
£3514 $6500 €5130 Bird (24x35cm-9x14in) s.d.56 polished grey stone incl black stone base. 12-Feb-4 Sotheby's, New York #145/R est:3000-5000
£4670 $8500 €6818 L'oiseau de feu (34x25cm-13x10in) s.d.59 white marble on black marble base. 29-Jun-4 Sotheby's, New York #509/R est:6000-8000
£8649 $16000 €12628 Tree (37x32cm-15x13in) s.d.59 marble incl black stone base. 12-Feb-4 Sotheby's, New York #144/R est:5000-7000

HAJEK, Otto Herbert (1927-) Czechoslovakian
Sculpture
£2200 $3938 €3300 Composition (26x13x9cm-10x5x4in) s.i. bronze. 15-May-4 Dr Sturies, Dusseldorf #60/R
£2937 $4993 €4200 Colour paths 65/1 (64x47x35cm-25x19x14in) s.d.65/1 col wood steel prov.exhib.lit. 27-Nov-3 Lempertz, Koln #165/R est:3000
£3636 $6182 €5200 Colour paths 63/18 (28cm-11in) s.i. col bronze Cast.H.Noack Berlin exhib. 27-Nov-3 Lempertz, Koln #164/R est:4000
£5333 $9547 €8000 Composition (30x34x8cm-12x13x3in) dark brown pat.bronze. 15-May-4 Bassenge, Berlin #6848/R est:7500
Works on paper
£704 $1218 €1000 Montevideo (50x75cm-20x30in) s.d.72 mixed media board. 13-Dec-3 Lempertz, Koln #146/R

HAJEK-HALKE, Heinz (1898-1983) ?
Photographs
£8108 $14514 €12000 Black-white nude (23x17cm-9x7in) s. verso silver gelatin lit. 8-May-4 Lempertz, Koln #112/R est:9000

HAKA, Janusz (1951-) ?
£2826 $4635 €3900 Untitled (10x150cm-4x59in) s. acrylic. 30-May-3 Farsetti, Prato #262 est:3900-4200

HAKALAHTI, Juhani (1934-) Finnish
Works on paper
£470 $874 €700 Three seasons (25x35cm-10x14in) s.d.96 gouache. 7-Mar-4 Bukowskis, Helsinki #329/R

HAKAVA, Aale (1909-) Finnish
£315 $587 €470 Ruska (70x90cm-28x35in) s.d.1947. 7-Mar-4 Bukowskis, Helsinki #330/R

HAKUIN, Ekaku (1685-1768) Japanese
Works on paper
£1600 $2672 €2336 Hossu (119x27cm-47x11in) ink. 12-Nov-3 Christie's, London #14/R est:1200-1800
£8696 $16000 €12696 Ebisu dancing (39x56cm-15x22in) ink hanging scroll prov. 23-Mar-4 Christie's, Rockefeller NY #99/R est:10000-15000
£38043 $70000 €55543 En no gyoja (120x38cm-47x15in) s.i.d.1744 ink hanging scroll prov.exhib. 23-Mar-4 Christie's, Rockefeller NY #101/R est:25000-30000
£40761 $75000 €59511 Daruma (121x56cm-48x22in) ink hanging scroll. 23-Mar-4 Christie's, Rockefeller NY #100/R est:20000-30000

HALAUSKA, Ludwig (1827-1882) German
£972 $1653 €1400 Landscape study (27x39cm-11x15in) s.d.23t August 861 paper on canvas. 28-Oct-3 Dorotheum, Vienna #262/R
£1192 $2181 €1800 Woodland path (25x29cm-10x11in) s.d.855 board. 8-Apr-4 Dorotheum, Vienna #149/R est:1800-2200
£2254 $3899 €3200 Sunny stream edge (35x47cm-14x19in) s.d.860. 10-Dec-3 Dorotheum, Vienna #35/R est:2500-3000
£3147 $5350 €4500 Near St Andra Wordern, NO (42x68cm-17x27in) s.d.8. 19-Nov-3 Dorotheum, Klagenfurt #15/R est:2500
£5705 $10668 €8500 Town on lakeshore (37x47cm-15x19in) s.i.d.Aug paper on board. 24-Feb-4 Dorotheum, Vienna #169/R est:2300-2700

HALBACH, David (1931-) American
Works on paper
£745 $1200 €1080 Canyon de Chelly (23x36cm-9x14in) W/C. 22-Aug-3 Altermann Galleries, Santa Fe #161

HALBART, Gustave (1846-1913) Belgian
£507 $958 €750 Fermiere et son troupeau (47x85cm-19x33in) s. 17-Feb-4 Galerie Moderne, Brussels #145/R
£1164 $1979 €1700 Still life of flowers (80x60cm-31x24in) s. 5-Nov-3 Hugo Ruef, Munich #1008/R est:800

HALBERG-KRAUSS (1874-1951) German
£3147 $5350 €4500 Fraueninsel, Chiemsee (68x99cm-27x39in) s.i. board. 20-Nov-3 Weidler, Nurnberg #300/R est:5000

HALBERG-KRAUSS, Fritz (1874-1951) German
£267 $485 €400 Forest interior with small pond (44x38cm-17x15in) s.i.d.18 board double-sided chl study verso. 1-Jul-4 Neumeister, Munich #2698
£278 $458 €400 Cows by water (30x37cm-12x15in) s. board. 3-Jul-3 Van Ham, Cologne #1220
£278 $458 €400 Chiemgau landscape (25x36cm-10x14in) s. board. 3-Jul-3 Van Ham, Cologne #1221
£300 $540 €450 Sunny wood (48x35cm-19x14in) i. i. verso board lit. 22-Apr-4 Allgauer, Kempten #3556/R
£345 $638 €500 Waterfall (40x28cm-16x11in) s. board. 12-Feb-4 Weidler, Nurnberg #304/R
£486 $802 €700 Cow pasture in Dachauer Moos (24x31cm-9x12in) s. 3-Jul-3 Van Ham, Cologne #1222
£633 $1014 €924 Peasant with ox cart in landscape (70x100cm-28x39in) s.i. 16-Sep-3 Philippe Schuler, Zurich #3360 (S.FR 1400)
£667 $1207 €1000 Summer pond (28x43cm-11x17in) i. board. 1-Apr-4 Van Ham, Cologne #1403
£680 $1218 €1000 Moor landscape (28x42cm-11x17in) s.i. board. 18-Mar-4 Neumeister, Munich #2677/R
£690 $1152 €1000 Haymaking (50x75cm-20x30in) s. board. 9-Jul-3 Hugo Ruef, Munich #104/R
£690 $1276 €1000 Dachauer Moos (35x51cm-14x20in) s.i. panel. 12-Feb-4 Weidler, Nurnberg #392/R
£724 $1158 €1057 Cows and crucifix in landscape (76x96cm-30x38in) s.i. 16-Sep-3 Philippe Schuler, Zurich #3359/R est:2000-2500 (S.FR 1600)
£872 $1605 €1300 Cows at lakeside (41x71cm-16x28in) s.i. board. 25-Mar-4 Dr Fritz Nagel, Stuttgart #710/R
£915 $1584 €1300 Cows by trees on rivershore (48x61cm-19x24in) s. 11-Dec-3 Dr Fritz Nagel, Stuttgart #522/R
£940 $1729 €1400 Hay harvest near Munich (18x24cm-7x9in) s. board. 24-Mar-4 Hugo Ruef, Munich #978/R
£1049 $1783 €1500 Summer landscape with pond (43x50cm-17x20in) i. board. 28-Nov-3 Wendl, Rudolstadt #3990/R est:1400
£1119 $1924 €1600 Winter evening on the Amper (65x95cm-26x37in) s.i. i. verso. 4-Dec-3 Neumeister, Munich #2752/R est:800
£1197 $2071 €1700 Landscape (26x43cm-10x17in) s. 13-Dec-3 Lempertz, Koln #24/R est:1500
£1253 $2294 €1829 River landscape with cows (64x90cm-25x35in) s.i. 9-Jun-4 Rasmussen, Copenhagen #1700/R est:15000-20000 (D.KR 14000)
£1267 $2318 €1900 Moor landscape with watering cows (60x89cm-24x35in) s.i. board. 5-Jun-4 Arnold, Frankfurt #592/R est:2400
£1389 $2264 €2000 Isar valley (70x101cm-28x40in) s.i. 24-Sep-3 Neumeister, Munich #436/R est:2600
£1538 $2646 €2200 Meadow with cows by water in evening (70x100cm-28x39in) s.i. 5-Dec-3 Michael Zeller, Lindau #629/R est:1800
£1644 $2795 €2400 The Isar near Bairawies (50x75cm-20x30in) s.i. i. verso board lit. 6-Nov-3 Allgauer, Kempten #3437/R est:2400
£1667 $2650 €2400 Cows by water (68x100cm-27x39in) s.i.d.1920. 11-Sep-3 Weidler, Nurnberg #305/R est:2500

£1776 $3268 €2700 Cows drinking at the waters edge (69x99cm-27x39in) s.i. cardboard. 25-Jun-4 Michael Zeller, Lindau #538/R est:2000
£1806 $2835 €2600 Isar near Wolfratshausen (42x64cm-17x25in) s. i. verso board. 30-Aug-3 Hans Stahl, Toestorf #8/R est:2700
£1818 $3127 €2600 Country scene with cows on the banks of the Main (50x70cm-20x28in) s.i. 3-Dec-3 Neumeister, Munich #586/R est:1500
£1958 $3368 €2800 Bodensee on summer day (65x92cm-26x36in) s.d.1920 board. 5-Dec-3 Michael Zeller, Lindau #630/R est:2400
£1972 $3411 €2800 Winter landscape with deer in a forest clearing (70x110cm-28x43in) s. canvas on canvas. 10-Dec-3 Hugo Ruef, Munich #2429/R est:2800
£2000 $3640 €3000 Moorland - near Murnau possibly (75x120cm-30x47in) s.d.1905. 30-Jun-4 Neumeister, Munich #555/R est:4000
£2200 $4004 €3300 Chiemsee (70x100cm-28x39in) s.i. panel. 30-Jun-4 Neumeister, Munich #556/R est:3500
£2292 $3735 €3300 Park landscape (57x80cm-22x31in) s. i. verso board. 24-Sep-3 Neumeister, Munich #435/R est:3000

HALBERSTADT, Ernst (1910-) American
£5988 $10000 €8742 Poker (51x69cm-20x27in) s. prov.exhib. 23-Oct-3 Shannon's, Milford #248/R est:1500-2500

HALD, Edward (1883-1980) Swedish
£1450 $2611 €2117 Women sunbathing (69x100cm-27x39in) s.d.1913 panel. 26-Apr-4 Bukowskis, Stockholm #23/R est:25000-30000 (S.KR 20000)

HALDENWANG, Friedrich (1800-1820) German
Works on paper
£541 $951 €800 Landscape with workers building house (26x37cm-10x15in) s.d.Marz 1816 pen wash prov. 22-May-4 Lempertz, Koln #1417/R

HALE, Elizabeth Frances (18/19th C) Canadian
Works on paper
£2600 $4342 €3796 View from the heights of Abraham looking over Quebec to the Island of Orleans (31x47cm-12x19in) s.i. W/C over pencil prov. 14-Oct-3 Sotheby's, London #199/R est:1500-2000

HALE, Kathleen (1898-) British
£5000 $9150 €7300 Bliss (28x37cm-11x15in) i.verso board. 8-Jul-4 Sotheby's, London #337/R est:6000-8000
Works on paper
£2500 $4575 €3650 Solo in the tree-tops (26x21cm-10x8in) s. pencil W/C. 8-Jul-4 Sotheby's, London #339/R est:3000-5000
£3000 $5490 €4380 Orlando and Grace skating (26x22cm-10x9in) s. pencil ink W/C. 8-Jul-4 Sotheby's, London #338/R est:4000-6000

HALE, Lilian Westcott (1881-1963) American
£18182 $32000 €26546 Song of the Spheres (133x114cm-52x45in) s. prov.exhib. 18-May-4 Christie's, Rockefeller NY #68/R est:40000-60000
Works on paper
£3352 $6000 €4894 Russian countess (72x56cm-28x22in) s. graphite. 14-May-4 Skinner, Boston #334/R est:7000-9000

HALE, Nathan Cabot (1925-) American
Sculpture
£1176 $2200 €1764 Evolution of man (81cm-32in) s. bronze. 24-Jul-4 Susanin's, Chicago #5052/R est:1000-1500

HALE, Philip L (1865-1931) American
£1374 $2500 €2006 Garden scene, Giverny (46cm-18in circular) s.d.1899 board. 29-Jun-4 Sotheby's, New York #236/R est:3000-5000
£17045 $30000 €24886 Sarah Bernhardt costumed as Princess Lointaine (102x76cm-40x30in) s. prov. 19-May-4 Sotheby's, New York #39/R est:30000-40000

HALE, William Matthew (1837-1929) British
£280 $507 €409 Fishing boat off a rocky coast (40x60cm-16x24in) s. 30-Mar-4 David Duggleby, Scarborough #88/R
£1486 $2750 €2170 Shipping scenes (18x38cm-7x15in) s. board three. 10-Mar-4 Doyle, New York #23/R est:2000-3000
Works on paper
£1800 $3114 €2628 Busy harbour scene at dusk (50x74cm-20x29in) s.d.1879 W/C. 11-Dec-3 Lyon & Turnbull, Edinburgh #85/R est:1000-1500

HALES, Gordon (1916-) British
£280 $518 €409 Bugby's Reach, tugs in a harbour (36x48cm-14x19in) s.d.1979 board. 9-Mar-4 Peter Francis, Wales #12/R

HALFNIGHT, Richard William (1855-1925) British
£3000 $5100 €4380 River landscape at sunset with punt amongst reeds (61x91cm-24x36in) s. 19-Nov-3 Tennants, Leyburn #1063/R est:2000-2500

HALFRICK, Frans (?) Belgian
£278 $464 €400 Kermesse (27x27cm-11x11in) s. panel. 21-Oct-3 Campo & Campo, Antwerp #138

HALICKA, Alice (1895-1975) Polish
£1325 $2411 €2000 Famille juive (21x27cm-8x11in) s. panel. 16-Jun-4 Claude Boisgirard, Paris #71/R est:2000-2200
£1333 $2426 €2000 Marcoussis in his studio (61x46cm-24x18in) s. 30-Jun-4 Calmels Cohen, Paris #7/R est:2000-3000
£2100 $3507 €3066 Trois danseuses (81x65cm-32x26in) s. 22-Oct-3 Sotheby's, Olympia #42/R est:2000-3000
£4967 $9040 €7500 Fillette jouant (61x46cm-24x18in) s. 15-Jun-4 Rossini, Paris #138/R est:4000-7000
£10345 $17276 €15000 Composition au violon (92x73cm-36x29in) s.d.1914. 17-Nov-3 Claude Boisgirard, Paris #35/R est:15000-20000
Works on paper
£379 $683 €550 Jardin des Tuileries (38x31cm-15x12in) s. gouache board exec c.1940. 25-Jan-4 Chayette & Cheval, Paris #142
£2252 $4098 €3400 Place avec maternite (33x27cm-13x11in) s. gouache. 15-Jun-4 Rossini, Paris #136/R est:1200-1800
£2318 $4219 €3500 Place animee (33x27cm-13x11in) s. gouache. 15-Jun-4 Rossini, Paris #135/R est:1200-1800
£2848 $5183 €4300 Femmes en conversation (33x26cm-13x10in) s. gouache. 15-Jun-4 Rossini, Paris #137/R est:1200-1800

HALINGRE, Marc (20th C) French
£428 $774 €650 Le retour de manege (87x115cm-34x45in) s.d.1988 canvas on panel. 18-Apr-4 Rouillac, Vendome #150

HALK, E (?) Russian
Sculpture
£1564 $2800 €2283 Two men with horses pulling a sled with stag (15x30cm-6x12in) s. bronze. 20-Mar-4 Selkirks, St. Louis #560/R est:2500-3000

HALKETT, Rene (1900-1983) German
£4545 $7727 €6500 Untitled (65x57cm-26x22in) s.d.27 s.i.d.27 verso. 29-Nov-3 Villa Grisebach, Berlin #209/R est:3500-4500

HALL, Anne Marie (1945-) Australian
£268 $488 €391 Portrait with cat. 1-Jul-4 Joel, Victoria #361 (A.D 700)
£383 $697 €559 Portrait. 1-Jul-4 Joel, Victoria #374 (A.D 1000)
£782 $1415 €1142 Circus. board. 1-Apr-4 Joel, Victoria #161 (A.D 1900)

HALL, Basil (attrib) (1788-1844) American
Works on paper
£1955 $3500 €2854 Moravian Missionary conversing with the Eskimos at Nain, Labrador (53x69cm-21x27in) W/C over pencil black ink after Maria Spilsbury lit. 18-Mar-4 Richard Opfer, Timonium #233/R est:5000-8500

HALL, Christopher (1930-) British
£300 $528 €438 Via Garibaldi, Montelupone (28x24cm-11x9in) s.d.1991 board prov. 18-May-4 Bonhams, Knightsbridge #90/R
£300 $528 €438 The Prince Alfred, Marylebone Lane (12x25cm-5x10in) s. board. 18-May-4 Woolley & Wallis, Salisbury #202/R
£330 $551 €482 Recanati Cathedral, Italy (34x27cm-13x11in) s.d.August 1956 board prov. 16-Oct-3 Christie's, Kensington #458
£500 $880 €730 Car dump at St Day, Cornwall (28x44cm-11x17in) s.d.1972 board. 18-May-4 Bonhams, Knightsbridge #14/R
£520 $915 €759 Marsala (21x30cm-8x12in) s.d.99 board. 18-May-4 Woolley & Wallis, Salisbury #87/R
£520 $915 €759 Snow at Enbourne (19x21cm-7x8in) board. 18-May-4 Woolley & Wallis, Salisbury #186/R
£560 $986 €818 West Woodhay (19x23cm-7x9in) s. board. 18-May-4 Woolley & Wallis, Salisbury #187/R
£700 $1232 €1022 San Gimignano (20x37cm-8x15in) s. board. 18-May-4 Woolley & Wallis, Salisbury #90/R
£700 $1232 €1022 Morning in Tunis (14x25cm-6x10in) s. board. 18-May-4 Woolley & Wallis, Salisbury #128/R

HALL, Clifford (1904-1973) British
£260 $424 €380 Sketch for the sun (24x34cm-9x13in) s.d.72 acrylic canvasboard. 24-Sep-3 Peter Wilson, Nantwich #44
£280 $442 €406 Model at portrait class (35x24cm-14x9in) board. 24-Jul-3 Lawrence, Crewkerne #977
£350 $627 €511 Boulogne (22x16cm-9x6in) s. board. 14-May-4 Christie's, Kensington #548
£360 $623 €526 Yachts at Brixham (14x20cm-6x8in) s. board. 9-Dec-3 Rosebery Fine Art, London #727/R
£380 $619 €555 Brighton, night (43x32cm-17x13in) s. s.i.d.1963 verso. 24-Sep-3 Peter Wilson, Nantwich #43
£400 $724 €584 Study of a nude (21x11cm-8x4in) s. panel. 30-Mar-4 Sworder & Son, Bishops Stortford #583/R
£400 $728 €584 Brixham quayside (16x22cm-6x9in) s.d.48 board. 1-Jul-4 Christie's, Kensington #111/R
£440 $695 €638 House and garden (75x75cm-30x30in) s. board prov. 7-Sep-3 Lots Road Auctions, London #359
£480 $864 €701 Street in Venice (36x24cm-14x9in) s. s.i.d.Sept 4.61 verso board. 20-Jan-4 Bonhams, Knightsbridge #69/R
£500 $795 €730 Cheyne Walk, Chelsea (14x22cm-6x9in) s. i.verso board. 10-Sep-3 Sotheby's, Olympia #215/R
£500 $835 €730 Antwerp (76x50cm-30x20in) 21-Oct-3 Bonhams, Knightsbridge #151/R
£600 $1074 €876 Cheyne Walk (15x22cm-6x9in) s. board. 14-May-4 Christie's, Kensington #550/R
£900 $1611 €1314 Portrait of Hannah Weil (30x41cm-12x16in) s. canvasboard. 14-May-4 Christie's, Kensington #549/R
£1200 $1908 €1752 Brushing hair (71x92cm-28x36in) s.d.56 board. 10-Sep-3 Sotheby's, Olympia #241/R est:1200-1600
£1700 $3043 €2482 Rue des Abbesses, Paris (47x33cm-19x13in) s. board exhib. 14-May-4 Christie's, Kensington #547/R est:1000-1500
£1800 $2862 €2628 Paignton (26x35cm-10x14in) s.i. i.d.1956 verso canvasboard. 10-Sep-3 Sotheby's, Olympia #230/R est:1500-2000
£2800 $5012 €4088 Dressmaker (51x40cm-20x16in) s. 16-Mar-4 Bonhams, New Bond Street #72/R est:1000-1500

HALL, Compton (1863-1937) British
£450 $765 €657 Italian hamlet with vines (30x37cm-12x15in) s. board. 30-Oct-3 Bracketts, Tunbridge Wells #1118/R

HALL, Cyrenius (1830-1904) South American
£14706 $27500 €21471 East of the gates (51x102cm-20x40in) s. exhib. 24-Jul-4 Coeur d'Alene, Hayden #159/R est:10000-20000

HALL, Dieter (1955-) Swiss
£543 $907 €793 Untitled (120x170cm-47x67in) s.d.1989 verso. 24-Jun-3 Germann, Zurich #973/R (S.FR 1200)

HALL, Edward (1922-1991) British
£800 $1304 €1168 No 2 - Interior (76x63cm-30x25in) s.d.64 i.verso. 24-Sep-3 Dreweatt Neate, Newbury #197/R

HALL, Frederick (1860-1948) British
£400 $748 €600 Alpine landscape (33x41cm-13x16in) s. wood panel. 22-Jul-4 Gorringes, Lewes #1986
£540 $918 €788 Under a spreading oak (32x40cm-13x16in) s.d.1921 board. 1-Dec-3 Bonhams, Bath #9/R
£650 $1105 €949 Summer landscape near Newbury (45x55cm-18x22in) s. sold with another by the same hand. 1-Dec-3 Bonhams, Bath #19
£720 $1224 €1051 Barbara as a baby (40x30cm-16x12in) s.i.d.1909. 1-Dec-3 Bonhams, Bath #15
£1050 $1785 €1533 Haycart in a farmyard (50x60cm-20x24in) s. 1-Dec-3 Bonhams, Bath #8 est:600-800
£1150 $1955 €1679 On Greenham Common (32x40cm-13x16in) s. panel. 1-Dec-3 Bonhams, Bath #14/R est:600-800
£1400 $2282 €2044 The Shambles, York (39x32cm-15x13in) s. board. 24-Sep-3 Dreweatt Neate, Newbury #107/R est:600-800
£1400 $2380 €2044 Porlock cottage (30x41cm-12x16in) i.verso panel sold with 3 further oils. 1-Dec-3 Bonhams, Bath #22 est:200-300
£1600 $2720 €2336 Rising moon (40x51cm-16x20in) s. 1-Dec-3 Bonhams, Bath #5 est:800-1200
£1850 $3145 €2701 Barbara, aged 13 (40x35cm-16x14in) s.i.d.1922. 1-Dec-3 Bonhams, Bath #17/R est:800-1200
£1850 $3145 €2701 Fairplay (40x30cm-16x12in) s.i.d.1895 board. 1-Dec-3 Bonhams, Bath #18/R est:1500-2500
£1869 $2953 €2710 Colonnade in a Gothic church, possibly Lincoln Cathedral (60x50cm-24x20in) s.i.d.1883. 2-Sep-3 Rasmussen, Copenhagen #1669/R est:20000 (D.KR 20000)
£1950 $3315 €2847 Homeward, work horses at the end of the day (30x39cm-12x15in) s. board. 1-Dec-3 Bonhams, Bath #7/R est:1500-2500
£2000 $3720 €2920 Guinea fowl before a cottage (32x39cm-13x15in) s. panel. 4-Mar-4 Christie's, Kensington #597/R est:2000-3000
£2100 $3570 €3066 Winterbourne Lane, near Newbury, Berks (33x40cm-13x16in) s. board. 1-Dec-3 Bonhams, Bath #10/R est:1500-2500
£2300 $3910 €3358 Guinea fowl in front of a cottage (31x40cm-12x16in) s. panel. 1-Dec-3 Bonhams, Bath #20 est:1500-2000
£2400 $3912 €3504 Cattle crossing a ford (53x69cm-21x27in) s. board. 24-Sep-3 Dreweatt Neate, Newbury #203/R est:1500-2000
£2500 $4250 €3650 Shan't or won't, Auntie Edith aged four (127x76cm-50x30in) s.d.95. 1-Dec-3 Bonhams, Bath #6/R est:2000-4000
£2600 $4420 €3796 Returning home (45x60cm-18x24in) s. 1-Dec-3 Bonhams, Bath #21 est:800-1200
£2800 $4760 €4088 Cattle grazing on a summer evening (51x63cm-20x25in) s. ply. 1-Dec-3 Bonhams, Bath #12/R est:3000-5000
£3200 $5888 €4672 Cattle fording a river on a winter's evening (40x48cm-16x19in) s. panel. 29-Mar-4 Bonhams, Bath #38/R est:3000-4000
£3800 $6992 €5548 Geese at a farm pond (32x40cm-13x16in) s. panel. 29-Mar-4 Bonhams, Bath #37/R est:2500-3500
£6200 $10540 €9052 Cattle drover on horseback (50x59cm-20x23in) intaglio sig. ply. 1-Dec-3 Bonhams, Bath #11/R est:4000-6000
£7200 $12240 €10512 Farm animals in a stable interior (69x89cm-27x35in) s. 1-Dec-3 Bonhams, Bath #13/R est:8000-12000
£11000 $20460 €16060 Portrait of Barbara Hall, the artist daughter aged 13 (41x36cm-16x14in) s.i.d.1922. 4-Mar-4 Christie's, Kensington #384/R est:3000-5000
£13200 $22440 €19272 Ducks on a pond (71x91cm-28x36in) s. 1-Dec-3 Bonhams, Bath #4/R est:7000-10000
Works on paper
£340 $578 €496 Self portrait (54x44cm-21x17in) s. pencil wax crayon. 1-Dec-3 Bonhams, Bath #3/R

HALL, George Henry (1825-1913) American
£412 $700 €602 Portrait of Goeorgia Maria Pickett Auld (43x33cm-17x13in) s.i.d.1884 prov. 21-Nov-3 Skinner, Boston #302/R
£591 $1100 €863 Portrait of a man (26x19cm-10x7in) s.d.1869 board oval. 5-Mar-4 Skinner, Boston #270/R
£600 $1032 €876 Cattle at pasture. Cattle grazing (50x76cm-20x30in) s.d.1884 pair. 3-Dec-3 Cheffins, Cambridge #628/R
£1765 $3000 €2577 Portrait of a gentleman (16x14cm-6x6in) s.i.verso oil paper on canvas prov. 21-Nov-3 Skinner, Boston #294/R est:800-1200
£2400 $4008 €3504 Still life of grapes and an apple (20x30cm-8x12in) s.d.1865 canvas laid down. 7-Oct-3 Bonhams, Knightsbridge #354/R est:1500-2000
£5714 $10000 €8342 Still life with grapes in a dish on a table (31x36cm-12x14in) s.d.67. 19-Dec-3 Sotheby's, New York #1102/R est:5000-7000
£10882 $18500 €15888 Hanging grapes (41x32cm-16x13in) s.d.1863 prov. 30-Oct-3 Phillips, New York #24/R est:15000-25000

HALL, Gustave (19th C) French
£1500 $2775 €2250 Still life of flowers in pots and a basket (80x64cm-31x25in) s.d.1886 exhib. 14-Jul-4 Sotheby's, Olympia #224/R est:1500-2000

HALL, H R (fl.1895-1902) British
£400 $716 €584 Highland cattle watering (39x60cm-15x24in) s. 11-May-4 Bonhams, Knightsbridge #53/R
£1800 $3240 €2628 Glencoe highland river landscape with cattle stood beside rocks (58x89cm-23x35in) s. 21-Apr-4 Brightwells, Leominster #675/R est:500-700

HALL, Hannah (1967-) Australian
£607 $978 €886 Morning, White Bay- Balmain (76x76cm-30x30in) init. i.verso prov. 25-Aug-3 Sotheby's, Paddington #356 (A.D 1500)

HALL, Harry (1814-1882) British
£1000 $1860 €1460 Plough team (25x41cm-10x16in) s.d.1854. 4-Mar-4 Christie's, Kensington #512/R est:500-800
£2113 $3655 €3000 Bay racehorse in a stable (43x53cm-17x21in) 10-Dec-3 Christie's, Amsterdam #866/R est:4000-6000
£2966 $5486 €4300 Blue gown (70x90cm-28x35in) 14-Jan-4 Castellana, Madrid #118/R est:3000
£3200 $5440 €4672 Gordon setter with mallard (58x76cm-23x30in) s.i.d.1845. 19-Nov-3 Sotheby's, Olympia #33/R est:2000-3000
£3409 $5659 €4943 La Reine (434x54cm-171x21in) s.d.1873 double-sided. 13-Jun-3 Zofingen, Switzerland #2361/R est:4000 (S.FR 7500)
£4000 $7320 €5840 Portrait of a horse with jockey up (49x59cm-19x23in) 28-Jul-4 Bonhams, Knightsbridge #120/R est:4000-6000
£6600 $11880 €9636 The racehorse Macaroni. The racehorse Silvio (41x51cm-16x20in) s.i. one d.1863 one d.1877 two. 21-Apr-4 Tennants, Leyburn #1175/R est:3500-4000
£9302 $16000 €13581 Bacchus, with jockey up, and his trainer Captain James Machell (71x92cm-28x36in) s.d.1863 prov. 5-Dec-3 Christie's, Rockefeller NY #5/R est:20000-30000
£20950 $37500 €30587 Mr John Bowe's Daniel O'Rourke with Frank Butler up (51x66cm-20x26in) 27-May-4 Sotheby's, New York #230/R est:20000-30000

HALL, Henry R (19th C) British
£850 $1522 €1241 Driving cattle, Loch Ness (61x91cm-24x36in) s. i.verso. 27-May-4 Christie's, Kensington #220/R
£1300 $2418 €1898 Highland cattle, Loch Ness (51x76cm-20x30in) s. s.i.verso. 4-Mar-4 Christie's, Kensington #48/R est:800-1200
£2500 $4500 €3650 Highland cattle, Loch Long. Highland cattle, Glen Rosa (61x89cm-24x35in) s. s.i.verso pair. 21-Jan-4 Sotheby's, Olympia #356/R est:1000-1500

HALL, John (19th C) British?
£1220 $2183 €1781 Rosenquist (30x30cm-12x12in) s.i.d.1987 verso acrylic prov.exhib. 27-May-4 Heffel, Vancouver #203/R est:2000-2500 (C.D 3000)

HALL, Jurriaan van (1962-) Dutch
£347 $549 €500 Model (70x50cm-28x20in) s.verso. 26-Apr-3 Auction Maastricht #181/R
£385 $654 €550 Self-portrait of the artist (100x80cm-39x31in) s.d.90. 24-Nov-3 Glerum, Amsterdam #199/R

HALL, Kenneth (1913-1946) British
£6000 $10740 €8760 Rue St Lazare (63x76cm-25x30in) s.i.d.38. 14-May-4 Christie's, Kensington #434/R est:6000-8000
Works on paper
£400 $716 €584 Crowd (38x28cm-15x11in) W/C pen black ink. 14-May-4 Christie's, Kensington #437/R
£1479 $2366 €2100 Studio interior (14x24cm-6x9in) s. W/C. 16-Sep-3 Whyte's, Dublin #202/R

HALL, Lindsay Bernard (1859-1935) Australian/British
£276 $430 €400 Pensive nun (59x45cm-23x18in) s. 1-Aug-2 Joel, Victoria #224 (A.D 800)
£520 $952 €759 Portrait of a lady standing by a vase of flowers (16x76cm-6x30in) s. 28-Jan-4 Dreweatt Neate, Newbury #64/R
£1300 $2379 €1898 Connoisseur (60x33cm-24x13in) s. 28-Jan-4 Dreweatt Neate, Newbury #56/R est:500-700
£1446 $2676 €2111 Contemplation (35x26cm-14x10in) s. canvas on board. 10-Mar-4 Deutscher-Menzies, Melbourne #342/R est:5000-7000 (A.D 3500)
£2099 $3821 €3065 Portrait of William Montgomery (51x40cm-20x16in) s. 16-Jun-4 Deutscher-Menzies, Melbourne #391/R est:2500-4000 (A.D 5500)

HALL, Nigel (1943-) British/Australian
£879 $1556 €1283 21.2.97 (71x101cm-28x40in) s.d.21.2.97 acrylic chl prov. 27-Apr-4 AB Stockholms Auktionsverk #935/R (S.KR 12000)
Sculpture
£3394 $5667 €4955 Untitled (127x103x74cm-50x41x29in) bronze prov. 24-Jun-3 Germann, Zurich #113/R est:9000-14000 (S.FR 7500)

HALL, Oliver (1869-1957) British
£300 $510 €438 Bardsea, Lancashire (30x39cm-12x15in) s. 26-Nov-3 Hamptons Fine Art, Godalming #163
£800 $1488 €1168 Bridge in a river landscape (56x81cm-22x32in) s. exhib. 4-Mar-4 Christie's, Kensington #490/R

HALL, Patrick (1906-1992) British
£811 $1532 €1200 Room with male dancer (76x51cm-30x20in) s.i.d.February 1983 verso exhib. 17-Feb-4 Whyte's, Dublin #83/R est:1800-2200
Works on paper
£480 $850 €701 Billingsgate fish market (40x50cm-16x20in) s.i. W/C. 27-Apr-4 Bonhams, Knightsbridge #106/R

HALL, Peter Adolphe (1739-1793) Swedish
Miniatures
£1156 $2070 €1700 Portrait of young woman with muff (8x6cm-3x2in) s.d.1789 W/C gouache ivory oval. 17-Mar-4 Neumeister, Munich #389/R est:1000

HALL, Peter Adolphe (attrib) (1739-1793) Swedish
Miniatures
£2000 $3340 €2900 Young woman as Flora (6cm-2in circular) gouache ivory gold frame lit. 14-Nov-3 Lempertz, Koln #529/R est:3000

HALL, Richard (1860-1943) French

£2000 $3700 €3000 Portrait of a young lady (156x113cm-61x44in) s.d.1906. 14-Jul-4 Sotheby's, Olympia #271/R est:2000-3000

HALL, Sydney Prior (1842-1922) British

£4200 $7434 €6132 Outside St Paul's Cathedral, London, figures in the foreground (104x74cm-41x29in) s. exhib. 30-Apr-4 Dee Atkinson & Harrison, Driffield #778 est:5000-8000

HALL, Thomas P (fl.1837-1867) British

£1350 $2147 €1958 Bringing in the milk (35x30cm-14x12in) mono.d.1835 i.verso. 12-Sep-3 ELR Auctions, Sheffield #323 est:1500-2000

HALL, Thomas P (attrib) (fl.1837-1867) British

£2300 $3910 €3358 Courtship under difficulties (66x53cm-26x21in) 19-Nov-3 Bonhams, New Bond Street #48/R est:2000-3000

HALL, Weeks (1895-1958) American

£9036 $15000 €13193 Night float, Mardi Gras (30x64cm-12x25in) s.d.June 1941 i.verso board. 4-Oct-3 Neal Auction Company, New Orleans #573/R est:20000-30000

HALL, William Henry (?-1880) British

£550 $919 €803 Valley of Varnun, Wales (25x41cm-10x16in) s. 13-Nov-3 Christie's, Kensington #143/R

HALLAM, Joseph Sydney (1898-1953) Canadian

£273 $445 €399 Morning light, Charlton Lake, Willisville (35x42cm-14x17in) s. s.i.verso board. 23-Sep-3 Ritchie, Toronto #77/R (C.D 600)
£625 $1075 €913 October afternoon (60x75cm-24x30in) s. 2-Dec-3 Joyner Waddington, Toronto #288/R (C.D 1400)

HALLBERG, Carl Peter (1809-1879) Swedish

£398 $640 €581 Pastoral landscape with figures (43x60cm-17x24in) s.indis.d. 25-Aug-3 Lilla Bukowskis, Stockholm #136 (S.KR 5200)

HALLE, Charles A (19th C) French

£940 $1748 €1400 Paysage au moulin (66x94cm-26x37in) s.d.1914. 7-Mar-4 Lesieur & Le Bars, Le Havre #64

HALLE, Noel (1711-1781) French

£26316 $48421 €40000 Savoyarde (64x53cm-25x21in) s.d.1757 prov.lit. 25-Jun-4 Piasa, Paris #47/R est:30000-40000

HALLE, Oscar (1850-1921) Belgian

£307 $561 €460 Young Dutch girl at the spinning wheel (104x89cm-41x35in) s.d.1889 canvas on canvas. 5-Jun-4 Arnold, Frankfurt #593
£592 $1089 €900 Young girl with doll (46x33cm-18x13in) s.d.1887 panel. 22-Jun-4 Christie's, Amsterdam #136/R

HALLENSLEBEN, Ruth (1898-1977) German

Photographs
£599 $1000 €875 Industrial image 20 (11x16cm-4x6in) num.20 gelatin silver print board exec.1930 prov. 17-Oct-3 Phillips, New York #143/R est:1000-1500

HALLER, Anna (1872-1924) Swiss

£339 $621 €495 Spring flowers (30x60cm-12x24in) s. 4-Jun-4 Zofingen, Switzerland #2823 (S.FR 780)
£391 $716 €571 The magic of flowers (60x40cm-24x16in) s. 4-Jun-4 Zofingen, Switzerland #2824 (S.FR 900)
£391 $716 €571 Flowers in a woodland clearing (45x65cm-18x26in) s. 4-Jun-4 Zofingen, Switzerland #2826 (S.FR 900)
£452 $769 €660 Country flowers (88x44cm-35x17in) s. 28-Nov-3 Zofingen, Switzerland #3906 (S.FR 1000)
£565 $1034 €825 Bouquet of flowers (65x95cm-26x37in) s. 4-Jun-4 Zofingen, Switzerland #2825 (S.FR 1300)

HALLER, Hermann (1880-1950) Swiss

Sculpture
£1357 $2348 €1981 Young woman with arms held high (37cm-15in) s. cement lit. 9-Dec-3 Sotheby's, Zurich #45/R est:1500-1800 (S.FR 3000)
£1455 $2415 €2110 Standing female nude (68cm-27in) s. cement. 13-Jun-3 Zofingen, Switzerland #2233/R est:2500 (S.FR 3200)
£1538 $2615 €2245 Standing female nude (68cm-27in) s. terracotta. 25-Nov-3 Germann, Zurich #126/R est:4000-6000 (S.FR 3400)
£1810 $3023 €2643 Stork (44x12x8cm-17x5x3in) s.i. bronze lit. 24-Jun-3 Germann, Zurich #77/R est:2500-3000 (S.FR 4000)
£2402 $4419 €3507 Standing male nude (61cm-24in) s. bronze prov. 8-Jun-4 Germann, Zurich #154/R est:6000-8000 (S.FR 5500)

HALLET, Andre (1890-1959) Belgian

£265 $482 €400 Peniche a quai (19x25cm-7x10in) s.d.19 panel. 16-Jun-4 Hotel des Ventes Mosan, Brussels #222
£280 $481 €400 Riviere au Congo (15x20cm-6x8in) s. panel. 2-Dec-3 Campo & Campo, Antwerp #164
£302 $559 €450 Maison enneigee aux environs de Liege (27x38cm-11x15in) s. panel exec.c.1919. 15-Mar-4 Horta, Bruxelles #162
£369 $687 €550 Snow landscape (60x70cm-24x28in) s. 4-Mar-4 Auction Maastricht #1059/R
£417 $696 €600 Riviere Semliki (40x50cm-16x20in) s. panel. 21-Oct-3 Galerie Moderne, Brussels #314/R
£467 $835 €700 Kitega (22x30cm-9x12in) s. board. 15-May-4 De Vuyst, Lokeren #154
£473 $847 €700 Chef Tutsi (40x33cm-16x13in) s. panel painted c.1934. 10-May-4 Horta, Bruxelles #156
£521 $828 €750 Cote Mediterraneene (70x80cm-28x31in) s. 15-Sep-3 Horta, Bruxelles #110
£544 $974 €800 Barrage N Zoro Kilo Moto (50x60cm-20x24in) s.i. panel. 17-Mar-4 Hotel des Ventes Mosan, Brussels #136
£559 $934 €800 Portrait de Madame Hallet (46x38cm-18x15in) s. cardboard. 13-Oct-3 Horta, Bruxelles #81
£629 $1145 €950 Bord de Mediterranee (37x44cm-15x17in) s. panel. 16-Jun-4 Hotel des Ventes Mosan, Brussels #197
£633 $1165 €950 Vues du lac Kivu (16x25cm-6x10in) s. panel two. 14-Jun-4 Horta, Bruxelles #314
£638 $1180 €950 Maison au bord du lac Kivu (38x48cm-15x19in) s. panel. 15-Mar-4 Horta, Bruxelles #160
£805 $1490 €1200 Chef Africain (64x48cm-25x19in) s. panel. 15-Mar-4 Horta, Bruxelles #161
£1049 $1752 €1500 View of Mechelen (60x50cm-24x20in) s. board. 11-Oct-3 De Vuyst, Lokeren #176 est:1100-1300
£1049 $1752 €1500 Reflection on Bruges (50x60cm-20x24in) s. 11-Oct-3 De Vuyst, Lokeren #176a/R est:1500-1800
£1118 $2024 €1700 Coucher de soleil sur les barques (60x50cm-24x20in) s. cardboard. 19-Apr-4 Horta, Bruxelles #69 est:1800-2200
£1224 $2192 €1800 La Dyle a Louvain (80x100cm-31x39in) s.d.27 panel. 17-Mar-4 Hotel des Ventes Mosan, Brussels #113 est:1400-1800
£1259 $2165 €1800 Vue de Pruse sur Mer, dans la Var (46x55cm-18x22in) s.d.1919 panel. 8-Dec-3 Horta, Bruxelles #96 est:2200-2400
£1325 $2411 €2000 Jardin fleuri a Bruges (55x45cm-22x18in) s. i.verso panel. 16-Jun-4 Hotel des Ventes Mosan, Brussels #253 est:2000-2500
£1931 $3572 €2800 Vue de la Dyle et de l'eglise Saint Lambertus-Muizen (52x118cm-20x46in) s.d.24 panel. 19-Jan-4 Horta, Bruxelles #161/R est:3000-3500
£2095 $3749 €3100 Femmes Kutu (60x50cm-24x20in) s. panel. 10-May-4 Horta, Bruxelles #155/R est:1800-2200
£2215 $4097 €3300 Bomputu, Congo, scene (80x100cm-31x39in) s. 13-Mar-4 De Vuyst, Lokeren #165/R est:1200-1600
£2238 $3737 €3200 Le Dyver a Bruges (70x80cm-28x31in) s.d.1927. 13-Oct-3 Horta, Bruxelles #80/R est:2500-3500
£2621 $4848 €3800 Danseuses aux environs de Coquilhatville (60x70cm-24x28in) s. 19-Jan-4 Horta, Bruxelles #162/R est:1800-2200
£3691 $6829 €5500 La Dyle au chateau d'Arenberg (50x60cm-20x24in) s. 15-Mar-4 Horta, Bruxelles #157/R est:5000-7000
£3931 $7272 €5700 Pagayeurs sur une pirogue au lac Kivu (100x80cm-39x31in) s. 19-Jan-4 Horta, Bruxelles #163/R est:2000-3000
£4444 $7067 €6400 Escale, Haute-Tchuapa (80x100cm-31x39in) s. 15-Sep-3 Horta, Bruxelles #109/R est:1500-2000
Works on paper
£278 $442 €400 Mere et enfant en Equatuer (59x45cm-23x18in) s.d.1935. 15-Sep-3 Horta, Bruxelles #112

HALLETT, Dorothy S (fl.1913-30) British

Works on paper
£387 $700 €565 Mr Vickers (34x22cm-13x9in) s.i. pastel. 30-Mar-4 Bonhams & Butterfields, San Francisco #124/R
£1600 $2720 €2336 Fei of Matsons, a Pekinese (29cm-11in circular) s.i. pencil pastel. 27-Nov-3 Christie's, Kensington #395/R est:600-800

HALLETT, Hendricks (1847-1921) American

£278 $500 €406 Landscape (46x30cm-18x12in) d.1881. 25-Apr-4 Locati, Maple Glen #470226/R
Works on paper
£621 $1000 €907 American fleet as Spanish fleet leaves Santiago harbour (58x91cm-23x36in) s. W/C. 20-Aug-3 James Julia, Fairfield #911/R

HALLEWELL, Lt Col Edmund Gilling (1822-1869) British

Works on paper
£460 $764 €672 Sebastopol Harbour from the east (33x61cm-13x24in) s.d.1864. 2-Oct-3 Neales, Nottingham #624

HALLEY, Peter (1953-) American

£2235 $4000 €3263 Untitled, 3/8/94 6A--1 (46x70cm-18x28in) s.d.1995 day-glo metallic acrylic computer paper prov. 14-May-4 Phillips, New York #351/R est:3000-4000
£2324 $4021 €3300 Untitled (45x60cm-18x24in) s.d.1996 glossex. 9-Dec-3 Artcurial Briest, Paris #175/R est:2500-2600
£2682 $4800 €3916 Untitled, 1/25/95 4 (46x70cm-18x28in) s.d.1995 day-glo metallic acrylic computer paper prov. 14-May-4 Phillips, New York #352/R est:3000-4000
£4022 $7200 €5872 Untitled, 12/1/93 65 1B (46x70cm-18x28in) s.d.1995 day-glo metallic acrylic computer paper prov.lit. 14-May-4 Phillips, New York #354/R est:3000-4000
£22346 $40000 €32625 Secret keeper (244x236cm-96x93in) s.d.2002 verso acrylic roll-a-tex prov. 14-May-4 Phillips, New York #235/R est:40000-60000
£23952 $40000 €34970 Untitled (198x212cm-78x83in) s.d.99 verso Day-Glo acrylic Roll-A-Tex 2 attached canvases prov. 12-Nov-3 Christie's, Rockefeller NY #630/R est:35000-45000
£32934 $55000 €48084 Before and After (152x325cm-60x128in) s.i.d.1986 verso Day-Glo acrylic Roll-A-Tex 3 3 attached prov. 12-Nov-3 Christie's, Rockefeller NY #627/R est:50000-70000
Works on paper
£1902 $3500 €2777 Untitled (46x57cm-18x22in) s.d.1990 gouache graphite tape prov. 10-Jun-4 Phillips, New York #461/R est:4000-6000
£2800 $5068 €4088 Untitled (28x22cm-11x9in) s.d.1997 metallic paint on paper. 1-Apr-4 Christie's, Kensington #272/R est:2000-3000
£23000 $38410 €33580 Nirvana (242x218cm-95x86in) day-glo acrylic roll-a-tex on canvas exec 1992 prov.exhib. 21-Oct-3 Sotheby's, London #423/R est:20000-30000
£33520 $60000 €48939 Keith (232x238cm-91x94in) day-glo acrylic roll-a-tex 2 parts exec 1992 prov.lit. 13-May-4 Sotheby's, New York #459/R est:40000-60000
£43413 $72500 €63383 Black cell (162x178cm-64x70in) s.i.d.1986 verso dayglo acrylic canvas two parts prov.exhib. 13-Nov-3 Sotheby's, New York #513/R est:50000-70000

HALLEZ, Germain Joseph (1769-1840) Belgian
Works on paper
£414 $766 €600 Notable de profil (49x39cm-19x15in) s.d.1825 pastel. 16-Feb-4 Horta, Bruxelles #337

HALLFORS-SIPILA, Greta (Johannes Church20...) Finnish
Works on paper
£486 $812 €700 Landscape, Drumso (23x31cm-9x12in) s.d.1926 gouache. 23-Oct-3 Hagelstam, Helsinki #914/R
£1761 $2817 €2500 In the evening the same day at Tiva and Halle (23x19cm-9x7in) s.d.1930 mixed media exhib. 18-Sep-3 Hagelstam, Helsinki #839 est:600
£2183 $3493 €3100 Johannes Church, Helsinki (27x27cm-11x11in) s. gouache exhib. 18-Sep-3 Hagelstam, Helsinki #840 est:600

HALLIDAY, Brian (?) New Zealander
£2174 $3522 €3152 Musterers Otago (52x122cm-20x48in) s. board. 31-Jul-3 International Art Centre, Auckland #78/R est:6000-8000 (NZ.D 6000)

HALLIDAY, Edward Irvine (1902-1984) British
£400 $668 €584 Portrait of a dog in an interior (22x30cm-9x12in) s. 11-Nov-3 Bonhams, Knightsbridge #191/R

HALLIDAY, Irene (1931-) British
£750 $1418 €1095 Symi courtyard, lemon trees (78x108cm-31x43in) s. board. 19-Feb-4 Lyon & Turnbull, Edinburgh #2

HALLIDAY, John (?) British
£300 $501 €438 Holyrood Park - winter (63x75cm-25x30in) s. 16-Oct-3 Lyon & Turnbull, Edinburgh #54
Works on paper
£300 $525 €438 The Nith, Dumfries (81x137cm-32x54in) d.98 pastel linen. 18-Dec-3 Bonhams, Edinburgh #374

HALLIER, Theodor (1908-1982) German
£280 $481 €400 Winter at Ritter-Raschen-Platz (80x65cm-31x26in) s. i.verso. 5-Dec-3 Bolland & Marotz, Bremen #365/R
£795 $1446 €1200 Night street scene (80x80cm-31x31in) s. 18-Jun-4 Bolland & Marotz, Bremen #350/R

HALLMAN, Adolf (1893-1968) Swedish
£580 $1044 €847 Untitled (66x90cm-26x35in) s.i.d.1951. 26-Apr-4 Bukowskis, Stockholm #224a/R (S.KR 8000)

HALLMANN, Anton (attrib) (1812-1845) German
Works on paper
£417 $679 €600 Minerva Temple ruins in Rome (23x33cm-9x13in) i.d.14 May 1836 pencil. 26-Sep-3 Venator & Hansten, Koln #843/R

HALLOWELL, George Hawley (1871-1926) American
£1438 $2300 €2099 Landscape, Egg Park Home (64x76cm-25x30in) s. painted c.1920. 17-May-3 Bunte, Elgin #1260 est:1500-2500
Works on paper
£3086 $5000 €4475 Katahdin from Wassataquoik (25x36cm-10x14in) s. W/C pencil gouache. 8-Aug-3 Barridorf, Portland #109/R est:5000-7000

HALLQUIST, J William (20th C) American
£732 $1200 €1061 Hollyhocks (13x20cm-5x8in) s.d. 7-Jun-3 Treadway Gallery, Cincinnati #1449

HALLS, John James (?-c.1834) British
£850 $1556 €1241 Portrait of Lieutenant Colonel Harris in uniform (30x25cm-12x10in) i.verso prov. 8-Jul-4 Duke & Son, Dorchester #278/R
£4054 $7500 €5919 Portrait of Vice Admiral Sir William H Essington in naval uniform (76x62cm-30x24in) prov. 10-Feb-4 Christie's, Rockefeller NY #156/R est:8000-12000

HALLSTROM, Carl (1850-1929) Swedish
£2027 $3628 €3000 Returning home (70x97cm-28x38in) s. 8-May-4 Bukowskis, Helsinki #397/R est:1500-1800

HALLSTROM, Eric (1893-1946) Swedish
£401 $738 €602 Summer landscape with cows (28x28cm-11x11in) s.d.33 panel. 14-Jun-4 Lilla Bukowskis, Stockholm #336 (S.KR 5500)
£480 $865 €701 Clearing away the snow (36x52cm-14x20in) s. panel. 26-Jan-4 Lilla Bukowskis, Stockholm #701 (S.KR 6400)
£765 $1231 €1117 Stocksund Station (21x28cm-8x11in) s. canvas on panel. 25-Aug-3 Lilla Bukowskis, Stockholm #623 (S.KR 10000)
£982 $1669 €1434 The speed sleigh (38x47cm-15x19in) s. panel. 5-Nov-3 AB Stockholms Auktionsverk #670/R (S.KR 13000)
£1109 $1984 €1619 Early spring - boy on kicking sleigh in garden (61x63cm-24x25in) s. 28-May-4 Uppsala Auktionskammare, Uppsala #312/R est:10000-12000 (S.KR 15000)
£1171 $1990 €1710 Timber floating (75x65cm-30x26in) s. 4-Nov-3 Bukowskis, Stockholm #124/R est:12000-15000 (S.KR 15500)
£1246 $2119 €1819 Evening over town (24x32cm-9x13in) s. panel lit. 4-Nov-3 Bukowskis, Stockholm #207/R est:12000-15000 (S.KR 16500)
£2266 $3852 €3308 Fishing-village (74x93cm-29x37in) s. exhib. 4-Nov-3 Bukowskis, Stockholm #122/R est:30000-35000 (S.KR 30000)
£2644 $4494 €3860 Winter view from the park (59x71cm-23x28in) s. exhib. 4-Nov-3 Bukowskis, Stockholm #123/R est:25000-30000 (S.KR 35000)
£9158 $16209 €13371 Italian market square (35x53cm-14x21in) painted c.1921-1922 lit. 27-Apr-4 AB Stockholms Auktionsverk #666/R est:125000-150000 (S.KR 125000)
£10256 $18154 €14974 Young woman - the artist's wife Marta (60x46cm-24x18in) s. panel painted 1920 prov.exhib.lit. 27-Apr-4 AB Stockholms Auktionsverk #848/R est:175000-200000 (S.KR 140000)
£13595 $23112 €19849 Italian village with figures (51x72cm-20x28in) s. cardboard lit. 4-Nov-3 Bukowskis, Stockholm #81/R est:200000-250000 (S.KR 180000)
Works on paper
£435 $784 €635 The cafe in Rejmyre (16x23cm-6x9in) s. W/C exhib. 26-Jan-4 Lilla Bukowskis, Stockholm #708 (S.KR 5800)
£798 $1436 €1197 The flower window (50x60cm-20x24in) s. pastel exhib. 25-Apr-4 Goteborg Auktionsverk, Sweden #341/R (S.KR 11000)
£1905 $3371 €2781 Carl Johan's Park, Norrkoping (47x64cm-19x25in) s. pastel exhib. 27-Apr-4 AB Stockholms Auktionsverk #716/R est:15000-18000 (S.KR 26000)

HALLSTROM, Staffan (1914-1976) Swedish
£466 $858 €699 Winter landscape (46x56cm-18x22in) mono. 14-Jun-4 Lilla Bukowskis, Stockholm #64 (S.KR 6400)
£489 $788 €714 Seated woman (73x66cm-29x26in) mono. 25-Aug-3 Lilla Bukowskis, Stockholm #111 (S.KR 6400)
£489 $788 €714 Coastal landscape (92x122cm-36x48in) panel. 25-Aug-3 Lilla Bukowskis, Stockholm #598 (S.KR 6400)
£586 $1037 €856 Composition (54x65cm-21x26in) init.d.61. 27-Apr-4 AB Stockholms Auktionsverk #1042/R (S.KR 8000)
£691 $1243 €1009 Flatfish (54x65cm-21x26in) s. exhib. 26-Jan-4 Lilla Bukowskis, Stockholm #261 (S.KR 9200)
£1330 $2381 €1942 The wood cutter (58x65cm-23x26in) mono. s.verso. 28-May-4 Uppsala Auktionskammare, Uppsala #315/R est:12000-15000 (S.KR 18000)
£1511 $2568 €2206 The scrubbing brush (54x65cm-21x26in) s. exhib. 5-Nov-3 AB Stockholms Auktionsverk #1066/R est:20000-25000 (S.KR 20000)
£2341 $3980 €3418 The approach (60x75cm-24x30in) mono. 5-Nov-3 AB Stockholms Auktionsverk #1057/R est:30000-40000 (S.KR 31000)
£13553 $23989 €19787 The drawing-room (107x137cm-42x54in) init. d.66 verso exhib.lit. 27-Apr-4 AB Stockholms Auktionsverk #921/R est:150000-175000 (S.KR 185000)
Works on paper
£550 $886 €803 Scene with animals (28x42cm-11x17in) s. pencil prov. 25-Aug-3 Lilla Bukowskis, Stockholm #240 (S.KR 7200)
£680 $1156 €993 Self-portrait (33x26cm-13x10in) init. mixed media lit. 5-Nov-3 AB Stockholms Auktionsverk #1049/R (S.KR 9000)
£879 $1556 €1283 Nobody's dogs (39x56cm-15x22in) s.d.69 mixed media. 27-Apr-4 AB Stockholms Auktionsverk #919/R (S.KR 12000)
£1172 $2075 €1711 Interior scene with figure (50x40cm-20x16in) init.d.70 W/C collage. 27-Apr-4 AB Stockholms Auktionsverk #1131/R est:20000-25000 (S.KR 16000)
£1905 $3371 €2781 The national coat of arms (26x30cm-10x12in) mono. mixed media panel lit. 27-Apr-4 AB Stockholms Auktionsverk #1077/R est:20000-25000 (S.KR 26000)

HALLY, E (19th C) British
£1100 $2024 €1606 Stable companions (46x61cm-18x24in) s. 10-Jun-4 Christie's, Kensington #64/R est:1000-1500

HALM, Pauline (1842-?) Austrian
£282 $504 €400 Still life with flowers (54x36cm-21x14in) s.i.d.30/7/1892 board lit. 8-Jan-4 Allgauer, Kempten #2402/R

HALMHUBER, Gustav (1862-1936) German
£6000 $10740 €9000 Bacchanal scene (100x201cm-39x79in) s.d.1894. 17-May-4 Finarte Semenzato, Rome #92/R est:10000-12000

HALMI, Arthur (1866-1939) Hungarian
£336 $601 €500 Venice (18x31cm-7x12in) s. 27-May-4 Dorotheum, Graz #21/R

HALONEN, Arttu (1885-1965) Finnish
Sculpture
£1549 $2680 €2200 Girl (30cm-12in) s.d.1914 bronze. 13-Dec-3 Hagelstam, Helsinki #10/R est:1500

HALONEN, Kalle (1899-1947) Finnish
£403 $673 €580 Washerwoman (52x47cm-20x19in) s.d.1923. 23-Oct-3 Hagelstam, Helsinki #988
£599 $958 €850 Winter's day (42x32cm-17x13in) s.d.1929. 18-Sep-3 Hagelstam, Helsinki #896

HALONEN, Pekka (1865-1933) Finnish
£2448 $4161 €3500 Landscape with Vesuvius (21x28cm-8x11in) s.d.1897 i.verso canvas on board. 29-Nov-3 Bukowskis, Helsinki #166/R est:4000-5000
£5068 $9071 €7500 Woodland brook (64x48cm-25x19in) s.d.1922 board. 8-May-4 Bukowskis, Helsinki #212/R est:10000-12000
£5986 $10356 €8500 Beach in summer (61x50cm-24x20in) s.d.1915. 13-Dec-3 Hagelstam, Helsinki #104/R est:14000
£6711 $12483 €10000 Wooded landscape (72x66cm-28x26in) s.d.1916. 7-Mar-4 Bukowskis, Helsinki #331/R est:10000
£6757 $12095 €10000 Madonna and Child and the Three Wise Men (76x50cm-30x20in) s. 8-May-4 Bukowskis, Helsinki #91/R est:10000-12000
£7692 $13077 €11000 Birch grove, early spring (61x46cm-24x18in) s.d.1929. 29-Nov-3 Bukowskis, Helsinki #45/R est:12000-15000
£7746 $13401 €11000 Spring landscape from Tusby (72x55cm-28x22in) s.d.1913 lit. 13-Dec-3 Hagelstam, Helsinki #105/R est:16000
£13333 $23867 €20000 Winter light, forest in March (58x48cm-23x19in) s.d.1917 exhib.lit. 15-May-4 Hagelstam, Helsinki #112/R est:20000
£14085 $24366 €20000 Kiln on the shore (57x41cm-22x16in) s.d.1922. 13-Dec-3 Hagelstam, Helsinki #106/R est:10000
£14685 $24965 €21000 Clear frosty morning in forest (69x50cm-27x20in) s.d.1921 lit. 29-Nov-3 Bukowskis, Helsinki #150/R est:17000-20000
£26573 $45175 €38000 Skaters (66x56cm-26x22in) s.d.1907 lit. 29-Nov-3 Bukowskis, Helsinki #136/R est:20000-25000
£28169 $48732 €40000 Winter landscape with sauna on the beach, Halosenniemi (82x49cm-32x19in) s.d.1903 exhib.lit. 13-Dec-3 Hagelstam, Helsinki #103/R est:40000

£48000 $85920 €72000 Winter view from Myllykyla (46x34cm-18x13in) s.d.1896. 15-May-4 Hagelstam, Helsinki #110/R est:30000
£62937 $106993 €90000 Winter landscape (117x63cm-46x25in) s.d.1903. 29-Nov-3 Bukowskis, Helsinki #164/R est:90000-120000

HALOZAN, Bertha A (20th C) American
£333 $600 €486 Statue of Liberty (33x43cm-13x17in) board. 24-Apr-4 Slotin Folk Art, Buford #728/R

HALPERT, Samuel (1884-1930) American
£4070 $7000 €5942 Brown jug with flowers (61x51cm-24x20in) s. indis d. 3-Dec-3 Doyle, New York #296/R est:5000-7000
£4360 $7500 €6366 Floral still life (51x64cm-20x25in) s. 3-Dec-3 Doyle, New York #295/R est:5000-7000
£50898 $85000 €74311 Greenwich village (65x81cm-26x32in) s. i.stretcher prov. 9-Oct-3 Christie's, Rockefeller NY #116/R est:12000-18000

HALPIN, Janet Cruise (20th C) Irish?
£333 $600 €500 Galway landscape (39x49cm-15x19in) s. 20-Apr-4 James Adam, Dublin #129/R

HALS, Dirck (attrib) (1591-1656) Dutch
Works on paper
£3014 $5123 €4400 Couple on a terrace, the woman with a telescope, and an old woman behind (14x19cm-6x7in) black chk stump prov. 4-Nov-3 Sotheby's, Amsterdam #76/R est:1500-2000

HALS, Frans (after) (16/17th C) Dutch
£1965 $3616 €2869 Laughing boy with flute (40x37cm-16x15in) canvas on panel. 14-Jun-4 Philippe Schuler, Zurich #4290/R est:4000-6000 (S.FR 4500)

HALS, Frans (circle) (16/17th C) Dutch
£29412 $47059 €42942 Portrait of man holding gloves (122x98cm-48x39in) i. 19-Sep-3 Koller, Zurich #3020/R est:70000-140000 (S.FR 65000)

HALS, Frans (elder) (c.1580-1666) Dutch
£104167 $177083 €150000 Portrait of man (32x28cm-13x11in) mono.d.1643 panel prov.lit. 28-Oct-3 Wiener Kunst Auktionen, Vienna #7/R est:150000-250000

HALS, Frans (style) (16/17th C) Dutch
£6111 $11000 €8922 Boy playing a violin (78x67cm-31x26in) panel prov.exhib.lit. 22-Jan-4 Sotheby's, New York #130/R est:15000-20000

HALS, Harmen (1611-1669) Dutch
£300 $555 €438 Peasant interior with boor lighting his clay pipe (37x26cm-15x10in) panel. 13-Jul-4 Rosebery Fine Art, London #572
£2431 $3840 €3500 Peasants seated outside a farmhouse (67x50cm-26x20in) bears sig panel lit. 2-Sep-3 Christie's, Amsterdam #128/R est:4000-6000

HALSALL, William Formby (1841-1919) American
£1176 $2000 €1717 Marine scenes (64x97cm-25x38in) one s. pair. 8-Nov-3 Van Blarcom, South Natick #171/R est:1500-2500
£2035 $3500 €2971 Gay Head, Martha's Vineyard (42x67cm-17x26in) s. 3-Dec-3 Doyle, New York #176/R est:2000-3000

HALSBAND, Gertrude (20th C) British
£260 $450 €380 Crowded street in front of a cottage (50x60cm-20x24in) s.i.d.79. 10-Dec-3 Ambrose, Loughton #1497/R
£260 $450 €380 Nightwatchman gazing into a brazier outside a restaurant (45x35cm-18x14in) s.d.1979. 10-Dec-3 Ambrose, Loughton #1498/R

HALSBY, Julian (1948-) British
£320 $563 €467 Watching the sunrise, Venice (25x35cm-10x14in) s. board. 18-May-4 Woolley & Wallis, Salisbury #24/R

HALSMAN, Philippe (1906-1972) American
Photographs
£1693 $3200 €2472 Winston Churchill (33x26cm-13x10in) s.i. gelatin silver print. 17-Feb-4 Christie's, Rockefeller NY #218/R est:2000-3000

HALSWELLE, Keeley (1832-1891) British
£280 $468 €409 Figures in a cathedral interior (41x61cm-16x24in) 7-Oct-3 Bonhams, Knightsbridge #190
£6000 $11160 €8760 Breezy day, Thorpeness (104x179cm-41x70in) s.d.1886 exhib. 4-Mar-4 Christie's, Kensington #79/R est:6000-8000
Works on paper
£300 $501 €438 Angler amongst the reeds (24x34cm-9x13in) init. W/C bodycol. 16-Oct-3 Christie's, Kensington #121/R
£480 $773 €701 Harvest scene with figures cutting corn and stacks stooks of corn (18x36cm-7x14in) init.d.78 W/C. 12-Aug-3 Canterbury Auctions, UK #188/R

HALSWELLE, Keeley (attrib) (1832-1891) British
£2632 $4842 €4000 Winter landscape with figures (64x76cm-25x30in) s.d.1862. 24-Jun-4 Dr Fritz Nagel, Stuttgart #717/R est:3500

HALTER, Jean H (1916-1981) American
£516 $950 €753 Seated girl holding a doll in her lap (25x20cm-10x8in) s. board. 9-Jun-4 Alderfer's, Hatfield #473/R est:800-1200
£1766 $3250 €2578 Colonial man watching boys at play (20x25cm-8x10in) s. 9-Jun-4 Alderfer's, Hatfield #472 est:800-1200
£2581 $4750 €3768 African American figures outside church building (20x25cm-8x10in) s. board. 9-Jun-4 Alderfer's, Hatfield #471/R est:1500-2000

HALTER, Marek (1936-) ?
£276 $500 €420 Vase fleuri (33x41cm-13x16in) s. 19-Apr-4 Horta, Bruxelles #503

HALTOM, Minnie Hollis (1889-1978) American
£419 $700 €612 Country scene with old house (25x36cm-10x14in) canvasboard. 18-Oct-3 David Dike, Dallas #261/R
£767 $1250 €1120 Bluebonnets in Texas hill country (23x30cm-9x12in) s. 28-Sep-3 Simpson's, Houston #165a/R

HALVORSEN, H (19/20th C) Norwegian
£430 $693 €628 Northern landscape with fjord (51x70cm-20x28in) s. 25-Aug-3 Blomqvist, Lysaker #1206 (N.KR 5000)

HAM, Geo (1900-1972) French
Works on paper
£6000 $10800 €8760 L'accident de la maison blanche (48x32cm-19x13in) s.d.27 W/C. 26-Apr-4 Bonhams, New Bond Street #261 est:2500-3200

HAMACHER, Willy (1865-1909) German
£272 $495 €400 Rocky coast (80x110cm-31x43in) s. 4-Feb-4 Neumeister, Munich #693
£336 $617 €500 Beach with houses (60x74cm-24x29in) s. 26-Mar-4 Altus, Berlin #598/R

HAMADA, Taisuke (1932-) Japanese
£236 $375 €345 Good fortune (45x38cm-18x15in) s. i.d.65 verso panel. 13-Sep-3 Weschler, Washington #713/R

HAMAGUCHI, Yozo (1909-) Japanese
£4521 $7685 €6600 Two lemons (24x40cm-9x16in) s.verso. 10-Nov-3 Horta, Bruxelles #50
Prints
£1882 $3200 €2748 Bottle with yellow lemons in darkness (63x48cm-25x19in) s.num.151/180 col mezzotint. 6-Nov-3 Swann Galleries, New York #558/R est:5000-8000
£1912 $3250 €2792 Bottle with lemons (62x48cm-24x19in) s. col mezzotint. 31-Oct-3 Sotheby's, New York #278/R
£2000 $3200 €2920 Twenty two cherries (54x23cm-21x9in) s.i. col mezzotint. 18-Sep-3 Swann Galleries, New York #287/R est:6000-9000
£2235 $3800 €3263 Bottle with lemons and red wall (63x48cm-25x19in) s.num.58/145 col mezzotint. 6-Nov-3 Swann Galleries, New York #556/R est:4000-6000
£2588 $4400 €3778 Rabbit (29x29cm-11x11in) s.num.48/50 col mezzotint. 6-Nov-3 Swann Galleries, New York #550/R est:1500-2500
£2706 $4600 €3951 Thirty-two cherries (20x20cm-8x8in) s.i. col mezzotint. 6-Nov-3 Swann Galleries, New York #554/R est:5000-8000
£3824 $6500 €5583 Twenty two cherries (54x23cm-21x9in) s.num.81/150 col mezzotint. 6-Nov-3 Swann Galleries, New York #563/R est:6000-9000
£5294 $9000 €7729 Watermelon (23x54cm-9x21in) s. col mezzotint exec.1981. 31-Oct-3 Sotheby's, New York #276/R

HAMAK, Herbert (1952-) German?
Sculpture
£1338 $2342 €1900 D466N (26x8x28cm-10x3x11in) s.i.d.1999 resin pigment canvas prov. 18-Dec-3 Cornette de St.Cyr, Paris #95/R est:1800-2000
£1408 $2465 €2000 D458N (25x8x28cm-10x3x11in) s.i.d.1999 resin pigment canvas prov. 18-Dec-3 Cornette de St.Cyr, Paris #94/R est:1800-2000
£1549 $2711 €2200 D457N (25x8x28cm-10x3x11in) s.i.d.1999 resin pigment canvas prov. 18-Dec-3 Cornette de St.Cyr, Paris #93/R est:1800-2000

HAMALAINEN, Vaino (1876-1940) Finnish
£839 $1427 €1200 Flowers in the park (65x55cm-26x22in) s.d.1930. 29-Nov-3 Bukowskis, Helsinki #44/R
£1133 $2029 €1700 Mountain slope (61x50cm-24x20in) s.d.1930. 15-May-4 Hagelstam, Helsinki #131/R est:2000
£1409 $2621 €2100 Tree covered in snow (39x32cm-15x13in) s.d.1919. 7-Mar-4 Bukowskis, Helsinki #338/R est:1500

HAMBIDGE, Jay (1867-1924) Canadian
£1855 $3413 €2708 Call to the spirits (84x56cm-33x22in) s. prov. 14-Jun-4 Waddingtons, Toronto #15/R est:4000-6000 (C.D 4600)

HAMBLEN, Robert (20th C) American
£243 $450 €355 Big Sur (51x61cm-20x24in) s. masonite. 15-Jul-4 Sotheby's, New York #64

HAMBLETT, Theora (1893-1977) American
£4696 $8500 €6856 Children game of blind man bluff (41x51cm-16x20in) s.d.73. 3-Apr-4 Neal Auction Company, New Orleans #565/R est:3000-5000
£4972 $9000 €7259 Two mothers and their children (41x51cm-16x20in) s.d.75. 3-Apr-4 Neal Auction Company, New Orleans #566/R est:3000-5000
£5000 $8500 €7300 Horse and colt going home (61x91cm-24x36in) s.d.64. 18-Nov-3 Doyle, New York #23/R est:2000-3000

HAMBLIN, Sturtevant J (fl.1837-1856) American
£45946 $85000 €67081 Portrait of a young boy with flowers (76x63cm-30x25in) painted c.1840 prov.exhib.lit. 16-Jan-4 Sotheby's, New York #29/R est:60000-80000

HAMBLING, Maggi (1945-) British

Works on paper

£580	$951	€841	Portrait of an elderly lady in bed with a kitten (38x28cm-15x11in) s.d.79 pencil. 28-May-3 Brightwells, Leominster #1074/R
£700	$1113	€1022	Sunset (49x61cm-19x24in) s.d.8.7.88 W/C. 10-Sep-3 Sotheby's, Olympia #291/R

HAMBOURG, Andre (1909-1999) French

£1047	$1800	€1529	Pluie a l'entree du port, Deauville (12x22cm-5x9in) s. init.i.verso prov. 3-Dec-3 Doyle, New York #134/R est:3000-5000
£1818	$3127	€2600	Mas Saint Paul (22x27cm-9x11in) s. 5-Dec-3 Maigret, Paris #100/R est:3000-4000
£1867	$3397	€2800	Venise (50x12cm-20x5in) s. 29-Jun-4 Gioffredo, Nice #334
£2113	$3697	€3000	Nu etendu (27x35cm-11x14in) s. d.1931. 16-Dec-3 Claude Aguttes, Neuilly #11/R est:3000-5000
£2113	$3697	€3000	Allee de chenes et paysage (20x26cm-8x10in) s.d.1931 pair. 16-Dec-3 Claude Aguttes, Neuilly #12 est:2000-3000
£2174	$4000	€3174	Concours Hippique (15x21cm-6x8in) s. prov. 27-Jun-4 Freeman, Philadelphia #60/R est:3000-5000
£2326	$4000	€3396	Beautemps en Mars a beauville (12x20cm-5x8in) s. i.verso prov. 3-Dec-3 Doyle, New York #135/R est:5000-7000
£2466	$4192	€3600	Bal masque (16x12cm-6x5in) s. panel. 9-Nov-3 Eric Pillon, Calais #145/R
£2617	$4685	€3900	Mas Saint-Paul (22x27cm-9x11in) s. i.d.1947 verso. 30-May-4 Eric Pillon, Calais #67/R
£2685	$4805	€4000	Deauville (12x22cm-5x9in) s. i.verso. 30-May-4 Eric Pillon, Calais #52/R
£2797	$4755	€4000	L'avant port de Honfleur (38x55cm-15x22in) s. painted c.1947. 28-Nov-3 Blanchet, Paris #116/R est:4000-5000
£3200	$5888	€4672	Maree haute (16x27cm-6x11in) s. s.d.1962 verso prov. 24-Mar-4 Sotheby's, Olympia #81/R est:1000-1500
£3521	$5669	€5000	Raisins blanc, noir et vin rouge (16x27cm-6x11in) s. s.i.verso. 22-Aug-3 Deauville, France #104/R est:5000-6000
£3846	$6423	€5500	Premier bouquet d'Arthur (35x27cm-14x11in) s. 29-Jun-3 Feletin, Province #92
£3873	$6778	€5500	Sur la plage (12x22cm-5x9in) s. 16-Dec-3 Claude Aguttes, Neuilly #15/R est:4000-6000
£4196	$7007	€6000	Maree haute (28x35cm-11x14in) s. mono.i.verso. 30-Jun-3 Artcurial Briest, Paris #753/R est:6000-8000
£4670	$8500	€6818	Temps couvert, en Septembre (27x46cm-11x18in) s. init.i.verso. 29-Jun-4 Sotheby's, New York #374/R est:8000-12000
£4749	$8500	€6934	Les voiles blanches (16x27cm-6x11in) s. i.verso. 6-May-4 Doyle, New York #75/R est:4000-6000
£4930	$8528	€7000	L'apres-midi, maree haute, Deauville (16x27cm-6x11in) s. mono.i.verso. 9-Dec-3 Chambelland & Giafferi, Paris #72/R est:6000-8000
£5000	$9000	€7500	Les planches a Deauville (22x35cm-9x14in) s. 26-Apr-4 Tajan, Paris #186/R est:8000-12000
£5000	$7850	€7300	Honfleur, la plage (38x55cm-15x22in) s. s.i.d.1949 verso. 20-Apr-3 Deauville, France #121/R est:4500-5000
£5215	$8500	€7614	Les mouettes en fin de jour (22x35cm-9x14in) s. init.i.verso. 25-Sep-3 Christie's, Rockefeller NY #540/R est:7000-9000
£5282	$9137	€7500	Marrakech (51x73cm-20x29in) s.d.1938 i.d.verso. 12-Dec-3 Piasa, Paris #128/R est:6000-8000
£5986	$10356	€8500	Plage animee l'apres-midi (22x35cm-9x14in) s. 14-Dec-3 Eric Pillon, Calais #140/R
£6135	$10000	€8957	Le bouquet aux feuilles d'automne (73x60cm-29x24in) s. s.i.d.1927 stretcher. 25-Sep-3 Christie's, Rockefeller NY #599/R est:12000-16000
£6623	$12119	€10000	Beau temps, maree basse (22x35cm-9x14in) s. init.i.d.1963 verso. 7-Apr-4 Fraysse & Associes, Paris #4/R est:10000-12000
£6748	$11000	€9852	Trois parasols par printemps (26x34cm-10x13in) s. init.i.verso. 25-Sep-3 Christie's, Rockefeller NY #542/R est:8000-10000
£6923	$11562	€9900	Regate devant la plage animee (22x35cm-9x14in) s. 29-Jun-3 Eric Pillon, Calais #186/R
£7000	$11130	€10150	Voiliers a Deauville (39x46cm-15x18in) s. s.i.d.1968 verso prov. 11-Sep-3 Christie's, Kensington #55/R est:4000-6000
£7746	$13401	€11000	Port breton (64x81cm-25x32in) s. painted 1954. 14-Dec-3 Eric Pillon, Calais #123/R
£7941	$13500	€11594	Sur la plage a maree montante (38x55cm-15x22in) s. i.verso. 19-Nov-3 Bonhams & Butterfields, San Francisco #162/R
£7947	$14464	€12000	Venise, bassin Saint-Marc (38x46cm-15x18in) s. 18-Jun-4 Piasa, Paris #180/R est:8000-10000
£8219	$12904	€12000	Fete de la mer a Honfleur (38x46cm-15x18in) s. mono.i.verso. 20-Apr-3 Deauville, France #120/R est:10000-12000
£8500	$15385	€12410	Beau temps, maree basse a Trouville (38x46cm-15x18in) s. init.i.verso. 1-Apr-4 Christie's, Kensington #24/R est:6000-8000
£9091	$15636	€13000	Maree basse (27x35cm-11x14in) s. s.i.d.1960 verso. 3-Dec-3 Tajan, Paris #380/R est:8000-10000
£9200	$16928	€13432	La plage a maree haute (38x46cm-15x18in) s. s.i.verso prov. 24-Mar-4 Sotheby's, Olympia #82/R est:2000-3000
£11189	$19245	€16000	La fete de la mer a Honfleur (46x55cm-18x22in) s. init.i.d.1969 verso prov.exhib. 2-Dec-3 Sotheby's, Amsterdam #90/R est:15000-20000
£12432	$23000	€18151	Parasoles a Maree Basse (54x65cm-21x26in) s. prov. 12-Feb-4 Sotheby's, New York #37/R est:12000-18000
£21333	$38827	€32000	Benediction de la mer, Trouville (45x64cm-18x25in) s. s.i.verso prov. 29-Jun-4 Sotheby's, Paris #16/R est:12000-18000
£21479	$34581	€30500	Dimanche a Trouville (60x82cm-24x32in) s.d.1952 s.i.d.verso. 22-Aug-3 Deauville, France #103/R est:25000-30000
£23313	$38000	€34037	Le port de Cannes (65x82cm-26x32in) s. s.i.d.1956 verso prov. 25-Sep-3 Christie's, Rockefeller NY #555/R est:25000-35000

Works on paper

£387	$670	€550	Remparts sur la mer, ville d'Afrique du Nord (16x24cm-6x9in) mono. pen black ink wash. 10-Dec-3 Rossini, Paris #17
£470	$860	€700	Petit Port (23x33cm-9x13in) s.i. Indian ink wash. 7-Jul-4 Artcurial Briest, Paris #34
£909	$1545	€1300	Paysage de Mougins, vu de la propriete de l'artiste (49x31cm-19x12in) s. pastel. 28-Nov-3 Blanchet, Paris #117/R est:600-800
£1678	$3003	€2500	Clocharde sur le boulevard (33x25cm-13x10in) s. Chinese ink wash dr. 30-May-4 Eric Pillon, Calais #149/R
£2606	$4195	€3700	Notre-Dame et les toits (45x51cm-18x20in) s.i. W/C gouache. 22-Aug-3 Deauville, France #4 est:3500-4500
£7534	$11829	€11000	Foire du Trone (88x178cm-35x70in) s.i.d.1959 gouache W/C. 20-Apr-3 Deauville, France #119/R est:10000-12000

HAMBRESIN, Albrecht (attrib) (1850-1937) Belgian

Sculpture

£1000	$1820	€1500	Town guard (76cm-30in) s. brown pat. bronze incl. marble plinth. 20-Jun-4 Wilkinson, Doncaster #157 est:1200-1800

HAMBUCHEN, Georg (20th C) German

£667	$1207	€1000	Dutch harbour (40x50cm-16x20in) s. 1-Apr-4 Van Ham, Cologne #1406
£1824	$3211	€2700	Old town of Dusseldorf (50x70cm-20x28in) s. 22-May-4 Lempertz, Koln #1523/R est:2000

HAMBUCHEN, Wilhelm (1869-1939) German

£430	$783	€650	Extensive coastal landscape with sailing boat (39x49cm-15x19in) s. board lit. 19-Jun-4 Bergmann, Erlangen #866
£490	$832	€700	Sailing ship on high seas (60x80cm-24x31in) s. 21-Nov-3 Reiss & Sohn, Konigstein #15/R
£567	$1031	€850	Sailing boat on the high seas (31x40cm-12x16in) s. 1-Jul-4 Van Ham, Cologne #1387
£600	$1086	€900	Windmill and farmstead near Nieuwport (48x69cm-19x27in) s. 1-Apr-4 Van Ham, Cologne #1409/R
£625	$1031	€900	Sailing ships on Dutch canal (40x50cm-16x20in) s. 3-Jul-3 Van Ham, Cologne #1223
£625	$1150	€950	Low tide (60x81cm-24x32in) indis.s. 22-Jun-4 Christie's, Amsterdam #204/R
£633	$1146	€950	Boats at anchor on Dutch canal (60x81cm-24x32in) s. 1-Apr-4 Van Ham, Cologne #1408
£909	$1545	€1300	Goats in meadow (44x60cm-17x24in) 20-Nov-3 Van Ham, Cologne #1611 est:1100
£1333	$2427	€2000	Fishermen on the mudflats of the North Sea (60x80cm-24x31in) s. 1-Jul-4 Van Ham, Cologne #1386 est:900
£2313	$4210	€3400	Fischer am strand von katwijk (60x80cm-24x31in) s. 3-Feb-4 Christie's, Amsterdam #389/R est:2500-3500
£2395	$4000	€3497	Fishing in the cove (89x102cm-35x40in) s. exhib. 23-Oct-3 Shannon's, Milford #198/R est:5000-7000
£3333	$5433	€4800	Beach with boats and figures (87x125cm-34x49in) s. 25-Sep-3 Dr Fritz Nagel, Stuttgart #1352/R est:2000

Works on paper

£467	$845	€700	Sailing boats at anchor on Dutch canal (52x66cm-20x26in) s. gouache. 1-Apr-4 Van Ham, Cologne #1407

HAMBURGER, Helen Augusta (1836-1919) Dutch

£6333	$11400	€9500	Still life with flowers and fruit (44x60cm-17x24in) init.d.1862 panel. 20-Apr-4 Sotheby's, Amsterdam #24/R est:4000-6000

HAMBURGER, Johann Konrad (1809-1871) German

Miniatures

£3000	$5190	€4380	Prince Henry Of Orange-Nassau in green coat (4cm-2in) s. gilt-wood frame oval. 9-Dec-3 Christie's, London #219/R est:600-800

HAMBURGER, Julius (1830-?) Austrian

£1243	$2300	€1815	Dog portrait (36x28cm-14x11in) s. 17-Jul-4 Brunk, Ashville #55a/R est:400-800

HAMDY-BEY, Osman (1842-1910) Turkish

£195000	$354900	€284700	Atik Valide Mosque, Uskudar (48x39cm-19x15in) s.d.75 prov. 15-Jun-4 Sotheby's, London #140/R est:100000-150000
£220000	$374000	€321200	Interior of mausoleum with man reading (55x38cm-22x15in) s.d.1881 prov. 18-Nov-3 Sotheby's, London #309/R

HAMEL, Jack (1890-1951) Dutch

£2069	$3455	€3000	Cote d'Azur (82x118cm-32x46in) s.d.1930. 13-Nov-3 Neumeister, Munich #338/R est:3500-3800

HAMEL, Otto (1866-1950) German

£345	$576	€500	Venice (19x26cm-7x10in) s. 9-Jul-3 Hugo Ruef, Munich #346
£503	$926	€750	Amsterdam (100x110cm-39x43in) s. 24-Mar-4 Hugo Ruef, Munich #979
£660	$1089	€950	Dutch canal landscape with ships (72x92cm-28x36in) s. 3-Jul-3 Dr Fritz Nagel, Stuttgart #497/R
£667	$1213	€1000	Sailing boat in Italian harbour (72x91cm-28x36in) s. 1-Jul-4 Neumeister, Munich #2699
£1597	$2603	€2300	Market in front of Bremen Town Hall (71x92cm-28x36in) s. 26-Sep-3 Bolland & Marotz, Bremen #541/R est:2500

HAMESSE, Adolphe-Jean (1849-1925) Belgian

£319	$533	€450	Cour de ferme (40x50cm-16x20in) s.d.1900. 17-Jun-3 Vanderkindere, Brussels #110

HAMILTON, Carl Wilhelm de (1668-1754) Austrian

£5369	$9879	€8000	Thistle, butterfly, dragonfly, lizard, snail and snake on forest floor (55x40cm-22x16in) prov. 24-Mar-4 Dorotheum, Vienna #248/R est:6000-9000
£6711	$11879	€10000	Sous bois still life with insects (33x25cm-13x10in) s. verso panel. 28-Apr-4 Wiener Kunst Auktionen, Vienna #6/R est:7000-15000
£40000	$69200	€58400	Forest floor still life with a snake. Forest floor still life with a lizard, snail and butterflies (29x21cm-11x8in) copper pair prov. 10-Dec-3 Bonhams, New Bond Street #2/R est:20000-30000

Works on paper

£3974	$7272	€6000	Bouvreuil perche sur une branche de groseiller (20x17cm-8x7in) gouache vellum. 7-Apr-4 Doutrebente, Paris #3/R est:1500-1800
£11258	$20603	€17000	Papillons, coccinelles et insectes. Papillon. gouache vellum two one sheet. 7-Apr-4 Doutrebente, Paris #2/R est:600-700
£15894	$29086	€24000	Libellules et papillons (12x26cm-5x10in) gouache vellum. 7-Apr-4 Doutrebente, Paris #1/R est:1000-1200

HAMILTON, Edward Wilbur Dean (c.1864-1948) American
£1229 $2200 €1794 Venezia (41x38cm-16x15in) s.i. s.i.d.1890 verso panel prov. 14-May-4 Skinner, Boston #310/R est:3500-5500
£4190 $7500 €6117 Market near the Rialto, Venice, Italy (30x20cm-12x8in) s.i. s.i.d.July of 1890 verso panel prov. 14-May-4 Skinner, Boston #308/R est:2000-4000
£4790 $8000 €6993 Rocky beach in Brittany (89x130cm-35x51in) s.d.89 prov. 7-Oct-3 Sotheby's, New York #193 est:8000-12000
£11628 $20000 €16977 Portrait of a seated lady (91x74cm-36x29in) s.d.1904 exhib. 7-Dec-3 Freeman, Philadelphia #166 est:2000-3000
£50279 $90000 €73407 Poppy fields (51x61cm-20x24in) s.i.d.89 prov. 14-May-4 Skinner, Boston #375/R est:45000-65000

HAMILTON, Ethel (1871-1936) American
£307 $500 €448 Laundry Day (38x28cm-15x11in) s.d.1896 canvasboard. 24-Sep-3 Jackson's, Cedar Falls #776/R

HAMILTON, Eugene (20th C) American
£437 $800 €656 Wisconsin waterfall no.4 (127x86cm-50x34in) acrylic on paper. 10-Jul-4 Hindman, Chicago #198/R

HAMILTON, Eva H (1880-1959) British
£1958 $3329 €2800 Figure on a path (14x17cm-6x7in) panel prov. 25-Nov-3 De Veres Art Auctions, Dublin #22/R est:3000-4000
Works on paper
£600 $978 €876 Master Edward Kelly (52x36cm-20x14in) pencil W/C exhib. 25-Sep-3 Mellors & Kirk, Nottingham #722/R

HAMILTON, Franz de (17th C) German
£4030 $6932 €5884 Still life of two game birds hanging on wall (66x60cm-26x24in) s. 3-Dec-3 Museumsbygningen, Copenhagen #151/R est:40000 (D.KR 43000)

HAMILTON, Gawen (attrib) (1697-1737) British
£6000 $10020 €8760 Portrait of a gentleman seated playing a cello (44x35cm-17x14in) 14-Oct-3 Sotheby's, London #433/R est:6000-8000

HAMILTON, Gustavus (1739-1775) Irish
Miniatures
£1800 $3240 €2628 Gentleman, possibly a Naval Officer (4cm-2in) s.d.1765 gold bracelet clasp frame oval exhib. 22-Apr-4 Bonhams, New Bond Street #32/R est:700-900

HAMILTON, H D (1739-1808) British
Works on paper
£1736 $2951 €2500 Portrait of a gent. Lady in a white dress (28x23cm-11x9in) pastel pair. 28-Oct-3 Mealy's, Castlecomer #491

HAMILTON, Hamilton (1847-1928) American/British
£1796 $3000 €2622 At the pond's edge (51x61cm-20x24in) s. 23-Oct-3 Shannon's, Milford #236/R est:2500-3500
£2793 $5000 €4078 Sunlit Connecticut landscape (64x76cm-25x30in) s. prov. 6-May-4 Shannon's, Milford #36/R est:4000-6000
£5587 $10000 €8157 California landscape (91x81cm-36x32in) s. painted c.1906. 6-May-4 Shannon's, Milford #37/R est:10000-15000

HAMILTON, Hugh Douglas (1739-1808) British
£480000 $859200 €700800 Double portrait of Mary, Countess of Erne with her daughter, Lady Caroline Crichton (170x131cm-67x52in) prov.exhib.lit. 14-May-4 Christie's, London #110/R est:500000-800000
Works on paper
£800 $1432 €1168 Portrait of William Power Keating Trench, 1st Earl of Clancarty (24x19cm-9x7in) pastel oval. 26-May-4 Sotheby's, Olympia #23/R
£920 $1647 €1343 Portrait of a gentleman (26x22cm-10x9in) s.d.1771 pastel oval. 26-May-4 Sotheby's, Olympia #25/R est:800-1200
£1181 $1924 €1700 Portrait of Miss Bathurst, half length wearing a blue dress (23x17cm-9x7in) pastel over pencil oval red chk drawing verso. 24-Sep-3 James Adam, Dublin #25/R est:1000-1500
£1400 $2506 €2044 Portrait of a gentleman, three-quarter-length, in a blue coat (23x19cm-9x7in) pencil pastel oval. 14-May-4 Christie's, London #118/R est:1500-2000
£1700 $3128 €2482 Portrait of a boy. Portrait of a young girl (26x20cm-10x8in) pastel oval pair. 25-Mar-4 Christie's, Kensington #7/R est:2000-3000
£2200 $4048 €3212 Queen Charlotte, wife of George III (26x21cm-10x8in) s.d.1770 pastel pencil oval. 29-Mar-4 Bonhams, Bath #2/R est:400-600
£2400 $4368 €3504 Portrait of a gentleman head and shoulders wearing a blue jacket (23x18cm-9x7in) pastel laid paper oval. 1-Jul-4 Sotheby's, London #130/R est:2000-3000
£2533 $4585 €3800 Portrait of a gentleman (20x25cm-8x10in) s.i.d.1778 pastel oval. 31-Mar-4 James Adam, Dublin #17/R est:2000-3000
£2800 $5012 €4088 Portrait of a gentleman, half length, in brown coat. Portrait of a gentleman (23x19cm-9x7in) one s.indis.d. pencil pastel oval two. 14-May-4 Christie's, London #116/R est:3000-5000
£3200 $5440 €4672 Portrait of Thomas Earl of Longford (23x18cm-9x7in) pastel over black chk prov. 27-Nov-3 Sotheby's, London #217/R est:2000-3000

HAMILTON, Hugh Douglas (attrib) (1739-1808) British
Works on paper
£475 $850 €694 Reclining gentleman beneath a tree (53x41cm-21x16in) pastel pen W/C exec.c.1795. 18-Mar-4 Richard Opfer, Timonium #218/R
£2000 $3680 €2920 Portrait of Sir Corbett Corbett (23x21cm-9x8in) pastel oval. 25-Mar-4 Christie's, Kensington #12/R est:600-800
£8000 $14560 €11680 Portrait of lady, probably Charlotte Myddelton the mother of Robert Myddelton (25x22cm-10x9in) pastel oval. 21-Jun-4 Christie's, London #61/R est:4000-6000

HAMILTON, James (1819-1878) American
£1377 $2300 €2010 Seascape at dusk (76x127cm-30x50in) bears sig. 20-Jun-3 Freeman, Philadelphia #146/R est:1500-2500
£1453 $2600 €2121 Noonday at sea (20x51cm-8x20in) s. i.d.1875 verso. 20-Mar-4 Sloans & Kenyon, Bethesda #1201/R est:1500-2500
£1750 $2800 €2555 Harbour scene (25x36cm-10x14in) s.i.verso. 20-Sep-3 Pook & Pook, Downington #389/R est:1500-2500
£1788 $3200 €2610 Seascape with two ships at sunset (53x89cm-21x35in) s.d.1872 verso. 20-Mar-4 Pook & Pook, Downington #544/R est:2500-3500
£2326 $4000 €3396 Ships at sunset (51x76cm-20x30in) s.i.d.1877 indis.i.verso. 7-Dec-3 Freeman, Philadelphia #164 est:3000-5000
£2471 $4250 €3608 Sunrise on the coast of Wales (30x51cm-12x20in) s.i.d.1870 verso board. 7-Dec-3 Freeman, Philadelphia #161 est:1000-1500
£4261 $7500 €6221 Seascape of a steamboat at sunset (61x91cm-24x36in) s. 21-May-4 Pook & Pook, Downington #134/R est:8000-9000
Works on paper
£1098 $1800 €1603 Sunset with wrecked boat on shore (15x25cm-6x10in) s. i.verso W/C bodycol prov. 31-May-3 Brunk, Ashville #343/R est:400-800

HAMILTON, James (attrib) (1819-1878) American
£3533 $6500 €5158 Coastal scene at dusk (41x64cm-16x25in) board. 25-Jun-4 Freeman, Philadelphia #142/R est:1000-1500

HAMILTON, James (1853-1894) British
£620 $1035 €905 Newmill from near Cupar (41x61cm-16x24in) s.d.1890. 16-Oct-3 Lyon & Turnbull, Edinburgh #4
£2400 $3768 €3480 Red doublet (56x21cm-22x8in) s.d.1880 panel prov. 27-Aug-3 Sotheby's, London #924/R est:1500-2000

HAMILTON, James Whitelaw (1860-1932) British
Works on paper
£300 $510 €438 On the river (25x30cm-10x12in) s. W/C. 28-Oct-3 Henry Adams, Chichester #378

HAMILTON, Johann Georg de (1672-1737) Flemish
£1888 $3153 €2700 Thistle with butterflies and other insects (69x56cm-27x22in) s. 30-Jun-3 Bloss, Merzhausen #1904/R est:2500
£17123 $29110 €25000 Houds watching the catch (89x99cm-35x39in) 4-Nov-3 Ansorena, Madrid #126/R est:25000

HAMILTON, John (1919-1993) British
£540 $988 €810 View of Tresco across the water (29x60cm-11x24in) s. board. 3-Jun-4 Lane, Penzance #47

HAMILTON, Juan (1945-) American
Sculpture
£1040 $1800 €1518 Untitled (51x43cm-20x17in) i.d.10-21-81 num.2/5 painted metal prov. 15-Dec-3 Hindman, Chicago #50/R est:1500-2000

HAMILTON, Ken (20th C) Irish
£300 $492 €438 Male study (28x20cm-11x8in) s. board. 4-Jun-3 John Ross, Belfast #91
£1050 $1722 €1533 Autumn dreamer (50x40cm-20x16in) s. 4-Jun-3 John Ross, Belfast #25
£1400 $2324 €2044 Sally (30x30cm-12x12in) mono. board. 1-Oct-3 John Ross, Belfast #34 est:1500-1800
£1400 $2408 €2044 Portrait of a girl (30x17cm-12x7in) mono. oil paper. 3-Dec-3 John Ross, Belfast #264 est:1400-1600
£1600 $2976 €2336 Female portrait (45x35cm-18x14in) s. 3-Mar-4 John Ross, Belfast #36 est:800-1000

HAMILTON, Letitia (1878-1964) British
£700 $1169 €1022 Boat on a river (25x36cm-10x14in) init. 20-Jun-3 Chrystals Auctions, Isle of Man #262/R
£1600 $2672 €2336 Through the trees (31x41cm-12x16in) init. canvasboard. 21-Oct-3 Bonhams, Knightsbridge #32/R est:1000-1500
£2300 $3703 €3335 Italian fishing boats (33x46cm-13x18in) init. panel. 13-Aug-3 Andrew Hartley, Ilkley #846/R est:2000-3000
£2535 $4386 €3600 Polo in the Phoenix Park (12x17cm-5x7in) board. 10-Dec-3 Bonhams & James Adam, Dublin #68/R est:3000-4000
£2535 $4386 €3600 Polo in the Phoenix Park (12x17cm-5x7in) init. board. 10-Dec-3 Bonhams & James Adam, Dublin #69/R est:3000-4000
£2600 $4342 €3796 Feeding time (30x41cm-12x16in) init. panel. 21-Oct-3 Bonhams, Knightsbridge #50/R est:2500-3000
£2819 $5046 €4200 Mountain view (19x25cm-7x10in) s. board. 26-May-4 James Adam, Dublin #108/R est:3000-4000
£2900 $4582 €4205 Wood in North France (50x61cm-20x24in) init. 3-Sep-3 Bonhams, Bury St Edmunds #417 est:1200-1800
£3380 $5848 €4800 Spring flowers (51x40cm-20x16in) board prov. 10-Dec-3 Bonhams & James Adam, Dublin #140/R est:4000-6000
£4000 $7240 €6000 Mountain road with figure on a donkey (28x38cm-11x15in) board. 31-Mar-4 James Adam, Dublin #122/R est:3000-4000
£5000 $7900 €7250 Italian town (50x61cm-20x24in) init. 3-Sep-3 Bonhams, Bury St Edmunds #418/R est:1500-2500
£5986 $9577 €8500 Dunbrody Abbey, County Wexford (30x40cm-12x16in) board prov. 16-Sep-3 Whyte's, Dublin #116/R est:8000-10000
£6081 $11493 €9000 Jura Valley (32x38cm-13x15in) init. i.verso board. 17-Feb-4 Whyte's, Dublin #55/R est:6000-8000
£6200 $9796 €8990 Toledo from Monte Rey (51x60cm-20x24in) init. 3-Sep-3 Bonhams, Bury St Edmunds #416/R est:2500-3500
£7042 $12183 €10000 Village through the trees (51x61cm-20x24in) init. 10-Dec-3 Bonhams & James Adam, Dublin #161/R est:10000-15000
£7746 $13401 €11000 Toledo from Monte Rey (50x61cm-20x24in) init. 10-Dec-3 Bonhams & James Adam, Dublin #104/R est:12000-16000
£8000 $14480 €12000 Fair day, Portarlington (38x39cm-15x15in) init. board prov.exhib. 30-Mar-4 De Veres Art Auctions, Dublin #45/R est:8000-10000

£8042	$13671	€11500	A wood in north France (51x61cm-20x24in) init. 18-Nov-3 Whyte's, Dublin #21/R est:8000-10000
£8389	$14849	€12500	Shillelagh, County Wicklow (51x61cm-20x24in) init. exhib. 27-Apr-4 Whyte's, Dublin #46/R est:12000-15000
£9000	$16110	€13140	The Pink House (39x51cm-15x20in) init. prov. 14-May-4 Christie's, London #10/R est:6000-8000
£9000	$16380	€13140	Landscape with figures on a winding road (31x40cm-12x16in) init.verso board. 1-Jul-4 Mellors & Kirk, Nottingham #843/R est:4000-6000
£9396	$16631	€14000	In the courtyard, Doge's Palace, Venice (56x66cm-22x26in) init. exhib. 27-Apr-4 Whyte's, Dublin #51/R est:10000-15000
£11000	$20020	€16060	Achill Island (29x40cm-11x16in) init.i. 1-Jul-4 Mellors & Kirk, Nottingham #844/R est:4000-6000
£11189	$19021	€16000	The upper town, Nazare (51x61cm-20x24in) s. exhib. 18-Nov-3 Whyte's, Dublin #31/R est:10000-12000
£11268	$18028	€16000	Cottages on Achill Island (42x47cm-17x19in) init. 16-Sep-3 Whyte's, Dublin #20/R est:15000-18000
£11268	$19493	€16000	Woman hanging clothes beneath trees with view to a distant town, France (50x61cm-20x24in) init. 10-Dec-3 Bonhams & James Adam, Dublin #67/R est:8000-12000
£12667	$22927	€19000	Hamilton family at Woodville House (51x61cm-20x24in) 30-Mar-4 De Veres Art Auctions, Dublin #77/R est:14000-18000
£13333	$24133	€20000	Roundstone, Connemara (50x60cm-20x24in) init. 31-Mar-4 James Adam, Dublin #76/R est:20000-30000
£14789	$25585	€21000	The Fair, Roundstone (65x90cm-26x35in) init. 10-Dec-3 Bonhams & James Adam, Dublin #70/R est:15000-20000
£16500	$30195	€24090	Bog Road (56x66cm-22x26in) init. 7-Apr-4 Woolley & Wallis, Salisbury #262/R est:3000-5000
£18667	$33787	€28000	Road to Roundstone (51x66cm-20x26in) init. prov.exhib. 30-Mar-4 De Veres Art Auctions, Dublin #24/R est:14000-18000
£28000	$50120	€40880	Canal scene in Venice (51x61cm-20x24in) init. prov. 13-May-4 Sotheby's, London #33/R est:12000-16000

HAMILTON, Letitia (attrib) (1878-1964) British

£480	$907	€701	Achill Island, Ireland (36x43cm-14x17in) bears.mono. board. 23-Feb-4 David Duggleby, Scarborough #702/R
£900	$1584	€1314	Coastal scene with cliffs, distant yacht and sea birds (28x30cm-11x12in) init. board. 18-May-4 Wotton Auction Rooms, Wotton #817

HAMILTON, Mac (20th C) ?

£960	$1565	€1402	Still life of glass and vegetables (100x130cm-39x51in) s.d.1996-97. 29-Sep-3 Lilla Bukowskis, Stockholm #525 (S.KR 12500)

HAMILTON, Mary Riter (1873-1954) Canadian

£982	$1689	€1434	Gondalas, Venice (37x46cm-15x18in) s.i. 2-Dec-3 Joyner Waddington, Toronto #343/R est:2000-3000 (C.D 2200)

HAMILTON, Philipp Ferdinand de (1664-1750) Flemish

£1733	$3103	€2600	Hunting still life of partridge, great tit, jay and robin in forest (9x12cm-4x5in) panel. 17-May-4 Christie's, Amsterdam #53/R est:1500-2000
£21000	$38430	€30660	Pheasants in a wooded glade (52x68cm-20x27in) pair. 7-Jul-4 Bonhams, New Bond Street #101/R est:10000-15000

HAMILTON, Philipp Ferdinand de (attrib) (1664-1750) Flemish

£2013	$3725	€3000	Hunting scene with dogs brining down a bear (53x67cm-21x26in) exhib. 15-Mar-4 Sotheby's, Amsterdam #31/R est:2000-3000
£2384	$4339	€3600	Pheasant in a landscape (74x76cm-29x30in) 16-Jun-4 Dorotheum, Vienna #337/R est:3500-4500
£4027	$7409	€6000	Shot wildfowl (53x64cm-21x25in) prov. 24-Mar-4 Dorotheum, Vienna #438/R est:6000-9000
£10490	$17517	€15000	Oiseau dans un parc (94x132cm-37x52in) 27-Jun-3 Millon & Associes, Paris #9/R est:15000-16000

HAMILTON, Philipp Ferdinand de (studio) (1664-1750) Flemish

£10067	$18523	€15000	Portrait of saddled and bridled white horse in park (44x60cm-17x24in) prov. 24-Mar-4 Dorotheum, Vienna #281/R est:2500-3500

HAMILTON, Ray (1919-) American

Works on paper			
£240	$400	€350	Red bulls (36x28cm-14x11in) ink. 15-Nov-3 Slotin Folk Art, Buford #367/R
£269	$450	€393	Orange cows (36x28cm-14x11in) ink. 15-Nov-3 Slotin Folk Art, Buford #368/R

HAMILTON, Richard (1922-) British

£2000	$3440	€2920	Tutti mercati d'arte moderna (30x21cm-12x8in) s. acrylic printed base. 3-Dec-3 Christie's, Kensington #772 est:2000-3000
Photographs			
£4500	$8190	€6570	Instant painting (70x56cm-28x22in) s.num.12/17 col Polaroid photo. 1-Jul-4 Sotheby's, London #394/R est:2500-3000
Prints			
£2000	$3640	€2920	Portrait of the artist by Francis Bacon (55x50cm-22x20in) s.i.num.107/140 col collotype screenprint. 1-Jul-4 Sotheby's, London #388/R est:500-700
£2200	$4004	€3212	Critic laughs (60x47cm-24x19in) s.num.41/125 col offset lithograph screenprint collage. 1-Jul-4 Sotheby's, London #369/R est:2500-3500
£2200	$4004	€3212	Lobby (34x48cm-13x19in) s.num.84/88 col collotype screenprint. 1-Jul-4 Sotheby's, London #379/R est:800-1200
£2200	$4004	€3212	Berlin interior (50x69cm-20x27in) s.num.19/100 photogravure engraving etching roulette. 1-Jul-4 Sotheby's, London #381/R est:2000-3000
£2200	$4004	€3212	In Horne's house (53x44cm-21x17in) s.i.num.116/120 etching aquatint engraving. 1-Jul-4 Sotheby's, London #391/R est:1000-1200
£2400	$4392	€3504	Interior with monochromes (48x53cm-19x21in) s.num.41/96 screenprint col collotype. 3-Jun-4 Christie's, Kensington #373/R est:700-900
£2400	$4392	€3504	Putting on de stilj (30x40cm-12x16in) s.num.37/90 screenprint col collotype. 3-Jun-4 Christie's, Kensington #374/R est:800-1000
£2600	$4732	€3796	Bronze by gold (53x43cm-21x17in) s.i.num.28/120 col aquatint engraving scraper. 1-Jul-4 Sotheby's, London #392/R est:2000-3000
£2657	$4517	€3800	I'm dreaming of a black Christmas (51x76cm-20x30in) s.i. col colotype serigraph board. 27-Nov-3 Lempertz, Koln #168/R est:1600
£2800	$4648	€4088	Swingeing London 67 poster (67x47cm-26x19in) s.num.14/50 photo-offset lithograph. 6-Oct-3 Sotheby's, London #227/R est:2200-2600
£2800	$5096	€4088	Interior with monochromes (50x70cm-20x28in) s.num.92/96 col collotype screenprint. 1-Jul-4 Sotheby's, London #382/R est:800-1200
£4000	$6800	€5840	I'm dreaming of a white Christmas (51x76cm-20x30in) s.i. col screenprint. 30-Oct-3 Christie's, Kensington #59/R est:3000-4000
£4000	$7280	€5840	Putting on de stilj (30x42cm-12x17in) s.num.22/90 col collotype screenprint. 1-Jul-4 Sotheby's, London #380/R est:2000-3000
£4500	$7470	€6570	Toaster (89x64cm-35x25in) s.i.d.1967 offset lithograph col silkscreen. 6-Oct-3 Sotheby's, London #226/R est:2500-2600
£4800	$8736	€7008	Patricia Knight III (24x18cm-9x7in) s.num.6/12 acrylic soft-lift step-bite aquatint. 1-Jul-4 Sotheby's, London #386/R est:4000-6000
£5882	$9824	€8588	My Marilyn (65x84cm-26x33in) s.d.66 num.23/75 col silkscreen. 16-Oct-3 Waddingtons, Toronto #90/R est:2000-3000 (C.D 13000)
£6500	$11830	€9490	Swinging London 67 (34x47cm-13x19in) s.num.15/70 etching aquatint metal imprints collage. 30-Jun-4 Christie's, Kensington #118/R est:1200-1600
£7000	$12740	€10220	Toaster (89x64cm-35x25in) s.num.29/75 col offset lithograph collage metalized polyester. 1-Jul-4 Sotheby's, London #371/R est:3000-4000
£7800	$14196	€11388	Release (70x94cm-28x37in) s.num.129/150 col screenprint collage. 1-Jul-4 Sotheby's, London #376/R est:4000-6000
£9040	$16000	€13198	Just what was it that made yesterday's homes so different so appealing (26x25cm-10x10in) s.num.21/25 col laser print. 30-Apr-4 Sotheby's, New York #345/R est:3000-4000
£11000	$20020	€16060	I'm dreaming of a black Christmas (51x76cm-20x30in) s.num.143/150 col screenprint collotype collage. 1-Jul-4 Sotheby's, London #375/R est:8000-10000
£12000	$21840	€17520	Fashion-plate (97x69cm-38x27in) s.num.53/70 col offset lithograph pochoir screenprint cosmetics. 1-Jul-4 Sotheby's, London #372/R est:3000-4000
£15000	$27300	€21900	Interior (48x60cm-19x24in) s.num.9/50 col screenprint. 1-Jul-4 Sotheby's, London #368/R est:4000-6000
£22000	$40040	€32120	Swingeing London III (68x86cm-27x34in) s.num.13/9 col screenprint collage. 1-Jul-4 Sotheby's, London #377/R est:6000-8000
Sculpture			
£3000	$4980	€4380	Guggenheim C - chrome (59x59cm-23x23in) s.num.87/750 verso silver plexiglas multiple box prov. 6-Oct-3 Sotheby's, London #228/R est:3000-3500
£3600	$5976	€5256	Guggenheim C - black (59x59cm-23x23in) s.num.87/750 verso black plexiglas multiple box prov. 6-Oct-3 Sotheby's, London #229/R est:3000-3500
Works on paper			
£3401	$6088	€5000	Composition d'apres Marcel Duchamp. s. mixed media glass. 19-Mar-4 Millon & Associes, Paris #212 est:200-300
£100000	$182000	€146000	Fashion-Plate (100x70cm-39x28in) collage pastel cosmetics lithographed paper prov.exhib.lit. 5-Feb-4 Sotheby's, London #26/R est:40000-60000

HAMILTON, Richard and ROTH, Dieter (20th C) British/German

Prints			
£14000	$25480	€20440	Strong sweet smell of incense. s.d.72 num.10/10 col screenprint collage sold with a drypoint. 1-Jul-4 Sotheby's, London #378/R est:3200-5000

HAMILTON, Vereker Monteith (1856-1931) British

£5500	$10230	€8030	Portrait of General sir Ian Stanish Monteith Hamilton (190x94cm-75x37in) init.d.1886. 4-Mar-4 Christie's, Kensington #387/R est:2000-3000

HAMILTON, Vereker Monteith (attrib) (1856-1931) British

£420	$672	€613	Study of a young Dorothy Swainson playing the piano (59x44cm-23x17in) painted c.1894. 20-Sep-3 Lacy Scott, Bury St.Edmunds #445/R

HAMILTON, William (1751-1801) British

£5556	$10000	€8112	Lavinia and her mother. Palaemon and Lavinia (45x51cm-18x20in) s.d.1795 pair prov. 23-Jan-4 Christie's, Rockefeller NY #137/R est:15000-20000
£7362	$12000	€10749	Portraits of Captain and Mrs Henry Holdridge. s.d.1838 pair. 27-Sep-3 Thomaston Place, Thomaston #165
Prints			
£1645	$3026	€2500	Eruptions (39x21cm-15x8in) engraving W/C exec.1776-79. 22-Jun-4 Sotheby's, Milan #167/R est:2500-3000
£1645	$3026	€2500	The Vesuvius seen from the sea (21x39cm-8x15in) engraving W/C exec.1776-79. 22-Jun-4 Sotheby's, Milan #175 est:2500-3000
£2632	$4842	€4000	View of the Vesuvius erupting (39x21cm-15x8in) engraving W/C. 22-Jun-4 Sotheby's, Milan #165/R est:3500-4500
Works on paper			
£280	$482	€409	Rural sports (25x25cm-10x10in) i. W/C. 3-Dec-3 Cheffins, Cambridge #556
£1000	$1670	€1460	Virtuous love (12x16cm-5x6in) pencil W/C prov. 16-Oct-3 Christie's, Kensington #7/R est:800-1200
£1000	$1830	€1460	Nine muses (7x14cm-3x6in) s.i. grey ink W/C three. 3-Jun-4 Christie's, London #100/R est:1000-1500

HAMILTON, William R (1810-?) American

£1648	$3000	€2406	Portrait of a young artist at work (94x74cm-37x29in) s. d.1855 verso. 29-Jun-4 Sotheby's, New York #184/R est:3000-5000

HAMLYN, Rhonda (1944-) Australian

£405	$652	€591	Morning (57x44cm-22x17in) s.d.66 verso prov.exhib.lit. 25-Aug-3 Sotheby's, Paddington #405/R (A.D 1000)

HAMM, Eugen (1885-1930) German

£1151	$2118	€1750	Still life with hyacinths and lemons. Still life with flowers in a green jug (53x64cm-21x25in) s.d.19 double-sided. 26-Jun-4 C & K, Leipzig #739/R est:900
£3741	$6810	€5500	At the brothel (46x38cm-18x15in) s.d.22. 3-Feb-4 Christie's, Amsterdam #463/R est:1500-2000

HAMMAD, Mahmoud (1923-1988) Syrian

£5000	$8850	€7300	Abstract in square. Figures in square. Gilgamesh figures. Arab men. Geometric squares (42x37cm-17x15in) s.d.81 set of five. 29-Apr-4 Bonhams, New Bond Street #569/R est:4000-8000

HAMMAN, Edouard-Jean-Conrad (1819-1888) Belgian
£2000 $3600 €3000 Family protection (120x160cm-47x63in) s.d.1886. 26-Apr-4 Bernaerts, Antwerp #25 est:3000-4000

HAMMAN, Edouard-Michel-Ferdinand (1850-?) French
£1400 $2548 €2100 Sheep grazing on a cliff top overlooking the sea (60x81cm-24x32in) 20-Jun-4 Wilkinson, Doncaster #320 est:2000-3000

HAMME, Alexis van (1818-1875) Belgian
£2639 $4169 €3800 Token of love (52x40cm-20x16in) s.d.1866 panel. 2-Sep-3 Christie's, Amsterdam #184/R est:6000-8000

HAMME, Peter van (1880-1936) German
£282 $504 €400 Nude female from behind (56x42cm-22x17in) s.i.d.24. 8-Jan-4 Allgauer, Kempten #2403/R

HAMMER, Edmund Guido (1821-1898) German
£270 $505 €405 Hind and two calves in woodland (12x10cm-5x4in) s. panel. 26-Jul-4 Bonhams, Bath #95/R

HAMMER, Erik (1853-?) German
£1007 $1872 €1500 Brother cellar master (45x55cm-18x22in) s.d.1899 panel. 6-Mar-4 Arnold, Frankfurt #737/R est:400

HAMMER, Guido (20th C) German
£537 $999 €800 Deer hunt (40x69cm-16x27in) s. i. stretcher. 5-Mar-4 Wendl, Rudolstadt #3680/R

HAMMER, Hans Jorgen (1815-1882) Danish
£391 $716 €571 Peasant and his two children on their way home from the fields (23x19cm-9x7in) 4-Jun-4 Zofingen, Switzerland #2348/R (S.FR 900)
£2647 $4578 €3865 The market in Arrica after sunset (20x31cm-8x12in) init. study. 9-Dec-3 Rasmussen, Copenhagen #1231/R est:10000-15000 (D.KR 28000)
£4297 $7864 €6274 The artist's studio in Nyhavn (34x41cm-13x16in) prov. 9-Jun-4 Rasmussen, Copenhagen #1573/R est:25000-35000 (D.KR 48000)

HAMMER, Johann-J (1842-1906) German/American
£381 $700 €556 The end of the day (58x84cm-23x33in) s. 25-Jun-4 Freeman, Philadelphia #308/R
£2732 $5000 €4098 Couple resting in a landscape (66x97cm-26x38in) canvas on board. 9-Jul-4 Du Mouchelle, Detroit #2004/R est:3000-5000

HAMMER, Nicolai (19/20th C) ?
£365 $580 €525 Church interior (64x51cm-25x20in) s.d.1908. 29-Apr-3 Durán, Madrid #72/R

HAMMER, William (1821-1889) German
£850 $1521 €1241 Still life of blue plums (16x24cm-6x9in) s.d.1861 cardboard on canvas. 25-May-4 Bukowskis, Stockholm #323/R (S.KR 11500)
£1880 $3440 €2745 Still life of cherries, melon and snail (40x48cm-16x19in) s. 9-Jun-4 Rasmussen, Copenhagen #1883/R est:15000-20000 (D.KR 21000)
£8889 $16000 €12978 Still life with fruits on a stone ledge (58x73cm-23x29in) s.d.1856 prov. 22-Apr-4 Christie's, Rockefeller NY #21/R est:20000-30000
£12587 $21399 €18000 Still life of flowers including roses, passion flowers, poppies (47x37cm-19x15in) s.d.1855. 20-Nov-3 Van Ham, Cologne #1613/R est:12000

HAMMERSHOI, Svend (1873-1948) Danish
£271 $486 €396 View from Borsen (46x38cm-18x15in) init. panel exhib. 10-May-4 Rasmussen, Vejle #476/R (D.KR 3000)
£374 $591 €542 St Nikolai's church's tower seen from Slotsholmen (46x38cm-18x15in) init.i.d.36 panel. 2-Sep-3 Rasmussen, Copenhagen #1793/R (D.KR 4000)
£379 $607 €550 From Oxford University, possibly Lincoln College (80x70cm-31x28in) 17-Sep-3 Kunsthallen, Copenhagen #451 (D.KR 4000)
£652 $1024 €952 Entrance to Frederiksberg Gardens (67x61cm-26x24in) mono.d.Dec 41. 30-Aug-3 Rasmussen, Havnen #2126/R (D.KR 7000)
£674 $1126 €984 With view towards the King's Garden and Rosenborg (170x81cm-67x32in) 25-Oct-3 Rasmussen, Havnen #2223/R (D.KR 7200)
£853 $1365 €1237 Village church (120x100cm-47x39in) 17-Sep-3 Kunsthallen, Copenhagen #471/R (D.KR 9000)
£870 $1583 €1270 Portrait of Vilhelm Hammershoi painted in Spurveskjul (58x66cm-23x26in) lit. 7-Feb-4 Rasmussen, Havnen #2043/R (D.KR 9500)
£898 $1671 €1311 View towards Kongen's Have and Rosenborg (170x81cm-67x32in) 2-Mar-4 Rasmussen, Copenhagen #1472/R (D.KR 10000)
£9452 $16352 €13800 Farm buildings, corn field in foreground (34x37cm-13x15in) prov. 9-Dec-3 Rasmussen, Copenhagen #1247/R est:25000-35000 (D.KR 100000)

HAMMERSHOI, Vilhelm (1864-1916) Danish
£4726 $8176 €6900 The artist's brother Svend Hammershoi (49x34cm-19x13in) prov. 9-Dec-3 Rasmussen, Copenhagen #1269/R est:50000-60000 (D.KR 50000)
£75614 $130813 €110396 From Frederiksholms Canal, hazy day in November (42x53cm-17x21in) painted 1892 prov.exhib.lit. 9-Dec-3 Rasmussen, Copenhagen #1294/R est:1000000-1200000 (D.KR 800000)
£264650 $457845 €386389 Dining room - with woman sewing at table - Strandgade 30 (50x45cm-20x18in) init. prov. 9-Dec-3 Rasmussen, Copenhagen #1258/R est:3000000-3500000 (D.KR 2800000)
£313339 $573411 €457475 Interior scene with the artist's wife Ida in their home in Strandgaden (55x46cm-22x18in) init. painted c.1905 prov.lit. 9-Jun-4 Rasmussen, Copenhagen #1452/R est:3500000-4000000 (D.KR 3500000)

HAMMERSTAD, John Olsen (1842-1925) American
£497 $900 €726 Coastal seascape with sloop at middle distance and steamship beyond (51x76cm-20x30in) s. 3-Apr-4 Nadeau, Windsor #294/R

HAMMERSTIEL, Robert (1933-) ?
£1986 $3316 €2800 The conversation (65x85cm-26x33in) mono. prov. 14-Oct-3 Dorotheum, Vienna #249/R est:1300-2000
£2695 $4501 €3800 Pieta (90x100cm-35x39in) mono. s.i.d.1.2.1994 verso prov. 14-Oct-3 Dorotheum, Vienna #310/R est:2800-3200

HAMMES, Christiaan Hendrik (1872-1965) Dutch
£347 $565 €500 Near mountain and valley (50x60cm-20x24in) s. 29-Sep-3 Sotheby's, Amsterdam #264

HAMMON, G Hamilton (fl.1895-1905) Australian
£388 $714 €566 Sydney Harbour from Vaucluse (52x75cm-20x30in) i. s.i.verso. 26-Mar-4 Lawson Menzies, Sydney #2202/R (A.D 950)

HAMMOND, Arthur Henry Knighton (1875-1970) British
£380 $703 €555 Gardener's wife (59x50cm-23x20in) s. board exhib. 14-Jan-4 Lawrence, Crewkerne #1440
£750 $1388 €1095 Artist's model (76x63cm-30x25in) 11-Feb-4 Sotheby's, Olympia #136/R
Works on paper
£300 $510 €438 Pastoral landscape with a shepherdess and flock (22x29cm-9x11in) s. W/C. 18-Nov-3 Bonhams, Leeds #23
£300 $510 €438 Farmyard Scene, Bodiam, Sussex (28x38cm-11x15in) s. W/C prov. 29-Oct-3 Hampton & Littlewood, Exeter #511/R
£320 $589 €467 View through trees to a palace (16x20cm-6x8in) s. W/C. 11-Jun-4 Keys, Aylsham #374/R
£350 $571 €511 Pal Labia and Cannaregio, Venice (33x51cm-13x20in) s. W/C. 24-Sep-3 Dreweatt Neate, Newbury #80
£361 $588 €527 An English beauty (52x36cm-20x14in) s.i. pastel. 23-Sep-3 Peter Webb, Auckland #161/R (NZ.D 1000)
£650 $1203 €949 Trafalgar Square, London (44x31cm-17x12in) s. pencil W/C. 11-Mar-4 Christie's, Kensington #177
£750 $1365 €1095 Flower Market, Venice (48x45cm-19x18in) s.i. W/C. 15-Jun-4 Bonhams, Oxford #59
£1300 $2366 €1898 Uffizi, Florence (49x45cm-19x18in) s. W/C. 15-Jun-4 Bonhams, Oxford #51 est:200-500

HAMMOND, Bill (1947-) New Zealander
£4104 $7101 €5992 Get it on, bang a gong, get it on, T Rex (30x37cm-12x15in) s.i.d.1986 enamel metallic paint aluminium. 9-Dec-3 Peter Webb, Auckland #51/R est:10000-15000 (NZ.D 11000)
£4340 $6901 €6336 Sea bird (35x27cm-14x11in) s.i.d.1990 acrylic canvas jute. 1-May-3 Dunbar Sloane, Wellington #21/R est:20000-30000 (NZ.D 12500)
£4513 $7356 €6589 Metal opera (34x39cm-13x15in) s.i.d.1987 acrylic metal. 23-Sep-3 Peter Webb, Auckland #67/R est:10000-15000 (NZ.D 12500)
£5725 $10420 €8359 Homesickness (63x91cm-25x36in) s.i.d.1983 oil paper on board. 16-Jun-4 Deutscher-Menzies, Melbourne #205/R est:10000-15000 (A.D 15000)
£10714 $19393 €15642 C.V service (71x106cm-28x42in) s.i.d.1991 acrylic on kauri panel. 30-Mar-4 Peter Webb, Auckland #48/R est:30000-40000 (NZ.D 30000)
£12635 $20596 €18447 Regional plate and gravy boat (70x90cm-28x35in) s.i.d.1991 enamel aluminium. 23-Sep-3 Peter Webb, Auckland #65/R est:35000-50000 (NZ.D 35000)
£15035 $27364 €21951 Snare (45x35cm-18x14in) s.i.d.1994. 29-Jun-4 Peter Webb, Auckland #50/R est:35000-45000 (NZ.D 43000)
£16045 $27757 €23426 Ball room (77x58cm-30x23in) s.i.d.2000 acrylic. 9-Dec-3 Peter Webb, Auckland #79/R est:28000-35000 (NZ.D 43000)
£17329 $28245 €25300 Zoomorphic detail (60x39cm-24x15in) s.i.d.1999. 23-Sep-3 Peter Webb, Auckland #66/R est:55000-65000 (NZ.D 48000)
£19930 $36273 €29098 Limbo Bay 3 (59x39cm-23x15in) s.i.d.2001. 29-Jun-4 Peter Webb, Auckland #49/R est:55000-75000 (NZ.D 57000)
£23466 $38249 €34260 Watching for Buller on waterfall rock (48x181cm-19x71in) s.i.d.1994 i.d.verso acrylic seven kauri panels prov. 23-Sep-3 Peter Webb, Auckland #55/R est:80000-150000 (NZ.D 65000)
£57762 $94152 €84333 Coast watchers, songbook (134x100cm-53x39in) s.i.d.1994 acrylic kauri and rimu panels prov. 23-Sep-3 Peter Webb, Auckland #54/R est:100000-150000 (NZ.D 160000)
£68592 $111805 €100144 All along the Heaphy Highway (107x145cm-42x57in) s.i.d.1998 prov.exhib.lit. 23-Sep-3 Peter Webb, Auckland #53/R est:190000-230000 (NZ.D 190000)
£89552 $154925 €130746 Whistlers mothers, sticks and stones (230x240cm-91x94in) s.i.d.2000 acrylic exhib. 9-Dec-3 Peter Webb, Auckland #49/R est:250000-300000 (NZ.D 240000)
Sculpture
£2099 $3821 €3065 Bad bad brain (34x24x6cm-13x9x2in) s.i.d.1982 hand painted wood assemblage. 16-Jun-4 Deutscher-Menzies, Melbourne #203/R est:6000-9000 (A.D 5500)
£2888 $4708 €4216 Seal with neckbrace (67x36x10cm-26x14x4in) s.i.d.1981 wood prov. 23-Sep-3 Peter Webb, Auckland #68/R est:6000-9000 (NZ.D 8000)
£4198 $7641 €6129 And I'm in the kitchen with the tombstone blues (35x50x5cm-14x20x2in) s.i.d.1982 hand painted assemblage. 16-Jun-4 Deutscher-Menzies, Melbourne #202/R est:8000-12000 (A.D 11000)
Works on paper
£297 $512 €434 Untitled (29x19cm-11x7in) s.d. ink. 3-Dec-3 Dunbar Sloane, Auckland #30/R (NZ.D 800)
£1161 $2136 €1695 Good drying day (40x27cm-16x11in) s.i.d.1978 pencil. 25-Mar-4 International Art Centre, Auckland #130/R est:1000-2000 (NZ.D 3250)
£4821 $8871 €7039 Untitled (75x55cm-30x22in) s.d.1993 W/C pencil. 25-Mar-4 International Art Centre, Auckland #70/R est:16000-24000 (NZ.D 13500)
£19643 $35554 €28679 Limbo Lodge and timeball (100x150cm-39x59in) s.i.d.2002 W/C. 30-Mar-4 Peter Webb, Auckland #42/R est:50000-60000 (NZ.D 55000)
£21277 $37660 €31064 Urban camoflage (127x96cm-50x38in) s.d.1997 W/C. 28-Apr-4 Dunbar Sloane, Auckland #30a/R est:60000-70000 (NZ.D 60000)

HAMMOND, Hermione Francis (1910-) British
£300 $477 €438 Family picnic (98x127cm-39x50in) 9-Sep-3 Sworder & Son, Bishops Stortford #442/R

HAMMOND, Jane (1950-) American
Works on paper
£405 $700 €591 All kinds (98x64cm-39x25in) s.i.d.1989 verso gouache brush ink graphite linoleum block print. 10-Dec-3 Phillips, New York #524/R
£3390 $5763 €4949 Tom Fiddlers ground (258x232cm-102x91in) s.i.d.1996 verso mixed media canvas. 24-Nov-3 Sotheby's, Melbourne #283/R est:8000-12000 (A.D 8000)

HAMMOND, John A (1843-1939) Canadian
£400 $692 €584 Morning, Bay of Fundy (17x17cm-7x7in) s. s.i.verso board. 9-Dec-3 Pinneys, Montreal #19 (C.D 900)
£400 $656 €584 Bay Shore, St John, NB (13x20cm-5x8in) i.verso board. 28-May-3 Maynards, Vancouver #15 (C.D 900)
£489 $846 €714 Willows (35x43cm-14x17in) s.i.verso board. 9-Dec-3 Pinneys, Montreal #145 (C.D 1100)
£804 $1382 €1174 By the lakeshore N B (27x32cm-11x13in) board prov. 2-Dec-3 Joyner Waddington, Toronto #189/R est:2000-2500 (C.D 1800)
£982 $1689 €1434 St Salute, Venice (40x50cm-16x20in) s.d.1927 canvasboard. 2-Dec-3 Joyner Waddington, Toronto #461 est:2000-3000 (C.D 2200)
£1126 $1914 €1644 Harbour activity (33x48cm-13x19in) s.d.1927 board. 21-Nov-3 Walker's, Ottawa #96/R est:2000-3000 (C.D 2500)
£1440 $2635 €2102 Low tide, Bay of Fundy (87x55cm-34x22in) s. board painted 1893 prov. 1-Jun-4 Joyner Waddington, Toronto #38/R est:3500-4500 (C.D 3600)
£2009 $3355 €2913 On the Seine (77x62cm-30x24in) s. i.verso prov. 17-Jun-3 Pinneys, Montreal #135 est:3500-4500 (C.D 4500)
£3125 $5375 €4563 Inward bound, Bay of Fundy (74x99cm-29x39in) s. board. 2-Dec-3 Joyner Waddington, Toronto #91/R est:7000-9000 (C.D 7000)

HAMMOND, Leon W (1869-?) American
£1145 $1900 €1672 Cabin in the forest, western landscape (89x127cm-35x50in) s. 4-Oct-3 Neal Auction Company, New Orleans #1144/R est:3000-5000

HAMMOND, Miss Gertrude Demain (1862-1953) British
Works on paper
£1600 $2672 €2336 Silver gown (42x28cm-17x11in) s. W/C. 12-Nov-3 Sotheby's, Olympia #109/R est:1000-1500

HAMMOND, Robert John (fl.1882-1911) British
£370 $699 €540 Doves before a Devonshire cottage (25x35cm-10x14in) s. 19-Feb-4 Christie's, Kensington #335/R
£550 $1018 €803 Children by a brook (52x34cm-20x13in) s.d.1893. 13-Jan-4 Bonhams, Knightsbridge #61/R
£800 $1336 €1168 Gathering reeds. Village track (24x35cm-9x14in) one s. pair. 12-Nov-3 Sotheby's, Olympia #78/R
£1600 $2960 €2336 Young girls outside a farm (40x60cm-16x24in) s. 13-Jan-4 Bonhams, Knightsbridge #73/R est:1500-2000
£4800 $8640 €7008 A Devonshire lane, young girl walking on a path beside a stream (41x61cm-16x24in) s.i. 21-Apr-4 Tennants, Leyburn #1144/R est:1000-1500

HAMMOND, Thomas William (1854-1935) British
Works on paper
£360 $601 €526 Old mill lock (25x58cm-10x23in) s. pastel. 12-Nov-3 Sotheby's, Olympia #48/R

HAMMONS, David (1943-) American
£22346 $40000 €32625 African - American flag (142x223cm-56x88in) s.d.90 dyed cotton fabric prov.exhib.lit. 13-May-4 Sotheby's, New York #356/R est:40000-60000
Sculpture
£11351 $21000 €16572 Duck Tape (41x16x35cm-16x6x14in) s.d.92 duck tape shoulder purse. 12-Feb-4 Sotheby's, New York #240/R est:3000-5000
£19553 $35000 €28547 Dream walking (102x15cm-40x6in) chicken feet wire lace prov. 12-May-4 Christie's, Rockefeller NY #397/R est:40000-60000
Works on paper
£10429 $17000 €15226 Untitled, green power (35x43cm-14x17in) s. pastel exec.c.1975 prov. 23-Sep-3 Christie's, Rockefeller NY #61/R est:4000-6000
£14724 $24000 €21497 Untitled, body print (59x74cm-23x29in) s.d.75 ground pigment prov. 23-Sep-3 Christie's, Rockefeller NY #126/R est:5000-7000

HAMNETT, Nina (1890-1956) British
£520 $822 €754 Portrait of a young man smoking a pipe (71x48cm-28x19in) s.d.26 exhib. 24-Jul-3 Lawrence, Crewkerne #966
Works on paper
£260 $434 €380 Portrait of a lady in a wide brimmed hat (35x25cm-14x10in) init. pen ink. 22-Oct-3 Cheffins, Cambridge #489/R

HAMON, Jean Louis (1821-1874) French
£1342 $2403 €2000 Enfants attaques par un aigle (90x116cm-35x46in) s. 25-May-4 Palais de Beaux Arts, Brussels #370/R est:2000-3000

HAMPE, Ernest Wilhelm (1806-1862) German
£530 $991 €800 Romantic landscape with figures fishing at dawn (68x97cm-27x38in) s. 23-Jul-4 Altus, Berlin #593/R

HAMPE, Guido (1839-1902) German
£709 $1184 €1000 Wooded landscape with small boat on a lake (77x112cm-30x44in) s. 20-Oct-3 Bernaerts, Antwerp #464
£1119 $1902 €1600 Spree landscape with ferry (75x96cm-30x38in) s. canvas on panel. 20-Nov-3 Van Ham, Cologne #1614/R est:2000
£1208 $2223 €1800 Lake Geneva (76x112cm-30x44in) s.d.76. 25-Mar-4 Dr Fritz Nagel, Stuttgart #712/R est:1800

HAMPEL, Angela (1956-) ?
Works on paper
£278 $464 €400 Untitled - two women with kangaroo (31x48cm-12x19in) s.d. Indian ink. 25-Oct-3 Dr Lehr, Berlin #181/R

HAMPEL, Carl (c.1887-1942) Australian
£242 $377 €351 Misty morn (39x49cm-15x19in) s. canvas on board. 1-Aug-2 Joel, Victoria #149 (A.D 700)
£259 $404 €376 Inlet (48x58cm-19x23in) s. canvas on board. 1-Aug-2 Joel, Victoria #286 (A.D 750)
£813 $1455 €1187 Still life with chrysanthemums in an oriental vase (62x75cm-24x30in) s. painted c.1935. 10-May-4 Joel, Victoria #271 est:2000-3000 (A.D 2000)

HAMPEL, Charlotte (1863-1945) Austrian
£890 $1514 €1300 Self portrait before dressing table mirror (45x37cm-18x15in) 5-Nov-3 Hugo Ruef, Munich #1007/R
£1027 $1747 €1500 Self portrait with dog and flowers (41x31cm-16x12in) panel. 5-Nov-3 Hugo Ruef, Munich #1006/R est:1500

HAMPEL, Charlotte (attrib) (1863-1945) Austrian
£1589 $2893 €2400 Self portrait at the dressing table with mirror (45x37cm-18x15in) 21-Jun-4 Dorotheum, Vienna #121/R est:2400-3000

HAMPEL, Sigmund Walter (1868-1949) Austrian
Works on paper
£671 $1235 €1000 Daughter of the artist aged fourteen (36x25cm-14x10in) mono. Indian ink pencil prov. 26-Mar-4 Dorotheum, Vienna #152/R
£1107 $1981 €1616 Vanitas (36x26cm-14x10in) s. W/C prov. 15-May-4 Christie's, Sydney #311/R (A.D 2800)

HAMPEY, E R V (?) ?
£561 $886 €813 Coastal landscape with figures by fishing village (71x92cm-28x36in) s. 2-Sep-3 Rasmussen, Copenhagen #1640/R (D.KR 6000)

HAMPSHIRE, Ernest Llewellyn (1882-?) British
Works on paper
£360 $659 €526 Market place, Bruges (36x29cm-14x11in) s.d.1914 W/C. 27-Jan-4 Bonhams, Knightsbridge #214/R

HAMPSON, Roger (?) British
£300 $537 €438 Canon Mill, Bolton (95x61cm-37x24in) s. s.i.verso board. 17-Mar-4 Bonhams, Chester #257

HAMSUN, Marianne Feiring (1925-) Norwegian
£275 $443 €402 Winter landscape with house (80x73cm-31x29in) s. 25-Aug-3 Blomqvist, Lysaker #1104 (N.KR 3200)

HAMSUN, Tore (1912-1995) Norwegian
£418 $765 €610 Landscape from Asker (49x74cm-19x29in) s. panel. 2-Feb-4 Blomqvist, Lysaker #1095/R (N.KR 5200)
£571 $1051 €834 Landscape (64x80cm-25x31in) s. 29-Mar-4 Blomqvist, Lysaker #1107/R (N.KR 7200)
£602 $1006 €879 Man with donkey (80x100cm-31x39in) s. 20-Oct-3 Blomqvist, Lysaker #1116 (N.KR 7000)

HAMZA, Hans (1879-1945) Austrian
£2523 $4213 €3658 Market scene (11x16cm-4x6in) s. panel. 23-Jun-3 Philippe Schuler, Zurich #3563/R est:5000-7000 (S.FR 5500)

HAMZA, Johann (1850-1927) German
£1325 $2411 €2000 Boy with basket of fruit (48x39cm-19x15in) s. prov. 18-Jun-4 Stadion, Trieste #362/R est:2000-3000
£3356 $6007 €5000 A cavelier (34x23cm-13x9in) s.i. panel. 27-May-4 Dorotheum, Vienna #51/R est:5000-7000
£5944 $10105 €8500 Waiting for father to come home (55x45cm-22x18in) s.i.d.874 lit. 28-Nov-3 Schloss Ahlden, Ahlden #1420/R est:8500
£6250 $10313 €9000 Woman with suitor in salon (37x27cm-15x11in) s. panel. 3-Jul-3 Van Ham, Cologne #1225/R est:9500
£17647 $30000 €25765 Old man reading. Lute player (21x16cm-8x6in) s. panel pair. 29-Oct-3 Christie's, Rockefeller NY #33/R est:40000-60000

HAN, H N (20th C) American
£3867 $7000 €5646 One Penn Plaza (244x173cm-96x68in) acrylic. 16-Apr-4 American Auctioneer #189/R est:10000-15000
Works on paper
£829 $1500 €1210 Aerial view of city street (97x150cm-38x59in) W/C. 16-Apr-4 American Auctioneer #187/R est:1500-2000

HANCOCK, Charles (1795-1868) British
£1400 $2324 €2044 Hunter and dog in a landscape (40x48cm-16x19in) 1-Oct-3 Woolley & Wallis, Salisbury #305/R est:800-1200
£6000 $11160 €8760 Portrait of Lord Kinnaird and Richard Williams deerstalking in Falah Forest (139x182cm-55x72in) s. prov.exhib. 4-Mar-4 Christie's, Kensington #35 est:6000-8000

HANCOCK, Charles (attrib) (1795-1868) British
£520 $884 €759 Queen of Trumps (29x38cm-11x15in) s. i.verso panel. 19-Nov-3 Sotheby's, Olympia #20/R

HAND, Molly Williams (1892-1951) American
£273 $500 €399 Magie house, Woodstock, NY (51x61cm-20x24in) s.i.d.1938 board. 5-Jun-4 Treadway Gallery, Cincinnati #682/R

HAND, Thomas (?-1804) British
£696 $1100 €1016 Gypsies in the woods (94x74cm-37x29in) s.d.94. 6-Sep-3 Quinn's, Falls Church #228

HANDEL-MAZZETTI, Eduard von (1885-1950) Austrian
£709 $1184 €1000 Winter in the Dolomites (70x50cm-28x20in) s.d.1934 board. 16-Oct-3 Dorotheum, Salzburg #621/R
Works on paper
£426 $711 €600 View from Monte Silvano (30x37cm-12x15in) s.d.1944 W/C. 16-Oct-3 Dorotheum, Salzburg #905/R

HANDLER, Richard (1932-) Austrian
£464 $848 €700 Flowers in glass vase with butterfly (40x30cm-16x12in) s. panel. 8-Apr-4 Dorotheum, Vienna #51
£524 $902 €750 Bouquet of flowers in a glass vase (70x60cm-28x24in) s. panel. 3-Dec-3 Neumeister, Munich #587/R
£563 $975 €800 Snow roses on forest floor (30x43cm-12x17in) s. panel. 10-Dec-3 Dorotheum, Vienna #205/R
£845 $1403 €1200 Flowers by river (30x50cm-12x20in) s. panel. 16-Jun-3 Dorotheum, Vienna #128/R
£1007 $1883 €1500 Flowers with butterfly (80x60cm-31x24in) s. panel. 24-Feb-4 Dorotheum, Vienna #294 est:1800-2000
£1111 $1833 €1600 Flowers in vase (69x56cm-27x22in) s. panel. 2-Jul-3 Neumeister, Munich #658/R
£1216 $2177 €1800 Still life of flowers with butterfly (57x48cm-22x19in) s. panel. 6-May-4 Michael Zeller, Lindau #687/R est:1800
£2238 $3737 €3200 Still life of flowers (98x67cm-39x26in) s. panel. 9-Oct-3 Michael Zeller, Lindau #585/R est:3200
£2238 $3849 €3200 Still life of flowers (118x79cm-46x31in) s. 5-Dec-3 Michael Zeller, Lindau #632/R est:3200
£2500 $4250 €3600 Flowers (90x72cm-35x28in) s. panel. 28-Oct-3 Dorotheum, Vienna #107/R est:2000-2400

HANDLER-STEINFEST, Herta (1940-) Austrian
£559 $934 €800 Still life with fruit (31x25cm-12x10in) mono. canvas on board. 9-Oct-3 Michael Zeller, Lindau #586/R

HANDLEY-READ, Edward Harry (1870-1935) British
£300 $555 €438 End of the evening (46x61cm-18x24in) s. 14-Jul-4 Christie's, Kensington #1159
Works on paper
£250 $455 €365 Landscape with piper (44x57cm-17x22in) init. W/C. 15-Jun-4 Bonhams, Knightsbridge #51

HANDMANN, Emanuel (1718-1781) Swiss
£699 $1272 €1021 Field camp (22x31cm-9x12in) s.d.1760 panel. 16-Jun-4 Fischer, Luzern #2156/R (S.FR 1600)
£1207 $2160 €1762 Portraits of Niclaus Gournel and wife (84x64cm-33x25in) s.d.1768 s.d.1769 verso two. 13-May-4 Stuker, Bern #166/R est:3000-4000 (S.FR 2800)
£1207 $2160 €1762 Portrait of Rosina Gournel (82x64cm-32x25in) s.i.d.1769 verso. 13-May-4 Stuker, Bern #167/R est:1400-1800 (S.FR 2800)

HANEL, Georg (1879-?) German
£1719 $2750 €2510 Unhitching the plough (116x95cm-46x37in) s.i. 21-Sep-3 Bonhams & Butterfields, San Francisco #2803/R est:2000-3000

HANEMANN, Wilhelm (1880-1962) Danish
£567 $1015 €828 Still life of roses in vase (75x75cm-30x30in) s. octagonal. 12-Jan-4 Rasmussen, Vejle #146/R (D.KR 6000)
£567 $1015 €828 Still life of lilacs in vase (81x63cm-32x25in) s. 12-Jan-4 Rasmussen, Vejle #147/R (D.KR 6000)

HANFSTANGL, Ernst (1840-1897) German
£1351 $2324 €1972 The tax collector (44x33cm-17x13in) s. panel. 8-Dec-3 Philippe Schuler, Zurich #3410/R est:1500-2000 (S.FR 3000)

HANFT, Willy (1888-?) German
£306 $483 €440 Fulda valley (70x100cm-28x39in) s. 19-Sep-3 Schloss Ahlden, Ahlden #1620/R

HANGER, Max (1874-1955) German
£267 $477 €400 Pre-alpine landscape with walkers on path (11x16cm-4x6in) s. panel. 13-May-4 Bassenge, Berlin #5566/R
£294 $550 €429 Barnyard fowl (15x23cm-6x9in) s. panel. 25-Feb-4 Doyle, New York #101/R
£306 $498 €440 Cock with two hens (9x13cm-4x5in) s. panel. 25-Sep-3 Neumeister, Munich #2782
£307 $561 €460 Chicken farm (10x21cm-4x8in) s. 5-Jun-4 Arnold, Frankfurt #594/R
£310 $518 €450 Poultry yard with peacock (16x23cm-6x9in) s. panel. 9-Jul-3 Hugo Ruef, Munich #102
£327 $594 €480 Poultry yard (13x24cm-5x9in) s.i. panel. 4-Feb-4 Neumeister, Munich #690/R
£336 $624 €500 Wild hen running towards a small pond (24x18cm-9x7in) s. cardboard. 5-Mar-4 Wendl, Rudolstadt #3674/R
£414 $691 €600 Poultry yard (17x23cm-7x9in) s. panel. 9-Jul-3 Hugo Ruef, Munich #101/R
£423 $731 €600 Hen yard (8x14cm-3x6in) s. panel. 12-Dec-3 Berlinghof, Heidelberg #1048/R
£439 $685 €650 Pheasant in the mountains (38x48cm-15x19in) s. 28-Mar-3 Behringer, Furth #1141/R
£450 $752 €657 Peacock and chickens (9x28cm-4x11in) s.i. panel. 12-Nov-3 Sotheby's, Olympia #198/R
£470 $864 €700 Poultry (18x24cm-7x9in) s.i. panel. 27-Mar-4 Geble, Radolfzell #725/R
£490 $832 €700 Hens, cockerels, ducks, geese and two peacocks by a pond (18x24cm-7x9in) s. panel. 28-Nov-3 Wendl, Rudolstadt #3988/R
£493 $789 €700 Pheasants (12x16cm-5x6in) s. panel lit. 19-Sep-3 Karlheinz Kaupp, Staufen #1940
£541 $930 €790 In the chicken run (9x13cm-4x5in) s. panel pair. 8-Dec-3 Philippe Schuler, Zurich #3446/R (S.FR 1200)
£559 $934 €800 Poultry yard (30x46cm-12x18in) s.i. barod. 26-Jun-3 Weidler, Nurnberg #330/R
£610 $951 €890 Chickens in meadow (13x17cm-5x7in) s. panel. 10-Apr-3 Weidler, Nurnberg #323/R
£662 $1212 €1000 Peacock in poultry yard (16x21cm-6x8in) s. panel. 8-Apr-4 Dorotheum, Vienna #77/R
£671 $1235 €1000 Poultry by pond (17x25cm-7x10in) s. lit. 25-Mar-4 Karlheinz Kaupp, Staufen #2475/R
£671 $1235 €1000 Poultry (24x17cm-9x7in) s. lit. 25-Mar-4 Karlheinz Kaupp, Staufen #2476/R
£676 $1209 €1000 Poultry (14x18cm-6x7in) s.i. panel. 6-May-4 Michael Zeller, Lindau #684/R
£733 $1313 €1100 Poultry yard (10x14cm-4x6in) s.i. panel lit. 14-May-4 Schloss Ahlden, Ahlden #2821/R
£733 $1313 €1100 Poultry yard (10x14cm-4x6in) s. panel lit. 14-May-4 Schloss Ahlden, Ahlden #2823/R
£743 $1330 €1100 Poultry yard on spring day (17x23cm-7x9in) s. panel. 6-May-4 Michael Zeller, Lindau #683/R
£800 $1448 €1200 Poultry (10x18cm-4x7in) s. panel. 1-Apr-4 Van Ham, Cologne #1400
£811 $1427 €1200 Landscape with pheasant, hens and duck (14x24cm-6x9in) s. panel. 22-May-4 Lempertz, Koln #1524
£1757 $3145 €2600 Poultry yard (23x30cm-9x12in) s. panel lit. 8-May-4 Schloss Ahlden, Ahlden #737/R est:1900
£2262 $3846 €3303 Poultry yards (19x27cm-7x11in) s. panel pair. 19-Nov-3 Fischer, Luzern #1170/R est:5000-6000 (S.FR 5000)

HANGER, Max (jnr) (1898-?) German
£374 $637 €546 Poultry yard (17x27cm-7x11in) s. panel. 5-Nov-3 Dobiaschofsky, Bern #624/R (S.FR 850)

HANICOTTE, Augustin (1870-1957) French
Works on paper
£470 $874 €700 Scene de kermesse (41x32cm-16x13in) s.i. W/C. 3-Mar-4 Ferri, Paris #203

HANIN, René (1873-1943) French
£922 $1540 €1300 Repos sur le banc de la medina (34x28cm-13x11in) s.i.d.1915 cardboard. 19-Oct-3 Raboudin & Choppin de Janvry, Paris #74/R

HANISCH, Alois (1866-1937) Austrian
£1275 $2385 €1900 Still life (35x91cm-14x36in) s.d.1920. 26-Feb-4 Cambi, Genoa #458/R est:600-800

HANKE, Hans (20th C) Austrian
£340 $609 €500 Itinerant musicians resting (40x30cm-16x12in) s. 18-Mar-4 Neumeister, Munich #2678/R

HANKE, Henry Aloysius (1901-1989) Australian
£4348 $7783 €6348 Arrival of First fleet, Sydney cove (114x126cm-45x50in) s.d.33 prov.lit. 15-May-4 Christie's, Sydney #490/R est:15000-25000 (A.D 11000)

HANKINS, Abraham (1903-1963) American
£217 $375 €317 Little town (28x61cm-11x24in) s. 10-Dec-3 Alderfer's, Hatfield #386/R
£267 $425 €390 Abstract still life (20x25cm-8x10in) s. board. 10-Sep-3 Alderfer's, Hatfield #315
£349 $600 €510 Still life (20x25cm-8x10in) s. canvasboard. 7-Dec-3 Freeman, Philadelphia #223
£438 $700 €639 Landscape with tree (64x99cm-25x39in) s. 19-Sep-3 Freeman, Philadelphia #94/R
£581 $1000 €848 Still life with mixed flowers (56x64cm-22x25in) s. 7-Dec-3 Freeman, Philadelphia #201

HANLEN, John (1922-) American
£250 $400 €365 Deep spring (183x122cm-72x48in) s. acrylic on masonite. 19-Sep-3 Freeman, Philadelphia #192/R

HANLON, Father Jack (1913-1968) Irish
£3662 $5859 €5200 Virgin and child (46x36cm-18x14in) s.d.1955. 16-Sep-3 Whyte's, Dublin #122/R est:2000-3000
£5035 $8559 €7200 Canticle to the sun (61x41cm-24x16in) s. i.verso canvas on board prov. 18-Nov-3 Whyte's, Dublin #16/R est:5000-6000
Works on paper
£950 $1511 €1387 Still life with lilac (30x23cm-12x9in) W/C prov. 10-Sep-3 Cheffins, Cambridge #500/R
£1000 $1590 €1460 Poppies and dahlias (22x29cm-9x11in) W/C prov. 10-Sep-3 Cheffins, Cambridge #499/R est:500-800
£1284 $2426 €1900 Holy Family (22x18cm-9x7in) W/C prov. 17-Feb-4 Whyte's, Dublin #10/R est:1500-2000
£1678 $2853 €2400 View of a house through trees (36x52cm-14x20in) W/C prov. 18-Nov-3 Whyte's, Dublin #14/R est:2500-3500
£2098 $3566 €3000 The sweeper (38x28cm-15x11in) W/C prov. 18-Nov-3 Whyte's, Dublin #9/R est:3000-4000
£2133 $3861 €3200 Model in Lhote's studio (56x33cm-22x13in) s. W/C. 31-Mar-4 James Adam, Dublin #162/R est:2500-3500
£2282 $4085 €3400 Girl with a hat (28x39cm-11x15in) s.d.43 W/C. 26-May-4 James Adam, Dublin #109/R est:2000-3000

£2800 $5068 €4200 Street scene, South of France (38x51cm-15x20in) s. W/C. 31-Mar-4 James Adam, Dublin #57/R est:2000-3000
£2847 $4641 €4100 Palazzo Interior (35x50cm-14x20in) s. W/C. 24-Sep-3 James Adam, Dublin #39/R est:3000-4000

HANLON, Marie (1948-) Irish?
£447 $804 €670 Tanka II (30x50cm-12x20in) s.verso acrylic board. 20-Apr-4 James Adam, Dublin #166/R
£453 $816 €680 Tanka I (30x50cm-12x20in) s.stretcher acrylic diptych. 20-Apr-4 James Adam, Dublin #165/R
£533 $960 €800 Secondo (35x66cm-14x26in) s.stretcher acrylic diptych. 20-Apr-4 James Adam, Dublin #158/R

HANLY, Patrick (1932-) New Zealander
£294 $526 €429 Tiki kite (150x150cm-59x59in) s.i. acrylic structure. 11-May-4 Peter Webb, Auckland #138/R (NZ.D 850)
£3261 $5250 €4761 Mt. Eden series (34x34cm-13x13in) s.d.74 board. 20-Aug-3 Dunbar Sloane, Auckland #38/R est:8000-16000 (NZ.D 9000)
£12500 $22625 €18250 Wintergarden 10am (90x90cm-35x35in) s.d.1974 s.i.d.verso enamel on board. 30-Mar-4 Peter Webb, Auckland #35/R est:45000-65000 (NZ.D 35000)
£13986 $25455 €20420 New age woman (60x60cm-24x24in) s.i.d.1988 enamel on board. 29-Jun-4 Peter Webb, Auckland #35/R est:40000-60000 (NZ.D 40000)
£14685 $26727 €21440 Torso, heart and eye composition (43x43cm-17x17in) s.d.1981 enamel on board. 29-Jun-4 Peter Webb, Auckland #36/R est:35000-45000 (NZ.D 42000)
£17730 $31383 €25886 Brown torso (48x43cm-19x17in) s.d.78 enamal board prov. 28-Apr-4 Dunbar Sloane, Auckland #25/R est:55000-65000 (NZ.D 50000)
£20979 $38182 €30629 Girl asleep no.9 (76x79cm-30x31in) s.d.1969. 29-Jun-4 Peter Webb, Auckland #29/R est:75000-95000 (NZ.D 60000)
£23929 $43311 €34936 Figure in light 2 (40x45cm-16x18in) s.i.d.1964. 30-Mar-4 Peter Webb, Auckland #37/R est:50000-60000 (NZ.D 67000)
£31469 $57273 €45945 Vessel attacked (120x120cm-47x47in) s.i.d.1987 enamel on board exhib. 29-Jun-4 Peter Webb, Auckland #34/R est:75000-95000 (NZ.D 90000)
£37313 $64552 €54477 Figures in light 8 (110x80cm-43x31in) s.i.d.1964 s.i.verso prov.exhib. 9-Dec-3 Peter Webb, Auckland #41/R est:100000-120000 (NZ.D 100000)
Works on paper
£1544 $2888 €2254 Bouquet of pieces (73x70cm-29x28in) s.d.1992 s.i.d.verso mixed media construction. 24-Feb-4 Peter Webb, Auckland #154/R est:3500-5000 (NZ.D 4200)
£1714 $3103 €2502 Escape vessel (58x64cm-23x25in) s.i.d.1983 pencil. 30-Mar-4 Peter Webb, Auckland #136/R est:5000-7000 (NZ.D 4800)
£1714 $3103 €2502 Awake aotearoa - fire series (58x68cm-23x27in) s.i.d.1983 pencil. 30-Mar-4 Peter Webb, Auckland #135/R est:5000-7000 (NZ.D 4800)
£3322 $6045 €4850 Flowers study (45x38cm-18x15in) W/C executed c.1967. 29-Jun-4 Peter Webb, Auckland #52/R est:10000-15000 (NZ.D 9500)

HANNAFORD, Charles E (1863-1955) British
Works on paper
£360 $576 €526 Fishing boats in the morning mist (20x53cm-8x21in) s. W/C. 18-Sep-3 Goldings, Lincolnshire #730/R
£444 $816 €648 Fishing boats leaving Ostende (45x69cm-18x27in) s.i. W/C. 9-Jun-4 Walker's, Ottawa #354/R (C.D 1100)
£750 $1365 €1095 Loch Coruisk, Isle of Skye (44x69cm-17x27in) s.i.d.1945 pencil W/C htd white. 1-Jul-4 Christie's, Kensington #116/R

HANNAFORD, Charles E (attrib) (1863-1955) British
Works on paper
£300 $498 €438 Sylvan Glen (22x29cm-9x11in) W/C. 1-Oct-3 Woolley & Wallis, Salisbury #107/R

HANNAH, Duncan (1952-) American?
£867 $1500 €1266 Crete (66x76cm-26x30in) prov. 10-Dec-3 Phillips, New York #515/R est:1500-2000

HANNAUX, Paul (1899-1954) French
£7801 $13028 €11000 Place animee devant la mosquee a Fes (73x100cm-29x39in) s.i. panel. 16-Jun-3 Gros & Delettrez, Paris #33/R est:6000-8000

HANNEMAN, Adriaen (1601-1671) Dutch
£3846 $7000 €5615 Portrait of a lady said to be Dorothea Countess of Sutherland (112x95cm-44x37in) 29-Jun-4 Sotheby's, New York #32/R est:6000-8000

HANNEMAN, Adriaen (circle) (1601-1671) Dutch
£8500 $15215 €12410 Portrait of Francis Potts seated with his gun and hound (110x89cm-43x35in) i. 22-Mar-4 Bonhams & Brooks, Norfolk #328/R est:4000-6000

HANNER, Hans (1883-) German
£1655 $2764 €2400 In the studio (122x66cm-48x26in) 15-Nov-3 Von Zezschwitz, Munich #55/R est:2500

HANNEY, Clifford (1890-1990) British
£300 $549 €438 Godrevy (49x60cm-19x24in) s. 3-Jun-4 Lane, Penzance #103

HANNIG, Henry (19/20th C) American
£256 $450 €374 Branches overlooking a small stream (25x36cm-10x14in) canvasboard prov. 23-May-4 Treadway Gallery, Cincinnati #561/R

HANNL, Maximilian Joseph (1694-1759) Austrian
£7500 $12975 €10950 Trompe l'Oeil self-portrait (74x60cm-29x24in) prov.lit. 11-Dec-3 Sotheby's, London #214/R est:8000-12000

HANNO, Carl von (1901-1953) Norwegian
£434 $724 €634 Cutting the Christmas tree (44x32cm-17x13in) s. panel. 17-Nov-3 Blomqvist, Lysaker #1106 (N.KR 5200)
£535 $889 €776 Sea spray, Hidra (38x47cm-15x19in) s. 16-Jun-3 Blomqvist, Lysaker #1317 (N.KR 6200)
£772 $1413 €1127 Interior scene with woman (70x49cm-28x19in) s. panel. 7-Jun-4 Blomqvist, Oslo #373/R (N.KR 9500)

HANNOTIAU, Alexandre (1863-1901) Belgian
£6174 $11423 €9200 Elegante regardant la carte des desserts (85x53cm-33x21in) s. 15-Mar-4 Horta, Bruxelles #114/R est:3500-5000

HANOTEAU, Hector (1823-1890) French
£534 $960 €800 La clairiere (55x46cm-22x18in) s. 26-Apr-4 Tajan, Paris #176
£789 $1453 €1200 Boeufs a la riviere (26x36cm-10x14in) s. panel. 23-Jun-4 Maigret, Paris #68/R
£1300 $2379 €1950 Chasseur (41x56cm-16x22in) s.d.1870 s.d.verso panel. 6-Jun-4 Osenat, Fontainebleau #247/R est:3000-3500
£1884 $3090 €2600 Promeneurs au bord du chemin (35x25cm-14x10in) s.d.1883 panel. 11-May-3 Osenat, Fontainebleau #207/R est:1500-1800

HANRAHAN, Kathleen Moors (1955-) Canadian
£475 $860 €694 Tapestries in gold frames (76x102cm-30x40in) s.i.verso prov. 18-Apr-4 Levis, Calgary #41a/R est:1000-1200 (C.D 1150)
£588 $982 €858 Untitled - riverbank in autumn (120x90cm-47x35in) s. acrylic. 17-Nov-3 Hodgins, Calgary #421/R est:750-1000 (C.D 1300)

HANS, Josefus Gerardus (1826-1891) Dutch
£922 $1540 €1300 La passage de la riviere (47x34cm-19x13in) s.d.68 panel. 17-Jun-3 Vanderkindere, Brussels #439
Works on paper
£710 $1300 €1037 Wooded landscape at Sorgvliet with a peasant near a stream (18x26cm-7x10in) s. s.i.verso W/C. 29-Jan-4 Swann Galleries, New York #203/R

HANS, Rolf (1938-1996) German
£769 $1285 €1100 Composition in red with dark surround (70x58cm-28x23in) s.i.d. verso study. 10-Oct-3 Winterberg, Heidelberg #1369/R
£1119 $1924 €1600 Dark Carmen (140x122cm-55x48in) s.i.d.1985 verso. 4-Dec-3 Van Ham, Cologne #181/R est:1500
Works on paper
£420 $722 €600 Black, blue violet (29x55cm-11x22in) s.i.d.1963 W/C ink. 4-Dec-3 Van Ham, Cologne #182

HANSCH, Anton (1813-1876) Austrian
£423 $701 €600 Old farmstead (19x25cm-7x10in) s. 12-Jun-3 Dorotheum, Graz #19
Works on paper
£437 $699 €620 Lucern (14x23cm-6x9in) mono.i. W/C. 18-Sep-3 Rieber, Stuttgart #4182

HANSCH, Anton (attrib) (1813-1876) Austrian
£403 $753 €600 Glacier (37x38cm-15x15in) board. 24-Feb-4 Dorotheum, Vienna #156
£436 $816 €650 Woodland (35x42cm-14x17in) 24-Feb-4 Dorotheum, Vienna #10/R

HANSCH, Johannes (1875-1945) German
£660 $1102 €950 Teufelssee in green wood (60x80cm-24x31in) s.d. i. stretcher. 25-Oct-3 Dr Lehr, Berlin #182/R

HANSEN, Al (1927-1995) American
Works on paper
£533 $976 €800 When I was little (30x23cm-12x9in) s.d.72 collage butterfly winds newspaper matchboz. 4-Jun-4 Lempertz, Koln #181/R

HANSEN, Ane Marie (1852-1941) Danish
£280 $439 €409 Still life (43x49cm-17x19in) s.d.1914. 30-Aug-3 Rasmussen, Havnen #2181 (D.KR 3000)

HANSEN, Armin Carl (1886-1957) American
£1118 $1900 €1632 Seascape (30x41cm-12x16in) s. 1-Nov-3 Susanin's, Chicago #5008/R est:800-1200
£1902 $3500 €2853 Portrait of Haakon Adelstein Jenssen (49x34cm-19x13in) s.d.15 board sketch verso. 8-Jun-4 Bonhams & Butterfields, San Francisco #4273/R est:5000-7000
£4348 $8000 €6522 View of a seaport. Self portrait (17x14cm-7x6in) init. board double-sided prov. 8-Jun-4 Bonhams & Butterfields, San Francisco #4272/R est:10000-15000
£7487 $14000 €10931 Idle fisher fleet (25x30cm-10x12in) s. board prov. 24-Jul-4 Coeur d'Alene, Hayden #69/R est:10000-15000
£97826 $180000 €146739 Seaward (76x106cm-30x42in) s.i. prov. 8-Jun-4 Bonhams & Butterfields, San Francisco #4274/R est:150000-200000
£102941 $175000 €150294 Afterdeck (46x56cm-18x22in) s. canvasboard. 29-Oct-3 Christie's, Los Angeles #9/R est:60000-80000
£174419 $300000 €254652 Decoration (86x100cm-34x39in) s. s.i.verso prov. 4-Dec-3 Christie's, Rockefeller NY #92/R est:300000-500000
Prints
£3867 $7000 €5646 Sardine barge (33x37cm-13x15in) s.i. etching. 19-Apr-4 Bonhams & Butterfields, San Francisco #27/R est:1200-1500

HANSEN, Arne L (1921-) Danish
£313 $533 €457 Composition in orange and red (24x30cm-9x12in) init. d.68 verso. 10-Nov-3 Rasmussen, Vejle #714 (D.KR 3400)
£348 $633 €508 Cold against warm - orange composition (50x73cm-20x29in) init.d.78. 7-Feb-4 Rasmussen, Havnen #4060 (D.KR 3800)

£427 $682 €623 From the world of industry (33x215cm-13x85in) init.d.78. 22-Sep-3 Rasmussen, Vejle #670/R (D.KR 4500)
£740 $1362 €1080 Winter scene with blue harvesting machine (50x73cm-20x29in) init. s.d.57 verso. 29-Mar-4 Rasmussen, Copenhagen #41/R (D.KR 8200)
£993 $1827 €1450 Varmland industry - Autumn (97x130cm-38x51in) init. s.d.74 verso. 29-Mar-4 Rasmussen, Copenhagen #384/R (D.KR 11000)

HANSEN, Asmus Christian (1901-?) Danish
£496 $829 €724 Seascape with the Battle at Helgoland 1864 (75x100cm-30x39in) s. 25-Oct-3 Rasmussen, Havnen #2548/R (D.KR 5300)

HANSEN, Bjarne (1890-1976) Norwegian
£396 $637 €578 Landscape from Jaeren (49x78cm-19x31in) s.d.1914. 25-Aug-3 Blomqvist, Lysaker #1105/R (N.KR 4600)

HANSEN, Bjorn T (1942-) Danish
£362 $648 €529 Composition in white (81x65cm-32x26in) s.d.85. 10-May-4 Rasmussen, Vejle #730/R (D.KR 4000)
£627 $1129 €915 Figure composition (140x100cm-55x39in) init.d.75. 24-Apr-4 Rasmussen, Havnen #4230/R (D.KR 7000)

HANSEN, Carel Lodewyk (1765-1840) Dutch
£495 $900 €723 Interior Dutch scene (36x43cm-14x17in) s.d.1812 panel. 7-Feb-4 Auctions by the Bay, Alameda #1512/R
£2533 $4535 €3800 Wooded landscape with travellers (83x107cm-33x42in) s.d.1827 prov. 17-May-4 Christie's, Amsterdam #113/R est:4000-6000

HANSEN, Carl (19/20th C) Scandinavian
£515 $860 €752 The young woman and death (86x105cm-34x41in) s. 25-Oct-3 Rasmussen, Havnen #2025 (D.KR 5500)

HANSEN, Carla Thonsgaard (?) Danish?
£1648 $3000 €2406 Circus star (45x65cm-18x26in) mono.d.73. 7-Feb-4 Rasmussen, Havnen #4230 est:1000-2000 (D.KR 18000)

HANSEN, Christ B (attrib) (19/20th C) American?
£1118 $1800 €1632 Classical ruins (150x201cm-59x79in) indis.sig. 21-Aug-3 Doyle, New York #31/R est:1000-1500

HANSEN, Constantin (1804-1880) Danish
£378 $654 €552 A seated nude man (25x21cm-10x8in) prov. 9-Dec-3 Rasmussen, Copenhagen #1333/R (D.KR 4000)
£614 $1063 €896 Portrait study of a young man (29x38cm-11x15in) s. d.1833 verso. 9-Dec-3 Rasmussen, Copenhagen #1327/R (D.KR 6500)
£662 $1145 €967 Scene from Homer's Iliaden (19x22cm-7x9in) painted c.1827 prov. 9-Dec-3 Rasmussen, Copenhagen #1325/R (D.KR 7000)
£1229 $2126 €1794 Small Neapolitan boy lying down (23x35cm-9x14in) 9-Dec-3 Rasmussen, Copenhagen #1326/R est:6000-8000 (D.KR 13000)

HANSEN, Constantin (attrib) (1804-1880) Danish
£496 $917 €724 Portrait of Kjerstine Fogh (47x40cm-19x16in) prov. 15-Mar-4 Rasmussen, Vejle #408/R (D.KR 5500)

HANSEN, Ejnar (1884-1965) American/Danish
£220 $400 €321 Valley landscape (36x43cm-14x17in) s. 19-Jun-4 Jeffery Burchard, Florida #196

HANSEN, Emiel (1878-1952) Danish
£360 $576 €526 Still life of fruit and bottles (55x70cm-22x28in) s. exhib. 22-Sep-3 Rasmussen, Vejle #680 (D.KR 3800)

HANSEN, Gordon (1904-1972) American
£216 $400 €315 Townscape (58x74cm-23x29in) s. 17-Jul-4 Outer Cape Auctions, Provincetown #112/R

HANSEN, Gotfred (20th C) Danish
£311 $566 €467 And we're dancing through woods, Lunden (56x76cm-22x30in) mono.d.1922. 19-Jun-4 Rasmussen, Havnen #2268/R (D.KR 3500)

HANSEN, Hans (1853-1947) British
Works on paper
£300 $480 €438 North African snake charmer (36x25cm-14x10in) s. W/C. 16-Sep-3 Gorringes, Bexhill #1523/R
£2200 $3982 €3212 An occasion of ceremony (18x25cm-7x10in) s. W/C. 19-Apr-4 Sotheby's, London #124/R est:1500-2000

HANSEN, Hans (1769-1828) Danish
£520 $899 €759 The Angel appearing to Josef (14x12cm-6x5in) s. metal after A R Mengs exhib.prov. 9-Dec-3 Rasmussen, Copenhagen #1632/R (D.KR 5500)

HANSEN, Hans Nikolaj (1853-1923) Danish
£433 $801 €632 Landscape from Frederiksborg with Th. Niss at the easel (43x34cm-17x13in) i.verso. 15-Mar-4 Rasmussen, Vejle #465/R (D.KR 4800)
£463 $829 €676 Wooded landscape with figures by river (71x104cm-28x41in) init.d.1906. 12-Jan-4 Rasmussen, Vejle #111/R (D.KR 4900)
£2410 $4000 €3519 Kronborg Castle (133x205cm-52x81in) init.d.1903. 30-Sep-3 Christie's, Rockefeller NY #446/R est:4000-6000
£2471 $4250 €3608 Fairy ring (64x79cm-25x31in) init.d.1891. 6-Dec-3 Neal Auction Company, New Orleans #235/R est:4000-6000

HANSEN, Harald (1890-1967) Danish
£282 $480 €412 Snake tamer at Djelma el Fna, Marrakech (100x120cm-39x47in) s.d.48-49. 26-Nov-3 Kunsthallen, Copenhagen #333 (D.KR 3000)
£541 $1001 €790 Matara - two bull fighters (75x80cm-30x31in) s.d.1926 exhib. 15-Mar-4 Rasmussen, Vejle #581/R (D.KR 6000)
£670 $1085 €972 Exterior with seated nurse (78x64cm-31x25in) s.d.17. 4-Aug-3 Rasmussen, Vejle #634/R (D.KR 7000)

HANSEN, Heinrich (1821-1890) Danish
£359 $668 €524 A monk in the crypt of Canterbury Cathedral (18x20cm-7x8in) panel prov. 2-Mar-4 Rasmussen, Copenhagen #1550 (D.KR 4000)
£654 $1034 €948 Church interior with monk (41x35cm-16x14in) init.d.75. 2-Sep-3 Rasmussen, Copenhagen #1667/R (D.KR 7000)
£945 $1635 €1380 Young woman fetching water (28x26cm-11x10in) init. 9-Dec-3 Rasmussen, Copenhagen #1351/R (D.KR 10000)
£5068 $8919 €7500 Scene in Rome (27x22cm-11x9in) init.d.85. 18-May-4 Sotheby's, Milan #243/R est:5000-8000
£5500 $10120 €8030 Fish market, Rome (53x42cm-21x17in) s. 25-Mar-4 Christie's, Kensington #121/R est:4000-6000
£26000 $47320 €37960 Frederiksborg Castle, departure of the royal falcon hunt (40x55cm-16x22in) init.d.61 prov. 15-Jun-4 Sotheby's, London #339/R est:14000-18000

HANSEN, Herman Wendelborg (1854-1924) American
Works on paper
£2874 $4800 €4196 Two cowboys on horseback (51x36cm-20x14in) s.d.02 W/C paper on board. 9-Oct-3 Christie's, Rockefeller NY #82/R est:6000-8000
£14706 $25000 €21471 Stolen cavalry horses (58x89cm-23x35in) s.d.20 W/C prov.lit. 1-Nov-3 Santa Fe Art, Santa Fe #34/R est:25000-35000
£16176 $27500 €23617 Fugitives (58x89cm-23x35in) s.d.1921 W/C prov.lit. 1-Nov-3 Santa Fe Art, Santa Fe #166/R est:25000-35000

HANSEN, I J (19/20th C) Scandinavian
£941 $1599 €1374 Town scene from Rothenburg (38x28cm-15x11in) s.i.d.1912. 29-Nov-3 Rasmussen, Havnen #2287/R (D.KR 10000)

HANSEN, Ian (1948-) Australian
£1093 $2000 €1596 Gretel vs Wetherley in the 1962 America's Cup race (60x91cm-24x36in) s. 29-Jul-4 Christie's, Rockefeller NY #53/R est:3000-5000
£4645 $8500 €6782 Schooner yacht - America 1851 (61x91cm-24x36in) s. 29-Jul-4 Christie's, Rockefeller NY #52/R est:3000-5000

HANSEN, Immanuel (1859-1940) Danish?
£895 $1638 €1307 Whale being cut up at Wilder's Place. Male model (56x65cm-22x26in) s.d.1889 double-sided exhib. 7-Jun-4 Museumsbygningen, Copenhagen #136/R (D.KR 10000)

HANSEN, J T (1848-1912) Danish
£469 $878 €685 View from Venice (30x68cm-12x27in) s.d.1886. 25-Feb-4 Museumsbygningen, Copenhagen #140 (D.KR 5200)
£716 $1311 €1045 View of Rothenburg (19cm-7in) s. sold with coastal landscape by C M Soya-Jensen. 9-Jun-4 Rasmussen, Copenhagen #1933/R (D.KR 8000)
£1432 $2621 €2091 Venetian street scene with small child (39x26cm-15x10in) 9-Jun-4 Rasmussen, Copenhagen #1895/R est:10000-15000 (D.KR 16000)

HANSEN, Jacoba Catherina Dorothea (attrib) (1825-1893) ?
£8054 $14416 €12000 Bouquet de fleurs et fruits sur une tablette de fenetre (87x70cm-34x28in) 25-May-4 Palais de Beaux Arts, Brussels #561/R est:11000-15000

HANSEN, Jakob (20th C) Danish
£1074 $1966 €1568 Views of Borghese park and garden, Rome (31x40cm-12x16in) pair. 9-Jun-4 Rasmussen, Copenhagen #1937/R est:6000-8000 (D.KR 12000)

HANSEN, Jorgen (1862-1937) Danish
£361 $667 €527 The little painter (38x41cm-15x16in) i.stretcher. 15-Mar-4 Rasmussen, Vejle #328 (D.KR 4000)
£387 $658 €565 Karen Vaever's kitchen during the war (47x63cm-19x25in) s.d.1918. 10-Nov-3 Rasmussen, Vejle #263/R (D.KR 4200)

HANSEN, Jorgen Teik (1947-) Danish
£724 $1296 €1057 Composition (133x160cm-52x63in) init.d.91 verso. 10-May-4 Rasmussen, Vejle #714 (D.KR 8000)

HANSEN, Josef Theodor (1848-1912) Danish
£658 $1211 €1000 Interior with bouquet (33x21cm-13x8in) s.d.87. 24-Jun-4 Christie's, Paris #143/R
£1308 $2067 €1897 Giardino cafe - Venetian canal view (31x25cm-12x10in) s.i.d.1884. 2-Sep-3 Rasmussen, Copenhagen #1666/R est:15000 (D.KR 14000)
£1791 $3277 €2615 From a wash-house in Jylland (63x83cm-25x33in) s.d.1870 exhib. 9-Jun-4 Rasmussen, Copenhagen #1574/R est:25000-35000 (D.KR 20000)
£1890 $3270 €2759 Town scene from Verona with Il Ponte della Pietra (45x29cm-18x11in) s.i.d.1897. 9-Dec-3 Rasmussen, Copenhagen #1350/R est:10000-15000 (D.KR 20000)
£2647 $4737 €3865 Mulini e Forno, Vico Storto, Pompeii (22x29cm-9x11in) s.d.1911. 12-Jan-4 Rasmussen, Vejle #385/R est:25000-30000 (D.KR 28000)
£3500 $5950 €5110 Interior at Pompei (52x26cm-20x10in) s.i.d.1884. 18-Nov-3 Sotheby's, London #335/R
£3581 $6553 €5228 Interior from Saint Peter's (52x32cm-20x13in) s.i.d.1884. 9-Jun-4 Rasmussen, Copenhagen #1579/R est:20000-30000 (D.KR 40000)
£5263 $9684 €8000 Mill and oven in Pompei (22x29cm-9x11in) s.i.d.1911. 24-Jun-4 Christie's, Paris #142/R est:8000-10000
£6000 $10920 €8760 Village scene in Rothenburg (28x38cm-11x15in) s.i.d.1910 prov. 15-Jun-4 Sotheby's, London #336/R est:6000-8000
£7000 $11900 €10220 Interior at Pompei (37x47cm-15x19in) s.i.d.1905. 18-Nov-3 Sotheby's, London #334/R
£8200 $14924 €11972 Acropolis, Athens (34x24cm-13x9in) s.d.1882 prov. 15-Jun-4 Sotheby's, London #332 est:7000-10000
£10000 $18200 €14600 House of the Vestal Virgins, Rome (24x37cm-9x15in) prov. 15-Jun-4 Sotheby's, London #333/R est:10000-15000

£12000 $21840 €17520 The Cloisters, Cefalu, Sicily (30x39cm-12x15in) s.i.d.1911 prov. 15-Jun-4 Sotheby's, London #34/R est:7000-10000
£18000 $32760 €26280 Patio de los Leones, Alhambra (38x49cm-15x19in) s.i.d.1908 prov. 15-Jun-4 Sotheby's, London #338/R est:18000-25000
Works on paper
£940 $1663 €1400 Pompei (23x33cm-9x13in) s.i. W/C. 30-Apr-4 Tajan, Paris #146 est:1500-2000

HANSEN, Lambertus Johannes (1803-1859) Dutch
£3404 $5685 €4800 Gentilhomme lisant a sa table dans un interieur (44x36cm-17x14in) s. i.verso prov. 23-Jun-3 Ribeyre & Baron, Paris #35/R est:3000-4500

HANSEN, Lys (c.1940-) British
£300 $501 €438 Figure (111x80cm-44x31in) s.d.85 acrylic on board. 16-Oct-3 Bonhams, Edinburgh #19

HANSEN, Mogens Gylling (20th C) Danish
£385 $662 €550 Still life of a model theatre (66x95cm-26x37in) mono.d.57. 6-Dec-3 Hans Stahl, Toestorf #52/R

HANSEN, Osmund (1908-1995) Danish
£469 $784 €685 Light and dark panel on red background (80x65cm-31x26in) init. s.d.1991 verso. 7-Oct-3 Rasmussen, Copenhagen #218 (D.KR 5000)

HANSEN, Peter (1868-1928) Danish
£327 $517 €474 The dancer (61x53cm-24x21in) mono.d.1918. 3-Sep-3 Museumsbygningen, Copenhagen #106 (D.KR 3500)
£515 $860 €752 Landscape with boy walking on road (42x60cm-17x24in) mono.d.1918. 25-Oct-3 Rasmussen, Havnen #4004/R (D.KR 5500)
£627 $1147 €915 Italian women digging out potatoes (79x98cm-31x39in) init. prov. 9-Jun-4 Rasmussen, Copenhagen #1724/R (D.KR 7000)
£748 $1181 €1085 Ship builders (47x54cm-19x21in) mono. 3-Sep-3 Museumsbygningen, Copenhagen #5/R (D.KR 8000)
£900 $1441 €1305 Cows by Vaengen, Faaborg (40x67cm-16x26in) mono. 17-Sep-3 Kunsthallen, Copenhagen #247/R (D.KR 9500)
£1083 $1993 €1581 Initiation at Faaborg Museum (43x63cm-17x25in) init. sketch. 29-Mar-4 Rasmussen, Copenhagen #484/R est:15000-20000 (D.KR 12000)
£1176 $2106 €1717 Woodland glade (58x74cm-23x29in) init. 10-May-4 Rasmussen, Vejle #543/R est:12000 (D.KR 13000)

HANSEN, Peter (attrib) (1868-1928) Danish
£316 $512 €458 Fjord landscape with beached punt (29x37cm-11x15in) init.d.1913. 4-Aug-3 Rasmussen, Vejle #322/R (D.KR 3300)

HANSEN, Sigvard (1859-1938) Danish
£272 $500 €397 Landscape with ducks in a meadow (36x46cm-14x18in) s.d.1923. 9-Jun-4 Alderfer's, Hatfield #354
£539 $1003 €787 Helsingor's pier, evening (18x29cm-7x11in) mono. panel painted c.1884. 2-Mar-4 Rasmussen, Copenhagen #1433/R (D.KR 6000)
£627 $1147 €915 Snow covered country road (48x75cm-19x30in) s.d.1915. 9-Jun-4 Rasmussen, Copenhagen #1753/R (D.KR 7000)
£654 $1034 €948 Winter landscape with man pulling sledge (17x13cm-7x5in) s. 2-Sep-3 Rasmussen, Copenhagen #1745/R (D.KR 7000)
£730 $1220 €1066 Landscape with farm by lake (88x128cm-35x50in) s. 25-Oct-3 Rasmussen, Havnen #2252/R (D.KR 7800)
£1025 $1610 €1497 Interior scene with woman in Wyese's sitting room, Ribe (56x66cm-22x26in) s.i.d.1912. 30-Aug-3 Rasmussen, Havnen #2136 (D.KR 11000)
£1075 $1935 €1570 Boy standing by edge of water in winter (49x72cm-19x28in) s.d.03. 24-Apr-4 Rasmussen, Havnen #2165/R est:3000-5000 (D.KR 12000)
£1579 $2558 €2290 View from the artist's home at Mols, Ebeltoft Bay (80x101cm-31x40in) s.d.1925. 4-Aug-3 Rasmussen, Vejle #327/R est:5000 (D.KR 16500)
£1701 $2943 €2483 Swedish fishing village, possibly Kullen (54x84cm-21x33in) mono.d.82/85. 9-Dec-3 Rasmussen, Copenhagen #1454/R est:20000-25000 (D.KR 18000)
£1803 $3336 €2632 Winter landscape with country road (84x127cm-33x50in) s.d.03. 15-Mar-4 Rasmussen, Vejle #461/R est:8000-10000 (D.KR 20000)
£1806 $3069 €2600 Winter in Engadin (43x60cm-17x24in) s. 28-Oct-3 Dorotheum, Vienna #42/R est:2600-3000

HANSEN, T M (19th C) Danish
Works on paper
£721 $1335 €1053 Ship's portrait - Kirstine of Fanoe (36x49cm-14x19in) indis.sig. gouache. 15-Mar-4 Rasmussen, Vejle #183/R (D.KR 8000)

HANSEN, Theodore Brooke (1890-1945) Australian
£810 $1304 €1183 Still life with flowers gum (40x49cm-16x19in) s. 13-Oct-3 Joel, Victoria #438 est:1500-2000 (A.D 2000)

HANSEN, Vald (?) Danish
£451 $834 €658 Schooner on tow in Copenhagen's Harbour (34x50cm-13x20in) s.d.95. 15-Mar-4 Rasmussen, Vejle #182/R (D.KR 5000)

HANSEN-JACOBSEN, Niels (1861-1941) Danish
Sculpture
£2817 $4704 €4113 The sae witch (19x26x17cm-7x10x7in) s.d.1893 led bronze lit. 7-Oct-3 Rasmussen, Copenhagen #136/R est:30000-40000 (D.KR 30000)

HANSEN-REISTRUP, Karl (1863-1929) Danish
£356 $594 €520 Canal view with mill (39x56cm-15x22in) s. 25-Oct-3 Rasmussen, Havnen #2195 (D.KR 3800)

HANSEN-SVANEKE, Bertel (1883-1937) Danish
£588 $953 €858 Young girl visiting the shoe-maker (45x45cm-18x18in) s.d.1907. 9-Aug-3 Hindemae, Ullerslev #123/R (D.KR 6200)
£1176 $2000 €1717 Cottage interior with a woman seated at her sewing machine (53x56cm-21x22in) s. 19-Nov-3 Bonhams & Butterfields, San Francisco #83

HANSET, Guido (1910-1992) Italian?
Works on paper
£302 $565 €450 View of Genoa (38x50cm-15x20in) W/C. 26-Feb-4 Cambi, Genoa #505a

HANSON, Albert J (1866-1914) Australian
£351 $597 €512 Bluegums with view of a pool (29x20cm-11x8in) s. board. 29-Oct-3 Lawson Menzies, Sydney #104/R (A.D 850)

HANSON, Duane (1925-1996) American
Sculpture
£128492 $230000 €187598 Executive. polyester resin fibreglass polychromed in oil prov.exhib.lit. 12-May-4 Sotheby's, New York #60/R est:220000-280000

HANSON, Léon William (1918-) Australian
£447 $702 €648 Spring morning Warburton (45x54cm-18x21in) s.d.51 s.i.verso. 27-Aug-3 Christie's, Sydney #760 (A.D 1100)
£650 $1021 €943 Morning near Hartley (45x55cm-18x22in) s. indis.sig.i.verso. 27-Aug-3 Christie's, Sydney #705 est:800-1200 (A.D 1600)

HANSON, Rolf (1953-) Swedish
£1538 $2646 €2245 Niboure - composition (149x122cm-59x48in) s.d.86 verso panel. 7-Dec-3 Uppsala Auktionskammare, Uppsala #293/R est:25000-30000 (S.KR 20000)
£1538 $2646 €2245 Boulsao (149x122cm-59x48in) s.d.86 verso panel. 7-Dec-3 Uppsala Auktionskammare, Uppsala #294/R est:25000-30000 (S.KR 20000)
£1888 $3210 €2756 Zomonga - composition (60x78cm-24x31in) s.d.87 panel. 5-Nov-3 AB Stockholms Auktionsverk #1021/R est:25000-30000 (S.KR 25000)
£2870 $4879 €4190 Dono Hue (160x135cm-63x53in) s.d.85 verso panel exhib.lit. 4-Nov-3 Bukowskis, Stockholm #575/R est:35000-40000 (S.KR 38000)
£3021 $5136 €4411 Oamaruo - composition (108x94cm-43x37in) s.d.1988 verso panel exhib.lit. 5-Nov-3 AB Stockholms Auktionsverk #975/R est:40000-50000 (S.KR 40000)
£4683 $7961 €6837 Faloue (122x113cm-48x44in) s.d.1992 panel exhib.lit. 4-Nov-3 Bukowskis, Stockholm #600/R est:35000-40000 (S.KR 62000)
£5665 $9630 €8271 Onkjau - composition (122x200cm-48x79in) s.d.1991 verso panel. 5-Nov-3 AB Stockholms Auktionsverk #932/R est:70000-80000 (S.KR 75000)
Works on paper
£1758 $3112 €2567 Portrait of Anne Reyl (90x105cm-35x41in) s.d.2001 verso mixed media panel. 27-Apr-4 AB Stockholms Auktionsverk #1106/R est:25000-30000 (S.KR 24000)

HANSTEEN, Nils (1855-1912) Norwegian
£241 $441 €352 From Skoyen (55x84cm-22x33in) s. 2-Feb-4 Blomqvist, Lysaker #1096 (N.KR 3000)
£278 $481 €406 Ship burning (24x34cm-9x13in) s. panel. 13-Dec-3 Blomqvist, Lysaker #1134 (N.KR 3200)
£500 $836 €730 Landscape from Selbo (12x12cm-5x5in) s. panel. 17-Nov-3 Blomqvist, Lysaker #1109/R (N.KR 6000)
£569 $1047 €854 Landscape from Selbo (32x43cm-13x17in) s. 14-Jun-4 Blomqvist, Lysaker #1133 (N.KR 7000)
£1626 $2976 €2374 Sailing boats in harbour (54x75cm-21x30in) s.d.1888. 7-Jun-4 Blomqvist, Oslo #283/R est:22000-26000 (N.KR 20000)
£1701 $3045 €2483 Harbour scene with vessels (40x50cm-16x20in) s.d.83. 12-Jan-4 Rasmussen, Vejle #1/R est:15000-20000 (D.KR 18000)
£1789 $3077 €2612 Old and new times (56x95cm-22x37in) s.d.1887. 8-Dec-3 Blomqvist, Oslo #461/R est:25000-30000 (N.KR 21000)
£3414 $6350 €4984 Norwegian fjord landscape with sailing ship off the coast (68x100cm-27x39in) s.d.1887. 2-Mar-4 Rasmussen, Copenhagen #1218/R est:40000-50000 (D.KR 38000)
£5537 $9523 €8084 Drying the sails (75x111cm-30x44in) s.d.1885. 8-Dec-3 Blomqvist, Oslo #442/R est:70000-90000 (N.KR 65000)
£6501 $11052 €9491 View of harbour with boats (38x60cm-15x24in) s.d.1888. 19-Nov-3 Grev Wedels Plass, Oslo #9/R est:70000-90000 (N.KR 76000)
Works on paper
£642 $1091 €937 Sailing ship in harbour (19x27cm-7x11in) s.d.86 W/C. 19-Nov-3 Grev Wedels Plass, Oslo #10/R (N.KR 7500)

HANSTEN, Ludwig (19th C) ?
£271 $486 €396 Mountain landscape (25x35cm-10x14in) s. 10-May-4 Rasmussen, Vejle #196/R (D.KR 3000)

HANTAI, Simon (1922-) French
£2105 $3874 €3200 Composition (25x34cm-10x13in) painted c.1950. 25-Jun-4 Millon & Associes, Paris #258/R est:2500-3500
£2632 $4842 €4000 Composition (23x35cm-9x14in) painted c.1950. 25-Jun-4 Millon & Associes, Paris #257/R est:2500-3500
£6667 $12267 €10000 Untitled (46x46cm-18x18in) mono.d.71 acrylic round prov. 9-Jun-4 Artcurial Briest, Paris #535/R est:6000-8000
£14966 $26790 €22000 Fertilite des champs (73x73cm-29x29in) s.d.1951 i.verso prov. 21-Mar-4 Calmels Cohen, Paris #48/R est:18000-20000
£15278 $25514 €22000 Sans titre (100x78cm-39x31in) mono.d.69 s.d.verso prov. 21-Oct-3 Artcurial Briest, Paris #608/R est:25000-30000
£20979 $35035 €30000 Untitled (94x80cm-37x31in) mono.d.1970 acrylic prov. 29-Jun-3 Versailles Encheres #116/R
£21333 $39253 €32000 Composition (104x146cm-41x57in) s.d.1957 d.verso. 9-Jun-4 Le Roux & Morel, Paris #43/R est:3000-4000
£31469 $52552 €45000 Peinture (146x218cm-57x86in) s.d.1958 prov. 29-Jun-3 Versailles Encheres #115/R
£49296 $85281 €70000 Meuns (222x186cm-87x73in) mono.d.63 prov. 9-Dec-3 Artcurial Briest, Paris #430/R est:80000-120000

HANTMAN, Carl (1935-) American
£692 $1100 €1010 Solitude (36x51cm-14x20in) s.d.79. 9-Sep-3 Arthur James, Florida #407
£692 $1100 €1010 Shoot out (30x41cm-12x16in) s.d.87. 9-Sep-3 Arthur James, Florida #408

£2793 $5000 €4078 Cowboys in saloon (81x104cm-32x41in) board. 15-May-4 Altermann Galleries, Santa Fe #116/R

HANTMAN, Murray (1904-1999) American
£2160 $3500 €3132 Untitled (99x91cm-39x36in) s. 8-Aug-3 Barridorf, Portland #226/R est:3000-5000

HANUM, V M (1927-1998) Russian
£559 $1000 €816 Still life with a jug (60x40cm-24x16in) painted 1983. 29-May-4 Shishkin Gallery, Moscow #31/R
£670 $1200 €978 Bukhara, Chor-Minor (68x49cm-27x19in) oil cardboard painted 1950's. 29-May-4 Shishkin Gallery, Moscow #30/R
£782 $1400 €1142 Landscape with the mosque (50x100cm-20x39in) painted 1950's. 29-May-4 Shishkin Gallery, Moscow #29/R
£1117 $2000 €1631 Decoration (50x70cm-20x28in) oil cardboard painted 1950's. 29-May-4 Shishkin Gallery, Moscow #32/R est:2000-3000

HANZEN, Aleksei Vasilievich (1876-1937) Russian
£1900 $3041 €2774 Coastal landscape with rocks (50x69cm-20x27in) s. 16-Sep-3 Philippe Schuler, Zurich #3361/R est:2500-3000 (S.FR 4200)
£2148 $3973 €3200 Motif de Doubrovnik (24x34cm-9x13in) s. 15-Mar-4 Claude Boisgirard, Paris #53/R est:3000-3500
£2282 $4221 €3400 Bord de mer Rocheux (24x34cm-9x13in) s. 15-Mar-4 Claude Boisgirard, Paris #52 est:3000-3500
£3472 $5729 €5000 Barques (64x77cm-25x30in) s. s.d.verso. 3-Jul-3 Claude Aguttes, Neuilly #101 est:300-400
£5000 $8950 €7300 View of Dubrovnik (34x43cm-13x17in) s. panel. 26-May-4 Sotheby's, London #102/R est:5000-7000
£6000 $10740 €8760 Seascape (32x41cm-13x16in) s.d.1931 verso. 26-May-4 Sotheby's, London #100/R est:5000-7000
£6000 $10740 €8760 Seashore (24x34cm-9x13in) s. 26-May-4 Sotheby's, Olympia #433/R est:3000-5000
£8000 $14320 €11680 Seascape (70x100cm-28x39in) s. s.d.1932 verso. 26-May-4 Sotheby's, London #101/R est:6000-8000
£8000 $14320 €11680 Seascape with rocks (54x76cm-21x30in) s. 26-May-4 Sotheby's, London #103/R est:5000-7000
£9000 $15300 €13140 Boats moored off the coast (63x76cm-25x30in) s. 19-Nov-3 Sotheby's, London #93/R est:8000-10000
£11793 $19694 €17100 Bateaux a voile sur l'Adriatique (70x95cm-28x37in) s. 17-Nov-3 Claude Boisgirard, Paris #36/R est:8000-10000
Works on paper
£667 $1227 €1000 Bord de fleuve (28x38cm-11x15in) s. W/C. 11-Jun-4 Claude Aguttes, Neuilly #54/R
£671 $1242 €1000 Stara Planina (19x28cm-7x11in) s. W/C. 15-Mar-4 Claude Boisgirard, Paris #55
£805 $1490 €1200 Eglise de Dubrovnik (18x23cm-7x9in) s. W/C. 15-Mar-4 Claude Boisgirard, Paris #56

HAPP, Sepp (1912-) German
£268 $491 €400 Still life with vase of flowers (79x58cm-31x23in) s.d.67 canvas on chipboard. 8-Jul-4 Allgauer, Kempten #2106/R

HAQUETTE, Georges Jean Marie (1854-1906) French
£1550 $2868 €2263 Mussel gatherers (46x55cm-18x22in) s. 15-Jan-4 Christie's, Kensington #826/R est:1000-1500

HARA, Jacques (1933-) French
£350 $602 €500 Chevaux dans l'enclos (22x27cm-9x11in) s. s.i.verso. 3-Dec-3 Tajan, Paris #268/R

HARARI, Hananiah (1912-) American
Works on paper
£1412 $2400 €2062 Nature of things (25x20cm-10x8in) s.d.1939 gouache. 9-Nov-3 Wright, Chicago #256 est:2000-3000

HARBOE, Eleonora Christine (1796-1860) Danish
£493 $789 €720 Portrait of Beatrice Cenci (63x49cm-25x19in) i.verso. 22-Sep-3 Rasmussen, Vejle #82/R (D.KR 5200)
£867 $1361 €1266 Woman with rolls of scripture (98x81cm-39x32in) s.d.1829 verso. 30-Aug-3 Rasmussen, Havnen #2052/R (D.KR 9300)

HARBURGER, Alice (1891-1942) German
£278 $453 €400 Lilies (37x46cm-15x18in) mono. board. 27-Sep-3 Dr Fritz Nagel, Stuttgart #9183/R
£278 $453 €400 Easter eggs (46x34cm-18x13in) mono. board. 27-Sep-3 Dr Fritz Nagel, Stuttgart #9193/R
£313 $509 €450 Summer flowers (88x56cm-35x22in) mono. board. 27-Sep-3 Dr Fritz Nagel, Stuttgart #9198/R
£382 $623 €550 Still life of fruit (60x80cm-24x31in) mono. board. 27-Sep-3 Dr Fritz Nagel, Stuttgart #9191/R
£382 $623 €550 Toys (42x57cm-17x22in) mono. board. 27-Sep-3 Dr Fritz Nagel, Stuttgart #9197/R
£417 $679 €600 Toys (46x34cm-18x13in) mono. board. 27-Sep-3 Dr Fritz Nagel, Stuttgart #9194/R
£451 $736 €650 Still life of flowers (69x50cm-27x20in) mono. board. 27-Sep-3 Dr Fritz Nagel, Stuttgart #9190/R
£486 $792 €700 Peonies in vase (80x50cm-31x20in) mono. board. 27-Sep-3 Dr Fritz Nagel, Stuttgart #9188/R
£486 $792 €700 Nils Holgerson (46x34cm-18x13in) mono. board. 27-Sep-3 Dr Fritz Nagel, Stuttgart #9192/R
£521 $849 €750 Zinnia (44x34cm-17x13in) mono. board. 27-Sep-3 Dr Fritz Nagel, Stuttgart #9185/R
£521 $849 €750 Danneckerstrasse studio (70x50cm-28x20in) mono. board. 27-Sep-3 Dr Fritz Nagel, Stuttgart #9189/R
£590 $962 €850 Doll's circus (46x34cm-18x13in) mono. board. 27-Sep-3 Dr Fritz Nagel, Stuttgart #9195/R
£694 $1132 €1000 Teddy bear (46x34cm-18x13in) mono.d.1922 board. 27-Sep-3 Dr Fritz Nagel, Stuttgart #9196/R

HARDEGG, Friedrich (1858-?) Austrian
£860 $1600 €1256 Still life with silver pitcher on a blue velvet drape (22x17cm-9x7in) s. board. 5-Mar-4 Skinner, Boston #225/R est:800-1200

HARDEN, Edmund Harris (fl.1851-1880) British
£1121 $1872 €1637 Wood gatherers. Cows by a waterside (48x78cm-19x31in) s. pair. 20-Oct-3 Stephan Welz, Johannesburg #190/R est:8000-12000 (SA.R 13000)

HARDENBERG, Cornelis van (1755-1843) Dutch
Works on paper
£959 $1630 €1400 View of the ruins of Delft after the explosion (20x28cm-8x11in) s. i.verso 1654 pen black ink wash. 4-Nov-3 Sotheby's, Amsterdam #133/R
£2568 $4519 €3800 White tailed trogon (24x20cm-9x8in) s. W/C gouache black chk prov. 19-May-4 Sotheby's, Amsterdam #233/R est:4500-5500

HARDENBERGH, Gerard R (1855-1915) American
£2201 $3500 €3213 Basket of smelts (41x56cm-16x22in) s. 9-Mar-3 William Jenack, New York #395 est:1500-2500

HARDERS (?) ?
Sculpture
£2200 $3806 €3212 Art deco table lamp modelled as an oriental fan dancer (68cm-27in) s. cold painted bronze ivory. 10-Dec-3 Wingetts, Wrexham #286/R est:800-1200

HARDERS, Johannes (1871-1950) German
£453 $816 €680 Fjord landscape (81x120cm-32x47in) s. 26-Apr-4 Rieber, Stuttgart #1319/R
£537 $988 €800 Harbour, probably Hamburg, with ships (70x100cm-28x39in) s. lit. 25-Mar-4 Karlheinz Kaupp, Staufen #2477/R
£1736 $2743 €2500 Cap Arcona (82x120cm-32x47in) s. 6-Sep-3 Schopman, Hamburg #843/R est:2500
£1748 $2920 €2500 Norwegian fjord with steamer (139x200cm-55x79in) s. 28-Jun-3 Bolland & Marotz, Bremen #656/R est:2200

HARDIE, Charles Martin (1858-1916) British
£500 $850 €730 Penning up the sheep at dusk (23x32cm-9x13in) init.d.1891. 4-Nov-3 Bristol Auction Rooms #521
£580 $1096 €847 Return of the huntsman (25x40cm-10x16in) init.i.d.22.8.84 board. 19-Feb-4 Lyon & Turnbull, Edinburgh #150
£600 $1086 €876 Sheep before ruined buildings (29x45cm-11x18in) mono. board. 3-Apr-4 Shapes, Edinburgh #430/R
£2096 $3500 €3060 Checkers (69x91cm-27x36in) board. 17-Oct-3 Du Mouchelle, Detroit #1018/R est:4000-5000
£2600 $4420 €3796 Young anglers (61x91cm-24x36in) s.d.1882. 30-Oct-3 Christie's, London #117/R est:3000-5000

HARDIE, Gwen (1962-) British
£750 $1298 €1095 Self portrait (117x87cm-46x34in) oil paper. 11-Dec-3 Lyon & Turnbull, Edinburgh #20/R

HARDIE, Martin (1875-1952) British
Works on paper
£740 $1362 €1080 View over a rural landscape (27x37cm-11x15in) s. W/C. 23-Mar-4 Bonhams, Knightsbridge #176/R

HARDIE, Robert Gordon (1854-1904) American
£5294 $9000 €7729 President Ulysses S Grant (137x102cm-54x40in) s.d.1880 exhib. 31-Oct-3 North East Auctions, Portsmouth #1797 est:5000-8000

HARDIME, Pieter (1677-1758) Flemish
£5479 $9315 €8000 Flowers in carved vase (128x92cm-50x36in) s.d.1696. 9-Nov-3 Finarte, Venice #19/R est:6500-7500
£6000 $10200 €8760 Roses, tulips and other flowers in a basket on a stone ledge (71x91cm-28x36in) 29-Oct-3 Christie's, London #55/R est:7000-10000
£7500 $13725 €10950 Still life with tulips, roses, carnation and other flowers in a glass vase on a stone ledge (46x61cm-18x24in) prov. 6-Jul-4 Sotheby's, Olympia #563/R est:6000-8000
£8054 $14980 €12000 Vase of flowers (71x68cm-28x27in) 2-Mar-4 Ansorena, Madrid #286/R est:9000
£21277 $34468 €30000 Vase of flowers (88x77cm-35x30in) 20-May-3 Ansorena, Madrid #103/R est:30000
£21477 $39946 €32000 Vase of flowers (83x68cm-33x27in) 2-Mar-4 Ansorena, Madrid #283/R est:20000
£27586 $45793 €40000 Vase of flowers (83x68cm-33x27in) 30-Sep-3 Ansorena, Madrid #35/R est:40000

HARDIME, Pieter (attrib) (1677-1758) Flemish
£6338 $11092 €9000 Nature morte au vase de fleurs (63x185cm-25x73in) 17-Dec-3 Piasa, Paris #31/R est:10000-12000

HARDIME, Simon (1672-1737) Flemish
£12000 $20760 €17520 Still life of roses, tulips, and other flowers in a basket on stone ledge (65x89cm-26x35in) prov. 11-Dec-3 Sotheby's, London #223/R est:8000-12000

HARDIN, Joseph (1921-1989) American
£389 $650 €568 Three nude figures (46x61cm-18x24in) acrylic prov. 15-Nov-3 Slotin Folk Art, Buford #407/R

HARDING, Chester (1792-1866) American
£2174 $3500 €3174 Portrait of a gentleman with bow tie (76x61cm-30x24in) prov. 20-Aug-3 James Julia, Fairfield #154/R est:6000-8000

£	$	€	Details
£7955	$14000	€11614	Seascape (71x91cm-28x36in) s.d.1832. 3-Jan-4 Brunk, Ashville #443/R est:4000-8000

HARDING, George Perfect (1780-1853) British

Works on paper

£400	$728	€584	Portrait of John Williams, the Dean of Westminster (23x19cm-9x7in) s.d.1810 W/C after C Jansen. 21-Jun-4 Bonhams, Bath #332

HARDING, J D (1798-1863) British

£217	$400	€317	Coastal scene (30x46cm-12x18in) board. 27-Jun-4 Hindman, Chicago #799/R

HARDING, James Duffield (1798-1863) British

Works on paper

£350	$585	€511	View in the Bernese Oberland (33x48cm-13x19in) pencil W/C sold with another by a different hand. 16-Oct-3 Christie's, Kensington #110/R
£450	$752	€657	Windsor Castle from the lower meadow (22x29cm-9x11in) W/C. 14-Oct-3 Bonhams, Knightsbridge #72/R
£450	$824	€657	Antibes (24x30cm-9x12in) init.i.d.1859 W/C pencil. 27-Jan-4 Bonhams, Knightsbridge #364/R
£460	$782	€672	Igtham Mote (43x58cm-17x23in) s. W/C. 25-Nov-3 Bonhams, Knightsbridge #7/R

HARDING, John (18th C) British

Works on paper

£480	$864	€701	Milking time. The visitor (41x34cm-16x13in) s. one d.1793 one d.1794 W/C pair. 21-Jan-4 Sotheby's, Olympia #131/R

HARDINGE, V (?) British?

£1700	$2924	€2482	Coming home (61x107cm-24x42in) s.d.81. 5-Dec-3 Chrystals Auctions, Isle of Man #254/R est:1500-2500

HARDMAN, J (19th C) British

£800	$1488	€1168	Stableyard scene with two coaching horses (46x66cm-18x26in) s.d.1807. 4-Mar-4 Amersham Auction Rooms, UK #298

HARDORFF, Herman Rudolf (1816-1907) German

£7692	$13077	€11000	River landscape with sailing ships at sunset (51x76cm-20x30in) s.d.1852. 24-Nov-3 Dorotheum, Vienna #161/R est:5000-6000

HARDRICK, John W (1891-1968) American

£1038	$1900	€1515	Colourful late summer landscape (61x76cm-24x30in) s. board. 5-Jun-4 Dan Ripley, Indianapolis #236

HARDT, Ernst (1869-1917) German

£375	$619	€540	Lower Rhine landscape (87x115cm-34x45in) s. 3-Jul-3 Van Ham, Cologne #1227

HARDTER, Andreas (?-1816) Austrian

Works on paper

£219	$400	€320	Sapienta, a female figure seated on a balustrade seem from below (19x24cm-7x9in) init.i. black chk. 29-Jan-4 Swann Galleries, New York #319/R

HARDWICK, Alice Roney (1876-?) American

£407	$750	€594	Autumn landscape (58x69cm-23x27in) s. 25-Jun-4 Freeman, Philadelphia #174/R

HARDWICK, John Jessop (1831-1917) British

Works on paper

£500	$910	€730	Roses (23x30cm-9x12in) s. W/C. 4-Feb-4 John Nicholson, Haslemere #42
£800	$1336	€1168	Apple blossom and nest (22x33cm-9x13in) s. W/C. 14-Oct-3 Bearnes, Exeter #340/R
£1000	$1810	€1460	Dixcart Well, Sark (16x25cm-6x10in) s.i.d.1898 W/C. 1-Apr-4 Martel Maides, Guernsey #230/R est:600-800

HARDWICK, Melbourne H (1857-1916) American

£235	$400	€343	Shore view with a distant church (25x35cm-10x14in) s. canvasboard. 21-Nov-3 Skinner, Boston #560/R
£280	$500	€409	Beached boat (23x30cm-9x12in) canvasboard. 18-Mar-4 Skinner, Bolton #796a/R
£339	$600	€495	Interior with woman and child (58x69cm-23x27in) s. 2-May-4 Grogan, Boston #34/R

Works on paper

£419	$700	€612	Sailboats off shore (33x48cm-13x19in) s. W/C paper on board. 18-Jun-3 Doyle, New York #37/R
£753	$1400	€1099	Fisherfolk (43x62cm-17x24in) s.d.97 W/C gouache. 5-Mar-4 Skinner, Boston #244/R est:600-800

HARDWICK, William Noble (attrib) (1805-1865) British

£503	$800	€729	The Bridge, view of Lyon (46x74cm-18x29in) s. 12-Sep-3 Aspire, Cleveland #33

HARDWICKE, Lindsey (1877-1961) American

£539	$900	€787	Willow (56x71cm-22x28in) 18-Oct-3 David Dike, Dallas #279/R

HARDY, Albert (fl.1887-1907) British

Works on paper

£300	$516	€438	Lady on a balcony overlooking the Thames (25x36cm-10x14in) s. W/C. 2-Dec-3 Gorringes, Lewes #2418

HARDY, Anna Eliza (1839-1934) American

£1613	$3000	€2355	Nasturtions (66x37cm-26x15in) s. canvas on board prov. 3-Mar-4 Christie's, Rockefeller NY #60/R est:3000-5000
£1899	$3000	€2773	Still life of white roses in a pitcher (33x43cm-13x17in) s. 6-Sep-3 Brunk, Ashville #425
£2429	$4250	€3546	Basket of flowers (34x26cm-13x10in) s. board. 19-Dec-3 Sotheby's, New York #1072/R est:5000-7000
£4630	$7500	€6714	Roses (29x44cm-11x17in) s. 8-Aug-3 Barridorf, Portland #59/R est:6000-9000

HARDY, Cyril (19th C) British

Works on paper

£310	$518	€453	Gate in a North African town (35x51cm-14x20in) s. W/C. 14-Oct-3 Rosebery Fine Art, London #580
£400	$640	€584	In old Algeria (20x48cm-8x19in) s. W/C. 16-Sep-3 Rosebery Fine Art, London #634
£410	$709	€599	North African street scene (36x26cm-14x10in) s. W/C. 9-Dec-3 Anderson & Garland, Newcastle #351/R

HARDY, David (fl.1855-1870) British

£3300	$6039	€4818	Family gathering for tea near open window (17x23cm-7x9in) s.d.1865 panel. 5-Jun-4 Windibank, Dorking #343 est:1000-1500

HARDY, David Whitaker III (1929-) American

£469	$750	€685	Cloth of gold; young woman arranging flowers at a table (119x56cm-47x22in) s.i. board. 20-Sep-3 Jeffery Burchard, Florida #68/R

HARDY, Dudley (1865-1922) British

£362	$605	€529	Arabs on a shaded terrace (50x76cm-20x30in) s. canvas on masonite. 17-Nov-3 Waddingtons, Toronto #96/R (C.D 800)
£800	$1464	€1168	Bullfight (29x21cm-11x8in) s.i. canvasboard. 6-Apr-4 Bonhams, Knightsbridge #167/R
£8824	$15000	€12883	Caravan (81x63cm-32x25in) s.i. panel. 28-Oct-3 Sotheby's, New York #91a/R est:15000-20000

Works on paper

£260	$481	€380	Shop window (30x23cm-12x9in) s.d.1902 ink dr. 10-Feb-4 David Lay, Penzance #585
£500	$850	€730	Question of price (35x26cm-14x10in) s. i.verso W/C gouache pair. 18-Nov-3 Sotheby's, Olympia #24/R
£600	$1092	€876	Traders in the desert (24x33cm-9x13in) s. bodycol. 1-Jul-4 Christie's, Kensington #344/R
£700	$1274	€1022	Bathers, Ambleteuse (18x25cm-7x10in) s. W/C bodycol. 1-Jul-4 Christie's, Kensington #475/R
£820	$1509	€1197	On the shore (24x34cm-9x13in) s. W/C. 23-Jun-4 Bonhams, Bury St Edmunds #351/R
£920	$1720	€1343	Snake charmer (12x17cm-5x7in) s. W/C. 25-Feb-4 Mallams, Oxford #358/R
£1100	$1936	€1606	Cottage interior, with young woman reading a book (25x33cm-10x13in) s. indis.d. W/C pastel. 18-May-4 Fellows & Sons, Birmingham #195/R est:1100-1500

HARDY, Frederick Daniel (1826-1911) British

£800	$1336	€1168	Figures and cat in kitchen (15x23cm-6x9in) s.d.1896. 17-Oct-3 Keys, Aylsham #807
£800	$1416	€1168	Little girl with her doll in a cottage interior (15x20cm-6x8in) board. 28-Apr-4 Halls, Shrewsbury #515/R
£1589	$2510	€2304	Farmyard with girl feeding chickens (40x30cm-16x12in) s.i.d.91 panel. 2-Sep-3 Rasmussen, Copenhagen #1840/R est:15000 (D.KR 17000)
£2700	$4266	€3915	Fireside conversation (46x61cm-18x24in) s.d.1880. 4-Sep-3 Christie's, Kensington #247/R est:3000-5000
£5000	$8500	€7300	Checkmate (53x46cm-21x18in) s.d.1872. 27-Nov-3 Sotheby's, London #334/R est:5000-7000
£6200	$10540	€9052	Little sweep (22x30cm-9x12in) s.d.1885 panel. 27-Nov-3 Clevedon Sale Rooms #114/R est:2000-3000

HARDY, George (1822-1909) British

£22000	$37400	€32120	Reading lesson (38x33cm-15x13in) s.d.1889 panel prov. 27-Nov-3 Sotheby's, London #400/R est:12000-16000

HARDY, George (attrib) (1822-1909) British

£450	$765	€657	Children on a path by a cottage (24x30cm-9x12in) indis.sig.d.52. 26-Nov-3 Hamptons Fine Art, Godalming #122

HARDY, Heywood (1843-1933) British

£1050	$1964	€1575	At Keynsham, Gloucestershire (16x37cm-6x15in) s.d.66. 26-Jul-4 Bonhams, Bath #68/R est:800-1200
£1413	$2600	€2063	Sunday morning hunt (51x76cm-20x30in) 25-Mar-4 Doyle, New York #21/R est:2000-3000
£4200	$7686	€6132	Escaping the fire (46x64cm-18x25in) s.d.1872. 28-Jan-4 Dreweatt Neate, Newbury #120/R est:5000-7000
£4600	$7820	€6716	On the sand dunes (25x31cm-10x12in) panel. 27-Nov-3 Sotheby's, London #375/R est:3000-5000
£5114	$9000	€7466	Trysting place (76x69cm-30x27in) s. i.verso. 18-May-4 Arthur James, Florida #103 est:10000-15000
£5676	$10500	€8287	Passing the coach (51x76cm-20x30in) s. i. stretcher. 10-Feb-4 Doyle, New York #229/R est:4000-6000
£6000	$10800	€8760	The morning ride (36x46cm-14x18in) s. 21-Apr-4 Tennants, Leyburn #1183/R est:5000-6000
£6500	$12025	€9490	Waiting for the master (56x46cm-22x18in) s. 14-Jul-4 Sotheby's, Olympia #98/R est:3000-4000
£7000	$11690	€10220	Portrait of lady with dog (79x65cm-31x26in) s.d.1897. 12-Nov-3 Sotheby's, Olympia #112/R est:4000-6000

£7558 $13000 €11035 Journey through the snow (27x46cm-11x18in) s. indis d. panel painted 1878 prov. 5-Dec-3 Christie's, Rockefeller NY #30/R est:12000-18000
£7821 $14000 €11419 Fox hunt (51x76cm-20x30in) s. 27-May-4 Sotheby's, New York #288/R est:15000-20000
£14000 $23800 €20440 Breaking cover (51x76cm-20x30in) s. 19-Nov-3 Bonhams, New Bond Street #78/R est:15000-20000
£14200 $26270 €20732 Huntsman's story (52x76cm-20x30in) s.d.1903. 10-Mar-4 Sotheby's, Olympia #212/R est:4000-6000
£14500 $26390 €21170 Daily ride (41x51cm-16x20in) s. prov. 16-Jun-4 Bonhams, New Bond Street #60/R est:12000-18000
£15000 $27600 €21900 An anxious moment (54x106cm-21x42in) s. prov. 11-Jun-4 Christie's, London #122/R est:8000-12000
£15934 $29000 €23264 Charming encounter (49x58cm-19x23in) s. 29-Jun-4 Sotheby's, New York #158/R est:20000-30000
£16000 $27200 €23360 Riding to the meet (51x76cm-20x30in) s. 19-Nov-3 Bonhams, New Bond Street #77/R est:15000-20000
£17000 $29920 €24820 Lady out hunting (62x58cm-24x23in) s.d.1899. 21-May-4 Christie's, London #33/R est:18000-25000
£18000 $30960 €26280 Mother and son (39x49cm-15x19in) s. prov. 3-Dec-3 Cheffins, Cambridge #613/R est:20000-30000
£18000 $31680 €26280 Squire (61x51cm-24x20in) s. i.verso prov. 21-May-4 Christie's, London #34/R est:20000-30000
£22000 $39600 €32120 Introduction to lady of the manor (44x67cm-17x26in) s. prov. 22-Apr-4 Lawrence, Crewkerne #934/R est:12000-18000
£25000 $40750 €36500 New Mount (46x61cm-18x24in) s. 24-Sep-3 Dreweatt Neate, Newbury #139/R est:10000-15000
£32000 $52160 €46720 Leaving for town (92x72cm-36x28in) s. 24-Sep-3 Dreweatt Neate, Newbury #140/R est:35000-40000
£38000 $69920 €55480 Cast shoe (51x76cm-20x30in) s.d.1917 prov. 11-Jun-4 Christie's, London #124/R est:20000-30000
£43605 $75000 €63663 Hounds of the Tickham hunt, Kent (76x165cm-30x65in) s. 5-Dec-3 Christie's, Rockefeller NY #67/R est:80000-120000
£44000 $80960 €64240 Her only playmates (96x75cm-38x30in) s.d.1870 prov.exhib. 11-Jun-4 Christie's, London #111/R est:40000-60000
£48000 $81600 €70080 Morning ride (105x85cm-41x33in) s.d.1902 prov. 19-Nov-3 Bonhams, New Bond Street #73/R est:30000-50000
£49000 $77910 €71540 Drawing Covert (90x120cm-35x47in) s. prov. 10-Sep-3 Cheffins, Cambridge #525/R est:30000-50000
Prints
£1118 $1800 €1632 Twin setters (48x64cm-19x25in) s. print. 20-Aug-3 James Julia, Fairfield #1006/R est:600-800
Works on paper
£850 $1530 €1241 Hacking home in snow (25x35cm-10x14in) s. W/C. 21-Apr-4 Cheffins, Cambridge #467/R

HARDY, Heywood (attrib) (1843-1933) British
£3077 $5292 €4492 Waiting for master (55x45cm-22x18in) s. 3-Dec-3 AB Stockholms Auktionsverk #2537/R est:12000-15000 (S.KR 40000)

HARDY, J (19th C) British
£460 $823 €672 Sheep at a stile, figures and a farm in the distance (34x29cm-13x11in) s. 22-Mar-4 Bearnes, Exeter #137

HARDY, James (19th C) British
£320 $544 €467 Saluting an old ally (40x51cm-16x20in) s. board. 6-Nov-3 Christie's, Kensington #868/R
£400 $640 €584 Shipping in choppy sea (29x40cm-11x16in) s. panel. 17-Sep-3 Henry Adams, Chichester #403
£420 $714 €613 King Charles II's visit to the fleet (60x91cm-24x36in) s. panel. 19-Nov-3 Christie's, Kensington #518/R
£500 $850 €730 Flagship arriving (40x51cm-16x20in) s. panel pair. 19-Nov-3 Christie's, Kensington #519/R
£500 $850 €730 Broadside attack (41x61cm-16x24in) s. panel. 19-Nov-3 Christie's, Kensington #516/R
£500 $850 €730 Naval bombardment (61x91cm-24x36in) s. panel. 19-Nov-3 Christie's, Kensington #517/R
£500 $920 €730 Marine scenes with sailing and fishing boats (30x41cm-12x16in) s. panel pair. 23-Mar-4 Wotton Auction Rooms, Wotton #812
£600 $1110 €876 View of Greenwich Naval College from across the Thames (56x83cm-22x33in) s. panel. 14-Jul-4 Christie's, Kensington #981/R
£909 $1564 €1300 Sailing boats (60x90cm-24x35in) s. 3-Dec-3 Stadion, Trieste #111/R

HARDY, James (jnr) (1832-1889) British
£300 $471 €435 Dutch barges off a coastal town (41x50cm-16x20in) s. board. 28-Aug-3 Christie's, Kensington #191
£3800 $6802 €5548 Playing marbles (28x24cm-11x9in) s.d.59 board. 26-May-4 Sotheby's, Olympia #138/R est:4000-6000
£5200 $9724 €7800 Bob's cherry (33x28cm-13x11in) s.d.1862 panel. 21-Jul-4 John Nicholson, Haslemere #199/R est:4000-6000
£8389 $15436 €12500 Day's bag, gun dogs and dead game in a landscape (38x52cm-15x20in) s.d.87. 23-Mar-4 Mealy's, Castlecomer #923/R est:8000-12000
£26000 $44200 €37960 Day's Bag (39x57cm-15x22in) s.d.82. 30-Oct-3 Christie's, London #59/R est:12000-18000
Works on paper
£420 $689 €613 Still life study of dead game birds on a kitchen table (42x31cm-17x12in) s. W/C. 3-Jun-3 Fellows & Sons, Birmingham #161/R
£440 $722 €642 Still life of game birds and wicker basket, strewn with holly and mistletoe (64x49cm-25x19in) s.d.1871 W/C htd white. 3-Jun-3 Fellows & Sons, Birmingham #163/R
£700 $1288 €1022 Scottish poacher with his dogs and bag (22x33cm-9x13in) s. indis d. W/C bodycol. 24-Jun-4 Locke & England, Leamington Spa #161/R
£18605 $32000 €27163 Gamekeeper (75x56cm-30x22in) s.d.81 pencil W/C bodycol htd white paper on card prov. 5-Dec-3 Christie's, Rockefeller NY #82/R est:30000-50000

HARDY, James (jnr-attrib) (1832-1889) British
Works on paper
£600 $1110 €876 A ghillie with two setters on the moor (25x34cm-10x13in) W/C bodycol. 16-Feb-4 Bonhams, Bath #52

HARDY, James (snr) (1801-1879) British
£550 $919 €803 Midday rest (17x25cm-7x10in) s. board. 16-Oct-3 Lawrence, Crewkerne #732
£2600 $4082 €3770 George Gordon Lennox aged nine (43x53cm-17x21in) s.i.d.1830. 27-Aug-3 Sotheby's, London #921/R est:2000-3000

HARDY, Kaspar Bernhard (attrib) (1726-1819) German
Sculpture
£1565 $2801 €2300 Voltaire (20x16cm-8x6in) i. verso wax wash lit. 17-Mar-4 Neumeister, Munich #191/R est:1500
£1769 $3166 €2600 Rousseau (21x17cm-8x7in) wax wash lit. 17-Mar-4 Neumeister, Munich #192/R est:1500

HARDY, Maria Smear (attrib) (1803-1864) British
Works on paper
£600 $1098 €876 Portrait of Robert Hardy, vicar of Walburton, Sussex (10x8cm-4x3in) W/C over pencil. 8-Jul-4 Duke & Son, Dorchester #134
£1000 $1830 €1460 Interior, probably at Walburton vicarage in Sussex (25x36cm-10x14in) W/C. 8-Jul-4 Duke & Son, Dorchester #133/R
£7000 $12810 €10220 Interior with members of the artist family and seated engaged in a variety of pursuits (48x69cm-19x27in) W/C. 8-Jul-4 Duke & Son, Dorchester #132/R

HARDY, Robert (1952-) British
£250 $450 €365 Journey (46x36cm-18x14in) s. s.i.d.2003 verso board. 20-Jan-4 Bonhams, Knightsbridge #305/R
£320 $573 €467 Tower (19x23cm-7x9in) s. board. 16-Mar-4 Bonhams, Knightsbridge #75/R
£400 $740 €584 Sailing boat and island (30x40cm-12x16in) s. acrylic board. 13-Jul-4 Bonhams, Knightsbridge #69/R
£400 $740 €584 Last train (30x40cm-12x16in) s. acrylic board. 13-Jul-4 Bonhams, Knightsbridge #71/R
£480 $859 €701 Meditrranean Landscape (30x40cm-12x16in) s. board. 16-Mar-4 Bonhams, Knightsbridge #74/R

HARDY, Roger (1969-) British
£250 $415 €365 Moving through blue (50x101cm-20x40in) s. i.verso acrylic. 2-Oct-3 Lane, Penzance #240/R

HARDY, Thomas Bush (1842-1897) British
£440 $708 €638 Fishing boats coming home (15x25cm-6x10in) s. board. 20-Aug-3 Brightwells, Leominster #885/R
£780 $1342 €1139 Pulling in the catch (41x56cm-16x22in) s.d.89 W/C gouache painted with studio. 2-Dec-3 Sotheby's, London #71/R
£1210 $2226 €1767 Wet day, Boston, Lincolnshire (51x77cm-20x30in) s.i. 14-Jun-4 Waddingtons, Toronto #138/R est:3000-4000 (C.D 3000)
£2400 $4536 €3504 Coming into Port (29x38cm-11x15in) s.d.1872 board. 17-Feb-4 Bonhams, New Bond Street #68/R est:400-600
£2800 $5124 €4088 On the Riva de Schiavoni, Venice (20x69cm-8x27in) s.i. 7-Apr-4 Andrew Hartley, Ilkley #1132/R est:2500-3500
Works on paper
£214 $400 €321 Towing a wreck (11x17cm-4x7in) s.i.d.1878 pencil W/C paper laid down prov. 25-Jul-4 Bonhams & Butterfields, San Francisco #6021/R
£272 $500 €397 Off Portsmouth (23x56cm-9x22in) s.i. W/C htd white. 25-Mar-4 Doyle, New York #22/R
£300 $549 €438 Sedge gatherers, Holland (46x71cm-18x28in) s.i. W/C. 3-Jun-4 Bonhams, Cornwall #239
£300 $552 €438 Weighing anchor (12x10cm-5x4in) s.d.1867 ink wash. 22-Jun-4 Bonhams, Knightsbridge #13/R
£320 $586 €467 Shipping at sea (13x15cm-5x6in) s.d.1893 W/C. 27-Jan-4 Gorringes, Lewes #1681
£320 $550 €467 Fishing boat (21x13cm-8x5in) W/C. 2-Dec-3 Sworder & Son, Bishops Stortford #482/R
£320 $525 €467 Pegwell Bay (61x38cm-24x15in) s.i.d.1882 W/C. 3-Jun-3 Fellows & Sons, Birmingham #162/R
£320 $550 €467 Falmouth harbour scene (22x15cm-9x6in) W/C. 2-Dec-3 Sworder & Son, Bishops Stortford #481/R
£340 $564 €496 View of castle ruins with figures and shelters (13x15cm-5x6in) s.d.1879 prov. W/C. 10-Jun-3 Canterbury Auctions, UK #129
£370 $692 €540 Busy shipping scene off a port (12x22cm-5x9in) s.d.1890 W/C. 20-Jul-4 Dreweatt Neate, Newbury #194/R
£380 $654 €555 Manorbeer Castle, Pembroke (23x32cm-9x13in) s.d.1879 pencil W/C. 3-Dec-3 Christie's, Kensington #190/R
£400 $636 €580 Scarborough Castle (17x24cm-7x9in) s.d.1890 W/C. 9-Sep-3 David Duggleby, Scarborough #139
£400 $680 €584 Fishing vessels off a pier (21x32cm-8x13in) s. W/C. 25-Nov-3 Bonhams, Knightsbridge #107
£403 $742 €588 Harbour, Boulogne. Arrival of the day's catch (22x69cm-9x27in) s.d.1895 W/C pair. 14-Jun-4 Waddingtons, Toronto #81/R est:1500-2500 (C.D 1000)
£450 $747 €657 Fishing cottages, Equitan (22x51cm-9x20in) s.i.d.1892 W/C. 1-Oct-3 Bonhams, Knightsbridge #55/R
£460 $782 €672 Off Boulogne (33x58cm-13x23in) s.i. W/C. 25-Nov-3 Bonhams, Knightsbridge #46/R
£480 $763 €696 Busy harbour scene with fishing fleet returning (16x29cm-6x11in) s.d.XI W/C. 9-Sep-3 David Duggleby, Scarborough #8/R
£480 $763 €696 Folkstone (23x24cm-9x9in) s.d.1899 W/C. 9-Sep-3 David Duggleby, Scarborough #222
£480 $816 €701 Off Dover (25x33cm-10x13in) s.i.d.1893 W/C. 26-Nov-3 Hamptons Fine Art, Godalming #74
£500 $815 €730 Waiting the turn of the tide (23x32cm-9x13in) s.i.d. below mount W/C. 23-Sep-3 Anderson & Garland, Newcastle #240/R
£500 $830 €730 At the mouth of the harbour, sailing vessel in rough sea (12x20cm-5x8in) s.d.1878 W/C. 2-Oct-3 Ewbank, Send #857
£520 $868 €759 Near Deal, Kent Coast (33x48cm-13x19in) s.i.d.1889 W/C scratching out. 14-Oct-3 Bearnes, Exeter #326/R
£550 $875 €803 Figures on a harbour wall with sea beyond (11x24cm-4x9in) s.d.1892 gouache. 12-Sep-3 Bracketts, Tunbridge Wells #913/R
£550 $946 €803 Marine scene - The Thames below Woolwich with sailing ships and barges in choppy sea (25x53cm-10x21in) s.i.d.1895 W/C. 2-Dec-3 Canterbury Auctions, UK #182
£580 $969 €847 Off Dover (42x67cm-17x26in) s.i.d.1891 pencil W/C over bodycol. 12-Nov-3 Sotheby's, Olympia #26/R

£580	$1056	€847	Morning Post (31x48cm-12x19in) s.i.d.1873 W/C htd touches white scratching out. 29-Jun-4 Bonhams, Knowle #37
£580	$1067	€847	Off Gravelines (50x75cm-20x30in) s.i. W/C. 10-Jun-4 Lyon & Turnbull, Edinburgh #77
£600	$996	€876	Old Portsmouth (27x59cm-11x23in) s.i. W/C. 1-Oct-3 Bonhams, Knightsbridge #59/R
£620	$1147	€905	Harbour scene with boats and figures (13x23cm-5x9in) s.d.92. 12-Feb-4 Andrew Hartley, Ilkley #781/R
£645	$1187	€942	Off the French coast. Off the Dutch coast (41x50cm-16x20in) one s.i.d.1890 one s.i.d.1891 W/C pair. 14-Jun-4 Waddingtons, Toronto #87/R est:2000-3000 (C.D 1600)
£650	$1118	€949	Shipping off a breakwater (23x30cm-9x12in) s. i.mount W/C. 4-Dec-3 Richardson & Smith, Whitby #419/R
£650	$1118	€949	Fishing boat landing on the beach (43x66cm-17x26in) s.d.1884 W/C. 2-Dec-3 Gorringes, Lewes #2543
£650	$1196	€949	Off the French coast (23x68cm-9x27in) s.i. pencil W/C. 25-Mar-4 Christie's, Kensington #265/R
£671	$1235	€1000	Off Penzance (23x51cm-9x20in) s.i.d.96 W/C. 29-Mar-4 Glerum, Amsterdam #134
£700	$1162	€1022	Mouth of the Thames (33x51cm-13x20in) s.i.d.1895. 1-Oct-3 Bonhams, Knightsbridge #50/R
£700	$1288	€1022	Shipping off a pier with a lighthouse (14x23cm-6x9in) s.i.d.IX90 W/C. 23-Mar-4 Rosebery Fine Art, London #730/R
£700	$1239	€1022	Repairing a Plack, Scheveningen (33x48cm-13x19in) s.i.d.1873 W/C htd bodycol. 27-Apr-4 Bonhams, Knowle #72/R
£700	$1288	€1022	On the Dutch Coast (22x33cm-9x13in) s.d.1879 W/C. 23-Mar-4 Anderson & Garland, Newcastle #270/R
£740	$1236	€1080	Marine scene with sailing ships, fishing boats and other shipping in choppy seas off Portsmouth (43x74cm-17x29in) W/C. 14-Oct-3 Canterbury Auctions, UK #128/R
£750	$1320	€1095	Folkestone (23x49cm-9x19in) s.i.d.1899 W/C. 19-May-4 John Bellman, Billingshurst #1846/R
£800	$1336	€1168	Nearing sunset (18x30cm-7x12in) s.i.d.1894 W/C prov. 18-Jun-3 John Nicholson, Haslemere #583/R
£800	$1472	€1168	Trading brig and other shipping in the Channel off Dover (24x44cm-9x17in) s.i.d.1891 pencil W/C prov. 25-Mar-4 Christie's, Kensington #267/R
£850	$1564	€1241	Fishing boat tacking out of the harbour (13x18cm-5x7in) pencil W/C prov. 25-Mar-4 Christie's, Kensington #270
£950	$1796	€1387	Entering harbour during a storm (23x46cm-9x18in) s.i.d.94 W/C. 19-Feb-4 Lyon & Turnbull, Edinburgh #16
£978	$1800	€1428	Rescued from Caister bank (64x53cm-25x21in) s.i.d.1890 W/C. 25-Jun-4 Freeman, Philadelphia #60/R est:1000-1500
£1000	$1700	€1460	Katwijk-am-Zee (43x69cm-17x27in) s.i. W/C bodycol. 19-Nov-3 Christie's, Kensington #330/R
£1000	$1840	€1460	Dutch fishing vessels on the North Sea (13x17cm-5x7in) s.i.d.1875 W/C. 23-Mar-4 Bonhams, Knightsbridge #67/R est:400-600
£1000	$1790	€1460	Scarborough fishing boats off Whitby (30x61cm-12x24in) s.d.1893 pencil W/C htd white. 26-May-4 Christie's, Kensington #428/R est:1000-1500
£1000	$1790	€1460	North Shields (18x36cm-7x14in) s. W/C. 13-May-4 Mitchells, Cockermouth #1038/R est:800-1200
£1100	$1892	€1606	San Giorgio Maggiore (22x27cm-9x11in) s.d.1889 W/C. 3-Dec-3 Cheffins, Cambridge #564/R est:800-1000
£1100	$1837	€1606	Le partel (30x46cm-12x18in) s.i.d.1876 W/C scratching out htd bodycol. 12-Nov-3 Halls, Shrewsbury #247 est:1000-1500
£1150	$1921	€1679	Low tide, Scheveningen (12x17cm-5x7in) s.i.d.1880 W/C. 20-Oct-3 Bonhams, Bath #113
£1200	$1920	€1752	Boats and figures in coastal scene (15x30cm-6x12in) s.d.1890 W/C pair. 16-Sep-3 Louis Taylor, Stoke on Trent #1064
£1200	$2004	€1752	Pegwell Bay (43x66cm-17x26in) s.i. W/C. 8-Oct-3 Rupert Toovey, Partridge Green #100/R est:1500-2000
£1200	$2064	€1752	Two decker unloading its crew (19x20cm-7x8in) s.d.1892 W/C gouache prov. 2-Dec-3 Sotheby's, London #68/R est:1500-2000
£1250	$2288	€1825	Scheveningen Beach, Holland (22x45cm-9x18in) s.d.1893 W/C. 27-Jan-4 Holloways, Banbury #343/R est:300-500
£1300	$2210	€1898	On the Maas (12x18cm-5x7in) s.i.d.1879 pencil ink W/C bodycol pair. 19-Nov-3 Christie's, Kensington #387/R
£1300	$2288	€1898	Fisherfolk and beached vessel with church (43x69cm-17x27in) s.indis.i. w. 20-May-4 Richardson & Smith, Whitby #672
£1350	$2228	€1971	Busy shipping lane (30x40cm-12x16in) s.d.1892 W/C board. 4-Jul-3 Honiton Galleries, Honiton #73/R est:1500-2000
£1400	$2520	€2044	Fishing vessels at low tide (22x51cm-9x20in) s.d.1892 W/C prov. 21-Apr-4 Cheffins, Cambridge #450/R est:500-800
£1400	$2506	€2044	Figures on a jetty with shipping beyond. Blustery day in the Channel off Dover (20x45cm-8x18in) s.d.1895 pencil W/C bodycol pair. 26-May-4 Christie's, Kensington #429/R est:1500-2000
£1450	$2683	€2117	Shipping off Calais (13x18cm-5x7in) s.i.d.1875 W/C. 10-Mar-4 Sotheby's, Olympia #72/R est:800-1200
£1550	$2527	€2263	North Shields, the Wellesly at anchor in the foreground (23x70cm-9x28in) s.i. W/C. 23-Sep-3 Anderson & Garland, Newcastle #239/R est:500-900
£1600	$3024	€2336	Kindsdown near Dover (23x33cm-9x13in) s.i. W/C scratching out. 17-Feb-4 Bonhams, New Bond Street #17/R est:700-1000
£1600	$2896	€2336	Hazy morning on the Dutch coast (36x68cm-14x27in) s.i.d.1874 W/C. 2-Apr-4 Moore Allen & Innocent, Cirencester #766/R est:1000-1500
£1600	$2944	€2336	Outward bound (28x74cm-11x29in) s.d.1889 W/C. 8-Jun-4 Gorringes, Lewes #2063/R est:700-1000
£1800	$3006	€2628	Fishing craft on the lagoon, Venice before the Dogana (22x31cm-9x12in) s.i.d.1878 pencil W/C. 16-Oct-3 Christie's, Kensington #57/R est:600-800
£1800	$3006	€2628	Figures shrimping in Pegwell Bay, Kent, shipping beyond (51x76cm-20x30in) s.d.1886 W/C. 19-Oct-3 Desmond Judd, Cranbrook #1001
£1800	$2862	€2628	Fishing and other boats off Calais (28x94cm-11x37in) s.d.1890 W/C. 1-May-3 John Nicholson, Haslemere #662/R est:1200-1500
£1800	$3402	€2628	Portsmouth (30x20cm-12x8in) s.i.d.1895 W/C scratching out. 17-Feb-4 Bonhams, New Bond Street #59/R est:1000-1500
£1900	$3401	€2774	Making for Newhaven harbour (40x54cm-16x21in) s.i.d.1878 W/C htd white scratching out. 26-May-4 Christie's, Kensington #425/R est:400-600
£1950	$3257	€2847	Busy shipping scene off the Dutch town of Flushing (23x71cm-9x28in) s.d.1896 W/C. 16-Nov-3 Desmond Judd, Cranbrook #1063
£2162	$3805	€3200	Boats at the mouth of the Maas (32x49cm-13x19in) s.i.d.1876 W/C black chk prov.exhib.lit. 19-May-4 Sotheby's, Amsterdam #189/R est:3000-4000
£2200	$3850	€3212	On the Medway. Mouth of the Thames (10x15cm-4x6in) s. one d.1875 W/C pair. 19-Dec-3 Mallams, Oxford #113/R est:800-1200
£2200	$4158	€3212	Venice (13x18cm-5x7in) s.d.1891 W/C. 17-Feb-4 Bonhams, New Bond Street #19/R est:2000-3000
£2250	$3825	€3285	Broken roads, low tide, figures on the beach by a breakwater (38x102cm-15x40in) s. 5-Nov-3 John Nicholson, Haslemere #508/R est:2500-5000
£2550	$4616	€3723	Fishing boats outside port (47x74cm-19x29in) s.d.1891 W/C htd white. 30-Mar-4 David Duggleby, Scarborough #130/R est:2000-3000
£2700	$4860	€3942	Fishing boat and other shipping in choppy seas off harbour (23x51cm-9x20in) s.d.1889. 20-Apr-4 Canterbury Auctions, UK #163/R est:400-600
£2800	$4480	€4088	Scheveningen (16x38cm-6x15in) s.i.d.1881 W/C htd white. 16-Sep-3 Bonhams, New Bond Street #24/R est:2000-3000
£3400	$6154	€4964	Beach scene with fishing vessels and many figures (46x72cm-18x28in) s.i.d.1881 W/C htd white bodycol. 2-Apr-4 Moore Allen & Innocent, Cirencester #762/R est:1500-2000
£3500	$6265	€5110	Boulogne. Leaving port (32x50cm-13x20in) s.i.d.1880 s.d. pencil W/C bodycol scratching out pair prov. 26-May-4 Christie's, Kensington #427/R est:3000-5000
£3600	$6660	€5256	Fresh breeze off Dover (30x48cm-12x19in) s.i.d.1878 W/C scratching out. 14-Jan-4 Lawrence, Crewkerne #1326/R est:1500-2000
£4800	$9072	€7008	Customs House and Tower of London (22x69cm-9x27in) s.i.d.1890 W/C htd white. 17-Feb-4 Bonhams, New Bond Street #60/R est:2500-3500

HARDY, Walter Manly (1877-1933) American

Works on paper

£223	$400	€326	Beached dory (33x48cm-13x19in) s. W/C. 8-Jan-4 James Julia, Fairfield #1059/R

HARDY, William F (19th C) British

£494	$850	€721	Farm scene with figure and chickens (41x69cm-16x27in) s. painted c.850. 7-Dec-3 Treadway Gallery, Cincinnati #567/R
£494	$850	€721	Autumn landscape (41x69cm-16x27in) s. painted c.1890. 7-Dec-3 Treadway Gallery, Cincinnati #568/R

HARDY, William Howard (?) British

£400	$640	€584	Cattle watering (28x58cm-11x23in) s. 15-May-3 Mitchells, Cockermouth #1013
£400	$640	€584	Cattle grazing (28x58cm-11x23in) s. 15-May-3 Mitchells, Cockermouth #1014

HARE, Dennis (20th C) American

£1470	$2500	€2146	Man reading (58x37cm-23x15in) s.d.90 oil on paper prov. 9-Nov-3 Bonhams & Butterfields, Los Angeles #4044/R

HARE, John (1908-1978) American

£440	$800	€642	Autumn, the Connecticut valley (51x41cm-20x16in) s. i.stretcher. 19-Jun-4 Jackson's, Cedar Falls #177/R
£798	$1300	€1165	Light and colour, Gloucester Bay (61x76cm-24x30in) s. 19-Jul-3 Outer Cape Auctions, Provincetown #95/R
£811	$1500	€1217	Harbour mist, Cape Cod (38x51cm-15x20in) s. board. 17-Jul-4 Outer Cape Auctions, Provincetown #33/R
£1257	$2100	€1835	Gloucester hare (61x76cm-24x30in) 16-Nov-3 CRN Auctions, Cambridge #11/R

Works on paper

£307	$550	€448	Dockside scene with boats and figures (41x36cm-16x14in) s. 15-May-4 Jeffery Burchard, Florida #219
£324	$550	€473	Untitled, harbour scene (30x23cm-12x9in) s. W/C. 9-Nov-3 Outer Cape Auctions, Provincetown #64/R
£368	$600	€537	Harbour at Gloucester (25x30cm-10x12in) s. W/C. 19-Jul-3 Outer Cape Auctions, Provincetown #108/R
£432	$800	€648	Provincetown waterfront (18x20cm-7x8in) s. W/C. 17-Jul-4 Outer Cape Auctions, Provincetown #81/R
£460	$750	€672	Townscape (25x30cm-10x12in) s. W/C. 19-Jul-3 Outer Cape Auctions, Provincetown #34/R
£605	$950	€883	Cape Cod lighthouse (43x33cm-17x13in) s. W/C. 20-Apr-3 Outer Cape Auctions, Provincetown #82/R
£746	$1350	€1089	Harbour haze (20x25cm-8x10in) s. W/C. 3-Apr-4 Outer Cape Auctions, Provincetown #50/R
£865	$1600	€1298	Harbour silhouette, Provincetown (41x30cm-16x12in) s. W/C. 17-Jul-4 Outer Cape Auctions, Provincetown #94/R

HARE, John Knowles (1884-1947) American

Works on paper

£282	$500	€412	Harbour with fishing boats (13x18cm-5x7in) s. pencil W/C. 2-May-4 Bonhams & Butterfields, San Francisco #1098/R
£335	$550	€486	Fishing boats, Provincetown (8x6cm-3x2in) s. W/C exec.c.1940. 7-Jun-3 Treadway Gallery, Cincinnati #1460
£346	$550	€505	Provincetown docks (49x39cm-19x15in) s. W/C. 12-Sep-3 Skinner, Boston #492/R
£528	$850	€771	Motif No 1 (36x41cm-14x16in) s. W/C. 20-Aug-3 James Julia, Fairfield #1723/R

HARE, Julius (1859-1932) British

£850	$1522	€1241	Breakwater Port St Mary (23x46cm-9x18in) s. 7-May-4 Chrystals Auctions, Isle of Man #302

HARE, St George (1857-1933) British

£2100	$3759	€3066	Portrait of a young lady wearing a white gauze gown and feather boa (76x61cm-30x24in) s. 22-Mar-4 Bonhams & Brooks, Norfolk #247/R est:700-1000
£14000	$25060	€20440	Fifty years since our wedding day (65x81cm-26x32in) s. s.indis.i.verso exhib.lit. 14-May-4 Christie's, London #139/R est:15000-20000

HARE, William (fl.1849-1852) American

£3279	$6000	€4787	Schooner Pearl off a lighthouse (60x69cm-24x27in) s.i. 29-Jul-4 Christie's, Rockefeller NY #238/R est:5000-7000
£3693	$6500	€5392	Ship portrait (53x66cm-21x26in) s.i. 22-May-4 Pook & Pook, Downington #545/R est:2000-2500

HAREUX, Ernest Victor (1847-1909) French

£451	$754	€650	La vase de Delft renverse (34x60cm-13x24in) s. peinture. 25-Oct-3 Binoche, Orleans #48

HARFAUT, Ferdinand (?) French?

£2446	$4012	€3400	Untitled (103x58cm-41x23in) 5-Jun-3 Adma, Formigine #413 est:2100-2200

HARGENS, Charles (1893-1996) American

£229	$425	€334	Dolphins, illustration for The Nerve of some animals (56x48cm-22x19in) s. board. 3-Mar-4 Alderfer's, Hatfield #404
£283	$450	€413	Spring (20x25cm-8x10in) s.i.verso board. 10-Sep-3 Alderfer's, Hatfield #414/R
£516	$950	€753	Delong barn, Carversville (25x36cm-10x14in) s. i.d.1945 verso canvasboard. 9-Jun-4 Alderfer's, Hatfield #476/R est:400-600
£518	$850	€751	Winter, landscape with cattle (33x25cm-13x10in) s. canvasboard. 4-Jun-3 Alderfer's, Hatfield #372
£543	$1000	€793	Irene (25x36cm-10x14in) s. i.d.1938 verso canvasboard. 9-Jun-4 Alderfer's, Hatfield #475/R est:1000-1200
£692	$1100	€1010	Pilgrimage of Grace (97x76cm-38x30in) s. 10-Sep-3 Alderfer's, Hatfield #410/R
£1159	$1900	€1681	Meadow, Col Richardson farm, New Hope, PA (30x41cm-12x16in) s. canvasboard. 4-Jun-3 Alderfer's, Hatfield #374/R est:2000-3000
£1766	$3250	€2578	Two prospectors and mules (51x71cm-20x28in) s. 9-Jun-4 Alderfer's, Hatfield #474/R est:2500-3500
£1882	$3500	€2748	Portrait of a bear and cubs confronting startled rider (53x66cm-21x26in) s. 3-Mar-4 Alderfer's, Hatfield #403/R est:3000-4000
£2044	$3250	€2984	Chisholm Trail (61x71cm-24x28in) s. d.1939 verso. 10-Sep-3 Alderfer's, Hatfield #409/R est:4000-6000
£3179	$5500	€4641	Illustration, Indian family on horseback approaching ranch house (46x81cm-18x32in) s. 10-Dec-3 Alderfer's, Hatfield #454/R est:800-1200
£3354	$5500	€4863	West of Abilene (64x53cm-25x21in) s. sold with book jacket. 4-Jun-3 Alderfer's, Hatfield #369/R est:5000-7000
Works on paper			
£246	$425	€359	Sylvan landscape (28x48cm-11x19in) s. i.verso W/C. 10-Dec-3 Alderfer's, Hatfield #457
£290	$475	€421	Days of 76 Rodeo, Deadwood, South Dakota (23x28cm-9x11in) s. pencil W/C. 4-Jun-3 Alderfer's, Hatfield #370/R
£305	$500	€442	Studio (30x23cm-12x9in) s. pencil W/C tempera. 4-Jun-3 Alderfer's, Hatfield #375
£1040	$1800	€1518	Portrait of bucking horse and thrown rider (33x46cm-13x18in) s. W/C. 10-Dec-3 Alderfer's, Hatfield #456 est:400-600

HARGITT, Edward (1835-1895) British

£1053	$1695	€1537	Highland cattle by the loch (50x75cm-20x30in) s. 13-Oct-3 Joel, Victoria #443 est:1000-1500 (A.D 2600)
Works on paper			
£480	$878	€701	Herding sheep (33x51cm-13x20in) s. W/C. 27-Jan-4 Bonhams, Knightsbridge #64/R

HARGREAVES, Thomas (1774-1846) British

Miniatures			
£2400	$3984	€3504	Two ladies wearing white dresses (11cm-4in) giltwood frame two in one frame. 2-Oct-3 Sotheby's, Olympia #28/R est:1000-1500
£2400	$4320	€3504	Lady in a pink cloak and coral necklace (8cm-3in) s.d.180 verso gilt mount rec. papier mache frame oval prov.exhib. 22-Apr-4 Bonhams, New Bond Street #139/R est:1200-1800
£4000	$7200	€5840	Lady in a white dress with lace trim and brooch (8cm-3in) s.d.1812 verso mono.verso gold frame oval prov.exhib.lit. 22-Apr-4 Bonhams, New Bond Street #136/R est:2000-3000
£4000	$7200	€5840	Portraits of a lady and gentleman (8cm-3in) s.i.d.1807 and 1808 verso gilt rec papier mache frame oval 2 prov. 22-Apr-4 Bonhams, New Bond Street #145/R est:2000-3000

HARING, Keith (1958-1990) American

£1189	$2021	€1700	Head birth (22x20cm-9x8in) s.i.d.89 feltpen. 29-Nov-3 Villa Grisebach, Berlin #789/R est:1400-1600
£3691	$6534	€5500	Untitled (96x126cm-38x50in) temperafelt pen board on panel. 30-Apr-4 Dr Fritz Nagel, Stuttgart #819/R est:5800
£14000	$25760	€21000	Untitled (70x100cm-28x39in) s.d.8.8.88 verso acrylic paper prov. 8-Jun-4 Artcurial Briest, Paris #252/R est:10000-15000
£14371	$24000	€20982	Dog (128x96cm-50x38in) acrylic silkscreen ink wood exec painted 1986 prov.lit. 12-Nov-3 Christie's, Rockefeller NY #623/R est:18000-22000
£20670	$37000	€30178	Untitled (28x35cm-11x14in) s.d.83 i.d.1984 verso acrylic marker incised panel prov. 14-May-4 Phillips, New York #340/R est:6000-8000
£30726	$55000	€44860	Untitled (97x127cm-38x50in) s.i.d.Jun 13 1982 verso acrylic paper prov. 14-May-4 Phillips, New York #210/R est:25000-35000
£83832	$140000	€122395	Untitled (229x232cm-90x91in) acrylic tarpaulin metal grommets two attached panels prov.exhib. 13-Nov-3 Sotheby's, New York #479a/R est:100000-150000
£145251	$260000	€212066	Untitled (152x152cm-60x60in) s.d.May 31 1988 overlap acrylic prov. 12-May-4 Christie's, Rockefeller NY #388/R est:120000-180000
£165000	$303600	€240900	Untitled (244x244cm-96x96in) s.i.d.Sept 7 86 acrylic oil on canvas prov.lit. 25-Jun-4 Christie's, London #199/R est:30000-40000
£178771	$320000	€261006	Untitled (152x152cm-60x60in) s.d.April 13 1984 verso acrylic nettle prov.exhib. 14-May-4 Phillips, New York #217/R est:100000-150000
£234637	$420000	€342570	Untitled (274x277cm-108x109in) s.d.Jan 16 1982 verso acrylic on vinyl tarp prov.exhib. 13-May-4 Phillips, New York #23/R est:400000-600000
£300000	$552000	€450000	Untitled (244x488cm-96x192in) s.d.1987 verso acrylic prov.exhib.lit. 11-Jun-4 Villa Grisebach, Berlin #82/R est:500000-700000
£307263	$550000	€448604	Untitled - People (305x457cm-120x180in) s.d.1/8/85 verso acrylic tarpaulin prov.exhib. 12-May-4 Sotheby's, New York #58/R est:400000-600000
Prints			
£1765	$3000	€2577	Untitled (63x99cm-25x39in) s. lithograph. 31-Oct-3 Sotheby's, New York #570/R
£1765	$3000	€2577	Three lithographs, one print (81x100cm-32x39in) s. lithograph. 31-Oct-3 Sotheby's, New York #568/R
£2210	$4000	€3227	Best buddies (56x70cm-22x28in) bears another sig.num.106/200 col silkscreen. 19-Apr-4 Bonhams & Butterfields, San Francisco #261/R est:3000-4000
£2230	$4214	€3300	Personnages (58x78cm-23x31in) s.num.43/150 col screenprint. 21-Feb-4 Cornette de St.Cyr, Paris #73/R est:2000-3000
£2401	$4250	€3505	Untitled (54x73cm-21x29in) s.d.1985 num.84/150 col screenprint. 30-Apr-4 Sotheby's, New York #346 est:3000-4000
£2703	$5108	€4000	Red tongue (81x100cm-32x39in) s.num.AP 7/20 col lithograph prov. 21-Feb-4 Cornette de St.Cyr, Paris #72 est:3000-4000
£3200	$5824	€4672	Blueprint drawings (100x192cm-39x76in) s.d.1990 num.11/33 screenprint. 30-Jun-4 Christie's, London #211 est:1500-2000
£3297	$5835	€4814	Untitled 2 (106x127cm-42x50in) s.num.76/100 col silkscreen prov.lit. 27-Apr-4 AB Stockholms Auktionsverk #1304/R est:45000-55000 (S.KR 45000)
£3529	$6000	€5152	Double man (56x76cm-22x30in) s. lithograph. 31-Oct-3 Sotheby's, New York #569/R
£3800	$6916	€5548	Blueprint drawings (136x103cm-54x41in) s.d.1990 num.11/33 screenprint. 30-Jun-4 Christie's, London #210/R est:1500-2000
£4000	$6640	€5840	Untitled (106x127cm-42x50in) s.d.1983 num.91/100 col silkscreen. 6-Oct-3 Sotheby's, London #230/R est:2000-2500
£5735	$9750	€8373	Untitled (20x20cm-8x8in) s. screenprint. 31-Oct-3 Sotheby's, New York #574/R
£6780	$12000	€9899	Untitled (81x100cm-32x39in) s.d.1985 num.63/80 red black lithograph set of three. 30-Apr-4 Sotheby's, New York #347/R est:8000-10000
£9040	$16000	€13198	Pop shop II (27x35cm-11x14in) s.d.1988 num.189/200 col screenprint set of four. 28-Apr-4 Christie's, Rockefeller NY #293/R est:5000-7000
£9412	$16000	€13742	Flowers suite (100x130cm-39x51in) s.d.1990 col screenprint set of 5. 4-Nov-3 Christie's, Rockefeller NY #242/R est:12000-16000
£11173	$20000	€16313	Untitled (138x248cm-54x98in) s.d.86 num.13/24 aquatint paper prov.lit. 12-May-4 Christie's, Rockefeller NY #393/R est:20000-30000
£12000	$21840	€17520	Retrospect (130x195cm-51x77in) s.d.1989 num.4/10 col screenprint. 30-Jun-4 Christie's, London #208/R est:7000-10000
£15537	$27500	€22684	Retrospect (116x201cm-46x79in) s.d.1989 num.38/75 col screenprint. 30-Apr-4 Sotheby's, New York #350/R est:20000-30000
£16949	$30000	€24746	Growing (76x102cm-30x40in) s.d.1988 num.80/100 screenprint portfolio of five. 30-Apr-4 Sotheby's, New York #348/R est:25000-35000
Sculpture			
£1300	$2249	€1898	Untitled, brooch (17x17cm-7x7in) st.num.171/200 yellow Continental metal conceived 1989 box. 11-Dec-3 Christie's, Kensington #255/R est:1500-2500
£2778	$4583	€4000	Chirro et torro (54x32cm-21x13in) glass plexiglas electric lamp pair. 2-Jul-3 Cornette de St.Cyr, Paris #226/R est:4000-5000
£15385	$26154	€22000	Three figures dancing (43cm-17in) s.d.1989 num.4/10 polyurethane paint aluminium. 28-Nov-3 Blanchet, Paris #225/R est:25000-30000
£23952	$40000	€34970	Untitled (51x85x54cm-20x33x21in) with sig.d.85 num.3-3 enamel on steel prov.lit. 12-Nov-3 Christie's, Rockefeller NY #622/R est:40000-60000
£29000	$48430	€42340	Untitled - Capuera Dancers (71x66x64cm-28x26x25in) s.d.86 num.1/3 verso baked enamel on aluminium prov. 21-Oct-3 Sotheby's, London #422/R est:18000-25000
£58000	$105560	€84680	Acrobats (126x82x76cm-50x32x30in) s.d.1986 num.1/7 baked enamel aluminium prov. 6-Feb-4 Sotheby's, London #259/R est:40000-60000
Works on paper			
£432	$800	€631	Dancing man (20x28cm-8x11in) s.d.88 Sumi ink. 13-Mar-4 Susanin's, Chicago #6080/R
£432	$800	€631	Dancing man (20x18cm-8x7in) s.d.88 Sumi ink. 13-Mar-4 Susanin's, Chicago #6081/R
£872	$1614	€1300	Composition (25x19cm-10x7in) s.d.87 felt-tip pen prov. 13-Mar-4 De Vuyst, Lokeren #168/R
£878	$1546	€1300	Haring man (18x14cm-7x6in) s.d.1987 felt-tip pen dr. prov. 18-May-4 Segre, Madrid #177/R
£1081	$1903	€1600	Babies (29x21cm-11x8in) s.d.1989 felt-tip pen dr. prov. 18-May-4 Segre, Madrid #178 est:900
£1149	$2022	€1700	Heart (16x18cm-6x7in) s. felt-tip pen dr exec.1987 prov. 18-May-4 Segre, Madrid #176/R est:800
£1176	$2000	€1717	Dancing figures (21x12cm-8x5in) s. ink. 21-Nov-3 Swann Galleries, New York #71/R est:1000-1500
£1399	$2406	€2000	Untitled (27x19cm-11x7in) s.d.89 felt tip pen cardboard. 4-Dec-3 Van Ham, Cologne #184/R est:2000
£1554	$2937	€2300	Stare at dog (15x10cm-6x4in) s.d.1989 felt pen. 21-Feb-4 Cornette de St.Cyr, Paris #303/R est:1500-2000
£2118	$3600	€3092	Jumping man. Standing dog (23x31cm-9x12in) s.d.1988 brush ink two. 21-Nov-3 Swann Galleries, New York #72/R est:2500-3500
£2432	$4597	€3600	Sans titre (28x21cm-11x8in) s. felt pen. 21-Feb-4 Cornette de St.Cyr, Paris #304/R est:2000-3000
£2797	$4671	€4000	Sans titre (48x38cm-19x15in) s.d.1985 felt. 11-Oct-3 Cornette de St.Cyr, Paris #120/R est:4000-5000
£2800	$5012	€4200	Rabbit (36x27cm-14x11in) s.i.d.89 felt-tip pen prov. 15-May-4 De Vuyst, Lokeren #155/R est:2500-3000
£2817	$4930	€4000	Untitled (47x66cm-19x26in) s.i.d.1983 silver felt pen on book page. 18-Dec-3 Cornette de St.Cyr, Paris #141/R est:6000-8000
£3000	$4770	€4350	Heated hands (35x51cm-14x20in) s.i.d.Jun 25 82 verso gouache prov. 11-Sep-3 Christie's, Kensington #225/R est:3000-4000
£3147	$5350	€4500	Flying man (30x24cm-12x9in) s. Indian ink. 26-Nov-3 Dorotheum, Vienna #287/R est:2000-2500
£3200	$5728	€4800	Maaike's jacket with dancing figures (27x14cm-11x6in) s.d.89 felt-tip pen jeans jacket prov. 15-May-4 De Vuyst, Lokeren #156/R est:1500-2000
£3930	$7232	€5855	Untitled (23x23cm-9x9in) s.d.1982 marker pen. 29-Mar-4 Cornette de St.Cyr, Paris #52/R est:6000-8000
£5245	$8759	€7500	Sans titre (23x23cm-9x9in) s.i.d.1983 silver marker. 11-Oct-3 Cornette de St.Cyr, Paris #106/R est:6000-8000
£5245	$8759	€7500	Sans titre (23x23cm-9x9in) s.i.d.1982 black marker. 11-Oct-3 Cornette de St.Cyr, Paris #107/R est:6000-8000
£6000	$11040	€8760	Subway drawing, wedding bandi (708x75cm-279x30in) chlk paper on paper exec.c.1982 prov. 24-Jun-4 Sotheby's, Olympia #600/R est:6000-8000
£7362	$12000	€10749	Twelve UN babies (58x48cm-23x19in) s.i.d.Nov.19 1984 felt tip marker prov. 23-Sep-3 Christie's, Rockefeller NY #162/R est:4000-9000
£7383	$13067	€11000	Subway drawing (214x113cm-84x44in) chk. 30-Apr-4 Dr Fritz Nagel, Stuttgart #818/R est:8000
£7639	$12451	€11000	Subway drawing (217x116cm-85x46in) chk. 27-Sep-3 Dr Fritz Nagel, Stuttgart #9550/R est:8000
£8824	$15000	€12883	Angels for Christmas decoration (20x63cm-8x25in) s.i.d.1989 gold ink set of nine. 21-Nov-3 Swann Galleries, New York #73/R est:8000-12000
£11000	$19910	€16060	Knokke (58x77cm-23x30in) s.i.d.July 5 1987 verso black ink on rice paper. 1-Apr-4 Christie's, Kensington #286/R est:6000-8000
£11000	$20020	€16060	Untitled (179x195cm-70x77in) s.d.87 indelible pen Hobie catamaran trampoline prov. 21-Jun-4 Bonhams, New Bond Street #104/R est:12000-15000
£11377	$19000	€16610	Untitled (61x75cm-24x30in) s.d.May 13-89 brush col ink prov. 13-Nov-3 Sotheby's, New York #611/R est:15000-20000
£12291	$22000	€17945	Madonna eye (63x75cm-25x30in) s.d.Nov 5 1989 verso ink gouache collage prov. 13-May-4 Sotheby's, New York #484/R est:15000-20000
£12500	$19750	€18000	Untitled (68x60cm-27x24in) ink exec.1989. 6-Sep-3 Meeting Art, Vercelli #618 est:10000
£14189	$24973	€21000	Skateboard (77x26cm-30x10in) s.d.1986 felt-tip pen board. 22-May-4 Galleria Pananti, Florence #528/R est:25000-30000
£14685	$24524	€21000	Sans titre (95x126cm-37x50in) s.d.1981 Sumi ink. 11-Oct-3 Cornette de St.Cyr, Paris #114/R est:20000-25000
£15000	$26850	€22500	Man, 3 dolphins and tv (57x77cm-22x30in) s.d.1987 verso brush black ink prov. 15-May-4 De Vuyst, Lokeren #527/R
£19461	$32500	€28413	Untitled (96x127cm-38x50in) s.d.Sept 16-89 verso sumi ink prov. 13-Nov-3 Sotheby's, New York #612/R est:30000-40000

£19632 $32000 €28663 Untitled, Mickey Mouse (47x63cm-19x25in) s.i.d.1983 ink prov.lit. 23-Sep-3 Christie's, Rockefeller NY #161/R est:22000-28000
£20950 $37500 €30587 Untitled (127x97cm-50x38in) s.d.Nov 17 1988 verso gouache. 13-May-4 Sotheby's, New York #483/R est:20000-30000
£26816 $48000 €39151 Untitled (49x70cm-19x28in) s.d.April 29 1982 verso ink prov. 12-May-4 Christie's, Rockefeller NY #392/R est:15000-20000
£106145 $190000 €154972 Blue print drawing (106x206cm-42x81in) s.d.Jan 28 1981 Sumi ink prov.exhib.lit. 13-May-4 Sotheby's, New York #359/R est:150000-200000

HARING, Keith and LA2 (20th C) American
£9441 $16049 €13500 Untitled (197x88cm-78x35in) paint. 28-Nov-3 Farsetti, Prato #331/R est:7000-10000
Works on paper
£5942 $9745 €8200 Untitled (191x50cm-75x20in) spray paint panel exec.1983. 30-May-3 Farsetti, Prato #315/R

HARING, Keith and ORR, Eric (20th C) American
Works on paper
£3022 $5500 €4412 Untitled - dog (28x22cm-11x9in) s.d.84 felt tip marker. 29-Jun-4 Sotheby's, New York #554/R est:3000-4000

HARING, Keith and ROY, Martin (20th C) American
Photographs
£1693 $3200 €2472 King Kong for a day (37x25cm-15x10in) s.d.1989 gelatin silver print. 17-Feb-4 Christie's, Rockefeller NY #273/R est:2000-3000

HARINGH, Daniel (attrib) (1636-1706) Flemish
£1007 $1852 €1500 Portrait de gentilhomme tenant un livre (38x31cm-15x12in) 24-Mar-4 Tajan, Paris #69 est:1500-2000

HARKORT, Gustav (19th C) German?
Works on paper
£403 $741 €600 Peasant couple talking on lake shore (18x25cm-7x10in) s.d.1827. 25-Mar-4 Karlheinz Kaupp, Staufen #2480/R
£470 $864 €700 River landscape with figures (18x25cm-7x10in) s.d.1826 gouache. 25-Mar-4 Karlheinz Kaupp, Staufen #2481/R

HARLAMOFF, Alexis (1842-1915) Russian
£16667 $30500 €25000 Portrait de jeune fille (55x46cm-22x18in) s. 6-Jun-4 Rouillac, Vendome #39
£37657 $68159 €54979 Portrait of a girl with mandolin (89x76cm-35x30in) s. prov. 1-Apr-4 Heffel, Vancouver #11/R est:80000-100000 (C.D 90000)
£44000 $78760 €64240 Day-dreams (47x36cm-19x14in) s. 28-May-4 Lyon & Turnbull, Edinburgh #50/R est:20000-30000
£58824 $100000 €85883 Absent lover (54x40cm-21x16in) s. prov. 29-Oct-3 Christie's, Rockefeller NY #41/R est:70000-90000
£68000 $123760 €99280 Portrait of a young girl (46x34cm-18x13in) s. prov. 15-Jun-4 Sotheby's, London #190/R est:25000-35000
£80000 $145600 €116800 Contemplation (46x34cm-18x13in) s. 17-Jun-4 Christie's, London #79/R est:15000-20000
£200000 $360000 €292000 Sisters (86x70cm-34x28in) s.d.1888 prov. 23-Apr-4 Sotheby's, New York #43/R est:220000-280000
Works on paper
£1867 $3435 €2800 Jeune fille dans un sous-bois (28x22cm-11x9in) s. chl. 11-Jun-4 Claude Aguttes, Neuilly #53/R est:2000-3000
£6500 $11830 €9490 Laughing gypsy (28x21cm-11x8in) s. W/C. 16-Jun-4 Christie's, Kensington #208/R est:4000-6000

HARLANDER, Hans (1880-1943) German
£324 $531 €450 Track in East Steinbek (16x12cm-6x5in) s. i. verso board. 4-Jun-3 Ketterer, Hamburg #62/R

HARLES, Victor Joseph (1894-1975) American
£369 $650 €539 Missouri farmstead in fall (41x51cm-16x20in) s. 22-May-4 Selkirks, St. Louis #568/R

HARLESTON, Edwin Augustus (attrib) (1882-1931) American
Works on paper
£690 $1250 €1007 Counting the blessings (41x61cm-16x24in) s.i. pencil. 16-Apr-4 James Julia, Fairfield #580/R est:1500-2000

HARLEY, David (1961-) Australian
£366 $574 €534 Painting (167x167cm-66x66in) s.verso acrylic. 27-Aug-3 Christie's, Sydney #598 (A.D 900)

HARLEY, Herbert E (fl.1884-1908) British
£600 $1098 €876 Portrait of Robert Harley as a boy with attendant hound, a horse and groom beyond (141x85cm-56x33in) s. 6-Jul-4 Bearnes, Exeter #500/R

HARLFINGER, Richard (1873-1943) Austrian
£4610 $7699 €6500 Shop fronts (75x100cm-30x39in) s.d.1919. 14-Oct-3 Dorotheum, Vienna #33/R est:7000-9000

HARLOW, George Henry (1787-1819) British
£250 $448 €365 Portrait of a young lady of the Gurney Family (30x25cm-12x10in) s.d.1806 verso. 22-Mar-4 Bonhams & Brooks, Norfolk #326/R
£750 $1395 €1095 Sleeping Bacchante. Lucy on the rocks (51x44cm-20x17in) board double-sided. 4-Mar-4 Christie's, Kensington #589/R
£4435 $8161 €6475 Two sisters (127x101cm-50x40in) 14-Jun-4 Waddingtons, Toronto #168/R est:10000-15000 (C.D 11000)
£6818 $12000 €9954 Master Thomas Ethride with a rabbit (76x63cm-30x25in) 18-May-4 Sotheby's, New York #29/R est:10000-15000

HARLOW, George Henry (attrib) (1787-1819) British
£670 $1152 €978 Portrait of a lady (61x51cm-24x20in) 2-Dec-3 Ritchie, Toronto #4/R (C.D 1500)
£1900 $3287 €2774 Group portrait of the four daughters of Arthur Houldsworth Brooking (94x81cm-37x32in) 10-Dec-3 Bonhams, Bury St Edmunds #594/R est:2000-3000
£3500 $6510 €5110 Portrait of a gentleman in black coat and white collar (76x63cm-30x25in) 4-Mar-4 Christie's, Kensington #346/R est:2000-3000

HARLOW, Louis Kinney (1850-1930) American
Works on paper
£867 $1500 €1266 Lighthouse harbour (23x43cm-9x17in) s. W/C. 10-Dec-3 Alderfer's, Hatfield #412/R est:200-400

HARMAN, Jean C (1897-?) American
£1912 $3250 €2792 High Sierras lake (97x112cm-38x44in) s. i.verso. 18-Nov-3 John Moran, Pasadena #76 est:3500-5000

HARMAN, Ruth (fl.1887) British
Works on paper
£340 $609 €496 Still life - Ancient salt cellar (53x41cm-21x16in) W/C. 7-May-4 Chrystals Auctions, Isle of Man #224

HARMAR, Fairlie (1876-1945) British
£900 $1674 €1314 Figures before a tavern, Andover (71x76cm-28x30in) s. 4-Mar-4 Christie's, Kensington #522/R

HARMON, Charles (1859-1936) American
£240 $400 €350 Poppys and lupin, San Juan, Bautista (10x36cm-4x14in) s. i.verso board. 11-Oct-3 Auctions by the Bay, Alameda #1611/R
£636 $1100 €929 Yosemite Valley (76x117cm-30x46in) s. prov. 10-Dec-3 Bonhams & Butterfields, San Francisco #6183/R
£776 $1250 €1133 The brook (41x51cm-16x20in) s. 20-Aug-3 James Julia, Fairfield #1724/R
£1236 $2250 €1805 Coastal scene (25x30cm-10x12in) s. canvasboard prov. 15-Jun-4 John Moran, Pasadena #19 est:2000-3000
£1497 $2500 €2186 Yosemite big trees. 15-Nov-3 Harvey Clar, Oakland #1190a
£1734 $3000 €2532 View of Yosemite from Inspiration Point (77x118cm-30x46in) s. prov. 10-Dec-3 Bonhams & Butterfields, San Francisco #6181/R est:3000-5000
£2457 $4250 €3587 View of Bridal Veil Falls with Half Dome in the distance (99x74cm-39x29in) s. canvas laid down prov. 10-Dec-3 Bonhams & Butterfields, San Francisco #6182/R est:2500-3500

HARNETT, Otto (19/20th C) German
£386 $603 €560 At the beach, France (31x48cm-12x19in) s. 26-Mar-3 Walker's, Ottawa #43/R est:1500-2000 (C.D 900)

HARNETT, William Michael (1848-1892) American
£22449 $40184 €33000 After the hunt - dead bird (37x29cm-15x11in) s.i.d.1883. 17-Mar-4 Neumeister, Munich #470/R est:4000
£145349 $250000 €212210 Still life on table top (38x46cm-15x18in) mono.d.1878 prov. 3-Dec-3 Sotheby's, New York #122/R est:250000-350000
£176136 $310000 €257159 New York Herald January 9 1880 (30x41cm-12x16in) mono.d.1880 prov.exhib.lit. 19-May-4 Sotheby's, New York #54/R est:150000-250000
£204545 $360000 €298636 Still life with mug, pipe and New York Herald - March 10 1880 (36x30cm-14x12in) mono.d.1880 prov.lit. 19-May-4 Sotheby's, New York #55/R est:150000-250000

HARNEY, Paul E (1850-1915) American
£610 $1050 €891 Chickens (25x30cm-10x12in) s. 6-Dec-3 Selkirks, St. Louis #184
£1221 $2100 €1783 Chickens feeding (18x18cm-7x7in) s.d.1907. 6-Dec-3 Selkirks, St. Louis #185/R est:1500-2000

HARPE, Marcel de la (20th C) American?
Works on paper
£726 $1300 €1060 Looking up West San Francisco Street Santa Fe (53x69cm-21x27in) s.i. W/C. 13-May-4 Dallas Auction Gallery, Dallas #211/R

HARPER, Adolf Friedrich (1725-1806) German
£4514 $7358 €6500 Still life of fruit in Roman ruins (85x153cm-33x60in) s.d.1772. 25-Sep-3 Dr Fritz Nagel, Stuttgart #1272/R est:9800

HARPER, Adolf Friedrich (attrib) (1725-1806) German
£2183 $4017 €3187 Landscape with ruins and figures under full moon (66x81cm-26x32in) s.d.1796. 14-Jun-4 Philippe Schuler, Zurich #4291/R est:5000-7000 (S.FR 5000)

HARPER, Charles (1943-) Irish
£933 $1689 €1400 In full costume (49x57cm-19x22in) s. oil paper. 30-Mar-4 De Veres Art Auctions, Dublin #144/R
£1761 $3046 €2500 Mountain (100x120cm-39x47in) s.d.1995 i.verso. 10-Dec-3 Bonhams & James Adam, Dublin #143/R est:2500-3500
Works on paper
£933 $1689 €1400 Red heads (38x56cm-15x22in) s.d.82 W/C. 30-Mar-4 De Veres Art Auctions, Dublin #194/R
£1200 $2064 €1752 Castigatory III (63x96cm-25x38in) s.d.1978 mixed media. 3-Dec-3 John Ross, Belfast #91 est:150-200
£1408 $2465 €2000 Bird (49x62cm-19x24in) s. mixed media. 16-Dec-3 James Adam, Dublin #248/R est:2000-3000

£1477	$2643	€2200	Citizens ambition (50x75cm-20x30in) s.i.d.79 gouache. 31-May-4 Hamilton Osborne King, Dublin #99/R est:1500-2000
£1745	$3089	€2600	Heads V (56x66cm-22x26in) s.i.d.1982 W/C pen ink. 27-Apr-4 Whyte's, Dublin #99/R est:2000-3000
£1806	$2943	€2600	Invinire (52x76cm-20x30in) s.d.1993 W/C Japanese paper. 24-Sep-3 James Adam, Dublin #59/R est:2000-3000
£1831	$2930	€2600	Man of Achill (53x72cm-21x28in) s.d.1978 W/C card. 16-Sep-3 Whyte's, Dublin #134/R est:2500-3500
£2517	$4280	€3600	Hearts (56x76cm-22x30in) s.i.d.1989 W/C pen ink. 18-Nov-3 Whyte's, Dublin #160/R est:2500-3500

HARPER, Edward Steel (1878-1951) British

£480	$893	€701	Morning glory (69x89cm-27x35in) mono.d.1913. 2-Mar-4 Bearnes, Exeter #454/R
£500	$930	€730	After Bannockburn, Dawn of Scottish Independence (50x75cm-20x30in) mono.d.1914. 2-Mar-4 Bearnes, Exeter #427/R
£1437	$2400	€2098	School girl (84x51cm-33x20in) s. 16-Nov-3 CRN Auctions, Cambridge #55/R

HARPER, Henry Andrew (1835-1900) British

Works on paper

£280	$476	€409	Walls of Maon, Israel (13x18cm-5x7in) s. i.verso W/C. 4-Nov-3 Bonhams, New Bond Street #84
£600	$1098	€876	Children gathering nuts in the wood (53x73cm-21x29in) s.d.1865 W/C. 7-Apr-4 Bonhams, Bury St Edmunds #422

HARPER, Melinda (1965-) Australian

£413	$731	€603	Untitled (30x25cm-12x10in) s.d.92 stretcher oil collage prov. 3-May-4 Christie's, Melbourne #245 (A.D 1000)
£2846	$4467	€4127	Untitled (122x102cm-48x40in) s.d.99 verso prov.exhib. 26-Aug-3 Christie's, Sydney #224/R est:7000-9000 (A.D 7000)
£3626	$6599	€5294	Untitled (183x150cm-72x59in) s.d.2000 verso. 16-Jun-4 Deutscher-Menzies, Melbourne #146/R est:10000-15000 (A.D 9500)
£4959	$9174	€7240	Untitled (183x152cm-72x60in) s.d.2003 stretcher verso. 10-Mar-4 Deutscher-Menzies, Melbourne #9/R est:11000-15000 (A.D 12000)
£5785	$9835	€8446	Untitled (182x152cm-72x60in) s.d.2002 verso. 29-Oct-3 Lawson Menzies, Sydney #3/R est:10000-12000 (A.D 14000)

HARPER, Thomas G (19th C) British

£329	$550	€480	Grapes, strawberries and pears tumbling from a basket (41x61cm-16x24in) s. 15-Nov-3 Sloans & Kenyon, Bethesda #134/R

HARPIGNIES, Henri (1819-1916) French

£699	$1189	€1000	Paysage (24x31cm-9x12in) s. cardboard. 23-Nov-3 Cornette de St.Cyr, Paris #309/R
£769	$1308	€1123	Woodland near Menton (15x11cm-6x4in) s.i.d.1909. 28-Nov-3 Zofingen, Switzerland #2465 est:800 (S.FR 1700)
£1121	$2006	€1637	Summer fields (36x57cm-14x22in) s. 12-May-4 Dobiaschofsky, Bern #592/R est:2600 (S.FR 2600)
£1131	$1810	€1651	Landscape with big tree (55x46cm-22x18in) s. 19-Sep-3 Koller, Zurich #3090/R est:2500-3500 (S.FR 2500)
£1238	$1981	€1795	Landscape with river (24x26cm-9x10in) s. panel. 15-May-3 Stuker, Bern #1278/R est:4000-5000 (S.FR 2600)
£1300	$2145	€1898	Countryside study (23x33cm-9x13in) s. panel. 1-Jul-3 Tayler & Fletcher, Cheltenham #8
£1329	$2285	€1900	Bord de mer (22x27cm-9x11in) s.i.d.1902. 7-Dec-3 Osenat, Fontainebleau #101 est:2000-2500
£1538	$2646	€2200	Soleil au couchant (16x25cm-6x10in) s.d.6 jan-vier 1901 s.i.verso panel. 7-Dec-3 Osenat, Fontainebleau #102 est:2000-2500
£1630	$3000	€2380	Driving cattle in a landscape (16x27cm-6x11in) s. indis.d. panel. 27-Jun-4 Freeman, Philadelphia #30/R est:3000-5000
£1769	$2812	€2600	Chaumiere dan un paysage (11x16cm-4x6in) s.d.1898 panel. 23-Mar-3 Mercier & Cie, Lille #222/R est:2200-2500
£1915	$3198	€2700	Etang (32x44cm-13x17in) s.d.1913. 20-Jun-3 Drouot Estimations, Paris #61 est:3000-4000
£1974	$3632	€3000	Le chemin aux grands arbres (55x38cm-22x15in) s. 28-Jun-4 Rossini, Paris #20/R est:2000-3000
£2000	$3640	€3000	Bord de riviere (27x41cm-11x16in) s. 4-Jul-4 Eric Pillon, Calais #12/R
£2333	$4270	€3500	Rue du village (16x26cm-6x10in) s. 6-Jun-4 Osenat, Fontainebleau #262 est:3500-4000
£2346	$3800	€3402	Montavan (22x31cm-9x12in) s. panel prov. 8-Aug-3 Barridorf, Portland #93/R est:3000-5000
£2394	$4142	€3400	Bridge across river (23x19cm-9x7in) s.d.1889 panel. 13-Dec-3 Hagelstam, Helsinki #40/R est:600
£2802	$5015	€4091	Summer woodland with stream (35x49cm-14x19in) s. paper on canvas. 12-May-4 Dobiaschofsky, Bern #591/R est:6000 (S.FR 6500)
£3022	$5500	€4412	Forest lake in spring (25x31cm-10x12in) s.d.98 panel. 29-Jun-4 Sotheby's, New York #80/R est:5000-7000
£3261	$5348	€4500	Paysage (22x35cm-9x14in) s.d.1901. 11-May-3 Osenat, Fontainebleau #104/R est:5000-5500
£3333	$6100	€5000	Oree du bois (33x22cm-13x9in) s. 6-Jun-4 Osenat, Fontainebleau #261/R est:5500-6000
£3750	$6000	€5475	Village landscape (21x44cm-8x17in) s.d.1883. 18-Sep-3 Swann Galleries, New York #294/R est:5000-8000
£3800	$7106	€5548	Wooded landscape with distant cottages (25x27cm-10x11in) s. panel. 21-Jul-4 Lyon & Turnbull, Edinburgh #129/R est:3000-5000
£4305	$7834	€6500	River landscape (99x72cm-39x28in) 18-Jun-4 Bolland & Marotz, Bremen #631/R est:3800
£4577	$7919	€6500	Pont sur la riviere (20x30cm-8x12in) s.d.67. 15-Dec-3 Bailly Pommery, Paris #104/R est:5000-6000
£5208	$8698	€7500	La chapelle sainte etienne (23x43cm-9x17in) s.d.76 prov.exhib. 21-Oct-3 Sotheby's, Amsterdam #220/R est:8000-12000
£5333	$9760	€8000	Bords de la Sarthe (27x31cm-11x12in) s.d.90. 6-Jun-4 Osenat, Fontainebleau #259/R est:9000-10000
£7394	$12275	€10500	Bord de l'Aumance (31x50cm-12x20in) s. 15-Jun-3 Peron, Melun #175
£13158	$24211	€20000	Allee de Famars (81x60cm-32x24in) s.d.87 prov.exhib. 24-Jun-4 Christie's, Paris #151/R est:10000-15000
£13529	$23000	€19752	Vue d'un village (53x82cm-21x32in) s.d.1882 panel prov. 29-Oct-3 Christie's, Rockefeller NY #89/R est:30000-40000

Works on paper

£235	$437	€350	Voilier pres du rivage (6x10cm-2x4in) s.d.97 Indian ink wash. 3-Mar-4 Tajan, Paris #19/R
£267	$477	€400	Sous-bois. wash. 16-May-4 other European Auctioneer #54a
£290	$475	€400	Soleil couchant (8x4cm-3x2in) s. W/C wash. 11-May-3 Osenat, Fontainebleau #9
£315	$541	€450	Artiste dessinant (14x9cm-6x4in) s.d.90 Chinese ink wash. 8-Dec-3 Claude Aguttes, Neuilly #14
£362	$615	€529	Paysage (10x14cm-4x6in) s.d.1902 w/C. 25-Nov-3 Germann, Zurich #797 (S.FR 800)
£364	$663	€550	Arbres dans un paysage (10x19cm-4x7in) s. pen black ink. 16-Jun-4 Piasa, Paris #208
£400	$728	€600	Sur la jetee un jour de vent (8x14cm-3x6in) s. ink wash. 30-Jun-4 Delvaux, Paris #47
£406	$698	€580	Le chasseur et son chien (12x16cm-5x6in) s.d.66 W/C. 7-Dec-3 Osenat, Fontainebleau #19
£507	$832	€700	L'oree du bois (12x13cm-5x5in) s.d.93 W/C. 11-May-3 Osenat, Fontainebleau #10
£532	$888	€750	Les sous-bois (25x35cm-10x14in) s.d.1913 W/C. 20-Jun-3 Drouot Estimations, Paris #45
£548	$932	€800	Arbres en bord de riviere (15x22cm-6x9in) s.d.1909 chl. 9-Nov-3 Eric Pillon, Calais #26/R
£559	$951	€800	Sous-bois (21x27cm-8x11in) s.d.1910 chl dr. 21-Nov-3 Lombrail & Teucquam, Paris #107
£559	$962	€800	Vue du port de Menton (8x12cm-3x5in) s.i.d.1900 Chinese ink wash. 8-Dec-3 Claude Aguttes, Neuilly #13
£563	$1030	€850	Paysage (9x12cm-4x5in) s.d.1888 W/C. 9-Apr-4 Claude Aguttes, Neuilly #6
£599	$1036	€850	Paysage vallonne aux arbres (26x32cm-10x13in) s. W/C. 10-Dec-3 Rossini, Paris #18
£600	$1104	€900	Silhouette dnas une barque sur une riviere (11x19cm-4x7in) s.i. W/C. 14-Jun-4 Tajan, Paris #8/R
£621	$1037	€900	La clairiere (20x33cm-8x13in) s.i.d.77 W/C. 17-Nov-3 Tajan, Paris #57
£664	$1129	€950	Riviere traversant la plaine (29x39cm-11x15in) s. Chinese ink dr. 21-Nov-3 Lombrail & Teucquam, Paris #108
£679	$1154	€991	Paysage (9x14cm-4x6in) s.d.1902 W/C. 25-Nov-3 Germann, Zurich #798 est:800-1200 (S.FR 1500)
£680	$1218	€1000	Homme se promenant sur une colline (17x11cm-7x4in) s. pen black ink grey wash. 19-Mar-4 Piasa, Paris #187/R
£700	$1099	€1015	Wooded landscape (25x23cm-10x9in) s.d.1900 pencil W/C. 28-Aug-3 Christie's, Kensington #422/R
£709	$1149	€1000	Les deux chevres (25x20cm-10x8in) s.d.79 W/C. 23-May-3 Sotheby's, Paris #20/R
£839	$1427	€1200	Grands arbres (41x32cm-16x13in) s.d.1901 W/C. 21-Nov-3 Coutau Begarie, Paris #53
£839	$1427	€1200	Chemin menant au hameau (12x16cm-5x6in) s.d.1862 W/C. 21-Nov-3 Lombrail & Teucquam, Paris #106/R
£933	$1717	€1400	Vallons au printemps (9x13cm-4x5in) s. W/C pair. 14-Jun-4 Tajan, Paris #9 est:600-800
£1000	$1810	€1500	Le parc de Saint-Cloud (17x13cm-7x5in) mono. W/C prov. 31-Mar-4 Sotheby's, Paris #117/R est:1500-2000
£1268	$2054	€1800	Paysge de l'Allier (15x22cm-6x9in) s. Indian ink wash. 11-Aug-3 Boscher, Cherbourg #830/R est:1500-2000
£1277	$2132	€1800	Personnage marchant sur la route (12x17cm-5x7in) s.d.95 pen grey ink wash. 19-Jun-3 Millon & Associes, Paris #1/R est:1800-2000
£1409	$2269	€2100	Les arbres en bord de mer (13x22cm-5x9in) s. W/C. 23-Feb-3 St-Germain-en-Laye Encheres #5/R est:2000-2500
£1469	$2526	€2100	Coucher de soleil (10x16cm-4x6in) s.d.89 W/C. 8-Dec-3 Claude Aguttes, Neuilly #15 est:1200
£1781	$3028	€2600	Paysage de campagne (16x27cm-6x11in) s. W/C. 6-Nov-3 Tajan, Paris #185/R
£1867	$3398	€2800	Path (50x35cm-20x14in) s. W/C. 30-Jun-4 Pierre Berge, Paris #68/R est:2500-3000
£3333	$6000	€4866	Figure on a path approaching a village (53x37cm-21x15in) s.d.1882 W/C prov. 23-Apr-4 Sotheby's, New York #9/R est:7000-9000
£3741	$6697	€5500	Chasse a courre (25x31cm-10x12in) s.i. W/C. 19-Mar-4 Millon & Associes, Paris #18/R est:3000-4000
£3889	$7000	€5678	Vue de la Villa d'Este (24x34cm-9x13in) s.i. W/C prov. 23-Apr-4 Sotheby's, New York #11/R est:8000-12000
£4085	$7066	€5800	Vallon au torrent a Herisson (24x33cm-9x13in) s.i.d.1871 W/C. 12-Dec-3 Piasa, Paris #57/R est:4000-6000
£4722	$8500	€6894	Crest of a hill (20x33cm-8x13in) s.i.d.77 pencil W/C prov. 22-Jan-4 Christie's, Rockefeller NY #143/R est:3000-5000
£4722	$8500	€6894	View of Paestum (15x31cm-6x12in) s.i.d.1851 W/C. 21-Jan-4 Sotheby's, New York #148/R est:8000-10000
£5000	$8500	€7300	Rocky landscape with a torrent of water (49x38cm-19x15in) s.d.83 W/C prov. 29-Oct-3 Christie's, Rockefeller NY #96/R est:10000-15000
£5467	$9895	€8200	Table a l'atelier (23x31cm-9x12in) mono. W/C. 30-Mar-4 Rossini, Paris #993/R est:1800-2500

HARPIGNIES, P (?) French?

£1258	$2290	€1900	Paysage. s. panel. 20-Jun-4 Versailles Encheres #32/R est:1500-2000

HARPLEY, Sydney (1927-) British

Sculpture

£1300	$2405	€1898	Grand Jette (23x23cm-9x9in) s.num.2/12 brown pat. bronze. 11-Mar-4 Christie's, Kensington #49/R est:600-800

HARR, Jan (1945-) Norwegian

£328	$545	€476	Morning (35x27cm-14x11in) s. panel. 16-Jun-3 Blomqvist, Lysaker #1069/R (N.KR 3800)
£344	$575	€502	Flower meadow (71x71cm-28x28in) s. 20-Oct-3 Blomqvist, Lysaker #1118/R (N.KR 4000)

HARR, Karl Erik (1940-) Norwegian

£666	$1226	€972	Dark (40x50cm-16x20in) s. 29-Mar-4 Blomqvist, Lysaker #1108 (N.KR 8400)
£801	$1433	€1169	Mountain landscape from Nordland (40x50cm-16x20in) s. i.stretcher. 22-Mar-4 Blomqvist, Oslo #670/R (N.KR 10000)
£5057	$9052	€7383	Mild weather at Kjerringoy (80x151cm-31x59in) s. i.stretcher lit. 25-May-4 Grev Wedels Plass, Oslo #107/R est:50000-70000 (N.KR 62000)

HARRADEN, Richard Bankes (1778-1862) British
£1400 $2604 €2044 Figures bathing in a canal with a town beyond (71x81cm-28x32in) 4-Mar-4 Christie's, Kensington #417/R est:1500-2000

HARRAH, June (20th C) American
Sculpture
£2077 $3800 €3032 Head of a horse (30cm-12in) s.d.19 green brown pat. bronze. 3-Jun-4 Christie's, Rockefeller NY #1040/R est:600-800

HARRATH, Joseph Anton (18th C) German
£1879 $3458 €2800 Deer hunt (71x91cm-28x36in) s. 24-Mar-4 Hugo Ruef, Munich #880/R est:2500
£2148 $3952 €3200 Wild boar hunt (71x91cm-28x36in) s. 24-Mar-4 Hugo Ruef, Munich #879/R est:2500

HARRI, Juhani (1939-2003) Finnish
Sculpture
£3077 $5231 €4400 On the last beach (82x92x11cm-32x36x4in) s.d.77 verso mixed media exhib. 29-Nov-3 Bukowskis, Helsinki #231/R est:4000-5000
Works on paper
£729 $1218 €1050 Untitled (100x80cm-39x31in) collage. 23-Oct-3 Hagelstam, Helsinki #915
£1733 $3103 €2600 Burned books (67x56cm-26x22in) collage. 15-May-4 Hagelstam, Helsinki #224/R est:1000

HARRIES, Hywel (1921-) British
£720 $1310 €1051 Dockside crane, Cardiff (41x48cm-16x19in) s. board. 21-Jun-4 Bonhams, Bath #348/R

HARRIET, Fulchran Jean (1778-1805) French
Works on paper
£3600 $6480 €5256 Studies of Herault-Sechelle and Marat (25x13cm-10x5in) i.d.31 Mai 1793 red chk two in trompe l'oeil mount. 20-Apr-4 Sotheby's, Olympia #153/R est:4000-6000

HARRINGTON, Charles (1865-1943) British
Works on paper
£360 $648 €526 Sussex, early summer, figures on the edge of a woodland (27x38cm-11x15in) s. W/C. 21-Apr-4 Rupert Toovey, Partridge Green #181
£400 $708 €584 Worcester meadows (27x37cm-11x15in) s.d.22 i.mount W/C. 27-Apr-4 Bonhams, Knowle #49
£450 $774 €657 A Norfolk river (28x36cm-11x14in) s. W/C. 5-Dec-3 Keys, Aylsham #563/R
£520 $827 €759 Sheep and cottage on a hilltop (25x33cm-10x13in) s. W/C. 9-Sep-3 Gorringes, Lewes #2071/R
£650 $1170 €949 June in Sussex meadows (34x47cm-13x19in) s.i. W/C. 21-Apr-4 Rupert Toovey, Partridge Green #188
£750 $1350 €1095 Coast repairs, Pagham, Sussex (27x37cm-11x15in) s. W/C. 21-Apr-4 Rupert Toovey, Partridge Green #182

HARRINGTON, R (1800-1882) British
£2099 $3800 €3065 Rose, Comus mare and Lady Fanny, Portrait of two bay and chestnut in an landscape (64x75cm-25x30in) s.d.1839 i.d.verso. 30-Mar-4 Christie's, Rockefeller NY #43/R est:3000-5000

HARRIS, Alyne (20th C) American
£306 $550 €447 Baptism (76x102cm-30x40in) acrylic. 24-Apr-4 Slotin Folk Art, Buford #666/R

HARRIS, Brent (1956-) Australian
£3719 $6583 €5430 Transference of Colin McCahon (122x65cm-48x26in) init.d.88 s.i.d.88 verso prov. 3-May-4 Christie's, Melbourne #243/R est:2000-4000 (A.D 9000)

HARRIS, Charles Gordon (1891-?) American
£559 $1000 €816 Newport coastal view (63x76cm-25x30in) s. prov. 14-May-4 Skinner, Boston #264/R
£899 $1700 €1313 Atmospheric sand dunes (36x36cm-14x14in) s. canvasboard prov. 17-Feb-4 John Moran, Pasadena #65a/R est:1500-2000

HARRIS, Edith M (?) British
£206 $375 €301 Floral still life (46x56cm-18x22in) s. 19-Jun-4 Jackson's, Cedar Falls #199/R

HARRIS, Edwin (1855-1906) British
£267 $461 €390 Landscape with cows (30x46cm-12x18in) s. 9-Dec-3 Maynards, Vancouver #157 (C.D 600)
£500 $920 €730 View towards Arundel Castle from the river (45x62cm-18x24in) s. 23-Jun-4 Bonhams, Bury St Edmunds #377/R
£5000 $8300 €7300 A cottage industry, old lady with spinning wheel in cottage interior (75x62cm-30x24in) s.d.1878. 2-Oct-3 Lane, Penzance #120/R est:5000-7000
£6250 $11500 €9500 Quiet contemplation (51x41cm-20x16in) s. 22-Jun-4 Christie's, Amsterdam #66/R est:3000-5000
£6600 $12210 €9636 Old woman reading in an interior (48x38cm-19x15in) s. 11-Mar-4 Duke & Son, Dorchester #145/R est:5000-8000
£12000 $21840 €17520 The letter (41x51cm-16x20in) s.d.1904. 15-Jun-4 Bonhams, New Bond Street #2/R est:10000-15000
£23651 $42336 €34530 Interior scene with girl doing needle-work and boy watching (92x71cm-36x28in) s.d.1891. 26-May-4 AB Stockholms Auktionsverk #2422/R est:25000-30000 (S.KR 320000)

HARRIS, George (19/20th C) British
£300 $549 €438 Logging in a forest (43x80cm-17x31in) s.d.1899. 7-Apr-4 Woolley & Wallis, Salisbury #251/R
£620 $1153 €905 Stapleton Bridge. Bridge on the Frome (54x80cm-21x31in) s. board pair. 4-Mar-4 Clevedon Sale Rooms #143

HARRIS, George Walter (fl.1864-1893) British
£400 $668 €584 Summer fruits (30x41cm-12x16in) s. prov. 13-Nov-3 Christie's, Kensington #365/R
£700 $1288 €1022 Still life of fruit (25x45cm-10x18in) s.d.1904. 8-Jun-4 Bonhams, Knightsbridge #326/R

HARRIS, Henry (1805-1865) British
£320 $534 €467 Tintern Abbey (34x67cm-13x26in) s. 12-Nov-3 Sotheby's, Olympia #13/R

HARRIS, Henry (1852-1926) British
£270 $505 €405 Blackberry picking (24x19cm-9x7in) s. 26-Jul-4 Bonhams, Bath #67/R
£440 $805 €642 Coming home - lumber cart on a rural track (52x65cm-20x26in) s. 27-Jan-4 Bristol Auction Rooms #640/R
£460 $727 €672 Riverside village at sunset (30x58cm-12x23in) 2-Sep-3 Bristol Auction Rooms #600/R
£580 $1038 €847 Near bridgwater (27x57cm-11x22in) s. 11-May-4 Dreweatt Neate, Newbury #481/R
£680 $1176 €993 Country scene, horse and cart passing Stapleton Mill (38x58cm-15x23in) s. 13-Dec-3 Nigel Ward, Hereford #1439
£700 $1281 €1022 Tintern Abbey from across the Wye (36x54cm-14x21in) s. 6-Apr-4 Bristol Auction Rooms #487/R
£820 $1468 €1197 On the Wye (75x56cm-30x22in) s. 11-May-4 Dreweatt Neate, Newbury #480/R
£950 $1615 €1387 Boy fishing before a ha penny bridge at Stapleton (67x47cm-26x19in) s. 4-Nov-3 Bristol Auction Rooms #519/R
£1000 $1700 €1460 Resting from gathering bracken in a wooded glen (84x56cm-33x22in) s. 4-Nov-3 Bristol Auction Rooms #520/R est:400-600
£1005 $1900 €1467 Landscapes with fishermen (20x36cm-8x14in) s. pair. 21-Feb-4 Jeffery Burchard, Florida #54/R
£1100 $1980 €1606 Snuff Mill Bridge, Stapleton. Near Seven Oaks (31x25cm-12x10in) bears indis.sig. i.verso pair. 21-Apr-4 Tennants, Leyburn #1131 est:350-450
£1400 $2576 €2044 In the highlands (76x148cm-30x58in) s. 29-Mar-4 Bonhams, Bath #75/R est:1000-1500
£1800 $3294 €2628 Country cottage with figures and horse beside the barn (73x150cm-29x59in) s.d.1910. 6-Apr-4 Bristol Auction Rooms #490/R est:1000-1500

HARRIS, James (jnr) (19th C) British
£1100 $1892 €1606 Fishing off Worms Head (30x51cm-12x20in) s.d.75. 2-Dec-3 Sotheby's, London #77/R est:800-1200

HARRIS, James (1810-1887) British
£2600 $4420 €3796 Stormy weather off Mumble's Head (29x40cm-11x16in) lit. 18-Nov-3 Sotheby's, Olympia #7/R est:2000-3000
£4000 $6800 €5840 Fishing off Worm's Head (61x107cm-24x42in) lit. 18-Nov-3 Sotheby's, Olympia #8/R est:4000-6000
Works on paper
£360 $612 €526 Clipper in open seas (29x49cm-11x19in) s.d.1867 W/C. 18-Nov-3 Sotheby's, Olympia #10/R
£1700 $2890 €2482 Sailing boat in stormy seas (30x55cm-12x22in) s. W/C set of 5. 18-Nov-3 Sotheby's, Olympia #15/R est:800-1500
£1800 $3060 €2628 High seas (15x25cm-6x10in) s. pencil W/C sepia wash set of 8. 18-Nov-3 Sotheby's, Olympia #16/R est:2000-3000

HARRIS, Jeffrey (1949-) New Zealander
£446 $767 €651 Study from an Italian Master (42x60cm-17x24in) board prov. 3-Dec-3 Dunbar Sloane, Auckland #64 (NZ.D 1200)
£743 $1279 €1085 Captive Slave (25x28cm-10x11in) s.i.d.1972 verso board prov. 3-Dec-3 Dunbar Sloane, Auckland #57 est:2000-3000 (NZ.D 2000)
£818 $1407 €1194 Mother and Daughter (36x35cm-14x14in) board painted 1971 prov. 3-Dec-3 Dunbar Sloane, Auckland #56 est:1000-2000 (NZ.D 2200)
£906 $1440 €1323 Self portrait (57x76cm-22x30in) s. 9-Sep-3 Watson's, Christchurch #44 (NZ.D 2500)
£909 $1427 €1318 Van Gogh landscape (50x61cm-20x24in) s.d.1973 acrylic. 27-Aug-3 Dunbar Sloane, Wellington #63/R (NZ.D 2500)
£1196 $1901 €1746 Two figures in a landscape (57x78cm-22x31in) s.d.1979 oil pastel. 9-Sep-3 Watson's, Christchurch #97 (NZ.D 3300)
£1268 $2156 €1851 Couple with baby (40x40cm-16x16in) i.d.1977 board. 4-Nov-3 Peter Webb, Auckland #30 est:3000-4000 (NZ.D 3500)
£1805 $2942 €2635 The rivermen (60x119cm-24x47in) s.i.d.August-November 1968 verso board. 23-Sep-3 Peter Webb, Auckland #90/R est:5000-7000 (NZ.D 5000)
£2527 $4119 €3689 On the slopes of the Kilimanjaro (123x125cm-48x49in) s.d.1980 verso board. 23-Sep-3 Peter Webb, Auckland #91/R est:6000-9000 (NZ.D 7000)
Works on paper
£362 $616 €529 Imogen's grave (55x76cm-22x30in) s.i.d.1978 pastel. 4-Nov-3 Peter Webb, Auckland #3/R est:400-800 (NZ.D 1000)
£608 $966 €888 For Judith for 1978 (64x90cm-25x35in) s.d.1979 pastel. 1-May-3 Dunbar Sloane, Wellington #83 est:2500-3500 (NZ.D 1750)
£662 $1238 €967 Figure in a landscape (57x76cm-22x30in) s. pastel. 24-Feb-4 Peter Webb, Auckland #4/R (NZ.D 1800)
£2832 $5155 €4135 What can I say for sharing one or two things (122x80cm-48x31in) s.i.d.1986 mixed media. 29-Jun-4 Peter Webb, Auckland #15/R est:3000-4000 (NZ.D 8100)

HARRIS, Lawren Stewart (1885-1970) Canadian
£4279 $7275 €6247 Untitled abstract 6 (30x38cm-12x15in) s. i.verso board prov. 18-Nov-3 Sotheby's, Toronto #63/R est:4000-5000 (C.D 9500)
£4505 $7658 €6577 Abstraction (77x60cm-30x24in) s. s.d.1958 verso masonite prov. 18-Nov-3 Sotheby's, Toronto #188/R est:10000-15000 (C.D 10000)
£5405 $9189 €7891 LSH Holdings, 118 (106x139cm-42x55in) prov.lit. 27-Nov-3 Heffel, Vancouver #177/R est:6000-8000 (C.D 12000)
£5488 $9823 €8012 L S H Holdings, number 87 (61x76cm-24x30in) s.i.d.1958 verso board prov.exhib.lit. 27-May-4 Heffel, Vancouver #45/R est:13000-16000 (C.D 13500)

£6757	$11486	€9865	LSH Holdings 25 (61x76cm-24x30in) board prov. 27-Nov-3 Heffel, Vancouver #208/R est:2500-3500 (C.D 15000)
£7317	$13098	€10683	Untitled (62x77cm-24x30in) s.i.d.1963 masonite prov. 31-May-4 Sotheby's, Toronto #29/R est:10000-15000 (C.D 18000)
£8482	$14589	€12384	Abstract (125x100cm-49x39in) prov. 2-Dec-3 Joyner Waddington, Toronto #84/R est:15000-18000 (C.D 19000)
£9350	$16736	€13651	L S H Holdings, number 76 (119x125cm-47x49in) i.verso prov. 27-May-4 Heffel, Vancouver #47/R est:6000-8000 (C.D 23000)
£12162	$20676	€17757	Untitled, abstract painting 117 (123x98cm-48x39in) s. i.verso prov.lit. 18-Nov-3 Sotheby's, Toronto #110/R est:30000-40000 (C.D 27000)
£15244	$27287	€22256	Field trees (26x30cm-10x12in) panel painted c.1916 prov. 27-May-4 Heffel, Vancouver #18/R est:25000-35000 (C.D 37500)
£18018	$30631	€26306	Melting snow, spring (28x30cm-11x12in) s.i.verso board prov. 18-Nov-3 Sotheby's, Toronto #189/R est:50000-70000 (C.D 40000)
£18293	$32744	€26708	Mountains east of Maligne Lake, Jasper, Colin Range IX (26x34cm-10x13in) s. s.i.verso panel painted c.1924-1928 lit. 27-May-4 Heffel, Vancouver #35/R est:50000-70000 (C.D 45000)
£23423	$39820	€34198	Tamarac, spruce and pine, Algoma (26x33cm-10x13in) s.i.d.1918-1919 verso panel prov. 27-Nov-3 Heffel, Vancouver #65/R est:60000-80000 (C.D 52000)
£27679	$47607	€40411	Mountains East of Maligne Lake (26x34cm-10x13in) s. panel prov.lit. 2-Dec-3 Joyner Waddington, Toronto #80/R est:40000-50000 (C.D 62000)
£31532	$53604	€46037	Mountain sketch, XLIII (30x38cm-12x15in) s.i.verso panel painted c.1928 prov.lit. 27-Nov-3 Heffel, Vancouver #38/R est:70000-90000 (C.D 70000)
£35714	$61429	€52142	North of Rossport, Lake Superior (26x35cm-10x14in) s. panel painted 1921 prov.lit. 2-Dec-3 Joyner Waddington, Toronto #67/R est:100000-125000 (C.D 80000)
£36036	$61261	€52613	North of Lake Superior (26x36cm-10x14in) s. s.i.verso panel prov. 18-Nov-3 Sotheby's, Toronto #42/R est:80000-100000 (C.D 80000)
£42793	$72748	€62478	Northern landscape (47x55cm-19x22in) s. s.verso prov.lit. 18-Nov-3 Sotheby's, Toronto #149/R est:90000-120000 (C.D 95000)
£45045	$76577	€65766	North shore, Lake Superior II (30x38cm-12x15in) s.i.verso panel prov. 18-Nov-3 Sotheby's, Toronto #90/R est:100000-125000 (C.D 100000)
£55556	$91111	€81112	Decorative landscape with barn (46x36cm-18x14in) d.1917 i.verso board. 28-May-3 Maynards, Vancouver #80/R est:150000-175000 (C.D 125000)
£58559	$99550	€85496	North of Lake Superior (37x37cm-15x15in) s.i.verso board prov.lit. 18-Nov-3 Sotheby's, Toronto #137/R est:100000-120000 (C.D 130000)
£66000	$120780	€96360	Lefroy Lake above Lake O'Hara (62x82cm-24x32in) s. board prov.lit. 1-Jun-4 Joyner Waddington, Toronto #39/R est:175000-225000 (C.D 165000)
£178571	$307143	€260714	Houses, winter (105x125cm-41x49in) s. painted c.1920-1921 prov.exhib.lit. 2-Dec-3 Joyner Waddington, Toronto #39/R est:500000-700000 (C.D 400000)
£188000	$344040	€274480	Lake in Temagami, Northern Sketch IX (30x37cm-12x15in) board. 1-Jun-4 Joyner Waddington, Toronto #74/R est:80000-100000 (C.D 470000)
£569106	$1018699	€830895	Winter in the northern woods (140x185cm-55x73in) s.i. i.verso prov.exhib.lit. 31-May-4 Sotheby's, Toronto #31/R est:1000000-1500000 (C.D 1400000)

Works on paper

£643	$1195	€939	Winter cabin (15x12cm-6x5in) i. pen ink. 2-Mar-4 Ritchie, Toronto #88/R (C.D 1600)
£964	$1793	€1407	Sketch (21x27cm-8x11in) i. graphite. 2-Mar-4 Ritchie, Toronto #90/R est:3000-4000 (C.D 2400)
£1220	$2183	€1781	Rocky Mountain scene (20x24cm-8x9in) i.verso graphite exec. c.1924-1930 prov.exhib.lit. 27-May-4 Heffel, Vancouver #34/R est:3500-4500 (C.D 3000)
£1321	$2365	€1929	Rocky Mountain (20x24cm-8x9in) i.verso exec. c.1924-1930 graphite prov.exhib. 27-May-4 Heffel, Vancouver #46/R est:3500-4500 (C.D 3250)
£1786	$3071	€2608	Arctic No. 6 Pangnirtung (16x24cm-6x9in) pencil prov. 2-Dec-3 Joyner Waddington, Toronto #174/R est:4000-5000 (C.D 4000)
£1802	$3063	€2631	Mountain sketch (27x21cm-11x8in) i. graphite prov. 18-Nov-3 Sotheby's, Toronto #54/R est:3000-5000 (C.D 4000)
£1802	$3063	€2631	Rocky Mountain, grey and blue (20x25cm-8x10in) i.verso pencil executed c.1923-1930 lit. 27-Nov-3 Heffel, Vancouver #17/R est:3000-4000 (C.D 4000)
£1840	$3367	€2686	Lake Superior 2 (19x25cm-7x10in) i. pencil prov. 1-Jun-4 Joyner Waddington, Toronto #159/R est:5000-6000 (C.D 4600)
£1915	$3255	€2796	Mountain sketch. Mountain sketch (20x25cm-8x10in) i. graphite two prov. 18-Nov-3 Sotheby's, Toronto #53/R est:5000-7000 (C.D 4250)
£1915	$3255	€2796	Rocky Mountains, 179 (20x24cm-8x9in) i.verso pencil executed c.1923-1930 lit. 27-Nov-3 Heffel, Vancouver #39/R est:3000-4000 (C.D 4250)
£2232	$3839	€3259	Mountain drawing No 5 (17x22cm-7x9in) i. pencil prov. 2-Dec-3 Joyner Waddington, Toronto #155/R est:5000-7000 (C.D 5000)
£2928	$4977	€4275	Rocky Mountain peak (20x24cm-8x9in) i.verso pencil executed c.1923-1930 lit. 27-Nov-3 Heffel, Vancouver #18/R est:3000-4000 (C.D 6500)
£3049	$5457	€4452	Houses, winter (21x27cm-8x11in) i.verso ink exec. c.1918 prov. 27-May-4 Heffel, Vancouver #55/R est:4000-6000 (C.D 7500)
£3252	$5821	€4748	Port Coldwell fish house, Lake Superior (19x21cm-7x8in) i.verso ink exec. c.1923 prov.lit. 27-May-4 Heffel, Vancouver #31/R est:4000-6000 (C.D 8000)
£4472	$8004	€6529	Snow covered trees (20x15cm-8x6in) i. gouache prov. 31-May-4 Sotheby's, Toronto #123/R est:3000-4000 (C.D 11000)

HARRIS, Lyndon Goodwin (1928-) British

Works on paper

£250	$455	€365	Sunlight and shadow over Cefn Bryn (36x55cm-14x22in) s.d.52 W/C. 21-Jun-4 Bonhams, Bath #313

HARRIS, Mabel Rollins (20th C) American

£520	$900	€759	Elk in a sunset landscape (21x15cm-8x6in) s. canvas on paperboard. 13-Dec-3 Auctions by the Bay, Alameda #1821/R

Works on paper

£1946	$3250	€2841	Nude woman pausing by flowering tree at lakeside (74x56cm-29x22in) s. pastel sold with card. 15-Nov-3 Illustration House, New York #144/R est:4000-6000

HARRIS, Marian D (1904-) American

£227	$425	€341	Young nude (76x56cm-30x22in) s. 25-Jul-4 Bonhams & Butterfields, San Francisco #6163/R
£235	$425	€343	Adirondacks (41x51cm-16x20in) s. s.i.verso. 2-Apr-4 Freeman, Philadelphia #42
£249	$450	€364	Zinnias - Mexican flowers (51x41cm-20x16in) s. s.i.d.1950 verso board. 2-Apr-4 Freeman, Philadelphia #17
£276	$500	€403	Self portrait (51x41cm-20x16in) s. s.i.d.1933 verso. 2-Apr-4 Freeman, Philadelphia #16
£276	$500	€403	Little Ruth (46x56cm-18x22in) s.d.33 s.i.d.verso. 2-Apr-4 Freeman, Philadelphia #32
£276	$500	€403	Nude with cigarette (58x36cm-23x14in) s. s.i.d.1940 verso. 2-Apr-4 Freeman, Philadelphia #33
£331	$600	€483	Solitaire (76x64cm-30x25in) s. s.i.d.1939 verso. 2-Apr-4 Freeman, Philadelphia #6
£331	$600	€483	Ballet motif (76x91cm-30x36in) s. s.i.verso. 2-Apr-4 Freeman, Philadelphia #13
£359	$650	€524	Ballet gossip (71x56cm-28x22in) s.i.verso. 2-Apr-4 Freeman, Philadelphia #44
£387	$700	€565	Still life (46x61cm-18x24in) s. s.i.d.1939 verso. 2-Apr-4 Freeman, Philadelphia #5
£442	$800	€645	October afternoon. Caspain Ave, Atlantic City. Batalo (64x76cm-25x30in) s. s.verso three. 2-Apr-4 Freeman, Philadelphia #2
£497	$900	€726	Still life with decanter and fruit (56x61cm-22x24in) s. 2-Apr-4 Freeman, Philadelphia #9
£497	$900	€726	High point (51x61cm-20x24in) s. s.i.d.63 verso. 2-Apr-4 Freeman, Philadelphia #30
£552	$1000	€806	Polishing the brass (102x114cm-40x45in) s. 2-Apr-4 Freeman, Philadelphia #3 est:150-250
£552	$1000	€806	Studio table (64x76cm-25x30in) s. s.d.1938 verso. 2-Apr-4 Freeman, Philadelphia #45
£718	$1300	€1048	Farmhouse, Chester Springs, PA (41x51cm-16x20in) s. s.i.d.1922 verso. 2-Apr-4 Freeman, Philadelphia #1 est:600-1000
£718	$1300	€1048	Waiting for rehersal (81x76cm-32x30in) s.d.71 s.i.d.verso. 2-Apr-4 Freeman, Philadelphia #40 est:200-300
£773	$1400	€1129	Pond (64x76cm-25x30in) s. s.i.d.1942 verso. 2-Apr-4 Freeman, Philadelphia #18 est:500-800
£994	$1800	€1451	Still life with fruit (56x61cm-22x24in) s. 2-Apr-4 Freeman, Philadelphia #37 est:300-500
£1436	$2600	€2097	Still life (64x76cm-25x30in) s. s.i.verso. 2-Apr-4 Freeman, Philadelphia #28 est:600-1000
£1547	$2800	€2259	Life study (81x51cm-32x20in) s. s.i.d.1925 verso pair. 2-Apr-4 Freeman, Philadelphia #34
£1796	$3250	€2622	Girl with scarf. Carol. Girl with kerchief (46x41cm-18x16in) s. s.i.d.25 verso set of three. 2-Apr-4 Freeman, Philadelphia #27 est:150-250
£3039	$5500	€4437	Outdoors model (56x51cm-22x20in) s.d.26 s.i.d.verso. 2-Apr-4 Freeman, Philadelphia #47

HARRIS, Mary L (19th C) British?

£270	$432	€394	Kittens playing in a barn (43x56cm-17x22in) indis.sig. possibly by Mary E Harris. 12-Jan-3 Desmond Judd, Cranbrook #759

HARRIS, Pam (20th C) Irish?

£556	$872	€800	Study for a barrier painting (46x46cm-18x18in) s.verso oil on paper. 26-Aug-3 James Adam, Dublin #147/R
£1319	$2072	€1900	Dialogue (66x66cm-26x26in) s.verso. 26-Aug-3 James Adam, Dublin #146/R est:1700-1900

HARRIS, Robert (1849-1919) Canadian

£405	$689	€591	Sailing boat at dusk (30x25cm-12x10in) s. paperboard. 23-Nov-3 Levis, Calgary #47/R (C.D 900)
£569	$1019	€831	In Victoria, BC (14x20cm-6x8in) s. i.d.1909 verso board. 27-May-4 Heffel, Vancouver #6 est:1200-1600 (C.D 1400)
£732	$1310	€1069	Vacant farmhouse, Holland Cove (14x20cm-6x8in) s. s.i.d.1916 verso board. 27-May-4 Heffel, Vancouver #79/R est:1500-2000 (C.D 1800)
£813	$1455	€1187	Portrait of Frances Gertrude Lawson (60x46cm-24x18in) i.verso oval. 31-May-4 Sotheby's, Toronto #23/R est:3000-5000 (C.D 2000)

Works on paper

£1250	$2150	€1825	Children at a water pump (24x32cm-9x13in) s. W/C. 2-Dec-3 Joyner Waddington, Toronto #245/R est:1500-2000 (C.D 2800)

HARRIS, Rolf (?) ?

Works on paper

£1200	$1920	€1740	Betty Boo and friends (74x104cm-29x41in) s. felt tip pen. 16-Sep-3 Bonhams, Knightsbridge #76/R est:600-800

HARRIS, Sam Hyde (1889-1977) American

£313	$500	€457	Summer landscape. s. 20-Sep-3 Harvey Clar, Oakland #1323
£549	$900	€802	California landscape (51x61cm-20x24in) s. 8-Feb-3 Auctions by the Bay, Alameda #347/R
£794	$1500	€1159	Farm in landscape (30x41cm-12x16in) masonite. 17-Feb-4 John Moran, Pasadena #46a/R est:1000-2000
£978	$1800	€1428	The barn (30x40cm-12x16in) s. i.verso masonite prov. 8-Jun-4 Bonhams & Butterfields, San Francisco #4243/R est:3000-5000
£1223	$2250	€1786	Hyde Park memory (40x50cm-16x20in) st.sig. i.verso canvasboard prov. 8-Jun-4 Bonhams & Butterfields, San Francisco #4314/R est:3000-5000
£1223	$2250	€1786	Colourful landscape (25x30cm-10x12in) s. canvasboard. 8-Jun-4 Bonhams & Butterfields, San Francisco #4348/R est:3000-5000
£1374	$2500	€2006	Fog bound (30x41cm-12x16in) s.i.verso canvasboard prov. 15-Jun-4 John Moran, Pasadena #95 est:2000-3000
£1471	$2500	€2148	Landscape (41x51cm-16x20in) estate st. canvasboard prov. 18-Nov-3 John Moran, Pasadena #96 est:2500-3500
£1471	$2500	€2148	Hyde Park memory (41x51cm-16x20in) estate st. s.verso canvasboard prov. 18-Nov-3 John Moran, Pasadena #97 est:2500-3500
£2198	$4000	€3209	Landscape with purple mountains (30x41cm-12x16in) masonite prov. 15-Jun-4 John Moran, Pasadena #96 est:2000-3000
£2381	$4500	€3476	Farm in eucalyptus landscape (41x51cm-16x20in) s. prov. 17-Feb-4 John Moran, Pasadena #173/R est:1500-2500
£2500	$4250	€3650	Springtime, landscape (30x41cm-12x16in) s. i.verso canvasboard prov. 18-Nov-3 John Moran, Pasadena #70 est:2500-3500
£2794	$4750	€4079	Old farmhouse (41x30cm-16x12in) s. i.verso canvasboard prov. 18-Nov-3 John Moran, Pasadena #22 est:1500-2000
£2794	$4750	€4079	Red and Gold (46x61cm-18x24in) s. i.verso masonite prov. 18-Nov-3 John Moran, Pasadena #102 est:3000-4000
£3297	$6000	€4814	Landscape near Cathedral city (41x51cm-16x20in) s.i.verso. 15-Jun-4 John Moran, Pasadena #32 est:3000-4000
£3297	$6000	€4814	Lonesome road (41x51cm-16x20in) s.i.verso canvasboard prov. 15-Jun-4 John Moran, Pasadena #94 est:2500-3500
£3468	$6000	€5063	Desert landscape (61x76cm-24x30in) prov. 10-Dec-3 Bonhams & Butterfields, San Francisco #6332/R est:3000-5000
£3757	$6500	€5485	Grove of trees near a country road leading to a valley (51x61cm-20x24in) prov. 10-Dec-3 Bonhams & Butterfields, San Francisco #6301/R est:3000-5000
£3824	$6500	€5583	Hilltop barn (41x51cm-16x20in) s. prov. 18-Nov-3 John Moran, Pasadena #34 est:4000-6000
£5882	$10000	€8588	Utah contrasts, in the vicinity of the Virgin River (51x61cm-20x24in) s. i.verso canvasboard. 18-Nov-3 John Moran, Pasadena #103 est:2000-3000

£6522 $12000 €9522 Barn in the mist (50x66cm-20x26in) s. prov. 8-Jun-4 Bonhams & Butterfields, San Francisco #4313/R est:5000-7000
£10405 $18000 €15191 View of a home on a hillside in California (61x76cm-24x30in) prov. 10-Dec-3 Bonhams & Butterfields, San Francisco #6300/R est:3000-5000
£12717 $22000 €18567 Backwater (63x76cm-25x30in) s.i.stretcher prov. 10-Dec-3 Bonhams & Butterfields, San Francisco #6299/R est:3000-5000

HARRIS, Steve (1953-) New Zealander
£1268 $2054 €1839 Peeling 1999 (29x39cm-11x15in) s. acrylic. 31-Jul-3 International Art Centre, Auckland #90/R est:3500-5000 (NZ.D 3500)
£2143 $3943 €3129 Pears (50x80cm-20x31in) s. acrylic. 25-Mar-4 International Art Centre, Auckland #12/R est:7000-10000 (NZ.D 6000)
£2236 $3510 €3242 Still life (57x74cm-22x29in) s. acrylic board. 27-Aug-3 Christie's, Sydney #689/R est:600-800 (A.D 5500)
£2679 $4929 €3911 Waitachuna Station (42x100cm-17x39in) s. painted c.1991 board. 25-Mar-4 International Art Centre, Auckland #18/R est:8000-12000 (NZ.D 7500)
Works on paper
£714 $1314 €1042 Green Island Railway Station (50x71cm-20x28in) s. pencil exec.c.1983. 25-Mar-4 International Art Centre, Auckland #22/R (NZ.D 2000)
£1033 $1911 €1508 Untitled still life (63x111cm-25x44in) synthetic polymer prov. 10-Mar-4 Deutscher-Menzies, Melbourne #512/R est:2000-3000 (A.D 2500)

HARRIS, Tomas (1908-1964) British
£450 $765 €657 Almond trees, Majorca (72x56cm-28x22in) d.54 prov.lit. 26-Nov-3 Sotheby's, Olympia #96/R

HARRIS, William E (1856-1929) British
£550 $1040 €803 Figures and sheep on a country lane in a panoramic English landscape (61x107cm-24x42in) 19-Feb-4 Rendalls, Ashburton #1603
£580 $986 €847 Loch scenes with figures (34x50cm-13x20in) s.d.1873. 4-Nov-3 Peter Webb, Auckland #14/R est:2000-3000 (NZ.D 1600)
£616 $962 €900 River landscape with anglers (51x77cm-20x30in) s.d.1888. 8-Apr-3 Il Ponte, Milan #606
£800 $1480 €1168 Extensive river landscape, thought be be near Broadway (48x68cm-19x27in) s.d.1884 canvasboard. 10-Feb-4 Bonhams, Knightsbridge #299/R
£1164 $2130 €1699 English village (39x77cm-15x30in) s.d.1889. 9-Jun-4 Rasmussen, Copenhagen #1682/R est:15000 (D.KR 13000)
£2400 $3792 €3480 Winding of the Llugwy, near Capel Curig (51x76cm-20x30in) s.d.1917. 4-Sep-3 Christie's, Kensington #184/R est:1000-1500
Works on paper
£350 $557 €508 Shipping on the Thames (24x34cm-9x13in) s.d.1894 W/C. 9-Sep-3 David Duggleby, Scarborough #130
£2291 $4101 €3345 Boats on the Thames (35x52cm-14x20in) s.d.1896 W/C. 26-May-4 AB Stockholms Auktionsverk #2471/R est:15000-20000 (S.KR 31000)

HARRISON, Ainsworth (19th C) New Zealander?
Works on paper
£417 $663 €609 Drinking at the pub (34x43cm-13x17in) s.d.1820 W/C. 1-May-3 Dunbar Sloane, Wellington #515 est:400-750 (NZ.D 1200)

HARRISON, Birge (1854-1929) American
£1099 $2000 €1605 New England street scene (56x48cm-22x19in) s. 15-Jun-4 John Moran, Pasadena #149 est:3000-5000
£1105 $2000 €1613 Colonial house in winter (51x41cm-20x16in) s. 16-Apr-4 James Julia, Fairfield #738/R est:1750-2250
£1524 $2500 €2210 Shady valley (20x25cm-8x10in) s.i.verso canvas laid down exec.c.1900. 7-Jun-3 Treadway Gallery, Cincinnati #1386 est:2000-3000
£4076 $7500 €5951 Woodstock stream (21x26cm-8x10in) s. canvas on board. 8-Jun-4 Bonhams & Butterfields, San Francisco #4053/R est:3000-5000

HARRISON, Charles Harmony (1842-1902) British
Works on paper
£260 $481 €380 Wherries on Oulton Broad at sunset (13x30cm-5x12in) s.d.1888 W/C. 13-Feb-4 Keys, Aylsham #579
£270 $451 €394 Angler (23x38cm-9x15in) s.d.1880 W/C. 17-Oct-3 Keys, Aylsham #647
£1000 $1850 €1460 Tranquil Norfolk river landscape (36x53cm-14x21in) s.d.1893 W/C. 13-Feb-4 Keys, Aylsham #626/R est:700-900
£1050 $1953 €1533 Gorlestone Beach and pier, Norfolk (35x53cm-14x21in) s.d.1887 W/C. 2-Mar-4 Bearnes, Exeter #330/R est:300-500
£1250 $2088 €1825 Coltishall (25x46cm-10x18in) s.d.1891 W/C. 17-Oct-3 Keys, Aylsham #658/R

HARRISON, Claude (1922-) British
£300 $552 €438 Teaching old dog new tricks (42x54cm-17x21in) s.d.1967 board. 23-Mar-4 Rosebery Fine Art, London #918/R
£400 $736 €584 Autumn dollies (29x38cm-11x15in) s.d.67 i.verso panel. 23-Mar-4 Rosebery Fine Art, London #917/R
£475 $836 €694 Fifteen (20x30cm-8x12in) s. board. 19-May-4 James Thompson, Kirby Lonsdale #11
£484 $890 €707 Harlequin revives (25x30cm-10x12in) s.d.96 s.d.verso masonite. 14-Jun-4 Waddingtons, Toronto #105/R est:1000-1500 (C.D 1200)
£645 $1187 €942 Different readings (27x30cm-11x12in) s.d.93 s.i.d.verso masonite. 14-Jun-4 Waddingtons, Toronto #134/R est:2000-3000 (C.D 1600)
£650 $1183 €949 Retired (38x20cm-15x8in) s. board. 1-Jul-4 Christie's, Kensington #191/R
£887 $1632 €1295 Trip to the island (30x42cm-12x17in) s.d.1996 s.i.d.verso. 14-Jun-4 Waddingtons, Toronto #135/R est:2000-3000 (C.D 2200)

HARRISON, Colin (20th C) Irish
£700 $1267 €1050 Making the most of the sun (38x30cm-15x12in) prov. 31-Mar-4 James Adam, Dublin #84/R
£1076 $1690 €1550 Private thoughts (46x38cm-18x15in) oil acrylic canvasboard prov. 26-Aug-3 James Adam, Dublin #63/R est:1500-2000
£1389 $2181 €2000 Lovers (40x40cm-16x16in) canvasboard prov. 26-Aug-3 James Adam, Dublin #62/R est:1500-2500

HARRISON, George (19/20th C) British
£260 $465 €380 Landscape scene with figure hedge laying and town beyond (33x43cm-13x17in) s. 16-Mar-4 Gildings, Market Harborough #397

HARRISON, J (19th C) British
£650 $1164 €949 Hunting party resting by a stream (42x53cm-17x21in) s.d. 16-Mar-4 Bonhams, Oxford #69

HARRISON, John Cyril (1898-1985) British
Works on paper
£250 $463 €365 Hen Montague brooding chicks. Redstart (13x15cm-5x6in) s. pencil W/C two. 13-Feb-4 Keys, Aylsham #593
£300 $552 €438 Crowned cranes off a river at Underberg, South Africa (32x46cm-13x18in) s. W/C. 23-Mar-4 Bonhams, Knightsbridge #76/R
£320 $544 €467 Pair of mallard overflying a lake (17x24cm-7x9in) s. W/C. 4-Nov-3 Dreweatt Neate, Newbury #48/R
£350 $585 €511 Black terns (23x30cm-9x12in) s. W/C. 17-Oct-3 Keys, Aylsham #527/R
£450 $824 €657 Grouse in flight (31x46cm-12x18in) s.d.1922 W/C. 28-Jul-4 Bonhams, Knightsbridge #61/R
£750 $1290 €1095 Grouse in flight (23x32cm-9x13in) s. W/C prov. 3-Dec-3 Bonhams, Knightsbridge #32/R
£800 $1328 €1168 Pink footed geese in flight (31x46cm-12x18in) s. W/C. 1-Oct-3 Sotheby's, Olympia #152/R
£852 $1500 €1244 Mallards at dusk (34x48cm-13x19in) s. pencil W/C. 18-May-4 Bonhams & Butterfields, San Francisco #179/R est:2000-3000
£852 $1500 €1244 Pink footed geese coming in to feed (36x49cm-14x19in) s. i.verso pencil W/C. 18-May-4 Bonhams & Butterfields, San Francisco #180/R est:2000-3000
£852 $1500 €1244 Pintails rising from the Broads (34x48cm-13x19in) s. pencil W/C. 18-May-4 Bonhams & Butterfields, San Francisco #181/R est:2000-3000
£900 $1548 €1314 Fishing eagle in flight over an African river (33x47cm-13x19in) s. W/C. 3-Dec-3 Bonhams, Knightsbridge #31/R
£950 $1739 €1387 Grouse in flight (33x47cm-13x19in) s. W/C. 28-Jul-4 Bonhams, Knightsbridge #63/R
£950 $1777 €1387 Winter landscape with a woodcock in flight in foreground (34x48cm-13x19in) s. pencil W/C. 22-Jul-4 Tennants, Leyburn #683
£1000 $1700 €1460 Rainbow trout caught on the Test (37x61cm-15x24in) s. pencil W/C htd white. 27-Nov-3 Christie's, Kensington #253/R est:1000-1500
£1000 $1700 €1460 Brown trout (44x71cm-17x28in) s.i. pencil W/C htd white. 27-Nov-3 Christie's, Kensington #255/R est:1000-1500
£1000 $1760 €1460 Driving partridge over a hedge (33x47cm-13x19in) s. W/C. 19-May-4 Dreweatt Neate, Newbury #7/R est:600-800
£1020 $1856 €1489 Black game over autumn bracken (33x46cm-13x18in) W/C. 19-Jun-4 Lacy Scott, Bury St.Edmunds #367/R
£1136 $2000 €1659 Covey of partridges in flight (34x48cm-13x19in) s. i.verso pencil W/C. 18-May-4 Bonhams & Butterfields, San Francisco #176/R est:2500-3500
£1136 $2000 €1659 Grouse in flight over moorland (34x48cm-13x19in) s. pencil W/C. 18-May-4 Bonhams & Butterfields, San Francisco #177/R est:2500-3500
£1136 $2000 €1659 Woodcock in flight (34x48cm-13x19in) s. pencil W/C. 18-May-4 Bonhams & Butterfields, San Francisco #178/R est:2500-3500
£1600 $2752 €2336 Hen harriers and grouse taking flight (56x79cm-22x31in) s. W/C. 3-Dec-3 Bonhams, Knightsbridge #33/R est:1500-2000
£1800 $3060 €2628 Snipe feeding, winter (32x22cm-13x9in) s. pencil W/C htd white prov. 30-Oct-3 Christie's, London #42/R est:1500-2500
£3000 $5100 €4380 Pheasant rising from bracken at the edge of the wood (56x78cm-22x31in) s. pencil W/C bodycol. 30-Oct-3 Christie's, London #41/R est:3000-5000
£3300 $5610 €4818 Golden Eagle with grouse (71x53cm-28x21in) s. pencil W/C htd white. 30-Oct-3 Christie's, London #48/R est:3000-5000
£3600 $6120 €5256 Driven red grouse (32x46cm-13x18in) s. pencil W/C touches bodycol prov. 30-Oct-3 Christie's, London #47/R est:2500-3500
£4400 $7480 €6424 Osprey fishing (56x72cm-22x28in) s. pencil W/C htd white prov. 30-Oct-3 Christie's, London #49/R est:2500-3500

HARRISON, Mark R (1819-1894) Canadian
£823 $1300 €1202 Woman and children with cows (56x43cm-22x17in) s.d.1883 panel. 6-Sep-3 Susanin's, Chicago #5039/R est:600-800

HARRISON, Sarah Cecilia (1863-1941) British
£1800 $3222 €2628 Moonlight (61x46cm-24x18in) prov. 14-May-4 Christie's, London #17/R est:2000-3000

HARRISON, Ted (1926-) Canadian
£520 $952 €759 Church of the attic (90x60cm-35x24in) s. acrylic painted 1994. 1-Jun-4 Joyner Waddington, Toronto #488 (C.D 1300)
£560 $1025 €818 Red bench (34x29cm-13x11in) s.d.75 acrylic canvasboard. 1-Jun-4 Joyner Waddington, Toronto #540 (C.D 1400)
£702 $1271 €1025 Green stove (46x36cm-18x14in) d.1973 acrylic hard board prov. 18-Apr-4 Levis, Calgary #44/R est:1200-1500 (C.D 1700)
£826 $1496 €1206 Summer night (61x51cm-24x20in) s. acrylic canvasboard prov. 18-Apr-4 Levis, Calgary #43/R est:2500-3000 (C.D 2000)
£1322 $2393 €1930 Parting (91x61cm-36x24in) s.d.1978 s.i.verso acrylic hard board prov. 18-Apr-4 Levis, Calgary #42/R est:3000-3500 (C.D 3200)
£1423 $2547 €2078 Winter days, Carcross (54x74cm-21x29in) s.d.1974 i.verso canvasboard. 27-May-4 Heffel, Vancouver #198/R est:3000-4000 (C.D 3500)
£2411 $4146 €3520 Black cat (90x120cm-35x47in) s. acrylic painted 1983. 2-Dec-3 Joyner Waddington, Toronto #304/R est:3000-4000 (C.D 5400)
£2477 $4212 €3616 Misty Islands (61x75cm-24x30in) s. i.verso acrylic prov. 27-Nov-3 Heffel, Vancouver #195 est:2750-3250 (C.D 5500)
£3153 $5360 €4603 Abandoned cabin (85x111cm-33x44in) s. s.i.d.1979 verso acrylic board. 27-Nov-3 Heffel, Vancouver #194/R est:3000-4000 (C.D 7000)

HARRISON, Thomas Alexander (1853-1930) American
£1395 $2400 €2037 Venice at dawn with sailboats (51x91cm-20x36in) s. 7-Dec-3 Hindman, Chicago #737/R est:3000-5000
£3077 $5231 €4400 Soir sur la mer (50x101cm-20x40in) s. 27-Nov-3 Millon & Associes, Paris #169/R est:2500-3000
£3911 $7000 €5710 Study, bathing scene (23x53cm-9x21in) s. 26-May-4 Doyle, New York #48/R est:5000-7000
£4469 $8000 €6525 Lower river (66x81cm-26x32in) s. prov. 6-May-4 Shannon's, Milford #53/R est:8000-12000

HARRITON, Abraham (1893-1986) American

£202	$375	€295	Still life (36x46cm-14x18in) s. 17-Jul-4 Outer Cape Auctions, Provincetown #20a/R
£250	$400	€365	Dock scene with boats (46x51cm-18x20in) s. 20-Sep-3 Bunte, Elgin #1258
£494	$800	€721	Confrontation (76x102cm-30x40in) s. 31-Jul-3 Eldred, East Dennis #884/R
£552	$1000	€806	Expressionistic golden misty landscape with horseman and figures (56x76cm-22x30in) s. 3-Apr-4 Nadeau, Windsor #89 est:1500-2000

HARRON, Rory (20th C) British?

Sculpture

£1333	$2400	€2000	Portrait bust of Samuel Beckett (43cm-17in) s.d.2001 bronze. 20-Apr-4 James Adam, Dublin #154/R est:1500-2000
£1567	$2820	€2350	Portrait bust of James Joyce (43cm-17in) s.d.2001 bronze. 20-Apr-4 James Adam, Dublin #153/R est:1500-2000

HARROWING, Walter (fl.1877-1904) British

£360	$652	€526	Portrait of chestnut mare (56x69cm-22x27in) s.d.1889. 31-Mar-4 Bonhams, Knightsbridge #69/R
£600	$1020	€876	At the water trough (46x41cm-18x16in) s.d.1900. 27-Nov-3 Christie's, Kensington #137/R

HARSANYI, Charles (1905-1973) American

£335	$600	€489	Gray day, Gloucester (63x76cm-25x30in) s. s.i.d.1945 verso. 14-May-4 Skinner, Boston #268/R

HART, Alfred A (1816-1906) American

£1766	$3250	€2649	Lush tropical landscape with a waterfall and mountains beyond (66x91cm-26x36in) s.d.1874 prov. 8-Jun-4 Bonhams & Butterfields, San Francisco #4026/R est:3000-5000

HART, Alfred A (attrib) (1816-1906) American

£1311	$2400	€1914	Leading the cows to drinks by the mill (71x89cm-28x35in) s. 6-Jun-4 Skinner, Boston #322/R est:1500-2500

HART, George Overbury (1868-1933) American

Works on paper

£349	$600	€510	Fruit juices, Oaxaca, Mexico (36x48cm-14x19in) s.i.d.27 W/C. 6-Dec-3 Neal Auction Company, New Orleans #600
£1196	$2200	€1746	Washing clothes. Oaxaco, Mexico (46x61cm-18x24in) s.i.d.1921 pencil W/C chl pair. 25-Mar-4 Doyle, New York #23/R est:200-400

HART, J T (fl.1833-1840) British

Works on paper

£3000	$5550	€4500	Night blowing cereus (71x51cm-28x20in) s.i.d.1834 pencil W/C bodycol. 15-Jul-4 Bonhams, New Bond Street #38/R est:3000-5000

HART, James MacDougal (1828-1901) American

£1353	$2300	€1975	Ram in a mountains landscape (18x25cm-7x10in) s. 31-Oct-3 North East Auctions, Portsmouth #1206
£1497	$2500	€2186	Watering hole (28x18cm-11x7in) s. prov. 7-Oct-3 Sotheby's, New York #178 est:2500-3500
£2446	$4500	€3571	The old pasture (76x55cm-30x22in) s.d.1882. 8-Jun-4 Bonhams & Butterfields, San Francisco #4020/R est:4000-6000
£3145	$5000	€4592	Figures beside a shrine in a country landscape (71x105cm-28x41in) s.i.d.1852. 13-Sep-3 Weschler, Washington #733/R est:3000-5000
£3825	$7000	€5585	Cows on a lane in a landscape (52x72cm-20x28in) s.d.1891. 3-Jun-4 Christie's, Rockefeller NY #840/R est:3000-5000
£5588	$9500	€8158	Pastoral scene of cows and flock of sheep (56x86cm-22x34in) s.i.d.1879. 31-Oct-3 North East Auctions, Portsmouth #1879
£6250	$10750	€9125	Cattle watering near a bridge (36x61cm-14x24in) s.d.1875 canvas on canvas. 6-Dec-3 Selkirks, St. Louis #178/R est:15000-20000
£12291	$22000	€17945	Cows watering (27x57cm-11x22in) s.d.1865 prov. 6-May-4 Shannon's, Milford #107/R est:20000-30000
£20359	$34000	€29724	River landscape (114x147cm-45x58in) s.d.1852. 23-Oct-3 Shannon's, Milford #162/R est:20000-25000

HART, James Turpin (1835-1899) British

Works on paper

£350	$627	€511	Harvest time (20x32cm-8x13in) W/C. 25-May-4 Bonhams, Knightsbridge #276/R

HART, Kevin Pro (1928-) Australian

£351	$621	€512	Flying insect (17x23cm-7x9in) s. board prov. 3-May-4 Christie's, Melbourne #394/R (A.D 850)
£367	$676	€536	Billabong at Dusk. 26-Mar-4 Lawson Menzies, Sydney #2258 (A.D 900)
£367	$676	€536	Landscape. board. 26-Mar-4 Lawson Menzies, Sydney #2227 (A.D 900)
£371	$671	€542	Whale beach (13x13cm-5x5in) s. i.verso board. 31-Mar-4 Goodman, Sydney #483 (A.D 900)
£388	$714	€566	Dragonfly. board. 26-Mar-4 Lawson Menzies, Sydney #2114 (A.D 950)
£417	$708	€609	Pick up truck in Australian landscape (14x14cm-6x6in) s. board. 4-Nov-3 Peter Webb, Auckland #214 est:400-600 (NZ.D 1150)
£449	$826	€656	Dragon fly. board. 26-Mar-4 Lawson Menzies, Sydney #2129 (A.D 1100)
£455	$773	€683	Landscape (16x16cm-6x6in) s. board. 28-Oct-3 Goodman, Sydney #375/R (A.D 1100)
£455	$773	€683	Painter's palette (30x40cm-12x16in) s.i. acrylic paper. 28-Oct-3 Goodman, Sydney #411/R (A.D 1100)
£455	$773	€683	Untitled (26x34cm-10x13in) s.d.66 board. 28-Oct-3 Goodman, Sydney #506 (A.D 1100)
£488	$766	€708	Scrubby landscape (30x20cm-12x8in) s. 26-Aug-3 Lawson Menzies, Sydney #375 est:800-1500 (A.D 1200)
£496	$917	€724	Landscape (15x15cm-6x6in) s. board. 10-Mar-4 Deutscher-Menzies, Melbourne #488/R est:1000-1500 (A.D 1200)
£517	$807	€750	Misty moonlight reflections (52x59cm-20x23in) s.d.64 board. 1-Aug-2 Joel, Victoria #254 est:1000-1500 (A.D 1500)
£569	$893	€825	Landscape (25x22cm-10x9in) s. board. 26-Aug-3 Lawson Menzies, Sydney #378 est:1000-2000 (A.D 1400)
£610	$958	€885	Waterbirds (29x29cm-11x11in) s. canvasboard. 26-Aug-3 Lawson Menzies, Sydney #376 est:1500-2500 (A.D 1500)
£643	$1073	€932	Dragon fly (17x19cm-7x7in) s. board. 30-Jun-3 Australian Art Auctions, Sydney #56 (A.D 1600)
£643	$1073	€932	Mine shaft (22x16cm-9x6in) s. board. 30-Jun-3 Australian Art Auctions, Sydney #139 (A.D 1600)
£683	$1140	€990	Dragon fly (17x29cm-7x11in) s. board. 30-Jun-3 Australian Art Auctions, Sydney #146 (A.D 1700)
£720	$1225	€1051	Men leaving Booligal (30x40cm-12x16in) s. bears i.verso composition board. 24-Nov-3 Sotheby's, Melbourne #175/R (A.D 1700)
£732	$1149	€1061	Dragonfly (28x28cm-11x11in) s.d.77 board. 26-Aug-3 Lawson Menzies, Sydney #377 est:2000-3000 (A.D 1800)
£785	$1452	€1146	Flowerscape (25x25cm-10x10in) s.d.1995 prov. 10-Mar-4 Deutscher-Menzies, Melbourne #486/R est:1800-2500 (A.D 1900)
£803	$1341	€1164	Playing in the bush (20x25cm-8x10in) s. board. 30-Jun-3 Australian Art Auctions, Sydney #86 (A.D 2000)
£809	$1399	€1181	Dragonfly (14x18cm-6x7in) s.i. board. 10-Dec-3 Shapiro, Sydney #10/R (A.D 1900)
£813	$1276	€1179	Sailing boats 1992 (23x35cm-9x14in) s. 26-Aug-3 Lawson Menzies, Sydney #114 est:2000-3000 (A.D 2000)
£859	$1607	€1289	Creek bed (55x61cm-22x24in) s. board. 20-Jul-4 Goodman, Sydney #115/R (A.D 2200)
£882	$1518	€1288	Waterbirds. board. 7-Dec-3 Joel, Victoria #109a/R (A.D 2100)
£884	$1476	€1282	Garden bush (22x16cm-9x6in) s. board. 30-Jun-3 Australian Art Auctions, Sydney #67 (A.D 2200)
£894	$1601	€1305	Landscape (22x29cm-9x11in) s. board. 10-May-4 Joel, Victoria #409 est:2000-3000 (A.D 2200)
£899	$1654	€1313	Valley muster (30x40cm-12x16in) s. board exhib. 28-Jun-4 Australian Art Auctions, Sydney #142 (A.D 2400)
£902	$1461	€1317	Ants (19x25cm-7x10in) s. board. 30-Jul-3 Goodman, Sydney #137/R (A.D 2200)
£902	$1461	€1317	Yabby hunters (21x20cm-8x8in) s. i.verso board. 30-Jul-3 Goodman, Sydney #147/R (A.D 2200)
£905	$1639	€1321	Newport beach (23x30cm-9x12in) s. i.verso canvasboard. 31-Mar-4 Goodman, Sydney #484 (A.D 2200)
£936	$1723	€1367	Amongst the scrub (30x40cm-12x16in) s. board exhib. 28-Jun-4 Australian Art Auctions, Sydney #143 (A.D 2500)
£939	$1728	€1371	Waterbird (24x28cm-9x11in) s. board. 29-Mar-4 Goodman, Sydney #183/R (A.D 2300)
£974	$1792	€1422	Uphill run (30x40cm-12x16in) s. board exhib. 28-Jun-4 Australian Art Auctions, Sydney #127 (A.D 2600)
£992	$1835	€1448	Orchids III (38x18cm-15x7in) s. board. 10-Mar-4 Deutscher-Menzies, Melbourne #487/R est:1800-2500 (A.D 2400)
£992	$1806	€1448	Bark Humpy (30x40cm-12x16in) s.i. board. 16-Jun-4 Deutscher-Menzies, Melbourne #516/R est:2500-4500 (A.D 2600)
£1016	$1899	€1524	Trappers house (21x34cm-8x13in) s. i.verso board. 20-Jul-4 Goodman, Sydney #130/R est:2000-3000 (A.D 2600)
£1030	$1895	€1504	Hillside muster (31x38cm-12x15in) s. board. 28-Jun-4 Australian Art Auctions, Sydney #88 (A.D 2750)
£1057	$1659	€1533	Damper cook (25x28cm-10x11in) s. board. 26-Aug-3 Christie's, Sydney #308/R est:1500-2000 (A.D 2600)
£1057	$1892	€1543	Mine (24x29cm-9x11in) s. board. 10-May-4 Joel, Victoria #371 est:2000-3000 (A.D 2600)
£1074	$1988	€1568	Gums (35x51cm-14x20in) s. board. 10-Mar-4 Deutscher-Menzies, Melbourne #331/R est:3000-4000 (A.D 2600)
£1079	$1802	€1619	Study from Holy Dan II (35x37cm-14x15in) s. i.verso. 27-Oct-3 Goodman, Sydney #188/R (A.D 2600)
£1092	$1879	€1594	Trees. board. 7-Dec-3 Joel, Victoria #158/R (A.D 2600)
£1138	$1787	€1650	Sydney beach (28x28cm-11x11in) s. 26-Aug-3 Christie's, Sydney #311/R est:1500-2000 (A.D 2800)
£1145	$2084	€1672	Morning study (50x61cm-20x24in) s. board. 16-Jun-4 Deutscher-Menzies, Melbourne #511/R est:2000-3000 (A.D 3000)
£1148	$1859	€1676	Shearing shed (29x29cm-11x11in) s. acrylic board study prov. 30-Jul-3 Goodman, Sydney #146/R (A.D 2800)
£1152	$2086	€1682	Old mine house (46x36cm-18x14in) s. 31-Mar-4 Goodman, Sydney #354/R est:2000-3000 (A.D 2800)
£1157	$2140	€1689	Paddock (40x46cm-16x18in) s. board. 10-Mar-4 Deutscher-Menzies, Melbourne #330/R est:2000-3000 (A.D 2800)
£1157	$2140	€1689	Hut at the diggings (30x45cm-12x18in) s. board. 10-Mar-4 Deutscher-Menzies, Melbourne #485/R est:2000-4000 (A.D 2800)
£1191	$2026	€1739	Dragonfly (30x37cm-12x15in) s. board painted c.1978 prov. 25-Nov-3 Christie's, Melbourne #187/R (A.D 2800)
£1200	$2100	€1752	Gums (41x58cm-16x23in) s.i. board sold with a letter. 19-Dec-3 Mallams, Oxford #222/R est:1000-1500
£1261	$2268	€1841	Fishing hole. board. 7-Dec-3 Joel, Victoria #99/R est:2000-3000 (A.D 3000)
£1301	$2328	€1899	Bush and locusts (55x37cm-22x15in) s. composition board. 4-May-4 Sotheby's, Melbourne #251/R est:1000-1500 (A.D 3200)
£1306	$2403	€1907	Dragonfly (35x30cm-14x12in) s.d.77 board. 29-Mar-4 Goodman, Sydney #224/R est:2500-4000 (A.D 3200)
£1310	$2044	€1900	Grasshoppers and plant (60x45cm-24x18in) s. board. 1-Aug-2 Joel, Victoria #166 est:2000-3000 (A.D 3800)
£1311	$2125	€1914	Landscape (44x60cm-17x24in) s. board painted 1977. 30-Jul-3 Goodman, Sydney #150/R est:1800-2500 (A.D 3200)
£1322	$2340	€1930	Mine (7x44cm-3x17in) s. board. 3-May-4 Christie's, Melbourne #300/R est:3000-5000 (A.D 3200)
£1322	$2340	€1930	Kangaroo hunter (42x59cm-17x23in) s. board. 3-May-4 Christie's, Melbourne #349 est:2000-3000 (A.D 3200)
£1360	$2475	€1986	Street football (30x30cm-12x12in) board. 5-Feb-4 Joel, Victoria #161 (A.D 3250)
£1379	$2152	€2000	Geebung polo club (59x66cm-23x26in) s.d.65 board. 1-Aug-2 Joel, Victoria #278 est:2000-3000 (A.D 4000)
£1464	$2665	€2137	At the Races (30x30cm-12x12in) board. 5-Feb-4 Joel, Victoria #65 (A.D 3500)
£1551	$2854	€2264	Miners shack (48x43cm-19x17in) s.d.68 board. 29-Mar-4 Goodman, Sydney #225/R est:2000-3000 (A.D 3800)
£1564	$2830	€2283	Gum billabong (60x59cm-24x23in) s.d.67 acrylic board. 31-Mar-4 Goodman, Sydney #362/R est:2000-3000 (A.D 3800)

£1577 $2633 €2366 Dragonfly (37x19cm-15x7in) s. board. 27-Oct-3 Goodman, Sydney #253/R est:2500-3500 (A.D 3800)
£1603 $2918 €2340 Rouseabout (42x54cm-17x21in) s.i. i.verso board. 16-Jun-4 Deutscher-Menzies, Melbourne #308/R est:2000-4000 (A.D 4200)
£1603 $2918 €2340 Sheep yards (26x43cm-10x17in) s.i. panel on board. 16-Jun-4 Deutscher-Menzies, Melbourne #512/R est:2000-3000 (A.D 4200)
£1619 $2607 €2364 Horsemen at waterhole (39x29cm-15x11in) s. canvasboard. 13-Oct-3 Joel, Victoria #232/R est:2000-2500 (A.D 4000)
£1633 $3004 €2384 Deserted mines (60x73cm-24x29in) s.d.67 s.i.verso board. 29-Mar-4 Goodman, Sydney #223/R est:4000-6000 (A.D 4000)
£1639 $2590 €2393 End of a day's work (25x29cm-10x11in) s. board. 2-Sep-3 Deutscher-Menzies, Melbourne #272/R est:2000-3000 (A.D 4000)
£1639 $2656 €2393 Song of the Artesian Water (39x49cm-15x19in) s. i.verso canvas on board. 30-Jul-3 Goodman, Sydney #153/R est:4000-6000 (A.D 4000)
£1660 $2772 €2490 Song of the Artesian Water (40x51cm-16x20in) s. canvas on board. 27-Oct-3 Goodman, Sydney #155/R est:3000-4000 (A.D 4000)
£1660 $2772 €2490 Study with water birds (61x61cm-24x24in) s.d.71 board. 27-Oct-3 Goodman, Sydney #189/R est:4000-6000 (A.D 4000)
£1660 $2772 €2490 Damper maker (50x30cm-20x12in) s. board. 27-Oct-3 Goodman, Sydney #255/R est:2500-3000 (A.D 4000)
£1680 $2722 €2453 Shearing time in the Outback (27x45cm-11x18in) s. board. 30-Jul-3 Goodman, Sydney #17/R est:4500-5500 (A.D 4100)
£1680 $2722 €2453 The claim (61x71cm-24x28in) s.d.71 board. 30-Jul-3 Goodman, Sydney #138/R est:4000-6000 (A.D 4100)
£1680 $2722 €2453 Grasshoppers (61x61cm-24x24in) s. acrylic board. 30-Jul-3 Goodman, Sydney #140/R est:4000-6000 (A.D 4100)
£1714 $2863 €2485 Picnic by the billabong (43x58cm-17x23in) s. acrylic board. 13-Jul-3 James Lawson, Sydney #482 est:4000-6000 (A.D 4200)
£1763 $2945 €2645 Birds on the fence (50x37cm-20x15in) s. canvasboard. 27-Oct-3 Goodman, Sydney #104a/R est:4000-6000 (A.D 4250)
£1822 $2933 €2660 Shearer (49x39cm-19x15in) s.d.78 board. 13-Oct-3 Joel, Victoria #405/R est:2500-3500 (A.D 4500)
£1829 $3275 €2670 Water birds (44x59cm-17x23in) s. board prov. 10-May-4 Joel, Victoria #193 est:3500-4500 (A.D 4500)
£1837 $3068 €2664 Nursemaid runs for help (48x57cm-19x22in) s. acrylic board. 13-Jul-3 James Lawson, Sydney #485 est:4500-5500 (A.D 4500)
£1867 $3118 €2801 Waterbird (76x56cm-30x22in) s. i.verso board. 27-Oct-3 Goodman, Sydney #252/R est:3000-4000 (A.D 4500)
£1870 $2936 €2712 Red mailbox (45x60cm-18x24in) s.i. board. 26-Aug-3 Lawson Menzies, Sydney #120 est:4000-6000 (A.D 4600)
£1908 $3473 €2786 Death of Jacky Jacky (61x61cm-24x24in) s.d.62 board. 16-Jun-4 Deutscher-Menzies, Melbourne #510/R est:4200-6000 (A.D 5000)
£1908 $3473 €2786 Water birds (44x59cm-17x23in) s. board. 16-Jun-4 Deutscher-Menzies, Melbourne #517/R est:2500-3500 (A.D 5000)
£1923 $3096 €2808 Muddy creek (48x58cm-19x23in) s.d.84 board. 13-Oct-3 Joel, Victoria #315a (A.D 4750)
£1951 $3063 €2829 Saltbush Bills gamecock (50x60cm-20x24in) s. i.verso board. 26-Aug-3 Lawson Menzies, Sydney #118 est:4500-6500 (A.D 4800)
£2041 $3755 €2980 Mine (50x61cm-20x24in) s. i.verso board. 29-Mar-4 Goodman, Sydney #147/R est:4000-6000 (A.D 5000)
£2114 $3319 €3065 Shop (44x60cm-17x24in) s.i. board. 26-Aug-3 Lawson Menzies, Sydney #121 est:4000-6000 (A.D 5200)
£2122 $3544 €3077 Restorer's yard (50x60cm-20x24in) s. acrylic board. 13-Jul-3 James Lawson, Sydney #489 est:5000-6000 (A.D 5200)
£2122 $3544 €3077 Sheepyards (50x60cm-20x24in) s. acrylic board. 13-Jul-3 James Lawson, Sydney #483 est:5000-6000 (A.D 5200)
£2127 $3617 €3105 Mulga Bill (40x49cm-16x19in) s. s.i. canvasboard prov. 26-Nov-3 Deutscher-Menzies, Melbourne #183/R est:5000-7000 (A.D 5000)
£2236 $3510 €3242 How Gilbert died (50x60cm-20x24in) s.d.1995 board. 26-Aug-3 Lawson Menzies, Sydney #119 est:4500-6500 (A.D 5500)
£2273 $4205 €3319 Homestead (40x45cm-16x18in) s.d.85 i.verso. 10-Mar-4 Deutscher-Menzies, Melbourne #492 est:2500-4500 (A.D 5500)
£2347 $4318 €3427 Chop picnic (58x76cm-23x30in) s. board. 29-Mar-4 Goodman, Sydney #184/R est:3000-4000 (A.D 5750)
£2367 $3953 €3432 Snakebite antidote (50x60cm-20x24in) s. acrylic board. 13-Jul-3 James Lawson, Sydney #486 est:5000-6000 (A.D 5800)
£2386 $3984 €3579 Kim Hart and friends camped at Nine Mile Creek (60x60cm-24x24in) s.i.d.29/1/79 board. 27-Oct-3 Goodman, Sydney #194/R est:4000-5000 (A.D 5750)
£2410 $4024 €3495 Sturt desert pea (91x37cm-36x15in) s. board. 30-Jun-3 Australian Art Auctions, Sydney #105 (A.D 6000)
£2436 $4142 €3557 Picnic by the Billabong (43x57cm-17x22in) s. board. 24-Nov-3 Sotheby's, Melbourne #233/R est:4000-6000 (A.D 5750)
£2479 $4215 €3619 Untitled - beach scene (34x82cm-13x32in) s. 29-Oct-3 Lawson Menzies, Sydney #114/R est:5000-7000 (A.D 6000)
£2531 $4226 €3670 Miners on Sunday (50x60cm-20x24in) s. acrylic board. 13-Jul-3 James Lawson, Sydney #484 est:5000-6000 (A.D 6200)
£2593 $4331 €3890 Camped by the river (44x60cm-17x24in) s.i. board. 27-Oct-3 Goodman, Sydney #165/R est:4500-6500 (A.D 6250)
£2672 $4863 €3901 Yabbie picnic (61x91cm-24x36in) s.i.d.70 i.verso board. 16-Jun-4 Deutscher-Menzies, Melbourne #298/R est:6500-9500 (A.D 7000)
£2686 $4566 €3922 Camp on the river (44x27cm-17x11in) s.d.89 two panel on board. 29-Oct-3 Lawson Menzies, Sydney #188/R est:4000-6000 (A.D 6500)
£2697 $4504 €4046 The fence menders (60x90cm-24x35in) s.i. board. 27-Oct-3 Goodman, Sydney #14/R est:5000-7000 (A.D 6500)
£2766 $4482 €4038 Stage coach and stock yards (59x59cm-23x23in) s. board prov. 30-Jul-3 Goodman, Sydney #149/R est:4000-6000 (A.D 6750)
£2811 $4695 €4076 Waterbirds along the riverbank (46x61cm-18x24in) s. board. 30-Jun-3 Australian Art Auctions, Sydney #122/R (A.D 7000)
£2893 $4917 €4224 Saltbush bills gamecock (45x60cm-18x24in) s.d.1995 i.verso board. 29-Oct-3 Lawson Menzies, Sydney #190/R est:4000-6000 (A.D 7000)
£2905 $4851 €4358 Yabbie Creek (61x87cm-24x34in) s.d.76 board. 27-Oct-3 Goodman, Sydney #153/R est:7000-9000 (A.D 7000)
£2931 $4572 €4250 Discussion under the dig tree (59x69cm-23x27in) s. board. 1-Aug-2 Joel, Victoria #271 est:2500-3500 (A.D 8500)
£2966 $5042 €4330 Mining Town (118x126cm-46x50in) s.d.88 composition board. 24-Nov-3 Sotheby's, Melbourne #241/R est:6000-8000 (A.D 7000)
£3099 $5269 €4525 Still life (90x60cm-35x24in) s. board. 29-Oct-3 Lawson Menzies, Sydney #115/R est:8000-10000 (A.D 7500)
£3306 $5620 €4827 Picnic (59x58cm-23x23in) s. board. 29-Oct-3 Lawson Menzies, Sydney #16/R est:4500-6500 (A.D 8000)
£3306 $6116 €4827 Camp (40x51cm-16x20in) s. board prov. 10-Mar-4 Deutscher-Menzies, Melbourne #306/R est:5000-7000 (A.D 8000)
£3513 $5971 €5129 Christening of maginnis (42x57cm-17x22in) s. i.verso board. 29-Oct-3 Lawson Menzies, Sydney #189/R est:4000-6000 (A.D 8500)
£3734 $6237 €5601 Catching the Christmas roast (60x60cm-24x24in) s.i. 27-Oct-3 Goodman, Sydney #1/R est:6500-8500 (A.D 9000)
£3745 $6891 €5468 Bush roses (40x60cm-16x24in) s. board. 28-Jun-4 Australian Art Auctions, Sydney #132/R (A.D 10000)
£3926 $6674 €5732 Miners with still life (44x44cm-17x17in) s. board. 29-Oct-3 Lawson Menzies, Sydney #111/R est:5000-7000 (A.D 9500)
£3926 $6674 €5732 Chop picnic (60x60cm-24x24in) s.i. board. 29-Oct-3 Lawson Menzies, Sydney #127/R est:4500-6500 (A.D 9500)
£4098 $6475 €5983 Crossing the creek from the Gold Rush (66x71cm-26x28in) s.d.1972 board prov. 2-Sep-3 Deutscher-Menzies, Melbourne #270/R est:9000-12000 (A.D 10000)
£4098 $6475 €5983 Down the home straight (40x50cm-16x20in) s. canvas on board. 2-Sep-3 Deutscher-Menzies, Melbourne #271/R est:5500-7500 (A.D 10000)
£4132 $7645 €6033 Celebrating Charlie Burt's birthday (57x77cm-22x30in) s.d.72 i.verso. 10-Mar-4 Deutscher-Menzies, Melbourne #307/R est:4500-6000 (A.D 10000)
£4149 $6929 €6224 Christmas handicap (60x60cm-24x24in) s. 27-Oct-3 Goodman, Sydney #190/R est:5000-7000 (A.D 10000)
£4149 $6929 €6224 Loading wool (60x75cm-24x30in) s.i.d.89 board. 27-Oct-3 Goodman, Sydney #256/R est:7000-10000 (A.D 10000)
£4237 $7203 €6186 Miner's Camp (120x135cm-47x53in) composition board. 24-Nov-3 Sotheby's, Melbourne #144/R est:10000-15000 (A.D 10000)
£4339 $7376 €6335 Sunday (60x74cm-24x29in) s.i. board. 29-Oct-3 Lawson Menzies, Sydney #17/R est:7000-10000 (A.D 10500)
£4472 $8004 €6529 Last week (90x90cm-35x35in) s.i.d.1977-79 board prov. 10-May-4 Joel, Victoria #200/R est:4000-5000 (A.D 11000)
£4681 $7957 €6834 Early Study, Broken Hill (91x122cm-36x48in) s.i.d.86. 26-Nov-3 Deutscher-Menzies, Melbourne #182/R est:10000-15000 (A.D 11000)
£4772 $7969 €7158 Mad hatters tea party (61x76cm-24x30in) s.i. board. 27-Oct-3 Goodman, Sydney #17/R est:10000-15000 (A.D 11500)
£5106 $8681 €7455 Eureka Stockade (56x108cm-22x43in) s. composition board. 26-Nov-3 Deutscher-Menzies, Melbourne #187/R est:12000-18000 (A.D 12000)
£5668 $9126 €8275 Simpson and his donkey (91x121cm-36x48in) s.i.d.1990. 13-Oct-3 Joel, Victoria #263/R est:4000-5000 (A.D 14000)
£5691 $8935 €8252 Shearers dream (120x183cm-47x72in) s.d.75 i.verso prov. 27-Aug-3 Christie's, Sydney #585/R est:12000-18000 (A.D 14000)
£5809 $9701 €8714 Preparing for the shearing season (91x122cm-36x48in) s.i.d.87 board. 27-Oct-3 Goodman, Sydney #197/R est:14000-20000 (A.D 14000)
£7660 $13021 €11184 St Kilda Beach (91x122cm-36x48in) s.i.d.3.10.88. 26-Nov-3 Deutscher-Menzies, Melbourne #181/R est:10000-15000 (A.D 18000)
£7724 $12126 €11200 Life in the outback (91x121cm-36x48in) s.d.66 board nine panels prov. 26-Aug-3 Christie's, Sydney #134/R est:12000-16000 (A.D 19000)
£10204 $18776 €14898 Four horse race (120x120cm-47x47in) s.d.79 i.verso. 29-Mar-4 Goodman, Sydney #215/R est:25000-35000 (A.D 25000)
Works on paper
£289 $512 €422 Country races (15x17cm-6x7in) s.d.86-87 W/C pencil crayon prov. 3-May-4 Christie's, Melbourne #390 (A.D 700)
£2481 $4515 €3622 Flowers (73x110cm-29x43in) s. synthetic polymer. 16-Jun-4 Deutscher-Menzies, Melbourne #299/R est:7000-10000 (A.D 6500)

HART, Maarten T (1950-) Dutch
£909 $1564 €1300 Binnenplaats met doorzicht (35x28cm-14x11in) s.d.1997 board. 2-Dec-3 Sotheby's, Amsterdam #266/R est:2000-3000
£3623 $5942 €5000 Interior of great church in Naarden (90x76cm-35x30in) s.d.1996 board prov. 27-May-3 Sotheby's, Amsterdam #351/R est:4000-6000

HART, Michael Bennallack (20th C) Irish?
Works on paper
£2000 $3580 €2920 The Blackwater, Lismore (73x79cm-29x31in) init. col pastels. 13-May-4 Sotheby's, London #113/R est:2000-3000

HART, Salomon Alexander (1806-1881) British
£1500 $2685 €2190 Hop pickers at Burswood, Kent (63x76cm-25x30in) s. exhib. 27-May-4 Christie's, Kensington #285/R est:2000-3000
Works on paper
£320 $576 €467 Figures (44x33cm-17x13in) s.d.1833 W/C. 21-Apr-4 John Bellman, Billingshurst #1733
£420 $773 €613 Inspection the waves (43x33cm-17x13in) s.d.1833 W/C. 8-Jun-4 Bonhams, Knightsbridge #20/R
£450 $765 €657 King John's funeral (25x32cm-10x13in) s. W/C. 25-Nov-3 Bonhams, Knightsbridge #71/R

HART, Thomas (?-1886) British
Works on paper
£300 $546 €438 Beach scene with fisherman during a storm (53x79cm-21x31in) W/C. 16-Jun-4 Andrew Hartley, Ilkley #975
£1900 $3154 €2774 Evening, St Michael's Mount (52x80cm-20x31in) s. W/C. 2-Oct-3 Lane, Penzance #65/R est:2000-2500

HART, Thomas (1830-1916) British
Works on paper
£800 $1384 €1168 Ship wreck on the Lizard coastline, Cornwall (31x23cm-12x9in) s. W/C. 11-Dec-3 Lane, Penzance #34
£1000 $1870 €1460 Panoramic view of the Lizard coastline, Cornwall (37x63cm-15x25in) s.d.1874 W/C. 26-Feb-4 Lane, Penzance #155/R est:1000-1500

HART, Thomas Gray (1797-1881) British
Works on paper
£400 $632 €580 Ships at anchor (18x23cm-7x9in) W/C. 24-Jul-3 Dominic Winter, Swindon #34/R

HART, William MacDougal (1823-1894) American
£938 $1500 €1369 Landscape with figures (56x76cm-22x30in) indis.sig.d. 20-Sep-3 Bunte, Elgin #1413 est:3000-5000
£1509 $2700 €2203 Path home (11x16cm-4x6in) s. canvasboard. 14-May-4 Skinner, Boston #74/R est:2000-3000
£1857 $3250 €2711 Cows resting by a stream (26x21cm-10x8in) s.d.1884. 19-Dec-3 Sotheby's, New York #1110/R est:3000-5000
£1879 $3250 €2743 Lake Windermere (30x46cm-12x18in) s.d.1852 panel. 13-Dec-3 Sloans & Kenyon, Bethesda #815/R est:3000-5000
£2000 $3500 €2920 Cows heading for a stream (26x36cm-10x14in) s.d.1888. 19-Dec-3 Sotheby's, New York #1107/R est:4000-6000
£2747 $5000 €4011 Two children reading (22x18cm-9x7in) s.d.1857 panel prov. 29-Jun-4 Sotheby's, New York #191/R est:5000-7000

£5028 $9000 €7341 Cattle watering (86x122cm-34x48in) s.d.1882. 26-May-4 Doyle, New York #20/R est:10000-15000
£6044 $11000 €8824 Nahant sunset (14x18cm-6x7in) init.d.57 panel prov. 29-Jun-4 Sotheby's, New York #192/R est:7000-9000
£7568 $14000 €11049 River landscape with cattle watering (56x102cm-22x40in) 13-Feb-4 Du Mouchelle, Detroit #2131/R est:8000-12000
£7784 $13000 €11365 Autumn on the lake (32x47cm-13x19in) s.d.1873 board. 9-Oct-3 Christie's, Rockefeller NY #4/R est:4000-6000
£9091 $16000 €13273 The Land, Keene Valley (34x59cm-13x23in) s. painted 1878 prov. 18-May-4 Christie's, Rockefeller NY #16/R est:15000-25000
£10795 $19000 €15761 Autumn in New Hampshire (46x36cm-18x14in) s. prov. 19-May-4 Sotheby's, New York #95/R est:15000-25000
£13125 $21000 €19163 Sunset over mountain lake (18x28cm-7x11in) s. 16-Sep-3 Lincoln, Orange #471
£20112 $36000 €29364 Nutting (20x16cm-8x6in) s.d.1857. 6-May-4 Shannon's, Milford #95/R est:40000-60000
£39773 $70000 €58069 Valley of the White Mountains, New Hampshire (81x122cm-32x48in) s.d.57 prov. 19-May-4 Sotheby's, New York #70/R est:25000-35000

HART, William MacDougal (attrib) (1823-1894) American
£265 $450 €387 Dark forest scene with two figures (33x25cm-13x10in) board. 21-Nov-3 Eldred, East Dennis #873/R
£629 $1000 €918 Landscape with cows resting in a shady field (13x26cm-5x10in) indis.d.Jan 18 1881 panel. 13-Sep-3 Weschler, Washington #729/R
£1882 $3500 €2748 Mountain landscape (56x76cm-22x30in) s. painted c.1870. 7-Mar-4 William Jenack, New York #157 est:3000-5000

HARTA, Felix Albrecht (1884-1970) Hungarian/Austrian
£2162 $3870 €3200 Summer flowers in vase (92x73cm-36x29in) s. lit. 8-May-4 Dawo, Saarbrucken #49/R est:2800

HARTENKAMPF, Gottlieb Theodor Kempf von (1871-1964) Austrian
Works on paper
£1074 $1976 €1600 Girl sewing seed in field (27x50cm-11x20in) s.d.97 W/C paper on board. 26-Mar-4 Dorotheum, Vienna #345 est:1000-1200

HARTH, Philipp (1885-1968) German
Sculpture
£1389 $2264 €2000 Pelican (17cm-7in) mono. brown pat.bronze. 27-Sep-3 Dr Fritz Nagel, Stuttgart #9563/R est:1900

HARTIG, Carl Christoph (1888-?) Swiss
£338 $605 €500 Spring day on the Bodensee (65x92cm-26x36in) s. 6-May-4 Michael Zeller, Lindau #690/R

HARTIG, Hans (1873-1936) German
£307 $561 €460 Summer river with bend and cows along the path (50x82cm-20x32in) s. 5-Jun-4 Arnold, Frankfurt #595/R
£1042 $1646 €1500 Sailing regatta on autumn morning (35x51cm-14x20in) s. i. verso board. 6-Sep-3 Schopman, Hamburg #844/R est:1700

HARTIGAN, Grace (1922-) American
£2473 $4500 €3611 August (72x57cm-28x22in) s.i.d.60 oilstick. 29-Jun-4 Sotheby's, New York #426/R est:3000-4000
£3571 $6500 €5214 July (72x57cm-28x22in) s.i.d.60 oilstick. 29-Jun-4 Sotheby's, New York #425/R est:3000-4000
Works on paper
£1744 $3000 €2546 Artisans (56x76cm-22x30in) s.d.75 painted paper collage prov. 3-Dec-3 Doyle, New York #83/R est:1500-2500

HARTING, Lloyd (1901-1976) American
Works on paper
£588 $1000 €858 Biting sands (28x36cm-11x14in) s. graphite W/C gouache prov. 1-Nov-3 Santa Fe Art, Santa Fe #228/R
£1099 $2000 €1605 Steam engine and crew at water tower (36x53cm-14x21in) s.i. W/C board prov. 15-Jun-4 John Moran, Pasadena #133 est:2000-3000

HARTINGER, Anton (1806-1890) Austrian
£46000 $83720 €67160 Roses, tulips and other flowers in a blue and white vase (95x79cm-37x31in) s.d.856. 15-Jun-4 Sotheby's, London #25/R est:25000-35000
Works on paper
£276 $458 €400 Yellow carto (45x28cm-18x11in) s. W/C. 30-Sep-3 Dorotheum, Vienna #238/R

HARTKANDT, Albert (19th C) ?
Works on paper
£867 $1569 €1300 Paysage (47x75cm-19x30in) s.d.1880 W/C. 30-Mar-4 Campo, Vlaamse Kaai #80

HARTLAND (1840-1893) Irish
£3448 $6379 €5000 Sailing boats believed to be in Cork Harbour (74x105cm-29x41in) s.d.1865. 11-Feb-4 Woodwards, Cork #11/R est:5000-7000

HARTLAND, Henry Albert (1840-1893) Irish
£1150 $2105 €1679 Peasant couple on a road through a village with thatched houses (48x76cm-19x30in) s.d.1876. 7-Apr-4 Gardiner & Houlgate, Bath #47/R est:200-300
Works on paper
£600 $1032 €876 Peat fields, County Cork landscape (33x48cm-13x19in) s.i. W/C. 4-Dec-3 Biddle & Webb, Birmingham #636
£647 $1170 €970 Turf stacks in an Irish landscape (34x51cm-13x20in) s.d.76 W/C. 30-Mar-4 De Veres Art Auctions, Dublin #122/R
£800 $1440 €1168 Ravine near Arthog, North Wales (34x49cm-13x19in) s.i. pencil W/C gouache htd white exhib. 21-Apr-4 Tennants, Leyburn #1053
£1250 $2275 €1825 Hot day in August (59x100cm-23x39in) s.i. W/C. 29-Jun-4 Bonhams, Knowle #38 est:300-500
£1319 $2151 €1900 Figure by a river (46x68cm-18x27in) s. W/C. 24-Sep-3 James Adam, Dublin #5/R est:2000-3000
£2535 $4056 €3600 Irish homestead (48x76cm-19x30in) s. W/C prov. 16-Sep-3 Whyte's, Dublin #112/R est:3500-4500

HARTLEY, Alfred (1855-1933) British
£850 $1530 €1241 Lock at Halford (24x29cm-9x11in) s. board. 22-Apr-4 Mellors & Kirk, Nottingham #1109/R

HARTLEY, Ben (c.1930-) British
Works on paper
£300 $546 €438 Green door (61x48cm-24x19in) bodycol. 15-Jun-4 David Lay, Penzance #656
£600 $1092 €876 Quack time (61x64cm-24x25in) bodycol. 15-Jun-4 David Lay, Penzance #655

HARTLEY, Jonathan Scott (1845-1912) American
Sculpture
£5988 $10000 €8742 Joy of life (40cm-16in) i.d.1910 green brown pat bronze prov. 7-Oct-3 Sotheby's, New York #170 est:4000-6000

HARTLEY, M (20th C) American
Works on paper
£815 $1500 €1190 Abstract forest scene (33x48cm-13x19in) s.d.43 W/C. 26-Jun-4 Susanin's, Chicago #6094/R est:600-800

HARTLEY, M (19th C) American
£17500 $28000 €25550 Portrait of the Fairmount pumper (43x61cm-17x24in) init.i. prov. 20-Sep-3 Pook & Pook, Downington #430/R est:20000-25000

HARTLEY, Marsden (1877-1943) American
£22093 $38000 €32256 Maine woods (10x16cm-4x6in) s. board prov. 4-Dec-3 Christie's, Rockefeller NY #81/R est:30000-50000
£29874 $47500 €43616 Rocky coast (25x36cm-10x14in) init. board. 12-Sep-3 Skinner, Boston #508/R est:50000
£45455 $80000 €66364 Still life with fruit (33x79cm-13x31in) canvas on board painted c.1923 prov.exhib. 18-May-4 Christie's, Rockefeller NY #117/R est:10000-150000
£73864 $130000 €107841 Dune Road - Sundown October (30x41cm-12x16in) i.d.1935 verso board prov. 18-May-4 Christie's, Rockefeller NY #133/R est:70000-100000
£85227 $150000 €124431 Mountainous landscape (33x79cm-13x31in) painted c.1922-1923 prov.exhib.lit. 19-May-4 Sotheby's, New York #145/R est:150000-250000
£85227 $150000 €124431 Still life with fruit and pitcher (51x41cm-20x16in) init. painted c.1911-12 prov. 19-May-4 Sotheby's, New York #151/R est:150000-250000
£104651 $180000 €152790 Gymnast (33x82cm-13x32in) painted c.1922-23 prov. 4-Dec-3 Christie's, Rockefeller NY #111/R est:30000-50000
£107955 $190000 €157614 Anemones (61x48cm-24x19in) s. i.stretcher prov.exhib. 19-May-4 Sotheby's, New York #152/R est:125000-175000
£130682 $230000 €190796 Bevi Poco (48x61cm-19x24in) s. i.stretcher prov.exhib. 19-May-4 Sotheby's, New York #144/R est:200000-300000
£162791 $280000 €237675 Embittered afternoon of November, Dogtown (46x62cm-18x24in) s.d.1931 i.verso board prov.exhib. 4-Dec-3 Christie's, Rockefeller NY #109/R est:200000-300000
£1220930 $2100000 €1782558 Storm down Pine Point Way, Old Orchard Beach (56x71cm-22x28in) masonite painted c.1941-43 prov.exhib.lit. 3-Dec-3 Sotheby's, New York #56/R est:700000-900000
Works on paper
£4000 $7000 €5840 Whales Jaw Rock, Dogtown (46x61cm-18x24in) pencil board prov. 19-Dec-3 Sotheby's, New York #1037/R est:3000-5000
£5429 $9500 €7926 Dogtown landscape (46x61cm-18x24in) pencil board prov. 19-Dec-3 Sotheby's, New York #1036/R est:4000-6000

HARTLEY, Rachel (1884-?) American
£1749 $3200 €2554 At home near Charleston (46x56cm-18x22in) i. board painted c.1940. 10-Apr-4 Cobbs, Peterborough #144/R

HARTMAN, Anne Franciscus (1904-1975) Dutch
£377 $640 €550 Still life with children's drawing and flowers (68x58cm-27x23in) s. 5-Nov-3 Vendue Huis, Gravenhage #402/R

HARTMAN, Emiel (?) Belgian?
£319 $533 €450 La chasse Africaine (90x120cm-35x47in) s. 17-Jun-3 Galerie Moderne, Brussels #348

HARTMAN, John (1950-) ?
£2902 $4991 €4237 Red Pool (60x162cm-24x64in) panel triptych painted 1996 prov.lit. 2-Dec-3 Joyner Waddington, Toronto #293/R est:3000-5000 (C.D 6500)
Works on paper
£1400 $2562 €2044 Pieta - Collins (65x134cm-26x53in) s.d.90 pastel triptych prov. 1-Jun-4 Joyner Waddington, Toronto #183/R est:3000-4000 (C.D 3500)

HARTMAN, Mauno (1930-) Finnish
Works on paper
£267 $477 €400 Varvinranta III (95x127cm-37x50in) s.d.1983-93 collage. 15-May-4 Hagelstam, Helsinki #223/R
£2027 $3628 €3000 The sun and the moon (200x154cm-79x61in) s.d.MCMLXXII mixed media. 8-May-4 Bukowskis, Helsinki #313/R est:4000-6000

HARTMAN, Wibbo (1903-) Dutch
£308 $524 €450 South European town (49x59cm-19x23in) s. 5-Nov-3 Vendue Huis, Gravenhage #403/R

HARTMANN, Bertram (1882-1960) American
£408 $750 €596 Spanish coast (15x20cm-6x8in) s.i. canvasboard. 10-Jun-4 Swann Galleries, New York #118/R
Works on paper
£272 $500 €397 R C A Building, New York City (36x28cm-14x11in) s.i.d.1949 W/C crayon. 10-Jun-4 Swann Galleries, New York #117/R
£346 $550 €505 Swans in Mecox Bay (56x76cm-22x30in) s. W/C. 9-Mar-3 William Jenack, New York #352

HARTMANN, Carl (1818-1857) German
Works on paper
£282 $487 €400 Juliana Princess of Thurn and Taxi with her daughter Sophie (30x26cm-12x10in) s.i.d.1840 pencil W/C. 10-Dec-3 Christie's, Amsterdam #202

HARTMANN, Erich (1886-?) German
£349 $618 €520 After the bath (79x52cm-31x20in) tempera mixed media. 28-Apr-4 Schopman, Hamburg #621/R
£872 $1632 €1300 Riverside farmstead (51x71cm-20x28in) s. s.d.IX 1927 verso board. 28-Feb-4 Bolland & Marotz, Bremen #308/R
Works on paper
£433 $784 €650 Boats in harbour (44x58cm-17x23in) s. W/C. 3-Apr-4 Hans Stahl, Hamburg #158/R
£605 $932 €950 Beach (46x63cm-18x25in) s.d.37. 4-Sep-2 Schopman, Hamburg #134/R

HARTMANN, Frans (20th C) Dutch
£724 $1210 €1057 Boy fishing in a village harbour (55x65cm-22x26in) s.d.46. 17-Nov-3 Waddingtons, Toronto #155/R (C.D 1600)

HARTMANN, Friedrich Hermann (1822-1902) German
£470 $864 €700 Huts in mountains (19x34cm-7x13in) s.d.18. 26-Mar-4 Bolland & Marotz, Bremen #529/R

HARTMANN, Hugo Friedrich (1870-1960) German
£561 $863 €880 Still life with apples, plate and knife (35x43cm-14x17in) s. board. 4-Sep-2 Schopman, Hamburg #137/R
£637 $981 €1000 Figure with horse in trees in front of farmstead (35x44cm-14x17in) s. board. 4-Sep-2 Schopman, Hamburg #136/R

HARTMANN, Johann Jacob (1680-1730) Czechoslovakian
£5634 $9746 €8000 Wooded landscape (33x36cm-13x14in) panel. 13-Dec-3 Lempertz, Koln #25/R est:4000
£20833 $32917 €30000 Hunters in woodland (32x38cm-13x15in) s. copper lit. 19-Sep-3 Schloss Ahlden, Ahlden #1424/R est:18500

HARTMANN, Johann Jacob (attrib) (1680-1730) Czechoslovakian
£3448 $5759 €5000 Figures enjoying the ice (69x86cm-27x34in) panel. 12-Jul-3 Bergmann, Erlangen #600/R est:6500
£3448 $5759 €5000 Enjoying the ice with horse drawn sledge (69x86cm-27x34in) panel. 12-Jul-3 Bergmann, Erlangen #601/R est:6500

HARTMANN, Joseph (1812-1885) German
£530 $964 €800 Portrait of Albertine Schopwinkel as a young girl (77x63cm-30x25in) s.i.d.1863 verso oval. 18-Jun-4 Bolland & Marotz, Bremen #632/R

HARTMANN, Karl (attrib) (1861-1927) German
£181 $308 €264 Rider in valley (12x32cm-5x13in) i. verso panel. 18-Nov-3 Hans Widmer, St Gallen #1076 (S.FR 400)

HARTMANN, Ludwig (1835-1902) German
£9000 $16380 €13140 A rest from work (30x56cm-12x22in) s. panel. 15-Jun-4 Sotheby's, London #37/R est:8000-12000
£12500 $20375 €18000 Midday rest (30x57cm-12x22in) s. panel. 24-Sep-3 Neumeister, Munich #440/R est:20000

HARTMANN, Oluf (1879-1910) Danish
£812 $1495 €1186 The witches from Macbeth dancing (26x27cm-10x11in) canvas on masonite prov. 29-Mar-4 Rasmussen, Copenhagen #486/R (D.KR 9000)

HARTMANN, Sadakichi (1869-1944) American
Works on paper
£279 $500 €407 Midnight stroll (25x36cm-10x14in) mono. i.verso gouache. 8-Jan-4 James Julia, Fairfield #1038/R

HARTMANN, Thomas (1950-) German
£662 $1205 €1000 Composition with green and brown (70x100cm-28x39in) s.i.d.96 verso. 18-Jun-4 Bolland & Marotz, Bremen #886/R

HARTMANN, W (?) ?
£348 $637 €508 In the artist's Paris studio (33x40cm-13x16in) s. i.verso cardboard. 4-Jun-4 Zofingen, Switzerland #2827 (S.FR 800)

HARTMANN, Werner (1903-1981) Swiss
£300 $516 €438 Still life of flowers (20x25cm-8x10in) s. 3-Dec-3 Andrew Hartley, Ilkley #1181

HARTOGENSIS, Joseph (1822-1865) Flemish
£2098 $3566 €3000 Dutch harvest (31x60cm-12x24in) s. 24-Nov-3 Dorotheum, Vienna #175/R est:3000-3500

HARTRICK, Archibald Standish (1864-1950) British
Works on paper
£1300 $2158 €1898 Prosper Le Gai rides forth (39x25cm-15x10in) s. W/C. 1-Oct-3 Sotheby's, Olympia #169/R est:800-1200

HARTSON, Walter C (1866-?) British
£1087 $1750 €1587 Prospect Mountain, Connecticut (71x91cm-28x36in) s. 20-Aug-3 James Julia, Fairfield #1450/R est:2000-4000

HARTUNG, H (?) ?
£1818 $3127 €2600 Children playing near farm in spring (70x100cm-28x39in) s. 4-Dec-3 Vendue Huis, Gravenhage #1024
£1818 $3127 €2600 Children playing near farm in spring (70x100cm-28x39in) s. 3-Dec-3 Auction Maastricht #1024/R est:1500-2000

HARTUNG, Hans (1904-1989) French/German
£1565 $2864 €2285 Town on the banks of the Rhine with ruins (42x55cm-17x22in) s.d.1917 cardboard. 4-Jun-4 Zofingen, Switzerland #2468/R est:4500 (S.FR 3600)
£1565 $2864 €2285 The Rhine near Koblenz with figures (42x56cm-17x22in) s.i.d.1917 verso cardboard. 4-Jun-4 Zofingen, Switzerland #2469 est:4500 (S.FR 3600)
£1667 $3067 €2500 Abstract (27x19cm-11x7in) exec. 1986 prov. 12-Jun-4 Villa Grisebach, Berlin #401/R est:4000-5000
£3497 $5944 €5000 HH2273 (22x17cm-9x7in) s.d.67 oil tempera card exhib. 24-Nov-3 Christie's, Milan #138/R est:3500-5000
£3667 $6563 €5500 T 1986 - E 10 (27x19cm-11x7in) d.23/2/86 stretcher acrylic oil prov. 15-May-4 Van Ham, Cologne #635/R est:7000
£5594 $9510 €8000 Composition 1977 - H 44 (46x60cm-18x24in) s.d.77 i. stretcher panel. 27-Nov-3 Lempertz, Koln #171/R est:10000-12000
£6338 $10965 €9000 T1986-R27 (65x81cm-26x32in) s.i.d.1986v. acrylic. 9-Dec-3 Artcurial Briest, Paris #421/R est:10000-15000
£6711 $12013 €10000 T 1975-R 36 (38x61cm-15x24in) s.mono.i.d.75 verso acrylic masonite prov. 25-May-4 Dorotheum, Vienna #84/R est:12000-15000
£7343 $12262 €10500 Composition P.1973 A5 (73x103cm-29x41in) s.d.73 acrylic cardboard prov. 29-Jun-3 Versailles Encheres #72/R
£7447 $12436 €10500 Sans titre, fond turquoise (81x100cm-32x39in) s.d.75 peinture. 19-Oct-3 Anaf, Lyon #170/R est:10000-12000
£7500 $12525 €10950 T1965 - E50 (46x65cm-18x26in) s.d.65 s.i.d.26.4.66 stretcher acrylic prov. 21-Oct-3 Sotheby's, London #394/R est:7000-10000
£7692 $13231 €11000 P 1967-118 (64x49cm-25x19in) s.d. paint vinyl ink cardboard exhib. 4-Dec-3 Piasa, Paris #90/R est:4000-6000
£9028 $15076 €13000 T1982 R 33 (81x60cm-32x24in) mono.d.82 i.verso acrylic prov. 21-Oct-3 Artcurial Briest, Paris #536/R est:12000-15000
£9091 $15636 €13000 T 1973 R 41 (38x61cm-15x24in) s.d.73 i.verso. 2-Dec-3 Calmels Cohen, Paris #72/R est:10000-12000
£9396 $17289 €14000 T1980-H25 (65x92cm-26x36in) s.d.1980 acrylic prov. 24-Mar-4 Joron-Derem, Paris #137/R est:18000-20000
£9500 $17290 €13870 T 1986-H24 (147x114cm-58x45in) s.d.86 s.i.stretcher acrylic prov. 6-Feb-4 Sotheby's, London #184/R est:8000-12000
£9650 $16406 €13800 T 1987 H6 (89x146cm-35x57in) mono.d.87 acrylic prov. 18-Nov-3 Pierre Berge, Paris #42/R est:10000-12000
£10000 $16700 €14600 T 1986-E15 (162x100cm-64x39in) init.d.86 acrylic prov. 21-Oct-3 Sotheby's, London #398/R est:8000-12000
£10417 $16458 €15000 Composition (50x65cm-20x26in) s.d.1960 i.verso acrylic grattage prov. 27-Apr-3 Versailles Encheres #45
£10738 $19221 €16000 T1982 R33 (81x60cm-32x24in) init.d.1982 acrylic lit. 30-May-4 Meeting Art, Vercelli #40 est:15000
£10738 $19221 €16000 T 1977-H42 (38x61cm-15x24in) i. verso acrylic masonite prov. 25-May-4 Dorotheum, Vienna #85/R est:16000-20000
£11000 $20020 €16060 T 1975-H47 (81x100cm-32x39in) s.d.75 s.i.d.stretcher acrylic prov.exhib. 6-Feb-4 Sotheby's, London #182/R est:15000-20000
£11189 $18685 €16000 Composition P.1793.A2 (72x101cm-28x40in) s.d.73 acrylic cardboard prov. 29-Jun-3 Versailles Encheres #71/R
£11189 $18685 €16000 T 1986 H7 (13x102cm-5x40in) s.d.1986 s.verso acrylic prov. 11-Oct-3 Cornette de St.Cyr, Paris #11/R est:10000-20000
£12000 $20040 €17520 T 1985-H13 (130x102cm-51x40in) init.d.85 i.d.stretcher d.1985 verso acrylic prov. 22-Oct-3 Christie's, London #31/R est:10000-12000
£13333 $24000 €20000 T-1983-H1 (102x130cm-40x51in) s.d.1983 acrylic. 24-Apr-4 Cornette de St.Cyr, Paris #565/R est:25000
£14474 $26632 €22000 T1971-E20 (50x73cm-20x29in) acrylic prov.lit. 27-Jun-4 Versailles Encheres #94/R est:20000-25000
£14667 $26987 €22000 T 1986-E 15 (163x100cm-64x39in) mono.d.86 s.i. verso acrylic prov.lit. 8-Jun-4 Artcurial Briest, Paris #271/R est:25000-30000
£14685 $24965 €21000 T 1985 H12 (130x102cm-51x40in) mono.d.1985 acrylic prov. 18-Nov-3 Pierre Berge, Paris #37/R est:12000-15000
£15972 $25236 €23000 Composition (50x65cm-20x26in) 6-Sep-3 Meeting Art, Vercelli #370 est:20000
£16000 $28800 €24000 Composition T-R41 (38x61cm-15x24in) s.d.1973 s.i.d.verso acrylic. 25-Apr-4 Versailles Encheres #97 est:28000-30000
£16438 $27945 €24000 Untitled (100x72cm-39x28in) s.d.82 acrylic. 4-Nov-3 Ansorena, Madrid #916/R est:24000
£16554 $29135 €24500 T 1985 H12 (130x102cm-51x40in) mono.d.1985 s.d. verso acrylic prov. 18-May-4 Tajan, Paris #64/R est:12000-15000
£17606 $30458 €25000 T 1963 - U 38 (61x46cm-24x18in) s.d.63 i. stretcher. 13-Dec-3 Lempertz, Koln #147/R est:15000
£19000 $34580 €27740 T 1964-E33 (65x81cm-26x32in) s.d.64 s.i.stretcher acrylic prov.lit. 6-Feb-4 Sotheby's, London #172/R est:18000-25000
£19000 $34580 €27740 T-1954-35 (24x41cm-9x16in) s.d.54 s.i.d.54 stretcher prov. 6-Feb-4 Sotheby's, London #174/R est:12000-15000
£19580 $32699 €28000 T 1980 K3 (180x180cm-71x71in) s.d.1980 acrylic prov. 11-Oct-3 Cornette de St.Cyr, Paris #15/R est:20000-25000
£20423 $35331 €29000 T 1980-E 48 (89x130cm-35x51in) s.d.1980 s.i.verso acrylic prov. 14-Dec-3 Versailles Encheres #108/R est:25000-30000
£20833 $33958 €30000 Untitled (100x73cm-39x29in) s.d.82 acrylic. 23-Sep-3 Durán, Madrid #61/R est:4000
£20979 $35035 €30000 T1966 R28 (92x65cm-36x26in) s.d.1966 acrylic prov. 11-Oct-3 Cornette de St.Cyr, Paris #5/R est:25000-30000

£21053	$38737	€32000	T1972-H1 (65x92cm-26x36in) acrylic prov.lit. 27-Jun-4 Versailles Encheres #108/R est:35000-40000
£22000	$36740	€32120	T 1963-H46 (100x81cm-39x32in) s.d.63 i.stretcher acrylic prov.exhib. 21-Oct-3 Sotheby's, London #393/R est:15000-20000
£22483	$41369	€33500	Composition (37x61cm-15x24in) s.d.1950 prov. 29-Mar-4 Cornette de St.Cyr, Paris #12/R est:35000-40000
£23000	$41860	€33580	T 1962 0 U49 (63x92cm-25x36in) s.d.62 i. stretcher prov. 5-Feb-4 Christie's, London #127/R est:15000-20000
£23000	$41630	€33580	T 1963-E35 (81x65cm-32x26in) s.i.d.1963 stretcher prov. 1-Apr-4 Christie's, Kensington #203/R est:15000-20000
£23077	$39231	€33000	PU28 (48x72cm-19x28in) oil pastel painted 1950 prov. 24-Nov-3 Christie's, Milan #236/R est:33000-36000
£23448	$37517	€34000	T 1882-H 49 (61x46cm-24x18in) s.d.1982 acrylic. 13-Mar-3 Galleria Pace, Milan #98/R est:40000-50000
£24476	$40874	€35000	T 1989 L 50 (154x250cm-61x98in) acrylic prov. 11-Oct-3 Cornette de St.Cyr, Paris #14/R est:30000-35000
£27465	$44493	€39000	Composition (119x78cm-47x31in) s.d.74 d.verso cardboard on canvas. 5-Aug-3 Tajan, Paris #60/R est:18000-25000
£28000	$51520	€40880	T 1965 - R21 (60x92cm-24x36in) s.d.65 s.i.d.stretcher acrylic prov. 25-Jun-4 Christie's, London #122/R est:18000-24000
£29333	$52800	€44000	Composition T-H18 (73x92cm-29x36in) s.d.1975 i.verso acrylic. 25-Apr-4 Versailles Encheres #106 est:50000-60000
£30000	$54600	€43800	T 1962-U4 (186x111cm-73x44in) s.i.stretcher acrylic prov.exhib.lit. 6-Feb-4 Sotheby's, London #162/R est:30000-40000
£34000	$56780	€49640	T 1963-R23 (102x130cm-40x51in) s.d.63 i.stretcher acrylic prov.exhib. 21-Oct-3 Sotheby's, London #391/R est:20000-30000
£37063	$61895	€53000	T 1973-R13 (154x250cm-61x98in) s.d.1973 acrylic prov. 11-Oct-3 Cornette de St.Cyr, Paris #6/R est:50000-60000
£40000	$66800	€58400	T 1962-R16 (180x141cm-71x56in) s.i.stretcher acrylic prov. 22-Oct-3 Christie's, London #32/R est:25000-35000
£45000	$75150	€65700	T 1955-40 (48x81cm-19x32in) s.d.55 i.stretcher prov. 22-Oct-3 Christie's, London #19/R est:50000-70000
£45947	$80866	€68000	Peinture T 61-65 (130x81cm-51x32in) s.d.1961 i. verso acrylic prov.lit. 18-May-4 Tajan, Paris #59/R est:70000-75000
£46000	$84640	€67160	T 1962-E28 (92x150cm-36x59in) s.d.62 i. verso acrylic. 24-Jun-4 Sotheby's, London #168/R est:40000-60000
£46667	$84933	€70000	T1962-R15 (92x250cm-36x98in) s.d.1962 acrylic prov. 29-Jun-4 Cornette de St.Cyr, Paris #44/R est:50000-60000
£73333	$134933	€110000	T 1952 - 3 (97x130cm-38x51in) s.d.52 prov.exhib. 8-Jun-4 Artcurial Briest, Paris #200/R est:25000-30000
£95070	$164472	€135000	T-1951-20 (50x73cm-20x29in) s.d.1951 prov.lit. 14-Dec-3 Versailles Encheres #119/R est:120000-140000
£134868	$248158	€205000	T56-13 (180x137cm-71x54in) s.d.1956 prov.exhib.lit. 27-Jun-4 Versailles Encheres #107/R est:200000-250000

Prints

£4977	$8312	€7266	Composition (77x56cm-30x22in) s.i.d.15-5-64 bears i. verso col chk pencil sold with another. 27-Jun-3 Falk & Falk, Zurich #450/R est:1800 (S.FR 11000)

Works on paper

£1268	$2218	€1800	Le mot de la fin (30x20cm-12x8in) s. wax pastel. 18-Dec-3 Cornette de St.Cyr, Paris #64/R est:2000-3000
£1901	$3289	€2700	Composition P5-1976-H24 (25x37cm-10x15in) s.d.1976 wax pastel. 10-Dec-3 Rossini, Paris #19/R
£2908	$4856	€4100	Composition (74x52cm-29x20in) s.d.1974 chl. 20-Jun-3 Drouot Estimations, Paris #117/R est:2000-2500
£3467	$6205	€5200	Untitled (25x25cm-10x10in) mono.i.d. mixed media paper on board. 13-May-4 Neumeister, Munich #634/R est:4000-5000
£3873	$6430	€5500	Composition (36x27cm-14x11in) s.d.1966 chk. 13-Jun-3 Hauswedell & Nolte, Hamburg #656/R est:6500
£4000	$6360	€5800	Sans titre (21x21cm-8x8in) s.d.71 pencil wax crayon paper on canvas. 11-Sep-3 Christie's, Kensington #213/R est:4000-6000
£4054	$7135	€6000	Untitled (37x52cm-15x20in) s.d.1972 W/C collage prov. 18-May-4 Tajan, Paris #61/R est:6000-8000
£4348	$7957	€6348	Abstract composition (47x63cm-19x25in) s.d.1954 pastel. 4-Jun-4 Zofingen, Switzerland #2467/R est:12000 (S.FR 10000)
£5333	$9600	€8000	Composition (23x31cm-9x12in) Chinese ink graphite gouache exec.1947 prov.exhib.lit. 25-Apr-4 Versailles Encheres #91 est:8000-10000
£5333	$9813	€8000	P.1960 - 253 (63x47cm-25x19in) s.d.60 col crayons lead pencil prov. 9-Jun-4 Artcurial Briest, Paris #454/R est:10000-15000
£6690	$11574	€9500	Composition (22x29cm-9x11in) mono.d.1947 Indian ink prov.exhib.lit. 14-Dec-3 Versailles Encheres #99/R est:8000-10000
£7000	$12740	€10220	P 1960 - 255 (65x50cm-26x20in) s.d.60 i.verso pastel prov. 5-Feb-4 Christie's, London #123/R est:8000-12000
£7183	$12427	€10200	Composition (21x22cm-8x9in) mono.d.1947 Indian ink prov.exhib.lit. 14-Dec-3 Versailles Encheres #101/R est:12000-15000
£7692	$13231	€11000	P 1958 15 (50x65cm-20x26in) s.d.58 pastel. 2-Dec-3 Calmels Cohen, Paris #71/R est:6000-8000
£8000	$14720	€12000	Untitled composition (63x48cm-25x19in) s.d.61 i.verso grease pencil pastel card. 24-Jun-4 Sotheby's, Olympia #567/R est:4000-6000
£8042	$13671	€11500	P1970-13 (80x58cm-31x23in) s.d.70 gouache mixed media paper on board. 24-Nov-3 Christie's, Milan #135/R est:10000-15000
£10000	$18200	€14600	P 1961-77 (60x80cm-24x31in) s.d.61 i.verso pastel chl pencil paperboard. 6-Feb-4 Sotheby's, London #158/R est:8000-12000
£10345	$19138	€15000	Composition (73x100cm-29x39in) s.d.1969 pastel wax crayon acrylic. 13-Feb-4 Charbonneaux, Paris #54/R est:10000-15000
£11189	$18685	€16000	Composition (50x73cm-20x29in) s.d.1960 pastel chl cardboard. 11-Oct-3 Cornette de St.Cyr, Paris #57/R est:15000-18000
£11538	$19615	€16500	P 1954-HH 5125 (47x65cm-19x26in) s.d.54 i.verso mixed media ink htd gouache varnish. 1-Dec-3 Camard, Paris #97/R est:7000-8000
£11972	$20711	€17000	Composition (10x14cm-4x6in) Indian ink ink wash pastel prov.lit. 14-Dec-3 Versailles Encheres #82/R est:15000-18000
£12238	$20437	€17500	Composition (10x14cm-4x6in) pastel Chinese ink W/C prov.exhib.lit. 29-Jun-3 Versailles Encheres #59/R
£12587	$21021	€18000	Composition (23x32cm-9x13in) mono.d.1947 pastel chl prov.exhib.lit. 29-Jun-3 Versailles Encheres #60/R
£12751	$23462	€19000	P 1953 1953 (65x48cm-26x19in) s.d.1953 wax pastel. 29-Mar-4 Cornette de St.Cyr, Paris #11/R est:20000-30000
£13000	$23920	€18980	P 1961-9 (72x50cm-28x20in) s.d.61 pastel card prov. 24-Jun-4 Sotheby's, London #180/R est:8000-12000
£13287	$22189	€19000	Composition HH4029 (45x56cm-18x22in) s.d.1959 pastel. 29-Jun-3 Versailles Encheres #81/R
£14493	$23768	€20000	P1958-13 (49x63cm-19x25in) s.d.1958 pastel. 29-May-3 Galleria Pace, Milan #123/R est:33000
£16000	$29440	€23360	P 1967-A54 (73x100cm-29x39in) s.d.67 i. verso pastel ink card. 24-Jun-4 Sotheby's, London #177/R est:8000-12000
£19444	$30722	€28000	Untitled (24x19cm-9x7in) s. graphite pastel tempera prov.lit. 27-Apr-3 Versailles Encheres #32
£21333	$38400	€32000	Composition (64x47cm-25x19in) s.d.1954 pastel paper on canvas prov.lit. 25-Apr-4 Versailles Encheres #85 est:30000-35000
£22819	$40846	€34000	Composition (65x49cm-26x19in) s.d.49 pastel gouache prov. 26-May-4 Christie's, Paris #69/R est:8000-12000

HARTUNG, Heinrich (1851-1919) German

£1854	$3393	€2800	Shepherd with flock on Luneburg heath (84x63cm-33x25in) s.d.81. 8-Apr-4 Dorotheum, Vienna #89/R est:3200-3800
£2297	$4043	€3400	Eiffel landscape with chapel (60x80cm-24x31in) s.d.1915. 22-May-4 Lempertz, Koln #1525/R est:3000
£3172	$5298	€4600	Eifel landscape in summer with peasants harvesting (92x83cm-36x33in) s.d.94. 15-Nov-3 Lempertz, Koln #1615/R est:4000
£6294	$10699	€9000	Awakening spring (27x35cm-11x14in) s.d.19 panel. 20-Nov-3 Van Ham, Cologne #1617/R est:10000

HARTUNG, Heinrich (1888-1966) German

£451	$745	€650	Boy's portrait (46x35cm-18x14in) s.d.1917. 3-Jul-3 Van Ham, Cologne #1230
£833	$1375	€1200	Eifel landscape (50x70cm-20x28in) s.d.1952. 3-Jul-3 Van Ham, Cologne #1229
£867	$1577	€1300	Landscape (86x86cm-34x34in) s.d.1948 s.i.d.verso panel. 1-Jul-4 Van Ham, Cologne #1391
£972	$1604	€1400	Portrait of young girl with red bow in hair (57x43cm-22x17in) s.d.1919. 3-Jul-3 Van Ham, Cologne #1231

HARTUNG, Johann (19th C) German

£3591	$6500	€5243	So I do to you, as you do to me (26x21cm-10x8in) s. panel pair. 30-Mar-4 Bonhams & Butterfields, San Francisco #97/R est:2800-3800

HARTUNG, Karl (1908-1967) German

Sculpture

£7746	$13401	€11000	Slice (19x37cm-7x15in) s. brown gold pat.bronze exhib.lit. 13-Dec-3 Lempertz, Koln #317/R est:8000-10000
£11189	$19021	€16000	Monument (57cm-22in) st.sig. brown pat.bronze Cast.Barth Berlin prov. 29-Nov-3 Villa Grisebach, Berlin #273/R est:18000-24000
£11333	$20853	€17000	Composition I (30x47cm-12x19in) s. bronze. 11-Jun-4 Hauswedell & Nolte, Hamburg #1296/R est:16000
£20979	$35664	€30000	Monumental woman's head (53cm-21in) anthracite green pat.bronze prov.exhib. 29-Nov-3 Villa Grisebach, Berlin #276/R est:30000-35000

Works on paper

£533	$955	€800	Still life with figure (24x34cm-9x13in) s.d. W/C. 15-May-4 Bassenge, Berlin #6852/R

HARTWELL, Charles Leonard (1873-1951) British

Sculpture

£2600	$4784	€3796	As he rode down to Camelot (44cm-17in) s.d.1914 brown pat. wooded plinth prov. 11-Jun-4 Christie's, London #84/R est:3000-5000

HARTWELL, George (attrib) (1815-1901) American

£3086	$5000	€4506	Young man with ivory embroidered vest (46x33cm-18x13in) board. 1-Aug-3 North East Auctions, Portsmouth #842/R est:5000-8000
£13580	$22000	€19827	Young blonde boy with rosy cheeks (36x25cm-14x10in) board prov. 1-Aug-3 North East Auctions, Portsmouth #838/R est:20000-30000
£18519	$30000	€27038	Girl in blue dress with coral beaded necklace (43x33cm-17x13in) board prov. 1-Aug-3 North East Auctions, Portsmouth #836/R est:20000-30000

HARTWICH, Herman (1853-1926) American

£1258	$2000	€1837	Back from the fields (36x66cm-14x26in) s. 12-Sep-3 Skinner, Boston #394/R
£1497	$2679	€2200	Little shepherd with sheep (32x44cm-13x17in) s. 17-Mar-4 Neumeister, Munich #471/R est:2200

HARTWICK, George Gunther (?-1899) American

£6587	$11000	€9617	Skating in a winter landscape (76x117cm-30x46in) prov. 23-Oct-3 Shannon's, Milford #149/R est:8000-12000

HARTWIG, Heinie (1937-) American

£212	$400	€310	Big lake encampment, Indians with canoe and tepees in autumn landscape (15x30cm-6x12in) s. masonite. 23-Feb-4 O'Gallerie, Oregon #729/R
£215	$400	€314	Wolf howling at the moon (46x56cm-18x22in) s. masonite. 6-Mar-4 Harvey Clar, Oakland #1312
£216	$400	€315	Indian encampment high above the mist (15x30cm-6x12in) s. masonite. 19-Jan-4 O'Gallerie, Oregon #794/R
£219	$400	€320	Sunset moonrise, an Indian encampment (15x30cm-6x12in) s. 7-Jun-4 O'Gallerie, Oregon #873/R
£233	$400	€340	By the lake. s. board. 6-Dec-3 Harvey Clar, Oakland #1171
£238	$450	€347	Still life with flowers, glass vase (41x51cm-16x20in) s. masonite. 23-Feb-4 O'Gallerie, Oregon #157/R
£240	$400	€350	Moonlight reflection. s. board. 15-Nov-3 Harvey Clar, Oakland #1600d
£265	$500	€387	North Dome, Yosemite (30x41cm-12x16in) s. masonite. 23-Feb-4 O'Gallerie, Oregon #91/R
£268	$475	€391	Lakeside camp (15x30cm-6x12in) s. i.verso. 3-May-4 O'Gallerie, Oregon #680
£270	$500	€394	Loring Bay, Revillagigedo Island (15x30cm-6x12in) s. 19-Jan-4 O'Gallerie, Oregon #78/R
£270	$500	€394	Landscape with a American bison (30x41cm-12x16in) s. masonite. 19-Jan-4 O'Gallerie, Oregon #118/R
£270	$500	€394	Summer landscape, nature's mood (30x41cm-12x16in) s.i. 19-Jan-4 O'Gallerie, Oregon #813/R
£396	$650	€578	View of Half Dome (30x61cm-12x24in) s. masonite. 8-Feb-3 Auctions by the Bay, Alameda #353/R
£397	$750	€580	Sunlit wall, still life with colour flowers in a vase (46x61cm-18x24in) s. masonite. 23-Feb-4 O'Gallerie, Oregon #781/R
£401	$750	€585	Indian encampment (23x28cm-9x11in) s. board. 25-Feb-4 Dallas Auction Gallery, Dallas #331/R
£417	$750	€609	Native American lakeside encampment (15x30cm-6x12in) s. masonite. 24-Apr-4 Weschler, Washington #619/R

£435	$800	€635	Indian encampment at dawn (28x38cm-11x15in) s. board. 26-Jun-4 Sloans & Kenyon, Bethesda #1078/R
£447	$800	€653	Indian encampment. s.i. board. 13-May-4 Dallas Auction Gallery, Dallas #340b/R
£455	$850	€664	Silver skies (13x28cm-5x11in) s. board. 25-Feb-4 Dallas Auction Gallery, Dallas #332/R
£559	$1000	€816	Indian encampment by the river. s. masonite. 10-Jan-4 Harvey Clar, Oakland #1225
£598	$1100	€873	Cooking in an Indian encampment (28x38cm-11x15in) s. board. 26-Jun-4 Sloans & Kenyon, Bethesda #1079/R est:800-1200
£683	$1100	€997	Mountain landscape with Indian encampment (46x61cm-18x24in) s. 18-Aug-3 O'Gallerie, Oregon #126/R
£710	$1300	€1037	Autumn haze (61x91cm-24x36in) s. masonite. 5-Jun-4 Neal Auction Company, New Orleans #822/R est:2000-3000
£778	$1400	€1136	Native American Camp at twilight (46x61cm-18x24in) s. masonite. 24-Apr-4 Weschler, Washington #617/R
£813	$1300	€1187	The way it was (193x170cm-76x67in) s. panel. 18-May-3 Auctions by the Bay, Alameda #1128/R
£838	$1400	€1223	Landscape with Indian encampment at sundown (46x61cm-18x24in) s. masonite. 27-Oct-3 O'Gallerie, Oregon #770/R est:1200-1600
£881	$1400	€1286	View of Mount Moran, Jackson Hole (79x61cm-31x24in) s. panel. 23-Mar-3 Auctions by the Bay, Alameda #855/R
£926	$1500	€1352	Native American camp at the edge of a mountain lake (74x104cm-29x41in) s. panel. 9-Aug-3 Auctions by the Bay, Alameda #1473/R
£1180	$1900	€1723	Mountain landscape with Indian encampment at Jackson Hole, Wyoming (61x76cm-24x30in) s. 18-Aug-3 O'Gallerie, Oregon #770 est:2000-3000
£1236	$2250	€1805	Indian encampment near a lake (46x61cm-18x24in) s. i.verso masonite. 15-Jun-4 John Moran, Pasadena #126 est:2000-3000
£1359	$2500	€1984	Indian winter encampment with mountains and lake (61x76cm-24x30in) s. masonite. 29-Mar-4 O'Gallerie, Oregon #138/R est:2000-3000
£1471	$2500	€2148	Indian camp in a winter mountain landscape (51x76cm-20x30in) s. masonite. 20-Nov-3 Auctions by the Bay, Alameda #1064/R
£1604	$3000	€2342	Winter encampment (51x76cm-20x30in) s. board. 25-Feb-4 Dallas Auction Gallery, Dallas #374/R
£1618	$2750	€2362	Majestic falls (74x58cm-29x23in) s. panel prov. 1-Nov-3 Santa Fe Art, Santa Fe #94/R est:3000-5000
£1676	$3000	€2447	Western sunset. s.i. board. 13-May-4 Dallas Auction Gallery, Dallas #250b/R est:1500-2500
£1734	$3000	€2532	In the far West (76x114cm-30x45in) s. masonite. 10-Dec-3 Bonhams & Butterfields, San Francisco #6136/R est:4000-6000
£1757	$3250	€2565	High plateau (61x91cm-24x36in) s. masonite. 19-Jan-4 O'Gallerie, Oregon #138/R est:3000-4000
£2647	$4500	€3865	Indian encampment (53x89cm-21x35in) s. panel prov. 1-Nov-3 Santa Fe Art, Santa Fe #95/R est:4000-6000

HARTWIG, Max (1873-1939) German

£272	$495	€400	Orchids (50x40cm-20x16in) s. 4-Feb-4 Neumeister, Munich #694
£353	$632	€530	Landscape with villages (22x7cm-9x3in) s. board. 14-May-4 Behringer, Furth #1576
£385	$642	€550	Upper Bavarian landscape (16x16cm-6x6in) s. board lit. 27-Jun-3 Auktionhaus Georg Rehm, Augsburg #8063/R
£699	$1203	€1000	View of the Schliersee (71x126cm-28x50in) s.i.d.08. 3-Dec-3 Neumeister, Munich #589/R

HARTZ, Lauritz (1903-1987) Danish

£387	$658	€565	Two women (60x80cm-24x31in) s. exhib.prov. 10-Nov-3 Rasmussen, Vejle #645/R (D.KR 4200)
£1534	$2869	€2240	Le Pont Neuf (38x55cm-15x22in) s. 25-Feb-4 Museumsbygningen, Copenhagen #96/R est:15000 (D.KR 17000)
£1690	$2823	€2467	Wooded area, Gronnehave (68x50cm-27x20in) init. exhib.prov. 7-Oct-3 Rasmussen, Copenhagen #321/R est:15000 (D.KR 18000)
£4883	$8154	€7129	Yellow flower in vase (69x49cm-27x19in) init. exhib.prov. 7-Oct-3 Rasmussen, Copenhagen #361/R est:12000 (D.KR 52000)

HARTZ, Louis (1869-1935) Dutch

£608	$1070	€900	Horse and cart on beach (54x45cm-21x18in) s.d.03. 21-May-4 Mehlis, Plauen #15114/R

HARUNOBU, Suzuki (1724-1770) Japanese

Prints

£1748	$2972	€2500	Abuna-e (19x25cm-7x10in) s. col print lit. 25-Nov-3 Sotheby's, Paris #15/R est:3000-4000
£2000	$3680	€2920	Parody of Ariwara No Narihira, the Eastern journey (28x21cm-11x8in) s. print lit. 8-Jun-4 Sotheby's, London #69/R est:2000-3000
£2000	$3680	€2920	Toi No Tamagawa from the series popular versions of the Six Jewel Rivers (66x12cm-26x5in) s. print exec. c.1768 lit. 8-Jun-4 Sotheby's, London #87/R est:2000-2500
£2098	$3566	€3000	Shunga (19x26cm-7x10in) col print. 25-Nov-3 Sotheby's, Paris #10/R est:2400-2800
£2448	$4161	€3500	Shunga (20x28cm-8x11in) col print exec.c.1770. 25-Nov-3 Sotheby's, Paris #11/R est:2400-2800
£2448	$4161	€3500	Ishiyama (26x19cm-10x7in) s. col print lit. 25-Nov-3 Sotheby's, Paris #38/R est:3000-4000
£2500	$4600	€3650	Osen at her tea stall (69x12cm-27x5in) s. print exec. c.1769 lit. 8-Jun-4 Sotheby's, London #89/R est:2500-3500
£2657	$4517	€3800	Shunga (21x28cm-8x11in) col print exhib.lit. 25-Nov-3 Sotheby's, Paris #9/R est:4500-5500
£2657	$4517	€3800	Wakamizu (32x15cm-13x6in) s. col print lit. 25-Nov-3 Sotheby's, Paris #29/R est:4500-5500
£2797	$4755	€4000	Oyasumi Dokoro-yorozuya (27x21cm-11x8in) s. col print prov.exhib.lit. 25-Nov-3 Sotheby's, Paris #18/R est:4500-5500
£2800	$5152	€4088	Beauty washing her feet (68x12cm-27x5in) s. print prov.lit. 8-Jun-4 Sotheby's, London #92/R est:2500-3000
£3000	$5520	€4380	The Jewel River at Toi (27x20cm-11x8in) s.i. print exec c.1767 lit. 8-Jun-4 Sotheby's, London #66/R est:3000-4000
£3497	$5944	€5000	Tokei (26x19cm-10x7in) col print lit. 25-Nov-3 Sotheby's, Paris #19/R
£3846	$6538	€5500	Courtisane debout dans un interieur. s. print. 25-Nov-3 Tajan, Paris #324/R est:2000-2200
£4200	$7728	€6132	Bijin emerging from a mosquito net (69x12cm-27x5in) s. print prov.lit. 8-Jun-4 Sotheby's, London #88/R est:2000-3000
£4545	$7727	€6500	Bucheronne et fils (27x20cm-11x8in) col print lit. 25-Nov-3 Sotheby's, Paris #21/R est:7500-8500
£5035	$8559	€7200	Courtisane (28x20cm-11x8in) s. col print prov.lit. 25-Nov-3 Sotheby's, Paris #39/R est:5500-6500
£5245	$8916	€7500	Komatsu-biki (27x21cm-11x8in) s. col print lit. 25-Nov-3 Sotheby's, Paris #35/R est:6000-7000
£5594	$9510	€8000	Koya (27x20cm-11x8in) s. col print prov.exhib.lit. 25-Nov-3 Sotheby's, Paris #31/R est:7500-8500
£6000	$11040	€8760	Ariwara No Narihira from the series of the thirty-six immortal poets (26x20cm-10x8in) s.i. print exec. c.1767-68 lit. 8-Jun-4 Sotheby's, London #75/R est:3000-4000
£7000	$12880	€10220	Mother and child (27x19cm-11x7in) s.i. print exec. c.1768 prov.lit. 8-Jun-4 Sotheby's, London #81/R est:3000-4000
£7343	$12483	€10500	Balles de coton (28x21cm-11x8in) s. col print lit. 25-Nov-3 Sotheby's, Paris #36/R est:12000-15000
£7500	$13800	€10950	Ki No Tsurayuki from the series of the thirty-six immortal poets (28x21cm-11x8in) s.i. print exec. c.1768 lit. 8-Jun-4 Sotheby's, London #76/R est:3000-4000
£7692	$13077	€11000	Kannazuki (28x21cm-11x8in) s. col print lit. 25-Nov-3 Sotheby's, Paris #32/R est:7500-8500
£7692	$13077	€11000	Scene musicale (25x39cm-10x15in) s. col print prov.lit. 25-Nov-3 Sotheby's, Paris #37/R est:12000-15000
£8000	$14720	€11680	Hotei gazing at the moon (27x20cm-11x8in) s. print lit. 8-Jun-4 Sotheby's, London #63/R est:5000-6000
£8042	$13671	€11500	Coucher de soleil (28x20cm-11x8in) s. col print lit. 25-Nov-3 Sotheby's, Paris #28/R est:6000-7000
£10140	$17238	€14500	Tenuguikake Kihan (27x21cm-11x8in) col print lit. 25-Nov-3 Sotheby's, Paris #20/R est:9000-12000
£10839	$18427	€15500	Dame (29x21cm-11x8in) col print lit. 25-Nov-3 Sotheby's, Paris #22/R est:9000-12000
£11175	$18997	€15980	Femme et garconnet (28x21cm-11x8in) s. col print prov.exhib. 25-Nov-3 Sotheby's, Paris #30/R est:18000-25000
£11860	$20162	€16960	Egoyomi (27x19cm-11x7in) colprint exec.1765 prov.exhib.lit. 25-Nov-3 Sotheby's, Paris #34/R est:6000-7000
£12000	$22080	€17520	The descending geese of the Koto bridges (28x20cm-11x8in) print exec. c.1766 prov.lit. 8-Jun-4 Sotheby's, London #71/R est:10000-15000
£16000	$29440	€23360	Erotic prints (28x21cm-11x8in) print album of eight. 8-Jun-4 Sotheby's, London #85/R est:10000-15000
£16000	$29440	€23360	Rain in May from the series Fuzoku Shiki Kasen (27x20cm-11x8in) s.i. print lit. 8-Jun-4 Sotheby's, London #65/R est:16000-20000
£16000	$29440	€23360	Ki No Tomonori from the series the thirty-six immortal poets (27x21cm-11x8in) s.i. print lit. 8-Jun-4 Sotheby's, London #82/R est:10000-15000
£19392	$32966	€27730	Ofuji (27x20cm-11x8in) col print lit. 25-Nov-3 Sotheby's, Paris #33/R est:24000-28000
£22000	$40480	€32120	Returning sails of the towel rack (28x21cm-11x8in) print exec. c.1766 lit. 8-Jun-4 Sotheby's, London #70/R est:8000-10000
£25553	$43439	€36540	Mitate (27x20cm-11x8in) col print prov.lit. 25-Nov-3 Sotheby's, Paris #26/R est:30000-40000
£26237	$44604	€37520	Kasamori Osen (27x21cm-11x8in) s. col print prov.exhib.lit. 25-Nov-3 Sotheby's, Paris #40/R est:24000-28000

HARUNOBU, Suzuki (attrib) (1724-1770) Japanese

Prints

£2000	$3680	€2920	Young girl on a veranda holding a fan with a man trying to pull open her bathrobe (67x12cm-26x5in) s. print exec. c.1770 prov.lit. 8-Jun-4 Sotheby's, London #86/R est:2000-2500
£3000	$5520	€4380	After her bath, the dream (20x12cm-8x5in) print exec.c.1768 lit. 8-Jun-4 Sotheby's, London #80/R est:700-900

HARUSHIGE, Suzuki (attrib) (1747-1818) Japanese

Prints

£2200	$4048	€3212	Interrupted koto playing (35x24cm-14x9in) print. 8-Jun-4 Sotheby's, London #100/R est:1500-2500
£5000	$9200	€7300	Calligraphy lesson (28x22cm-11x9in) print prov.lit. 8-Jun-4 Sotheby's, London #99/R est:2500-3500

HARVENT, Rene (1925-) Belgian

Sculpture

£3108	$5874	€4600	Buste de Niki (42cm-17in) s.d.1925 green pat bronze sold with marble socle and glass column. 17-Feb-4 Vanderkindere, Brussels #159 est:400-600

HARVEY, Bessie (1929-) American

£419	$700	€612	Six faces (124x97cm-49x38in) paint board prov. 15-Nov-3 Slotin Folk Art, Buford #292/R

HARVEY, Bruce (20th C) New Zealander

£525	$846	€767	Rain Forest Toucan (90x60cm-35x24in) s. board. 12-Aug-3 Peter Webb, Auckland #154/R (NZ.D 1450)

HARVEY, Charles (20th C) Irish?

£539	$993	€820	Narcissi (41x31cm-16x12in) s. board prov. 22-Jun-4 De Veres Art Auctions, Dublin #226/R

HARVEY, Charles W (1895-1970) British

£733	$1320	€1100	Harbour in Brittany (50x60cm-20x24in) s. 20-Apr-4 James Adam, Dublin #116/R

HARVEY, Edmund (1907-1994) Australian

£826	$1529	€1206	North west Europe (44x59cm-17x23in) s.d.31 oil pencil pen ink. 10-Mar-4 Deutscher-Menzies, Melbourne #464/R est:2000-4000 (A.D 2000)

HARVEY, G (20th C) American

£4118	$7000	€6012	Coming in (33x23cm-13x9in) 1-Nov-3 Altermann Galleries, Santa Fe #84
£4706	$8000	€6871	Peaceful days (23x15cm-9x6in) board. 1-Nov-3 Altermann Galleries, Santa Fe #83
£9412	$16000	€13742	Working vaquero (61x91cm-24x36in) 1-Nov-3 Altermann Galleries, Santa Fe #82

£35706 $63913 €52131 Back home (66x97cm-26x38in) 15-May-4 Altermann Galleries, Santa Fe #92/R

HARVEY, Gail (1954-) British
£500 $945 €730 Cliff tops, moonlight (105x115cm-41x45in) 19-Feb-4 Lyon & Turnbull, Edinburgh #151

HARVEY, George (1835-c.1920) American
Works on paper
£430 $800 €628 Marine views (19x40cm-7x16in) s.d.83 W/C two. 5-Mar-4 Skinner, Boston #318/R

HARVEY, George Wainwright (1855-1930) American
£1006 $1600 €1469 Dieppe harbour (40x61cm-16x24in) s.d.87. 12-Sep-3 Skinner, Boston #306/R

HARVEY, Gerald (1933-) American
£9412 $16000 €13742 Open gate (76x102cm-30x40in) s. prov. 1-Nov-3 Santa Fe Art, Santa Fe #96/R est:20000-25000
£18717 $35000 €27327 Through golden Aspens (76x61cm-30x24in) s.d.1987 prov. 24-Jul-4 Coeur d'Alene, Hayden #88/R est:20000-30000

HARVEY, Gerald (attrib) (1933-) American
Sculpture
£1117 $2000 €1631 Wall eyed (28cm-11in) bronze edn of 150. 15-May-4 Altermann Galleries, Santa Fe #2/R

HARVEY, Harold (1874-1941) British
£1500 $2385 €2190 Interior study of a young girl sitting on a Cornish wooden window seat (36x43cm-14x17in) s. 30-Apr-3 Peter Wilson, Nantwich #56/R est:1500-2000
£5000 $9100 €7300 Shellfish gatherer (41x30cm-16x12in) s.d.1926 lit. 15-Jun-4 David Lay, Penzance #556/R est:3000-4000
£13000 $22100 €18980 Red silk shawl (76x63cm-30x25in) s.d.32 exhib.lit. 21-Nov-3 Christie's, London #36/R est:7000-10000
£29000 $52780 €42340 The road (76x76cm-30x30in) s.d.1919. 15-Jun-4 Bonhams, New Bond Street #8/R est:10000-15000
£38000 $64600 €55480 Three fishermen (44x51cm-17x20in) s.d.09 prov.lit. 21-Nov-3 Christie's, London #42/R est:40000-60000

HARVEY, Henry T (19th C) American
£414 $750 €604 Duck pond (38x48cm-15x19in) s.i. stretcher. 16-Apr-4 James Julia, Fairfield #624j/R
£428 $800 €625 Duck pond. Old cottage (51x41cm-20x16in) s. i.stretcher pair. 25-Feb-4 Doyle, New York #5/R
£824 $1500 €1203 Feeding time (97x71cm-38x28in) s. 19-Jun-4 Jackson's, Cedar Falls #49/R est:800-1200

HARVEY, Herbert Johnson (1884-1928) British
£320 $598 €467 Daffodils, tulip and other flowers in a cut glass vase (61x51cm-24x20in) s. prov. 24-Feb-4 Bonhams, Knowle #111

HARVEY, Marianne (attrib) (?-1812) British?
Works on paper
£4400 $7876 €6424 Pike was taken Nov 7th 1807 by Wlm Dring, in the river at Saxlingham, Norfolk (23x99cm-9x39in) bears sig.i. W/C prov. 22-Mar-4 Bonhams & Brooks, Norfolk #128/R est:120-180

HARVEY, Marion Roger Hamilton (1886-1971) British
£984 $1800 €1437 Spaniels (51x61cm-20x24in) s. board exhib. 5-Jun-4 Neal Auction Company, New Orleans #780 est:1000-1500
£1400 $2296 €2044 Portrait of a tabby cat, in a basket with a ball of wool (43x53cm-17x21in) s. 29-May-3 Neales, Nottingham #838/R est:1000-1400
£2700 $4941 €3942 Terrier and a spaniel (50x60cm-20x24in) s. i. verso. 8-Jul-4 Lawrence, Crewkerne #1658/R est:1000-1500
Works on paper
£260 $481 €380 Portrait of a Buzz (36x32cm-14x13in) s. pastel. 9-Mar-4 Bonhams, Knightsbridge #46/R
£820 $1509 €1197 Wire haired terrier (34x25cm-13x10in) s.d.193- pastel. 10-Jun-4 Lyon & Turnbull, Edinburgh #107

HARVEY, Reginald L (1888-1963) Canadian
£271 $453 €396 Confluence of mistaya and Saskatchewan Rivers (45x60cm-18x24in) s.i. board. 17-Nov-3 Hodgins, Calgary #87/R (C.D 600)
£407 $680 €594 Mt. Edith Cavell (60x80cm-24x31in) s.i. board. 17-Nov-3 Hodgins, Calgary #342/R (C.D 900)
£407 $680 €594 Untitled - mountain peaks (60x80cm-24x31in) s. board. 17-Nov-3 Hodgins, Calgary #376/R (C.D 900)

HARVEY, Robert Martin (1924-) American
£227 $400 €331 January lagoon, Stinson beach (180x119cm-71x47in) s.d.1960. 23-May-4 Treadway Gallery, Cincinnati #769/R
£270 $475 €394 Untitled (119x180cm-47x71in) s.d.1959. 23-May-4 Treadway Gallery, Cincinnati #768/R

HARWEY, J (20th C) ?
£1697 $2935 €2478 Riding horses on the campagna in Rome (45x74cm-18x29in) s. 12-Dec-3 Kieselbach, Budapest #131/R (H.F 650000)

HARWOOD, A (19/20th C) British
Works on paper
£280 $445 €406 Ship's portrait - Scarborough trawler the a Spence MacDonald (36x54cm-14x21in) s.d.1919 W/C. 9-Sep-3 David Duggleby, Scarborough #140/R

HARWOOD, James Taylor (1860-1940) American
£8092 $14000 €11814 Bountiful Utah, Burnham Duck Club (53x81cm-21x32in) s.d.28 i.verso prov. 10-Dec-3 Bonhams & Butterfields, San Francisco #6043/R est:10000-15000

HARWOOD, Lloyd (20th C) New Zealander
£797 $1291 €1156 Crown and k9 (17x13cm-7x5in) s. board. 31-Jul-3 International Art Centre, Auckland #6/R est:1000-2000 (NZ.D 2200)
£1598 $2716 €2333 Mixed metaphors (79x79cm-31x31in) s. board painted 2001. 27-Nov-3 International Art Centre, Auckland #53/R est:3500-4500 (NZ.D 4250)

HARY, Gyula (1864-1946) Hungarian
£1229 $2176 €1794 Naphegy (60x80cm-24x31in) s. 28-Apr-4 Kieselbach, Budapest #28/R (H.F 460000)
£1457 $2652 €2200 View of Lake Como (66x95cm-26x37in) s. 17-Jun-4 Finarte Semenzato, Milan #350/R est:2000-3000
£1470 $2601 €2146 Tihany (60x80cm-24x31in) s. 28-Apr-4 Kieselbach, Budapest #7/R (H.F 550000)
£1737 $3074 €2536 View of Hallstadt (60x80cm-24x31in) s.i. 28-Apr-4 Kieselbach, Budapest #30/R (H.F 650000)
Works on paper
£1001 $1812 €1461 View of the Buda Castle (36x52cm-14x20in) s. mixed media. 16-Apr-4 Mu Terem Galeria, Budapest #20/R (H.F 380000)

HASBROUCK, Dubois Fenelon (1860-1934) American
£718 $1300 €1048 The Esopus Creek at Mt Pleasant NY (25x36cm-10x14in) s.d.86 panel. 2-Apr-4 Eldred, East Dennis #876/R
£5429 $9500 €7926 Wintry twilight (41x56cm-16x22in) s.d.1889. 19-Dec-3 Sotheby's, New York #1106/R est:3000-5000

HASCH, Carl (1834-1897) Austrian
£775 $1340 €1100 View over Gosausee to the upper Dachstein (32x42cm-13x17in) s. 10-Dec-3 Dorotheum, Vienna #113/R
£1056 $1827 €1500 Mountain landscape with wild valley stream (67x95cm-26x37in) s.d.1882. 12-Dec-3 Berlinghof, Heidelberg #1049/R
£1831 $3168 €2600 Summer landscape with travellers by the saw-mill (28x39cm-11x15in) s. panel. 13-Dec-3 De Vuyst, Lokeren #171/R est:2200-2600

HASCH, Victor (1945-) ?
£417 $696 €600 Andy Warhol (65x50cm-26x20in) s. 25-Oct-3 Cornette de St.Cyr, Paris #697

HASE, Ernst (1889-?) German
£315 $541 €450 Working harbour (24x57cm-9x22in) s. board. 5-Dec-3 Bolland & Marotz, Bremen #1454

HASEGAWA, Kiyoshi (1891-1980) Japanese
£5034 $9363 €7500 Village (65x81cm-26x32in) s.d.25. 3-Mar-4 Tajan, Paris #71/R est:8000-12000

HASEGAWA, Shoichi (1929-) Japanese
Works on paper
£1200 $2208 €1800 Landscape (130x89cm-51x35in) s. bears artist st. W/C paper on canvas. 9-Jun-4 Le Roux & Morel, Paris #77/R est:1500

HASELTINE, Herbert (1877-1962) American
Sculpture
£6250 $11000 €9125 Un puyazo (33cm-13in) i. brown pat. bronze st.f.C Valsuani lit. 18-May-4 Sotheby's, New York #196/R est:4000-6000
£17045 $30000 €24886 Toro de miura (15cm-6in) i.num.4 gold pat. bronze lit. 18-May-4 Sotheby's, New York #197/R est:2500-3500
£19886 $35000 €29034 Thoroughbred horse (25cm-10in) i. brown pat bronze exhib.lit. 18-May-4 Sotheby's, New York #200/R est:5000-7000
£21307 $37500 €31108 Polo pony, Perfection (23cm-9in) i. num.III dark brown pat. bronze marble base. 18-May-4 Sotheby's, New York #198/R est:5000-7000
£26163 $45000 €38198 Combourg, a horse (55cm-22in) i. bronze executed 1912 prov.lit. 5-Dec-3 Christie's, Rockefeller NY #32/R est:20000-30000
£28409 $50000 €41477 Horse heads (16cm-6in) i. green pat. bronze marble base pair st.f.C Valsani cire perdue. 18-May-4 Sotheby's, New York #195/R est:4000-6000

HASELTINE, James Henry (1833-1907) American
Sculpture
£1786 $3250 €2608 Portrait of a young woman (66x47cm-26x19in) i. white marble. 29-Jun-4 Sotheby's, New York #185/R est:2500-3500
£8125 $13000 €11863 America victorious (43cm-17in) s.i. bronze prov. 20-Sep-3 Pook & Pook, Downington #355/R est:3000-5000

HASELTINE, William Stanley (1835-1900) American
£1198 $2000 €1749 Mill-Schwyz, Switzerland (25x33cm-10x13in) paper on canvas prov. 23-Oct-3 Shannon's, Milford #2445/R est:2000-3000
£2957 $5500 €4317 Woodland interior (51x69cm-20x27in) oil paper prov. 5-Mar-4 Skinner, Boston #301/R est:12000-18000
£7429 $13000 €10846 Pulpit Rock, Nahant (23x30cm-9x12in) init.d.63 s.indis.i. verso board. 19-Dec-3 Sotheby's, New York #1065/R est:6000-8000
£9497 $17000 €15946 Young boy in a scow fishing next to a farmhouse (38x53cm-15x21in) s.d.1861. 20-Mar-4 Pook & Pook, Downington #222/R est:15000-25000
£20455 $36000 €29864 Evening scene (58x42cm-23x17in) init. 18-May-4 Christie's, Rockefeller NY #32/R est:20000-30000
£51136 $90000 €74659 Rocky Coast, Capri (66x99cm-26x39in) mono.d.1874. 19-May-4 Sotheby's, New York #102/R est:50000-70000

Works on paper
£346 $550 €505 Tivoli (38x52cm-15x20in) ink wash pencil. 13-Sep-3 Weschler, Washington #747/R
£2054 $3800 €2999 New England coast (34x50cm-13x20in) ink pencil exec.c.1864-1865 prov.exhib. 11-Mar-4 Christie's, Rockefeller NY #6/R est:6000-8000

HASEMANN, Wilhelm Gustav Friederich (1850-1913) German
£1389 $2319 €2000 Walkers in landscape (19x27cm-7x11in) s. panel. 22-Oct-3 Neumeister, Munich #704 est:300
£2639 $4407 €3800 Blossoming gorse in mountain landscape (66x87cm-26x34in) s. 22-Oct-3 Neumeister, Munich #703 est:300
£8392 $14014 €12000 Young woman on country path near farmstead (22x16cm-9x6in) s. panel. 10-Oct-3 Winterberg, Heidelberg #593/R est:15800
£24000 $43440 €36000 After church (104x81cm-41x32in) 2-Apr-4 Winterberg, Heidelberg #428/R est:38000

HASENFRATZ, Walter (1904-1983) German
£448 $749 €654 Emigrant II (60x92cm-24x36in) s.d.37 s.i. verso. 24-Oct-3 Hans Widmer, St Gallen #95/R (S.FR 1000)

HASENPFLUG, Carl George Adolph (1802-1858) German
£24887 $42308 €36335 Falkenstein ruins in winter (89x79cm-35x31in) s.d.1847 prov. 19-Nov-3 Fischer, Luzern #1143/R est:55000-65000 (S.FR 55000)

HASIM (?) ?
£340 $609 €500 Indonesian dancer (90x63cm-35x25in) s.d.61. 16-Mar-4 Christie's, Amsterdam #61

HASIOR, Wladyslaw (1928-1999) Polish
Works on paper
£2143 $3837 €3129 Full speed (104x122cm-41x48in) s.verso mixed media. 28-May-4 Uppsala Auktionskammare, Uppsala #337/R est:5000-6000 (S.KR 29000)
£2956 $5292 €4316 A single rose (127x65cm-50x26in) s.d.1958 mixed media. 28-May-4 Uppsala Auktionskammare, Uppsala #339 est:3000-4000 (S.KR 40000)

HASKELL, Ida C (1861-1932) American
£4192 $7000 €6120 Mother Love (69x56cm-27x22in) s. prov.exhib. 23-Oct-3 Shannon's, Milford #258/R est:5000-7000

HASLAM, Ron (20th C) American?
£374 $700 €546 Impressionist harbour scene with sailboat (48x58cm-19x23in) s. 28-Feb-4 Thomaston Place, Thomaston #345/R

HASLEGRAVE, Adelaide L (fl.1901) British
Works on paper
£290 $499 €423 An April morning, going to work (51x74cm-20x29in) s. i.verso W/C board. 2-Dec-3 Ritchie, Toronto #32/R (C.D 650)

HASLEM, John (1808-1884) British
Miniatures
£2200 $3960 €3212 Portrait of the artist (8x6cm-3x2in) s.d.1852 oval. 22-Apr-4 Mellors & Kirk, Nottingham #945/R est:800-1200

HASLUND, Ludvig (1847-1902) Norwegian
£341 $545 €494 Woman on country road (18x24cm-7x9in) s. 22-Sep-3 Blomqvist, Lysaker #1092/R (N.KR 4000)

HASLUND, Otto (1842-1917) Danish
£301 $553 €439 Farm yard with chickens (35x47cm-14x19in) s. 10-Jun-4 Grev Wedels Plass, Oslo #179/R (N.KR 3700)

HASS, Sigfred (1848-1908) Danish/German
£559 $900 €816 Landscape with autumn hardwoods and stream with fishermen in boat (69x79cm-27x31in) s. 24-Feb-3 O'Gallerie, Oregon #845a
£760 $1383 €1110 Wooded landscape with lake (95x130cm-37x51in) s.d.02. 7-Feb-4 Rasmussen, Havnen #2079 (D.KR 8300)
£1163 $2000 €1698 Walking on a rural road. s.d.04. 7-Dec-3 Hindman, Chicago #771/R est:1600-2000

HASSALL, John (1868-1948) British
Works on paper
£550 $875 €803 French washerwoman (53x28cm-21x11in) i. ink W/C. 9-Sep-3 Gorringes, Lewes #1804/R
£3200 $5920 €4672 War (39x50cm-15x20in) s. exhib. 10-Mar-4 Sotheby's, Olympia #108/R est:600-800

HASSAM, Childe (1859-1935) American
£4375 $7000 €6388 Coastal view (20x25cm-8x10in) bears sig. 21-Sep-3 William Jenack, New York #232 est:800-1200
£13953 $24000 €20371 Clouds (13x22cm-5x9in) s. panel prov.exhib. 4-Dec-3 Christie's, Rockefeller NY #62/R est:20000-30000
£24865 $46000 €37298 Child in landscape with rabbits (41x152cm-16x60in) s.d.1922 panel prov. 14-Jul-4 American Auctioneer #490224/R est:70000-90000
£27933 $50000 €40782 Nocturne, Provincetown, Massachusetts (56x41cm-22x16in) s.d.1900 init.d.verso prov.exhib. 26-May-4 Doyle, New York #94/R est:60000-80000
£31977 $55000 €46686 Under the willows (17x12cm-7x5in) s. indis d. init.d.1904 verso panel prov. 3-Dec-3 Doyle, New York #203/R est:15000-25000
£110465 $190000 €161279 Autumn landscape East Hampton (100x190cm-39x75in) s.d.1931 prov. 4-Dec-3 Christie's, Rockefeller NY #91/R est:100000-150000
£136364 $240000 €199091 September (64x76cm-25x30in) s.d.1906 prov.exhib. 19-May-4 Sotheby's, New York #17/R est:250000-350000
£139535 $240000 €203721 Andover, Massachusetts (76x192cm-30x76in) s.d.1930 prov.exhib.lit. 4-Dec-3 Christie's, Rockefeller NY #80/R est:200000-300000
£164773 $290000 €240569 Home sweet home cottage (51x61cm-20x24in) s.d.1916 i.d.verso prov.exhib.lit. 19-May-4 Sotheby's, New York #16/R est:200000-300000
£187500 $330000 €273750 Pont-Aven (74x56cm-29x22in) s.d.1897 prov.exhib.lit. 19-May-4 Sotheby's, New York #40/R est:250000-350000
£255814 $440000 €373488 In the doorway (46x37cm-18x15in) s.d.1888 board prov.exhib.lit. 4-Dec-3 Christie's, Rockefeller NY #58/R est:250000-350000
£352273 $620000 €514319 Rainy day (62x46cm-24x18in) s. indis.d. prov.exhib.lit. 18-May-4 Christie's, Rockefeller NY #83/R est:300000-500000
£380682 $670000 €555796 Stone Bridge, Old Lyme (76x84cm-30x33in) s.d.1904 i.stretcher prov.lit. 19-May-4 Sotheby's, New York #13/R est:400000-600000
£553977 $975000 €808806 Sailing on calm seas, Gloucester Harbour (51x61cm-20x24in) s.d.1900 prov.exhib. 19-May-4 Sotheby's, New York #32/R est:300000-500000
Prints
£1657 $3000 €2419 Old lace (18x17cm-7x7in) s. with cypher etching. 19-Apr-4 Bonhams & Butterfields, San Francisco #28 est:2000-3000
£1955 $3500 €2854 Big horse chestnut tree, Easthampton (23x30cm-9x12in) s.i. etching. 4-May-4 Doyle, New York #178/R est:2500-3500
£2118 $3600 €3092 Easthampton (18x29cm-7x11in) cypher sig.i. etching. 6-Nov-3 Swann Galleries, New York #567/R est:3000-5000
£2353 $4000 €3435 Big horse chestnut tree, Easthampton (23x30cm-9x12in) cypher sig.i. etching. 6-Nov-3 Swann Galleries, New York #568/R est:2500-3500
£3955 $7000 €5774 Fifth Avenue, noon (25x18cm-10x7in) s.i. etching drypoint. 30-Apr-4 Sotheby's, New York #12/R est:3000-5000
£4294 $7000 €6269 Lion Gardiner House, Easthampton (33x44cm-13x17in) s.i. etching. 24-Sep-3 Christie's, Rockefeller NY #12/R est:7000-9000
£4749 $8500 €6934 Fifth Avenue, noon (25x19cm-10x7in) s.i. etching drypoint. 4-May-4 Doyle, New York #177/R est:3000-5000
£7647 $13000 €11165 Writing desk (25x18cm-10x7in) cypher sig.i. etching. 6-Nov-3 Swann Galleries, New York #569/R est:8000-12000
Works on paper
£3243 $6000 €4735 Rocks by the ocean (22x27cm-9x11in) s.d.1908 pencil col pencil prov. 11-Mar-4 Christie's, Rockefeller NY #34/R est:7000-10000
£7764 $12500 €11335 The marriage (46x33cm-18x13in) s. W/C gouache. 20-Aug-3 James Julia, Fairfield #1235/R est:15000-25000
£8919 $16500 €13379 In the park (25x30cm-10x12in) s.d.1902 pastel prov. 14-Jul-4 American Auctioneer #490229/R est:10000-15000
£8939 $16000 €13051 Water carrier, Anvers-sur-Oise (36x25cm-14x10in) s.i. W/C pencil. 14-May-4 Skinner, Boston #299/R est:15000-20000
£14054 $26000 €20519 Along the shoreline (36x25cm-14x10in) s.d.1899 W/C prov. 11-Mar-4 Christie's, Rockefeller NY #33/R est:10000-15000
£19886 $35000 €29034 The Seine at Chatou (25x36cm-10x14in) s. W/C exec c.1889 prov.exhib. 19-May-4 Sotheby's, New York #4/R est:12000-18000
£27273 $48000 €39819 Chicken yard back of the Holley House (25x28cm-10x11in) s.d.1902 pastel paperboard prov.exhib. 18-May-4 Christie's, Rockefeller NY #74/R est:40000-60000
£31250 $55000 €45625 Cos cob (25x28cm-10x11in) s.d.1902 pastel paperboard prov.exhib. 18-May-4 Christie's, Rockefeller NY #73/R est:40000-60000
£31977 $55000 €46686 Thunderstorm on the Oregon Trail (42x56cm-17x22in) s.d.1908 W/C prov.exhib. 4-Dec-3 Christie's, Rockefeller NY #63/R est:25000-35000
£494186 $850000 €721512 Home of the hummingbird (35x26cm-14x10in) s.d.1893 W/C. 3-Dec-3 Sotheby's, New York #9/R est:1000000-1500000

HASSE, Christian (1913-) German
£886 $1382 €1400 Monte Klia (91x123cm-36x48in) s.d.94 panel. 18-Oct-2 Von Zezschwitz, Munich #117/R

HASSE, Hermann Georg (?) ?
Sculpture
£1705 $3000 €2489 Nude maiden seated atop a water buffalo (58cm-23in) s.i. bronze pedestal support. 22-May-4 Selkirks, St. Louis #783/R est:2000-3000

HASSEBRAUK, Ernst (1905-1974) German
£451 $754 €650 Woman's portrait (94x62cm-37x24in) s. 25-Oct-3 Dr Lehr, Berlin #183/R
£567 $1020 €850 Head and vase (42x59cm-17x23in) s. i. verso col chk board. 24-Apr-4 Dr Lehr, Berlin #144/R
Works on paper
£524 $902 €750 Playing cards and green glove (30x40cm-12x16in) mono. col pastel pencil. 2-Dec-3 Hauswedell & Nolte, Hamburg #252/R
£2000 $3600 €3000 Portrait of Charlotte Hassebrauk (55x37cm-22x15in) s.i.d. verso pastel graphite board. 24-Apr-4 Dr Lehr, Berlin #143/R est:3000

HASSELHORST, Johann Heinrich (1825-1904) German
£3311 $6026 €5000 Italian girl in the shade by a fountain (43x30cm-17x12in) s. 19-Jun-4 Hans Stahl, Hamburg #56/R est:7500

HASSELL, Edward (fl.1827-1852) ?
Works on paper
£480 $883 €701 Fishing in a punt (26x48cm-10x19in) s.d.51 W/C. 22-Jun-4 Bonhams, Knightsbridge #24/R

HASSELL, Hilton Macdonald (1910-1980) Canadian
£413 $752 €603 Afternoon, Polperro (30x51cm-12x20in) s. i.d.1961 verso board prov. 5-Feb-4 Heffel, Vancouver #40/R (C.D 1000)
£432 $704 €631 Blue Mountain houses (46x61cm-18x24in) s. masonite. 23-Sep-3 Ritchie, Toronto #141/R est:700-900 (C.D 950)
£620 $1122 €905 Late winter, Beaver Pool (46x56cm-18x22in) s. hard board prov. 18-Apr-4 Levis, Calgary #45/R est:1500-2000 (C.D 1500)
£960 $1757 €1402 Rue d'Auteuil, Quebec (45x55cm-18x22in) s. board. 1-Jun-4 Joyner Waddington, Toronto #163/R est:2000-2500 (C.D 2400)
£1600 $2928 €2336 Vernal migration (80x105cm-31x41in) s. acrylic board. 1-Jun-4 Joyner Waddington, Toronto #310/R est:3000-4000 (C.D 4000)

HASSELT, Willem van (1882-1963) Dutch
£1958 $3270 €2800 Bord de riviere (46x55cm-18x22in) s. 30-Jun-3 Artcurial Briest, Paris #754/R est:1200-1500
£2000 $3640 €3000 Prairie animee en bord de mer (61x73cm-24x29in) s. 4-Jul-4 Eric Pillon, Calais #205/R

HASSENKAMP, Kurt (1886-1917) German
£676 $1054 €1000 Seascape (83x119cm-33x47in) s.d.1916 paper on canvas. 31-Mar-3 Bloss, Merzhausen #1556/R
Works on paper
£400 $720 €600 Warships off Tenerife (38x46cm-15x18in) s.i. gouache. 26-Apr-4 Rieber, Stuttgart #1304/R

HASSENTEUFEL, Hans (1887-1943) German
£1172 $1958 €1700 Young Arabian woman with waterjug on shoulder (85x60cm-33x24in) s.d.1924. 9-Jul-3 Hugo Ruef, Munich #347/R est:1000
£1500 $2775 €2190 Portrait of a young lady with flowers in her hair (100x70cm-39x28in) s.i. 10-Feb-4 Bonhams, Knightsbridge #273/R est:1500-2000
£2603 $4425 €3800 Young woman posing in front of wall (99x69cm-39x27in) s. 5-Nov-3 Hugo Ruef, Munich #1240/R est:1300

HASSLER, Carl von (1887-1962) American
£3235 $5500 €4723 Autumn landscape (66x89cm-26x35in) s. prov. 1-Nov-3 Santa Fe Art, Santa Fe #140/R est:5000-7000

HASTIE, Grace H (fl.1874-1927) British
Works on paper
£234 $425 €342 Peonies (23x51cm-9x20in) s.d.1925 W/C. 7-Feb-4 Sloans & Kenyon, Bethesda #1249/R
£300 $555 €438 Crofters cottage (25x36cm-10x14in) s.d.1908. 9-Mar-4 Gorringes, Lewes #2039
£317 $529 €463 Still life of flowers (29x22cm-11x9in) s.d.1883 W/C. 17-Nov-3 Waddingtons, Toronto #37/R (C.D 700)
£380 $623 €555 Common objects of the seashore (16x9cm-6x4in) i.verso W/C. 3-Jun-3 Fellows & Sons, Birmingham #36/R
£380 $703 €555 Mother and child on a lane (23x18cm-9x7in) s.d.1911. 9-Mar-4 Gorringes, Lewes #2038
£380 $695 €555 In the Harbour, Boscastle, North Cornwall (21x33cm-8x13in) s.d.1908 W/C over pencil htd bodycol. 6-Jul-4 Peter Wilson, Nantwich #81/R
£750 $1373 €1095 Saleries, Guernsey, the Channel Islands (22x32cm-9x13in) s.d.1911 W/C htd bodycol. 6-Jul-4 Peter Wilson, Nantwich #82/R

HASUI, Kawase (1883-1957) Japanese
£274 $466 €400 Oban of young Japanese lady (27x40cm-11x16in) s.d.1925 seal. 8-Nov-3 Dr Fritz Nagel, Stuttgart #2226/R
Prints
£1748 $2972 €2500 Haru (39x27cm-15x11in) s. col print. 25-Nov-3 Sotheby's, Paris #41/R est:3000-4000
£2322 $4250 €3390 Shiobara arayuji (19x47cm-7x19in) s. print. 6-Apr-4 Bonhams & Butterfields, San Francisco #3084/R est:2500-4000
£2657 $4517 €3800 Yuki (26x39cm-10x15in) s. col print. 25-Nov-3 Sotheby's, Paris #42/R est:1500-1800
£7104 $13000 €10372 Shiobara okaneji (47x18cm-19x7in) s.i.d.1919 print. 6-Apr-4 Bonhams & Butterfields, San Francisco #3085/R est:2000-3000
£8696 $16000 €12696 Snow at Shiba great gate. Evening moon. Central market. Sumiyoshi shrine. Spring Tsukuda (34x24cm-13x9in) s. woodcut set of six. 23-Mar-4 Christie's, Rockefeller NY #46/R est:2000-3000

HASWELL, John (1855-1925) British
£300 $489 €438 Autumn morning (91x69cm-36x27in) 23-Sep-3 John Nicholson, Haslemere #283

HASZARD, Rhona (1901-1931) New Zealander
£8741 $15909 €12762 Cock - Sark (32x43cm-13x17in) s.d.1926 prov. 29-Jun-4 Peter Webb, Auckland #61/R est:25000-35000 (NZ.D 25000)

HATCH, Doug (20th C) American
£232 $425 €348 Small town birdwatch with daisies (122x91cm-48x36in) 10-Jul-4 Hindman, Chicago #207/R

HATCH, Emily Nicols (1871-1959) American
Works on paper
£217 $350 €317 Isle Adam (13x23cm-5x9in) s. gouache. 20-Aug-3 James Julia, Fairfield #1805/R

HATHAWAY, Bruce (20th C) British?
£1043 $1700 €1523 Wayside chat (60x100cm-24x39in) s. 28-Sep-3 Bonhams & Butterfields, Los Angeles #7019 est:2000-3000

HATHAWAY, George M (1852-1903) American
£339 $550 €492 Casco Bay II (16x27cm-6x11in) s. board. 8-Aug-3 Barridorf, Portland #328/R
£401 $650 €581 Casco Bay I (23x30cm-9x12in) s. board. 8-Aug-3 Barridorf, Portland #329/R
£617 $1000 €895 White head (15x25cm-6x10in) s. board. 8-Aug-3 Barridorf, Portland #326/R est:1200-1800
£679 $1100 €985 Portland Head light (15x26cm-6x10in) s. board. 8-Aug-3 Barridorf, Portland #331/R est:2000-3000
£679 $1100 €985 Pearl House at Orr's Island (15x25cm-6x10in) s. i.verso academy board painted c.1900. 26-Jul-3 Thomaston Place, Thomaston #13/R
£874 $1600 €1276 View of the bandstand on the coastline off Cushing, Maine (10x23cm-4x9in) s. board. 6-Jun-4 Skinner, Boston #208 est:800-1200
£994 $1600 €1451 Maine coastal landscape (15x25cm-6x10in) s. 20-Aug-3 James Julia, Fairfield #1380/R est:1000-1500
£1173 $1900 €1701 Evergreen Landing Peaks Island (15x25cm-6x10in) i.verso academy board painted c.1900. 26-Jul-3 Thomaston Place, Thomaston #24/R
£1193 $2100 €1742 Maine coastal scene with light house (13x20cm-5x8in) mono. board. 21-May-4 North East Auctions, Portsmouth #633/R
£1543 $2500 €2237 Spring Point and Portland Head (15x25cm-6x10in) s. board. 8-Aug-3 Barridorf, Portland #327/R est:2000-3000
£1863 $3000 €2720 Coastal landscapes (15x30cm-6x12in) s. board two. 20-Aug-3 James Julia, Fairfield #1379/R est:2000-3000

HATHERELL, William (1855-1928) British
Works on paper
£300 $531 €438 Shepherds beside a river (23x36cm-9x14in) s. W/C. 29-Apr-4 Gorringes, Lewes #2336

HATOUM, Mona (1952-) Palestinian
Photographs
£14970 $25000 €21856 Performance still (76x110cm-30x43in) black white photo aluminum edition 12 of 15 prov.exhib.lit. 13-Nov-3 Sotheby's, New York #417/R est:20000-30000
Sculpture
£55866 $100000 €81564 Pin carpet (3x124x188cm-1x49x74in) stainless steel pins canvas glue edn of 3 exec 1999 prov.exhib. 11-May-4 Christie's, Rockefeller NY #60/R est:100000-150000
Works on paper
£1522 $2800 €2222 Milk strainer (27x38cm-11x15in) s.d.1996 verso punctured Japanese wax paper prov. 10-Jun-4 Phillips, New York #424/R est:3000-4000
£1522 $2800 €2222 Grater (27x38cm-11x15in) s.verso punctured Japanese wax paper prov. 10-Jun-4 Phillips, New York #425/R est:3000-4000
£1739 $3200 €2539 Flat colander (40x54cm-16x21in) s.verso punctured Japanese wax paper prov. 10-Jun-4 Phillips, New York #656/R est:4000-6000
£1739 $3200 €2539 Shaker colander (40x54cm-16x21in) s.verso punctured Japanese wax paper prov. 10-Jun-4 Phillips, New York #657/R est:4000-6000

HATTAM, Katherine (1950-) Australian
Works on paper
£455 $841 €664 House (152x102cm-60x40in) s. i.d.1989 verso mixed media prov. 15-Mar-4 Sotheby's, Melbourne #42 est:400-600 (A.D 1100)
£1322 $2446 €1930 Return of the repressed, pinky orange (158x120cm-62x47in) s. s.verso mixed media triptych executed 2000 exhib. 15-Mar-4 Sotheby's, Melbourne #43 est:1500-2500 (A.D 3200)

HATTEM, Arie van (1860-1924) Dutch
£408 $743 €600 Sergeant of the 3rd Hussars (48x27cm-19x11in) s. plywood. 3-Feb-4 Christie's, Amsterdam #263

HATTERSLEY, F W (19/20th C) British
Works on paper
£2000 $3700 €2920 Shore scene with figures, horse and cart, boats beyond (36x51cm-14x20in) W/C. 14-Jan-4 Brightwells, Leominster #808 est:300-500

HATTERSLEY, Frederick William (1859-?) British
Works on paper
£360 $673 €526 Changing pastures (10x13cm-4x5in) s. W/C. 24-Feb-4 Canterbury Auctions, UK #187/R
£1057 $1892 €1543 Comparing the catch. How do you catch them. Lobster gatherers. Snettesham Beach (25x35cm-10x14in) each s. W/C four. 10-May-4 Joel, Victoria #331 est:2500-3500 (A.D 2600)
£1300 $2457 €1898 Sorting the fish (25x46cm-10x18in) s. W/C htd white. 17-Feb-4 Bonhams, New Bond Street #7/R est:1200-1800
£1600 $3024 €2336 First load (25x46cm-10x18in) s. W/C htd white. 17-Feb-4 Bonhams, New Bond Street #8/R est:1200-1800
£2500 $4175 €3650 Fishing boats and figures (34x52cm-13x20in) s.d.1920 pair. 22-Oct-3 Wingetts, Wrexham #378/R est:2000-3000

HATTICH, Petrus van (attrib) (17th C) Dutch
£543 $1000 €793 Shepherds by the river (36x41cm-14x16in) panel. 13-Jun-4 Bonhams & Butterfields, Los Angeles #7005/R est:1500-2500

HATVANY, Ferencz (1881-1958) Hungarian
£4276 $7568 €6243 Lady with pearls (105x85cm-41x33in) s. 28-Apr-4 Kieselbach, Budapest #181/R (H.F 1600000)

HATZIS, Vassilios (1870-1915) Greek
£2200 $3850 €3212 Promenade by the shore (22x19cm-9x7in) s. cardboard. 16-Dec-3 Bonhams, New Bond Street #6/R est:800-1000

HATZOPOULOS, Georgios (1859-1935) Greek
£6200 $10850 €9052 Resting at the beach (25x37cm-10x15in) s. 16-Dec-3 Bonhams, New Bond Street #8/R est:5000-6000

HAUBENSAK, Pierre (1935-) Swiss
£604 $1027 €882 Doors for Perception (65x50cm-26x20in) s.d.73 verso acrylic chl prov. 5-Nov-3 AB Stockholms Auktionsverk #951/R (S.KR 8000)
Works on paper
£1131 $1889 €1651 Door of perception (81x61cm-32x24in) s.i.d. verso chl acrylic prov.exhib.lit. 24-Jun-3 Germann, Zurich #112/R est:3000-4000 (S.FR 2500)

HAUBTMANN, Michael (1843-1921) German/Czech
£521 $859 €750 Off Capri (20x43cm-8x17in) s. canvas on board. 3-Jul-3 Van Ham, Cologne #1232
£1119 $1902 €1600 Rocky coast line (49x63cm-19x25in) s.d.1874. 20-Nov-3 Van Ham, Cologne #1619/R est:1800

HAUCK, Friedrich Ludwig (1718-1801) German
£526 $968 €800 Portrait of Maria Christina von Keget (83x66cm-33x26in) i. verso canvas on board. 24-Jun-4 Dr Fritz Nagel, Stuttgart #667/R
£1733 $3103 €2600 Portrait of Mr Petrus Wierdsma. Portait of Jelje Wierdsma (30x22cm-12x9in) s.d.1773 pair prov. 17-May-4 Glerum, Amsterdam #39/R est:1000-1500

HAUCK, J P (18th C) Swiss
£2128 $3447 €3000 Nobleman (78x63cm-31x25in) s.d.1756 verso prov.lit. 23-May-3 Karlheinz Kaupp, Staufen #1714/R est:2000

HAUDEBOURT-LESCOT, Antoinette (1784-1845) French
£7746 $13401 €11000 Compte avec l'hote (32x40cm-13x16in) s.d.1822 exhib. 10-Dec-3 Beaussant & Lefèvre, Paris #55/R est:4000-5000
Works on paper
£461 $847 €700 La main chaude (18x25cm-7x10in) s. W/C prov. 23-Jun-4 Millon & Associes, Paris #60

HAUEISEN, Albert (1872-1954) German
£470 $864 €700 Capri (41x48cm-16x19in) s.i.d.94 board lit. 25-Mar-4 Karlheinz Kaupp, Staufen #2487/R
Works on paper
£300 $537 €450 Woman sewing (13x25cm-5x10in) s.d.16 col chk htd white board. 15-May-4 Bassenge, Berlin #6853

HAUER, Christa (1925-) Austrian
£5705 $10097 €8500 Untitled (80x100cm-31x39in) s. s.d. verso exhib.lit. 28-Apr-4 Wiener Kunst Auktionen, Vienna #241/R est:7000-9000

HAUER, Leopold (1896-1984) Austrian
£921 $1695 €1400 Still life of flowers (39x37cm-15x15in) s.d.29. 22-Jun-4 Wiener Kunst Auktionen, Vienna #205/R
£987 $1816 €1500 Italian city (34x20cm-13x8in) mono. board. 22-Jun-4 Wiener Kunst Auktionen, Vienna #209/R est:1500
Works on paper
£563 $986 €800 Mountains, trees (25x35cm-10x14in) mono. pencil oil. 19-Dec-3 Dorotheum, Vienna #136/R

HAUG, Kristian (1862-1953) Norwegian
£300 $546 €450 Deer resting in a forest clearing (29x38cm-11x15in) s. 1-Jul-4 Van Ham, Cologne #1392
£700 $1239 €1022 Stag in a winter forest (80x61cm-31x24in) s. 29-Apr-4 Christie's, Kensington #280/R
£705 $1198 €1029 Deer in snowy landscape (45x36cm-18x14in) s. board. 5-Nov-3 Dobiaschofsky, Bern #628/R (S.FR 1600)

HAUG, Robert von (1857-1922) German
£709 $1184 €1000 Woman on horse (97x55cm-38x22in) s. 16-Oct-3 Dorotheum, Salzburg #565/R

HAUGE, Halfdan (1892-1976) Norwegian
£256 $409 €371 Old houses from Old Lofoten, Svolvaer (31x36cm-12x14in) indis sig. panel. 22-Sep-3 Blomqvist, Lysaker #1094 (N.KR 3000)
£341 $545 €494 Old trading boat of 1870 (39x56cm-15x22in) s. panel. 22-Sep-3 Blomqvist, Lysaker #1095/R (N.KR 4000)
£341 $545 €494 Grey day (27x41cm-11x16in) s. 22-Sep-3 Blomqvist, Lysaker #1096/R (N.KR 4000)
£374 $688 €561 The battle at Trollfjord (68x69cm-27x27in) s. 14-Jun-4 Blomqvist, Lysaker #1140/R (N.KR 4600)
£504 $927 €756 Sunset (64x101cm-25x40in) s. 14-Jun-4 Blomqvist, Lysaker #1142 (N.KR 6200)

HAUGEN-SORENSEN, Arne (1932-) Danish
£1701 $3045 €2483 Composition (65x80cm-26x31in) s.d.64. 12-Jan-4 Rasmussen, Vejle #581/R est:20000 (D.KR 18000)
£2708 $4982 €3954 Figure composition (130x97cm-51x38in) s. prov. 29-Mar-4 Rasmussen, Copenhagen #114/R est:30000 (D.KR 30000)
Works on paper
£271 $506 €396 Composition (30x46cm-12x18in) s. W/C. 25-Feb-4 Kunsthallen, Copenhagen #25 (D.KR 3000)
£282 $480 €412 Composition (50x61cm-20x24in) s.d.81 W/C. 26-Nov-3 Kunsthallen, Copenhagen #23 (D.KR 3000)

HAUGHTON, Wilfred (1921-) Irish
£320 $595 €467 Water reflections (50x61cm-20x24in) s.d.58. 3-Mar-4 John Ross, Belfast #191

HAUKEBO, Gunnar (1909-1993) Norwegian
£313 $542 €457 Woodland interior (42x51cm-17x20in) s. exhib. 13-Dec-3 Blomqvist, Lysaker #1144 (N.KR 3600)
£330 $603 €482 Summer's day (55x61cm-22x24in) s. 2-Feb-4 Blomqvist, Lysaker #1100 (N.KR 4100)
£432 $717 €626 From Grip (41x47cm-16x19in) s. panel. 16-Jun-3 Blomqvist, Lysaker #1319 (N.KR 5000)

HAUKELAND, Arnold (1920-1983) Norwegian
Sculpture
£2129 $3663 €3108 Mother and child (33x16x11cm-13x6x4in) s.d.53 bronze. 8-Dec-3 Blomqvist, Oslo #525/R est:15000-18000 (N.KR 25000)

HAUMONT, Emile Richard (19/20th C) French
£342 $582 €500 Seine in Paris with bateau lavoir (23x32cm-9x13in) s. canvas on board lit. 6-Nov-3 Allgauer, Kempten #3442/R

HAUNOLD, Carl (1832-1911) Austrian
£1342 $2510 €2000 Untersberg, Salzburg (33x47cm-13x19in) i. verso board. 24-Feb-4 Dorotheum, Vienna #66 est:1600-1800

HAUPT, Matti (1912-1999) Finnish
Sculpture
£1007 $1852 €1500 Seated girl (20cm-8in) s. gilded bronze. 25-Mar-4 Hagelstam, Helsinki #762/R est:850
£1049 $1783 €1500 Woman churning (27cm-11in) s. bronze. 29-Nov-3 Bukowskis, Helsinki #6/R
Works on paper
£372 $665 €550 Model (50x70cm-20x28in) s. mixed media. 8-May-4 Bukowskis, Helsinki #204/R

HAUPTMANN, Ivo (1886-1973) German
£769 $1308 €1100 Still life with fruit (38x46cm-15x18in) s.d.1951. 28-Nov-3 Wendl, Rudolstadt #3994/R
£769 $1308 €1100 Still life with fruit (38x46cm-15x18in) mono.d.49. 28-Nov-3 Wendl, Rudolstadt #3995/R
£4514 $7132 €6500 Midday sun on the Elbe (75x91cm-30x36in) s.d.1922. 6-Sep-3 Arnold, Frankfurt #575/R est:1600
£7000 $12670 €10500 Hamburg Blankensee - Baur's Park on the Elbe (81x100cm-32x39in) s.d.1956. 3-Apr-4 Hans Stahl, Hamburg #163/R est:5500
Works on paper
£369 $683 €535 Nine anglers (32x48cm-13x19in) s. W/C. 14-Feb-4 Hans Stahl, Hamburg #146
£371 $637 €530 Blankensee (32x41cm-13x16in) W/C chl. 2-Dec-3 Hauswedell & Nolte, Hamburg #255/R
£462 $794 €660 Fishing harbour (38x47cm-15x19in) W/C. 6-Dec-3 Hans Stahl, Toestorf #116/R
£532 $888 €750 Narcissi in glass jug (47x38cm-19x15in) s.d.1963 W/C. 21-Jun-3 Hans Stahl, Hamburg #90
£546 $912 €770 Tulips in glass (46x38cm-18x15in) s.d.1964 w/C. 21-Jun-3 Hans Stahl, Hamburg #86
£547 $989 €820 Still life with red and yellow tulips in vase (44x36cm-17x14in) s.d.1968 W/C. 3-Apr-4 Hans Stahl, Hamburg #162/R
£607 $1123 €880 Sylt (31x48cm-12x19in) s.d.1950 W/C. 14-Feb-4 Hans Stahl, Hamburg #143
£615 $1028 €880 Swiss village (37x45cm-15x18in) s.d.1958 W/C. 11-Oct-3 Hans Stahl, Hamburg #104/R
£615 $1058 €880 Bathers in front of the Teufelsbruck (32x50cm-13x20in) st.sig. W/C. 6-Dec-3 Hans Stahl, Toestorf #113
£633 $1146 €950 Baltic beach with cliffs (32x47cm-13x19in) s.d.1952 W/C. 3-Apr-4 Hans Stahl, Hamburg #161/R
£655 $1212 €950 Ships on the Elbe (22x28cm-9x11in) W/C. 14-Feb-4 Hans Stahl, Hamburg #145/R
£655 $1212 €950 Sylt (31x48cm-12x19in) W/C. 14-Feb-4 Hans Stahl, Hamburg #148/R
£692 $1156 €990 Bodensee (37x45cm-15x18in) W/c. 11-Oct-3 Hans Stahl, Hamburg #103/R
£692 $1191 €990 Beach scene with sand dunes and village in distance (31x48cm-12x19in) s.d.1950 W/C. 6-Dec-3 Hans Stahl, Toestorf #117/R
£733 $1327 €1100 Coastal landscape (35x43cm-14x17in) W/C. 3-Apr-4 Hans Stahl, Hamburg #159
£839 $1443 €1200 Harbour (25x36cm-10x14in) s.d.1911 W/C pencil. 2-Dec-3 Hauswedell & Nolte, Hamburg #254/R
£839 $1443 €1200 List (25x43cm-10x17in) s.i.d.50 W/C. 4-Dec-3 Schopman, Hamburg #729/R
£867 $1560 €1300 Beaulieu harbour (32x49cm-13x19in) s.i.d. w/C on chk. 24-Apr-4 Dr Lehr, Berlin #146/R
£1083 $1668 €1700 Flowers (38x46cm-15x18in) s.d.1964 W/C chl. 4-Sep-2 Schopman, Hamburg #141/R est:1950
£1167 $2112 €1750 Sylt (33x50cm-13x20in) W/C. 3-Apr-4 Hans Stahl, Hamburg #160/R est:800
£1170 $1954 €1650 Ships in harbour of southern French city (37x46cm-15x18in) s.d.1963 W/C. 21-Jun-3 Hans Stahl, Hamburg #89/R est:800
£1200 $2208 €1800 Ile de Paris (33x51cm-13x20in) mono.d.8.IX.12 W/C on pencil. 10-Jun-4 Hauswedell & Nolte, Hamburg #258/R est:1500

HAUPTMANN, K (1880-1947) German
£1810 $3077 €2643 Mountain landscape in winter (69x96cm-27x38in) s. 19-Nov-3 Fischer, Luzern #1203/R est:4000-5000 (S.FR 4000)

HAUPTMANN, Karl (1880-1947) German
£459 $766 €666 Wayside cross in the mountains (70x51cm-28x20in) s.d.30. 23-Jun-3 Philippe Schuler, Zurich #8598 (S.FR 1000)
£1014 $1581 €1500 Extensive Black Forest valley (51x63cm-20x25in) s. 31-Mar-3 Bloss, Merzhausen #1559/R
£1049 $1783 €1500 Snowy Black Forest landscape (28x39cm-11x15in) s. panel. 19-Nov-3 Dorotheum, Klagenfurt #16/R est:1000
£1127 $1803 €1600 View of Loffelschmiede (25x35cm-10x14in) s. lit. 19-Sep-3 Karlheinz Kaupp, Staufen #2021/R est:1200
£1216 $1897 €1800 Extensive Black Forest landscape in early summer (57x78cm-22x31in) s. 31-Mar-3 Bloss, Merzhausen #1557/R
£1216 $1897 €1800 Black Forest valley in spring (71x90cm-28x35in) s. 31-Mar-3 Bloss, Merzhausen #1558/R
£1342 $2470 €2000 Snowy pine trees in Black Forest landscape (27x35cm-11x14in) s. board lit. 25-Mar-4 Karlheinz Kaupp, Staufen #2492/R est:600
£1560 $2528 €2200 Sunny winter's day in the Black Forest (40x56cm-16x22in) s. i. verso board lit. 23-May-3 Karlheinz Kaupp, Staufen #1773/R est:1700

£1972 $3155 €2800 Sunny winter landscape (35x49cm-14x19in) s. lit. 19-Sep-3 Karlheinz Kaupp, Staufen #1958/R est:1800
£2465 $3944 €3500 Snowy slope with pine trees (37x34cm-15x13in) s. lit. 19-Sep-3 Karlheinz Kaupp, Staufen #2141/R est:1500
£2517 $4280 €3600 Black Forest autumnal landscape with house (70x90cm-28x35in) s. 28-Nov-3 Schloss Ahlden, Ahlden #1537/R est:2800
£2584 $4754 €3850 First snow in October (30x40cm-12x16in) s. masonite lit. 25-Mar-4 Karlheinz Kaupp, Staufen #2489/R est:2000
£3200 $5760 €4800 Snowy Black Forest (60x70cm-24x28in) s. 26-Apr-4 Rieber, Stuttgart #1190/R est:4500
£3333 $6033 €5000 Morning in the Black Forest (51x76cm-20x30in) s. 1-Apr-4 Frank Peege, Freiburg #1201/R est:4000
£3380 $5408 €4800 Sunner winter's day in Todtmoos Bernau (70x90cm-28x35in) i. verso lit. 19-Sep-3 Karlheinz Kaupp, Staufen #2059/R est:3500
£3490 $6421 €5200 Feldberg pines in the snow (46x59cm-18x23in) s. panel lit. 25-Mar-4 Karlheinz Kaupp, Staufen #2490/R est:3600
£4236 $6693 €6100 Winter landscape near Bernau (70x90cm-28x35in) s.d.37. 19-Sep-3 Schloss Ahlden, Ahlden #1694/R est:5800
£5106 $8272 €7200 Snow covered farmsteads in landscape (70x90cm-28x35in) s. lit. 23-May-3 Karlheinz Kaupp, Staufen #1967 est:8000
£7746 $12394 €11000 Black Forest farmstead by pond (110x140cm-43x55in) s.d.1923 lit. 19-Sep-3 Karlheinz Kaupp, Staufen #2026/R est:8000

HAUPTMANN, Sven (1911-1984) Danish
Works on paper
£496 $928 €724 Composition (50x37cm-20x15in) s. collage. 25-Feb-4 Kunsthallen, Copenhagen #28 (D.KR 5500)

HAUSCHILD, Max (1810-1895) German
£524 $892 €750 Altar in the San Antonio basilica, Padua (34x24cm-13x9in) htd bodycol wash pencil board sold with four others. 21-Nov-3 Reiss & Sohn, Konigstein #206/R

HAUSDORF, Georg (20th C) German
£2235 $4000 €3263 Carousel (41x51cm-16x20in) s. prov. 6-May-4 Shannon's, Milford #211/R est:4000-6000

HAUSE, Rudolf (1877-1961) German
£284 $474 €400 Bathers by lake (70x60cm-28x24in) s. i. verso. 14-Oct-3 Dorotheum, Vienna #104/R
£319 $533 €450 Bathers (70x60cm-28x24in) s. i. verso. 14-Oct-3 Dorotheum, Vienna #105/R

HAUSEN, Werner von (1870-1951) Finnish
£278 $464 €400 Old tree (41x55cm-16x22in) s.d.1914. 26-Oct-3 Bukowskis, Helsinki #344/R

HAUSER, Carry (1895-1985) Austrian
£2013 $3725 €3000 In the water (38x33cm-15x13in) mono.d.84 panel. 9-Mar-4 Dorotheum, Vienna #208/R est:2400-3400
Works on paper
£470 $869 €700 Woman with cat (30x26cm-12x10in) mono. pen Indian ink. 9-Mar-4 Dorotheum, Vienna #71/R
£496 $829 €700 Bookshop (33x23cm-13x9in) mono. Indian ink htd white. 16-Oct-3 Dorotheum, Salzburg #995/R
£570 $1055 €850 Travelling youth (19x17cm-7x7in) s. pen Indian ink pencil W/C gouache. 9-Mar-4 Dorotheum, Vienna #53/R
£769 $1323 €1100 Death as a girl - a dream (38x26cm-15x10in) mono.i. Indian ink W/C. 2-Dec-3 Hauswedell & Nolte, Hamburg #257/R
£839 $1443 €1200 Child worker (25x14cm-10x6in) mono.i.d.1921 W/C pencil. 2-Dec-3 Hauswedell & Nolte, Hamburg #256/R
£845 $1479 €1200 Ingeborg Bachmann (29x21cm-11x8in) s.i.d.1955 mixed media board. 19-Dec-3 Dorotheum, Vienna #185/R
£851 $1421 €1200 Girl in summer landscape (32x26cm-13x10in) s.mono.d.46 gouache. 14-Oct-3 Dorotheum, Vienna #130/R
£1745 $3123 €2600 Joseph and Photiphar's wife (19x19cm-7x7in) s.i.d.22 W/C over pencil. 25-May-4 Karl & Faber, Munich #315/R est:2200
£2685 $4805 €4000 Diamond dealer (18x18cm-7x7in) s.i.d.22 W/C over pencil. 25-May-4 Karl & Faber, Munich #314/R est:2400
£3125 $5313 €4500 Lovers under palm trees (28x21cm-11x8in) s.d.18 gouache. 28-Oct-3 Wiener Kunst Auktionen, Vienna #68/R est:2000-5000

HAUSER, Eric (1930-) German
Sculpture
£6000 $11040 €9000 Steel construction (69cm-27in) s.i. steel exec. 1965 prov. 12-Jun-4 Villa Grisebach, Berlin #353/R est:9000-12000
Works on paper
£282 $451 €400 Line composition (61x86cm-24x34in) s.d.Juli 63 chl lit. 19-Sep-3 Karlheinz Kaupp, Staufen #2191
£317 $507 €450 Composition (60x84cm-24x33in) s.d.28.11.62 chl. 19-Sep-3 Karlheinz Kaupp, Staufen #2205

HAUSER, F (19th C) ?
£1408 $2437 €2000 Allegorical representation (55x74cm-22x29in) s.d.1854. 10-Dec-3 Dorotheum, Vienna #18/R est:2000-2400

HAUSER, John (1859-1918) American
£1471 $2500 €2148 Joe Black Fox, Sioux (17x11cm-7x4in) s.i.d.1902 wood panel prov. 18-Nov-3 John Moran, Pasadena #119 est:4000-6000
£5294 $9000 €7729 Mounted Indian brave with rifle (36x25cm-14x10in) s.d.1909 panel prov. 1-Nov-3 Santa Fe Art, Santa Fe #167/R est:5000-7000
£7647 $13000 €11165 Suspicious noise (30x45cm-12x18in) s.d.1912 s.i.d.verso board prov. 29-Oct-3 Christie's, Los Angeles #23/R est:10000-15000
Works on paper
£497 $800 €721 Cheyenne camp (13x23cm-5x9in) W/C. 22-Aug-3 Altermann Galleries, Santa Fe #87
£1029 $1750 €1502 Boy on a horse in a landscape (10x13cm-4x5in) s.d.1902 gouache board prov. 18-Nov-3 John Moran, Pasadena #119a est:2500-4000
£2825 $5000 €4125 San Ildefonso medicine man (40x25cm-16x10in) s.i.d.99 W/C gouache paper on board. 28-Apr-4 Christie's, Los Angeles #30/R est:6000-8000
£3293 $5500 €4808 Oklahoma buck (35x25cm-14x10in) s.d.1901 i.verso gouache board. 7-Oct-3 Sotheby's, New York #196 est:5000-7000
£4706 $8000 €6871 Scouting (33x23cm-13x9in) s.d.1904 gouache prov.lit. 1-Nov-3 Santa Fe Art, Santa Fe #168/R est:6000-8000

HAUSER, Karl Ludwig (1810-1873) German
£511 $950 €746 Table top still life (56x69cm-22x27in) s. painted c.1890. 7-Mar-4 Treadway Gallery, Cincinnati #494/R

HAUSER, Nadine (20th C) German
£280 $476 €400 Still life with summer flowers (40x30cm-16x12in) s.d.54 i.verso panel. 28-Nov-3 Schloss Ahlden, Ahlden #1558/R

HAUSER, Renée-Yolande (1919-) Swiss
£259 $463 €378 Still life with flowers in water glass (49x20cm-19x8in) s. panel. 12-May-4 Dobiaschofsky, Bern #3634 (S.FR 600)
£431 $772 €629 Bouquet des bois (36x24cm-14x9in) s. i.d.1980 verso panel. 12-May-4 Dobiaschofsky, Bern #3636 (S.FR 1000)

HAUSHOFER, Alfred (1872-1943) German
Works on paper
£1067 $1941 €1600 Chiemsee (40x56cm-16x22in) s.d.1923 gouache. 30-Jun-4 Neumeister, Munich #414/R est:1200

HAUSHOFER, Marie (19/20th C) ?
£537 $988 €800 Still life of flowers (80x65cm-31x26in) s. 24-Mar-4 Hugo Ruef, Munich #982
£805 $1482 €1200 Frauenchiemsee (30x43cm-12x17in) s. verso board. 24-Mar-4 Hugo Ruef, Munich #983

HAUSHOFER, Maximilian (1811-1866) Austrian
£6463 $11568 €9500 Young peasant girls drying washing on Chiemsee shore (28x34cm-11x13in) s. 17-Mar-4 Neumeister, Munich #472/R est:10000
£8333 $13583 €12000 Mountain landscape (57x72cm-22x28in) s. 24-Sep-3 Neumeister, Munich #441/R est:15000

HAUSLEITHNER, Rudolf (1840-1918) Austrian
£1745 $3228 €2600 Frieden und Krieg (91x74cm-36x29in) s. 15-Mar-4 Sotheby's, Amsterdam #57/R est:2500-3500

HAUSMAN, Manfred (1892-1955) German
£940 $1748 €1400 S'olla-Deia Beach, Majorca (60x79cm-24x31in) s. 2-Mar-4 Ansorena, Madrid #138/R

HAUSMANN, Friedrich Karl (1825-1886) German
£700 $1267 €1050 Figures resting in southern mountain landscape (28x42cm-11x17in) 2-Apr-4 Winterberg, Heidelberg #430/R

HAUSMANN, Raoul (1886-1971) Austrian
£1958 $3329 €2800 Abstract composition (92x73cm-36x29in) mono.d.1961 prov. 26-Nov-3 Lempertz, Koln #695/R est:3500
Photographs
£2027 $3628 €3000 Tree trumps in the sand, Sylt (38x30cm-15x12in) s. silver gelatin lit. 8-May-4 Lempertz, Koln #123/R est:3500
£2400 $4224 €3600 Nude (40x30cm-16x12in) s.i.d.1931 verso card printed 1955 prov. 21-May-4 Bloomsbury, London #95/R est:2000-3000
£3497 $5944 €5000 Jeux mecaniques (17x23cm-7x9in) i. verso bromide silver gelatin lit.exhib. 27-Nov-3 Villa Grisebach, Berlin #1207/R est:800-1200
£6364 $10945 €9100 Nu (8x5cm-3x2in) photo. 6-Dec-3 Renaud, Paris #144/R

HAUSSEN, Carl von (1887-1962) American?
£4348 $8000 €6348 New Mexico winter scene (66x76cm-26x30in) s. 26-Jun-4 Susanin's, Chicago #6063/R est:2000-4000

HAUSSWOLF, Annika von (1967-) Swedish
Photographs
£2466 $4438 €3600 The best stories are the once which are not told (110x138cm-43x54in) s.d.1999 verso C print prov. 26-Apr-4 Bukowskis, Stockholm #535/R est:40000-50000 (S.KR 34000)

HAUSTRAETE, Gaston (1878-1949) Belgian
£464 $844 €700 Le vieux marche en hiver (50x60cm-20x24in) s. 15-Jun-4 Galerie Moderne, Brussels #166/R
£517 $957 €750 Nature morte aux homards (80x92cm-31x36in) s.d.1929. 13-Jan-4 Vanderkindere, Brussels #77
£537 $993 €800 Hechtel landscape (48x78cm-19x31in) s.i.d.1899. 13-Mar-4 De Vuyst, Lokeren #172
£800 $1432 €1200 Boats at Zeebrugge (70x80cm-28x31in) s.d.1920 s.i.d.1920 verso. 15-May-4 De Vuyst, Lokeren #158
£972 $1624 €1400 Place des Barricades (80x100cm-31x39in) s. 21-Oct-3 Galerie Moderne, Brussels #214/R
£986 $1725 €1400 Le Parc de Bruxelles (65x80cm-26x31in) s. 16-Dec-3 Galerie Moderne, Brussels #763/R
£1081 $1903 €1600 Rue des Olives a Bruxelles (70x80cm-28x31in) s. 18-May-4 Galerie Moderne, Brussels #159/R est:1000-1500
£1103 $2041 €1600 L'allumeur de reverberes (65x80cm-26x31in) s.d.1910. 19-Jan-4 Horta, Bruxelles #371 est:1000-1500

£1197 $2095 €1700 Still life of flowers (75x60cm-30x24in) s.indis.d. 19-Dec-3 Dorotheum, Vienna #119/R est:1500-2000
£2000 $3680 €3000 In front of the mirror (105x90cm-41x35in) s.d.1922. 9-Jun-4 Christie's, Amsterdam #84/R est:3000-5000
£2200 $4004 €3212 Seated nude (40x30cm-16x12in) s.d.1922. 21-Jun-4 Bonhams, New Bond Street #11/R est:3000-4000
£2695 $4501 €3800 Nu assis de dos (113x87cm-44x34in) s.d.1920 oval. 14-Oct-3 Vanderkindere, Brussels #110

HAUTH, Emil van (1899-1974) German
£1667 $3067 €2500 Landscape (46x64cm-18x25in) s.d.1927 panel prov. 12-Jun-4 Villa Grisebach, Berlin #241/R est:3500-4500
£5000 $9200 €7500 Portrait of a lady (88x54cm-35x21in) s.d.1926 panel prov. prov.lit. 12-Jun-4 Villa Grisebach, Berlin #242/R est:5000-7000

HAUTRIVE, Mathilde Marguerite (1881-1963) French
£474 $857 €720 Vue de Venise (38x42cm-15x17in) s. 18-Apr-4 Rouillac, Vendome #151

HAVE, Henrik (20th C) Danish
£517 $880 €755 Composition (90x70cm-35x28in) s.d.01. 26-Nov-3 Kunsthallen, Copenhagen #177/R (D.KR 5500)

HAVEKOST, Eberhard (1967-) American
£19500 $35880 €28470 Hobbs, industries 5 (50x70cm-20x28in) s.i.d.01 prov. 25-Jun-4 Christie's, London #235/R est:8000-12000

HAVELKA, Roman (1877-1950) Czechoslovakian
£394 $654 €575 Spring at Stary Bitov (33x45cm-13x18in) s. board. 4-Oct-3 Dorotheum, Prague #58/R est:10000-15000 (C.KR 18000)
£577 $1072 €842 Winter mood (37x51cm-15x20in) s. board. 6-Mar-4 Dorotheum, Prague #92 est:20000-30000 (C.KR 28000)
£657 $1090 €959 Winter late afternoon (31x49cm-12x19in) s.d.1923 board. 4-Oct-3 Dorotheum, Prague #68/R est:15000-25000 (C.KR 30000)

HAVELL, Alfred C (1855-1928) British
£1000 $1800 €1460 Horse Pepita in a stable (42x52cm-17x20in) s. 20-Apr-4 Rowley Fine Art, Newmarket #444/R

HAVELL, Edmund (jnr-attrib) (1819-1894) British
£2900 $5307 €4234 Portrait of Richard Roake seated on a grey hunter surrounded by hounds (58x74cm-23x29in) 28-Jul-4 Mallams, Oxford #395/R est:3000-4000

HAVELL, William (1782-1857) British
Works on paper
£460 $846 €672 Chinese vessels on river (5x15cm-2x6in) pen ink wash. 23-Mar-4 Bonhams, Knightsbridge #257
£640 $1184 €934 View of Bolton Abbey with cattle watering (38x51cm-15x20in) s. 12-Feb-4 Andrew Hartley, Ilkley #790
£1150 $2151 €1725 Shepherds reposing (76x102cm-30x40in) W/C. 26-Jul-4 Bonhams, Bath #1/R est:600-800

HAVELL, William (attrib) (1782-1857) British
Works on paper
£450 $833 €657 Towards Rome (13x23cm-5x9in) W/C. 10-Feb-4 David Lay, Penzance #134/R
£800 $1336 €1168 View of Windsor Castle (17x25cm-7x10in) W/C prov. 16-Oct-3 Christie's, Kensington #28/R

HAVEN, Franklin de (1856-1934) American
£283 $450 €413 Country church (76x64cm-30x25in) s. 4-May-3 William Jenack, New York #215
£432 $800 €631 Country road in fall landscape (41x51cm-16x20in) s. 13-Mar-4 DeFina, Austinburg #725/R
£559 $900 €816 Forest landscape with water (76x61cm-30x24in) s. 20-Aug-3 James Julia, Fairfield #1712/R
£594 $1100 €867 Fall landscape (23x25cm-9x10in) s. 18-Jul-4 Bonhams & Butterfields, Los Angeles #7029/R
£919 $1700 €1342 Landscape (61x76cm-24x30in) s. 13-Mar-4 DeFina, Austinburg #796 est:2000-3000
£1321 $2100 €1929 Moonlit landscape (91x122cm-36x48in) s.d.1893. 9-Mar-3 William Jenack, New York #176 est:4000-6000
£2432 $4500 €3551 Camp in the woods (61x76cm-24x30in) s. 13-Mar-4 DeFina, Austinburg #908/R est:1500-2500

HAVERKAMP, Gerrit (1872-1926) Dutch
£414 $691 €600 Still life of flowers (39x29cm-15x11in) s. 11-Nov-3 Vendu Notarishuis, Rotterdam #572/R

HAVERMAET, Charles van (fl.1895-1911) British
£3099 $5361 €4400 Le petit dejeuner (47x72cm-19x28in) s. 9-Dec-3 Campo, Vlaamse Kaai #455/R est:4000-6000

HAVERMANN, Hendrik Johannes (1857-1928) Dutch
Works on paper
£306 $550 €447 Mother and child (33x25cm-13x10in) s. W/C. 24-Apr-4 Weschler, Washington #566/R

HAVERTY, Joseph Patrick (1794-1864) British
£38000 $68020 €55480 Group portrait of a family, thought to be the Reilly family of Scarvagh (122x155cm-48x61in) indis.s. prov.lit. 14-May-4 Christie's, London #67/R est:25000-35000

HAVLICEK, Karel (1907-1988) Austrian
Works on paper
£867 $1595 €1300 Poskakujici Ptak (43x30cm-17x12in) mono.i.d.49 lead pencil. 9-Jun-4 Artcurial Briest, Paris #401/R est:800-1000

HAVLICEK, Vincenz (1864-1914) Austrian
Works on paper
£537 $988 €800 Donau with Leopold and Kahlenberg (19x25cm-7x10in) s.d.94 W/C. 26-Mar-4 Dorotheum, Vienna #300/R
£690 $1145 €1000 St Maria in Wolkensein, Grodner valley (21x28cm-8x11in) s.i.d.04 W/C bodycol. 30-Sep-3 Dorotheum, Vienna #348/R
£872 $1605 €1300 Klosterneubrug (19x30cm-7x12in) s.i.d.97 W/C. 26-Mar-4 Dorotheum, Vienna #234/R

HAVSTEEN-MIKKELSEN, Sven (1912-1999) Danish
£948 $1744 €1384 Risin (24x35cm-9x14in) init. s.stretcher. 29-Mar-4 Rasmussen, Copenhagen #504/R (D.KR 10500)
£1038 $1910 €1515 The Annunciation (38x26cm-15x10in) init. 29-Mar-4 Rasmussen, Copenhagen #562/R (D.KR 11500)
£1083 $2025 €1581 Winter landscape (60x72cm-24x28in) init. 25-Feb-4 Kunsthallen, Copenhagen #189/R est:12000 (D.KR 12000)
£1083 $2025 €1581 Summer landscape with view towards the fjord (56x83cm-22x33in) init. 25-Feb-4 Kunsthallen, Copenhagen #225/R est:7000 (D.KR 12000)
£1242 $2111 €1813 Landscape, Gulbrandsdalen (40x51cm-16x20in) init. 26-Nov-3 Kunsthallen, Copenhagen #292/R est:10000 (D.KR 13200)
£1374 $2199 €1992 Landscape, Ulvemarken (38x46cm-15x18in) init. 17-Sep-3 Kunsthallen, Copenhagen #243/R est:5000 (D.KR 14500)
£1557 $2833 €2273 Scottish landscape (27x46cm-11x18in) init. s.verso. 7-Feb-4 Rasmussen, Havnen #4120/R est:3000-5000 (D.KR 17000)
£1625 $3038 €2373 Summer landscape (73x92cm-29x36in) init.d.42. 25-Feb-4 Kunsthallen, Copenhagen #211/R est:10000 (D.KR 18000)
£1760 $3238 €2570 Evening sun over roof tops (33x46cm-13x18in) init. 29-Mar-4 Rasmussen, Copenhagen #506/R est:12000 (D.KR 19500)

HAWAY, Georges (1941-) Belgian
£321 $600 €469 Marine landscape (30x41cm-12x16in) s. 25-Feb-4 Dallas Auction Gallery, Dallas #527/R

HAWKER, Derrick (1936-) British
£1700 $3043 €2482 Late evening, Belfast Lough (91x91cm-36x36in) s.d.68 s.i.overlap. 14-May-4 Christie's, Kensington #456/R est:600-800

HAWKER, Thomas (1640-1725) British
£4800 $8832 €7008 Portrait of Charles, Lord Wilmot, son of Henry Earl of Rochester, when a child (71x58cm-28x23in) i. painted cartouche prov.lit. 26-Mar-4 Sotheby's, London #6/R est:4000-6000

HAWKESWORTH, J H (19th C) British
£1119 $1902 €1600 Man with gun and young boy on a country path (13x11cm-5x4in) s. panel sold with a companion. 18-Nov-3 Mealy's, Castlecomer #1356/R est:1600-2000

HAWKINS, George (jnr) (1819-1852) British
Works on paper
£700 $1288 €1022 Residence of Joseph Calrow (30x39cm-12x15in) s.d.1831 W/C. 22-Jun-4 Bonhams, Knightsbridge #20/R

HAWKINS, H F Weaver (1893-1977) Australian/British
£307 $485 €448 Abstract (30x25cm-12x10in) s.d.58 board. 2-Sep-3 Deutscher-Menzies, Melbourne #314/R (A.D 750)
£410 $647 €599 Free unity (44x38cm-17x15in) s.d.59 s.i. verso board. 2-Sep-3 Deutscher-Menzies, Melbourne #313/R (A.D 1000)
£533 $842 €778 Harvesting (45x38cm-18x15in) s.d.58 board. 2-Sep-3 Deutscher-Menzies, Melbourne #288/R est:4500-6500 (A.D 1300)
£820 $1295 €1197 Kitchen plate (25x30cm-10x12in) s. s.i. verso board. 2-Sep-3 Deutscher-Menzies, Melbourne #304/R est:2600-3400 (A.D 2000)
£1639 $2656 €2393 Abstract C2 (71x51cm-28x20in) s.d.53 i.verso board. 30-Jul-3 Goodman, Sydney #58/R est:2500-3500 (A.D 4000)
£1653 $3058 €2413 Pittwater (71x51cm-28x20in) s.d.59 board prov.exhib. 10-Mar-4 Deutscher-Menzies, Melbourne #319/R est:4000-6000 (A.D 4000)
Works on paper
£1012 $1630 €1478 Rhythmic Activity (55x37cm-22x15in) init.d.71 ink W/C prov. 25-Aug-3 Sotheby's, Paddington #467/R est:2500-3500 (A.D 2500)

HAWKINS, Louis Welden (1849-1910) British
£1915 $3198 €2700 Jeune garcon a la couronne de lierre (20x17cm-8x7in) s. panel. 12-Oct-3 St-Germain-en-Laye Encheres #36/R est:2000-2500
£3147 $5350 €4500 Portrait of presumably Mademoiselle Hawkins (55x46cm-22x18in) s. 1-Dec-3 Camard, Paris #13/R est:4500-5000
Works on paper
£510 $913 €750 Le pique-nique (19x39cm-7x15in) s. W/C gouache black pencil. 19-Mar-4 Piasa, Paris #195a
£699 $1168 €1000 Jeune femme dans le sous-bois (35x22cm-14x9in) s. W/C gouache. 29-Jun-3 Eric Pillon, Calais #10/R
£699 $1168 €1000 Mere et fille dans un jardin (29x23cm-11x9in) s. W/C gouache. 29-Jun-3 Eric Pillon, Calais #9/R
£6358 $11000 €9283 Priestess (94x62cm-37x24in) s. pastel. 11-Dec-3 Sotheby's, New York #171/R est:6000-8000

HAWKINS, O John (1935-) Canadian
£1786 $3071 €2608 Melting icefield (60x160cm-24x63in) s. acrylic diptych. 2-Dec-3 Joyner Waddington, Toronto #309/R est:2500-3000 (C.D 4000)

HAWKINS, Rocky (1950-) American
£1341 $2200 €1944 Lover's rose (46x36cm-18x14in) s. board painted c.1980. 7-Jun-3 Treadway Gallery, Cincinnati #1526 est:1000-2000

HAWKINS, William (1895-1990) American
£4790 $8000 €6993 Eagle and snake (48x86cm-19x34in) acrylic board prov. 15-Nov-3 Slotin Folk Art, Buford #128/R est:8000-15000
£5389 $9000 €7868 Building (91x107cm-36x42in) enamel posterboard prov. 15-Nov-3 Slotin Folk Art, Buford #127/R est:10000-20000
£8611 $15500 €12572 Christmas tree (89x64cm-35x25in) acrylic board. 24-Apr-4 Slotin Folk Art, Buford #275/R est:10000-15000
£17365 $29000 €25353 Alligator with lover number 2 (117x142cm-46x56in) enamel fibreboard prov.lit. 15-Nov-3 Slotin Folk Art, Buford #126/R est:20000-40000
Works on paper
£222 $400 €324 Rolls Royce, 1979 (8x13cm-3x5in) pencil. 24-Apr-4 Slotin Folk Art, Buford #277/R
£359 $600 €524 Running rabbit (36x43cm-14x17in) graphite prov. 15-Nov-3 Slotin Folk Art, Buford #130/R
£509 $850 €743 Camel (46x53cm-18x21in) graphite prov. 15-Nov-3 Slotin Folk Art, Buford #129/R

HAWKSETT, John (19th C) British
£2238 $3804 €3200 The visionary (41x32cm-16x13in) i.verso. 18-Nov-3 Whyte's, Dublin #117/R est:1500-2000

HAWKSWORTH, Joseph Haslam (1827-1908) British?
£399 $646 €579 Fishing in the river (26x38cm-10x15in) s. board. 31-Jul-3 International Art Centre, Auckland #160/R est:1200-1800 (NZ.D 1100)

HAWKSWORTH, Joseph Haslam (attrib) (1827-1908) British?
£1600 $2672 €2336 Farmstead scene with approaching shower (69x89cm-27x35in) s. 16-Oct-3 Lawrence, Crewkerne #733 est:800-1200

HAWKSWORTH, William Thomas Martin (1853-1935) British
Works on paper
£473 $832 €700 View of Gravesend, Kent (14x22cm-6x9in) W/C black chk prov. 19-May-4 Sotheby's, Amsterdam #187/R

HAWLEY, Hughson (1850-1936) American
Works on paper
£432 $700 €631 West Haven Armory (11x20cm-4x8in) s. W/C. 31-Jul-3 Eldred, East Dennis #1200/R

HAWORTH, Bobs Cogill (1904-1988) Canadian
£200 $366 €292 Cape North, Cape Breton (28x37cm-11x15in) s. oil acrylic board prov. 1-Jun-4 Joyner Waddington, Toronto #358/R (C.D 500)
£300 $469 €435 Winter white (51x63cm-20x25in) s.i. acrylic on board prov. 26-Mar-3 Walker's, Ottawa #425/R (C.D 700)
£300 $549 €438 Newhaven, Cape Breton Island (50x63cm-20x25in) s.i. acrylic board. 1-Jun-4 Hodgins, Calgary #157/R (C.D 750)
£357 $614 €521 Coastal fog, CBI - Miel's harbour (56x77cm-22x30in) s. acrylic board painted 1975 prov. 2-Dec-3 Joyner Waddington, Toronto #190/R (C.D 800)

HAWRANEK, Friedrich (1821-1899) Czechoslovakian
£14000 $25760 €20440 Village life (62x90cm-24x35in) s.d.1846. 25-Mar-4 Christie's, Kensington #182/R est:12000-18000
Works on paper
£306 $509 €447 Trees study (36x26cm-14x10in) col pencil. 4-Oct-3 Dorotheum, Prague #263/R est:8000-12000 (C.KR 14000)

HAWTHORNE, Charles W (1872-1930) American
£4620 $8500 €6745 Hauling sea weed (35x61cm-14x24in) s. prov. 27-Jun-4 Freeman, Philadelphia #87/R est:4000-6000
£8380 $15000 €12235 Orange and red (56x46cm-22x18in) s.d.1903 prov. 26-May-4 Doyle, New York #80/R est:10000-15000
£13081 $22500 €19098 Portrait of a young girl (55x42cm-22x17in) i. canvas on board. 3-Dec-3 Doyle, New York #237/R est:12000-18000
£18519 $30000 €26853 Waiting (102x101cm-40x40in) s. board prov.exhib. 8-Aug-3 Barridorf, Portland #118/R est:30000-50000

HAWTHORNE, Edith Garregues (1874-1949) American
£449 $750 €656 Landscape with blue foothills (36x46cm-14x18in) indis.sig. 26-Oct-3 Bonhams & Butterfields, San Francisco #6510/R

HAWTHORNE, John S (20th C) American
£262 $425 €383 Waldoboro from the south. mono.d.Aug 1932. 26-Jul-3 Thomaston Place, Thomaston #394/R

HAXTON, Elaine Alys (1909-1999) Australian
£3239 $5215 €4729 Bathers (58x73cm-23x29in) s. board. 25-Aug-3 Sotheby's, Paddington #257/R est:9000-12000 (A.D 8000)
£4858 $7822 €7093 Mediterranean beach scene (49x59cm-19x23in) s. composition board prov. 25-Aug-3 Sotheby's, Paddington #372/R est:12000-16000 (A.D 12000)
£6612 $12231 €9654 Harlequin and horse (90x45cm-35x18in) s.d.1969 board. 10-Mar-4 Deutscher-Menzies, Melbourne #270/R est:20000-25000 (A.D 16000)

HAY, Bernard (1864-?) British/Italian
£296 $473 €420 Bearded man smoking pipe (40x25cm-16x10in) s.i. lit. 19-Sep-3 Karlheinz Kaupp, Staufen #1985/R
£1096 $1863 €1600 Capri (24x38cm-9x15in) s. lit. 6-Nov-3 Allgauer, Kempten #3443/R est:1500
£1150 $2093 €1679 Venetian Canal scene (69x46cm-27x18in) s.d.1909. 16-Jun-4 Andrew Hartley, Ilkley #1084/R est:900-1200
£1867 $3435 €2800 Taormin, Siciy (31x50cm-12x20in) s.d.1909. 10-Jun-4 Christie's, Rome #75/R est:2300-2800
£2044 $3250 €2984 Venetian canal (72x45cm-28x18in) s.i.d.1909. 12-Sep-3 Skinner, Boston #312/R est:2000
£2667 $4827 €4000 Capri (54x35cm-21x14in) s. 1-Apr-4 Van Ham, Cologne #1412/R est:2200
£3056 $5042 €4400 Children playing on Naples beach. Fishermen in Bay of Naples (25x40cm-10x16in) s. two. 3-Jul-3 Van Ham, Cologne #1233/R est:4200
£18000 $32760 €26280 Grand Canal, Venice (61x96cm-24x38in) s. 1-Jul-4 Sotheby's, London #338/R est:20000-30000

HAY, Emily (19/20th C) British
Works on paper
£500 $835 €730 View of Morton Corbett Hall (33x51cm-13x20in) s.i.d.1874 W/C. 12-Nov-3 Halls, Shrewsbury #249/R

HAY, James Hamilton (1874-1916) British
Works on paper
£500 $850 €730 Fishing boats and other shipping in a harbour (21x27cm-8x11in) s.d.1907 pencil W/C prov. 19-Nov-3 Tennants, Leyburn #870

HAY, Jill (20th C) New Zealander?
£293 $542 €428 Queenstown (90x59cm-35x23in) s. 9-Mar-4 Watson's, Christchurch #198 (NZ.D 800)

HAY, William M (fl.1852-1881) British
£811 $1395 €1184 Poor Mary (50x61cm-20x24in) mono.d.65. 8-Dec-3 Philippe Schuler, Zurich #3411/R (S.FR 1800)
£5500 $9845 €8030 Maid of the inn (29x25cm-11x10in) s.d.81 i.verso board exhib. 27-May-4 Christie's, Kensington #328/R est:800-1200

HAYCOCK, Frederick J (?) British
£694 $1104 €1000 Farming horses (74x48cm-29x19in) board. 10-Sep-3 James Adam, Dublin #82 est:1000-2000

HAYD, Karl (1882-1945) Austrian
£315 $535 €450 Gosausee Guest House (33x48cm-13x19in) s. board. 27-Nov-3 Dorotheum, Linz #485/R
£333 $597 €500 Red roses (34x48cm-13x19in) s. board. 13-May-4 Dorotheum, Linz #476/R
£385 $654 €550 Still life of flowers (53x45cm-21x18in) s. board. 27-Nov-3 Dorotheum, Linz #467/R
£420 $713 €600 Peonies in pot (68x98cm-27x39in) s. panel. 27-Nov-3 Dorotheum, Linz #509/R

HAYDEN, Adrian Murray (1931-1975) Irish
£986 $1577 €1400 Dublin Bay from the Wicklow mountains (61x98cm-24x39in) s. board. 16-Sep-3 Whyte's, Dublin #188/R est:1200-1500

HAYDEN, Charles Henry (1856-1901) American
£1582 $2800 €2310 Sheep grazing in a meadow (14x18cm-6x7in) s. 2-May-4 Bonhams & Butterfields, San Francisco #1113/R est:2500-3500
£13559 $24000 €19796 Winter sunrise (45x75cm-18x30in) s.d.1891 prov. 28-Apr-4 Christie's, Los Angeles #44/R est:6000-8000

HAYDEN, Edward Parker (1858-1922) American
£410 $750 €599 Autumn (76x64cm-30x25in) s. painted c.1920. 5-Jun-4 Treadway Gallery, Cincinnati #564/R
£2419 $4500 €3532 Landscape with a stream (51x76cm-20x30in) s. painted c.1880. 7-Mar-4 Treadway Gallery, Cincinnati #531/R est:2500-3500

HAYDEN, Henri (1883-1970) French
£526 $953 €800 Paysage provencal (23x32cm-9x13in) s.i.verso cardboard. 19-Apr-4 Boscher, Cherbourg #804
£530 $964 €800 Paysage de Mougins (32x46cm-13x18in) s. s.i.d.mars 43 verso cardboard. 18-Jun-4 Charbonneaux, Paris #173
£629 $1151 €950 Vase de fleurs (34x41cm-13x16in) s. 9-Apr-4 Bailly Pommery, Paris #93
£1259 $2140 €1800 Paysage de compagne (27x35cm-11x14in) s. cardboard. 28-Nov-3 Blanchet, Paris #110 est:1500-1800
£1389 $2320 €2000 L'entree du port (38x47cm-15x19in) s. painted c.1930. 21-Oct-3 Artcurial Briest, Paris #256/R est:1800-2200
£1399 $2378 €2000 Still life of flowers with roses and gladioli (73x56cm-29x22in) s.d.30. 24-Nov-3 Glerum, Amsterdam #4/R est:2500-3000
£1413 $2600 €2063 Untitled - Landscape (33x46cm-13x18in) s.d.62 prov. 27-Jun-4 Freeman, Philadelphia #61/R est:1500-2500
£1512 $2600 €2208 Vue sur Beauval (61x79cm-24x31in) s.d.60 i.stretcher prov. 7-Dec-3 Freeman, Philadelphia #55 est:3000-5000
£1890 $3250 €2759 Marnet en verte (58x81cm-23x32in) s.d.52 prov. 7-Dec-3 Freeman, Philadelphia #54 est:3000-5000
£1890 $3250 €2759 Nature morte au panier (38x56cm-15x22in) s.d.63 prov. 7-Dec-3 Freeman, Philadelphia #63 est:2000-3000
£1987 $3616 €3000 Tete de femme (35x27cm-14x11in) s. 15-Jun-4 Rossini, Paris #146 est:2500-3500
£2069 $3828 €3000 Nature morte a la carafe et aux coquillages (60x73cm-24x29in) s.d.62. 13-Feb-4 Charbonneaux, Paris #73/R est:2500-3000
£2400 $4008 €3504 Chemin de Fay le Bac, bord de Marne (54x65cm-21x26in) s.d.56. 22-Oct-3 Sotheby's, Olympia #103/R est:3000-4000
£2448 $4210 €3500 Village de Meyroune, Lot (60x73cm-24x29in) s.d. 3-Dec-3 Beaussant & Lefèvre, Paris #39/R est:3000-4000
£2583 $4701 €3900 Le village (60x73cm-24x29in) s. 16-Jun-4 Claude Boisgirard, Paris #72/R est:4000-5000
£2667 $4800 €4000 Le village (54x73cm-21x29in) s.d.31. 26-Apr-4 Tajan, Paris #151/R est:4000-6000

£2800	$4844	€4088	Chamigny, rouge (54x73cm-21x29in) s.d.64 i.d.1964 stretcher. 11-Dec-3 Christie's, Kensington #177/R est:1500-2000
£2800	$5152	€4088	La marne a Ussy-sur-Marne (38x46cm-15x18in) s.d.57 board. 24-Mar-4 Sotheby's, Olympia #75/R est:3000-4000
£2937	$5052	€4200	Landscape (61x71cm-24x28in) s.d.1935 prov. 2-Dec-3 Sotheby's, Amsterdam #79/R est:3000-4000
£3333	$5433	€4800	Paysage de Provence (37x44cm-15x17in) s. cardboard on canvas. 26-Sep-3 Rabourdin & Choppin de Janvry, Paris #48/R est:5000-6000
£3775	$6870	€5700	Nature morte a la bouteille de Chianti (81x65cm-32x26in) s.d.1955. 16-Jun-4 Claude Boisgirard, Paris #73/R est:5000-6000
£5999	$11040	€9000	Nature morte table rouge (60x73cm-24x29in) s.d.57 exhib.lit. 8-Jun-4 Artcurial Briest, Paris #197/R est:4000-6000
£6294	$10825	€9000	Les deux vases roses (65x81cm-26x32in) s.d.69 exhib. 3-Dec-3 Beaussant & Lefèvre, Paris #41/R est:4000-5000
£6333	$11654	€9500	Route de Jaignes (60x81cm-24x32in) s.d.59 lit. 8-Jun-4 Artcurial Briest, Paris #198/R est:4000-6000
£10738	$19007	€16000	Port de Sanary (54x65cm-21x26in) s. painted c.1930. 27-Apr-4 Artcurial Briest, Paris #156/R est:15000-18000
£14570	$26517	€22000	Red interior (55x46cm-22x18in) s.d.1914. 15-Jun-4 Rossini, Paris #144/R est:15000-20000
£22069	$36855	€32000	Femme au chapeau (61x50cm-24x20in) s.d.1915 lit. 17-Nov-3 Claude Boisgirard, Paris #39/R est:10000-12000
£28188	$52430	€42000	Composition au pain et au verre de vin (38x45cm-15x18in) s. s.d.1920 verso prov. 2-Mar-4 Artcurial Briest, Paris #147/R est:25000-30000
£42000	$76440	€61320	Nature morte aux artichauts (100x72cm-39x28in) s. painted 1914 prov.exhib. 4-Feb-4 Sotheby's, London #260/R est:40000-60000
£46980	$86913	€70000	Composition (64x81cm-25x32in) s. 15-Mar-4 Claude Boisgirard, Paris #59/R est:80000-100000
£51397	$92000	€75040	Still life of a bottle and some fruit (54x65cm-21x26in) s.d.1914 prov.exhib. 5-May-4 Christie's, Rockefeller NY #290/R est:60000-80000
£100559	$180000	€146816	Composition (92x60cm-36x24in) s.d.1919 prov.exhib. 18-Mar-4 Sotheby's, New York #101/R est:180000-220000
Works on paper			
£600	$1002	€876	Ship offshore (55x40cm-22x16in) s.d.57 crayon W/C. 21-Oct-3 Bonhams, Knightsbridge #149/R
£652	$1200	€952	Dimple bottle (38x46cm-15x18in) s.d.67 gouache prov. 27-Jun-4 Freeman, Philadelphia #59/R
£950	$1748	€1387	Les collines vues depuis d'Ussy-sur-Marne (35x52cm-14x20in) s.d.66 gouache on board. 24-Mar-4 Sotheby's, Olympia #76/R
£1300	$2405	€1898	Still life with teapot (38x46cm-15x18in) s.d.68 gouache. 13-Jul-4 Bonhams, Knightsbridge #73/R est:800-1200
£1419	$2682	€2100	Paysage de la Marne (29x47cm-11x19in) s.d.1958 gouache. 21-Feb-4 Cornette de St.Cyr, Paris #205/R est:2000-2500
£3500	$6370	€5110	Les Collines vues depuis la Plaine d'Ussy-sur-Marne (33x51cm-13x20in) s.d.64 gouache board prov. 4-Feb-4 Sotheby's, Olympia #94/R est:2000-3000

HAYDEN, Palmer (1890-1973) American

£1397	$2250	€2040	Roust-about (41x36cm-16x14in) 20-Aug-3 James Julia, Fairfield #81/R est:2000-4000

HAYDEN, Reg (?) British

£280	$512	€409	Bar interior, Millbank (38x58cm-15x23in) s.i.verso. 7-Apr-4 Gardiner & Houlgate, Bath #275/R

HAYDON, Benjamin Robert (1786-1846) British

£500	$895	€730	Portrait of Robert Hawkes, holding a letter and spectacles (71x51cm-28x20in) 27-May-4 Christie's, Kensington #83/R

HAYEK, Hans von (1869-1940) Austrian

£340	$626	€510	Summer landscape (35x51cm-14x20in) s. board. 11-Jun-4 Wendl, Rudolstadt #4065/R
£342	$582	€500	Winter landscape with stream (34x50cm-13x20in) s. 5-Nov-3 Hugo Ruef, Munich #1009
£480	$883	€720	Cattle drinking at a stream (60x80cm-24x31in) s. 11-Jun-4 Wendl, Rudolstadt #4064/R
£943	$1500	€1377	Flock of grazing sheep with trees in background (91x69cm-36x27in) s. 10-Sep-3 Alderfer's, Hatfield #287 est:1200-1400
£1376	$2298	€1995	Beach scene on the Baltic (35x50cm-14x20in) s. s.i. verso board. 23-Jun-3 Philippe Schuler, Zurich #3564 est:2500-3000 (S.FR 3000)

HAYER, Florine (1868-1936) American?

£528	$850	€771	Still life with roses on a table (46x74cm-18x29in) s. canvas on board painted c.1914. 22-Feb-3 Bunte, Elgin #1248

HAYES (?) British

£260	$434	€380	Moonlit shipping scene (18x32cm-7x13in) s. board. 21-Oct-3 Bruton Knowles, Cheltenham #442

HAYES, Claude (1852-1922) British

£420	$773	€613	Harvesting near Arundel (24x34cm-9x13in) s. i.verso board. 23-Mar-4 Anderson & Garland, Newcastle #417
£764	$1245	€1100	River landscape with flock of birds landing (51x81cm-20x32in) s. 23-Sep-3 De Veres Art Auctions, Dublin #331/R
£1000	$1670	€1460	Children on a bridge with a cottage (61x51cm-24x20in) 7-Oct-3 Bonhams, Knightsbridge #101/R est:500-700
£1500	$2580	€2190	Gulls by the river (50x83cm-20x33in) s. 3-Dec-3 John Ross, Belfast #207 est:1600-1800
Works on paper			
£270	$491	€394	Sheepfold (25x35cm-10x14in) s. W/C htd bodycol scratching out. 29-Jun-4 Bonhams, Knowle #64
£280	$504	€409	Sheep grazing beside a coastline (23x35cm-9x14in) s. pencil W/C. 21-Apr-4 Tennants, Leyburn #927
£320	$509	€464	Royal Common, Surrey (23x33cm-9x13in) s. W/C exec.c.1880. 23-Mar-3 Desmond Judd, Cranbrook #1036
£323	$594	€472	Haying scene (23x34cm-9x13in) s. W/C. 14-Jun-4 Waddingtons, Toronto #171/R (C.D 800)
£329	$605	€500	The hay gatherers (25x33cm-10x13in) s. W/C prov. 22-Jun-4 De Veres Art Auctions, Dublin #183/R
£350	$644	€511	Cattle watering (25x35cm-10x14in) s. W/C. 23-Mar-4 Bonhams, Knightsbridge #206/R
£360	$598	€526	On the Ouse near Houghton (18x23cm-7x9in) s. W/C prov. 10-Jun-3 Canterbury Auctions, UK #128/R
£380	$707	€555	Tending sheep (25x35cm-10x14in) s. W/C. 3-Mar-4 John Ross, Belfast #129
£400	$756	€584	Edge of New Forest (24x35cm-9x14in) s. W/C. 23-Feb-4 David Duggleby, Scarborough #603/R
£400	$728	€584	Landscape with village and cattle grazing (22x34cm-9x13in) s. W/C. 15-Jun-4 Bonhams, Leeds #29
£400	$748	€584	View of Camber Castle (26x42cm-10x17in) pencil W/C. 22-Jul-4 Tennants, Leyburn #746
£500	$850	€730	Berkshire Common. Landscape (24x34cm-9x13in) s. W/C pair. 18-Nov-3 Bonhams, Leeds #28
£500	$900	€730	Hampshire landscape, shepherd and flock near a path (44x58cm-17x23in) s. i.verso W/C. 21-Apr-4 Rupert Toovey, Partridge Green #116
£550	$1007	€803	Windmill in Sussex (37x52cm-15x20in) s. i.verso W/C. 27-Jan-4 Holloways, Banbury #299/R
£600	$984	€876	Break in the harvest, figures crossing a bridge, a farmhand watering horse (23x36cm-9x14in) s. W/C htd white. 29-May-3 Neales, Nottingham #726/R
£600	$1080	€876	Figures with a horse and cart on a moor (16x25cm-6x10in) s. pencil W/C. 21-Apr-4 Tennants, Leyburn #926
£620	$1122	€905	Edge of New Forest (23x33cm-9x13in) s. W/C. 16-Apr-4 Keys, Aylsham #475/R
£700	$1302	€1022	View of Sudland Bay, Dorset (50x66cm-20x26in) s. W/C. 3-Mar-4 John Ross, Belfast #59
£720	$1332	€1051	Shepherd and his flock (24x35cm-9x14in) s. W/C. 10-Mar-4 Sotheby's, Olympia #94/R
£750	$1388	€1095	Reaper's lunch (34x52cm-13x20in) s. W/C pencil prov. sold with two by different artists three prov. 10-Mar-4 Sotheby's, Olympia #149/R
£850	$1471	€1241	Shepherd tending his flock. W/C. 11-Dec-3 Rendalls, Ashburton #1728
£860	$1436	€1256	Harvesters in an extensive landscape (49x71cm-19x28in) s. W/C. 17-Nov-3 Waddingtons, Toronto #138/R est:1500-1800 (C.D 1900)
£1050	$1659	€1523	Loiterers, woman with geese by a greenhouse in a back garden (36x70cm-14x28in) s. W/C. 2-Sep-3 Bonhams, Oxford #48/R est:1000-1500
£1200	$2160	€1752	Harvesting (23x34cm-9x13in) s. W/C. 23-Jan-4 British Auctioneer #498/R est:200-300

HAYES, Colin (1919-) British

£300	$555	€450	Salamanca II, the new cathedral (50x74cm-20x29in) s. 14-Jul-4 John Bellman, Billingshurst #1734
£700	$1232	€1022	On the road to Kimi Evvia, Greece (41x51cm-16x20in) s. 18-May-4 Bonhams, Knightsbridge #1/R

HAYES, David (20th C) American?

Works on paper			
£333	$613	€500	Untitled (20x57cm-8x22in) s.i.d. W/C Indian ink. 11-Jun-4 Hauswedell & Nolte, Hamburg #1297/R

HAYES, Edward (1797-1864) British

Works on paper			
£503	$926	€750	Young boy and girl with goat (38x28cm-15x11in) s.i. W/C. 23-Mar-4 Mealy's, Castlecomer #1119/R
£1200	$2004	€1752	Portrait of an officers of the 16th Lancers (44x34cm-17x13in) s. W/C over pencil htd bodycol. 14-Oct-3 Sotheby's, London #498/R est:600-800

HAYES, Edwin (1820-1904) British

£670	$1200	€978	Ships at sea (30x46cm-12x18in) s. board. 8-May-4 Susanin's, Chicago #6150/R est:1000-2000
£750	$1193	€1095	Sailing boats at dusk (38x46cm-15x18in) s.d.80. 12-Sep-3 Gardiner & Houlgate, Bath #145/R
£750	$1275	€1095	Coastal shipping scenes with boats and figures in calm and stormy waters (13x15cm-5x6in) one s. board pair. 6-Nov-3 Biddle & Webb, Birmingham #821
£1118	$1800	€1632	Sketch in Holland (25x41cm-10x16in) s. board. 20-Aug-3 James Julia, Fairfield #1099/R est:2000-3000
£1200	$2172	€1800	Coastal landscape with figures on a pier (19x31cm-7x12in) s. i.verso oil paper on board. 30-Mar-4 De Veres Art Auctions, Dublin #252 est:600-900
£2000	$3220	€2900	Harbour mouth with shipping (43x79cm-17x31in) s.d.1879. 13-Aug-3 Andrew Hartley, Ilkley #847/R est:2000-3000
£2200	$3960	€3212	Squally weather, Seaford (40x67cm-16x26in) s.d.1886. 21-Apr-4 Cheffins, Cambridge #498/R est:1200-1800
£2847	$4641	€4100	Vessels leaving Portsmouth Harbour (29x19cm-11x7in) s. canvas board. 24-Sep-3 James Adam, Dublin #6/R est:2500-4000
£3500	$6615	€5110	Trading brig entering port on the tide (29x42cm-11x17in) s.d.51. 17-Feb-4 Bonhams, New Bond Street #49/R est:2500-3500
£3611	$5886	€5200	Coastal scene with boats and figures (14x23cm-6x9in) s. board. 24-Sep-3 James Adam, Dublin #1/R est:2500-4000
£4469	$8000	€6704	Stormy ships in port (119x69cm-47x27in) s.d.1879. 16-May-4 Abell, Los Angeles #208
£4930	$8528	€7000	Fishermen at sea at sunrise (39x60cm-15x24in) s. 10-Dec-3 Bonhams & James Adam, Dublin #1/R est:6000-8000
£5000	$8600	€7300	Wreck of a vessel on the Bray Strand (60x92cm-24x36in) s.d.1863 exhib. 3-Dec-3 AB Stockholms Auktionsverk #2583/R est:15000-20000 (S.KR 65000)
£6504	$11642	€9496	Rounding the buoy (63x103cm-25x41in) s. canvas on masonite. 4-May-4 Ritchie, Toronto #19/R est:3000-5000 (C.D 16000)
£6800	$12852	€9928	Off to the fishing grounds (46x81cm-18x32in) s. 17-Feb-4 Bonhams, New Bond Street #47/R est:3000-5000
£8000	$13600	€11680	Dutch barges (48x84cm-19x33in) s.d.1869. 22-Nov-3 Bonhams, Chester #332 est:4000-5000
£10000	$17900	€14600	Yarmouth lugger, Dublin Bay. Ship on the Goodwin Sands (25x38cm-10x15in) s.i.verso pair prov. 26-May-4 Sotheby's, Olympia #59/R est:5000-7000
£10500	$17850	€15330	Fishing fleet heading out (61x106cm-24x42in) s.d.1870 prov. 27-Nov-3 Sotheby's, London #389/R est:5000-7000
£19333	$34993	€29000	Wreck of a vessel on Bray Strand (59x89cm-23x35in) s.d.1869 exhib. 31-Mar-4 James Adam, Dublin #10/R est:10000-15000
Works on paper			
£300	$567	€438	Sailing boats and steamer in choppy seas (11x23cm-4x9in) W/C. 18-Feb-4 John Bellman, Billingshurst #1891
£599	$1036	€850	Fishing boats (44x20cm-17x8in) s. W/C. 10-Dec-3 Bonhams & James Adam, Dublin #2/R
£625	$1169	€938	The Thames off Erith (10x18cm-4x7in) W/C. 21-Jul-4 John Nicholson, Haslemere #59
£640	$1024	€934	Beached ship on a storm washed coast (33x48cm-13x19in) s. W/C. 8-Jan-3 Biddle & Webb, Birmingham #770

£676 $1277 €1000 Hay barge off Gravesend (15x19cm-6x7in) s.i. pencil pen ink. 17-Feb-4 Whyte's, Dublin #166/R est:1000-1500
£1000 $1840 €1460 Boats off the coast (11x15cm-4x6in) s. W/C. 23-Jun-4 Bonhams, Bury St Edmunds #339/R est:400-600
£1200 $2220 €1752 Leaving harbour (21x28cm-8x11in) W/C. 9-Mar-4 Bonhams, New Bond Street #79/R est:1200-1500
£1733 $3137 €2600 Sailing boats in seascape at sunset (14x28cm-6x11in) s. W/C. 31-Mar-4 James Adam, Dublin #136/R est:1500-2000
£1800 $3222 €2628 Putting out to sea (21x48cm-8x19in) s.d.1862 pencil W/C gum arabic htd bodycol scratching out prov. 14-May-4 Christie's, London #89/R est:700-1000
£2113 $3655 €3000 Fishing boats in coastal seascape (16x33cm-6x13in) s.indis.d.1869 W/C. 10-Dec-3 Bonhams & James Adam, Dublin #20/R est:3000-4000

HAYES, Ernest (1914-1978) British
£764 $1245 €1100 Portrait of a lady, half length in red dress (58x42cm-23x17in) s. 24-Sep-3 James Adam, Dublin #114/R est:1000-2000
£1049 $1783 €1500 Country cottage with blue shutters (41x46cm-16x18in) s. 18-Nov-3 Whyte's, Dublin #97/R est:1500-2000
£1329 $2259 €1900 Light on the haystacks (51x61cm-20x24in) s.d.1936. 18-Nov-3 Whyte's, Dublin #96/R est:2000-2500
£1667 $2717 €2400 Farmhouse in landscape (45x68cm-18x27in) s.d.1935. 24-Sep-3 James Adam, Dublin #116/R est:1000-2000

HAYES, F William (1848-1918) British
£1840 $3000 €2686 Cottage in the English countryside (76x114cm-30x45in) s. board. 28-Sep-3 Simpson's, Houston #239/R
Works on paper
£340 $568 €496 View of docks, possibly Liverpool (10x15cm-4x6in) s. W/C. 15-Oct-3 Brightwells, Leominster #947

HAYES, J W (19th C) British
£3200 $5216 €4672 Distant thoughts (76x63cm-30x25in) s.d.1882. 24-Sep-3 Dreweatt Neate, Newbury #163/R est:1000-1500
£7761 $13891 €11331 Mary Stuart and Darnley (111x86cm-44x34in) s/ prov. 25-May-4 Bukowskis, Stockholm #358/R est:40000-50000 (S.KR 105000)

HAYES, Michael Angelo (1820-1877) British
£350 $595 €511 London Coach (18x25cm-7x10in) init.d.1840 board. 18-Nov-3 Sotheby's, Olympia #46/R
£1974 $3632 €3000 London coach and four packed travelling at speed (18x25cm-7x10in) init.d.1840 board. 22-Jun-4 Mealy's, Castlecomer #791/R est:800-1500
Works on paper
£320 $531 €467 Infantry on the edge of a village (29x41cm-11x16in) s. W/C. 1-Oct-3 Woolley & Wallis, Salisbury #67/R
£1197 $1915 €1700 Guard turn out. Three untitled (17x24cm-7x9in) one mono.d.1838 one mono.d.1839 W/C bodycol four. 16-Sep-3 Whyte's, Dublin #101/R est:2000-3000

HAYET, Louis (1854-1940) French
£2013 $3705 €3000 Au marche (27x40cm-11x16in) st.verso. 24-Mar-4 Binoche, Paris #103 est:3000-4000
Works on paper
£319 $517 €450 Village dans un paysage (13x22cm-5x9in) bears st.sig. W/C. 21-May-3 Daguerre, Paris #22

HAYEZ, Francesco (1791-1882) Italian
£26846 $48054 €40000 Portrait of the artist's wife Vincenza Scaccia (64x50cm-25x20in) lit. 25-May-4 Finarte Semenzato, Milan #182/R est:28000-32000
£31915 $53298 €45000 Vittor Pisani freed from prison (47x38cm-19x15in) s. board lit. 14-Oct-3 Finarte Semenzato, Milan #172/R est:50000
Works on paper
£3947 $7263 €6000 Portrait of seated man (30x24cm-12x9in) i. pencil. 23-Jun-4 Finarte Semenzato, Rome #10/R est:3000-4000

HAYLLAR, James (1829-1920) British
£1000 $1660 €1460 Guilty or not guilty (26x20cm-10x8in) s.d.1876 board. 1-Oct-3 Sotheby's, Olympia #52/R est:700-1000
£1500 $2745 €2190 Quiet nap (45x34cm-18x13in) s. 6-Jul-4 Bearnes, Exeter #491/R est:1500-2000
£1800 $3330 €2628 Young girl with doll (29x24cm-11x9in) s. panel. 14-Jul-4 Bonhams, Chester #442/R est:2000-3000
£2500 $4650 €3650 In the rocky valley, near Tintagel, Cornwall (20x28cm-8x11in) init.d.16.94 board. 4-Mar-4 Christie's, Kensington #156/R est:3000-5000
£3000 $5010 €4380 Never had no learning (91x71cm-36x28in) 21-Oct-3 Gorringes, Lewes #1975/R est:3000-5000
Works on paper
£1200 $2208 €1752 Little eavesdropper (49x33cm-19x13in) s.d.1867 pencil W/C. 25-Mar-4 Christie's, Kensington #234/R est:800-1200
£2517 $4280 €3600 Soup for granny, young girl bringing soup to her granny in bed (48x34cm-19x13in) s.d.1868 W/C. 18-Nov-3 Mealy's, Castlecomer #1001/R est:2800-3500

HAYMAN, Francis (1708-1776) British
£6000 $10200 €8760 Don Quixote (50x60cm-20x24in) set of three. 27-Nov-3 Sotheby's, London #203/R est:6000-8000
£12000 $20040 €17520 Portrait of a gentleman, possibly Mr Goodyear St. John, wearing a green suit (76x56cm-30x22in) prov.lit. 14-Oct-3 Sotheby's, London #446/R est:10000-15000

HAYMAN, Karen (1959-) Australian
£763 $1389 €1114 Sea swirl (101x86cm-40x34in) s.d.02. 16-Jun-4 Deutscher-Menzies, Melbourne #366/R est:2200-2800 (A.D 2000)

HAYMAN, Mrs N (19th C) British
Works on paper
£1000 $1770 €1460 Beach, Mauritius (18x25cm-7x10in) s. W/C sold with three sketches by same hand. 27-Apr-4 Bonhams, New Bond Street #83/R est:800-1200

HAYMAN, Patrick (1915-1988) British
£340 $622 €496 Dark buildings (15x23cm-6x9in) s. board. 6-Jul-4 Bearnes, Exeter #480
£700 $1169 €1022 Solitary mister, for Dylan Thomas (25x19cm-10x7in) s. board. 16-Oct-3 Christie's, Kensington #607

HAYN, Ernst von (attrib) (1822-1896) German
Works on paper
£268 $494 €400 Swabian landscape (30x45cm-12x18in) i. W/C. 25-Mar-4 Dr Fritz Nagel, Stuttgart #508

HAYNES, Alice M (fl.1903-1904) British
£320 $586 €467 Spring flowers (29x34cm-11x13in) init. 6-Apr-4 Bristol Auction Rooms #457/R

HAYNES, Douglas Hector (1936-) Canadian
£248 $449 €362 Untitled - historical house, Edmonton (40x30cm-16x12in) s. s.i.d.1957 canvasboard prov. 18-Apr-4 Levis, Calgary #308/R (C.D 600)

HAYNES, John William (fl.1852-1882) British
£924 $1654 €1349 The mother's hope (20x25cm-8x10in) init.d.59 panel exhib. 25-May-4 Bukowskis, Stockholm #356/R (S.KR 12500)
£2800 $4424 €4060 Humble fare (41x50cm-16x20in) s.d.70. 4-Sep-3 Christie's, Kensington #265/R est:2000-3000

HAYS, Barton S (attrib) (1826-1914) American
£881 $1400 €1286 Still life (30x46cm-12x18in) s. 14-Sep-3 Susanin's, Chicago #6117/R est:800-1200

HAYS, George Arthur (1854-1945) American
£479 $800 €699 Westport shanties (20x25cm-8x10in) s. board. 16-Nov-3 CRN Auctions, Cambridge #8/R
£508 $900 €742 Farmer with his cow (12x16cm-5x6in) s. i.d.1901 verso. 2-May-4 Bonhams & Butterfields, San Francisco #1137/R
£1145 $2050 €1672 Plowing in the pasture (41x61cm-16x24in) s. s.i.d.1920 verso. 8-Jan-4 James Julia, Fairfield #803/R est:1500-2500

HAYS, William Jacob (snr-attrib) (1830-1875) American
£335 $600 €489 Rural path with stage coach (23x30cm-9x12in) bears sig. 20-Mar-4 Selkirks, St. Louis #146

HAYSOM, Melville (1900-1976) Australian
£1653 $2926 €2413 Boating party (43x53cm-17x21in) s.d.31 canvasboard. 3-May-4 Christie's, Melbourne #370/R est:4000-6000 (A.D 4000)

HAYTER, Charles (1761-1835) British
Works on paper
£2000 $3340 €2920 Royal Exchange fireman (42x30cm-17x12in) s.d.1832 pencil W/C. 16-Oct-3 Christie's, Kensington #157/R est:2000-3000
£3200 $5440 €4672 Captain James Bradshaw. His wife (7cm-3in) s.d.1816 oval pair. 18-Nov-3 Bonhams, New Bond Street #123/R est:1000-1500

HAYTER, Simon (20th C) ?
Works on paper
£403 $713 €600 Untitled (61x94cm-24x37in) s.d.53 felt-tip pen wax crayon. 29-Apr-4 David Kahn, Paris #191

HAYTER, Sir George (1792-1871) British
£256 $450 €374 Portrait of a woman in a mauve dress (76x64cm-30x25in) 21-May-4 North East Auctions, Portsmouth #528/R
£1988 $3500 €2902 Portrait of a lady (91x71cm-36x28in) prov. 18-May-4 Bonhams & Butterfields, San Francisco #151/R est:4000-6000
£4500 $8055 €6570 Tribute money (117x170cm-46x67in) indis sig.d. 27-May-4 Christie's, Kensington #262/R est:5000-8000
£50279 $90000 €73407 Portrait of lady (239x148cm-94x58in) prov. 27-May-4 Sotheby's, New York #283/R est:100000-150000
Works on paper
£380 $699 €555 Mary Adelaide, daughter of Adolphus Frederick, Duke of Cambridge (60x45cm-24x18in) s.i. pencil htd white brown paper. 14-Jun-4 Bonhams, Bath #16

HAYTER, Sir George (attrib) (1792-1871) British
£300 $474 €435 Mrs ogle (13x18cm-5x7in) i.verso oil ivory painted c.1810-1820. 27-Apr-3 Desmond Judd, Cranbrook #1084

HAYTER, Stanley William (1901-1988) British
£1200 $2184 €1752 Abstract (65x53cm-26x21in) indis.s.d.52. 1-Jul-4 Christie's, Kensington #383/R est:1000-1500
£1333 $2400 €2000 Composition (73x53cm-29x21in) s. d.1967 verso prov. 25-Apr-4 Versailles Encheres #39 est:2000-3000
£1469 $2497 €2100 Composition (64x50cm-25x20in) s.d.1959 prov. 23-Nov-3 Cornette de St.Cyr, Paris #136/R est:1000-1500
£1645 $3026 €2500 Composition (64x50cm-25x20in) s. s.d.1959 verso. 27-Jun-4 Versailles Encheres #57/R est:2500-3000
£1864 $3300 €2721 Composition (30x15cm-12x6in) s.d.18.9.38 acrylic panel. 2-May-4 William Jenack, New York #399 est:1000-1500
£2667 $4853 €4000 Alba red stream (81x100cm-32x39in) s. painted 1963 prov. 29-Jun-4 Cornette de St.Cyr, Paris #32/R est:3500-4500
£3600 $6192 €5256 Abstract composition (129x80cm-51x31in) s.d.50. 3-Dec-3 Christie's, Kensington #780/R est:4000-6000

£5102 $9133 €7500 Untitled (30x42cm-12x17in) s.d.35 wood. 21-Mar-4 Calmels Cohen, Paris #17/R est:8000-10000
Prints
£2824 $4800 €4123 Ceres (61x39cm-24x15in) s.i.d.1947-48 num.47/50 col engraving etching scorper. 6-Nov-3 Swann Galleries, New York #574/R est:1000-1500
£3176 $5400 €4637 Unstable woman (38x50cm-15x20in) s.i.d.1946-47 num.31/50 col engraving etching scorper. 6-Nov-3 Swann Galleries, New York #572/R est:1000-1500
£3294 $5600 €4809 Falling figure (45x38cm-18x15in) s.i.d.1947 num.8/50 col engraving etching scorper. 6-Nov-3 Swann Galleries, New York #573/R est:1000-1500
£3495 $6500 €5103 Tropic of cancer (54x70cm-21x28in) s.i.d.1949 num.1/50 engraving etching roulette soft ground. 2-Mar-4 Swann Galleries, New York #237/R est:3000-5000
£3529 $6000 €5152 Cinq personnages (38x60cm-15x24in) s.i.d.3-10-46 col engraving etching scorper. 6-Nov-3 Swann Galleries, New York #571/R est:1500-2500
£4190 $7500 €6117 Amazon (62x40cm-24x16in) s.i.d.1945 num.1/50 soft ground engraving. 6-May-4 Swann Galleries, New York #468/R est:2500-3500
Works on paper
£1000 $1820 €1500 Dancing figures (56x72cm-22x28in) s.i.d.1946 W/C pen ink. 2-Jul-4 Bloomsbury, London #146/R est:1500-2000
£1800 $3312 €2628 Plaza Nationale (36x27cm-14x11in) s.i.d.37 i.verso gouache pencil board prov. 24-Jun-4 Sotheby's, Olympia #544/R est:1800-2200
£2000 $3700 €2920 Untitled (43x56cm-17x22in) s.i.d.45 ink W/C. 10-Mar-4 Sotheby's, Olympia #115/R est:1800-2500
£4400 $8008 €6600 Greek dancers (64x76cm-25x30in) s.i.d.3.19.44 pen ink. 2-Jul-4 Bloomsbury, London #142/R est:1000-1500

HAYTER, William (20th C) British?
£1549 $2680 €2200 Gerbe (72x60cm-28x24in) s.d.1960. 14-Dec-3 Versailles Encheres #28/R est:1200-1500

HAYWARD, A F W (1856-1939) British
£360 $576 €526 Study of white chrysanthemums in a vase (49x39cm-19x15in) s. 16-Sep-3 Holloways, Banbury #298

HAYWARD, Alfred Frederick William (1856-1939) British
£260 $411 €377 Auricula in a glass (21x15cm-8x6in) s. 4-Sep-3 Christie's, Kensington #334/R
£290 $534 €423 Still life of pansies in a vase (19x21cm-7x8in) s. 10-Jun-4 Morphets, Harrogate #506/R
£320 $509 €467 Tree peonies in a vase (61x36cm-24x14in) s.d.1902. 12-Sep-3 Gardiner & Houlgate, Bath #166/R
£420 $714 €613 Still life of flowers (33x43cm-13x17in) s.d.1891. 30-Oct-3 Duke & Son, Dorchester #219
£750 $1350 €1095 Still life of white chrysanthemums (51x41cm-20x16in) s. 20-Jan-4 Bonhams, Knightsbridge #73/R
£1200 $2220 €1752 Still life of roses in a glass (38x30cm-15x12in) s. 11-Feb-4 Sotheby's, Olympia #118/R est:600-800

HAYWARD, Alfred Robert (1875-1971) British
£280 $468 €409 Gondola (48x67cm-19x26in) s.d.64 board. 11-Nov-3 Rosebery Fine Art, London #1046
£280 $518 €409 Pink roses in a blue and white bowl (51x63cm-20x25in) s.d.1956. 11-Mar-4 Christie's, Kensington #119
£700 $1253 €1022 Fishing boats in the early morning mist (25x30cm-10x12in) s. board. 14-May-4 Christie's, Kensington #532/R
£2000 $3340 €2920 Romance in Italy (72x82cm-28x32in) s. 16-Oct-3 Christie's, Kensington #446/R est:2000-3000
£20000 $34000 €29200 In the sunlit garden (77x51cm-30x20in) s. i.on stretcher. 25-Nov-3 Christie's, London #121/R est:20000-30000

HAYWARD, Arthur (1889-1971) British
£480 $874 €701 Portrait of a lady (91x71cm-36x28in) s. 15-Jun-4 David Lay, Penzance #692
£1400 $2338 €2044 November day, St. Ives (27x37cm-11x15in) s. i.on stretcher. 14-Oct-3 Bearnes, Exeter #411/R est:800-1200
£1800 $2952 €2628 The Old Sloop Inn, St Ives, Cornwall (34x25cm-13x10in) s. i.verso board. 3-Jun-3 Fellows & Sons, Birmingham #20/R est:500-800
£1900 $3458 €2774 Harbour, St Ives (23x32cm-9x13in) s. board. 1-Jul-4 Christie's, Kensington #87/R est:2000-3000
£5500 $10065 €8030 Morning, St Ives (28x23cm-11x9in) s. s.i.verso panel exhib. 4-Jun-4 Christie's, London #60/R est:6000-8000
£7800 $14352 €11388 Near the harbour wall, St Ives. Boats in St Ives harbour (21x24cm-8x9in) s. board pair. 24-Mar-4 Hamptons Fine Art, Godalming #307/R

HAYWARD, Johnson (fl.1911-1925) British
£520 $962 €759 Jug of daffodils (44x25cm-17x10in) s. 14-Jan-4 Lawrence, Crewkerne #1436/R

HAYWARD, Lucy F (fl.1891-1916) British
£660 $1181 €964 A morning call, a cat at the bedroom door (48x33cm-19x13in) s. 11-May-4 Dreweatt Neate, Newbury #495/R

HAZARD, William Garnet (1903-1987) Canadian
£366 $655 €534 Cabin in early spring (48x39cm-19x15in) s. board prov. 6-May-4 Heffel, Vancouver #67/R (C.D 900)
Works on paper
£302 $556 €441 East Coast fishing boats (28x38cm-11x15in) s. W/C. 9-Jun-4 Walker's, Ottawa #92/R (C.D 750)
£363 $668 €530 Grand Manan, New Brunswick (34x45cm-13x18in) s. i.d.1962 verso W/C. 9-Jun-4 Walker's, Ottawa #93/R (C.D 900)

HAZELHUST, Ernest William (1866-1949) British
Works on paper
£350 $585 €511 Spring flowers (36x53cm-14x21in) s. W/C. 12-Nov-3 Halls, Shrewsbury #277/R

HAZELL, Frank (1883-1958) American
£506 $800 €739 Low tide (23x28cm-9x11in) s.d.1914 canvas on board. 7-Sep-3 Treadway Gallery, Cincinnati #633/R

HAZLEDINE, Alfred (1876-1954) Belgian
£400 $716 €600 Jardine anime (67x82cm-26x32in) s.d.1935. 16-May-4 MonsAntic, Maisieres #421
£680 $1218 €1000 L'approvisionnement en eau (60x90cm-24x35in) s. 16-Mar-4 Vanderkindere, Brussels #9
£728 $1326 €1100 Scene de marche (64x78cm-25x31in) s. panel. 21-Jun-4 Bernaerts, Antwerp #70
£759 $1403 €1100 Les travaux au potager (67x62cm-26x24in) s.d.1935. 16-Feb-4 Horta, Bruxelles #236
£864 $1434 €1253 Women with needlework in evening light (71x80cm-28x31in) s. 16-Jun-3 Blomqvist, Lysaker #1072/R (N.KR 10000)
£931 $1722 €1350 Lavandieres pres du pont (46x61cm-18x24in) s. 19-Jan-4 Horta, Bruxelles #234
£966 $1786 €1400 Le retour des champs (75x100cm-30x39in) s. 16-Feb-4 Horta, Bruxelles #235
£986 $1706 €1400 Scene de jardin (78x71cm-31x28in) s.d.1939. 10-Dec-3 Hotel des Ventes Mosan, Brussels #212
£3380 $5848 €4800 Evening in Brugge (71x79cm-28x31in) s. 13-Dec-3 De Vuyst, Lokeren #552/R est:5000-6000
Works on paper
£521 $828 €750 Enfants sur le petit pont (22x29cm-9x11in) s.d.1941 W/C. 15-Sep-3 Horta, Bruxelles #511

HAZLEHURST, Thomas (1740-1821) British
Miniatures
£1100 $1969 €1606 Nicholas Hurry, in a blue coat (7cm-3in) init. gilt metal frame lock of hair seed pearls. 25-May-4 Christie's, London #141/R est:800-1200
£3400 $5780 €4964 Gentleman (8cm-3in) init. oval. 18-Nov-3 Bonhams, New Bond Street #117/R est:2000-3000
£8000 $14400 €11680 Gentleman in a black coat (8cm-3in) init. mono.verso gold frame oval prov.exhib. 22-Apr-4 Bonhams, New Bond Street #140/R est:2000-3000

HAZLETON, Mart S (19/20th C) American
£335 $550 €489 Still life with raspberries and clover (20x25cm-8x10in) s.d.1884. 9-Jun-3 O'Gallerie, Oregon #22/R

HE BAILI (1945-) Chinese
Works on paper
£6564 $10961 €9583 Morning boats, early birds (23x28cm-9x11in) s. ink scrolls set of two. 26-Oct-3 Christie's, Hong Kong #262/R est:50000-70000 (HK.D 85000)
£9957 $17923 €14537 Blue mountain series (17x22cm-7x9in) s. ink col scroll silk set of four. 25-Apr-4 Christie's, Hong Kong #99/R est:60000-80000 (HK.D 140000)
£19915 $35846 €29076 Autumn valley (47x122cm-19x48in) s.i.d.2004 ink col scroll. 25-Apr-4 Christie's, Hong Kong #94/R est:100000-150000 (HK.D 280000)

HEADE, Martin Johnson (1819-1904) American
£63953 $110000 €93371 Glass of roses on gold cloth (55x35cm-22x14in) s. prov.exhib.lit. 3-Dec-3 Doyle, New York #180/R est:100000-150000
£93023 $160000 €135814 Palm trees, Florida (16x31cm-6x12in) s.d.1896 board. 3-Dec-3 Sotheby's, New York #111/R est:30000-50000
£108696 $200000 €158696 Cherokee roses in a tumbler (46x25cm-18x10in) s. 9-Jun-4 Alderfer's, Hatfield #376/R est:60000-80000
£244318 $430000 €356704 Cattle in the marsh near a fence (33x66cm-13x26in) s. painted c.1866-76 prov.lit. 19-May-4 Sotheby's, New York #103/R est:300000-500000
£482955 $850000 €705114 Single magnolia on red velvet (38x62cm-15x24in) s. prov. 18-May-4 Christie's, Rockefeller NY #29/R est:700000-900000
Works on paper
£3681 $6000 €5374 Still life of a white rose (25x20cm-10x8in) s. W/C. 27-Sep-3 Charlton Hall, Columbia #513/R est:3000-5000

HEADLAM, Kristin (1953-) Australian
£287 $453 €419 The sick rose (152x122cm-60x48in) s.d.96 s.i.d.1995/96 verso linen prov. 2-Sep-3 Deutscher-Menzies, Melbourne #260/R (A.D 700)
£744 $1376 €1086 Love mills (76x121cm-30x48in) s.d.1988 i.verso prov. 15-Mar-4 Sotheby's, Melbourne #55 est:800-1200 (A.D 1800)
£3049 $4786 €4421 Four trees (152x213cm-60x84in) s.i.d.1990 verso prov.exhib. 27-Aug-3 Christie's, Sydney #510/R est:3000-5000 (A.D 7500)

HEALY, Christine (1955-) Australian
£2236 $3510 €3265 Jaune (167x244cm-66x96in) s.i.d.1996 verso acrylic oil wax. 27-Aug-3 Christie's, Sydney #698 est:500-800 (A.D 5500)

HEALY, Francis D (1861-1948) American
£417 $750 €609 Arizona desert landscape (51x76cm-20x30in) s.d.36. 24-Apr-4 Weschler, Washington #615/R

HEALY, George Peter Alexander (1813-1894) American
£375 $600 €548 Portrait of William Fry (61x51cm-24x20in) i.verso. 19-Sep-3 Freeman, Philadelphia #139/R
£376 $700 €549 Portrait of a young woman (60x50cm-24x20in) s.d.1874. 5-Mar-4 Skinner, Boston #262/R
£710 $1300 €1037 Portrait of Anne Elizabeth Wheaton Haven (61x76cm-24x30in) i.verso. 5-Jun-4 Neal Auction Company, New Orleans #449/R est:1800-2400
£2869 $5250 €4189 Joseph Hume (112x86cm-44x34in) s.d.1845. 5-Jun-4 Neal Auction Company, New Orleans #348/R est:3000-5000
£3107 $5500 €4536 Mystic marriage of St Catherine (124x117cm-49x46in) s.i.d.1884 after Van Dyck. 2-May-4 Bonhams & Butterfields, San Francisco #1063/R est:4000-6000

HEALY, Henry (1909-1985) Irish?
£493 $908 €750 Farm buildings (34x45cm-13x18in) s. canvas on board. 22-Jun-4 De Veres Art Auctions, Dublin #129/R

£750	$1245	€1095	Farmstead (35x45cm-14x18in) s. board. 1-Oct-3 John Ross, Belfast #105
£760	$1421	€1110	Hanging the washing (64x74cm-25x29in) s. 26-Feb-4 Mallams, Cheltenham #215
£903	$1472	€1300	Leeson Street bridge (61x51cm-24x20in) s. i.verso canvasboard. 23-Sep-3 De Veres Art Auctions, Dublin #147/R
£1118	$2058	€1700	Hanging out the washing (63x75cm-25x30in) s. 22-Jun-4 De Veres Art Auctions, Dublin #25/R est:2000-3000
£1806	$2943	€2600	View of Rathmines from the canal (60x50cm-24x20in) s. board. 24-Sep-3 James Adam, Dublin #129/R est:2000-4000
£2162	$4086	€3200	Leeson Street bridge, Dublin (61x51cm-24x20in) s. i.verso canvasboard. 17-Feb-4 Whyte's, Dublin #5/R est:2000-3000

HEALY, Michael (1873-1941) British

£278	$453	€400	Study, five apples (19x22cm-7x9in) canvasboard. 23-Sep-3 De Veres Art Auctions, Dublin #73
£278	$453	€400	County Dublin landscape (17x17cm-7x7in) canvasboard. 23-Sep-3 De Veres Art Auctions, Dublin #4
£278	$453	€400	County Dublin landscape (16x30cm-6x12in) canvasboard. 23-Sep-3 De Veres Art Auctions, Dublin #11
£278	$453	€400	Still life (19x16cm-7x6in) canvasboard. 23-Sep-3 De Veres Art Auctions, Dublin #15
£278	$453	€400	County Dublin landscape (21x27cm-8x11in) canvasboard. 23-Sep-3 De Veres Art Auctions, Dublin #18
£278	$453	€400	Still life (16x23cm-6x9in) canvasboard. 23-Sep-3 De Veres Art Auctions, Dublin #21/R
£278	$453	€400	County Dublin landscape (19x26cm-7x10in) canvasboard. 23-Sep-3 De Veres Art Auctions, Dublin #26
£278	$453	€400	Landscape with river (18x23cm-7x9in) canvasboard. 23-Sep-3 De Veres Art Auctions, Dublin #68
£278	$453	€400	Wicklow landscape (21x22cm-8x9in) canvasboard. 23-Sep-3 De Veres Art Auctions, Dublin #69
£292	$475	€420	Sky studies, trees and cottage (21x24cm-8x9in) canvasboard. 23-Sep-3 De Veres Art Auctions, Dublin #59
£313	$509	€450	County Dublin landscape (14x22cm-6x9in) canvasboard. 23-Sep-3 De Veres Art Auctions, Dublin #5
£313	$509	€450	County Dublin landscape (14x20cm-6x8in) canvasboard. 23-Sep-3 De Veres Art Auctions, Dublin #16
£313	$509	€450	County Dublin landscape (19x22cm-7x9in) canvasboard. 23-Sep-3 De Veres Art Auctions, Dublin #23
£313	$509	€450	County Dublin landscape (19x25cm-7x10in) canvasboard. 23-Sep-3 De Veres Art Auctions, Dublin #25
£313	$509	€450	County Dublin landscape (19x22cm-7x9in) canvasboard. 23-Sep-3 De Veres Art Auctions, Dublin #37
£313	$509	€450	County Dublin landscape (18x24cm-7x9in) canvasboard. 23-Sep-3 De Veres Art Auctions, Dublin #50/R
£347	$566	€500	Study, two apples (14x20cm-6x8in) canvasboard. 23-Sep-3 De Veres Art Auctions, Dublin #72
£347	$566	€500	Still life (19x16cm-7x6in) canvasboard. 23-Sep-3 De Veres Art Auctions, Dublin #14/R
£347	$566	€500	County Dublin landscape (37x46cm-15x18in) canvasboard. 23-Sep-3 De Veres Art Auctions, Dublin #20/R
£347	$566	€500	County Dublin landscape (19x25cm-7x10in) canvasboard. 23-Sep-3 De Veres Art Auctions, Dublin #28/R
£347	$566	€500	County Dublin landscape (17x23cm-7x9in) canvasboard. 23-Sep-3 De Veres Art Auctions, Dublin #29
£347	$566	€500	County Dublin landscape (18x22cm-7x9in) canvasboard. 23-Sep-3 De Veres Art Auctions, Dublin #30
£347	$566	€500	Tree study, Wicklow (18x22cm-7x9in) canvasboard. 23-Sep-3 De Veres Art Auctions, Dublin #65
£347	$566	€500	Landscape, North Dublin with houses in distance (25x30cm-10x12in) canvasboard. 23-Sep-3 De Veres Art Auctions, Dublin #74
£361	$589	€520	Field of corn stooks, North Dublin (20x23cm-8x9in) canvasboard. 23-Sep-3 De Veres Art Auctions, Dublin #63
£382	$623	€550	County Dublin landscape (20x30cm-8x12in) canvasboard. 23-Sep-3 De Veres Art Auctions, Dublin #9/R
£382	$623	€550	County Dublin landscape (18x23cm-7x9in) canvasboard. 23-Sep-3 De Veres Art Auctions, Dublin #32
£417	$679	€600	County Dublin landscape (18x23cm-7x9in) canvasboard. 23-Sep-3 De Veres Art Auctions, Dublin #22
£417	$679	€600	In the wood at Orlagh College, Co Dublin (51x41cm-20x16in) i.verso canvasboard. 23-Sep-3 De Veres Art Auctions, Dublin #71
£451	$736	€650	Haycocks with houses (19x22cm-7x9in) canvasboard. 23-Sep-3 De Veres Art Auctions, Dublin #61/R
£486	$792	€700	County Dublin landscape (38x46cm-15x18in) canvasboard. 23-Sep-3 De Veres Art Auctions, Dublin #51
£486	$792	€700	Snowscene (21x25cm-8x10in) canvasboard. 23-Sep-3 De Veres Art Auctions, Dublin #75/R
£521	$849	€750	Still life (19x16cm-7x6in) canvasboard. 23-Sep-3 De Veres Art Auctions, Dublin #13/R
£521	$849	€750	Wicklow fields (19x23cm-7x9in) canvasboard. 23-Sep-3 De Veres Art Auctions, Dublin #67
£590	$962	€850	County Dublin landscape (20x29cm-8x11in) canvasboard. 23-Sep-3 De Veres Art Auctions, Dublin #8/R
£625	$1019	€900	County Dublin landscape (19x29cm-7x11in) canvasboard. 23-Sep-3 De Veres Art Auctions, Dublin #1/R
£694	$1132	€1000	County Dublin landscape (22x29cm-9x11in) canvasboard. 23-Sep-3 De Veres Art Auctions, Dublin #12/R
£764	$1245	€1100	County Dublin landscape (21x33cm-8x13in) canvasboard. 23-Sep-3 De Veres Art Auctions, Dublin #2
£972	$1585	€1400	Coastal landscape with three figures (23x34cm-9x13in) canvasboard. 23-Sep-3 De Veres Art Auctions, Dublin #90
Works on paper			
£292	$475	€420	Corn stooks with trees (12x17cm-5x7in) W/C. 23-Sep-3 De Veres Art Auctions, Dublin #82/R
£313	$509	€450	Beach scene, North Dublin (12x17cm-5x7in) W/C. 23-Sep-3 De Veres Art Auctions, Dublin #76
£313	$509	€450	Sand dunes and clouds (12x17cm-5x7in) W/C. 23-Sep-3 De Veres Art Auctions, Dublin #77
£382	$623	€550	Cattle near trees (12x17cm-5x7in) W/C. 23-Sep-3 De Veres Art Auctions, Dublin #84/R
£417	$679	€600	Cattle in pasture with trees (12x17cm-5x7in) W/C. 23-Sep-3 De Veres Art Auctions, Dublin #81/R

HEAPHY, Chris (20th C) New Zealander

£507	$862	€740	Upraised hand II (20x20cm-8x8in) s.d.1997 s.i.d.verso. 4-Nov-3 Peter Webb, Auckland #251/R est:600-1200 (NZ.D 1400)
£1715	$2795	€2504	Abstract composition (38x111cm-15x44in) s.d.1993 acrylic pastel four sheets of paper. 23-Sep-3 Peter Webb, Auckland #10/R est:4000-6000 (NZ.D 4750)

HEARD, H Percy (fl.1886-1914) British

£560	$935	€818	Azalea blooms (17x92cm-7x36in) s. 20-Oct-3 Bonhams, Bath #226

HEARD, Joseph (1799-1859) British

£5307	$9500	€7748	Outward bound Barque - Shuttle - passing Holyhead (71x102cm-28x40in) s. 16-Mar-4 Bonhams & Butterfields, San Francisco #6125/R est:6000-8000
£12000	$21480	€17520	Departing paddle steamer Victoria off the perch rock fort and lighthouse, Liverpool (66x91cm-26x36in) init.d.1838. 26-May-4 Sotheby's, Olympia #61/R est:10000-15000

HEARD, Joseph (attrib) (1799-1859) British

£4748	$8500	€6932	British paddle steamer towing a becalmed sailing ship out of danger (71x102cm-28x40in) bears indis.sig. 16-Mar-4 Bonhams & Butterfields, San Francisco #6124/R est:10000-15000

HEARD, Joseph (circle) (1799-1859) British

£650	$1190	€949	East Indiaman offshore in a light breeze (29x50cm-11x20in) 6-Jul-4 Bearnes, Exeter #477/R

HEARD, Ralph (19/20th C) American

£223	$400	€326	Fall landscape with red maple tree (56x66cm-22x26in) s. 10-Jan-4 CRN Auctions, Cambridge #103

HEARMAN, Louise (1963-) Australian

£2672	$4863	€3901	Untitled no.849 (53x45cm-21x18in) s. i.d.00 verso board. 16-Jun-4 Deutscher-Menzies, Melbourne #157/R est:8000-10000 (A.D 7000)
£4453	$7170	€6501	Untitled - Night scene (91x68cm-36x27in) s.d.95 verso board. 25-Aug-3 Sotheby's, Paddington #375/R est:7000-10000 (A.D 11000)
Works on paper			
£638	$1085	€931	Untitled No.633 (22x27cm-9x11in) i.d.1997 verso pastel exhib.prov. 25-Nov-3 Christie's, Melbourne #114/R (A.D 1500)

HEARN, Joseph (18th C) British

Works on paper			
£7000	$12880	€10220	Gostinoy Dvor, ou les Boutiques public, la Perspective de Nevsky (45x59cm-18x23in) bears i.verso W/C prov. 8-Jun-4 Bonhams, New Bond Street #25/R est:7000-10000

HEARNE, Thomas (1744-1817) British

Works on paper			
£6000	$10200	€8760	Elvet Bridge, Durham, with a washerwoman in the foreground (21x26cm-8x10in) pencil W/C prov.lit. 20-Nov-3 Christie's, London #19/R est:5000-8000

HEARSEY, Peter (20th C) American

£216	$350	€313	Rolls thru the door. s.d.1990. 1-Aug-3 Bonhams & Butterfields, San Francisco #804/R

HEATH, Adrian (1920-1992) British

£2800	$4452	€4088	Still life (51x61cm-20x24in) s.d.59. 10-Sep-3 Sotheby's, Olympia #308/R est:3000-5000
£4000	$6680	€5840	Abstract (51x41cm-20x16in) s.d.59 verso. 16-Oct-3 Christie's, Kensington #716/R est:2500-3500
Works on paper			
£900	$1530	€1314	Drawing V1 (73x53cm-29x21in) gouache. 18-Nov-3 Bonhams, Knightsbridge #91
£1300	$2405	€1898	Black and orange abstract (74x54cm-29x21in) s.d.61 W/C brush ink col chk. 11-Mar-4 Christie's, Kensington #377/R est:1500-2000
£1300	$2405	€1898	Black and brown abstract (74x54cm-29x21in) s.d.61 W/C brush ink col chk. 11-Mar-4 Christie's, Kensington #380/R est:1500-2000
£1800	$3222	€2628	July (76x56cm-30x22in) s. W/C bodycol brush black ink prov.exhib. 14-May-4 Christie's, Kensington #629/R est:1000-1500

HEATH, David (20th C) American

Photographs			
£4311	$7200	€6294	Portrait of Erin (19x22cm-7x9in) s. s.i.d.1963 verso gelatin silver print lit. 17-Oct-3 Phillips, New York #75/R est:3000-5000

HEATH, E (?) ?

£1044	$1900	€1566	Recumbent lion with mate (56x76cm-22x30in) s. 20-Jun-4 Charlton Hall, Columbia #689/R est:800-1200

HEATH, Frank Gascoigne (1873-1936) British

£11000	$20130	€16060	Mousehole harbour (24x33cm-9x13in) s. board. 3-Jun-4 Lane, Penzance #90/R est:7500-8500

HEATH, Margaret A (1886-1914) British

Works on paper			
£720	$1346	€1051	Feeding the chickens (49x38cm-19x15in) s. W/C. 20-Jul-4 Sworder & Son, Bishops Stortford #712/R

HEATH, William (1795-1840) British
Works on paper
£820 $1517 €1197 Dover Packet (17x25cm-7x10in) s.d.1835 pen ink. 10-Mar-4 Sotheby's, Olympia #49/R
£1647 $2750 €2388 Master Dogberry. Noblest Roman of them all. Take care of your pockets (61x89cm-24x35in) pen ink W/C drs two s.pseudonym Paul Pry three sold with etching. 25-Jun-3 Butterfields, San Francisco #3122 est:2000-3000
£2400 $4008 €3504 Portrait of General the Hon, Edward Pyndar Lygon (84x65cm-33x26in) s. W/C bodycol gum arabic. 14-Oct-3 Sotheby's, London #50 est:2000-3000

HEATON, E (?) British
£636 $1189 €929 Landscape with peasant woman (35x23cm-14x9in) s. cardboard painted c.1900. 24-Feb-4 Louis Morton, Mexico #29/R est:15000-20000 (M.P 13000)

HEBBAR, Kattingeri Krishna (1911-1996) Indian
£815 $1500 €1190 Evening catch (11x14cm-4x6in) s.d.74 oil paper. 24-Mar-4 Sotheby's, New York #177/R est:1500-2000
£2989 $5500 €4364 Dance (58x74cm-23x29in) 24-Mar-4 Sotheby's, New York #160/R est:5000-8000
Works on paper
£1223 $2250 €1786 Untitled (56x39cm-22x15in) s.d.75 pen ink. 24-Mar-4 Sotheby's, New York #163/R est:1500-2000

HEBERER, Charles (fl.1887-1910) American
£1620 $2900 €2365 Shepherdess with flock of sheep in spring landscape (41x33cm-16x13in) s. 20-Mar-4 Selkirks, St. Louis #154/R est:3500-4500

HEBERT, Adrien (1890-1967) Canadian
£407 $728 €594 Eglise de Quebec (31x25cm-12x10in) i.verso canvasboard prov. 6-May-4 Heffel, Vancouver #68/R (C.D 1000)
£4065 $7276 €5935 Montreal Harbour (51x61cm-20x24in) s. canvas on masonite. 31-May-4 Sotheby's, Toronto #150/R est:10000-12000 (C.D 10000)

HEBERT, Antoine Auguste Ernest (1817-1908) French
£1863 $3000 €2720 Water carriers at the well (116x72cm-46x28in) s.i. 14-Jan-4 Christie's, Rockefeller NY #38/R est:4000-6000

HEBERT, Edmond Ernest Paulin (1824-?) French
£942 $1545 €1300 La pointe de Saint-Valery-sur-Somme (49x35cm-19x14in) s.i. 11-May-3 Osenat, Fontainebleau #167/R

HEBERT, Louis Philippe (1850-1917) Canadian
Sculpture
£3111 $5382 €4542 Chute (30cm-12in) s.i.d.1902 pat bronze marble base. 9-Dec-3 Pinneys, Montreal #103 est:6000-8000 (C.D 7000)
£4444 $7689 €6488 Demoiselle de Vercheres (49cm-19in) s. brown pat bronze. 15-Dec-3 Iegor de Saint Hippolyte, Montreal #19 (C.D 10000)

HECHLE, Hilda (fl.1902-1938) British
Works on paper
£7200 $11952 €10512 Come buy from us with a golden curl (49x39cm-19x15in) sd.1914 W/C prov.exhib. 1-Oct-3 Sotheby's, Olympia #189/R est:2500-3500

HECHT, Hendrick van der (1841-1901) Belgian
£532 $888 €750 Paysage enneige (90x70cm-35x28in) s. 17-Jun-3 Vanderkindere, Brussels #139
£915 $1584 €1300 Vaches dans la clairiere (32x40cm-13x16in) s.d.65. 9-Dec-3 Vanderkindere, Brussels #178
£2238 $3804 €3200 Paysage de Campine avec berger le long d'un ruisseau (115x90cm-45x35in) s. 1-Dec-3 Palais de Beaux Arts, Brussels #324/R est:2800-3600

HECK, Robert (1831-1889) German
£884 $1583 €1300 Wild vine (63x78cm-25x31in) s.d.1883 board. 17-Mar-4 Neumeister, Munich #473/R

HECKE, Arthur van (1924-) French
£845 $1462 €1200 Cote rocheuse (50x61cm-20x24in) s. 14-Dec-3 Eric Pillon, Calais #210/R

HECKE, Jan van den (elder) (1620-1684) Belgian
£4800 $8160 €7008 Roses, carnation and other flowers in an earthenware vase on a table top (72x52cm-28x20in) 29-Oct-3 Bonhams, New Bond Street #70/R est:4000-6000
£13793 $24828 €20000 Vase of flowers (72x52cm-28x20in) 26-Jan-4 Ansorena, Madrid #64/R est:20000

HECKE, Willem van (1893-1976) Belgian
£347 $580 €500 Tete (50x40cm-20x16in) s.d.1974 oil paper. 21-Oct-3 Campo, Vlaamse Kaai #597
£369 $683 €550 Figure on coloured background (27x22cm-11x9in) s. paper on panel lit. 13-Mar-4 De Vuyst, Lokeren #550
£403 $745 €600 Torso (28x19cm-11x7in) s.d.1964 paper on panel lit. 13-Mar-4 De Vuyst, Lokeren #350
£500 $895 €750 Still life (35x28cm-14x11in) s.d.1966 paper on panel. 15-May-4 De Vuyst, Lokeren #356
£533 $955 €800 Abstract people (36x27cm-14x11in) s.d.1962 paper on panel. 15-May-4 De Vuyst, Lokeren #355
£537 $993 €800 Composition with figures (24x36cm-9x14in) s.d.1965 paper on panel lit. 13-Mar-4 De Vuyst, Lokeren #348/R
£594 $993 €850 Two heads (22x27cm-9x11in) s.d.1964 paper. 11-Oct-3 De Vuyst, Lokeren #369
£604 $1117 €900 Figure (29x19cm-11x7in) s.d.1964 paper on panel lit. 13-Mar-4 De Vuyst, Lokeren #349/R
£733 $1313 €1100 Structure (39x21cm-15x8in) s. paper. 15-May-4 De Vuyst, Lokeren #352/R
£769 $1285 €1100 Three unity; man, woman and child (18x28cm-7x11in) s.d.1955 paper on panel. 11-Oct-3 De Vuyst, Lokeren #368/R
£800 $1432 €1200 Composition (29x38cm-11x15in) s.d.1962 paper on panel. 15-May-4 De Vuyst, Lokeren #354
£1056 $1827 €1500 Still life (36x70cm-14x28in) s.d.1966 paper on panel. 13-Dec-3 De Vuyst, Lokeren #347/R est:1800-2000
£1056 $1827 €1500 Standing figure (80x32cm-31x13in) s.d.1964 paper on panel. 13-Dec-3 De Vuyst, Lokeren #350/R est:1500-1800
£1303 $2254 €1850 Christ (59x42cm-23x17in) s.d.1965 paper lit. 13-Dec-3 De Vuyst, Lokeren #348/R est:1800-2000
£1373 $2376 €1950 Figure (36x27cm-14x11in) s.d.1969 paper. 13-Dec-3 De Vuyst, Lokeren #349/R est:1600-1900
£1831 $3168 €2600 Structure (72x56cm-28x22in) s.d.1966 paper. 13-Dec-3 De Vuyst, Lokeren #346/R est:2400-2800
Works on paper
£278 $464 €400 Nu (18x12cm-7x5in) s.d.1955 mixed media. 21-Oct-3 Campo, Vlaamse Kaai #595
£278 $464 €400 Composition (20x27cm-8x11in) s.d.1962 mixed media. 21-Oct-3 Campo, Vlaamse Kaai #596
£282 $487 €400 Two figures (31x25cm-12x10in) s. wax crayon. 13-Dec-3 De Vuyst, Lokeren #351
£340 $609 €500 Paysage a la maison (12x16cm-5x6in) mono. mixed media ink. 19-Mar-4 Millon & Associes, Paris #125/R
£408 $731 €600 Marine (22x28cm-9x11in) s.d.1945 mixed media ink. 19-Mar-4 Millon & Associes, Paris #122
£451 $754 €650 Deux figures dans un paysage (13x21cm-5x8in) s.d.1947 mixed media. 21-Oct-3 Campo, Vlaamse Kaai #594
£467 $840 €700 Face (32x40cm-13x16in) s.d.1974 mixed media. 26-Apr-4 Bernaerts, Antwerp #587
£510 $913 €750 En famille (32x23cm-13x9in) s.d.49 mixed media ink. 19-Mar-4 Millon & Associes, Paris #123/R
£544 $974 €800 Maison (16x23cm-6x9in) s.d.1943 mixed media ink. 19-Mar-4 Millon & Associes, Paris #126/R
£544 $974 €800 Pere, la mere et la fille (16x21cm-6x8in) s.d.46 mixed media ink. 19-Mar-4 Millon & Associes, Paris #127
£680 $1218 €1000 Paysage (28x32cm-11x13in) s.d.1936 mixed media ink. 19-Mar-4 Millon & Associes, Paris #121/R

HECKEL, Erich (1883-1970) German
£6944 $11597 €10000 Sleeping figure - Siddi Heckel (56x36cm-22x14in) s.i.d. W/C bodycol over col pen board. 24-Oct-3 Ketterer, Hamburg #369/R est:12000-14000
£10000 $17900 €15000 Woman in studio (37x34cm-15x13in) s.d. oil crayon wash prov. 14-May-4 Ketterer, Munich #137/R est:9000-12000
£24667 $45387 €37000 Huts on beach (27x34cm-11x13in) s.i.d.1911 W/C pencil. 10-Jun-4 Hauswedell & Nolte, Hamburg #260/R est:30000
£25000 $40750 €36000 Landscape in southern France (83x96cm-33x38in) s.d.1958 i.d. stretcher tempera. 27-Sep-3 Dr Fritz Nagel, Stuttgart #9548/R est:22000
£34965 $59441 €50000 Sea near Kampen (70x80cm-28x31in) mono.d.34 s.d.34 verso s.i.d.1934 stretcher tempera prov. 29-Nov-3 Villa Grisebach, Berlin #237/R est:30000-40000
£150000 $276000 €219000 Roter Steinbruch - Red quarry (83x96cm-33x38in) s.i. stretcher painted 1916 prov.exhib.lit. 23-Jun-4 Christie's, London #169/R est:150000-200000
£174825 $297203 €250000 Still life with blue vase (48x55cm-19x22in) s.d.12 s.i. verso prov. 28-Nov-3 Villa Grisebach, Berlin #37/R est:280000-340000
£320000 $588800 €467200 Standing female nude (84x39cm-33x15in) s.d.1913 s.d.verso prov. 22-Jun-4 Christie's, London #46/R est:250000-350000
Prints
£1207 $2160 €1762 Street (17x20cm-7x8in) s.mono.d.10 etching. 13-May-4 Stuker, Bern #169/R est:1000-1500 (S.FR 2800)
£1333 $2453 €2000 Siblings (41x30cm-16x12in) s.d.1913 woodcut one of 40. 12-Jun-4 Villa Grisebach, Berlin #218/R est:2500-3500
£1667 $3067 €2500 Young man (36x29cm-14x11in) s.d.1917 woodcut. 12-Jun-4 Villa Grisebach, Berlin #219/R est:2500-3500
£2000 $3680 €3000 Two women on beach (58x42cm-23x17in) s.d.1920 lithograph. 10-Jun-4 Hauswedell & Nolte, Hamburg #271/R est:3500
£2000 $3680 €3000 Sunrise (25x32cm-10x13in) s.d.1914 woodcut. 10-Jun-4 Hauswedell & Nolte, Hamburg #287/R est:3000
£2000 $3640 €2920 Jugendlicher kopf (18x14cm-7x6in) s.d.08 drypoint. 1-Jul-4 Sotheby's, London #183/R est:2500-3500
£2158 $3540 €3000 Woman by table (27x31cm-11x12in) s.mono.i.d. lithograph. 4-Jun-3 Ketterer, Hamburg #462/R est:3500-4500
£2400 $4416 €3600 Portrait of E H (26x29cm-10x11in) s.i.d.1917 woodcut. 10-Jun-4 Hauswedell & Nolte, Hamburg #288/R est:3000
£2448 $4161 €3500 Fisherman (27x21cm-11x8in) s.d. lithograph. 29-Nov-3 Villa Grisebach, Berlin #201/R est:4000-6000
£2550 $4693 €3800 Stralsund (31x36cm-12x14in) s.i.d. woodcut. 26-Mar-4 Ketterer, Hamburg #450/R est:3800-4500
£2620 $4769 €3825 Portrait of Asta Nielsen. s.d.19 woodcut. 17-Jun-4 Kornfeld, Bern #411/R est:6000 (S.FR 6000)
£2661 $4443 €3858 Reclining figure. s.d.13 col woodcut. 19-Jun-3 Kornfeld, Bern #463 est:6000 (S.FR 5800)
£2937 $5052 €4200 Actress (15x10cm-6x4in) s.mono.i.d.1905 woodcut. 2-Dec-3 Hauswedell & Nolte, Hamburg #266/R est:4500
£3057 $5563 €4463 Factory in Dresden. s.d.08 woodcut. 17-Jun-4 Kornfeld, Bern #407/R est:7500 (S.FR 7000)
£3333 $5967 €5000 Street by harbour (17x20cm-7x8in) s.mono.d. drypoint paper on board. 14-May-4 Ketterer, Munich #138/R est:5000-5600
£3497 $5944 €5000 Drunkard (19x13cm-7x5in) s.i.d. woodcut. 26-Nov-3 Lempertz, Koln #707/R est:4800
£3566 $6134 €5100 Woman at table (27x31cm-11x12in) s.i.d.1907 lithograph. 2-Dec-3 Hauswedell & Nolte, Hamburg #263/R est:6500
£3691 $6607 €5500 Three girls on beach (30x25cm-12x10in) s.i.d.19 drypoint. 25-May-4 Karl & Faber, Munich #319/R est:6000-8000
£4118 $7000 €6012 Portrait (36x29cm-14x11in) s.d.1917 woodcut. 31-Oct-3 Sotheby's, New York #283/R
£4336 $7457 €6200 Bathers by pond (20x15cm-8x6in) s.i. woodcut. 2-Dec-3 Hauswedell & Nolte, Hamburg #268/R est:2500
£4667 $8587 €7000 Ball game (19x27cm-7x11in) s.d.1911 woodcut. 10-Jun-4 Hauswedell & Nolte, Hamburg #284/R est:8000
£5333 $9813 €8000 The Millmann trio (32x27cm-13x11in) s.i.d.1910 lithograph. 11-Jun-4 Villa Grisebach, Berlin #1533/R est:12000-15000
£5467 $10059 €8200 Bearded man (44x47cm-17x19in) s.i.d.08 lithograph. 10-Jun-4 Hauswedell & Nolte, Hamburg #269/R est:9000

£6294	$10699	€9000	Tightropeartists (19x24cm-7x9in) s.i.d.1909 lithograph prov. 28-Nov-3 Villa Grisebach, Berlin #21/R est:9000-12000
£6550	$11921	€9563	By the stone - two girls by water. s.i.d.14 lithograph. 17-Jun-4 Kornfeld, Bern #424 est:6000 (S.FR 15000)
£8734	$15895	€12752	A girl. s.d.10 lithograph. 17-Jun-4 Kornfeld, Bern #423/R est:20000 (S.FR 20000)
£9607	$17485	€14026	Shooting gallery (17x21cm-7x8in) s.d.09 col woodcut. 18-Jun-4 Kornfeld, Bern #54/R est:25000 (S.FR 22000)
£10432	$17108	€14500	Two girls in studio (18x24cm-7x9in) s.i.d. woodcut. 4-Jun-3 Ketterer, Hamburg #460/R est:4000-5000
£12000	$21480	€18000	In front of the mirror (22x16cm-9x6in) col woodcut prov. 14-May-4 Ketterer, Munich #143/R est:18000-24000
£15385	$26154	€22000	Sleeping black woman (25x33cm-10x13in) s.i.d.1910 woodcut prov. 28-Nov-3 Villa Grisebach, Berlin #23/R est:20000-25000
£16084	$27664	€23000	Two women in studio (18x24cm-7x9in) s.i.d.1910 woodcut. 2-Dec-3 Hauswedell & Nolte, Hamburg #267/R est:25000
£27333	$50293	€41000	Young girl (58x42cm-23x17in) s.d.12/13 lithograph. 11-Jun-4 Villa Grisebach, Berlin #1536/R est:15000-20000
Works on paper			
£2000	$3200	€2920	Bauernhaus (52x40cm-20x16in) s. brush ink. 18-Sep-3 Swann Galleries, New York #303/R est:5000-8000
£3237	$5309	€4500	Couple (13x10cm-5x4in) s. verso col chk pencil. 4-Jun-3 Ketterer, Hamburg #458/R est:4000-5000
£3267	$5945	€4900	Landscape by Untersee (51x70cm-20x28in) s.d.44 W/C. 3-Jul-4 Geble, Radolfzell #441/R est:800
£3667	$6747	€5500	Couple (13x10cm-5x4in) s. verso pencil col chk. 10-Jun-4 Hauswedell & Nolte, Hamburg #259/R est:7500
£3706	$6301	€5300	Three nudes on beach (36x47cm-14x19in) s.d.19 W/C over pencil. 29-Nov-3 Bassenge, Berlin #6746/R est:6000
£3873	$6701	€5500	Cyclamen (47x28cm-19x11in) s.i.d.59 W/C gouache pencil. 13-Dec-3 Lempertz, Koln #151/R est:4500
£4000	$7360	€6000	Still life with flowers in vase and statuette (50x42cm-20x17in) s.i.d.1946 w/C gouache. 10-Jun-4 Hauswedell & Nolte, Hamburg #264/R est:8000
£4577	$7919	€6500	Alpine lakes II (46x60cm-18x24in) s.i.d.57 W/C chl W/C. 13-Dec-3 Lempertz, Koln #150/R est:5000-6000
£4667	$8540	€7000	Portrait of E H - Self portrait (43x30cm-17x12in) s.i.d.49 W/C pencil board prov. 5-Jun-4 Lempertz, Koln #756/R est:7000-8000
£4895	$8322	€7000	High mountains (48x63cm-19x25in) s.i.d.55 W/C chk over pencil. 26-Nov-3 Lempertz, Koln #704/R est:8000
£5000	$9200	€7300	Blaue berge (48x61cm-19x24in) s.i.d.23 W/C over pencil col crayons prov. 24-Mar-4 Sotheby's, Olympia #36/R est:5000-7000
£5000	$9200	€7300	Im Gesprach (54x49cm-21x19in) s.i.d.24 W/C crayon prov. 24-Jun-4 Christie's, London #380/R est:7000-10000
£5000	$9200	€7500	Seamstress (54x44cm-21x17in) s.i.d.1922 Indian ink. 10-Jun-4 Hauswedell & Nolte, Hamburg #262/R est:6000
£5500	$10010	€8030	Young girl (34x26cm-13x10in) s.i.d.11 chl prov.exhib. 4-Feb-4 Sotheby's, London #431/R est:3500-4500
£5594	$9510	€8000	Sailing ship (44x35cm-17x14in) s.i.d.37 W/C over pencil. 26-Nov-3 Lempertz, Koln #700/R est:10000
£5594	$9510	€8000	Zinnia (67x54cm-26x21in) s.i.d.40 W/C. 26-Nov-3 Lempertz, Koln #701/R est:10000-12000
£5594	$9510	€8000	Path between meadows (46x60cm-18x24in) s.i.d.23 W/C over pencil. 29-Nov-3 Villa Grisebach, Berlin #231/R est:5000-7000
£5594	$9510	€8000	Mudflats (546x70cm-215x28in) s.i.d.50 W/C chk. 29-Nov-3 Villa Grisebach, Berlin #234/R est:8000-10000
£5594	$9510	€8000	Dunes on Sylt (56x68cm-22x27in) s.i.d.33 W/C chk prov. 29-Nov-3 Villa Grisebach, Berlin #235/R est:8000-10000
£5895	$10729	€8607	Sleeping figure (33x42cm-13x17in) s.i.d.13 pencil. 17-Jun-4 Kornfeld, Bern #405/R est:15000 (S.FR 13500)
£5944	$10105	€8500	View of sea (49x63cm-19x25in) s.i.d.53 W/C on pencil. 29-Nov-3 Villa Grisebach, Berlin #236/R est:9000-11000
£5986	$9577	€8500	Karnten landscape (48x63cm-19x25in) s.i.d.42 W/C over pencil. 19-Sep-3 Karlheinz Kaupp, Staufen #2200/R est:8500
£6040	$11114	€9000	Untersee (54x68cm-21x27in) s.i.d. W/C gouache chk. 26-Mar-4 Ketterer, Hamburg #449/R est:9000-12000
£6643	$11427	€9500	Harvest time (56x70cm-22x28in) s.i.d.1935 W/C over pencil. 2-Dec-3 Hauswedell & Nolte, Hamburg #260/R est:10000
£7000	$12530	€10500	Landscape (56x69cm-22x27in) s.i.d. W/C on chk prov. 14-May-4 Ketterer, Munich #194/R est:9000-12000
£8000	$13840	€11680	Blumenvasen (49x33cm-19x13in) s.d.14 pencil W/C gouache prov. 11-Dec-3 Christie's, Kensington #102/R est:8000-12000
£8000	$14720	€12000	Lovely day (58x46cm-23x18in) s.d.1922 i. verso W/C on pencil. 10-Jun-4 Hauswedell & Nolte, Hamburg #261/R est:12000
£8000	$14720	€12000	Landscape in Schleswig (55x69cm-22x27in) s.i.d.1940 W/C col wax chk. 10-Jun-4 Hauswedell & Nolte, Hamburg #263/R est:14000
£8297	$15100	€12114	Woman sitting on the beach (35x45cm-14x18in) s.i.d.22 W/C pencil. 18-Jun-4 Kornfeld, Bern #53/R est:17500 (S.FR 19000)
£8392	$14266	€12000	Untersee (44x49cm-17x19in) s.i.d.48 W/C bodycol prov. 26-Nov-3 Lempertz, Koln #703/R est:12000-15000
£8392	$14266	€12000	Glacier and mountains (48x63cm-19x25in) s.i.d.58 W/C chk. 26-Nov-3 Lempertz, Koln #705/R est:14000
£9091	$15636	€13000	North Sea (55x59cm-22x23in) si.d.1925 W/C chk. 2-Dec-3 Hauswedell & Nolte, Hamburg #259/R est:8000
£10823	$19372	€15802	Wall with houses (49x60cm-19x24in) s.i.d. W/C over chl. 22-Mar-4 Philippe Schuler, Zurich #4020/R est:19800-23100 (S.FR 25000)
£13000	$23920	€18980	Dahlias (63x46cm-25x18in) s.i.d.1923 gouache wash chl prov. 24-Jun-4 Christie's, London #381/R est:15000-20000
£14685	$25259	€21000	Dahlia blooms (49x40cm-19x16in) s.i.d.1948 W/C opaque white prov. 5-Dec-3 Ketterer, Munich #110/R est:10000-15000
£17958	$31067	€25500	In the studio (60x37cm-24x15in) s.d.21 W/C over pencil. 13-Dec-3 Lempertz, Koln #149/R est:8000-10000

HECKEN, Samuel van den (17th C) Flemish

£19397	$35690	€28320	Floers (106x74cm-42x29in) s. panel prov. 26-Mar-4 Koller, Zurich #3025/R est:30000-50000 (S.FR 45000)

HECKENDORF, Franz (1888-1962) German

£267	$480	€400	Tea roses in vase (55x45cm-22x18in) s. W/C. 26-Apr-4 Rieber, Stuttgart #1134/R
£940	$1682	€1400	Mountain lake with pine trees (60x81cm-24x32in) s.d.48. 25-May-4 Karl & Faber, Munich #320/R
£2083	$3479	€3000	Houses on mountain lake (60x81cm-24x32in) s.d. cotton. 24-Oct-3 Ketterer, Hamburg #374/R est:3000-3500
£2128	$3553	€3000	Peonies in vase (100x80cm-39x31in) s.d.42 panel. 17-Oct-3 Behringer, Furth #1489/R est:900
£3497	$5944	€5000	Still life of flowers (63x52cm-25x20in) s.d.23. 29-Nov-3 Villa Grisebach, Berlin #250/R est:5000-7000
£5000	$9200	€7500	Still life with flowers (97x79cm-38x31in) s.d.55 masonite. 12-Jun-4 Villa Grisebach, Berlin #332/R est:6000-8000
£9091	$15455	€13000	Landscape with drawbridge (60x80cm-24x31in) s.d.28. 29-Nov-3 Villa Grisebach, Berlin #248/R est:7000-9000
Works on paper			
£433	$776	€650	River crossing (30x41cm-12x16in) s.d.12 col chk. 15-May-4 Bassenge, Berlin #6861
£470	$860	€700	Sun over a mountain village (42x46cm-17x18in) s.d.19 pastel. 8-Jul-4 Allgauer, Kempten #1985/R
£559	$951	€800	Donau bridge (31x43cm-12x17in) s.d.53 i. verso W/C bodycol. 29-Nov-3 Villa Grisebach, Berlin #564/R
£625	$1044	€900	Mediterranean landscape (40x49cm-16x19in) s.d. gouache on pencil. 24-Oct-3 Ketterer, Hamburg #804/R
£629	$1145	€950	Country landscape with mountains in the distance (50x60cm-20x24in) s.d.51 W/C. 16-Jun-4 Hugo Ruef, Munich #1160/R
£662	$1205	€1000	Tessin landscape (38x46cm-15x18in) s.d.51 W/C. 16-Jun-4 Hugo Ruef, Munich #1159/R
£733	$1313	€1100	Landscape with anglers (31x41cm-12x16in) s.d.53 w/C lit. 14-May-4 Schloss Ahlden, Ahlden #2957/R
£733	$1342	€1100	Roses (53x46cm-21x18in) s. W/C. 5-Jun-4 Lempertz, Koln #760/R
£800	$1472	€1200	Forest interior (64x49cm-25x19in) s. W/C gouache. 12-Jun-4 Villa Grisebach, Berlin #565/R
£878	$1572	€1300	River promenade (37x47cm-15x19in) s.d.60 w/C pencil lit. 8-May-4 Schloss Ahlden, Ahlden #832/R
£1067	$1909	€1600	Monaco (35x50cm-14x20in) s.d.27 W/C. 15-May-4 Bassenge, Berlin #6860/R est:1500
£1259	$2140	€1800	Still life of flowers (48x36cm-19x14in) s.d.51 W/C gouache. 29-Nov-3 Villa Grisebach, Berlin #563/R est:1800-2400

HECKERT, Hans (1926-) Austrian

£326	$597	€476	Le chat (65x41cm-26x16in) s.d.75. 5-Jun-4 Galerie du Rhone, Sion #333 (S.FR 750)

HECKROTH, Hein (1901-1970) German

£2500	$3975	€3650	Theatergoers use shell (76x114cm-30x45in) s.stretcher. 10-Sep-3 Sotheby's, Olympia #79/R est:400-600

HECQ, Émile (1924-) French

£403	$713	€600	Ile de Re (102x80cm-40x31in) s. 28-Apr-4 Charbonneaux, Paris #173/R
£604	$1069	€900	Ile de Re (80x100cm-31x39in) s. 28-Apr-4 Charbonneaux, Paris #172/R
£1172	$2169	€1700	Taquine (150x75cm-59x30in) s.d.1970 oil mixed media. 13-Feb-4 Charbonneaux, Paris #78/R est:800-1000
Works on paper			
£268	$475	€400	Composition lune bleue (63x48cm-25x19in) s. gouache exec.c.1960. 28-Apr-4 Charbonneaux, Paris #171

HEDA, Willem Claesz (style) (1594-1680) Dutch

£6000	$10980	€8760	Still life of a nautilus cup, tazza, pie and two wine glass on a table top (77x59cm-30x23in) 6-Jul-4 Sotheby's, Olympia #550/R est:5000-7000

HEDBERG, Hans (1917-) Swedish

Sculpture			
£1600	$2960	€2400	Little apple (13cm-5in) s. painted ceramic exec.1994 prov. 18-Jul-4 Sotheby's, Paris #217/R est:1000-1500

HEDBERG, Kalle (1894-1959) Swedish

£471	$815	€688	Yellow bowl on blue mat (54x73cm-21x29in) s. 15-Dec-3 Lilla Bukowskis, Stockholm #215 (S.KR 6000)

HEDDEGHEM, Alice van (fl.1906-1927) British

£600	$1122	€876	Still life of flowers (40x118cm-16x46in) s. 22-Jul-4 Tennants, Leyburn #888

HEDELIN, Carl (1861-1894) Swedish

£20695	$37044	€30215	Oskar II walking at Norrbro (95x121cm-37x48in) s.d.1891 lit. 25-May-4 Bukowskis, Stockholm #11/R est:175000-200000 (S.KR 280000)

HEDGECOCK, Derek Albert (1932-1999) British

£260	$468	€380	Fishing boats at Dungeness (81x97cm-32x38in) s. 20-Apr-4 Canterbury Auctions, UK #138
£580	$1044	€847	Coast near Lands End (76x84cm-30x33in) s. 20-Apr-4 Canterbury Auctions, UK #137

HEDINGER, Elise (1854-?) American

£473	$847	€700	Nature morte au homard (26x33cm-10x13in) s.d.1885 panel. 10-May-4 Horta, Bruxelles #387

HEDLEY, Ralph (c.1851-1913) British

£550	$919	€803	Young boy cooking muscles (48x38cm-19x15in) s. 17-Oct-3 Keys, Aylsham #759
£2600	$4238	€3796	Full-length portrait of Robert Charles Duncombe Shafto as a boy, with pony (135x110cm-53x43in) 23-Sep-3 Anderson & Garland, Newcastle #345/R est:1000-2000
£3000	$5460	€4380	Butter churn (69x51cm-27x20in) s.d.97 exhib. 16-Jun-4 Bonhams, New Bond Street #66/R est:3000-5000
£3300	$6072	€4818	Home sweet home (32x41cm-13x16in) s.d.03 panel. 23-Mar-4 Anderson & Garland, Newcastle #432/R est:3000-4000
£3600	$6552	€5256	Lonely road (38x31cm-15x12in) s.d.1904 panel. 16-Jun-4 Bonhams, New Bond Street #67/R est:4000-6000
£6200	$11408	€9052	Sheep shearer (39x31cm-15x12in) s.d.1906 board exhib. 23-Mar-4 Anderson & Garland, Newcastle #431/R est:3000-4000
£11765	$20000	€17177	Animal market (124x89cm-49x35in) s.d.1886. 28-Oct-3 Sotheby's, New York #138/R est:10000-15000

£22000	$40480	€32120	Truant's log (106x92cm-42x36in) s.d.1899 prov.exhib. 23-Mar-4 Bonhams, New Bond Street #55/R est:15000-20000
£36000	$66240	€52560	The tournament (83x103cm-33x41in) s.d.98 prov.exhib.lit. 23-Mar-4 Bonhams, New Bond Street #53/R est:20000-30000
Works on paper			
£380	$680	€555	Portrait of the artist's nephew (46x37cm-18x15in) s.d.August 1907 pastel. 16-Mar-4 Bonhams, Leeds #655
£1350	$2417	€1971	Young girl with a water pail (28x21cm-11x8in) s.d.1884 pencil W/C. 16-Mar-4 Bonhams, Leeds #654 est:300-400

HEDLEY, Ralph (attrib) (c.1851-1913) British

£350	$585	€511	Road to London (31x41cm-12x16in) 16-Oct-3 Lawrence, Crewkerne #741

HEDLICKA, Alfred (1928-) ?

Sculpture			
£1884	$3090	€2600	Power block (35cm-14in) init. num.13/20 bronze prov.lit. 27-May-3 Sotheby's, Amsterdam #529/R est:1000-1500

HEEBNER, Abraham (1802-1877) American

Works on paper			
£1818	$3200	€2654	Schwenkfelder Fraktur, nighttime and daytime (20x15cm-8x6in) W/C. 21-May-4 Pook & Pook, Downington #250/R est:3000-5000

HEEBNER, Mary (1951-) American

Works on paper			
£333	$613	€500	Near to far (17x15cm-7x6in) s.d. W/C on paper collage. 11-Jun-4 Hauswedell & Nolte, Hamburg #1299/R

HEEKS, Willy (1951-) American

£324	$550	€473	Untitled (152x137cm-60x54in) s.i.d.1985. 21-Nov-3 Swann Galleries, New York #75/R

HEEL, Jan van (1898-1991) Dutch

£1088	$1981	€1600	Still life with fruits, sunflowers and ginger jar (40x50cm-16x20in) s.d.60. 3-Feb-4 Christie's, Amsterdam #476 est:1000-1500
£1189	$2045	€1700	House with pretty fence in Paris (35x28cm-14x11in) s. board. 8-Dec-3 Glerum, Amsterdam #129/R est:1200-1500
£1370	$2329	€2000	Spain (49x59cm-19x23in) s.d.57. 5-Nov-3 Vendue Huis, Gravenhage #464/R est:2000-2500
£1447	$2663	€2200	Stuffed bird (60x50cm-24x20in) s. s.i.d.1960 verso. 22-Jun-4 Christie's, Amsterdam #609/R est:1800-2200
£2098	$3608	€3000	Circus monkey (100x70cm-39x28in) s. 8-Dec-3 Glerum, Amsterdam #99/R est:2500-3000
£2098	$3608	€3000	Bird in cage (60x50cm-24x20in) s. 8-Dec-3 Glerum, Amsterdam #106/R est:1000-1500
£2098	$3608	€3000	Clown (50x60cm-20x24in) s.d.79 s.d.verso. 2-Dec-3 Sotheby's, Amsterdam #271/R est:3000-4000
£3000	$5520	€4500	Museum Zaal (80x100cm-31x39in) s.d.78 s.i.d. stretcher. 8-Jun-4 Sotheby's, Amsterdam #275/R est:4000-6000
£3014	$5123	€4400	Tin soldiers under glass dome (49x58cm-19x23in) s.d.75. 5-Nov-3 Vendue Huis, Gravenhage #463/R est:2000-3000
£3767	$6404	€5500	Carnival (100x80cm-39x31in) s.d.66 lit. 5-Nov-3 Vendue Huis, Gravenhage #465/R est:4000-6000
£4452	$7568	€6500	White chair (48x63cm-19x25in) s.d.70 lit. 5-Nov-3 Vendue Huis, Gravenhage #467b/R est:5000-7000
£4795	$8151	€7000	Ortisei, Dolomiti (100x89cm-39x35in) s.d.76. 5-Nov-3 Vendue Huis, Gravenhage #466/R est:4000-6000
£6643	$11427	€9500	Unemployed (100x70cm-39x28in) s. exhib. 8-Dec-3 Glerum, Amsterdam #98/R est:10000-15000
Works on paper			
£276	$461	€400	Shells (30x23cm-12x9in) s. gouache. 11-Nov-3 Vendu Notarishuis, Rotterdam #67
£276	$461	€400	City view (30x22cm-12x9in) s. gouache. 11-Nov-3 Vendu Notarishuis, Rotterdam #69
£490	$842	€700	Clown (34x28cm-13x11in) s.i. W/C htd white. 8-Dec-3 Glerum, Amsterdam #336/R
£524	$902	€750	Clown (18x10cm-7x4in) s. ink W/C prov. 8-Dec-3 Glerum, Amsterdam #338/R
£816	$1486	€1200	Ingang cirque d'hiver, Paris (30x20cm-12x8in) s.i.d.47 ink W/C. 3-Feb-4 Christie's, Amsterdam #480 est:400-600
£872	$1614	€1300	Untitled (30x48cm-12x19in) s.d.70 ink W/C. 15-Mar-4 Sotheby's, Amsterdam #228/R est:1000-1500
£1382	$2542	€2100	Soldier (48x30cm-19x12in) s.d.68 ink W/C gouache. 22-Jun-4 Christie's, Amsterdam #606/R est:1200-1600
£2133	$3925	€3200	Haan (62x48cm-24x19in) s.d.51 gouache lit. 8-Jun-4 Sotheby's, Amsterdam #276/R est:2000-3000

HEEM, Cornelis de (1631-1695) Dutch

£23776	$40895	€34000	Still life with peaches, plums, grapes and hazelnuts (47x39cm-19x15in) 3-Dec-3 Neumeister, Munich #470/R est:36000
£34483	$57241	€50000	Still life with fruit and glass of wine (40x30cm-16x12in) s. panel. 1-Oct-3 Dorotheum, Vienna #164/R est:50000-60000
£35000	$63000	€51100	Still life of peaches, plums, grapes and other fruits on a stone ledge (47x39cm-19x15in) s. prov. 22-Apr-4 Sotheby's, London #21/R est:25000-35000
£47945	$81507	€70000	Festoon of fruits, peppers and woodsnails tied with a ribbon (69x56cm-27x22in) prov. 4-Nov-3 Sotheby's, Amsterdam #25/R est:15000-20000
£90909	$151818	€130000	Still life with lemon, grapes and oranges (28x38cm-11x15in) lit. 30-Jun-3 Ansorena, Madrid #185/R est:130000
£99329	$185745	€148000	Garland. Still life of flowers and fruit (68x55cm-27x22in) s. pair. 25-Feb-4 Porro, Milan #63/R est:148000

HEEM, Cornelis de (attrib) (1631-1695) Dutch

£20690	$34345	€30000	Still life with fruit, Venetian glass and silver sugar castor (50x40cm-20x16in) 1-Oct-3 Dorotheum, Vienna #163/R est:30000-50000

HEEM, Cornelis de (style) (1631-1695) Dutch

£8500	$13855	€12410	Grapes, peach, butterfly and orange on a porcelain plate and roemer of wine (37x30cm-15x12in) paper on canvas. 26-Sep-3 Christie's, Kensington #95/R est:600-800

HEEM, J D de (1606-1684) Dutch

£12245	$22286	€18000	Still life with melons, grapes and figs (83x68cm-33x27in) i. verso. 4-Feb-4 Neumeister, Munich #648/R est:2500

HEEM, Jan Davidsz de (1606-1684) Dutch

£140000	$256200	€204400	Still life of wine glass on parcel-gilt stand, beaker and lobster, clay pipe and lemons (43x56cm-17x22in) s.d.1642 panel prov. 7-Jul-4 Sotheby's, London #11/R est:150000-200000

HEEM, Jan Davidsz de (attrib) (1606-1684) Dutch

£11207	$20060	€16362	Still life (67x53cm-26x21in) 12-May-4 Dobiaschofsky, Bern #594/R est:36000 (S.FR 26000)

HEEM, Jan Davidsz de (studio) (1606-1684) Dutch

£27778	$45278	€40000	Flower garland (82x106cm-32x42in) i. 25-Sep-3 Dr Fritz Nagel, Stuttgart #1211/R est:26000

HEEMSKERK, Egbert van (17/18th C) Dutch

£1300	$2340	€1898	Peasants singing outside an inn (20x17cm-8x7in) s. panel. 21-Apr-4 Bonhams, New Bond Street #56a/R est:1500-2000
£1308	$2249	€1910	Burlesque figure of a man (19x15cm-7x6in) init. panel. 2-Dec-3 Bukowskis, Stockholm #366/R est:15000-18000 (S.KR 17000)

HEEMSKERK, Egbert van (attrib) (17/18th C) Dutch

£1399	$2406	€2000	Interieur de taverne avec paysans buvant (63x75cm-25x30in) 3-Dec-3 Palais de Beaux Arts, Brussels #1276/R est:2000-2500
£1409	$2465	€2000	Scene d'interieur de taverne avec des paysans (27x25cm-11x10in) 18-Dec-3 Tajan, Paris #82 est:2000-3000
£1500	$2445	€2190	Peasants carousing in an interior (39x54cm-15x21in) 26-Sep-3 Christie's, Kensington #74/R est:1500-2000
£2685	$4940	€4000	Peasants dancing in tavern (34x60cm-13x24in) panel. 25-Mar-4 Dr Fritz Nagel, Stuttgart #602/R est:4000
£3500	$5950	€5110	Village kermesse (70x103cm-28x41in) 31-Oct-3 Christie's, Kensington #57/R est:4000-6000

HEEMSKERK, Egbert van (elder) (1610-1680) Dutch

£733	$1313	€1100	School class (29x38cm-11x15in) panel. 17-May-4 Glerum, Amsterdam #24/R
£6711	$12349	€10000	Merry party in tavern (72x87cm-28x34in) 24-Mar-4 Dorotheum, Vienna #124/R est:12000-15000

HEEMSKERK, Egbert van (younger) (1634-1704) Dutch

£420	$769	€613	Hermit in contemplation (36x31cm-14x12in) s. 6-Jul-4 Bonhams, Knightsbridge #21
£700	$1113	€1015	Monkey school with a cat and an ass disciplining two monkey's and a monkey reading (35x30cm-14x12in) bears sig. 9-Sep-3 Bonhams, Knightsbridge #215/R
£1342	$2483	€2000	Family praying at a table in an interior (41x48cm-16x19in) s. 15-Mar-4 Sotheby's, Amsterdam #42/R est:2000-3000
£1600	$2928	€2336	Interior with two Boors playing cards (15x13cm-6x5in) copper. 6-Jul-4 Sotheby's, Olympia #527/R est:1500-2000
£1736	$2743	€2500	Boors drinking in a tavern (66x56cm-26x22in) 2-Sep-3 Christie's, Amsterdam #24/R est:800-1200
£1761	$3081	€2500	Smokers (15x12cm-6x5in) s.d.1696 panel. 19-Dec-3 Pierre Berge, Paris #41/R est:1500-2000
£2027	$3568	€3000	Interior with three drunk peasants (25x20cm-10x8in) mono. prov. 22-May-4 Lempertz, Koln #1060/R est:4000
£3500	$6405	€5110	Interior with figures playing backgammon. Interior with figures playing cards (21x25cm-8x10in) s. copper set of four. 6-Jul-4 Sotheby's, Olympia #482/R est:4000-6000
£6000	$10980	€8760	An alchemist in his study. Dentist in his surgery (35x30cm-14x12in) s. panel oval pair. 6-Jul-4 Sotheby's, Olympia #483/R est:4000-6000
£10000	$18300	€14600	Tavern interior with pipe-player and merry company (81x107cm-32x42in) 8-Jul-4 Sotheby's, London #271/R est:8000-12000
£14000	$25620	€20440	Doctor's surgery (64x77cm-25x30in) mono. prov. 8-Jul-4 Sotheby's, London #270/R est:10000-15000

HEEMSKERK, Egbert van (younger-attrib) (1634-1704) Dutch

£1100	$2057	€1606	Peasants drinking and making music in an interior (49x67cm-19x26in) panel. 27-Feb-4 Christie's, Kensington #89/R est:700-1000
£1223	$2250	€1786	Peasants in tavern (22x28cm-9x11in) mono. panel. 14-Jun-4 Philippe Schuler, Zurich #4294/R est:3000-5000 (S.FR 2800)
£1800	$3114	€2628	Portrait of a man in a plumed cap (76x63cm-30x25in) 12-Dec-3 Christie's, Kensington #91/R est:2000-3000

HEEMSKERK, Jacob Eduard van Beest (1828-1894) Dutch

£1399	$2336	€2000	Sailing vessels at sea (120x150cm-47x59in) s. 30-Jun-3 Sotheby's, Amsterdam #282
£4000	$7200	€6000	Shipping off the coast (59x107cm-23x42in) s. 20-Apr-4 Sotheby's, Amsterdam #44/R est:3000-4000
£6207	$10366	€9000	Ships in Batavia (57x107cm-22x42in) s. 15-Nov-3 Lempertz, Koln #1616/R est:5000

HEEMSKERK, Marten Jacobsz van Veen (attrib) (1498-1574) Dutch

£2759	$4579	€4000	Portrait of man in black cap (68x53cm-27x21in) panel. 1-Oct-3 Dorotheum, Vienna #274/R est:7000-10000

HEEMSKERK, Marten van (17th C) Dutch

£34000	$61200	€49640	Judgement of Paris (27x33cm-11x13in) panel prov.lit. 21-Apr-4 Christie's, London #48/R est:15000-20000
Works on paper			
£5479	$9315	€8000	St Luke (24x18cm-9x7in) bears i.d.1549 pen brown ink. 4-Nov-3 Sotheby's, Amsterdam #6/R est:8000-12000

HEEMSKERK, Sebastiaen (?-1748) Dutch

£1200	$2076	€1752	Drovers and their animals beside a ruin (31x25cm-12x10in) mono. panel. 9-Dec-3 Sotheby's, Olympia #357/R est:1500-2000

HEEMSTEDE-OBELT, C van (20th C) Dutch

£306	$548	€450	Wayang puppets (85x70cm-33x28in) s.d.1915. 16-Mar-4 Christie's, Amsterdam #15

HEENCK, Jabez (1752-1782) French

Works on paper			
£816	$1461	€1200	Un colibri et un rouge-gorge pose sur une branche (41x27cm-16x11in) black chk pen ink W/C. 18-Mar-4 Christie's, Paris #327/R
£1081	$1903	€1600	Golden pheasant in a landscape. Minerva with a cockerel and owl (12x18cm-5x7in) s.i.d.1775 mono.verso pen black ink W/C double-sided. 19-May-4 Sotheby's, Amsterdam #238/R est:500-700

HEER, Gerrit Adriaensz de (1634-1681) Dutch

Works on paper			
£2400	$4392	€3504	Village scene with peasants relaxing under a tree to the left (33x43cm-13x17in) s. pen ink framing lines. 6-Jul-4 Christie's, London #168/R est:2000-4000
£3288	$5589	€4800	Village scene with gypsies, peasants and figures round a May pole (33x43cm-13x17in) s. pen brown ink wash vellum. 4-Nov-3 Sotheby's, Amsterdam #71/R est:7000-9000

HEERBRANT, Henri (1913-1982) Belgian

Works on paper			
£369	$683	€550	Untitled (29x39cm-11x15in) s.d.53 mixed media panel. 13-Mar-4 De Vuyst, Lokeren #173

HEERDEN, Louis van (1941-) South African

£743	$1330	€1085	Lemon girl (72x59cm-28x23in) s. s.i.d.2003 verso. 31-May-4 Stephan Welz, Johannesburg #608 (SA.R 9000)
£1379	$2303	€2013	White still life, Gladioli (72x59cm-28x23in) s. s.i.d.2003 verso. 20-Oct-3 Stephan Welz, Johannesburg #366/R est:9000-12000 (SA.R 16000)
£1652	$2956	€2412	Blue irises (99x84cm-39x33in) s. s.i.d.2003 verso. 31-May-4 Stephan Welz, Johannesburg #513/R est:15000-20000 (SA.R 20000)

HEERDEN, Piet van (1917-1991) South African

£325	$552	€475	Small dwellings in a Namaqualand landscape (21x28cm-8x11in) s. board. 4-Nov-3 Stephan Welz, Johannesburg #620 est:4000-6000 (SA.R 3800)
£385	$654	€562	Namaqualand landscape with a house (19x29cm-7x11in) s. canvas on board. 4-Nov-3 Stephan Welz, Johannesburg #618 est:3000-5000 (SA.R 4500)
£739	$1338	€1079	Landscape, Hex River valley (25x34cm-10x13in) s.d.40 board. 30-Mar-4 Stephan Welz, Johannesburg #453 est:5000-8000 (SA.R 8800)
£908	$1626	€1326	Cape farmstead with figures (34x44cm-13x17in) s. indis.d.50 s.i.verso. 31-May-4 Stephan Welz, Johannesburg #500 (SA.R 11000)
£991	$1774	€1447	Still life with fruit, a bottle and a bowl (49x39cm-19x15in) s. canvasboard. 31-May-4 Stephan Welz, Johannesburg #521 (SA.R 12000)
£1121	$1872	€1637	Cottages, Elm Mission Station (26x44cm-10x17in) s.d.78 canvas on board. 20-Oct-3 Stephan Welz, Johannesburg #344/R est:9000-12000 (SA.R 13000)
£1121	$1872	€1637	Landscape, Western Cape (25x30cm-10x12in) s. board. 20-Oct-3 Stephan Welz, Johannesburg #639 est:3000-5000 (SA.R 13000)
£1190	$2226	€1737	Western Cape farm worker's cottage with figures in the foreground (34x43cm-13x17in) s.d.1958/59 canvas on board. 24-Feb-4 Cannon & Cannon, Pietermaritzburg #274 (SA.R 15000)
£1638	$2735	€2391	Landscape with houses, a stone pine in the foreground (34x60cm-13x24in) s. canvas on board. 20-Oct-3 Stephan Welz, Johannesburg #339/R est:8000-12000 (SA.R 19000)
£1724	$2879	€2517	Overberg landscape (39x49cm-15x19in) s. board. 20-Oct-3 Stephan Welz, Johannesburg #258/R est:9000-12000 (SA.R 20000)
£2064	$3695	€3013	Cape Dutch farmhouse (62x72cm-24x28in) s.d.54. 31-May-4 Stephan Welz, Johannesburg #507/R est:15000-20000 (SA.R 25000)
£2241	$3743	€3272	Overberg landscape (20x60cm-8x24in) s. canvas on board. 20-Oct-3 Stephan Welz, Johannesburg #342 est:7000-10000 (SA.R 26000)
£2241	$3743	€3272	Klein Drakenstein (23x26cm-9x10in) s. canvas on board. 20-Oct-3 Stephan Welz, Johannesburg #345/R est:9000-12000 (SA.R 26000)
£2414	$4031	€3524	View of Philadelphia, Cape (37x59cm-15x23in) s.d.79 canvas on board. 20-Oct-3 Stephan Welz, Johannesburg #318/R est:12000-16000 (SA.R 28000)
£2521	$4563	€3681	Namaqualand landscape in spring (34x44cm-13x17in) s. canvasboard. 30-Mar-4 Stephan Welz, Johannesburg #465/R est:12000-18000 (SA.R 30000)
Works on paper			
£924	$1673	€1349	Cottages in a mountainous landscape (24x29cm-9x11in) s.d.53 pastel. 30-Mar-4 Stephan Welz, Johannesburg #193 est:2000-3000 (SA.R 11000)

HEERE, Lucas de (circle) (1534-1584) Flemish

£5517	$9159	€8000	Rebecca and Eliezer at the well (64x89cm-25x35in) panel prov. 1-Oct-3 Dorotheum, Vienna #129/R est:8000-13000

HEEREBAART, Georgius (1829-1915) Dutch

£3800	$6346	€5548	Dutch canal scene (26x41cm-10x16in) s. panel. 12-Nov-3 Sotheby's, Olympia #164/R est:1000-1500

HEEREMANS, Thomas (fl.1660-1697) Dutch

£3406	$5995	€4973	Riverside festival (26x35cm-10x14in) s.d.1686 panel prov. 22-May-4 Galerie Gloggner, Luzern #55/R est:8000-9000 (S.FR 7800)
£3800	$6840	€5548	Fishermen inspecting their catch with figures on a path (29x37cm-11x15in) s. indis d. panel. 21-Apr-4 Bonhams, New Bond Street #46/R est:2000-3000
£4800	$8784	€7008	Winter landscape with skaters (48x42cm-19x17in) indis.sig. panel. 9-Jul-4 Christie's, Kensington #81 est:4000-6000
£4967	$9040	€7500	Dutch winter landscape with ice skaters on a frozen river (22x26cm-9x10in) panel prov. 16-Jun-4 Dorotheum, Vienna #41/R est:7500-9000
£6333	$11337	€9500	Winter landscape with townsfolk skating and sledging on a frozen river (74x58cm-29x23in) s.d.1665 panel prov. 17-May-4 Christie's, Amsterdam #111/R est:8000-12000
£8784	$15459	€13000	Winter landscape with skaters and a horse-drawn sleigh near walls (24x32cm-9x13in) indis sig.d.1668 panel. 18-May-4 Sotheby's, Amsterdam #107/R est:5000-7000
£10000	$18000	€14600	Dutch parties along a canal (68x55cm-27x22in) s.d.1689. 21-Jan-4 Doyle, New York #87/R est:10000-15000
£10000	$18100	€15000	Landscape covered in snow (60x84cm-24x33in) s.d.1682. 30-Mar-4 Segre, Madrid #45/R est:15000
£11258	$20490	€17000	Spare time in a Dutch village (46x64cm-18x25in) s.d.16 panel. 16-Jun-4 Dorotheum, Vienna #87/R est:15000-20000
£12414	$20607	€18000	Peasants and horsemen with cart in village (60x84cm-24x33in) s. panel. 1-Oct-3 Dorotheum, Vienna #150/R est:18000-25000
£13158	$24211	€20000	Estaury landscape (45x67cm-18x26in) s.d.1664 panel. 25-Jun-4 Piasa, Paris #25/R est:15000-20000
£13423	$24966	€20000	Rural scene with boats (48x66cm-19x26in) s.d.1677 prov. 2-Mar-4 Ansorena, Madrid #299/R est:12000
£13699	$23288	€20000	Landscape with river and boats (48x66cm-19x26in) s.d.1677 prov. 4-Nov-3 Ansorena, Madrid #102/R est:19000
£15500	$26815	€22630	Winter landscape with figures skating on a frozen river by a town (65x88cm-26x35in) s. indis.d.16. 11-Dec-3 Sotheby's, London #154/R est:12000-18000
£16084	$26860	€23000	River landscape with peasants on boat (48x66cm-19x26in) prov. 30-Jun-3 Ansorena, Madrid #181/R
£25000	$45000	€36500	Riverside village with figures unloading sailing boats (46x62cm-18x24in) s.d.1669 panel. 22-Apr-4 Sotheby's, London #75/R est:15000-20000

HEEREMANS, Thomas (circle) (fl.1660-1697) Dutch

£5556	$8778	€8000	View of the Zwaenseiland and the River Zwaenhals, Rotterdam (72x97cm-28x38in) indis sig. panel prov. 2-Sep-3 Christie's, Amsterdam #38/R est:3000-5000

HEEREMANS, Thomas (style) (fl.1660-1679) Dutch

£7500	$13500	€10950	Frozen river landscape with skaters by a walled town (45x55cm-18x22in) indis.sig. panel. 23-Apr-4 Christie's, Kensington #72/R est:4000-6000

HEERFORDT, Anna Cathrine Christine (1839-1910) Danish

£422	$725	€616	Yellow roses on ledge (16x23cm-6x9in) init. 3-Dec-3 Museumsbygningen, Copenhagen #149 (D.KR 4500)
£887	$1588	€1295	Water lilies on pond (42x54cm-17x21in) s.d.1882. 25-May-4 Bukowskis, Stockholm #322/R (S.KR 12000)

HEERFORDT, Ida Marie Margrethe (1834-1887) Danish

£398	$637	€581	From Lykkeholm near Ravnholt (20x28cm-8x11in) s. 22-Sep-3 Rasmussen, Vejle #403/R (D.KR 4200)
£1592	$2658	€2324	Still life of strawberries and butterflies (29x24cm-11x9in) s. 25-Oct-3 Rasmussen, Havnen #2110/R est:4000-6000 (D.KR 17000)

HEERSCHOP, Hendrik (1620-1672) Flemish

£8784	$15459	€13000	Venus, Adonis and Cupid, together with hounds (143x105cm-56x41in) s.d.1652 prov. 18-May-4 Sotheby's, Amsterdam #79/R est:10000-15000

HEERUP, Henry (1907-1993) Danish

£284	$518	€426	Portrait of an old man (71x51cm-28x20in) s. 19-Jun-4 Rasmussen, Havnen #4020 (D.KR 3200)
£493	$887	€720	Landscape (33x45cm-13x18in) s.d.1938 verso. 24-Apr-4 Rasmussen, Havnen #4178/R (D.KR 5500)
£1033	$1725	€1508	Landscape with windmill (80x100cm-31x39in) s. painted c.1936 prov. 7-Oct-3 Rasmussen, Copenhagen #329/R (D.KR 11000)
£1176	$2106	€1717	Tidal wave (48x65cm-19x26in) s.d.66 masonite. 10-May-4 Rasmussen, Vejle #596/R est:15000-20000 (D.KR 13000)
£1374	$2500	€2006	Summer day at Vangede flower meadow (35x59cm-14x23in) s.d.1955 prov. 7-Feb-4 Rasmussen, Havnen #4065 est:15000 (D.KR 15000)
£1976	$3358	€2885	Composition (30x26cm-12x10in) s.d.57. 26-Nov-3 Kunsthallen, Copenhagen #156/R est:20000 (D.KR 21000)
£2535	$4234	€3701	Children playing (90x110cm-35x43in) s. painted c.1950. 7-Oct-3 Rasmussen, Copenhagen #13/R est:40000 (D.KR 27000)
£2540	$4318	€3708	Composition (38x46cm-15x18in) s.d.64 plywood. 26-Nov-3 Kunsthallen, Copenhagen #64/R est:30000 (D.KR 27000)
£2708	$4982	€3954	Erotic scene with satyr and woman (34x50cm-13x20in) s. painted c.1952. 29-Mar-4 Rasmussen, Copenhagen #8/R est:15000-18000 (D.KR 30000)
£3156	$5839	€4608	Wiseman and children (60x57cm-24x22in) s. 15-Mar-4 Rasmussen, Vejle #504/R est:40000 (D.KR 35000)
£3481	$5917	€5082	The drop - composition (110cm-43in circular) s.d.83 panel. 26-Nov-3 Kunsthallen, Copenhagen #102/R est:40000 (D.KR 37000)
£4225	$7056	€6169	Man's only hope - Tree of Peace (122x147cm-48x58in) s.d.1959 s.i.verso plywood prov. 7-Oct-3 Rasmussen, Copenhagen #62/R est:80000 (D.KR 45000)
£5644	$9595	€8240	The wave of love (100x90cm-39x35in) s. tempera. 26-Nov-3 Kunsthallen, Copenhagen #55/R est:60000 (D.KR 60000)
£11289	$19191	€16482	Composition. Composition painted by Erik Ortvad (74x89cm-29x35in) s.d.48 double-sided. 26-Nov-3 Kunsthallen, Copenhagen #14/R est:125000 (D.KR 120000)
£15343	$28231	€22401	Symbolic figure composition with woman, man and small children (130x145cm-51x57in) s.d.44 prov. 29-Mar-4 Rasmussen, Copenhagen #113/R est:200000-250000 (D.KR 170000)
Sculpture			
£1625	$2989	€2373	Woman kneeling (39cm-15in) granite exec.c.1950 prov. 29-Mar-4 Rasmussen, Copenhagen #7/R est:25000-35000 (D.KR 18000)
£2817	$4704	€4113	Millstone decorated with face, sun and fantasy animals (40x40cm-16x16in) granite partly painted exec.c.1955 circular prov. 7-Oct-3 Rasmussen, Copenhagen #33/R est:30000-40000 (D.KR 30000)

£7109 $11374 €10308 Figure (48cm-19in) granite exec.c.1949-50. 17-Sep-3 Kunsthallen, Copenhagen #10/R est:80000 (D.KR 75000)
£11733 $21588 €17130 Seated gnome and bell (76x48cm-30x19in) painted carved granite exec.c.1950 prov. 29-Mar-4 Rasmussen, Copenhagen #29/R est:80000-120000 (D.KR 130000)
£12635 $23249 €18447 Cyclist and bell (47x68cm-19x27in) painted carved stone relief exec.c.1950 prov. 29-Mar-4 Rasmussen, Copenhagen #16/R est:60000-80000 (D.KR 140000)
£19856 $36534 €28990 Figure (100cm-39in) granite exec.c.1950 prov. 29-Mar-4 Rasmussen, Copenhagen #9/R est:150000-200000 (D.KR 220000)
£19856 $36534 €28990 Woman squatting (83cm-33in) granite exec.c.1950. 29-Mar-4 Rasmussen, Copenhagen #23/R est:80000-120000 (D.KR 220000)
Works on paper
£338 $565 €493 Man fishing, using starfish as bait, horse in background (27x39cm-11x15in) s.i.d.8 juli 56 crayon. 7-Oct-3 Rasmussen, Copenhagen #264/R (D.KR 3600)
£394 $659 €575 Olympia - figures with wagon (26x28cm-10x11in) s.i.d.10 jun 54 crayon sketch. 7-Oct-3 Rasmussen, Copenhagen #293 (D.KR 4200)
£800 $1456 €1200 The right toys (48x68cm-19x27in) s. 10 febr 1952 pencil crayon lit. 19-Jun-4 Rasmussen, Havnen #4160/R (D.KR 9000)
£993 $1856 €1450 The blue knight (29x44cm-11x17in) s.d.26 Juli 58 crayon. 25-Feb-4 Kunsthallen, Copenhagen #113/R (D.KR 11000)
£993 $1856 €1450 The gnome is moving with you (28x45cm-11x18in) s.i.d.27-28 Juli 1958 crayon. 25-Feb-4 Kunsthallen, Copenhagen #115/R (D.KR 11000)
£1173 $2159 €1713 Portrait of Erik and Susanna Olesen with heart and target (44cm-17in circular) s.d.71 col pencil prov. 29-Mar-4 Rasmussen, Copenhagen #32/R est:8000 (D.KR 13000)
£1264 $2363 €1845 Bird (52x67cm-20x26in) s.d.67 liquorice collage. 25-Feb-4 Kunsthallen, Copenhagen #43/R est:25000 (D.KR 14000)

HEES, Gustav Adolf van (1862-?) German
£6250 $10188 €9000 Sailing ships and fishing boats in Venice (150x114cm-59x45in) s. 26-Sep-3 Bolland & Marotz, Bremen #542/R est:6500

HEFELE, J F (?-1710) German
Works on paper
£1389 $2500 €2028 Parrot on a ledge pecking at cherries, with a grasshopper below (19x24cm-7x9in) s. bodycol. 22-Jan-4 Christie's, Rockefeller NY #197/R est:3000-5000

HEFFNER, Karl (1849-1925) German
£360 $666 €526 Sunset (7x12cm-3x5in) s. panel. 10-Mar-4 Sotheby's, Olympia #230/R
£367 $671 €550 Avenue of birch trees by high water in Niederhein (70x96cm-28x38in) s. 5-Jun-4 Arnold, Frankfurt #596/R
£400 $716 €584 On the estuary at dusk (10x34cm-4x13in) s. board. 18-Mar-4 Christie's, Kensington #521/R
£559 $951 €800 On the moors (35x46cm-14x18in) s.i.d.1875 canvas on board lit. 28-Nov-3 Schloss Ahlden, Ahlden #1563/R
£600 $1110 €876 Early sunrise near Brotzen, in the South Tyrol (15x26cm-6x10in) s.i.d.75 board sold with a companion. 10-Feb-4 Bonhams, Knightsbridge #216/R
£604 $1069 €900 Italian village landscape (9x11cm-4x4in) s. cardboard lit. 30-Apr-4 Auktionhaus Georg Rehm, Augsburg #7521/R
£789 $1453 €1200 Extensive landscape with village by river (55x85cm-22x33in) s. 24-Jun-4 Dr Fritz Nagel, Stuttgart #712/R
£884 $1583 €1300 Fishing boats in Dutch harbour (70x96cm-28x38in) s. 17-Mar-4 Neumeister, Munich #474/R
£1056 $1891 €1500 View of Rotterdam harbour in the evening light (71x96cm-28x38in) s. lit. 8-Jan-4 Allgauer, Kempten #2409/R est:900
£1250 $2063 €1800 Harbour on Baltic Sea (70x95cm-28x37in) s. 2-Jul-3 Neumeister, Munich #661/R est:1500
£1300 $2366 €1898 Peaceful moorland landscape (91x130cm-36x51in) s. 4-Feb-4 John Nicholson, Haslemere #158/R est:1500-2000
£1477 $2717 €2200 Roman farmstead by river (70x95cm-28x37in) s. 27-Mar-4 L & B, Essen #127/R est:1500
£1867 $3397 €2800 Footpath lined with birches in a Dutch landscape (71x95cm-28x37in) s. 1-Jul-4 Van Ham, Cologne #1393/R est:2500
£1972 $3411 €2800 View of harbour city of Ostsee (70x95cm-28x37in) s. 10-Dec-3 Dorotheum, Vienna #243/R est:3800-4200
£2267 $4103 €3400 Shepherd with flock in rainy Dutch landscape (65x117cm-26x46in) s. 1-Apr-4 Van Ham, Cologne #1413/R est:1200
£2933 $5309 €4400 Lower Rhine (63x139cm-25x55in) s. 1-Apr-4 Van Ham, Cologne #1414/R est:2800

HEFFNER, Karl (attrib) (1849-1925) German
£310 $518 €450 Wooded shore in cloudy landscape (30x65cm-12x26in) i. verso lit. 10-Jul-3 Allgauer, Kempten #2524/R

HEFNER, Hugh M (1926-) American
Works on paper
£3314 $5800 €4838 Man is she stacked (15x23cm-6x9in) init. ink. 17-Dec-3 Christie's, Rockefeller NY #1/R est:2000-3000

HEGEDUS, Endre (1913-) Hungarian
£2219 $3838 €3240 Self portrait with the artist's bride (80x80cm-31x31in) 12-Dec-3 Kieselbach, Budapest #193/R (H.F 850000)

HEGENBARTH, Emanuel (1868-1923) German
£800 $1448 €1200 Two hares on snowy heath (37x47cm-15x19in) s. 1-Apr-4 Van Ham, Cologne #1415

HEGENBARTH, Josef (1884-1962) German
£694 $1160 €1000 Road junction (46x37cm-18x15in) s. tempera board double-sided. 25-Oct-3 Dr Lehr, Berlin #187/R
£972 $1624 €1400 Cats (24x32cm-9x13in) s. Indian ink brush. 25-Oct-3 Dr Lehr, Berlin #188/R
£3533 $6360 €5300 Hen running (32x50cm-13x20in) s. oil distemper board double-sided. 24-Apr-4 Dr Lehr, Berlin #148/R est:4000
£5208 $8698 €7500 Circus scene - Chinese artistes (51x41cm-20x16in) s. s.i. verso oil distemper board. 25-Oct-3 Dr Lehr, Berlin #185/R est:8000
Works on paper
£268 $481 €400 Circus scene (16x20cm-6x8in) Indian ink. 25-May-4 Karl & Faber, Munich #321
£268 $481 €400 Brawl (14x20cm-6x8in) s. Indian ink. 25-May-4 Karl & Faber, Munich #322
£417 $679 €600 Rubezahl (24x22cm-9x9in) s. pen. 26-Sep-3 Venator & Hansten, Koln #1477/R
£694 $1132 €1000 Schlossberg near Bohmisch Kamnitz (32x42cm-13x17in) s.i. mixed media chk wash Indian ink brush. 26-Sep-3 Venator & Hansten, Koln #1475
£833 $1392 €1200 Standing female nude (49x24cm-19x9in) s. Indian ink brush W/C board. 25-Oct-3 Dr Lehr, Berlin #189/R
£1333 $2387 €2000 Cat grooming itself (38x49cm-15x19in) s. brush board. 15-May-4 Bassenge, Berlin #6866/R est:2500
£1389 $2264 €2000 Two bears (42x35cm-17x14in) s. mixed media board. 27-Sep-3 Dr Fritz Nagel, Stuttgart #9545/R est:2000
£1733 $3103 €2600 Fox (36x25cm-14x10in) s. brush. 15-May-4 Bassenge, Berlin #6865/R est:2500
£2222 $3711 €3200 For the ballet - Devil in the village (48x37cm-19x15in) s. distemper board double-sided. 25-Oct-3 Dr Lehr, Berlin #186/R est:2500
£2657 $4517 €3800 In the restaurant (31x44cm-12x17in) s. i.d. verso brush distemper board. 29-Nov-3 Bassenge, Berlin #6758 est:2500
£3007 $5112 €4300 Woman with black dog (46x37cm-18x15in) s. i. verso brush distemper board. 29-Nov-3 Bassenge, Berlin #6759/R est:2500
£3333 $5967 €5000 Conversation (40x51cm-16x20in) s.i.d. W/C gouache prov. 14-May-4 Ketterer, Munich #31/R est:2000-3000

HEGER, Heinrich Anton (1832-1888) German
£2238 $3804 €3200 Le cabinet du collectionneur (45x61cm-18x24in) s. panel. 18-Nov-3 Vanderkindere, Brussels #35 est:1500-2500

HEGEWISCH, Erika (20th C) German
Works on paper
£550 $919 €798 On the balcony (50x36cm-20x14in) s.d.91 chl. 19-Jun-3 Kornfeld, Bern #475 (S.FR 1200)

HEGG, Teresa (fl.1872-1893) British
Works on paper
£280 $510 €409 Wild flowers on a mossy bank (23x15cm-9x6in) s. W/C. 16-Jun-4 Andrew Hartley, Ilkley #1009

HEGGTVEIT, Bruce (1917-2003) Canadian
£193 $301 €280 Gatineau spring (28x41cm-11x16in) s.i. 26-Mar-3 Walker's, Ottawa #404 (C.D 450)
£258 $402 €374 Quiet spring evening (41x51cm-16x20in) s.i.d. board. 26-Mar-3 Walker's, Ottawa #435/R (C.D 600)
£302 $556 €441 Evening glow, Fortune Lake (40x50cm-16x20in) s. s.i.d.1993 verso board. 9-Jun-4 Walker's, Ottawa #14/R (C.D 750)
£444 $816 €648 Winter twilight, Quebec (61x76cm-24x30in) s.i.d.1993 verso board. 9-Jun-4 Walker's, Ottawa #38/R (C.D 1100)
£450 $766 €657 MacLarens Gristmaill, Wakefield (46x61cm-18x24in) s. s.i.d.1988 verso board. 21-Nov-3 Walker's, Ottawa #70/R (C.D 1000)
Works on paper
£383 $705 €559 Homeward bound, Quebec (45x61cm-18x24in) s. s.i.d.1991 pastel. 9-Jun-4 Walker's, Ottawa #27/R (C.D 950)

HEGGTVEIT, Oyvind (1884-1967) Norwegian
£366 $673 €534 Coastal landscape with house and lilacs (50x60cm-20x24in) s. 10-Jun-4 Grev Wedels Plass, Oslo #183/R (N.KR 4500)

HEGNDAL, Valdemar Foersom (1916-) Danish
Sculpture
£1805 $3321 €2635 Standing nude female model (102cm-40in) init.d.1936 pat.bronze. 29-Mar-4 Rasmussen, Copenhagen #36/R est:15000 (D.KR 20000)

HEIBERG, Astri Welhaven (1881-1967) Norwegian
£488 $898 €732 From Rondane, Straumbo farm (60x73cm-24x29in) s. panel. 14-Jun-4 Blomqvist, Lysaker #1145 (N.KR 6000)

HEIBERG, Jean (1884-1976) Norwegian
£275 $481 €402 Landscape (45x55cm-18x22in) s. i.verso. 16-Dec-3 Grev Wedels Plass, Oslo #167/R (N.KR 3200)
£333 $613 €486 Landscape one summer evening (45x64cm-18x25in) s. prov. 29-Mar-4 Blomqvist, Lysaker #1117/R (N.KR 4200)
£515 $901 €752 Archipelago (50x61cm-20x24in) s. panel. 16-Dec-3 Grev Wedels Plass, Oslo #165/R (N.KR 6000)
£584 $975 €853 Woodland study (53x64cm-21x25in) s. panel. 17-Nov-3 Blomqvist, Lysaker #1116 (N.KR 7000)
£732 $1346 €1098 Seascape study for regatta II (60x73cm-24x29in) s. panel. 14-Jun-4 Blomqvist, Lysaker #1146/R (N.KR 9000)
£1264 $2325 €1845 After sunset (53x68cm-21x27in) s.d.1955 canvas on panel exhib. 29-Mar-4 Rasmussen, Copenhagen #475/R est:10000-12000 (D.KR 14000)

HEICKE, Franz (19th C) Austrian
£861 $1575 €1300 Animals on lakeshore (55x58cm-22x23in) s. 8-Apr-4 Dorotheum, Vienna #40/R

HEICKE, Joseph (1811-1861) Austrian
£1690 $2924 €2400 Resting in the alpine meadow (42x53cm-17x21in) s.d.846. 10-Dec-3 Dorotheum, Vienna #144/R est:3000-3500
£2381 $4262 €3500 Oriental horse (45x35cm-18x14in) s.d.850. 17-Mar-4 Neumeister, Munich #476/R est:2000

HEICKELL, Arthur (1873-1958) Finnish
£272 $495 €400 Evening sun (50x60cm-20x24in) s. 8-Feb-4 Bukowskis, Helsinki #360/R
£278 $464 €400 View towards the sea (49x67cm-19x26in) s. 26-Oct-3 Bukowskis, Helsinki #352/R
£282 $451 €400 Hemholmen (41x50cm-16x20in) s. 21-Sep-3 Bukowskis, Helsinki #347/R
£296 $473 €420 View from Paijanne (40x50cm-16x20in) s. 21-Sep-3 Bukowskis, Helsinki #348/R
£300 $552 €450 Coastal meadow (48x78cm-19x31in) s,. 9-Jun-4 Bukowskis, Helsinki #405/R
£306 $557 €450 Coastal landscape (40x50cm-16x20in) s. 8-Feb-4 Bukowskis, Helsinki #362/R
£320 $589 €480 Reading lamp (46x66cm-18x26in) s. 9-Jun-4 Bukowskis, Helsinki #406/R
£324 $518 €460 Still life (44x64cm-17x25in) s. 18-Sep-3 Hagelstam, Helsinki #774
£326 $544 €476 Hawk on branch (60x50cm-24x20in) s. 12-Oct-3 Uppsala Auktionskammare, Uppsala #302 (S.KR 4200)
£333 $557 €480 Sunset (46x66cm-18x26in) s. 26-Oct-3 Bukowskis, Helsinki #347/R
£333 $613 €500 Autumn landscape with birch by sea (47x74cm-19x29in) s. 9-Jun-4 Bukowskis, Helsinki #408/R
£333 $613 €500 Old road (49x65cm-19x26in) s. 9-Jun-4 Bukowskis, Helsinki #409/R
£400 $736 €600 Coastal landscape (56x80cm-22x31in) s. 9-Jun-4 Bukowskis, Helsinki #407/R
£400 $736 €600 Beached boat (49x65cm-19x26in) s. 9-Jun-4 Bukowskis, Helsinki #410/R
£417 $696 €600 Landscape (61x81cm-24x32in) s. 23-Oct-3 Hagelstam, Helsinki #971
£417 $696 €600 Still life (40x50cm-16x20in) s. 26-Oct-3 Bukowskis, Helsinki #346/R
£417 $696 €600 View from Koli (46x65cm-18x26in) s. 26-Oct-3 Bukowskis, Helsinki #351/R
£431 $719 €620 February (46x66cm-18x26in) s. 26-Oct-3 Bukowskis, Helsinki #349/R
£500 $835 €720 Beach in autumn (60x100cm-24x39in) s. 26-Oct-3 Bukowskis, Helsinki #354/R
£503 $926 €750 Karl XII on horseback (110x85cm-43x33in) s. 25-Mar-4 Hagelstam, Helsinki #966
£514 $858 €740 Pine trees on the shore (55x90cm-22x35in) s. 26-Oct-3 Bukowskis, Helsinki #353/R
£570 $1050 €850 Landscape from Lapland (48x66cm-19x26in) s. 25-Mar-4 Hagelstam, Helsinki #948
£1040 $1935 €1550 Sailing in the skerries, evening (50x80cm-20x31in) s. 7-Mar-4 Bukowskis, Helsinki #334/R est:800

HEIDE, Johannes Wilhelm van der (1878-1957) Dutch
£315 $526 €450 Seaweed collector with horse and cart by sea (26x34cm-10x13in) s. board. 9-Oct-3 Michael Zeller, Lindau #589
£450 $828 €657 Young shepherd (48x72cm-19x28in) s. 8-Jun-4 Bonhams, Knightsbridge #171/R
£694 $1200 €1013 Field work (15x18cm-6x7in) s. 13-Dec-3 Auctions by the Bay, Alameda #1818/R

HEIDELBACH, Karl (1923-) German
£1467 $2625 €2200 Robot (125x100cm-49x39in) s.d.60 panel. 15-May-4 Van Ham, Cologne #648/R est:1000

HEIDER, Fritz von (1868-1933) German
£267 $485 €401 Winter landscape with faggot gatherer by river (48x62cm-19x24in) s. 19-Jun-4 Rasmussen, Havnen #2150/R (D.KR 3000)

HEIDER, Hans (1861-1947) German
£310 $574 €450 Snowy wooded landscape with river (80x90cm-31x35in) s. lit. 13-Feb-4 Auktionhaus Georg Rehm, Augsburg #8041

HEIDER, Hans von (1867-1952) German
£382 $623 €550 Urach landscape (120x95cm-47x37in) s.d.1911. 27-Sep-3 Dr Fritz Nagel, Stuttgart #9206/R

HEIDER-SCHWEINITZ, Maria von (1894-1974) German
£1600 $2864 €2400 Still life of flowers (99x71cm-39x28in) s.d.37. 15-May-4 Van Ham, Cologne #649/R est:2500

HEIDERSCHEID, Henri (?) French?
£267 $483 €400 Conversation (50x61cm-20x24in) mono. 3-Apr-4 Neret-Minet, Paris #30/R
£280 $476 €400 Guinguette (60x50cm-24x20in) mono. 29-Nov-3 Neret-Minet, Paris #236/R

HEIDINGSFELD, Fritz (1907-) German
£440 $801 €660 Building the Tower of Babel (99x69cm-39x27in) s.d.1962. 1-Jul-4 Weidler, Nurnberg #7062
£467 $849 €700 Harbour scene (97x67cm-38x26in) s. 1-Jul-4 Weidler, Nurnberg #7061

HEIL, Axel (1951-) German
£433 $784 €650 Several (38x30cm-15x12in) s.d. verso. 2-Apr-4 Winterberg, Heidelberg #1085/R

HEIL, Daniel van (1604-1662) Flemish
£10638 $17234 €15000 Incendio nocturno en una ciudad (72x48cm-28x19in) 20-May-3 Ansorena, Madrid #100/R est:15000
£10738 $19758 €16000 Winter landscape with faggot gatherers, elegant horsemen and sleighs (80x125cm-31x49in) 24-Mar-4 Dorotheum, Vienna #149/R est:20000-25000

HEIL, Daniel van (attrib) (1604-1662) Flemish
£3028 $5300 €4300 La prise de la Ville de Troie (108x178cm-43x70in) 18-Dec-3 Tajan, Paris #93/R est:4000-6000

HEIL, Theodore van (fl.1668-1692) Flemish
£8242 $15000 €12033 Winter landscape with villagers conversing on a path (69x88cm-27x35in) prov. 17-Jun-4 Christie's, Rockefeller NY #12/R est:20000-30000

HEILBUTH, Ferdinand (1826-1889) French
£2171 $3995 €3300 Partie de badminton (35x57cm-14x22in) s. 22-Jun-4 Ribeyre & Baron, Paris #48 est:1000-1500
£2980 $5424 €4500 Jeune femme assise dans un parc (32x41cm-13x16in) s. panel. 18-Jun-4 Piasa, Paris #76/R est:6000-8000
£9412 $16000 €13742 Conveying the news (115x126cm-45x50in) s.d.1858. 29-Oct-3 Christie's, Rockefeller NY #153/R est:18000-25000
Works on paper
£690 $1276 €1000 Nymphes dans un paysage (38x46cm-15x18in) s. W/C. 16-Feb-4 Horta, Bruxelles #418
£2398 $4076 €3500 Promenade en bateau (19x24cm-7x9in) s. gouache. 6-Nov-3 Tajan, Paris #184/R

HEILEMANN, Ernst (1870-?) German
Works on paper
£514 $812 €745 Young blond girl wearing grey dress and red jacket (100x68cm-39x27in) s.d.16 pastel. 2-Sep-3 Rasmussen, Copenhagen #1712/R (D.KR 5500)
£1563 $2609 €2282 Female nude (81x52cm-32x20in) s.d.28 W/C. 19-Oct-3 Agra, Warsaw #39/R est:4000 (P.Z 10000)

HEILIGER, Bernhard (1915-1995) German
Sculpture
£6867 $12291 €10300 Upright female torso (70cm-28in) concrete. 15-May-4 Bassenge, Berlin #6869/R est:4500
£10490 $17832 €15000 Head of Carl Hofer. mono. brown pat.bronze. 27-Nov-3 Lempertz, Koln #174/R est:16000
£10811 $20000 €15784 Seraph II (81cm-32in) s. back green pat bronze incl granite base exec 1953 prov.exhib. 12-Feb-4 Sotheby's, New York #193/R est:3000-5000
£15385 $26154 €22000 Ferryman (92cm-36in) brown pat.bronze prov. 29-Nov-3 Villa Grisebach, Berlin #295/R est:15000-20000
Works on paper
£267 $477 €400 Kneeling female nude (58x68cm-23x27in) s.i.d. pencil wash. 13-May-4 Neumeister, Munich #639/R
£278 $464 €400 Untitled - abstract composition (32x24cm-13x9in) s.d. mixed media. 25-Oct-3 Dr Lehr, Berlin #194/R
£417 $696 €600 Untitled (54x70cm-21x28in) s.d. graphite W/C board. 25-Oct-3 Dr Lehr, Berlin #193/R
£533 $981 €800 Two female nudes (35x54cm-14x21in) s.d. wash chl pencil. 11-Jun-4 Hauswedell & Nolte, Hamburg #1302/R
£667 $1193 €1000 Two standing figures (42x53cm-17x21in) s.d. pencil. 15-May-4 Bassenge, Berlin #6870
£2667 $4773 €4000 Berlin by the sea - with steamer (36x46cm-14x18in) mono.d. Indian ink brush. 15-May-4 Bassenge, Berlin #6874/R est:4000

HEILMAN, Mary (1940-) American
£5517 $9214 €8000 Dark alley (153x107cm-60x42in) init.d.1984 verso. 13-Nov-3 Finarte Semenzato, Rome #429/R est:9000-10000
£7186 $12000 €10492 Blue bazaar (76x56cm-30x22in) i.d.1997 prov. 14-Nov-3 Phillips, New York #223/R est:8000-12000
£17877 $32000 €26100 Yellow blue of the square pair (122x122cm-48x48in) s.i.d.1976 verso prov. 14-May-4 Phillips, New York #130/R est:10000-15000

HEILMANN, Anton Paul (1830-1912) Austrian
Works on paper
£414 $687 €600 Lake Garda (37x51cm-15x20in) s.d.1909 mixed media. 30-Sep-3 Dorotheum, Vienna #357/R

HEILMANN, Flora (1872-1944) Danish
£539 $1003 €787 Flowers in a vase (47x39cm-19x15in) init.d.1912-13. 2-Mar-4 Rasmussen, Copenhagen #1519/R (D.KR 6000)

HEILMANN, Gerhard (1859-1946) Danish
£427 $682 €623 Landscape with farms by fjord (51x74cm-20x29in) mono.d.1895. 22-Sep-3 Rasmussen, Vejle #365/R (D.KR 4500)
£440 $800 €642 Landscape from Mov (83x73cm-33x29in) init. 7-Feb-4 Rasmussen, Havnen #2026 (D.KR 4800)
£748 $1181 €1085 Still life of fruit on dish and flowers in vase (110x100cm-43x39in) init. 2-Sep-3 Rasmussen, Copenhagen #1999/R (D.KR 8000)

HEILMANN, Karl (1881-?) German
£426 $689 €600 Black Forest landscape in winter (30x42cm-12x17in) s. 23-May-3 Karlheinz Kaupp, Staufen #1735
£426 $689 €600 Black Forest in spring (50x70cm-20x28in) s. 23-May-3 Karlheinz Kaupp, Staufen #1886

HEILMANN, Max (1869-?) German
£2238 $3804 €3200 By the village stream (90x63cm-35x25in) s.d.89. 24-Nov-3 Dorotheum, Vienna #149/R est:3200-3800

HEILMAYER, Karl (1829-1908) German
£733 $1327 €1100 Moonlit river landscape (95x75cm-37x30in) s.i. lit. 1-Apr-4 Frank Peege, Freiburg #1122/R
£805 $1490 €1200 Paysages montagneux crepusculaires. s. i.verso panel pair. 15-Mar-4 Horta, Bruxelles #230

£805 $1482 €1200 Rowing boat at night (45x35cm-18x14in) s. board. 25-Mar-4 Dr Fritz Nagel, Stuttgart #713/R
£805 $1506 €1200 High Alpine landscape with lake (34x44cm-13x17in) s.d.1884 panel. 27-Feb-4 Altus, Berlin #452/R
£933 $1680 €1400 Moonlit sea cliffs (45x68cm-18x27in) s.d.1888 lit. 22-Apr-4 Allgauer, Kempten #3562/R
£1250 $1975 €1800 Moonlit Gulf of Naples (82x117cm-32x46in) s.d.1872 lit. 19-Sep-3 Schloss Ahlden, Ahlden #1520/R est:1900

HEIM, François Joseph (attrib) (1787-1865) French
Works on paper
£544 $975 €800 Portrait of Louis Radziwill in profile (23x18cm-9x7in) black crayon. 17-Mar-4 Tajan, Paris #100

HEIM, Heinz (1859-1895) German
Works on paper
£867 $1577 €1300 Seated young man carrying a scimitar (47x31cm-19x12in) s.i.d.1887 red chk lit. 3-Jul-4 Geble, Radolfzell #443/R
£1000 $1820 €1500 Seated man (47x31cm-19x12in) s.i.d.1887 red chk lit. 3-Jul-4 Geble, Radolfzell #442/R
£2000 $3640 €3000 Portrait of a lady. Portrait of a gentleman. red chk exec. 1887-1891 pair sold with book. 3-Jul-4 Geble, Radolfzell #444/R est:150

HEIMA, Tatshuhiko (20th C) Japanese?
£490 $832 €700 Composition (80x73cm-31x29in) s.d.58 exhib. 28-Nov-3 Blanchet, Paris #241/R

HEIMANN, Max (1909-) American?
£300 $500 €438 Still life with musical instruments (66x91cm-26x36in) s. board. 26-Oct-3 Bonhams & Butterfields, San Francisco #6591/R

HEIMBACH, Christian Wolfgang (1613-1678) German
£6081 $10703 €9000 Barber scene (26x29cm-10x11in) panel prov.lit. 22-May-4 Lempertz, Koln #1061/R est:10000
£91216 $163277 €135000 Equestrian portrait of Prince Bishop Christoph Bernhard von Galen (171x133cm-67x52in) s.i.d.1674 prov.exhib.lit. 5-May-4 Sotheby's, Amsterdam #304/R est:20000-30000

HEIMBURG, E von (19th C) German
£3514 $6289 €5200 Figures outside tavern in upper Bavaria (52x78cm-20x31in) s.d.1863. 6-May-4 Michael Zeller, Lindau #692/R est:4000

HEIMERL, Josef (19/20th C) Austrian
£273 $436 €396 Two kittens (21x27cm-8x11in) s. 22-Sep-3 Blomqvist, Lysaker #1318 (N.KR 3200)
£345 $576 €500 Cat family (37x58cm-15x23in) s. lit. 10-Jul-3 Allgauer, Kempten #2526/R

HEIMIG, Walter (1881-1955) German
£292 $461 €420 Lady engaged in handcraft (30x30cm-12x12in) s. board. 5-Sep-3 Wendl, Rudolstadt #3407/R
£629 $1051 €900 Man resting (65x65cm-26x26in) s. 28-Jun-3 Bolland & Marotz, Bremen #770

HEIMLICH, Herman (1904-1986) Canadian?
£289 $500 €422 Still life (41x51cm-16x20in) s. board. 9-Dec-3 Pinneys, Montreal #126 (C.D 650)

HEIN, Eduard (19th C) German
£524 $892 €750 Boat in water on winter evening (16x12cm-6x5in) s. panel. 20-Nov-3 Van Ham, Cologne #1621
£795 $1446 €1200 Homecoming hunter in a winter landscape (94x75cm-37x30in) s.i. 21-Jun-4 Dorotheum, Vienna #159
£1389 $2292 €2000 Rhine at Boppard (40x60cm-16x24in) s. 3-Jul-3 Van Ham, Cologne #1235/R est:2200

HEINE, Friedrich Wilhelm (1845-1921) German
Works on paper
£242 $400 €353 Untitled, treaty pact between Native Americans and American forces (18x46cm-7x18in) s.d.1918 W/C. 7-Jul-3 Schrager Galleries, Milwaukee #1547
£242 $400 €353 Untitled, palace guardsman relaxing with a stein of beer (48x36cm-19x14in) init.d.Nov.10 1880 W/C. 7-Jul-3 Schrager Galleries, Milwaukee #1551

HEINE, Harry (1928-) Canadian
Works on paper
£225 $383 €329 Evening at Steveston, British Columbia (33x51cm-13x20in) s. W/C prov. 23-Nov-3 Levis, Calgary #471/R (C.D 500)
£280 $512 €409 Salmon Troller, Debbie J (45x66cm-18x26in) s. W/C prov. 3-Jun-4 Heffel, Vancouver #29/R (C.D 700)
£480 $878 €701 Standing out to westward (49x69cm-19x27in) s.i. W/C. 1-Jun-4 Hodgins, Calgary #127/R (C.D 1200)
£496 $898 €724 Dodman's store (46x67cm-18x26in) s. W/C prov. 18-Apr-4 Levis, Calgary #46/R est:1000-1200 (C.D 1200)

HEINE, Johann Adalbert (1850-?) German
£278 $439 €400 Peasant couple in a mountain landscape (23x18cm-9x7in) s. panel. 5-Sep-3 Wendl, Rudolstadt #3410/R
£306 $483 €440 Man offering a woman some flowers through the open window (23x18cm-9x7in) s. panel. 5-Sep-3 Wendl, Rudolstadt #3409/R
£2013 $3705 €3000 Elegant couple playing chess. Elegant couple in salon (13x11cm-5x4in) s.i. pair. 25-Mar-4 Dr Fritz Nagel, Stuttgart #714/R est:900

HEINE, Ludwig (fl.1816-1834) German
£699 $1272 €1021 Female slave (44x33cm-17x13in) s. cardboard. 16-Jun-4 Fischer, Luzern #2163/R (S.FR 1600)

HEINE, Thomas Theodor (1867-1948) German
£4196 $7133 €6000 Children in wood (53x37cm-21x15in) mono.d.1904 i. verso panel prov.exhib.lit. 26-Nov-3 Lempertz, Koln #716/R est:6000-7000
Works on paper
£667 $1227 €1000 The correct strength (18x36cm-7x14in) s.i.d.95 grey black brush over pencil board. 12-Jun-4 Villa Grisebach, Berlin #567/R

HEINEFETTER, Johann (1815-1902) German
£302 $556 €450 Procession to country chapel (32x42cm-13x17in) board. 29-Mar-4 Bloss, Merzhausen #1504/R

HEINEL, Eduard (1835-1895) German
£4933 $8979 €7400 Bridge over steep river gorge (88x66cm-35x26in) s.d.1871. 30-Jun-4 Neumeister, Munich #565/R est:7000

HEINEMANN, Margarete von (1856-?) German
£252 $456 €368 Semova (72x118cm-28x46in) s.i.d.1900. 30-Mar-4 Stephan Welz, Johannesburg #411 est:3000-5000 (SA.R 3000)

HEINEMANN, Reinhardt (1895-1967) German
£282 $480 €412 Coastal landscape with large cliffs in foreground (50x63cm-20x25in) cardboard. 26-Nov-3 Kunsthallen, Copenhagen #336 (D.KR 3000)
£470 $800 €686 Coastal landscape with Trevose Head and Lighthouse (50x63cm-20x25in) s.i.d.july 5th 1925 cardboard. 26-Nov-3 Kunsthallen, Copenhagen #337 (D.KR 5000)
£486 $812 €700 Still life (32x38cm-13x15in) s.d. board. 24-Oct-3 Ketterer, Hamburg #805/R

HEINEN, Hans (1860-?) German
£333 $613 €500 Forest pond with trees and marshes (73x99cm-29x39in) s. 11-Jun-4 Wendl, Rudolstadt #4070/R

HEINESEN, William (1900-1991) Icelandic
£1354 $2491 €1977 Breakfast outside (81x69cm-32x27in) init.d.34 plywood. 29-Mar-4 Rasmussen, Copenhagen #235/R est:15000-20000 (D.KR 15000)
Works on paper
£812 $1495 €1186 Landscape with house (63x52cm-25x20in) init.d.53 prov. pastel chk. 29-Mar-4 Rasmussen, Copenhagen #266 (D.KR 9000)
£993 $1827 €1450 Birds in flight by the sea (66x52cm-26x20in) init.d.54 i.d.juni 1954 verso pastel chk prov. 29-Mar-4 Rasmussen, Copenhagen #233 (D.KR 11000)

HEINESEN, Zakarias (1936-) Danish
£542 $996 €791 Reynagarden abstraction (40x48cm-16x19in) init.d.76. 29-Mar-4 Rasmussen, Copenhagen #253 (D.KR 6000)
£632 $1162 €923 House in blue (40x45cm-16x18in) init.d.72. 29-Mar-4 Rasmussen, Copenhagen #268/R (D.KR 7000)
£762 $1371 €1113 Composition with houses (72x51cm-28x20in) init. plywood. 24-Apr-4 Rasmussen, Havnen #4152/R (D.KR 8500)
£1489 $2740 €2174 Town scene, Torshavn (61x84cm-24x33in) s.d.87. 29-Mar-4 Rasmussen, Copenhagen #236/R est:7000-10000 (D.KR 16500)

HEINISCH, Karl Adam (1847-1923) German
£563 $901 €800 Outside the village (19x24cm-7x9in) s. 18-Sep-3 Rieber, Stuttgart #823/R
£726 $1300 €1060 German mountain scene (28x36cm-11x14in) board. 12-May-4 South Bay, Long Island #473399/R
£805 $1482 €1200 Farmstead with woman and cow (18x28cm-7x11in) s. board. 24-Mar-4 Hugo Ruef, Munich #991/R
£1879 $3458 €2800 Peasant driving cattle along track (22x38cm-9x15in) s.i. 25-Mar-4 Dr Fritz Nagel, Stuttgart #718/R est:1500
£2333 $4223 €3500 Autumn afternoon (40x61cm-16x24in) s.d.90. 1-Apr-4 Van Ham, Cologne #1417/R est:2600
£2585 $4627 €3800 Winter landscape with ox cart (19x25cm-7x10in) s.i.d.94 panel. 17-Mar-4 Neumeister, Munich #478/R est:3000

HEINONEN, Aarre (1906-2003) Finnish
£347 $580 €500 Still life of bread (38x46cm-15x18in) s. 26-Oct-3 Bukowskis, Helsinki #357/R
£417 $696 €600 Still life (38x46cm-15x18in) s. 26-Oct-3 Bukowskis, Helsinki #356/R

HEINRICH, Franz (1802-1890) German
Works on paper
£3611 $6500 €5272 Sala dell'Iliade in the Galleria Palatina at the Palazzo Pitti, Florence (42x60cm-17x24in) s. black lead W/C bodycol. 22-Jan-4 Christie's, Rockefeller NY #154/R est:7000-10000

HEINRICH, Otto (1891-?) German
£1408 $2521 €2000 Rainy day in Berlin with figures (30x39cm-12x15in) s. board lit. 8-Jan-4 Allgauer, Kempten #2411/R est:4700

HEINRICH, Theodor (19th C) Austrian
Works on paper
£828 $1374 €1200 New sister (28x41cm-11x16in) s. W/C. 30-Sep-3 Dorotheum, Vienna #204/R

HEINRICH-HANSEN, Adolf (1859-1925) Danish

£327	$517	€474	Italian church interior (60x46cm-24x18in) s.d.14. 2-Sep-3 Rasmussen, Copenhagen #1886 (D.KR 3500)
£359	$668	€524	From the inner palace courtyard, Frederiksborg (53x38cm-21x15in) s. 2-Mar-4 Rasmussen, Copenhagen #1486/R (D.KR 4000)
£627	$1147	€915	Horses with Sunday harness in street at Tonder (47x60cm-19x24in) init. 9-Jun-4 Rasmussen, Copenhagen #1707/R (D.KR 7000)

HEINS, John Theodore (snr) (1697-1756) British

£5200	$8840	€7592	Portrait of Lucy, Lady Gage, daughter of William Knight (75x60cm-30x24in) s.d.1748 prov. 25-Nov-3 Christie's, London #13/R est:3000-5000

HEINSDORFF, Emil Ernst (1887-1948) German

£800	$1456	€1200	Meadow flowers (24x30cm-9x12in) s.d.1924 panel. 30-Jun-4 Neumeister, Munich #568/R

HEINSIUS, Johann Ernst (1740-1812) German

£533	$981	€800	Portrait de femme (61x49cm-24x19in) s.d.178. 11-Jun-4 Maigret, Paris #70/R
£7237	$13316	€11000	Cheval tenu par valet dans un paysage (70x85cm-28x33in) s.d.1787. 23-Jun-4 Sotheby's, Paris #35/R est:8000-10000
£10638	$17234	€15000	Portrait de Marie Adelaide de France (65x54cm-26x21in) s.d.1786. 21-May-3 Daguerre, Paris #45/R est:7500-9000

HEINSIUS, Johann Julius (18th C) German

£5944	$10224	€8500	Portrait of a man said to be Pierre Gando (73x59cm-29x23in) s.d.1780. 2-Dec-3 Christie's, Paris #143/R est:10000-15000

HEINTZ, Henrik (1896-1955) Hungarian?

£783	$1355	€1143	Park with a horse (69x99cm-27x39in) s. cardboard. 12-Dec-3 Kieselbach, Budapest #23/R (H.F 300000)

HEINTZ, Joseph (16/17th C) Swiss

Works on paper			
£16319	$27253	€23500	Le vieux, nymphes et allegories de fleuves (61x61cm-24x24in) pen brown ink brown wash col gouache cardboard two sheets. 25-Oct-3 Binoche, Orleans #59

HEINTZ, Joseph (elder) (1564-1609) Swiss

£60000	$103800	€87600	Entombment (50x39cm-20x15in) copper. 11-Dec-3 Sotheby's, London #16/R est:60000-80000

HEINTZ, Joseph (elder-attrib) (1564-1609) Swiss

£729	$1189	€1050	Man and two women (25x33cm-10x13in) i. pen wash double-sided. 26-Sep-3 Bolland & Marotz, Bremen #442/R est:1800
£13514	$23784	€20000	Abigail before King David (173x280cm-68x110in) prov. 22-May-4 Lempertz, Koln #1062/R est:25000-30000

HEINTZ, Joseph (elder-style) (1564-1609) Swiss

£4667	$8353	€7000	Winter scene (75x101cm-30x40in) 12-May-4 Finarte Semenzato, Milan #38/R est:5000-7000

HEINTZ, Joseph (younger-attrib) (1600-1678) Swiss

£7285	$13258	€11000	Spell (47x68cm-19x27in) 16-Jun-4 Christie's, Rome #399/R est:10000-15000

HEINTZ, Richard (1871-1929) Belgian

£250	$450	€365	ALlesse Redu, Ardenne, Belgium (23x31cm-9x12in) s.i.d.1923 verso. 20-Jan-4 Rosebery Fine Art, London #575
£278	$506	€420	Fermette a Sy (14x21cm-6x8in) s. panel. 16-Jun-4 Hotel des Ventes Mosan, Brussels #230
£397	$723	€600	Coin a Mortehan (14x19cm-6x7in) panel. 16-Jun-4 Hotel des Ventes Mosan, Brussels #218
£662	$1205	€1000	La meule (42x33cm-17x13in) s. 16-Jun-4 Hotel des Ventes Mosan, Brussels #214
£894	$1627	€1350	Coin sur l'Ourthe (18x13cm-7x5in) s. s.i.verso panel. 16-Jun-4 Hotel des Ventes Mosan, Brussels #242
£1060	$1928	€1600	Soir de mars (24x33cm-9x13in) s.d.1916 panel. 16-Jun-4 Hotel des Ventes Mosan, Brussels #221 est:800-1200
£1060	$1928	€1600	Bord de l'Ourthe a Sauheid (51x39cm-20x15in) s.d.94. 16-Jun-4 Hotel des Ventes Mosan, Brussels #224 est:1300-1500
£1528	$2429	€2200	Porte a Ravello (44x64cm-17x25in) s. 15-Sep-3 Horta, Bruxelles #75 est:1200-1800
£1633	$2922	€2400	Rochers a Sy (40x50cm-16x20in) s. s.i.d.avril-mai 1929 verso. 17-Mar-4 Hotel des Ventes Mosan, Brussels #132/R est:2800-3000
£1915	$3198	€2700	Vale de Scano (51x51cm-20x20in) s. 15-Oct-3 Hotel des Ventes Mosan, Brussels #226/R est:3000-3500
£2119	$3857	€3200	Moulin a Furnes (65x50cm-26x20in) s.d.1906. 16-Jun-4 Hotel des Ventes Mosan, Brussels #237 est:3500-4500
£3311	$6026	€5000	Automne a Sy (71x54cm-28x21in) s. 16-Jun-4 Hotel des Ventes Mosan, Brussels #246/R est:6000-8000
£3642	$6629	€5500	Chapelle a Lesse (50x61cm-20x24in) s. i.d.1918 verso. 16-Jun-4 Hotel des Ventes Mosan, Brussels #238/R est:6000-8000
£12500	$19875	€18000	La roche noire (80x90cm-31x35in) s. s.i.d.1925 verso. 15-Sep-3 Horta, Bruxelles #74/R est:6000-8000

HEINZ, Charles L (1885-1953) American

£1288	$2100	€1880	Landscape (102x64cm-40x25in) s. exhib. 19-Jul-3 Outer Cape Auctions, Provincetown #65/R

HEINZ, Wolfgang (?) German

£559	$934	€800	Harvest time on Mainau Island, Bodensee (70x100cm-28x39in) s. 28-Jun-3 Bolland & Marotz, Bremen #772/R

HEINZE, Adolph (1887-1958) American

£387	$700	€565	Mountain landscape (69x81cm-27x32in) 16-Apr-4 American Auctioneer #197/R

HEIRING, Harald (1906-1995) Danish

£361	$667	€527	Interior scene with seated model (99x79cm-39x31in) s.d.34. 15-Mar-4 Rasmussen, Vejle #622/R (D.KR 4000)

HEIRMAN, Edmond (1869-1957) Belgian

£306	$557	€450	La Rade d'Anvers (58x115cm-23x45in) 9-Feb-4 Amberes, Antwerp #262
£403	$749	€600	The Hoogbrug at Mechelen (60x80cm-24x31in) s. 8-Mar-4 Bernaerts, Antwerp #606/R
£946	$1788	€1400	Pont a Gand (80x120cm-31x47in) s. 17-Feb-4 Vanderkindere, Brussels #1

HEIS, Ehrentraud (1939-) Austrian

£300	$540	€450	Butterfly (64x69cm-25x27in) s.d.1981 masonite. 21-Apr-4 Dorotheum, Vienna #185/R

HEIS, Franz (1934-) Austrian

£533	$960	€800	Still life (44x60cm-17x24in) mono. masonite. 21-Apr-4 Dorotheum, Vienna #183

HEISIG, Bernhard (1925-) Polish

£14000	$25760	€21000	Icarus (79x120cm-31x47in) s. i.verso sketch painted 1966-70 prov.exhib.lit. 12-Jun-4 Villa Grisebach, Berlin #421/R est:18000-24000
Works on paper			
£347	$580	€500	Barn in bushes (28x37cm-11x15in) s. Indian ink. 25-Oct-3 Dr Lehr, Berlin #196/R
£800	$1440	€1200	Portrait of Gudrun (59x42cm-23x17in) s. graphite board. 24-Apr-4 Dr Lehr, Berlin #153/R

HEISKA, Joonas (1873-1937) Finnish

£333	$557	€480	Kevaiset kentat (27x34cm-11x13in) s.d.1930. 23-Oct-3 Hagelstam, Helsinki #818
£805	$1482	€1200	Laplander (43x35cm-17x14in) s. 25-Mar-4 Hagelstam, Helsinki #934
Works on paper			
£326	$545	€470	Cows (22x34cm-9x13in) s.d.1929 mixed media. 23-Oct-3 Hagelstam, Helsinki #1007
£845	$1462	€1200	Itinerant peddler visiting (42x52cm-17x20in) s.d.1907 W/C. 13-Dec-3 Hagelstam, Helsinki #141/R

HEISS, Johann (1640-1704) German

£3000	$5400	€4380	Mars and Venus (54x65cm-21x26in) 20-Apr-4 Sotheby's, Olympia #307/R est:3000-4000
£6500	$11245	€9490	Rape of the Sabines (115x135cm-45x53in) prov.lit. 11-Dec-3 Sotheby's, London #128/R est:7000-10000
£9000	$15300	€13140	Triumph of Neptune and Amphitrite (103x110cm-41x43in) 30-Oct-3 Sotheby's, Olympia #144/R est:3000-5000
£9500	$16435	€13870	Alexander and the Gymnosophists (130x165cm-51x65in) s. prov.lit. 11-Dec-3 Sotheby's, London #126/R est:10000-15000
£10135	$17838	€15000	Death of Dido (82x99cm-32x39in) prov. 22-May-4 Lempertz, Koln #1063/R est:15000
£17000	$29410	€24820	Belshazzar's Feast (120x137cm-47x54in) s. bears date 1702 prov.lit. 11-Dec-3 Sotheby's, London #127/R est:10000-15000
£20000	$34600	€29200	Dido and Aeneas in the Temple (130x195cm-51x77in) s.d.1702 prov.lit. 11-Dec-3 Sotheby's, London #125/R est:15000-20000
£20000	$36600	€29200	Allegory of Spring. Allegory of Summer (98x106cm-39x42in) s. pair prov.lit. 8-Jul-4 Sotheby's, London #256/R est:20000-30000
£26000	$44980	€37960	Allegory of time (125x118cm-49x46in) s. prov.lit. 11-Dec-3 Sotheby's, London #123/R est:15000-20000
£28000	$48440	€40880	Allegory of Art and Commerce (108x160cm-43x63in) s. prov.lit. 11-Dec-3 Sotheby's, London #124/R est:20000-30000

HEISS, Johann (attrib) (1640-1704) German

£1600	$2928	€2400	Apollus in Volcano's cave (68x82cm-27x32in) canvas on masonite. 1-Jun-4 Sotheby's, Milan #36/R est:1500-2000
Works on paper			
£541	$951	€800	Martyrdom of St Laurentius (38x30cm-15x12in) d.18. Marz 1679 verso pen wash htd white prov. 22-May-4 Lempertz, Koln #1285

HEIST, Bartholomeus van der (1611-1670) Dutch

£4375	$7000	€6388	Portrait of a man (76x61cm-30x24in) s.d.1659. 20-Sep-3 Bunte, Elgin #1401 est:8000-12000

HEITER, Guillermo (1915-) Czechoslovakian

£542	$840	€791	Calendula (60x46cm-24x18in) s. 3-Nov-2 Subastas Odalys, Caracas #82/R
£570	$900	€832	Clown (100x100cm-39x39in) s. 1-Dec-2 Subastas Odalys, Caracas #62/R

HEITINGER, Paul (1841-1920) German

£1232	$1972	€1750	Large house in park landscape (37x57cm-15x22in) s. lit. 19-Sep-3 Karlheinz Kaupp, Staufen #2157/R est:1400

HEJNA, Vaclav (1914-1985) Czechoslovakian

£633	$1114	€950	Kitchen still life (75x59cm-30x23in) s.d.1940. 22-May-4 Dorotheum, Prague #178/R est:20000-30000 (C.KR 30000)

HEKKING, William M (1885-1970) American
Works on paper
£864 $1400 €1253 Manana in January (51x75cm-20x30in) s. W/C. 8-Aug-3 Barridorf, Portland #104/R est:1500-2500

HELANDER, Sven Victor (attrib) (1839-1901) Swedish
£470 $850 €686 Der besuch. indis sig. panel. 3-Apr-4 Harvey Clar, Oakland #1535e

HELBERGER, Alfred Hermann (1871-?) German
£431 $772 €629 Winter landscape in the mountains (70x89cm-28x35in) s. 12-May-4 Dobiaschofsky, Bern #596/R (S.FR 1000)
£433 $797 €650 Vase of flowers (54x65cm-21x26in) s. oval. 11-Jun-4 Wendl, Rudolstadt #4071/R
£667 $1193 €1000 Engelberg, Vosges 1915 (70x90cm-28x35in) s.d.1915 lit. 14-May-4 Schloss Ahlden, Ahlden #2941/R

HELBIG, Bud (1915-) American
Works on paper
£621 $1000 €900 High country team (14x17cm-6x7in) chl. 22-Aug-3 Altermann Galleries, Santa Fe #126

HELBIG, Margaret A (1884-?) American
£782 $1400 €1142 Morning, Gloucester harbour (51x58cm-20x23in) s. i.verso board. 7-May-4 Sloans & Kenyon, Bethesda #1711/R

HELBIG, Peter (1841-1896) German
£350 $584 €500 Summer landscape (69x100cm-27x39in) s. 28-Jun-3 Bolland & Marotz, Bremen #658

HELBIG, Walter (1878-1965) German
£455 $755 €660 Girl's portrait (18x13cm-7x5in) s. board. 13-Jun-3 Zofingen, Switzerland #2874 (S.FR 1000)
£814 $1385 €1188 On Lago Maggiorer (67x84cm-26x33in) s. d.1949 verso. 19-Nov-3 Fischer, Luzern #2127/R (S.FR 1800)
£1041 $1769 €1520 Ruins of Falkenstein (71x90cm-28x35in) s.d.43 i. stretcher. 18-Nov-3 Hans Widmer, St Gallen #1078/R est:1600-3000 (S.FR 2300)
£2667 $4907 €4000 Still life with flowers (70x49cm-28x19in) s. 12-Jun-4 Villa Grisebach, Berlin #305/R est:4000-6000

HELCK, Peter (1893-1988) American
£5988 $10000 €8742 66th Street L Station, New York City (91x91cm-36x36in) s. prov.exhib. 23-Oct-3 Shannon's, Milford #195/R est:2000-3000
Works on paper
£3631 $6500 €5301 Champion, artist's studio with model car and bottle of scotch (41x38cm-16x15in) s. 15-May-4 Illustration House, New York #47/R est:3000-6000

HELCKE, Arnold (fl.1865-1911) British
£500 $915 €730 Heathland with the sea visible in the distance (58x109cm-23x43in) s.d.1894. 8-Jul-4 Duke & Son, Dorchester #221/R

HELD, Al (1928-) American
£1882 $3200 €2748 Triangle square, circle (26x71cm-10x28in) s.i. brush ink. 21-Nov-3 Swann Galleries, New York #76/R est:2000-3000
£16467 $27500 €24042 Out (91x91cm-36x36in) s.d.66 verso acrylic prov. 13-Nov-3 Sotheby's, New York #185/R est:20000-30000
£25449 $42500 €37156 West-northwest (152x152cm-60x60in) acrylic prov.exhib. 13-Nov-3 Sotheby's, New York #134/R est:10000-15000
Works on paper
£2432 $4500 €3551 D Series No 5 (58x89cm-23x35in) India ink prov. 13-Jul-4 Christie's, Rockefeller NY #17/R est:2000-3000

HELD, Alma M (1898-1988) American
£522 $950 €762 Early fall (46x61cm-18x24in) s. painted c.1924. 19-Jun-4 Jackson's, Cedar Falls #3a/R
£522 $950 €762 Allegory of the Arts (107x46cm-42x18in) s. painted c.1928 sold with preparatory drawings. 19-Jun-4 Jackson's, Cedar Falls #182/R
£522 $950 €762 September landscape (13x18cm-5x7in) s. board. 19-Jun-4 Jackson's, Cedar Falls #294/R

HELD, John (jnr) (1889-1958) American
Works on paper
£695 $1300 €1015 Standing gesturing flapper (18x18cm-7x7in) s. pen ink W/C. 26-Feb-4 Illustration House, New York #91
£958 $1600 €1399 Elegant ladies receive lessons from portly dance instructor (23x33cm-9x13in) s. i.verso pen ink. 15-Nov-3 Illustration House, New York #56/R est:1800-2600
£1078 $1800 €1574 Ballet dancer Novikoff as Roman soldier. Pavlova as Amarilla. The Fauns (15x10cm-6x4in) pen ink exec.c.1920 three. 15-Nov-3 Illustration House, New York #54/R est:2000-3000
£1341 $2400 €1958 Women's hairdos from around the world (13x33cm-5x13in) s. pen ink W/C. 15-May-4 Illustration House, New York #144/R est:1500-2400
£1955 $3500 €2854 Making the scene (33x25cm-13x10in) pen ink W/C board prov. 26-May-4 Doyle, New York #149/R est:2000-3000

HELD, Margarethe (1894-1981) German
Works on paper
£334 $614 €500 Untitled (41x27cm-16x11in) mono. lead pencil. 9-Jun-4 Artcurial Briest, Paris #389
£564 $975 €800 Gestorbene (42x27cm-17x11in) mono. i.verso graphite exec.c.1950 prov.lit. 9-Dec-3 Artcurial Briest, Paris #477
£867 $1595 €1300 Untitled (42x27cm-17x11in) mono. col wax crayon exec c.1950. 9-Jun-4 Artcurial Briest, Paris #385/R est:1000-1200
£1007 $1802 €1500 Head (41x27cm-16x11in) pencil prov. 25-May-4 Dorotheum, Vienna #298/R est:1500-1800

HELDNER, Collette Pope (1902-1996) American
£291 $500 €425 Swamp idyll, Louisiana Bayou County (74x28cm-29x11in) s. 6-Dec-3 Neal Auction Company, New Orleans #952/R
£301 $500 €439 Courtyard of the Little Theatre, St Peter Street, Old French Quarter, New O. (15x10cm-6x4in) s. s.i.d.1933 verso board. 4-Oct-3 Neal Auction Company, New Orleans #1118
£349 $600 €510 Swamp idyll, Louisiana Bayou County (69x79cm-27x31in) s. s.i.verso. 6-Dec-3 Neal Auction Company, New Orleans #1347
£357 $650 €521 Swamp Idyl, Louisiana Bayou Country (76x91cm-30x36in) s. s.i.verso. 7-Feb-4 Neal Auction Company, New Orleans #785
£378 $650 €552 Swamp idyll, Louisiana Bayou County (74x28cm-29x11in) s. 6-Dec-3 Neal Auction Company, New Orleans #951
£385 $700 €562 Swamp Idyll, Louisiana Bayou Country (51x91cm-20x36in) s. s.i.verso. 7-Feb-4 Neal Auction Company, New Orleans #786
£385 $700 €562 Swamp Idyll, Louisiana Bayou Country (48x38cm-19x15in) s. canvasboard. 7-Feb-4 Neal Auction Company, New Orleans #797
£482 $800 €704 Swamp Idyl, Louisiana Bayou country (46x91cm-18x36in) s.i.verso. 4-Oct-3 Neal Auction Company, New Orleans #1114/R
£549 $1000 €802 Patio, Old Brulator Patio, French Quarter, Old New Orleans (41x51cm-16x20in) s. s.i.verso canvasboard. 7-Feb-4 Neal Auction Company, New Orleans #789 est:400-600
£625 $1000 €913 Latin Quarter, Paris (61x76cm-24x30in) s.i.d.1929. 20-Sep-3 New Orleans Auction, New Orleans #148
£714 $1300 €1042 Swamp Idyll, Louisiana Bayou Country (41x51cm-16x20in) s. s.i.verso canvasboard pair. 7-Feb-4 Neal Auction Company, New Orleans #790/R
£798 $1300 €1165 Old Spanish Cabildo, French Quarter (41x51cm-16x20in) s.d.1933 canvasboard. 24-Sep-3 Jackson's, Cedar Falls #755/R
£1099 $2000 €1605 Swamp Idyll, Louisiana Bayou Country (102x127cm-40x50in) s. s.i.verso. 7-Feb-4 Neal Auction Company, New Orleans #526/R est:3000-5000
£1111 $1800 €1622 Vieux carre courtyard (25x18cm-10x7in) s.i.d.1935 board. 2-Aug-3 Neal Auction Company, New Orleans #553 est:800-1200
£1145 $1900 €1672 Swamp Idyll, Louisiana Bayou country (89x119cm-35x47in) s. s.i.verso. 4-Oct-3 Neal Auction Company, New Orleans #1116/R est:2000-3000
£2907 $5000 €4244 Court of the Wisteria Vine, Chartres St, Vieux Carre, New Orleans (51x41cm-20x16in) s.d.1936 s.i.d.1936 verso board. 6-Dec-3 Neal Auction Company, New Orleans #608/R est:2500-3500
£3023 $5200 €4414 Black women on a French Quarter street (51x41cm-20x16in) s. canvasboard. 6-Dec-3 Neal Auction Company, New Orleans #607/R est:2500-4000

HELDNER, Knute (1884-1952) American
£814 $1400 €1188 Ploughing the fields (20x25cm-8x10in) s. i.verso board. 6-Dec-3 Neal Auction Company, New Orleans #610/R est:1000-1500
£823 $1300 €1202 Arrowhead country (61x76cm-24x30in) s. i. on stretcher. 7-Sep-3 Treadway Gallery, Cincinnati #623/R
£1913 $3500 €2793 Sail boat in the mist (61x76cm-24x30in) s. 5-Jun-4 Neal Auction Company, New Orleans #396/R est:4000-6000
£2439 $4000 €3537 Hillside birches, Deluth (25x36cm-10x14in) s. board painted c.1925. 7-Jun-3 Treadway Gallery, Cincinnati #1445 est:3000-5000
£2761 $4750 €4031 Shrimp boats at the canal (36x41cm-14x16in) s. 6-Dec-3 Neal Auction Company, New Orleans #567/R est:5000-6000
£3453 $6250 €5041 Cabins on the bayou (61x76cm-24x30in) s. 3-Apr-4 Neal Auction Company, New Orleans #452/R est:3000-5000
£4067 $6750 €5938 Shrimp boats (58x74cm-23x29in) s. prov. 4-Oct-3 Neal Auction Company, New Orleans #570/R est:5000-7000
£5202 $9000 €7595 On the docks (118x99cm-46x39in) s. prov.exhib. 10-Dec-3 Bonhams & Butterfields, San Francisco #6071/R est:6000-8000
£5488 $9000 €7958 Sunset (91x107cm-36x42in) s. panel painted c.1925. 7-Jun-3 Treadway Gallery, Cincinnati #1315 est:4000-6000

HELDT, Werner (1904-1954) German
£3147 $5350 €4500 Carneval scene - Old Berlin Ball (37x45cm-15x18in) mono.d.27 s. verso panel prov.exhib. 29-Nov-3 Villa Grisebach, Berlin #211/R est:5000-7000
£10490 $17832 €15000 Uprising (37x41cm-15x16in) canvas on panel. 29-Nov-3 Bassenge, Berlin #6765/R est:10000
£34965 $59441 €50000 Afternoon - still life near window (35x42cm-14x17in) mono.d.50 s.i. verso nettle on panel prov.exhib. 28-Nov-3 Villa Grisebach, Berlin #76/R est:45000-55000
£48951 $83217 €70000 Still life with white circle (55x65cm-22x26in) mono.d.52 prov.exhib. 26-Nov-3 Lempertz, Koln #717/R est:70000-80000
£50000 $92000 €75000 Still life by the window (56x98cm-22x39in) mono.d.53 prov.exhib. 11-Jun-4 Villa Grisebach, Berlin #68/R est:80000-100000
Works on paper
£567 $1014 €850 Ruins (21x29cm-8x11in) pencil. 15-May-4 Bassenge, Berlin #6880
£667 $1193 €1000 Square at night (19x25cm-7x10in) pen. 15-May-4 Bassenge, Berlin #6879/R
£800 $1432 €1200 Summer night (30x24cm-12x9in) pencil chl. 15-May-4 Bassenge, Berlin #6878/R
£1049 $1783 €1500 Crucifix (31x23cm-12x9in) mono.i. chl prov. 29-Nov-3 Villa Grisebach, Berlin #791/R est:1500-2000
£1333 $2400 €2000 Ruins by canal (37x29cm-15x11in) mono.d. chl. 24-Apr-4 Dr Lehr, Berlin #156/R est:3000
£1733 $3103 €2600 House (63x47cm-25x19in) mono. 15-May-4 Bassenge, Berlin #6877/R est:3500
£2297 $4250 €3354 Revolution (33x47cm-13x19in) init. chl prov. 12-Feb-4 Sotheby's, New York #2/R est:7000-9000
£2667 $4773 €4000 Revolution (36x51cm-14x20in) W/C col chks on pencil board. 15-May-4 Bassenge, Berlin #6871/R est:6000
£2703 $5000 €3946 Untitled (21x29cm-8x11in) init.d.46 ink wash W/C prov. 12-Feb-4 Sotheby's, New York #69/R est:8000-12000
£2797 $4755 €4000 House fronts (24x43cm-9x17in) W/C board. 29-Nov-3 Bassenge, Berlin #6766/R est:3000
£3846 $6538 €5500 Cityscape (37x48cm-15x19in) s.d.53 Indian ink brush. 29-Nov-3 Bassenge, Berlin #6767/R est:4000
£8392 $14266 €12000 Medallion on window ledge (38x51cm-15x20in) mono.d.48 chl W/C prov.exhib. 29-Nov-3 Villa Grisebach, Berlin #267/R est:14000-18000
£9790 $16643 €14000 Houses (47x62cm-19x24in) s.d.47 chl. 29-Nov-3 Bassenge, Berlin #6768/R est:4000

HELE, Ivor Henry Thomas (1912-1993) Australian
Works on paper
£457 $854 €667 Jean in armchair doing her nails (27x37cm-11x15in) pencil exhib. 27-Feb-4 Lawson Menzies, Sydney #2053/R (A.D 1100)
£2273 $4205 €3319 Nude in stockings (46x33cm-18x13in) s. pastel chl. 10-Mar-4 Deutscher-Menzies, Melbourne #183/R est:3500-4500 (A.D 5500)

HELENIUS, Ester (1875-1955) Finnish
£493 $853 €700 Still life of flowers (51x64cm-20x25in) s.d.1943. 13-Dec-3 Hagelstam, Helsinki #140/R

HELENIUS, Jorma (1955-) Finnish
£986 $1577 €1400 Birch grove (35x46cm-14x18in) s.d.1988. 18-Sep-3 Hagelstam, Helsinki #865/R
£1216 $2177 €1800 Light in the woods (34x46cm-13x18in) s.d.88. 8-May-4 Bukowskis, Helsinki #137/R est:1700-2200
£1268 $2028 €1800 Forest (54x42cm-21x17in) s. 18-Sep-3 Hagelstam, Helsinki #864 est:2000

HELFF, Josef (19th C) Austrian
Works on paper
£838 $1500 €1223 Wild rocky country overgrown with gnarled trees with waterfall (76x56cm-30x22in) s.d.1850 W/C prov. 11-May-4 Roland's, New York #473317/R

HELFFERICH, Frans (1871-1941) Dutch
£1275 $2257 €1900 Bathers on beach (60x70cm-24x28in) s. panel. 28-Apr-4 Schopman, Hamburg #546/R est:1650
£1678 $2887 €2400 Ducks by the ditch (19x27cm-7x11in) s. panel. 8-Dec-3 Glerum, Amsterdam #79/R est:3000-5000
£7092 $11844 €10000 Busy cafe in The Hague (35x45cm-14x18in) s. 20-Oct-3 Glerum, Amsterdam #173/R est:2500-3500

HELFIN, Tom (1934-) American
£419 $700 €612 Nearing Buffalo Front (58x43cm-23x17in) s. 11-Oct-3 Nadeau, Windsor #150/R

HELIKER, John Edward (1909-2000) American
£1257 $2250 €1835 Quarry near Barre, Vermont (51x81cm-20x32in) s. masonite prov. 26-May-4 Doyle, New York #156/R est:3000-5000
£1347 $2250 €1967 Beach and Driftwood (46x61cm-18x24in) s. masonite prov.exhib. 23-Oct-3 Shannon's, Milford #10/R est:1200-1800
£1599 $2750 €2335 Still life with potted plant (64x102cm-25x40in) s. prov. 3-Dec-3 Doyle, New York #300/R est:5000-7000
£2138 $3400 €3121 Double portrait, Rome (118x112cm-46x44in) s. prov. 13-Sep-3 Weschler, Washington #782/R est:4000-6000
£2395 $4000 €3497 Boatyard in Spring (76x102cm-30x40in) s. prov.exhib. 23-Oct-3 Shannon's, Milford #12/R est:2000-3000
£7407 $12000 €10740 Kitchen interior, Maine (140x114cm-55x45in) s. prov. 8-Aug-3 Barridorf, Portland #229/R est:9000-12000

HELINCK, Gustave (1884-1954) Belgian
£362 $655 €550 Vase fleuri de pivoines (90x66cm-35x26in) s. 19-Apr-4 Horta, Bruxelles #460
£532 $888 €750 Nature morte aux fleurs et cerises (65x70cm-26x28in) s. 17-Jun-3 Vanderkindere, Brussels #91

HELION, Jean (1904-1987) French
£1149 $2056 €1700 Maison du douanier (22x53cm-9x21in) mono.d.56 paper on canvas prov. 4-May-4 Calmels Cohen, Paris #158/R est:2000-3000
£1409 $2437 €2000 Sur la terrasse (16x22cm-6x9in) mono.d.61 cardboard. 9-Dec-3 Artcurial Briest, Paris #558/R est:2500-3000
£1608 $2734 €2300 Bateaux de peche a Belle-Isle (27x21cm-11x8in) s. s.d.64 verso. 28-Nov-3 Blanchet, Paris #186/R est:2500-3000
£1689 $3193 €2500 Besus (40x65cm-16x26in) s.d.Mai 1956 verso prov. 21-Feb-4 Cornette de St.Cyr, Paris #208/R est:3000-4000
£1944 $3072 €2800 Palais, Belle-Ile (23x35cm-9x14in) mono.d.1959 i.verso cardboard. 27-Apr-3 Versailles Encheres #63
£1974 $3632 €3000 Sentier (64x35cm-25x14in) s.d.58. 25-Jun-4 Millon & Associes, Paris #189/R est:2500-3500
£2148 $3952 €3200 Portrait de jeune femme (37x27cm-15x11in) mono.d. 1961 s.d.verso board. 24-Mar-4 Joron-Derem, Paris #163/R est:4000-5000
£2318 $4219 €3500 Fete de nuit a belli-ile (33x46cm-13x18in) s.i.d.1966 verso cardboard on isorel. 15-Jun-4 Blanchet, Paris #188/R est:4000-4500
£2448 $4161 €3500 Portrait de femme (37x39cm-15x15in) s. 23-Nov-3 Cornette de St.Cyr, Paris #641/R est:4000-5000
£4027 $7409 €6000 Entree trombonniere (65x46cm-26x18in) mono.d.1968 s.i.d.verso. 24-Mar-4 Binoche, Paris #87/R est:7000-8000
£4762 $8667 €7000 Suite maraichere (46x55cm-18x22in) init.d.73 s.i.verso. 8-Feb-4 Anaf, Lyon #195/R est:7000-8000
£5705 $10497 €8500 Duo luxembourgeois (46x65cm-18x26in) mono.d.1967 s.i.d.verso. 24-Mar-4 Binoche, Paris #86/R est:7000-8000
£7237 $13316 €11000 Monuments pour un passant (89x130cm-35x51in) mono.d.1965 s.i.d.verso prov. 27-Jun-4 Versailles Encheres #119/R est:12000-15000
£7639 $12069 €11000 Composition (32x45cm-13x18in) s.d.1934 acrylic paper prov. 27-Apr-3 Versailles Encheres #51
£9211 $16947 €14000 Toits (115x145cm-45x57in) s.d.1959 verso prov. 27-Jun-4 Versailles Encheres #120/R est:15000-20000
£188235 $320000 €274823 Figure Claire (163x119cm-64x47in) s.d.1936 verso prov. 6-Nov-3 Sotheby's, New York #277/R est:300000-400000
Works on paper
£405 $766 €600 Gondoliers (31x24cm-12x9in) s.i. graphite col crayon. 21-Feb-4 Cornette de St.Cyr, Paris #207
£533 $955 €800 Marche aux puces (27x211cm-11x83in) s. dr. exec.1927. 15-May-4 Renaud, Paris #109
£600 $1080 €900 Divan (49x64cm-19x25in) s. gouache. 25-Apr-4 Versailles Encheres #132
£664 $1129 €950 Trois etudes de nu de profil (65x50cm-26x20in) s.d.79 chl white chk gouache. 1-Dec-3 Rieunier, Paris #17/R
£795 $1446 €1200 Suite puciere a la main (31x45cm-12x18in) s.d.27/11/78 i.verso pastel. 15-Jun-4 Blanchet, Paris #186/R
£795 $1446 €1200 Choeur de journaliers (44x28cm-17x11in) s.d.51 chl. 15-Jun-4 Blanchet, Paris #187/R
£1400 $2548 €2044 Untitled (28x21cm-11x8in) s.d.33 W/C pencil prov. 4-Feb-4 Sotheby's, Olympia #173/R est:1500-2000
£1678 $2970 €2500 Mannequinerie (23x30cm-9x12in) s.d.50 W/C ink. 28-Apr-4 Artcurial Briest, Paris #250/R est:2500-3000
£1806 $3015 €2600 Le perroquet (23x24cm-9x9in) init.d.75 W/C ink pencil prov. 21-Oct-3 Christie's, Paris #127/R est:1400-1600
£2041 $3653 €3000 Untitled (31x44cm-12x17in) s.d.81 mixed media prov. 21-Mar-4 Calmels Cohen, Paris #132/R est:3000-4000
£2517 $4330 €3600 Untitled (29x22cm-11x9in) s.d.34 Indian ink w/ wash. 2-Dec-3 Calmels Cohen, Paris #25/R est:4000-5000
£2533 $4661 €3800 Untitled (59x42cm-23x17in) s.i.d.XII/73 gouache. 10-Jun-4 Camard, Paris #189/R est:3800-4800
£2697 $4963 €4100 Homme au journal (63x45cm-25x18in) s.d.1952 gouache. 28-Jun-4 Joron-Derem, Paris #184/R est:5000-6000
£2800 $5152 €4200 Figure dressee (38x28cm-15x11in) s.d.36 W/C ink wash prov. 8-Jun-4 Artcurial Briest, Paris #77/R est:4000-5000
£3379 $6048 €5000 Equilibre (22x31cm-9x12in) s.d.34 ink crayon W/C. 4-May-4 Calmels Cohen, Paris #165/R est:6000-8000
£3873 $6701 €5500 Composition (22x17cm-9x7in) s.i.d.1934 W/C. 14-Dec-3 Versailles Encheres #94/R est:5000-6000
£3893 $7162 €5800 Homme au journal (63x45cm-25x18in) s.d.1952 gouache. 24-Mar-4 Joron-Derem, Paris #164/R est:7000-8000
£4236 $6693 €6100 Composition (24x31cm-9x12in) s.i.d.1935 ink W/C prov. 27-Apr-3 Versailles Encheres #53
£5667 $10200 €8500 Equilibre complexe (19x25cm-7x10in) s. Chinese ink, W/C. 25-Apr-4 Versailles Encheres #122 est:7000-8000
£7368 $13558 €11200 Equilibre complexe (20x27cm-8x11in) s.d.1934 W/C ink prov. 27-Jun-4 Versailles Encheres #78/R est:8000-10000
£7394 $12940 €10500 Equilibre (25x34cm-10x13in) s. gouache W/C ink. 18-Dec-3 Cornette de St.Cyr, Paris #16/R est:12000-15000
£8252 $13780 €11800 Untitled (17x19cm-7x7in) s.d.1936 W/C Chinese ink. 29-Jun-3 Versailles Encheres #76/R
£16197 $28021 €23000 Homme assis (128x80cm-50x31in) s.d.47 W/C ink prov.exhib.lit. 9-Dec-3 Artcurial Briest, Paris #297/R est:25000-35000

HELL, Johan van (1889-1952) Dutch
£2041 $3714 €3000 Mijn oude vrind Tikoes - my old friend Tikoes (100x110cm-39x43in) s.i.d.1934. 3-Feb-4 Christie's, Amsterdam #484 est:800-1200
£20667 $37820 €31000 Window cleaner at work (100x75cm-39x30in) s.d.1927 prov. 7-Jun-4 Glerum, Amsterdam #27/R est:8000-12000

HELLABY, Richard Sydney (1887-?) British
£400 $716 €584 Winter mountain landscape with man on a path before a hut (39x36cm-15x14in) s. 17-Mar-4 Bonhams, Chester #396

HELLDORF, Ferdinand (20th C) Austrian
£423 $676 €600 Self portrait at blacksmiths (80x63cm-31x25in) s.d.1936 panel. 18-Sep-3 Rieber, Stuttgart #1370

HELLEMANS, Pierre (1787-1845) Belgian
£1879 $3477 €2800 Landscape with shepherd (35x48cm-14x19in) s.d.1815 panel. 13-Mar-4 De Vuyst, Lokeren #174/R est:1500-1800
£6993 $11888 €10000 Deer in a forest clearing (58x48cm-23x19in) s. panel lit. 28-Nov-3 Schloss Ahlden, Ahlden #1473/R est:12000

HELLER, Edmund (1878-1921) Hungarian
£5594 $9622 €8000 Four children in a living room blowing bubbles (55x69cm-22x27in) s. 3-Dec-3 Neumeister, Munich #592/R est:3000

HELLER, Samuel S (19/20th C) American
£377 $600 €550 View of a European canal (39x21cm-15x8in) s. panel. 13-Sep-3 Weschler, Washington #769/R

HELLESEN, Hanne (1801-1844) Danish
£4299 $6793 €6234 Flowers on e ledge (19x25cm-7x10in) s.d.1842 panel. 2-Sep-3 Rasmussen, Copenhagen #1569/R est:30000 (D.KR 46000)
£5000 $9000 €7500 Spring blossom in a glass on a marble ledge (32x24cm-13x9in) s.d.1843 panel. 21-Apr-4 Christie's, Amsterdam #166/R est:8000-12000
£6667 $12000 €10000 Pink roses and forget-me-nots in a glass on a marble ledge (37x31cm-15x12in) s.d.1842. 21-Apr-4 Christie's, Amsterdam #167/R est:5000-7000
£6704 $12000 €9788 Still life of fruit and flowers in basket and peaches on marble ledge (39x47cm-15x19in) s.d.1838. 27-May-4 Sotheby's, New York #75/R est:6000-8000

HELLESEN, Thorwald (1888-1937) Danish
£5333 $9547 €8000 Composition (50x59cm-20x23in) init.d.21 tempera. 12-May-4 Stadion, Trieste #738/R est:1500-2000

HELLEU, Jean (1894-1985) French
£530 $964 €800 La Seine a Saint-Cloud (33x46cm-13x18in) s.d.1945 i.verso panel. 16-Jun-4 Renaud, Paris #47

HELLEU, Paul-Cesar (1859-1927) French
£3221 $5928 €4800 Portrait d'enfant (40x32cm-16x13in) s.d.78. 26-Mar-4 Pierre Berge, Paris #45/R est:6000-7000
£30000 $54600 €43800 Navires des voiles (47x80cm-19x31in) s. prov. 4-Feb-4 Sotheby's, London #229/R est:35000-45000
£34444 $62000 €50288 Le bassin de Deauville (77x58cm-30x23in) s. 22-Apr-4 Christie's, Rockefeller NY #177/R est:40000-60000
£51676 $96118 €77000 Le yacht (58x72cm-23x28in) s. 8-Mar-4 Artcurial Briest, Paris #34/R est:18000-22000
£70000 $128800 €102200 Le grand pavois (65x81cm-26x32in) s. painted c.1901 prov. 23-Jun-4 Christie's, London #110/R est:80000-120000
£167598 $300000 €244693 Madame Helleu sur son yacht, L'Etoile (81x65cm-32x26in) painted c.1898-1900 prov.exhib.lit. 6-May-4 Sotheby's, New York #241/R est:300000-400000

£184564 $339597 €275000 Madame Helleu et son fils en mer (81x65cm-32x26in) s. 24-Mar-4 Binoche, Paris #85/R est:200000-300000
Prints
£2055 $3493 €3000 Femme en buste. s. col drypoint. 6-Nov-3 Piasa, Paris #103
£2055 $3493 €3000 Femme en buste. s.i. drypoint. 6-Nov-3 Piasa, Paris #109
£2055 $3493 €3000 Madame Gaudet. drypoint. 6-Nov-3 Piasa, Paris #108
£2192 $3726 €3200 Femme en buste. s.i. drypoint. 6-Nov-3 Piasa, Paris #105
£2192 $3726 €3200 Fillette en buste. drypoint. 6-Nov-3 Piasa, Paris #107/R
£2386 $4200 €3579 Le noed bleu, Miss Madeleine Dolley (53x33cm-21x13in) col sepia drypoint edition 80. 21-May-4 North East Auctions, Portsmouth #75
£2467 $4489 €3700 Portrait of a young woman in profile (72x52cm-28x20in) s. col drypoint. 1-Jul-4 Van Ham, Cologne #1394/R est:3500
£2600 $4472 €3796 Etude d'apres (33x25cm-13x10in) s. drypoint. 2-Dec-3 Christie's, London #150/R est:2000-3000
£3600 $6192 €5256 Madame Helleu devant les Watteau du Louvre (30x40cm-12x16in) s. drypoint executed c.1895. 2-Dec-3 Christie's, London #151/R est:3000-5000
£3672 $6500 €5361 Le visage encadre. Femme au chapeau (51x29cm-20x11in) s. drypoints prints two sold with another. 30-Apr-4 Sotheby's, New York #103/R est:3000-4000
£3767 $6404 €5500 Femme rousse. s.i. drypoint. 6-Nov-3 Piasa, Paris #102
£4118 $7000 €6012 Dessins de Watteau au Louvre (30x40cm-12x16in) s.i. painted drypoint. 31-Oct-3 Sotheby's, New York #285/R
£5548 $9432 €8100 Madame Marguerite Labady. s.i. drypoint. 6-Nov-3 Piasa, Paris #104/R
£6507 $11062 €9500 Noeud bleu. col drypoint. 6-Nov-3 Piasa, Paris #110/R
Works on paper
£545 $905 €790 Maternite (29x39cm-11x15in) s. W/C pencil. 13-Jun-3 Zofingen, Switzerland #2457/R (S.FR 1200)
£795 $1400 €1161 Mademoiselle Dauriac (25x30cm-10x12in) s. chl pastel. 28-May-4 Aspire, Cleveland #121/R est:2000-4000
£1800 $3312 €2628 Portrait de Jean Helleu a dix ans (28x23cm-11x9in) s. black white sanguine chk. 25-Mar-4 Christie's, Kensington #39/R est:2000-3000
£1974 $3632 €3000 Buste de femme (43x37cm-17x15in) s. crayon dr. 23-Jun-4 Sotheby's, Paris #91/R est:3000-5000
£3000 $4800 €4380 Etudes des costumes, femmes au dos (27x24cm-11x9in) s.i. col chk exec.c.1895. 18-Sep-3 Swann Galleries, New York #307/R est:5000-8000
£3841 $6991 €5800 Jeune femme alanguie (45x52cm-18x20in) s. crayon dr oval. 19-Jun-4 St-Germain-en-Laye Encheres #88/R est:8000
£4392 $7730 €6500 Elegant lady with a big hat (75x55cm-30x22in) s. black red chk prov.exhib. 19-May-4 Sotheby's, Amsterdam #369/R est:8000-12000
£4930 $8183 €7000 Portrait d'elegante en robe (74x56cm-29x22in) s.i.d.3 septembre col crayon. 16-Jun-3 E & Eve, Paris #73/R
£4930 $8183 €7000 Portrait de jeune elegante et un enfant. s. col crayon. 16-Jun-3 E & Eve, Paris #74/R
£5000 $9100 €7300 Une femme etendue (51x76cm-20x30in) s. pencil col chk. 16-Jun-4 Christie's, Kensington #263/R est:2500-3500
£5282 $8768 €7500 Portrait d'Helene au chapeau (38x30cm-15x12in) s. crayon sanguine dr. 15-Jun-3 Peron, Melun #4
£5442 $9741 €8000 Jeune femme etendue sous une ombrelle (61x62cm-24x24in) s. col chk. 18-Mar-4 Christie's, Paris #182/R est:8000-12000
£5500 $10120 €8030 Anticipation (73x46cm-29x18in) s. pencil sanguine black white chk. 25-Mar-4 Christie's, Kensington #40/R est:4000-6000
£6803 $12177 €10000 Portrait of Madame de Guerin friend of the artist (63x47cm-25x19in) s. three col crayons. 17-Mar-4 Tajan, Paris #152/R est:10000-12000
£7000 $12880 €10220 Mrs Fenwick (74x56cm-29x22in) s. pencil sanguine black white chk. 25-Mar-4 Christie's, Kensington #42/R est:4000-6000
£7151 $12300 €10440 Elegante au chapeau (60x47cm-24x19in) s. crayon sanguine. 3-Dec-3 Naón & Cia, Buenos Aires #19/R est:3000-5000
£13000 $23920 €18980 Elegant lady. Blonde beauty (72x56cm-28x22in) s. pencil sanguine col chk double-sided. 25-Mar-4 Christie's, Kensington #41/R est:4000-6000

HELLEU, Paulette (20th C) French
£336 $624 €500 Estuaire (27x38cm-11x15in) s. isorel exhib. 8-Mar-4 Artcurial Briest, Paris #35/R

HELLGREWE, Rudolf (1860-1935) German
£358 $655 €523 Sunset over heather fields on outskirts of wood (75x130cm-30x51in) s. 9-Jun-4 Rasmussen, Copenhagen #1692/R (D.KR 4000)
£839 $1401 €1200 At sunset (95x145cm-37x57in) s. i. verso. 28-Jun-3 Bolland & Marotz, Bremen #659/R
Works on paper
£567 $1043 €850 Markisch Lake (36x60cm-14x24in) s. gouache board. 12-Jun-4 Villa Grisebach, Berlin #568/R

HELLHOF, Heinrich (1868-1914) German
£521 $823 €750 Fisherman and young boys looking out to sea (120x73cm-47x29in) indis.s. 5-Sep-3 Wendl, Rudolstadt #3412/R

HELLIER, Dermont James John (1916-) Australian
£316 $566 €474 Australian Club, William Street, Melbourne (24x29cm-9x11in) s. i.verso canvas on plywood panel. 17-May-4 Sotheby's, Melbourne #588 (A.D 800)
£325 $582 €475 Yarra at Warrandyte (59x75cm-23x30in) s. 10-May-4 Joel, Victoria #272 (A.D 800)
£569 $1019 €831 Boy with the red shirt (60x72cm-24x28in) s. painted c.1960 board. 10-May-4 Joel, Victoria #289 est:1500-2000 (A.D 1400)

HELLMAN, Ake (1915-) Finnish
£387 $620 €550 Still life (50x70cm-20x28in) s. 18-Sep-3 Hagelstam, Helsinki #857/R

HELLMEIER, Otto (1908-) German
£323 $600 €472 Coastal village (38x58cm-15x23in) s. board painted c.1950. 7-Mar-4 Treadway Gallery, Cincinnati #630/R
£367 $675 €550 Chiemgau landscape in autumn (46x59cm-18x23in) s. masonite. 9-Jun-4 Dorotheum, Salzburg #595/R
£590 $962 €850 Cap Nero near S Remo (70x80cm-28x31in) s. i. verso. 26-Sep-3 Bolland & Marotz, Bremen #656/R
£1016 $1696 €1483 At the seaside. s. painted c.1930. 19-Oct-3 Agra, Warsaw #51/R est:5000 (P.Z 6500)
£1200 $2184 €1800 Fish market in Venice (36x56cm-14x22in) i.verso. 1-Jul-4 Neumeister, Munich #2706 est:2000

HELLWAG, Rudolf (1867-1942) German
£709 $1184 €1000 Street in winter (43x56cm-17x22in) s. 16-Oct-3 Dorotheum, Salzburg #572/R

HELMAN, Robert (1910-) French
£500 $910 €730 Untitled (115x88cm-45x35in) s. 4-Feb-4 Sotheby's, Olympia #185/R
£680 $1217 €1000 Untitled (100x81cm-39x32in) s. prov. 21-Mar-4 Calmels Cohen, Paris #133/R
Works on paper
£268 $499 €400 Composition (77x57cm-30x22in) s. W/C gouache. 3-Mar-4 Artcurial Briest, Paris #451a

HELMANTEL, Henk (1945-) Dutch
£8042 $13671 €11500 Still life with glazed vase and garlic on a base-board (34x36cm-13x14in) s.d.1994 board. 24-Nov-3 Glerum, Amsterdam #272/R est:14000-18000
£8276 $13241 €12000 Still life with bottles and dish (45x45cm-18x18in) s.d.1983 board. 12-Mar-3 Auction Maastricht #1047/R est:20000
£9333 $17173 €14000 Still life with shells (43x55cm-17x22in) s.d.1975 s.d. verso board. 8-Jun-4 Sotheby's, Amsterdam #25/R est:12000-18000
£9589 $16301 €14000 Still life with bottle and fruit (27x34cm-11x13in) s.d.1994. 5-Nov-3 Vendue Huis, Gravenhage #392/R est:14000-18000
£16667 $27333 €23000 Still life with apples (38x59cm-15x23in) s.d.2002 masonite exhib. 27-May-3 Sotheby's, Amsterdam #348/R est:20000-30000
£16667 $30667 €25000 Still life with grapes (45x36cm-18x14in) s.d.1976 s.d.1979 verso masonite prov. 8-Jun-4 Sotheby's, Amsterdam #32/R est:15000-20000

HELMBERGER, A (20th C) ?
£2041 $3653 €3000 Winter mountain wood (75x99cm-30x39in) s.d.1914. 17-Mar-4 Dorotheum, Vienna #1/R est:700

HELMBERGER, Adolf (1885-1967) Austrian
£1067 $1963 €1600 Furberg on Wolfgangsee (30x36cm-12x14in) s.d.1944 board. 9-Jun-4 Dorotheum, Salzburg #605/R est:2000-3000
£1700 $3111 €2482 Alpine scene in early Spring (75x85cm-30x33in) s. 7-Jul-4 George Kidner, Lymington #153/R est:500-600

HELMBREKER, Theodor (attrib) (1633-1696) Flemish
£2800 $4760 €4088 Peasants feasting outside a tavern with a beggar woman, her baby and son (74x97cm-29x38in) 29-Oct-3 Bonhams, New Bond Street #27/R est:3000-4000

HELME, Helge (1894-1987) Danish
£337 $550 €492 Coastal landscape with nude woman (46x38cm-18x15in) s.d.43. 27-Sep-3 Rasmussen, Havnen #2279 (D.KR 3600)
£341 $546 €498 Young girl holding mirror (22x17cm-9x7in) s. 22-Sep-3 Rasmussen, Vejle #35/R (D.KR 3600)
£361 $675 €527 A nymph (110x110cm-43x43in) s.d.30 exhib. 25-Feb-4 Kunsthallen, Copenhagen #291 (D.KR 4000)
£364 $589 €528 Interior scene with seated ballet dancer (33x41cm-13x16in) s. 4-Aug-3 Rasmussen, Vejle #71/R (D.KR 3800)
£373 $585 €545 Interior scene with seated ballet girl (50x33cm-20x13in) s. 30-Aug-3 Rasmussen, Havnen #2211 (D.KR 4000)
£379 $607 €553 Tying ribbons on the hat (31x23cm-12x9in) s. 22-Sep-3 Rasmussen, Vejle #37/R (D.KR 4000)
£398 $637 €581 Morning toilet (33x25cm-13x10in) s. 22-Sep-3 Rasmussen, Vejle #40/R (D.KR 4200)
£507 $862 €740 Portrait of female nude seated by brook (120x110cm-47x43in) s.d.41. 10-Nov-3 Rasmussen, Vejle #157/R (D.KR 5500)

HELME, Helge (attrib) (1894-1987) Danish
£1471 $2500 €2148 Girl at window (53x38cm-21x15in) 29-Nov-3 Carlsen Gallery, Greenville #635/R

HELME, Jane (20th C) British?
£250 $463 €365 Still life of cherries, and tureen (26x41cm-10x16in) s. board. 13-Feb-4 Sworder & Son, Bishops Stortford #127/R
£340 $629 €496 Still life with a bowl, a jar and feathers (46x60cm-18x24in) s. 13-Feb-4 Sworder & Son, Bishops Stortford #128/R
£400 $740 €584 Sunny square in St Guilhem-le-Desert (38x55cm-15x22in) s. canvasboard. 13-Feb-4 Sworder & Son, Bishops Stortford #125/R

HELMER, Phillip (1846-1912) German
£490 $817 €700 Portrait of young girl wearing white headscarf (30x21cm-12x8in) s. 9-Oct-3 Michael Zeller, Lindau #591
£600 $942 €870 Scholarly rabbi (20x16cm-8x6in) s. panel. 28-Aug-3 Christie's, Kensington #58/R

HELMERSEN, Odd (1922-1964) Norwegian
£442 $809 €645 From Svolvaer (62x50cm-24x20in) s. 2-Feb-4 Blomqvist, Lysaker #1105 (N.KR 5500)
£459 $766 €670 From Svolvaer (38x46cm-15x18in) s. 17-Nov-3 Blomqvist, Lysaker #1119 (N.KR 5500)
£514 $941 €750 Fishermen with nets (55x76cm-22x30in) s. 2-Feb-4 Blomqvist, Lysaker #1107 (N.KR 6400)
£659 $1206 €962 Skrova - with fishing boats and figures (65x85cm-26x33in) s. 2-Feb-4 Blomqvist, Lysaker #1106/R (N.KR 8200)
£820 $1362 €1189 Trollfjord battle (119x89cm-47x35in) s. after Gunnar Berg. 16-Jun-3 Blomqvist, Lysaker #1321/R (N.KR 9500)

HELMICK, Howard (1845-1907) American
£532 $850 €777 Tired out (23x18cm-9x7in) s. s.i.verso wood panel. 20-Sep-3 Bunte, Elgin #1423
£15000 $24900 €21900 The Magic Trick (60x82cm-24x32in) s.d.85. 1-Oct-3 Sotheby's, Olympia #16/R est:1000-1500

HELMONT, Lucas van Gassel (c.1480-c.1570) Flemish
£48000 $87840 €70080 Landscape with penitent Saint Jerome (63x75cm-25x30in) panel prov.lit. 8-Jul-4 Sotheby's, London #110/R est:40000-60000

HELMONT, Matheus van (1623-1679) Flemish
£10345 $17276 €15000 Slaughtered pig (58x84cm-23x33in) prov. 15-Nov-3 Lempertz, Koln #1061/R est:15000-20000

HELMONT, Matheus van (attrib) (1623-1679) Flemish
£2345 $4338 €3400 Interieur d'auberge anime (50x64cm-20x25in) panel. 13-Jan-4 Vanderkindere, Brussels #33/R est:2500-4000

HELMSTADT, Samuel (attrib) (1827-1902) German
£1333 $2427 €2000 Coastal landscape (47x63cm-19x25in) 1-Jul-4 Van Ham, Cologne #1395 est:2000

HELNWEIN, Gottfried (1948-) Austrian
£1133 $2085 €1700 Empty face (98x71cm-39x28in) s.i. oil acrylic board. 9-Jun-4 Dorotheum, Salzburg #722/R est:2800-4000
Works on paper
£400 $720 €600 Landscape (12x8cm-5x3in) s.d.79 Indian ink transparent paper. 21-Apr-4 Dorotheum, Vienna #257

HELOK, C Peter (1893-?) American
Works on paper
£541 $1000 €812 Vintage auto racer. s.i. W/C. 18-Jan-4 Carlsen Gallery, Greenville #125/R

HELPMAN, John Robert Crichton (1814-?) British
Works on paper
£380 $699 €555 Plains of Troy (17x25cm-7x10in) s W/C. 22-Jun-4 Bonhams, Knightsbridge #85/R
£700 $1190 €1022 Tower in Corfu (17x24cm-7x9in) W/C over pencil htd white. 18-Nov-3 Sotheby's, London #134/R

HELPS, Francis (fl.1910-1940) British
£350 $648 €511 Portrait of a lady in a straw hat (61x46cm-24x18in) i. 11-Mar-4 Christie's, Kensington #43
£420 $722 €613 Children playing in landscape (49x49cm-19x19in) i.verso prov. 3-Dec-3 Cheffins, Cambridge #638/R
£480 $883 €701 Washing line (39x29cm-15x11in) 13-Jun-4 Lots Road Auctions, London #370
£800 $1408 €1168 Figures in a landscape (51x51cm-20x20in) prov. 19-May-4 Sotheby's, Olympia #187/R

HELSBY, Alfredo (1862-1933) Chilean
£874 $1600 €1276 Landscape (33x25cm-13x10in) 31-Jan-4 South Bay, Long Island #261
£1100 $1969 €1606 South French scene with figures promenading by a river, perhaps Chile (25x33cm-10x13in) s. paper on board. 13-May-4 Scarborough Perry Fine Arts, Hove #622

HELST, Bartholomeus van der (attrib) (1613-1670) Dutch
£6538 $11246 €9545 Girl with bunch of grapes (73x61cm-29x24in) s.d.1654. 3-Dec-3 AB Stockholms Auktionsverk #2674/R est:80000-100000 (S.KR 85000)

HELSTED, Axel (1847-1907) Danish
£327 $517 €474 From Johanitternes Hospital, Jerusalem (39x29cm-15x11in) init.d.90. 3-Sep-3 Museumsbygningen, Copenhagen #192 (D.KR 3500)
£716 $1311 €1045 The botanist (50x61cm-20x24in) s. prov. 9-Jun-4 Rasmussen, Copenhagen #1653/R (D.KR 8000)
£902 $1668 €1317 Johanitterne's Hospice in Jerusalem (39x29cm-15x11in) mono.d.90. 15-Mar-4 Rasmussen, Vejle #377/R (D.KR 10000)

HELSTROM, Bessie (20th C) American
£333 $600 €486 Flowers in urn (76x99cm-30x39in) s. board oval. 25-Apr-4 Hindman, Chicago #1593/R

HELWIG, Arthur Louis (1899-1976) American
£255 $475 €372 Ship in a harbour (61x76cm-24x30in) s. board painted c.1950. 7-Mar-4 Treadway Gallery, Cincinnati #698/R
£593 $1050 €866 Nocturn la mer (17x23cm-7x9in) 1-May-4 Dan Ripley, Indianapolis #562

HEM, Louise de (1866-1922) Belgian
£743 $1330 €1100 Etude de femme de profil (47x39cm-19x15in) s. canvas on panel. 10-May-4 Horta, Bruxelles #5

HEM, Piet van der (1885-1961) Dutch
£733 $1342 €1100 Portrait of a woman in a black hat (69x59cm-27x23in) s. 7-Jun-4 Glerum, Amsterdam #97/R
£1333 $2453 €2000 Portrait of a dandy (54x43cm-21x17in) cardboard prov. 8-Jun-4 Sotheby's, Amsterdam #189/R est:2000-3000
£2533 $4636 €3800 Hare in the snow (60x86cm-24x34in) s. 7-Jun-4 Glerum, Amsterdam #67/R est:4000-5000
£6294 $10699 €9000 Oldehove, Leewarden (91x110cm-36x43in) s. painted c.1940. 25-Nov-3 Christie's, Amsterdam #190/R est:9000-12000
Works on paper
£789 $1453 €1200 Street scene, Paris (24x25cm-9x10in) s.i. pencil gouache. 22-Jun-4 Christie's, Amsterdam #438/R
£1389 $2264 €2000 Lady on a terrace (59x47cm-23x19in) s. black chk htd W/C. 29-Sep-3 Sotheby's, Amsterdam #252/R
£2667 $4907 €4000 Zandvoort (29x23cm-11x9in) s.i. gouache W/C. 8-Jun-4 Sotheby's, Amsterdam #169/R est:2000-3000

HEMCHE, Abdelhalim (1906-1979) Algerian
£638 $1066 €900 Mosquee (25x31cm-10x12in) s.d.1928 cardboard. 19-Oct-3 Rabourdin & Choppin de Janvry, Paris #134/R

HEMERLEIN, Carl Johann Nepomuk (1807-1884) German
£1818 $3091 €2600 Allegorical portrayal of helpfulness (63x54cm-25x21in) s. 22-Nov-3 Arnold, Frankfurt #547/R est:3000

HEMESSEN, Jan van (1504-1566) Flemish
£19000 $32870 €27740 Lucretia (42x35cm-17x14in) panel fragment prov. 10-Dec-3 Christie's, London #24/R est:15000-25000

HEMESSEN, Jan van (attrib) (1504-1566) Flemish
£40000 $69200 €58400 An allegory of love and music (109x96cm-43x38in) panel. 10-Dec-3 Christie's, London #25/R est:40000-60000

HEMING, Arthur (1870-1940) Canadian
£1584 $2486 €2297 Mountie washing his clothes (51x61cm-20x24in) s. prov. 30-Aug-3 Heffel, Vancouver #13 est:2500-3000 (C.D 3500)
£1705 $2779 €2489 Buffalo in autumn landscape (76x60cm-30x24in) s.d.31 prov. 23-Sep-3 Ritchie, Toronto #145/R est:1800-2000 (C.D 3750)

HEMINGWAY, Charles (fl.1932-1937) British
£320 $534 €467 Coastal road (56x71cm-22x28in) s.d.35. 12-Nov-3 Halls, Shrewsbury #326/R

HEMKEN, Willem de Haas (attrib) (1831-1911) Dutch
£2778 $4639 €4000 Townsfolk in the streets of Amsterdam (38x28cm-15x11in) 21-Oct-3 Sotheby's, Amsterdam #54/R est:3000-5000

HEMMRICH, Georg (1896-?) German
£300 $471 €435 Gathering outside an alpine tavern (18x27cm-7x11in) s. board. 28-Aug-3 Christie's, Kensington #100/R
£300 $540 €450 Village tavern (14x18cm-6x7in) s. panel. 22-Apr-4 Allgauer, Kempten #3566/R
£369 $679 €550 Post coach in front of tavern (23x17cm-9x7in) s. panel. 24-Mar-4 Hugo Ruef, Munich #993/R
£414 $691 €600 Garmisch (18x26cm-7x10in) s. panel. 9-Jul-3 Hugo Ruef, Munich #105

HEMPEL, Heinrich (20th C) German
£468 $731 €740 Boy (75x50cm-30x20in) s.i.21.9.32 stretcher. 18-Oct-2 Von Zezschwitz, Munich #55/R

HEMPFING, Wilhelm (1886-1951) German
£300 $552 €438 Sunlit summer landscape with a female figure on a bridge (78x96cm-31x38in) s. 25-Mar-4 Locke & England, Leamington Spa #103/R
£486 $768 €700 Greek coast from Corfu (33x45cm-13x18in) s. board. 6-Sep-3 Schopman, Hamburg #796/R
£503 $926 €750 Granada (49x39cm-19x15in) s.i. board lit. 25-Mar-4 Karlheinz Kaupp, Staufen #2499/R
£531 $888 €760 Yellow roses (60x50cm-24x20in) s.d.1917. 28-Jun-3 Bolland & Marotz, Bremen #773/R
£733 $1327 €1100 Duet (72x60cm-28x24in) s. 1-Apr-4 Van Ham, Cologne #1421
£780 $1303 €1100 Figures in the medina (75x55cm-30x22in) s. 19-Oct-3 Rabourdin & Choppin de Janvry, Paris #49/R
£905 $1538 €1321 Peonies (80x102cm-31x40in) s. 19-Nov-3 Fischer, Luzern #2130/R est:1200-1500 (S.FR 2000)
£2351 $4350 €3432 Female nude sitting on a chair, with a blanket over shoulders (105x93cm-41x37in) 14-Mar-4 Agra, Warsaw #67/R (P.Z 17000)

HEMPWORTH, Dorothy (20th C) American
Sculpture
£939 $1700 €1371 Untitled (109x84cm-43x33in) laminated wood floor sculpture. 3-Apr-4 David Rago, Lambertville #239/R est:900-1400

HEMSLEY, William (1819-1906) British
£1000 $1790 €1460 New baby (30x25cm-12x10in) s. 18-Mar-4 Christie's, Kensington #494/R est:1000-1500
£1200 $2196 €1752 Little shrimpers (31x25cm-12x10in) 6-Jul-4 Bonhams, Knightsbridge #195/R est:1200-1800
£1264 $2150 €1845 Boy and dog in the field (30cm-12in circular) s.d.1863. 29-Oct-3 Louis Morton, Mexico #46/R est:18000-20000 (M.P 24000)
£1300 $2067 €1898 Pet Lamb (20x16cm-8x6in) s.i.verso panel. 18-Mar-3 Anderson & Garland, Newcastle #539/R est:600-1000
£1400 $2380 €2044 Feeding time (13x10cm-5x4in) s. panel. 1-Dec-3 Bonhams, Bath #112/R est:1000-1500
£1796 $3000 €2622 Feeding the baby birds (26x20cm-10x8in) s. panel prov. 7-Oct-3 Sotheby's, New York #103 est:3000-4000

HEMY (?) ?

£434	$724	€620	Homeward Bounty (30x50cm-12x20in) s. i. verso. 9-Oct-3 Michael Zeller, Lindau #592

HEMY, Bernard Benedict (1845-1913) British

£270	$491	€394	Shipping off Tynemouth (44x58cm-17x23in) s. 15-Jun-4 Bonhams, Leeds #116
£282	$480	€412	Shipwreck off the coast (61x50cm-24x20in) s. 29-Nov-3 Rasmussen, Havnen #2087 (D.KR 3000)
£460	$846	€672	Fishermen repairing a boat in North Shields Harbour (29x44cm-11x17in) s. 23-Mar-4 Anderson & Garland, Newcastle #400
£480	$782	€701	Shipping at the mouth of the Tyne at evening (60x44cm-24x17in) s. 23-Sep-3 Anderson & Garland, Newcastle #408
£480	$883	€701	Morning - Collingham Shore near Berwick (17x30cm-7x12in) s. 23-Mar-4 Anderson & Garland, Newcastle #402/R
£500	$795	€730	Cullercoats Bay (25x35cm-10x14in) s. 18-Mar-3 Anderson & Garland, Newcastle #277/R
£600	$1122	€876	Fishing boats at a harbour entrance (36x23cm-14x9in) s. 25-Feb-4 Mallams, Oxford #382
£670	$1092	€978	Lobster fishermen in an open boat (44x54cm-17x21in) s. 23-Sep-3 Anderson & Garland, Newcastle #409/R
£700	$1288	€1022	Herring drifter unloading its catch in North Shields Harbour (25x39cm-10x15in) s. prov. 23-Mar-4 Anderson & Garland, Newcastle #403/R
£920	$1500	€1343	Cullercoats bay with fishing cobles putting to sea (50x75cm-20x30in) s. 23-Sep-3 Anderson & Garland, Newcastle #366/R
£950	$1644	€1387	Tramp steamer unloading in North Shields harbour (50x75cm-20x30in) s. 9-Dec-3 Anderson & Garland, Newcastle #468/R
£1600	$2560	€2336	Shipping on the Tyne (61x91cm-24x36in) s. 16-Sep-3 Gorringes, Bexhill #1593/R est:1000-1500
Works on paper			
£580	$1067	€847	Hulk towed by tugs on the Tyne (46x72cm-18x28in) s. W/C. 22-Jun-4 Bonhams, Knightsbridge #8/R

HEMY, Charles Napier (1841-1917) British

£600	$996	€876	Windy Day (28x38cm-11x15in) s. 1-Oct-3 Sotheby's, Olympia #27/R
£661	$1123	€965	Model ship (46x61cm-18x24in) s. 5-Nov-3 Dobiaschofsky, Bern #632/R est:14000 (S.FR 1500)
£880	$1602	€1285	Old fisher boat, Salmon Station on the Tyne (27x47cm-11x19in) mono.d.1865 i.d.verso. 15-Jun-4 Rosebery Fine Art, London #455
£1200	$2112	€1752	Cottage garden - twilight (47x77cm-19x30in) i.verso. 19-May-4 Christie's, Kensington #557/R est:700-1000
£1800	$3060	€2628	Running for home (44x67cm-17x26in) s. board. 19-Nov-3 Christie's, Kensington #584/R
£3175	$6000	€4636	Parlock Bay (28x48cm-11x19in) s.d.1891 s.i.verso. 21-Feb-4 Jeffery Burchard, Florida #22a/R
£3800	$6460	€5548	Boat houses at Mylor Creek (49x34cm-19x13in) oil on paper. 25-Nov-3 Christie's, London #167/R est:2500-3500
£4200	$7140	€6132	Leaving harbour (50x75cm-20x30in) s.i.d.1880 i.verso. 1-Dec-3 Bonhams, Bath #120/R est:800-1200
£7500	$13725	€10950	Fair wind out, Little Hampton harbour (51x76cm-20x30in) s.i.d.1880. 3-Jun-4 Lane, Penzance #230/R est:7500-9500
Works on paper			
£250	$455	€365	Low tide on the estuary (33x46cm-13x18in) mono.d.79 W/C. 1-Jul-4 Christie's, Kensington #470
£300	$552	€438	Pulling the ropes (9x9cm-4x4in) s.d.1862 W/C pair in one frame. 22-Jun-4 Bonhams, Knightsbridge #14/R
£380	$600	€555	Coastal landscape study of a rocky headland and distant lighthouse (36x61cm-14x24in) mono. W/C. 4-Apr-3 Biddle & Webb, Birmingham #133
£580	$1061	€847	Rocks and sea (31x41cm-12x16in) init.d.1899 W/C. 7-Apr-4 Bonhams, Bury St Edmunds #398/R
£620	$1135	€905	Sea fog (33x49cm-13x19in) init.d.1899 W/C. 7-Apr-4 Bonhams, Bury St Edmunds #397/R
£1000	$1600	€1460	Entrance to Falmouth harbour from Pendennis (23x31cm-9x12in) init. W/C htd white. 16-Sep-3 Bonhams, New Bond Street #36/R est:1000-1500
£1700	$2839	€2482	Fishing boats on the Cornish coast (46x66cm-18x26in) init.d.1908 W/C bodycol. 14-Oct-3 David Lay, Penzance #265/R est:800-1400
£3586	$6563	€5200	Le maquettiste (51x76cm-20x30in) s. peinture. 31-Jan-4 Robin & Fattori, Granville #107a
£3800	$6954	€5548	Near Monkseaton, Northumberland (16x25cm-6x10in) s.d.1862 pencil W/C bodycol buff coloured paper prov. 3-Jun-4 Christie's, London #25/R est:2000-3000
£4234	$7790	€6182	Waiting (51x76cm-20x30in) s.i.d.1895 W/C gouache. 14-Jun-4 Waddingtons, Toronto #99/R est:8000-10000 (C.D 10500)

HEMY, Thomas Marie (1852-1937) British

£920	$1592	€1343	North Shields Harbour with the Wellesley and the Satellite at anchor (50x75cm-20x30in) s.indis.d. 9-Dec-3 Anderson & Garland, Newcastle #467/R
Works on paper			
£550	$935	€803	Shipping on a busy river, possibly Mersey (44x34cm-17x13in) s.indis.d. pencil W/C prov. 19-Nov-3 Tennants, Leyburn #879
£1050	$1785	€1533	Fishing boats at Burnmouth, near Berwick (50x75cm-20x30in) s.d.1875 W/C. 18-Nov-3 Bonhams, Leeds #30 est:700-1000

HENARD, Charles (1757-c.1812) French/British

Miniatures			
£2600	$4498	€3796	Young lady (7cm-3in circular) gilt-metal mount. 9-Dec-3 Christie's, London #90/R est:1000-1500

HENCZE, Tamas (1938-) Hungarian

£1305	$2258	€1905	Dynamic structure (100x70cm-39x28in) s.verso cardboard. 12-Dec-3 Kieselbach, Budapest #107/R (H.F 500000)
£1305	$2258	€1905	Dynamic structure - green blue (100x70cm-39x28in) s.d.1970 cardboard. 12-Dec-3 Kieselbach, Budapest #106/R (H.F 500000)

HENDERSON OF WHITBY, William (fl.1880-1894) British

£1400	$2226	€2030	Confrontation between geese and kittens (20x28cm-8x11in) s. board pair. 9-Sep-3 David Duggleby, Scarborough #300/R est:1000-1500

HENDERSON, Allan (20th C) British

£280	$515	€409	Buckhaven Harbour. 25-Mar-4 Bonhams, Edinburgh #303

HENDERSON, Charles Cooper (1803-1877) British

£552	$1000	€806	London to York coaches passing (30x48cm-12x19in) init.d.1866 board. 30-Mar-4 Christie's, Rockefeller NY #38/R est:2000-3000
£660	$1234	€964	Coach travelling in the snow (30x49cm-12x19in) 24-Feb-4 Bonhams, Knowle #113
Works on paper			
£700	$1288	€1022	Rouen Havre Paris stagecoach (17x27cm-7x11in) mono. W/C prov. 10-Jun-4 Christie's, Kensington #120/R

HENDERSON, James (1871-1951) Canadian

£1818	$3291	€2654	Untitled - Qu'Appelle Valley (31x41cm-12x16in) bears sig prov. 18-Apr-4 Levis, Calgary #47/R est:4000-4500 (C.D 4400)
£4444	$7378	€6488	Close of day (51x61cm-20x24in) s. s.i.verso prov. 5-Oct-3 Levis, Calgary #42a/R est:12000-14000 (C.D 10000)

HENDERSON, John (1860-1924) British

£800	$1384	€1168	Seascape (30x46cm-12x18in) s. 9-Dec-3 Maynards, Vancouver #156 est:1000-1500 (C.D 1800)
£1000	$1570	€1450	Picnic beside the river (20x35cm-8x14in) s. 27-Aug-3 Sotheby's, London #1072/R est:1000-1500
£1400	$2562	€2044	Highland river (50x65cm-20x26in) s. 8-Apr-4 Bonhams, Edinburgh #93 est:1200-1800
£2200	$3454	€3190	Summer paddling (23x30cm-9x12in) s. board. 27-Aug-3 Sotheby's, London #1119/R est:1200-1800
£6000	$9420	€8700	Returning from school (46x61cm-18x24in) s. 27-Aug-3 Sotheby's, London #1099/R est:3000-5000
£7500	$11775	€10875	Summer picnic in the countryside (101x127cm-40x50in) s. 27-Aug-3 Sotheby's, London #1120/R est:6000-8000

HENDERSON, Joseph (1832-1908) British

£541	$1000	€790	Couple strolling a wooded lane with water and mountains in background (33x28cm-13x11in) mono.d.1874. 19-Jan-4 Winter Associates, Plainville #140/R
£740	$1236	€1080	Girls picking flowers on the west coast (17x13cm-7x5in) s. canvasboard. 16-Oct-3 Bonhams, Edinburgh #171/R
£769	$1323	€1123	Seascape with boats at sunset (32x44cm-13x17in) s. 7-Dec-3 Uppsala Auktionskammare, Uppsala #188/R (S.KR 10000)
£1150	$2059	€1679	Coastal scene with rowing boat (30x43cm-12x17in) s. 17-May-4 David Duggleby, Scarborough #691/R est:1200-1800
£1200	$2148	€1752	Off the West Coast (30x46cm-12x18in) s. 26-May-4 Sotheby's, Olympia #232/R est:1500-2000
£1400	$2562	€2044	Deserted cove, Argyll (97x72cm-38x28in) s. 8-Apr-4 Bonhams, Edinburgh #108 est:1500-2000
£1800	$3060	€2628	Waves (51x76cm-20x30in) s. 30-Oct-3 Christie's, London #109/R est:2000-3000
£1900	$3173	€2774	Mother and children on a beach (46x61cm-18x24in) 21-Oct-3 Gorringes, Lewes #1955/R est:800-1200
£2600	$4706	€3796	Fresh breeze off Kintyre (36x56cm-14x22in) s. s.i.stretcher. 19-Apr-4 Sotheby's, London #120/R est:3000-4000
£3500	$6335	€5110	Choppy seas (99x72cm-39x28in) s. prov. 19-Apr-4 Sotheby's, London #99/R est:4000-6000
£3600	$6192	€5256	Threading the line (51x92cm-20x36in) s. 6-Dec-3 Shapes, Edinburgh #404 est:1500-2000
£3600	$6516	€5256	Near Ballantrae (46x61cm-18x24in) s. prov. 19-Apr-4 Sotheby's, London #121/R est:3000-4000
£3965	$6740	€5789	Mussel collectors (46x61cm-18x24in) s. 5-Nov-3 Dobiaschofsky, Bern #633/R est:14000 (S.FR 9000)
£4000	$6800	€5840	Yacht Race (46x77cm-18x30in) s. i.verso. 30-Oct-3 Christie's, London #107/R est:4000-6000
£5000	$8350	€7300	Baiting the line (63x94cm-25x37in) s. 13-Nov-3 Christie's, Kensington #278/R est:4000-6000
£5000	$9050	€7300	Threading the line (51x91cm-20x36in) s. 19-Apr-4 Sotheby's, London #114/R est:5000-7000
£16000	$27200	€23360	Fishing from the rocks (72x99cm-28x39in) s. exhib. 30-Oct-3 Christie's, London #106/R est:8000-12000
Works on paper			
£11000	$19910	€16060	Looking out to sea (46x61cm-18x24in) s. 19-Apr-4 Sotheby's, London #107/R est:4000-6000

HENDERSON, Joseph Morris (1863-1936) British

£380	$692	€555	View of a stream and rock pool (18x23cm-7x9in) indis sig. 15-Jun-4 Canterbury Auctions, UK #87
£400	$748	€584	River landscape (35x45cm-14x18in) s. 22-Jul-4 Bonhams, Edinburgh #329
£600	$1080	€876	Autumn on the moor (44x60cm-17x24in) s. 22-Apr-4 Bonhams, Edinburgh #328
£750	$1403	€1095	On the cart (45x60cm-18x24in) s. 22-Jul-4 Bonhams, Edinburgh #323
£800	$1336	€1168	Horses fording a burn (25x35cm-10x14in) s. 19-Jun-3 Bonhams, Edinburgh #313
£1200	$1884	€1740	Coastal meadow (19x29cm-7x11in) s. board. 27-Aug-3 Sotheby's, London #1082/R est:1500-2000
£1200	$2004	€1752	Lochailort shore (50x75cm-20x30in) s. 16-Oct-3 Bonhams, Edinburgh #174/R est:1000-1500
£1400	$2408	€2044	Ayrshire Cove (45x68cm-18x27in) s. 4-Dec-3 Bonhams, Edinburgh #80/R est:1500-2000
£1400	$2562	€2044	Tumbledown croft (50x60cm-20x24in) s. 8-Apr-4 Bonhams, Edinburgh #94 est:1200-1800
£2200	$3454	€3190	Along the coast (30x46cm-12x18in) s. 27-Aug-3 Sotheby's, London #1071/R est:1500-2000
£2200	$3454	€3190	Corn stooks (46x61cm-18x24in) s. prov. 27-Aug-3 Sotheby's, London #1129/R est:2000-3000
£2500	$4525	€3650	Picnic in the dunes (30x46cm-12x18in) s. 19-Apr-4 Sotheby's, London #103/R est:2500-3500
£2800	$5068	€4088	At Benderloch, Argyllshire (61x76cm-24x30in) s. 19-Apr-4 Sotheby's, London #102/R est:3000-4000
£3000	$4710	€4350	Seagulls on the beach (67x100cm-26x39in) s. 27-Aug-3 Sotheby's, London #1076/R est:3000-5000

£3000 $5460 €4380 Landscape with stream and children picking wild flowers (43x61cm-17x24in) s. 30-Jun-4 Neal & Fletcher, Woodbridge #289/R est:1500-2000
£6500 $11765 €9490 Breezy skies (51x76cm-20x30in) s. 19-Apr-4 Sotheby's, London #122/R est:3000-4000

HENDERSON, Keith (1883-?) British
Works on paper
£270 $497 €394 Cereus in flower (18x22cm-7x9in) s. pastel. 11-Jun-4 Keys, Aylsham #330
£1258 $2000 €1837 Two girls playing in roses (38x33cm-15x13in) s. W/C. 10-Sep-3 Alderfer's, Hatfield #362 est:300-500
£2200 $3542 €3190 Alasdiar and Angus (35x48cm-14x19in) s. W/C gouache exhib. 21-Aug-3 Bonhams, Edinburgh #1169/R est:500-800

HENDERSON, Leslie (1895-1988) American
£531 $850 €775 Spring landscape (51x41cm-20x16in) s.d.1934. 19-Sep-3 Freeman, Philadelphia #198/R

HENDERSON, Lola (20th C) American
£389 $700 €568 School dancer (51x61cm-20x24in) canvasboard. 24-Apr-4 Slotin Folk Art, Buford #254/R

HENDERSON, Louise (1912-1994) New Zealander
£752 $1278 €1098 Afternoon glow (55x76cm-22x30in) s. board. 27-Nov-3 International Art Centre, Auckland #64/R (NZ.D 2000)
£1306 $2259 €1907 Cubist abstract composition (50x65cm-20x26in) s.d.1961. 9-Dec-3 Peter Webb, Auckland #156/R est:3000-5000 (NZ.D 3500)
£3147 $5727 €4595 Cubist abstract composition (119x90cm-47x35in) s.d.1973 board. 29-Jun-4 Peter Webb, Auckland #123/R est:12000-18000 (NZ.D 9000)
£3249 $5296 €4744 Still life before a window (60x53cm-24x21in) s.d.1936. 23-Sep-3 Peter Webb, Auckland #25/R est:7000-9000 (NZ.D 9000)
£7609 $12250 €11109 Canterbury Foot Hills (37x43cm-15x17in) s. board prov. 20-Aug-3 Dunbar Sloane, Auckland #25/R est:12000-18000 (NZ.D 21000)
Works on paper
£320 $543 €467 Waitakeres (30x33cm-12x13in) s.d.1965 verso W/C. 27-Nov-3 International Art Centre, Auckland #139/R (NZ.D 850)
£688 $1183 €1004 Disco (38x53cm-15x21in) s.d.83 mixed media. 3-Dec-3 Dunbar Sloane, Auckland #84/R (NZ.D 1850)
£1250 $2300 €1825 Original study for Southern Cross (41x66cm-16x26in) pencil mixed media prov. 25-Mar-4 International Art Centre, Auckland #69/R est:4500-7000 (NZ.D 3500)
£1986 $3236 €2900 Arthur's Pass (26x27cm-10x11in) s. pencil W/C exec. c.1940. 23-Sep-3 Peter Webb, Auckland #105/R est:4000-6000 (NZ.D 5500)
£2679 $4929 €3911 Cubist bird study (48x63cm-19x25in) s.d.1982 mixed media. 25-Mar-4 International Art Centre, Auckland #26/R est:7000-10000 (NZ.D 7500)

HENDERSON, Louise (attrib) (1912-1994) New Zealander
Works on paper
£277 $496 €404 Palestine (25x17cm-10x7in) i.d.1958 col pencil. 11-May-4 Peter Webb, Auckland #37/R (NZ.D 800)

HENDERSON, Maurice (20th C) Irish?
£300 $549 €438 Male portrait (23x20cm-9x8in) s.d.1989 board. 2-Jun-4 John Ross, Belfast #133
£319 $521 €460 Cliffs at Moher, Co Clare (41x51cm-16x20in) s.i.verso. 23-Sep-3 De Veres Art Auctions, Dublin #248

HENDERSON, Neville (20th C) British
£800 $1440 €1200 Kinsale, Co Cork (44x54cm-17x21in) s.d.1999. 20-Apr-4 James Adam, Dublin #192/R

HENDERSON, William Penhallow (1877-1943) American
£814 $1400 €1188 Kitchen study (33x43cm-13x17in) oil paperboard painted c.1910 prov. 7-Dec-3 Treadway Gallery, Cincinnati #501/R
Works on paper
£254 $475 €371 Portrait of Roy McWilliams (13x5cm-5x2in) pastel prov. 29-Feb-4 Grogan, Boston #83/R
£489 $900 €714 Waiting, woman in blue (23x13cm-9x5in) mono. col pastel pencil. 10-Jun-4 Swann Galleries, New York #119/R
£1347 $2290 €1967 Lemon and gold, morning on the drive (25x18cm-10x7in) s. pastel prov. 1-Nov-3 Santa Fe Art, Santa Fe #188/R est:2000-3000
£1471 $2500 €2148 New Mexico landscape (13x18cm-5x7in) s.d.18 W/C prov. 1-Nov-3 Santa Fe Art, Santa Fe #242/R est:2000-3000

HENDRICH, Hermann (1856-1931) German
£267 $480 €400 Evening landscape with sleeping Brunhilde (71x100cm-28x39in) s. lit. 22-Apr-4 Allgauer, Kempten #3567/R
£728 $1326 €1100 Flute player on rocky coast (48x67cm-19x26in) s. s.i.d.1919 verso panel. 19-Jun-4 Dannenberg, Berlin #567/R
£1467 $2655 €2200 Faust and Mephisto on Walpurgis night (58x72cm-23x28in) s. 3-Apr-4 Hans Stahl, Hamburg #36/R est:2200

HENDRICKX, Henri François Joseph (1817-1894) Belgian
£811 $1451 €1200 Still life with roses (66x90cm-26x35in) 10-May-4 Amberes, Antwerp #273

HENDRICKX, Michel (1847-1906) Dutch
£1500 $2490 €2190 Flower still lifes (32x23cm-13x9in) s. panel two. 1-Oct-3 Sotheby's, Olympia #234/R est:1500-2500

HENDRIKS, G (19th C) Dutch
£1400 $2646 €2044 Dutch barges in an estuary (41x54cm-16x21in) s. 19-Feb-4 Lyon & Turnbull, Edinburgh #114 est:800-1200

HENDRIKS, Lieven (1970-) Dutch
£1333 $2453 €2000 Table (150x200cm-59x79in) s. init.d.2000 verso acrylic. 9-Jun-4 Christie's, Amsterdam #396/R est:1000-1500

HENDRIKS, Willem (1828-1891) Dutch
£282 $519 €412 Autumn (30x40cm-12x16in) s. masonite. 14-Jun-4 Waddingtons, Toronto #220/R (C.D 700)
£550 $990 €803 Cattle in autumn landscape (41x51cm-16x20in) s. 21-Jan-4 Sotheby's, Olympia #471/R

HENDRIKS, Willem (1888-1966) Dutch
£567 $948 €800 Nature morte aux tomates (55x70cm-22x28in) s.d.41. 17-Jun-3 Galerie Moderne, Brussels #360
£586 $995 €856 Cows in a sunny glade (61x81cm-24x32in) s. 21-Nov-3 Walker's, Ottawa #208/R (C.D 1300)
£724 $1209 €1057 Polder landscape, autumn (61x71cm-24x28in) s. prov. 17-Nov-3 Waddingtons, Toronto #161/R (C.D 1600)
£905 $1511 €1321 Springtime (50x71cm-20x28in) s. prov. 17-Nov-3 Waddingtons, Toronto #163/R est:2000-3000 (C.D 2000)

HENDRIKS, Wybrand (1744-1831) Dutch
£1733 $3137 €2600 Still life with chrysanthemums (56x44cm-22x17in) s. lit. 1-Apr-4 Frank Peege, Freiburg #1115/R est:600
£3500 $6300 €5110 Portrait of gentleman with recorder. Portrait of lady at a harpsicord (36x28cm-14x11in) s.d.1787 panel oval pair. 23-Apr-4 Christie's, Kensington #127/R est:4000-6000
£7243 $12965 €10575 Interior scene with figures merrymaking (44x56cm-17x22in) s. panel. 28-May-4 Uppsala Auktionskammare, Uppsala #75/R est:80000-100000 (S.KR 98000)

HENDSCHEL, Albert (1834-1883) German
Works on paper
£1189 $2021 €1700 The ambush (30x35cm-12x14in) i. pencil board. 21-Nov-3 Reiss & Sohn, Konigstein #209/R est:500

HENEIN, Adam (1929-) Egyptian
Works on paper
£1700 $3009 €2482 Cairo. Bottles (39x29cm-15x11in) s. gouache two. 29-Apr-4 Bonhams, New Bond Street #593/R est:1800-2400

HENG, Euan (1945-) British
Works on paper
£932 $1585 €1361 On a street where we live (54x72cm-21x28in) s.verso W/C prov. 24-Nov-3 Sotheby's, Melbourne #68/R est:2000-3000 (A.D 2200)

HENGGE, Joseph (1890-1970) German
£280 $504 €420 Shepherd with lamb (57x48cm-22x19in) s. lit. 22-Apr-4 Allgauer, Kempten #3570/R

HENGSBACH, Franz (1814-1883) German
£17606 $30810 €25000 View of Losanna Valley (107x173cm-42x68in) s.d.1855. 17-Dec-3 Il Ponte, Milan #654/R est:25000-30000

HENGSTENBERG, Wulfried (20th C) German
£306 $510 €440 Reclining female nude on red cloth (58x76cm-23x30in) mono.d. panel. 25-Oct-3 Dr Lehr, Berlin #202/R

HENKEL, Irmin (1921-) South African
£1681 $3042 €2454 Lourens River (64x85cm-25x33in) s.d.70 i.verso. 30-Mar-4 Stephan Welz, Johannesburg #440/R est:9000-12000 (SA.R 20000)
£3966 $6622 €5790 Still life with roses and pawpaws (48x58cm-19x23in) s.d.73. 20-Oct-3 Stephan Welz, Johannesburg #255/R est:10000-14000 (SA.R 46000)

HENKES, Dolf (1903-1989) Dutch
£987 $1816 €1500 Landscape with houses and trees (40x60cm-16x24in) mono. two. 22-Jun-4 Christie's, Amsterdam #601/R est:1200-1600

HENKES, Dolf (attrib) (1903-1989) Dutch
£759 $1267 €1100 Fair and buildings on the river (36x89cm-14x35in) board. 11-Nov-3 Vendu Notarishuis, Rotterdam #42/R

HENKES, Gerke (1844-1927) Dutch
Works on paper
£567 $948 €800 The latest news (53x44cm-21x17in) s. gouache. 20-Oct-3 Glerum, Amsterdam #42/R

HENLEY, William (attrib) (1819-1895) British
£2500 $4625 €3650 Interior scene with two boys playing draughts (50x64cm-20x25in) 13-Feb-4 Bracketts, Tunbridge Wells #716/R est:2500-3500

HENNAH, Joseph Edward (1897-?) British
£260 $481 €380 Cornish harbour, possibly Polperro (36x43cm-14x17in) s. board. 11-Mar-4 Duke & Son, Dorchester #140
£280 $445 €409 Newport Levels, pollards willows by a stream (61x76cm-24x30in) s. 9-Sep-3 Peter Francis, Wales #4

HENNEBERG, Rudolf (attrib) (1825-1876) German
£919 $1700 €1342 Allegorical scene with nude, soldier and death (81x173cm-32x68in) s. 24-Jan-4 Jeffery Burchard, Florida #60/R

HENNEBERGER, August Philipp (1902-) German
Works on paper
£329 $549 €470 Peasant in lower Bavarian village (36x51cm-14x20in) s. W/C Indian ink brush. 10-Oct-3 Winterberg, Heidelberg #1409

HENNEBICQ, Andre (attrib) (1836-1904) Belgian
£428 $787 €650 Portrait de Madame Raquez (77x54cm-30x21in) 22-Jun-4 Palais de Beaux Arts, Brussels #260

HENNELL, Thomas (1903-1945) British
Works on paper
£500 $885 €730 Overgrown river backwater (48x63cm-19x25in) s. indis d. W/C. 27-Apr-4 Bonhams, Knightsbridge #187/R

HENNEMANN, Karl (1884-?) German
Works on paper
£573 $883 €900 Harvest time in Mecklenburg (37x46cm-15x18in) s. W/C. 4-Sep-2 Schopman, Hamburg #143/R

HENNEMANN-BARTSCH, Helene (20th C) German
Works on paper
£318 $490 €500 Mecklenburg farmstead in spring (40x50cm-16x20in) s. W/C. 4-Sep-2 Schopman, Hamburg #144/R

HENNEQUIN, Philippe Auguste (1762-1833) French
Works on paper
£559 $962 €800 Apollon sur son char (22x16cm-9x6in) i.verso crayon wash. 5-Dec-3 Gros & Delettrez, Paris #7

HENNER, Jean Jacques (1829-1905) French
£397 $723 €600 Portrait (13x22cm-5x9in) cardboard. 20-Jun-4 Versailles Encheres #37
£483 $806 €700 Jeune femme allongee a demi-nu (22x33cm-9x13in) s. 17-Nov-3 Tajan, Paris #89
£750 $1230 €1095 Petite fille aux cheveux a la titan (31x38cm-12x15in) s. i. stretcher. 3-Jun-3 Fellows & Sons, Birmingham #3/R
£853 $1500 €1245 Lady in a red dress (48x33cm-19x13in) s. 23-May-4 Hindman, Chicago #56/R est:3000-5000
£1176 $2000 €1717 Reclining female nude (21x32cm-8x13in) s. panel. 21-Nov-3 Skinner, Boston #251/R est:3000-5000
£1438 $2445 €2100 Etude (15x24cm-6x9in) exhib. 6-Nov-3 Sotheby's, Paris #142/R est:1000-1500
£1676 $3000 €2447 Red haired woman in profile (27x21cm-11x8in) panel prov. 6-May-4 Doyle, New York #48/R est:4000-6000
£1931 $3225 €2800 L'Alsacienne (27x21cm-11x8in) s. panel. 17-Nov-3 Tajan, Paris #91/R est:2000-3000
£2128 $3447 €3000 Nymphe appuyee contre un rocher ou une fontaine (22x16cm-9x6in) s. panel prov.lit. 23-May-3 Sotheby's, Paris #35/R est:3000-4000
£2238 $3804 €3200 Portrait de femme (27x22cm-11x9in) s. panel. 27-Nov-3 Millon & Associes, Paris #149/R est:1200-1500
£2394 $4286 €3400 Portrait de femme (32x27cm-13x11in) s. panel. 11-Jan-4 Rouillac, Vendome #351
£2448 $4161 €3500 Jeune femme rousse en buste (41x33cm-16x13in) s. 28-Nov-3 Blanchet, Paris #47/R est:4500-5000
£2781 $5090 €4200 Femme nue allongee (34x46cm-13x18in) s. 9-Apr-4 Claude Aguttes, Neuilly #9 est:3000-4000
£2837 $4596 €4000 Nymphe couchee de dos (26x38cm-10x15in) bears studio st. cardboard prov.lit. 23-May-3 Sotheby's, Paris #32/R est:3000-4000
£3147 $5413 €4500 Portrait of a lady, head and shoulders (40x32cm-16x13in) s. panel. 2-Dec-3 Christie's, Paris #139/R est:3000-5000
£3333 $6100 €5000 Portrait de Maria Heilbronn Vicomtesse de la Panouse (46x36cm-18x14in) 6-Jun-4 Osenat, Fontainebleau #233/R est:4500-5000
£3889 $7000 €5678 La fontaine (81x68cm-32x27in) s. 21-Jan-4 Sotheby's, New York #184/R est:5000-7000
£4615 $7938 €6600 Portrait de jeune femme rousse de profil (27x22cm-11x9in) s. panel. 7-Dec-3 Osenat, Fontainebleau #157 est:5000-6000
£4783 $7843 €6600 Jeune femme rousse de profil (33x24cm-13x9in) s. 11-May-3 Osenat, Fontainebleau #181/R est:7000-8000
£6471 $11000 €9448 Melancholie (65x46cm-26x18in) s. prov. 29-Oct-3 Christie's, Rockefeller NY #133/R est:10000-15000
£9396 $16819 €14000 Portrait de Juana Romani (130x70cm-51x28in) s.i. panel. 25-May-4 Chambelland & Giafferi, Paris #65/R est:20000-30000
Works on paper
£408 $731 €600 Portrait de femme portant un chapeau (10x8cm-4x3in) s. chl estompe. 19-Mar-4 Piasa, Paris #190
£1197 $2095 €1700 Portrait de Jacques Watelin enfant (47x36cm-19x14in) s. chl. 17-Dec-3 Delorme & Bocage, Paris #38/R est:1500-2000

HENNER, Jean Jacques (attrib) (1829-1905) French
£1549 $2680 €2200 Profile portrait of a lady in red (27x19cm-11x7in) i. 10-Dec-3 Dorotheum, Vienna #219/R est:1800-2200

HENNESSEY, Frank Charles (1893-1941) Canadian
£402 $683 €587 Autumn afternoon, the Laurentian Hills (41x51cm-16x20in) i.verso masonite prov. 6-Nov-3 Heffel, Vancouver #60/R (C.D 900)
£811 $1378 €1184 The red punt (41x51cm-16x20in) s. i.verso pastel prov. 21-Nov-3 Walker's, Ottawa #2/R est:900-1200 (C.D 1800)
Works on paper
£440 $805 €642 Trail to the lake (22x29cm-9x11in) s.d.39 panel. 1-Jun-4 Joyner Waddington, Toronto #8/R (C.D 1100)
£536 $921 €783 Early Spring on the Gatineau (22x29cm-9x11in) s. pastel prov. 2-Dec-3 Joyner Waddington, Toronto #417 (C.D 1200)
£580 $998 €847 River sweeper (56x64cm-22x25in) s.d.31 pastel. 2-Dec-3 Joyner Waddington, Toronto #474 (C.D 1300)
£645 $1187 €942 Gatineau winter (22x30cm-9x12in) s.d.38 pastel. 9-Jun-4 Walker's, Ottawa #8/R (C.D 1600)

HENNESSY, Patrick (1915-1980) Irish
£399 $650 €583 Farewell to Ireland (127x102cm-50x40in) s. 24-Sep-3 Jackson's, Cedar Falls #797/R
£1259 $2140 €1800 Patsy (21x21cm-8x8in) s. card on board prov. 25-Nov-3 De Veres Art Auctions, Dublin #10/R est:2000-3000
£2027 $3831 €3000 Self portrait (46x37cm-18x15in) oil gesso board painted c.1938. 17-Feb-4 Whyte's, Dublin #155/R est:4000-6000
£2148 $3844 €3200 Conch Shell (35x21cm-14x8in) s. board. 31-May-4 Hamilton Osborne King, Dublin #179/R est:2000-3000
£2297 $4342 €3400 Abandoned houses seen through an archway (43x29cm-17x11in) canvas on board. 17-Feb-4 Whyte's, Dublin #43/R est:3000-4000
£2800 $5068 €4200 On the shore (37x63cm-15x25in) s. prov. 31-Mar-4 James Adam, Dublin #40/R est:3000-4000
£3490 $6247 €5200 Still life with flowers and conch shell (61x51cm-24x20in) s. 26-May-4 James Adam, Dublin #54/R est:4000-6000
£3618 $6658 €5500 Spanish castle (56x47cm-22x19in) s. prov. 22-Jun-4 De Veres Art Auctions, Dublin #21/R est:6000-8000
£3667 $6637 €5500 Clonmacnoise (84x61cm-33x24in) exhib. 30-Mar-4 De Veres Art Auctions, Dublin #13/R est:5000-7000
£4685 $7965 €6700 Yellow roses (40x55cm-16x22in) s. painted c.1958 prov.exhib. 25-Nov-3 De Veres Art Auctions, Dublin #14/R est:7000-10000
£6711 $12013 €10000 ORACLE (62x88cm-24x35in) S. P. 26-May-4 James Adam, Dublin #76/R est:10000-15000
£7203 $12245 €10300 Madame butterfly (31x19cm-12x7in) s. canvasboard prov. 25-Nov-3 De Veres Art Auctions, Dublin #185/R est:6000-9000
£7292 $11885 €10500 Serenade (63x91cm-25x36in) s. prov. 24-Sep-3 James Adam, Dublin #93/R est:8000-12000
£8800 $16016 €12848 Boy and horses on the seashore (62x100cm-24x39in) s. prov. 15-Jun-4 Bonhams, Knightsbridge #220/R est:3000-5000
£9028 $14715 €13000 Bouquet (30x22cm-12x9in) s. board. 24-Sep-3 James Adam, Dublin #74/R est:6000-10000
£13423 $24027 €20000 Magic Mountain (63x89cm-25x35in) s. prov. 26-May-4 James Adam, Dublin #53/R est:10000-15000
£13514 $25541 €20000 Farewell to Ireland (127x102cm-50x40in) s. prov. 17-Feb-4 Whyte's, Dublin #97/R est:8000-10000
£29000 $51910 €42340 Still life with sea chest (63x88cm-25x35in) s. prov. 14-May-4 Christie's, London #217/R est:10000-15000

HENNIG, Albert (1907-1998) German
Works on paper
£268 $494 €400 Composition (9x14cm-4x6in) s.d.70 W/C. 27-Mar-4 L & B, Essen #267/R
£268 $494 €400 Composition (21x28cm-8x11in) s.d.67 W/C. 27-Mar-4 L & B, Essen #268/R
£301 $511 €430 Landscape with pine trees (13x17cm-5x7in) s.d.80 W/C over feltpen board. 29-Nov-3 Bassenge, Berlin #6770
£467 $845 €700 Geometric composition (19x13cm-7x5in) s.d. mixed media. 2-Apr-4 Winterberg, Heidelberg #1092/R
£1084 $1810 €1550 City (24x34cm-9x13in) s.d. pastel. 10-Oct-3 Winterberg, Heidelberg #1410/R est:1200

HENNIG, Erich (1875-?) German
£280 $481 €400 The pianist Max Becker in full flight (94x114cm-37x45in) s.d.1907. 6-Dec-3 Dannenberg, Berlin #787/R
£498 $796 €727 Esther in the mirror (72x57cm-28x22in) s. s.i. verso canvas on board. 16-Sep-3 Philippe Schuler, Zurich #5444 (S.FR 1100)
£2000 $3580 €2920 Start of the day (71x57cm-28x22in) s. 26-May-4 Sotheby's, Olympia #322/R est:2000-3000

HENNIG, Gustav Adolph (attrib) (1797-1869) German
£867 $1569 €1300 Biedermeier portrait - Agnes Wilhelmina (42x33cm-17x13in) 3-Apr-4 Badum, Bamberg #81/R

HENNIGS, Gosta von (1866-1941) Swedish
£538 $876 €785 Figures on the quay (50x61cm-20x24in) s.d.1904. 29-Sep-3 Lilla Bukowskis, Stockholm #15 (S.KR 7000)
Works on paper
£393 $679 €574 Friends (55x40cm-22x16in) s.d.1935 gouache exhib.lit. 15-Dec-3 Lilla Bukowskis, Stockholm #555 (S.KR 5000)
£952 $1686 €1390 The tight-rope walker (43x29cm-17x11in) init.d.1927 W/C. 27-Apr-4 AB Stockholms Auktionsverk #728/R (S.KR 13000)
£2069 $3704 €3021 Female manege-rider (40x50cm-16x20in) init.d.1933 W/C. 25-May-4 Bukowskis, Stockholm #17/R est:10000-12000 (S.KR 28000)

HENNING, Gerhard (1880-1967) Swedish
Sculpture
£1323 $2369 €1932 Woman with hair put on top (38cm-15in) pat plaster prov. 12-Jan-4 Rasmussen, Vejle #718/R est:1500 (D.KR 14000)
£2723 $4547 €3976 Female model standing (28cm-11in) s.d.1923, 1951 black pat.bronze incl. wood socle cire perdue. 7-Oct-3 Rasmussen, Copenhagen #141/R est:20000 (D.KR 29000)
Works on paper
£1212 $1902 €1770 Erotic studies of nude girls. pencil Indian ink W/C four. 30-Aug-3 Rasmussen, Havnen #4261 est:5000 (D.KR 13000)

HENNING, J S (19th C) British
£4000 $6680 €5840 Portrait of Johnny Hannan, the boxer (39x29cm-15x11in) 14-Oct-3 Sotheby's, London #456/R est:3000-4000

HENNING, Robert (20th C) German
£839 $1401 €1200 Portraits (113x65cm-44x26in) one s. one mono. pair. 28-Jun-3 Bolland & Marotz, Bremen #661/R

HENNINGER, Manfred (1894-1986) German
£300 $540 €450 Bathers on Max Eyth See (56x75cm-22x30in) s.d.1971 W/C. 26-Apr-4 Rieber, Stuttgart #1059/R
£676 $1162 €987 Landscape with lake and sailing boats (50x70cm-20x28in) s. 8-Dec-3 Philippe Schuler, Zurich #3447/R (S.FR 1500)
£764 $1245 €1100 Figures (46x64cm-18x25in) s.d.1970 tempera. 27-Sep-3 Dr Fritz Nagel, Stuttgart #9182/R
£1056 $1690 €1500 Male nudes (37x54cm-15x21in) s.d.1954. 18-Sep-3 Rieber, Stuttgart #777/R est:2200
£1748 $3007 €2500 Autumn landscape, probably Tessin (73x92cm-29x36in) s. board. 5-Dec-3 Michael Zeller, Lindau #637/R est:2500
£1761 $2817 €2500 Bathers on Mediterranean coast (75x100cm-30x39in) s. 18-Sep-3 Rieber, Stuttgart #883/R est:2700
£2083 $3479 €3000 Southern landscape - Riva (70x85cm-28x33in) s.d. linene. 24-Oct-3 Ketterer, Hamburg #376/R est:3500-4000
£2847 $4641 €4100 Lago Maggiore (73x90cm-29x35in) s.d.1948. 27-Sep-3 Dr Fritz Nagel, Stuttgart #9555/R est:4500
Works on paper
£278 $464 €400 Riva (31x45cm-12x18in) s.i.d. W/C sold with offset lithograph. 24-Oct-3 Ketterer, Hamburg #806/R

HENNINGS, Ernest Martin (1886-1956) American
£1808 $3200 €2640 Portrait of Marie Hennings (47x38cm-19x15in) s. prov. 28-Apr-4 Christie's, Los Angeles #65/R est:4000-6000
£2907 $5000 €4244 Female figure study (89x97cm-35x38in) painted c.1914 prov. 7-Dec-3 Treadway Gallery, Cincinnati #496/R est:6000-8000
£3672 $6500 €5361 Venetian canal (34x30cm-13x12in) s. i.verso canvas on board prov. 28-Apr-4 Christie's, Los Angeles #61/R est:6000-8000
£4360 $7500 €6366 Male figure study (89x74cm-35x29in) painted c.1914 prov. 7-Dec-3 Treadway Gallery, Cincinnati #495/R est:6000-8000
£4545 $8500 €6636 Pueblo village (18x25cm-7x10in) s. canvas on board prov. 24-Jul-4 Coeur d'Alene, Hayden #251/R est:5000-10000
£13369 $25000 €19519 Sagebrush and billowing clouds (33x33cm-13x13in) s. board prov. 24-Jul-4 Coeur d'Alene, Hayden #44/R est:8000-12000
£13529 $23000 €19752 Friendly discussion (64x76cm-25x30in) s. pr. 1-Nov-3 Santa Fe Art, Santa Fe #195/R est:25000-35000
£17380 $32500 €25375 Taos Pueble Indian (46x36cm-18x14in) s. prov. 24-Jul-4 Coeur d'Alene, Hayden #204/R est:30000-50000
£21390 $40000 €31229 Black Olla (20x25cm-8x10in) s. canvasboard prov. 24-Jul-4 Coeur d'Alene, Hayden #72/R est:40000-60000
£25401 $47500 €37085 Green corn necklace (20x25cm-8x10in) s. canvasboard prov. 24-Jul-4 Coeur d'Alene, Hayden #73/R est:40000-60000
£28409 $50000 €41477 Vined entrance (76x64cm-30x25in) s. prov.exhib. 19-May-4 Sotheby's, New York #198/R est:60000-80000
£32086 $60000 €46846 Indian music (20x25cm-8x10in) s. canvasboard prov. 24-Jul-4 Coeur d'Alene, Hayden #71/R est:40000-60000
£32086 $60000 €46846 Bow and arrow (20x25cm-8x10in) s. canvasboard prov. 24-Jul-4 Coeur d'Alene, Hayden #74/R est:40000-60000
£32086 $60000 €46846 Aspen view (36x36cm-14x14in) s. canvas on board prov. 24-Jul-4 Coeur d'Alene, Hayden #121/R est:10000-15000
£72674 $125000 €106104 Along the Rio Hondo Stream (76x91cm-30x36in) s. 6-Dec-3 Selkirks, St. Louis #193/R est:150000-175000
£215909 $380000 €315227 At the water hole (91x91cm-36x36in) s. prov. 19-May-4 Sotheby's, New York #196/R est:250000-350000
£274567 $475000 €400868 Indian horsemen (91x102cm-36x40in) prov. 10-Dec-3 Bonhams & Butterfields, San Francisco #6096/R est:400000-600000
Prints
£1618 $2750 €2362 Across the sage (20x23cm-8x9in) s.num.1/25 lithograph prov. 1-Nov-3 Santa Fe Art, Santa Fe #3/R est:2500-3500
£4412 $7500 €6442 Three Indian riders in landscape (9x10cm-4x4in) s. col monotype. 18-Nov-3 John Moran, Pasadena #117a est:3000-5000
Works on paper
£206 $350 €301 Figure study (23x13cm-9x5in) s. ink prov. 1-Nov-3 Santa Fe Art, Santa Fe #184/R

HENNINGS, Johann Friedrich (1838-1899) German
£1325 $2424 €2000 Sunday in the park (29x40cm-11x16in) s. panel. 7-Apr-4 Dorotheum, Salzburg #119/R est:4000-6000
£2254 $3899 €3200 Idyllic scene at the stream (76x95cm-30x37in) s. 10-Dec-3 Dorotheum, Vienna #74/R est:3600-4000

HENNINGSEN, Erik (1855-1930) Danish
£467 $738 €677 Young lady (24x18cm-9x7in) mono. 2-Sep-3 Rasmussen, Copenhagen #1882/R (D.KR 5000)
£611 $1040 €892 Portrait of woman (39x29cm-15x11in) 29-Nov-3 Rasmussen, Havnen #2144/R (D.KR 6500)
£905 $1620 €1321 The letter from America (54x45cm-21x18in) s. 10-May-4 Rasmussen, Vejle #428/R (D.KR 10000)
£6289 $11698 €9182 Fire - early morning in Mariager (72x62cm-28x24in) s.d.1918 exhib. 2-Mar-4 Rasmussen, Copenhagen #1253/R est:50000-75000 (D.KR 70000)
£18904 $32703 €27600 Morning at the information office building (74x97cm-29x38in) s.d.1881 exhib.prov. 9-Dec-3 Rasmussen, Copenhagen #1296/R est:200000-250000 (D.KR 200000)
£20143 $36862 €29409 The town's musicians (85x104cm-33x41in) s.d.1926 exhib.prov. 9-Jun-4 Rasmussen, Copenhagen #1496/R est:250000-300000 (D.KR 225000)
£22684 $39244 €33119 Children playing hopscotch being interrupted by absent-minded gentleman (45x55cm-18x22in) s.d.1925 exhib. 9-Dec-3 Rasmussen, Copenhagen #1295/R est:250000-300000 (D.KR 240000)
Works on paper
£258 $451 €377 The angel (20x13cm-8x5in) s. pen wash. 16-Dec-3 Grev Wedels Plass, Oslo #33/R (N.KR 3000)

HENNINGSEN, Frants (1850-1908) Danish
£369 $627 €539 Wooded landscape with country road (65x55cm-26x22in) mono. 10-Nov-3 Rasmussen, Vejle #92/R (D.KR 4000)
£403 $737 €588 Coastal landscape with view from Hellebaek (48x66cm-19x26in) d.21.10.93. 9-Jun-4 Rasmussen, Copenhagen #1954/R (D.KR 4500)
£430 $774 €628 Portrait of a dragoon (72x44cm-28x17in) init. 24-Apr-4 Rasmussen, Havnen #2175/R (D.KR 4800)
£449 $709 €651 Baby's christening (40x30cm-16x12in) mono.d.85 pastel. 2-Sep-3 Rasmussen, Copenhagen #1881/R (D.KR 4800)
£467 $738 €677 Interior scene with elegant lady in pink dress (57x40cm-22x16in) mono.d.90. 2-Sep-3 Rasmussen, Copenhagen #1706/R (D.KR 5000)
£888 $1403 €1288 Two hussars on horseback guarding (29x19cm-11x7in) mono.d.1902. 2-Sep-3 Rasmussen, Copenhagen #1696/R (D.KR 9500)
£1323 $2289 €1932 Seascape with view from Hellebaek towards Kullen (32x48cm-13x19in) init. 9-Dec-3 Rasmussen, Copenhagen #1497/R est:6000 (D.KR 14000)
£2679 $4341 €3885 Interior scene with two boys seated at table (55x46cm-22x18in) mono.d.92 exhib. 4-Aug-3 Rasmussen, Vejle #83/R est:20000 (D.KR 28000)
£3205 $5833 €4679 Landscape from Gisselfeld with young man pulling two horses across waterway (63x95cm-25x37in) mono.i.d.1886. 7-Feb-4 Rasmussen, Havnen #2269/R est:15000 (D.KR 35000)
£3249 $6076 €4744 Jaegersborg Avenue in Charlottelund (52x67cm-20x26in) mono.d.1879. 25-Feb-4 Kunsthallen, Copenhagen #531/R est:50000 (D.KR 36000)

HENNO, Louis (1907-1990) Belgian
£390 $651 €550 Bord d'etang anime (70x90cm-28x35in) s. 17-Jun-3 Vanderkindere, Brussels #130

HENOCQUE, Narcisse (1879-1952) French
£1241 $2061 €1800 Paysage enneige (24x35cm-9x14in) s. panel. 1-Oct-3 Millon & Associes, Paris #158/R
£2349 $4322 €3500 Bord de Seine (67x82cm-26x32in) s. 28-Mar-4 Anaf, Lyon #138/R est:4000-5000
£2685 $4940 €4000 Le ponton (73x92cm-29x36in) s. 28-Mar-4 Anaf, Lyon #139/R est:4000-5000

HENRI, Adrian (1932-) British
£420 $722 €613 Pere Ubu in Liverpool (152x152cm-60x60in) s.i.d.Sept 1968 verso board exhib. 3-Dec-3 Christie's, Kensington #688

HENRI, Émile (?) French?
Sculpture
£1250 $2299 €1900 Roman gladiator (55cm-22in) s.i. green pat bronze incl. marble base. 22-Jun-4 Sotheby's, Amsterdam #100/R est:1000-1500

HENRI, Robert (1865-1929) American
£3333 $6000 €4866 Portrait of Butler King Couper Junior (20x14cm-8x6in) canvasboard prov. 24-Apr-4 Weschler, Washington #639/R est:5000-7000
£4706 $8000 €6871 In the Tuilleries, Paris (10x15cm-4x6in) s.i. panel double-sided. 30-Oct-3 Phillips, New York #67/R est:8000-12000
£10440 $19000 €15242 Charenton Bridge, raining (22x15cm-9x6in) s.i. panel prov. 29-Jun-4 Sotheby's, New York #306/R est:12000-18000
£21739 $40000 €31739 Storm cloud, Boothbay Harbor (20x25cm-8x10in) s. pencil prov. 10-Jun-4 Sotheby's, New York #140/R est:8000-12000
£24419 $42000 €35652 Sunlight, girl on a beach (46x62cm-18x24in) painted 1893 prov.exhib. 4-Dec-3 Christie's, Rockefeller NY #79/R est:20000-30000
Works on paper
£217 $400 €317 Full length study of a man (33x25cm-13x10in) black crayon prov. 25-Jun-4 Freeman, Philadelphia #41/R
£235 $400 €343 Man in hat (10x18cm-4x7in) black crayon. 7-Nov-3 Selkirks, St. Louis #472
£259 $425 €376 Mountain scene with building (18x25cm-7x10in) estate st. pen blue ink dr. 2-Jun-3 Grogan, Boston #693
£299 $500 €437 Nude woman (28x20cm-11x8in) s. blue crayon. 16-Nov-3 CRN Auctions, Cambridge #4/R
£608 $1100 €888 Portrait of a woman (48x38cm-19x15in) s. pastel. 16-Apr-4 James Julia, Fairfield #888/R est:800-1200
£615 $1100 €898 Standing draped figure (28x18cm-11x7in) ink wash. 20-Mar-4 Rachel Davis, Shaker Heights #174/R est:500-700
£1117 $2000 €1631 Caught in a compromising position (25x30cm-10x12in) s. chl prov. 6-May-4 Shannon's, Milford #218/R est:2500-3500
£1270 $2350 €1905 Meenaune Cliffs, Achill Island, County Mayo, Ireland (18x30cm-7x12in) s. s.d.Sept 1913 verso W/C prov. 14-Jul-4 American Auctioneer #490258/R est:1500-2500
£1537 $2750 €2244 Nude. Dandy. City from the park (18x23cm-7x9in) s. one W/C one ink one chl three prov. 6-May-4 Shannon's, Milford #224/R est:2000-3000
£1573 $2910 €2360 Fete Day, Concarneau (23x15cm-9x6in) s. W/C exec. 1894 prov. 14-Jul-4 American Auctioneer #490233/R est:1500-2500
£1676 $3000 €2447 Majorie with hat. Girl with folded hands. Isadora Duncan. Through a window. s. pencil col pencil ink four prov. 6-May-4 Shannon's, Milford #219/R est:1500-2500
£1816 $3250 €2651 Reclining nude (30x43cm-12x17in) estate st.verso pastel prov. 6-May-4 Shannon's, Milford #223/R est:3000-5000
£1816 $3250 €2651 Nude with black background (13x15cm-5x6in) estate st. ink prov. 6-May-4 Shannon's, Milford #236/R est:1500-2500
£2000 $3500 €2920 Reclining nude (32x48cm-13x19in) s. gouache. 19-Dec-3 Sotheby's, New York #1034/R est:5000-7000

HENRICHSEN, Carsten (1824-1897) Danish
£293 $533 €428 View from outskirts of wood (21x28cm-8x11in) mono. panel. 7-Feb-4 Rasmussen, Havnen #2035 (D.KR 3200)
£337 $563 €492 Landscape with house and figures (37x54cm-15x21in) mono.d.1867. 25-Oct-3 Rasmussen, Havnen #2206/R (D.KR 3600)
£374 $591 €542 Landscape with sheep and man with wheelbarrow, Jylland (50x73cm-20x29in) mono.d.1886. 2-Sep-3 Rasmussen, Copenhagen #1612/R (D.KR 4000)
£383 $620 €555 Wooded landscape with sea and sailing boat (70x59cm-28x23in) init.d.1875. 4-Aug-3 Rasmussen, Vejle #339/R (D.KR 4000)
£498 $891 €727 Danish summer landscape with lake (36x47cm-14x19in) mono.d.1859. 10-May-4 Rasmussen, Vejle #90/R (D.KR 5500)
£521 $834 €761 River landscape with angler, North Sjaelland (39x55cm-15x22in) mono.d.1860. 22-Sep-3 Rasmussen, Vejle #401/R (D.KR 5500)
£588 $940 €858 Wooded landscape with man walking, view of town through trees (51x71cm-20x28in) mono.d.1875. 22-Sep-3 Rasmussen, Vejle #329/R (D.KR 6200)
£701 $1107 €1016 Landscape with children playing under large tree (44x56cm-17x22in) init. 2-Sep-3 Rasmussen, Copenhagen #1992/R (D.KR 7500)
£1168 $2173 €1705 Peasant girl taking a rest on country path near lake (69x95cm-27x37in) mono.d.1874. 2-Mar-4 Rasmussen, Copenhagen #1336/R est:10000-15000 (D.KR 13000)

£1343 $2457 €1961 Sunset over lake (52x77cm-20x30in) mono.d.1861. 9-Jun-4 Rasmussen, Copenhagen #1643/R est:8000-10000 (D.KR 15000)
£1797 $3342 €2624 Summer landscape with houses, trees and harvester (50x72cm-20x28in) init.d.1873. 2-Mar-4 Rasmussen, Copenhagen #1384/R est:10000 (D.KR 20000)

HENRICHSEN-BREMSEN, Charles (1854-1924) Danish
£383 $620 €555 Landscape with barn by river (30x40cm-12x16in) s.d.1890. 4-Aug-3 Rasmussen, Vejle #324/R (D.KR 4000)

HENRICI, John H (1874-1958) American
£939 $1700 €1371 Portrait of a young boy with dog (33x23cm-13x9in) s. board. 14-Apr-4 Dallas Auction Gallery, Dallas #104/R est:800-1200

HENRIETTE, Jules Joseph (1879-?) Belgian
£1517 $2807 €2200 Marche a Bruges (50x70cm-20x28in) s.d.1909. 16-Feb-4 Horta, Bruxelles #48 est:1200-1500

HENRIKSEN, Peder (20th C) Danish?
£448 $819 €654 Summer's day in the garden with lady reading (73x62cm-29x24in) s.d.1917. 9-Jun-4 Rasmussen, Copenhagen #1951/R (D.KR 5000)

HENRIKSEN, Ulrik (1891-1960) Norwegian
£1361 $2436 €1987 The town seen from my window, Oslo (85x79cm-33x31in) s.d.58 i.verso. 22-Mar-4 Blomqvist, Oslo #396/R est:15000-18000 (N.KR 17000)

HENRIKSEN, William (1880-1964) Danish
£362 $648 €529 Good friends (45x40cm-18x16in) s.i.d.1923. 10-May-4 Rasmussen, Vejle #324/R (D.KR 4000)
£462 $841 €693 Interior (64x55cm-25x22in) s. 19-Jun-4 Rasmussen, Havnen #2166/R (D.KR 5200)
£794 $1255 €1151 Interior in grey and pink (68x51cm-27x20in) s. 2-Sep-3 Rasmussen, Copenhagen #1970/R (D.KR 8500)

HENRION, Armand (1875-?) Belgian
£391 $716 €571 Pierrot avec pipe (18x14cm-7x6in) s. panel. 4-Jun-4 Zofingen, Switzerland #2473 (S.FR 900)
£531 $950 €775 Head of a clown (18x13cm-7x5in) s. board. 21-Mar-4 Hindman, Chicago #793 est:800-1200
£930 $1600 €1358 Clown smoking cigar (18x13cm-7x5in) s. panel. 7-Dec-3 Hindman, Chicago #872/R est:800-1200
£1081 $1935 €1600 Clown laughing (18x14cm-7x6in) s. panel. 10-May-4 Giraudeau, Tours #148
£1149 $2056 €1700 Clown smoking (18x14cm-7x6in) s. panel. 10-May-4 Giraudeau, Tours #147
£1477 $2746 €2200 Pierrot riant. Pierrot fumant (18x14cm-7x6in) s. panel pair. 3-Mar-4 Ferri, Paris #71/R est:1000-1200

HENRIQUES, Nathan Ruben (1820-1846) Danish
£1418 $2538 €2070 A blind musician and his children at the entrance to Dyrehaven (55x72cm-22x28in) s. exhib. 12-Jan-4 Rasmussen, Vejle #78/R est:15000 (D.KR 15000)

HENRY D'ARLES, Jean (attrib) (1734-1784) French
£845 $1462 €1200 Paysage portuaire mediterraneen (37x45cm-15x18in) canvas on panel. 12-Dec-3 Libert, Castor, Paris #40

HENRY, Barclay (fl.1891-1940) British
£280 $448 €409 Lobster fishers (39x65cm-15x26in) s. 15-May-3 Bonhams, Edinburgh #323
£300 $498 €438 Crofters drying their nets (23x38cm-9x15in) s.d.1916. 6-Oct-3 David Duggleby, Scarborough #226
£1250 $2088 €1825 Crabers (38x56cm-15x22in) s. 16-Oct-3 Bonhams, Edinburgh #129 est:1000-1500

HENRY, Charles (20th C) French
£307 $549 €460 Marine en Bretagne (40x80cm-16x31in) s. panel. 16-May-4 Thierry & Lannon, Brest #323

HENRY, Charles Trumbo (1902-) American
Works on paper
£196 $350 €286 Coal yard and river (41x51cm-16x20in) s.d.1927 W/C. 8-Jan-4 James Julia, Fairfield #1053/R

HENRY, E (?) ?
£894 $1600 €1305 Tress by the river (79x119cm-31x47in) s. 8-May-4 Susanin's, Chicago #6122/R est:800-1200

HENRY, Edward Lamson (1841-1919) American
£2353 $4000 €3435 Townhouse with carriage (18x15cm-7x6in) s.d.79. 1-Nov-3 Skinner, Boston #189/R est:8000-12000
£4118 $7000 €6012 217 East 10th Street, New York (53x36cm-21x14in) init.d.72 oil paper on board. 30-Oct-3 Phillips, New York #26/R est:4000-6000
£6918 $11000 €10100 Going to church (21x15cm-8x6in) s.d.1871 panel prov.exhib. 13-Sep-3 Weschler, Washington #742/R est:7000-10000
£12291 $22000 €17945 Coach awaits (30x41cm-12x16in) s.indis.i. 26-May-4 Doyle, New York #14/R est:20000-25000
£27933 $50000 €40782 In the early sixties, Main St, Johnstown (38x58cm-15x23in) s.d.1917 masonite prov.exhib. 6-May-4 Shannon's, Milford #80/R est:50000-75000
Works on paper
£2419 $4500 €3532 Carriage ride (64x51cm-25x20in) s.d.1886 pencil W/C htd white paper on canvas. 3-Mar-4 Christie's, Rockefeller NY #49/R est:5000-7000

HENRY, Émile (1822-1920) French
Works on paper
£461 $847 €700 Seascape (25x42cm-10x17in) s.d.1906 W/C. 22-Jun-4 Chassaing Rivet, Toulouse #299
£559 $951 €800 La Sacamore. Le Newmark (20x45cm-8x18in) s. W/C pair. 27-Nov-3 Millon & Associes, Paris #62

HENRY, George (1859-1943) British
£290 $464 €423 Portrait of a gentleman (91x70cm-36x28in) s.d.1903. 18-Sep-3 Bonhams, Edinburgh #322
£700 $1099 €1015 Amongst the bracken in the woods (71x81cm-28x32in) s.d.1907. 28-Aug-3 Christie's, Kensington #176/R
£700 $1302 €1022 Amongst the bracken and wood (71x81cm-28x32in) s.d.1907. 4-Mar-4 Christie's, Kensington #148/R
£2800 $5208 €4088 Portrait of Audrey Innes, wife of John Alfred Innes (102x76cm-40x30in) s. 4-Mar-4 Christie's, Kensington #20/R est:800-1200
£4000 $7440 €5840 Portrait of Mrs Agnes Innes wearing a blue embroidered kimono, holding a fan (91x71cm-36x28in) s.d.1913. 4-Mar-4 Christie's, Kensington #21/R est:700-1000
£4459 $8250 €6689 Summer by the river (41x48cm-16x19in) s. prov.exhib. 14-Jul-4 American Auctioneer #490259/R est:5000-7000
£5000 $7850 €7250 Girls gathering cowslips (40x61cm-16x24in) s. prov. 27-Aug-3 Sotheby's, London #1029/R est:5000-7000
£15000 $25950 €21900 Goatherd (25x22cm-10x9in) s.d.86 panel. 11-Dec-3 Lyon & Turnbull, Edinburgh #56/R est:3000-5000
£19500 $35295 €28470 Resting by the lake (64x76cm-25x30in) s.d.1918. 19-Apr-4 Sotheby's, London #44/R est:10000-15000
Works on paper
£450 $824 €657 Figures with sheep in a copse (27x27cm-11x11in) s. W/C crayon. 7-Apr-4 Woolley & Wallis, Salisbury #98/R
£2900 $4553 €4205 On Goodwood Downs (17x24cm-7x9in) gouache prov.exhib. 27-Aug-3 Sotheby's, London #1022/R est:3000-5000

HENRY, George (attrib) (1859-1943) British
£580 $1079 €847 Portrait of John Alfred Innes, as an officer of the Red Cross (76x63cm-30x25in) 4-Mar-4 Christie's, Kensington #22/R

HENRY, Grace (1868-1953) British
£621 $1148 €900 Autumn landscape (27x39cm-11x15in) s. board. 11-Feb-4 Woodwards, Cork #1/R
£3467 $6275 €5200 Ballybunion (36x44cm-14x17in) s.i. s.d.1947 verso board prov. 30-Mar-4 De Veres Art Auctions, Dublin #59a/R est:5000-7000
£3611 $5886 €5200 Woman wearing a black shawl (60x44cm-24x17in) 24-Sep-3 James Adam, Dublin #62/R est:4000-5000
£4333 $7843 €6500 Gardener (51x59cm-20x23in) s. board. 30-Mar-4 De Veres Art Auctions, Dublin #151/R est:7000-10000
£4336 $7371 €6200 Boats at Chioggia (26x36cm-10x14in) init. canvas on board. 25-Nov-3 De Veres Art Auctions, Dublin #100a/R est:4000-5000
£4895 $8322 €7000 Still life, roses in a bowl (14x18cm-6x7in) s. canvas on board. 25-Nov-3 De Veres Art Auctions, Dublin #54/R est:5000-7000

HENRY, James Levin (1855-?) British
£580 $1027 €847 The orchard (30x40cm-12x16in) s.d. 27-Apr-4 Henry Adams, Chichester #769

HENRY, L (?) ?
£1043 $1710 €1450 Fishermen leaving shore (24x35cm-9x14in) s.d.1851. 10-Jun-3 Pandolfini, Florence #60/R est:1500-1700

HENRY, Louise (1798-1839) German
Works on paper
£444 $800 €648 Self portrait (17x14cm-7x6in) pencil executed c.1825. 21-Jan-4 Sotheby's, New York #50/R

HENRY, Marjorie (1900-1974) British?
£400 $664 €584 Still life (45x35cm-18x14in) s. board. 1-Oct-3 John Ross, Belfast #112a
£400 $664 €584 Still life (30x25cm-12x10in) s. board. 1-Oct-3 John Ross, Belfast #272
£420 $689 €613 Thatched cottage (10x17cm-4x7in) s. board. 4-Jun-3 John Ross, Belfast #23
£600 $996 €876 Still life (61x50cm-24x20in) s. 1-Oct-3 John Ross, Belfast #118
£1127 $1972 €1600 Achill Island, Co Mayo. Co Down farm (16x21cm-6x8in) s. board pair. 16-Dec-3 James Adam, Dublin #251/R est:300-400
£1400 $2604 €2044 Connemara (23x28cm-9x11in) s. board. 3-Mar-4 John Ross, Belfast #20 est:800-1000
£1900 $3154 €2774 In the Rosses, Donegal (14x20cm-6x8in) s. board pair. 1-Oct-3 John Ross, Belfast #23a est:800-1000

HENRY, Maurice (1907-1984) French
Works on paper
£315 $535 €450 Sans titre (15x13cm-6x5in) s. ink graphite prov. 23-Nov-3 Cornette de St.Cyr, Paris #142
£1748 $3007 €2500 Charles Trenet (73x54cm-29x21in) s. gouache exec.c.1943. 6-Dec-3 Renaud, Paris #148/R

HENRY, Michel (1928-) French
£316 $500 €461 Interior still life with flowers (38x30cm-15x12in) s. 6-Apr-3 William Jenack, New York #201
£479 $800 €695 Verdure (20x25cm-8x10in) s. prov. 22-Jun-3 Simpson's, Houston #23
£845 $1479 €1200 Bouquet de fleurs sur fond bleu (92x65cm-36x26in) s. 19-Dec-3 Delvaux, Paris #51
£861 $1610 €1300 Soleil couchant au pont Marie (38x46cm-15x18in) s. 25-Jul-4 Feletin, Province #81
£986 $1725 €1400 Bouquet de fleurs sur fond rouge (92x65cm-36x26in) s. 19-Dec-3 Delvaux, Paris #52/R

£1007	$1883	€1500	Sur le jardin (129x87cm-51x34in) s. 29-Feb-4 Versailles Encheres #152 est:500-600

HENRY, Olive (1902-1989) British

Works on paper

£450	$837	€657	Boats, no.2 (30x40cm-12x16in) s. W/C. 3-Mar-4 John Ross, Belfast #69

HENRY, Paul (20th C) Canadian

£383	$651	€559	Farmhouse and hay bales (51x61cm-20x24in) s. s.i.d.1995 verso. 21-Nov-3 Walker's, Ottawa #69/R (C.D 850)

HENRY, Paul (1876-1958) Irish

£8800	$16456	€12848	Sugar Loaf Mountain (33x40cm-13x16in) s. panel. 20-Jul-4 Sworder & Son, Bishops Stortford #738/R est:8000-12000
£12937	$21993	€18500	Killary harbour (21x28cm-8x11in) s. board. 25-Nov-3 De Veres Art Auctions, Dublin #18/R est:15000-20000
£14000	$24640	€20440	Pullough Bay, Achill (35x42cm-14x17in) s. prov. 19-May-4 Dreweatt Neate, Newbury #48/R est:15000-20000
£20000	$35800	€29200	Evening on an Irish Bog (25x30cm-10x12in) s. board painted c.1932-6 prov. 13-May-4 Sotheby's, London #46/R est:15000-20000
£21429	$38786	€31286	Evening in the mountains (32x40cm-13x16in) s. board painted c.1914-15 prov. 30-Mar-4 Peter Webb, Auckland #117/R est:45000-65000 (NZ.D 60000)
£24000	$42960	€35040	Reflections, Killary Bay (36x41cm-14x16in) s. painted c.1920-5 prov. 14-May-4 Christie's, London #212/R est:20000-30000
£25000	$44750	€36500	The pear tree (82x70cm-32x28in) s. canvas on board prov.exhib.lit. 13-May-4 Sotheby's, London #42/R est:25000-35000
£28873	$49951	€41000	West of Ireland landscape with cottage (30x26cm-12x10in) s. 10-Dec-3 Bonhams & James Adam, Dublin #159/R est:20000-30000
£34722	$56597	€50000	Connemara (36x45cm-14x18in) s. i.verso prov. 24-Sep-3 James Adam, Dublin #102/R est:50000-80000
£36000	$64440	€52560	Landscape with cottages (38x46cm-15x18in) s. painted c.1928-38 prov.exhib. 14-May-4 Christie's, London #209/R est:40000-60000
£37000	$66230	€54020	Cottages by a still lough (30x35cm-12x14in) s. painted 1930-5 prov.exhib. 14-May-4 Christie's, London #210/R est:30000-50000
£37500	$69000	€57000	West of Ireland bogland (40x50cm-16x20in) s. i.verso canvas on board. 22-Jun-4 De Veres Art Auctions, Dublin #75/R est:50000-70000
£40789	$75053	€62000	Road in Kerry (36x40cm-14x16in) s.i. stretcher. 22-Jun-4 De Veres Art Auctions, Dublin #27/R est:50000-60000
£41667	$67917	€60000	Incoming Tide, Achill (41x61cm-16x24in) s. prov.exhib. 24-Sep-3 James Adam, Dublin #54/R est:60000-80000
£52000	$93080	€75920	Turf stacks in the West (41x62cm-16x24in) s. painted 1934-6 prov.exhib. 14-May-4 Christie's, London #149/R est:50000-80000
£55000	$98450	€80300	Roadside village, Connemara (34x39cm-13x15in) s. s.i.verso panel painted 1935-40 prov. 14-May-4 Christie's, London #150/R est:40000-60000
£59859	$103556	€85000	Red earth (63x51cm-25x20in) s. painted c.1914/15 prov.exhib.lit. 10-Dec-3 Bonhams & James Adam, Dublin #98/R est:70000-90000
£83893	$150168	€125000	Evening on Achill (35x81cm-14x32in) s. 26-May-4 James Adam, Dublin #118/R est:80000-120000
£101333	$183413	€152000	Lobster fishermen, west of ireland (31x40cm-12x16in) s. canvas on board prov. 30-Mar-4 De Veres Art Auctions, Dublin #61/R est:40000-60000
£130000	$232700	€189800	Achill landscape (66x80cm-26x31in) s.d.1912 prov. 13-May-4 Sotheby's, London #22/R est:100000-150000
£140000	$250600	€204400	The edge of the lake (61x71cm-24x28in) s. canvas on board prov.exhib. 13-May-4 Sotheby's, London #47/R est:80000-120000
£220000	$393800	€321200	A Connemara village (76x91cm-30x36in) s. s.i.verso panel prov.exhib.lit. 14-May-4 Christie's, London #148/R est:100000-150000

Works on paper

£15000	$26850	€21900	The storm (38x44cm-15x17in) s. chl col crayon exec.c.1910-13 prov.exhib. 14-May-4 Christie's, London #44/R est:7000-10000

HENRY, Pierre (1924-) French

£284	$500	€415	Table d'Automne (23x33cm-9x13in) s.d.62 prov. 23-May-4 Hindman, Chicago #978/R

HENRY, R (20th C) American

Works on paper

£1923	$3096	€2808	Victorian Colonial militia training in the Mont Albert District on the outskirts of Melbourne (26x35cm-10x14in) s.d.29/5/93 W/C set of four. 13-Oct-3 Joel, Victoria #265 (A.D 4750)

HENRY, William (1812-1884) British

Works on paper

£269	$500	€393	Mercado (41x51cm-16x20in) s. i.d.1952 verso casein board. 7-Mar-4 Treadway Gallery, Cincinnati #644/R

HENS, Frans (1856-1928) Belgian

£320	$579	€480	Het zwarte kalf (44x46cm-17x18in) s.verso. 30-Mar-4 Campo & Campo, Antwerp #132/R
£400	$680	€584	Towards the end of the day (76x95cm-30x37in) s. 6-Nov-3 Christie's, Kensington #780
£521	$870	€750	Fermier a la charrette (111x141cm-44x56in) s. s.verso. 21-Oct-3 Campo & Campo, Antwerp #142/R
£1342	$2456	€2000	Sur l'Escaut (40x44cm-16x17in) s. panel. 8-Jul-4 Campo, Vlaamse Kaai #139/R est:1000-1200
£1812	$3352	€2700	Matin sur l'escaut (57x68cm-22x27in) s. s.i.verso panel. 13-Mar-4 De Vuyst, Lokeren #179/R est:1700-2000

HENSCHE, Ada Rayner (1901-1984) American

£235	$400	€343	Still life (23x13cm-9x5in) s. board. 9-Nov-3 Outer Cape Auctions, Provincetown #109/R
£460	$750	€672	Untitled - landscape (15x20cm-6x8in) s. board. 19-Jul-3 Outer Cape Auctions, Provincetown #93/R
£491	$800	€717	Untitled - landscape (15x20cm-6x8in) s. board. 19-Jul-3 Outer Cape Auctions, Provincetown #77/R
£500	$850	€730	Still life (51x41cm-20x16in) s. board. 9-Nov-3 Outer Cape Auctions, Provincetown #131/R
£771	$1250	€1126	Chinese jar filled with flowers (51x61cm-20x24in) s. i. verso panel. 31-Jul-3 Eldred, East Dennis #873/R

HENSCHE, Henry (1901-1992) American

£1963	$3200	€2866	Portrait of William Shea (64x46cm-25x18in) s. board exhib. 19-Jul-3 Outer Cape Auctions, Provincetown #45/R
£2037	$3300	€2974	Landscape (9x11cm-4x4in) s. panel. 31-Jul-3 Eldred, East Dennis #1089/R est:2000-3000
£3067	$5000	€4478	Still life (66x56cm-26x22in) s. 19-Jul-3 Outer Cape Auctions, Provincetown #90/R
£4118	$7000	€6012	Still life with copper fire pot (36x46cm-14x18in) s. masonite. 21-Nov-3 Eldred, East Dennis #826/R est:3500-4000
£4140	$6500	€6044	Still life (66x56cm-26x22in) s. 20-Apr-3 Outer Cape Auctions, Provincetown #80
£5882	$10000	€8588	Early summer no 3 (51x61cm-20x24in) s. board. 9-Nov-3 Outer Cape Auctions, Provincetown #80/R
£7393	$12050	€10794	Townscape (61x51cm-24x20in) s. board. 19-Jul-3 Outer Cape Auctions, Provincetown #55/R

Works on paper

£514	$950	€750	Still life (30x48cm-12x19in) s. W/C. 15-Feb-4 Outer Cape Auctions, Provincetown #73/R

HENSCHKE, Johann Gottlieb (1771-1850) German

£753	$1281	€1100	Vue de l'hermitage du Jardin du prince Antoine a Dresde (23x34cm-9x13in) s.d.1798 W/C. 4-Nov-3 Hartung & Hartung, Munich #3053/R

HENSEL, Maurice (1890-?) French

£552	$916	€800	Portrait de femme au chapeau (41x33cm-16x13in) s. 1-Oct-3 Millon & Associes, Paris #91
£897	$1488	€1300	Nu. (52x37cm-20x15in) s. cardboard. 1-Oct-3 Millon & Associes, Paris #90

HENSEL, Stephen Hopkins (1921-1979) American

£2545	$4250	€3716	Ice cream parlour (53x86cm-21x34in) s.d.49 prov.exhib.lit. 7-Oct-3 Sotheby's, New York #227 est:7000-10000

HENSELER, Josef (19th C) ?

£1589	$2909	€2400	Hunters' visit (85x115cm-33x45in) s.d.1889. 8-Apr-4 Dorotheum, Vienna #76/R est:2600-3000

HENSHALL, John Henry (1856-1928) British

Works on paper

£605	$1113	€883	Last Bawbee (27x37cm-11x15in) s. W/C. 14-Jun-4 Waddingtons, Toronto #94/R est:2000-3000 (C.D 1500)
£610	$1091	€891	Gleam of light (27x19cm-11x7in) s.i. W/C exhib. 4-May-4 Ritchie, Toronto #7/R est:1500-2000 (C.D 1500)
£3800	$6954	€5700	Sympathy (29x22cm-11x9in) s. W/C. 27-Jul-4 Henry Adams, Chichester #394/R est:2000-3000
£4400	$7348	€6424	First grief (47x30cm-19x12in) s.d.06 W/C exhib. 12-Nov-3 Sotheby's, Olympia #93/R est:1500-2000

HENSHAW, F H (1807-1891) British

£800	$1288	€1160	Sandy road at Corwen with figure and dog on track (51x76cm-20x30in) i. 20-Aug-3 Brightwells, Leominster #879
£850	$1445	€1241	Bolsover Castle, Derbyshire (23x32cm-9x13in) board. 26-Nov-3 Peter Wilson, Nantwich #103/R

HENSHAW, Frederick Henry (1807-1891) British

£259	$463	€378	Wooded landscape with figures on bridge (46x60cm-18x24in) s.indis.d.1858. 28-May-4 Uppsala Auktionskammare, Uppsala #111 (S.KR 3500)
£450	$833	€657	Cottages in a mountainous landscape (28x22cm-11x9in) s. 10-Feb-4 Bonhams, Knightsbridge #142/R
£1800	$3294	€2628	Raglan Castle (18x14cm-7x6in) panel. 7-Jul-4 George Kidner, Lymington #159/R est:2000-2500
£5800	$10382	€8468	Kenilworth Castle from Woodhall Road, Warwickshire (71x122cm-28x48in) i.verso exhib. 27-May-4 Christie's, Kensington #160/R est:4000-6000

Works on paper

£450	$752	€657	Last farthing (29x22cm-11x9in) s. W/C. 14-Oct-3 Bonhams, Knightsbridge #151/R
£500	$805	€725	Landscape with figures, river and windmill (23x18cm-9x7in) W/C. 20-Aug-3 Brightwells, Leominster #857/R
£750	$1253	€1095	Cottage home (37x25cm-15x10in) s. W/C. 14-Oct-3 Bonhams, Knightsbridge #152/R

HENSHAW, Frederick Henry (attrib) (1807-1891) British

£320	$534	€467	Angler in a rocky river landscape (48x76cm-19x30in) 8-Oct-3 Christie's, Kensington #872
£337	$550	€492	The Old Hall, Packington, Warwickshire (53x36cm-21x14in) bears init. paper on canvas. 24-Sep-3 Doyle, New York #41

HENSHAW, Frederick Henry and PRATT, Jonathan (19th C) British

£1800	$3006	€2628	Feeding the chicks (48x37cm-19x15in) s. 13-Nov-3 Christie's, Kensington #276/R est:2000-3000

HENSHAW, Glenn Cooper (1881-1946) American

Works on paper

£316	$575	€461	Cityscape, possibly Indianapolis (28x38cm-11x15in) s. pastel. 7-Feb-4 Dan Ripley, Indianapolis #6

HENSLEY, Jackson (1940-) American
Works on paper
£565 $1000 €825 Flood gate (25x30cm-10x12in) s. i.verso W/C board painted mid 1980's. 28-Apr-4 Christie's, Los Angeles #17/R

HENSON, Bill (1955-) Australian
Photographs
£2542 $4322 €3711 Untitled (81x67cm-32x26in) C-type photograph exec 1983/84. 24-Nov-3 Sotheby's, Melbourne #78/R est:5000-7000 (A.D 6000)
£4878 $7659 €7073 Untitled (82x70cm-32x28in) s.d.1983/84 type C photo edition 10. 26-Aug-3 Christie's, Sydney #62/R est:12000-18000 (A.D 12000)

HENSTENBURGH, Anton (1695-1781) Dutch
Works on paper
£18919 $33297 €28000 Seven butterflies (28x42cm-11x17in) init. pen black ink W/C gouache vellum prov.exhib. 19-May-4 Sotheby's, Amsterdam #193/R est:6000-8000
£20270 $35676 €30000 Eight butterflies and moths (29x40cm-11x16in) init. pen black ink W/C gouache vellum prov.exhib. 19-May-4 Sotheby's, Amsterdam #192/R est:8000-12000

HENSTENBURGH, Herman (1667-1726) Dutch
Works on paper
£5500 $9515 €8030 Floral heart (30x26cm-12x10in) s.i. black chk W/C bodycol vellum prov. 12-Dec-3 Christie's, Kensington #530/R est:1200-1800
£5556 $10000 €8112 Urn, garland with flowers, on a terrace, with shells in the foreground (42x30cm-17x12in) W/C gouache on vellum prov. 21-Jan-4 Sotheby's, New York #75/R est:10000-15000
£8333 $15000 €12166 Roller on a branch (35x24cm-14x9in) s. bodycol vellum. 22-Jan-4 Christie's, Rockefeller NY #202/R est:5000-8000
£108108 $190270 €160000 Vanitas still life, with skull, flowers, candle and hour glass on a ledge (40x33cm-16x13in) s. W/C gouache vellum prov.exhib.lit. 19-May-4 Sotheby's, Amsterdam #199/R est:60000-80000

HENTON, George Moore (1861-1924) British
Works on paper
£300 $501 €438 Greyfriars Tower (38x51cm-15x20in) s.d.1916 W/C. 17-Oct-3 Keys, Aylsham #516
£750 $1298 €1095 Country cottage with mother and child in a doorway (30x25cm-12x10in) s. W/C. 9-Dec-3 Clarke Gammon, Guildford #5/R

HENTSCHEL, Hans Rudolf (1869-1951) German
£386 $645 €560 Evening (52x39cm-20x15in) s. canvas on masonite. 15-Nov-3 Von Zezschwitz, Munich #45/R
£2930 $5245 €4278 Flower meadow with woman and child picking flowers (42x65cm-17x26in) s. 12-Jan-4 Rasmussen, Vejle #362/R est:6000 (D.KR 31000)

HENWOOD, Jacqui (1946-) Australian
Works on paper
£407 $728 €594 Summer balcony at Mona Road (75x50cm-30x20in) s.i. gouache W/C ink exhib. 4-May-4 Sotheby's, Melbourne #241 (A.D 1000)

HENWOOD, T (fl.1842-1855) British
£5400 $9828 €7884 Hereford bull in landscape setting (61x74cm-24x29in) s.d.1850 i.verso. 3-Feb-4 Gorringes, Bexhill #955/R est:1000-1500

HENWOOD, Thomas (fl.1842-1855) British
£700 $1288 €1022 Old Druid, with Richard King Sampson Esq and John Presse (57x46cm-22x18in) s.d.1845 s.d.verso. 10-Jun-4 Christie's, Kensington #56
£5000 $8950 €7300 Prize bull (64x76cm-25x30in) s.d.1856 s.d.verso. 26-May-4 Sotheby's, Olympia #105/R est:5000-7000

HENZE, Ingfried (1925-1972) German
£240 $425 €350 Landscape (48x66cm-19x26in) s. 1-May-4 Susanin's, Chicago #5040/R

HENZELL, Isaac (1815-1876) British
£1600 $2928 €2336 Woman carrying the catch (58x48cm-23x19in) s.d.1846. 7-Apr-4 Gardiner & Houlgate, Bath #255/R est:1800-2700

HEPBURN, Katharine (1907-2003) American
£2989 $5500 €4364 Seascapes with lighthouses (8x20cm-3x8in) board two. 10-Jun-4 Sotheby's, New York #332/R est:300-500
£3261 $6000 €4761 View of a palm tree, Jamaica (20x8cm-8x3in) board. 10-Jun-4 Sotheby's, New York #367/R est:300-500
£3804 $7000 €5554 View of a tree (18x13cm-7x5in) board. 10-Jun-4 Sotheby's, New York #368/R est:700-900
£3804 $7000 €5554 Hotel stairs to the beach, Jamaica (30x15cm-12x6in) init. board. 10-Jun-4 Sotheby's, New York #366/R est:300-500
£4076 $7500 €5951 Lighthouses of Old Saybrook (25x61cm-10x24in) two different sizes. 10-Jun-4 Sotheby's, New York #399/R est:300-500
£4348 $8000 €6348 Untitled (23x15cm-9x6in) W/C pencil set of three. 10-Jun-4 Sotheby's, New York #457/R est:300-500
£4348 $8000 €6348 Untitled (18x25cm-7x10in) W/C set of three. 10-Jun-4 Sotheby's, New York #610/R est:300-500
£4620 $8500 €6745 Figures by the ocean (15x23cm-6x9in) board. 10-Jun-4 Sotheby's, New York #364/R est:400-600
£4891 $9000 €7141 Woman by the sea (20x15cm-8x6in) board. 10-Jun-4 Sotheby's, New York #389/R est:500-700
£5163 $9500 €7538 Sesacpes (25x10cm-10x4in) board set of five different sizes. 10-Jun-4 Sotheby's, New York #297/R est:400-600
£5978 $11000 €8728 Still life with flowers on a tile (20x30cm-8x12in) board painted c.1965. 10-Jun-4 Sotheby's, New York #517/R est:400-600
£5978 $11000 €8728 Still life with flowers (15x20cm-6x8in) board. 10-Jun-4 Sotheby's, New York #519/R est:400-600
£5978 $11000 €8728 Landscapes (10x25cm-4x10in) board set of three different sizes. 10-Jun-4 Sotheby's, New York #576/R est:300-500
£6522 $12000 €9522 Landscape scenes (10x25cm-4x10in) board set of three. 10-Jun-4 Sotheby's, New York #293/R est:300-500
£6522 $12000 €9522 Still life with flowers (18x20cm-7x8in) board. 10-Jun-4 Sotheby's, New York #518/R est:400-600
£7065 $13000 €10315 Seascapes (20x25cm-8x10in) board set of four different sizes. 10-Jun-4 Sotheby's, New York #246/R est:400-600
£7065 $13000 €10315 View from the bed (10x13cm-4x5in) oil on cigar box lid. 10-Jun-4 Sotheby's, New York #365/R est:400-600
£7609 $14000 €11109 Two ladies on the beach with black umbrellas (23x15cm-9x6in) board. 10-Jun-4 Sotheby's, New York #388/R est:400-600
£7609 $14000 €11109 Untitled - flowers (15x23cm-6x9in) board. 10-Jun-4 Sotheby's, New York #516/R est:400-600
£8696 $16000 €12696 Still life of a basket of fruit (13x15cm-5x6in) acrylic W/C. 10-Jun-4 Sotheby's, New York #495/R est:500-700
£8696 $16000 €12696 New York cityscape (51x41cm-20x16in) after George Bellows. 10-Jun-4 Sotheby's, New York #601/R est:600-800
£9239 $17000 €13489 California landscape with lawn chairs (15x20cm-6x8in) board. 10-Jun-4 Sotheby's, New York #443/R est:500-700
£9239 $17000 €13489 Still life with peaches (30x41cm-12x16in) 10-Jun-4 Sotheby's, New York #494/R est:600-800
£9783 $18000 €14283 Format paintings (18x13cm-7x5in) board two. 10-Jun-4 Sotheby's, New York #492/R est:500-700
£10870 $20000 €15870 View of Los Angeles home with clothesline (28x36cm-11x14in) board painted c.1965. 10-Jun-4 Sotheby's, New York #446/R est:400-600
£11413 $21000 €16663 Landscape of the California Hills (36x28cm-14x11in) s. 10-Jun-4 Sotheby's, New York #445/R est:800-1200
£11413 $21000 €16663 Still life with flowers (25x36cm-10x14in) board painted c.1965. 10-Jun-4 Sotheby's, New York #514/R est:700-900
£11957 $22000 €17457 Self portrait on the beach (18x25cm-7x10in) board. 10-Jun-4 Sotheby's, New York #387/R est:300-500
£12500 $23000 €18250 House in the Los Angeles Hills, (13x23cm-5x9in) board painted c.1965. 10-Jun-4 Sotheby's, New York #444/R est:400-600
£14946 $27500 €21821 Portrait of Phyllis Wilbourn (51x30cm-20x12in) 10-Jun-4 Sotheby's, New York #255/R est:400-600
£16304 $30000 €23804 Still life with fruit (20x30cm-8x12in) s.verso board painted c.1960. 10-Jun-4 Sotheby's, New York #490/R est:500-700
£16304 $30000 €23804 Fenwick gulls (41x51cm-16x20in) 10-Jun-4 Sotheby's, New York #503/R est:2000-3000
£19022 $35000 €27772 Hills in Beverly Hills (48x41cm-19x16in) sold with a letter. 10-Jun-4 Sotheby's, New York #442/R est:1000-1500
£29891 $55000 €43641 Los Angeles bedroom interior (25x36cm-10x14in) 10-Jun-4 Sotheby's, New York #608/R est:500-700
£35326 $65000 €51576 Portrait of Spencer Tracy (20x15cm-8x6in) s.verso canvasboard painted c.1965. 10-Jun-4 Sotheby's, New York #456/R est:800-1200
Sculpture
£40761 $75000 €59511 Angel on a wave (23cm-9in) brown pat. bronze green glass in two parts lit. 10-Jun-4 Sotheby's, New York #232/R est:2000-4000
£149457 $275000 €218207 Portrait of Spencer Tracy (8cm-3in) bronze green base. 10-Jun-4 Sotheby's, New York #460/R est:3000-5000
Works on paper
£3261 $6000 €4761 Australian landscapes and seascapes (13x18cm-5x7in) W/C acrylic seven. 10-Jun-4 Sotheby's, New York #211/R est:600-800
£3804 $7000 €5554 Self portrait (71x56cm-28x22in) pencil dr. on canvas. 10-Jun-4 Sotheby's, New York #605 est:200-400
£4891 $9000 €7141 Seascapes and landscapes (30x23cm-12x9in) W/C set of seven different sizes. 10-Jun-4 Sotheby's, New York #604/R est:400-600
£5163 $9500 €7538 View of a sail boat on Long Island Sound, Stratford, Connecticut (15x43cm-6x17in) W/C. 10-Jun-4 Sotheby's, New York #331/R est:200-400
£5435 $10000 €7935 Seascapes in Stratford, Connecticut (33x25cm-13x10in) W/C set of six different sizes. 10-Jun-4 Sotheby's, New York #330/R est:400-600
£5978 $11000 €8728 Still lifes paintings with flowers (28x23cm-11x9in) W/C set of four. 10-Jun-4 Sotheby's, New York #491/R est:400-600
£6522 $12000 €9522 View of the Barrenjoey Lighthouse and Broken Bay, Sydney Australia (13x18cm-5x7in) W/C. 10-Jun-4 Sotheby's, New York #213/R est:300-500
£6522 $12000 €9522 Still lifes with flowers (56x38cm-22x15in) W/C two. 10-Jun-4 Sotheby's, New York #496/R est:300-500
£7065 $13000 €10315 Two views of the Barrenjoey Lighthouse sitting atop Broken Bay, Sydney, Australia (18x23cm-7x9in) W/C two. 10-Jun-4 Sotheby's, New York #214/R est:600-800
£7065 $13000 €10315 Seascapes Stratford, Connecticut, 1957 (30x46cm-12x18in) W/C pencil ink set of four. 10-Jun-4 Sotheby's, New York #328/R est:300-500
£7609 $14000 €11109 Untitled (28x20cm-11x8in) pencil sketch book. 10-Jun-4 Sotheby's, New York #578/R est:300-500
£7609 $14000 €11109 Sailing boats at sunset at Fenwick on Long Island Sound (8x38cm-3x15in) W/C. 10-Jun-4 Sotheby's, New York #603/R est:400-600
£8152 $15000 €11902 Water scenes (18x25cm-7x10in) W/C set of five. 10-Jun-4 Sotheby's, New York #602/R est:400-600
£8696 $16000 €12696 Stratford, Connecticut seascapes (25x30cm-10x12in) W/C set of four different sizes. 10-Jun-4 Sotheby's, New York #291/R est:800-1200
£8696 $16000 €12696 Self portraits (25x18cm-10x7in) W/C set of 14 different sizes. 10-Jun-4 Sotheby's, New York #333/R est:800-1200
£9783 $18000 €14283 Connecticut landscape (23x30cm-9x12in) board set of four. 10-Jun-4 Sotheby's, New York #294/R est:300-500
£9783 $18000 €14283 Views of sailboats in Stratford (23x28cm-9x11in) W/C two. 10-Jun-4 Sotheby's, New York #295/R est:400-600
£9783 $18000 €14283 Beverly Hills patio views (36x51cm-14x20in) W/C set of three. 10-Jun-4 Sotheby's, New York #447/R est:600-800
£9783 $18000 €14283 Landscapes (25x18cm-10x7in) W/C set of five different sizes. 10-Jun-4 Sotheby's, New York #577/R est:500-700
£10326 $19000 €15076 Self portrait (30x23cm-12x9in) W/C ink. 10-Jun-4 Sotheby's, New York #329/R est:200-400
£10326 $19000 €15076 Self portrait (51x23cm-20x9in) i. pencil W/C executed c.1960. 10-Jun-4 Sotheby's, New York #515/R est:400-600
£10870 $20000 €15870 View of boat and boat club, Housatonic River, Stratford (33x23cm-13x9in) s. W/C. 10-Jun-4 Sotheby's, New York #327/R est:800-1200
£11413 $21000 €16663 Untitled (10x15cm-4x6in) one s. W/C pen ink set of six different sizes. 10-Jun-4 Sotheby's, New York #579/R est:600-800
£12228 $22500 €17853 Cuban views (25x36cm-10x14in) W/C set of six different sizes. 10-Jun-4 Sotheby's, New York #363/R est:1200-1800
£13587 $25000 €19837 Self portraits from a matter of gravity (30x23cm-12x9in) W/C dr. set of five different sizes. 10-Jun-4 Sotheby's, New York #544/R est:400-600
£14946 $27500 €21821 Breakfast in bed, self portrait in Brisbane, Australia (20x15cm-8x6in) pencil W/C. 10-Jun-4 Sotheby's, New York #212/R est:600-800

£14946 $27500 €21821 Figures by the ocean (20x23cm-8x9in) W/C set of five different sizes. 10-Jun-4 Sotheby's, New York #400/R est:700-900
£29891 $55000 €43641 Self portrait with Spencer Tracy (28x20cm-11x8in) s. W/C ink executed c.1960. 10-Jun-4 Sotheby's, New York #455/R est:800-1200

HEPPENER, Johannes Jacobus (1826-1898) Dutch
£280 $515 €420 Sailing boat (16x21cm-6x8in) s. panel. 11-Jun-4 Wendl, Rudolstadt #4075/R
£1399 $2406 €2000 Gathering wood (63x91cm-25x36in) s.d.1862. 7-Dec-3 Sotheby's, Amsterdam #625
£2083 $3396 €3000 Town view, possibly Delft (62x80cm-24x31in) s. 29-Sep-3 Sotheby's, Amsterdam #62/R
£3497 $6014 €5000 Bords du canal a la Haye (47x76cm-19x30in) s.d.1871. 7-Dec-3 Osenat, Fontainebleau #173 est:4000-4500

HEPPER, George (attrib) (1839-1868) British
£360 $666 €526 Portrait of a young girl with a tabby cat (25x20cm-10x8in) indis.sig.d.65 panel. 9-Mar-4 Bonhams, Knightsbridge #298/R

HEPPLE, John Wilson (1886-1939) British
Works on paper
£280 $510 €409 Landscape with figures on a stone bride (28x38cm-11x15in) s.d.1914 W/C. 5-Feb-4 Gorringes, Worthing #426/R

HEPPLE, Robert Norman (1908-1994) British
£480 $802 €701 Il rendetore (30x41cm-12x16in) s. 16-Oct-3 Christie's, Kensington #357
£1300 $2210 €1898 Portrait of a young lady with a green hat (61x50cm-24x20in) s.indis.i. 19-Nov-3 Tennants, Leyburn #1267 est:150-200
£2100 $3717 €3066 Ponte Vecchio, Florence (75x63cm-30x25in) s. 27-Apr-4 Bonhams, Knowle #131/R est:800-1200

HEPPLE, Wilson (1853-1937) British
£480 $763 €701 Farm girl guiding calves through a gate (24x29cm-9x11in) s. 18-Mar-3 Anderson & Garland, Newcastle #460
£850 $1386 €1241 Portrait of a horse (50x70cm-20x28in) s.d.1894. 24-Sep-3 Peter Wilson, Nantwich #11
£920 $1536 €1343 Four kittens hiding in a box (26x37cm-10x15in) s.d.1894. 21-Oct-3 Gildings, Market Harborough #510/R
£1400 $2422 €2044 Tabby cat and her kitten (21x31cm-8x12in) s. 9-Dec-3 Anderson & Garland, Newcastle #408/R
£3000 $5190 €4380 Bigg Market, Old Newcastle, with carts parked in front of the Inns (70x100cm-28x39in) s. 9-Dec-3 Anderson & Garland, Newcastle #432/R est:2000-3000
£3700 $6401 €5402 Two kittens playing with a pearl necklace (29x39cm-11x15in) s. 9-Dec-3 Anderson & Garland, Newcastle #407/R est:2500-3500
Works on paper
£2200 $3652 €3212 Artist's apprentice (26x36cm-10x14in) s.d.1930 W/C. 1-Oct-3 Sotheby's, Olympia #132/R est:800-1200

HEPWORTH, Dame Barbara (1903-1975) British
£26000 $44720 €37960 Stringed figure (40x30cm-16x12in) s.i.d. 1976 prov.exhib. 2-Dec-3 Bonhams, New Bond Street #157/R est:10000-15000
£28249 $50000 €41244 Group for a stone relief (29x22cm-11x9in) s.d.1953 oil pencil board prov.exhib.lit. 2-May-4 Bonhams & Butterfields, Los Angeles #3032/R est:10000-15000
Sculpture
£11173 $20000 €16313 Single form (57cm-22in) num.4/7 base polished bronze conceived 1937 prov.lit. 5-May-4 Christie's, Rockefeller NY #311/R est:20000-30000
£17568 $32500 €25649 Small Mincarlo (17cm-7in) num.2/3 brass string exec.1971 prov. 11-Feb-4 Sotheby's, New York #55/R est:15000-20000
£17647 $30000 €25765 Disk with strings - moon (48x48cm-19x19in) num.4/9 aluminum string prov. 9-Nov-3 Bonhams & Butterfields, Los Angeles #4102/R est:20000-30000
£20000 $36400 €29200 Vertical form (65cm-26in) num.1/7 green pat bronze conceived 1962 prov.lit. 3-Feb-4 Christie's, London #276/R est:15000-20000
£24000 $43920 €35040 Four hemispheres (16cm-6in) s. quartz lit. 4-Jun-4 Christie's, London #144/R est:20000-30000
£28000 $50960 €40880 Disc with strings (49cm-19in) num.5/9 verso aluminium string conceived 1969 lit. 3-Feb-4 Christie's, London #274/R est:18000-22000
£33824 $57500 €49383 Maquette for Monolith (33cm-13in) i. num.2/9 brown green pat bronze Cast Morris Singer prov.lit. 6-Nov-3 Sotheby's, New York #247/R est:30000-40000
£72000 $132480 €105120 Maquette for winged figure (61cm-24in) brass metal string concrete base exec 1957 edn 5/8 prov.lit. 22-Jun-4 Sotheby's, London #201/R est:30000-40000
£78212 $140000 €114190 Maquette for dual form (51cm-20in) s.d.1966 num.0/9 green brown pat bronze Cast London prov.lit. 5-May-4 Christie's, Rockefeller NY #343/R est:40000-60000
£83799 $150000 €122347 Forms in movement - Pavan (76x109cm-30x43in) s.d.1956 num.5/7 green pat bronze Cast f.Morris Singer prov.lit. 5-May-4 Christie's, Rockefeller NY #342/R est:40000-60000
£91176 $155000 €133117 Orpheus - Maquette I (43cm-17in) brass string exec 1956 edn of 8 lit. 6-Nov-3 Sotheby's, New York #238/R est:50000-70000
£117318 $210000 €171284 Young girl - Figure 6 from the Family of Man (173cm-68in) s. i.f.Morris Singer num.3/4 brown green pat bronze prov.lit. 5-May-4 Christie's, Rockefeller NY #344/R est:150000-200000
£140000 $238000 €204400 Reclining figure II (61cm-24in) scented guarea caved 1955-56 prov.exhib.lit. 21-Nov-3 Christie's, London #182/R est:60000-80000
£170000 $309400 €248200 Torso I (133cm-52in) s.d.1958 green pat bronze incl. base one of six prov.lit. 15-Jun-4 Bonhams, New Bond Street #96/R est:60000-80000
£185000 $338550 €270100 Two forms- forms to touch (85cm-33in) serravezza marble black stone base prov.exhib.lit. 4-Jun-4 Christie's, London #145/R est:150000-250000
Works on paper
£4000 $7400 €5840 Operating theatre study (35x25cm-14x10in) s.d.12/47 red chk exhib. 11-Mar-4 Christie's, Kensington #173/R est:2000-3000
£18000 $32940 €26280 Two figures (38x27cm-15x11in) s.d.47 pen ink crayon pencil prov.exhib. 2-Jun-4 Sotheby's, London #69/R est:10000-15000
£56757 $105000 €82865 Chord (29x47cm-11x19in) s.d.1946 s.i.d.verso gouache pencil paper on card prov.exhib. 11-Feb-4 Sotheby's, New York #54/R est:15000-20000

HER, Theodor (1838-1892) German
£395 $726 €600 Two women with child and dog in landscape (51x40cm-20x16in) s.i. 24-Jun-4 Dr Fritz Nagel, Stuttgart #715/R

HERALD, James Watterson (1859-1914) British
£4200 $6762 €6090 By the river (31x28cm-12x11in) panel. 21-Aug-3 Bonhams, Edinburgh #1188/R est:1200-1800
Works on paper
£450 $851 €657 Figures by lamplight (23x17cm-9x7in) s. pastel. 19-Feb-4 Lyon & Turnbull, Edinburgh #61
£800 $1488 €1168 Self portrait, fancy dress ball (15x16cm-6x6in) i. 4-Mar-4 Christie's, Kensington #116/R
£800 $1488 €1168 On the river Orwell (16x16cm-6x6in) s. monochrome wash. 4-Mar-4 Christie's, Kensington #117/R
£800 $1488 €1168 Baby in a high chair (15x23cm-6x9in) pen ink. 4-Mar-4 Christie's, Kensington #118/R
£1550 $2899 €2263 Figure on a path with distant mountains (7x10cm-3x4in) s. W/C. 25-Feb-4 Mallams, Oxford #142/R est:500-700
£2000 $3220 €2900 Mending the nets (24x32cm-9x13in) s. W/C. 21-Aug-3 Bonhams, Edinburgh #1081/R est:1200-1800
£2000 $3140 €2900 Ipswich (34x24cm-13x9in) s.i.d.99 W/C. 27-Aug-3 Sotheby's, London #1040/R est:1200-1800
£2000 $3460 €2920 Waiting for the fleet (34x25cm-13x10in) s. pastel. 11-Dec-3 Lyon & Turnbull, Edinburgh #90 est:2000-3000
£2700 $4347 €3915 Fishing fleet setting out (24x32cm-9x13in) s. W/C. 21-Aug-3 Bonhams, Edinburgh #1080/R est:1000-1500
£2800 $4760 €4088 Museum Street, Arbroath (39x28cm-15x11in) s.d.95 pencil W/C gum arabic htd white. 30-Oct-3 Christie's, London #127/R est:2000-3000
£4200 $7140 €6132 Museum Street, Montrose, rainy day (32x23cm-13x9in) W/C prov. 30-Oct-3 Christie's, London #130/R est:2000-3000
£6200 $10540 €9052 Violin player (342x620cm-135x244in) s. W/C. 30-Oct-3 Christie's, London #129/R est:2500-3500

HERAMB, Thore (1916-) Norwegian
£861 $1386 €1257 Colour composition (50x65cm-20x26in) s. exhib. 25-Aug-3 Blomqvist, Lysaker #1110/R (N.KR 10000)
£959 $1602 €1400 Composition (50x65cm-20x26in) s. 17-Nov-3 Blomqvist, Lysaker #1120/R (N.KR 11500)
£1001 $1671 €1461 Snow in the forest (32x42cm-13x17in) s. panel. 17-Nov-3 Blomqvist, Lysaker #1121 est:12000-15000 (N.KR 12000)
£3203 $5733 €4676 Composition (65x81cm-26x32in) s.d.85. 22-Mar-4 Blomqvist, Oslo #616/R est:30000-40000 (N.KR 40000)
£3363 $6019 €4910 Sitkagran (73x92cm-29x36in) s/d/63 exhib. 22-Mar-4 Blomqvist, Oslo #663/R est:40000-60000 (N.KR 42000)

HERARD, H (?) ?
£1034 $1862 €1500 Cardinal's visit (27x34cm-11x13in) s. copper. 26-Jan-4 Durán, Madrid #610/R est:600

HERAS, Gaetano de la (19/20th C) Spanish
£17647 $30000 €25765 In the Cafe (55x60cm-22x24in) s.d.1902. 28-Oct-3 Sotheby's, New York #12/R est:30000-40000

HERAUT, Henri (1894-1981) French
£268 $475 €400 Scene familiale (54x45cm-21x18in) s. 29-Apr-4 David Kahn, Paris #213

HERBECK, Edward (20th C) American
Works on paper
£219 $400 €329 Plants, pots and stones (66x97cm-26x38in) W/C. 10-Jul-4 Hindman, Chicago #210/R

HERBELIN, Louis (19th C) French
£950 $1644 €1387 Porteuses d'eau (65x100cm-26x39in) s.i. 12-Dec-3 Galerie du Rhone, Sion #153 (S.FR 2100)

HERBERT, Alfred (?-1861) British
Works on paper
£540 $956 €788 Extensive stormy beach scene with figures attending a shipwreck (33x66cm-13x26in) s. W/C. 27-Apr-4 Lawrences, Bletchingley #1559
£600 $1062 €876 Ship wrecking with figures on the shore (30x79cm-12x31in) s.d.48 W/C. 29-Apr-4 Gorringes, Lewes #2377
£1120 $2050 €1635 Man of war, off Dover (38x61cm-15x24in) s.d.1845 W/C. 1-Jun-4 Hodgins, Calgary #118/R est:2000-2500 (C.D 2800)

HERBERT, H (20th C) British
£1200 $2208 €1752 On the footbridge (22x30cm-9x12in) s. 8-Jun-4 Bonhams, Knightsbridge #319/R est:600-800

HERBERT, Harold Brocklebank (1892-1945) Australian
Works on paper
£287 $453 €419 Angelsea river and beach (22x24cm-9x9in) s. W/C. 2-Sep-3 Deutscher-Menzies, Melbourne #355/R (A.D 700)
£345 $538 €500 Buffalo boulders (36x34cm-14x13in) s.d.1933 W/C. 1-Aug-2 Joel, Victoria #202 est:1000-1500 (A.D 1000)
£383 $697 €559 Victorian coastline. W/C. 1-Jul-4 Joel, Victoria #301/R (A.D 1000)
£410 $647 €599 It seemed more politic to buy knives (25x19cm-10x7in) i. pencil. 2-Sep-3 Deutscher-Menzies, Melbourne #356/R (A.D 1000)
£500 $850 €730 At Osburn's Flat near Tawonga, Victoria (33x40cm-13x16in) s.d.1931 W/C. 31-Oct-3 Moore Allen & Innocent, Cirencester #452
£500 $905 €730 Australian Landscape (33x41cm-13x16in) W/C exec 1926. 17-Apr-4 Dickins, Middle Claydon #34
£648 $1043 €946 Road to Tallarock (36x42cm-14x17in) s.d.1942 W/C. 13-Oct-3 Joel, Victoria #322 est:1500-2000 (A.D 1600)
£820 $1295 €1197 Old sluicing works, Buninyong, near Ballarat (27x25cm-11x10in) s. W/C. 2-Sep-3 Deutscher-Menzies, Melbourne #295/R est:2500-3500 (A.D 2000)

HERBERT, John Rogers (1810-1890) British
£1900 $3173 €2774 New World in the west for Spain or for England (117x194cm-46x76in) s.i.d.86. 7-Oct-3 Bonhams, Knightsbridge #281/R est:2000-3000
£20000 $34000 €29200 Valley of Moses, in the desert of Sinai (86x168cm-34x66in) s.i.d.1866 prov.exhib. 25-Nov-3 Christie's, London #162/R est:20000-30000

HERBERT, Sidney (1854-1914) British
£550 $869 €798 Deer in a beech wood (91x71cm-36x28in) s.d.1895. 4-Sep-3 Christie's, Kensington #163/R
£750 $1253 €1095 Dutch fisher girl (51x41cm-20x16in) s. 11-Nov-3 Bonhams, Knightsbridge #113/R
£1450 $2639 €2117 Ruins of Rome (61x92cm-24x36in) s. 29-Jun-4 Bonhams, Knowle #93 est:800-1200
£3231 $5557 €4717 Constantine the Great crossing the Alps (77x127cm-30x50in) s. 2-Dec-3 Bukowskis, Stockholm #293/R est:20000-22000 (S.KR 42000)

HERBERTE, E B (fl.1860-1893) British
£791 $1400 €1155 Jumping fence (36x25cm-14x10in) s.d.1883. 2-May-4 Grogan, Boston #57/R
£791 $1400 €1155 Hunt scene (36x25cm-14x10in) s.d.1883. 2-May-4 Grogan, Boston #58/R
£1300 $2340 €1898 Farmyard scene with horses, sheep, chickens, geese and other animals (25x35cm-10x14in) s. 21-Apr-4 Tennants, Leyburn #1192/R est:600-800

HERBERTE, Edward Benjamin (fl.1860-1893) British
£447 $800 €653 Pursuit (15x25cm-6x10in) board. 6-May-4 Doyle, New York #11/R
£660 $1234 €964 The meet (23x30cm-9x12in) s. board. 24-Feb-4 Bonhams, Knowle #75
£750 $1290 €1095 Before the off, into the ditch! (31x46cm-12x18in) s.d.1876. 3-Dec-3 Bonhams, Knightsbridge #167
£900 $1530 €1314 The brook (29x49cm-11x19in) s. 1-Dec-3 Bonhams, Bath #109/R
£2000 $3400 €2920 Meet. Kill (25x36cm-10x14in) s.d.1880 pair. 27-Nov-3 Christie's, Kensington #23/R est:2000-3000
£5000 $9150 €7300 Hunt (35x53cm-14x21in) all s. four. 28-Jul-4 Bonhams, Knightsbridge #104/R est:5000-7000

HERBERTE, Sandy (1960-) Australian
£1053 $1695 €1537 Brisbane house (122x383cm-48x151in) board prov. 25-Aug-3 Sotheby's, Paddington #427/R est:1500-3000 (A.D 2600)

HERBET, Jean (20th C) French
Works on paper
£524 $892 €750 Etude de trois tetes de chiens, braque, setter gordon, setter lord braque (45x61cm-18x24in) s.d.1943 W/C. 20-Nov-3 Millon & Associes, Paris #94/R

HERBIG, Otto (1889-1971) German
Works on paper
£667 $1227 €1000 Putto with amaryllis (67x48cm-26x19in) s. pastel. 12-Jun-4 Villa Grisebach, Berlin #569/R

HERBIN, Auguste (1882-1960) French
£1321 $2140 €1929 Eros (35x24cm-14x9in) s. pencil double-sided. 24-May-3 Burkhard, Luzern #149/R est:3500-4000 (S.FR 2800)
£6000 $11040 €9000 Mountain landscape, Corsica (37x47cm-15x19in) s. painted 1907. 8-Jun-4 Sotheby's, Amsterdam #62/R est:15000-20000
£7343 $12629 €10500 Composition (55x46cm-22x18in) s.d.1938 oil paper on canvas prov.lit. 4-Dec-3 Piasa, Paris #94/R est:12000-18000
£8652 $14450 €12200 Les Coteaux - Haute Isle, Seine et Oise (60x73cm-24x29in) 20-Jun-3 Drouot Estimations, Paris #170/R est:15000-18000
£11333 $20853 €17000 Chateau a Vaison-la-Romaine (93x73cm-37x29in) s. prov.lit. 9-Jun-4 Tajan, Paris #19/R est:30000-40000
£14085 $24648 €20000 Sentier sur la colline Sainte Croix a Cassis (55x65cm-22x26in) s. exhib.lit. 18-Dec-3 Cornette de St.Cyr, Paris #5/R est:20000-25000
£14094 $26356 €21000 Hamburg harbour (60x73cm-24x29in) s. 28-Feb-4 Quittenbaum, Hamburg #69/R est:18000
£17687 $31660 €26000 Pont (46x38cm-18x15in) s. 19-Mar-4 Millon & Associes, Paris #85/R est:15000-20000
£20290 $33275 €28000 Vase de fleurs (60x35cm-24x14in) s. board on panel prov.lit. 27-May-3 Sotheby's, Amsterdam #310/R est:12000-15000
£22059 $37500 €32206 Apres la pluie a la Roche-Guyon (60x73cm-24x29in) s. painted 1906 prov.exhib.lit. 6-Nov-3 Sotheby's, New York #153/R est:30000-40000
£27000 $45090 €39420 Paysage a ceret (60x81cm-24x32in) s.d.1920 prov.exhib.lit. 21-Oct-3 Sotheby's, London #56/R est:30000-40000
£28000 $50960 €40880 Nature morte a la lampe (47x55cm-19x22in) s. canvas on board painted c.1905 prov. 4-Feb-4 Sotheby's, London #235/R est:30000-40000
£28384 $51659 €41441 Notre-Dame de Paris (60x73cm-24x29in) s. painted 1908 prov. 18-Jun-4 Kornfeld, Bern #56/R est:75000 (S.FR 65000)
£32353 $55000 €47235 Coteaux a haute Isle (59x73cm-23x29in) s. painted 1906. 6-Nov-3 Sotheby's, New York #142/R est:30000-40000
£33566 $57063 €48000 Fleur (81x65cm-32x26in) s.i.d.1945. 28-Nov-3 Blanchet, Paris #200/R est:40000-50000
£43437 $72105 €63418 Small town (74x101cm-29x40in) s. 4-Oct-3 Kieselbach, Budapest #112/R (H.F 16000000)
£45000 $82800 €65700 Paysage au cours d'eau (55x46cm-22x18in) s. painted 1908 prov.exhib.lit. 22-Jun-4 Sotheby's, London #155/R est:50000-70000
£57042 $98683 €81000 Parfum III (130x96cm-51x38in) s.i.d.1954 prov.exhib.lit. 14-Dec-3 Versailles Encheres #128/R est:90000-110000
£104895 $178322 €150000 Une place a Bastia (73x60cm-29x24in) s. i. stretcher prov.lit. 26-Nov-3 Lempertz, Koln #720/R est:100000-120000
£245810 $440000 €358883 Une place a Bastia - le 14 Juillet (73x60cm-29x24in) s. painted 1907 prov.lit. 6-May-4 Sotheby's, New York #282/R est:180000-220000
Works on paper
£420 $713 €600 Bouquet (14x5cm-6x2in) bears sig. gouache prov. 23-Nov-3 Cornette de St.Cyr, Paris #155
£455 $759 €650 Composition (24x13cm-9x5in) s. crayon dr. 29-Jun-3 Versailles Encheres #16
£559 $951 €800 Triptyque (31x70cm-12x28in) s. W/C three in one frame. 23-Nov-3 Cornette de St.Cyr, Paris #154
£2083 $3437 €3000 Composition geometrique (35x25cm-14x10in) s. W/C. 3-Jul-3 Piasa, Paris #94/R est:6000-8000
£2465 $4265 €3500 Paysage a Ceret (17x21cm-7x8in) s. Chinese ink crayon dr prov. 9-Dec-3 Artcurial Briest, Paris #226a/R est:2500-3000
£2535 $4208 €3600 Composition (32x23cm-13x9in) s. W/C. 16-Jun-3 E & Eve, Paris #103/R
£3088 $5250 €4508 Composition (22x34cm-9x13in) s.d.1942 gouache pencil sold with letter prov. 9-Nov-3 Bonhams & Butterfields, Los Angeles #4023/R
£3289 $6084 €4900 Composition (34x26cm-13x10in) s.d.38 gouache. 15-Mar-4 Blanchet, Paris #117/R est:6000-8000
£3379 $5946 €5000 Volute (24x31cm-9x12in) s. gouache crayon prov. 18-May-4 Tajan, Paris #24/R est:5000-6000
£3667 $6747 €5500 Composition fleurs (31x23cm-12x9in) s. gouache W/C exec. 1920 prov. 8-Jun-4 Artcurial Briest, Paris #76/R est:6000-8000
£3691 $6607 €5500 Composition (20x33cm-8x13in) s.d.1942 gouache. 30-May-4 Eric Pillon, Calais #305/R
£4200 $7644 €6132 Composition sur le nom propre herbin no 2 (27x35cm-11x14in) s.d.1942 gouache prov. 6-Feb-4 Sotheby's, London #148/R est:4000-6000
£5000 $8350 €7300 Tete volute (34x22cm-13x9in) s.d.38 gouache prov. 21-Oct-3 Sotheby's, London #70/R est:4000-6000
£6000 $10020 €8760 Untitled - study for synochomie en blue fonce (21x24cm-8x9in) s.d.41 gouache prov. 21-Oct-3 Sotheby's, London #334/R est:5000-7000
£6000 $10020 €8760 Victor (37x25cm-15x10in) s.i.d.1948 gouache. 21-Oct-3 Sotheby's, London #338/R est:6000-8000
£6500 $11830 €9490 Untitled (36x26cm-14x10in) s.d.1942 gouache prov. 6-Feb-4 Sotheby's, London #149/R est:4000-6000
£8726 $14137 €12740 Reine (38x31cm-15x12in) s.i.d.1953 gouache board. 24-May-3 Burkhard, Luzern #151/R est:17000-20000 (S.FR 18500)

HERBO, Fernand (1905-1995) French
£483 $801 €700 Etang en hiver (65x50cm-26x20in) s. panel. 1-Oct-3 Millon & Associes, Paris #112/R
£839 $1552 €1250 Peniches a Conflans-Sainte-Honorine (27x34cm-11x13in) s. panel. 14-Mar-4 Eric Pillon, Calais #169/R
£1000 $1840 €1500 Embarcations en mer (46x61cm-18x24in) s. 14-Jun-4 Tajan, Paris #98 est:1500-2000
£1103 $2019 €1600 A la godille (55x38cm-22x15in) s. 31-Jan-4 Neret-Minet, Paris #144/R est:1000
£1141 $2122 €1700 Sortie du port d'Honfleur (60x73cm-24x29in) s. 3-Mar-4 Ferri, Paris #121 est:1000-1500
£1208 $2235 €1800 Bord de riviere (65x50cm-26x20in) s. 14-Mar-4 Eric Pillon, Calais #176/R
£1342 $2497 €2000 Le port par gros temps (38x46cm-15x18in) s. panel. 3-Mar-4 Ferri, Paris #120 est:1000-1500
£1538 $2646 €2200 The port of Havre (60x81cm-24x32in) s. 2-Dec-3 Christie's, Paris #356/R est:2200-2800
£1745 $3088 €2600 Montmartre - Rue de l'Abreuvoir (60x81cm-24x32in) s. 27-Apr-4 Artcurial Briest, Paris #194 est:2000-3000
£3758 $6953 €5600 Dieppe (81x100cm-32x39in) s. 14-Mar-4 Eric Pillon, Calais #153/R
£4577 $8011 €6500 Regate a Douarnenez (60x84cm-24x33in) s. 21-Dec-3 Thierry & Lannon, Brest #168/R est:3000-4000
£7333 $13493 €11000 Le vieux bassin a Honfleur (114x146cm-45x57in) s.i. 14-Jun-4 Tajan, Paris #97/R est:10000-12000
Works on paper
£269 $475 €400 Jeune femme assise (30x26cm-12x10in) s.d.1931 W/C chl. 27-Apr-4 Artcurial Briest, Paris #40
£270 $484 €400 Entree du port a Honfleur (24x32cm-9x13in) s. W/C. 5-May-4 Coutau Begarie, Paris #48h
£274 $430 €400 Honfleur, le vieux bassin (10x21cm-4x8in) s. W/C. 20-Apr-3 Deauville, France #16
£284 $474 €400 Bateaux dans un port a maree basse (23x32cm-9x13in) s. W/C. 19-Jun-3 Millon & Associes, Paris #253
£284 $474 €400 Clichy (35x62cm-14x24in) s.i.d.1939 W/C. 20-Jun-3 Drouot Estimations, Paris #161
£300 $540 €450 Entree du port de Honfleur (25x44cm-10x17in) s.i.d.1936 W/C. 26-Apr-4 Tajan, Paris #38
£301 $473 €440 Port de Honfleur (11x20cm-4x8in) s. W/C conte. 20-Apr-3 Deauville, France #15
£315 $535 €450 Honfleur, l'estuaire (11x16cm-4x6in) s. W/C graphite. 27-Nov-3 Millon & Associes, Paris #60
£319 $533 €450 Conflans Sainte Honorine (30x48cm-12x19in) s.i. W/C. 20-Jun-3 Drouot Estimations, Paris #160
£329 $516 €480 Honfleur, le port (13x21cm-5x8in) s. W/C. 20-Apr-3 Deauville, France #14
£336 $621 €500 Petit village (19x31cm-7x12in) s. W/C. 14-Mar-4 Eric Pillon, Calais #179/R
£336 $624 €500 Montmartre (21x28cm-8x11in) s. W/C. 3-Mar-4 Ferri, Paris #119
£420 $722 €600 Noirmoutier, le vieux port (49x63cm-19x25in) W/C. 5-Dec-3 Gros & Delettrez, Paris #70
£423 $731 €600 Honfleur (24x31cm-9x12in) s. W/C. 10-Dec-3 Millon & Associes, Paris #65/R
£563 $975 €800 Peniches a quai (47x63cm-19x25in) s. W/C. 12-Dec-3 Piasa, Paris #181/R
£600 $1110 €900 Les navires au port (32x52cm-13x20in) s. W/C. 14-Jul-4 Livinec, Gaudcheau & Jezequel, Rennes #94
£621 $1117 €900 Port de Honfleur (50x64cm-20x25in) s. W/C. 25-Jan-4 Chayette & Cheval, Paris #253
£845 $1361 €1200 Conflans Saint-Honorine (30x49cm-12x19in) s.i. W/C chl. 22-Aug-3 Deauville, France #5/R
£872 $1623 €1300 Peniches a quai (48x6cm-19x2in) s. W/C. 7-Mar-4 Lesieur & Le Bars, Le Havre #66/R
£1096 $1721 €1600 Port (48x64cm-19x25in) s. W/C gouache. 20-Apr-3 Deauville, France #19 est:1200-1500
£1208 $2162 €1800 Port de Honfleur (48x63cm-19x25in) s. W/C. 30-May-4 Eric Pillon, Calais #14/R
£1233 $1936 €1800 Le Havre. Bretagne (14x25cm-6x10in) s.i.d.1931 W/C pair. 20-Apr-3 Deauville, France #13 est:1000-1500
£1370 $2151 €2000 Camaret (29x45cm-11x18in) s.d.1930 W/C. 20-Apr-3 Deauville, France #17 est:2000-2500
£1600 $2864 €2400 Vapeur a St Denis (42x51cm-17x20in) s.d.1937 W/C. 16-May-4 Thierry & Lannon, Brest #54/R est:2200-2500

HERBO, Léon (1850-1907) Belgian
£280 $467 €400 Jeune Orientale au collier de perles (35x27cm-14x11in) s. panel. 13-Oct-3 Horta, Bruxelles #28
£413 $761 €620 Jeune fille de profil (36x27cm-14x11in) s. 14-Jun-4 Horta, Bruxelles #312
£704 $1218 €1000 Portrait of man with moustache (82x65cm-32x26in) s.d.1899. 15-Dec-3 Bernaerts, Antwerp #67/R
£769 $1323 €1100 Portrait of a young oriental (18x14cm-7x6in) s. panel. 8-Dec-3 Tajan, Paris #286/R est:1200-1500
£900 $1413 €1305 Tune for a loved one (46x32cm-18x13in) s.d.76 canvas on panel. 28-Aug-3 Christie's, Kensington #65/R
£1135 $1895 €1600 Portrait of a lady (82x65cm-32x26in) s.d.1898. 20-Oct-3 Bernaerts, Antwerp #26/R est:1500-1800
£1773 $2961 €2500 Oiseleur (52x39cm-20x15in) s.d.1879 panel. 14-Oct-3 Vanderkindere, Brussels #1/R
£2817 $4873 €4000 Sphinx (100x85cm-39x33in) s.i. 13-Dec-3 De Vuyst, Lokeren #545/R est:4500-6000
£3243 $5805 €4800 Portrait en pied d'un jeune fille (140x72cm-55x28in) s.d.1883 canvas on panel. 10-May-4 Horta, Bruxelles #177 est:3000-5000
£6250 $11313 €9500 Elegante dans une serre (66x52cm-26x20in) s. panel. 19-Apr-4 Horta, Bruxelles #108/R est:10000-12000
£16000 $26720 €23360 Odalisque (110x144cm-43x57in) s. 14-Oct-3 Sotheby's, London #50/R est:10000-15000

HERBST, Adolf (1909-1983) Swiss
£526 $879 €768 Umbrian landscape (32x41cm-13x16in) s.i. canvas on board prov. 15-Nov-3 Galerie Gloggner, Luzern #68/R (S.FR 1200)
£724 $1231 €1057 Wine bottles, glass and pipe (55x46cm-22x18in) s.d.56. 19-Nov-3 Fischer, Luzern #2131/R (S.FR 1600)
£2183 $4017 €3187 Seated nude (93x61cm-37x24in) s.d.1944. 8-Jun-4 Germann, Zurich #120/R est:6000-8000 (S.FR 5000)
£2252 $3874 €3288 Festival (54x65cm-21x26in) s. painted 1973 lit. 8-Dec-3 Philippe Schuler, Zurich #3336/R est:5000-6000 (S.FR 5000)
£4525 $7828 €6607 Vallee de la Chevreuse (64x91cm-25x36in) s.d.1958 lit. 9-Dec-3 Sotheby's, Zurich #63/R est:10000-14000 (S.FR 10000)
Works on paper
£317 $538 €463 Bull against tree (17x25cm-7x10in) s. W/C Indian ink. 19-Nov-3 Fischer, Luzern #2631 (S.FR 700)
£341 $566 €494 Self portrait (25x19cm-10x7in) s. Indian ink wash. 13-Jun-3 Zofingen, Switzerland #2876 (S.FR 750)
£570 $1049 €832 Three dancers on red ground (19x12cm-7x5in) gouache. 23-Jun-4 Koller, Zurich #3047 (S.FR 1300)
£721 $1240 €1053 Reclining nude (28x40cm-11x16in) i. Indian ink htd white. 2-Dec-3 Koller, Zurich #3022 est:1200-1800 (S.FR 1600)

HERBST, Frank C (1912-1970) American
£870 $1400 €1270 Near the New Jersey shore (41x51cm-16x20in) s. 20-Aug-3 James Julia, Fairfield #1714/R est:1500-2000

HERBST, Thomas (1848-1915) German
£699 $1168 €1000 Reclining cow in meadow (48x66cm-19x26in) board. 28-Jun-3 Bolland & Marotz, Bremen #662/R
£1500 $2505 €2190 Gondolas before the Dogana, Venice (40x60cm-16x24in) s.d.1900. 8-Oct-3 Christie's, Kensington #793/R est:1500-2000
£4200 $7644 €6300 Farmstead by water (38x56cm-15x22in) board. 30-Jun-4 Neumeister, Munich #571/R est:1500

HERBURGER, Julius (1900-1973) German
£267 $480 €400 Two female nudes in park landscape (35x29cm-14x11in) s.d.48 canvas on board lit. 22-Apr-4 Allgauer, Kempten #3572/R

HERCKENRATH, Julius (1858-1910) Dutch
£789 $1453 €1200 Winter landscape with figures on the ice (15x31cm-6x12in) s. panel. 28-Jun-4 Sotheby's, Amsterdam #47/R

HERDMAN, Robert (1828-1888) British
£700 $1260 €1022 Conventicle preacher (29x49cm-11x19in) mono.d.1874. 21-Jan-4 Sotheby's, Olympia #274/R
£1239 $2106 €1809 Allegorical subject of an innocent looking upward (61x46cm-24x18in) s.d.1853. 21-Nov-3 Walker's, Ottawa #267/R est:2000-3000 (C.D 2750)
£5800 $9860 €8468 Heather from the Hills - Arran (60x46cm-24x18in) mono.d.1864 panel. 30-Oct-3 Christie's, London #99/R est:5000-7000

HERDMAN, William Gavin (1805-1882) British
Works on paper
£360 $659 €526 Everton, with the old toffee shop (23x39cm-9x15in) s.d.1878 W/C. 2-Feb-4 Bonhams, Chester #891
£400 $688 €584 Albert Dock, Liverpool (26x33cm-10x13in) init. W/C. 2-Dec-3 Sotheby's, London #30/R
£400 $736 €600 Bootle Church (13x28cm-5x11in) init. W/C lit. 23-Jun-4 Byrne's, Chester #595/R
£700 $1288 €1050 Saint Nicholas Church (20x15cm-8x6in) init. W/C prov.lit. 23-Jun-4 Byrne's, Chester #593/R
£700 $1288 €1050 Shaw's Brow (15x28cm-6x11in) init. W/C prov.lit. 23-Jun-4 Byrne's, Chester #597/R
£1100 $2024 €1650 Herculaneum potteries and shore (15x28cm-6x11in) init. W/C lit. 23-Jun-4 Byrne's, Chester #586/R est:300-500
£1350 $2484 €2025 View from Sparling Street (25x28cm-10x11in) init.d.1870 W/C prov. 23-Jun-4 Byrne's, Chester #596 est:300-500
£1450 $2668 €2175 Exchange, Bridewell (25x41cm-10x16in) init. W/C prov.lit. 23-Jun-4 Byrne's, Chester #592/R est:300-500
£1600 $2944 €2400 Old Custom House and castle (25x38cm-10x15in) init. W/C prov. 23-Jun-4 Byrne's, Chester #583/R est:300-500
£1600 $2944 €2400 Lord Street (25x38cm-10x15in) init. W/C lit. 23-Jun-4 Byrne's, Chester #588/R est:300-500
£1700 $3128 €2550 Hackins Hey (23x20cm-9x8in) init. W/C exec.1858 prov. 23-Jun-4 Byrne's, Chester #582/R est:300-500
£1700 $3128 €2550 Saint Nicholas Church and George's Basin (20x43cm-8x17in) init. W/C prov.lit. 23-Jun-4 Byrne's, Chester #585/R est:300-500
£1800 $3312 €2700 Old Exchange (25x41cm-10x16in) init. W/C lit. 23-Jun-4 Byrne's, Chester #594 est:300-500
£1900 $3496 €2850 Liverpool from Lime Street (23x43cm-9x17in) init. W/C lit. 23-Jun-4 Byrne's, Chester #591 est:300-500
£1950 $3588 €2925 Chapel Street (15x28cm-6x11in) init. W/C lit. 23-Jun-4 Byrne's, Chester #587/R est:300-500
£1950 $3588 €2925 Lord Street (28x38cm-11x15in) init. W/C lit. 23-Jun-4 Byrne's, Chester #590/R est:300-500
£2000 $3680 €3000 Top of old Shores Brow (28x46cm-11x18in) s.d.1853 W/C prov. 23-Jun-4 Byrne's, Chester #581/R est:400-600
£2200 $4048 €3300 Hanover Street towards Canning Dock (33x28cm-13x11in) init.indis.d. W/C. 23-Jun-4 Byrne's, Chester #580/R est:500-700
£2200 $4048 €3300 Royal Bank Buildings (25x36cm-10x14in) s.d.74 W/C prov. 23-Jun-4 Byrne's, Chester #589/R est:400-600
£3100 $5704 €4650 Southport (51x74cm-20x29in) s.i.d.1862 W/C prov.lit. 23-Jun-4 Byrne's, Chester #598/R est:1000-1500
£4200 $7560 €6132 Views of Liverpool (17x21cm-7x8in) s. two d.1857 pen grey ink W/C over pencil seven. 21-Jan-4 Sotheby's, Olympia #146/R est:800-1200

HERDMAN-SMITH, Robert (1879-?) British
Works on paper
£282 $519 €412 Bootham Bar, York (35x25cm-14x10in) s. W/C. 9-Jun-4 Walker's, Ottawa #368/R (C.D 700)

HERDOIT, Gerard (attrib) (19/20th C) American?
£333 $600 €486 Stag by the river (81x66cm-32x26in) bears sig. 24-Apr-4 Slotin Folk Art, Buford #253/R

HERDT, Jan de (attrib) (17th C) Flemish
£10000 $18300 €14600 Man and woman playing mandolin and tambourine at table (74x98cm-29x39in) 8-Jul-4 Sotheby's, London #309/R est:10000-15000

HERDTLE, Hermann (1819-1889) German
£420 $722 €600 View of saint Gilgen (16x23cm-6x9in) s.d.1851 board. 3-Dec-3 Stadion, Trieste #703
£1111 $1811 €1600 Torbole, Lake Garda (57x69cm-22x27in) s. 25-Sep-3 Dr Fritz Nagel, Stuttgart #1357/R est:1100

HERDTLE, Richard (1866-1943) German
£372 $654 €550 Country path with two oxen pulling a wagon (56x84cm-22x33in) s. 22-May-4 Sigalas, Stuttgart #431/R

HEREAU, Jules (1839-1879) French
£1000 $1890 €1460 Pulling a barge at the end of the day (46x56cm-18x22in) s. 19-Feb-4 Christie's, Kensington #134/R est:1200-1800

HEREDIA, Alberto (20th C) Argentinian
Works on paper
£1657 $3000 €2419 Untitled (46x32cm-18x13in) mixed media collage. 30-Mar-4 Arroyo, Buenos Aires #28
£2210 $4000 €3227 Untitled (37x27cm-15x11in) mixed media pair. 30-Mar-4 Arroyo, Buenos Aires #17

HEREMANS, Paul (?) Belgian
£1622 $2903 €2400 Jeunes femmes faisant signe a un jeune homme au bord d'un cours d'eau (80x120cm-31x47in) s. 10-May-4 Horta, Bruxelles #158/R est:3000-5000

HERGET, Herbert (1885-1950) American
Works on paper
£595 $1100 €869 Indian Chief. Colorado river (30x23cm-12x9in) each s. W/C pair prov. 15-Jul-4 Sotheby's, New York #61/R

HERING, George Edwards (1805-1879) British
£350 $651 €511 Falls of Terni (21x15cm-8x6in) s. i.verso. 4-Mar-4 Christie's, Kensington #572/R
£1757 $3092 €2600 Monastery garden on Lake Orta, Piemont (62x98cm-24x39in) s. 22-May-4 Lempertz, Koln #1527/R est:2000
£2600 $4810 €3796 Lake Maggiore (51x86cm-20x34in) 10-Feb-4 Bonhams, Knightsbridge #346/R est:2000-3000
£3472 $5799 €5000 View of an Italian lake (73x130cm-29x51in) 21-Oct-3 Sotheby's, Amsterdam #53/R est:5000-7000
£6600 $12078 €9636 Evening in Greece, ruined temple, Cape Colonna (74x130cm-29x51in) 28-Jul-4 Mallams, Oxford #365/R est:3000-4000
£7500 $13800 €10950 Daybreak, night storm have stolen away and nothing now upon the shore (90x140cm-35x55in) s.d.1870 prov.exhib. 11-Jun-4 Christie's, London #97a/R est:7000-10000

HERING, Harry (1887-1949) American
£314 $500 €458 Southwestern scene with figures and sheep in foreground (74x84cm-29x33in) s. board. 10-Sep-3 Alderfer's, Hatfield #300/R

HERIZOG, L E (?) ?
£1000 $1790 €1500 View of San Simeone, Venice (74x101cm-29x40in) s. 12-May-4 Stadion, Trieste #638/R est:700-1000

HERKELMAN, A (19th C) ?
£586 $979 €850 Enjoying the ice (76x99cm-30x39in) s. st.sig. verso panel. 12-Jul-3 Bergmann, Erlangen #688/R

HERKENRATH, Peter (1900-1992) German

£1400	$2506	€2100	Containers (70x89cm-28x35in) s.d.60 board. 15-May-4 Van Ham, Cologne #656/R est:3000
£3200	$5728	€4800	Still life with containers (90x70cm-35x28in) s.d.90 s.d.89 verso. 15-May-4 Van Ham, Cologne #655/R est:5500
£4196	$7133	€6000	Composition (131x100cm-52x39in) s.d.1959. 29-Nov-3 Arnold, Frankfurt #279/R est:1600

HERKOMER, Hubert von (1849-1914) British

£300	$549	€438	Portrait of a gentleman in a black frock coat (140x102cm-55x40in) init.d.82. 8-Apr-4 Christie's, Kensington #54/R
£400	$740	€584	After bathing (23x15cm-9x6in) mono.d.92 panel. 14-Jul-4 Christie's, Kensington #950
£488	$873	€712	Portrait of an Italian girl (60x47cm-24x19in) init.d.1879. 4-May-4 Ritchie, Toronto #14/R est:1000-1500 (C.D 1200)
£2318	$4219	€3500	Portrait of Baroness Ellen Franziska of Heldburg (105x78cm-41x31in) s.d.1906. 16-Jun-4 Hugo Ruef, Munich #984/R est:1500
£15000	$27300	€21900	Moorish girl (46x36cm-18x14in) init.d.1881 s.i.verso. 17-Jun-4 Christie's, London #106/R est:15000-20000
Works on paper			
£650	$1151	€949	Italian shepherd (69x51cm-27x20in) s.d.1889 W/C. 28-Apr-4 Halls, Shrewsbury #473/R
£660	$1181	€964	Head and shoulders portrait of a young woman wearing a laurel garland (51x38cm-20x15in) s. mixed media. 22-Mar-4 Mullucks Wells, Bishop's Stortford #462/R
£806	$1500	€1177	Thinking it over (23x25cm-9x10in) init.d.1876 W/C sold with an etching. 5-Mar-4 Skinner, Boston #221/R est:800-1200
£900	$1548	€1314	Miller and the sweep (13x10cm-5x4in) W/C htd bodycol. 2-Dec-3 Canterbury Auctions, UK #167/R
£1300	$2041	€1885	Penitent Magdalene (39x30cm-15x12in) s.d.1878 pencil W/C scratching out gum arabic. 28-Aug-3 Christie's, Kensington #370/R est:300-500
£1300	$2431	€1898	The wheelwright (16x24cm-6x9in) init.d.85 pencil W/C gouache htd white. 22-Jul-4 Tennants, Leyburn #707 est:400-500
£3311	$6026	€5000	Portrait of Prince Georgs II. mono.i.d.1904 mixed media. 16-Jun-4 Hugo Ruef, Munich #983/R est:1500

HERLAND, Emma (1856-1947) French

£317	$555	€450	Bretonne devant le portail (34x27cm-13x11in) s. panel. 21-Dec-3 Thierry & Lannon, Brest #325
£331	$619	€500	Bouquet de dahlias (35x27cm-14x11in) s. 24-Jul-4 Thierry & Lannon, Brest #178
£437	$764	€620	Passage Lanriec a Concarneau (24x33cm-9x13in) s. panel. 21-Dec-3 Thierry & Lannon, Brest #324
£3867	$6921	€5800	Jeune fille au bol (56x36cm-22x14in) s.d.1883. 16-May-4 Thierry & Lannon, Brest #143/R est:2000-3000
Works on paper			
£296	$518	€420	Barques au sec (20x28cm-8x11in) s. W/C. 21-Dec-3 Thierry & Lannon, Brest #232
£423	$739	€600	Interieur d'eglise (41x31cm-16x12in) s. pastel. 21-Dec-3 Thierry & Lannon, Brest #253

HERM-SOHN, Nicolai Peters (1766-1825) ?

Works on paper			
£2177	$3897	€3200	Faucon et sa chasse (47x61cm-19x24in) s.d.1810 gouache. 17-Mar-4 Tajan, Paris #89/R est:4000

HERMAN, Josef (1911-1999) British

£480	$802	€701	Man in the field (28x35cm-11x14in) s.i. verso board. 16-Oct-3 Christie's, Kensington #628/R
£1200	$2148	€1752	The Avenue (14x23cm-6x9in) board prov. 16-Mar-4 Bonhams, New Bond Street #62/R est:1000-1500
£1300	$2340	€1898	Three figures (20x25cm-8x10in) oil pastel W/C. 20-Jan-4 Bonhams, Knightsbridge #127/R est:400-600
£2400	$4008	€3504	Mexican peasant (25x30cm-10x12in) s.i. verso. 16-Oct-3 Christie's, Kensington #627/R est:1800-2500
£2600	$4472	€3796	Road past the oasthouse (25x30cm-10x12in) s.verso prov. 2-Dec-3 Bonhams, New Bond Street #109/R est:2000-3000
£3000	$5010	€4380	Woman and donkey (25x35cm-10x14in) s.i.verso. 16-Oct-3 Christie's, Kensington #623/R est:2500-3500
£3000	$5010	€4380	Mexican scene (25x35cm-10x14in) s.i. verso. 16-Oct-3 Christie's, Kensington #629/R est:2500-3500
£3200	$5216	€4672	Four standing miners (18x25cm-7x10in) card. 24-Sep-3 Dreweatt Neate, Newbury #89/R est:400-600
£3500	$5845	€5110	Mexican donkey cart (30x41cm-12x16in) s.d.1964 verso prov. 16-Oct-3 Christie's, Kensington #626/R est:4000-6000
£3871	$7123	€5652	Man on a donkey (46x61cm-18x24in) s.d.1963 prov. 14-Jun-4 Waddingtons, Toronto #156/R est:6000-8000 (C.D 9600)
£4500	$7740	€6570	Mexican girl (89x74cm-35x29in) s.i.d.1974 verso board. 3-Dec-3 Christie's, Kensington #640/R est:2500-3500
£6000	$10980	€8760	Welsh miner, sunset (76x91cm-30x36in) s.verso board prov. 2-Jun-4 Sotheby's, London #93/R est:6000-8000
£8000	$13760	€11680	Man and woman on the road (50x65cm-20x26in) s.i.verso prov. 2-Dec-3 Bonhams, New Bond Street #130/R est:5000-7000
£10000	$17200	€14600	Standing miners (44x64cm-17x25in) indis sig. board prov. 2-Dec-3 Bonhams, New Bond Street #108/R est:8000-12000
£10000	$18200	€14600	Portuguese fisherman (71x91cm-28x36in) prov. 1-Jul-4 Christie's, Kensington #324/R est:12000-16000
Works on paper			
£280	$496	€409	Oil lamp on a table (15x10cm-6x4in) pen ink. 27-Apr-4 Bonhams, Knightsbridge #204/R
£380	$654	€555	Old man with a cat (23x18cm-9x7in) pen bush black ink. 3-Dec-3 Christie's, Kensington #726
£380	$673	€555	Three women (20x24cm-8x9in) pen ink. 27-Apr-4 Bonhams, Knightsbridge #300/R
£420	$722	€613	Seagulls in flight (20x25cm-8x10in) s.i.d.1989 pencil W/C gouache. 2-Dec-3 Bonhams, New Bond Street #117/R
£420	$764	€613	Midday shade, Mexico (16x22cm-6x9in) pencil pen brush blk ink prov. 1-Jul-4 Christie's, Kensington #325
£450	$833	€657	Seated man with birds (24x18cm-9x7in) s.d.1984 verso brush ink W/C. 11-Mar-4 Christie's, Kensington #262
£500	$860	€730	Bearded man (16x20cm-6x8in) s. pen ink wash. 2-Dec-3 Bonhams, New Bond Street #114/R
£500	$860	€730	Head (25x19cm-10x7in) s. W/C. 2-Dec-3 Bonhams, New Bond Street #118/R
£500	$860	€730	Mother and children (25x19cm-10x7in) s.i. ink wash. 2-Dec-3 Bonhams, New Bond Street #123/R
£550	$897	€803	Studies of peasants with milk (22x16cm-9x6in) pencil pen ink monochromatic washes. 24-Sep-3 Dreweatt Neate, Newbury #16/R
£550	$919	€803	Woman in the fields (19x25cm-7x10in) s.i.d.1978 verso pencil pen black ink W/C. 16-Oct-3 Christie's, Kensington #24/R
£550	$946	€803	Singer (22x16cm-9x6in) s. pen ink. 2-Dec-3 Bonhams, New Bond Street #115/R
£550	$1012	€803	Mother and child (10x7cm-4x3in) ink wash. 11-Jun-4 Keys, Aylsham #458
£600	$1032	€876	Looking out to sea (18x23cm-7x9in) W/C brush black ink. 3-Dec-3 Christie's, Kensington #738
£600	$1020	€876	Full moon (20x25cm-8x10in) pencil pen ink wash. 18-Nov-3 Sotheby's, Olympia #201/R
£620	$1011	€899	Figure group (24x19cm-9x7in) W/C pen. 23-Sep-3 Bonhams, Leeds #100
£680	$1238	€993	Fish seller with his basket (20x24cm-8x9in) pen ink. 15-Jun-4 Bonhams, Knightsbridge #13/R
£750	$1290	€1095	Village street (18x24cm-7x9in) d.17.4.76 ink W/C. 2-Dec-3 Bonhams, New Bond Street #126/R
£800	$1336	€1168	Two female nudes lying (17x22cm-7x9in) pen ink sold with another by same hand. 21-Oct-3 Bonhams, Knightsbridge #178/R
£800	$1376	€1168	In the outskirts of Jerusalem (20x25cm-8x10in) s.d.1954 ink W/C. 2-Dec-3 Bonhams, New Bond Street #125/R
£800	$1360	€1168	Miners (17x22cm-7x9in) pencil pen ink. 18-Nov-3 Sotheby's, Olympia #197/R
£800	$1408	€1168	Anchor (19x24cm-7x9in) W/C pencil executed 1978. 19-May-4 Sotheby's, Olympia #278/R
£850	$1462	€1241	Loading the donkey (19x25cm-7x10in) s.i.d.1972 ink W/C. 2-Dec-3 Bonhams, New Bond Street #122/R
£850	$1522	€1241	Figure study (25x20cm-10x8in) s.verso pen ink pastel. 28-May-4 Lyon & Turnbull, Edinburgh #32/R
£900	$1503	€1314	In the fields (16x22cm-6x9in) s.i.d.1976 verso pen brush black ink W/C pastel. 16-Oct-3 Christie's, Kensington #625
£900	$1548	€1314	Seated woman (23x17cm-9x7in) s. ink wash. 2-Dec-3 Bonhams, New Bond Street #113/R
£900	$1548	€1314	Market scene. Melody (16x20cm-6x8in) s.i. ink wash two. 2-Dec-3 Bonhams, New Bond Street #119/R
£900	$1548	€1314	Lone figure (24x19cm-9x7in) s.i.d.1978 pencil W/C gouache. 2-Dec-3 Bonhams, New Bond Street #124/R
£900	$1548	€1314	Group of miners (20x25cm-8x10in) s.i. pencil W/C. 2-Dec-3 Bonhams, New Bond Street #128/R
£1100	$1870	€1606	Horse and cart (17x22cm-7x9in) pencil ink wash. 26-Nov-3 Sotheby's, Olympia #83/R est:800-1200
£1200	$2064	€1752	Family (20x25cm-8x10in) s.i. pencil W/C. 2-Dec-3 Bonhams, New Bond Street #127/R est:600-800
£1200	$2076	€1752	Husband and wife (25x20cm-10x8in) s. pen ink W/C. 11-Dec-3 Lyon & Turnbull, Edinburgh #75/R est:1200-1600
£1400	$2338	€2044	On the surface of the colliery (25x20cm-10x8in) pencil pen brush black ink W/C. 16-Oct-3 Christie's, Kensington #622/R est:500-700
£1400	$2590	€2044	Bringing home the catch (24x19cm-9x7in) s. pen ink W/C. 11-Mar-4 Christie's, Kensington #261/R est:500-700
£1700	$2924	€2482	Dusk (18x24cm-7x9in) s.i.d.1978 pencil W/C pastel. 2-Dec-3 Bonhams, New Bond Street #110/R est:600-800
£1800	$2862	€2628	Glass of wine (23x17cm-9x7in) s. W/C ink gouache. 10-Sep-3 Sotheby's, Olympia #283/R est:1800-2500
£2100	$3885	€3066	Peasant woman (20x15cm-8x6in) s.verso pen ink W/C. 11-Feb-4 Sotheby's, Olympia #272/R est:1200-1800
£2200	$3784	€3212	Shepherd (25x20cm-10x8in) s.i. W/C. 2-Dec-3 Bonhams, New Bond Street #121/R est:500-700
£2600	$4420	€3796	Man in fish and chips shop (23x19cm-9x7in) W/C pen ink. 26-Nov-3 Sotheby's, Olympia #82/R est:2000-3000
£4400	$8008	€6424	Two Purim players (36x33cm-14x13in) s.d.42 s.i.d.verso pastel prov. 15-Jun-4 Bonhams, New Bond Street #75/R est:3000-4000
£4500	$7740	€6570	Where to now ? (46x34cm-18x13in) s.i.d.1943 chl W/C. 2-Dec-3 Bonhams, New Bond Street #112/R est:4000-6000
£8500	$14620	€12410	Memory of a pogrom (41x50cm-16x20in) s.i.d.1943 chl W/C gouache. 2-Dec-3 Bonhams, New Bond Street #111/R est:4000-6000

HERMAN, Josef (attrib) (1911-1999) British

Works on paper			
£250	$458	€375	Suffolk scene (12x19cm-5x7in) W/C ink. 30-Jul-4 Dreweatt Neate, Newbury #22
£260	$476	€390	Figure driving tractor (17x22cm-7x9in) W/C ink. 30-Jul-4 Dreweatt Neate, Newbury #29/R

HERMAN, Roger (1947-) American

£647	$1100	€945	Small paint cans I (58x53cm-23x21in) s.d.87 verso. 9-Nov-3 Bonhams & Butterfields, Los Angeles #4053/R
£941	$1600	€1374	Joust (122x122cm-48x48in) s.i.d.89 verso. 9-Nov-3 Bonhams & Butterfields, Los Angeles #4095/R est:4000-6000

HERMAN, Sali (1898-1993) Australian/Swiss

£345	$538	€500	Gentle giant (48x42cm-19x17in) s.d.24. 1-Aug-2 Joel, Victoria #257 est:2000-3000 (A.D 1000)
£729	$1173	€1064	Country town (31x19cm-12x7in) s.d.67 board. 13-Oct-3 Joel, Victoria #313 est:1000-1500 (A.D 1800)
£1162	$1940	€1743	Fisherman (37x30cm-15x12in) s.d.70. 27-Oct-3 Goodman, Sydney #202/R (A.D 2800)
£1447	$2459	€2113	Street Urchin (38x30cm-15x12in) s.d.66. 26-Nov-3 Deutscher-Menzies, Melbourne #250/R est:3000-4000 (A.D 3400)
£1660	$2772	€2490	Bowl of fruit (52x61cm-20x24in) s.d.58 board. 27-Oct-3 Goodman, Sydney #211/R est:4000-6000 (A.D 4000)
£2282	$3811	€3423	Mikinos (38x51cm-15x20in) s.d.76. 27-Oct-3 Goodman, Sydney #157/R est:4000-6000 (A.D 5500)
£3239	$5215	€4729	Country Store (45x60cm-18x24in) s.d.86 i.verso. 25-Aug-3 Sotheby's, Paddington #495/R est:8000-12000 (A.D 8000)
£4065	$6382	€5894	Cornwall (69x89cm-27x35in) s.d.80. 26-Aug-3 Christie's, Sydney #95a/R est:10000-15000 (A.D 10000)
£4472	$7020	€6484	Red door (62x80cm-24x31in) 26-Aug-3 Christie's, Sydney #27/R est:10000-15000 (A.D 11000)
£5500	$9845	€8030	Backyard (46x56cm-18x22in) s.52 exhib. 11-May-4 Sotheby's, Olympia #605/R est:6000-8000

£6224	$10394	€9336	Cello (137x91cm-54x36in) s. 27-Oct-3 Goodman, Sydney #147/R est:15000-20000 (A.D 15000)
£7287	$11733	€10639	French Village (80x105cm-31x41in) s. indis.d.78 or 79 prov.exhib. 25-Aug-3 Sotheby's, Paddington #177/R est:18000-25000 (A.D 18000)
£7692	$12385	€11230	St Clement Danes (76x98cm-30x39in) s.d.53 prov.exhib. 25-Aug-3 Sotheby's, Paddington #170/R est:18000-25000 (A.D 19000)
£8097	$13036	€11822	Harbourside houses (70x90cm-28x35in) s.d.68 prov.exhib. 25-Aug-3 Sotheby's, Paddington #133/R est:20000-28000 (A.D 20000)
£8097	$13036	€11822	Bridge (86x136cm-34x54in) s.d.79 prov. 25-Aug-3 Sotheby's, Paddington #196/R est:20000-25000 (A.D 20000)
£9350	$16736	€13651	Feeding the cats (50x78cm-20x31in) s.d.83. 4-May-4 Sotheby's, Melbourne #47/R est:20000-30000 (A.D 23000)
£9924	$18061	€14489	Suburbia (45x61cm-18x24in) s.d.55 exhib. 16-Jun-4 Deutscher-Menzies, Melbourne #79/R est:28000-36000 (A.D 26000)
£11157	$20640	€16289	Lovers lane Paddington (45x66cm-18x26in) s.d.65. 10-Mar-4 Deutscher-Menzies, Melbourne #129/R est:18000-24000 (A.D 27000)
£11915	$20255	€17396	Paddington (50x60cm-20x24in) s.d.60 prov. 25-Nov-3 Christie's, Melbourne #52/R est:18000-25000 (A.D 28000)
£12000	$21480	€17520	In the park (63x84cm-25x33in) s.d.52. 11-May-4 Sotheby's, Olympia #604/R est:6000-8000

HERMANJAT, Abraham (1862-1932) Swiss

£1086	$1846	€1586	Lac Leman (50x60cm-20x24in) s.d.1924. 28-Nov-3 Zofingen, Switzerland #3015 est:2000 (S.FR 2400)
£2241	$4012	€3272	Paysage alpestre, environs des Diablerets (55x33cm-22x13in) s.d.1901 cardboard. 13-May-4 Pierre Berge, Paris #12/R est:5000-6000 (S.FR 5200)

HERMANN, H (19/20th C) German

£317	$567	€450	Winter landscape with ducks in stream and mountains in background (18x24cm-7x9in) s. panel. 8-Jan-4 Allgauer, Kempten #2414/R

HERMANN, Hans (1813-1890) German

£451	$713	€650	Fishing boats in harbour (32x23cm-13x9in) s.i.d.1883 board. 6-Sep-3 Arnold, Frankfurt #580
Works on paper			
£966	$1612	€1400	Villa park on Lake Como (32x41cm-13x16in) s.d.1924 gouache board. 15-Nov-3 Lempertz, Koln #1489/R est:1500

HERMANN, Johann (1794-1880) Austrian

£520	$936	€759	Study of a musician seated (42x36cm-17x14in) s.d.1918. 20-Apr-4 Rosebery Fine Art, London #475/R

HERMANN, Ludwig (1812-1881) German

£1477	$2643	€2200	Vue d'une ville le long d'une riviere (50x82cm-20x32in) s. 25-May-4 Palais de Beaux Arts, Brussels #95/R est:2500-3500
£1800	$2988	€2628	Jetty on the river (42x59cm-17x23in) s.d.1837 panel. 1-Oct-3 Sotheby's, Olympia #197/R est:2000-4000
£2465	$4264	€3500	Fantasy town at dusk (70x97cm-28x38in) s.d.1853. 10-Dec-3 Christie's, Amsterdam #678/R est:2000-3000
£5000	$8000	€7250	Departing from the banks of the estuary (69x96cm-27x38in) s. 18-Sep-3 Christie's, Kensington #55/R est:5000-7000
£6500	$11830	€9490	Figures on a quay before a town (68x96cm-27x38in) s. prov. 16-Jun-4 Bonhams, New Bond Street #22/R est:5000-7000
Works on paper			
£662	$1205	€1000	Old quarter of Strasbourg with a synagogue (50x36cm-20x14in) s.d.853 W/C. 18-Jun-4 Bolland & Marotz, Bremen #637/R

HERMANNES, Carl (1874-1955) German

£280	$467	€400	Sunny morning (69x59cm-27x23in) s. i. verso. 28-Jun-3 Bolland & Marotz, Bremen #663

HERMANNS, Heinrich (1862-1942) German

£340	$609	€500	October sun with view of Caub am Rhein (25x35cm-10x14in) s.d.34 i. verso board. 18-Mar-4 Neumeister, Munich #2687/R
£490	$832	€700	North German dune landscape (46x60cm-18x24in) s. canvas on board. 20-Nov-3 Van Ham, Cologne #1623
£625	$987	€900	Woman collecting wood in the forest with a child (37x50cm-15x20in) s. 5-Sep-3 Wendl, Rudolstadt #3415/R
£667	$1193	€1000	Sous-bois (64x90cm-25x35in) s. 11-May-4 Vanderkindere, Brussels #76
£667	$1213	€1000	Young mother and her two children spending time at the forest's edge (47x35cm-19x14in) s. 1-Jul-4 Van Ham, Cologne #1399
£833	$1375	€1200	Summer trees casting shadows in front of church (48x58cm-19x23in) s. 3-Jul-3 Van Ham, Cologne #1239/R
£2550	$4565	€3800	Flower market in Old-Delft (43x60cm-17x24in) s. 27-May-4 Dorotheum, Vienna #180/R est:3800-4000
£2896	$4836	€4228	The high altar, Toledo Cathedral (154x134cm-61x53in) s. 17-Nov-3 Waddingtons, Toronto #246/R est:3000-5000 (C.D 6400)
£3889	$6417	€5600	Vegetable market in Amsterdam (61x81cm-24x32in) s. 3-Jul-3 Van Ham, Cologne #1238/R est:3000
£5333	$9600	€8000	At the flower market (61x81cm-24x32in) s. 20-Apr-4 Sotheby's, Amsterdam #154/R est:8000-12000
£7586	$12669	€11000	Amsterdam street (60x80cm-24x31in) s. prov. 15-Nov-3 Lempertz, Koln #1617/R est:8000
Works on paper			
£333	$607	€500	Interior of a church (48x36cm-19x14in) s. gouache. 1-Jul-4 Van Ham, Cologne #1397
£667	$1213	€1000	Interior view of the Capella Palatino in Palermo (47x39cm-19x15in) s. gouache paper on board. 1-Jul-4 Van Ham, Cologne #1398/R
£690	$1152	€1000	Capella Palatina in Palermo (44x37cm-17x15in) s. gouache W/C prov. 15-Nov-3 Lempertz, Koln #1488/R

HERMANS, Charles (1839-1924) Belgian

Works on paper			
£333	$613	€500	L'etal du boucher (47x50cm-19x20in) s. W/C. 14-Jun-4 Horta, Bruxelles #281

HERMANS, Paul (1898-1972) Belgian

£272	$487	€400	Portrait d'homme (90x73cm-35x29in) s.d.26. 16-Mar-4 Vanderkindere, Brussels #390
£436	$811	€650	Venice (38x46cm-15x18in) s.d.1951 panel. 6-Mar-4 Arnold, Frankfurt #740/R

HERMANSEN, O A (1849-1897) Danish

£281	$469	€410	Nature morte with bird and cranberries (43x28cm-17x11in) mono. 25-Oct-3 Rasmussen, Havnen #2230/R (D.KR 3000)
£649	$1201	€948	Nature morte with bird caught in berry trap (43x28cm-17x11in) mono. i.verso. 15-Mar-4 Rasmussen, Vejle #205/R (D.KR 7200)
£1308	$2067	€1897	Winter's day in Fiol street with church and university (25x28cm-10x11in) mono.d.77. 2-Sep-3 Rasmussen, Copenhagen #1791/R est:15000 (D.KR 14000)

HERMANSEN, Olaf August (1849-1897) Danish

£944	$1700	€1378	Still life of poppies (46x36cm-18x14in) mono.d.1883 prov. 21-Jan-4 Sotheby's, New York #236/R est:2500-3500
£1478	$2646	€2158	Still life of flowers (25x20cm-10x8in) s.d.1858. 25-May-4 Bukowskis, Stockholm #321/R est:10000-12000 (S.KR 20000)
£3223	$5898	€4706	Ferns, birds, snails and insects on woodland ground (55x70cm-22x28in) mono.d.1876 prov. 9-Jun-4 Rasmussen, Copenhagen #1868/R est:40000-50000 (D.KR 36000)
£4308	$7409	€6290	Still life of flowers (76x57cm-30x22in) indis.sig. 3-Dec-3 AB Stockholms Auktionsverk #2569/R est:60000-80000 (S.KR 56000)

HERMANUS, Paul (1859-1911) Belgian

£1655	$3062	€2400	Village hollandaise enneige (28x40cm-11x16in) s. panel. 19-Jan-4 Horta, Bruxelles #181 est:1200-1500
£1944	$3247	€2800	Village hollandais (73x93cm-29x37in) s.d.1892. 21-Oct-3 Galerie Moderne, Brussels #372/R
Works on paper			
£662	$1145	€967	Winter's day in town with canals (63x82cm-25x32in) s. gouache. 9-Dec-3 Rasmussen, Copenhagen #1590/R (D.KR 7000)
£800	$1432	€1200	Vue de ville animee en Hollande (29x37cm-11x15in) s. gouache W/C. 11-May-4 Vanderkindere, Brussels #3

HERMELIN, Olof (1827-1913) Swedish

£318	$569	€464	Lonely wanderer on path (19x32cm-7x13in) s. canvas on panel. 28-May-4 Uppsala Auktionskammare, Uppsala #229 (S.KR 4300)
£389	$700	€568	Harvesting (27x39cm-11x15in) s. 23-Apr-4 Weschler, Washington #130/R
£692	$1191	€1010	Autumn landscape (53x79cm-21x31in) s. 7-Dec-3 Uppsala Auktionskammare, Uppsala #190/R (S.KR 9000)
£901	$1622	€1315	Autumn landscape (81x54cm-32x21in) s.d.1907. 26-Jan-4 Lilla Bukowskis, Stockholm #373 (S.KR 12000)
£961	$1720	€1403	Morning by Sollefte river (51x79cm-20x31in) s.d.1898. 26-May-4 AB Stockholms Auktionsverk #2097/R (S.KR 13000)
£1109	$1984	€1619	Lake landscape with farm (42x60cm-17x24in) s.d.1886. 26-May-4 AB Stockholms Auktionsverk #2182/R est:20000-25000 (S.KR 15000)
£1166	$2146	€1749	Over the bridge (34x57cm-13x22in) s. 14-Jun-4 Lilla Bukowskis, Stockholm #272 est:20000-25000 (S.KR 16000)
£1183	$2117	€1727	Harvesting landscape (38x66cm-15x26in) s.d.97. 28-May-4 Uppsala Auktionskammare, Uppsala #217/R est:8000-10000 (S.KR 16000)
£1192	$2051	€1740	Spring landscape with horses grazing (22x33cm-9x13in) s.d.1883 panel prov. 3-Dec-3 AB Stockholms Auktionsverk #2476/R est:8000-10000 (S.KR 15500)
£1231	$2117	€1797	Lake landscape with figure and boats (53x80cm-21x31in) s.d.1890. 3-Dec-3 AB Stockholms Auktionsverk #2255/R est:12000-15000 (S.KR 16000)
£1231	$2117	€1797	Autumn landscape (53x79cm-21x31in) s.d.95. 7-Dec-3 Uppsala Auktionskammare, Uppsala #191/R est:10000-12000 (S.KR 16000)
£1414	$2277	€2064	Spring landscape (40x55cm-16x22in) s.d.1900. 25-Aug-3 Lilla Bukowskis, Stockholm #739 est:12000-15000 (S.KR 18500)
£1846	$3175	€2695	Harvesting the hay (57x99cm-22x39in) s.d.1869. 2-Dec-3 Bukowskis, Stockholm #169/R est:30000-40000 (S.KR 24000)
£2365	$4234	€3453	Red Riding Hood and the wolf (55x33cm-22x13in) s. 26-May-4 AB Stockholms Auktionsverk #2271/R est:20000-25000 (S.KR 32000)
£2615	$4498	€3818	First day of spring (72x101cm-28x40in) s.d.1902. 2-Dec-3 Bukowskis, Stockholm #130/R est:25000-30000 (S.KR 34000)
£3400	$6086	€4964	Lake landscape in summer (59x92cm-23x36in) s.d.1891. 25-May-4 Bukowskis, Stockholm #120/R est:20000-30000 (S.KR 46000)
£3462	$5954	€5055	Summer landscape with woman (78x52cm-31x20in) s.d.1909. 2-Dec-3 Bukowskis, Stockholm #128/R est:40000-45000 (S.KR 45000)
£3843	$6880	€5611	Summer landscape with shepherd boy and sheep (42x61cm-17x24in) s. 25-May-4 Bukowskis, Stockholm #115/R est:30000-35000 (S.KR 52000)
£4308	$7409	€6290	Couple resting by waterway (42x61cm-17x24in) s.d.1879. 2-Dec-3 Bukowskis, Stockholm #170/R est:30000-35000 (S.KR 56000)
£6000	$10320	€8760	From a park (132x91cm-52x36in) s.d.14/9 1894 exhib. 2-Dec-3 Bukowskis, Stockholm #62/R est:30000-35000 (S.KR 78000)
£6308	$10849	€9210	Woman in the avenue (110x76cm-43x30in) s.d.1901. 3-Dec-3 AB Stockholms Auktionsverk #2316/R est:50000-60000 (S.KR 82000)

HERMELIN, Olof (attrib) (1827-1913) Swedish

£604	$1111	€900	Archipelago (51x76cm-20x30in) s.d.1894. 25-Mar-4 Hagelstam, Helsinki #831/R

HERMES, Johannes (attrib) (1842-1901) German

£265	$450	€387	Landscape with birch trees and stream (56x74cm-22x29in) 1-Dec-3 O'Gallerie, Oregon #793/R

HERMOSILLA, Concha (1940-) Spanish

£759	$1366	€1100	Homage to Buster Keaton (47x38cm-19x15in) 26-Jan-4 Durán, Madrid #172/R

HERNADI-HANDMANN, Adolf (1873-1944) Hungarian

£748	$1324	€1092	Still life (74x100cm-29x39in) s.d.1912. 28-Apr-4 Kieselbach, Budapest #100/R (H.F 280000)

HERNANDEZ AMORES, German (1823-1894) Spanish
£3451 $5970 €4900 Washerwoman (100x60cm-39x24in) s. 15-Dec-3 Ansorena, Madrid #286/R est:1500

HERNANDEZ COP, Francisco (1944-) Spanish
Works on paper
£395 $714 €600 Tulips (58x44cm-23x17in) s.d.83 pastel. 14-Apr-4 Ansorena, Madrid #357/R

HERNANDEZ GUERRA, Carlos (1939-) South American?
£248 $405 €362 Untitled (73x58cm-29x23in) s. panel painted 1963. 20-Jul-3 Subastas Odalys, Caracas #135
£3276 $5570 €4783 Apure (80x100cm-31x39in) s. painted 1985. 23-Nov-3 Subastas Odalys, Caracas #81/R est:4000

HERNANDEZ LOPEZ, Rafael (1854-1917) Spanish
£448 $807 €650 Fisherman on the beach (39x79cm-15x31in) s. 26-Jan-4 Ansorena, Madrid #147/R

HERNANDEZ MOMPO, Manuel (1927-1992) Spanish
£7483 $13619 €11000 Musician (38x46cm-15x18in) s.d.1960. 3-Feb-4 Segre, Madrid #203/R est:13200
£8805 $14000 €12855 Pequeno mercado (53x66cm-21x26in) s.i.d.1965. 4-May-3 William Jenack, New York #366 est:3000-5000
£10638 $17766 €15000 Composition (50x70cm-20x28in) s. panel lit. 23-Jun-3 Durán, Madrid #217/R est:15000
£10870 $17826 €15000 Composition (50x70cm-20x28in) s.d.66 card lit. 27-May-3 Durán, Madrid #172/R est:15000
Sculpture
£6338 $11092 €9000 Wings 5 (32x32x32cm-13x13x13in) s.d.1976 oil plexiglas. 16-Dec-3 Segre, Madrid #148/R est:7200
Works on paper
£822 $1488 €1250 Seascape with boats (23x33cm-9x13in) s. W/C. 14-Apr-4 Ansorena, Madrid #361/R
£833 $1417 €1200 Two figures (16x10cm-6x4in) s.d.1957 W/C collage. 28-Oct-3 Segre, Madrid #171/R
£1528 $2597 €2200 Flute player (11x24cm-4x9in) i.d.1960 wash prov. 28-Oct-3 Segre, Madrid #172/R est:2000
£2083 $3396 €3000 Composition (25x17cm-10x7in) s.d.61 mixed media card. 16-Jul-3 Durán, Madrid #113/R est:3000
£2083 $3396 €3000 Composition (25x17cm-10x7in) s.d.61 mixed media card. 16-Jul-3 Durán, Madrid #114/R est:3000
£2658 $4200 €3881 Abstract, Mallorca (48x69cm-19x27in) s. W/C prov. 6-Apr-3 William Jenack, New York #258 est:1500-2500
£2721 $4952 €4000 Composition (24x34cm-9x13in) s.d.1971 gouache pencil. 3-Feb-4 Segre, Madrid #235/R est:4000
£3099 $5423 €4400 Untitled (32x46cm-13x18in) s.d.1983 W/C prov. 16-Dec-3 Segre, Madrid #219/R est:2500
£3819 $6493 €5500 Composition (24x34cm-9x13in) s.d.61 W/C. 28-Oct-3 Segre, Madrid #147/R est:4500
£4874 $8968 €7116 Composition (67x47cm-26x19in) s.d.70 collage Indian ink. 29-Mar-4 Rasmussen, Copenhagen #174/R est:40000 (D.KR 54000)
£4965 $8291 €7000 Composition (39x43cm-15x17in) s.d.74 mixed media. 20-Oct-3 Durán, Madrid #139/R
£5903 $9622 €8500 Women putting linen to dry (27x35cm-11x14in) s.d.73 mixed media. 23-Sep-3 Durán, Madrid #64/R est:5000
£8966 $14972 €13000 Composition (50x70cm-20x28in) s.d.66 mixed media card lit. 17-Nov-3 Durán, Madrid #235/R est:13000
£8966 $14972 €13000 Composition (49x70cm-19x28in) s.d.66 mixed media paper on board lit. 17-Nov-3 Durán, Madrid #234/R est:13000

HERNANDEZ MONJO, Francesc (1862-1937) Spanish
£837 $1423 €1222 Mercado annual (18x12cm-7x5in) s. board. 5-Nov-3 Dobiaschofsky, Bern #636/R (S.FR 1900)
£1103 $1986 €1600 Storm at sea (32x17cm-13x7in) s. board. 26-Jan-4 Durán, Madrid #131/R est:1400
£1944 $3169 €2800 Marina (39x70cm-15x28in) s. 16-Jul-3 Durán, Madrid #117/R est:2800
£2138 $3934 €3250 Eating on the beach (18x31cm-7x12in) s. board. 22-Jun-4 Durán, Madrid #169/R est:2800
£2482 $4145 €3500 Seascape with battle ships (35x55cm-14x22in) s. 20-Oct-3 Durán, Madrid #152/R
£2961 $5359 €4500 Seascape (60x40cm-24x16in) s. 14-Apr-4 Ansorena, Madrid #54/R est:4500
Works on paper
£423 $739 €600 Seascape (25x35cm-10x14in) s. W/C. 16-Dec-3 Durán, Madrid #585/R
£592 $1089 €900 Seascape with boats (17x21cm-7x8in) s. W/C. 22-Jun-4 Durán, Madrid #625/R
£966 $1738 €1400 Beach in the Baleares (25x35cm-10x14in) s. W/C. 26-Jan-4 Ansorena, Madrid #306/R
£993 $1609 €1400 Port (29x24cm-11x9in) s. W/C. 20-May-3 Ansorena, Madrid #963/R

HERNANDEZ PIJUAN, Juan (1931-) Spanish
£676 $1209 €1000 Groc de Napols (12x29cm-5x11in) s.d.90 paper. 4-May-4 Calmels Cohen, Paris #240
£1014 $1814 €1500 Folquer (19x33cm-7x13in) s.d.88 prov. 4-May-4 Calmels Cohen, Paris #241 est:1000-1500
£1831 $2930 €2600 Untitled (142x75cm-56x30in) s.d.1986 acrylic paper prov.exhib. 16-Sep-3 Segre, Madrid #135/R
Works on paper
£3448 $6207 €5000 Landscape 6 (81x100cm-32x39in) s.d.1963 mixed media. 26-Jan-4 Durán, Madrid #204/R est:5000

HERNANDEZ SANZ, Agustin (1931-) Spanish
£671 $1255 €1000 Woman begging (86x68cm-34x27in) s. 24-Feb-4 Durán, Madrid #194/R
£993 $1658 €1400 Landscape (54x65cm-21x26in) s. 20-Oct-3 Durán, Madrid #214/R

HERNANDEZ XOCHITIOTZIN, Desidero (1922-) Mexican
£7263 $13000 €10604 Christmas fair (81x61cm-32x24in) s.d.1952 masonite prov.exhib. 26-May-4 Sotheby's, New York #86/R est:10000-15000

HERNANDEZ, Daniel (1856-1932) Peruvian
£4310 $7716 €6293 Two women on park bench (59x80cm-23x31in) s.i. 12-May-4 Dobiaschofsky, Bern #599/R est:14000 (S.FR 10000)
£4310 $7716 €6293 Goose maid (44x30cm-17x12in) s. canvas on board. 12-May-4 Dobiaschofsky, Bern #600/R est:10000 (S.FR 10000)

HERNANDEZ, Jose (1944-) Spanish
Works on paper
£445 $757 €650 Becerro (25x25cm-10x10in) s.d.1969 ink dr. 4-Nov-3 Ansorena, Madrid #209
£845 $1479 €1200 Human study (50x35cm-20x14in) s.d.1982 pencil col pastel dr. 16-Dec-3 Segre, Madrid #193

HERNANDEZ, Lucho (1973-) Spanish?
Works on paper
£490 $842 €700 La guitarra herrida (52x70cm-20x28in) s. mixed media. 5-Dec-3 Chochon-Barre & Allardi, Paris #109

HERNANDEZ, Miguel (1893-1957) Spanish
£999 $1819 €1500 Two feminine figures (27x21cm-11x8in) s.d.51 paper. 30-Jun-4 Calmels Cohen, Paris #82/R est:500-600
£1067 $1941 €1600 Female figures (27x21cm-11x8in) s.d.51 paper. 30-Jun-4 Calmels Cohen, Paris #88/R est:500-600

HERNANDEZ, Pico (20th C) ?
£900 $1467 €1305 Cotton picking in Brazil (16x24cm-6x9in) s. board. 21-Jul-3 Sotheby's, London #146

HERNANDEZ, Sergio (1957-) Mexican
£2000 $3500 €2920 Animal (60x50cm-24x20in) s.d.1994 verso. 19-Dec-3 Sotheby's, New York #1211/R est:6000-8000
£7263 $13000 €10604 Mates (120x80cm-47x31in) s.d.83. 26-May-4 Sotheby's, New York #185/R est:10000-15000
£22346 $40000 €32625 Bread tree (180x300cm-71x118in) i.verso oil sand linen painted 1995 prov. 26-May-4 Sotheby's, New York #47/R est:50000-70000
£22353 $38000 €32635 Sin titulo - untitled (190x280cm-75x110in) s.i. oil sand painted 1998 prov. 18-Nov-3 Christie's, Rockefeller NY #13/R est:25000-30000
Works on paper
£474 $806 €692 Untitled (29x38cm-11x15in) s. mixed media. 30-Oct-3 Louis Morton, Mexico #137/R (M.P 9000)
£843 $1433 €1231 Untitled (28x37cm-11x15in) s. mixed media. 30-Oct-3 Louis Morton, Mexico #19/R est:20000 (M.P 16000)

HERNANDEZ, Vicente (1971-) Cuban
£4706 $8000 €6871 El ultimo vuelo de matias y sus amigos (102x76cm-40x30in) s.d.03 exhib. 19-Nov-3 Sotheby's, New York #170/R est:10000-15000

HERNDON, Lawrence (1883-?) American
£535 $1000 €781 Man ice sailing (91x71cm-36x28in) s. painted c.1930. 26-Feb-4 Illustration House, New York #93

HERNICK, Alois (1870-1939) Austrian
£280 $476 €400 Traunsee (57x76cm-22x30in) s. board. 27-Nov-3 Dorotheum, Linz #436/R
£367 $656 €550 Trafoi on Stilfser Joch (37x46cm-15x18in) s. i. verso board. 13-May-4 Dorotheum, Linz #457/R
£548 $932 €800 Danae (71x100cm-28x39in) s.d.1925 lit. 6-Nov-3 Allgauer, Kempten #3451/R

HEROLD, Georg (1947-) German
Works on paper
£4895 $8322 €7000 Untitled (130x160cm-51x63in) s.d.90 verso caviar acrylic varnish canvas prov. 27-Nov-3 Lempertz, Koln #178/R est:7500

HEROLD, J (19th C) Austrian
Miniatures
£798 $1300 €1165 Europa and the bull (20x10cm-8x4in) s. ivorine gilt metal frame easel backing. 19-Jul-3 Skinner, Boston #436/R est:1200-1800

HEROLD, Jacques (1910-1987) Rumanian
£576 $944 €800 Composition (63x48cm-25x19in) s. oil paper. 6-Jun-3 David Kahn, Paris #30
£909 $1545 €1300 Il n'y a pas de raison (52x63cm-20x25in) s. i.d.1969 verso prov. 23-Nov-3 Cornette de St.Cyr, Paris #156/R
£4000 $7280 €5840 Retour de Londres (80x100cm-31x39in) s.i.d.58 stretcher prov. 4-Feb-4 Sotheby's, Olympia #188/R est:4000-6000
Sculpture
£7483 $13395 €11000 Femmoiselle (45cm-18in) plaster exec 1945 prov.exhib.lit. 21-Mar-4 Calmels Cohen, Paris #33/R est:5000-7000
£16176 $27500 €23617 Femmoiselle (111cm-44in) i. num.3/8 green pat bronze st.f.Bacquel prov. 6-Nov-3 Sotheby's, New York #281/R est:10000-15000

Works on paper			
£395	$726	€600	Composition (64x49cm-25x19in) s. mixed media. 27-Jun-4 Versailles Encheres #130/R
£680	$1217	€1000	Untitled (27x18cm-11x7in) i.d.1951 ink wax. 21-Mar-4 Calmels Cohen, Paris #68/R
£1958	$3368	€2800	Untitled (50x65cm-20x26in) s.d.42 gouache prov. 2-Dec-3 Calmels Cohen, Paris #31/R est:2000-2500

HEROLD-GRAFF, Johanna Helena (1668-?) German

Works on paper			
£10135	$17838	€15000	Poppy in three stages of flowering, with caterpillar, pupa and butterfly (38x30cm-15x12in) W/C gouache black chk vellum prov.lit. 19-May-4 Sotheby's, Amsterdam #197/R est:12000-18000
£18919	$33297	€28000	Tulips, hyacinth, tuffett and its pupa, and caterpillar (37x30cm-15x12in) pen black ink W/C gouache black chk vellum prov.exhib. 19-May-4 Sotheby's, Amsterdam #198/R est:14000-18000

HERON, Hilary (1923-) Irish

Sculpture			
£2517	$4280	€3600	Adam and Eve (29cm-11in) i.d.July 51 carved wood pair prov. 25-Nov-3 De Veres Art Auctions, Dublin #105/R est:2000-3000

HERON, James (fl.1880-1919) British

£703	$1300	€1026	Preparing for the day (61x102cm-24x40in) s.d.1882. 10-Mar-4 Doyle, New York #24/R
Works on paper			
£307	$500	€448	Stone bridge (15x20cm-6x8in) s. W/C board. 28-Sep-3 Simpson's, Houston #162/R
£320	$522	€467	Coastal scene with beached boats and figures (28x51cm-11x20in) s. W/C. 27-Sep-3 Rogers Jones, Clwyd #28
£340	$561	€496	Gill Snu Mill (44x30cm-17x12in) s.d.1908 W/C. 5-Jul-3 Shapes, Edinburgh #365

HERON, Patrick (1920-1999) British

£20000	$34400	€29200	Lamp and lemon (37x37cm-15x15in) s.d.48 panel prov. 2-Dec-3 Bonhams, New Bond Street #154/R est:10000-15000
£35000	$64050	€51100	London window, evening (63x132cm-25x52in) s. prov. 2-Jun-4 Sotheby's, London #99/R est:20000-30000
£52000	$89440	€75920	Shostakovitch, Reds and Greens (152x152cm-60x60in) s.i.d. May 1981. 2-Dec-3 Bonhams, New Bond Street #196/R est:12000-18000
£63000	$107100	€91980	Mainly ultramarine and venetian, November 1966 (183x213cm-72x84in) s. i.verso prov.exhib.lit. 21-Nov-3 Christie's, London #186/R est:30000-40000
Prints			
£2000	$3660	€2920	Interlocking pink and vermillion with blues (58x78cm-23x31in) s.num.7/100 col screenprint. 3-Jun-4 Christie's, Kensington #367/R est:1000-1500
£2100	$3570	€3066	Abstract composition (70x102cm-28x40in) s.d.1970 num.15/100 silkscreen. 1-Dec-3 Bonhams, New Bond Street #214/R est:800-1200
Works on paper			
£440	$717	€638	Portrait of Roger Hilton (25x20cm-10x8in) s.i.d.December 30th 56 pencil dr. 23-Sep-3 Bonhams, Leeds #96a
£4200	$7770	€6132	22 July 1995 I (30x40cm-12x16in) gouache prov. 11-Mar-4 Christie's, Kensington #385/R est:3000-5000
£4200	$7518	€6132	May 1 (18x23cm-7x9in) s.d.May I 1976 gouache prov. 14-May-4 Christie's, Kensington #646/R est:3000-5000
£4800	$8784	€7008	Green, red and blue (39x56cm-15x22in) gouache. 2-Jun-4 Sotheby's, London #108/R est:7000
£5000	$9250	€7300	22 Juky 1995 II (30x40cm-12x16in) gouache prov. 11-Mar-4 Christie's, Kensington #389/R est:3000-5000
£5500	$9350	€8030	January 15, 1983 I (42x51cm-17x20in) gouache prov. 21-Nov-3 Christie's, London #185/R est:4000-6000
£5500	$9845	€8030	May III (18x23cm-7x9in) s.d.May III 1976 verso gouache prov. 14-May-4 Christie's, Kensington #644/R est:4000-6000
£5800	$10556	€8468	May 11 1986 I (33x47cm-13x19in) gouache prov. 1-Jul-4 Christie's, Kensington #408/R est:4000-6000
£6000	$10020	€8760	Pink, blue, brown interlock (18x23cm-7x9in) gouache prov. 16-Oct-3 Christie's, Kensington #707/R est:2000-3000
£6600	$12078	€9636	Violet and blue flooding olive (18x23cm-7x9in) gouache exec. February 1968. 28-Jul-4 Mallams, Oxford #274/R est:2000-3000
£7500	$11925	€10950	Muted red, brown and orange with lemon (57x77cm-22x30in) gouache. 10-Sep-3 Sotheby's, Olympia #318/R est:2000-3000
£9000	$14310	€13140	Irregular diagonals, blues, brown, red (17x23cm-7x9in) gouache. 10-Sep-3 Sotheby's, Olympia #319/R est:2500-3500
£12000	$21480	€17520	Dark pink in cobalt with egg yellow (58x79cm-23x31in) gouache prov. 16-Mar-4 Bonhams, New Bond Street #85/R est:7000-10000
£95000	$173850	€138700	Dahlias on a gas stove (41x51cm-16x20in) s.d.46 i.stretcher pencil oil on canvas prov. 4-Jun-4 Christie's, London #121/R est:30000-50000

HEROULT, Antoine Desire (1802-1853) French

Works on paper			
£2200	$3938	€3212	French merchant frigate Chile preparing to set sail (61x91cm-24x36in) s. brown ink W/C bodycol. 26-May-4 Christie's, Kensington #412/R est:1500-2000

HERP, Willem van (elder) (1614-1677) Flemish

£6000	$10980	€8760	Angels preparing the Virgin (68x98cm-27x39in) copper prov. 9-Jul-4 Christie's, Kensington #2/R est:4000-6000
£9000	$16200	€13140	Adoration of the Shepherds (74x53cm-29x21in) copper. 21-Apr-4 Christie's, London #16/R est:8000-12000
£26000	$47580	€37960	Bilocation of Saint Anthony of Padua (78x110cm-31x43in) s. copper. 8-Jul-4 Sotheby's, London #255/R est:15000-20000
£50336	$93624	€75000	Izaac blessing Jacob (137x210cm-54x83in) 2-Mar-4 Ansorena, Madrid #275/R est:75000

HERP, Willem van (elder-circle) (1614-1677) Flemish

£5500	$10065	€8030	Triumph of David (112x154cm-44x61in) i. 9-Jul-4 Christie's, Kensington #69/R est:6000-8000

HERP, Willem van (elder-studio) (1614-1677) Flemish

£17000	$28900	€24820	Isaac blessing Jacob (138x206cm-54x81in) 30-Oct-3 Sotheby's, Olympia #48/R est:6000-8000

HERPIGNY (?) ?

£355	$592	€500	Kermesse. 17-Jun-3 Galerie Moderne, Brussels #443

HERPIN, Léon (1841-1880) French

£1028	$1717	€1450	Port de Socoa (34x52cm-13x20in) s. 22-Jun-3 Versailles Encheres #25/R

HERRAEZ Y RODRIGUEZ, Felix (1891-1976) Spanish

£276	$497	€400	Wood (22x29cm-9x11in) s. board. 26-Jan-4 Ansorena, Madrid #136/R

HERRAN, Carlos de la (1930-) Spanish

£268	$502	€400	Homage to Cezanne (35x21cm-14x8in) s. s.i.d.2003 verso board. 24-Feb-4 Durán, Madrid #32/R

HERREGOUTS, Jan Baptist (c.1640-1721) Flemish

Works on paper			
£959	$1630	€1400	Mythological scene (25x38cm-10x15in) pen brown ink wash red chk over black chk. 4-Nov-3 Sotheby's, Amsterdam #157/R

HERREMANS, L (1858-1921) Belgian

£5068	$9071	€7500	Scene nocturne de rue a Bruxelles (72x48cm-28x19in) 10-May-4 Amberes, Antwerp #274

HERREMANS, Lievin (1858-1921) Belgian

£250	$393	€363	Portrait of a lady seated wearing a hat and burgundy coat (61x50cm-24x20in) s. panel. 28-Aug-3 Christie's, Kensington #49
£333	$597	€500	Bords du Rhin animes a Sankt-Goar (28x42cm-11x17in) s. panel. 11-May-4 Vanderkindere, Brussels #248
£347	$552	€500	Portrait de la mariee (49x36cm-19x14in) s. panel. 9-Sep-3 Vanderkindere, Brussels #21
£694	$1104	€1000	Dans les coulisses du cirque (92x61cm-36x24in) s. 9-Sep-3 Vanderkindere, Brussels #10
Works on paper			
£667	$1207	€1000	Le beguinage de Bruges (59x84cm-23x33in) s. pastel. 30-Mar-4 Palais de Beaux Arts, Brussels #608

HERRER, Cesar de (1868-1919) Spanish

£694	$1104	€1000	Pergola a Venise (36x26cm-14x10in) s. cardboard. 15-Sep-3 Horta, Bruxelles #304
£1060	$1928	€1600	Venice (30x14cm-12x6in) s.i.d.97 panel. 19-Jun-4 Dannenberg, Berlin #568/R est:1500
£1305	$2258	€1905	Nude with red draperies (58x88cm-23x35in) s.d.1916. 12-Dec-3 Kieselbach, Budapest #176/R (H.F 500000)
£1581	$2861	€2308	Venetian scene (34x28cm-13x11in) s. 16-Apr-4 Mu Terem Galeria, Budapest #128/R (H.F 600000)
£2036	$3380	€2973	View of Venice (54x43cm-21x17in) s. 4-Oct-3 Kieselbach, Budapest #10/R (H.F 750000)
£3056	$5042	€4400	Palaces on Lagoon, Venice (28x48cm-11x19in) s. 3-Jul-3 Van Ham, Cologne #1241/R est:5800

HERRERA, Arturo (1959-) Venezuelan

£14525	$26000	€21207	From the road (216x192cm-85x76in) s.d.2001 verso acrylic paper collage on paper prov.lit. 14-May-4 Phillips, New York #108/R est:15000-20000
Works on paper			
£598	$1100	€873	Untitled (61x48cm-24x19in) init.d.2000 verso collage W/C prov. 10-Jun-4 Phillips, New York #702/R
£707	$1300	€1032	Untitled (61x48cm-24x19in) init.d.2000 verso W/C prov. 10-Jun-4 Phillips, New York #483/R est:1500-2000
£870	$1600	€1270	Untitled (60x48cm-24x19in) init.d.2000 verso collage W/C prov. 10-Jun-4 Phillips, New York #481/R est:1500-2000
£1033	$1900	€1508	Untitled (59x48cm-23x19in) init.d.2000 verso collage W/C prov. 10-Jun-4 Phillips, New York #479/R est:1500-2000
£8380	$15000	€12235	Study for when alone again/Hammer Museum (119x207cm-47x81in) s.i.d.2001 col pencil tracing paper prov. 14-May-4 Phillips, New York #338/R est:8000-12000
£16471	$28000	€24048	Behind the house I - two units (258x358cm-102x141in) col felt exec. 1999 prov.exhib.lit. 18-Nov-3 Christie's, Rockefeller NY #2/R est:15000-20000
£26816	$48000	€39151	I am yours (161x457cm-63x180in) wool felt executed 2000 prov. 13-May-4 Phillips, New York #55/R est:20000-30000

HERRERA, Carlos Maria (1875-1914) Uruguayan

£2614	$4600	€3816	Little girl (61x83cm-24x33in) exhib.lit. 5-Jan-4 Galeria y Remates, Montevideo #125/R est:6000-8000
Works on paper			
£5294	$9000	€7729	Peasant man (56x36cm-22x14in) s.d. 25-Nov-3 Galeria y Remates, Montevideo #133/R
£6176	$10500	€9017	Peasant man (46x36cm-18x14in) s.d.1907 pastel. 25-Nov-3 Galeria y Remates, Montevideo #134/R

HERRERA, Francisco (elder) (1576-1656) Spanish

Works on paper			
£8500	$15555	€12410	Man in a cloak (15x11cm-6x4in) black chk blue wash prov. 6-Jul-4 Christie's, London #96/R est:2000-4000

HERRERA, Jose (1943-) Spanish

£348	$637	€508	Deux bustes feminins (58x36cm-23x14in) s. i.verso. 5-Jun-4 Galerie du Rhone, Sion #336 (S.FR 800)

HERRERA, Octavio (1952-) Venezuelan

£330	$535	€482	Relief descriptive rouge-vert (45x22cm-18x9in) s.i.d.1993 verso acrylic canvas on board panel. 24-May-3 Burkhard, Luzern #95/R (S.FR 700)

HERRERO SOLANO, Luis (20th C) Spanish

Works on paper

£278	$442	€400	Corrida de toros (40x60cm-16x24in) s. W/C. 29-Apr-3 Durán, Madrid #738/R

HERRERO, Mari Puri (1942-) Spanish

£1944	$3306	€2800	Zebra crossing (46x55cm-18x22in) s.d.1973. 28-Oct-3 Segre, Madrid #185/R est:2800

HERRFELDT, Marcel René von (1890-1965) French

£582	$990	€850	Young girl naked on sofa (35x51cm-14x20in) s. board. 5-Nov-3 Hugo Ruef, Munich #1242
£621	$1000	€900	Red shoes (30x65cm-12x26in) s. board. 24-Aug-3 Bonhams & Butterfields, Los Angeles #7034 est:2000-3000
£795	$1446	€1200	Nude gypsy (60x50cm-24x20in) s. 16-Jun-4 Hugo Ruef, Munich #1200
£890	$1514	€1300	Nude in English Garden (60x49cm-24x19in) s. 5-Nov-3 Hugo Ruef, Munich #1244
£1096	$1863	€1600	Nude girl with young man (31x22cm-12x9in) s. 5-Nov-3 Hugo Ruef, Munich #1243/R est:800
£1333	$2427	€2000	Reclining nude on a rock (70x90cm-28x35in) s. 1-Jul-4 Weidler, Nurnberg #315/R est:1900
£1457	$2652	€2200	Female nude (90x70cm-35x28in) s. 16-Jun-4 Hugo Ruef, Munich #1199/R est:900
£1733	$3120	€2600	Woman in rowing boat (55x44cm-22x17in) s. 22-Apr-4 Weidler, Nurnberg #330/R est:1500
£1736	$2899	€2500	Female nude (80x110cm-31x43in) s. lit. 25-Oct-3 Bergmann, Erlangen #974/R est:2500
£1773	$2961	€2500	Nude girl on beach (3x123cm-1x48in) s. 17-Oct-3 Behringer, Furth #1597/R est:1400

HERRICK, Arthur R (1897-1970) American

£252	$400	€368	The back road (41x51cm-16x20in) s. canvasboard. 10-Sep-3 Alderfer's, Hatfield #359

HERRICK, William Salter (fl.1852-1888) British

£1200	$2148	€1752	Little flower girl (60x49cm-24x19in) s.d.1860. 16-Mar-4 Bonhams, Oxford #52 est:400-600

HERRIMAN, George (1880-1944) American

Works on paper

£3352	$6000	€4894	Krazy is serenaded at Ignatz instigation who winds up in jail (51x46cm-20x18in) s. pen ink. 15-May-4 Illustration House, New York #56/R est:6000-8000

HERRING, Benjamin (19th C) British

£300	$531	€438	Ploughmen at work (43x61cm-17x24in) 29-Apr-4 Gorringes, Lewes #2552

HERRING, Benjamin (jnr) (1830-1871) British

£3000	$5520	€4380	Steeplechasing (17x23cm-7x9in) s. board pair. 23-Mar-4 Bonhams, New Bond Street #37/R est:3000-5000

HERRING, Benjamin (snr) (1806-1830) British

£83799	$150000	€122347	Southampton and London Royal Mail Coach (72x122cm-28x48in) s.d.1829 prov.exhib.lit. 27-May-4 Sotheby's, New York #221/R est:30000-40000

HERRING, J F (19/20th C) British

£2500	$4675	€3650	Study of the racehorse Ellis, winner of the St Leger 1836 (33x43cm-13x17in) s. 26-Feb-4 Mallams, Cheltenham #246/R est:300-500

Works on paper

£1000	$1760	€1460	Farmyard scenes (25x42cm-10x17in) W/C pair. 19-May-4 James Thompson, Kirby Lonsdale #182

HERRING, J F (jnr) (1815-1907) British

£1000	$1840	€1460	Figures with horses and farm cart in a lane (12x18cm-5x7in) bears sig. 11-Jun-4 Keys, Aylsham #699/R est:1000-1200

HERRING, J F (snr) (1795-1865) British

£3145	$5000	€4592	Bay Middleton 1836 Derby Winner, bred by The Earl of Jersey. 25-Feb-3 Bunch, West Chester #486a/R

HERRING, John Frederick (19/20th C) British

£1667	$2883	€2434	Horses and farmyard animals outside the barn (52x76cm-20x30in) s. 9-Dec-3 Pinneys, Montreal #65 est:6000-8000 (C.D 3750)
£8800	$16016	€12848	Farmyard scene in winter (35x51cm-14x20in) bears sig. prov. 1-Jul-4 Sotheby's, London #348/R est:8000-12000
£10500	$19110	€15330	Hay cart (30x46cm-12x18in) s. prov. 1-Jul-4 Sotheby's, London #347/R est:7000-10000

HERRING, John Frederick (attrib) (19/20th C) British

£1471	$2500	€2148	Stable scene with rabbits (26x30cm-10x12in) board. 25-Nov-3 Galeria y Remates, Montevideo #185/R
£5000	$8500	€7300	Stable scene (50x76cm-20x30in) s. 25-Nov-3 Galeria y Remates, Montevideo #184/R

HERRING, John Frederick (jnr) (1815-1907) British

£3500	$5950	€5110	Farmyard scene (29x44cm-11x17in) s. 29-Oct-3 Bonhams, Chester #517/R est:3000-5000
£4400	$6952	€6380	Three horses outside a stable (30x46cm-12x18in) s. 3-Sep-3 Bonhams, Bury St Edmunds #442/R est:3000-5000
£4651	$8000	€6790	Horses, pigs and ducks in a farmyard (36x51cm-14x20in) s. prov. 5-Dec-3 Christie's, Rockefeller NY #43/R est:10000-15000
£4800	$8160	€7008	Horse and pigs in a farmyard (32x47cm-13x19in) s. prov. 25-Nov-3 Christie's, London #117/R est:4000-6000
£5500	$8690	€7975	Plough team (41x41cm-16x16in) s. painted circle prov. 4-Sep-3 Christie's, Kensington #310/R est:6000-8000
£6000	$11040	€8760	Mare and foal with a pack of hounds (46x61cm-18x24in) 10-Jun-4 Christie's, Kensington #92/R est:6000-8000
£6400	$11264	€9344	Hereford bull in a farmyard (44x60cm-17x24in) s.d.1845. 18-May-4 Woolley & Wallis, Salisbury #182/R est:4000-6000
£6704	$12000	€9788	Cart horses in a yard (61cm-24in circular) mono.d.1854 prov. 27-May-4 Sotheby's, New York #257/R est:15000-25000
£7500	$13875	€10950	Huntsman and hounds at the kennels (40x61cm-16x24in) s. 10-Mar-4 Sotheby's, Olympia #188/R est:6000-8000
£7800	$12948	€11388	Farmyard friends (45x59cm-18x23in) s. prov. 1-Oct-3 Sotheby's, Olympia #38/R est:8000-12000
£7930	$13480	€11578	Farmstead (61x92cm-24x36in) s. 5-Nov-3 Dobiaschofsky, Bern #637/R est:18000 (S.FR 18000)
£8500	$14450	€12410	Horses and cattle in a farmyard (32x47cm-13x19in) s. prov. 25-Nov-3 Christie's, London #116/R est:6000-8000
£8500	$15640	€12410	At the ford (38x51cm-15x20in) s.d.1854. 26-Mar-4 Sotheby's, London #44/R est:6000-8000
£10000	$17000	€14600	Plough team (51x76cm-20x30in) s. 25-Nov-3 Christie's, London #115/R est:8000-12000
£10000	$18400	€14600	Farmyard companions (71x91cm-28x36in) s. 11-Jun-4 Christie's, London #125/R est:10000-15000
£10067	$17819	€15000	Stable yard with two horses and a foal, a riverine landscape beyond (38x51cm-15x20in) s.d.1854. 27-Apr-4 Whyte's, Dublin #56/R est:10000-12000
£10465	$18000	€15279	Full cry (47x75cm-19x30in) s. prov. 5-Dec-3 Christie's, Rockefeller NY #66/R est:25000-35000
£11828	$22000	€17269	At the Barnyard door. The Watering Pond (30x46cm-12x18in) s. pair prov. 6-Mar-4 North East Auctions, Portsmouth #1117/R est:15000-25000
£20000	$34000	€29200	Farmyard scene with horses, pigs, cattle and poultry (64x92cm-25x36in) bears sig.d. 19-Nov-3 Bonhams, New Bond Street #44/R est:20000-30000
£44693	$80000	€65252	Mundig with William Scott up (56x76cm-22x30in) s.i.d.1835 prov. 27-May-4 Sotheby's, New York #234/R est:80000-120000

Works on paper

£300	$501	€438	Fall at the ditch (18x28cm-7x11in) s. ink wash. 12-Nov-3 Halls, Shrewsbury #254/R
£600	$1020	€876	Crossing the burn (21x31cm-8x12in) s. W/C. 19-Nov-3 Sotheby's, Olympia #51/R
£820	$1394	€1197	Disastrous fence. Farmer O'Phat and Squire McLean (19x26cm-7x10in) s. one i. W/C pair. 19-Nov-3 Sotheby's, Olympia #50/R
£880	$1496	€1285	Casting for scent. Breaking for cover (21x31cm-8x12in) s. W/C pair. 19-Nov-3 Sotheby's, Olympia #49/R
£1200	$2040	€1752	Horses grazing (19x29cm-7x11in) s. W/C gouache. 19-Nov-3 Sotheby's, Olympia #52/R est:400-600

HERRING, John Frederick (jnr-attrib) (1815-1907) British

£1700	$3128	€2482	Horses, ducks and a goat, in a farmyard (35x34cm-14x13in) painted oval. 10-Jun-4 Christie's, Kensington #90/R est:2000-3000
£6471	$11000	€9448	Barnyard (45x76cm-18x30in) s.i. prov. 21-Nov-3 Skinner, Boston #222/R est:6000-8000

HERRING, John Frederick (snr) (1795-1865) British

£2793	$5000	€4078	End of the day (51x61cm-20x24in) s. 6-May-4 Doyle, New York #8/R est:8000-10000
£4651	$8000	€6790	Grey mare and chestnut foal by a stable (25x30cm-10x12in) s.d.1853 panel prov. 5-Dec-3 Christie's, Rockefeller NY #41/R est:10000-15000
£5500	$9350	€8030	Carriage horse and groom in a stable (31x36cm-12x14in) prov. 25-Nov-3 Christie's, London #97/R est:6000-8000
£9000	$16560	€13140	Grey Arab mare outside a stable in an extensive river landscape (56x76cm-22x30in) 26-Mar-4 Sotheby's, London #43/R est:10000-15000
£10000	$17600	€14600	Cotherstone - a bay racehorse in a stable (56x76cm-22x30in) prov. 21-May-4 Christie's, London #48/R est:12000-18000
£10000	$17600	€14600	Music, a white bull in a landscape (38x51cm-15x20in) s.indis.d. prov. 18-May-4 Woolley & Wallis, Salisbury #159/R est:4000-6000
£11000	$19360	€16060	Grey pony with a dog by a stable door (25x36cm-10x14in) init.d.1855 prov. 21-May-4 Christie's, London #53/R est:8000-12000
£13966	$25000	€20390	Bloomsbury (63x76cm-25x30in) s.d.1839. 27-May-4 Sotheby's, New York #228/R est:20000-30000
£14000	$25760	€20440	Goose and gosling in a landscape, figures beyond (25x30cm-10x12in) s.d.1855 panel. 11-Jun-4 Christie's, London #70/R est:10000-15000
£16000	$26560	€23360	Sow and five piglets near a sty (24x29cm-9x11in) s.d.1854 panel. 1-Oct-3 Woolley & Wallis, Salisbury #327/R est:3000-5000
£19000	$33440	€27740	Mare and foal by a bothy (25x30cm-10x12in) s.d.1854 board. 21-May-4 Christie's, London #52/R est:10000-15000
£20000	$34000	€29200	Filho Da Puta, dark bay racehorse with Thomas Goodisson up (35x45cm-14x18in) s.i. 27-Nov-3 Sotheby's, London #212/R est:20000-30000
£24000	$44160	€35040	Mr H M Greaves's liver chestnut hunter, tethered to a gate at Page Hall, Yorkshire (55x76cm-22x30in) panel prov. 11-Jun-4 Christie's, London #67/R est:10000-15000
£26000	$44200	€37960	Portrait of James Hartley with a grey carriage horse, in an extensive river landscape (71x91cm-28x36in) s.d.1838 prov. 25-Nov-3 Christie's, London #100/R est:30000-50000
£30000	$55200	€43800	Morning. preparing to plough (47x72cm-19x28in) s.d.1848 prov. 11-Jun-4 Christie's, London #69/R est:30000-50000
£53719	$91322	€78430	In the highlands - rest during the a day's sport (72x94cm-28x37in) s.d.1857 prov. 29-Oct-3 Lawson Menzies, Sydney #39/R est:200000-300000 (A.D 130000)
£80000	$136000	€116800	Three horses at a stable door with pigs and doves (80x80cm-31x31in) s.d.1848 prov. 25-Nov-3 Christie's, London #92/R est:80000-120000
£150838	$270000	€220223	Charles XII, winner of the Saint-Leger (71x91cm-28x36in) s.d.1839 prov.exhib. 27-May-4 Sotheby's, New York #235/R est:250000-350000
£460000	$809600	€671600	Matilda and Mameluke - The finish of the 1827 St Leger (16x91cm-6x36in) s.d.1827 prov. 21-May-4 Christie's, London #47/R est:150000-250000

HERRING, John Frederick (snr-after) (1795-1865) British
Prints
£85000 $144500 €124100 Portraits of the winners of the Great Saint Leger and Derby Stakes (59x42cm-23x17in) aquatint prints album. 1-Dec-3 Bonhams, New Bond Street #102/R est:40000-60000

HERRING, John Frederick (snr-attrib) (1795-1865) British
£1371 $2523 €2002 Racehorse with jockey up (36x46cm-14x18in) s. 14-Jun-4 Waddingtons, Toronto #124/R est:3000-5000 (C.D 3400)
£2353 $4000 €3435 Mr H M Greaves's hunter at Page Hall, Yorkshire (57x77cm-22x30in) s.d.1821 panel prov. 21-Nov-3 Skinner, Boston #227/R est:8000-10000
£2465 $4264 €3500 Head to head, grey and colt in a field at Bolton (25x32cm-10x13in) i.verso panel pair. 10-Dec-3 Christie's, Amsterdam #867/R est:3000-5000
£3488 $6000 €5092 Bay Middleton, with James Robinson up (38x46cm-15x18in) with sig.d.1836 prov. 5-Dec-3 Christie's, Rockefeller NY #18/R est:5000-7000
£18000 $28260 €26100 In the highlands (102x127cm-40x50in) 27-Aug-3 Sotheby's, London #1015/R est:18000-25000
Works on paper
£441 $750 €644 Stables scenes (19x29cm-7x11in) s.i. one d.1849 W/C pair. 21-Nov-3 Skinner, Boston #220/R

HERRLICH, Philipp (1818-1868) German
£2917 $4608 €4200 The convalescent child (30x25cm-12x10in) s.d.1843 panel. 5-Sep-3 Wendl, Rudolstadt #3416/R est:2800

HERRMANN (20th C) ?
£3007 $5022 €4300 Ville du nord animee (70x97cm-28x38in) s. 29-Jun-3 St-Germain-en-Laye Encheres #4/R est:4500

HERRMANN, Alexander (1814-1845) German
Works on paper
£567 $1014 €850 Font in St Zeno Church, Verona (31x24cm-12x9in) i.d.1839 W/C. 13-May-4 Bassenge, Berlin #5571/R

HERRMANN, Carl Gustav (1857-?) German
£816 $1461 €1200 Still life with grapes (34x48cm-13x19in) s. panel. 17-Mar-4 Neumeister, Munich #481/R

HERRMANN, Curt (1854-1929) German
£2568 $4596 €3800 Study of a woman (48x32cm-19x13in) mono. i. verso oil pencil lit. 8-May-4 Schloss Ahlden, Ahlden #813/R est:2600

HERRMANN, Curt (attrib) (1854-1929) German
£1573 $2500 €2297 In the field (58x46cm-23x18in) 12-Sep-3 Skinner, Boston #428/R est:5000-7000

HERRMANN, Ernst Paul (1870-?) German
£699 $1168 €1000 View over the Elbe of Dresden (61x95cm-24x37in) s.d.1938. 28-Jun-3 Bolland & Marotz, Bremen #664/R

HERRMANN, Frank S (1866-1942) American
Works on paper
£656 $1200 €958 Spring flowers (58x71cm-23x28in) gouache executed c.1930. 5-Jun-4 Treadway Gallery, Cincinnati #643/R est:2000-3000

HERRMANN, Gottfried (1907-) German
£267 $480 €400 Red flowers (79x35cm-31x14in) mono.d. board. 24-Apr-4 Dr Lehr, Berlin #157/R

HERRMANN, Hans (1858-1942) German
£1408 $2437 €2000 Amsterdam street (35x41cm-14x16in) s. board prov. 13-Dec-3 Lempertz, Koln #220/R est:1500
Works on paper
£898 $1500 €1311 Dockyard scene (34x50cm-13x20in) s. pencil W/C. 26-Oct-3 Bonhams & Butterfields, San Francisco #6467/R

HERRMANN, Paul (1864-1940) German
£2133 $3819 €3200 Figures in park (97x128cm-38x50in) s. lit. 14-May-4 Schloss Ahlden, Ahlden #2795/R est:2800

HERRMANN, Peter (1937-) German
£800 $1440 €1200 Boxes (45x65cm-18x26in) mono.d. mono.i.d. stretcher. 24-Apr-4 Dr Lehr, Berlin #159/R
£1067 $1920 €1600 Artist (55x50cm-22x20in) mono.d. mono.i.d. stretcher. 24-Apr-4 Dr Lehr, Berlin #158/R est:600

HERRMANN, Philipp (fl.1910) German
£599 $1090 €880 Female nude wearing pearl necklace (54x43cm-21x17in) s. 3-Feb-4 Sigalas, Stuttgart #559/R

HERRMANN, Philipp Ludwig (1841-1894) German
£433 $793 €650 Holy path with steeple (25x35cm-10x14in) 5-Jun-4 Arnold, Frankfurt #600

HERRMANN, Theodor (1884-1926) German
£403 $741 €600 On the Hamme (70x79cm-28x31in) s.d.22. 26-Mar-4 Bolland & Marotz, Bremen #331/R

HERRMANN, Willy (1895-1963) German
£503 $921 €750 Trees in coastal landscape in summer (50x70cm-20x28in) s. i.verso fibreboard lit. 8-Jul-4 Allgauer, Kempten #2112/R
£1267 $2293 €1900 Birches on moor in autumn (100x150cm-39x59in) s. 1-Apr-4 Van Ham, Cologne #1427 est:500

HERRMANN-ALLGAU, August (?) German
£699 $1272 €1021 Basket with white and blue grapes (62x47cm-24x19in) s.i. 16-Jun-4 Fischer, Luzern #2168/R (S.FR 1600)

HERRMANN-LEON, Charles (1838-1908) French
£900 $1647 €1350 Arret (36x28cm-14x11in) s. 6-Jun-4 Osenat, Fontainebleau #254/R

HERSCH, Lee F (20th C) American
£214 $400 €321 Self portrait (81x60cm-32x24in) s.d.30 prov.exhib. 25-Jul-4 Bonhams & Butterfields, San Francisco #6104/R

HERSCHEL, Otto (1871-1937) German
£221 $400 €323 Lute player (53x43cm-21x17in) s.d.1906. 3-Apr-4 Neal Auction Company, New Orleans #677

HERSCHEND, Oscar (1853-1891) Danish
£312 $558 €456 Coastal landscape (24x32cm-9x13in) mono. 12-Jan-4 Rasmussen, Vejle #32/R (D.KR 3300)
£323 $523 €472 Heather hills near Silkeborg (63x111cm-25x44in) s.i.d.87. 9-Aug-3 Hindemae, Ullerslev #73/R (D.KR 3400)
£412 $750 €602 Man in rowing boat (28x44cm-11x17in) s.i.d.89. 7-Feb-4 Rasmussen, Havnen #2291 (D.KR 4500)
£650 $1203 €949 Shipping in the Sund with view toward Kronborg Castle, Denmark (23x35cm-9x14in) 10-Feb-4 Bonhams, Knightsbridge #122/R
£1040 $1799 €1518 The lifeboat going out (50x84cm-20x33in) s.i.d.89. 9-Dec-3 Rasmussen, Copenhagen #1488/R (D.KR 11000)

HERSENT, Yves (1925-1987) French
£300 $546 €450 Cache corset rose (97x47cm-38x19in) studio st.verso board. 5-Jul-4 Millon & Associes, Paris #234
£300 $546 €450 Echecs (89x130cm-35x51in) studio st.verso. 5-Jul-4 Millon & Associes, Paris #235
£300 $546 €450 Atelier de Vermeuil (124x166cm-49x65in) studio st.verso. 5-Jul-4 Millon & Associes, Paris #238
£333 $607 €500 Etude pour fantasmes (104x47cm-41x19in) studio st.verso board. 5-Jul-4 Millon & Associes, Paris #253/R
£333 $607 €500 Miroir (130x97cm-51x38in) studio st.verso. 5-Jul-4 Millon & Associes, Paris #239
£367 $667 €550 Robe rouge (65x50cm-26x20in) studio st.verso. 5-Jul-4 Millon & Associes, Paris #195
£400 $728 €600 Chaussettes rouges (46x55cm-18x22in) studio st.verso. 5-Jul-4 Millon & Associes, Paris #189
£467 $849 €700 Couverture rouge (60x96cm-24x38in) studio st.verso. 5-Jul-4 Millon & Associes, Paris #245
£533 $971 €800 Grand nu etendu (55x155cm-22x61in) s. 5-Jul-4 Millon & Associes, Paris #226/R
£600 $1092 €900 Puce a la photo (70x41cm-28x16in) studio st.verso. 5-Jul-4 Millon & Associes, Paris #233/R
£700 $1274 €1050 Fleurs d'Annette (81x60cm-32x24in) 5-Jul-4 Millon & Associes, Paris #246/R
£2000 $3640 €3000 Canape bleu (89x130cm-35x51in) studio st.verso. 5-Jul-4 Millon & Associes, Paris #252

HERSEY, Dick (20th C) American
£1359 $2500 €2039 Caged tiger (101x76cm-40x30in) s. 8-Jun-4 Bonhams & Butterfields, San Francisco #4367/R est:3000-5000

HERSEY, Karen R (1941-) Canadian
£800 $1464 €1168 Rockwall, Floe Lake (60x75cm-24x30in) s.i. 1-Jun-4 Hodgins, Calgary #58/R est:1750-2250 (C.D 2000)

HERSHBERG, Israel (1948-) Israeli
£5587 $10000 €8157 Tree portrait (44x53cm-17x21in) init.d.86 exhib. 18-Mar-4 Sotheby's, New York #47a/R est:15000-20000
£13966 $25000 €20390 French flusher (62x61cm-24x24in) s.d.1998 verso oil panel prov. 18-Mar-4 Sotheby's, New York #48/R est:22000-28000

HERSHEY, Samuel Franklin (1904-1959) American
£273 $500 €399 On the breakwater (25x30cm-10x12in) s.i.d.1937 verso canvasboard. 5-Jun-4 Treadway Gallery, Cincinnati #627/R
£519 $950 €758 Hoberg's House, Rockport (30x36cm-12x14in) s. i.d.1937 canvasboard prov. 5-Jun-4 Treadway Gallery, Cincinnati #625/R

HERSTEIN, Adolf Edward (1869-1932) Polish
£380 $684 €555 Portrait of a lady in a hat (66x90cm-26x35in) s. 20-Jan-4 Bonhams, Knightsbridge #188/R

HERTEL, Albert (1843-1912) German
£743 $1330 €1100 Riva/Lake Garda (46x70cm-18x28in) s.i.d.84 board. 6-May-4 Michael Zeller, Lindau #698/R
£2685 $5020 €4000 Landscape near Rome (52x92cm-20x36in) mono. 24-Feb-4 Dorotheum, Vienna #177/R est:4500-5500
£2877 $4890 €4200 Hunting still life (160x113cm-63x44in) s. 5-Nov-3 Hugo Ruef, Munich #1012/R est:3000

Works on paper

£400	$716	€600	Coastal landscape with two lakes (16x38cm-6x15in) mono.i.d.69 W/C. 13-May-4 Bassenge, Berlin #5573/R

HERTEL, Carl Conrad Julius (1837-1895) German

£2533	$4611	€3800	At the fountain in Kaiserswerth (63x80cm-25x31in) s. 1-Jul-4 Van Ham, Cologne #1402/R est:3500

HERTER, Albert (1871-1950) American

Works on paper

£5882	$10000	€8588	Nativity (32x53cm-13x21in) mono. W/C triptych. 21-Nov-3 Skinner, Boston #375/R est:2500-3500

HERTERVIG, Lars (1830-1902) Norwegian

Works on paper

£6814	$11721	€9948	Fjord landscape with mountains in background (33x49cm-13x19in) s.d.1856 and 1874 W/C gouache exhib.lit. 8-Dec-3 Blomqvist, Oslo #458/R est:150000-200000 (N.KR 80000)
£11073	$19046	€16167	Fjord landscape with two large stones and two rowing boats by shore (32x50cm-13x20in) s.d.1856 exhib.lit. 8-Dec-3 Blomqvist, Oslo #459/R est:150000-200000 (N.KR 130000)

HERTH, Francis (1943-) Belgian

Works on paper

£267	$488	€400	Composition avec figure (74x104cm-29x41in) s.d.1973 ink prov. 7-Jun-4 Palais de Beaux Arts, Brussels #130

HERTLING, Wilhelm Jakob (1849-1926) German

£993	$1808	€1500	Landscape (87x118cm-34x46in) s. 16-Jun-4 Hugo Ruef, Munich #985/R est:1500

Works on paper

£567	$1020	€850	Ox cart in village street (13x19cm-5x7in) W/C on Indian ink pencil. 24-Apr-4 Reiss & Sohn, Konigstein #5498/R
£1111	$1811	€1600	River landscape (58x69cm-23x27in) s. gouache over pencil. 24-Sep-3 Neumeister, Munich #278/R est:1600

HERTZ, Mogens (1909-1990) Danish

£300	$500	€438	From the herring smokery at Bornholm (65x80cm-26x31in) s.d.43. 25-Oct-3 Rasmussen, Havnen #4184/R (D.KR 3200)
£398	$637	€577	Summer's day by Ostersoen (60x73cm-24x29in) 17-Sep-3 Kunsthallen, Copenhagen #261 (D.KR 4200)
£408	$652	€596	Interior scene with Knut Hamsun's daughter and grandchild (81x100cm-32x39in) s.d.46. 22-Sep-3 Rasmussen, Vejle #619/R (D.KR 4300)
£451	$844	€658	Bridge across canal, Venice (65x54cm-26x21in) 25-Feb-4 Kunsthallen, Copenhagen #215 (D.KR 5000)
£455	$728	€660	Mother and child (65x81cm-26x32in) s.d.50 exhib. 17-Sep-3 Kunsthallen, Copenhagen #273 (D.KR 4800)
£469	$764	€685	Smoke-cured herrings, Bornholm (65x80cm-26x31in) s.d.43. 27-Sep-3 Rasmussen, Havnen #4076/R (D.KR 5000)
£551	$1003	€827	View in Bornholm with the herring smokery (65x80cm-26x31in) s.d.43. 19-Jun-4 Rasmussen, Havnen #4013/R (D.KR 6200)
£622	$1008	€902	View across town, sea in background (27x46cm-11x18in) s. 4-Aug-3 Rasmussen, Vejle #595/R (D.KR 6500)
£638	$1066	€931	View across red roofs, Gudhjem (46x55cm-18x22in) s. 7-Oct-3 Rasmussen, Copenhagen #298 (D.KR 6800)
£682	$1092	€989	Canal scene, Venice (87x72cm-34x28in) 17-Sep-3 Kunsthallen, Copenhagen #262 (D.KR 7200)
£758	$1213	€1099	Street scene with figures (72x92cm-28x36in) s.d.44. 17-Sep-3 Kunsthallen, Copenhagen #288/R (D.KR 8000)
£777	$1244	€1127	Street scene with figures (35x41cm-14x16in) s. panel. 17-Sep-3 Kunsthallen, Copenhagen #266 (D.KR 8200)
£903	$1661	€1318	Still life of fruit (65x81cm-26x32in) s.d.47 sacking. 29-Mar-4 Rasmussen, Copenhagen #521/R (D.KR 10000)
£948	$1517	€1375	Summer landscape with farm by the sea, Bornholm (55x65cm-22x26in) s/. 17-Sep-3 Kunsthallen, Copenhagen #237/R (D.KR 10000)
£1264	$2325	€1845	Farm yard with figure in foreground (60x81cm-24x32in) s.d.56. 29-Mar-4 Rasmussen, Copenhagen #494/R est:10000-12000 (D.KR 14000)
£1317	$2239	€1923	View of Salene Bay (60x92cm-24x36in) s. 26-Nov-3 Kunsthallen, Copenhagen #296/R est:12000 (D.KR 14000)
£1354	$2491	€1977	Winter landscape, Salene Bay, Gudhjem (50x81cm-20x32in) s. 29-Mar-4 Rasmussen, Copenhagen #498/R est:10000 (D.KR 15000)
£1517	$2427	€2200	Evening by the smokery, Gudhjem (97x135cm-38x53in) 17-Sep-3 Kunsthallen, Copenhagen #256/R est:15000 (D.KR 16000)
£1613	$2903	€2355	Street scene, Bornholm with figures (60x81cm-24x32in) 24-Apr-4 Rasmussen, Havnen #4232/R est:10000 (D.KR 18000)
£1613	$2903	€2355	From Bornholm's Round Church with figures (80x70cm-31x28in) s. 24-Apr-4 Rasmussen, Havnen #4260/R est:10000-15000 (D.KR 18000)

HERVAS, Fernando (20th C) Spanish?

£355	$574	€500	Composition with apple tree (100x73cm-39x29in) 20-May-3 Ansorena, Madrid #387/R

HERVE, Isabelle (20th C) French

£300	$543	€450	Les recolteurs de vent (50x50cm-20x20in) s. acrylic. 3-Apr-4 Neret-Minet, Paris #17/R
£350	$594	€500	Un vent d'eternite (80x40cm-31x16in) s. acrylic. 29-Nov-3 Neret-Minet, Paris #61
£455	$773	€650	Le moment (60x30cm-24x12in) s. acrylic. 29-Nov-3 Neret-Minet, Paris #212/R
£559	$951	€800	La noce (80x80cm-31x31in) s. acrylic. 29-Nov-3 Neret-Minet, Paris #121/R
£700	$1267	€1050	L'envolee mauve (80x80cm-31x31in) s. acrylic. 3-Apr-4 Neret-Minet, Paris #119/R

HERVE, Jules R (1887-1981) French

£539	$900	€787	Fin d'audience (22x27cm-9x11in) s. s.i.verso prov. 7-Oct-3 Sotheby's, New York #314
£563	$975	€800	Pecheur au bord du fleuve (27x22cm-11x9in) s. 10-Dec-3 Millon & Associes, Paris #101
£592	$1089	€900	Gouter des enfants (18x24cm-7x9in) s. panel. 24-Jun-4 Credit Municipal, Paris #47
£800	$1440	€1168	Tuileries (22x27cm-9x11in) s. 20-Jan-4 Bonhams, Knightsbridge #2/R
£800	$1440	€1168	Place de la Concorde (22x27cm-9x11in) s. 20-Jan-4 Bonhams, Knightsbridge #5/R
£820	$1492	€1197	View of the Seine towards Notre Dame (9x11cm-4x4in) s. i. verso. 5-Feb-4 Amersham Auction Rooms, UK #221
£851	$1421	€1200	Danseuses dans le Foyer de l'opera (22x27cm-9x11in) s. 19-Oct-3 Peron, Melun #326
£861	$1567	€1300	Bouquinistes pres de Notre-Dame (27x22cm-11x9in) s. s.verso. 15-Jun-4 Rossini, Paris #172
£897	$1497	€1300	Enfants jouant dans le bassin des Tuileries (22x27cm-9x11in) s. prov. 17-Nov-3 Charbonneaux, Paris #208
£900	$1647	€1314	Children by the Seine (32x24cm-13x9in) s. 1-Feb-4 Lots Road Auctions, London #362
£901	$1532	€1315	Bassin du Louvre (22x27cm-9x11in) s. s.i.verso prov. 21-Nov-3 Walker's, Ottawa #227/R est:2000-2500 (C.D 2000)
£958	$1600	€1399	Still life with roses (39x33cm-15x13in) s. 26-Oct-3 Bonhams & Butterfields, San Francisco #6577/R
£993	$1808	€1500	Notre-Dame sous la neige (22x27cm-9x11in) s. cardboard. 18-Jun-4 Piasa, Paris #150 est:1500-2000
£1027	$1747	€1500	Scene de chasse a courre (22x27cm-9x11in) s. panel. 9-Nov-3 Eric Pillon, Calais #144/R
£1060	$1928	€1600	Quai aux fleurs (27x22cm-11x9in) s. s.verso. 15-Jun-4 Rossini, Paris #171 est:1200-1800
£1118	$2058	€1700	La Garde Republicaine devant le Grand Palais a Paris (38x46cm-15x18in) s. 25-Jun-4 Daguerre, Paris #162/R est:1500-2000
£1137	$1900	€1660	Still life of flowers (27x22cm-11x9in) s. 16-Nov-3 Bonhams & Butterfields, Los Angeles #7073/R est:800-1000
£1198	$2000	€1749	Wooded landscape with ducks by a stream (55x65cm-22x26in) s. 26-Oct-3 Bonhams & Butterfields, San Francisco #6472/R
£1215	$2200	€1774	Les petits amis (23x28cm-9x11in) s.verso. 3-Apr-4 Neal Auction Company, New Orleans #48 est:300-500
£1300	$2353	€1898	Jeunes filles sur les bords de Seine (22x27cm-9x11in) s. prov. 1-Apr-4 Christie's, Kensington #32/R est:1000-1500
£1312	$2191	€1916	Les petits amis (26x21cm-10x8in) s. s.i. verso prov. 17-Nov-3 Waddingtons, Toronto #205/R est:2000-3000 (C.D 2900)
£1333	$2453	€2000	A la fontaine, hameau en montagne (46x55cm-18x22in) s. prov. 9-Jun-4 Beaussant & Lefèvre, Paris #169/R est:2000-2500
£1389	$2264	€2000	Pique-nique en foret (54x65cm-21x26in) s. 29-Sep-3 Charbonneaux, Paris #231 est:2500-3000
£1406	$2250	€2053	Les Tuilleries, Paris (56x69cm-22x27in) s. board. 18-May-3 Auctions by the Bay, Alameda #1006/R
£1455	$2415	€2110	La sortie de la messe (38x46cm-15x18in) s. 13-Jun-3 Zofingen, Switzerland #2461/R est:2000 (S.FR 3200)
£1486	$2750	€2170	Fontaine, Concorde (33x41cm-13x16in) s. i.stretcher prov. 12-Feb-4 Sotheby's, New York #57/R est:1500-2000
£1492	$2745	€2178	Jardin des Tuilleriers (27x21cm-11x8in) s. s.verso. 14-Jun-4 Waddingtons, Toronto #282/R est:3000-4000 (C.D 3700)
£1497	$2500	€2186	Outside the cottage (55x47cm-22x19in) s. 26-Oct-3 Bonhams & Butterfields, San Francisco #6573/R
£1497	$2500	€2186	View of the Institute of France (46x53cm-18x21in) s. 26-Oct-3 Bonhams & Butterfields, San Francisco #6578/R
£1513	$2784	€2300	Place de la Madeleine (22x27cm-9x11in) s. s.verso. 25-Jun-4 Millon & Associes, Paris #179 est:400-500
£1534	$2500	€2240	Pont Alexandre III under the snow, Le Traineau (33x41cm-13x16in) s. s.verso. 28-Sep-3 Bonhams & Butterfields, Los Angeles #7031 est:2000-3000
£1600	$2944	€2400	Fin d'Audience (23x27cm-9x11in) s. s.i. verso. 8-Jun-4 Sotheby's, Amsterdam #201/R est:2000-3000
£1613	$2968	€2355	Ballerinas (22x27cm-9x11in) s. s.verso. 14-Jun-4 Waddingtons, Toronto #284/R est:4000-4500 (C.D 4000)
£1622	$3000	€2368	Coastal landscape (66x81cm-26x32in) s. 17-Jul-4 New Orleans Auction, New Orleans #424/R est:3500-5000
£1644	$2581	€2400	Bouquinistes devant Notre-Dame (22x27cm-9x11in) s. 20-Apr-3 Deauville, France #131/R est:2000-2500
£1647	$2750	€2405	Notre Dame under snow. Children in a drawing room (23x27cm-9x11in) s. pair. 26-Oct-3 Bonhams & Butterfields, San Francisco #6560/R
£1744	$3000	€2546	Place de la Concorde (61x71cm-24x28in) s. s.verso. 3-Dec-3 Doyle, New York #144/R est:5000-7000
£1796	$3000	€2622	Children at the basin in the Tuilleries (63x80cm-25x31in) s. 26-Oct-3 Bonhams & Butterfields, San Francisco #6569/R
£1796	$3000	€2622	Mothers and children at a table set for tea (81x66cm-32x26in) s. 26-Oct-3 Bonhams & Butterfields, San Francisco #6571/R
£1818	$3036	€2600	Danseuses (22x27cm-9x11in) s. panel. 29-Jun-3 Feletin, Province #106/R
£1899	$3400	€2773	Recital, elegant interior with figures around a piano (53x66cm-21x26in) s.verso. 29-May-4 Brunk, Ashville #107/R
£1935	$3561	€2825	Les artistes sur le quais a Paris (22x27cm-9x11in) s. s.verso. 14-Jun-4 Waddingtons, Toronto #283/R est:3000-4000 (C.D 4800)
£1946	$3250	€2841	Children with their boats at the basin, Tuilleries (63x80cm-25x31in) s. 26-Oct-3 Bonhams & Butterfields, San Francisco #6575/R
£1972	$3411	€2800	Ballade en foret sous la neige (46x55cm-18x22in) s. 15-Dec-3 Charbonneaux, Paris #193/R est:2500-3000
£1974	$3632	€3000	Foyer de l'Opera (38x46cm-15x18in) s.s.verso. 25-Jun-4 Millon & Associes, Paris #178/R est:1200-1500
£2000	$3640	€3000	Annonce du garde-champetre (38x46cm-15x18in) s. 4-Jul-4 Eric Pillon, Calais #74/R
£2065	$3800	€3015	Paris park scene (61x74cm-24x29in) s. 27-Jun-4 Hindman, Chicago #843a/R est:3000-5000
£2119	$3878	€3200	Passage du facteur a Langres (41x33cm-16x13in) s. i.verso. 7-Apr-4 Piasa, Paris #74 est:3000-4000
£2168	$3620	€3100	Dans la loge a l'opera (27x22cm-11x9in) s. 29-Jun-3 Eric Pillon, Calais #187/R
£2245	$3750	€3278	Tuillerie gardens (49x61cm-19x24in) s. 26-Oct-3 Bonhams & Butterfields, San Francisco #6562/R
£2295	$4200	€3351	Courtyard cafe (38x46cm-15x18in) s. 5-Jun-4 Neal Auction Company, New Orleans #96 est:800-1200
£2340	$3909	€3300	Printemps, jeunes enfants (41x33cm-16x13in) s. s.d.1933 verso. 19-Oct-3 Anaf, Lyon #172/R est:2000-2500
£2400	$4320	€3600	Place de la Concorde sortie des Tuileries (46x55cm-18x22in) s. 26-Apr-4 Tajan, Paris #183/R est:3000-4000
£2486	$4500	€3630	Rainy day (38x46cm-15x18in) s.verso. 3-Apr-4 Neal Auction Company, New Orleans #47/R est:800-1200

£2514	$4500	€3670	La grille en fer in the Tulleries. s.i. 13-May-4 Dallas Auction Gallery, Dallas #285/R est:2000-4000
£2545	$4250	€3716	Tuillerie gardens under snowfall (55x65cm-22x26in) s. 16-Nov-3 Bonhams & Butterfields, Los Angeles #7048/R est:4000-6000
£2545	$4250	€3716	Figures on the riverbank (46x55cm-18x22in) s. 16-Nov-3 Bonhams & Butterfields, Los Angeles #7066/R est:800-1200
£2545	$4250	€3716	Figures by a stream (46x55cm-18x22in) s. 16-Nov-3 Bonhams & Butterfields, Los Angeles #7067/R est:800-1200
£2545	$4250	€3716	Figures bathing in a stream. Children in a rowboat (23x27cm-9x11in) s. two. 16-Nov-3 Bonhams & Butterfields, Los Angeles #7068/R est:1600-2000
£2545	$4250	€3716	Reclining nude. Seated nude (22x27cm-9x11in) s. 16-Nov-3 Bonhams & Butterfields, Los Angeles #7070/R est:1200-1600
£2609	$4800	€3809	Paris park scene (56x46cm-22x18in) s. s.verso. 27-Jun-4 Hindman, Chicago #843b/R est:2000-4000
£2624	$4382	€3700	Bouquinistes sur le Pont Neuf (46x55cm-18x22in) s. 19-Jun-3 Millon & Associes, Paris #243/R est:4000-5000
£2632	$4842	€4000	Grand escalier (38x46cm-15x18in) s.s.verso. 25-Jun-4 Millon & Associes, Paris #180/R est:1200-1500
£2793	$5000	€4078	View of the River Lieze with figures. s.i. 13-May-4 Dallas Auction Gallery, Dallas #239/R est:2500-4500
£2844	$4750	€4152	Children playing in the stream (12x81cm-5x32in) s. 26-Oct-3 Bonhams & Butterfields, San Francisco #6567/R
£2844	$4750	€4152	Figures by the Bouquinistes (46x55cm-18x22in) s. 16-Nov-3 Bonhams & Butterfields, Los Angeles #7064/R est:1000-1500
£2844	$4750	€4152	Snow falling on the right bank (46x55cm-18x22in) s. 16-Nov-3 Bonhams & Butterfields, Los Angeles #7065/R est:1000-1500
£2966	$4923	€4300	Ballerines au foyer (46x55cm-18x22in) s. s.verso. 1-Oct-3 Millon & Associes, Paris #144/R
£2994	$5000	€4371	Garden table (102x81cm-40x32in) s. 26-Oct-3 Bonhams & Butterfields, San Francisco #6564/R
£2994	$5000	€4371	View of the river Lieze with figures (46x55cm-18x22in) s. 16-Nov-3 Bonhams & Butterfields, Los Angeles #7063/R est:800-1200
£3020	$5587	€4500	Paris les Tuileries (46x55cm-18x22in) s. 14-Mar-4 Eric Pillon, Calais #126/R
£3288	$5589	€4800	Paris, bouquinistes et cite (46x55cm-18x22in) s. 9-Nov-3 Eric Pillon, Calais #141/R
£3293	$5500	€4808	Bouquinistes along the Seine. Le marche aux fleurs on the Isle de la Cite (38x46cm-15x18in) s. two different sizes. 16-Nov-3 Bonhams & Butterfields, Los Angeles #7058/R est:2000-3000
£3294	$5500	€4809	Sunday afternoon at the Tuilleries (81x102cm-32x40in) s. 26-Oct-3 Bonhams & Butterfields, San Francisco #6566/R
£3380	$5848	€4800	Aux compagnons de la Belle Table (33x41cm-13x16in) s. s.i.verso. 10-Dec-3 Rossini, Paris #80/R
£3497	$5839	€5000	La Brocante (50x60cm-20x24in) s. 25-Jun-3 Rabourdin & Choppin de Janvry, Paris #21/R est:5500-6000
£3677	$6250	€5368	Paris l'Eglise de la Medeleine et les Magazin des Trois quartiers (51x51cm-20x20in) s.i.verso. 22-Nov-3 New Orleans Auction, New Orleans #668/R est:6000-9000
£3867	$6999	€5800	Musiciens dans les rues de Paris (50x60cm-20x24in) s. 30-Mar-4 Gioffredo, Nice #146/R
£3892	$6500	€5682	La grille en fer in the Tuilleries. Barc du carousel under snow (34x41cm-13x16in) s. two different sizes. 16-Nov-3 Bonhams & Butterfields, Los Angeles #7059/R est:2000-3000
£3892	$6500	€5682	Figures riding in a forest. Landscape of Langres (38x46cm-15x18in) s. two different sizes. 16-Nov-3 Bonhams & Butterfields, Los Angeles #7061/R est:2000-3000
£4491	$7500	€6557	Langres under snowfall. Street scene under rain. Rive gauche under snow (41x33cm-16x13in) s. three different sizes. 16-Nov-3 Bonhams & Butterfields, Los Angeles #7060/R est:3000-5000
£4545	$7727	€6500	Vue de l'eglise de la Madeleine (60x73cm-24x29in) s. 20-Nov-3 Gioffredo, Nice #34/R
£4636	$8437	€7000	Marche aux fleurs anime a la Madeleine (65x81cm-26x32in) s. 15-Jun-4 Vanderkindere, Brussels #78 est:750-1250
£5090	$8500	€7431	Lunch table, Cottage door. Vegetable garden (22x27cm-9x11in) s. set of three. 16-Nov-3 Bonhams & Butterfields, Los Angeles #7069/R est:1600-2000

HERVE, Juliane (1921-) French

£1644	$2795	€2400	Cyclades (97x130cm-38x51in) s. 9-Nov-3 Eric Pillon, Calais #201/R

HERVE-MATHE, Jules Alfred (1868-1953) French

£483	$883	€700	Le port de la Rochelle (27x35cm-11x14in) s. panel. 31-Jan-4 Neret-Minet, Paris #145/R
£629	$1083	€900	Retour des marins a Concarneau (45x38cm-18x15in) s. cardboard. 3-Dec-3 Tajan, Paris #336
£1200	$2208	€1800	Beaulieu-sur-Mer (33x41cm-13x16in) s.d.1921 prov. 11-Jun-4 Pierre Berge, Paris #223/R est:2000-3000
£2727	$4555	€3900	Port de La Rochelle (46x38cm-18x15in) s. panel. 29-Jun-3 Eric Pillon, Calais #139/R

Works on paper

£563	$986	€800	Plage des Sables Blancs a Treboul (31x46cm-12x18in) s.d.1970. 21-Dec-3 Thierry & Lannon, Brest #233

HERVENS, Jacques (1890-1928) Belgian

£350	$601	€500	Chemin ensoleille (51x57cm-20x22in) s.d.24 panel. 8-Dec-3 Horta, Bruxelles #299
£355	$592	€500	Printemps (38x80cm-15x31in) s. 17-Jun-3 Vanderkindere, Brussels #125

HERVIER, Adolphe (1818-1879) French

£940	$1729	€1400	Travellers resting by wooded river (54x45cm-21x18in) s. lit. 25-Mar-4 Karlheinz Kaupp, Staufen #2501/R
£3000	$5430	€4500	Moulins sur la route de Migny (43x59cm-17x23in) s. exhib. 30-Mar-4 Rossini, Paris #261/R est:4000-7000
£3000	$5460	€4500	Farmhouse in Normandy (38x46cm-15x18in) s.d.1866 lit. 1-Jul-4 Van Ham, Cologne #1403/R est:2500

Works on paper

£319	$593	€475	Saint Germain en Laye (15x12cm-6x5in) s. W/C. 7-Mar-4 Lesieur & Le Bars, Le Havre #69
£347	$590	€500	La Ruelle au Hameau (12x15cm-5x6in) s.d.1870 W/C. 30-Oct-3 Artus Associes, Paris #49
£629	$1051	€900	Femme et enfant (12x15cm-5x6in) s.i.d.1870 ink wash W/C. 25-Jun-3 Maigret, Paris #44

HERVIEU, Louise (1878-1954) French

Works on paper

£816	$1461	€1200	Jeune femme tenant une Vierge a l'Enfant (117x86cm-46x34in) s. chl. 19-Mar-4 Oger, Dumont, Paris #12

HERVO, Vaino (1894-1974) Finnish

£278	$464	€400	Still life (50x61cm-20x24in) s.d.1946. 23-Oct-3 Hagelstam, Helsinki #958/R
£400	$716	€600	Still life of fruit on table (60x70cm-24x28in) s.d.1956. 15-May-4 Hagelstam, Helsinki #173/R

HERWERDEN, Jacob Dirk van (1806-1879) Dutch

£8163	$14612	€12000	View in West Java (40x53cm-16x21in) lit. 16-Mar-4 Christie's, Amsterdam #1/R est:12000-16000

HERWIG, Ferdinand (19/20th C) German

£517	$947	€750	Lake Garda (87x100cm-34x39in) s. 27-Jan-4 Dorotheum, Vienna #106/R

HERWIJNEN, Jan van (1889-1965) Dutch

£592	$1089	€900	Still life with yellow and orange flowers in a vase (75x80cm-30x31in) s.d.63. 22-Jun-4 Christie's, Amsterdam #462/R
£658	$1211	€1000	Flower still life (55x58cm-22x23in) s.d.50. 28-Jun-4 Sotheby's, Amsterdam #220/R
£748	$1362	€1100	Still life with white and pink flowers in a vase (77x80cm-30x31in) s.d.53 s.verso canvas on board. 3-Feb-4 Christie's, Amsterdam #428 est:700-900
£921	$1695	€1400	Still life with jug, bottle and pears (76x81cm-30x32in) s. exhib. 22-Jun-4 Christie's, Amsterdam #460/R
£972	$1585	€1400	The factory Enci, St Petersberg (96x124cm-38x49in) s. 29-Sep-3 Sotheby's, Amsterdam #379/R
£1579	$2905	€2400	Flower still life (103x81cm-41x32in) s. 28-Jun-4 Sotheby's, Amsterdam #252/R est:2000-3000
£1888	$3248	€2700	Still life with flowers (79x76cm-31x30in) init.d.34. 2-Dec-3 Sotheby's, Amsterdam #236/R est:3000-4000
£2800	$5152	€4200	Landscape at sunset (82x14cm-32x6in) painted 1921 prov. 9-Jun-4 Christie's, Amsterdam #65/R est:2000-3000

HERZ, Emil W (1877-?) German

£839	$1443	€1200	Dog looking at goldfish (73x57cm-29x22in) s. 4-Dec-3 Schopman, Hamburg #679/R

HERZIG, Edouard (1860-1926) ?

£1267	$2318	€1900	Cascades a Tlemcen (78x58cm-31x23in) s.i. 3-Jun-4 Tajan, Paris #279/R est:3000-4000

Works on paper

£267	$491	€400	La maitre d'ecole coranique (35x56cm-14x22in) s. gouache. 14-Jun-4 Gros & Delettrez, Paris #437
£533	$981	€800	La fileuse, Bou-Saada (29x23cm-11x9in) s.i. W/C. 14-Jun-4 Gros & Delettrez, Paris #250
£1189	$2045	€1700	Enluminure (46x37cm-18x15in) s. gouache polychrome gilding. 8-Dec-3 Tajan, Paris #285/R est:1800-2000
£2238	$3849	€3200	Marchand d'oranges dans la Kasbah (57x42cm-22x17in) s. chl pastel gouache. 8-Dec-3 Tajan, Paris #288/R est:2300-2800

HERZIG, Heinrich (1887-1964) Swiss

£226	$385	€330	Wimmet in Berneck (24x21cm-9x8in) s. i. verso panel. 18-Nov-3 Hans Widmer, St Gallen #1092 (S.FR 500)
£407	$692	€594	Zermatt and Matterhorn (14x10cm-6x4in) s. s.i. verso board. 18-Nov-3 Hans Widmer, St Gallen #1084 (S.FR 900)
£415	$763	€606	Storm over Bodensee (27x34cm-11x13in) s.d.1946 board. 8-Jun-4 Germann, Zurich #804 (S.FR 950)
£452	$769	€660	Appenzell landscape with houses (28x35cm-11x14in) s.d.1940. 18-Nov-3 Hans Widmer, St Gallen #1094 (S.FR 1000)
£679	$1154	€991	Rhine valley in summer (30x38cm-12x15in) s.d.1938 i. verso board. 18-Nov-3 Hans Widmer, St Gallen #1087 est:1400-2800 (S.FR 1500)
£1480	$2471	€2161	Appenzell country, Santis and Altmann (39x51cm-15x20in) s. s.i. verso board. 24-Oct-3 Hans Widmer, St Gallen #74/R est:3000-5500 (S.FR 3300)
£1704	$2846	€2488	Appenzell landscape (55x67cm-22x26in) s. s.i. verso panel. 24-Oct-3 Hans Widmer, St Gallen #78/R est:3000-5500 (S.FR 3800)
£2063	$3445	€3012	Tree in bloom (30x40cm-12x16in) s. s.i. verso board. 24-Oct-3 Hans Widmer, St Gallen #72/R est:1600-3500 (S.FR 4600)

Works on paper

£226	$385	€330	Berneck (33x31cm-13x12in) s.d.46 W/C. 18-Nov-3 Hans Widmer, St Gallen #1093/R (S.FR 500)
£271	$462	€396	Houses by water in mountain landscape (27x20cm-11x8in) s. WC chl paper on board. 18-Nov-3 Hans Widmer, St Gallen #1085 (S.FR 600)
£409	$733	€597	In the vineyards (23x17cm-9x7in) s. chl W/C. 12-May-4 Dobiaschofsky, Bern #604/R (S.FR 950)
£545	$905	€790	Bodensee landscape (28x39cm-11x15in) d.1932 s.i. verso board. 13-Jun-3 Zofingen, Switzerland #2877 (S.FR 1200)
£679	$1154	€991	Rome (25x35cm-10x14in) s.d.1924 W/C pen. 18-Nov-3 Hans Widmer, St Gallen #1086/R est:1200-1800 (S.FR 1500)

HERZIG, Wolfgang (1941-) German

£6944	$11806	€10000	The last rites (98x126cm-39x50in) mono.d.1969 i. verso. 28-Oct-3 Wiener Kunst Auktionen, Vienna #267/R est:10000-13000

Works on paper

£4167	$7083	€6000	Cafe sketch (174x118cm-69x46in) chk. 28-Oct-3 Wiener Kunst Auktionen, Vienna #274/R est:6000-10000

HERZIG, Yvonne (20th C) French
Works on paper
£2098 $3608 €3000 Fountain (41x55cm-16x22in) s. gouache. 8-Dec-3 Tajan, Paris #287/R est:2200-2400

HERZING, Minni (1883-?) German
£385 $654 €550 Summer bouquet of flowers (100x84cm-39x33in) s. board. 28-Nov-3 Wendl, Rudolstadt #4002/R
£533 $981 €800 Mountain landscape (99x84cm-39x33in) s. board. 11-Jun-4 Wendl, Rudolstadt #4077/R
£1007 $1872 €1500 Meadow with flowers in a mountain landscape with lake in background (90x110cm-35x43in) s. panel. 5-Mar-4 Wendl, Rudolstadt #3697/R est:650

HERZMANOVSKY-ORLANDO, Fritz von (1877-1954) Austrian
Works on paper
£284 $474 €400 Papageno (20x24cm-8x9in) mono.d.1920 pencil. 16-Oct-3 Dorotheum, Salzburg #1031/R
£1342 $2403 €2000 Lovesick (23x19cm-9x7in) mono.i.d.1.April 1919 pencil col pen prov. 25-May-4 Dorotheum, Vienna #162/R est:2000-2600
£1745 $3123 €2600 Commedia dell'Arte (22x28cm-9x11in) mono. pencil col pen prov. 25-May-4 Dorotheum, Vienna #163/R est:2000-2600
£2098 $3566 €3000 Onslaught of the Trinacrie (25x20cm-10x8in) s.d.18 Juli 1919 i. verso pencil col pen prov. 26-Nov-3 Dorotheum, Vienna #129/R est:2000-2800
£2098 $3566 €3000 Evening leisure (25x20cm-10x8in) i.d.31 Aug 1919 i. verso pencil col pen prov. 26-Nov-3 Dorotheum, Vienna #130/R est:1900-2600
£2378 $4042 €3400 Two writers and two flying horses (20x25cm-8x10in) s.d.6 Juli 1919 i. verso prov. 26-Nov-3 Dorotheum, Vienna #131/R est:2000-2800

HERZOG, August (1885-1959) German
£388 $694 €566 Alpine landscape in winter with small hut (46x55cm-18x22in) s.d.1927. 12-May-4 Dobiaschofsky, Bern #605/R (S.FR 900)
£390 $651 €566 St Saphorin (32x55cm-13x22in) s. 23-Jun-3 Philippe Schuler, Zurich #8434 (S.FR 850)
£1633 $2922 €2400 Kallmunz (38x48cm-15x19in) s.i.d.1923 i. stretcher. 17-Mar-4 Neumeister, Munich #482/R est:1200

HERZOG, C (19th C) German?
£1007 $1852 €1500 Burg Rheinstein near Rudesheim (75x101cm-30x40in) s.d.1871. 25-Mar-4 Karlheinz Kaupp, Staufen #2502/R est:1400

HERZOG, Hermann (1832-1932) American/German
£559 $1000 €937 Farmyard pond (36x48cm-14x19in) s. canvas on panel. 20-Mar-4 Pook & Pook, Downington #600/R
£938 $1500 €1369 Pastoral landscape with cows grazing beneath a birch tree (30x23cm-12x9in) s. 20-Sep-3 Pook & Pook, Downington #521/R est:2000-4000
£1181 $1924 €1700 Mountain stream (54x51cm-21x20in) s.d.1868 panel. 24-Sep-3 Neumeister, Munich #444 est:2200
£2381 $4500 €3476 Cows in wooded landscape (53x71cm-21x28in) s. 17-Feb-4 John Moran, Pasadena #53/R est:5000-7000
£2600 $4758 €3900 Italian landscape (57x82cm-22x32in) s. 5-Jun-4 Arnold, Frankfurt #601/R est:800
£2647 $4578 €3865 Mountain landscape with reindeer, Lapland (31x41cm-12x16in) s.d.1871. 9-Dec-3 Rasmussen, Copenhagen #1577/R est:15000-20000 (D.KR 28000)
£2793 $5000 €4078 Alpine landscape with figure and dog in foreground (51x71cm-20x28in) s. 29-May-4 Brunk, Ashville #445/R
£3297 $6000 €4814 Squall at sea (56x68cm-22x27in) s. 29-Jun-4 Sotheby's, New York #188/R est:10000-15000
£4012 $6500 €5817 Afternoon pasture (36x49cm-14x19in) s. 8-Aug-3 Barridorf, Portland #344/R est:5000-7000
£4348 $7000 €6305 Old watermill (27x43cm-11x17in) 22-Aug-3 Altermann Galleries, Santa Fe #144
£4469 $8000 €6525 Coast at Vinal Haven, Maine (46x58cm-18x23in) s. prov. 6-May-4 Shannon's, Milford #154/R est:7000-9000
£5028 $9000 €8442 Landscape with women walking through tall grass towards a cabin (51x43cm-20x17in) s. 20-Mar-4 Pook & Pook, Downington #291/R est:3000-5000
£5090 $8500 €7431 Forest landscape with pond and ducks (46x61cm-18x24in) s. 23-Oct-3 Shannon's, Milford #161/R est:8000-12000
£5091 $8500 €7433 Feeding the geese (53x74cm-21x29in) prov. 23-Oct-3 Shannon's, Milford #115/R est:8000-12000
£5938 $9500 €8669 Landscape with inlet on Lake George (38x53cm-15x21in) s.i. 20-Sep-3 Pook & Pook, Downington #520/R est:4000-6000
£7186 $12000 €10492 Eagle above the river (69x56cm-27x22in) s. prov. 23-Oct-3 Shannon's, Milford #21/R est:12000-18000
£7186 $12000 €10492 Fly fishing (69x56cm-27x22in) s. prov. 23-Oct-3 Shannon's, Milford #22/R est:12000-18000
£12570 $22500 €18352 Cascade with fisherman (51x41cm-20x16in) s. indis.i.stretcher. 26-May-4 Doyle, New York #17/R est:15000-25000
£15000 $24000 €21900 Southern landscape with river and canoe (48x38cm-19x15in) s. 20-Sep-3 Pook & Pook, Downington #500/R est:6000-8000
£17919 $31000 €26162 Wheat harvesting beside a river (84x121cm-33x48in) s. 13-Dec-3 Weschler, Washington #562 est:30000-50000
£20349 $35000 €29710 Fishing in Alpine lake (53x79cm-21x31in) s.d.1873 prov. 4-Dec-3 Christie's, Rockefeller NY #11/R est:30000-50000
£25815 $47500 €37690 Bear approaching a forest stream (68x55cm-27x22in) s. prov. 8-Jun-4 Bonhams & Butterfields, San Francisco #4024/R est:20000-30000
£29070 $50000 €42442 Forest interior with waterfall (92x80cm-36x31in) s. 3-Dec-3 Doyle, New York #163/R est:15000-25000
£40698 $70000 €59419 Morining fisherman (100x82cm-39x32in) s.d.1882 prov. 3-Dec-3 Doyle, New York #178/R est:20000-30000
Works on paper
£326 $600 €476 Atlantic City (10x15cm-4x6in) i. pencil. 10-Jun-4 Swann Galleries, New York #122/R

HERZOG, Jakob (1867-1959) Swiss
£293 $504 €428 Nussbaumersee (38x45cm-15x18in) s.d.1928 board. 8-Dec-3 Philippe Schuler, Zurich #5927 (S.FR 650)
£352 $651 €510 Isar meadows with view of Frauenkirche, Munich (69x88cm-27x35in) s.d.1896. 12-Feb-4 Weidler, Nurnberg #6501/R
£352 $651 €510 Isar meadows with figures (60x88cm-24x35in) s. i. verso. 12-Feb-4 Weidler, Nurnberg #6502/R

HERZOG, Oswald (20th C) ?
Sculpture
£867 $1595 €1300 Sitting (21cm-8in) mono. brown pat bronze. 12-Jun-4 Villa Grisebach, Berlin #571/R est:800-1000

HESLING, Bernard (1905-1987) Australian
£535 $968 €781 Two faces. enamel on tin. 1-Apr-4 Joel, Victoria #156 (A.D 1300)

HESON, Jan (1869-?) Czechoslovakian
£909 $1545 €1300 Nude with boy (76x50cm-30x20in) s. 20-Nov-3 Van Ham, Cologne #1626/R est:1400

HESPEL, Gregoire (1961-) French
£486 $900 €710 Untitled (96x130cm-38x51in) s.d.VII90 prov. 12-Feb-4 Sotheby's, New York #354/R

HESS, Bruno (1888-1949) Austrian
£667 $1200 €1000 Kitzsteinhorn (73x60cm-29x24in) s.d.1936 i. verso. 21-Apr-4 Dorotheum, Vienna #93/R
Works on paper
£759 $1388 €1100 Tree border (38x27cm-15x11in) s. W/C gouache prov. 27-Jan-4 Dorotheum, Vienna #77

HESS, Carl Adolph Heinrich (1769-1849) German
£320 $573 €480 Napoleon on horseback (48x44cm-19x17in) 14-May-4 Bassenge, Berlin #6436
Works on paper
£28743 $48000 €41965 Ural cossacks with their Ataman DM Borodin during the Swiss campaign (60x87cm-24x34in) s.d.1799 gouache lit. 21-Oct-3 Christie's, Rockefeller NY #87 est:50000-70000

HESS, Hildi (1911-) Swiss
Sculpture
£2620 $4690 €3825 Woman's head (25cm-10in) mono. plaster. 26-May-4 Sotheby's, Zurich #55/R est:1500-2000 (S.FR 6000)

HESS, Ludwig (1760-1800) Swiss
£4525 $7692 €6607 Romantic river landscape with ruins (29x41cm-11x16in) s.d.1782 panel. 19-Nov-3 Fischer, Luzern #1226/R est:10000-12000 (S.FR 10000)

HESS, Marcel (1878-1948) Belgian
£533 $955 €800 Bouquet de pivoines (100x90cm-39x35in) s. 16-May-4 MonsAntic, Maisieres #427
£1267 $2267 €1900 Nu feminin de dos se mirant (135x85cm-53x33in) s. 16-May-4 MonsAntic, Maisieres #424 est:1500-2000

HESS, Peter von (1792-1871) German
£800 $1440 €1200 Retreat of Napoleon's army from Russia (49x76cm-19x30in) s.d.1861 lit. 22-Apr-4 Allgauer, Kempten #3574/R
£2639 $4354 €3800 Farewell ouside the Osteria (53x60cm-21x24in) s.d.1827. 2-Jul-3 Neumeister, Munich #663/R est:3000
Works on paper
£385 $642 €550 Soldier with head injury and sleeping soldier (16x23cm-6x9in) s. pencil. 10-Oct-3 Winterberg, Heidelberg #598

HESS, Sara M (1880-1960) American
£722 $1300 €1054 Passing clouds (63x63cm-25x25in) s. i.verso. 24-Apr-4 Weschler, Washington #606/R

HESSE, Bruno (1905-) Swiss
Works on paper
£435 $796 €635 Landscape with a country house (24x29cm-9x11in) mono.i.d.5 Juni 1925 W/C. 4-Jun-4 Zofingen, Switzerland #2841/R (S.FR 1000)

HESSE, Eva (1936-1970) American
£56886 $95000 €83054 Untitled (92x91cm-36x36in) painted c.1960 prov. 13-Nov-3 Sotheby's, New York #192/R est:50000-70000
£75419 $135000 €110112 Boxes (60x50cm-24x20in) s.d.1964 acrylic gouache pen ink collage on paper prov.exhib.lit. 13-May-4 Phillips, New York #42/R est:80000-120000
Works on paper
£14970 $25000 €21856 Untitled (28x21cm-11x8in) gouache ink folded paper exec 1961 prov. 12-Nov-3 Christie's, Rockefeller NY #603/R est:35000-45000

HESSE, Georg (1845-1920) German
£1111 $1833 €1600 Hilly summer landscape in evening light (79x130cm-31x51in) s.d.81. 3-Jul-3 Van Ham, Cologne #1243 est:2000
£5369 $10040 €8000 Hilly summer landscape in the evening (79x130cm-31x51in) s.d.81. 24-Feb-4 Dorotheum, Vienna #84/R est:3800-4000

HESSE, Henri-Joseph (1781-1849) French
£2000 $3620 €3000 Portrait du Duc d'Orleans, futur Louis-Philippe (24x19cm-9x7in) painted c.1825. 30-Mar-4 Rossini, Paris #56/R est:3000-5000

HESSE, Hermann (1877-1962) German

Works on paper

£524	$954	€765	Tremor (11x13cm-4x5in) i. W/C lit. 16-Jun-4 Fischer, Luzern #2778/R (S.FR 1200)
£550	$919	€803	Death of a child (17x18cm-7x7in) i. W/C. 20-Jun-3 Kornfeld, Bern #7 (S.FR 1200)
£688	$1149	€1004	Letter (5x6cm-2x2in) s. W/C over ink. 20-Jun-3 Kornfeld, Bern #46 (S.FR 1500)
£922	$1494	€1300	Tessin landscape (6x8cm-2x3in) mono.d.33 W/C pen. 23-May-3 Altus, Berlin #546/R
£963	$1609	€1406	Letters (7x8cm-3x3in) i. W/c two. 20-Jun-3 Kornfeld, Bern #39 (S.FR 2100)
£963	$1609	€1406	Letter (6x7cm-2x3in) s. W/C over ink. 20-Jun-3 Kornfeld, Bern #42 (S.FR 2100)
£1009	$1685	€1473	Letter (7x8cm-3x3in) s. W/C over pencil. 20-Jun-3 Kornfeld, Bern #41 (S.FR 2200)
£1009	$1685	€1473	Letter (5x7cm-2x3in) s. W/C over ink. 20-Jun-3 Kornfeld, Bern #44 (S.FR 2200)
£1088	$1731	€1600	Tessin landscape (6x8cm-2x3in) mono.d.31 W/C. 28-Feb-3 Altus, Berlin #469/R est:1900
£1101	$1839	€1607	Letter (7x9cm-3x4in) s. W/C over ink. 20-Jun-3 Kornfeld, Bern #31 (S.FR 2400)
£1147	$1915	€1675	Early light (5x6cm-2x2in) s.i. W/C over ink. 20-Jun-3 Kornfeld, Bern #21 est:2500 (S.FR 2500)
£1147	$1915	€1675	Letter (6x8cm-2x3in) s. W/C over ink. 20-Jun-3 Kornfeld, Bern #35 est:3000 (S.FR 2500)
£1193	$1992	€1742	Good health, Frau Welt (6x6cm-2x2in) s. W/C over ink. 20-Jun-3 Kornfeld, Bern #19 est:3000 (S.FR 2600)
£1193	$1992	€1742	Letter (8x14cm-3x6in) s. W/C over Indian ink. 20-Jun-3 Kornfeld, Bern #23/R est:3000 (S.FR 2600)
£1193	$1992	€1742	Letter (8x11cm-3x4in) s. W/C over ink. 20-Jun-3 Kornfeld, Bern #26/R est:4000 (S.FR 2600)
£1193	$1992	€1742	Letter (7x8cm-3x3in) s. W/C over ink. 20-Jun-3 Kornfeld, Bern #28 est:3000 (S.FR 2600)
£1193	$1992	€1742	Letter (7x8cm-3x3in) s. W/C over ink. 20-Jun-3 Kornfeld, Bern #30 est:3000 (S.FR 2600)
£1239	$2068	€1809	Playing the flute (18x14cm-7x6in) s.i. W/C two. 20-Jun-3 Kornfeld, Bern #16/R est:3000 (S.FR 2700)
£1239	$2068	€1809	Tessin village (9x14cm-4x6in) i. verso W/C over Indian ink. 20-Jun-3 Kornfeld, Bern #47/R est:2000 (S.FR 2700)
£1284	$2145	€1875	Poems and pictures (22x15cm-9x6in) s.i. W/C over ink. 20-Jun-3 Kornfeld, Bern #15 est:2500 (S.FR 2800)
£1333	$2453	€2000	Summer heat (5x8cm-2x3in) i. W/C pen ink sold with typed script two. 12-Jun-4 Villa Grisebach, Berlin #572/R est:1800-2000
£1357	$2308	€1981	Spring day (6x7cm-2x3in) s.i. W/C Indian ink. 28-Nov-3 Zofingen, Switzerland #3019/R est:3500 (S.FR 3000)
£1422	$2375	€2076	Letter (7x9cm-3x4in) W/C over ink. 20-Jun-3 Kornfeld, Bern #24 est:3000 (S.FR 3100)
£1422	$2375	€2076	Letter (7x9cm-3x4in) s. W/C over ink. 20-Jun-3 Kornfeld, Bern #34/R est:3000 (S.FR 3100)
£1514	$2528	€2210	Letter (9x10cm-4x4in) s. W/C over ink. 20-Jun-3 Kornfeld, Bern #37 est:3000 (S.FR 3300)
£1560	$2605	€2278	Steps (8x7cm-3x3in) mono.i. W/C over pen. 20-Jun-3 Kornfeld, Bern #218 est:3000 (S.FR 3400)
£1577	$2712	€2302	Letter dated 1 Mai 1942. s. W/C. 2-Dec-3 Koller, Zurich #3093 est:2200-2800 (S.FR 3500)
£1606	$2681	€2345	Viglio in Tessin (23x26cm-9x10in) s.i.d.1 August 29 pencil. 20-Jun-3 Kornfeld, Bern #50 est:3000 (S.FR 3500)
£1743	$2911	€2545	End of August 1929 (7x8cm-3x3in) i.d. W/C ink. 20-Jun-3 Kornfeld, Bern #5/R est:3000 (S.FR 3800)
£1789	$2988	€2612	In the garden (26x17cm-10x7in) i. W/C. 20-Jun-3 Kornfeld, Bern #13/R est:5000 (S.FR 3900)
£1835	$3064	€2679	Poems and prose (6x6cm-2x2in) s.i. W/C over ink five. 20-Jun-3 Kornfeld, Bern #1/R est:5000 (S.FR 4000)
£1927	$3217	€2813	Letter (7x8cm-3x3in) s. W/C over ink. 20-Jun-3 Kornfeld, Bern #38/R est:4000 (S.FR 4200)
£2110	$3524	€3081	Letter (7x8cm-3x3in) s. W/C over pencil. 20-Jun-3 Kornfeld, Bern #29/R est:5000 (S.FR 4600)
£2172	$3692	€3171	Easter greetings (5x5cm-2x2in) mono.i. Indian ink W/C. 18-Nov-3 Hans Widmer, St Gallen #1095/R est:3000-4800 (S.FR 4800)
£2385	$3983	€3482	Scenes from old park in Tessin (22x17cm-9x7in) s.i. W/C two. 20-Jun-3 Kornfeld, Bern #14 est:5000 (S.FR 5200)
£2752	$4596	€4018	Church tower in Tessin landscape (17x24cm-7x9in) s.d.1926 W/C over pencil. 20-Jun-3 Kornfeld, Bern #49 est:5000 (S.FR 6000)
£3020	$5406	€4500	Untitled (27x22cm-11x9in) s.d.1933 pen W/C. 25-May-4 Dorotheum, Vienna #173/R est:3000-4000
£3440	$5745	€5022	Sylvester (6x8cm-2x3in) s.i.d. W/C ink. 20-Jun-3 Kornfeld, Bern #8/R est:5000 (S.FR 7500)
£5263	$9684	€7684	House in Montagnola (20x25cm-8x10in) mono.d.1931 prov. 23-Jun-4 Koller, Zurich #3072/R est:12000-15000 (S.FR 12000)
£6881	$11491	€10046	Poems and pictures (17x17cm-7x7in) i. W/C ink. 20-Jun-3 Kornfeld, Bern #10/R est:17500 (S.FR 15000)
£9174	$15321	€13394	Poems and pictures (23x18cm-9x7in) i. W/C 28. 20-Jun-3 Kornfeld, Bern #2/R est:20000 (S.FR 20000)
£9174	$15321	€13394	The seasons (24x16cm-9x6in) i. W/C 10. 20-Jun-3 Kornfeld, Bern #11 est:25000 (S.FR 20000)
£10092	$16853	€14734	Pictor's transformation (22x17cm-9x7in) W/C 15. 20-Jun-3 Kornfeld, Bern #3/R est:25000 (S.FR 22000)
£18807	$31408	€27458	Tessin villages (22x18cm-9x7in) one s. W/C 12. 20-Jun-3 Kornfeld, Bern #48/R est:35000 (S.FR 41000)

HESSE, Nicolas Auguste (1795-1869) French

Works on paper

£629	$1083	€900	Portrait d'un jeune garcon (33x24cm-13x9in) s.d.1849 W/C. 5-Dec-3 Chochon-Barre & Allardi, Paris #111/R

HESSE, Rudolf (1871-?) German

£696	$1086	€1100	Convent sitting (55x71cm-22x28in) s. panel. 18-Oct-2 Von Zezschwitz, Munich #40/R

HESSELBOM, Otto (1848-1913) Swedish

£1185	$1908	€1730	Landscape at sunset (33x53cm-13x21in) s.d.1911. 25-Aug-3 Lilla Bukowskis, Stockholm #94 est:8000-10000 (S.KR 15500)
£2217	$3969	€3237	Drying hurdles (61x93cm-24x37in) s.d.1909. 25-May-4 Bukowskis, Stockholm #100/R est:30000-35000 (S.KR 30000)
£4308	$7409	€6290	Winter landscape at dusk (81x61cm-32x24in) s. exhib. 3-Dec-3 AB Stockholms Auktionsverk #2243/R est:30000-35000 (S.KR 56000)
£10385	$17862	€15162	View in morning light from Dalsland (115x185cm-45x73in) s. exhib.lit. 2-Dec-3 Bukowskis, Stockholm #167/R est:150000-200000 (S.KR 135000)

HESSELIUS, John (1728-1778) American

£5625	$9000	€8213	Portraits of Elizabeth Brown and her husband Robert Seal (76x64cm-30x25in) pair prov. 20-Sep-3 Sloans & Kenyon, Bethesda #1191/R est:12000-15000

HESSEN, Hans (1913-) Swiss

£498	$846	€727	Light green composition (92x73cm-36x29in) s.i.d.1961. 28-Nov-3 Zofingen, Switzerland #3020 (S.FR 1100)

HESSING, Gustav (1909-1981) Rumanian

£4965	$8291	€7000	Landscape with houses, tower and tree (72x94cm-28x37in) s.d.40. 14-Oct-3 Dorotheum, Vienna #124/R est:7000-10000

Works on paper

£486	$792	€700	Landscape (45x57cm-18x22in) s.d.50 W/C. 23-Sep-3 Wiener Kunst Auktionen, Vienna #55/R
£486	$792	€700	Landscape with church (48x60cm-19x24in) mono.d.40 W/C. 23-Sep-3 Wiener Kunst Auktionen, Vienna #59/R
£759	$1388	€1100	Village (48x60cm-19x24in) s.d.52 W/C prov. 27-Jan-4 Dorotheum, Vienna #127/R
£867	$1560	€1300	Landscape (46x57cm-18x22in) s. W/C. 21-Apr-4 Dorotheum, Vienna #229/R
£867	$1560	€1300	Houses (42x54cm-17x21in) s. w/C. 21-Apr-4 Dorotheum, Vienna #230/R

HESSL, Gustav August (1849-1926) Austrian

£268	$499	€400	The diver - Schiller (29x14cm-11x6in) s. i. verso. 6-Mar-4 Arnold, Frankfurt #741/R

HESSMERT, Karl (1869-1928) German

£415	$743	€610	Stream in evening (35x54cm-14x21in) s. i.d.1903 stretcher. 17-Mar-4 Neumeister, Munich #484/R
£556	$883	€800	Winter landscape with river (47x70cm-19x28in) s. board. 11-Sep-3 Weidler, Nurnberg #6565
£707	$1300	€1032	Summer landscape (48x69cm-19x27in) s. board. 25-Jun-4 Freeman, Philadelphia #226/R est:800-1200
£839	$1401	€1200	Grey winter's day (56x72cm-22x28in) s. i. stretcher. 28-Jun-3 Dannenberg, Berlin #696/R
£1434	$2437	€2050	Castle in Schivelbein (62x78cm-24x31in) s. i.verso lit. 28-Nov-3 Schloss Ahlden, Ahlden #1543/R est:2400

HESSOVA, Boza (1899-1981) American

£714	$1300	€1042	Dome of the largest worlds telescope on Palomar (41x51cm-16x20in) s. i.d.1955 verso. 15-Jun-4 John Moran, Pasadena #49

HESTER, Joy (1920-1960) Australian

Works on paper

£3390	$5763	€4949	Sweeney (31x20cm-12x8in) bears studio st. ink wash exhib. 24-Nov-3 Sotheby's, Melbourne #74/R est:8000-10000 (A.D 8000)
£4681	$7957	€6834	Portrait of John and Sunday Reed (25x15cm-10x6in) s.d.55 ink prov.lit. 25-Nov-3 Christie's, Melbourne #45/R est:8000-12000 (A.D 11000)

HESTHAL, William Jurgen (1908-1985) American

Works on paper

£242	$450	€353	Amusement park (53x38cm-21x15in) s.d.1939 gouache exhib. 6-Mar-4 Harvey Clar, Oakland #1273

HETHERINGTON, Ivystan (fl.1875-1904) British

Works on paper

£1250	$2288	€1825	Quiet Haven, View of Bosham (75x126cm-30x50in) s.d.1891 W/C. 28-Jan-4 Henry Adams, Chichester #245/R est:400-600

HETTNER, Sabine (1907-1986) French

£504	$937	€750	Composition (73x60cm-29x24in) s. painted c.1950. 3-Mar-4 Artcurial Briest, Paris #452

HETZEL, George (1826-1899) American

£7821	$14000	€11119	Wooded landscape (36x58cm-14x23in) s.d.1885. 11-Jan-4 William Jenack, New York #127 est:4000-6000

HEUBACH, Walter (1865-1923) German

£347	$552	€500	Horse (50x65cm-20x26in) s. 11-Sep-3 Weidler, Nurnberg #6537

HEUBERGER, Felix (20th C) ?

£483	$883	€700	Mountain landscape (50x61cm-20x24in) s. tempera board. 27-Jan-4 Dorotheum, Vienna #67/R

HEUBNER, Friedrich Leonhard (1876-1974) German

£1275	$2283	€1900	Studio (70x90cm-28x35in) s.d. tempera pencil exhib. 25-May-4 Karl & Faber, Munich #326/R est:1200

HEUDE, J S (18th C) ?

£7667	$13953	€11500	Trompe-l'oeil allegorique de la Famille Royale (35x29cm-14x11in) s.d.1785. 30-Jun-4 Pierre Berge, Paris #89/R est:300-3500

HEUDEBERT, Raymonde (1905-) French
£1429 $2557 €2100 Musiciens africains (72x60cm-28x24in) s. 21-Mar-4 St-Germain-en-Laye Encheres #95/R est:2000-2500
Works on paper
£272 $487 €400 Guerrier au chasse-mouches (36x18cm-14x7in) mono. graphite dr. 21-Mar-4 St-Germain-en-Laye Encheres #97/R

HEULLANT, Felix Armand (1834-?) French
£3800 $6346 €5548 Flower girls (67x100cm-26x39in) s. panel. 12-Nov-3 Sotheby's, Olympia #230/R est:4000-6000

HEUNERT, Wilhelm (19th C) German
£280 $467 €400 Figures in street (32x48cm-13x19in) s.d.1870. 28-Jun-3 Bolland & Marotz, Bremen #665/R

HEURIS, Alfred A (attrib) (19th C) British?
£560 $885 €818 Old hulks at Devonport (25x30cm-10x12in) indis.sig. painted c.1850-1860. 27-Apr-3 Desmond Judd, Cranbrook #1040

HEURTAUX, Andre Gaston (1898-1983) French
£529 $899 €772 Composition au tringle violet (10x21cm-4x8in) paper. 5-Nov-3 AB Stockholms Auktionsverk #1097/R (S.KR 7000)

HEUSCH, Jacob de (1657-1701) Dutch
£24161 $44456 €36000 Landscape in Lazio (133x173cm-52x68in) lit. 27-Mar-4 Farsetti, Prato #335/R est:40000

HEUSCH, Jacob de (attrib) (1657-1701) Dutch
Works on paper
£467 $859 €700 Vue de Monte Sabine (27x41cm-11x16in) i. graphite grey wash pen. 11-Jun-4 Maigret, Paris #3/R

HEUSCH, Willem de (1638-1692) Dutch
£2308 $3969 €3370 Italianate landscape with travelling figures (41x57cm-16x22in) s. panel. 2-Dec-3 Bukowskis, Stockholm #388/R est:40000-50000 (S.KR 30000)

HEUSCH, Willem de (attrib) (1638-1692) Dutch
£3803 $6655 €5400 Berger et son troupeau (59x46cm-23x18in) indis.sig. panel. 17-Dec-3 Piasa, Paris #21/R est:4000-5000

HEUSER, C (19th C) German
£1111 $2000 €1622 Untitled, rustic gentleman with a pipe (18x13cm-7x5in) s. panel prov. 25-Jan-4 Hindman, Chicago #1025/R est:200-400

HEUSER, Carl (19th C) German
£700 $1260 €1022 Good read (6x12cm-2x5in) s. panel. 21-Jan-4 Sotheby's, Olympia #438/R
£900 $1620 €1314 Good read. Good smoke (16x12cm-6x5in) s. panel pair framed as one. 21-Jan-4 Sotheby's, Olympia #432/R est:1000-1500
£900 $1620 €1314 Sip of wine. Good smoke (16x12cm-6x5in) s. panel pair framed as one. 21-Jan-4 Sotheby's, Olympia #437/R est:1000-1500
£950 $1710 €1387 Pipe smoker (16x12cm-6x5in) s. panel. 21-Jan-4 Sotheby's, Olympia #433/R est:600-800
£1000 $1830 €1500 Portrait of gentleman. Portrait of lady (17x12cm-7x5in) s. panel pair. 27-Jul-4 Henry Adams, Chichester #455/R est:800-1200
£1050 $1859 €1533 Portrait of an old man with pipe (12x15cm-5x6in) panel. 28-Apr-4 Crow, Dorking #720/R est:580-650
£1400 $2520 €2044 Couple in traditional Alpine costume (16x12cm-6x5in) s. panel pair framed as one. 21-Jan-4 Sotheby's, Olympia #434/R est:1000-1500
£1400 $2520 €2044 Good smoke (20x19cm-8x7in) s panel. 21-Jan-4 Sotheby's, Olympia #435/R est:600-800

HEUSER, Christian (1862-1942) German
£650 $1086 €949 Portrait of an old man, smoking a pipe (17x13cm-7x5in) panel. 22-Oct-3 Cheffins, Cambridge #525/R
£2009 $3455 €2933 Gentleman with carved pipe. Woman in fur hat (16x12cm-6x5in) s. panel pair prov. 2-Dec-3 Ritchie, Toronto #125/R est:5000-7000 (C.D 4500)

HEUSS, Eduard von (1808-1880) German
£350 $584 €500 Maria Gloriosa (82cm-32in circular) s.d.1869 tondo. 28-Jun-3 Bolland & Marotz, Bremen #666

HEUSSER, Harry (1881-1944) Polish
£1745 $3123 €2600 Warship Budapest under way (164x110cm-65x43in) s.d.1909. 27-May-4 Dorotheum, Graz #22/R est:1300

HEUSSLER, Ernst Georg (1903-) ?
£294 $500 €429 Anenomes (35x29cm-14x11in) mono. i. verso panel. 28-Nov-3 Zofingen, Switzerland #3021 (S.FR 650)

HEUTENBORG, Willem (19/20th C) Dutch
£529 $899 €772 Winter scene with horse sleigh (40x50cm-16x20in) s. panel. 5-Nov-3 Dobiaschofsky, Bern #639/R (S.FR 1200)

HEUVEL, Karel Jan van den (1913-1991) Dutch
£347 $580 €500 Boat on the river (80x100cm-31x39in) s. 21-Oct-3 Campo & Campo, Antwerp #305
£367 $664 €550 Vue portuaire (80x100cm-31x39in) s. 30-Mar-4 Campo, Vlaamse Kaai #184
£400 $724 €600 La table dressee (65x80cm-26x31in) s. 30-Mar-4 Campo, Vlaamse Kaai #183
£467 $845 €700 Portrait de jeune fille (65x80cm-26x31in) s. 30-Mar-4 Campo, Vlaamse Kaai #182

HEUVEL, Theodore Bernard de (1817-1906) Flemish
£651 $1106 €950 Lavandiere (45x37cm-18x15in) s. canvas on panel. 10-Nov-3 Horta, Bruxelles #371
£13793 $23034 €20000 Curious magpie (55x66cm-22x26in) s.d.1871 panel. 15-Nov-3 Lempertz, Koln #1619/R est:20000

HEUZE, Edmond (1884-1967) French
£280 $467 €400 Self-portrait (32x27cm-13x11in) s. panel. 7-Oct-3 Livinec, Gaudcheau & Jezequel, Rennes #141
£287 $516 €430 Clowns (46x55cm-18x22in) s. panel. 24-Apr-4 Cornette de St.Cyr, Paris #370
Works on paper
£285 $464 €410 Nu allonge (34x52cm-13x20in) s. pastel. prov. 18-Jul-3 Charbonneaux, Paris #187

HEWARD, Prudence (1896-1947) Canadian
£11261 $19144 €16441 Bermuda house (56x63cm-22x25in) s. i.d.1938-9 on stretcher prov.exhib. 18-Nov-3 Sotheby's, Toronto #3/R est:8000-10000 (C.D 25000)

HEWITT, Henry (1818-1875) British
Works on paper
£1200 $2040 €1752 Brockley Combe from Backwell Hill, near Bristol (25x35cm-10x14in) s.d.1855 bodycol. 4-Nov-3 Bonhams, New Bond Street #90/R est:800-1200

HEWKIN, Andrew (20th C) American
Works on paper
£2286 $4000 €3338 Rabbit Head (107x102cm-42x40in) s.d.1991 W/C pastel ink printed paper collage exhib. 17-Dec-3 Christie's, Rockefeller NY #296/R est:1000-1500

HEWLAND, Elsie Dalton (1901-) British
£602 $1023 €879 Little Woods Burtons Lane Chalfont St Giles, Bucks (76x100cm-30x39in) s. 27-Nov-3 International Art Centre, Auckland #192/R (NZ.D 1600)

HEWLETT, James (1768-1836) British
Works on paper
£1676 $3000 €2447 Still life of flower with a bird on a branch (31x41cm-12x16in) init. one d.1818 gouache W/C over pencil on board two. 6-May-4 Doyle, New York #27/R est:2000-3000

HEWSON, Ann (1933-) British
£420 $756 €613 Watching (51x41cm-20x16in) s. s.i.d.1991 stretcher. 20-Jan-4 Bonhams, Knightsbridge #220

HEWTON, Randolph Stanley (1888-1960) Canadian
£887 $1632 €1295 Winter, Lower St Lawrence (25x30cm-10x12in) prov. 9-Jun-4 Walker's, Ottawa #26/R est:2500-3500 (C.D 2200)
£1778 $3076 €2596 Cove, Newfoundland (51x61cm-20x24in) s. painted c.1925. 9-Dec-3 Maynards, Vancouver #227 est:3000-4000 (C.D 4000)
£4464 $7679 €6517 Winter landscape (43x47cm-17x19in) s. 2-Dec-3 Joyner Waddington, Toronto #494 est:4000-5000 (C.D 10000)
£4800 $8784 €7008 Horses and hounds (65x75cm-26x30in) s. oil sketch verso prov. 1-Jun-4 Joyner Waddington, Toronto #114/R est:12000-15000 (C.D 12000)
£6000 $10980 €8760 Quebec village (50x60cm-20x24in) s. prov. 1-Jun-4 Joyner Waddington, Toronto #91/R est:15000-20000 (C.D 15000)
£26423 $47297 €38578 Street scene with figures (50x60cm-20x24in) s. board prov.lit. 31-May-4 Sotheby's, Toronto #126/R est:20000-30000 (C.D 65000)

HEY, Paul (1867-1952) German
£1000 $1810 €1500 Early summer landscape on the Amper (83x144cm-33x57in) s. board. 1-Apr-4 Van Ham, Cologne #1430 est:2000
£1067 $1952 €1600 Valley in summer with wall on edge of field (53x78cm-21x31in) s. 5-Jun-4 Arnold, Frankfurt #602/R est:1000
Works on paper
£319 $505 €460 Panorama of Rothenburg with church in distance (50x67cm-20x26in) s. 5-Sep-3 Wendl, Rudolstadt #3417/R
£455 $759 €650 Village in evening with angels in the sky (14x9cm-6x4in) s. W/C. 28-Jun-3 Dannenberg, Berlin #697/R
£1007 $1852 €1500 Peasant woman and children in horse drawn cart (23x21cm-9x8in) s. W/C lit. 25-Mar-4 Karlheinz Kaupp, Staufen #2504/R est:1500
£1354 $2207 €1950 Mother with child greeting soldiers (22x35cm-9x14in) s. gouache. 27-Sep-3 Dannenberg, Berlin #551/R est:600

HEYBOER, Anton (1924-) Dutch
£385 $643 €550 Woorden Sea (80x110cm-31x43in) s. acrylic. 30-Jun-3 Sotheby's, Amsterdam #482/R
£733 $1342 €1100 The man is on his head (37x49cm-15x19in) s.d.1989. 7-Jun-4 Glerum, Amsterdam #314
£867 $1586 €1300 Figures (37x48cm-15x19in) s. paper. 7-Jun-4 Glerum, Amsterdam #229/R
£1067 $1952 €1600 Trio (55x65cm-22x26in) s.d.1978. 7-Jun-4 Glerum, Amsterdam #317/R est:1500-1800
£2657 $4438 €3800 Composition (100x130cm-39x51in) s.indi.i.d.1976 i.d.1976 verso. 30-Jun-3 Sotheby's, Amsterdam #528/R
Works on paper
£293 $525 €440 Four brides (79x106cm-31x42in) s. gouache pastel. 15-May-4 De Vuyst, Lokeren #163

£293 $525 €440 Hen (106x79cm-42x31in) s. W/C. 15-May-4 De Vuyst, Lokeren #164
£300 $549 €450 Figures on the sand (35x62cm-14x24in) s. W/C. 7-Jun-4 Glerum, Amsterdam #313/R
£315 $525 €450 Untitled (53x78cm-21x31in) s.d.1989 mixed media. 30-Jun-3 Sotheby's, Amsterdam #521
£349 $650 €510 Birth of a chicken (74x61cm-29x24in) s. mixed media executed c.1970. 7-Mar-4 Treadway Gallery, Cincinnati #732/R

HEYDE, Herman Henri op der (1813-1857) Dutch
£7095 $12486 €10500 Dutch coat (62x85cm-24x33in) s. prov. 22-May-4 Lempertz, Koln #1526/R est:6000-8000

HEYDEN, A van de (?) ?
£436 $811 €650 View of Rotterdam harbour (40x50cm-16x20in) s. 4-Mar-4 Auction Maastricht #1135/R

HEYDEN, August Jakob Theodor von (1827-1897) German
£1119 $1902 €1600 The patriot (50x35cm-20x14in) s. 20-Nov-3 Van Ham, Cologne #1627/R est:2200

HEYDEN, Carl (1845-1933) German
£800 $1448 €1200 Portrait of young woman by fountain (92x47cm-36x19in) s. 1-Apr-4 Van Ham, Cologne #1428

HEYDEN, Pieter van der (1530-?) Flemish
Prints
£6769 $12319 €9883 Four seasons. copperplate. 17-Jun-4 Kornfeld, Bern #67 est:3000 (S.FR 15500)

HEYDENDAHL, Friedrich Joseph Nicolai (1844-1906) German
£400 $724 €600 Looking for food (60x80cm-24x31in) s. 1-Apr-4 Van Ham, Cologne #1429
£467 $854 €700 Winter landscape with wild boars (61x80cm-24x31in) s.i. 5-Jun-4 Arnold, Frankfurt #604/R
£629 $1070 €900 Winter landscape in evening (32x50cm-13x20in) s. 20-Nov-3 Weidler, Nurnberg #6512/R
£667 $1220 €1000 Evening in Lower Rhein winter landscape (65x47cm-26x19in) s. 5-Jun-4 Arnold, Frankfurt #603/R
£671 $1188 €1000 Hunting dog carrying dead hare in mouth (73x58cm-29x23in) mono. 28-Apr-4 Schopman, Hamburg #482/R
£1458 $2304 €2100 Wildboar in winter wood (22x80cm-9x31in) s. lit. 19-Sep-3 Schloss Ahlden, Ahlden #1578/R est:2300

HEYER, Arthur (1872-1931) German
£405 $750 €591 Cattle in a field at dusk (79x94cm-31x37in) s. 15-Jul-4 Doyle, New York #44/R
£407 $680 €594 White Persian cat playing with a ball (40x50cm-16x20in) s. 17-Nov-3 Waddingtons, Toronto #252/R (C.D 900)
£420 $713 €600 Angora cat (40x50cm-16x20in) s. lit. 28-Nov-3 Schloss Ahlden, Ahlden #1440/R
£650 $1105 €949 Cattle before a windmill at dusk (55x68cm-22x27in) s. 6-Nov-3 Christie's, Kensington #770/R
£720 $1202 €1044 Kittens at play, interior scene (58x79cm-23x31in) s. 14-Jul-3 Trembath Welch, Great Dunmow #550/R
£735 $1250 €1073 Ready to pounce (45x57cm-18x22in) s. 21-Nov-3 Skinner, Boston #13/R est:2000-4000
£1800 $3222 €2628 Ready to pounce (56x69cm-22x27in) s. 26-May-4 Sotheby's, Olympia #289/R est:2000-3000
£2500 $4625 €3650 Best of friends (50x71cm-20x28in) s. 14-Jul-4 Sotheby's, Olympia #234/R est:2500-3500
£2500 $4625 €3650 Washing his coat (68x55cm-27x22in) s.d.15. 14-Jul-4 Sotheby's, Olympia #239/R est:3000-5000

HEYERDAHL, Hans Olaf (1857-1913) Norwegian
£1601 $2866 €2337 Portrait of Mrs Diriks (73x59cm-29x23in) s.i.indis.d.96 exhib. 22-Mar-4 Blomqvist, Oslo #311/R est:35000-45000 (N.KR 20000)
£6748 $12349 €9852 Girl with blue hat and red berries (42x32cm-17x13in) s.indis.d. panel lit. 7-Jun-4 Blomqvist, Oslo #313/R est:100000-120000 (N.KR 83000)

HEYERMANS, Jean Arnould (1837-1892) Belgian
£350 $601 €500 Scene domestique avec chat (41x51cm-16x20in) s. 2-Dec-3 Campo & Campo, Antwerp #169
£1500 $2505 €2190 He loves me, love me not (60x45cm-24x18in) s.i. 11-Nov-3 Bonhams, Knightsbridge #98d/R est:1500-2000

HEYL, Marinus (1836-1931) Dutch
£1766 $3250 €2578 River Amstel, Amsterdam (45x75cm-18x30in) s. s.i. verso panel prov. 27-Jun-4 Freeman, Philadelphia #15/R est:3000-5000

HEYLIGERS, Antoon François (1828-1897) Dutch
£2980 $5424 €4500 Scene with figures in narrow street (35x46cm-14x18in) s.d.1858 panel. 15-Jun-4 Claude Aguttes, Neuilly #29/R est:5000-7000
£6500 $11635 €9490 Girl seated at a spinning wheel in an interior scene with doves (36x28cm-14x11in) s. panel. 7-May-4 Christopher Matthews, Yorkshire #305 est:2500-3500

HEYLIGERS, Hendrik (1877-1967) Dutch
£2813 $4500 €4107 Interior scene (64x79cm-25x31in) 19-Sep-3 Du Mouchelle, Detroit #2001/R est:3000-5000
£2937 $5052 €4200 Boulevard (76x63cm-30x25in) s. s.i.verso. 7-Dec-3 Sotheby's, Amsterdam #676/R
£3235 $5500 €4723 Still life of white roses (55x46cm-22x18in) s. 20-Nov-3 Auctions by the Bay, Alameda #1017/R

HEYMAN, Steven (1952-) American
Works on paper
£219 $400 €320 Bathers from Berlin (150x127cm-59x50in) pastel. 10-Jul-4 Hindman, Chicago #213/R

HEYMANS, A J (1839-1921) Flemish
£9524 $17333 €14000 Vachere avec troupeau pres de l'abreuvoir (83x146cm-33x57in) 9-Feb-4 Amberes, Antwerp #264/R

HEYMANS, Adriaan Josef (1839-1921) Flemish
£676 $1277 €1000 Marines (15x24cm-6x9in) s. pair. 17-Feb-4 Vanderkindere, Brussels #72
£676 $1209 €1000 La conduite du troupeau (23x38cm-9x15in) s.d.1896 panel. 10-May-4 Horta, Bruxelles #89
£1197 $2071 €1700 La Clairiere (47x60cm-19x24in) s. panel. 10-Dec-3 Hotel des Ventes Mosan, Brussels #222 est:1200-1500
£1333 $2400 €2000 Harvest landscape (18x26cm-7x10in) s. board. 26-Apr-4 Rieber, Stuttgart #1224/R est:2800
£1538 $2569 €2200 Rue animee en hiver (40x47cm-16x19in) s. 13-Oct-3 Horta, Bruxelles #74/R est:3000-4000
£1958 $3270 €2800 Blanchisseuses au bord d'une riviere (26x35cm-10x14in) s. panel. 11-Oct-3 De Vuyst, Lokeren #422/R est:3000-4000
£2533 $4535 €3800 Paysage au moulin a vent (40x60cm-16x24in) s. 11-May-4 Vanderkindere, Brussels #90/R est:3000-5000

HEYMANS, Karel (20th C) Belgian?
£417 $663 €600 Vegetable market (52x63cm-20x25in) s. 15-Sep-3 Bernaerts, Antwerp #732/R
£600 $1086 €900 Promenade au marche (53x64cm-21x25in) s. 30-Mar-4 Campo & Campo, Antwerp #133/R

HEYMANS, Louis (1890-1977) Dutch
£1429 $2557 €2100 Harbour scene (50x66cm-20x26in) 17-Mar-4 De Zwann, Amsterdam #4659/R est:400-600

HEYMANS, Pieternella Johanna Maria (1825-1854) Dutch
£1678 $3138 €2500 Still life of fruit with melon, peaches and grapes (29x38cm-11x15in) s.d.1848 panel. 24-Feb-4 Dorotheum, Vienna #155/R est:3600-4000

HEYN, Karl (1834-1906) German
£455 $782 €650 Chapel in a mountain landscape (64x43cm-25x17in) s.i. grisaille. 3-Dec-3 Neumeister, Munich #597/R

HEYNDRICKX, Charles Louis (?) Belgian
£828 $1374 €1200 Portrait of man (116x97cm-46x38in) 6-Oct-3 Amberes, Antwerp #225

HEYNEMANN, David (1903-) Argentinian
£447 $800 €653 Costanera (24x30cm-9x12in) canvas on board. 11-May-4 Arroyo, Buenos Aires #50

HEYRAULT, Louis Robert (19th C) French
£2333 $4247 €3500 Promenade a cheval. s.d.1853. 29-Jun-4 Sotheby's, Paris #42/R est:5000-7000
£9722 $15264 €14000 Cheval de course trottant dans une clairiere (80x100cm-31x39in) s.d.1882. 29-Aug-3 Deauville, France #120 est:15000-18000

HEYRAULT, Louis Robert (attrib) (19th C) French
£2400 $4152 €3504 Whippet seated on a rug beside a ball (71x58cm-28x23in) s.d.1851. 10-Dec-3 Rupert Toovey, Partridge Green #140/R est:1500-2500

HEYRMAN, Hugo (1942-) Belgian
£486 $812 €700 Model and painter (180x180cm-71x71in) s. d.1989 verso tempera. 21-Oct-3 Campo & Campo, Antwerp #145
£851 $1421 €1200 Girl at the beach (20x20cm-8x8in) s.d.77 verso. 20-Oct-3 Bernaerts, Antwerp #227/R

HEYSEN, Nora (1911-) Australian
£1870 $3347 €2730 Camellias (38x33cm-15x13in) s.d.1939. 4-May-4 Sotheby's, Melbourne #240/R est:5000-8000 (A.D 4600)
£2400 $4248 €3504 Flowers in glass (55x45cm-22x18in) s. board. 27-Apr-4 Bonhams, New Bond Street #7/R est:2000-3000
£2672 $4863 €3901 Portrait of a girl (45x35cm-18x14in) s. prov. 16-Jun-4 Deutscher-Menzies, Melbourne #124/R est:8000-12000 (A.D 7000)
£5929 $10613 €8894 Zinnias (40x31cm-16x12in) s.d.1933 s.i.verso exhib. 17-May-4 Sotheby's, Melbourne #594/R est:9000-12000 (A.D 15000)
£8779 $15977 €12817 Still life with fuchsias (51x40cm-20x16in) s.d.1939 board prov. 16-Jun-4 Deutscher-Menzies, Melbourne #100/R est:28000-35000 (A.D 23000)
£9091 $16091 €13273 Still life (44x36cm-17x14in) s.d.1946 canvasboard prov. 3-May-4 Christie's, Melbourne #100/R est:8000-12000 (A.D 22000)
£9924 $18061 €14489 Spring flowers (48x44cm-19x17in) s. i.verso canvas on board prov. 16-Jun-4 Deutscher-Menzies, Melbourne #125/R est:20000-25000 (A.D 26000)
£12295 $19426 €17951 Flowers in a window (51x40cm-20x16in) s.d.1938 prov. 2-Sep-3 Deutscher-Menzies, Melbourne #56/R est:14000-18000 (A.D 30000)

HEYSEN, Sir Hans (1877-1968) Australian
£681 $1157 €994 Outskirts, Paris (19x31cm-7x12in) composition board. 26-Nov-3 Deutscher-Menzies, Melbourne #175/R (A.D 1600)
£786 $1234 €1148 Liverpool Range (17x28cm-7x11in) s. W/C col chk gouache pencil. 24-Nov-2 Goodman, Sydney #64/R est:1200-1800 (A.D 2200)
£1229 $1942 €1794 Landscape, Florence (19x31cm-7x12in) canvas on board prov. 2-Sep-3 Deutscher-Menzies, Melbourne #3443/R est:1800-2500 (A.D 3000)
£1527 $2779 €2229 Seine, Paris (25x33cm-10x13in) s.d.1892 canvas on board. 16-Jun-4 Deutscher-Menzies, Melbourne #269/R est:3000-5000 (A.D 4000)
£5285 $8297 €7663 White gums (31x41cm-12x16in) s. 27-Aug-3 Christie's, Sydney #541/R est:18000-25000 (A.D 13000)

£8714	$14552	€13071	Dappled light (32x40cm-13x16in) s.d.1925 W/C. 27-Oct-3 Goodman, Sydney #113/R est:12000-18000 (A.D 21000)
£11719	$21914	€17579	Druids Range far North Central Australia (40x70cm-16x28in) s.d.1932. 20-Jul-4 Goodman, Sydney #30/R (A.D 30000)

Works on paper

£400	$736	€584	Snow capped mountains (28x36cm-11x14in) s. pencil W/C htd white. 25-Mar-4 Christie's, Kensington #134
£407	$728	€594	Hahndorf Pastoral (28x38cm-11x15in) pencil. 10-May-4 Joel, Victoria #212 est:1000-2000 (A.D 1000)
£539	$901	€809	Poplars in the Torrens (22x15cm-9x6in) pencil. 27-Oct-3 Goodman, Sydney #112/R (A.D 1300)
£729	$1173	€1064	Mill at Encounter Bay (12x19cm-5x7in) pencil. 13-Oct-3 Joel, Victoria #248 est:2000-2500 (A.D 1800)
£1702	$2894	€2485	Bronzed Wings (30x36cm-12x14in) s. chl prov. 26-Nov-3 Deutscher-Menzies, Melbourne #213/R est:5000-7000 (A.D 4000)
£1724	$2690	€2500	Copse (25x33cm-10x13in) s.d.07 W/C. 1-Aug-2 Joel, Victoria #296 est:6000-8000 (A.D 5000)
£1724	$2690	€2500	Hilltop study (25x17cm-10x7in) s. W/C. 1-Aug-2 Joel, Victoria #274 est:5000-6000 (A.D 5000)
£1957	$3327	€2857	Running Water, Waterfall Gully (24x34cm-9x13in) s.d.1903 W/C prov. 26-Nov-3 Deutscher-Menzies, Melbourne #214/R est:4500-6000 (A.D 4600)
£2043	$3472	€2983	Creek, Waterfall Gully (25x34cm-10x13in) s.d.1904 W/C prov. 26-Nov-3 Deutscher-Menzies, Melbourne #215/R est:4500-6500 (A.D 4800)
£2553	$4340	€3727	Bare Ridges, Flinders Ranges (16x29cm-6x11in) s.d.1957 W/C prov. 26-Nov-3 Deutscher-Menzies, Melbourne #216/R est:3500-5000 (A.D 6000)
£2834	$4563	€4138	Pastoral, Ambleside (32x37cm-13x15in) s. W/C prov. 25-Aug-3 Sotheby's, Paddington #471/R est:8000-12000 (A.D 7000)
£2846	$4467	€4127	Haystacks, Woodside (30x38cm-12x15in) s.d.1930 W/C. 27-Aug-3 Christie's, Sydney #588/R est:9000-15000 (A.D 7000)
£2905	$4851	€4358	The plough team (32x39cm-13x15in) s.d.1917 W/C pencil. 27-Oct-3 Goodman, Sydney #114/R est:6000-9000 (A.D 7000)
£2979	$5064	€4349	Sydney Harbour (21x26cm-8x10in) s.d.1906 W/C. 25-Nov-3 Christie's, Melbourne #265/R est:3000-5000 (A.D 7000)
£3036	$4889	€4433	Creek crossing (24x30cm-9x12in) s.d.99 W/C. 25-Aug-3 Sotheby's, Paddington #415/R est:7000-9000 (A.D 7500)
£3099	$5269	€4525	Pastoral scene (30x40cm-12x16in) s.d.Dec 1925 pencil W/C. 29-Oct-3 Lawson Menzies, Sydney #107/R est:6000-8000 (A.D 7500)
£3284	$5583	€4795	Ambleside (32x39cm-13x15in) s.i.d.40 W/C. 24-Nov-3 Sotheby's, Melbourne #198/R est:7000-10000 (A.D 7750)
£3305	$5619	€4825	Ambleside (34x28cm-13x11in) s.d.1924 W/C prov. 24-Nov-3 Sotheby's, Melbourne #184/R est:10000-15000 (A.D 7800)
£3306	$6116	€4827	Into the morning light (38x33cm-15x13in) s. chl pastel prov. 10-Mar-4 Deutscher-Menzies, Melbourne #170/R est:8000-12000 (A.D 8000)
£3441	$5540	€5024	Young saplings (39x30cm-15x12in) s.d.1915 W/C. 25-Aug-3 Sotheby's, Paddington #336/R est:8000-12000 (A.D 8500)
£3906	$7305	€5859	No 4 the Red Range Aroona, the Wilpenas in the distance (24x37cm-9x15in) s.d.1945 W/C. 20-Jul-4 Goodman, Sydney #27a/R est:10000-12000 (A.D 10000)
£4564	$7622	€6846	By the roadside, Ambleside, Mount Barker South (32x40cm-13x16in) s.d.23 W/C. 27-Oct-3 Goodman, Sydney #116/R est:8000-12000 (A.D 11000)
£4661	$7924	€6805	Turkeys, the dress parade (37x41cm-15x16in) s.d.1914 s.i.verso W/C prov.exhib. 24-Nov-3 Sotheby's, Melbourne #222/R est:5000-8000 (A.D 11000)
£5078	$9496	€7617	Aroona (30x39cm-12x15in) s.i.d.1949 W/C. 20-Jul-4 Goodman, Sydney #13/R est:12000-15000 (A.D 13000)
£5785	$10702	€8446	Ambleside landscape (32x40cm-13x16in) s.d.34 i.verso W/C. 10-Mar-4 Deutscher-Menzies, Melbourne #132/R est:12000-15000 (A.D 14000)
£5785	$10240	€8446	Cattle amongst the gums, Hahndorf (30x39cm-12x15in) s. W/C prov. 3-May-4 Christie's, Melbourne #275/R est:5000-8000 (A.D 14000)
£6198	$10971	€9049	Early morning, Hahndorf landscape (45x58cm-18x23in) s.d.1913 W/C prov. 3-May-4 Christie's, Melbourne #116/R est:10000-12000 (A.D 15000)
£7025	$12434	€10257	Two red gums (32x40cm-13x16in) s.d.1938 W/C prov. 3-May-4 Christie's, Melbourne #109/R est:6000-8000 (A.D 17000)
£7851	$14525	€11462	Three gums (58x47cm-23x19in) s.d.1920 chl. 10-Mar-4 Deutscher-Menzies, Melbourne #133/R est:16000-22000 (A.D 19000)
£13008	$20423	€18862	Near Hahndorf (52x70cm-20x28in) s.d.54 W/C. 27-Aug-3 Christie's, Sydney #586/R est:15000-20000 (A.D 32000)

HEYVAERT, Pierre (1934-1974) Canadian

Sculpture

£833	$1492	€1216	Equa-Tria No 14 (48x23cm-19x9in) st.sig.d.1970 painted metal prov. 22-Mar-4 Waddingtons, Toronto #601/R est:200-300 (C.D 2000)

HEYWOOD-HARDY, Tom (fl.1882-1913) British

£900	$1656	€1314	Head of an English setter (31x23cm-12x9in) s.d.1910 canvasboard. 10-Jun-4 Christie's, Kensington #394/R

HEYWORTH, Alfred (1926-1976) British

£380	$619	€555	Nude posing on a bed in the artist's studio (122x152cm-48x60in) board prov. 24-Sep-3 Dreweatt Neate, Newbury #180
£1000	$1720	€1460	Park benches (120x120cm-47x47in) board prov.exhib. 3-Dec-3 Cheffins, Cambridge #655/R est:800-1200

Works on paper

£540	$880	€788	Towards Southwold from Walberswick. East wind Walberswick (47x49cm-19x19in) s. W/C pair. 23-Sep-3 Bonhams, Leeds #122/R

HEZAVEHI, Josef (1905-1992) Egyptian

£667	$1227	€1000	Balloon seller on beach (50x60cm-20x24in) s. 9-Jun-4 Dorotheum, Salzburg #643/R

HIBBARD, Aldro Thompson (1886-1972) American

£1022	$1900	€1492	Squally Venice (22x26cm-9x10in) s.d.17 canvasboard. 5-Mar-4 Skinner, Boston #328/R est:3000-5000
£1353	$2300	€1975	Rocky coast (45x66cm-18x26in) s. board. 21-Nov-3 Skinner, Boston #547/R est:3000-5000
£2160	$3500	€3154	Snowy river scene (9x11cm-4x4in) s. board. 31-Jul-3 Eldred, East Dennis #1192/R est:2000-3000
£2957	$5500	€4317	Mt Mansfield, Vermont (43x60cm-17x24in) s. canvasboard prov. 5-Mar-4 Skinner, Boston #497/R est:6000-8000
£3352	$6000	€4894	Winter landscape with distant farm (45x61cm-18x24in) s. canvasboard. 14-May-4 Skinner, Boston #220/R est:6000-8000
£3492	$6250	€5098	Winter landscape with sugaring shack (61x76cm-24x30in) with sig. 20-Mar-4 Selkirks, St. Louis #162/R est:4000-6000
£3495	$6500	€5103	Mountain landscape, winter (45x60cm-18x24in) s. canvasboard. 5-Mar-4 Skinner, Boston #492/R est:5000-7000
£4032	$7500	€5887	Winter landscape with distant mountains (45x61cm-18x24in) s. canvasboard prov. 5-Mar-4 Skinner, Boston #484/R est:5000-6000
£4118	$7000	€6012	Hillside farm, winter (46x60cm-18x24in) s. canvasboard prov. 21-Nov-3 Skinner, Boston #503/R est:5000-7000
£5031	$8000	€7345	New England, winter (61x82cm-24x32in) s. 12-Sep-3 Skinner, Boston #457/R est:8000
£5202	$9000	€7595	Stream in winter (45x66cm-18x26in) s. i.verso canvas on board prov. 10-Dec-3 Bonhams & Butterfields, San Francisco #6035/R est:8000-12000
£5588	$9500	€8158	Spring thaw, mountain landscape (41x51cm-16x20in) s. canvasboard prov. 21-Nov-3 Skinner, Boston #504/R est:6000-8000
£5780	$10000	€8439	Winter stream (76x91cm-30x36in) s. prov. 10-Dec-3 Bonhams & Butterfields, San Francisco #6033/R est:8000-12000
£6587	$11000	€9617	Cold weather (77x91cm-30x36in) s. prov. 9-Oct-3 Christie's, Rockefeller NY #67/R est:12000-18000
£8380	$15000	€12235	Winter landscape (22x32cm-9x13in) s. 6-May-4 Shannon's, Milford #100/R est:10000-15000
£10440	$19000	€15242	Vermont bridge (68x90cm-27x35in) s. prov. 29-Jun-4 Sotheby's, New York #239/R est:15000-25000
£12346	$20000	€17902	Mt. Rundle, Vermilion Lakes (91x107cm-36x42in) prov. 8-Aug-3 Barridorf, Portland #355/R est:20000-30000
£15294	$26000	€22329	Wooden bridge (72x91cm-28x36in) s. prov. 21-Nov-3 Skinner, Boston #470/R est:7000-9000
£25698	$46000	€37519	Country auction (61x71cm-24x28in) s. i.verso painted c.1930. 16-Mar-4 Matthew's, Oregon #28/R est:12000-18000

HIBBERT, Phyllis I (1903-) British

Works on paper

£250	$455	€365	June (43x55cm-17x22in) s. pencil W/C. 1-Jul-4 Mellors & Kirk, Nottingham #736
£320	$509	€467	Still life of cornflowers, carnations and nasturtiums in a jug (42x38cm-17x15in) s. W/C. 10-Sep-3 Cheffins, Cambridge #476
£580	$922	€847	Still life of delphiniums, roses, peonies, cornflowers and ferns (55x76cm-22x30in) s. W/C. 10-Sep-3 Cheffins, Cambridge #475/R
£620	$986	€905	Still life of carnations, roses and gypsophila (74x54cm-29x21in) s. 10-Sep-3 Cheffins, Cambridge #474/R

HIBBITS, Forrest (1905-) American

£378	$650	€552	Nemesis (84x20cm-33x8in) s.d.1953 board. 7-Dec-3 Treadway Gallery, Cincinnati #725/R

HIBEL, Edna (1917-) American

£2032	$3250	€2967	Japanese girl (104x76cm-41x30in) s. masonite panel. 20-Sep-3 Bunte, Elgin #1216 est:1500-2500

Works on paper

£472	$750	€689	Dancer in white tutu (18x10cm-7x4in) s. W/C ink. 10-Sep-3 Alderfer's, Hatfield #303

HICK, Jacqueline (1920-) Australian

£741	$1341	€1082	Carnival scene (32x47cm-13x19in) s. board. 31-Mar-4 Goodman, Sydney #366/R (A.D 1800)
£1405	$2599	€2051	Evening at Andamooka (63x91cm-25x36in) s. board prov. 10-Mar-4 Deutscher-Menzies, Melbourne #463/R est:2200-3200 (A.D 3400)

HICKEL, Joseph (1736-1807) Austrian

£7500	$12975	€10950	Portrait of Maria-Theresia, Altgrafin Zu Salmreifferscheidt-Raitz, half length (75x58cm-30x23in) i.verso prov. 11-Dec-3 Sotheby's, London #216/R est:8000-12000

HICKEY, Dale (1937-) Australian

Works on paper

£300	$554	€438	Seymour 56 (23x30cm-9x12in) s.i. mixed media executed 1991 prov. 15-Mar-4 Sotheby's, Melbourne #196 (A.D 725)
£533	$842	€778	Drawing No 56 (42x41cm-17x16in) s.d.94 pastel prov. 2-Sep-3 Deutscher-Menzies, Melbourne #257/R est:1500-2000 (A.D 1300)

HICKEY, Desmond (20th C) British?

£537	$961	€800	Achill landscape, Dooagh (29x35cm-11x14in) s. board. 26-May-4 James Adam, Dublin #87/R
£625	$1019	€900	Afternoon traffic in O'Connell Street, Dublin (51x61cm-20x24in) s.i.verso canvasboard. 23-Sep-3 De Veres Art Auctions, Dublin #334

HICKEY, Patrick (1927-1999) Irish

£2817	$4873	€4000	Winter forestry no 11 (101x76cm-40x30in) s. prov. 10-Dec-3 Bonhams & James Adam, Dublin #171/R est:4000-6000
£4161	$7448	€6200	Italian sea (49x59cm-19x23in) s.i.verso board exhib. 26-May-4 James Adam, Dublin #116/R est:1500-2000
£4306	$7018	€6200	County Wicklow landscape (76x101cm-30x40in) s. prov. 24-Sep-3 James Adam, Dublin #57/R est:4000-6000
£6944	$11319	€10000	Fairground, Booterstown (107x152cm-42x60in) s. prov. 24-Sep-3 James Adam, Dublin #66/R est:10000-15000

HICKEY, Thomas (attrib) (1741-1824) British

£7000	$11690	€10220	Portrait of a gentleman. Portrait of a lady (28x23cm-11x9in) pair oval prov. 14-Oct-3 Sotheby's, London #450/R est:2500-4000

HICKIN, George (fl.1858-1877) British

£540	$848	€788	Cockerel and his flock scratching in the fields (28x44cm-11x17in) s. 16-Apr-3 Bamfords, Derby #656/R

HICKIN, George Arthur (19th C) British

£260	$419	€377	Landscape with ducks entering stream (28x38cm-11x15in) s. 20-Aug-3 Brightwells, Leominster #899/R

HICKLING, Ross (20th C) British
£400 $692 €584 Nude (56x77cm-22x30in) s. board exhib. sold with two framed photographs. 9-Dec-3 Rosebery Fine Art, London #665/R

HICKMAN, Nathaniel (19/20th C) British
£2000 $3580 €2920 Haymaking, Norton near Worcester, with figures. s.i.d.1880 verso. 5-May-4 John Nicholson, Haslemere #542/R est:1500-2000

HICKS, George Elgar (1824-1914) British
£20000 $34000 €29200 Her pet (61x46cm-24x18in) s.d.04 prov. 27-Nov-3 Sotheby's, London #339/R est:15000-20000
£29000 $49300 €42340 Haymaking (46x36cm-18x14in) mono.d.1855 prov.lit. 25-Nov-3 Christie's, London #118/R est:12000-18000
£36000 $65520 €52560 Gypsy girl (43x35cm-17x14in) s.d.1899 board prov. 1-Jul-4 Sotheby's, London #312/R est:30000-50000

HICKS, Jason (20th C) New Zealander
£489 $831 €714 Shine (68x118cm-27x46in) 26-Nov-3 Dunbar Sloane, Wellington #142 est:500-1500 (NZ.D 1300)

HICKS, Nicola (1960-) British
Sculpture
£11500 $20930 €16790 Nice little earner (104x86cm-41x34in) init.d.88 num.6/6 grey pat bronze prov. 4-Feb-4 Sotheby's, Olympia #89/R est:7000-9000
Works on paper
£1000 $1850 €1460 Seated dog (114x95cm-45x37in) s.d.99 chl col chk. 11-Mar-4 Christie's, Kensington #163/R est:1500-2000

HICKS, Thomas (1823-1890) American
£6630 $12000 €9680 No place like home (55x72cm-22x28in) s.d.1877 prov.exhib. 31-Mar-4 Sotheby's, New York #83/R est:15000-25000

HIDALGO DE CAVIEDES, Hipolito (1902-1996) Spanish
£775 $1356 €1100 Musician (74x46cm-29x18in) s.d.1901. 16-Dec-3 Durán, Madrid #116
£1064 $1723 €1500 La carga (50x65cm-20x26in) s. 20-May-3 Ansorena, Madrid #302/R est:2000
£1418 $2298 €2000 Planideras II (65x50cm-26x20in) s. i.verso panel. 20-May-3 Ansorena, Madrid #301/R est:2000
Works on paper
£267 $485 €400 Guarapo Dulse (18x15cm-7x6in) s.d.1936 W/C pencil. 29-Jun-4 Segre, Madrid #289/R

HIDALGO DE CAVIEDES, Rafael (1864-1950) Spanish
£709 $1184 €1000 Study for Rea Silvia (40x44cm-16x17in) s.i.d.1888. 20-Oct-3 Durán, Madrid #182/R

HIDALGO Y PADILLA, Felix Resurreccion (1853-1913) Spanish
£249462 $399140 €364215 La Parisienne (93x54cm-37x21in) s.d.1887 lit. 18-May-3 Sotheby's, Singapore #78/R est:380000-550000 (S.D 696000)

HIDAYAT, S P (1969-) Oriental
£2451 $4436 €3578 Kuda lumping (140x140cm-55x55in) s.d.03 s.i.d.verso. 4-Apr-4 Sotheby's, Singapore #180/R est:5500-7500 (S.D 7500)
£2604 $4349 €3802 Mother and child (130x100cm-51x39in) s.d.02 s.i.d.verso. 12-Oct-3 Sotheby's, Singapore #189/R est:4000-6000 (S.D 7500)

HIDEMASA (19th C) Japanese
Sculpture
£4500 $7515 €6525 Woman and young boy (20cm-8in) s. ivory. 18-Jun-3 Christie's, London #147/R est:4000-6000

HIDER, Frank (1861-1933) British
£260 $471 €380 Scottish loch and mountain landscape at sunset (28x48cm-11x19in) s. 16-Apr-4 Keys, Aylsham #782
£260 $465 €380 Pastoral scene (39x60cm-15x24in) s. 11-May-4 Bonhams, Ipswich #258
£260 $478 €380 Rocky coastal scene (51x76cm-20x30in) 8-Jun-4 Bonhams, Ipswich #374
£280 $529 €409 Golden autumn (30x49cm-12x19in) s. i.verso. 18-Feb-4 Peter Wilson, Nantwich #51
£280 $512 €409 Cottage by a river (23x45cm-9x18in) s. 6-Jul-4 Bonhams, Knightsbridge #57/R
£300 $543 €438 Stormy weather (28x48cm-11x19in) s. 31-Mar-4 Brightwells, Leominster #973
£320 $586 €467 The waning of the year (41x61cm-16x24in) s. i.verso. 7-Apr-4 Gardiner & Houlgate, Bath #239/R
£360 $587 €526 In a Welsh Valley (29x50cm-11x20in) s. i.verso. 24-Sep-3 Peter Wilson, Nantwich #12
£391 $700 €571 Calmly the day departs (30x51cm-12x20in) s. 15-May-4 Jeffery Burchard, Florida #60
£400 $756 €584 Tide at the ebb (30x50cm-12x20in) s. i.verso. 18-Feb-4 Peter Wilson, Nantwich #34
£400 $756 €584 On the banks of Derwentwater (29x49cm-11x19in) s. i.verso. 18-Feb-4 Peter Wilson, Nantwich #52
£400 $680 €584 High tide near Land's End (29x49cm-11x19in) s.i. 26-Nov-3 Peter Wilson, Nantwich #107
£660 $1195 €964 Coastal views with fisherfolk and boats (28x48cm-11x19in) s. pair. 16-Apr-4 Keys, Aylsham #781/R

HIDER, Frank (attrib) (1861-1933) British
£560 $1025 €818 River landscape scenes with distant hills (29x39cm-11x15in) each s. pair. 8-Jul-4 Lawrence, Crewkerne #1652

HIDER, Frederic (19/20th C) British
£280 $484 €409 Summer evening in the Highlands (46x36cm-18x14in) 12-Dec-3 Bracketts, Tunbridge Wells #814

HIEBLOT, Eugene (1886-1953) French?
£400 $728 €600 Portrait de paquebot (32x45cm-13x18in) s. 3-Jul-4 Neret-Minet, Paris #176/R
£556 $928 €800 Normandie (31x44cm-12x17in) s. panel. 26-Oct-3 Lesieur & Le Bars, Le Havre #245
£625 $1044 €900 Paquebot Ile de France (30x45cm-12x18in) s. panel. 26-Oct-3 Lesieur & Le Bars, Le Havre #246
£972 $1624 €1400 Le Minaewaska et son bateau pilote au Havre (54x73cm-21x29in) s.d.34. 26-Oct-3 Lesieur & Le Bars, Le Havre #47

HIEN, J W (fl.1755-1775) Dutch?
Works on paper
£1892 $3330 €2800 Portrait of a man (58x47cm-23x19in) s.d.1755 pastel vellum. 19-May-4 Sotheby's, Amsterdam #262/R est:1800-2200

HIENL-MERRE, Franz (1870-1943) German
£272 $487 €400 Horse racing (28x38cm-11x15in) s. board. 18-Mar-4 Neumeister, Munich #2691/R
£308 $529 €440 Horse drawn sleigh race in the mountains (71x60cm-28x24in) s.i. 4-Dec-3 Neumeister, Munich #2762
£333 $597 €500 Apres-midi de detente (29x40cm-11x16in) s. cardboard. 11-May-4 Vanderkindere, Brussels #49
£664 $1129 €950 Cavaliers sautant un obstacle (61x81cm-24x32in) s. 18-Nov-3 Vanderkindere, Brussels #71
Works on paper
£426 $711 €600 Fete nocturne (46x38cm-18x15in) s. gouache W/C. 14-Oct-3 Vanderkindere, Brussels #65

HIER, Auguste van (19/20th C) Dutch?
£315 $536 €460 Clam gatherers on the beach (36x46cm-14x18in) s. paper on canvas prov. 21-Nov-3 Walker's, Ottawa #218/R (C.D 700)

HIERCK, Huub (1917-1970) Dutch
£308 $524 €450 Landscape in Italy (42x62cm-17x24in) s. board. 5-Nov-3 Vendue Huis, Gravenhage #440/R
£455 $782 €650 Still life with flowers (47x37cm-19x15in) s. board. 8-Dec-3 Glerum, Amsterdam #337/R
£3014 $5123 €4400 Carnaval (90x110cm-35x43in) s.d.75. 5-Nov-3 Vendue Huis, Gravenhage #441/R est:2500-3000

HIERONYMI, Ernst W (1823-1897) German
£1806 $2979 €2600 Mill by stream (36x32cm-14x13in) s.d.1857. 3-Jul-3 Dr Fritz Nagel, Stuttgart #491/R est:2900

HIETANEN, Reino (1932-) Finnish
£1867 $3341 €2800 Sullottu (70x90cm-28x35in) s.d.1968 canvas on board exhib. 15-May-4 Hagelstam, Helsinki #227/R est:2400
£2230 $3991 €3300 Cosmos (108x88cm-43x35in) s.d.68-74 board. 8-May-4 Bukowskis, Helsinki #256/R est:2500-3000
Works on paper
£317 $548 €450 Dark room (20x20cm-8x8in) s.d.1970 mixed media. 13-Dec-3 Hagelstam, Helsinki #193/R
£333 $597 €500 Curtains (114x65cm-45x26in) s.d.1977 mixed media. 15-May-4 Hagelstam, Helsinki #226/R

HIGGINS, Eugene (1874-1958) American
£380 $700 €555 Flight (41x51cm-16x20in) s. board. 9-Jun-4 Alderfer's, Hatfield #407
£407 $700 €594 Descent from the Cross (61x51cm-24x20in) s. exhib. 7-Dec-3 William Jenack, New York #362
£516 $950 €753 Lunchtime. Home at last (36x25cm-14x10in) s. board two. 25-Mar-4 Doyle, New York #26/R
£598 $1100 €873 Sinking of the Vestris. Jesus silencing the water (25x36cm-10x14in) s. board two prov.exhib. 23-Jun-4 Doyle, New York #5037/R
£795 $1446 €1200 Nature morte cubiste (41x33cm-16x13in) s.d.48. 16-Jun-4 Renaud, Paris #53
£1033 $1900 €1508 Brawl. Flight (41x51cm-16x20in) one s. one s.d.1935. 25-Mar-4 Doyle, New York #25/R est:800-1200
£1033 $1900 €1508 Old man and the setting sun. Wagons on the prairie (38x28cm-15x11in) s. board two different sizes. 25-Mar-4 Doyle, New York #30/R est:800-1200
£1087 $2000 €1587 Watering place. Poor fisherman (41x51cm-16x20in) s. two. 25-Mar-4 Doyle, New York #28/R est:800-1200
Works on paper
£543 $1000 €793 Picking up the scent. Coming home (28x38cm-11x15in) s. W/C pencil htd white two. 25-Mar-4 Doyle, New York #27/R est:800-1200

HIGGINS, George F (19th C) American
£343 $550 €501 Bridge over stream (76x51cm-30x20in) s. 21-Sep-3 Grogan, Boston #95/R
£1497 $2500 €2186 New Hampshire landscape (61x91cm-24x36in) s. 16-Nov-3 CRN Auctions, Cambridge #22/R

HIGGINS, Michael (1949-) American?
Works on paper
£270 $500 €394 Board Track (58x74cm-23x29in) china marker exec 1975 prov. 13-Jul-4 Christie's, Rockefeller NY #154/R

HIGGINS, R B (1943-) British
£1267 $2280 €1900 Near Ardara, Co Donegal (59x89cm-23x35in) s. 20-Apr-4 James Adam, Dublin #85/R est:2500-3500

HIGGINS, Robert B (1943-) British
£265 $482 €400 Shell Hill, Last Drive, Greyabbey, County Down (44x60cm-17x24in) s. 15-Jun-4 James Adam, Dublin #84/R
£300 $558 €438 Scrabo. Co Down (50x76cm-20x30in) s.d.1986. 3-Mar-4 John Ross, Belfast #82

HIGGINS, Victor (1884-1949) American
£13369 $25000 €19519 Bak trees (23x28cm-9x11in) s. board prov. 24-Jul-4 Coeur d'Alene, Hayden #158/R est:12000-16000
£14706 $25000 €21471 Sarah with her horse (36x51cm-14x20in) s. panel painted c.1923 prov.lit. 1-Nov-3 Santa Fe Art, Santa Fe #52/R est:30000-40000
£45455 $85000 €66364 Meadow with cattle (30x43cm-12x17in) s. board prov. 24-Jul-4 Coeur d'Alene, Hayden #156/R est:20000-30000
Works on paper
£16176 $27500 €23617 New Mexico landscape (36x51cm-14x20in) s. W/C exec.c.1930-1940 prov.lit. 1-Nov-3 Santa Fe Art, Santa Fe #201/R est:40000-50000
£24457 $45000 €35707 Untitled (70x52cm-28x20in) W/C. 24-Jun-4 Sotheby's, New York #170/R est:15000-25000
£29412 $55000 €42942 Fish ponds (43x56cm-17x22in) s. W/C prov. 24-Jul-4 Coeur d'Alene, Hayden #157/R est:15000-25000

HIGGINSON, Augustus (19/20th C) American
Works on paper
£455 $800 €664 Architectural rendering for a midwest rectory (53x33cm-21x13in) W/C exec.c.1903 prov. 23-May-4 Treadway Gallery, Cincinnati #294/R
£568 $1000 €829 Architectural rendering for a Chicago North Shore Estate (64x33cm-25x13in) mono. W/C exec.c.1905 prov. 23-May-4 Treadway Gallery, Cincinnati #296/R
£625 $1100 €913 Architectural rendering for a midwest Arts and Crafts building (56x33cm-22x13in) W/C exec.c.1903 prov. 23-May-4 Treadway Gallery, Cincinnati #292/R
£852 $1500 €1244 Architectural rendering for the E Fechheimer home in Winnetka, IL (53x28cm-21x11in) i.verso W/C exec.c.1903 prov. 23-May-4 Treadway Gallery, Cincinnati #293/R est:1000-1500
£1648 $2900 €2406 Architectural rendering for D S Look residence of Santa Barbara (56x30cm-22x12in) i.verso W/C exec.c.1909 prov. 23-May-4 Treadway Gallery, Cincinnati #297/R est:900-1200
£1705 $3000 €2489 Architectural rendering for S M Coe residence of Montecito, CA (56x30cm-22x12in) W/C exec.c.1909 prov. 23-May-4 Treadway Gallery, Cincinnati #295/R est:9000-12000

HIGGS, Cecil (1906-1986) South African
£924 $1673 €1349 Street group (35x25cm-14x10in) 30-Mar-4 Stephan Welz, Johannesburg #501/R est:8000-12000 (SA.R 11000)
£1176 $2129 €1717 Camelia (32x27cm-13x11in) s.d.59 exhib. 30-Mar-4 Stephan Welz, Johannesburg #528 est:4000-6000 (SA.R 14000)
£3529 $6388 €5152 Still life (45x55cm-18x22in) init.d.50 five. 30-Mar-4 Stephan Welz, Johannesburg #527/R est:12000-16000 (SA.R 42000)
Works on paper
£248 $443 €362 Fire II (51x49cm-20x19in) s.d.72 mixed media exhib. 31-May-4 Stephan Welz, Johannesburg #410 (SA.R 3000)
£259 $432 €378 Sea and rocks (47x56cm-19x22in) s.d.72 mixed media. 20-Oct-3 Stephan Welz, Johannesburg #577 est:3000-5000 (SA.R 3000)
£454 $813 €663 Marine composition (38x56cm-15x22in) s.d.72 mixed media. 31-May-4 Stephan Welz, Johannesburg #234 (SA.R 5500)

HIGGS, Joshua (fl.1880s) Australian
£840 $1528 €1226 Entrance to Lanena, Tasmania (20x51cm-8x20in) s.d.96 i.verso. 16-Jun-4 Deutscher-Menzies, Melbourne #208/R est:2500-3500 (A.D 2200)

HIGGS, Paul David (1954-) Australian
£494 $894 €721 Binary (92x124cm-36x49in) s. i.d.1980 verso acrylic liquitex sprayed matt varnish. 30-Mar-4 Lawson Menzies, Sydney #19 est:1500-2000 (A.D 1200)
£741 $1341 €1082 Parc Guell sequence (137x121cm-54x48in) i.verso. 30-Mar-4 Lawson Menzies, Sydney #24 est:1500-2500 (A.D 1800)
£988 $1788 €1442 Untitled (168x198cm-66x78in) i.verso. 30-Mar-4 Lawson Menzies, Sydney #67/R est:1500-2500 (A.D 2400)

HIGGS, Warwick (1956-) British
Works on paper
£300 $516 €438 Robin seated on a snowy wire (25x33cm-10x13in) d.1980 gouache. 3-Dec-3 Brightwells, Leominster #1252/R

HIGHAM, Bernard (fl.1917-1919) British
Works on paper
£2703 $5000 €3946 To a higher plane (74x74cm-29x29in) s.d.1917 s.i.verso W/C board. 24-Jan-4 Jeffery Burchard, Florida #12a/R

HIGHMORE, Joseph (1692-1780) British
£2133 $3904 €3200 Portrait of gentleman in landscape (51x37cm-20x15in) en grisaille prov. 1-Jun-4 Sotheby's, Milan #94/R est:3000-4000
£3200 $5760 €4672 Portrait of George Leycester (72x60cm-28x24in) oval. 21-Jan-4 Sotheby's, Olympia #17/R est:2500-4000
£9200 $15640 €13432 Portrait of a young girl wearing a cream dress (39x29cm-15x11in) 27-Nov-3 Sotheby's, London #132/R est:4000-6000

HIGHMORE, Joseph (attrib) (1692-1780) British
£4790 $8000 €6993 Seated woman (119x147cm-47x58in) 14-Nov-3 Du Mouchelle, Detroit #2024/R est:8000-12000
£4800 $8880 €7008 Portrait of lady, identified as Jane Shore (89x69cm-35x27in) 14-Jan-4 Lawrence, Crewkerne #1383/R est:3000-5000

HIGHSTEIN, Jene (1942-) American
Sculpture
£1757 $3250 €2565 Untitled (183x89x68cm-72x35x27in) carved elm wood exec 1988 prov.exhib. 12-Feb-4 Sotheby's, New York #228/R est:4000-5000
Works on paper
£444 $800 €648 Untitled (32x23cm-13x9in) init.d.1975 ink. 24-Apr-4 David Rago, Lambertville #519/R
£889 $1600 €1298 Untitled (32x22cm-13x9in) init.d.1975 chl. 24-Apr-4 David Rago, Lambertville #265/R est:200-400
£2222 $4000 €3244 Untitled (22x30cm-9x12in) s.d.1971 graphite. 24-Apr-4 David Rago, Lambertville #343/R est:200-400

HIGHT, Beryl (?) ?
£1007 $1852 €1500 Night in Greccio (95x95cm-37x37in) board. 24-Mar-4 Il Ponte, Milan #541/R est:1600-1800

HIGHT, Michael (20th C) New Zealander
£3172 $5487 €4631 Mangatawhiri hives no 2 (50x220cm-20x87in) s.i.d.1994 verso. 9-Dec-3 Peter Webb, Auckland #117/R est:5000-8000 (NZ.D 8500)
£3383 $5752 €4939 Ahuriri Pass (50x150cm-20x59in) s.i.d.2001-02 verso. 27-Nov-3 International Art Centre. Auckland #47/R est:8000-12000 (NZ.D 9000)
£5714 $10343 €8342 Oakley Creek (80x279cm-31x110in) i.d.2.VII.99 s.i.d.stretcher verso. 30-Mar-4 Peter Webb, Auckland #57/R est:16000-22000 (NZ.D 16000)
£9386 $15300 €13704 Clyde (110x250cm-43x98in) i.d.17.X.00 s.i.d.verso. 23-Sep-3 Peter Webb, Auckland #81/R est:20000-25000 (NZ.D 26000)

HIGUERO, Enrique Marin (1876-?) Spanish
£1111 $1811 €1600 Street in Granada (32x17cm-13x7in) s. board. 23-Sep-3 Durán, Madrid #180/R est:1400
£1319 $2151 €1900 View in Granada (32x17cm-13x7in) s.i. board. 23-Sep-3 Durán, Madrid #181/R
Sculpture
£4577 $8011 €6500 Future teller (190cm-75in) i. marble lit. 16-Dec-3 Durán, Madrid #307/R est:1200
Works on paper
£345 $621 €500 Tower, Seville (20x16cm-8x6in) s. W/C. 26-Jan-4 Durán, Madrid #39/R
£379 $630 €550 View of Toledo (13x9cm-5x4in) s. W/C. 1-Oct-3 Ansorena, Madrid #342/R
£379 $630 €550 Street in Toledo (13x9cm-5x4in) s.i. W/C. 1-Oct-3 Ansorena, Madrid #341/R
£379 $683 €550 Landscape (24x19cm-9x7in) s. W/C. 26-Jan-4 Durán, Madrid #40/R
£423 $731 €600 Granada (13x9cm-5x4in) s. W/C. 15-Dec-3 Ansorena, Madrid #173/R
£436 $781 €650 View of Granada (13x9cm-5x4in) s. W/C. 25-May-4 Durán, Madrid #53/R
£436 $781 €650 View of granada (14x9cm-6x4in) s. W/C. 25-May-4 Durán, Madrid #52/R
£483 $806 €700 View of Seville (26x17cm-10x7in) s. W/C. 17-Nov-3 Durán, Madrid #1279/R
£517 $864 €750 Houses (26x17cm-10x7in) s. W/C. 17-Nov-3 Durán, Madrid #1280/R
£966 $1738 €1400 Street in Toledo (37x27cm-15x11in) s. W/C. 26-Jan-4 Durán, Madrid #124/R
£1596 $2665 €2250 El Generalife, Granada (43x34cm-17x13in) s. W/C. 23-Jun-3 Durán, Madrid #183/R est:2250
£1812 $2971 €2500 Patio granadino (46x32cm-18x13in) s. W/C. 27-May-3 Durán, Madrid #175/R est:1500
£1950 $3257 €2750 La Alhambra (51x35cm-20x14in) s. W/C. 23-Jun-3 Durán, Madrid #163/R est:2250

HIIRONEN, Eero (1938-) Finnish
Sculpture
£2297 $4112 €3400 Shapes (100x60cm-39x24in) s.d.87 bronze. 8-May-4 Bukowskis, Helsinki #222/R est:3000-4000

HIIVANAINEN, Frans (1884-1944) Finnish
£320 $589 €480 In the harbour (46x56cm-18x22in) s.d.1935. 9-Jun-4 Bukowskis, Helsinki #412/R

HILAIRE, Camille (1916-1988) French
£1057 $1797 €1543 Le canape rouge (16x27cm-6x11in) s. i.d.1961 verso. 5-Nov-3 Dobiaschofsky, Bern #640/R est:1900 (S.FR 2400)
£1118 $1900 €1632 Deauville (64x53cm-25x21in) s. prov. 22-Nov-3 Jackson's, Cedar Falls #389/R est:500-750
£1176 $2000 €1717 Race horses (46x25cm-18x10in) s. prov. 22-Nov-3 Jackson's, Cedar Falls #388/R est:1000-1500
£1351 $2500 €1972 Before the race (38x46cm-15x18in) s. prov. 10-Mar-4 Doyle, New York #73/R est:1200-1600
£1812 $3371 €2700 Le lever (38x46cm-15x18in) s. i.verso. 2-Mar-4 Artcurial Briest, Paris #254/R est:2500-3500
£2013 $3604 €3000 Paddock (33x55cm-13x22in) s. 30-May-4 Eric Pillon, Calais #130/R
£2051 $3631 €2994 La Course (39x80cm-15x31in) s. 27-Apr-4 AB Stockholms Auktionsverk #1174/R est:30000-40000 (S.KR 28000)
£2676 $4630 €3800 Reflets d'automne (38x55cm-15x22in) s. 14-Dec-3 Eric Pillon, Calais #284/R
£3020 $5617 €4500 Jazz, le quatuor (60x92cm-24x36in) s. 3-Mar-4 Ferri, Paris #160/R est:4000-4500
£3356 $6007 €5000 Rio a Venise (54x65cm-21x26in) s. 30-May-4 Eric Pillon, Calais #112/R

£3893 $6968 €5800 Venise (54x65cm-21x26in) s. 30-May-4 Eric Pillon, Calais #113/R
£3893 $7240 €5800 Pesage a Deauville (73x92cm-29x36in) s. 3-Mar-4 Ferri, Paris #161/R est:5000-6000
£4895 $8322 €7000 Au Mont Boron (89x116cm-35x46in) s. s.i.verso painted c.1968 prov.exhib.lit. 18-Nov-3 Pierre Berge, Paris #64/R est:10000-12000
£6977 $12000 €10186 Paddock at Deauville (74x91cm-29x36in) s. s.i.verso. 5-Dec-3 Christie's, Rockefeller NY #134/R est:12000-18000

Works on paper

£369 $687 €550 Nu aux bas noirs (47x36cm-19x14in) s. brown ink ink wash. 2-Mar-4 Artcurial Briest, Paris #255
£560 $1003 €818 Houses in Venice (43x65cm-17x26in) s. W/C. 12-May-4 Dobiaschofsky, Bern #607/R (S.FR 1300)
£633 $1159 €950 Nu allongee (49x63cm-19x25in) s. W/C. 6-Jun-4 Rouillac, Vendome #41
£872 $1623 €1300 Composition (47x65cm-19x26in) s. W/C. 3-Mar-4 Ferri, Paris #159
£2013 $3604 €3000 Chasse a courre (47x63cm-19x25in) s. W/C gouache. 30-May-4 Eric Pillon, Calais #132/R

HILAIRE, Jean Baptiste (1753-1822) French

£7333 $13127 €11000 Flora (85x113cm-33x44in) s.d.1787. 17-May-4 Finarte Semenzato, Rome #75/R est:12000-14000

HILAIRE, Jean Baptiste (attrib) (1753-1822) French

£2961 $5447 €4500 Concert champetre (37x46cm-15x18in) prov. 24-Jun-4 Christie's, Paris #131/R est:4000-6000

HILBERT, Georges (1900-1982) French

Sculpture

£890 $1513 €1300 Pony (20x24x12cm-8x9x5in) s. num.1/10 pat bronze. 5-Nov-3 Tajan, Paris #19/R

HILBERT, Gustav (1900-1981) German

£533 $976 €800 Wooded coast with dunes and sailing boats (60x82cm-24x32in) s.d.22 prov. 5-Jun-4 Lempertz, Koln #762/R

HILBERTH, Ilona (?) ?

£750 $1380 €1095 Relaxing by the lamp (87x73cm-34x29in) s. 23-Mar-4 Rosebery Fine Art, London #930/R

HILBERTH, Iren (1872-1925) Hungarian

£5879 $10406 €8583 Girl in a dress with green ribbon (157x62cm-62x24in) s.d.1894. 28-Apr-4 Kieselbach, Budapest #74/R (H.F 2200000)

HILDEBRANDT, Eduard (1818-1869) German

£1208 $2223 €1800 Brazilian landscape with storks (32x42cm-13x17in) s. lit. 25-Mar-4 Karlheinz Kaupp, Staufen #2506/R est:1800
£1806 $3015 €2600 Figures in a harbour at low tide (28x37cm-11x15in) mono. 21-Oct-3 Sotheby's, Amsterdam #86/R est:2500-3500
£1931 $3225 €2800 Canal landscape with sailing boat (29x39cm-11x15in) s. 15-Nov-3 Lempertz, Koln #1620/R est:3000
£3067 $5520 €4600 Brazilian landscape (68x102cm-27x40in) s. 26-Apr-4 Rieber, Stuttgart #110/R est:4500
£4500 $6974 €6570 Loo Rock and Pontinha, Madeira, sunset (84x117cm-33x46in) s. i.on stretcher. 26-Sep-2 Christie's, London #106/R est:3000-5000
£11111 $18111 €16000 Grand Canal, Venice in the evening (78x115cm-31x45in) s.d.1852. 26-Sep-3 Bolland & Marotz, Bremen #546/R est:16000
£48000 $78240 €70080 Ein heiliger See in Birma (84x117cm-33x46in) s. s.i.stretcher prov.exhib. 25-Sep-3 Christie's, London #464/R est:30000-50000

Works on paper

£451 $736 €650 Cleopatra's Needle near Alexandria (26x35cm-10x14in) s.i.d.1862 W/C. 25-Sep-3 Neumeister, Munich #279/R
£500 $885 €730 Bangkok (24x34cm-9x13in) i. pencil W/C. 29-Apr-4 Christie's, Kensington #114
£564 $998 €840 Arab group with horses in mountain landscape (24x32cm-9x13in) s. W/C. 28-Apr-4 Schopman, Hamburg #483/R
£650 $1086 €949 Street in South America (16x25cm-6x10in) studio st. W/C. 8-Oct-3 Christie's, Kensington #1105/R
£699 $1203 €1000 Fisherwomen on the beach (12x21cm-5x8in) s.d.1842 W/C. 3-Dec-3 Neumeister, Munich #395/R
£1379 $2303 €2000 Church of St Michael in Seville (18x26cm-7x10in) s.d.1849 W/C. 15-Nov-3 Lempertz, Koln #1491/R est:1300

HILDEBRANDT, Eduard (attrib) (1818-1869) German

Works on paper

£800 $1456 €1200 Hong Kong harbour (23x32cm-9x13in) s.i.d.1894 W/C. 1-Jul-4 Van Ham, Cologne #1404/R

HILDEBRANDT, Friedrich Fritz (1819-1885) German

£355 $635 €518 Coastal landscape with boats and figures (41x57cm-16x22in) s.indis.d.1849 prov. 28-May-4 Uppsala Auktionskammare, Uppsala #161 (S.KR 4800)
£671 $1235 €1000 Barque de peche sous le vent a l'entree du port (35x55cm-14x22in) s.d.53. 28-Mar-4 Anaf, Lyon #159

HILDENBRAND, Adolf (1881-1944) German

£331 $603 €500 Summer landscape near Lake Constance (70x104cm-28x41in) mono.d.38. 17-Jun-4 Frank Peege, Freiburg #1168/R

HILDER, Edith (1904-) British

Works on paper

£360 $572 €526 Shell nature studies (64x46cm-25x18in) ink W/C gouache printed note. 10-Sep-3 Sotheby's, Olympia #110/R

HILDER, J J (1881-1916) Australian

Works on paper

£936 $1591 €1367 Lennox Bridge (15x20cm-6x8in) s.d.1911 W/C. 26-Nov-3 Deutscher-Menzies, Melbourne #178/R est:2000-2500 (A.D 2200)
£1021 $1736 €1491 Moreton Bay (12x18cm-5x7in) s. W/C exec 1916. 26-Nov-3 Deutscher-Menzies, Melbourne #179/R (A.D 2400)
£1065 $1683 €1555 Bondi (10x19cm-4x7in) s.i.d.1906 W/C. 2-Sep-3 Deutscher-Menzies, Melbourne #204/R est:3500-4500 (A.D 2600)
£1319 $2243 €1926 Children at the beach (10x15cm-4x6in) s. W/C. 26-Nov-3 Deutscher-Menzies, Melbourne #177/R est:1800-2500 (A.D 3100)
£6383 $10851 €9319 Bush Scene, landscape with sheep (53x42cm-21x17in) s.d.1912 W/C prov.exhib.lit. 26-Nov-3 Deutscher-Menzies, Melbourne #64/R est:18000-22000 (A.D 15000)

HILDER, Jesse Jewhurst (1881-1916) Australian

Works on paper

£1000 $1770 €1460 Sheep grazing on bushland (23x30cm-9x12in) s. W/C. 27-Apr-4 Bonhams, New Bond Street #11/R est:800-1200
£1245 $2079 €1868 Dora Creek (18x17cm-7x7in) s. W/C. 27-Oct-3 Goodman, Sydney #131 est:800-1200 (A.D 3000)
£2075 $3465 €3113 Reflection (28x16cm-11x6in) s.d.1908 W/C. 27-Oct-3 Goodman, Sydney #111/R est:5000-7000 (A.D 5000)
£4878 $7659 €7073 Jetty (16x26cm-6x10in) s. W/C. 27-Aug-3 Christie's, Sydney #532/R est:8000-12000 (A.D 12000)

HILDER, John (19th C) British

£1200 $1992 €1752 Horse and cart on a wooded track (78x64cm-31x25in) s. 1-Oct-3 Sotheby's, Olympia #9/R est:600-800

HILDER, Richard (1813-1852) British

£244 $450 €356 Landscape with hay cart on track, figures in distance and wooded hillside (41x30cm-16x12in) s. 9-Jun-4 Alderfer's, Hatfield #347
£950 $1739 €1387 Figures outside a thatched cottage, children playing next to a stream (23cm-9in circular) init. board. 8-Apr-4 Christie's, Kensington #90/R
£1100 $2035 €1606 Extensive country landscape at dusk with figure and horses (27x37cm-11x15in) s. panel. 13-Jan-4 Bonhams, Knightsbridge #307/R est:1000-1500

HILDER, Rowland (1905-1993) British

£2200 $4070 €3212 Winter landscape (51x76cm-20x30in) s. 11-Feb-4 Sotheby's, Olympia #148/R est:2500-3500
£3600 $5724 €5256 Winter landscape in Kent (60x81cm-24x32in) s. board. 10-Sep-3 Sotheby's, Olympia #181/R est:2000-3000

Works on paper

£280 $510 €409 Evening, small lake, Rutland (18x23cm-7x9in) s. W/C. 1-Jul-4 Christie's, Kensington #464
£300 $546 €438 Autumn landscape, Kent (21x28cm-8x11in) s. W/C. 15-Jun-4 Bonhams, Knightsbridge #7/R
£360 $572 €526 Grosvenor Buildings (30x53cm-12x21in) s.d.1929 pencil black chk ink W/C. 10-Sep-3 Sotheby's, Olympia #92/R
£360 $648 €526 Quayside, coastal view with houses and moored sailing boats (17x25cm-7x10in) s. i.verso pencil ink W/C. 21-Jan-4 Rupert Toovey, Partridge Green #101/R
£448 $749 €654 Barn interior, Porlock, Somerset (50x73cm-20x29in) s. W/C. 20-Oct-3 Stephan Welz, Johannesburg #212/R est:5000-8000 (SA.R 5200)
£550 $891 €798 Old Portsmouth (28x41cm-11x16in) s. W/C wash htd white. 30-Jul-3 Hamptons Fine Art, Godalming #94
£580 $1044 €847 Flooded landscape (16x24cm-6x9in) s. i.verso pencil ink W/C. 21-Jan-4 Rupert Toovey, Partridge Green #99/R
£600 $1038 €876 Coast near Mullion Cove, Cornwall (31x40cm-12x16in) s. i.verso W/C. 10-Dec-3 Bonhams, Bury St Edmunds #470
£600 $1098 €876 Sailing ships in the estuary (28x36cm-11x14in) s.i.verso. 7-Apr-4 Andrew Hartley, Ilkley #1001
£600 $1062 €876 Cargo ship nearing port (51x61cm-20x24in) s. 27-Apr-4 Bonhams, Knightsbridge #11/R
£700 $1323 €1022 Shoreham by Sea, Sussex (34x51cm-13x20in) s. i.verso pencil ink W/C. 18-Feb-4 Rupert Toovey, Partridge Green #75/R
£720 $1332 €1051 Valley (18x23cm-7x9in) s. W/C. 10-Feb-4 David Lay, Penzance #133
£900 $1431 €1314 Artists at work (37x31cm-15x12in) one s. pencil ink W/C two framed as one. 10-Sep-3 Sotheby's, Olympia #109/R
£900 $1656 €1314 Penny Flats farm. W/C gouache. 28-Jun-4 British Auctioneer #371/R
£1000 $1760 €1460 Old toll bridge, Shoreham-on-sea (33x51cm-13x20in) s. W/C gouache pen ink. 19-May-4 Sotheby's, Olympia #85/R est:1000-1500
£1300 $2210 €1898 Extensive landscape with cattle grazing, cottages, farms and windmill (45x62cm-18x24in) i.verso pencil chl pastel wash. 19-Nov-3 Tennants, Leyburn #995a est:1000-1200
£1550 $2682 €2263 Myconos, Cyclades, view over the town and bay from a hillside church (52x71cm-20x28in) s. W/C. 9-Dec-3 Bonhams, Oxford #77/R est:600-800
£1600 $2816 €2336 Oast houses, Kent (35x52cm-14x20in) s. W/C. 18-May-4 Bonhams, Knightsbridge #2/R est:1200-1800
£2642 $4730 €3857 February landscape (53x72cm-21x28in) s. pencil chl W/C prov.lit. 31-May-4 Stephan Welz, Johannesburg #456 est:30000-50000 (SA.R 32000)
£2800 $4816 €4088 Winter landscape (51x70cm-20x28in) s. pen ink W/C. 2-Dec-3 Bonhams, New Bond Street #36/R est:1500-2000
£4000 $7160 €5840 Oast houses in Kent (50x75cm-20x30in) s. pencil W/C gouache. 16-Mar-4 Bonhams, New Bond Street #59/R est:4000-6000
£6500 $12025 €9490 Morning shadows over a country track (53x73cm-21x29in) s. W/C. 11-Feb-4 Sotheby's, Olympia #149/R est:3000-4000

HILER, Hilaire (1898-1966) American/French

Works on paper

£7821 $14000 €11419 Bronson Gold (30x46cm-12x18in) s.d.1931 gouache prov.exhib. 16-May-4 Wright, Chicago #159/R est:18000-22000

HILES, Bartram (1872-1927) British

£280 $468 €409 Country landscape with a figure beside a stream (52x18cm-20x7in) s. i.verso W/C htd white. 7-Oct-3 Fellows & Sons, Birmingham #540/R

Works on paper

£250 $418 €365 Landscape (28x46cm-11x18in) s. W/C bodycol. 14-Oct-3 David Lay, Penzance #450

£250 $463 €365 Figures on a jetty welcoming the fishing fleet (37x26cm-15x10in) s. gouache. 16-Feb-4 Bonhams, Bath #148

£540 $859 €788 Busy street scene (50x36cm-20x14in) s. gouache. 18-Mar-3 Anderson & Garland, Newcastle #140/R

HILGERS, Carl (1818-1890) German

£398 $677 €581 Transporting the relics (28x24cm-11x9in) 28-Nov-3 Zofingen, Switzerland #2467/R (S.FR 880)

£769 $1308 €1100 Small boy with flowers (12x11cm-5x4in) s.d.74 panel. 20-Nov-3 Van Ham, Cologne #1631 est:1000

£3217 $5469 €4600 On the coast in winter with riders round campfire (24x32cm-9x13in) s.d.77 panel. 20-Nov-3 Van Ham, Cologne #1630/R est:5500

£5556 $10000 €8112 Hunters with their dogs on a frozen stream by a castle (30x46cm-12x18in) s.d.1858 prov. 22-Apr-4 Christie's, Rockefeller NY #25/R est:15000-20000

HILKER, Reinhard (1899-1961) German

Works on paper

£933 $1671 €1400 Figure by table (20x12cm-8x5in) s.d. i. verso W/C over pencil prov. 14-May-4 Ketterer, Munich #33/R est:1000-1500

HILL, Adrian (1897-1977) British

£320 $566 €467 Low tide, Itchenor (64x77cm-25x30in) s. board exhib. 27-Apr-4 Bonhams, Knightsbridge #184/R

£380 $711 €555 Mont St. Eloi - View of the war damaged farmhouse (15x25cm-6x10in) s.i.d.17 i.verso. 24-Feb-4 Tayler & Fletcher, Cheltenham #1

£1176 $2000 €1717 By the Barbican, Plymouth (51x61cm-20x24in) s. exhib. 19-Nov-3 Bonhams & Butterfields, San Francisco #153/R

HILL, Andrew Putnam (attrib) (1853-1922) American

£1421 $2600 €2075 Santa Clara Mission in 1849 (81x119cm-32x47in) prov. 5-Jun-4 Neal Auction Company, New Orleans #434/R est:2000-3000

HILL, Anthony (1930-) British

Sculpture

£4000 $7320 €5840 Relief construction (91x91cm-36x36in) s.i.d.69 plastic aluminium prov.exhib. 2-Jun-4 Sotheby's, London #121/R est:8000

HILL, Arthur (19th C) British

£5000 $8950 €7300 Reflection (63x37cm-25x15in) s.d.86. 27-May-4 Christie's, Kensington #312/R est:4000-6000

£6557 $12000 €9573 Dancer (175x76cm-69x30in) s.i. 5-Jun-4 Neal Auction Company, New Orleans #270/R est:7000-10000

HILL, Berrisford (19/20th C) British

£700 $1253 €1022 Wooded winter landscape with pheasants (61x74cm-24x29in) s. 13-May-4 Grant, Worcester #380

HILL, Carl Frederik (1849-1911) Swedish

£4582 $8203 €6690 Landscape in evening light (29x40cm-11x16in) painted c.1874-75. 25-May-4 Bukowskis, Stockholm #113/R est:50000-60000 (S.KR 62000)

£384331 $687953 €561123 Heath landscape, horse and wagon (60x73cm-24x29in) s. painted 1878 prov.exhib.lit. 26-May-4 AB Stockholms Auktionsverk #2185/R est:4500000-5000000 (S.KR 5200000)

Works on paper

£352 $566 €514 Town scene (18x22cm-7x9in) pencil crayon prov. 25-Aug-3 Lilla Bukowskis, Stockholm #653 (S.KR 4600)

£615 $1058 €898 Theatre scene (9x11cm-4x4in) chk exhib. 2-Dec-3 Bukowskis, Stockholm #41c/R (S.KR 8000)

£665 $1191 €971 Woman and horses (23x31cm-9x12in) col chk. 26-May-4 AB Stockholms Auktionsverk #2346/R (S.KR 9000)

£2217 $3969 €3237 Rocky landscape with trees (46x61cm-18x24in) s.indis.d.77 chl prov. 26-May-4 AB Stockholms Auktionsverk #2247/R est:30000-35000 (S.KR 30000)

£2385 $4102 €3482 Exotic landscape I (24x31cm-9x12in) chk exhib. 2-Dec-3 Bukowskis, Stockholm #41a/R est:25000-30000 (S.KR 31000)

£2661 $4763 €3885 The cathedral raising against the waves (21x32cm-8x13in) s. crayon. 28-May-4 Uppsala Auktionskammare, Uppsala #173/R est:20000-25000 (S.KR 36000)

£2923 $5028 €4268 O A I (17x21cm-7x8in) chk exhib. 2-Dec-3 Bukowskis, Stockholm #145/R est:15000-18000 (S.KR 38000)

£2923 $5028 €4268 Temple made of rocks by river (17x21cm-7x8in) chk exhib. 2-Dec-3 Bukowskis, Stockholm #146/R est:15000-18000 (S.KR 38000)

£5026 $8996 €7338 Pine tree in a storm (21x34cm-8x13in) s. chk exhib.prov. 25-May-4 Bukowskis, Stockholm #111/R est:40000-50000 (S.KR 68000)

£6800 $12171 €9928 Landscape with black tree, palms and elephants on red mountain (21x35cm-8x14in) s. col chk chl lit. 26-May-4 AB Stockholms Auktionsverk #2249/R est:100000-125000 (S.KR 92000)

HILL, Daryl (1930-) Australian

£364 $618 €520 Sysyphus (91x63cm-36x25in) s. 20-Nov-3 Claude Aguttes, Neuilly #154/R

HILL, David Octavius (1802-1870) British

Works on paper

£440 $805 €642 Witch's Pool, St. Andrews (24x35cm-9x14in) s.i. W/C bodycol exhib. 8-Apr-4 Bonhams, Edinburgh #144/R

HILL, Derek (1916-2000) British

£669 $1157 €950 Rocky outcrop (26x21cm-10x8in) i.d.1985 verso board. 10-Dec-3 Bonhams & James Adam, Dublin #172/R

£900 $1530 €1314 Portrait of Raymond Mortimer (20x20cm-8x8in) init. panel sold with a painting by Rodrigo Moynihan. 21-Nov-3 Christie's, London #52/R

£1600 $2864 €2336 Landscape (23x35cm-9x14in) init. board. 14-May-4 Christie's, Kensington #367/R est:800-1200

£3500 $6265 €5110 Portrait of Yehudi playing the violin (51x76cm-20x30in) 11-May-4 Sotheby's, Olympia #552/R est:4000-6000

£4336 $7371 €6200 Tor Mor (71x122cm-28x48in) i.verso prov.exhib. 18-Nov-3 Whyte's, Dublin #57/R est:6000-8000

£5000 $8950 €7300 Tory Gully (91x51cm-36x20in) init. prov. 14-May-4 Christie's, London #92/R est:5000-7000

HILL, Diana (?-1844) British

Miniatures

£3400 $6018 €4964 Portrait of a child and spaniel (8x5cm-3x2in) s.d.1786 W/C ivory. 29-Apr-4 Gorringes, Lewes #2267 est:500-700

HILL, Edward (1843-1923) American

£376 $700 €549 Pasture scene of sheep alongside an old stone wall (46x36cm-18x14in) prov.exhib. 6-Mar-4 North East Auctions, Portsmouth #557/R

£2554 $4750 €3729 Twilight in the White Mountains (25x36cm-10x14in) s.d.87. 6-Mar-4 North East Auctions, Portsmouth #558/R

£2857 $5000 €4171 Sierra Blanca (35x56cm-14x22in) s.d.94 s.i. on stretcher. 19-Dec-3 Sotheby's, New York #1081/R est:4000-6000

£3911 $7000 €6566 Woman holding parasol in wooded landscape. Gentleman on horseback (38x28cm-15x11in) one s.d.1879 two. 20-Mar-4 Pook & Pook, Downington #193/R est:1500-2000

£6522 $12000 €9522 Untitled (76x48cm-30x19in) 24-Jun-4 Sotheby's, New York #169/R est:2000-3000

HILL, Edward (attrib) (1843-1923) American

£559 $900 €816 Hudson River landscape (51x69cm-20x27in) init. 20-Aug-3 James Julia, Fairfield #253/R

£1902 $3500 €2777 Skyrockets and a crescent moon (38x53cm-15x21in) prov. 8-Jun-4 Bonhams & Butterfields, San Francisco #4017/R est:3000-5000

HILL, Edward Rufus (1852-c.1908) American

£549 $1000 €824 View of El Capitan, Yosemite National Park (79x97cm-31x38in) s. painted c.1900-1910. 16-Jun-4 Wolf's, New York #486706/R

£609 $950 €889 Bridalveil Fall, Yosemite (46x25cm-18x10in) s. board. 12-Apr-3 Auctions by the Bay, Alameda #258/R

£1445 $2500 €2110 El Capitan. Bridal Veil Falls (23x15cm-9x6in) both s. paper board. 10-Dec-3 Bonhams & Butterfields, San Francisco #6184/R est:2500-3500

£1836 $3250 €2681 Mt hood as seen from high mountain lake with Indians at campfire (91x51cm-36x20in) s. 3-May-4 O'Gallerie, Oregon #162/R est:3000-4000

HILL, George Snow (1898-1969) American

Works on paper

£1280 $2100 €1856 Lindbergh in Paris (20x58cm-8x23in) s. s.i.verso gouache ink masonite exec.c.1940. 7-Jun-3 Treadway Gallery, Cincinnati #1490 est:2500-3500

HILL, George William (1862-1934) Canadian

Sculpture

£1339 $2237 €1942 George Etienne Cartier (28cm-11in) s.i. bronze. 17-Jun-3 Pinneys, Montreal #97 est:3500-4500 (C.D 3000)

HILL, Hattie Hutchcraft (1847-1921) American

£1148 $2100 €1676 Fishing boats (71x112cm-28x44in) s.i.d.1894. 5-Jun-4 Treadway Gallery, Cincinnati #647/R est:4500-6500

HILL, Howard (19th C) American

£569 $950 €831 Evening, roosters and three hens (10x15cm-4x6in) s. i.verso board. 18-Jun-3 Doyle, New York #40/R

£1705 $3000 €2489 Hens and cockerels in a barnyard. Hens and cockerels on a grassy knoll (13x18cm-5x7in) s. panel two. 24-May-4 Winter Associates, Plainville #100/R est:2000-3000

£2793 $5000 €4078 Two English setter (43x76cm-17x30in) s. 16-May-4 CRN Auctions, Cambridge #16/R

£4268 $7000 €6189 Pair of partridges (61x81cm-24x32in) s. painted c.1860. 7-Jun-3 Treadway Gallery, Cincinnati #1335 est:5000-7000

HILL, Ivan (20th C) New Zealander

£433 $774 €632 Debby Healey picking African marigolds (84x95cm-33x37in) s.i.d.1983 acrylic on board. 11-May-4 Peter Webb, Auckland #64/R est:1500-2500 (NZ.D 1250)

£471 $801 €688 Sir Toss Woollaston at Greymouth 1950 (125x138cm-49x54in) s.i. s.d.1991 verso acrylic on board. 4-Nov-3 Peter Webb, Auckland #224/R est:1800-2500 (NZ.D 1300)

HILL, J E (19/20th C) British?

£3901 $6514 €5500 Jeune fille au plateau de fleurs. Jeune musicienne a la jetee de roses (63x38cm-25x15in) s.d.1904 panel pair. 19-Oct-3 Rabourdin & Choppin de Janvry, Paris #58/R est:10000-12000

HILL, J W (1812-1879) American

£1307 $2300 €1908 Landscape. 1-Jan-4 Fallon, Copake #76/R est:2500-2800

HILL, James John (1811-1882) British

£460 $750 €672 Young girl with her pet dog in a coastal landscape (30x30cm-12x12in) s. canvas on panel. 26-Sep-3 Bigwood, Stratford on Avon #426

£1300 $2418 €1898 Nearest way home (32x47cm-13x19in) s.i.d.1875. 4-Mar-4 Christie's, Kensington #506/R est:1500-2000
£1500 $2685 €2190 Young shepherd boy (33x46cm-13x18in) s.i.verso. 18-Mar-4 Christie's, Kensington #497/R est:600-800
£2000 $3680 €2920 Family group at a spring (94x130cm-37x51in) s. 29-Mar-4 Bonhams, Bath #97/R est:2000-3000
Works on paper
£620 $1110 €905 Knitting is hard (41x31cm-16x12in) s.d.68 W/C. 11-May-4 Dreweatt Neate, Newbury #452/R

HILL, James John (circle) (1811-1882) British
£1000 $1850 €1460 Girl with corn stalks (76x63cm-30x25in) 10-Mar-4 Sotheby's, Olympia #182/R est:1000-1500

HILL, Jean (19th C) British
£497 $904 €750 Le retour des pecheurs sur la plage d'Ostende (23x32cm-9x13in) s. 15-Jun-4 Vanderkindere, Brussels #31
£556 $883 €800 Souvenir d'excursion a Ostende (23x32cm-9x13in) s.d.1886 s.verso. 15-Sep-3 Horta, Bruxelles #436
£709 $1184 €1000 Dyle a Malines (41x70cm-16x28in) s. 14-Oct-3 Vanderkindere, Brussels #46

HILL, John (19th C) British
Miniatures
£2123 $3800 €3100 British Light Infantry officer in American Campaign uniform (3cm-1in) s. mother of pearl gilt wrist locket oval exec.c.1777. 18-Mar-4 Richard Opfer, Timonium #35/R est:3200-3500

HILL, John Henry (1839-1922) American/British
£1050 $1900 €1533 Early morning landscape (25x20cm-10x8in) s. board prov. 3-Apr-4 Charlton Hall, Columbia #551/R est:1200-1800

HILL, John William (1812-1879) American
Works on paper
£550 $990 €803 Still life with apples and plums (35x44cm-14x17in) bears sig.d.1874 W/C. 21-Jan-4 Sotheby's, Olympia #341/R
£2235 $4000 €3263 Stranded ashore (30x41cm-12x16in) s. W/C prov. 6-May-4 Shannon's, Milford #190/R est:5000-7000
£2762 $5000 €4033 White water (33x25cm-13x10in) s.d.1873 W/C prov.exhib. 31-Mar-4 Sotheby's, New York #65/R est:8000-12000
£6818 $12000 €9954 Hudson river at Caldwell (20x33cm-8x13in) s.d.1866 W/C prov. 19-May-4 Sotheby's, New York #66/R est:10000-15000
£9091 $16000 €13273 Fishing (15x13cm-6x5in) s. W/C exec c.1865 exhib. 18-May-4 Christie's, Rockefeller NY #23/R est:12000-18000

HILL, John William (after) (1812-1879) American
Prints
£3243 $6000 €4735 New York (74x128cm-29x50in) hand coloring aquatint. 15-Jan-4 Sotheby's, New York #136/R est:4000-6000
£3514 $6500 €5130 New York (74x128cm-29x50in) hand coloring aquatint. 15-Jan-4 Sotheby's, New York #137/R est:4000-5000

HILL, John William and John Henry (19th C) American
Works on paper
£6704 $12000 €9788 Miscellaneous. W/C pen ink pencil thirty-four album. 26-May-4 Doyle, New York #1/R est:6000-8000
£8380 $15000 €12235 Miscellaneous. W/C pen ink pencil thirty-four album. 26-May-4 Doyle, New York #2/R est:6000-8000

HILL, Mabel M (1872-1956) New Zealander
£362 $583 €529 Early Auckland houses (36x46cm-14x18in) s. 20-Aug-3 Dunbar Sloane, Auckland #112 est:500-700 (NZ.D 1000)

HILL, Michael John (20th C) British
£1163 $2000 €1698 The kissing trees at dawn (76x102cm-30x40in) s.i. 7-Dec-3 Susanin's, Chicago #6050/R est:1500-2500

HILL, Raymond Leroy (1891-1980) American
£396 $650 €578 Landscape with windmill, buildings and distant shore (25x30cm-10x12in) s. canvas on masonite prov. 31-May-3 Brunk, Ashville #223/R

HILL, Robin (1932-) Australian
Works on paper
£260 $465 €380 Galahs perched on a branch (48x36cm-19x14in) s.d.65 W/C. 7-May-4 Mallams, Oxford #244/R
£448 $699 €650 Pink and white cockatoo (60x51cm-24x20in) s.i.d.68 W/C. 1-Aug-2 Joel, Victoria #204 est:1000-1200 (A.D 1300)

HILL, Rowland (1919-) British
£260 $426 €380 Carnalea (22x33cm-9x13in) s.d.1936 board. 4-Jun-3 John Ross, Belfast #60
£380 $623 €555 Cottages (30x61cm-12x24in) s. board. 4-Jun-3 John Ross, Belfast #33
£550 $902 €803 Cottages, Donegal (35x55cm-14x22in) s. board. 4-Jun-3 John Ross, Belfast #182
£600 $1032 €876 Cushendun, County Antrim (35x50cm-14x20in) s. 3-Dec-3 John Ross, Belfast #117
£750 $1290 €1095 Cottages in Donegal (35x50cm-14x20in) s. board. 3-Dec-3 John Ross, Belfast #27
£800 $1312 €1168 Sailing (61x91cm-24x36in) s. 4-Jun-3 John Ross, Belfast #111
£1400 $2380 €2044 Showery day. Muckish mountain (31x43cm-12x17in) s. one i.verso canvasboard pair. 26-Nov-3 Sotheby's, Olympia #67/R est:1000-1500
£2254 $3899 €3200 Old cottage on Marble Hill, Co Donegal (41x61cm-16x24in) s. i.verso. 10-Dec-3 Bonhams & James Adam, Dublin #66/R est:2000-3000
Works on paper
£340 $626 €496 Sheep grazing in mountain landscape by a bridge (9x13cm-4x5in) s. W/C. 11-Jun-4 Keys, Aylsham #226/R
£350 $651 €511 Mulroy Bay, Co. Donegal (22x35cm-9x14in) s. W/C. 3-Mar-4 John Ross, Belfast #146
£520 $941 €759 Sunset over heath and woodland (23x30cm-9x12in) s.d.1930 W/C. 1-Apr-4 Amersham Auction Rooms, UK #310
£550 $1007 €803 Farmyard scene with a figure standing beside haystacks (13x20cm-5x8in) s.d.1921 W/C. 3-Jun-4 Amersham Auction Rooms, UK #343
£820 $1484 €1197 Farmyard scene with a figure standing beside haystacks (13x20cm-5x8in) s.d.1921 W/C. 1-Apr-4 Amersham Auction Rooms, UK #309

HILL, Rowland Henry (1873-1952) British
£360 $576 €526 Goatland, landscape (15x23cm-6x9in) s.d.1900. 18-Sep-3 Goldings, Lincolnshire #851/R
£480 $883 €701 English village, thatched roof houses and church tower in the middle ground (14x22cm-6x9in) s.d.1899. 26-Jun-4 Thos Mawer, Lincoln #115
£5200 $8268 €7540 Pickering Moor, North Yorkshire (86x104cm-34x41in) s.d.1923. 12-Sep-3 ELR Auctions, Sheffield #310 est:1500-2000
Works on paper
£380 $631 €555 Loading Windjammer at the dockside (53x37cm-21x15in) s.d.1912 W/C pencil. 1-Oct-3 Bonhams, Knightsbridge #86
£380 $688 €555 Goathland moor (18x31cm-7x12in) s.i. W/C. 30-Mar-4 David Duggleby, Scarborough #227/R
£380 $692 €555 Crosshaven, nr Cork, Ireland (21x31cm-8x12in) s.d.1907 pencil W/C. 15-Jun-4 Bonhams, Leeds #165/R
£420 $668 €609 Byland Abbey ruins with cottages beyond (33x23cm-13x9in) s.d.1924 W/C. 9-Sep-3 David Duggleby, Scarborough #142/R
£460 $837 €672 HMS Warspite (26x38cm-10x15in) s.i.d.1933 W/C pastel. 15-Jun-4 Bonhams, Leeds #166
£500 $810 €725 Horseguards parade (25x36cm-10x14in) s.d.1930. 26-Jan-3 Desmond Judd, Cranbrook #876
£780 $1342 €1139 Rural landscape with farmhouse, path and sheep grazing (25x33cm-10x13in) s.d.1927 W/C. 5-Dec-3 ELR Auctions, Sheffield #699
£880 $1399 €1276 Inn at Ellerby (20x31cm-8x12in) s.d.1936 W/C. 9-Sep-3 David Duggleby, Scarborough #134/R
£950 $1587 €1387 Whitby (13x18cm-5x7in) s.d.1934 W/C. 10-Oct-3 Richardson & Smith, Whitby #101/R
£1050 $1901 €1533 Moorland crossroads (18x25cm-7x10in) s.d.1932 W/C. 30-Mar-4 David Duggleby, Scarborough #175/R est:400-600
£1400 $2380 €2044 North Yorkshire village in winter, with horses and cart passing cottages (29x25cm-11x10in) s.d.1925 indis.i.verso pencil W/C. 19-Nov-3 Tennants, Leyburn #972a est:500-700
£1450 $2407 €2117 Fishermen emptying nets on a beach (43x25cm-17x10in) s. W/C. 2-Oct-3 Biddle & Webb, Birmingham #882
£1800 $3060 €2628 Coasters coaling (38x53cm-15x21in) s.d.1925 pencil W/C. 19-Nov-3 Tennants, Leyburn #869/R est:1200-1500
£2000 $3580 €2920 Carting the hay (25x36cm-10x14in) s.d.1927 W/C. 28-May-4 Tring Auctions, Tring #380/R est:800-1000
£2200 $3674 €3212 Ugthorpe Mill, near Whitby (25x36cm-10x14in) s.d.1932 i.verso W/C. 10-Oct-3 Richardson & Smith, Whitby #102 est:800-1200
£2800 $5180 €4088 Ponte di Rialto (36x51cm-14x20in) s.i.d.1912 W/C gouache scratching out. 13-Jan-4 Woolley & Wallis, Salisbury #276/R est:200-300
£2900 $5249 €4234 Robins Hood Bay looking towards Ravenscar (25x30cm-10x12in) s. W/C. 30-Mar-4 David Duggleby, Scarborough #14/R est:1000-1500

HILL, Thomas (1829-1908) American
£4913 $8500 €7173 Boat on Calm seas at Dusk (13x42cm-5x17in) s. prov.lit. 10-Dec-3 Bonhams & Butterfields, San Francisco #6142/R est:4000-6000
£5367 $9500 €7836 Encampment in the Sierras (20x36cm-8x14in) s. oil paper. 28-Apr-4 Christie's, Los Angeles #6/R est:5000-7000
£6878 $13000 €10042 Rider on horseback and two figures in view of Mt Shasta from Castle Lake (41x61cm-16x24in) s. prov. 17-Feb-4 John Moran, Pasadena #147/R est:12000-18000
£13587 $25000 €19837 Figures at the base of a glacier (62x74cm-24x29in) s.d.1896 prov. 8-Jun-4 Bonhams & Butterfields, San Francisco #4171/R est:30000-50000
£17341 $30000 €25318 Mount Shasta from Castle Lake at evening (41x60cm-16x24in) s. i.verso prov. 10-Dec-3 Bonhams & Butterfields, San Francisco #6155/R est:30000-50000
£20000 $34000 €29200 Trial scene from the Merchant of Venice (94x140cm-37x55in) s.i.d.1863 prov.exhib.lit. 29-Oct-3 Christie's, Los Angeles #33/R est:10000-15000
£24566 $42500 €35866 Lake Tahoe - A man with an oar sitting on a bluff (53x39cm-21x15in) s. paper on panel prov.exhib. 10-Dec-3 Bonhams & Butterfields, San Francisco #6141/R est:15000-20000
£24566 $42500 €35866 Native American at Bridal Veil Falls, Yosemite (76x51cm-30x20in) s. prov. 10-Dec-3 Bonhams & Butterfields, San Francisco #6147/R est:30000-50000
£81522 $150000 €119022 Yosemite Valley (87x63cm-34x25in) s. prov. 27-Jun-4 Freeman, Philadelphia #94/R est:40000-60000
£132948 $230000 €194104 Hetch Hetchy Valley, deer in foreground and Mount Conness beyond (91x132cm-36x52in) s.d.1884 prov. 10-Dec-3 Bonhams & Butterfields, San Francisco #6148/R est:150000-200000
Works on paper
£410 $664 €599 Little firewood gather (110x25cm-43x10in) s.d.1885 chl monochrome. 5-Aug-3 Bonhams, Knowle #156

HILL, Thomas (attrib) (1829-1908) American
£1730 $3200 €2526 Waterfalls (46x61cm-18x24in) s. 12-Mar-4 Jackson's, Cedar Falls #775/R est:2000-3000
£3352 $6000 €4894 Snowy scene with trees at mountain edge (36x48cm-14x19in) s. 7-May-4 Sloans & Kenyon, Bethesda #1712/R est:900-1200

HILL, Tom (1922-) American
£14804 $26500 €21614 Waterfall (61x41cm-24x16in) 15-May-4 Altermann Galleries, Santa Fe #137/R

Works on paper

£437 $800 €638 Man carrying sacks (36x53cm-14x21in) s.i. W/C executed c.1940. 5-Jun-4 Treadway Gallery, Cincinnati #612/R

£1914 $3100 €2775 Basket market in Ocotian (53x74cm-21x29in) W/C. 23-May-3 Altermann Galleries, Santa Fe #183

HILL, Vernon (1887-?) British

Works on paper

£800 $1480 €1200 Stylized angel above four doves. mono. pencil ink W/C sold with an etching and drawings. 14-Jul-4 Rupert Toovey, Partridge Green #38/R

HILLEGAERT, Pauwels van (c.1596-1640) Dutch

£4027 $7208 €6000 Landscape (114x163cm-45x64in) s. 25-May-4 Durán, Madrid #87/R est:3000

Works on paper

£3425 $5822 €5000 Wooded landscape (23x32cm-9x13in) pen brown ink col wash over black chk. 4-Nov-3 Sotheby's, Amsterdam #30/R est:3000-5000

HILLEGAERT, Pauwels van (attrib) (c.1596-1640) Dutch

£1000 $1700 €1460 Equestrian portrait of Prince Frederick Heinrich of the Netherlands (38x32cm-15x13in) panel prov. 30-Oct-3 Sotheby's, Olympia #102/R est:2000-3000

HILLEMACHER, Eugène Ernest (1818-1887) French

£4027 $7409 €6000 French nobleman with two Italian peasant girls (80x100cm-31x39in) s.d.1864. 25-Mar-4 Dr Fritz Nagel, Stuttgart #715/R est:2400

HILLEMACHER, Frederic Desire (1811-1914) Belgian

£562 $967 €821 Figures by large well in a Southern European square (40x32cm-16x13in) s.d.1848. 3-Dec-3 Museumsbygningen, Copenhagen #189/R (D.KR 6000)

HILLEN, John Francis Edward (1819-1865) American

£2711 $4500 €3958 Civil War skirmish in the forest (56x69cm-22x27in) s. 4-Oct-3 Neal Auction Company, New Orleans #364/R est:4000-6000

HILLENIUS, Jaap (1934-1999) Dutch

£884 $1610 €1300 Composition (35x40cm-14x16in) s.d.1973 sold with another by same hand. 3-Feb-4 Christie's, Amsterdam #599 est:600-800

£2667 $4880 €4000 The secret II (110x90cm-43x35in) s.d.1980 lit. 7-Jun-4 Glerum, Amsterdam #258/R est:3000-4000

HILLER, Anton (20th C) ?

Sculpture

£2098 $3566 €3000 Female figure, statuette II (41cm-16in) s. verso brown pat.bronze. 29-Nov-3 Villa Grisebach, Berlin #362/R est:3500-4500

HILLER, Heinrich (19th C) German

£486 $768 €700 Three master in Sonderburg harbour (40x60cm-16x24in) s. 6-Sep-3 Schopman, Hamburg #845/R

£567 $1026 €850 Rhine at Andernach (19x15cm-7x6in) s. canvas on board. 1-Apr-4 Van Ham, Cologne #1431

£933 $1689 €1400 On the water in Venice (32x25cm-13x10in) s. panel. 1-Apr-4 Van Ham, Cologne #1433/R

£1111 $1811 €1600 Riverside mill (77x67cm-30x26in) s. 24-Sep-3 Neumeister, Munich #447/R est:1800

£1259 $2140 €1800 Lower alpine landscape with old farmhouse (62x88cm-24x35in) s.d.72. 27-Nov-3 Dorotheum, Linz #420/R est:3600-5000

£1399 $2378 €2000 Windmill. Peasant with horse and cart (48x42cm-19x17in) s.d.71 two. 20-Nov-3 Van Ham, Cologne #1632/R est:2500

HILLER, Karol (1891-1939) Polish

Works on paper

£2825 $5113 €4125 Composition (30x27cm-12x11in) mixed media photographic paper exec 1936-37. 4-Apr-4 Agra, Warsaw #4/R (P.Z 20000)

HILLER-BAUMANN, Leonore (1881-?) German

£299 $545 €440 Bodensee with farmstead (60x80cm-24x31in) s. masonite. 6-Feb-4 Paul Kieffer, Pforzhiem #7878

HILLER-FOELL, Maria (1880-1943) German

£451 $736 €650 Still life with shrimps (30x34cm-12x13in) s. i. verso. 27-Sep-3 Dr Fritz Nagel, Stuttgart #9218/R

£634 $1014 €900 Two Russian saints (95x74cm-37x29in) s. 18-Sep-3 Rieber, Stuttgart #1363/R

£671 $1188 €1000 Still life with flowers including tulips and narcissi (47x33cm-19x13in) s. 30-Apr-4 Dr Fritz Nagel, Stuttgart #245/R

HILLERSBERG, Lars (1937-) Swedish

Works on paper

£566 $963 €826 It's up to you my friend! (36x51cm-14x20in) s.d.71 mixed media. 4-Nov-3 Bukowskis, Stockholm #544/R (S.KR 7500)

£624 $1123 €911 Gustav VI Adolf (54x42cm-21x17in) s.d.73 mixed media collage. 26-Apr-4 Bukowskis, Stockholm #489/R (S.KR 8600)

£906 $1541 €1323 The palm mark (58x79cm-23x31in) mixed media. 4-Nov-3 Bukowskis, Stockholm #545/R (S.KR 12000)

HILLESTROM, Carl Peter (1760-1812) Swedish

Works on paper

£1385 $2382 €2022 View of Haga Park from Old Haga (40x56cm-16x22in) s. wash W/C prov. 3-Dec-3 AB Stockholms Auktionsverk #2339/R est:18000-20000 (S.KR 18000)

HILLESTROM, Per (1733-1816) Swedish

£2069 $3704 €3021 Caritas Humana (40x32cm-16x13in) panel. 26-May-4 AB Stockholms Auktionsverk #2133/R est:25000-30000 (S.KR 28000)

£3538 $6086 €5165 Interior from a copper mine with melting copper in progress, Falun (40x32cm-16x13in) panel lit. 3-Dec-3 AB Stockholms Auktionsverk #2502/R est:35000-40000 (S.KR 46000)

£6800 $12171 €9928 Still life of fish, onions and wine on table (34x45cm-13x18in) 26-May-4 AB Stockholms Auktionsverk #2255/R est:50000-60000 (S.KR 92000)

£16260 $29106 €23740 Young woman sweeping and girl untyding (39x30cm-15x12in) painted 1774 prov.lit. 26-May-4 AB Stockholms Auktionsverk #2260/R est:250000-300000 (S.KR 220000)

£27692 $47631 €40430 The broken plate (54x43cm-21x17in) painted c.1776 prov.lit. 2-Dec-3 Bukowskis, Stockholm #318/R est:200000-250000 (S.KR 360000)

HILLEVELD, Adrianus David (1838-1869) Dutch

£2431 $4059 €3500 Summer landscape with ships in a waterway (42x59cm-17x23in) init.d.58. 21-Oct-3 Sotheby's, Amsterdam #70/R est:3000-5000

HILLHOUSE, May (1908-1989) South African

£378 $684 €552 Triangles round the moon (91x91cm-36x36in) s.d.79 exhib. 30-Mar-4 Stephan Welz, Johannesburg #512 est:5000-8000 (SA.R 4500)

HILLIARD, Nicholas (1547-1619) British

Miniatures

£110000 $198000 €160600 Henry Wriothesely, 3rd Earl of Southampton (5cm-2in) i.verso vellum card silver gilt frame oval prov.exhib.lit. 22-Apr-4 Bonhams, New Bond Street #1/R est:70000-90000

HILLIARD, William Henry (1836-1905) American

£391 $700 €571 Woman on a path (51x30cm-20x12in) s. 16-May-4 CRN Auctions, Cambridge #28/R

£435 $780 €635 Dawn on the pond (36x61cm-14x24in) 8-Jan-4 James Julia, Fairfield #970/R

£484 $900 €707 French country house with figure of a woman (58x41cm-23x16in) s. canvas on board painted c.1882. 7-Mar-4 Treadway Gallery, Cincinnati #490/R

HILLIER, H Deacon (19th C) British

£1600 $2752 €2336 Loch Lomond, Dumbartonshire (30x45cm-12x18in) s. s.i.verso. 4-Dec-3 Mellors & Kirk, Nottingham #936/R est:1200-1800

HILLIER, Tristram (1905-1983) British

£1900 $3363 €2774 Beached fishing boats (41x51cm-16x20in) s.d.1970 board. 29-Apr-4 Gorringes, Lewes #2531 est:1200-1800

£2700 $4293 €3942 Skulls (35x45cm-14x18in) s.d.56 exhib. 10-Sep-3 Sotheby's, Olympia #111/R est:3000-5000

£3261 $6000 €4761 Cork trees of Alentejo, Portugal (13x18cm-5x7in) s.d.1948 panel. 10-Jun-4 Sotheby's, New York #316/R est:2500-3500

£5500 $8745 €8030 Shell nature fossils cover design (35x25cm-14x10in) s. board. 10-Sep-3 Sotheby's, Olympia #112/R est:800-1200

£5500 $8745 €8030 Reptiles and amphibians (35x46cm-14x18in) s. exhib. 10-Sep-3 Sotheby's, Olympia #113/R est:6000-8000

£6500 $10335 €9490 August bees and wasps (36x46cm-14x18in) mono.i. exhib. 10-Sep-3 Sotheby's, Olympia #114/R est:7000-9000

£8200 $14678 €11972 Mijas (15x23cm-6x9in) init. i.d.1952 verso panel. 16-Mar-4 Bonhams, New Bond Street #46/R est:5000-7000

£9000 $16110 €13140 Provence (63x76cm-25x30in) s.d.1936 i.d.stretcher prov. 16-Mar-4 Bonhams, New Bond Street #45/R est:10000-15000

£10000 $17200 €14600 Clewer (40x50cm-16x20in) s.d.43 prov. 2-Dec-3 Bonhams, New Bond Street #75/R est:7000-10000

HILLINGFORD, Robert Alexander (1825-1904) British

£2000 $3700 €2920 Last days of Sir Philip Sidney (116x178cm-46x70in) s.d.1882 i.overlap exhib. 9-Mar-4 Bonhams, Knightsbridge #193/R est:2000-3000

£3000 $4890 €4380 Not forgotten in Marlborough's time (44x60cm-17x24in) s. 25-Sep-3 Mellors & Kirk, Nottingham #787/R est:3000-4000

£3100 $5270 €4526 Napoleans retreat after the Battle of Waterloo (50x76cm-20x30in) s. 25-Nov-3 Bonhams, Knowle #251/R est:2000-3000

£8000 $13600 €11680 Italian serenade, man playing a guitar with figures and dog round a table (66x91cm-26x36in) s.i. 5-Nov-3 John Nicholson, Haslemere #657/R est:10000-15000

£8500 $15810 €12410 Adventures of Baron Munchausen (58x90cm-23x35in) mono. 4-Mar-4 Christie's, Kensington #614/R est:4000-6000

HILLINGFORD, Robert Alexander (attrib) (1825-1904) British

£700 $1106 €1015 Falstaff in an inn (36x46cm-14x18in) 4-Sep-3 Christie's, Kensington #245/R

HILLS, Anna A (1882-1930) American

£1630 $3000 €2380 Old houses by the sea, St Ives, England (36x47cm-14x19in) s.d.1910 i.verso. 8-Jun-4 Bonhams & Butterfields, San Francisco #4338/R est:3000-5000

£1786 $3250 €2608 Brittany boat scene (18x25cm-7x10in) s. canvasboard prov. 15-Jun-4 John Moran, Pasadena #142 est:3000-5000

£2023 $3500 €2954 High fog in the Canyon (25x35cm-10x14in) s. i.verso masonite prov. 10-Dec-3 Bonhams & Butterfields, San Francisco #6234/R est:5000-7000

£4335 $7500 €6329 House at Laguna Beach (18x25cm-7x10in) s. board. 10-Dec-3 Bonhams & Butterfields, San Francisco #6235/R est:5000-7000

£4670 $8500 €6818 Orange County Park, California (18x13cm-7x5in) s. i.d.1915 verso board. 15-Jun-4 John Moran, Pasadena #142a est:2500-3500

£4762 $9000 €6953 Coastal waves and rocks (30x41cm-12x16in) s. board. 17-Feb-4 John Moran, Pasadena #42b/R est:4000-6000

£5291 $10000 €7725 Spring on the desert (36x46cm-14x18in) s.d.1923 i.d. verso board. 17-Feb-4 John Moran, Pasadena #30b/R est:7000-9000

Works on paper

£607	$1100	€886	Wood gatherer (24x16cm-9x6in) s. W/C. 18-Apr-4 Bonhams & Butterfields, Los Angeles #7026 est:1000-1500
£1000	$1700	€1460	Cabin by the lake (20x25cm-8x10in) s. W/C prov. 18-Nov-3 John Moran, Pasadena #87b est:1500-2500

HILLS, Laura Coombs (1859-1952) American

£2500	$4250	€3650	Portrait of a young girl, possibly Lizzie Hills, the artist sister (51x61cm-20x24in) s.stretcher. 21-Nov-3 Skinner, Boston #393/R est:4000-6000
£5028	$9000	€7341	Chrysanthemums (61x53cm-24x21in) s. prov. 6-May-4 Shannon's, Milford #49/R est:12000-18000

Works on paper

£5308	$9500	€7750	Purple and white petunias (27x30cm-11x12in) s. pastel paperboard prov. 14-May-4 Skinner, Boston #386/R est:6000-8000
£5376	$10000	€7849	White freesia (46x38cm-18x15in) s. pastel exec c.1935 prov. 6-Mar-4 North East Auctions, Portsmouth #546/R est:10000-15000
£5376	$10000	€7849	Petunias in celadon vase (53x41cm-21x16in) s. pastel prov. 6-Mar-4 North East Auctions, Portsmouth #547/R est:10000-15000
£7317	$12000	€10610	Floral still life (41x41cm-16x16in) s. pastel artist board on matboard. 2-Jun-3 Grogan, Boston #644/R
£7527	$14000	€10989	Yellow iris (53x46cm-21x18in) s. pastel exec c.1934 prov. 6-Mar-4 North East Auctions, Portsmouth #545/R est:10000-15000
£7547	$12000	€11019	Yellow pansies (25x20cm-10x8in) s. pastel prov. 12-Sep-3 Skinner, Boston #361/R est:8000
£7547	$12000	€11019	Zinnias and pink velvet (50x39cm-20x15in) s. pastel prov. 12-Sep-3 Skinner, Boston #359/R est:15000
£7821	$14000	€11419	Pansies and red (38x32cm-15x13in) s. pastel paperboard prov. 14-May-4 Skinner, Boston #384/R est:5000-7000
£9581	$16000	€13988	Canterbury Bells (53x46cm-21x18in) s.i.verso pastel prov. 23-Oct-3 Shannon's, Milford #98/R est:15000-25000
£13125	$21000	€19163	Still life of roses in a pottery basket (15x23cm-6x9in) s. pastel sold with the original pottery basket. 21-Sep-3 Grogan, Boston #24
£25140	$45000	€36704	Peonies and velvet (72x58cm-28x23in) s. pastel paperboard. 14-May-4 Skinner, Boston #347/R est:4000-6000

HILLS, Laura Coombs (attrib) (1859-1952) American

Miniatures

£932	$1500	€1361	Still life with vase of flowers and elephant (8x5cm-3x2in) s. ivory wood frame. 20-Aug-3 James Julia, Fairfield #1550/R est:1500-2000

HILLS, Robert (1769-1844) British

Works on paper

£300	$540	€438	Drover and cattle in a wooded lane (11x14cm-4x6in) W/C over pencil. 21-Jan-4 Sotheby's, Olympia #162/R
£335	$600	€489	Stags in woods (20x13cm-8x5in) d.1827 W/C. 12-May-4 South Bay, Long Island #473458/R
£400	$668	€584	Sevenoaks, Kent (15x24cm-6x9in) pencil W/C. 16-Oct-3 Christie's, Kensington #179
£420	$727	€613	Cattle drinking (8x11cm-3x4in) W/C. 11-Dec-3 Bruton Knowles, Cheltenham #79
£580	$1067	€847	Cattle resting in a farmyard (7x11cm-3x4in) W/C prov. 23-Jun-4 Bonhams, Bury St Edmunds #308/R
£650	$1203	€949	Trees at the water's edge (20x30cm-8x12in) i. W/C pencil prov. 14-Jul-4 Sotheby's, Olympia #42/R
£780	$1349	€1139	Cattle grazing (28x41cm-11x16in) one s. sepia W/C pair. 11-Dec-3 Mitchells, Cockermouth #896/R
£1900	$3230	€2774	Cottage children (27x20cm-11x8in) W/C exhib. 4-Nov-3 Bonhams, New Bond Street #26/R est:2000-3000

HILLS, Robert (attrib) (1769-1844) British

Works on paper

£850	$1462	€1241	Cows grazing in a wooded landscape (16x24cm-6x9in) pencil W/C prov. 3-Dec-3 Christie's, Kensington #13/R

HILLSMITH, Fannie (1911-) American

£696	$1100	€1016	Talking dolphin (91x124cm-36x49in) s. 6-Sep-3 Brunk, Ashville #298

HILSING, Werner (20th C) German

Works on paper

£287	$519	€430	Revaluation (14x21cm-6x8in) s. collage tempera oil. 2-Apr-4 Winterberg, Heidelberg #1099

HILSOE, Hans (20th C) Danish

£276	$470	€403	Clouds over hill heath landscape (63x95cm-25x37in) s.d.1914. 10-Nov-3 Rasmussen, Vejle #533 (D.KR 3000)
£320	$544	€467	Woman standing in an interior, looking out of a window (68x53cm-27x21in) s.d.1918. 27-Nov-3 Greenslade Hunt, Taunton #1033
£358	$655	€523	Interior from Bakkehuset's green drawing room (50x61cm-20x24in) s.d.35. 9-Jun-4 Rasmussen, Copenhagen #2000/R (D.KR 4000)
£667	$1213	€1001	Interior (51x40cm-20x16in) s. 19-Jun-4 Rasmussen, Havnen #2065/R (D.KR 7500)
£1078	$2005	€1574	Interior scene with view of the green sitting room from the pink one (53x58cm-21x23in) s. 2-Mar-4 Rasmussen, Copenhagen #1641/R est:8000 (D.KR 12000)
£1900	$3496	€2774	Music room (57x44cm-22x17in) s. 25-Mar-4 Christie's, Kensington #178/R est:2000-3000

HILTON, Arthur Cyril (1897-1960) British

Works on paper

£380	$695	€555	Three torsos (35x41cm-14x16in) s.i.d.1955 ink wash. 6-Jul-4 Peter Wilson, Nantwich #113/R

HILTON, Colin C (?) British

£350	$641	€511	Fishing smachs in harbour (58x84cm-23x33in) s. board. 6-Apr-4 Capes Dunn, Manchester #842/R

HILTON, John William (1904-1983) American

£347	$600	€507	Desert landscape with mountains (30x41cm-12x16in) s. 10-Dec-3 Boos Gallery, Michigan #517/R
£347	$600	€507	Desert landscape with mountains (30x41cm-12x16in) s. 10-Dec-3 Boos Gallery, Michigan #518
£380	$700	€555	Golden dreams (46x61cm-18x24in) s. board. 13-Jun-4 Bonhams & Butterfields, Los Angeles #7040/R
£440	$700	€642	Desert flowers. s. panel. 5-May-3 O'Gallerie, Oregon #91/R
£516	$950	€753	Capristrano gold (28x38cm-11x15in) s.d.1951 board. 10-Jun-4 Swann Galleries, New York #123/R
£543	$1000	€793	Hawaiian checkers (51x76cm-20x30in) s. board. 13-Jun-4 Bonhams & Butterfields, Los Angeles #7041/R est:1500-2500
£769	$1400	€1123	Snow-capped mountain landscape (66x81cm-26x32in) s.d.49 board prov. 15-Jun-4 John Moran, Pasadena #162a est:2000-3000
£847	$1600	€1237	Night in the dunes (30x41cm-12x16in) s. i. verso panel prov. 17-Feb-4 John Moran, Pasadena #195/R est:800-1200
£1044	$1900	€1524	Royal robes of sundown (41x51cm-16x20in) s. masonite prov. 15-Jun-4 John Moran, Pasadena #201 est:1000-2000
£1236	$2250	€1805	Southwest landscape (76x91cm-30x36in) s. 15-Jun-4 John Moran, Pasadena #145a est:2000-3000
£1676	$3000	€2447	Desert primroses (30x41cm-12x16in) s. canvasboard. 14-May-4 Skinner, Boston #204/R est:2000-4000
£1984	$3750	€2897	The friendly dunes - verbena dunes landscape (51x86cm-20x34in) s. i. verso panel prov. 17-Feb-4 John Moran, Pasadena #146/R est:2500-3500
£3352	$6000	€4894	Sundown trail (72x97cm-28x38in) s. 14-May-4 Skinner, Boston #205/R est:6000-8000

HILTON, Roger (1911-1975) British

Works on paper

£450	$752	€657	Male abstract (26x31cm-10x12in) s.d.73 chl ink. 21-Oct-3 Bonhams, Knightsbridge #30/R
£750	$1320	€1095	Woman planting (25x20cm-10x8in) i.d.April 1966 pen ink prov. 19-May-4 Sotheby's, Olympia #271/R
£800	$1480	€1168	Female nude (25x20cm-10x8in) pencil. 11-Mar-4 Christie's, Kensington #193/R
£900	$1503	€1314	Seated nude (20x15cm-8x6in) pencil sold with a letter prov. 16-Oct-3 Christie's, Kensington #551/R
£1736	$2950	€2535	Untitled (25x34cm-10x13in) s. gouache. 29-Oct-3 Lawson Menzies, Sydney #249/R est:4500-6500 (A.D 4200)
£1860	$3161	€2716	Untitled (27x42cm-11x17in) s.d.73 mixed media. 29-Oct-3 Lawson Menzies, Sydney #247/R est:5000-6000 (A.D 4500)
£2100	$3822	€3066	Pony (25x20cm-10x8in) s.d.68 mixed media. 15-Jun-4 David Lay, Penzance #573/R est:2000-3000
£2200	$3784	€3212	Standing female nude (32x19cm-13x7in) init. d.73 charcoal crayon gouache. 2-Dec-3 Bonhams, New Bond Street #164/R est:1500-2000
£3000	$4770	€4380	Reclining nude (17x42cm-7x17in) init.d.73 gouache pencil. 10-Sep-3 Sotheby's, Olympia #322/R est:3000-5000
£3600	$6192	€5256	Peacock (25x20cm-10x8in) s.d.73 charcoal gouache. 2-Dec-3 Bonhams, New Bond Street #163/R est:2000-3000
£3600	$6192	€5256	Abstract 73 (26x32cm-10x13in) init.d.73 gouache blk chk prov. 3-Dec-3 Sotheby's, London #95/R est:2000-3000
£5500	$9460	€8030	Crouching form (47x57cm-19x22in) init. chl gouache prov. 3-Dec-3 Christie's, Kensington #784/R est:4000-6000
£6000	$10980	€8760	Untitled, 1967 (38x56cm-15x22in) chl gouache executed 1967 prov. 4-Jun-4 Christie's, London #118/R est:4000-6000

HILTON, Rose (1931-) British

£450	$752	€657	Girl in the studio (61x51cm-24x20in) s s.i.verso. 16-Oct-3 Christie's, Kensington #578
£516	$950	€753	Yellow nude (38x33cm-15x13in) s.d.71 panel. 25-Jun-4 Freeman, Philadelphia #264/R
£1000	$1590	€1460	Nude in red chair (50x40cm-20x16in) s. s.i.verso. 10-Sep-3 Sotheby's, Olympia #307/R est:800-1200
£1000	$1670	€1460	Blue nude (61x72cm-24x28in) s. s.i.verso. 16-Oct-3 Christie's, Kensington #601/R est:800-1200
£1350	$2376	€1971	St. Elvyns, Hayle (61x76cm-24x30in) s.i.verso. 19-May-4 Sotheby's, Olympia #252/R est:1500-2000
£2000	$3660	€2920	Wistful woman, nude seated on a bed (49x29cm-19x11in) s. s.i.verso. 3-Jun-4 Lane, Penzance #292 est:1200-1500

HILVERDINK, Eduard Alexander (1846-1891) Dutch

£1399	$2336	€2000	Sailing vessels at sea (17x25cm-7x10in) s.d.1868 panel. 30-Jun-3 Sotheby's, Amsterdam #84/R
£4749	$8500	€6934	Canal scene in Dutch city (33x43cm-13x17in) s.d.1868 panel. 7-May-4 Sloans & Kenyon, Bethesda #1644/R est:1500-2000
£5667	$10200	€8500	Canal in a Dutch town (65x56cm-26x22in) s. 20-Apr-4 Sotheby's, Amsterdam #5/R est:4000-6000

HILVERDINK, Johannes (1813-1902) Dutch

£2027	$3628	€3000	Winter landscape with figures (50x60cm-20x24in) s. lit. 8-May-4 Schloss Ahlden, Ahlden #751/R est:1800
£6803	$12381	€10000	Fisherfamily standing by a river on a sunny day (37x54cm-15x21in) s.d.1858. 3-Feb-4 Christie's, Amsterdam #71/R est:3000-5000

Works on paper

£356	$651	€530	Rocky coast with two figures and sailing boats (28x35cm-11x14in) s.d.1865 chl oval. 8-Jul-4 Allgauer, Kempten #1988/R
£403	$737	€600	Two travellers on the steep shore (31x43cm-12x17in) s.d.1857 monochrome W/C oval. 8-Jul-4 Allgauer, Kempten #1990/R
£436	$798	€650	Shepherd and flock in front of ruins (32x37cm-13x15in) s.d.1861 chl oval. 8-Jul-4 Allgauer, Kempten #1989/R
£570	$1044	€850	Traveller in a river landscape with ruins (34x29cm-13x11in) s.d.1872 W/C oval lit. 8-Jul-4 Allgauer, Kempten #1987/R
£1000	$1800	€1500	Calm at sunset (34x52cm-13x20in) s. pencil W/C. 21-Apr-4 Christie's, Amsterdam #39/R est:1500-2000

HINCK, Willy (1915-2002) German

£521	$849	€750	Warft in the Marsh near Dangast (37x48cm-15x19in) s.d.74 i. verso canvas on panel. 26-Sep-3 Bolland & Marotz, Bremen #329/R

HINCKLEY, Thomas H (1813-1896) American

£698 $1200 €1019 Woodland scene with hunter and dog (36x51cm-14x20in) s.d.1847 board. 7-Dec-3 Susanin's, Chicago #6044/R
£8025 $13000 €11717 Portrait of young boy from Milton, Massachusetts (30x25cm-12x10in) s. verso. 31-Jul-3 Eldred, East Dennis #995/R est:3000-5000

HINDER, Francis Henry Critchley (1906-1992) Australian

£691 $1237 €1009 Casting yard (13x19cm-5x7in) s.d.58 composition board. 4-May-4 Sotheby's, Melbourne #149 (A.D 1700)
£1057 $1892 €1543 City building (14x19cm-6x7in) s.d.57 bears i.verso board. 4-May-4 Sotheby's, Melbourne #142/R est:2000-3000 (A.D 2600)
Works on paper
£364 $587 €531 Seated nude (44x31cm-17x12in) s.d.37 pencil. 25-Aug-3 Sotheby's, Paddington #414 (A.D 900)
£447 $800 €653 Constructivist study (17x22cm-7x9in) s.d.39 pencil col pencil exhib. 4-May-4 Sotheby's, Melbourne #151 (A.D 1100)
£769 $1238 €1123 C.R.T.S. (24x17cm-9x7in) s.i.d.1948 pencil prov. 25-Aug-3 Sotheby's, Paddington #398/R (A.D 1900)

HINDS, Will (20th C) American

£1477 $2600 €2156 Untitled pasture scene (30x51cm-12x20in) s. masonite. 23-May-4 Hindman, Chicago #1024/R est:2500-5000
£1977 $3400 €2886 I want that carrot (33x25cm-13x10in) s. panel. 6-Dec-3 Neal Auction Company, New Orleans #604/R est:3800-4500

HINE, Harry T (1845-1941) British

Works on paper
£620 $1128 €905 View of Durham cathedral (33x51cm-13x20in) s.d.1878 W/C. 15-Jun-4 Canterbury Auctions, UK #122/R

HINE, Henry George (1811-1895) British

£360 $601 €526 Dunstable (18x25cm-7x10in) 21-Oct-3 Gorringes, Lewes #2035/R
£380 $635 €555 Landscape with chapel on a hillside. 21-Oct-3 Gorringes, Lewes #2036
Works on paper
£320 $544 €467 Village scene (23x33cm-9x13in) s. W/C bodycol. 25-Nov-3 Bonhams, Knowle #156
£700 $1260 €1022 Afterglow (24x34cm-9x13in) s.d.1884 pencil W/C hw/ exhib. 22-Apr-4 Mellors & Kirk, Nottingham #1037/R est:400-600
£1700 $3111 €2482 Downlands near Eastbourne (26x56cm-10x22in) s.d.1869 W/C pencil scratching out. 8-Jul-4 Lawrence, Crewkerne #1541/R est:1500-2500
£4000 $7320 €5840 Downs near Eastbourne (35x61cm-14x24in) s.d.1869 pencil W/C scratching out prov. 3-Jun-4 Christie's, London #18/R est:3000-5000
£5500 $10065 €8030 Chain Pier, Brighton during the hurricane 24 November 1824 (23x69cm-9x27in) s. W/C scratching prov.exhib. 3-Jun-4 Christie's, London #24/R est:2500-3500

HINE, Lewis W (1879-1940) American

Photographs
£6878 $13000 €10042 Empire State Building - Icarus (24x19cm-9x7in) i. verso silver print. 17-Feb-4 Swann Galleries, New York #47/R est:15000-20000
£6878 $13000 €10042 Empire State Building (19x24cm-7x9in) silver print. 17-Feb-4 Swann Galleries, New York #48/R est:10000-15000
£8982 $15000 €13114 Empire State Building (25x20cm-10x8in) silver print. 21-Oct-3 Swann Galleries, New York #130/R est:20000-30000
£41667 $75000 €60834 Girl working in a Carolina cotton mill (19x24cm-7x9in) gelatin silver print mounted on board exhib.lit. 22-Apr-4 Phillips, New York #22/R est:50000-70000

HINE, William Egerton (1926-) British

Works on paper
£480 $826 €701 Kentish farmhouse (29x45cm-11x18in) s.d.1876 pencil W/C prov. 3-Dec-3 Christie's, Kensington #113/R

HINEARD, Hubert (19th C) ?

£400 $740 €584 Chestnut hunter with a dog in an extensive landscape (33x43cm-13x17in) s.d.1880. 11-Mar-4 Duke & Son, Dorchester #198

HINES, Frederick (19/20th C) British

£1339 $2237 €1942 Near Leith Hill, Surrey (51x76cm-20x30in) s.d.1902 s.i.d.verso. 17-Jun-3 Pinneys, Montreal #46 est:3500-4500 (C.D 3000)
Works on paper
£280 $476 €409 Silver birches (53x36cm-21x14in) s.d.1894 W/C. 21-Nov-3 Dee Atkinson & Harrison, Driffield #759
£280 $442 €409 The old homestead (38x55cm-15x22in) s.d.1900 W/C. 5-Sep-3 Honiton Galleries, Honiton #28
£280 $512 €409 Fagot gathering (54x37cm-21x15in) s. W/C. 7-Apr-4 Dreweatt Neate, Newbury #4
£360 $670 €526 Homestead, lady feeding doves by a gate (38x55cm-15x22in) s. W/C. 2-Mar-4 Bonhams, Oxford #270
£380 $646 €555 Girl under blossom tree (53x37cm-21x15in) s. W/C htd bodycol. 25-Nov-3 Bonhams, Knightsbridge #57/R

HINES, Richard (?) American

£380 $600 €551 Country gentleman (61x91cm-24x36in) s. 27-Jul-3 Simpson's, Houston #345

HINES, Theodore (fl.1876-1889) British

£750 $1178 €1088 By Katrine's margin, the Trossacks (35x46cm-14x18in) s. i.verso. 28-Aug-3 Christie's, Kensington #163/R
£3800 $7030 €5548 On the Lockay, Killin, NB (51x76cm-20x30in) s. 9-Mar-4 Gorringes, Lewes #2212 est:1000-1500

HINKLE, Clarence Keiser (1880-1960) American

£1156 $2000 €1688 Aftermath (67x123cm-26x48in) s.d.42 tempera board exhib. 10-Dec-3 Bonhams & Butterfields, San Francisco #6283/R est:3000-5000
£1324 $2250 €1933 Still life, pomegranates (30x23cm-12x9in) s. i.verso canvasboard prov. 18-Nov-3 John Moran, Pasadena #52b est:2000-2500
£1589 $2750 €2320 Chinatown, San Francisco (25x36cm-10x14in) s.d.04 canvasboard. 10-Dec-3 Bonhams & Butterfields, San Francisco #6166/R est:3000-5000
£1765 $3000 €2577 Still life, fruit, vegetables and copper kettle (30x38cm-12x15in) s. masonite prov. 18-Nov-3 John Moran, Pasadena #52a est:3000-4000
£2310 $4250 €3373 Still life with yellow roses in a vase (45x35cm-18x14in) s. canvasboard prov. 8-Jun-4 Bonhams & Butterfields, San Francisco #4249/R est:3000-5000
£2941 $5000 €4294 Still life with fruit (51x61cm-20x24in) s. 20-Nov-3 Auctions by the Bay, Alameda #1109/R
Works on paper
£2235 $3800 €3263 Santa Barbara pier. Santa Barbara beach (23x30cm-9x12in) ink wash oil crayon two prov. 29-Oct-3 Christie's, Los Angeles #50/R est:3000-5000
£2457 $4250 €3587 Still life with fruit. Santa Barbara beach and pier. Preparing to sail (23x28cm-9x11in) mixed media three. 10-Dec-3 Bonhams & Butterfields, San Francisco #6303/R est:3000-5000
£2457 $4250 €3587 Santa Barbara beach. Sunny Santa Barbara. Study of an Indian woman (25x22cm-10x9in) mixed media three. 10-Dec-3 Bonhams & Butterfields, San Francisco #6304/R est:3000-5000

HINMAN, Charles (1932-) American

£500 $850 €730 Hesiod (69x122cm-27x48in) s.i.d.1979 acrylic. 9-Nov-3 Wright, Chicago #438
£578 $1000 €844 Crystal (66x86cm-26x34in) acrylic emulsion prov. 15-Dec-3 Hindman, Chicago #94/R est:2000-3000
£578 $1000 €844 Two volumes (163x109cm-64x43in) acrylic emulsion prov. 15-Dec-3 Hindman, Chicago #95/R est:2000-3000
£636 $1100 €929 No 7 (58x81cm-23x32in) acrylic emulsion prov. 15-Dec-3 Hindman, Chicago #97/R
£765 $1300 €1117 Changing course (117x183cm-46x72in) s.d.1973 verso acrylic. 9-Nov-3 Wright, Chicago #437 est:1500-2000
£867 $1500 €1266 Two volumes turning (163x264cm-64x104in) acrylic emulsion prov. 15-Dec-3 Hindman, Chicago #96/R est:3000-5000

HINNA, Bernhard (1871-1951) Norwegian

£1057 $1945 €1586 Winter covered buildings (60x75cm-24x30in) s. 14-Jun-4 Blomqvist, Lysaker #1150/R est:15000-18000 (N.KR 13000)

HINOJOSA, Paloma (1947-) Spanish

£355 $574 €500 Nino con bicicleta (16x50cm-6x20in) s. panel prov. 20-May-3 Segre, Madrid #284/R
£2397 $4075 €3500 Feast (81x100cm-32x39in) s. s.i.verso. 4-Nov-3 Ansorena, Madrid #53/R est:3500

HINRICKSEN, Kurt (1901-) Swiss

£573 $974 €837 Le potager (59x73cm-23x29in) s. i. verso panel. 5-Nov-3 Dobiaschofsky, Bern #643/R (S.FR 1300)

HINSBERGER, Alexis (1907-1996) ?

Works on paper
£333 $597 €500 Trois chevaux sauvages (62x94cm-24x37in) s. W/C. 11-May-4 Vanderkindere, Brussels #88

HINTERBERGER, Paul (20th C) Swiss

£226 $385 €330 Appenzell landscape with Sanits chain (50x89cm-20x35in) s.d.69 pavatex. 18-Nov-3 Hans Widmer, St Gallen #1098 (S.FR 500)

HINTERHOLZER, Franz (1851-?) German?

£319 $533 €450 Sunflowers (30x20cm-12x8in) s. board. 16-Oct-3 Dorotheum, Salzburg #555/R
£567 $1043 €850 Autumn evening with view of Untersberg (19x29cm-7x11in) s. board. 9-Jun-4 Dorotheum, Salzburg #534/R

HINTERMEISTER, Henry (1897-1972) American

£1564 $2800 €2283 Boy to the rescue as a young girl chases ball into street (76x56cm-30x22in) s. 15-May-4 Illustration House, New York #69/R est:2500-4000
£1620 $2900 €2365 Fisherman reeling in catch (43x30cm-17x12in) s. 15-May-4 Illustration House, New York #71/R est:2500-3500
£2695 $4500 €3935 Mother bear and cubs fishing, one distracted by beehive (76x61cm-30x24in) s. 15-Nov-3 Illustration House, New York #155/R est:2500-3500

HINTERREITER, Hans (1902-1989) Swiss

£1176 $2000 €1717 Study 388 (15x20cm-6x8in) s.i.d.1938 tempera paper prov. 22-Nov-3 Burkhard, Luzern #184/R est:2600-3000 (S.FR 2600)
£1179 $1910 €1721 Study 303 BB (12x17cm-5x7in) s.i.d.1957 tempera prov. 24-May-3 Burkhard, Luzern #89/R est:2600-3000 (S.FR 2500)
£1810 $3077 €2643 Study for Opus 112 (27x33cm-11x13in) s.i.d.1959/1973 tempera exhib. 25-Nov-3 Germann, Zurich #36/R est:6000-7000 (S.FR 4000)
£2009 $3696 €2933 SW 131 (33x27cm-13x11in) s.i.d. s.i.d. verso tempera. 8-Jun-4 Germann, Zurich #56/R est:5000-7000 (S.FR 4600)
£2096 $3857 €3060 Study 297 A (14x19cm-6x7in) s.i.d.1941 tempera. 8-Jun-4 Germann, Zurich #54/R est:5000-6000 (S.FR 4800)
£2172 $3692 €3171 Study 222 B (14x19cm-6x7in) s.i.d.1949 tempera. 25-Nov-3 Germann, Zurich #37/R est:5000-6000 (S.FR 4800)
£2183 $4017 €3187 Opus 57F, 1943-81 (36x30cm-14x12in) s.i.d. caparol. 8-Jun-4 Germann, Zurich #55/R est:6000-7000 (S.FR 5000)
£2262 $3846 €3303 Untitled (14x19cm-6x7in) s.d.1949 verso tempera. 25-Nov-3 Germann, Zurich #38/R est:5000-6000 (S.FR 5000)
£5677 $10445 €8288 Opus 79 (82x82cm-32x32in) s.i.d.1958 verso tempera pavatex exhib. 8-Jun-4 Germann, Zurich #57/R est:20000-30000 (S.FR 13000)
£7240 $12308 €10570 Opus 10 (83x72cm-33x28in) mono.d.1951 verso tempera pavatex exhib. 25-Nov-3 Germann, Zurich #39/R est:20000-30000 (S.FR 16000)

HINTON, Walter Haskell (20th C) American

£306	$550	€447	Cascading river n a mountain landscape (51x61cm-20x24in) s. prov. 24-Apr-4 Weschler, Washington #622/R

HINTZ, Julius (1805-1862) German

£3800	$7030	€5548	Port of Dieppe (39x61cm-15x24in) s.i. board. 10-Feb-4 Bonhams, Knightsbridge #316/R est:2500-3500

HINZE, Walter (?) German?

£769	$1285	€1100	Landscape with six putti (91x194cm-36x76in) s.d.1923 after Rubens. 27-Jun-3 Altus, Berlin #486/R

HIPSHER, Charles (20th C) American

£273	$500	€399	Fall out (127x97cm-50x38in) oil on paper. 10-Jul-4 Hindman, Chicago #215/R

HIQUILY, Philippe (1925-) French

Sculpture			
£2657	$4438	€3800	Meridienne (41x41x12cm-16x16x5in) mono. tin exec.1990 lit. 29-Jun-3 Versailles Encheres #193/R
£3846	$6615	€5500	Untitled (55cm-22in) copper iron exec.c.1980. 2-Dec-3 Calmels Cohen, Paris #64/R est:6000-8000
£3867	$7037	€5800	Chrysalide (52x24cm-20x9in) s. num.1/1 tin exec.1988 lit. 29-Jun-4 Cornette de St.Cyr, Paris #146/R est:6000-8000
£4225	$7310	€6000	L'Olympia (104x180cm-41x71in) s. brass wood screenprint panel. 14-Dec-3 Versailles Encheres #188/R est:7000-8000
£7113	$12305	€10100	La Celestine (108x57cm-43x22in) s. num.6/8 brown green pat bronze. 9-Dec-3 Chambelland & Giafferi, Paris #76/R est:10000-12000
£7333	$13493	€11000	Femme cave a cigares (38x50cm-15x20in) s. gold brass. 10-Jun-4 Camard, Paris #178/R est:12000-15000

HIRAGA, Kamesuke (1890-1971) Japanese

£546	$1000	€797	Vue generale de Montemaggiore (64x79cm-25x31in) s. painted 1931. 6-Jun-4 American Auctioneer #475766/R
£1133	$2074	€1700	Lavandieres pres du port (46x61cm-18x24in) s.d.1930 panel. 6-Jun-4 Anaf, Lyon #391/R est:1000-1200

HIRAKAWA, Isamu (1921-) Japanese

£272	$500	€397	Passage de L'Atlas (53x66cm-21x26in) s.d.1965. 26-Jun-4 Susanin's, Chicago #6076/R

HIRANKUL, Sujarit (1956-1982) Thai

£1700	$2738	€2482	Houses on the river (74x84cm-29x33in) s.d.1969. 13-Oct-3 Joel, Victoria #365 est:1500-2000 (A.D 4200)

HIRD, Mary (20th C) American

£248	$450	€362	Shepherds with sheep (25x38cm-10x15in) s. 16-Apr-4 James Julia, Fairfield #624i/R

HIREMY-HIRSCHL, Adolph (1860-1933) Hungarian

£20000	$34400	€29200	Venus reclining in the waves (109x274cm-43x108in) s. 3-Dec-3 Christie's, London #69/R est:25000-35000
£39526	$70751	€57708	Ahasuerus (139x229cm-55x90in) s.indis.d.1888 prov. 15-May-4 Christie's, Sydney #175/R est:40000-60000 (A.D 100000)
Works on paper			
£789	$1453	€1200	Landscape with cliffs (34x47cm-13x19in) mixed media. 23-Jun-4 Finarte Semenzato, Rome #43/R
£851	$1379	€1200	Loggia a Capodistria (38x41cm-15x16in) s. W/C prov. 22-May-3 Stadion, Trieste #381/R
£1471	$2500	€2148	Portrait of the artist's daughter Maud (42x25cm-17x10in) graphite blk chk stumping. 28-Oct-3 Sotheby's, New York #103/R est:3000-4000

HIRLEMANN, Charles (20th C) ?

£1513	$2784	€2300	Villa, les Algues a Villers (81x99cm-32x39in) s.d.1934. 23-Jun-4 Maigret, Paris #70/R est:2300-3000

HIRN, Jean Georges (1777-1839) French

£10000	$18201	€15000	Corbeille de vannerie (71x60cm-28x24in) s.d.1824 copper. 30-Jun-4 Pierre Berge, Paris #39/R est:20000-30000

HIROSHIGE (19th C) Japanese

Prints			
£1734	$3190	€2600	Island. s. print. 11-Jun-4 Tajan, Paris #211/R est:1800-2000
£1867	$3434	€2800	Figures in landscape. s. print. 11-Jun-4 Tajan, Paris #203/R est:1800-2000
£2200	$4048	€3300	Winter landscape. s. print. 11-Jun-4 Tajan, Paris #201/R est:1500-2000
£2934	$5398	€4400	Winter landscape. s. print. 11-Jun-4 Tajan, Paris #214/R est:1800-2000
£2934	$5398	€4400	View. s. print. 11-Jun-4 Tajan, Paris #209/R est:4500-5000
£3667	$6747	€5500	Landscape with figures. s. print. 11-Jun-4 Tajan, Paris #208/R est:3500-4000

HIROSHIGE II (1826-1869) Japanese

Prints			
£2238	$3804	€3200	Akasaka (35x23cm-14x9in) s. col print. 25-Nov-3 Sotheby's, Paris #78/R est:2400-2800
£2657	$4517	€3800	Ocha no Mizu (37x25cm-15x10in) s. col print. 25-Nov-3 Sotheby's, Paris #79/R est:3000-4000
£3497	$5944	€5000	Shinsu (36x24cm-14x9in) s. col print lit. 25-Nov-3 Sotheby's, Paris #82/R est:3800-4500

HIROSHIGE, Ando I (1797-1858) Japanese

Prints			
£1748	$2972	€2500	Annaka (23x36cm-9x14in) s. col print lit. 25-Nov-3 Sotheby's, Paris #57/R est:2400-2800
£2105	$3811	€3200	Figures in landscape. i. 16-Apr-4 Dorotheum, Vienna #327/R est:800-1000
£2119	$3857	€3200	Waterfall. s.d.1855. 19-Jun-4 Klefisch, Cologne #130/R
£2238	$3804	€3200	Mariko (18x24cm-7x9in) s. col print. 25-Nov-3 Sotheby's, Paris #54/R est:900-1200
£2448	$4161	€3500	Tsunohazu (38x26cm-15x10in) s. col print lit. 25-Nov-3 Sotheby's, Paris #72/R est:3000-4000
£2518	$4280	€3600	Bateaux approchant de la rive de Sumida la nuit. s.d.1857 print. 25-Nov-3 Tajan, Paris #427/R est:1500-1800
£2657	$4517	€3800	Sumidagawa (22x28cm-9x11in) s. col print. 25-Nov-3 Sotheby's, Paris #51/R est:4500-5500
£2797	$4755	€4000	Pont parmi les clycine et pins. s.d.1856 print. 25-Nov-3 Tajan, Paris #431/R est:800-1000
£2797	$4811	€4000	Atake viewed through the driving rain from the Ohashi bridge. i.d.1857 col woodcut. 5-Dec-3 Lempertz, Koln #701/R est:5000
£2800	$5152	€4088	Lobster and prawns (25x36cm-10x14in) s. print exec. early 1830's. 8-Jun-4 Sotheby's, London #404/R est:1800-2200
£2937	$4993	€4200	Pluie la nuit sur Karasaki. s. print. 25-Nov-3 Tajan, Paris #433 est:2200-2500
£2989	$5500	€4364	Surimono with mica embellishment (22x40cm-9x16in) s. print prov. 23-Mar-4 Christie's, Rockefeller NY #18/R est:1000-1500
£3147	$5350	€4500	O (22x35cm-9x14in) s. col print lit. 25-Nov-3 Sotheby's, Paris #61/R est:2400-2800
£3147	$5350	€4500	Fukagawa Kiba (35x23cm-14x9in) s. col print lit. 25-Nov-3 Sotheby's, Paris #74/R est:2800
£3147	$5350	€4500	Meguro (35x23cm-14x9in) s. col print lit. 25-Nov-3 Sotheby's, Paris #76/R est:2400-2800
£3357	$5706	€4800	Oki Hono (36x24cm-14x9in) s. col print prov. 25-Nov-3 Sotheby's, Paris #46/R est:2000-3000
£3357	$5706	€4800	Horikiri (36x24cm-14x9in) s. col print exhib.lit. 25-Nov-3 Sotheby's, Paris #71/R est:4500-5500
£3357	$5706	€4800	Untitled. s. print. 25-Nov-3 Tajan, Paris #422/R est:3500-4000
£3357	$5706	€4800	Le temple Kinryuzan a Asakusa. s.d.1856 print. 25-Nov-3 Tajan, Paris #434/R est:2000-2200
£3846	$6538	€5500	Katada (25x36cm-10x14in) s. col print lit. 25-Nov-3 Sotheby's, Paris #58/R est:6000-7000
£3846	$6538	€5500	Untitled. s. print. 25-Nov-3 Tajan, Paris #424/R est:3000-4000
£4545	$7727	€6500	Kawaguchi (35x24cm-14x9in) s. col print exhib.lit. 25-Nov-3 Sotheby's, Paris #68/R est:7500-8500
£5594	$9510	€8000	Takanawa (36x24cm-14x9in) s. col print exhib.lit. 25-Nov-3 Sotheby's, Paris #67/R est:6000-8000
£5600	$10304	€8176	Still life with paper bag and cord with tassels (19x17cm-7x7in) s.i. print exec. early 1820's prov. 8-Jun-4 Sotheby's, London #478/R est:700-900
£7692	$13077	€11000	Hakone Sanchu (21x28cm-8x11in) s. col print prov.lit. 25-Nov-3 Sotheby's, Paris #52/R est:12000-15000
£7692	$13077	€11000	Yotsugidori (35x24cm-14x9in) s. col print exhib.lit. 25-Nov-3 Sotheby's, Paris #73/R est:3000-4000
£20000	$36800	€29200	The fifty-three stations of the Tokaido Road (23x36cm-9x14in) s.i. print album of 53 exec. c.1833. 8-Jun-4 Sotheby's, London #397/R est:20000-25000
£22133	$37626	€31650	Chouette (37x13cm-15x5in) s. col print prov.lit. 25-Nov-3 Sotheby's, Paris #62/R est:35000-40000
£26574	$45175	€38000	Les cinquantes trois stations de la route du Tokaido. s. print. 25-Nov-3 Tajan, Paris #440/R est:25000-30000
Works on paper			
£769	$1308	€1100	Study (34x24cm-13x9in) ink exhib. 25-Nov-3 Sotheby's, Paris #170/R est:700-900
£979	$1664	€1400	Apres la tempete (24x34cm-9x13in) s. ink exhib. 25-Nov-3 Sotheby's, Paris #165/R est:1400-1700
£1259	$2140	€1800	Study (34x24cm-13x9in) s. ink exhib. 25-Nov-3 Sotheby's, Paris #171/R est:700-900
£1399	$2378	€2000	Study (34x24cm-13x9in) s. ink exhib. 25-Nov-3 Sotheby's, Paris #168/R est:700-900
£1538	$2615	€2200	Relais (24x34cm-9x13in) ink. 25-Nov-3 Sotheby's, Paris #166/R est:700-900
£1902	$3500	€2777	Peacock (128x24cm-50x9in) s. ink hanging scroll. 23-Mar-4 Christie's, Rockefeller NY #124/R est:3500-4000
£2797	$4755	€4000	Relais (24x34cm-9x13in) ink. 25-Nov-3 Sotheby's, Paris #167/R est:700-900
£2797	$4755	€4000	Study (34x24cm-13x9in) ink lit. 25-Nov-3 Sotheby's, Paris #172/R est:1400-1700
£2937	$4993	€4200	Relais (24x33cm-9x13in) ink. 25-Nov-3 Sotheby's, Paris #164/R est:1700-2000

HIRSCH, A E (?) American

£255	$400	€372	Yankee clipper (41x51cm-16x20in) double-sided. 20-Apr-3 Outer Cape Auctions, Provincetown #159/R

HIRSCH, Auguste Alexandre (1833-1912) French

£1049	$1783	€1500	Parisian woman wearing corsage (110x85cm-43x33in) s. 20-Nov-3 Dorotheum, Salzburg #154/R est:3000-4500
£15385	$26154	€22000	Hommage a la lingere (142x108cm-56x43in) s.d.1890. 30-Nov-3 Anaf, Lyon #118/R est:18000-20000

HIRSCH, Debora (1967-) Brazilian

£6993	$11888	€10000	Darkness upon the face of the deep (240x130cm-94x51in) s.d.2001 acrylic. 28-Nov-3 Farsetti, Prato #280/R est:10000-14000

HIRSCH, Joseph (1910-1981) American

£9239	$17000	€13489	Wrestlers (41x51cm-16x20in) s.d.32 exhib. 27-Jun-4 Freeman, Philadelphia #129/R est:6000-10000

HIRSCHBERG, Carl (1854-1923) American

£1117 $2000 €1631 East Hampton (18x30cm-7x12in) board prov. 26-May-4 Doyle, New York #141/R est:3000-4000

HIRSCHFELD, Al (1903-2003) American

Prints

£1816 $3250 €2651 Elvis (35x27cm-14x11in) s.num.90/150 etching aquatint. 4-May-4 Doyle, New York #184/R est:2000-3000
£1840 $3000 €2686 Marlene Dietrich sings Lili Marlene (41x51cm-16x20in) s.num.28/100 etching. 25-Sep-3 Swann Galleries, New York #39
£1840 $3000 €2686 Slaughter on Tenth Avenue, Suzanne Ferrell and Arthur Mitchell (66x53cm-26x21in) s. lithograph. 25-Sep-3 Swann Galleries, New York #104
£1963 $3200 €2866 Elvis (30x25cm-12x10in) s.num.xxi/xxx etching. 25-Sep-3 Swann Galleries, New York #42/R
£1963 $3200 €2866 La serviette au cou (41x30cm-16x12in) s. lithograph. 25-Sep-3 Swann Galleries, New York #105
£2209 $3600 €3225 W C Fields (33x25cm-13x10in) s.num.11/150 etching. 25-Sep-3 Swann Galleries, New York #44
£2209 $3600 €3225 Railway Station, Kharkov, USSR (41x30cm-16x12in) s.num.13/15 lithograph. 25-Sep-3 Swann Galleries, New York #98
£2454 $4000 €3583 Marilyn (43x33cm-17x13in) s.i. etching. 25-Sep-3 Swann Galleries, New York #88
£3190 $5200 €4657 Martha Graham (51x51cm-20x20in) s.i. etching. 25-Sep-3 Swann Galleries, New York #50
£11413 $21000 €16663 Spencer and Kate (38x38cm-15x15in) s. num. etching. 10-Jun-4 Sotheby's, New York #464/R est:1000-1500
£14674 $27000 €21424 Katharine Hepburn and Spencer Tracy (56x46cm-22x18in) s. num.14/750 etching. 10-Jun-4 Sotheby's, New York #600/R est:1500-2000

Works on paper

£736 $1200 €1075 Fred Allen (36x33cm-14x13in) s. pen ink. 25-Sep-3 Swann Galleries, New York #2
£920 $1500 €1343 Fred Allen (51x36cm-20x14in) s. pen ink. 25-Sep-3 Swann Galleries, New York #2a
£1227 $2000 €1791 Keith Baxter in Corpse (69x53cm-27x21in) s.i. pen ink board. 25-Sep-3 Swann Galleries, New York #10
£1227 $2000 €1791 Mary McCarthy in Anna Christie (76x56cm-30x22in) s. pen ink board. 25-Sep-3 Swann Galleries, New York #86
£1257 $2100 €1835 Ricardo Montablan and Herve Villechaize from Fantasy Island (38x30cm-15x12in) s. gouache. 15-Nov-3 Illustration House, New York #47/R est:5000-7000
£1472 $2400 €2149 Annie get your gun, Ethel Merman and Harry Belaver (41x51cm-16x20in) s. pen ink board. 25-Sep-3 Swann Galleries, New York #3
£1472 $2400 €2149 The Boy Friend, with Twiggy and Thum Friends (53x74cm-21x29in) s. pen ink. 25-Sep-3 Swann Galleries, New York #29
£1557 $2600 €2258 Genie in a bottle (69x55cm-27x22in) s. ink on board. 22-Jun-3 Freeman, Philadelphia #128/R est:1000-1500
£1667 $3000 €2434 Connoisseurs (43x66cm-17x26in) ink. 24-Apr-4 Du Mouchelle, Detroit #3136/R est:1000-2000
£1946 $3250 €2841 Judgement at Nuremburg (53x76cm-21x30in) s. pen ink board. 14-Oct-3 Bonhams & Butterfields, San Francisco #5063/R est:4000-6000
£1963 $3200 €2866 Shirley Booth in A Tree Grows in Brooklyn (36x33cm-14x13in) s. pen ink board. 25-Sep-3 Swann Galleries, New York #28
£2086 $3400 €3046 Hallelujah, Baby, Leslie Uggams, Alan Weeks and others (43x74cm-17x29in) s. pen board. 25-Sep-3 Swann Galleries, New York #56
£2096 $3500 €3060 Leila Hadley Luce (53x43cm-21x17in) s. pen ink. 15-Nov-3 Illustration House, New York #57/R est:3500-4500
£2331 $3800 €3403 Quadrille and Fanny (38x66cm-15x26in) s. pen ink board. 25-Sep-3 Swann Galleries, New York #97
£2331 $3800 €3403 Ziegfeld Follies, with Beatrice Lille in foreground (51x64cm-20x25in) s. pen ink. 25-Sep-3 Swann Galleries, New York #119
£2454 $4000 €3583 Of thee I sing (53x74cm-21x29in) s. pen ink board. 25-Sep-3 Swann Galleries, New York #92
£2454 $4000 €3583 The war between men and women, Jason Robards, B Harris, J Lemmon (56x76cm-22x30in) pen ink board. 25-Sep-3 Swann Galleries, New York #115
£2577 $4200 €3762 The Millionairess, with Cyril Ritchard, Katherine Hepburn, Robert Helpmann (53x56cm-21x22in) s. pen ink board. 25-Sep-3 Swann Galleries, New York #89
£2822 $4600 €4120 Buster Keaton (18x13cm-7x5in) s. pen ink board. 25-Sep-3 Swann Galleries, New York #71
£3067 $5000 €4478 Creative minds, S J Perelman, Elizabeth Taylor and Richard (51x53cm-20x21in) s. pen ink. 25-Sep-3 Swann Galleries, New York #38
£3190 $5200 €4657 Elizabeth Taylor in Ash Wednesday (58x53cm-23x21in) pen ink. 25-Sep-3 Swann Galleries, New York #111
£3293 $5500 €4808 Julie Andrews performing a song and dance number (41x66cm-16x26in) s. pen brush ink. 15-Nov-3 Illustration House, New York #55/R est:6000-8000
£3313 $5400 €4837 Jack Benny with violin (61x38cm-24x15in) s. pen ink board. 25-Sep-3 Swann Galleries, New York #11
£3681 $6000 €5374 John Barrymore as Hamlet (46x38cm-18x15in) pen ink board. 25-Sep-3 Swann Galleries, New York #9
£3681 $6000 €5374 Hermione Gingold (61x41cm-24x16in) s. pen ink gouache acetate board. 25-Sep-3 Swann Galleries, New York #48
£3892 $6500 €5682 Sergeants 3 (53x64cm-21x25in) s. pen ink board. 14-Oct-3 Bonhams & Butterfields, San Francisco #5062/R est:4000-6000
£3988 $6500 €5822 Camino Real (41x66cm-16x26in) s. pen ink board. 25-Sep-3 Swann Galleries, New York #35
£4294 $7000 €6269 Liberace (46x41cm-18x16in) s. gouache board. 25-Sep-3 Swann Galleries, New York #84
£4294 $7000 €6269 Laurence Olivier in the Entertainer (56x76cm-22x30in) pen ink board. 25-Sep-3 Swann Galleries, New York #93
£5215 $8500 €7614 Preliminary drawings for Charleston. gouache double-sided. 25-Sep-3 Swann Galleries, New York #37
£5215 $8500 €7614 The Great Sebastians, with Lunt and Fontanne (51x56cm-20x22in) s. pen ink board. 25-Sep-3 Swann Galleries, New York #52
£5215 $8500 €7614 Elvis Presley (71x56cm-28x22in) s. pen ink board. 25-Sep-3 Swann Galleries, New York #95
£5521 $9000 €8061 Golden boy, Sammy Davis Jr and Paula Wayne (33x23cm-13x9in) pen ink. 25-Sep-3 Swann Galleries, New York #49
£6135 $10000 €8957 Ethel Barrymore as a 101 year old woman in Whiteoaks (38cm-15in) black chl white gouache. 25-Sep-3 Swann Galleries, New York #8
£6135 $10000 €8957 The visit, with Lunt and Fontanne (48x74cm-19x29in) s. pen ink board. 25-Sep-3 Swann Galleries, New York #114
£7065 $13000 €10315 Katharine Hepburn and Nick Nolte. s. ink. 10-Jun-4 Sotheby's, New York #609/R est:4000-6000
£7362 $12000 €10749 Self portrait in barber chair (28x20cm-11x8in) s. gouache ink board exec.c.1957. 25-Sep-3 Swann Galleries, New York #102
£7609 $14000 €11109 Spencer Tracy, the old man and the sea (51x66cm-20x26in) s.i. pen ink dr. 10-Jun-4 Sotheby's, New York #466/R est:4000-6000
£8589 $14000 €12540 Diamond Lil, Mae West (36x46cm-14x18in) s. pen ink board. 25-Sep-3 Swann Galleries, New York #116
£9202 $15000 €13435 Bob Hope (53x41cm-21x16in) s. gouache board. 25-Sep-3 Swann Galleries, New York #57
£10870 $20000 €15870 Katharine Hepburn and Dorothy Loudon - West Side Waltz (64x46cm-25x18in) s. ink. 10-Jun-4 Sotheby's, New York #593/R est:4000-6000
£17178 $28000 €25080 TV totem pole, Lucille Ball, Desi Arnaz, J Gleason, J Webb, Groucho Marx (53x41cm-21x16in) s. gouache board. 25-Sep-3 Swann Galleries, New York #110
£18405 $30000 €26871 Broadway at night, Broadway on a Saturday night (25x51cm-10x20in) pen ink blue W/C htd gouache board. 25-Sep-3 Swann Galleries, New York #30

HIRSCHFELD, Emil Benediktoff (1867-1922) Russian

£940 $1682 €1400 Effet de lune sur la mer (54x72cm-21x28in) s. 25-May-4 Chambelland & Giafferi, Paris #44/R

HIRSCHHORN, Thomas (1957-) Swiss

Sculpture

£17964 $30000 €26227 Fahrplan 2000, agents de l'extreme (161x244x22cm-63x96x9in) s.i.d.2000 photograph fluorescent light packing tape diptych. 13-Nov-3 Phillips, New York #56/R est:25000-35000

Works on paper

£6500 $10855 €9490 Providing crying I-IV (49x59cm-19x23in) i. s.i.d.2003 verso felt tip pen cut out collage tape 4 prov. 22-Oct-3 Christie's, London #125/R est:10000-15000

HIRSH, Alice (1888-1935) American

£1324 $2250 €1933 Children on pier, with boats (20x25cm-8x10in) indis.sig. board. 18-Nov-3 John Moran, Pasadena #10 est:1000-1500

HIRSHFIELD, Morris (1872-1946) American

£27616 $47500 €40319 Garden stand and birds (53x63cm-21x25in) s.d.1945 prov. 3-Dec-3 Sotheby's, New York #65/R est:15000-20000

HIRST, Claude Raguet (1855-1942) American

£16471 $28000 €24048 Peaches on a tabletop (23x35cm-9x14in) s.i. 30-Oct-3 Phillips, New York #11/R est:30000-50000

Works on paper

£938 $1500 €1369 Still life (36x30cm-14x12in) s. W/C. 21-Sep-3 Grogan, Boston #19/R

HIRST, Damien (1965-) British

£3200 $5792 €4672 Untitled (29x21cm-11x8in) s. acrylic pencil executed c.1993. 1-Apr-4 Christie's, Kensington #352/R est:3000-5000
£5500 $10120 €8030 Time (23cm-9in circular) s. gloss paint card clock surface prov. 24-Jun-4 Sotheby's, Olympia #429/R est:3000-4000
£7000 $12880 €10220 Untitled, spin painting (46cm-18in circular) acrylic prov. 24-Jun-4 Sotheby's, Olympia #404/R est:4000-6000
£16500 $29865 €24090 Untitled (23x21cm-9x8in) s.i.verso gloss household paint on canvas painted c.1994. 1-Apr-4 Christie's, Kensington #353/R est:8000-12000
£22346 $40000 €32625 Butyric anhydride (23x23cm-9x9in) s.verso gloss household paint prov.lit. 14-May-4 Phillips, New York #110/R est:30000-40000
£60000 $110400 €87600 Aspartic Acid Di-T-Butylester (46x41cm-18x16in) s.i. verso household gloss paint painted 1995 prov.lit. 24-Jun-4 Sotheby's, London #120/R est:20000-30000
£110000 $200200 €160600 I'm only sleeping (122x122cm-48x48in) household gloss paint pharmaceutical drugs resin canvas prov. 5-Feb-4 Sotheby's, London #49/R est:80000-120000
£120000 $218400 €175200 Untitled - spot painting (91x91cm-36x36in) s.verso gloss household paint painted 1992 prov. 5-Feb-4 Christie's, London #217/R est:90000-120000
£150898 $252000 €220311 Amnioantipyrine (203x222cm-80x87in) gloss household paint painted 1992 prov.lit. 12-Nov-3 Christie's, Rockefeller NY #517/R est:250000-350000
£170000 $309400 €248200 Beautiful, four cheese, spicy, quatro, staggioni, florentine, michelangelo (213cm-84in circular) i.verso gloss household paint on canvas painted 1997 prov. 4-Feb-4 Christie's, London #37/R est:100000-150000
£170000 $312800 €248200 Morphine sulfate (145x223cm-57x88in) s.verso gloss household paint on canvas prov.lit. 24-Jun-4 Christie's, London #43/R est:180000-220000
£210000 $382200 €306600 Beautiful thing to do (108x130cm-43x51in) butterflies household gloss paint canvas exec 2003 prov. 5-Feb-4 Sotheby's, London #2/R est:120000-150000
£270000 $496800 €394200 Untitled no.3 (91x91cm-36x36in) s.i. verso gloss household paint prov. 25-Jun-4 Christie's, London #229a/R est:100000-150000
£299401 $500000 €437125 4-Chlororesorcinol - PFS (76x179cm-30x70in) household gloss four panels painted 1999 prov. 11-Nov-3 Christie's, Rockefeller NY #45/R est:400000-600000

Photographs

£1796 $3000 €2622 Valium (127x127cm-50x50in) s. num.301/500 verso col photo. 21-Oct-3 Bonhams & Butterfields, San Francisco #1324/R
£18000 $33120 €26280 With dead head (57x76cm-22x30in) black and white photo on aluminium exec 1981-1991 prov.lit. 24-Jun-4 Sotheby's, London #124/R est:15000-20000
£20958 $35000 €30599 With dead head (57x76cm-22x30in) black white photograph on aluminum prov.exhib.lit. 13-Nov-3 Phillips, New York #46/R est:40000-60000
£22455 $37500 €32784 With dead head (57x76cm-22x30in) black white photo aluminum edition of 15 prov.lit. 13-Nov-3 Sotheby's, New York #414/R est:30000-40000

Prints

£1818 $3091 €2600 From 'The Last Supper' (73x99cm-29x39in) s. col serigraph. 29-Nov-3 Villa Grisebach, Berlin #793/R est:1800-2400
£1818 $3091 €2600 From 'The Last Supper' (150x86cm-59x34in) s. col serigraph. 29-Nov-3 Villa Grisebach, Berlin #794/R est:1800-2400
£2000 $3700 €2920 Last Supper Steak and Kidney (152x102cm-60x40in) s. edn of 150 screenprint exec 1999. 13-Jul-4 Bonhams, Knightsbridge #77/R est:2000-3000
£2721 $4952 €4000 Lysergic Acid Diethylamide. s. num.229/300 verso serigraph. 3-Feb-4 Segre, Madrid #223/R est:4000
£2800 $5152 €4088 Lycergic acid diethylamide (106x126cm-42x50in) s.num.283/300 verso lambda print Fuji gloss paper prov. 24-Jun-4 Sotheby's, Olympia #407/R est:2500-3500
£4200 $7644 €6132 Opium (48x43cm-19x17in) s. num.136/500 verso lambda print exec 2000. 4-Feb-4 Sotheby's, Olympia #40/R est:800-1200
£17365 $29000 €25353 Last supper (152x102cm-60x40in) s. 13 colour screenprint executed 1999 prov.lit. 14-Nov-3 Phillips, New York #124/R est:20000-30000
£19461 $32500 €28413 Last supper (152x102cm-60x40in) s. col screenprints paper 13 prov. 13-Nov-3 Sotheby's, New York #535/R est:20000-30000

Sculpture			
£5587	$10000	€8157	Love will tear us apart (36x51x22cm-14x20x9in) plastic plexiglas cabinet needles syringes edition of 30 prov. 14-May-4 Phillips, New York #103/R est:15000-20000
£30726	$55000	€44860	Pharmaceutical wall painting, five blacks. enamel paint box tins brushes compass edition of 10 prov.lit. 14-May-4 Phillips, New York #105/R est:50000-70000
£60000	$110400	€87600	Oy (38x76x15cm-15x30x6in) glass MDF drug packaging executed 1997 prov. 24-Jun-4 Christie's, London #3/R est:60000-80000
£120000	$218400	€175200	Charity - Maquette (102cm-40in) acrylic paint on bronze exec 2003 prov. 5-Feb-4 Sotheby's, London #1/R est:100000-150000
£307263	$550000	€448604	Still pursuing impossible desires (221x205x213cm-87x81x84in) steel glass rubber gloss paint canvas butterflies prov.exhib.lit. 12-May-4 Sotheby's, New York #40/R est:600000-800000
£530726	$950000	€774860	We are afraid of nothing (183x274x30cm-72x108x12in) mdf glass steel pharmaceutical drug containers ladder. 13-May-4 Phillips, New York #10/R est:500000-700000
£628743	$1050000	€917965	Something solid beneath the surface of all creatures great and small (205x376x122cm-81x148x48in) animal skeletons glass display unit executed 2001 prov.exhib.lit. 13-Nov-3 Phillips, New York #11/R est:800000-1200000
Works on paper			
£4000	$7360	€5840	Charity - it begins at home (25x18cm-10x7in) s.i. felt tip pen prov. 24-Jun-4 Sotheby's, Olympia #402/R est:3000-4000
£5500	$10120	€8030	Prodigal son (29x20cm-11x8in) s.i. biro prov.exhib. 24-Jun-4 Sotheby's, Olympia #401/R est:3000-4000
£9000	$16380	€13140	Study for the acquired inability to escape divided (59x84cm-23x33in) s.i.d.93 pencil prov. 5-Feb-4 Christie's, London #219/R est:6000-8000
£18000	$32760	€26280	Beautiful obliterating accelerating psychotic drawing (59x42cm-23x17in) s.d.93 ink wax crayon biro prov. 5-Feb-4 Christie's, London #200/R est:7000-9000
£30000	$55200	€43800	Away from the flock (51x73cm-20x29in) s.i.d.93/4 pencil prov.exhib.lit. 24-Jun-4 Sotheby's, London #119/R est:10000-15000
£191617	$320000	€279761	Caesium carbide 89 (193x153cm-76x60in) s. i.d.1997 verso dayglo acrylic on canvas prov. 12-Nov-3 Sotheby's, New York #36/R est:350000-450000

HIRST, Proteo (1930-1985) Italian

Sculpture			
£1119	$1924	€1600	Bust of woman (65cm-26in) bronze. 3-Dec-3 Stadion, Trieste #1086/R est:1500-2000
£1278	$2287	€1915	Prisoner (74x92cm-29x36in) s. pat bronze. 12-May-4 Stadion, Trieste #808/R est:2500-3500
£1667	$2983	€2500	Sense (143cm-56in) pat bronze. 12-May-4 Stadion, Trieste #803/R est:2500-3500

HIRT, Friedrich Wilhelm (1721-1772) German

£3030	$5424	€4424	River landscape with herders and grazing animals (39x51cm-15x20in) s.d.1766 prov. 22-Mar-4 Philippe Schuler, Zurich #4410/R est:8000-10000 (S.FR 7000)

HIRT, Heinrich (1841-1902) German

£3077	$5231	€4400	Hunter with two girls (72x83cm-28x33in) s. 20-Nov-3 Van Ham, Cologne #1632a/R est:5000
£4422	$7915	€6500	Small girl with rabbits (40x29cm-16x11in) s.i. panel. 17-Mar-4 Neumeister, Munich #483/R est:6000

HIRTH DU FRENES, Rudolf (1846-1916) German

£451	$754	€650	Entertainers in front of tavern (24x31cm-9x12in) s. 22-Oct-3 Neumeister, Munich #710
£972	$1604	€1400	Portrait of Horst Hacker (59x51cm-23x20in) s. 2-Jul-3 Neumeister, Munich #665/R
£3357	$5773	€4800	Travelling entertainers practising in a barn (76x90cm-30x35in) s.d.1883. 3-Dec-3 Neumeister, Munich #598/R est:4000
Works on paper			
£490	$842	€700	Portrait of a young woman (56x40cm-22x16in) s. pastel. 3-Dec-3 Neumeister, Munich #397/R

HIRTZ, Albert (?) ?

£294	$490	€420	Calvaire en bord de mer en Bretagne (55x46cm-22x18in) s. 7-Oct-3 Livinec, Gaudcheau & Jezequel, Rennes #82
£313	$509	€450	Nice, promenade des Anglais, l'ancien casino. s. 29-Sep-3 Charbonneaux, Paris #233

HIS, René Charles Edmond (1877-1960) French

£750	$1253	€1095	Fishermen off a Mediterranean coastline (45x65cm-18x26in) s. prov. 21-Oct-3 Bonhams, Knightsbridge #11/R
£900	$1503	€1314	Stream (34x53cm-13x21in) s. 16-Oct-3 Bonhams, Edinburgh #65
£1100	$1837	€1606	Springtime (37x45cm-15x18in) s. 12-Nov-3 Sotheby's, Olympia #232/R est:1000-1500
£2000	$3700	€2920	Sunny river landscape (60x81cm-24x32in) s. 10-Feb-4 Bonhams, Knightsbridge #323/R est:2000-3000
£2676	$4630	€3800	Vagues et rochers en Mediterranee (38x55cm-15x22in) s. i.d.1936 verso pair. 12-Dec-3 Libert, Castor, Paris #68/R est:4000-6000
£2800	$5012	€4088	Bord de l'eure (51x66cm-20x26in) s. 26-May-4 Sotheby's, Olympia #343/R est:2000-3000
£3200	$5056	€4672	Autumn tints (59x80cm-23x31in) s. i.verso. 2-Sep-3 Gildings, Market Harborough #441/R est:2000-3000
£4200	$6972	€6132	River landscape (65x91cm-26x36in) s. 1-Oct-3 Sotheby's, Olympia #290/R est:2500-3500
£4500	$8055	€6570	Wild flowers by the river (61x82cm-24x32in) s.i.stretcher. 26-May-4 Sotheby's, Olympia #342/R est:3000-5000
£6000	$10740	€8760	Path along the river (46x56cm-18x22in) s. 26-May-4 Sotheby's, Olympia #344/R est:2000-3000
£7400	$13246	€10804	Woodland pool (114x161cm-45x63in) s. 11-May-4 Bonhams, Knightsbridge #266/R est:2000-4000
£50000	$92000	€75000	Campement au bord de l'oued (132x225cm-52x89in) s. 11-Jun-4 Claude Aguttes, Neuilly #142/R est:50000-60000

HISAO, Domoto (1928-) American?

£297	$550	€434	Solution de continuite (19x47cm-7x19in) s.i.d.1963-64 verso prov. 13-Jul-4 Christie's, Rockefeller NY #47/R

HISHIKAWA MORONOBU (c.1618-1694) Chinese

Prints			
£2098	$3608	€3000	Lovers reclining on a futon, watched by another man (26x37cm-10x15in) col engraving. 5-Dec-3 Lempertz, Koln #552/R est:2000

HISLOP, Helga (20th C) British

Works on paper			
£800	$1480	€1168	Snowdrops (46x52cm-18x20in) s.d.1992 W/C. 13-Feb-4 Sworder & Son, Bishops Stortford #95/R
£800	$1480	€1168	Crab apples in a basket (16x21cm-6x8in) s.i.d. W/C. 13-Feb-4 Sworder & Son, Bishops Stortford #97/R

HISSARD, Henri (20th C) French

Works on paper			
£470	$869	€700	Etudes de Marocains et de Marocaines (23x31cm-9x12in) s.i.d.1932 chl htd gouache. 15-Mar-4 Gros & Delettrez, Paris #41/R
£537	$993	€800	Marocains pres de Sale (23x31cm-9x12in) s.i.d.1932 chl gouache. 15-Mar-4 Gros & Delettrez, Paris #42/R

HITCHCOCK, George (1850-1913) American

£6989	$13000	€10204	Rotterdam Mill (55x43cm-22x17in) s. 5-Mar-4 Skinner, Boston #510/R est:5000-7000
£12291	$22000	€17945	Pandora (66x56cm-26x22in) s. prov. 14-May-4 Skinner, Boston #343/R est:30000-50000
£16176	$27500	€23617	View of tulips beds in bloom, Holland (36x43cm-14x17in) s.i.d.1915 canvas on board. 19-Nov-3 Bonhams & Butterfields, San Francisco #148/R
£24581	$44000	€35888	Swans by a bridge, Holland (84x71cm-33x28in) s.d.98 prov. 6-May-4 Shannon's, Milford #89/R est:25000-35000
£42614	$75000	€62216	Dutch bride (76x61cm-30x24in) s. painted c.1895-98 prov.exhib.lit. 19-May-4 Sotheby's, New York #30/R est:60000-80000
Works on paper			
£1098	$1900	€1603	Off the coast of Chicago (33x56cm-13x22in) s.d.1879 W/C. 13-Dec-3 Charlton Hall, Columbia #524/R est:2000-2500

HITCHCOCK, Harold (1914-) British

£900	$1638	€1314	In the woods (41x44cm-16x17in) mono.d.01. 1-Jul-4 Christie's, Kensington #244/R
£1362	$2356	€1989	Mediterranean village (51x61cm-20x24in) mono. acrylic prov. 10-Dec-3 Shapiro, Sydney #57/R est:2000-4000 (A.D 3200)
Works on paper			
£550	$935	€803	Harbour (49x59cm-19x23in) mono.d.1966 W/C. 26-Nov-3 Sotheby's, Olympia #179/R
£649	$1200	€948	Capriccio. The harvester (51x71cm-20x28in) init.d.1965 W/C second tempera on paper on masonite two. 15-Jul-4 Sotheby's, New York #126/R
£749	$1250	€1094	Landscape (99x152cm-39x60in) init.d.1966 W/C paper on masonite. 20-Oct-3 Sotheby's, New York #201/R
£778	$1300	€1136	Landscape (76x101cm-30x40in) init.d.70 i.verso W/C board. 20-Oct-3 Sotheby's, New York #203/R
£800	$1408	€1168	Woodland fantasy (54x75cm-21x30in) mono.d.1963 W/C gouache prov. 19-May-4 Sotheby's, Olympia #265/R
£850	$1590	€1241	Figure reaching in a fantasy landscape (57x75cm-22x30in) mono.d.1964 W/C. 26-Feb-4 Lane, Penzance #283
£900	$1548	€1314	Sea madonna (49x58cm-19x23in) mono.d.1965 pencil W/C prov. 3-Dec-3 Christie's, Kensington #656/R

HITCHCOCK, Malcolm J (1929-1998) British

£280	$510	€409	Railway at Erzbergbahn (30x40cm-12x16in) s.d.1973 board. 1-Jul-4 Christie's, Kensington #297/R

HITCHENS, Alfred (1861-?) British

Works on paper			
£400	$680	€584	Portrait of Denis Verity as a boy (67x49cm-26x19in) s. pastel. 18-Nov-3 Bearnes, Exeter #573

HITCHENS, Ivon (1893-1979) British

£12000	$20040	€17520	Surroundings of water (41x75cm-16x30in) s.d.72 prov. 16-Oct-3 Christie's, Kensington #652/R est:10000-15000
£13000	$23790	€18980	Woodcutter (75x41cm-30x16in) s. prov. 4-Jun-4 Christie's, London #98/R est:12000-18000
£16000	$29280	€23360	Woman seated at a window (37x41cm-15x16in) s. canvas on board prov. 4-Jun-4 Christie's, London #99/R est:8000-12000
£18000	$32940	€26280	Gamekeeper's cottage (41x75cm-16x30in) s. prov. 4-Jun-4 Christie's, London #109/R est:15000-20000
£20000	$36400	€29200	Hampshire Water (40x74cm-16x29in) s.d.73 prov. 15-Jun-4 Bonhams, New Bond Street #100/R est:10000-15000
£22000	$40040	€32120	Serenade for winter (40x75cm-16x30in) s.d.75 prov. 15-Jun-4 Bonhams, New Bond Street #99/R est:10000-15000
£24000	$40800	€35040	Green walks (46x109cm-18x43in) s. 21-Nov-3 Christie's, London #17/R est:20000-30000
£24000	$40800	€35040	Arched trees (40x90cm-16x35in) s. prov.lit. 26-Nov-3 Sotheby's, Olympia #165/R est:10000-15000
£28000	$51240	€40880	Spring still life, red bowl (51x76cm-20x30in) s. painted c.1937 prov. 4-Jun-4 Christie's, London #100/R est:30000-50000
£28000	$51240	€40880	Woodland landscape (43x109cm-17x43in) s. painted 1957 prov. 4-Jun-4 Christie's, London #110/R est:25000-35000
£29000	$49300	€42340	Ruined canal gates, evening (51x84cm-20x33in) s. s.i.on stretcher painted c.1951 prov. 21-Nov-3 Christie's, London #18/R est:15000-20000
£38000	$69540	€55480	Foliage by water 8 (61x165cm-24x65in) s. 2-Jun-4 Sotheby's, London #104/R est:20000-30000
£38000	$69160	€55480	November wood (41x109cm-16x43in) s. prov. 15-Jun-4 Bonhams, New Bond Street #98/R est:18000-25000
£40000	$73200	€58400	Larchwood (51x76cm-20x30in) s.d.41 prov. 4-Jun-4 Christie's, London #108/R est:30000-50000

£48000 $87840 €70080 Avington water 1 (51x117cm-20x46in) s. prov.exhib. 2-Jun-4 Sotheby's, London #103/R est:20000-30000
£48000 $87840 €70080 Flowers, black, blue and yellow (46x17cm-18x7in) s. painted 1966 prov. 2-Jun-4 Sotheby's, London #106/R est:25000-35000
£62000 $113460 €90520 Orange bush 1 (46x76cm-18x30in) s. prov. 2-Jun-4 Sotheby's, London #105/R est:30000-40000
£92000 $156400 €134320 Orange boy, John by Jordan no.3 (41x75cm-16x30in) s. painted 1942 prov.exhib. 21-Nov-3 Christie's, London #65/R est:25000-35000
£150000 $255000 €219000 Boy at breakfast (64x91cm-25x36in) s. painted 1943 prov.exhib. 21-Nov-3 Christie's, London #64/R est:40000-60000
Works on paper
£750 $1388 €1095 Sheet of nine reclining females figures (57x39cm-22x15in) s.d.63 pen ink prov. 11-Mar-4 Christie's, Kensington #199/R

HITCHENS, John (1940-) British
£300 $549 €438 Landscape, Heyshott, west wind (51x104cm-20x41in) s. 8-Jul-4 Duke & Son, Dorchester #173
£400 $668 €584 Hill under large cloud (46x91cm-18x36in) s.d.64 s.i.d.1964 stretcher. 16-Oct-3 Christie's, Kensington #611
£500 $850 €730 Blues and orange (35x45cm-14x18in) s.d.1967 s.i.verso. 26-Nov-3 Sotheby's, Olympia #182/R
£550 $1001 €803 Green Hill (51x91cm-20x36in) s.d.1963 s.i.d. stretcher. 1-Jul-4 Christie's, Kensington #348/R
£800 $1408 €1168 Loose light (63x76cm-25x30in) s. s.i.d.1968 stretcher. 19-May-4 Sotheby's, Olympia #327/R
£900 $1584 €1314 Autumn dusk (55x91cm-22x36in) s. painted 1974. 18-May-4 Bonhams, Knightsbridge #57/R

HITCHINGS, Henry (?-1902) American
£367 $650 €536 Homestead with woman at work (28x43cm-11x17in) s.d.1887. 2-May-4 Grogan, Boston #76/R
Works on paper
£197 $350 €288 Homestead with ducks (30x48cm-12x19in) s.d.1887 W/C. 2-May-4 Grogan, Boston #75/R

HITZ, Dora (1856-?) German
£3289 $5954 €5000 Bather in a brook in the forest (93x116cm-37x46in) s. 19-Apr-4 Glerum, Amsterdam #301/R est:3500-4500

HITZLER, Franz (1946-) German
£1831 $3168 €2600 Untitled (90x60cm-35x24in) s.d.1986 verso. 13-Dec-3 Lempertz, Koln #152/R est:500
Works on paper
£345 $576 €500 Untitled (57x40cm-22x16in) mixed media board. 15-Nov-3 Von Zezschwitz, Munich #190/R
£533 $955 €800 Untitled (127x116cm-50x46in) s.d. verso mixed media board. 13-May-4 Neumeister, Munich #643/R
£704 $1218 €1000 Untitled (106x59cm-42x23in) chl acrylic board prov. 13-Dec-3 Lempertz, Koln #318

HJERLOW, Ragnvald (1863-1947) Norwegian
£1126 $1880 €1644 From Asker (37x52cm-15x20in) s. 17-Nov-3 Blomqvist, Lysaker #1123/R est:8000-12000 (N.KR 13500)

HJERSING, Arne (1860-1926) Norwegian
£289 $530 €422 Coastal landscape (45x69cm-18x27in) s. 2-Feb-4 Blomqvist, Lysaker #1110 (N.KR 3600)
£2238 $4096 €3267 View of Oslo (100x200cm-39x79in) s.i.d.1914. 9-Jun-4 Rasmussen, Copenhagen #1586/R est:35000 (D.KR 25000)

HJERTEN, Sigrid (1885-1948) Swedish
£3021 $5136 €4411 Mulatto woman wearing turban - Aicha (33x24cm-13x9in) with sig.verso panel exhib.lit. 4-Nov-3 Bukowskis, Stockholm #89/R est:40000-50000 (S.KR 40000)
£4206 $7571 €6141 Youths (27x35cm-11x14in) s. 26-Apr-4 Bukowskis, Stockholm #102/R est:40000-50000 (S.KR 58000)
£7977 $14358 €11646 Southern townscape (67x53cm-26x21in) s. panel. 26-Apr-4 Bukowskis, Stockholm #107/R est:100000-125000 (S.KR 110000)
£8308 $14124 €12130 Salso Maggiore (72x91cm-28x36in) s. panel exhib. 5-Nov-3 AB Stockholms Auktionsverk #656/R est:150000-175000 (S.KR 110000)
£11240 $20232 €16410 Still life (47x38cm-19x15in) s. painted 1914. 26-Apr-4 Bukowskis, Stockholm #122/R est:150000-175000 (S.KR 155000)
£13553 $23989 €19787 Female nude with blue dressing gown (60x73cm-24x29in) s. painted 1935 exhib. 27-Apr-4 AB Stockholms Auktionsverk #806/R est:100000-125000 (S.KR 185000)
£14286 $25286 €20858 Sicke and Svenne (81x72cm-32x28in) panel exhib.lit. 27-Apr-4 AB Stockholms Auktionsverk #861/R est:250000-300000 (S.KR 195000)
£16994 $28890 €24811 Under the blossom of the apple tree (81x65cm-32x26in) s. exhib. 4-Nov-3 Bukowskis, Stockholm #177/R est:150000-175000 (S.KR 225000)
£22659 $38520 €33082 Ivan wearing a French soldier's cap (75x42cm-30x17in) s. i.verso exhib. 5-Nov-3 AB Stockholms Auktionsverk #685/R est:300000-350000 (S.KR 300000)
£47583 $80891 €69471 Ivan playing in the heap of sand (45x38cm-18x15in) painted 1913 exhib. 4-Nov-3 Bukowskis, Stockholm #15/R est:450000-500000 (S.KR 630000)
£105149 $189268 €153518 The red hoisting cranes at Stadsgaarden (92x73cm-36x29in) s. panel exhib.lit. 26-Apr-4 Bukowskis, Stockholm #106/R est:1000000-1500000 (S.KR 1450000)
Works on paper
£2198 $3890 €3209 Seated female nude (66x49cm-26x19in) s. W/C. 27-Apr-4 AB Stockholms Auktionsverk #690/R est:25000-30000 (S.KR 30000)
£3223 $5705 €4706 The white hat (41x33cm-16x13in) gouache. 27-Apr-4 AB Stockholms Auktionsverk #745/R est:15000-20000 (S.KR 44000)
£8059 $14264 €11766 Ivan at the cafe (46x35cm-18x14in) s. W/C. 27-Apr-4 AB Stockholms Auktionsverk #746/R est:100000-120000 (S.KR 110000)
£35896 $64612 €52408 Kornhamstorg - market scene with figures (98x116cm-39x46in) W/C executed 1913 exhib.prov. 26-Apr-4 Bukowskis, Stockholm #64/R est:600000-700000 (S.KR 495000)

HJERTSEN, Sverre (1909-1968) Norwegian
£1027 $1745 €1499 Negro woman (86x64cm-34x25in) s.d.58. 19-Nov-3 Grev Wedels Plass, Oslo #91/R est:15000-20000 (N.KR 12000)

HJORTH, Bror (1894-1968) Swedish
£24176 $42791 €35297 The old Rattviks road in Sjugare (61x50cm-24x20in) s. prov.lit. 27-Apr-4 AB Stockholms Auktionsverk #687/R est:200000-225000 (S.KR 330000)
Sculpture
£1378 $2480 €2012 Girl with masks (32cm-13in) s.num.1 gold pat.bronze Cast Bergman. 26-Apr-4 Bukowskis, Stockholm #271/R est:25000-30000 (S.KR 19000)
£2190 $3724 €3197 Reclining girl (24cm-9in) s.num.6/9 painted terracotta. 4-Nov-3 Bukowskis, Stockholm #76/R est:15000-18000 (S.KR 29000)
£60423 $102719 €88218 Lady of the woods and the fiddler (84x50cm-33x20in) s.d.1947 sculpted painted black oak prov.exhib.lit. 5-Nov-3 AB Stockholms Auktionsverk #769/R est:300000-400000 (S.KR 800000)
Works on paper
£361 $625 €527 Lioness (19x28cm-7x11in) s. i.verso pencil prov. 15-Dec-3 Lilla Bukowskis, Stockholm #754 (S.KR 4600)
£1183 $2117 €1727 Female nude (72x49cm-28x19in) s. chl. 28-May-4 Uppsala Auktionskammare, Uppsala #286/R est:15000-18000 (S.KR 16000)
£5076 $9137 €7411 Violin player on horseback (18x21cm-7x8in) s.i. mixed media. 26-Apr-4 Bukowskis, Stockholm #93a/R est:30000-40000 (S.KR 70000)

HJORTH-NIELSEN, S (1901-1983) Danish
£469 $878 €685 Southern harbour (81x100cm-32x39in) init. painted c.1933-34. 25-Feb-4 Kunsthallen, Copenhagen #201/R (D.KR 5200)

HJORTH-NIELSEN, Soren (1901-1983) Danish
£722 $1329 €1054 Boats at Gammel Strand (60x81cm-24x32in) init. s.i.d.1952 verso. 29-Mar-4 Rasmussen, Copenhagen #559/R (D.KR 8000)
£1083 $1993 €1581 View across roof tops (82x100cm-32x39in) init. 29-Mar-4 Rasmussen, Copenhagen #460/R est:12000-15000 (D.KR 12000)
£1083 $1993 €1581 The harbour in Laesoe (89x117cm-35x46in) init. s.i.d.1956 verso. 29-Mar-4 Rasmussen, Copenhagen #556/R est:15000 (D.KR 12000)
£1176 $1999 €1717 Field landscape with hay stooks (68x82cm-27x32in) init. 29-Nov-3 Rasmussen, Havnen #4076/R est:8000-10000 (D.KR 12500)
£1986 $3653 €2900 Harbour view (80x100cm-31x39in) init. 29-Mar-4 Rasmussen, Copenhagen #507/R est:25000 (D.KR 22000)
£2629 $4391 €3838 View of houses (89x117cm-35x46in) init. 7-Oct-3 Rasmussen, Copenhagen #303/R est:12000-15000 (D.KR 28000)

HJORTZBERG, Olle (1872-1959) Swedish
£323 $526 €472 Southern landscape with figures (50x61cm-20x24in) s. 29-Sep-3 Lilla Bukowskis, Stockholm #415 (S.KR 4200)
£566 $1018 €849 The church in Assisi (65x54cm-26x21in) s. 25-Apr-4 Goteborg Auktionsverk, Sweden #350/R (S.KR 7800)
£1021 $1767 €1491 Umbrian landscape (65x54cm-26x21in) s.d.1950. 15-Dec-3 Lilla Bukowskis, Stockholm #386 (S.KR 13000)
£1035 $1852 €1511 Pelargonium in pot (46x37cm-18x15in) s.d.1935 panel. 26-May-4 AB Stockholms Auktionsverk #2142/R est:20000-25000 (S.KR 14000)
£1848 $3307 €2698 Southern mountain town (61x50cm-24x20in) s. 26-May-4 AB Stockholms Auktionsverk #2167/R est:8000-10000 (S.KR 25000)
£2956 $5292 €4316 Still life of yellow roses in blue vase (61x50cm-24x20in) s.d.1943 panel. 26-May-4 AB Stockholms Auktionsverk #2143/R est:50000-60000 (S.KR 40000)
£3077 $5292 €4492 Still life of figurine and potted plant (65x54cm-26x21in) s.d.1945 panel prov. 2-Dec-3 Bukowskis, Stockholm #151/R est:50000-70000 (S.KR 40000)
£3077 $5292 €4492 Still life of yellow roses (66x54cm-26x21in) s.d.1941 panel. 2-Dec-3 Bukowskis, Stockholm #152/R est:50000-70000 (S.KR 40000)
£3077 $5292 €4492 Still life of pink roses in silver vase (66x54cm-26x21in) s.d.44 panel. 2-Dec-3 Bukowskis, Stockholm #172/R est:50000-60000 (S.KR 40000)
£4582 $8203 €6690 Still life of roses in silver vase (67x57cm-26x22in) s.d.1945 panel. 28-May-4 Uppsala Auktionskammare, Uppsala #261/R est:50000-60000 (S.KR 62000)
£4769 $8203 €6963 The artist and his wife (79x78cm-31x31in) s.d.1901 exhib. 7-Dec-3 Uppsala Auktionskammare, Uppsala #175/R est:30000-40000 (S.KR 62000)
£5385 $9262 €7862 Still life of roses in silver vase (65x54cm-26x21in) s.d.1945 panel. 2-Dec-3 Bukowskis, Stockholm #171/R est:60000-70000 (S.KR 70000)
£5769 $9923 €8423 Still life of yellow roses in silver bowl (54x65cm-21x26in) s.d.1943 panel. 3-Dec-3 AB Stockholms Auktionsverk #2266/R est:50000-60000 (S.KR 75000)
£6154 $10585 €8985 Still life of apples and silver vase (50x60cm-20x24in) s.d.47 panel. 2-Dec-3 Bukowskis, Stockholm #1/R est:60000-70000 (S.KR 80000)
£6154 $10585 €8985 Still life of summer flowers (55x46cm-22x18in) s.d.1940 panel. 2-Dec-3 Bukowskis, Stockholm #63/R est:80000-100000 (S.KR 80000)
£6800 $12171 €9928 Still life of roses in Delft vase (66x55cm-26x22in) s.d.45 panel. 25-May-4 Bukowskis, Stockholm #117/R est:75000-100000 (S.KR 92000)
£10347 $18522 €15107 Still life of amaryllis (65x81cm-26x32in) s.d.1941 panel. 26-May-4 AB Stockholms Auktionsverk #2141/R est:75000-100000 (S.KR 140000)
£11826 $21168 €17266 Still life of roses in silver vase (92x73cm-36x29in) s.d.1944 panel. 26-May-4 AB Stockholms Auktionsverk #2099/R est:125000-150000 (S.KR 160000)
£25868 $46305 €37767 Still life of chrysanthemums (100x81cm-39x32in) s.d.1955 panel prov. 25-May-4 Bukowskis, Stockholm #119/R est:150000-200000 (S.KR 350000)
£30303 $54242 €44242 Wild flowers in dish (50x61cm-20x24in) s.d.51. 25-May-4 Bukowskis, Stockholm #1/R est:100000-125000 (S.KR 410000)
Works on paper
£308 $529 €450 Still life of flowers (32x40cm-13x16in) s.d.1951 mixed media. 7-Dec-3 Uppsala Auktionskammare, Uppsala #221/R (S.KR 4000)

HLADIK, Frantisek (1887-1944) Czechoslovakian
£329 $560 €480 Study of nudes and a figure (26x22cm-10x9in) s. canvas on cardboard. 29-Nov-3 Dorotheum, Prague #46/R est:15000-23000 (C.KR 15000)
£591 $1039 €887 Autumn (65x82cm-26x32in) s. 22-May-4 Dorotheum, Prague #80/R est:18000-28000 (C.KR 28000)

HLAVACEK, Anton (1842-1926) Austrian
£590 $1003 €850 Arnsdorf on the Donau (14x22cm-6x9in) s. i. verso board. 28-Oct-3 Dorotheum, Vienna #207/R
£872 $1562 €1300 In Pustertal (50x41cm-20x16in) mono. i.s.verso cardboard. 27-May-4 Hassfurther, Vienna #50a
£1958 $3329 €2800 View of Karawanken with Mittagskogel (32x42cm-13x17in) s. 25-Nov-3 Hassfurther, Vienna #44/R est:2400-2800

Works on paper

£276 $458 €400 House in landscape near Nussdorf (27x49cm-11x19in) s.i. W/C board. 30-Sep-3 Dorotheum, Vienna #351/R

HLINA, Ladislav (1947-) German

Sculpture

£1049 $1783 €1500 Wild boar (57cm-22in) s. dark brown pat bronze. 28-Nov-3 Schloss Ahlden, Ahlden #535/R est:1600

£1597 $2524 €2300 Young angler with water spear (142cm-56in) dark brown pat.bronze. 19-Sep-3 Schloss Ahlden, Ahlden #777/R est:1900

£1597 $2524 €2300 Girl with ducklings (115cm-45in) dark brown pat.bronze. 19-Sep-3 Schloss Ahlden, Ahlden #779/R est:1900

£1748 $2972 €2500 Young flute player sitting on a barrel (103cm-41in) s. brown pat bronze wood. 28-Nov-3 Schloss Ahlden, Ahlden #534/R est:2800

£1818 $3091 €2600 Girl carrying a lamb (112cm-44in) s. dark brown pat bronze. 28-Nov-3 Schloss Ahlden, Ahlden #536/R est:1900

HLITO, Alfredo (1923-1993) Argentinian

£6077 $11000 €8872 Untitled (50x35cm-20x14in) cardboard. 30-Mar-4 Arroyo, Buenos Aires #62

£10588 $18000 €15458 Construction (70x50cm-28x20in) s.i.d.45 verso prov.exhib. 19-Nov-3 Sotheby's, New York #146/R est:20000-25000

£17486 $32000 €25530 Ghost (70x120cm-28x47in) acrylic. 1-Jun-4 Arroyo, Buenos Aires #66

HNIZDOVSKY, Jacques (1915-1985) American

Works on paper

£412 $750 €602 Tree truck (53x38cm-21x15in) s.d.1966 pen ink. 19-Jun-4 Rachel Davis, Shaker Heights #636

£495 $900 €723 Irises (51x38cm-20x15in) s.d.1966 pen ink. 19-Jun-4 Rachel Davis, Shaker Heights #634 est:750-850

£604 $1100 €882 Tree without leaves (51x43cm-20x17in) s.d.1966 pen ink. 19-Jun-4 Rachel Davis, Shaker Heights #635 est:750-850

HO HUU THU (1943-) Vietnamese

£2536 $3931 €3703 Portrait I (80x70cm-31x28in) s.d.1996. 6-Oct-2 Sotheby's, Singapore #96/R est:7000-9000 (S.D 7000)

£3261 $5054 €4761 Two sisters (100x85cm-39x33in) s.d.1991. 6-Oct-2 Sotheby's, Singapore #103/R est:9000-12000 (S.D 9000)

£3871 $6194 €5652 Sisters (106x86cm-42x34in) s.d.90. 18-May-3 Sotheby's, Singapore #116/R est:9000-12000 (S.D 10800)

HOAD, Jeremiah (1924-1999) Irish?

£660 $1075 €950 Winter, Donegal (45x59cm-18x23in) s.i.verso board. 23-Sep-3 De Veres Art Auctions, Dublin #235

£2639 $4301 €3800 Lighthouse on the Coast (46x61cm-18x24in) s. board prov. 24-Sep-3 James Adam, Dublin #56/R est:2000-2500

HOAGLAND, Mary Adams (attrib) (19/20th C) American

£396 $650 €574 River landscape (43x53cm-17x21in) indis.sig. painted c.1905. 7-Jun-3 Treadway Gallery, Cincinnati #1385

HOAR, Steve (20th C) Canadian

Sculpture

£950 $1720 €1387 Scout (47x41x17cm-19x16x7in) s.d. num bronze wood plinth prov. 18-Apr-4 Levis, Calgary #48a/R est:2000-2500 (C.D 2300)

£1446 $2618 €2111 High Ridin (62x39x23cm-24x15x9in) s.i.d.1978 num bronze wood plinth prov. 18-Apr-4 Levis, Calgary #48/R est:3000-3500 (C.D 3500)

HOARE, William (1706-1799) British

£2000 $3580 €2920 Portrait of George Burges (78x64cm-31x25in) s.indis d. i.verso prov. 26-May-4 Sotheby's, Olympia #21/R est:2000-3000

£17500 $29750 €25550 Double portrait of Elizabeth and Thomas Trower in a landscape, with their dog (137x109cm-54x43in) indis.sig.d.1773. 25-Nov-3 Christie's, London #26/R est:15000-20000

Works on paper

£500 $910 €730 Portrait of a lady in a bonnet (62x47cm-24x19in) i.verso pastel. 3-Feb-4 Sworder & Son, Bishops Stortford #256/R

£620 $1116 €905 Portrait of a lady (61x41cm-24x16in) pastel paper on canvas. 21-Jan-4 Sotheby's, Olympia #101/R

£4200 $7518 €6132 Portrait of a lady wearing a pearl choker (60x44cm-24x17in) pastel. 22-Mar-4 Bonhams & Brooks, Norfolk #184/R est:4000-6000

HOARE, William (attrib) (1706-1799) British

£1200 $2232 €1752 Portrait of Mrs Mary Knowles, in a blue dress (55x46cm-22x18in) 4-Mar-4 Christie's, Kensington #321/R est:1200-1800

Works on paper

£581 $1000 €848 Portrait of woman with hat. Portrait of man holding pen (11x11cm-4x4in) chk pair. 2-Dec-3 Christie's, Rockefeller NY #151/R

£703 $1300 €1026 Portrait of a young lady (58x46cm-23x18in) pastel. 15-Jul-4 Sotheby's, New York #12/R

HOBART OF MONKS ELEIGH, J R (fl.1829-1858) British

£500 $790 €725 Horse and dog (50x61cm-20x24in) s.d.1813. 3-Sep-3 Bonhams, Bury St Edmunds #429

£2400 $4296 €3504 Mr Chaplin on horseback on the road to Hadleigh (20x28cm-8x11in) s. 22-Mar-4 Bonhams & Brooks, Norfolk #246/R est:600-800

HOBART OF MONKS ELEIGH, John R (fl.1829-1858) British

£3005 $5500 €4387 Gentleman mounted on his chestnut hunter with a greyhound (42x52cm-17x20in) s.d.1859 prov. 7-Apr-4 Sotheby's, New York #82/R est:3000-4000

HOBART, A (19th C) ?

£839 $1427 €1200 Farmsteads by alpine river (18x31cm-7x12in) s. panel. 20-Nov-3 Dorotheum, Salzburg #122/R

HOBART, Clark (1868-1948) American

£13228 $25000 €19313 Monterey coastal (41x61cm-16x24in) s. s.i. verso prov. 17-Feb-4 John Moran, Pasadena #46/R est:10000-15000

HOBBEMA, M (1638-1709) Dutch

£4878 $8000 €7122 Landscape with figures on a road, hunters and dogs (102x135cm-40x53in) bears sig.verso prov. 31-May-3 Brunk, Ashville #426/R est:5000-10000

HOBBEMA, Meindert (1638-1709) Dutch

£130000 $237900 €189800 Wooded landscape with a hunter and other figures on a path (31x40cm-12x16in) s. panel prov.lit. 7-Jul-4 Christie's, London #43/R est:150000-250000

HOBBEMA, Meindert (style) (1638-1709) Dutch

£2431 $4059 €3500 Horse drawn cart in landscape (59x90cm-23x35in) panel prov. 24-Oct-3 Ketterer, Hamburg #717/R est:4000-5000

HOBBS, Morris Henry (1898-1967) American

Works on paper

£226 $375 €330 Florida landscape (15x23cm-6x9in) s.d.1923 s.i.d.verso pastel. 4-Oct-3 Neal Auction Company, New Orleans #1087

£949 $1500 €1386 Gardenias in a blue vase (30x23cm-12x9in) s. W/C. 7-Sep-3 Treadway Gallery, Cincinnati #639/R est:700-900

£1530 $2800 €2234 Bromeliad and female cardinal (51x36cm-20x14in) s.i.d.Feb 15 1966 W/C. 5-Jun-4 Neal Auction Company, New Orleans #391/R est:2500-3500

£1776 $3250 €2593 Bromeliad and blue bird (51x36cm-20x14in) s.d.Feb 15.1966 W/C. 5-Jun-4 Neal Auction Company, New Orleans #390/R est:2500-3500

HOBDELL, Roy (1911-1961) British

£450 $752 €657 Gothic trompe l'oeil (59x49cm-23x19in) s. board prov. 22-Oct-3 Cheffins, Cambridge #552/R

HOBERMAN, Nicky (1967-) South African

£3000 $5520 €4380 Mermaid II (152x244cm-60x96in) s.i.d.97 overlap prov.exhib. 24-Jun-4 Sotheby's, London #301/R est:3000-4000

£8500 $15640 €12410 Confetti cluster (212x212cm-83x83in) s.d.97 overlap i. stretcher prov. 24-Jun-4 Sotheby's, London #302/R est:4000-6000

HOBSON, Alice Mary (1860-1954) British

Works on paper

£250 $393 €363 Sketch from Monaco (30x39cm-12x15in) s.d.1912 pencil W/C exhib. 28-Aug-3 Christie's, Kensington #437/R

HOBSON, Henry E (fl.1857-1866) British

Works on paper

£300 $489 €435 Portrait of a gentleman (23x18cm-9x7in) init.d.1865 pencil W/C. 23-Sep-3 Bonhams, Knightsbridge #36/R

£360 $644 €526 Peasant girl picking flowers (35x25cm-14x10in) s.d.1865 W/C. 16-Mar-4 Bonhams, Oxford #15

£380 $699 €555 Awaiting the ferry (52x41cm-20x16in) s. W/C. 14-Jun-4 Bonhams, Bath #137

£660 $1102 €964 Country girls (43x30cm-17x12in) s. W/C pair. 16-Oct-3 Mallams, Cheltenham #202/R

£1000 $1820 €1460 Stile (45x35cm-18x14in) s. pencil W/C htd white. 1-Jul-4 Mellors & Kirk, Nottingham #697 est:800-1200

£1000 $1820 €1460 Well (37x27cm-15x11in) s. pencil W/C htd white. 1-Jul-4 Mellors & Kirk, Nottingham #698/R est:800-1200

HOCH, Hannah (1889-1979) German

£9333 $17173 €14000 Head (75x65cm-30x26in) mono. s.verso i.verso stretcher painted c.1946 prov. 12-Jun-4 Villa Grisebach, Berlin #271/R est:10000-15000

£10667 $19627 €16000 Children (49x37cm-19x15in) mono. s.i.verso prov.exhib. 8-Jun-4 Artcurial Briest, Paris #190/R est:8000-12000

Photographs

£11111 $21000 €16222 Untitled (25x16cm-10x6in) photo collage. 17-Feb-4 Swann Galleries, New York #41/R est:15000-25000

Works on paper

£417 $696 €600 Native with child (16x7cm-6x3in) mono. s.d. verso W/C bodycol over Indian ink board. 25-Oct-3 Dr Lehr, Berlin #205/R

£1733 $3103 €2600 Flowers (62x48cm-24x19in) mono.d.43 gouache chl. 15-May-4 Van Ham, Cologne #658/R est:3500

£1733 $3189 €2600 Composition (19x26cm-7x10in) mono.d.1966 gouache board. 12-Jun-4 Villa Grisebach, Berlin #573/R est:1200-1500

£3221 $5766 €4800 Vegetabiles (49x62cm-19x24in) mono. W/C bodycol. 25-May-4 Karl & Faber, Munich #331/R est:5500

£3672 $6500 €5361 Summer. Untitled. Untitled (70x47cm-28x19in) init. one s.verso one s.i.verso mixed media three prov. 2-May-4 Bonhams & Butterfields, Los Angeles #3019/R est:1500-2000

HOCHARD, Gaston (1863-1913) French

£3421 $6295 €5200 Soiree de Vernissage (65x53cm-26x21in) s. wood. 28-Jun-4 Joron-Derem, Paris #248 est:1500-2000

HOCK, Daniel (1858-1934) Austrian

£675 $1100 €986 Cupid (53x102cm-21x40in) s.d.1904. 24-Sep-3 Doyle, New York #42

£1690 $2924 €2400 The cavalier (74x46cm-29x18in) s.d.1888. 10-Dec-3 Dorotheum, Vienna #100/R est:2200-3000
£5944 $9927 €8500 The little misereant (115x81cm-45x32in) s.i.d.1880 i. verso. 9-Oct-3 Michael Zeller, Lindau #599/R est:8500

HOCKELMANN, Antonius (1937-) German
£567 $1014 €850 Racehorse (62x102cm-24x40in) s. W/C. 15-May-4 Van Ham, Cologne #659 est:1000

HOCKEN, Marion Grace (1922-1987) British
£350 $627 €511 Still life of chrysanthemums in a glass vase, a statue of herons to the side (64x76cm-25x30in) s.d.1947 i.verso. 18-Mar-4 Christie's, Kensington #720

HOCKER, William (1918-) American
£449 $750 €656 Hay manger (76x56cm-30x22in) masonite. 18-Oct-3 David Dike, Dallas #311/R

HOCKEY, Patrick (1948-1992) Australian
£909 $1682 €1327 After the meeting (61x75cm-24x30in) s.d.73 i.verso board. 10-Mar-4 Deutscher-Menzies, Melbourne #297/R est:2500-3500 (A.D 2200)
£2357 $3818 €3441 Before council meeting (91x121cm-36x48in) s.d.75 board prov. 30-Jul-3 Goodman, Sydney #25/R est:6000-8000 (A.D 5750)
£4102 $7670 €6153 Waterbirds (122x184cm-48x72in) s. board. 20-Jul-4 Goodman, Sydney #61/R est:5000-7000 (A.D 10500)

HOCKNER, Rudolf (1864-1942) German
£369 $653 €550 Landscape (11x18cm-4x7in) s. board. 28-Apr-4 Schopman, Hamburg #627/R
£403 $713 €600 Little autumn wood (14x19cm-6x7in) s. board. 28-Apr-4 Schopman, Hamburg #626/R
£486 $768 €700 Holstein farmstead in trees (20x26cm-8x10in) s. panel. 6-Sep-3 Schopman, Hamburg #755/R
£490 $842 €700 Landscape (17x26cm-7x10in) s. board. 4-Dec-3 Schopman, Hamburg #733a/R
£530 $964 €800 Path through the fields (21x30cm-8x12in) s. board. 19-Jun-4 Quittenbaum, Hamburg #21/R
£590 $933 €850 Stream in winter landscape (15x20cm-6x8in) s. 6-Sep-3 Schopman, Hamburg #757/R
£872 $1632 €1300 Houses in Wedel (18x28cm-7x11in) s. board. 28-Feb-4 Quittenbaum, Hamburg #71/R
£1049 $1752 €1500 Sand dunes in Wedel wood (34x48cm-13x19in) s.d.1930 board. 28-Jun-3 Bolland & Marotz, Bremen #668/R est:2000
£1067 $1931 €1600 Wedeler pasture in high summer (14x21cm-6x8in) s. board on panel. 3-Apr-4 Hans Stahl, Hamburg #165/R est:1400
£1192 $2170 €1800 Country road with a horse and cart near Wendel (15x21cm-6x8in) s. cardboard on panel. 19-Jun-4 Hans Stahl, Hamburg #137/R est:2200
£1329 $2285 €1900 On the banks of the Alster (22x32cm-9x13in) s. cardboard. 6-Dec-3 Quittenbaum, Hamburg #91/R est:1900
£1611 $2851 €2400 Bridge over small stream in old town (30x46cm-12x18in) s. board. 28-Apr-4 Schopman, Hamburg #625/R est:2700
£1611 $2964 €2400 Path in winter wood (40x50cm-16x20in) i. 29-Mar-4 Dr Fritz Nagel, Stuttgart #7001/R est:500
£1818 $3036 €2600 Hamburg (14x20cm-6x8in) s. board. 11-Oct-3 Hans Stahl, Hamburg #110 est:2800
£2028 $3488 €2900 Country landscape near Hamburg (35x50cm-14x20in) s.d.1936. 6-Dec-3 Quittenbaum, Hamburg #92/R est:3200
£2349 $4393 €3500 Old Hamburg (51x66cm-20x26in) s.d.1910. 28-Feb-4 Quittenbaum, Hamburg #70/R est:3800
£4459 $6866 €7000 Old town (28x45cm-11x18in) s.i. i. verso board. 4-Sep-2 Schopman, Hamburg #147/R est:7500

HOCKNEY, David (1937-) British
£17500 $30800 €25550 Bolton Junction, Eccleshill (71x91cm-28x36in) painted 1956 prov.exhib.lit. 18-May-4 Woolley & Wallis, Salisbury #4/R est:6000-8000
£90000 $163800 €131400 Tyger Painting No.2 (101x63cm-40x25in) s. board painted 1960 prov. 5-Feb-4 Sotheby's, London #28/R est:50000-70000
£418994 $750000 €611731 Antheriums (105x135cm-41x53in) s.i.d.1995 verso prov.exhib. 12-May-4 Christie's, Rockefeller NY #191/R est:400000-600000
£1257485 $2100000 €1835928 Portrait of Nick Wilder (183x183cm-72x72in) s. i.d.1966 verso acrylic prov.exhib.lit. 12-Nov-3 Sotheby's, New York #54/R est:2000000-3000000

Photographs
£4790 $8000 €6993 Paul explaining pictures to Mie Makigahara (89x113cm-35x44in) s.i.d.Feb 1983 num.2 col photo collage board series of 15 lit. 13-Nov-3 Sotheby's, New York #284/R est:8000-12000
£6500 $11830 €9490 Gregory and Shinro on the train (95x105cm-37x41in) s.i.d.1983 num.7 photo-montage board prov.lit. 4-Feb-4 Sotheby's, Olympia #78/R est:4000-6000
£6500 $11830 €9490 Gregory reading in Kyoto (100x110cm-39x43in) s.i.d.Feb 1983 num.4 photo-montage on board prov.lit. 4-Feb-4 Sotheby's, Olympia #79/R est:4000-6000
£9581 $16000 €13988 Graffiti palace, New York (122x147cm-48x58in) s.i.d.Dec 1983 num.6 col photo collage board series of 15 prov. 13-Nov-3 Sotheby's, New York #285/R est:18000-25000

Prints
£1622 $3000 €2368 Warm start (49x57cm-19x22in) s.d.94 num.63/68 col lithograph. 12-Feb-4 Christie's, Rockefeller NY #95/R est:2000-3000
£1765 $3000 €2577 My pool and terrace (60x90cm-24x35in) s. col aquatint etching. 31-Oct-3 Sotheby's, New York #593/R
£1765 $3000 €2577 Three black flowers (28x21cm-11x8in) s. print. 31-Oct-3 Sotheby's, New York #597/R
£1765 $3000 €2577 Red chair (28x22cm-11x9in) s.d.1986 col print. 4-Nov-3 Christie's, Rockefeller NY #267/R est:3500-4500
£1786 $3250 €2608 Eine (112x80cm-44x31in) s.d.91 num.2/35 col lithograph. 29-Jun-4 Sotheby's, New York #651/R est:2000-3000
£1796 $3000 €2622 Two peppers (25x39cm-10x15in) s.i.d.1973 col etching. 21-Oct-3 Bonhams & Butterfields, San Francisco #1326/R
£1808 $3200 €2640 Olympische Spiele Munchen (88x65cm-35x26in) s.d.1970 num.80/200 col lithograph. 28-Apr-4 Christie's, Rockefeller NY #296/R est:2000-3000
£2000 $3660 €2920 What is Picasso (34x42cm-13x17in) s.num.58/200 col etching aquatint. 3-Jun-4 Christie's, Kensington #402/R est:1500-2000
£2059 $3500 €3006 Tres, end of triple (112x80cm-44x31in) s. col lithograph. 31-Oct-3 Sotheby's, New York #598/R
£2059 $3500 €3006 Perspective lesson (76x56cm-30x22in) s.d.1985 col lithograph. 4-Nov-3 Christie's, Rockefeller NY #260/R est:3500-4500
£2060 $3750 €3008 New and the old and the new (75x107cm-30x42in) s.d.91 num.4/50 lithograph. 29-Jun-4 Sotheby's, New York #649/R est:2000-3000
£2060 $3750 €3008 Rampant (67x97cm-26x38in) s.d.91 num.1/50 col lithograph. 29-Jun-4 Sotheby's, New York #650/R est:1800-2200
£2147 $3500 €3135 Celia - Adjusting her eyelash (58x79cm-23x31in) s.d.1979 num.96/100 lithograph on Twinrocker. 24-Sep-3 Christie's, Rockefeller NY #256/R est:2800-3500
£2331 $3800 €3403 Apples, Grapes, Lemons on a table (43x56cm-17x22in) s.d.1988 num.52/91 diptych print office colour paper. 24-Sep-3 Christie's, Rockefeller NY #257/R est:3000-4000
£2353 $4000 €3435 Red pot (35x21cm-14x8in) s.d.1986 col print. 4-Nov-3 Christie's, Rockefeller NY #268/R est:5000-7000
£2373 $4200 €3465 Anne combing her hair (60x80cm-24x31in) s.d.1979 num.38/75 lithograph. 28-Apr-4 Christie's, Rockefeller NY #299/R est:3000-5000
£2446 $4500 €3571 Photograph of a photograph with photograph, July 10 (89x111cm-35x44in) s.d.1995 num.45 digital inkjet print prov. 10-Jun-4 Phillips, New York #692/R est:3000-4000
£2500 $4250 €3650 Paper pools (26x22cm-10x9in) s.d.1980 col lithograph. 30-Oct-3 Christie's, Kensington #83/R est:1000-1500
£2500 $4250 €3650 Pembroke studio chairs (47x55cm-19x22in) s. col lithograph. 31-Oct-3 Sotheby's, New York #588/R
£2647 $4500 €3865 Henry seated (107x75cm-42x30in) s.d.1976 col lithograph. 4-Nov-3 Christie's, Rockefeller NY #245/R est:5000-8000
£2695 $4500 €3935 Vase of flowers (72x50cm-28x20in) s.i.d.70 num. 60/200 col lithograph. 20-Oct-3 Sotheby's, New York #179/R est:6000-8000
£2712 $4800 €3960 Dog, num 3 (30x35cm-12x14in) s.d.1998 num.29/35 etching. 28-Apr-4 Christie's, Rockefeller NY #306/R est:2500-3500
£2797 $4755 €4000 Yves Marie (63x49cm-25x19in) s.i.d. lithograph. 29-Nov-3 Villa Grisebach, Berlin #328/R est:4000-5000
£2800 $4760 €4088 Halleluja God is love Jesus saves (15x20cm-6x8in) etching aquatint. 30-Oct-3 Christie's, Kensington #75/R est:2000-3000
£2800 $5096 €4088 Two plants (36x43cm-14x17in) s.d.1988 num.35/75 home-made print office paper. 1-Jul-4 Sotheby's, London #400/R est:2500-3000
£2824 $4800 €4123 Blue hang cliff (58x77cm-23x30in) s.d.1993 col lithograph screenprint. 4-Nov-3 Christie's, Rockefeller NY #270/R est:2500-3500
£2941 $5000 €4294 Painted environment I (79x99cm-31x39in) s. col laser print. 31-Oct-3 Sotheby's, New York #601/R
£3000 $5100 €4380 For blondes (15x20cm-6x8in) etching aquatint. 30-Oct-3 Christie's, Kensington #76/R est:2000-3000
£3067 $5489 €4600 Picture of a still life in silver frame (70x56cm-28x22in) s.i.d. col lithograph. 15-May-4 Dr Sturies, Dusseldorf #68/R
£3107 $5500 €4536 Lightning (79x65cm-31x26in) s.i.d.1973 num.15/98 lithograph. 28-Apr-4 Christie's, Rockefeller NY #297/R est:3000-5000
£3200 $5312 €4672 Snow (102x85cm-40x33in) s.i.d.1973 num.77/98 col lithograph. 6-Oct-3 Sotheby's, London #247/R est:2000-3000
£3200 $5824 €4672 Steel stool with newspaper (73x52cm-29x20in) s.d.1998 num.11/35 etching aquatint. 30-Jun-4 Christie's, London #231/R est:4000-6000
£3235 $5500 €4723 Pembroke studio (47x56cm-19x22in) s.d.84 col lithograph. 4-Nov-3 Christie's, Rockefeller NY #255/R est:6000-8000
£3235 $5500 €4723 Self portrait (56x22cm-22x9in) s.d.1986 col print. 4-Nov-3 Christie's, Rockefeller NY #264/R est:3500-4500
£3235 $5500 €4723 Snail's space (89x110cm-35x43in) s.d.1995 col laser print. 4-Nov-3 Christie's, Rockefeller NY #271/R est:3000-5000
£3356 $6174 €5000 Lillies - still life (62x49cm-24x19in) s.i.d. col lithograph. 26-Mar-4 Ketterer, Hamburg #461/R est:4000-4500
£3400 $5780 €4964 Student - from homage to Picasso (57x44cm-22x17in) s.d.73 num.11/XV etching aquatint prov. 18-Nov-3 Bonhams, Knightsbridge #99/R est:2500-3500
£3400 $5780 €4964 Painted environment 2 (70x90cm-28x35in) s.d.1993 num.13/25 sixteen col laser printed photos on board. 18-Nov-3 Bonhams, Knightsbridge #101/R est:3000-5000
£3672 $6500 €5361 Flowers, apple and pear (56x43cm-22x17in) s.d.1986 num.10/59 col handmade print 4 sheets office copier. 28-Apr-4 Christie's, Rockefeller NY #304/R est:5000-8000
£3672 $6500 €5361 Living room and terrace (43x56cm-17x22in) s.d.1986 num.22/60 col handmade print two sheets office copier. 28-Apr-4 Christie's, Rockefeller NY #305/R est:4000-6000
£3824 $6500 €5583 Conversation in the studio (61x72cm-24x28in) s.d.1984 col lithograph. 4-Nov-3 Christie's, Rockefeller NY #253/R est:6000-8000
£3824 $6500 €5583 White porcelain (48x56cm-19x22in) s.d.1985-86 offset lithograph col etching. 4-Nov-3 Christie's, Rockefeller NY #262/R est:6000-8000
£4118 $7000 €6012 Painted environment II (79x99cm-31x39in) s. col laser print. 31-Oct-3 Sotheby's, New York #602/R
£4133 $7605 €6200 Mist (73x63cm-29x25in) s.i.d.1973 col lithograph card one of 98. 12-Jun-4 Villa Grisebach, Berlin #396/R est:5000-7000
£4200 $6972 €6132 Flowers made of paper and black (99x95cm-39x37in) s.i.d.1971 num.40/50 lithograph. 6-Oct-3 Sotheby's, London #241/R est:3000-4000
£4294 $7000 €6269 Celia - musing (103x74cm-41x29in) s.d.1979 num.97/100 lithograph on Japon. 24-Sep-3 Christie's, Rockefeller NY #255/R est:3000-4000
£4412 $7500 €6442 Vases in the Louvre (74x74cm-29x29in) s. col etching. 31-Oct-3 Sotheby's, New York #581/R
£4412 $7500 €6442 Potted daffodils (113x76cm-44x30in) s.d.1980 lithograph. 4-Nov-3 Christie's, Rockefeller NY #248/R est:8000-12000
£4412 $7500 €6442 Number one chair (56x47cm-22x19in) s.d.1985-6 lithograph etching. 4-Nov-3 Christie's, Rockefeller NY #263/R est:5000-7000
£4706 $8000 €6871 Water (74x88cm-29x35in) s. col lithograph. 31-Oct-3 Sotheby's, New York #584/R
£4800 $8736 €7008 Rue de Seine (53x43cm-21x17in) d.1972 etching. 30-Jun-4 Christie's, London #222/R est:4000-6000
£5000 $8300 €7300 Wind (80x60cm-31x24in) s.i.d.1973 num.77/98 col lithograph. 6-Oct-3 Sotheby's, London #246/R est:3000-4000
£5000 $8500 €7300 Arrival (15x20cm-6x8in) etching aquatint. 30-Oct-3 Christie's, Kensington #74/R est:6000-8000
£5000 $8500 €7300 Wave (68x96cm-27x38in) s. col lithograph. 31-Oct-3 Sotheby's, New York #599/R
£5000 $9150 €7300 Godetia (59x42cm-23x17in) s.d.1973 num.50/100 col etching aquatint. 3-Jun-4 Christie's, Kensington #389/R est:3500-4000
£5588 $9500 €8158 Celia smoking (99x72cm-39x28in) s.i.d.1973 lithograph. 4-Nov-3 Christie's, Rockefeller NY #244/R est:8000-12000
£5882 $10000 €8588 Still life with book (69x55cm-27x22in) s. col lithograph. 31-Oct-3 Sotheby's, New York #578/R
£5882 $10000 €8588 Black tulips (112x76cm-44x30in) s.d.1980 lithograph. 4-Nov-3 Christie's, Rockefeller NY #247/R est:12000-15000
£7059 $12000 €10306 Water (75x88cm-30x35in) s. col lithograph. 31-Oct-3 Sotheby's, New York #603/R

£7345	$13000	€10724	An image of Gregory (221x107cm-87x42in) s.d.1984-85 num.49/75 lithograph diptych. 30-Apr-4 Sotheby's, New York #353/R est:12000-15000
£8200	$14924	€11972	Contrejour in the French style (75x74cm-30x29in) s.num.1/75 col etching aquatint. 1-Jul-4 Sotheby's, London #399/R est:6000-8000
£8235	$14000	€12023	Water (66x88cm-26x35in) s. col lithograph. 31-Oct-3 Sotheby's, New York #582/R
£8500	$14195	€12410	Celia with green hat 1985 (75x56cm-30x22in) s.num.36/98 lithograph prov.exhib. 14-Oct-3 Sotheby's, London #522/R est:6000-8000
£9000	$15480	€13140	Celia (89x72cm-35x28in) s.i.d.73 lithograph. 4-Dec-3 Sotheby's, London #241/R est:5000-7000
£9000	$16380	€13140	Coloured flowers made of paper and ink (99x95cm-39x37in) s.i.d.1971 col lithograph. 1-Jul-4 Sotheby's, London #403/R est:8000-12000
£9040	$16000	€13198	Celia elegant (102x73cm-40x29in) s.d.1979 num.53/100 lithograph. 28-Apr-4 Christie's, Rockefeller NY #300/R est:4000-6000
£9040	$16000	€13198	Big Celia print no 2 (134x147cm-53x58in) s.d.81 num.67/100 lithograph. 28-Apr-4 Christie's, Rockefeller NY #301/R est:10000-15000
£9412	$16000	€13742	Celia in armchair (102x122cm-40x48in) s.d.1980-1 lithograph. 4-Nov-3 Christie's, Rockefeller NY #250/R est:8000-12000
£9605	$17000	€14023	Celia with green plant (75x100cm-30x39in) s.d.1981 num.52/90 col lithograph. 30-Apr-4 Sotheby's, New York #351/R est:10000-15000
£10000	$16600	€14600	Illustrations for poems (59x42cm-23x17in) s.d.66 etching aquatint twelve album. 6-Oct-3 Sotheby's, London #233/R est:5000-7000
£10000	$17000	€14600	Water (67x87cm-26x34in) s.d.1978-80 lithograph. 4-Nov-3 Christie's, Rockefeller NY #246/R est:12000-15000
£10000	$17000	€14600	View of Hotel Well I (80x105cm-31x41in) s.d.1984-85 col lithograph. 4-Nov-3 Christie's, Rockefeller NY #258/R est:18000-22000
£10000	$18200	€14600	Blue guitar (53x46cm-21x18in) s.num.APXXXII/XXXV etching aquatint portfolio of 20. 30-Jun-4 Christie's, London #227/R est:12000-16000
£10169	$18000	€14847	Water made of lines, crayon and two blue washes without green wash (76x87cm-30x34in) s.d.1978-80 num.27/36 col lithograph. 30-Apr-4 Sotheby's, New York #357/R est:12000-15000
£10588	$18000	€15458	Pembroke studio interior (103x126cm-41x50in) s.d.87 col lithograph. 4-Nov-3 Christie's, Rockefeller NY #256/R est:15000-20000
£12429	$22000	€18146	Tyler dining room (74x95cm-29x37in) s.d.84 num.7/98 col lithograph. 28-Apr-4 Christie's, Rockefeller NY #303/R est:14000-18000
£14706	$25000	€21471	Hotel Acatlan (73x193cm-29x76in) s. col lithograph. 31-Oct-3 Sotheby's, New York #590/R
£16176	$27500	€23617	Hotel Acatlan (73x188cm-29x74in) s. col lithograph. 31-Oct-3 Sotheby's, New York #591/R
£17647	$30000	€25765	View of Hotel Well III (145x117cm-57x46in) s.d.1984-5 col lithograph. 4-Nov-3 Christie's, Rockefeller NY #259/R est:35000-45000
£18824	$32000	€27483	Afternoon swimming (79x101cm-31x40in) s.d.79 col lithograph. 4-Nov-3 Christie's, Rockefeller NY #249/R est:40000-50000
£18824	$32000	€27483	Hotel Acatlan (73x189cm-29x74in) s.d.84-5 col lithograph. 4-Nov-3 Christie's, Rockefeller NY #257/R est:22000-28000
£20904	$37000	€30520	Amaryllis in vase (127x92cm-50x36in) s.d.1985 num.11/80 col lithograph. 30-Apr-4 Sotheby's, New York #352/R est:35000-45000
£21469	$38000	€31345	Amaryllis in vase (117x83cm-46x33in) s.d.84 num.35/80 col lithograph. 28-Apr-4 Christie's, Rockefeller NY #302/R est:25000-35000
£22059	$37500	€32206	Walking past chairs (72x116cm-28x46in) s. col lithograph. 31-Oct-3 Sotheby's, New York #594/R
£24706	$42000	€36071	Amaryllis in vase (127x91cm-50x36in) s.d.84 col lithograph. 4-Nov-3 Christie's, Rockefeller NY #254/R est:25000-35000
£26471	$45000	€38648	Amaryllis in vase (127x92cm-50x36in) s. col lithograph. 31-Oct-3 Sotheby's, New York #587/R
£27000	$44820	€39420	Illustrations for fairy tales from the Brothers Grimm (48x66cm-19x26in) s.num.40/100 etching thirty-nine portfolio. 6-Oct-3 Sotheby's, London #240/R est:18000-22000
£32353	$55000	€47235	Rake's progress (50x63cm-20x25in) s.i. etching aquatint set of 16. 4-Nov-3 Christie's, Rockefeller NY #243/R est:40000-50000
£35294	$60000	€51529	Image of Celia (166x122cm-65x48in) s. col lithograph screenprint. 31-Oct-3 Sotheby's, New York #592/R
£35294	$60000	€51529	Image of Celia (174x122cm-69x48in) s.d.1984-86 col lithograph screenprint. 4-Nov-3 Christie's, Rockefeller NY #261/R est:70000-90000

Works on paper

£380	$703	€555	Three brothers (20x19cm-8x7in) i. pencil. 13-Jul-4 Bonhams, Knightsbridge #80
£930	$1600	€1358	Head of Patrick Proctor (18x20cm-7x8in) i. ink prov. 3-Dec-3 Doyle, New York #61/R est:1000-1500
£1500	$2550	€2190	Portrait of Richard Buckle (26x20cm-10x8in) s.d.VII.63 verso pencil prov. 18-Nov-3 Bonhams, Knightsbridge #97/R est:1200-1800
£2568	$4750	€3749	My mother sleeping, Los Angeles, December 1992 (57x57cm-22x22in) s.i. photocollage cardboard exec 1982 prov. 12-Feb-4 Sotheby's, New York #326/R est:5000-7000
£4121	$7500	€6017	Tea time Los Angeles (71x91cm-28x36in) s.i.d.April 16th 1983 photocollage on cardboard. 29-Jun-4 Sotheby's, New York #549/R est:6000-8000
£4651	$8000	€6790	Chapter six (25x32cm-10x13in) init.d.62 pencil col chk double-sided prov. 3-Dec-3 Doyle, New York #59/R est:9000-12000
£6000	$10320	€8760	Beiruit (31x24cm-12x9in) s.i.d.66 pen black ink. 3-Dec-3 Christie's, Kensington #770/R est:6000-8000
£6000	$10860	€8760	Gregory and Shinro on the train to Nara (95x105cm-37x41in) s.i.d.1983 num.8 photo-montage mounted on board prov.lit. 1-Apr-4 Christie's, Kensington #308/R est:4000-6000
£7000	$11690	€10220	Study for floor and teapot (48x61cm-19x24in) init.d.79 pencil wax crayon prov. 16-Oct-3 Christie's, Kensington #690/R est:10000-15000
£7200	$12240	€10512	Paul (43x34cm-17x13in) init.i.d.March 1971 pen ink. 1-Dec-3 David Duggleby, Scarborough #238/R est:4000-6000
£9441	$16049	€13500	Russ writing postcard in Venice (32x25cm-13x10in) init.i. Chinese ink exec.1966 exhib. 20-Nov-3 Finarte Semenzato, Milan #230/R est:11000-12000
£11377	$19000	€16610	Mother in check dress, Wales (43x36cm-17x14in) init.i.d.77 pen ink prov.exhib. 13-Nov-3 Sotheby's, New York #200/R est:20000-30000
£11656	$19000	€17018	Lawn sprays (35x42cm-14x17in) init.i.d.67 col crayon graphite prov. 23-Sep-3 Christie's, Rockefeller NY #98/R est:6000-8000
£11976	$20000	€17485	Kieth St. Mawes (25x32cm-10x13in) init.i.d.1966 ink. 12-Nov-3 Christie's, Rockefeller NY #392/R est:20000-30000
£12000	$21840	€17520	Ossie Clark, Powis Terrace, London (42x35cm-17x14in) init.i.d.Jan 68 pencil prov. 30-Jun-4 Christie's, Kensington #115/R est:15000-20000
£16000	$29120	€23360	Peter Langham in his kitchen at Odids (43x35cm-17x14in) init.d.1969 ink prov. 5-Feb-4 Christie's, London #173/R est:15000-20000
£17877	$32000	€26100	Chair in Henry's House (43x35cm-17x14in) s.i.d.1976 ink prov. 12-May-4 Christie's, Rockefeller NY #162/R est:25000-35000
£32000	$58880	€46720	Celia sleeping (35x43cm-14x17in) i. indis d.1972 ink prov.exhib. 25-Jun-4 Christie's, London #101/R est:15000-20000
£36000	$66240	€52560	My room - my window (43x35cm-17x14in) init.d.73 col cryons pencil prov. 25-Jun-4 Christie's, London #102/R est:20000-30000
£75000	$138000	€109500	Study of Louvre window, no.1 (100x73cm-39x29in) init.d. col pencil prov.exhib.lit. 23-Jun-4 Sotheby's, London #12/R est:60000-80000
£80000	$147200	€116800	Gregory in the pool (81x127cm-32x50in) init.d.78 hand pressed col pulp prov.lit. 25-Jun-4 Christie's, London #203/R est:55000-75000

HOD, Edmund (fl.1871-1886) Austrian

£350	$594	€500	Am Cheimsee (20x46cm-8x18in) s.i.d.1882 verso. 27-Nov-3 Dorotheum, Linz #424/R
£625	$1000	€913	Figure on forest path (43x33cm-17x13in) s.d.1880. 20-Sep-3 Sloans & Kenyon, Bethesda #141/R est:1250-1750

HODE, Pierre (1889-1942) French

£1608	$2734	€2300	Place a Montmartre (50x61cm-20x24in) s. 28-Nov-3 Drouot Estimations, Paris #194 est:2200-2500
£1678	$3121	€2500	Nature morte au violon (54x65cm-21x26in) s. 2-Mar-4 Artcurial Briest, Paris #218 est:1500-2000
£2083	$3479	€3000	Paris, Notre-Dame vue des quais (54x65cm-21x26in) s. 21-Oct-3 Artcurial Briest, Paris #196/R est:3000-3500
£4000	$7360	€6000	Nature morte au chapeau haut de forme (61x50cm-24x20in) s. s.d.1921 verso prov. 11-Jun-4 Pierre Berge, Paris #200 est:6000-8000
£15493	$27113	€22000	Bateaux a quai (54x65cm-21x26in) 16-Dec-3 Claude Aguttes, Neuilly #17/R est:10000-15000

HODEL, Ernst (elder) (1852-1902) Swiss

£294	$500	€429	Cattle (46x38cm-18x15in) s. 28-Nov-3 Zofingen, Switzerland #3023 (S.FR 650)

HODEL, Ernst (younger) (1881-1955) Swiss

£281	$477	€410	Hexenhaus Engelberg (56x66cm-22x26in) s. 19-Nov-3 Fischer, Luzern #2139/R (S.FR 620)
£339	$577	€495	Mountain stream in spring (41x50cm-16x20in) s. board. 19-Nov-3 Fischer, Luzern #2135/R (S.FR 750)
£780	$1302	€1131	Two young animals in shadow of tree (64x74cm-25x29in) s. 23-Jun-3 Philippe Schuler, Zurich #3395/R (S.FR 1700)
£860	$1462	€1256	Summer evening (73x94cm-29x37in) s. 19-Nov-3 Fischer, Luzern #2136/R (S.FR 1900)
£1310	$2345	€1913	Cows drinking (60x80cm-24x31in) s. 26-May-4 Sotheby's, Zurich #12/R est:3000-5000 (S.FR 3000)

HODGDON, Sylvester Phelps (1830-1906) American

£1956	$3500	€2856	Path to the coast (42x67cm-17x26in) s.d.1873. 14-May-4 Skinner, Boston #67/R est:1500-3000

HODGE, Simon Prince (1903-1973) British

Works on paper

£300	$546	€438	St Mark's Square in the rain (44x65cm-17x26in) s. W/C. 1-Jul-4 Christie's, Kensington #313/R

HODGE, Thomas (fl.1880-1895) British

Works on paper

£1250	$2288	€1825	The slogger, portrait of Robert Clark (11x9cm-4x4in) i. pencil card. 12-Jul-4 Lyon & Turnbull, Edinburgh #418/R est:300-500
£1400	$2562	€2044	The diver, Portrait of Freddie Tait, Step Rock, St Andrews (24x16cm-9x6in) i. pencil W/C. 12-Jul-4 Lyon & Turnbull, Edinburgh #423/R est:1000-1500

HODGES, Charles Howard (1764-1837) British

Works on paper

£1275	$2346	€1900	Portrait of Anna Petronella Gerlings, wife of Mr Jacob Crommelin (25x22cm-10x9in) pastel oval. 29-Mar-4 Glerum, Amsterdam #26 est:800-1200
£1544	$2840	€2300	Portrait of Johanna Catharina Paneras Clifford (25x22cm-10x9in) pastel oval. 29-Mar-4 Glerum, Amsterdam #28 est:800-1200
£1678	$3087	€2500	Portrait of Herman Arnoldus Crommelin (25x22cm-10x9in) pastel oval. 29-Mar-4 Glerum, Amsterdam #27 est:800-1200

HODGES, Christopher (1954-) Australian

£370	$670	€540	Victims (174x111cm-69x44in) s.d.1984 verso. 30-Mar-4 Lawson Menzies, Sydney #188 est:500-800 (A.D 900)

HODGES, J E (19th C) British

Works on paper

£1200	$1884	€1740	Still lives of tulips, peonies and other flowers in an urn on a ledge (51x37cm-20x15in) s.i. pencil bodycol pair prov. 28-Aug-3 Christie's, Kensington #450/R est:500-700

HODGES, Jim (1957-) American

Sculpture

£98802	$165000	€144251	Trembling and Joy. metal chains exec 1994 prov. 12-Nov-3 Christie's, Rockefeller NY #507/R est:35000-45000

Works on paper

£5215	$8500	€7614	Blue love (91x81cm-36x32in) s.i.d.1992 verso ink paper napkins 21 prov.exhib. 23-Sep-3 Christie's, Rockefeller NY #72/R est:8000-12000

HODGES, William (1744-1797) British

£20000	$32600	€29200	View of the Palace of Nawab Asaf-ud-daulah at Lucknow (43x53cm-17x21in) prov.exhib.lit. 24-Sep-3 Christie's, London #3/R est:7000-10000
£24000	$39120	€35040	View of the Fort of Pateeta, near Chunar (61x102cm-24x40in) prov.exhib.lit. 24-Sep-3 Christie's, London #1/R est:15000-20000
£28000	$45640	€40880	View of the north end of the fort of Chunar Gur (64x76cm-25x30in) prov.exhib.lit. 24-Sep-3 Christie's, London #2/R est:15000-20000

HODGINS, Robert (1920-) South African

£661 $1182 €965 Friends Head IV (20x14cm-8x6in) s.d.01/02 i.verso canvas on board. 31-May-4 Stephan Welz, Johannesburg #565 (SA.R 8000)
£1486 $2661 €2170 Fruit spectrum (81x95cm-32x37in) init.d.74 i.verso board. 31-May-4 Stephan Welz, Johannesburg #523/R est:20000-30000 (SA.R 18000)
£1897 $3167 €2770 Five faces (180x45cm-71x18in) s.d.1993/1998 i.verso board. 20-Oct-3 Stephan Welz, Johannesburg #387/R est:25000-35000 (SA.R 22000)
£2414 $4031 €3524 Boy between banners (90x90cm-35x35in) s. i.d.1999/2001 verso. 20-Oct-3 Stephan Welz, Johannesburg #390/R est:30000-40000 (SA.R 28000)
£6606 $11825 €9645 J'accuse (90x120cm-35x47in) s.i.d.1995/6 verso. 31-May-4 Stephan Welz, Johannesburg #596/R est:50000-80000 (SA.R 80000)

HODGKIN, Eliot (1905-1987) British

£600 $960 €870 Portrait of Stanley Bud Farmiloe with the Acropolis beyond (46x35cm-18x14in) s.d.39. 16-Sep-3 Bonhams, Knightsbridge #65/R
£750 $1365 €1095 Landscape at Villias (33x22cm-13x9in) s.d.54 board. 15-Jun-4 Bonhams, New Bond Street #72/R
£1100 $2002 €1606 Pink and white May (11x11cm-4x4in) s.d.17/V/58 tempera board prov. 15-Jun-4 Bonhams, New Bond Street #69/R est:1200-1800
£3593 $6000 €5246 Untitled (25x29cm-10x11in) s.d.59 tempera masonite. 20-Oct-3 Sotheby's, New York #117/R est:6000-8000
£4250 $7608 €6205 Two brioche on a paper bag (18x30cm-7x12in) s.d.14.I.67 tempera. 5-May-4 John Nicholson, Haslemere #459/R est:6000-8000
£4250 $7608 €6205 Quinces on a pewter dish (33x61cm-13x24in) s.d.16.II.63 tempera prov. 5-May-4 John Nicholson, Haslemere #461/R est:6000-8000
£6500 $11180 €9490 April (7x25cm-3x10in) s.i.d.54 tempera on board prov. 2-Dec-3 Bonhams, New Bond Street #66/R est:5000-7000
£7000 $12950 €10220 Autumn leaves (16x16cm-6x6in) s.d.6.IX.69 tempera. 11-Mar-4 Christie's, Kensington #122/R est:7000-10000
£7000 $12530 €10220 Red berries in a punnet (13x18cm-5x7in) s.d.28.VII.74 tempera. 5-May-4 John Nicholson, Haslemere #457/R est:6000-8000
£7000 $12530 €10220 Corms, three different angles of corms (10x20cm-4x8in) s.d.2.I.67 tempera. 5-May-4 John Nicholson, Haslemere #458/R est:6000-8000
£7500 $12900 €10950 December (8x25cm-3x10in) s.i.d.53 tempera on board prov. 2-Dec-3 Bonhams, New Bond Street #67/R est:5000-7000
£7500 $12900 €10950 Penny Bun (11x13cm-4x5in) init. canvas on board. 3-Dec-3 Sotheby's, London #46/R est:2000-3000
£7500 $13425 €10950 Two lemons, one partly peeled on a pewter dish (18x30cm-7x12in) s.d.13.IX.72 tempera. 5-May-4 John Nicholson, Haslemere #460/R est:6000-8000
£8000 $13760 €11680 Ingredients for plum pudding (31x27cm-12x11in) s.d.30 III 61 tempera on board. 2-Dec-3 Bonhams, New Bond Street #68/R est:8000-12000
£14000 $25620 €20440 La famille brioche (25x29cm-10x11in) s.d.2.1.59 s.i.verso tempera on board prov. 4-Jun-4 Christie's, London #137/R est:7000-10000

Works on paper

£280 $456 €409 Landscape with buildings (30x40cm-12x16in) s. W/C gouache prov. 24-Sep-3 Dreweatt Neate, Newbury #79
£4000 $6920 €5840 Autumn leaves (15x15cm-6x6in) s.d.1969 W/C. 11-Dec-3 Bruton Knowles, Cheltenham #70 est:200-300

HODGKIN, Howard (1932-) British

£17000 $29240 €24820 Chopin etudes opus 10 and 25 (40x33cm-16x13in) board. 2-Dec-3 Bonhams, New Bond Street #195/R est:10000-15000
£68000 $123080 €99280 Portrait of Mr and Mrs Kasmin (106x127cm-42x50in) s.verso i.d.1964-66 stretcher. 1-Apr-4 Christie's, Kensington #300/R est:25000-35000
£80000 $145600 €116800 After dinner at Smith Square (79x104cm-31x41in) board painted 1980-81 prov.exhib.lit. 5-Feb-4 Sotheby's, London #29/R est:80000-120000

Prints

£2000 $3640 €2920 David Pool (64x80cm-25x31in) init.d.1985 hand col etching aquatint. 1-Jul-4 Sotheby's, London #337/R est:2500-3500
£2200 $3740 €3212 Lotus (72x92cm-28x36in) s.d.1980 col screenprint. 30-Oct-3 Christie's, Kensington #87/R est:1500-2000
£2200 $4026 €3212 Lotus (112x140cm-44x55in) s.d.1980 num.55/100 col screenprint. 3-Jun-4 Christie's, Kensington #407/R est:2000-3000
£2486 $4400 €3630 Here we are in Croydon (57x75cm-22x30in) s.d.1979 num.3/100 hand col black W/C gouache lithograph. 28-Apr-4 Christie's, Rockefeller NY #308/R est:2500-3500
£2510 $4544 €3665 Monsoon (106x134cm-42x53in) init.d.1987 num.33/83 lithograph. 1-Apr-4 Heffel, Vancouver #55/R est:2000-3000 (C.D 6000)
£2586 $4319 €3776 For Bernard Jacobson (105x151cm-41x59in) s.d.79 num80/80 col lithograph. 20-Oct-3 Stephan Welz, Johannesburg #227/R est:30000-40000 (SA.R 30000)
£3000 $5160 €4380 Moonlight (112x140cm-44x55in) init.d.1980 num.81/100 col lithograph. 4-Dec-3 Sotheby's, London #244/R est:3000-4000
£3107 $5500 €4536 For Bernard Jacobson (105x150cm-41x59in) s.d.1979 col hand col gouache crayon lithograph two sheets. 28-Apr-4 Christie's, Rockefeller NY #307/R est:5000-7000
£4351 $7832 €6352 Palm and windows (149x120cm-59x47in) s.num.15/55 col.etching carborundum hand col exec.c.1990-91. 26-Apr-4 Bukowskis, Stockholm #354/R est:60000-70000 (S.KR 60000)
£4412 $7500 €6442 For Bernard Jacobson (105x150cm-41x59in) s. col lithograph. 31-Oct-3 Sotheby's, New York #604/R

Works on paper

£8000 $14720 €11680 Palm (45x53cm-18x21in) s.i.d.1978 verso textile dye handmade paper prov.exhib.lit. 24-Jun-4 Sotheby's, Olympia #576/R est:4000-6000

HODGKINS, Frances (1869-1947) New Zealander

Works on paper

£1128 $1917 €1647 European river scene (24x24cm-9x9in) W/C prov. 26-Nov-3 Dunbar Sloane, Wellington #71/R est:2000-4000 (NZ.D 3000)
£1410 $2397 €2059 Ladies in the shade (41x32cm-16x13in) W/C. 26-Nov-3 Dunbar Sloane, Wellington #70/R est:3000-5000 (NZ.D 3750)
£2400 $3744 €3480 Crossroads (25x33cm-10x13in) s.d.1935 W/C. 20-Oct-2 Desmond Judd, Cranbrook #847
£2536 $4083 €3703 Woolsheds near Oamaru (18x24cm-7x9in) init. W/C prov. 20-Aug-3 Dunbar Sloane, Auckland #47/R est:10000-15000 (NZ.D 7000)
£3000 $4680 €4350 Farm pond Denham (36x56cm-14x22in) s.d.1943 W/C dr. 20-Oct-2 Desmond Judd, Cranbrook #821
£4511 $7669 €6586 Market, Tangier (17x11cm-7x4in) s.d.1903 W/C. 27-Nov-3 International Art Centre, Auckland #81/R est:14000-20000 (NZ.D 12000)
£7624 $14105 €11131 Still life with hydrangea's, 1930 (50x53cm-20x21in) s.i. gouache. 13-Jul-4 Watson's, Christchurch #20/R est:25000-40000 (NZ.D 21500)
£8550 $14706 €12483 Still life with eggs in bowl (53x41cm-21x16in) s. W/C exec c.1929 prov. 3-Dec-3 Dunbar Sloane, Auckland #24/R est:30000-50000 (NZ.D 23000)
£9441 $17182 €13784 Picnic (28x28cm-11x11in) s. W/C prov. 29-Jun-4 Peter Webb, Auckland #72/R est:20000-30000 (NZ.D 27000)
£13091 $20553 €18982 French street scene, south of France (52x44cm-20x17in) s. W/C pencil exec.c.1928. 27-Aug-3 Dunbar Sloane, Wellington #36/R est:45000-55000 (NZ.D 36000)
£18214 $33514 €26592 Washerwomen, Morrocco (23x20cm-9x8in) s.d.1902 W/C prov. 25-Mar-4 International Art Centre, Auckland #75/R est:35000-45000 (NZ.D 51000)
£27778 $44167 €40556 Picnic (42x52cm-17x20in) s. W/C executed 1920. 1-May-3 Dunbar Sloane, Wellington #35/R est:80000-110000 (NZ.D 80000)
£30797 $49891 €44656 In Hyde Park (27x18cm-11x7in) s.d.1901 W/C exhib. 31-Jul-3 International Art Centre, Auckland #33/R est:65000-85000 (NZ.D 85000)

HODGKINS, Frances and KEAN, Cissie (19/20th C) New Zealander/British

Works on paper

£1736 $2760 €2535 Chipping Campden Village scene (36x32cm-14x13in) W/C prov. 1-May-3 Dunbar Sloane, Wellington #50/R est:3000-6000 (NZ.D 5000)

HODGKINS, William Matthew (1833-1898) New Zealander

Works on paper

£364 $571 €528 Pine trees waving high (33x22cm-13x9in) init.i. W/C. 27-Aug-3 Dunbar Sloane, Wellington #291 (NZ.D 1000)
£940 $1598 €1372 Valley gloom and mountain glory, Hollyford Valley (58x37cm-23x15in) s. W/C. 27-Nov-3 International Art Centre, Auckland #90/R (NZ.D 2500)
£1573 $2864 €2297 Beach scene with boat wreck (35x62cm-14x24in) s. W/C. 29-Jun-4 Peter Webb, Auckland #134/R est:6000-8000 (NZ.D 4500)

HODGKINSON, Alexander (20th C) British

£380 $608 €555 Still life with gas lamp (102x71cm-40x28in) board. 16-Sep-3 Bonhams, Knightsbridge #110/R

HODGKINSON, Frank (1919-2001) Australian

£254 $475 €381 Billy goat (50x67cm-20x26in) s. oil pastel wash. 20-Jul-4 Goodman, Sydney #129/R (A.D 650)
£311 $570 €467 Running emus. oil paper. 3-Jun-4 Joel, Victoria #167 (A.D 800)
£311 $520 €467 Deaf adder track (11x21cm-4x8in) s. board. 27-Oct-3 Goodman, Sydney #70/R (A.D 750)
£661 $1170 €965 Untitled, landscape (83x101cm-33x40in) s.d.72 prov. 3-May-4 Christie's, Melbourne #237 (A.D 1600)
£1570 $2779 €2292 Abstract (100x87cm-39x34in) s.d.83 prov. 3-May-4 Christie's, Melbourne #223 est:1500-2500 (A.D 3800)
£2344 $4383 €3516 Lake Eyre reflections (181x152cm-71x60in) s. s.i.verso. 20-Jul-4 Goodman, Sydney #67/R est:8000-12000 (A.D 6000)

Works on paper

£284 $446 €412 Via Dei Calzaidi (28x38cm-11x15in) s.i.d.96 W/C. 27-Aug-3 Christie's, Sydney #722 (A.D 700)
£325 $511 €471 Yellow waters, Kakadu (55x74cm-22x29in) s.i.d.79 gouache feathers exhib. 26-Aug-3 Christie's, Sydney #362 (A.D 800)
£649 $1181 €948 After the wet (55x74cm-22x29in) s.i.d.80 W/C synthetic polymer pastel. 16-Jun-4 Deutscher-Menzies, Melbourne #607/R est:1000-2000 (A.D 1700)
£1311 $2125 €1914 Ganderbal festival (64x103cm-25x41in) s.i.d.88 mixed media. 30-Jul-3 Goodman, Sydney #64/R est:800-1200 (A.D 3200)
£1660 $2772 €2490 Symbol man and Olga Wuhl Wuhl (57x75cm-22x30in) s.d.83 mixed media. 27-Oct-3 Goodman, Sydney #75/R est:1500-2500 (A.D 4000)
£2439 $3829 €3537 Kakadu, last of the wet (54x74cm-21x29in) s.d.89 s.i.d.verso W/C gouache prov.exhib.lit. 27-Aug-3 Christie's, Sydney #756 est:600-1000 (A.D 6000)

HODGSON, Charles (1769-1825) British

£750 $1343 €1095 Figures in a church interior (38x30cm-15x12in) panel. 22-Mar-4 Bonhams & Brooks, Norfolk #225/R

HODGSON, David (1798-1864) British

£360 $601 €526 Old Norwich (44x60cm-17x24in) 22-Oct-3 Cheffins, Cambridge #515/R
£1050 $1659 €1523 Debris of the old fish market, Norwich (21x26cm-8x10in) 3-Sep-3 Bonhams, Bury St Edmunds #437/R est:600-1000

HODGSON, George (1847-1921) British

£280 $476 €409 Woodcutter by a rustic water mill (37x55cm-15x22in) s. board. 30-Oct-3 Bracketts, Tunbridge Wells #1047/R

Works on paper

£347 $552 €507 Portrait of a child (28x22cm-11x9in) s.d.1879 W/C. 1-May-3 Dunbar Sloane, Wellington #706/R est:200-500 (NZ.D 1000)
£400 $748 €584 Man cutting wood beside a watermill with a stream in the foreground (36x53cm-14x21in) s. pencil W/C. 22-Jul-4 Tennants, Leyburn #749
£1200 $2208 €1752 Valley on the Teme and Castle at Ludlow (66x100cm-26x39in) s. W/C. 8-Jun-4 Bonhams, Knightsbridge #34/R est:1200-1500

HODGSON, John Evan (1831-1895) British

£805 $1506 €1200 English countryside (50x67cm-20x26in) s.d.1870. 26-Feb-4 Cambi, Genoa #552/R

HODGSON, William Scott (1864-?) British

£1350 $2147 €1958 Fishing boats leaving Whitby Harbour (70x90cm-28x35in) s. 9-Sep-3 David Duggleby, Scarborough #395/R est:800-1200

HODICKE, Karl Horst (1938-) German

£3571 $6500 €5214 Jaguar (170x230cm-67x91in) s.i.d.83 verso prov. 29-Jun-4 Sotheby's, New York #553/R est:5000-7000
£8099 $14011 €11500 Composition with figure and snakes (170x115cm-67x45in) s.i.d.83 acrylic cotton. 13-Dec-3 Lempertz, Koln #153/R est:5000-7000

HODIENER, Hugo (1886-c.1935) German
£414 $757 €600 Rocky slope with cave (69x59cm-27x23in) s. tempera board prov. 27-Jan-4 Dorotheum, Vienna #72/R
£1172 $2146 €1700 Dachstein (70x62cm-28x24in) s. tempera board prov. 27-Jan-4 Dorotheum, Vienna #70/R est:1200-1600
£1197 $2095 €1700 The Matterhorn (72x63cm-28x25in) s. tempera board prov. 19-Dec-3 Dorotheum, Vienna #79/R est:1400-2000
£1690 $2958 €2400 Das Breitham (114x102cm-45x40in) i.verso oil tempera. 19-Dec-3 Dorotheum, Vienna #81/R est:1600-2200

HODINA, Hugo (1886-?) Austrian
£979 $1684 €1400 Cimone de la Pala (120x108cm-47x43in) s.d.1904. 4-Dec-3 Dorotheum, Graz #15/R
£993 $1549 €1450 Mountains with figures (100x120cm-39x47in) s. 10-Apr-3 Weidler, Nurnberg #7090

HODLER, Ferdinand (1853-1918) Swiss
£2477 $4261 €3616 Souvenir landscape of Lake Thun (43x30cm-17x12in) i. verso board exhib. lit. 2-Dec-3 Koller, Zurich #3003/R est:7000-9000 (S.FR 5500)
£35808 $65170 €52280 Glance into eternity (59x36cm-23x14in) s.d.1916 study of second figure prov.exhib.lit. 18-Jun-4 Kornfeld, Bern #59/R est:100000 (S.FR 82000)
£41485 $75502 €60568 Glance into eternity (59x36cm-23x14in) s. study exec c. 1915/16 prov.exhib.lit. 18-Jun-4 Kornfeld, Bern #61/R est:100000 (S.FR 95000)
£99548 $169231 €220000 Stream and tree (90x80cm-35x31in) s. painted 1910 lit. 25-Nov-3 Pierre Berge, Paris #17/R est:150000-200000
£239130 $437609 €349130 Thunersee as seen from Leissigen (55x46cm-22x18in) s. prov.lit. 7-Jun-4 Christie's, Zurich #63/R est:600000-800000 (S.FR 550000)
£403587 $657848 €589237 Lake Thun with Stockhorn (65x88cm-26x35in) s.d.1910 prov. 29-Sep-3 Christie's, Zurich #56/R est:1200000-1800000 (S.FR 900000)
£538117 $877130 €785651 Woman (170x85cm-67x33in) s. prov. 29-Sep-3 Christie's, Zurich #38/R est:1200000-1800000 (S.FR 1200000)
Prints
£2632 $4842 €3843 Holy hour (40x75cm-16x30in) s. num.81/100 photogravure. 23-Jun-4 Koller, Zurich #3249/R est:4000-6000 (S.FR 6000)
Works on paper
£500 $830 €725 Walking figure (40x22cm-16x9in) pencil. 13-Jun-3 Zofingen, Switzerland #2879 (S.FR 1100)
£655 $1192 €956 Portrait study of Valentine Gode-Darel (17x13cm-7x5in) i. Indian ink. 17-Jun-4 Kornfeld, Bern #428 est:1500 (S.FR 1500)
£679 $1154 €991 Untitled (31x18cm-12x7in) s. pencil. 25-Nov-3 Germann, Zurich #801 est:1200-1500 (S.FR 1500)
£696 $1273 €1016 Two studies of figures (24x15cm-9x6in) pencil two. 7-Jun-4 Christie's, Zurich #35/R est:1500-2500 (S.FR 1600)
£811 $1395 €1184 Looking into eternity (28x10cm-11x4in) i. pencil. 2-Dec-3 Koller, Zurich #3007/R est:1300-1800 (S.FR 1800)
£819 $1466 €1196 Study for The Holy Hour (35x20cm-14x8in) pencil squared paper. 14-May-4 Dobiaschofsky, Bern #57/R est:3000 (S.FR 1900)
£866 $1550 €1264 Woman's portrait (22x19cm-9x7in) pencil squared paper prov. 22-Mar-4 Philippe Schuler, Zurich #4174/R est:800-900 (S.FR 2000)
£881 $1498 €1286 Study for Jena (28x43cm-11x17in) Indian ink. 7-Nov-3 Dobiaschofsky, Bern #48/R (S.FR 2000)
£991 $1685 €1447 Two reclining women (28x41cm-11x16in) chl. 7-Nov-3 Dobiaschofsky, Bern #50/R (S.FR 2250)
£1131 $1957 €1651 Study of a figure view of infinity (40x22cm-16x9in) st.sig. pencil. 9-Dec-3 Sotheby's, Zurich #44/R est:2500-3500 (S.FR 2500)
£1397 $2501 €2040 Taking an oath (41x17cm-16x7in) s. pencil. 26-May-4 Sotheby's, Zurich #26/R est:2500-3000 (S.FR 3200)
£1397 $2543 €2040 Figure study (57x22cm-22x9in) carpenter's pencil. 17-Jun-4 Kornfeld, Bern #429 est:4000 (S.FR 3200)
£1659 $2970 €2422 Design for a warrior (31x23cm-12x9in) pencil col pencil ink. 26-May-4 Sotheby's, Zurich #25/R est:3000-5000 (S.FR 3800)
£1810 $3241 €2643 Figure study for unanimity (38x20cm-15x8in) s. pencil. 14-May-4 Dobiaschofsky, Bern #56/R est:3500 (S.FR 4200)
£2183 $3974 €3187 Composition sketch for 'Battle at Murten' (43x58cm-17x23in) chl. 17-Jun-4 Kornfeld, Bern #430 est:6000 (S.FR 5000)
£2620 $4690 €3825 Girl standing (36x23cm 14x9in) s. pencil exhib. 26-May-4 Sotheby's, Zurich #21/R est:6000-8000 (S.FR 6000)
£2620 $4690 €3825 Back view of male nude (34x19cm-13x7in) s. pencil ink. 26-May-4 Sotheby's, Zurich #22/R est:3000-5000 (S.FR 6000)
£3363 $5482 €4910 Portrait of Adrian Lachenal (47x41cm-19x16in) st.sig.i. pencil. 29-Sep-3 Christie's, Zurich #25/R est:2500-3500 (S.FR 7500)
£5000 $9150 €7300 Study of Die Wahrheit (29x28cm-11x11in) pencil prov. 7-Jun-4 Christie's, Zurich #38/R est:12000-15000 (S.FR 11500)
£7860 $14070 €11476 Woman sitting (42x24cm-17x9in) mono. pencil W/C prov. 26-May-4 Sotheby's, Zurich #24/R est:18000-25000 (S.FR 18000)
£8696 $15913 €12696 Study of Empfindung I (53x34cm-21x13in) ink prov. 7-Jun-4 Christie's, Zurich #46/R est:20000-25000 (S.FR 20000)
£10403 $19141 €15500 Female nude holding cloth over bust (35x21cm-14x8in) s. i. verso chk. 26-Mar-4 Venator & Hansten, Koln #1731/R est:1800
£11659 $19004 €17022 Study of woman (46x22cm-18x9in) i. verso brush over pencil prov. 29-Sep-3 Christie's, Zurich #39/R est:20000-25000 (S.FR 26000)
£14912 $27439 €21772 La Mere Royaume (59x30cm-23x12in) mono. ink wash W/C prov.lit. 23-Jun-4 Koller, Zurich #3044/R est:30000-40000 (S.FR 34000)
£47826 $87522 €69826 Berthe Hodler (35x26cm-14x10in) mono. pencil ink prov. 7-Jun-4 Christie's, Zurich #49/R est:30000-50000 (S.FR 110000)

HODSON, Samuel John (1836-1908) British
Works on paper
£450 $747 €657 Step of San Marco, Venice (52x37cm-20x15in) s. W/C. 1-Oct-3 Sotheby's, Olympia #51/R

HOEBER, Arthur (1854-1915) American
£1796 $3000 €2622 Summer landscape (36x58cm-14x23in) s. prov. 23-Oct-3 Shannon's, Milford #176/R est:2500-3500
£2035 $3500 €2971 Sail at sunset (50x75cm-20x30in) s. 3-Dec-3 Doyle, New York #181/R est:5000-7000
£2235 $4000 €3263 Berkshire Hills (41x51cm-16x20in) s. i.verso painted c.1904 prov. 26-May-4 Doyle, New York #77/R est:4000-6000
£5028 $9000 €7341 Quiet hour (51x76cm-20x30in) s. s.i.verso prov. 6-May-4 Shannon's, Milford #10/R est:8000-12000
£5714 $10000 €8342 Long Island landscape (53x43cm-21x17in) s.i. canvas on panel. 19-Dec-3 Sotheby's, New York #1129/R est:4000-6000
£6486 $12000 €9470 Shinnecock landscape (26x36cm-10x14in) s. 11-Mar-4 Christie's, Rockefeller NY #2/R est:4000-6000

HOECKE, Caspar van den (1595-1648) Flemish
£3642 $6629 €5500 L'enlevement de Prosperine (114x136cm-45x54in) 21-Jun-4 Tajan, Paris #55/R est:3000-5000

HOECKE, Caspar van den (attrib) (1595-1648) Flemish
£1500 $2700 €2190 Sibyl (103x76cm-41x30in) 23-Apr-4 Christie's, Kensington #25/R est:2000-3000
£21918 $37260 €32000 Adoration of the Magi (55x81cm-22x32in) panel. 4-Nov-3 Sotheby's, Amsterdam #47/R est:15000-20000

HOECKE, Caspar van den (circle) (1595-1648) Flemish
£117318 $210000 €171284 Esther before Ahasuerus (105x165cm-41x65in) panel lit. 18-Mar-4 Sotheby's, New York #244/R est:80000-100000

HOECKE, Jan van den (1611-1651) Flemish
£2897 $4837 €4200 Le serpent en cuivre (30x42cm-12x17in) copper. 17-Nov-3 Bernaerts, Antwerp #84/R est:1000-1500

HOECKE, Raymond van (?) Belgian?
£532 $888 €750 Still life with bottle and vegetable. s. 20-Oct-3 Bernaerts, Antwerp #183/R

HOEF, Abraham van der (fl.1613-1649) Dutch
£5000 $9150 €7300 Cavalry skirmish on a plain (48x63cm-19x25in) panel. 7-Jul-4 Bonhams, New Bond Street #2/R est:5000-8000

HOEFER, Wade (20th C) American
£706 $1200 €1031 Campus (91x91cm-36x36in) s.i.d.2000 oil on linen. 21-Nov-3 Swann Galleries, New York #89/R est:2000-3000

HOEFFLER, Adolf (1826-1898) German
£533 $976 €800 Niddabiegung with trees (18x30cm-7x12in) s. 5-Jun-4 Arnold, Frankfurt #605/R
£1389 $2264 €2000 Autumnal landscape with birch trees (5x46cm-2x18in) s. 25-Sep-3 Dr Fritz Nagel, Stuttgart #1354/R est:2900

HOEFNAGEL, Jacob (attrib) (1575-1630) Flemish
£38803 $69457 €56652 Portrait of Queen Maria Eleonora (25x20cm-10x8in) panel oval. 25-May-4 Bukowskis, Stockholm #400/R est:100000-125000 (S.KR 525000)

HOEGH-GULDBERG, Emmerik (1807-1881) Danish
£606 $951 €885 Sheep by an old mill (26x39cm-10x15in) init.d.1836 verso. 30-Aug-3 Rasmussen, Havnen #2094 (D.KR 6500)

HOEHME, Gerhard (1920-1990) German
£11000 $20130 €16500 Portinguez (96x68cm-38x27in) s.d.58 oil gouache resin paper collage prov.exhib. 4-Jun-4 Lempertz, Koln #197/R est:16000-18000
£20979 $35664 €30000 Genuine place - genuine yellow (100x100cm-39x39in) s.i.d.1957 verso oil plaster masonite prov.exhib.lit. 27-Nov-3 Lempertz, Koln #190/R est:32000
£45455 $78182 €65000 Paravent A (200x500cm-79x197in) s.d. acrylic prov. 5-Dec-3 Ketterer, Munich #332/R est:70000-90000
£45455 $78182 €65000 Paravent B (200x500cm-79x197in) s.d. acrylic prov. 5-Dec-3 Ketterer, Munich #334/R est:70000-90000
Works on paper
£400 $716 €600 Untitled (30x23cm-12x9in) s.d.85 W/C pencil. 15-May-4 Van Ham, Cologne #662/R
£559 $962 €800 Space - ear (36x26cm-14x10in) s.i.d. W/C pencil. 5-Dec-3 Ketterer, Munich #346/R
£1000 $1840 €1500 Small fire god (61x43cm-24x17in) s.d.80 s.i.d.1980 W/C. 12-Jun-4 Villa Grisebach, Berlin #742/R est:1800-2400
£1310 $2410 €1913 Untitled (62x48cm-24x19in) s.d.1962 W/C silkpaper on paper. 8-Jun-4 Germann, Zurich #109/R est:3500-4000 (S.FR 3000)
£1667 $2983 €2500 Untitled (40x50cm-16x20in) s.d. W/C pencil opaque white col chk double-sided prov. 14-May-4 Ketterer, Munich #280/R est:2400-2600

HOEK, Hans van (1947-) Dutch
£10490 $18042 €15000 Buddha with vase surrounded with flowers (130x170cm-51x67in) s.d.80-81 i.stretcher. 2-Dec-3 Sotheby's, Amsterdam #181/R est:15000-20000
Works on paper
£2000 $3680 €3000 Kruisiging I (105x74cm-41x29in) s. verso W/C blk chk prov. 8-Jun-4 Sotheby's, Amsterdam #298/R est:3000-3500

HOELZL, Andreas (18th C) German
£2500 $4325 €3650 Portraits of Josephus Casparus de Jaquemod and Maria Anna de Jaquemod (88x67cm-35x26in) pair. 12-Dec-3 Christie's, Kensington #128/R est:3000-5000

HOEN, Cornelis Peter (1814-1880) Dutch
£1224 $2192 €1800 Dutch landscape in winter (22x30cm-9x12in) s. panel. 17-Mar-4 Neumeister, Munich #485/R est:2000
£8000 $14400 €12000 Figures on the ice at dusk (41x54cm-16x21in) s.d.46 panel. 21-Apr-4 Christie's, Amsterdam #28/R est:5000-7000

HOENIGER, Paul (1865-?) German
£1399 $2336 €2000 Bridge at Baumwall, Hamburg (73x60cm-29x24in) s.d.05 i. stretcher. 28-Jun-3 Bolland & Marotz, Bremen #844/R est:2700

HOENIGSMANN, Rela (1865-?) German
£1088 $1948 €1600 Summer courtyard (52x36cm-20x14in) s.i.d.1892. 17-Mar-4 Neumeister, Munich #486/R est:1500

HOENTESCHEL, Georges (1855-1915) ?
Sculpture
£1643 $2744 €2350 Untitled. sandstone enamel six squares panel. 24-Jun-3 Millon & Associes, Paris #194/R est:2500-3000

HOEPFNER, Franz (19th C) German
£300 $552 €438 Extensive coastal landscape with encampment in the foreground (14x23cm-6x9in) s. panel. 8-Jun-4 Bonhams, Knightsbridge #293/R
£440 $814 €642 On the canal near Birmingham (30x46cm-12x18in) s. s.i.d.verso. 15-Jan-4 Christie's, Kensington #910/R
£560 $963 €818 Hay making on the River Glas, Ballanard (30x46cm-12x18in) s.d.90 i.verso. 5-Dec-3 Chrystals Auctions, Isle of Man #272
£1400 $2618 €2044 Figures on a coastal path before a cottage. Fisherfolk by a coastal cottage (46x61cm-18x24in) s. one d.1879 one d.1888 pair. 24-Feb-4 Bonhams, Knowle #69 est:800-1200

HOEPKER, Thomas (1936-) German?
Photographs
£2500 $4400 €3750 Muhammad Ali Chicago River Bridge (117x178cm-46x70in) gelatin silver print. 18-May-4 Bonhams, New Bond Street #439/R est:2500-3500
£4722 $8500 €6894 Muhammad Ali (38x28cm-15x11in) i.verso gelatin silver print. 24-Apr-4 Phillips, New York #74/R est:4000-6000

HOERLE, Heinrich (1895-1936) German
£10490 $17832 €15000 Still life of tulips (47x42cm-19x17in) s. prov. 26-Nov-3 Lempertz, Koln #722/R est:15000-20000
£62937 $106993 €90000 Couple (49x57cm-19x22in) s.i.d.1931/9 panel prov.exhib. 26-Nov-3 Lempertz, Koln #721/R est:35000-45000
Works on paper
£2400 $4296 €3600 Man in wood - self portrait standing (19x9cm-7x4in) pencil. 15-May-4 Van Ham, Cologne #665/R est:3500
£4615 $7846 €6600 Double portrait (22x21cm-9x8in) s.mono.d.1923/9 W/C Indian ink pencil board prov. 26-Nov-3 Lempertz, Koln #723/R est:3500-4000

HOERMAN, Carl (1885-1955) American
£939 $1700 €1371 Coachella (84x92cm-33x36in) s. 18-Apr-4 Bonhams & Butterfields, Los Angeles #7038 est:1800-2500
£1347 $2250 €1967 Sunset mood near Saugatuck (71x79cm-28x31in) 17-Oct-3 Du Mouchelle, Detroit #2013/R est:1500-2500

HOERNIG, Laura (20th C) American
£227 $400 €331 Path on the outskirts of Taos Pueblo (41x51cm-16x20in) painted c.1940. 23-May-4 Treadway Gallery, Cincinnati #596/R
£227 $400 €331 Taos Pueblo with mountain in the distance (41x51cm-16x20in) painted c.1940. 23-May-4 Treadway Gallery, Cincinnati #597/R
£227 $400 €331 Portrait of a girl (51x41cm-20x16in) painted c.1940. 23-May-4 Treadway Gallery, Cincinnati #598/R
£227 $400 €331 View in Taos (61x51cm-24x20in) painted c.1940. 23-May-4 Treadway Gallery, Cincinnati #601/R
£227 $400 €331 Figures by a building, Taos (41x51cm-16x20in) painted c.1940. 23-May-4 Treadway Gallery, Cincinnati #606/R
£232 $425 €339 New Mexico landscape (46x56cm-18x22in) s. painted c.1940. 5-Jun-4 Treadway Gallery, Cincinnati #616/R
£313 $550 €457 Taos pueblo with mountain in the distance (41x51cm-16x20in) painted c.1940. 23-May-4 Treadway Gallery, Cincinnati #605/R

HOESE, Jean de la (1846-1917) Belgian
£638 $1066 €900 Bibi (45x34cm-18x13in) panel exhib. 20-Oct-3 Bernaerts, Antwerp #481
£1268 $2193 €1800 Young woman in red dress (27x19cm-11x7in) s.d.1903. 13-Dec-3 De Vuyst, Lokeren #106/R est:1000-1400
£43046 $78344 €65000 La chaise brisee (100x150cm-39x59in) s. 15-Jun-4 Vanderkindere, Brussels #155/R est:20000-30000

HOET, Gerard (attrib) (17/18th C) Dutch
£3667 $6673 €5500 Acis and Galatea (34x44cm-13x17in) panel. 30-Jun-4 Neumeister, Munich #457/R est:5500

HOET, Gerard (circle) (17/18th C) Dutch
£4977 $8462 €7266 Hermes presenting Herse to the assembled Olympians (31x41cm-12x16in) copper. 19-Nov-3 Fischer, Luzern #1021/R est:8000-12000 (S.FR 11000)

HOET, Gerard (elder) (1648-1733) Dutch
£3400 $6222 €4964 Cephalus and Procris (36x27cm-14x11in) s. 6-Jul-4 Sotheby's, Olympia #433/R est:3000-4000
£30000 $54000 €43800 Market scene with a commedia dell'arte performance (63x88cm-25x35in) s. 21-Apr-4 Christie's, London #49/R est:12000-18000

HOETERICKX, Émile (1858-1923) Belgian
£552 $922 €800 La toupie (21x16cm-8x6in) s.d.1881 panel. 17-Nov-3 Tajan, Paris #103
£1049 $1752 €1500 In the studio (46x56cm-18x22in) s.d.1893. 11-Oct-3 De Vuyst, Lokeren #182/R est:1800-2200
Works on paper
£270 $511 €400 Femme a la coiffe blanche, assise (52x37cm-20x15in) s. 17-Feb-4 Vanderkindere, Brussels #64
£423 $731 €600 Vue des quais a Paris (20x11cm-8x4in) s.d.1882 W/C gouache traces blk crayon. 10-Dec-3 Piasa, Paris #150
£1399 $2378 €2000 Vue de Londres (33x24cm-13x9in) s. W/C. 1-Dec-3 Palais de Beaux Arts, Brussels #263/R est:2000-3000

HOETGER, Bernhard (1874-1949) German
Sculpture
£1119 $1902 €1600 Mendiant (26cm-10in) s. pat bronze Cast Andro. 25-Nov-3 Millon & Associes, Paris #15/R est:1200-1500
£1918 $3260 €2800 Pleureuse (27cm-11in) s. dark pat.bronze Cast.Eug. Blot Paris. 8-Nov-3 Quittenbaum, Munich #260/R est:3000
£2098 $3566 €3000 Mother, kissing child (29cm-11in) s.d.1936 bronze Cast.Guss Heinze and Barth Berlin exhib. 26-Nov-3 Lempertz, Koln #725/R est:2800
£2759 $4607 €4000 La pleureuse (27cm-11in) s.st.f. black pat bronze lit. 17-Nov-3 Tajan, Paris #121/R est:4000-5000
£7000 $12810 €10220 Fecondite (47cm-19in) pat bronze lit. 9-Jul-4 Sotheby's, London #163/R est:9000
£7587 $12670 €11000 Les musiciens (44x46x30cm-17x18x12in) s. black pat bronze lit. 17-Nov-3 Tajan, Paris #147/R est:12000-15000
£8667 $15860 €13000 Hausweber - man, seated (68x31x34cm-27x12x13in) s.d.1903 bronze exhib. 5-Jun-4 Lempertz, Koln #766/R est:10000-12000
£11888 $20210 €17000 Fountain - child (109x50cm-43x20in) bronze prov.exhib.lit. 26-Nov-3 Lempertz, Koln #724/R est:20000-22000

HOEVE, Jan van (?) Dutch
£330 $538 €475 Still life (50x61cm-20x24in) s. board. 23-Sep-3 Durán, Madrid #570/R

HOEY, Isaak de (17th C) Belgian
£8000 $13840 €11680 Dead Christ lamented by angels in a mountainous landscape (17x21cm-7x8in) s.d.1623 copper. 12-Dec-3 Christie's, Kensington #2/R est:8000-12000

HOEY, Judith (20th C) Belgian?
£250 $458 €365 Still life, strawberries (22x22cm-9x9in) s.d.2001 board. 2-Jun-4 John Ross, Belfast #222

HOEYDONCK, Paul van (1925-) Belgian
£517 $931 €750 Lichtwerk (60x70cm-24x28in) s.verso panel. 20-Jan-4 Galerie Moderne, Brussels #289/R
Sculpture
£1141 $2019 €1700 Tete de femme et boulle (53cm-21in) s. bronze. 27-Apr-4 Campo & Campo, Antwerp #242/R est:1000-1500
£2013 $3564 €3000 Vierge electronique (210x122cm-83x48in) s.d.1966 sculpture. 27-Apr-4 Campo, Vlaamse Kaai #625 est:3000-3500

HOFBAUER, Ferdinand (1801-1864) Austrian
£800 $1440 €1200 Village with buildings by mountain lake (68x106cm-27x42in) s. lit. 22-Apr-4 Allgauer, Kempten #3577/R

HOFBAUER, Josef (1907-1998) German
£385 $642 €550 Three kittens playing (13x18cm-5x7in) s. panel lit. 27-Jun-3 Auktionhaus Georg Rehm, Augsburg #8077/R
£420 $701 €600 Hen with chicks by fence (13x18cm-5x7in) s. s.verso panel. 28-Jun-3 Dannenberg, Berlin #706/R
£420 $722 €600 Duck family and hens at village pond (13x18cm-5x7in) panel. 6-Dec-3 Dannenberg, Berlin #794/R
£543 $923 €793 Family of ducks. Two cats (13x18cm-5x7in) s. panel two. 1-Dec-3 Koller, Zurich #6483 (S.FR 1200)

HOFBAUER, Josef (jnr) (1948-) German
£315 $541 €450 Chiemsee with view of Staudeninsel (15x29cm-6x11in) s.i.verso panel. 6-Dec-3 Dannenberg, Berlin #790/R
£345 $576 €500 Figures with hay wagon by village pond (14x29cm-6x11in) s. panel. 10-Jul-3 Allgauer, Kempten #2537/R
£347 $566 €500 Sunday outing on Tegernsee (18x24cm-7x9in) s. s.i. verso panel. 27-Sep-3 Dannenberg, Berlin #553/R
£347 $566 €500 Village pond (18x24cm-7x9in) s. s.i. verso panel. 27-Sep-3 Dannenberg, Berlin #554/R
£347 $566 €500 Tegernsee with view of Wallberg (18x24cm-7x9in) s. s.i. verso panel. 27-Sep-3 Dannenberg, Berlin #555/R
£347 $566 €500 Starnberger See with Zugspitze (18x24cm-7x9in) s. s.i. verso panel. 27-Sep-3 Dannenberg, Berlin #556/R
£347 $566 €500 Grand Canal, Venice (18x24cm-7x9in) s. s.i. verso panel. 27-Sep-3 Dannenberg, Berlin #557/R
£347 $566 €500 Summer landscape with figures (13x18cm-5x7in) s. panel. 27-Sep-3 Dannenberg, Berlin #558/R
£350 $584 €500 Children playing by stream (18x24cm-7x9in) s. s.i. verso panel. 28-Jun-3 Dannenberg, Berlin #703/R
£350 $584 €500 Sylt (20x40cm-8x16in) s. s.i. verso panel. 28-Jun-3 Dannenberg, Berlin #705/R
£350 $584 €500 Grape harvest (17x23cm-7x9in) s. s.i. verso panel. 28-Jun-3 Dannenberg, Berlin #701/R
£455 $759 €650 Country cattle market (17x23cm-7x9in) s. panel. 9-Oct-3 Michael Zeller, Lindau #606
£458 $819 €650 Haymaking with lake and mountains in background (18x24cm-7x9in) s. panel. 8-Jan-4 Allgauer, Kempten #2418/R
£528 $945 €750 Cafe terrace on the shores of Lake Starnberger (18x24cm-7x9in) s. panel. 8-Jan-4 Allgauer, Kempten #2417/R
£559 $934 €800 Tegernsee with view of Wallberg (17x23cm-7x9in) s. i. verso panel. 9-Oct-3 Michael Zeller, Lindau #604
£559 $934 €800 Chiemsee with view of Staudeninsel (17x23cm-7x9in) s. i. verso panel. 9-Oct-3 Michael Zeller, Lindau #605
£559 $962 €800 Hay harvest by Tegernsee with view of Wallberg (19x39cm-7x15in) s. i. verso panel. 5-Dec-3 Michael Zeller, Lindau #644/R
£559 $962 €800 Alpine peaks and Waxenstein (17x23cm-7x9in) s. i. verso panel. 5-Dec-3 Michael Zeller, Lindau #645/R

HOFBAUR, Johann Nepomuk (19/20th C) German
£739 $1323 €1079 On the battle field (25x36cm-10x14in) mono. 28-May-4 Uppsala Auktionskammare, Uppsala #130/R (S.KR 10000)

HOFELICH, Friedrich Ludwig (1842-1903) German

£267	$480	€400	Edge of the wood (31x41cm-12x16in) s. board. 26-Apr-4 Rieber, Stuttgart #850/R

HOFER, Candida (1944-) German

£4581	$8200	€6688	BNF Paris III (85x85cm-33x33in) c-print edition of six prov.lit. 14-May-4 Phillips, New York #300/R est:5000-7000
Photographs			
£2235	$4000	€3263	Funkhaus Koln I (51x61cm-20x24in) s.i.d.1985 1999 num.5/6 cibachrome print prov. 13-May-4 Sotheby's, New York #383/R est:5000-7000
£2550	$4565	€3800	Voralberger Naturschau Dornbirn I (59x59cm-23x23in) num.4/6 cibachrome. 26-May-4 Christie's, Paris #133/R est:4000-6000
£2994	$5000	€4371	Universitat Oslo (85x85cm-33x33in) s.i. num.6 verso c-print prov. 14-Nov-3 Phillips, New York #198/R est:5000-7000
£3000	$5100	€4380	Deutsches hygiene museum, Dresden I (60x60cm-24x24in) s.i.d.2000 num.2/6 chromogenic print. 18-Nov-3 Christie's, Kensington #240/R est:3000-5000
£3125	$5156	€4500	Teatro olimpico (36x53cm-14x21in) s.num.1/10 verso photo prov. 2-Jul-3 Cornette de St.Cyr, Paris #207/R est:3000-4000
£3133	$5609	€4700	NY Carlsberg Glyptothek Copenhagen II (60x60cm-24x24in) s.i.d.2000 verso c print. 14-May-4 Van Ham, Cologne #88/R est:5000
£4200	$7014	€6132	Riba London I (38x57cm-15x22in) s.i.d.1993 num.3/6 verso cibachrome print prov.lit. 21-Oct-3 Sotheby's, London #325/R est:3000-4000
£4358	$7800	€6363	BNF Paris XIII (85x85cm-33x33in) s.d.1999 verso c-print prov.lit. 14-May-4 Phillips, New York #293/R est:5000-7000
£4469	$8000	€6525	Bibliothek der Kunsthalle Basel II (85x85cm-33x33in) s. verso cibachrome print on foamcore exec 1999 6 edn 6 prov. 13-May-4 Sotheby's, New York #382/R est:6000-8000
£4491	$7500	€6557	Kunsthaus bregenz II (152x153cm-60x60in) s.verso c-print executed 1999 prov. 14-Nov-3 Phillips, New York #324/R est:6000-8000
£4500	$7515	€6570	Voralberger landesbibliothek bregenz I (60x60cm-24x24in) s.verso col coupler print edition 6 of 6 prov. 22-Oct-3 Christie's, London #166/R est:5000-7000
£5090	$8500	€7431	Etablissement thermal enghien les bains (152x153cm-60x60in) s.verso c-print executed 1999 prov. 14-Nov-3 Phillips, New York #325/R est:6000-8000
£5988	$10000	€8742	Konigliche bibliotek Kopenhagen (50x60cm-20x24in) s.i.d.1995 num.APII verso c-print. 13-Nov-3 Sotheby's, New York #504/R est:6000-8000
£6000	$10020	€8760	College Saint Augustin Bitche III (119x118cm-47x46in) s.i.d.1999 num.E.D.A I verso colour photograph prov. 21-Oct-3 Sotheby's, London #320/R est:5000-7000
£8000	$14720	€11680	Milchor Nuremberg II (120x120cm-47x47in) s. colour photograph prov. 24-Jun-4 Sotheby's, London #274/R est:8000-12000
£8939	$16000	€13051	Neue Nationalgalerie II, Berlin (154x154cm-61x61in) c-print edition of six prov. 14-May-4 Phillips, New York #304/R est:8000-12000
£9581	$16000	€13988	Kunsthistoriches Museum Wien - Franz West (38x38cm-15x15in) s. c-prints set of four executed 1990 prov. 14-Nov-3 Phillips, New York #190/R est:15000-20000
£14525	$26000	€21207	Museum for Volkerkunde Dresden II (120x120cm-47x47in) s.i.d.1999 verso col coupler print edition of 6 prov. 12-May-4 Christie's, Rockefeller NY #445/R est:10000-15000
Prints			
£2162	$4000	€3157	Konglche bibliothek Schweden, Stockholm II (30x30cm-12x12in) s.i.d.1983 num.6/6 C-print. 12-Feb-4 Sotheby's, New York #252/R est:3000-4000

HOFER, Heinrich (attrib) (1825-1878) German

£8054	$14416	€12000	View of the Jungfrau with figures in the foreground (61x86cm-24x34in) s. 27-May-4 Dorotheum, Vienna #193/R est:4000-5000

HOFER, Ignaz (19th C) ?

£634	$1052	€900	Still life (3x42cm-1x17in) s.d.1834 canvas on board. 12-Jun-3 Dorotheum, Graz #24/R
£4027	$7208	€6000	Still life (33x42cm-13x17in) s.d.1834. 27-May-4 Dorotheum, Vienna #199/R est:6000-7000

HOFER, K (?) ?

£15000	$27300	€21900	Stilleben melone und kurbisse still life with melon and pumpkins (34x70cm-13x28in) mono.d.33. 4-Feb-4 Sotheby's, London #261/R est:25000-35000

HOFER, Karl (1878-1955) German

£4196	$7133	€6000	Imaginary animal (26x22cm-10x9in) mono. 29-Nov-3 Bassenge, Berlin #6775/R est:8000
£16667	$30667	€25000	Seated woman wearing a yellow blouse (67x43cm-26x17in) mono. painted c.1942 prov. 12-Jun-4 Villa Grisebach, Berlin #311/R est:25000-30000
£17333	$31720	€26000	Girl's portrait (70x50cm-28x20in) mono.d.53 prov. 5-Jun-4 Lempertz, Koln #769/R est:26000-28000
£20000	$36400	€29200	Pfirsichstilleben - still life with peaches (28x35cm-11x14in) mono.d.37 board exhib. 3-Feb-4 Christie's, London #211/R est:15000-20000
£20979	$35664	€30000	Landscape with sailing boat (100x71cm-39x28in) mono. board on panel exhib. 26-Nov-3 Lempertz, Koln #726/R est:30000-35000
£24161	$43248	€36000	Indian girl - Gewri (70x52cm-28x20in) mono. board prov.lit. 25-May-4 Dorotheum, Vienna #48/R est:36000-42000
£25352	$43859	€36000	Nude Indian girl (26x33cm-10x13in) mono. i. stretcher prov. 13-Dec-3 Lempertz, Koln #319/R est:12000-15000
£38000	$69920	€55480	Montagnola (80x100cm-31x39in) mono. painted 1940 prov.exhib. 22-Jun-4 Sotheby's, London #271/R est:40000-60000
£40000	$73600	€60000	Girl playing the lute (97x70cm-38x28in) mono.i.d.33 cardboard prov.exhib. 11-Jun-4 Villa Grisebach, Berlin #1570/R est:50000-70000
£41958	$71329	€60000	Masks - demons, three half figures (81x61cm-32x24in) mono.d.41 i. stretcher lit. 26-Nov-3 Lempertz, Koln #728/R est:40000-50000
£52448	$89161	€75000	Female nude with raised arm (90x57cm-35x22in) mono.d.41 prov. 28-Nov-3 Villa Grisebach, Berlin #67/R est:70000-90000
£55944	$95105	€80000	Tessin landscape (58x84cm-23x33in) mono. prov. 28-Nov-3 Villa Grisebach, Berlin #73/R est:60000-80000
£60000	$110400	€90000	Two girls, friendship (100x65cm-39x26in) mono. i. on stretcher prov.exhib. 11-Jun-4 Villa Grisebach, Berlin #59/R est:50000-70000
£61333	$112853	€92000	Orange picker (126x81cm-50x32in) mono.d.1943 prov. 11-Jun-4 Villa Grisebach, Berlin #54/R est:60000-80000
£62937	$106993	€90000	Woman reading (96x69cm-38x27in) mono. i. verso prov.exhib. 28-Nov-3 Villa Grisebach, Berlin #44/R est:90000-120000
£63333	$116533	€95000	Sleeping nude (50x70cm-20x28in) s.d.08 prov. 11-Jun-4 Villa Grisebach, Berlin #15/R est:60000-80000
£66667	$119333	€100000	Two girls with fruit (56x47cm-22x19in) s.mono. prov.exhib.lit. 14-May-4 Ketterer, Munich #183/R est:20000-30000
£80000	$147200	€116800	Zwei Madchen, Akte, vor einem Vorhang - Two young nudes in front of a curtain (117x90cm-46x35in) init. painted c.1927 prov.exhib. 23-Jun-4 Christie's, London #171/R est:100000-150000
£245614	$451930	€358596	The masquerade (109x87cm-43x34in) mono. prov.exhib.lit. 23-Jun-4 Koller, Zurich #3030/R est:450000-600000 (S.FR 560000)
Works on paper			
£671	$1235	€1000	Two heads (24x15cm-9x6in) mono. pencil wash board. 26-Mar-4 Ketterer, Hamburg #925/R
£699	$1189	€1000	Sleeping figure (36x38cm-14x15in) chk. 29-Nov-3 Villa Grisebach, Berlin #570/R est:1000-1500
£828	$1382	€1200	Loving couple (36x28cm-14x11in) mono.d.1913 brown wash over chk board double-sided. 13-Nov-3 Neumeister, Munich #344/R
£972	$1624	€1400	Figure reading (60x42cm-24x17in) mono. Indian ink brush board. 25-Oct-3 Dr Lehr, Berlin #212/R
£1000	$1790	€1500	Faces (37x24cm-15x9in) mono. pencil. 15-May-4 Van Ham, Cologne #670/R est:500
£1000	$1790	€1500	Standing female nude (38x19cm-15x7in) mono. Indian ink on pencil. 13-May-4 Neumeister, Munich #374/R est:1000-1500
£1049	$1783	€1500	Two figures (51x37cm-20x15in) W/C double-sided. 29-Nov-3 Villa Grisebach, Berlin #569/R est:1500-2000
£1049	$1783	€1500	Figure walking (42x27cm-17x11in) bears mono. chl double-sided. 29-Nov-3 Villa Grisebach, Berlin #573/R est:1500-2000
£1133	$2085	€1700	Reclining nude (31x23cm-12x9in) mono. W/C double-sided. 12-Jun-4 Villa Grisebach, Berlin #574/R est:1500-2000
£1333	$2440	€2000	View of Taverne - Tessin (31x47cm-12x19in) mono.i. pencil wash. 5-Jun-4 Lempertz, Koln #770/R est:2500
£1600	$2864	€2400	Young woman (43x33cm-17x13in) mono. Indian ink. 15-May-4 Van Ham, Cologne #668/R est:3000
£1958	$3329	€2800	Figures in landscape (37x51cm-15x20in) mono. chl. 29-Nov-3 Villa Grisebach, Berlin #572/R est:2000-3000
£2098	$3566	€3000	Standing nude (32x23cm-13x9in) mono. W/C double-sided prov. 29-Nov-3 Villa Grisebach, Berlin #238/R est:3000-4000
£2098	$3566	€3000	Standing nude with hand towel (51x41cm-20x16in) mono. pencil. 29-Nov-3 Villa Grisebach, Berlin #239/R est:3000-4000
£2098	$3566	€3000	Female nude with arms crossed (43x50cm-17x20in) mono. chk double-sided. 29-Nov-3 Bassenge, Berlin #6776/R est:3000
£2448	$4161	€3500	Two sisters (31x43cm-12x17in) mono. Indian ink brush double-sided. 26-Nov-3 Lempertz, Koln #732/R est:4000
£3649	$6531	€5400	Couple (40x30cm-16x12in) s.i. lit. 8-May-4 Schloss Ahlden, Ahlden #840/R est:3800
£4545	$7727	€6500	Man's head with open mouth (48x40cm-19x16in) mono. pen W/C gouache sketch verso. 26-Nov-3 Lempertz, Koln #734/R est:6500
£5467	$10059	€8200	Female nude (61x47cm-24x19in) mono. chl exec. 1924 prov.exhib.lit. 11-Jun-4 Villa Grisebach, Berlin #1573/R est:3000-4000
£6711	$11879	€10000	Two heads (49x35cm-19x14in) mono. W/C Indian ink prov. 30-Apr-4 Dr Fritz Nagel, Stuttgart #838/R est:9800
£7000	$12740	€10220	Seated nude (34x26cm-13x10in) mono. W/C pencil exec.1911 prov. 4-Feb-4 Sotheby's, London #430/R est:4000-6000
£15734	$26748	€22500	Girl at table (35x32cm-14x13in) mono. carpenter's pencil lit. 29-Nov-3 Villa Grisebach, Berlin #240/R est:6000-8000

HOFER, Konrad (1928-) Swiss

£330	$562	€482	Untitled (81x73cm-32x29in) s.d.60 acrylic. 5-Nov-3 Dobiaschofsky, Bern #3476 (S.FR 750)

HOFF, Carl Heinrich (19th C) German

£4028	$6646	€5800	Coastal landscape with palace ruins lit by evening light (48x73cm-19x29in) s. 2-Jul-3 Neumeister, Munich #666/R est:4800

HOFF, Margo (1912-) American

£407	$650	€594	Journey into spring. s. s.i.verso. 20-Sep-3 Bunte, Elgin #300
Works on paper			
£599	$1000	€875	Runic alphabets (119x89cm-47x35in) s. collage. 19-Oct-3 Susanin's, Chicago #6079/R est:500-700

HOFF, Tor (1925-1976) Norwegian

£1121	$2006	€1637	Composition (80x66cm-31x26in) s.d.50. 22-Mar-4 Blomqvist, Oslo #605/R est:15000-18000 (N.KR 14000)

HOFFBAUER, Charles (1875-1957) French

£405	$750	€591	Italian garden (30x23cm-12x9in) estate st. 13-Mar-4 DeFina, Austinburg #966a/R
£824	$1400	€1203	City street (23x31cm-9x12in) board. 21-Nov-3 Skinner, Boston #584/R est:1500-2500
£8721	$15000	€12733	New York at night (50x40cm-20x16in) s. exhib. 3-Dec-3 Doyle, New York #270/R est:20000-30000
£15988	$27500	€23342	Wintry evening in Times Square (45x60cm-18x24in) painted c.1927 prov. 3-Dec-3 Doyle, New York #269/R est:15000-25000

HOFFIE, Patricia (1953-) Australian

£453	$819	€661	Voodoo phunk bebe (180x180cm-71x71in) i.verso. 30-Mar-4 Lawson Menzies, Sydney #170/R est:1500-2500 (A.D 1100)

HOFFLANDER, Jack (20th C) American

£389	$650	€568	Creole Belle (20x3cm-8x1in) 18-Oct-3 David Dike, Dallas #81/R

HOFFMAN, Adrian (19th C) German

£500	$915	€730	Still life of flowers in a vase on a ledge (91x61cm-36x24in) s. 7-Apr-4 Woolley & Wallis, Salisbury #211/R
£661	$1182	€965	Still life of flowers (90x69cm-35x27in) s. board. 31-May-4 Stephan Welz, Johannesburg #77 (SA.R 8000)

HOFFMAN, Frank B (1888-1958) American

£1734	$3000	€2532	No dinner tonight (23x30cm-9x12in) canvasboard prov. 10-Dec-3 Bonhams & Butterfields, San Francisco #6118/R est:4000-6000

£1734 $3000 €2532 Time for a snack (25x36cm-10x14in) s. canvasboard. 10-Dec-3 Bonhams & Butterfields, San Francisco #6119/R est:4000-6000
£1955 $3500 €2854 Surprise (30x41cm-12x16in) board. 15-May-4 Altermann Galleries, Santa Fe #73/R
£2890 $5000 €4219 Midi (61x76cm-24x30in) s. canvas on masonite prov. 10-Dec-3 Bonhams & Butterfields, San Francisco #6123/R est:3000-5000
£7487 $14000 €10931 At camp (46x61cm-18x24in) s. board prov. 24-Jul-4 Coeur d'Alene, Hayden #248/R est:8000-12000
£8556 $16000 €12492 Trapper (76x51cm-30x20in) s. oil en grisaille. 24-Jul-4 Coeur d'Alene, Hayden #211/R est:8000-12000
£8556 $16000 €12492 Cowboy camp (46x61cm-18x24in) s. canvasboard prov. 24-Jul-4 Coeur d'Alene, Hayden #249/R est:8000-12000
£8671 $15000 €12660 Rim fire (92x100cm-36x39in) s. prov. 10-Dec-3 Bonhams & Butterfields, San Francisco #6122/R est:8000-12000
£9249 $16000 €13504 Race Horse (102x127cm-40x50in) prov. 10-Dec-3 Bonhams & Butterfields, San Francisco #6121/R est:10000-15000
£12717 $22000 €18567 No dinner tonight (71x91cm-28x36in) s. masonite prov. 10-Dec-3 Bonhams & Butterfields, San Francisco #6117/R est:15000-25000
Works on paper
£267 $500 €390 Cowboy on a bucking horse (25x33cm-10x13in) pen ink prov. 24-Jul-4 Coeur d'Alene, Hayden #241/R

HOFFMAN, Harry Leslie (1871-1964) American
£4469 $8000 €6525 Under the Wisteria (10x8cm-4x3in) s.d.15 board prov. 6-May-4 Shannon's, Milford #119/R est:5000-7000
£5308 $9500 €7750 Amongst the hollyhocks (25x20cm-10x8in) s.indis.d. board prov. 6-May-4 Shannon's, Milford #51/R est:5000-7000
£6704 $12000 €9788 In the garden (25x20cm-10x8in) s.indis.d. board prov. 6-May-4 Shannon's, Milford #86/R est:5000-7000

HOFFMAN, Malvina (1887-1966) American
Sculpture
£1836 $3250 €2681 Shiver, la frileuse (25cm-10in) s. green pat. bronze. 2-May-4 Grogan, Boston #49/R
£3226 $6000 €4710 Daboa (37cm-15in) i.d.1933 base brown red pat bronze prov.lit. 3-Mar-4 Christie's, Rockefeller NY #2/R est:4000-6000
£3693 $6500 €5392 Modesty (20cm-8in) i.num.VII brown pat. bronze st.f.Roman. 18-May-4 Sotheby's, New York #96/R est:1500-2000
£4651 $8000 €6790 Head of Sioux indian (20cm-8in) i. pat bronze. 2-Dec-3 Christie's, Rockefeller NY #77/R est:3000-5000
£17442 $30000 €25465 La frileuse - shivering girl (96cm-38in) i. brown green pat. bronze lit. 3-Dec-3 Sotheby's, New York #37/R est:25000-30000

HOFFMAN, Martin (1935-) American
£857 $1500 €1251 Woman Eternal (170x170cm-67x67in) s.i. a. painted 1972 lit. 17-Dec-3 Christie's, Rockefeller NY #252/R est:3000-5000
£2171 $3800 €3170 Woman Eternal (170x122cm-67x48in) s.i. a. painted 1972. 17-Dec-3 Christie's, Rockefeller NY #251/R est:3000-5000

HOFFMAN, Vlastimil (1881-1970) Polish
£963 $1599 €1406 Angel watching over two children (14x32cm-6x13in) s. cardboard painted c.1935. 15-Jun-3 Agra, Warsaw #34/R est:6000 (P.Z 6000)
£1250 $2088 €1825 Portraits (40x90cm-16x35in) s.d.1958 cardboard triptych. 19-Oct-3 Agra, Warsaw #44/R est:5000 (P.Z 8000)
£1447 $2663 €2200 Mother and child (57x68cm-22x27in) s.d.1915 board. 22-Jun-4 Wiener Kunst Auktionen, Vienna #71/R est:2400
£3261 $6000 €4761 Recipient of the Sacrament (60x140cm-24x55in) s.d.1921 prov. 8-Jun-4 Auctions by the Bay, Alameda #1149/R
£3529 $6000 €5152 Recipient of the Sacrament (60x140cm-24x55in) s.d.1921 prov. 20-Nov-3 Auctions by the Bay, Alameda #1116/R

HOFFMAN, William (1924-) American
£349 $600 €510 Seascape at dusk (61x122cm-24x48in) s. 6-Dec-3 Neal Auction Company, New Orleans #1349/R

HOFFMANN, Adam (1918-2001) Polish
£1724 $2690 €2517 Old man and angel (25x35cm-10x14in) s. plywood painted c.1930. 30-Mar-3 Agra, Warsaw #29/R est:10000 (P.Z 11000)
Works on paper
£223 $384 €326 Couple under the trees (51x36cm-20x14in) s.d.1973 chk ink wash. 4-Dec-3 Agra, Warsaw #24/R (P.Z 1500)
£310 $518 €450 Fantasy scene (30x42cm-12x17in) mono.i.d.1975 pastel chk. 16-Nov-3 Agra, Warsaw #22/R

HOFFMANN, Anker (1904-1985) Danish
Sculpture
£1083 $1993 €1581 Woman standing (54cm-21in) s.d.1971 num.7 dark pat.bronze. 29-Mar-4 Rasmussen, Copenhagen #529/R est:10000-12000 (D.KR 12000)
£1354 $2491 €1977 Reclining female nude (25x42cm-10x17in) mono.d.45 dark pat.bronze incl.teak plinth. 29-Mar-4 Rasmussen, Copenhagen #449/R est:10000-12000 (D.KR 15000)
£1625 $2989 €2373 Reclining female nude (26x41cm-10x16in) mono.d.84 num.4/7 dark green pat.bronze cire perdue. 29-Mar-4 Rasmussen, Copenhagen #469/R est:8000-10000 (D.KR 18000)
£1787 $3039 €2609 Girl seated with bent knees (33x47cm-13x19in) mono.d.61 bronze. 26-Nov-3 Kunsthallen, Copenhagen #400/R est:8000 (D.KR 19000)

HOFFMANN, Anton (1863-1938) German
£1049 $1804 €1500 Medieval military camp (56x88cm-22x35in) s. 5-Dec-3 Michael Zeller, Lindau #646/R est:1500
£2188 $3653 €3194 Wandering troops during summer war (61x81cm-24x32in) s. painted c.1900. 19-Oct-3 Agra, Warsaw #28/R est:14000 (P.Z 14000)
Works on paper
£467 $845 €700 Bavarian cavalry in winter landscape (32x49cm-13x19in) s. W/C htd white. 3-Apr-4 Hans Stahl, Hamburg #39/R

HOFFMANN, Eduardo (1957-) Argentinian
£8824 $15000 €12883 Sin titulo (200x130cm-79x51in) s.d.2002 verso acrylic vellum prov. 19-Nov-3 Sotheby's, New York #156/R est:12000-18000

HOFFMANN, Ernst (1879-?) German
£4362 $7809 €6500 Wedding congratulations (80x119cm-31x47in) s. 27-May-4 Dorotheum, Vienna #53/R est:6500-7500

HOFFMANN, H (?) ?
£900 $1530 €1314 Portrait of a young beauty, holding a fan (55x46cm-22x18in) s. 6-Nov-3 Christie's, Kensington #732/R

HOFFMANN, Hans (attrib) (16th C) German
£17450 $32107 €26000 Ecce Homo (42x41cm-17x16in) panel prov. 24-Mar-4 Dorotheum, Vienna #210/R est:9000-12000

HOFFMANN, Jacob (?) ?
£738 $1373 €1100 Altkonig in spring (38x57cm-15x22in) s.i.d.April 1903 board. 6-Mar-4 Arnold, Frankfurt #742/R

HOFFMANN, Josef (1831-1904) Austrian
Works on paper
£493 $863 €700 Untitled (21x27cm-8x11in) mono.d.47 pencil. 19-Dec-3 Dorotheum, Vienna #196/R
£524 $892 €750 Drawing for tin (21x27cm-8x11in) mono. mixed media. 27-Nov-3 Wiener Kunst Auktionen, Vienna #265/R
£524 $892 €750 Sketch for teapot (21x29cm-8x11in) mono. mixed media. 27-Nov-3 Wiener Kunst Auktionen, Vienna #266/R
£1049 $1783 €1500 Sketches (30x21cm-12x8in) mono. three. 27-Nov-3 Wiener Kunst Auktionen, Vienna #264/R est:1500-3500
£4027 $7208 €6000 Plans for Palais Stoclet. i. col pen pencil eleven exhib. 25-May-4 Dorotheum, Vienna #12/R est:2000-2600

HOFFMANN, Karl (1841-1910) German
£317 $538 €463 Still life of flowers with fruit (53x42cm-21x17in) s. 28-Nov-3 Zofingen, Switzerland #2606 (S.FR 700)

HOFFMANN, Oskar Adolfovitch (1851-1913) Russian
£289 $500 €422 Summer harvest (58x79cm-23x31in) s. 13-Dec-3 Charlton Hall, Columbia #90/R
£6944 $11458 €10000 Russian village street in evening light (67x121cm-26x48in) s. 3-Jul-3 Van Ham, Cologne #1254/R est:11000

HOFFMANN, Otto (after) (1885-1915) German
Sculpture
£4396 $8000 €6594 Columbine dancing (30cm-12in) i. pat bronze ivory marble base exec. 1920. 16-Jun-4 Sotheby's, New York #261/R est:4000-6000

HOFFMANN-FALLERSLEBEN, Franz (1855-1927) German
£532 $862 €750 Christmas wood (38x32cm-15x13in) s.d.1916 board lit. 23-May-3 Karlheinz Kaupp, Staufen #1893
£567 $1026 €850 Woodland pond in autumn (31x41cm-12x16in) s.d.23 canvas on board. 1-Apr-4 Van Ham, Cologne #1435
£1014 $1724 €1450 Country house (36x27cm-14x11in) s.d.08 i.verso canvas on board lit. 28-Nov-3 Schloss Ahlden, Ahlden #1562/R

HOFFMEISTER, Adolf (1902-) Czechoslovakian
Works on paper
£658 $1119 €961 Leaving for emigration (30x50cm-12x20in) mono.d.38 ink collage text. 29-Nov-3 Dorotheum, Prague #173/R est:30000-45000 (C.KR 30000)

HOFFSTEN, Albert (?) ?
Works on paper
£378 $642 €552 Woman wearing summer hat (30x25cm-12x10in) s.d.17 W/C. 4-Nov-3 Bukowskis, Stockholm #174/R (S.KR 5000)

HOFINGER, Oskar E (1935-) Austrian
Sculpture
£1844 $3079 €2600 St Florian (33cm-13in) s.i.d.1985 sandstone. 14-Oct-3 Dorotheum, Vienna #303/R est:4500-6500
£1844 $3079 €2600 St George (33cm-13in) s.i.d.1988 sandstone. 14-Oct-3 Dorotheum, Vienna #304/R est:4500-6500
£4895 $8322 €7000 Reclining figure with crossed over leg (22x50x11cm-9x20x4in) s.d.1990 pat.bronze. 26-Nov-3 Dorotheum, Vienna #327/R est:9000-12000

HOFKER, Willem Gerard (1902-1981) Dutch
£3125 $5219 €4563 Self portrait, the young Hofker as a dandy (27x21cm-11x8in) s.i.verso mahogany panel. 12-Oct-3 Sotheby's, Singapore #30/R est:5000-7000 (S.D 9000)
£3441 $5505 €5024 Seated nude (26x15cm-10x6in) s. board prov. 18-May-3 Sotheby's, Singapore #26/R est:8000-10000 (S.D 9600)
£5442 $9905 €8000 Reguliersgracht hoek Keizersgracht (50x40cm-20x16in) s.d.1958 i.verso. 3-Feb-4 Christie's, Amsterdam #330/R est:4000-6000
£8172 $13075 €11931 Still life (69x55cm-27x22in) s.i.d.1953 s.i.d.1953 verso. 18-May-3 Sotheby's, Singapore #25/R est:10000-12000 (S.D 22800)
£12091 $21764 €17653 Various flower in a vase (41x60cm-16x24in) s.d.1952 prov. 25-Apr-4 Christie's, Hong Kong #510/R est:150000-200000 (HK.D 170000)
£17761 $29660 €25931 Cherry blossom and other flowers (57x50cm-22x20in) s.d.1954 i.on stretcher prov. 26-Oct-3 Christie's, Hong Kong #20/R est:120000-160000 (HK.D 230000)
£31944 $53347 €46638 Balinese girl (32x24cm-13x9in) s.d.1948 s.verso canvas on board. 12-Oct-3 Sotheby's, Singapore #18/R est:45000-65000 (S.D 92000)

Prints

£3261 $5054 €4761 Grace and charm, Bali. Atmosphere and enchantment, Bali (74x46cm-29x18in) lithograph two lit. 6-Oct-2 Sotheby's, Singapore #47/R est:5000-7000 (S.D 9000)

Works on paper

£743 $1308 €1100 Houses on the Nieuwezijds Voorburgwal, Amsterdam (49x37cm-19x15in) s.i.d.1970 col chk grey wash lit. 19-May-4 Sotheby's, Amsterdam #380/R
£878 $1546 €1300 Zuiderkerk, Amsterdam (38x28cm-15x11in) s.i.d.1968 col chk col wash. 19-May-4 Sotheby's, Amsterdam #381/R
£1141 $2099 €1700 Herengracht at corner of Leidse Gracht, Amsterdam (37x55cm-15x22in) s.d.1974 black chk prov. 29-Mar-4 Glerum, Amsterdam #14 est:1000-1500
£1377 $2134 €2010 Portrait of a girl (40x30cm-16x12in) s.i. pastel. 6-Oct-2 Sotheby's, Singapore #25/R est:2000-3000 (S.D 3800)
£1634 $2958 €2386 Nude (31x13cm-12x5in) s.d.1936 pastel. 4-Apr-4 Sotheby's, Singapore #34/R est:3000-5000 (S.D 5000)
£1812 $2808 €2646 Girl (40x30cm-16x12in) s.d.1962 pastel. 6-Oct-2 Sotheby's, Singapore #26/R est:5000-7000 (S.D 5000)
£2721 $4952 €4000 Young ballerina (48x33cm-19x13in) s.d.1950 black chk chl pastel htd white. 3-Feb-4 Christie's, Amsterdam #205/R est:800-1200
£2721 $4871 €4000 Portrait of Maria, Oeboed abangan Bali. Portrait of Maria (32x43cm-13x17in) s.i.d.Juli 1943 pencil pastel two. 16-Mar-4 Christie's, Amsterdam #93/R est:2000-3000
£3819 $6378 €5576 Klooster san Francesco Assisi. Views of Wells. Study of nude. Portrait of of a Chinese Lady (42x30cm-17x12in) all s. pastel five. 12-Oct-3 Sotheby's, Singapore #33/R est:9000-12000 (S.D 11000)
£4086 $6538 €5966 Cortenbach. Chiesa e Porte, San Petro. Nude (33x22cm-13x9in) s. two i. one d.54 one d.1955 one d.1965 pastel three. 18-May-3 Sotheby's, Singapore #53/R est:8000-12000 (S.D 11400)
£5797 $8986 €8464 Dancer (46x25cm-18x10in) s.i. pastel. 6-Oct-2 Sotheby's, Singapore #27/R est:3500-5500 (S.D 16000)
£6178 $10317 €9020 Ni Dabling and Ni Tjawan (24x17cm-9x7in) s.i.d.1943 pencil col chk prov. 26-Oct-3 Christie's, Hong Kong #24/R est:120000-200000 (HK.D 80000)
£13333 $21333 €19466 Ni Kentjoeng (44x30cm-17x12in) s.i.d.1942. 18-May-3 Sotheby's, Singapore #7/R est:12000-15000 (S.D 37200)
£13889 $23194 €20278 Bali offers, Banten (46x28cm-18x11in) s.d.1939 pastel cardboard. 12-Oct-3 Sotheby's, Singapore #26/R est:25000-35000 (S.D 40000)
£13900 $23212 €20294 Balinese girl on the steps of a temple entrance (48x31cm-19x12in) d.4 Juli 1942 col chk W/C prov. 26-Oct-3 Christie's, Hong Kong #25/R est:200000-280000 (HK.D 180000)
£45752 $82810 €66798 Ni Tjawan (46x30cm-18x12in) indis sig.i.d. W/C cardboard. 4-Apr-4 Sotheby's, Singapore #29/R est:15000-20000 (S.D 140000)

HOFKER-RUETER, Maria (1902-1999) Dutch

Works on paper

£272 $487 €400 Roses (39x27cm-15x11in) s.d.89 W/C. 16-Mar-4 Christie's, Amsterdam #94

HOFLEHNER, Rudolf (1916-1995) Austrian

Works on paper

£256 $450 €374 Untitled, sculpture sketches (64x43cm-25x17in) s.d.1964 ink W/C prov. 22-May-4 Selkirks, St. Louis #784

HOFLER, Max (1892-1963) British

£250 $408 €365 Landscape with Barnard Castle beyond (36x40cm-14x16in) board. 24-Sep-3 Dreweatt Neate, Newbury #189
£500 $895 €730 Summertime canal loch scene (30x38cm-12x15in) s. board. 28-May-4 Tring Auctions, Tring #401/R
£550 $985 €803 Notre Dame, Paris (41x51cm-16x20in) s. i.d.July 1960 verso board. 18-Mar-4 Christie's, Kensington #636/R
£780 $1303 €1139 St Paul's Cathedral from Gateway House (55x75cm-22x30in) s. board. 20-Oct-3 Bonhams, Bath #115

HOFMAN, Aad (1944-) Dutch

£433 $793 €650 Still life with margaritas (30x24cm-12x9in) s.d.83 prov. 7-Jun-4 Glerum, Amsterdam #343

HOFMANN, A (19/20th C) ?

£9000 $16110 €13140 Collecting the hay (59x79cm-23x31in) s. 26-May-4 Sotheby's, London #79/R est:7000-9000

HOFMANN, Egon (1884-1972) Austrian

£420 $722 €600 Still life with flowers and fruit (92x72cm-36x28in) s. 4-Dec-3 Dorotheum, Graz #16/R
£667 $1193 €1000 Flowers in vase (31x38cm-12x15in) s. board. 13-May-4 Dorotheum, Linz #464/R
£1333 $2387 €2000 Rodner valley (35x48cm-14x19in) s. i. verso board. 13-May-4 Dorotheum, Linz #498/R est:2800-3200
£1733 $3103 €2600 Alberfeldkogel (53x60cm-21x24in) s.d.37 panel. 13-May-4 Dorotheum, Linz #499/R est:3600-4500

HOFMANN, Hans (1880-1966) American/German

£7027 $13000 €10259 Last Sun Ray (22x26cm-9x10in) s.d.60 board prov. 12-Feb-4 Sotheby's, New York #89/R est:10000-15000
£17964 $30000 €26227 Untitled (48x60cm-19x24in) s.d.45 tempera W/C gouache paper prov.exhib. 13-Nov-3 Sotheby's, New York #167/R est:18000-22000
£19461 $32500 €28413 Nocturne (51x41cm-20x16in) s.d.50 s.i.d.50 verso panel prov.exhib. 13-Nov-3 Sotheby's, New York #170/R est:25000-35000
£38922 $65000 €56826 Untitled no.25 (63x76cm-25x30in) board painted 1939 prov. 12-Nov-3 Christie's, Rockefeller NY #348/R est:40000-60000
£52695 $88000 €76935 Landscape (76x90cm-30x35in) panel painted 1942 prov.exhib. 12-Nov-3 Christie's, Rockefeller NY #306/R est:80000-100000
£56886 $95000 €83054 Colour volume III (76x61cm-30x24in) s.d.50 prov.exhib. 13-Nov-3 Sotheby's, New York #182/R est:60000-80000
£113772 $190000 €166107 Splendor (127x102cm-50x40in) s.s.i.d.1962 verso prov.exhib. 12-Nov-3 Christie's, Rockefeller NY #307/R est:120000-180000
£122905 $220000 €179441 Arcade (95x81cm-37x32in) s.d.61 s.i.d.verso plywood prov.exhib. 12-May-4 Christie's, Rockefeller NY #129/R est:180000-220000
£209581 $350000 €305988 Violin concerto (127x102cm-50x40in) s.d.62 s.i.d.verso prov.exhib. 12-Nov-3 Sotheby's, New York #59/R est:350000-450000
£335196 $600000 €489386 Conjuntis Viribus (183x152cm-72x60in) s.d.63 prov.exhib.lit. 12-May-4 Sotheby's, New York #28/R est:600000-800000
£391061 $700000 €570949 Tourbillon (122x118cm-48x46in) s.d.60 s.i.d.1960 verso board prov.exhib.lit. 11-May-4 Christie's, Rockefeller NY #26/R est:450000-650000
£586826 $980000 €856766 In upper regions (152x122cm-60x48in) s.d.63 i.d.1963 verso prov.exhib. 12-Nov-3 Sotheby's, New York #16/R est:400000-600000

Prints

£2235 $4000 €3263 Composition (25x25cm-10x10in) s.d.1961 num.38/50 col oil photolithograph. 4-May-4 Doyle, New York #186/R est:1000-1500

Works on paper

£698 $1200 €1019 Untitled (21x27cm-8x11in) s.d.32 India ink prov. 3-Dec-3 Doyle, New York #3 est:1200-1800
£872 $1500 €1273 Untitled - in the car (21x27cm-8x11in) init.d.32 India ink prov. 3-Dec-3 Doyle, New York #2/R est:1500-2000
£1397 $2500 €2040 Harbor, Provincetown (21x27cm-8x11in) s. India ink. 6-May-4 Doyle, New York #111/R est:1500-2000
£1786 $3250 €2608 Provincetown landscape (23x27cm-9x11in) s. ink executed c.1941 prov.exhib. 29-Jun-4 Sotheby's, New York #453/R est:2500-3500
£2023 $3500 €2954 Untitled (28x22cm-11x9in) num.933/345 verso India ink prov. 10-Dec-3 Phillips, New York #438/R est:4000-6000
£2258 $4200 €3297 Untitled (21x27cm-8x11in) s.d.1956 W/C. 2-Mar-4 Swann Galleries, New York #263/R est:5000-8000
£7200 $13104 €10512 Untitled (43x36cm-17x14in) s.d.43 W/C prov. 21-Jun-4 Bonhams, New Bond Street #79/R est:10000-15000
£19632 $32000 €28663 Untitled (60x48cm-24x19in) s. gouache exec.c.1944 prov.exhib. 23-Sep-3 Christie's, Rockefeller NY #38/R est:15000-20000
£26816 $48000 €39151 Untitled (44x60cm-17x24in) gouache exec 1943 prov.exhib. 12-May-4 Christie's, Rockefeller NY #121/R est:25000-35000
£27174 $50000 €39674 Untitled (57x72cm-22x28in) s. gouache exec c.1954 prov. 27-Jun-4 Freeman, Philadelphia #216/R est:25000-40000

HOFMANN, Hans (attrib) (1880-1966) American/German

£520 $900 €759 Abstract (127x160cm-50x63in) board. 11-Dec-3 Lane, Penzance #351

HOFMANN, Hermann (1920-) Swiss

£354 $651 €517 Early spring I (92x81cm-36x32in) s.d. masonite. 14-Jun-4 Philippe Schuler, Zurich #5728 (S.FR 810)
£376 $628 €545 Toscana (120x110cm-47x43in) s. 23-Jun-3 Philippe Schuler, Zurich #8435 (S.FR 820)

HOFMANN, Jasinicka (20th C) ?

£748 $1339 €1100 Deux jeunes femmes a la terrasse (81x60cm-32x24in) s.d.28 after Renoir. 16-Mar-4 Vanderkindere, Brussels #374

HOFMANN, Karl (1852-?) Austrian

£1119 $1902 €1600 Italian garden (50x62cm-20x24in) s.i.d.1892. 19-Nov-3 Dorotheum, Klagenfurt #17/R est:500

HOFMANN, Ludwig von (1861-1945) German

£347 $580 €500 Seated female nude (25x18cm-10x7in) mono. ochre. 24-Oct-3 Ketterer, Hamburg #813/R
£2587 $4399 €3700 Homeward journey of the riders (55x65cm-22x26in) s. lit. 28-Nov-3 Schloss Ahlden, Ahlden #1595/R est:3500
£4196 $7133 €6000 Supraporte - study (28x62cm-11x24in) mono. 29-Nov-3 Villa Grisebach, Berlin #108/R est:3000-4000
£8392 $14266 €12000 Five boys on rocks (117x107cm-46x42in) s. prov. 29-Nov-3 Villa Grisebach, Berlin #107/R est:12000-15000
£9000 $14940 €13140 Bathers (64x77cm-25x30in) mono. 30-Sep-3 Sotheby's, London #21/R est:5000-7000
£33566 $57063 €48000 Three women bathing (74x97cm-29x38in) s. s. stretcher prov. 29-Nov-3 Villa Grisebach, Berlin #106/R est:15000-18000

Works on paper

£262 $446 €383 Two youths bathing (23x23cm-9x9in) mono. chl col chk. 18-Nov-3 Hans Widmer, St Gallen #1101 (S.FR 580)
£267 $491 €400 Female nude kneeling (29x43cm-11x17in) mono. red ochre black chk brown paper. 12-Jun-4 Villa Grisebach, Berlin #576/R
£280 $476 €400 Standing female nude (49x35cm-19x14in) mono. chk. 29-Nov-3 Bassenge, Berlin #6780
£300 $537 €450 Bathing (12x21cm-5x8in) mono. chk. 15-May-4 Bassenge, Berlin #6895
£490 $842 €700 Horse rustlers (22x31cm-9x12in) col chk. 2-Dec-3 Hauswedell & Nolte, Hamburg #285/R
£570 $1050 €850 Dance scene (19x33cm-7x13in) col chk. 26-Mar-4 Ketterer, Hamburg #465/R
£667 $1193 €1000 Women carrying jugs (23x37cm-9x15in) mono. pastel chk double-sided. 13-May-4 Neumeister, Munich #377/R
£1208 $2223 €1800 Harpist (39x26cm-15x10in) mono. col chk. 26-Mar-4 Ketterer, Hamburg #464/R est:1200-1400
£1400 $2324 €2044 Figures in a landscape (25x18cm-10x7in) mono. blk chk W/C. 30-Sep-3 Sotheby's, London #308/R est:1500-2000
£2000 $3580 €3000 March sun (32x43cm-13x17in) s.d. pastel chk paper on board. 13-May-4 Neumeister, Munich #376/R est:2000-2500

HOFMANN, Otto (1907-) German?

£567 $1020 €850 Two figures (73x55cm-29x22in) s.d. verso. 24-Apr-4 Dr Lehr, Berlin #170/R

HOFMANN, Richard (20th C) German

£448 $749 €650 Extensive landscape (127x178cm-50x70in) s. i. verso board lit. 12-Jul-3 Bergmann, Erlangen #685/R

HOFMANN, Robert (1889-1987) American/Austrian

£302 $556 €441 Chess game (23x29cm-9x11in) s. board. 14-Jun-4 Waddingtons, Toronto #24/R (C.D 750)

HOFMANN, Rudolf (1820-1882) German
£453 $816 €680 Girl by fountain watched by peasant boys (26x18cm-10x7in) panel. 26-Apr-4 Rieber, Stuttgart #1132/R

HOFMANN, Vlastislav (1884-1964) Czechoslovakian
Works on paper
£1329 $2259 €1900 Alban Berg: Vojcek-U Rybnika - moonlit pond (51x76cm-20x30in) s.i.d.1923 mixed media collage board prov. 26-Nov-3 Dorotheum, Vienna #127/R

HOFMANN-GROTZINGEN, Gustav (1889-?) German
£284 $460 €400 Extensive valley with small villages (85x104cm-33x41in) s.d.1922 lit. 23-May-3 Karlheinz Kaupp, Staufen #1745/R

HOFMANS, Pieter (1642-1692) Flemish
£8667 $15860 €13000 Battles (30x46cm-12x18in) pair. 1-Jun-4 Sotheby's, Milan #82/R est:13000-16000

HOFMEISTER, Johannes (1914-1990) Danish
£721 $1335 €1053 Figure in hilly landscape (30x40cm-12x16in) init. panel. 15-Mar-4 Rasmussen, Vejle #636 (D.KR 8000)
£857 $1585 €1251 Coastal landscape with figure (27x41cm-11x16in) init. 15-Mar-4 Rasmussen, Vejle #660/R (D.KR 9500)
£860 $1539 €1256 Landscape with farm (18x34cm-7x13in) init. panel. 10-May-4 Rasmussen, Vejle #668/R (D.KR 9500)
£1060 $1802 €1548 Figures in landscape (40x50cm-16x20in) init. 10-Nov-3 Rasmussen, Vejle #644/R (D.KR 11500)
£1128 $2110 €1647 Landscape (34x39cm-13x15in) init. masonite. 25-Feb-4 Kunsthallen, Copenhagen #196/R est:10000 (D.KR 12500)
£1444 $2657 €2108 Three figures in landscape (43x53cm-17x21in) init. cardboard on canvas. 29-Mar-4 Rasmussen, Copenhagen #44/R est:12000 (D.KR 16000)
£1511 $2750 €2267 Coastal landscape with figure and houses (50x61cm-20x24in) init. masonite. 19-Jun-4 Rasmussen, Havnen #4022/R est:15000 (D.KR 17000)
£1517 $2427 €2200 Winter landscape with figure by houses, Hjorringe Bjerge (52x65cm-20x26in) init. masonite. 17-Sep-3 Kunsthallen, Copenhagen #271/R est:10000 (D.KR 16000)
£1579 $2558 €2290 Landscape with figure (39x46cm-15x18in) init. panel. 4-Aug-3 Rasmussen, Vejle #592/R est:10000 (D.KR 16500)
£1685 $2815 €2460 Landscape (45x55cm-18x22in) init. masonite. 25-Oct-3 Rasmussen, Havnen #4230/R est:5000 (D.KR 18000)
£1693 $2879 €2472 Figures in landscape (50x61cm-20x24in) init. 26-Nov-3 Kunsthallen, Copenhagen #329/R est:15000 (D.KR 18000)
£1801 $2882 €2629 Landscape with church (125x180cm-49x71in) init. 22-Sep-3 Rasmussen, Vejle #549/R est:20000 (D.KR 19000)
£2180 $3488 €3161 Figure in harbour (68x78cm-27x31in) init. 17-Sep-3 Kunsthallen, Copenhagen #301/R est:20000 (D.KR 23000)
£2457 $4399 €3587 Houses and figures by the sea (51x69cm-20x27in) init. 12-Jan-4 Rasmussen, Vejle #502/R est:12000-15000 (D.KR 26000)
£2938 $4701 €4289 Coastal landscape with figures and houses (125x400cm-49x157in) init. 22-Sep-3 Rasmussen, Vejle #550/R est:40000-50000 (D.KR 31000)
£3033 $4853 €4428 Coastal landscape with figures (125x251cm-49x99in) init. 22-Sep-3 Rasmussen, Vejle #551/R est:30000 (D.KR 32000)

HOFNER, Johann Baptist (1832-1913) German
£1689 $2973 €2500 Outside farmstead (50x65cm-20x26in) mono. canvas on panel. 22-May-4 Lempertz, Koln #1530/R est:1500

HOFNER, Otto (?) Austrian
Sculpture
£2484 $4000 €3627 Charging bull (27cm-11in) bronze cast by Erzgiesserai A G. 14-Jan-4 Christie's, Rockefeller NY #303/R est:2500-3500

HOFRICHTER, Martha (1872-?) Czechoslovakian
£5000 $8300 €7300 Lady with lyre (65x71cm-26x28in) s. 1-Oct-3 Sotheby's, Olympia #186/R est:1500-2000

HOFSCHEN, Edgar (1941-) German
£610 $1000 €891 Modification XXXXI (62x73cm-24x29in) s.i.d.71 verso green tent cloth prov. 28-May-3 Sotheby's, Amsterdam #170/R

HOGBERG, Fritz (1899-1956) Swedish
£513 $908 €749 Bridge across the Seine, Paris (26x35cm-10x14in) i.d.1926 verso panel. 27-Apr-4 AB Stockholms Auktionsverk #700/R (S.KR 7000)

HOGBERG, Karl (1901-1981) Scandinavian
£314 $574 €458 Sketch for wall decoration at Oslo Town Hall (72x150cm-28x59in) s.verso painted c.1941. 2-Feb-4 Blomqvist, Lysaker #1116 (N.KR 3900)

HOGER, Joseph (1801-1877) Austrian
Works on paper
£800 $1432 €1200 Village street in Austria (26x40cm-10x16in) s.d.1825 W/C. 13-May-4 Bassenge, Berlin #5576/R

HOGER, Rudolf A (1877-1930) Austrian
£657 $1090 €959 Stage coach (75x100cm-30x39in) s. 4-Oct-3 Dorotheum, Prague #40/R est:30000-50000 (C.KR 30000)
£1690 $2958 €2400 Garden dance (90x124cm-35x49in) s. 19-Dec-3 Dorotheum, Vienna #11/R est:2400-3200
£2685 $4940 €4000 Birth of Venus (105x148cm-41x58in) s. 24-Mar-4 Hugo Ruef, Munich #994/R est:3000

HOGFELDT, Robert (1894-1986) Swedish
Works on paper
£266 $476 €388 It's not as easy as that (29x35cm-11x14in) s. W/C. 28-May-4 Uppsala Auktionskammare, Uppsala #320 (S.KR 3600)
£333 $595 €486 The trespasser's den (26x34cm-10x13in) s. mixed media. 26-May-4 AB Stockholms Auktionsverk #2323/R (S.KR 4500)
£392 $705 €588 Joke picture (27x22cm-11x9in) s. mixed media. 25-Apr-4 Goteborg Auktionsverk, Sweden #307/R (S.KR 5400)
£480 $860 €701 A quiet story (21x26cm-8x10in) s. W/C. 28-May-4 Uppsala Auktionskammare, Uppsala #189 (S.KR 6500)
£692 $1191 €1010 The Sunday walk (20x31cm-8x12in) s. W/C. 3-Dec-3 AB Stockholms Auktionsverk #2482/R (S.KR 9000)
£976 $1757 €1425 The beggar woman (34x48cm-13x19in) s. W/C. 26-Jan-4 Lilla Bukowskis, Stockholm #753 (S.KR 13000)

HOGFORD, John (?) British
Works on paper
£500 $915 €750 Hubbard's Mill, Lincolnshire (32x49cm-13x19in) s. W/C. 27-Jul-4 Henry Adams, Chichester #384

HOGGAN, Jack (?) British
£1500 $2505 €2190 Amongst the bents (30x25cm-12x10in) s. 16-Oct-3 Lyon & Turnbull, Edinburgh #68 est:300-500

HOGGATT, William (1880-1961) British
£1200 $2124 €1752 Cottage in a coastal landscape (17x23cm-7x9in) s. board. 27-Apr-4 Bonhams, Knightsbridge #108/R est:600-800
£1300 $2236 €1898 Manx Farm (18x25cm-7x10in) card. 5-Dec-3 Chrystals Auctions, Isle of Man #299a est:2000-3000
£2000 $3340 €2920 Moorland glendown (23x30cm-9x12in) s. panel. 20-Jun-3 Chrystals Auctions, Isle of Man #202/R est:1000-1500
£2400 $4008 €3504 Old and new (20x25cm-8x10in) board. 20-Jun-3 Chrystals Auctions, Isle of Man #261/R est:1000-1600
£3700 $6771 €5402 From the artist's garden (15x19cm-6x7in) s. oil sketch paper. 8-Jul-4 Lawrence, Crewkerne #1662/R est:1000-2000
£3900 $6708 €5694 Castletown Square (33x33cm-13x13in) s. board. 5-Dec-3 Chrystals Auctions, Isle of Man #256 est:3000-4000
£5600 $9520 €8176 Artist's garden, Darrag, Isle of Man (50x60cm-20x24in) s. 29-Oct-3 Bonhams, Chester #361/R est:3000-5000
£6600 $12078 €9636 A village courtship, figures outside a cottage (45x60cm-18x24in) s. 5-Jun-4 Windibank, Dorking #336 est:500-800
Works on paper
£510 $918 €745 Calf of man (10x15cm-4x6in) s. W/C. 21-Jan-4 James Thompson, Kirby Lonsdale #24
£600 $1032 €876 Port Erin (13x15cm-5x6in) s. W/C. 5-Dec-3 Chrystals Auctions, Isle of Man #299b
£700 $1204 €1022 Silverburn River (15x20cm-6x8in) s. W/C. 5-Dec-3 Chrystals Auctions, Isle of Man #299c
£1300 $2171 €1898 St John's Valley, Tower Foxdale, Isle of Man (39x56cm-15x22in) s. W/C. 16-Oct-3 Lyon & Turnbull, Edinburgh #75 est:200-300
£1400 $2408 €2044 Burnham Beeches (30x23cm-12x9in) s.i. W/C. 5-Dec-3 Chrystals Auctions, Isle of Man #258 est:600-900
£2200 $3674 €3212 Silver burn (41x56cm-16x22in) s. W/C. 20-Jun-3 Chrystals Auctions, Isle of Man #291
£2500 $4625 €3650 Farm maid feeding geese. Horse drawn cart laden with seaweed on the shore (20x25cm-8x10in) s. W/C pair. 9-Mar-4 Capes Dunn, Manchester #614/R
£2900 $5307 €4234 Hyacinth Wood, Bailrigg (43x58cm-17x23in) s. 27-Jan-4 Gorringes, Lewes #1728/R est:3000-4000
£5600 $10024 €8176 Hyacinth wood bailrigg (46x61cm-18x24in) s. W/C. 7-May-4 Chrystals Auctions, Isle of Man #281 est:4000-6000

HOGLE, Ann (20th C) American
£273 $500 €410 Hills of Hiway 280 (91x122cm-36x48in) 10-Jul-4 Hindman, Chicago #217/R

HOGLEY, Stephen E (fl.1874-1893) British
£392 $675 €572 Landscape with cattle watering (41x66cm-16x26in) s. 6-Dec-3 Selkirks, St. Louis #106/R

HOGUE, Alexandre (1898-1994) American
£2395 $4000 €3497 Live oaks, Glen Rose, Texas (15x20cm-6x8in) board. 18-Oct-3 David Dike, Dallas #195/R est:4000-6000
£4192 $7000 €6120 On the Paluxy (15x20cm-6x8in) board. 18-Oct-3 David Dike, Dallas #193/R est:4000-6000
Prints
£7784 $13000 €11365 End of the trail (23x33cm-9x13in) lithograph. 18-Oct-3 David Dike, Dallas #47/R est:8000-10000

HOGUET, Charles (1821-1870) French
£569 $910 €831 Landscape with buildings and washerwomen by water (37x50cm-15x20in) with sig. verso. 22-Sep-3 Rasmussen, Vejle #398/R (D.KR 6000)
£795 $1446 €1200 Breton fisherman's family on the beach (25x19cm-10x7in) panel. 18-Jun-4 Bolland & Marotz, Bremen #638/R
£2133 $3861 €3200 Kitchen still life with saucepan on little stove (15x13cm-6x5in) s.d. panel. 1-Apr-4 Van Ham, Cologne #1437/R est:1200
£5000 $8350 €7300 Chateau kitchen (74x65cm-29x26in) s.d.1863. 12-Nov-3 Sotheby's, Olympia #155/R est:5000-7000
Works on paper
£302 $556 €450 Retour de peche (12x12cm-5x5in) mono.d.1843 W/C. 24-Mar-4 Joron-Derem, Paris #241

HOGUET, Louis (1825-?) German
£5263 $9685 €8000 Navire de peche (65x81cm-26x32in) s. 24-Jun-4 Tajan, Paris #78/R est:6000-8000

HOHENBERG, Marguerite (1883-?) American

Works on paper

£	$	€	
£941	$1600	€1374	Chronological 219 (51x66cm-20x26in) init. gouache. 9-Nov-3 Wright, Chicago #267 est:1000-1500

HOHENBERG, Wagner (19th C) Austrian

£	$	€	
£4545	$8000	€6636	Question of money (69x100cm-27x39in) s. prov. 18-May-4 Bonhams & Butterfields, San Francisco #100/R est:4000-6000

HOHENLEITER, Francisco (1889-1968) Spanish

£	$	€	
£9859	$17254	€14000	Procession, Seville (80x60cm-31x24in) s.d.MCMXLIV. 16-Dec-3 Durán, Madrid #197/R est:12000
£13043	$21391	€18000	Procesion de La Macarena, Sevilla (80x60cm-31x24in) s. 27-May-3 Durán, Madrid #227/R est:12000
£19928	$32681	€27500	Fiesta en el Puente de Toledo (80x100cm-31x39in) s. 27-May-3 Durán, Madrid #226/R est:20000

HOHENSTEIN, Adolf (1854-?) Russian

£	$	€	
£236	$425	€345	Recitation (20x30cm-8x12in) s. panel. 23-Jan-4 Freeman, Philadelphia #219/R

HOHLENBERG, Johannes Edouard (1881-1960) Danish

£	$	€	
£2705	$5005	€3949	Small girl and cat in garden (81x65cm-32x26in) s.d.1914. 15-Mar-4 Rasmussen, Vejle #58/R est:30000 (D.KR 30000)

HOHLWEIN, Ludwig (1879-1949) German

Works on paper

£	$	€	
£298	$542	€450	Stag and deer in a winter landscape (18x18cm-7x7in) s. W/C pencil. 16-Jun-4 Hugo Ruef, Munich #1163
£350	$601	€500	Woman wearing hat (31x27cm-12x11in) s.i. W/C. 5-Dec-3 Michael Zeller, Lindau #649/R
£417	$688	€600	Deer by wood (35x45cm-14x18in) s.i. W/C over pencil. 2-Jul-3 Neumeister, Munich #464
£1173	$2100	€1713	Woman and two men having drinks (30x30cm-12x12in) s.i.d.1917 gouache W/C. 15-May-4 Illustration House, New York #96/R est:1500-3000

HOHNECK, Adolf (1812-1878) German

£	$	€	
£2222	$3622	€3200	Extensive winter landscape with frozen lake (53x72cm-21x28in) s.i. 25-Sep-3 Dr Fritz Nagel, Stuttgart #1356/R est:1800

HOHNEL, Wilhelm (1871-1941) Austrian

£	$	€	
£455	$773	€650	Dogs (29x42cm-11x17in) s. board. 27-Nov-3 Dorotheum, Linz #491

HOHNSTEDT, Peter Lanz (1872-1957) American

£	$	€	
£291	$500	€425	Autumn in Texas (30x41cm-12x16in) s. board painted c.1930. 7-Dec-3 Treadway Gallery, Cincinnati #552/R
£479	$800	€699	Landscape (46x61cm-18x24in) board. 18-Oct-3 David Dike, Dallas #177/R
£1582	$2500	€2294	Wooded landscape (30x41cm-12x16in) s. 27-Jul-3 Simpson's, Houston #380

HOHR, Franz Xaver Ludwig (1766-1848) French

Works on paper

£	$	€	
£3800	$6954	€5700	Apollon et les neuf muses (15x20cm-6x8in) s.d.1788 gouache prov. 6-Jun-4 Rouillac, Vendome #11

HOIN, Claude (1750-1817) French

Works on paper

£	$	€	
£352	$616	€500	Etude de perdrix (24x29cm-9x11in) i. pierre noire htd white. 19-Dec-3 Pierre Berge, Paris #10/R
£408	$715	€580	Etude d'arbres (26x32cm-10x13in) i. pierre noire htd white. 19-Dec-3 Pierre Berge, Paris #13
£423	$739	€600	Pont avec paysage au loin (25x31cm-10x12in) i. pierre noire htd white. 19-Dec-3 Pierre Berge, Paris #22
£458	$801	€650	Paysage avec arbre et pont (30x25cm-12x10in) i. pierre noire htd white. 19-Dec-3 Pierre Berge, Paris #17/R
£493	$863	€700	Etude d'arbres (25x31cm-10x12in) i. pierre noire htd white. 19-Dec-3 Pierre Berge, Paris #18
£507	$887	€720	Paysage (31x26cm-12x10in) i. pierre noire htd white. 19-Dec-3 Pierre Berge, Paris #20/R

HOIN, Claude (attrib) (1750-1817) French

Works on paper

£	$	€	
£272	$433	€400	Jeune fille a la guitare (15x9cm-6x4in) W/C gouache over crayon. 23-Mar-3 St-Germain-en-Laye Encheres #7
£816	$1461	€1200	Scene galante dans un parc (33x25cm-13x10in) grey wash htd gouache sold with dr by French School. 19-Mar-4 Piasa, Paris #75/R
£1056	$1827	€1500	Portrait de femme (41x53cm-16x21in) pierre noire sanguine htd white chk. 15-Dec-3 Bailly Pommery, Paris #27/R est:1500-2500

HOINKIS, Ewald (1897-1960) German

Photographs

£	$	€	
£2174	$3565	€3000	Untitled (27x20cm-11x8in) s. prov.lit. 30-May-3 Villa Grisebach, Berlin #1201/R est:800-1000
£2778	$4722	€4000	George Grosz (11x8cm-4x3in) gelatin silver prov. 30-Oct-3 Van Ham, Cologne #89/R est:1800
£3533	$6501	€5300	Street scene, Berlin (11x15cm-4x6in) vintage gelatin silver i. verso prov. 11-Jun-4 Bassenge, Berlin #4190/R est:900

HOIT, Albert Gallatin (1809-1856) American

£	$	€	
£6790	$11000	€9913	Portrait of Daniel Webster (64x43cm-25x17in) s. prov.lit. 1-Aug-3 North East Auctions, Portsmouth #940/R est:6000-9000

HOIT, Albert Gallatin (attrib) (1809-1856) American

£	$	€	
£7407	$12000	€10814	Portrait of George Otis Lawrence aged six with spaniel (114x81cm-45x32in) bears i.stretcher. 1-Aug-3 North East Auctions, Portsmouth #826/R est:12000-18000

HOITSU, Sakai (1761-1828) Japanese

Works on paper

£	$	€	
£51630	$95000	€75380	Chofu Jewel River (71x28cm-28x11in) s.d.1785 ink hanging scroll. 23-Mar-4 Christie's, Rockefeller NY #117/R est:20000-30000

HOKE, Giselbert (1927-) Austrian

Works on paper

£	$	€	
£3497	$5944	€5000	Glasing, Burgenland (50x70cm-20x28in) s.i.d.1985 gouache. 28-Nov-3 Wiener Kunst Auktionen, Vienna #631/R est:3500-6000
£4196	$7133	€6000	Picture (79x58cm-31x23in) s.d.10.2.1970 W/C gouache. 26-Nov-3 Dorotheum, Vienna #270/R est:4000-5500

HOKKEI, Totoya (1780-1850) Japanese

Prints

£	$	€	
£1748	$2972	€2500	Surimono (20x18cm-8x7in) s. col print lit. 25-Nov-3 Sotheby's, Paris #85/R est:2400-2800
£2800	$5152	€4088	Still life with a white radish (21x18cm-8x7in) s. i. print exec. c.1820 lit. 8-Jun-4 Sotheby's, London #459/R est:1000-1500
£2800	$5152	€4088	Surimono (20x18cm-8x7in) s. i. print exec. 1829. 8-Jun-4 Sotheby's, London #463/R est:1800-2200
£3000	$5520	€4380	Plaited shell container wrapped in a blue furoshiki (20x18cm-8x7in) s.i. exec. 1833. 8-Jun-4 Sotheby's, London #458/R est:1800-2200
£3400	$6256	€4964	Still life with an egg in a porcelain bowl, stalks of asparagus and more eggs (19x17cm-7x7in) s.i. print exec. c.1817. 8-Jun-4 Sotheby's, London #461/R est:1800-2200
£5000	$9200	€7300	Still life of a interior scene (20x18cm-8x7in) s. print exec. 1834. 8-Jun-4 Sotheby's, London #462/R est:1800-2200
£5400	$9936	€7884	Still life with a bowl, a tobacco pouch, a pipeholder and a box (21x18cm-8x7in) s.i. print exec. early 1820's lit. 8-Jun-4 Sotheby's, London #460/R est:1800-2200

HOKUGA, Katsushika (19th C) Japanese

Prints

£	$	€	
£3400	$6256	€4964	Sewing box with a pin cushion as its lid (20x18cm-8x7in) s. print exec. c.1820. 8-Jun-4 Sotheby's, London #456/R est:900-1200

HOKUSAI (1760-1849) Japanese

£	$	€	
£6500	$11245	€9490	Going around waterfalls in various provinces (38x25cm-15x10in) s. oban. 11-Dec-3 Sotheby's, Olympia #34/R est:8000-10000

Prints

£	$	€	
£1667	$3066	€2500	Figures by river. s. print. 11-Jun-4 Tajan, Paris #189/R est:2500-3000
£1800	$3312	€2700	Poet. s. print. 11-Jun-4 Tajan, Paris #186 est:1300-1500
£1800	$3312	€2700	Poet. s. print. 11-Jun-4 Tajan, Paris #181/R est:1800-2000
£2000	$3680	€3000	Mount Fuji. s. print. 11-Jun-4 Tajan, Paris #188/R est:2500-3000
£2400	$4416	€3600	Mount Fuji. s. print. 11-Jun-4 Tajan, Paris #182/R est:2500-3000
£6000	$11040	€9000	Mount Fuji. s. print. 11-Jun-4 Tajan, Paris #183/R est:6500-7000

HOKUSAI, Katsushika (1760-1849) Japanese

£	$	€	
£6993	$11888	€10000	Koshu (26x38cm-10x15in) s. col print lit. 25-Nov-3 Sotheby's, Paris #98/R est:6500-8500

Prints

£	$	€	
£1748	$2972	€2500	Surimono (20x26cm-8x10in) s. col print exhib. 25-Nov-3 Sotheby's, Paris #86/R est:3000-4000
£1748	$2972	€2500	Bishu (24x34cm-9x13in) s. col print exhib.lit. 25-Nov-3 Sotheby's, Paris #100/R est:1500-2000
£1748	$2972	€2500	Soshu (34x35cm-13x14in) s. col print exhib.lit. 25-Nov-3 Sotheby's, Paris #99/R est:750-1200
£1818	$3091	€2600	Le pont Yahagi a Okazaki sur la route du Tokaido. s. print. 25-Nov-3 Tajan, Paris #369/R est:2000-2200
£1958	$3328	€2800	Senju de la province Murashi. s. print. 25-Nov-3 Tajan, Paris #376 est:1500-1600
£1958	$3328	€2800	En mer au large de Kazusa, deux grandes jonques en mer. s. print. 25-Nov-3 Tajan, Paris #380 est:2000-3000
£2098	$3567	€3000	Le Fuji de Kajikazawa dans la province de Kai. s. print. 25-Nov-3 Tajan, Paris #378/R est:2000-2200
£2119	$3857	€3200	Travellers crossing the dangerous Oi River, Mount Fuji in the distance. s.d.1830-32. 19-Jun-4 Klefisch, Cologne #84/R
£2200	$4048	€3212	The coast at Noboto (25x37cm-10x15in) s. print exec. 1830-1834 lit. 8-Jun-4 Sotheby's, London #368/R est:1500-2000
£2200	$4048	€3212	Water surface at Misaka in Kai province (25x37cm-10x15in) s. print exec. 1830-1834 lit. 8-Jun-4 Sotheby's, London #369/R est:2200-2500
£2500	$4600	€3650	Fuji seen from under Mannen bridge at Fukagawa (24x36cm-9x14in) s. print exec. 1830-1834 lit. 8-Jun-4 Sotheby's, London #343/R est:1800-2200
£2600	$4784	€3796	In the mountains of Totomi Province (25x37cm-10x15in) s. print exec. 1830-1834 lit. 8-Jun-4 Sotheby's, London #354/R est:2600-3000
£2797	$4755	€4000	Joshu Ushibori (25x38cm-10x15in) s. col print lit. 25-Nov-3 Sotheby's, Paris #91/R est:3000-4000
£2800	$5152	€4088	Hodogaya on the Tokaida (25x36cm-10x14in) s. print exec. 1830-1834 lit. 8-Jun-4 Sotheby's, London #370/R est:2600-3000
£3000	$5520	€4380	The Hanging Cloud Bridge at Gyodo mountain in Ashikaga (25x36cm-10x14in) s. print exec. 1833 prov.lit. 8-Jun-4 Sotheby's, London #376/R est:2400-2800

£3007	$5172	€4300	The Mishma Pass in the province of Kai. i. exec. c.1831 col woodcut. 5-Dec-3 Lempertz, Koln #587/R est:1000
£3147	$5350	€4500	Soshu (24x36cm-9x14in) s. col print exhib.lit. 25-Nov-3 Sotheby's, Paris #97/R est:3800-4000
£3200	$5888	€4672	Senju in Musashi province (25x37cm-10x15in) s. print exec. 1830-1834 lit. 8-Jun-4 Sotheby's, London #344/R est:1800-2200
£3200	$5888	€4672	Distant view of Ejiri on the Tokaido and Tago beach (26x38cm-10x15in) s. print exec. 1830-1834 lit. 8-Jun-4 Sotheby's, London #361/R est:3200-3500
£3200	$5888	€4672	Tenpozan in the mouth of the Aji River in Settsu Province (25x37cm-10x15in) s. print exec. 1833 lit. 8-Jun-4 Sotheby's, London #374/R est:3200-3500
£3400	$6256	€4964	Surugadai in the eastern capital (25x37cm-10x15in) s. print exec. 1830-1834 lit. 8-Jun-4 Sotheby's, London #345/R est:3200-3800
£3600	$6624	€5256	Fuji viewing plains in Owari province (25x37cm-10x15in) s. print exec.1830-1834 lit. 8-Jun-4 Sotheby's, London #347/R est:3000-3500
£3600	$6624	€5256	To the left of Umezawa in Sagami province (26x38cm-10x15in) s. print exec. 1830-1834 lit. 8-Jun-4 Sotheby's, London #350/R est:1800-2200
£3600	$6624	€5256	Enoshima in Sagami Province (24x36cm-9x14in) s. print exec. 1830-1834 lit. 8-Jun-4 Sotheby's, London #358/R est:2800-3200
£3800	$6992	€5548	Ushibori in Hitachi Province (26x38cm-10x15in) s. print exec. 1830-1834 lit. 8-Jun-4 Sotheby's, London #355/R est:2800-3200
£3800	$6992	€5548	The sea route from Kazusa (25x37cm-10x15in) s. print exec. 1830-1834 lit. 8-Jun-4 Sotheby's, London #364/R est:2600-3000
£4000	$7360	€5840	Lake Suwa in Shinano Province (25x37cm-10x15in) s. print exec. 1830-1834 lit. 8-Jun-4 Sotheby's, London #352/R est:3500-3800
£4200	$7728	€6132	Pleasure boats on the Sumida River (25x37cm-10x15in) s. print exec. 1835 lit. 8-Jun-4 Sotheby's, London #379/R est:2800-3200
£4500	$8280	€6570	Yoshida on the Tokaido (25x37cm-10x15in) s. print exec. 1830-1834 lit. 8-Jun-4 Sotheby's, London #362/R est:4500-5000
£4800	$8832	€7008	Tsukuda island in Musashi province (25x37cm-10x15in) s. print exec. 1830-1834 lit. 8-Jun-4 Sotheby's, London #348/R est:2800-3200
£4800	$8832	€7008	Group of hunters warming themselves in winter (25x37cm-10x15in) s. print exec. 1835 lit. 8-Jun-4 Sotheby's, London #378/R est:3400-3800
£4895	$8322	€7000	Gohyaku (25x37cm-10x15in) s. col print lit. 25-Nov-3 Sotheby's, Paris #95/R est:5000-6000
£5000	$9200	€7300	Enoshima in Sagami Province (25x37cm-10x15in) s. print exec. 1830-1834 lit. 8-Jun-4 Sotheby's, London #359/R est:5000-5500
£5400	$9936	€7884	The suspension bridge on the border between the provinces of Hida and Etchu (26x38cm-10x15in) s. print exec. 1833 lit. 8-Jun-4 Sotheby's, London #377/R est:2800-3200
£6000	$11040	€8760	Mishima Pass in Kai Province (25x37cm-10x15in) s. print exec. 1830-1834 lit. 8-Jun-4 Sotheby's, London #351/R est:3400-3800
£6294	$10700	€9000	Vent frais par matin clair, le Fuji rouge. s. print. 25-Nov-3 Tajan, Paris #372/R est:4000-6000
£6500	$11960	€9490	Lower Meguro (25x37cm-10x15in) s. print exec. 1830-1834 lit. 8-Jun-4 Sotheby's, London #356/R est:4500-4800
£6500	$11960	€9490	The Drum Bridge at Kameido Shrine (25x37cm-10x15in) s. print exec. 1833 lit. 8-Jun-4 Sotheby's, London #372/R est:3800-4200
£8392	$14266	€12000	Sous la vague au large de Kanagawa. s. print. 25-Nov-3 Tajan, Paris #373/R est:3500-4500
£8500	$15640	€12410	Sudden shower below the mountain (24x35cm-9x14in) s. print exec. 1830-1834 lit. 8-Jun-4 Sotheby's, London #346/R est:8000-10000
£9000	$16560	€13140	Village of Sekiya on the Sumida River (25x37cm-10x15in) s. print exec. 1830-1834 lit. 8-Jun-4 Sotheby's, London #367/R est:6500-7000
£9091	$15455	€13000	Lys oranges et roses (25x36cm-10x14in) s. col print lit. 25-Nov-3 Sotheby's, Paris #103/R est:15000-18000
£9091	$15455	€13000	Pluie d'orage sous le sommet, l'eclair. s. print. 25-Nov-3 Tajan, Paris #374/R est:2000-3000
£18021	$30636	€25770	Volubilis et grenouille (24x36cm-9x14in) s. col print lit. 25-Nov-3 Sotheby's, Paris #102/R est:30000-40000
£41986	$71376	€60040	Gaifu Kaisei (26x37cm-10x15in) s. col print exhib.lit. 25-Nov-3 Sotheby's, Paris #89/R est:25000-30000
£42671	$72541	€61020	Koshu (25x38cm-10x15in) s. col print exhib.lit. 25-Nov-3 Sotheby's, Paris #93/R est:50000-70000

Works on paper

£490	$832	€700	Blaireau (16x11cm-6x4in) ink W/C. 25-Nov-3 Sotheby's, Paris #180/R
£699	$1189	€1000	Deux paysans (9x14cm-4x6in) ink. 25-Nov-3 Sotheby's, Paris #181/R
£769	$1308	€1100	Etudes. ink lit. set of 3. 25-Nov-3 Sotheby's, Paris #197/R
£839	$1427	€1200	Etudes (13x10cm-5x4in) ink exhib.lit. three. 25-Nov-3 Sotheby's, Paris #200/R est:600-800
£979	$1664	€1400	Untitled (13x10cm-5x4in) ink exhib. pair. 25-Nov-3 Sotheby's, Paris #196/R est:500-600
£1049	$1783	€1500	Personnage assis (16x22cm-6x9in) ink lit. 25-Nov-3 Sotheby's, Paris #187/R est:1700-2300
£1049	$1783	€1500	Etudes (19x27cm-7x11in) ink exhib. 25-Nov-3 Sotheby's, Paris #192/R est:1400-1700
£1259	$2140	€1800	Homme assis (10x12cm-4x5in) ink exhib. 25-Nov-3 Sotheby's, Paris #191/R est:1200-1700
£2238	$3804	€3200	Deux hommes agenouilles (13x25cm-5x10in) ink. 25-Nov-3 Sotheby's, Paris #185/R est:1000-1400
£2238	$3804	€3200	Etudes (12x11cm-5x4in) ink set of 4. 25-Nov-3 Sotheby's, Paris #189/R est:1000-1400
£3077	$5231	€4400	Guerrier et bebe (38x27cm-15x11in) ink W/C exhib.lit. 25-Nov-3 Sotheby's, Paris #178/R est:5200-6300
£3636	$6182	€5200	Pieds et formes (10x13cm-4x5in) ink lit. 25-Nov-3 Sotheby's, Paris #182/R est:1000-1400
£4196	$7133	€6000	Arrestation (15x18cm-6x7in) ink exhib. 25-Nov-3 Sotheby's, Paris #188/R est:700-900
£4545	$7727	€6500	Animaux et insectes (29x39cm-11x15in) ink. 25-Nov-3 Sotheby's, Paris #186/R est:1000-1400
£4545	$7727	€6500	Scenes de campagne (14x10cm-6x4in) ink dr pair. 25-Nov-3 Sotheby's, Paris #183/R est:1400-1700
£5245	$8916	€7500	Vieille femme et vieil homme (23x39cm-9x15in) ink exhib.lit. 25-Nov-3 Sotheby's, Paris #190/R est:4400-5200
£5245	$8916	€7500	Etudes (23x14cm-9x6in) ink lit. 25-Nov-3 Sotheby's, Paris #198/R est:1400-1700
£5944	$10105	€8500	Untitled (11x13cm-4x5in) ink pair. 25-Nov-3 Sotheby's, Paris #194/R est:1400-1700
£6993	$11888	€10000	Homme accroupi (7x10cm-3x4in) ink. 25-Nov-3 Sotheby's, Paris #179/R est:1000-1400
£7692	$13077	€11000	Etudes d'hommes (27x40cm-11x16in) ink exhib.lit. 25-Nov-3 Sotheby's, Paris #193/R est:2800-3200
£8152	$15000	€11902	Morning glory (12x40cm-5x16in) s. ink fan mounted on hanging scroll exhib. 23-Mar-4 Christie's, Rockefeller NY #121/R est:15000-20000
£9790	$16643	€14000	Femme de profil (30x23cm-12x9in) ink lit. 25-Nov-3 Sotheby's, Paris #199/R est:4400-5200
£17336	$29471	€24790	Jonque chinoise (27x38cm-11x15in) ink lit. 25-Nov-3 Sotheby's, Paris #184/R est:4400-5200
£20077	$34131	€28710	Combat (17x24cm-7x9in) ink. 25-Nov-3 Sotheby's, Paris #201/R est:2800-3200
£31031	$52754	€44375	Cent poemes (26x38cm-10x15in) ink lit. 25-Nov-3 Sotheby's, Paris #195/R est:10400-13800

HOL, Dag (1951-) Norwegian

£261	$451	€381	Karmoyloe (18x39cm-7x15in) s. panel. 13-Dec-3 Blomqvist, Lysaker #1151 (N.KR 3000)

HOLBAK, Niels (1884-1954) Danish

£295	$501	€431	Dune landscape with farm and figures (43x61cm-17x24in) s. exhib. 10-Nov-3 Rasmussen, Vejle #198 (D.KR 3200)
£298	$550	€435	Landscape from Fanoe (42x56cm-17x22in) s. 15-Mar-4 Rasmussen, Vejle #315 (D.KR 3300)
£299	$500	€437	Old woman spinning in a cottage interior (43x48cm-17x19in) s.i. s.on stretcher. 15-Nov-3 Sloans & Kenyon, Bethesda #478/R
£379	$701	€553	Cottage interior (78x56cm-31x22in) s. 15-Mar-4 Rasmussen, Vejle #421/R (D.KR 4200)

HOLBECH, Niels Peter (1804-1889) Danish

£2692	$4631	€3930	Two brothers (39x31cm-15x12in) mono.d.1843. 3-Dec-3 AB Stockholms Auktionsverk #2542/R est:35000-40000 (S.KR 35000)

HOLBEIN, Eduard Carl Friedrich (1807-1875) German

Works on paper

£417	$679	€600	Martyrdom of the Maccabeen brothers (22x29cm-9x11in) s.i.d.1839 pencil pen W/C. 26-Sep-3 Venator & Hansten, Koln #849/R

HOLBEIN, Hans (after) (15/16th C) German

£8392	$14434	€12000	Portrait de gentilhomme assis (71x52cm-28x20in) i. panel. 8-Dec-3 Rossini, Paris #37/R est:12000-15000

HOLBEIN, Hans (style) (15/16th C) German

£16000	$27200	€23360	Portrait of Sir Nicholas Poyntz (57x41cm-22x16in) i. panel prov.lit. 27-Nov-3 Sotheby's, London #128/R est:5000-7000

HOLBEIN, Hans (younger) (1497-1543) German

£12500	$22375	€18500	Portrait of elegant man (39x31cm-15x12in) panel prov. lit. 8-May-4 Schloss Ahlden, Ahlden #671/R est:7500

HOLBO, Halvdan (1907-1996) Norwegian

£317	$529	€463	Cottage interior (65x81cm-26x32in) s. 17-Nov-3 Blomqvist, Lysaker #1124/R (N.KR 3800)
£409	$707	€597	Landscape (38x46cm-15x18in) s. 13-Dec-3 Blomqvist, Lysaker #1152 (N.KR 4700)
£870	$1504	€1270	Gamleveien (38x46cm-15x18in) s. 13-Dec-3 Blomqvist, Lysaker #1153 (N.KR 10000)

HOLBO, Kristen (1869-1953) Norwegian

£858	$1502	€1253	June evening in Vaagaa (46x55cm-18x22in) s.d.40 s.i.stretcher. 16-Dec-3 Grev Wedels Plass, Oslo #172/R (N.KR 10000)
£861	$1437	€1257	Hay harvest (45x55cm-18x22in) s. 20-Oct-3 Blomqvist, Lysaker #1128/R (N.KR 10000)
£991	$1824	€1447	Landscape from Bessheim (38x46cm-15x18in) s. panel. 29-Mar-4 Blomqvist, Lysaker #1120/R est:8000-10000 (N.KR 12500)

HOLBROOK, Peter Greene (1940-) American

£601	$1100	€877	Chinese snow pea (76x76cm-30x30in) masonite. 10-Jul-4 Hindman, Chicago #218/R est:800-1200
£1200	$2100	€1752	Many faces of Murder (93x93cm-37x37in) acrylic graphite nine attached masonite panels exhib.lit. 17-Dec-3 Christie's, Rockefeller NY #210/R est:1000-1500

Works on paper

£818	$1300	€1194	Grand Canyon from the air (79x104cm-31x41in) W/C acrylic. 14-Sep-3 Susanin's, Chicago #6028/R est:300-500

HOLCK, Julius (1845-1911) Norwegian

£417	$696	€609	Salmon fishing (28x53cm-11x21in) s. 17-Nov-3 Blomqvist, Lysaker #1126/R (N.KR 5000)
£476	$875	€695	Salmon fisherman (28x53cm-11x21in) s. 29-Mar-4 Blomqvist, Lysaker #1121/R (N.KR 6000)
£488	$898	€712	Landscape from Laurvigs area (42x58cm-17x23in) s.d.77 s.i.d.stretcher. 10-Jun-4 Grev Wedels Plass, Oslo #187/R (N.KR 6000)

HOLD, Abel (1815-1891) British

£280	$524	€409	Bird's nest (25x30cm-10x12in) s.d.1881 panel. 20-Jul-4 Holloways, Banbury #310/R
£450	$707	€657	Fallen grouse in a moorland landscape (17x21cm-7x8in) 31-Aug-3 Paul Beighton, Rotherham #497

Works on paper

£320	$576	€467	Still life of a bird's nest with eggs (23x28cm-9x11in) s. W/C gouache htd white. 21-Apr-4 Tennants, Leyburn #991
£560	$952	€818	Bird's nest on a bank (21x27cm-8x11in) s. W/C. 18-Nov-3 Bonhams, Leeds #34

HOLD, Abel (attrib) (1815-1891) British

£900	$1665	€1314	Three grouse at the edge of a woodland, river alongside (25x36cm-10x14in) s. 9-Mar-4 Capes Dunn, Manchester #677/R

HOLDEN, Albert William (1848-1932) British
£368 $688 €537 Friends (21x14cm-8x6in) s. 24-Feb-4 Peter Webb, Auckland #173/R (NZ.D 1000)
£400 $740 €584 Tambourine girl (76x51cm-30x20in) s. 15-Jan-4 Christie's, Kensington #850
£441 $825 €644 Glass of wine (21x14cm-8x6in) i. 24-Feb-4 Peter Webb, Auckland #170/R (NZ.D 1200)
£1780 $3025 €2599 Tempora mutantur - dressed for the occasion (96x50cm-38x20in) s. 24-Nov-3 Sotheby's, Melbourne #284 est:2000-3000 (A.D 4200)

HOLDEN, John (20th C) British
Works on paper
£850 $1352 €1233 Beached fishing smacks, Isle of Man (51x82cm-20x32in) s. pastel. 9-Sep-3 David Duggleby, Scarborough #67

HOLDEN, Raymond James (1901-) American
Works on paper
£549 $900 €796 New England snow (11x15cm-4x6in) s. W/C exec.c.1948. 7-Jun-3 Treadway Gallery, Cincinnati #1464

HOLDEN, S B (19th C) ?
£1250 $1975 €1825 Miss Donovan nee McKay, two years of age holding her dolls (69x49cm-27x19in) s.d.1898. 6-Sep-3 Shapes, Edinburgh #336/R est:800-1200

HOLDER, Edward Henry (fl.1864-1917) British
£310 $533 €453 Coastal view with figure by a cottage in foreground (20x36cm-8x14in) s. 5-Dec-3 Keys, Aylsham #766
£483 $893 €700 Landscape with lake and castle (20x50cm-8x20in) s. 12-Feb-4 Weidler, Nurnberg #383/R
£600 $948 €870 Children playing on a hillside path (56x69cm-22x27in) s. 4-Sep-3 Christie's, Kensington #144/R
£600 $1062 €876 Rural river scene with figures fishing (66x53cm-26x21in) s. 27-Apr-4 Lawrences, Bletchingley #1697/R
£620 $1011 €905 Summertime (44x34cm-17x13in) s. 25-Sep-3 Mellors & Kirk, Nottingham #752/R
£700 $1190 €1022 Patterdale and deepdale (29x45cm-11x18in) s.i.d.97. 26-Nov-3 Peter Wilson, Nantwich #81/R
£894 $1600 €1305 Summer country landscape with cottage and figures (36x46cm-14x18in) s. 21-Mar-4 Jeffery Burchard, Florida #20/R
£950 $1587 €1387 Sheep and cattle grazing in a landscape (32x68cm-13x27in) s.d.97. 7-Oct-3 Bonhams, Knightsbridge #355/R
£1100 $2057 €1606 River landscape with man fishing from a boat (51x76cm-20x30in) s.indis.d. 22-Jul-4 Tennants, Leyburn #823 est:600-800
£1350 $2498 €1971 First glean, early morning Reigate Heath (33x86cm-13x34in) s.d.1894. 11-Mar-4 Morphets, Harrogate #282/R est:400-600
£1429 $2586 €2086 Valley town (29x44cm-11x17in) s.d.96. 30-Mar-4 Stephan Welz, Johannesburg #406/R est:5000-8000 (SA.R 17000)
£1800 $3330 €2628 Cliveden on Thames. Figure fishing from a punt (28x44cm-11x17in) s.d.1893 pair. 11-Mar-4 Morphets, Harrogate #283 est:500-700
£1800 $3222 €2628 First gleam, early morning on Reigate Heath (33x86cm-13x34in) s.d.94 i.verso. 27-May-4 Christie's, Kensington #177/R est:1800-2200
£2336 $3692 €3387 Waterway through gorge (61x45cm-24x18in) s.indis.d.1880. 2-Sep-3 Rasmussen, Copenhagen #1799/R est:15000 (D.KR 25000)

HOLDER, Edwin (fl.1856-1864) British
£2000 $3160 €2900 Orphan family (33x38cm-13x15in) s.d.1858. 4-Sep-3 Christie's, Kensington #315/R est:2500-3500

HOLDER, Gottlieb (19th C) Austrian
Works on paper
£470 $864 €700 Portrait of woman wearing off the shoulder white dress (8x6cm 3x2in) s.d.841 i. verso W/C ivory one of pair. 26-Mar-4 Dorotheum, Vienna #368/R

HOLDER, Gottlieb (attrib) (19th C) Austrian
Works on paper
£664 $1129 €950 Emilie Khun. Friedrich Khun (8x7cm-3x3in) i. verso W/C ivory two. 20-Nov-3 Dorotheum, Salzburg #258/R
£769 $1308 €1100 Karl and Emil Khun with book (9x7cm-4x3in) W/C ivory. 20-Nov-3 Dorotheum, Salzburg #259/R

HOLDER, Kathleen (20th C) American
Works on paper
£232 $425 €348 Sympathetic magix no.8 (127x97cm-50x38in) pastel. 10-Jul-4 Hindman, Chicago #219a/R

HOLDER, Kenneth Allen (1936-) American
£410 $750 €615 Jan's garden (152x213cm-60x84in) acrylic. 10-Jul-4 Hindman, Chicago #220/R

HOLDERNESS, Mark Clark (20th C) American
£359 $600 €524 Washington cathedral stone cutters yard (56x102cm-22x40in) i.verso board. 15-Nov-3 Sloans & Kenyon, Bethesda #119/R

HOLDING, Henry James (1833-1872) British
£7500 $13800 €10950 Logging wagon (88x128cm-35x50in) s.d.1858 prov. 11-Jun-4 Christie's, London #113/R est:8000-12000

HOLDREDGE, Ransome G (1836-1899) American
£838 $1500 €1223 In the Tropics (19x24cm-7x9in) s.d.1870 i.verso board prov. 21-Mar-4 Bonhams & Butterfields, Los Angeles #7328a/R est:2000-3000
£989 $1800 €1444 River in wooded landscape (51x76cm-20x30in) s. 15-Jun-4 John Moran, Pasadena #120 est:2500-3500
£1563 $2750 €2282 Clearing in the snow (51x91cm-20x36in) s. canvasboard prov. 22-May-4 Harvey Clar, Oakland #2434
£2188 $3500 €3194 Mount Hood. s. board. 20-Sep-3 Harvey Clar, Oakland #1537
£3390 $6000 €4949 The cottage yard (50x91cm-20x36in) s. 28-Apr-4 Christie's, Los Angeles #58/R est:2000-3000
£3529 $6000 €5152 Landscape with Indian encampment (51x91cm-20x36in) s. 1-Dec-3 O'Gallerie, Oregon #784/R est:3000-4000
£6358 $11000 €9283 Sacramento Delta (76x127cm-30x50in) s. 10-Dec-3 Bonhams & Butterfields, San Francisco #6158/R est:6000-8000

HOLDSTOCK, Alfred Worsley (1820-1901) Canadian
Works on paper
£338 $574 €493 Ravine near Muskoka River (48x62cm-19x24in) s.i. pastel prov. 21-Nov-3 Walker's, Ottawa #101/R (C.D 750)
£533 $923 €778 Esquimaux River, Quibec (35x52cm-14x20in) s.i. pastel. 9-Dec-3 Pinneys, Montreal #144 (C.D 1200)
£560 $1025 €818 Loggers by a lake, a steamer in the distance (35x51cm-14x20in) pastel. 1-Jun-4 Joyner Waddington, Toronto #349/R (C.D 1400)
£893 $1536 €1304 Indian encampment near the rapids (37x51cm-15x20in) indis.i. pastel. 2-Dec-3 Joyner Waddington, Toronto #132/R est:2000-3000 (C.D 2000)
£893 $1536 €1304 Indian encampment with rapids and distant mountains (37x50cm-15x20in) pastel. 2-Dec-3 Joyner Waddington, Toronto #133/R est:2000-3000 (C.D 2000)
£893 $1536 €1304 Indian encampement (20x32cm-8x13in) s.i. W/C. 2-Dec-3 Joyner Waddington, Toronto #341/R est:2000-3000 (C.D 2000)

HOLESCH, Denes de (1910-) Hungarian
£660 $1036 €950 Chevaux du bonheur (55x65cm-22x26in) s. 29-Aug-3 Deauville, France #184/R

HOLFELD, Hippolyte (1804-1872) French
£4733 $8567 €7100 En hommage a l'empereur, Paris (26x39cm-10x15in) s.d.1863 cardboard oval. 30-Mar-4 Rossini, Paris #815/R est:1000-1500

HOLGATE, Edwin Headley (1892-1977) Canadian
£3000 $5490 €4380 On the Simon River near Morin Heights (21x26cm-8x10in) init. panel prov. 1-Jun-4 Joyner Waddington, Toronto #40/R est:8000-10000 (C.D 7500)
£3600 $6588 €5256 Ste Rose du Nord, Saguenay (21x26cm-8x10in) init. board painted 1956 prov. 1-Jun-4 Joyner Waddington, Toronto #137/R est:10000-12000 (C.D 9000)
£4800 $8784 €7008 Beach logs (21x26cm-8x10in) s. panel painted 1960 prov. 1-Jun-4 Joyner Waddington, Toronto #62/R est:12000-15000 (C.D 12000)
£5405 $9189 €7891 La riviere a Simon Morin Heights (22x27cm-9x11in) init. s.i.verso panel prov. 18-Nov-3 Sotheby's, Toronto #161/R est:12000-15000 (C.D 12000)
£12195 $21829 €17805 Mutton Bay, PQ (22x27cm-9x11in) s.i.d.1930 verso prov.exhib. 31-May-4 Sotheby's, Toronto #5/R est:15000-20000 (C.D 30000)
£27027 $45946 €39459 Laurentian Farm (51x56cm-20x22in) s.i.d.52 board prov. 18-Nov-3 Sotheby's, Toronto #1/R est:40000-50000 (C.D 60000)
Prints
£1931 $3456 €2819 Totems (15x12cm-6x5in) s. num.19 woodblock prov. 27-May-4 Heffel, Vancouver #155 est:2000-2500 (C.D 4750)
Works on paper
£640 $1171 €934 Reposing nude (22x28cm-9x11in) s. ink chl exec. 1940 prov. 1-Jun-4 Hodgins, Calgary #107/R (C.D 1600)
£732 $1310 €1069 Portrait study (29x20cm-11x8in) s.d.1960 i.d.verso ink prov. 27-May-4 Heffel, Vancouver #75/R est:1000-1500 (C.D 1800)

HOLGATE, Ernest (20th C) British
Works on paper
£300 $480 €438 Fleet Street, St Paul's Cathedral, London (48x43cm-19x17in) s.d.1918 i.verso W/C. 16-Sep-3 Capes Dunn, Manchester #840/R
£450 $720 €657 Impressionistic view, possibly Venice (48x74cm-19x29in) s. bodycol chk. 16-Sep-3 Capes Dunn, Manchester #845/R

HOLIDAY, Gilbert (1879-1937) British
£5500 $9185 €8030 Leppin fantasia, Grand National. 21-Oct-3 Gorringes, Lewes #2094/R est:5000-7000
Works on paper
£1700 $3094 €2482 Ireland (37x53cm-15x21in) s. pastel. 15-Jun-4 Bonhams, New Bond Street #20/R est:1000-1500

HOLIDAY, Henry (1839-1927) British
Works on paper
£1383 $2476 €2019 Dante and Beatrice (16x23cm-6x9in) black white chk brown paper exec 1883 prov. 15-May-4 Christie's, Sydney #305/R est:3000-5000 (A.D 3500)
£1600 $2928 €2336 View in the Lake District (30x46cm-12x18in) pencil W/C scratching out prov. 3-Jun-4 Christie's, London #32/R est:2000-3000

HOLL, Frank (1845-1888) British
£4500 $8280 €6570 Boulogne fisher girl (56x41cm-22x16in) s.d.2/66 exhib. 23-Mar-4 Bonhams, New Bond Street #51/R est:4000-6000
£76000 $139840 €110960 Absconded (76x110cm-30x43in) s.d.1879 prov.exhib.lit. 9-Jun-4 Christie's, London #24/R est:40000-60000

HOLLAENDER, Alphons (1845-1923) German
£1325 $2411 €2000 Village fair (33x41cm-13x16in) s. board. 17-Jun-4 Finarte Semenzato, Milan #277/R est:2000-3000

HOLLAMS, F Mabel (1877-1963) British
£550 $935 €803 Lady Luck, bridled grey hunter (30x42cm-12x17in) s.d.1928 panel. 27-Nov-3 Christie's, Kensington #145/R
£550 $1012 €803 Seagull, a bridled hunter (31x42cm-12x17in) s.i. panel. 29-Mar-4 Bonhams, Bath #89/R

£550 $1012 €803 Marconi, a grey (32x22cm-13x9in) init.i. panel. 29-Mar-4 Bonhams, Bath #92/R
£600 $1104 €876 Batsey, a saddled hunter (31x42cm-12x17in) s.i.d.1931 panel. 29-Mar-4 Bonhams, Bath #91/R
£620 $1141 €905 Patricia, a bridled hunter (29x39cm-11x15in) s.i. panel. 29-Mar-4 Bonhams, Bath #90/R
£650 $1105 €949 Bridled dark brown horse (32x44cm-13x17in) s.i. panel. 27-Nov-3 Christie's, Kensington #143a
£750 $1373 €1095 Robin (33x43cm-13x17in) s.d.1937 panel. 8-Jul-4 Duke & Son, Dorchester #216/R
£760 $1360 €1110 Marigold, portrait of a bay hunter. s.i. panel. 16-Mar-4 Bonhams, Oxford #74/R
£780 $1435 €1139 Jessie, head study (30x45cm-12x18in) i. panel. 29-Mar-4 Bonhams, Bath #88/R
£820 $1435 €1197 Spinster, brown ladies hunter (33x43cm-13x17in) s.i. wood panel. 19-Dec-3 Mallams, Oxford #223/R
£850 $1420 €1241 James Gray, a portrait of a grey hunter standing in a stable interior (32x44cm-13x17in) s. board. 9-Oct-3 Greenslade Hunt, Taunton #497/R
£850 $1607 €1241 Charles, a bridled brown hunter (34x45cm-13x18in) s.i.d.43. 19-Feb-4 Christie's, Kensington #328/R
£980 $1529 €1431 Sheba, great Dane on a drive (34x45cm-13x18in) s.i.d.47 board. 28-Mar-3 Greenslade Hunt, Taunton #504/R
£1000 $1580 €1450 Tommy, a bridled chestnut hunter (40x50cm-16x20in) s.i. panel. 24-Jul-3 Dominic Winter, Swindon #100/R est:700-1000
£1150 $2082 €1679 Toffee (32x46cm-13x18in) s.i. panel. 2-Apr-4 Bracketts, Tunbridge Wells #467/R est:500-700
£1250 $2075 €1825 Hilary, a dark bay thoroughbred hunter (30x43cm-12x17in) s.d.37 panel. 3-Oct-3 Mallams, Oxford #225/R est:800-1200
£1250 $2263 €1825 Duke (35x46cm-14x18in) s.i. panel. 2-Apr-4 Bracketts, Tunbridge Wells #468/R est:600-1000
£1297 $2400 €1894 Bruno (33x43cm-13x17in) s.i.d.50 panel. 10-Feb-4 Doyle, New York #168/R est:1500-2500
£1300 $2054 €1885 Bay mare with chestnut foal standing under a tree in a sunlit landscape (33x44cm-13x17in) s.d.1926 panel. 2-Sep-3 Bonhams, Oxford #74/R est:400-500
£1450 $2668 €2117 Equestrian portraits (30x41cm-12x16in) s. panel pair. 8-Jun-4 Peter Francis, Wales #28a est:250-350
£1500 $2505 €2190 Head portrait of the hunter, Cock Robin (12x17cm-5x7in) s.i.d.1932 board. 9-Oct-3 Greenslade Hunt, Taunton #500/R est:800-1200
£1500 $2760 €2190 Peat, the head of a black hunter (34x46cm-13x18in) s.i.d.40 board. 10-Jun-4 Christie's, Kensington #173/R est:1200-1800
£1600 $2880 €2336 Delight (31x43cm-12x17in) s.i.d.1929 panel. 21-Jan-4 Sotheby's, Olympia #357/R est:1000-1500
£1600 $2880 €2336 Dry Toast (33x45cm-13x18in) s.i.d.33 panel. 21-Jan-4 Sotheby's, Olympia #358/R est:1000-1500
£1800 $3060 €2628 Rose Park, chestnut racehorse in a paddock (63x76cm-25x30in) s.d.58. 27-Nov-3 Christie's, Kensington #143/R est:2000-3000
£1800 $3294 €2628 Lady Ursula (33x43cm-13x17in) s.d.1936 panel. 8-Jul-4 Duke & Son, Dorchester #215/R
£2000 $3580 €2920 Chokey - hunter pony. Toby - polo pony (33x46cm-13x18in) s. panels pair. 7-May-4 Chrystals Auctions, Isle of Man #273 est:1800-2400
£2200 $4048 €3212 Susie, a Terrier (33x24cm-13x9in) s.i.d.1928 panel. 10-Jun-4 Christie's, Kensington #363/R est:300-500
£6000 $10200 €8760 Monmouthshire hunt (80x100cm-31x39in) s.d.37. 27-Nov-3 Christie's, Kensington #29/R est:6000-8000

HOLLAND, Brad (1944-) American
£457 $800 €667 Ribald Classic - The Little Peasant (55x42cm-22x17in) ink a. board painted 1970. 17-Dec-3 Christie's, Rockefeller NY #253/R est:1000-1500
£800 $1400 €1168 Ribald Classic - To Wrestle an Angel (90x30cm-35x12in) a. masonite painted c.1974. 17-Dec-3 Christie's, Rockefeller NY #255/R

HOLLAND, Catherine (20th C) British
Works on paper
£320 $589 €467 Self portrait (22x15cm-9x6in) s. W/C. 23-Mar-4 Bonhams, Knightsbridge #252

HOLLAND, Edward (20th C) British
£1300 $2171 €1898 Speedway (46x36cm-18x14in) s. painted c.1950. 16-Oct-3 Christie's, Kensington #693/R est:300-500

HOLLAND, George Herbert Buckingham (1901-) British
£260 $481 €380 Three quarter length portrait of a seated young school boy (80x62cm-31x24in) s.d.1925. 10-Feb-4 Bonhams, Knowle #221

HOLLAND, James (1800-1870) British
£380 $600 €555 Study of a stream flowing through a forest glade from distant waterfall (53x41cm-21x16in) s.d.1873. 4-Apr-3 Biddle & Webb, Birmingham #145
£550 $1018 €803 Palace de la Reine Blanche (34x28cm-13x11in) i.d.1840 verso oil paper. 10-Feb-4 Bonhams, Knightsbridge #111/R
£750 $1388 €1095 Venetian canal scene (38x56cm-15x22in) indis.mono. indis.i.verso. 9-Mar-4 Bonhams, Knightsbridge #170/R
£780 $1404 €1139 Piazzetta, Venice (71x41cm-28x16in) mono. exhib. 21-Jan-4 Sotheby's, Olympia #328/R est:800-1200
£2817 $4873 €4000 On a Venetian quay (51x68cm-20x27in) s.i.d.1860 prov. 10-Dec-3 Christie's, Amsterdam #671a/R est:4000-6000
£3333 $6000 €5000 View of Venice (76x126cm-30x50in) s. 20-Apr-4 Sotheby's, Amsterdam #6/R est:4000-6000
£15294 $26000 €22329 Chiesa di Gesuati, Venezia (41x76cm-16x30in) mono.d.1863 s.i.verso prov. 29-Oct-3 Christie's, Rockefeller NY #241/R est:15000-20000
Works on paper
£280 $512 €409 Study of a statue of a knight on horseback (26x18cm-10x7in) init.i. pencil wash. 3-Jun-4 Lane, Penzance #309
£420 $664 €609 Posy of flowers (15x20cm-6x8in) s. W/C prov. 3-Sep-3 Bonhams, Bury St Edmunds #311
£600 $1020 €876 France from an English farmyard at Dover (26x17cm-10x7in) mono.i. pencil W/C htd white prov. 20-Nov-3 Christie's, London #84/R
£700 $1288 €1022 Balcony overlooking the Rialto Bridge, Venice (41x28cm-16x11in) pencil W/C bodycol exhib. 25-Mar-4 Christie's, Kensington #83/R
£1550 $2806 €2263 Figures on a Venetian quay (34x48cm-13x19in) s.d.1864 W/C. 1-Apr-4 Martel Maides, Guernsey #267/R est:1500-2000
£2400 $4320 €3504 Verona (24x17cm-9x7in) mono.i. pencil W/C. 21-Apr-4 Tennants, Leyburn #923/R est:1500-2000

HOLLAND, James (attrib) (1800-1870) British
£364 $618 €520 Study of roses (28x17cm-11x7in) i.verso board. 26-Nov-3 James Adam, Dublin #32/R
£629 $1170 €918 Boats and gondolas on a canal in Venice (26x36cm-10x14in) 2-Mar-4 Rasmussen, Copenhagen #1306/R (D.KR 7000)
£1447 $2532 €2113 Sunset on the Bosporus (69x119cm-27x47in) 19-Dec-3 Lawson Menzies, Sydney #2116 est:2000-3000 (A.D 3400)

HOLLAND, John (18/19th C) British
£450 $792 €657 Desert mill (50x76cm-20x30in) s.i.d.1865 stretcher verso. 19-May-4 Christie's, Kensington #531/R
£1000 $1670 €1460 Shipwreck of the crown on rocky Manx Coast (46x79cm-18x31in) s. 20-Jun-3 Chrystals Auctions, Isle of Man #183/R est:400-600
£1875 $3000 €2738 Country landscape with figures and children by a stream (86x152cm-34x60in) s.i.d.1872. 21-Sep-3 Bonhams & Butterfields, San Francisco #2796/R est:1500-2000
£2000 $3340 €2920 Peel fishing boats off Bradda Head. s. 20-Jun-3 Chrystals Auctions, Isle of Man #240c est:1500-2500

HOLLAND, John (attrib) (18/19th C) British
£425 $769 €621 Sunset with sailing boats on a craggy coastline with figures (23x30cm-9x12in) 30-Mar-4 Rogers Jones, Clwyd #127/R

HOLLAND, John (snr) (fl.1831-1879) British
£1300 $2327 €1898 Portrait of a young girl by a fence (53x43cm-21x17in) mono.d.1864. 22-Mar-4 Bonhams & Brooks, Norfolk #263/R est:800-1000
£1300 $2431 €1950 Isle of Sark, Channel Islands, with lobstermen on the shore (30x46cm-12x18in) s. 22-Jul-4 Gorringes, Lewes #2009/R est:1000-1500
£10500 $18795 €15330 Outside the Canterbury Arms Hotel (91x132cm-36x52in) s. 26-May-4 Sotheby's, Olympia #71/R est:6000-9000

HOLLAND, Sebastopol Samuel (fl.1877-1911) British
£250 $400 €365 Figures by a country road towards a Nottinghamshire Church (31x46cm-12x18in) s.d.1888 i.verso. 16-Sep-3 Bonhams, Knowle #82
£400 $656 €584 North Wales, summer river scene with angler (41x61cm-16x24in) s. indis.i.d.1882 verso. 29-May-3 Neales, Nottingham #821
£420 $764 €613 Holland in a spring morning at Gedling (29x44cm-11x17in) s.d.1888 s.i.d.stretcher. 5-Feb-4 Mellors & Kirk, Nottingham #591
£500 $915 €730 Figures on a beach, a town beyond (40x66cm-16x26in) s.d.81. 7-Apr-4 Woolley & Wallis, Salisbury #325/R
£620 $1141 €930 Landscapes on the Isle of Man (23x30cm-9x12in) s.d.84 pair. 23-Jun-4 Byrne's, Chester #621/R
£650 $1079 €949 On the Trent (38x58cm-15x23in) s.d.1881. 2-Oct-3 Neales, Nottingham #728/R

HOLLANDER, Hendrik (1823-1884) Dutch
£1788 $3200 €2610 Interior scene of man and woman at a table with an infant, child and servant (74x56cm-29x22in) s. 14-May-4 Eldred, East Dennis #543/R est:1600-2000

HOLLAR, Wencelaus (1606-1677) Hungarian
Works on paper
£26000 $47580 €37960 View of Regensburg (4x13cm-2x5in) s.i. black chk pen ink wash. 6-Jul-4 Christie's, London #171/R est:5000-7000

HOLLAR, Wencelaus (attrib) (1606-1677) Hungarian
Works on paper
£507 $958 €750 Vue d'un Chateau-fort (19x30cm-7x12in) pencil ink. 17-Feb-4 Vanderkindere, Brussels #59

HOLLEGHA, Wolfgang (1929-) Austrian
£10417 $17708 €15000 Untitled (125x117cm-49x46in) s. 28-Oct-3 Wiener Kunst Auktionen, Vienna #239/R est:15000-23000
£14765 $26134 €22000 Untitled (130x125cm-51x49in) s. 28-Apr-4 Wiener Kunst Auktionen, Vienna #275/R est:15000-25000
£17361 $29514 €25000 Untitled (150x105cm-59x41in) s. acrylic. 28-Oct-3 Wiener Kunst Auktionen, Vienna #244/R est:16000-25000

HOLLEMAN, Frida (1908-1999) Dutch
Works on paper
£839 $1443 €1200 Doll's basket (34x46cm-13x18in) s. W/C. 8-Dec-3 Glerum, Amsterdam #357/R

HOLLENBERG, Felix (1868-1946) German
£567 $1020 €850 Landscape (17x25cm-7x10in) mono.d.1912 board. 26-Apr-4 Rieber, Stuttgart #1165/R
£570 $1050 €850 Forest interior (70x70cm-28x28in) s. 25-Mar-4 Dr Fritz Nagel, Stuttgart #722/R

HOLLENSHAW, F and PRATT, J (19th C) British
£1400 $2198 €2044 Feeding the chicks (48x36cm-19x14in) s. 15-Dec-2 Desmond Judd, Cranbrook #827

HOLLER, Alfred (1888-?) German
£306 $504 €440 Maar on the Eifel (58x58cm-23x23in) s. 3-Jul-3 Van Ham, Cologne #1256
£521 $859 €750 Krefeld (31x26cm-12x10in) s. board. 3-Jul-3 Van Ham, Cologne #1257

HOLLEY, Lonnie (1951-) American
£222 $400 €324 Butterfly, 1993 (66x104cm-26x41in) oil giller on paper. 24-Apr-4 Slotin Folk Art, Buford #540/R

£444 $800 €648 Universe 1995 (124x130cm-49x51in) oil on paper. 24-Apr-4 Slotin Folk Art, Buford #538/R

HOLLICK, Elizabeth (1944-) Canadian

£240 $439 €350 Jessica (15x20cm-6x8in) s. s.i.d.1984 verso board prov. 3-Jun-4 Heffel, Vancouver #32/R (C.D 600)

HOLLINGS, Anna (?) ?

£313 $497 €457 Cultural objects (40x40cm-16x16in) s.d.2001. 1-May-3 Dunbar Sloane, Wellington #109 (NZ.D 900)
£761 $1210 €1111 Small sacrifice (49x59cm-19x23in) s.d.2060. 9-Sep-3 Watson's, Christchurch #55 (NZ.D 2100)
£906 $1467 €1314 Moulin Rouge (91x61cm-36x24in) s.d.2001. 31-Jul-3 International Art Centre, Auckland #114/R est:2400-2800 (NZ.D 2500)

HOLLINGS, Russell (20th C) New Zealander

£446 $767 €651 Roses (44x33cm-17x13in) s.d.1995 board. 7-Dec-3 International Art Centre, Auckland #247/R (NZ.D 1200)

HOLLINGSWORTH, William R (1910-1944) American

Works on paper
£4475 $7250 €6534 Rural cabin scene (51x33cm-20x13in) s.d.1940 W/C. 2-Aug-3 Neal Auction Company, New Orleans #408/R est:3000-5000

HOLLINS, John (1798-1855) British

£1600 $2864 €2336 Portrait of Emily, wife of Carteret John William Ellis (129x104cm-51x41in) s. indis d. 11-May-4 Bonhams, Knightsbridge #95/R est:800-1200

HOLLIS, R Wallace (19th C) British

£500 $905 €730 Highland scenes (71x92cm-28x36in) s.d.1882 pair. 2-Apr-4 Bracketts, Tunbridge Wells #490/R

HOLLO, Laszlo (1887-1976) Hungarian

£1015 $1797 €1482 Girl with apples (75x60cm-30x24in) s.d.1959. 28-Apr-4 Kieselbach, Budapest #127/R (H.F 380000)

HOLLOSY, Simon (1857-1918) Hungarian

£70585 $117171 €103054 Pub scene, pledge (65x86cm-26x34in) s. 4-Oct-3 Kieselbach, Budapest #53/R (H.F 26000000)

HOLLOWAY, Edgar A (1914-) British

Works on paper
£300 $501 €438 Hampstead Heath (23x33cm-9x13in) s.i. W/C ink. 7-Oct-3 Bonhams, Knightsbridge #23/R

HOLLOWAY, Edward Stratton (?-1939) American

£8696 $16000 €12696 Virginia Beach (76x127cm-30x50in) s. 27-Jun-4 Freeman, Philadelphia #77/R est:5000-7000

HOLLY, J (?) British

£3000 $5430 €4380 Chiddingfield and Leconfield hunt meeting in the grounds of Puttenham Priory (58x92cm-23x36in) s. 31-Mar-4 Bonhams, Knightsbridge #84/R est:2000-3000

HOLLYER, Eva (1865-1948) British

£1305 $2350 €1958 The letter - young woman reading (53x34cm-21x13in) s. panel. 25-Apr-4 Goteborg Auktionsverk, Sweden #163/R est:10000 (S.KR 18000)

HOLLYER, Frederick (?) British

Prints
£1976 $3538 €2885 Crudelitas and Saevita (16x31cm-6x12in) i. platinum print paper after E Burne-Jones prov. 15-May-4 Christie's, Sydney #428/R est:4000-6000 (A.D 5000)

HOLLYER, Gregory (19/20th C) British

£1105 $2000 €1613 Barn scene with sheep (51x76cm-20x30in) s. 14-Apr-4 Dallas Auction Gallery, Dallas #255/R est:750-1250

HOLLYER, W P (1834-1922) British

£850 $1530 €1241 Highland cattle (30x41cm-12x16in) s.i. 21-Apr-4 Tennants, Leyburn #1118
£1100 $2013 €1606 Head of gundog (20x25cm-8x10in) s. pair. 8-Apr-4 Christie's, Kensington #138/R est:400-600
£1450 $2712 €2117 In the lowlands. Highland farm (61x91cm-24x36in) s. s.i.verso pair. 22-Jul-4 Tennants, Leyburn #822/R est:1500-2000

HOLLYWOOD, William (20th C) British

£480 $878 €701 Belfast Lough from Cavenhill (61x86cm-24x34in) s. 2-Jun-4 John Ross, Belfast #90
£500 $820 €730 Foreshore, Donegal (50x61cm-20x24in) s.d.64. 4-Jun-3 John Ross, Belfast #102
£500 $820 €730 Returning with the catch (40x55cm-16x22in) s. 4-Jun-3 John Ross, Belfast #150
£8000 $14400 €11680 Mallard playing on a lake. Teal at low tide (50x75cm-20x30in) s. pair. 21-Apr-4 Cheffins, Cambridge #502/R est:3000-4000

HOLM (?) ?

£543 $906 €793 Interior scene with woman and child by fire (75x62cm-30x24in) s.d.60. 12-Oct-3 Uppsala Auktionskammare, Uppsala #96 (S.KR 7000)

HOLM, Anders (1770-1828) Swedish

£4000 $6880 €5840 River landscape with figures and boats (64x82cm-25x32in) s.d.1800. 2-Dec-3 Bukowskis, Stockholm #315/R est:30000-40000 (S.KR 52000)

HOLM, Astrid (1876-1937) Danish

£677 $1245 €988 Still life of fruit (45x59cm-18x23in) s. 29-Mar-4 Rasmussen, Copenhagen #550 (D.KR 7500)

HOLM, F (?) ?

£2000 $3400 €2920 German liner Lahn at Bremen (68x103cm-27x41in) s. pair. 19-Nov-3 Christie's, Kensington #581/R est:2000-3000

HOLM, H G F (1803-1861) Danish

Works on paper
£1611 $2949 €2352 Gate of honour for the soldiers return (21x27cm-8x11in) s.d.1851 W/C pen pencil prov. 9-Jun-4 Rasmussen, Copenhagen #2051/R est:20000-25000 (D.KR 18000)

HOLM, Julie and Line (19th C) Danish

£8953 $16383 €13071 Still life of fruit in Greek bowl. Still life of flowers on stone ledge (32x41cm-13x16in) s.d.1839 panel pair. 9-Jun-4 Rasmussen, Copenhagen #1884/R est:125000 (D.KR 100000)

HOLM, Line (19th C) Danish

£895 $1638 €1307 Exotic bird on branch (39x30cm-15x12in) s.d.1840 panel. 9-Jun-4 Rasmussen, Copenhagen #1880/R (D.KR 10000)

HOLM, Ludvig (1884-1954) Danish

£376 $677 €549 Interior scene with woman (47x37cm-19x15in) s.d.1925. 24-Apr-4 Rasmussen, Havnen #2194 (D.KR 4200)
£590 $986 €850 Interior (38x48cm-15x19in) s. 24-Oct-3 Ketterer, Hamburg #180/R

HOLM, Milton W (1903-) American

£538 $1000 €785 Untitled (64x76cm-25x30in) 6-Mar-4 Page, Batavia #128

HOLM, Niels Emil Severin (1823-1863) Danish

£5235 $9789 €7643 View towards Catania with Etna in background, Sicily (37x56cm-15x22in) init.d.1867. 25-Feb-4 Kunsthallen, Copenhagen #501/R est:30000 (D.KR 58000)

HOLM, P C (1823-1888) Danish/German

£936 $1564 €1367 Ship's portrait of the barque Carl Wilhelm (46x64cm-18x25in) s.d.1863. 25-Oct-3 Rasmussen, Havnen #2645/R (D.KR 10000)

HOLM, P C and PETERSEN, H (19th C) Danish/German

£800 $1336 €1168 William Melhuish on its journey from Buenos Ayres to Calloo (45x63cm-18x25in) s.i. 7-Oct-3 Bonhams, Knightsbridge #334/R est:800-1200

HOLM, Per Daniel (1835-1903) Swedish

£1067 $1941 €1601 Mountain landscape (34x62cm-13x24in) s.verso panel. 19-Jun-4 Rasmussen, Havnen #2270/R est:8000-12000 (D.KR 12000)

HOLM, Peter Christian and PETERSEN, Lorenz (attrib) (19th C) Danish/German

£984 $1800 €1437 Dutch barque Voolph in the Sound off Kronborg (46x63cm-18x25in) indis.s.d. i. 29-Jul-4 Christie's, Rockefeller NY #241/R est:2000-3000

HOLM, Wilhelm Lorens (1810-1870) Swedish

£887 $1588 €1295 Still life of wine glass, bread and meat (40x32cm-16x13in) s.d.1849. 28-May-4 Uppsala Auktionskammare, Uppsala #12/R (S.KR 12000)

HOLMAN, Edwin Charles Pascoe (fl.1918-1939) British

Works on paper
£280 $442 €409 Drover with cattle on a bridge (26x37cm-10x15in) s. W/C. 5-Sep-3 Honiton Galleries, Honiton #19

HOLMAN, Francis (1729-1790) British

£55000 $100100 €80300 Action between Lord Hood and the Count de Grasse (98x183cm-39x72in) s. prov.exhib. 1-Jul-4 Sotheby's, London #6/R est:60000-80000

HOLMBERG, August (1851-1911) German

£3974 $7232 €6000 Allegory of the beautiful arts (190x110cm-75x43in) s.d.1875. 16-Jun-4 Hugo Ruef, Munich #990/R est:1500
£6000 $10020 €8760 Rehearsal (109x82cm-43x32in) s. 12-Nov-3 Sotheby's, Olympia #235/R est:4000-4500

HOLMBERG, Gustaf-Werner (1830-1860) Finnish

Works on paper
£1757 $3145 €2600 In the forest (34x29cm-13x11in) s.d.57 pencil. 8-May-4 Bukowskis, Helsinki #210/R est:1500-1800

HOLMBOE, Thorolf (1866-1935) Norwegian

£407 $748 €594 Park landscape with house (65x79cm-26x31in) s.d.1919. 10-Jun-4 Grev Wedels Plass, Oslo #190/R (N.KR 5000)
£435 $752 €635 Two men seated by the sea (38x26cm-15x10in) s. 13-Dec-3 Blomqvist, Lysaker #1156/R (N.KR 5000)

£813 $1488 €1187 Seascape with vessel in rough seas (40x60cm-16x24in) s. 7-Jun-4 Blomqvist, Oslo #229/R (N.KR 10000)
£813 $1496 €1187 Spring landscape with brook (44x66cm-17x26in) s. 10-Jun-4 Grev Wedels Plass, Oslo #189/R (N.KR 10000)
£894 $1646 €1341 Sailing boat at sunset (46x54cm-18x21in) s. panel. 14-Jun-4 Blomqvist, Lysaker #1152/R (N.KR 11000)
£965 $1765 €1409 Summer evening by the fjord (50x65cm-20x26in) s. 2-Feb-4 Blomqvist, Lysaker #1112 (N.KR 12000)
£1220 $2232 €1781 Rowing boat (58x78cm-23x31in) s.d.1901. 7-Jun-4 Blomqvist, Oslo #290/R est:24000-28000 (N.KR 15000)
£1281 $2139 €1870 Archipelago (50x65cm-20x26in) s. 13-Oct-3 Blomqvist, Oslo #288/R est:20000-25000 (N.KR 15000)
£1288 $2253 €1880 Street scene with two figures in moonlight (50x65cm-20x26in) s.d.1905. 16-Dec-3 Grev Wedels Plass, Oslo #351/R est:20000-30000 (N.KR 15000)
£1348 $2481 €1968 Landscape with Lofotveggen (69x99cm-27x39in) s. 29-Mar-4 Blomqvist, Lysaker #1123/R est:25000-30000 (N.KR 17000)
£1721 $2874 €2513 Ducks on mountain lake (95x121cm-37x48in) s/. 20-Oct-3 Blomqvist, Lysaker #1129/R est:40000-50000 (N.KR 20000)
£1876 $3358 €2739 Coastal landscape, Stotthola in Nordland (45x65cm-18x26in) s. i.stretcher. 25-May-4 Grev Wedels Plass, Oslo #13/R est:15000-20000 (N.KR 23000)
£2177 $4006 €3178 Boats off a windswept shoreline (70x89cm-28x35in) s. 14-Jun-4 Waddingtons, Toronto #346/R est:4500-5000 (C.D 5400)
£2435 $4212 €3555 Fishing for coalfish (67x98cm-26x39in) s. 13-Dec-3 Blomqvist, Lysaker #1157/R est:30000-35000 (N.KR 28000)
£2500 $4625 €3650 Boats at the North Cape (57x88cm-22x35in) s. prov. 14-Jul-4 Sotheby's, Olympia #249/R est:3000-4000
£2726 $4688 €3980 Boats along the coast (86x121cm-34x48in) s. 8-Dec-3 Blomqvist, Oslo #493/R est:45000-55000 (N.KR 32000)
£2936 $5256 €4287 Midnight sun at Lofoten (73x101cm-29x40in) s. 25-May-4 Grev Wedels Plass, Oslo #14/R est:30000 (N.KR 36000)
£2994 $5090 €4371 Seascape with bird life and boats in the skerries (65x80cm-26x31in) s. 19-Nov-3 Grev Wedels Plass, Oslo #62/R est:30000-40000 (N.KR 35000)
£4804 $8599 €7014 Sunshine on the coast (109x109cm-43x43in) s.d.1916. 22-Mar-4 Blomqvist, Oslo #399/R est:50000-60000 (N.KR 60000)
£6525 $11680 €9527 Bare rock-face and boats (70x90cm-28x35in) s. 25-May-4 Grev Wedels Plass, Oslo #66/R est:50000-70000 (N.KR 80000)
£6800 $12580 €9928 Midnight sun at the North Cape (114x164cm-45x65in) s. prov. 14-Jul-4 Sotheby's, Olympia #250/R est:3000-4000
£9565 $16548 €13965 Christmas shopping on Karl Johan, Oslo (55x43cm-22x17in) s. 13-Dec-3 Blomqvist, Lysaker #1155 est:40000-50000 (N.KR 110000)

Works on paper
£258 $451 €377 Mountain landscape (36x45cm-14x18in) s. mixed media. 16-Dec-3 Grev Wedels Plass, Oslo #39/R (N.KR 3000)
£402 $736 €587 Manor farm (78x69cm-31x27in) s. mixed media prov. 2-Feb-4 Blomqvist, Lysaker #1113 (N.KR 5000)
£435 $752 €635 Manor house (78x69cm-31x27in) s. mixed media. 13-Dec-3 Blomqvist, Lysaker #1158/R (N.KR 5000)
£500 $836 €730 Hanko (46x62cm-18x24in) s. W/C. 17-Nov-3 Blomqvist, Lysaker #1127/R (N.KR 6000)
£674 $1240 €984 Landscape from Hanko (46x62cm-18x24in) s. W/C. 29-Mar-4 Blomqvist, Lysaker #1127/R (N.KR 8500)
£709 $1184 €1035 Off the coast (45x69cm-18x27in) s. W/C. 17-Nov-3 Blomqvist, Lysaker #1128/R (N.KR 8500)
£1269 $2335 €1853 Boats from Nordland in fresh breeze - borders decorated with fish and octopus (37x63cm-15x25in) s. W/C. 29-Mar-4 Blomqvist, Lysaker #1124/R est:6000-8000 (N.KR 16000)

HOLMENS, Gerard (1934-1995) Belgian
Sculpture
£1667 $2783 €2400 Composition (124cm-49in) marble. 21-Oct-3 Campo, Vlaamse Kaai #446/R est:3000-3500
£6000 $10740 €9000 Fish (72x155cm-28x61in) Rose de Bourgogne marble one of one. 15-May-4 De Vuyst, Lokeren #499/R est:8500-9500
£7333 $13127 €11000 Communication (190x65cm-75x26in) white Carrara marble arduin base one of one. 15-May-4 De Vuyst, Lokeren #513/R est:10000-12000

HOLMES, Catherine Sancroft (19th C) British
Works on paper
£320 $573 €467 Head study of a spaniel (11cm-4in circular) s.i.verso black white chk prov. 22-Mar-4 Bonhams & Brooks, Norfolk #162/R

HOLMES, Dwight (1900-1988) American
£310 $550 €453 Autumn afternoon (91x46cm-36x18in) s.d.45. 2-May-4 Grogan, Boston #83/R
£378 $700 €552 Ruidosa snow (61x74cm-24x29in) s.i. 14-Jul-4 Dallas Auction Gallery, Dallas #335/R
£447 $800 €653 Mountainous landscape. s. 13-May-4 Dallas Auction Gallery, Dallas #2
£838 $1400 €1223 Bluebonnets (38x48cm-15x19in) board. 18-Oct-3 David Dike, Dallas #323/R
£889 $1600 €1298 Lizard Mt, Alpine. South of Pisano Mt Alpine. Alpine, Texas (51x61cm-20x24in) s.i. masonite. 25-Jan-4 Bonhams & Butterfields, San Francisco #3591/R est:700-1000
£2395 $4000 €3497 Fall, Langford Ranch NW of Kerrville, TX (41x51cm-16x20in) canvasboard. 18-Oct-3 David Dike, Dallas #275/R est:3500-4500

HOLMES, Edith Lilla (1893-1973) Australian
£298 $507 €435 Landscape (52x47cm-20x19in) s. canvas on board prov. 26-Nov-3 Deutscher-Menzies, Melbourne #245/R (A.D 700)

HOLMES, Edward (?-1893) British
£979 $1536 €1429 Wooded landscape with young woman and two girls carrying faggots (52x69cm-20x27in) s. 30-Aug-3 Rasmussen, Havnen #2188 (D.KR 10500)

HOLMES, Frank Graham (jnr) (?-1981) American
£648 $1050 €946 Still life with blue vase and fruit on tapestry (76x91cm-30x36in) s. 31-Jul-3 Eldred, East Dennis #872/R

HOLMES, George (18/19th C) British
Works on paper
£250 $425 €365 Avon gorge with the New Hotwell sea wall (28x41cm-11x16in) i. monochrome wash. 4-Nov-3 Bristol Auction Rooms #578

HOLMES, George Augustus (?-1911) British
£820 $1533 €1230 Rude awakening (25x19cm-10x7in) 26-Jul-4 Bonhams, Bath #85/R
£982 $1600 €1434 Pleased to meet you (61x91cm-24x36in) s. 24-Sep-3 Doyle, New York #43 est:2000-3000
£2200 $4092 €3212 Rivals (23x18cm-9x7in) init. 4-Mar-4 Christie's, Kensington #644/R est:1800-2200
£6000 $9480 €8700 But they who come mid frost and flood, peeping from bank (46x56cm-18x22in) init.d.68 painted oval. 4-Sep-3 Christie's, Kensington #306/R est:4000-6000

HOLMES, John J (20th C) British
£300 $552 €438 Racing yacht Irex in the Solent off Norris Castle (60x90cm-24x35in) board. 23-Mar-4 Anderson & Garland, Newcastle #407
£400 $736 €584 Kariad Racing Cicely in the Clyde (60x90cm-24x35in) s. 23-Mar-4 Anderson & Garland, Newcastle #406/R
£680 $1176 €993 J class yachts in the Solent off the Needles (80x100cm-31x39in) 9-Dec-3 Anderson & Garland, Newcastle #472/R
£750 $1290 €1095 Gloucester schooners (86x106cm-34x42in) s. i.on overlap. 2-Dec-3 Sotheby's, London #137/R
£820 $1410 €1197 Discovery, Davaar Cicely and Mariquita on the Thames (61x91cm-24x36in) s. i.on stretcher. 2-Dec-3 Sotheby's, London #128/R
£850 $1522 €1241 Windward leg - Germania leading Britannia and Velsheda (61x91cm-24x36in) s. 26-May-4 Christie's, Kensington #507/R
£950 $1701 €1387 Westward, Astra and Candida racing to windward in the Solent (61x91cm-24x36in) s. 26-May-4 Christie's, Kensington #508/R
£1500 $2580 €2190 Nyria and Rainbow off Norris Castle (61x91cm-24x36in) s. i.on stretcher. 2-Dec-3 Sotheby's, London #129/R est:800-1200

HOLMES, Ralph (1876-1963) American
£344 $650 €502 Dawn at Mt Williamson (20x25cm-8x10in) i. stretcher prov. 17-Feb-4 John Moran, Pasadena #5/R
£437 $800 €638 Mountain town landscape (25x20cm-10x8in) s. paperboard. 10-Apr-4 Auctions by the Bay, Alameda #1581/R
£437 $800 €638 Mountain town landscape (25x20cm-10x8in) s. painted c.1915. 10-Jul-4 Auctions by the Bay, Alameda #544/R
£934 $1700 €1364 California coastal landscape with Channel Island view (61x71cm-24x28in) s. board prov. 15-Jun-4 John Moran, Pasadena #37 est:2000-3000
£963 $1800 €1406 Pink hills (46x56cm-18x22in) s. board prov. 29-Feb-4 Bonhams & Butterfields, San Francisco #4542 est:2000-3000

HOLMES, Walter (20th C) European
£380 $619 €555 Grasmere (34x49cm-13x19in) s.i. 23-Sep-3 Anderson & Garland, Newcastle #377a
Works on paper
£250 $398 €365 Bamburgh beach with the castle in the distance (36x54cm-14x21in) s. pastel. 18-Mar-3 Anderson & Garland, Newcastle #125/R
£440 $700 €642 Cullercoats Bay (35x52cm-14x20in) s. pastel. 18-Mar-3 Anderson & Garland, Newcastle #127/R
£510 $811 €745 Theatre Royal, Newcastle (35x53cm-14x21in) s. pastel. 18-Mar-3 Anderson & Garland, Newcastle #123/R

HOLMES, William H (1846-1933) American
Works on paper
£950 $1700 €1387 Harbour view through wisteria (38x51cm-15x20in) W/C board. 26-May-4 Doyle, New York #66/R est:2000-3000
£1117 $2000 €1631 Hills in bloom. Summertime near Rockville, Maryland (38x51cm-15x20in) one s.verso one init. i.verso W/C paperboard pair. 26-May-4 Doyle, New York #65/R est:3000-5000

HOLMGREN, Vilhelm (1863-1943) Swedish
£853 $1424 €1245 Portrait of Jeanne d'Aragon, married to Prince Ascanio (120x95cm-47x37in) after Raphael painted c.1898. 12-Oct-3 Uppsala Auktionskammare, Uppsala #19 (S.KR 11000)

HOLMLUND, Josephina (1827-1905) Swedish
£813 $1455 €1187 Summer landscape, Northern Sweden (40x58cm-16x23in) s. 26-May-4 AB Stockholms Auktionsverk #2170/R (S.KR 11000)
£1115 $1918 €1628 Coastal landscape (42x61cm-17x24in) s.d.69. 3-Dec-3 AB Stockholms Auktionsverk #2326/R (S.KR 14500)
£1231 $2117 €1797 Summer landscape with country girl and cow at dusk (55x74cm-22x29in) s.d.1870 oval. 3-Dec-3 AB Stockholms Auktionsverk #2356/R est:12000-15000 (S.KR 16000)
£1308 $2249 €1910 Fjord landscape with figures on the shore (63x93cm-25x37in) s.d.88. 3-Dec-3 AB Stockholms Auktionsverk #2522/R est:10000-12000 (S.KR 17000)
£1458 $2682 €2187 Summer in the skerries (91x55cm-36x22in) s.d.99. 14-Jun-4 Lilla Bukowskis, Stockholm #993 est:10000-12000 (S.KR 20000)
£1769 $3043 €2583 Moonlit landscape (60x89cm-24x35in) s.indis.d. 3-Dec-3 AB Stockholms Auktionsverk #2355/R est:10000-12000 (S.KR 23000)

HOLMSTEDT, J (19/20th C) Scandinavian
£459 $739 €670 Fjord landscape (58x79cm-23x31in) s. 25-Aug-3 Lilla Bukowskis, Stockholm #160 (S.KR 6000)

HOLMSTEDT, Johann (1851-1929) Swedish
£355 $592 €500 Steamer in fjord (72x100cm-28x39in) s. 16-Oct-3 Dorotheum, Salzburg #562/R
£420 $722 €600 Lac de montagne (60x81cm-24x32in) s. 3-Dec-3 Beaussant & Lefèvre, Paris #36/R

HOLMSTRAND, Cajsa (1951-) Swedish
£453 $770 €661 Abstract composition (100x100cm-39x39in) s.d.1986. 5-Nov-3 AB Stockholms Auktionsverk #948/R (S.KR 6000)

HOLMSTROM, Tora Vega (1880-1967) Swedish
£314 $544 €458 Eiderducks (53x56cm-21x22in) s. 15-Dec-3 Lilla Bukowskis, Stockholm #432 (S.KR 4000)
£353 $612 €515 Still life of flowers and fruit (50x40cm-20x16in) s.d.41 panel. 15-Dec-3 Lilla Bukowskis, Stockholm #34 (S.KR 4500)

HOLMWOOD, John (1910-1987) New Zealander
£399 $642 €583 Street scene with wheat stack, hops, tree and sun (180x430cm-71x169in) s.d.1971 four-panel mural. 20-Aug-3 Peter Webb, Auckland #2084 (NZ.D 1100)
£761 $1225 €1111 Harbour scene with horse and cart, Maori and Pakeha figures (200x451cm-79x178in) s.d.1971 five-panel mural. 20-Aug-3 Peter Webb, Auckland #2082 (NZ.D 2100)
£1923 $3500 €2808 Quick and the dead (75x55cm-30x22in) s.d.1953 i.verso canvasboard prov. 29-Jun-4 Peter Webb, Auckland #150/R est:8000-12000 (NZ.D 5500)
£5435 $8750 €7935 Captain Cook (200x500cm-79x197in) s.d.1967 five-panel mural. 20-Aug-3 Peter Webb, Auckland #2083 est:1000-2000 (NZ.D 15000)

HOLMYARD, James (1929-) Australian
£250 $393 €365 Tangled nets, St. Ives, Cornwall (26x33cm-10x13in) s. board. 24-Nov-2 Goodman, Sydney #46/R (A.D 700)
£464 $729 €677 Winter, Mt. Hotham (49x67cm-19x26in) s. board. 24-Nov-2 Goodman, Sydney #18/R est:600-800 (A.D 1300)

HOLSOE, Carl (1863-1935) Danish
£359 $668 €524 Heather covered heath (64x80cm-25x31in) s. exhib.prov. 2-Mar-4 Rasmussen, Copenhagen #1241/R (D.KR 4000)
£761 $1400 €1111 Landscape (38x53cm-15x21in) s. panel. 28-Mar-4 Carlsen Gallery, Greenville #375/R
£898 $1671 €1311 Landscape with view of meadow (53x53cm-21x21in) s. 2-Mar-4 Rasmussen, Copenhagen #1390/R (D.KR 10000)
£1343 $2457 €1961 Danish landscape with cattle and milkmaid in meadow (52x58cm-20x23in) s. 9-Jun-4 Rasmussen, Copenhagen #1662/R est:18000 (D.KR 15000)
£1364 $2319 €1991 Still life of herring, hare and pheasants (100x78cm-39x31in) s. 29-Nov-3 Rasmussen, Havnen #2293/R est:15000-20000 (D.KR 14500)
£2175 $3916 €3263 Interior scene with large urn (37x26cm-15x10in) s. 25-Apr-4 Goteborg Auktionsverk, Sweden #226/R est:30000 (S.KR 30000)
£2991 $4725 €4337 Interior scene with chest of drawers, chair, cello and iron stove (33x40cm-13x16in) s. panel. 2-Sep-3 Rasmussen, Copenhagen #1540/R est:20000-30000 (D.KR 32000)
£3081 $4929 €4498 Interior scene with woman seated at table (46x54cm-18x21in) 22-Sep-3 Rasmussen, Vejle #55/R est:30000 (D.KR 32500)
£6075 $9598 €8809 Interior scene with different ornaments on chest of drawers in front of painting (66x55cm-26x22in) s. 2-Sep-3 Rasmussen, Copenhagen #1539/R est:50000-60000 (D.KR 65000)
£8953 $16383 €13071 Interior scene with open door (56x50cm-22x20in) s. prov. 9-Jun-4 Rasmussen, Copenhagen #1461/R est:100000-150000 (D.KR 100000)
£9000 $16380 €13140 Interior with a cello (33x41cm-13x16in) s. panel. 15-Jun-4 Sotheby's, London #356/R est:6000-8000
£10280 $16243 €14906 Interior scene with young girl standing by window (66x52cm-26x20in) s. 2-Sep-3 Rasmussen, Copenhagen #1541/R est:150000-200000 (D.KR 110000)
£12000 $21840 €17520 The open window (73x60cm-29x24in) s. exhib. 15-Jun-4 Sotheby's, London #328/R est:10000-15000
£14000 $25480 €20440 Interior with a bureau (65x61cm-26x24in) s. 15-Jun-4 Sotheby's, London #359/R est:15000-20000
£15123 $26163 €22080 Interior scene with mother and baby by window (57x45cm-22x18in) s. 9-Dec-3 Rasmussen, Copenhagen #1262/R est:250000-350000 (D.KR 160000)
£16260 $29106 €23740 Interior scene with woman reading (38x30cm-15x12in) s. 26-May-4 AB Stockholms Auktionsverk #2376/R est:150000-175000 (S.KR 220000)
£18847 $33736 €27517 Interior scene with woman by mirror (51x42cm-20x17in) s. 25-May-4 Bukowskis, Stockholm #320/R est:150000-175000 (S.KR 255000)
£19696 $36043 €28756 The artist's wife holding their baby daughter looking out of window (57x45cm-22x18in) s. 9-Jun-4 Rasmussen, Copenhagen #1444/R est:250000-300000 (D.KR 220000)
£20000 $34000 €29200 Girl reading by open window (82x63cm-32x25in) s. 18-Nov-3 Sotheby's, London #336/R
£22684 $39244 €33119 Girl reading by window (49x52cm-19x20in) s.d.1909. 9-Dec-3 Rasmussen, Copenhagen #1273/R est:300000 (D.KR 240000)
£26858 $49150 €39213 Interior scene with woman sewing by window (61x50cm-24x20in) s. 9-Jun-4 Rasmussen, Copenhagen #1495/R est:100000-150000 (D.KR 300000)
£38000 $65360 €55480 Mother and child in an interior (79x76cm-31x30in) s. 3-Dec-3 Christie's, London #83/R est:25000-35000
£42056 $66449 €60981 Interior scene with woman reading by window (60x48cm-24x19in) s. mahogany. 2-Sep-3 Rasmussen, Copenhagen #1549/R est:300000-350000 (D.KR 450000)
£42677 $79380 €62308 Interior scene with the artist's wife seated on chair, sunshine coming through (79x68cm-31x27in) S. 2-Mar-4 Rasmussen, Copenhagen #1221/R est:500000-600000 (D.KR 475000)
£48000 $87360 €70080 Mother and child in a dinning room (75x68cm-30x27in) s. 16-Jun-4 Bonhams, New Bond Street #24/R est:30000-50000
£65000 $118300 €94900 Lady reading (70x62cm-28x24in) s. panel. 15-Jun-4 Sotheby's, London #358/R est:30000-40000

HOLSOE, Carl (attrib) (1863-1935) Danish
£2175 $3916 €3263 Sitting room interior (80x70cm-31x28in) 25-Apr-4 Goteborg Auktionsverk, Sweden #225/R est:35000 (S.KR 30000)

HOLSOE, Niels (1865-1928) Danish
£325 $527 €471 Interior (52x44cm-20x17in) s.d.1917 panel. 4-Aug-3 Rasmussen, Vejle #92/R (D.KR 3400)

HOLST, Bjarne (1944-1993) Norwegian
£1098 $2020 €1647 Still life of a cigarette (71x101cm-28x40in) s. 14-Jun-4 Blomqvist, Lysaker #1154/R est:6000-8000 (N.KR 13500)
£1138 $2094 €1707 A picture about Knut W (70x100cm-28x39in) s. 14-Jun-4 Blomqvist, Lysaker #1153/R est:6000-8000 (N.KR 14000)
£1382 $2543 €2073 Figure in a landscape (70x90cm-28x35in) s. 14-Jun-4 Blomqvist, Lysaker #1155/R est:6000-8000 (N.KR 17000)

HOLST, Johan Gustaf von (1841-1917) Swedish
£813 $1455 €1187 The little puppy (33x41cm-13x16in) s. 25-May-4 Bukowskis, Stockholm #211/R (S.KR 11000)

HOLST, Johannes (1880-1965) German
£671 $1235 €1000 Cutter from Finkenwerd on stormy sea (22x33cm-9x13in) s.d.1915. 26-Mar-4 Ketterer, Hamburg #14/R
£1119 $1924 €1600 Fishing smack (36x26cm-14x10in) s.d.1918. 5-Dec-3 Bolland & Marotz, Bremen #723/R est:1000
£1342 $2470 €2000 Cutter from Finkenwerd in full sail (36x48cm-14x19in) s.d.1917. 26-Mar-4 Ketterer, Hamburg #15/R est:1800-2000
£1389 $2264 €2000 Three master at sea (70x60cm-28x24in) s.d.28. 24-Sep-3 Neumeister, Munich #449/R est:2200
£1399 $2336 €2000 Torpedo boat A19 (37x47cm-15x19in) s.d.1916 canvas on board. 11-Oct-3 Hans Stahl, Hamburg #141/R est:1800
£1399 $2336 €2000 Mouth of the Elb with Finkenwarder fishing boats (56x87cm-22x34in) s.d.1918. 11-Oct-3 Hans Stahl, Hamburg #142/R est:2500
£1511 $2478 €2100 Schooner on the high seas (64x96cm-25x38in) s.d. 4-Jun-3 Ketterer, Hamburg #8/R est:2500-3000
£1987 $3616 €3000 The Four-master Passat (57x80cm-22x31in) s.d.1947 board. 18-Jun-4 Bolland & Marotz, Bremen #812/R est:3300
£2781 $5062 €4200 Three master on quiet waters (40x60cm-16x24in) s.d.1938. 19-Jun-4 Hans Stahl, Hamburg #141/R est:3200
£3217 $5469 €4600 Four master accompanied by steamer and fishing boat (80x120cm-31x47in) s.d.1945. 22-Nov-3 Arnold, Frankfurt #552/R est:2000
£3642 $6629 €5500 The four master Admiral Karpfanger (70x100cm-28x39in) s.d.1937. 19-Jun-4 Hans Stahl, Hamburg #140/R est:3500
£3901 $6514 €5500 Three master at sea (65x100cm-26x39in) s.d.1912. 21-Jun-3 Hans Stahl, Hamburg #126/R est:4000
£4965 $8291 €7000 Flying Cloud in full sail (60x80cm-24x31in) s.i.d.1937. 21-Jun-3 Hans Stahl, Hamburg #125/R est:6000

HOLST, L (1848-1934) Danish
£1278 $2198 €1866 Coastal town prospect, possibly Hammerfest (31x45cm-12x18in) s.indis.d.18. metal. 8-Dec-3 Blomqvist, Oslo #405/R est:18000-20000 (N.KR 15000)

HOLST, Laurits (1848-1934) Danish
£1613 $3000 €2355 Ship and other vessels along a coast, the storm has passed (58x94cm-23x37in) s.i.d.1870. 5-Mar-4 Skinner, Boston #320/R est:800-1200

HOLSTAYN, Josef (20th C) German
£6944 $11319 €10000 Still life of flowers, grapes, birds nest and lizard (75x60cm-30x24in) s.i. 24-Sep-3 Neumeister, Munich #450/R est:16000

HOLSTEIN, Bent (1942-) Danish
£587 $1079 €857 Green Nubian III (90x90cm-35x35in) s.d.1986 verso. 29-Mar-4 Rasmussen, Copenhagen #343/R (D.KR 6500)

HOLSTEIN, Gustav (1876-?) Russian
£664 $1109 €950 High mountains (120x145cm-47x57in) s.d.21 i. stretcher. 28-Jun-3 Bolland & Marotz, Bremen #673/R

HOLSTEYN, Pieter (elder) (1580-1662) Dutch
Works on paper
£800 $1448 €1200 Elster (15x20cm-6x8in) mono. W/C Indian ink on pencil. 2-Apr-4 Winterberg, Heidelberg #155/R
£839 $1401 €1200 Seated monkey (15x21cm-6x8in) mono. W/C Indian ink over pencil. 10-Oct-3 Winterberg, Heidelberg #315/R
£839 $1401 €1200 Goose (16x20cm-6x8in) mono. i. verso W/C Indian ink over pencil. 10-Oct-3 Winterberg, Heidelberg #317/R
£933 $1689 €1400 Bird (15x20cm-6x8in) mono. W/C Indian ink over pencil. 2-Apr-4 Winterberg, Heidelberg #159/R
£1538 $2569 €2200 White stork (14x18cm-6x7in) mono. bears i. W/C Indian ink over pencil. 10-Oct-3 Winterberg, Heidelberg #316/R est:2500
£1678 $2803 €2400 Bird (14x20cm-6x8in) mono. i. verso W/C Indian ink over pencil. 10-Oct-3 Winterberg, Heidelberg #314/R est:2500
£1733 $3137 €2600 Lucky cat (14x18cm-6x7in) mono. W/C Indian ink over pencil. 2-Apr-4 Winterberg, Heidelberg #158/R est:2500

HOLSTEYN, Pieter (younger) (1614-1687) Flemish
Works on paper
£1014 $1784 €1500 White duck (15x20cm-6x8in) mono. i.verso pen grey ink W/C gouache. 19-May-4 Sotheby's, Amsterdam #124/R est:1500-2000
£1081 $1903 €1600 Ruff in summer plumage (16x20cm-6x8in) mono. i.verso pen grey ink wash W/C gouache exhib. 19-May-4 Sotheby's, Amsterdam #125/R est:2400-2800
£1736 $2899 €2500 Tulip (30x17cm-12x7in) i. W/C Indian ink. 24-Oct-3 Ketterer, Hamburg #73/R est:2500-3000
£1736 $2899 €2500 Tulip (29x19cm-11x7in) i. W/C Indian ink. 24-Oct-3 Ketterer, Hamburg #74/R est:2500-3000
£1736 $2899 €2500 Tulip (29x14cm-11x6in) i. W/C Indian ink. 24-Oct-3 Ketterer, Hamburg #75/R est:2500-3000
£2466 $4192 €3600 Black tailed godwit (16x20cm-6x8in) mono. i.verso pen black ink W/C. 4-Nov-3 Sotheby's, Amsterdam #144/R est:1500-2000
£5500 $10065 €8030 Tulip - Semper Augustus (31x21cm-12x8in) i. W/C bodycol over traces blk chk prov.exhib.lit. 8-Jul-4 Sotheby's, London #164/R est:2000-3000
£6000 $10980 €8760 Wall lizard (12x20cm-5x8in) s. black chk pen ink wash W/C bodycol framing lines. 6-Jul-4 Christie's, London #172/R est:3000-5000

HOLT, Alf Krohg (1919-) Norwegian
£268 $499 €400 Paysage de montagnes (50x60cm-20x24in) 8-Mar-4 Rieunier, Paris #79

£282 $524 €420 Paysage de campagne (38x61cm-15x24in) s. 8-Mar-4 Rieunier, Paris #34/R
£302 $562 €450 Homme ecrivant (38x46cm-15x18in) 8-Mar-4 Rieunier, Paris #37
£302 $562 €450 Homme aux lunettes a son bureau (45x38cm-18x15in) 8-Mar-4 Rieunier, Paris #39
£302 $562 €450 Village de montagne (47x39cm-19x15in) 8-Mar-4 Rieunier, Paris #45
£302 $562 €450 Village au creux du vallon (41x46cm-16x18in) 8-Mar-4 Rieunier, Paris #54
£302 $562 €450 Arbres au pied de la montagne (61x38cm-24x15in) 8-Mar-4 Rieunier, Paris #61
£302 $562 €450 Village au pied de la montagne (46x55cm-18x22in) 8-Mar-4 Rieunier, Paris #77
£369 $687 €550 Paysage du midi (33x46cm-13x18in) 8-Mar-4 Rieunier, Paris #41
£369 $687 €550 Bord de mer (38x54cm-15x21in) 8-Mar-4 Rieunier, Paris #70/R
£396 $637 €578 Stone quarry (60x73cm-24x29in) s. 25-Aug-3 Blomqvist, Lysaker #1115/R (N.KR 4600)
£403 $749 €600 Village au creux des montagnes sous ciel d'orage (54x65cm-21x26in) 8-Mar-4 Rieunier, Paris #67
£537 $999 €800 Village montagneux au milieu des arbres (46x65cm-18x26in) 8-Mar-4 Rieunier, Paris #75
£570 $1061 €850 Oliviers aux pieds des montagnes (50x60cm-20x24in) 8-Mar-4 Rieunier, Paris #63/R
£570 $1061 €850 Chaise (73x50cm-29x20in) 8-Mar-4 Rieunier, Paris #65
£671 $1248 €1000 Homme assis (81x54cm-32x21in) 8-Mar-4 Rieunier, Paris #69
£671 $1248 €1000 Femme a la toilette (46x38cm-18x15in) 8-Mar-4 Rieunier, Paris #35
£738 $1373 €1100 Nature morte aux pinceaux (81x52cm-32x20in) 8-Mar-4 Rieunier, Paris #68/R
Works on paper
£365 $632 €533 Pavement restaurant (46x55cm-18x22in) s. 13-Dec-3 Blomqvist, Lysaker #1159/R (N.KR 4200)

HOLT, E F (19th C) British
£1500 $2775 €2190 Cows in a landscape (39x59cm-15x23in) s.indis.i.d.1904. 9-Mar-4 Bonhams, Knightsbridge #353/R est:1500-2000
£2000 $3700 €2920 View of a village, with figures and pony and trap (39x59cm-15x23in) s.indis.i.d.1907. 9-Mar-4 Bonhams, Knightsbridge #352/R est:2000-3000

HOLT, Edwin Frederick (fl.1864-1897) British
£407 $728 €594 Views of Hopgood's dairy farm, near Dunstable (51x77cm-20x30in) s.d.1908 two. 4-May-4 Ritchie, Toronto #44/R est:1500-2000 (C.D 1000)
£1400 $2590 €2044 Sportsman's rendezvous (69x51cm-27x20in) s.i.d.1878 i.verso. 10-Feb-4 Bonhams, Knightsbridge #89/R est:600-800
£6077 $11000 €8872 Dan, a specila poodle (64x80cm-25x31in) s.i.d.1879. 30-Mar-4 Bonhams & Butterfields, San Francisco #131/R est:6000-8000

HOLT, Fernando (18th C) ?
£300 $552 €438 Elegant gentleman from 18th Century conversing with lady outside a shop (30x25cm-12x10in) s. 23-Mar-4 Wotton Auction Rooms, Wotton #751

HOLT, Frank (1911-1987) American
£455 $800 €664 Tomorrow comes today (41x51cm-16x20in) s. board painted c.1960. 23-May-4 Treadway Gallery, Cincinnati #741/R

HOLT, Geoffrey (1882-1977) American
£369 $650 €539 Four sentinels (67x86cm-26x34in) s.d.56 board exhib. 23-May-4 Bonhams & Butterfields, San Francisco #6613/R
£401 $750 €602 Venetian waters (61x91cm-24x36in) s. 25-Jul-4 Bonhams & Butterfields, San Francisco #6097/R
£838 $1500 €1223 Native American boy on horseback (61x76cm-24x30in) s. 14-May-4 Skinner, Boston #210/R est:1000-1500

HOLT, Herbert (1849-?) British
£600 $1062 €876 Flowers in red pots (60x50cm-24x20in) s. 27-Apr-4 Bonhams, Knightsbridge #202/R

HOLT, John (20th C) British
Works on paper
£300 $510 €438 Evening cafe, St Tropez (54x44cm-21x17in) s. pastel prov. 19-Nov-3 Tennants, Leyburn #935

HOLT, Lilian (1898-1983) British
£400 $668 €584 London river (84x107cm-33x42in) s.d.1969 prov. 14-Oct-3 Rosebery Fine Art, London #534

HOLTER, Rigmor (1906-) Norwegian
£330 $572 €482 Mountain landscape (49x61cm-19x24in) s. panel. 13-Dec-3 Blomqvist, Lysaker #1160/R (N.KR 3800)
£417 $696 €609 The blue town (81x100cm-32x39in) s. 17-Nov-3 Blomqvist, Lysaker #1129/R (N.KR 5000)

HOLTORF, Hans (1899-1984) German
£403 $632 €580 Summer flowers in stone garden (84x59cm-33x23in) s.d.35 lit. 30-Aug-3 Hans Stahl, Toestorf #74/R
£833 $1308 €1200 Moonlit clouds (84x70cm-33x28in) s.d.62 board. 30-Aug-3 Hans Stahl, Toestorf #72/R

HOLTRUP, Jan (1917-1995) Dutch
£987 $1786 €1500 Farm on forest edge, Acterhoek (35x45cm-14x18in) s. i. on stretcher. 19-Apr-4 Glerum, Amsterdam #232/R est:700-900
£1053 $1905 €1600 Autumn on the Veluwe, near de Steeg (35x45cm-14x18in) s. i. on stretcher. 19-Apr-4 Glerum, Amsterdam #217 est:700-900
£1370 $2329 €2000 Hay wagon (34x44cm-13x17in) s. 5-Nov-3 Vendue Huis, Gravenhage #227/R est:3000-4000
£1447 $2620 €2200 Old Waal-arm (48x67cm-19x26in) s. i. on stretcher. 19-Apr-4 Glerum, Amsterdam #226/R est:400-600
£1745 $3228 €2600 View of a landscape (41x61cm-16x24in) s.d.48. 15-Mar-4 Sotheby's, Amsterdam #123/R est:800-1200
£2632 $4763 €4000 Hay wagon on country path in Limburg (60x50cm-24x20in) s. i. on stretcher. 19-Apr-4 Glerum, Amsterdam #214/R est:1500-2000
£2632 $4763 €4000 Potato pickers with horse and cart (70x60cm-28x24in) s. 19-Apr-4 Glerum, Amsterdam #216/R est:1000-1500
£3288 $5589 €4800 Landscape near Doetichem (48x88cm-19x35in) s. 5-Nov-3 Vendue Huis, Gravenhage #228/R est:4000-6000

HOLTY, Carl (1900-1973) American
£1519 $2750 €2218 Football pyramid (35x28cm-14x11in) s.d.46 s.i.verso masonite prov. 31-Mar-4 Sotheby's, New York #151/R est:600-900
£1934 $3500 €2824 Untitled (35x28cm-14x11in) s.d.45 indis.sig.i.verso masonite prov. 31-Mar-4 Sotheby's, New York #158/R est:600-900
£2486 $4500 €3630 Adria (28x36cm-11x14in) s.d.45 indis.sig.i.verso oil chl masonite prov. 31-Mar-4 Sotheby's, New York #157/R est:600-900
Works on paper
£615 $1100 €898 Untitled (43x28cm-17x11in) s.d.1933 pencil prov. 16-May-4 Wright, Chicago #149/R
£2326 $4000 €3396 Untitled (18x25cm-7x10in) s. brush India ink set of six. 3-Dec-3 Doyle, New York #4/R est:1200-1800

HOLTZ, Erich Theodor (1885-1956) German
£972 $1604 €1400 Factories in Bochum (38x45cm-15x18in) s.d.1926 board. 3-Jul-3 Van Ham, Cologne #1260

HOLTZMAN, Fanny (1895-1980) American
£1599 $2750 €2335 Times Square, New York City (50x60cm-20x24in) s. prov. 3-Dec-3 Doyle, New York #275/R est:4000-6000

HOLTZMAN, Shimshon (1907-1986) Israeli
£355 $650 €518 Reclining female nude (50x65cm-20x26in) s. oil on cardboard. 1-Jun-4 Ben-Ami, Tel Aviv #4920/R
£385 $700 €578 Female nude (50x65cm-20x26in) s. cardboard. 1-Jul-4 Ben-Ami, Tel Aviv #4935/R

HOLUB, Georg (1861-1919) Czechoslovakian
£3497 $5944 €5000 Nymphe Kalisto (100x172cm-39x68in) 24-Nov-3 Dorotheum, Vienna #225/R est:3000-3800

HOLUB, Josef (1870-?) Czechoslovakian
£985 $1635 €1438 Rape field (44x62cm-17x24in) s.d.03. 4-Oct-3 Dorotheum, Prague #61/R est:26000-40000 (C.KR 45000)

HOLWECK, Oskar (1924-) German
Sculpture
£427 $700 €623 The 58-X62 (41x36cm-16x14in) s.i. perforated paper exec.1962 one of 100 prov. 28-May-3 Sotheby's, Amsterdam #132/R

HOLY, Adrien (1898-1978) Swiss
£328 $603 €479 Village (28x46cm-11x18in) s.d.1942 pavatex. 8-Jun-4 Germann, Zurich #806 (S.FR 750)
£381 $610 €552 Portrait of woman in artist's studio (41x33cm-16x13in) s.d.47 pavatex. 15-May-3 Stuker, Bern #1299 (S.FR 800)
£474 $849 €692 Pecheurs au bord de l'Arve (33x46cm-13x18in) s.d.43. 14-May-4 Dobiaschofsky, Bern #87/R (S.FR 1100)
Works on paper
£390 $651 €566 Vieux bateaux immobilises, Oslo (36x57cm-14x22in) s.d. gouache. 21-Jun-3 Galerie du Rhone, Sion #385/R (S.FR 850)

HOLYOAKE, Robert (?) British
£300 $501 €438 Young girl seated reading book by garden (51x41cm-20x16in) s. 17-Oct-3 Keys, Aylsham #758

HOLYOAKE, William (1834-1894) British
£25000 $45000 €36500 Patience (96x122cm-38x48in) s. prov. 22-Apr-4 Christie's, Rockefeller NY #76/R est:50000-70000

HOLZ, Albert (1884-1954) German
£333 $610 €500 Middle mountain landscape with wild deer (100x140cm-39x55in) s.i. 5-Jun-4 Arnold, Frankfurt #608
£979 $1664 €1400 Fox in a winter landscape (60x81cm-24x32in) s.i. lit. 28-Nov-3 Schloss Ahlden, Ahlden #1529/R

HOLZ, Johann Daniel (1867-1945) German
£458 $732 €650 Cows watering (50x80cm-20x31in) s. 18-Sep-3 Rieber, Stuttgart #1179/R
£544 $974 €800 Cows by water (40x61cm-16x24in) s. 17-Mar-4 Neumeister, Munich #490
£1528 $2521 €2200 Peasant woman with cow and goat (88x104cm-35x41in) s. 2-Jul-3 Neumeister, Munich #668/R est:2500
£1881 $2934 €2746 Pasture scene (88x120cm-35x47in) s. painted c.1900. 30-Mar-3 Agra, Warsaw #27/R est:12000 (P.Z 12000)

HOLZAPFEL, Hans (20th C) German
£216 $387 €315 On the way home (38x48cm-15x19in) s. s.i. verso. 22-Mar-4 Philippe Schuler, Zurich #6153 (S.FR 500)

HOLZAPFEL, Ludwig (20th C) German
£625 $1100 €913 Courtyard scene (30x20cm-12x8in) one s. s.i. verso masonite pair. 18-May-4 Arthur James, Florida #105 est:800-1200

HOLZEL, Adolf (1853-1934) German
£278 $464 €400 Figure composition (11x14cm-4x6in) graphite. 25-Oct-3 Dr Lehr, Berlin #210/R
£1000 $1800 €1500 Untitled - mother with children (14x11cm-6x4in) pastel graphite board. 24-Apr-4 Dr Lehr, Berlin #165/R est:1500
£1528 $2551 €2200 Composition (31x21cm-12x8in) col chk. 25-Oct-3 Dr Lehr, Berlin #209/R est:2400
£2778 $4528 €4000 Awakening II (111x123cm-44x48in) s. 27-Sep-3 Dr Fritz Nagel, Stuttgart #9566/R
£5667 $10200 €8500 Capodistria (50x61cm-20x24in) s.i. double-sided. 26-Apr-4 Rieber, Stuttgart #1199/R est:12800
Works on paper
£336 $594 €500 Figure composition (14x14cm-6x6in) mono w/C prov. 30-Apr-4 Dr Fritz Nagel, Stuttgart #832/R
£504 $826 €700 Sketch of landscape with trees (16x19cm-6x7in) chl prov. 3-Jun-3 Sigalas, Stuttgart #495/R
£537 $950 €800 Nude studies. pencil two prov. 30-Apr-4 Dr Fritz Nagel, Stuttgart #828/R
£667 $1200 €1000 Untitled abstract composition (11x14cm-4x6in) pastel postcard. 24-Apr-4 Dr Lehr, Berlin #164/R
£671 $1188 €1000 Figure composition (43x32cm-17x13in) col pen prov. 30-Apr-4 Dr Fritz Nagel, Stuttgart #833/R
£738 $1307 €1100 Worship (24x17cm-9x7in) pencil two prov. 30-Apr-4 Dr Fritz Nagel, Stuttgart #829/R
£805 $1426 €1200 Sketch for crucifixion (84x67cm-33x26in) mono.d. chl canvas prov.lit. 30-Apr-4 Dr Fritz Nagel, Stuttgart #830/R
£851 $1345 €1200 Wander year (15x21cm-6x8in) Indian ink prov. 22-Jul-3 Sigalas, Stuttgart #296/R
£899 $1475 €1250 Figure sketch (14x18cm-6x7in) chl chk prov. 3-Jun-3 Sigalas, Stuttgart #494/R
£1208 $2138 €1800 Meeting (53x65cm-21x26in) s.d. chl board. 30-Apr-4 Dr Fritz Nagel, Stuttgart #826/R est:800
£1477 $2613 €2200 Figures in landscape (33x42cm-13x17in) col chk col pen pencil prov. 30-Apr-4 Dr Fritz Nagel, Stuttgart #824/R est:1500
£1733 $3120 €2600 Untitled - lovers in moonlit landscape (14x11cm-6x4in) pastel on ink. 24-Apr-4 Dr Lehr, Berlin #163/R est:1800
£3333 $6133 €5000 Composition (10x13cm-4x5in) mono. pastel exec. after 1930. 12-Jun-4 Villa Grisebach, Berlin #228/R est:5000-7000
£3356 $5940 €5000 Composition (24x34cm-9x13in) pastel. 28-Apr-4 Wiener Kunst Auktionen, Vienna #125/R est:6000-12000
£4027 $7128 €6000 Idea for stained glass window (27x12cm-11x5in) pastel. 28-Apr-4 Wiener Kunst Auktionen, Vienna #126/R est:4000-8000
£4027 $7128 €6000 From the series ' Colourful tones' (14x18cm-6x7in) pastel. 28-Apr-4 Wiener Kunst Auktionen, Vienna #127/R est:4000-8000
£4027 $7128 €6000 Composition (24x34cm-9x13in) pastel. 30-Apr-4 Dr Fritz Nagel, Stuttgart #823/R est:4000
£5034 $8909 €7500 From the series ' Colourful tones' (18x23cm-7x9in) pastel. 28-Apr-4 Wiener Kunst Auktionen, Vienna #123/R est:5000-10000
£5667 $10200 €8500 Untitled landscape composition (25x34cm-10x13in) s. i. verso pastel board. 24-Apr-4 Dr Lehr, Berlin #162/R est:7000
£5944 $10105 €8500 Landscape with figures (19x23cm-7x9in) s. pastel chk paper on board. 29-Nov-3 Villa Grisebach, Berlin #178/R est:6000-8000
£7000 $12880 €10500 Composition (47x28cm-19x11in) pastel exec. 1932 prov.exhib. 12-Jun-4 Villa Grisebach, Berlin #229/R est:10000-15000
£7746 $13401 €11000 Adoration (30x20cm-12x8in) pastel graphite transparent paper. 13-Dec-3 Lempertz, Koln #154/R est:6000-8000
£10000 $18300 €15000 Composition (52x70cm-20x28in) pastel prov. 5-Jun-4 Lempertz, Koln #765/R est:18000-20000

HOLZEL, Adolf (circle) (1853-1934) German
£1389 $2319 €2000 Biblical scene with two angels (68x84cm-27x33in) mono.d. sack cloth. 25-Oct-3 Dr Lehr, Berlin #211/R est:3000

HOLZER, Adi (1936-) Austrian?
£467 $859 €700 Full moon over the Traunstein and Altmunster (130x97cm-51x38in) s.d.80. 9-Jun-4 Dorotheum, Salzburg #715/R

HOLZER, Jenny (1950-) American
£3631 $6500 €5301 Selection for the living series (53x58cm-21x23in) num.2/5 enamel aluminium prov. 16-May-4 Wright, Chicago #339/R est:5000-7000
Sculpture
£10056 $18000 €14682 Untitled (13x74x11cm-5x29x4in) electronic LED sign red diodes exec 1986 edn 15/50 prov. 13-May-4 Sotheby's, New York #460/R est:15000-20000
£14970 $25000 €21856 Truism footstool (41x58x40cm-16x23x16in) baltic brown granite edition 12 of 40 prov. 13-Nov-3 Sotheby's, New York #147/R est:15000-20000
£20958 $35000 €30599 I am a man (284x24x11cm-112x9x4in) LED sign col diodes edition 2 of 4 prov.exhib. 13-Nov-3 Sotheby's, New York #493/R est:35000-45000

HOLZER, Johann Evangelist (attrib) (1709-1740) German
Works on paper
£267 $483 €400 Martyrdom of St Sebastian (12x12cm-5x5in) i. i. verso pencil. 2-Apr-4 Winterberg, Heidelberg #318

HOLZER, Joseph (1824-1876) Austrian
£11888 $20210 €17000 Zellersee with Kitzsteinhorn (70x94cm-28x37in) s.d.1854. 24-Nov-3 Dorotheum, Vienna #25/R est:11000-13000

HOLZHANDLER, Dora (1928-) British/French
£380 $684 €555 Flower shop (45x35cm-18x14in) s.d.76 board. 22-Apr-4 Mellors & Kirk, Nottingham #1065
£850 $1420 €1241 Judgement of Paris (86x76cm-34x30in) s.d.85 studio st.verso. 16-Oct-3 Christie's, Kensington #614/R
Works on paper
£320 $582 €467 Jerusalem and Rabbis (37x31cm-15x12in) s. W/C. 15-Jun-4 Bonhams, Knightsbridge #75

HOLZHAUER, Emil Eugen (1887-1986) American
£884 $1600 €1291 Coden, Alabama casein (51x66cm-20x26in) s. 3-Apr-4 Neal Auction Company, New Orleans #542/R est:2500-3500
£1209 $2200 €1765 Fort Walton Beach, West Florida (58x79cm-23x31in) s.d.66 masonite. 7-Feb-4 Neal Auction Company, New Orleans #493/R est:3000-5000
£1878 $3400 €2742 Asheville, North Carolina (48x71cm-19x28in) s.i.verso masonite. 3-Apr-4 Neal Auction Company, New Orleans #541/R est:3000-5000
£2088 $3800 €3048 At Bayou La Batre, Alabama (76x64cm-30x25in) s. masonite. 7-Feb-4 Neal Auction Company, New Orleans #494/R est:3000-5000
Works on paper
£414 $750 €604 Black neighborhood scene (53x38cm-21x15in) W/C. 3-Apr-4 Neal Auction Company, New Orleans #564/R

HOLZMANN, Adolf (1890-?) Swiss
£318 $528 €461 The red dress (55x40cm-22x16in) s.d.1912. 13-Jun-3 Zofingen, Switzerland #2881 (S.FR 700)
£405 $697 €591 Girl with doll (48x35cm-19x14in) mono. 8-Dec-3 Philippe Schuler, Zurich #5929 (S.FR 900)

HOM, Poul (1905-1994) Danish
£356 $594 €520 Study of female nude (88x61cm-35x24in) s. 25-Oct-3 Rasmussen, Havnen #4120 (D.KR 3800)
£493 $887 €720 Mother nursing baby (46x60cm-18x24in) s. 24-Apr-4 Rasmussen, Havnen #4237/R (D.KR 5500)
£504 $917 €736 Girl with cat (59x47cm-23x19in) s. 7-Feb-4 Rasmussen, Havnen #4049 (D.KR 5500)
£941 $1599 €1374 Interior scene with small girl (65x65cm-26x26in) s. 26-Nov-3 Kunsthallen, Copenhagen #348/R (D.KR 10000)
£992 $1776 €1448 Interior scene with two girls enjoying the sunshine by window (100x80cm-39x31in) s. 12-Jan-4 Rasmussen, Vejle #664 (D.KR 10500)
£1971 $3548 €2878 Passage of life - composition with figures (205x150cm-81x59in) s.d.40. 24-Apr-4 Rasmussen, Havnen #4275/R est:20000 (D.KR 22000)
£2708 $4982 €3954 Kirsten - the artist's wife (150x98cm-59x39in) s. exhib.prov. 29-Mar-4 Rasmussen, Copenhagen #45/R est:20000-25000 (D.KR 30000)

HOMBERG, Dirk (1885-1952) Dutch
£664 $1110 €950 Camels resting in the desert (32x42cm-13x17in) s.i. panel. 30-Jun-3 Sotheby's, Amsterdam #125/R

HOME, Robert (attrib) (1752-1834) British
£22222 $40000 €32444 Portrait of Edmund Pytts Middleton Esq, accompanied by servants, in an Indian landscape (230x138cm-91x54in) i.d.1800. 23-Jan-4 Christie's, Rockefeller NY #60/R est:30000-50000

HOMER, Winslow (1836-1910) American
£255682 $450000 €373296 Young man reading (36x41cm-14x16in) init. painted 1873 prov.exhib. 18-May-4 Christie's, Rockefeller NY #41/R est:600000-800000
£581395 $1000000 €848837 Last days of harvest (31x51cm-12x20in) s.d.1874 prov.exhib.lit. 4-Dec-3 Christie's, Rockefeller NY #47/R est:1500000-2500000
£1193182 $2100000 €1742046 Farmer with a pitchfork (24x34cm-9x13in) board painted c.1874 prov.exhib. 18-May-4 Christie's, Rockefeller NY #22/R est:700000-1000000
Prints
£17647 $30000 €25765 Saved (58x83cm-23x33in) s. etching exec.1889. 31-Oct-3 Sotheby's, New York #188/R
£17647 $30000 €25765 Life line (33x45cm-13x18in) s.d.1884 etching. 4-Nov-3 Christie's, Rockefeller NY #6/R est:30000-40000
£21469 $38000 €31345 Eight bells (49x63cm-19x25in) s. etching. 30-Apr-4 Sotheby's, New York #15/R est:30000-50000
Works on paper
£3704 $6000 €5371 Boy with cap (9x8cm-4x3in) s. chl gouache prov. 8-Aug-3 Barridorf, Portland #276/R est:6000-9000
£5696 $9000 €8316 Old fisherman (30x25cm-12x10in) s. ink. 7-Sep-3 Treadway Gallery, Cincinnati #562/R est:4000-6000
£261628 $450000 €381977 Young woman (24x35cm-9x14in) s.d.1880 W/C gouache pencil prov.lit. 4-Dec-3 Christie's, Rockefeller NY #26/R est:500000-700000
£441860 $760000 €645116 Boy with blue dory (23x43cm-9x17in) s.d.80 W/C pencil prov. 3-Dec-3 Sotheby's, New York #26/R est:300000-500000
£872093 $1500000 €1273256 In the garden (23x17cm-9x7in) s.d.1874 W/C gouache. 3-Dec-3 Sotheby's, New York #18/R est:1500000-2500000

HOMITZKY, Peter (20th C) ?
£1105 $2000 €1613 Farm panorama (157x183cm-62x72in) 16-Apr-4 American Auctioneer #205/R est:2000-3000

HOMMEL, Conrad (1883-?) German
£377 $640 €550 Portrait of Dr Lersch (115x70cm-45x28in) s. 5-Nov-3 Hugo Ruef, Munich #1021/R

HON, P L (19th C) ?
£1200 $2040 €1752 Fishing fleet running out on the tide (52x74cm-20x29in) s.d.46 panel. 19-Nov-3 Christie's, Kensington #528/R est:1200-1800

HONDECOETER, Gysbert Gillisz de (1604-1653) Dutch
£4000 $7240 €6000 Peasant woman with cows and sheep by canal (434x54cm-171x21in) mono.d.1652 panel. 1-Apr-4 Van Ham, Cologne #1202/R est:6000
£15000 $27000 €21900 Garden of Eden (42x65cm-17x26in) s.d.1644 panel. 22-Jan-4 Sotheby's, New York #191/R est:20000-30000
£15894 $28927 €24000 Orpheus enchanting the animals and trees (66x105cm-26x41in) s.d.1642 panel prov. 16-Jun-4 Dorotheum, Vienna #92/R est:6000-10000

HONDECOETER, Melchior de (1636-1695) Dutch

£9722	$16236	€14000	Cock with hens and chick (63x85cm-25x33in) init. prov.exhib. 22-Oct-3 Finarte Semenzato, Milan #35/R
£22759	$40966	€33000	Landscape with birds (130x164cm-51x65in) s. 26-Jan-4 Ansorena, Madrid #52/R est:33000
£55944	$96224	€80000	Poultry in a garden (126x164cm-50x65in) s.d.1670 prov. 2-Dec-3 Christie's, Paris #411/R est:50000-70000

HONDECOETER, Melchior de (attrib) (1636-1695) Dutch

£3824	$6500	€5583	Barnyard squabble, chickens and ducks (74x71cm-29x28in) s. 31-Oct-3 North East Auctions, Portsmouth #1199
£4667	$8400	€7000	Cock fight (93x122cm-37x48in) panel. 24-Apr-4 Reiss & Sohn, Konigstein #5344/R est:1000

HONDECOETER, Melchior de (style) (1636-1695) Dutch

£3709	$6750	€5415	Proud Rooster (94x112cm-37x44in) 7-Feb-4 Neal Auction Company, New Orleans #186/R est:5000-7000
£5000	$9150	€7300	Farmyard scene with bantam cockerel, hens and chicks (76x64cm-30x25in) 6-Jul-4 Sotheby's, Olympia #481/R est:6000-8000
£5736	$9750	€8375	Fighting cockerel, fowl and spaniel in a garden (119x102cm-47x40in) 22-Nov-3 New Orleans Auction, New Orleans #361/R est:10000-15000
£6154	$10585	€8985	Park landscape with birds (102x125cm-40x49in) 7-Dec-3 Uppsala Auktionskammare, Uppsala #28/R est:100000-150000 (S.KR 80000)
£9877	$17877	€14420	Peacock, rooster and birds by an urn, a baroque palace beyond (212x140cm-83x55in) 30-Mar-4 Christie's, Melbourne #429/R est:8000-12000 (A.D 24000)
£16000	$27200	€23360	Farmyard scene with cockerel, hens, pigeon and turkey (101x94cm-40x37in) prov.exhib. 30-Oct-3 Sotheby's, Olympia #69/R est:6000-8000

HONDECOETER, Melchior de and WEENIX, Jan Baptist (17th C) Dutch

£40268	$74094	€60000	Green parrot with silver tazza. Two monkeys with grapes (156x77cm-61x30in) pair prov. 24-Mar-4 Dorotheum, Vienna #189/R est:60000-90000

HONDIUS, Abraham (1625-1695) Dutch

£979	$1635	€1400	The chase (16x20cm-6x8in) s. panel. 30-Jun-3 Sotheby's, Amsterdam #22/R
£2800	$4760	€4088	Landscape with a hunting party by a stream (63x87cm-25x34in) init. 29-Oct-3 Bonhams, New Bond Street #64/R est:3000-5000
£2937	$5052	€4200	Hunting the flamingo (30x35cm-12x14in) s.d.1686 board. 2-Dec-3 Sotheby's, Milan #69/R est:3500-4500

HONDIUS, Abraham (attrib) (1625-1695) Dutch

£3819	$6302	€5500	Hunting dog with bird rising from reeds (85x77cm-33x30in) i. 2-Jul-3 Neumeister, Munich #550/R est:4500

HONDIUS, Gerrit (1891-1970) American/Dutch

£223	$400	€326	Two figures (70x61cm-28x24in) masonite. 14-May-4 Skinner, Boston #359/R
£223	$400	€326	Two women (76x61cm-30x24in) masonite. 14-May-4 Skinner, Boston #361/R
£242	$450	€353	Two women (76x60cm-30x24in) s. 5-Mar-4 Skinner, Boston #389/R
£250	$425	€365	Portrait of a young lady (76x61cm-30x24in) s. masonite. 21-Nov-3 Skinner, Boston #424/R
£272	$500	€397	Portrait of a lady (51x41cm-20x16in) s. masonite prov. 25-Jun-4 Freeman, Philadelphia #241/R
£276	$500	€403	Untitled portrait (107x61cm-42x24in) s. board. 3-Apr-4 Outer Cape Auctions, Provincetown #71/R
£297	$550	€434	Townsfolk (51x41cm-20x16in) s.verso oil paper on board. 17-Jul-4 Outer Cape Auctions, Provincetown #55/R
£297	$550	€434	Circus clowns (51x41cm-20x16in) s. board. 17-Jul-4 Outer Cape Auctions, Provincetown #87/R
£430	$800	€628	Circus performers (41x30cm-16x12in) s. board painted c.1940. 7-Mar-4 Treadway Gallery, Cincinnati #647/R
£460	$750	€672	Still life (51x41cm-20x16in) s. board. 19-Jul-3 Outer Cape Auctions, Provincetown #58/R
£486	$900	€710	Circus figures. Two women (76x61cm-30x24in) each s. two prov. 13-Jul-4 Christie's, Rockefeller NY #119/R
£541	$1000	€790	Two ladies (76x61cm-30x24in) s. 17-Jul-4 Outer Cape Auctions, Provincetown #26/R
£594	$950	€867	Portrait of a woman (76x51cm-30x20in) s. board. 20-Sep-3 Bunte, Elgin #1218
£682	$1200	€996	Provincetown Wharf (30x41cm-12x16in) s. board. 3-Jan-4 Outer Cape Auctions, Provincetown #61a/R
£914	$1700	€1334	Halloween (60x76cm-24x30in) s. masonite. 5-Mar-4 Skinner, Boston #391/R est:800-1200
£1000	$1850	€1460	Lady with chair (107x61cm-42x24in) s. board. 15-Feb-4 Outer Cape Auctions, Provincetown #75/R

HONDIUS, Hendrik (elder) (1573-1650) Dutch

Works on paper

£5556	$10000	€8112	Farmstead with windmill by a pond (12x17cm-5x7in) d.1625 pen brown ink grey wash prov.exhib. 22-Jan-4 Christie's, Rockefeller NY #116/R est:10000-15000

HONDIUS, Jodocus (16/17th C) Dutch

Prints

£3056	$5103	€4400	Carte de l'Europe. d.1631 col engraving. 21-Oct-3 Galerie Moderne, Brussels #154 est:100-150

HONDT, Lambert de (17th C) Flemish

£1528	$2414	€2200	Wooded landscape with a cavalry skirmish (47x62cm-19x24in) indis sig. 2-Sep-3 Christie's, Amsterdam #66/R est:800-1200

HONDT, Lambert de and TENIERS, David (younger) (17th C) Flemish

£5172	$8586	€7500	Huntsmen resting in interior (60x44cm-24x17in) bears sig. prov. 1-Oct-3 Dorotheum, Vienna #173/R est:10000-15000

HONE, Evie (1894-1955) Irish

£18310	$29296	€26000	Windowsill still life with oil lamp and chrysanthemums (61x91cm-24x36in) s. i.verso prov. 16-Sep-3 Whyte's, Dublin #24/R est:20000-30000

Prints

£3662	$5859	€5200	Man with accordion (42x25cm-17x10in) pochoir silkscreen gouache lit. 16-Sep-3 Whyte's, Dublin #21/R est:3000-5000

Works on paper

£347	$566	€500	Design for stained glass window, Greystones (23x9cm-9x4in) gouache prov. 23-Sep-3 De Veres Art Auctions, Dublin #318
£385	$654	€550	Horseman and hound, study for stained glass window (19x10cm-7x4in) s. 25-Nov-3 De Veres Art Auctions, Dublin #183
£420	$713	€600	Head of a Saint, for stained glass window (22x14cm-9x6in) Indian ink W/C. 25-Nov-3 De Veres Art Auctions, Dublin #184
£573	$975	€820	Study for stained glass window (21x9cm-8x4in) gouache prov. 25-Nov-3 De Veres Art Auctions, Dublin #223
£769	$1308	€1100	Cockerel, study for stained glass window (26x19cm-10x7in) gouache. 25-Nov-3 De Veres Art Auctions, Dublin #180/R est:600-900
£909	$1545	€1300	Study for a stained glass window - Tullabeg (38x10cm-15x4in) gouache. 25-Nov-3 De Veres Art Auctions, Dublin #179/R est:800-1200
£909	$1545	€1300	Nativity, study for stained glass window (26x8cm-10x3in) gouache. 25-Nov-3 De Veres Art Auctions, Dublin #182/R est:500-700
£1049	$1783	€1500	Seascape (19x33cm-7x13in) gouache prov. 25-Nov-3 De Veres Art Auctions, Dublin #21/R est:1500-2000
£1119	$1902	€1600	Ascension, study for stained glass window (21x5cm-8x2in) gouache diptych. 25-Nov-3 De Veres Art Auctions, Dublin #181/R est:800-1200
£1216	$2299	€1800	Marriage feast of Cana and the Parable of the Virgins and the lamps (38x11cm-15x4in) gouache board prov. 17-Feb-4 Whyte's, Dublin #12/R est:1000-2200
£1399	$2378	€2000	Garden view (22x28cm-9x11in) W/C exhib. 18-Nov-3 Whyte's, Dublin #13/R est:2000-3000
£2050	$3834	€2993	St Francis and lady Poverty (33x18cm-13x7in) s. W/C bodycol. 20-Jul-4 Sworder & Son, Bishops Stortford #709/R est:300-500
£2200	$3938	€3212	Head of Christ (85x66cm-33x26in) gouache. 14-May-4 Christie's, Kensington #448/R est:1200-1800
£7000	$12530	€10220	Cubist composition (51x71cm-20x28in) gouache prov. 14-May-4 Christie's, London #11/R est:7000-10000

HONE, Geraldine (?) Irish?

£1600	$2896	€2400	Coastal landscape (61x76cm-24x30in) s. 30-Mar-4 De Veres Art Auctions, Dublin #197/R est:2000-3000
£1818	$3091	€2600	Edge of the pond (61x56cm-24x22in) s. 25-Nov-3 De Veres Art Auctions, Dublin #172 est:1400-1800

HONE, Horace (1756-1825) British

Miniatures

£1800	$3222	€2628	Gentleman called Mr Mullen, in brown coat (7cm-3in) init.d.1796 silver gilt frame plaited hair. 25-May-4 Christie's, London #146/R est:2000-3000
£2000	$3460	€2920	Sir Thomas Apprede (8cm-3in) s.d.1795 oval prov. 9-Dec-3 Christie's, London #169/R est:2000-3000
£2200	$3806	€3212	Gentleman in brown coat (8cm-3in) mono.d.1796 oval. 9-Dec-3 Christie's, London #168/R est:2000-3000
£2800	$4844	€4088	Gentleman in brown coat (7cm-3in) mono.d.1793 oval. 9-Dec-3 Christie's, London #166/R est:2000-3000
£3356	$6007	€5000	Portrait of Joseph Hone in military uniform (7x6cm-3x2in) W/C on ivory. 26-May-4 James Adam, Dublin #15/R est:5000-7000
£3356	$6007	€5000	Portrait of Nathaniel Hone (4x3cm-2x1in) W/C on ivory gilt locket prov. 26-May-4 James Adam, Dublin #16
£4500	$8100	€6570	Lieutenant Sir Richard McQuire (7cm-3in) gold frame oval exhib. 22-Apr-4 Bonhams, New Bond Street #121/R est:3000-5000
£4698	$8409	€7000	Portrait of Joseph Hone (7x6cm-3x2in) W/C on ivory gold locket. 26-May-4 James Adam, Dublin #17/R est:5000-7000
£5800	$9860	€8468	John Philip Kemble (8cm-3in) mono.d.1786 verso octagonal prov. 18-Nov-3 Bonhams, New Bond Street #173/R est:3000-5000
£8500	$15300	€12410	Lieutenant and Captain the Hon William George Crofton (7cm-3in) mono.d.1814 gold frame oval exhib. 22-Apr-4 Bonhams, New Bond Street #123/R est:5000-7000

Works on paper

£2100	$3570	€3066	George IV (23cm-9in) s.i.d.1812 verso pencil W/C card prov. 18-Nov-3 Bonhams, New Bond Street #144/R est:2000-3000

HONE, Nathaniel I (1718-1784) British

£10500	$17850	€15330	Portrait of Master Meynell wearing van Dyck dress (74x62cm-29x24in) oval. 27-Nov-3 Sotheby's, London #142/R est:6000-8000
£20000	$35800	€29200	Portrait of a lady, believed to be Lady Juliana Colyer (76x63cm-30x25in) init.d.1757. 22-Mar-4 Bonhams & Brooks, Norfolk #369/R est:20000-30000
£23000	$41170	€33580	Portrait of a lady, half-length, wearing a shawl (50x40cm-20x16in) mono.d.1771. 13-May-4 Sotheby's, London #3/R est:8000-12000
£105000	$187950	€153300	Portrait of the artist, half-length, in a brown coat, holding a canvas and pen (76x63cm-30x25in) prov.exhib. 14-May-4 Christie's, London #107/R est:30000-50000

Miniatures

£1300	$2327	€1898	Young gentleman, facing right in gold-bordered blue velvet coat (3cm-1in) mono.d.1758 enamel oval gilt-metal bracelet clasp frame prov. 14-May-4 Christie's, London #64/R est:1000-1500
£1300	$2327	€1898	Gentleman, Admiral Keith Stewart, facing left in gold-bordered blue coat (3cm-1in) mono.d.1760 oval gold bracelet clasp frame prov. 14-May-4 Christie's, London #65/R est:400-600
£1500	$2685	€2190	Gentleman, believed to be John, 7th Earl of Galloway, facing right (3cm-1in) mono.d.1759 oval gold bracelet clasp frame prov. 14-May-4 Christie's, London #63/R est:800-1200
£1700	$2890	€2482	Gentleman (5cm-2in) s.d.1750 enamel oval. 18-Nov-3 Bonhams, New Bond Street #40/R est:1500-2000

Works on paper

£1342	$2376	€2000	Head of a lady (15x12cm-6x5in) indis.i.verso pencil red chl rag paper prov.lit. 27-Apr-4 Whyte's, Dublin #129/R est:1200-1500

HONE, Nathaniel I (attrib) (1718-1784) British

£8000	$13600	€11680	Portrait of a young girl in a pink dress, peering from behind a green curtain (61x47cm-24x19in) 25-Nov-3 Christie's, London #34/R est:3000-5000

£8721 $15000 €12733 Portrait of a lady, half length, in a decollete dress (79x64cm-31x25in) prov. 7-Dec-3 Freeman, Philadelphia #13 est:4000-6000

HONE, Nathaniel I (circle) (1718-1784) British
£7500 $13425 €10950 Portrait of a young boy, possibly Master Ridley, three-quarter-length (76x63cm-30x25in) prov. 14-May-4 Christie's, London #117/R est:4000-6000

HONE, Nathaniel II (1831-1917) Irish
£2763 $5084 €4200 Coastal landscape (18x26cm-7x10in) canvasboard prov. 22-Jun-4 De Veres Art Auctions, Dublin #111/R est:3500-4500
£3900 $6981 €5694 Sheep under trees (20x27cm-8x11in) canvasboard prov. 14-May-4 Christie's, London #16/R est:2000-3000
£4085 $7066 €5800 Sea and brig (25x37cm-10x15in) prov. 10-Dec-3 Bonhams & James Adam, Dublin #32/R est:5000-7000
£4161 $7448 €6200 Cows in landscape (60x90cm-24x35in) 26-May-4 James Adam, Dublin #41/R est:6000-10000
£4500 $8055 €6570 Figures under a tree (38x46cm-15x18in) prov. 14-May-4 Christie's, London #15/R est:5000-8000
£5594 $9510 €8000 Cattle in pasture, Malahide (26x36cm-10x14in) init. canvas on board prov. 25-Nov-3 De Veres Art Auctions, Dublin #32/R est:7000-10000
£5594 $9510 €8000 Coastal landscape, Malahide (29x46cm-11x18in) init. canvas on board. 25-Nov-3 De Veres Art Auctions, Dublin #51/R est:9000-12000
£10067 $17819 €15000 Silver birch (43x69cm-17x27in) init. prov. 27-Apr-4 Whyte's, Dublin #119/R est:15000-20000
£15436 $27631 €23000 Cows at Malahide (36x52cm-14x20in) 26-May-4 James Adam, Dublin #40/R est:12500-18500
Works on paper
£538 $915 €770 Hilly pasture (12x17cm-5x7in) W/C. 25-Nov-3 De Veres Art Auctions, Dublin #99/R
£799 $1302 €1150 Path under green trees (24x17cm-9x7in) studio st. W/C prov. 24-Sep-3 James Adam, Dublin #22/R est:600-800

HONE, Robert (attrib) (18th C) ?
£25166 $46053 €38000 Portrait d'un jeune garcon en rouge et de ses deux soeurs (150x110cm-59x43in) 7-Apr-4 Libert, Castor, Paris #23/R est:6000-10000

HONEDER, Walter (1906-) Austrian
£638 $1066 €900 Evening Dolomites (66x50cm-26x20in) s. i.d.1988 verso oil mixed media board. 16-Oct-3 Dorotheum, Salzburg #811/R
£851 $1421 €1200 Rossl in the Au (37x55cm-15x22in) s. 16-Oct-3 Dorotheum, Salzburg #689/R
£1645 $3026 €2500 Beach in Italy (56x80cm-22x31in) s. i.verso panel. 22-Jun-4 Wiener Kunst Auktionen, Vienna #59/R est:2500
Works on paper
£828 $1514 €1200 Trains, railway lines at night (74x51cm-29x20in) s. pastel prov. 27-Jan-4 Dorotheum, Vienna #123/R

HONEGGER, Gottfried (1917-) Swiss
£1435 $2440 €2095 Etude (56x56cm-22x22in) s.i.d.1983 acrylic prov. 5-Nov-3 AB Stockholms Auktionsverk #1151/R est:20000-25000 (S.KR 19000)
£2190 $3724 €3197 Etude 20 (42x42cm-17x17in) s.d.1979 verso acrylic prov. 5-Nov-3 AB Stockholms Auktionsverk #944/R est:15000-20000 (S.KR 29000)
£2266 $3852 €3308 Z593 (103x78cm-41x31in) s.i.d.1969 oil on glass fibre prov. 5-Nov-3 AB Stockholms Auktionsverk #985/R est:20000-30000 (S.KR 30000)
£5430 $9068 €7928 Z91 (140x60cm-55x24in) s.i.d.1977 acrylic two parts. 24-Jun-3 Germann, Zurich #82/R est:10000-12000 (S.FR 12000)
£7424 $13659 €10839 Z 785 (150x150cm-59x59in) s.d.1977 verso exhib. 8-Jun-4 Germann, Zurich #65/R est:13000-18000 (S.FR 17000)
£10044 $17978 €14664 PZ 17 (100x100cm-39x39in) s.i.d.1962-63 verso tableau-relief oil plate exhib. 26-May-4 Sotheby's, Zurich #158/R est:8000-12000 (S.FR 23000)
Sculpture
£1465 $2593 €2139 Fragment 18 (41cm-16in) s.num.2/2 steel prov. 27-Apr-4 AB Stockholms Auktionsverk #1015/R est:20000-25000 (S.KR 20000)
Works on paper
£282 $454 €400 Esquisse pour vitraux (64x49cm-25x19in) s.i.d.1991 col crayon prov. 11-May-3 Versailles Encheres #193
£667 $1226 €1000 Composition (104x74cm-41x29in) s.d.79 verso col felt pen crayon board. 9-Jun-4 Artcurial Briest, Paris #537/R est:1500-2000

HONG LING (1955-) Chinese
£2614 $4732 €3816 Torrent of snow (80x100cm-31x39in) s.d.2003 lit. 3-Apr-4 Glerum, Singapore #84/R est:9000-12000 (S.D 8000)
£7112 $12802 €10384 Snowy bamboo and latent hut (70x200cm-28x79in) s.d.2003. 25-Apr-4 Christie's, Hong Kong #729/R est:100000-120000 (HK.D 100000)

HONG TONG (1920-1987) Chinese
Works on paper
£15444 $25792 €22548 Festival (138x43cm-54x17in) s. mixed media paper on board lit. 26-Oct-3 Christie's, Hong Kong #110/R est:250000-300000 (HK.D 200000)
£34749 $58031 €50734 Phoenix and lion (62x122cm-24x48in) mixed media on board executed c.1972-76. 26-Oct-3 Christie's, Hong Kong #111/R est:300000-400000 (HK.D 450000)

HONGYI (1880-1942) Chinese
Works on paper
£4267 $7681 €6230 Calligraphy in standard script (68x33cm-27x13in) s.i. ink scroll. 25-Apr-4 Christie's, Hong Kong #15/R est:10000-12000 (HK.D 60000)

HONIGBERGER, Ernst (?) German
£470 $864 €700 Still life of flowers in vase on table (60x90cm-24x35in) s.d.31. 27-Mar-4 Dannenberg, Berlin #571/R
£738 $1358 €1100 Landscape with trees and small town (60x50cm-24x20in) s. panel lit. 25-Mar-4 Karlheinz Kaupp, Staufen #2510/R

HONOUR, W Basil (20th C) New Zealander
£297 $512 €434 Landscape with trees (50x60cm-20x24in) s. board. 7-Dec-3 International Art Centre, Auckland #237/R (NZ.D 800)

HONTHORST, Gerrit van (1590-1656) Dutch
£2533 $4661 €3800 Portrait de femme aux perles (74x59cm-29x23in) s.d.1644 panel. 11-Jun-4 Maigret, Paris #48/R est:2500-3500
Works on paper
£1038 $1900 €1515 Crucifixion of St Peter. Man holding a post (25x20cm-10x8in) pen ink double-sided. 29-Jan-4 Swann Galleries, New York #161/R est:1500-2500

HONTHORST, Gerrit van (studio) (1590-1656) Dutch
£11189 $19021 €16000 St Hieronymus (92x116cm-36x46in) lit.prov. 20-Nov-3 Van Ham, Cologne #1347/R est:9000

HONTHORST, Gerrit van (style) (1590-1656) Dutch
£5500 $10065 €8030 St. Sebastian (97x118cm-38x46in) 6-Jul-4 Sotheby's, Olympia #432/R est:6000-8000

HOOCH, Horatius de (17th C) Dutch
£2600 $4420 €3796 Group portrait of a family in an Italianate landscape (91x121cm-36x48in) s. 29-Oct-3 Bonhams, New Bond Street #50/R est:3000-4000
£5000 $9100 €7500 Southern river landscape with a bridge and figures (85x102cm-33x40in) s. 1-Jul-4 Van Ham, Cologne #1077/R est:10000
£11189 $18685 €16000 Italianate landscape (81x106cm-32x42in) 30-Jun-3 Ansorena, Madrid #201/R

HOOCH, Pieter de (1629-1681) Dutch
£1100000 $2013000 €1606000 Card players at table (107x93cm-42x37in) s. prov.exhib.lit. 7-Jul-4 Sotheby's, London #20/R est:1000000-1500000

HOOCH, Pieter de (style) (1629-1681) Dutch
£15363 $27500 €22430 Woman receiving man at door (72x64cm-28x25in) prov.exhib.lit. 27-May-4 Sotheby's, New York #17/R est:15000-20000

HOOD, Cherry (20th C) Australian?
Works on paper
£1953 $3652 €2930 Timmy (95x80cm-37x31in) s. i.stretcher mixed media canvas. 20-Jul-4 Goodman, Sydney #53/R est:5000-7000 (A.D 5000)
£2893 $5351 €4224 Finnish lapphund (76x57cm-30x22in) s.d.2002 verso W/C prov. 10-Mar-4 Deutscher-Menzies, Melbourne #18/R est:3000-5000 (A.D 7000)
£3484 $5504 €5087 Julian (153x102cm-60x40in) W/C oil glazes paper prov. 2-Sep-3 Deutscher-Menzies, Melbourne #22/R est:8000-12000 (A.D 8500)
£4065 $6382 €5894 Portrait of a boy (153x101cm-60x40in) W/C gouache prov. 26-Aug-3 Christie's, Sydney #59/R est:10000-15000 (A.D 10000)

HOOD, Ernest Burnett (1932-1988) British
Works on paper
£250 $418 €365 Greyfriars churchyard (29x31cm-11x12in) s.d.81 gouache. 16-Oct-3 Bonhams, Edinburgh #52

HOOD, George Washington (1869-1949) American
£670 $1200 €978 Seated woman in cave weaving (43x30cm-17x12in) s. board. 15-May-4 Illustration House, New York #73/R est:1600-2400

HOOD, Kenneth Edwin (1928-) Australian
£412 $745 €602 Still life. board. 1-Apr-4 Joel, Victoria #222 (A.D 1000)

HOODLESS, Harry (1913-1997) British
£350 $595 €511 Brancaster, with fishing boats at low tide (39x59cm-15x23in) s.d.80 s.i.verso tempera on wood. 29-Oct-3 Bonhams, Chester #378a

HOOF, Jef van (1928-1986) Belgian
£3873 $6236 €5500 Pagliaio (100x120cm-39x47in) 8-May-3 Farsetti, Prato #24 est:6500-7500

HOOFT, Cornelis Gerardus (1866-1936) Dutch
£245 $409 €350 The stern of a seventeenth century ships model (45x32cm-18x13in) s.d.1928 panel. 30-Jun-3 Sotheby's, Amsterdam #291

HOOFT, Ina (1894-?) Dutch
£278 $439 €400 Still life with white flowers in a blue jar (50x41cm-20x16in) s.d.78. 2-Sep-3 Christie's, Amsterdam #358
£278 $453 €400 Still life with chestnuts (40x50cm-16x20in) s. 29-Sep-3 Sotheby's, Amsterdam #278
£548 $932 €800 Still life with flowers and pears (59x49cm-23x19in) s.d.41. 5-Nov-3 Vendue Huis, Gravenhage #418

HOOG, Bernard de (1867-1943) Dutch
£526 $953 €800 A mother sewing and her child at a table in an interior (22x17cm-9x7in) s. panel. 19-Apr-4 Glerum, Amsterdam #242/R
£667 $1213 €1000 Still life with sunflowers (94x47cm-37x19in) s. 1-Jul-4 Van Ham, Cologne #1407
£700 $1260 €1022 Still life of flowers (36x46cm-14x18in) s. 21-Jan-4 Sotheby's, Olympia #499/R
£1000 $1830 €1460 Motherly love (25x20cm-10x8in) s. panel. 6-Apr-4 Bonhams, Knightsbridge #233 est:700-1000
£1778 $3076 €2596 Devant la fenetre (71x91cm-28x36in) s. 15-Dec-3 Iegor de Saint Hippolyte, Montreal #63 (C.D 4000)

£1867 $3360 €2800 Mother and her children in an interior (50x66cm-20x26in) s. 20-Apr-4 Sotheby's, Amsterdam #110/R est:3000-5000
£1875 $3000 €2738 Interior scene with figures at table (56x71cm-22x28in) s. 20-Sep-3 Bunte, Elgin #1447 est:4000-6000
£2174 $4000 €3174 Young lady reading at a table (41x30cm-16x12in) s. 9-Jun-4 Alderfer's, Hatfield #355/R est:5000-7000
£2318 $4266 €3384 Mending the garment (40x35cm-16x14in) s. prov. 9-Jun-4 Walker's, Ottawa #300/R est:5000-6000 (C.D 5750)
£2400 $4368 €3504 Mother and child (25x20cm-10x8in) s. panel pair. 16-Jun-4 Christie's, Kensington #170/R est:3000-4000
£2500 $4175 €3600 Mother and her children in an interior (60x51cm-24x20in) s. 21-Oct-3 Sotheby's, Amsterdam #148/R est:4000-6000
£2557 $4500 €3733 Maternal love (76x61cm-30x24in) s. 18-May-4 Bonhams & Butterfields, San Francisco #75/R est:4000-6000
£3000 $5610 €4380 Interior scene with girl seated beside a window preparing fruit (40x30cm-16x12in) s. 22-Jul-4 Tennants, Leyburn #892 est:3000-4000
£3167 $5290 €4624 A favourite doll (50x61cm-20x24in) s. 17-Nov-3 Waddingtons, Toronto #166/R est:6000-8000 (C.D 7000)
£3333 $6000 €5000 Tea time (60x75cm-24x30in) s. 20-Apr-4 Sotheby's, Amsterdam #148/R est:7000-9000
£4000 $7160 €5840 Bedtime story (75x60cm-30x24in) s. 26-May-4 Sotheby's, Olympia #282/R est:4000-6000
£4027 $7450 €6000 Lunch time (49x39cm-19x15in) s. 10-Mar-4 James Adam, Dublin #4/R est:4000-6000
£4362 $8070 €6500 Small child and toddler (48x38cm-19x15in) s. 10-Mar-4 James Adam, Dublin #9/R est:4000-6000
£4637 $8532 €6770 Mother darning (66x51cm-26x20in) s. prov. 14-Jun-4 Waddingtons, Toronto #253/R est:7000-9000 (C.D 11500)
£4762 $8667 €7000 Busy hands (48x40cm-19x16in) s. 3-Feb-4 Christie's, Amsterdam #225/R est:7000-9000
£8054 $14255 €12000 Femme de pecheur et ses enfants attendant le retour des pecheurs (96x125cm-38x49in) s. 27-Apr-4 Campo, Vlaamse Kaai #381/R est:9000-11000
£12000 $21600 €18000 Playing in the dunes (65x85cm-26x33in) s. 21-Apr-4 Christie's, Amsterdam #149/R est:8000-12000
Works on paper
£671 $1235 €1000 Care of the draught horse (30x41cm-12x16in) s. W/C. 29-Mar-4 Glerum, Amsterdam #161

HOOG, Bernard de (attrib) (1867-1943) Dutch
£315 $500 €460 Reading (34x22cm-13x9in) indis.sig. 12-Sep-3 Skinner, Boston #232/R

HOOG, Birger (1899-1929) Swedish
£17404 $31327 €25410 Masquerade (81x60cm-32x24in) painted c.1927-28. 26-Apr-4 Bukowskis, Stockholm #26/R est:175000-200000 (S.KR 240000)

HOOGBRUIN, Johannes Matthys (1819-1891) Dutch
£4861 $8264 €7000 Figures skating on a frozen river (46x57cm-18x22in) s. panel. 28-Oct-3 Christie's, Amsterdam #103/R est:7000-9000

HOOGSTEYNS, Jan (1935-) Belgian
£333 $557 €480 Winter landscape (60x70cm-24x28in) s. 21-Oct-3 Campo & Campo, Antwerp #148
£340 $619 €500 Still life with fruit and a teapot (65x80cm-26x31in) s. s.on stretcher. 3-Feb-4 Christie's, Amsterdam #617/R
£633 $1134 €950 Winter wind (65x80cm-26x31in) s. 15-May-4 De Vuyst, Lokeren #167/R

HOOGSTRATEN, Jan van (c.1629-1654) Dutch
£2185 $3978 €3300 Un marchand de legumes (20x17cm-8x7in) mono. panel. 21-Jun-4 Tajan, Paris #39/R est:4000-6000

HOOGSTRATEN, Samuel van (1627-1678) Flemish
£22000 $40260 €32120 Portrait of a young man in a brocade lined cloak and velvet black cap (52x44cm-20x17in) prov.lit. 7-Jul-4 Christie's, London #46/R est:25000-35000

HOOGSTRATEN, Samuel van (attrib) (1627-1678) Flemish
Works on paper
£267 $477 €400 Interior with woman reading (11x11cm-4x4in) bears mono. ochre. 13-May-4 Bassenge, Berlin #5181

HOOK, James Clarke (1819-1907) British
£500 $910 €730 Study of children climbing rocks by the sea (33x42cm-13x17in) 19-Jun-4 Lacy Scott, Bury St.Edmunds #409/R
£1018 $1700 €1486 Pretty maiden by the sea (91x61cm-36x24in) mono. 29-Jun-3 William Jenack, New York #322 est:1000-1500
£1250 $2150 €1825 The day's catch (69x109cm-27x43in) mono.d.1866 prov. 2-Dec-3 Ritchie, Toronto #45/R est:4000-6000 (C.D 2800)
£7500 $13800 €10950 Unloading the catch (52x82cm-20x32in) mono.d.1883. 11-Jun-4 Christie's, London #192/R est:4000-6000
£15000 $27600 €21900 Cow tending (87x136cm-34x54in) mono.d.1874 prov.exhib.lit. 11-Jun-4 Christie's, London #106/R est:15000-20000
£26000 $47840 €37960 Olivia and Viola (60x74cm-24x29in) s.i.verso panel prov.exhib.lit. 11-Jun-4 Christie's, London #166/R est:15000-20000

HOOK, James Clarke (attrib) (1819-1907) British
£2000 $3680 €2920 Mother and children on a beach (28x23cm-11x9in) mono.d.1863. 8-Jun-4 Gorringes, Lewes #2034/R est:2000-3000

HOOK, Sandy (1879-1960) French
£1118 $2024 €1700 Cargo en manche (28x36cm-11x14in) s.d.59 W/C. 17-Apr-4 Deburaux, Boulogne #217
Works on paper
£868 $1450 €1250 Cargo en Patagonie (29x36cm-11x14in) s. gouache. 26-Oct-3 Lesieur & Le Bars, Le Havre #152
£937 $1566 €1350 Bateau (24x36cm-9x14in) s. gouache. 26-Oct-3 Lesieur & Le Bars, Le Havre #149
£1007 $1682 €1450 Cargo (25x36cm-10x14in) s. gouache. 26-Oct-3 Lesieur & Le Bars, Le Havre #150
£1042 $1740 €1500 Dechargement (25x36cm-10x14in) s. gouache. 26-Oct-3 Lesieur & Le Bars, Le Havre #151
£1944 $3247 €2800 Cargos et jonques (21x37cm-8x15in) gouache pair. 26-Oct-3 Lesieur & Le Bars, Le Havre #153

HOOPER, John Horace (fl.1877-1899) British
£470 $855 €686 Near Boulters Lock (29x49cm-11x19in) s.d.96. 5-Feb-4 Mellors & Kirk, Nottingham #563
£750 $1373 €1095 View of a cornfield from across a pond (40x55cm-16x22in) s. 6-Apr-4 Bonhams, Knightsbridge #189/R
£833 $1325 €1200 Landscape (74x100cm-29x39in) s. 9-Sep-3 Vanderkindere, Brussels #91
£1150 $2128 €1679 Haymaking near Gt Marlow (60x100cm-24x39in) s. s.i. verso. 14-Jul-4 Bonhams, Chester #448/R est:1200-1600
£1231 $2117 €1797 Coming through the lock (60x106cm-24x42in) 7-Dec-3 Uppsala Auktionskammare, Uppsala #99/R est:12000-15000 (S.KR 16000)
£1500 $2505 €2190 Near Mapledurham. Near Streatley-on-Thames (41x29cm-16x11in) s. s.i.verso pair. 8-Oct-3 Christie's, Kensington #764 est:200-300
£1700 $3043 €2482 Summer evening on the Thames, below Reading. Peaceful day on the river (46x81cm-18x32in) i.verso pair. 27-May-4 Christie's, Kensington #166/R est:2000-3000
£2273 $4022 €3319 On the river (61x105cm-24x41in) s. 3-May-4 Christie's, Melbourne #277/R est:4000-6000 (A.D 5500)

HOOPER, William G (19/20th C) British
Works on paper
£300 $519 €438 Flowing to the Mill, landscape with cattle (20x28cm-8x11in) s.d.1883 W/C. 11-Dec-3 Neales, Nottingham #557

HOOPLE, Warner (20th C) American
Works on paper
£1347 $2250 €1967 Off shore oil rig (46x58cm-18x23in) gouache W/C. 18-Oct-3 David Dike, Dallas #196/R est:1000-1500

HOOPSTAD, Elisabeth Iosetta (1787-1847) Dutch
£2778 $4639 €4000 Still life with basket of fruit (65x55cm-26x22in) s.i.d.1840. 24-Oct-3 Ketterer, Hamburg #47/R est:5000-6000

HOORN, Johannes Huibertus van (1897-1964) Dutch
£526 $968 €800 A bird's nest (35x37cm-14x15in) s.d.58. 22-Jun-4 Christie's, Amsterdam #465/R

HOORN, Jordanus (1753-1833) Dutch
Works on paper
£811 $1427 €1200 View of copper mills near Amersfoort (27x33cm-11x13in) pen brush grey ink wash prov. 19-May-4 Sotheby's, Amsterdam #250/R
£1333 $2387 €2000 Portrait of two children and their dog (70x53cm-28x21in) s.d.1792 pastel. 17-May-4 Glerum, Amsterdam #60/R est:1000-1500

HOORN, Kirk van (?) Dutch
£306 $492 €447 Harbour view (50x40cm-20x16in) s. 25-Aug-3 Lilla Bukowskis, Stockholm #261 (S.KR 4000)

HOORN, Ralph van (1970-) Dutch
£278 $439 €400 Pink tree (60x60cm-24x24in) s.d.1999 panel. 26-Apr-3 Auction Maastricht #160/R

HOOSTE, Jozef van (1884-1940) Belgian
£528 $914 €750 Caravans (65x76cm-26x30in) s. 13-Dec-3 De Vuyst, Lokeren #354
£570 $1055 €850 Old houses in the evening (66x81cm-26x32in) s. 13-Mar-4 De Vuyst, Lokeren #355

HOOVEN, Herbert Nelson (1898-?) American
£809 $1400 €1181 Autumn landscape with buildings at streamside (41x36cm-16x14in) s. board. 10-Dec-3 Alderfer's, Hatfield #461/R est:700-900

HOPE, E Lyn (fl.1940-1958) British
Works on paper
£302 $559 €450 Rotunda Hospital, Dublin (52x75cm-20x30in) s.d.1947 W/C. 10-Mar-4 James Adam, Dublin #33/R

HOPE, Gabrielle (1916-) New Zealander
Works on paper
£1224 $2227 €1787 Donkey picnic (53x61cm-21x24in) s. W/C gouache prov. 29-Jun-4 Peter Webb, Auckland #92/R est:2000-3000 (NZ.D 3500)

HOPE, Henry (?) New Zealander
£319 $590 €466 Fisherman, Lake Alexandrina (60x80cm-24x31in) s. board. 13-Jul-4 Watson's, Christchurch #21/R (NZ.D 900)

HOPE, James (1818-1892) American
£46296 $75000 €67129 Army of the Potomac at Cumberland landing on the Pamunky River VA. 26-Jul-3 Thomaston Place, Thomaston #75/R

HOPE, Laurence (1928-) Australian
£1832 $3334 €2675 Untitled (63x76cm-25x30in) s.d.62. 16-Jun-4 Deutscher-Menzies, Melbourne #276/R est:5000-7500 (A.D 4800)

HOPE, Robert (1869-1936) British
£900 $1701 €1314 Fishing boats, Crail (25x21cm-10x8in) s. board. 19-Feb-4 Lyon & Turnbull, Edinburgh #52
£1000 $1810 €1460 The boatyard (23x29cm-9x11in) s. panel. 3-Apr-4 British Auctioneer #266
£1150 $1886 €1679 Young lady with parrot (23x23cm-9x9in) s. 6-Jun-3 Biddle & Webb, Birmingham #264
£1700 $2669 €2465 Girl and a quetzal (25x25cm-10x10in) s. prov. 27-Aug-3 Sotheby's, London #1138/R est:1000-1500
£1800 $2826 €2610 Idle hours (35x51cm-14x20in) s. prov. 27-Aug-3 Sotheby's, London #1137/R est:1800-2500
£3000 $4710 €4350 At the mirror (57x47cm-22x19in) s. i.verso. 27-Aug-3 Sotheby's, London #1134/R est:3000-5000

HOPF, Fredy (1875-1943) Swiss
£345 $617 €504 Eiger, Monch and Jungfrau (32x51cm-13x20in) s. canvas on board. 13-May-4 Stuker, Bern #678/R (S.FR 800)

HOPFER, Daniel (1470-1536) Dutch
Prints
£4118 $7000 €6012 Crucifixion (34x22cm-13x9in) etching executed c.1525. 6-Nov-3 Swann Galleries, New York #22/R est:8000-12000

HOPFER, Georg (attrib) (fl.1559-1595) Dutch
Works on paper
£2055 $3493 €3000 Adoration of the shepherds (13x10cm-5x4in) init.i.mount d.1595 pen brown black ink prov. 4-Nov-3 Sotheby's, Amsterdam #5/R est:3000-4000

HOPFFNER, T W (18th C) German
£3716 $6652 €5500 Portrait of Frederick the Great (83x66cm-33x26in) i.d.1756 verso. 8-May-4 Schloss Ahlden, Ahlden #687/R est:4500

HOPFGARTEN, August Ferdinand (1807-1896) German
£1275 $2257 €1900 Young Neapolitan women (59x58cm-23x23in) s.d.1849. 27-Apr-4 Durán, Madrid #162/R est:1500

HOPKIN, Robert (1832-1909) American
£719 $1200 €1050 Landscape (15x18cm-6x7in) panel. 17-Oct-3 Du Mouchelle, Detroit #2280/R
£1250 $2000 €1825 Seascape (61x91cm-24x36in) 19-Sep-3 Du Mouchelle, Detroit #2007/R est:2000-3000
£1563 $2500 €2282 Seascape (79x114cm-31x45in) 19-Sep-3 Du Mouchelle, Detroit #2006/R est:3000-5000
£1720 $3200 €2511 Shiping offshore in rough winters (66x102cm-26x40in) s.d.72 canvas on board. 3-Mar-4 Christie's, Rockefeller NY #22/R est:1000-1500
£1875 $3000 €2738 In the channel (61x46cm-24x18in) 19-Sep-3 Du Mouchelle, Detroit #2008/R est:2500-3500

HOPKINS, Arthur (1848-1930) British
£1050 $1670 €1533 Daphne, all if fair and sweet (29x39cm-11x15in) s. 18-Mar-3 Anderson & Garland, Newcastle #218/R est:900-1200
Works on paper
£580 $1044 €847 Headland, Coverack (24x33cm-9x13in) s. W/C exhib. 21-Jan-4 Sotheby's, Olympia #226/R
£800 $1480 €1168 Daphne - all is fair and sweet (28x39cm-11x15in) s. W/C. 14-Jul-4 Bonhams, Chester #476
£2200 $3674 €3212 In the day of Cromwell (49x35cm-19x14in) s.d.1912 W/C. 14-Oct-3 Bearnes, Exeter #339/R est:800-1200
£4600 $8510 €6716 Young girl carrying violets (46x37cm-18x15in) s. W/C. 9-Mar-4 Bonhams, New Bond Street #111/R est:1500-2000

HOPKINS, Elisabeth Margaret (1894-1991) Canadian?
Works on paper
£156 $266 €228 Fungus (24x35cm-9x14in) s.d.1980 ink W/C. 6-Nov-3 Heffel, Vancouver #61/R (C.D 350)
£156 $266 €228 The cat's garden party (24x35cm-9x14in) s.d.1979 ink W/C. 6-Nov-3 Heffel, Vancouver #62/R (C.D 350)

HOPKINS, Frances Anne (1838-1919) British
Works on paper
£1440 $2635 €2102 Pastoral scene with cattle and farm workers (34x47cm-13x19in) init. W/C lit. 1-Jun-4 Joyner Waddington, Toronto #176/R est:4000-5000 (C.D 3600)

HOPKINS, Milton W (1789-1844) American
£108108 $200000 €157838 Portrait of Virginia Ada Wright (107x66cm-42x26in) painted c.1830 prov.exhib.lit. 16-Jan-4 Sotheby's, New York #32/R est:60000-80000

HOPKINS, William H (?-1892) British
£5405 $10000 €7891 Pug (74x84cm-29x33in) s. lit. 10-Feb-4 Doyle, New York #259/R est:12000-14000

HOPKINSON, Charles Sydney (1869-1962) American
Works on paper
£442 $800 €645 Waikiki beach scene with palm trees, figures and rowers (36x53cm-14x21in) s. W/C. 2-Apr-4 Eldred, East Dennis #966/R

HOPKINSON, Glen Spencer (1946-) American
£300 $471 €435 Indian scout wading through a river on horseback (40x51cm-16x20in) s. 28-Aug-3 Christie's, Kensington #356/R
£549 $1000 €802 Indian on horseback (41x51cm-16x20in) s. 7-Feb-4 Auctions by the Bay, Alameda #1569/R

HOPKINSON, John (1941-) British
£350 $637 €511 Pool Game (63x81cm-25x32in) s. acrylic board. 4-Feb-4 Sotheby's, Olympia #134/R
£1200 $2184 €1752 Schoolyard (127x127cm-50x50in) s. board. 4-Feb-4 Sotheby's, Olympia #131/R est:600-800

HOPKINSON, William John (1887-?) Canadian
£785 $1429 €1146 Haliburton Village, Early Spring (25x30cm-10x12in) s. i.d.1944 verso prov. 5-Feb-4 Heffel, Vancouver #42/R (C.D 1900)

HOPLEY, Edward William John (1816-1869) British
£679 $1086 €991 Portrait of a musician (82x67cm-32x26in) mono. 16-Sep-3 Philippe Schuler, Zurich #3337 est:2000-2500 (S.FR 1500)

HOPPE, C A W (fl.1836-1860) German
£1656 $3013 €2500 Still life of fruit with wine glass (32x27cm-13x11in) s.d.1863. 21-Jun-4 Dorotheum, Vienna #331/R est:2500-2800

HOPPE, Carl (1897-1981) American
£539 $900 €787 Oaks at San Antonio river (41x51cm-16x20in) 18-Oct-3 David Dike, Dallas #306/R

HOPPE, Erik (1897-1968) Danish
£496 $917 €724 House gable by the sea (81x76cm-32x30in) s. panel. 15-Mar-4 Rasmussen, Vejle #652 (D.KR 5500)
£1418 $2538 €2070 Summer landscape from Sondermarken with two young girls (61x71cm-24x28in) s. 12-Jan-4 Rasmussen, Vejle #514/R est:20000 (D.KR 15000)
£1787 $3039 €2609 Landscape with figure in Sondermarken (50x70cm-20x28in) s. 29-Nov-3 Rasmussen, Havnen #4210/R est:15000-20000 (D.KR 19000)
£1881 $3198 €2746 Landscape from Sondermarken (61x51cm-24x20in) s. 29-Nov-3 Rasmussen, Havnen #4091/R est:20000 (D.KR 20000)
£2160 $3607 €3154 Sunset over Sondermarken (65x85cm-26x33in) s. 7-Oct-3 Rasmussen, Copenhagen #308/R est:15000-20000 (D.KR 23000)
£2166 $3986 €3162 Landscape from Sondermarken (51x61cm-20x24in) s/. 29-Mar-4 Rasmussen, Copenhagen #567/R est:20000-25000 (D.KR 24000)
£2254 $3763 €3291 Walking in Sondermarken (67x80cm-26x31in) s. prov. 7-Oct-3 Rasmussen, Copenhagen #322/R est:25000 (D.KR 24000)
£4332 $8101 €6325 Figure in Sondermarken, sunshine (81x100cm-32x39in) s. 25-Feb-4 Kunsthallen, Copenhagen #272/R est:50000 (D.KR 48000)
£4513 $8303 €6589 Summer's day in Sondermarken (51x66cm-20x26in) s.i. exhib.prov. 29-Mar-4 Rasmussen, Copenhagen #1/R est:20000-25000 (D.KR 50000)
Works on paper
£474 $758 €687 Figure in Sondermarken (42x54cm-17x21in) s. W/C. 17-Sep-3 Kunsthallen, Copenhagen #250/R (D.KR 5000)

HOPPE, Ferdinand Bernhard (1841-1922) Dutch
£658 $1191 €1000 Blossoming orchard in front of a farm (40x50cm-16x20in) s. 19-Apr-4 Glerum, Amsterdam #236/R

HOPPE, Ferdinand Theodor (1848-1890) German
£833 $1375 €1200 Portrait of young woman collecting mussels on the beach (60x50cm-24x20in) s.d.88 canvas on panel. 3-Jul-3 Van Ham, Cologne #1263

HOPPE, Harry (19/20th C) Danish?
£271 $500 €396 Picnic on an island with rowing boat, calm day (33x38cm-13x15in) s.d.1916. 15-Mar-4 Rasmussen, Vejle #452/R (D.KR 3000)

HOPPE, Jenny Bernier (20th C) Belgian
£1067 $1909 €1600 Nature morte aux fleurs et aux fruits (50x39cm-20x15in) s. 11-May-4 Vanderkindere, Brussels #52 est:700-900

HOPPEN, Gerard (1885-1928) Dutch
Sculpture
£1189 $2021 €1700 Figure of a fisherwoman (46cm-18in) mono. oak exec.c.1930 lit. 18-Nov-3 Christie's, Amsterdam #328/R est:1200-1500

HOPPENBROUWERS, Johannes Franciscus (1819-1866) Dutch
£1007 $1802 €1500 Paysage de montagne anime (35x16cm-14x6in) mono.indis.d. panel. 26-May-4 Blanchet, Paris #177/R est:1200-1500
£1333 $2400 €2000 Traveller in an extensive landscape at dusk (19x26cm-7x10in) s. panel. 21-Apr-4 Christie's, Amsterdam #6/R est:2000-3000
£1736 $2830 €2500 Winter landscape with ice skaters (38x46cm-15x18in) s. panel. 26-Sep-3 Bolland & Marotz, Bremen #550/R est:3300
£2721 $4952 €4000 Smoking eels on a river in moonlight (39x56cm-15x22in) s.d.54 panel. 3-Feb-4 Christie's, Amsterdam #95/R est:4000-6000
Works on paper
£302 $553 €450 Homecoming shepherd near a house behind a group of trees (17x24cm-7x9in) s.d.48 W/C lit. 8-Jul-4 Allgauer, Kempten #1993/R
£2838 $4995 €4200 Winter landscape (23x32cm-9x13in) init.d.6 December 54 W/C prov.lit. 19-May-4 Sotheby's, Amsterdam #341/R est:2000-3000

HOPPENBROUWERS, Johannes Franciscus (attrib) (1819-1866) Dutch
£1667 $2750 €2400 Dutch landscape with farmstead (46x65cm-18x26in) i. panel. 3-Jul-3 Van Ham, Cologne #1264/R est:900

HOPPENBROUWERS, Johannes Franciscus and ROCHUSSEN, Charles (19th C) Dutch
£3472 $5799 €5000 Elegant figures in the landscape of Montferlant, Gelderland (37x52cm-15x20in) s. indis d. panel acrylic prov. 21-Oct-3 Sotheby's, Amsterdam #7/R est:5000-8000

HOPPENRATH, Clara (19/20th C) French
£738 $1358 €1100 Still life with fruit and wicker basket (68x98cm-27x39in) s. board. 27-Mar-4 Dannenberg, Berlin #572/R

HOPPENSACH, Emilius (1834-1913) Danish
£448 $806 €654 Landscape from Noddebo Church (28x37cm-11x15in) init.d.21 august 52. 24-Apr-4 Rasmussen, Havnen #2051 (D.KR 5000)

HOPPER, Charles W (fl.1893-1902) British
Works on paper
£650 $1196 €949 Cottage garden (23x33cm-9x13in) s. W/C. 22-Jun-4 Bonhams, Knightsbridge #1/R

HOPPER, Edward (1882-1967) American
Prints
£28443 $47500 €41527 Cat boat (20x25cm-8x10in) s.i. etching. 21-Oct-3 Bonhams & Butterfields, San Francisco #1055/R
£31073 $55000 €45367 Evening wind (17x21cm-7x8in) s.i. etching. 30-Apr-4 Sotheby's, New York #17/R est:35000-45000
£33898 $60000 €49491 Cat boat (20x25cm-8x10in) s.i. etching. 30-Apr-4 Sotheby's, New York #16/R est:35000-45000
£38235 $65000 €55823 American landscape (34x46cm-13x18in) s.i. etching exec.1920. 4-Nov-3 Christie's, Rockefeller NY #8/R est:30000-40000
Works on paper
£352273 $620000 €514319 Shacks at Pamet Head (51x56cm-20x22in) s. W/C exec 1937 prov.exhib.lit. 19-May-4 Sotheby's, New York #146/R est:500000-700000

HOPPER, Floyd D (1909-1984) American
Works on paper
£226 $400 €330 Sailboats (10x22cm-4x9in) s. W/C. 1-May-4 Dan Ripley, Indianapolis #575

HOPPER, H (19th C) British
Sculpture
£10180 $17000 €14863 Neoclassical female figures (195cm-77in) s.d.1815 wooden base painted plaster pair. 18-Oct-3 Sotheby's, New York #85/R est:2000-30000

HOPPIN, Helen I (attrib) (20th C) American
£299 $500 €437 Impressionistic summer landscape (20x25cm-8x10in) s. 14-Jul-3 O'Gallerie, Oregon #754/R

HOPPNER, John (1758-1810) British
£4000 $7400 €5840 Portrait of Rev Beiley Porteus DD, Bishop of London (74x61cm-29x24in) 14-Jan-4 Lawrence, Crewkerne #1385/R est:4000-6000
£13966 $25000 €20390 Portrait of Henry Wellesley, Baron Cowley (76x63cm-30x25in) prov.exhib.lit. 27-May-4 Sotheby's, New York #250/R est:10000-15000
£21500 $36550 €31390 Portrait of Eleanor Agnes, wife of Robert, 4th Earl of Buckingham, in a wooded landscape (127x102cm-50x40in) prov. 25-Nov-3 Christie's, London #36/R est:10000-15000
£150000 $255000 €219000 Portrait of a lady as Evelina (68x53cm-27x21in) prov.exhib.lit. 27-Nov-3 Sotheby's, London #10/R est:40000-60000

HOPPNER, John (attrib) (1758-1810) British
£6250 $10000 €9125 Portrait of Lady Berwick (152x122cm-60x48in) 19-Sep-3 Du Mouchelle, Detroit #2296/R est:12000-15000
£6587 $11000 €9617 Portrait of Lady Barrie (74x61cm-29x24in) init. 19-Oct-3 Susanin's, Chicago #6023/R est:6000-8000

HOPPOCK, Kay (20th C) American
Works on paper
£383 $700 €575 Pitcher of zinnias (58x79cm-23x31in) W/C. 10-Jul-4 Hindman, Chicago #222/R

HOPS, Tom (1906-1976) German
£362 $615 €529 Hamburg 13 (48x63cm-19x25in) s.d.64. 19-Nov-3 Fischer, Luzern #2146/R (S.FR 800)
£1793 $3317 €2600 Spring on the Alster (48x63cm-19x25in) s.d.64 i. verso. 14-Feb-4 Hans Stahl, Hamburg #154/R est:2400

HOPTON, Gwendoline M (fl.1897-1913) British
£300 $555 €438 Evening pipe (77x61cm-30x24in) s.i.verso. 10-Feb-4 Bonhams, Knightsbridge #221/R
£540 $1010 €788 Drying the sails, St Ives (24x34cm-9x13in) s. panel. 26-Feb-4 Lane, Penzance #217
£1000 $1820 €1460 St. Ives Harbour (51x61cm-20x24in) s. 15-Jun-4 David Lay, Penzance #126 est:1000-1500

HOPWOOD, Henry Silkstone (1860-1914) British
£1300 $2080 €1898 Draught players, Tunis (22x28cm-9x11in) s. canvasboard. 16-Sep-3 Rosebery Fine Art, London #612/R est:600-900
£1600 $2560 €2336 A Tunis doorway (28x22cm-11x9in) s. canvasboard. 16-Sep-3 Rosebery Fine Art, London #613/R est:600-900
Works on paper
£4600 $8372 €6716 Cottage prayer meeting (23x25cm-9x10in) s.d.1898 W/C. 17-Jun-4 Gorringes, Worthing #759/R est:1000-1500

HORACEK, Rudolf (1915-1986) ?
Works on paper
£667 $1226 €1000 In Mannsworth (41x30cm-16x12in) s. col crayon lead pencil prov.lit. 9-Jun-4 Artcurial Briest, Paris #369/R

HORACIO (1912-1972) Mexican
£1836 $3250 €2681 Portrait of a young girl with a village and figures in the distance (60x45cm-24x18in) s. 2-May-4 Bonhams & Butterfields, Los Angeles #3095/R est:2000-3000
£4645 $8500 €6782 Portrait of a little girl in a red dress holding a cardinal (60x46cm-24x18in) s.i. painted 1879. 3-Jun-4 Christie's, Rockefeller NY #1280/R est:5000-6000

HORADAM, Franz (1846-1925) German
£451 $736 €650 Landscape with cows (57x42cm-22x17in) s. board. 25-Sep-3 Neumeister, Munich #2789
£903 $1472 €1300 Evening landscape (43x73cm-17x29in) s. 25-Sep-3 Neumeister, Munich #2787/R

HORBERG, Pehr (1746-1816) Swedish
£1257 $2174 €1835 Bacchus and Orpheus (62x79cm-24x31in) pair. 15-Dec-3 Lilla Bukowskis, Stockholm #395 est:20000-25000 (S.KR 16000)

HORE, James (fl.1828-1837) Irish
£23000 $41170 €33580 View of the Quays with the Customs House beyond, Dublin (41x56cm-16x22in) prov.exhib. 14-May-4 Christie's, London #71/R est:20000-30000

HORE, Somnath (1920-) Indian
£3533 $6500 €5158 Wounds (48x60cm-19x24in) s.d.1979 handmade cast paper four. 24-Mar-4 Sotheby's, New York #193/R est:7000-10000

HOREMANS, Jan Josef (18th C) Flemish
£1667 $3033 €2500 Women and men sitting outside tavern (70x92cm-28x36in) 30-Jun-4 Neumeister, Munich #458/R est:2200
£16200 $28349 €23000 Concert dans l'entree d'un palais classique (67x83cm-26x33in) s.d.1725. 18-Dec-3 Tajan, Paris #25/R est:15000-20000

HOREMANS, Jan Josef (attrib) (18th C) Flemish
£1528 $2812 €2231 Haircut (49x55cm-19x22in) s. 14-Jun-4 Philippe Schuler, Zurich #4301/R est:4000-6000 (S.FR 3500)

HOREMANS, Jan Josef (elder) (1682-1759) Flemish
£1049 $1751 €1500 Village scene with a man pushing a cart (38x30cm-15x12in) 30-Jun-3 Sotheby's, Amsterdam #11/R
£3819 $6035 €5500 Elegant company dancing and feasting on a terrace (47x60cm-19x24in) s.d.1719 prov. 2-Sep-3 Christie's, Amsterdam #88/R est:2500-3500
£25140 $45000 €36704 Interior scene with figures by hearth. Interior scene with figures at table (46x59cm-18x23in) s. pair prov. 27-May-4 Sotheby's, New York #29/R est:30000-40000
£39189 $68973 €58000 Farm scene with woman putting apples in a basket. Market scene with vendor selling fruit (54x62cm-21x24in) s.d.1756 pair. 18-May-4 Sotheby's, Amsterdam #26/R est:60000-80000

HOREMANS, Jan Josef (elder-attrib) (1682-1759) Flemish
£1259 $2140 €1800 La rixe dans l'auberge (25x30cm-10x12in) panel. 18-Nov-3 Vanderkindere, Brussels #203 est:1500-2000

HOREMANS, Jan Josef (younger) (1714-1790) Flemish
£1986 $3316 €2800 La classe (50x58cm-20x23in) 17-Oct-3 Tajan, Paris #59 est:3000-4000
£3000 $5490 €4500 Kitchen interior with figures (45x56cm-18x22in) 1-Jun-4 Sotheby's, Milan #90/R est:7000
£3699 $6288 €5400 Inn interior (63x76cm-25x30in) prov. 4-Nov-3 Ansorena, Madrid #105/R est:5400
£3767 $6404 €5500 Company smoking and conversing in a kitchen (40x31cm-16x12in) 5-Nov-3 Christie's, Amsterdam #66/R est:4000-6000
£13475 $22504 €19000 Scenes d'interieurs paysans (39x32cm-15x13in) s. pair. 17-Oct-3 Tajan, Paris #50/R est:18000-20000
£19000 $34200 €27740 Sliced melon, apples, pears and plums, two pewter plates, wicker basket hanging from the wall (44x60cm-17x24in) s. prov. 21-Apr-4 Christie's, London #18/R est:12000-18000

HORGNIES, Norbert Joseph (19th C) Belgian
£3200 $5760 €4672 Fish sellers (49x37cm-19x15in) s. 21-Jan-4 Sotheby's, Olympia #408/R est:800-1200

HORIK, Vladimir (1939-) Canadian
£848 $1459 €1238 Paysage St-Urbain (40x50cm-16x20in) s. board. 2-Dec-3 Joyner Waddington, Toronto #322/R est:800-1200 (C.D 1900)
£889 $1538 €1298 Un coin d'un village au bord du fleuve (76x101cm-30x40in) s. s.i.verso isorel. 15-Dec-3 Iegor de Saint Hippolyte, Montreal #20 (C.D 2000)
£901 $1532 €1315 St Lawrence Seaway blues (51x71cm-20x28in) s. s.i.verso board. 23-Nov-3 Levis, Calgary #49/R est:2500-3000 (C.D 2000)

HORL, Ottmar (1950-) German
Sculpture
£2292 $3735 €3300 Might (94x224x19cm-37x88x7in) plexiglas steel fluorescent light. 27-Sep-3 Dr Fritz Nagel, Stuttgart #9570/R est:3000

HORLOR, George W (fl.1849-1891) British
£640 $1100 €934 Cows and farmers in a landscape (30x46cm-12x18in) s. 7-Dec-3 Hindman, Chicago #732/R
£820 $1443 €1197 Two calves and a dog. Milkmaid in a landscape with a cottage (25x35cm-10x14in) one canvas one board two. 18-May-4 Woolley & Wallis, Salisbury #178/R
£1600 $2944 €2336 Spaniels with the day's bag (25x35cm-10x14in) s. 10-Jun-4 Christie's, Kensington #395/R est:1500-2000
£1800 $3312 €2628 Sheep in a mountain landscape (66cm-26in circular) 8-Jun-4 Bonhams, Knightsbridge #238/R est:2000-3000
£2500 $4250 €3650 Ghillie, smoking his pipe beside a day's bag (46x62cm-18x24in) s.d.1895 prov. 30-Oct-3 Christie's, London #73/R est:2500-3500
£3800 $6460 €5548 Waiting for master (55x75cm-22x30in) s.d.1846. 27-Nov-3 Christie's, Kensington #94/R est:1500-2500
£23000 $36110 €33350 Setters in a highland landscape (86x112cm-34x44in) s.d.1866 prov. 27-Aug-3 Sotheby's, London #1182/R est:30000-40000
£38000 $64600 €55480 Day's Bag (113x151cm-44x59in) s.d.1855 exhib. 30-Oct-3 Christie's, London #79/R est:40000-60000

HORLOR, Joseph (1809-1887) British
£250 $405 €363 Cader Idris, North Wales (14x30cm-6x12in) bears i. board. 30-Jul-3 Hamptons Fine Art, Godalming #279
£360 $601 €526 Fisherman resting (30x50cm-12x20in) s.d.63. 12-Nov-3 Sotheby's, Olympia #37/R
£400 $732 €584 Welsh upland scene with river and fisherman (46x81cm-18x32in) 27-Jan-4 Peter Francis, Wales #12/R
£460 $846 €672 Waterfall in a Highland landscape (29x89cm-11x35in) s.d.73. 23-Mar-4 Rosebery Fine Art, London #821
£700 $1169 €1022 View from Wyncliffe on the Wye (27x35cm-11x14in) s.d.1834. 14-Oct-3 Bearnes, Exeter #383/R
£1000 $1820 €1460 Highland landscape, with woman and cattle crossing a bridge (58x102cm-23x40in) s. 16-Jun-4 John Nicholson, Haslemere #755 est:800-1500
£1500 $2760 €2190 Wooded river landscape with figure in the foreground (46x66cm-18x26in) s.d.60. 23-Mar-4 Bonhams, New Bond Street #34/R est:1500-2000
£2300 $4232 €3358 Landscape near Bath (13x18cm-5x7in) s. indis i.verso board set of four. 23-Jun-4 Bonhams, Bury St Edmunds #395/R

HORLOR, Joseph (attrib) (1809-1887) British
£628 $1087 €917 Watering pool near Bath (47x67cm-19x26in) s. 15-Dec-3 Lilla Bukowskis, Stockholm #488 (S.KR 8000)
£1100 $1837 €1606 Collie and flock on a mountain ridge (51x68cm-20x27in) pair. 16-Oct-3 Bonhams, Edinburgh #219/R est:1200-1800

HORMANN, Theodor von (1840-1895) Austrian
£1067 $1941 €1600 Mill by stream (36x16cm-14x6in) d.11.9.1885 board. 30-Jun-4 Neumeister, Munich #574/R
£2961 $5447 €4500 Study of Dorfbrand (20x31cm-8x12in) canvas on board. 22-Jun-4 Wiener Kunst Auktionen, Vienna #54/R est:3000
£3819 $6493 €5500 Tyrolean landscape (38x31cm-15x12in) 28-Oct-3 Wiener Kunst Auktionen, Vienna #41/R est:5000-12000

HORMUTH-KALLMORGEN, Margarethe (1858-1916) German
£3020 $5557 €4500 Still life of flowers (108x67cm-43x26in) s. lit. 25-Mar-4 Karlheinz Kaupp, Staufen #2511/R est:350

HORN, Adam (1717-1778) Swedish
Works on paper
£654 $1125 €955 Revolution (25x34cm-10x13in) s.d.1765 i.verso wash. 3-Dec-3 AB Stockholms Auktionsverk #2341/R (S.KR 8500)

HORN, Harry (20th C) American
£983 $1700 €1435 Canal and walking path (61x46cm-24x18in) mono. canvasboard. 10-Dec-3 Alderfer's, Hatfield #497/R est:1600-1800

HORN, J W (19th C) British?
Works on paper
£520 $931 €759 Portrait of the Rous children, standing in a landscape (38x30cm-15x12in) s.i. W/C. 22-Mar-4 Bonhams & Brooks, Norfolk #137/R

HORN, Karen (20th C) American
Works on paper
£546 $1000 €819 Table and flower, rhododendrons (84x58cm-33x23in) W/C. 10-Jul-4 Hindman, Chicago #224/R est:2300-2500

HORN, Rebecca (1944-) German
Photographs
£2000 $3680 €2920 Unicorns are everywhere (50x60cm-20x24in) s.i.d.17.2.84 verso black white photo prov. 24-Jun-4 Sotheby's, Olympia #456/R est:1500-2000
Sculpture
£3000 $5520 €4500 Buster's bedroom (30cm-12in) i. s.i.d.1989 verso plexiglas aluminium col paint. 12-Jun-4 Villa Grisebach, Berlin #746/R est:2000-3000
£5689 $9500 €8306 Seamless (105x71x19cm-41x28x7in) s.i.d.1990 wood spools thermometer other objects prov. 12-Nov-3 Christie's, Rockefeller NY #573/R est:10000-15000
£16000 $29440 €23360 Brush machine (68x36x19cm-27x14x7in) paintbrushes electric motors exec 1993 edn 1/10 prov. 24-Jun-4 Sotheby's, London #291/R est:10000-12000
£27000 $49680 €39420 Libelle (127cm-50in) s.d.86 electric motor wire metal feathers prov. 25-Jun-4 Christie's, London #264/R est:10000-15000
Works on paper
£2036 $3462 €2973 Untitled (68x98cm-27x39in) d.1978 mixed media pencil col pen fingerprints collage polaroids. 25-Nov-3 Germann, Zurich #143/R est:5000-7000 (S.FR 4500)

HORN, Roni (1944-) American
£7784 $13000 €11365 Untitled, pigment drawings (40x49cm-16x19in) s. pigment varnish pencil one s.d.1986 oil paper pair prov. 13-Nov-3 Sotheby's, New York #570/R est:8000-12000
£8939 $16000 €13051 The XXIX (63x80cm-25x31in) s.i. acrylic paper collage on paper prov. 14-May-4 Phillips, New York #294/R est:8000-12000
Prints
£10778 $18000 €15736 Dead owl (57x57cm-22x22in) s.d.1997 num.15 iris print prov.lit. 14-Nov-3 Phillips, New York #280/R est:10000-15000
£15000 $27600 €21900 Still water - River Thames, for example - images C, G, J (77x105cm-30x41in) three offset lithograph prov. 25-Jun-4 Christie's, London #225/R est:15000-20000

HORNBROOK, Thomas L (1780-1850) British
£4000 $6800 €5840 Aftermath of the Great Gale - frigate in distress in Plymouth Sounds (29x39cm-11x15in) panel board prov. 25-Nov-3 Christie's, London #79/R est:4000-6000
£5000 $8500 €7300 Frist making her way down Plymouth Sounds in a still breeze with Drake's Island (31x41cm-12x16in) panel board prov. 25-Nov-3 Christie's, London #80/R est:5000-8000

HORNBROOK, Thomas L (attrib) (1780-1850) British
Works on paper
£317 $555 €450 View of Irun (22x28cm-9x11in) W/C double-sided. 16-Dec-3 Segre, Madrid #4/R

HORNE, Laura Trevitte (1891-1951) American
£260 $447 €380 December along the Hudson (51x61cm-20x24in) s. board. 2-Dec-3 Gorringes, Lewes #2459

HORNE, Sir William van (1843-1915) Canadian
£4955 $8423 €7234 Autumn woods and meadows (71x55cm-28x22in) s.d.1893. 27-Nov-3 Heffel, Vancouver #150/R est:2000-3000 (C.D 11000)
£5405 $9189 €7891 Passamaquoddy Bay (106x177cm-42x70in) s.d.1910. 27-Nov-3 Heffel, Vancouver #190/R est:2500-3500 (C.D 12000)

HORNEL, Edward Atkinson (1864-1933) British
£2000 $3440 €2920 Bluebell wood (66x86cm-26x34in) prov. 4-Dec-3 Bonhams, Edinburgh #73/R est:1000-1500
£7800 $13260 €11388 Girls in a wood (51x61cm-20x24in) s.d.1918. 30-Oct-3 Christie's, London #146/R est:7000-10000
£9058 $14583 €13225 Apple blossom, Galloway (59x50cm-23x20in) s.d.1918. 20-Aug-3 Dunbar Sloane, Auckland #32/R est:50000-80000 (NZ.D 25000)
£9500 $16340 €13870 Two geishas (92x77cm-36x30in) prov. 4-Dec-3 Bonhams, Edinburgh #72/R est:10000-15000
£13000 $23790 €18980 Picking blossom (64x77cm-25x30in) s.d.1918 prov. 8-Apr-4 Bonhams, Edinburgh #192/R est:10000-15000
£14000 $21980 €20300 Toy boat (77x92cm-30x36in) s.d.1919. 27-Aug-3 Sotheby's, London #1019/R est:15000-25000
£14500 $22910 €21170 Sea Breeze (61x61cm-24x24in) s.d.1913 round. 27-Apr-3 Wilkinson, Doncaster #341/R
£19000 $34390 €27740 Galloway maidens (77x36cm-30x14in) s.d.1900 prov.exhib. 19-Apr-4 Sotheby's, London #41/R est:7000-10000
£20000 $34000 €29200 Balloons in the woods (63x76cm-25x30in) s.d.1916. 30-Oct-3 Christie's, London #145/R est:25000-35000
£20000 $36200 €29200 Little goat herd (63x80cm-25x31in) s.d.1912 prov. 19-Apr-4 Sotheby's, London #42/R est:15000-20000
£23000 $39100 €33580 In the woods (51x41cm-20x16in) s.d.1904. 30-Oct-3 Christie's, London #144/R est:25000-35000

HORNEMAN, Christian (attrib) (1765-1844) Danish
£1060 $1928 €1600 Young gentleman looking at a statue (80x63cm-31x25in) 16-Jun-4 Hugo Ruef, Munich #905 est:600

HORNEMANN, Friedrich Adolf (1813-1890) German
£4196 $7133 €6000 Peasant at weekly market with fruit, poultry and flowers (126x115cm-50x45in) s. 22-Nov-3 Arnold, Frankfurt #556/R est:1600

HORNER, Friedrich (1800-1864) Swiss
£2087 $3819 €3047 View towards Genua (41x55cm-16x22in) mono. metal. 4-Jun-4 Zofingen, Switzerland #2350/R est:6000 (S.FR 4800)

HORNER, John (fl.1876-1891) British
Works on paper
£1400 $2618 €2044 Fountains Abbey (52x72cm-20x28in) pencil W/C. 22-Jul-4 Tennants, Leyburn #665 est:700-800

HORNLY, T (19th C) British
£2778 $4528 €4000 Thames shore, London (40x61cm-16x24in) s. 26-Sep-3 Bolland & Marotz, Bremen #552/R est:2800

HORNUNG, Joseph (attrib) (1792-1870) Swiss
£371 $676 €542 Portrait of Miss Recordon (32x27cm-13x11in) 16-Jun-4 Fischer, Luzern #2186/R (S.FR 850)

HORNUNG, Preben (1919-1989) Danish
£611 $1040 €892 From the sea (37x55cm-15x22in) mono. 26-Nov-3 Kunsthallen, Copenhagen #35/R (D.KR 6500)
£890 $1531 €1299 Abstract composition (27x46cm-11x18in) mono.d.62 s.d.62 verso. 3-Dec-3 Museumsbygningen, Copenhagen #56 (D.KR 9500)
£898 $1607 €1311 Composition (66x95cm-26x37in) 12-Jan-4 Rasmussen, Vejle #516/R (D.KR 9500)
£918 $1532 €1340 Composition (37x45cm-15x18in) mono. 25-Oct-3 Rasmussen, Havnen #4055/R (D.KR 9800)
£1448 $2592 €2114 At water's edge (60x73cm-24x29in) mono. s.d.82 verso. 10-May-4 Rasmussen, Vejle #535/R est:15000-20000 (D.KR 16000)
£1646 $2799 €2403 Water surface (60x73cm-24x29in) mono. 26-Nov-3 Kunsthallen, Copenhagen #12/R est:18000 (D.KR 17500)

£1693 $2879 €2472 Relations, Milan (66x141cm-26x56in) mono. triptych. 26-Nov-3 Kunsthallen, Copenhagen #44/R est:25000 (D.KR 18000)
£1706 $2730 €2474 On the water's surface (60x73cm-24x29in) mono. 17-Sep-3 Kunsthallen, Copenhagen #54/R est:20000 (D.KR 18000)
£2347 $3920 €3427 Composition (50x65cm-20x26in) s.d.78 verso. 7-Oct-3 Rasmussen, Copenhagen #93/R est:25000-30000 (D.KR 25000)
£2540 $4318 €3708 Composition in black and white (74x112cm-29x44in) mono. 29-Nov-3 Rasmussen, Havnen #4296/R est:20000-25000 (D.KR 27000)
£3481 $5917 €5082 Studio picture (130x93cm-51x37in) mono.i. verso. 26-Nov-3 Kunsthallen, Copenhagen #148/R est:40000 (D.KR 37000)
£3756 $6272 €5484 Composition (112x79cm-44x31in) mono. 7-Oct-3 Rasmussen, Copenhagen #77/R est:20000-25000 (D.KR 40000)
£4516 $7676 €6593 Sergel's birds - shape is made up (157x125cm-62x49in) mono. 26-Nov-3 Kunsthallen, Copenhagen #36/R est:40000 (D.KR 48000)
£4883 $8154 €7129 White composition (220x145cm-87x57in) mono. 7-Oct-3 Rasmussen, Copenhagen #169/R est:35000 (D.KR 52000)
Works on paper
£300 $502 €438 Do you think I'm joking? (85x113cm-33x44in) mono.d.64 crayon. 7-Oct-3 Rasmussen, Copenhagen #252/R (D.KR 3200)
£379 $607 €550 Compositions. mono.d.10/3/57 crayon two in one frame. 17-Sep-3 Kunsthallen, Copenhagen #114 (D.KR 4000)

HORNUNG-JENSEN, C (1882-1960) Danish
£280 $439 €409 Farmyard with chickens (45x67cm-18x26in) s. 30-Aug-3 Rasmussen, Havnen #2281 (D.KR 3000)
£421 $664 €610 The artist's wife Ellen at the summer house in Hornbaek (43x53cm-17x21in) prov. 2-Sep-3 Rasmussen, Copenhagen #1748/R (D.KR 4500)

HORNYANSKY, Nicholas (1896-1965) Canadian
£357 $614 €521 Little go Home Bay (40x30cm-16x12in) s. panel. 2-Dec-3 Joyner Waddington, Toronto #445 (C.D 800)
£357 $614 €521 Kakabeka Falls (30x40cm-12x16in) s. board. 2-Dec-3 Joyner Waddington, Toronto #484 (C.D 800)

HOROWITZ, Brenda (20th C) American
£398 $700 €581 Pilgrim Lake (53x71cm-21x28in) s. acrylic painted c.1983. 3-Jan-4 Outer Cape Auctions, Provincetown #85/R

HORRACH, Ramon Nadal (1913-1999) Spanish
£7248 $13482 €10800 Majorca (33x28cm-13x11in) s.d.1942 board. 2-Mar-4 Ansorena, Madrid #67/R est:10800

HORRAK, Johann (1815-1870) Austrian
Works on paper
£897 $1488 €1300 Portrait of woman wearing light blue dress (16x14cm-6x6in) s.d.April 850 W/C. 30-Sep-3 Dorotheum, Vienna #391/R

HORRIX, Hendrikus Mattheus (1845-1932) Dutch
£1250 $2263 €1900 Early love, Zeeland (32x48cm-13x19in) s. canvas on panel. 19-Apr-4 Glerum, Amsterdam #230/R est:2000-3000
£3947 $7145 €6000 Two girls from Zeeuw in national costume with flowers (75x57cm-30x22in) s. 19-Apr-4 Glerum, Amsterdam #130/R est:3000-4000

HORSCHELT, Theodor (1829-1871) German
£23684 $43579 €36000 Battle scene with cossacks in mountain landscape (107x87cm-42x34in) s.d.1853. 24-Jun-4 Dr Fritz Nagel, Stuttgart #724/R est:800
Works on paper
£17013 $29433 €24839 Cossacks - Vier Kaukas, Reiter (44x34cm-17x13in) s.d.1866 W/C pencil. 9-Dec-3 Rasmussen, Copenhagen #1529/R est:15000-20000 (D.KR 180000)

HORSFALL, Charles M (fl.1893-1914) German
Works on paper
£333 $544 €480 Portrait of Hugo Mendelssohn Bartholdy (32x41cm-13x16in) s.d.1900 pastel. 29-Sep-3 Sotheby's, Amsterdam #18

HORSFALL, Robert Bruce (1869-?) American
Works on paper
£549 $1000 €802 Wolf (41x61cm-16x24in) s.d.1922 gouache. 19-Jun-4 Rachel Davis, Shaker Heights #171 est:1200-1800

HORSLEY, John (20th C) New Zealander?
£2166 $3531 €3162 View across Auckland Harbour towards North Head (27x45cm-11x18in) s.d.1884. 23-Sep-3 Peter Webb, Auckland #23/R est:6000-8000 (NZ.D 6000)

HORSLEY, John Callcott (1817-1903) British
£1000 $1800 €1460 Unexpected visitor (30x39cm-12x15in) s.d.1884. 21-Jan-4 Sotheby's, Olympia #284/R est:1000-1500
£1550 $2774 €2263 Scene from Kenilworth, by Sir Walter Scott (19x20cm-7x8in) s.d.1852 i.verso panel. 26-May-4 Sotheby's, Olympia #83/R est:1000-1500
£2809 $5027 €4101 Interior scene with chemists (71x101cm-28x40in) s.i.d.1863. 26-May-4 AB Stockholms Auktionsverk #2369/R est:40000-50000 (S.KR 38000)
£6500 $11830 €9490 Hunting morning (54x65cm-21x26in) s.d.1861 exhib. 1-Jul-4 Sotheby's, London #321/R est:6000-8000

HORST, Emil (attrib) (1854-1910) German
£303 $500 €442 Untitled, five ducks at a pond (48x64cm-19x25in) s. 7-Jul-3 Schrager Galleries, Milwaukee #1266

HORST, Franz (1862-1956) Austrian
£658 $1211 €1000 Austrian landscape with figures and barn (24x31cm-9x12in) s. 25-Jun-4 Michael Zeller, Lindau #533/R

HORST, Horst P (1906-1999) German
Photographs
£1695 $3000 €2475 Gloria Vanderbilt, 1940 (23x19cm-9x7in) i.d. num.14112 gelatin silver print. 27-Apr-4 Christie's, Rockefeller NY #138/R est:4000-6000
£1808 $3200 €2640 Marlene Dietrich (24x20cm-9x8in) s. s.i.d.1942 verso gelatin silver print. 27-Apr-4 Christie's, Rockefeller NY #135/R est:3000-5000
£2515 $4200 €3672 Round the clock I, NY (29x23cm-11x9in) s.i.d.1987 verso gelatin silver print lit. 20-Oct-3 Christie's, Rockefeller NY #91/R est:3000-5000
£2778 $4722 €4000 Lisa with hat and gloves (45x33cm-18x13in) s.i.d. verso gelatin silver print prov.lit. 31-Oct-3 Lempertz, Koln #157/R est:4000-4500
£2778 $5000 €4056 Vogue (33x27cm-13x11in) i.verso gelatin silver print prov. 23-Apr-4 Phillips, New York #139/R est:5000-7000
£2797 $4755 €4000 The Mainbocher Corset, Paris (30x22cm-12x9in) s.i. verso silver gelatin lit.exhib. 27-Nov-3 Villa Grisebach, Berlin #1229/R est:4000-6000
£2797 $4755 €4000 Round the clock I, New York (29x23cm-11x9in) s.i. verso silver gelatin lit.exhib. 27-Nov-3 Villa Grisebach, Berlin #1240/R est:4000-6000
£2825 $5000 €4125 Gabrielle, Coco, Chanel (23x17cm-9x7in) s.i. num.verso photo printed c.1955 prov. 28-Apr-4 Sotheby's, New York #218/R est:5000-8000
£3293 $5500 €4808 Lisa Fonssagrives, fashion shot, New York (49x40cm-19x16in) s. num.3/25 verso platinum print exec.1951 printed later prov. 17-Oct-3 Sotheby's, New York #240/R est:4000-6000
£3800 $6954 €5548 Mainbocher corset, Paris (29x22cm-11x9in) s. silver print 1939 printed later prov.lit. 8-Jul-4 Sotheby's, London #468/R est:3000-5000
£4237 $7500 €6186 Mainbocher corset, 1939 (30x22cm-12x9in) s.i.d. gelatin silver print. 27-Apr-4 Christie's, Rockefeller NY #130/R est:4000-6000
£5000 $8500 €7300 Mainbocher corset, Paris (61x50cm-24x20in) s.i.d.verso silver print exec.1939 printed later lit. 19-Nov-3 Sotheby's, Olympia #210/R est:4000-6000
£6800 $11560 €9928 Lisa, Fonssagrives, with turban NY (61x50cm-24x20in) s.i.d.verso silver print exec.c.1940 printed later lit. 19-Nov-3 Sotheby's, Olympia #211/R est:3000-4000
£7500 $12750 €10950 Odalisque I, N Y (61x50cm-24x20in) st.sig.i.d.verso silver print exec.1943 printed later lit. 19-Nov-3 Sotheby's, Olympia #208/R est:3000-4000
£9040 $16000 €13198 Barefoot beauty, New York, 1941 (61x48cm-24x19in) s. platinum print on canvas prov.lit. 27-Apr-4 Christie's, Rockefeller NY #132/R est:9000-12000
£10870 $17826 €15000 Lisa with money plant (25x21cm-10x8in) i. verso vintage silver gelatin contact. 30-May-3 Villa Grisebach, Berlin #1207/R est:15000-18000
£10870 $17826 €15000 American nude (19x19cm-7x7in) s.i. verso silver gelatin lit. 30-May-3 Villa Grisebach, Berlin #1209/R est:18000-20000

HORST, Ludwig (1829-1891) German
£1042 $1698 €1500 Portrait of young woman wearing red dress (137x88cm-54x35in) s.d.1887. 25-Sep-3 Dr Fritz Nagel, Stuttgart #1361/R est:1100

HORST, Nicolaus van der (1598-1646) Flemish
Works on paper
£408 $731 €600 La conversaion de Constantin (17x11cm-7x4in) pen brown ink wash black crayon. 19-Mar-4 Piasa, Paris #37

HORST, Theo van der (1921-) Dutch
£308 $524 €450 Landscape with farm (79x99cm-31x39in) init.d.75. 5-Nov-3 Vendue Huis, Gravenhage #504/R

HORSTOK, J P van (1745-1825) Dutch
£3147 $5350 €4500 Le nettoyage de cuivre (33x27cm-13x11in) panel. 1-Dec-3 Amberes, Antwerp #316

HORTER, Earl (1881-1940) American
£344 $550 €502 Figures in a landscape (43x64cm-17x25in) s.verso tempera on board. 19-Sep-3 Freeman, Philadelphia #5/R
Works on paper
£264 $475 €385 Seated nude (38x28cm-15x11in) init. chl. 23-Jan-4 Freeman, Philadelphia #79/R
£472 $850 €689 Woman with cow (36x51cm-14x20in) init.i. W/C. 23-Jan-4 Freeman, Philadelphia #61/R

HORTON, Etty (fl.1882-1905) British
£260 $426 €380 Landscape with horse drawn cart and figures (25x36cm-10x14in) s. 6-Jun-3 Biddle & Webb, Birmingham #140
£260 $465 €380 Stepping stones (38x51cm-15x20in) s. 27-May-4 Christie's, Kensington #186/R
£280 $468 €409 Country landscape with children, sheep and a pond (54x43cm-21x17in) s. 7-Oct-3 Bonhams, Knightsbridge #319/R
£330 $611 €482 Figures on a riverside path by thatched cottage (48x74cm-19x29in) s. 13-Feb-4 Keys, Aylsham #637
£340 $568 €496 Rural landscape with cottage and figures to a pathway (75x49cm-30x19in) s. 7-Oct-3 Fellows & Sons, Birmingham #411/R
£581 $1000 €848 Cattle watering at a river's edge (30x61cm-12x24in) s. 6-Dec-3 Neal Auction Company, New Orleans #217

HORTON, George (1859-1950) British
£260 $413 €380 Cullercoats from Tynemouth (31x49cm-12x19in) s. board. 18-Mar-3 Anderson & Garland, Newcastle #466
Works on paper
£260 $478 €380 Black Middens, Tynemouth (8x15cm-3x6in) s. W/C. 23-Mar-4 Anderson & Garland, Newcastle #238
£270 $491 €394 Dutch street scene with figures (36x25cm-14x10in) s. pencil W/C chk. 15-Jun-4 Bonhams, Leeds #49
£300 $540 €438 Coastal scene at low tide with figures unloading a large boat (17x26cm-7x10in) s. W/C. 21-Apr-4 Tennants, Leyburn #939
£310 $570 €453 Figures on a beach on a blustery day (15x11cm-6x4in) s. W/C. 23-Mar-4 Anderson & Garland, Newcastle #239
£320 $592 €467 Near Rotterdam (25x35cm-10x14in) s.i. W/C. 9-Mar-4 Bonhams, Knightsbridge #10/R
£360 $612 €526 Fishing boats in a harbour (26x21cm-10x8in) s. W/C. 27-Nov-3 Greenslade Hunt, Taunton #980/R

£360 $662 €526 In Holland (24x32cm-9x13in) s.i. W/C. 23-Mar-4 Anderson & Garland, Newcastle #233
£420 $773 €613 On the Bents, South Shields (21x36cm-8x14in) s. W/C. 23-Mar-4 Anderson & Garland, Newcastle #236
£460 $846 €672 Street scene with a clock tower (33x25cm-13x10in) s. W/C. 23-Mar-4 Anderson & Garland, Newcastle #234
£550 $1012 €803 St Mary's Church, Stokenewington (34x25cm-13x10in) s.i. W/C. 23-Mar-4 Anderson & Garland, Newcastle #235/R
£778 $1291 €1136 Harbour scene (56x63cm-22x25in) W/C. 2-Oct-3 Heffel, Vancouver #20 (C.D 1750)
£925 $1656 €1351 Extensive coastal scene with lighthouse (56x89cm-22x35in) s. i.verso W/C. 6-May-4 Biddle & Webb, Birmingham #909

HORTON, John M (1935-) Canadian
£1000 $1830 €1460 Waiting packers at Port Renfrew (61x91cm-24x36in) s. i.verso acrylic prov. 3-Jun-4 Heffel, Vancouver #33/R est:3000-4000 (C.D 2500)

HORTON, Percy (1897-1970) British
£300 $528 €438 Corner of Dulwich Common (50x33cm-20x13in) 19-May-4 Christie's, Kensington #753

HORTON, William Samuel (1865-1936) American
£757 $1400 €1105 Village of Headcorn, Kent (38x46cm-15x18in) s. i.d.1906 verso panel. 10-Mar-4 Doyle, New York #28/R
£3125 $5000 €4563 Gstaad, Switzerland (43x53cm-17x21in) s.d.1912 verso panel. 20-Sep-3 Sloans & Kenyon, Bethesda #1193/R est:5000-7000
£5587 $10000 €8157 Tuileries, Paris (63x75cm-25x30in) s. board prov. 14-May-4 Skinner, Boston #307/R est:15000-25000
£17318 $31000 €25284 Blackbirds and falling snow (63x76cm-25x30in) s. board prov. 14-May-4 Skinner, Boston #303/R est:35000-45000
Works on paper
£620 $1128 €905 Group of fisher folk on a sunlit beach (32cm-13in) s. black crayon gouache. 15-Jun-4 Rosebery Fine Art, London #495/R

HORVAT, Frank (1928-) ?
£352 $609 €500 Landscape with trees (35x50cm-14x20in) s. cardboard. 9-Dec-3 Finarte Semenzato, Milan #5/R

HORVAT, Mirko (1955-) Yugoslavian
£629 $1083 €900 Still life with bowl of pears (43x43cm-17x17in) s.d.1976. 4-Dec-3 Van Ham, Cologne #220/R

HORWOOD, Charles (20th C) British
£280 $476 €409 Elegant figures under parasols at the seaside (30x41cm-12x16in) s.i.d.1966 verso. 6-Nov-3 Christie's, Kensington #891
£580 $986 €847 The finish (31x40cm-12x16in) s.verso. 19-Nov-3 Sotheby's, Olympia #131/R
£700 $1260 €1022 Cornish seascape (41x30cm-16x12in) s. 21-Apr-4 Brightwells, Leominster #788/R

HORY, Elmyr de (1905-1978) French
£685 $1164 €1000 Woman (55x46cm-22x18in) s. 4-Nov-3 Ansorena, Madrid #953/R
£852 $1500 €1244 Portrait of a lady (76x63cm-30x25in) s.d.1970 verso after Amadeo Modigliani. 23-May-4 Bonhams & Butterfields, Los Angeles #7074/R
£852 $1500 €1244 Mother and daughter in a garden (61x86cm-24x34in) s.d.1971 after Claude Monet. 23-May-4 Bonhams & Butterfields, Los Angeles #7075/R
£852 $1500 €1244 Woman seated at a table (61x81cm-24x32in) s.d.1970 verso after Henri Matisse. 23-May-4 Bonhams & Butterfields, Los Angeles #7076/R
£2282 $4244 €3400 Woman (100x85cm-39x33in) s. 2-Mar-4 Ansorena, Madrid #828/R est:1200
Works on paper
£369 $653 €550 Woman (20x27cm-8x11in) s. dr. 27-Apr-4 Durán, Madrid #1134

HOSAEUS, Kurt Hermann (1875-?) German
Sculpture
£1027 $1747 €1500 Greek fighter on horse drinking water (47x50cm-19x20in) s. bronze marble socle Cast Gladenbeck, Friedrichshagen lit. 6-Nov-3 Allgauer, Kempten #3043/R est:1800

HOSCH, Edouard (1843-1908) Swiss
£3084 $5242 €4503 Kramgasse and Zytglogge (73x59cm-29x23in) s.d.1880. 7-Nov-3 Dobiaschofsky, Bern #72/R est:8000 (S.FR 7000)

HOSCH, Friedrich Karl (19th C) German
£2467 $4415 €3700 Watchmaker in an interior studying a wrist watch (53x59cm-21x23in) s.d.1858. 14-May-4 Behringer, Furth #1511/R est:2000

HOSCH, Karl (1900-1972) Swiss
£173 $310 €253 Girl holding candle in hand (61x50cm-24x20in) s.d. 22-Mar-4 Philippe Schuler, Zurich #6019 (S.FR 400)
£289 $483 €419 Village in mountain landscape (50x70cm-20x28in) s.d. 23-Jun-3 Philippe Schuler, Zurich #3397 (S.FR 630)
£649 $1162 €948 View of Zurichsee from Oberrieden (120x59cm-47x23in) s.d. 22-Mar-4 Philippe Schuler, Zurich #4336 (S.FR 1500)
£814 $1385 €1188 Hirzel (79x102cm-31x40in) s.d.1930. 25-Nov-3 Germann, Zurich #44/R est:2200-2600 (S.FR 1800)
£905 $1511 €1321 Landscape (81x100cm-32x39in) s.d.1941. 24-Jun-3 Germann, Zurich #159/R est:2500-3000 (S.FR 2000)

HOSCHEDE-MONET, Blanche (1865-1947) French
£5000 $9100 €7500 Lac de montagne (60x74cm-24x29in) s. painted c.1920. 30-Jun-4 Delvaux, Paris #38/R est:10000-15000
£6376 $11859 €9500 Nature morte au vase de dahlias (61x73cm-24x29in) s. 3-Mar-4 Ferri, Paris #384/R est:4000-6000
£8108 $15000 €11838 Jardins de Claude Monet, Giverny (74x93cm-29x37in) s.d.28. 11-Feb-4 Sotheby's, New York #15/R est:18000-25000
£20270 $37500 €29594 Roseraie du jardin Monet a Giverny (65x81cm-26x32in) s.d.27 exhib. 11-Feb-4 Sotheby's, New York #21/R est:20000-30000

HOSEMANN, Theodor (1807-1875) German
£559 $951 €800 Fruit seller with small cart on street corner (17x18cm-7x7in) mono.d.1859 W/C paper on board. 20-Nov-3 Van Ham, Cologne #1636
£4000 $6680 €5800 Shepherd having fun (44x37cm-17x15in) mono.d.1846 prov. 15-Nov-3 Lempertz, Koln #1624/R est:6000
Works on paper
£267 $477 €400 Mother returning home with children (15x12cm-6x5in) pencil W/C. 13-May-4 Bassenge, Berlin #5577
£313 $497 €450 Merry outing (16x27cm-6x11in) s. 11-Sep-3 Weidler, Nurnberg #382/R

HOSENFELDER, Christian Friedrich (1706-1780) German
£554 $992 €809 Portrait of horse (20x20cm-8x8in) s. panel. 26-May-4 AB Stockholms Auktionsverk #2545/R (S.KR 7500)

HOSHI, Joichi (1913-1979) Japanese
Prints
£2375 $3800 €3468 Red tree (42x56cm-17x22in) s.d.73 col woodcut. 18-Sep-3 Swann Galleries, New York #308a/R est:2500-3500

HOSIASSON, Philippe (1898-1978) French
£1184 $2179 €1800 Composition (46x55cm-18x22in) s.d.1948 s.d.48 verso. 27-Jun-4 Versailles Encheres #26/R est:2000-3000
£1888 $3153 €2700 On the Eve (30x89cm-12x35in) s.d.1958 s.i.d.verso prov. 29-Jun-3 Versailles Encheres #38/R
£1958 $3270 €2800 Composition (92x73cm-36x29in) s.s.1959 s.d.verso prov. 29-Jun-3 Versailles Encheres #37/R
£2349 $4158 €3500 Composition (81x65cm-32x26in) s.d.64. 28-Apr-4 Artcurial Briest, Paris #275/R est:2500-3000

HOSKINS, Gayle Porter (1887-1962) American
£5975 $9500 €8724 Trail ride (91x61cm-36x24in) s. bears another sig.i.verso. 14-Sep-3 Susanin's, Chicago #6088/R est:8000-10000

HOSKINS, John (17th C) British
Miniatures
£9000 $16110 €13140 Sir Arthur Hesilrige, in gilt studded armour (6cm-2in) init.d.1652 vellum silver gilt frame prov.exhib.lit. 25-May-4 Christie's, London #62/R est:6000-8000

HOSKYNS, Ben (20th C) British
Works on paper
£270 $494 €394 Hare in a winter landscape (43x30cm-17x12in) s. W/C. 7-Jun-4 Cumbria Auction Rooms, Carlisle #221/R
£310 $527 €453 Grouse in flight (31x40cm-12x16in) s. W/C. 24-Nov-3 Tiffin King & Nicholson, Carlisle #200/R

HOSMER, Florence Ames (19/20th C) American
£315 $500 €460 Millhouse (20x26cm-8x10in) s. board. 12-Sep-3 Skinner, Boston #395/R

HOSOTTE, Georges (1936-) French
£2413 $4150 €3450 Les alpilles (92x73cm-36x29in) s. 7-Dec-3 Feletin, Province #102

HOST, Marianne (1865-1943) Danish
£325 $601 €475 An inn in Sonderho (40x49cm-16x19in) s.d.1901 exhib. 15-Mar-4 Rasmussen, Vejle #447/R (D.KR 3600)

HOST, Oluf (1884-1966) Danish
£469 $764 €685 Evening landscape at Bornholm (17x23cm-7x9in) init. canvas on board. 27-Sep-3 Rasmussen, Havnen #4129/R (D.KR 5000)
£851 $1523 €1242 Houses at Bornholm (17x26cm-7x10in) s.verso. 12-Jan-4 Rasmussen, Vejle #679 (D.KR 9000)
£1878 $3136 €2742 September landscape, Roe (50x71cm-20x28in) init.d.9-21 prov. 7-Oct-3 Rasmussen, Copenhagen #316/R est:25000-30000 (D.KR 20000)
£2031 $3736 €2965 Landscape from Helleland (34x56cm-13x22in) mono.d.19-8-56 prov. 29-Mar-4 Rasmussen, Copenhagen #212/R (D.KR 22500)
£2256 $4152 €3294 Bathers, Suserenden (27x46cm-11x18in) init.d.37 prov. 29-Mar-4 Rasmussen, Copenhagen #208/R est:25000-30000 (D.KR 25000)
£2817 $4704 €4113 Bognemark - cowshed (73x100cm-29x39in) prov. 7-Oct-3 Rasmussen, Copenhagen #335/R est:30000 (D.KR 30000)
£3339 $6144 €4875 Sunlit road in Gudhjem Plantation (65x54cm-26x21in) mono.d.39. 29-Mar-4 Rasmussen, Copenhagen #216/R est:30000 (D.KR 37000)
£3763 $6397 €5494 Sunset over the sea (64x95cm-25x37in) init.i.d.20 exhib. 26-Nov-3 Kunsthallen, Copenhagen #370/R (D.KR 40000)
£4327 $7357 €6317 Model bathing from cliffs, Bornholm (60x82cm-24x32in) init. s.i.d.1950 verso. 26-Nov-3 Kunsthallen, Copenhagen #340/R est:30000 (D.KR 46000)
£5415 $9964 €7906 View over the sea, Gudhjem, Bornholm (54x62cm-21x24in) mono. s.verso prov. 29-Mar-4 Rasmussen, Copenhagen #213/R est:40000-50000 (D.KR 60000)
£5634 $9408 €8226 Bognemark - scene from slaughter (73x130cm-29x51in) mono.d.63 prov. 7-Oct-3 Rasmussen, Copenhagen #149/R est:60000 (D.KR 60000)
£6137 $11292 €8960 View over Gudhjem from Bokul (54x81cm-21x32in) mono. s.verso prov. 29-Mar-4 Rasmussen, Copenhagen #209/R est:50000-75000 (D.KR 68000)
£6769 $12455 €9883 The farm is burning, Gudhjem (28x71cm-11x28in) init. plywood prov. 29-Mar-4 Rasmussen, Copenhagen #192/R est:75000-100000 (D.KR 75000)

£7401 $13617 €10805 Sunset after rain (73x100cm-29x39in) mono. exhib.prov. 29-Mar-4 Rasmussen, Copenhagen #202/R est:80000-100000 (D.KR 82000)
£7981 $13329 €11652 Sunset, winter (96x130cm-38x51in) mono.indis.d.52 prov. 7-Oct-3 Rasmussen, Copenhagen #146/R est:80000 (D.KR 85000)
£14440 $26570 €21082 Oesterlars round church (73x92cm-29x36in) mono. prov. 29-Mar-4 Rasmussen, Copenhagen #194/R est:150000-200000 (D.KR 160000)
£15433 $28397 €22532 Winter day in our garden (81x146cm-32x57in) init.d.55. 29-Mar-4 Rasmussen, Copenhagen #191/R est:200000-250000 (D.KR 171000)
£34296 $63105 €50072 Bognemark (81x130cm-32x51in) mono. s.verso prov. 29-Mar-4 Rasmussen, Copenhagen #207/R est:250000-300000 (D.KR 380000)
Works on paper
£280 $523 €409 Two studies. mono. pen crayon two in one frame. 25-Feb-4 Kunsthallen, Copenhagen #217 (D.KR 3100)

HOSTE, Constant P (1873-1917) Belgian
£638 $1180 €950 Barque dans un paysage automnal (66x90cm-26x35in) s. 15-Mar-4 Horta, Bruxelles #441

HOTERE, Ralph (1931-) New Zealander
£2747 $5083 €4011 Untitled (81x61cm-32x24in) acrylic on board. 9-Mar-4 Watson's, Christchurch #35 est:10000-18000 (NZ.D 7500)
£2857 $5257 €4171 Fusion II (28x28cm-11x11in) s.d.1964 board. 25-Mar-4 International Art Centre, Auckland #30/R est:10000-20000 (NZ.D 8000)
£3759 $6391 €5488 Ulysses (55x43cm-22x17in) s.d.1965 verso board. 27-Nov-3 International Art Centre, Auckland #78/R est:10000-15000 (NZ.D 10000)
£4135 $7030 €6037 Tourettes Surlong, France (30x54cm-12x21in) s.d.January 1963 oil paper. 27-Nov-3 International Art Centre, Auckland #51/R est:5000-7000 (NZ.D 11000)
£4135 $7030 €6037 Black (38x36cm-15x14in) board. 27-Nov-3 International Art Centre, Auckland #52/R est:6000-10000 (NZ.D 11000)
£5536 $9910 €8083 February May and the birds of ice, the moon drowns in its voices of water (36x54cm-14x21in) s.d.7/70 acrylic on paper. 12-May-4 Dunbar Sloane, Wellington #21/R est:20000-30000 (NZ.D 16000)
£8922 $15346 €13026 Drawing for Song Cycle (51x38cm-20x15in) s.i.d.76 paper. 3-Dec-3 Dunbar Sloane, Auckland #52 est:40000-48000 (NZ.D 24000)
£18051 $29422 €26354 Karanga (52x40cm-20x16in) i. init.i.verso enamel board prov. 23-Sep-3 Peter Webb, Auckland #56/R est:45000-65000 (NZ.D 50000)
£18545 $29116 €26890 Avignon (62x52cm-24x20in) s.i.d.July 1978 i.verso. 27-Aug-3 Dunbar Sloane, Wellington #35/R est:60000-80000 (NZ.D 51000)
£28881 $47076 €42166 Koputai (58x78cm-23x31in) s.i.d.1976 verso enamel hardboard. 23-Sep-3 Peter Webb, Auckland #57/R est:90000-120000 (NZ.D 80000)
£28881 $47076 €42166 Black painting (107x107cm-42x42in) s.i.d.1976 verso. 23-Sep-3 Peter Webb, Auckland #58/R est:90000-150000 (NZ.D 80000)
£30075 $51128 €43910 Black painting II (178x71cm-70x28in) s.i.d.1970 oil acrylic. 27-Nov-3 International Art Centre, Auckland #77/R est:110000-150000 (NZ.D 80000)
£31469 $57273 €45945 Test piece red and black (78x58cm-31x23in) s.i.d.1977 enamel on board. 29-Jun-4 Peter Webb, Auckland #31/R est:70000-90000 (NZ.D 90000)
£58182 $91345 €84364 Untitled, Baby iron series. Sketch for a Mungo painting (86x77cm-34x30in) s.d.1983 enamel burnished stainless steel double-sided. 27-Aug-3 Dunbar Sloane, Wellington #26/R est:160000-200000 (NZ.D 160000)
£62500 $99375 €91250 Black painting I from malady (177x71cm-70x28in) s. i.d.1970 verso acrylic prov. 1-May-3 Dunbar Sloane, Wellington #28/R est:160000-200000 (NZ.D 180000)
£82090 $142015 €119851 Baby iron (120x85cm-47x33in) s.d.1983 acrylic steel nails sash window board prov. 9-Dec-3 Peter Webb, Auckland #34/R est:220000-280000 (NZ.D 220000)
Prints
£1636 $2569 €2372 Black rainbow (57x38cm-22x15in) s.i.d.20/08/1986 artists proof. 27-Aug-3 Dunbar Sloane, Wellington #10 est:4000-6000 (NZ.D 4500)
£2448 $4455 €3574 Anzac II (54x37cm-21x15in) s.i.d.1990 lithograph. 29-Jun-4 Peter Webb, Auckland #112/R est:6500-8500 (NZ.D 7000)
£2500 $4600 €3650 At Matauri Bay (55x44cm-22x17in) s.d.1988 num.2/30 lithograph. 25-Mar-4 International Art Centre, Auckland #127/R est:7000-9000 (NZ.D 7000)
£2527 $4119 €3689 Round midnight September (57x75cm-22x30in) s.i.d.2000 num.18/24 lithograph. 23-Sep-3 Peter Webb, Auckland #27/R est:6500-8500 (NZ.D 7000)
£2536 $4109 €3677 January evening (72x50cm-28x20in) s.d.1991 lithograph. 31-Jul-3 International Art Centre, Auckland #10/R est:5000-8000 (NZ.D 7000)
£2622 $4773 €3828 Jerusalem (49x37cm-19x15in) s.d.2002 lithograph. 29-Jun-4 Peter Webb, Auckland #114/R est:6500-7500 (NZ.D 7500)
£2627 $4229 €3835 This is a black Union Jack (52x37cm-20x15in) s.d.88 lithograph. 20-Aug-3 Dunbar Sloane, Auckland #14/R est:4500-8000 (NZ.D 7250)
£2632 $4474 €3843 Manhires midnight windows II (53x38cm-21x15in) s.d.1980 num.10/10 etching. 27-Nov-3 International Art Centre, Auckland #41/R est:7500-11000 (NZ.D 7000)
£2632 $4474 €3843 Manhires midnight windows III (53x38cm-21x15in) s,d,1980 num.10/10 etching. 27-Nov-3 International Art Centre, Auckland #42/R est:7500-11000 (NZ.D 7000)
£2797 $5091 €4084 Song of Soloman (75x53cm-30x21in) s.i.d.1991 lithograph. 29-Jun-4 Peter Webb, Auckland #116/R est:7000-9000 (NZ.D 8000)
£2857 $5257 €4171 La cruz, window in Spain (68x49cm-27x19in) s.d.1992 lithograph. 25-Mar-4 International Art Centre, Auckland #40/R est:7000-10000 (NZ.D 8000)
£2899 $4609 €4233 Purple (75x57cm-30x22in) s.i.d.97 num. lithograph. 9-Sep-3 Watson's, Christchurch #34 (NZ.D 8000)
£2946 $5333 €4301 Winter solstice - Carey's Bay (76x52cm-30x20in) s.i.d.1991 num.14/18 lithograph. 30-Mar-4 Peter Webb, Auckland #129/R est:9000-12000 (NZ.D 8250)
£3008 $5113 €4392 La cruz II (74x53cm-29x21in) s.d.1992 num.8/18 lithograph. 27-Nov-3 International Art Centre, Auckland #26/R est:8000-12000 (NZ.D 8000)
£3008 $5113 €4392 Untitled (74x53cm-29x21in) s. num.8/18. 27-Nov-3 International Art Centre, Auckland #27/R est:8000-12000 (NZ.D 8000)
£3008 $5113 €4392 Winter solstice, Carrys Bay (75x53cm-30x21in) s.d.1998 num.8/18 lithograph. 27-Nov-3 International Art Centre, Auckland #28/R est:8000-12000 (NZ.D 8000)
£3497 $6364 €5106 Window in Spain (69x48cm-27x19in) s.i.d.1992 lithograph oilstick. 29-Jun-4 Peter Webb, Auckland #10/R est:7000-9000 (NZ.D 10000)
£3497 $6364 €5106 Keep NZ out of Iraq (77x56cm-30x22in) s.d.2003 num.26/40 lithograph. 29-Jun-4 Peter Webb, Auckland #115/R est:8000-12000 (NZ.D 10000)
£3663 $6777 €5348 Window in Spain (74x52cm-29x20in) s.i.d.92 num. 2/18 lithograph. 9-Mar-4 Watson's, Christchurch #92 est:11000-15000 (NZ.D 10000)
£3791 $6179 €5535 Window in Spain (72x52cm-28x20in) s.i.d.1992 num.9/50 lithograph. 23-Sep-3 Peter Webb, Auckland #31/R est:7000-9000 (NZ.D 10500)
£3979 $7123 €5809 This is a Black Union Jack (50x35cm-20x14in) s.i.d.88 lithograph. 12-May-4 Dunbar Sloane, Wellington #12/R est:6000-10000 (NZ.D 11500)
£5410 $9360 €7899 Window in Spain (76x58cm-30x23in) s.i.d.1996 num.19/24 lithograph gold leaf. 9-Dec-3 Peter Webb, Auckland #59/R est:12000-15000 (NZ.D 14500)
£5776 $9415 €8433 Window in Spain (76x58cm-30x23in) s.i.d.1996 num.13/24 lithograph goldleaf. 23-Sep-3 Peter Webb, Auckland #59/R est:12000-16000 (NZ.D 16000)
£5978 $9685 €8668 Yellow (75x56cm-30x22in) s.d.1997 lithograph num.22/22. 31-Jul-3 International Art Centre, Auckland #2/R est:5000-8000 (NZ.D 16500)
Works on paper
£727 $1142 €1054 R M (40x28cm-16x11in) i.d.11/8/1990 ink dr lithograph. 27-Aug-3 Dunbar Sloane, Wellington #51 (NZ.D 2000)
£846 $1438 €1235 Nude (40x28cm-16x11in) d.11.VIII.90 ink dr. 26-Nov-3 Dunbar Sloane, Wellington #15a est:2500-5000 (NZ.D 2250)
£1857 $3361 €2711 Reclining nude female figure study (25x20cm-10x8in) s.d.1963 pencil. 30-Mar-4 Peter Webb, Auckland #139/R est:4000-6000 (NZ.D 5200)
£2239 $3873 €3269 Untitled, composition (36x26cm-14x10in) s.d.13.11.91 pastel oil stick. 9-Dec-3 Peter Webb, Auckland #74/R est:8000-12000 (NZ.D 6000)
£2256 $3835 €3294 Anatomy of a dance, song cycle, sound movement theatre programme (25x38cm-10x15in) W/C ink on print. 26-Nov-3 Dunbar Sloane, Wellington #15/R est:6000-9000 (NZ.D 6000)
£2422 $4336 €3536 How much is that Dali in the window (33x25cm-13x10in) s.d.86 chl prov. 12-May-4 Dunbar Sloane, Wellington #55/R est:6000-8000 (NZ.D 7000)
£2545 $3996 €3690 Oedipus drawing for Baxter's Temptations of Oedipus (26x18cm-10x7in) s.i. ink. 27-Aug-3 Dunbar Sloane, Wellington #43/R est:7000-10000 (NZ.D 7000)
£2727 $4282 €3954 Set design for Whitings, The Devil, Globe Theatre, Denedin (33x44cm-13x17in) s.i.d.November 1973 W/C ink. 27-Aug-3 Dunbar Sloane, Wellington #59/R est:7000-10000 (NZ.D 7500)
£3287 $5884 €4799 Les Saintes Maries de la mer, Aromoana XII 80 (36x25cm-14x10in) s.i.d.80 pastel. 12-May-4 Dunbar Sloane, Wellington #22/R est:12000-15000 (NZ.D 9500)
£3571 $6071 €5214 Reclining nude (37x30cm-15x12in) s.d.1970 W/C. 27-Nov-3 International Art Centre, Auckland #22/R est:10000-15000 (NZ.D 9500)
£3986 $6417 €5820 Girl in a hat (38x27cm-15x11in) s.i.d.76 pencil dr. prov. 20-Aug-3 Dunbar Sloane, Auckland #24/R est:11000-16000 (NZ.D 11000)
£4286 $7757 €6258 Black window (23x30cm-9x12in) s.i.d.8.80 W/C acrylic. 30-Mar-4 Peter Webb, Auckland #19/R est:10000-15000 (NZ.D 12000)
£4332 $7061 €6325 London (36x25cm-14x10in) s.d.1988 collage pastel. 23-Sep-3 Peter Webb, Auckland #75/R est:15000-20000 (NZ.D 12000)
£4364 $6851 €6328 Window in Spain (32x23cm-13x9in) s.i.d.1978 W/C. 27-Aug-3 Dunbar Sloane, Wellington #40/R est:13000-18000 (NZ.D 12000)
£4511 $7669 €6586 Winter solstice, Carey's Bay (20x13cm-8x5in) s.i.d.1992 pastel. 26-Nov-3 Dunbar Sloane, Wellington #22/R est:10000-15000 (NZ.D 12000)
£4874 $7944 €7116 Song of Solomon (62x49cm-24x19in) s.i.d. Feb 1991 mixed media collage. 23-Sep-3 Peter Webb, Auckland #20/R est:12000-18000 (NZ.D 13500)
£5245 $9545 €7658 Drawing for a tin painting (75x55cm-30x22in) s.i.d.1985 pencil pastel ink. 29-Jun-4 Peter Webb, Auckland #25/R est:20000-30000 (NZ.D 15000)
£5357 $9857 €7821 Window in Spain (32x23cm-13x9in) s.i.d.4/1978 W/C. 25-Mar-4 International Art Centre, Auckland #42/R est:8000-12000 (NZ.D 15000)
£6522 $10565 €9457 Nude drawings's no.2 and 6 (20x28cm-8x11in) s.d.1971 W/C pair. 31-Jul-3 International Art Centre, Auckland #31/R est:20000-30000 (NZ.D 18000)
£6993 $12727 €10210 Drawing for Te Whiti series (58x39cm-23x15in) s.i.d.8.72 W/C. 29-Jun-4 Peter Webb, Auckland #76/R est:18000-24000 (NZ.D 20000)
£7519 $12782 €10978 Sapwood and milk (76x42cm-30x17in) s. W/C publicity poster by Hone Tuwhare. 26-Nov-3 Dunbar Sloane, Wellington #18/R est:20000-30000 (NZ.D 20000)
£7971 $12833 €11638 Untitled (37x27cm-15x11in) s.d.93 mixed media. 20-Aug-3 Dunbar Sloane, Auckland #40/R est:22000-35000 (NZ.D 22000)
£8727 $13702 €12654 Reclining nude (28x20cm-11x8in) s. ink exec.c.1980. 27-Aug-3 Dunbar Sloane, Wellington #50/R est:15000-25000 (NZ.D 24000)
£9091 $16545 €13273 London (35x25cm-14x10in) s.d.10.88 collage pastel. 29-Jun-4 Peter Webb, Auckland #118/R est:12000-18000 (NZ.D 26000)
£10490 $19091 €15315 Pathway to the sea, drawing for Ian Wedde (55x76cm-22x30in) s.i.d.1975 W/C ink pencil crayon. 29-Jun-4 Peter Webb, Auckland #51/R est:35000-45000 (NZ.D 30000)
£10714 $19393 €15642 Requiem for Tony (37x54cm-15x21in) s.i.d.1974 W/C ink pencil on card diptych prov.exhib. 30-Mar-4 Peter Webb, Auckland #46/R est:30000-40000 (NZ.D 30000)
£14286 $26286 €20858 Pine no 8 (71x51cm-28x20in) s.d.1974 W/C prov. 25-Mar-4 International Art Centre, Auckland #60/R est:38000-48000 (NZ.D 40000)
£16263 $29111 €23744 Cyanidefects, aluminpolitik (74x54cm-29x21in) s.d.80 W/C acrylic. 12-May-4 Dunbar Sloane, Wellington #37/R est:40000-60000 (NZ.D 47000)
£25271 $41191 €36896 Port Chalmers (54x41cm-21x16in) s.i.d.1983 paper burnished steel acrylic. 23-Sep-3 Peter Webb, Auckland #60/R est:45000-65000 (NZ.D 70000)

HOTERE, Ralph and McFARLANE, Mary (20th C) New Zealander
Works on paper
£7143 $12929 €10429 Binisafua II (45x76cm-18x30in) s.d.1999 verso silver leadhead nails coin metal on mirror. 30-Mar-4 Peter Webb, Auckland #138/R est:20000-30000 (NZ.D 20000)

HOTTINGER, Johann Konrad (1788-1828) Austrian
Works on paper
£671 $1235 €1000 River landscape with shepherd in foreground. River landscape with sailing boats (37x48cm-15x19in) s.d.1804 pen ink W/C two. 29-Mar-4 Glerum, Amsterdam #136

HOTTOT, Louis (1834-1905) French
Sculpture
£1096 $1831 €1600 Young oriental woman holding playing cards (67cm-26in) s. pat.bronze ivory prov. 15-Nov-3 Galerie Gloggner, Luzern #69/R est:2500-2800 (S.FR 2500)
£1200 $2172 €1800 Orientale filant (51x18x13cm-20x7x5in) s. col pat alloy. 1-Apr-4 Credit Municipal, Paris #90 est:1500-1800
£1243 $2300 €1815 An Arab card receiver (109cm-43in) zinc pat. traces polychrome. 12-Mar-4 Jackson's, Cedar Falls #927/R est:1500-2000
£14184 $23688 €20000 Couple d'orientaux tenant un plateau (107cm-42in) s. polychrome rec. socle pair. 16-Jun-3 Gros & Delettrez, Paris #48/R est:20000-25000

HOTZENDORFF, Theodor von (1898-1974) German
£625 $987 €900 Extensive summer landscape (55x80cm-22x31in) mono. lit. 19-Sep-3 Schloss Ahlden, Ahlden #1617/R
£634 $1096 €900 Grassau-Hindling (55x112cm-22x44in) 10-Dec-3 Hugo Ruef, Munich #2435/R
£1208 $2223 €1800 Bergen moor (72x98cm-28x39in) mono. s.i. verso panel. 24-Mar-4 Hugo Ruef, Munich #1231/R est:1800

HOUARI (1950-) ?
Sculpture
£1184 $2179 €1800 Tension (80x30x25cm-31x12x10in) s. num.1/8 steel exec.1991 prov. 27-Jun-4 Versailles Encheres #164/R est:2500-3000

HOUASSE, Michel-Ange (attrib) (1680-1730) French
£7143 $13000 €10429 Portrait of a young gentleman, said to be an infant of Spain (104x69cm-41x27in) prov.lit. 17-Jun-4 Christie's, Rockefeller NY #32/R est:10000-15000

HOUASSE, René-Antoine (1645-1710) French
£1854 $3375 €2800 Les angelots moissonneurs (15x18cm-6x7in) paper on cardboard. 21-Jun-4 Tajan, Paris #93/R est:2500-3500

HOUBEN, Charles (1871-1931) Belgian
£306 $556 €447 River landscape with fishing boats (81x116cm-32x46in) s. 16-Jun-4 Fischer, Luzern #2187 (S.FR 700)

HOUBEN, Henri (1858-1931) Belgian
£1361 $2476 €2000 Guiding home the flock (55x75cm-22x30in) s. 3-Feb-4 Christie's, Amsterdam #279/R est:2000-3000
£2961 $5447 €4500 Retour a la bergerie (116x180cm-46x71in) s. 22-Jun-4 Palais de Beaux Arts, Brussels #262/R est:5000-7000
£3152 $5421 €4602 Le retour des pecheurs (97x134cm-38x53in) s. 8-Dec-3 Blomqvist, Oslo #418/R est:40000-60000 (N.KR 37000)
£7383 $13658 €11000 Le retour des pecheurs (96x133cm-38x52in) s. 13-Mar-4 De Vuyst, Lokeren #423/R est:10000-12000
£10440 $19000 €15242 Aphrodite presenting a rose to cupid (94x127cm-37x50in) s. 7-Feb-4 Neal Auction Company, New Orleans #397/R est:15000-25000

HOUCHIN, Jackie (20th C) American
Works on paper
£297 $550 €434 Pueblo sweetheart (61x46cm-24x18in) s. pastel masonite. 13-Mar-4 Susanin's, Chicago #6066/R

HOUCKGEEST, Gerard (1600-1661) Dutch
£1317 $2200 €1923 Interior of old kerk Amsterdam (53x64cm-21x25in) 19-Oct-3 Susanin's, Chicago #6031/R est:3000-5000

HOUDON (after) (?) French
Sculpture
£7692 $12846 €11000 Bust of Benjamin Franklin (49cm-19in) i.verso terracotta piedouche. 24-Jun-3 Christie's, Paris #405/R est:5000-8000

HOUDON, Jean Antoine (1741-1828) French
Sculpture
£4823 $7813 €6800 Portrait de femme inconnue (84x48x31cm-33x19x12in) st.verso plaster exec.c.1775 lit. 21-May-3 Daguerre, Paris #278/R est:6000-8000

HOUDON, Jean Antoine (after) (1741-1828) French
Sculpture
£4605 $8474 €7000 Frileuse (25cm-10in) bears sig. pat bronze lit. 23-Jun-4 Sotheby's, Paris #110/R est:7000-10000

HOUDON, Jean Antoine (studio) (1741-1828) French
Sculpture
£7333 $13273 €11000 Buste de Claudine Houdon enfant (51cm-20in) pat plaster incl. marble base lit. 31-Mar-4 Sotheby's, Paris #46/R est:7000-9000
£10000 $18400 €14600 Bust of Voltaire (52cm-20in) s.d.1778 brown pat bronze socle plinth marble base lit. 10-Jun-4 Christie's, London #149/R est:5000-8000

HOUEL, Jean (?) French
£6294 $10511 €9000 Scene paysanne (46x64cm-18x25in) i.d.1789 verso. 26-Jun-3 Artcurial Briest, Paris #491 est:8000-12000

HOUEL, Jean Pierre (1735-1813) French
Works on paper
£634 $1096 €900 Halt au relais de poste (18x26cm-7x10in) pen blk ink brown grey wash. 10-Dec-3 Piasa, Paris #58

HOUGAARD, Henning (1922-1995) Swedish
£386 $676 €564 Bullfinches (45x65cm-18x26in) s. 16-Dec-3 Grev Wedels Plass, Oslo #176/R (N.KR 4500)
£442 $809 €645 Winter landscape with hare (50x60cm-20x24in) s. 2-Feb-4 Blomqvist, Lysaker #1115 (N.KR 5500)

HOUGH, Jennine (1948-) American
Works on paper
£519 $950 €758 Summer garden (107x74cm-42x29in) W/C. 10-Jul-4 Hindman, Chicago #227/R est:700-900

HOUGH, William (fl.1857-1894) British
£2500 $3950 €3625 Pears and plums on a mossy bank (77x64cm-30x25in) s.d.1875. 4-Sep-3 Christie's, Kensington #318/R est:3000-5000
Works on paper
£450 $788 €657 Bird's nest and primroses against a mossy bank (25x33cm-10x13in) s. W/C. 16-Dec-3 Capes Dunn, Manchester #722
£640 $1184 €934 Grapes and peach (17x25cm-7x10in) s. W/C. 14-Jul-4 Bonhams, Chester #529
£650 $1105 €949 Still life of plums and peaches before a mossy bank (20x25cm-8x10in) s. W/C. 29-Oct-3 Hampton & Littlewood, Exeter #519/R
£1100 $1980 €1606 Still life with plums (25x35cm-10x14in) s. W/C. 21-Jan-4 Sotheby's, Olympia #336/R
£1500 $2700 €2190 Still life of cherry blossoms and bird's nest (26x38cm-10x15in) s. W/C gouache. 21-Jan-4 Sotheby's, Olympia #207/R est:1500-2000

HOUGH, William and MYLES, J (19th C) British
Works on paper
£780 $1443 €1139 Still life with birds nest and primroses (25x36cm-10x14in) s. 12-Feb-4 Andrew Hartley, Ilkley #764

HOUGUE, Jean de la (1874-1959) French
£347 $573 €500 Bord de mer (24x19cm-9x7in) s. panel. 3-Jul-3 Claude Aguttes, Neuilly #103
£2371 $4362 €3462 Woman reading (41x33cm-16x13in) s. 26-Mar-4 Koller, Zurich #525/R est:2000-3000 (S.FR 5500)

HOURDE, Daniel (1947-) French
Works on paper
£839 $1427 €1200 Untitled (190x95cm-75x37in) s.d.2001 chl collage wood. 27-Nov-3 Calmels Cohen, Paris #83/R

HOURTAL, Henri (19/20th C) French
£403 $745 €600 Paysage anime au Maroc (20x14cm-8x6in) oil on paper. 15-Mar-4 Gros & Delettrez, Paris #63/R
£634 $1096 €900 Marocains dans le souk (20x15cm-8x6in) paper. 15-Dec-3 Gros & Delettrez, Paris #489/R
£1361 $2163 €2000 Rue Quinquempois a Paris (53x45cm-21x18in) s. 21-Mar-3 Bailly Pommery, Paris #113 est:2000
Works on paper
£423 $731 €600 Rue de casbah, Maroc (32x25cm-13x10in) chl W/C. 15-Dec-3 Gros & Delettrez, Paris #140/R
£493 $853 €700 Marocaines devant la ville (21x23cm-8x9in) W/C chl. 15-Dec-3 Gros & Delettrez, Paris #136/R
£493 $853 €700 Marocaine en balade (31x23cm-12x9in) W/C chl. 15-Dec-3 Gros & Delettrez, Paris #490/R
£496 $829 €700 Trois femmes assises (24x31cm-9x12in) W/C gouache chl. 16-Jun-3 Gros & Delettrez, Paris #165
£528 $914 €750 Marocain devant son echoppe (32x26cm-13x10in) s. W/C chl. 15-Dec-3 Gros & Delettrez, Paris #491/R
£537 $993 €800 Marocaines assises (23x31cm-9x12in) W/C chl. 15-Mar-4 Gros & Delettrez, Paris #97/R
£563 $975 €800 Devant Fes (32x47cm-13x19in) w chl. 15-Dec-3 Gros & Delettrez, Paris #138/R
£634 $1096 €900 Marocains discutant (32x25cm-13x10in) s. chl gouache. 15-Dec-3 Gros & Delettrez, Paris #141/R
£709 $1184 €1000 Trois femmes voilees (31x24cm-12x9in) s. W/C gouache chl. 16-Jun-3 Gros & Delettrez, Paris #174/R
£1135 $1895 €1600 Deux marocains (31x24cm-12x9in) s. W/C gouache chl. 16-Jun-3 Gros & Delettrez, Paris #177/R est:800-1000

HOUSE, H Elmer (1877-1969) American
£241 $430 €352 Oldtimer (71x56cm-28x22in) s. painted c.1930. 16-Mar-4 Matthew's, Oregon #7/R
Works on paper
£209 $375 €305 Old white stucco mission (25x28cm-10x11in) s. with pen name Remle pastel. 16-Mar-4 Matthew's, Oregon #4/R

HOUSEMAN, Edith Giffard (1875-?) British
Works on paper
£400 $708 €584 Bury Hill, looking north (34x44cm-13x17in) s. W/C. 27-Apr-4 Henry Adams, Chichester #582

HOUSER, Allan C (1915-1994) American
Sculpture
£3529 $6000 €5152 Southwest dance shield (36x36x3cm-14x14x1in) s.num.13/24 bronze st.f. prov.lit. 1-Nov-3 Santa Fe Art, Santa Fe #42/R est:6000-9000
£4940 $8250 €7212 Buffalo hunt (112x152cm-44x60in) num.7/15 bronze 3 parts. 11-Oct-3 Nadeau, Windsor #45/R est:12500-20000
£7059 $12000 €10306 Sacred rain arrow II (30x15x15cm-12x6x6in) s.d.80 num.17/20 bronze st.f. prov.lit. 1-Nov-3 Santa Fe Art, Santa Fe #41/R est:10000-15000

HOUSEWORTH, Thomas (1828-1915) American
Photographs
£3846 $6538 €5500 City of San Francisco (25x33cm-10x13in) i. albumen lit. 28-Nov-3 Bassenge, Berlin #4055/R est:1200

HOUSMAN, Laurence (1865-1959) British
Works on paper
£550 $1001 €803 Cain (20x15cm-8x6in) init.i. black ink. 1-Jul-4 Christie's, Kensington #487/R

HOUSSARD, Charles Claude (1884-1958) Belgian
£460 $727 €672 Landscape of wooded avenue (84x95cm-33x37in) s. 27-Apr-3 Wilkinson, Doncaster #281/R

HOUSSAYE, Josephine (1840-?) French
£333 $557 €480 La lettre (34x25cm-13x10in) s. panel. 25-Oct-3 Binoche, Orleans #49

HOUSSER, Bess (1890-1969) Canadian
£723 $1345 €1056 Mountain torrent (30x38cm-12x15in) s.i. board exhib. 2-Mar-4 Ritchie, Toronto #121/R est:1000-1200 (C.D 1800)
£772 $1383 €1127 Baie St Paul. Houses (26x31cm-10x12in) one s.i.d.1926 verso one i.verso panel two. 6-May-4 Heffel, Vancouver #63/R (C.D 1900)

HOUSSER, Yvonne McKague (1898-1996) Canadian
£756 $1239 €1104 Autumn contrasts (33x41cm-13x16in) s. board. 28-May-3 Maynards, Vancouver #63/R (C.D 1700)
Works on paper
£636 $1037 €929 Georgian Bay (28x39cm-11x15in) s. chl. 23-Sep-3 Ritchie, Toronto #152/R est:1400-1600 (C.D 1400)
£3455 $6185 €5044 Spring fantasy (63x50cm-25x20in) s.i.d.47 verso mixed media paper on masonite prov.exhib. 31-May-4 Sotheby's, Toronto #8/R est:3000-5000 (C.D 8500)

HOUSSIN, Edouard (1847-1917) French
Sculpture
£6000 $10380 €8760 Bust of Louise (46cm-18in) s. white marble grey onyx base lit. 12-Dec-3 Sotheby's, London #245/R est:3000-5000

HOUSSOT, Louis (1824-1890) French
£1034 $1914 €1500 L'enroulement de la bobine ou le galant a genoux (16x50cm-6x20in) s. 13-Feb-4 Rossini, Paris #13/R est:1500-2000
£3500 $6020 €5110 Le chaussure manque (23x16cm-9x6in) s. panel. 4-Dec-3 Christie's, Kensington #15/R est:1500-2000

HOUSTON, Alastair D (20th C) British
Works on paper
£320 $544 €467 The 57-footer Senga in the Clyde (52x72cm-20x28in) s.i.d.90 pencil W/C. 19-Nov-3 Christie's, Kensington #412/R
£1093 $2000 €1596 Moonbeam and Tuiga (38x53cm-15x21in) s.d.96 W/C. 29-Jul-4 Christie's, Rockefeller NY #51/R est:4000-6000
£1093 $2000 €1596 Big reacher (33x44cm-13x17in) s.d.01 W/C gouache. 29-Jul-4 Christie's, Rockefeller NY #54/R est:4000-6000

HOUSTON, George (1869-1947) British
£400 $680 €584 Self portrait of the artist (45x34cm-18x13in) s.d.April 1945 panel. 6-Nov-3 Ambrose, Loughton #13/R
£650 $1196 €949 Gorse on the lochside (40x60cm-16x24in) s. board. 10-Jun-4 Lyon & Turnbull, Edinburgh #110
£1000 $1670 €1460 Snow capped peaks, probably Arran (46x61cm-18x24in) s. 16-Oct-3 Bonhams, Edinburgh #183 est:1000-1500
£1300 $2171 €1898 Near Loch Fyne (44x59cm-17x23in) s. 19-Jun-3 Bonhams, Edinburgh #332 est:800-1200
£1350 $2525 €1971 Misty morning, Ayrshire (44x59cm-17x23in) s. 22-Jul-4 Bonhams, Edinburgh #300 est:1000-1500
£1700 $2669 €2465 Highland gorse (46x61cm-18x24in) s. 27-Aug-3 Sotheby's, London #1086/R est:1500-2000
£2000 $3620 €2920 Bridge at Stradbally (46x61cm-18x24in) s. 19-Apr-4 Sotheby's, London #92/R est:3000-4000
£2064 $3695 €3013 Road alongside a lake (68x88cm-27x35in) s. 31-May-4 Stephan Welz, Johannesburg #440/R est:10000-15000 (SA.R 25000)
£2300 $3979 €3358 Loch Fyne (45x61cm-18x24in) s. 11-Dec-3 Lyon & Turnbull, Edinburgh #4/R est:1500-2000
£2700 $4941 €3942 River landscape with trees (69x91cm-27x36in) s. 28-Jul-4 Mallams, Oxford #341/R est:1500-2000
£2800 $4760 €4088 Port Bahn, Iona (71x93cm-28x37in) s. 30-Oct-3 Christie's, London #206/R est:2500-3500
£3000 $5100 €4380 Summer landscape near the Rest and be Thankful, Argyll (71x91cm-28x36in) s. 30-Oct-3 Christie's, London #208/R est:2500-3500
£3200 $5440 €4672 Stormy sea (71x91cm-28x36in) s. 30-Oct-3 Christie's, London #209/R est:1500-2500
£4200 $7140 €6132 Snow on the hill, Argyll (35x46cm-14x18in) s. panel. 30-Oct-3 Christie's, London #207/R est:3000-5000
£5000 $8050 €7250 Bridge at Inveraray (71x91cm-28x36in) s. 21-Aug-3 Bonhams, Edinburgh #1198/R est:3000-5000
£6000 $10800 €8760 Scottish river landscape (71x91cm-28x36in) s. prov. 21-Apr-4 Tennants, Leyburn #1137/R est:3000-4000
£6800 $12308 €9928 Spring snows at Loch Fyne (71x91cm-28x36in) s. prov. 19-Apr-4 Sotheby's, London #101/R est:6000-8000
£9000 $15300 €13140 Loch Fyne side (71x91cm-28x36in) s. prov. 30-Oct-3 Christie's, London #205/R est:7000-10000
Works on paper
£500 $895 €730 Stepping stones (24x32cm-9x13in) s.d.95 pastel. 28-May-4 Lyon & Turnbull, Edinburgh #8
£620 $998 €899 Mother and child by a cottage (17x23cm-7x9in) s. W/C. 21-Aug-3 Bonhams, Edinburgh #1178
£750 $1178 €1088 Views of the Naver, Sutherlandshire (38x54cm-15x21in) s. pencil W/C bodycol pair prov. 28-Aug-3 Christie's, Kensington #414/R
£820 $1501 €1197 On the Naver (38x56cm-15x22in) s. W/C pair. 29-Jan-4 Bonhams, Edinburgh #345

HOUSTON, Ian (1934-) British
£330 $604 €482 Kyle of Lochalsh (16x24cm-6x9in) s. board prov. 8-Jul-4 Lawrence, Crewkerne #1665
£350 $585 €511 Swansea marina (23x28cm-9x11in) s. board. 16-Oct-3 Christie's, Kensington #474
£400 $688 €584 Fishing boats on the slipway, Pellestrina, Venetian lagoon (25x23cm-10x9in) s. 5-Dec-3 Keys, Aylsham #583
£400 $740 €584 View from the bridge, Sacavem, Lisbon (25x23cm-10x9in) s,. 13-Feb-4 Keys, Aylsham #600
£420 $760 €613 Avenue of poplars (25x38cm-10x15in) s. 16-Apr-4 Keys, Aylsham #687/R
£450 $752 €657 Morning sunlight, Leigh-on-Sea (23x28cm-9x11in) board. 14-Oct-3 David Lay, Penzance #66/R
£460 $750 €667 Beach scene, storm clouds breaking up (28x38cm-11x15in) s. board. 23-Sep-3 Bonhams, Leeds #133
£520 $894 €759 Sunlight on a winter afternoon (28x41cm-11x16in) s. 5-Dec-3 Keys, Aylsham #582/R
£1050 $1932 €1533 On Cromer Beach (19x29cm-7x11in) s. 11-Jun-4 Keys, Aylsham #603/R est:400-600

HOUSTON, J A (1812-1884) British
£2000 $3200 €2900 Arcadi the blessed (60x90cm-24x35in) 17-Sep-3 James Thompson, Kirby Lonsdale #149/R

HOUSTON, James Archibald (1921-) North American
Works on paper
£450 $766 €657 Untitled, on the ice at Tehkjuak Baffin Island (27x20cm-11x8in) s. one d.51 one d.1953 ink pair. 3-Nov-3 Waddingtons, Toronto #507/R (C.D 1000)

HOUSTON, John (1930-) British
£310 $561 €453 Wave breaking, Varengeville (25x30cm-10x12in) s.i. 2-Apr-4 Moore Allen & Innocent, Cirencester #422/R
£420 $773 €613 Green landscape (26x36cm-10x14in) s. 10-Jun-4 Lyon & Turnbull, Edinburgh #40
£820 $1492 €1197 Red cows and reeds (71x92cm-28x36in) s. 15-Jun-4 Bonhams, Knightsbridge #103/R
£850 $1556 €1241 Reclining figure (25x36cm-10x14in) exhib. 28-Jul-4 Mallams, Oxford #279/R
£1300 $2171 €1898 Flowers and night sky (92x101cm-36x40in) s. s.i.on stretcher. 16-Oct-3 Bonhams, Edinburgh #23/R est:1500-2000
£1500 $2835 €2190 Early morning skies (127x152cm-50x60in) s.d.1964. 19-Feb-4 Lyon & Turnbull, Edinburgh #96 est:1500-2000
£1900 $3059 €2755 Ca D'Oro, Venice (18x23cm-7x9in) s. prov. 21-Aug-3 Bonhams, Edinburgh #1048 est:700-900
£2200 $3806 €3212 Early morning rain (102x152cm-40x60in) s. 11-Dec-3 Lyon & Turnbull, Edinburgh #15/R est:1500-2000
£2200 $4048 €3212 Flowers, birds and nightsky (62x76cm-24x30in) s.d.1962. 29-Mar-4 Thomson Roddick & Medcalf, Edinburgh #257/R est:800-1200
£2600 $4186 €3770 Bird, bush and yellow sun (25x35cm-10x14in) s. s.i.d.1961 on stretcher prov. 21-Aug-3 Bonhams, Edinburgh #1051/R est:700-1000
£2600 $4082 €3770 Aviary (76x102cm-30x40in) s.d.1961. 27-Aug-3 Sotheby's, London #1153/R est:3000-5000
£2800 $5012 €4088 Rock coast, dusk (71x91cm-28x36in) s. prov. 28-May-4 Lyon & Turnbull, Edinburgh #29/R est:1500-2000
£3000 $4710 €4350 Summer sea, Gullane (122x122cm-48x48in) s. i.verso. 27-Aug-3 Sotheby's, London #1150/R est:3000-4000
Works on paper
£300 $549 €438 Rose head (15x13cm-6x5in) W/C exhib. 28-Jul-4 Mallams, Oxford #280/R
£380 $612 €551 Blue necklace (15x11cm-6x4in) s.d.1982 W/C prov. 21-Aug-3 Bonhams, Edinburgh #1038
£400 $644 €580 Reclining figure (11x16cm-4x6in) s. W/C prov. 21-Aug-3 Bonhams, Edinburgh #1013
£520 $983 €759 Botanical garden (15x21cm-6x8in) s.d.1962 gouache. 19-Feb-4 Lyon & Turnbull, Edinburgh #51
£550 $1001 €803 Dune, sea and sky (23x28cm-9x11in) s. W/C exec 1995 prov. 1-Jul-4 Christie's, Kensington #304/R

HOUSTON, John Adam (1812-1884) British
£1500 $2790 €2190 Evening thoughts (27x21cm-11x8in) s.d.1877 board. 4-Mar-4 Christie's, Kensington #90/R est:1500-2000
£2600 $4706 €3796 Light and shade (69x51cm-27x20in) s.d.1860. 19-Apr-4 Sotheby's, London #2/R est:2500-3000
£2800 $5152 €4088 Eastern question (44x58cm-17x23in) s.d.1880 i.verso. 25-Mar-4 Christie's, Kensington #212/R est:3000-5000
£3200 $5792 €4672 His favourite toy (79x58cm-31x23in) s.d.1867. 19-Apr-4 Sotheby's, London #3/R est:3000-4000
£4800 $7728 €6960 Expectancy (44x41cm-17x16in) s.i.d.1850 verso panel. 21-Aug-3 Bonhams, Edinburgh #1124/R est:2000-3000
Works on paper
£1633 $2922 €2400 View of Ben Nevis (26x40cm-10x16in) mono. W/C htd gouache double-sided. 17-Mar-4 Maigret, Paris #23/R est:1200-1800

HOUSTON, John R (1856-1932) British
£320 $512 €467 Granny reading (46x34cm-18x13in) s. 15-May-3 Bonhams, Edinburgh #390
£430 $770 €628 Harvesters (25x36cm-10x14in) s. 6-Jan-4 Gildings, Market Harborough #428/R
Works on paper
£300 $537 €438 Wheelwrights's working and forge (35x44cm-14x17in) s. W/C. 17-Mar-4 Bonhams, Chester #368
£580 $1021 €847 Fireside chores (50x60cm-20x24in) s. W/C. 20-May-4 Bonhams, Edinburgh #305

HOUSTON, Robert (1891-1942) British
£1600 $2864 €2336 Arrochar, Loch Long, Argyll (63x75cm-25x30in) s. 27-May-4 Christie's, Kensington #223/R est:800-1200

HOUSTON, William (19th C) American?
Works on paper
£410 $750 €599 Tennessee landscape no.144 (33x53cm-13x21in) W/C. 10-Jul-4 Hindman, Chicago #229/R

HOUSTOUN, Donald Mackay (1916-) Canadian
£446 $768 €651 Hills after rain, Quebec (40x50cm-16x20in) s. board. 2-Dec-3 Joyner Waddington, Toronto #212/R (C.D 1000)

HOUT, Oskar van (1883-?) Polish
£805 $1482 €1200 Nude boy on mountain background (155x135cm-61x53in) s.d.18. 24-Mar-4 Hugo Ruef, Munich #1233/R

HOUT, Pieter (1879-1965) Dutch
£296 $545 €450 Cockerel on a window ledge (7x9cm-3x4in) s. panel. 22-Jun-4 Mealy's, Castlecomer #341

HOUTEN, Barbara van (1862-1950) Dutch
Works on paper
£1361 $2476 €2000 Summer flowers (70x52cm-28x20in) s. pencil conte W/C bodycol. 3-Feb-4 Christie's, Amsterdam #172/R est:2000-3000

HOUTEN, G van (?) ?
£431 $698 €625 Couple flirting (115x90cm-45x35in) indis.sig. i.d.18 Avril 1921 verso. 4-Aug-3 Rasmussen, Vejle #84/R (D.KR 4500)

HOUTEN, Henricus Leonardus van den (1801-1879) Australian/Dutch
£2767 $4953 €4040 Nera Macedon, Victoria. Camping out at Fernshaw near Warragul (44x60cm-17x24in) pair prov. 15-May-4 Christie's, Sydney #479/R est:6000-8000 (A.D 7000)

HOUTH, Annette (1888-1956) Danish
£301 $512 €439 Interior scene with ballet dancer (110x102cm-43x40in) exhib. 29-Nov-3 Rasmussen, Havnen #4432 (D.KR 3200)

HOUTHUESEN, Albert (1903-1979) British
£500 $900 €730 Portrait in blue (45x35cm-18x14in) init. board. 22-Apr-4 Lawrence, Crewkerne #951
£560 $1008 €818 Hampstead heath (28x35cm-11x14in) init.d.17 March 1931 prov. 22-Apr-4 Lawrence, Crewkerne #949
£620 $1116 €905 Ghosts, on the coast, ghosts a clown and circus horse (40x50cm-16x20in) s.i.d.1967 verso. 22-Apr-4 Lawrence, Crewkerne #950/R
£2800 $4928 €4088 Incoming tide (40x51cm-16x20in) s. canvasboard painted 1967 prov. 19-May-4 Sotheby's, Olympia #328/R est:800-1200

HOUTHUESEN, J C P (?) ?
£544 $974 €800 Geishas near trellis-work (40x33cm-16x13in) d.09. 17-Mar-4 De Zwann, Amsterdam #4630/R

HOUWAERT, L (1873-?) Belgian
£5500 $9900 €8030 Figures on a country road with horses watering outside an inn. Figures strolling beside a meadow (27x35cm-11x14in) s.d.1793 panel pair prov. 21-Apr-4 Bonhams, New Bond Street #122/R est:4000-6000

HOUWALD, Werner von (1901-) German
£280 $504 €420 Landscape (55x73cm-22x29in) s. 26-Apr-4 Rieber, Stuttgart #1068/R
£1079 $1770 €1500 Two pine trees in flower garden (100x80cm-39x31in) s. 4-Jun-3 Ketterer, Hamburg #485/R est:1500-2000

HOUYOUX, Léon (1856-?) Belgian
£347 $580 €500 Vue de parc (43x54cm-17x21in) s. 21-Oct-3 Campo, Vlaamse Kaai #870a
£667 $1193 €1000 The big market of Hertogenbos (41x54cm-16x21in) s. panel. 15-May-4 De Vuyst, Lokeren #169
£816 $1461 €1200 Les naiades (80x100cm-31x39in) s. 17-Mar-4 Hotel des Ventes Mosan, Brussels #147

HOVE, Bartholomeus Johannes van (1790-1880) Dutch
£559 $962 €800 Dinner time (46x37cm-18x15in) s. panel. 7-Dec-3 Sotheby's, Amsterdam #641/R
£3400 $5440 €4930 Figures by a Dutch canal (20x29cm-8x11in) s. panel. 18-Sep-3 Christie's, Kensington #53/R est:2000-3000
£6358 $11000 €9283 Church courtyard (23x25cm-9x10in) s. panel. 13-Dec-3 Charlton Hall, Columbia #82/R est:2000-3000
£7639 $12986 €11000 View of the Mauritshuis and the Torentje, The Hague (34x42cm-13x17in) s. panel prov.exhib. 28-Oct-3 Christie's, Amsterdam #53/R est:12000-16000
£22378 $38042 €32000 Une port de Brunswick sous la neige, et au printemps (41x35cm-16x14in) s.d.1824 panel pair. 30-Nov-3 Anaf, Lyon #119/R est:35000-40000
Works on paper
£345 $576 €500 Vue d'une rue de village animee (19x15cm-7x6in) s.d.1837 W/C. 17-Nov-3 Delorme & Bocage, Paris #97/R
£1517 $2519 €2200 Haarlem canal (18x26cm-7x10in) s. W/C. 30-Sep-3 Dorotheum, Vienna #266/R est:1200-1400
£2953 $5434 €4400 View of town in summer with canal activity (45x62cm-18x24in) s. W/C. 29-Mar-4 Glerum, Amsterdam #157 est:5000-7000

HOVE, Bartholomeus Johannes van (attrib) (1790-1880) Dutch
Works on paper
£500 $910 €750 Figures by a church in a Dutch town (25x18cm-10x7in) pencil W/C. 1-Jul-4 Christie's, Amsterdam #449/R

HOVE, Hubertus van (1814-1865) Dutch
£1477 $2643 €2200 Mother with child in entrance hall (19x24cm-7x9in) s.indis.i. i.verso panel. 27-May-4 Dorotheum, Vienna #13/R est:3000-3500
Works on paper
£900 $1503 €1314 Getting dressed (38x51cm-15x20in) s.i. pencil W/C. 8-Oct-3 Christie's, Kensington #1126/R

HOVE, P L van (19th C) ?
Works on paper
£833 $1500 €1216 View of a canal (16x22cm-6x9in) black chk pen brown ink W/C bodycol. 22-Jan-4 Christie's, Rockefeller NY #253/R est:1500-2000

HOVE, Victor van (1825-1891) Belgian
£1701 $3044 €2500 Lecture a l'ombre (35x26cm-14x10in) s. panel. 17-Mar-4 Hotel des Ventes Mosan, Brussels #86/R est:3500-4500

HOVEN, Gottfried von (1868-1921) German
£278 $439 €400 City in Holland (70x100cm-28x39in) s. 6-Sep-3 Arnold, Frankfurt #585
£490 $832 €700 View of Venice (71x51cm-28x20in) s.d.95 lit. 28-Nov-3 Schloss Ahlden, Ahlden #1542/R

HOVEN, Herman de (1865-?) Dutch
£745 $1200 €1088 Young mother sewing at her kitchen table with sunlight through a window (46x66cm-18x26in) s. 24-Feb-3 O'Gallerie, Oregon #805a/R

HOVENDEN, Thomas (1840-1895) American/Irish
Works on paper
£543 $1000 €793 Stables (24x34cm-9x13in) mono. W/C. 8-Jun-4 Auctions by the Bay, Alameda #1057/R

HOVENER, Jan (1936-) Dutch?
£290 $484 €420 Harbour view with cranes (59x79cm-23x31in) s. panel. 11-Nov-3 Vendu Notarishuis, Rotterdam #560
£483 $806 €700 View of Rotterdam with the White House (59x79cm-23x31in) s. panel. 11-Nov-3 Vendu Notarishuis, Rotterdam #547

HOVI, Mikko (1879-1962) Finnish
Sculpture
£1333 $2387 €2000 Woman with jug (34cm-13in) s. bronze. 15-May-4 Hagelstam, Helsinki #15/R est:500
£1611 $2964 €2400 Dreaming (43cm-17in) s. bronze. 25-Mar-4 Hagelstam, Helsinki #769 est:400
£2267 $4057 €3400 Eel (60cm-24in) s.d.1958 bronze. 15-May-4 Hagelstam, Helsinki #10/R est:850

HOVY, Elisabeth (1873-1957) Dutch
Works on paper
£2128 $3553 €3000 Servants doing handwork by lamp light (42x30cm-17x12in) s.d.94 pastel. 20-Oct-3 Glerum, Amsterdam #95/R est:800-1000

HOW, Ada Mary (?) British?
£800 $1360 €1168 Schoolroom (62x121cm-24x48in) after Thomas Webster. 26-Nov-3 Hamptons Fine Art, Godalming #110

HOW, Beatrice (1867-1932) British
£950 $1530 €1378 Parakeet (40x51cm-16x20in) exhib. 21-Aug-3 Bonhams, Edinburgh #1162
£1100 $1969 €1606 Man with a cat (51x38cm-20x15in) prov. 14-May-4 Christie's, Kensington #490/R est:1000-1500

HOWARD, Charlotte (20th C) American
£259 $425 €378 City scene with children playing and view of a bridge (76x86cm-30x34in) s.d.1947. 4-Jun-3 Alderfer's, Hatfield #306

HOWARD, Donald J (20th C) American
£636 $1100 €929 Cape May Point, winters landscape (41x51cm-16x20in) s. canvasboard. 10-Dec-3 Alderfer's, Hatfield #498/R est:600-800

HOWARD, Edith Lucile (1885-1960) American
£347 $600 €507 Still life with flowers and figurines (64x76cm-25x30in) s. 10-Dec-3 Boos Gallery, Michigan #510

HOWARD, George James (1843-1911) British
Works on paper
£850 $1335 €1233 View of Rome from the Pincio (16x34cm-6x13in) pencil W/C htd white prov. 28-Aug-3 Christie's, Kensington #409/R

HOWARD, George James (attrib) (1843-1911) British
Works on paper
£280 $484 €409 Profile portrait, Winifred (15x13cm-6x5in) crayon. 11-Dec-3 Mitchells, Cockermouth #931

HOWARD, Henry (1769-1847) British
£450 $819 €657 Lake within a mountainous landscape with grasses in foreground (74x58cm-29x23in) mono.d.1895. 4-Feb-4 Brightwells, Leominster #961/R

HOWARD, Hugh Huntington (1860-1927) American
£223 $400 €326 Landscape (74x102cm-29x40in) s. 15-May-4 Jeffery Burchard, Florida #196

HOWARD, Humbert (1905-1990) American

£349	$650	€510	Yellow pear (13x15cm-5x6in) s.d.70 board. 3-Mar-4 Alderfer's, Hatfield #342
£538	$1000	€785	Still life of yellow flowers in pink pitcher (58x46cm-23x18in) s.d.69 board. 3-Mar-4 Alderfer's, Hatfield #336 est:1000-1500
£538	$1000	€785	Yellow pears (28x43cm-11x17in) s.d.70 board. 3-Mar-4 Alderfer's, Hatfield #337/R est:800-1200
£591	$1100	€863	Strawberries (23x28cm-9x11in) s.d.68 board. 3-Mar-4 Alderfer's, Hatfield #339 est:500-700
£814	$1400	€1188	Bathers (91x76cm-36x30in) s. 7-Dec-3 Freeman, Philadelphia #227
£2222	$4000	€3244	Girl with rose bud (81x53cm-32x21in) s.d.79 board. 23-Jan-4 Freeman, Philadelphia #290/R est:1500-2500
Works on paper			
£295	$550	€431	Girl with black cat (71x56cm-28x22in) s.d.76 W/C. 3-Mar-4 Alderfer's, Hatfield #338
£323	$600	€472	Still life with yellow flowers in a white vase (58x79cm-23x31in) s.d.69 pastel on panel. 3-Mar-4 Alderfer's, Hatfield #335

HOWARD, Josephine (19th C) American?

£297	$550	€434	Still life with grapes (36x41cm-14x16in) s.d.87. 13-Mar-4 Susanin's, Chicago #6190/R

HOWARD, Ken (1932-) British

£350	$602	€511	Seated female nude (48x38cm-19x15in) 3-Dec-3 Christie's, Kensington #497
£360	$583	€522	View from a field towards a farmhouse (62x76cm-24x30in) s.d.78 i.on stretcher. 30-Jul-3 Hamptons Fine Art, Godalming #212
£380	$635	€555	Poplars (35x41cm-14x16in) s. 16-Oct-3 Christie's, Kensington #449/R
£400	$668	€584	Fruit stall (39x30cm-15x12in) 16-Oct-3 Christie's, Kensington #447
£400	$668	€584	Vineyards (51x58cm-20x23in) 16-Oct-3 Christie's, Kensington #445
£480	$802	€701	Newlyn harbour (16x23cm-6x9in) s. board. 16-Oct-3 Christie's, Kensington #316
£500	$910	€730	Bright light, Bergun (23x16cm-9x6in) s. board prov.exhib. 1-Jul-4 Christie's, Kensington #269/R
£520	$946	€759	Green windbreak (16x21cm-6x8in) s. i.verso board. 21-Jun-4 Bonhams, Bath #435
£550	$919	€803	Figures in a street (41x51cm-16x20in) 16-Oct-3 Christie's, Kensington #456/R
£586	$1037	€856	Rotherhite Number 4 (31x41cm-12x16in) s.d.66 prov. 27-Apr-4 AB Stockholms Auktionsverk #1224/R (S.KR 8000)
£750	$1350	€1095	On Paul Hill, Midday (31x21cm-12x8in) s. board. 20-Jan-4 Bonhams, Knightsbridge #80
£780	$1303	€1139	Valerie (25x20cm-10x8in) s. board. 14-Oct-3 David Lay, Penzance #387
£800	$1376	€1168	Still life with Olympia (76x61cm-30x24in) 3-Dec-3 Christie's, Kensington #631/R
£850	$1420	€1241	Trawler, Newlyn harbour (26x30cm-10x12in) s. canvasboard. 16-Oct-3 Christie's, Kensington #451/R
£900	$1665	€1314	Mediterranean village (21x25cm-8x10in) s. canvas on board. 11-Feb-4 Sotheby's, Olympia #203/R est:1000-1500
£950	$1615	€1387	Poplars in Provence (51x61cm-20x24in) s. 26-Nov-3 Sotheby's, Olympia #110/R
£950	$1757	€1387	Mousehole (26x35cm-10x14in) s. board. 11-Feb-4 Sotheby's, Olympia #193/R est:800-1200
£1000	$1870	€1460	Beached dinghy and figures on a beach (22x25cm-9x10in) init. 26-Feb-4 Lane, Penzance #325 est:800-1000
£1050	$1911	€1533	Figures on the beach at Mousehole (20x25cm-8x10in) s. board. 21-Jun-4 Bonhams, Bath #434/R est:800-1200
£1100	$1837	€1606	Windbreaks (25x30cm-10x12in) s. 16-Oct-3 Christie's, Kensington #429/R est:600-800
£1100	$1837	€1606	Thames, towards Chelsea (51x61cm-20x24in) s. 16-Oct-3 Christie's, Kensington #450/R est:800-1200
£1100	$1837	€1606	Mousehole (51x61cm-20x24in) s. 16-Oct-3 Christie's, Kensington #452/R est:1000-1500
£1100	$1870	€1606	Mousehole (30x39cm-12x15in) s. canvas on board. 26-Nov-3 Sotheby's, Olympia #113/R est:1000-1500
£1100	$1969	€1606	Venice (30x39cm-12x15in) s. 17-May-4 David Duggleby, Scarborough #678/R est:400-500
£1100	$2002	€1606	Mousehole (18x23cm-7x9in) s. board. 21-Jun-4 Bonhams, Bath #433 est:500-700
£1150	$1955	€1679	Piazza San Marco, Venice (24x29cm-9x11in) s. board. 26-Nov-3 Hamptons Fine Art, Godalming #234/R est:800-1200
£1150	$1955	€1679	Old Charing Cross Hospital, London on the Strand, street scene with figures (60x47cm-24x19in) s. 28-Nov-3 Bigwood, Stratford on Avon #303/R
£1150	$2093	€1679	Light breaks towards Penzance (21x26cm-8x10in) s. board prov.exhib. 1-Jul-4 Christie's, Kensington #267/R est:500-700
£1200	$2004	€1752	Piazza San Marco, Florence (51x61cm-20x24in) s. board. 16-Oct-3 Christie's, Kensington #454/R est:1200-1800
£1200	$2064	€1752	From the steps of the Duomo, Florence (49x60cm-19x24in) s. 3-Dec-3 Christie's, Kensington #491/R est:1200-1800
£1200	$2112	€1752	Cosuende, Arragon (61x30cm-24x12in) s. 18-May-4 Woolley & Wallis, Salisbury #83/R est:750-1000
£1200	$2112	€1752	Mousehole (30x40cm-12x16in) s. canvasboard. 19-May-4 Sotheby's, Olympia #214/R est:800-1200
£1200	$2196	€1752	Traffic circle (51x61cm-20x24in) s. 4-Jun-4 Christie's, London #4/R est:600-800
£1250	$2125	€1825	Winter at Sampford Spiney, Nr Tavistock, Devon (51x61cm-20x24in) s. i.stretcher. 25-Nov-3 Bonhams, Knowle #257 est:700-1000
£1300	$2171	€1898	Roadworks (51x61cm-20x24in) s.d.61. 16-Oct-3 Christie's, Kensington #453/R est:1000-1500
£1300	$2249	€1898	Penzance (25x35cm-10x14in) s.i.d.May 90 verso. 10-Dec-3 Bonhams, Bury St Edmunds #575/R est:1000-1500
£1300	$2210	€1898	Santa Maria della Salute, Venice (20x25cm-8x10in) s. canvas on board. 26-Nov-3 Sotheby's, Olympia #138/R est:700-900
£1400	$2380	€2044	Dora (29x39cm-11x15in) s. i.d.96 verso canvas on board. 26-Nov-3 Sotheby's, Olympia #98/R est:1000-1500
£1500	$2640	€2190	Early morning light, Venice (24x29cm-9x11in) s. board. 18-May-4 Woolley & Wallis, Salisbury #121/R est:400-600
£1600	$2960	€2336	Old school, Sampford Spiney (51x61cm-20x24in) s.d.76 prov. 11-Feb-4 Sotheby's, Olympia #199/R est:1000-1500
£1700	$3145	€2482	Winter ski resort (51x61cm-20x24in) s. 11-Feb-4 Sotheby's, Olympia #227/R est:800-1200
£1800	$3168	€2628	Seated female (30x20cm-12x8in) s. canvasboard. 19-May-4 Sotheby's, Olympia #222/R est:1000-1500
£1800	$3312	€2628	London roof tops (81x122cm-32x48in) s. 8-Jun-4 Gorringes, Lewes #2222 est:500-800
£1850	$3145	€2701	Mornington Crescent (51x61cm-20x24in) s. 25-Nov-3 Bonhams, Knowle #255/R est:1000-1500
£2000	$3180	€2920	Newlyn, the quay (50x63cm-20x25in) s. 10-Sep-3 Sotheby's, Olympia #260/R est:1000-1500
£2200	$4048	€3212	Crowded beach scene (46x59cm-18x23in) s. 23-Mar-4 Rosebery Fine Art, London #856/R est:1000-1500
£2200	$4026	€3212	Santa Maria della Salute, Venice (25x36cm-10x14in) s. 4-Jun-4 Christie's, London #33/R est:500-700
£2500	$4300	€3650	Fish market, Venice (61x50cm-24x20in) s. prov. 3-Dec-3 Christie's, Kensington #489/R est:2500-3500
£2600	$4758	€3796	St. Mark's, Venice (20x25cm-8x10in) s. linen on board. 4-Jun-4 Christie's, London #32/R est:500-700
£3000	$5490	€4380	Porthcurno, midday light (51x61cm-20x24in) s. exhib. 4-Jun-4 Christie's, London #64/R est:800-1200
£3500	$6475	€5110	Reclining nude (25x30cm-10x12in) s. 11-Feb-4 Sotheby's, Olympia #223/R est:1500-2000
£3800	$6726	€5548	Black stockings (61x51cm-24x20in) s. prov. 27-Apr-4 Bonhams, Knightsbridge #148/R est:4000-6000
£4000	$6360	€5840	Bath towel (61x51cm-24x20in) s. exhib. 10-Sep-3 Sotheby's, Olympia #263/R est:3000-5000
£4200	$7434	€6132	Figure on a bed (61x51cm-24x20in) s. 27-Apr-4 Bonhams, Knightsbridge #147/R est:3000-5000
£4800	$8784	€7008	Duomo, Florence (41x30cm-16x12in) s. 4-Jun-4 Christie's, London #31 est:4000-6000
£5000	$9150	€7300	Lorraine Allongee (41x81cm-16x32in) s. 4-Jun-4 Christie's, London #136/R est:6000-8000
£8000	$13280	€11680	Summer haze, Sennon Cove, Cornwall (101x122cm-40x48in) s. 2-Oct-3 Lane, Penzance #25/R est:8000-9000
£12000	$21120	€17520	Artist and model, Bo Hilton at an easel in the background (122x101cm-48x40in) s. 18-May-4 Woolley & Wallis, Salisbury #81/R est:6000-8000
Works on paper			
£280	$515	€409	River scene with mosque and stone bridge (17x21cm-7x8in) s. pencil W/C. 23-Mar-4 Rosebery Fine Art, London #740
£300	$552	€438	Turmanabad (17x24cm-7x9in) s. pencil W/C. 23-Mar-4 Rosebery Fine Art, London #741
£380	$654	€555	Venice (13x16cm-5x6in) s. W/C bodycol. 3-Dec-3 Christie's, Kensington #495
£500	$835	€730	Untitled (13x18cm-5x7in) s.d.18.9.86 W/C. 18-Jun-3 John Nicholson, Haslemere #672
£640	$1043	€928	Nude posing on a bed (26x17cm-10x7in) s. pencil W/C. 23-Sep-3 Bonhams, Leeds #168/R
£800	$1480	€1168	Morning on the Giudecca (18x21cm-7x8in) s. pencil W/C gouache exhib. 11-Feb-4 Sotheby's, Olympia #195/R
£1200	$2004	€1752	Venetian harbour scene (25x30cm-10x12in) s. W/C. 18-Jun-3 John Nicholson, Haslemere #670 est:250-500
£2000	$3520	€2920	Homage to Christa Gaa, the artist's wife (55x55cm-22x22in) s. mixed media. 18-May-4 Woolley & Wallis, Salisbury #248/R est:500-700

HOWARD, Lucile (1885-1960) American

£353	$650	€515	Lake landscape (64x76cm-25x30in) 23-Jun-4 Doyle, New York #5039/R
£353	$650	€515	Irish landscape (76x61cm-30x24in) s. 23-Jun-4 Doyle, New York #5041/R
£761	$1400	€1111	Coastal village (76x61cm-30x24in) s. 23-Jun-4 Doyle, New York #5042/R est:1000-1500
£1766	$3250	€2578	Drama in gray, Mont Saint Michel (99x124cm-39x49in) s. exhib. 23-Jun-4 Doyle, New York #5040/R est:2000-3000
Works on paper			
£870	$1600	€1270	Storm beyond sleive-na-mon, Ireland (33x48cm-13x19in) s. W/C. 9-Jun-4 Alderfer's, Hatfield #408/R est:500-700

HOWARD, Margaret Maitland (1898-?) British

£550	$990	€803	Portrait of a lady in a classical setting (66x50cm-26x20in) s. 20-Jan-4 Bonhams, Knightsbridge #75/R

HOWARD, Nellie C Hopps (1855-1956) American

£1630	$3000	€2445	Corner of a tea house, Myanashita, Japan (76x38cm-30x15in) s. prov. 8-Jun-4 Bonhams & Butterfields, San Francisco #4204/R est:3000-5000

HOWARD, William (17th C) British

£700	$1274	€1022	White Hart Inn at Sonning on Thames (61x84cm-24x33in) s. 15-Jun-4 Rosebery Fine Art, London #563/R
£860	$1608	€1256	Figures by a woodland pond (70x116cm-28x46in) s. 24-Feb-4 Bonhams, Knowle #59
£950	$1758	€1387	Bruges canal scene (61x91cm-24x36in) s. 13-Jan-4 Bonhams, Knightsbridge #80/R
£1200	$2220	€1752	Busy continental harbour (76x127cm-30x50in) s. 9-Mar-4 Bonhams, Knightsbridge #250/R est:1200-1800
£1500	$2685	€2190	Whitby (61x92cm-24x36in) s. 26-May-4 Sotheby's, Olympia #64/R est:1000-1500
£2400	$4200	€3504	Dutch harbour set in a town with fishing and other small boats (76x127cm-30x50in) s. prov. 18-Dec-3 John Nicholson, Haslemere #1156/R est:2500-3000

HOWARD-JONES, Ray (1903-) British

Works on paper			
£280	$524	€409	Picton Point, Pembrokeshire (9x12cm-4x5in) s.d.67 W/C gouache black chk exhib. 25-Feb-4 Mallams, Oxford #213
£500	$935	€730	Skomer Island (12x19cm-5x7in) s.d.1952 W/C. 25-Feb-4 Mallams, Oxford #214/R

HOWE, Anthony (20th C) American

Works on paper			
£296	$550	€432	Woodlands (28x42cm-11x17in) s.d.80 W/C. 5-Mar-4 Skinner, Boston #482/R

HOWE, L van (19th C) Dutch

£521	$823	€750	Medieval harbour city (69x55cm-27x22in) s. 6-Sep-3 Arnold, Frankfurt #591/R
£1111	$1889	€1600	Grand Canal, Venice (55x68cm-22x27in) s. canvas on board. 28-Oct-3 Dorotheum, Vienna #3/R est:1600-2000
£3200	$5920	€4672	Continental town views (100x161cm-39x63in) s. two. 14-Jul-4 Christie's, Kensington #917/R est:3000-5000

HOWE, William Henry (1846-1929) American

£645	$1200	€942	On the beach Egmond Holland (61x81cm-24x32in) s. 7-Mar-4 William Jenack, New York #198 est:1500-2000
£1519	$2750	€2218	Country lane (30x41cm-12x16in) s. 16-Apr-4 James Julia, Fairfield #875/R est:2500-3500
£2174	$3500	€3174	Day's end (61x81cm-24x32in) s.d.97. 14-Jan-4 Christie's, Rockefeller NY #18/R est:3000-5000

HOWELL, Felicie (1897-1968) American

Works on paper

£2206	$3750	€3221	Pigeon Cove (29x39cm-11x15in) s. indis d. gouache. 21-Nov-3 Skinner, Boston #561/R est:2500-3000

HOWELL, Peter (1932-) British

£310	$502	€453	Horses in the snow (50x60cm-20x24in) s.d.78. 27-Jan-3 Bristol Auction Rooms #486
£320	$518	€467	Mares and foals (75x90cm-30x35in) s.d.78. 27-Jan-3 Bristol Auction Rooms #488
£340	$551	€496	The sale ring, Tattersalls, Newmarket (44x59cm-17x23in) s. 27-Jan-3 Bristol Auction Rooms #485
£900	$1530	€1314	Mares in the snow (51x61cm-20x24in) s.d.78. 27-Nov-3 Christie's, Kensington #158/R
£1181	$1853	€1700	Horses racing (60x75cm-24x30in) s. 26-Aug-3 James Adam, Dublin #117/R est:800-1200
£1424	$2235	€2050	Racing in sunlight. s.d.75. 26-Aug-3 James Adam, Dublin #231/R est:400-600
£1458	$2290	€2100	Horses racing (60x75cm-24x30in) s. 26-Aug-3 James Adam, Dublin #116/R est:800-1200
£1667	$2617	€2400	Horses racing (60x75cm-24x30in) s. 26-Aug-3 James Adam, Dublin #114/R est:800-1200
£3194	$5015	€4600	Horseracing (101x126cm-40x50in) s. 26-Aug-3 James Adam, Dublin #83/R est:1200-1500

HOWES, Jerome (20th C) American

£278	$450	€406	Wes Beach Beverly, Mass at sunset (30x61cm-12x24in) s. 31-Jul-3 Eldred, East Dennis #228/R
£339	$550	€495	The Island Home (51x76cm-20x30in) s. 31-Jul-3 Eldred, East Dennis #793/R
£353	$600	€515	Steamboat (76x122cm-30x48in) s. 21-Nov-3 Eldred, East Dennis #599/R
£546	$1000	€819	Portrait of the sailing ship New Hampshire with the Nantucket Lightship (38x56cm-15x22in) s. panel. 29-Jul-4 Eldred, East Dennis #498/R
£765	$1300	€1117	Yachts racing (81x104cm-32x41in) s. 21-Nov-3 Eldred, East Dennis #560/R est:1000-1500

HOWES, John Townsend (19th C) British?

Works on paper

£187	$350	€273	From Heidelberg over the Necktar (23x33cm-9x13in) i.verso pencil Chinese white prov. 29-Feb-4 Grogan, Boston #26/R

HOWES, Kenneth (?) British

£1450	$2552	€2117	Violin, books, Wedgwood pot and pewter ewer on a table (51x61cm-20x24in) s. 19-May-4 Christie's, Kensington #681/R est:1200-1500

HOWES, W H (1856-1911) ?

£1382	$2170	€2018	Fairy bower, manly (14x34cm-6x13in) s. board. 26-Aug-3 Christie's, Sydney #298 est:2000-3000 (A.D 3400)

HOWET, Marie (1897-1984) Belgian

£769	$1285	€1100	Vers Corli (50x60cm-20x24in) s. 13-Oct-3 Horta, Bruxelles #192
£828	$1490	€1200	Paysage hivernal (50x60cm-20x24in) s. 20-Jan-4 Galerie Moderne, Brussels #268/R
£1014	$1814	€1500	Les geraniums (56x62cm-22x24in) s. 10-May-4 Horta, Bruxelles #380 est:1200-1800
£1067	$1920	€1600	Nature morte aux fleurs (60x70cm-24x28in) s. 20-Apr-4 Galerie Moderne, Brussels #385/R est:800-1000
£1081	$1935	€1600	Vase fleuri (62x48cm-24x19in) s. cardboard. 10-May-4 Horta, Bruxelles #381 est:1200-1500

HOWEY, John William (1873-1938) British

£900	$1629	€1314	Cottage in the trees (25x30cm-10x12in) s. panel. 15-Apr-4 Richardson & Smith, Whitby #110/R
£1000	$1810	€1460	Low Morley, Tyne (25x33cm-10x13in) s. i.verso board. 15-Apr-4 Richardson & Smith, Whitby #91/R est:1000-1500

HOWEY, Robert Leslie (1900-1981) British

£620	$1135	€905	Derwentwater (49x59cm-19x23in) s. board. 2-Feb-4 Bonhams, Chester #952
£680	$1224	€993	Borrowdale. Elta Water and Langdale Pikes (49x71cm-19x28in) s. board pair. 20-Apr-4 Bonhams, Leeds #338

Works on paper

£320	$579	€467	Teesmouth from Seaton beach (10x15cm-4x6in) s. W/C. 30-Mar-4 David Duggleby, Scarborough #159/R
£360	$652	€526	Mountainous lakeland landscape (15x23cm-6x9in) s. W/C htd white. 15-Apr-4 Richardson & Smith, Whitby #75
£400	$724	€584	St Johns Chapel, Weardale (29x26cm-11x10in) s.d.44 pastel. 30-Mar-4 David Duggleby, Scarborough #45/R
£460	$828	€672	Durham (40x49cm-16x19in) s. pastel dr. 21-Apr-4 Tennants, Leyburn #965
£900	$1683	€1314	Huntsmen on horseback with foxhounds (36x44cm-14x17in) s.d.73 pencil W/C gouache bodycol htd white. 22-Jul-4 Tennants, Leyburn #675
£940	$1739	€1372	Fishing boats in harbour (20x25cm-8x10in) s. pair. 12-Feb-4 Andrew Hartley, Ilkley #796
£1120	$1781	€1624	Fishing boats and sea gulls in Whitby Harbour (22x28cm-9x11in) s. W/C htd white. 9-Sep-3 David Duggleby, Scarborough #204/R est:400-600

HOWIS, William (1804-1882) Irish

£3194	$5207	€4600	The salmon leap, Leixlip (52x71cm-20x28in) 24-Sep-3 James Adam, Dublin #9/R est:2000-3000

HOWITT, John Newton (1885-1958) American

£366	$600	€531	The hill, Pawling (30x41cm-12x16in) s. s.i.verso canvasboard. 4-Jun-3 Alderfer's, Hatfield #289
£419	$750	€612	Mt Hope road, Greenville, NY (23x30cm-9x12in) s.i.d.February 18, 1950. 11-Jan-4 William Jenack, New York #123
£3106	$5000	€4535	Duck pond (76x102cm-30x40in) s. 20-Aug-3 James Julia, Fairfield #1525/R est:3000-5000

HOWITT, Samuel (1765-1822) British

Works on paper

£1200	$2208	€1752	Huntsmen and dogs shooting over a cornfield (18x26cm-7x10in) s. W/C. 10-Jun-4 Christie's, Kensington #238/R est:700-1000
£1300	$2366	€1898	Coaches and horses before the White Hart Inn (14x21cm-6x8in) pencil W/C black ink. 1-Jul-4 Christie's, Kensington #19/R est:700-900
£2653	$4749	€3900	Des chiens chassant des cerfs et des lapins (35x54cm-14x21in) s.d.1812 black chk pen brown ink col wash prov. 18-Mar-4 Christie's, Paris #323/R est:1500-2000
£4600	$8464	€6716	Huntsmen and dogs hare coursing in rocky landscape. Huntsmen and dogs with hare (22x32cm-9x13in) s. pen ink W/C over pencil pair. 26-Mar-4 Sotheby's, London #97/R est:2000-3000

HOWITT, Samuel (attrib) (1765-1822) British

£480	$864	€701	Hawk and plover (49x61cm-19x24in) 21-Jan-4 Sotheby's, Olympia #130/R
£4969	$8000	€7255	Gone to ground (94x122cm-37x48in) 14-Jan-4 Christie's, Rockefeller NY #49/R est:7000-9000

Works on paper

£221	$375	€323	Two horses in a stable with a groom (26x34cm-10x13in) s.d.1802 W/C prov. 21-Nov-3 Skinner, Boston #229/R
£380	$673	€570	Partridge shootint (17x27cm-7x11in) pencil brown wash. 27-Apr-4 Holloways, Banbury #203/R

HOWLAND, A C (1838-1909) American

£958	$1600	€1399	On the campus, Ithaca, NY, trees and sunset (20x25cm-8x10in) board. 14-Nov-3 Douglas, South Deerfield #3

HOWLAND, Alfred Cornelius (1838-1909) American

£1326	$2400	€1936	Mother and child on a country path (27x41cm-11x16in) s.i. indis d. 65 panel. 30-Mar-4 Christie's, Rockefeller NY #91/R est:1000-1500
£4491	$7500	€6557	Resting along the side of the river (46x69cm-18x27in) s.d.76 prov. 23-Oct-3 Shannon's, Milford #6/R est:5000-7000

HOWLEY, John Richard (1931-) Australian

£1016	$1595	€1473	Looking up (128x128cm-50x50in) s. s.i.d.91 verso. 26-Aug-3 Christie's, Sydney #406 est:3000-4000 (A.D 2500)

HOWORTH, C H (1856-1945) New Zealander

£3114	$5574	€4546	Fishing cottage, Stewart Island (29x44cm-11x17in) s. board prov. 12-May-4 Dunbar Sloane, Wellington #18/R est:5000-10000 (NZ.D 9000)
£4152	$7433	€6062	Hongi's track, near Rotorua (60x49cm-24x19in) s. board. 12-May-4 Dunbar Sloane, Wellington #17/R est:8000-15000 (NZ.D 12000)

HOWORTH, Charles Henry (1856-1945) New Zealander

£752	$1278	€1098	Early morning, Golden Bay, Patersen Inlet, Stewart Island (44x59cm-17x23in) s.i.d.1902. 27-Nov-3 International Art Centre, Auckland #103/R (NZ.D 2000)
£7143	$13143	€10429	Lake Rotokakahi and Lake Tikitapu, the Green and Blue Lakes Rotorua (60x90cm-24x35in) s. 25-Mar-4 International Art Centre, Auckland #76/R est:25000-35000 (NZ.D 20000)

HOWSE (19th C) British

£4200	$7266	€6132	Druid, portrait of a bloodhound (84x105cm-33x41in) 9-Dec-3 Bonhams, Oxford #123/R est:800-1200

HOWSE, George (?-1860) British

Works on paper

£1700	$3128	€2482	Figures unloading fishing boats on the shore (26x49cm-10x19in) W/C pencil htd bodycol. 26-Mar-4 Sotheby's, London #136/R est:2000-3000

HOWSON, Mark Henry (1961-) Australian

£453	$819	€661	Untitled (77x53cm-30x21in) s.d.85 oil on paper. 30-Mar-4 Lawson Menzies, Sydney #58 est:800-1000 (A.D 1100)
£648	$1043	€946	Two swimmers (111x137cm-44x54in) s.d.2000 s.i.d.verso. 25-Aug-3 Sotheby's, Paddington #277/R (A.D 1600)
£681	$1157	€994	Moonless night (137x111cm-54x44in) s.d.99 s.i.d.1999 verso linen prov. 25-Nov-3 Christie's, Melbourne #253/R (A.D 1600)
£1145	$2084	€1672	Reclining nude (71x91cm-28x36in) s. i.d.2001 verso. 16-Jun-4 Deutscher-Menzies, Melbourne #365/R est:3500-4500 (A.D 3000)

HOWSON, Peter (1958-) British

£300 $516 €438 Portrait of a man (24cm-9in circular) oil china plate. 3-Dec-3 Christie's, Kensington #671
£1000 $1720 €1460 Boxer (33x23cm-13x9in) s. board. 3-Dec-3 Christie's, Kensington #661/R est:700-1000
£1800 $3096 €2628 Untitled (23x56cm-9x22in) s. prov. 3-Dec-3 Christie's, Kensington #663/R est:2000-3000
£2200 $3674 €3212 Timeless March (61x91cm-24x36in) s.i. on stretcher. 16-Oct-3 Bonhams, Edinburgh #69/R est:2000-3000
£7200 $12240 €10512 Face of Britain IV (213x152cm-84x60in) s. painted 1991. 30-Oct-3 Christie's, London #237/R est:8000-12000
£7500 $12750 €10950 Riding the Gauntlet (244x183cm-96x72in) s. prov. 18-Nov-3 Bonhams, Knightsbridge #108/R est:8000-10000
£9000 $16290 €13140 Women on the mind (60x45cm-24x18in) s. col chks. 19-Apr-4 Sotheby's, London #156/R est:2000-3000

Works on paper

£300 $549 €438 Tea and doughnuts (28x20cm-11x8in) pencil prov. 8-Apr-4 Bonhams, Edinburgh #4
£389 $650 €568 Man portrait (41x30cm-16x12in) s. pastel. 25-Oct-3 Rachel Davis, Shaker Heights #574/R
£480 $826 €701 Quarry gladiators (18x15cm-7x6in) s. pastel. 3-Dec-3 Christie's, Kensington #662
£550 $946 €803 Three figures in an industrial landscape (31x24cm-12x9in) s. pastel. 3-Dec-3 Christie's, Kensington #673
£550 $1023 €803 Lowland hero 23 (29x20cm-11x8in) s. pastel executed 1993 prov.exhib. 4-Mar-4 Christie's, Kensington #268/R
£600 $1032 €876 Portrait of Dean Lemmon (58x51cm-23x20in) s.d.58 chl. 3-Dec-3 Christie's, Kensington #676
£600 $1062 €876 Profile portrait of a man (28x20cm-11x8in) s. pastel. 1-May-4 Shapes, Edinburgh #430/R
£650 $1118 €949 White city series XIII (22x16cm-9x6in) s. chl col chk. 3-Dec-3 Christie's, Kensington #664
£700 $1302 €1022 Lowland hero 10 (28x19cm-11x7in) s. si.d.1993 verso crayon prov.exhib. 4-Mar-4 Christie's, Kensington #270/R
£750 $1395 €1095 Head study (28x20cm-11x8in) s. pastel. 4-Mar-4 Christie's, Kensington #272/R
£750 $1365 €1095 Portrait Head 9 (27x19cm-11x7in) s. pastel prov. 1-Jul-4 Christie's, Kensington #200/R
£800 $1376 €1168 Progress of a rake begins (41x12cm-16x5in) s.d.95 pencil chl prov. 3-Dec-3 Christie's, Kensington #665/R
£840 $1487 €1226 Portrait of a vagrant (27x20cm-11x8in) s. pastel. 1-May-4 Shapes, Edinburgh #431/R
£900 $1638 €1314 Dancer (29x28cm-11x11in) s. pastel. 1-Jul-4 Christie's, Kensington #198/R
£1200 $2232 €1752 Sons of thunder 2 (63x49cm-25x19in) s. pastel executed 1997 prov. 4-Mar-4 Christie's, Kensington #269/R est:1200-1800
£1600 $2976 €2336 Three drummers (46x59cm-18x23in) s. pastel. 4-Mar-4 Christie's, Kensington #262/R est:1400-1800

HOY, Edward John (20th C) British

£311 $500 €454 The white dog (41x61cm-16x24in) s. 20-Aug-3 James Julia, Fairfield #1004/R

HOYER, C F (1775-1855) Danish

£2268 $3924 €3311 Cupid visiting Anakreon (73x99cm-29x39in) painted c.1808-1811. 9-Dec-3 Rasmussen, Copenhagen #1324/R est:15000-25000 (D.KR 24000)

HOYER, Edward (19th C) British

£1000 $1670 €1460 Marine study (74x124cm-29x49in) s.d. 26-Oct-3 Tayler & Fletcher, Cheltenham #4
£1050 $1754 €1533 Sail and steam (74x122cm-29x48in) s.d. 26-Oct-3 Tayler & Fletcher, Cheltenham #5/R
£1350 $2147 €1958 Shipping off an Eastern port (41x64cm-16x25in) s.d.77. 9-Sep-3 David Duggleby, Scarborough #388 est:1500-2000
£4200 $7014 €6132 Moonlight over Constantinople (31x41cm-12x16in) s. 14-Oct-3 Sotheby's, London #9/R est:4000-6000

HOYER, Peter (19th C) British

£540 $956 €788 Shipping in heavy seas. Moonlit vessels in heavy seas (20x30cm-8x12in) s.d.1873 pair. 27-Apr-4 Bonhams, Knowle #101

HOYLAND, Francis (1930-) British

£280 $456 €409 Art Class (64x76cm-25x30in) init. board. 24-Sep-3 Dreweatt Neate, Newbury #178

HOYLAND, John (1934-) British

£700 $1267 €1022 Untitled (84x60cm-33x24in) s.d.71 acrylic paper. 2-Apr-4 Moore Allen & Innocent, Cirencester #424/R
£1200 $2220 €1752 Composition VIII (55x76cm-22x30in) s.d.69 oil on paper prov.exhib. 11-Mar-4 Christie's, Kensington #379/R est:600-800
£1500 $2430 €2175 Clearing (61x46cm-24x18in) s.i.d.1997 acrylic on paper. 30-Jul-3 Hamptons Fine Art, Godalming #128 est:1500-1800
£1800 $3006 €2628 27.8.72 (168x152cm-66x60in) s.d.27.8.72 overlap acrylic prov.exhib. 16-Oct-3 Christie's, Kensington #717/R est:2000-3000
£3200 $5824 €4672 Voluptuous night (50x76cm-20x30in) acrylic. 15-Jun-4 Bonhams, New Bond Street #123/R est:2000-3000
£3200 $5824 €4672 Abstract composition (50x76cm-20x30in) acrylic. 15-Jun-4 Bonhams, New Bond Street #124/R est:2000-3000
£3500 $6370 €5110 Untitled 1970 (183x76cm-72x30in) s. acrylic. 1-Jul-4 Christie's, Kensington #397/R est:2500-3500
£7000 $12040 €10220 Untitled (167x184cm-66x72in) acrylic. 2-Dec-3 Bonhams, New Bond Street #168/R est:4000-6000
£9500 $17385 €13870 7.7.75 (229x203cm-90x80in) s.i. acrylic painted 1975. 2-Jun-4 Sotheby's, London #130/R est:5000-7000

Works on paper

£381 $700 €556 Untitled (53x74cm-21x29in) s.d.67 W/C gouache. 25-Jun-4 Freeman, Philadelphia #37/R

HOYLES, William R (fl.1906-1929) British

Works on paper

£280 $515 €409 Picking flowers (25x35cm-10x14in) s. W/C. 22-Jun-4 Bonhams, Knightsbridge #57
£375 $611 €548 Banks of the River Conway with woman and child (20x53cm-8x21in) s. W/C. 27-Sep-3 Rogers Jones, Clwyd #35

HOYNE, Thomas Maclay (1924-1989) American

£12973 $24000 €18941 Widow maker (61x77cm-24x30in) s.d.1979 board prov.exhib. 10-Feb-4 Christie's, Rockefeller NY #250/R est:8000-10000

HOYNINGEN-HUENE, George (1900-1968) British

Photographs

£5090 $8500 €7431 Bathing suits (29x22cm-11x9in) i.d.1930 verso gelatin silver print prov.lit. 17-Oct-3 Phillips, New York #209/R est:4000-6000

HOYRUP, Carl (1893-1961) Danish

£284 $455 €415 Stag in woodland glade with flowers (100x135cm-39x53in) s.d.1958. 22-Sep-3 Rasmussen, Vejle #245/R (D.KR 3000)

HOYT, Waite (20th C) American

£335 $550 €486 Buildings and figures (13x18cm-5x7in) s. board painted c.1950. 7-Jun-3 Treadway Gallery, Cincinnati #1512

HOYTE, John Barr Clarke (1835-1913) New Zealander

Works on paper

£376 $639 €549 Unloading barge, Waikato river. Small river entrance with canoe (14x21cm-6x8in) W/C pair. 27-Nov-3 International Art Centre, Auckland #100/R (NZ.D 1000)
£451 $767 €658 North Island settlement with flagpole on peninsula, buildings, boats and figures (16x23cm-6x9in) W/C. 27-Nov-3 International Art Centre, Auckland #97/R (NZ.D 1200)
£634 $1027 €919 Mt. Cook and Tasman Valley (19x36cm-7x14in) s. W/C. 31-Jul-3 International Art Centre, Auckland #109/R est:1600-2400 (NZ.D 1750)
£800 $1256 €1160 Mitre Peak landscape (19x38cm-7x15in) s. W/C. 27-Aug-3 Dunbar Sloane, Wellington #150 (NZ.D 2200)
£900 $1610 €1314 Rangitoto (17x32cm-7x13in) init. W/C. 11-May-4 Peter Webb, Auckland #168/R est:3000-5000 (NZ.D 2600)
£1241 $2109 €1812 Blue Mountains, NSW (32x19cm-13x7in) s. W/C. 27-Nov-3 International Art Centre, Auckland #145/R est:2500-3500 (NZ.D 3300)
£1250 $2300 €1825 Queen Charlotte Sound (25x42cm-10x17in) s. W/C. 25-Mar-4 International Art Centre, Auckland #155/R est:3800-4800 (NZ.D 3500)
£2068 $3515 €3019 Whangarei (30x57cm-12x22in) s. W/C. 26-Nov-3 Dunbar Sloane, Wellington #41/R est:6000-9000 (NZ.D 5500)
£2364 $3711 €3428 Whangarei heads (37x68cm-15x27in) s. W/C. 27-Aug-3 Dunbar Sloane, Wellington #69/R est:11000-15000 (NZ.D 6500)
£3297 $6099 €4814 Surveyors, Taramakau River (23x41cm-9x16in) init. W/C. 9-Mar-4 Watson's, Christchurch #42 est:7500-12500 (NZ.D 9000)
£5000 $9200 €7300 Northland homestead (27x54cm-11x21in) s. W/C. 25-Mar-4 International Art Centre, Auckland #85/R est:15000-20000 (NZ.D 14000)
£5263 $8947 €7684 Pink terraces, Rotomahana (30x55cm-12x22in) s. W/C. 27-Nov-3 International Art Centre, Auckland #125/R est:14000-20000 (NZ.D 14000)
£5357 $9857 €7821 Mitre peak and Milford Sound (39x64cm-15x25in) s. W/C. 25-Mar-4 International Art Centre, Auckland #57/R est:14000-20000 (NZ.D 15000)
£6294 $11455 €9189 Auckland from Park Road (37x62cm-15x24in) s. W/C prov. 29-Jun-4 Peter Webb, Auckland #82/R est:22000-27000 (NZ.D 18000)
£6469 $11773 €9445 Coromandel Harbour (32x52cm-13x20in) s. W/C prov. 29-Jun-4 Peter Webb, Auckland #83/R est:20000-26000 (NZ.D 18500)
£7246 $11739 €10507 Pink terraces, Rotomahana (35x58cm-14x23in) s. W/C. 31-Jul-3 International Art Centre, Auckland #59/R est:15000-20000 (NZ.D 20000)
£8392 $15273 €12252 Whakamanu Geyser, Whakarewarewa, Rotorua (29x49cm-11x19in) i. W/C prov. 29-Jun-4 Peter Webb, Auckland #81/R est:20000-25000 (NZ.D 24000)
£8681 $13802 €12674 Coromandel (34x54cm-13x21in) s. indis d. W/C. 1-May-3 Dunbar Sloane, Wellington #31/R est:25000-35000 (NZ.D 25000)
£8727 $13702 €12654 Dunedin (35x55cm-14x22in) s. W/C. 27-Aug-3 Dunbar Sloane, Wellington #29/R est:18000-25000 (NZ.D 24000)
£11273 $17698 €16346 Rowing, Wanganui river (33x61cm-13x24in) s. W/C. 27-Aug-3 Dunbar Sloane, Wellington #22/R est:25000-35000 (NZ.D 31000)
£12500 $23000 €18750 New Zealand landscapes (41x69cm-16x27in) s.d.1873 W/C pair. 25-Jun-4 Bigwood, Stratford on Avon #252/R
£22925 $41036 €34388 View from Parnell, Auckland, New Zealand (44x75cm-17x30in) s.d.1872 W/C. 17-May-4 Sotheby's, Melbourne #606/R est:12000-18000 (A.D 58000)

HOYTEMA, Theodoor van (1863-1917) Dutch

£559 $951 €800 Waterfowl (40x80cm-16x31in) i. 18-Nov-3 Christie's, Amsterdam #312/R

Works on paper

£490 $832 €700 Ducks on a pond (28x22cm-11x9in) s. col chk. 18-Nov-3 Christie's, Amsterdam #303/R
£559 $951 €800 Six pelicans fighting over a fish (35x48cm-14x19in) black chk. 18-Nov-3 Christie's, Amsterdam #272/R
£559 $951 €800 Chicken near a pond (31x42cm-12x17in) s. col pastel cardboard sold with another by the same hand. 18-Nov-3 Christie's, Amsterdam #285/R
£559 $951 €800 Tropical garden (39x64cm-15x25in) init.d.27 april 1916 W/C cardboard. 18-Nov-3 Christie's, Amsterdam #311/R
£839 $1427 €1200 Butterfly in garden (62x37cm-24x15in) s.d.1916 W/C. 18-Nov-3 Christie's, Amsterdam #297/R
£979 $1664 €1400 Three toucans (18x34cm-7x13in) s. black col chk. 18-Nov-3 Christie's, Amsterdam #310/R
£1189 $2021 €1700 Five chickens going to roost (15x26cm-6x10in) mono. col crayon W/C. 18-Nov-3 Christie's, Amsterdam #270/R est:1200-1600
£1399 $2378 €2000 Thistles (76x63cm-30x25in) s.d.1916 col pastel. 18-Nov-3 Christie's, Amsterdam #316/R est:2000-3000
£1538 $2615 €2200 Crocodile (35x54cm-14x21in) s. black chk W/C. 18-Nov-3 Christie's, Amsterdam #286/R est:2000-3000
£2098 $3566 €3000 Curlews (35x24cm-14x9in) s.i. col pastel. 18-Nov-3 Christie's, Amsterdam #317/R est:4000-6000
£2797 $4755 €4000 Wenken bij het schilderen (50x33cm-20x13in) s.i.d.24 dec 1893 i.verso W/C pen ink lit. 18-Nov-3 Christie's, Amsterdam #269 est:1500-2000
£2797 $4755 €4000 Twee pelikanen, een reiger en eenden (26x32cm-10x13in) s. black col chk W/C pair lit. 18-Nov-3 Christie's, Amsterdam #313/R est:3000-4000

£2797	$4755	€4000	Two bearded vultures (57x43cm-22x17in) s. W/C black chk. 18-Nov-3 Christie's, Amsterdam #315/R est:4000-6000
£3357	$5706	€4800	Landschap op Texel (35x63cm-14x25in) s. pencil col chk W/C cardboard lit. 18-Nov-3 Christie's, Amsterdam #271/R est:1500-2000
£3846	$6538	€5500	Two crown pigeons (44x54cm-17x21in) s. col crayon W/C lit. 18-Nov-3 Christie's, Amsterdam #314/R est:5000-7000

HOYTON, Inez E (1903-1983) British

Works on paper

£350	$602	€511	Portloe, Cornwall (50x39cm-20x15in) s. pencil W/C pen brush black ink. 3-Dec-3 Christie's, Kensington #609

HRADIL, C (19th C) ?

£1275	$2346	€1900	Telling children a story (23x29cm-9x11in) s.d.98 panel. 24-Mar-4 Hugo Ruef, Munich #997/R est:600

HRDLICKA, Alfred (1928-) Austrian

£31250	$53125	€45000	Returning aristocracy assaulting the corpse of the revolution (200x160cm-79x63in) s.d.1985 oil chl exhib.lit. 28-Oct-3 Wiener Kunst Auktionen, Vienna #263/R est:28000-60000

Sculpture

£1067	$1963	€1600	Death of Marat (10x13x6cm-4x5x2in) gold pat.bronze. 11-Jun-4 Hauswedell & Nolte, Hamburg #1310/R est:1600
£1333	$2453	€2000	Schubert (15x19x12cm-6x7x5in) gold pat.bronze. 11-Jun-4 Hauswedell & Nolte, Hamburg #1308/R est:1600
£1467	$2640	€2200	Portrait B (23cm-9in) mono. light brown pat.bronze Cat.A Zottl, Wien. 21-Apr-4 Dorotheum, Vienna #161/R est:2000-3000
£1533	$2806	€2300	Kaiser Avenue (39cm-15in) st.mono. brown brass col pat.bronze. 4-Jun-4 Lempertz, Koln #205/R est:2200
£1667	$2717	€2400	Sappho (28cm-11in) s.i.d.1957 brown pat.bronze Cast.Venturi Arte. 27-Sep-3 Dr Fritz Nagel, Stuttgart #9561/R est:1800
£1972	$3273	€2800	Standing female nude (38cm-15in) mono.i. dark pat.bronze. 12-Jun-3 Dorotheum, Graz #209/R est:2200
£8042	$13671	€11500	Upright male figure (69cm-27in) mono.i.d.1968 brown pat.bronze. 27-Nov-3 Lempertz, Koln #195/R est:6000-8000

Works on paper

£1184	$2179	€1800	Untitled (45x60cm-18x24in) s.d.1971 ink. 22-Jun-4 Wiener Kunst Auktionen, Vienna #321/R est:2000
£1900	$3477	€2850	Untitled (62x48cm-24x19in) s.d.1971 col chk pencil prov. 4-Jun-4 Lempertz, Koln #208/R est:3800
£2000	$3660	€3000	Untitled - erotic scene (49x67cm-19x26in) s.d.1974 pastel chk pencil. 4-Jun-4 Lempertz, Koln #209/R est:3000
£2098	$3566	€3000	Three nudes (46x61cm-18x24in) s.d.1968 mixed media. 28-Nov-3 Wiener Kunst Auktionen, Vienna #664/R est:2000-5000
£2467	$4539	€3700	Figures (48x65cm-19x26in) s.d. chk w/C. 11-Jun-4 Hauswedell & Nolte, Hamburg #1312/R est:2500
£2657	$4517	€3800	Chatila - study for slaughter (50x65cm-20x26in) s.d.1982 chk pastel prov.exhib. 27-Nov-3 Lempertz, Koln #194/R est:3600
£3007	$5112	€4300	Turkish war (48x67cm-19x26in) s.d.1983 pastel chk. 27-Nov-3 Lempertz, Koln #196/R est:3800
£3077	$5231	€4400	Peasant wark (49x67cm-19x26in) s.d.1986 pastel chk. 27-Nov-3 Lempertz, Koln #197/R est:3800
£4000	$7360	€6000	Untitled (67x49cm-26x19in) s.d.1982 pastel sold with another pastel two. 8-Jun-4 Sotheby's, Amsterdam #57/R est:6000-9000

HRDLICKA, Heinrich R (20th C) Austrian

£342	$582	€500	Composition (50x70cm-20x28in) 5-Nov-3 Dorotheum, Vienna #21/R

HRENOV, Alexander Sergeevich (1860-1926) Russian

Works on paper

£2096	$3500	€3060	Hunting scene (41x58cm-16x23in) s. pencil W/C. 21-Oct-3 Christie's, Rockefeller NY #95 est:2000-3000

HRONEK, Joseph (20th C) American

£219	$400	€320	Painting of western landscape no.5 (58x33cm-23x13in) panel with glass. 10-Jul-4 Hindman, Chicago #232/R

HRUBY, Sergius (1869-1943) Austrian

Works on paper

£250	$448	€365	The four old men (21x21cm-8x8in) s.d.31 W/C. 25-May-4 Bonhams, Knightsbridge #182/R
£915	$1602	€1300	Siren (43x22cm-17x9in) s.d.32 pencil W/C gouache. 19-Dec-3 Dorotheum, Vienna #116/R

HSI HU (1942-) Chinese

£9804	$17745	€14314	Eight immortals (90x134cm-35x53in) s. diptych. 4-Apr-4 Sotheby's, Singapore #197/R est:25000-35000 (S.D 30000)

HSIAO CHIN (1935-) Chinese

£313	$522	€450	Nove (70x90cm-28x35in) s.d.1963. 21-Oct-3 Campo, Vlaamse Kaai #448
£503	$931	€750	Untitled (19x19cm-7x7in) s. mixed media paper on canvas. 13-Mar-4 Meeting Art, Vercelli #78
£1049	$1783	€1500	Cut 2 (50x60cm-20x24in) s.i.d.1973 acrylic. 24-Nov-3 Christie's, Milan #71/R est:1500-2000
£1100	$1969	€1606	Untitled (89x69cm-35x27in) 6-May-4 Sotheby's, London #147/R est:1500-2000
£1189	$2021	€1700	Best wishes, Poland (75x100cm-30x39in) s. acrylic. 24-Nov-3 Christie's, Milan #113/R est:1000-1500
£1216	$2141	€1800	Composition (176x30cm-69x12in) s.d.59 tempera paper on canvas. 24-May-4 Christie's, Milan #71/R est:1800-2500
£1793	$2994	€2600	Big black cloud (112x187cm-44x74in) s. i.verso. 13-Nov-3 Finarte Semenzato, Rome #251/R est:2800-3500

Works on paper

£500	$920	€750	Untitled (40x56cm-16x22in) s.d.1960 mixed media card on canvas. 12-Jun-4 Meeting Art, Vercelli #451/R
£500	$920	€750	Untitled (19x19cm-7x7in) s. mixed media paper on board. 12-Jun-4 Meeting Art, Vercelli #699/R
£839	$1427	€1200	Tsuei (120x60cm-47x24in) s.d.1963 i.verso ink oil. 25-Nov-3 Christie's, Amsterdam #122/R

HSIAO JU-SUNG (1922-1992) Chinese

Works on paper

£37066	$61900	€54116	Scene of the windows (71x100cm-28x39in) s. W/C exhib.lit. 26-Oct-3 Christie's, Hong Kong #126/R est:400000-500000 (HK.D 480000)

HU NIANZU (1927-) Chinese

Works on paper

£782	$1400	€1142	Waterfall (49x135cm-19x53in) s.d.1967 ink. 10-May-4 Bonhams & Butterfields, San Francisco #4395/R

HU PEIHENG (1892-1965) Chinese

Works on paper

£3698	$6657	€5399	Sailing in autumn (16x101cm-6x40in) s.i.d.1951 ink col. 26-Apr-4 Sotheby's, Hong Kong #551/R est:25000-35000 (HK.D 52000)
£6046	$10882	€8827	Monastery in Zhejiang (148x43cm-58x17in) s.i.d.1953 ink col hanging scroll. 26-Apr-4 Sotheby's, Hong Kong #556/R est:35000-45000 (HK.D 85000)

HU SHUANGAN (1916-1988) Chinese

Works on paper

£743	$1308	€1100	Growling tiger in the grass (65x66cm-26x26in) s.i. seal Indian ink col hanging scroll. 21-May-4 Dr Fritz Nagel, Stuttgart #1198/R
£1622	$2854	€2400	Two tigers (98x32cm-39x13in) s.i. seal Indian ink col hanging scroll. 21-May-4 Dr Fritz Nagel, Stuttgart #1196/R est:450
£1892	$3330	€2800	Tiger in mountain landscape (150x83cm-59x33in) s.i. seal Indian ink col hanging scroll. 21-May-4 Dr Fritz Nagel, Stuttgart #1195/R est:1000
£2500	$4400	€3700	Three tigers in landscape (135x64cm-53x25in) s.d.1946 seals Indian ink col hanging scroll. 21-May-4 Dr Fritz Nagel, Stuttgart #1197/R est:500

HU WEI (20th C) Chinese

Works on paper

£1284	$2259	€1900	Two horses (79x83cm-31x33in) s. seal Indian ink silk. 21-May-4 Dr Fritz Nagel, Stuttgart #1217/R est:2200

HU YEFO (1908-) Chinese

Works on paper

£1991	$3585	€2907	Watching the waterfall (68x32cm-27x13in) s.i.d.1940 ink col hanging scroll. 25-Apr-4 Christie's, Hong Kong #149/R est:18000-20000 (HK.D 28000)
£2703	$4514	€3946	Lady holding a fan. Calligraphy (18x49cm-7x19in) s.i.d.1944 ink col folding fan double-sided. 26-Oct-3 Christie's, Hong Kong #371/R est:25000-35000 (HK.D 35000)

HU YONGKAI (1945-) Chinese

Works on paper

£3089	$5158	€4510	Enjoying tea (73x71cm-29x28in) s. ink col scroll. 26-Oct-3 Christie's, Hong Kong #268/R est:45000-55000 (HK.D 40000)

HU YUKUN (1607-?) Chinese

Works on paper

£119691	$199884	€174749	Countryside (19x28cm-7x11in) s.i.d.1652 ink col twelve leaves album prov. 27-Oct-3 Sotheby's, Hong Kong #322/R est:1200000-1500000 (HK.D 1550000)

HU, Santos (?) ?

£268	$502	€400	Roses (38x20cm-15x8in) s.d.2002 board. 24-Feb-4 Durán, Madrid #30/R

HUA JIN (17/18th C) Chinese

Works on paper

£5690	$10242	€8307	Washing the ink stone (97x46cm-38x18in) s.i. ink col hanging scroll silk. 25-Apr-4 Christie's, Hong Kong #377/R est:50000-70000 (HK.D 80000)

HUA YAN (1682-1756) Chinese

£2013	$3604	€3000	Landscape. s. paint. 27-May-4 Beaussant & Lefèvre, Paris #268/R est:3500-4000

Works on paper

£3861	$6448	€5637	Composing poems by bamboo grove (121x30cm-48x12in) s.i. ink col. 26-Oct-3 Christie's, Hong Kong #482/R (HK.D 50000)
£227596	$409673	€332290	Scenes of Yansu Garden (175x49cm-69x19in) s.i. ink col hanging scroll silk set of twelve. 25-Apr-4 Christie's, Hong Kong #383/R est:3600000-4800000 (HK.D 3200000)

HUA YILAN (19th C) Chinese

Works on paper

£1849	$3329	€2700	Landscape (131x32cm-52x13in) s.i.d.1850 ink hanging scroll after Huang Gongwang. 25-Apr-4 Christie's, Hong Kong #404/R est:30000-40000 (HK.D 26000)

HUANG BINHONG (1864-1955) Chinese

Works on paper

£3912	$7041	€5712	Landscape (21x29cm-8x11in) seal of artist ink col hanging scroll. 25-Apr-4 Christie's, Hong Kong #119/R est:20000-30000 (HK.D 55000)
£4267	$7681	€6230	Couplet calligraphy in archaic script (156x27cm-61x11in) s.i.d.1929 ink hanging scroll pair. 25-Apr-4 Christie's, Hong Kong #12/R est:15000-20000 (HK.D 60000)
£4979	$8962	€7269	Calligraphy in archaic script (80x32cm-31x13in) s.i.d.1947 ink hanging scroll. 25-Apr-4 Christie's, Hong Kong #13/R est:10000-12000 (HK.D 70000)
£5334	$9602	€7788	Mount Hiuang (76x41cm-30x16in) s.i. ink col hanging scroll. 25-Apr-4 Christie's, Hong Kong #118/R est:60000-80000 (HK.D 75000)
£5405	$9027	€7891	Landscape (107x39cm-42x15in) s.i. ink col hanging scroll. 26-Oct-3 Christie's, Hong Kong #232/R est:50000-70000 (HK.D 70000)
£6757	$12162	€9865	Landscape (77x37cm-30x15in) s.i. ink col. 26-Apr-4 Sotheby's, Hong Kong #632/R est:80000-120000 (HK.D 95000)
£9266	$15475	€13528	Landscape (122x47cm-48x19in) s.i.d.1940 ink col hanging scroll. 26-Oct-3 Christie's, Hong Kong #231/R est:60000-80000 (HK.D 120000)
£9266	$15475	€13528	Reading in a studio (65x34cm-26x13in) s.i.d. ink col hanging scroll prov. 27-Oct-3 Sotheby's, Hong Kong #335/R est:120000-150000 (HK.D 120000)
£17070	$30725	€24922	Secluded retreat (105x40cm-41x16in) s.i. ink col hanging scroll. 26-Apr-4 Sotheby's, Hong Kong #633/R est:200000-250000 (HK.D 240000)
£19915	$35846	€29076	Sichuan landscape (92x42cm-36x17in) s.i. ink col hanging scroll. 26-Apr-4 Sotheby's, Hong Kong #557/R est:70000-90000 (HK.D 280000)
£19915	$35846	€29076	Summer scene (90x32cm-35x13in) s.i.d.1951 ink col hanging scroll. 26-Apr-4 Sotheby's, Hong Kong #625/R est:160000-200000 (HK.D 280000)
£24182	$43528	€35306	Landscape in the shores (109x41cm-43x16in) s.i. ink col hanging scroll. 25-Apr-4 Christie's, Hong Kong #5/R est:50000-60000 (HK.D 340000)
£38610	$64479	€56371	Spring landscape (104x59cm-41x23in) s.i. ink col hanging scroll. 27-Oct-3 Sotheby's, Hong Kong #218/R est:300000-400000 (HK.D 500000)
£117354	$211238	€171337	Autumn landscape (87x37cm-34x15in) s.i.d.1952 ink col hanging scroll. 26-Apr-4 Sotheby's, Hong Kong #583/R est:220000-280000 (HK.D 1650000)

HUANG JUNBI (1898-1991) Chinese

Works on paper

£1486	$2616	€2200	Landscape (172x35cm-68x14in) s.i.d.1949 Indian ink col hanging scroll. 21-May-4 Dr Fritz Nagel, Stuttgart #1101/R est:2200
£2845	$5121	€4154	Listening to the streams (106x30cm-42x12in) s.i.d.1941 ink col hanging scroll. 25-Apr-4 Christie's, Hong Kong #6/R est:30000-35000 (HK.D 40000)
£2987	$5377	€4361	Landscape (82x37cm-32x15in) s.i.d.1933 ink col scroll. 25-Apr-4 Christie's, Hong Kong #52/R est:20000-30000 (HK.D 42000)
£9957	$17923	€14537	Waterfall (60x120cm-24x47in) s.i.d.1984 ink col scroll. 25-Apr-4 Christie's, Hong Kong #54/R est:80000-100000 (HK.D 140000)

HUANG RUNHUA (1932-) Chinese

Works on paper

£753	$1281	€1100	Evening view of Yen'an (67x45cm-26x18in) s.i.d.1977 seal hanging scroll. 7-Nov-3 Dr Fritz Nagel, Stuttgart #974/R

HUANG SHEN (1682-1772) Chinese

Works on paper

£3475	$5803	€5074	Plum blossoms (81x45cm-32x18in) s.i. ink col. 26-Oct-3 Christie's, Hong Kong #484/R (HK.D 45000)
£4979	$8962	€7269	Flower seller (111x41cm-44x16in) s.i.d.1727 ink col hanging scroll. 25-Apr-4 Christie's, Hong Kong #429a/R est:40000-60000 (HK.D 70000)
£32432	$54162	€47351	Scenes from travels (25x41cm-10x16in) s.i. ink col set of 12. 26-Oct-3 Christie's, Hong Kong #462/R (HK.D 420000)

HUANG YONGYU (1924-) Chinese

Works on paper

£3861	$6448	€5637	Ethnic girl (54x40cm-21x16in) s.d.Octoboer 1959 ink col. 27-Oct-3 Sotheby's, Hong Kong #374/R est:50000-70000 (HK.D 50000)

HUANG ZHONG YANG (1949-) Chinese

£479	$800	€699	Jesus and the old peasant (61x122cm-24x48in) s.d. 11-Oct-3 Nadeau, Windsor #4/R

Works on paper

£240	$400	€350	Tibet market place 1 (43x58cm-17x23in) s.d. W/C. 11-Oct-3 Nadeau, Windsor #5/R
£359	$600	€524	Tibet market place 2 (53x74cm-21x29in) s.d. W/C. 11-Oct-3 Nadeau, Windsor #3/R
£719	$1200	€1050	In sunshine (43x66cm-17x26in) s.d. W/C. 11-Oct-3 Nadeau, Windsor #6/R
£719	$1200	€1050	Song of childhood (66x89cm-26x35in) s.d. W/C. 11-Oct-3 Nadeau, Windsor #7/R

HUANG ZHOU (1925-1997) Chinese

Works on paper

£4189	$7373	€6200	Donkeys (94x49cm-37x19in) s.i.d.1959 seals Indian ink hanging scroll. 21-May-4 Dr Fritz Nagel, Stuttgart #1194/R est:900

HUANG, Anton (1935-1985) Javanese

£4248	$7690	€6202	Kupu - Kupu di Taman (41x56cm-16x22in) s.d.80 s.i.d.Sept 1980 verso. 3-Apr-4 Glerum, Singapore #32/R est:8000-11000 (S.D 13000)

HUARD, Frans (19th C) French

Works on paper

£500	$880	€730	The bravo (65x45cm-26x18in) s. W/C arched top. 20-May-4 Bonhams, Edinburgh #345

HUASOS, Chillan (19/20th C) New Zealander?

£521	$828	€761	At a wayside inn (15x21cm-6x8in) d.1895 verso. 1-May-3 Dunbar Sloane, Wellington #329 (NZ.D 1500)

HUAULT, Pierre (younger) (1647-1698) Swiss

Miniatures

£1000	$1730	€1460	Young gentleman in blue silk gown and purple silk cloak (3cm-1in) s.d.1682 on gold oval prov. 9-Dec-3 Christie's, London #11 est:1000-1500

HUBACEK, William (19th C) American

£2989	$5500	€4364	Still life with apples, plums, bananas and watermelon (50x86cm-20x34in) s.d.1911 prov. 8-Jun-4 Bonhams & Butterfields, San Francisco #4195/R est:6000-8000

HUBACHER, Hermann (1885-1976) Swiss

Sculpture

£961	$1720	€1403	Mother and child (15cm-6in) s. st.f.m Pastori bronze lit. 26-May-4 Sotheby's, Zurich #94/R est:1800-2500 (S.FR 2200)
£1048	$1876	€1530	Horse's head (17cm-7in) mono. bronze lit. 26-May-4 Sotheby's, Zurich #117/R est:1500-2000 (S.FR 2400)
£1572	$2814	€2295	Girl with mirror (24cm-9in) s. st.f.M Pastori bronze lit. 26-May-4 Sotheby's, Zurich #56/R est:2000-2500 (S.FR 3600)

HUBACHER, Rena (1916-1987) Swiss

£323	$579	€472	Day in Kenya (90x110cm-35x43in) s. 12-May-4 Dobiaschofsky, Bern #623/R (S.FR 750)

HUBBARD, Bennett (attrib) (1806-1870) British

£884	$1600	€1291	Palomino horse in a mountainous landscape (58x69cm-23x27in) 30-Mar-4 Christie's, Rockefeller NY #44/R est:1000-1500

HUBBARD, Eric Hesketh (1892-1957) British

£1200	$1908	€1752	Panorama of Arundel (39x107cm-15x42in) s. 10-Sep-3 Sotheby's, Olympia #161/R est:700-1000

HUBBARD, J (19th C) ?

£1000	$1580	€1450	King Lear and Cordelia on the heath (112x142cm-44x56in) 4-Sep-3 Christie's, Kensington #239/R est:1000-1500

HUBBARD, John (1931-) American

Works on paper

£330	$551	€482	Spring colours (26x25cm-10x10in) s.d.1983 mixed media prov. 16-Oct-3 Lawrence, Crewkerne #759

HUBBARD, Lydia M B (1849-1911) American

£2235	$4000	€3263	Yellow flowers on a tabletop (43x56cm-17x22in) s.d.99. 6-May-4 Shannon's, Milford #226/R est:2000-3000

HUBBARD, Richard William (1817-1888) American

£2060	$3750	€3008	Landscape (36x61cm-14x24in) s.d.1885. 7-Feb-4 Sloans & Kenyon, Bethesda #1313/R est:3000-4000

HUBBARD, Whitney Myron (1875-1965) American

£929	$1700	€1356	Two ladies by the water (25x20cm-10x8in) board. 31-Jan-4 South Bay, Long Island #126
£1215	$2200	€1774	Beach scene (20x25cm-8x10in) oil on cardboard exhib. 3-Apr-4 South Bay, Long Island #123
£1381	$2500	€2016	Seascape (30x41cm-12x16in) exhib. 3-Apr-4 South Bay, Long Island #122
£1628	$2800	€2377	Seascape (41x51cm-16x20in) s. board. 6-Dec-3 South Bay, Long Island #137/R

Works on paper

£640	$1100	€934	Rocks and surf, Montauk (28x33cm-11x13in) s.verso W/C. 6-Dec-3 South Bay, Long Island #273/R

HUBBELL, Charles H (20th C) American

£459	$850	€670	North American 0-47 (46x61cm-18x24in) s.d.1937 canvasboard. 13-Mar-4 DeFina, Austinburg #960/R

HUBBELL, Henry Salem (1870-1949) American

£349	$600	€510	Beginning of the trail (30x20cm-12x8in) s.i.d.1895 canvas on board. 6-Dec-3 Neal Auction Company, New Orleans #623
£2793	$5000	€4078	Portrait of Ricard W Sears (145x97cm-57x38in) s. 21-Mar-4 Hindman, Chicago #792/R est:6000-8000
£7880	$14500	€11820	Landscape river view from Alton Bluffs (76x89cm-30x35in) s. 26-Jun-4 Selkirks, St. Louis #154/R est:6000-8000

HUBBUCH, Karl (1891-1979) German

£3333	$6133	€5000	Roundabout (44x82cm-17x32in) s.i. panel painted c.1960. 12-Jun-4 Villa Grisebach, Berlin #300/R est:6000-8000
£32000	$58880	€46720	Afternoon tea (21x31cm-8x12in) s. verso panel painted 1933-35 prov.exhib.lit. 22-Jun-4 Sotheby's, London #173/R est:25000-35000

Works on paper

£267	$477	€400	The outing (12x22cm-5x9in) mono. lit. 14-May-4 Schloss Ahlden, Ahlden #2923/R
£267	$477	€400	Sketch for illustration for fairy tale (27x19cm-11x7in) i. Indian ink W/C lit. 14-May-4 Schloss Ahlden, Ahlden #2934/R
£350	$594	€500	Figure sketch (17x22cm-7x9in) mono. biro feltpen. 29-Nov-3 Villa Grisebach, Berlin #583/R
£382	$623	€550	Hilde (42x31cm-17x12in) mono. Indian ink col pen. 27-Sep-3 Dr Fritz Nagel, Stuttgart #9222/R
£467	$840	€700	Interior - table and chairs (38x38cm-15x15in) st.sig. verso graphite board double-sided. 24-Apr-4 Dr Lehr, Berlin #175/R

£733 $1320 €1100 Martha sitting in chair (22x27cm-9x11in) pen wash. 24-Apr-4 Dr Lehr, Berlin #174/R
£872 $1562 €1300 Before bathing (42x33cm-17x13in) s. i.d.1931 verso pen prov. 25-May-4 Dorotheum, Vienna #182/R
£887 $1401 €1250 For happy souls (29x47cm-11x19in) s. Indian ink W/C. 22-Jul-3 Sigalas, Stuttgart #299/R

HUBER, Carl Rudolf (1839-1896) Austrian
£5667 $10257 €8500 Hunting dogs (64x79cm-25x31in) s. bars d. 1-Apr-4 Van Ham, Cologne #1444/R est:3300

HUBER, Conrad (1752-1830) German
£2552 $4261 €3700 The last supper (69x89cm-27x35in) s.i.d.1825 verso lit. 10-Jul-3 Allgauer, Kempten #2539/R est:3500
£3819 $6226 €5500 Jacob and Rachel (52x70cm-20x28in) s.d.1810. 25-Sep-3 Dr Fritz Nagel, Stuttgart #1276/R est:10300

HUBER, Conrad (attrib) (1752-1830) German
£533 $960 €800 Noli me tangere - Risen Christ appearing to Mary Magdalen (60x41cm-24x16in) lit. 22-Apr-4 Allgauer, Kempten #3581/R

HUBER, E (?) ?
£4027 $7409 €6000 Italian coastline (38x63cm-15x25in) s. 25-Mar-4 Dr Fritz Nagel, Stuttgart #720/R est:900

HUBER, Eduard (19/20th C) Austrian
£295 $490 €428 Peacock with hens before barn (24x34cm-9x13in) s.i.d.1915 board. 13-Jun-3 Zofingen, Switzerland #2465/R (S.FR 650)

HUBER, Enrico (19th C) Italian?
£4698 $8644 €7000 Fishing boats in Bay of Naples (50x67cm-20x26in) s. 25-Mar-4 Dr Fritz Nagel, Stuttgart #719/R est:900

HUBER, Ernst (1895-1960) Austrian
£1477 $2732 €2200 Landscape with dark clouds (32x42cm-13x17in) s.d.22 board. 9-Mar-4 Dorotheum, Vienna #32/R est:4400-5800
£2961 $5447 €4500 Zinkenbach on Wolfgang Lake (40x50cm-16x20in) s.d.38. 22-Jun-4 Wiener Kunst Auktionen, Vienna #80/R est:4500
£3352 $6000 €4894 Village amid rolling hills (60x82cm-24x32in) s. masonite. 6-May-4 Doyle, New York #67/R est:6000-8000
£3472 $5903 €5000 Still life of flowers (79x59cm-31x23in) s.d.46. 28-Oct-3 Wiener Kunst Auktionen, Vienna #101/R est:7000-14000
£3901 $6514 €5500 Village in Muhlviertel (34x42cm-13x17in) i. 14-Oct-3 Dorotheum, Vienna #77/R est:3600-5000
£4225 $7394 €6000 Country people resting (70x100cm-28x39in) s.i.d.1933 verso prov. 19-Dec-3 Dorotheum, Vienna #106/R est:5000-8000
£4545 $7727 €6500 Village in winter (50x60cm-20x24in) s. prov. 26-Nov-3 Dorotheum, Vienna #16/R est:6000-10000
£4667 $8400 €7000 Resting after the harvest (48x70cm-19x28in) s.d.23. 21-Apr-4 Dorotheum, Vienna #55/R est:6000-8000
£5944 $10105 €8500 Later summer day in the country (60x80cm-24x31in) s. 26-Nov-3 Dorotheum, Vienna #187/R est:4500-7000
£6040 $10812 €9000 Freistadt in winter (92x73cm-36x29in) s.i.d.1928. 27-May-4 Hassfurther, Vienna #51/R est:10000-15000
£8667 $15600 €13000 South Seas (56x73cm-22x29in) s.d.25 board prov. 21-Apr-4 Dorotheum, Vienna #73/R est:5000-8000
Works on paper
£280 $476 €400 Village street (22x30cm-9x12in) s. pencil. 27-Nov-3 Dorotheum, Linz #564
£355 $592 €500 Landscape (34x52cm-13x20in) s.i.d.1933 W/C gouache. 14-Oct-3 Dorotheum, Vienna #102/R
£355 $592 €500 Old farmer house in Florida (34x42cm-13x17in) mono.i. Indian ink bodycol. 16-Oct-3 Dorotheum, Salzburg #889/R
£526 $968 €800 Near Tucson, Arizona. Naples (47x63cm-19x25in) one mono. one mono.i.d.25 W/C double-sided. 22-Jun-4 Wiener Kunst Auktionen, Vienna #120/R
£532 $888 €750 Huts in snowy wooded landscape (44x53cm-17x21in) s. wash Indian ink brush htd white. 16-Oct-3 Dorotheum, Salzburg #1006/R
£533 $960 €800 Old Donau (43x58cm-17x23in) mono. w/C. 21-Apr-4 Dorotheum, Vienna #148/R
£669 $1198 €950 Mountain village with figures (50x65cm-20x26in) s. mixed media lit. 8-Jan-4 Allgauer, Kempten #2423/R
£845 $1479 €1200 Harbour (47x63cm-19x25in) s. W/C. 19-Dec-3 Dorotheum, Vienna #137/R
£855 $1574 €1300 Castle Orth (44x60cm-17x24in) s.i.d.42 W/C. 22-Jun-4 Wiener Kunst Auktionen, Vienna #118/R
£933 $1671 €1400 Freistadt (43x58cm-17x23in) s. W/C. 13-May-4 Dorotheum, Linz #550/R
£987 $1816 €1500 Traunsee (43x56cm-17x22in) s.i.d.1942 W/C. 22-Jun-4 Wiener Kunst Auktionen, Vienna #119/R est:1500
£1208 $2235 €1800 Barn in Salzburg (48x62cm-19x24in) mono.i. verso. 9-Mar-4 Dorotheum, Vienna #115/R est:2000-2500
£1408 $2465 €2000 View of a seaside village (44x60cm-17x24in) collage board. 19-Dec-3 Dorotheum, Vienna #52/R est:2000-2800
£1418 $2369 €2000 Wagrain (45x60cm-18x24in) s.i.d.1938 W/C gouache. 14-Oct-3 Dorotheum, Vienna #101/R est:900-1200
£1477 $2732 €2200 Wagrein (41x52cm-16x20in) s. W/C col chk. 9-Mar-4 Dorotheum, Vienna #78/R est:2000-2600

HUBER, Hermann (1888-1968) Swiss
£271 $462 €396 Portrait of a man (86x71cm-34x28in) 25-Nov-3 Germann, Zurich #811 (S.FR 600)
£318 $528 €461 Girl in garden (53x47cm-21x19in) s. i. verso prov. 13-Jun-3 Zofingen, Switzerland #2883/R (S.FR 700)
£339 $567 €495 Strawberry strands (27x32cm-11x13in) s.d.1944. 24-Jun-3 Germann, Zurich #980 (S.FR 750)
£367 $613 €532 Apple harvest (127x95cm-50x37in) s. 23-Jun-3 Philippe Schuler, Zurich #8436 (S.FR 800)
£611 $1125 €892 Flowers (42x55cm-17x22in) s.d.1942. 8-Jun-4 Germann, Zurich #811 (S.FR 1400)
£661 $1123 €965 Still life of flowers in stone jug (74x60cm-29x24in) s.d.41. 7-Nov-3 Dobiaschofsky, Bern #161/R (S.FR 1500)
£724 $1158 €1057 Summer landscape (90x71cm-35x28in) 16-Sep-3 Philippe Schuler, Zurich #5623 est:2000-3000 (S.FR 1600)
£961 $1768 €1403 Adam and Eve (50x40cm-20x16in) prov. 14-Jun-4 Philippe Schuler, Zurich #4212 (S.FR 2200)
£961 $1768 €1403 DAvid and Goliath (52x35cm-20x14in) board prov. 14-Jun-4 Philippe Schuler, Zurich #4213/R (S.FR 2200)
£1614 $2696 €2356 Early spring landscape (55x48cm-22x19in) s. i. stretcher. 24-Oct-3 Hans Widmer, St Gallen #138/R est:2000-3800 (S.FR 3600)
£1900 $3231 €2774 Landscape (100x58cm-39x23in) mono. prov. 25-Nov-3 Germann, Zurich #46/R est:3000-5000 (S.FR 4200)

HUBER, Ika (1953-) German
£1042 $1740 €1500 Untitled (150x130cm-59x51in) s.i.d.X/89 verso acrylic. 24-Oct-3 Ketterer, Hamburg #384/R est:1500-2000

HUBER, Johann Rudolf (1668-1748) Swiss
£786 $1431 €1148 Portrait of a young woman in a red dress (79x62cm-31x24in) 16-Jun-4 Fischer, Luzern #2188/R (S.FR 1800)
£1034 $1852 €1510 Portrait of man as hunter (80x65cm-31x26in) s.d.1719 verso. 13-May-4 Stuker, Bern #184/R est:1400-1800 (S.FR 2400)
Works on paper
£862 $1543 €1259 Landscapes in the Canton of Solothurn (20x39cm-8x15in) s. W/C over pencil two. 13-May-4 Stuker, Bern #9286 est:2000-3000 (S.FR 2000)

HUBER, Léon (1858-1928) French
£1267 $2318 €1900 Chatons surpris par les ecrevisses (39x45cm-15x18in) s. 6-Jun-4 Osenat, Fontainebleau #245 est:2000-2500
£1690 $2958 €2400 Composition aux fruits et a la bouteille (38x46cm-15x18in) s. 21-Dec-3 Thierry & Lannon, Brest #327 est:1500-2000
£2353 $4000 €3435 Still life with fruit, cheese and wine on a table (49x65cm-19x26in) s. 19-Nov-3 Bonhams & Butterfields, San Francisco #111/R
£2961 $5359 €4500 Jeunes chats, lutrin profane (54x65cm-21x26in) s.d.10 exhib. 19-Apr-4 Horta, Bruxelles #134/R est:3000-4000
£3024 $5565 €4415 Kittens and a brass cauldron (51x63cm-20x25in) s.d.1917. 14-Jun-4 Waddingtons, Toronto #293/R est:8000-12000 (C.D 7500)

HUBER, Max (1919-1992) Swiss
Works on paper
£1399 $2378 €2000 Study for fabric (47x34cm-19x13in) s.verso collage tempera. 26-Nov-3 Pandolfini, Florence #512/R est:1000-1200
£2238 $3804 €3200 Study for fabric (44x34cm-17x13in) s.verso collage tempera Chinese ink. 26-Nov-3 Pandolfini, Florence #513/R est:1000-1200

HUBER, Rudolf (1770-1844) Swiss
Prints
£2371 $4244 €3462 Panorama from Heiligenlandhubel near Affoltern (33x116cm-13x46in) i. col lithograph. 14-May-4 Dobiaschofsky, Bern #25/R est:9000 (S.FR 5500)
Works on paper
£7759 $14276 €11328 View from Bozberg of Aare valley with Brugg and other mountains (43x135cm-17x53in) s.i. W/C. 26-Mar-4 Koller, Zurich #3319/R est:18000-20000 (S.FR 18000)

HUBER, Wilhelm (1787-1871) German
Works on paper
£734 $1226 €1050 Italian square (31x46cm-12x18in) wash pencil. 10-Oct-3 Winterberg, Heidelberg #604/R

HUBER-AUDORF, Eduard (1877-1965) German
£333 $600 €500 Lilacs in vase (73x93cm-29x37in) s.i.d. board oval lit. 22-Apr-4 Allgauer, Kempten #3582/R

HUBER-SULZEMOOS, Hans (1873-1951) German
£293 $534 €440 Small church on the hill (35x40cm-14x16in) s. i.verso panel. 1-Jul-4 Neumeister, Munich #2717

HUBERT, Ernest (1899-1988) Swiss
£323 $550 €472 Still life with onions (27x22cm-11x9in) s.d.1949. 21-Nov-3 Skinner, Boston #373/R
£409 $733 €597 Paysage a Menton - Le Borrigo (50x65cm-20x26in) s. i.d.1932 stretcher. 12-May-4 Dobiaschofsky, Bern #626/R (S.FR 950)

HUBNER, Anton (1818-1892) Austrian
£1678 $2853 €2400 High alp near Tavis with view of Karn Alps (74x100cm-29x39in) s. 20-Nov-3 Dorotheum, Salzburg #138/R est:2200-3000

HUBNER, Carl Wilhelm (1814-1879) German
£217 $400 €317 A tender farewell (66x53cm-26x21in) s. 25-Jun-4 Freeman, Philadelphia #285/R
£559 $962 €800 Smuggler in rocky mountain valley (90x16cm-35x6in) s.d.1849. 4-Dec-3 Neumeister, Munich #2773/R
£699 $1189 €1000 Winter pleasures (19x23cm-7x9in) s. 20-Nov-3 Van Ham, Cologne #1637/R
£2530 $4200 €3694 Farewell (60x76cm-24x30in) s.d.1856 panel. 30-Sep-3 Christie's, Rockefeller NY #465/R est:3000-5000

HUBNER, Franz (18th C) ?
Works on paper
£500 $785 €725 Grapes, pears and other fruits in a basket on a ledge (36x30cm-14x12in) s. bodycol htd white. 28-Aug-3 Christie's, Kensington #452/R

HUBNER, Gerhard (20th C) German?
£676 $1209 €1000 Children playing in the sand dunes (124x157cm-49x62in) s.d.1928 oabek. 8-May-4 Hans Stahl, Toestorf #65/R

HUBNER, Heinrich (1869-1945) German
£490 $832 €700 Path towards the lake (64x65cm-25x26in) mono. lit. 28-Nov-3 Schloss Ahlden, Ahlden #713/R

HUBNER, Julius (1842-1874) German
Works on paper
£306 $504 €440 The day (22x28cm-9x11in) mono.i.d.1845 ochresketch verso. 3-Jul-3 Neumeister, Munich #2680/R

HUBNER, Ulrich (1872-1932) German
£1333 $2427 €2000 View of Travemunde (80x100cm-31x39in) s.d.1910 lit. 3-Jul-4 Badum, Bamberg #47/R est:2500
£1987 $3616 €3000 River landscape with sailing boat (60x80cm-24x31in) s.d.1913. 18-Jun-4 Bolland & Marotz, Bremen #640/R est:3300
£2500 $3975 €3625 Dutch canal (69x93cm-27x37in) s. 11-Sep-3 Christie's, Kensington #23/R est:2000-4000
£2667 $4907 €4000 View of the harbour and church spire (54x65cm-21x26in) s.d.1918 s.i.verso. 12-Jun-4 Villa Grisebach, Berlin #145/R est:3500-4500
£5333 $9813 €8000 Courtyard with trees (81x70cm-32x28in) s.d.1908. 12-Jun-4 Villa Grisebach, Berlin #146/R est:5000-7000
£5667 $10427 €8500 Canal scene in Potsdam (69x92cm-27x36in) s. 12-Jun-4 Villa Grisebach, Berlin #157/R est:9000-12000

HUBRECHT, Amalda (1855-1913) Dutch
Works on paper
£578 $1052 €850 Sheep shearing (39x43cm-15x17in) s.d.87 pencil W/C htd white. 3-Feb-4 Christie's, Amsterdam #223

HUC, Eugene (1891-?) French
£483 $869 €700 Les pivoines (24x29cm-9x11in) s. panel exhib. 26-Jan-4 Gros & Delettrez, Paris #22

HUCHTENBURGH, Jan van (1647-1733) Dutch
£851 $1421 €1200 Combat entre Musulmans et Chretiens (42x45cm-17x18in) s. 17-Jun-3 Galerie Moderne, Brussels #339/R
£4054 $7135 €6000 Cavalry battle scene near a bridge (97x127cm-38x50in) 18-May-4 Sotheby's, Amsterdam #22/R est:7000-9000
£7000 $12600 €10220 Cavalry skirmish in a wooded landscape (49x63cm-19x25in) s.d.1717. 22-Apr-4 Sotheby's, London #100/R est:7000-10000
£8000 $14400 €11680 Battle scene with cavalry skirmishing before a walled town (50x67cm-20x26in) s.indis.d. 22-Apr-4 Sotheby's, London #99/R est:8000-12000
£8000 $14640 €11680 Cavalry engagement in a landscape (76x101cm-30x40in) s. 6-Jul-4 Sotheby's, Olympia #480/R est:7000-10000

HUCHTENBURGH, Jan van (attrib) (1647-1733) Dutch
£4200 $7266 €6132 Cavalry skirmish (64x89cm-25x35in) 11-Dec-3 Lyon & Turnbull, Edinburgh #99/R est:2000-3000

HUCHTENBURGH, Jan van (circle) (1647-1733) Dutch
£7000 $11900 €10220 Cavalry skirmish before ruins (163x113cm-64x44in) 29-Oct-3 Bonhams, New Bond Street #26/R est:8000-12000

HUDDLE, Nannie Zenobia (1860-1951) American
£2994 $5000 €4371 Indian paint, view of Austin (25x30cm-10x12in) board. 18-Oct-3 David Dike, Dallas #167/R est:1500-3000

HUDDLESTON, Gertie (c.1930-) Australian
Works on paper
£1953 $3652 €2930 Untitled, Ngukurr landscape (94x126cm-37x50in) synthetic polymer paint canvas prov. 26-Jul-4 Sotheby's, Melbourne #280/R est:5000-8000 (A.D 5000)
£4492 $8400 €6738 Untitled, Ngukurr landscape (92x124cm-36x49in) synthetic polymer paint canvas prov. 26-Jul-4 Sotheby's, Melbourne #281/R est:6000-8000 (A.D 11500)

HUDECEK, Antonin (1872-1941) Czechoslovakian
£788 $1308 €1150 Bouquet in vase (64x68cm-25x27in) board. 4-Oct-3 Dorotheum, Prague #121/R est:26000-38000 (C.KR 36000)
£2531 $4455 €3797 Brook in forest (95x135cm-37x53in) s. 22-May-4 Dorotheum, Prague #63/R est:80000-120000 (C.KR 120000)

HUDLER, August (1868-1905) German
Sculpture
£2238 $3737 €3200 Bailleur (53cm-21in) s.d.1900 pat bronze. 7-Oct-3 Livinec, Gaudcheau & Jezequel, Rennes #160

HUDON, Normand (1929-1997) Canadian
£402 $671 €583 L'impossible partie d'eches (41x51cm-16x20in) s.d.66. 17-Jun-3 Pinneys, Montreal #4 (C.D 900)
£1563 $2609 €2266 Le medecin de campagne (40x51cm-16x20in) s.i.d.84 board. 17-Jun-3 Pinneys, Montreal #120 est:1400-1800 (C.D 3500)

HUDSON RIVER SCHOOL, American
£5294 $9000 €7729 Excursion (71x91cm-28x36in) 29-Nov-3 Carlsen Gallery, Greenville #575/R

HUDSON, Benjamin (attrib) (fl.1847-1862) British
£14000 $22820 €20440 Portrait of Maharajah Bahadur Jotindra Tagore, wearing a jamewar shawl (76x61cm-30x24in) 24-Sep-3 Christie's, London #77/R est:12000-16000

HUDSON, Charles Bradford (1865-1938) American
£2310 $4250 €3373 Laguna sunset (51x76cm-20x30in) s. i. stretcher. 8-Jun-4 Bonhams & Butterfields, San Francisco #4320/R est:3000-5000

HUDSON, Eric (1864-1932) American
£5083 $9200 €7421 Schooner (61x71cm-24x28in) s. 16-Apr-4 James Julia, Fairfield #34/R est:1000-2000

HUDSON, Grace Carpenter (1865-1937) American
£978 $1800 €1428 Woman walking a dog in a field (23x18cm-9x7in) s. board prov. 8-Jun-4 Bonhams & Butterfields, San Francisco #4227/R est:3000-5000
£1190 $2250 €1737 Chumash Indian reed hut with kneeling figure (18x13cm-7x5in) s. board prov. 17-Feb-4 John Moran, Pasadena #123a/R est:2000-3000
£1341 $2400 €1958 Sun house (20x25cm-8x10in) s. i.verso board prov. 16-Mar-4 Matthew's, Oregon #92/R est:1200-1500
£4545 $8500 €6636 Annie (15x13cm-6x5in) s. board lit. 24-Jul-4 Coeur d'Alene, Hayden #272/R est:5000-10000
£7821 $14000 €11419 Guarding the baby (18x13cm-7x5in) s.d.1905 s.i.verso board. 14-May-4 Skinner, Boston #213/R est:3000-5000
£8696 $16000 €12696 Abalone (35x27cm-14x11in) s.i.d.08 prov.lit. 8-Jun-4 Bonhams & Butterfields, San Francisco #4167/R est:12000-16000
£10588 $18000 €15458 Little piper (25x15cm-10x6in) s.d.95 canvas on board prov.lit. 1-Nov-3 Santa Fe Art, Santa Fe #169/R est:20000-25000
Works on paper
£750 $1200 €1095 Girl sitting on a fence (61x46cm-24x18in) s.d.81 pencil W/C. 18-May-3 Auctions by the Bay, Alameda #1139/R

HUDSON, Hannah Maria (19th C) British?
£568 $1000 €829 Portrait of Mrs S A Butterfield (46x36cm-18x14in) 21-May-4 North East Auctions, Portsmouth #636/R

HUDSON, John Bradley (jnr) (1832-1903) American
£1235 $2000 €1791 View of Casco Bay (25x34cm-10x13in) s.d.August 31 1880. 8-Aug-3 Barridorf, Portland #69/R est:2000-3000

HUDSON, Thomas (1701-1779) British
£3611 $6500 €5272 Portrait of a lady (67x52cm-26x20in) prov. 21-Jan-4 Doyle, New York #109/R est:4000-6000
£4500 $8280 €6570 Portrait of gentleman, wearing grey coat (76x63cm-30x25in) painted oval. 26-Mar-4 Sotheby's, London #10/R est:4000-6000
£5556 $10000 €8112 Portrait of Right Hon Sir Thomas Parker (141x114cm-56x45in) s.d.1749 prov. 24-Apr-4 Weschler, Washington #547/R est:10000-15000
£9000 $16380 €13140 Portrait of a lady (125x100cm-49x39in) 1-Jul-4 Sotheby's, London #118/R est:10000-15000
£12000 $20400 €17520 Portrait of George Booth, 2nd earl of Warrington (124x101cm-49x40in) i. 27-Nov-3 Sotheby's, London #140/R est:6000-8000
£13889 $23611 €20000 Duke of Kent (124x100cm-49x39in) i. prov. 28-Oct-3 Wiener Kunst Auktionen, Vienna #2/R est:20000-50000
£19000 $32300 €27740 Portrait of Sir Watkin William Wynn, 3rd Bt. wearing dark blue coat and red trousers (126x102cm-50x40in) i.verso prov. 25-Nov-3 Christie's, London #27/R est:12000-18000

HUDSON, Thomas (attrib) (1701-1779) British
£1946 $3250 €2841 Portrait of a lady, said to be Miss Scotts (76x64cm-30x25in) 20-Jun-3 Freeman, Philadelphia #240/R est:1000-1500
£2113 $3507 €3000 Portrait femme en buste au tricorne fleuri (74x62cm-29x24in) 16-Jun-3 E & Eve, Paris #55/R
£12000 $21600 €17520 Portrait of a boy with his dog (165x105cm-65x41in) 21-Jan-4 Sotheby's, Olympia #49/R est:6000-8000

HUDSON, Thomas (style) (1701-1779) British
£9000 $15030 €13140 Portrait of three children, and their pet dog (112x163cm-44x64in) 14-Oct-3 Sotheby's, London #445/R est:4000-6000

HUDSON, William J L (1779-1834) British
Miniatures
£1630 $3000 €2380 British military officer bearing a Union Jack (10x8cm-4x3in) d.1826 rectangular frame. 27-Mar-4 New Orleans Auction, New Orleans #981/R est:1800-2500

HUE, Charles Desire (1825-?) French
£6954 $12725 €10500 Le marchand de tissus (46x64cm-18x25in) s.d.1864 panel. 9-Apr-4 Claude Aguttes, Neuilly #49/R est:5000-7000

HUE, Madelaine (1882-1943) French
£1457 $2652 €2200 Le port de Rouen (63x86cm-25x34in) 15-Jun-4 Blanchet, Paris #125 est:400-500

HUEBER, Pierre Paul (20th C) French
£323 $579 €472 Paysage de Provence avec cabanon de Jean Moulin (24x35cm-9x14in) s. i. stretcher. 12-May-4 Dobiaschofsky, Bern #3657 (S.FR 750)

HUEBER, Wolfgang (1950-) German
£389 $700 €568 Dunkelbraunes (74x56cm-29x22in) oil pastel on paper prov. 24-Apr-4 Slotin Folk Art, Buford #370/R
£556 $1000 €812 Keene anxd (56x74cm-22x29in) oil pastel graphite prov. 24-Apr-4 Slotin Folk Art, Buford #369/R est:1000-3000

HUEBLER, Douglas (1924-1997) American
Works on paper
£2083 $3750 €3041 Untitled (12x13cm-5x5in) s.d.1978 graphite ink col pencil. 24-Apr-4 David Rago, Lambertville #114/R est:600-1200

HUEBSCHER, Konrad (1858-1941) Swiss
£281 $477 €410 Avenue (27x38cm-11x15in) mono. vedute. 28-Nov-3 Zofingen, Switzerland #3030 (S.FR 620)

HUET, Christophe (1694-1759) French
£8333 $15000 €12166 Spaniel retrieving a duck from a pond (95x127cm-37x50in) s.d.1728 prov. 23-Jan-4 Christie's, Rockefeller NY #2/R est:10000-15000
Works on paper
£2925 $5236 €4300 Singe predicateur dans un basse-cour, renards desguises en cure caches (29x36cm-11x14in) gouache. 18-Mar-4 Christie's, Paris #246/R est:3000-5000

HUET, Christophe (attrib) (1694-1759) French
Works on paper
£510 $913 €750 Tetes de loup et de singe (25x16cm-10x6in) sanguine. 17-Mar-4 Maigret, Paris #53/R

HUET, Ernestine (19th C) French
£1667 $2833 €2400 Flute lesson (64x48cm-25x19in) bears sig. 28-Oct-3 Dorotheum, Vienna #168/R est:2000-2500

HUET, Jacques (20th C) French?
£403 $749 €600 Peniches sur la Seine (54x65cm-21x26in) s. 7-Mar-4 Lesieur & Le Bars, Le Havre #141
£470 $874 €700 Peniches a Rouen (60x73cm-24x29in) s. 7-Mar-4 Lesieur & Le Bars, Le Havre #140
£503 $936 €750 Le port de Rouen (54x73cm-21x29in) s. 7-Mar-4 Lesieur & Le Bars, Le Havre #142
£586 $979 €850 La Seine a Duclair (46x65cm-18x26in) s. 11-Nov-3 Lesieur & Le Bars, Le Havre #64

HUET, Jean Baptiste (1745-1811) French
Works on paper
£437 $800 €638 Studies of sheep (18x25cm-7x10in) s.d.1802 brush brown ink wash. 29-Jan-4 Swann Galleries, New York #239/R
£728 $1326 €1100 Ane, mouton et chevres au repos (37x50cm-15x20in) s. black crayon htd white gouache. 16-Jun-4 Piasa, Paris #116
£861 $1567 €1300 Tete de coq (14x11cm-6x4in) d.17 sebre 1787 sanguine black crayon prov. 16-Jun-4 Piasa, Paris #115/R
£909 $1545 €1300 Cows and sheep in landscape (14x13cm-6x5in) s.d.1769 pen wash. 27-Nov-3 Bassenge, Berlin #5448/R
£1268 $2193 €1800 Cour de ferme animee (28x43cm-11x17in) s.d.1789 black crayon white chk. 12-Dec-3 Renaud, Paris #44/R est:1500-2000
£1818 $3091 €2600 Two sheep's heads (13x30cm-5x12in) bears i. ochre. 27-Nov-3 Bassenge, Berlin #5447/R est:2400
£1892 $3330 €2800 The toilet. Bath of Venus (14x9cm-6x4in) one s.d.1789 pen brwn ink grey wash black chk pair exhib.lit. 19-May-4 Sotheby's, Amsterdam #157/R est:1800-2200
£2113 $3655 €3000 Trophee, un coq (40x25cm-16x10in) s. black crayon pastel. 12-Dec-3 Renaud, Paris #43/R est:3000-4000
£2238 $3849 €3200 Putti trayant une chevre. Une jeune femme jouant du tambourin (8x33cm-3x13in) blk chk pair prov. 2-Dec-3 Christie's, Paris #516 est:600-800
£2500 $4575 €3650 Wooded autumn landscape with shepherds and their flock (34x45cm-13x18in) s.d.1768 blk chk brown green wash prov. 8-Jul-4 Sotheby's, London #156/R est:3000-5000
£2550 $4693 €3800 Paysan et troupeau (23x28cm-9x11in) s.d.1772 pierre noire sanguine prov. 24-Mar-4 Claude Boisgirard, Paris #21/R est:2000
£3889 $7000 €5678 Pair of shepherds resting by a tree, and by a fountain (14x17cm-6x7in) s.d.1786 pen brown ink wash pair prov.lit. 22-Jan-4 Christie's, Rockefeller NY #99/R est:5000-7000
£7483 $13395 €11000 Bouquet de fleurs (33x28cm-13x11in) s.d.1770 col crayon. 19-Mar-4 Piasa, Paris #83/R est:4000-5000
£19048 $34095 €28000 Bouquet de fleurs (33x28cm-13x11in) s.d.1770 col crayon. 19-Mar-4 Piasa, Paris #86/R est:4000-5000

HUET, Jean Baptiste (attrib) (1745-1811) French
Works on paper
£700 $1211 €1022 Five studies of a goat's head (18x24cm-7x9in) red chk. 12-Dec-3 Christie's, Kensington #449
£2059 $3500 €3006 Animals and woman (23x31cm-9x12in) chk prov. 25-Nov-3 Christie's, Rockefeller NY #511/R est:1000-1500

HUET, Nicolas (younger) (1770-?) French
Works on paper
£24000 $43920 €35040 American cougar (31x45cm-12x18in) s.d.1811 graphite W/C bodycol htd gum arabic. 6-Jul-4 Christie's, London #148/R est:20000-40000

HUET, Paul (1803-1869) French
£400 $724 €600 Les talus de petit ravin (19x15cm-7x6in) 30-Mar-4 Rossini, Paris #401
£486 $871 €720 Pluie d'orage en montagne (21x29cm-8x11in) s. i.verso canvas on panel. 5-May-4 Coutau Begarie, Paris #45
£933 $1689 €1400 Rochers en foret de Fontainebleau (32x50cm-13x20in) painted c.1849 lit. 30-Mar-4 Rossini, Paris #436/R
£933 $1689 €1400 Chaville, effet d'orage vu de sa fenetre (23x33cm-9x13in) cardboard. 30-Mar-4 Rossini, Paris #583/R
£933 $1708 €1400 Eaux de Royat (21x20cm-8x8in) panel. 6-Jun-4 Osenat, Fontainebleau #35
£1000 $1810 €1500 Cavalier au clair de lune (26x37cm-10x15in) panel painted c.1861-62. 30-Mar-4 Rossini, Paris #599/R est:1500-2500
£1067 $1931 €1600 Deux chevaux de cirque (11x22cm-4x9in) canvas on cardboard painted c.1826. 30-Mar-4 Rossini, Paris #422/R est:600-1000
£1133 $2051 €1700 Village a la Lisiere des Bois (11x25cm-4x10in) canvas on cardboard. 30-Mar-4 Rossini, Paris #491 est:500-800
£1200 $2172 €1800 Paysage d'Auvergne, vers le Mont Dore (21x31cm-8x12in) st.verso canvas on panel. 30-Mar-4 Rossini, Paris #414/R est:1000-1500
£1200 $2172 €1800 Normandie, arc-en-ciel (16x27cm-6x11in) panel. 30-Mar-4 Rossini, Paris #459/R est:800-1200
£1200 $2172 €1800 Crepuscule avec personnage en pantalaon rouge (18x27cm-7x11in) oil paper on canvas. 30-Mar-4 Rossini, Paris #525/R est:800-1500
£1267 $2293 €1900 Etude de figures pour l'inondation a Saint-Cloud et le gouffre (50x61cm-20x24in) 30-Mar-4 Rossini, Paris #550/R est:800-1200
£1333 $2413 €2000 L'echelle et le panier (23x33cm-9x13in) st. W/C. 30-Mar-4 Rossini, Paris #415 est:600-1000
£1333 $2413 €2000 Vieilles maisons en Auvergne, Monferrand (34x25cm-13x10in) s. 30-Mar-4 Rossini, Paris #500/R est:2000-3000
£1333 $2413 €2000 Le Mont Dore (16x43cm-6x17in) exhib. 30-Mar-4 Rossini, Paris #594/R est:1800-3000
£1467 $2655 €2200 Soir a Trouville (26x32cm-10x13in) s. 30-Mar-4 Rossini, Paris #579/R est:1000-1500
£1594 $2614 €2200 Edmee sur son ane, la fille de Paul Huet (36x42cm-14x17in) s. panel painted c.1852. 11-May-3 Osenat, Fontainebleau #80/R est:2200-2500
£1667 $3017 €2500 Le retour du troupeau, foret de Barbizon (24x39cm-9x15in) oil paper on panel. 30-Mar-4 Rossini, Paris #479/R est:700-1000
£1800 $3258 €2700 En Ile de France, soir d'orage, vallee de la Seine (11x25cm-4x10in) st. W/C. 30-Mar-4 Rossini, Paris #589/R est:600-1000
£2133 $3861 €3200 Parc de Saint-cloud (23x49cm-9x19in) cardboard prov.exhib. 30-Mar-4 Rossini, Paris #602/R est:2500-4000
£2333 $4223 €3500 Enfants Bretons, Douarnenez (38x28cm-15x11in) cardboard exhib.lit. 30-Mar-4 Rossini, Paris #531/R est:1500-2500
£2400 $4344 €3600 Vieielles maisons a Rouen (41x32cm-16x13in) exhib. 30-Mar-4 Rossini, Paris #418/R est:2000-3000
£2533 $4585 €3800 Paysage (29x40cm-11x16in) oil paper on canvas exhib. 30-Mar-4 Rossini, Paris #509/R est:1500-2500
£2533 $4585 €3800 La route de Sceaux vers Fontenay-aux-Roses (15x25cm-6x10in) st.i. W/C. 30-Mar-4 Rossini, Paris #605/R est:700-1200
£2536 $4159 €3500 Les pins en Normandie (29x38cm-11x15in) s.i.d.1868 panel. 11-May-3 Osenat, Fontainebleau #81/R est:4500-4800
£2667 $4827 €4000 Talus a Chaville (34x50cm-13x20in) cardboard on canvas exhib. 30-Mar-4 Rossini, Paris #588/R est:1200-1800
£2781 $5062 €4200 Interferences (26x34cm-10x13in) paper. 18-Jun-4 Piasa, Paris #57/R est:2500-2800
£3067 $5551 €4600 La cabane de l'Ile Seguin (24x32cm-9x13in) cardboard lit. 30-Mar-4 Rossini, Paris #442/R est:1800-3000
£3200 $5792 €4800 Orage debutant sur la manche (26x40cm-10x16in) oil paper on cardboard. 30-Mar-4 Rossini, Paris #406/R est:1000-1500
£3333 $6033 €5000 La laita a maree haute dans la foret de Quimperle (34x51cm-13x20in) panel lit. 30-Mar-4 Rossini, Paris #427/R est:3000-5000
£3333 $6033 €5000 Soleil couchant, Trouville (27x37cm-11x15in) painted c.1858 exhib.lit. 30-Mar-4 Rossini, Paris #493/R est:1200-1800
£3333 $6033 €5000 Lavoir en foret, pres de Pont-Audemer, effet d'automne (34x55cm-13x22in) panel prov.exhib.lit. 30-Mar-4 Rossini, Paris #558/R est:2000-3000
£3667 $6637 €5500 L'allee des Ormes au parc de Saint-Cloud (40x52cm-16x20in) cardboard on panel painted c.1822 exhib. 30-Mar-4 Rossini, Paris #561/R est:3000-5000
£3867 $6999 €5800 Fleurs (33x41cm-13x16in) painted c.1828-1830 prov. 30-Mar-4 Rossini, Paris #522/R est:2000-3000
£4000 $7240 €6000 La plaine de Caen vue des Falaises des Dives (52x78cm-20x31in) s. 30-Mar-4 Rossini, Paris #606/R est:6000-9000
£4333 $7843 €6500 Etude de hetre, sous-bois Compiegne (19x15cm-7x6in) canvas on panel painted c.1838. 30-Mar-4 Rossini, Paris #469/R est:1000-1500
£4800 $8688 €7200 Villa Massimo (33x51cm-13x20in) s. sold with three anonymous studies on one sheet. 30-Mar-4 Rossini, Paris #477/R est:6000-10000
£4800 $8688 €7200 Lisiere en foret de Compiegne (21x27cm-8x11in) cardboard painted c.1832. 30-Mar-4 Rossini, Paris #547/R est:1200-1800
£4867 $8809 €7300 La mare, foret de Compiegne (23x34cm-9x13in) s. painted c.1837. 30-Mar-4 Rossini, Paris #504/R est:3000-5000
£5333 $9653 €8000 L'orage a la find du jour ou le cavalier (46x68cm-18x27in) canvas on panel exhib.lit. 30-Mar-4 Rossini, Paris #538/R est:5000-8000
£5733 $10377 €8600 Souvenir d'Auvergne, soleil couchant dans les montagnes (29x44cm-11x17in) s. oil paper on canvas exhib.lit. 30-Mar-4 Rossini, Paris #534/R est:3000-5000
£5867 $10619 €8800 Soleil du matin, Ile Seguin (31x48cm-12x19in) exhib. 30-Mar-4 Rossini, Paris #565/R est:1800-3000
£8000 $14480 €12000 Bouquet (38x51cm-15x20in) s. panel. 30-Mar-4 Rossini, Paris #437/R est:4000-7000
£8000 $14480 €12000 Nature, soleil levant pres Rouen (26x37cm-10x15in) 30-Mar-4 Rossini, Paris #580/R est:3000-5000
£8333 $15083 €12500 La Laita, Bretagne (33x55cm-13x22in) exhib. 30-Mar-4 Rossini, Paris #485/R est:3000-5000
£9667 $17497 €14500 Le bois de la Haye (47x73cm-19x29in) s. prov.exhib.lit. 30-Mar-4 Rossini, Paris #512/R est:5000-8000
£10000 $18100 €15000 Bas Meudon, Le Bac (22x41cm-9x16in) s. 30-Mar-4 Rossini, Paris #498/R est:2000-3000
£10667 $19307 €16000 Vue de la Meuse a Dordrecht, Hollande (46x77cm-18x30in) s. exhib.lit. 30-Mar-4 Rossini, Paris #461/R est:4000-7000
£10667 $19307 €16000 La lisiere des etangs a Chaville (32x55cm-13x22in) painted c.1865 exhib.lit. 30-Mar-4 Rossini, Paris #530/R est:3000-5000
£13333 $24133 €20000 La cathedrale de Rouen (195x112cm-77x44in) s. exhib. 30-Mar-4 Rossini, Paris #575/R est:20000-30000
£16000 $28960 €24000 Les ormes de Saint-Cloud (36x27cm-14x11in) s. panel painted c.1823 exhib.lit. 30-Mar-4 Rossini, Paris #411/R est:4000-7000
£21333 $38613 €32000 Etude de mer dans la Manche (35x66cm-14x26in) s. panel exhib.lit. 30-Mar-4 Rossini, Paris #447/R est:8000-12000
Works on paper
£252 $403 €350 Chevaux atrteles a une charrette (11x20cm-4x8in) pen brown ink. 16-May-3 Tajan, Paris #127
£267 $483 €400 Nicois et enfant (30x23cm-12x9in) st. graphite. 30-Mar-4 Rossini, Paris #591
£267 $483 €400 Les saules (13x20cm-5x8in) pen brown ink. 30-Mar-4 Rossini, Paris #593/R
£300 $543 €450 La tour (19x10cm-7x4in) st. black crayon W/C wash. 30-Mar-4 Rossini, Paris #435
£300 $543 €450 Ane au chemin (14x10cm-6x4in) st. black crayon htd red gouache. 30-Mar-4 Rossini, Paris #438
£318 $579 €480 Paysage aux falaises (23x37cm-9x15in) crayon. 17-Jun-4 Marie & Robert, Paris #27
£320 $579 €480 Chaos (17x27cm-7x11in) st. W/C. 30-Mar-4 Rossini, Paris #586/R

£320	$579	€480	Bapteme du Christ (31x20cm-12x8in) st. pen brown ink. 30-Mar-4 Rossini, Paris #607/R
£333	$603	€500	Bergers et troupeau en bord de mer (11x17cm-4x7in) st. chl estompe. 30-Mar-4 Rossini, Paris #470
£333	$603	€500	Le pommier (11x20cm-4x8in) st. graphite. 30-Mar-4 Rossini, Paris #486/R
£333	$603	€500	Marecage ou le voyageur (9x12cm-4x5in) st. pen brown ink. 30-Mar-4 Rossini, Paris #523
£347	$627	€520	Apt (22x36cm-9x14in) st. pen brown ink wash graphite. 30-Mar-4 Rossini, Paris #457/R
£347	$627	€520	Mare aux deux arbres (8x10cm-3x4in) st. pen brownk ink. 30-Mar-4 Rossini, Paris #466
£347	$627	€520	Bort-les-Orgues (16x12cm-6x5in) st. graphite. 30-Mar-4 Rossini, Paris #526/R
£347	$627	€520	Personnage, etude pour le gouffre (28x30cm-11x12in) st. black crayon W/C. 30-Mar-4 Rossini, Paris #551
£367	$664	€550	Le cavalier (18x31cm-7x12in) st. graphite pen brown ink. 30-Mar-4 Rossini, Paris #409
£367	$664	€550	Paysage d'Italie (16x23cm-6x9in) st. pen brown ink wash. 30-Mar-4 Rossini, Paris #478
£367	$664	€550	Porteuse d'eau Nicoise (31x21cm-12x8in) st. pen brown ink wash. 30-Mar-4 Rossini, Paris #487
£367	$664	€550	L'oree du bois (11x19cm-4x7in) st. pen brown ink. 30-Mar-4 Rossini, Paris #501
£367	$664	€550	Baigneuse tressant une couronne de fleurs (29x23cm-11x9in) st. pierre noire htd white chk. 30-Mar-4 Rossini, Paris #567
£400	$632	€580	Rouen from Monte St Catherine (10x19cm-4x7in) W/C. 2-Sep-3 Bonhams, Oxford #19
£400	$724	€600	La grotte de Santa Croce, Nice (22x34cm-9x13in) st. pen brown ink. 30-Mar-4 Rossini, Paris #403/R
£400	$724	€600	Pont a Rouen. Paysage (22x18cm-9x7in) st. pencil W/C graphite double-sided. 30-Mar-4 Rossini, Paris #600/R
£433	$784	€650	Chemin a la ferme (10x13cm-4x5in) st. pen brown ink wash. 30-Mar-4 Rossini, Paris #458
£433	$784	€650	Reflets dans l'eau, le Rhone (17x23cm-7x9in) st. pen brown ink exec.c.1841. 30-Mar-4 Rossini, Paris #495
£433	$784	€650	Voilier a quai (28x15cm-11x6in) st. black crayon two sheets. 30-Mar-4 Rossini, Paris #499
£467	$845	€700	Les moulins de Clamart pres Bagneux (23x35cm-9x14in) chl white chk. 30-Mar-4 Rossini, Paris #494/R
£467	$845	€700	Paysage anime (13x21cm-5x8in) st. pen brown ink wash. 30-Mar-4 Rossini, Paris #520
£500	$905	€750	Les bois de Sevres (21x23cm-8x9in) st. W/C. 30-Mar-4 Rossini, Paris #443/R
£500	$905	€750	Barque et peupliers (13x20cm-5x8in) st. brown ink. 30-Mar-4 Rossini, Paris #513
£533	$965	€800	Bateau et maison en vallee (10x28cm-4x11in) st.i. pen brown ink exec.c.1833-1836. 30-Mar-4 Rossini, Paris #412
£533	$965	€800	Torrent et chapelle (22x35cm-9x14in) st. pen brown ink. 30-Mar-4 Rossini, Paris #425/R
£533	$965	€800	Les Marais Pointins, paysage d'Italie (28x45cm-11x18in) st. pierre noire gouache exec.c.1841-42. 30-Mar-4 Rossini, Paris #581/R
£567	$1026	€850	Vieilles maisons Normandes (24x24cm-9x9in) st. W/C exhib. 30-Mar-4 Rossini, Paris #420/R
£567	$1026	€850	Chenes (13x21cm-5x8in) st. graphite. 30-Mar-4 Rossini, Paris #440/R
£600	$1086	€900	Chaumiere et absse-cour (27x44cm-11x17in) st. black crayon. 30-Mar-4 Rossini, Paris #465/R
£600	$1086	€900	Les chenes, entree du dormoir (18x28cm-7x11in) st. chl. 30-Mar-4 Rossini, Paris #577/R
£667	$1207	€1000	Arbres et rochers pres du dormoire en foret de Fontainebleau (28x45cm-11x18in) st. pierre noire white chk exec.c.1865. 30-Mar-4 Rossini, Paris #416/R
£667	$1207	€1000	Les romarins bleus (22x35cm-9x14in) st.i. W/C exec.c.1862 exhib.lit. 30-Mar-4 Rossini, Paris #455/R
£667	$1207	€1000	Rochers de la vallee d'Apt (22x34cm-9x13in) st.i. W/C. 30-Mar-4 Rossini, Paris #460/R est:600-1000
£667	$1207	€1000	Ruisseau et rochers (23x34cm-9x13in) st. i.verso pen brown ink wash. 30-Mar-4 Rossini, Paris #570
£689	$1151	€1000	Paysanne Italienne (31x23cm-12x9in) studio st. W/C gouache prov. 17-Nov-3 Tajan, Paris #1/R
£733	$1327	€1100	Paysan a la barriere (15x12cm-6x5in) st. brown ink wash. 30-Mar-4 Rossini, Paris #428/R
£733	$1327	€1100	Le braconnier (22x35cm-9x14in) st. graphite black crayon brown ink wash. 30-Mar-4 Rossini, Paris #510/R
£733	$1327	€1100	Le vieux chene, Parc de Saint-Cloud (20x25cm-8x10in) st.i. pen brown ink wash. 30-Mar-4 Rossini, Paris #555
£800	$1448	€1200	Paysage compose (22x35cm-9x14in) st. brown ink wash. 30-Mar-4 Rossini, Paris #519/R
£800	$1448	€1200	Paysanne levant sa cruche, Bearn (35x24cm-14x9in) st. W/C exhib. 30-Mar-4 Rossini, Paris #527
£800	$1448	€1200	Les oliviers de la colline du Mont Alban avec personnages, Nice (19x29cm-7x11in) st. pen brown ink exhib. 30-Mar-4 Rossini, Paris #574/R
£867	$1569	€1300	Deux voiliers (6x10cm-2x4in) st. W/C. 30-Mar-4 Rossini, Paris #446/R
£867	$1569	€1300	Fontainebleau, le Nid de l'Aigle (21x30cm-8x12in) st.i. W/C. 30-Mar-4 Rossini, Paris #539/R
£900	$1629	€1350	Le passage difficile (31x51cm-12x20in) st. black crayon htd white. 30-Mar-4 Rossini, Paris #431/R
£933	$1689	€1400	Cascade du Mont Dorse (17x13cm-7x5in) st. W/C. 30-Mar-4 Rossini, Paris #473/R
£933	$1689	€1400	Ollioules pres Toulon, route de Marseille (25x45cm-10x18in) st.i. W/C exec.c.1838-39 exhib. 30-Mar-4 Rossini, Paris #507/R
£933	$1689	€1400	Les Pierres Druidiques, Stonehenge (22x35cm-9x14in) st. brown ink wash exhib. 30-Mar-4 Rossini, Paris #524/R
£933	$1689	€1400	Vallee d'Auvergne (11x19cm-4x7in) st. W/C. 30-Mar-4 Rossini, Paris #556/R
£1000	$1810	€1500	Le moulin Normand (25x26cm-10x10in) st. W/C exec.c.1835. 30-Mar-4 Rossini, Paris #408/R est:400-700
£1000	$1810	€1500	Une cour a Vizille, Isere (32x32cm-13x13in) st.i. W/C. 30-Mar-4 Rossini, Paris #471/R est:600-1000
£1000	$1810	€1500	L'Ile aux Anglais, Seine Port (24x32cm-9x13in) st. black crayon W/C. 30-Mar-4 Rossini, Paris #488/R est:500-800
£1000	$1810	€1500	Les Nourrices Nicoises (13x20cm-5x8in) st. W/C gouache exec.c.1838. 30-Mar-4 Rossini, Paris #492/R est:700-1200
£1000	$1810	€1500	La vallee du Mont Dore et le Puy de Dome (10x23cm-4x9in) st. W/C exec.c.1833-36. 30-Mar-4 Rossini, Paris #533/R est:600-1000
£1000	$1810	€1500	Paysage imaginaire (27x7cm-11x3in) st. W/C exhib. 30-Mar-4 Rossini, Paris #571/R est:250-350
£1000	$1810	€1500	Paysage des Alpes, Lors du Voyage de la Grande Chartreuse (16x24cm-6x9in) st. W/C. 30-Mar-4 Rossini, Paris #592/R est:600-1000
£1067	$1931	€1600	Sous-bois (13x21cm-5x8in) pen brown ink wash. 30-Mar-4 Rossini, Paris #553/R est:250-400
£1067	$1931	€1600	Nicoise (33x20cm-13x8in) st. W/C. 30-Mar-4 Rossini, Paris #559/R est:600-1000
£1067	$1931	€1600	Le retour du marche, esquisse Normande (22x37cm-9x15in) st. pastel exec.c.1825. 30-Mar-4 Rossini, Paris #562/R est:1000-1500
£1067	$1931	€1600	Personnages Nicois (38x32cm-15x13in) s. W/C. 30-Mar-4 Rossini, Paris #590/R est:1200-1800
£1133	$2051	€1700	Griffonage (29x22cm-11x9in) st. pen brown ink W/C. 30-Mar-4 Rossini, Paris #462/R est:400-700
£1133	$2051	€1700	Foret de Compiegne, mare sous les arbres (46x31cm-18x12in) bears sig. W/C. 30-Mar-4 Rossini, Paris #506/R est:1000-1500
£1133	$2051	€1700	Toulon, vue generale (34x19cm-13x7in) st. black crayon W/C. 30-Mar-4 Rossini, Paris #543/R est:1200-1800
£1133	$2051	€1700	Etretat, falaise monstrueuse (17x25cm-7x10in) st. W/C. 30-Mar-4 Rossini, Paris #564/R est:600-1000
£1133	$2051	€1700	Land's End Cap Corno (23x36cm-9x14in) st. brown ink wash exec.c.1862 exhib. 30-Mar-4 Rossini, Paris #603/R est:1000-1500
£1200	$2172	€1800	Entree d'un port Normand (8x15cm-3x6in) W/C exhib. 30-Mar-4 Rossini, Paris #584/R est:800-2000
£1200	$2172	€1800	Le treport (15x50cm-6x20in) st.i. W/C. 30-Mar-4 Rossini, Paris #585/R est:1000-1500
£1267	$2293	€1900	Le Plessis-Robinson, anciennement le Plessis-Piquet (22x35cm-9x14in) s.st.i. W/C. 30-Mar-4 Rossini, Paris #432/R est:1500-2500
£1267	$2293	€1900	Les eaux-bonnes, Pyrenees-Atlantiques (33x40cm-13x16in) st. W/C. 30-Mar-4 Rossini, Paris #434/R est:800-1200
£1267	$2293	€1900	Les rochers, Carabasco (29x47cm-11x19in) st. W/C exec.c.1837-1838. 30-Mar-4 Rossini, Paris #497/R est:800-1500
£1333	$2413	€2000	L'inondation a l'Ile Seguin (20x30cm-8x12in) st. pen brown ink wash. 30-Mar-4 Rossini, Paris #490/R est:400-700
£1333	$2413	€2000	Etude de tetes (22x35cm-9x14in) st. pen brown ink after les Maitres Anciens. 30-Mar-4 Rossini, Paris #546/R est:300-500
£1351	$2378	€2000	Extensive mountainous landscape near Nice (18x26cm-7x10in) W/C black chk prov.exhib. 19-May-4 Sotheby's, Amsterdam #363/R est:600-800
£1400	$2534	€2100	Impalpable univers (29x45cm-11x18in) st. pierre noire htd white exhib. 30-Mar-4 Rossini, Paris #410/R est:500-800
£1400	$2534	€2100	La Tour Constance a Aigues-Mortes (20x27cm-8x11in) st. W/C exhib. 30-Mar-4 Rossini, Paris #548/R est:800-1200
£1467	$2655	€2200	Nice, chemin anime (16x28cm-6x11in) st.i. W/C. 30-Mar-4 Rossini, Paris #552/R est:1000-1500
£1467	$2655	€2200	Avignon, vue generale prise de Villeneuve-les-Avignon (28x44cm-11x17in) st. W/C. 30-Mar-4 Rossini, Paris #576/R est:1400-2200
£1533	$2775	€2300	La mer aux environs de Nice (20x36cm-8x14in) st. W/C. 30-Mar-4 Rossini, Paris #541/R est:1200-2000
£1600	$2896	€2400	La Mediterranee, etude de ciel (14x16cm-6x6in) st. pastel exec.c.1844. 30-Mar-4 Rossini, Paris #429 est:3000-5000
£1667	$3017	€2500	Trouville (24x41cm-9x16in) st. black crayon white chk. 30-Mar-4 Rossini, Paris #453/R est:1000-1500
£1667	$3017	€2500	Le soleil (13x19cm-5x7in) st. W/C. 30-Mar-4 Rossini, Paris #472/R est:600-1000
£1667	$3017	€2500	Les rives enchantees (20x36cm-8x14in) st. W/C exec.c.1845 exhib. 30-Mar-4 Rossini, Paris #517/R est:500-800
£1733	$3137	€2600	Paysage de l'abbaye dans le bois (23x37cm-9x15in) st. pastel exhib. 30-Mar-4 Rossini, Paris #452/R est:700-1200
£1800	$3258	€2700	Trouville, temps orageux, voilier (12x23cm-5x9in) st. W/C exhib. 30-Mar-4 Rossini, Paris #402/R est:600-1000
£1867	$3379	€2800	Envol de canards (17x30cm-7x12in) s. brown ink wash. 30-Mar-4 Rossini, Paris #484/R est:500-800
£1867	$3379	€2800	Quatre grands arbres, foret de Fontainebleau (33x48cm-13x19in) st. pierre noire htd W/C exec.c.1855. 30-Mar-4 Rossini, Paris #542/R est:1000-1500
£1933	$3499	€2900	Andilly, paysanne dans un champ (20x32cm-8x13in) st. W/C. 30-Mar-4 Rossini, Paris #535/R est:1000-1500
£2000	$3620	€3000	La passerelle pres de Cagnes-sur-Mer (19x31cm-7x12in) st. W/C exhib. 30-Mar-4 Rossini, Paris #516/R est:1000-1500
£2067	$3741	€3100	Vue generale de Nice (23x42cm-9x17in) st. W/C exhib. 30-Mar-4 Rossini, Paris #451/R est:2000-3500
£2067	$3741	€3100	Rouen, le Gros Horloge (20x16cm-8x6in) st. W/C exec.c.1826 exhib. 30-Mar-4 Rossini, Paris #514/R est:1200-1800
£2333	$4223	€3500	Le pont du Gard (16x32cm-6x13in) st. W/C exec.c.1841. 30-Mar-4 Rossini, Paris #421/R est:1000-1500
£2333	$4223	€3500	Crepuscule a Etretat (14x22cm-6x9in) st. W/C. 30-Mar-4 Rossini, Paris #537/R est:800-1200
£2533	$4585	€3800	Le Charlemagne, Fontainebleau (34x52cm-13x20in) st.i. black crayon W/C. 30-Mar-4 Rossini, Paris #413/R est:1000-1500
£2533	$4585	€3800	Montagnes et lac en Auvergne (19x28cm-7x11in) st.indis.i. W/C. 30-Mar-4 Rossini, Paris #426/R est:800-1200
£2533	$4585	€3800	Granville (13x35cm-5x14in) st. W/C. 30-Mar-4 Rossini, Paris #554/R est:600-1000
£2533	$4585	€3800	Chateau de Pierrefonds en cours de restauration (25x35cm-10x14in) st.i. W/C prov.exhib. 30-Mar-4 Rossini, Paris #560/R est:1200-1800
£2533	$4585	€3800	Les Ormes a Saint-Cloud a l'automne (16x11cm-6x4in) st. W/C. 30-Mar-4 Rossini, Paris #566/R est:500-800
£2600	$4706	€3900	Les environs d'Antibes (17x33cm-7x13in) st. W/C exec.c.1855. 30-Mar-4 Rossini, Paris #439/R est:1000-1500
£2667	$4827	€4000	Hauteurs sur la Cote de Nice (28x47cm-11x19in) st. W/C. 30-Mar-4 Rossini, Paris #417/R est:1200-1800
£2667	$4827	€4000	Impression marine (18x22cm-7x9in) st. W/C. 30-Mar-4 Rossini, Paris #482/R est:500-800
£2667	$4827	€4000	Bords riviere, plaine en contre-jour, lumiere d'orage (15x29cm-6x11in) st. brown ink wash W/C wash double-sided exhib. 30-Mar-4 Rossini, Paris #595/R est:500-800
£2667	$4827	€4000	Chemin (15x24cm-6x9in) st. i.verso W/C. 30-Mar-4 Rossini, Paris #598/R est:500-800
£2800	$5068	€4200	Soleil couchant, soir d'orage (12x28cm-5x11in) st. W/C. 30-Mar-4 Rossini, Paris #430/R est:600-1000
£2800	$5068	€4200	Granville au crepuscule (17x37cm-7x15in) st. W/C. 30-Mar-4 Rossini, Paris #502/R est:800-1200
£3000	$5430	€4500	Le Monte Calvo dominant Nice (22x36cm-9x14in) st. W/C. 30-Mar-4 Rossini, Paris #480/R est:900-1400
£3000	$5430	€4500	Vue generale de Rouen (20x30cm-8x12in) W/C. 30-Mar-4 Rossini, Paris #481/R est:1500-2500
£3200	$5792	€4800	Lumieres sur la plage Normande, Trouville-Deauville (17x27cm-7x11in) st. W/C exec.c.1828 exhib.lit. 30-Mar-4 Rossini, Paris #601/R est:1000-1500
£3333	$6033	€5000	Lac d'Auvergne (17x29cm-7x11in) st.i. W/C. 30-Mar-4 Rossini, Paris #569/R est:800-1200
£3667	$6637	€5500	Etang en foret de Compiegne (52x83cm-20x33in) st. pen brown ink wash exhib. 30-Mar-4 Rossini, Paris #508/R est:2000-3000
£3867	$6999	€5800	Les falaises a Fecamp (21x30cm-8x12in) st. W/C. 30-Mar-4 Rossini, Paris #404/R est:1000-1600

£4133 $7481 €6200 Bateau pour le Havre (9x21cm-4x8in) st. W/C. 30-Mar-4 Rossini, Paris #515/R est:800-1200
£4133 $7481 €6200 Le Pays de Lumieres dans la Brie (20x36cm-8x14in) st.i. i.verso W/C exec.c.1856 lit. 30-Mar-4 Rossini, Paris #568/R est:1000-1500
£4333 $7843 €6500 Terrasse de Saint-Germain et aqueduc de Marly (44x28cm-17x11in) st. W/C. 30-Mar-4 Rossini, Paris #521/R est:700-1200
£4400 $7964 €6600 Jetee de Honfleur (16x24cm-6x9in) st. W/C. 30-Mar-4 Rossini, Paris #456/R est:1000-1500
£4667 $8447 €7000 Matinee d'hiver pres du Pont Neuf (12x17cm-5x7in) st. W/C exhib.lit. 30-Mar-4 Rossini, Paris #489/R est:1000-1500
£5000 $9050 €7500 Le bain des chevaux avec Paris dans le lointain (19x27cm-7x11in) st. W/C exec.c.1835. 30-Mar-4 Rossini, Paris #464/R est:1200-1800

HUET, Paul (attrib) (1803-1869) French
£267 $477 €400 Paysage vers Pont-Audemer (48x31cm-19x12in) panel. 16-May-4 other European Auctioneer #32
£319 $533 €450 Animaux au bord d'un etang (104x66cm-41x26in) 19-Oct-3 Daniel Herry, Beaune #7

HUETOS, Domingo (1928-) Spanish
£379 $683 €550 Young fisherwoman (82x65cm-32x26in) s. 26-Jan-4 Ansorena, Madrid #91/R

HUEY, George R (19/20th C) American
Sculpture
£4282 $7750 €6252 Merganser decoy (38x15cm-15x6in) s. painted wood. 16-Apr-4 James Julia, Fairfield #517/R est:3000-5000

HUF, Fritz (1888-1970) Swiss
Works on paper
£711 $1187 €1031 Reclining nude (38x56cm-15x22in) pencil. 19-Jun-3 Kornfeld, Bern #484 est:1500 (S.FR 1550)

HUFFEL, Frans van (19th C) Belgian
£345 $638 €500 Vue de village anime (60x90cm-24x35in) s. 13-Jan-4 Vanderkindere, Brussels #76
£800 $1448 €1200 Paysage avec fermiere et moulin a eau (80x120cm-31x47in) s. 30-Mar-4 Campo & Campo, Antwerp #309

HUG, Fritz Rudolf (1921-1989) Swiss
£219 $391 €320 Girl from Lambarene (24x19cm-9x7in) s. 22-Mar-4 Philippe Schuler, Zurich #6021 (S.FR 505)
£308 $524 €450 Donkey with foal (27x34cm-11x13in) s. board. 5-Nov-3 Dobiaschofsky, Bern #655 (S.FR 700)
£317 $538 €463 From the Braunwald (46x65cm-18x26in) s. i. stretcher. 19-Nov-3 Fischer, Luzern #2150/R (S.FR 700)
£323 $579 €472 Summer lakeshore with boathouses (45x55cm-18x22in) s. panel. 12-May-4 Dobiaschofsky, Bern #629/R (S.FR 750)
£606 $1085 €885 Foals in meadow (120x59cm-47x23in) s. 22-Mar-4 Philippe Schuler, Zurich #4337 (S.FR 1400)
£655 $1192 €956 Cockfight (50x100cm-20x39in) s. 16-Jun-4 Fischer, Luzern #2192/R (S.FR 1500)
£948 $1697 €1384 Rhone glacier (80x100cm-31x39in) s. 14-May-4 Dobiaschofsky, Bern #203/R est:3500 (S.FR 2200)
£1310 $2410 €1913 Two cocks fighting (72x100cm-28x39in) s. 14-Jun-4 Philippe Schuler, Zurich #4216/R est:3000-4000 (S.FR 3000)
£1364 $2264 €1978 Three chimps (50x100cm-20x39in) s. 13-Jun-3 Zofingen, Switzerland #2885/R est:3500 (S.FR 3000)
£1586 $2696 €2316 Badger family (60x80cm-24x31in) s.d.86. 7-Nov-3 Dobiaschofsky, Bern #134/R est:5500 (S.FR 3600)
£2087 $3819 €3047 Bird of prey with its catch (81x101cm-32x40in) s. 4-Jun-4 Zofingen, Switzerland #2846/R est:5500 (S.FR 4800)
£2091 $3471 €3032 King of the Skies (70x65cm-28x26in) s. 13-Jun-3 Zofingen, Switzerland #2884/R est:4800 (S.FR 4600)
£3017 $5401 €4405 Flower garden (100x80cm-39x31in) s. 14-May-4 Dobiaschofsky, Bern #202/R est:9000 (S.FR 7000)
£3448 $6172 €5034 Owls (75x200cm-30x79in) s.i. 14-May-4 Dobiaschofsky, Bern #201/R est:10000 (S.FR 8000)

HUG, Karl Georg (attrib) (19th C) Swiss
£734 $1226 €1064 Elegant scene (32x24cm-13x9in) s.i.d.1836 panel. 23-Jun-3 Philippe Schuler, Zurich #3528/R (S.FR 1600)

HUG, Nicolaus (1771-1852) Swiss
Works on paper
£296 $545 €450 Having a party on the lakeshore (25x45cm-10x18in) W/C. 26-Jun-4 Karrenbauer, Konstanz #1733

HUG, Pya (1922-) Swiss
Works on paper
£724 $1231 €1057 Children's fete (42x54cm-17x21in) s.d.85 collage panel. 18-Nov-3 Hans Widmer, St Gallen #1242/R est:1200-2400 (S.FR 1600)

HUGENTOBLER, Ivan Edwin (1886-1972) Swiss
£1310 $2384 €1913 Two ploughing horses being attached to the plough (60x77cm-24x30in) s.d.1936. 16-Jun-4 Fischer, Luzern #1318/R est:3500-4500 (S.FR 3000)
Works on paper
£271 $462 €396 Two horses in field (24x25cm-9x10in) s. W/C gouache. 18-Nov-3 Hans Widmer, St Gallen #1103 (S.FR 600)
£271 $462 €396 Hussar on horseback (25x27cm-10x11in) s. gouache W/C. 18-Nov-3 Hans Widmer, St Gallen #1104 (S.FR 600)
£271 $462 €396 Military rider jumping obstacle (24x25cm-9x10in) mono. W/C gouache. 18-Nov-3 Hans Widmer, St Gallen #1105/R (S.FR 600)
£271 $462 €396 Three German hunters in field (26x26cm-10x10in) mono. W/C. 18-Nov-3 Hans Widmer, St Gallen #1106 (S.FR 600)
£294 $500 €429 Mounted cavalryman (26x26cm-10x10in) s. W/C. 18-Nov-3 Hans Widmer, St Gallen #1107/R (S.FR 650)
£295 $490 €428 Horses in the Pussta (22x26cm-9x10in) s.d.1955 W/C. 13-Jun-3 Zofingen, Switzerland #2887/R (S.FR 650)
£295 $490 €428 Two despatch riders (23x26cm-9x10in) s.d.1947 W/C. 13-Jun-3 Zofingen, Switzerland #2889 (S.FR 650)
£318 $528 €461 Horse's head (27x19cm-11x7in) s.d.1927 W/C. 13-Jun-3 Zofingen, Switzerland #2888 (S.FR 700)
£339 $543 €495 Garde reuplicaine (38x30cm-15x12in) s.i.d.1950 W/C chl. 16-Sep-3 Philippe Schuler, Zurich #3154 (S.FR 750)
£345 $617 €504 Artillery (12x42cm-5x17in) mono. Indian ink W/C. 12-May-4 Dobiaschofsky, Bern #1712/R (S.FR 800)
£349 $636 €510 Two four horse wagons (20x23cm-8x9in) s.d.1931 mixed media. 16-Jun-4 Fischer, Luzern #2782/R (S.FR 800)
£430 $731 €628 Horse's head (17x19cm-7x7in) s.d.1950 wash Indian ink brush. 18-Nov-3 Hans Widmer, St Gallen #1109/R (S.FR 950)
£478 $875 €698 Farmer and his team of horses (42x30cm-17x12in) s. gouache. 4-Jun-4 Zofingen, Switzerland #2851 (S.FR 1100)
£905 $1538 €1321 Mounted Zurich officer, 1775 (30x39cm-12x15in) s.d.1958 W/C. 18-Nov-3 Hans Widmer, St Gallen #1108 est:1800-2800 (S.FR 2000)

HUGGINS, James Miller (fl.1836-1849) British
£3000 $5100 €4380 Blazing frigate off Mediterranean citadel. Napoleonic frigate action (38x63cm-15x25in) one s.d.1837 pair. 19-Nov-3 Christie's, Kensington #447/R est:3000-4000

HUGGINS, William (1820-1884) British
£500 $880 €730 Cow, calf and goat (35x46cm-14x18in) 19-May-4 Christie's, Kensington #519
£550 $880 €803 Head of an ox (22cm-9in circular) s.d.1864 board. 16-Sep-3 Rosebery Fine Art, London #610/R
£850 $1420 €1241 Portrait of a gentleman seated (99x76cm-39x30in) 11-Nov-3 Bonhams, Knightsbridge #178/R
£1150 $2151 €1679 Study of the head of a cow (22cm-9in circular) s. board. 20-Jul-4 Sworder & Son, Bishops Stortford #679/R est:600-800
Works on paper
£250 $463 €365 Roaring tiger (53x46cm-21x18in) s. black white chk. 9-Mar-4 Peter Francis, Wales #25/R
£720 $1332 €1051 Lioness (18x25cm-7x10in) pencil W/C. 10-Mar-4 Sotheby's, Olympia #153/R
£950 $1710 €1387 Lion (18x24cm-7x9in) pencil col chk. 22-Apr-4 Lawrence, Crewkerne #768/R

HUGGINS, William John (1781-1845) British
£800 $1480 €1168 Hens in a landscape (25x31cm-10x12in) s.d.1872 board oval. 10-Feb-4 Bonhams, Knightsbridge #72/R
£10000 $17000 €14600 Blackwall frigate Madagascar off Dover (91x130cm-36x51in) s.d.1841. 27-Nov-3 Sotheby's, London #390/R est:10000-15000
£11500 $18285 €16790 East Indiaman Earl Balcarres, dripping a Pilot off Dover (65x93cm-26x37in) s.d.1832. 10-Sep-3 Edgar Horn, Eastbourne #375/R est:5000-7000

HUGHES, Arthur (1832-1915) British
£3755 $6721 €5482 Gurnard's Head from St Ives (17x29cm-7x11in) s. i.verso wood panel prov. 15-May-4 Christie's, Sydney #301/R est:8000-12000 (A.D 9500)
£6000 $10200 €8760 Pet of the farm (61x42cm-24x17in) s. panel prov.exhib.lit. 19-Nov-3 Bonhams, New Bond Street #64/R est:7000-10000
£7500 $12750 €10950 Lady of Shalott (17x23cm-7x9in) mono.i. panel prov.exhib.lit. 25-Nov-3 Christie's, London #148/R est:8000-12000
£18786 $32500 €27428 Mower (54x35cm-21x14in) s. panel prov.lit. 11-Dec-3 Sotheby's, New York #37/R est:25000-35000
£26000 $44200 €37960 Overthrowing of the rusty knight (52x43cm-20x17in) s. panel exhib.lit. 27-Nov-3 Sotheby's, London #317/R est:25000-35000
£50000 $85000 €73000 Sir Galahad (89x113cm-35x44in) s. prov.lit. 25-Nov-3 Christie's, London #147/R est:60000-80000

HUGHES, Arthur Ford (1856-?) British
£2000 $3340 €2920 Farmyard doves (62x47cm-24x19in) s.d.1873. 7-Oct-3 Fellows & Sons, Birmingham #414/R est:2000-3000
Works on paper
£290 $525 €423 Village scene with church tower and old woman carrying bucket (38x28cm-15x11in) s. pencil W/C. 17-Apr-4 Jim Railton, Durham #991
£330 $604 €482 Musical exercise (23x15cm-9x6in) s. W/C over pencil htd white. 8-Jul-4 Lawrence, Crewkerne #1551
£380 $635 €555 An impromptu concert (32x50cm-13x20in) s. W/C. 14-Oct-3 Bonhams, Knightsbridge #36/R
£1200 $2244 €1752 Below stairs (46x28cm-18x11in) s. W/C. 20-Jul-4 Sworder & Son, Bishops Stortford #701/R est:1200-1800

HUGHES, Bill (1932-1992) American
£2793 $5000 €4078 Lost mission (91x122cm-36x48in) 15-May-4 Altermann Galleries, Santa Fe #139/R
£8939 $16000 €13051 Passing of the Ancient One (94x152cm-37x60in) 15-May-4 Altermann Galleries, Santa Fe #138/R
£10000 $17000 €14600 Summer camp (137x183cm-54x72in) 1-Nov-3 Altermann Galleries, Santa Fe #185

HUGHES, Christopher Wyndham (1881-1961) British
£380 $646 €555 Hacking home, Bourton on the water (56x38cm-22x15in) s. 30-Oct-3 Grant, Worcester #561/R
Works on paper
£550 $963 €803 Symonds Yat, landscape with a flock of sheep (43x55cm-17x22in) s.i. W/C. 19-Dec-3 Bigwood, Stratford on Avon #350

HUGHES, Daisy Marguerite (1883-1968) American
£257 $475 €375 Untitled, house (30x41cm-12x16in) s. 17-Jul-4 Outer Cape Auctions, Provincetown #32a/R
£377 $600 €550 Provincetown (31x41cm-12x16in) s. 12-Sep-3 Skinner, Boston #513/R

£398 $625 €581 Wreckage, John King's Barn, Provincetown (36x46cm-14x18in) s. 20-Apr-3 Outer Cape Auctions, Provincetown #60/R
£455 $800 €664 Provincetown rooftops (41x51cm-16x20in) s. 3-Jan-4 Outer Cape Auctions, Provincetown #75/R
£588 $1000 €858 Old fishing boat (41x51cm-16x20in) s. 9-Nov-3 Outer Cape Auctions, Provincetown #56/R

HUGHES, David Gordon (1957-) Irish
£300 $516 €438 Errigal, Donegal (30x30cm-12x12in) mono. board. 3-Dec-3 John Ross, Belfast #98
£350 $581 €511 Moonlight, Donegal (25x35cm-10x14in) mono. board. 1-Oct-3 John Ross, Belfast #189
£350 $581 €511 Still life (40x40cm-16x16in) mono. oil gold leaf. 1-Oct-3 John Ross, Belfast #215
£350 $602 €511 Still life (38x38cm-15x15in) mono. oil gold leaf. 3-Dec-3 John Ross, Belfast #57
£380 $623 €555 Still life of poppies (30x25cm-12x10in) mono. gold leaf oil. 4-Jun-3 John Ross, Belfast #16
£380 $631 €555 La mer, Cap Ferrat (81x81cm-32x32in) mono.d.01 verso board. 1-Oct-3 John Ross, Belfast #81
£420 $781 €613 Farm, Co.Antrim (20x22cm-8x9in) mono. board. 3-Mar-4 John Ross, Belfast #139
£420 $781 €613 Cliffs of Moher (43x43cm-17x17in) mono. board. 3-Mar-4 John Ross, Belfast #195
£450 $837 €657 Still life (45x45cm-18x18in) mono. board. 3-Mar-4 John Ross, Belfast #221
£640 $1171 €934 Fairhead by moonlight (50x50cm-20x20in) mono. board. 2-Jun-4 John Ross, Belfast #93

HUGHES, Edmund (fl.1874-1879) British
£480 $758 €696 Sheep grazing in a mountainous lake landscape (41x66cm-16x26in) s.d.1874. 4-Sep-3 Christie's, Kensington #180/R

HUGHES, Edward (1832-1908) British
£270 $489 €394 Bust portrait of a bearded gentleman (48x58cm-19x23in) s.d.1892. 17-Apr-4 Jim Railton, Durham #1670

HUGHES, Edward John (1913-) Canadian
£7207 $12252 €10522 Mill Bay road (82x102cm-32x40in) s.d.1975 s.i.d. verso on stretcher prov. 18-Nov-3 Sotheby's, Toronto #98/R est:20000-25000 (C.D 16000)
£8108 $13784 €11838 Looking east over Cowichan Bay (61x91cm-24x36in) s.d.1976 s.i.d. verso on stretcher prov. 18-Nov-3 Sotheby's, Toronto #96/R est:15000-20000 (C.D 18000)
£9910 $16847 €14469 Looking North over Osborne Bay (63x82cm-25x32in) s.d.1990 s.i.d. verso on stretcher prov. 18-Nov-3 Sotheby's, Toronto #158/R est:15000-20000 (C.D 22000)
£11261 $19144 €16441 East of Chilliwack (64x81cm-25x32in) s.d.1983 s.i.d. stretcher verso prov. 18-Nov-3 Sotheby's, Toronto #88/R est:15000-20000 (C.D 25000)
£13211 $23648 €19288 Kootenay Lake (63x81cm-25x32in) s.d.74 s.i.d. stretcher prov. 31-May-4 Sotheby's, Toronto #168/R est:25000-30000 (C.D 32500)
£27027 $45946 €39459 Above Kootenay Lake (63x81cm-25x32in) s.d.1968 s.i.d.verso prov.exhib.lit. 27-Nov-3 Heffel, Vancouver #64/R est:60000-80000 (C.D 60000)
£31532 $53604 €46037 St Mary's Lake, Salt Spring Island (61x91cm-24x36in) s.d.1969 s.i.d.verso prov. 27-Nov-3 Heffel, Vancouver #30/R est:60000-80000 (C.D 70000)
£48780 $87317 €71219 Kootenay Lake, from Riondel (61x91cm-24x36in) s.d.1968 s.i.d.verso prov. 27-May-4 Heffel, Vancouver #40/R est:60000-80000 (C.D 120000)
£77236 $138252 €112765 South Thompson Valley at Chase, BC (63x81cm-25x32in) s. s.i.d.1957 verso prov.lit. 27-May-4 Heffel, Vancouver #36/R est:100000-125000 (C.D 190000)
£113821 $203740 €166179 Departure from Nanaimo (81x122cm-32x48in) s.d.1964 s.i.verso prov.exhib. 31-May-4 Sotheby's, Toronto #175/R est:100000-150000 (C.D 280000)

Works on paper
£450 $766 €657 Looking north on University Avenue, Toronto (27x37cm-11x15in) s. i.d.1956 verso pencil prov. 27-Nov-3 Heffel, Vancouver #159/R (C.D 1000)
£488 $873 €712 Two freighters at Cowichan Bay (22x29cm-9x11in) s. s.i.d.1967 verso pencil prov. 27-May-4 Heffel, Vancouver #37/R (C.D 1200)
£528 $946 €771 Sooke Harbour (22x30cm-9x12in) s. s.i.d.1948 verso pencil. 27-May-4 Heffel, Vancouver #39/R (C.D 1300)
£528 $946 €771 Oil tanker at Refuge Cove (22x30cm-9x12in) init.i.d.1953 s.i.d.verso pencil. 27-May-4 Heffel, Vancouver #38/R (C.D 1300)
£610 $1091 €891 The maple grove at Cowichan Bay (23x31cm-9x12in) s. s.i.d.1963 verso pencil prov. 27-May-4 Heffel, Vancouver #154/R (C.D 1500)
£785 $1429 €1146 Vancouver School of Art, Autograph Book (10x16cm-4x6in) s. W/C prov. 5-Feb-4 Heffel, Vancouver #44/R (C.D 1900)
£1126 $1914 €1644 Saint Boniface (24x35cm-9x14in) s. i.d.1956 verso pencil prov. 27-Nov-3 Heffel, Vancouver #157/R est:800-1200 (C.D 2500)

HUGHES, Edward Robert (1851-1914) British
Miniatures
£13000 $23400 €18980 William Holman Hunt OM, full bearded (4cm-2in) zircon ruby diamond beryl topaz silver frame oval prov.exhib.lit. 22-Apr-4 Bonhams, New Bond Street #164/R est:15000-20000

Works on paper
£300 $552 €438 Portrait of a lady (34x27cm-13x11in) s.d.1912 red chk. 25-Mar-4 Christie's, Kensington #129
£6936 $12000 €10127 Portrait of Anthony Freeman (31x26cm-12x10in) s.d.1903 W/C gouache board prov. 11-Dec-3 Sotheby's, New York #33/R est:6000-8000
£20000 $34000 €29200 Coward (45x33cm-18x13in) s.d.1898 s.i.verso col chk W/C. 27-Nov-3 Sotheby's, London #315/R est:20000-30000
£62000 $114080 €90520 Night.abstrait Day (25x18cm-10x7in) s. pencil W/C htd gold bodycol prov. pair. 9-Jun-4 Christie's, London #25/R est:60000-80000

HUGHES, Ethel (19/20th C) British
Works on paper
£552 $900 €806 Cottage (22x30cm-9x12in) s. W/C. 17-Jul-3 Naón & Cia, Buenos Aires #14/R
£780 $1396 €1139 Autumn flowers (25x17cm-10x7in) s. W/C. 17-Mar-4 Bonhams, Chester #247

HUGHES, George (19/20th C) British
£214 $400 €312 Woman and young boy hitchhiking (76x46cm-30x18in) s. hardboard painted c.1950. 26-Feb-4 Illustration House, New York #95
£220 $400 €330 Still life of flowers (74x102cm-29x40in) s.d.1927 board. 16-Jun-4 Wolf's, New York #486586/R

HUGHES, George Frederick (fl.1859-1883) British
Works on paper
£320 $589 €467 Sheep in an English landscape (35x60cm-14x24in) s. W/C. 8-Jun-4 Bonhams, Knightsbridge #29/R

HUGHES, George H (fl.1894-1909) British
Works on paper
£320 $544 €467 Old cottage garden (45x33cm-18x13in) s. W/C. 18-Nov-3 Bonhams, Leeds #73

HUGHES, John (attrib) (1806-1878) British
£3500 $6265 €5110 Schooner yacht America to windward of other competitors (33x48cm-13x19in) board. 26-May-4 Christie's, Kensington #490/R est:4000-6000

HUGHES, John Joseph (?-1909) British
£450 $824 €675 Extensive Welsh landscape (48x74cm-19x29in) 27-Jul-4 Henry Adams, Chichester #460
£487 $882 €711 St. Martins, Wareham (40x65cm-16x26in) s. i.verso. 30-Mar-4 Stephan Welz, Johannesburg #397 est:5000-8000 (SA.R 5800)
£600 $1110 €876 St. Michaels church, Old Handsworth, Bimingham (48x58cm-19x23in) s. 13-Feb-4 Keys, Aylsham #706/R
£934 $1700 €1364 Windsor Castle with sheep and soldiers (36x48cm-14x19in) s. 7-Feb-4 Sloans & Kenyon, Bethesda #1258/R est:800-1000

HUGHES, John Joseph (attrib) (?-1909) British
£320 $534 €467 Edenbridge, Kent (37x48cm-15x19in) init. i.on stretcher. 16-Oct-3 Lawrence, Crewkerne #736

HUGHES, Lester (20th C) American
£220 $400 €321 Southwestern landscape with cowhands and cattle (61x91cm-24x36in) s. 19-Jun-4 Jeffery Burchard, Florida #260

HUGHES, Patrick (1939-) British
£275 $437 €402 Uneven balance (28x61cm-11x24in) prov. 1-May-3 John Nicholson, Haslemere #695

Works on paper
£600 $1116 €876 Rainbows (56x78cm-22x31in) s.d.77 gouache. 7-Mar-4 Lots Road Auctions, London #345

HUGHES, Paul (?) ?
£368 $678 €560 Bateaux au port (37x44cm-15x17in) s. panel. 27-Jun-4 Feletin, Province #105

HUGHES, S (19th C) British?
£1280 $2304 €1869 Street scene at Bangor near Castle Hotel, with coach, horses and figures (36x51cm-14x20in) s. 24-Apr-4 Rogers Jones, Clwyd #150/R

HUGHES, Talbot (1869-1942) British
£1000 $1850 €1460 Arrest (107x80cm-42x31in) s. 10-Mar-4 Sotheby's, Olympia #211/R est:2000-3000
£8000 $13360 €11680 Story of the hare that got away (51x61cm-20x24in) s.d.98 panel. 13-Nov-3 Christie's, Kensington #296/R est:4000-6000

Works on paper
£3500 $5950 €5110 Starlight (28x22cm-11x9in) s.d.1905 col chks buff paper. 20-Nov-3 Christie's, London #142/R est:2500-3500

HUGHES, William (1842-1901) British
£531 $850 €775 Gloucester Harbour dock scene with figures (61x91cm-24x36in) s. 20-Sep-3 Jeffery Burchard, Florida #20a/R
£650 $1190 €949 Apples, a pear and a bunch of grapes on a mossy bank (23x31cm-9x12in) s. 8-Apr-4 Christie's, Kensington #232/R
£1500 $2505 €2190 Grapes, apples and a wicker basket (30x41cm-12x16in) s.d.1869. 13-Nov-3 Christie's, Kensington #364/R est:1500-1800
£1500 $2745 €2190 Still life with grapes and peaches (39x47cm-15x19in) s.d.1875. 7-Apr-4 Woolley & Wallis, Salisbury #207/R est:1200-1800
£1900 $3173 €2774 Still life with game (91x76cm-36x30in) s.d.1885. 12-Nov-3 Sotheby's, Olympia #59/R est:1000-1500

HUGHES, William (attrib) (1842-1901) British
£500 $835 €730 Still life with peaches, raspberries and grapes on a table top (33cm-13in circular) canvas on board. 12-Nov-3 Halls, Shrewsbury #310

HUGHES-STANTON, Sir Herbert (1870-1937) British
£350 $595 €511 Road up to Cagnes (63x74cm-25x29in) s.d.1930. 6-Nov-3 Christie's, Kensington #848/R
£380 $680 €555 Cattle resting and watering beside a river in an open landscape (21x28cm-8x11in) s. 16-Mar-4 Bonhams, Leeds #661
£600 $978 €876 Landscape near Cagnes (46x61cm-18x24in) s.d.1930. 24-Sep-3 Dreweatt Neate, Newbury #195
£900 $1530 €1314 Washing in the river (51x68cm-20x27in) s.d.1911. 26-Nov-3 Sotheby's, Olympia #45/R

Works on paper
£380 $619 €555 The Valley, Montreuil (36x51cm-14x20in) s.d.1909 W/C exhib. 24-Sep-3 Dreweatt Neate, Newbury #42/R
£500 $835 €730 View of Tamatoukuri, Japan (35x50cm-14x20in) s. W/C over pencil htd bodycol. 14-Oct-3 Sotheby's, London #171/R

£560 $918 €818 Dunes, looking towards Hardelot, France (36x51cm-14x20in) s.d.1912 W/C. 29-May-3 Neales, Nottingham #739/R
£700 $1169 €1022 Torri gate, Japan (51x72cm-20x28in) s. W/C over pencil htd bodycol. 14-Oct-3 Sotheby's, London #169/R
£700 $1169 €1022 Inland sea, Japan (49x74cm-19x29in) s. W/C over pencil htd scratching out. 14-Oct-3 Sotheby's, London #170/R
£2800 $4760 €4088 Greek views (48x65cm-19x26in) s.d.1935 W/C set of 4. 18-Nov-3 Sotheby's, London #136/R est:3000-4000

HUGNET, Georges (1906-1974) French
Works on paper
£254 $457 €371 Untitled (23x15cm-9x6in) collage on cardboard. 26-Apr-4 Bukowskis, Stockholm #548/R (S.KR 3500)
£254 $457 €371 Untitled (22x18cm-9x7in) init.verso collage cardboard. 26-Apr-4 Bukowskis, Stockholm #549/R (S.KR 3500)
£254 $457 €371 Untitled (22x18cm-9x7in) init. collage photographic paper on cardboard. 26-Apr-4 Bukowskis, Stockholm #550/R (S.KR 3500)
£254 $457 €371 Untitled (20x15cm-8x6in) init. collage. 26-Apr-4 Bukowskis, Stockholm #552/R (S.KR 3500)
£254 $457 €371 Untitled (42x25cm-17x10in) init.d.1961 collage paper on cardboard. 26-Apr-4 Bukowskis, Stockholm #554/R (S.KR 3500)
£254 $457 €371 Untitled (24x25cm-9x10in) init.d.1961 collage cardboard. 26-Apr-4 Bukowskis, Stockholm #556/R (S.KR 3500)
£471 $848 €688 Untitled (22x16cm-9x6in) init.verso collage photographic paper. 26-Apr-4 Bukowskis, Stockholm #547/R (S.KR 6500)
£544 $979 €794 Untitled (23x15cm-9x6in) init.verso collage. 26-Apr-4 Bukowskis, Stockholm #551/R (S.KR 7500)
£872 $1605 €1300 Green owl (26x19cm-10x7in) studio st. pastel. 24-Mar-4 Joron-Derem, Paris #88/R
£940 $1729 €1400 Baiser Canard (25x23cm-10x9in) studio st. collage. 24-Mar-4 Joron-Derem, Paris #89
£1000 $1790 €1500 Collage (34x20cm-13x8in) collage. 15-May-4 Renaud, Paris #121
£1818 $3127 €2600 Un Pape main levee, laquelle semble porter une femme a l'air inquiet (25x25cm-10x10in) st.verso collage. 6-Dec-3 Renaud, Paris #164/R
£2103 $3785 €3070 Untitled (23x17cm-9x7in) init. verso collage. 26-Apr-4 Bukowskis, Stockholm #553/R est:5000-7000 (S.KR 29000)
£12000 $22080 €17520 Qui inventa (56x40cm-22x16in) s.i.d.1936 paper collage board prov.exhib. 24-Jun-4 Christie's, London #369/R est:4000-6000

HUGO, Georges Victor (1868-1925) French
£338 $595 €500 View of village at dusk (38x46cm-15x18in) s.i.d.1902. 19-May-4 Il Ponte, Milan #530

HUGO, Jean (1894-1984) French
£313 $498 €457 Urban scene (33x49cm-13x19in) panel. 29-Apr-3 Louis Morton, Mexico #77/R (M.P 5200)
£1243 $2300 €1865 Le Mazet en ruine (25x33cm-10x13in) s. i.verso painted 1971. 14-Jul-4 American Auctioneer #490124/R est:800-1200
£1608 $2766 €2300 Paysage des Cotwolds (22x33cm-9x13in) s. panel. 2-Dec-3 Calmels Cohen, Paris #10/R est:2000-2500
£3867 $7115 €5800 Le puits (66x81cm-26x32in) s. 9-Jun-4 Beaussant & Lefèvre, Paris #166/R est:5000-6000
Works on paper
£433 $789 €650 Le Labour (9x13cm-4x5in) s. gouache. 30-Jun-4 Calmels Cohen, Paris #17/R
£433 $789 €650 Remorqueur dans le port (7x12cm-3x5in) s. gouache. 30-Jun-4 Calmels Cohen, Paris #26/R
£466 $849 €700 Walk by the lake (11x6cm-4x2in) s. gouache. 30-Jun-4 Calmels Cohen, Paris #16/R
£466 $849 €700 Bateaux a Sec (7x12cm-3x5in) s. gouache. 30-Jun-4 Calmels Cohen, Paris #29/R
£500 $910 €750 Village (12x8cm-5x3in) s. gouache. 30-Jun-4 Calmels Cohen, Paris #21/R
£533 $970 €800 Village et clocher (10x8cm-4x3in) s. gouache. 30-Jun-4 Calmels Cohen, Paris #23/R
£533 $970 €800 Pont sur la riviere (7x11cm-3x4in) s. gouache. 30-Jun-4 Calmels Cohen, Paris #24/R
£537 $950 €800 Seine a Villequiez (7x12cm-3x5in) s. gouache prov. 27-Apr-4 Artcurial Briest, Paris #90
£594 $1022 €850 Village (6x10cm-2x4in) s. gouache. 2-Dec-3 Calmels Cohen, Paris #21/R
£599 $1091 €900 Entrance to the port (6x14cm-2x6in) s. gouache. 30-Jun-4 Calmels Cohen, Paris #18/R
£599 $1091 €900 Fishermen (7x12cm-3x5in) s. gouache. 30-Jun-4 Calmels Cohen, Paris #28/R
£667 $1227 €1000 Maquette originale Ruy Blas, Comedie Francaise (34x18cm-13x7in) i. W/C exec. 1938. 11-Jun-4 Pierre Berge, Paris #148
£1000 $1830 €1460 Village scene (10x12cm-4x5in) s. W/C. 7-Apr-4 Woolley & Wallis, Salisbury #72/R est:200-300
£1338 $2315 €1900 Sortie du port (5x8cm-2x3in) s. gouache. 14-Dec-3 Eric Pillon, Calais #230/R
£1408 $2437 €2000 Bateaux pres des cotes (8x13cm-3x5in) s. W/C gouache. 14-Dec-3 Eric Pillon, Calais #231/R
£2128 $3553 €3000 Le kiosque au bord du Loing (13x18cm-5x7in) s.d.27 gouache. 19-Jun-3 Millon & Associes, Paris #58/R est:1000-1500
£2449 $4384 €3600 Grand mas avec oliviers et vignes (26x43cm-10x17in) s. W/C pastel. 17-Mar-4 Maigret, Paris #130/R est:1900-2500
£2500 $3975 €3625 Village (20x15cm-8x6in) s. gouache. 11-Sep-3 Christie's, Kensington #80/R est:2000-3000
£4000 $6360 €5800 Le casino de Boulogne-sur-mer (20x25cm-8x10in) s. i.verso gouache on card prov. 11-Sep-3 Christie's, Kensington #82/R est:4000-6000

HUGO, Madame Victor (19th C) French
Works on paper
£367 $675 €550 Portrait d'une jeune fille en bandeaux et robe blanche (18x15cm-7x6in) s.d.1839 graphite. 9-Jun-4 Piasa, Paris #117

HUGO, Valentine (1890-1968) French
Works on paper
£400 $736 €600 Maquette du costume de Genevieive (43x27cm-17x11in) i. col crayon. 9-Jun-4 Piasa, Paris #119
£800 $1472 €1200 Pour l'Opera Comique, Pelleas et Melisande, une foret, acte I scene I (37x21cm-15x8in) s.i.d.1947 pastel. 11-Jun-4 Pierre Berge, Paris #130/R

HUGO, Valentine and BRETON, Andre (20th C) French
Works on paper
£16000 $28640 €24000 Cadavre exquis (32x24cm-13x9in) col crayon exec. with Paul Eluard, Nusch Eluard. 15-May-4 Renaud, Paris #339/R

HUGO, Victor (1802-1885) French
Works on paper
£243 $450 €355 Statue of Liberty (48x38cm-19x15in) s.d.1976 W/C. 17-Jul-4 Outer Cape Auctions, Provincetown #67a/R
£3521 $6303 €5000 Chateau (4x6cm-2x2in) mono. ink wash. 11-Jan-4 Rouillac, Vendome #59
£12222 $22000 €17844 Castle seen across a lake (10x15cm-4x6in) s.d.1863 pen brown ink col wash prov. 22-Jan-4 Christie's, Rockefeller NY #142/R est:15000-20000
£44444 $80000 €64888 Ruins in an imaginary landscape (9x26cm-4x10in) i.verso pen brown ink wash prov. 22-Jan-4 Christie's, Rockefeller NY #141/R est:30000-50000

HUGUENIN, Paul (1870-1919) Swiss
Works on paper
£588 $1018 €858 Lac de Geronde (32x49cm-13x19in) s.i.d.02 W/C gouache. 12-Dec-3 Galerie du Rhone, Sion #511 (S.FR 1300)

HUGUENIN, Viretaux-Henri-Edouard (1878-1958) Swiss
£264 $449 €385 Chapelle de Maria (34x44cm-13x17in) s.d.40 i. stretcher. 5-Nov-3 Dobiaschofsky, Bern #659/R (S.FR 600)
£302 $540 €441 Mountain lake with chalet (50x61cm-20x24in) s. 12-May-4 Dobiaschofsky, Bern #633/R (S.FR 700)
£306 $556 €447 Motif de la Foret d'Aletsch-Le Spaarhorn, le Schienhorn et l'Oberaletsch (46x54cm-18x21in) s. 16-Jun-4 Fischer, Luzern #2193/R (S.FR 700)
£326 $564 €476 Glacier d'Aletsch (46x38cm-18x15in) s.d.1937 panel. 12-Dec-3 Galerie du Rhone, Sion #506 (S.FR 720)
£352 $599 €514 Aletsch glacier (37x55cm-15x22in) s. 5-Nov-3 Dobiaschofsky, Bern #657/R (S.FR 800)
£352 $599 €514 Sunny alpine landscape in Wallis (34x44cm-13x17in) s.d.1947 board. 5-Nov-3 Dobiaschofsky, Bern #658/R (S.FR 800)
£381 $610 €552 Vue de l'Hotel Jungfrau sur Bellwald (38x46cm-15x18in) s.d.33 i. verso. 15-May-3 Stuker, Bern #1307 (S.FR 800)
£529 $899 €772 Vue de la Goppisbergalp (46x55cm-18x22in) s.d.1909 i. stretcher. 5-Nov-3 Dobiaschofsky, Bern #660/R (S.FR 1200)

HUGUENIN-LASSANGUETTE, Fritz Eduard (1842-1926) Swiss
£323 $579 €472 Winter wood (41x32cm-16x13in) s. 13-May-4 Stuker, Bern #186 (S.FR 750)
£409 $733 €597 Le Cergneux (33x46cm-13x18in) s. i.d.1919 stretcher. 12-May-4 Dobiaschofsky, Bern #632 (S.FR 950)
£688 $1149 €998 Fileuse, Val d'Herens (40x30cm-16x12in) s. painted c.1916. 21-Jun-3 Galerie du Rhone, Sion #387/R est:1000-1500 (S.FR 1500)
Works on paper
£226 $391 €330 Chablais au couchant (34x51cm-13x20in) W/C. 12-Dec-3 Galerie du Rhone, Sion #508 (S.FR 500)
£271 $470 €396 Ascona (25cm-10in) s. i.d.1903 W/C paper on cardboard. 12-Dec-3 Galerie du Rhone, Sion #509 (S.FR 600)
£362 $626 €529 Bretaye (30x45cm-12x18in) s.i. W/C. 12-Dec-3 Galerie du Rhone, Sion #507 (S.FR 800)

HUGUENIN-LASSANGUETTE, Fritz Eduard (attrib) (1842-1926) Swiss
Works on paper
£226 $391 €330 Vallee de Zermatt (39x56cm-15x22in) W/C htd gouache. 12-Dec-3 Galerie du Rhone, Sion #510 (S.FR 500)

HUGUES, Paul Jean (1891-?) French
£1800 $3330 €2628 Study of an interior (55x47cm-22x19in) s. 14-Jul-4 Christie's, Kensington #903/R est:1000-1500
£2096 $3500 €3060 Interior (41x33cm-16x13in) s. 16-Nov-3 CRN Auctions, Cambridge #54/R
£3800 $7106 €5548 Salon interiors (53x61cm-21x24in) s. pair exhib. 26-Feb-4 Bruton Knowles, Cheltenham #72/R est:3000-5000
Works on paper
£828 $1514 €1200 La commode (27x22cm-11x9in) s. gouache. 31-Jan-4 Gerard, Besancon #5
£1103 $2019 €1600 Angle du salon Empire (22x26cm-9x10in) s.i.d.1945 gouache. 31-Jan-4 Gerard, Besancon #4

HUGUET, Victor Pierre (1835-1902) French
£2098 $3608 €3000 Cuisine au campement (37x59cm-15x23in) s.d.1863 panel. 8-Dec-3 Tajan, Paris #289/R est:3000-4500
£3179 $5817 €4800 La halte des cavaliers (24x32cm-9x13in) s. 9-Apr-4 Claude Aguttes, Neuilly #132/R est:3000-4000
£3500 $5845 €5110 Caravan crossing a stream (38x46cm-15x18in) s. 14-Oct-3 Sotheby's, London #39/R est:4000-6000
£4085 $7066 €5800 Tempete de sable (35x44cm-14x17in) s. wood. 12-Dec-3 Renaud, Paris #145/R est:8000-10000
£6000 $10980 €9000 Cavaliers devant la grande porte (60x40cm-24x16in) s. 3-Jun-4 Tajan, Paris #270/R est:7000-10000
£7334 $13421 €11000 Cavaliers au pied d'une falaise (46x37cm-18x15in) s. i.verso panel. 3-Jun-4 Tajan, Paris #264/R est:6000-8000
£21277 $35532 €30000 La chasse aux faucons (59x72cm-23x28in) s. 16-Jun-3 Gros & Delettrez, Paris #90/R est:30000-50000

HUHN, Karl Theodor Fidorovitch (1830-1877) Russian

£4514	$7448	€6500	Leon sur Mer harbour (71x99cm-28x39in) s.cyrillic i. 3-Jul-3 Van Ham, Cologne #1267/R est:9000

HUHNEN, Fritz (1895-1981) German

Works on paper

£333	$597	€500	Woman on couch (33x41cm-13x16in) s.d. W/C on pencil chl. 15-May-4 Dr Sturies, Dusseldorf #73/R
£347	$621	€520	Figures (54x41cm-21x16in) s.d. chl. 15-May-4 Dr Sturies, Dusseldorf #75/R
£427	$764	€640	Dog attack (30x40cm-12x16in) s.i. bears d. W/C bodycol on pencil. 15-May-4 Dr Sturies, Dusseldorf #74/R
£1600	$2864	€2400	Self as heavy smoker (38x26cm-15x10in) s.i.d. graphite col pen. 15-May-4 Dr Sturies, Dusseldorf #7y/R
£3200	$5728	€4800	Couple in front of landscape (41x32cm-16x13in) s.d. w/C. 15-May-4 Dr Sturies, Dusseldorf #72/R

HUIDEKOPER, Christiaan (1878-1939) Dutch

£538	$899	€770	Street festival with bullfight, possibly Pamplona (49x59cm-19x23in) s.d.06 prov. 11-Oct-3 Hans Stahl, Hamburg #41/R

HUIDEKOPER, Geertruida Margaretha Jacoba (1824-1884) Dutch

£4255	$7106	€6000	Still life of flowers (38x30cm-15x12in) init. 20-Oct-3 Glerum, Amsterdam #1/R est:2000-3000

HUILLIOT, Pierre Nicolas (1674-1751) French

£1656	$3030	€2500	Cols-verts et batraciens. Pigeons et gallinace (80x72cm-31x28in) one s. oval. 7-Apr-4 Doutrebente, Paris #12/R est:2500-3000
£12048	$20000	€17590	Flowers in a vase with foliage in an urn, and fruit on a ledge (153x145cm-60x57in) prov. 30-Sep-3 Christie's, Rockefeller NY #408/R est:20000-30000

HUILLIOT, Pierre Nicolas (attrib) (1674-1751) French

£15569	$26000	€22731	Still life of flowers in vases with birds (46x37cm-18x15in) pair prov. 7-Oct-3 Sotheby's, New York #53/R est:10000-15000

HUILLIOT, Pierre Nicolas (circle) (1674-1751) French

£8621	$14397	€12500	Trompe l'oeil still life (66x80cm-26x31in) canvas on board. 15-Nov-3 Lempertz, Koln #1067/R est:6000

HUISMAN, Jopie (20th C) Dutch

£12667	$23307	€19000	Still life with a pot of paint (29x24cm-11x9in) s.d.1986 panel prov. 9-Jun-4 Christie's, Amsterdam #224/R est:10000-15000

HUISMAN, Klaas (1885-1973) Dutch

£280	$467	€400	Village near the waterside (40x80cm-16x31in) s. 30-Jun-3 Sotheby's, Amsterdam #263

HUITTI, Ilmari (1897-1960) Finnish

£310	$496	€440	Hayfield (31x40cm-12x16in) s.d.1944. 18-Sep-3 Hagelstam, Helsinki #797
£313	$570	€460	View of farm (61x74cm-24x29in) 8-Feb-4 Bukowskis, Helsinki #433/R
£333	$557	€480	Cloudy day (35x27cm-14x11in) s.d.44. 26-Oct-3 Bukowskis, Helsinki #362/R
£389	$649	€560	Calm day (26x32cm-10x13in) s.d.44. 26-Oct-3 Bukowskis, Helsinki #363/R

HUJAR, Peter (1934-1987) American

Photographs

£2500	$4500	€3650	Bruce de Saint Croix (37x37cm-15x15in) i.d.1976 gelatin silver print prov.lit. 23-Apr-4 Phillips, New York #154/R est:5000-7000
£2825	$5000	€4125	Electric cow (37x37cm-15x15in) s.i.d.1978 num.6/15 verso gelatin silver print prov. 27-Apr-4 Christie's, Rockefeller NY #347/R est:4000-6000
£4006	$7250	€5849	Candy darling on her death bed (36x36cm-14x14in) s.verso gelatin silver print exec. 1973. 19-Apr-4 Daniel Cooney, Brooklyn #469265/R
£6215	$11000	€9074	Candy darling (37x37cm-15x15in) s.i.d.1979 num.22/50 gelatin silver print prov.lit. 27-Apr-4 Christie's, Rockefeller NY #175/R est:7000-9000
£10734	$19000	€15672	Chloe Finch, 1981 (37x37cm-15x15in) s.num.1/15 i.d.1981 verso gelatin silver print lit. 27-Apr-4 Christie's, Rockefeller NY #346/R est:10000-15000

HULDAH, Cherry Jeffe (1901-2001) American

£297	$475	€434	Spectre de la rose (25x20cm-10x8in) s. s.i.verso. 20-Sep-3 Bunte, Elgin #1300e
£361	$650	€527	Girl's head (25x20cm-10x8in) s. s.i.d.1945 verso. 20-Jan-4 Arthur James, Florida #171
£389	$700	€568	Relaxing by the lake (20x25cm-8x10in) s. s.i.d.1988 verso prov. 20-Apr-4 Arthur James, Florida #19/R

HULETT, Ralph (19/20th C) American

Works on paper

£718	$1300	€1048	Mexican village (56x76cm-22x30in) s. W/C. 18-Apr-4 Bonhams & Butterfields, Los Angeles #7099 est:500-700
£1374	$2500	€2006	Mammoth Valley landscape (56x76cm-22x30in) s. i.verso W/C prov. 15-Jun-4 John Moran, Pasadena #137 est:1500-2000
£1923	$3500	€2808	Panamint Range (53x69cm-21x27in) s.d.49 i.verso W/C prov. 15-Jun-4 John Moran, Pasadena #133a est:2000-3000
£2513	$4750	€3669	Mill Valley (53x71cm-21x28in) s. W/C prov. 17-Feb-4 John Moran, Pasadena #87/R est:2500-3500

HULINGS, Clark (1922-) American

£5294	$9000	€7729	Fresh fruit (20x25cm-8x10in) s.d.1974 prov. 1-Nov-3 Santa Fe Art, Santa Fe #49/R est:10500-12500
£5587	$10000	€8157	Man with donkey (23x30cm-9x12in) 15-May-4 Altermann Galleries, Santa Fe #144/R
£10465	$18000	€15279	Dolores hidalgo, Mexico (50x75cm-20x30in) s.d.1968 prov. 3-Dec-3 Doyle, New York #254/R est:25000-35000
£26471	$45000	€38648	Backyards San Francisco St. Santa Fe New Mexico (61x91cm-24x36in) masonite. 1-Nov-3 Altermann Galleries, Santa Fe #169

Works on paper

£838	$1500	€1223	Burro with man (20x25cm-8x10in) pen ink. 15-May-4 Altermann Galleries, Santa Fe #145/R
£1176	$2000	€1717	Gateway in Istanbul (30x43cm-12x17in) s. W/C prov. 1-Nov-3 Santa Fe Art, Santa Fe #186/R est:2500-4000
£1471	$2500	€2148	Mostar, Yugoslavia (30x43cm-12x17in) s.i. W/C prov. 1-Nov-3 Santa Fe Art, Santa Fe #185/R est:3000-5000

HULK, A (jnr) (1851-1922) British

£250	$395	€365	Wooded rural scene with sheep grazing beside a distant church (58x38cm-23x15in) s. 4-Apr-3 Biddle & Webb, Birmingham #147

HULK, Abraham (19th C) Dutch

£529	$899	€772	Zuiderzee (26x34cm-10x13in) s. panel. 5-Nov-3 Dobiaschofsky, Bern #661/R (S.FR 1200)
£669	$1111	€950	Fishing boats of Dutch coast (17x26cm-7x10in) s. panel. 12-Jun-3 Dorotheum, Graz #25/R
£986	$1766	€1450	Marine (20x23cm-8x9in) s. panel. 16-Mar-4 Vanderkindere, Brussels #21
£1818	$3036	€2600	Shipping in a calm (16x24cm-6x9in) s. panel. 30-Jun-3 Sotheby's, Amsterdam #65/R
£1875	$2963	€2700	Fishing boats off coast with lighthouse (25x36cm-10x14in) s. panel. 6-Sep-3 Schopman, Hamburg #848/R est:2700
£2000	$3460	€2920	Barges off the Dutch coast (40x61cm-16x24in) s. 11-Dec-3 Lyon & Turnbull, Edinburgh #86/R est:2000-3000
£2523	$4213	€3658	Coastal landscape with sailing ships and town (18x25cm-7x10in) s. panel. 23-Jun-3 Philippe Schuler, Zurich #3529/R est:3500-4000 (S.FR 5500)
£3333	$5500	€4800	Seascape (16x25cm-6x10in) s. panel. 2-Jul-3 Neumeister, Munich #670/R est:1500
£4000	$7200	€6000	Sailing vessels on a calm river at dusk (35x46cm-14x18in) s. 21-Apr-4 Christie's, Amsterdam #2/R est:3000-5000
£4000	$7160	€5840	Stiff breeze offshore (43x61cm-17x24in) s. 26-May-4 Christie's, Kensington #657/R est:3500-5000
£7383	$13584	€11000	Seashore with sailing boats in breakers (25x35cm-10x14in) s. panel lit. 25-Mar-4 Karlheinz Kaupp, Staufen #2513/R est:300
£7500	$13875	€10950	Dutch fishing boats in an estuary at sunset (56x84cm-22x33in) s. prov. 11-Mar-4 Duke & Son, Dorchester #175/R est:5000-10000
£13750	$24613	€20075	Fishing boats on the Scheldt. Fishing barges in an onshore breeze (18x25cm-7x10in) s. panel pair. 26-May-4 Christie's, Kensington #658/R est:8000-12000
£14000	$24080	€20440	Fishing boats on an estuary, Fishing boats in a calm (17x25cm-7x10in) s. panel pair. 3-Dec-3 Christie's, London #14/R est:15000-20000

HULK, Abraham (jnr) (1851-1922) British

£280	$512	€409	Wooded riverbank (38x59cm-15x23in) s. 6-Jul-4 Bonhams, Knightsbridge #37/R
£400	$640	€584	Country landscape with figures by stream (75x125cm-30x49in) s. 17-Sep-3 Bonhams, Brooks & Langlois, Jersey #64/R
£400	$680	€584	Young girl at the edge of a stream near Gomshall, Surrey (61x41cm-24x16in) s. 5-Nov-3 John Nicholson, Haslemere #649
£550	$886	€798	Extensive landscape with shepherd and sheep in a lane by cottages (48x74cm-19x29in) s. 15-Aug-3 Keys, Aylsham #704
£556	$906	€800	Peasant woman near the river (15x22cm-6x9in) s. panel. 29-Sep-3 Sotheby's, Amsterdam #83/R
£600	$1110	€876	Figure in a summer landscape (91x70cm-36x28in) s. 10-Feb-4 Bonhams, Knightsbridge #326/R
£601	$1100	€877	Landscape in Albury Park, Surrey (56x46cm-22x18in) s.i. board. 5-Jun-4 Neal Auction Company, New Orleans #523/R est:1500-2500
£650	$1086	€949	Figure in a landscape collecting firewood (75x48cm-30x19in) s. sold with a companion. 7-Oct-3 Bonhams, Knightsbridge #155/R
£700	$1295	€1022	View of a farmstead. River landscape (73x48cm-29x19in) s. pair. 9-Mar-4 Bonhams, Knightsbridge #261/R
£726	$1300	€1219	Landscapes (23x15cm-9x6in) s. panel two. 20-Mar-4 Pook & Pook, Downington #589
£773	$1400	€1129	Near Abinger half Surrey. s. 14-Apr-4 Dallas Auction Gallery, Dallas #190/R est:1000-1500
£782	$1400	€1142	A country path (51x41cm-20x16in) s. 10-Jan-4 Harvey Clar, Oakland #1581
£839	$1443	€1200	Alburry Park, Surrey (62x92cm-24x36in) s.d.1881. 2-Dec-3 Campo & Campo, Antwerp #182/R
£909	$1600	€1327	Landscapes in Surrey (20x30cm-8x12in) pair prov. 23-May-4 Hindman, Chicago #43/R est:2000-3000
£950	$1539	€1378	Near Haslemere (77x128cm-30x50in) s. i.verso. 30-Jul-3 Hamptons Fine Art, Godalming #231

HULK, Abraham (snr) (1813-1897) Dutch

£1500	$2550	€2190	Lugger in heavy seas (32x42cm-13x17in) s.indis.d. 19-Nov-3 Christie's, Kensington #531/R
£1528	$2490	€2200	Shipping in calm waters (16x29cm-6x11in) s. panel. 29-Sep-3 Sotheby's, Amsterdam #95/R
£2800	$5096	€4088	Off to the fishing grounds (30x45cm-12x18in) s. 16-Jun-4 Bonhams, New Bond Street #7/R est:3000-5000
£2917	$4871	€4200	Fishing boats in choppy waters (40x61cm-16x24in) s. 21-Oct-3 Sotheby's, Amsterdam #9/R est:4000-6000
£3000	$5100	€4380	Fishermen setting sail off the harbour mouth (47x63cm-19x25in) s.d.1846 panel. 19-Nov-3 Christie's, Kensington #532/R
£4018	$6710	€5866	Fishermen at work (18x25cm-7x10in) s. panel. 17-Jun-3 Maynards, Vancouver #314 est:6000-8000 (C.D 9000)
£4554	$7604	€6649	Fishing vessels (18x25cm-7x10in) s. panel. 17-Jun-3 Maynards, Vancouver #315 est:6000-8000 (C.D 10200)
£5000	$8950	€7300	Barges in a stiff breeze. Barges in a calm (17x25cm-7x10in) both s. panel pair. 26-May-4 Christie's, Kensington #656/R est:6000-8000
£5208	$8854	€7500	Calm - rowing the tender to shore (15x20cm-6x8in) s. panel. 28-Oct-3 Christie's, Amsterdam #4/R est:5000-7000
£6376	$11795	€9500	Shipping off the shore in high winds (46x67cm-18x26in) s. panel prov. 15-Mar-4 Sotheby's, Amsterdam #69/R est:6000-8000
£6800	$11696	€9928	Shipping off a harbour (40x60cm-16x24in) s. pair. 2-Dec-3 Sotheby's, London #48/R est:5000-7000

£9000 $16110 €13140 Calm waters at dawn. Boats in a swell (41x61cm-16x24in) s. canvas on board pair. 26-May-4 Sotheby's, Olympia #272/R est:10000-15000
£9333 $16800 €14000 Shipping in a calm (37x54cm-15x21in) s. 20-Apr-4 Sotheby's, Amsterdam #11/R est:6000-8000
£9722 $16528 €14000 Shipping in a calm estuary (20x31cm-8x12in) s. 28-Oct-3 Christie's, Amsterdam #235/R est:15000-20000
£11806 $20069 €17000 Shipping in a calm (25x32cm-10x13in) s. panel. 28-Oct-3 Christie's, Amsterdam #75/R est:12000-16000
£12000 $21840 €17520 Sailing in calm waters (58x88cm-23x35in) s. prov. 15-Jun-4 Sotheby's, London #154/R est:15000-25000
£14634 $26195 €21366 Sunset on the Mersey. Fishers on the beach at low tide (30x45cm-12x18in) s. two prov. 4-May-4 Ritchie, Toronto #66/R est:6000-9000 (C.D 36000)
£23333 $42000 €35000 Shipping off the Dutch coast (65x93cm-26x37in) s. 20-Apr-4 Sotheby's, Amsterdam #195/R est:35000-40000
£25000 $45500 €36500 Shipping in a calm (37x54cm-15x21in) s.i. 17-Jun-4 Christie's, London #10/R est:25000-35000

HULK, Abraham (snr-attrib) (1813-1897) Dutch
£1000 $1700 €1460 Dutch fishing boats in a calm (24x35cm-9x14in) bears sig. 29-Oct-3 Bonhams, Chester #480 est:700-1000

HULK, Hendrik (1842-1937) Dutch
£1250 $2037 €1800 Moored sailing vessel (18x30cm-7x12in) s. 29-Sep-3 Sotheby's, Amsterdam #63/R
£1267 $2293 €1900 Voilier pres d'un rivage pres d'un moulin (18x30cm-7x12in) s. 4-Apr-4 Salle des ventes Pillet, Lyon la Foret #37/R est:2000-2500
£1397 $2250 €2040 Dutch canal scene (30x46cm-12x18in) s. 20-Aug-3 James Julia, Fairfield #944/R est:1800-2800
£2215 $3920 €3300 Fishing boats at Arnheim. Fishing boats at Haarlem (30x46cm-12x18in) s. pair. 28-Apr-4 Schopman, Hamburg #668/R est:3300
£2762 $4750 €4033 Boats in an estuary (43x66cm-17x26in) s. 7-Dec-3 Freeman, Philadelphia #20 est:1500-2500
£3125 $5219 €4500 Shipping near the coast (45x68cm-18x27in) s. prov. 21-Oct-3 Sotheby's, Amsterdam #60a/R est:5000-7000
£4195 $7006 €6000 Moored sailing vessel (45x67cm-18x26in) s. 30-Jun-3 Sotheby's, Amsterdam #195/R

Works on paper
£355 $592 €500 City canal with moored boats (13x17cm-5x7in) s. W/C. 20-Oct-3 Glerum, Amsterdam #57/R

HULK, John Frederick (jnr) (1855-1913) Dutch
£3500 $6370 €5110 Bustling Dutch street scenes (27x21cm-11x8in) s. panel pair. 16-Jun-4 Christie's, Kensington #178/R est:3000-5000

HULK, John Frederick (snr) (1829-1911) Dutch
£1736 $2743 €2500 Cattle ferry on a river by a village (21x27cm-8x11in) s. panel. 2-Sep-3 Christie's, Amsterdam #168/R est:2500-3000

HULK, William F (1852-1906) British
£382 $615 €558 Herder boy with cows (36x25cm-14x10in) s. canvas on panel. 25-Aug-3 Lilla Bukowskis, Stockholm #411 (S.KR 5000)
£450 $774 €657 Wood gatherer on a path (20x13cm-8x5in) s. 5-Dec-3 Keys, Aylsham #611/R
£450 $833 €657 Cattle by and watering at a river, farm building beyond (48x38cm-19x15in) s. 13-Feb-4 Keys, Aylsham #663/R
£460 $833 €672 Cattle in a water meadow (40x38cm-16x15in) s. 2-Apr-4 Bracketts, Tunbridge Wells #461/R
£500 $860 €730 Drover and cattle in a lane (28x23cm-11x9in) s. 5-Dec-3 Keys, Aylsham #595/R
£759 $1305 €1108 Going home (61x77cm-24x30in) bears sig. exhib. 2-Dec-3 Ritchie, Toronto #64/R (C.D 1700)
£800 $1464 €1168 Cattle watering. Returning home (30x23cm-12x9in) s. pair. 27-Jan-4 Gorringes, Lewes #1618/R
£1250 $2250 €1825 Cattle watering (30x22cm-12x9in) s. canvasboard pair. 21-Jan-4 Sotheby's, Olympia #373/R est:800-1200

HULL, Clementina M (fl.1881-1908) British
Works on paper
£460 $782 €672 Springtime in the park, St Albans (29x23cm-11x9in) s. W/C bodycol. 25-Nov-3 Bonhams, Knowle #182

HULL, Edward (19th C) British
Works on paper
£480 $883 €701 Watermill (30x43cm-12x17in) s. W/C. 8-Jun-4 Gorringes, Lewes #480
£2400 $4008 €3504 The 2nd Life Guards on Manoeuvres (23x33cm-9x13in) W/C over pencil htd bodycol. 14-Oct-3 Sotheby's, London #499 est:400-600

HULL, Frederick William (1867-1953) British?
£350 $574 €511 Waiter on the Minnowburn (40x50cm-16x20in) s. board. 4-Jun-3 John Ross, Belfast #75
£430 $783 €650 Figures strolling along canal path (25x35cm-10x14in) s. board. 15-Jun-4 James Adam, Dublin #142/R
£533 $965 €800 Mixed bunch (46x36cm-18x14in) s. 31-Mar-4 James Adam, Dublin #152/R

HULL, Gregory (1950-) American
£870 $1600 €1270 Still life with fruit (107x81cm-42x32in) s. 26-Jun-4 Susanin's, Chicago #6135/R est:2000-3000

HULL, Richard (1955-) American
£420 $664 €609 Young female by window (30x25cm-12x10in) indis.sig.d.1907. 27-Jul-3 Desmond Judd, Cranbrook #1141

HULLGREN, Oscar (1869-1948) Swedish
£549 $1027 €802 Fishing vessel at Lofoten (73x99cm-29x39in) s. 29-Feb-4 Uppsala Auktionskammare, Uppsala #395 (S.KR 7500)

HULME, Alice L (fl.1877-1890) British
£460 $731 €672 Still life of nasturtiums in a vase (28x38cm-11x15in) s.d.90 board. 9-Sep-3 Gorringes, Lewes #2080

HULME, Frederick William (1816-1884) British
£5500 $10175 €8030 Shepherd resting with his flock (51x76cm-20x30in) s.d.1871. 14-Jul-4 Sotheby's, Olympia #62/R est:4000-6000
£5913 $10584 €8633 River landscape with children playing (57x75cm-22x30in) s.d.1858. 25-May-4 Bukowskis, Stockholm #363/R est:30000-40000 (S.KR 80000)
£8000 $14720 €11680 Near the common, Working, Surrey (51x67cm-20x26in) s.d.1859 prov.exhib. 11-Jun-4 Christie's, London #115/R est:10000-15000
£9800 $18130 €14308 Shepherd and his flock (60x51cm-24x20in) s.d.1873. 14-Jul-4 Sotheby's, Olympia #63/R est:2000-3000

Works on paper
£2700 $4914 €3942 On the Llugwy, vale of Bettws, North Wales (75x126cm-30x50in) s.d.1871 i.verso. 21-Jun-4 Bonhams, Bath #312/R est:3000-5000

HULSDONCK, Jacob van (1582-1647) Flemish
£17105 $31474 €26000 Raisins and plums in bowl on wooden ledge (40x49cm-16x19in) panel. 24-Jun-4 Christie's, Paris #27/R est:15000-20000
£89655 $165862 €130000 Still life with basket of fruit (27x37cm-11x15in) lit. 16-Feb-4 Giraudeau, Tours #46
£243421 $447895 €370000 Still life with prunes and apricots in a basket (41x64cm-16x25in) indis.sig. panel. 25-Jun-4 Piasa, Paris #15/R est:150000-200000
£391061 $700000 €570949 Still life of fruit in basket and flowers in basket (49x65cm-19x26in) s. panel. 27-May-4 Sotheby's, New York #26/R est:700000-900000

HULST, Frans de (1610-1661) Flemish
£4422 $7915 €6500 Riverside castle with towers and landing jetty with sailing boats (55x82cm-22x32in) panel. 17-Mar-4 Neumeister, Munich #351/R est:6500
£5298 $9642 €8000 River landscape with anchoring boats (30cm-12in circular) indis.i.d.1637 panel prov. 16-Jun-4 Dorotheum, Vienna #458/R est:1800-2500
£16552 $27641 €24000 River landscape with tower. Monastery by river (62x85cm-24x33in) panel prov.lit. 15-Nov-3 Lempertz, Koln #1068/R est:25000

HULST, Maerten Frans van der (17th C) Dutch
£6111 $11000 €8922 Travelers on a coastal road (26x40cm-10x16in) panel. 21-Jan-4 Sotheby's, New York #82/R est:8000-12000

Works on paper
£1781 $3027 €2600 Two figures fishing from a bridge over a stream (15x22cm-6x9in) mono.d.1643 black chk. 4-Nov-3 Sotheby's, Amsterdam #35/R est:1500-2000

HULSTYN, Cornelis Johannes van (1813-1879) Dutch
£533 $965 €800 La jeune tricoteuse (37x23cm-15x9in) s. panel. 30-Mar-4 Campo, Vlaamse Kaai #201
£1055 $1856 €1583 Flowers (39x28cm-15x11in) s.d.1871. 22-May-4 Dorotheum, Prague #11/R est:30000-45000 (C.KR 50000)

HULSWIT, Jan (1766-1822) Dutch
£5500 $10285 €8250 Shepherd and sheep on roadway (46x56cm-18x22in) s. 21-Jul-4 John Nicholson, Haslemere #194/R est:5000-8000

HULTEN, Carl Otto (1916-) Swedish
£906 $1541 €1323 Composition (39x46cm-15x18in) s. 5-Nov-3 AB Stockholms Auktionsverk #807/R (S.KR 12000)
£1330 $2381 €1942 Tropical landscape (92x73cm-36x29in) s.d.76. 28-May-4 Uppsala Auktionskammare, Uppsala #313/R est:10000-12000 (S.KR 18000)
£2719 $4622 €3970 Dialogue with landscape (83x100cm-33x39in) s. exhib. 4-Nov-3 Bukowskis, Stockholm #238/R est:12000-15000 (S.KR 36000)
£3408 $6135 €4976 The red watchman (100x81cm-39x32in) s.d.76 prov.exhib.lit. 26-Apr-4 Bukowskis, Stockholm #233/R est:20000-25000 (S.KR 47000)
£10196 $17334 €14886 The wall (144x168cm-57x66in) exhib.lit. 4-Nov-3 Bukowskis, Stockholm #229/R est:40000-50000 (S.KR 135000)

Works on paper
£680 $1156 €993 Figure composition (45x60cm-18x24in) s.d.53 mixed media. 5-Nov-3 AB Stockholms Auktionsverk #724/R (S.KR 9000)
£1964 $3338 €2867 What is the green aimed at? (70x100cm-28x39in) s. gouache exhib. 5-Nov-3 AB Stockholms Auktionsverk #808/R est:12000-15000 (S.KR 26000)

HULTON, William S (1852-1921) British
£800 $1296 €1160 Gondolier on the Venetian canal (30x18cm-12x7in) s.d.1893 wood panel. 25-May-3 Desmond Judd, Cranbrook #1033

HUMANN, O Victor (1874-1951) American
£782 $1400 €1142 Winter splendour, Worcester, Mass (81x96cm-32x38in) s. board. 14-May-4 Skinner, Boston #221/R est:1500-2000

HUMBERT DE SUPERVILLE, David Pierre Giottino (1770-1849) Dutch
Works on paper
£3056 $5500 €4462 Seated woman holding a plate. Angel with a carafe. Draped bearded man (22x15cm-9x6in) s. pen brown ink three. 22-Jan-4 Christie's, Rockefeller NY #133/R est:2500-3500

HUMBERT, Charles Auguste (1891-1958) Swiss
£505 $843 €732 Nature morte aux pivoines (100x82cm-39x32in) s.d. 21-Jun-3 Galerie du Rhone, Sion #388/R (S.FR 1100)

HUMBERT, Jacques Fernand (1842-1934) French
£699 $1203 €1000 Le coffret a bijoux (40x31cm-16x12in) s.d.85 panel. 8-Dec-3 Rossini, Paris #103/R
£2300 $4255 €3358 Portrait of a young lady (35x27cm-14x11in) s.d.76. 10-Mar-4 Sotheby's, Olympia #299/R est:2000-3000

HUMBERT, Jacques Fernand (attrib) (1842-1934) French
£467 $835 €700 Paix et jeune soldat (59x35cm-23x14in) 16-May-4 other European Auctioneer #39

HUMBERT, Jean-Charles-Ferdinand (1813-1881) Swiss
£524 $954 €765 Fisherman preparing their nets on the lakeside (41x27cm-16x11in) s.d.1873. 16-Jun-4 Fischer, Luzern #2194/R (S.FR 1200)
£946 $1627 €1381 Bull and cows by lake (46x60cm-18x24in) s. 2-Dec-3 Koller, Zurich #3001/R est:1600-2200 (S.FR 2100)

HUMBLOT, Robert (1907-1962) French
£671 $1248 €1000 Rose blanche dans un vase (38x25cm-15x10in) s. 3-Mar-4 Ferri, Paris #333
£972 $1624 €1400 Nature morte aux rascasses (38x62cm-15x24in) s. 21-Oct-3 Christie's, Paris #178/R
£1342 $2403 €2000 Les baux (38x61cm-15x24in) s. 25-May-4 Chambelland & Giafferi, Paris #75/R est:2000-2500
£1379 $2524 €2000 Bateaux echoues (65x92cm-26x36in) s. 1-Feb-4 Feletin, Province #110
£1611 $2996 €2400 Paysage du Midi (36x60cm-14x24in) s.d.56. 3-Mar-4 Ferri, Paris #365 est:1000-1500
£1678 $3003 €2500 Vase de roses (38x25cm-15x10in) s. 30-May-4 Eric Pillon, Calais #56/R
£2448 $4210 €3500 Nature morte au bouquet de roses (73x59cm-29x23in) s.d.56. 2-Dec-3 Calmels Cohen, Paris #51/R est:3500-4000

HUMBOLDT, Wilhelm (19th C) German?
Works on paper
£255 $392 €400 Portrait (28x24cm-11x9in) Indian ink silver htd white. 4-Sep-2 Schopman, Hamburg #16/R

HUMBORG, Adolf (1847-1913) Austrian
£2610 $4515 €3811 Fair with side show (64x88cm-25x35in) s.d.1894. 12-Dec-3 Kieselbach, Budapest #145/R (H.F 1000000)
£4700 $7990 €6862 Monastery kitchen (49x65cm-19x26in) s. panel. 22-Nov-3 Bonhams, Chester #329 est:2000-2500

HUME, Edith (fl.1862-1906) British
£780 $1303 €1139 Timely rescue (36x46cm-14x18in) mono.d.1859. 16-Nov-3 Desmond Judd, Cranbrook #1145
£2900 $5336 €4234 Time for a drink (30x23cm-12x9in) s. panel. 29-Mar-4 Bonhams, Bath #101/R est:2000-3000
£3600 $6012 €5256 Gathering wild flowers (30x24cm-12x9in) s. panel prov. 13-Nov-3 Christie's, Kensington #266/R est:1500-2000
Works on paper
£620 $980 €905 Children fishing off a rock (20x15cm-8x6in) s. W/C. 3-Sep-3 Bonhams, Bury St Edmunds #335/R

HUME, Gary (1962-) British
£8696 $16000 €12696 Magnolia door three (254x163cm-100x64in) s.i.d.1989 verso gloss paint prov. 10-Jun-4 Phillips, New York #415/R est:15000-20000
£19553 $35000 €28547 Beautiful - Kate Moss (117cm-46in circular) gloss paint on aluminum executed 2002 prov.exhib. 13-May-4 Phillips, New York #51/R est:50000-70000
£67039 $120000 €97877 Song (208x117cm-82x46in) s.i.d.1998 verso enamel on aluminum prov.lit. 13-May-4 Phillips, New York #9/R est:60000-80000
Works on paper
£217 $400 €317 Untitled (19x13cm-7x5in) s.d.2000 W/C prov. 10-Jun-4 Phillips, New York #662/R
£360 $644 €526 London Plane leaves (19x12cm-7x5in) s. Indian ink prov. 16-Mar-4 Bonhams, Knightsbridge #92/R

HUME, J Henry (c.1858-1881) British
£800 $1464 €1168 Sewing practice in a cottage yard (40x26cm-16x10in) s. 6-Jul-4 Bearnes, Exeter #539/R

HUMME, Julius (1825-1889) Canadian
£720 $1318 €1051 Road North of Orillia (29x44cm-11x17in) mono. board prov. 1-Jun-4 Joyner Waddington, Toronto #258/R est:2500-3500 (C.D 1800)
£1080 $1976 €1577 Sunset on the Upper Black River (29x44cm-11x17in) mono. prov. 1-Jun-4 Joyner Waddington, Toronto #259/R est:2300-3500 (C.D 2700)
£1440 $2635 €2102 Basket weaving on the Black River (52x40cm-20x16in) mono. prov. 1-Jun-4 Joyner Waddington, Toronto #254/R est:3000-5000 (C.D 3600)
Works on paper
£1689 $2871 €2466 Portrait of an Indian Chief (34x26cm-13x10in) s. W/C lit. 21-Nov-3 Walker's, Ottawa #102/R est:800-1200 (C.D 3750)

HUMMEL, Carl (1821-1907) German
£839 $1401 €1200 Mountain stream (31x47cm-12x19in) 10-Oct-3 Winterberg, Heidelberg #605
Works on paper
£268 $494 €400 Landscape near Tivoli (36x54cm-14x21in) s.i. pencil wash. 26-Mar-4 Venator & Hansten, Koln #1595/R
£278 $453 €400 Landscape in Italian Alps (37x49cm-15x19in) s.d.65 W/C. 25-Sep-3 Dr Fritz Nagel, Stuttgart #1150/R
£403 $741 €600 Rocky high mountain landscape near Obersee in Switzerland. i.d.12/8 50 brush pencil board. 26-Mar-4 Venator & Hansten, Koln #1593/R
£455 $759 €650 Trees on slope (20x32cm-8x13in) s.i.d.6.Mai pencil. 10-Oct-3 Winterberg, Heidelberg #606
£503 $926 €750 Pine trees (43x28cm-17x11in) s.i.d.1850 brush on pencil board. 26-Mar-4 Venator & Hansten, Koln #1594/R
£646 $1157 €950 Paysage de montagne au chateau fort (20x30cm-8x12in) s.d.68 W/C. 17-Mar-4 Maigret, Paris #21/R
£699 $1168 €1000 Southern landscape with river (24x38cm-9x15in) s.d.1862. 28-Jun-3 Dannenberg, Berlin #709/R

HUMMEL, Eugen (1812-?) Austrian
£2252 $4121 €3400 Girl with soldiers on battlefield (55x44cm-22x17in) 7-Apr-4 Dorotheum, Salzburg #93/R est:3000-4000

HUMMEL, Fritz (1828-1905) German
£6643 $11294 €9500 Portrait of Kaiser Friedrich III in uniform (137x91cm-54x36in) s. 20-Nov-3 Van Ham, Cologne #1639/R est:1900

HUMMEL, Theodor (1864-1939) German
£417 $696 €600 Fishing boats in Hamburg harbour (59x50cm-23x20in) s. 22-Oct-3 Neumeister, Munich #717/R

HUMPHREY, Jack Weldon (1901-1967) Canadian
£960 $1757 €1402 Portrait of a lady with a vase of flowers (60x50cm-24x20in) st.sig. portrait gentleman verso double-sided. 1-Jun-4 Joyner Waddington, Toronto #205/R est:2000-3000 (C.D 2400)
£3659 $6549 €5342 Still life with old saxon violin (61x76cm-24x30in) s. i.verso painted c.1933 double-sided prov. 27-May-4 Heffel, Vancouver #129/R est:4000-6000 (C.D 9000)
Works on paper
£273 $445 €399 Mexican village (33x28cm-13x11in) s. lithographic crayon prov. 23-Sep-3 Ritchie, Toronto #149/R (C.D 600)
£446 $768 €651 Fishing boats at the Wharf (36x52cm-14x20in) s. W/C. 2-Dec-3 Joyner Waddington, Toronto #463 (C.D 1000)
£602 $1120 €879 Trout files no 1 (38x56cm-15x22in) s. i.verso W/C ink prov. 2-Mar-4 Ritchie, Toronto #149/R (C.D 1500)
£625 $1075 €913 Cottages near the water (36x49cm-14x19in) s. W/C prov. 2-Dec-3 Joyner Waddington, Toronto #462 (C.D 1400)

HUMPHREY, Ozias (1742-1810) British
Miniatures
£5405 $10000 €7891 Mrs Sarah Hill (5x3cm-2x1in) oval. 12-Mar-4 Du Mouchelle, Detroit #2032/R est:1000-2000
Works on paper
£9000 $15300 €13140 Portrait of George Earl Macartney, the first Ambassador to China (58x49cm-23x19in) pastel. 27-Nov-3 Sotheby's, London #219/R est:10000-15000

HUMPHREY, Ozias (attrib) (1742-1810) British
£6000 $10200 €8760 Portrait of an officer (32x19cm-13x7in) panel prov. 27-Nov-3 Sotheby's, London #149 est:2000-3000

HUMPHREY, Ralph (1932-1990) American
£1444 $2600 €2108 Untitled (20x20cm-8x8in) s.i.d.1962 prov.exhib. 24-Apr-4 David Rago, Lambertville #547/R est:800-1200
£2639 $4750 €3853 Untitled (18x24cm-7x9in) acrylic paper collage. 24-Apr-4 David Rago, Lambertville #239/R est:800-1200
£3056 $5500 €4462 Rio II (60x60cm-24x24in) s.d.1969 acrylic day-glo prov.exhib. 24-Apr-4 David Rago, Lambertville #525/R est:1000-2000
£6667 $12000 €9734 Untitled (36x36cm-14x14in) s. prov.exhib. 24-Apr-4 David Rago, Lambertville #347/R est:2000-3000
Sculpture
£3000 $5460 €4380 Untitled (162x115x15cm-64x45x6in) acrylic modelling paste exec 1974-75 prov. 4-Feb-4 Sotheby's, Olympia #189/R est:3000-4000
£3243 $6000 €4735 Flick (24x28x14cm-9x11x6in) s.i.d.1979-80 inside acrylic modelling paste over wood prov. 12-Feb-4 Sotheby's, New York #207/R est:3000-3500
Works on paper
£889 $1600 €1298 Untitled, from the Window Series (44x30cm-17x12in) chl prov. 24-Apr-4 David Rago, Lambertville #35/R est:800-1200

HUMPHREYS, Ian (20th C) British
£728 $1326 €1100 Westwind (15x30cm-6x12in) s. board. 15-Jun-4 James Adam, Dublin #122/R

HUMPHRIES, Barry John (1934-) Australian
£840 $1528 €1226 Self portrait (46x46cm-18x18in) s.i.d.04. 16-Jun-4 Deutscher-Menzies, Melbourne #14a/R est:3000-5000 (A.D 2200)
Works on paper
£890 $1513 €1299 Bigscape (39x49cm-15x19in) synthetic polymer paint composition board prov.exhib. 24-Nov-3 Sotheby's, Melbourne #100/R (A.D 2100)

HUMPHRISS, Charles Henry (1867-1934) British
Sculpture
£1622 $3000 €2368 American Indian astride a horse (41cm-16in) s. bronze marble base. 13-Mar-4 DeFina, Austinburg #557/R est:6000-9000
£10335 $18500 €15089 Appeal to the Great Spirit (76cm-30in) s.d.1906 verdigris brown pat bronze st.f. Roman Bronze Works. 8-Jan-4 James Julia, Fairfield #689/R est:6000-8000

HUNAEUS, Andreas (1814-1866) Danish
£562 $967 €821 Portraits of F.Chr. Emil Dahlstrom and his wife Sophie Wilhelmine (26x20cm-10x8in) one s.d.1846 pair. 2-Dec-3 Kunsthallen, Copenhagen #549/R (D.KR 6000)
£2383 $3765 €3455 Portrait of Oscar Frederik Mollerup as a child (46x35cm-18x14in) s.d.1846. 3-Sep-3 Museumsbygningen, Copenhagen #205/R est:8000-10000 (D.KR 25500)

HUNDAHL, P (19th C) Danish

£356 $647 €534 Ship's portrait of Cecilie of Arosjobing (43x54cm-17x21in) s. panel. 19-Jun-4 Rasmussen, Havnen #2338 (D.KR 4000)
£379 $607 €553 Seascape with the schooner Cecilie of Aeroskjobing (48x69cm-19x27in) panel. 22-Sep-3 Rasmussen, Vejle #307/R (D.KR 4000)

HUNDERTWASSER, Friedrich (1928-2000) Austrian

£9928 $18267 €14495 Nana Hyaku Mizu. s.num.132/200 seven woodcuts in colour lit. 29-Mar-4 Rasmussen, Copenhagen #166/R est:100000-125000 (D.KR 110000)
£36000 $60120 €52560 Erste spirale im guten sinne des buddhistschen zeichens (91x117cm-36x46in) s.d.1961 tempera oil brick rice paper chk on jute prov.exhib.lit. 21-Oct-3 Sotheby's, London #395/R est:35000-45000
£240000 $441600 €350400 La tour de Babel perfore le solel un spiraloid - tower of Babel (130x162cm-51x64in) s.d.1959 s.i.d.verso oil egg tempera W/C wrapping paper chk PV. 23-Jun-4 Sotheby's, London #22/R est:70000-90000

Prints
£1765 $3000 €2577 Last tears (61x42cm-24x17in) s. col woodcut. 31-Oct-3 Sotheby's, New York #292/R
£1765 $3000 €2577 The rain falls far from us (43x53cm-17x21in) s. col woodcut. 31-Oct-3 Sotheby's, New York #290/R
£1800 $3312 €2700 Sea rise II, travel to the sea and with the train (63x50cm-25x20in) s.i.d.1967 col lithograph one of 267. 12-Jun-4 Villa Grisebach, Berlin #749/R est:2000-3000
£1824 $3266 €2700 Fall in cloud, fall in fog, fall out (29x35cm-11x14in) s. num.680/999 col serigraph plexiglas. 4-May-4 Calmels Cohen, Paris #253/R est:3000-4000
£1912 $3250 €2792 Tears of artist (57x43cm-22x17in) s. col woodcut. 31-Oct-3 Sotheby's, New York #291/R
£2000 $3580 €3000 Flight (41x59cm-16x23in) s.i. col silkscreen board. 15-May-4 Van Ham, Cologne #677/R est:3500
£2000 $3640 €2920 Window out of the pond, window into the pond (40x33cm-16x13in) s.i.d.1978 num.103/280 col etching aquatint. 1-Jul-4 Sotheby's, London #187/R est:2500-3000
£2029 $3328 €2800 Town in town 801, Koschatzky 78 (56x76cm-22x30in) s. num.XLVII/LXXI col silkscreen one of 421. 27-May-3 Sotheby's, Amsterdam #606/R est:3500-4500
£2067 $3720 €3100 See journey (63x50cm-25x20in) s.i.d.1967 col lithograph board. 24-Apr-4 Dr Lehr, Berlin #178/R est:2200
£2067 $3699 €3100 Kolumbus rainy day in India (45x59cm-18x23in) s. col serigraph. 15-May-4 Bassenge, Berlin #6903/R est:2500
£2067 $3803 €3100 Kolumbus rainy day in India (46x59cm-18x23in) s. col serigraph metal board one of 300. 12-Jun-4 Villa Grisebach, Berlin #752/R est:1800-2400
£2133 $3925 €3200 Mit dem Liebe warten tut weh, wenn die liebe woanders ist - Rainy day (36x60cm-14x24in) s.i.col serigraph board one of 300. 12-Jun-4 Villa Grisebach, Berlin #750/R est:2000-3000
£2148 $3844 €3200 Night train (51x73cm-20x29in) s.d.19 Mai 1978 col silkscreen. 25-May-4 Dorotheum, Vienna #264/R est:3200-3400
£2200 $3938 €3300 Night train (55x73cm-22x29in) s.d. col silkscreen. 15-May-4 Van Ham, Cologne #680/R est:3000
£2200 $4026 €3212 Waiting houses (30x40cm-12x16in) s.d.1969 num.52/200 col woodcut. 3-Jun-4 Christie's, Kensington #413/R est:2500-3000
£2215 $4075 €3300 Composition with spiral (14x19cm-6x7in) s.i.d.1962 etching. 26-Mar-4 Ketterer, Hamburg #466/R est:2800-3200
£2238 $3804 €3200 Boy with the green hair (52x37cm-20x15in) s.d.1967 lithograph. 26-Nov-3 Dorotheum, Vienna #240/R est:3600-3800
£2271 $4020 €3316 Good-bye from Africa (46x62cm-18x24in) s.num.17/90 CLX col silkscreen lit. 27-Apr-4 AB Stockholms Auktionsverk #1308/R est:20000-25000 (S.KR 31000)
£2282 $4085 €3400 Rainy day on loves waves (40x60cm-16x24in) s.i. col silkscreen. 25-May-4 Dorotheum, Vienna #261/R est:3400-3600
£2333 $4177 €3500 City-city (44x64cm-17x25in) s. col silkscreen. 15-May-4 Van Ham, Cologne #681/R est:4500
£2353 $4000 €3435 Olympic Games, Munich (103x65cm-41x26in) s.i.d.1971 col screenprint. 31-Oct-3 Sotheby's, New York #288/R
£2353 $4000 €3435 Two to thirteen windows (37x51cm-15x20in) s.d.1979 col woodcut. 31-Oct-3 Sotheby's, New York #293/R
£2533 $4535 €3800 It hurts to wait with love when love is elsewhere (49x67cm-19x26in) s.i. col silkscreen board. 15-May-4 Van Ham, Cologne #676/R est:4000
£2533 $4661 €3800 Small palace of illness (34x24cm-13x9in) s.i.d. col woodcut. 11-Jun-4 Hauswedell & Nolte, Hamburg #1314/R est:4000
£2670 $4458 €3898 Town in town (56x76cm-22x30in) s. col serigraph lit. 24-Jun-3 Germann, Zurich #416/R est:6000-7000 (S.FR 5900)
£2685 $4805 €4000 Island of the lost wishes (22x18cm-9x7in) s. col woodcut silver. 25-May-4 Karl & Faber, Munich #348/R est:3500
£2759 $4607 €4000 Rainy day (66x42cm-26x17in) s.d.1968 col serigraph gold. 9-Jul-3 Hugo Ruef, Munich #389 est:300
£2958 $4910 €4200 Rainy day with Walter Kampmann (41x58cm-16x23in) s.i.d.1969 col serigraph. 13-Jun-3 Hauswedell & Nolte, Hamburg #677/R est:4000
£3000 $5460 €4380 Tears of an artist (45x34cm-18x13in) s.num90A col woodcut. 30-Jun-4 Christie's, London #236/R est:3000-5000
£3125 $5219 €4500 Two trees on the Regentag ship (37x51cm-15x20in) col woodcut gold silver. 24-Oct-3 Ketterer, Hamburg #385/R est:5000-6000
£3200 $5728 €4800 Testament in yellow (51x73cm-20x29in) s. col silkscreen board. 15-May-4 Van Ham, Cologne #675/R est:2500
£3239 $5377 €4600 Testament in yellow (52x74cm-20x29in) s.i.d.24.Mai 1971 col serigraph. 13-Jun-3 Hauswedell & Nolte, Hamburg #678/R est:5000
£3333 $5967 €5000 Do not wait houses-move (50x37cm-20x15in) s.d. col woodcut. 15-May-4 Van Ham, Cologne #683/R est:4000
£3497 $5944 €5000 The explosion (66x80cm-26x31in) s.d. col lithograph. 26-Nov-3 Dorotheum, Vienna #242/R est:5000-5500
£3667 $6563 €5500 Counting raindrops (56x76cm-22x30in) s.d. col lithograph col silkscreen. 15-May-4 Van Ham, Cologne #682/R est:6000
£3691 $6607 €5500 Testament in yellow (52x74cm-20x29in) s.d.30 april 1971 col silkscreen on silver foil on board. 25-May-4 Dorotheum, Vienna #262/R est:6000-8000
£3803 $6313 €5400 King Kong (60x47cm-24x19in) s.i.d.1968 col serigraph. 13-Jun-3 Hauswedell & Nolte, Hamburg #676/R est:5000
£3819 $6226 €5500 Water on roof (52x39cm-20x15in) s.i.d.19. April 1987 col woodcut. 27-Sep-3 Dr Fritz Nagel, Stuttgart #9553/R est:5900
£4500 $8190 €6570 Yellow last will (51x73cm-20x29in) s.d.1971 num.117/475 offset col lithograph. 1-Jul-4 Sotheby's, London #189/R est:5000-6000
£6040 $10691 €9000 Water on the rooftops (57x41cm-22x16in) s.i.d.19.April 1987 col woodcut. 30-Apr-4 Dr Fritz Nagel, Stuttgart #841/R est:4700
£16779 $29698 €25000 Nana Hyaku Mizu portfolio (67x54cm-26x21in) s.i.d. woodcut lit. 28-Apr-4 Wiener Kunst Auktionen, Vienna #293/R est:28000-40000

Works on paper
£2939 $5407 €4291 Boat (30x44cm-12x17in) mono.d.1990 mixed media. 29-Mar-4 Goodman, Sydney #121/R est:2500-3500 (A.D 7200)
£4196 $7217 €6000 Composition (23x12cm-9x5in) s. W/C collage. 3-Dec-3 Hauswedell & Nolte, Hamburg #810/R est:4000
£31250 $53125 €45000 Grassy raindrops (66x48cm-26x19in) W/C prov.exhib.lit. 28-Oct-3 Wiener Kunst Auktionen, Vienna #236/R est:30000-80000
£42000 $76440 €61320 Les nuages sur contretemps Ill de Paris (34x56cm-13x22in) s.i.d.1965 i.verso W/C paper suchard foil paper collage prov.lit. 5-Feb-4 Christie's, London #101/R est:30000-40000
£45000 $82800 €65700 Count down (56x49cm-22x19in) s.i.d.1980-82 s.i.d.verso W/C egg tempera lacquer on board. 25-Jun-4 Christie's, London #125/R est:40000-60000
£47486 $85000 €69330 Rio Negro (53x43cm-21x17in) s.i.d.1977 W/C oil lacquer Chinese ink paper on linen prov. 13-May-4 Sotheby's, New York #125/R est:60000-80000
£65000 $108550 €94900 Lauf in die Sonne (36x100cm-14x39in) s.indis.i.d.1964 s.i.d.1964 W/C gold paint prov.exhib. 22-Oct-3 Christie's, London #35/R est:40000-60000
£69444 $118056 €100000 Come and go walking with me - conversation (51x73cm-20x29in) s.i.d.1970 i. verso oil col pen W/C egg sand polyvinyl exhib. 28-Oct-3 Wiener Kunst Auktionen, Vienna #245/R est:100000-150000

HUNDT, Hermann Baptist (1894-1974) German

£1259 $2165 €1800 Circus scene (100x77cm-39x30in) s. 4-Dec-3 Van Ham, Cologne #227/R est:2200

HUNG, Francisco (1937-) Chinese

£430 $690 €628 Homage to landscape (80x100cm-31x39in) s. 16-Mar-3 Subastas Odalys, Caracas #37
£497 $810 €726 Untitled (49x40cm-19x16in) s. acrylic. 20-Jul-3 Subastas Odalys, Caracas #76
£509 $875 €743 Untitled (60x50cm-24x20in) s. painted 1979. 7-Dec-3 Subastas Odalys, Caracas #50/R
£570 $900 €832 Untitled (100x80cm-39x31in) s. painted 1991. 1-Dec-2 Subastas Odalys, Caracas #75/R
£616 $1145 €899 Untitled (60x40cm-24x16in) s. painted 1986. 14-Mar-4 Subastas Odalys, Caracas #92
£654 $1125 €955 Untitled (49x39cm-19x15in) s. painted 1979. 7-Dec-3 Subastas Odalys, Caracas #34
£674 $1125 €984 Prelude to a storm (70x60cm-28x24in) s. painted 1998. 13-Jul-3 Subastas Odalys, Caracas #37/R
£709 $1305 €1064 Untitled (80x62cm-31x24in) s. acrylic painted 1960. 27-Jun-4 Subastas Odalys, Caracas #83
£1076 $1980 €1614 Basket (80x100cm-31x39in) s. acrylic painted 2000. 27-Jun-4 Subastas Odalys, Caracas #131
£1383 $2310 €2019 Fragrance (121x191cm-48x75in) s. acrylic painted 1988. 13-Jul-3 Subastas Odalys, Caracas #68
£1600 $2720 €2336 Fragrance (121x191cm-48x75in) s. acrylic painted 1988. 23-Nov-3 Subastas Odalys, Caracas #56/R
£2462 $4480 €3693 Untitled (114x108cm-45x43in) s. painted 1969. 21-Jun-4 Subastas Odalys, Caracas #91/R
£2582 $4390 €3770 Floating figure (120x80cm-47x31in) s. painted 1980. 23-Nov-3 Subastas Odalys, Caracas #105/R est:4000
£3407 $5860 €4974 Untitled (120x140cm-47x55in) s. painted 1968. 7-Dec-3 Subastas Odalys, Caracas #66/R est:7000
£4213 $7035 €6151 Floating figure (161x111cm-63x44in) s. painted 1968. 19-Oct-3 Subastas Odalys, Caracas #7/R est:5000

Works on paper
£475 $750 €694 Untitled (76x50cm-30x20in) s. mixed media panel. 27-Apr-3 Subastas Odalys, Caracas #18

HUNN, Tom (fl.1878-1908) British

Works on paper
£250 $460 €365 On the Thames (31x67cm-12x26in) s.d.1903 W/C. 23-Mar-4 Bonhams, Knightsbridge #199/R
£320 $506 €464 Water mill (33x22cm-13x9in) s. W/C. 3-Sep-3 Bonhams, Bury St Edmunds #336
£375 $676 €548 Peacock in an English park (37x54cm-15x21in) s.d.1909 W/C. 26-Jan-4 Lilla Bukowskis, Stockholm #740 (S.KR 5000)
£380 $635 €555 Tranquil mill pond (20x26cm-8x10in) s.d.85 W/C. 14-Oct-3 Rosebery Fine Art, London #550
£380 $657 €555 St. Peter and St. Paul, West Clandon (36x25cm-14x10in) s.d.98 W/C. 9-Dec-3 Clarke Gammon, Guildford #25

HUNSCHE (?) Dutch?

£1923 $3308 €2808 By the Munttoren in Amsterdam (40x30cm-16x12in) s. prov. 2-Dec-3 Bukowskis, Stockholm #277a/R est:30000-35000 (S.KR 25000)

HUNT, Alfred (fl.1870-1874) British

£820 $1451 €1197 Fishing vessel in choppy seas off the shore (51x78cm-20x31in) s.d.1876. 27-Apr-4 Bonhams, Knowle #100/R

HUNT, Alfred William (1830-1896) British

£44000 $80960 €64240 When the leave begin to turn (44x38cm-17x15in) init. prov.exhib. 11-Jun-4 Christie's, London #93/R est:3000-5000

Works on paper
£750 $1350 €1095 Near Athens (18x24cm-7x9in) W/C prov. 21-Jan-4 Sotheby's, Olympia #183/R
£2200 $4026 €3212 Nocturne - fishing boats at twilight (27x39cm-11x15in) W/C scratching out prov. 3-Jun-4 Christie's, London #10/R est:2000-3000
£2500 $4575 €3650 Goring Lock, stormy day (23x37cm-9x15in) init.i. verso pencil W/C scratching out prov. 3-Jun-4 Christie's, London #7/R est:3000-5000
£2600 $4758 €3796 Upper Thames (21x35cm-8x14in) init.d.1870 pencil W/C scratching out prov. 3-Jun-4 Christie's, London #9/R est:2000-3000
£4000 $7320 €5840 Mill on the Coquet, Northumberland (28x39cm-11x15in) s.d.1887 i. verso pencil W/C scratching out prov. 3-Jun-4 Christie's, London #8/R est:3000-5000

HUNT, Arthur Ackland (fl.1863-1913) British

Works on paper
£1650 $2987 €2409 Interior of Gouliot caves, Sark (25x18cm-10x7in) s.i.d.1894 W/C. 1-Apr-4 Martel Maides, Guernsey #247 est:600-800

£2150 $4021 €3139 Dixcart Bay, Sark (29x24cm-11x9in) s.i.d.1894 W/C. 22-Jul-4 Martel Maides, Guernsey #175/R est:1000-1500

HUNT, Bryan (1947-) American

Sculpture

£1622 $3000 €2368 Untitled (854x29x12cm-336x11x5in) brown pat bronze. 12-Feb-4 Sotheby's, New York #214/R est:4000-6000
£23952 $40000 €34970 E III, E series (20x162x20cm-8x64x8in) wood silk foil lacquer prov. 13-Nov-3 Sotheby's, New York #135/R est:40000-60000
£35928 $60000 €52455 Arch falls (259x152x122cm-102x60x48in) cast bronze limestone base prov. 13-Nov-3 Sotheby's, New York #139/R est:35000-45000
£44693 $80000 €65252 Daphne (358x58x53cm-141x23x21in) with sig.d.78 num.2/3 green pat bronze. 13-May-4 Sotheby's, New York #203/R est:30000-40000
£56886 $95000 €83054 Shift (305cm-120in) bronze edition 1 of 3 prov.exhib. 13-Nov-3 Sotheby's, New York #138/R est:30000-40000

Works on paper

£599 $1000 €875 Airship Placement drawing no 5 (60x74cm-24x29in) s.d.75 graphite linseed oil paper collage prov. 12-Nov-3 Christie's, Rockefeller NY #607/R
£1757 $3250 €2565 Separation I (76x59cm-30x23in) s.d.10 7 82 pencil conte crayon linseed oil prov. 12-Feb-4 Sotheby's, New York #260/R est:1500-2000

HUNT, Cecil Arthur (1873-1965) British

£800 $1480 €1168 Apennines (51x76cm-20x30in) s. i. verso. 14-Jul-4 Christie's, Kensington #1039/R

Works on paper

£250 $430 €365 Trepani and Mount Eyre (30x36cm-12x14in) s.d.1922 verso W/C. 5-Dec-3 Keys, Aylsham #455/R
£260 $481 €380 Taomina (28x36cm-11x14in) s. W/C. 13-Feb-4 Keys, Aylsham #446
£280 $468 €409 View of Dartmoor (26x74cm-10x29in) s. W/C bodycol. 14-Oct-3 Bonhams, Knightsbridge #46/R
£560 $1008 €818 Hills of Skye (28x42cm-11x17in) s.i. gouache. 22-Apr-4 Lawrence, Crewkerne #808/R
£600 $1002 €876 Gravesend Reach the Thames (23x33cm-9x13in) s. W/C. 12-Nov-3 Halls, Shrewsbury #242/R
£1000 $1840 €1460 Trapani with Mount Erice beyond, Sicily (30x37cm-12x15in) s. W/C. 8-Jun-4 Bonhams, New Bond Street #135/R est:800-1200
£1050 $1964 €1533 Glen Dochart (27x38cm-11x15in) s. W/C. 21-Jul-4 Bonhams, New Bond Street #157/R est:300-500
£1100 $1870 €1606 Rain on the hills, Scotland (11x16cm-4x6in) s.i.verso W/C bodycol scratching out buff paper. 20-Nov-3 Christie's, London #165/R est:1000-1500
£1100 $1870 €1606 Jura mountains, France (23x29cm-9x11in) s.i.verso W/C bodycol scratching out. 20-Nov-3 Christie's, London #169/R est:1200-1800
£1300 $2210 €1898 Bridge at Sospel, Alpes Maritimes, Provence (28x38cm-11x15in) s.i. pencil W/C htd white buff paper exhib. 20-Nov-3 Christie's, London #173/R est:1200-1800
£1400 $2380 €2044 Isle of Skye (21x30cm-8x12in) s.i. pencil W/C bodycol scratching out. 20-Nov-3 Christie's, London #162/R est:1500-2000
£1400 $2380 €2044 Valescure, near St Raphael, Var, Southern France (24x34cm-9x13in) s.i.verso pencil W/C scratching out. 20-Nov-3 Christie's, London #172/R est:1000-1500
£1400 $2576 €2044 Dunollie Castle, Oban, Argyllshire (27x37cm-11x15in) s.i. W/C bodycol prov. 25-Mar-4 Christie's, Kensington #195/R est:1500-2500
£1600 $2720 €2336 Ruined church at Coleville, Cambridgshire (28x38cm-11x15in) s. pencil pen brown in, W/C htd bodycol. 20-Nov-3 Christie's, London #167/R est:1500-2000
£2200 $3740 €3212 Trees by the waters edge (36x54cm-14x21in) s. W/C bodycol scratching out. 20-Nov-3 Christie's, London #171/R est:1500-2000
£2400 $4080 €3504 Storm on Loch Awe,. Argyllshire (27x36cm-11x14in) s. W/C htd bodycol scratching out prov.exhib. 20-Nov-3 Christie's, London #164/R est:1200-1800

HUNT, Charles (jnr) (1829-1900) British

£700 $1253 €1022 Young guitarist (46x35cm-18x14in) s.d.1878 oval. 27-May-4 Christie's, Kensington #307/R
£1100 $1826 €1606 Squirrel (30x25cm-12x10in) s.d.84. 1-Oct-3 Sotheby's, Olympia #26/R est:1000-1500
£1400 $2604 €2044 Dollies on a donkey (29x22cm-11x9in) init. panel prov. 4-Mar-4 Christie's, Kensington #627/R est:1500-2000
£3800 $6840 €5548 Playtime (60x91cm-24x36in) s.d.79. 21-Jan-4 Sotheby's, Olympia #288/R est:2500-4500

HUNT, Charles D (1840-1914) American

£270 $500 €394 Fishing on a mountain lake (25x36cm-10x14in) s. canvas on plywood. 15-Jul-4 Doyle, New York #46/R

HUNT, Charles Henry (1857-1938) Australian

£2024 $3259 €2955 Head gardener (29x21cm-11x8in) s.d.87 board prov.exhib. 13-Oct-3 Joel, Victoria #237 est:1500-2000 (A.D 5000)

HUNT, Edgar (1876-1953) British

£3800 $6916 €5548 Farmyard friends (19x26cm-7x10in) s. board. 29-Jun-4 Bonhams, Knowle #72 est:4000-6000
£6000 $10200 €8760 Pigeons by a terracotta pot (18x25cm-7x10in) s.d.1913. 25-Nov-3 Bonhams, Knowle #261/R est:3500-4500
£9500 $16150 €13870 Friendly confrontation (28x38cm-11x15in) s.d.1943 board. 27-Nov-3 Sotheby's, London #376/R est:6000-8000
£10000 $17000 €14600 Cockerel, chickens and doves outside a barn, with chicks playing with a pea pod (30x32cm-12x13in) s. 25-Nov-3 Christie's, London #204/R est:10000-15000
£11261 $19369 €16441 Girl feeding the goats (46x61cm-18x24in) s.d.1888. 8-Dec-3 Philippe Schuler, Zurich #3414/R est:20000-25000 (S.FR 25000)
£12000 $20400 €17520 Chickens by a rabbit hutch (20x28cm-8x11in) s.d.1923. 19-Nov-3 Bonhams, New Bond Street #103/R est:7000-10000
£12000 $20400 €17520 Hen and chicks in a barn (20x28cm-8x11in) s.d.1924. 19-Nov-3 Bonhams, New Bond Street #104/R est:7000-10000
£14000 $22960 €20440 Chickens and ducks feeding on cabbages and vegetables by barn door (37x27cm-15x11in) s.d.1924. 3-Jun-3 Fellows & Sons, Birmingham #82/R est:12000-18000
£15000 $25050 €21900 Farmyard friends (28x38cm-11x15in) s.d.1922 prov. 13-Nov-3 Christie's, Kensington #229/R est:15000-20000
£16000 $27200 €23360 Goats, a rabbit and chickens in a barn. Donkey and geese feeding (28x38cm-11x15in) s.d.1951 board pair. 25-Nov-3 Christie's, London #202/R est:12000-18000
£23000 $39100 €33580 Feathered friends (91x61cm-36x24in) s.d.1904. 27-Nov-3 Sotheby's, London #377/R est:25000-35000
£25000 $42500 €36500 Goats, ducks and pigeons in a stable doorway (51x76cm-20x30in) s.d.1907 prov. 25-Nov-3 Christie's, London #201/R est:15000-20000
£30000 $54600 €43800 Farmyard neighbours. Outside world (35x30cm-14x12in) each s.d.1926 two. 1-Jul-4 Sotheby's, London #353/R est:15000-20000
£32000 $54400 €46720 Farmyard scene with donkeys and poultry (51x76cm-20x30in) s.d.1925 prov. 19-Nov-3 Bonhams, New Bond Street #102/R est:15000-20000

HUNT, Edward Aubrey (1855-1922) British

£1100 $1837 €1606 Noonday rest (31x44cm-12x17in) s. 16-Oct-3 Bonhams, Edinburgh #189 est:800-1200
£1200 $2196 €1752 Fishing vessels off Venice (20x30cm-8x12in) init. 7-Apr-4 Woolley & Wallis, Salisbury #306/R est:750-1000
£1300 $2171 €1898 Moorish fishermen (34x44cm-13x17in) s. 16-Oct-3 Bonhams, Edinburgh #188/R est:800-1200
£1600 $2768 €2336 Gate of the town (44x34cm-17x13in) s.i. panel. 11-Dec-3 Lyon & Turnbull, Edinburgh #3/R est:1000-1500

HUNT, Esther (1875-1951) American

Works on paper

£419 $700 €612 Young girl with fan. s. W/C. 15-Nov-3 Harvey Clar, Oakland #1330
£882 $1500 €1288 Chinese girl holding umbrella (20x13cm-8x5in) s. W/C prov. 18-Nov-3 John Moran, Pasadena #65 est:2000-3000
£1720 $3250 €2511 Portrait of Chinese girl holding paper parasol (28x18cm-11x7in) bears s.i. W/C. 17-Feb-4 John Moran, Pasadena #60b/R est:1500-2000

HUNT, Georgina (1922-) British

£900 $1503 €1314 Harmony of opposites, no 33 (122x122cm-48x48in) s. acrylic. 16-Oct-3 Christie's, Kensington #718/R

HUNT, Holman (?) British

£1000 $1730 €1460 The forbidden fruit. after Pre-Raphaelite School. 14-Dec-3 Desmond Judd, Cranbrook #1137

HUNT, Lynn Bogue (1878-1960) American

£1744 $3000 €2546 Grouse eating bittersweet berries (38x30cm-15x12in) s. 6-Dec-3 South Bay, Long Island #29/R

HUNT, Millson (fl.1875-1900) British

£300 $549 €438 Shipping scene (23x38cm-9x15in) 28-Jul-4 Mallams, Oxford #316/R
£400 $692 €584 Lifeboat and sailing smack going to the assistance of a dis-masted brig (24x44cm-9x17in) s.d.90. 9-Dec-3 Anderson & Garland, Newcastle #476
£460 $833 €672 On the Cornish Coast, ship wreck in stormy seas (48x74cm-19x29in) 31-Mar-4 Brightwells, Leominster #485
£800 $1328 €1168 On the Llugwy. Mountain stream (18x39cm-7x15in) s.d.1873 two. 1-Oct-3 Woolley & Wallis, Salisbury #255/R

HUNT, Peter and WHORF, Nancy (20th C) American

£271 $425 €396 Boston and Main Railroad (33x20cm-13x8in) s. tin. 20-Apr-3 Outer Cape Auctions, Provincetown #61/R

HUNT, R (19th C) British

£1611 $2964 €2400 Boy with animals by water (77x128cm-30x50in) s.d.81. 25-Mar-4 Dr Fritz Nagel, Stuttgart #724/R est:1800

HUNT, Reuben (19th C) British

£650 $1170 €949 Study of a goat eating cabbage leaves from a bucket (18x12cm-7x5in) s. board. 21-Apr-4 Tennants, Leyburn #1186
£3200 $5056 €4640 Tea party (46x61cm-18x24in) s.d.98. 4-Sep-3 Christie's, Kensington #291/R est:2000-3000

HUNT, Richard Howard (1935-) American

Sculpture

£929 $1700 €1356 Winged hybrid (23cm-9in) init. polished bronze. 10-Jul-4 Susanin's, Chicago #5126/R est:600-800
£2286 $4000 €3338 Tri-Motion (184x81x43cm-72x32x17in) s.d.95 stainless steel lit. 17-Dec-3 Christie's, Rockefeller NY #298/R est:4000-6000
£5346 $8500 €7805 Hybrid (61x71x48cm-24x28x19in) s.d.64 welded steel. 14-Sep-3 Susanin's, Chicago #6129/R est:6000-8000
£17610 $28000 €25711 Growing orbit (216x145cm-85x57in) welded bronze. 14-Sep-3 Susanin's, Chicago #6061/R est:40000-60000

HUNT, Thomas Lorraine (1882-1938) American

£3757 $6500 €5485 Nocturnal Harbour (76x81cm-30x32in) s. 10-Dec-3 Bonhams & Butterfields, San Francisco #6250/R est:7000-9000

HUNT, Walter (1861-1941) British

£1277 $2170 €1864 Farmyard (47x61cm-19x24in) s.d.80 canvas on board. 25-Nov-3 Christie's, Melbourne #195/R est:3000-5000 (A.D 3000)
£1600 $2720 €2336 Head of a hound (18x23cm-7x9in) s. canvasboard. 27-Nov-3 Christie's, Kensington #385/R est:2000-3000
£11500 $21045 €16790 Meal time with Jack Russell puppies (24x35cm-9x14in) s. indis.d. 10-Jun-4 Neales, Nottingham #590 est:4000-5000
£15000 $25500 €21900 Corner of the farm (51x77cm-20x30in) s.d.1901 i.verso. 19-Nov-3 Bonhams, New Bond Street #101/R est:10000-15000
£16000 $29760 €23360 Clves watering (30x41cm-12x16in) s.d.1925 pair. 4-Mar-4 Christie's, Kensington #487/R est:15000-25000
£20000 $34000 €29200 Calves feeding, with chickens and doves beside a barn (77x115cm-30x45in) s.d.1918. 25-Nov-3 Christie's, London #203/R est:15000-20000
£20500 $36695 €29930 Breakfast time (51x76cm-20x30in) s.d.1911 i.verso. 27-May-4 Christie's, Kensington #199/R est:10000-15000

HUNT, William (19th C) British

Works on paper

£280	$468	€409	Still life of a birds nest, flowers and insects on a mossy bank (26x18cm-10x7in) s.d.1850 W/C htd white oval. 7-Oct-3 Fellows & Sons, Birmingham #538/R
£300	$519	€438	Apples and grapes (8x12cm-3x5in) s. W/C. 11-Dec-3 Bruton Knowles, Cheltenham #74

HUNT, William Henry (1790-1864) British

£600	$1104	€876	Hard at work (20x15cm-8x6in) init. s.verso board. 23-Mar-4 Bonhams, New Bond Street #29/R
£700	$1323	€1022	Peaches and grapes on a mossy bank (25x30cm-10x12in) s. board prov. 19-Feb-4 Christie's, Kensington #297

Works on paper

£325	$582	€475	Still life, grapes, orange and raspberries on a rocky base (15x13cm-6x5in) s. W/C oval. 5-May-4 John Nicholson, Haslemere #351
£460	$814	€672	Green grapes and an apple (19cm-7in circular) s. W/C htd white. 27-Apr-4 Bonhams, Knowle #42
£500	$835	€730	Cottages at St Albans (18x25cm-7x10in) pencil W/C. 16-Oct-3 Christie's, Kensington #51/R
£580	$1067	€847	Rural landscape (7x10cm-3x4in) W/C. 23-Mar-4 Bonhams, Knightsbridge #289/R
£600	$1032	€876	Magnum bonum and orleans plums (20x28cm-8x11in) s. W/C bodycol. 3-Dec-3 Christie's, Kensington #201/R
£650	$1060	€949	Still life, an apple, blueberries and red berries, flower and leaves (15x10cm-6x4in) s. W/C. 23-Sep-3 John Nicholson, Haslemere #90/R
£800	$1336	€1168	Young girl reclining on a sofa (25x28cm-10x11in) pencil W/C oval. 16-Oct-3 Christie's, Kensington #79/R
£1500	$2730	€2190	Still life with nectarines, plums, grapes and forget-me-nots on a mossy bank (19x27cm-7x11in) s. W/C over pencil htd bodycol gum arabic oval. 1-Jul-4 Sotheby's, London #245/R est:2000-3000
£1600	$2944	€2336	Fancy dress (26x13cm-10x5in) s. pencil W/C prov. 25-Mar-4 Christie's, Kensington #228/R est:800-1200
£1700	$3128	€2482	Asking for trouble (69x74cm-27x29in) pencil W/C bodycol. 25-Mar-4 Christie's, Kensington #229/R est:1000-2000
£1800	$3006	€2628	Young boy viewing a picture by candlelight (28x21cm-11x8in) s. pencil W/C prov. 16-Oct-3 Christie's, Kensington #87/R est:2000-3000
£2500	$4550	€3650	Still life with a jug, a cabbage in basket and a gherkin (19x26cm-7x10in) s. W/C over pencil htd scratching out gum arabic. 1-Jul-4 Sotheby's, London #249/R est:3000-5000
£2500	$4550	€3650	Still life with sea shells on a mossy bank (13x17cm-5x7in) s. W/C over pencil htd bodycol. 1-Jul-4 Sotheby's, London #250/R est:3000-5000
£3800	$6916	€5548	Still life with grapes, a tankard and a sprig of holly (15x11cm-6x4in) s. W/C bodycol. 1-Jul-4 Christie's, Kensington #262/R est:1000-1500
£5000	$9150	€7300	Interior of a barn with chickens (31x45cm-12x18in) pencil W/C gum arabic htd bodycol scratching out prov. 3-Jun-4 Christie's, London #150/R est:3500-4500
£22000	$37400	€32120	Eavesdropper (73x55cm-29x22in) pencil W/C bodycol gum arabic scratching out. 20-Nov-3 Christie's, London #107/R est:15000-20000

HUNT, William Henry (attrib) (1790-1864) British

£540	$1004	€788	Still lifes of birds' nests with apple blossom or primroses, on mossy banks (34x24cm-13x9in) bears sig. pair. 2-Mar-4 Bristol Auction Rooms #302/R

HUNT, William Holman (1827-1910) British

£15000	$25500	€21900	Piazza della Constituzione by night, Athens (37x50cm-15x20in) s.d.92 i.verso i. paper on millboard prov.exhib.lit. 27-Nov-3 Sotheby's, London #318/R est:15000-20000

Works on paper

£450	$833	€657	Study of angels (15x11cm-6x4in) pen ink prov. 9-Mar-4 Bonhams, New Bond Street #76/R
£2000	$3400	€2920	Cornish coast (1x24cm-0x9in) mono.d.1860 W/C. 4-Nov-3 Bonhams, New Bond Street #95/R est:2000-3000
£2800	$4760	€4088	Walls of Jerusalem. Descent to Tomb of David. House built on the water, Damietta, Egypt (18x25cm-7x10in) all i. one d.1854 pencil three prov.exhib. 20-Nov-3 Christie's, London #155/R est:4000-6000

HUNT, William Howes (1806-1879) British

Works on paper

£800	$1432	€1168	Moored sailing barges (30x53cm-12x21in) s.d.1862 W/C. 17-May-4 David Duggleby, Scarborough #612/R

HUNT, William Morris (1824-1879) American

£883	$1500	€1289	Seated dog portrait (31x41cm-12x16in) mono. 21-Nov-3 Skinner, Boston #180/R est:3000-5000
£2045	$3600	€2986	House by the sea (13x28cm-5x11in) s.d.1864 panel prov. 3-Jan-4 Collins, Maine #36/R est:800-1200
£2353	$4000	€3435	Young girl at table with sculpture (25x35cm-10x14in) 30-Oct-3 Phillips, New York #7/R est:4000-6000
£2386	$4200	€3484	Windblown shade tree (30x41cm-12x16in) prov.exhib. 3-Jan-4 Collins, Maine #34/R est:2000-3000

HUNTEN, Emil Johann (1827-1902) German

£556	$917	€800	Infantry in hand to hand battle (41x32cm-16x13in) s. bears d. canvas on board. 3-Jul-3 Van Ham, Cologne #1266
£861	$1575	€1300	Prussian soldier on horseback (37x47cm-15x19in) s.d.76. 8-Apr-4 Dorotheum, Vienna #35/R
£1267	$2293	€1900	Prussian hunter and hussar (59x59cm-23x23in) s. 1-Apr-4 Van Ham, Cologne #1445/R est:3300
£5479	$9315	€8000	The disturbed picnic (63x83cm-25x33in) s. 5-Nov-3 Vendue Huis, Gravenhage #91/R est:4000-6000
£6667	$12000	€9734	The search (61x104cm-24x41in) s.d.1867 canvas on panel prov. 22-Apr-4 Christie's, Rockefeller NY #42/R est:15000-20000

HUNTEN, Emil Johann (attrib) (1827-1902) German

£299	$536	€440	Cavalry battle (28x38cm-11x15in) d.10.11.50 i. stretcher. 18-Mar-4 Neumeister, Munich #2694/R

HUNTEN, Franz Johann Wilhelm (1822-1887) German

£839	$1401	€1200	Ship in stormy seas (64x96cm-25x38in) s.d. canvas on panel. 28-Jun-3 Bolland & Marotz, Bremen #675/R

HUNTEN, Richard (1867-1952) German

£417	$658	€600	Helgoland (30x40cm-12x16in) s. board. 6-Sep-3 Schopman, Hamburg #847/R
£664	$1143	€950	Breakers on the coast near Bornholm (46x63cm-18x25in) s.i.d.1893 canvas on board. 6-Dec-3 Hans Stahl, Toestorf #129/R

HUNTER, Clementine (1887-1988) American

£718	$1300	€1048	Sister with a red and blue headdress (41x51cm-16x20in) mono. 3-Apr-4 Neal Auction Company, New Orleans #873/R est:1500-2500
£769	$1400	€1123	Watermelon (30x38cm-12x15in) mono. canvasboard. 7-Feb-4 Neal Auction Company, New Orleans #798 est:1500-2500
£889	$1600	€1298	Woman washing clothes (15x20cm-6x8in) acrylic board painted c.1960. 24-Apr-4 Slotin Folk Art, Buford #287/R est:2000-3000
£1024	$1700	€1495	My brother smoking behind the trees (41x30cm-16x12in) mono. canvasboard. 4-Oct-3 Neal Auction Company, New Orleans #1092/R est:2000-3000
£1024	$1700	€1495	Releasing red bird (41x30cm-16x12in) mono. 4-Oct-3 Neal Auction Company, New Orleans #1093/R est:2000-3000
£1033	$1900	€1508	Watermelon slice (36x41cm-14x16in) wooden board shaped. 27-Mar-4 New Orleans Auction, New Orleans #875 est:1800-2500
£1125	$1800	€1643	Wedding (30x41cm-12x16in) mono. board prov. 20-Sep-3 New Orleans Auction, New Orleans #864/R
£1163	$2000	€1698	Zinnias (41x30cm-16x12in) mono. 6-Dec-3 Neal Auction Company, New Orleans #601/R est:1500-2500
£1326	$2400	€1936	Traveling by mule (74x46cm-29x18in) mono. 3-Apr-4 Neal Auction Company, New Orleans #872/R est:2500-3500
£1374	$2500	€2006	Flower pickers (38x48cm-15x19in) mono. canvasboard. 7-Feb-4 Neal Auction Company, New Orleans #792/R est:2500-3500
£1446	$2400	€2111	Cotton picking (46x61cm-18x24in) mono. canvasboard. 4-Oct-3 Neal Auction Company, New Orleans #602/R est:2500-3500
£1529	$2600	€2232	African house (36x36cm-14x14in) mono. masonite. 22-Nov-3 New Orleans Auction, New Orleans #1257/R est:1500-2500
£1529	$2600	€2232	Funeral at Saint Augustine Church (41x51cm-16x20in) mono. canvasboard. 22-Nov-3 New Orleans Auction, New Orleans #1259/R est:2000-4000
£1566	$2600	€2286	Birthday Party (41x51cm-16x20in) mono. canvasboard. 4-Oct-3 Neal Auction Company, New Orleans #600/R est:3000-4000
£1566	$2600	€2286	Saturday Night (41x51cm-16x20in) mono. canvasboard. 4-Oct-3 Neal Auction Company, New Orleans #601/R est:3000-4000
£1570	$2700	€2292	Funeral (30x38cm-12x15in) mono. canvasboard. 6-Dec-3 Neal Auction Company, New Orleans #592a/R est:1500-2500
£1625	$2600	€2373	Ignoring the ducks (30x41cm-12x16in) mono. board. 20-Sep-3 New Orleans Auction, New Orleans #865/R
£1625	$2600	€2373	Saturday night (41x61cm-16x24in) mono. board prov. 20-Sep-3 New Orleans Auction, New Orleans #861/R
£1744	$3000	€2546	Baptism (30x38cm-12x15in) mono. canvasboard. 6-Dec-3 Neal Auction Company, New Orleans #593/R est:1500-2500
£1744	$3000	€2546	Yucca House, Melrose Plantation (36x46cm-14x18in) mono. 6-Dec-3 Neal Auction Company, New Orleans #602 est:2500-3500
£1750	$2800	€2555	Leaving church (30x41cm-12x16in) mono. board prov. 20-Sep-3 New Orleans Auction, New Orleans #863/R
£1768	$3200	€2581	Wash day (41x58cm-16x23in) mono. board. 3-Apr-4 Neal Auction Company, New Orleans #449 est:1200-2000
£1768	$3200	€2581	Cotton pickers (41x58cm-16x23in) mono. board. 3-Apr-4 Neal Auction Company, New Orleans #450 est:1200-2000
£1882	$3200	€2748	Ladies playing cards (30x76cm-12x30in) mono. canvasboard. 22-Nov-3 New Orleans Auction, New Orleans #1256/R est:3000-5000
£2000	$3500	€2920	Cotton picking (46x61cm-18x24in) init. canvasboard prov. 19-Dec-3 Sotheby's, New York #1030/R est:2500-3500
£2072	$3750	€3025	Picking cotton at Melrose Plantation (46x61cm-18x24in) mono. 3-Apr-4 Neal Auction Company, New Orleans #453/R est:2500-3500
£2118	$3600	€3092	Ginning cotton (41x51cm-16x20in) mono. canvasboard. 22-Nov-3 New Orleans Auction, New Orleans #1255/R est:3500-5000
£2125	$3400	€3103	Hauling cotton (41x61cm-16x24in) mono. prov. 20-Sep-3 New Orleans Auction, New Orleans #860/R
£2331	$3800	€3380	Red cotton gin (41x51cm-16x20in) mono. board. 19-Jul-3 New Orleans Auction, New Orleans #926/R est:2500-4000
£2353	$4000	€3435	Wash day (41x61cm-16x24in) mono. board prov. 22-Nov-3 New Orleans Auction, New Orleans #1254/R est:3500-5000
£3235	$5500	€4723	Cotton pickin (41x51cm-16x20in) mono. board. 22-Nov-3 New Orleans Auction, New Orleans #1253/R est:3500-5000
£3333	$6000	€4866	Saturday night juke joint (58x69cm-23x27in) acrylic board painted c.1960. 24-Apr-4 Slotin Folk Art, Buford #285/R est:7000-10000
£5000	$9000	€7300	Funeral (41x61cm-16x24in) board painted c.1958. 24-Apr-4 Slotin Folk Art, Buford #286/R est:5000-8000
£6944	$12500	€10138	Melrose plantation (53x69cm-21x27in) canvasboard. 24-Apr-4 Slotin Folk Art, Buford #284/R est:7000-10000

Works on paper

£1429	$2500	€2086	Untitled (30x38cm-12x15in) init. gouache prov. 19-Dec-3 Sotheby's, New York #1029/R est:2000-3000

HUNTER, Colin (1841-1904) British

£300	$567	€438	Waves breaking on a deserted coast (30x55cm-12x22in) s. 19-Feb-4 Lyon & Turnbull, Edinburgh #26
£550	$1018	€803	Harbour view (58x46cm-23x18in) s. 10-Feb-4 Bonhams, Knightsbridge #297/R
£1600	$2912	€2336	Pennyween, Fifeshire (28x38cm-11x15in) s.d.1899 canvasboard. 3-Feb-4 Gorringes, Bexhill #1043/R est:1000-1500
£2500	$3925	€3625	Gathering bracken (46x72cm-18x28in) s.d.1869. 27-Aug-3 Sotheby's, London #936/R est:2000-3000
£2500	$3925	€3625	West coast jetty (38x76cm-15x30in) s.d.1876 prov. 27-Aug-3 Sotheby's, London #1108/R est:2500-3500

HUNTER, Frances Tipton (1896-1957) American

Works on paper

£838	$1500	€1223	Young boy life guard and dog (48x33cm-19x13in) s. W/C. 15-May-4 Illustration House, New York #70/R est:2000-3000

£1747 $3250 €2551 Young girl calling for her dog (71x53cm-28x21in) s. W/C gouache executed c.1920. 7-Mar-4 Treadway Gallery, Cincinnati #678/R est:800-1200

HUNTER, Fred Leo (1858-1943) American
£741 $1400 €1082 Shipa at sea - The whaling bark Wanderer (36x51cm-14x20in) s.d.192 prov. 17-Feb-4 John Moran, Pasadena #170/R est:800-1200

HUNTER, George Leslie (1877-1931) British
£5000 $7850 €7250 Still life with roses and delphiniums (50x40cm-20x16in) s. 27-Aug-3 Sotheby's, London #1225/R est:5000-7000
£8500 $13345 €12325 Fife cottages (30x50cm-12x20in) s. 27-Aug-3 Sotheby's, London #1226/R est:3000-5000
£24000 $43440 €35040 Fife landscape (25x51cm-10x20in) s. prov. 19-Apr-4 Sotheby's, London #72/R est:15000-20000
£28000 $47600 €40880 Still life with bottles and fruit (51x61cm-20x24in) s. prov.exhib. 30-Oct-3 Christie's, London #172/R est:30000-50000
£32000 $51520 €46400 Still life of pink roses and fruit (40x35cm-16x14in) s. board. 21-Aug-3 Bonhams, Edinburgh #1031/R est:20000-30000
£33000 $53130 €47850 Red sail, Largo harbour (25x35cm-10x14in) s. canvasboard. 21-Aug-3 Bonhams, Edinburgh #1105/R est:15000-20000
£38000 $59660 €55100 Still life with anemones and apples (56x46cm-22x18in) s. prov. 27-Aug-3 Sotheby's, London #1222/R est:25000-35000
£39000 $67080 €56940 Still life of marigolds and fruit (39x34cm-15x13in) s. board. 4-Dec-3 Bonhams, Edinburgh #45/R est:20000-30000
£40000 $62800 €58000 Still life with apples and a rose (67x54cm-26x21in) s. 27-Aug-3 Sotheby's, London #1224/R est:40000-60000
£75000 $117750 €108750 Still life with tulips and fruit (56x46cm-22x18in) s. board prov. 27-Aug-3 Sotheby's, London #1223/R est:50000-70000
Works on paper
£450 $752 €657 Curtain call (20x12cm-8x5in) pen ink. 16-Oct-3 Bonhams, Edinburgh #150
£1600 $2720 €2336 Mill Dam, Fife (23x34cm-9x13in) pen blk ink col crayon. 30-Oct-3 Christie's, London #171/R est:1500-2000
£1900 $3230 €2774 Breakwater, Lower Largo (24x28cm-9x11in) init. pen blk ink col crayon. 30-Oct-3 Christie's, London #176/R est:1500-2000
£2600 $4420 €3796 Cottage in Fife (28x37cm-11x15in) s. pen blk ink col crayon. 30-Oct-3 Christie's, London #169/R est:2000-3000
£3000 $4830 €4350 St. Monan's (46x59cm-18x23in) s. W/C prov. 21-Aug-3 Bonhams, Edinburgh #1092/R est:3000-5000
£3200 $5440 €4672 Mother and child on the shore (20x25cm-8x10in) pen blk ink wash col crayon. 30-Oct-3 Christie's, London #177/R est:1500-2000
£3400 $5474 €4930 Cottages, Ceres, Fife (15x28cm-6x11in) s. black ink crayon. 21-Aug-3 Bonhams, Edinburgh #1029/R est:2500-3500
£3500 $5495 €5075 Yellow chair (43x36cm-17x14in) pencil pen ink col crayon prov. 27-Aug-3 Sotheby's, London #1229/R est:2000-3000
£3800 $6460 €5548 Figures amongst boats (30x38cm-12x15in) pen blk ink col crayon. 30-Oct-3 Christie's, London #175/R est:3000-5000
£4000 $7240 €5840 Grand piano (53x43cm-21x17in) s. W/C crayon prov. 19-Apr-4 Sotheby's, London #70/R est:4000-6000
£6500 $11050 €9490 Largo Harbour with figures (30x38cm-12x15in) pen blk ink col crayon. 30-Oct-3 Christie's, London #170/R est:4000-6000
£8500 $13345 €12325 Balcony with a sea view (44x34cm-17x13in) pencil pen ink col crayon prov. 27-Aug-3 Sotheby's, London #1228/R est:3000-5000
£8500 $14450 €12410 Juan les Pins (30x37cm-12x15in) s. pen brush blk ink col crayon prov. 30-Oct-3 Christie's, London #174/R est:4000-6000
£9000 $16290 €13140 Beach, South of France (33x43cm-13x17in) s. W/C ink over chl pencil. 19-Apr-4 Sotheby's, London #71/R est:2000-3000

HUNTER, George Leslie (attrib) (1877-1931) British
£460 $823 €672 Still life fruit on a ledge (23x53cm-9x21in) s. board. 7-May-4 Mallams, Oxford #305a/R

HUNTER, George Sherwood (1846-1919) British
£281 $458 €410 Oarsman (31x46cm-12x18in) s. 27-Sep-3 Rasmussen, Havnen #2181/R (D.KR 3000)
£704 $1169 €1000 Venice from Guidecca (36x51cm-14x20in) 16-Jun-3 Dorotheum, Vienna #97/R
£1757 $3250 €2565 George V Coronation Procession (30x46cm-12x18in) s.i. prov. 12-Feb-4 Sotheby's, New York #3/R est:4000-6000
£10500 $17850 €15330 Emptying a salmon net (101x76cm-40x30in) s.d.1880 prov.exhib. 25-Nov-3 Christie's, London #171/R est:7000-10000

HUNTER, John (?) British?
£1700 $2924 €2482 Sailing boats in a choppy estuary (38x55cm-15x22in) board. 3-Dec-3 John Ross, Belfast #152 est:800-1000

HUNTER, John F (1893-1951) British
Works on paper
£340 $622 €496 Path to the river (28x22cm-11x9in) s.d.1930 W/C. 2-Jun-4 John Ross, Belfast #191
£580 $1061 €847 Winter trees (38x28cm-15x11in) s. W/C. 2-Jun-4 John Ross, Belfast #73

HUNTER, John Young (1874-1955) British
£1300 $2158 €1898 Estuary landscape (45x89cm-18x35in) s.d.1893 prov. 1-Oct-3 Woolley & Wallis, Salisbury #317/R est:800-1200

HUNTER, Leslie (1877-1931) British
£22000 $38060 €32120 Still life of chrysanthemums (55x46cm-22x18in) s. 11-Dec-3 Lyon & Turnbull, Edinburgh #83/R est:18000-25000
Works on paper
£580 $969 €847 Set design for Evergreen (17x22cm-7x9in) ink crayon prov. 16-Oct-3 Bonhams, Edinburgh #175

HUNTER, Mason (1854-1921) British
£340 $595 €496 Yachts off a town (30x37cm-12x15in) s. board. 18-Dec-3 Bonhams, Edinburgh #341
£500 $815 €730 Morning tide. 17-Jul-3 Bonhams, Edinburgh #305
£600 $1032 €876 Fishing boats (74x48cm-29x19in) i.verso. 3-Dec-3 Andrew Hartley, Ilkley #1173
£1600 $2864 €2336 Riders in a mountain pass (72x92cm-28x36in) s. s.verso. 26-May-4 Sotheby's, Olympia #228/R est:1200-1800
Works on paper
£2900 $5249 €4234 I put with the tide (51x66cm-20x26in) s.d.1907 W/C. 19-Apr-4 Sotheby's, London #118/R est:1500-2000

HUNTER, Philip (1958-) Australian
£2066 $3512 €3016 Untitled no.1 (126x112cm-50x44in) s.d.98 verso linen. 29-Oct-3 Lawson Menzies, Sydney #158/R est:4000-8000 (A.D 5000)
£2119 $3602 €3094 Untitled no.2 (120x180cm-47x71in) s.d.98 verso. 24-Nov-3 Sotheby's, Melbourne #66/R est:4000-5000 (A.D 5000)
£2632 $4237 €3843 Untitled No. 3 (121x184cm-48x72in) s.d.98 verso. 25-Aug-3 Sotheby's, Paddington #378/R est:3500-4500 (A.D 6500)
£6275 $10103 €9162 Cloud (198x167cm-78x66in) s.d.98-99 i.verso. 25-Aug-3 Sotheby's, Paddington #437/R est:5000-8000 (A.D 15500)

HUNTER, Robert (fl.1745-1803) Irish
£25000 $44750 €36500 Portrait of James Fitzgerald, 20th Earl of Kildare (127x102cm-50x40in) prov. 13-May-4 Sotheby's, London #54/R est:25000-35000

HUNTER, Robert (1947-) Australian
£9091 $16091 €13273 Untitled (122x244cm-48x96in) init.d.94 verso enamel board prov. 3-May-4 Christie's, Melbourne #31/R est:20000-30000 (A.D 22000)
Works on paper
£1803 $2849 €2632 Untitled (122x244cm-48x96in) s.d.83-4 verso synthetic polymer board prov. 2-Sep-3 Deutscher-Menzies, Melbourne #101/R est:4000-6000 (A.D 4400)

HUNTER, Robert Douglas (1928-) American
£409 $650 €597 Tom Never's Head Nantucket (20x38cm-8x15in) s. d.1967 verso masonite. 12-Sep-3 Skinner, Boston #504/R
£1243 $2200 €1815 Pewter tureen (16x30cm-6x12in) s. 2-May-4 Bonhams & Butterfields, San Francisco #1154/R est:2500-3500
£1956 $3500 €2856 Russian copper and English brass (38x58cm-15x23in) s.d.76. 14-May-4 Skinner, Boston #381/R est:2000-4000
£3107 $5500 €4536 Copper urn and crabapples (24x40cm-9x16in) s. 2-May-4 Bonhams & Butterfields, San Francisco #1153/R est:2500-3500

HUNTER, William (c.1890-1967) British
£725 $1160 €1059 Terrier dog (51x41cm-20x16in) s. 8-Jan-3 Biddle & Webb, Birmingham #900
£1933 $3500 €2822 Morag, a favourite Westie (51x40cm-20x16in) s. 30-Mar-4 Bonhams & Butterfields, San Francisco #102/R est:4000-6000

HUNTER, William D (20th C) American
Sculpture
£958 $1600 €1399 Joe Foss (163x56x41cm-64x22x16in) num.1/40 bronze incl. stand. 11-Oct-3 Nadeau, Windsor #180/R est:6000-10000

HUNTINGTON, Anna Hyatt (1876-1973) American
Sculpture
£1105 $1900 €1613 Cobra and mongoose (25cm-10in) i.d.1955 aluminium. 2-Dec-3 Christie's, Rockefeller NY #73/R est:2000-4000
£3779 $6500 €5517 Ship of the desert (76cm-30in) i.d.1950 aluminium. 2-Dec-3 Christie's, Rockefeller NY #74/R est:3000-5000
£8000 $14720 €12000 Duex oursons jouant et un petit chien rongeant son os (146cm-57in) s. terracotta. 10-Jun-4 Camard, Paris #49/R est:15000-20000
£12228 $22500 €17853 Yawning tiger (21cm-8in) s.st.f. Gorham brown pat. bronze prov. 8-Jun-4 Bonhams & Butterfields, San Francisco #4044/R est:25000-35000

HUNTINGTON, Chris (20th C) American
£1852 $3000 €2685 Sea garden, Mohegan Island (36x51cm-14x20in) s.i.d.1977 s.verso prov. 8-Aug-3 Barridorf, Portland #207/R est:3000-5000

HUNTINGTON, Daniel (1816-1906) American
£3911 $7000 €5710 My pleasure ground (46x36cm-18x14in) s. prov. 6-May-4 Shannon's, Milford #26/R est:8000-12000
£78488 $135000 €114592 George Washington and Christopher Gist on the Allegheny River (51x61cm-20x24in) prov.exhib. 3-Dec-3 Sotheby's, New York #96/R est:15000-25000

HUNTINGTON, Dwight W (19/20th C) American
Works on paper
£1512 $2600 €2208 English setters in a wood (35x48cm-14x19in) s.d.1905 i.verso pencil W/C bodycol paper on card. 5-Dec-3 Christie's, Rockefeller NY #84/R est:3000-5000

HUNTLY, Moira (1932-) British
Works on paper
£460 $842 €672 Blaneau Fjestinog (55x65cm-22x26in) s. W/C gouache. 31-Jan-4 Shapes, Edinburgh #343
£520 $915 €759 Campo de la Pescaria (43x62cm-17x24in) s. W/C gouache. 18-May-4 Woolley & Wallis, Salisbury #254/R
£750 $1320 €1095 Boats at Staithes (50x63cm-20x25in) s. W/C gouache. 18-May-4 Woolley & Wallis, Salisbury #247/R

HUNTRESS, Alfred William (19th C) ?
£520 $832 €759 River North Italy. 16-Sep-3 Lawrences, Bletchingley #1828

HUNZIKER, Edwin (1901-1986) Swiss

£390	$697	€569	Seaside town (60x1cm-24x0in) s. 22-Mar-4 Philippe Schuler, Zurich #6022 (S.FR 900)
£437	$803	€638	Landscape with tree in bloom (74x61cm-29x24in) s. 14-Jun-4 Philippe Schuler, Zurich #5731 (S.FR 1000)

HUNZIKER, Frieda (1908-1966) Dutch

Works on paper

£1884	$3090	€2600	Untitled (45x55cm-18x22in) s.d.51 s.d.50 verso gouache. 27-May-3 Sotheby's, Amsterdam #549/R est:1800-2400

HUNZIKER, Max (1901-1976) Swiss

£216	$387	€315	Self portrait (46x38cm-18x15in) s. 22-Mar-4 Philippe Schuler, Zurich #6023 (S.FR 500)
£407	$692	€594	Keep (45x46cm-18x18in) s.d.1935 panel. 25-Nov-3 Germann, Zurich #814 (S.FR 900)

HUNZIKER, Robert (1876-1951) ?

£387	$643	€550	Saint Mark's Square and cathedral (18x25cm-7x10in) i.verso card. 11-Jul-3 Finarte, Venice #259/R

HUOT, Charles Edouard (1855-1930) Canadian

£290	$485	€421	Le juge cyrus pelletier (66x53cm-26x21in) s. 17-Jun-3 Pinneys, Montreal #90 (C.D 650)
£536	$895	€777	Coucher de soleil (41x67cm-16x26in) s. 17-Jun-3 Pinneys, Montreal #19 est:800-1200 (C.D 1200)

HURARD, Joseph Marius (1887-1956) French

£1275	$2359	€1900	Martigues, soleil levant (48x65cm-19x26in) s. panel. 14-Mar-4 Eric Pillon, Calais #181/R
£2222	$3711	€3200	Martigues (61x46cm-24x18in) s. 25-Oct-3 Dianous, Marseille #393

Works on paper

£347	$552	€500	Vue du pont (34x62cm-13x24in) s. mixed media cardboard. 15-Sep-3 Horta, Bruxelles #489

HURD, Peter (1904-1984) American

£4190	$7500	€7034	Portrait of a horse (53x66cm-21x26in) s. panel. 20-Mar-4 Pook & Pook, Downington #541/R est:8000-10000

Works on paper

£436	$750	€637	Hilly landscape (23x28cm-9x11in) s. W/C pencil. 2-Dec-3 Christie's, Rockefeller NY #100/R
£1000	$1700	€1460	Cowboys on horseback in atmospheric landscape (7x10cm-3x4in) s.i. W/C prov. 18-Nov-3 John Moran, Pasadena #118a est:1000-2000
£1397	$2500	€2040	Western scene with figures, river and man on a horse (18x28cm-7x11in) s.i. 8-Jan-4 James Julia, Fairfield #506/R est:2000-3000
£3240	$5800	€4730	Hondo valley on a hazy afternoon (28x43cm-11x17in) W/C. 15-May-4 Altermann Galleries, Santa Fe #175/R
£3471	$5900	€5068	An afternoon in summer (25x48cm-10x19in) W/C. 1-Nov-3 Altermann Galleries, Santa Fe #151

HURKA, Otakar (1889-?) Czechoslovakian

£355	$592	€500	Single house in winter landscape (25x33cm-10x13in) s. panel. 14-Oct-3 Dorotheum, Vienna #109/R

HURLEY, Frank (1885-1962) Australian

Photographs

£4472	$7020	€6484	Correll on the edge of a ravine in the ice-sheet, Adelie Land (57x44cm-22x17in) carbon print photo prov.lit. 26-Aug-3 Christie's, Sydney #309 est:8000-12000 (A.D 11000)
£5500	$8524	€8030	Adrift in the moving ice (15x20cm-6x8in) i. gelatin silver print. 25-Sep-2 Christie's, London #227/R est:3000-5000

HURLEY, Robert Newton (1894-1980) Canadian

Works on paper

£200	$366	€292	South Saskatchewan (26x36cm-10x14in) s. W/C. 1-Jun-4 Hodgins, Calgary #467/R (C.D 500)
£227	$411	€331	Untitled - lake (24x33cm-9x13in) s.d.1957 W/C paper board prov. 18-Apr-4 Levis, Calgary #476/R (C.D 550)
£240	$439	€350	Field and distant town (29x37cm-11x15in) s.d.1963 W/C. 1-Jun-4 Hodgins, Calgary #11/R (C.D 600)
£240	$439	€350	View of a town across the river (26x38cm-10x15in) s.d.1964 W/C. 1-Jun-4 Hodgins, Calgary #12/R (C.D 600)
£383	$651	€559	Grain elevators in Spring (29x36cm-11x14in) s.d.1960 W/C board prov. 23-Nov-3 Levis, Calgary #473/R (C.D 850)

HURMERINTA, Olavi (1928-) Finnish

£293	$532	€430	Landscape from Tenerife (80x100cm-31x39in) s.d.72. 8-Feb-4 Bukowskis, Helsinki #367/R
£302	$556	€450	Landscape (30x30cm-12x12in) s.d.1987. 25-Mar-4 Hagelstam, Helsinki #1013
£322	$593	€480	River landscape in autumn (65x85cm-26x33in) s.d.1989. 25-Mar-4 Hagelstam, Helsinki #861/R
£324	$518	€460	Autumn (54x65cm-21x26in) 18-Sep-3 Hagelstam, Helsinki #838
£479	$766	€680	Winter's day (54x65cm-21x26in) s.d.1991. 18-Sep-3 Hagelstam, Helsinki #837/R

HURRELL, George (1904-1992) American

Photographs

£6522	$12000	€9522	Portraits of Katharine Hepburn (23x18cm-9x7in) s.d.1938 gelatin silver print set of three. 10-Jun-4 Sotheby's, New York #94/R est:1500-2500
£8152	$15000	€11902	Portraits of Katharine Hepburn (20x15cm-8x6in) s.d.1938 gelatin silver print set of three. 10-Jun-4 Sotheby's, New York #93/R est:1500-2500

HURRY, Leslie (1909-1978) British

Works on paper

£400	$640	€580	Boathouse in the trees (38x52cm-15x20in) s.d.1939 W/C. 16-Sep-3 Bonhams, Knightsbridge #23/R
£420	$714	€613	Three figures (29x33cm-11x13in) pen ink W/C prov. 26-Nov-3 Sotheby's, Olympia #120/R
£480	$888	€701	Untitled I (56x45cm-22x18in) pen ink W/C gouache prov. 11-Feb-4 Sotheby's, Olympia #263/R
£500	$935	€730	View of a village green with church (15x19cm-6x7in) s.d.36 W/C. 25-Feb-4 Mallams, Oxford #357/R
£1000	$1720	€1460	Welsh figures (27x21cm-11x8in) s.d.1944 pencil pen black ink W/C prov. 3-Dec-3 Christie's, Kensington #651 est:2000-3000

HURSON, Michael (20th C) American

Works on paper

£419	$700	€612	Study of a man reading a newspaper (64x32cm-25x13in) s. pencil pastel conte crayon. 19-Oct-3 Bonhams & Butterfields, Los Angeles #7096
£472	$850	€689	Portrait of Daniel Weinberg (29x23cm-11x9in) s. stabilo pencil pastel conte crayon prov. 24-Apr-4 David Rago, Lambertville #207/R

HURST, Hal (1863-1938) British

£360	$569	€522	Portrait of Charles Chetwynd, seated in officers uniform (102x76cm-40x30in) 4-Sep-3 Christie's, Kensington #77/R
£440	$814	€642	The launching (74x99cm-29x39in) indis.s. 16-Feb-4 Bonhams, Bath #66
£598	$1100	€873	Figures on a garden staircase (56x33cm-22x13in) s. board. 23-Mar-4 Arthur James, Florida #157/R est:1000-1500

HURST, Hal (attrib) (1863-1938) British

£417	$750	€609	Figures on a garden staircase (56x33cm-22x13in) bears sig. board. 25-Jan-4 Bonhams & Butterfields, San Francisco #3574/R

HURT, Louis B (1856-1929) British

£850	$1369	€1233	Arran (13x24cm-5x9in) i.d.29.8.03 canvasboard. 21-Aug-3 Bonhams, Edinburgh #1058
£880	$1417	€1276	Buchaille Etive (16x24cm-6x9in) i. d.Sep 92 verso canvasboard. 21-Aug-3 Bonhams, Edinburgh #1060
£880	$1417	€1276	At Sligachan, Skye (12x21cm-5x8in) init.d.13/7/06 panel. 21-Aug-3 Bonhams, Edinburgh #1062
£950	$1530	€1378	Cattle in mountain landscape (30x38cm-12x15in) init.i. oil sketch. 15-Aug-3 Keys, Aylsham #724
£1000	$1670	€1460	Highland cattle on a riverside path (32x42cm-13x17in) init.i. board. 13-Nov-3 Christie's, Kensington #200/R est:1200-1800
£1150	$1852	€1668	In Glencoe (12x21cm-5x8in) init.i. panel. 21-Aug-3 Bonhams, Edinburgh #1059/R est:400-600
£1150	$1852	€1668	Landscape and loch (36x56cm-14x22in) s.verso panel. 21-Aug-3 Bonhams, Edinburgh #1061 est:400-600
£2600	$4758	€3796	October, a bye lane (61x102cm-24x40in) s.d.1884. 8-Jul-4 Duke & Son, Dorchester #210/R est:2000-4000
£3000	$4980	€4380	North Derbyshire moorland (46x76cm-18x30in) s.d.1881 s.i.d.verso. 1-Oct-3 Sotheby's, Olympia #87/R est:3000-4000
£3000	$5580	€4380	Sound of Noss, Shetland (13x23cm-5x9in) s.i. i.verso panel. 4-Mar-4 Christie's, Kensington #77/R est:2000-3000
£3800	$6802	€5548	Afternoon on a Perthshire moorland (30x46cm-12x18in) s. i.verso. 27-May-4 Christie's, Kensington #203/R est:2500-3500
£4000	$7320	€5840	Highland cattle watering (32x47cm-13x19in) with sig. 8-Apr-4 Bonhams, Edinburgh #105/R est:1500-2000
£4200	$6762	€6090	Highland calves watering (36x56cm-14x22in) s. board. 21-Aug-3 Bonhams, Edinburgh #1057/R est:1500-2000
£6100	$10370	€8906	Highland cattle by a loch (41x56cm-16x22in) s. 25-Nov-3 Bonhams, Knowle #253/R est:1000-1500
£7000	$11900	€10220	Hills of Skye (81x102cm-32x40in) s.d.1905 prov. 30-Oct-3 Christie's, London #86/R est:9000-12000
£9000	$14130	€13050	Evening in the highlands (61x91cm-24x36in) s. i.verso. 27-Aug-3 Sotheby's, London #946/R est:10000-15000
£9000	$15930	€13140	By the loch side (39x60cm-15x24in) s. 28-Apr-4 Hampton & Littlewood, Exeter #571 est:10000-12000
£14000	$25340	€20440	In Glencoe (67x108cm-26x43in) s. canvas on board. 19-Apr-4 Sotheby's, London #23/R est:12000-18000
£20000	$34000	€29200	Highland cattle and drovers in a valley (76x128cm-30x50in) s.d.1894. 30-Oct-3 Christie's, London #89/R est:20000-30000
£25000	$39250	€36250	Head of the loch, showery weather (61x101cm-24x40in) s. i.verso. 27-Aug-3 Sotheby's, London #963/R est:22000-28000
£70000	$109900	€101500	Sunshine and shower (128x102cm-50x40in) s.d.1897 prov. 27-Aug-3 Sotheby's, London #1180/R est:80000-120000

HURT, Louis B (attrib) (1856-1929) British

£2800	$4760	€4088	Highland cattle in a Scottish glen (71x95cm-28x37in) 19-Nov-3 Tennants, Leyburn #1078/R est:2500-3500

HURTADO ARNAUDON, Fabio (1960-) Spanish

Works on paper

£461	$770	€650	Figures (32x35cm-13x14in) s.d.93 wax crayon. 23-Jun-3 Durán, Madrid #1294/R

HURTADO, Angel (1927-) Venezuelan

Works on paper

£684	$1095	€999	Untitled (51x67cm-20x26in) s. mixed media exec.1952. 21-Sep-3 Subastas Odalys, Caracas #6

HURTEAU, Philippe (20th C) French

£403	$713	€600	Etude pour peintre (116x89cm-46x35in) s.i.d.1987 verso prov.exhib. 28-Apr-4 Artcurial Briest, Paris #518
£403	$713	€600	Etude pour Mutus Lieber Museum (116x89cm-46x35in) s.i.d.1987 verso exhib. 28-Apr-4 Artcurial Briest, Paris #520/R

HURTUBISE, Jacques (1939-) Canadian

£2489	$3907	€3634	Celine (121x121cm-48x48in) s.i.d.67 acrylic. 26-Aug-3 Iegor de Saint Hippolyte, Montreal #90 (C.D 5500)

HURTUNA GIRALT, Jose (1913-1978) Spanish

£1354	$2234	€1950	Abstract composition (92x60cm-36x24in) s. s.verso. 2-Jul-3 Ansorena, Madrid #932/R

HUSAIN, Maqbool Fida (1915-) Indian

£3823	$6500	€5582	Farmer (43x69cm-17x27in) s.i.verso acrylic. 9-Nov-3 Bonhams & Butterfields, Los Angeles #4042/R
£5882	$10000	€8588	Untitled - blue figure and horse (66x66cm-26x26in) s.d.64 verso acrylic. 9-Nov-3 Bonhams & Butterfields, Los Angeles #4041/R
£7059	$12000	€10306	Untitled - two horse and a female figure (66x135cm-26x53in) s.i. s.verso acrylic. 9-Nov-3 Bonhams & Butterfields, Los Angeles #4040/R
£10669	$19203	€15577	Couple (60x44cm-24x17in) s.d. 25-Apr-4 Christie's, Hong Kong #596/R est:70000-80000 (HK.D 150000)
£10870	$20000	€15870	Maya with Hanuman (76x102cm-30x40in) s.d.80 i.verso acrylic. 24-Mar-4 Sotheby's, New York #189/R est:25000-30000
£15217	$28000	€22217	Horses (41x50cm-16x20in) s. 25-Mar-4 Christie's, Rockefeller NY #222/R est:9000-12000
£17391	$32000	€25391	Procession (58x141cm-23x56in) s. 25-Mar-4 Christie's, Rockefeller NY #221/R est:25000-30000
£18000	$30060	€26280	Blue woman with monkey (136x53cm-54x21in) s. 17-Oct-3 Christie's, Kensington #507/R est:12000-15000
£20000	$33400	€29200	Untitled (97x46cm-38x18in) s.d.63. 17-Oct-3 Christie's, Kensington #509/R est:10000-15000
£20000	$33400	€29200	Orchestra (59x100cm-23x39in) s.d.60 prov. 17-Oct-3 Christie's, Kensington #511/R est:10000-12000
£20652	$38000	€30152	Lady (140x85cm-55x33in) s. 25-Mar-4 Christie's, Rockefeller NY #216/R est:35000-40000
£22760	$40967	€33230	Horse (92x66cm-36x26in) s. 25-Apr-4 Christie's, Hong Kong #604/R est:150000-200000 (HK.D 320000)
£27027	$48649	€39459	Untitled (72x121cm-28x48in) s. acrylic. 25-Apr-4 Christie's, Hong Kong #605/R est:180000-240000 (HK.D 380000)
£29891	$55000	€43641	Musicians (83x123cm-33x48in) s.d.62. 25-Mar-4 Christie's, Rockefeller NY #214/R est:30000-35000
£34139	$61451	€49843	Krishna (91x148cm-36x58in) s. acrylic. 25-Apr-4 Christie's, Hong Kong #606/R est:360000-400000 (HK.D 480000)
£35326	$65000	€51576	Mother Theresa (168x234cm-66x92in) diptych exhib. 24-Mar-4 Sotheby's, New York #188/R est:65000-85000
£40761	$75000	€59511	Ganga (69x160cm-27x63in) s. 25-Mar-4 Christie's, Rockefeller NY #217/R est:30000-35000
Works on paper			
£3912	$7041	€5712	Untitled (53x74cm-21x29in) s.d.72 W/C marker paper on card. 25-Apr-4 Christie's, Hong Kong #598/R est:50000-60000 (HK.D 55000)
£5334	$9602	€7788	Bhishma - 10th day kurukshetra (35x53cm-14x21in) s.i. W/C paper on card. 25-Apr-4 Christie's, Hong Kong #597/R est:55000-65000 (HK.D 75000)
£5435	$10000	€7935	Portrait of an umbrella - two (37x54cm-15x21in) s.i. W/C black marker. 25-Mar-4 Christie's, Rockefeller NY #218/R est:7000-9000

HUSE, Marion (1896-?) American

£294	$500	€429	Hillside cottage (33x42cm-13x17in) s. board. 21-Nov-3 Skinner, Boston #461/R

HUSER, A (19th C) ?

£1972	$3273	€2800	Sunny wood (103x128cm-41x50in) s.d.96. 16-Jun-3 Dorotheum, Vienna #232/R est:2400-3000

HUSNER, Paul (1942-) Swiss

£1910	$3189	€2789	Temple entrance (48x65cm-19x26in) s.d.03. 12-Oct-3 Sotheby's, Singapore #40/R est:3000-4000 (S.D 5500)
£1935	$3097	€2825	Sea festival in Bali (70x90cm-28x35in) s.d.2002 s.d.02-13 2002. 18-May-3 Sotheby's, Singapore #13/R est:3000-4000 (S.D 5400)
£2162	$3611	€3157	Landscape of Bali, Iseh (56x71cm-22x28in) s. s.d.2001 verso. 26-Oct-3 Christie's, Hong Kong #76/R est:15000-20000 (HK.D 28000)
£2941	$5324	€4294	Planting of the new rice in Iseh, Bali (83x123cm-33x48in) s.i.d.03. 3-Apr-4 Glerum, Singapore #25/R est:7000-9000 (S.D 9000)
£3414	$6145	€4984	Temple ritual in Tabanan (71x91cm-28x36in) s.i.d.03. 25-Apr-4 Christie's, Hong Kong #504/R est:18000-30000 (HK.D 48000)
£3922	$7098	€5726	Landscape with temples in Tabanan, Bali (70x90cm-28x35in) s.d.03 s.i.d.verso. 4-Apr-4 Sotheby's, Singapore #16/R est:4000-6000 (S.D 12000)

HUSSEM, Willem (1900-1974) Dutch

£1027	$1747	€1500	Abstract still life (50x62cm-20x24in) s.d.47. 5-Nov-3 Vendue Huis, Gravenhage #439 est:1500-2000
£4196	$7217	€6000	Compositie (90x141cm-35x56in) init.d.65 oil on hessian. 2-Dec-3 Sotheby's, Amsterdam #180/R est:10000-15000
£4348	$7130	€6000	Untitled (60x100cm-24x39in) init.d.60 prov.exhib. 27-May-3 Sotheby's, Amsterdam #428/R est:6000-8000
£7692	$13231	€11000	Compositie (140x110cm-55x43in) i.d.1962 s.stretcher prov. 2-Dec-3 Sotheby's, Amsterdam #183/R est:10000-15000
£10145	$16638	€14000	Untitled (80x110cm-31x43in) init.d.64 exhib. 27-May-3 Sotheby's, Amsterdam #430/R est:8000-12000
£13333	$24533	€20000	Untitled (150x200cm-59x79in) prov. 8-Jun-4 Sotheby's, Amsterdam #127/R est:20000-25000

HUSSENOT, Joseph (1827-1896) French

Works on paper			
£550	$952	€803	Young Annibale and Agostino Carracci in their father's tailor shop (19x25cm-7x10in) s.i.d.1846 pen black ink brown wash. 12-Dec-3 Christie's, Kensington #504

HUSSEY, Philip (attrib) (1713-1782) British

£11000	$18260	€16060	Portrait of Matthew Lynch, Co Galway. Portrait of M Lynch's wife Miss Martyn (61x51cm-24x20in) pair. 30-Sep-3 Sotheby's, London #362/R est:12000-18000

HUSSMANN, Albert Heinrich (1874-1946) German

Sculpture			
£1626	$2911	€2374	Horse's head (61cm-24in) s. pat.bronze incl. stone socle. 26-May-4 AB Stockholms Auktionsverk #2474/R est:6000-8000 (S.KR 22000)
£1689	$3024	€2500	Three year old stallion Fried (40cm-16in) s.i. dark brown pat.bronze lit. 8-May-4 Schloss Ahlden, Ahlden #1052/R est:1600
£1867	$3435	€2800	Two jousters on horseback (37cm-15in) s.st.f. Gladenbeck brown pat. bronze oval marble base. 11-Jun-4 Wendl, Rudolstadt #1828/R est:1800

HUSSON, Leon (?) French?

£559	$934	€800	Gircourt-sur-Mouzon (81x63cm-32x25in) 12-Oct-3 Teitgen, Nancy #70

HUSTWICK, Francis (18/19th C) British

£2400	$4296	€3504	Full-rigged ship Duisburg flying her number at sea (51x61cm-20x24in) 26-May-4 Christie's, Kensington #622/R est:2000-3500
£3000	$5100	€4380	Royal Charter in-bound for Liverpool (61x91cm-24x36in) lit. 19-Nov-3 Christie's, Kensington #470/R

HUSZAR, Vilmos (1884-1960) Dutch

£1316	$2421	€2000	Red herring on a pewter plate (35x39cm-14x15in) s. 22-Jun-4 Christie's, Amsterdam #456/R est:800-1200
£8000	$14720	€12000	Seated lady (68x89cm-27x35in) s. board painted c.1932-33 prov. 8-Jun-4 Sotheby's, Amsterdam #16/R est:9000-12000

HUTCHENS, Frank Townsend (1869-1937) American

£1087	$2000	€1587	Portrait of woman (15x23cm-6x9in) s. board. 28-Mar-4 Carlsen Gallery, Greenville #565/R

HUTCHINS, Glen (20th C) New Zealander

£335	$575	€489	The silent T (148x119cm-58x47in) s.d.2001. 7-Dec-3 International Art Centre, Auckland #293/R (NZ.D 900)

HUTCHINSON, George Musther (1934-) British

Works on paper			
£280	$510	€409	Crawleyside towards Stanhope (33x53cm-13x21in) s.i. verso W/C. 29-Jun-4 Anderson & Garland, Newcastle #131
£320	$582	€467	Towards Burnhope from near Tow Law (40x60cm-16x24in) s. i. verso. 29-Jun-4 Anderson & Garland, Newcastle #129/R
£340	$619	€496	Millers Farm near Castleside (41x60cm-16x24in) s. i. verso W/C. 29-Jun-4 Anderson & Garland, Newcastle #127/R
£380	$692	€555	Towards Muggleswick, Derwent Valley (41x60cm-16x24in) s.i. i. verso W/C. 29-Jun-4 Anderson & Garland, Newcastle #128/R

HUTCHINSON, J (19/20th C) British

Sculpture			
£17000	$27370	€24650	Robert of Bruce (130cm-51in) i. bronze. 21-Aug-3 Bonhams, Edinburgh #893/R est:8000-12000

HUTCHINSON, John E (19th C) British

£1243	$2250	€1815	Pointer in a landscape. Setter with game (23x30cm-9x12in) s. board pair. 30-Mar-4 Bonhams & Butterfields, San Francisco #56/R est:1500-2200

HUTCHINSON, Leonard (1896-1980) Canadian

£360	$659	€526	Shore side still life (27x32cm-11x13in) s. panel. 1-Jun-4 Joyner Waddington, Toronto #368/R (C.D 900)

HUTCHINSON, Nick Hely (1955-) Irish

Works on paper			
£260	$458	€380	South of France interior (37x55cm-15x22in) s.verso gouache. 4-Jan-4 Lots Road Auctions, London #370
£1056	$1690	€1500	La colombe d'or, St Paul de Venice (46x61cm-18x24in) init. W/C gouache prov. 16-Sep-3 Whyte's, Dublin #200/R est:1500-1800
£1329	$2259	€1900	Approaching storm, Easky (44x52cm-17x20in) init. gouache oil pastel prov. exhib. 18-Nov-3 Whyte's, Dublin #7/R est:2000-3000

HUTCHINSON, Peter (1932-) British

Works on paper			
£333	$613	€500	Long point project (35x28cm-14x11in) s.i.d.1969/89 collage three photos. 12-Jun-4 Villa Grisebach, Berlin #755/R
£333	$613	€500	Roman Empire series no VI (70x650cm-28x256in) s.i. s.d.1980 verso collage photos felt-tip. 12-Jun-4 Villa Grisebach, Berlin #756/R

HUTCHISON, Frederick William (1871-1953) Canadian

£800	$1464	€1168	Farm house, Baie St Paul (30x40cm-12x16in) prov. 1-Jun-4 Joyner Waddington, Toronto #11/R est:2000-3000 (C.D 2000)
£1200	$2196	€1752	Houses and landscape - Baie St Paul (20x25cm-8x10in) s. board. 1-Jun-4 Joyner Waddington, Toronto #199/R est:3500-4500 (C.D 3000)
£1520	$2782	€2219	Old house and poplars (30x40cm-12x16in) s. prov. 1-Jun-4 Joyner Waddington, Toronto #182/R est:4000-5000 (C.D 3800)
£2411	$4146	€3520	Home from the village (12x18cm-5x7in) s. panel prov. 2-Dec-3 Joyner Waddington, Toronto #478 est:1000-1500 (C.D 5400)
£4200	$7686	€6132	Quebec village (41x51cm-16x20in) s. prov. 1-Jun-4 Joyner Waddington, Toronto #109/R est:8000-10000 (C.D 10500)

Works on paper
£560 $1025 €818 Street scene in winter, Ste Urbain, PQ (10x14cm-4x6in) studio st. ink W/C prov. 1-Jun-4 Joyner Waddington, Toronto #300/R (C.D 1400)
£4018 $6911 €5866 Valley of Baie St Paul. Paie St Paul. Road to Baie St Paul (17x21cm-7x8in) each init. gouache three prov. 2-Dec-3 Joyner Waddington, Toronto #479 est:1200-1500 (C.D 9000)

HUTCHISON, Robert Gemmell (1855-1936) British
£1500 $2805 €2190 View of an old Scottish cottage with a figure standing beside doorway (13x18cm-5x7in) init. i.verso board prov. 22-Jul-4 Tennants, Leyburn #841/R est:1500-2500
£2200 $3542 €3190 Carnoustie (21x25cm-8x10in) s. board. 21-Aug-3 Bonhams, Edinburgh #1011/R est:800-1200
£2200 $3740 €3212 Nook in a cornfield (46x30cm-18x12in) s.d.1877. 30-Oct-3 Christie's, London #111/R est:2500-3500
£4800 $8160 €7008 Among the seagrass (37x27cm-15x11in) s. board exhib. 8-Nov-3 Shapes, Edinburgh #469/R est:3000-5000
£5000 $9150 €7300 Preparing the midday meal (44x59cm-17x23in) s. indis i. 8-Apr-4 Bonhams, Edinburgh #166/R est:5000-8000
£5500 $9900 €8030 Children playing on the beach at Carnoustie (14x19cm-6x7in) s. board prov. 21-Apr-4 Tennants, Leyburn #1217/R est:4000-6000
£7000 $13020 €10220 Dutch boy (28x18cm-11x7in) s. canvasboard. 4-Mar-4 Christie's, Kensington #152/R est:7000-10000
£8000 $14480 €11680 Washing her socks (25x35cm-10x14in) s. 19-Apr-4 Sotheby's, London #57/R est:8000-12000
£8000 $14400 €12000 Departure (122x158cm-48x62in) s. 26-Apr-4 Bernaerts, Antwerp #47/R est:12500-15000
£8500 $13685 €12325 Young horticulturist (9x14cm-4x6in) s. board. 21-Aug-3 Bonhams, Edinburgh #1104/R est:7000-10000
£10000 $15700 €14500 Polishing the kettle (41x32cm-16x13in) s. board prov. 27-Aug-3 Sotheby's, London #1196/R est:10000-15000
£10200 $18666 €14892 Building sandcastle (24x34cm-9x13in) s. canvasboard prov. 8-Apr-4 Bonhams, Edinburgh #161/R est:6000-8000
£11000 $17270 €15950 Hot potatoes (14x11cm-6x4in) s. panel. 27-Aug-3 Sotheby's, London #1195/R est:5000-7000
£12000 $21840 €17520 Mother and child (78x64cm-31x25in) s. 3-Feb-4 Sworder & Son, Bishops Stortford #301/R est:12000-15000
£12000 $21720 €17520 Balloon (35x46cm-14x18in) s. panel. 19-Apr-4 Sotheby's, London #59/R est:12000-18000
£13000 $23530 €18980 By the side of the Zuiderzee (22x30cm-9x12in) s. board. 3-Apr-4 British Auctioneer #267
£15000 $23550 €21750 Pans, Machrihanish (25x36cm-10x14in) s. board prov. 27-Aug-3 Sotheby's, London #1193/R est:10000-15000
£15000 $26850 €21900 Shrimping (22x29cm-9x11in) s. board. 27-May-4 Christie's, Kensington #334/R est:8000-12000
£16000 $28960 €23360 Stormy sea at Carnoustie (73x102cm-29x40in) s. prov. 19-Apr-4 Sotheby's, London #60/R est:15000-20000
£20000 $31400 €29000 Kitten's milk (36x39cm-14x15in) s. panel prov.exhib. 27-Aug-3 Sotheby's, London #1197/R est:15000-20000
£20000 $34000 €29200 In Tow (35x53cm-14x21in) s. 30-Oct-3 Christie's, London #141/R est:15000-20000
£30000 $54300 €43800 Peeling potatoes (61x51cm-24x20in) s. 19-Apr-4 Sotheby's, London #61/R est:20000-30000
Works on paper
£320 $534 €467 Rustic toilet (19x14cm-7x6in) init. pen ink. 19-Jun-3 Bonhams, Edinburgh #330
£920 $1739 €1343 Children paddling by the seashore (16x22cm-6x9in) s. W/C. 17-Feb-4 Fellows & Sons, Birmingham #121/R
£1500 $2730 €2190 Young girl holding a basket seated on a beach (18x13cm-7x5in) s. W/C htd white. 29-Jun-4 Rowley Fine Art, Newmarket #361/R
£2800 $5208 €4088 Girl knitting (40x29cm-16x11in) s. W/C. 4-Mar-4 Christie's, Kensington #153/R est:3000-5000
£2900 $4843 €4234 Looking to Jura (29x41cm-11x16in) pastel prov. 16-Oct-3 Bonhams, Edinburgh #145/R est:2000-3000
£6000 $10320 €8760 Young waders (45x35cm-18x14in) s. pencil W/C htd white prov. 4-Dec-3 Bonhams, Edinburgh #19/R est:6000-8000

HUTCHISON, William Oliphant (1889-c.1971) British
£530 $837 €769 Spanish village (45x37cm-18x15in) s. canvasboard. 4-Sep-3 Bonhams, Cornwall #476

HUTEAU, Marie (19/20th C) French?
£355 $592 €500 Fleurs (50x61cm-20x24in) s.d.1902. 15-Oct-3 Neret-Minet, Paris #5/R
£496 $829 €700 Nora et Duminet (77x61cm-30x24in) s.d.1904. 15-Oct-3 Neret-Minet, Paris #2

HUTH, Franz (1876-?) German
£972 $1585 €1400 Summer flowers (70x88cm-28x35in) 29-Sep-3 Dr Fritz Nagel, Stuttgart #7195/R
Works on paper
£333 $603 €500 Flowers (40x60cm-16x24in) s. pastel. 2-Apr-4 Winterberg, Heidelberg #1127
£387 $670 €550 View of Colmar (30x22cm-12x9in) s.d.1959 pastel. 12-Dec-3 Berlinghof, Heidelberg #1057/R
£423 $731 €600 Passage in Schwetzinger Castle Park (38x25cm-15x10in) s. pastel. 12-Dec-3 Berlinghof, Heidelberg #1058/R
£458 $792 €650 Amorbach with church interior (29x23cm-11x9in) s. pastel. 12-Dec-3 Berlinghof, Heidelberg #1056/R
£458 $792 €650 View of Wurzburg (31x23cm-12x9in) s.d.1937 pastel. 12-Dec-3 Berlinghof, Heidelberg #1059/R
£593 $1092 €890 Colourful vase of flowers on the window sill (68x83cm-27x33in) s. pastel. 11-Jun-4 Wendl, Rudolstadt #4091/R

HUTH, Julius (1838-1892) German
£1000 $1850 €1460 Unloading the catch, Katwijk Aan Zee (21x31cm-8x12in) s. 10-Mar-4 Sotheby's, Olympia #240/R est:1000-1500

HUTH, Willy Robert (1890-1977) German
£533 $955 €800 Street in small southern town (51x66cm-20x26in) mono.d. board. 15-May-4 Bassenge, Berlin #7344/R
Works on paper
£280 $476 €400 Still life of fruit (29x41cm-11x16in) mono.d.48 bodycol board. 29-Nov-3 Bassenge, Berlin #6785/R

HUTHER, Julius (1881-1954) German
£315 $541 €450 In the vineyard (65x88cm-26x35in) s.d.1925. 4-Dec-3 Van Ham, Cologne #231
£400 $716 €600 Three heads (52x36cm-20x14in) s.d. 13-May-4 Neumeister, Munich #381/R
£483 $806 €700 Sunflowers (23x30cm-9x12in) s.d.1943 board on paper. 13-Nov-3 Neumeister, Munich #351/R
£570 $1050 €850 Sunflowers (69x49cm-27x19in) s.d.36. 24-Mar-4 Hugo Ruef, Munich #1236/R
£1007 $1852 €1500 Flower garden (58x73cm-23x29in) s.d.1931 panel. 24-Mar-4 Hugo Ruef, Munich #1235/R est:1500
£1049 $1783 €1500 Arab boy before oriental town (63x56cm-25x22in) s. 20-Nov-3 Weidler, Nurnberg #6510/R est:1300
£1250 $2088 €1800 Still life of flowers (51x60cm-20x24in) s.d. 24-Oct-3 Ketterer, Hamburg #396/R est:2000-2200

HUTLE, Carl (fl.1856-1862) ?
£1589 $2909 €2400 Tired travellers (93x78cm-37x31in) s. 8-Apr-4 Dorotheum, Vienna #180/R est:1300-1500

HUTRI, Armas (1922-) Finnish
Sculpture
£9441 $16049 €13500 Swans in flight (35x105cm-14x41in) s.d.80 bronze three. 29-Nov-3 Bukowskis, Helsinki #15/R est:6500-8000

HUTSCHENREUTHER, Arthur (?) ?
£2222 $3778 €3200 Studying (56x65cm-22x26in) s. 28-Oct-3 Dorotheum, Vienna #146/R est:2600-3000

HUTSON, Marshall C (fl.1930-40) British
£1319 $2151 €1900 Birthday flowers (58x48cm-23x19in) board exhib. 24-Sep-3 James Adam, Dublin #94/R est:2000-3000

HUTTE, Axel (1951-) ?
Photographs
£2222 $4000 €3244 Rio muerte II, Coasta Rica (157x287cm-62x113in) num.1/4 chromogenic colour print. 23-Apr-4 Phillips, New York #234/R est:7000-10000
£4667 $8587 €7000 Brunifirm (94x128cm-37x50in) s.i.d.1997 num.3/4 verso colour photograph. 8-Jun-4 Sotheby's, Amsterdam #159/R est:8000-12000
£4762 $9000 €6953 Punta della Salute from the Xanten (115x171cm-45x67in) gelatin silver print. 17-Feb-4 Christie's, Rockefeller NY #279/R est:4000-6000
£15363 $27500 €22430 Goch - Phlanzen (166x201cm-65x79in) s.i.d.2000 num.1/4 verso cibachrome print prov.exhib. 13-May-4 Sotheby's, New York #387/R est:20000-30000

HUTTER, Wolfgang (1928-) Austrian
Works on paper
£987 $1816 €1500 Surreal composition (27x24cm-11x9in) s.d.1946 lit. mixed media. 22-Jun-4 Wiener Kunst Auktionen, Vienna #312/R est:1500
£987 $1816 €1500 Surreal composition (31x16cm-12x6in) mono.d.1946 mixed media. 22-Jun-4 Wiener Kunst Auktionen, Vienna #313/R est:1500

HUTTON, Thomas S (c.1865-1935) British
£420 $668 €613 Cockle gatherers, Cullercoats (24x33cm-9x13in) s. 18-Mar-3 Anderson & Garland, Newcastle #343
£920 $1463 €1343 North coast scene with a castle on a headland (42x59cm-17x23in) s. 18-Mar-3 Anderson & Garland, Newcastle #342/R
Works on paper
£250 $460 €365 Seagull in flight off the North East Coast (54x75cm-21x30in) s. W/C. 23-Mar-4 Anderson & Garland, Newcastle #296/R
£260 $465 €380 Brindle Bay, Bamburgh (32x51cm-13x20in) s.i.d.1893 W/C. 17-Mar-4 Bonhams, Chester #331
£350 $637 €511 Bamburgh village with a shepherd and flock in the foreground (23x34cm-9x13in) s.i. 29-Jun-4 Anderson & Garland, Newcastle #253/R
£380 $619 €555 Waves breaking in a rocky Yorkshire bay (53x76cm-21x30in) s. W/C. 23-Sep-3 Anderson & Garland, Newcastle #287
£400 $652 €584 In from the North Sea, an East Coast harbour (22x32cm-9x13in) s. i.verso W/C. 23-Sep-3 Anderson & Garland, Newcastle #286/R
£400 $692 €584 Old Hartley with Blyth in the distance (27x52cm-11x20in) s. W/C. 9-Dec-3 Anderson & Garland, Newcastle #314/R
£400 $736 €584 Seagulls in flight along a rocky coast (66x53cm-26x21in) s. W/C. 23-Mar-4 Anderson & Garland, Newcastle #297
£420 $764 €613 Cullercoats Bay (16x31cm-6x12in) s. W/C. 29-Jun-4 Anderson & Garland, Newcastle #254
£500 $875 €730 Cullercoats (28x71cm-11x28in) s. W/C. 19-Dec-3 Mallams, Oxford #144/R
£500 $910 €730 St Mary's Island (16x30cm-6x12in) s. W/C. 29-Jun-4 Anderson & Garland, Newcastle #255
£520 $957 €759 Old Hartley with Blyth Harbour in the distance (25x54cm-10x21in) s. W/C. 23-Mar-4 Anderson & Garland, Newcastle #295
£550 $919 €803 Beach tents (25x53cm-10x21in) init. W/C. 14-Oct-3 David Lay, Penzance #67/R
£560 $1030 €818 Two figures walking in Holywell Dene, Seaton Sluice (16x32cm-6x13in) s. W/C. 23-Mar-4 Anderson & Garland, Newcastle #292
£600 $1104 €876 Mouth of the Tyne (18x32cm-7x13in) s.i. W/C. 23-Mar-4 Anderson & Garland, Newcastle #293/R
£750 $1373 €1095 View of Robin Hood's bay (32x48cm-13x19in) s. W/C. 29-Jul-4 Locke & England, Leamington Spa #123/R
£750 $1373 €1095 Figures on beach (33x53cm-13x21in) s. W/C. 29-Jul-4 Locke & England, Leamington Spa #124/R
£820 $1509 €1197 Seaton Sluice, Northumberland (28x51cm-11x20in) s. W/C. 23-Mar-4 Anderson & Garland, Newcastle #291/R

HUTTON, Walter (19/20th C) British
£2762 $5000 €4033 Two sisters by a garden gate (198x132cm-78x52in) s. 3-Apr-4 Neal Auction Company, New Orleans #289/R est:7500-12500

HUTTY, Alfred (1877-1954) American
£41436 $75000 €60497 Wash day (76x61cm-30x24in) s. 3-Apr-4 Neal Auction Company, New Orleans #418/R est:30000-50000
Prints
£1744 $3000 €2546 Cabbage row (20x25cm-8x10in) s.i. etching. 6-Dec-3 Neal Auction Company, New Orleans #524/R est:3000-4000
£1796 $3000 €2622 Street scene, Charleston (20x25cm-8x10in) s.d.1941 drypoint. 11-Nov-3 Doyle, New York #271a/R est:1000-1500
£1807 $3000 €2638 Charleston Spires, St Philip's Church (41x33cm-16x13in) mono.i. etching drypoint. 4-Oct-3 Neal Auction Company, New Orleans #474/R est:3000-4000
£1916 $3200 €2797 Young blacks (20x20cm-8x8in) drypoint. 25-Oct-3 Du Mouchelle, Detroit #3154/R est:200-400
£1928 $3200 €2815 Rural South (20x25cm-8x10in) s.i. drypoint exec 1939 edn of 75. 4-Oct-3 Neal Auction Company, New Orleans #475/R est:3000-4000
£2315 $3750 €3380 Low country cabin (28x36cm-11x14in) mono.i. etching. 2-Aug-3 Neal Auction Company, New Orleans #414/R est:2500-3500
£3704 $6000 €5408 Towards a new day (28x38cm-11x15in) mono.i. drypoint. 2-Aug-3 Neal Auction Company, New Orleans #413/R est:2500-3500
Works on paper
£16201 $29000 €23653 Around the campfire (28x34cm-11x13in) s. W/C go. paperboard. 14-May-4 Skinner, Boston #259/R est:300-500

HUXLEY, Paul (1938-) British
£809 $1400 €1181 No 105 (239x239cm-94x94in) prov. 15-Dec-3 Hindman, Chicago #115/R est:2000-4000

HUYGENS, François Joseph (1820-1908) Belgian
£629 $1051 €900 Tableau de chasse (18x16cm-7x6in) s. panel pair. 13-Oct-3 Horta, Bruxelles #453
£1333 $2440 €2000 Fraises de bois dans une corbeille (36x52cm-14x20in) s.d.1891. 7-Jun-4 Palais de Beaux Arts, Brussels #68/R est:2000-3000
£4520 $8000 €6599 Still life with roses, flowers, butterfly and bird's nest (56x46cm-22x18in) s.d.1850. 2-May-4 Bonhams & Butterfields, San Francisco #1032/R est:8000-12000
£4651 $8000 €6790 Vase of flowers with plums and nest (70x54cm-28x21in) s.d.1846 panel. 2-Dec-3 Christie's, Rockefeller NY #35/R est:7000-9000

HUYGENS, J (1833-1911) Dutch
£1119 $1902 €1600 Vase chinois garni de roses (80x60cm-31x24in) s. 18-Nov-3 Galerie Moderne, Brussels #821 est:400-600

HUYGENS, Léon (19/20th C) Belgian
£397 $723 €600 L'Yser (33x41cm-13x16in) s.d.1916 panel. 15-Jun-4 Vanderkindere, Brussels #586
£490 $842 €700 Nature morte aux huitres (35x44cm-14x17in) s.d.1884 panel. 8-Dec-3 Horta, Bruxelles #380

HUYGHES, Pierre (20th C) French?
Works on paper
£1200 $2160 €1800 Untitled (82x82cm-32x32in) s.verso mixed media. 24-Apr-4 Cornette de St.Cyr, Paris #569/R est:1200-1500

HUYGHUE, Samuel Douglas Smith (1815-1891) Australian/Canadian
Works on paper
£632 $1132 €948 Grass tree, eureka diggings. Young gum tree (9x15cm-4x6in) one i.d.Oct 24 1852 one i.d.May 1852 ink pair. 17-May-4 Sotheby's, Melbourne #579 (A.D 1600)
£992 $1806 €1448 Site of the Eureka Stockade (16x23cm-6x9in) s.i.d.1855 pencil. 16-Jun-4 Deutscher-Menzies, Melbourne #210/R est:3000-5000 (A.D 2600)

HUYS, Bernhard (1885-1973) German
£282 $519 €420 Winter in Worpswede (25x35cm-10x14in) s. board. 26-Mar-4 Bolland & Marotz, Bremen #337a/R
£331 $603 €500 Canal scene (49x69cm-19x27in) s. board. 18-Jun-4 Bolland & Marotz, Bremen #353/R
£350 $601 €500 Peat cutting in the moor (35x50cm-14x20in) s. board. 5-Dec-3 Bolland & Marotz, Bremen #370/R
£436 $803 €650 Winter on the Weyerberg (25x34cm-10x13in) board. 26-Mar-4 Bolland & Marotz, Bremen #338/R
£470 $864 €700 Lilienthal (49x65cm-19x26in) s.d.1964 panel. 26-Mar-4 Bolland & Marotz, Bremen #337/R
£629 $1145 €950 Landscape with a small wooden bridge (50x70cm-20x28in) s.d.51 board. 18-Jun-4 Bolland & Marotz, Bremen #352/R

HUYS, Modeste (1875-1932) Belgian
£4698 $8691 €7000 Calm slate and flax workers (38x50cm-15x20in) s. panel. 13-Mar-4 De Vuyst, Lokeren #535/R est:6000-8000
£13287 $22587 €19000 Snow and flood (60x70cm-24x28in) s. s.i.verso. 25-Nov-3 Christie's, Amsterdam #205/R est:15000-20000
£69930 $118881 €100000 In de lente (96x120cm-38x47in) s.d.1910 verso. 1-Dec-3 Palais de Beaux Arts, Brussels #77/R est:100000-150000

HUYSMANS, Cornelis (1648-1727) Flemish
£6897 $11448 €10000 Landscape with classical figures (52x62cm-20x24in) exhib. 30-Sep-3 Ansorena, Madrid #62/R est:10000
£16667 $29833 €25000 Landscapes with nymphs and shepherds (74x90cm-29x35in) pair. 17-May-4 Finarte Semenzato, Rome #118/R est:30000-35000

HUYSMANS, Cornelis (attrib) (1648-1727) Flemish
£5103 $8523 €7400 Sous-bois anime de bergers au repos (74x95cm-29x37in) 17-Nov-3 Bernaerts, Antwerp #171/R est:5000-6000

HUYSMANS, Jacob (circle) (1633-1680) Flemish
£12500 $22375 €18250 Portrait of a young girl, believed to be Mary Gulston. Portrait of her sister (76x63cm-30x25in) pair. 22-Mar-4 Bonhams & Brooks, Norfolk #340/R est:6000-8000

HUYSMANS, Jan Baptist (1826-1906) Belgian
£5656 $9615 €8258 Woman resting in harem (21x27cm-8x11in) s. panel. 19-Nov-3 Fischer, Luzern #1111/R est:4000-5000 (S.FR 12500)

HUYSMANS, Jan Baptist (1654-1716) Flemish
£6897 $11448 €10000 Landscape with hunters (64x76cm-25x30in) 30-Sep-3 Ansorena, Madrid #55/R est:10000

HUYSUM, Jacob van (1686-1740) Dutch
Works on paper
£4200 $7770 €6132 Hibiscus syriacus. Bladder-nut (50x34cm-20x13in) pencil W/C three. 15-Jul-4 Bonhams, New Bond Street #39/R est:3000-5000

HUYSUM, Jan van (1682-1749) Dutch
£608 $1070 €900 Arcadian landscape with figures (15x20cm-6x8in) s. pen wash prov. 22-May-4 Lempertz, Koln #1289/R
£5333 $9707 €8000 Italian river landscape (65x79cm-26x31in) s. 30-Jun-4 Neumeister, Munich #459/R est:9000
£18121 $32436 €27000 Vase de fleurs dans une niche (69x50cm-27x20in) s. 25-May-4 Palais de Beaux Arts, Brussels #554/R est:30000-40000
£2700000 $4671000 €3942000 Still life of flowers in a terracotta vase upon a marble ledge before a niche (81x61cm-32x24in) s.d.1734 panel prov.exhib.lit. 11-Dec-3 Sotheby's, London #74/R est:1200000-1800000
£4400000 $7612000 €6424000 Still life of fruit in a basket with flowers and other fruit all upon a marble ledge (80x60cm-31x24in) panel prov.exhib.lit. 11-Dec-3 Sotheby's, London #75/R est:1000000-1500000
Works on paper
£467 $835 €700 Italian landscape with fortress and figures (19x31cm-7x12in) chk. 13-May-4 Bassenge, Berlin #5403
£969 $1648 €1415 Flowers (40x31cm-16x12in) s. ochre. 5-Nov-3 Dobiaschofsky, Bern #1135/R (S.FR 2200)

HUYSUM, Jan van (style) (1682-1749) Dutch
£5913 $10584 €8633 Still life of flowers (93x68cm-37x27in) 26-May-4 AB Stockholms Auktionsverk #2517/R est:40000-60000 (S.KR 80000)
£6500 $11700 €9490 Flowers in an urn on a marble ledge with butterflies (74x60cm-29x24in) mono. 23-Apr-4 Christie's, Kensington #124/R est:2000-4000
£7500 $13500 €10950 Still life with roses, irises, tulips and other flowers in a terracotta urn on a stone ledge (53x42cm-21x17in) bears sig panel. 20-Apr-4 Sotheby's, Olympia #365/R est:2500-3500
£10596 $19285 €16000 Still life with flowers and fruit (79x59cm-31x23in) i.d.1752 panel. 16-Jun-4 Dorotheum, Vienna #70/R est:5000-7000

HUYSUM, Justus van (17/18th C) Dutch
£14084 $24648 €20000 Nature morte au vase de fleurs sur un entablement (64x53cm-25x21in) s. 18-Dec-3 Tajan, Paris #31/R est:10000-15000

HUZE, Guy (?) ?
Works on paper
£578 $1035 €850 Danseurs a la batterie (47x65cm-19x26in) s. gouache. 21-Mar-4 St-Germain-en-Laye Encheres #111/R
£782 $1400 €1150 Danse a Capetown (47x61cm-19x24in) s.i. gouache. 21-Mar-4 St-Germain-en-Laye Encheres #63/R

HUZEL (19th C) French
Sculpture
£824 $1400 €1203 Rapunzel (33cm-13in) i. gilt bronze. 22-Nov-3 Jackson's, Cedar Falls #205/R est:1000-1500

HYAKUNEN, Suzuki (1825-1891) Japanese
Works on paper
£629 $1083 €900 One hundred okamis performing various seasonal tasks (120x50cm-47x20in) s. ink col silk hanging scroll. 5-Dec-3 Lempertz, Koln #776/R

HYAKUSEN, Sakaki (1698-1753) Japanese
Works on paper
£2600 $4342 €3796 Foreigners (119x25cm-47x10in) s.d.1751 ink col set of 3. 12-Nov-3 Christie's, London #58/R est:3000-5000

HYAMS, William (1878-1952) British
Works on paper
£380 $688 €555 Three masted sailing ship at sea (36x48cm-14x19in) s. W/C. 16-Apr-4 Keys, Aylsham #506

HYATT, Derek (1931-) British
£320 $582 €467 Moonlight, green (22x22cm-9x9in) acrylic hardboard. 15-Jun-4 Bonhams, Leeds #45
£340 $602 €496 Evening forms, Lyme (39x52cm-15x20in) i.verso board prov. 27-Apr-4 Bonhams, Knowle #130
£360 $655 €526 Collingham cloudscape (22x29cm-9x11in) oil plywood. 15-Jun-4 Bonhams, Leeds #43

£380	$692	€555	Snow shower (21x24cm-8x9in) acrylic board. 15-Jun-4 Bonhams, Leeds #44/R

HYBERT, Fabrice (1961-) French?

£4667	$8587	€7000	Vortex (114x146cm-45x57in) s.d.1990 verso oil pastel prov. 9-Jun-4 Artcurial Briest, Paris #560/R est:6000-8000
£6338	$11092	€9000	Hermetique (130x130cm-51x51in) s.i.d.24.01.97 oil chl collage. 18-Dec-3 Cornette de St.Cyr, Paris #47/R est:10000-12000
Sculpture			
£2568	$4519	€3800	Pof No. 3, M Balancoire a la menthe (280x40x20cm-110x16x8in) elastic resin edn of 8 exe 1992. 18-May-4 Tajan, Paris #186/R est:3000-4000
Works on paper			
£1056	$1827	€1500	Telepherique (29x40cm-11x16in) s.i.d.2002 W/C pastel prov. 14-Dec-3 Versailles Encheres #219 est:1500-2000
£1549	$2680	€2200	Bacterian war (55x75cm-22x30in) s.d.1999 wax pastel acrylic. 9-Dec-3 Artcurial Briest, Paris #184/R est:1500-1600
£3716	$6540	€5500	Trans-Action (100x100cm-39x39in) s.i.d.2001 mixed media canvas prov. 18-May-4 Tajan, Paris #149/R est:5500-6000
£4667	$8587	€7000	Sange de l'homme de Bessine (16x114cm-6x45in) s.i.d.1996 verso mixed media canvas prov. 9-Jun-4 Artcurial Briest, Paris #559/R est:6000-8000
£8667	$16033	€13000	Balle verte (200x200cm-79x79in) chl oil W/C paper on canvas exec.2000 prov.exhib. 18-Jul-4 Sotheby's, Paris #277/R est:8000-12000
£9333	$16987	€14000	Hu-meur (130x162cm-51x64in) s.i.d.1996 verso prov. 29-Jun-4 Cornette de St.Cyr, Paris #160/R est:10000-12000

HYDE, Doug (1946-) American

Sculpture			
£1324	$2250	€1933	Blanket trader (25x30x13cm-10x12x5in) s.num.11/21 bronze prov. 1-Nov-3 Santa Fe Art, Santa Fe #43/R est:3000-4000
£1765	$3000	€2577	Grandma, Kitty and me (66cm-26in) alabaster. 1-Nov-3 Altermann Galleries, Santa Fe #123

HYDE, Frank (fl.1872-1916) British

£500	$815	€730	Procession of comical monks sliding on an icy path (40x30cm-16x12in) s.d.85 panel. 25-Sep-3 Clevedon Sale Rooms #226

HYDE, Helen (?) ?

£860	$1600	€1256	Still life of purple flowers in a green vase (61x46cm-24x18in) board. 3-Mar-4 Alderfer's, Hatfield #300 est:1000-1500

HYDE, Russell T (1886-?) American

£1524	$2500	€2225	Woman at the lake (79x107cm-31x42in) d.1923 i.stretcher. 7-Jun-3 Auctions by the Bay, Alameda #530/R

HYDMAN-VALLIEN, Ulrika (1938-) Swedish

£554	$992	€809	Female head with snakes (55x46cm-22x18in) s. panel. 28-May-4 Uppsala Auktionskammare, Uppsala #346/R (S.KR 7500)
£702	$1257	€1025	Still life of tulips (80x65cm-31x26in) s. 28-May-4 Uppsala Auktionskammare, Uppsala #344/R (S.KR 9500)
£725	$1305	€1088	Mother, children, birds (65x54cm-26x21in) s. acrylic. 25-Apr-4 Goteborg Auktionsverk, Sweden #1265/R (S.KR 10000)

HYGEN, Bernitz (?) Norwegian?

£261	$451	€381	Norwegian coastal landscape (36x52cm-14x20in) s. 13-Dec-3 Blomqvist, Lysaker #1032 (N.KR 3000)

HYLAND, Benedict A (19th C) British

£432	$800	€631	Recumbent Saint Bernard in stable (38x51cm-15x20in) s. 10-Feb-4 Doyle, New York #164/R

HYLANDER, Einar (1913-1989) Swedish

Works on paper			
£2039	$3467	€2977	Once upon a time (58x38cm-23x15in) init.d.78 collage prov. 5-Nov-3 AB Stockholms Auktionsverk #1046/R est:6000-8000 (S.KR 27000)
£2417	$4109	€3529	Jasmin (109x87cm-43x34in) init.d.1972 mixed media panel exhib. 4-Nov-3 Bukowskis, Stockholm #538/R est:18000-20000 (S.KR 32000)

HYLL, Jul (20th C) Scandinavian

£363	$668	€530	Beech tree in winter (125x99cm-49x39in) s. 9-Jun-4 Walker's, Ottawa #311a/R (C.D 900)

HYNARD, Sally A (1959-) British

Works on paper			
£300	$501	€438	Little lamb with the boy (20x24cm-8x9in) s. W/C. 22-Oct-3 Cheffins, Cambridge #504
£420	$668	€613	Zebra (48x30cm-19x12in) s. cromacolour. 10-Sep-3 Cheffins, Cambridge #502/R

HYNCKES, Raoul (1893-1973) Dutch

£533	$965	€800	Port de peche (42x55cm-17x22in) panel. 30-Mar-4 Campo, Vlaamse Kaai #85
£940	$1757	€1400	Le port (46x58cm-18x23in) s. panel. 29-Feb-4 Osenat, Fontainebleau #207
£1667	$3050	€2500	Mountain landscape with houses (51x64cm-20x25in) s. 7-Jun-4 Glerum, Amsterdam #84/R est:2500-3000
£2013	$3725	€3000	Le depart du vapeur pres de la jetee (66x101cm-26x40in) s. 15-Mar-4 Horta, Bruxelles #96 est:800-1200
£5000	$9200	€7500	Amitie (65x88cm-26x35in) painted 1952 exhib. 9-Jun-4 Christie's, Amsterdam #223/R est:7000-9000

HYNCKES-ZAHN, Marguerite (1897-1978) Dutch

£490	$832	€700	Still life with plums in a bowl (35x50cm-14x20in) mono. 24-Nov-3 Glerum, Amsterdam #100/R

HYNEMAN, Herman (1859-1907) American

£367	$675	€550	Crepuscule sur l'Escaut (50x61cm-20x24in) s. 14-Jun-4 Horta, Bruxelles #429

HYNER, Arend (1866-1916) Dutch

£1935	$3561	€2825	Preparing the meal (56x45cm-22x18in) s. prov. 14-Jun-4 Waddingtons, Toronto #246/R est:2500-3000 (C.D 4800)

HYNES, Stephen (1944-) Canadian

£200	$366	€292	Early evening solace (30x40cm-12x16in) s.i.d.2003. 1-Jun-4 Hodgins, Calgary #152/R (C.D 500)
£320	$586	€467	Englishman's Falls (30x40cm-12x16in) s.i. 1-Jun-4 Hodgins, Calgary #151/R (C.D 800)

HYRE, Laurent de la (attrib) (1606-1656) French

Works on paper			
£612	$973	€900	Architecture animee (34x23cm-13x9in) pen ink wash crayon. 21-Mar-3 Bailly Pommery, Paris #42
£75658	$139211	€115000	L'Assomption de la Vierge (50x37cm-20x15in) i. graphite htd white. 25-Jun-4 Doutrebente, Paris #3/R est:3000-4000

IACOVLEFF, Alexandre (1887-1938) French/Russian

£2600	$4420	€3796	Man carrying a basket (87x57cm-34x22in) s.d.1937 board. 19-Nov-3 Sotheby's, London #152/R est:3000-5000
£4324	$8000	€6313	Head of an Asian man (41x33cm-16x13in) 10-Mar-4 Doyle, New York #58/R est:1000-1500
£6000	$10740	€8760	Flowers in a vase (71x52cm-28x20in) s.i.d.1938. 26-May-4 Sotheby's, London #124/R est:6000-8000
£7000	$12530	€10220	Flower in a green pot (61x45cm-24x18in) s.d.1937 board. 26-May-4 Sotheby's, London #123/R est:7000-9000
£7059	$12000	€10306	Bazaar at Ghazini (103x76cm-41x30in) s.d.1933. 21-Nov-3 Skinner, Boston #320/R est:1200-1800
£25000	$42500	€36500	Diana the Huntress (100x49cm-39x19in) s.d.1928. 19-Nov-3 Sotheby's, London #156/R est:15000-25000
£28000	$50120	€40880	Bazaar at Ghazini (102x76cm-40x30in) s.d.1939 tempera. 26-May-4 Sotheby's, London #128/R est:8000-12000
£50000	$89500	€73000	Still life with musical instruments (84x70cm-33x28in) s.i.d.1923 tempera prov. 26-May-4 Sotheby's, London #134/R est:60000-80000
£70000	$119000	€102200	Marionettes (85x76cm-33x30in) tempera. 19-Nov-3 Sotheby's, London #143/R est:7000-9000
£120000	$214800	€175200	Pierrot (163x111cm-64x44in) s.d.1923. 26-May-4 Sotheby's, London #251/R est:120000-180000
Works on paper			
£880	$1523	€1250	Tete d'homme de trois-quarts (46x36cm-18x14in) s. sanguine. 12-Dec-3 Piasa, Paris #130
£1149	$1792	€1700	Rue de ville du Sud (26x43cm-10x17in) s.d.1923 gouache cardboard. 25-Mar-3 Brissoneau, France #62/R est:1000-1400
£2500	$4250	€3650	Female nude (63x50cm-25x20in) s. artist st. sanguine. 19-Nov-3 Sotheby's, London #151/R est:2500-3500
£2770	$4876	€4100	Portrait de Madame de Grammont (132x68cm-52x27in) studio st. gouache. 19-May-4 Camard, Paris #109 est:2500-3500
£3200	$5728	€4672	Portrait of a Kashmiri (35x27cm-14x11in) s.d.1931 pastel. 26-May-4 Sotheby's, Olympia #456/R est:1500-2000
£3600	$6444	€5256	Chinese river landscape (36x54cm-14x21in) s.d.1932 gouache on card. 26-May-4 Sotheby's, London #129/R est:4000-6000
£3867	$7076	€5800	Afghan (60x50cm-24x20in) i.d.1931 sanguine prov. 6-Jun-4 Rouillac, Vendome #42/R
£4200	$7140	€6300	Portrait of Kyrgyz. Portrait of Mongol (52x36cm-20x14in) s.i.d.1931 one pastel chk one lithograph two. 25-Nov-3 Christie's, London #201/R est:3000-4000
£4500	$7650	€6570	Negro in a head-dress (49x63cm-19x25in) s. indis.i.d.1925 brown blk chl gouache. 19-Nov-3 Sotheby's, London #150/R est:5000-7000
£8000	$14320	€11680	Settlement on the hilltop (52x69cm-20x27in) s. gouache on board. 26-May-4 Sotheby's, London #131/R est:5000-7000
£8889	$16000	€12978	Wrestling the minotaur (53x51cm-21x20in) gouache prov. 23-Apr-4 Sotheby's, New York #61/R est:15000-20000
£13889	$25000	€20278	Corbeille avec raisins (104x69cm-41x27in) s.d.1937 mixed media prov.exhib. 23-Apr-4 Sotheby's, New York #62/R est:25000-35000
£26923	$42000	€	Portrait of Tatiana Riabouchinska (76x58cm-30x23in) s.d.1936 col chk paper on cardboard exhib. 11-Apr-3 Christie's, Rockefeller NY #34/R est:12000-16000

IACURTO, Francesco (1908-) Canadian

£1000	$1890	€1460	Autumn in Canada (61x76cm-24x30in) s.d.1969. 19-Feb-4 Christie's, Kensington #228/R est:300-500
£1786	$2982	€2590	Vue de Quebec (51x61cm-20x24in) s.d.1963. 17-Jun-3 Pinneys, Montreal #125 est:3000-4000 (C.D 4000)
£2439	$4366	€3561	Sous bois, Montmorency River (76x61cm-30x24in) s. s.i.verso. 6-May-4 Heffel, Vancouver #71/R est:4500-5500 (C.D 6000)
£2703	$4595	€3946	Rickshaws (50x61cm-20x24in) s.d.1965 prov. 27-Nov-3 Heffel, Vancouver #90/R est:2000-3000 (C.D 6000)

IAKOUBOV, Rady (1926-) Russian

£300	$540	€450	Summer colours (59x74cm-23x29in) s. 26-Apr-4 Millon & Associes, Paris #29/R

IALENTI, Antonio (1937-) Italian

£333	$613	€500	Intelvi Valley (70x50cm-28x20in) s. painted 2004 lit. 12-Jun-4 Meeting Art, Vercelli #148/R
£333	$613	€500	Countryside in Molise (50x70cm-20x28in) s. s.i.verso painted 2003 lit. 12-Jun-4 Meeting Art, Vercelli #676/R
£333	$613	€500	Spring in Molise (50x70cm-20x28in) s. s.i.verso painted 2004. 12-Jun-4 Meeting Art, Vercelli #927/R
£336	$621	€500	Vase of flowers (70x50cm-28x20in) s. painted 1998. 13-Mar-4 Meeting Art, Vercelli #221
£347	$549	€500	Tuscan countryside (50x70cm-20x28in) 6-Sep-3 Meeting Art, Vercelli #400

£352 $585 €500 Campagna Molisana (50x70cm-20x28in) s. s.i.d.2003 verso. 14-Jun-3 Meeting Art, Vercelli #638/R
£367 $675 €550 Wood in Lombardy (50x70cm-20x28in) s. s.i.verso painted 2003. 12-Jun-4 Meeting Art, Vercelli #194/R
£367 $675 €550 Intelvi Valley (70x50cm-28x20in) s. painted 2003. 12-Jun-4 Meeting Art, Vercelli #195/R
£367 $675 €550 Flowers with seascape beyond (60x80cm-24x31in) s. painted 2004. 12-Jun-4 Meeting Art, Vercelli #337/R
£367 $675 €550 Seascape in Liguria (60x80cm-24x31in) s. painted 2004. 12-Jun-4 Meeting Art, Vercelli #564/R
£367 $675 €550 Countryside in Tuscany (50x70cm-20x28in) s. s.i.verso painted 2004 lit. 12-Jun-4 Meeting Art, Vercelli #562/R
£387 $643 €550 Campagna Molisana (50x70cm-20x28in) s. s.i.verso. 14-Jun-3 Meeting Art, Vercelli #618
£417 $658 €600 Countryside in Abruzzo with vase of flowers (70x50cm-28x20in) 6-Sep-3 Meeting Art, Vercelli #445
£433 $797 €650 Farm in Varzi (50x70cm-20x28in) s. painted 2003. 12-Jun-4 Meeting Art, Vercelli #308/R
£436 $807 €650 River Ticino (45x65cm-18x26in) s. s.i.verso painted 2003. 13-Mar-4 Meeting Art, Vercelli #183
£436 $807 €650 Cherry tree (30x40cm-12x16in) s. s.i.verso lit. 13-Mar-4 Meeting Art, Vercelli #497
£451 $713 €650 Field with cherry tree in bloom (50x70cm-20x28in) painted 2003. 6-Sep-3 Meeting Art, Vercelli #678
£500 $920 €750 Chiana Valley (70x100cm-28x39in) s. painted 2003. 12-Jun-4 Meeting Art, Vercelli #219/R
£537 $993 €800 Red field covered in snow (80x60cm-31x24in) s. s.i.verso painted 2003. 13-Mar-4 Meeting Art, Vercelli #502

IAMS, Richard (1950-) American
£294 $550 €429 Approaching rain in the Grand Canyon (48x99cm-19x39in) s. 25-Feb-4 Dallas Auction Gallery, Dallas #467/R

IANELLI, Arcangelo (1922-) Brazilian
£6484 $11476 €9726 Abstract (80x100cm-31x39in) s.d.1977. 27-Apr-4 Bolsa de Arte, Rio de Janeiro #116/R (B.R 35400)
£6502 $11898 €9753 Untitled (130x100cm-51x39in) s.d.1989. 6-Jul-4 Bolsa de Arte, Rio de Janeiro #166/R (B.R 35500)
Works on paper
£1007 $1843 €1511 Untitled (37x31cm-15x12in) s.d.1966 gouache. 6-Jul-4 Bolsa de Arte, Rio de Janeiro #84/R (B.R 5500)

IANNI, Guglielmo (1937-) Italian
£4406 $7490 €6300 Prelate (56x28cm-22x11in) tempera on asbestos painted 1937. 18-Nov-3 Babuino, Rome #147/R est:1800-2200

I'ANSON, C (19th C) British?
£385 $654 €562 Two women by a lake (62x101cm-24x40in) s. 4-Nov-3 Stephan Welz, Johannesburg #567 est:5000-7000 (SA.R 4500)

IBANEZ DE ALDECOA, Julian (1866-1952) Spanish
£470 $874 €700 Basques (17x15cm-7x6in) s. cardboard. 2-Mar-4 Ansorena, Madrid #156/R
£1164 $1979 €1700 Basque shepherd (34x43cm-13x17in) s. cardboard. 4-Nov-3 Ansorena, Madrid #68/R est:1700

IBANEZ, Concha (1929-) Spanish
£900 $1638 €1350 Landscape (54x65cm-21x26in) s.d.1974. 29-Jun-4 Segre, Madrid #105/R

IBARROLA, Agustin (20th C) ?
Works on paper
£272 $495 €400 Figures (32x22cm-13x9in) s. collage wax crayon. 3-Feb-4 Segre, Madrid #243/R
£510 $929 €750 Figures (23x30cm-9x12in) s. collage wax col crayon prov. 3-Feb-4 Segre, Madrid #242/R

IBARZ ROCA, Miguel (1920-1987) Spanish
£426 $711 €600 Landscape (97x130cm-38x51in) s. s.i.d.1981 verso. 23-Jun-3 Durán, Madrid #53/R
£578 $1052 €850 Fruit bowls and sparrow. s. s.i.d.1972 verso prov. 3-Feb-4 Segre, Madrid #135/R

IBBETSON, Julius Caesar (1759-1817) British
£500 $895 €730 Extensive landscape with figures, timber house and farm buildings (43x53cm-17x21in) s. 11-May-4 Bonhams, Knightsbridge #36/R
£1100 $1870 €1606 Peasants on a country road with donkeys in a landscape (11x16cm-4x6in) init. panel. 27-Nov-3 Sotheby's, London #189 est:1200-1800
£1806 $2943 €2600 Lively English village (22x31cm-9x12in) s.d.1804 panel. 27-Sep-3 Dannenberg, Berlin #560/R est:400
£1840 $3000 €2668 Landscape with cattle drovers (61x76cm-24x30in) s. 19-Jul-3 New Orleans Auction, New Orleans #210/R est:5000-8000
£4000 $7280 €5840 Distant view of Llantrisant Castle, Glamorganshire with figures seated (32x44cm-13x17in) s.i.d.1817 prov. 1-Jul-4 Sotheby's, London #141/R est:5000-7000
£5500 $9350 €8030 Two peasants on the bank of a lake. Two fishermen on the bank of an estuary (25x30cm-10x12in) pair. 27-Nov-3 Sotheby's, London #188/R est:6000-8000
Works on paper
£26000 $47580 €37960 Fashionable figures promenading on the Mall, London (19x26cm-7x10in) pencil W/C prov. 3-Jun-4 Christie's, London #80/R est:8000-12000

IBBETSON, Julius Caesar (attrib) (1759-1817) British
£1500 $2775 €2190 View of Middleham Castle, Yorkshire with drover and her cattle (26x44cm-10x17in) prov. 14-Jul-4 Sotheby's, Olympia #20/R est:2000-3000

IBELS, Henri Gabriel (1867-1936) French
£2183 $3820 €3100 Paysage au bord de l'eau (28x46cm-11x18in) s. 21-Dec-3 Thierry & Lannon, Brest #169 est:2200-2400
Works on paper
£879 $1600 €1283 Haystacks (46x57cm-18x22in) s. pastel prov. 29-Jun-4 Sotheby's, New York #338/R est:4000-6000

IBSEN, Henrik (1828-1906) Norwegian
£1176 $2000 €1717 Pastoral landscape with a hut and a tree (32x41cm-13x16in) s. board. 19-Nov-3 Bonhams & Butterfields, San Francisco #82/R

ICART, Louis (1888-1950) French
£1200 $1920 €1740 Les elegantes sur l'herbe (56x68cm-22x27in) s. board. 18-Sep-3 Christie's, Kensington #26/R est:1500-2000
£3007 $5112 €4300 Elegante a sa fenetre (41x33cm-16x13in) s. 21-Nov-3 Coutau Begarie, Paris #55/R est:3000-3500
£3103 $5183 €4500 Automne (28x16cm-11x6in) s. i.verso panel. 14-Nov-3 Claude Boisgirard, Paris #25/R est:5000-6000
£3421 $6295 €5200 Caleche (33x41cm-13x16in) s. 25-Jun-4 Millon & Associes, Paris #137 est:4000-5000
£3758 $6953 €5600 La caleche (50x61cm-20x24in) s. init.i.verso. 15-Mar-4 Blanchet, Paris #78/R est:7000-9000
£5590 $9000 €8161 Promenade a l'automne (51x61cm-20x24in) i. verso prov. 20-Aug-3 James Julia, Fairfield #627/R est:8000-12000
£6338 $10268 €9000 Femme pensive (73x60cm-29x24in) s. 5-Aug-3 Tajan, Paris #20/R est:5000-7000
£28000 $51240 €42000 Carnaval a Venise (195x130cm-77x51in) s.i. prov. 6-Jun-4 Anaf, Lyon #393/R est:60000-80000
Prints
£1629 $2720 €2378 Au bar, gay trio (49x29cm-19x11in) s. col drypoint etching lit. 16-Oct-3 Waddingtons, Toronto #123/R est:3000-4000 (C.D 3600)
£1705 $3000 €2489 Symphonie en bleu (58x48cm-23x19in) s. etching drypoint. 22-May-4 Selkirks, St. Louis #851/R est:1200-1600
£1758 $3200 €2567 Spanish dancer observing the auditorium (53x36cm-21x14in) s. monotype. 20-Jun-4 Charlton Hall, Columbia #578/R est:2000-3000
£1879 $3250 €2743 Before the raid (44x54cm-17x21in) s.num.265 drypoint aquatint. 11-Dec-3 Sotheby's, New York #219/R est:1500-2000
£2395 $4000 €3497 Martini (33x46cm-13x18in) s. hand col drypoint. 11-Nov-3 Doyle, New York #273/R est:800-1200
Works on paper
£302 $553 €450 Lady in carnival costume (45x35cm-18x14in) s. pastel chl lit. 8-Jul-4 Allgauer, Kempten #1994/R
£302 $553 €450 Young lady with umbrella (45x35cm-18x14in) s. pastel chl. 8-Jul-4 Allgauer, Kempten #1995/R
£400 $668 €584 Seated woman (43x33cm-17x13in) s. pastel. 14-Oct-3 David Lay, Penzance #389
£412 $750 €618 Mother and child (28x23cm-11x9in) s.i. pencil wash. 16-Jun-4 Wolf's, New York #487429/R
£450 $752 €657 Woman with a pierrot doll (43x33cm-17x13in) s. pastel. 14-Oct-3 David Lay, Penzance #390/R
£452 $756 €660 After the bath (45x33cm-18x13in) s. chl htd white. 17-Nov-3 Waddingtons, Toronto #204/R (C.D 1000)
£544 $975 €800 Portrait de femme tenant un chapeau (37x29cm-15x11in) chl pastel. 17-Mar-4 Tajan, Paris #178
£615 $1058 €898 Woman with book resting (34x43cm-13x17in) s. chk. 7-Dec-3 Uppsala Auktionskammare, Uppsala #216/R (S.KR 8000)
£674 $1125 €950 Elegante au chapeau (42x31cm-17x12in) s. pastel. 15-Oct-3 Rabourdin & Choppin de Janvry, Paris #1
£805 $1498 €1200 Une jeune femme cueillant des pommes (32x25cm-13x10in) s. W/C. 4-Mar-4 Claude Aguttes, Neuilly #115/R
£1073 $1900 €1567 Portrait of an elegant lady with a hat (43x33cm-17x13in) s. col chk. 2-May-4 Bonhams & Butterfields, San Francisco #1043/R est:1500-2000
£2308 $3923 €3300 Ballerine (109x78cm-43x31in) s. chl chk dr. 21-Nov-3 Lombrail & Teucquam, Paris #137 est:3000-3200
£3784 $7000 €5525 Le trophee (44x26cm-17x10in) s.i.d. chl W/C. 11-Mar-4 Sotheby's, New York #116/R est:7000-10000

ICART, Louis (attrib) (1888-1950) French
Works on paper
£756 $1300 €1104 Reclining female nude with flowers in her hair (33x46cm-13x18in) graphite W/C. 6-Dec-3 Skinner, Boston #84/R est:1500-2500
£930 $1600 €1358 Reclining female nude (64x48cm-25x19in) s. graphite W/C. 6-Dec-3 Skinner, Boston #97/R est:1500-2500

ICAZA, Ernesto (1866-1935) Mexican
£1706 $2696 €2491 Horse taming (11x15cm-4x6in) s. cardboard. 24-Jul-3 Louis Morton, Mexico #285/R (M.P 28000)
£7903 $13435 €11538 Waiting for the master (55x94cm-22x37in) canvas on board. 29-Oct-3 Louis Morton, Mexico #44/R est:60000-80000 (M.P 150000)

ICHE, René (1897-1954) French
Sculpture
£6250 $11500 €9500 Jeune Tarentine (40x85x38cm-16x33x15in) s. marble lit. 24-Jun-4 Credit Municipal, Paris #75/R est:12000-15000

ICKS, Walter (1901-?) German
£567 $1014 €850 Untitled (72x92cm-28x36in) s.d.22.4.1954 board. 15-May-4 Van Ham, Cologne #684
£833 $1392 €1200 Abstract composition (60x78cm-24x31in) s.d. masonite. 24-Oct-3 Ketterer, Hamburg #397/R

IEFIMENKO, Viktor (1952-) Russian
£600 $1080 €900 Brother and sister (50x61cm-20x24in) 26-Apr-4 Bernaerts, Antwerp #968
£833 $1358 €1200 Sunny day (61x50cm-24x20in) s. 23-Sep-3 Durán, Madrid #675/R
£903 $1472 €1300 Resting in the garden (69x84cm-27x33in) s. 23-Sep-3 Durán, Madrid #674/R

IEGOROV, Alexei (1966-) Russian
£560 $1003 €818 In the garden (50x60cm-20x24in) s. i. verso. 12-May-4 Dobiaschofsky, Bern #670/R (S.FR 1300)

IEPEREN, Johan Hendrik van (1909-1995) Dutch
£455 $782 €650 Old scour (25x34cm-10x13in) s. board. 8-Dec-3 Glerum, Amsterdam #291/R
£559 $962 €800 Dark landscape (57x70cm-22x28in) acrylic board. 8-Dec-3 Glerum, Amsterdam #298/R
£822 $1397 €1200 Bouquet (80x50cm-31x20in) s. board. 5-Nov-3 Vendue Huis, Gravenhage #490/R
£839 $1443 €1200 Kop Zeerover (40x30cm-16x12in) s.d.27 lit. 8-Dec-3 Glerum, Amsterdam #240/R
£884 $1610 €1300 Boslaan - forest path (47x60cm-19x24in) s. s.i.verso board. 3-Feb-4 Christie's, Amsterdam #477 est:600-800
£1020 $1857 €1500 Stilleven met blauwen lap - still life with blue cloth (40x60cm-16x24in) s. cardboard. 3-Feb-4 Christie's, Amsterdam #538 est:700-900
£1027 $1747 €1500 Bunch of flowers (97x70cm-38x28in) s. board. 5-Nov-3 Vendue Huis, Gravenhage #491 est:2000-3000
£1189 $2045 €1700 Haystacks by moonlight (29x36cm-11x14in) s. board. 8-Dec-3 Glerum, Amsterdam #309/R est:800-1200
£1370 $2329 €2000 Village (78x98cm-31x39in) s. board exhib. 5-Nov-3 Vendue Huis, Gravenhage #494/R est:2000-3000
£1507 $2562 €2200 Shrimp boat (80x100cm-31x39in) s. board. 5-Nov-3 Vendue Huis, Gravenhage #493/R est:2000-2500
£1678 $2887 €2400 Still life with red cloth (50x70cm-20x28in) s. board exhib. 8-Dec-3 Glerum, Amsterdam #317/R est:2000-2500
£1818 $3127 €2600 Tower (61x73cm-24x29in) s. board exhib.lit. 8-Dec-3 Glerum, Amsterdam #287/R est:2000-2500
£1958 $3368 €2800 River Maas near Rotterdam in the winter (62x98cm-24x39in) s. board. 8-Dec-3 Glerum, Amsterdam #155/R est:1200-1500
£1958 $3368 €2800 Green landscape (48x68cm-19x27in) s. board. 8-Dec-3 Glerum, Amsterdam #267/R est:1800-2200
£2238 $3849 €3200 The woods (72x96cm-28x38in) s. board exhib. 8-Dec-3 Glerum, Amsterdam #307/R est:3000-5000
Works on paper
£280 $481 €400 Farm in between trees (21x26cm-8x10in) s. pastel. 8-Dec-3 Glerum, Amsterdam #296/R
£350 $601 €500 Winter landscape with farms (28x40cm-11x16in) s. gouache. 8-Dec-3 Glerum, Amsterdam #300/R
£1818 $3127 €2600 Illuminated houses (45x65cm-18x26in) s. gouache. 8-Dec-3 Glerum, Amsterdam #303/R est:800-1200

IEVGRAFOV, Dmitrii (1967-) Russian
£278 $442 €400 En el muelle de la Fontanka de San Petesburgo (46x61cm-18x24in) s. 29-Apr-3 Durán, Madrid #804/R
£333 $543 €480 Coming out of the theatre (46x61cm-18x24in) s. 23-Sep-3 Durán, Madrid #678/R
£400 $652 €584 After the rain in Saint Petersburg (46x61cm-18x24in) s. 28-Sep-3 John Nicholson, Haslemere #138
£403 $657 €580 Grand Opera, Paris (46x60cm-18x24in) s. 23-Sep-3 Durán, Madrid #677/R
£451 $736 €650 Boulevard Nevsky (55x66cm-22x26in) s. 23-Sep-3 Durán, Madrid #679/R

IFFLAND, Franz (19th C) German
Sculpture
£1887 $3435 €2850 Young mother with baby (69cm-27in) s.d.1887brown pat.bronze Cast.Gladenbeck Berlin - Friedrichshagen. 19-Jun-4 Dannenberg, Berlin #187/R est:2000

IGLER, Gustav (1842-1908) Hungarian
£21774 $40065 €31790 Playing mother (91x61cm-36x24in) s.d.1887 prov. 14-Jun-4 Waddingtons, Toronto #315/R est:20000-25000 (C.D 54000)

IGLESIAS SANZ, Antonio (1935-) Spanish
£350 $584 €500 Aran Valley (38x46cm-15x18in) s. 30-Jun-3 Ansorena, Madrid #292/R
£350 $584 €500 Dusk in the mountains (42x54cm-17x21in) s. board. 30-Jun-3 Ansorena, Madrid #293/R
£411 $699 €600 Guadalajara fields (38x61cm-15x24in) s. s.i.verso. 4-Nov-3 Ansorena, Madrid #331/R
£423 $731 €600 Landscape (22x27cm-9x11in) s. board. 15-Dec-3 Ansorena, Madrid #258/R
£448 $749 €650 Cantabrico, Asturia (38x61cm-15x24in) s. s.i.d.96 verso. 17-Nov-3 Durán, Madrid #85/R
£528 $914 €750 Mountainous landscape (54x81cm-21x32in) s. i.verso. 15-Dec-3 Ansorena, Madrid #273/R
£532 $888 €750 Amor Lake (55x65cm-22x26in) s. 20-Oct-3 Durán, Madrid #644/R
£559 $934 €800 Boats (50x60cm-20x24in) s. board. 30-Jun-3 Ansorena, Madrid #270/R
£608 $1070 €900 Gondolas in Venice (38x61cm-15x24in) s. s.i.d.2000 verso. 18-May-4 Segre, Madrid #102/R
£655 $1094 €950 Fishing amongst rocks (42x64cm-17x25in) s. lit. 17-Nov-3 Durán, Madrid #84/R
£800 $1456 €1200 Feriolo Aleps - Italia (60x63cm-24x25in) s. s.i.d.2004 verso. 29-Jun-4 Segre, Madrid #313/R

IGNATIEFF, Alex (1913-1997) American
Works on paper
£344 $650 €502 Fishermen mending nets - San Pedro (25x33cm-10x13in) s. mixed media. 17-Feb-4 John Moran, Pasadena #90b/R
£503 $950 €734 Figures - Los Angeles street scene (36x48cm-14x19in) mixed media. 17-Feb-4 John Moran, Pasadena #90a/R

IHLEE, Rudolph (1883-1968) British
£2000 $3640 €2920 Landscape (51x61cm-20x24in) s.d.1925. 15-Jun-4 Bonhams, New Bond Street #57/R est:1200-1600

IHLEFELD, Henry (1859-1932) American
Works on paper
£248 $400 €362 Portrait of a young girl (38x28cm-15x11in) s.d.1890 W/C. 22-Feb-3 Bunte, Elgin #1221

IHLENFELD, Klaus (20th C) American?
Sculpture
£898 $1500 €1311 Exotic plants (30x28cm-12x11in) welded copper verdigris pat bronze. 25-Oct-3 David Rago, Lambertville #387 est:1500-2000
£1326 $2400 €1936 Bamboo (36x15cm-14x6in) bronze. 3-Apr-4 David Rago, Lambertville #77/R est:1500-2000

IHLY, Daniel (1854-1910) Swiss
£1810 $3077 €2643 Line of horses carrying military supplies in the mountains (28x46cm-11x18in) s. board. 19-Nov-3 Fischer, Luzern #1270/R est:3000-4000 (S.FR 4000)
£2466 $4020 €3600 Marche a la Place de Plainpalais (64x68cm-25x27in) s. 29-Sep-3 Christie's, Zurich #64/R est:4000-6000 (S.FR 5500)

IHRAN, Manne (1877-1917) Swedish
£739 $1323 €1079 Skytteanum (55x65cm-22x26in) s.d.1915. 28-May-4 Uppsala Auktionskammare, Uppsala #227/R (S.KR 10000)

IKEGAMI SHUHO (1874-1944) Japanese
Works on paper
£1781 $3027 €2600 Girl from Kanbun era (114x41cm-45x16in) s. seal Indian ink seal silk hanging scroll. 8-Nov-3 Dr Fritz Nagel, Stuttgart #1999/R est:900

IKEMURA, Leiko (1951-) ?
£543 $923 €793 Untitled (38x46cm-15x18in) s. cotton painted 1980 prov.exhib. 22-Nov-3 Burkhard, Luzern #219/R (S.FR 1200)
£600 $1080 €900 Red tree and animal (165x121cm-65x48in) acrylic painted 1982 prov. 26-Apr-4 Tajan, Paris #231

IKKIDLUAK, Lucassie (1949-) North American
Sculpture
£1081 $1838 €1578 Musk ox with horns (38cm-15in) s. mottled green soapstone. 3-Nov-3 Waddingtons, Toronto #42/R est:2500-3500 (C.D 2400)

IKSIKTAARYUK, Luke (1909-1977) North American
Sculpture
£2027 $3446 €2959 Six Inuit figures (43cm-17in) caribou antler base. 3-Nov-3 Waddingtons, Toronto #181/R est:5000-7000 (C.D 4500)
£4505 $7658 €6577 Drummer holding a drum and beater, together with eleven figures (33cm-13in) caribou antler wood gut sinew antler base. 3-Nov-3 Waddingtons, Toronto #183a est:20000-25000 (C.D 10000)
£6306 $10721 €9207 Drummer holding a drum and beater with five figures (30cm-12in) caribou antler wood gut sinew base two parts. 3-Nov-3 Waddingtons, Toronto #169/R est:20000-25000 (C.D 14000)

ILIADIS, Costas (1903-1991) Greek
Works on paper
£2000 $3500 €2920 Theatre scene (119x92cm-47x36in) s.d.51 gouache paper on canvas. 16-Dec-3 Bonhams, New Bond Street #116/R est:2000-3000

ILLENZ, Lipot (1882-?) Rumanian
£921 $1695 €1400 Portrait of girl, bay beyond (60x80cm-24x31in) s. 22-Jun-4 Babuino, Rome #529/R

ILLES, Aladar (1870-1958) Hungarian
£400 $740 €584 Grapes, pears and a silver salver before a vase of flowers on draped table (61x51cm-24x20in) s. 15-Jan-4 Christie's, Kensington #1063/R
£835 $1445 €1219 Birch trees in sunshine (24x18cm-9x7in) s. cardboard. 12-Dec-3 Kieselbach, Budapest #2/R (H.F 320000)

ILLIES, Arthur (1870-1952) German
£2308 $3969 €3300 Female nude (100x65cm-39x26in) 4-Dec-3 Schopman, Hamburg #734/R est:5000
£3333 $5967 €5000 Zinnia (71x115cm-28x45in) 15-May-4 Van Ham, Cologne #688 est:6000
£3333 $5967 €5000 Tulips (70x110cm-28x43in) 15-May-4 Van Ham, Cologne #686/R est:6000
£3333 $5967 €5000 Hyacinths (68x110cm-27x43in) 15-May-4 Van Ham, Cologne #687/R est:6000
£3510 $6388 €5300 Autumnal landscape (49x67cm-19x26in) s.d.1918 cardboard. 19-Jun-4 Hans Stahl, Hamburg #144/R est:3000

ILLIG, Carl (?) American?
£430 $800 €628 Untitled (46x61cm-18x24in) board. 6-Mar-4 Page, Batavia #200

ILLINGWORTH, Michael (1932-1988) New Zealander
£1123 $1909 €1640 Abstract composition (59x49cm-23x19in) canvasboard prov. 4-Nov-3 Peter Webb, Auckland #269 est:1000-2000 (NZ.D 3100)
£1128 $1917 €1647 Two figures (27x21cm-11x8in) acrylic paper. 27-Nov-3 International Art Centre, Auckland #179/R est:500-1000 (NZ.D 3000)

£7463	$12910	€10896	Self portrait. Cityscape (59x44cm-23x17in) init.d.1960 board double-sided. 9-Dec-3 Peter Webb, Auckland #39/R est:20000-25000 (NZ.D 20000)
£15884	$25892	€23191	The photographer (36x31cm-14x12in) s.d.1968 verso. 23-Sep-3 Peter Webb, Auckland #52/R est:25000-35000 (NZ.D 44000)
£26786	$48482	€39108	Pah Hill (106x90cm-42x35in) painted c.1971 exhib. 30-Mar-4 Peter Webb, Auckland #43/R est:75000-90000 (NZ.D 75000)
£35448	$61325	€51754	Director (57x51cm-22x20in) s.i.d.1985 i.verso exhib. 9-Dec-3 Peter Webb, Auckland #36/R est:45000-65000 (NZ.D 95000)
£44776	$77463	€65373	Portrait of a flower (112x91cm-44x36in) s.i.d.1968 verso prov.exhib. 9-Dec-3 Peter Webb, Auckland #35/R est:120000-160000 (NZ.D 120000)
Works on paper			
£1504	$2556	€2196	Bride and groom in a field (23x29cm-9x11in) W/C acrylic. 27-Nov-3 International Art Centre, Auckland #180/R est:800-1200 (NZ.D 4000)

ILLNER, Walther (1874-?) German

£385	$654	€550	Still life with flowers (62x65cm-24x26in) s.d.1932. 28-Nov-3 Wendl, Rudolstadt #4013/R

ILMONI, Einar (1880-1946) Finnish

£1408	$2437	€2000	Landscape, Vehonas (50x42cm-20x17in) lit. 13-Dec-3 Hagelstam, Helsinki #130/R est:2000
£2168	$3685	€3100	Landscape with cliffs (38x49cm-15x19in) 29-Nov-3 Bukowskis, Helsinki #29/R est:3000-3500
£2535	$4386	€3600	Twinflowers (42x31cm-17x12in) canvas on board exhib.lit. 13-Dec-3 Hagelstam, Helsinki #128/R est:3500
£2535	$4386	€3600	Coastal landscape, Standalar, Porto (38x55cm-15x22in) s. exhib.lit. 13-Dec-3 Hagelstam, Helsinki #129/R est:3500

ILSTED, Peter Vilhelm (1861-1933) Danish

£1444	$2700	€2108	En Skaermydsel - interior scene with married couple - she's seated, he's standing (43x33cm-17x13in) s. grisaille. 25-Feb-4 Museumsbygningen, Copenhagen #175/R est:15000-20000 (D.KR 16000)
£4513	$8439	€6589	Interior scene with seated female model by oil lamp (46x38cm-18x15in) s.d.1890. 25-Feb-4 Museumsbygningen, Copenhagen #177/R est:60000-80000 (D.KR 50000)
£5198	$8993	€7589	Pelargonium in flower, Capri (66x51cm-26x20in) s.d.1891 exhib.prov. 9-Dec-3 Rasmussen, Copenhagen #1243/R est:75000-100000 (D.KR 55000)
£5249	$9395	€7664	Girl standing by garden table by house (44x38cm-17x15in) mono.d.1904. 10-May-4 Rasmussen, Vejle #394/R est:60000-80000 (D.KR 58000)
£12287	$21994	€17939	Interior scene with the artist's wife Ingeborg at breakfast table, Italy (67x51cm-26x20in) s. prov. 12-Jan-4 Rasmussen, Vejle #144/R est:100000-150000 (D.KR 130000)
£46553	$85192	€67967	Girl reading by window (58x50cm-23x20in) mono.d.1901. 9-Jun-4 Rasmussen, Copenhagen #1462/R est:300000-400000 (D.KR 520000)
Prints			
£2156	$4011	€3148	The red room at Liselund with seated woman (49x49cm-19x19in) s.num.50/37 mezzotint in colour. 2-Mar-4 Rasmussen, Copenhagen #1697/R est:20000-25000 (D.KR 24000)
£2366	$4400	€3454	Little girl with flat cap (48x48cm-19x19in) s.num.40/10 col mezzotint. 2-Mar-4 Swann Galleries, New York #275/R est:3000-5000
£2538	$4569	€3705	Interior scene with woman standing (42x39cm-17x15in) s.i.num.100/75 mezzotint. 26-Apr-4 Bukowskis, Stockholm #359/R est:15000-18000 (S.KR 35000)

IMAI, Hisashi (20th C) Japanese

£2000	$3640	€3000	Fleur eclatee (80x110cm-31x43in) s.d.1974 paper on canvas. 5-Jul-4 Le Mouel, Paris #53/R est:2500-3500

IMAI, Toshimitau (1928-) Japanese

£1325	$2411	€2000	Cigares de Havane (64x104cm-25x41in) s.i.d.17 fev 2001 acrylic collage paper. 18-Jun-4 Charbonneaux, Paris #97/R est:2300-2500
£3427	$5825	€4900	Composition (73x116cm-29x46in) s.d.Mars-Avril 1958 verso prov. 23-Nov-3 Cornette de St.Cyr, Paris #159/R est:1000-1500
£6338	$10965	€9000	Ironie romatique (120x160cm-47x63in) s.d.1961 verso prov. 9-Dec-3 Artcurial Briest, Paris #411/R est:3000-4000

IMANDT, Willem (1882-1967) Dutch

£272	$487	€400	Storm at sea (41x80cm-16x31in) s. 16-Mar-4 Christie's, Amsterdam #86
£284	$474	€400	Volcano (90x120cm-35x47in) s. 20-Oct-3 Bernaerts, Antwerp #256/R
£374	$670	€550	View on a sawah at dusk (35x40cm-14x16in) s. 16-Mar-4 Christie's, Amsterdam #34
£411	$699	€600	Indian landscape (48x68cm-19x27in) s. 5-Nov-3 Vendue Huis, Gravenhage #536/R
£476	$852	€700	Boerangkran bij Tankoebanprauw bandoeng (40x60cm-16x24in) s. 16-Mar-4 Christie's, Amsterdam #95
£816	$1461	€1200	Gondano salaman (55x60cm-22x24in) s. i.stretcher. 16-Mar-4 Christie's, Amsterdam #29 est:800-1200
£890	$1514	€1300	Tropical forest (79x58cm-31x23in) s. 5-Nov-3 Vendue Huis, Gravenhage #537/R
£959	$1630	€1400	Eastern city (76x85cm-30x33in) s. 5-Nov-3 Vendue Huis, Gravenhage #538/R
£980	$1775	€1431	Meer van Lelles - TTen Z Van Garolt.Java (41x50cm-16x20in) s. 4-Apr-4 Sotheby's, Singapore #3/R est:5000-7000 (S.D 3000)
£1020	$1827	€1500	Mountainous landscape (68x78cm-27x31in) s. prov. 16-Mar-4 Christie's, Amsterdam #41/R est:1500-2000
£1020	$1827	€1500	Bay (84x130cm-33x51in) s. canvas on board. 16-Mar-4 Christie's, Amsterdam #109 est:500-700
£1156	$2070	€1700	Sawah under a cloudy sky (79x68cm-31x27in) s. prov. 16-Mar-4 Christie's, Amsterdam #43/R est:1000-1500
£1224	$2192	€1800	Sawahs at sunset (58x78cm-23x31in) s. prov. 16-Mar-4 Christie's, Amsterdam #39/R est:1000-1500
£1250	$2263	€1900	Baie en Indonesie (48x75cm-19x30in) s. 19-Apr-4 Horta, Bruxelles #156 est:500-700
£2857	$5114	€4200	Waringin tree (54x54cm-21x21in) s. canvas on board prov. 16-Mar-4 Christie's, Amsterdam #46/R est:2000-3000
£4795	$8151	€7000	Banyan-tree (85x76cm-33x30in) s. 5-Nov-3 Vendue Huis, Gravenhage #539/R est:800-1200

IMHOF, Hans Rudolf (1935-) Swiss

£476	$762	€690	Street (49x70cm-19x28in) s. 15-May-3 Stuker, Bern #1308 (S.FR 1000)

IMHOF, Joseph A (1871-1955) American

£706	$1200	€1031	Acoma pueblo (30x23cm-12x9in) s. canvas on board prov. 1-Nov-3 Santa Fe Art, Santa Fe #22/R
Works on paper			
£1899	$3000	€2773	Taos Pueblo (51x66cm-20x26in) s. W/C. 7-Sep-3 Treadway Gallery, Cincinnati #587/R est:2000-3000

IMKAMP, Wilhelm (1906-1990) German

£470	$832	€700	Composition (19x9cm-7x4in) s.d. 30-Apr-4 Dr Fritz Nagel, Stuttgart #845/R
£872	$1544	€1300	Composition (25x20cm-10x8in) s. prov. 30-Apr-4 Dr Fritz Nagel, Stuttgart #846/R
£3497	$6014	€5000	Abstract composition (58x40cm-23x16in) s.d.1960 board. 4-Dec-3 Van Ham, Cologne #233/R est:5000
Works on paper			
£556	$928	€800	Abstract composition (10x15cm-4x6in) s.d. W/C oil pencil Indian ink. 24-Oct-3 Ketterer, Hamburg #818/R

IMMENDORF, Jorg (1945-) German

£3056	$5500	€4462	Cafe Deutschland (16x11cm-6x4in) s.d.1979 acrylic paper prov. 24-Apr-4 David Rago, Lambertville #195/R est:800-1200
£3077	$5231	€4400	For all the love in the world (9x76cm-4x30in) s.i.d.67 verso masonite prov. 27-Nov-3 Lempertz, Koln #204/R est:1000
£4000	$7360	€6000	Seduction (99x80cm-39x31in) s.d. acrylic. 11-Jun-4 Hauswedell & Nolte, Hamburg #1318/R est:6000
£4333	$7757	€6500	Cafe Deutschland/Ostschnee (30x22cm-12x9in) s.d.78 oil W/C. 15-May-4 Van Ham, Cologne #690/R est:3500
£6711	$12013	€10000	M. Goose (80x100cm-31x39in) s.d.85. 25-May-4 Dorotheum, Vienna #385/R est:10000-15000
£6993	$11888	€10000	Self portrait with nude and rose (100x80cm-39x31in) s.d.91. 26-Nov-3 Dorotheum, Vienna #103/R est:8000-14000
£9310	$15548	€13500	Cafe Flore, self with Joseph Beuys (100x80cm-39x31in) s.d.1991. 13-Nov-3 Neumeister, Munich #560/R est:20000-22000
Prints			
£2657	$4571	€3800	Heuler (156x202cm-61x80in) s.d.1990 i.verso red black linocut blue canvas. 5-Dec-3 Ketterer, Munich #187/R est:5000-7000
£6667	$12200	€10000	Cafe Deutschland (155x208cm-61x82in) s.d. col linocut acrylic paper on canvas. 4-Jun-4 Lempertz, Koln #218/R est:9000
Sculpture			
£1267	$2267	€1900	Alter ego (39x27x38cm-15x11x15in) s.i. bronze two parts. 15-May-4 Van Ham, Cologne #692/R est:2000
£3356	$6174	€5000	Immendorf in the Reichstag (82x128x91cm-32x50x36in) s.d. col plaster thread paper. 26-Mar-4 Ketterer, Hamburg #481/R est:4000-5000
Works on paper			
£979	$1664	€1400	Depesche 1.7.79 - the President is not my President (41x29cm-16x11in) s.i.d.79 gouache. 27-Nov-3 Lempertz, Koln #206/R
£1748	$2972	€2500	Cafe Deutschland (41x30cm-16x12in) s.i.d.78 gouache. 29-Nov-3 Villa Grisebach, Berlin #799/R est:2500-3000
£5333	$9760	€8000	Lidlstadt takes shape - city plan IX (70x90cm-28x35in) s.d.68 chk panel prov. 4-Jun-4 Lempertz, Koln #216/R est:4500
£5333	$9760	€8000	Lidlstadt takes shape - city plan X (70x90cm-28x35in) s.d.68 chk panel prov. 4-Jun-4 Lempertz, Koln #217/R est:4500

IMPENS, Josse (1840-1905) Belgian

£369	$679	€550	Le joueur de cornemuse (26x15cm-10x6in) s. panel. 23-Mar-4 Galerie Moderne, Brussels #311/R
£403	$745	€600	Au coin du poele (32x40cm-13x16in) s. 15-Mar-4 Horta, Bruxelles #318
£670	$1200	€978	Stable interior (30x41cm-12x16in) s. panel. 7-May-4 Sloans & Kenyon, Bethesda #1643/R
£1119	$1869	€1600	Les artisans au bistrot (29x38cm-11x15in) s. 13-Oct-3 Horta, Bruxelles #480 est:600-800
£3873	$6701	€5500	Domestic happiness (37x52cm-15x20in) s. panel. 13-Dec-3 De Vuyst, Lokeren #434/R est:5000-6000

IMPERIALI, Francesco (18th C) Italian

£22819	$41987	€34000	Scene of sacrifice in front of ancient ruins with dancers (74x135cm-29x53in) s.i. verso prov. 24-Mar-4 Dorotheum, Vienna #18/R est:10000-15000

IMSCHOOT, Jules van (1821-1884) Flemish

£634	$1096	€900	Soldier back from the Prussian War (22x16cm-9x6in) s.d.71 panel. 15-Dec-3 Bernaerts, Antwerp #66

INCE, Joseph Murray (1806-1859) British

£1800	$3006	€2628	Beating to windward (20x33cm-8x13in) 21-Oct-3 Gorringes, Lewes #1968 est:800-1200
Works on paper			
£240	$450	€350	Queens College, Cambridge (23x33cm-9x13in) s.d.1846 W/C. 29-Feb-4 Grogan, Boston #27/R

INCHBOLD, John William (1830-1888) British

Works on paper			
£420	$714	€613	Parkland landscape with mausoleum, thought to be Castle Howard, Yorkshire (24x34cm-9x13in) W/C. 18-Nov-3 Bonhams, Leeds #101
£520	$952	€759	Yorkshire Coast (34x50cm-13x20in) W/C htd white. 28-Jan-4 Dreweatt Neate, Newbury #3/R
£700	$1190	€1022	Continental street scene with figures, probably Switzerland (34x24cm-13x9in) W/C. 18-Nov-3 Bonhams, Leeds #99/R

£800 $1360 €1168 Trait Montreux (23x34cm-9x13in) s.i.d.1882 W/C. 18-Nov-3 Bonhams, Leeds #98/R
£950 $1615 €1387 Vouverie, mountain landscape (23x35cm-9x14in) s.i. indis d.1880 W/C. 18-Nov-3 Bonhams, Leeds #103
£960 $1632 €1402 Extensive river landscape at twilight (17x26cm-7x10in) bears i. W/C. 18-Nov-3 Bonhams, Leeds #100
£1850 $3145 €2701 Alpine lake landscape (24x35cm-9x14in) W/C. 18-Nov-3 Bonhams, Leeds #102 est:300-500
£2000 $3400 €2920 Saint Martin in the Alps (17x24cm-7x9in) mono.i. W/C bodycol scratching out. 20-Nov-3 Christie's, London #160/R est:2000-3000
£2600 $4810 €3796 Greenwich Park (34x52cm-13x20in) pencil W/C gouache paper on canvas. 10-Mar-4 Sotheby's, Olympia #171/R est:400-600
£2600 $4758 €3796 Swiss mountain scene (26x25cm-10x10in) s. pencil W/C htd touches white prov. 3-Jun-4 Christie's, London #28/R est:3000-5000

INCHBOLD, Stanley (1856-?) British
Works on paper
£2100 $3822 €3066 Whitby at dawn (37x50cm-15x20in) s. pencil W/C htd white. 5-Feb-4 Mellors & Kirk, Nottingham #515/R est:300-400

INDACO, Jacopo da (attrib) (1476-1526) Italian
£9500 $17385 €13870 Hercules and Nemean lion (29x41cm-11x16in) panel prov.exhib.lit. 7-Jul-4 Christie's, London #5/R est:10000-15000

INDEN, Rudi (20th C) German?
£833 $1517 €1250 Summer landscape with the Castle of Reifferscheidt (60x80cm-24x31in) s. board. 1-Jul-4 Van Ham, Cologne #1411

INDENBAUM, Léon (1892-1980) Russian
Sculpture
£2448 $4161 €3500 Tete de femme au bandeau (30cm-12in) s.st.f.C. Valsuani black pat bronze. 24-Nov-3 Tajan, Paris #31/R est:3500-4500
£3517 $6331 €5100 Modele nu se coiffant (39cm-15in) s. base pat terracotta. 25-Jan-4 Chayette & Cheval, Paris #150/R est:5000-6000

INDERMAUR, Robert (1947-) Swiss
Works on paper
£633 $1058 €924 Untitled (99x69cm-39x27in) s.d.1988 gouache. 24-Jun-3 Germann, Zurich #982 (S.FR 1400)

INDIA, Bernardino (1528-1590) Italian
Works on paper
£2500 $4500 €3650 Design for a ceiling decoration with Venice and Cupid embracing (12x20cm-5x8in) pen brown ink wash prov. 21-Jan-4 Sotheby's, New York #9/R est:4500-6500

INDIAN SCHOOL, 17th C
£5435 $10000 €7935 Dancing couple (16x10cm-6x4in) i.verso paint on album mount double-sided exec.c.1660 prov. 25-Mar-4 Christie's, Rockefeller NY #198/R est:10000-15000
Works on paper
£6803 $12177 €10000 Untitled (18x10cm-7x4in) i.verso gouache gold. 19-Mar-4 Claude Boisgirard, Paris #224/R
£8163 $14612 €12000 Untitled (15x10cm-6x4in) i.verso gouache gold. 19-Mar-4 Claude Boisgirard, Paris #223/R

INDIAN SCHOOL, 18th/19th C
Works on paper
£30000 $53100 €43800 Life of Krishna (273x251cm-107x99in) gouache htd gold and silver cloth. 30-Apr-4 Christie's, Kensington #350/R est:1500-2000

INDIAN SCHOOL, 19th C
Works on paper
£6000 $10620 €8760 Burmese Ambassador with courtiers and attendants (35x26cm-14x10in) gouache transparent wash htd gold exec.c.1810-20. 28-Apr-4 Sotheby's, London #58/R est:6000-8000

INDIANA, Robert (1928-) American
£10811 $20000 €15784 From the set of Red Eye of Love (183x183cm-72x72in) st.sig. verso acrylic oil ink canvas on panel. 13-Jul-4 Christie's, Rockefeller NY #32/R est:20000-30000
£14595 $27000 €21309 From the set of Red Eye of Love (183x183cm-72x72in) st.sig. verso acrylic oil ink canvas on panel. 13-Jul-4 Christie's, Rockefeller NY #33/R est:20000-30000
£14595 $27000 €21309 From the set of Red Eye of Love (183x183cm-72x72in) st.sig. verso acrylic oil ink canvas on panel. 13-Jul-4 Christie's, Rockefeller NY #34/R est:20000-30000
£15951 $26000 €23288 From the set of Red Eye of Love, Beef (183x183cm-72x72in) st.sig.verso canvas on panel prov. 23-Sep-3 Christie's, Rockefeller NY #136/R est:30000-40000
£15951 $26000 €23288 From the set of Red Eye of Love, meat (183x183cm-72x72in) st.sig.verso acrylic canvas on panel prov. 23-Sep-3 Christie's, Rockefeller NY #137/R est:30000-40000
£36313 $65000 €53017 Two (31x31cm-12x12in) s.i.d.66 acrylic prov.lit. 12-May-4 Christie's, Rockefeller NY #140/R est:30000-40000
£36471 $62000 €53248 Die deutsche liebe - the German love (30x30cm-12x12in) s.d.1967 verso acrylic. 22-Nov-3 New Orleans Auction, New Orleans #1348/R est:25000-40000
£83799 $150000 €122347 Chief (61x56cm-24x22in) i. s.d.1969 overlap prov. 13-May-4 Sotheby's, New York #160/R est:80000-120000
£106145 $190000 €154972 USA fun (130x130cm-51x51in) s.i.d.1964-5 overlap prov. 12-May-4 Christie's, Rockefeller NY #134/R est:150000-250000
£139665 $250000 €203911 Love (31x31cm-12x12in) st.sig. d.1965 verso prov. 13-May-4 Sotheby's, New York #154/R est:80000-120000
Prints
£9040 $16000 €13198 Decade (101x83cm-40x33in) s.num. col screenprint set of ten album. 28-Apr-4 Christie's, Rockefeller NY #310/R est:7000-10000
£15819 $28000 €23096 Numbers (66x50cm-26x20in) s.d.num. col screenprint set of ten album. 28-Apr-4 Christie's, Rockefeller NY #309/R est:6000-9000
Sculpture
£12291 $22000 €17945 Art - Red (46x46x25cm-18x18x10in) st.sig.d.2000 num.3/8 painted aluminium prov.lit. 12-May-4 Christie's, Rockefeller NY #164/R est:25000-35000
£14583 $24063 €21000 Nine (44x45x25cm-17x18x10in) s.num.2/8 paint aluminium. 2-Jul-3 Cornette de St.Cyr, Paris #83/R est:20000-25000
£15642 $28000 €22837 Six (45x46x25cm-18x18x10in) st.sig.d.1980-96 num.3/8 painted aluminium steel base prov.lit. 12-May-4 Christie's, Rockefeller NY #209/R est:25000-35000
£20958 $35000 €30599 Eight (44x46x25cm-17x18x10in) st.sig.d.1980-1997 num.7/8 base enamel on steel. 12-Nov-3 Christie's, Rockefeller NY #407/R est:25000-35000
£22346 $40000 €32625 Five (45x46x25cm-18x18x10in) st.sig.d.1980-97 num.7/8 painted aluminium steel base prov.lit. 12-May-4 Christie's, Rockefeller NY #208/R est:25000-35000
£31944 $53347 €46000 Love (45x45x22cm-18x18x9in) s.num.7/8 painted aluminium enamel exec 1966-2000. 25-Oct-3 Cornette de St.Cyr, Paris #698/R est:50000-60000
£62874 $105000 €91796 Love (46x46x23cm-18x18x9in) st.sig.d.1966-1999 num.5/8 enamel on steel. 12-Nov-3 Christie's, Rockefeller NY #405/R est:60000-80000
£110000 $200200 €160600 Love - Red/Blue (91x91x46cm-36x36x18in) st.sig.d.1966-1998 num.6/6 painted aluminium prov. 5-Feb-4 Sotheby's, London #24/R est:100000-150000
£170000 $312800 €248200 Love (183x183x91cm-72x72x36in) enamel on steel executed 1990 prov. 24-Jun-4 Christie's, London #39/R est:170000-250000
£234637 $420000 €342570 Love blue red (183x183x91cm-72x72x36in) i.sig. d.1995 num.2/6 painted aluminium prov. 12-May-4 Sotheby's, New York #47/R est:400000-600000

INDONESIAN SCHOOL, 20th C
Works on paper
£21622 $38054 €32000 Bare breasted girl seated by tree (105x51cm-41x20in) s. seals Indian ink oil board. 21-May-4 Dr Fritz Nagel, Stuttgart #1407/R est:1500

INDONI, Filippo (1800-1884) Italian
£11154 $19185 €16285 Flirting in the countryside (159x124cm-63x49in) s.d.1875 prov. 2-Dec-3 Bukowskis, Stockholm #280/R est:125000-150000 (S.KR 145000)
Works on paper
£800 $1360 €1168 Man lighting his pipe, girl carrying an umbrella leaning on a post (51x36cm-20x14in) s. 5-Nov-3 John Nicholson, Haslemere #495/R
£1022 $1900 €1492 Waiting by the old wall, portrait of a peasant girl (54x36cm-21x14in) s. W/C paper on board. 5-Mar-4 Skinner, Boston #236/R est:1800-2200
£1250 $2300 €1825 Discussion (35x54cm-14x21in) s. W/C. 8-Jun-4 Bonhams, New Bond Street #21/R est:1000-1500
£1400 $2338 €2044 Gypsy girl leaning against a wall. Gypsy girl carrying wood (51x36cm-20x14in) s. pencil W/C pair. 8-Oct-3 Christie's, Kensington #1124/R est:1000-1500
£1867 $3435 €2800 Peasants in Vesta temple (75x55cm-30x22in) s. W/C card. 10-Jun-4 Christie's, Rome #138/R est:2500-3000

INDONI, Filippo (jnr) (1842-1908) Italian
Works on paper
£2346 $4200 €3425 Portrait of a man. Portrait of a woman (51x33cm-20x13in) s. W/C pair. 20-Mar-4 Pook & Pook, Downington #381/R est:1500-2500

INDREBO, Tone (1954-) Norwegian
£1107 $1905 €1616 Composition (51x51cm-20x20in) s.d.96. 8-Dec-3 Blomqvist, Oslo #562/R est:12000-15000 (N.KR 13000)

INDRIKOVICS, Ivan (fl.1840s) Hungarian
£1317 $2384 €1923 Fruit still life (42x53cm-17x21in) s. 16-Apr-4 Mu Terem Galeria, Budapest #27/R (H.F 500000)

INDSETH, Rolf (1900-1951) Norwegian
£267 $446 €390 Portrait of a boy wearing a sailor suit (112x67cm-44x26in) s. 17-Nov-3 Blomqvist, Lysaker #1131/R (N.KR 3200)

INDUNI, Eduardo (19/20th C) Argentinian
£1457 $2652 €2200 Quiet shipbuilding yard (109x133cm-43x52in) s. 18-Jun-4 Bolland & Marotz, Bremen #648/R est:1600

INDUNO, Domenico (1815-1878) Italian
£6944 $11458 €10000 In love - girl on sofa (39x30cm-15x12in) s. 3-Jul-3 Van Ham, Cologne #1269/R est:11000
Works on paper
£6159 $10101 €8500 Player begging (55x46cm-22x18in) s.d.1878 W/C wash paper on cardboard. 29-May-3 Galleria Pace, Milan #92/R est:10000-13000

INDUNO, Domenico (attrib) (1815-1878) Italian
£1028 $1717 €1450 I pensieri della mamma (23x18cm-9x7in) s.verso. 21-Jun-3 Stadion, Trieste #194/R
Works on paper
£545 $927 €780 Hunter and dog (17x13cm-7x5in) s. W/C pencil. 19-Nov-3 Finarte Semenzato, Milan #517/R

INDUNO, Gerolamo (1827-1890) Italian
£5072 $8319 €7000 Garibaldi soldier resting. s. board. 29-May-3 Galleria Pace, Milan #93/R est:10000
£7042 $11690 €10000 La battaglia della Cernaia (40x74cm-16x29in) s. 11-Jun-3 Christie's, Rome #286/R est:10000-15000
£23944 $39746 €34000 Return of the soldier (75x95cm-30x37in) s. 11-Jun-3 Christie's, Rome #285/R est:16000-20000
£24648 $42641 €35000 Little Japanese (44x34cm-17x13in) s. lit. 10-Dec-3 Sotheby's, Milan #115/R est:35000-45000
£42254 $73099 €60000 Portrait of Giovan Battista Botero (40x30cm-16x12in) s.d.1851 cardboard. 10-Dec-3 Sotheby's, Milan #142/R est:55000-75000
Works on paper
£780 $1303 €1100 Garibaldi in Volturno. Man with sword (27x14cm-11x6in) i. pencil double-sided. 14-Oct-3 Finarte Semenzato, Milan #156/R

£1224 $2192 €1800 Landscape (19x25cm-7x10in) s. sepia ink pencil lead exhib. 22-Mar-4 Sant Agostino, Torino #260/R est:2000

INGALL, J Spence (?) ?
Works on paper
£397 $723 €600 Fey Gate, Tangiers (25x35cm-10x14in) s. W/C. 21-Jun-4 Pandolfini, Florence #246/R

INGANNI, Angelo (1807-1880) Italian
£3521 $6092 €5000 Tamer (21x26cm-8x10in) s.d.1858 board. 10-Dec-3 Sotheby's, Milan #108/R est:2000-4000
£33629 $60196 €49098 Interior from the Cathedral in Milan (45cm-18in circular) s.d.1843. 25-May-4 Bukowskis, Stockholm #352/R est:80000-100000 (S.KR 455000)

INGELS, Domien (1881-1946) ?
Sculpture
£811 $1500 €1184 Draft horse (20cm-8in) s.i. brown pat.bronze. 10-Feb-4 Doyle, New York #225/R est:1000-1500
£3099 $5361 €4400 Duck (34x30cm-13x12in) s.i. brown green pat bronze marble base. 13-Dec-3 De Vuyst, Lokeren #474/R est:4400-5000
£3357 $5773 €4800 Le centaure (48x36cm-19x14in) s.st.f.Vindevogel black pat bronze marble socle. 8-Dec-3 Horta, Bruxelles #129 est:1800-2200

INGEMANN, Lucie (1792-1868) Danish
£1250 $2037 €1800 Still life with summer flowers and porcelain vase (26x30cm-10x12in) mono. i. stretcher. 24-Sep-3 Neumeister, Munich #451/R est:2000
£1944 $3247 €2800 Flowers on stone ledge (15x21cm-6x8in) mono.d.1837 panel. 24-Oct-3 Ketterer, Hamburg #76/R est:3000-3500

INGEN, Hendrik van (1833-1898) Dutch
£438 $700 €639 Portrait of a gentleman (53x74cm-21x29in) i.verso board. 20-Sep-3 Sloans & Kenyon, Bethesda #153/R

INGEN, Hendrikus Alexander van (1846-1920) Dutch
£417 $658 €600 Cows by rocky shore (25x38cm-10x15in) s. 6-Sep-3 Arnold, Frankfurt #587/R
£433 $776 €650 Cows watering (13x23cm-5x9in) s. board. 11-May-4 Vendu Notarishuis, Rotterdam #198
£1119 $1869 €1600 Resting cows (55x86cm-22x34in) s. 30-Jun-3 Sotheby's, Amsterdam #183/R

INGENMEY, Franz Maria (1830-1878) German
£6294 $10699 €9000 Three children in park (79x57cm-31x22in) s.d.1863. 20-Nov-3 Van Ham, Cologne #1640/R est:3500

INGERL, Kurt (1935-1999) Austrian
£352 $616 €500 Sequence 09 (50x50cm-20x20in) s.i.d.1974 verso lacquer masonite. 19-Dec-3 Dorotheum, Vienna #291/R

INGHAM, Alan (?) British
Works on paper
£360 $655 €526 At ease in the country (34x53cm-13x21in) s. W/C. 29-Jun-4 Bonhams, Knowle #56

INGHAM, Bryan (1936-1997) British
£5200 $9308 €7592 Still life at the Lizard (41x43cm-16x17in) s.i.d.1986/7 backboard oil pencil collage. 16-Mar-4 Bonhams, New Bond Street #81/R est:3000-5000
£7200 $13104 €10512 Large Porthleven with clocktower III (178x38cm-70x15in) s.i.d.1989 oil pencil chl collage prov. 15-Jun-4 Bonhams, New Bond Street #102/R est:6000-8000
Sculpture
£3400 $6188 €4964 Untitled (35x88cm-14x35in) painted wood relief prov. 15-Jun-4 Bonhams, Knightsbridge #169/R est:400-600
Works on paper
£300 $546 €438 San Sebastian - Galero - Basque Series (6x13cm-2x5in) s.i.d.1988 verso collage prov. 15-Jun-4 Bonhams, Knightsbridge #166/R
£380 $692 €555 Basque Series, San Sebastian - Cabal (18x15cm-7x6in) s.i.d.1988 collage prov. 15-Jun-4 Bonhams, Knightsbridge #162/R
£4000 $7280 €5840 Summer evening Kynance Suite (12x41cm-5x16in) s.i.d.1985 verso collage. 15-Jun-4 Bonhams, Knightsbridge #164/R est:600-800
£13000 $23660 €18980 Large view of Tuscany and Pisa (134x120cm-53x47in) s.i.d.1993-1996 mixed media collage prov. 15-Jun-4 Bonhams, New Bond Street #101/R est:4000-6000

INGLE, John S (1933-) American
Works on paper
£1519 $2750 €2218 Suite of pears-13 (20x25cm-8x10in) W/C. 16-Apr-4 American Auctioneer #214/R est:3000-5000
£1657 $3000 €2419 Suite of pears-2 (30x38cm-12x15in) gouache. 16-Apr-4 American Auctioneer #213/R est:3000-5000
£21547 $39000 €31459 Tomatoes in a jar (104x74cm-41x29in) W/C. 16-Apr-4 American Auctioneer #215/R est:30000-40000

INGLES, George Scott (1871-?) British
Works on paper
£270 $489 €394 Whitby harbour with paddle steamer (25x35cm-10x14in) i.verso W/C. 30-Mar-4 David Duggleby, Scarborough #153/R

INGLES, Marie (?) ?
£400 $632 €584 Still life with a pot of pink godetias (38x33cm-15x13in) board. 27-Apr-3 Wilkinson, Doncaster #300/R

INGLIS, Jane (?-1916) British
Works on paper
£280 $501 €409 River landscape (32x50cm-13x20in) s. W/C. 25-May-4 Bonhams, Knightsbridge #279/R

INGLIS, Peter (20th C) American
£223 $400 €326 Wollaston station at night (19x35cm-7x14in) s.d.1/14/90. 14-May-4 Skinner, Boston #295/R

INGRES, Jean Auguste Dominique (1780-1867) French
£455556 $820000 €665112 Virgin with the crown (70x51cm-28x20in) s. panel prov.exhib.lit. 23-Apr-4 Sotheby's, New York #49/R est:500000-700000
Works on paper
£1560 $2605 €2262 Hand study with stick. Hand study with parts of head (10x13cm-4x5in) pencil two. 19-Jun-3 Kornfeld, Bern #487 est:2000 (S.FR 3400)
£18000 $32940 €26280 Portrait of a young woman wearing a lace bonnet (8x8cm-3x3in) s. pencil beige blue wash paper on card round. 8-Jul-4 Sotheby's, London #142/R est:20000-30000
£205479 $349315 €300000 Portrait de Napoleon empereur (29x19cm-11x7in) s. pen ink wash prov.exhib.lit. 6-Nov-3 Tajan, Paris #103/R est:300000

INGUIMBERTY, Joseph (1896-1971) French
£1119 $1902 €1600 Paysage basque (73x92cm-29x36in) s. 27-Nov-3 Millon & Associes, Paris #232/R est:1500-2000
£6178 $10317 €9020 View along the river bank (60x110cm-24x43in) s. 26-Oct-3 Christie's, Hong Kong #44/R est:90000-140000 (HK.D 80000)
Works on paper
£1236 $2063 €1805 Two ladies under a banana tree (68x50cm-27x20in) s. col ink. 26-Oct-3 Christie's, Hong Kong #42/R est:20000-28000 (HK.D 16000)
£19355 $30968 €28258 Peasants in the rice fields (200x300cm-79x118in) seal sig. mixed media paper on canvas. 18-May-3 Sotheby's, Singapore #109/R est:50000-60000 (S.D 54000)

INGVARSSON, Jarl (1955-) Swedish
Works on paper
£1888 $3210 €2756 Who am I (128x122cm-50x48in) s.d.86 verso mixed media panel exhib. 5-Nov-3 AB Stockholms Auktionsverk #993/R est:15000-18000 (S.KR 25000)

INIESTA, Antonio (19/20th C) Spanish
£544 $974 €800 Pastoral scene (140x76cm-55x30in) s.d.1942 s.i.d.verso. 22-Mar-4 Durán, Madrid #631/R

INIMA (?) Brazilian?
£2015 $3566 €3023 Parisian landscape (49x65cm-19x26in) s. board. 27-Apr-4 Bolsa de Arte, Rio de Janeiro #54/R (B.R 11000)
£4396 $7780 €6594 View of the rooftops (50x61cm-20x24in) s. 27-Apr-4 Bolsa de Arte, Rio de Janeiro #62/R (B.R 24000)
£5128 $9385 €7692 Village scene (64x80cm-25x31in) s.d.1972 masonite. 6-Jul-4 Bolsa de Arte, Rio de Janeiro #137/R (B.R 28000)
£5495 $9725 €8243 Street scene with houses (73x60cm-29x24in) s.i.verso. 27-Apr-4 Bolsa de Arte, Rio de Janeiro #59/R (B.R 30000)

INJALBERT, Jean Antoine (1845-1933) French
Sculpture
£894 $1600 €1305 Lion and Cupid (43cm-17in) s. bronze. 8-May-4 Susanin's, Chicago #6005/R est:3000-5000

INLANDER, Henry (1925-1983) British
£460 $727 €667 Landscape (74x62cm-29x24in) s.d.59. 24-Jul-3 Lawrence, Crewkerne #978
£800 $1416 €1168 On the surface (96x96cm-38x38in) exhib. 27-Apr-4 Bonhams, Knightsbridge #303/R
£1000 $1790 €1460 Summer river no 1 (147x198cm-58x78in) prov. 14-May-4 Christie's, Kensington #591/R est:700-900

INMAN, Henry (1801-1846) American
£4802 $8500 €7011 Portraits of Samuel Brown and Maria Crosby Brown (84x71cm-33x28in) painted c.1839 pair. 27-Apr-4 Doyle, New York #15 est:8000-12000

INMAN, John O'Brien (1828-1896) American
£5114 $9000 €7466 Villager on the street (64x147cm-25x58in) prov. 23-May-4 Hindman, Chicago #145/R est:9000-12000
£13636 $24000 €19909 Napping (26x34cm-10x13in) s.i.d.69 board prov. 18-May-4 Christie's, Rockefeller NY #25/R est:12000-18000
Works on paper
£269 $450 €393 In the forest (30x23cm-12x9in) s. W/C exhib. 29-Jun-3 William Jenack, New York #401

INNES, Callum (1962-) British
£8152 $15000 €11902 Monologue (228x202cm-90x80in) prov. 10-Jun-4 Phillips, New York #462/R est:5000-7000
Works on paper
£650 $1183 €949 Evidence (50x65cm-20x26in) W/C together with three related screenprints. 21-Jun-4 Bonhams, New Bond Street #169/R

INNES, James Dickson (1887-1914) British
£6000 $10980 €8760 Girl reading in landscape (40x61cm-16x24in) s.d.13. 2-Jun-4 Sotheby's, London #28/R est:6000-8000

£7500 $13725 €10950 Collioure (27x35cm-11x14in) s.d.1911 panel prov.exhib. 4-Jun-4 Christie's, London #57/R est:4000-6000
£14000 $25060 €20440 Heavy cloud, Arenig (30x40cm-12x16in) panel prov. 16-Mar-4 Bonhams, New Bond Street #11/R est:4000-6000
Works on paper
£320 $515 €464 Windmill (23x38cm-9x15in) pen wash W/C exhib. 13-Aug-3 Andrew Hartley, Ilkley #751
£420 $722 €613 Muret-Le-Chateau, Pyrenees (27x38cm-11x15in) s.i.d.04 pencil W/C exhib. 3-Dec-3 Christie's, Kensington #550
£2514 $4500 €3670 Mountain and waterfall (27x39cm-11x15in) s.d.1910 W/C pencil on board. 6-May-4 Doyle, New York #44/R est:3000-4000

INNES, John (1863-1941) Canadian
£543 $852 €787 Mountie on horseback (25x20cm-10x8in) s. 30-Aug-3 Heffel, Vancouver #17 est:1500-2000 (C.D 1200)
£724 $1137 €1050 Cowboys on horseback in the Rockies (25x20cm-10x8in) s. 30-Aug-3 Heffel, Vancouver #15 est:1500-2000 (C.D 1600)
£3153 $5360 €4603 Early snow, Coast Range (45x61cm-18x24in) s. i.verso prov. 27-Nov-3 Heffel, Vancouver #110/R est:3000-4000 (C.D 7000)

INNESS, George (1825-1894) American
£5249 $9500 €7664 Landscape (36x66cm-14x26in) 16-Apr-4 Du Mouchelle, Detroit #2083/R est:7000-9000
£8939 $16000 €13051 Pastoral landscape (33x56cm-13x22in) s.d.1860. 26-May-4 Doyle, New York #64/R est:15000-20000
£10937 $19250 €15968 Soldiers return (23x33cm-9x13in) s. canvas on board. 28-May-4 Aspire, Cleveland #16/R est:7500-15000
£11173 $20000 €16313 Leaning double birch (30x46cm-12x18in) 6-May-4 Shannon's, Milford #142/R est:12000-18000
£29070 $50000 €42442 North Conway (30x46cm-12x18in) s. painted 1875. 4-Dec-3 Christie's, Rockefeller NY #11/R
£37791 $65000 €55175 River landscape (25x36cm-10x14in) s. painted 1877-78 prov. 4-Dec-3 Christie's, Rockefeller NY #3/R est:50000
£102273 $180000 €149319 Golden Glow (56x86cm-22x34in) s.d.1883 canvas on board prov.exhib.lit. 18-May-4 Christie's, Rockefeller NY #35/R est:150000-250000
Works on paper
£366 $600 €531 Autumn landscape (38x30cm-15x12in) bears sig.d. W/C. 7-Jun-3 Treadway Gallery, Cincinnati #1347

INNESS, George (attrib) (1825-1894) American
£2156 $3600 €3148 Sunset (20x25cm-8x10in) s. canvas on canvas. 27-Oct-3 Schrager Galleries, Milwaukee #1187/R

INNESS, George (jnr) (1853-1926) American
£1359 $2500 €1984 Landscape with central figure in field (41x61cm-16x24in) s. 9-Jun-4 Alderfer's, Hatfield #377 est:2000-4000

INNESS, George (jnr-attrib) (1853-1926) American
£359 $650 €524 Autumn landscape (25x33cm-10x13in) panel. 3-Apr-4 Charlton Hall, Columbia #550/R

INNOCENT, Ferenc (1859-?) Hungarian
£411 $699 €600 Portrait study of young woman (48x38cm-19x15in) s. lit. 6-Nov-3 Allgauer, Kempten #3457/R
£616 $1048 €900 Portrait of young woman (69x49cm-27x19in) s.i. 6-Nov-3 Allgauer, Kempten #3458/R
£1457 $2666 €2200 Astrid (69x49cm-27x19in) s. 8-Apr-4 Dorotheum, Vienna #129/R est:2200-2600
£1854 $3375 €2800 Portrait of a young lady with red hair (48x38cm-19x15in) s. 21-Jun-4 Dorotheum, Vienna #255/R est:2400-2800

INNOCENT, Franck (1912-1983) French?
£300 $510 €438 Still life of jug of flower, basket of eggs (53x64cm-21x25in) s. 5-Nov-3 Brightwells, Leominster #1013
£350 $594 €500 Chaumiere et chapelle (38x46cm-15x18in) s.d.1962. 30-Nov-3 Salle des ventes Pillet, Lyon la Foret #128
£450 $810 €657 Bordes de la Soie (54x64cm-21x25in) s.d.1966 verso exhib. 21-Apr-4 Cheffins, Cambridge #514/R
£1064 $1777 €1500 La maison de Paul Faure, les Andelys a travers les arbres (65x81cm-26x32in) s.d.64 s.i.d.verso. 19-Oct-3 Imberdis, Pont Audemer #37

INNOCENTI, Bruno (1906-1986) Italian
£680 $1218 €1000 Farm in Tuscany (34x44cm-13x17in) s.d.1941 cardboard. 22-Mar-4 Sant Agostino, Torino #199/R

INNOCENTI, Camillo (1871-1961) Italian
£957 $1599 €1350 Violin player in forest (22x16cm-9x6in) s. panel. 15-Oct-3 Neret-Minet, Paris #10/R
£1724 $3086 €2517 Farmstead with small girl (65x85cm-26x33in) mono. 12-May-4 Dobiaschofsky, Bern #637/R est:5500 (S.FR 4000)
£1736 $2743 €2500 Flower seller and suitor (41x30cm-16x12in) s.i.d.60 panel lit. 19-Sep-3 Schloss Ahlden, Ahlden #1480/R est:2200
£1853 $3095 €2650 Repas pres de l'atre (21x27cm-8x11in) s. panel. 29-Jun-3 Eric Pillon, Calais #63/R
£24000 $43680 €36000 Young girl listening to a story (67x62cm-26x24in) s. exhib. 1-Jul-4 Van Ham, Cologne #1412/R est:4000

INNOCENTI, Camillo (attrib) (1871-1961) Italian
£688 $1149 €998 Peasants dancing in fields (38x46cm-15x18in) s. paper on panel. 23-Jun-3 Philippe Schuler, Zurich #8604 (S.FR 1500)

INNOCENTI, Guglielmo (19th C) Italian
£526 $953 €800 L'amateur d'Estampes (17x11cm-7x4in) s.i.d.97 panel prov. 19-Apr-4 Glerum, Amsterdam #28/R

INNOCENTI, Sergio (1925-) Italian
£671 $1188 €1000 Mount Rosa from Macugnaga (50x70cm-20x28in) s. i.verso board. 1-May-4 Meeting Art, Vercelli #498

INO, Pierre (1909-) French
£400 $724 €600 L'ile perdue (81x65cm-32x26in) s. 5-Apr-4 Marie & Robert, Paris #115

INOKUMA, Genichiro (1902-1993) Japanese
£6977 $12000 €10186 Broadway (119x122cm-47x48in) s.i.d.1966 verso acrylic prov.exhib. 7-Dec-3 Freeman, Philadelphia #86 est:10000-15000

INSAM, Ernst (1927-) Austrian
£987 $1816 €1500 Kitzbuhl (57x78cm-22x31in) s. tempera. 22-Jun-4 Wiener Kunst Auktionen, Vienna #234/R est:1500
£987 $1816 €1500 Mountain landscape (57x77cm-22x30in) s. tempera. 22-Jun-4 Wiener Kunst Auktionen, Vienna #235/R est:1500
Works on paper
£267 $491 €400 Lunz am See - N O (38x56cm-15x22in) s.i.d.84 W/C. 9-Jun-4 Dorotheum, Vienna #185

INSHAW, David (1943-) British
£2400 $4128 €3504 Mozart piano concertos (43x43cm-17x17in) 2-Dec-3 Bonhams, New Bond Street #194/R est:2000-3000

INSKIP, John Henry (?-1947) British
£610 $1092 €891 Poppies (23x16cm-9x6in) board. 10-May-4 Joel, Victoria #211/R est:1000-1500 (A.D 1500)

INSLEY, Albert (1842-1937) American
£563 $900 €822 View in Orange County, NY (20x28cm-8x11in) s. board. 21-Sep-3 William Jenack, New York #96
£941 $1600 €1374 Near Ridgefield, Connecticut (43x33cm-17x13in) s.d.1925 board. 21-Nov-3 Skinner, Boston #440/R est:1500-3000
£1087 $2000 €1587 Atlantic from Acadia, Maine (35x51cm-14x20in) prov. 27-Jun-4 Freeman, Philadelphia #83/R est:2000-3000
£2500 $4000 €3650 View in Orange County (36x51cm-14x20in) s. 21-Sep-3 William Jenack, New York #212 est:2500-4000
£4469 $8000 €6525 Sunset landscape (51x81cm-20x32in) s. prov.exhib. 6-May-4 Shannon's, Milford #56/R est:8000-12000

INTERLANDI, Phil (20th C) American
Works on paper
£971 $1700 €1418 Why can't you just greet me with cocktails the way other wives do (42x33cm-17x13in) gouache illus board exec May 1960. 17-Dec-3 Christie's, Rockefeller NY #69/R est:1000-1500
£1714 $3000 €2502 Watch it with that pick will you, Mr Crippen (38x29cm-15x11in) s. W/C illus board exec Oct 1964. 17-Dec-3 Christie's, Rockefeller NY #137/R est:1000-1500

INTRAINA, Enrico Edoardo (1870-?) ?
£922 $1540 €1300 Osigo and the Grigna (24x36cm-9x14in) s. board. 14-Oct-3 Finarte Semenzato, Milan #114

INUIT, Mark (1953-) Canadian
Sculpture
£800 $1328 €1168 Fisherman (47x37x30cm-19x15x12in) s.i.d.1999 soapstone bone quartz. 5-Oct-3 Levis, Calgary #48/R est:3000-3500 (C.D 1800)
£1022 $1697 €1492 Bear (22x46x18cm-9x18x7in) s.i.d.2001 black soapstone. 5-Oct-3 Levis, Calgary #49/R est:3000-3500 (C.D 2300)
£1067 $1771 €1558 Dancing bear (46x25x27cm-18x10x11in) s.i.d.2002 black soapstone. 5-Oct-3 Levis, Calgary #47/R est:3000-3500 (C.D 2400)

INUKPUK, Johnny (1911-) North American
Sculpture
£1351 $2297 €1972 Inuit mother carrying her child in her amaut and holding a dipper (33cm-13in) i. mottled grey soapstone. 3-Nov-3 Waddingtons, Toronto #157/R est:3500-4500 (C.D 3000)
£1464 $2488 €2137 Mother with her child (46cm-18in) s. marbled dark soapstone. 3-Nov-3 Waddingtons, Toronto #147/R est:3000-5000 (C.D 3250)

INUKPUK, Johnny (jnr) (1930-1984) North American
Sculpture
£1081 $1838 €1578 Kneeling Inuit mother, softening a skin (33cm-13in) s. mottled dark soapstone exec.c.1965. 3-Nov-3 Waddingtons, Toronto #154/R est:2500-3500 (C.D 2400)

INVERA, Irene (1919-) Italian
£604 $1069 €900 Il paradiso (35x45cm-14x18in) s.d.1973. 28-Apr-4 Schopman, Hamburg #547/R

INVERNI, Francesco (1935-1991) Italian
£567 $1043 €850 Courtyard (60x50cm-24x20in) s. 11-Jun-4 Farsetti, Prato #461

INZA, Joaquin X (18/19th C) Spanish
£2747 $5000 €4011 Portrait of a Spainish gentleman, said to be Senor Sebastian Martinez (98x73cm-39x29in) 29-Jun-4 Sotheby's, New York #53/R est:6000-8000

INZA, Joaquin X (attrib) (18/19th C) Spanish
£2466 $4192 €3600 James fighting on horseback (73x62cm-29x24in) 4-Nov-3 Ansorena, Madrid #46/R est:3600

IOANNIDIS, Evangelos (1868-1942) Greek
Works on paper
£2400 $4200 €3504 Portraits of Bibi, friend of the artist (35x24cm-14x9in) one init. crayon pencil pair. 16-Dec-3 Bonhams, New Bond Street #59/R est:2000-3000

IOKI, Bunsai (1863-1906) Japanese
Works on paper
£1100 $2024 €1606 Outside a Japanese temple (66x50cm-26x20in) s.i. W/C. 10-Jun-4 Lyon & Turnbull, Edinburgh #111 est:150-250

IONESCU, Gheorges (1912-1971) Rumanian
£865 $1600 €1263 In the garden (33x41cm-13x16in) s. 17-Jan-4 New Orleans Auction, New Orleans #513/R est:1500-2500

I'ONS, Frederick Timpson (1802-1887) South African
£1156 $2069 €1688 Two Xhosa women (35x27cm-14x11in) s.d.1885 panel. 31-May-4 Stephan Welz, Johannesburg #590/R (SA.R 14000)

IPCAR, Dahlov (1917-) American
£5864 $9500 €8503 Winter workout (69x122cm-27x48in) s. prov. 8-Aug-3 Barridorf, Portland #175/R est:9000-12000
£6049 $9800 €8771 Greyhounds (41x89cm-16x35in) s.d.1985. 8-Aug-3 Barridorf, Portland #219/R est:6000-9000

IPEELEE, Osuitok (1923-) North American
Sculpture
£1216 $2068 €1775 Bird (36cm-14in) s. mottled green soapstone. 3-Nov-3 Waddingtons, Toronto #627/R est:2000-3000 (C.D 2700)
£1351 $2297 €1972 Duck eating a clam (29cm-11in) mottled green soapstone exec.c.1969. 3-Nov-3 Waddingtons, Toronto #113/R est:2500-3500 (C.D 3000)
£1802 $3063 €2631 Walrus with tusks (20cm-8in) s. mottled green soapstone ivory exec.c.1965. 3-Nov-3 Waddingtons, Toronto #315/R est:2500-3500 (C.D 4000)
£2342 $3982 €3419 Mother with her child in an amaut (15cm-6in) mottled dark soapstone exec.c.1955. 3-Nov-3 Waddingtons, Toronto #117/R est:3000-5000 (C.D 5200)
£2703 $4595 €3946 Reclining caribou with antlers (48cm-19in) s. marbled green soapstone. 3-Nov-3 Waddingtons, Toronto #97/R est:4000-6000 (C.D 6000)
£3266 $5551 €4768 Owl standing with outstretched wings (61cm-24in) mottled dark green soapstone. 3-Nov-3 Waddingtons, Toronto #934 est:4000-6000 (C.D 7250)
£3378 $5743 €4932 Mother polar bear with her young (48cm-19in) mottled green soapstone. 3-Nov-3 Waddingtons, Toronto #95/R est:6000-9000 (C.D 7500)
£3604 $6126 €5262 Caribou head with antlers (48cm-19in) s. marbled dark green soapstone. 3-Nov-3 Waddingtons, Toronto #323/R est:5000-7000 (C.D 8000)
£3716 $6317 €5425 Falcon (38cm-15in) s. marbled green soapstone. 3-Nov-3 Waddingtons, Toronto #90/R est:5000-7000 (C.D 8250)
£4730 $8041 €6906 Running Inuit woman (26cm-10in) s. marbled green soapstone exec.c.1975. 3-Nov-3 Waddingtons, Toronto #92/R est:3000-4000 (C.D 10500)
£5856 $9955 €8550 Standing caribou with antlers (69cm-27in) s. mottled green soapstone. 3-Nov-3 Waddingtons, Toronto #106/R est:10000-15000 (C.D 13000)

IPELLIE, Nuveeya (1920-) North American
Sculpture
£901 $1532 €1315 Musk ox (43cm-17in) s. mottled dark soapstone. 3-Nov-3 Waddingtons, Toronto #56/R est:2500-3500 (C.D 2000)

IPOUSTEGUY, Jean (1920-) French
Sculpture
£1486 $2750 €2170 Figure (37cm-15in) s.d.1959 num.2/6 brown black pat bronze st.f.Valsuani cire perdue. 12-Feb-4 Sotheby's, New York #141/R est:2000-4000
£3514 $6500 €5130 Helmeted Head (41x53cm-16x21in) dark brown pat bronze edn of 6 st.f.Valsuani prov.exhib. 12-Feb-4 Sotheby's, New York #184/R est:2500-3500
£4014 $7184 €5900 Masque mobile. s.d.1966 num.8/9 blk pat bronze. 19-Mar-4 Millon & Associes, Paris #204/R est:3500-4500

IPPOLITO, Angelo (1922-2002) American
£361 $650 €527 Untitled (40x40cm-16x16in) s.d.62. 25-Apr-4 Bonhams & Butterfields, San Francisco #5648/R
£368 $600 €537 Landscape with blue (102x122cm-40x48in) s.i.d.78 verso exhib. 20-Jul-3 Jeffery Burchard, Florida #49
£429 $700 €626 Winter drawing number 3 (56x76cm-22x30in) s.d.57 oil W/C graphite paper exhib. 20-Jul-3 Jeffery Burchard, Florida #55
£460 $750 €672 Indiana (124x127cm-49x50in) s.d.65 exhib. 20-Jul-3 Jeffery Burchard, Florida #48a
£552 $900 €806 Winter drawing number 2 (56x71cm-22x28in) s.d.57 oil marker board exhib. 20-Jul-3 Jeffery Burchard, Florida #50b
£1626 $2650 €2374 Trespiano (152x201cm-60x79in) s.d.60 exhib. 20-Jul-3 Jeffery Burchard, Florida #48

IPSEN, Ernest Ludwig (1869-1951) American
£8140 $14000 €11884 Gloucester docks (50x40cm-20x16in) s.d.97 prov. 3-Dec-3 Doyle, New York #214/R est:8000-12000

IPSEN, Poul Janus (1936-) Danish
£376 $627 €549 The hot summer I (100x90cm-39x35in) s.verso. 7-Oct-3 Rasmussen, Copenhagen #186/R (D.KR 4000)
£682 $1092 €989 The hungry (71x51cm-28x20in) s.verso. 17-Sep-3 Kunsthallen, Copenhagen #93 (D.KR 7200)
£812 $1495 €1186 Holberg Portrait Year 1984 (130x90cm-51x35in) s.i.d.30/84 verso. 29-Mar-4 Rasmussen, Copenhagen #328/R (D.KR 9000)

IQULIQ, Tuna (1935-) North American
Sculpture
£785 $1413 €1178 Mother with her child in her amaut (29cm-11in) s. grey soapstone. 26-Apr-4 Waddingtons, Toronto #71/R est:1500-2000 (C.D 1900)

IRAMAIN, Demetrio (?) Argentinian?
Works on paper
£223 $400 €326 Fair in Santiago (33x43cm-13x17in) mixed media. 11-May-4 Arroyo, Buenos Aires #51

IRAZABAL, Victor Hugo (20th C) ?
£386 $610 €564 Seascape (46x47cm-18x19in) s. diptych painted 1996. 1-Dec-2 Subastas Odalys, Caracas #14

IRAZU, Pello (1963-) Spanish
Works on paper
£946 $1665 €1400 London II (100x74cm-39x29in) s.d.1989 W/C glue prov. 18-May-4 Segre, Madrid #238/R
£1156 $2105 €1700 Enchanted series (65x50cm-26x20in) s.d.39 gouache ink felt-tip pen sticky tape prov.exhib.lit. 3-Feb-4 Segre, Madrid #196/R est:1500

IRELAND, James (fl.1885-1896) British
Works on paper
£500 $815 €730 Village children by a gate and stile with village and church in background (36x53cm-14x21in) s.i. W/C. 27-Sep-3 Rogers Jones, Clwyd #115

IRELAND, Thomas Tayler (fl.1880-c.1927) British
Works on paper
£260 $465 €380 Forest pond (52x34cm-20x13in) s. W/C. 26-May-4 Outhwaite & Litherland, Liverpool #291
£280 $501 €409 Woodland river (33x51cm-13x20in) s. W/C. 17-Mar-4 Bonhams, Chester #303
£340 $632 €496 Beech tree on wooded riverbank (52x34cm-20x13in) s. W/C. 2-Mar-4 Bearnes, Exeter #328/R
£357 $614 €521 Autumn mist in the forest (35x53cm-14x21in) s. W/C. 2-Dec-3 Ritchie, Toronto #37/R (C.D 800)
£420 $781 €613 Swans in woodland glade (52x34cm-20x13in) s. W/C. 2-Mar-4 Bearnes, Exeter #327

IRISH SCHOOL, 18th C
£4737 $8716 €7200 Cattle, sheep and drover on a path in an extensive landscape (39x50cm-15x20in) 22-Jun-4 Mealy's, Castlecomer #373/R est:3500-4500
£6690 $11574 €9500 Wooded landscape with figures and dogs (69x90cm-27x35in) 10-Dec-3 Bonhams & James Adam, Dublin #12/R est:8000-12000
£8553 $15737 €13000 Extensive panoramic landscape (114x148cm-45x58in) 22-Jun-4 Mealy's, Castlecomer #794/R est:15000-25000

IRISH SCHOOL, 19th C
£4000 $7240 €6000 View in the Dargle. View towards the Sugar Loaf, Co Wicklow (23x33cm-9x13in) init.d.1805 verso board pair possibly by John H Campbell. 31-Mar-4 James Adam, Dublin #8/R est:6000-8000
£5500 $9845 €8030 Group portrait of the two Ladies White and William, 4th Earl of Bantry and dog (133x163cm-52x64in) 14-May-4 Christie's, London #119/R est:4000-6000

IRMER, Carl (1834-1900) German
£268 $494 €400 Landscape with farmstead in Teutoburg Wood (15x20cm-6x8in) bears i. verso panel. 26-Mar-4 Bolland & Marotz, Bremen #536/R
£1189 $2021 €1700 River by full moon (40x31cm-16x12in) s.d.75. 20-Nov-3 Van Ham, Cologne #1642/R est:1900

IRMINGER, Valdemar (1850-1938) Danish
£269 $484 €393 A Danish soldier (26x38cm-10x15in) init.d.81. 24-Apr-4 Rasmussen, Havnen #2146 (D.KR 3000)
£344 $558 €499 The plague (42x57cm-17x22in) init.d.07 i.verso. 4-Aug-3 Rasmussen, Vejle #437/R (D.KR 3600)
£374 $591 €542 Stillness - room with candles and floor covered in wreaths (41x32cm-16x13in) init.d.97 exhib.prov. 2-Sep-3 Rasmussen, Copenhagen #1710/R (D.KR 4000)
£395 $672 €577 From the Jungle Book (37x53cm-15x21in) init.d.08. 29-Nov-3 Rasmussen, Havnen #2253/R (D.KR 4200)
£496 $917 €724 Forest interior with pine trees and fungi (100x127cm-39x50in) init.d.28. 15-Mar-4 Rasmussen, Vejle #464/R (D.KR 5500)
£674 $1253 €984 Small devils climbing up a wall to steal grapes (42x33cm-17x13in) init. prov. 2-Mar-4 Rasmussen, Copenhagen #1608/R (D.KR 7500)
£2056 $3249 €2981 The girl and the kitten (67x60cm-26x24in) init.d.95. 2-Sep-3 Rasmussen, Copenhagen #1548/R est:15000-20000 (D.KR 22000)

IROLLI, Vincenzo (1860-1949) Italian
£1781 $2778 €2600 Peasant woman with hen (40x28cm-16x11in) s. 8-Apr-3 Il Ponte, Milan #604
£2819 $5046 €4200 Little Madonna (53x38cm-21x15in) s. prov.lit. 25-May-4 Finarte Semenzato, Milan #226/R est:6000-6500
£3804 $7000 €5554 Praying time (92x79cm-36x31in) s. 22-Jun-4 Galeria y Remates, Montevideo #29/R
£4800 $8880 €7008 Young beauty (64x48cm-25x19in) s. prov. 11-Mar-4 Duke & Son, Dorchester #225/R est:5000-10000
£5403 $9563 €8105 Motherhood (69x48cm-27x19in) s.d.1898. 27-Apr-4 Bolsa de Arte, Rio de Janeiro #27/R (B.R 29500)
£6081 $10703 €9000 Saint Mark's Square (80x70cm-31x28in) s. 18-May-4 Segre, Madrid #82/R est:9000
£6522 $10696 €9000 Portrait of a boy (34x30cm-13x12in) s. 27-May-3 Finarte Semenzato, Milan #106/R est:8000-9000

£12000 $22080 €17520 Portrait of a boy with a goat (55x41cm-22x16in) s. prov. 23-Mar-4 Bonhams, New Bond Street #86/R est:12000-18000
£21277 $35532 €30000 Jokes (101x68cm-40x27in) s. lit. 14-Oct-3 Finarte Semenzato, Milan #159/R est:45000-50000
£22000 $40040 €32120 Young beauty (110x90cm-43x35in) s. 17-Jun-4 Christie's, London #82/R est:20000-30000
£34667 $63787 €52000 Sunday morning (91x152cm-36x60in) s. 8-Jun-4 Sotheby's, Milan #134/R est:50000-70000
£38889 $70000 €56778 In a bed of flowers (27x38cm-11x15in) s. prov. 23-Apr-4 Sotheby's, New York #76/R est:30000-40000
Works on paper
£1477 $2613 €2200 Pupil (36x29cm-14x11in) s. W/C. 1-May-4 Meeting Art, Vercelli #239 est:2000
£4930 $8183 €7000 Giovane venditrice di ciliege (47x30cm-19x12in) s. W/C cardboard. 11-Jun-3 Christie's, Rome #202/R est:8000-10000

IROLLI, Vincenzo (attrib) (1860-1949) Italian
£800 $1448 €1200 Portrait of a girl (41x26cm-16x10in) s. board. 2-Apr-4 Farsetti, Prato #526
£1797 $3342 €2624 Nude beauty posing in a boudoir (37x45cm-15x18in) init. 2-Mar-4 Rasmussen, Copenhagen #1574/R est:10000 (D.KR 20000)

IRONSIDE, Christopher (20th C) British
Works on paper
£300 $546 €438 Lansdowne circus in winter (25x35cm-10x14in) s.d.1926 pencil chl W/C. 15-Jun-4 Bonhams, Knightsbridge #68

IRVIN, Albert (1922-) British
£600 $1002 €876 Abstract (78x78cm-31x31in) board. 16-Oct-3 Christie's, Kensington #663

IRVINE, Greg (1946-) Australian
£242 $377 €351 Indian courtyard (121x182cm-48x72in) mono. s.verso. 1-Aug-2 Joel, Victoria #194 (A.D 700)
£267 $486 €390 Daisy rising to heaven (127x127cm-50x50in) init. i.verso prov. 16-Jun-4 Deutscher-Menzies, Melbourne #582/R (A.D 700)
£573 $1042 €837 Penny farthing (106x106cm-42x42in) init. s.i.verso prov. 16-Jun-4 Deutscher-Menzies, Melbourne #583/R est:1000-2000 (A.D 1500)

IRVINE, Wilson (1869-1936) American
£950 $1700 €1387 Coast of Maine (56x71cm-22x28in) s. i.stretcher. 14-May-4 Skinner, Boston #239/R est:3500-5500
£1676 $3000 €2447 Rocky coastline (58x81cm-23x32in) s. 14-May-4 Skinner, Boston #233/R est:3000-5000
£4469 $8000 €6525 Wooded grove (61x69cm-24x27in) s. prov. 6-May-4 Shannon's, Milford #187/R est:8000-12000
£7186 $12000 €10492 Path to the River (61x69cm-24x27in) s. 23-Oct-3 Shannon's, Milford #136/R est:12000-18000
£7821 $14000 €11419 Woodcutter in a fall landscape (66x84cm-26x33in) s. prov. 6-May-4 Shannon's, Milford #176/R est:8000-12000
£9143 $16000 €13349 Spring landscape (61x68cm-24x27in) s. 19-Dec-3 Sotheby's, New York #1090/R est:4000-6000
£27027 $50000 €39459 Selden's Cove (82x102cm-32x40in) s. s.i.stretcher painted c.1914-1918. 11-Mar-4 Christie's, Rockefeller NY #68/R est:30000-50000
Works on paper
£246 $450 €359 Landscape (30x43cm-12x17in) s. W/C double-sided. 5-Jun-4 Treadway Gallery, Cincinnati #650/R
£316 $500 €461 Expansive landscape (33x46cm-13x18in) s. W/C double-sided. 7-Sep-3 Treadway Gallery, Cincinnati #626/R
£373 $600 €545 The White Mountains (33x46cm-13x18in) s. W/C double-sided. 20-Aug-3 James Julia, Fairfield #1806/R

IRVING, Brian (20th C) British
Works on paper
£280 $524 €409 Sheep grazing on a hillside in Coverdale, North Yorkshire (20x34cm-8x13in) s. pencil W/C htd white scatching out. 22-Jul-4 Tennants, Leyburn #695
£360 $648 €526 A Dales landscape with figures harvesting (36x54cm-14x21in) s. pencil W/C. 21-Apr-4 Tennants, Leyburn #994
£380 $711 €555 Shepherd and his dog with sheep in an upland pasture (16x24cm-6x9in) s. pencil W/C. 22-Jul-4 Tennants, Leyburn #696
£700 $1260 €1022 Yorkshire Dales landscape. Sheep in a moorland landscape (51x37cm-20x15in) s. pencil W/C. 21-Apr-4 Tennants, Leyburn #995

IRVING, J Thwaite (fl.1888-1893) British
£691 $1250 €1009 English country scene with figures tending a garden (20x30cm-8x12in) s. 3-Apr-4 Nadeau, Windsor #231 est:400-600

IRVING, James (fl.1880-1890) British
£320 $512 €467 Village scene with pony and trap (21x31cm-8x12in) s. panel. 19-May-3 Bruton Knowles, Cheltenham #235/R

IRVING, Jean (20th C) American
Works on paper
£366 $600 €531 Figure near the coast (36x51cm-14x20in) s. W/C gouache exec.c.1950. 7-Jun-3 Treadway Gallery, Cincinnati #1495

IRVING, Jennette Bowman (20th C) American
£276 $500 €403 Gloucester harbor (46x36cm-18x14in) s. board. 16-Apr-4 James Julia, Fairfield #916/R

IRVING, Joan Brandt (1916-1995) American
Works on paper
£341 $600 €498 Heavy surf (28x36cm-11x14in) s.i. W/C. 23-May-4 Bonhams & Butterfields, Los Angeles #7004/R

IRVING, William C (1866-1943) British
£480 $763 €701 Cattle watering in the river before Warkworth Castle, Northumberland (50x75cm-20x30in) s. board. 18-Mar-3 Anderson & Garland, Newcastle #520/R
£550 $995 €803 Amorous huntsman (41x33cm-16x13in) s. 31-Mar-4 Bonhams, Knightsbridge #82/R

IRWE, Knut (1912-) Swedish
£508 $914 €762 Coastal landscape with sailing boat (50x61cm-20x24in) s. 25-Apr-4 Goteborg Auktionsverk, Sweden #321/R (S.KR 7000)
£1051 $1893 €1577 Landscape with figures on road (55x65cm-22x26in) s. 25-Apr-4 Goteborg Auktionsverk, Sweden #403/R est:15000 (S.KR 14500)
Works on paper
£254 $457 €381 Sailing boats in the skerries (36x44cm-14x17in) s. pastel. 25-Apr-4 Goteborg Auktionsverk, Sweden #396/R (S.KR 3500)
£261 $470 €392 Coastal landscape with boats by jetty (44x58cm-17x23in) s. pastel. 25-Apr-4 Goteborg Auktionsverk, Sweden #397/R (S.KR 3600)

IRWIN, Benoni (1840-1896) American
£699 $1300 €1021 The lute player (67x54cm-26x21in) s. canvasboard oval. 5-Mar-4 Skinner, Boston #224/R est:1000-1500
Works on paper
£1025 $1650 €1497 Portrait of young woman (43x33cm-17x13in) s. W/C. 20-Aug-3 James Julia, Fairfield #1769/R est:1500-2500

IRWIN, Flavia (20th C) British
Works on paper
£550 $1018 €803 Drift VIII (152x101cm-60x40in) s.i. pencil oil on canvas. 11-Mar-4 Christie's, Kensington #233

IRWIN, Wesley Fraser (1897-1976) Canadian
Works on paper
£214 $364 €312 Boathouse, White Mud Creek (26x36cm-10x14in) s. s.i.d.1943 W/C prov. 23-Nov-3 Levis, Calgary #481/R (C.D 475)

ISAAC, P (20th C) Haitian
£820 $1500 €1197 Peasants in a courtyard (60x86cm-24x34in) s. 3-Jun-4 Christie's, Rockefeller NY #1121/R est:500-700

ISAACHSEN, Olaf (1835-1893) Norwegian
£1626 $2976 €2374 View from Venemyr near Kristiansand (31x50cm-12x20in) mono. 7-Jun-4 Blomqvist, Oslo #301/R est:25000-30000 (N.KR 20000)

ISAAKSZ, Pieter Franz (1569-1625) Dutch
£12570 $22500 €18352 Venus and Cupid (32x24cm-13x9in) copper. 27-May-4 Sotheby's, New York #24/R est:20000-30000

ISABEY, Eugène (1803-1886) French
£280 $481 €400 Sailing boat in open sea before the thunderstorm (13x19cm-5x7in) mono. 5-Dec-3 Bolland & Marotz, Bremen #574/R
£1467 $2655 €2200 Paysage (28x40cm-11x16in) mono. paper on canvas. 1-Apr-4 Credit Municipal, Paris #41a est:2000-2500
£1500 $2400 €2175 Street in a French town (33cm-13in circular) s. card. 18-Sep-3 Christie's, Kensington #13/R est:1800-2200
£1733 $3137 €2600 Ferme Saint Simeon (32x42cm-13x17in) mono.d.1860 panel. 1-Apr-4 Credit Municipal, Paris #41b/R est:3500-4000
£2133 $3861 €3200 Passage voute dans la Casbah d'Alger (28x20cm-11x8in) st. cardboard lit. 30-Mar-4 Rossini, Paris #314/R est:2500-4000
£2333 $4223 €3500 Reception de la Reine Victoria au Treport (28x41cm-11x16in) bears i. exhib.lit. 30-Mar-4 Rossini, Paris #311/R est:4000-6000
£2649 $4954 €4000 Scene de bataille, cavalier de dos (38x46cm-15x18in) 24-Jul-4 Thierry & Lannon, Brest #181/R est:3500-4000
£2844 $4750 €4152 La procession ou le retour de Christophe Colomb (74x58cm-29x23in) s.d.58 prov.lit. 7-Oct-3 Sotheby's, New York #106 est:8000-12000
£4056 $6895 €5800 La Haye (38x46cm-15x18in) s.i.d.1840. 27-Nov-3 Millon & Associes, Paris #128/R est:7500-10000
£4167 $6958 €6000 Beach scene (18x24cm-7x9in) mono.d.63 panel prov.exhib. 21-Oct-3 Sotheby's, Amsterdam #224/R est:6000-8000
£4362 $7721 €6500 Tempete (48x77cm-19x30in) 28-Apr-4 Marc Kohn, Paris #141/R est:10000-12000
£4533 $8205 €6800 Les deux moulins (24x37cm-9x15in) mono. panel lit. 30-Mar-4 Rossini, Paris #315/R est:2500-4000
£5000 $9000 €7300 La defense du chateau (83x58cm-33x23in) s.d.68 canvas on panel prov.lit. 22-Apr-4 Christie's, Rockefeller NY #157/R est:10000-15000
£6000 $10860 €9000 Etude de ciel, Bretagne (31x25cm-12x10in) peinture paper on cardboard lit. 30-Mar-4 Rossini, Paris #312/R est:4000-7000
£6333 $11463 €9500 Tentation de Saint-Antoine (103x83cm-41x33in) mono.d.68 exhib.lit. 30-Mar-4 Rossini, Paris #313/R est:10000-15000
£8333 $13917 €12000 Harbour scene in a town (28x40cm-11x16in) s. panel prov. 21-Oct-3 Sotheby's, Amsterdam #221/R est:8000-12000
£8500 $14620 €12410 L'auberge de l'Ecu de France (74x60cm-29x24in) s.d.57 prov.exhib.lit. 4-Dec-3 Christie's, Kensington #16/R est:8000-12000
£11000 $19910 €16500 Brick sur les rochers (42x59cm-17x23in) s.d.1851 panel exhib.lit. 30-Mar-4 Rossini, Paris #310/R est:6000-9000
Works on paper
£278 $453 €400 Sailing ships off rocky coast (10x22cm-4x9in) s.i. verso pencil htd white. 26-Sep-3 Bolland & Marotz, Bremen #443/R
£733 $1327 €1100 Le combat du Texel (10x14cm-4x6in) graphite lit. 30-Mar-4 Rossini, Paris #1002
£800 $1448 €1200 Cezembre, bord de mer (25x34cm-10x13in) i. col crayon. 30-Mar-4 Rossini, Paris #317
£979 $1664 €1400 Navire dans la tempete (22x31cm-9x12in) bears sig.d.1839 W/C gouache prov. 26-Nov-3 Daguerre, Paris #39/R

£1338 $2315 €1900 Interieur d'eglise a Fecamp (33x24cm-13x9in) s. W/C gouache blk crayon. 10-Dec-3 Piasa, Paris #83/R est:2000
£1733 $3137 €2600 Vieille rue a Dinan (25x31cm-10x12in) s.i. W/C gouache lit. 30-Mar-4 Rossini, Paris #316/R est:1500-2500

ISABEY, Eugène (attrib) (1803-1886) French
£986 $1706 €1400 Scene de bataille (55x64cm-22x25in) 12-Dec-3 Piasa, Paris #67/R
£1467 $2655 €2200 Flotille de peche par gros temps (32x40cm-13x16in) lit. 30-Mar-4 Rossini, Paris #1006/R est:2500-3500
£1600 $2896 €2400 Nature morte a la soupiere (22x29cm-9x11in) oil paper on cardboard painted c.1830 exhib.lit. 30-Mar-4 Rossini, Paris #1007/R est:2000-3000
£1879 $3458 €2800 Four elegantly dressed girls on terrace (24x34cm-9x13in) s.d.1843 panel. 25-Mar-4 Dr Fritz Nagel, Stuttgart #727/R est:2100
Works on paper
£400 $724 €600 Vieille rue a Paris (25x16cm-10x6in) W/C htd white lit. 30-Mar-4 Rossini, Paris #1009
£1633 $2922 €2400 Portrait d'homme (15x13cm-6x5in) graphite pen black ink W/C. 18-Mar-4 Christie's, Paris #263/R est:700-900

ISABEY, Jean Baptiste (1767-1855) French
Miniatures
£1342 $2470 €2000 Homme de qualite en redingote bleue, gilet et cravate blancs (5x4cm-2x2in) exec. c.1800 oval bronze sculpted frame prov.lit. 26-Mar-4 Pierre Berge, Paris #94/R est:2000-3000
£1748 $3007 €2500 Portrait de femme (13x9cm-5x4in) s. on vellum. 4-Dec-3 E & Eve, Paris #47/R
£1800 $3114 €2628 Young lady facing right (21x16cm-8x6in) s.d.1836 card. 9-Dec-3 Christie's, London #185/R est:1800-2200
£3289 $6053 €5000 Portrait d'homme a la legion d'honneur (13x10cm-5x4in) s. oval. 25-Jun-4 Daguerre, Paris #199/R est:4000-5000
£9500 $17005 €13870 Young lady holding a riding whip (8cm-3in circular) s. gilt wood frame. 25-May-4 Christie's, London #185/R est:8000-12000
£10000 $18000 €14600 Napoleon, Emperor of the French (5cm-2in) s.d.1811 enamel gold mount rec. gilt metal mount oval exhib.lit. 22-Apr-4 Bonhams, New Bond Street #129/R est:4000-6000
Works on paper
£667 $1207 €1000 Le plaisir l'emportant sur la raison (13x14cm-5x6in) s.d.1825 brown wash black crayon. 30-Mar-4 Rossini, Paris #33/R
£1724 $3172 €2517 Park landscape (18x23cm-7x9in) s. W/C on pen htd white. 26-Mar-4 Koller, Zurich #3088/R est:4000-5000 (S.FR 4000)
£13889 $25000 €20278 Le vie de l'homme du monde, scenes of the times of the day (7x9cm-3x4in) s.d.1816 graphite brown wash set of 12. 21-Jan-4 Sotheby's, New York #140/R est:10000-15000

ISABEY, Jean Baptiste (attrib) (1767-1855) French
£5369 $9504 €8000 Portrait de M.lle de Caumont (42x32cm-17x13in) prov.exhib. 30-Apr-4 Tajan, Paris #85/R est:8000-10000
Miniatures
£2013 $3745 €3000 Jeune femme en bust sur fond de nuages (9cm-4in circular) gilt brass frame round. 8-Mar-4 Artcurial Briest, Paris #95/R est:1000-1200
Works on paper
£280 $481 €400 Portrait of the artist Jacques Luc Barbier Wallbonne smoking a pipe (27x22cm-11x9in) blk white chk htd white. 2-Dec-3 Christie's, Paris #505
£604 $1069 €900 Napoleon III aged 4 (26x18cm-10x7in) pencil wash. 29-Apr-4 Dorotheum, Vienna #41/R

ISAILOFF, Alexandre (1869-?) Russian?
£377 $640 €550 Village provencal (40x32cm-16x13in) s. panel. 9-Nov-3 Eric Pillon, Calais #116/R
£795 $1446 €1200 Place du Chatelet, Paris (15x24cm-6x9in) s. panel. 18-Jun-4 Piasa, Paris #100
£3611 $6500 €5272 View of Venice (32x41cm-13x16in) s. panel. 23-Apr-4 Sotheby's, New York #40/R est:4000-6000

ISAKSEN, Christen Holm (1877-1935) Danish
£709 $1269 €1035 Coastal landscape with figures on cliffs, Faroe Islands (69x108cm-27x43in) s. 12-Jan-4 Rasmussen, Vejle #85/R (D.KR 7500)

ISAKSON, Karl (1878-1922) Swedish
£6798 $11556 €9925 Still life of marigolds in vase (60x63cm-24x25in) exhib.prov. 4-Nov-3 Bukowskis, Stockholm #21/R est:100000-125000 (S.KR 90000)
£16117 $28527 €23531 Still life of tulips and oranges (68x52cm-27x20in) 27-Apr-4 AB Stockholms Auktionsverk #670/R est:175000-200000 (S.KR 220000)

ISBEY, Annette (20th C) New Zealander
£709 $1312 €1035 Portraits (24x37cm-9x15in) init. double-sided. 13-Jul-4 Watson's, Christchurch #32/R est:1750-2500 (NZ.D 2000)

ISBRAND, Victor (1897-1989) Danish
£451 $830 €658 View - Skodsborg (41x35cm-16x14in) s.d.19 canvas on plywood prov. 29-Mar-4 Rasmussen, Copenhagen #458 (D.KR 5000)

ISELI, Rolf (1934-) Swiss
£1584 $2692 €2313 Landscape (38x33cm-15x13in) mono.d.1963 verso. 25-Nov-3 Germann, Zurich #2/R est:3000-4000 (S.FR 3500)
£2028 $3286 €2961 Untitled (45x35cm-18x14in) mono.d.64 jute prov. 24-May-3 Burkhard, Luzern #3/R est:2500-3000 (S.FR 4300)
Works on paper
£409 $679 €593 All aboard (29x21cm-11x8in) s.i.d.1973 mixed media. 13-Jun-3 Zofingen, Switzerland #2892 (S.FR 900)
£450 $775 €657 Untitled (62x48cm-24x19in) s.i.d.1962 verso gouache. 8-Dec-3 Philippe Schuler, Zurich #3204 (S.FR 1000)
£519 $841 €758 Untitled (31x22cm-12x9in) s. bears i.d.1962 gouache prov. 24-May-3 Burkhard, Luzern #9/R (S.FR 1100)
£769 $1308 €1123 Gagarin (62x48cm-24x19in) s.i.d.1961 verso W/C prov. 22-Nov-3 Burkhard, Luzern #23/R (S.FR 1700)
£849 $1375 €1240 Gagarin (62x48cm-24x19in) s.i.d.1961 verso W/C prov. 24-May-3 Burkhard, Luzern #44/R (S.FR 1800)
£860 $1462 €1256 Homme champignon (32x24cm-13x9in) s.i.d.1972 mixed media collage. 25-Nov-3 Germann, Zurich #816/R est:2000-2500 (S.FR 1900)
£1176 $2000 €1717 Composition (32x27cm-13x11in) s.i.d.1975 mixed media. 25-Nov-3 Germann, Zurich #1/R est:2500-3500 (S.FR 2600)
£1226 $1987 €1790 Untitled (62x48cm-24x19in) s.i.d.4.1964 W/C prov. 24-May-3 Burkhard, Luzern #40/R (S.FR 2600)
£1233 $2097 €1800 Bovist, end landscape (37x50cm-15x20in) s.i.d.74earth W/C. 7-Nov-3 Dobiaschofsky, Bern #275/R est:4000 (S.FR 2800)
£1310 $2384 €1913 Homme champignon (26x19cm-10x7in) s.i.d.73 Indian ink W/C. 17-Jun-4 Kornfeld, Bern #439/R est:3000 (S.FR 3000)
£1415 $2292 €2066 Untitled (76x55cm-30x22in) s. verso gouache collage prov. 24-May-3 Burkhard, Luzern #47/R est:2500-3000 (S.FR 3000)
£1454 $2471 €2123 Boyards series (15x14cm-6x6in) s.i.d.77 or 85 four. 7-Nov-3 Dobiaschofsky, Bern #251/R est:4500 (S.FR 3300)
£1454 $2471 €2123 Earth picture (76x107cm-30x42in) s.d.76 earth W/C. 7-Nov-3 Dobiaschofsky, Bern #277/R est:6000 (S.FR 3300)
£1850 $3145 €2701 Untitled (63x48cm-25x19in) s.d.63 verso gouache. 7-Nov-3 Dobiaschofsky, Bern #276/R est:3000 (S.FR 4200)
£2262 $3846 €3303 Mushroom man (65x48cm-26x19in) pencil W/C earth prov.exhib.lit. 25-Nov-3 Germann, Zurich #89/R est:6000-8000 (S.FR 5000)
£3620 $6154 €5285 Untitled (52x66cm-20x26in) s.d.79 W/C sand col clk prov. 22-Nov-3 Burkhard, Luzern #25/R est:8000-12000 (S.FR 8000)

ISENBART (?) French
£1135 $1895 €1600 Paysage (35x56cm-14x22in) s. 21-Jun-3 Peron, Melun #67

ISENBART, E (?) French?
£3014 $5034 €4250 Paysanne sur le chemin (48x64cm-19x25in) s. 21-Jun-3 Peron, Melun #71

ISENBART, Marie Victor Émile (1846-1921) French
£2222 $3711 €3200 La vallee de la Loue (38x51cm-15x20in) s. 23-Oct-3 Credit Municipal, Paris #100 est:800-1000
£2692 $4631 €3930 Pastoral landscape with cattle and figure (96x134cm-38x53in) s. 2-Dec-3 Bukowskis, Stockholm #286/R est:50000-55000 (S.KR 35000)
£3000 $5010 €4380 Neuchatel lake (48x64cm-19x25in) s. 12-Nov-3 Sotheby's, Olympia #169/R est:2500-3500

ISENBRANDT, Adriaen (studio) (1490-1551) Flemish
£23026 $42368 €35000 Saint Jerome in landscape (28x25cm-11x10in) panel prov.lit. 24-Jun-4 Christie's, Paris #5/R est:8000-12000

ISEPP, Sebastian (attrib) (1884-1954) Austrian
£2000 $3680 €3000 Snow covered high mountain landscape (49x69cm-19x27in) board. 9-Jun-4 Dorotheum, Salzburg #590/R est:6000-7000

ISER, Iosif (1881-1958) Hungarian
£966 $1786 €1400 Seated North African (22x31cm-9x12in) s. d.1921 verso board. 14-Feb-4 Hans Stahl, Hamburg #43/R

ISFAHAN SCHOOL (17th C) Persian
£85000 $150450 €124100 Portrait of a fashionable young man (151x89cm-59x35in) 27-Apr-4 Christie's, London #85/R est:60000-80000

ISGRO, Emilio (1936-) Spanish
£379 $607 €550 L (29x24cm-11x9in) s.i. oil collage card. 13-Mar-3 Galleria Pace, Milan #46/R
£467 $859 €700 Raphael (29x25cm-11x10in) mixed media card. 10-Jun-4 Galleria Pace, Milan #1/R
£3623 $5942 €5000 Letter M (50x70cm-20x28in) s.d.1971 verso acrylic. 30-May-3 Farsetti, Prato #434/R
£4054 $7135 €6000 After the bomb (21x30cm-8x12in) s.i.d.1973 verso. 22-May-4 Galleria Pananti, Florence #313/R est:1000-2000
£4362 $7809 €6500 Henricus Kissinger, EX (125x160cm-49x63in) s.i.d.1974 verso oil ink. 25-May-4 Sotheby's, Milan #152/R est:2000
£4467 $8219 €6700 Full painting (40x60cm-16x24in) s.d.1972 verso book on wood. 8-Jun-4 Finarte Semenzato, Milan #359/R est:5000-6000
Sculpture
£3636 $6182 €5200 Untitled (40x60cm-16x24in) s.d.1972 verso book plexiglas. 20-Nov-3 Finarte Semenzato, Milan #33/R est:4000-4500
Works on paper
£278 $439 €400 Artist and mistake (29x23cm-11x9in) mixed media board on cardboard. 6-Sep-3 Meeting Art, Vercelli #256
£278 $439 €400 Artist and mistake (29x24cm-11x9in) mixed media card. 6-Sep-3 Meeting Art, Vercelli #511
£282 $468 €400 L'artista e l'errore (29x23cm-11x9in) s. mixed media panel on board. 14-Jun-3 Meeting Art, Vercelli #531
£367 $675 €550 Artist and error (30x24cm-12x9in) s.i. mixed media cardboard. 12-Jun-4 Meeting Art, Vercelli #106
£379 $633 €550 Untitled (29x24cm-11x9in) s. mixed media card. 13-Nov-3 Galleria Pace, Milan #22/R
£399 $654 €550 L (29x24cm-11x9in) s. mixed media cardboard. 29-May-3 Galleria Pace, Milan #6/R
£403 $745 €600 Untitled (29x24cm-11x9in) s. mixed media card. 11-Mar-4 Galleria Pace, Milan #36/R
£450 $832 €670 Artist and mistake (29x24cm-11x9in) s.i. mixed media cardboard on card. 13-Mar-4 Meeting Art, Vercelli #313
£667 $1207 €1000 Artist and honour (29x24cm-11x9in) s.i. mixed media cardboard. 2-Apr-4 Farsetti, Prato #65/R

ISHERWOOD, Lawrence (1917-1988) British

£260	$424	€380	Head of a miner (40x30cm-16x12in) s. board. 23-Sep-3 Bonhams, Chester #984
£280	$456	€409	Paignton - figures on the shore (31x41cm-12x16in) s. i.verso canvasboard. 23-Sep-3 Bonhams, Chester #985
£280	$512	€409	Buckinghamshire landscape (33x43cm-13x17in) s. i.verso board. 6-Apr-4 Bonhams, Chester #992
£300	$489	€435	Lancashire miner (49x39cm-19x15in) s.d.58 i.verso board. 23-Sep-3 Bonhams, Leeds #135
£300	$489	€438	Creole (45x35cm-18x14in) s. i.verso board. 23-Sep-3 Bonhams, Chester #979
£300	$537	€438	Grandmother's hight button boots (65x77cm-26x30in) s.d.56 s.i.d.1956 verso board. 14-May-4 Christie's, Kensington #583/R
£320	$522	€464	Cornflowers (35x24cm-14x9in) s. i.verso board sold with another by the same artist. 23-Sep-3 Bonhams, Leeds #134
£320	$522	€467	Family on a beach (48x61cm-19x24in) s.d.58 board. 23-Sep-3 Bonhams, Chester #972
£320	$522	€467	Crowning glory (45x69cm-18x27in) s. i.verso board. 23-Sep-3 Bonhams, Chester #974
£320	$586	€467	Orchard daffodils Knowlsely Estate (34x44cm-13x17in) s. i.d.1973 verso board. 6-Apr-4 Bonhams, Chester #990
£320	$589	€467	Pits near Wigan (30x44cm-12x17in) s. i.verso board. 8-Jun-4 Bonhams, Chester #1027
£320	$586	€467	Woodland scene with stream in foreground (24x34cm-9x13in) s. indis.i. verso board. 6-Jul-4 Peter Wilson, Nantwich #32/R
£340	$554	€496	Lord Street, Southport (34x45cm-13x18in) s.d.59 i.d.verso board. 23-Sep-3 Bonhams, Chester #977
£360	$587	€522	Lancs, nude (49x39cm-19x15in) s.d.59 i.d.verso board. 23-Sep-3 Bonhams, Leeds #136
£380	$718	€555	Newburgh Church (37x53cm-15x21in) s.d.58 i.verso board. 18-Feb-4 Peter Wilson, Nantwich #13
£400	$732	€584	Miners Mosley Common Pit (38x49cm-15x19in) s. i.verso board. 6-Apr-4 Bonhams, Chester #993
£420	$689	€613	Watch Tower, Arbroath (60x45cm-24x18in) s. i.verso board. 3-Jun-3 Fellows & Sons, Birmingham #4/R
£420	$701	€613	Dover cliffs (41x60cm-16x24in) s.i.verso board. 24-Jun-3 Bonhams, Chester #938
£420	$701	€613	Beach and sky (59x39cm-23x15in) s. i.verso board. 7-Oct-3 Fellows & Sons, Birmingham #368/R
£420	$685	€613	Fishing boats in a port (46x56cm-18x22in) s. board. 23-Sep-3 Bonhams, Chester #973
£430	$787	€628	Mother's funeral people with detached Rector (30x41cm-12x16in) i.d.1972 board. 6-Apr-4 Capes Dunn, Manchester #846/R
£460	$768	€672	Untitled (49x39cm-19x15in) s. i.verso board. 7-Oct-3 Fellows & Sons, Birmingham #369
£480	$850	€701	Daffodils (50x40cm-20x16in) s.d.74 i.verso board. 28-Apr-4 Peter Wilson, Nantwich #44
£500	$795	€730	Susan (49x37cm-19x15in) s.d.1975 s.verso. 30-Apr-3 Peter Wilson, Nantwich #57
£550	$985	€803	Natives, Wigan (61x48cm-24x19in) s.d.56 canvasboard. 14-May-4 Christie's, Kensington #582/R
£580	$934	€847	Patti Boyd at Epstein's funeral (48x36cm-19x14in) board. 19-Feb-3 Peter Wilson, Nantwich #55
£680	$1204	€993	Rain horse guards parade Whitehall, London (44x60cm-17x24in) s.i.verso board. 28-Apr-4 Peter Wilson, Nantwich #40
£800	$1312	€1168	The sky and beach (49x39cm-19x15in) s. i.verso board. 3-Jun-3 Fellows & Sons, Birmingham #5/R
£860	$1402	€1247	Mevagissey, Cornwall (48x59cm-19x23in) s. i.verso board. 23-Sep-3 Bonhams, Leeds #137/R

ISHIKAWA, Kinichiro (1871-1945) Japanese

Works on paper

£2134	$3841	€3116	Landscape in Paris (40x24cm-16x9in) s.i. W/C silk. 25-Apr-4 Christie's, Hong Kong #762/R est:30000-50000 (HK.D 30000)

ISHIKAWA, Shigehiko (20th C) Japanese

£222	$408	€324	Nakiri no ie - horse of Nakiri (47x38cm-19x15in) s. i.verso prov. 14-Jun-4 Waddingtons, Toronto #341/R (C.D 550)

ISHULUTAQ, Jaco (1951-) North American

Sculpture

£811	$1378	€1184	Inuit legend of Lumak and the whale (38cm-15in) walrus tusk green soapstone base. 3-Nov-3 Waddingtons, Toronto #419/R est:2000-3000 (C.D 1800)

ISKANDAR, Popo (1927-2000) Javanese

£1373	$2484	€2005	Kukuruyuk (31x31cm-12x12in) 4-Apr-4 Sotheby's, Singapore #140/R est:2000-3000 (S.D 4200)
£1806	$2890	€2637	Still life (61x48cm-24x19in) s.d.91. 18-May-3 Sotheby's, Singapore #164/R est:6000-8000 (S.D 5040)
£1935	$3097	€2825	Two bouquettes (60x40cm-24x16in) s.d.68 s.i.d.1968 verso. 18-May-3 Sotheby's, Singapore #162/R est:3000-5000 (S.D 5400)
£1961	$3549	€2863	Alam Benda (65x60cm-26x24in) s.d.1967 lit. 4-Apr-4 Sotheby's, Singapore #161/R est:6000-8000 (S.D 6000)
£2174	$3370	€3174	Kucing (40x48cm-16x19in) s.d.86 canvas on board. 6-Oct-2 Sotheby's, Singapore #174/R est:4000-6000 (S.D 6000)
£2237	$3578	€3266	Beach (90x70cm-35x28in) s.d.68 s.i.d.1968 verso. 18-May-3 Sotheby's, Singapore #163/R est:3000-4000 (S.D 6240)
£2899	$4493	€4233	Nude (30x50cm-12x20in) s.d.68 exhib. 6-Oct-2 Sotheby's, Singapore #130/R est:4000-6000 (S.D 8000)
£3623	$5616	€5290	Kosamba boats (100x95cm-39x37in) s.d.77. 6-Oct-2 Sotheby's, Singapore #158/R est:10000-12000 (S.D 10000)
£3986	$6178	€5820	Cat (66x70cm-26x28in) s.d.76. 6-Oct-2 Sotheby's, Singapore #73/R est:6000-9000 (S.D 11000)
£4633	$7737	€6764	At the beach (80x100cm-31x39in) s.d.76 prov. 26-Oct-3 Christie's, Hong Kong #83/R est:32000-42000 (HK.D 60000)
£4902	$8873	€7157	Kucing hitam (80x96cm-31x38in) s.d.90. 4-Apr-4 Sotheby's, Singapore #164/R est:18000-25000 (S.D 15000)
£5072	$7862	€7405	Cat (100x95cm-39x37in) s.d.97 lit. 6-Oct-2 Sotheby's, Singapore #171/R est:12000-18000 (S.D 14000)
£5161	$8258	€7535	Nude (113x82cm-44x32in) s.d.87. 18-May-3 Sotheby's, Singapore #181/R est:12000-15000 (S.D 14400)
£5435	$8424	€7935	The dream (100x100cm-39x39in) s.d.98 lit. 6-Oct-2 Sotheby's, Singapore #166/R est:12000-15000 (S.D 15000)
£5556	$9278	€8112	Nude (90x70cm-35x28in) s.d.61 lit. 12-Oct-3 Sotheby's, Singapore #155/R est:5000-7000 (S.D 16000)
£6522	$10109	€9522	Nude (101x93cm-40x37in) s.d.63. 6-Oct-2 Sotheby's, Singapore #152/R est:7000-9000 (S.D 18000)
£8535	$15363	€12461	Dua macan dan matahari - two leopards (90x100cm-35x39in) s.d.77. 25-Apr-4 Christie's, Hong Kong #569/R est:45000-75000 (HK.D 120000)
£9266	$15475	€13528	Cheetah (95x146cm-37x57in) s.d.90. 26-Oct-3 Christie's, Hong Kong #82/R est:40000-80000 (HK.D 120000)
£12043	$19269	€17583	Cockerel (125x100cm-49x39in) s.d.97 lit. 18-May-3 Sotheby's, Singapore #171/R est:18000-25000 (S.D 33600)

ISKOWITZ, Gershon (1921-1988) Canadian

£407	$728	€594	Winter landscape (48x59cm-19x23in) s.d.1955. 6-May-4 Heffel, Vancouver #76/R (C.D 1000)
£447	$800	€653	Autumn scene (43x58cm-17x23in) s.d.1955 board. 6-May-4 Heffel, Vancouver #72/R (C.D 1100)
£1802	$3063	€2631	Sky (101x81cm-40x32in) s.d.65 i.d. verso prov. 18-Nov-3 Sotheby's, Toronto #131/R est:4000-6000 (C.D 4000)
£2236	$4002	€3265	Midnight No.6 (102x85cm-40x33in) s.i.d.1986 verso prov. 31-May-4 Sotheby's, Toronto #95/R est:4000-6000 (C.D 5500)
£7207	$12252	€10522	New greens (114x101cm-45x40in) s.i.d.1975 verso prov. 18-Nov-3 Sotheby's, Toronto #164/R est:7000-9000 (C.D 16000)

Works on paper

£407	$728	€594	K S (43x55cm-17x22in) s.i.d.1977 W/C prov. 6-May-4 Heffel, Vancouver #73/R (C.D 1000)

ISMAEL, Juan (20th C) Spanish

£800	$1448	€1200	Fish (41x67cm-16x26in) s.d.1964 oil sand copper on board. 30-Mar-4 Segre, Madrid #331/R

ISMAIL, Muhammad (18th C) Iranian

Works on paper

£10000	$17700	€14600	Gul-o bulbul, bulbul perched on a hazelnut sprig with a caterpillar (28x18cm-11x7in) gouache. 27-Apr-4 Christie's, London #77/R est:5000-7000

ISMAIL, Naim (1930-1979) Syrian

£1800	$3186	€2628	Faces (38x48cm-15x19in) s.d.1977. 29-Apr-4 Bonhams, New Bond Street #572/R est:1500-2000

ISNARD, Vivien (1946-) French?

£1316	$2421	€2000	Peinture S123 (76x56cm-30x22in) s.d.1989 paint mixed media paper prov. 27-Jun-4 Versailles Encheres #172/R est:800-1000

Works on paper

£909	$1563	€1300	Sans titre (107x87cm-42x34in) s.d.1992 verso mixed media canvas. 3-Dec-3 Tajan, Paris #468/R est:1500-2000

ISOE, Gustavo (1954-) Japanese

£2432	$4281	€3600	Untitled - Still life (70x92cm-28x36in) s. board painted 1993 exhib.lit. 18-May-4 Segre, Madrid #231/R est:3600

ISOLA, Giancarlo (1927-) Italian

£323	$594	€472	Fishing boats (49x100cm-19x39in) prov. 14-Jun-4 Waddingtons, Toronto #324/R (C.D 800)

ISOM, Graham (1945-) British

£300	$519	€438	Jockey racing (29x39cm-11x15in) s. 9-Dec-3 Bristol Auction Rooms #444
£380	$657	€555	Two jockeys racing neck to neck (29x39cm-11x15in) s. 9-Dec-3 Bristol Auction Rooms #445
£410	$709	€599	Hunting vignettes (49x67cm-19x26in) s. 9-Dec-3 Bristol Auction Rooms #443/R
£900	$1530	€1314	Queen Anne Stakes (51x61cm-20x24in) s. 27-Nov-3 Christie's, Kensington #182/R
£1300	$2210	€1898	On the scent (49x75cm-19x30in) s. 27-Nov-3 Christie's, Kensington #42/R est:700-900
£1700	$3128	€2482	Lowther stakes, York 1998 (51x66cm-20x26in) s. 10-Jun-4 Christie's, Kensington #208 est:1200-1800

Works on paper

£900	$1656	€1314	Fox, the hound and huntsman (51x67cm-20x26in) s. bodycol. 10-Jun-4 Christie's, Kensington #191/R

ISRAELS, Isaac (1865-1934) Dutch

£4000	$7200	€6000	En profile (32x24cm-13x9in) s. plywood prov. 21-Apr-4 Christie's, Amsterdam #128/R est:6000-8000
£4167	$7083	€6000	Friend of the artist in his studio, standing in front of a painting of a donkeyride (32x21cm-13x8in) s. panel. 28-Oct-3 Christie's, Amsterdam #180/R est:6000-8000
£15278	$25972	€22000	Selfportrait in the artist's studio. Young beauty (32x23cm-13x9in) s. panel double-sided. 28-Oct-3 Christie's, Amsterdam #179/R est:18000-24000
£19858	$33163	€28000	Portrait of a young woman (80x52cm-31x20in) s. prov.lit. 20-Oct-3 Glerum, Amsterdam #97/R est:30000-50000
£24306	$40590	€35000	Soldier with two children (51x27cm-20x11in) s.d.1881 panel prov. 21-Oct-3 Sotheby's, Amsterdam #231/R est:35000-45000
£24306	$40590	€35000	Portrait of an actress in a hat (154x101cm-61x40in) s. 21-Oct-3 Sotheby's, Amsterdam #250/R est:50000-80000
£25000	$41750	€36000	Reclining female nude (33x55cm-13x22in) s. 21-Oct-3 Sotheby's, Amsterdam #95/R est:25000-35000
£27778	$46389	€40000	In the artist's studio (51x60cm-20x24in) s. prov. 21-Oct-3 Sotheby's, Amsterdam #241/R est:40000-60000
£30000	$54000	€45000	Reclining girl looking at a print (15x24cm-6x9in) s. panel prov. 20-Apr-4 Sotheby's, Amsterdam #200/R est:20000-30000
£32000	$57600	€48000	Finishing touch (85x50cm-33x20in) s. painted c.1905 lit. 21-Apr-4 Christie's, Amsterdam #126/R est:40000-60000
£33333	$60000	€50000	Lady in a beach chair (50x60cm-20x24in) s. 20-Apr-4 Sotheby's, Amsterdam #233/R est:50000-70000
£45139	$76736	€65000	Dancing girl (101x66cm-40x26in) s. painted c.1920-1925 prov.exhib. 28-Oct-3 Christie's, Amsterdam #177/R est:70000-90000

£46667 $84000 €70000 Donkey ride (46x56cm-18x22in) s. board prov.lit. 20-Apr-4 Sotheby's, Amsterdam #204/R est:40000-60000
£48239 $80077 €68500 Amazone at Rotten Row (50x40cm-20x16in) s. prov. 12-Jun-3 Auction Maastricht #806/R
£48611 $81181 €70000 After the dance (71x91cm-28x36in) s. prov.lit. 21-Oct-3 Sotheby's, Amsterdam #211/R est:70000-90000
£59028 $98576 €85000 Reclining female nude reading (40x65cm-16x26in) s. prov.lit. 21-Oct-3 Sotheby's, Amsterdam #238/R est:40000-60000
£60000 $108000 €90000 At the fitting room, Paquin (78x56cm-31x22in) studio st. board on panel prov. 20-Apr-4 Sotheby's, Amsterdam #198/R est:70000-90000
£72917 $121771 €105000 Hyde Park, Rotten Row, London (64x76cm-25x30in) s. prov. 21-Oct-3 Sotheby's, Amsterdam #233/R est:120000-150000
£83333 $139167 €120000 Female nude reading on a bed (56x81cm-22x32in) s. prov.lit. 21-Oct-3 Sotheby's, Amsterdam #216/R est:100000-150000
£97222 $165278 €140000 Busy morning on a canal bridge, Amsterdam (90x105cm-35x41in) s. painted c.1894. 28-Oct-3 Christie's, Amsterdam #172/R est:150000-180000
£120000 $216000 €180000 Getting dressed for the show at the Scala Theatre, The Hague (101x76cm-40x30in) s. prov.exhib. 20-Apr-4 Sotheby's, Amsterdam #213/R est:150000-200000
£246667 $444000 €370000 Midinettes on the place Vendome, Paris (65x81cm-26x32in) s. prov.exhib.lit. 20-Apr-4 Sotheby's, Amsterdam #225/R est:250000-350000
Works on paper
£274 $466 €400 Two girls behind the wing of the stage (25x18cm-10x7in) studio st. pencil prov. 5-Nov-3 Vendue Huis, Gravenhage #399a
£676 $1189 €1000 Park landscape. View of the Marmorbat. Landscapes (13x21cm-5x8in) i. pencil two double-sided sheets lit. 19-May-4 Sotheby's, Amsterdam #346/R
£1489 $2487 €2100 Girl resting (75x43cm-30x17in) Indian ink. 20-Oct-3 Glerum, Amsterdam #98/R est:3000-4000
£2016 $3750 €2943 Sketch with three figures (44x53cm-17x21in) s. chl. 5-Mar-4 Skinner, Boston #417/R est:1500-2500
£2148 $3952 €3200 Visitors to monkey rock in Artis (25x33cm-10x13in) s. black chk. 29-Mar-4 Glerum, Amsterdam #55 est:1500-2000
£2416 $4446 €3600 Portrait of a lady (30x23cm-12x9in) black chk. 29-Mar-4 Glerum, Amsterdam #56 est:2500-3000
£2550 $4693 €3800 Square. Figure study (34x21cm-13x8in) s. black chk double-sided. 29-Mar-4 Glerum, Amsterdam #109 est:2000-2500
£2639 $4407 €3800 Egg market in Bern (29x37cm-11x15in) s. W/C. 21-Oct-3 Sotheby's, Amsterdam #135/R est:4000-6000
£3262 $5448 €4600 Men in a cafe. Card players (16x26cm-6x10in) s. chl double-sided. 20-Oct-3 Glerum, Amsterdam #225/R est:2500-3000
£4027 $7409 €6000 Self portrait with cigarette (30x22cm-12x9in) s. pencil. 29-Mar-4 Glerum, Amsterdam #59 est:3000-5000
£4762 $8524 €7000 In the Kraton, Solo (36x50cm-14x20in) s. W/C executed c.1920-21. 16-Mar-4 Christie's, Amsterdam #9/R est:6000-8000
£6250 $11313 €9500 Salesman with basket under his arm on the Viareggio Beach (49x37cm-19x15in) s. W/C. 19-Apr-4 Glerum, Amsterdam #186/R est:8000-12000
£8000 $14400 €12000 Gamalan player (34x50cm-13x20in) s. pencil W/C prov. 21-Apr-4 Christie's, Amsterdam #140/R est:12000-16000
£8389 $15436 €12500 Many figures in front of a podium with musicians (40x55cm-16x22in) studio st. W/C. 29-Mar-4 Glerum, Amsterdam #182 est:10000-15000
£13514 $23784 €20000 Girl sketching (48x35cm-19x14in) pastel prov.lit. 19-May-4 Sotheby's, Amsterdam #350/R est:40000-60000
£21333 $38400 €32000 Cafe Chantant (42x49cm-17x19in) s. pastel black chk exhib.lit. 20-Apr-4 Sotheby's, Amsterdam #98/R est:6000-8000
£26389 $44861 €38000 Hoedenatelier (49x37cm-19x15in) s. pastel prov.exhib. 28-Oct-3 Christie's, Amsterdam #182/R est:40000-60000

ISRAELS, J (1824-1911) Dutch
Works on paper
£1259 $2165 €1800 Children playing (20x14cm-8x6in) s. W/C. 4-Dec-3 Vendue Huis, Gravenhage #900
£1259 $2165 €1800 Children playing (20x14cm-8x6in) s. W/C. 3-Dec-3 Auction Maastricht #900/R est:2000-3500

ISRAELS, Josef (1824-1911) Dutch
£2333 $4200 €3500 Shipwrecked (35x47cm-14x19in) s. prov.exhib.lit. 21-Apr-4 Christie's, Amsterdam #97/R est:4000-6000
£2333 $4200 €3500 Terpsychore, muse of music and dance (32x27cm-13x11in) s. panel prov.exhib. 21-Apr-4 Christie's, Amsterdam #108/R est:4000-6000
£3125 $5219 €4500 Mother and her child returning home (40x29cm-16x11in) s. panel. 21-Oct-3 Sotheby's, Amsterdam #153/R est:5000-7000
£3500 $6020 €5110 Retour du marche (32x42cm-13x17in) s. board. 4-Dec-3 Christie's, Kensington #197/R est:3000-5000
£3819 $6378 €5500 At the window (38x27cm-15x11in) s. panel. 21-Oct-3 Sotheby's, Amsterdam #113/R est:6000-8000
£13333 $24000 €20000 Sick neighbour (101x130cm-40x51in) s. prov.exhib.lit. 21-Apr-4 Christie's, Amsterdam #102/R est:15000-20000
£13575 $22670 €19820 Girl knitting in the sand dunes looking out to sea (43x35cm-17x14in) s. panel. 17-Nov-3 Waddingtons, Toronto #177/R est:15000-20000 (C.D 30000)
£15294 $26000 €22329 Anxiously waiting (58x74cm-23x29in) s. prov. 29-Oct-3 Christie's, Rockefeller NY #10/R est:20000-30000
£19444 $33056 €28000 Les emigrants (79x132cm-31x52in) s. prov. 28-Oct-3 Christie's, Amsterdam #123/R est:35000-45000
£66667 $120000 €97334 Mother and children by the shore (91x132cm-36x52in) s. 23-Apr-4 Sotheby's, New York #32/R est:60000-80000
Works on paper
£380 $600 €551 Der Toweg (10x13cm-4x5in) s. chl dr. 27-Jul-3 Simpson's, Houston #163
£927 $1687 €1400 Fisherman's wife and child at the seaside (26x21cm-10x8in) s. ink pen. 18-Jun-4 Bolland & Marotz, Bremen #549/R
£1333 $2387 €2000 Woman sewing (50x33cm-20x13in) s. chk htd white board. 13-May-4 Bassenge, Berlin #5579/R est:3000
£3000 $5400 €4500 Patron at the orphanage (27x20cm-11x8in) s. pencil W/C htd white. 21-Apr-4 Christie's, Amsterdam #100/R est:2500-3500
£3200 $5760 €4800 Guiding the flock home (45x37cm-18x15in) s. black chk W/C prov.lit. 21-Apr-4 Christie's, Amsterdam #89/R est:3500-4500
£3667 $6600 €5500 Awaiting the fishermen's return (13x16cm-5x6in) s. W/C. 20-Apr-4 Sotheby's, Amsterdam #131/R est:2000-3000
£6956 $12798 €10156 Feeding the chickens (59x88cm-23x35in) s. gouache prov.exhib.lit. 14-Jun-4 Waddingtons, Toronto #217/R est:20000-25000 (C.D 17250)

ISRAELS, Josef (attrib) (1824-1911) Dutch
Works on paper
£1210 $2226 €1767 Burgomaster (46x30cm-18x12in) s. W/C prov. 14-Jun-4 Waddingtons, Toronto #215/R est:3000-5000 (C.D 3000)

ISSAIEV, Nicolas (1897-1977) French/Russian
£331 $596 €480 Paysage (54x64cm-21x25in) s. 25-Jan-4 Chayette & Cheval, Paris #209
£633 $1146 €950 Paysage (41x47cm-16x19in) s. i.verso cardboard. 5-Apr-4 Marie & Robert, Paris #84
£1060 $1928 €1600 Composition aux arches (57x44cm-22x17in) s. isorel. 16-Jun-4 Claude Boisgirard, Paris #75/R est:1200-1500
£2685 $4966 €4000 Composition (46x38cm-18x15in) s. isorel. 15-Mar-4 Claude Boisgirard, Paris #60 est:1100-1200
£3000 $5100 €4380 Still life with tulips in a blue vase (60x80cm-24x31in) s. 19-Nov-3 Sotheby's, London #119/R est:3000-5000

ISSELMANN, Dik (20th C) American?
£449 $750 €656 Still life with red lilies. 15-Nov-3 Harvey Clar, Oakland #1149

ISSUPOFF, Alessio (1889-1957) Russian
£704 $1218 €1000 Nude in green (24x14cm-9x6in) s. board. 11-Dec-3 Christie's, Rome #6
£800 $1472 €1200 Boy at table (20x20cm-8x8in) s. cardboard. 10-Jun-4 Christie's, Rome #196a
£1333 $2453 €2000 Caravane (14x25cm-6x10in) s. board. 8-Jun-4 Sotheby's, Milan #67/R est:2000-4000
£1408 $2437 €2000 Horse (18x33cm-7x13in) s. board. 10-Dec-3 Sotheby's, Milan #92/R est:2000-4000
£1678 $3138 €2500 Black horse and white horse (65x80cm-26x31in) 26-Feb-4 Cambi, Genoa #439/R est:2000-3000
£1690 $2924 €2400 Peasants women in the fields (30x50cm-12x20in) s. board. 11-Dec-3 Christie's, Rome #16/R est:2000-3000
£1972 $3411 €2800 Farmer and horse (30x50cm-12x20in) s. board. 11-Dec-3 Christie's, Rome #18/R est:2000-3000
£2098 $3608 €3000 Horse and riders in the snow (35x43cm-14x17in) s. cardboard. 3-Dec-3 Stadion, Trieste #1175/R est:2000-3000
£2667 $4907 €4000 Horses resting (25x33cm-10x13in) s. board. 8-Jun-4 Sotheby's, Milan #66/R est:4000-6000
£2848 $5325 €4300 Chevaux a l'abreuvoir (28x37cm-11x15in) s. panel. 20-Jul-4 Gioffredo, Nice #10/R
£5070 $8417 €7200 Il tombolo (75x95cm-30x37in) s. i.verso prov. 11-Jun-3 Christie's, Rome #188/R est:5000-8000
£9220 $15397 €13000 Winter landscape (104x76cm-41x30in) s. 14-Oct-3 Finarte Semenzato, Milan #186/R
£12676 $21042 €18000 Lilac (100x70cm-39x28in) s. lit. 11-Jun-3 Christie's, Rome #250/R est:11000-13000
£27778 $50000 €40556 Woman with a parrot (98x70cm-39x28in) s. 23-Apr-4 Sotheby's, New York #100/R est:40000-60000
£32000 $57280 €46720 Still life with lilacs (100x70cm-39x28in) s.d.1951. 26-May-4 Sotheby's, London #182/R est:25000-30000
£34000 $60860 €49640 Dance (60x79cm-24x31in) panel. 26-May-4 Sotheby's, London #199/R est:10000-15000
Works on paper
£734 $1248 €1050 Horse and stag (20x29cm-8x11in) s. ink. 19-Nov-3 Finarte Semenzato, Milan #539/R
£4829 $8500 €7050 View of the courtyard if Til-a-Kari Mosque, Samarkand (52x42cm-20x17in) s.d.1920 mixed media on board. 18-May-4 Bonhams & Butterfields, San Francisco #86/R est:3000-5000

ISSUPOFF, Alessio (attrib) (1889-1957) Russian
£284 $474 €400 Ussari sul Don (40x50cm-16x20in) s. 21-Jun-3 Stadion, Trieste #514/R
£4070 $7000 €5942 Festival Scene (66x79cm-26x31in) masonite. 7-Dec-3 Freeman, Philadelphia #33 est:1500-2500

ISTRATI, Alexandre (1915-1991) Rumanian
£265 $485 €400 Composition (55x46cm-22x18in) s. 7-Apr-4 Le Roux & Morel, Paris #8
£298 $545 €450 Composition verte et grise (16x27cm-6x11in) 7-Apr-4 Le Roux & Morel, Paris #6
£313 $564 €470 Composition (19x24cm-7x9in) s. s.verso. 25-Apr-4 Versailles Encheres #3
£322 $577 €480 Composition (29x19cm-11x7in) s.d.62 oil gouache. 27-May-4 Christie's, Paris #132/R
£331 $606 €500 Composition (27x35cm-11x14in) s.i. s.d.1991 verso. 7-Apr-4 Le Roux & Morel, Paris #5
£331 $606 €500 Composition (114x88cm-45x35in) 7-Apr-4 Le Roux & Morel, Paris #14
£331 $606 €500 Composition (60x60cm-24x24in) 7-Apr-4 Le Roux & Morel, Paris #10
£397 $727 €600 Composition (97x80cm-38x31in) s. s.verso. 7-Apr-4 Le Roux & Morel, Paris #15
£470 $841 €700 Echappe a toute description (50x61cm-20x24in) s. s.i.d.1961 verso prov.exhib. 27-May-4 Christie's, Paris #135/R
£497 $909 €750 Composition jaune et verte (38x46cm-15x18in) s. s.d.76 verso. 7-Apr-4 Le Roux & Morel, Paris #20/R
£552 $950 €806 Composition (59x72cm-23x28in) s. s.i.on stretcher prov. 3-Dec-3 Doyle, New York #77
£556 $928 €800 Composition (92x73cm-36x29in) s. s.d.1952 verso. 21-Oct-3 Artcurial Briest, Paris #421
£556 $928 €800 Tondo (99x99cm-39x39in) s.d.91 i.d.1961 verso oval prov. 21-Oct-3 Artcurial Briest, Paris #427
£556 $928 €800 Composition - rouge (65x54cm-26x21in) s. s.d.1965 verso. 21-Oct-3 Artcurial Briest, Paris #439
£596 $1091 €900 Composition (114x88cm-45x35in) 7-Apr-4 Le Roux & Morel, Paris #13
£596 $1091 €900 Composition (54x37cm-21x15in) d.1965 verso. 7-Apr-4 Le Roux & Morel, Paris #39/R
£599 $1000 €875 Untitled (56x46cm-22x18in) s. s.d.1957 verso. 25-Oct-3 Rachel Davis, Shaker Heights #576/R
£609 $1115 €920 Composition (33x41cm-13x16in) 7-Apr-4 Le Roux & Morel, Paris #7

£662	$1212	€1000	Composition rouge et jaune (46x55cm-18x22in) s. s.d.75. 7-Apr-4 Le Roux & Morel, Paris #18/R
£662	$1212	€1000	Composition (67x31cm-26x12in) mono.d.62 mono.verso canvas on panel. 7-Apr-4 Le Roux & Morel, Paris #38
£662	$1212	€1000	Composition blanche, noire et ocre (75x50cm-30x20in) s.d.60 canvas on panel. 7-Apr-4 Le Roux & Morel, Paris #41/R
£667	$1200	€1000	Composition (73x60cm-29x24in) s.d.1977 verso. 24-Apr-4 Cornette de St.Cyr, Paris #571
£728	$1333	€1100	Composition (146x114cm-57x45in) s. s.d.1988 verso. 7-Apr-4 Le Roux & Morel, Paris #16
£728	$1333	€1100	Composition polychrome (38x46cm-15x18in) s. s.d.68 verso. 7-Apr-4 Le Roux & Morel, Paris #30/R
£795	$1454	€1200	Composition rose (54x46cm-21x18in) s. s.d.56 verso. 7-Apr-4 Le Roux & Morel, Paris #19/R
£861	$1575	€1300	Composition geometrique (42x55cm-17x22in) s. d.52 verso exhib. 7-Apr-4 Le Roux & Morel, Paris #11
£872	$1500	€1273	Composition (92x73cm-36x29in) s. s.i.verso prov. 3-Dec-3 Doyle, New York #56/R est:1500-2500
£927	$1697	€1400	Composition (92x73cm-36x29in) s. s.d.88. 7-Apr-4 Le Roux & Morel, Paris #17/R
£927	$1697	€1400	Composition geometrique (61x49cm-24x19in) s. s.d.1951 verso. 7-Apr-4 Le Roux & Morel, Paris #33/R
£972	$1624	€1400	Composition bleu et jaune (81x65cm-32x26in) s.d.1951 verso. 21-Oct-3 Artcurial Briest, Paris #433 est:800-1200
£1060	$1939	€1600	Composition (91x73cm-36x29in) s.d.70 verso. 7-Apr-4 Le Roux & Morel, Paris #12 est:450-600
£1060	$1939	€1600	Composition sepia (46x38cm-18x15in) s. s.d.1965 verso. 7-Apr-4 Le Roux & Morel, Paris #37/R est:300-350
£1060	$1939	€1600	Composition bleue et grise (55x38cm-22x15in) s.d.52 s.d.verso. 7-Apr-4 Le Roux & Morel, Paris #34/R est:300-350
£1225	$2242	€1850	Composition geometrique (92x73cm-36x29in) s. s.d.1953 verso. 7-Apr-4 Le Roux & Morel, Paris #31 est:550-700
£1225	$2242	€1850	Composition (81x100cm-32x39in) s. s.d.1990 verso. 7-Apr-4 Le Roux & Morel, Paris #28/R est:550-700
£1319	$2203	€1900	Tropique du capricorne (116x73cm-46x29in) s.i.d.1961 verso prov. 21-Oct-3 Artcurial Briest, Paris #416/R est:2000-2500
£1319	$2203	€1900	Composition jaune et rose (73x92cm-29x36in) s. d.1952 verso. 21-Oct-3 Artcurial Briest, Paris #423 est:1000-1500
£1319	$2203	€1900	Composition (200x100cm-79x39in) s.d.1962. 21-Oct-3 Artcurial Briest, Paris #456 est:1500-2000
£1382	$2542	€2100	Composition (50x61cm-20x24in) s. s.i.d.1961 verso prov. 27-Jun-4 Versailles Encheres #62/R est:2000-3000
£1589	$2909	€2400	Composition (81x100cm-32x39in) s. s.d.90 verso. 7-Apr-4 Le Roux & Morel, Paris #27/R est:650-850
£1597	$2668	€2300	Espace vegetal (162x130cm-64x51in) s.d.61 s.i.d.1961 verso. 21-Oct-3 Artcurial Briest, Paris #453/R est:2500-3500
£1788	$3272	€2700	Composition geometrique (73x92cm-29x36in) s. s.d.1952 verso. 7-Apr-4 Le Roux & Morel, Paris #21/R est:550-700
£1788	$3272	€2700	Composition. s.d.59 exhib. 7-Apr-4 Le Roux & Morel, Paris #23/R est:950-1200
£1921	$3515	€2900	Composition geometrique (37x46cm-15x18in) s. 7-Apr-4 Le Roux & Morel, Paris #36/R est:300-350
£1944	$3247	€2800	Soleil (145x114cm-57x45in) s.d.1961 s.i.d.1961 verso prov.exhib.lit. 21-Oct-3 Artcurial Briest, Paris #447/R est:2500-3500
£1987	$3636	€3000	Composition (130x97cm-51x38in) s.d.1962. 7-Apr-4 Le Roux & Morel, Paris #22/R est:1500-2000
£2053	$3757	€3100	Composition geometrique (46x56cm-18x22in) s. s.d.48 verso. 7-Apr-4 Le Roux & Morel, Paris #35/R est:300-350
£2252	$4121	€3400	Composition geometrique (100x81cm-39x32in) s. d.1953 verso. 7-Apr-4 Le Roux & Morel, Paris #29/R est:550-700
£2292	$3827	€3300	Composition en vert (73x92cm-29x36in) s. s.i.d.1956 verso exhib. 21-Oct-3 Artcurial Briest, Paris #418/R est:2000-2500
£2583	$4726	€3900	Composition (89x115cm-35x45in) s. s.d.61 verso exhib. 7-Apr-4 Le Roux & Morel, Paris #26/R est:1500-2000
£2685	$4913	€4000	Composition (194x130cm-76x51in) s. s.d.1968 verso prov. 7-Jul-4 Artcurial Briest, Paris #280b est:4000-5000
£2917	$4871	€4200	Composition aux disques (140x112cm-55x44in) s.d.1948. 21-Oct-3 Artcurial Briest, Paris #443 est:2500-3000
£3179	$5817	€4800	Composition rouge (195x175cm-77x69in) s. s.d.1987 verso. 7-Apr-4 Le Roux & Morel, Paris #25/R est:2200-2700
£3642	$6666	€5500	Composition bleue (195x130cm-77x51in) s. d.1987 verso. 7-Apr-4 Le Roux & Morel, Paris #24/R est:1500-2000
Works on paper			
£397	$727	€600	Composition (45x34cm-18x13in) s. ink gouache. 7-Apr-4 Le Roux & Morel, Paris #9
£397	$727	€600	Composition (25x34cm-10x13in) s. gouache ink. 7-Apr-4 Le Roux & Morel, Paris #40

ISTVANFFY, Gabrielle Rainer (1877-1964) Hungarian

£405	$750	€591	Cat and kitten lapping milk (51x61cm-20x24in) s. 24-Jan-4 Jeffery Burchard, Florida #52/R
£420	$714	€613	Well deserved rest (30x41cm-12x16in) s. 6-Nov-3 Christie's, Kensington #911/R
£420	$794	€613	Stand off (21x27cm-8x11in) s. oil pencil col chk. 19-Feb-4 Christie's, Kensington #349/R
£550	$935	€803	Bedtime (50x70cm-20x28in) s. 6-Nov-3 Christie's, Kensington #915/R
£1351	$2419	€2000	Fluffy black dog (41x50cm-16x20in) s. 6-May-4 Michael Zeller, Lindau #828/R est:900
£1800	$3330	€2628	White cat (45x70cm-18x28in) s.d.1915. 14-Jul-4 Sotheby's, Olympia #238/R est:2000-3000
Works on paper			
£350	$641	€511	Sleeping papillon (19x30cm-7x12in) s. col chk oil on paper. 8-Apr-4 Christie's, Kensington #141/R
£403	$713	€600	Angora cat eyeing beetle (22x27cm-9x11in) s. gouache tempera mixed media. 28-Apr-4 Schopman, Hamburg #575/R

ITALIAANDER, Gisela (1936-) German

£1447	$2663	€2200	Sunflowers (100x100cm-39x39in) s.d.96. 25-Jun-4 Michael Zeller, Lindau #611/R

ITALIAN SCHOOL

£6648	$11700	€9706	Landscape with ruins and figures (27x44cm-11x17in) panel. 23-May-4 Agra, Warsaw #10/R (P.Z 47000)
£13000	$24050	€18980	Still life of vase of flowers (74x56cm-29x22in) 14-Jan-4 Brightwells, Leominster #905 est:3000-5000
Sculpture			
£5929	$10613	€8656	Bust of Julius Caesar (54cm-21in) marble after the antique prov. 15-May-4 Christie's, Sydney #455/R est:15000-20000 (A.D 15000)
£6993	$11888	€10000	Dancer (230cm-91in) green pat.bronze prov. 26-Nov-3 Dorotheum, Vienna #72/R est:12000-16000
£13423	$23758	€20000	Berlin Adorante (38cm-15in) pat bronze. 29-Apr-4 Sotheby's, Paris #113/R est:1200-1800

ITALIAN SCHOOL, 15th C

£5000	$9000	€7300	Lamentation (30x25cm-12x10in) tempera panel prov. 20-Apr-4 Sotheby's, Olympia #207/R est:4000-6000
£18519	$30000	€26853	Madonna and Child with Saints (48x37cm-19x15in) oil gold leaf on board. 8-Aug-3 Barridorf, Portland #124/R est:6000-9000

ITALIAN SCHOOL, 16th C

£5500	$10065	€8030	Portrait of Copernicus (101x79cm-40x31in) panel lit. 8-Jul-4 Sotheby's, London #193/R est:4000-6000
£6525	$10571	€9200	The Virgin and Infant in a landscape scene (51x37cm-20x15in) panel. 21-May-3 Artcurial Briest, Paris #278/R est:500-8000
£9955	$16923	€14534	Portrait of noblewoman (70x53cm-28x21in) 19-Nov-3 Fischer, Luzern #1009/R est:5000-7000 (S.FR 22000)
£10563	$18486	€15000	Madonna and Child and Saints (161x145cm-63x57in) board triptych. 17-Dec-3 Il Ponte, Milan #299/R est:18000-20000
£11650	$19806	€16660	Trick (95x128cm-37x50in) 1-Dec-3 Babuino, Rome #95/R est:10000-12000
£14789	$25880	€21000	Ascension (179x83cm-70x33in) board. 17-Dec-3 Il Ponte, Milan #264/R est:18000-22000
Sculpture			
£5689	$9500	€8306	Pacing bull (13cm-5in) pat bronze. 18-Oct-3 Sotheby's, New York #80/R est:7000-9000
£6587	$11000	€9617	Antinous (27cm-11in) pat bronze. 18-Oct-3 Sotheby's, New York #68/R est:4000-6000
£17365	$29000	€25353	Venus (19cm-7in) pat bronze. 18-Oct-3 Sotheby's, New York #66/R est:4000-6000
Works on paper			
£4261	$7500	€6221	Hades passing in his chariot while Persephone picks flowers (19x46cm-7x18in) ink wash chl squared transfer. 18-May-4 Sotheby's, New York #98/R est:5000-7000

ITALIAN SCHOOL, 16th/17th C

£3889	$7000	€5678	Portrait of Andrea del Sarto, seated drawing (183x140cm-72x55in) lit. 23-Jan-4 Christie's, Rockefeller NY #104/R est:20000-30000
£5333	$9707	€8000	Maria with Child and Infant St John (122x95cm-48x37in) panel. 30-Jun-4 Neumeister, Munich #461/R est:6000
£14000	$25060	€21000	Samson victorieux (125x92cm-49x36in) 16-May-4 Joron-Derem, Paris #39/R est:20000-25000
Works on paper			
£10556	$19000	€15412	Perseus and Andromeda (25x17cm-10x7in) i. bodycol. 23-Jan-4 Christie's, Rockefeller NY #183/R est:20000-30000

ITALIAN SCHOOL, 17th C

£2778	$5000	€4056	Assumption of the Virgin (15x11cm-6x4in) oil on alabaster oval. 23-Jan-4 Christie's, Rockefeller NY #190/R est:3000-5000
£3846	$6538	€5615	St Sebastian (65x828cm-26x326in) 19-Nov-3 Fischer, Luzern #1017/R est:5000-7000 (S.FR 8500)
£4861	$8264	€7000	Holy Family in Nazareth (97x110cm-38x43in) 29-Oct-3 Il Ponte, Milan #712/R
£4895	$8175	€7000	La rencontre d'Eliezer et de Rebecca (71x62cm-28x24in) 26-Jun-3 Artcurial Briest, Paris #467 est:4000-6000
£5000	$8950	€7500	Big still life (88x118cm-35x46in) 12-May-4 Stadion, Trieste #594/R est:7000-8000
£5028	$9000	€7341	Esther before King Ahasuerus (116x150cm-46x59in) 14-May-4 Skinner, Boston #8/R est:800-1200
£5240	$9537	€7650	Madonna before Mount Carmel with the Holy Child (113x161cm-44x63in) mono. 16-Jun-4 Fischer, Luzern #1020/R est:12000-15000 (S.FR 12000)
£5442	$9741	€8000	Perseus and Andromeda (42x31cm-17x12in) i. verso. 17-Mar-4 Neumeister, Munich #354/R est:2300
£5667	$10257	€8500	Jephte comeback (142x205cm-56x81in) 30-Mar-4 Babuino, Rome #47/R est:8000
£5727	$9736	€8361	Caritas with two boys (86x67cm-34x26in) 5-Nov-3 Dobiaschofsky, Bern #667/R est:15000 (S.FR 13000)
£5986	$9577	€8500	Proserpina kidnapped (183x277cm-72x109in) 21-Sep-3 Finarte, Venice #7/R
£6335	$10136	€9249	Holy Family (23x19cm-9x7in) panel. 19-Sep-3 Koller, Zurich #3053/R est:5000-7000 (S.FR 14000)
£7391	$13230	€10791	Still life of fruit (70x54cm-28x21in) 26-May-4 AB Stockholms Auktionsverk #2515/R est:30000-40000 (S.KR 100000)
£7761	$13891	€11331	Teseus fight with the Amazones (128x177cm-50x70in) 25-May-4 Bukowskis, Stockholm #443/R est:80000-100000 (S.KR 105000)
£8054	$14819	€12000	Peter's denial (95x132cm-37x52in) canvas on board. 24-Mar-4 Finarte Semenzato, Rome #172/R est:14000
£9050	$15385	€13213	Daedalus and Icarus (74x93cm-29x37in) prov. 19-Nov-3 Fischer, Luzern #1019/R est:3000-4000 (S.FR 20000)
£9375	$15937	€13500	Baskets of flowers (47x63cm-19x25in) pair. 28-Oct-3 Il Ponte, Milan #322/R
£10360	$17820	€15126	River landscape with hunters and dogs (61x88cm-24x35in) oval. 8-Dec-3 Philippe Schuler, Zurich #3416/R est:12000-16000 (S.FR 23000)
£10596	$19285	€16000	Portrait d'Emmanuel de Rohan (104x78cm-41x31in) 21-Jun-4 Tajan, Paris #17/R est:6000-8000
£10811	$19351	€16000	Mary with child (141x118cm-56x46in) 8-May-4 Schloss Ahlden, Ahlden #668/R est:16500
£11921	$21815	€18000	Loth et ses filles (115x148cm-45x58in) 7-Apr-4 Libert, Castor, Paris #7/R est:6000-8000
£12081	$22228	€18000	Still life with musical instruments and hour glass (82x130cm-32x51in) prov. 24-Mar-4 Dorotheum, Vienna #73/R est:18000-25000
£13158	$24211	€20000	Battle on the bridge (129x204cm-51x80in) lit. 22-Jun-4 Babuino, Rome #40/R est:6000-8000
£14912	$24904	€21772	Venus and Cupid (120x93cm-47x37in) prov. 15-Nov-3 Galerie Gloggner, Luzern #71/R est:20000-25000 (S.FR 34000)
£15232	$27722	€23000	Titus (131x106cm-52x42in) 15-Jun-4 Claude Aguttes, Neuilly #11/R est:10000-15000

£16892	$30236	€25000	Mary with Jesus and Infant St John (45x34cm-18x13in) board. 8-May-4 Dawo, Saarbrucken #1/R est:1800
£19000	$34010	€28500	Still lives of flowers (79x101cm-31x40in) pair. 16-May-4 Joron-Derem, Paris #136/R est:30000
£22222	$40000	€32444	Stills lifes of lilies and other flowers in a vase (65x48cm-26x19in) pair. 22-Jan-4 Sotheby's, New York #222/R est:30000-40000
£37572	$65000	€54855	Cardsharps (104x176cm-41x69in) 13-Dec-3 Weschler, Washington #508 est:2000-3000
£57047	$104966	€85000	St George (139x110cm-55x43in) prov. 25-Mar-4 Dr Fritz Nagel, Stuttgart #641/R est:7000
£210526	$387368	€320000	Allegory of the Five Senses (71x125cm-28x49in) s.d.1634. 24-Jun-4 Christie's, Paris #53/R est:20000-30000
Sculpture			
£5319	$8883	€7500	Roman emperor (85cm-33in) marble prov. 15-Oct-3 Sotheby's, Paris #220/R
£6000	$10380	€8760	Hercules (60cm-24in) brown pat. bronze lit. 11-Dec-3 Christie's, London #52/R est:8000-12000
£7000	$12110	€10220	Pan and syrinx (39cm-15in) hall mark silver lit. 12-Dec-3 Sotheby's, London #196/R est:10000-15000
£15000	$25950	€21900	Reclining putto allegorical of sleep (35x73x43cm-14x29x17in) white marble lit. 12-Dec-3 Sotheby's, London #212/R est:20000-30000
£15000	$25950	€21900	Baptism of Christ (61cm-24in) giltwood base lit. 12-Dec-3 Sotheby's, London #217/R est:15000-20000
£16901	$29239	€24000	Saint George. Saint Paul (33x26cm-13x10in) bronze marble base pair lit. 15-Dec-3 Sotheby's, Paris #42/R est:25000-40000
£22000	$38060	€32120	Reclining putto allegorical of dawn (30x72x60cm-12x28x24in) white marble. 12-Dec-3 Sotheby's, London #211/R est:20000-30000
Works on paper			
£9155	$15838	€13000	St Agatha (25x20cm-10x8in) ochre chk htd white. 11-Dec-3 Dr Fritz Nagel, Stuttgart #363/R est:200

ITALIAN SCHOOL, 17th/18th C

£4469	$8000	€6525	Formal floral stil life with tulips, carnations and morning glories (64x110cm-25x43in) 14-May-4 Skinner, Boston #1/R est:2500-3500
£6608	$11233	€9648	Fall of the phaeton (44x31cm-17x12in) panel. 5-Nov-3 Dobiaschofsky, Bern #668/R est:6000 (S.FR 15000)
£6780	$12000	€9899	Madonna and Child (69x53cm-27x21in) panel prov. 2-May-4 Van Blarcom, South Natick #57
£11231	$20889	€16397	View of Rome seen from the Tiber (33x64cm-13x25in) 2-Mar-4 Rasmussen, Copenhagen #1292/R est:50000 (D.KR 125000)
£18156	$32500	€26508	Portrait of bewigged gentleman holding a ring, said to be the wedding portrait of Jacob Carvalho (206x188cm-81x74in) prov.exhib.lit. 18-Mar-4 Sotheby's, New York #245/R est:50000-70000
£18341	$33380	€26778	Flowers in an urn with a parrot, a monkey and a squirrel (118x160cm-46x63in) 16-Jun-4 Fischer, Luzern #1047/R est:35000-40000 (S.FR 42000)
£37162	$66520	€55000	Allegory of Autumn (200x170cm-79x67in) prov. 8-May-4 Hans Stahl, Toestorf #103/R est:7000
Sculpture			
£3892	$6500	€5682	Saint Jerome (35cm-14in) bronze prov. 18-Oct-3 Sotheby's, New York #65/R est:2500-4500
£20423	$35740	€29000	Jeune maure (54x48cm-21x19in) black marble prov. 17-Dec-3 Tajan, Paris #74/R est:35000-50000
£68056	$115694	€98000	Coppia di putti. white marble pair. 28-Oct-3 Della Rocca, Turin #351/R est:15000-18000
Miniatures			
£6200	$11098	€9052	Francesco, King of the two Sicilies, in white coat yellow collar (6cm-2in circular) gilt metal mount rectangular wood frame. 25-May-4 Christie's, London #122/R est:600-800

ITALIAN SCHOOL, 18th C

£3476	$6500	€5214	Capriccio of classical ruins with figures (91x74cm-36x29in) 25-Jul-4 Bonhams & Butterfields, San Francisco #6003/R est:3000-5000
£4444	$8000	€6488	Hunters resting in a forest with an extensive landscape (107x177cm-42x70in) 21-Jan-4 Sotheby's, New York #140/R est:3000-5000
£4802	$8500	€7011	City landscape scene with classical ruins, figures and livestock (71x94cm-28x37in) 2-May-4 Van Blarcom, South Natick #68
£5071	$8873	€7200	Nature morte au bouquet de fleurs, lievre, fruits et oiseaux (124x99cm-49x39in) 16-Dec-3 Artcurial Briest, Paris #220/R est:8000-10000
£5400	$9180	€7884	Town scene with figures (23x30cm-9x12in) 29-Oct-3 Mallams, Oxford #692/R est:600-800
£5495	$10000	€8023	Capriccio view of a walled garden with elegant figures (113x143cm-44x56in) 4-Feb-4 Christie's, Rockefeller NY #82/R est:3000-5000
£5594	$9510	€8000	Portrait de femme au masque de carnaval (79x61cm-31x24in) 20-Nov-3 Gioffredo, Nice #182
£5938	$9500	€8669	Capriccio (69x97cm-27x38in) 20-Sep-3 New Orleans Auction, New Orleans #219/R
£5944	$9927	€8500	Roasted chestnuts (15x20cm-6x8in) board. 7-Oct-3 Pandolfini, Florence #482 est:1500-1800
£6000	$10200	€8760	Still lifes with various flowers in vases (57x43cm-22x17in) pair. 30-Oct-3 Sotheby's, Olympia #131/R est:3000-5000
£6338	$11092	€9000	Buildings (109x167cm-43x66in) 16-Dec-3 Durán, Madrid #178/R est:9000
£6500	$11050	€9490	Classical palace with a fountain and duck pond. Classical palace with an ornamental rose garden (102x128cm-40x50in) pair. 30-Oct-3 Sotheby's, Olympia #154/R est:4000-6000
£6690	$11574	€9500	Still life with grapes and fruit. Still life with grapes, flowers and bird (48x70cm-19x28in) pair. 11-Dec-3 Dr Fritz Nagel, Stuttgart #426/R est:5800
£7639	$12069	€11000	Kitchen still life (150x191cm-59x75in) 19-Sep-3 Schloss Ahlden, Ahlden #1421/R est:12500
£7800	$14274	€11388	Bacchanalian scene with naked figures an a classical landscape (36x48cm-14x19in) 28-Jul-4 Mallams, Oxford #252/R est:700-900
£7801	$13028	€11000	Il Parnaso (68x83cm-27x33in) 18-Jun-3 Christie's, Rome #447/R est:4000-6000
£8333	$13583	€12000	Still life of pomegranates, figs, flowers and guinea pig (51x101cm-20x40in) 25-Sep-3 Dr Fritz Nagel, Stuttgart #1261/R est:15000
£8681	$14323	€12500	Still life with flowers and fruit (91x117cm-36x46in) 2-Jul-3 Neumeister, Munich #55/R est:3000
£9200	$15364	€13432	Holy Family (87x69cm-34x27in) panel. 11-Nov-3 Bonhams, Knightsbridge #240/R est:800-1200
£9502	$16154	€13873	Saint Hieronymus (56x47cm-22x19in) i. 19-Nov-3 Fischer, Luzern #2155/R est:1800-2500 (S.FR 21000)
£10000	$18000	€14600	Capriccio view of the Tiber, with the Castel Sant'Angelo (119x123cm-47x48in) 23-Apr-4 Christie's, Kensington #259/R est:6000-8000
£10067	$18523	€15000	Izaac's sacrifice (108x83cm-43x33in) 24-Mar-4 Finarte Semenzato, Rome #199/R est:3000
£10526	$17579	€15368	River landscape with figures (55x73cm-22x29in) canvas on panel prov. 15-Nov-3 Galerie Gloggner, Luzern #73/R est:1800-2500 (S.FR 24000)
£11806	$19479	€17000	Madonna with child (60x45cm-24x18in) 2-Jul-3 Neumeister, Munich #554/R est:2000
£13889	$22639	€20000	Still life with flowers and pheasant (183x136cm-72x54in) pair. 25-Sep-3 Dr Fritz Nagel, Stuttgart #1264/R est:40000
£14480	$24181	€21141	Portrait of a Turk (43x36cm-17x14in) 17-Nov-3 Waddingtons, Toronto #273/R est:4000-6000 (C.D 32000)
£27397	$46575	€40000	Still life of flowers and fruit (63x116cm-25x46in) lit. 7-Nov-3 Farsetti, Prato #548/R est:30000-35000
£58000	$105560	€84680	View of Constantinople from the east (73x174cm-29x69in) i. 15-Jun-4 Sotheby's, London #149a/R est:40000-60000
£62000	$112840	€90520	Panoramic view of Constantinople from the north (73x174cm-29x69in) i. 15-Jun-4 Sotheby's, London #149/R est:40000-60000
Sculpture			
£5000	$9200	€7300	Bust of Socrates (53cm-21in) marble socle after the Antique prov. 10-Jun-4 Christie's, London #174/R est:3000-5000
£5479	$9315	€8000	Putto (70cm-28in) bronze. 8-Nov-3 Finarte, Venice #151/R est:9000-14000
£5944	$9926	€8500	Philisopher (62x38x25cm-24x15x10in) brown pat bronze col marble socle. 24-Jun-3 Christie's, Paris #412/R est:7000-10000
£7500	$13500	€10950	Rape of Europa (9x14cm-4x6in) tortoiseshell relief ivory veneered panel four sections prov. 21-Apr-4 Sotheby's, London #19/R est:4000-6000
£7647	$13000	€11165	Busts of emperors (43cm-17in) bronze pair prov. 25-Nov-3 Christie's, Rockefeller NY #76/R est:5000-8000
£10490	$18042	€15000	Homme en priere, Saint Jerome (43cm-17in) terracotta. 8-Dec-3 Horta, Bruxelles #83 est:5000-7000
£10563	$18486	€15000	Diana (89cm-35in) marble. 16-Dec-3 Christie's, Paris #209/R est:15000-25000
£11377	$19000	€16610	Moors (75cm-30in) bronze pair. 18-Oct-3 Sotheby's, New York #40/R est:7000-9000
£11921	$21696	€18000	Venus. Meleagre (54cm-21in) bronze marble base pair prov. 16-Jun-4 Tajan, Paris #167/R est:9000-12000
£11921	$21695	€18000	Women (113cm-44in) carved painted wood pair. 15-Jun-4 Sotheby's, Milan #28/R est:1800-25000
£14000	$25760	€20440	Bust of Julius Caesar (98cm-39in) porphyry marble socle after the Antique. 10-Jun-4 Christie's, London #72/R est:5000-8000
£16000	$29440	€23360	Equestrian group of Marcus Aurelius (59cm-23in) i. green brown pat bronze white marble pedestal after the Antique. 10-Jun-4 Christie's, London #150/R est:20000-30000
£16892	$29730	€25000	Hercules Farnese (42cm-17in) bronze lit.prov. 22-May-4 Lempertz, Koln #1210/R est:10500
£18310	$32042	€26000	Proserpine (90cm-35in) marble. 16-Dec-3 Christie's, Paris #208/R est:15000-25000
£42000	$77280	€61320	Rape of the Sabines (88x122cm-35x48in) marble relief probably Venetian prov.lit. 10-Jun-4 Christie's, London #74/R est:40000-60000
£180000	$311400	€262800	Sleeping Venus (55x32x23cm-22x13x9in) marble possibly Florentine Grand Ducal workshop lit. 11-Dec-3 Christie's, London #103/R est:70000-100000
Miniatures			
£19000	$34010	€27740	Prince Carlo Felice of Savoy and his brother Prince Giuseppe Placido, as young boys (6cm-2in) gilt metal mount. 25-May-4 Christie's, London #76/R est:2000-3000

ITALIAN SCHOOL, 18th/19th C

£7895	$14526	€12000	Diana the Huntress with dogs and landscape beyond (61x81cm-24x32in) 22-Jun-4 Mealy's, Castlecomer #786/R est:3000-4000
£15000	$27000	€21900	The three fates, Clotho, Atropos and Lachesis (121x211cm-48x83in) 21-Apr-4 Tennants, Leyburn #1083/R est:1800-2500
Sculpture			
£6711	$12550	€10000	Young woman (110cm-43in) silver. 29-Feb-4 Finarte, Venice #162/R est:8000-12000
Works on paper			
£6674	$12280	€10011	Allegorical depiction of the many facets of life and history within the Roman Empire (48x86cm-19x34in) W/C. 23-Mar-4 American Auctioneer #453750/R

ITALIAN SCHOOL, 19th C

£3889	$7000	€5678	On the Mediterranean (71x99cm-28x39in) 24-Apr-4 Weschler, Washington #580/R est:5000-7000
£4362	$8027	€6500	Still life of fruit with dead game (147x186cm-58x73in) 24-Mar-4 Finarte Semenzato, Rome #191/R est:7000
£4698	$8785	€7000	View of the Coliseum (137x239cm-54x94in) 28-Feb-4 Finarte, Venice #205/R est:6000-8000
£5667	$10257	€8500	Portrait of young Sanvitale (150x98cm-59x39in) 31-Mar-4 Finarte Semenzato, Milan #555/R est:4000-5000
£6667	$11933	€10000	Alexander and Diogenes (175x236cm-69x93in) 17-May-4 Finarte Semenzato, Rome #91/R est:12000-14000
£7801	$13028	€11000	Giunone. Venere. Cerere. Galatea (40x30cm-16x12in) four. 18-Jun-3 Christie's, Rome #386 est:3000-4000
£7955	$14000	€11614	View of St. Peter's Square, Rome (71x94cm-28x37in) prov. 18-May-4 Bonhams & Butterfields, San Francisco #51/R est:12000-20000
£8333	$14917	€12500	View of Campo Vaccino (119x98cm-47x39in) 17-May-4 Finarte Semenzato, Rome #105/R est:10000-12000
£8667	$15773	€13000	Jupiter room in the Palazzo Pitti, Florence (65x75cm-26x30in) one of pair. 30-Jun-4 Neumeister, Munich #580/R est:3500
£9333	$16987	€14000	Mars room in the Palazzo Pitti, Florence (65x76cm-26x30in) bears sig. one of pair. 30-Jun-4 Neumeister, Munich #579/R est:3500
£12184	$20956	€17789	Prospect views of Pompeii (18x23cm-7x9in) cardboard 22 prov. 2-Dec-3 Kunsthallen, Copenhagen #542/R est:15000 (D.KR 130000)
£16260	$29106	€23740	Riva Degli Sciavoni in Venice (46x68cm-18x27in) bears mono. 25-May-4 Bukowskis, Stockholm #530/R est:30000-40000 (S.KR 220000)
£18403	$31285	€26500	Grand Canal (70x90cm-28x35in) 28-Oct-3 Il Ponte, Milan #308/R
£34483	$57586	€50000	View of San Pietro, Rome (25x46cm-10x18in) 12-Nov-3 Sotheby's, Milan #177/R est:20000-30000
£45000	$75150	€65700	Panoramic view of Constantinople (28x275cm-11x108in) i. oil on paper prov. 14-Oct-3 Sotheby's, London #21/R est:50000-70000
Sculpture			
£5479	$9315	€8000	Winged putto (80x48x43cm-31x19x17in) marble. 8-Nov-3 Finarte, Venice #217/R est:9000-12000

£5705	$10097	€8500	Minerve Giustiniani (47cm-19in) pat bronze lit. 29-Apr-4 Sotheby's, Paris #150/R est:2000-3000
£5944	$10224	€8500	Bust of Seneca (81cm-32in) white col marble wooden column white marble base. 2-Dec-3 Christie's, Paris #2/R est:6000-9000
£6164	$10479	€9000	Diana after the bath (135cm-53in) marble. 4-Nov-3 Ansorena, Madrid #798/R est:9000
£6335	$10136	€9249	Venus and Cupid (108cm-43in) marble prov. 19-Sep-3 Koller, Zurich #1195/R est:12000-18000 (S.FR 14000)
£6667	$11933	€10000	Venere de' Medici (110cm-43in) white marble. 17-May-4 Finarte Semenzato, Rome #194/R est:10000-12000
£6711	$11879	€10000	Mercurius seated (51cm-20in) bears sig pat bronze. 29-Apr-4 Sotheby's, Paris #16/R est:6000-8000
£8145	$13032	€11892	Pauline Borghese (79x126cm-31x50in) marble lit. 19-Sep-3 Koller, Zurich #1251/R est:18000-28000 (S.FR 18000)
£9655	$16028	€14000	Putti in concert (63x90cm-25x35in) white marble. 1-Oct-3 Della Rocca, Turin #76/R
£10333	$18807	€15500	Neo-classical figures (230cm-91in) pat bronze pair. 4-Jul-4 Finarte, Venice #39/R est:2500-3500
£12000	$21480	€18000	Caesar Augustus (134cm-53in) white marble sold with base. 17-May-4 Finarte Semenzato, Rome #871/R est:18000-20000
£13333	$24000	€19466	Surmounted by Venus, allegorical figures, and dancing mermaids (100cm-39in) bronze fountain marble plinth. 23-Apr-4 Christie's, Rockefeller NY #89/R est:15000-25000
£13333	$24000	€19466	Bust of Marcus Aurelius (200cm-79in) marble rouge marble pedestal prov. 23-Apr-4 Christie's, Rockefeller NY #170/R est:8000-12000
£20000	$36800	€29200	Figure of Thetis pouring water from a jug (192cm-76in) marble base wood pedestal prov. 10-Jun-4 Christie's, London #171/R est:10000-15000
£23154	$42372	€34500	Bust of noble man (66x70cm-26x28in) marble. 6-Jul-4 Marc Kohn, Paris #52/R
£27000	$49680	€39420	Leda and the swan (169x157cm-67x62in) marble plinth wood pedestal prov. 10-Jun-4 Christie's, London #170/R est:20000-30000
£59441	$101049	€85000	Vittoria della Rovere. Marie-Madeleine of Austria (95x90cm-37x35in) white marble pair. 24-Nov-3 Marc Kohn, Paris #20/R
£91867	$152500	€134126	Amore and Psyche (170x58x91cm-67x23x36in) s.i.d.1887 base carrara marble. 4-Oct-3 Neal Auction Company, New Orleans #282/R est:50000-75000

ITALIAN SCHOOL, 19th/20th C

Sculpture

£5556	$10000	€8112	Figure of Hebe (160cm-63in) white marble square base after Bertel Thorvaldsen. 23-Apr-4 Christie's, Rockefeller NY #3/R est:8000-12000
£5556	$10000	€8112	Seated girl playing a lute (153cm-60in) s. alabaster pedestal. 23-Apr-4 Christie's, Rockefeller NY #101/R est:5000-7000
£5882	$10000	€8588	Female bather (109cm-43in) marble. 28-Oct-3 Christie's, Rockefeller NY #100/R
£8075	$13000	€11790	Blackamoor term figure (229cm-90in) polychrome. 14-Jan-4 Christie's, Rockefeller NY #321/R est:10000-15000
£21111	$38000	€30822	Cupid and Psyche (218cm-86in) s. alabaster verde antico marble pedestal. 23-Apr-4 Christie's, Rockefeller NY #106/R est:20000-30000

ITALIAN SCHOOL, 20th C

£6667	$12267	€10000	Praying at sunset (99x150cm-39x59in) bears sig. 8-Jun-4 Sotheby's, Milan #93/R est:10000-15000

Sculpture

£8725	$15443	€13000	Cleopatra (59x82cm-23x32in) marble lit. 29-Apr-4 Sotheby's, Paris #140/R est:12000-16000

ITALIANER, Flory (1938-) ?

Sculpture

£1159	$1901	€1600	Nude squatter (30cm-12in) bronze one of one. 27-May-3 Sotheby's, Amsterdam #526/R est:1500-2000

ITATANI, Michiko (1948-) American

£383	$700	€559	Untitled (213x213cm-84x84in) acrylic. 10-Jul-4 Hindman, Chicago #242/R

ITAYA, Foussa (1919-) French

£302	$553	€450	Jeune fille au chien (27x23cm-11x9in) s.i. 7-Jul-4 Artcurial Briest, Paris #64a
£479	$800	€699	La cite (71x91cm-28x36in) s.d.1960. 29-Jun-3 William Jenack, New York #413

ITEN, Hans (1874-1930) Swiss/British

£750	$1320	€1095	Ploughed field, Bevoir Park (15x21cm-6x8in) s. board. 19-May-4 Sotheby's, Olympia #114/R
£2100	$3843	€3066	Co. Down Coast (25x35cm-10x14in) s. board. 2-Jun-4 John Ross, Belfast #56 est:1400-1600
£2587	$4399	€3700	Marigolds (61x46cm-24x18in) s. exhib. 25-Nov-3 De Veres Art Auctions, Dublin #187/R est:3500-5000
£2600	$4472	€3796	Pond in Belvoir Park (15x20cm-6x8in) s. board. 3-Dec-3 John Ross, Belfast #21a
£2797	$4755	€4000	St. Remy (33x41cm-13x16in) s. board exhib. 25-Nov-3 De Veres Art Auctions, Dublin #151/R est:4000-6000
£3497	$5944	€5000	Carnations (42x34cm-17x13in) s.d.1909 canvas on board prov. 18-Nov-3 Whyte's, Dublin #49/R est:3000-5000
£3800	$6954	€5548	Bluebell wood at Holywood (40x30cm-16x12in) s. board. 2-Jun-4 John Ross, Belfast #36 est:3000-3500
£4500	$7380	€6570	Fair Head (48x66cm-19x26in) s. board. 4-Jun-3 John Ross, Belfast #150a
£5600	$10416	€8176	Still life, roses (50x76cm-20x30in) s.d.1905. 3-Mar-4 John Ross, Belfast #122 est:5000-7000
£6200	$11346	€9052	Picking bluebells, Belvoir Park (30x40cm-12x16in) s. board. 2-Jun-4 John Ross, Belfast #149 est:2000-3000
£18000	$32220	€26280	Rhododendrons in a lustre bowl (51x66cm-20x26in) s. 13-May-4 Sotheby's, London #94/R est:8000-12000

ITO, Shinsui (1898-1972) Japanese

Prints

£1912	$3500	€2792	Shato no yuki - snow at a shrine. s.i.d.1930 print. 6-Apr-4 Bonhams & Butterfields, San Francisco #3090/R est:1000-1500
£2049	$3750	€2992	Katada ukimido (32x21cm-13x8in) s.i.d.May 1918 print. 6-Apr-4 Bonhams & Butterfields, San Francisco #3089/R est:2000-3000
£4372	$8000	€6383	Fubaki - snowstorm. s.i.d.December 1932 print. 6-Apr-4 Bonhams & Butterfields, San Francisco #3091/R est:1400-2000

Works on paper

£600	$1098	€876	Beauty and a clock. Blue kimono with orange obi. s. W/C two. 7-Apr-4 Sotheby's, Olympia #26/R

ITRUNRTES, Fred Y (?) ?

£379	$702	€550	Cows in landscape (50x75cm-20x30in) s. 12-Feb-4 Weidler, Nurnberg #6646

ITTEN, Johannes (1888-1967) Swiss

Works on paper

£350	$601	€500	Composition (29x21cm-11x8in) pencil. 4-Dec-3 Van Ham, Cologne #239/R
£459	$766	€666	Child with school book (25x26cm-10x10in) pencil. 19-Jun-3 Kornfeld, Bern #491 est:1000 (S.FR 1000)
£2067	$3699	€3100	I is joy (29x21cm-11x8in) i. pencil col chk prov. 14-May-4 Ketterer, Munich #387/R est:2500-3000

ITTENBACH, Franz (1813-1879) German

£1325	$2411	€2000	Mary being taken into heaven (28x14cm-11x6in) s.d.1860. 17-Jun-4 Frank Peege, Freiburg #1106/R est:800

Works on paper

£507	$892	€750	Madonna with child holding book (29x23cm-11x9in) pencil prov. 22-May-4 Lempertz, Koln #1422/R

ITTMAN, Hans (1914-) Dutch

£2303	$4237	€3500	Abstract composition (90x100cm-35x39in) s. 28-Jun-4 Sotheby's, Amsterdam #190/R est:2000-3000

ITURRIA, Ignacio de (1949-) Uruguayan

£739	$1300	€1079	Table (23x28cm-9x11in) s.d.92. 5-Jan-4 Galeria y Remates, Montevideo #26/R
£941	$1600	€1374	Grandmother (21x28cm-8x11in) s.d.82. 25-Nov-3 Galeria y Remates, Montevideo #27/R
£1193	$2100	€1742	Soldier and stag (20x30cm-8x12in) s.verso. 5-Jan-4 Galeria y Remates, Montevideo #25/R est:2500-3500
£1294	$2200	€1889	Harbour workers (28x35cm-11x14in) s.d.82. 25-Nov-3 Galeria y Remates, Montevideo #28/R
£1359	$2500	€1984	Rural landscape (13x52cm-5x20in) s.d.82 board. 22-Jun-4 Galeria y Remates, Montevideo #90/R est:2500-3000
£2045	$3600	€2986	Untitled (30x24cm-12x9in) s.d.93 cardboard on canvas. 5-Jan-4 Galeria y Remates, Montevideo #24/R est:3000-4000
£2045	$3600	€2986	Cadaques, Spain (46x38cm-18x15in) s.d.80. 5-Jan-4 Galeria y Remates, Montevideo #23/R est:3500-4000
£2610	$4750	€3811	Watering hole with horse and swimmers. Composition with circus performers (48x63cm-19x25in) s. oil paper pair. 29-Jun-4 Sotheby's, New York #673/R est:3000-5000
£2646	$5000	€3863	Cadaques (73x60cm-29x24in) s.d.91. 22-Feb-4 Galeria y Remates, Montevideo #117/R est:8000
£3054	$5100	€4459	Rural landscape with cows (60x73cm-24x29in) s.d.89. 7-Oct-3 Galeria y Remates, Montevideo #105/R est:5500
£3059	$5200	€4466	Angler (132x100cm-52x39in) s.d.81. 25-Nov-3 Galeria y Remates, Montevideo #80
£3647	$6200	€5325	Model (74x61cm-29x24in) s.d.80. 25-Nov-3 Galeria y Remates, Montevideo #78/R
£3714	$6500	€5422	Untitled (26x198cm-10x78in) s.d.94 prov. 19-Dec-3 Sotheby's, New York #1209/R est:6000-8000
£3765	$6400	€5497	Boy and bike (73x60cm-29x24in) s.d.80. 25-Nov-3 Galeria y Remates, Montevideo #77/R
£3824	$6500	€5583	Waiting (60x73cm-24x29in) s.d.82. 25-Nov-3 Galeria y Remates, Montevideo #79/R
£5163	$9500	€7538	Houses in Cadaques (93x120cm-37x47in) s.d.78. 22-Jun-4 Galeria y Remates, Montevideo #89/R est:10000-12000
£6286	$11000	€9178	Untitled (81x99cm-32x39in) s.d.95 prov. 19-Dec-3 Sotheby's, New York #1192/R est:8000-12000
£8000	$14000	€11680	Bel canto (96x133cm-38x52in) prov. 19-Dec-3 Sotheby's, New York #1186/R est:15000-18000
£10056	$18000	€14682	Field with horse on the table (60x73cm-24x29in) s. painted 1990 prov. 26-May-4 Sotheby's, New York #177/R est:15000-20000
£32353	$55000	€47235	Mesa contacitas (100x209cm-39x82in) s.d.93 prov. 19-Nov-3 Sotheby's, New York #175/R est:30000-40000

ITURRINO, Francisco de (1864-1924) Spanish

Works on paper

£1241	$2061	€1800	Arab street (25x19cm-10x7in) s. W/C. 30-Sep-3 Ansorena, Madrid #4/R est:1800
£2289	$4005	€3250	Arabian street (25x19cm-10x7in) s. W/C. 16-Dec-3 Durán, Madrid #105/R est:1300
£5263	$9684	€8000	Party in the fields (30x39cm-12x15in) s. W/C. 22-Jun-4 Durán, Madrid #167/R est:4600

IVANEC, Stjepan (1953-) Yugoslavian

£355	$592	€500	My Podrawina (54x59cm-21x23in) s.d.76 behind glass. 16-Oct-3 Dorotheum, Salzburg #981/R

IVANISIN, Katarina (1975-) British?

£1800	$3276	€2628	Untitled (200x300cm-79x118in) s.d.2000 verso prov. 4-Feb-4 Sotheby's, Olympia #190/R est:2000-3000

IVANKOVICH, Basi (1815-1898) ?

£1312	$2414	€1968	Ship's portrait of Charlotta fran Goteborg (45x73cm-18x29in) s.i.d.1879. 14-Jun-4 Lilla Bukowskis, Stockholm #578/R est:15000-20000 (S.KR 18000)

IVANOFF, Serge (1893-1983) Bulgarian

£265	$482	€400	Elegante au chapeau (46x33cm-18x13in) s. cardboard. 16-Jun-4 Claude Boisgirard, Paris #77
£3200	$5440	€4800	Apology (45x61cm-18x24in) s. 25-Nov-3 Christie's, London #215/R est:3000-5000

IVANOFF, Vassil (1897-1973) Russian?

Sculpture

£1049	$1783	€1500	Homme couche (18x23cm-7x9in) s. brown sandstone. 20-Nov-3 Camard, Paris #127/R est:2000-2200

IVANOFF, Victor Archipovich (1909-1988) South African

£347	$621	€507	Busy street scene (70x55cm-28x22in) s.d.65 board. 31-May-4 Stephan Welz, Johannesburg #268 (SA.R 4200)

IVANOV, S I (1922-) Russian

£272	$500	€397	Old man with a pipe (38x31cm-15x12in) painted late 1940's. 27-Mar-4 Shishkin Gallery, Moscow #13/R
£272	$500	€397	The pitman (94x74cm-37x29in) painted 1950's. 27-Mar-4 Shishkin Gallery, Moscow #16/R
£543	$1000	€793	In the sculptor studio (118x79cm-46x31in) painted late 1940's. 27-Mar-4 Shishkin Gallery, Moscow #19/R
£778	$1400	€1136	Steel maker (65x47cm-26x19in) 24-Apr-4 Shishkin Gallery, Moscow #57/R est:2000-3000
£1833	$3300	€2676	Steel checking (26x156cm-10x61in) 24-Apr-4 Shishkin Gallery, Moscow #58/R est:7000-8000

IVANOV, Vasili Filipovich (1928-c.1970) Russian

£1923	$3500	€2808	Fond farewell (69x86cm-27x34in) s.d.51. 7-Feb-4 Sloans & Kenyon, Bethesda #1266/R est:3000-5000

IVANOV, Vladimir (1917-1986) Russian

Works on paper

£2800	$5012	€4088	Zolotoi petushok - golden cockerel (48x69cm-19x27in) s.i.d.1932 gouache on card. 26-May-4 Sotheby's, London #208/R est:3000-5000

IVARSON, Ivan (1900-1939) Swedish

£806	$1426	€1177	Adam and Eve - poetic (25x28cm-10x11in) panel prov. 27-Apr-4 AB Stockholms Auktionsverk #869/R (S.KR 11000)
£1612	$2853	€2354	Three tulips - for my love (25x28cm-10x11in) panel prov. 27-Apr-4 AB Stockholms Auktionsverk #683/R est:10000-12000 (S.KR 22000)
£2795	$4751	€4081	Ploughing, France (41x41cm-16x16in) i.verso exhib. 4-Nov-3 Bukowskis, Stockholm #187/R est:50000-55000 (S.KR 37000)
£3191	$5743	€4659	Flowers (34x27cm-13x11in) s. 26-Apr-4 Bukowskis, Stockholm #30/R est:40000-50000 (S.KR 44000)
£3399	$5778	€4963	Garden with sunflowers (30x37cm-12x15in) s. 5-Nov-3 AB Stockholms Auktionsverk #666/R est:60000-80000 (S.KR 45000)
£8702	$15664	€12705	Girl with red rosette (62x46cm-24x18in) s. panel prov. 26-Apr-4 Bukowskis, Stockholm #48/R est:150000-175000 (S.KR 120000)
£9063	$15408	€13232	Summer in Stenungsund (56x66cm-22x26in) s. 4-Nov-3 Bukowskis, Stockholm #22/R est:150000-175000 (S.KR 120000)
£9158	$16209	€13371	Still life of bouquet of flowers (50x35cm-20x14in) s. 27-Apr-4 AB Stockholms Auktionsverk #738/R est:125000-150000 (S.KR 125000)
£10574	$17976	€15438	Still life of flowers (95x61cm-37x24in) s. 4-Nov-3 Bukowskis, Stockholm #20/R est:130000-140000 (S.KR 140000)
£12690	$22843	€18527	Autumn landscape from France (56x64cm-22x25in) prov. 26-Apr-4 Bukowskis, Stockholm #145/R est:150000-175000 (S.KR 175000)
£27946	$47508	€40801	Girls bathing (52x45cm-20x18in) s. exhib. 4-Nov-3 Bukowskis, Stockholm #100/R est:300000-350000 (S.KR 370000)
£75529	$128399	€110272	Mother and child by the sea, Stenungson (110x96cm-43x38in) s. prov.exhib.lit. 4-Nov-3 Bukowskis, Stockholm #106/R est:1000000-1500000 (S.KR 1000000)

Works on paper

£306	$563	€459	Fishing from the quay (20x26cm-8x10in) s. chk. 14-Jun-4 Lilla Bukowskis, Stockholm #51 (S.KR 4200)
£340	$578	€496	Town scene with figure (15x19cm-6x7in) mixed media. 5-Nov-3 AB Stockholms Auktionsverk #732/R (S.KR 4500)
£1511	$2568	€2206	Coastal landscape with bathers (25x34cm-10x13in) s. mixed media. 4-Nov-3 Bukowskis, Stockholm #23/R est:25000-30000 (S.KR 20000)

IVASCHENKO, Tatiana Anatolievna (20th C) Russian

£1923	$3500	€2808	Femme fatale (122x91cm-48x36in) s. i.verso. 19-Jun-4 Jackson's, Cedar Falls #268/R est:2000-3000

IVASENKO, Anatoli (1936-) Russian

£1400	$2520	€2044	Hot Day (90x147cm-35x58in) s.i.d.1958 verso. 20-Jan-4 Bonhams, Knightsbridge #1/R est:1500-2000

IVERD, Eugene (1893-c.1938) American

£3702	$6700	€5405	Man seated in train (89x69cm-35x27in) 16-Apr-4 American Auctioneer #217/R est:4000-6000

IVERSEN, Kraesten (1886-1955) Danish

£287	$465	€416	Road through landscape (100x130cm-39x51in) init. 4-Aug-3 Rasmussen, Vejle #664 (D.KR 3000)
£316	$581	€461	Coastal landscape, morning sunshine, Svaneke (45x64cm-18x25in) init. 29-Mar-4 Rasmussen, Copenhagen #540 (D.KR 3500)
£361	$667	€527	Coastal landscape with cliffs (72x92cm-28x36in) mono. 15-Mar-4 Rasmussen, Vejle #661/R (D.KR 4000)
£376	$640	€549	Coastal landscape, Bornholm (75x99cm-30x39in) init. 29-Nov-3 Rasmussen, Havnen #4308/R (D.KR 4000)
£451	$830	€658	Rocky cliffs by Svaneke lighthouse (91x127cm-36x50in) init. 29-Mar-4 Rasmussen, Copenhagen #495/R (D.KR 5000)
£559	$878	€816	Fjord landscape with rowing boats (92x120cm-36x47in) init. 30-Aug-3 Rasmussen, Havnen #4353/R (D.KR 6000)
£722	$1329	€1054	View of Svaneke along the coast (93x120cm-37x47in) init. s.i.verso. 29-Mar-4 Rasmussen, Copenhagen #481/R (D.KR 8000)
£751	$1254	€1096	Landscape view towards the sea (90x130cm-35x51in) init. 7-Oct-3 Rasmussen, Copenhagen #309/R (D.KR 8000)

IVES, Chauncey Bradley (1810-1894) American

Sculpture

£39535	$68000	€57721	Ino and Bacchus (136cm-54in) s.i. marble prov.exhib. 4-Dec-3 Christie's, Rockefeller NY #51/R est:60000-80000
£136364	$240000	€199091	Undine receives her mortal soul (154cm-61in) s. marble incl red marble base exec 1880-4. 18-May-4 Christie's, Rockefeller NY #31/R est:150000-250000

IVES, Hazel Beauregard (fl.1915-c.1980) American

Works on paper

£926	$1500	€1352	Still lifes with flowers (23x25cm-9x10in) s. pair. 31-Jul-3 Eldred, East Dennis #899/R est:1500-2000

IVES, Percy (1864-1928) American

£599	$1000	€875	Portrait of Theodore A McGraw (81x74cm-32x29in) 17-Oct-3 Du Mouchelle, Detroit #2119/R

IVEY, John Joseph (1842-1910) American

Works on paper

£257	$475	€375	Mountain landscape with stone bridge. W/C. 19-Jan-4 O'Gallerie, Oregon #111/R

IWILL, Joseph (1850-1923) French

£1200	$2208	€1752	Venitian canal scene (34x47cm-13x19in) s. 23-Mar-4 Rosebery Fine Art, London #793
£1319	$2203	€1900	Coucher de soleil sur Venise (32x48cm-13x19in) s.i. 23-Oct-3 Credit Municipal, Paris #64 est:1000-1200
£1600	$2560	€2320	Venetian lagoon at night (51x65cm-20x26in) i.d.93. 18-Sep-3 Christie's, Kensington #79/R est:1500-2000
£1667	$3000	€2500	Stretch of coastline at dusk (34x60cm-13x24in) s.indis.i.d.1900. 21-Apr-4 Christie's, Amsterdam #50/R est:2000-3000
£2069	$3455	€3000	Sur la lagune (50x115cm-20x45in) s.i.d.1921 verso. 11-Jul-3 Rabourdin & Choppin de Janvry, Paris #15/R
£2098	$3608	€3000	Vue du Port Saint-Vaast (48x33cm-19x13in) s.i. 8-Dec-3 Christie's, Paris #61/R est:3000-5000
£2465	$4264	€3500	Soleil couchant sur le port (36x61cm-14x24in) s. 14-Dec-3 Eric Pillon, Calais #35/R
£2535	$4208	€3600	Vue de Venise (34x48cm-13x19in) s. pair. 16-Jun-3 E & Eve, Paris #78
£3892	$6500	€5682	La Boresca, Venice (60x92cm-24x36in) s.I Will prov.lit. 7-Oct-3 Sotheby's, New York #322 est:3000-4000

IYUNA, James (1959-) Australian

Works on paper

£391	$730	€587	Wayuk, waterlillies, at Dilebang (126x71cm-50x28in) bears name.verso earth pigments eucalyptus bark exec.c.1999. 26-Jul-4 Sotheby's, Melbourne #545 (A.D 1000)
£488	$771	€708	Buluwana, ancestor from Ngandarrayo (155x46cm-61x18in) earth pigments eucalyptus bark prov. 28-Jul-3 Sotheby's, Paddington #453/R (A.D 1200)
£2422	$4529	€3633	Ngalyod, the rainbow serpent (264x90cm-104x35in) pigment eucalyptus bark exec. 1993 prov. 21-Jul-4 Shapiro, Sydney #17/R est:6000-8000 (A.D 6200)

IZQUIERDO, Cesar (1973-) Guatemalan

£184	$305	€267	Espiritu apasionado (139x100cm-55x39in) d.1973. 12-Jun-3 Louis Morton, Mexico #130 est:2000-2500 (M.P 3200)
£430	$714	€624	Los guardianes (136x197cm-54x78in) d.1973. 12-Jun-3 Louis Morton, Mexico #134/R est:2500-3000 (M.P 7500)

IZQUIERDO, Domingo (?) ?

Sculpture

£884	$1600	€1291	Wing (147x23x10cm-58x9x4in) stainless steel. 3-Apr-4 David Rago, Lambertville #79/R est:1500-2000

IZQUIERDO, J J (20th C) Venezuelan

£1274	$2000	€1860	Still life (34x52cm-13x20in) s. cardboard on canvas. 23-Nov-2 Subastas Odalys, Caracas #40/R est:1200
£2611	$4100	€3812	Fruit (106x63cm-42x25in) s. 23-Nov-2 Subastas Odalys, Caracas #18/R

IZQUIERDO, Maria (1906-1950) Mexican

Works on paper

£11176	$19000	€16317	Mujer y caballo - Woman with horse (21x28cm-8x11in) s.d.38 gouache prov.exhib. 18-Nov-3 Christie's, Rockefeller NY #98/R est:15000-20000

IZSAK SIPOS, Szilard (1977-) Hungarian

£679	$1174	€991	Flowers (195x120cm-77x47in) s.d.2002 verso. 12-Dec-3 Kieselbach, Budapest #168/R (H.F 260000)
£855	$1514	€1248	Flowers (140x100cm-55x39in) s.d.03. 28-Apr-4 Kieselbach, Budapest #190/R (H.F 320000)

IZUMI, Sei Raku Ju (19th C) Japanese
Sculpture
£4452 $7568 €6500 Hen and cockerel (28cm-11in) i. brown pat.bronze pair. 8-Nov-3 Dr Fritz Nagel, Stuttgart #1886/R est:3800

IZZARD, Daniel J (1923-) Canadian
£228 $365 €333 Along the Lillooet River no.1 (25x30cm-10x12in) s.d.1982 board. 16-Sep-3 Maynards, Vancouver #367 (C.D 500)
£257 $436 €375 View from the studio (51x61cm-20x24in) s.d.1979 masonite. 19-Nov-3 Maynards, Vancouver #3b (C.D 570)
£267 $437 €390 On the beach; Marciana Marina, Elbe (61x76cm-24x30in) s. 28-May-3 Maynards, Vancouver #12 (C.D 600)
£267 $437 €390 Thieves Bay, Pender Island (30x36cm-12x14in) s. board. 28-May-3 Maynards, Vancouver #48 (C.D 600)

J C (?) ?
£3103 $5183 €4500 Deux elegantes (100x65cm-39x26in) mono. painted c.1920. 17-Nov-3 Claude Boisgirard, Paris #40/R est:1500-2000

J G (?) ?
£600 $1092 €876 Still life with fruit and flowers on a ledge (127x61cm-50x24in) mono. 4-Feb-4 John Nicholson, Haslemere #181

JAAKOLA, Alpo (1929-1997) Finnish
£739 $1183 €1050 Pyrokinetic self portrait (89x59cm-35x23in) s.d.1983. 18-Sep-3 Hagelstam, Helsinki #909/R
£1014 $1814 €1500 Friends (46x90cm-18x35in) s.d.1972. 8-May-4 Bukowskis, Helsinki #234/R est:100-1300
£1111 $1856 €1600 Pallomainen kulkija - Abstract composition (70x30cm-28x12in) s.d.1964. 23-Oct-3 Hagelstam, Helsinki #850/R est:2000
£1189 $2021 €1700 The white tower rising (29x61cm-11x24in) s.d.66 board exhib. 29-Nov-3 Bukowskis, Helsinki #262/R est:1700-2000
£1333 $2387 €2000 Before the evening (80x70cm-31x28in) s.d.1967. 15-May-4 Hagelstam, Helsinki #206/R est:2000
£1399 $2378 €2000 Caligulas as young (120x65cm-47x26in) s.d.1976 acrylic. 29-Nov-3 Bukowskis, Helsinki #288/R est:2000-2500
£1748 $2972 €2500 Grey chairs (85x108cm-33x43in) s.d.1972 board. 29-Nov-3 Bukowskis, Helsinki #256/R est:2000-2500

JAAR, Alfredo (1956-) American
Photographs
£2335 $4250 €3409 Gold in the morning (25x82cm-10x32in) s.d.93 verso c-type print prov. 29-Jun-4 Sotheby's, New York #634/R est:2500-3500
Sculpture
£6704 $12000 €9788 Cries and whispers (47x245x17cm-19x96x7in) lightbox projection 2 parts exec 1988 prov. 13-May-4 Sotheby's, New York #416/R est:12000-18000

JABIN, Georg (1828-1864) German
£662 $1205 €1000 Mountain landscape (38x53cm-15x21in) s.d.6 Juni 62. 18-Jun-4 Bolland & Marotz, Bremen #653/R

JABONEAU, Albert (19th C) French
£769 $1285 €1100 Remorqueur dans un port anime (40x60cm-16x24in) s. 13-Oct-3 Horta, Bruxelles #57

JABURG, Oltmann (1830-1908) German
£7292 $12031 €10500 Three master in stormy seas (58x87cm-23x34in) s.d.1865. 3-Jul-3 Dr Fritz Nagel, Stuttgart #492/R est:7500

JACCARD, Christian (1939-) French
£704 $1218 €1000 Empreinte et son objet (52x97cm-20x38in) s.i. acrylic string prov. 9-Dec-3 Artcurial Briest, Paris #574
£1667 $3066 €2500 Couple toile / outil echelle, empreinte (238x200cm-94x79in) acrylic canvas book cords painted c.1973. 9-Jun-4 Artcurial Briest, Paris #532/R est:3000-4000

JACK, Joanassie (20th C) North American
Sculpture
£988 $1600 €1442 Bear attacking seal (38x30cm-15x12in) grey soapstone base. 26-Jul-3 Thomaston Place, Thomaston #562/R

JACK, Kenneth (1924-) Australian
£1545 $2425 €2240 Untitled, Silverton (60x90cm-24x35in) s.d.1964 board prov. 27-Aug-3 Christie's, Sydney #566/R est:2000-4000 (A.D 3800)
Works on paper
£1157 $2140 €1689 Twilight Queens Square, Sydney (57x100cm-22x39in) s.d.1981 W/C prov. 10-Mar-4 Deutscher-Menzies, Melbourne #498/R est:3000-3500 (A.D 2800)
£1489 $2532 €2174 Karang (51x71cm-20x28in) s.d.1992 W/C. 25-Nov-3 Christie's, Melbourne #303a est:3500-4500 (A.D 3500)

JACK, Lieutenant Colonel Alexander (1805-1857) British
Works on paper
£1000 $1630 €1460 Kot Kangrar (41x28cm-16x11in) pencil W/C prov.exhib. 24-Sep-3 Christie's, London #44/R est:800-1200

JACK, Richard (1866-1952) Canadian/British
£294 $491 €429 Near Mt. Tremblant (34x49cm-13x19in) s.i. board. 17-Nov-3 Hodgins, Calgary #282/R (C.D 650)
£360 $601 €526 Chiswick Mall (25x35cm-10x14in) s.indis.d.1903 panel. 7-Oct-3 Bonhams, Knightsbridge #73/R
£1728 $3093 €2523 Humber River, Newfoundland (76x102cm-30x40in) s.i. prov. 31-May-4 Sotheby's, Toronto #151/R est:4000-6000 (C.D 4250)
£80000 $136000 €116800 Toast (153x213cm-60x84in) s.i.d.Jan 1913 prov.exhib. 26-Nov-3 Christie's, London #35/R est:70000-100000

JACKIEWICZ, Wladyslaw (1924-) Polish
£367 $665 €551 Nude from behind (101x82cm-40x32in) s. 4-Apr-4 Agra, Warsaw #1/R (P.Z 2600)

JACKLIN, Bill (1943-) British
£4800 $8784 €7008 The bar, Coney Island (40x51cm-16x20in) s.i. 2-Jun-4 Sotheby's, London #140/R est:5000-7000
£10000 $17200 €14600 Meatpackers, Washington Street, II (91x76cm-36x30in) s.i.d.86 verso. 3-Dec-3 Sotheby's, London #101/R est:6000-8000

JACKLIN, Marjorie (1895-1984) British
Works on paper
£320 $573 €467 Haddon Hall looking down the garden steps (46x68cm-18x27in) s.d.1915 W/C. 17-May-4 David Duggleby, Scarborough #719/R

JACKMAN, Iris (20th C) British?
£280 $496 €409 Christmas roses (44x34cm-17x13in) s. canvasboard. 27-Apr-4 Bonhams, Knightsbridge #121/R

JACKMAN, Reva (1892-1966) American
£1223 $2250 €1786 Jardin de Luxembourg (53x64cm-21x25in) s.d.1926 i.verso prov. 8-Jun-4 Bonhams & Butterfields, San Francisco #4340/R est:2000-3000

JACKOWSKI, Andrzej (1947-) British
£1400 $2338 €2044 Holding the tree (302x127cm-119x50in) s. i.d.1988 verso prov. 21-Oct-3 Bonhams, Knightsbridge #65/R est:1000-1500

JACKS, Robert (1943-) Australian
£826 $1463 €1206 Summer (91x71cm-36x28in) s.i.d.1990 verso prov. 3-May-4 Christie's, Melbourne #244/R est:2000-3000 (A.D 2000)
£1957 $3327 €2857 Bound time 1967 (76x53cm-30x21in) i.verso exhib. 26-Nov-3 Deutscher-Menzies, Melbourne #158/R est:2000-4000 (A.D 4600)
£2290 $4168 €3343 Guitar (183x152cm-72x60in) s.i.d.2000 verso prov.exhib. 16-Jun-4 Deutscher-Menzies, Melbourne #51/R est:8000-12000 (A.D 6000)
£2642 $4148 €3831 Blue for Pablo (152x122cm-60x48in) s.i.d.1996 verso. 27-Aug-3 Christie's, Sydney #600/R est:8000-12000 (A.D 6500)
£2846 $5093 €4155 To tie a bow (183x152cm-72x60in) s.d.2001 i.verso. 4-May-4 Sotheby's, Melbourne #186/R est:7000-12000 (A.D 7000)
£2893 $5120 €4224 Leaning harlequin (182x152cm-72x60in) s.i.d.1997 verso. 3-May-4 Christie's, Melbourne #5/R est:8000-12000 (A.D 7000)
£3320 $5544 €4980 Untitled (91x223cm-36x88in) s.d.1996 verso two panels. 27-Oct-3 Goodman, Sydney #108/R est:8000-12000 (A.D 8000)
£3926 $7262 €5732 Consort neglected (182x151cm-72x59in) s.d.1988 i.verso prov.exhib. 15-Mar-4 Sotheby's, Melbourne #62/R est:10000-15000 (A.D 9500)
£4468 $7596 €6523 Barcelona night (152x122cm-60x48in) s.i.d.5 June-July 1999 verso. 25-Nov-3 Christie's, Melbourne #85/R est:9000-12000 (A.D 10500)
£5344 $9725 €7802 Rays of rhyme, ways, days, Blaze (198x297cm-78x117in) s. i.d.1982 verso prov. 16-Jun-4 Deutscher-Menzies, Melbourne #142/R est:10000-15000 (A.D 14000)

JACKSON OF LEEDS, Albert (19th C) British
£650 $1216 €975 Cockerel pecking at a cabbage leaf with hens and pigeons nearby (20x25cm-8x10in) s. board. 22-Jul-4 Tennants, Leyburn #876
£800 $1360 €1168 Farmyard scene with blacksmith at a forge (58x102cm-23x40in) s. 19-Nov-3 Tennants, Leyburn #1070/R

JACKSON, A (19th C) British?
£601 $1081 €877 Pastoral landscapes with cattle (20x28cm-8x11in) s.d.85 panel pair. 26-Jan-4 Lilla Bukowskis, Stockholm #357 (S.KR 8000)

JACKSON, A Y (1882-1974) Canadian
£1850 $3090 €2701 Logging teams on woodland road (48x36cm-19x14in) bears sig. 17-Oct-3 Keys, Aylsham #716

JACKSON, Alexander Young (1882-1974) Canadian
£4032 $7419 €5887 Fields in June, St Cezaire, Quebec (26x34cm-10x13in) s. s.i.verso panel painted late 1940's prov. 9-Jun-4 Walker's, Ottawa #68/R est:10000-15000 (C.D 10000)
£4241 $7295 €6192 Before rain, Yellowknife (26x34cm-10x13in) s. panel prov. 2-Dec-3 Joyner Waddington, Toronto #150/R est:7000-9000 (C.D 9500)
£4254 $7827 €6211 Winter, Shefferville, Quebec (26x34cm-10x13in) s.i.d.1961 verso panel prov. 9-Jun-4 Walker's, Ottawa #6/R est:10000-15000 (C.D 10550)
£4254 $7827 €6211 Autumn hills, Lake Superior (26x34cm-10x13in) panel prov. 9-Jun-4 Walker's, Ottawa #42 est:10000-15000 (C.D 10550)
£4472 $8004 €6529 Algoma Lake (26x34cm-10x13in) s. s.i.d.1955 verso board prov. 27-May-4 Heffel, Vancouver #164/R est:10000-12000 (C.D 11000)
£4505 $7658 €6577 Street, Yellowknife (26x34cm-10x13in) s. s.i.verso panel prov. 18-Nov-3 Sotheby's, Toronto #27/R est:10000-12000 (C.D 10000)
£4505 $7658 €6577 Farm at Wilno, Ont (27x34cm-11x13in) s. s.i.d.1966 verso panel prov. 18-Nov-3 Sotheby's, Toronto #141/R est:8000-10000 (C.D 10000)
£4505 $7658 €6577 Combermere, Ontario (26x34cm-10x13in) s. i.d.1960 verso panel. 21-Nov-3 Walker's, Ottawa #27/R est:10000-12000 (C.D 10000)
£4878 $8732 €7122 Tangled trees in autumn (22x27cm-9x11in) panel prov. 31-May-4 Sotheby's, Toronto #131/R est:12000-15000 (C.D 12000)
£4955 $8423 €7234 Winter, Quebec (22x27cm-9x11in) panel prov. 18-Nov-3 Sotheby's, Toronto #25/R est:8000-10000 (C.D 11000)
£4955 $8423 €7234 Porcupine Hills at Pincher Creek, Alberta (26x34cm-10x13in) s. s.i.d. October 1949 verso panel prov.lit. 27-Nov-3 Heffel, Vancouver #207/R est:7000-9000 (C.D 11000)
£5285 $9459 €7716 Barns, l'Islet Ste Louise (21x26cm-8x10in) s. s.i.verso panel prov. 27-May-4 Heffel, Vancouver #26/R est:10000-15000 (C.D 13000)
£5285 $9459 €7716 Carhaix evening (21x26cm-8x10in) s. i.d.1911 verso panel prov. 27-May-4 Heffel, Vancouver #169/R est:8000-10000 (C.D 13000)

£5285 $9459 €7716 Barn near Combermere, Ontario, Rockingham (27x34cm-11x13in) s. s.i.d.1961 verso. 31-May-4 Sotheby's, Toronto #163/R est:12000-15000 (C.D 13000)
£5285 $9459 €7716 Gatineau river (26x34cm-10x13in) s.i.d.1948 verso. 31-May-4 Sotheby's, Toronto #164/R est:10000-15000 (C.D 13000)
£5357 $9107 €7821 County near Bancroft, Ontario (27x34cm-11x13in) s. s.i.d.1953 verso panel prov. 6-Nov-3 Heffel, Vancouver #67/R est:10000-12000 (C.D 12000)
£5405 $9189 €7891 Lake at Clontarf, Ont (27x34cm-11x13in) s. s.i. verso prov. 18-Nov-3 Sotheby's, Toronto #138/R est:12000-15000 (C.D 12000)
£5600 $10248 €8176 Algoma Woods (21x26cm-8x10in) s. panel. 1-Jun-4 Joyner Waddington, Toronto #7/R est:12000-15000 (C.D 14000)
£5600 $10248 €8176 Onward Ranch May 1949 (26x34cm-10x13in) s. panel painted 1949 prov. 1-Jun-4 Joyner Waddington, Toronto #87/R est:10000-15000 (C.D 14000)
£5691 $10187 €8309 Palmey Rapids, Madawaska River (26x34cm-10x13in) s. s.i.d.1960 verso panel prov. 27-May-4 Heffel, Vancouver #114/R est:8000-10000 (C.D 14000)
£5691 $10187 €8309 Barren lands, Tershierpi Hills (26x34cm-10x13in) s.d.1959 verso prov.lit. 31-May-4 Sotheby's, Toronto #130/R est:12000-15000 (C.D 14000)
£5856 $9955 €8550 Georgian Bay (27x34cm-11x13in) s. paper prov. 18-Nov-3 Sotheby's, Toronto #182/R est:12000-15000 (C.D 13000)
£5882 $9824 €8588 Devils warehouse Island, lake Superior (26x34cm-10x13in) s.i.d.1965 panel. 17-Nov-3 Hodgins, Calgary #381/R est:14000-17000 (C.D 13000)
£6000 $10980 €8760 Hills at Arundel, Quebec (26x34cm-10x13in) s. panel painted 1958 prov. 1-Jun-4 Joyner Waddington, Toronto #110/R est:10000-15000 (C.D 15000)
£6250 $10750 €9125 Baffin Island - Mount Asgard (40x50cm-16x20in) s. painted 1965. 2-Dec-3 Joyner Waddington, Toronto #85/R est:15000-20000 (C.D 14000)
£6250 $10750 €9125 Early snow, North Gower, Ontario (26x34cm-10x13in) s. panel painted 1955. 2-Dec-3 Joyner Waddington, Toronto #140/R est:8000-10000 (C.D 14000)
£6306 $10721 €9207 Farm near Actinolite, Ont (27x34cm-11x13in) s. s.i.d.1967 verso panel prov. 18-Nov-3 Sotheby's, Toronto #140/R est:14000-16000 (C.D 14000)
£6306 $10721 €9207 Chapel in Venice (22x27cm-9x11in) s. i.d.1909 verso panel prov. 18-Nov-3 Sotheby's, Toronto #180/R est:7000-9000 (C.D 14000)
£6504 $11642 €9496 Barns at Combermere, Ont, Barry's Bay (27x34cm-11x13in) s. s.i.d.Oct 1961 verso panel prov. 31-May-4 Sotheby's, Toronto #4/R est:12000-15000 (C.D 16000)
£6757 $11486 €9865 Evening, Combermere, Ontario (27x34cm-11x13in) s.i.d.1962 verso panel prov. 18-Nov-3 Sotheby's, Toronto #24/R est:15000-20000 (C.D 15000)
£6787 $10656 €9909 Lake in LaClocke Hills (26x34cm-10x13in) s.d. 6 Oct 1940 s.i.d.verso board. 26-Aug-3 Iegor de Saint Hippolyte, Montreal #91 (C.D 15000)
£6911 $12370 €10090 Spring, Algoma, Grace Lake (26x34cm-10x13in) s. s.i.d.1938 verso panel prov.lit. 27-May-4 Heffel, Vancouver #53/R est:10000-15000 (C.D 17000)
£7200 $13176 €10512 Visit to Camp Ahmek 17 July 64 (26x34cm-10x13in) s. panel painted 1964. 1-Jun-4 Joyner Waddington, Toronto #185/R est:8000-10000 (C.D 18000)
£7317 $13098 €10683 Hills at Kluene Lake, Alaska Highway (26x34cm-10x13in) s. panel painted 1943 prov.lit. 27-May-4 Heffel, Vancouver #88/R est:13000-16000 (C.D 18000)
£7658 $13018 €11181 Farm in Kamloops, BC (26x34cm-10x13in) s. i.d.September 1944 verso panel prov. 27-Nov-3 Heffel, Vancouver #87/R est:8000-10000 (C.D 17000)
£8000 $14640 €11680 Lake in a La Cloche Hills (26x34cm-10x13in) s. panel painted 1940. 1-Jun-4 Joyner Waddington, Toronto #105/R est:15000-18000 (C.D 20000)
£8065 $14839 €11775 Mount Asgard, Baffin Island (40x50cm-16x20in) s. s.i.d.July 1965 verso. 9-Jun-4 Walker's, Ottawa #28/R est:20000-30000 (C.D 20000)
£8065 $14839 €11775 Farm at Comberemre, Ontario (40x50cm-16x20in) s. i.verso lit. 9-Jun-4 Walker's, Ottawa #53/R est:20000-25000 (C.D 20000)
£8130 $14553 €11870 Georgian Bay (21x26cm-8x10in) s.d.1920 double-sided. 31-May-4 Sotheby's, Toronto #137/R est:12000-15000 (C.D 20000)
£8482 $14589 €12384 Birches (26x34cm-10x13in) s. panel double-sided prov. 2-Dec-3 Joyner Waddington, Toronto #191/R est:15000-20000 (C.D 19000)
£8597 $14357 €12552 Georgian Bay (26x33cm-10x13in) s.i.d.1920. 17-Nov-3 Hodgins, Calgary #112/R est:15000-18000 (C.D 19000)
£8800 $16104 €12848 Comermere pastoral (52x62cm-20x24in) s. 1-Jun-4 Joyner Waddington, Toronto #45/R est:25000-30000 (C.D 22000)
£8929 $15357 €13036 Birches (21x26cm-8x10in) s.i.verso prov. 2-Dec-3 Joyner Waddington, Toronto #22/R est:20000-25000 (C.D 20000)
£9009 $15315 €13153 Port Munro, Lake Superior (21x26cm-8x10in) s. i.d.1925 verso panel prov.lit. 27-Nov-3 Heffel, Vancouver #68/R est:12000-15000 (C.D 20000)
£9821 $16893 €14339 Grain elevators, Pincher Creek, Alberta (30x40cm-12x16in) s. board prov. 2-Dec-3 Joyner Waddington, Toronto #128/R est:10000-15000 (C.D 22000)
£12162 $20676 €17757 Still life with red dahlias (33x40cm-13x16in) s. board painted 1912 prov. 27-Nov-3 Heffel, Vancouver #27/R est:20000-25000 (C.D 27000)
£12387 $21059 €18085 Still life, sweet peas, Etaples, Pas-de-Calais (33x40cm-13x16in) i.d.1912 verso board prov. 27-Nov-3 Heffel, Vancouver #129/R est:13000-16000 (C.D 27500)
£12800 $23424 €18688 The meeting of the Peace and Smokey Rivers (75x100cm-30x39in) s.i.d.1952 tempera paper. 1-Jun-4 Hodgins, Calgary #401/R est:25000-35000 (C.D 32000)
£13211 $23648 €19288 Snow in September, Bar X Ranch, near Pincher Creek (26x33cm-10x13in) s. i.d.1937 verso panel prov.lit. 27-May-4 Heffel, Vancouver #9/R est:20000-25000 (C.D 32500)
£13393 $23036 €19554 Eastern Arctic (21x26cm-8x10in) s.d.1930 prov. 2-Dec-3 Joyner Waddington, Toronto #53/R est:20000-30000 (C.D 30000)
£19144 $32545 €27950 Farm house, Petite Riviere (27x34cm-11x13in) s. s.i.verso panel prov.lit. 18-Nov-3 Sotheby's, Toronto #46/R est:20000-25000 (C.D 42500)
£19309 $34563 €28191 Smallwood Mine from Carol Hill, Schefferville, Quebec (63x81cm-25x32in) s. s.i.d.1962 verso prov. 27-May-4 Heffel, Vancouver #67/R est:45000-55000 (C.D 47500)
£21111 $34622 €30822 April, Baie St Paul (20x25cm-8x10in) s.d.1923 s.i.verso panel prov. 28-May-3 Maynards, Vancouver #77/R est:30000-35000 (C.D 47500)
£22358 $40020 €32643 Lake Rouviere, NWT (51x61cm-20x24in) s. s.i.d.1961 verso prov.lit. 31-May-4 Sotheby's, Toronto #165/R est:35000-45000 (C.D 55000)
£22523 $38288 €32884 Somme River at Picquigny, France (53x63cm-21x25in) s. i.verso canvas on board painted April - May 1912 prov.exhib. 27-Nov-3 Heffel, Vancouver #82/R est:40000-50000 (C.D 50000)
£24000 $43920 €35040 Hills at Ste Adele (62x82cm-24x32in) s. 1-Jun-4 Joyner Waddington, Toronto #71/R est:60000-80000 (C.D 60000)
£26786 $46071 €39108 Laurentian Hills at Ste Adele (62x82cm-24x32in) s. 2-Dec-3 Joyner Waddington, Toronto #29/R est:50000-60000 (C.D 60000)
£27027 $45946 €39459 Lockhart River, the deserted village (51x61cm-20x24in) s. init.i.verso prov.lit. 27-Nov-3 Heffel, Vancouver #80/R est:30000-40000 (C.D 60000)
£29279 $49775 €42747 Castle River, Alberta (65x80cm-26x31in) s. s.i. stretcher verso prov. 18-Nov-3 Sotheby's, Toronto #51/R est:30000-50000 (C.D 65000)
£31250 $53750 €45625 Encampment, Eastern Arctic (50x65cm-20x26in) s. lit. 2-Dec-3 Joyner Waddington, Toronto #52/R est:60000-80000 (C.D 70000)
£32000 $58560 €46720 Deese Bay, Great Bear Lake (65x75cm-26x30in) s. prov. 1-Jun-4 Joyner Waddington, Toronto #61/R est:40000-60000 (C.D 80000)
£44715 $80041 €65284 Skeena Crossing, BC (21x26cm-8x10in) s.i.verso panel painted 1926 prov.lit. 27-May-4 Heffel, Vancouver #145/R est:35000-45000 (C.D 110000)
£112613 $191441 €164415 Quebec village on the St Lawrence in winter (53x67cm-21x26in) s. prov.lit. 18-Nov-3 Sotheby's, Toronto #59/R est:100000-125000 (C.D 250000)

Works on paper
£262 $482 €383 Rocky beach (22x30cm-9x12in) conte prov. 9-Jun-4 Walker's, Ottawa #100/R (C.D 650)
£536 $921 €783 Quebec village with horse and rider. French Canadian family home beyond (7x10cm-3x4in) both i. ink htd white two. 2-Dec-3 Joyner Waddington, Toronto #381/R (C.D 1200)
£982 $1689 €1434 Port Dover (22x29cm-9x11in) s.i. pencil prov. 2-Dec-3 Joyner Waddington, Toronto #199/R est:2500-3000 (C.D 2200)
£1138 $2037 €1661 Rolling hills (29x37cm-11x15in) s. graphite prov. 31-May-4 Sotheby's, Toronto #155/R est:3000-4000 (C.D 2800)
£2143 $3686 €3129 Eastern Arctic (21x27cm-8x11in) s.d. pencil sketch. 2-Dec-3 Joyner Waddington, Toronto #54/R est:3000-5000 (C.D 4800)
£2477 $4212 €3616 Fishing on the River Seine, Paris (24x26cm-9x10in) s.d.1907 W/C prov. 27-Nov-3 Heffel, Vancouver #83/R est:3500-4500 (C.D 5500)

JACKSON, Ashley (1940-) British
Works on paper
£320 $509 €464 Vale of York from Grewelthorpe Moor (26x35cm-10x14in) s.i.verso W/C. 9-Sep-3 David Duggleby, Scarborough #166
£320 $550 €467 Moorland coast, Wessenden Moor (36x53cm-14x21in) s.i.d.1990 W/C. 3-Dec-3 Andrew Hartley, Ilkley #1134
£380 $608 €555 Blackshaw Edge, Hebden Moor. s.d.1978 W/C. 18-Sep-3 Goldings, Lincolnshire #834/R
£500 $795 €725 Hawkswell's Farm, Low Birk Hatt (38x52cm-15x20in) s.d.1979 W/C. 9-Sep-3 David Duggleby, Scarborough #49/R
£560 $935 €818 Movement of light (36x53cm-14x21in) s.i.verso W/C. 8-Oct-3 Andrew Hartley, Ilkley #1096
£820 $1410 €1197 Down Flush House Lane (36x53cm-14x21in) s.i.d.1987 verso W/C. 3-Dec-3 Andrew Hartley, Ilkley #1135

JACKSON, C (19th C) British
£1647 $2750 €2405 Bay horse and dog in an extensive landscape (66x77cm-26x30in) s.d.1833. 22-Oct-3 Doyle, New York #103 est:2000-3000

JACKSON, Erna Nook (1886-?) Canadian
£360 $659 €526 Mountain landscape (20x25cm-8x10in) s. board. 1-Jun-4 Hodgins, Calgary #302/R (C.D 900)

JACKSON, Frederick Hamilton (1848-1923) British
Works on paper
£3162 $5660 €4617 Religious Ceremony (39x68cm-15x27in) s.d.1888 W/C. 15-May-4 Christie's, Sydney #73/R est:8000-12000 (A.D 8000)

JACKSON, Frederick William (1859-1918) British
£350 $616 €511 Thatched farmstead (28x33cm-11x13in) init. board. 20-May-4 Richardson & Smith, Whitby #665
£904 $1600 €1320 Figures strolling on a country lane. Fishing near the homestead (20x41cm-8x16in) s. pair. 2-May-4 Grogan, Boston #70/R
£2000 $3620 €2920 Fishing cobbles at Staithes (11x19cm-4x7in) mono. i.verso. 30-Mar-4 David Duggleby, Scarborough #92/R est:400-600
£5200 $9360 €7592 Hollyhocks (34x34cm-13x13in) indis.sig. board exhib. 21-Jan-4 Sotheby's, Olympia #338/R est:2000-3000
Works on paper
£280 $451 €409 Sheep grazing on heathered mountainous moorland (34x46cm-13x18in) s. W/C. 19-Feb-3 Peter Wilson, Nantwich #62
£350 $644 €511 Moors, Whitby (18x27cm-7x11in) s. W/C. 26-Mar-4 ELR Auctions, Sheffield #310
£350 $655 €511 Coastal village (25x33cm-10x13in) mono.d.1914 W/C. 23-Jul-4 Tring Auctions, Tring #265/R
£400 $724 €584 Rome from Pincian Hill (24x34cm-9x13in) s. i.verso W/C. 30-Mar-4 David Duggleby, Scarborough #63/R
£420 $764 €613 Moorland landscape with purple heather (12x17cm-5x7in) s. pencil W/C. 15-Jun-4 Bonhams, Leeds #173
£1050 $1911 €1533 Cattle grazing in a pasture (12x21cm-5x8in) s.d.1913 W/C. 15-Jun-4 Bonhams, Leeds #172/R
£1800 $3330 €2628 The Souk (26x38cm-10x15in) s. W/C gouache prov. 11-Feb-4 Sotheby's, Olympia #108/R est:600-800
£2500 $3975 €3625 Lansdowne cottage Runswick Bay (37x24cm-15x9in) s.d.1901 W/C. 9-Sep-3 David Duggleby, Scarborough #1/R est:1000-1500

JACKSON, G and RICHARDSON, William (19th C) British
£1500 $2550 €2190 River landscape with figures and dog beside a cottage (61x91cm-24x36in) s.d.1856. 19-Nov-3 Tennants, Leyburn #1100/R est:1000-1500

JACKSON, Geneva A (20th C) Canadian
£670 $1152 €978 Up the 3rd Range Road, from Ski House, St Adele (29x34cm-11x13in) s.d.1954 panel. 2-Dec-3 Joyner Waddington, Toronto #492 (C.D 1500)

JACKSON, George (19th C) British
£633 $1000 €924 Forest interior with sheep (56x91cm-22x36in) s.d.1896. 7-Sep-3 Treadway Gallery, Cincinnati #643/R

JACKSON, Gordena Parker (1900-1992) American
Works on paper
£924 $1700 €1349 Young lady reading with a cat by her side (59x44cm-23x17in) s.d.38 pencil W/C. 8-Jun-4 Bonhams & Butterfields, San Francisco #4371/R est:2000-3000

JACKSON, Harry (1924-) American
Sculpture
£1033 $1900 €1508 The seeker (35cm-14in) s.d.1978 brown pat. bronze incl. base st.f. Italia prov. 8-Jun-4 Bonhams & Butterfields, San Francisco #4145/R est:2500-3500
£1087 $2000 €1587 Pony express (26cm-10in) s.d.63 num.33 brown pat. bronze incl. base prov. 8-Jun-4 Bonhams & Butterfields, San Francisco #4144/R est:2500-3500
£1676 $3000 €2447 Trapper II (30cm-12in) bronze. 15-May-4 Altermann Galleries, Santa Fe #88/R

£2059 $3500 €3006 Chief Washakie II (48cm-19in) bronze. 1-Nov-3 Altermann Galleries, Santa Fe #121
£2431 $4400 €3549 Hazin in the leaders (33x28x10cm-13x11x4in) sig.d.59 bronze. 3-Apr-4 Neal Auction Company, New Orleans #80/R est:3000-5000
£2793 $5000 €4078 Chief Washakie II (46cm-18in) bronze edn of 50. 15-May-4 Altermann Galleries, Santa Fe #86/R
£4491 $7500 €6557 Ropin (41x46cm-16x18in) s.d.1959 dark brown pat. bronze. 16-Nov-3 Simpson's, Houston #98/R
£5689 $9500 €8306 Trapper (57cm-22in) s.d.1970 black brown pat bronze black marble base lit. 9-Oct-3 Christie's, Rockefeller NY #79/R est:4000-6000
£6816 $12200 €9951 Indian mother and child (64x91cm-25x36in) d.1980/81 polychrome bronze. 20-Mar-4 Selkirks, St. Louis #189/R est:15000-20000
£8235 $14000 €12023 Frontiersman (56cm-22in) bronze. 1-Nov-3 Altermann Galleries, Santa Fe #27
£11377 $19000 €16610 Pony express (52cm-20in) s.d.1967 num.16p polychromed bronze lit. 9-Oct-3 Christie's, Rockefeller NY #81/R est:10000-15000
£11976 $20000 €17485 Cowboy's meditation (58cm-23in) s.d.64 num.2 polychromed bronze black marble base lit. 9-Oct-3 Christie's, Rockefeller NY #80/R est:10000-15000

JACKSON, James Ranalph (1882-1975) Australian
£658 $1192 €961 Molonglo river (45x55cm-18x22in) s. 31-Mar-4 Goodman, Sydney #475 (A.D 1600)
£828 $1291 €1201 Rigging the boats, Sydney Harbour (36x44cm-14x17in) s. canvas on board. 1-Aug-2 Joel, Victoria #338 est:2000-3000 (A.D 2400)
£902 $1461 €1317 Landscape with blue mountains (34x44cm-13x17in) s. board prov. 30-Jul-3 Goodman, Sydney #114/R (A.D 2200)
£1328 $2484 €1992 Moonlit landscape (24x29cm-9x11in) s. 20-Jul-4 Goodman, Sydney #122/R est:1500-2000 (A.D 3400)
£1463 $2620 €2136 Evening sky (500x700cm-197x276in) s. d.18.12.44 verso. 10-May-4 Joel, Victoria #400 est:5000-7000 (A.D 3600)
£1626 $2911 €2374 Landscape (49x60cm-19x24in) s. 4-May-4 Sotheby's, Melbourne #107/R est:4000-6000 (A.D 4000)
£1680 $2722 €2453 Berrys Bay (28x38cm-11x15in) s. board prov. 30-Jul-3 Goodman, Sydney #108/R est:4000-5000 (A.D 4100)
£1957 $3327 €2857 Sydney Harbour shipping (48x50cm-19x20in) s. 26-Nov-3 Deutscher-Menzies, Melbourne #172/R est:5000-8000 (A.D 4600)
£2400 $4248 €3504 Chinaman's beach, Sydney harbour (61x91cm-24x36in) s.i. 29-Apr-4 Christie's, Kensington #80/R est:2000-3000
£2734 $5113 €4101 Sydney harbour (46x56cm-18x22in) s. 20-Jul-4 Goodman, Sydney #103/R est:8000-10000 (A.D 7000)
£2754 $4682 €4021 Autumn morning - Middle Harbour, Sydney (44x54cm-17x21in) s. board. 24-Nov-3 Sotheby's, Melbourne #191/R est:5000-8000 (A.D 6500)
£2893 $5351 €4224 Sydney Harbour (56x66cm-22x26in) s. 10-Mar-4 Deutscher-Menzies, Melbourne #315/R est:10000-15000 (A.D 7000)
£2893 $5351 €4224 Careel Bay near Palm Beach (38x45cm-15x18in) s. i.verso board. 10-Mar-4 Deutscher-Menzies, Melbourne #316/R est:5000-7000 (A.D 7000)
£3049 $4786 €4421 Cremorne Point, Sydney harbour (60x75cm-24x30in) s.d.56 prov. 27-Aug-3 Christie's, Sydney #533/R est:5000-7000 (A.D 7500)
£3306 $5851 €4827 Artist's home, Mosman (50x40cm-20x16in) s.d.13. 3-May-4 Christie's, Melbourne #378/R est:8000-12000 (A.D 8000)
£3719 $6583 €5430 Sydney Harbour and South Head from Dobroyd Point (59x81cm-23x32in) s.d.55 prov. 3-May-4 Christie's, Melbourne #384/R est:9000-12000 (A.D 9000)
£4800 $8784 €7008 Marley Beach, Sidney (41x51cm-16x20in) s. 27-Jan-4 Gorringes, Lewes #1581/R est:2000-3000
£7438 $13760 €10859 Spit Bridge, Sydney (66x96cm-26x38in) s. 10-Mar-4 Deutscher-Menzies, Melbourne #134/R est:20000-25000 (A.D 18000)
£8907 $14340 €13004 Boating (48x38cm-19x15in) s.d.18 canvas on board prov. 25-Aug-3 Sotheby's, Paddington #149/R est:15000-20000 (A.D 22000)

JACKSON, John (attrib) (1778-1831) British
£600 $1098 €876 Portrait of Earl of Harewood, wearing ceremonial robes (57x41cm-22x16in) 6-Jul-4 Bonhams, Knightsbridge #166/R

JACKSON, John (studio) (1778-1831) British
£4600 $8280 €6716 Portrait of Antonio Canova (77x64cm-30x25in) 21-Jan-4 Sotheby's, Olympia #48/R est:3000-5000

JACKSON, John Adams (1825 1879) American
Sculpture
£2914 $4750 €4254 Greek slave, a classical nude woman (165cm-65in) s.d.1864 white marble green marble socle incl. marble pedestal. 19-Jul-3 Skinner, Boston #378 est:2500-3500

JACKSON, Kurt (1961-) British
Works on paper
£400 $728 €584 Merlin's Cave (36x25cm-14x10in) s. W/C. 15-Jun-4 David Lay, Penzance #374/R
£400 $728 €584 Green stream (18x20cm-7x8in) s. i.verso mixed media. 15-Jun-4 David Lay, Penzance #377
£400 $732 €584 Dusk in the valley (18x27cm-7x11in) s.i.d.8/10/87 W/C bodycol. 3-Jun-4 Lane, Penzance #69
£780 $1443 €1139 Stream (23x23cm-9x9in) s.i.d.1997 verso mixed media. 10-Feb-4 David Lay, Penzance #344
£800 $1456 €1168 Towards White Island, St Martins, Scilly (18x18cm-7x7in) s. i.verso mixed media. 15-Jun-4 David Lay, Penzance #170
£1000 $1820 €1460 Lane to Higher Kerowe and Higher Trye (28x28cm-11x11in) s.d.01 i.verso mixed media. 15-Jun-4 David Lay, Penzance #463 est:400-600
£1200 $2220 €1752 Lazy wave (25x30cm-10x12in) s.d.1989 W/C. 10-Feb-4 David Lay, Penzance #268/R est:1000-1200
£1300 $2366 €1898 Evening tide (56x76cm-22x30in) s.i.d.93 mixed media. 15-Jun-4 David Lay, Penzance #630/R est:1200-1800

JACKSON, Lee (1909-) American
£2762 $5000 €4033 Dancers of the Moiseyev Ballet (36x61cm-14x24in) s. s.i.verso masonite prov. 31-Mar-4 Sotheby's, New York #174/R est:2000-3000

JACKSON, Lesley Elizabeth (1866-1958) American
£1167 $2100 €1704 Feeding the chickens (17x26cm-7x10in) s.d.189. 24-Apr-4 Weschler, Washington #595/R est:2000-3000

JACKSON, Major Ralph Temple (20th C) American
£488 $800 €712 African invasion (51x79cm-20x31in) s.i. W/C gouache board. 2-Jun-3 Grogan, Boston #675/R

JACKSON, Martin (1919-1986) American
£406 $650 €593 Carousel (30x84cm-12x33in) s. board. 19-Sep-3 Freeman, Philadelphia #82/R

JACKSON, Mary (1936-) British
£300 $528 €438 Evening light, Peloponese (12x18cm-5x7in) board. 18-May-4 Woolley & Wallis, Salisbury #80/R
£360 $634 €526 Winter in St Mary Bourne (25x30cm-10x12in) board. 18-May-4 Woolley & Wallis, Salisbury #77/R
Works on paper
£360 $634 €526 High tide at the pier (34x52cm-13x20in) s. W/C htd white. 18-May-4 Woolley & Wallis, Salisbury #284/R

JACKSON, Michael (1961-) British
£500 $920 €730 Leopard with her cubs (46x56cm-18x22in) s.d.1993. 10-Jun-4 Christie's, Kensington #289/R

JACKSON, Raymond Allen (1927-) British
Works on paper
£300 $543 €438 I don't care if you did it at Ascot and Lord's, you're not playing tennis here in that hat (43x54cm-17x21in) s. pencil ink wash. 30-Mar-4 Sworder & Son, Bishops Stortford #503/R
£320 $579 €467 I don't care what the police say I feel alot safer on the tube with the Guardian Angels! (43x54cm-17x21in) s.d.31 Jan 1989 pencil ink wash. 30-Mar-4 Sworder & Son, Bishops Stortford #504/R
£580 $998 €847 It was those damn cathedral bells over Truro (43x54cm-17x21in) s.i. pencil black ink. 3-Dec-3 Christie's, Kensington #305/R

JACKSON, Richard (20th C) ?
Works on paper
£595 $1100 €869 Untitled (89x114cm-35x45in) s.d.75 pencil oil. 13-Jul-4 Christie's, Rockefeller NY #135/R est:600-800

JACKSON, Ronald (1902-1992) Canadian
£222 $384 €324 Centre bay (41x51cm-16x20in) s. board. 9-Dec-3 Maynards, Vancouver #224 (C.D 500)
£273 $445 €399 Salmon trawler, BC. s. prov. 23-Sep-3 Ritchie, Toronto #138/R (C.D 600)
£294 $491 €429 Quadra Island (30x40cm-12x16in) s.i. board. 17-Nov-3 Hodgins, Calgary #38/R (C.D 650)
£317 $529 €463 Johnston Strait no.10 (45x60cm-18x24in) s.i. board. 17-Nov-3 Hodgins, Calgary #272/R (C.D 700)
£387 $630 €565 Perez Sound, North West Coast (45x61cm-18x24in) s. i.verso masonite. 23-Sep-3 Ritchie, Toronto #139/R (C.D 850)

JACKSON, Ross (20th C) Australian
£407 $638 €594 Pastorale II (170x229cm-67x90in) s.i.d.1973 i.d.verso acrylic prov. 27-Aug-3 Christie's, Sydney #668 (A.D 1000)

JACKSON, Samuel (1794-1869) British
Works on paper
£750 $1275 €1095 Near Cader Idis, North Wales (18x26cm-7x10in) s.d.May 1st 1867 verso W/C. 4-Nov-3 Rowley Fine Art, Newmarket #368/R
£850 $1445 €1241 Skiddaw and Derwent Water (22x32cm-9x13in) W/C. 4-Nov-3 Rowley Fine Art, Newmarket #369/R
£1300 $2405 €1898 Avon Gorge from Clifton Down, looking towards the Severn Estuary (21x30cm-8x12in) W/C. 9-Mar-4 Bonhams, New Bond Street #38/R est:1500-2000
£1300 $2405 €1898 Beach at Clevedon, Bristol (21x29cm-8x11in) W/C pencil. 9-Mar-4 Bonhams, New Bond Street #39/R est:1500-2000
£2000 $3260 €2920 Chapel Porth, North Cornwall (61x100cm-24x39in) s.i.d.1889 verso. 25-Sep-3 Clevedon Sale Rooms #176/R est:2000-3000
£2800 $4760 €4088 Porth-yr-Ogof, Ystradfellte, Vale of Neath, South Wales (29x39cm-11x15in) pencil W/C scratching out prov. 20-Nov-3 Christie's, London #46/R est:3000-5000
£4310 $7931 €6293 View of the Eiger, Monch and Jungfrau (35x51cm-14x20in) s. W/C. 26-Mar-4 Koller, Zurich #3312/R est:2500-3500 (S.FR 10000)

JACKSON, Samuel (attrib) (1794-1869) British
Works on paper
£350 $648 €511 Figure walking through an extensive landscape (23x34cm-9x13in) ink wash scratching out. 10-Mar-4 Sotheby's, Olympia #59/R

JACKSON, Samuel Phillips (1830-1904) British
Works on paper
£250 $418 €365 Castle ruins, Cornwall (27x53cm-11x21in) s.d.70 pencil W/C. 16-Oct-3 Christie's, Kensington #158
£250 $433 €365 King Arthur's Castle, Tintagel, Cornwall with figures on shoreline and boats (31x54cm-12x21in) s. pencil W/C. 9-Dec-3 Bonhams, Oxford #60
£300 $483 €435 Heavy sea on the harbour wall (33x61cm-13x24in) s. W/C. 15-Aug-3 Keys, Aylsham #515
£300 $552 €438 Seaweed covered rocks at low tide (24x51cm-9x20in) s. pencil W/C. 25-Mar-4 Christie's, Kensington #250
£340 $578 €496 Lifeboat rescue off Tynemouth (34x51cm-13x20in) s. W/C. 29-Oct-3 Bonhams, Chester #424
£400 $736 €584 Filey beach (17x34cm-7x13in) s. W/C. 22-Jun-4 Bonhams, Knightsbridge #86/R
£400 $736 €584 Beached fishing vessel (48x76cm-19x30in) s.d.1858 W/C. 22-Jun-4 Bonhams, Knightsbridge #192/R

£420	$739	€613	Derelict mill (30x48cm-12x19in) s.d.1852 W/C. 31-Dec-3 Lambrays, Wadebridge #680
£500	$910	€730	Approaching the lock (35x58cm-14x23in) s.d.1877 pencil W/C scratching out. 1-Jul-4 Christie's, Kensington #246/R
£550	$935	€803	Beached (7x13cm-3x5in) s. W/C bodycol. 18-Nov-3 Sotheby's, Olympia #18/R
£650	$1229	€949	Low Tide (14x30cm-6x12in) s.d.84 W/C htd white. 17-Feb-4 Bonhams, New Bond Street #4/R
£700	$1169	€1022	Whitby, from opposite side of harbour with cliffs and ruined church (30x48cm-12x19in) s.i.d. W/C exec.1862. 18-Jun-3 John Nicholson, Haslemere #592
£800	$1336	€1168	Whitby Sands towards the Abbey (33x51cm-13x20in) s. W/C. 10-Oct-3 Richardson & Smith, Whitby #70/R

JACKSON, Samuel Phillips (attrib) (1830-1904) British

Works on paper

£270	$486	€394	Fisherfolk with a boat in a cove, other vessels offshore (35x50cm-14x20in) W/C htd bodycol. 22-Apr-4 Lawrence, Crewkerne #748
£420	$764	€613	A study of fishes (14x25cm-6x10in) W/C sold with quantity by other hands. 1-Jul-4 Christie's, Kensington #276/R

JACKSON, William Franklin (1850-1936) American

£434	$750	€634	Old Gosling Ranch (10x16cm-4x6in) s.i.verso oil graphite. 13-Dec-3 Auctions by the Bay, Alameda #1835/R
£4121	$7500	€6017	Flower fields in a coastal landscape (25x36cm-10x14in) s. prov. 15-Jun-4 John Moran, Pasadena #164 est:7000-9000

JACOB, Alexandre (1876-1972) French

£291	$487	€420	Paysage d'hiver (14x22cm-6x9in) s.i. board. 21-Oct-3 Artcurial Briest, Paris #160
£634	$1096	€900	Lever de lune sur la Seine a Asniere (50x65cm-20x26in) s. 13-Dec-3 Martinot & Savignat, Pontoise #219/R
£775	$1340	€1100	Matin d'hiver sur la Seine, pres d'Asniere (46x65cm-18x26in) s. 13-Dec-3 Martinot & Savignat, Pontoise #218/R
£839	$1401	€1200	Bord de riviere (46x55cm-18x22in) s. 29-Jun-3 Eric Pillon, Calais #129/R
£979	$1635	€1400	Attelage (22x22cm-9x9in) s. panel. 29-Jun-3 Eric Pillon, Calais #131/R
£1200	$2208	€1752	Tranquil moment on the river (43x32cm-17x13in) board. 25-Mar-4 Christie's, Kensington #8/R est:1000-1500
£1259	$2102	€1800	Peupliers au bord de la riviere (30x27cm-12x11in) s.i.verso panel. 29-Jun-3 Eric Pillon, Calais #132/R
£1500	$2760	€2190	Village view (40x38cm-16x15in) s.i.verso. 25-Mar-4 Christie's, Kensington #10/R est:1500-2000
£1600	$2896	€2336	Au bord de la Loire (40x32cm-16x13in) board. 2-Apr-4 Bracketts, Tunbridge Wells #489/R est:800-1200
£1800	$2862	€2610	Village pres de Mareuil (46x56cm-18x22in) s. 11-Sep-3 Christie's, Kensington #49/R est:1500-2000
£2657	$4438	€3800	Moulin en bord de riviere (54x65cm-21x26in) s. 29-Jun-3 Eric Pillon, Calais #128/R
£2950	$5104	€4307	Rustic figure in punt on the marais at eventide (38x41cm-15x16in) s. 14-Dec-3 Desmond Judd, Cranbrook #1107
£2950	$5104	€4307	Rustic figure in punt on the marais, early morning (38x41cm-15x16in) s. 14-Dec-3 Desmond Judd, Cranbrook #1108
£3400	$6256	€4964	Le pecheur (28x30cm-11x12in) s. 25-Mar-4 Christie's, Kensington #9/R est:1000-1500
£6600	$11418	€9636	Farmer and work horses entering farm on old stone bridge over river Marne (53x53cm-21x21in) s. 14-Dec-3 Desmond Judd, Cranbrook #1054
£7258	$13355	€10597	Neige dans vallee de L'ourcq (51x56cm-20x22in) s. s.i.stretcher. 14-Jun-4 Waddingtons, Toronto #278/R est:1500-2000 (C.D 18000)

JACOB, Ernst Emanuel (1917-1966) Swiss

£814	$1360	€1188	Untitled (61x50cm-24x20in) 24-Jun-3 Germann, Zurich #147/R (S.FR 1800)
£1629	$2720	€2378	Things (73x100cm-29x39in) s. exhib. 24-Jun-3 Germann, Zurich #146/R est:4000-6000 (S.FR 3600)
£2262	$3846	€3303	Painting I (146x146cm-57x57in) s. 25-Nov-3 Germann, Zurich #77/R est:6000-8000 (S.FR 5000)

JACOB, Julius (younger) (1842-1929) German

£1970	$3604	€2876	Venetian scene in evening (32x48cm-13x19in) s.i.d.77. 9-Jun-4 Rasmussen, Copenhagen #1853/R est:20000-25000 (D.KR 22000)

JACOB, Max (1876-1944) French

Works on paper

£269	$475	€400	Portement de croix (21x26cm-8x10in) s. ink lead pencil paper on board. 27-Apr-4 Artcurial Briest, Paris #78
£333	$613	€500	Deposition de croix (17x26cm-7x10in) s.i. pen. 9-Jun-4 Piasa, Paris #121
£347	$638	€520	Oedipe et le Sphinx (21x27cm-8x11in) s.i. pen. 9-Jun-4 Piasa, Paris #123
£400	$688	€584	Racecourse (23x33cm-9x13in) s. W/C. 2-Dec-3 Gorringes, Lewes #2394
£432	$708	€600	Autoportrait. s.i. ink. 6-Jun-3 David Kahn, Paris #54
£464	$844	€700	Les voiles blanches (24x30cm-9x12in) s. gouache. 18-Jun-4 Piasa, Paris #127
£470	$832	€700	Roi des eaux (15x9cm-6x4in) s.i. brown ink. 27-Apr-4 Artcurial Briest, Paris #79
£533	$981	€800	Un moine en priere (28x22cm-11x9in) s. chl. 9-Jun-4 Piasa, Paris #122
£661	$1123	€965	Visitation (21x32cm-8x13in) s.d.38 Indian ink w/C chk pencil. 5-Nov-3 Dobiaschofsky, Bern #1684/R (S.FR 1500)
£699	$1189	€1000	Paddock (24x33cm-9x13in) s. W/C. 21-Nov-3 Coutau Begarie, Paris #68
£833	$1392	€1200	Paysage - Le lac d'Enghein (25x34cm-10x13in) s.d.1920 gouache. 21-Oct-3 Artcurial Briest, Paris #83/R
£1944	$3247	€2800	Personnages de theatre (16x18cm-6x7in) s.d.17 gouache. 21-Oct-3 Artcurial Briest, Paris #82/R est:1500-2000
£2133	$3925	€3200	Orphee et les pelicans (20x20cm-8x8in) s. W/C. 9-Jun-4 Piasa, Paris #120/R est:1300-1500

JACOB, Walter (1893-1964) German

£4200	$7518	€6300	Lower mountain landscape with farmsteads (63x89cm-25x35in) s.d. study verso prov. 14-May-4 Ketterer, Munich #35/R est:5000-7000
£5944	$10105	€8500	Agg - landscape (71x96cm-28x38in) s.d.27 exhib.lit. 26-Nov-3 Lempertz, Koln #737/R est:8000
£18000	$33120	€27000	Cemetery in Eberbach (70x74cm-28x29in) mono.i.d.20 prov.exhib. 12-Jun-4 Villa Grisebach, Berlin #224/R est:30000-40000
Works on paper			
£559	$951	€800	To the sun (49x40cm-19x16in) mnoo.d.1920 i. verso chk. 29-Nov-3 Villa Grisebach, Berlin #584/R

JACOBAEUS, Cecilie (20th C) Danish?

£373	$585	€545	Branch of grapes (43x49cm-17x19in) s. 30-Aug-3 Rasmussen, Havnen #2131 (D.KR 4000)
£654	$1034	€948	Golden cornfield with flowers in foreground (48x54cm-19x21in) s. exhib. 2-Sep-3 Rasmussen, Copenhagen #1725/R (D.KR 7000)
£1325	$2424	€2000	Cornflowers on side of field track (48x54cm-19x21in) s. i. verso. 8-Apr-4 Dorotheum, Vienna #90/R est:2400-2800

JACOBBER, Moise (1786-1863) French

£4363	$8027	€6500	Nature morte au vase de fleurs et nid d'oiseau sur un entablement (44x36cm-17x14in) s. panel exhib. 24-Mar-4 Tajan, Paris #50/R est:4000-6000

JACOBE, Neil (1924-) American

Works on paper

£769	$1400	€1123	Figures on a pier (15x23cm-6x9in) s. W/C prov. 15-Jun-4 John Moran, Pasadena #136 est:800-1200

JACOBEY, Karoly (1825-1891) Hungarian

£2715	$4507	€3964	At school (58x78cm-23x31in) s.d.1866. 4-Oct-3 Kieselbach, Budapest #181/R (H.F 1000000)

JACOBI, Lotte (1896-1990) American

Photographs

£2119	$3750	€3094	Photogenic, dimensions no 11 (28x35cm-11x14in) s. i.verso photo exec.c.1950. 28-Apr-4 Sotheby's, New York #177/R est:4000-6000
£2174	$3565	€3000	Untitled - photogenic (24x19cm-9x7in) s. vintage silver gelatin on board lit. 30-May-3 Villa Grisebach, Berlin #1214/R est:3000-3500

JACOBI, Lotte and KALLIN-FISCHER, Grit (20th C) American

Photographs

£9581	$16000	€13988	Portraits, Karl Vallentin and Hilde Rantzsch (17x16cm-7x6in) one s.i. one i.verso photo exec.1930 and exec.c.1927 two prov. 17-Oct-3 Sotheby's, New York #228/R est:5000-8000

JACOBI, Marcus (1891-1969) Swiss

£366	$656	€534	Summer landscape (60x81cm-24x32in) s. 13-May-4 Stuker, Bern #206 (S.FR 850)
£603	$1080	€880	Lake Thun with Stockhorn chain (69x86cm-27x34in) s.d.1936. 14-May-4 Dobiaschofsky, Bern #128/R (S.FR 1400)
£659	$1094	€956	Lake Thun landscape (61x69cm-24x27in) s. 13-Jun-3 Zofingen, Switzerland #2895 (S.FR 1450)
£705	$1198	€1029	Young undressed woman at window (112x85cm-44x33in) s. 5-Nov-3 Dobiaschofsky, Bern #689/R (S.FR 1600)
£776	$1389	€1133	Lake Thun with Niesen (80x95cm-31x37in) s.d.1936. 14-May-4 Dobiaschofsky, Bern #126/R est:2200 (S.FR 1800)
£795	$1320	€1153	Merligen with view of lake and Stockhorn (55x48cm-22x19in) s. 13-Jun-3 Zofingen, Switzerland #2894 est:1800 (S.FR 1750)
£1207	$2160	€1762	Lake Thun in autumn (75x92cm-30x36in) s.d.1935. 13-May-4 Stuker, Bern #204/R est:1500-2000 (S.FR 2800)

JACOBI, Otto Reinhard (1812-1901) German/Canadian

£293	$497	€428	Summertime pleasures (46x38cm-18x15in) s.d.1862 oval. 21-Nov-3 Walker's, Ottawa #93/R (C.D 650)
£522	$971	€762	The forge (24x30cm-9x12in) s. board. 2-Mar-4 Ritchie, Toronto #42/R (C.D 1300)
£960	$1757	€1402	Cottage in the forest (22x30cm-9x12in) s.d.1887 board. 1-Jun-4 Joyner Waddington, Toronto #342/R est:2500-3000 (C.D 2400)
£1696	$2918	€2476	Consolation (27x36cm-11x14in) s.d.1860 cradled panel. 2-Dec-3 Joyner Waddington, Toronto #225/R est:3000-3500 (C.D 3800)
£2703	$4595	€3946	Ste Anne river, Quebec (74x104cm-29x41in) s.d.1872. 18-Nov-3 Sotheby's, Toronto #171/R est:7000-9000 (C.D 6000)
£7658	$13018	€11181	Indian encampment (66x104cm-26x41in) s.d.1854 prov. 18-Nov-3 Sotheby's, Toronto #100/R est:10000-15000 (C.D 17000)
Works on paper			
£248	$451	€362	Seine (61x44cm-24x17in) s. W/C prov. 5-Feb-4 Heffel, Vancouver #45/R (C.D 600)
£826	$1496	€1206	Untitled - mountain scene with rocky stream (25x41cm-10x16in) s.d.1869 W/C. 18-Apr-4 Levis, Calgary #51/R est:2500-3000 (C.D 2000)

JACOBI, Rudolf (1889-1972) American

£1268	$2028	€1800	Industrial city (65x81cm-26x32in) s. 18-Sep-3 Rieber, Stuttgart #1146/R est:1980
Works on paper			
£500	$895	€750	Fishing huts by river (49x64cm-19x25in) s.d.31 gouache. 15-May-4 Van Ham, Cologne #693
£629	$1070	€900	Southern city with moon (48x62cm-19x24in) s.d.1925 i.d. verso W/C chl. 29-Nov-3 Villa Grisebach, Berlin #586/R est:800-1000
£664	$1129	€950	Narrow street (62x48cm-24x19in) s.d.1925 W/C over chl. 29-Nov-3 Villa Grisebach, Berlin #585/R est:800-1000
£733	$1342	€1100	Paris (48x65cm-19x26in) s.i.d.1927 W/C. 5-Jun-4 Lempertz, Koln #773/R

JACOBS, Adolphe (1859-1940) Belgian
£667 $1207 €1000 Deux chiots au repos (25x35cm-10x14in) s.d.1890. 30-Mar-4 Campo & Campo, Antwerp #141/R
£933 $1671 €1400 Fermiere et ses vaches (36x45cm-14x18in) s. 16-May-4 MonsAntic, Maisieres #430
£1818 $3091 €2600 Charette tiree par deux vaches (86x92cm-34x36in) s.d.1900. 18-Nov-3 Vanderkindere, Brussels #125 est:1500-2000

JACOBS, Bruno (20th C) German
£497 $929 €750 Forest worker in Ferch Forest near Potsdam (120x95cm-47x37in) s. i.verso. 23-Jul-4 Altus, Berlin #554/R

JACOBS, Gerard (1865-1958) Belgian
£704 $1218 €1000 Marine au vapeur (63x78cm-25x31in) s. 9-Dec-3 Campo, Vlaamse Kaai #333

JACOBS, Helen Mary (fl.1910-1928) British
Works on paper
£698 $1200 €1019 Illustration for - The land of Never Grow Old (38x23cm-15x9in) s. W/C ink traces pencil lit. 7-Dec-3 Freeman, Philadelphia #137 est:2000-3000

JACOBS, Herman (1936-) Belgian
£408 $731 €600 Clown (78x59cm-31x23in) 22-Mar-4 Amberes, Antwerp #214

JACOBS, Herman (1921-1994) Belgian
£470 $832 €700 Femme cubiste (39x33cm-15x13in) s.d.1957. 27-Apr-4 Campo & Campo, Antwerp #123

JACOBS, Jacob Albertus Michael (1812-1879) Belgian
£642 $1149 €950 Peniche accostee (28x41cm-11x16in) mono. 10-May-4 Horta, Bruxelles #309
£760 $1307 €1110 Kitchen interior with fisherman presenting catch to a lady of the house young boy looking on (38x43cm-15x17in) s.d.1833 panel. 2-Dec-3 Canterbury Auctions, UK #159/R
£2000 $3620 €3000 Smuggler by racing mountain river (92x123cm-36x48in) s.d.1857 panel. 1-Apr-4 Van Ham, Cologne #1453/R est:3400

JACOBS, Jacob Albertus Michael (attrib) (1812-1879) Belgian
£270 $511 €400 Tour de guet en Mediterranee (18x27cm-7x11in) oil paper on canvas prov. 17-Feb-4 Vanderkindere, Brussels #468

JACOBS, Louis Adolphe (1855-1929) Belgian
£567 $1014 €850 Fishermen on the beach (35x29cm-14x11in) s. 15-May-4 De Vuyst, Lokeren #170
£775 $1340 €1100 Cows in meadow (57x77cm-22x30in) s.d.1913. 15-Dec-3 Bernaerts, Antwerp #245/R

JACOBS, Michel (1877-1958) American
£682 $1200 €996 Two gent stamp (30x30cm-12x12in) s.d.1906 board. 22-May-4 New Orleans Auction, New Orleans #829/R est:1800-2500

JACOBSEN, A (19th C) ?
£737 $1253 €1076 Woodland lake (67x65cm-26x26in) s. 10-Nov-3 Rasmussen, Vejle #90/R (D.KR 8000)

JACOBSEN, Antonio (1850-1921) American
£2100 $3780 €3066 Governor Robie of New York (29x46cm-11x18in) s.d.1916 board. 22-Apr-4 Lawrence, Crewkerne #897/R est:300-500
£3279 $6000 €4787 Steam sail ship at sea (45x70cm-18x28in) 29-Jul-4 Christie's, Rockefeller NY #244/R est:5000-7000
£3353 $5800 €4895 Yorkshire (46x76cm-18x30in) s.d.1916 board. 13-Dec-3 Charlton Hall, Columbia #519/R est:8000-12000
£3552 $6500 €5186 Steam ship, Antilia (53x38cm-21x15in) s.d.1904. 10-Apr-4 Cobbs, Peterborough #14/R
£3593 $6000 €5246 American ship, L Schepp, in a typhoon off Bellona Reef, New Caledonia (61x107cm-24x42in) s.indis.i.d.1889 prov. 7-Oct-3 Sotheby's, New York #169 est:4000-6000
£3727 $6000 €5441 Schooner on high seas (18x13cm-7x5in) 20-Aug-3 James Julia, Fairfield #578/R est:6000-8000
£3757 $6500 €5485 Charles H Marshall (46x76cm-18x30in) s.d.1916 board. 13-Dec-3 Charlton Hall, Columbia #520/R est:9000-14000
£3784 $7000 €5525 The James Foster Jr under reduced sail at sea (43x74cm-17x29in) s.d.1911 board. 10-Feb-4 Christie's, Rockefeller NY #215/R est:8000-12000
£4184 $7573 €6109 La Provence (71x120cm-28x47in) s.d.1909 board prov. 1-Apr-4 Heffel, Vancouver #58/R est:15000-20000 (C.D 10000)
£4372 $8000 €6383 Antilles at sea (46x76cm-18x30in) s.d.1900/31 board. 29-Jul-4 Christie's, Rockefeller NY #246/R est:8000-12000
£5405 $10000 €7891 The Black Ball packet ship Charles H Marshall (44x76cm-17x30in) s.d.1915 board lit. 10-Feb-4 Christie's, Rockefeller NY #209/R est:10000-12000
£5405 $10000 €7891 The Fidelia under full sail (45x76cm-18x30in) s.d.1916 board lit. 10-Feb-4 Christie's, Rockefeller NY #214/R est:10000-12000
£5442 $9741 €8000 Vaderland en route pour les Etats-Unis (56x92cm-22x36in) s.d.1905. 21-Mar-4 St-Germain-en-Laye Encheres #9/R est:6000
£5518 $9214 €8000 La touraine (52x92cm-20x36in) s.i.d.1894 prov. 17-Nov-3 Tajan, Paris #63/R est:8000-10000
£5587 $10000 €8157 Black Ball Packet ship - Columbia II (46x76cm-18x30in) s.i.d.1917. 16-Mar-4 Bonhams & Butterfields, San Francisco #6143/R est:4000-6000
£5587 $10000 €9381 S S New York after her refit in 1903 (53x89cm-21x35in) s.i.d.1907 panel. 20-Mar-4 Pook & Pook, Downington #547/R est:9000-12000
£5946 $11000 €8681 The French liner, La Touraine, in heavy seas (53x89cm-21x35in) s.i.d.1894 lit. 10-Feb-4 Christie's, Rockefeller NY #33/R est:7000-10000
£6145 $11000 €8972 American steamer - Navahoe (46x76cm-18x30in) s.i.d.1909 board. 16-Mar-4 Bonhams & Butterfields, San Francisco #6144/R est:6000-8000
£6145 $11000 €8972 S S Manhattan (22x36cm-9x14in) prov. 6-May-4 Shannon's, Milford #125/R est:10000-15000
£6211 $10000 €9068 Portrait of a steam powered yacht (56x91cm-22x36in) s. board prov. 20-Aug-3 James Julia, Fairfield #577/R est:6000-8000
£6486 $12000 €9470 The French liner, La Touraine, outward bound for America (76x127cm-30x50in) s.i.d.1900 lit. 10-Feb-4 Christie's, Rockefeller NY #36/R est:15000-25000
£6704 $12000 €9788 Ship portrait of the Winchester II with Winchester Bowl (56x91cm-22x36in) s.d.1910 board. 8-Jan-4 James Julia, Fairfield #439/R est:1000-2000
£6790 $11000 €9846 Steam yacht, Cristina (61x89cm-24x35in) s.i.d.1912-13 board. 1-Aug-3 Bonhams & Butterfields, San Francisco #688/R est:12000-18000
£7186 $12000 €10492 M S Dollar (56x91cm-22x36in) s.i.d.1901 canvas on board prov. 23-Oct-3 Shannon's, Milford #45/R est:10000-15000
£7453 $12000 €10881 Ship portrait of the North Land (51x91cm-20x36in) s. board prov. 20-Aug-3 James Julia, Fairfield #576/R est:12000-16000
£7821 $14000 €11419 Four-masted American Barque - Manga Reva (46x76cm-18x30in) s.i.d.1909 board. 16-Mar-4 Bonhams & Butterfields, San Francisco #6142/R est:10000-15000
£8380 $15000 €12235 British Auxiliary steamer, Cornwall approaching New York (56x91cm-22x36in) s.i.d.1877. 16-Mar-4 Bonhams & Butterfields, San Francisco #6141/R est:10000-15000
£11173 $20000 €16313 Steamship Oregon (56x91cm-22x36in) s.i.d.1878. 11-Jan-4 William Jenack, New York #152 est:20000-25000
£11628 $20000 €16977 Lusitania met by the pilot boat New York (5x87cm-2x34in) s.i.d.1908 board. 3-Dec-3 Doyle, New York #256/R est:20000-30000
£11801 $19000 €17229 Schooner James T Maxwell jr (51x79cm-20x31in) s. board prov. 20-Aug-3 James Julia, Fairfield #575/R est:20000-25000
£12346 $20000 €17902 The Cornwall (56x91cm-22x36in) s. prov. 8-Aug-3 Barridorf, Portland #74/R est:18000-22000
£13580 $22000 €19691 Schooner Marie Gilbert (56x91cm-22x36in) s.i.d.1907 board prov. 8-Aug-3 Barridorf, Portland #72/R est:15000-20000
£13975 $22500 €20404 Portrait of the schooner 'Mannie Swan' (122x71cm-48x28in) s. board. 20-Aug-3 James Julia, Fairfield #578a/R est:15000-20000
£15135 $28000 €22097 Mayflower and Galatea neck and neck during America's Cup Race (25x40cm-10x16in) s.d.1887. 10-Feb-4 Christie's, Rockefeller NY #201/R est:10000-15000
£20000 $34000 €29200 Portrait of the yacht Marguerite (56x91cm-22x36in) s.d.1907 board prov. 1-Nov-3 Skinner, Boston #136/R est:35000-45000
£37838 $70000 €55243 New York Yacht Club member's race between Estelle and Clio (62x108cm-24x43in) s.d.1879. 10-Feb-4 Christie's, Rockefeller NY #199/R est:50000-70000
£45000 $72000 €65700 American schooner, possibly the Grayling, trailing the leader (71x102cm-28x40in) s.i.d.1883 prov. 16-Sep-3 Bonhams, New Bond Street #84/R est:30000-50000

JACOBSEN, Antonio (attrib) (1850-1921) American
£1647 $2800 €2405 El dorado (41cm-16in circular) s. board. 22-Nov-3 Jackson's, Cedar Falls #93/R est:2000-3000

JACOBSEN, August (1868-1955) Norwegian
£338 $615 €507 Wooded landscape with waterway (58x92cm-23x36in) s. 19-Jun-4 Rasmussen, Havnen #2124/R (D.KR 3800)
Prints
£2566 $4363 €3746 View with four churches, Stavanger (70x80cm-28x31in) s. lit. 19-Nov-3 Grev Wedels Plass, Oslo #3/R est:30000-40000 (N.KR 30000)

JACOBSEN, August (attrib) (1868-1955) Norwegian
£450 $733 €657 Summer's day by woodland lake (60x93cm-24x37in) s. 27-Sep-3 Rasmussen, Havnen #2124/R (D.KR 4800)
£469 $764 €685 Summer's day in the woods (65x99cm-26x39in) s. 27-Sep-3 Rasmussen, Havnen #2123/R (D.KR 5000)

JACOBSEN, David (1821-1871) Danish
£416 $744 €607 Interior scene with woman standing by bird cage (24x19cm-9x7in) s. 12-Jan-4 Rasmussen, Vejle #137/R (D.KR 4400)

JACOBSEN, Egill (1910-1998) Danish
£316 $581 €461 Erik Olesen as child playing at table with his siblings (55x62cm-22x24in) s.d.21 prov. 29-Mar-4 Rasmussen, Copenhagen #560/R (D.KR 3500)
£3700 $6809 €5402 Orange mask composition (28x21cm-11x8in) init.d.82 verso. 29-Mar-4 Rasmussen, Copenhagen #125/R est:35000 (D.KR 41000)
£5164 $8624 €7539 Mask composition (41x31cm-16x12in) init.d.1989 verso. 7-Oct-3 Rasmussen, Copenhagen #47/R est:40000-50000 (D.KR 55000)
£5446 $9095 €7951 Mask composition (65x50cm-26x20in) init.d.70 verso. 7-Oct-3 Rasmussen, Copenhagen #59/R est:60000 (D.KR 58000)
£5822 $9722 €8500 White mask (41x32cm-16x13in) init.d.70 verso prov. 7-Oct-3 Rasmussen, Copenhagen #48/R est:50000 (D.KR 62000)
£6890 $11162 €9991 Composition (42x65cm-17x26in) mono. init.d.88 verso. 4-Aug-3 Rasmussen, Vejle #531/R est:60000-80000 (D.KR 72000)
£7512 $12545 €10968 Conventional mask composition with yellow and green spiral eyes (63x49cm-25x19in) s.i.verso painted c.1938 exhib.prov. 7-Oct-3 Rasmussen, Copenhagen #7/R est:100000 (D.KR 80000)
£9928 $18267 €14495 Mask in green (65x46cm-26x18in) init.d.62 verso prov.exhib.lit. 29-Mar-4 Rasmussen, Copenhagen #132/R est:100000 (D.KR 110000)
£10900 $17441 €15805 Mask composition (81x65cm-32x26in) init.i.d.78 verso. 17-Sep-3 Kunsthallen, Copenhagen #3/R est:100000 (D.KR 115000)
£11289 $19191 €16482 Fire bird III (81x65cm-32x26in) init.d.85 verso lit. 26-Nov-3 Kunsthallen, Copenhagen #29/R est:125000 (D.KR 120000)
£12184 $22419 €17789 Lyrical improvisation (81x65cm-32x26in) init.verso painted 1958 exhib.prov. 29-Mar-4 Rasmussen, Copenhagen #122/R est:100000-125000 (D.KR 135000)
£12207 $20385 €17822 Mask in blue (92x73cm-36x29in) init.d.65 verso prov. 7-Oct-3 Rasmussen, Copenhagen #24/R est:125000-150000 (D.KR 130000)
£12207 $20385 €17822 Mask composition (81x65cm-32x26in) init.verso painted 1973. 7-Oct-3 Rasmussen, Copenhagen #63a (D.KR 130000)
£13170 $22389 €19228 Green mask (81x65cm-32x26in) init.d.78 verso lit. 26-Nov-3 Kunsthallen, Copenhagen #3/R est:100000 (D.KR 140000)
£13170 $22389 €19228 Mask composition (100x81cm-39x32in) init.d.80 verso lit. 26-Nov-3 Kunsthallen, Copenhagen #82/R est:150000 (D.KR 140000)
£13641 $23189 €19916 Blue room (100x73cm-39x29in) init.d.82 lit. 26-Nov-3 Kunsthallen, Copenhagen #70/R est:125000 (D.KR 145000)
£14581 $24788 €21288 Dwarf (100x73cm-39x29in) painted 1986 lit. 26-Nov-3 Kunsthallen, Copenhagen #108/R est:125000 (D.KR 155000)
£17840 $29793 €26046 Mask composition (100x75cm-39x30in) init.d.64 verso prov. 7-Oct-3 Rasmussen, Copenhagen #57/R est:150000-200000 (D.KR 190000)
£20657 $34498 €30159 Happy mask in green (92x65cm-36x26in) init.d.67 verso prov. 7-Oct-3 Rasmussen, Copenhagen #63/R est:150000-175000 (D.KR 220000)

£37559 $62723 €54836 Masked figure in green (93x67cm-37x26in) s.d.1946 verso lit. 7-Oct-3 Rasmussen, Copenhagen #35/R est:400000 (D.KR 400000)
£42419 $78051 €61932 Spring II (84x70cm-33x28in) init.d.45 verso exhib.prov. 29-Mar-4 Rasmussen, Copenhagen #109/R est:400000-500000 (D.KR 470000)
Works on paper
£448 $806 €654 Mask composition (31x21cm-12x8in) init.d.81 crayon. 24-Apr-4 Rasmussen, Havnen #4186 (D.KR 5000)
£1083 $1993 €1581 Happy mask composition (28x20cm-11x8in) init.d.12/3 69 crayon Indian ink prov. 29-Mar-4 Rasmussen, Copenhagen #435/R est:8000 (D.KR 12000)
£2174 $3565 €3000 Untitled (29x22cm-11x9in) one s.i. one init.d.54 col crayon two. 27-May-3 Sotheby's, Amsterdam #543/R est:3000-4000

JACOBSEN, Ludvig (1890-1957) Danish
£276 $470 €403 Cooking chestnuts in Toledo (67x55cm-26x22in) s. 10-Nov-3 Rasmussen, Vejle #637/R (D.KR 3000)
£280 $476 €400 Girl with doll (37x29cm-15x11in) s. lit. 28-Nov-3 Schloss Ahlden, Ahlden #1597/R
£286 $486 €418 Olive pickers, Majorca (76x59cm-30x23in) s. 10-Nov-3 Rasmussen, Vejle #636/R (D.KR 3100)
£287 $465 €416 Interior scene with two girls playing (52x54cm-20x21in) s. 4-Aug-3 Rasmussen, Vejle #522 (D.KR 3000)
£299 $473 €434 Jacob von Tyboe (60x79cm-24x31in) s. 2-Sep-3 Rasmussen, Copenhagen #1931/R (D.KR 3200)
£320 $531 €467 Boy seated at a table with a bottle and fruit (56x46cm-22x18in) s. 4-Oct-3 Finan Watkins & Co, Mere #149
£327 $517 €474 Brother and sister playing at table (47x56cm-19x22in) s. 2-Sep-3 Rasmussen, Copenhagen #1930/R (D.KR 3500)
£327 $517 €474 Selling fish in the south (80x107cm-31x42in) s. 2-Sep-3 Rasmussen, Copenhagen #1995/R (D.KR 3500)
£361 $675 €527 Courtesans conversing (35x23cm-14x9in) s. 25-Feb-4 Museumsbygningen, Copenhagen #2 (D.KR 4000)
£361 $667 €527 Kristian and Kirsten - the artist's children (55x46cm-22x18in) s. panel. 15-Mar-4 Rasmussen, Vejle #648/R (D.KR 4000)
£414 $704 €604 Family at dinner table (58x62cm-23x24in) s. 29-Nov-3 Rasmussen, Havnen #2122/R (D.KR 4400)
£433 $736 €632 Breakfast outside (62x76cm-24x30in) s. 29-Nov-3 Rasmussen, Havnen #2123/R (D.KR 4600)
£461 $783 €673 Well dressed gentleman flirting with young girl in town (65x55cm-26x22in) s. 10-Nov-3 Rasmussen, Vejle #638/R (D.KR 5000)
£562 $938 €821 Market place in Palma, Majorca (86x112cm-34x44in) s. 25-Oct-3 Rasmussen, Havnen #2148/R (D.KR 6000)
£654 $1177 €955 Plaza del Conde Toledo (100x130cm-39x51in) s. 24-Apr-4 Rasmussen, Havnen #2008 (D.KR 7300)

JACOBSEN, Robert (1912-1993) Danish
£753 $1279 €1099 Composition (92x61cm-36x24in) s. acrylic Japan paper. 26-Nov-3 Kunsthallen, Copenhagen #166/R (D.KR 8000)
£1418 $2538 €2070 Composition (80x60cm-31x24in) s. acrylic oil. 12-Jan-4 Rasmussen, Vejle #592/R est:10000-15000 (D.KR 15000)
Sculpture
£1597 $2667 €2300 La loi eternelle (24x24x13cm-9x9x5in) soldered metal prov. 25-Oct-3 Cornette de St.Cyr, Paris #705 est:2000-3000
£2266 $3852 €3308 Composition (10cm-4in) init. black iron prov. 5-Nov-3 AB Stockholms Auktionsverk #1109/R est:25000-30000 (S.KR 30000)
£2347 $4388 €3427 Life and death (31cm-12in) init. iron. 25-Feb-4 Kunsthallen, Copenhagen #119/R est:25000 (D.KR 26000)
£2676 $4469 €3907 Untitled (42cm-17in) init. exec.c.1960 pat iron. 7-Oct-3 Rasmussen, Copenhagen #244/R est:35000-40000 (D.KR 28500)
£3159 $5812 €4612 Prag 68 - doll (42cm-17in) mono. iron. 29-Mar-4 Rasmussen, Copenhagen #5/R est:40000 (D.KR 35000)
£3497 $5944 €5000 Untitled (58x40cm-23x16in) init. welded iron exec c.1952-1957 prov. 25-Nov-3 Christie's, Amsterdam #151/R est:5500-6500
£3776 $6420 €5513 Composition (58cm-23in) init.num.240 black iron prov. 5-Nov-3 AB Stockholms Auktionsverk #1107/R est:60000-80000 (S.KR 50000)
£3791 $6975 €5535 Stationary vibration (14x33x23cm-6x13x9in) init. black painted iron prov. 29-Mar-4 Rasmussen, Copenhagen #126/R est:30000 (D.KR 42000)
£3873 $6701 €5500 Sans titre (23x8cm-9x3in) mono. soldered iron prov. 14-Dec-3 Versailles Encheres #207/R est:5000-6000
£4206 $6645 €6099 Theme chinois-fin (32cm-13in) init. black painted iron incl.white wood base. 3-Sep-3 Museumsbygningen, Copenhagen #152/R est:15000-18000 (D.KR 45000)
£4693 $8635 €6852 Mask composition (75x58cm-30x23in) iron relief. 29-Mar-4 Rasmussen, Copenhagen #143/R est:40000 (D.KR 52000)
£4964 $9134 €7247 Concrete sculpture (16cm-6in) init. iron incl.light stone socle exec.c.1950. 29-Mar-4 Rasmussen, Copenhagen #42/R est:20000 (D.KR 55000)
£5359 $8681 €7771 The Holy Family (56cm-22in) init. gilded iron exhib. 4-Aug-3 Rasmussen, Vejle #516/R est:50000 (D.KR 56000)
£6042 $10272 €8821 Hulla Hoop (35cm-14in) welded iron exhib.prov. 5-Nov-3 AB Stockholms Auktionsverk #1147/R est:18000-20000 (S.KR 80000)
£7401 $13839 €10805 Construction (65cm-26in) iron executed 1960s. 25-Feb-4 Kunsthallen, Copenhagen #49/R est:80000 (D.KR 82000)
£7512 $12545 €10968 Construction (61x50x30cm-24x20x12in) mono. red pat iron exec.c.1954. 7-Oct-3 Rasmussen, Copenhagen #92/R est:100000 (D.KR 80000)
£7671 $14346 €11200 Doll (100cm-39in) init. iron exec.c.1952. 25-Feb-4 Kunsthallen, Copenhagen #60/R est:70000 (D.KR 85000)
£9953 $15924 €14432 Figure (38x35x28cm-15x14x11in) soapstone exhib. exec.c.1944. 17-Sep-3 Kunsthallen, Copenhagen #14/R est:100000 (D.KR 105000)
£13538 $24910 €19765 Doll (64cm-25in) iron exec.c.1955 prov. 29-Mar-4 Rasmussen, Copenhagen #136/R est:125000-150000 (D.KR 150000)
£14440 $26570 €21082 Concrete sculpture (50x34cm-20x13in) init. pat iron exec.c.1953. 29-Mar-4 Rasmussen, Copenhagen #33/R est:75000-100000 (D.KR 160000)
£14440 $26570 €21082 Anti sculpture - construction (80x55x55cm-31x22x22in) mono. pat iron exec.c.1958. 29-Mar-4 Rasmussen, Copenhagen #115/R est:100000 (D.KR 160000)
£16901 $28225 €24675 Pinco (53x47cm-21x19in) init. iron exec.c.1952-53 exhib.prov. 7-Oct-3 Rasmussen, Copenhagen #97/R est:200000-250000 (D.KR 180000)
£23944 $39986 €34958 Jakob's Ladder (70x35x45cm-28x14x18in) st.mono.d.1949/50 black painted iron. 7-Oct-3 Rasmussen, Copenhagen #88/R est:200000 (D.KR 255000)
£29783 $54801 €43483 Drawing in the air - concrete sculpture (37x40cm-15x16in) init. black painted iron exec.c.1949. 29-Mar-4 Rasmussen, Copenhagen #20/R est:125000-150000 (D.KR 330000)
£52347 $96318 €76427 Construction (60x60x45cm-24x24x18in) black painted iron exec.c.1950. 29-Mar-4 Rasmussen, Copenhagen #4/R est:200000-250000 (D.KR 580000)
Works on paper
£416 $744 €607 Composition (28x27cm-11x11in) s. W/C. 12-Jan-4 Rasmussen, Vejle #667 (D.KR 4400)
£542 $996 €791 Composition (25x32cm-10x13in) s. gouache. 29-Mar-4 Rasmussen, Copenhagen #357/R (D.KR 6000)
£586 $1037 €856 Composition (36x47cm-14x19in) st.sig. gouache. 27-Apr-4 AB Stockholms Auktionsverk #1187/R (S.KR 8000)
£614 $1100 €896 Composition (64x49cm-25x19in) s. mixed media. 12-Jan-4 Rasmussen, Vejle #596/R (D.KR 6500)
£632 $1162 €923 Composition (65x49cm-26x19in) s. gouache. 29-Mar-4 Rasmussen, Copenhagen #430/R (D.KR 7000)
£709 $1269 €1035 Boy on rocking horse (49x64cm-19x25in) s. W/C pastel. 12-Jan-4 Rasmussen, Vejle #593/R (D.KR 7500)
£1597 $2524 €2300 Composition (45x54cm-18x21in) s.d.1958 pastel prov.exhib. 27-Apr-3 Versailles Encheres #10

JACOBSEN, Sophus (1833-1912) Norwegian
£1201 $2150 €1753 Fence in the forest (40x55cm-16x22in) s. canvas on panel. 22-Mar-4 Blomqvist, Oslo #354/R est:20000-30000 (N.KR 15000)
£2365 $4234 €3453 Winter landscape with cottage (37x59cm-15x23in) s.d.66. 25-May-4 Bukowskis, Stockholm #333/R est:40000-50000 (S.KR 32000)
£5208 $8594 €7500 Fishing by moonlight on forest lake (101x150cm-40x59in) s. 3-Jul-3 Van Ham, Cologne #1275 est:5000
£7240 $12453 €10570 Spear fishing (100x150cm-39x59in) s. 8-Dec-3 Blomqvist, Oslo #471/R est:80000-90000 (N.KR 85000)

JACOBSON, Albert (20th C) American
Works on paper
£240 $400 €350 Coastal rocks (29x45cm-11x18in) s. gouache. 26-Oct-3 Bonhams & Butterfields, San Francisco #6554/R

JACOBSON, Elisabeth (1852-1886) Swedish
£6000 $10320 €8760 Interior scene with children (169x127cm-67x50in) s.d.85 exhib. 3-Dec-3 AB Stockholms Auktionsverk #2386/R est:30000-40000 (S.KR 78000)

JACOBSON, Oscar Brousse (1882-1966) American
£988 $1700 €1442 Bottomless pit (46x61cm-18x24in) s. i.d.1924 verso board. 7-Dec-3 Grogan, Boston #116/R

JACOBSZ, Lambert (c.1598-1636) Dutch
£36154 $62185 €52785 The prophet Nathan and King David (102x120cm-40x47in) 2-Dec-3 Bukowskis, Stockholm #379/R est:400000-500000 (S.KR 470000)

JACOBY, A A (?) ?
£420 $659 €613 First snow, figures before a thatched cottage (29x44cm-11x17in) s. 10-Dec-2 Bamfords, Derby #773/R

JACOBY, Paul (1844-1899) German
£935 $1477 €1356 Genre scene with young couple, he's reading, she's knitting (76x62cm-30x24in) s.d.1867. 2-Sep-3 Rasmussen, Copenhagen #1709/R (D.KR 10000)

JACOMB-HOOD, George Percy (1857-1937) British
£5500 $10120 €8030 Emblems of spring (51x41cm-20x16in) prov. 11-Jun-4 Christie's, London #191/R est:7000-10000

JACOMIN, Alfred (1842-1913) French
£17647 $30000 €25765 Baptism (130x202cm-51x80in) s. 28-Oct-3 Sotheby's, New York #155/R est:50000-70000

JACOPO DA FIRENZE (14/15th C) Italian
£27933 $50000 €40782 Madonna and Child surrounded by eight saints (75x53cm-30x21in) tempera panel gold ground arched top. 27-May-4 Sotheby's, New York #58/R est:20000-30000

JACOPO DI PAOLO (14th C) Italian
£70922 $118440 €100000 Madonna and Child with thirteen angels (72x60cm-28x24in) tempera gold board lit. 17-Jun-3 Finarte Semenzato, Milan #466/R est:150000

JACOPS, Joseph (1808-?) Belgian
£764 $1245 €1100 Fishermen and women on beach at sunset (49x64cm-19x25in) s. panel. 24-Sep-3 Neumeister, Munich #455/R

JACOT, Don (1949-) American
£13423 $24027 €20000 Commuter trains, Union station, Chicago (91x122cm-36x48in) s.d.91 prov. 27-May-4 Sotheby's, Paris #258/R est:10000-15000

JACOT-GUILLARMOD, Jules Jacques (1828-1889) Swiss
£707 $1300 €1032 Wash Day (31x51cm-12x20in) s. 27-Jun-4 Freeman, Philadelphia #32/R est:1500-2500

JACOULET, Paul (1902-1960) French
Prints
£1863 $3000 €2701 Butterflies of the tropics. s.num.129/350 verso print. 20-Aug-3 Eldred, East Dennis #56 est:3000-4000
£3416 $5500 €4953 Tattooed woman of Falalap. s.num.166/350 verso print. 20-Aug-3 Eldred, East Dennis #21 est:6000-8000
£7453 $12000 €10807 Parisian lady. s.num.64/150 verso print. 20-Aug-3 Eldred, East Dennis #13 est:15000-20000
£7453 $12000 €10807 Modern Japanese beauty. s.num.24/150 verso print. 20-Aug-3 Eldred, East Dennis #23 est:14000-18000
Works on paper
£1977 $3500 €2886 Portrait de Ramon (50x36cm-20x14in) s.d.1940 s.i.d.verso mixed media. 2-May-4 Bonhams & Butterfields, Los Angeles #3016/R est:2000-3000

JACQ, Augustin (20th C) French?

£352	$616	€500	Vague (54x65cm-21x26in) s.d.88. 21-Dec-3 Thierry & Lannon, Brest #394
£387	$678	€550	Grande Tomenie (65x81cm-26x32in) s.d.88. 21-Dec-3 Thierry & Lannon, Brest #393

JACQUE, Charles Émile (1813-1894) French

£450	$833	€657	Chickens in a barn (16x22cm-6x9in) s. panel. 15-Jan-4 Christie's, Kensington #885
£646	$1157	€950	Bouvier et ses cochons (22x34cm-9x13in) s. canvas on panel. 19-Mar-4 Millon & Associes, Paris #39/R
£661	$1123	€965	Poultry yard (13x24cm-5x9in) s. panel. 5-Nov-3 Dobiaschofsky, Bern #690/R (S.FR 1500)
£797	$1307	€1100	Les cochons, la porcherie (19x25cm-7x10in) s. panel. 11-May-3 Osenat, Fontainebleau #61
£850	$1420	€1241	Shepherd and his flock at the edge of a forest (17x27cm-7x11in) s. panel. 8-Oct-3 Christie's, Kensington #805/R
£950	$1710	€1387	The sheepfold (61x53cm-24x21in) s.i. panel prov. 21-Apr-4 Tennants, Leyburn #1196/R
£1862	$3110	€2700	Le poulailler (22x34cm-9x13in) s.d.78 oil paper on canvas. 17-Nov-3 Tajan, Paris #48/R est:3000-4000
£1974	$3632	€3000	Fermiere et ses poules (32x40cm-13x16in) s. panel. 22-Jun-4 Calmels Cohen, Paris #42/R est:3000-3500
£2069	$3455	€3000	Cueillette pres de la mare (22x25cm-9x10in) s. panel. 17-Nov-3 Tajan, Paris #46/R est:3000-4000
£2484	$4000	€3602	Ducks and chickens (13x20cm-5x8in) s. panel. 17-Aug-3 Jeffery Burchard, Florida #60
£2517	$4580	€3800	Shepherd and flocks and a dog in an extensive landscape (44x66cm-17x26in) s. 19-Jun-4 Hans Stahl, Hamburg #58/R est:3200
£3333	$6100	€5000	Poulailler (28x40cm-11x16in) s. 6-Jun-4 Osenat, Fontainebleau #200/R est:7000-8000
£3357	$5606	€4800	Moutons dans une etable (31x46cm-12x18in) s. panel. 25-Jun-3 Maigret, Paris #78/R est:2200-2800
£4000	$7240	€6000	Le troupeau de porcs (21x27cm-8x11in) s. cardboard exhib.lit. 30-Mar-4 Rossini, Paris #306/R est:2000-3000
£4491	$7500	€6557	Relaxing among the flock (31x51cm-12x20in) s. panel. 7-Oct-3 Sotheby's, New York #157 est:5000-7000
£4545	$7818	€6500	Coq et poules pres de la ferme (34x45cm-13x18in) s. i.verso painted c.1860-65. 7-Dec-3 Osenat, Fontainebleau #53 est:7000-8000
£4667	$8447	€7000	Troupeau de moutons dans la plaine de Chailly (54x73cm-21x29in) prov.exhib.lit. 30-Mar-4 Rossini, Paris #305/R est:4000-6000
£4928	$8081	€6800	Bergere et ses moutons (25x34cm-10x13in) s. 11-May-3 Osenat, Fontainebleau #60/R est:8000-10000
£6014	$9864	€8300	Bergere et ses moutons a Barbizon, Bellecroix (37x46cm-15x18in) s. panel. 11-May-3 Osenat, Fontainebleau #59/R est:10000-12000
£7042	$11690	€10000	Coq et poules (46x67cm-18x26in) s. 15-Jun-3 Peron, Melun #183
£7222	$13000	€10544	Un berger avec son troupeau (47x39cm-19x15in) s. prov. 22-Apr-4 Christie's, Rockefeller NY #99/R est:12000-18000
£7333	$13420	€11000	Bergere et moutons (67x100cm-26x39in) s. lit. 6-Jun-4 Osenat, Fontainebleau #102/R est:14000-16000
£8333	$15000	€12166	Paysage avec moutons (43x70cm-17x28in) s. prov. 22-Apr-4 Christie's, Rockefeller NY #102/R est:15000-20000
£9000	$15480	€13140	Shepherd and his dog with cattle and sheep in a field (75x100cm-30x39in) s. 4-Dec-3 Christie's, Kensington #20/R est:7000-10000
£33333	$60000	€48666	Un berger se reposant avec ses moutons (81x110cm-32x43in) s. prov. 22-Apr-4 Christie's, Rockefeller NY #93/R est:70000-90000
£52778	$95000	€77056	Le printemps (107x77cm-42x30in) s.d.59 prov. 23-Apr-4 Sotheby's, New York #3/R est:70000-90000
Works on paper			
£594	$1022	€850	Etude de moutons. s. graphite wax crayon. 7-Dec-3 Osenat, Fontainebleau #13
£629	$1083	€900	La boisiere en foret (13x21cm-5x8in) s. pen black ink. 7-Dec-3 Osenat, Fontainebleau #12/R
£670	$1200	€978	Shepherd and his flock (31x22cm-12x9in) s. black chk htd white. 6-May-4 Doyle, New York #34/R est:2000-3000
£1667	$2733	€2300	Le repas des laboureurs (20x26cm-8x10in) mono. Indian ink wash. 11-May-3 Osenat, Fontainebleau #63/R est:1800-2000

JACQUE, Charles Emile (attrib) (1813-1894) French

£529	$899	€772	Girl with herd of sheep by wood (50x65cm-20x26in) 5-Nov-3 Dobiaschofsky, Bern #691/R (S.FR 1200)
£574	$1085	€850	Bergere et son troupeau au bord de l'eau (19x24cm-7x9in) bears sig. panel. 17-Feb-4 Vanderkindere, Brussels #36

JACQUE, Émile (1848-1912) French

£1449	$2377	€2000	Troupeau de moutons a l'oree du bois (35x27cm-14x11in) s. 11-May-3 Osenat, Fontainebleau #65/R est:2700-3000
£2083	$3292	€3000	Working horses pausing for a drink in a river (50x67cm-20x26in) s. 2-Sep-3 Christie's, Amsterdam #177/R est:2000-3000

JACQUE, Frederic (1859-?) French

£315	$535	€450	La barque (38x46cm-15x18in) s. 24-Nov-3 Boscher, Cherbourg #783

JACQUE, Mariel (20th C) French

Works on paper			
£306	$550	€447	Barbizon style (41x25cm-16x10in) s. chl. 25-Jan-4 Hindman, Chicago #1024/R

JACQUEMART, A (19th C) French

Sculpture			
£1267	$2267	€1900	Chien et tortue (15cm-6in) s. brown pat bronze. 12-May-4 Coutau Begarie, Paris #255/R est:1900-2000

JACQUEMART, Alfred (1824-1896) French

Sculpture			
£1418	$2369	€2000	Chien Saint Hubert et son petit (22cm-9in) s. green pat bronze. 12-Oct-3 St-Germain-en-Laye Encheres #46/R est:2200-2500
£1514	$2800	€2210	Standing hound (18x20x28cm-7x8x11in) s. brown pat.bronze. 10-Feb-4 Doyle, New York #158/R est:3000-5000
£2059	$3500	€3006	Bloodhound studying tortoise (14cm-6in) s. pat bronze. 28-Oct-3 Christie's, Rockefeller NY #227/R

JACQUEMART, Andre (?) French?

Sculpture			
£1138	$1900	€1661	Thoroughbred race horse (38cm-15in) s. cast bronze green marble base. 16-Nov-3 CRN Auctions, Cambridge #69/R

JACQUEMART, Nelie (1841-1912) French

£2759	$4607	€4000	Autoportrait presume (61x50cm-24x20in) s.d.1859. 17-Nov-3 Delorme & Bocage, Paris #129/R est:1200-1800

JACQUEMON, Pierre (1936-2002) French

£300	$546	€450	Orchestre de jazz (31x23cm-12x9in) d.1954 panel. 29-Jun-4 Chenu & Scrive, Lyon #104/R
£500	$910	€750	New York, la nuit (14x23cm-6x9in) s.d.1958 paper. 29-Jun-4 Chenu & Scrive, Lyon #105/R

JACQUES, Emile (1874-1937) Belgian

£2133	$3819	€3200	Chevaux au pres du porche (23x30cm-9x12in) s. 16-May-4 Lombrail & Teucquam, Paris #141/R

JACQUES, François-Louis (1877-1937) Swiss

£330	$562	€482	Etable (38x50cm-15x20in) s. i. verso. 5-Nov-3 Dobiaschofsky, Bern #696/R (S.FR 750)

JACQUES, Nicolas (1780-1844) French

Miniatures			
£5500	$9515	€8030	Comte de Flahaut in blue coat with black collar (6x5cm-2x2in) s. gilt-metal mount. 9-Dec-3 Christie's, London #141/R est:2000-3000
£12000	$20760	€17520	Louis Philippe of Orleans, King of the French. Madame Adelaide (7cm-3in) s.d.1818 gilt-bronze frame oval pair prov.exhib. 9-Dec-3 Christie's, London #205/R est:10000-15000

JACQUET, Alain (1939-) French

£903	$1507	€1300	Composition (18x38cm-7x15in) s.i.63 verso acrylic board prov. 21-Oct-3 Artcurial Briest, Paris #556 est:1200-1500
£2667	$4907	€4000	Portrait of man (162x114cm-64x45in) s.i.d.1964 acrylic prov. 14-Jun-4 Porro, Milan #41/R est:3200-4000
£9000	$16560	€13500	Camouflage image d'epinal une gondole a Venise (192x190cm-76x75in) s.d.1962 i.verso acrylic prov.lit. 8-Jun-4 Artcurial Briest, Paris #229/R est:15000-20000
£16197	$28021	€23000	Camouflage lingerie (196x114cm-77x45in) s.d.64 s.verso prov.exhib. 9-Dec-3 Artcurial Briest, Paris #362/R est:25000-30000
£16784	$28532	€24000	Le dejeuner sur l'herbe (174x194cm-69x76in) s.i.d.1964 verso acrylic panel diptych. 25-Nov-3 Tajan, Paris #56/R est:25000-30000
Prints			
£2222	$3712	€3200	First breakfast (118x163cm-46x64in) s.d.72 verso screenprint canvas exhib.lit. 21-Oct-3 Artcurial Briest, Paris #494/R est:3500-4000
£2300	$4186	€3358	First breakfast (119x151cm-47x59in) s.i.d.1978 verso col silkscreen. 1-Jul-4 Sotheby's, London #410/R est:2500-3000
£2800	$5096	€4088	L'ane (114x162cm-45x64in) s.i. col silkscreen. 1-Jul-4 Sotheby's, London #412/R est:3000-4000
£2817	$4873	€4000	Plage des Antilles (97x158cm-38x62in) s.verso serigraph on canvas prov.exhib. 9-Dec-3 Artcurial Briest, Paris #370/R est:2500-3000
£3521	$6092	€5000	Untitled (122x183cm-48x72in) serigraph on plexiglass exec.1967 prov. 9-Dec-3 Artcurial Briest, Paris #365/R est:5000-7000
£3873	$6701	€5500	Portrait d'homme (162x114cm-64x45in) s.i.d.1964 verso print on canvas prov.exhib.lit. 9-Dec-3 Artcurial Briest, Paris #363/R est:6000-8000
£3873	$6701	€5500	Jeune fille aux boules (195x114cm-77x45in) s.i.verso serigraph on canvas. 9-Dec-3 Artcurial Briest, Paris #367/R est:4500-6000
£4578	$7920	€6500	Portrait d'homme (162x114cm-64x45in) s.d.1964 num.1/30 verso serigraph prov.exhib.lit. 9-Dec-3 Artcurial Briest, Paris #364/R est:6000-8000
£4578	$7920	€6500	Tub (130x80cm-51x31in) s.d.65 serigraph. 9-Dec-3 Artcurial Briest, Paris #369/R est:4000-6000
£4671	$8595	€7100	Gabrielle d'Estree (114x162cm-45x64in) s. s.i.d.1965 verso serigraph on canvas. 27-Jun-4 Versailles Encheres #142/R est:8000-10000
£4930	$8528	€7000	Bat girl (122x183cm-48x72in) s.d.67 serigraph prov. 9-Dec-3 Artcurial Briest, Paris #373/R est:4000-6000
£5903	$9858	€8500	Portrait d'un homme (162x114cm-64x45in) s.d.64 verso trichromie cellulosique canvas prov.exhib.lit. 21-Oct-3 Artcurial Briest, Paris #480/R est:6000-8000
£6338	$10965	€9000	Gabrielle d'Estree (114x162cm-45x64in) s.d.65 serigraph on canvas prov. 9-Dec-3 Artcurial Briest, Paris #368/R est:4000-6000
£7770	$13676	€11500	Gabrielle d'Estree (115x162cm-45x64in) s.d.1965 serigraph prov. 18-May-4 Tajan, Paris #121/R est:8000-10000
£28275	$48916	€40150	Grues (183x122cm-72x48in) s.d.67 serigraph on plexiglass prov. 9-Dec-3 Artcurial Briest, Paris #371/R est:4000-6000
Works on paper			
£564	$975	€800	Estafette Renault (35x53cm-14x21in) s.d.1969 mixed media collage prov. 9-Dec-3 Artcurial Briest, Paris #376
£6250	$10438	€9000	Portrait d'un homme (162x114cm-64x45in) s.d.64 cellulosique canvas prov.exhib.lit. 21-Oct-3 Artcurial Briest, Paris #481/R est:6000-8000
£6944	$11597	€10000	Portrait d'homme (162x114cm-64x45in) s.d.64 cellulosique canvas lit. 21-Oct-3 Artcurial Briest, Paris #482/R est:6000-8000
£12676	$22183	€18000	Dejeuner sur l'herbe (175x197cm-69x78in) s.i.d.1964 verso ink serigraph paper on canvas. 18-Dec-3 Cornette de St.Cyr, Paris #129/R est:20000-25000

JACQUET, Gustave-Jean (1846-1909) French

£1544	$2733	€2300	Portrait de femme (30x25cm-12x10in) s. 30-Apr-4 Tajan, Paris #167/R est:1500-2000
£1667	$3033	€2500	Jeune fille (46x33cm-18x13in) s. panel. 4-Jul-4 Eric Pillon, Calais #78/R
£1765	$3000	€2577	Portrait of a woman with ruffled collar (33x25cm-13x10in) s. panel. 31-Oct-3 North East Auctions, Portsmouth #1198 est:3000-5000

£3200 $5120 €4640 On the balcony of the Hotel Crillon, Paris (81x63cm-32x25in) st.sig. canvas on panel. 18-Sep-3 Christie's, Kensington #170/R est:2500-3500
£3727 $6000 €5441 Young beauty (33x25cm-13x10in) s. 14-Jan-4 Christie's, Rockefeller NY #12/R est:7000-9000
£3800 $6992 €5548 Card seller (33x21cm-13x8in) s. panel prov. 25-Mar-4 Christie's, Kensington #68a/R est:4000-6000
£4076 $7500 €5951 Portrait of a young lady (30x23cm-12x9in) s. panel. 26-Jun-4 Selkirks, St. Louis #425/R est:6000-8000
£12000 $20400 €17520 Musical interlude (88x63cm-35x25in) s.d.1873 prov. 18-Nov-3 Sotheby's, London #320/R
£26471 $45000 €38648 Portrait of a young woman in a black hat and red feathers (81x66cm-32x26in) s. prov. 28-Oct-3 Sotheby's, New York #55/R est:50000-70000

JACQUET, Gustave-Jean (attrib) (1846-1909) French
£640 $1190 €934 Coquettish young lady (31x23cm-12x9in) bears sig. panel. 2-Mar-4 Bristol Auction Rooms #311/R

JACQUETTE, Julia (1964-) American
£1156 $2000 €1688 Diana (38x38cm-15x15in) enamel wood prov. 10-Dec-3 Phillips, New York #544/R est:3000-4000

JACQUETTE, Yvonne (1934-) American
£13580 $22000 €19691 Town of Skowegon II (198x163cm-78x64in) prov. 8-Aug-3 Barridorf, Portland #231/R est:12000-18000

JACQUIARD, Max (20th C) Canadian
£356 $583 €520 Northern Pacific in Montana (46x61cm-18x24in) s. 28-May-3 Maynards, Vancouver #21 (C.D 800)
£744 $1354 €1086 CN 6013 Near Inkitsaph, Fraser Canyon (51x76cm-20x30in) s. i.verso acrylic. 5-Feb-4 Heffel, Vancouver #46/R (C.D 1800)

JACQUIER, M (20th C) French
£845 $1479 €1200 Passage Lanriec a Concarneau (27x22cm-11x9in) s. panel. 21-Dec-3 Thierry & Lannon, Brest #329

JACQUIER, Marcel (1877-?) French
£2028 $3387 €2900 Pardon en Bretagne (13x15cm-5x6in) s. panel. 29-Jun-3 Eric Pillon, Calais #147/R

JADIN, Louis Godefroy (1805-1882) French
£464 $844 €700 Portrait d'un chien King Charles (28x23cm-11x9in) mono. i.verso cardboard oval. 20-Jun-4 Salle des ventes Pillet, Lyon la Foret #24/R
£1958 $3368 €2800 La grand allee de Rambouillet (141x106cm-56x42in) s.d.1832. 7-Dec-3 Osenat, Fontainebleau #106

JAECKEL, Henry (19th C) German
£3056 $4981 €4400 Sunny city on upper Italian lake (70x96cm-28x38in) s. i. verso. 25-Sep-3 Dr Fritz Nagel, Stuttgart #1358/R est:2400
£11724 $19579 €17000 Santa Maria della Salute, Venice (57x83cm-22x33in) s. prov. 15-Nov-3 Lempertz, Koln #1627/R est:4000
£13194 $22431 €19000 Cafe Giardina mit der Salute in Vendig (83x99cm-33x39in) s. 28-Oct-3 Christie's, Amsterdam #193/R est:10000-15000

JAECKEL, Henry (attrib) (19th C) German
£1458 $2377 €2100 Southern landscape with fountain and figures (60x48cm-24x19in) 24-Sep-3 Neumeister, Munich #456/R est:2500

JAECKEL, Willy (1888-1944) German
£1467 $2640 €2200 Peonies (81x66cm-32x26in) s.d. 24-Apr-4 Dr Lehr, Berlin #179/R est:1800
£2185 $3977 €3300 White lilac in blue vase (90x80cm-35x31in) s.d.36. 19-Jun-4 Dannenberg, Berlin #576/R est:3000
£2395 $4000 €3497 Portrait of a woman (71x61cm-28x24in) s. prov. 23-Oct-3 Shannon's, Milford #247/R est:3000-5000
£2738 $4983 €3997 Still life with flowers in a vase on draped cloth (71x55cm-28x22in) s.d.43. 20-Jun-4 Agra, Warsaw #14/R (P.Z 19000)
£3245 $5906 €4900 White lilies in vase (81x70cm-32x28in) s. 19-Jun-4 Dannenberg, Berlin #575/R est:4000
£13986 $23776 €20000 Reclining nude (98x146cm-39x57in) s. prov.exhib.lit. 29-Nov-3 Villa Grisebach, Berlin #213/R est:10000-15000
£20000 $36600 €30000 Dancer in red (118x119cm-46x47in) s.d.29 exhib.lit. 5-Jun-4 Lempertz, Koln #774/R est:15000-18000
Works on paper
£267 $480 €400 Prometheus (37x29cm-15x11in) s. Indian ink brush board. 24-Apr-4 Dr Lehr, Berlin #180/R

JAECKS, Joel (20th C) American
Works on paper
£273 $500 €410 Red azaleas (99x147cm-39x58in) W/C. 10-Jul-4 Hindman, Chicago #244/R

JAEGER, Friedrich Wilhelm Johannes (1833-1888) German
£1667 $2717 €2400 Peasant on horseback by water pump with peasant girl and dog (67x93cm-26x37in) s.i. 24-Sep-3 Neumeister, Munich #457/R est:2200

JAEGER, Gotthilf (1871-?) German
Sculpture
£1133 $2063 €1700 Swordsman (56cm-22in) i. bronze. 1-Jul-4 Van Ham, Cologne #1034 est:600
£1300 $2327 €1898 Reclining female nude (47cm-19in) s. pat bronze. 13-May-4 Christie's, Kensington #305/R est:1500-2000

JAEGER, Stefan de (1957-) Belgian
Works on paper
£5517 $10207 €8000 Figure et ombre (256x215cm-101x85in) s.d.1981 collage Polaroid panel sold with a monograph and a book. 16-Feb-4 Horta, Bruxelles #194/R est:5000-7000

JAENISCH, Hans (1907-1989) German
£839 $1427 €1200 Composition (28x40cm-11x16in) mono. 29-Nov-3 Bassenge, Berlin #6788/R
Sculpture
£1467 $2699 €2200 AFrican cow (12x14x12cm-5x6x5in) bronze. 11-Jun-4 Hauswedell & Nolte, Hamburg #1319/R est:1500

JAENSSON, Carl Wilhelm (1853-1931) Swedish
£363 $653 €545 Boat builders, Bryggholmen (80x56cm-31x22in) s. exhib. 25-Apr-4 Goteborg Auktionsverk, Sweden #177/R (S.KR 5000)

JAFFE, Lee (1957-) American
Works on paper
£366 $648 €534 Untitled (75x58cm-30x23in) mixed media prov. 27-Apr-4 AB Stockholms Auktionsverk #1205/R (S.KR 5000)
£508 $914 €742 Untitled (106x76cm-42x30in) mixed media collage prov. 26-Apr-4 Bukowskis, Stockholm #619/R (S.KR 7000)
£1088 $1958 €1588 Apache - ? (101x78cm-40x31in) s.d.93 mixed media paper on panel prov. 26-Apr-4 Bukowskis, Stockholm #620/R est:20000-30000 (S.KR 15000)

JAFFE, Shirley (1923-) American
Works on paper
£1056 $1828 €1500 Poste restante (33x25cm-13x10in) gouache W/C prov. 9-Dec-3 Artcurial Briest, Paris #569 est:2000-2500
£1223 $2250 €1786 Untitled (75x54cm-30x21in) s. gouache. 8-Jun-4 Germann, Zurich #817 est:1000-1200 (S.FR 2800)

JAGER, Franz (1893-1985) German
£267 $480 €400 Still life with cactus and wooden horse (61x49cm-24x19in) s. 24-Apr-4 Dr Lehr, Berlin #181/R

JAGER, Franz Wilhelm (1861-1928) Austrian
£300 $489 €438 Peasant women chatting with houses in background (68x56cm-27x22in) s. 27-Sep-3 Rasmussen, Havnen #2177 (D.KR 3200)

JAGER, Frederic (1957-) French?
Sculpture
£1933 $3557 €2900 Enfant cavalier (53x53cm-21x21in) s. num.1/8 pat bronze. 8-Jun-4 Livinec, Gaudcheau & Jezequel, Rennes #183/R

JAGER, Margot de (1956-) Dutch
£667 $1227 €1000 Nieuwbouw (140x150cm-55x59in) s.i.d.1998 verso. 9-Jun-4 Christie's, Amsterdam #381/R

JAGGER, David (fl.1917-1940) British
£680 $1238 €993 Portrait of a lady in a silk scarf (92x74cm-36x29in) s.d. 15-Jun-4 Bonhams, Knightsbridge #82/R

JAHN, Adolf (1858-?) ?
Sculpture
£1034 $1862 €1500 Nathan le Sage (43cm-17in) s. alabaster marble base. 21-Jan-4 Tajan, Paris #91/R est:1500-2500

JAHN, Gustav (1879-1919) Austrian
£500 $910 €750 Grossglockner (60x47cm-24x19in) s. panel. 1-Jul-4 Neumeister, Munich #2720

JAHN, Hans Emil (1834-1902) Norwegian
£580 $1044 €870 Lake landscape with figures by farm (93x125cm-37x49in) s.d.4/3 1897. 25-Apr-4 Goteborg Auktionsverk, Sweden #179/R (S.KR 8000)

JAHN-HEILIGENSTADT, Albert (1885-1961) German
£438 $727 €639 From Berlin (65x55cm-26x22in) s. 4-Oct-3 Dorotheum, Prague #82/R est:60000-90000 (C.KR 20000)

JAHNKE, Robert (20th C) New Zealander?
Sculpture
£1805 $2942 €2635 This is not a customary rights issue, this is a Koha (40x71cm-16x28in) i. bronze kauri. 23-Sep-3 Peter Webb, Auckland #18/R est:3000-4000 (NZ.D 5000)

JAHNS, Rudolf (1896-1983) German
£10738 $19221 €16000 Composition R 9 (25x20cm-10x8in) s.i.d.28 tempera exhib. 25-May-4 Karl & Faber, Munich #350/R est:22000-24000

JAIMES SANCHEZ, Humberto (1930-) South American
£1311 $2190 €1914 Sea wall (80x70cm-31x28in) s.verso painted 1971. 13-Jul-3 Subastas Odalys, Caracas #28/R
£1935 $3000 €2825 Entrance (48x94cm-19x37in) s. painted 1953. 3-Nov-2 Subastas Odalys, Caracas #84/R est:3000

JAIN, Michael (20th C) ?
£320 $586 €467 Salt lake, Camargue (60x91cm-24x36in) s. i.d.1965 verso. 7-Apr-4 Dreweatt Neate, Newbury #113/R

JAKAB, Zoltan (1883-1925) Hungarian
£1148 $1987 €1676 Nagybanya (72x66cm-28x26in) s. 12-Dec-3 Kieselbach, Budapest #58/R (H.F 440000)

JAKAMARRA, Jack Ross (c.1925-) Australian
Works on paper
£340 $579 €496 Luwarrinki Jukurrpa - lizard dreaming (61x76cm-24x30in) s.i.verso synthetic polymer paint linen prov. 25-Nov-3 Christie's, Melbourne #288 (A.D 800)

JAKOBIDES, Georg (1853-1932) Greek
£17450 $32456 €26000 Still life of fruit on plate (39x50cm-15x20in) s. 6-Mar-4 Arnold, Frankfurt #753/R est:2400
£20000 $35000 €29200 Recalling the past (77x58cm-30x23in) s.d.1931 prov. 16-Dec-3 Bonhams, New Bond Street #39/R est:20000-30000
£49000 $83300 €71540 Portrait of the young Stampoulopoulou (125x80cm-49x31in) s.d.1902 prov.exhib.lit. 18-Nov-3 Sotheby's, London #24/R est:50000-70000

JAKOBIDES, Georg (attrib) (1853-1932) Greek
£2069 $3455 €3000 Portrait de fillette (47x38cm-19x15in) bears sig. 17-Nov-3 Tajan, Paris #108/R est:2000-3000

JAKOBSEN, Erik Lagoni (1930-2000) Danish
£1444 $2657 €2108 Surrealistic landscape (170x130cm-67x51in) s.d.88-89 verso exhib. 29-Mar-4 Rasmussen, Copenhagen #324/R est:20000 (D.KR 16000)

JAKOBSSON, Fritz (1940-) Finnish
£2448 $4161 €3500 Still life (39x45cm-15x18in) s.d.1979. 29-Nov-3 Bukowskis, Helsinki #193/R est:3500-4000
£3784 $6773 €5600 Still life of jug and plums (38x60cm-15x24in) s. 8-May-4 Bukowskis, Helsinki #208/R est:4000-5000
£4054 $7257 €6000 Still life of chanterelles (65x95cm-26x37in) s.d.1987. 8-May-4 Bukowskis, Helsinki #153/R est:6000-8000
Works on paper
£1622 $2903 €2400 Chanterelles (36x44cm-14x17in) s.d.2000 W/C. 8-May-4 Bukowskis, Helsinki #130/R est:2000-2500
£1812 $3370 €2700 Apple-tree in blossom (55x76cm-22x30in) s.d.1990 W/C. 7-Mar-4 Bukowskis, Helsinki #340/R est:2000

JAKOWLEFF, Michael (1880-1942) Russian
£1200 $2040 €1752 Beach, Heyst, Belgium (30x40cm-12x16in) s.i. board. 19-Nov-3 Sotheby's, London #114/R est:1500-2000

JALDON, Juan Rodriguez (1890-1967) Spanish
£2069 $3455 €3000 Preparing the horses (69x100cm-27x39in) s. 17-Nov-3 Durán, Madrid #222/R est:2500

JAMAR, Armand (1870-1946) Belgian
£276 $510 €400 Arbres au littoral (46x38cm-18x15in) s.d.1933 panel. 19-Jan-4 Horta, Bruxelles #501
£298 $542 €450 Paysage ardennais (30x37cm-12x15in) s. panel. 15-Jun-4 Galerie Moderne, Brussels #335
£306 $548 €450 Marine (29x39cm-11x15in) s.d.1933 panel. 16-Mar-4 Vanderkindere, Brussels #161
£313 $497 €450 Cote Sauvage animee (85x96cm-33x38in) s.d.1941. 9-Sep-3 Vanderkindere, Brussels #99
£318 $579 €480 La mare (50x75cm-20x30in) s. 16-Jun-4 Hotel des Ventes Mosan, Brussels #209
£323 $600 €472 Figure in an interior (28x36cm-11x14in) s.d.1918 board. 7-Mar-4 Treadway Gallery, Cincinnati #707/R
£331 $603 €500 Paysage hivernal (55x74cm-22x29in) s.d.1928. 16-Jun-4 Hotel des Ventes Mosan, Brussels #202
£352 $609 €500 Premiers beaux jours, La Malignee (29x37cm-11x15in) s. i.verso. 10-Dec-3 Millon & Associes, Paris #106
£377 $640 €550 Les dunes (37x45cm-15x18in) s.d.1946. 5-Nov-3 Vendue Huis, Gravenhage #170
£403 $749 €600 Street in Bruges (75x55cm-30x22in) s.d.1936. 8-Mar-4 Bernaerts, Antwerp #608/R
£430 $783 €650 L'oree du bois (50x70cm-20x28in) 16-Jun-4 Hotel des Ventes Mosan, Brussels #208
£451 $754 €650 Landscape in Provence (70x100cm-28x39in) s.d.1931. 21-Oct-3 Campo & Campo, Antwerp #151
£486 $900 €710 New York Harbor (20x28cm-8x11in) s.d.1919 canvas on panel. 15-Jul-4 Doyle, New York #49/R
£548 $932 €800 Vue portuaire au clair de lune (55x75cm-22x30in) s. 4-Nov-3 Servarts Themis, Bruxelles #582/R
£563 $975 €800 Venise (55x45cm-22x18in) s.d.1922. 10-Dec-3 Millon & Associes, Paris #105
£582 $990 €850 Port de Quiberon (55x75cm-22x30in) s. 4-Nov-3 Servarts Themis, Bruxelles #581/R
£594 $1010 €850 Marine orientaliste (30x37cm-12x15in) s. cardboard. 18-Nov-3 Galerie Moderne, Brussels #826/R
£733 $1349 €1100 Coucher de soleil a Venise (55x75cm-22x30in) s.d.1933. 14-Jun-4 Horta, Bruxelles #55
£753 $1281 €1100 Harmonie en rouge (60x50cm-24x20in) s.d.43. 10-Nov-3 Horta, Bruxelles #30
£839 $1427 €1200 Bateaux en Mer du Nord (70x100cm-28x39in) s.d.1937. 1-Dec-3 Palais de Beaux Arts, Brussels #79
£839 $1443 €1200 Promenade dans le parc publique (55x45cm-22x18in) s.d.1923. 8-Dec-3 Horta, Bruxelles #377
£1611 $2851 €2400 Pont de Venise (55x75cm-22x30in) s.d.1924. 27-Apr-4 Campo & Campo, Antwerp #127/R est:1750-2000
£1667 $2783 €2400 Venise (75x55cm-30x22in) s.d.1928. 21-Oct-3 Campo & Campo, Antwerp #152/R est:2250-2500
£2113 $3697 €3000 Doge's Palace in Venice (55x75cm-22x30in) s.d.1933. 19-Dec-3 Dorotheum, Vienna #102/R est:4000-5000

JAMBERS, Theodorus (1804-?) Belgian
£596 $1085 €900 Le conteur (37x46cm-15x18in) s. 15-Jun-4 Vanderkindere, Brussels #12

JAMBOR, Louis (1884-1955) American
£599 $1000 €875 Abstract congregation. one s.d.1910 board two. 18-Oct-3 Harvey Clar, Oakland #1504
£1380 $2250 €2015 Woman with flowers (74x56cm-29x22in) s. 24-Sep-3 Doyle, New York #50 est:3000-5000
£8982 $15000 €13114 Travellers by moonlight. s. 18-Oct-3 Harvey Clar, Oakland #1466
£9581 $16000 €13988 Remembrance. s. 18-Oct-3 Harvey Clar, Oakland #1464

JAMBULULA (c.1908-1960) Australian
Works on paper
£1719 $3214 €2579 Dancing Mimih (45x23cm-18x9in) bears name.i.verso earth pigment eucalyptus bark exec.c.1957 prov. 26-Jul-4 Sotheby's, Melbourne #291/R est:1200-1800 (A.D 4400)

JAMES, Charlie -Sculptor (attrib) (20th C) ?
Sculpture
£5435 $10000 €8153 Kwakiutl totem pole (71cm-28in) ceder wood. 14-Jun-4 Bonhams & Butterfields, San Francisco #1127/R est:2000-3000

JAMES, David (fl.1881-1898) British
£389 $650 €568 Cornish coast. s. 15-Nov-3 Harvey Clar, Oakland #1153
£400 $680 €584 Lonely Ocean (20x30cm-8x12in) s.d.83. 19-Nov-3 Christie's, Kensington #585/R
£605 $1113 €883 Mount's Bay, Cornwall (30x51cm-12x20in) s.d.84 i.verso. 14-Jun-4 Waddingtons, Toronto #118/R est:1500-2500 (C.D 1500)
£900 $1647 €1314 Coastal landscape (46x76cm-18x30in) s.d.82. 6-Apr-4 Bonhams, Knightsbridge #226/R
£1300 $2405 €1898 Shipping in open seas (76x127cm-30x50in) s.d.1871. 13-Jan-4 Bonhams, Knightsbridge #315/R est:600-800
£1600 $3024 €2336 Coastal Scene (46x76cm-18x30in) s.d.90. 17-Feb-4 Bonhams, New Bond Street #9/R est:1000-1500
£2100 $3360 €3066 Off the Scilly Isles (46x91cm-18x36in) s. i. verso. 16-Sep-3 Bonhams, New Bond Street #67/R est:1000-1500
£2235 $4000 €3263 Choppy seas off Dover (74x124cm-29x49in) s.d.83 canvas laid down. 16-Mar-4 Bonhams & Butterfields, San Francisco #6134/R est:4000-6000
£3200 $6048 €4672 Tide coming in at Bude (46x76cm-18x30in) s.d.87 prov. 17-Feb-4 Bonhams, New Bond Street #11/R est:2000-3000
£4000 $7160 €5840 Vice-Admiral Phipps Hornby's squadron streaming through the Dardanelles (76x127cm-30x50in) s.d.1878. 26-May-4 Christie's, Kensington #677/R est:5000-7000
£8000 $13760 €11680 Portsmouth Harbour (76x127cm-30x50in) s.d.1886. 2-Dec-3 Sotheby's, London #145/R est:6000-9000
£16000 $27200 €23360 Atlantic rollers (63x127cm-25x50in) s. s.d.96 on stretcher prov. 25-Nov-3 Christie's, London #166/R est:20000-30000

JAMES, David (attrib) (fl.1881-1898) British
£1200 $2064 €1752 Fishing boats in stormy weather (45x76cm-18x30in) bears sig.d. 2-Dec-3 Sotheby's, London #67/R est:1200-1800

JAMES, Edwin P (?) American?
£217 $350 €317 New boat (20x30cm-8x12in) s. board. 24-Aug-3 Bonhams & Butterfields, Los Angeles #7064

JAMES, Louis Robert (1920-1997) Australian
£360 $612 €526 Park (30x30cm-12x12in) s.d.66 s.i.d.verso composition board. 24-Nov-3 Sotheby's, Melbourne #243 (A.D 850)
£393 $726 €574 Coast III (17x25cm-7x10in) s.d.60 s.i.d.verso board prov. 10-Mar-4 Deutscher-Menzies, Melbourne #467/R (A.D 950)
£800 $1464 €1168 Landscape (23x48cm-9x19in) s.d.58 board. 28-Jul-4 Mallams, Oxford #258/R
£1053 $1695 €1537 Red Journey (62x75cm-24x30in) s. s.i.d.71 verso composition board. 25-Aug-3 Sotheby's, Paddington #322/R est:2000-3000 (A.D 2600)
£2273 $4205 €3319 Landscape, village (76x114cm-30x45in) s.d.59 s.i.d.verso prov.exhib. 10-Mar-4 Deutscher-Menzies, Melbourne #209/R est:7000-12000 (A.D 5500)
£2686 $4754 €3922 Terra Nova, 2 (101x127cm-40x50in) s.d.62 s.i.d.63 verso. 3-May-4 Christie's, Melbourne #381/R est:4000-6000 (A.D 6500)
Works on paper
£344 $625 €502 Blue garden (32x21cm-13x8in) s.d.64 gouache pastel. 16-Jun-4 Deutscher-Menzies, Melbourne #630/R (A.D 900)
£369 $598 €539 Red Landscape (51x61cm-20x24in) s.d.61 s.i.d.verso mixed media. 30-Jul-3 Goodman, Sydney #4/R (A.D 900)
£620 $1147 €905 Backyard II (75x49cm-30x19in) s.d.90 pastel. 10-Mar-4 Deutscher-Menzies, Melbourne #517/R est:1000-1500 (A.D 1500)

JAMES, Michael (20th C) British
£450 $765 €657 German shepherd (49x60cm-19x24in) s. acrylic on board. 27-Nov-3 Christie's, Kensington #361/R

JAMES, William (fl.1754-1771) British
£2000 $3740 €2920 Santa maria della salute, Venice. s.d.71 pair. 20-Jul-4 Sworder & Son, Bishops Stortford #678/R est:2000-3000
£28000 $51240 €40880 Grand Canal, Venice, looking towards the south east with Santo Stea (60x96cm-24x38in) 7-Jul-4 Bonhams, New Bond Street #55/R est:10000-15000

£30000	$51900	€43800	Grand Canal, Venice, looking towards the south east Santo Stale and the Fabbriche Nuove (60x96cm-24x38in) 10-Dec-3 Bonhams, New Bond Street #43/R est:10000-15000
£38889	$70000	€56778	View of the entrance to the Cannareggio (41x64cm-16x25in) prov. 22-Jan-4 Sotheby's, New York #72/R est:80000-120000
£50000	$86500	€73000	Thames at Lambeth Palace, with St. Paul's Cathedral and Westminster Bridge (76x127cm-30x50in) 10-Dec-3 Bonhams, New Bond Street #50/R est:15000-20000
£56000	$96880	€81760	Thames at Westminster with Old Westminster Bridge and the shot tower, Somerset House, London (76x127cm-30x50in) 10-Dec-3 Bonhams, New Bond Street #49/R est:15000-20000
£66667	$121333	€100000	Grand Canal, Venice (38x63cm-15x25in) 4-Jul-4 Finarte, Venice #60/R est:12000-145000

JAMES, William (attrib) (fl.1754-1771) British

£13986	$23776	€20000	View of the Doge Palace, Venice (57x92cm-22x36in) 21-Nov-3 Coutau Begarie, Paris #128/R est:15000-20000
£14000	$25620	€20440	Grand Canal, Venice (69x109cm-27x43in) prov. 8-Jul-4 Duke & Son, Dorchester #241/R

JAMES, William (style) (fl.1754-1771) British

£12000	$18960	€17400	Royal barges passing beneath Westminster Bridge (71x117cm-28x46in) 4-Sep-3 Christie's, Kensington #83/R est:8000-12000
£14000	$22120	€20300	Old Westminster Bridge (71x116cm-28x46in) 4-Sep-3 Christie's, Kensington #86/R est:6000-8000

JAMESON, F E (?) British?

£320	$515	€464	Scottish river and mountain landscape with figures by cottages in foreground (41x61cm-16x24in) s. 15-Aug-3 Keys, Aylsham #669

JAMESON, Frank (1898-1968) British

£350	$655	€511	Foreshore (34x44cm-13x17in) s. canvasboard. 26-Feb-4 Lane, Penzance #212
£800	$1496	€1168	St Mawes harbour (33x46cm-13x18in) s. board. 26-Feb-4 Lane, Penzance #213
£850	$1590	€1241	Low tide St Ives harbour (39x48cm-15x19in) s. 26-Feb-4 Lane, Penzance #214
£1000	$1830	€1460	Bathe in a woodland pool (58x48cm-23x19in) s. 3-Jun-4 Lane, Penzance #191 est:1000-1250
£1250	$2163	€1825	The quiet pool (49x60cm-19x24in) s. 11-Dec-3 Lane, Penzance #165/R est:1250-1500

JAMESON, James Arthur Henry (fl.1883-1923) British

Works on paper

£285	$447	€410	Bridge near Dumber (30cm-12in) mono.d. W/C. 26-Aug-3 Thomas Adams, Dublin #5

JAMESON, Joan (fl.1933-1938) British

£650	$1164	€949	Still life with carnations in a vase (63x51cm-25x20in) s. 14-May-4 Christie's, Kensington #388/R

Works on paper

£733	$1327	€1100	Shadow of the mountain (36x43cm-14x17in) s. mixed media. 30-Mar-4 De Veres Art Auctions, Dublin #114/R

JAMESON, T A (19th C) ?

£2000	$3140	€2900	Gathering in the corn at Inverary Castle (48x65cm-19x26in) s.d.1841. 27-Aug-3 Sotheby's, London #917/R est:2000-3000

JAMESONE, George (attrib) (1587-1644) British

£1900	$3420	€2774	Portrait of Patrick Leslie, 1st Lord Lindores (65x52cm-26x20in) 21-Jan-4 Sotheby's, Olympia #62/R est:800-1200

JAMIESON, Alexander (1873-1937) British

£330	$528	€482	By the river. s.d.1912 panel. 18-Sep-3 Bonhams, Edinburgh #311
£460	$791	€672	River scene with bridge (36x28cm-14x11in) s. 4-Dec-3 Biddle & Webb, Birmingham #878
£1000	$1860	€1460	Laburnum, the old mill, Weston Turville, Buckinghamshire (32x41cm-13x16in) s. board. 4-Mar-4 Christie's, Kensington #157/R est:1500-2000
£1800	$3348	€2628	Autumn landscape (86x112cm-34x44in) s.d.1932 s.i.verso. 4-Mar-4 Christie's, Kensington #155/R est:2000-3000
£2000	$3140	€2900	Amboise Castle on the Loire, France (32x41cm-13x16in) s.d.1912 i.verso panel. 27-Aug-3 Sotheby's, London #1068/R est:2000-3000
£4000	$6360	€5840	Spring in Weston Turville (89x128cm-35x50in) s.d.1929. 10-Sep-3 Sotheby's, Olympia #167/R est:2000-3000
£5200	$8840	€7592	Le Quai de Rosaire, Bruges (76x61cm-30x24in) s.d.1921 s.i.d.verso prov. 30-Oct-3 Christie's, London #151/R est:3000-5000

JAMIESON, F E (1895-1950) British

£1100	$1969	€1606	Figures on a path in a highland landscape (50x75cm-20x30in) s. pair. 11-May-4 Bonhams, Knightsbridge #155/R est:600-800

JAMIESON, Frances E (1895-1950) British

£471	$800	€688	Highland scene with cottage in distance (41x61cm-16x24in) s. 22-Nov-3 New Orleans Auction, New Orleans #316/R
£500	$850	€730	Highland scene (41x61cm-16x24in) s.i.verso. 22-Nov-3 New Orleans Auction, New Orleans #317

JAMIESON, Frank (1834-1899) British

£359	$600	€524	Landscape with cottage (41x61cm-16x24in) 17-Oct-3 Du Mouchelle, Detroit #2008/R

JAMIESON, Gil (1938-) Australian

£395	$737	€577	Farmyard (135x212cm-53x83in) s. board. 27-Feb-4 Lawson Menzies, Sydney #2138 (A.D 950)

JAMIESON, Mitchell (1915-) American

£219	$400	€320	Nude (51x41cm-20x16in) s. 31-Jul-4 Sloans & Kenyon, Bethesda #1210/R

JAMIN, Paul Joseph (1853-1903) French

£6383	$10660	€9000	Le Brenn a Rome (113x145cm-44x57in) 19-Jun-3 Millon & Associes, Paris #143/R est:10000-12000

JAMINJI, Paddy (c.1912-) Australian

Works on paper

£5579	$9484	€8145	Mount house (80x115cm-31x45in) natural earth pigment on board prov. 29-Oct-3 Lawson Menzies, Sydney #55/R est:10000-12000 (A.D 13500)

JAMISON, Philip (1925-) American

£1183	$2200	€1727	Farmhouse in winter (27x55cm-11x22in) s. board. 3-Mar-4 Christie's, Rockefeller NY #41/R est:1000-1500

Works on paper

£265	$450	€387	Still life, Windsor chair (27x20cm-11x8in) s. W/C prov. 21-Nov-3 Skinner, Boston #415/R
£299	$500	€437	Three vases of daisies (28x36cm-11x14in) s. W/C. 20-Jun-3 Freeman, Philadelphia #79/R
£707	$1300	€1032	Main Street, Vinal Haven - Maine (46x69cm-18x27in) s. W/C. 26-Jun-4 Sloans & Kenyon, Bethesda #1025/R
£1321	$2100	€1929	Lilies and daisies in a vase. W/C. 25-Feb-3 Bunch, West Chester #478a/R

JAMMES, Louis and ROSA, Herve di (20th C) French?

Works on paper

£1543	$2732	€2300	Salope Putain Seceuse Poufiasse Chienne tu me degouttes (108x103cm-43x41in) s. both artists collage of photos mixed media panel. 28-Apr-4 Artcurial Briest, Paris #407 est:1500-2000

JAMOIS, Edmond (1876-?) French

£1268	$2218	€1800	Vers la Pardon de Tremeur, Le Guilvinec (46x61cm-18x24in) s. 21-Dec-3 Thierry & Lannon, Brest #328 est:1200-1500

JAN, Elvire (1904-1996) French/Bulgarian

£789	$1453	€1200	Composition (38x61cm-15x24in) s.d.1987 lit. 27-Jun-4 Versailles Encheres #32/R
£993	$1808	€1500	Composition (30x37cm-12x15in) s. s.d.1960 verso panel. 18-Jun-4 Charbonneaux, Paris #148/R est:800-1000
£1831	$3168	€2600	Sans titre (32x40cm-13x16in) s. 14-Dec-3 Versailles Encheres #47/R est:1500-2000
£1974	$3632	€3000	Composition (46x38cm-18x15in) s.d.1949 prov. 27-Jun-4 Versailles Encheres #20/R est:3000-4000
£3662	$6335	€5200	Composition (73x92cm-29x36in) s. s.d.1958 verso prov. 14-Dec-3 Versailles Encheres #42/R est:4000-4500
£5921	$10895	€9000	Composition (117x145cm-46x57in) s.d.1952 s.verso prov.lit. 27-Jun-4 Versailles Encheres #55/R est:5000-6000

Works on paper

£336	$628	€500	Composition (34x21cm-13x8in) s.d.1963 ink W/C. 29-Feb-4 Versailles Encheres #254/R
£775	$1340	€1100	Composition (36x36cm-14x14in) s.d.1959 gouache prov. 14-Dec-3 Versailles Encheres #17

JANCE, Paul Claude (1840-?) French

£2000	$3600	€3000	Portraits de famille (47x39cm-19x15in) s.d.1875 and 1877 two. 25-Apr-4 Daniel Herry, Beaune #105

JANCO, Marcel (1895-1984) Israeli/Rumanian

£1235	$2100	€1803	Abstract (34x49cm-13x19in) s. cardboard painted early 1950's prov. 1-Dec-3 Ben-Ami, Tel Aviv #4314/R est:3000-4000
£1444	$2700	€2108	Abstract composition (34x49cm-13x19in) s. canvas on board painted c.1950. 1-Mar-4 Ben-Ami, Tel Aviv #4667/R est:3000-4000
£1630	$2950	€2380	Parisian street lamp with a bouquet of flowers (34x49cm-13x19in) s. cardboard on board painted c.1950. 1-Apr-4 Ben-Ami, Tel Aviv #4723/R est:2500-3000
£3916	$6500	€5717	Cubes dominos (50x70cm-20x28in) s. canvas on masonite. 2-Oct-3 Christie's, Tel Aviv #69/R est:7000-9000

Works on paper

£440	$800	€660	Landscape (24x33cm-9x13in) s. W/C. 1-Jul-4 Ben-Ami, Tel Aviv #4925/R
£765	$1400	€1117	View of the Kineret, Sea of Galilee (34x49cm-13x19in) s. mixed media exec.c.1950. 1-Feb-4 Ben-Ami, Tel Aviv #4645/R est:2000-3000

JANCSEK, Antal (1907-) Hungarian

£420	$713	€600	On the beach (60x50cm-24x20in) s. 28-Nov-3 Schloss Ahlden, Ahlden #1580/R

JANCZAK, Jan (1938-) Polish

£315	$542	€460	Na drodze (80x100cm-31x39in) s.d.1969. 8-Dec-3 Philippe Schuler, Zurich #5857 (S.FR 700)

JANDANY, Hector (1929-) Australian

Works on paper

£941	$1685	€1374	Warrawurrinji Hills (71x51cm-28x20in) earth pigments Belgian linen prov. 25-May-4 Lawson Menzies, Sydney #2/R (A.D 2400)

£1647 $2948 €2405 Two Sharp Holes in Nangunearth (92x60cm-36x24in) natural earth pigments on Belgian linen exec c.1993. 25-May-4 Lawson Menzies, Sydney #157/R est:2500-4500 (A.D 4200)

JANDI, David (1893-1944) Hungarian
Works on paper
£641 $1135 €936 Nagybanya (34x50cm-13x20in) s.d.925 pastel. 28-Apr-4 Kieselbach, Budapest #5/R (H.F 240000)
£1581 $2861 €2308 River Zazar (30x48cm-12x19in) s. pastel. 16-Apr-4 Mu Terem Galeria, Budapest #29/R (H.F 600000)
£1581 $2861 €2308 Lying nude (32x49cm-13x19in) s. pastel. 16-Apr-4 Mu Terem Galeria, Budapest #55/R (H.F 600000)
£2898 $5246 €4231 Street in Nagybanya (34x47cm-13x19in) s. pastel. 16-Apr-4 Mu Terem Galeria, Budapest #62/R (H.F 1100000)
£3952 $7153 €5770 Big still life with melon (70x100cm-28x39in) s. pastel. 16-Apr-4 Mu Terem Galeria, Budapest #67/R (H.F 1500000)

JANEBE (1907-2000) Swiss
£690 $1234 €1007 L'assiette de cerises (21x34cm-8x13in) s.d.78 i. stretcher panel. 14-May-4 Dobiaschofsky, Bern #109/R est:2600 (S.FR 1600)
£2155 $3858 €3146 Young woman pouring water out of jug (108x65cm-43x26in) s. panel. 14-May-4 Dobiaschofsky, Bern #108/R est:6000 (S.FR 5000)

JANECEK, Ota (1919-1996) Czechoslovakian
£218 $350 €318 Ecce Homo (46x30cm-18x12in) s.d.1964. 22-Feb-3 Bunte, Elgin #1160
£759 $1336 €1139 Flowers (31x20cm-12x8in) s.d.50 cardboard. 22-May-4 Dorotheum, Prague #170/R est:20000-30000 (C.KR 36000)
Works on paper
£359 $631 €539 Nude girl (27x22cm-11x9in) s.d.80 pastel pencil. 22-May-4 Dorotheum, Prague #255/R est:9000-15000 (C.KR 17000)

JANENSCH, Gerhard Adolf (1860-1933) German
Sculpture
£2270 $3790 €3200 Le forgeron (97cm-38in) s.i.d.1897 brown pat bronze. 15-Oct-3 Hotel des Ventes Mosan, Brussels #155b est:2700-2900

JANES, Norman (1892-1980) British
£400 $632 €580 Spring in Hampstead (40x49cm-16x19in) board painted c. 1935. 7-Sep-3 Lots Road Auctions, London #348

JANET, Ange Louis (1815-1872) French
£1748 $2920 €2500 Portrait de jeune homme romantique (144x98cm-57x39in) s. 29-Jun-3 St-Germain-en-Laye Encheres #9/R est:3000

JANGALA, Abie (c.1919-2002) Australian
Works on paper
£781 $1461 €1172 Ngapa, water, dreaming (55x61cm-22x24in) bears name.i.d.1996 verso synthetic polymer paint canvas prov. 26-Jul-4 Sotheby's, Melbourne #467 (A.D 2000)
£941 $1685 €1374 Rainbow dreaming (54x85cm-21x33in) s. verso synthetic polymer paint canvas exec 1993 prov. 25-May-4 Lawson Menzies, Sydney #207/R (A.D 2400)
£1172 $2191 €1758 Ngapa, water, dreaming (72x54cm-28x21in) bears name.i.d.1996 verso synthetic polymer paint canvas prov. 26-Jul-4 Sotheby's, Melbourne #465/R est:3000-4000 (A.D 3000)
£1373 $2457 €2005 Water dreaming (56x91cm-22x36in) i. verso synthetic polymer paint canvas exec 1993 prov. 25-May-4 Lawson Menzies, Sydney #208/R est:3500-4500 (A.D 3500)
£1563 $2922 €2345 Ngapa, water, dreaming (99x56cm-39x22in) bears name.i.d.1996 verso synthetic polymer paint canvas prov. 26-Jul-4 Sotheby's, Melbourne #466/R est:4000-6000 (A.D 4000)
£1953 $3652 €2930 Water dreaming (85x59cm-33x23in) synthetic polymer paint canvas prov. 26-Jul-4 Sotheby's, Melbourne #272/R est:5000-7000 (A.D 5000)
£3529 $6318 €5152 Ngapa - Water dreaming (77x153cm-30x60in) synthetic polymer paint linen exec 1997 prov. 25-May-4 Lawson Menzies, Sydney #206/R est:10000-12000 (A.D 9000)

JANGARRA, Ignatia (c.1930-?) Australian
Works on paper
£781 $1461 €1172 Two wanjina (63x23cm-25x9in) earth pigments eucalyptus bark exec.c.1985 prov. 26-Jul-4 Sotheby's, Melbourne #462/R (A.D 2000)
£813 $1285 €1187 Wanjina (17x15cm-7x6in) i.verso earth pigments eucalyptus bark exec.c.1987 pair. 28-Jul-3 Sotheby's, Paddington #468 est:1500-2500 (A.D 2000)
£894 $1413 €1305 Wanjina (40x23cm-16x9in) earth pigments eucalyptus bark prov. 28-Jul-3 Sotheby's, Paddington #555 est:900-1200 (A.D 2200)
£1301 $2055 €1899 Wanjina (43x20cm-17x8in) earth pigments eucalyptus bark prov. 28-Jul-3 Sotheby's, Paddington #556 est:700-900 (A.D 3200)

JANIKOWSKI, Mieczyslaw Tadeusz (1912-1968) Polish
£434 $737 €620 Composition jaune (27x16cm-11x6in) s.verso. 23-Nov-3 Cornette de St.Cyr, Paris #161

JANINET, Jean François (1752-1814) French
Prints
£4582 $8203 €6690 La toilette de Venus (38x340cm-15x134in) col engraving executed 1783 prov.lit. 25-May-4 Bukowskis, Stockholm #561/R est:20000-25000 (S.KR 62000)

JANK, Angelo (1868-1940) German
£268 $475 €400 Hunt jumping hedge (70x90cm-28x35in) s. 30-Apr-4 Dr Fritz Nagel, Stuttgart #261/R
£280 $476 €400 Portrait of Field Marshall Hindenburg (41x36cm-16x14in) s.d.1915. 20-Nov-3 Van Ham, Cologne #1657
£385 $654 €550 Three horses jumping hedge and water during fox hunt (55x75cm-22x30in) s. 22-Nov-3 Arnold, Frankfurt #559/R
£417 $696 €600 Fox hunting (55x75cm-22x30in) s. 24-Oct-3 Ketterer, Hamburg #185/R
£940 $1467 €1372 Horses and riders jumping over a fence (55x75cm-22x30in) s. painted c.1930. 30-Mar-3 Agra, Warsaw #46/R est:6000 (P.Z 6000)
£1224 $2229 €1800 Woman on horse jumping fence (73x58cm-29x23in) s. 4-Feb-4 Neumeister, Munich #705/R est:700
£1297 $2360 €1894 Horse race (55x76cm-22x30in) s. painted 1930. 20-Jun-4 Agra, Warsaw #15/R (P.Z 9000)
£1818 $3127 €2600 Woman riding a horse in the hall at a riding school (50x30cm-20x12in) s. 3-Dec-3 Neumeister, Munich #605/R est:1800
£2292 $3781 €3300 Horse racing (41x47cm-16x19in) s. 2-Jul-3 Neumeister, Munich #674/R est:1500

JANK, Angelo (attrib) (1868-1940) German
£408 $731 €600 Hunter on horseback (50x64cm-20x25in) s. canvas on panel lit. 20-Mar-4 Bergmann, Erlangen #1115

JANKOWSKI, J W (fl.1825-1861) Austrian
£1060 $1928 €1600 River landscape with a river and a church on a hilltop (52x66cm-20x26in) s. 16-Jun-4 Hugo Ruef, Munich #993 est:2000

JANKOWSKI, J Wilhelm (fl.1825-1861) Austrian
£1042 $1771 €1500 Lake landscape (55x69cm-22x27in) s. 28-Oct-3 Dorotheum, Vienna #95/R est:1600-1800
£1800 $3294 €2628 Doges Palace, Venice, the Grand Canal beyond (46x90cm-18x35in) s. 6-Jul-4 Bonhams, Knightsbridge #187/R est:1500-2000
£2345 $3916 €3400 Old city of Lucern (107x135cm-42x53in) s. pair. 12-Jul-3 Bergmann, Erlangen #631/R est:3000
£2778 $4389 €4000 Venice (48x93cm-19x37in) s. lit. 19-Sep-3 Schloss Ahlden, Ahlden #1519/R est:4600

JANKOWSKI, J Wilhelm (attrib) (fl.1825-1861) Austrian
£634 $1052 €900 Landscape with figures (55x68cm-22x27in) 12-Jun-3 Dorotheum, Graz #27

JANMOT, Anne François Louis (1814-1892) French
£816 $1486 €1200 Etude pour une fillette (43x37cm-17x15in) cardboard. 8-Feb-4 Anaf, Lyon #198

JANNECK, Franz Christoph (1703-1761) Austrian
£13103 $21883 €19000 Old Testament scenes (13x19cm-5x7in) copper prov. two. 15-Nov-3 Lempertz, Koln #1071/R est:10000
£14000 $25620 €20440 Crucifixion (50x41cm-20x16in) s. copper. 6-Jul-4 Sotheby's, Olympia #568/R est:4000-6000
£38158 $70211 €58000 Depart du Fils Prodigue. Fils Prodigue chez les filles (39x54cm-15x21in) panel pair. 25-Jun-4 Piasa, Paris #9/R est:12000-15000
£230000 $414000 €335800 Elegant company, with figures playing musical instruments (40x58cm-16x23in) s. copper. 22-Apr-4 Sotheby's, London #101/R est:40000-60000

JANNECK, Franz Christoph (attrib) (1703-1761) Austrian
£3020 $5557 €4500 Interiors (32x25cm-13x10in) pair. 25-Mar-4 Dr Fritz Nagel, Stuttgart #671/R est:7200
£6000 $10800 €8760 Bacchus and Ariadne (45x62cm-18x24in) 22-Apr-4 Sotheby's, London #102/R est:6000-8000

JANNEL, Jean (1894-?) French
£728 $1362 €1100 Nu de dos (61x46cm-24x18in) s. 24-Jul-4 Thierry & Lannon, Brest #182/R

JANNIOT, Alfred Auguste (1889-1969) French
Sculpture
£3222 $5992 €4800 Apollon (91cm-36in) pat studio plaster prov. 4-Mar-4 Tajan, Paris #106/R est:2500-3000
£6197 $10721 €8800 L'antilope (70x70cm-28x28in) s.num.1/8 gold pat bronze st.f. Coubertin lit. 13-Dec-3 Martinot & Savignat, Pontoise #82/R est:9000-10000
Works on paper
£800 $1488 €1168 Hercules (45x28cm-18x11in) indis.sig.i.d.1942 chl W/C gold paint. 4-Mar-4 Christie's, London #312/R
£5944 $10105 €8500 Untitled (140x82cm-55x32in) s. crayon. 26-Nov-3 Christie's, Paris #53/R est:3500-4500

JANNY, Georg (1864-1946) Austrian
£1700 $3128 €2482 Mystical gorge (47x32cm-19x13in) s.d.1921 board. 25-Mar-4 Christie's, Kensington #50/R est:2000-3000
Works on paper
£403 $741 €600 Rax, Siebenbrunner meadows (15x19cm-6x7in) s.i. W/C. 26-Mar-4 Dorotheum, Vienna #313/R
£528 $945 €750 Peasant's bedroom baby's cot (49x64cm-19x25in) s.d.1921 W/C gouache lit. 8-Jan-4 Allgauer, Kempten #2095/R
£604 $1111 €900 Grinzing (14x19cm-6x7in) s.i. W/C. 26-Mar-4 Dorotheum, Vienna #288/R

JANS, Edouard de (1855-?) Belgian
£1007 $1872 €1500 Laundress near ditch (57x72cm-22x28in) s.d.1885. 8-Mar-4 Bernaerts, Antwerp #749/R est:1500-1750
£1127 $1949 €1600 Southern street with boy on steps (30x19cm-12x7in) s.d.1880. 11-Dec-3 Dr Fritz Nagel, Stuttgart #524/R est:2200

JANS, Knud (1916-1985) Danish
£496 $928 €724 Composition (110x77cm-43x30in) s.d.54. 25-Feb-4 Kunsthallen, Copenhagen #82 (D.KR 5500)

JANSCH, Heather (1948-) British
Sculpture
£8000 $14080 €11680 Nightmare and Daydream. driftwood metal. 18-May-4 Woolley & Wallis, Salisbury #387/R est:10000-15000

JANSCHA, Lorenz (1749-1812) Austrian
Works on paper
£851 $1421 €1200 Landscape with Schloss Schalabach (28x43cm-11x17in) bears sig. verso. 17-Oct-3 Altus, Berlin #504/R

JANSEM, Jean (1920-1990) French
£839 $1401 €1200 Deux femmes, un enfant et un ane (27x22cm-11x9in) s. 25-Jun-3 Digard, Paris #75/R
£2535 $4386 €3600 Vase de fleurs et tasse (50x65cm-20x26in) s. mixed media paper on canvas prov. 13-Dec-3 Touati, Paris #127/R est:4500
£2657 $4571 €3800 La procession (33x24cm-13x9in) s. prov. 2-Dec-3 Sotheby's, Amsterdam #211/R est:2500-3500
£2703 $4838 €4000 Mere et enfant (40x23cm-16x9in) s. 4-May-4 Calmels Cohen, Paris #159/R est:2500-3000
£2762 $4750 €4033 Profile of a dancer (35x24cm-14x9in) s. i.on overlap prov. 3-Dec-3 Doyle, New York #150/R est:2000-3000
£2819 $5046 €4200 Jeune femme se coiffant (27x22cm-11x9in) s. 30-May-4 Eric Pillon, Calais #241/R
£3200 $5760 €4800 Trois vieilles femmes au panier (33x46cm-13x18in) s.i.verso. 20-Apr-4 Chenu & Scrive, Lyon #105/R est:4500-5000
£4161 $7448 €6200 Jeune fille assise et pensive (51x33cm-20x13in) s. 30-May-4 Eric Pillon, Calais #242/R
£4362 $7809 €6500 Jeune marchand assis (35x27cm-14x11in) s. 30-May-4 Eric Pillon, Calais #240/R
£4430 $8195 €6600 Jeune pecheur (61x49cm-24x19in) s. 14-Mar-4 Eric Pillon, Calais #205/R
£5435 $9946 €7935 La marchande de fruits (129x162cm-51x64in) s. prov.exhib. 5-Jun-4 Galerie du Rhone, Sion #569/R est:10000-15000 (S.FR 12500)
£5556 $10000 €8112 Woman in window (127x94cm-50x37in) s. 20-Jan-4 Arthur James, Florida #106
£6294 $10825 €9000 Arlequin et Colombine (25x33cm-10x13in) s. 2-Dec-3 Sotheby's, Amsterdam #227/R est:3000-4000
£6643 $11427 €9500 Procession (65x81cm-26x32in) s. painted 1977. 2-Dec-3 Sotheby's, Amsterdam #228/R est:6000-9000
£7919 $13699 €11562 Danseuse assise (100x81cm-39x32in) s. prov. 12-Dec-3 Galerie du Rhone, Sion #192/R est:10000-15000 (S.FR 17500)
£8021 $15000 €11711 Scene de rue avec enfants (104x140cm-41x55in) s. painted c.1957 prov. 25-Feb-4 Christie's, Rockefeller NY #86/R est:15000-20000
£20280 $33867 €29000 Nature morte au vase bleu (130x162cm-51x64in) s. 25-Jun-3 Digard, Paris #98/R est:15000-20000
Prints
£2381 $3786 €3500 Jeune danseuse (38x49cm-15x19in) s. num.30/50 lithograph. 18-Mar-3 Adjug'art, Brest #78
Works on paper
£391 $700 €571 Portrait (23x18cm-9x7in) s. ink wash. 21-Mar-4 Jeffery Burchard, Florida #8
£433 $780 €650 La maison (30x23cm-12x9in) s. ink wash. 26-Apr-4 Tajan, Paris #76
£704 $1218 €1000 Portrait de femme (65x50cm-26x20in) s. ink wash gouache. 13-Dec-3 Touati, Paris #125/R
£884 $1583 €1300 Mere et enfant (37x28cm-15x11in) s. wash htd W/C. 20-Mar-4 Binoche, Orleans #30
£951 $1645 €1350 Modele au drap dans l'atelier (62x34cm-24x13in) s. ink wash. 13-Dec-3 Touati, Paris #128/R
£1107 $1982 €1650 Femme assise (64x49cm-25x19in) s. chl col crayon. 30-May-4 Eric Pillon, Calais #262/R
£1197 $2071 €1700 Nu allonge (50x66cm-20x26in) s. ink wash. 13-Dec-3 Touati, Paris #126/R est:1500
£1217 $2228 €1777 Danseuse assise (66x50cm-26x20in) s. mixed media. 5-Jun-4 Galerie du Rhone, Sion #337/R est:2500-3500 (S.FR 2800)
£1227 $2000 €1791 Femme tricote (71x49cm-28x19in) s. pen brush black ink. 25-Sep-3 Christie's, Rockefeller NY #600/R est:2000-3000
£1267 $2192 €1850 Nu sur chaise (65x50cm-26x20in) s. mixed media prov. 12-Dec-3 Galerie du Rhone, Sion #111/R est:2500-3500 (S.FR 2800)
£1901 $3289 €2700 Modele au bas rouge (64x49cm-25x19in) s. ink wash. 13-Dec-3 Touati, Paris #124/R est:2500
£1989 $3500 €2904 Danseuse (66x51cm-26x20in) s. W/C ink prov. 18-May-4 Arthur James, Florida #152 est:2000-3000
£2937 $5052 €4200 Ballerina seated (65x49cm-26x19in) s. W/C ink. 2-Dec-3 Sotheby's, Amsterdam #209/R est:2000-3000

JANSEN, Egbert A (1877-1957) Dutch
£1136 $2000 €1659 Harbour scene with figures (66x102cm-26x40in) s. painted c.1920. 23-May-4 Treadway Gallery, Cincinnati #538/R est:2000-4000

JANSEN, Hans (1896-1987) German
Works on paper
£238 $426 €347 Untitled (50x60cm-20x24in) s.i.d.79 verso mixed media. 22-Mar-4 Philippe Schuler, Zurich #6160 (S.FR 550)

JANSEN, Hendrik Willebrord (1855-1908) Dutch
£872 $1614 €1300 Man standing beside a boat (42x61cm-17x24in) s. 15-Mar-4 Sotheby's, Amsterdam #110 est:1200-1500

JANSEN, Willem George Frederick (1871-1949) Dutch
£423 $731 €600 Village view (15x21cm-6x8in) s. cardboard. 10-Dec-3 Hugo Ruef, Munich #2437/R
£594 $1022 €850 Landscape with horse and carriage (40x60cm-16x24in) s. 7-Dec-3 Sotheby's, Amsterdam #672
£748 $1362 €1100 Brabantsch landschap, chickens on a country path (40x30cm-16x12in) s. 3-Feb-4 Christie's, Amsterdam #366 est:1000-1500
£816 $1486 €1200 In the dunes (70x131cm-28x52in) one s. pair. 3-Feb-4 Christie's, Amsterdam #201 est:1500-2000
£900 $1665 €1314 Drover and sheep outside a barn (71x58cm-28x23in) s. 9-Mar-4 Bonhams, Knightsbridge #177/R
£979 $1664 €1400 Dutch landscape (25x35cm-10x14in) s. panel. 20-Nov-3 Van Ham, Cologne #1658
£1126 $1914 €1644 Farmer and horse with laden cart (94x76cm-37x30in) s. 21-Nov-3 Walker's, Ottawa #206/R est:3000-5000 (C.D 2500)
£1151 $2083 €1680 Cows by the barn (45x59cm-18x23in) s. prov. 1-Apr-4 Heffel, Vancouver #59/R est:1200-1600 (C.D 2750)
£1156 $2105 €1700 Cowherdress by a shed (40x50cm-16x20in) s. 3-Feb-4 Christie's, Amsterdam #256/R est:1200-1600
£1399 $2336 €2000 Moored sailing vessels (40x50cm-16x20in) s. 30-Jun-3 Sotheby's, Amsterdam #148
£1560 $2606 €2200 View of city, possibly Alkmaar (40x55cm-16x22in) s. 20-Oct-3 Glerum, Amsterdam #136/R est:2800-3200
£1736 $2743 €2500 Milking time , leading the cows into the barn (61x91cm-24x36in) s. 2-Sep-3 Christie's, Amsterdam #286 est:2000-3000
£2177 $3962 €3200 Cattle in a polder landscape (71x101cm-28x40in) s. 3-Feb-4 Christie's, Amsterdam #190/R est:4000-6000
£2500 $4600 €3800 View of a landscape with windmill (35x26cm-14x10in) s. 28-Jun-4 Sotheby's, Amsterdam #54/R est:4000-6000
£2632 $4842 €4000 A peasant woman on a wooded path by a meadow (121x96cm-48x38in) s. 22-Jun-4 Christie's, Amsterdam #103/R est:4000-6000
£2857 $5200 €4200 Ferry across a river, Arcen (40x80cm-16x31in) s. 3-Feb-4 Christie's, Amsterdam #368/R est:1500-2000
£4333 $7800 €6500 View of Haelingen Harbour (30x40cm-12x16in) s. 20-Apr-4 Sotheby's, Amsterdam #106/R est:4000-6000
£6044 $11000 €8824 Shrimper (37x63cm-15x25in) s. prov. 29-Jun-4 Sotheby's, New York #145/R est:3000-5000
£10417 $17396 €15000 View of the Prinsengracht with the Westerkerk, Amsterdam (60x100cm-24x39in) s. 21-Oct-3 Sotheby's, Amsterdam #108/R est:8000-12000
Works on paper
£1342 $2497 €2000 Port of Harlingen (34x47cm-13x19in) s. gouache. 4-Mar-4 Auction Maastricht #1127/R est:2000-3000

JANSEN-HULLEMAN, Gerritje (1936-) Dutch
Works on paper
£377 $640 €550 Abstract composition (172x63cm-68x25in) mixed media. 5-Nov-3 Vendue Huis, Gravenhage #477/R

JANSON, Johannes (1729-1784) Dutch
£1300 $2327 €1898 Dutch landscape with figures and cattle on a canal towpath (30x41cm-12x16in) s. panel. 7-May-4 Christopher Matthews, Yorkshire #306 est:500-600
£5028 $9000 €7341 Winter landscape with skaters (26x35cm-10x14in) s. panel prov. 27-May-4 Sotheby's, New York #68/R est:10000-15000

JANSON, Johannes Christian (1763-1823) Dutch
£700 $1295 €1022 Interior with elderly lady and young boy before a fire (39x33cm-15x13in) panel. 9-Mar-4 Bonhams, Knightsbridge #253/R

JANSON, Marc (1930-) French
£315 $526 €450 Composition (53x75cm-21x30in) s. paper on canvas prov. 29-Jun-3 Versailles Encheres #4
£336 $614 €500 Hommage a Odilon Reddon (100x100cm-39x39in) prov. 7-Jul-4 Artcurial Briest, Paris #283
£352 $609 €500 L'ete fastueux (88x131cm-35x52in) s. i.d.78 verso. 10-Dec-3 Hotel des Ventes Mosan, Brussels #281
£367 $671 €550 Nuees accourues (80x100cm-31x39in) s.d.67 verso prov. 7-Jun-4 Palais de Beaux Arts, Brussels #131
£470 $860 €700 Projet de jardin, hommage a Gustave Moreau (92x149cm-36x59in) painted 1985 prov. 7-Jul-4 Artcurial Briest, Paris #284
£1049 $1783 €1500 Au noeud du jour et de la nuit (73x100cm-29x39in) s. 27-Nov-3 Calmels Cohen, Paris #115/R est:1500-2000
£1200 $2160 €1800 Tous les couteaux du monde (114x146cm-45x57in) s. s.i.d.1965 verso prov.exhib. 25-Apr-4 Versailles Encheres #44 est:1000-1500
£1867 $3360 €2800 Composition (27x41cm-11x16in) s.d.1956. 25-Apr-4 Versailles Encheres #57 est:2500-3000

JANSONS, Ivars (1939-) ?
£363 $660 €530 Evening reflection (40x50cm-16x20in) s. i.verso. 16-Jun-4 Deutscher-Menzies, Melbourne #617/R (A.D 950)
£483 $753 €705 Rendez-vous (43x55cm-17x22in) s. board. 1-Aug-2 Joel, Victoria #272 est:800-1000 (A.D 1400)
£552 $861 €800 At north Adelaide (49x59cm-19x23in) s. 1-Aug-2 Joel, Victoria #314 est:800-1000 (A.D 1600)

JANSSAUD, Mathurin (1857-1940) French
Works on paper
£733 $1313 €1100 Famille Bretonne en bord de mer (33x24cm-13x9in) pastel. 16-May-4 Osenat, Fontainebleau #27/R
£1000 $1790 €1500 Dentellieres devant la ville close (22x30cm-9x12in) s. pastel. 16-May-4 Thierry & Lannon, Brest #255 est:1500-2000
£1067 $1909 €1600 Retour de peche (19x24cm-7x9in) s. pastel. 16-May-4 Renault-Aubry, Pontivy #459
£1399 $2336 €2000 Femmes de pecheurs sur la greve (26x34cm-10x13in) s. pastel. 29-Jun-3 Eric Pillon, Calais #140/R
£1761 $3046 €2500 Retour de peche (24x33cm-9x13in) s. pastel. 12-Dec-3 Piasa, Paris #114/R est:2500-3000
£2215 $3566 €3300 Soleil couchant, baie de Concarneau (37x60cm-15x24in) s. pastel. 23-Feb-3 St-Germain-en-Laye Encheres #70/R est:3200-3500
£2817 $4930 €4000 Dechargement du poisson a Concarneau (31x39cm-12x15in) s. pastel. 21-Dec-3 Thierry & Lannon, Brest #93/R est:2500-3000

JANSSEN, Gerhard (1636-1725) Dutch

Prints

£2098 $3566 €3000 Pastoral landscape with ruins and a ford (16x21cm-6x8in) etching. 27-Nov-3 Bassenge, Berlin #5164/R est:4500
£3147 $5350 €4500 Pastoral landscape with ruins and shepherds (16x21cm-6x8in) etching. 27-Nov-3 Bassenge, Berlin #5165/R est:4500

JANSSEN, Horst (1929-1995) German

£2013 $3705 €3000 Svanshall reversed (21x29cm-8x11in) s.i.d. W/C pencil. 26-Mar-4 Ketterer, Hamburg #483/R est:2800-3200
£3472 $5799 €5000 Still life (62x44cm-24x17in) tempera Indian ink pencil prov. 24-Oct-3 Ketterer, Hamburg #398/R est:5500-6500

Prints

£2133 $3925 €3200 Birdcage (26x24cm-10x9in) s.i.d. col woodcut. 11-Jun-4 Hauswedell & Nolte, Hamburg #1334/R est:2500
£2333 $4177 €3500 Railway (47x63cm-19x25in) s.d. col woodcut. 15-May-4 Van Ham, Cologne #700/R est:6300
£2937 $4993 €4200 Fire brigade (79x49cm-31x19in) col woodcut board. 29-Nov-3 Bassenge, Berlin #6790/R est:6000
£3497 $6014 €5000 Nuns (47x63cm-19x25in) s.i.d. woodcut. 3-Dec-3 Hauswedell & Nolte, Hamburg #836/R est:6000
£5594 $9510 €8000 Skaters (80x50cm-31x20in) s.d. col woodcut. 29-Nov-3 Villa Grisebach, Berlin #365/R est:9000-12000

Works on paper

£267 $491 €400 Landscape (10x16cm-4x6in) mono.d. W/C over pencil. 11-Jun-4 Hauswedell & Nolte, Hamburg #1327/R
£280 $481 €400 Cat and bone (6x26cm-2x10in) i.d. pencil. 3-Dec-3 Hauswedell & Nolte, Hamburg #819/R
£469 $806 €670 Rondo? (23x16cm-9x6in) mono.i.d. pencil col pen. 3-Dec-3 Hauswedell & Nolte, Hamburg #822/R
£503 $866 €720 Self portrait for Gisela (29x21cm-11x8in) s.i.d.1970 pencil. 6-Dec-3 Hans Stahl, Toestorf #375
£526 $853 €763 Surrealistic composition with eye and trees (24x31cm-9x12in) mono.i. pencil crayon. 4-Aug-3 Rasmussen, Vejle #619/R (D.KR 5500)
£533 $960 €800 Composition (21x29cm-8x11in) s.i.d.Dez 86 W/C. 24-Apr-4 Dr Lehr, Berlin #183/R
£567 $1043 €850 Female figure (25x20cm-10x8in) mono.d. Indian ink col pen. 11-Jun-4 Hauswedell & Nolte, Hamburg #1326/R
£600 $1080 €900 Sketch for book jacket (19x21cm-7x8in) s.i. brush bodycol board. 24-Apr-4 Dr Lehr, Berlin #182/R
£629 $1070 €900 Standing female nude (30x21cm-12x8in) s.i.d.13.10.76 wash pen col pen board. 21-Nov-3 Reiss & Sohn, Konigstein #578/R
£629 $1083 €900 E T A Hoffmann from me to him (19x11cm-7x4in) s.i.d. pencil. 3-Dec-3 Hauswedell & Nolte, Hamburg #825/R
£629 $1083 €900 Landscape 23.08.77 (18x24cm-7x9in) mono.d. col Indian ink pen brush. 3-Dec-3 Hauswedell & Nolte, Hamburg #829/R
£679 $1133 €991 Gottfried Keller (34x20cm-13x8in) bears i. verso Indian ink prov.exhib.lit. 24-Jun-3 Germann, Zurich #986/R est:1600-2000 (S.FR 1500)
£738 $1321 €1100 Female nude (21x32cm-8x13in) mono. pencil. 25-May-4 Dorotheum, Vienna #344/R
£764 $1276 €1100 Maria needs 900 Marks (21x30cm-8x12in) s.i.d.26.2.91 W/C ink board. 25-Oct-3 Dr Lehr, Berlin #223/R
£863 $1416 €1200 Landscape with willow (16x24cm-6x9in) s.i.d. col pen pencil. 4-Jun-3 Ketterer, Hamburg #508/R
£867 $1595 €1300 Composition (8x21cm-3x8in) s.i.d. pencil col pen collage. 11-Jun-4 Hauswedell & Nolte, Hamburg #1325/R
£921 $1695 €1400 Self portrait (20x20cm-8x8in) s.d.76 red pen. 25-Jun-4 Michael Zeller, Lindau #830/R
£979 $1684 €1400 Self with Chagall effect (34x21cm-13x8in) s.i.d. Indian ink wash. 3-Dec-3 Hauswedell & Nolte, Hamburg #828/R
£979 $1684 €1400 Self-portrait (16x14cm-6x6in) s.d. col Indian ink. 3-Dec-3 Hauswedell & Nolte, Hamburg #830/R
£1000 $1790 €1500 Self portrait (38x27cm-15x11in) s.d.21/7/74 pencil W/C. 15-May-4 Bassenge, Berlin #6905 est:900
£1049 $1804 €1500 Luciferig - landscape study (21x26cm-8x10in) mono.i.d. col pen pencil. 3-Dec-3 Hauswedell & Nolte, Hamburg #831/R est:1800
£1067 $1920 €1600 Untitled tree study (35x66cm-14x26in) s.i.d. pen. 24-Apr-4 Dr Lehr, Berlin #184/R est:800
£1067 $1963 €1600 Coastline (18x34cm-7x13in) mono.i.d.1974 pencil col pen. 11-Jun-4 Hauswedell & Nolte, Hamburg #1321/R est:1200
£1127 $1870 €1600 Landscape with sailing ships (14x21cm-6x8in) s.d.1977 pen w/C. 13-Jun-3 Hauswedell & Nolte, Hamburg #692/R est:1200
£1141 $2099 €1700 Sunset (10x18cm-4x7in) s.d. pencil oil chk. 26-Mar-4 Ketterer, Hamburg #482/R est:1100-1200
£1200 $2148 €1800 Lady come (65x45cm-26x18in) i. biro col pen. 15-May-4 Van Ham, Cologne #699/R est:1900
£1389 $2319 €2000 Untitled - landscape (17x28cm-7x11in) s.d.8.9.93 W/C bodycol Indian ink. 25-Oct-3 Dr Lehr, Berlin #224/R est:1000
£1399 $2336 €2000 Self-portrait (19x19cm-7x7in) s.i.d.4.4.71 ink brush. 10-Oct-3 Winterberg, Heidelberg #1463/R est:2500
£1408 $2338 €2000 Self-portrait (29x23cm-11x9in) s.d.1981 pencil col pen. 13-Jun-3 Hauswedell & Nolte, Hamburg #693/R est:2500
£1655 $2714 €2300 Untitled (62x82cm-24x32in) s.d. W/C over pencil. 4-Jun-3 Ketterer, Hamburg #510/R est:3000-5000
£1818 $3127 €2600 City landscape of Guardi (16x25cm-6x10in) s.i.d. fibretip wash. 3-Dec-3 Hauswedell & Nolte, Hamburg #832/R est:3000
£1933 $3538 €2900 Untitled - self portrait, seated (23x23cm-9x9in) mono.d.81 pencil col pen board. 4-Jun-4 Lempertz, Koln #222/R est:2500
£2013 $3604 €3000 Letter to Birgit Jacobsen (20x29cm-8x11in) mono.d.24.7.74.8 brio pencil col pen. 25-May-4 Dorotheum, Vienna #343/R est:4000-5000
£2098 $3608 €3000 Self portrait with Birgit Jacobsen (32x21cm-13x8in) mono.d. pencil col pen. 3-Dec-3 Hauswedell & Nolte, Hamburg #827/R est:2000
£2378 $4042 €3400 Phyllis (33x46cm-13x18in) i. bears s. pencil Indian ink W/C. 29-Nov-3 Villa Grisebach, Berlin #367/R est:4000-6000
£2657 $4571 €3800 For mothers' day (28x29cm-11x11in) s.i.d. pencil col pen. 3-Dec-3 Hauswedell & Nolte, Hamburg #818/R est:3000
£2667 $4907 €4000 Lovers (50x34cm-20x13in) s.i.d.66 pencil crayon. 11-Jun-4 Villa Grisebach, Berlin #1568/R est:3000-4000
£3873 $6430 €5500 Ice cream (52x39cm-20x15in) s.i.d.1966 pencil col pen. 13-Jun-3 Hauswedell & Nolte, Hamburg #690/R est:7500
£4333 $7930 €6500 Portrait of Charles Laughton (21x16cm-8x6in) mono.i.d.82 pencil pastel gouache lit. 4-Jun-4 Lempertz, Koln #224/R est:7000
£5369 $9611 €8000 Nature morte (22x34cm-9x13in) mono.d.24.3.87 W/C pen prov. 25-May-4 Dorotheum, Vienna #342/R est:10000-15000
£6667 $12267 €10000 Self portrait (50x35cm-20x14in) s.i.d.7.7.80 pencil col chk. 11-Jun-4 Hauswedell & Nolte, Hamburg #1328/R est:12000
£8667 $15947 €13000 M G N L Svanshall (43x43cm-17x17in) s.i. pencil col felt tip W/C prov. 12-Jun-4 Villa Grisebach, Berlin #422/R est:5000-7000
£9333 $17173 €14000 Bobethanien, 31 December 1990 (32x43cm-13x17in) i.d. Indian ink pencil W/C tempera. 11-Jun-4 Hauswedell & Nolte, Hamburg #1333/R est:7500
£10000 $18400 €15000 Bobethanien, 14 November 1990 (33x48cm-13x19in) s.i.d. Indian ink W/C. 11-Jun-4 Hauswedell & Nolte, Hamburg #1331/R est:8000
£10000 $18400 €15000 Bobethanien 17 November 1990 (30x46cm-12x18in) s.i.d. Indian ink W/C. 11-Jun-4 Hauswedell & Nolte, Hamburg #1332/R est:8000
£11333 $20853 €17000 Self portrait - paranoia (37x20cm-15x8in) mono.d. col chk pencil. 11-Jun-4 Hauswedell & Nolte, Hamburg #1329/R est:20000
£11538 $19846 €16500 Self-portrait (43x33cm-17x13in) s.d. W/C on pencil. 3-Dec-3 Hauswedell & Nolte, Hamburg #833/R est:15000
£12000 $22080 €18000 Self portrait (48x34cm-19x13in) s.i.d.74 black chk col chk prov. 12-Jun-4 Villa Grisebach, Berlin #423/R est:14000-18000
£13333 $24533 €20000 Self portrait (43x25cm-17x10in) s.d.10.7.71 pencil col chk. 11-Jun-4 Hauswedell & Nolte, Hamburg #1322/R est:20000
£16084 $27664 €23000 Self-portrait (47x30cm-19x12in) s.i.d. pencil col pen double-sided. 3-Dec-3 Hauswedell & Nolte, Hamburg #826/R est:12000
£16667 $30667 €25000 Bobethanien, 19 September 1990 (32x43cm-13x17in) s.i.d. Indian ink W/C. 11-Jun-4 Hauswedell & Nolte, Hamburg #1330/R est:8000

JANSSEN, Jacob (19th C) ?

Works on paper

£11067 $19810 €16601 View of the entrance to Jackson's Bay (25x45cm-10x18in) s.d.1848 i.verso W/C. 17-May-4 Sotheby's, Melbourne #567/R est:8000-12000 (A.D 28000)

JANSSEN, Ludovic (1888-1954) Belgian

£296 $512 €420 Eiffel (17x26cm-7x10in) s.i.d.juin 1925 panel. 10-Dec-3 Hotel des Ventes Mosan, Brussels #164
£310 $536 €440 Le Beffroi de Bruges (33x24cm-13x9in) s. canvas on panel. 10-Dec-3 Hotel des Ventes Mosan, Brussels #200
£352 $609 €500 Menet et son lac, Auvergen (39x58cm-15x23in) s. i.verso. 10-Dec-3 Hotel des Ventes Mosan, Brussels #162
£510 $913 €750 Declin du jour (40x60cm-16x24in) s. s.i.d.2-31 verso. 17-Mar-4 Hotel des Ventes Mosan, Brussels #111
£993 $1808 €1500 Soleil du soir (60x74cm-24x29in) s. s.i.verso. 16-Jun-4 Hotel des Ventes Mosan, Brussels #258 est:1000-1200

JANSSEN, Luplau (1869-1927) Danish

£321 $583 €469 Learning homework (19x18cm-7x7in) s. panel. 7-Feb-4 Rasmussen, Havnen #2248 (D.KR 3500)
£326 $512 €476 Autumn landscape with young woman (56x45cm-22x18in) s.d.1892. 30-Aug-3 Rasmussen, Havnen #2015 (D.KR 3500)
£556 $1000 €812 Mother and child seated on bench next to a pram (48x53cm-19x21in) s. 24-Apr-4 Rasmussen, Havnen #2307/R (D.KR 6200)
£750 $1290 €1095 The artist's wife and son with goat in garden (95x123cm-37x48in) s. 2-Dec-3 Kunsthallen, Copenhagen #570/R (D.KR 8000)
£750 $1290 €1095 Interior scene with the artist's wife and baby (90x115cm-35x45in) s.d.1913 exhib. 2-Dec-3 Kunsthallen, Copenhagen #574/R (D.KR 8000)
£889 $1618 €1334 Interior scene with Augusta Rist and daughter Ebba. Study of a gentleman (33x45cm-13x18in) s.d.92 double-sided. 19-Jun-4 Rasmussen, Havnen #2190/R (D.KR 10000)
£2240 $4032 €3270 Children around table (61x71cm-24x28in) s. 24-Apr-4 Rasmussen, Havnen #2128/R est:8000-10000 (D.KR 25000)
£6238 $10792 €9107 Young girl with a few sheep (173x225cm-68x89in) s.d.1897 exhib. 9-Dec-3 Rasmussen, Copenhagen #1435/R est:75000 (D.KR 66000)

JANSSEN, Peter (1844-1908) German

£1333 $2453 €2000 Figures on bicycles (90x100cm-35x39in) s.d.61 s.i.d.verso. 12-Jun-4 Villa Grisebach, Berlin #346/R est:2500-3500

JANSSENS, Hieronymus (1624-1693) Flemish

£11513 $21184 €17500 Interior scene with dancers (56x80cm-22x31in) 25-Jun-4 Piasa, Paris #7/R est:25000-30000
£15000 $27450 €21900 Interior with elegant company (59x85cm-23x33in) s. 8-Jul-4 Sotheby's, London #273/R est:15000-20000
£23129 $36776 €34000 L'ouverture du bal (57x81cm-22x32in) 23-Mar-3 Mercier & Cie, Lille #175b est:30000-35000

JANSSENS, Jacques (19th C) Belgian

£1477 $2746 €2200 Landscape (50x70cm-20x28in) s. s.i.d. verso. 8-Mar-4 Bernaerts, Antwerp #620/R est:2200-2400

JANSSENS, René (1870-1936) Belgian

£280 $507 €420 Porte donnant sur une cour (73x49cm-29x19in) s.d.1900. 30-Mar-4 Palais de Beaux Arts, Brussels #623
£284 $474 €400 La chambre a coucher (60x70cm-24x28in) 17-Jun-3 Galerie Moderne, Brussels #326
£300 $543 €450 Vestibule et escalier (54x41cm-21x16in) s.d.1897. 30-Mar-4 Campo, Vlaamse Kaai #89

JANSSENS, Victor Emile (1807-1845) German

£2198 $4000 €3209 Preparing dinner (62x49cm-24x19in) s.d.69 panel. 29-Jun-4 Sotheby's, New York #117/R est:4000-6000

JANSSON, Alfred (1863-1931) American/Swedish

£988 $1700 €1442 Winter in Iowa (51x41cm-20x16in) s.d.1929 board. 6-Dec-3 Neal Auction Company, New Orleans #622/R est:1200-1800
£1304 $2100 €1904 Landscape (46x66cm-18x26in) s.d.1909 canvas on board. 22-Feb-3 Bunte, Elgin #1274

JANSSON, Alvar (1922-1990) Scandinavian

£604 $1027 €882 Still life of vegetables and fruit (44x60cm-17x24in) init.d.83. 4-Nov-3 Bukowskis, Stockholm #197/R (S.KR 8000)

JANSSON, August Fredrik (1851-1915) Swedish
£322 $599 €480 Landscape from Lapland (73x118cm-29x46in) s. 7-Mar-4 Bukowskis, Helsinki #493/R

JANSSON, Eugène (1862-1915) Swedish
£350 $644 €525 Gripsholm study (45x36cm-18x14in) s. 14-Jun-4 Lilla Bukowskis, Stockholm #398 (S.KR 4800)
£25868 $46305 €37767 Outskirts of town (81x140cm-32x55in) s. painted 1896 prov.exhib.lit. 25-May-4 Bukowskis, Stockholm #95/R est:400000-500000 (S.KR 350000)

JANSSON, Rune (1918-) Swedish
£291 $468 €425 Blue stripes (38x68cm-15x27in) s.d.76. 25-Aug-3 Lilla Bukowskis, Stockholm #605 (S.KR 3800)
£1026 $1815 €1498 Cross and red lines (49x54cm-19x21in) s.d.59 lit. 27-Apr-4 AB Stockholms Auktionsverk #759/R (S.KR 14000)
£1026 $1815 €1498 Fluttering (41x50cm-16x20in) s.d.60 verso exhib.lit. 27-Apr-4 AB Stockholms Auktionsverk #760/R (S.KR 14000)

JANSSON, Tove (1914-2001) Finnish
£2465 $4264 €3500 Still life of flowers and pots (65x55cm-26x22in) s.d.1946. 13-Dec-3 Hagelstam, Helsinki #180/R est:4000
Works on paper
£521 $870 €750 Farm (30x43cm-12x17in) s.d.1948 chl. 23-Oct-3 Hagelstam, Helsinki #981

JANSZ, Pieter (1612-1672) Dutch
Works on paper
£2603 $4425 €3800 Abraham dismissing Hagar and Ismael (19x16cm-7x6in) bears i. pen brown ink brown grey wash black chk prov.exhib.lit. 4-Nov-3 Sotheby's, Amsterdam #83/R est:2000-3000

JANVIER, Alex (1935-) Canadian
£2127 $3552 €3105 Resident of Crooked River (60x90cm-24x35in) s.i.d.1979. 17-Nov-3 Hodgins, Calgary #295/R est:2000-3000 (C.D 4700)
Works on paper
£225 $383 €329 Carried into the sunset (22x58cm-9x23in) i. gouache prov. 23-Nov-3 Levis, Calgary #483/R (C.D 500)
£848 $1442 €1238 Fishing by nets (38x51cm-15x20in) s. gouache prov. 6-Nov-3 Heffel, Vancouver #68/R est:1200-1500 (C.D 1900)

JANZ, Franz (1946-) Austrian
Works on paper
£638 $1180 €950 Composition (107x76cm-42x30in) s.i.d.1929 mixed media board. 9-Mar-4 Dorotheum, Vienna #243/R
£738 $1366 €1100 Composition (99x70cm-39x28in) s.i.d.1991 mixed media board. 9-Mar-4 Dorotheum, Vienna #242/R

JANZON, Nils Gustaf (1850-1926) Swedish
£780 $1256 €1139 Girl on a three wheeler (53x43cm-21x17in) s.d.1890. 25-Aug-3 Lilla Bukowskis, Stockholm #651 (S.KR 10200)

JAPANANGKA, Harry Dixon (20th C) Australian
Works on paper
£690 $1255 €1007 Numuj - Witchety - Dreaming (196x135cm-77x53in) synthetic polymer paint canvas sold with photo. 1-Jul-4 Joel, Victoria #2 (A.D 1800)

JAPANESE SCHOOL
Works on paper
£4518 $7500 €6596 Japanese Buddhist hanging scroll (56x115cm-22x45in) hanging scroll, ink colour gold on silk. 30-Sep-3 Bonhams & Butterfields, San Francisco #4367/R est:1500-2500

JAPANESE SCHOOL, 18th C
Sculpture
£16000 $29440 €23360 Figure of Tekkai Sennin (12cm-5in) wood. 9-Jun-4 Sotheby's, London #1132/R est:3500-4000

JAPANESE SCHOOL, 19th C
Sculpture
£8000 $14720 €11680 Archer kneeling as he releases an arrow (66cm-26in) bronze base. 9-Jun-4 Sotheby's, London #1076/R est:8000-10000
Works on paper
£24000 $40080 €35040 Western ladies by lake (111x40cm-44x16in) ink col silk pair. 12-Nov-3 Christie's, London #9/R

JAPY, Louis Aime (1840-1916) French
£431 $772 €629 Arbres en fleurs (18x27cm-7x11in) s. i. verso board. 12-May-4 Dobiaschofsky, Bern #666/R (S.FR 1000)
£969 $1648 €1415 Summer lake (41x27cm-16x11in) s. bears i. 5-Nov-3 Dobiaschofsky, Bern #695/R (S.FR 2200)
£969 $1648 €1415 Landscape with flock of sheep (41x65cm-16x26in) s. 5-Nov-3 Dobiaschofsky, Bern #694/R (S.FR 2200)
£1223 $2250 €1786 Cattle grazing along the river's edge (23x41cm-9x16in) s.d.04 panel. 9-Jun-4 Doyle, New York #3099/R est:1500-2500
£1248 $2334 €1860 La chaumiere pres du lac (13x22cm-5x9in) s. panel. 29-Feb-4 Osenat, Fontainebleau #214
£2000 $3680 €3000 Le torrent (31x41cm-12x16in) s. panel. 9-Jun-4 Beaussant & Lefèvre, Paris #172/R est:3000-3200
£2536 $4159 €3500 La clairiere (38x46cm-15x18in) s. 11-May-3 Osenat, Fontainebleau #33/R est:3000-3500
£2538 $4366 €3705 Paysage avec bergers et ses moutons (41x32cm-16x13in) s. panel. 3-Dec-3 AB Stockholms Auktionsverk #2625/R est:25000-30000 (S.KR 33000)
£2958 $4910 €4200 Arbres en fleurs (41x33cm-16x13in) s. panel. 15-Jun-3 Peron, Melun #99
£3200 $5920 €4672 Ferrying the flock (65x81cm-26x32in) s.d.91. 10-Mar-4 Sotheby's, Olympia #243/R est:2000-3000
£4336 $7457 €6200 La gardienne de troupeau (32x40cm-13x16in) s. panel. 7-Dec-3 Osenat, Fontainebleau #65 est:5000-5500
£4600 $7636 €6716 River landscape (81x101cm-32x40in) s. 1-Oct-3 Sotheby's, Olympia #272/R est:4000-6000
£5000 $9000 €7300 Sunset landscape (47x55cm-19x22in) s.d.92 prov. 22-Apr-4 Christie's, Rockefeller NY #113/R est:10000-15000

JAQUELART, L (?) ?
£2162 $3870 €3200 Bergere tricotant avec chevres (58x46cm-23x18in) 10-May-4 Amberes, Antwerp #280/R

JAQUES, Francis Lee (1887-?) American
£8380 $15000 €12235 Two cranes against an orange sky (76x61cm-30x24in) s. 15-May-4 Illustration House, New York #63/R est:2000-4000

JAQUES, Pierre (1913-) French
£396 $674 €578 Lac de Divonne (19x24cm-7x9in) s.d.75 i. verso prov. 7-Nov-3 Dobiaschofsky, Bern #77/R (S.FR 900)
£690 $1234 €1007 Autumn woodland (73x81cm-29x32in) s. 12-May-4 Dobiaschofsky, Bern #667/R est:2200 (S.FR 1600)

JAQUET, Cecilia (fl.1889-1893) British?
Works on paper
£260 $434 €380 Sailing out of harbour (18x27cm-7x11in) s. W/C. 14-Oct-3 Bonhams, Knightsbridge #173/R

JARAY, Tess (1937-) British
£1050 $1911 €1533 Untitled (90x71cm-35x28in) all s. one d.1984 two d.1986 acrylic four. 4-Feb-4 Sotheby's, Olympia #127/R est:600-800

JARDIEL, Jose (1928-2000) Spanish
£306 $550 €447 Children playing (114x76cm-45x30in) s.d.60. 23-Jan-4 Freeman, Philadelphia #257/R
£3947 $7263 €6000 Young people sitting by columns (162x114cm-64x45in) s.d.77 s.i.d.verso. 22-Jun-4 Durán, Madrid #197/R est:6000

JARDIN, Alida du (19th C) Belgian?
£374 $681 €550 Nature morte au vase de fleurs (46x33cm-18x13in) 9-Feb-4 Amberes, Antwerp #253

JARDINE, Aeta (fl.1917-1940) British
£1493 $2494 €2180 Winter afternoon sunshine, Hammersmith (45x55cm-18x22in) s. s.i.d.1940 stretcher exhib. 17-Nov-3 Waddingtons, Toronto #149/R est:3500-4000 (C.D 3300)

JARDINES, Jose Maria (1862-?) Spanish
£2536 $4159 €3500 Landscape with rural church (54x66cm-21x26in) s. 27-May-3 Durán, Madrid #177/R est:3000
£5282 $9243 €7500 Landscape with river (60x73cm-24x29in) s. 16-Dec-3 Segre, Madrid #85a/R est:1900

JAREMA, Maria (1908-1958) Polish
Prints
£4483 $7486 €6500 Sketch for female nude (29x36cm-11x14in) i.d.1953 verso monotype. 16-Nov-3 Agra, Warsaw #32/R est:1000
Works on paper
£720 $1311 €1051 Woman seated (20x16cm-8x6in) W/C exec 1940. 20-Jun-4 Agra, Warsaw #16/R (P.Z 5000)
£759 $1267 €1100 Still life (29x21cm-11x8in) W/C pencil exec. 1932-33. 16-Nov-3 Agra, Warsaw #26/R

JARITZ, Jozsa (1893-1986) Hungarian
£588 $1041 €858 Girl with red scarf (96x75cm-38x30in) s.d.1922. 28-Apr-4 Kieselbach, Budapest #194/R (H.F 220000)
£3474 $6149 €5072 Boy in blue shirt (83x45cm-33x18in) s. 28-Apr-4 Kieselbach, Budapest #164/R (H.F 1300000)
£12006 $20770 €17529 By the table (125x135cm-49x53in) 12-Dec-3 Kieselbach, Budapest #43/R (H.F 4600000)
£13574 $22533 €19818 Nude in the studio (105x175cm-41x69in) s. painted c.1918. 4-Oct-3 Kieselbach, Budapest #28/R (H.F 5000000)

JARKI, Youri Alexandrovitch (1938-) Russian
£433 $780 €650 Rodeo (74x92cm-29x36in) s. 26-Apr-4 Millon & Associes, Paris #298/R
£867 $1560 €1300 Corde Raide (100x80cm-39x31in) s.i.verso. 26-Apr-4 Millon & Associes, Paris #299/R

JARL, Otto (1856-1915) Swedish
Sculpture
£1877 $3116 €2722 Hippo family (18x30cm-7x12in) s.i. dark pat.bronze Cast.A.G. Wien/Oesterr.Gesellsch. 13-Jun-3 Zofingen, Switzerland #2270/R est:5500 (S.FR 4130)

£2162 $3870 €3200 Indian elephant lamp base (84cm-33in) s. mono. dark brown pat. bronze. 8-May-4 Schloss Ahlden, Ahlden #1051/R est:3500

JARMAN, Derek (1942-1994) British
£260 $486 €390 Knight takes the Queen (25x33cm-10x13in) s. board. 22-Jul-4 Gorringes, Lewes #1805
£2200 $4004 €3212 Cool water series (183x254cm-72x100in) 1-Jul-4 Christie's, Kensington #385/R est:1000-1500

JARMAN, Henry Thomas (?) ?
£380 $619 €555 Garden of dreams (38x46cm-15x18in) s. s.i.verso. 25-Sep-3 Mellors & Kirk, Nottingham #769
£480 $782 €701 Vegetable garden (51x61cm-20x24in) s. 25-Sep-3 Mellors & Kirk, Nottingham #768
£900 $1467 €1314 Picking apples (61x51cm-24x20in) 25-Sep-3 Mellors & Kirk, Nottingham #767/R

JARNEFELT, Eero (1863-1937) Finnish
£4000 $7160 €6000 Birch wood in autumn (45x52cm-18x20in) s. 15-May-4 Hagelstam, Helsinki #72/R est:6000
£4000 $7160 €6000 Evening twilight (22x38cm-9x15in) s. 15-May-4 Hagelstam, Helsinki #73/R est:5000
£6294 $10699 €9000 Flowering trees (35x43cm-14x17in) s.d.1912 canvas on board exhib. 29-Nov-3 Bukowskis, Helsinki #120/R est:7000-8000
£6757 $12095 €10000 Evening sky (29x41cm-11x16in) s.d.91 board prov. 8-May-4 Bukowskis, Helsinki #270/R est:10000-13000
£17483 $29720 €25000 Winter landscape with silver birch tree trunks (48x33cm-19x13in) s.d.1905. 29-Nov-3 Bukowskis, Helsinki #41/R est:25000-28000
£18000 $32220 €27000 The artist's sister-in-law Nelma Sibelius at Tusby marsh (72x64cm-28x25in) s.d.1908. 15-May-4 Hagelstam, Helsinki #68/R est:25000
£46667 $83533 €70000 Larin Paraske (44x48cm-17x19in) s.d.1893 exhib.lit. 15-May-4 Hagelstam, Helsinki #70/R est:50000
£53333 $95467 €80000 Nelma Sibelius (22x29cm-9x11in) s.i.d.1899 lit. 15-May-4 Hagelstam, Helsinki #69/R est:35000
Works on paper
£553 $1018 €830 Evening glow (12x23cm-5x9in) W/C exhib. 9-Jun-4 Bukowskis, Helsinki #414/R
£733 $1349 €1100 Cloud (18x28cm-7x11in) W/C exhib. 9-Jun-4 Bukowskis, Helsinki #416/R
£767 $1411 €1150 Pine tree (34x24cm-13x9in) W/C exhib. 9-Jun-4 Bukowskis, Helsinki #415/R
£880 $1408 €1250 Autumn colours (28x26cm-11x10in) s.d.1906 gouache. 21-Sep-3 Bukowskis, Helsinki #358/R
£1197 $1915 €1700 Bridge, Budapest (29x46cm-11x18in) s.d.1934 W/C. 18-Sep-3 Hagelstam, Helsinki #869/R est:2000
£2400 $4296 €3600 Pine trees on the shore (47x34cm-19x13in) s.d.1933 gouache. 15-May-4 Hagelstam, Helsinki #75/R est:2500
£2400 $4296 €3600 Girl (24x17cm-9x7in) s.d.1914 gouache. 15-May-4 Hagelstam, Helsinki #76/R est:2500
£2685 $4993 €4000 View across the water (29x20cm-11x8in) s.d.1893 W/C. 7-Mar-4 Bukowskis, Helsinki #345/R est:4000
£3497 $5944 €5000 Foaming river (38x55cm-15x22in) s.d.1923 gouache. 29-Nov-3 Bukowskis, Helsinki #142/R est:4000-4500
£3667 $6563 €5500 Factories (40x55cm-16x22in) s.d.1928 gouache. 15-May-4 Hagelstam, Helsinki #74/R est:5000
£4930 $8528 €7000 Twilight (25x44cm-10x17in) s.d.1891 pastel. 13-Dec-3 Hagelstam, Helsinki #127/R est:2500
£8042 $13671 €11500 Leda and the swan (46x63cm-18x25in) s.d.1926 pastel. 29-Nov-3 Bukowskis, Helsinki #86/R est:4000-5000

JARNEFELT, Laura (1904-1985) Finnish
£302 $556 €450 Amaryllis (33x27cm-13x11in) s.d.1947. 25-Mar-4 Hagelstam, Helsinki #870
£880 $1408 €1250 Beach flowers (50x63cm-20x25in) s. 21-Sep-3 Bukowskis, Helsinki #360/R
Works on paper
£423 $676 €600 Landscape with reeds (34x32cm-13x13in) s. gouache. 21-Sep-3 Bukowskis, Helsinki #359/R
£541 $968 €800 Toeloe Bay (31x48cm-12x19in) s. gouache. 8-May-4 Bukowskis, Helsinki #37/R

JAROS, Peter J (1859-1929) Czechoslovakian
£285 $485 €416 Willows (60x48cm-24x19in) s. cardboard. 29-Nov-3 Dorotheum, Prague #38/R est:8000-15000 (C.KR 13000)
£455 $759 €650 Landscape with stream and ducks (96x75cm-38x30in) s.d.1918 board lit. 27-Jun-3 Auktionhaus Georg Rehm, Augsburg #8093

JAROSZ, Jozef (1890-1966) Polish
£963 $1599 €1406 View of Wisla with castle (62x49cm-24x19in) s. 15-Jun-3 Agra, Warsaw #38/R est:500 (P.Z 6000)

JAROSZ, Romain (1889-1932) French
£897 $1488 €1300 Forains. s. i.verso. 1-Oct-3 Millon & Associes, Paris #77/R

JAROSZYNSKI, Tadeusz (1933-) South African
Works on paper
£500 $835 €730 Three figures and a dog in an interior (49x37cm-19x15in) s. gouache. 20-Oct-3 Stephan Welz, Johannesburg #379 est:3000-5000 (SA.R 5800)

JARRY, Gaston (1889-1974) Argentinian
£782 $1400 €1142 View of Paris (60x50cm-24x20in) s. 4-May-4 Arroyo, Buenos Aires #10/R
£782 $1400 €1142 Fish (50x60cm-20x24in) 11-May-4 Arroyo, Buenos Aires #52
£1099 $2000 €1605 Nude (60x50cm-24x20in) s. 5-Jul-4 Arroyo, Buenos Aires #53/R est:2000

JARVIS, Don (1923-2001) Canadian
£222 $364 €324 Hillside (69x86cm-27x34in) s.d.53. 28-May-3 Maynards, Vancouver #30 (C.D 500)
£361 $672 €527 Autumn theme (120x90cm-47x35in) s. i.d.1992 verso acrylic prov. 4-Mar-4 Heffel, Vancouver #21/R (C.D 900)

JARVIS, Georgia (1944-1990) Canadian
£2715 $4534 €3964 Saskatchewan sleigh ride (45x60cm-18x24in) s.i.d.1986 board. 17-Nov-3 Hodgins, Calgary #324/R est:3000-4000 (C.D 6000)

JARVIS, W Frederick (?) ?
£2096 $3500 €3060 Texas landscape (61x76cm-24x30in) 18-Oct-3 David Dike, Dallas #266/R est:4000-6000

JARVIS, W Howard (fl.1950) British
£280 $512 €409 Looking over the Thames (40x51cm-16x20in) 7-Apr-4 Woolley & Wallis, Salisbury #157/R
£450 $824 €657 Moonlit Bembridge Harbour, Isle of Wight (55x74cm-22x29in) s. 7-Apr-4 Woolley & Wallis, Salisbury #307/R

JASCHA, Hans Werner (1942-) Austrian
£333 $597 €500 Spring sea (66x50cm-26x20in) s.d.10.8.94.12.51 acrylic graphite col pen. 13-May-4 Dorotheum, Linz #599/R
£350 $594 €500 Keen eye (66x50cm-26x20in) s.d.99 acrylic graphite col pencil. 27-Nov-3 Dorotheum, Linz #642/R
Works on paper
£333 $600 €500 Aquamarine (59x42cm-23x17in) s.d.83 graphite. 21-Apr-4 Dorotheum, Vienna #262/R
£367 $660 €550 4404 from 'head' cycle (59x42cm-23x17in) s. graphite. 21-Apr-4 Dorotheum, Vienna #263

JASCHIK, Almos (1885-1950) Hungarian
£1871 $3311 €2732 In the forest (43x32cm-17x13in) tempera paper. 28-Apr-4 Kieselbach, Budapest #12/R (H.F 700000)
Works on paper
£1566 $2709 €2286 Shipmen with ghosts (34x24cm-13x9in) mixed media. 12-Dec-3 Kieselbach, Budapest #111/R (H.F 600000)
£1827 $3161 €2667 Monsters and ghosts (34x23cm-13x9in) mixed media. 12-Dec-3 Kieselbach, Budapest #112/R (H.F 700000)
£3207 $5676 €4682 Dream and death (50x40cm-20x16in) mixed media canvas. 28-Apr-4 Kieselbach, Budapest #67/R (H.F 1200000)
£3258 $5408 €4757 Noah's Ark (71x49cm-28x19in) s.d.1926 mixed media. 4-Oct-3 Kieselbach, Budapest #62/R (H.F 1200000)

JASCHKE, Franz (1775-1842) Austrian
Works on paper
£483 $801 €700 St Leonhard im Pongau (23x35cm-9x14in) s.i.d.828 verso W/C. 30-Sep-3 Dorotheum, Vienna #255/R

JASINSKI, Feliks Stanislaw (1858-1901) Polish
Prints
£2767 $4953 €4040 Golden stairs (62x27cm-24x11in) s. both artists engraving vellum after E Burne-Jones prov.lit. 15-May-4 Christie's, Sydney #286/R est:3000-5000 (A.D 7000)

JASKIERSKI, Zbigniew (1928-1969) Polish
£1172 $1958 €1700 Landscape (240x154cm-94x61in) s.d.1964 s.i.d.verso. 16-Nov-3 Agra, Warsaw #99/R est:1000

JASTRAM, Jo (1928-) German
Sculpture
£3472 $5799 €5000 Mongolian rider (44x33x22cm-17x13x9in) s. bronze. 25-Oct-3 Dr Lehr, Berlin #248/R est:4000

JAUDON, Valerie (1945-) American
£6936 $12000 €10127 Kosciusko (183x183cm-72x72in) prov.exhib. 15-Dec-3 Hindman, Chicago #100/R est:6000-8000

JAUMANN, Rudolf Alfred (1859-?) German
£524 $892 €750 Vixen with kill (23x45cm-9x18in) i.d.15.2.97 canvas on board. 20-Nov-3 Dorotheum, Salzburg #115/R

JAUNBERSIN, J (?) ?
£2695 $5013 €3935 Rococo lounge in golden colours (77x115cm-30x45in) s. 2-Mar-4 Rasmussen, Copenhagen #1659/R est:20000 (D.KR 30000)

JAUSLIN, Karl (1842-1904) Swiss
£2586 $4629 €3776 Napoleon receiving Oberst von Affri (64x85cm-25x33in) prov. 13-May-4 Stuker, Bern #9510/R est:6000-9000 (S.FR 6000)

JAVIER, Maximino (20th C) Mexican
Works on paper
£369 $627 €539 Bull (26x37cm-10x15in) s.d.1981 mixed media card. 30-Oct-3 Louis Morton, Mexico #132/R (M.P 7000)

JAVOR, Pal (1880-1923) Hungarian

£2200 $4070 €3212 Sweet dreams (84x105cm-33x41in) s. 15-Jan-4 Christie's, Kensington #852/R est:2000-3000

JAVUREK, Karel (1815-1909) Czechoslovakian

£445 $757 €650 Academic in study (47x34cm-19x13in) mono.d.1901 lit. 6-Nov-3 Allgauer, Kempten #3460/R

JAWLENSKY, Alexej von (1864-1941) Russian

£18000 $33120 €26280 Grosse Meditation, Herr, Befiel. Great meditation (24x20cm-9x8in) init.d.36 i.verso linen-finish paper on board prov.exhib.lit. 23-Jun-4 Christie's, London #173/R est:20000-30000
£18667 $34347 €28000 Meditation (18x13cm-7x5in) s. paper on board prov. 11-Jun-4 Villa Grisebach, Berlin #32/R est:20000-30000
£25000 $45500 €36500 Grosse Meditation, im Dickicht (24x19cm-9x7in) init.i.d.37 linen-finish paper on cardboard prov.lit. 3-Feb-4 Christie's, London #217/R est:25000-35000
£32127 $54615 €46905 Meditation (25x16cm-10x6in) mono.d.37 s.i.d.verso cardboard prov.exhib.lit. 22-Nov-3 Burkhard, Luzern #114/R est:90000-110000 (S.FR 71000)
£35000 $64400 €51100 Large meditation (25x17cm-10x7in) init.d.36 linen finish paper on card prov.exhib.lit. 22-Jun-4 Sotheby's, London #175/R est:25000-35000
£50279 $90000 €73407 Meditation (20x17cm-8x7in) s.d.34 paper on artist board prov. 6-May-4 Sotheby's, New York #322/R est:40000-60000
£65000 $118300 €94900 Variation (35x27cm-14x11in) init. oil linen on card painted c.1918 prov.lit. 3-Feb-4 Sotheby's, London #24/R est:60000-80000
£70000 $128800 €105000 Large still life, bouquet of carnations and gentian bowl (25x21cm-10x8in) mono.d.36 paintboard on board prov.lit. 11-Jun-4 Villa Grisebach, Berlin #31/R est:70000-90000
£76667 $141067 €115000 Vase of flowers (35x26cm-14x10in) s.d.15 oil pencil prov. 11-Jun-4 Villa Grisebach, Berlin #1550/R est:70000-90000
£92000 $167440 €134320 Abstrakter kopf - abstract head (31x24cm-12x9in) s.d.32 s.i.verso oil linen on board prov.exhib.lit. 4-Feb-4 Sotheby's, London #274/R est:80000-100000
£94406 $160490 €135000 Variation: maturity and youth (36x27cm-14x11in) mono. canvasboard prov.exhib.lit. 26-Nov-3 Lempertz, Koln #739/R est:40000
£170000 $309400 €248200 Mystischer kopf, madchenkope - mystical head of a girl (27x24cm-11x9in) init. board painted c.1918 prov.exhib.lit. 3-Feb-4 Sotheby's, London #10/R est:100000-150000
£349650 $594406 €500000 Saviour's face: black buddha (36x27cm-14x11in) mono. paper on board prov.exhib.lit. 28-Nov-3 Villa Grisebach, Berlin #58/R est:300000-400000
£4352941 $7400000 €6355294 Schokko - Schokko mit tellerhut (76x65cm-30x26in) init. cardboard on canvas painted 1910 prov.exhib.lit. 5-Nov-3 Sotheby's, New York #20/R est:5000000-7000000

Prints
£4126 $7014 €5900 Movement (44x37cm-17x15in) lithograph. 26-Nov-3 Lempertz, Koln #741/R est:3500-4000
£4196 $7217 €6000 Head II (50x39cm-20x15in) s.d.1922 lithograph one of 80. 4-Dec-3 Van Ham, Cologne #253/R est:3500
£5505 $9193 €7982 Head III. s.i. W/C lithograph. 19-Jun-3 Kornfeld, Bern #507 est:15000 (S.FR 12000)

Works on paper
£1748 $2972 €2500 Portrait of Mrs K (21x17cm-8x7in) s.i.d.28.XI.27 Indian ink. 29-Nov-3 Villa Grisebach, Berlin #587/R est:1500-2000
£2958 $5117 €4200 Reclining female nude (24x32cm-9x13in) pencil. 13-Dec-3 Lempertz, Koln #157/R est:4000
£6993 $12028 €10000 Still life of flowers (12x9cm-5x4in) mono.i. W/C over pencil exec.1927/28 prov. 5-Dec-3 Ketterer, Munich #109/R est:10000-15000
£10000 $18200 €14600 Portrat einer frau - Portrait of a woman (42x29cm-17x11in) s. blue crayon exec.1921-22 prov. 4-Feb-4 Sotheby's, London #538/R est:3000-4000

JAWLENSKY, Andreas (1902-1984) Polish

Works on paper
£679 $1086 €991 Mimosa tree (40x27cm-16x11in) s.i.d.1959 feltpen. 16-Sep-3 Philippe Schuler, Zurich #3029 est:1500-2000 (S.FR 1500)

JAXA-MALACHOWSKI, Soter (1867-1952) Polish

Works on paper
£415 $768 €606 Ocean (49x69cm-19x27in) W/C. 14-Mar-4 Agra, Warsaw #55/R (P.Z 3000)

JAY, Florence (fl.1905-1920) British

£580 $1044 €847 Daisy (51x61cm-20x24in) s.d.1898. 21-Jan-4 Sotheby's, Olympia #323/R
£900 $1503 €1314 Two fox terriers on a bank (23x12cm-9x5in) s. board. 9-Oct-3 Greenslade Hunt, Taunton #491/R
£1150 $2105 €1679 End of day - horses watering in a woodland pool (70x91cm-28x36in) s.d.1905. 10-Jun-4 Neales, Nottingham #594/R est:400-800

Works on paper
£300 $549 €450 Herbaceous border at Close House (48x36cm-19x14in) s. pencil W/C. 30-Jul-4 Jim Railton, Durham #575
£360 $666 €526 Head of an Irish setter (25x36cm-10x14in) s. W/C. 9-Mar-4 Gorringes, Lewes #2158

JAY, Hamilton (fl.1875-1913) British

£289 $524 €422 Untitled - stolen pleasure (20x15cm-8x6in) s.d.1897 prov. 18-Apr-4 Levis, Calgary #211/R (C.D 700)

JEAN, Baptiste Jean (1953-) Haitian

£377 $600 €550 Saint Honore day procession (61x76cm-24x30in) s. masonite prov. 13-Sep-3 Weschler, Washington #717/R

JEAN, Marcel (1900-) French

Works on paper
£490 $832 €700 La fantome de la liberte (29x20cm-11x8in) s.d.1975 pastel. 23-Nov-3 Cornette de St.Cyr, Paris #162

JEAN, Philippe (1755-1802) British

Miniatures
£1100 $1980 €1606 Francis Reynolds Moreton, Baron Ducie of Tortworth (7cm-3in) i.verso gold plated mount oval prov.exhib. 22-Apr-4 Bonhams, New Bond Street #93/R est:1000-1500
£2800 $5040 €4088 Gentleman wearing a brown coat with coloured collar (5cm-2in) blue enamel gold fausse-montre frame oval exhib.lit. 22-Apr-4 Bonhams, New Bond Street #63/R est:1200-1800
£3243 $6000 €4735 Tyres Family member (8x5cm-3x2in) oval. 12-Mar-4 Du Mouchelle, Detroit #2031/R est:2000-3000
£4800 $7680 €7008 Naval officer in dress tunic (8x6cm-3x2in) 17-Sep-3 Bonhams, Brooks & Langlois, Jersey #119 est:3000-4000
£7500 $13500 €10950 Lady wearing a white dress with lilac waistband (8cm-3in) gold frame oval prov.exhib.lit. 22-Apr-4 Bonhams, New Bond Street #91/R est:4000-6000

JEANCLOS, Georges (1933-1997) French

Sculpture
£3662 $6335 €5200 Cecile (42x20x13cm-17x8x5in) s.i. bronze prov. 9-Dec-3 Artcurial Briest, Paris #551/R est:4000-6000
£4225 $7310 €6000 Untitled (62x52x45cm-24x20x18in) terracotta exec.c.1980 prov.exhib. 9-Dec-3 Artcurial Briest, Paris #403/R est:6000-8000

JEANES, Sigismond (1863-?) French

£315 $535 €450 Sur le Walen Stadherberg, Suisse (32x41cm-13x16in) s.d.1910 panel. 28-Nov-3 Doutrebente, Paris #30

JEANMAIRE, Edouard (1847-1916) Swiss

£862 $1543 €1259 Soleil levant sur le Wildhorn (58x40cm-23x16in) s. i.d.1903 verso board. 12-May-4 Dobiaschofsky, Bern #668/R est:2400 (S.FR 2000)
£1233 $2097 €1800 Lac de Tanay - a la Pointe de Peney (58x41cm-23x16in) s.i.d.1890 board. 7-Nov-3 Dobiaschofsky, Bern #46/R est:5000 (S.FR 2800)
£1762 $2996 €2573 Le Mont Blanc avec le cours de l'Arve avant Etrembieres (32x54cm-13x21in) s.d.1881 i. verso. 7-Nov-3 Dobiaschofsky, Bern #39/R est:8000 (S.FR 4000)
£1861 $3332 €2717 En foret, a la Joux-Peret (106x71cm-42x28in) s. i.d. verso exhib. 22-Mar-4 Philippe Schuler, Zurich #4338/R est:2600-4000 (S.FR 4300)
£3478 $6365 €5078 Paturage d'ete a la Joux-Perret (49x79cm-19x31in) s. s.i.d.aout 1914 verso prov. 5-Jun-4 Galerie du Rhone, Sion #531/R est:8000-10000 (S.FR 8000)
£8182 $13582 €11946 Joux Perret (140x115cm-55x45in) s.d.1889 s.i. verso. 13-Jun-3 Zofingen, Switzerland #2897/R est:4000 (S.FR 18000)

JEANNEAU, Fernand (20th C) French

£278 $520 €420 Retour de peche (32x24cm-13x9in) s. panel. 24-Jul-4 Thierry & Lannon, Brest #383

JEANNERET, Gustave (1847-1927) Swiss

£396 $674 €578 Girl with cattle by mountain lake (30x46cm-12x18in) mono.d.1865. 5-Nov-3 Dobiaschofsky, Bern #697/R (S.FR 900)

JEANNEST, Louis Francois (1810-1850) French

Sculpture
£2676 $4630 €3800 Cupid (26x26cm-10x10in) s.d.1811 bronze round. 10-Dec-3 Hugo Ruef, Munich #2782/R est:1500

JEANNIN, Georges (1841-1925) French

£364 $663 €550 Jetee de fleurs sur le sol (38x46cm-15x18in) s. cardboard. 20-Jun-4 Versailles Encheres #66
£1467 $2640 €2200 Still life with peaches (26x35cm-10x14in) s.i. board. 26-Apr-4 Rieber, Stuttgart #856/R
£2333 $4270 €3500 Jetee de roses (38x46cm-15x18in) s. 6-Jun-4 Osenat, Fontainebleau #80 est:3500-4000
£3357 $5606 €4800 Jetee de pivoines (65x81cm-26x32in) s. 7-Oct-3 Livinec, Gaudcheau & Jezequel, Rennes #134/R
£3497 $5839 €5000 Jetee de roses (46x55cm-18x22in) s. 29-Jun-3 Eric Pillon, Calais #99/R
£3803 $6579 €5400 Flowers and still life (22x34cm-9x13in) s.d.1918 board. 13-Dec-3 Lempertz, Koln #158/R est:2000
£5634 $9352 €8000 Corbeille de roses et cerises (50x65cm-20x26in) s. 15-Jun-3 Peron, Melun #104

JEANNIOT, Pierre Alexandre (1826-1892) French

£2096 $3857 €3060 Landscape (75x117cm-30x46in) s.d. 14-Jun-4 Philippe Schuler, Zurich #5859 est:2500-3000 (S.FR 4800)

JEANNIOT, Pierre Georges (1848-1934) French

£483 $893 €700 Paris, Place de la Concorde (24x32cm-9x13in) s.d.1900 panel. 11-Feb-4 Beaussant & Lefèvre, Paris #191

JEANRON, Philippe Auguste (1809-1877) French

£414 $766 €600 Plage animee (16x21cm-6x8in) s. panel. 13-Jan-4 Vanderkindere, Brussels #46

JEAURAT, Étienne (attrib) (1699-1789) French

£2818 $4931 €4000 Un jeune buveur de vin (43x33cm-17x13in) 18-Dec-3 Tajan, Paris #118/R est:3000-4000

Works on paper
£646 $1157 €950 Une femme assise regardant vers le haut avec des etudes subsidiares (37x26cm-15x10in) i. red white chk. 18-Mar-4 Christie's, Paris #245/R

JECT-KEY, David Wu (1890-1968) Chinese
£1062 $1900 €1551 Seaside cottage (51x87cm-20x34in) s. prov. 14-May-4 Skinner, Boston #258/R est:1200-1500

JEDRINSKY, Vladimir (20th C) Russian
Works on paper
£1000 $1790 €1460 Costume design (30x23cm-12x9in) s.i. W/C set of four. 26-May-4 Sotheby's, Olympia #406/R est:1200-1800

JEFFCOCK, Robert Salisbury (19/20th C) British
£480 $816 €701 Kitty, skewbald (23x29cm-9x11in) s.d.1895 canvasboard. 27-Nov-3 Christie's, Kensington #162/R

JEFFERIS, Lindsay (20th C) New Zealander?
£879 $1626 €1283 Benmore reflection (54x99cm-21x39in) s.d.2003. 9-Mar-4 Watson's, Christchurch #50 est:1500-3500 (NZ.D 2400)

JEFFERSON, Henrich (?) American?
£798 $1300 €1197 Luminous Hudson Valley (46x76cm-18x30in) s. 28-Sep-3 Carlsen Gallery, Greenville #295/R

JEFFERSON, Joseph (1829-1905) American
£335 $550 €486 Landscape with flowering field and house in distance (61x51cm-24x20in) s. 4-Jun-3 Alderfer's, Hatfield #280

JEFFERY, George (1864-1930) American
£272 $500 €397 Three sisters, Oregon at sunset (122x84cm-48x33in) 29-Mar-4 O'Gallerie, Oregon #730/R
£978 $1800 €1428 Rooster Rock, Columbia river, Oregon (56x91cm-22x36in) painted c.1910. 29-Mar-4 O'Gallerie, Oregon #194/R est:400-600

JEFFERYS, Charles William (1869-1951) Canadian
Works on paper
£383 $705 €559 Apple trees by the lake, Toronto (17x25cm-7x10in) s. s.i.verso W/C. 9-Jun-4 Walker's, Ottawa #74/R (C.D 950)
£537 $978 €784 Niagara Falls (37x51cm-15x20in) s. W/C prov. 5-Feb-4 Heffel, Vancouver #47/R (C.D 1300)

JEFFERYS, Marcel (1872-1924) Belgian
£278 $464 €400 Bruyere (20x40cm-8x16in) s. cardboard. 21-Oct-3 Campo, Vlaamse Kaai #450
£1342 $2376 €2000 Nature morte au vase de fleurs et a l'eventail (55x60cm-22x24in) s. exhib. 27-Apr-4 Campo, Vlaamse Kaai #461/R est:5000-6000
£2361 $3943 €3400 Pavots d'islande (65x77cm-26x30in) s. exhib. 21-Oct-3 Campo, Vlaamse Kaai #451/R est:4500-5500
£5103 $9441 €7400 Le bol de pavots (63x76cm-25x30in) bears mono. d.1917-1918 verso exhib. 13-Jan-4 Vanderkindere, Brussels #92/R est:5000-7500
Works on paper
£1862 $3445 €2700 Interieur de restaurant parisien (25x25cm-10x10in) mono.d.1912 chl W/C gouache. 13-Jan-4 Vanderkindere, Brussels #113 est:500-750
£2324 $4020 €3300 La couture (34x37cm-13x15in) mono. W/C gouache prov. 13-Dec-3 De Vuyst, Lokeren #181/R est:1800-2200

JEGERLEHNER, Hans (1907-1974) Swiss
£495 $852 €723 Cadiz (50x60cm-20x24in) i.verso stretcher. 8-Dec-3 Philippe Schuler, Zurich #5934 (S.FR 1100)
£647 $1157 €945 Girl in garden (70x80cm-28x31in) s. i. stretcher. 14-May-4 Dobiaschofsky, Bern #206/R est:2500 (S.FR 1500)
£1322 $2247 €1930 Svajatoslav Richter at piano (60x72cm-24x28in) s. 5-Nov-3 Dobiaschofsky, Bern #699/R est:1400 (S.FR 3000)

JEGOROV, A (19/20th C) Russian
£2300 $4186 €3358 Winter street scene with horse-drawn sleigh (36x48cm-14x19in) indis sig. board. 15-Jun-4 Canterbury Auctions, UK #112/R est:300-400

JEHAN, Christophe (1961-) French
£342 $582 €500 Trois personnages (50x50cm-20x20in) s. 9-Nov-3 Eric Pillon, Calais #267/R
£403 $721 €600 Chat (50x50cm-20x20in) s. 30-May-4 Eric Pillon, Calais #310/R

JEIHAN (1938-) Javanese
£3011 $4817 €4396 Melati (100x90cm-39x35in) s.d.86 s.d.1986 verso. 18-May-3 Sotheby's, Singapore #166/R est:4000-9000 (S.D 8400)
£3623 $5616 €5290 Mother and child (99x98cm-39x39in) s.d.78. 6-Oct-2 Sotheby's, Singapore #146/R est:10000-15000 (S.D 10000)
£5229 $9464 €7634 Nursiti (141x141cm-56x56in) s.d.82-3 s.i.verso. 4-Apr-4 Sotheby's, Singapore #163/R est:8000-10000 (S.D 16000)
£5435 $8424 €7935 Bariah (140x120cm-55x47in) s.d.91 s.i.verso. 6-Oct-2 Sotheby's, Singapore #147/R est:15000-20000 (S.D 15000)

JELINEK, Franz A (1890-1977) Czechoslovakian
£577 $1072 €842 Still life with armour (85x115cm-33x45in) s. 6-Mar-4 Dorotheum, Prague #82/R est:28000-45000 (C.KR 28000)

JELINEK, Josef (1871-1945) Czechoslovakian
£285 $485 €416 Paris (18x20cm-7x8in) s. cardboard. 29-Nov-3 Dorotheum, Prague #40/R est:8000-15000 (C.KR 13000)

JELINEK, Rudolf (1880-?) Austrian
£1200 $2184 €1800 A visit to the antiques dealer (61x88cm-24x35in) s. 1-Jul-4 Van Ham, Cologne #1428/R est:1500

JELINGER, Henri Adriaan (1895-1961) Dutch
£1074 $1997 €1600 Church in Maastricht (84x95cm-33x37in) s. 4-Mar-4 Auction Maastricht #1090/R est:1000-1500
£1241 $1986 €1800 Market in Tongerem (69x79cm-27x31in) s. 12-Mar-3 Auction Maastricht #1146/R est:2000-2600

JELINGER, Henri Adriaan (attrib) (1895-1961) Dutch
Works on paper
£322 $553 €460 Canal in Brugge (16x23cm-6x9in) s.d.1955 W/C. 4-Dec-3 Vendue Huis, Gravenhage #1007
£322 $553 €460 Canal in Brugge (16x23cm-6x9in) s.d.1955 W/C. 3-Dec-3 Auction Maastricht #1007/R

JELLETT, Mainie (1897-1944) Irish
£1042 $1698 €1500 Wicklow landscape (29x39cm-11x15in) board. 24-Sep-3 James Adam, Dublin #18/R est:1500-2000
£7500 $13425 €10950 Cubist composition (38x114cm-15x45in) s. panel. 14-May-4 Christie's, London #12/R est:8000-12000
£19000 $34010 €27740 Three elements (91x71cm-36x28in) prov.exhib. 13-May-4 Sotheby's, London #30/R est:10000-15000
£20000 $35800 €29200 Abstract composition (183x92cm-72x36in) s.d.1926 prov.lit. 13-May-4 Sotheby's, London #31/R est:20000-30000
Works on paper
£769 $1308 €1100 Composition with three elements. Rug design (20x27cm-8x11in) pencil prov.exhib. pair. 18-Nov-3 Whyte's, Dublin #17/R
£909 $1545 €1300 Composition (17x22cm-7x9in) ink wash board prov. 18-Nov-3 Whyte's, Dublin #15/R
£912 $1724 €1350 Abstract composition (27x17cm-11x7in) pencil. 17-Feb-4 Whyte's, Dublin #11/R est:1000-1500
£986 $1725 €1400 Mountainous landscape with donkey (22x30cm-9x12in) monochrome wash. 16-Dec-3 James Adam, Dublin #32/R
£1389 $2264 €2000 Figure composition (23x18cm-9x7in) gouache. 24-Sep-3 James Adam, Dublin #126/R est:2000-3000
£1400 $2618 €2100 Abstract (13x15cm-5x6in) s.d.1925. 21-Jul-4 John Nicholson, Haslemere #135 est:500-1000
£2685 $4752 €4000 Artist at her easel in the Life Room at the Westminster School of Art (23x18cm-9x7in) s.d.1918 W/C pencil prov. 27-Apr-4 Whyte's, Dublin #28/R est:3000-4000
£3000 $5370 €4380 Madonna and Child (25x11cm-10x4in) s.d.25 gouache pencil prov. 13-May-4 Sotheby's, London #101/R est:3000-4000
£3077 $5231 €4400 Figure composition (23x18cm-9x7in) gouache exhib. 18-Nov-3 Whyte's, Dublin #11/R est:3000-4000
£3099 $5361 €4400 Digging the turf Connemara (21x30cm-8x12in) monochrome wash prov. 10-Dec-3 Bonhams & James Adam, Dublin #166/R est:1200-1500
£3636 $6182 €5200 Study for bog and sea (27x36cm-11x14in) s.d.1940 gouache prov.exhib. 18-Nov-3 Whyte's, Dublin #10/R est:3000-4000
£3893 $6890 €5800 Waterfall (30x19cm-12x7in) s.d.1937 i.verso gouache board exhib. 27-Apr-4 Whyte's, Dublin #29/R est:6000-8000
£4000 $7240 €6000 Untitled (13x26cm-5x10in) s.d.1926 gouache prov. 30-Mar-4 De Veres Art Auctions, Dublin #15/R est:4500-6000
£4196 $7133 €6000 Babbin and Betty at home in Fitzwilliam Square (24x21cm-9x8in) s.d.1918 gouache. 25-Nov-3 De Veres Art Auctions, Dublin #31/R est:6000-8000
£4698 $8315 €7000 Woman in summer hat (16x15cm-6x6in) s.d.1918 W/C pencil prov.exhib.lit. 27-Apr-4 Whyte's, Dublin #27/R est:3000-4000
£5000 $8950 €7300 Figure composition (52x21cm-20x8in) s.d.36 gouache prov. 14-May-4 Christie's, London #13/R est:3000-5000
£8200 $14678 €11972 Study for Achill Horses II (22x37cm-9x15in) s.d.1939 s.i. on backboard pencil gouache. 14-May-4 Christie's, London #220/R est:7000-10000

JELLEY, James Valentine (fl.1878-1942) British
£480 $792 €701 Study of turkeys and chickens at feeding time in a farm field (18x20cm-7x8in) s. canvas on panel. 1-Jul-3 Tayler & Fletcher, Cheltenham #1
£550 $919 €803 Kingfisher (25x30cm-10x12in) s.d.02. 13-Nov-3 Christie's, Kensington #324/R
Works on paper
£450 $832 €657 Daffodils (19x13cm-7x5in) mono.i. W/C bodycol. prov. 10-Mar-4 Sotheby's, Olympia #83/R
£500 $925 €730 Study of Daphne (30x13cm-12x5in) s.i. pencil W/C gouache. 10-Mar-4 Sotheby's, Olympia #82/R

JEMIERCO, Alexander (20th C) British?
£420 $714 €613 Shire horse and farm workers (112x152cm-44x60in) s.d.1971. 4-Nov-3 Dreweatt Neate, Newbury #130

JENDRASSIK, Jeno (1860-1919) Hungarian
£400 $720 €600 Portrait of woman wearing white dress (52x41cm-20x16in) s.d.1889 lit. 22-Apr-4 Allgauer, Kempten #3593/R

JENE, Edgar (1904-1984) Austrian
£359 $600 €524 Castle courtyard (54x64cm-21x25in) s.d.57 lit. 7-Oct-3 Sotheby's, New York #323
Works on paper
£333 $613 €500 Mediterranean island (45x66cm-18x26in) s.d.30 gouache. 9-Jun-4 Dorotheum, Salzburg #599/R
£356 $651 €530 Stallions fighting (64x49cm-25x19in) s.d.1961 gouache mixed media. 9-Jul-4 Dawo, Saarbrucken #181/R
£470 $869 €700 Sailing boats (64x50cm-25x20in) i. verso gouache. 9-Mar-4 Dorotheum, Vienna #82/R
£470 $869 €700 Sails (50x62cm-20x24in) i. verso gouache. 9-Mar-4 Dorotheum, Vienna #83/R

JENEY, Viktor de (1902-1996) American/Hungarian
£581 $1000 €848 Haystacks in winter (64x46cm-25x18in) s.d.1971. 6-Dec-3 Selkirks, St. Louis #209

JENIN, Jonathan (19th C) American
Works on paper
£1359 $2500 €1984 School room (43x51cm-17x20in) W/C graphite crayon prov. 22-Jun-4 Sotheby's, New York #198/R est:2500-3500

JENKIN, William (19th C) British
Works on paper
£250 $425 €365 Birds feeding in the nest (16x20cm-6x8in) s.d.1894 W/C. 25-Nov-3 Bonhams, Knightsbridge #122

JENKINS, Blanche (fl.1872-1915) British
£880 $1610 €1285 Simple child (52x41cm-20x16in) s.d.1885. 6-Apr-4 Bristol Auction Rooms #463/R

JENKINS, G H (?) ?
£486 $900 €710 Welsh mountain stream (33x48cm-13x19in) s.i. 14-Jan-4 Dallas Auction Gallery, Dallas #479/R

JENKINS, George Henry (1843-1914) British
£320 $554 €467 Gathering flotsam on the Devonshire coast (25x41cm-10x16in) s.d.1874 board. 11-Dec-3 Lane, Penzance #102
£343 $631 €501 Fisherman at a rapids (51x76cm-20x30in) s. prov. 14-Jun-4 Waddingtons, Toronto #103/R (C.D 850)
£360 $659 €526 Fishing boats off the coast at sunset (39x65cm-15x26in) s. 6-Apr-4 Bristol Auction Rooms #495/R
£400 $640 €584 Hawthorn near Bickleigh, Devon (23x36cm-9x14in) s. painted c.1880. 21-Sep-3 Desmond Judd, Cranbrook #1077
£440 $761 €642 Boats at anchor, the Barbican, Plymouth (22x35cm-9x14in) s. board. 11-Dec-3 Lane, Penzance #103
£450 $833 €657 Coastal landscape (56x91cm-22x36in) s. 9-Mar-4 Bonhams, Knightsbridge #209/R
£500 $915 €730 Fisherman in a quiet cove on the Devon coast (24x41cm-9x16in) s.d.1879 board. 3-Jun-4 Lane, Penzance #10/R
£860 $1522 €1256 Salcombe Castle, South Devon (51x47cm-20x19in) s.d.81. 27-Apr-4 Bonhams, Knowle #76/R
£1200 $2184 €1752 Across the bay (53x90cm-21x35in) s. 21-Jun-4 Bonhams, Bath #443/R est:500-700
Works on paper
£260 $429 €380 Dartmoor scene (26x46cm-10x18in) s. W/C. 4-Jul-3 Honiton Galleries, Honiton #72

JENKINS, John Eliot (1868-1937) American
£539 $900 €787 Quiet stream (30x41cm-12x16in) board. 18-Oct-3 David Dike, Dallas #264/R

JENKINS, Michael (20th C) American
Works on paper
£307 $550 €448 Detail number 35 (36x28cm-14x11in) fabric felt prov. 16-May-4 Wright, Chicago #372/R

JENKINS, Paul (1923-) American
£805 $1498 €1200 Phenomena under maypole (78x57cm-31x22in) s. acrylic paper. 3-Mar-4 Artcurial Briest, Paris #455
£909 $1545 €1300 Untitled (40x50cm-16x20in) acrylic painted 1989 exhib. 25-Nov-3 Christie's, Amsterdam #108/R
£939 $1568 €1371 Composition (109x78cm-43x31in) s. W/C paper on canvas. 7-Oct-3 Rasmussen, Copenhagen #239/R (D.KR 10000)
£979 $1664 €1400 Phenomena Chinese window (55x33cm-22x13in) s. s.d.89-90 verso acrylic prov. 18-Nov-3 Pierre Berge, Paris #43/R
£1007 $1873 €1500 Untitled (77x57cm-30x22in) s.i.d.1962-1964 acrylic paper two. 3-Mar-4 Artcurial Briest, Paris #459 est:400-500
£1007 $1844 €1500 Phenomena Panning Told (75x105cm-30x41in) s. acrylic paper painted 1972 prov. 7-Jul-4 Artcurial Briest, Paris #285 est:1000-1500
£1074 $1997 €1600 Untitled (57x77cm-22x30in) s.i.d.1962-1965 acrylic two. 3-Mar-4 Artcurial Briest, Paris #458 est:400-500
£1133 $2062 €1700 Phenomena Shaman Seen (46x38cm-18x15in) s.i.d.1989-90 verso acrylic prov. 30-Jun-4 Calmels Cohen, Paris #83/R est:1500-1800
£1275 $2372 €1900 Untitled (78x57cm-31x22in) s.i.d.1962-1964 acrylic paper three. 3-Mar-4 Artcurial Briest, Paris #457 est:600-800
£1630 $3000 €2380 Phenomena over far (97x162cm-38x64in) s. s.i.d.1966 verso acrylic. 27-Jun-4 Freeman, Philadelphia #138/R est:3000-5000
£1744 $3000 €2546 Phenomena lucifer hump (96x129cm-38x51in) s. s.i.d.1962 overlap. 3-Dec-3 Doyle, New York #87/R est:2500-3500
£2533 $4661 €3800 Phenomena of resusitation (147x89cm-58x35in) s. s.i.d.1960 verso. 11-Jun-4 Pierre Berge, Paris #74 est:4000-5000
£2658 $4518 €3800 Phenomena flight of the wild jander (96x129cm-38x51in) s.i.d.1982 verso acrylic prov. 25-Nov-3 Tajan, Paris #23/R est:3000-4000
£2794 $4750 €4079 Phenomena steep incline (163x97cm-64x38in) s.i.d.1967 verso acrylic prov. 9-Nov-3 Wright, Chicago #448 est:2500-3500
£2795 $4751 €4081 Phenomena Monet's Second - Rouen (162x121cm-64x48in) s.i.d.1985 verso acrylic. 5-Nov-3 AB Stockholms Auktionsverk #1174/R est:40000-50000 (S.KR 37000)
£2973 $5500 €4341 Phenomena by Welsh Green (127x95cm-50x37in) acrylic plastic painted 1966 prov. 13-Jul-4 Christie's, Rockefeller NY #18/R est:3000-5000
£3067 $5000 €4478 Phenomena with blue moving in (122x127cm-48x50in) s. s.i.d.1965 verso acrylic prov. 23-Sep-3 Christie's, Rockefeller NY #120/R est:4000-6000
£3073 $5500 €4487 Phenomena prism citadel (164x122cm-65x48in) s. s.i.d.1993 overlap acrylic. 6-May-4 Doyle, New York #116/R est:3000-5000
£3099 $5423 €4400 Phenomena pealing of balls (97x130cm-38x51in) s. s.i.d.1989 verso prov. 18-Dec-3 Cornette de St.Cyr, Paris #139/R est:3000-4000
£3147 $5413 €4500 Phenomena on the way (120x56cm-47x22in) s. s.i.d.1965 verso acrylic prov. 5-Dec-3 Ketterer, Munich #173a/R est:4000-6000
£3593 $6000 €5246 Phenomena Katherine's guardian (161x94cm-63x37in) s. s.i.overlap acrylic prov. 7-Oct-3 Sotheby's, New York #401 est:3000-5000
£4054 $7135 €6000 Untitled (120x100cm-47x39in) s. acrylic prov. 18-May-4 Tajan, Paris #71/R est:6000-8000
£4076 $7500 €5951 Phenomena fourth turn (100x100cm-39x39in) s. i. verso prov. 27-Jun-4 Freeman, Philadelphia #139/R est:2000-3000
£4121 $7500 €6017 Phenomena (84x84cm-33x33in) s. s.i.d.1966 overlap acrylic prov. 29-Jun-4 Sotheby's, New York #519/R est:6000-8000
£4360 $7500 €6366 Phenomena Veronica (161x97cm-63x38in) s. s.i.d.1968 on overlap. 3-Dec-3 Doyle, New York #86/R est:4000-6000
£4469 $8000 €6525 Phenomena heaven shield (97x163cm-38x64in) s. s.i.d.1966 overlap prov. 6-May-4 Doyle, New York #115/R est:2500-3500
£10270 $19000 €14994 Phenomena Port of Call (196x325cm-77x128in) s. s.i.d.1984 verso. 13-Jul-4 Christie's, Rockefeller NY #20/R est:7000-9000
£14054 $26000 €20519 Phenomena 190 Degree Prism (196x332cm-77x131in) s. s.i.d.1985 verso. 13-Jul-4 Christie's, Rockefeller NY #19/R est:7000-9000
Works on paper
£336 $625 €500 Phenomena sun worshipper (77x56cm-30x22in) s. s.i.d.1962 verso W/C prov. 3-Mar-4 Artcurial Briest, Paris #456
£376 $650 €549 Rockefeller Arch (77x57cm-30x22in) s. W/C prov. 13-Dec-3 Weschler, Washington #593
£403 $749 €600 Phenomena prism orator (28x21cm-11x8in) s. s.i.d.1989 verso W/C. 3-Mar-4 Artcurial Briest, Paris #454
£645 $1097 €942 Composition (76x106cm-30x42in) s. W/C. 10-Nov-3 Rasmussen, Vejle #568/R (D.KR 7000)
£839 $1443 €1200 Phenomena oracle wait (76x55cm-30x22in) s. i. verso W/C. 3-Dec-3 Hauswedell & Nolte, Hamburg #891/R
£1222 $2250 €1784 Phenomena eclipse light. Untitled (76x107cm-30x42in) s. W/C two. 28-Mar-4 Bonhams & Butterfields, San Francisco #2758 est:1000-1500
£1250 $2250 €1825 Phenomena mineral body. Untitled (76x106cm-30x42in) s. W/C two. 25-Apr-4 Bonhams & Butterfields, San Francisco #5655/R est:1000-1500

JENKINS, Robert (fl.1890s) Australian
£1417 $2281 €2069 Harvesting (71x140cm-28x55in) s. 13-Oct-3 Joel, Victoria #373 est:3500-4500 (A.D 3500)
Works on paper
£324 $521 €473 Harvest time (41x62cm-16x24in) s. W/C. 13-Oct-3 Joel, Victoria #384 (A.D 800)

JENKINS, Wilfred (fl.1875-1888) British
£260 $481 €380 Figures by moonlight (20x36cm-8x14in) s. board. 15-Jul-4 Richardson & Smith, Whitby #423/R
£280 $521 €409 Twilight scene, Whitby harbour (38x58cm-15x23in) s. 5-Mar-4 Dee Atkinson & Harrison, Driffield #639
£360 $666 €526 Traveller passing a country cottage at sunset (20x33cm-8x13in) s. 13-Feb-4 Keys, Aylsham #819
£400 $740 €584 Moonlit street scene (25x41cm-10x16in) s.d.1934 board. 12-Feb-4 Andrew Hartley, Ilkley #871
£480 $830 €701 Moonlit dock scene (40x61cm-16x24in) s. 10-Dec-3 Edgar Horn, Eastbourne #289/R
£650 $1203 €949 Vies of Whitby harbour by moonlight (18x25cm-7x10in) s. board pair. 9-Mar-4 Capes Dunn, Manchester #694
£780 $1240 €1131 Whitby Harbour. View of Whitby (19x36cm-7x14in) board pair. 9-Sep-3 David Duggleby, Scarborough #323

JENNER, Isaac Walter (1836-1901) Australian/British
£687 $1250 €1003 Portsmouth Arm of Shoreham Harbour (15x28cm-6x11in) s. i.verso painted c.1882. 16-Jun-4 Deutscher-Menzies, Melbourne #226/R est:2000-3000 (A.D 1800)
£851 $1447 €1242 Pilot Cutter off the East Point, Devon. To Brighton, Sussex (15x23cm-6x9in) both s.d.1890 i.verso pair academy board. 26-Nov-3 Deutscher-Menzies, Melbourne #176/R (A.D 2000)
£1450 $2640 €2117 Seascape with man-of-war (30x61cm-12x24in) s.d.1876. 16-Jun-4 Deutscher-Menzies, Melbourne #227/R est:4000-6000 (A.D 3800)
£1450 $2640 €2117 River Ouse at Newhaven (30x45cm-12x18in) s.d.1889 i.verso. 16-Jun-4 Deutscher-Menzies, Melbourne #229/R est:4000-6000 (A.D 3800)
£1800 $3402 €2628 On the fishing banks (61x102cm-24x40in) s. 17-Feb-4 Bonhams, New Bond Street #42/R est:2000-3000
£1908 $3473 €2786 Sunset sea (26x45cm-10x18in) s.d.1899 board prov. 16-Jun-4 Deutscher-Menzies, Melbourne #228/R est:4000-6000 (A.D 5000)
£3252 $5106 €4715 Portsmouth (20x40cm-8x16in) mono. board painted c.1881 prov.exhib.lit. 26-Aug-3 Christie's, Sydney #330/R est:8000-12000 (A.D 8000)

JENNER, Isaac Walter (attrib) (1836-1901) Australian/British
£400 $664 €584 Shipping off Cherbourg at sunset (17x34cm-7x13in) board. 1-Oct-3 Bonhams, Knightsbridge #141/R
£1100 $1826 €1606 Vessels off St Michaels Mount. Shipping off Bridport (14x30cm-6x12in) board pair. 1-Oct-3 Bonhams, Knightsbridge #132/R est:1200-1800

JENNEWEIN, Carl Paul (1890-1978) American
£588 $1000 €858 Sail ship and tug in harbour (15x20cm-6x8in) s.verso board. 18-Nov-3 John Moran, Pasadena #12b
Sculpture
£5405 $10000 €7891 Over the waves (31cm-12in) s. green brown pat bronze black marble base prov.lit. 11-Mar-4 Christie's, Rockefeller NY #29/R est:12000-18000

JENNEY, Neil (1945-) American
£11173 $20000 €16313 Intercoastal (125x74cm-49x29in) s.d.83 verso canvasboard prov.exhib.lit. 12-May-4 Christie's, Rockefeller NY #466/R est:35000-45000
£21557 $36000 €31473 Morning (47x83cm-19x33in) s.d.1996 panel prov. 14-Nov-3 Phillips, New York #135/R est:35000-45000
£26946 $45000 €39341 Morning (46x82cm-18x32in) s.d.1990 verso acrylic masonite prov. 12-Nov-3 Christie's, Rockefeller NY #629/R est:30000-40000

JENNINGS, James Harold (1931-) American
£278 $500 €406 Police woman rides man to jail (46x48cm-18x19in) painted wood cut out. 24-Apr-4 Slotin Folk Art, Buford #428/R
Sculpture
£611 $1100 €892 Self portrait with bus (43x48x15cm-17x19x6in) paint cut out wood. 24-Apr-4 Slotin Folk Art, Buford #427/R est:1000-2000
£833 $1500 €1216 Jennings environment with self portrait (89x76cm-35x30in) painted wood construction. 24-Apr-4 Slotin Folk Art, Buford #426/R est:1000-2000
£2500 $4500 €3650 Mini skirt girl gang raids the man's pool house (46x102cm-18x40in) painted caved wood. 24-Apr-4 Slotin Folk Art, Buford #425/R est:2000-3000

JENNINGS, Walter Robin (1927-) British
£320 $509 €467 Fishing the Severn below Bewdley (51x61cm-20x24in) s. 12-Sep-3 Halls, Shrewsbury #732

JENNY, Arnold (1831-1881) Swiss
£393 $715 €574 View over Lake Lauerzer (51x70cm-20x28in) s.d.79. 16-Jun-4 Fischer, Luzern #2197/R (S.FR 900)

JENOUR, Charles (fl.1825-1832) British
Works on paper
£550 $1001 €803 Portrait of Lieutenant William Innes (19x15cm-7x6in) s.i. pastel. 1-Jul-4 Mellors & Kirk, Nottingham #739/R

JENRIN, Edmond (19th C) French
Works on paper
£616 $1048 €900 Portrait d'un enfant avec chiens (45x35cm-18x14in) s. chl gouache. 6-Nov-3 Tajan, Paris #208

JENSEN, Alfred (1903-1981) American
£4324 $8000 €6313 God and Man (25x38cm-10x15in) s.i.d.1959 verso board prov. 12-Feb-4 Sotheby's, New York #91/R est:6000-8000
£9581 $16000 €13988 Magneto - Optical Study No 13 (53x89cm-21x35in) s.i.d.1974 verso prov. 12-Nov-3 Christie's, Rockefeller NY #360/R est:12000-16000
£23952 $40000 €34970 Correspondence of Function of Magnet and Prism (127x213cm-50x84in) each s.i.d.1961 verso two attached canvases prov.exhib. 12-Nov-3 Christie's, Rockefeller NY #352/R est:50000-70000
£26946 $45000 €39341 Earth, Moon, Sun and Venus (127x183cm-50x72in) each s.i.d.1968 two attached canvases prov.exhib. 12-Nov-3 Christie's, Rockefeller NY #351/R est:50000-70000

JENSEN, Alfred (1859-1935) Danish
£236 $375 €345 Landscape with lake in valley surrounded by wooded hills (69x97cm-27x38in) 10-Sep-3 Alderfer's, Hatfield #284
£265 $482 €400 Sailing boat leaving the harbour (23x31cm-9x12in) s.d.1910 canvas on board. 19-Jun-4 Quittenbaum, Hamburg #25
£336 $617 €500 Cutter off Hamburg (24x36cm-9x14in) s. 26-Mar-4 Bolland & Marotz, Bremen #538a/R
£443 $784 €660 Ships in mouth of the Elbe (12x25cm-5x10in) s.d.1898. 28-Apr-4 Schopman, Hamburg #669/R
£470 $800 €686 Harbour scene with many vessels (55x80cm-22x31in) s.d.1916. 29-Nov-3 Rasmussen, Havnen #2102/R (D.KR 5000)
£477 $877 €710 Four masted bark with tugs in Hamburg harbour (54x80cm-21x31in) s. 26-Mar-4 Bolland & Marotz, Bremen #538/R
£486 $812 €700 Fishing boat off chalk cliffs (30x40cm-12x16in) s. 24-Oct-3 Ketterer, Hamburg #16/R
£497 $919 €720 Three master with fishing boat at mouth of Elbe (86x60cm-34x24in) s.d.1910. 14-Feb-4 Hans Stahl, Hamburg #155
£497 $904 €750 Harbour landscape with boats out at sea (79x100cm-31x39in) s. 18-Jun-4 Bolland & Marotz, Bremen #654/R
£521 $870 €750 Steamer in stormy seas (24x29cm-9x11in) s. board. 24-Oct-3 Ketterer, Hamburg #14/R
£521 $870 €750 Fishing boat SBII in choppy seas (24x36cm-9x14in) s. 24-Oct-3 Ketterer, Hamburg #15/R
£537 $983 €784 Seascape with three master in evening (80x120cm-31x47in) s. 9-Jun-4 Rasmussen, Copenhagen #1831/R (D.KR 6000)
£615 $1100 €898 Maritime, frigate and other sailing vessels (81x119cm-32x47in) s. i.verso. 29-May-4 Brunk, Ashville #474/R
£671 $1235 €1000 Hamburg harbour with dock and Cap Polonio (79x119cm-31x47in) s. 26-Mar-4 Ketterer, Hamburg #17/R
£694 $1160 €1000 Three fishing boats at sea in evening (80x120cm-31x47in) s. 24-Oct-3 Ketterer, Hamburg #12/R
£766 $1418 €1118 Seascape with sailing vessels (81x119cm-32x47in) s. 15-Mar-4 Rasmussen, Vejle #179/R (D.KR 8500)
£804 $1343 €1150 Ship in harbour (12x18cm-5x7in) s.d.1899 i. verso panel. 11-Oct-3 Hans Stahl, Hamburg #146/R
£1119 $1869 €1600 Ships leaving Hamburg harbour (70x99cm-28x39in) s. 28-Jun-3 Bolland & Marotz, Bremen #678/R est:1100
£1500 $2550 €2190 Danish paddle yacht passing through The Sound off Kronborg Castle (85x135cm-33x53in) s.d.1896. 19-Nov-3 Christie's, Kensington #571/R est:2000-3000
£1538 $2569 €2200 Ships off rocky coast (80x120cm-31x47in) s.d.1906. 28-Jun-3 Bolland & Marotz, Bremen #677/R est:2200
£2188 $3653 €3194 Sailing vessel on the open seas (54x81cm-21x32in) s. painted c.1910. 19-Oct-3 Agra, Warsaw #29/R est:6000 (P.Z 14000)

JENSEN, Alfred V (19/20th C) Danish
£322 $547 €460 Harbour scene with large steam ship (51x70cm-20x28in) s. i.verso. 28-Nov-3 Wendl, Rudolstadt #4020/R

JENSEN, Arup (1906-) Danish
£275 $500 €402 Evening by the sea (67x93cm-26x37in) s. 7-Feb-4 Rasmussen, Havnen #2252/R (D.KR 3000)
£515 $860 €752 Naval battle (71x100cm-28x39in) s. 25-Oct-3 Rasmussen, Havnen #2549/R (D.KR 5500)

JENSEN, Augusta (1858-1936) Swedish
£400 $728 €600 Sailing boat docked at a village quay, with storms approaching (52x77cm-20x30in) s.d.1902. 1-Jul-4 Van Ham, Cologne #1429/R

JENSEN, Axel P (1885-1972) Danish
£276 $470 €403 Landscape with houses (65x92cm-26x36in) s.d.42. 10-Nov-3 Rasmussen, Vejle #620/R (D.KR 3000)
£351 $561 €512 Summer landscape with flowers (73x100cm-29x39in) s.d.54. 22-Sep-3 Rasmussen, Vejle #609/R (D.KR 3700)
£358 $645 €523 Wooded landscape with figures (170x225cm-67x89in) s.d.31. 24-Apr-4 Rasmussen, Havnen #4276/R (D.KR 4000)
£423 $706 €618 Dunes near the sea (95x82cm-37x32in) s.d.31 study. 7-Oct-3 Rasmussen, Copenhagen #311/R (D.KR 4500)
£451 $830 €658 Dune landscape with the sea in background (174x260cm-69x102in) s.d.1956. 29-Mar-4 Rasmussen, Copenhagen #480/R (D.KR 5000)
£542 $996 €791 Dune landscape with farms in background (174x260cm-69x102in) s.d.1956. 29-Mar-4 Rasmussen, Copenhagen #444/R (D.KR 6000)
£632 $1162 €923 Large meadows (116x162cm-46x64in) s.d.36 lit. 29-Mar-4 Rasmussen, Copenhagen #493/R (D.KR 7000)
Works on paper
£357 $596 €521 Haystacks alongside a lake (56x81cm-22x32in) s. 17-Jun-3 Maynards, Vancouver #336 (C.D 800)

JENSEN, Berit (1956-) Danish
£1075 $1935 €1570 Compositions with elephants (100x80cm-39x31in) s.d.1995 three. 24-Apr-4 Rasmussen, Havnen #4239/R est:15000 (D.KR 12000)

JENSEN, Bill (1945-) American
£611 $1100 €892 Drawing for heavy painting (30x22cm-12x9in) s.i.d.1972 verso oil paper. 24-Apr-4 David Rago, Lambertville #406/R
£4595 $8500 €6709 Untitled (245x197cm-96x78in) s.d.1973 verso oil sand. 12-Feb-4 Sotheby's, New York #120/R est:5000-7000
Works on paper
£611 $1100 €892 Untitled (15x11cm-6x4in) ink wash prov.exhib. 24-Apr-4 David Rago, Lambertville #179/R est:400-800
£1806 $3250 €2637 Untitled (23x19cm-9x7in) s.i.d.1975 verso graphite vellum. 24-Apr-4 David Rago, Lambertville #319/R est:1000-2000

JENSEN, Christian Albrecht (1792-1870) Danish
£6542 $10336 €9486 Bertel Thorvaldsen seated in a chair (29x23cm-11x9in) s. panel prov. 2-Sep-3 Rasmussen, Copenhagen #1584/R est:75000-125000 (D.KR 70000)

JENSEN, Cilia (20th C) Danish
£406 $759 €593 Harbour scene (62x81cm-24x32in) s.d.1938. 25-Feb-4 Kunsthallen, Copenhagen #263 (D.KR 4500)

JENSEN, Edvard Michael (1822-1915) Danish
£275 $500 €402 Vicar on the way to church (65x59cm-26x23in) mono. 7-Feb-4 Rasmussen, Havnen #2114/R (D.KR 3000)
£383 $620 €555 Wooded landscape with woman and game by lake (34x47cm-13x19in) mono.d.1869. 4-Aug-3 Rasmussen, Vejle #320/R (D.KR 4000)
£614 $1100 €896 Landscape from Dyrehaven with thatched house and deer (71x105cm-28x41in) mono. 12-Jan-4 Rasmussen, Vejle #89/R (D.KR 6500)

JENSEN, Eric (?) ?
£699 $1203 €1000 Favorite au harem (68x55cm-27x22in) s.d.97. 2-Dec-3 Claude Aguttes, Neuilly #16

JENSEN, George (1878-?) American
£238 $425 €347 Moonlit landscape (30x30cm-12x12in) s. board. 21-Mar-4 Hindman, Chicago #832/R
£328 $600 €492 Lakeside rest (41x30cm-16x12in) 9-Jul-4 Du Mouchelle, Detroit #2017/R
£479 $800 €699 Sprint landscape with figure on a road (76x97cm-30x38in) s. 20-Jun-3 Freeman, Philadelphia #178/R
£1223 $2250 €1786 Along the Juniata River (46x61cm-18x24in) s. board. 9-Jun-4 Alderfer's, Hatfield #409/R est:1200-1800

JENSEN, Helge (1899-1986) Danish
£280 $439 €409 View across the sea, house in foreground (64x83cm-25x33in) s.d.51. 30-Aug-3 Rasmussen, Havnen #4359 (D.KR 3000)

JENSEN, Holger W (1880-?) American/Danish
Works on paper
£270 $475 €394 Rock river vista, Grand Detour, Dixon, Illinois (23x25cm-9x10in) s.i. gouache exec.c.1920. 23-May-4 Treadway Gallery, Cincinnati #640/R

JENSEN, J P (19th C) Danish
£473 $818 €691 From the drawing cabin at the Art Museum (42x51cm-17x20in) s.d.91. 9-Dec-3 Rasmussen, Copenhagen #1651 (D.KR 5000)

JENSEN, J-L (1800-1856) Danish
£537 $983 €784 Still life of birds and hunting bag on tree trunk (13x19cm-5x7in) s.d.1844 panel. 7-Jun-4 Museumsbygningen, Copenhagen #47/R (D.KR 6000)
£1354 $2532 €1977 Fuchsia in flower (14x22cm-6x9in) s. panel. 25-Feb-4 Kunsthallen, Copenhagen #509/R est:12000 (D.KR 15000)
£1438 $2674 €2099 White lilies and pink roses (18x13cm-7x5in) s. panel. 2-Mar-4 Rasmussen, Copenhagen #1537/R est:15000 (D.KR 16000)

JENSEN, Jens Thomsen (1862-1925) Danish
£909 $1473 €1318 Flowering meadow near river, Skanderborg (82x107cm-32x42in) s.d.1888. 4-Aug-3 Rasmussen, Vejle #304/R (D.KR 9500)

JENSEN, Johan-Laurents (1800-1856) Danish
£904 $1500 €1320 Spring bouquet (22x18cm-9x7in) board. 30-Sep-3 Christie's, Rockefeller NY #439/R est:3000-5000
£1600 $2752 €2336 Carnations (20x15cm-8x6in) s. 4-Dec-3 Christie's, Kensington #88/R est:1200-1800
£3000 $5520 €4380 Summer flowers on a marble ledge (15x21cm-6x8in) s.d.1844. 25-Mar-4 Christie's, Kensington #78/R est:3000-4000
£5198 $8993 €7589 Pink and white roses (22x29cm-9x11in) s. 9-Dec-3 Rasmussen, Copenhagen #1205/R est:40000 (D.KR 55000)
£5372 $9830 €7843 White and blue flowers (21x29cm-8x11in) s. mahogany prov. 9-Jun-4 Rasmussen, Copenhagen #1429/R est:50000-60000 (D.KR 60000)
£5500 $10010 €8030 Tulips (30x23cm-12x9in) s. panel prov. 15-Jun-4 Sotheby's, London #306/R est:4000-6000

£9452	$16352	€13800	Still life of plant in clay pot (59x43cm-23x17in) s.d.1843 panel. 9-Dec-3 Rasmussen, Copenhagen #1223/R est:100000-150000 (D.KR 100000)
£13084	$20673	€18972	Roses in basket and small bouquet of wild flowers (40x62cm-16x24in) s. 2-Sep-3 Rasmussen, Copenhagen #1568/R est:150000-200000 (D.KR 140000)
£15219	$27851	€22220	Pink roses in a champagne glass (32x24cm-13x9in) s. mahogany prov. 9-Jun-4 Rasmussen, Copenhagen #1431/R est:120000-150000 (D.KR 170000)
£16115	$29490	€23528	Bouquet of flowers in glass (36x27cm-14x11in) s. mahogany prov. 9-Jun-4 Rasmussen, Copenhagen #1428/R est:150000-200000 (D.KR 180000)
£17010	$31128	€24835	Pink roses in a basket (34x45cm-13x18in) s. mahogany prov. 9-Jun-4 Rasmussen, Copenhagen #1414/R est:150000-200000 (D.KR 190000)
£17905	$32766	€26141	Roses in a Greek bowl (24x34cm-9x13in) s. mahogany prov. 9-Jun-4 Rasmussen, Copenhagen #1415/R est:150000-200000 (D.KR 200000)
£22381	$40958	€32676	Still life of fruit in basket with flowers (55x69cm-22x27in) s.d.1842. 9-Jun-4 Rasmussen, Copenhagen #1437/R est:250000-300000 (D.KR 250000)
£23629	$40879	€34498	Still life of hyacinths, amaryllis and gardenia in pots on ledge (79x66cm-31x26in) possibly painted by school prov. 9-Dec-3 Rasmussen, Copenhagen #1224/R est:250000 (D.KR 250000)
£37601	$68809	€54897	Camellias in a Greek vase (57x44cm-22x17in) s.d.1843 mahogany prov. 9-Jun-4 Rasmussen, Copenhagen #1432/R est:200000-300000 (D.KR 420000)
£50998	$91286	€74457	Still life of flowers and basket of fruit (102x78cm-40x31in) s.d.1848. 28-May-4 Uppsala Auktionskammare, Uppsala #91/R est:350000-400000 (S.KR 690000)

JENSEN, Johan-Laurents (attrib) (1800-1856) Danish

£675	$1100	€986	Still life with rose (13x23cm-5x9in) indis.sig.d. panel. 24-Sep-3 Doyle, New York #49a
£1439	$2360	€2000	Still life of flowers (42x41cm-17x16in) 4-Jun-3 Ketterer, Hamburg #66/R est:2000-2500
£1769	$3043	€2583	Hunting still life (47x35cm-19x14in) panel. 3-Dec-3 AB Stockholms Auktionsverk #2566/R est:25000-30000 (S.KR 23000)
£1797	$3342	€2624	Pink roses and white berries in glass vase (35x27cm-14x11in) prov. 2-Mar-4 Rasmussen, Copenhagen #1538/R est:10000-15000 (D.KR 20000)
£3000	$5550	€4380	Passion flowers and hummingbird (45x33cm-18x13in) s. panel. 14-Jul-4 Sotheby's, Olympia #220/R est:2000-3000

JENSEN, Johan-Laurents (school) (1800-1856) Danish

£292	$475	€420	Rose crown (30x39cm-12x15in) canvas on panel. 26-Sep-3 Bolland & Marotz, Bremen #554
£940	$1729	€1400	Roses, carnations, grapes and cherries (30x45cm-12x18in) pair. 26-Mar-4 Bolland & Marotz, Bremen #539/R

JENSEN, Karl (1851-1933) Danish

£379	$607	€553	Interior scene with old woman reading (25x32cm-10x13in) init. 22-Sep-3 Rasmussen, Vejle #50/R (D.KR 4000)
£569	$910	€831	Woodland scene in sunshine (40x60cm-16x24in) init.d.1884 exhib. 22-Sep-3 Rasmussen, Vejle #341/R (D.KR 6000)

JENSEN, Louis Isak Napolean (1858-1908) Danish

£3311	$6026	€5000	Coastal landscape with huts (47x59cm-19x23in) s.d.1904. 19-Jun-4 Hans Stahl, Hamburg #59/R est:5000

JENSEN, Max (fl.1887) German

£315	$526	€450	High seas (93x126cm-37x50in) 10-Oct-3 Stadion, Trieste #162
£382	$603	€550	Frigate off the coast (40x79cm-16x31in) s. 5-Sep-3 Wendl, Rudolstadt #3439/R

JENSEN, Simony (1864-1932) Danish

£310	$559	€450	Cat playing with wool (50x36cm-20x14in) s. 26-Jan-4 Durán, Madrid #685/R
£361	$675	€527	Reading the letter (49x40cm-19x16in) s. 25-Feb-4 Kunsthallen, Copenhagen #570 (D.KR 4000)
£369	$627	€539	Cellar interior with monks merrymaking (40x50cm-16x20in) s.d.1904. 10-Nov-3 Rasmussen, Vejle #429/R (D.KR 4000)
£382	$630	€550	Two monks in conversation (52x41cm-20x16in) s. 3-Jul-3 Neumeister, Munich #2854/R

JENSEN, Soren Georg (1917-1982) Danish

Sculpture

£1444	$2657	€2108	Untitled (21cm-8in) mono.d.76 num.1/25 black green pat.bronze incl.granite socle. 29-Mar-4 Rasmussen, Copenhagen #413/R est:8000-10000 (D.KR 16000)
£1625	$2989	€2373	Untitled (21cm-8in) mono.d.76 num.3/25 brown pat.bronze incl.granite socle. 29-Mar-4 Rasmussen, Copenhagen #412/R est:8000-10000 (D.KR 18000)
£2817	$4704	€4113	Constructive sculpture (24x52cm-9x20in) mono. stoneware exec.c.1955. 7-Oct-3 Rasmussen, Copenhagen #195/R est:12000-15000 (D.KR 30000)

JENSEN, Ulf Valde (1945-) Norwegian

Works on paper

£258	$416	€377	Composition (105x75cm-41x30in) s. W/C. 25-Aug-3 Blomqvist, Lysaker #1123/R (N.KR 3000)

JENSSEN, Olav Christopher (1954-) Norwegian

£2135	$3565	€3117	Composition (70x90cm-28x35in) s.i.d.1989 verso exhib. 13-Oct-3 Blomqvist, Oslo #332/R est:40000-50000 (N.KR 25000)
£2711	$4798	€3958	Untitled composition (70x90cm-28x35in) s.i.d.1989. 27-Apr-4 AB Stockholms Auktionsverk #944/R est:25000-30000 (S.KR 37000)

Works on paper

£366	$648	€534	Untitled. s.d.1987 mixed media pair. 27-Apr-4 AB Stockholms Auktionsverk #1133/R (S.KR 5000)

JENTSCH, Adolph (1888-1977) German

£8258	$14781	€12057	Landscape Namibia (68x98cm-27x39in) s.d.1940 prov. 31-May-4 Stephan Welz, Johannesburg #497/R est:100000-140000 (SA.R 100000)
£10009	$17216	€14613	Extensive landscape, Namibia (69x99cm-27x39in) init.d.1943. 3-Dec-3 Stephan Welz, Johannesburg #35/R est:80000-120000 (SA.R 110000)

Works on paper

£372	$665	€543	Suid West Afrika (10x23cm-4x9in) init.d.1943 i.verso W/C. 31-May-4 Stephan Welz, Johannesburg #138 (SA.R 4500)
£372	$665	€543	South West Africa (27x12cm-11x5in) init.d.1949 W/C. 31-May-4 Stephan Welz, Johannesburg #139 (SA.R 4500)
£537	$961	€784	Suid West Afrika (17x30cm-7x12in) init.d.1952 s.i.verso W/C. 31-May-4 Stephan Welz, Johannesburg #141 (SA.R 6500)
£603	$1008	€880	Landscape, Namibia (18x35cm-7x14in) init.d.1955 s.i.on mount W/C. 20-Oct-3 Stephan Welz, Johannesburg #362 est:5000-7000 (SA.R 7000)
£733	$1224	€1070	Wooded landscape, Namibia (18x26cm-7x10in) init.d.1940 W/C. 20-Oct-3 Stephan Welz, Johannesburg #361 est:6000-9000 (SA.R 8500)
£784	$1404	€1145	Suid West Afrika (18x26cm-7x10in) init.d.1948 s.i.verso W/C. 31-May-4 Stephan Welz, Johannesburg #142 (SA.R 9500)
£10924	$19773	€15949	South West Africa (27x19cm-11x7in) init.d.1950 i.verso W/C. 30-Mar-4 Stephan Welz, Johannesburg #468 est:4000-6000 (SA.R 130000)

JENTZSCH, Johannes Gabriel (1862-?) German

£917	$1532	€1330	The duet (60x80cm-24x31in) s. 23-Jun-3 Philippe Schuler, Zurich #3530/R (S.FR 2000)

JEPSEN, Morten (1826-1903) Danish

£2059	$3768	€3006	Roman street scene near Via Sistina (24x30cm-9x12in) mono. 9-Jun-4 Rasmussen, Copenhagen #1904/R est:20000-25000 (D.KR 23000)

JEPSON, Keith (?) British?

£500	$915	€730	Mermaid and Loire (50x75cm-20x30in) s.i. 2-Feb-4 Bonhams, Chester #969

JERACE, Gaetano (1860-1940) Italian

£1111	$1889	€1600	View of Naples (24x31cm-9x12in) s. board. 1-Nov-3 Meeting Art, Vercelli #44

JERAM, Edward (20th C) American

£4420	$8000	€6453	Variety of machine age themes and motifs (109x94cm-43x37in) s.d.1935. 3-Apr-4 David Rago, Lambertville #83/R est:3500-4000

JERANIAN, Richard (1928-) ?

£369	$687	€550	Bouquet violet (75x60cm-30x24in) s. s.i.d.verso. 3-Mar-4 Tajan, Paris #193

JERECZEK, Christian (20th C) German

£490	$817	€700	Flower stalls in market (50x60cm-20x24in) s. 9-Oct-3 Michael Zeller, Lindau #617/R
£946	$1693	€1400	Street with flowers stall and figures (68x80cm-27x31in) s. 6-May-4 Michael Zeller, Lindau #713/R

JERICHAU, Harald Adolf Nikolai (1851-1878) Danish

£391	$712	€587	Summer landscape with ruin (33x26cm-13x10in) mono.i.d.72 panel. 19-Jun-4 Rasmussen, Havnen #2333 (D.KR 4400)
£1522	$2785	€2222	Italian landscape with shepherd resting (26x39cm-10x15in) mono. 9-Jun-4 Rasmussen, Copenhagen #1924/R est:15000 (D.KR 17000)
£1611	$2949	€2352	Sunset by Dolma Bagdche (17x28cm-7x11in) init. 9-Jun-4 Rasmussen, Copenhagen #1917/R est:10000-15000 (D.KR 18000)
£2857	$4857	€4171	River landscape with boats and figures, Constantinoples in background (25x54cm-10x21in) mono. 10-Nov-3 Rasmussen, Vejle #13/R est:10000-15000 (D.KR 31000)
£7500	$12750	€10950	Overlooking the acropolis (40x54cm-16x21in) init.i.d.73. 18-Nov-3 Sotheby's, London #71/R est:4000-6000
£13477	$25067	€19676	View of Constantinople from the graveyard outside town (41x58cm-16x23in) 2-Mar-4 Rasmussen, Copenhagen #1309/R est:15000-25000 (D.KR 150000)

JERICHAU, Holger H (1861-1900) Danish

£313	$573	€457	Italian landscape with monk in town (37x27cm-15x11in) s. prov. 9-Jun-4 Rasmussen, Copenhagen #1893/R (D.KR 3500)
£313	$573	€457	Two Italian women with donkey and dog by well (48x64cm-19x25in) s. 9-Jun-4 Rasmussen, Copenhagen #1938/R (D.KR 3500)
£358	$655	€523	Villa in evening light in mountains (50x40cm-20x16in) s. 9-Jun-4 Rasmussen, Copenhagen #1896 (D.KR 4000)
£378	$654	€552	Young girl in a loggia (29x19cm-11x7in) s. panel. 9-Dec-3 Rasmussen, Copenhagen #1551/R (D.KR 4000)
£378	$677	€552	Wooded landscape with country road (62x75cm-24x30in) s. prov. 12-Jan-4 Rasmussen, Vejle #98/R (D.KR 4000)
£473	$818	€691	Spanish harbour scene (16x20cm-6x8in) s.i.d.76. 9-Dec-3 Rasmussen, Copenhagen #1468/R (D.KR 5000)
£493	$799	€720	Norwegian landscape (49x63cm-19x25in) s.i. 9-Aug-3 Hindemae, Ullerslev #59/R (D.KR 5200)
£496	$928	€724	Italian beach landscape with fishing boat and yellow houses in background (32x70cm-13x28in) s/. 25-Feb-4 Museumsbygningen, Copenhagen #202/R (D.KR 5500)
£526	$853	€763	Southern landscape with woman on stone steps (55x36cm-22x14in) s. 4-Aug-3 Rasmussen, Vejle #358/R (D.KR 5500)
£531	$967	€775	Coastal landscape from Capri with children bathing (30x56cm-12x22in) s.i. 7-Feb-4 Rasmussen, Havnen #2000/R (D.KR 5800)
£567	$981	€828	Summer's day in Lovrena, Italy (59x41cm-23x16in) s.i.d.1898. 9-Dec-3 Rasmussen, Copenhagen #1550/R (D.KR 6000)
£632	$1181	€923	View of an Italian bay with fishermen and nets (30x46cm-12x18in) s. 25-Feb-4 Museumsbygningen, Copenhagen #280 (D.KR 7000)
£664	$1062	€969	Peat bog with windmill in background (38x61cm-15x24in) s. 22-Sep-3 Rasmussen, Vejle #363/R (D.KR 7000)
£714	$1164	€1042	Coastal landscape from Capri (33x44cm-13x17in) s. panel. 29-Sep-3 Lilla Bukowskis, Stockholm #1044 (S.KR 9300)
£1037	$1918	€1514	Arabian camp (41x63cm-16x25in) s. panel. 15-Mar-4 Rasmussen, Vejle #321/R (D.KR 11500)
£1704	$2930	€2488	Evening by the lake near mountains (93x137cm-37x54in) s.d.1889. 8-Dec-3 Blomqvist, Oslo #438/R est:30000-40000 (N.KR 20000)
£2686	$4915	€3922	Courtyard with monk scolding two small children (81x54cm-32x21in) s.i.d.1895. 9-Jun-4 Rasmussen, Copenhagen #1891/R est:20000 (D.KR 30000)
£2741	$4742	€4002	Meeting in an Italian pergola (52x77cm-20x30in) s. 9-Dec-3 Rasmussen, Copenhagen #1682/R est:12000 (D.KR 29000)

£3311 $6026 €5000 Terrase near Solent (101x68cm-40x27in) 21-Jun-4 Dorotheum, Vienna #203/R est:4500-5000

JERICHAU, Jens Adolf (1816-1883) Danish
Sculpture
£1488 $2752 €2172 Hunting panther (70cm-28in) pat.bronze Cast Rasmussen. 15-Mar-4 Rasmussen, Vejle #969/R est:8000 (D.KR 16500)

JERICHAU, Jens Adolf (1890-1916) Danish
£18051 $33213 €26354 Bathing girls (65x80cm-26x31in) s. painted 1916 prov.exhib.lit. 29-Mar-4 Rasmussen, Copenhagen #188/R est:200000-250000 (D.KR 200000)
Works on paper
£316 $591 €461 The meeting in heaven (22x29cm-9x11in) pastel pencil. 25-Feb-4 Kunsthallen, Copenhagen #199/R (D.KR 3500)
£378 $654 €552 Model study of man (22x18cm-9x7in) s. pencil. 9-Dec-3 Rasmussen, Copenhagen #1743/R (D.KR 4000)

JERICHAU-BAUMANN, Elisabeth (1819-1881) Danish
£364 $589 €528 Portrait of gentleman with fur hat (51x42cm-20x17in) s.d.1851 i.verso. 4-Aug-3 Rasmussen, Vejle #4/R (D.KR 3800)
£4348 $7522 €6348 Mother and her baby (82x92cm-32x36in) s.d.52 exhib.prov. 9-Dec-3 Rasmussen, Copenhagen #1384/R est:30000-40000 (D.KR 46000)
£9017 $16682 €13165 A Turkish pipe boy, Tschibuktschi (62x50cm-24x20in) lit. 15-Mar-4 Rasmussen, Vejle #56/R est:75000 (D.KR 100000)

JERKEN, Erik (1898-1947) Swedish
£277 $510 €416 View of Stockholm (65x55cm-26x22in) s. 14-Jun-4 Lilla Bukowskis, Stockholm #89 (S.KR 3800)
£398 $640 €581 Hammarbyleden (60x73cm-24x29in) s.d.1931. 25-Aug-3 Lilla Bukowskis, Stockholm #442 (S.KR 5200)
£421 $757 €632 Boat houses, view from Smogen (55x46cm-22x18in) s. 25-Apr-4 Goteborg Auktionsverk, Sweden #369/R (S.KR 5800)
Works on paper
£276 $451 €403 Tyne Docks, Newcastle on Tyne (44x54cm-17x21in) s.i.d.1936 W/C. 29-Sep-3 Lilla Bukowskis, Stockholm #211 (S.KR 3600)

JERNBERG, August (1826-1896) Swedish
£1000 $1720 €1460 Still life of vegetables (32x40cm-13x16in) s. cardboard. 2-Dec-3 Bukowskis, Stockholm #150/R (S.KR 13000)
£3030 $5424 €4424 Playing the clarinet (47x38cm-19x15in) s. 25-May-4 Bukowskis, Stockholm #210/R est:20000-25000 (S.KR 41000)
£3385 $5822 €4942 Still life of fruit (62x50cm-24x20in) s. 2-Dec-3 Bukowskis, Stockholm #149/R est:20000-25000 (S.KR 44000)

JERNBERG, Olof (1855-1935) Swedish
£267 $480 €400 Fishing boat anchored on beach (47x35cm-19x14in) s. board. 26-Apr-4 Rieber, Stuttgart #998/R
£556 $906 €800 Summer landscape (51x61cm-20x24in) s. 24-Sep-3 Neumeister, Munich #459
£665 $1191 €971 Coastal landscape (27x41cm-11x16in) s. panel. 26-May-4 AB Stockholms Auktionsverk #23120/R (S.KR 9000)
£800 $1472 €1200 Flock of sheep under a tree (59x79cm-23x31in) s. 11-Jun-4 Wendl, Rudolstadt #4098/R
£1133 $2040 €1700 Holland. Dune landscape (31x39cm-12x15in) s. canvas on board. 26-Apr-4 Rieber, Stuttgart #997/R est:980
£2847 $4641 €4100 Potato harvest on lower Rhine (77x92cm-30x36in) s. 26-Sep-3 Bolland & Marotz, Bremen #555/R est:2300
Works on paper
£833 $1317 €1200 Woman field worker (45x33cm-18x13in) s. W/C lit. 19-Sep-3 Schloss Ahlden, Ahlden #1630/R

JERNDORFF, August (1846-1906) Danish
£7089 $12264 €10350 Gerda and Elin in the garden (169x123cm-67x48in) mono.d.98 exhib.prov. 9-Dec-3 Rasmussen, Copenhagen #1416/R est:75000 (D.KR 75000)

JERNDORFF, Povl (1885-1935) Danish
£271 $506 €396 Landscape with farms (65x75cm-26x30in) s.d.1917. 25-Feb-4 Kunsthallen, Copenhagen #200/R (D.KR 3000)
£667 $1213 €1001 Adam and Eve in the Garden of Eden (33x27cm-13x11in) panel. 19-Jun-4 Rasmussen, Havnen #4127 (D.KR 7500)

JEROME, Ambrosini (attrib) (fl.1840-1871) British
£700 $1281 €1022 Portrait of a young child, believed to be Edwin Collins (61x51cm-24x20in) 6-Apr-4 Bonhams, Knightsbridge #129/R

JEROME, G (19th C) American
£13000 $21710 €18980 Figures by a river in a tropical landscape (76x127cm-30x50in) s. board. 14-Oct-3 Sotheby's, London #244/R est:6000-8000

JERREMS, Carol (1949-1980) Australian
Photographs
£4000 $7040 €6000 Vale Street, 1975 (15x20cm-6x8in) s.i.d.1975 num.2/9 gelatin silver print. 18-May-4 Bonhams, New Bond Street #495/R est:4000-5000

JERVAS, Charles (1675-1739) British
£1109 $1984 €1619 Portrait of lady wearing blue (77x64cm-30x25in) oval. 25-May-4 Bukowskis, Stockholm #517/R est:20000-25000 (S.KR 15000)
£3500 $5950 €5110 Portrait of John Willes, chief justice of Chester (126x101cm-50x40in) 27-Nov-3 Sotheby's, London #138/R est:4000-6000

JERVAS, Charles (attrib) (1675-1739) British
£2100 $3906 €3066 Portrait of Miss Howell, nee Hamilton (73x60cm-29x24in) painted oval. 2-Mar-4 Bearnes, Exeter #479/R est:2000-3000
£2600 $4654 €3796 Portrait of Sir Edward Bacon (127x101cm-50x40in) 22-Mar-4 Bonhams & Brooks, Norfolk #212/R est:2500-3500

JERZEY, Victor (20th C) American
£296 $550 €432 Wrestling (102x76cm-40x30in) s. 7-Mar-4 Treadway Gallery, Cincinnati #649/R

JERZY, Richard (1943-2001) American
£1078 $1800 €1574 Back garden (43x30cm-17x12in) masonite. 17-Oct-3 Du Mouchelle, Detroit #2021/R est:1500-2500
£1590 $2750 €2321 Christmas (61x51cm-24x20in) 12-Dec-3 Du Mouchelle, Detroit #2029/R est:3750-5000
Works on paper
£578 $1000 €844 Tiger lily with thistle (69x46cm-27x18in) W/C. 12-Dec-3 Du Mouchelle, Detroit #2/R
£751 $1300 €1096 Still life with fruit and flowers (71x99cm-28x39in) W/C. 12-Dec-3 Du Mouchelle, Detroit #3/R

JESPERS, Floris (1889-1965) Belgian
£278 $464 €400 Arbres devant la ville (34x49cm-13x19in) s. cardboard on panel. 21-Oct-3 Campo & Campo, Antwerp #155
£331 $603 €500 Paysage a Our (38x49cm-15x19in) s.d.39 canvas on panel. 21-Jun-4 Bernaerts, Antwerp #83/R
£333 $603 €500 Petite eglise a Our (36x50cm-14x20in) s. 30-Mar-4 Campo, Vlaamse Kaai #95
£350 $584 €500 Palma, Majorca (15x21cm-6x8in) s.d.64 paper. 11-Oct-3 De Vuyst, Lokeren #195
£352 $616 €500 Femme a sa toilette (38x28cm-15x11in) s. 16-Dec-3 Galerie Moderne, Brussels #669/R
£461 $770 €650 African interior (57x73cm-22x29in) s. oil paper. 20-Oct-3 Bernaerts, Antwerp #213/R
£490 $817 €700 African woman (52x25cm-20x10in) s. 11-Oct-3 De Vuyst, Lokeren #192
£521 $870 €750 Nu de dos (20x28cm-8x11in) s. 21-Oct-3 Galerie Moderne, Brussels #346/R
£556 $928 €800 Porteuses. s. panel. 21-Oct-3 Campo, Vlaamse Kaai #455e
£616 $1048 €900 Vaches au paturage (60x80cm-24x31in) s. 4-Nov-3 Servarts Themis, Bruxelles #584/R
£671 $1248 €1000 The cow stable (35x45cm-14x18in) s. panel. 8-Mar-4 Bernaerts, Antwerp #833/R
£709 $1184 €1000 Arlequin (28x19cm-11x7in) s. eglomise. 15-Oct-3 Hotel des Ventes Mosan, Brussels #178/R
£822 $1397 €1200 Vue de village (43x60cm-17x24in) s. 10-Nov-3 Horta, Bruxelles #25
£833 $1392 €1200 Deux petites figures. s. 21-Oct-3 Campo, Vlaamse Kaai #455c
£897 $1614 €1300 Africaine (56x39cm-22x15in) s. panel. 20-Jan-4 Galerie Moderne, Brussels #329/R
£903 $1508 €1300 Image d'Epinal (75x55cm-30x22in) s.d.1931 panel. 21-Oct-3 Campo & Campo, Antwerp #153/R
£927 $1687 €1400 Femmes africaines (40x50cm-16x20in) s. 16-Jun-4 Hotel des Ventes Mosan, Brussels #254
£1000 $1790 €1500 View of the Ardennes (50x60cm-20x24in) s. 15-May-4 De Vuyst, Lokeren #171/R est:1500-2000
£1042 $1698 €1500 Femmes africaines (50x45cm-20x18in) s. cardboard. 23-Sep-3 Galerie Moderne, Brussels #757/R
£1064 $1777 €1500 African water carriers (50x66cm-20x26in) s. oil paper. 20-Oct-3 Bernaerts, Antwerp #211/R est:400-500
£1074 $1901 €1600 Paysage a Our (51x66cm-20x26in) s.d.1941 panel. 27-Apr-4 Campo, Vlaamse Kaai #462 est:2000-2500
£1135 $1895 €1600 Landscape with African water carriers (50x60cm-20x24in) s. cardboard. 20-Oct-3 Bernaerts, Antwerp #294 est:1100-1300
£1141 $2111 €1700 Still life with violin (41x57cm-16x22in) s. oil pastel paper on board exhib. 13-Mar-4 De Vuyst, Lokeren #198/R est:1500-1800
£1208 $2138 €1800 Congolaises (54x72cm-21x28in) s. paper. 27-Apr-4 Campo, Vlaamse Kaai #466 est:1800-2000
£1250 $2088 €1800 Composition abstraite. s. panel. 21-Oct-3 Campo, Vlaamse Kaai #455d
£1329 $2259 €1900 Vase de fleurs (46x40cm-18x16in) s. 18-Nov-3 Vanderkindere, Brussels #163 est:2000-3000
£1389 $2181 €2000 La ballerine (50x45cm-20x18in) s. 26-Aug-3 Galerie Moderne, Brussels #338/R est:1000-1500
£1408 $2437 €2000 View of Cagnes Sur Mer (44x56cm-17x22in) s. paper on canvas. 13-Dec-3 De Vuyst, Lokeren #183/R est:3000-4000
£1611 $2980 €2400 View of a moored boat in a polder landscape (45x65cm-18x26in) s. 15-Mar-4 Sotheby's, Amsterdam #147/R est:1000-2000
£1667 $2783 €2400 Porteuses. s. cardboard. 21-Oct-3 Campo, Vlaamse Kaai #455b
£1745 $3228 €2600 Two woman from the Congo (82x102cm-32x40in) s.d.51 paper on panel exhib. 13-Mar-4 De Vuyst, Lokeren #196/R est:3000-4000
£1745 $3228 €2600 Three bathers (60x50cm-24x20in) s. 13-Mar-4 De Vuyst, Lokeren #197/R est:2400-2800
£2113 $3655 €3000 Landscape in the Ardennes (41x60cm-16x24in) s. prov.exhib. 13-Dec-3 De Vuyst, Lokeren #184/R est:3500-4000
£2797 $4811 €4000 En flandre (49x58cm-19x23in) s. s.i.d.30 verso panel. 2-Dec-3 Sotheby's, Amsterdam #45/R est:6000-8000
£3200 $5728 €4800 African market (70x88cm-28x35in) s. paper. 15-May-4 De Vuyst, Lokeren #486/R est:4000-5000
£3333 $6133 €5000 Spring landscape (88x130cm-35x51in) s. board exhib. 8-Jun-4 Sotheby's, Amsterdam #206/R est:7000-9000
£3401 $6088 €5000 Porteuses Africaines (87x64cm-34x25in) s. panel. 17-Mar-4 Hotel des Ventes Mosan, Brussels #112 est:1400-1800
£3472 $5799 €5000 Village Ardennais, Suxy (84x190cm-33x75in) s. d.1941 verso. 21-Oct-3 Campo, Vlaamse Kaai #452/R est:5000-7000
£4545 $7727 €6500 Maisonettes au bord de 'etang (55x75cm-22x30in) s.d.1931. 1-Dec-3 Palais de Beaux Arts, Brussels #272/R est:8000-12000
£4895 $8322 €7000 Paysage aux saules (90x114cm-35x45in) s.d.32. 1-Dec-3 Palais de Beaux Arts, Brussels #278/R est:7500-10000
£64189 $114899 €95000 Les maries (133x106cm-52x42in) s.d.26 i.d.verso. 10-May-4 Horta, Bruxelles #92/R est:15000-25000

Works on paper
£284 $474 €400 African woman (40x25cm-16x10in) s.d.56 mixed media. 20-Oct-3 Bernaerts, Antwerp #209/R
£364 $663 €550 Les africaines (35x27cm-14x11in) s. W/C. 15-Jun-4 Galerie Moderne, Brussels #171/R
£528 $914 €750 Landscape with cows (34x44cm-13x17in) s. pastel. 13-Dec-3 De Vuyst, Lokeren #185
£733 $1320 €1100 African woman (53x42cm-21x17in) s. W/C oil. 26-Apr-4 Bernaerts, Antwerp #534/R
£972 $1624 €1400 La robe congolaise. s. gouache. 21-Oct-3 Campo, Vlaamse Kaai #455a

JESPERS, Floris (attrib) (1889-1965) Belgian
£467 $835 €700 Femmes Congolaises (36x50cm-14x20in) panel. 16-May-4 MonsAntic, Maisieres #432

JESPERS, Oscar (1887-1970) Belgian
Sculpture
£1600 $2864 €2400 Baby's head (13x14cm-5x6in) s. light brown pat bronze marble base lit. 15-May-4 De Vuyst, Lokeren #473/R est:2000-3000

JESPERSEN, Henrik (1853-1936) Danish
£286 $486 €418 Wooded landscape (45x73cm-18x29in) init. 10-Nov-3 Rasmussen, Vejle #111/R (D.KR 3100)
£314 $500 €458 Coastal scene with distant mountains (36x61cm-14x24in) init. 13-Sep-3 Selkirks, St. Louis #487
£314 $565 €458 Ducks on water (28x42cm-11x17in) init.d.1923. 24-Apr-4 Rasmussen, Havnen #2184/R (D.KR 3500)
£335 $543 €486 Landscape near Karup (43x63cm-17x25in) s. 4-Aug-3 Rasmussen, Vejle #313/R (D.KR 3500)
£361 $584 €527 Heath landscape (65x100cm-26x39in) s. 9-Aug-3 Hindemae, Ullerslev #77/R (D.KR 3800)
£421 $664 €610 Heath landscape, Tyrol, October (70x110cm-28x43in) s. 2-Sep-3 Rasmussen, Copenhagen #1892/R (D.KR 4500)
£425 $736 €621 Woodland with old oak tree (77x57cm-30x22in) s.d.1902. 9-Dec-3 Rasmussen, Copenhagen #1430/R (D.KR 4500)
£433 $801 €632 Park landscape with lake and sun-dial (52x78cm-20x31in) s. 15-Mar-4 Rasmussen, Vejle #473/R (D.KR 4800)
£451 $834 €658 Lake Como seen from a villa (53x79cm-21x31in) mono.d.1914. 15-Mar-4 Rasmussen, Vejle #322/R (D.KR 5000)
£664 $1062 €969 Summer by waterway (53x78cm-21x31in) s. 22-Sep-3 Rasmussen, Vejle #339/R (D.KR 7000)
£721 $1335 €1053 View of an Italian town (49x73cm-19x29in) mono. 15-Mar-4 Rasmussen, Vejle #54/R (D.KR 8000)
£1253 $2294 €1829 Italian mountains with blue irises in garden (70x100cm-28x39in) s. 9-Jun-4 Rasmussen, Copenhagen #1850/R est:15000-20000 (D.KR 14000)

JESSE, Gaston (19th C) French
£5921 $10895 €9000 Bergers et troupeau sur la cote amalfitaine (66x97cm-26x38in) s.d.1848. 25-Jun-4 Piasa, Paris #129/R est:8000-12000

JESSEN, Carl Ludwig (1833-1917) Danish/German
£1014 $1814 €1500 Portrait of Hinrich Hansen from Deetzbull (34x31cm-13x12in) s.d.1886 board. 8-May-4 Hans Stahl, Toestorf #68/R est:2600

JESSUP, Frederick (1920-) Australian
£247 $450 €361 Floral still life (53x33cm-21x13in) s.d.1965. 19-Jun-4 Charlton Hall, Columbia #105
£247 $450 €361 Floral still life (46x61cm-18x24in) s.d.55. 19-Jun-4 Charlton Hall, Columbia #130/R
£879 $1600 €1283 Panier estyal (79x79cm-31x31in) s. 19-Jun-4 Charlton Hall, Columbia #99 est:500-700
£1322 $2248 €1930 Schizophrenic coming out of Insulin coma (39x29cm-15x11in) s. board painted c.1943. 29-Oct-3 Lawson Menzies, Sydney #171/R est:1500-2000 (A.D 3200)

JESSURUN DE MESQUITA, Samuel (20th C) ?
Works on paper
£2381 $4333 €3500 Untitled (49x64cm-19x25in) s.d.1927 s.i.verso pencil W/C. 3-Feb-4 Christie's, Amsterdam #483/R est:2000-3000

JETELOWA, Magdalena (1946-) ?
Sculpture
£3533 $6466 €5300 Chair (45x34x31cm-18x13x12in) s.d.73 bronze. 4-Jun-4 Lempertz, Koln #229/R est:5500

JETTEL, Eugen (1845-1901) Austrian
£1599 $2750 €2335 An der kuste, 1899 (33x44cm-13x17in) s.i. board prov. 3-Dec-3 Doyle, New York #117/R est:5000-7000
£7000 $12740 €10220 Geese before a farmstead (41x59cm-16x23in) board prov. 16-Jun-4 Christie's, Kensington #24/R est:3000-5000
£8500 $15470 €12410 Normandy landscape (44x92cm-17x36in) s.i. panel prov. 16-Jun-4 Christie's, Kensington #23/R est:8000-12000
£16667 $28333 €24000 Dutch river landscape with farmsteads (42x60cm-17x24in) s. panel lit. 28-Oct-3 Wiener Kunst Auktionen, Vienna #47/R est:22000-35000

JETTEL, Eugen (attrib) (1845-1901) Austrian
£1000 $1810 €1500 Vue de Rio (29x46cm-11x18in) indis.s. 5-Apr-4 Marie & Robert, Paris #71/R est:1500-2000

JETTMAR, Rudolf (1869-1939) Austrian
£1379 $2524 €2000 Child killing, Bethlehem (120x94cm-47x37in) i. 27-Jan-4 Dorotheum, Vienna #18/R est:4000-6000
£2308 $3969 €3300 Endless (46x125cm-18x49in) 3-Dec-3 Stadion, Trieste #1061/R est:3500-4500
£2550 $4693 €3800 Black horses racing across mudflats (115x130cm-45x51in) s.d.1936 lit. 25-Mar-4 Karlheinz Kaupp, Staufen #2523/R est:2000

JEUNE, James le (1910-1983) Irish
£1867 $3379 €2800 Portrait of a young woman, Monica Schultz (75x60cm-30x24in) s. 31-Mar-4 James Adam, Dublin #142/R est:2500-4000
£8741 $14860 €12500 At the races (28x46cm-11x18in) s. i.verso board prov. 18-Nov-3 Whyte's, Dublin #32/R est:8000-10000
Works on paper
£667 $1207 €1000 Near Clifden (35x54cm-14x21in) s. s.i.verso W/C. 30-Mar-4 De Veres Art Auctions, Dublin #124/R

JEWELL, Ruth (20th C) American
£188 $350 €274 Still life with petunias (50x40cm-20x16in) s. 5-Mar-4 Skinner, Boston #387/R

JEWELS, Mary (1886-1977) British
£1200 $2184 €1752 Shipping in Mousehole Harbour (36x46cm-14x18in) s. i.verso board. 15-Jun-4 David Lay, Penzance #310/R est:1500-2500
£2600 $4342 €3796 Newlyn fishing boat (23x51cm-9x20in) s.i.d.1964 verso. 14-Oct-3 David Lay, Penzance #488/R est:800-1000
£2900 $5278 €4234 Flowers (51x56cm-20x22in) 15-Jun-4 David Lay, Penzance #585/R est:800-1200
Works on paper
£300 $546 €438 Landscape with trees (25x36cm-10x14in) s.d.1926 W/C bodycol. 15-Jun-4 David Lay, Penzance #311/R
£520 $972 €759 Houses in a wooded landscape (29x37cm-11x15in) s. W/C bodycol. 26-Feb-4 Lane, Penzance #46

JEWETT, William Smith (1812-1873) American
£419 $700 €612 Gentle Grieve - the vacant cage. s.i.d.1867. 15-Nov-3 Harvey Clar, Oakland #1466
£16304 $30000 €23804 Jupiter's Spires, Yosemite Valley (108x137cm-43x54in) painted 1861 prov. 8-Jun-4 Bonhams & Butterfields, San Francisco #4176/R est:15000-20000

JEWETT, William and WALDO, Samuel Lovett (19th C) American
£1676 $3100 €2514 Portrait of the Reverend Stephan N Rowan (89x69cm-35x27in) s.i.d.July 1827 panel. 14-Jul-4 American Auctioneer #490218/R est:3000-5000

JEX, Garnet W (1895-1979) American
£938 $1500 €1369 Pierce mill, Rock Creek Park, D.C (36x41cm-14x16in) s.d.1928. 20-Sep-3 Sloans & Kenyon, Bethesda #1188/R est:1750-2250

JI DACHUN (1968-) Chinese
Works on paper
£3556 $6401 €5192 Converse Hollywood (150x150cm-59x59in) mixed media collage canvas. 25-Apr-4 Christie's, Hong Kong #731/R est:50000-60000 (HK.D 50000)

JIA YOUFU (1943-) Chinese
Works on paper
£959 $1630 €1400 Evening in Yuelu Park in Changsha (51x34cm-20x13in) s.i.d.1975 seal Indian ink col. 7-Nov-3 Dr Fritz Nagel, Stuttgart #975/R
£1622 $2854 €2400 Autumn on Emei mountain (68x45cm-27x18in) s.i. Indian ink col seal hanging scroll. 21-May-4 Dr Fritz Nagel, Stuttgart #1109/R est:250
£1849 $3329 €2700 Returning in the sunset (27x92cm-11x36in) s.i.d.1984 ink col scroll. 25-Apr-4 Christie's, Hong Kong #96/R est:30000-40000 (HK.D 26000)

JIANG GA (18/19th C) Chinese
Works on paper
£445 $757 €650 Painting of fruits, vegetables and vessels (25x338cm-10x133in) s. seals Indian ink col hand scroll prov. 7-Nov-3 Dr Fritz Nagel, Stuttgart #834/R

JIANG HANTING (1903-1963) Chinese
Works on paper
£2317 $3869 €3383 Lotus and dragonfly (100x49cm-39x19in) s. ink col hanging scroll. 27-Oct-3 Sotheby's, Hong Kong #312/R est:30000-50000 (HK.D 30000)
£3000 $5370 €4380 Bird perched among prunus and magnolia (112x48cm-44x19in) s.d.1943 col ink hanging scroll. 6-May-4 Sotheby's, London #105/R est:800-1200

JIANG JIA SHENG (1955-) Chinese
£268 $475 €400 Hangar 27, Antwerpen (75x110cm-30x43in) s. 27-Apr-4 Campo & Campo, Antwerp #135/R
£300 $540 €450 Antwerp opera (60x70cm-24x28in) s.d.04. 26-Apr-4 Bernaerts, Antwerp #1008/R

JIANG JUN (1847-1919) Chinese
Works on paper
£372 $654 €550 Chrysanthemums and fence (129x65cm-51x26in) i.d.1915 seals. 21-May-4 Dr Fritz Nagel, Stuttgart #1202/R

JIANG TINGXI (1669-1732) Chinese
Works on paper
£78236 $140825 €114225 Birds and flowers (13x21cm-5x8in) ink colour eight leaves albums pair. 26-Apr-4 Christie's, Hong Kong #963/R est:200000-300000 (HK.D 1100000)

JIANG ZHAOSHEN (1925-) Chinese
Works on paper
£2703 $4514 €3946 Hermitage (30x98cm-12x39in) s.i.d.1988 ink col handscroll. 27-Oct-3 Sotheby's, Hong Kong #292/R est:35000-45000 (HK.D 35000)

JIANGUO SUI (1956-) Chinese
Sculpture
£1117 $2000 €1631 Structure series number 1 (38x30cm-15x12in) prov.lit. 16-May-4 Wright, Chicago #424/R est:700-900
£1285 $2300 €1876 Structure series number 2 (25x38cm-10x15in) prov.lit. 16-May-4 Wright, Chicago #423/R est:700-900

JIAO BINGZHEN (1606-c.1687) Chinese
Works on paper
£22760 $40967 €33230 Lady admiring flowers (154x97cm-61x38in) s. ink col hanging scroll silk. 25-Apr-4 Christie's, Hong Kong #430/R est:80000-100000 (HK.D 320000)

JIAO BINGZHEN (attrib) (1606-c.1687) Chinese
Works on paper
£2937 $5052 €4200 Mountain landscape with Wang Xizhi writing in a pavillion in foreground (149x80cm-59x31in) i.d.1701 ink silk hanging scroll. 5-Dec-3 Lempertz, Koln #239/R est:1200

JIMENEZ Y ARANDA, Jose (1837-1903) Spanish
£7059 $12000 €10306 Don Quixote and Sancho Panza (56x42cm-22x17in) s.i. 29-Oct-3 Christie's, Rockefeller NY #199/R est:10000-15000
Works on paper
£1020 $1827 €1500 Scene from the Don Quixote (19x28cm-7x11in) s. gouache. 22-Mar-4 Durán, Madrid #168/R est:1500
£1034 $1862 €1500 Untitled (18x19cm-7x7in) s. wash. 26-Jan-4 Durán, Madrid #660/R est:1500
£1135 $1895 €1600 Male nude (24x16cm-9x6in) s.d.1873 chl dr. 20-Oct-3 Durán, Madrid #5/R

JIMENEZ Y ARANDA, Luis (1845-1928) Spanish
£4138 $7655 €6000 The painter's study (34x26cm-13x10in) s. 14-Jan-4 Castellana, Madrid #247/R est:3000
£4828 $8014 €7000 Goat keeper (33x20cm-13x8in) s.d.1890. 30-Sep-3 Ansorena, Madrid #78/R est:6200
£4828 $8690 €7000 Goat keeper (33x20cm-13x8in) s.i.d.1890. 26-Jan-4 Ansorena, Madrid #227/R est:6000
£6950 $11260 €9800 The goatherdess (33x20cm-13x8in) s.d.1890. 20-May-3 Ansorena, Madrid #153/R est:9800
£26471 $45000 €38648 Dancing lesson (73x99cm-29x39in) s.d.1888. 29-Oct-3 Christie's, Rockefeller NY #204/R est:50000-70000
£34483 $57586 €50000 Conversation in the park (32x24cm-13x9in) s.d.1879 panel. 15-Nov-3 Lempertz, Koln #1630/R est:15000

JIMENEZ Y FERNANDEZ, Federico (1841-?) Spanish
£1141 $2134 €1700 Unpredicted (40x75cm-16x30in) s. 24-Feb-4 Durán, Madrid #183/R est:1500
£2355 $3862 €3250 Unexpected (40x75cm-16x30in) s. 27-May-3 Durán, Madrid #146/R est:2500
£5060 $9159 €7590 Still life with rabbit, lobster and turkeys (113x76cm-44x30in) s. 30-Mar-4 Segre, Madrid #96/R est:9000
£5102 $9133 €7500 Hens (70x96cm-28x38in) s. 22-Mar-4 Durán, Madrid #221/R est:5000
Works on paper
£428 $774 €650 Study of goats (23x28cm-9x11in) s. pencil dr. 14-Apr-4 Ansorena, Madrid #403/R
£1988 $3200 €2902 Spanish dancer. Toast (36x50cm-14x20in) one s.i. one s. pencil W/C paper on board pair. 14-Jan-4 Christie's, Rockefeller NY #40/R est:1000-1500

JIMENEZ Y MARTIN, Juan (1858-1901) Spanish
£1087 $1783 €1500 Avila (15x23cm-6x9in) s. panel. 27-May-3 Durán, Madrid #173/R est:1500
Works on paper
£483 $801 €700 Fishing at dusk (37x63cm-15x25in) s. W/C. 30-Sep-3 Dorotheum, Vienna #276/R
£1510 $2824 €2250 Oriental scene (53x39cm-21x15in) s. W/C. 24-Feb-4 Durán, Madrid #228/R est:2250

JIMENEZ, Patricio (1949-) Chilean
£4469 $8000 €6525 Still life (83x118cm-33x46in) s.d.1993. 26-May-4 Sotheby's, New York #146/R est:10000-15000

JIMENEZ-BALAGUER, Laurent (attrib) (1938-) French
£280 $467 €400 Vers un point omega (129cm-51in) s.i.d.1980 verso triptych. 25-Jun-3 Rabourdin & Choppin de Janvry, Paris #158

JIMMY LIAO (1958-) Chinese
Works on paper
£4623 $8321 €6750 Windows of happiness (17x74cm-7x29in) s.d.2004 verso W/C acrylic. 26-Apr-4 Sotheby's, Hong Kong #519/R est:12000-18000 (HK.D 65000)
£4979 $8962 €7269 Last melody of a butterfly (17x74cm-7x29in) s.d.2004 verso W/C acrylic. 26-Apr-4 Sotheby's, Hong Kong #520/R est:12000-18000 (HK.D 70000)

JIN CHENG (1878-1926) Chinese
Works on paper
£3089 $5158 €4510 Corn and pea (23x69cm-9x27in) s.i.d.1922 ink col fan painting. 27-Oct-3 Sotheby's, Hong Kong #313/R est:18000-25000 (HK.D 40000)

JIN KUN (fl.1662-1746) Chinese
Works on paper
£270270 $486486 €394594 Historical figures (9x10cm-4x4in) ink album twelve leaves lit. 26-Apr-4 Christie's, Hong Kong #964/R est:180000-220000 (HK.D 3800000)

JIN KUN and LIANG SHIZHENG (17/18th C) Chinese
Works on paper
£1671408 $3008535 €2440256 Emperor Qianlong's review of the Grand Parade of Troops (68cm-27in) i. handscroll ink col gold silk exec with court painters lit. 26-Apr-4 Christie's, Hong Kong #1011/R (HK.D 23500000)

JIN NONG (1687-c.1764) Chinese
Works on paper
£99573 $179232 €145377 Sixteen Arhats (39x27cm-15x11in) s.i.d.1759 ink col leaves silk sixteen album. 25-Apr-4 Christie's, Hong Kong #425/R est:1000000-1200000 (HK.D 1400000)

JIRA, Josef (1929-) Czechoslovakian
£788 $1308 €1150 Lilies of the Valley (30x40cm-12x16in) s.d.74. 4-Oct-3 Dorotheum, Prague #144/R est:16000-25000 (C.KR 36000)

JIRINCOVA, Ludmila (1912-1994) Czechoslovakian
Works on paper
£875 $1453 €1278 Alone (25x18cm-10x7in) s. mixed media. 4-Oct-3 Dorotheum, Prague #333/R est:10000-15000 (C.KR 40000)

JIRLOW, Lennart (1936-) Swedish
£1360 $2311 €1986 Paris (23x19cm-9x7in) s. panel. 4-Nov-3 Bukowskis, Stockholm #303/R est:25000-30000 (S.KR 18000)
£1978 $3501 €2888 Blue mountains, Provence (19x24cm-7x9in) s. panel. 27-Apr-4 AB Stockholms Auktionsverk #865/R est:25000-30000 (S.KR 27000)
£3443 $6095 €5027 Flowers in the window (41x30cm-16x12in) s. cardboard. 27-Apr-4 AB Stockholms Auktionsverk #693/R est:40000-50000 (S.KR 47000)
£3474 $5906 €5072 The gardener (24x19cm-9x7in) s. panel. 5-Nov-3 AB Stockholms Auktionsverk #845/R est:20000-25000 (S.KR 46000)
£7100 $12069 €10366 On the terrace, Province (46x38cm-18x15in) s. 4-Nov-3 Bukowskis, Stockholm #306/R est:40000-50000 (S.KR 94000)
£7175 $12198 €10476 The violinist (49x65cm-19x26in) s. 4-Nov-3 Bukowskis, Stockholm #299/R est:80000-100000 (S.KR 95000)
£9063 $15408 €13232 In the restaurant (54x65cm-21x26in) s. 4-Nov-3 Bukowskis, Stockholm #298/R est:100000-125000 (S.KR 120000)
£9063 $15408 €13232 The French house (74x81cm-29x32in) s. 4-Nov-3 Bukowskis, Stockholm #305/R est:125000-150000 (S.KR 120000)
£9441 $16050 €13784 The market garden (90x116cm-35x46in) s. 4-Nov-3 Bukowskis, Stockholm #307/R est:150000-175000 (S.KR 125000)
£11707 $19902 €17092 Man with parrots (90x117cm-35x46in) s. 4-Nov-3 Bukowskis, Stockholm #304/R est:200000-250000 (S.KR 155000)
£19217 $34590 €28057 The restaurant's kitchen (54x73cm-21x29in) s. 26-Apr-4 Bukowskis, Stockholm #216/R est:100000-125000 (S.KR 265000)
£33358 $60044 €48703 Grand Hotel des Palmiers (115x225cm-45x89in) s. 26-Apr-4 Bukowskis, Stockholm #217/R est:400000-450000 (S.KR 460000)
Works on paper
£544 $979 €794 Memorandum from La Coupole, Paris (19x8cm-7x3in) s. mixed media. 26-Apr-4 Bukowskis, Stockholm #214/R (S.KR 7500)
£831 $1412 €1213 Portrait of a clown (23x16cm-9x6in) s. gouache. 5-Nov-3 AB Stockholms Auktionsverk #846/R (S.KR 11000)
£1057 $1798 €1543 Tabac (34x26cm-13x10in) s. gouache. 4-Nov-3 Bukowskis, Stockholm #302/R (S.KR 14000)
£1284 $2183 €1875 Le Figaro (37x33cm-15x13in) s.i.d.1990 hand col page of newspaper. 5-Nov-3 AB Stockholms Auktionsverk #739/R est:12000-15000 (S.KR 17000)
£2417 $4109 €3529 Still life of flowers (59x44cm-23x17in) s. gouache. 5-Nov-3 AB Stockholms Auktionsverk #844/R est:40000-50000 (S.KR 32000)
£2564 $4538 €3743 Boat in the skerries (23x18cm-9x7in) s.d.1996 gouache. 27-Apr-4 AB Stockholms Auktionsverk #906/R est:10000-12000 (S.KR 35000)
£2756 $4960 €4024 Sitting in the arbour (41x32cm-16x13in) s. gouache. 26-Apr-4 Bukowskis, Stockholm #214a/R est:30000-40000 (S.KR 38000)
£11965 $21537 €17469 Le sommelier (64x54cm-25x21in) s. gouache executed 1990 lit. 26-Apr-4 Bukowskis, Stockholm #215/R est:100000-125000 (S.KR 165000)

JISTER, L (18th C) Swiss
£4605 $8474 €7000 L'Ermite Nicolas de Flue apaisant des querelles a la Diete de Stans en 1481 (55x92cm-22x36in) s.d.1795. 25-Jun-4 Rossini, Paris #57/R est:4000-5000

JOANOVITCH, Paul (1859-1957) Austrian
£4518 $7500 €6596 Greek sentinel (66x44cm-26x17in) s. 30-Sep-3 Christie's, Rockefeller NY #451/R est:7000-9000
£5245 $8916 €7500 Interior with figures (13x17cm-5x7in) s. study panel. 24-Nov-3 Dorotheum, Vienna #52/R est:4000-5500
£9396 $16819 €14000 Toast to a lady (42x58cm-17x23in) 27-May-4 Dorotheum, Vienna #5/R est:3400-4000
£10738 $19221 €16000 Midday meal (42x58cm-17x23in) s. 27-May-4 Dorotheum, Vienna #4/R est:3400-4000

JOBBINS, William H (fl.1872-1893) British
£1000 $1860 €1460 Time for supper (41x58cm-16x23in) s.i.d.83. 4-Mar-4 Christie's, Kensington #610/R est:1000-1500

JOBERT, Paul (1863-1942) French
£2534 $4636 €3800 Biskra (70x90cm-28x35in) s.i. 3-Jun-4 Tajan, Paris #255/R est:3000-4000

JOBLING, Robert (1841-1923) British
£260 $473 €380 Moorland view (49x64cm-19x25in) s. indis.i. 29-Jun-4 Anderson & Garland, Newcastle #489
£760 $1315 €1110 Staithes fisher girls on the shore (23x33cm-9x13in) board. 9-Dec-3 Anderson & Garland, Newcastle #454/R
£780 $1349 €1139 Cumberland Tarn in sunlight (45x59cm-18x23in) s.i.verso exhib. 9-Dec-3 Anderson & Garland, Newcastle #452
£780 $1412 €1139 South Shields harbour (29x44cm-11x17in) s. 30-Mar-4 David Duggleby, Scarborough #194/R
£880 $1522 €1285 Fisher girls on Cullercoats sands with fishing cobles beyond (30x44cm-12x17in) s. 9-Dec-3 Anderson & Garland, Newcastle #455/R
£1400 $2534 €2044 Fishing boats at sea (34x63cm-13x25in) s. 30-Mar-4 David Duggleby, Scarborough #35/R est:500-800
£3000 $5010 €4380 Milkmaid in a meadow (58x84cm-23x33in) s.d.1883. 13-Nov-3 Christie's, Kensington #123/R est:3000-5000
£3400 $6256 €4964 North Eastern fishing cobles landing a catch (50x67cm-20x26in) s. 23-Mar-4 Anderson & Garland, Newcastle #415/R est:3000-5000
£5469 $9790 €7985 Harbour view (118x88cm-46x35in) s.d.1912. 26-May-4 AB Stockholms Auktionsverk #2435/R est:25000-30000 (S.KR 74000)
£9100 $14469 €13286 Three Cullercoats fighergirls near Cliff House under a starry sky (60x49cm-24x19in) s. 18-Mar-3 Anderson & Garland, Newcastle #532/R est:3000-5000
Works on paper
£280 $445 €409 Cullercoats (19x15cm-7x6in) s.i.d.November 1889 pen ink. 18-Mar-3 Anderson & Garland, Newcastle #347
£560 $913 €818 Barges on the Thames before St Paul's Cathedral (18x25cm-7x10in) s. W/C. 23-Sep-3 Anderson & Garland, Newcastle #278/R
£580 $1067 €847 Dawn - fisher folk on a beach preparing cobles for sea (23x33cm-9x13in) mono. W/C. 23-Mar-4 Anderson & Garland, Newcastle #302
£650 $1125 €949 Three girls paddling in a woodland stream (26x21cm-10x8in) s. W/C. 9-Dec-3 Anderson & Garland, Newcastle #449/R
£700 $1113 €1022 Cullercoats Bay (25x22cm-10x9in) grey wash htd white. 18-Mar-3 Anderson & Garland, Newcastle #280/R
£800 $1384 €1168 Four girls on North Shields quay with trawlers and the Wesley at anchor nearby (17x25cm-7x10in) init. W/C. 9-Dec-3 Anderson & Garland, Newcastle #348
£900 $1656 €1314 Durham Cathedral from the river (62x49cm-24x19in) s. W/C. 23-Mar-4 Anderson & Garland, Newcastle #303/R

JOBSON, John (1941-) British
£336 $601 €500 Orchard (50x27cm-20x11in) s. board. 31-May-4 Hamilton Osborne King, Dublin #92
£633 $1146 €950 Prospector (26x24cm-10x9in) mono. 30-Mar-4 De Veres Art Auctions, Dublin #37/R
£850 $1522 €1241 Cherry trees in a sandpit (16x19cm-6x7in) init. s.i.d.01 verso board. 14-May-4 Christie's, Kensington #413/R
£921 $1695 €1400 Winter Hill, Wicklow (28x32cm-11x13in) s.i.verso board. 22-Jun-4 De Veres Art Auctions, Dublin #73/R
£1056 $1690 €1500 Whitethorn (25x30cm-10x12in) mono. board. 16-Sep-3 Whyte's, Dublin #198/R est:1500-2000
£1351 $2554 €2000 Foffany School Lane, County Down (35x30cm-14x12in) mono.i.d.2002 s.i.d.verso board. 17-Feb-4 Whyte's, Dublin #189/R est:2000-3000
£1867 $3379 €2800 Rescue (51x60cm-20x24in) mono. i.verso. 30-Mar-4 De Veres Art Auctions, Dublin #5/R est:3000-4000
£1900 $3401 €2774 Night drive (51x61cm-20x24in) init. s.i.d.04 verso board. 14-May-4 Christie's, Kensington #412/R est:2000-2500
£5594 $9510 €8000 Pike Lane (94x125cm-37x49in) s.i. s.verso board. 25-Nov-3 De Veres Art Auctions, Dublin #224 est:4000-6000

JOCHEMS, Frans (1880-1949) Belgian
Sculpture
£870 $1600 €1270 Elephant (36x36cm-14x14in) s. bronze. 27-Mar-4 New Orleans Auction, New Orleans #636/R est:1000-1500
£1250 $2088 €1800 Faisan dore (46cm-18in) s. pat plaster. 21-Oct-3 Campo & Campo, Antwerp #157/R est:450-550
£1348 $2250 €1900 Art Deco figure of a bowman (67cm-26in) s. brown pat bronze. 20-Oct-3 Bernaerts, Antwerp #205/R est:1000-1250

JOCHHEIM, Auguste (19th C) ?
£1189 $1985 €1700 Venice: fruit sellers and gondoliers on narrow canal (48x38cm-19x15in) i. strechter. 11-Oct-3 Hans Stahl, Hamburg #16/R est:1000

JOCHIMS, Reimer (1934-) German
£533 $955 €800 Violet and blue-black (40x74cm-16x29in) s.i.d. verso spray on panel. 13-May-4 Neumeister, Munich #656/R
Works on paper
£490 $842 €700 I (36x36cm-14x14in) s.i.d.stretcher col pen. 3-Dec-3 Hauswedell & Nolte, Hamburg #950/R

JOCQUE, Willy (1900-1960) Belgian
£372 $665 €550 Bord de riviere (68x70cm-27x28in) s. canvas on panel. 10-May-4 Horta, Bruxelles #307

JODE, Hans de (attrib) (17th C) Dutch
£1000 $1700 €1460 Wooded landscape with travellers on a path (38x32cm-15x13in) bears sig panel prov. 30-Oct-3 Sotheby's, Olympia #85/R est:1200-1800

JODICE, Mimmo (1934-) Italian
Photographs
£6500 $10855 €9490 Trentaremi (70x210cm-28x83in) s.d.2003 num.2/3 verso photo three lit. 21-Oct-3 Christie's, London #77/R est:5000-7000

JOENSEN-MIKINES, S (1906-1979) Danish
Works on paper
£361 $675 €527 Danish landscape with farm (22x28cm-9x11in) s.d.41 W/C pencil. 25-Feb-4 Museumsbygningen, Copenhagen #42 (D.KR 4000)

JOENSEN-MIKINES, Samuel (1906-1979) Danish
£1444 $2657 €2108 Garden view with house (84x112cm-33x44in) s.d.43. 29-Mar-4 Rasmussen, Copenhagen #261/R est:25000 (D.KR 16000)
£1878 $3136 €2742 Ascetic - man seated with female nudes behind (68x50cm-27x20in) s.d.38 prov. 7-Oct-3 Rasmussen, Copenhagen #356/R est:18000 (D.KR 20000)
£2256 $4152 €3294 Family in summer garden (72x95cm-28x37in) s.d.43. 29-Mar-4 Rasmussen, Copenhagen #225/R est:20000 (D.KR 25000)
£2871 $4651 €4163 Coastal landscape with figures (80x120cm-31x47in) s.d.59 i.verso. 4-Aug-3 Rasmussen, Vejle #599/R est:30000-40000 (D.KR 30000)
£3159 $5812 €4612 Landscape from Hesto, Faroe Islands (80x100cm-31x39in) s.d.70 lit. 29-Mar-4 Rasmussen, Copenhagen #276/R est:20000 (D.KR 35000)
£4152 $7639 €6062 Killing of whales (80x100cm-31x39in) s.d.61 artistboard. 29-Mar-4 Rasmussen, Copenhagen #274/R est:40000-50000 (D.KR 46000)
£4513 $8303 €6589 Sunset over Vesterhavet, Bovbjerg (80x99cm-31x39in) init.i.d.1962 lit. 29-Mar-4 Rasmussen, Copenhagen #232/R est:30000-40000 (D.KR 50000)
£4513 $8303 €6589 Velbestad rural district, Faroe Islands, grey day (105x125cm-41x49in) s.d.64 lit. 29-Mar-4 Rasmussen, Copenhagen #278/R est:50000 (D.KR 50000)
£5634 $9408 €8226 From Mykines - summer night (122x152cm-48x60in) s.d.37 plywood exhib.lit. 7-Oct-3 Rasmussen, Copenhagen #153/R est:60000-80000 (D.KR 60000)
£6769 $12455 €9883 View from Mykines with figures in foreground (106x126cm-42x50in) s.d.61. 29-Mar-4 Rasmussen, Copenhagen #237/R est:75000 (D.KR 75000)
£10830 $19928 €15812 Evening (175x139cm-69x55in) s.d.39 exhib.lit. 29-Mar-4 Rasmussen, Copenhagen #260/R est:125000-150000 (D.KR 120000)
Works on paper
£717 $1290 €1047 Kattinge Lake (42x57cm-17x22in) s.d.67 W/C. 24-Apr-4 Rasmussen, Havnen #4153/R (D.KR 8000)

JOFFE, Chantal (1969-) British
£1100 $2002 €1606 Semi nude woman (25x35cm-10x14in) 21-Jun-4 Bonhams, New Bond Street #140/R
£4500 $8190 €6570 Twins (240x268cm-94x106in) 21-Jun-4 Bonhams, New Bond Street #135/R est:5000-7000

JOHANN, Hermann (1821-1884) German
£289 $483 €419 River landscape with cows and sailing ships (45x64cm-18x25in) s.d.1841. 23-Jun-3 Philippe Schuler, Zurich #8609 (S.FR 630)
£704 $1218 €1000 Landscape with pond and village church (63x50cm-25x20in) s. prov. 13-Dec-3 Lempertz, Koln #221/R

JOHANNESEN, Arne (1908-?) Danish
£293 $533 €428 Hay field (55x87cm-22x34in) init. 7-Feb-4 Rasmussen, Havnen #4045 (D.KR 3200)

JOHANNESSEN, Erik Harry (1902-1980) Norwegian
£1060 $1898 €1548 Landscape from Aasgaardstrand II (38x46cm-15x18in) init. s.i.d.1948 verso. 25-May-4 Grev Wedels Plass, Oslo #91/R (N.KR 13000)
£1283 $2181 €1873 Madonna (61x50cm-24x20in) init. si.d.1949 verso panel. 19-Nov-3 Grev Wedels Plass, Oslo #100/R est:15000-20000 (N.KR 15000)
£1369 $2327 €1999 Landscape from Tofte, Gudbrandsdalen (70x70cm-28x28in) init. s.i.d.1977 verso. 19-Nov-3 Grev Wedels Plass, Oslo #101/R est:15000-20000 (N.KR 16000)
£1704 $2930 €2488 Composition (70x60cm-28x24in) init. i.d.1961 verso. 8-Dec-3 Blomqvist, Oslo #513/R est:20000-25000 (N.KR 20000)
£2002 $3583 €2923 Composition (100x70cm-39x28in) init. i.d.1968 verso. 22-Mar-4 Blomqvist, Oslo #615/R est:30000-40000 (N.KR 25000)
£2764 $5059 €4035 Fishermen with closing net (75x80cm-30x31in) init. s.i.d.1957 verso. 7-Jun-4 Blomqvist, Oslo #411/R est:25000-30000 (N.KR 34000)
£6661 $11124 €9725 Three figures and toy sailing boat in landscape (100x100cm-39x39in) init. 13-Oct-3 Blomqvist, Oslo #308/R est:70000-90000 (N.KR 78000)

JOHANNESSEN, Jens (1934-) Norwegian
£407 $748 €594 Landscape (16x27cm-6x11in) init. 10-Jun-4 Grev Wedels Plass, Oslo #193/R (N.KR 5000)
£11976 $20359 €17485 Composition (46x38cm-18x15in) init.d.71. 19-Nov-3 Grev Wedels Plass, Oslo #104/R est:100000-120000 (N.KR 140000)
Works on paper
£515 $948 €752 Landscape (20x26cm-8x10in) s. W/C. 29-Mar-4 Blomqvist, Lysaker #1138/R (N.KR 6500)
£687 $1202 €1003 Composition (32x40cm-13x16in) init. W/C. 16-Dec-3 Grev Wedels Plass, Oslo #177/R (N.KR 8000)
£773 $1352 €1129 Town (32x40cm-13x16in) init. W/C. 16-Dec-3 Grev Wedels Plass, Oslo #178/R (N.KR 9000)
£834 $1393 €1218 Froya - 7 daughters (30x22cm-12x9in) s. mixed media. 17-Nov-3 Blomqvist, Lysaker #1140/R (N.KR 10000)
£1487 $2721 €2171 No.10.J.E.D. - from Tydalsuiten (28x38cm-11x15in) s. W/C. 2-Feb-4 Blomqvist, Lysaker #1122/R est:8000-12000 (N.KR 18500)

JOHANNOT, Alfred (1800-1837) French
Works on paper
£537 $988 €800 Cromwell et sa famille (44x36cm-17x14in) s.d. W/C exhib. 29-Mar-4 Rieunier, Paris #4

JOHANNSEN, Albert (1890-1975) German
£433 $784 €650 Mudflats in spring (60x80cm-24x31in) s. 1-Apr-4 Van Ham, Cologne #1456
£833 $1308 €1200 Evening sea (49x70cm-19x28in) s. board. 30-Aug-3 Hans Stahl, Toestorf #78/R
£2055 $3493 €3000 North Friesian hallway (60x72cm-24x28in) s. 8-Nov-3 Hans Stahl, Toestorf #70/R est:3000

JOHANSEN, Anders D (20th C) Danish/American
Works on paper
£339 $600 €495 Nude ladies among the white birches (38x51cm-15x20in) s. pencil W/C. 2-May-4 Bonhams & Butterfields, San Francisco #1039/R

JOHANSEN, Anna Moller (19th C) Danish
£281 $484 €410 Garland of roses on table (11x14cm-4x6in) panel painted c.1855. 2-Dec-3 Kunsthallen, Copenhagen #551 (D.KR 3000)

JOHANSEN, Axel (1872-1938) Danish
£281 $458 €410 From Frederiksholm's Canal (28x34cm-11x13in) s/d/1925. 27-Sep-3 Rasmussen, Havnen #2022 (D.KR 3000)
£289 $534 €422 Kastrup Works seen from the harbour (39x48cm-15x19in) s.d.1916. 15-Mar-4 Rasmussen, Vejle #681/R (D.KR 3200)
£289 $534 €422 Mundelstrup acid factory (48x68cm-19x27in) s.d.1916. 15-Mar-4 Rasmussen, Vejle #682/R (D.KR 3200)
£362 $648 €529 Watermill near Pompeii (36x42cm-14x17in) s.d.1920. 10-May-4 Rasmussen, Vejle #212/R (D.KR 4000)
£468 $782 €683 View from Gammel Strand with Slotsholms Canal (52x58cm-20x23in) s. 25-Oct-3 Rasmussen, Havnen #2211 (D.KR 5000)
£756 $1375 €1134 Summer landscape in front of Slotskirken near Christiansborg (49x59cm-19x23in) s.d.1928 exhib. 19-Jun-4 Rasmussen, Havnen #2251 (D.KR 8500)
£890 $1451 €1299 Landscape from Dragoer (72x65cm-28x26in) s.d.1917. 27-Sep-3 Rasmussen, Havnen #2075/R (D.KR 9500)

JOHANSEN, Hans Lorentz (19th C) Danish
Works on paper
£425 $736 €621 Hesselo Lighthouse (30x42cm-12x17in) s.d.1862 gouache. 9-Dec-3 Rasmussen, Copenhagen #1728 (D.KR 4500)

JOHANSEN, John C (1876-1964) American
£3593 $6000 €5246 Little trio (81x117cm-32x46in) s.d.1926 prov.exhib.lit. 7-Oct-3 Sotheby's, New York #223 est:2000-4000

JOHANSEN, Otto (1866-1934) Norwegian
£418 $765 €610 In the vegetable garden (46x52cm-18x20in) s. panel. 2-Feb-4 Blomqvist, Lysaker #1124 (N.KR 5200)
£772 $1421 €1158 Landscape with small buildings (47x53cm-19x21in) s. 14-Jun-4 Blomqvist, Lysaker #1176 (N.KR 9500)
£2135 $3565 €3117 Children picking fruit (98x84cm-39x33in) s.d.11. 13-Oct-3 Blomqvist, Oslo #291/R est:25000-30000 (N.KR 25000)

JOHANSEN, Svend (1890-1970) Danish
£485 $761 €708 Still life of jug, vase and fruit (54x64cm-21x25in) init. 30-Aug-3 Rasmussen, Havnen #4397 (D.KR 5200)
£3971 $7426 €5798 View from Hotel des Colonies, South of France (116x88cm-46x35in) painted c.1923 exhib. 25-Feb-4 Kunsthallen, Copenhagen #223/R est:60000 (D.KR 44000)
£7220 $13285 €10541 Street scene - Lille Kongensgade from Kongen's Nytorv (97x75cm-38x30in) init.d.27 exhib.lit. 29-Mar-4 Rasmussen, Copenhagen #196/R est:80000-100000 (D.KR 80000)
Works on paper
£387 $658 €565 To Comedia dell arte figure (59x45cm-23x18in) mono. gouache exhib. 10-Nov-3 Rasmussen, Vejle #688/R (D.KR 4200)

JOHANSEN, Viggo (1851-1935) Danish
£325 $527 €471 Garden scene with pavilion (45x70cm-18x28in) prov. 4-Aug-3 Rasmussen, Vejle #279 (D.KR 3400)
£376 $688 €549 Horse and foal in field (61x69cm-24x27in) init.d.09. 7-Jun-4 Museumsbygningen, Copenhagen #39 (D.KR 4200)
£427 $682 €623 Half-timbered house in woodland glade (50x65cm-20x26in) s. 22-Sep-3 Rasmussen, Vejle #414/R (D.KR 4500)
£452 $768 €660 Wooded landscape (67x91cm-26x36in) s. 29-Nov-3 Rasmussen, Havnen #2138 (D.KR 4800)
£614 $1063 €896 Cottage at Middelfart (47x73cm-19x29in) s.d.1900. 9-Dec-3 Rasmussen, Copenhagen #1388/R (D.KR 6500)
£651 $1054 €944 Landscape from Capri (46x30cm-18x12in) init.i. 4-Aug-3 Rasmussen, Vejle #359/R (D.KR 6800)
£662 $1184 €967 Landscape with cows grazing, Dragor (44x61cm-17x24in) s.i.d.1903. 12-Jan-4 Rasmussen, Vejle #97/R (D.KR 7000)
£664 $1062 €969 Interior scene with old women (33x36cm-13x14in) init.d.1882. 22-Sep-3 Rasmussen, Vejle #137/R (D.KR 7000)
£674 $1253 €984 Street scene towards Blegen in Dragoer (37x56cm-15x22in) s.i.d.1897 exhib.prov. 2-Mar-4 Rasmussen, Copenhagen #1548/R (D.KR 7500)
£748 $1181 €1085 Self-portrait in the studio, model in background (24x21cm-9x8in) init.d.02 i.verso. 3-Sep-3 Museumsbygningen, Copenhagen #241/R (D.KR 8000)
£861 $1395 €1248 Landscape from Skagen Brickyard (43x55cm-17x22in) mono. 4-Aug-3 Rasmussen, Vejle #340/R (D.KR 9000)
£960 $1565 €1402 Moonlight over Tyreso, Stockholm (74x93cm-29x37in) s.d.1905. 29-Sep-3 Lilla Bukowskis, Stockholm #307 (S.KR 12500)
£993 $1856 €1450 Young girl wearing black outfit standing in landscape (20x13cm-8x5in) s. i.verso study. 25-Feb-4 Museumsbygningen, Copenhagen #195/R (D.KR 11000)
£1083 $2025 €1581 Sheep grazing by the beach (26x39cm-10x15in) s.i.d.86. 25-Feb-4 Kunsthallen, Copenhagen #547/R est:5000 (D.KR 12000)
£1357 $2430 €1981 Portrait of the artist Hans Smidth (46x38cm-18x15in) i.verso. 10-May-4 Rasmussen, Vejle #411/R est:15000-18000 (D.KR 15000)
£2330 $4194 €3402 Summer landscape from Skagen, man walking by cornfield (41x64cm-16x25in) init.i.d.87. 24-Apr-4 Rasmussen, Havnen #2087/R est:8000-10000 (D.KR 26000)
£2836 $4905 €4141 Beached boats at Aero Shore (46x70cm-18x28in) s. painted c.1916-1917 exhib.prov. 9-Dec-3 Rasmussen, Copenhagen #1451/R est:12000-15000 (D.KR 30000)
£8507 $14716 €12420 Happy Christmas (58x63cm-23x25in) study exhib.prov. 9-Dec-3 Rasmussen, Copenhagen #1272/R est:40000 (D.KR 90000)
Works on paper
£467 $738 €677 Horses in meadow (24x31cm-9x12in) mono.i.d.1910 pencil W/C. 2-Sep-3 Rasmussen, Copenhagen #2028 (D.KR 5000)

JOHANSEN, Viggo (attrib) (1851-1935) Danish
£541 $1001 €790 Cherries on a dish (14x18cm-6x7in) study. 15-Mar-4 Rasmussen, Vejle #199/R (D.KR 6000)

JOHANSON-THOR, Emil (1889-1958) Swedish
£407 $728 €594 Houses in winter, Skaane (39x55cm-15x22in) s.d.1951. 28-May-4 Uppsala Auktionskammare, Uppsala #230 (S.KR 5500)

JOHANSSON, Albert (1926-1998) Swedish
Works on paper
£982 $1669 €1434 Fysionomik 12 (52x30cm-20x12in) s.d.1969 verso mixed media. 5-Nov-3 AB Stockholms Auktionsverk #790/R (S.KR 13000)
£1172 $2075 €1711 Indra II (100x100cm-39x39in) s.d.1959 verso mixed media panel. 27-Apr-4 AB Stockholms Auktionsverk #761/R est:20000-25000 (S.KR 16000)
£1172 $2075 €1711 Aniara II - Homage a Harry Martinson (100x200cm-39x79in) s.d.1959 verso mixed media panel. 27-Apr-4 AB Stockholms Auktionsverk #883/R est:25000-30000 (S.KR 16000)

JOHANSSON, Arvid (1862-1923) Swedish
£1357 $2172 €1981 Sailing ship on the high seas (81x100cm-32x39in) s.d.1890. 19-Sep-3 Koller, Zurich #3124/R est:3000-5000 (S.FR 3000)

JOHANSSON, Carl (1863-1944) Swedish
£615 $1058 €898 Winter day by Ljungan (42x61cm-17x24in) s.d.1928. 3-Dec-3 AB Stockholms Auktionsverk #2377/R (S.KR 8000)
£754 $1305 €1101 Coastal landscape (54x81cm-21x32in) s.d.1919. 15-Dec-3 Lilla Bukowskis, Stockholm #794 (S.KR 9600)
£923 $1588 €1348 Winter landscape (20x30cm-8x12in) s.d.95 panel. 3-Dec-3 AB Stockholms Auktionsverk #2251/R (S.KR 12000)
£1014 $1824 €1480 Winter at Sollentunaholm (74x101cm-29x40in) s.indis.d. 26-Jan-4 Lilla Bukowskis, Stockholm #481 (S.KR 13500)
£1500 $2580 €2190 Carrefour parisien (60x73cm-24x29in) s.d.4 Januari 1894. 3-Dec-3 AB Stockholms Auktionsverk #2275/R est:20000-25000 (S.KR 19500)
£1538 $2646 €2245 Summer evening - landscape from Medelpad (90x135cm-35x53in) s.d.1906. 3-Dec-3 AB Stockholms Auktionsverk #2261/R est:20000-25000 (S.KR 20000)
£1552 $2778 €2266 Montigny-sur-Loing (32x45cm-13x18in) s.d.92. 25-May-4 Bukowskis, Stockholm #4/R est:12000-15000 (S.KR 21000)
£2462 $4234 €3595 River landscape in spring (54x82cm-21x32in) s.d.89. 3-Dec-3 AB Stockholms Auktionsverk #2268/R est:40000-50000 (S.KR 32000)
£2809 $5027 €4101 View from Waldemarsudde (74x111cm-29x44in) s. 25-May-4 Bukowskis, Stockholm #12/R est:30000-35000 (S.KR 38000)

JOHANSSON, Eric (1896-1979) German
Works on paper
£280 $476 €400 Composition (34x26cm-13x10in) col chks. 29-Nov-3 Bassenge, Berlin #6803/R

JOHANSSON, Johan (1879-1951) Swedish
£650 $1046 €949 River landscape in evening glow (58x88cm-23x35in) s.d.91. 25-Aug-3 Lilla Bukowskis, Stockholm #9 (S.KR 8500)
£1233 $2219 €1800 Landscape from Glumslovs hills (61x78cm-24x31in) s. 26-Apr-4 Bukowskis, Stockholm #6/R est:10000-15000 (S.KR 17000)

JOHANSSON, Stefan (1876-1955) Swedish
Works on paper
£1846 $3175 €2695 Woodland glade (38x31cm-15x12in) s.d.31 W/C canvas. 3-Dec-3 AB Stockholms Auktionsverk #2244/R est:30000-40000 (S.KR 24000)
£3695 $6615 €5395 Summer night - landscape from Eksharad, Varmland (36x50cm-14x20in) s.d.00 mixed media. 25-May-4 Bukowskis, Stockholm #101/R est:30000-40000 (S.KR 50000)
£7692 $13231 €11230 Street lights (37x32cm-15x13in) s.d.37 W/C canvas. 2-Dec-3 Bukowskis, Stockholm #15/R est:60000-80000 (S.KR 100000)

JOHANSSON, Sven-Erik (1925-) Swedish
£378 $642 €552 Changing arena (21x29cm-8x11in) s.d.1966 panel. 5-Nov-3 AB Stockholms Auktionsverk #811/R (S.KR 5000)
£529 $953 €794 The baron's morning ride (38x50cm-15x20in) s.d.97 tempera paper. 25-Apr-4 Goteborg Auktionsverk, Sweden #405/R (S.KR 7300)
£1133 $1926 €1654 The fairy-story of the wheel (60x120cm-24x47in) s.d.59 panel. 5-Nov-3 AB Stockholms Auktionsverk #859/R est:18000-20000 (S.KR 15000)

JOHN, Augustus (1878-1961) British
£2400 $4080 €3504 Gypsy (68x51cm-27x20in) s. 26-Nov-3 Sotheby's, Olympia #25/R
£3000 $4770 €4380 Reclining nudes in a landscape (33x43cm-13x17in) s. 1-May-3 John Nicholson, Haslemere #703/R est:2000-3000
£7500 $12750 €10950 Portrait of a young woman in a red tunic (81x61cm-32x24in) s. painted c.1922 prov. 21-Nov-3 Christie's, London #90/R est:7000-10000
£9000 $14310 €13140 Portrait of Mrs Gribble (92x71cm-36x28in) s.d.17 prov. 10-Sep-3 Sotheby's, Olympia #180/R est:5000-8000
£10500 $17850 €15330 Chrysanthemums (101x76cm-40x30in) s. prov.lit. 26-Nov-3 Sotheby's, Olympia #43/R est:6000-8000
£12000 $20400 €17520 Fanny Fletcher (45x32cm-18x13in) s. panel prov. 21-Nov-3 Christie's, London #7/R est:7000-10000
£26000 $44200 €37960 Portrait of Mrs Eve Fleming (107x86cm-42x34in) s. painted c.1922 exhib. 21-Nov-3 Christie's, London #91/R est:30000-50000
Prints
£5000 $9200 €7300 Gwen (14x19cm-6x7in) s. etching. 28-Jun-4 Bonhams, New Bond Street #175 est:250-350
Works on paper
£280 $468 €409 Portrait of a lady (41x36cm-16x14in) s. chk. 10-Oct-3 Richardson & Smith, Whitby #247

£300	$516	€438	Portrait of Villiers David (23x35cm-9x14in) pencil. 3-Dec-3 Cheffins, Cambridge #600
£400	$740	€584	Head of a boy (15x11cm-6x4in) pen ink prov. 11-Mar-4 Christie's, Kensington #118
£480	$826	€701	Portrait of a girl (16x20cm-6x8in) pencil. 3-Dec-3 Christie's, Kensington #429/R
£500	$830	€730	Kentish farm workers (30x38cm-12x15in) s.d.1921 pencil. 5-Oct-3 Lots Road Auctions, London #354
£500	$935	€730	Study of a standing female nude (40x28cm-16x11in) s. pencil. 24-Feb-4 Rowley Fine Art, Newmarket #440/R
£600	$996	€876	Female life study, probably of his daughter Poppet (28x18cm-11x7in) s. chl sketch. 4-Oct-3 Finan Watkins & Co, Mere #147
£680	$1102	€986	Religious cartoon with figures (22x17cm-9x7in) sepia wash. 30-Jul-3 Hamptons Fine Art, Godalming #46
£700	$1281	€1022	Nude study (38x20cm-15x8in) s. 27-Jan-4 Gorringes, Lewes #1528
£700	$1169	€1022	Female nude (27x18cm-11x7in) s. red chk. 16-Oct-3 Christie's, Kensington #226/R
£800	$1272	€1168	Standing male nude (63x48cm-25x19in) s. chl brown chk. 10-Sep-3 Sotheby's, Olympia #116/R
£1000	$1620	€1450	Portrait of a lady (19x16cm-7x6in) s. pencil col crayon. 30-Jul-3 Hamptons Fine Art, Godalming #47/R est:600-1000
£1025	$1671	€1497	Young girl (23x18cm-9x7in) s. pencil dr prov. 27-Sep-3 Rogers Jones, Clwyd #59
£1100	$1936	€1606	Portrait of Mary Keene (12x11cm-5x4in) s. black chk. 19-May-4 Sotheby's, Olympia #78/R est:1000-1500
£1200	$2244	€1800	Two Gitanas (41x28cm-16x11in) s. chl. 22-Jul-4 Gorringes, Lewes #1772/R est:2000-3000
£1234	$2135	€1802	Fisher girl of Equihen (31x18cm-12x7in) s. black pencil exec.c.1900. 10-Dec-3 Shapiro, Sydney #62/R est:3000-5000 (A.D 2900)
£1300	$2366	€1898	Age and innocence no.2 (21x11cm-8x4in) s. pen brush blk brown ink htd white prov. 1-Jul-4 Christie's, Kensington #15/R est:1000-1500
£1400	$2268	€2030	Artist model (23x18cm-9x7in) sepia pen ink sketch. 30-Jul-3 Hamptons Fine Art, Godalming #45/R est:1000-1500
£1400	$2380	€2044	Two sketches of a baby (23x30cm-9x12in) s. pencil sketches verso prov. 20-Nov-3 Christie's, London #179/R est:800-1200
£1450	$2610	€2117	Study of a standing boy (37x19cm-15x7in) s. pencil. 23-Apr-4 Charterhouse, Sherborne #653/R
£1500	$2550	€2190	Fishergirl at Equihen (33x25cm-13x10in) pencil exec c.1907. 20-Nov-3 Christie's, London #175/R est:1500-2000
£1600	$2672	€2336	Standing nude (43x15cm-17x6in) s. pen black ink prov. 16-Oct-3 Christie's, Kensington #224/R est:600-800
£1600	$2816	€2336	Study for peasants in altercation (24x34cm-9x13in) s. pencil wash prov. 18-May-4 Woolley & Wallis, Salisbury #286/R est:1500-2000
£1800	$2862	€2628	Study of a nude (44x22cm-17x9in) s. pencil. 10-Sep-3 Sotheby's, Olympia #128/R est:2000-3000
£2000	$3400	€2920	Two Canadian Soldiers, one with raised head (35x23cm-14x9in) blk ink prov. 20-Nov-3 Christie's, London #176/R est:2000-3000
£2200	$3740	€3212	Standing female nude with hands behind her back (45x28cm-18x11in) s. pencil prov. 20-Nov-3 Christie's, London #180/R est:1200-1800
£2300	$3910	€3358	Study of a female nude (45x30cm-18x12in) s. pencil sketch. 31-Oct-3 Moore Allen & Innocent, Cirencester #485/R est:2000-3000
£3000	$5370	€4380	Study of a Canadian Soldier no 5 (25x35cm-10x14in) s. pencil exhib. 14-May-4 Christie's, Kensington #495/R est:2000-3000
£3200	$5824	€4672	Portrait studies of a child (29x22cm-11x9in) s. pencil. 1-Jul-4 Christie's, Kensington #17/R est:2000-3000
£5028	$9000	€7341	Dorelia smoking (35x26cm-14x10in) s. sepia chk prov. 6-May-4 Doyle, New York #112/R est:2000-3000
£8000	$14320	€11680	Shawled girls, Galway (44x30cm-17x12in) s. pen black ink W/C prov. 13-May-4 Sotheby's, London #87/R est:8000-12000

JOHN, Augustus (attrib) (1878-1961) British

£6200	$11284	€9052	Self portrait of the artist wearing a blue jumper (75x63cm-30x25in) 29-Jun-4 Rowley Fine Art, Newmarket #352/R

JOHN, Gwen (1876-1939) British

Works on paper

£270	$464	€394	Girl holding flower (23x15cm-9x6in) s. pencil dr. 3-Dec-3 Andrew Hartley, Ilkley #1050
£1800	$3168	€2628	Study of a cat (16x11cm-6x4in) s. W/C pencil prov.exhib. 19-May-4 Sotheby's, Olympia #76/R est:2000-3000
£3200	$5504	€4672	Seated girl (15x12cm-6x5in) st.sig. pencil exhib. 3-Dec-3 Christie's, Kensington #425/R est:1800-2500
£3500	$6475	€5110	Portrait of a lady (16x12cm-6x5in) with studio st. pencil exhib. 11-Mar-4 Christie's, Kensington #13/R est:2500-3000

JOHN, Hans (1888-?) German

£694	$1097	€1000	Friedrich II in Sanssouci Park (95x67cm-37x26in) mono.d.1923 panel double-sided lit. 19-Sep-3 Schloss Ahlden, Ahlden #1549/R

JOHN, Joseph (1833-1877) American

£3261	$6000	€4761	Village fair (46x84cm-18x33in) s.d.1876. 27-Jun-4 Freeman, Philadelphia #69/R est:5000-8000

JOHN, Vivien (1915-1994) British

£350	$595	€511	Provence (33x46cm-13x18in) s.d.37 canvas on board. 4-Nov-3 Dreweatt Neate, Newbury #149/R
£520	$915	€759	Figures in a park (50x60cm-20x24in) s.d.1937. 18-May-4 Bonhams, Knightsbridge #11/R

JOHN, Wilhelm (1813-?) German

£1399	$2378	€2000	Winter landscape with Drachenfels (38x47cm-15x19in) s.d.1842. 20-Nov-3 Van Ham, Cologne #1659/R est:2800

JOHNS, Ambrose Bowden (1776-1858) British

£480	$864	€701	View of Mount Edgcumbe and Plymouth Sound (91x71cm-36x28in) panel. 21-Jan-4 Sotheby's, Olympia #78/R

JOHNS, Greg (1952-) Australian

Sculpture

£8163	$15020	€11918	Excavator II (265x150x36cm-104x59x14in) init.d.97/98 corten steel prov. 29-Mar-4 Goodman, Sydney #32/R est:14000-20000 (A.D 20000)

JOHNS, Jasper (1930-) American

£10734	$19000	€15672	Corpse and mirror (69x93cm-27x37in) s.d.1976 num.54/58 lithograph. 28-Apr-4 Christie's, Rockefeller NY #324/R est:20000-30000
£167665	$280000	€244791	Untitled (81x65cm-32x26in) s.i.d.86-87 prov.lit. 12-Nov-3 Christie's, Rockefeller NY #384/R est:300000-400000

Prints

£1613	$3000	€2355	Untitled (45x30cm-18x12in) s.d.1998 num.74/75 etching. 2-Mar-4 Swann Galleries, New York #289/R est:2000-3000
£1808	$3200	€2640	Light bulb (17x22cm-7x9in) s.d.67-69 num.14/40 black grey etching aquatint. 28-Apr-4 Christie's, Rockefeller NY #319/R est:3000-4000
£1977	$3500	€2886	Evian (112x74cm-44x29in) s.d.1971-2 num.58/64 col lithograph. 28-Apr-4 Christie's, Rockefeller NY #322/R est:5000-7000
£2000	$3580	€3000	Knee (37x39cm-15x15in) s.i.d. col lithograph. 15-May-4 Dr Sturies, Dusseldorf #95/R
£2027	$3568	€3000	Handfootsockfloor (79x57cm-31x22in) s. num.30/48 col lithograph on vellum lit. 18-May-4 Tajan, Paris #159/R est:3000-3500
£2054	$3800	€2999	Cups 4 Picasso (56x81cm-22x32in) s.d.1972 num.16/39 col lithograph. 12-Feb-4 Christie's, Rockefeller NY #102/R est:2000-3000
£2246	$3750	€3279	Critic smiles (33x28cm-13x11in) s.i.d.1966 num.31/40 lithograph. 11-Nov-3 Doyle, New York #275/R est:4000-6000
£2267	$4171	€3400	Torso (37x47cm-15x19in) s.d. col lithograph. 11-Jun-4 Hauswedell & Nolte, Hamburg #1365/R est:3000
£2282	$4085	€3400	Buttocks (37x39cm-15x15in) s.d.74 col lithograph. 25-May-4 Dorotheum, Vienna #350/R est:3400-3600
£2333	$4177	€3500	Figure 2 (70x55cm-28x22in) s.d. lithograph. 15-May-4 Van Ham, Cologne #703/R est:5000
£2373	$4200	€3465	0 through 9 (8x6cm-3x2in) s.d.76 num.43/63 lithograph. 28-Apr-4 Christie's, Rockefeller NY #325/R est:4000-6000
£2401	$4250	€3505	Untitled (8x6cm-3x2in) s.d.1981 num.27/78 col etching aquatint. 30-Apr-4 Sotheby's, New York #362 est:3000-4000
£2454	$4000	€3583	Untitled (66x47cm-26x19in) s.d.1995 num.24/37 mezzotint on Lana Gravure. 24-Sep-3 Christie's, Rockefeller NY #264/R est:5000-7000
£2542	$4500	€3711	Figure 4 (69x54cm-27x21in) s.d.1968 num.63/70 lithograph. 28-Apr-4 Christie's, Rockefeller NY #317/R est:4000-5000
£2577	$4200	€3762	Alphabet (79x94cm-31x37in) s.d.1969 num.31/70 lithograph wove paper. 24-Sep-3 Christie's, Rockefeller NY #263/R est:3000-4000
£2825	$5000	€4125	Figure 2 (70x54cm-28x21in) s.d.1968 num.37/70 lithograph. 28-Apr-4 Christie's, Rockefeller NY #316/R est:4000-5000
£2941	$5000	€4294	Painted bronze (9x9cm-4x4in) s.d.64-69 et photoengraving. 31-Oct-3 Sotheby's, New York #607/R
£2941	$5000	€4294	Zone (111x48cm-44x19in) s.d.1972 col lithograph. 4-Nov-3 Christie's, Rockefeller NY #275/R est:3000-4000
£3107	$5500	€4536	No (118x71cm-46x28in) s.d.1969 num.14/80 lithograph embossing lead collage. 28-Apr-4 Christie's, Rockefeller NY #320/R est:4000-5000
£3200	$5824	€4672	Face from casts from untitled (37x33cm-15x13in) s.d.1974 num.17/49 col lithograph. 30-Jun-4 Christie's, Kensington #131/R est:1800-2000
£3390	$6000	€4949	Target (22x15cm-9x6in) s.num.13/50 lithograph stamp objects. 28-Apr-4 Christie's, Rockefeller NY #321/R est:3000-4000
£3513	$6289	€5200	Untitled (98x79cm-39x31in) s. num.44/72 col lithograph exec.1992. 4-May-4 Calmels Cohen, Paris #111/R est:6000-8000
£3763	$7000	€5494	Untitled (65x47cm-26x19in) s.d.1996 num.29/39 col mezzotint. 2-Mar-4 Swann Galleries, New York #288/R est:6000-9000
£3824	$6500	€5583	Target (61x41cm-24x16in) s.d.1973 lithograph. 4-Nov-3 Christie's, Rockefeller NY #276/R est:3000-5000
£4133	$7399	€6200	Man's portrait - self portrait (53x37cm-21x15in) s.i.d. lithograph. 15-May-4 Dr Sturies, Dusseldorf #97/R
£4237	$7500	€6186	Figure 5 (93x75cm-37x30in) s.d.1968 num.63/70 black tones lithograph. 30-Apr-4 Sotheby's, New York #358/R est:4000-6000
£4412	$7500	€6442	Target (96x68cm-38x27in) s. screenprint. 31-Oct-3 Sotheby's, New York #610/R
£4520	$8000	€6599	Untitled (24x24cm-9x9in) s.d.1977 num.98/130 col screenprint. 28-Apr-4 Christie's, Rockefeller NY #328/R est:4000-6000
£4595	$8500	€6709	Evian black state (112x77cm-44x30in) s.d.1972 num.11/18 black grey lithograph. 12-Feb-4 Christie's, Rockefeller NY #101/R est:5000-8000
£5085	$9000	€7424	Two flags (100x75cm-39x30in) s.d.1980 num.18/45 lithograph. 28-Apr-4 Christie's, Rockefeller NY #333/R est:8000-12000
£5294	$9000	€7729	Untitled (24x24cm-9x9in) s. col screenprint. 31-Oct-3 Sotheby's, New York #613/R
£5650	$10000	€8249	Device (75x52cm-30x20in) s.i.d.1962 lithograph. 28-Apr-4 Christie's, Rockefeller NY #312/R est:10000-15000
£6215	$11000	€9074	Two flags (102x83cm-40x33in) s.d.1980 num.38/56 lithograph. 28-Apr-4 Christie's, Rockefeller NY #331/R est:8000-12000
£6471	$11000	€9448	Target with four faces (91x66cm-36x26in) s.d.1968 num.10/100 col screenprint. 21-Nov-3 Swann Galleries, New York #95/R est:7000-10000
£7647	$13000	€11165	Flags II (70x90cm-28x35in) s.d.1973 col screenprint. 4-Nov-3 Christie's, Rockefeller NY #277/R est:15000-20000
£9040	$16000	€13198	Flags (87x65cm-34x26in) s.d.67-68 num.16/43 col lithograph rubber stamps. 28-Apr-4 Christie's, Rockefeller NY #315/R est:15000-20000
£9040	$16000	€13198	Periscope I (127x92cm-50x36in) s.d.1979 num.12/65 col lithograph. 28-Apr-4 Christie's, Rockefeller NY #329/R est:12000-18000
£10734	$19000	€15672	Targets (88x66cm-35x26in) s.d.67-68 num.9/42 col lithograph. 28-Apr-4 Christie's, Rockefeller NY #314/R est:12000-15000
£10734	$19000	€15672	Target with four faces (92x67cm-36x26in) s.d.1968 num.66/100 col screenprint. 28-Apr-4 Christie's, Rockefeller NY #318/R est:12000-18000
£10734	$19000	€15672	Untitled (62x94cm-24x37in) s.d.1977 num.40/53 col lithograph. 28-Apr-4 Christie's, Rockefeller NY #326/R est:18000-25000
£11176	$19000	€16317	Target with four faces (92x67cm-36x26in) s. col screenprint. 31-Oct-3 Sotheby's, New York #606/R
£11176	$19000	€16317	Usuyuki (116x37cm-46x15in) s. col screenprint. 31-Oct-3 Sotheby's, New York #615/R
£11765	$20000	€17177	Two flags (63x50cm-25x20in) s. lithograph. 31-Oct-3 Sotheby's, New York #609/R
£11765	$20000	€17177	Usuyuki (132x51cm-52x20in) s. col screenprint. 31-Oct-3 Sotheby's, New York #614/R
£12000	$21840	€17520	Target with four faces (60x46cm-24x18in) s.d.1979 num.37/88 col etching aquatint. 1-Jul-4 Sotheby's, London #335/R est:10000-12000
£13559	$24000	€19796	Usuyuki (117x36cm-46x14in) s.d.1980 num.50/57 col lithograph. 28-Apr-4 Christie's, Rockefeller NY #332/R est:15000-20000
£16471	$28000	€24048	0 through 9 (77x60cm-30x24in) s.d.1970 embossed lead relief. 4-Nov-3 Christie's, Rockefeller NY #274/R est:22000-28000
£16949	$30000	€24746	Painting with two balls (99x70cm-39x28in) s.num.36/59 col screenprint. 30-Apr-4 Sotheby's, New York #359/R est:15000-20000
£17514	$31000	€25570	Untitled (87x77cm-34x30in) s.d.77-80 num.29/60 col lithograph. 28-Apr-4 Christie's, Rockefeller NY #330/R est:18000-25000

£26471 $45000 €38648 Usuyuki (70x115cm-28x45in) s. col screenprint. 31-Oct-3 Sotheby's, New York #616/R
£29412 $50000 €42942 Decoy (104x78cm-41x31in) s. lithograph. 31-Oct-3 Sotheby's, New York #608/R
£30882 $52500 €45088 Corpse and mirror (78x101cm-31x40in) s. col lithograph. 31-Oct-3 Sotheby's, New York #612/R
£32934 $55000 €48084 False start (46x35cm-18x14in) s.d.1962 col lithograph. 11-Nov-3 Christie's, Rockefeller NY #141/R est:70000-90000
£38235 $65000 €55823 False start II (46x35cm-18x14in) s. lithograph. 31-Oct-3 Sotheby's, New York #605/R
£38922 $65000 €56826 0 through 9 (62x48cm-24x19in) s.d.1960 num.18/35 lithograph. 11-Nov-3 Christie's, Rockefeller NY #140/R est:40000-60000
£39548 $70000 €57740 Two maps (64x51cm-25x20in) s.i.d.1966 num.5/30 black lithograph. 28-Apr-4 Christie's, Rockefeller NY #313/R est:70000-90000
£42373 $75000 €61865 Savarin (97x71cm-38x28in) s.d.1977 num.30/50 col lithograph. 28-Apr-4 Christie's, Rockefeller NY #327/R est:50000-70000
£58824 $100000 €85883 Target (89x70cm-35x28in) s.d.1974 col screenprint. 4-Nov-3 Christie's, Rockefeller NY #278/R est:100000-150000
Works on paper
£155689 $260000 €227306 Litanies of the Chariot (13x9cm-5x4in) s.d.61 pencil graphite wash prov.exhib.lit. 11-Nov-3 Christie's, Rockefeller NY #14/R est:120000-180000
£530726 $950000 €774860 Map (49x62cm-19x24in) s.d.71 graphite graphite wash prov.exhib. 11-May-4 Christie's, Rockefeller NY #44/R est:1000000-1500000
£658683 $1100000 €961677 Figure 3 (66x51cm-26x20in) s.d.61 verso sculptmetal collage canvas prov.lit. 11-Nov-3 Christie's, Rockefeller NY #44/R est:1200000-1600000
£1564246 $2800000 €2283799 Corpse and mirror (43x54cm-17x21in) s.d.75-76 W/C prov.exhib.lit. 12-May-4 Sotheby's, New York #22/R est:2000000-3000000
£2814371 $4700000 €4108982 Grey Numbers (71x56cm-28x22in) s.d.1957 verso encaustic canvas prov.exhib.lit. 11-Nov-3 Christie's, Rockefeller NY #15/R est:5000000-7000000

JOHNSEN, Hjalmar (1852-1901) Norwegian
£515 $901 €752 Seascape with man in rowing boat (40x60cm-16x24in) s/. 16-Dec-3 Grev Wedels Plass, Oslo #180/R (N.KR 6000)
£559 $901 €816 From Citadel Island (35x40cm-14x16in) s. panel. 25-Aug-3 Blomqvist, Lysaker #1135 (N.KR 6500)
£650 $1197 €949 Evening in the skerries (27x41cm-11x16in) s. panel. 29-Mar-4 Blomqvist, Lysaker #1153/R (N.KR 8200)
£870 $1504 €1270 From Stavern (14x19cm-6x7in) s. panel. 13-Dec-3 Blomqvist, Lysaker #1184/R (N.KR 10000)
£2129 $3663 €3108 Sailing boats along the coast (79x125cm-31x49in) s.d.1884. 8-Dec-3 Blomqvist, Oslo #413/R est:50000-70000 (N.KR 25000)
£3834 $6862 €5598 Seascape with paddle steamer and sailing vessel (90x124cm-35x49in) s.d.1887. 25-May-4 Grev Wedels Plass, Oslo #9/R est:20000-30000 (N.KR 47000)

JOHNSEN, Johannes (1890-1965) Norwegian
£311 $516 €451 Outside Mandal (39x56cm-15x22in) s. 16-Jun-3 Blomqvist, Lysaker #1326/R (N.KR 3600)
£447 $818 €653 Seascape with steam ship (40x60cm-16x24in) s. 7-Jun-4 Blomqvist, Oslo #286/R (N.KR 5500)
£528 $972 €792 Vessel by the coast (52x67cm-20x26in) s/. 14-Jun-4 Blomqvist, Lysaker #1177 (N.KR 6500)

JOHNSON (?) British?
£865 $1600 €1263 Snowscape with river (61x76cm-24x30in) 12-Mar-4 Du Mouchelle, Detroit #2139/R est:1800-2800

JOHNSON, A Hale (?) American
£1132 $2050 €1653 Looman's barn (36x46cm-14x18in) s. panel. 16-Apr-4 James Julia, Fairfield #561/R est:1500-2500
£1243 $2250 €1815 Fresh produce (36x71cm-14x28in) panel. 16-Apr-4 James Julia, Fairfield #560/R est:2000-4000

JOHNSON, Andrew (20th C) British
Works on paper
£1800 $2862 €2628 Air, sea and land (76x114cm-30x45in) gouache. 10-Sep-3 Sotheby's, Olympia #66/R est:300-500

JOHNSON, Barbara (fl.1897-1933) British
£380 $718 €555 Tulips, lilac and other flowers in a glass vase (61x50cm-24x20in) s. 19-Feb-4 Christie's, Kensington #283/R
£650 $1203 €949 Old Ash (28x21cm-11x8in) s. 10-Mar-4 Sotheby's, Olympia #98/R

JOHNSON, Basil (20th C) British
Works on paper
£360 $583 €526 West Vale, view of a country house garden (51x141cm-20x56in) s.i.d.12 triptych W/C. 27-Jan-3 Bristol Auction Rooms #458

JOHNSON, Buffie (1912-) American
£703 $1300 €1026 Eastern Garden (42x83cm-17x33in) s. s.i. verso. 13-Jul-4 Christie's, Rockefeller NY #110/R

JOHNSON, C Everett (attrib) (1866-?) American
£363 $650 €545 Landscape with river (61x41cm-24x16in) bears sig. 29-May-4 Brunk, Ashville #164/R

JOHNSON, Candice (20th C) British?
Works on paper
£315 $535 €450 Oberon, Jayla (35x35cm-14x14in) s. mixed media board. 29-Nov-3 Neret-Minet, Paris #163/R

JOHNSON, Charles Edward (1832-1913) British
£900 $1431 €1305 Barges on a river (71x102cm-28x40in) 9-Sep-3 Bonhams, Knightsbridge #76/R
£2000 $3720 €2920 Misty day near Glencoe (86x122cm-34x48in) s.d.1903. 4-Mar-4 Christie's, Kensington #51/R est:800-1200
£3200 $5024 €4640 Grouse shoot (35x61cm-14x24in) s.d.1890. 27-Aug-3 Sotheby's, London #1004/R est:2000-3000

JOHNSON, Christine (1959-) Australian
£305 $479 €442 Glade (76x57cm-30x22in) s.i.d.1993 verso oil paper. 27-Aug-3 Christie's, Sydney #511 (A.D 750)

JOHNSON, Christopher (?) British?
£500 $800 €730 Connemara (81x121cm-32x48in) board. 19-May-3 Bruton Knowles, Cheltenham #206

JOHNSON, Content (1871-1949) American
£1599 $2750 €2335 Rug maker (65x55cm-26x22in) s. prov. 3-Dec-3 Doyle, New York #286/R est:5000-7000

JOHNSON, David (1827-1908) American
£2206 $3750 €3221 Afternoon (26x36cm-10x14in) mono. s.i.d.1882 verso board. 21-Nov-3 Skinner, Boston #260/R est:5000-7000
£3779 $6500 €5517 Cattle by a river (23x30cm-9x12in) init. s.verso. 7-Dec-3 Freeman, Philadelphia #111 est:4000-6000
£4749 $8500 €6934 Wallkill at Montgomery (25x36cm-10x14in) init. s.i.verso prov. 6-May-4 Shannon's, Milford #13/R est:5000-7000
£5682 $10000 €8296 House in the Adirondacks (46x41cm-18x16in) init.d.1851. 19-May-4 Sotheby's, New York #93/R est:15000-25000
£9412 $16000 €13742 Ossipee Lake (19x32cm-7x13in) init.d.72 i.verso panel prov. 30-Oct-3 Phillips, New York #19/R est:15000-25000
£9581 $16000 €13988 Adirondack lake (12x23cm-5x9in) init. board prov.lit. 9-Oct-3 Christie's, Rockefeller NY #8/R est:8000-12000
£9581 $16000 €13988 View of the Narrows, Lake George (13x19cm-5x7in) init. board prov. 9-Oct-3 Christie's, Rockefeller NY #10/R est:10000-15000
£9877 $16000 €14322 Mount Mansfield, Vermont (33x46cm-13x18in) mono.i. i.on stretcher. 8-Aug-3 Barridorf, Portland #132/R est:20000-30000
£14365 $26000 €20973 On the Housatonic River, Connecticut (36x56cm-14x22in) s.d.1877 s.i.d.1877 verso panel prov. 31-Mar-4 Sotheby's, New York #45/R est:20000-30000
£20950 $37500 €30587 Afternoon along the banks of a river (30x51cm-12x20in) init. 26-May-4 Doyle, New York #21/R est:30000-40000
£50279 $90000 €73407 View of Lancaster, NH (36x56cm-14x22in) init.d.1869 s.i.d.verso prov.exhib. 6-May-4 Shannon's, Milford #72/R est:25000-35000
£209302 $360000 €305581 Scene at cold spring, Hudson River (57x86cm-22x34in) s.d.57 s.i.d.verso prov. 3-Dec-3 Sotheby's, New York #102/R est:200000-300000

JOHNSON, E B (19th C) American?
£881 $1400 €1286 Still life of pears (18x28cm-7x11in) s.d.1885. 14-Sep-3 Susanin's, Chicago #6005/R est:400-600

JOHNSON, Eastman (1824-1906) American
£6286 $11000 €9178 Golden October, Catskills (26x38cm-10x15in) init. i.d.1869 on stretcher prov. 19-Dec-3 Sotheby's, New York #1062/R est:12000-18000
£22093 $38000 €32256 Little boy on a stool (22x17cm-9x7in) init.d.67 prov. 4-Dec-3 Christie's, Rockefeller NY #24/R
£115591 $215000 €168763 Embers (43x36cm-17x14in) s.d.1879 board prov.lit. 6-Mar-4 North East Auctions, Portsmouth #231/R est:80000-120000
£116279 $200000 €169767 Little soldier (39x32cm-15x13in) board prov. 4-Dec-3 Christie's, Rockefeller NY #46/R est:70000-90000
Works on paper
£442 $800 €645 Landscape (28x43cm-11x17in) chk white chk. 16-Apr-4 Du Mouchelle, Detroit #2115/R

JOHNSON, Edward Killingworth (1825-1923) British
Works on paper
£300 $489 €438 Cavalier (23x18cm-9x7in) s.d.1864 pencil W/C htd white. 25-Sep-3 Mellors & Kirk, Nottingham #702
£1800 $3330 €2628 Pet Bird (31x21cm-12x8in) init.d.1864 W/C. 10-Mar-4 Sotheby's, Olympia #162/R est:1000-2000
£2400 $4128 €3504 Watching the butterflies (67x47cm-26x19in) s.d.1881 pencil W/C bodycol. 3-Dec-3 Christie's, Kensington #84/R est:2500-3000

JOHNSON, Ernest Borough (1867-1949) British
£260 $481 €380 A springtime walk (61x50cm-24x20in) init.indis.d. 13-Jan-4 Bonhams, Ipswich #269
£327 $517 €474 Children and puppy with parasol under flowering tree (61x43cm-24x17in) 2-Sep-3 Rasmussen, Copenhagen #1944/R (D.KR 3500)
£514 $812 €745 Young lady on bench under tree in park (41x33cm-16x13in) s/d/1942. 2-Sep-3 Rasmussen, Copenhagen #1771/R (D.KR 5500)
£900 $1674 €1314 Under the parasol. Still life of flowers and fruit (61x43cm-24x17in) s.96 two. 4-Mar-4 Christie's, Kensington #652/R

JOHNSON, F Morton (1846-1921) ?
£667 $1193 €1000 Village amongst trees (54x65cm-21x26in) s. 12-May-4 Brissoneau, France #86

JOHNSON, Francis Norton (1878-1931) American
£3357 $5774 €4800 Le jardin public (54x65cm-21x26in) s. 3-Dec-3 Tajan, Paris #301/R est:4000-5000
£5705 $10497 €8500 Parc (50x61cm-20x24in) s. 24-Mar-4 Joron-Derem, Paris #55/R est:10000-12000

JOHNSON, Frank Tenney (1874-1939) American
£3529 $6000 €5152 Buttes of Little Colorado, Arizona (30x41cm-12x16in) s.d.1933 canvas on board prov.lit. 1-Nov-3 Santa Fe Art, Santa Fe #24/R est:8000-12000
£4375 $7000 €6388 Quaking aspens (41x51cm-16x20in) s.d.1930 i.verso canvas on board. 20-Sep-3 Bunte, Elgin #1461 est:10000-15000
£11765 $20000 €17177 Navajo (28x20cm-11x8in) s. canvas on panel prov.lit. 1-Nov-3 Santa Fe Art, Santa Fe #125/R est:25000-35000

£53476 $100000 €78075 Hour of slumber (64x76cm-25x30in) s. prov.exhib.lit. 24-Jul-4 Coeur d'Alene, Hayden #175/R est:75000-150000
£90909 $170000 €132727 Moon-bathed night (41x30cm-16x12in) s. board prov. 24-Jul-4 Coeur d'Alene, Hayden #26/R est:30000-50000
£90909 $170000 €132727 Unexpected visitor (64x76cm-25x30in) s. prov.exhib.lit. 24-Jul-4 Coeur d'Alene, Hayden #114/R est:75000-150000
£97826 $180000 €142826 On the drive (76x101cm-30x40in) s.d.1938 i. stretcher prov.exhib.lit. 8-Jun-4 Bonhams & Butterfields, San Francisco #4126/R est:175000-225000
Works on paper
£2235 $4000 €3263 Man with hat smoking (30x23cm-12x9in) chl. 15-May-4 Altermann Galleries, Santa Fe #71/R
£19118 $32500 €27912 Cowboy on horseback (53x36cm-21x14in) s.d.1907 W/C board prov.lit. 1-Nov-3 Santa Fe Art, Santa Fe #33/R est:35000-45000

JOHNSON, G F Waldo (fl.1893-1894) British
£600 $1110 €876 Portrait of a greyhound in a field (51x66cm-20x26in) s.d.1893. 9-Mar-4 Gorringes, Lewes #2004

JOHNSON, George Henry (1926-) New Zealander
£494 $894 €721 Red and grey triangle construction (56x46cm-22x18in) s.d.87. 30-Mar-4 Lawson Menzies, Sydney #154/R est:1000-2000 (A.D 1200)
£1646 $2979 €2403 Red triangle construction no.8 (183x152cm-72x60in) s.d.88 exhib. 30-Mar-4 Lawson Menzies, Sydney #155/R est:2500-3500 (A.D 4000)

JOHNSON, Guy (1927-) American
£1224 $2192 €1800 Wedding of my mothers cousin (34x62cm-13x24in) s. paper on panel painted 1972. 19-Mar-4 Millon & Associes, Paris #208 est:600-800
£1837 $3288 €2700 Main street (38x56cm-15x22in) s. paper on panel. 19-Mar-4 Millon & Associes, Paris #209 est:500-600
£2282 $4085 €3400 Watching TV (42x59cm-17x23in) s. paper on cardboard prov. 27-May-4 Sotheby's, Paris #28/R est:1000-1500
£2282 $4085 €3400 Last dirigeable to heaven (90x70cm-35x28in) s. paper on aluminium painted 1989 prov. 27-May-4 Sotheby's, Paris #282/R est:500-600
£3221 $5766 €4800 California moon (63x69cm-25x27in) s. paper on aluminium prov. 27-May-4 Sotheby's, Paris #283/R est:500-700
Works on paper
£1429 $2557 €2100 Dirigeable en flamme (34x50cm-13x20in) s. mixed media panel. 19-Mar-4 Millon & Associes, Paris #207/R est:500-600

JOHNSON, Harry John (1826-1884) British
£486 $900 €710 Lake of the Four Cantons (48x81cm-19x32in) canvas laid down. 12-Mar-4 Du Mouchelle, Detroit #2136/R
Works on paper
£362 $587 €525 Inner harbour, Rhodes (31x42cm-12x17in) s. W/C. 31-Jul-3 International Art Centre, Auckland #151/R est:500-1000 (NZ.D 1000)

JOHNSON, Harvey W (1920-) American
£1429 $2300 €2072 Trailing north (51x66cm-20x26in) board. 22-Aug-3 Altermann Galleries, Santa Fe #20

JOHNSON, Isaac (fl.1799-1816) British
Works on paper
£260 $465 €380 Gateway to Hadleigh Parsonage (16x19cm-6x7in) i. pen ink W/C. 22-Mar-4 Bonhams & Brooks, Norfolk #148/R
£900 $1611 €1314 Langley Abbey cross, Langley Common, Norfolk (33x20cm-13x8in) s.i.d.1783 W/C sold with W/C by John Johnson. 22-Mar-4 Bonhams & Brooks, Norfolk #149/R
£900 $1611 €1314 Langley Abbey, Norfolk (15x28cm-6x11in) s.i.d.1788 W/C. 22-Mar-4 Bonhams & Brooks, Norfolk #152/R
£920 $1647 €1343 South west view of Woodbridge church in Suffolk (127x35cm-50x14in) s.i. ink wash engrisaille. 22-Mar-4 Bonhams & Brooks, Norfolk #145/R
£1050 $1880 €1533 Oak south of Langley churchyard, Norfolk (28x33cm-11x13in) s.i.d.1788 W/C. 22-Mar-4 Bonhams & Brooks, Norfolk #150/R est:400-600

JOHNSON, Kaare Espolin (1907-1994) Norwegian
Prints
£2159 $3584 €3131 Spring in Telemark (35x77cm-14x30in) s.num.30/290 col lithograph. 16-Jun-3 Blomqvist, Lysaker #1092/R est:20000-25000 (N.KR 25000)
£2371 $4340 €3462 Peder at Rosthavet - man in boat (48x61cm-19x24in) s.num.66/260 lithograph. 2-Feb-4 Blomqvist, Lysaker #1128/R est:30000-40000 (N.KR 29500)
£2669 $4457 €3897 Peder in small boat at Rost Ocean (48x61cm-19x24in) s.num.1/260 col lithograph. 17-Nov-3 Blomqvist, Lysaker #1148/R est:30000-35000 (N.KR 32000)
£3670 $6128 €5358 Fishermen cheating (51x86cm-20x34in) s.num.122/200 col lit. 17-Nov-3 Blomqvist, Lysaker #1149/R est:40000-50000 (N.KR 44000)
£5336 $8910 €7791 Cheating at fishing I (52x86cm-20x34in) s.num.59/200 col lithograph. 20-Oct-3 Blomqvist, Lysaker #1151/R est:40000-50000 (N.KR 62000)
Works on paper
£1363 $2344 €1990 Roest (26x39cm-10x15in) s.i.d.1957 mixed media. 8-Dec-3 Blomqvist, Oslo #523/R est:18000-22000 (N.KR 16000)
£1533 $2637 €2238 Mountain landscape, Trollfjorden (21x18cm-8x7in) s.i. mixed media. 8-Dec-3 Blomqvist, Oslo #521/R est:12000-15000 (N.KR 18000)
£1739 $3009 €2539 Roest (38x55cm-15x22in) s. mixed media scraping out. 13-Dec-3 Blomqvist, Lysaker #1178/R est:15000-20000 (N.KR 20000)
£2783 $4814 €4063 Per Anders (49x32cm-19x13in) s. mixed media scraping out. 13-Dec-3 Blomqvist, Lysaker #1179/R est:15000-20000 (N.KR 32000)
£2896 $4981 €4228 A tragedy at the Polar circle (24x32cm-9x13in) s. i.verso mixed media. 8-Dec-3 Blomqvist, Oslo #522/R est:18000-20000 (N.KR 34000)

JOHNSON, Ken (1950-) Australian
£539 $1009 €787 Clouded dunes I, II (113x80cm-44x31in) S. AC. 27-Feb-4 Lawson Menzies, Sydney #2072/R (A.D 1300)

JOHNSON, Lester (1919-) American
Works on paper
£391 $700 €571 Original design for an exhibition (35x25cm-14x10in) s.i. gouache chk on pencil executed c.1962. 6-May-4 Doyle, New York #110/R
£1912 $3250 €2792 Untitled - still life. Untitled - Portrait (28x43cm-11x17in) s. ink oil on paper. 9-Nov-3 Wright, Chicago #414 est:1200-1500

JOHNSON, Louisa (fl.1865) British
£800 $1480 €1168 Sulpher crested cockatoo (28x23cm-11x9in) s.d.1869. 13-Feb-4 Keys, Aylsham #644/R

JOHNSON, Marshall (1850-1921) American
£695 $1300 €1015 Lake and mountain scene with red roofed house (25x36cm-10x14in) s.d.88. 28-Feb-4 Thomaston Place, Thomaston #97a/R
£1311 $2400 €1914 Shipping in a calm (46x35cm-18x14in) s. 29-Jul-4 Christie's, Rockefeller NY #275/R est:3000-5000
£1573 $2500 €2297 Sailing vessels (63x76cm-25x30in) s. 12-Sep-3 Skinner, Boston #303/R
£2322 $4250 €3483 Shipping (25x36cm-10x14in) s. 29-Jul-4 Eldred, East Dennis #292/R est:4000-5000

JOHNSON, Matthew Franklin (1963-) Australian
£447 $702 €648 Spring (41x37cm-16x15in) s.d.89 oil pastel paper prov. 26-Aug-3 Christie's, Sydney #235/R (A.D 1100)
£3252 $5106 €4715 Stages of a summer day (152x152cm-60x60in) s.i.d.2001 verso linen prov. 26-Aug-3 Christie's, Sydney #24/R est:8000-12000 (A.D 8000)
Works on paper
£2024 $3259 €2955 Untitled (152x122cm-60x48in) mixed media canvas. 25-Aug-3 Sotheby's, Paddington #267/R est:5000-7000 (A.D 5000)

JOHNSON, Michael (1938-) Australian
£8264 $14628 €12065 Vasu (122x91cm-48x36in) s.i.d.1996 verso linen prov. 3-May-4 Christie's, Melbourne #7/R est:20000-30000 (A.D 20000)
£10656 $16836 €15558 Cattai Revisit (122x366cm-48x144in) s.d.1989 verso prov. 2-Sep-3 Deutscher-Menzies, Melbourne #73/R est:35000-45000 (A.D 26000)
£14170 $22814 €20688 Inuit (153x122cm-60x48in) s.d.1999 i.verso prov. 25-Aug-3 Sotheby's, Paddington #145/R est:26000-30000 (A.D 35000)
£26483 $45021 €38665 Untitled (122x366cm-48x144in) s.verso prov. 24-Nov-3 Sotheby's, Melbourne #42/R est:45000-55000 (A.D 62500)
Works on paper
£1860 $3440 €2716 Mosman I (75x58cm-30x23in) init.d.1996 gouache prov. 10-Mar-4 Deutscher-Menzies, Melbourne #264/R est:5000-7000 (A.D 4500)

JOHNSON, Minnie Wolaver (1874-1954) American
£539 $900 €787 Bluebonnets (46x61cm-18x24in) 18-Oct-3 David Dike, Dallas #221/R

JOHNSON, Neville (1911-1999) British
£2000 $3320 €2920 Enigmatic landscape (40x50cm-16x20in) s.d.78 acrylic. 1-Oct-3 John Ross, Belfast #167 est:2000-2500
£2027 $3831 €3000 Enigmatic landscape (41x51cm-16x20in) s.d.1978 i.verso. 17-Feb-4 Whyte's, Dublin #26/R est:4000-5000
£9274 $17065 €13540 Nurses (69x122cm-27x48in) s. s.i.d.1953 verso masonite exhib. 14-Jun-4 Waddingtons, Toronto #176/R est:8000-12000 (C.D 23000)

JOHNSON, R (20th C) Australian
£1700 $3128 €2482 Tying his shoe laces (28x20cm-11x8in) s. canvasboard. 24-Mar-4 Hamptons Fine Art, Godalming #303/R

JOHNSON, Ray (1927-1995) American
Works on paper
£7362 $12000 €10749 Kiss the lotus (42x39cm-17x15in) s.i.d.1969 ink W/C collage cardboard on board prov. 23-Sep-3 Christie's, Rockefeller NY #53/R est:7000-9000

JOHNSON, Richard (19th C) Irish
£1605 $2600 €2343 Abstract composition (183x152cm-72x60in) init.d.79. 2-Aug-3 Neal Auction Company, New Orleans #395/R est:4000-6000

JOHNSON, Robert (1890-1964) Australian
£250 $393 €363 Constantine Cornwall (9x11cm-4x4in) board. 27-Aug-3 Mallams, Oxford #631/R
£415 $743 €606 View through boat sheds (31x39cm-12x15in) s.d. board. 12-May-4 Dunbar Sloane, Wellington #224 est:500-1000 (NZ.D 1200)
£562 $939 €815 Garden sun (38x45cm-15x18in) s. board. 30-Jun-3 Australian Art Auctions, Sydney #109/R (A.D 1400)
£576 $1043 €841 Spring morning Capertree (71x91cm-28x36in) s.i. prov. 31-Mar-4 Goodman, Sydney #402 (A.D 1400)
£679 $1065 €991 Burragorang Valley (36x29cm-14x11in) s.d.1928 canvas on board. 24-Nov-2 Goodman, Sydney #23/R est:1200-1800 (A.D 1900)
£732 $1149 €1061 Cattle creek (43x53cm-17x21in) s. prov. 27-Aug-3 Christie's, Sydney #545/R est:2500-4500 (A.D 1800)
£742 $1388 €1113 Country road (29x37cm-11x15in) s. canvasboard. 21-Jul-4 Goodman, Sydney #231 (A.D 1900)
£749 $1378 €1094 Artist garden (37x45cm-15x18in) s. board. 28-Jun-4 Australian Art Auctions, Sydney #116 (A.D 2000)
£894 $1404 €1296 Mount Genowlan Capertee Valley (70x90cm-28x35in) s. i.stretcher. 27-Aug-3 Christie's, Sydney #540/R est:3000-5000 (A.D 2200)
£902 $1534 €1317 Wellington (19x24cm-7x9in) s. canvas on board painted c.1930. 26-Nov-3 Dunbar Sloane, Wellington #103/R est:2000-3000 (NZ.D 2400)
£1134 $1825 €1656 Deserted Cottage (30x37cm-12x15in) s. canvasboard. 25-Aug-3 Sotheby's, Paddington #460/R est:1500-2000 (A.D 2800)
£1134 $1825 €1656 Old gum (37x44cm-15x17in) s. i.verso painted c.1945. 13-Oct-3 Joel, Victoria #251 est:1500-2500 (A.D 2800)
£1393 $2187 €2034 Sydney street scene - City from Darling Harbour 1933 (34x44cm-13x17in) s. canvasboard. 24-Nov-2 Goodman, Sydney #40/R est:2200-3200 (A.D 3900)
£1832 $3334 €2675 Gorge, New South Wales (44x55cm-17x22in) s. i.verso canvasboard. 16-Jun-4 Deutscher-Menzies, Melbourne #265/R est:4000-6000 (A.D 4800)

£2300 $4140 €3358 Near Cambrewarra, New South Wales (44x54cm-17x21in) s. prov. 21-Apr-4 Cheffins, Cambridge #510/R est:2500-3000

£2642 $4729 €3857 Autumn afternoon, Wattamolla Valley (36x44cm-14x17in) s. board. 10-May-4 Joel, Victoria #360/R est:4000-5000 (A.D 6500)

£2766 $4702 €4038 Whale Beach (38x45cm-15x18in) s. canvas on board painted c.1940. 26-Nov-3 Deutscher-Menzies, Melbourne #171/R est:7000-9000 (A.D 6500)

£7927 $14189 €11573 Valley of the Hawkesbury (69x89cm-27x35in) s.d.1928. 10-May-4 Joel, Victoria #296/R est:18000-22000 (A.D 19500)

JOHNSON, Robert Barbour (20th C) American

Works on paper

£700 $1295 €1022 Berwick on Tweed (61x84cm-24x33in) s. W/C. 9-Mar-4 Gorringes, Lewes #2271

JOHNSON, Sargent (1889-1967) American

Sculpture

£5814 $10000 €8488 Mother and child (46x18x15cm-18x7x6in) s. glazed painted terracotta exec.c.1965. 7-Dec-3 Treadway Gallery, Cincinnati #678/R

£15294 $26000 €22329 Mother and child (39cm-15in) s.d.47 verso painted terracotta exhib. 9-Nov-3 Bonhams & Butterfields, Los Angeles #4100/R est:10000-15000

JOHNSON, Sidney Yates (fl.1901-1910) British

£250 $433 €365 Haymaking scene. s. i.verso. 13-Dec-3 Nigel Ward, Hereford #1436

£250 $418 €365 The Old Mill Basingstoke (28x69cm-11x27in) s. 18-Oct-3 Nigel Ward, Hereford #1390

£310 $518 €453 Coastal scene (61x30cm-24x12in) s.d.1915. 11-Nov-3 Bonhams, Ipswich #214

£550 $935 €803 Figures harvesting beside a hay cart pulled by two horses (30x60cm-12x24in) s.d.1906. 19-Nov-3 Tennants, Leyburn #1068

£688 $1300 €1004 Old Mile, Busingstoke (30x71cm-12x28in) s. s.i.verso. 21-Feb-4 Jeffery Burchard, Florida #26/R

£850 $1522 €1241 Mountainous river landscape (46x81cm-18x32in) s.d.1899 pair. 27-May-4 Christie's, Kensington #184/R

JOHNSON, Sir William Elliott (1862-1932) Australian/British

£900 $1503 €1314 Eldon bluff, Tasmania. s. 14-Oct-3 Sotheby's, London #184/R

JOHNSON, Tim (1947-) Australian

£1626 $2553 €2358 Untitled (91x61cm-36x24in) acrylic prov.exhib. 26-Aug-3 Christie's, Sydney #61/R est:4000-6000 (A.D 4000)

£4132 $7314 €6033 Shambala (183x152cm-72x60in) s.i.d.97 verso acrylic prov. 3-May-4 Christie's, Melbourne #35/R est:10000-15000 (A.D 10000)

Works on paper

£329 $596 €480 Untitled (39x30cm-15x12in) mixed media canvas. 31-Mar-4 Goodman, Sydney #356 (A.D 800)

£1271 $2161 €1856 Kintore (91x121cm-36x48in) s.d.87 verso synthetic polymer paint canvas. 24-Nov-3 Sotheby's, Melbourne #67/R est:3000-5000 (A.D 3000)

JOHNSON, Tony (1941-) Australian

£347 $552 €507 Wheat fields of Suffolk (61x74cm-24x29in) s. board. 1-May-3 Dunbar Sloane, Wellington #70 est:500-1000 (NZ.D 1000)

JOHNSON, W Noel (fl.1887-1914) British

Works on paper

£260 $481 €380 Cottage and figures on the Anglesey coast (37x53cm-15x21in) s. W/C. 14-Jul-4 Bonhams, Chester #345

JOHNSON, Wesley (20th C) American

£249 $450 €364 River scene (28x36cm-11x14in) s.d.87. 18-Apr-4 Bonhams & Butterfields, Los Angeles #7010

JOHNSON, William (fl.c.1780) British

£2100 $3759 €3066 Portrait of Henrietta Nelson, seated in an interior wearing blue gown (43x34cm-17x13in) sold with a book. 22-Mar-4 Bonhams & Brooks, Norfolk #347/R est:500-800

JOHNSON, William Henry (1901-1970) American

£3069 $5646 €4481 Portrait of the artist Regner Lange (35x35cm-14x14in) s. prov. 29-Mar-4 Rasmussen, Copenhagen #511/R est:20000 (D.KR 34000)

JOHNSSON, Lasse (1899-1992) Swedish

£270 $486 €394 Fields and meadows, Hven (73x80cm-29x31in) s.d.1963. 26-Jan-4 Lilla Bukowskis, Stockholm #575 (S.KR 3600)

JOHNSTON, Alexander (1815-1891) British

£1800 $3348 €2628 Highland Jennie (71x91cm-28x36in) s.d.1840. 4-Mar-4 Christie's, Kensington #44/R est:2000-3000

JOHNSTON, Alexander (attrib) (1815-1891) British

£1900 $3173 €2774 Unwelcome suitor (23x31cm-9x12in) board companion pair. 16-Oct-3 Lyon & Turnbull, Edinburgh #29 est:600-800

JOHNSTON, Alfred W (1885-1961) American

£1099 $2000 €1605 Flower field (61x74cm-24x29in) s. i.verso. 15-Jun-4 John Moran, Pasadena #92a est:2000-3000

JOHNSTON, David (1946-) British

Works on paper

£600 $1110 €876 Vincent Amazon Macaws (44x29cm-17x11in) i. pencil W/C. 11-Mar-4 Christie's, Kensington #135/R

£1000 $1850 €1460 Lears Macaws (48x37cm-19x15in) s. pencil W/C bodycol. 11-Mar-4 Christie's, Kensington #136/R est:1000-1500

£1000 $1850 €1460 Blue headed Macaws (49x36cm-19x14in) s. pencil W/C bodycol. 11-Mar-4 Christie's, Kensington #138/R est:1000-1500

JOHNSTON, Frank Hans (1888-1949) Canadian

£556 $961 €812 Decorative panel (41x99cm-16x39in) board painted c.1920. 9-Dec-3 Maynards, Vancouver #251 est:1800-2000 (C.D 1250)

£1321 $2365 €1929 Landscape (15x11cm-6x4in) s. tempera paper on board prov. 27-May-4 Heffel, Vancouver #168/R est:3000-4000 (C.D 3250)

£1696 $2918 €2476 Winding Road (19x25cm-7x10in) s. board. 2-Dec-3 Joyner Waddington, Toronto #435 est:2000-3000 (C.D 3800)

£1920 $3514 €2803 Winter stream (21x26cm-8x10in) s. board. 1-Jun-4 Joyner Waddington, Toronto #3/R est:3000-5000 (C.D 4800)

£1964 $3379 €2867 Trees in a rolling landscape (20x24cm-8x9in) tempera. 2-Dec-3 Joyner Waddington, Toronto #466 est:2000-3000 (C.D 4400)

£2033 $3638 €2968 View of lake through the trees (25x36cm-10x14in) s. s.verso board prov. 31-May-4 Sotheby's, Toronto #133/R est:5000-7000 (C.D 5000)

£2172 $3627 €3171 Wolf River (25x30cm-10x12in) s. board prov. 17-Nov-3 Hodgins, Calgary #345/R est:3500-5000 (C.D 4800)

£2236 $4002 €3265 Before the storm (33x26cm-13x10in) s. i.verso board. 27-May-4 Heffel, Vancouver #158/R est:5000-7000 (C.D 5500)

£2236 $4002 €3265 Cross country journey, trail to Lake O'Hara, Banff (31x34cm-12x13in) s. i.verso board prov. 27-May-4 Heffel, Vancouver #171/R est:4500-5500 (C.D 5500)

£2846 $5093 €4155 Algoma (13x13cm-5x5in) s. tempera paper on board painted c.1919 prov. 27-May-4 Heffel, Vancouver #157/R est:4000-6000 (C.D 7000)

£2902 $4991 €4237 Rolling road to Penetang (30x39cm-12x15in) s. board. 2-Dec-3 Joyner Waddington, Toronto #281/R est:2000-3000 (C.D 6500)

£3125 $5375 €4563 Young man in the North (40x50cm-16x20in) s. board prov. 2-Dec-3 Joyner Waddington, Toronto #193/R est:3500-4000 (C.D 7000)

£3600 $6588 €5256 Blue and gold (39x50cm-15x20in) s. panel prov.exhib. 1-Jun-4 Joyner Waddington, Toronto #100/R est:12000-15000 (C.D 9000)

£3604 $6126 €5262 Bright sun of spring (25x30cm-10x12in) s. s.i.verso board prov. 27-Nov-3 Heffel, Vancouver #98/R est:4500-5500 (C.D 8000)

£4065 $7276 €5935 The veil (27x22cm-11x9in) s. i.verso tempera paper on board painted c.1919 prov. 27-May-4 Heffel, Vancouver #162/R est:6000-8000 (C.D 10000)

£4241 $7295 €6192 Spring on Silver Island, Great Bear Lake, N.W.T. (25x30cm-10x12in) s.i. canvas on board painted 1939 exhib.lit. 2-Dec-3 Joyner Waddington, Toronto #241/R est:3000-4000 (C.D 9500)

£4241 $7295 €6192 Through the channel, Bryce's Island on the right, lake of the woods (15x21cm-6x8in) s. prov. 2-Dec-3 Joyner Waddington, Toronto #433 est:2000-3000 (C.D 9500)

£4472 $8004 €6529 Pleasant paths (40x30cm-16x12in) s. s.i.verso board. 27-May-4 Heffel, Vancouver #22/R est:7000-9000 (C.D 11000)

£4556 $7471 €6652 Spring (51x61cm-20x24in) s. board. 28-May-3 Maynards, Vancouver #79/R est:8000-10000 (C.D 10250)

£4955 $8423 €7234 50 below zero (30x40cm-12x16in) s. i.verso board prov. 27-Nov-3 Heffel, Vancouver #96/R est:4500-6500 (C.D 11000)

£5357 $9214 €7821 McAlpine Channel, July morning, Great Bear Lake (50x60cm-20x24in) s. board exhib.lit. painted 1939. 2-Dec-3 Joyner Waddington, Toronto #151/R est:8000-10000 (C.D 12000)

£5691 $10187 €8309 The laughing valley (50x40cm-20x16in) s. s.i.verso board prov. 27-May-4 Heffel, Vancouver #160/R est:10000-12000 (C.D 14000)

£5804 $9982 €8474 Snowy riverbank on a winter's day (60x75cm-24x30in) s. board. 2-Dec-3 Joyner Waddington, Toronto #7/R est:8000-12000 (C.D 13000)

£5804 $9982 €8474 Woodland (50x60cm-20x24in) init. painted c.1918-1924 exhib.lit. 2-Dec-3 Joyner Waddington, Toronto #167/R est:8000-12000 (C.D 13000)

£5856 $9955 €8550 Woodland pool (28x36cm-11x14in) s. panel prov. 18-Nov-3 Sotheby's, Toronto #163/R est:3000-5000 (C.D 13000)

£5856 $9955 €8550 Spring song in the sugar bush (64x82cm-25x32in) s. s.i.verso board prov. 27-Nov-3 Heffel, Vancouver #193/R est:7000-9000 (C.D 13000)

£6400 $11712 €9344 Signal (30x39cm-12x15in) s.d.27 panel. 1-Jun-4 Joyner Waddington, Toronto #17/R est:7000-9000 (C.D 16000)

£7207 $12252 €10522 Trees (30x25cm-12x10in) board prov. 18-Nov-3 Sotheby's, Toronto #4/R est:9000-12000 (C.D 16000)

£7600 $13908 €11096 Spring on the Penetang Road (60x75cm-24x30in) s. board. 1-Jun-4 Joyner Waddington, Toronto #112/R est:12000-15000 (C.D 19000)

£7600 $13908 €11096 Hints of fall (25x33cm-10x13in) s. board prov. 1-Jun-4 Joyner Waddington, Toronto #122/R est:9000-12000 (C.D 19000)

£7658 $13018 €11181 Autumn elm (34x25cm-13x10in) s. i.verso tempera painted c.1919 prov. 27-Nov-3 Heffel, Vancouver #147/R est:4000-6000 (C.D 17000)

£8000 $14640 €11680 Long shadows - Onoman lake (25x30cm-10x12in) s. board. 1-Jun-4 Joyner Waddington, Toronto #187/R est:5000-7000 (C.D 20000)

£8333 $15250 €12166 Shadowed pools on the Wye (48x70cm-19x28in) s. panel. 27-Jan-4 Iegor de Saint Hippolyte, Montreal #17 (C.D 20000)

£8929 $15357 €13036 Spring chores (55x70cm-22x28in) s. board. 2-Dec-3 Joyner Waddington, Toronto #76/R est:8000-10000 (C.D 20000)

£10135 $17230 €14797 On the road to spring (55x71cm-22x28in) s. s.i.verso prov. 27-Nov-3 Heffel, Vancouver #95/R est:10000-12000 (C.D 22500)

£12195 $21829 €17805 Arabesque, lake of the woods (27x33cm-11x13in) s.i.d.1922 board prov. 31-May-4 Sotheby's, Toronto #54/R est:9000-12000 (C.D 30000)

£16000 $29280 €23360 Northern Lake (75x100cm-30x39in) s.d.32 board. 1-Jun-4 Joyner Waddington, Toronto #31/R est:40000-60000 (C.D 40000)

£16892 $28716 €24662 Lake Louise (51x61cm-20x24in) s. i.verso prov.lit. 21-Nov-3 Walker's, Ottawa #79/R est:40000-60000 (C.D 37500)

£18293 $32744 €26708 Orient Bay, Lake Nipigon (76x101cm-30x40in) s. s.i.d.1933 verso board exhib.lit. 27-May-4 Heffel, Vancouver #51/R est:20000-30000 (C.D 45000)

£19643 $33786 €28679 Halcyon Morn (75x100cm-30x39in) s. board prov. 2-Dec-3 Joyner Waddington, Toronto #101/R est:30000-40000 (C.D 44000)

£102679 $176607 €149911 Autumn, Algoma (151x131cm-59x52in) s. lit. 2-Dec-3 Joyner Waddington, Toronto #97/R est:125000-150000 (C.D 230000)

Works on paper

£340 $622 €496 Path into the woods (23x17cm-9x7in) init. gouache W/C. 1-Jun-4 Hodgins, Calgary #131/R (C.D 850)

£455 $741 €664 Landscape study (48x15cm-19x6in) col pencil graphite. 23-Sep-3 Ritchie, Toronto #148/R est:400-600 (C.D 1000)

£480 $878 €701 Shoreline (11x16cm-4x6in) gouache. 1-Jun-4 Joyner Waddington, Toronto #463 (C.D 1200)

JOHNSTON, Henrietta (attrib) (?-c.1728) American
Works on paper
£500 $910 €750 Portrait of a gentleman, thought to be Mr Geekie, bust-length (28x20cm-11x8in) col chk. 1-Jul-4 Christie's, Kensington #12/R

JOHNSTON, John R (19th C) American
£753 $1400 €1099 Sketch on the Rhine (33x26cm-13x10in) s.i.d.1868 verso board sold with another. 5-Mar-4 Skinner, Boston #300/R est:800-1200

JOHNSTON, Robert E (1885-1933) American
£741 $1200 €1082 Ship at sea (38x51cm-15x20in) s. panel. 2-Aug-3 Neal Auction Company, New Orleans #178 est:1200-1800

JOHNSTON, Sir Harry (1858-1927) British
Works on paper
£300 $501 €438 Ragwort and heather (46x30cm-18x12in) mono. pencil W/C bodycol. 16-Oct-3 Christie's, Kensington #198/R

JOHNSTON, Ynez (1920-) American
Works on paper
£335 $600 €489 A city square (36x56cm-14x22in) gouache prov. 8-May-4 Auctions by the Bay, Alameda #487/R
£824 $1400 €1203 Little zoo (33x51cm-13x20in) s. casein prov. 9-Nov-3 Wright, Chicago #296 est:1500-2000
£978 $1800 €1428 Sun drawing (69x48cm-27x19in) s.d.1972 mixed media. 10-Jun-4 Swann Galleries, New York #125/R est:2000-3000

JOHNSTONE, Celestine Gustave (1911-) American
£380 $700 €570 Still life. 11-Jun-4 David Rago, Lambertville #355/R

JOHNSTONE, Dorothy (1892-?) British
£280 $448 €409 Killin (55x101cm-22x40in) s.d.1964. 15-May-3 Bonhams, Edinburgh #376

JOHNSTONE, George Whitton (1849-1901) British
£370 $681 €540 Near Blairgowrie (25x35cm-10x14in) s.d.86. 23-Jun-4 Bonhams, Bury St Edmunds #368/R

JOHNSTONE, Henry James (1835-1907) British
£850 $1581 €1241 Swaffham, Norfolk (10x16cm-4x6in) s.d.1880 i.verso oil on paper. 4-Mar-4 Christie's, Kensington #499/R
£1626 $2911 €2374 Change of clothes (39x29cm-15x11in) s. prov. 4-May-4 Sotheby's, Melbourne #329/R est:6000-10000 (A.D 4000)
£3125 $5500 €4563 Hunter in the Macedonian Range, Victoria, Australia (29x20cm-11x8in) s. board. 18-May-4 Bonhams & Butterfields, San Francisco #163/R est:4000-6000
Works on paper
£2000 $3400 €2920 Young girl gathering spring flowers (25x17cm-10x7in) s. W/C. 4-Nov-3 Bonhams, New Bond Street #138/R est:1200-1500

JOHNSTONE, Henry John (fl.1881-1900) British
£2800 $5208 €4088 In the valley of the Thames (38x30cm-15x12in) s.d.1880 i.verso. 4-Mar-4 Christie's, Kensington #462/R est:3000-5000

JOHNSTONE, John Young (1887-1930) Canadian
£1339 $2304 €1955 Village in Flanders (24x19cm-9x7in) s. panel. 2-Dec-3 Joyner Waddington, Toronto #370/R est:2000-2500 (C.D 3000)
£1626 $2911 €2374 White farm house, summer (12x17cm-5x7in) s.verso prov. 31-May-4 Sotheby's, Toronto #128/R est:3000-5000 (C.D 4000)
£2120 $3647 €3095 Beach Scene (25x35cm-10x14in) s.d.15. 2-Dec-3 Joyner Waddington, Toronto #248/R est:3500-4000 (C.D 4750)

JOHNSTONE, William (1897-1981) British
£700 $1113 €1022 Composition (61x76cm-24x30in) s.d.69 verso. 10-Sep-3 Sotheby's, Olympia #310/R
£900 $1449 €1305 Bust portrait (19x14cm-7x6in) s. board. 21-Aug-3 Bonhams, Edinburgh #1154
£1100 $1749 €1606 Blue composition (71x91cm-28x36in) s.verso. 10-Sep-3 Sotheby's, Olympia #311/R est:800-1200
£2600 $4654 €3796 Northern Gothic (30x41cm-12x16in) s.verso board prov. 14-May-4 Christie's, Kensington #595/R est:1500-2000

JOINER, Harvey (1852-?) American
£581 $1000 €848 Sunlit forest path (20x41cm-8x16in) canvasboard. 6-Dec-3 Selkirks, St. Louis #179

JOINVILLE, Antoine Victor Edmond (1801-1849) French
£2817 $4873 €4000 Vue du Campo Vaccino a Rome (41x57cm-16x22in) s.d.1827. 10-Dec-3 Maigret, Paris #51/R est:2000-3000

JOIRE, Jean (1862-?) French
Sculpture
£1667 $3017 €2500 Chien de berger (25cm-10in) s.st.f.Susse pat bronze. 1-Apr-4 Millon & Associes, Paris #6/R est:1000-1500

JOKI, Olli (1943-) Finnish
£268 $499 €400 Bay (22x40cm-9x16in) s.d.1982. 7-Mar-4 Bukowskis, Helsinki #342/R
£278 $464 €400 Mother and child (30x33cm-12x13in) s.d.1990. 23-Oct-3 Hagelstam, Helsinki #883/R
£329 $612 €490 Southern town scene (40x30cm-16x12in) s. 7-Mar-4 Bukowskis, Helsinki #341/R
£336 $617 €500 Winter landscape (40x50cm-16x20in) s.d.1982. 25-Mar-4 Hagelstam, Helsinki #857
£479 $766 €680 Archipelago with fisherman's cottage (28x42cm-11x17in) s.d.1990. 18-Sep-3 Hagelstam, Helsinki #888/R

JOLI, Antonio (1700-1770) Italian
£36111 $65000 €52722 Cappriccio of Roman ruins with classical figures (104x114cm-41x45in) 22-Jan-4 Sotheby's, New York #179/R est:30000-50000
£180000 $311400 €262800 Tiber, Rome, looking downstream with Castle and Ponte Sant Angelo (38x71cm-15x28in) prov. 10-Dec-3 Christie's, London #48/R est:100000-150000
£900000 $1557000 €1314000 Calle de Alcala, Madrid (77x120cm-30x47in) prov. 10-Dec-3 Christie's, London #64/R est:250000-350000

JOLI, Antonio (attrib) (1700-1770) Italian
£19310 $32248 €28000 View of Naples Bay (37x63cm-15x25in) i.on stretcher. 12-Nov-3 Sotheby's, Milan #150/R est:25000-35000
£23743 $42500 €34665 Trajan's column. Column of Marcus Aurelius, Rome (97x72cm-38x28in) pair prov. 27-May-4 Sotheby's, New York #115/R est:40000-60000

JOLI, Antonio (circle) (1700-1770) Italian
£5036 $8259 €7000 Seascape with sailing ships (48x100cm-19x39in) 4-Jun-3 Sotheby's, Milan #50/R est:7000-10000
£45000 $76500 €65700 Tiber, Rome, looking downstream with the castle and ponte Sant Angelo (98x134cm-39x53in) 31-Oct-3 Christie's, Kensington #165/R est:10000-15000

JOLI, Antonio (style) (1700-1770) Italian
£4444 $8000 €6488 Architectural capriccio with waterfalls (126x100cm-50x39in) 21-Jan-4 Sotheby's, New York #119/R est:6000-8000
£13000 $23790 €18980 The Tiber in Rome (101x126cm-40x50in) prov. 9-Jul-4 Christie's, Kensington #197/R est:8000-12000
£18000 $30600 €26280 Rome, view of the Forum (99x136cm-39x54in) 30-Oct-3 Sotheby's, Olympia #184/R est:10000-15000

JOLIN, Einar (1890-1976) Swedish
£310 $518 €453 Mountain landscape with reindeer (38x46cm-15x18in) s.d.1962. 12-Oct-3 Uppsala Auktionskammare, Uppsala #183 (S.KR 4000)
£310 $518 €453 Landscape with stags (55x65cm-22x26in) s.d.1941. 12-Oct-3 Uppsala Auktionskammare, Uppsala #355/R (S.KR 4000)
£399 $651 €583 Girl from Tallberg (54x46cm-21x18in) s.d.1966. 29-Sep-3 Lilla Bukowskis, Stockholm #709 (S.KR 5200)
£465 $777 €679 Moonlit landscape with hare (66x53cm-26x21in) s.d.1948. 12-Oct-3 Uppsala Auktionskammare, Uppsala #354/R (S.KR 6000)
£604 $1027 €882 Landscape with bears (27x35cm-11x14in) s.d.1960. 5-Nov-3 AB Stockholms Auktionsverk #886/R (S.KR 8000)
£628 $1087 €917 Model study (61x50cm-24x20in) s.d.1933. 15-Dec-3 Lilla Bukowskis, Stockholm #394/R (S.KR 8000)
£630 $1027 €920 Still life of tulips, lilies and shell (61x50cm-24x20in) s.d.1961. 29-Sep-3 Lilla Bukowskis, Stockholm #338 (S.KR 8200)
£733 $1245 €1070 Spring landscape with oak trees (38x55cm-15x22in) s.d.maj 1926. 5-Nov-3 AB Stockholms Auktionsverk #749/R (S.KR 9700)
£806 $1426 €1177 Girl wearing national costume (55x46cm-22x18in) s.d.1960. 27-Apr-4 AB Stockholms Auktionsverk #810/R (S.KR 11000)
£911 $1676 €1367 Rowing in moonlight (50x60cm-20x24in) s.d.1948. 14-Jun-4 Lilla Bukowskis, Stockholm #22 (S.KR 12500)
£948 $1743 €1422 Still life (63x50cm-25x20in) s.d.1966. 14-Jun-4 Lilla Bukowskis, Stockholm #367/R (S.KR 13000)
£982 $1669 €1434 Portrait of young girl (62x50cm-24x20in) s.d.1942. 5-Nov-3 AB Stockholms Auktionsverk #654/R (S.KR 13000)
£1075 $1753 €1570 Interior scene with Japanese lady (55x46cm-22x18in) s.d.1963. 29-Sep-3 Lilla Bukowskis, Stockholm #578 est:10000-12000 (S.KR 14000)
£1269 $2284 €1853 Still life of figurine and fruit (55x46cm-22x18in) s.d.1968. 26-Apr-4 Bukowskis, Stockholm #4/R est:15000-20000 (S.KR 17500)
£1450 $2611 €2117 Still life of mimosa and dish (46x55cm-18x22in) s.d.1969. 26-Apr-4 Bukowskis, Stockholm #3/R est:15000-20000 (S.KR 20000)
£1511 $2568 €2206 Riddarholmen Church, winter scene from Stockholm (46x38cm-18x15in) s.d.1971. 5-Nov-3 AB Stockholms Auktionsverk #653/R est:25000-30000 (S.KR 20000)
£1523 $2741 €2224 Still life of flowering twigs (46x38cm-18x15in) s.d.1942 panel. 26-Apr-4 Bukowskis, Stockholm #61/R est:15000-18000 (S.KR 21000)
£1612 $2853 €2354 Geisha (61x50cm-24x20in) s.d.1963. 27-Apr-4 AB Stockholms Auktionsverk #656/R est:12000-15000 (S.KR 22000)
£1612 $2853 €2354 Seated model with mirror (46x55cm-18x22in) s.d.1954. 27-Apr-4 AB Stockholms Auktionsverk #733/R est:18000-20000 (S.KR 22000)
£1662 $2825 €2427 Still life of flowers and peach (38x46cm-15x18in) s.i. prov. 4-Nov-3 Bukowskis, Stockholm #2/R est:12000-15000 (S.KR 22000)
£1685 $2982 €2460 Still life of flowers and mirror (46x55cm-18x22in) s/d/1968. 27-Apr-4 AB Stockholms Auktionsverk #668/R est:20000-25000 (S.KR 23000)
£1758 $3112 €2567 Still life of mirror and flowers (46x55cm-18x22in) s.d.1968. 27-Apr-4 AB Stockholms Auktionsverk #664/R est:15000-20000 (S.KR 24000)
£1813 $3082 €2647 Still life of letter and carafe (55x46cm-22x18in) s.d.1941 panel. 4-Nov-3 Bukowskis, Stockholm #86/R est:20000-25000 (S.KR 24000)
£1813 $3263 €2647 Still life (41x33cm-16x13in) s.d.1937 panel. 26-Apr-4 Bukowskis, Stockholm #119/R est:25000-30000 (S.KR 25000)
£1832 $3242 €2675 Still life of yellow roses (46x55cm-18x22in) s.d.1969. 27-Apr-4 AB Stockholms Auktionsverk #639/R est:15000-20000 (S.KR 25000)
£1905 $3371 €2781 Pheasants by Chinese Palace (46x55cm-18x22in) s.d.1964. 27-Apr-4 AB Stockholms Auktionsverk #847/R est:12000-15000 (S.KR 26000)
£2041 $3755 €3062 View towards Skeppsbron (50x60cm-20x24in) s.d.1964. 14-Jun-4 Lilla Bukowskis, Stockholm #339 est:15000-20000 (S.KR 28000)
£2870 $4879 €4190 View of Skeppsbron and Stor Church (51x61cm-20x24in) s.d.1975. 4-Nov-3 Bukowskis, Stockholm #214/R est:20000-25000 (S.KR 38000)
£3474 $5906 €5072 Naval cadets on Skeppsholm Bridge (22x27cm-9x11in) s.d.1939 panel. 4-Nov-3 Bukowskis, Stockholm #3/R est:15000-20000 (S.KR 46000)
£3474 $5906 €5072 View towards Stockholm Palace and Skeppsbron (33x55cm-13x22in) s.d.1963. 4-Nov-3 Bukowskis, Stockholm #85/R est:25000-30000 (S.KR 46000)
£3625 $6163 €5293 View towards Riddarholmen (46x55cm-18x22in) s.d.1942 panel. 4-Nov-3 Bukowskis, Stockholm #87/R est:25000-30000 (S.KR 48000)
£3927 $6677 €5733 Boys playing bandy (46x55cm-18x22in) s.d.1944. 4-Nov-3 Bukowskis, Stockholm #129/R est:18000-20000 (S.KR 52000)
£3927 $6677 €5733 Skaters in front of Dramaten (46x55cm-18x22in) s.d.1964. 4-Nov-3 Bukowskis, Stockholm #215/R est:15000-20000 (S.KR 52000)

£4641 $8354 €6776 Cart full of snow (22x27cm-9x11in) s.d.1934 panel. 26-Apr-4 Bukowskis, Stockholm #175/R est:8000-10000 (S.KR 64000)
£4683 $7961 €6837 View of Riddarholmen and the old town (61x51cm-24x20in) s.d.1941 panel. 4-Nov-3 Bukowskis, Stockholm #154/R est:30000-35000 (S.KR 62000)
£4683 $7961 €6837 Skeppsbron and the old town (65x50cm-26x20in) s.d.1948. 4-Nov-3 Bukowskis, Stockholm #157/R est:30000-35000 (S.KR 62000)
£4786 $8615 €6988 Horse riding at Brunnsviken (54x65cm-21x26in) s.d.1971. 26-Apr-4 Bukowskis, Stockholm #103/R est:25000-30000 (S.KR 66000)
£7106 $12578 €10375 Officer on horseback (55x46cm-22x18in) s.d.1931. 27-Apr-4 AB Stockholms Auktionsverk #804/R est:60000-80000 (S.KR 97000)
£7931 $13482 €11579 Riddarholmen's church (100x73cm-39x29in) s.d.1931 lit. 4-Nov-3 Bukowskis, Stockholm #5/R est:70000-80000 (S.KR 105000)
Prints
£1037 $1690 €1514 Oriental still life with shell and vase (41x33cm-16x13in) s.d.1953. 29-Sep-3 Lilla Bukowskis, Stockholm #210 (S.KR 13500)
Works on paper
£415 $676 €606 Circus acrobats (24x32cm-9x13in) s.d.1947 W/C. 29-Sep-3 Lilla Bukowskis, Stockholm #496 (S.KR 5400)
£504 $841 €736 Pheasant by Drottningholm Palace (28x47cm-11x19in) s.d.1961. 12-Oct-3 Uppsala Auktionskammare, Uppsala #430 (S.KR 6500)
£642 $1091 €937 Girl by shock (37x54cm-15x21in) s.d.1956 W/C. 5-Nov-3 AB Stockholms Auktionsverk #887/R (S.KR 8500)
£901 $1622 €1315 Rattvik (37x55cm-15x22in) s.d.april 1960 W/C exhib. 26-Jan-4 Lilla Bukowskis, Stockholm #742 (S.KR 12000)
£943 $1631 €1377 View of Marstrand's fort (34x49cm-13x19in) s.i.d.Aug.1931 W/C. 15-Dec-3 Lilla Bukowskis, Stockholm #681 (S.KR 12000)
£2611 $4699 €3812 View of Stockholm from Djurgarden (30x47cm-12x19in) s.d.1923 W/C. 26-Apr-4 Bukowskis, Stockholm #58/R est:20000-25000 (S.KR 36000)

JOLIN, Ellen (1854-1939) Swedish
Works on paper
£495 $892 €723 Still life (58x100cm-23x39in) s.d.1907 W/C. 26-Jan-4 Lilla Bukowskis, Stockholm #754 (S.KR 6600)

JOLLAIN, Nicolas René (younger-attrib) (1732-1804) French
£5298 $9642 €8000 Nymphe endormie dans un paysage (63x78cm-25x31in) 15-Jun-4 Claude Aguttes, Neuilly #50/R est:8000-10000
£7895 $14526 €12000 Allegorie de la Peinture. Allegorie de l'Architecture (85x99cm-33x39in) pair. 23-Jun-4 Sotheby's, Paris #32/R est:12000-18000

JOLLEY, Martin Gwilt (1859-?) British
£3000 $5550 €4380 Serenada above the Bay of Naples (41x70cm-16x28in) s. 15-Jan-4 Christie's, Kensington #952/R est:1500-2000
£3500 $6440 €5110 Campagnia, summer morning (53x35cm-21x14in) s. s.i.verso. 23-Mar-4 Bonhams, New Bond Street #129/R est:1000-1500

JOLY DE BEYNAC, René (1870-?) French
£578 $1000 €844 Tolede (54x65cm-21x26in) s. 15-Dec-3 Iegor de Saint Hippolyte, Montreal #86 (C.D 1300)

JOLY, Alexis Victor (1798-1874) French
£776 $1389 €1133 Figures in cemetery (30x54cm-12x21in) s. panel. 12-May-4 Dobiaschofsky, Bern #672/R est:2000 (S.FR 1800)

JOLY, Jean Rene (20th C) French
£1342 $2376 €2000 Vehicule hydraulique (81x116cm-32x46in) s. 29-Apr-4 Claude Aguttes, Neuilly #256 est:2000-2200

JOMANTAS, Vincas (1922-2001) Australian
Sculpture
£1271 $2161 €1856 Beacon III (74x96x31cm-29x38x12in) wood exhib. 24-Nov-3 Sotheby's, Melbourne #242/R est:3500-5500 (A.D 3000)
£1423 $2233 €2078 Tower II (113x106x50cm-44x42x20in) s.d.February 1992 laminated wood prov.exhib. 27-Aug-3 Christie's, Sydney #726/R est:2000-3000 (A.D 3500)

JOMOUTON, Frederic (1858-?) Belgian
£338 $605 €500 Le Botanique a Bruxelles (38x67cm-15x26in) s. 10-May-4 Horta, Bruxelles #356
£372 $665 €550 Enfants au bord de la mer (31x51cm-12x20in) 10-May-4 Horta, Bruxelles #357
£473 $847 €700 Les cabines sur la plage (46x65cm-18x26in) sold with another oil. 10-May-4 Horta, Bruxelles #354
£1486 $2661 €2200 A la lage (47x63cm-19x25in) s. 10-May-4 Horta, Bruxelles #355 est:600-800
Works on paper
£503 $931 €750 Marche aux fleurs a la Grand Place (30x51cm-12x20in) s. W/C. 15-Mar-4 Horta, Bruxelles #323

JON ONE (20th C) ?
£470 $869 €700 Ice bull (126x86cm-50x34in) i.d.1990 verso acrylic. 15-Mar-4 Blanchet, Paris #186/R
£470 $869 €700 Do or die (75x67cm-30x26in) s.i.verso acrylic. 15-Mar-4 Blanchet, Paris #188
£805 $1490 €1200 Turmoil down below (158x200cm-62x79in) s.i.d.1991 verso acrylic. 15-Mar-4 Blanchet, Paris #187
£944 $1605 €1350 Untitled (170x92cm-67x36in) s.verso acrylic. 28-Nov-3 Blanchet, Paris #252
£1469 $2497 €2100 Turmoil down below (160x200cm-63x79in) s.verso acrylic marker. 28-Nov-3 Blanchet, Paris #251/R est:800-1000

JON-AND, John (1889-1941) Swedish
£870 $1566 €1270 Still life of wine carafe (52x46cm-20x18in) s. d.18 verso. 26-Apr-4 Bukowskis, Stockholm #108a/R (S.KR 12000)
£906 $1632 €1359 Harbour view with figures in boat (33x40cm-13x16in) init.d.09. 25-Apr-4 Goteborg Auktionsverk, Sweden #356/R (S.KR 12500)
£1057 $1798 €1543 Still life of flowers on window ledge (39x27cm-15x11in) init.d.14 panel. 5-Nov-3 AB Stockholms Auktionsverk #763/R est:8000-10000 (S.KR 14000)
£1099 $1945 €1605 Coast (38x47cm-15x19in) st.sig. 27-Apr-4 AB Stockholms Auktionsverk #864/R est:30000-40000 (S.KR 15000)
£1392 $2464 €2032 Interior scene with Per Erik and Agnes Cleve (50x35cm-20x14in) s. panel on panel. 27-Apr-4 AB Stockholms Auktionsverk #849/R est:30000-40000 (S.KR 19000)
£1511 $2568 €2206 Still life V (58x45cm-23x18in) s. panel. 4-Nov-3 Bukowskis, Stockholm #170/R est:30000-35000 (S.KR 20000)
£1740 $3133 €2540 Per-Erik with his boat (73x54cm-29x21in) s. d.1922 verso. 26-Apr-4 Bukowskis, Stockholm #51/R est:40000-50000 (S.KR 24000)
£2051 $3631 €2994 Shipwreck (35x35cm-14x14in) init.d.13. 27-Apr-4 AB Stockholms Auktionsverk #862/R est:30000-40000 (S.KR 28000)
£2175 $3916 €3176 Skier in landscape (84x112cm-33x44in) s. panel. 26-Apr-4 Bukowskis, Stockholm #109/R est:60000-80000 (S.KR 30000)
£2644 $4494 €3860 View of Lorensberg (77x98cm-30x39in) s. 5-Nov-3 AB Stockholms Auktionsverk #762/R est:30000-35000 (S.KR 35000)
£2644 $4494 €3860 Woman in armchair (40x28cm-16x11in) st.sig. pastel. 4-Nov-3 Bukowskis, Stockholm #160/R est:35000-40000 (S.KR 35000)
£3263 $5874 €4764 Cubist model (86x60cm-34x24in) s. 26-Apr-4 Bukowskis, Stockholm #110/R est:50000-60000 (S.KR 45000)
Works on paper
£1160 $2088 €1694 The boats in Palermo (33x43cm-13x17in) st.sig.d.10 jan 22 mixed media. 26-Apr-4 Bukowskis, Stockholm #171/R est:22000-25000 (S.KR 16000)
£1208 $2054 €1764 Cubist figure (25x16cm-10x6in) s.d.15 Indian ink. 5-Nov-3 AB Stockholms Auktionsverk #719/R est:10000-12000 (S.KR 16000)
£1305 $2350 €1905 Girl wearing hat (36x29cm-14x11in) st.sig. mixed media painted c.1916. 26-Apr-4 Bukowskis, Stockholm #164/R est:25000-30000 (S.KR 18000)
£1450 $2611 €2117 The card game (28x36cm-11x14in) s. chk painted c.1917-18. 26-Apr-4 Bukowskis, Stockholm #165/R est:20000-25000 (S.KR 20000)
£2198 $3890 €3209 Figures by Trollhatte Canal (59x45cm-23x18in) s. pastel. 27-Apr-4 AB Stockholms Auktionsverk #850/R est:20000-25000 (S.KR 30000)
£2870 $4879 €4190 London (55x67cm-22x26in) s. Indian ink. 4-Nov-3 Bukowskis, Stockholm #164/R est:40000-50000 (S.KR 38000)

JONAS, Henri Charles (1878-1944) Dutch
£671 $1248 €1000 Madonna and Child (38x30cm-15x12in) s. panel. 4-Mar-4 Auction Maastricht #1106/R est:400-600
£959 $1630 €1400 Woman at the river (29x30cm-11x12in) init. 5-Nov-3 Vendue Huis, Gravenhage #336/R
£5655 $9048 €8200 Suzanne and the old men (200x126cm-79x50in) s.i. painted c.1930. 12-Mar-3 Auction Maastricht #1073 est:5000-7000

JONAS, Lucien (1880-1947) French
£1972 $3411 €2800 Muezzin de Bou-Saada (38x55cm-15x22in) s.i.d.1934 i.verso. 15-Dec-3 Gros & Delettrez, Paris #234 est:2500-3500

JONAS, Rudolf (attrib) (1822-1888) German
£282 $504 €400 View of St Peter's church near the castle of Tirol (13x17cm-5x7in) panel lit. 8-Jan-4 Allgauer, Kempten #2425/R

JONASON, Lennart (1927-1992) Swedish
£2417 $4109 €3529 Geometric composition (33x24cm-13x9in) mono. d.15.8.51 verso lit. 5-Nov-3 AB Stockholms Auktionsverk #902/R est:20000-25000 (S.KR 32000)

JONCHERIE, Gabriele Germain (19th C) French
£5263 $9685 €8000 Nature morte au panier d'oeufs (64x77cm-25x30in) 24-Jun-4 Tajan, Paris #66/R est:8000-10000

JONCHERY, Charles (1873-?) French
Sculpture
£2098 $3503 €3000 Persian cat (34x58cm-13x23in) s. white marble. 11-Oct-3 De Vuyst, Lokeren #200/R est:3000-4000

JONCIERES, Leonce J V de (1871-1947) French
£379 $702 €550 Oeillets au vase verts (48x26cm-19x10in) s.i.d.1909 cardboard. 11-Feb-4 Beaussant & Lefèvre, Paris #196/R
£436 $750 €637 Lazy afternoon (66x51cm-26x20in) s.d.1943. 6-Dec-3 Neal Auction Company, New Orleans #1094

JONES OF NANTWICH, Herbert St John (19th C) British
£1000 $1810 €1460 Champion tandem team, Hopwood Spark and Hopwood Horace (25x51cm-10x20in) s.d.1907. 31-Mar-4 Bonhams, Knightsbridge #65/R est:600-800
£1000 $1810 €1460 Heathfield Squire by Wildfire and Ophelia, winner of over 600 first prize (30x45cm-12x18in) s.i.d.1907. 31-Mar-4 Bonhams, Knightsbridge #66a/R est:600-800
£1050 $1901 €1533 Hopwood Spark and Hopwood Horace (30x46cm-12x18in) s.i.d.1907. 31-Mar-4 Bonhams, Knightsbridge #66/R est:600-800

JONES, Adrian (1845-1938) British
Sculpture
£1700 $2686 €2465 Study of the champion racehorse, Ormonde, with Fred Archer up (33cm-13in) i. bronze. 27-Apr-3 Desmond Judd, Cranbrook #573

JONES, Allan D (jnr) (1915-) American
Sculpture
£2162 $3719 €3157 Breast plate (56x30x16cm-22x12x6in) s. PCV leather metal. 2-Dec-3 Koller, Zurich #3345 est:1800-2500 (S.FR 4800)

JONES, Allen (1937-) British
£1600 $2912 €2336 Sunset (35x46cm-14x18in) s.i.d.87 overlap. 1-Jul-4 Christie's, Kensington #332/R est:1000-1500
£10000 $15900 €14600 Focus (61x101cm-24x40in) s.d.91 overlap prov.lit. 10-Sep-3 Sotheby's, Olympia #343/R est:10000-15000

Sculpture
£5500 $10065 €8030 Man loosing his head (80cm-31in) painted steel exec.1988. 2-Jun-4 Sotheby's, London #133/R est:6000-8000
£6200 $11346 €9052 Face (65cm-26in) steel exec.1988. 2-Jun-4 Sotheby's, London #119/R est:6000-8000
Works on paper
£600 $1092 €876 Grenada (18x25cm-7x10in) s.i.d.85 W/C. 1-Jul-4 Christie's, Kensington #335/R
£600 $1032 €876 Acropolis (23x26cm-9x10in) s.i.d.75 W/C. 3-Dec-3 Christie's, Kensington #727/R
£950 $1587 €1387 Study for split figure (54x73cm-21x29in) s.d.69 pencil blue biro. 16-Oct-3 Christie's, Kensington #549/R
£1700 $3145 €2482 Embryo (56x73cm-22x29in) s.i.d.70 pencil col crayon. 11-Feb-4 Sotheby's, Olympia #301/R est:1500-2000
£4500 $7155 €6570 Harmony (101x152cm-40x60in) s.d.97 W/C prov. 10-Sep-3 Sotheby's, Olympia #342/R est:4000-6000
£4500 $8325 €6570 Untitled (57x77cm-22x30in) s.d.72 brush ink W/C prov. 11-Mar-4 Christie's, Kensington #197/R est:3000-5000

JONES, Aneurin M (20th C) British
Works on paper
£1600 $2944 €2336 Welsh cob with handler (43x56cm-17x22in) s. gouache. 8-Jun-4 Peter Francis, Wales #2 est:1500-2000

JONES, Angus (1962-) Australian
£424 $720 €619 Priest and the Priest's apprentice (119x33cm-47x13in) s.d.94-95 i.verso on metal two panels. 24-Nov-3 Sotheby's, Melbourne #239 (A.D 1000)
Works on paper
£1116 $2064 €1629 Drawing (50x239cm-20x94in) synthetic polymer plywood panel. 15-Mar-4 Sotheby's, Melbourne #99 est:1500-2500 (A.D 2700)

JONES, Arne (1914-1976) Swedish
Sculpture
£1511 $2568 €2206 Fly (46x45cm-18x18in) s.d.60 num.2/3 brass pewter incl. wood base lit. 5-Nov-3 AB Stockholms Auktionsverk #699/R est:10000-12000 (S.KR 20000)

JONES, Brian J (19/20th C) British
£900 $1530 €1314 White Heather II and Britannia (61x91cm-24x36in) s. 19-Nov-3 Christie's, Kensington #420/R
£1200 $2040 €1752 Shamrock (61x76cm-24x30in) s. 19-Nov-3 Christie's, Kensington #421/R
£1300 $2210 €1898 Astra and Candida (76x102cm-30x40in) s. 19-Nov-3 Christie's, Kensington #424/R
£1500 $2685 €2190 Valkyrie and Defender at the start of the first race for the America's cup 1895 (41x61cm-16x24in) s. 26-May-4 Christie's, Kensington #515/R est:1500-2500
£1600 $2720 €2336 America's Cup (40x51cm-16x20in) s. 19-Nov-3 Christie's, Kensington #423/R
£1800 $3060 €2628 Sceptre (51x76cm-20x30in) s. 19-Nov-3 Christie's, Kensington #422/R
£2200 $3784 €3212 15 metre class with Sonya in the van of the fleet, Cowes 1911 (51x76cm-20x30in) s. 2-Dec-3 Sotheby's, London #134/R est:2000-3000
£2500 $4300 €3650 Britannia leading the big class, 1926 (51x76cm-20x30in) 2-Dec-3 Sotheby's, London #133/R est:2000-3000
£4000 $7160 €5840 Velsheda, Candida, Shamrock, Astra and Britannia under spinnakers (76x127cm-30x50in) s. 26-May-4 Christie's, Kensington #516/R est:1500-2500

JONES, Charles (1836-1892) British
£1200 $1992 €1752 Highlander with his dog and a horse carrying a dead deer (29x45cm-11x18in) s. 1-Oct-3 Woolley & Wallis, Salisbury #229/R est:1200-1800
£1800 $3348 €2628 Monarch of the glen (23x17cm-9x7in) mono, i.verso panel. 4-Mar-4 Christie's, Kensington #62/R est:1500-2000
£2239 $3873 €3269 Highland cattle drinking from a river (29x50cm-11x20in) mono.d.1879. 9-Dec-3 Peter Webb, Auckland #82/R est:6000-8000 (NZ.D 6000)
£3300 $5841 €4818 Sheep on a bank. Sheep in a meadow (30x41cm-12x16in) mono.d.1871 two. 28-Apr-4 Halls, Shrewsbury #497/R est:2500-3000
£6667 $12000 €10000 Resting cattle, sheep and deer, a farm beyond (77x127cm-30x50in) mono.d.1871. 20-Apr-4 Sotheby's, Amsterdam #187/R est:15000-20000
Works on paper
£2650 $4903 €3869 Flock of sheep grazing in a meadow with hills in the background (46x59cm-18x23in) init.d.1889 W/C. 10-Feb-4 Dickinson, Davy & Markham, Brigg #813 est:1000-1500

JONES, Charles (1866-1959) British
Photographs
£1796 $3000 €2622 Runner bean (14x10cm-6x4in) init.i.verso gelatin silver print exec. c.1902 prov. 17-Oct-3 Phillips, New York #139/R est:4000-6000
£3713 $6200 €5421 Tomato perfection (10x15cm-4x6in) init.i.verso gelatin silver print exec. c.1902 prov. 17-Oct-3 Phillips, New York #140/R est:4000-6000

JONES, Charlotte (attrib) (1768-1847) British
Miniatures
£1550 $2852 €2263 William Frederick, 2nd Duke of Gloucester, standing (23cm-9in) black wood frame rec. prov. 24-Jun-4 Bonhams, New Bond Street #117/R est:800-1200

JONES, Chet (1957-) American
£382 $600 €558 Captain's house (30x30cm-12x12in) s. 20-Apr-3 Outer Cape Auctions, Provincetown #118
£860 $1350 €1256 Winter house (46x51cm-18x20in) s. 20-Apr-3 Outer Cape Auctions, Provincetown #69/R

JONES, Daniel Adolphe Robert (1806-1874) Belgian
£1850 $3145 €2701 Cattle and cockerel in a byre (26x35cm-10x14in) s. panel. 4-Nov-3 Holloways, Banbury #501/R est:1500-2000

JONES, David (1895-1974) British
Works on paper
£1200 $1944 €1740 Tom's cat (26x21cm-10x8in) init.d.49 pencil htd red crayon. 30-Jul-3 Hamptons Fine Art, Godalming #131/R est:1000-1500
£4800 $8256 €7008 Town scene (56x38cm-22x15in) W/C prov. 2-Dec-3 Bonhams, New Bond Street #88/R est:6000-8000
£12000 $21960 €17520 Dusk is growing (75x55cm-30x22in) s.d.47 w gouache chk pencil prov. 2-Jun-4 Sotheby's, London #71/R est:10000-15000

JONES, Deborah (1921-) British
£360 $666 €526 Nursery Room (51x76cm-20x30in) s.d. 9-Mar-4 Bonhams, Knowle #278
£440 $792 €642 Dolls, teddy bear, toys, ornaments and cards on a pine shelf (76x51cm-30x20in) s.d.1975. 20-Apr-4 Canterbury Auctions, UK #116
£530 $901 €774 Cupboard with curios (91x45cm-36x18in) s.d.MCMLXXV. 27-Nov-3 Greenslade Hunt, Taunton #1042/R

JONES, Eleanor Ferri (20th C) American
£221 $400 €323 Route (41x51cm-16x20in) s. acrylic. 3-Apr-4 Outer Cape Auctions, Provincetown #74/R

JONES, Francis Coates (1857-1932) American
£5946 $11000 €8681 Coffin's Beach, Annisquam (36x51cm-14x20in) s. panel painted c.1890 prov. 11-Mar-4 Christie's, Rockefeller NY #3/R est:7000-10000
£9375 $15000 €13688 Garden scene with two women and swans (69x48cm-27x19in) s. 17-May-3 Bunte, Elgin #1214 est:8000-12000
Works on paper
£4972 $9000 €7259 Tea time. Female figure (30x33cm-12x13in) s. pastel double-sided. 18-Apr-4 Jeffery Burchard, Florida #120/R

JONES, Fred Cecil (1891-1956) British
Works on paper
£400 $716 €584 York (19x56cm-7x22in) s.i.d.1941 pencil W/C. 16-Mar-4 Bonhams, Leeds #594
£900 $1530 €1314 Sowerby Bridge, Yorkshire (67x43cm-26x17in) s.d.1937 pencil pen W/C htd white. 18-Nov-3 Bonhams, Leeds #74/R

JONES, Frederick D (1914-) American
£1000 $1700 €1460 Two veiled ladies (33x23cm-13x9in) board. 9-Nov-3 Wright, Chicago #323 est:2000-3000
£1647 $2800 €2405 Nude on horse (25x20cm-10x8in) s. 9-Nov-3 Wright, Chicago #321 est:2500-3500
£2059 $3500 €3006 Lady with plate of fish (30x25cm-12x10in) s.d. 9-Nov-3 Wright, Chicago #322 est:3000-4000
Works on paper
£323 $600 €472 Eleven faces (5x38cm-2x15in) s. W/C card executed c.1948. 7-Mar-4 Treadway Gallery, Cincinnati #712/R
£457 $850 €667 Woman seated at a table (30x23cm-12x9in) s. W/C executed c.1960. 7-Mar-4 Treadway Gallery, Cincinnati #713/R
£457 $850 €667 Spear fishing (33x23cm-13x9in) s. W/C ink. 7-Mar-4 Treadway Gallery, Cincinnati #714/R
£464 $850 €677 Heads (5x51cm-2x20in) W/C executed c.1960. 5-Jun-4 Treadway Gallery, Cincinnati #777/R
£882 $1500 €1288 Mother and child (33x20cm-13x8in) s. W/C. 9-Nov-3 Wright, Chicago #319 est:2000-3000
£941 $1600 €1374 Two harlequins on horseback (20x30cm-8x12in) s. W/C. 9-Nov-3 Wright, Chicago #320 est:2000-3000
£1047 $1800 €1529 Woman with flowers (51x18cm-20x7in) s. W/C exec.c.1948. 7-Dec-3 Treadway Gallery, Cincinnati #679/R est:1500-2500
£1471 $2500 €2148 Balloon man and two ladies (33x25cm-13x10in) s. gouache W/C. 9-Nov-3 Wright, Chicago #324 est:3000-5000

JONES, George (1786-1869) British
£3000 $5580 €4380 Bristol Harbour. Pont Royal, Paris (17x22cm-7x9in) indis sig.d.1825 oil paper on canvas pair. 4-Mar-4 Christie's, Kensington #560/R est:1500-2500

JONES, Glyn (fl.1930-1934) British
£280 $476 €409 Dusk, Athens (35x42cm-14x17in) exhib. 26-Nov-3 Sotheby's, Olympia #55/R

JONES, H F (?) British?
£1000 $1670 €1460 London to Brighton stage coach by night (30x61cm-12x24in) s. 11-Nov-3 Bonhams, Knightsbridge #63/R est:1000-1500

JONES, Herbert H (19/20th C) ?
£580 $922 €847 Wrexham, winner of 2nd prize, polo pony show (25x36cm-10x14in) s.d.1896. 30-Apr-3 Peter Wilson, Nantwich #52/R

JONES, Herbert John (19/20th C) British
£650 $1079 €949 Orphan Bowden Choice (28x41cm-11x16in) s.d.1917. 3-Oct-3 Mallams, Oxford #264/R
£1500 $2445 €2190 Old Lamb Hotel, Hospital Street, Nantwich (28x44cm-11x17in) s.i.d.1913 verso. 24-Sep-3 Peter Wilson, Nantwich #23/R
Works on paper
£280 $512 €409 Moreton Old Hall (27x21cm-11x8in) s. i. W/C htd bodycol. 6-Jul-4 Peter Wilson, Nantwich #74/R
£280 $512 €409 Durham - with rowing boat in foreground, Durham Cathedral beyond (27x21cm-11x8in) s.i. W/C htd. bodycol. 6-Jul-4 Peter Wilson, Nantwich #75/R
£380 $695 €555 Dysart Buildings, Nantwich (21x27cm-8x11in) s.i. W/C htd bodycol. 6-Jul-4 Peter Wilson, Nantwich #73/R

JONES, Hugh Bolton (1848-1927) American
£2275 $3800 €3322 Forest road (43x33cm-17x13in) s. 9-Oct-3 Christie's, Rockefeller NY #41/R est:4000-6000
£3294 $5500 €4809 Distant mountains (61x76cm-24x30in) s. canvas. 23-Oct-3 Shannon's, Milford #266/R est:5000-7000
£3846 $7000 €5615 Landscape (40x61cm-16x24in) s. 29-Jun-4 Sotheby's, New York #197/R est:8000-12000
£5882 $10000 €8588 Early September (51x61cm-20x24in) s. 30-Oct-3 Phillips, New York #54/R est:12000-18000
£7182 $13000 €10486 Riverside landscapes (18x30cm-7x12in) s. one d.1871 canvas on panel pair. 31-Mar-4 Sotheby's, New York #100/R est:4000-6000
£15135 $28000 €22097 Saint Michaels, Maryland (25x41cm-10x16in) s. painted c.1880 prov. 11-Mar-4 Christie's, Rockefeller NY #21/R est:10000-15000
£27616 $47500 €40319 Adams County, Pennsylvania (76x136cm-30x54in) s.d.1870 prov. 3-Dec-3 Sotheby's, New York #103/R est:40000-60000

JONES, J Haydn (?) British
Works on paper
£390 $690 €569 Church Lane Nantwich (25x18cm-10x7in) s.i. W/C. 28-Apr-4 Peter Wilson, Nantwich #130

JONES, J Llewellyn (fl.1880-1924) Australian
£813 $1455 €1187 Coastal landscape (22x29cm-9x11in) s.d.1921 board. 10-May-4 Joel, Victoria #372 est:1000-2000 (A.D 2000)
£1224 $2253 €1787 Evening on the beach, summer holiday (15x25cm-6x10in) s. s.i.verso. 29-Mar-4 Goodman, Sydney #98/R est:3000-5000 (A.D 3000)
£1245 $2079 €1868 Manly (14x22cm-6x9in) s. board. 27-Oct-3 Goodman, Sydney #174/R est:3000-5000 (A.D 3000)
£1660 $2772 €2490 Old steam ferry at the wharf (15x23cm-6x9in) i. board. 27-Oct-3 Goodman, Sydney #172/R est:4000-6000 (A.D 4000)

JONES, Joe (1909-1963) American
£405 $750 €591 Elk Basin (76x102cm-30x40in) s. i.stretcher. 10-Mar-4 Doyle, New York #35/R
£455 $800 €664 Still life with Asian vases (61x46cm-24x18in) s. 22-May-4 Selkirks, St. Louis #581/R
£645 $1200 €942 Portrait of a woman with a hat (46x33cm-18x13in) s. canvasboard painted c.1930. 7-Mar-4 Treadway Gallery, Cincinnati #663/R est:2000-3000
£988 $1700 €1442 Beach at Brielle (76x102cm-30x40in) s. i.stretcher prov. 3-Dec-3 Doyle, New York #288/R est:1200-1800
£988 $1700 €1442 Orchard on the Hudson (76x102cm-30x40in) s. i.stretcher. 3-Dec-3 Doyle, New York #289/R est:1200-1800
£2286 $4000 €3338 Winter landscape (51x61cm-20x24in) s. 19-Dec-3 Sotheby's, New York #1145/R est:2500-3500
£2695 $4500 €3935 Regatta, Barnegat Bay, New Jersey (56x102cm-22x40in) s. oil chl prov.exhib.lit. 7-Oct-3 Sotheby's, New York #230 est:1000-1500
Works on paper
£568 $1000 €829 Man with scythe (25x33cm-10x13in) s.d.41 ink. 22-May-4 Selkirks, St. Louis #582/R

JONES, John Edward (19th C) Irish
Sculpture
£7639 $12986 €11000 Archibald Montgomerie, 13th Earl of Eglinton with his wife (76cm-30in) s.d.1854 pair of marble busts. 28-Oct-3 Mealy's, Castlecomer #328

JONES, Josiah Clinton (1848-1936) British
£950 $1549 €1387 Glengarry Castle Oich, Scotland. Bettws-y-Coed, North Wales (50x75cm-20x30in) s. one s.i.stretcher pair. 24-Sep-3 Peter Wilson, Nantwich #6

JONES, Leon Foster (1871-1934) American
£471 $800 €688 Powder house, Somerset (25x18cm-10x7in) s. 21-Nov-3 Eldred, East Dennis #872/R

JONES, Leonard (19/20th C) British?
£540 $918 €788 Half rigged fishing smacks in a harbour. Shipping off Dover. pair. 28-Oct-3 Lawrences, Bletchingley #1755

JONES, Liam (20th C) Irish
£537 $961 €800 Renvyle (50x75cm-20x30in) s.d.03. 31-May-4 Hamilton Osborne King, Dublin #71/R

JONES, Lois Mailou (1905-1988) American
£8092 $14000 €11814 Voodoo (62x75cm-24x30in) s.i. oil gold leaf. 13-Dec-3 Weschler, Washington #598 est:2000-3000

JONES, Lucy (1955-) British
£444 $816 €648 River Thames. Riverside (46x56cm-18x22in) i.d.1993 s. two. 14-Jun-4 Waddingtons, Toronto #100/R est:600-800 (C.D 1100)

JONES, Paul (1921-1998) Australian
Works on paper
£711 $1274 €1067 Camellia, Lilian Pitts (28x21cm-11x8in) s.d.47 i.verso W/C gouache. 17-May-4 Sotheby's, Melbourne #589 (A.D 1800)
£2290 $4168 €3343 Camellia (31x22cm-12x9in) s.d.51 W/C. 16-Jun-4 Deutscher-Menzies, Melbourne #326/R est:5500-7500 (A.D 6000)

JONES, Paul (19th C) British
£360 $569 €526 Beyond reach (20x25cm-8x10in) s. painted c.1850-1860. 7-Sep-3 Desmond Judd, Cranbrook #719
£432 $800 €631 Longing for their master, two spaniels in an interior (20x25cm-8x10in) s.d.1856. 10-Feb-4 Doyle, New York #211/R
£550 $1012 €803 In sight of the quarry (20x25cm-8x10in) s.d.1857. 10-Jun-4 Christie's, Kensington #409/R
£1200 $2040 €1752 Spaniels putting a mallard up (23x30cm-9x12in) s.d.1880. 27-Nov-3 Christie's, Kensington #422/R est:1200-1600
£1550 $2635 €2263 Spaniels in an interior (20x25cm-8x10in) s.d.1857 pair. 18-Nov-3 Bonhams, Leeds #169/R est:700-900
£1800 $3366 €2700 Spaniel in an interior. Pointer with a grouse (20x25cm-8x10in) s.d.1855 pair. 26-Jul-4 Bonhams, Bath #72/R est:800-1200
£2800 $5208 €4088 Rest at the fence. The day's bag (19x13cm-7x5in) s.d.1873 panel pair. 4-Mar-4 Christie's, Kensington #626/R est:2000-3000
£3200 $5504 €4672 Waiting for master. Fallen stag (20x30cm-8x12in) s. pair. 3-Dec-3 Bonhams, Knightsbridge #86/R est:2000-3000
£3591 $6500 €5243 Setters in a landscape. Terriers (20x30cm-8x12in) s. one d.1872 one d.1873 pair. 30-Mar-4 Bonhams & Butterfields, San Francisco #44/R est:4000-6000
£5200 $8372 €7800 Scottish highland scenes (20x30cm-8x12in) s.d.1868 pair. 12-Aug-3 Canterbury Auctions, UK #156/R est:2000-3000

JONES, Pelham (20th C) British
Works on paper
£950 $1701 €1387 Giroflee in the Channel. Motor yacht Jumbo (25x35cm-10x14in) s.d.1932 second i. pencil W/C htd white other by same hand three. 26-May-4 Christie's, Kensington #520/R

JONES, R Benjamin (20th C) American
£359 $600 €524 Wild roses (23x79cm-9x31in) 11-Oct-3 Nadeau, Windsor #143/R
£833 $1350 €1216 Edgartown light (41x56cm-16x22in) s. board. 31-Jul-3 Eldred, East Dennis #874/R

JONES, Ray Howard (1903-1996) British
£350 $641 €511 Abstract in fiery colours (122x102cm-48x40in) exhib. 27-Jan-4 Peter Francis, Wales #5

JONES, Rev Calvert Richard (c.1804-1877) British
Works on paper
£550 $935 €803 Father playing with children (16x24cm-6x9in) d. pencil htd white. 18-Nov-3 Sotheby's, Olympia #30/R
£900 $1530 €1314 H.M.S. Leopold (36x53cm-14x21in) s.i.d.1860 pencil wash set of 3. 18-Nov-3 Sotheby's, Olympia #14/R
£900 $1530 €1314 H.M.S. Prince Regent (36x53cm-14x21in) s.d.1853 pencil W/C. 18-Nov-3 Sotheby's, Olympia #13/R

JONES, Richard (1767-1840) British
£1933 $3500 €2822 Clumber spaniel in a wood (28x38cm-11x15in) 30-Mar-4 Bonhams & Butterfields, San Francisco #24/R est:3500-4500
£10465 $18000 €15279 Going out. Finding. Coursing. Death (36x48cm-14x19in) i.on stretcher set of four prov.exhib.lit. 5-Dec-3 Christie's, Rockefeller NY #15/R est:20000-30000

JONES, Robert (fl.1906-1940) British
£260 $486 €380 Gulls on a western rock, Isles of Scilly (16x43cm-6x17in) init. i.verso artist board. 26-Feb-4 Lane, Penzance #51
£300 $561 €438 The beach (60x44cm-24x17in) init. artist board. 26-Feb-4 Lane, Penzance #22
£300 $549 €438 Sea and cows, St Agnes, Isles of Scilly (33x23cm-13x9in) s.i. 3-Jun-4 Lane, Penzance #159
£350 $655 €511 Foxgloves above the sea (34x16cm-13x6in) init. 26-Feb-4 Lane, Penzance #18
Works on paper
£650 $1203 €949 Cornish coast (58x81cm-23x32in) s.d.1990 mixed media. 10-Feb-4 David Lay, Penzance #552

JONES, Robert Edmond (1887-1954) American
Works on paper
£769 $1400 €1123 Guest of infanta. Bennolio masquerade (26x21cm-10x8in) s.i. gouache ink pencil on board set of three. 29-Jun-4 Sotheby's, New York #293/R est:1500-2000
£1236 $2250 €1805 Romeo and Juliet on the way to the ball (46x56cm-18x22in) s.i.d.1923 gouache ink on board. 29-Jun-4 Sotheby's, New York #290/R est:2500-3500
£2198 $4000 €3209 Saint, act 1 (38x51cm-15x20in) i. W/C pencil. 29-Jun-4 Sotheby's, New York #292/R est:1000-1500
£7609 $14000 €11109 Living room, the Philadelphia Story (23x53cm-9x21in) s.d.1939 W/C. 10-Jun-4 Sotheby's, New York #95/R est:2000-3000

JONES, Ronald (20th C) American
£236 $425 €345 We imagine that in catastrophic situations (30x30cm-12x12in) s.d.1985 zince plate. 24-Apr-4 David Rago, Lambertville #218/R

JONES, S L (20th C) American
Sculpture
£1167 $2100 €1704 Woman's face. carved painted wood. 24-Apr-4 Slotin Folk Art, Buford #325/R est:1000-2000
£3611 $6500 €5272 Brunette's bust (36x23x23cm-14x9x9in) carved painted wood. 24-Apr-4 Slotin Folk Art, Buford #324/R est:4000-6000
£4444 $8000 €6488 Woman's bust with blue eyes (33x25x30cm-13x10x12in) carved painted wood prov. 24-Apr-4 Slotin Folk Art, Buford #323/R est:5000-8000

JONES, Samuel John Egbert (attrib) (fl.1820-1855) British
£500 $790 €725 Gentleman shooting over pointers in a moorland landscape (20x30cm-8x12in) panel. 3-Sep-3 Bonhams, Bury St Edmunds #432/R
£3000 $5100 €4380 Putting up pheasants (63x89cm-25x35in) 19-Nov-3 Sotheby's, Olympia #23/R est:3000-5000

JONES, Selwyn (?) British
£380 $703 €555 Bodorgan chapel (46x58cm-18x23in) s.verso board exhib. 13-Feb-4 Halls, Shrewsbury #801

JONES, Seth C (1853-1930) American
£360 $623 €526 Sheep at feeding time (23x38cm-9x15in) s. 10-Dec-3 Bonhams, Bury St Edmunds #546
Works on paper
£296 $550 €432 Frederick Mill (28x41cm-11x16in) W/C. 6-Mar-4 Page, Batavia #89

JONES, Steven (1959-) British
£280 $501 €409 Paddling (48x58cm-19x23in) s. board. 7-May-4 Chrystals Auctions, Isle of Man #324
£1093 $2000 €1596 Great expectations (122x81cm-48x32in) 10-Jul-4 Hindman, Chicago #249/R est:2000-3000

JONES, Thomas (1742-1803) British
£9500 $17480 €13870 Wooded river landscape with figures by a ford (29x40cm-11x16in) s. indis d. panel prov.exhib. 11-Jun-4 Christie's, London #42/R est:6000-8000

JONES, William (c.1798-1860) British
£4200 $7560 €6132 Pointers on the scent. Spaniels flushing out (20x25cm-8x10in) pair. 21-Apr-4 Christie's, Kensington #136/R est:4000-6000

JONES, William (attrib) (fl.1744-1747) Irish
£32000 $57280 €46720 Young girl in bed (82x101cm-32x40in) 14-May-4 Christie's, London #106/R est:20000-30000

JONES, William E (19th C) British
£1300 $2340 €1898 Resting on a woodland track (49x75cm-19x30in) s.d.1875. 21-Jan-4 Sotheby's, Olympia #310/R est:700-900

JONG, Antonie Gerardus de (1860-1932) Dutch
£552 $921 €800 Landscape with farm (19x32cm-7x13in) s. panel. 11-Nov-3 Vendu Notarishuis, Rotterdam #13/R
£2447 $4209 €3500 Cattle market (37x52cm-15x20in) s. 7-Dec-3 Sotheby's, Amsterdam #622/R

JONG, Erik de (1958-) Dutch
£559 $951 €800 De Processie (47x29cm-19x11in) s.d.1991 panel prov. 24-Nov-3 Glerum, Amsterdam #210/R

JONG, Germ de (1886-1967) Dutch
£1259 $2165 €1800 Mountain village (60x81cm-24x32in) s.d.1929 prov. 2-Dec-3 Sotheby's, Amsterdam #239/R est:2000-3000
£1667 $3067 €2500 View at a village (65x55cm-26x22in) s.d.1930. 8-Jun-4 Sotheby's, Amsterdam #190/R est:2500-3500
£3000 $5520 €4500 Still life with sunflowers in a blue vase (99x79cm-39x31in) s.d.1921. 9-Jun-4 Christie's, Amsterdam #12/R est:4000-6000

JONG, Hens de (1927-2003) Dutch
£503 $866 €720 Landscape with train (100x80cm-39x31in) s.d.1996 prov. 8-Dec-3 Glerum, Amsterdam #271/R
Sculpture
£2119 $3857 €3200 Couple (41x37cm-16x15in) st.sig.d.68 stoneware prov.exhib. 15-Jun-4 Christie's, Amsterdam #352/R est:700-900

JONG, Johannes de (1864-1901) Dutch
£400 $728 €600 Farm village (82x49cm-32x19in) s. 30-Jun-4 Vendue Huis, Gravenhage #163
£417 $679 €600 Cottage interior (44x56cm-17x22in) s. 29-Sep-3 Sotheby's, Amsterdam #104
£671 $1242 €1000 Street scene (65x36cm-26x14in) s. 15-Mar-4 Sotheby's, Amsterdam #82/R est:1000-1500
Works on paper
£263 $476 €400 Rowing boat by edge of water (54x36cm-21x14in) s.d.92 W/C. 19-Apr-4 Glerum, Amsterdam #118/R

JONG, Toon J de (1879-?) Dutch
£296 $536 €450 Larens interior (28x34cm-11x13in) s. panel. 19-Apr-4 Glerum, Amsterdam #116/R

JONG, W de (19th C) Dutch
£2933 $5251 €4400 Italian landscape with hunting scene. Italian landscape with riders (30x36cm-12x14in) one s. two. 17-May-4 Glerum, Amsterdam #21/R est:3000-5000

JONGE, Johan Antonio de (1864-1927) Dutch
Works on paper
£350 $601 €500 Sandy path through dunes of Schevening (24x33cm-9x13in) mono. W/C. 8-Dec-3 Glerum, Amsterdam #83/R

JONGELINGHS, Karel (?) Belgian
£541 $968 €800 Scene dans une salle de bain (49x33cm-19x13in) panel. 10-May-4 Amberes, Antwerp #281

JONGERE, M de (1912-1978) Dutch
Works on paper
£769 $1285 €1100 Maas harbour in Rotterdam (39x79cm-15x31in) mixed media. 24-Jun-3 Vendu Notarishuis, Rotterdam #244

JONGERE, Marinus de (1912-1978) Dutch
£408 $743 €600 Windmill in a polder landscape near Ridderkerk (50x70cm-20x28in) s. i.stretcher. 3-Feb-4 Christie's, Amsterdam #378
£586 $979 €850 Harbour view (39x59cm-15x23in) s. 11-Nov-3 Vendu Notarishuis, Rotterdam #7/R
£800 $1432 €1200 Harbour scene (39x79cm-15x31in) s. 11-May-4 Vendu Notarishuis, Rotterdam #82/R
£822 $1397 €1200 View of harbour with grain lifters (99x59cm-39x23in) s. 5-Nov-3 Vendue Huis, Gravenhage #185
£850 $1522 €1241 Busy Dutch harbour, probably Rotterdam (61x101cm-24x40in) s. 26-May-4 Christie's, Kensington #733/R
£880 $1628 €1285 By Schronhoven (57x97cm-22x38in) s. 16-Feb-4 Bonhams, Bath #21
£921 $1695 €1400 Harbourview (40x80cm-16x31in) s. 28-Jun-4 Sotheby's, Amsterdam #103/R
£930 $1600 €1358 Busy Dutch port (58x99cm-23x39in) s. 7-Dec-3 Freeman, Philadelphia #71 est:1500-2500
£1049 $1751 €1500 Sailing vessel in the Rotterdam harbour (40x60cm-16x24in) s. 30-Jun-3 Sotheby's, Amsterdam #210
£1053 $1905 €1600 View of Bergse Lake with Hillegersberg in the distance (50x80cm-20x31in) s. 19-Apr-4 Glerum, Amsterdam #169/R est:1000-1500
£1189 $1985 €1700 Harbour of Rotterdam (40x60cm-16x24in) s. 30-Jun-3 Sotheby's, Amsterdam #209/R
£1233 $2096 €1800 Sea port (39x80cm-15x31in) s. 5-Nov-3 Vendue Huis, Gravenhage #186/R est:1500-2000
£1277 $2132 €1800 Haulier at full steam in Rotterdam harbour (40x61cm-16x24in) s. board. 20-Oct-3 Glerum, Amsterdam #105/R est:1800-2000
£1414 $2361 €2050 Maas harbour in Rotterdam (29x49cm-11x19in) s.i.verso. 11-Nov-3 Vendu Notarishuis, Rotterdam #127/R est:1500-2000
£1497 $2724 €2200 Windmill de slaper with the village of Berkel in the distance (50x80cm-20x31in) s. i.d.November 63 stretcher. 3-Feb-4 Christie's, Amsterdam #381 est:1000-1500
£1560 $2606 €2200 Coal carrying boats in Rotterdam harbour (61x91cm-24x36in) s. 20-Oct-3 Glerum, Amsterdam #106/R est:2500-3500
£1586 $2649 €2300 Harbour view (39x59cm-15x23in) s. 11-Nov-3 Vendu Notarishuis, Rotterdam #93/R est:1000-1500
£1600 $2864 €2400 Harbour scene (39x59cm-15x23in) s. 11-May-4 Vendu Notarishuis, Rotterdam #176/R est:2000-2500
£1931 $3225 €2800 Activity in a Rotterdam harbour (59x99cm-23x39in) 11-Nov-3 Vendu Notarishuis, Rotterdam #60/R est:1800-2000
Works on paper
£345 $576 €500 Schooner in the harbour (39x48cm-15x19in) W/C. 11-Nov-3 Vendu Notarishuis, Rotterdam #64
£1067 $1909 €1600 Harbour scene (47x66cm-19x26in) s. mixed media. 11-May-4 Vendu Notarishuis, Rotterdam #178/R est:1500-2000

JONGH, Ernst de (1934-) South African
£259 $432 €378 Agapanthus (60cm-24in circular) s.d.1981 oil gold leaf on panel. 20-Oct-3 Stephan Welz, Johannesburg #802 est:3000-5000 (SA.R 3000)
£276 $461 €403 Strelitzia Regina (60cm-24in circular) s.d.1981 oil gold leaf on panel exhib. 20-Oct-3 Stephan Welz, Johannesburg #801 est:3000-5000 (SA.R 3200)
£302 $504 €441 Rainbow aspidstra (60cm-24in circular) s.d.1981 oil gold leaf on panel. 20-Oct-3 Stephan Welz, Johannesburg #803 est:3000-5000 (SA.R 3500)
£302 $504 €441 Abstract (30x30cm-12x12in) s.d.70 canvas on board. 20-Oct-3 Stephan Welz, Johannesburg #918 est:1800-2400 (SA.R 3500)

JONGH, Gabriel de (1913-) South African?
£294 $532 €429 Mountains with river in foreground (44x59cm-17x23in) s. 30-Mar-4 Cannon & Cannon, Pietermaritzburg #225/R (SA.R 3500)
£299 $509 €437 Ebb and flow, wilderness (59x90cm-23x35in) s. indis d.1978 s.i.d.on stretcher verso. 4-Nov-3 Stephan Welz, Johannesburg #603 est:3500-5000 (SA.R 3500)
£302 $504 €441 Cottage in a mountain landscape (25x30cm-10x12in) s. 20-Oct-3 Stephan Welz, Johannesburg #886 est:2200-3000 (SA.R 3500)
£336 $608 €491 Pool in a mountainous landscape (45x60cm-18x24in) s. 30-Mar-4 Stephan Welz, Johannesburg #442 est:3500-5000 (SA.R 4000)
£347 $621 €507 Lake with a grey heron (59x90cm-23x35in) s. 31-May-4 Stephan Welz, Johannesburg #127 (SA.R 4200)
£347 $621 €507 At Robertson, Cape (44x62cm-17x24in) s. 31-May-4 Stephan Welz, Johannesburg #159 (SA.R 4200)
£380 $684 €555 Cape Dutch homes with mountains beyond (46x62cm-18x24in) s. 20-Jan-4 Bonhams, Knightsbridge #191/R
£420 $761 €613 View of Hout Bay (32x47cm-13x19in) s. 30-Mar-4 Stephan Welz, Johannesburg #432/R est:3000-5000 (SA.R 5000)
£420 $761 €613 Cape homestead in mountainous landscape (44x59cm-17x23in) s. canvasboard. 30-Mar-4 Stephan Welz, Johannesburg #441 est:3000-5000 (SA.R 5000)
£462 $837 €675 Thatched cottage in the mountains (32x47cm-13x19in) s. 30-Mar-4 Stephan Welz, Johannesburg #195 est:2500-3500 (SA.R 5500)
£507 $822 €735 Cape farm in mountainous landscape (59x60cm-23x24in) s. 31-Jul-3 International Art Centre, Auckland #171/R est:1000-1500 (NZ.D 1400)
£581 $1064 €848 Untitled (45x60cm-18x24in) 6-Jul-4 Dales, Durban #3 (SA.R 6500)
£769 $1308 €1123 Blyvooruitzight, Constantia, Cape (67x100cm-26x39in) s.d.57 i.verso. 4-Nov-3 Stephan Welz, Johannesburg #679 est:4000-6000 (SA.R 9000)
£798 $1445 €1165 Bosch Kloof, Clanwilliam, C.P (67x100cm-26x39in) s. 30-Mar-4 Stephan Welz, Johannesburg #445 est:6000-10000 (SA.R 9500)
£939 $1719 €1371 Untitled (60x90cm-24x35in) 6-Jul-4 Dales, Durban #6 (SA.R 10500)
£939 $1719 €1371 Untitled (60x90cm-24x35in) 6-Jul-4 Dales, Durban #4 (SA.R 10500)
£940 $1598 €1372 Table Mountain from Melkbosstrand (60x90cm-24x35in) s. 4-Nov-3 Stephan Welz, Johannesburg #615 est:4000-6000 (SA.R 11000)
£1297 $2373 €1894 Untitled (67x100cm-26x39in) 6-Jul-4 Dales, Durban #5 (SA.R 14500)
Works on paper
£276 $461 €403 View of a river (33x48cm-13x19in) s. W/C. 20-Oct-3 Stephan Welz, Johannesburg #893 est:2000-3000 (SA.R 3200)
£336 $608 €491 Cottage in a mountainous landscape (30x40cm-12x16in) s.d.40 pencil W/C. 30-Mar-4 Stephan Welz, Johannesburg #192 est:1500-2000 (SA.R 4000)

JONGH, Ludolf de (1616-1679) Dutch
£1020 $1857 €1500 Portrait of a vicar, aged 34 in a black costume (70x61cm-28x24in) s.i.d.1667. 3-Feb-4 Christie's, Amsterdam #14/R est:1200-1600

JONGH, Oene Romkes de (1812-1896) Dutch
£1579 $2858 €2400 Figures on a path along side houses with a village in the background (43x53cm-17x21in) s. 19-Apr-4 Glerum, Amsterdam #52/R est:1500-2000
£5333 $9600 €8000 Dutch canal scene in summer. Figures on a frozen canal in a Dutch town (67x55cm-26x22in) s. pair. 21-Apr-4 Christie's, Amsterdam #14/R est:8000-12000
£10000 $18000 €15000 View of the Brouwersgracht in Amsterdam on a winter day (70x87cm-28x34in) s. 20-Apr-4 Sotheby's, Amsterdam #13/R est:10000-15000

JONGH, Tinus de (1885-1942) Dutch
£431 $720 €629 View of a river (44x62cm-17x24in) s. 20-Oct-3 Stephan Welz, Johannesburg #794 est:3000-5000 (SA.R 5000)
£450 $833 €657 Cottage in a mountainous landscape (31x51cm-12x20in) s. 13-Jan-4 Bonhams, Knightsbridge #212/R
£480 $840 €701 Sunset over the Cape Mountains (30x46cm-12x18in) s. 19-Dec-3 Mallams, Oxford #229
£537 $961 €784 Cape cottage in a mountainous landscape (22x29cm-9x11in) s. 31-May-4 Stephan Welz, Johannesburg #165 (SA.R 6500)
£572 $1053 €835 Shaded farmhouse in trees (21x30cm-8x12in) 8-Jun-4 Dales, Durban #1 (SA.R 6800)
£661 $1182 €965 Mountainous river landscape (24x29cm-9x11in) s. prov. 31-May-4 Stephan Welz, Johannesburg #207 (SA.R 8000)
£661 $1182 €965 Footpath beneath the mountain (22x30cm-9x12in) s. 25-May-4 Cannon & Cannon, Pietermaritzburg #447 (SA.R 8000)
£714 $1293 €1042 Thatched cottage in the mountains (24x30cm-9x12in) s. 30-Mar-4 Stephan Welz, Johannesburg #443 est:3500-5000 (SA.R 8500)
£743 $1330 €1085 Cape coastal landscape (23x29cm-9x11in) s. 31-May-4 Stephan Welz, Johannesburg #501 (SA.R 9000)
£812 $1380 €1186 Farmhouse dappled in afternoon shade (22x29cm-9x11in) s. canvas on board. 4-Nov-3 Stephan Welz, Johannesburg #678 est:3500-5000 (SA.R 9500)
£819 $1368 €1196 Mountain landscape with a river (25x30cm-10x12in) s. 20-Oct-3 Stephan Welz, Johannesburg #237 est:5000-7000 (SA.R 9500)
£908 $1626 €1326 Mountain landscape with a cottage amongst trees (23x29cm-9x11in) s. 31-May-4 Stephan Welz, Johannesburg #209 (SA.R 11000)
£908 $1626 €1326 Tulbach's Valley (23x29cm-9x11in) s. 31-May-4 Stephan Welz, Johannesburg #210 (SA.R 11000)
£948 $1584 €1384 Near Ceres (25x29cm-10x11in) 20-Oct-3 Stephan Welz, Johannesburg #779/R est:4000-6000 (SA.R 11000)
£1429 $2586 €2086 Cottages beyond an avenue of trees (30x49cm-12x19in) s. 30-Mar-4 Stephan Welz, Johannesburg #454/R est:6000-10000 (SA.R 17000)
£1486 $2661 €2170 Calm river at the foot of a mountain (31x50cm-12x20in) s. 31-May-4 Stephan Welz, Johannesburg #482/R est:6000-8000 (SA.R 18000)
£1486 $2661 €2170 Wilderness, Cape coast (29x48cm-11x19in) s. prov. 31-May-4 Stephan Welz, Johannesburg #503 est:5000-7000 (SA.R 18000)
£2064 $3695 €3013 Extensive mountainous landscape (32x47cm-13x19in) s. 31-May-4 Stephan Welz, Johannesburg #536/R est:12000-18000 (SA.R 25000)
£2184 $3756 €3189 Cape cottages in the late afternoon (32x47cm-13x19in) s. 3-Dec-3 Stephan Welz, Johannesburg #26/R est:10000-14000 (SA.R 24000)
£2312 $4139 €3376 Sunset in the Karoo (32x46cm-13x18in) s. i.verso. 31-May-4 Stephan Welz, Johannesburg #496/R est:15000-20000 (SA.R 28000)
£2941 $5324 €4294 Panoramic view of Clifton and the Twelve Apostles (60x90cm-24x35in) s. 30-Mar-4 Stephan Welz, Johannesburg #458/R est:18000-24000 (SA.R 35000)

JONGHE, Gustave de (1829-1893) Belgian
£3497 $5944 €5000 Jeune femme au harem (46x38cm-18x15in) s. panel. 18-Nov-3 Vanderkindere, Brussels #147/R est:3000-4500
£12000 $20640 €17520 Secret whisper (81x65cm-32x26in) s. 3-Dec-3 Christie's, London #9/R est:12000-16000
£27000 $49140 €39420 Le baiser (61x49cm-24x19in) s. panel. 15-Jun-4 Sotheby's, London #192/R est:12000-18000

JONGHE, Jan Baptiste de and VERBOECKHOVEN, Eugène (19th C) Flemish
£14085 $24366 €20000 Bord de riviere anime de cavaliers (47x65cm-19x26in) s.d.1826 panel. 14-Dec-3 St-Germain-en-Laye Encheres #21/R est:20000-22000

JONGKIND, Johan Barthold (1819-1891) Dutch
£530 $964 €800 Moulin (17x15cm-7x6in) st.sig. graphite dr. 15-Jun-4 Rossini, Paris #25
£4500 $8235 €6570 Moonlight marine, with boats and windmills (38x46cm-15x18in) s. 8-Jul-4 Duke & Son, Dorchester #284/R est:2000-4000
£10268 $18894 €15300 Bateau a quai, Hollande (33x41cm-13x16in) s. lit. 24-Mar-4 Binoche, Paris #84/R est:20000-25000
£11333 $20400 €17000 Coucher du soleil au bord du Schie (24x33cm-9x13in) s.d.1870 prov.lit. 21-Apr-4 Christie's, Amsterdam #104/R est:18000-22000
£13333 $24000 €20000 Rue de village, Hollande (19x24cm-7x9in) s.i.d.1888 panel prov.exhib.lit. 20-Apr-4 Sotheby's, Amsterdam #224/R est:20000-30000
£26573 $45175 €38000 Lyon, Fourviere vue des quais de Saone (33x52cm-13x20in) s.d.1875 lit. 30-Nov-3 Anaf, Lyon #120/R est:35000-45000
£34722 $59028 €50000 Brick et Barques a l'embouchure d'un fleuve - Antwerpen De Schelde (33x46cm-13x18in) s.d.1866 prov.exhib.lit. 28-Oct-3 Christie's, Amsterdam #134/R est:30000-50000
£40000 $72000 €60000 Scene d'hiver en Hollande (23x32cm-9x13in) s.d.1878 prov.exhib.lit. 21-Apr-4 Christie's, Amsterdam #91/R est:40000-60000
£59028 $98576 €85000 View of the hoofdpoort, Rotterdam (33x52cm-13x20in) s.d.1878 prov.exhib. 21-Oct-3 Sotheby's, Amsterdam #229/R est:35000-45000
£72000 $131040 €105120 Navire norvegien sortant du port de Honfleur (33x47cm-13x19in) s.d.1865 prov.lit. 3-Feb-4 Christie's, London #102/R est:40000-60000

Works on paper
£493 $853 €700 Bateaux a quai (16x18cm-6x7in) s. ink W/C wash. 9-Dec-3 Artcurial Briest, Paris #74
£685 $1164 €1000 Ships at dusk (31x43cm-12x17in) s. W/C lit. 6-Nov-3 Allgauer, Kempten #3294/R
£1000 $1790 €1460 Canal scene, Holland (20x29cm-8x11in) s. W/C. 25-May-4 Bonhams, Knightsbridge #297/R est:1000-1500
£1007 $1873 €1500 Moulin au bord d'une riviere, Rotterdam (24x35cm-9x14in) st.sig.i.d.58 graphite. 2-Mar-4 Artcurial Briest, Paris #3/R est:1500-2000
£1300 $2340 €1898 Views of a French town (11x17cm-4x7in) s. black chk col wash double-sided. 20-Apr-4 Sotheby's, Olympia #190/R est:600-800
£1316 $2421 €2000 Chemin des ornieres vertes (16x25cm-6x10in) d.1881 W/C graphite prov. 22-Jun-4 Ribeyre & Baron, Paris #60/R est:2000-3000
£1316 $2421 €2000 Etude de paysage (10x16cm-4x6in) st.sig. crayon W/C. 22-Jun-4 Calmels Cohen, Paris #35/R est:2000-2500
£1867 $3341 €2800 Three-master at anker in Rotterdam harbour (21x19cm-8x7in) s. W/C. 11-May-4 Vendu Notarishuis, Rotterdam #239/R est:3000-4000
£2000 $3580 €3000 Les deux peupliers derriere la ferme (24x15cm-9x6in) s. chl W/C. 16-May-4 Osenat, Fontainebleau #32/R est:3000-4000
£2119 $3878 €3200 Paysage a la porteuse de fagot et paysage (16x24cm-6x9in) s. d.1885 verso W/C double-sided. 9-Apr-4 Claude Aguttes, Neuilly #8 est:2500-3500
£2128 $3553 €3000 La route (11x17cm-4x7in) s.d.1871 chl gouache exhib. 19-Oct-3 Anaf, Lyon #174/R est:3000-3500
£2200 $3938 €3300 Un cerisier (15x24cm-6x9in) st.sig.d.11 oct 1881 chl W/C. 16-May-4 Osenat, Fontainebleau #29/R est:3000-4000
£2333 $4177 €3500 Entree de village (17x25cm-7x10in) s.d.25 feb 1880 chl W/C crayon graphite. 16-May-4 Osenat, Fontainebleau #28/R est:3000-4000
£2414 $4031 €3500 Paysage (11x18cm-4x7in) st.sig.d.26 fevrier 1886 pencil W/C. 17-Nov-3 Delorme & Bocage, Paris #109/R est:3000-4000
£2800 $5152 €4200 La route de Balbins (15x23cm-6x9in) st.sig. W/C gouache lit. 9-Jun-4 Beaussant & Lefèvre, Paris #170/R est:3000
£3133 $5609 €4700 Paysage de campagne (24x15cm-9x6in) s.d.4 nov 1881 W/C chl double-sided. 16-May-4 Osenat, Fontainebleau #31/R est:5000-6000
£3333 $5333 €4833 Houses by water (11x14cm-4x6in) s. W/C. 15-May-3 Stuker, Bern #1323/R est:2500-3000 (S.FR 7000)
£5000 $8950 €7500 Bateaux au port, Bruxelles (25x37cm-10x15in) s.d.1866 W/C. 16-May-4 Osenat, Fontainebleau #30/R est:8000-10000
£8500 $15470 €12410 Route de village (16x25cm-6x10in) st.sig.d.1879 W/C gouache chl prov. 4-Feb-4 Sotheby's, London #405/R est:7000-9000

JONGKIND, Johan Barthold (attrib) (1819-1891) Dutch
Works on paper
£1322 $2247 €1930 Dutch river landscape (22x30cm-9x12in) i.d.1869 W/C over pencil. 5-Nov-3 Dobiaschofsky, Bern #701/R est:5000 (S.FR 3000)

JONGSMA, Jacob Lucas (1893-1926) Dutch
£600 $1092 €900 House of Hoorn, Ryswyk (38x58cm-15x23in) s. 30-Jun-4 Vendue Huis, Gravenhage #332/R

JONIC, Milos (1916-) French
£231 $415 €337 West Hampton beach (57x74cm-22x29in) s. acrylic paper painted 1987. 25-Apr-4 Subastas Odalys, Caracas #16/R
£283 $520 €413 Untitled (58x77cm-23x30in) s. acrylic paper painted 1990. 28-Mar-4 Subastas Odalys, Caracas #4/R
£514 $935 €771 Untitled (60x75cm-24x30in) s. acrylic painted 1977. 21-Jun-4 Subastas Odalys, Caracas #47/R

JONK, Nic (1928-1994) Dutch
Sculpture
£1399 $2406 €2000 Getij (36cm-14in) i.d.1981 bronze. 2-Dec-3 Sotheby's, Amsterdam #286/R est:2800-3500
£1600 $2928 €2400 Nereide op Triton II (13cm-5in) s.d.1981 num.5/12 silver. 7-Jun-4 Glerum, Amsterdam #182/R est:1200-1600
£1748 $2972 €2500 Rhythm (29cm-11in) s.d.1981 bronze incl bronze base conceived 1981. 25-Nov-3 Christie's, Amsterdam #145/R est:2000-3000
£2238 $3804 €3200 Nude with drape (33cm-13in) s.d.55 bronze incl brone base conceived 1955. 25-Nov-3 Christie's, Amsterdam #133/R est:2000-3000
£2319 $3803 €3200 Exercise (15cm-6in) i.d.1953 bronze. 27-May-3 Sotheby's, Amsterdam #524/R est:2000-3000
£6643 $11294 €9500 Pacific (56cm-22in) s.d.num.Ed-7-12 bronze incl bronze base conceived 1993. 25-Nov-3 Christie's, Amsterdam #146/R est:7000-9000
£12587 $21399 €18000 Nereide op Triton II (75cm-30in) s. bronze incl bronze base edn of seven prov.lit. 25-Nov-3 Christie's, Amsterdam #141/R est:6000-8000

JONNART, L (19/20th C) ?
£1000 $1840 €1500 Lavandieres dans l'oued de M'Sila, Algerie (35x64cm-14x25in) s. 14-Jun-4 Gros & Delettrez, Paris #81/R est:1600-2000

JONNEVOLD, Carl Henrik (1856-1930) American
£294 $491 €429 In the California Sierras (13x18cm-5x7in) s. i.verso board. 17-Nov-3 Waddingtons, Toronto #8/R (C.D 650)
£531 $950 €775 In the California Sierras (13x18cm-5x7in) s. board. 10-Jan-4 Harvey Clar, Oakland #1589
£599 $1000 €875 Autumn in California (36x51cm-14x20in) s. i.verso panel. 26-Oct-3 Bonhams & Butterfields, San Francisco #6514/R
£938 $1500 €1369 Sunlight on the forest floor. s. 20-Sep-3 Harvey Clar, Oakland #1333
£2457 $4250 €3587 Marin landscape, Sunny Day (33x43cm-13x17in) s. board. 10-Dec-3 Bonhams & Butterfields, San Francisco #6169/R est:4000-6000
£2601 $4500 €3797 California Coast, Marin. Shepherd and his flock (30x36cm-12x14in) all s. one panel two canvas three. 10-Dec-3 Bonhams & Butterfields, San Francisco #6168/R est:4000-6000

JONNIAUX, Alfred (1882-1974) Belgian
£1000 $1790 €1460 Portrait of Diana Gould (39x32cm-15x13in) s. sold with a oil sketch of the same subject by another hand. 11-May-4 Sotheby's, Olympia #550/R est:300-500

JONSON, Cornelis (1593-1664) Dutch
£2800 $4760 €4088 Portrait of a lady in a black dress with white lace collar (78x65cm-31x26in) i. prov. 29-Oct-3 Bonhams, New Bond Street #61/R est:3000-4000
£4167 $7500 €6084 Portrait of lady Jane Sanwell (79x62cm-31x24in) init.d.1623 panel painted oval prov. 23-Jan-4 Christie's, Rockefeller NY #133/R est:5000-7000
£8200 $13940 €11972 Portrait of a lady (24x20cm-9x8in) copper. 27-Nov-3 Sotheby's, London #112/R est:2500-4000
£9500 $17385 €13870 Portrait of lady wearing a orange silk dress (75x61cm-30x24in) s.d.1657. 6-Jul-4 Sotheby's, Olympia #454/R est:6000-8000
£10000 $18300 €14600 Portrait of gentleman wearing black tunic (66x50cm-26x20in) s.d.1630 panel oval. 6-Jul-4 Sotheby's, Olympia #453/R est:5000-7000
£15500 $28210 €22630 Portrait of a gentleman wearing a black doublet and a white lace ruff (74x64cm-29x25in) panel. 1-Jul-4 Sotheby's, London #101/R est:4000-6000

Miniatures

£16500	$29700	€24090	Gentleman, wearing black doublet with white lace ruff (9cm-4in) s.d.1628 oil copper silver frame oval exhib.lit. 22-Apr-4 Bonhams, New Bond Street #7/R est:4000-6000

JONSON, Cornelis (attrib) (1593-1664) Dutch

Miniatures

£1700	$3060	€2482	Young gentleman, in a black doublet with small white collar (5cm-2in) oil copper silver frame oval prov.exhib.lit. 22-Apr-4 Bonhams, New Bond Street #14/R est:800-1200

JONSON, Raymond (1891-1982) American

£389	$650	€568	Oil no.3-1955, abstract (43x58cm-17x23in) s.i.d.1955 verso masonite. 25-Oct-3 David Rago, Lambertville #159
£559	$1000	€816	Oil no 3 (46x61cm-18x24in) s.i.d.1955 prov. 16-May-4 Wright, Chicago #219/R
£894	$1600	€1305	Polymer no 24 (74x43cm-29x17in) s.d.1958 s.i.d.1958 verso acrylic polymer emulsion masonite prov. 16-May-4 Wright, Chicago #220/R est:2000-3000
£4237	$7500	€6186	Oil no.3 (50x35cm-20x14in) s.i.d.1946 verso prov. 28-Apr-4 Christie's, Los Angeles #80/R est:8000-12000
£8939	$16000	€13051	Chromatic contrasts no 23, oil no 15 (102x102cm-40x40in) s.d.1947 s.i.d.1947 verso. 16-May-4 Wright, Chicago #221/R est:20000-30000
£11111	$18000	€16111	Oil no.2-1942 (102x102cm-40x40in) prov.exhib. 8-Aug-3 Barridorf, Portland #263/R est:20000-30000
£12941	$22000	€18894	Oil no.4-1942 (102x102cm-40x40in) s.i.on stretcher oil on linen prov. 9-Nov-3 Wright, Chicago #233 est:25000-35000
£15988	$27500	€23342	Growth variant no. V (96x69cm-38x27in) s.d.29 s. on stretcher prov. 3-Dec-3 Sotheby's, New York #78/R est:20000-30000

Prints

£2746	$4750	€4009	Near Abiquiu no.2 (44x57cm-17x22in) s.d.33 lithographic crayon paper. 10-Dec-3 Bonhams & Butterfields, San Francisco #6078/R est:2000-4000

Works on paper

£569	$950	€831	Polymer no.24-1958, abstract (74x43cm-29x17in) s.i.d.1958 verso polymer masonite. 25-Oct-3 David Rago, Lambertville #158

JONSON, Sven (1902-1981) Danish

£459	$739	€670	The old farm (14x55cm-6x22in) s. panel exhib. 25-Aug-3 Lilla Bukowskis, Stockholm #158 (S.KR 6000)
£513	$908	€749	Portrait of the artist friend Esaias Thoren (42x31cm-17x12in) s.i.d.25 Nov. 27-Apr-4 AB Stockholms Auktionsverk #638/R (S.KR 7000)
£523	$900	€764	Walking in the wood (27x35cm-11x14in) s. 7-Dec-3 Uppsala Auktionskammare, Uppsala #278/R (S.KR 6800)
£903	$1563	€1318	Harbour of night (22x27cm-9x11in) s. 15-Dec-3 Lilla Bukowskis, Stockholm #83/R (S.KR 11500)
£938	$1689	€1369	Shadow play I (22x27cm-9x11in) s.d.47. 26-Jan-4 Lilla Bukowskis, Stockholm #138 (S.KR 12500)
£1133	$1926	€1654	The night came in through my open window (33x41cm-13x16in) s.d.49. 4-Nov-3 Bukowskis, Stockholm #145/R est:15000-18000 (S.KR 15000)
£1185	$1908	€1730	Red porch (19x24cm-7x9in) s.d.51. 25-Aug-3 Lilla Bukowskis, Stockholm #747 est:10000-12000 (S.KR 15500)
£1208	$2054	€1764	Night picture (19x24cm-7x9in) s. 4-Nov-3 Bukowskis, Stockholm #49/R est:10000-12000 (S.KR 16000)
£1662	$2825	€2427	Tree in moonlight (22x27cm-9x11in) s.d.51. 5-Nov-3 AB Stockholms Auktionsverk #636/R est:15000-18000 (S.KR 22000)
£1662	$2825	€2427	Dawn - composition (55x46cm-22x18in) s.d.48. 5-Nov-3 AB Stockholms Auktionsverk #751/R est:25000-30000 (S.KR 22000)
£2266	$3852	€3308	Lily-of-the-valley (25x35cm-10x14in) s.d.42. 5-Nov-3 AB Stockholms Auktionsverk #744/R est:30000-35000 (S.KR 30000)
£2266	$3852	€3308	Evening by the sea (34x41cm-13x16in) s. 4-Nov-3 Bukowskis, Stockholm #144/R est:18000-20000 (S.KR 30000)
£2795	$4751	€4081	Light night (46x55cm-18x22in) s.d.47. 5-Nov-3 AB Stockholms Auktionsverk #759/R est:35000-40000 (S.KR 37000)
£3150	$5576	€4599	The rainbow (60x45cm-24x18in) s.d.40 panel. 27-Apr-4 AB Stockholms Auktionsverk #741/R est:35000-40000 (S.KR 43000)
£3191	$5743	€4659	The old Oster bridge (48x70cm-19x28in) s. prov. 26-Apr-4 Bukowskis, Stockholm #75/R est:40000-50000 (S.KR 44000)
£7326	$12967	€10696	The light night (65x80cm-26x31in) s. 27-Apr-4 AB Stockholms Auktionsverk #637/R est:40000-50000 (S.KR 100000)
£8425	$14912	€12301	The statue in a landscape (40x50cm-16x20in) s.d.32 lit. 27-Apr-4 AB Stockholms Auktionsverk #742/R est:125000-150000 (S.KR 115000)
£9063	$15408	€13232	The cathedral (133x163cm-52x64in) s.d.51. 4-Nov-3 Bukowskis, Stockholm #48/R est:80000-100000 (S.KR 120000)

Works on paper

£596	$960	€870	Vallgatan - street scene (14x12cm-6x5in) s. W/C exhib.prov. 25-Aug-3 Lilla Bukowskis, Stockholm #755 (S.KR 7800)

JONSSON, Asgrimur (1876-1958) Icelandic

£406	$747	€593	Portrait of an old man (31x25cm-12x10in) canvas on board painted c.1908. 29-Mar-4 Rasmussen, Copenhagen #231/R (D.KR 4500)
£2166	$3986	€3162	Sketch from Tjorsa (23x36cm-9x14in) init.d.1904 board prov. 29-Mar-4 Rasmussen, Copenhagen #277/R est:20000-25000 (D.KR 24000)
£2254	$3763	€3291	View towards Tingvalla and Aimannagja (26x34cm-10x13in) init.d.1903. 7-Oct-3 Rasmussen, Copenhagen #142/R est:30000-40000 (D.KR 24000)
£6769	$12455	€9883	Cattle grazing at Stigagil near Hornafjorthur, Iceland (94x128cm-37x50in) s. exhib.prov. 29-Mar-4 Rasmussen, Copenhagen #252/R est:75000-100000 (D.KR 75000)

JONSSON, Erik (1893-1950) Swedish

£1319	$2334	€1926	Street scene - from L'Hay-les-Roses, Paris (41x33cm-16x13in) s.d.19. 27-Apr-4 AB Stockholms Auktionsverk #671/R est:8000-10000 (S.KR 18000)

JONSSON, Kers Erik (19th C) Swedish

£1070	$1723	€1562	Jesus talking to the King from Capernaum (118x90cm-46x35in) cardboard. 25-Aug-3 Lilla Bukowskis, Stockholm #665 (S.KR 14000)

JONSSON, Lars (1952-) Swedish

£7761	$13891	€11331	Pair of ducks by water (89x130cm-35x51in) s.d.83 exhib. 26-May-4 AB Stockholms Auktionsverk #2111/R est:50000-60000 (S.KR 105000)

Works on paper

£1769	$3043	€2583	Blackheaded gulls and terns (16x46cm-6x18in) s.i.d.81 W/C. 3-Dec-3 AB Stockholms Auktionsverk #2481/R est:6000-8000 (S.KR 23000)

JONXIS, Jan Lodewijk (1789-1867) Dutch

Works on paper

£513	$873	€750	View of river (18x23cm-7x9in) wash. 6-Nov-3 Tajan, Paris #227

JONZEN, Basil (1913-1967) British

£1300	$2171	€1898	Patio at Hoya Grande (64x76cm-25x30in) 21-Oct-3 Gorringes, Lewes #1971

JONZEN, Karin (1914-1998) British

Sculpture

£5500	$9680	€8030	Seated female nude (49cm-19in) init, green pat. bronze. 19-May-4 Sotheby's, Olympia #164/R est:5000-7000

JOONG, Kim en (1940-) ?

£759	$1267	€1100	Composition (120x95cm-47x37in) s.d.92-98 acrylic. 17-Nov-3 Charbonneaux, Paris #210

JOOP, Wolfgang (20th C) German

Works on paper

£1301	$2250	€1899	Drawing cocktail dress (40x28cm-16x11in) s. crayon W/C gouache. 12-Dec-3 Sotheby's, New York #356/R
£1329	$2300	€1940	Drawing jeans (48x28cm-19x11in) s. crayon W/C gouache. 12-Dec-3 Sotheby's, New York #354/R
£2312	$4000	€3376	Drawing, evening dress (40x28cm-16x11in) s. crayon W/C gouache. 12-Dec-3 Sotheby's, New York #357/R
£5491	$9500	€8017	Drawing man with red sweater. gray suit (48x30cm-19x12in) s. crayon W/C gouache. 12-Dec-3 Sotheby's, New York #355/R

JOORS, Eugeen (1850-1910) Belgian

£397	$723	€600	Portrait de femme a la rose (30x25cm-12x10in) s. 15-Jun-4 Galerie Moderne, Brussels #32

JOOSTENS, Paul (1889-1960) Belgian

£2013	$3564	€3000	Untitled (94x62cm-37x24in) s.d.1955 panel. 27-Apr-4 Campo, Vlaamse Kaai #470 est:3000-3300

Works on paper

£604	$1069	€900	Grunewald (35x26cm-14x10in) s.d.1955 dr. exhib. 27-Apr-4 Campo, Vlaamse Kaai #469
£694	$1160	€1000	Poezeloes (50x63cm-20x25in) s.d.1953 dr. 21-Oct-3 Campo & Campo, Antwerp #158
£1000	$1830	€1500	Figure (34x18cm-13x7in) s.d.1957 collage. 7-Jun-4 Palais de Beaux Arts, Brussels #367/R est:2000-3000

JOPLING, Joseph Middleton (1831-1884) British

Works on paper

£600	$1122	€900	Miss Ashton seated at the piano (46x32cm-18x13in) s.d.1857 W/C. 26-Jul-4 Bonhams, Bath #3/R

JORDAENS, Hans III (1595-1643) Flemish

£9500	$16435	€13870	Israelites worshipping the golden calf (127x236cm-50x93in) 12-Dec-3 Christie's, Kensington #1/R est:7000-10000

JORDAENS, Hans III (attrib) (1595-1643) Flemish

£2000	$3580	€3000	Dance of Miriam (52x80cm-20x31in) panel prov. 17-May-4 Christie's, Amsterdam #1/R est:2500-3500

JORDAENS, Jacob (1593-1678) Flemish

£4375	$7000	€6388	Study of an Evangelist. 20-Sep-3 Harvey Clar, Oakland #1418
£16760	$30000	€24470	Pan and Syrinx (175x135cm-69x53in) painted with his studio prov.exhib.lit. 27-May-4 Sotheby's, New York #65/R est:40000-60000
£18421	$33895	€28000	Miraculous catching (51x68cm-20x27in) panel. 24-Jun-4 Tajan, Paris #11/R est:30000-40000
£37931	$62966	€55000	Painter and his model (117x96cm-46x38in) lit.exhib.prov. 1-Oct-3 Dorotheum, Vienna #123/R est:15000-20000
£100000	$183000	€146000	Portrait of the artist's daughter (74x59cm-29x23in) prov.exhib.lit. 7-Jul-4 Sotheby's, London #29/R est:80000-120000

Works on paper

£2222	$4000	€3244	Three women playing music in an interior, a dog in the foreground (14x20cm-6x8in) col chk. 22-Jan-4 Christie's, Rockefeller NY #125/R est:4000-6000
£5000	$9150	€7300	Group of penitents taking communion (22x36cm-9x14in) bears i. blk red chk pen brown ink wash prov. 8-Jul-4 Sotheby's, London #78/R est:5000-7000

JORDAENS, Jacob (after) (1593-1678) Flemish

£6419	$11297	€9500	The king drinks (78x93cm-31x37in) 22-May-4 Lempertz, Koln #1082/R est:10000

JORDAENS, Jacob (attrib) (1593-1678) Flemish

£3664	$6558	€5349	Head of an apostle (41x32cm-16x13in) paper on canvas. 13-May-4 Stuker, Bern #207 est:12000-16000 (S.FR 8500)

£22000 $37400 €32120 Head of a bearded man (48x34cm-19x13in) 29-Oct-3 Christie's, London #15/R est:6000-8000
Works on paper
£410 $750 €599 Lot and his daughters (23x27cm-9x11in) i.verso col chk. 29-Jan-4 Swann Galleries, New York #162/R
£600 $1074 €900 Garland of flowers (26x7cm-10x3in) pen ink chk wash prov. 11-May-4 Christie's, Paris #116/R
£3889 $7000 €5678 Deposition (47x57cm-19x22in) red black chk bodycol three joined sheets prov.lit. 22-Jan-4 Christie's, Rockefeller NY #124/R est:7000-10000

JORDAENS, Jacob (circle) (1593-1678) Flemish
£6081 $10703 €9000 Peasant eating porridge at a table together with mother and child (206x217cm-81x85in) prov. 18-May-4 Sotheby's, Amsterdam #53/R est:10000-15000

JORDAENS, Jacob (studio) (1593-1678) Flemish
£15278 $27500 €22306 Four Fathers of the latin church (182x243cm-72x96in) prov.exhib.lit. 22-Jan-4 Sotheby's, New York #134/R est:20000-30000

JORDAN, Colin George (1935-) Australian
£264 $414 €385 Blue black stack (137x137cm-54x54in) s.i.d.1/71 verso acrylic canvas on board. 27-Aug-3 Christie's, Sydney #669 (A.D 650)

JORDAN, Jack (1925-) American
£601 $1100 €902 Moonlight sentinel (51x41cm-20x16in) 9-Jul-4 Du Mouchelle, Detroit #2104/R
£984 $1800 €1476 Apache scouts (56x71cm-22x28in) 9-Jul-4 Du Mouchelle, Detroit #2010/R est:1500-1800
£1038 $1900 €1557 Dog soldiers (61x76cm-24x30in) 9-Jul-4 Du Mouchelle, Detroit #2013/R est:1500-2000

JORDAN, Robert (20th C) American
£221 $400 €323 Interior (58x79cm-23x31in) 16-Apr-4 American Auctioneer #224/R

JORDAN, Rudolf (1810-1887) German
£1329 $2259 €1900 Young pleasure (27x32cm-11x13in) mono. 20-Nov-3 Van Ham, Cologne #1661 est:2100

JORDAN, Wilhelm (1871-?) German
£541 $834 €850 Mediterranean coast in the last rays of sun (68x100cm-27x39in) s. 4-Sep-2 Schopman, Hamburg #253/R

JORDE, Lars (1865-1939) Norwegian
£1119 $1868 €1634 Landscape from Ringebu (42x49cm-17x19in) s. panel. 20-Oct-3 Blomqvist, Lysaker #1153/R est:10000-12000 (N.KR 13000)
£1301 $2380 €1899 Summer landscape (46x55cm-18x22in) s.d.30 panel. 7-Jun-4 Blomqvist, Oslo #369/R est:15000-18000 (N.KR 16000)
Works on paper
£604 $1003 €876 Barn (36x26cm-14x10in) s. gouache. 16-Jun-3 Blomqvist, Lysaker #1094 (N.KR 7000)

JORDON, Eithne (1954-) Irish
£484 $890 €707 Portrait of a woman, Dublin (142x122cm-56x48in) 14-Jun-4 Waddingtons, Toronto #172/R est:1000-1500 (C.D 1200)

JORGENS, Alex (?) Norwegian?
£894 $1431 €1296 By the coast (44x71cm-17x28in) s. 22-Sep-3 Blomqvist, Lysaker #1137/R (N.KR 10500)

JORGENSEN, Aksel (1883-1957) Danish
£397 $711 €580 Studio with figures (39x33cm-15x13in) s. 12-Jan-4 Rasmussen, Vejle #136/R (D.KR 4200)
£574 $930 €832 Entrance to the Dancing Saloon Aftenstjernen (51x66cm-20x26in) init.d.1908 s.i.verso. 4-Aug-3 Rasmussen, Vejle #260/R (D.KR 6000)
£724 $1296 €1057 Town scene with houses and figures (68x74cm-27x29in) s.d.1918. 10-May-4 Rasmussen, Vejle #638/R (D.KR 8000)
£753 $1279 €1099 Street scene, Osterbrogade (78x82cm-31x32in) s.d.1909. 29-Nov-3 Rasmussen, Havnen #2249 (D.KR 8000)
Works on paper
£300 $502 €438 Portrait of Mr Haahr, Amaliegade (53x31cm-21x12in) s.d.1908 pastel chk exhib. 7-Oct-3 Rasmussen, Copenhagen #357 (D.KR 3200)
£696 $1203 €1016 Composition with figures, shell and peacock (22x16cm-9x6in) s. W/C. 13-Dec-3 Blomqvist, Lysaker #1190/R (N.KR 8000)

JORGENSEN, Borge (1926-1998) Danish
Sculpture
£1502 $2509 €2193 Untitled (45cm-18in) stainless steel on granite socle. 7-Oct-3 Rasmussen, Copenhagen #212/R est:18000 (D.KR 16000)
£1690 $2823 €2467 Untitled (48cm-19in) s.d.79 stainless steel. 7-Oct-3 Rasmussen, Copenhagen #172/R est:18000 (D.KR 18000)

JORGENSEN, Christian (1860-1935) American
£5294 $9000 €7729 Cypress near Blue Water, point Lobos (66x102cm-26x40in) s.d.1929 i.verso prov. 18-Nov-3 John Moran, Pasadena #64 est:10000-15000
Works on paper
£1087 $2000 €1587 Church bells (32x21cm-13x8in) s. W/C prov. 8-Jun-4 Bonhams & Butterfields, San Francisco #4255/R est:3000-5000
£1796 $3000 €2622 Waterfall in Yosemite (30x18cm-12x7in) s. W/C. 26-Oct-3 Bonhams & Butterfields, San Francisco #6495/R
£2174 $4000 €3174 Vernal Falls, Yosemite (48x31cm-19x12in) s.d.1900 pencil W/C prov. 8-Jun-4 Bonhams & Butterfields, San Francisco #4183/R est:5000-7000
£2717 $5000 €3967 Woodlands with a stream (37x26cm-15x10in) s.d.1916 pencil W/C prov. 8-Jun-4 Bonhams & Butterfields, San Francisco #4182/R est:5000-7000
£3529 $6000 €5152 High Sierra landscape (46x28cm-18x11in) s.d. W/C. 18-Nov-3 John Moran, Pasadena #64a est:4000-5500

JORGENSEN, Jacob (1879-1948) Danish
£614 $1100 €896 Landscape (48x64cm-19x25in) s.d.1909. 12-Jan-4 Rasmussen, Vejle #125/R (D.KR 6500)

JORGENSEN, Knut (1937-1991) Norwegian
£1201 $2150 €1753 Geometry and light (46x55cm-18x22in) init.d.1969. 22-Mar-4 Blomqvist, Oslo #674/R est:20000-25000 (N.KR 15000)
£1631 $2920 €2381 Woman and man (38x30cm-15x12in) s.d.1982 panel. 25-May-4 Grev Wedels Plass, Oslo #121/R est:20000-30000 (N.KR 20000)
£2529 $4526 €3692 Composition with floating figures and bird (61x75cm-24x30in) s.indis.i.d.1982 panel. 25-May-4 Grev Wedels Plass, Oslo #122/R est:20000-30000 (N.KR 31000)
£3074 $5134 €4488 The discovery (51x70cm-20x28in) s.d.1989 s.i.d.stretcher exhib. 13-Oct-3 Blomqvist, Oslo #313/R est:40000-50000 (N.KR 36000)
£4003 $6886 €5844 Composition with squares (40x33cm-16x13in) s.d.1987 panel. 8-Dec-3 Blomqvist, Oslo #557/R est:25000-35000 (N.KR 47000)
Works on paper
£344 $575 €502 Genealogical tree (28x19cm-11x7in) s. mixed media. 20-Oct-3 Blomqvist, Lysaker #1157 (N.KR 4000)
£1201 $2150 €1753 A fable (29x43cm-11x17in) s.d.1968-69 W/C prov. 22-Mar-4 Blomqvist, Oslo #660/R est:20000-25000 (N.KR 15000)
£3843 $6418 €5611 The embrace (74x54cm-29x21in) s.d.1988 W/C. 13-Oct-3 Blomqvist, Oslo #380/R est:60000-70000 (N.KR 45000)
£11209 $20064 €16365 Alhambra (69x98cm-27x39in) s.d.1983-85 i.verso W/C. 22-Mar-4 Blomqvist, Oslo #621/R est:120000-150000 (N.KR 140000)
£17933 $29949 €26182 Alhambra (72x100cm-28x39in) s.d.78-1979 W/C. 13-Oct-3 Blomqvist, Oslo #373/R est:100000-120000 (N.KR 210000)

JORGENSEN, Sandra (20th C) American
Works on paper
£205 $375 €308 Illuminated pool II (48x64cm-19x25in) pastel. 10-Jul-4 Hindman, Chicago #251/R

JORGENSEN, Willer (20th C) Danish
£537 $983 €784 Spring landscape (79x120cm-31x47in) s. 9-Jun-4 Rasmussen, Copenhagen #1693/R (D.KR 6000)

JORGENSON, Flemming (20th C) American
£232 $425 €339 Farmland (61x74cm-24x29in) s. board. 5-Jun-4 Susanin's, Chicago #5032/R

JORI, Marcello (1951-) Italian
£634 $1052 €900 Untitled (50x70cm-20x28in) s. canvas on panel. 14-Jun-3 Meeting Art, Vercelli #72/R
Works on paper
£704 $1169 €1000 Untitled (70x70cm-28x28in) s. mixed media canvas on panel. 14-Jun-3 Meeting Art, Vercelli #523/R

JORIS, Pio (1843-1921) Italian
£3659 $6000 €5306 Italian woman in yard feeding chickens (36x56cm-14x22in) indis.sig. 4-Jun-3 Alderfer's, Hatfield #243/R est:2500-3500
Works on paper
£909 $1518 €1300 Study of man (58x43cm-23x17in) s. graphite. 24-Jun-3 Finarte Semenzato, Rome #43/R
£1127 $1949 €1600 Path in the park (30x45cm-12x18in) s. W/C card. 11-Dec-3 Christie's, Rome #17/R est:1000-1200

JORN, Asger (1914-1973) Danish
£2798 $5148 €4085 Small composition (12x26cm-5x10in) panel painted c.1940-41 lit. 29-Mar-4 Rasmussen, Copenhagen #117/R est:20000-25000 (D.KR 31000)
£6993 $11888 €10000 Head (29x28cm-11x11in) s.d.68 paper on board. 25-Nov-3 Christie's, Amsterdam #247/R est:10000-15000
£7089 $12689 €10350 At the time (40x30cm-16x12in) s.d.67 acrylic paper on canvas. 12-Jan-4 Rasmussen, Vejle #571/R est:80000-100000 (D.KR 75000)
£8057 $12891 €11683 The snowman - portrait of Borge Birch (50x40cm-20x16in) i.verso prov.exhib.lit. 17-Sep-3 Kunsthallen, Copenhagen #51/R est:125000 (D.KR 85000)
£9000 $15030 €13140 Linking class girl (35x27cm-14x11in) s. s.i.verso executed 1961 prov.exhib. 22-Oct-3 Bonhams, New Bond Street #82/R est:7000-10000
£11333 $20853 €17000 Startled doves (42x49cm-17x19in) s.i.d.1952 verso board prov.exhib.lit. 9-Jun-4 Christie's, Amsterdam #303/R est:15000-20000
£11400 $20748 €17100 Faccia di scimmia (71x51cm-28x20in) s.d.1971 acrylic paper on canvas exhib. 5-Jul-4 Le Mouel, Paris #66/R est:18000-25000
£11733 $21588 €17130 The bride (40x26cm-16x10in) s.i.d.1951 verso hardboard prov.lit. 29-Mar-4 Rasmussen, Copenhagen #107/R est:100000-125000 (D.KR 130000)
£13000 $20670 €18850 Composition (117x86cm-46x34in) s.d.68 acrylic on board. 11-Sep-3 Christie's, Kensington #230/R est:6000-8000
£16084 $27664 €23000 Composition (39x28cm-15x11in) s.d.45 oil on cardboard prov.lit. 2-Dec-3 Sotheby's, Amsterdam #141/R est:25000-35000
£19014 $33275 €27000 Les enfants s'engueulent (29x39cm-11x15in) s.d.53 prov.exhib. 16-Dec-3 Porro, Milan #33/R est:18000-22000
£23223 $37156 €33673 Composition (24x33cm-9x13in) s.d.71 lit. 17-Sep-3 Kunsthallen, Copenhagen #6/R est:200000 (D.KR 245000)
£25850 $46272 €38000 Composition (54x65cm-21x26in) s.d.67. 19-Mar-4 Millon & Associes, Paris #170/R est:20000-25000
£26000 $47320 €37960 La Strega (54x65cm-21x26in) s.d.66 i. verso prov. 5-Feb-4 Christie's, London #149/R est:30000-40000
£26601 $49211 €38837 Life (40x60cm-16x24in) s.d.52 prov.lit. 15-Mar-4 Rasmussen, Vejle #509/R est:300000 (D.KR 295000)
£28000 $46760 €40880 Untitled (66x59cm-26x23in) s.d.44 prov.lit. 21-Oct-3 Sotheby's, London #411/R est:28000-35000
£29371 $50517 €42000 No hard feelings (65x54cm-26x21in) s. s.d.66 verso prov. 2-Dec-3 Sotheby's, Amsterdam #136/R est:30000-40000

£32000 $58240 €46720 Extrovision d'une introvision (65x54cm-26x21in) s. s.i.d.68 verso prov. 5-Feb-4 Christie's, London #150/R est:30000-40000
£32864 $54883 €47981 Figurative scene (65x50cm-26x20in) s. painted c.1960-61. 7-Oct-3 Rasmussen, Copenhagen #8/R est:400000 (D.KR 350000)
£34123 $54597 €49478 Gofs-Lygybri (84x100cm-33x39in) s.d.43 prov.exhib.lit. 17-Sep-3 Kunsthallen, Copenhagen #48/R est:400000 (D.KR 360000)
£36101 $66426 €52707 Figures composition (55x70cm-22x28in) s. s.d.42 verso prov.exhib.lit. 29-Mar-4 Rasmussen, Copenhagen #119/R est:500000-600000 (D.KR 400000)
£36667 $67467 €55000 Composition (55x46cm-22x18in) s. painted c.1963-64 lit. 9-Jun-4 Christie's, Amsterdam #315/R est:45000-60000
£40000 $73600 €60000 Aspirations (60x45cm-24x18in) s. s.i.d.69 verso prov.lit. 14-Jun-4 Porro, Milan #27/R est:60000-70000
£55000 $101200 €80300 Untitled (100x75cm-39x30in) s.d.46 prov.lit. 24-Jun-4 Sotheby's, London #209/R est:60000-80000
£56338 $94085 €82253 Fine desires (60x80cm-24x31in) s. s.d.66 verso. 7-Oct-3 Rasmussen, Copenhagen #23/R est:600000-800000 (D.KR 600000)
£60000 $107400 €90000 Sanoyara (100x80cm-39x31in) s. s.i.d.58 verso. 14-May-4 Ketterer, Munich #260/R est:90000-120000
£70000 $128800 €102200 Voleur volant (116x90cm-46x35in) s. i.stretcher painted 1958 prov.lit. 25-Jun-4 Christie's, London #147/R est:60000-80000
£91080 $152103 €132977 Murder in the Alps - Les spectateurs et l'assassin de l'Urs (54x102cm-21x40in) s. painted 1953 prov.exhib.lit. 7-Oct-3 Rasmussen, Copenhagen #46/R est:1000000-1200000 (D.KR 970000)
£216607 $398556 €316246 Fantasy Fair (100x85cm-39x33in) painted 1941 prov.exhib.lit. 29-Mar-4 Rasmussen, Copenhagen #27/R est:3000000-4000000 (D.KR 2400000)
£225632 $415162 €329423 Summer land - Didaska figure composition (97x130cm-38x51in) s.d.44 exhib.prov. 29-Mar-4 Rasmussen, Copenhagen #10/R est:3000000-4000000 (D.KR 2500000)
£319249 $533146 €466104 That's obvious - Det viser seg (116x89cm-46x35in) s. s.i.d.71 verso prov.exhib.lit. 7-Oct-3 Rasmussen, Copenhagen #31/R est:3000000 (D.KR 3400000)
£436019 $697630 €632228 Titania I (100x125cm-39x49in) s.d.1940 verso exhib.lit. 17-Sep-3 Kunsthallen, Copenhagen #28/R est:5000000 (D.KR 4600000)

Sculpture

£3610 $6643 €5271 Figures (29x29cm-11x11in) s.d.1953 num.78 burned leather. 29-Mar-4 Rasmussen, Copenhagen #155/R est:30000-40000 (D.KR 40000)

Works on paper

£664 $1143 €950 Untitled (14x20cm-6x8in) s. ink wash. 2-Dec-3 Calmels Cohen, Paris #40/R
£1134 $2030 €1656 Composition with head (25x20cm-10x8in) s. Indian ink. 12-Jan-4 Rasmussen, Vejle #563/R est:6000-8000 (D.KR 12000)
£1502 $2509 €2193 Figure composition (24x31cm-9x12in) s.d.41 Indian ink. 7-Oct-3 Rasmussen, Copenhagen #71/R est:15000-20000 (D.KR 16000)
£1667 $3000 €2500 Untitled (31x24cm-12x9in) s.d.1942 ink wash. 25-Apr-4 Versailles Encheres #67 est:2500-3000
£1715 $3207 €2504 The girl in the fire (17x22cm-7x9in) s. pencil thin paper prov. 25-Feb-4 Kunsthallen, Copenhagen #51/R est:20000 (D.KR 19000)
£2000 $3340 €2920 Owl (23x18cm-9x7in) s.d.44 crayon pencil. 21-Oct-3 Sotheby's, London #410/R est:2000-3000
£2297 $3721 €3331 Composition (32x24cm-13x9in) s.d.71 mixed media. 4-Aug-3 Rasmussen, Vejle #532/R est:30000-40000 (D.KR 24000)
£2517 $4330 €3600 Untitled (32x24cm-13x9in) s. W/C ink prov. 2-Dec-3 Sotheby's, Amsterdam #321/R est:4000-6000
£2667 $4907 €4000 Composition I (2x28cm-1x11in) s.verso Chinese ink card exec.1955. 10-Jun-4 Galleria Pace, Milan #134/R est:6000
£2728 $4638 €3983 Figure composition (11x14cm-4x6in) s.d.50 W/C Indian ink. 26-Nov-3 Kunsthallen, Copenhagen #1/R est:25000 (D.KR 29000)
£3159 $5907 €4612 L'homme velu (49x41cm-19x16in) s.d.1951 study W/C pastel prov.lit. 25-Feb-4 Kunsthallen, Copenhagen #8/R est:25000 (D.KR 35000)
£3986 $6536 €5500 Untitled (36x26cm-14x10in) one s.d.44 ink two. 27-May-3 Sotheby's, Amsterdam #541/R est:3000-4000
£4061 $7473 €5929 Surrealistic composition (24x20cm-9x8in) s.i.d.37 gouache prov. 29-Mar-4 Rasmussen, Copenhagen #120/R est:25000-35000 (D.KR 45000)
£4200 $7014 €6132 Untitled (57x46cm-22x18in) s.d.68 gouache crayon over lithograph. 22-Oct-3 Bonhams, New Bond Street #80/R est:3500-4500
£6667 $11933 €10000 Untitled (37x26cm-15x10in) s.d.1944 ink dr pair. 15-May-4 Renaud, Paris #50/R
£6993 $12028 €10000 Untitled (34x25cm-13x10in) s. indis d. gouache. 2-Dec-3 Sotheby's, Amsterdam #300/R est:10000-15000

JORON, Maurice Paul (1883-1937) French

£3741 $6697 €5500 Tempting offer (54x64cm-21x25in) s. 17-Mar-4 Neumeister, Munich #492/R est:1200
£4000 $7360 €5840 Une drole d'histoire (66x81cm-26x32in) s.d.26. 23-Mar-4 Bonhams, New Bond Street #106/R est:4000-6000

JORRES, Carl (1872-1947) German

£313 $509 €450 Cornstooks on Weyerberg (59x58cm-23x23in) s. 26-Sep-3 Bolland & Marotz, Bremen #337
£407 $692 €594 Trees in bloom (70x80cm-28x31in) s.i. verso. 28-Nov-3 Zofingen, Switzerland #2610 (S.FR 900)

JORSKOV, Ivan (19th C) ?

£282 $487 €400 Marine (24x32cm-9x13in) s.d.1893. 9-Dec-3 Vanderkindere, Brussels #101

JORWITZ, Ferdinand (1897-1979) Belgian?

£382 $607 €550 Winter landscape (140x160cm-55x63in) s.d. 15-Sep-3 Bernaerts, Antwerp #716

JOS, Julien (?) ?

£710 $1300 €1037 Haying season (55x45cm-22x18in) s. 10-Jul-4 Auctions by the Bay, Alameda #404/R

JOSEPH, Albert (1868-1952) French

£3988 $6500 €5822 Printemps en Bougogne (46x61cm-18x24in) s. prov. 25-Sep-3 Christie's, Rockefeller NY #538/R est:3000-4000

JOSEPH, Jasmin (1924-) Haitian

£218 $350 €318 La nuit (58x89cm-23x35in) s. acrylic. 17-May-3 Bunte, Elgin #685

JOSEPH, Julian (1882-1964) American

£4192 $7000 €6120 Impressionist harbour scene (81x99cm-32x39in) i.verso. 19-Oct-3 Jeffery Burchard, Florida #32

JOSEPHSON, Ernst (1851-1906) Swedish

£403 $737 €588 Southern woman with long black hair and tambourine (48x38cm-19x15in) s. panel prov. 9-Jun-4 Rasmussen, Copenhagen #1624/R (D.KR 4500)
£10769 $18523 €15723 Portrait of the artist Severin Nilson (49x39cm-19x15in) s.i. prov.lit. 3-Dec-3 AB Stockholms Auktionsverk #2260/R est:60000-70000 (S.KR 140000)
£31781 $56888 €46400 Molly Magnus - portrait of a dog (26x44cm-10x17in) s.d.84 panel prov.exhib.lit. 25-May-4 Bukowskis, Stockholm #116/R est:300000-400000 (S.KR 430000)

Works on paper

£517 $926 €755 The blind Homeros (36x22cm-14x9in) s. Indian ink exhib. 26-May-4 AB Stockholms Auktionsverk #2331/R (S.KR 7000)
£615 $1058 €898 Word to Carl XII's march at Narva (37x22cm-15x9in) s. Indian ink. 7-Dec-3 Uppsala Auktionskammare, Uppsala #148/R (S.KR 8000)
£922 $1502 €1346 Emperor Augustus (23x30cm-9x12in) s. W/C. 29-Sep-3 Lilla Bukowskis, Stockholm #316 (S.KR 12000)
£1154 $1985 €1685 On the bridge (34x22cm-13x9in) s. Indian ink. 2-Dec-3 Bukowskis, Stockholm #144/R est:15000-20000 (S.KR 15000)
£1421 $2316 €2075 The beggar - from Fanrik Staal's legends (34x21cm-13x8in) s. Indian ink prov. 29-Sep-3 Lilla Bukowskis, Stockholm #315 est:12000-15000 (S.KR 18500)
£1848 $3307 €2698 Woman resting in landscape (33x20cm-13x8in) s. Indian ink. 26-May-4 AB Stockholms Auktionsverk #2248/R est:20000-25000 (S.KR 25000)
£2000 $3440 €2920 Napoleon II (34x20cm-13x8in) s. Indian ink prov. 3-Dec-3 AB Stockholms Auktionsverk #2415/R est:25000-30000 (S.KR 26000)
£2000 $3440 €2920 Richard Wagner (34x20cm-13x8in) s. pencil prov. 3-Dec-3 AB Stockholms Auktionsverk #2416/R est:25000-30000 (S.KR 26000)
£2217 $3969 €3237 Couple dancing (22x17cm-9x7in) s. Indian ink. 25-May-4 Bukowskis, Stockholm #109/R est:30000-35000 (S.KR 30000)
£2365 $4234 €3453 Song for Norway (33x19cm-13x7in) hand-written poem verso Indian ink exhib. 25-May-4 Bukowskis, Stockholm #110/R est:30000-35000 (S.KR 32000)
£2661 $4763 €3885 Figure with hat (33x20cm-13x8in) s. Indian ink. 25-May-4 Bukowskis, Stockholm #108/R est:40000-50000 (S.KR 36000)
£3548 $6350 €5180 Queen with three ladies in waiting (23x31cm-9x12in) Indian ink crayon. 25-May-4 Bukowskis, Stockholm #112/R est:50000-60000 (S.KR 48000)

JOSEPHSON, Ken (1932-) American

Photographs

£2096 $3500 €3060 Chicago (15x23cm-6x9in) s.i.verso gelatin silver print lit. 16-Oct-3 Phillips, New York #184/R est:6000-8000

JOSEPHU, Josef (1889-?) Austrian

Sculpture

£1042 $1656 €1500 The kiss (28cm-11in) i.d.1922 verso pat.bronze onyx socle. 15-Sep-3 Dorotheum, Vienna #188/R est:1600-2000

JOSIC, Mladen (1897-1972) Yugoslavian

£345 $621 €500 Composition (50x72cm-20x28in) s.d.1966. 25-Jan-4 Chayette & Cheval, Paris #224/R

JOST, Eugen (19/20th C) Swiss

Works on paper

£688 $1149 €998 Biasca (38x53cm-15x21in) s.i.d. chl W/C. 21-Jun-3 Galerie du Rhone, Sion #392/R est:1500-2000 (S.FR 1500)

JOST, Joseph (1888-?) Austrian

£7000 $11200 €10150 Tea table (64x81cm-25x32in) s. panel. 18-Sep-3 Christie's, Kensington #31/R est:6000-8000

JOTTI, Carlo (1826-1905) Italian

£625 $1031 €900 Near Molin Grasso (26x31cm-10x12in) s. cardboard. 1-Jul-3 Il Ponte, Milan #137
£5333 $9813 €8000 Scipione Castle (43x57cm-17x22in) s.i. 8-Jun-4 Sotheby's, Milan #63/R est:8000-12000

JOUANT, Jules (19th C) French

Sculpture

£3400 $6086 €5100 Femme ax pavots (42cm-17in) s. pat bronze pair. 17-May-4 Sotheby's, Paris #56/R est:4000-6000

JOUAS, Edouard Etienne (19th C) French

£1724 $2879 €2500 Printemps, les poules (76x112cm-30x44in) s. 17-Nov-3 Tajan, Paris #56 est:3000-4000

JOUAULT, Andre Gustave (1904-) French

£209 $350 €305 Children on a garden path (65cm-26in circular) s. 16-Nov-3 Bonhams & Butterfields, Los Angeles #7049/R

JOUBERT, Léon (19th C) French

£738 $1381 €1100 Coastal landscape (26x35cm-10x14in) s. i. verso panel. 24-Feb-4 Dorotheum, Vienna #215/R
£3521 $6092 €5000 Outside the town (61x76cm-24x30in) s. 13-Dec-3 Lempertz, Koln #26/R est:4000
£4670 $8500 €6818 Vetheuil (90x130cm-35x51in) s. 29-Jun-4 Arroyo, Buenos Aires #43/R est:7000

JOUBIN, Georges (1888-1983) French
£284 $474 €400 La couturiere (64x49cm-25x19in) s. oil paper laid down. 23-Jun-3 Lombrail & Teucquam, Paris #25
£340 $569 €480 Une loge. Composition. s. panel double-sided. 23-Jun-3 Lombrail & Teucquam, Paris #48
£355 $592 €500 La cousseuse (82x65cm-32x26in) s. panel. 23-Jun-3 Lombrail & Teucquam, Paris #5
£355 $592 €500 La vieille robe (146x114cm-57x45in) s. panel. 23-Jun-3 Lombrail & Teucquam, Paris #22
£355 $592 €500 Jeune femme lisant (81x65cm-32x26in) s. 23-Jun-3 Lombrail & Teucquam, Paris #23
£355 $592 €500 La vieille robe (99x81cm-39x32in) s. panel. 23-Jun-3 Lombrail & Teucquam, Paris #50
£361 $589 €520 Le lectrice (46x38cm-18x15in) s. oil paper on canvas. 29-Sep-3 Charbonneaux, Paris #236
£369 $616 €520 Nu assis (92x73cm-36x29in) s. panel. 23-Jun-3 Lombrail & Teucquam, Paris #6
£426 $711 €600 Mon atelier aux fusains (92x73cm-36x29in) s. i.verso. 23-Jun-3 Lombrail & Teucquam, Paris #4
£426 $711 €600 La robe (99x132cm-39x52in) s. 23-Jun-3 Lombrail & Teucquam, Paris #58
£426 $711 €600 Le collier (116x89cm-46x35in) s. 23-Jun-3 Lombrail & Teucquam, Paris #62
£461 $770 €650 La vieille cabane (73x92cm-29x36in) s. 23-Jun-3 Lombrail & Teucquam, Paris #14
£569 $928 €820 Femme assise (64x49cm-25x19in) s. 18-Jul-3 Charbonneaux, Paris #196
£733 $1297 €1070 The harbour in Villefranche (49x64cm-19x25in) s. i.d.1955 verso panel. 27-Apr-4 AB Stockholms Auktionsverk #1223/R (S.KR 10000)
£872 $1623 €1300 Poupee (65x55cm-26x22in) s. panel. 3-Mar-4 Tajan, Paris #186 est:1500-2000

JOUDERVILLE, Isaac de (attrib) (1612-1645) Flemish
£9239 $16537 €13489 Man wearing turban decorated with feather (48x36cm-19x14in) panel. 25-May-4 Bukowskis, Stockholm #478/R est:80000-100000 (S.KR 125000)

JOUENNE, Michel (1933-) French
£634 $1096 €900 Petits chalutiers (30x60cm-12x24in) s. painted 1967. 14-Dec-3 Eric Pillon, Calais #213/R
£1333 $2427 €2000 Foret (100x73cm-39x29in) s. 4-Jul-4 Eric Pillon, Calais #263/R
£1690 $2924 €2400 Rivage breton a maree basse (38x55cm-15x22in) s. 14-Dec-3 Eric Pillon, Calais #212/R
£3014 $5123 €4400 Paysage de Provence (90x90cm-35x35in) s. 9-Nov-3 Eric Pillon, Calais #247/R
£3154 $5646 €4700 Retour de peche (73x100cm-29x39in) s. 30-May-4 Eric Pillon, Calais #145/R

JOUENNE, Sylviane (20th C) French
£350 $594 €500 Automne joyeux (46x55cm-18x22in) 30-Nov-3 Teitgen, Nancy #96

JOUFFROY, Pierre (18th C) French
£2349 $4323 €3500 Portrait de jeune femme tenant une guirlande de fleurs (81x65cm-32x26in) s.d.1756. 24-Mar-4 Tajan, Paris #101/R est:4000-6000

JOUFFROY, Pierre (1912-2000) French
£347 $580 €500 L'automne (39x50cm-15x20in) s.d.1931. 21-Oct-3 Christie's, Paris #166/R
£1533 $2775 €2300 Nature morte a la cruche (73x92cm-29x36in) s. 3-Apr-4 Gerard, Besancon #54

JOUKOVSKI, Stanislav (1873-1944) Russian
£1875 $3131 €2738 Forest scene (29x42cm-11x17in) s. 19-Oct-3 Agra, Warsaw #34/R est:9000 (P.Z 12000)
£4483 $7486 €6500 Les Tatras (34x48cm-13x19in) s. cardboard. 17-Nov-3 Claude Boisgirard, Paris #111/R est:5000-6000
£17568 $31446 €26000 Stream in winter forest (62x74cm-24x29in) s.d.1934. 8-May-4 Bukowskis, Helsinki #458/R est:4000-5000

JOUKOVSKY, C (19/20th C) ?
£4076 $7500 €5951 Winter landscape (25x64cm-10x25in) bears sig.d.1903. 25-Jun-4 Freeman, Philadelphia #275/R est:2000-3000

JOULLAIN, François (1697-1778) French
Works on paper
£1200 $2172 €1800 Nus feminins (21x29cm-8x11in) black crayon sanguine pair. 30-Mar-4 Rossini, Paris #18 est:1500-2000

JOULLIN, Amadee (1862-1917) American
£1190 $2250 €1737 Pond in atmospheric autumn landscape (15x23cm-6x9in) s. panel prov. 17-Feb-4 John Moran, Pasadena #1/R est:1000-1500

JOUNI, Hassan (1942-) Lebanese
£1800 $3186 €2628 Cafe scene (36x76cm-14x30in) s. 29-Apr-4 Bonhams, New Bond Street #549/R est:1200-1800

JOURDAIN, F (18th C) French
Works on paper
£443 $794 €647 Allegorical figure scene with Louis XVI (38x22cm-15x9in) s.d.1788 Indian ink wash. 25-May-4 Bukowskis, Stockholm #549/R (S.KR 6000)

JOURDAIN, Roger Joseph (1845-1918) French
£642 $1072 €931 In the Orient (30x18cm-12x7in) s.i. panel. 23-Jun-3 Philippe Schuler, Zurich #3531/R (S.FR 1400)
£5500 $8800 €7975 En attendant l'audition (46x61cm-18x24in) s. 18-Sep-3 Christie's, Kensington #178/R est:6000-8000
£38000 $69160 €55480 L'entrepot a bateaux (81x111cm-32x44in) s. prov. 15-Jun-4 Sotheby's, London #188/R est:20000-30000

JOURDAN, Adolphe (1825-1889) French
£18497 $32000 €27006 Mother and child (119x91cm-47x36in) s. 13-Dec-3 Weschler, Washington #514 est:5000-10000
Works on paper
£1100 $2002 €1606 The sound of the sea (25x18cm-10x7in) s. chl. 1-Jul-4 Christie's, Kensington #420/R est:600-800

JOURDAN, Émile (1860-1931) French
£15000 $27300 €21900 Les voiliers rouges (84x115cm-33x45in) s.d.89. 3-Feb-4 Christie's, London #165/R est:15000-20000

JOURDAN, Jacques Jean Raoul (1880-1916) French
£872 $1623 €1300 Boats in the harbour (46x38cm-18x15in) s. 5-Mar-4 Wendl, Rudolstadt #3720/R

JOURDAN, Louis (1872-1948) French
£2800 $5068 €4200 Lande Bretonne (125x192cm-49x76in) s. 30-Mar-4 Rossini, Paris #1016 est:800-1200

JOURDEUIL, Louis-Adrien (1849-1907) Russian/French
£805 $1474 €1200 Coastal landscape with a windmill (36x58cm-14x23in) i. 9-Jul-4 Dawo, Saarbrucken #48/R
£1745 $3263 €2600 Fishing boats on beach (28x38cm-11x15in) s.i. panel. 24-Feb-4 Dorotheum, Vienna #34/R est:2800-3400

JOURNIAC, Michel (1943-) French
£1000 $1800 €1500 Self-portrait (130x97cm-51x38in) s. d.1965 verso. 24-Apr-4 Cornette de St.Cyr, Paris #575/R est:1500

JOURNOD, Monique (1935-) French
£599 $1036 €850 Coupe d'anemones (46x55cm-18x22in) s. 14-Dec-3 Eric Pillon, Calais #201/R
£664 $1109 €950 Vase de fleurs des champs (65x81cm-26x32in) s. 29-Jun-3 Eric Pillon, Calais #226/R

JOURTAL (19th C) ?
£1329 $2259 €1900 Atelier de Cormon (17x23cm-7x9in) s.d.1887 verso panel. 1-Dec-3 Palais de Beaux Arts, Brussels #354/R est:2000-3000

JOUVE (20th C) French
Works on paper
£2378 $4090 €3400 Panthere assise (32x24cm-13x9in) s. dr. 3-Dec-3 Coutau Begarie, Paris #222/R est:2300-2500

JOUVE, Paul (1880-1973) French
£1448 $2650 €2100 Couple d'aigles (43x54cm-17x21in) s. panel. 31-Jan-4 Gerard, Besancon #49
£2727 $4636 €3900 Panthere (15x23cm-6x9in) s. oil ink wash crayon. 27-Nov-3 Claude Aguttes, Neuilly #60 est:3000-3500
£3497 $5839 €5000 Notre-Dame de Paris (62x66cm-24x26in) s. 24-Jun-3 Millon & Associes, Paris #4/R est:6000-7000
£11189 $19245 €16000 Elephants dans les marais (66x96cm-26x38in) s. oil paper on panel exhib.lit. 3-Dec-3 Oger, Dumont, Paris #35/R est:10000-12000
£16484 $30000 €24067 Study of a tiger (107x71cm-42x28in) s. oil gouache chl paper on paper board prov. 15-Jun-4 Christie's, Rockefeller NY #156/R est:30000-50000
£142857 $260000 €208571 Miroir aure boussois (193x254cm-76x100in) s. nine glass panel exhib.lit. 15-Jun-4 Christie's, Rockefeller NY #157/R est:150000-250000
Prints
£2400 $3984 €3504 Leopard with a snake (49x70cm-19x28in) etching. 30-Sep-3 Sotheby's, London #409/R est:2500-3500
£5278 $8603 €7600 La panthere (62x78cm-24x31in) s.num.6/52 lithograph. 18-Jul-3 Feletin, Province #97
Sculpture
£1333 $2453 €2000 Mouflon couche (20x26cm-8x10in) s.d.04 brown pat. bronze. 10-Jun-4 Camard, Paris #25/R est:2000-3000
£3276 $5995 €4750 Le singe et l'idole (16cm-6in) s. black green pat bronze marble socle Cast Alexis Rudier. 31-Jan-4 Gerard, Besancon #245
£17931 $29766 €26000 Lion marchant (72cm-28in) s.i. pat bronze. 2-Oct-3 Sotheby's, Paris #150/R est:30000
Works on paper
£1867 $3341 €2800 Panthere assise (32x24cm-13x9in) s. 12-May-4 Coutau Begarie, Paris #185/R est:2300-2500
£2215 $3920 €3300 Lionne couchee (30x24cm-12x9in) s. Chinese ink crayon stump. 27-Apr-4 Claude Aguttes, Neuilly #44/R est:4000
£2318 $4242 €3500 Tigre s'abreuvant (40x50cm-16x20in) s. chl. 7-Apr-4 Fraysse & Associes, Paris #7/R est:1500-2000
£2587 $4399 €3700 Panthere couchee (21x33cm-8x13in) s. Chinese ink stump. 27-Nov-3 Claude Aguttes, Neuilly #59 est:3000-3500
£6667 $11933 €10000 Deux lionnes (44x93cm-17x37in) s.i. chl. 17-May-4 Sotheby's, Paris #3/R est:10000-12000
£7500 $12450 €10950 Black jaguar (102x72cm-40x28in) s. chl gold leaf surround. 30-Sep-3 Sotheby's, London #406/R est:10000-15000

JOUVENET, Jean Baptiste (1644-1717) French
Works on paper
£1311 $2400 €1914 Deposition (37x26cm-15x10in) brush brown ink wash. 29-Jan-4 Swann Galleries, New York #208/R est:3000-5000

JOUVENET, Jean Baptiste (attrib) (1644-1717) French
£3220 $5860 €4860 Saint Paul (73x59cm-29x23in) 21-Jun-4 Tajan, Paris #90/R est:5000-7000
Works on paper
£1133 $2051 €1700 Academie d'homme debout (43x27cm-17x11in) i. sanguine. 30-Mar-4 Rossini, Paris #9/R est:1500-2000

JOUY, Joseph Nicolas (1809-?) French
£1067 $1931 €1600 Portrait de Michelet (65x54cm-26x21in) s.d.1832 exhib. 30-Mar-4 Rossini, Paris #818/R est:700-1000

JOVANOVIC, Pajo (1859-1913) Yugoslavian
£52632 $96842 €80000 The fencing hour (100x150cm-39x59in) s. 22-Jun-4 Wiener Kunst Auktionen, Vienna #16/R est:25000
£66000 $120120 €96360 The resting sentinel (74x51cm-29x20in) s. 15-Jun-4 Sotheby's, London #126/R est:25000-35000

JOVENEAU, Jean (1888-?) French
£300 $483 €438 French landscape (53x64cm-21x25in) s. 17-Aug-3 Lots Road Auctions, London #331
£465 $800 €679 Gueridon a la carte de France (61x91cm-24x36in) s. 6-Dec-3 Neal Auction Company, New Orleans #1071/R

JOVER CASANOVA, Francisco (c.1830-1890) Spanish
£1448 $2607 €2100 Female toreador (56x46cm-22x18in) s.d.1875 oval. 26-Jan-4 Ansorena, Madrid #242/R est:2100

JOVINGE, Torsten (1898-1936) Swedish
£11240 $20232 €16410 The Town Hall, Stockholm (62x51cm-24x20in) s. 26-Apr-4 Bukowskis, Stockholm #118/R est:175000-200000 (S.KR 155000)

JOWETT, Frank B (fl.1915-1938) British
Works on paper
£500 $915 €730 Figures and cattle on a path in an extensive landscape (26x39cm-10x15in) s. W/C. 7-Apr-4 Woolley & Wallis, Salisbury #123/R

JOWETT, Percy Hague (1882-1955) British
£500 $885 €730 Tress by the Seine (56x81cm-22x32in) s. 29-Apr-4 Gorringes, Lewes #2472
£1100 $1826 €1606 Holy Family. Virgin Mary and an angel (41x46cm-16x18in) s.d.1915 board pair. 1-Oct-3 Woolley & Wallis, Salisbury #336/R est:600-800

JOY, George William (1844-1925) British
£44000 $69080 €63800 Drummer by of the Royal Scots Dragoons (180x107cm-71x42in) s. 27-Aug-3 Sotheby's, London #910/R est:10000-15000
£46000 $73600 €67160 First Union Jack (178x142cm-70x56in) s.d.1891 prov.exhib. 16-Sep-3 Bonhams, New Bond Street #72/R est:40000-60000

JOY, John (1925-) Canadian
£180 $329 €263 Ossington Avenue (20x15cm-8x6in) s. acrylic board. 1-Jun-4 Joyner Waddington, Toronto #538 (C.D 450)
£201 $345 €293 Sullivan St (20x25cm-8x10in) s. acrylic board. 2-Dec-3 Joyner Waddington, Toronto #543 (C.D 450)
£245 $422 €358 Kensington Ave (25x20cm-10x8in) s.d.00 board. 2-Dec-3 Joyner Waddington, Toronto #544 (C.D 550)
£280 $512 €409 Pape Avenue (27x37cm-11x15in) s.d.86 acrylic board. 1-Jun-4 Joyner Waddington, Toronto #521 (C.D 700)
£313 $522 €454 Manning Avenue (23x30cm-9x12in) s. i.verso board. 17-Jun-3 Pinneys, Montreal #163 (C.D 700)
£446 $768 €651 Bellvue Avenue (40x50cm-16x20in) s. acrylic board prov. 2-Dec-3 Joyner Waddington, Toronto #540 (C.D 1000)

JOY, William (1803-1867) British
Works on paper
£490 $842 €700 Trois mats dans la rade (55x29cm-22x11in) s.d.1859 W/C. 5-Dec-3 Gros & Delettrez, Paris #44
£2200 $3652 €3212 Dutch fishing boats at anchor off an estuary (17x26cm-7x10in) W/C. 1-Oct-3 Bonhams, Knightsbridge #74/R est:1500-2000
£2200 $3520 €3212 HMS Narcissus shortening sail ahead of a squall (27x39cm-11x15in) W/C htd white. 16-Sep-3 Bonhams, New Bond Street #37/R est:2000-3000
£3000 $4800 €4380 HMS London at anchor at Spithead (30x42cm-12x17in) s.d.1857 W/C htd white. 16-Sep-3 Bonhams, New Bond Street #39/R est:3000-5000
£3000 $4800 €4380 HMS Ganges underway in Spithead (29x42cm-11x17in) s.d.1857 W/C. 16-Sep-3 Bonhams, New Bond Street #65/R est:3000-5000
£3200 $5824 €4672 Still day, two warships at anchor with much other shipping (28x38cm-11x15in) s.d.1857 W/C. 15-Jun-4 David Lay, Penzance #101/R est:2500-3500
£3500 $6370 €5110 Line of battleship and frigate getting under way, sunrise bright morning (25x36cm-10x14in) s.d.1854 W/C. 15-Jun-4 David Lay, Penzance #100/R est:2500-3500
£5000 $8650 €7300 British war ships at anchor and other shipping in a calm anchorage (28x39cm-11x15in) s.d.1857 W/C. 11-Dec-3 Lane, Penzance #65/R est:4500-5500
£5000 $8650 €7300 British war ships and other shipping under sail in a stiff breeze (26x36cm-10x14in) s.d.1854 W/C. 11-Dec-3 Lane, Penzance #66/R est:4500-5500

JOY, William (attrib) (1803-1867) British
Works on paper
£337 $550 €492 Vessels on blustery seas (23x28cm-9x11in) W/C ink with tooling prov. 19-Jul-3 Skinner, Boston #390

JOY, William and John Cantiloe (19th C) British
Works on paper
£700 $1253 €1022 Men-o'war running past the anchorage (21x29cm-8x11in) pencil brown ink W/C. 26-May-4 Christie's, Kensington #378/R
£769 $1400 €1154 Man overboard (36x51cm-14x20in) W/C exec. c.1850. 16-Jun-4 Wolf's, New York #486554/R
£2400 $4008 €3504 Man-o-war and other shipping in an estuary (24x34cm-9x13in) W/C. 21-Oct-3 Sworder & Son, Bishops Stortford #308/R est:1500-2500
£4000 $6400 €5840 HM ships Duke of Wellington and Queen at the naval review at Spithead, 1853 (22x37cm-9x15in) W/C htd white arched top. 16-Sep-3 Bonhams, New Bond Street #35/R est:4000-6000
£4500 $8280 €6570 Frigate and other shipping off a coast (11x17cm-4x7in) s.d.1853 W/C. 11-Jun-4 Keys, Aylsham #591/R est:3500-4500

JOYA, Jose (1931-1995) Philippino
£1562 $2609 €2281 Abstract (36x58cm-14x23in) s.d.Dec 10 1974 paper on board. 12-Oct-3 Sotheby's, Singapore #57/R est:4500-6500 (S.D 4500)
£1806 $2890 €2637 Blue lake (37x57cm-15x22in) s.d.July 30 1974 s.i.d.verso oil paper on board. 18-May-3 Sotheby's, Singapore #76/R est:4500-6500 (S.D 5040)
£3268 $5915 €4771 Four seasons (23x39cm-9x15in) s.d.1960 oil on paper set of four. 4-Apr-4 Sotheby's, Singapore #96/R est:7000-9000 (S.D 10000)
£3871 $6194 €5652 Awit sa umaga (76x76cm-30x30in) s.d.1976 s.i.d.1976 verso. 18-May-3 Sotheby's, Singapore #93/R est:6500-8500 (S.D 10800)
£6452 $10323 €9420 Untitled (84x114cm-33x45in) s.d.61. 18-May-3 Sotheby's, Singapore #68/R est:15000-25000 (S.D 18000)
£10870 $16848 €15870 Abstract (83x121cm-33x48in) s.d.1963 board. 6-Oct-2 Sotheby's, Singapore #69/R est:12000-20000 (S.D 30000)
£15914 $25462 €23234 Untitled (116x152cm-46x60in) s.d.59 canvas on board. 18-May-3 Sotheby's, Singapore #79/R est:22000-28000 (S.D 44400)

JOYANT, Jules Romain (1803-1854) French
£1119 $1869 €1600 Vue de ruelle a Venise (22x15cm-9x6in) panel. 12-Oct-3 Salle des ventes Pillet, Lyon la Foret #41/R
£4384 $6882 €6400 Vue du pont du Rialto a Venise (41x33cm-16x13in) s. 20-Apr-3 Deauville, France #74/R est:5000-6000
£6757 $11892 €10000 Venice, Campo SS. Giovanni and Paolo (46x65cm-18x26in) s.d.1838. 18-May-4 Sotheby's, Milan #531/R est:6000-8000

JOYCE, Marshall W (1912-1998) American
£617 $1000 €901 Winter landscape near water (20x24cm-8x9in) s. board. 31-Jul-3 Eldred, East Dennis #1176a/R

JOYNER, M (19th C) British
£1600 $2864 €2336 Sheltering from the approaching storm (62x92cm-24x36in) s. 27-May-4 Christie's, Kensington #201/R est:2000-3000

JU JEONG (20th C) Chinese
£1242 $2198 €1850 L'amour (100cm-39in circular) s.verso acrylic. 29-Apr-4 Claude Aguttes, Neuilly #254 est:1900-2000

JU LIAN (1828-1904) Chinese
Works on paper
£927 $1547 €1353 Birds (18x54cm-7x21in) s.i.d.1876 ink col fan. 27-Oct-3 Sotheby's, Hong Kong #276/R est:15000-20000 (HK.D 12000)
£2471 $4127 €3608 Two fish (18x54cm-7x21in) s.i. ink col hanging scroll fan painting. 27-Oct-3 Sotheby's, Hong Kong #275/R est:20000-30000 (HK.D 32000)

JU MING (1938-) Chinese
Sculpture
£2317 $3869 €3383 Musician (14cm-6in) s.d.1982 pottery pair. 27-Oct-3 Sotheby's, Hong Kong #372/R est:30000-50000 (HK.D 30000)
£13127 $21923 €19165 Wu song (49cm-19in) carved sig.d.82 camphor wood executed 1982. 26-Oct-3 Christie's, Hong Kong #154/R est:100000-150000 (HK.D 170000)
£14225 $25605 €20769 Taiji arch (24x19cm-9x7in) s.d.92 camphor wood. 25-Apr-4 Christie's, Hong Kong #725/R est:200000-300000 (HK.D 200000)
£24893 $44808 €36344 Thrust (49cm-19in) s.d.82 champhor wood. 25-Apr-4 Christie's, Hong Kong #724/R est:250000-300000 (HK.D 350000)
£24893 $44808 €36344 Taichi (60x50x38cm-24x20x15in) s.d.1989 wood. 26-Apr-4 Sotheby's, Hong Kong #522/R est:350000-450000 (HK.D 350000)
£29344 $49004 €42842 Taichi (42x66x30cm-17x26x12in) s.d.1989 wood. 27-Oct-3 Sotheby's, Hong Kong #369/R est:350000-450000 (HK.D 380000)
£32432 $54162 €47351 Taiji - preparation for underarm strike (65cm-26in) carved sig. camphor wood executed 2002. 26-Oct-3 Christie's, Hong Kong #152/R est:300000-400000 (HK.D 420000)
£35562 $64011 €51921 Taichi arch (71x108x35cm-28x43x14in) s.d.1986 num.17/20 bronze. 26-Apr-4 Sotheby's, Hong Kong #527/R est:350000-500000 (HK.D 500000)
£50193 $83822 €73282 Taiji shadow boxing (76cm-30in) s.d.91 num.16/20 green pat. bronze pair. 26-Oct-3 Christie's, Hong Kong #153/R est:300000-400000 (HK.D 650000)
£85349 $153627 €124610 Thrust (99cm-39in) s.d.91 camphor wood. 25-Apr-4 Christie's, Hong Kong #723/R est:600000-800000 (HK.D 1200000)

JUAN DE BORGONA (elder-attrib) (c.1470-1535) Spanish
£4276 $7868 €6500 Arrestation de Saint-Etienne (100x71cm-39x28in) panel prov. 24-Jun-4 Christie's, Paris #11/R est:10000-15000

JUAN, Ronaldo de (1930-) Argentinian
£280 $476 €400 Composition (100x75cm-39x30in) s. oil paper. 27-Nov-3 Calmels Cohen, Paris #108/R

JUCHSER, Hans (1894-1977) ?
£2000 $3600 €3000 Portrait of B Z (80x60cm-31x24in) s.d. s.i.d. verso panel. 24-Apr-4 Dr Lehr, Berlin #211/R est:4000
£4533 $8160 €6800 Small figure lying on white cushion (42x56cm-17x22in) s.d. s.i.d. verso panel. 24-Apr-4 Dr Lehr, Berlin #212/R est:5000
£5208 $8698 €7500 Garden with mallow and larkspur (64x80cm-25x31in) s.d. double-sided. 25-Oct-3 Dr Lehr, Berlin #251/R est:8000

JUDD, Deforrest (1916-1993) American
£1198 $2000 €1749 Pier, Port Lavaca (76x122cm-30x48in) acrylic masonite. 18-Oct-3 David Dike, Dallas #94/R est:2000-4000
£1647 $2750 €2405 Cholia (122x91cm-48x36in) masonite. 18-Oct-3 David Dike, Dallas #96/R est:2000-4000

JUDD, Donald (1928-1994) American
£18000 $32760 €26280 Woodblock (66x41cm-26x16in) s.d.2.76 verso wood prov. 5-Feb-4 Christie's, London #181/R est:18000-22000
Prints
£2270 $4200 €3314 Untitled, S 296 (60x80cm-24x31in) s.num.13/25 verso black red woodcut. 12-Feb-4 Christie's, Rockefeller NY #107/R est:3000-5000
£2331 $3800 €3403 Untitled (60x80cm-24x31in) s.verso num.PP 3/4 woodcut on Japanese wove Toso Hanga. 24-Sep-3 Christie's, Rockefeller NY #267/R est:3000-5000
£2432 $4500 €3551 Untitled, S 295 (60x80cm-24x31in) s.num.13/25 verso col woodcut. 12-Feb-4 Christie's, Rockefeller NY #106/R est:3000-5000
£2454 $4000 €3583 Untitled (60x80cm-24x31in) s.verso num.PP 3/4 woodcut Japanese wove Toso Hanga. 24-Sep-3 Christie's, Rockefeller NY #266/R est:3000-5000
£3889 $7000 €5678 Untitled (30x30cm-12x12in) s.i.d.1969 woodblock. 24-Apr-4 David Rago, Lambertville #386/R est:800-1200
£12000 $20640 €17520 Untitled (85x67cm-33x26in) s.i.verso black woodcuts ten portfolio. 4-Dec-3 Sotheby's, London #245/R est:8000-10000
Sculpture
£2800 $5124 €4200 Untitled (6x51x61cm-2x20x24in) s.i. steel. 4-Jun-4 Lempertz, Koln #230/R est:2000-2500
£6936 $12000 €10127 Untitled (7x51x61cm-3x20x24in) folded stainless steel one of 200 sold with proofs prov. 10-Dec-3 Phillips, New York #404/R est:3000-4000
£8696 $16000 €12696 Untitled (7x51x61cm-3x20x24in) stainless steel edition of 200. 10-Jun-4 Phillips, New York #404/R est:10000-15000
£10615 $19000 €15498 Untitled (10x58x69cm-4x23x27in) s.d.1971 num. of 50 stainless steel plexiglas prov. 14-May-4 Phillips, New York #249/R est:10000-15000
£18000 $33120 €26280 Folded meters (100x100x1cm-39x39x0in) st.sig. d.1982 num 81-101.54 verso cold rolled steel prov.lit. 24-Jun-4 Sotheby's, London #148/R est:8000-12000
£38000 $63460 €55480 Untitled, Lehni 85-047/100 (30x60x30cm-12x24x12in) st.sig.num.85-047/100 verso pulverized aluminium prov. 22-Oct-3 Christie's, London #71/R est:40000-60000
£41916 $70000 €61197 Untitled (29x60x30cm-11x24x12in) s.d.89 pulver aluminum prov. 13-Nov-3 Sotheby's, New York #517/R est:35000-45000
£74850 $125000 €109281 Desk Set (84x147x76cm-33x58x30in) st.JUDD d.1989 Douglas fir one desk two chairs prov. 12-Nov-3 Christie's, Rockefeller NY #601/R est:70000-90000
£83832 $140000 €122395 Untitled (15x69x61cm-6x27x24in) brass green plexiglass exec 1969 prov.exhib.lit. 12-Nov-3 Christie's, Rockefeller NY #594/R est:120000-180000
£94972 $170000 €138659 Untitled (100x100x50cm-39x39x20in) Cor-ten steel exec 1989 prov.exhib. 13-May-4 Sotheby's, New York #194/R est:140000-180000
£100559 $180000 €146816 Untitled (25x100x25cm-10x39x10in) st.sig.d.91 num.91-127 aluminium orange Plexiglas prov. 13-May-4 Sotheby's, New York #188/R est:80000-100000
£101796 $170000 €148622 Untitled (16x69x62cm-6x27x24in) s.d.1965 galvanized iron prov.exhib.lit. 13-Nov-3 Phillips, New York #29/R est:150000-200000
£143713 $240000 €209821 Untitled (15x67x61cm-6x26x24in) blue lacquer galvanized iron prov.exhib.lit. 13-Nov-3 Sotheby's, New York #565/R est:200000-300000
£153631 $275000 €224301 Untitled, 89-09 lascaux (30x180x30cm-12x71x12in) st.sig.d.89-90 verso pulver aluminum galvanised iron prov.exhib. 12-May-4 Christie's, Rockefeller NY #410/R est:150000-200000
£170000 $312800 €248200 Untitled (15x69x61cm-6x27x24in) s.d.68 stainless steel amber plexiglas prov.exhib.lit. 24-Jun-4 Christie's, London #17/R est:80000-120000
£178771 $320000 €261006 Untitled (13x102x23cm-5x40x9in) blue lacquer galvanised steel exec 1967-69 prov.lit. 12-May-4 Sotheby's, New York #53/R est:180000-250000
£209581 $350000 €305988 Untitled (13x65x22cm-5x26x9in) copper executed September 23 1970 prov.lit. 12-Nov-3 Sotheby's, New York #48/R est:300000-400000
£251397 $450000 €367040 Untitled (15x281x15cm-6x111x6in) st.sig.d.90-06 interior black anodised aluminium prov. 12-May-4 Sotheby's, New York #49/R est:400000-600000
£380000 $699200 €554800 Untitled - DSS225 (16x281x15cm-6x111x6in) clear anodized and purple anodized aluminum executed 1970. 24-Jun-4 Christie's, London #18/R est:400000-600000
£391061 $700000 €570949 Untitled - DSS 107 (13x175x23cm-5x69x9in) blue lacquer on galvanised iron exec 1967 prov.exhib.lit. 11-May-4 Christie's, Rockefeller NY #43/R est:700000-900000
£558659 $1000000 €815642 Untitled. galvanised iron blue plexiglass 10 parts exec 1980 prov.exhib. 12-May-4 Sotheby's, New York #13/R est:800000-1200000
Works on paper
£5100 $9282 €7446 Untitled (34x48cm-13x19in) init.d.12 Feb 87 pencil prov.exhib. 4-Feb-4 Sotheby's, Olympia #11/R est:3000-4000
£8939 $16000 €13051 Untitled (58x78cm-23x31in) s.d.74 pencil prov. 13-May-4 Sotheby's, New York #172/R est:10000-15000
£10056 $18000 €14682 Untitled (58x78cm-23x31in) s.d.74 pencil prov. 13-May-4 Sotheby's, New York #173/R est:10000-15000
£391061 $700000 €570949 Untitled - DSS 18 (123x153cm-48x60in) liquitex sand masonite exec 1961 prov.exhib.lit. 11-May-4 Christie's, Rockefeller NY #52/R est:350000-450000

JUDE, Mervyn (20th C) British
£1600 $2720 €2336 His last Grand National, Red Rum at Bechers Brook (60x85cm-24x33in) s.d.78 s.i.verso. 19-Nov-3 Sotheby's, Olympia #134/R est:800-1200

JUDEICH, Therese (c.1831-1914) German
£6711 $12013 €10000 The Werner Chapel in Oberwesel on the Rhein (57x76cm-22x30in) s.d.1857. 27-May-4 Dorotheum, Vienna #163/R est:10000-12000

JUDERSLEBEN, Georg Arthur (20th C) German?
£294 $499 €420 Blossoming orchard (55x66cm-22x26in) s. 28-Nov-3 Wendl, Rudolstadt #4023/R

JUDKIN, Rev Thomas James (1788-1871) British
£2000 $3160 €2900 Stoke Poges (71x91cm-28x36in) s.i.d.1847. 4-Sep-3 Christie's, Kensington #138/R est:2000-3000

JUDSON, William Lees (1842-1928) American
£516 $950 €753 Pasadena cottage (20x36cm-8x14in) s. canvas on board. 13-Jun-4 Bonhams & Butterfields, Los Angeles #7045/R est:1000-1500
£1357 $2267 €1981 Women and children on a lakeside path (51x87cm-20x34in) s. 17-Nov-3 Waddingtons, Toronto #10/R est:1000-1500 (C.D 3000)
£2273 $4000 €3319 Coastal scene (61x140cm-24x55in) s.d.1881. 23-May-4 Treadway Gallery, Cincinnati #518/R est:7000-9000
£2500 $4250 €3650 Perris country (15x25cm-6x10in) s. i.verso canvas on canvas prov. 18-Nov-3 John Moran, Pasadena #120 est:2500-3500

JUEL, Jens (1745-1802) Danish
£9346 $14766 €13552 Portrait of a blond girl with blue eyes (36x29cm-14x11in) oval. 2-Sep-3 Rasmussen, Copenhagen #1567/R est:100000-125000 (D.KR 100000)
£24367 $41912 €35576 Sigismund Ludvig Schulin as a child (73x57cm-29x22in) oval prov.exhib.lit. 2-Dec-3 Kunsthallen, Copenhagen #544/R est:200000 (D.KR 260000)
£51925 $95022 €75811 Portrait of Frederich von der Maase and his wife Vilhelmine (69x50cm-27x20in) oval pair painted c.1800. 9-Jun-4 Rasmussen, Copenhagen #1433/R est:400000 (D.KR 580000)
Works on paper
£806 $1474 €1177 Portrait of Jacob Damkier (37x27cm-15x11in) i. pastel. 9-Jun-4 Rasmussen, Copenhagen #2067/R (D.KR 9000)
£4537 $7849 €6624 Sophie Hedvig Adeler as a child (30x24cm-12x9in) pastel oval prov. 9-Dec-3 Rasmussen, Copenhagen #1215/R est:25000 (D.KR 48000)

JUEL, Jens (attrib) (1745-1802) Danish
Works on paper
£797 $1370 €1164 Portrait of a gentleman (34x26cm-13x10in) gouache prov. 3-Dec-3 Museumsbygningen, Copenhagen #181/R (D.KR 8500)
£984 $1693 €1437 Portrait of gentleman (39x27cm-15x11in) pastel. 2-Dec-3 Kunsthallen, Copenhagen #548/R (D.KR 10500)

JUEL-SOOP, Brita (20th C) Swedish
£351 $657 €512 Portrait of King Maij and other figures (84x95cm-33x37in) s.d.1967 verso. 29-Feb-4 Uppsala Auktionskammare, Uppsala #92 (S.KR 4800)

JUELL, Tore (1942-) Norwegian
£412 $759 €602 Landscape by the sea (65x100cm-26x39in) s. 29-Mar-4 Blomqvist, Lysaker #1155/R (N.KR 5200)

JUELL-GLEDITSCH, Rolf (1892-1984) Norwegian
£691 $1272 €1009 Ljungan near Torpshammar (103x134cm-41x53in) s.d.1931 s.i.d.stretcher exhib. 10-Jun-4 Grev Wedels Plass, Oslo #176/R (N.KR 8500)
£1334 $2229 €1948 View from Roros (70x100cm-28x39in) s. 17-Nov-3 Blomqvist, Lysaker #1076/R est:12000-15000 (N.KR 16000)

JUGADAI, Daisy Napaltjarri (c.1955-) Australian
Works on paper
£3320 $6209 €4980 Ulampawurru ikuntji (151x198cm-59x78in) bears name.verso synthetic polymer paint linen prov. 26-Jul-4 Sotheby's, Melbourne #148/R est:10000-15000 (A.D 8500)

JUGADAI, Molly (1953-) Australian
Works on paper
£471 $842 €688 Untitled (76x92cm-30x36in) synthetic polymer paint canvas exec 2002. 25-May-4 Lawson Menzies, Sydney #104/R (A.D 1200)

JUGADAI, Naputa Nungala (c.1933-) Australian
Works on paper
£1647 $2948 €2405 Salt lake and Hills Kintore (124x153cm-49x60in) synthetic polymer paint canvas prov. 25-May-4 Lawson Menzies, Sydney #106/R est:6000-8000 (A.D 4200)
£1758 $3287 €2637 Kaarkurujintja (137x183cm-54x72in) i.verso synthetic polymer linen exec. 1999 prov. 21-Jul-4 Shapiro, Sydney #130/R est:5000-7000 (A.D 4500)

JUGELET, Jean-Marie (1805-1875) French
£805 $1482 €1200 Scene de tempete pres de Falaise (23x31cm-9x12in) s. paper. 24-Mar-4 Tajan, Paris #182
£1233 $2096 €1800 Marines (9x13cm-4x5in) s. canvas on glass pair. 10-Nov-3 Horta, Bruxelles #373 est:1000-1200

JUHEL, Jean Luc (?) French?
£420 $713 €600 Laissez-la parler (110x85cm-43x33in) s.d.91 acrylic. 29-Nov-3 Neret-Minet, Paris #175/R

JUILLERAT, Jacques-Henri (1770-1860) Swiss
Works on paper
£733 $1348 €1070 Vue de la Verrerie de Rocher pres de Moutier (38x49cm-15x19in) s.i.d.1813 W/C over pencil. 26-Mar-4 Koller, Zurich #3328/R est:1500-2000 (S.FR 1700)
£1034 $1852 €1510 La Sorne (40x53cm-16x21in) i. verso W/C. 13-May-4 Stuker, Bern #9291/R est:2000-3000 (S.FR 2400)

JULES, Marc (?) French?
£493 $883 €740 Two French soldiers on a sandy path (32x22cm-13x9in) panel. 11-May-4 Vendu Notarishuis, Rotterdam #172/R

JULES, Mervin (1912-) American
£276 $500 €403 Trio (46x61cm-18x24in) acrylic board. 16-Apr-4 American Auctioneer #226/R
£324 $525 €520 Christmas tree vendor, Province Town Mass (64x76cm-25x30in) board painted c.1930s. 26-May-3 Quinn's, Falls Church #212/R
£398 $700 €581 Young boy with dandelions (61x30cm-24x12in) s. masonite painted c.1950. 23-May-4 Treadway Gallery, Cincinnati #703/R

JULI, Mabel (c.1944-) Australian
Works on paper
£1176 $2106 €1717 Living Water site (79x120cm-31x47in) natural earth pigments synthetic polymer paint exec 1994 prov. 25-May-4 Lawson Menzies, Sydney #164a/R est:3500-4500 (A.D 3000)
£1289 $2411 €1934 Wandarrang, Darrajayn country (100x140cm-39x55in) i.verso pigment canvas prov. 21-Jul-4 Shapiro, Sydney #24/R est:3500-5000 (A.D 3300)

JULI, Marlene (1975-) Australian
Works on paper
£588 $1053 €858 Pandamus, Fishing Hole Texas (100x80cm-39x31in) natural ochre pigments canvas exec 2002. 25-May-4 Lawson Menzies, Sydney #171/R (A.D 1500)

JULIA VENTURA, Francisco (1900-?) Spanish
£387 $678 €550 Autumnal landscape (50x61cm-20x24in) s. board. 16-Dec-3 Durán, Madrid #32/R

JULIA Y CARRERE, Luis (19th C) Spanish
£1549 $2711 €2200 Segundo. Rosquillero. Garrion (24x34cm-9x13in) s. cardboard set of 3. 16-Dec-3 Segre, Madrid #299/R est:1200
£1549 $2711 €2200 Calabozo. Hortelano. Hormigon (25x34cm-10x13in) s. cardboard set of 3 prov. 16-Dec-3 Segre, Madrid #298/R est:1200
£2241 $4034 €3250 Bulls in the field (44x71cm-17x28in) s. 26-Jan-4 Durán, Madrid #151/R est:2800

JULIA, Luis (?-1908) Spanish
£300 $552 €450 Mountain landscape with grazing bulls (75x40cm-30x16in) s. 11-Jun-4 Wendl, Rudolstadt #4100/R

JULIANA Y ALBERT, Jose (1844-1890) Spanish
£1064 $1723 €1500 Personajes en la fuente (47x39cm-19x15in) s. 20-May-3 Ansorena, Madrid #196/R est:1500
Works on paper
£260 $465 €380 A scolding (36x25cm-14x10in) s.i.d.1876. 25-May-4 Bonhams, Knightsbridge #214a

JULIARD, Nicolas Jacques (1715-1790) French
£8000 $14400 €11680 Pastoral landscape with shepherd, shepherdess and farmhouse (23x35cm-9x14in) s.d.1748 panel prov. 22-Apr-4 Sotheby's, London #119/R est:8000-12000
£105556 $190000 €154112 Figures resting on river banks (83x102cm-33x40in) s.d.1752 pair. 22-Jan-4 Sotheby's, New York #93/R est:100000-150000

JULIEN, Jean Antoine (attrib) (1736-1799) French
£1429 $2600 €2086 Glory Crowing the Muse of Painting (73x60cm-29x24in) 4-Feb-4 Christie's, Rockefeller NY #6/R est:4000-6000

JULIEN, René (1937-) Belgian
£347 $580 €500 Elle (60x47cm-24x19in) s. d.1970 verso panel. 21-Oct-3 Campo, Vlaamse Kaai #557
£417 $696 €600 Personnages dans un paysage (25x58cm-10x23in) s.d.1959 panel. 21-Oct-3 Campo, Vlaamse Kaai #886
£556 $883 €800 Portrait a la mer (28x15cm-11x6in) s.d.60 panel. 15-Sep-3 Horta, Bruxelles #275
£634 $1096 €900 L'Avicultrice (116x73cm-46x29in) s. i.verso. 10-Dec-3 Hotel des Ventes Mosan, Brussels #265
£671 $1188 €1000 La manade de bois (40x33cm-16x13in) s. d.1972 verso. 27-Apr-4 Campo & Campo, Antwerp #136/R
£769 $1285 €1100 Le marche du ciel (40x30cm-16x12in) s.d.1972 verso. 13-Oct-3 Horta, Bruxelles #476
Sculpture
£1181 $1972 €1700 FemmCelliste (26cm-10in) s. num.3/8 pat bronze. 21-Oct-3 Campo & Campo, Antwerp #159/R est:2600-2800
Works on paper
£496 $829 €700 Les colombes envolees (73x53cm-29x21in) s. i.d.1969 verso mixed media panel. 15-Oct-3 Hotel des Ventes Mosan, Brussels #285

JULIN, Johan Fredrik (1798-1843) Swedish
Works on paper
£270 $486 €394 Vreta monastery (38x49cm-15x19in) W/C paper on canvas prov. 26-Jan-4 Lilla Bukowskis, Stockholm #136 (S.KR 3600)

JULIO, E B D Fabrino (1843-1879) American
£47059 $80000 €68706 Bayou landscape (23x36cm-9x14in) s.d.1877 prov. 22-Nov-3 New Orleans Auction, New Orleans #1063/R est:8000-12000

JUMELET, Jan (1924-) Dutch
£582 $990 €850 Cyclists on a dike (38x49cm-15x19in) s. 5-Nov-3 Vendue Huis, Gravenhage #305/R

JUNCKER, Franz (1899-1980) German?
£1419 $2540 €2100 Street scene with two men, dog and female nude in red hat (60x80cm-24x31in) mono.d. 8-May-4 Dawo, Saarbrucken #257/R est:2800

JUNCKER, Justus (1703-1767) German
£4795 $8151 €7000 Kitchen interior with a maid and child conversing. Kitchen interior with a maid and a man conversing (33x26cm-13x10in) panel pair. 5-Nov-3 Christie's, Amsterdam #64/R est:5000-7000
£10717 $19183 €15647 Still life of flowers in vase (28x22cm-11x9in) s.d.1764 panel pair. 25-May-4 Bukowskis, Stockholm #525/R est:25000-30000 (S.KR 145000)

JUNEAU, Denis (1925-) Canadian
£763 $1419 €1114 Monement en couleur (51x51cm-20x20in) s.i.d.76 verso acrylic. 2-Mar-4 Ritchie, Toronto #194/R est:1500-2000 (C.D 1900)
£1118 $2001 €1632 Deux pendules en couleur superposee (174x37cm-69x15in) s.i.d.1972 verso oil acrylic canvas on panel with metal grommets. 31-May-4 Sotheby's, Toronto #94/R est:3000-4000 (C.D 2750)
Works on paper
£210 $390 €307 Composition (28x20cm-11x8in) s.d.60 gouache. 2-Mar-4 Ritchie, Toronto #195/R (C.D 520)
£221 $411 €323 Untitled (30x23cm-12x9in) s.d.63 i.verso gouache collage. 2-Mar-4 Ritchie, Toronto #190/R (C.D 550)
£342 $635 €499 Rythmes (58x66cm-23x26in) s.i.d.58 verso collage. 2-Mar-4 Ritchie, Toronto #186/R (C.D 850)
£482 $896 €704 Deux demi circles noirs (49x49cm-19x19in) s.d.56 s.i.d.1954-56 verso gouache. 2-Mar-4 Ritchie, Toronto #187/R (C.D 1200)

JUNES, David (1874-1938) Tunisian
£2167 $3922 €3250 Dans l'atelier du peintre (46x38cm-18x15in) s. 5-Apr-4 Marie & Robert, Paris #89 est:1500-2000

JUNG, Carl (1852-?) German?
£833 $1358 €1200 Hunter with dog (52x68cm-20x27in) s.d.1894. 26-Sep-3 Bolland & Marotz, Bremen #558/R est:1000

JUNG, Charles Jacob (?) ?
£11176 $19000 €16317 Winter morning, view of the mills on the Delaware River (79x101cm-31x40in) exhib. 21-Nov-3 Skinner, Boston #500/R est:8000-12000

JUNG, Georg (attrib) (1899-1957) Austrian
£828 $1382 €1200 Man's portrait (84x67cm-33x26in) i. verso. 9-Jul-3 Hugo Ruef, Munich #115

JUNG, Otto (fl.1909-1913) German
£302 $556 €450 Mountain stream (85x115cm-33x45in) 29-Mar-4 Dr Fritz Nagel, Stuttgart #6937/R
£333 $557 €480 Spring sun (95x75cm-37x30in) s.d.1899 i. verso lit. 25-Oct-3 Bergmann, Erlangen #942/R
£500 $900 €750 Woodland path (95x76cm-37x30in) s.i.d.1899 verso lit. 22-Apr-4 Allgauer, Kempten #3595/R
£957 $1599 €1350 Landscape with eight men (123x80cm-48x31in) s.d.1925 panel. 21-Jun-3 Klittich Pfankuch, Braunschweig #30

JUNG, Theodore (1803-1865) French
£1126 $2049 €1700 Sa majeste Charles X a Mulhouse en 1828 examinant le canal Monsieur (38x55cm-15x22in) 21-Jun-4 Tajan, Paris #125/R est:2000-3000
Works on paper
£1224 $1947 €1800 Campagne d'Algerie (27x41cm-11x16in) s. W/C. 23-Mar-3 St-Germain-en-Laye Encheres #33/R

JUNG-ILSENHEIM, Franz Xaver (1883-1963) Austrian
Works on paper
£284 $474 €400 Sailing boats on the Attersee (50x80cm-20x31in) s. mixed media masonite. 16-Oct-3 Dorotheum, Salzburg #813/R
£1067 $1963 €1600 Wild horse hunt (30x42cm-12x17in) s. mixed media paper on board. 9-Jun-4 Dorotheum, Salzburg #640/R est:520-700

JUNGBLUT, Johann (1860-1912) German
£317 $538 €463 Fjord landscape (26x36cm-10x14in) s. 19-Nov-3 Fischer, Luzern #2268/R (S.FR 700)
£432 $708 €600 River landscape with mill (18x48cm-7x19in) s. 4-Jun-3 Ketterer, Hamburg #67/R
£437 $795 €638 Fjord landscape (60x80cm-24x31in) s. 16-Jun-4 Fischer, Luzern #2230/R (S.FR 1000)
£510 $785 €800 Norwegian fjord (82x118cm-32x46in) s. 4-Sep-2 Schopman, Hamburg #255/R
£529 $883 €755 Romantic winter landscape in moonlight (27x21cm-11x8in) mono. panel lit. 27-Jun-3 Auktionhaus Georg Rehm, Augsburg #8096/R
£537 $988 €800 Two anglers in boat on fjord (55x81cm-22x32in) s. lit. 25-Mar-4 Karlheinz Kaupp, Staufen #2527/R
£699 $1189 €1000 Summer fjord (37x54cm-15x21in) s. 20-Nov-3 Van Ham, Cologne #1666/R
£704 $1218 €1000 Woman in wood (25x20cm-10x8in) s. panel. 13-Dec-3 Lempertz, Koln #223
£733 $1320 €1100 Evening winter landscape with figures (18x47cm-7x19in) s. panel. 21-Apr-4 Neumeister, Munich #2659/R
£833 $1317 €1200 Winter landscape with figures on frozen river (70x100cm-28x39in) s.pseudonym R Hibler lit. 19-Sep-3 Schloss Ahlden, Ahlden #1582/R
£839 $1427 €1200 Fjord landscape with figures on shore (80x120cm-31x47in) s. lit. 28-Nov-3 Schloss Ahlden, Ahlden #1492/R

£863 $1416 €1200 Norwegian fjord with sailing boats and figures (80x120cm-31x47in) s.pseudonym J Sander. 3-Jun-3 Sigalas, Stuttgart #422/R
£933 $1680 €1400 Wild boar in the snow (65x70cm-26x28in) s. 26-Apr-4 Rieber, Stuttgart #1270/R
£972 $1624 €1400 Norwegian landscape (17x24cm-7x9in) s. bears i. verso panel. 24-Oct-3 Ketterer, Hamburg #79/R
£979 $1664 €1400 Autumn waterside (23x18cm-9x7in) s. panel. 20-Nov-3 Van Ham, Cologne #1664
£1060 $1928 €1600 Winter evening ice-skating (81x61cm-32x24in) s. 18-Jun-4 Bolland & Marotz, Bremen #655/R est:2000
£1084 $1864 €1550 Driving sheep home from the moor (60x80cm-24x31in) s. 5-Dec-3 Bolland & Marotz, Bremen #577/R est:1700
£1111 $1811 €1600 Northern landscape (81x121cm-32x48in) s. 23-Sep-3 Durán, Madrid #177/R est:1500
£1133 $2051 €1700 Lower Rhine landscape in late summer (60x80cm-24x31in) s. 1-Apr-4 Van Ham, Cologne #1458/R est:2000
£1133 $2074 €1700 Evening time over Eisfischen on village edge (80x120cm-31x47in) s. 5-Jun-4 Arnold, Frankfurt #615/R est:2000
£1141 $2134 €1700 Northern landscape (81x121cm-32x48in) s. 24-Feb-4 Durán, Madrid #224/R est:750
£1181 $1948 €1700 Sailing boats on sunny fjord (79x104cm-31x41in) s. 3-Jul-3 Van Ham, Cologne #1278
£1333 $2427 €2000 Potato harvest (60x80cm-24x31in) s. canvas on board. 1-Jul-4 Van Ham, Cologne #1431/R est:1800
£1467 $2655 €2200 Two girls collecting wood in autumn (55x82cm-22x32in) s. 1-Apr-4 Van Ham, Cologne #1459/R est:3000
£1467 $2669 €2200 Two farmer women by a forest stream by moonlight (81x55cm-32x22in) s. 1-Jul-4 Van Ham, Cologne #1433/R est:1300
£1761 $3046 €2500 Walking home in winter (77x56cm-30x22in) s. 10-Dec-3 Christie's, Amsterdam #681/R est:1800-2200
£2098 $3566 €3000 Lower Rhine in autumn (18x84cm-7x33in) s. 20-Nov-3 Van Ham, Cologne #1663/R est:2500
£2937 $4993 €4200 Frozen river lit by evening sun (94x75cm-37x30in) s. 20-Nov-3 Van Ham, Cologne #1665/R est:4800
£3873 $6701 €5500 Figures on a snow covered country road (81x120cm-32x47in) s. 10-Dec-3 Christie's, Amsterdam #683/R est:2500-3500
£4800 $8688 €7200 Winter evening in Dutch town (81x121cm-32x48in) s. 1-Apr-4 Van Ham, Cologne #1457/R est:5200

JUNGBLUT, Johann (attrib) (1860-1912) German
£2128 $3553 €3000 Ice fishing in evening winter landscape (53x80cm-21x31in) s. 21-Jun-3 Hans Stahl, Hamburg #23/R est:3000

JUNGER, C (fl.1815) ?
Miniatures
£1700 $2890 €2482 Salome Koechlin as a child (11cm-4in) s.verso wood frame oval. 18-Nov-3 Bonhams, New Bond Street #159/R est:1200-1500

JUNGHANNS, Julius Paul (1876-1958) Austrian
£307 $558 €460 Mare with foal (35x30cm-14x12in) s.d.56. 1-Jul-4 Neumeister, Munich #2723
£455 $759 €650 Man with horses by Tyrolean village church (18x18cm-7x7in) s. s.i.d.04 veso board. 28-Jun-3 Bolland & Marotz, Bremen #679/R
£524 $892 €750 Three coach horses in city street (18x26cm-7x10in) mono.d.08 board on panel. 20-Nov-3 Van Ham, Cologne #1668
£800 $1456 €1200 Sleeping goatherd (44x60cm-17x24in) s. 1-Jul-4 Van Ham, Cologne #1434/R
£1200 $2184 €1800 Young girl watching the goats at the forest edge (25x40cm-10x16in) s. panel. 1-Jul-4 Van Ham, Cologne #1435/R est:2000
£1250 $2063 €1800 Young herder resting with goats (25x40cm-10x16in) s. panel. 3-Jul-3 Van Ham, Cologne #1282/R est:2600
£1329 $2285 €1900 Peasants with a horse drawn sleigh in a winter mountain landscape (39x66cm-15x26in) s. panel. 3-Dec-3 Neumeister, Munich #606/R est:1500
£1467 $2655 €2200 In the Alps (31x48cm-12x19in) s. panel. 1-Apr-4 Van Ham, Cologne #1460 est:1600
£3846 $6538 €5500 Four horses pulling cart (54x77cm-21x30in) s. 20-Nov-3 Van Ham, Cologne #1670/R est:7000

JUNGHEIM, Carl (1803-1886) German
£972 $1585 €1400 Procession of monks in monastery garden (60x80cm-24x31in) s.d.55. 25-Sep-3 Dr Fritz Nagel, Stuttgart #1362/R
£1197 $2143 €1700 Successful hunt in the Dolomite mountains (76x104cm-30x41in) s. lit. 8-Jan-4 Allgauer, Kempten #2428/R est:1700
£14865 $26162 €22000 Fishermen on Capri (108x154cm-43x61in) s.d.1865 exhib.prov.lit. 22-May-4 Lempertz, Koln #1533/R est:15000

JUNGHEIM, Julius (20th C) German
£300 $543 €450 Late summer's day (61x50cm-24x20in) s. 1-Apr-4 Van Ham, Cologne #1461

JUNGMANN, Maarten Johannes Balthasar (1877-1964) Dutch
£833 $1358 €1200 Winter landscape (70x92cm-28x36in) s. prov. 29-Sep-3 Sotheby's, Amsterdam #303/R

JUNGMANN, Nico W (1872-1935) British/Dutch
£900 $1665 €1314 Ride a cock horse (25x36cm-10x14in) mono. panel. 13-Jan-4 Bonhams, Knightsbridge #150/R
Works on paper
£700 $1169 €1022 Portrait of a girl with a doll (24x18cm-9x7in) mono.i. W/C pencil. 14-Oct-3 Bonhams, Knightsbridge #193/R

JUNGNICKEL, Ludwig Heinrich (1881-1965) German
£3147 $5350 €4500 Cat's head (22x17cm-9x7in) s. canvas on board. 19-Nov-3 Dorotheum, Klagenfurt #18/R est:2000
£4861 $8264 €7000 Wild cat (36x47cm-14x19in) 28-Oct-3 Wiener Kunst Auktionen, Vienna #88/R est:7000-14000
£5921 $10895 €9000 Southern town with palm trees (38x46cm-15x18in) s. 22-Jun-4 Wiener Kunst Auktionen, Vienna #56/R est:5000
£23776 $40420 €34000 Landscape near Castelgandolfo (68x105cm-27x41in) s. bears d. prov. 26-Nov-3 Dorotheum, Vienna #135/R est:18000-26000
Prints
£3221 $5766 €4800 Tiger's head (30x30cm-12x12in) s.d.1908 col woodcut lit. 27-May-4 Hassfurther, Vienna #53/R est:800-1200
£3691 $6607 €5500 Parrot wood (42x39cm-17x15in) col woodcut. 25-May-4 Dorotheum, Vienna #142/R est:5000-6000
Works on paper
£319 $533 €450 Dog (46x31cm-18x12in) st.sig. chl. 14-Oct-3 Dorotheum, Vienna #126/R
£369 $683 €550 Cats (39x54cm-15x21in) chk. 9-Mar-4 Dorotheum, Vienna #72/R
£379 $694 €550 Gazelle (32x23cm-13x9in) chk. 27-Jan-4 Dorotheum, Vienna #60/R
£493 $863 €700 Gazelle (32x23cm-13x9in) s.i. black chk. 19-Dec-3 Dorotheum, Vienna #111
£528 $924 €750 Preditory cat lying on his back (23x30cm-9x12in) s. black chk W/C. 19-Dec-3 Dorotheum, Vienna #63/R
£532 $888 €750 Seated female nude (31x38cm-12x15in) s.d.1912 pencil. 14-Oct-3 Dorotheum, Vienna #6/R
£532 $888 €750 Female nude (33x43cm-13x17in) st.sig. chl. 14-Oct-3 Dorotheum, Vienna #97
£655 $1199 €950 Gazelle (33x46cm-13x18in) chk pencil W/C. 27-Jan-4 Dorotheum, Vienna #61/R
£694 $1132 €1000 Head (48x37cm-19x15in) s. pencil. 23-Sep-3 Wiener Kunst Auktionen, Vienna #77/R
£694 $1132 €1000 Monkeys (42x30cm-17x12in) s. pencil. 23-Sep-3 Wiener Kunst Auktionen, Vienna #80/R
£789 $1453 €1200 Squirrel (20x22cm-8x9in) mixed media. 22-Jun-4 Wiener Kunst Auktionen, Vienna #84/R
£800 $1440 €1200 Leopard (25x39cm-10x15in) s. chl W/C prov. 21-Apr-4 Dorotheum, Vienna #10/R
£878 $1546 €1300 Monkeys playing (39x29cm-15x11in) s. W/C. 19-May-4 Dorotheum, Klagenfurt #47/R
£915 $1602 €1300 Gazelle (33x31cm-13x12in) s. chl chk W/C. 19-Dec-3 Dorotheum, Vienna #110/R
£987 $1816 €1500 Roedeer and roebuck (40x27cm-16x11in) s. mixed media. 22-Jun-4 Wiener Kunst Auktionen, Vienna #86/R est:1500
£993 $1658 €1400 Portrait of a girl (43x37cm-17x15in) s. chl chk. 14-Oct-3 Dorotheum, Vienna #127/R
£1000 $1800 €1500 Two pekes (36x45cm-14x18in) s. chl W/C prov. 21-Apr-4 Dorotheum, Vienna #61/R est:1700-2000
£1250 $2037 €1800 Head (48x37cm-19x15in) s. pencil. 23-Sep-3 Wiener Kunst Auktionen, Vienna #75/R est:1000-2000
£1528 $2490 €2200 Nude sitting (48x37cm-19x15in) pencil. 23-Sep-3 Wiener Kunst Auktionen, Vienna #74/R est:1000-2000
£1831 $3204 €2600 Three Dachshund (23x29cm-9x11in) s. chl W/C. 19-Dec-3 Dorotheum, Vienna #109/R est:800-1200
£1879 $3364 €2800 Two leopards (42x38cm-17x15in) s. mixed media prov. 25-May-4 Dorotheum, Vienna #187/R est:2200-3000
£1944 $3169 €2800 Portrait of a lady (48x37cm-19x15in) s. pencil. 23-Sep-3 Wiener Kunst Auktionen, Vienna #72/R est:1000-2000
£1958 $3329 €2800 Parrot (38x27cm-15x11in) s. pencil W/C. 28-Nov-3 Wiener Kunst Auktionen, Vienna #492/R est:2000-5000
£2148 $3844 €3200 Prowling wild cat (36x45cm-14x18in) s. chl W/C prov. 25-May-4 Dorotheum, Vienna #184/R est:2000-2600
£2207 $4039 €3200 Two donkeys (29x36cm-11x14in) s. chk W/C. 27-Jan-4 Dorotheum, Vienna #62/R est:1400-2000
£2533 $4560 €3800 Cat and parrot (58x43cm-23x17in) mono.d.36 chl chk W/C prov. 21-Apr-4 Dorotheum, Vienna #81/R est:3000-4500
£2778 $4528 €4000 Back view of a nude sitting (52x38cm-20x15in) s. pencil W/C. 23-Sep-3 Wiener Kunst Auktionen, Vienna #73/R est:1000-2000
£3020 $5406 €4500 Girl with pillow (36x46cm-14x18in) s.d.1915 pencil gouache W/C prov. 25-May-4 Dorotheum, Vienna #6/R est:3400-5000
£4605 $8474 €7000 Two donkeys (30x40cm-12x16in) s. mixed media. 22-Jun-4 Wiener Kunst Auktionen, Vienna #85/R est:1500

JUNGSTEDT, Axel (1859-1933) Swedish
£1231 $2117 €1797 Three girls wrapping up parcels (32x33cm-13x13in) init.indis.d.96 grisaille. 3-Dec-3 AB Stockholms Auktionsverk #2298/R est:18000-20000 (S.KR 16000)
£2439 $4366 €3561 Kontraband (93x139cm-37x55in) s.verso after A G Hafstrom. 26-May-4 AB Stockholms Auktionsverk #2355/R est:30000-40000 (S.KR 33000)

JUNGSTEDT, Kurt (1894-1963) Swedish
£443 $794 €647 Malar Square (54x65cm-21x26in) s. d.45 verso. 28-May-4 Uppsala Auktionskammare, Uppsala #323 (S.KR 6000)

JUNGURRAYI, Jimija (1961-) Australian
Works on paper
£664 $1242 €996 Pamapardu jukurrpa, flying ant dreaming (71x55cm-28x22in) bears name.verso synthetic polymer paint canvasboard prov. 26-Jul-4 Sotheby's, Melbourne #417/R (A.D 1700)

JUNGWIRTH, Josef (1869-1950) Austrian
£479 $800 €699 Going fishing (43x36cm-17x14in) 14-Nov-3 Du Mouchelle, Detroit #2092/R
£1538 $2646 €2245 Spring landscape with girls playing (62x76cm-24x30in) s.indis.d.190. 3-Dec-3 AB Stockholms Auktionsverk #2618/R est:20000-25000 (S.KR 20000)

JUNGWIRTH, Martha (1940-) Austrian
Works on paper
£709 $1184 €1000 Untitled (41x29cm-16x11in) s.d.87 W/C gouache. 14-Oct-3 Dorotheum, Vienna #266/R
£1399 $2378 €2000 Untitled (70x100cm-28x39in) mono.d.1967 W/C. 28-Nov-3 Wiener Kunst Auktionen, Vienna #649/R est:2000-4000

JUNIPER, Robert (1929-1983) Australian
£1245 $2079 €1868 Untitled (70x60cm-28x24in) s.d.76 board. 27-Oct-3 Goodman, Sydney #88/R est:2000-3000 (A.D 3000)

£1245	$2079	€1868	Untitled (30x38cm-12x15in) s. canvas on board. 27-Oct-3 Goodman, Sydney #90/R est:2000-3000 (A.D 3000)
£1306	$2403	€1907	Untitled (25x31cm-10x12in) s.d.75 canvas on board prov. 29-Mar-4 Goodman, Sydney #4/R est:3000-4000 (A.D 3200)
£1500	$2550	€2190	Sunrise 555 (90x135cm-35x53in) s.d.66 board prov. 26-Nov-3 Sotheby's, Olympia #160/R est:600-800
£2128	$3617	€3107	Image of Kal No.4 (90x89cm-35x35in) s.d.1959 s.i.verso board. 25-Nov-3 Christie's, Melbourne #162/R est:6000-8000 (A.D 5000)
£2273	$4205	€3319	Desert wind (60x80cm-24x31in) s.d.73 canvas on board. 10-Mar-4 Deutscher-Menzies, Melbourne #351/R est:6000-8000 (A.D 5500)
£2341	$3979	€3418	Shadows (45x62cm-18x24in) s.d.63 composition board. 26-Nov-3 Deutscher-Menzies, Melbourne #252/R est:1600-2400 (A.D 5500)
£6098	$9573	€8842	Quandong (119x137cm-47x54in) s.d.96. 26-Aug-3 Christie's, Sydney #93/R est:15000-20000 (A.D 15000)
£6504	$10211	€9431	Burn off (170x178cm-67x70in) s.d.69 prov.exhib.lit. 27-Aug-3 Christie's, Sydney #576/R est:20000-30000 (A.D 16000)

JUNK, Rudolf (1880-1943) Austrian

£4196	$7133	€6000	Forest clearing (66x51cm-26x20in) s. 26-Nov-3 Dorotheum, Vienna #133/R est:6000-8000

JUNKER, Hermann (19/20th C) German

£467	$854	€700	Riders on horseback on the side of the racecourse (122x114cm-48x45in) s.d.1901. 5-Jun-4 Arnold, Frankfurt #618

JUNTTILA, Einari (1901-1975) Finnish

Works on paper

£282	$519	€420	Landscape (25x32cm-10x13in) s. W/C. 25-Mar-4 Hagelstam, Helsinki #971
£286	$520	€420	Sunny day in Lapland (29x37cm-11x15in) s. W/C. 8-Feb-4 Bukowskis, Helsinki #370/R

JUNYENT SANS, Olegario (1876-1956) Spanish

£1469	$2452	€2100	Basket with grapes (54x65cm-21x26in) s.d.52. 30-Jun-3 Ansorena, Madrid #376/R est:2100

JURGENS, Grethe (1899-1981) German

Works on paper

£1477	$2643	€2200	Portrait of Gustav Schenk (64x48cm-25x19in) s. W/C. 25-May-4 Karl & Faber, Munich #358/R est:4000

JURGENS, Johann Wilhelm (1845-1906) German

£312	$521	€440	Holstein winter landscape in the evening (46x86cm-18x34in) s.d.95. 21-Jun-3 Hans Stahl, Hamburg #67/R

JURGENSEN, Sophus M (1873-1958) Danish

£806	$1474	€1177	Female nude on beach at sunset (66x74cm-26x29in) s. 9-Jun-4 Rasmussen, Copenhagen #1978/R (D.KR 9000)

JURNEY, David (20th C) American?

£262	$450	€383	Figure on path (10x20cm-4x8in) s. panel. 2-Dec-3 Christie's, Rockefeller NY #99/R

JURRES, Johannes Hendricus (1875-1946) Dutch

£588	$982	€858	Horsemen at dusk (46x40cm-18x16in) s.d.07 panel. 17-Nov-3 Waddingtons, Toronto #154/R (C.D 1300)
£1701	$3095	€2500	Rest from the ride (70x90cm-28x35in) s. 3-Feb-4 Christie's, Amsterdam #164/R est:2500-3500
£2747	$5000	€4011	Samson and Delilah (92x118cm-36x46in) s. 29-Jun-4 Sotheby's, New York #142/R est:6000-9000
£4698	$8691	€7000	Hannibal crossing the Alps (86x129cm-34x51in) s.d.23. 15-Mar-4 Sotheby's, Amsterdam #44/R est:1500-2000

JURY, Anne P (1907-1995) Irish

£450	$774	€657	Homestead and little farm in Connemara (28x35cm-11x14in) s. canvas on board. 3-Dec-3 John Ross, Belfast #56
£450	$774	€657	Clady River, Donegal (25x33cm-10x13in) s. canvas on board. 3-Dec-3 John Ross, Belfast #71
£520	$853	€759	Donegal (30x35cm-12x14in) s. canvas on board. 4-Jun-3 John Ross, Belfast #9
£526	$968	€800	Gathering storm near Leenan, County Galway (24x31cm-9x12in) canvasboard prov. 22-Jun-4 De Veres Art Auctions, Dublin #215/R
£650	$1066	€949	White dog tooth, violets and primula (33x25cm-13x10in) s. canvas on board. 4-Jun-3 John Ross, Belfast #53
£650	$1079	€949	Cliffs, West of Ireland (35x45cm-14x18in) s. canvas on board. 1-Oct-3 John Ross, Belfast #52
£750	$1230	€1095	Whitepark Bay (30x38cm-12x15in) s. canvas on board. 4-Jun-3 John Ross, Belfast #28
£800	$1312	€1168	Fair Head (30x38cm-12x15in) s. canvas on board. 4-Jun-3 John Ross, Belfast #136
£850	$1462	€1241	Fairhead, Ballycastle (25x30cm-10x12in) s. canvas on board. 3-Dec-3 John Ross, Belfast #13
£950	$1558	€1387	Flowers (25x33cm-10x13in) s. canvas on board. 4-Jun-3 John Ross, Belfast #221
£950	$1739	€1387	Fairhead (30x40cm-12x16in) s. canvas on board. 2-Jun-4 John Ross, Belfast #60
£1500	$2580	€2190	Muckish on a cold spring day (35x45cm-14x18in) s. canvas on board. 3-Dec-3 John Ross, Belfast #118a est:700-900
£1800	$3222	€2628	Slieve More, Achill Island (30x39cm-12x15in) s. board. 14-May-4 Christie's, Kensington #374/R est:1000-1500
£2300	$3703	€3335	Muckish mountain from the Horn Head Road (28x48cm-11x19in) s. 15-Aug-3 Keys, Aylsham #776/R est:600-800

JUSSEL, Eugen (1912-1997) Austrian

£897	$1498	€1310	Harbour in a city in South Africa (62x73cm-24x29in) s.d.65 board. 24-Oct-3 Hans Widmer, St Gallen #89/R est:1500-3500 (S.FR 2000)
£4698	$8691	€7000	Feldkirch (80x90cm-31x35in) s.d.58. 9-Mar-4 Dorotheum, Vienna #98/R est:7000-9000

JUSTE, Juste de (1505-1559) French

Prints

£17333	$31027	€26000	Pyramid of five male nudes (27x20cm-11x8in) etching. 13-May-4 Bassenge, Berlin #5194/R est:6000

JUSTE, Rene (?) Spanish?

£490	$842	€700	Ferme en hiver (46x55cm-18x22in) s. 5-Dec-3 Maigret, Paris #9

JUSZKO, Bela (1877-1969) Hungarian

£486	$802	€700	Herders with horses watering in Hungarian Pussta (61x101cm-24x40in) s. 3-Jul-3 Neumeister, Munich #2856/R
£700	$1295	€1022	Ready to ride (99x119cm-39x47in) s.d.928. 15-Jan-4 Christie's, Kensington #889/R est:800-1200
£973	$1800	€1421	Drover with cattle (94x122cm-37x48in) s. 15-Jul-4 Doyle, New York #50/R est:1000-1500

JUTREM, Arne Jon (1929-) Norwegian

£261	$451	€381	Red country (65x81cm-26x32in) s. 13-Dec-3 Blomqvist, Lysaker #1186 (N.KR 3000)

JUTSUM, Henry (1816-1869) British

£500	$920	€730	Figures on a wooded road, an estuary beyond (32x48cm-13x19in) s. 8-Jun-4 Bonhams, Knightsbridge #162/R
£950	$1767	€1387	Figures in an extensive landscape (41x61cm-16x24in) s.d.60. 4-Mar-4 Christie's, Kensington #458/R
£1800	$3330	€2628	Cows being driven across a stone bridge (27x37cm-11x15in) s.d.1859. 14-Jul-4 Bonhams, Chester #446/R est:800-1200

Works on paper

£450	$747	€657	Richmond Park (32x49cm-13x19in) s. W/C. 1-Oct-3 Sotheby's, Olympia #101/R
£1400	$2590	€2044	Corn harvesters in a field (24x36cm-9x14in) s.d.1859 W/C htd pencil. 14-Jan-4 Lawrence, Crewkerne #1319/R est:400-600

JUTTNER, Brune (1880-?) Scandinavian

£319	$505	€460	Fishermen and boats at the quayside with village in background (47x65cm-19x26in) s. board. 5-Sep-3 Wendl, Rudolstadt #3441/R
£738	$1358	€1100	Shrimp fishermen returning home (91x193cm-36x76in) i. verso lit. 25-Mar-4 Karlheinz Kaupp, Staufen #2530/R est:100

JUTZ, Carl (elder) (1838-1916) German

£4444	$7022	€6400	Poultry yard (23x40cm-9x16in) s. panel lit. 19-Sep-3 Schloss Ahlden, Ahlden #1585/R est:6500
£5430	$9231	€7928	Poultry yard. Waterbirds by pond (31x40cm-12x16in) s.d.1860 panel. 19-Nov-3 Fischer, Luzern #1171/R est:12000-14000 (S.FR 12000)
£6597	$10885	€9500	Stork and ducks by pond with gathering storm (27x22cm-11x9in) s. 3-Jul-3 Van Ham, Cologne #1283/R est:15000
£6667	$12133	€10000	Harvest near Flintsbach (58x77cm-23x30in) s.d.1900 lit. 30-Jun-4 Neumeister, Munich #582/R est:10000
£10738	$19758	€16000	Ducks on edge of pond (36x57cm-14x22in) s. 25-Mar-4 Dr Fritz Nagel, Stuttgart #725/R est:30000
£12000	$21840	€18000	Ducks on the edge of a pond (13x16cm-5x6in) s.d.00 panel. 1-Jul-4 Van Ham, Cologne #1438/R est:8000

JUTZ, Carl (younger) (1873-1915) German

£1119	$1924	€1600	Poultry (19x23cm-7x9in) s. board. 4-Dec-3 Schopman, Hamburg #628/R est:1400

JUUEL, Andreas (1817-1868) Danish

£762	$1371	€1113	Seascape with sailing vessels at sunset (21x30cm-8x12in) s.d.1848 panel. 24-Apr-4 Rasmussen, Havnen #2296/R (D.KR 8500)
£797	$1370	€1164	Large stone near Duppol, Broager Church in background (33x41cm-13x16in) s. 3-Dec-3 Museumsbygningen, Copenhagen #119/R (D.KR 8500)

JUUL, Ole (1852-1927) Norwegian

£290	$463	€421	Northern coastal landscape (35x28cm-14x11in) s. 22-Sep-3 Blomqvist, Lysaker #1141 (N.KR 3400)
£325	$598	€488	By water's edge (39x32cm-15x13in) s. panel. 14-Jun-4 Blomqvist, Lysaker #1187 (N.KR 4000)
£480	$802	€701	Lake view with mountains (37x58cm-15x23in) s. 22-Oct-3 Cheffins, Cambridge #543/R
£652	$1128	€952	Midnight sun (30x49cm-12x19in) s. panel. 13-Dec-3 Blomqvist, Lysaker #1187/R (N.KR 7500)
£732	$1346	€1098	Dark night (38x63cm-15x25in) s. 14-Jun-4 Blomqvist, Lysaker #1189 (N.KR 9000)
£732	$1346	€1098	Buildings by the fjord (30x46cm-12x18in) s. panel. 14-Jun-4 Blomqvist, Lysaker #1188 (N.KR 9000)
£777	$1290	€1127	Along the coast (38x62cm-15x24in) s. 16-Jun-3 Blomqvist, Lysaker #1333/R (N.KR 9000)
£813	$1496	€1220	Winter landscape (49x71cm-19x28in) s. 14-Jun-4 Blomqvist, Lysaker #1191 (N.KR 10000)
£935	$1720	€1403	Summer night (45x65cm-18x26in) 14-Jun-4 Blomqvist, Lysaker #1190 (N.KR 11500)
£1041	$1863	€1520	Northern light, coastal landscape (22x33cm-9x13in) s. panel. 22-Mar-4 Blomqvist, Oslo #300/R est:15000-18000 (N.KR 13000)
£1065	$1704	€1544	Winter light over a Northern harbour (42x67cm-17x26in) s. 22-Sep-3 Blomqvist, Lysaker #1142/R (N.KR 12500)
£2439	$4463	€3561	Fishing village in Lofoten (39x60cm-15x24in) s. 7-Jun-4 Blomqvist, Oslo #308/R est:20000-25000 (N.KR 30000)

JUVELA, Lennu (1886-1979) Finnish

£470	$874	€700	Old croft (27x39cm-11x15in) s.d.1918. 7-Mar-4 Bukowskis, Helsinki #343/R

JUVENELL, Paul (elder) (1579-1643) German
£533 $971 €800 John the Evangelist (38x29cm-15x11in) i.verso. 1-Jul-4 Weidler, Nurnberg #6556/R

JUVENELL, Paul (elder-circle) (1579-1643) German
£5500 $9515 €8030 Ecce Homo (37x50cm-15x20in) panel. 10-Dec-3 Bonhams, New Bond Street #108/R est:6000-8000

JYNGE, Gert (1904-1994) Norwegian
£1326 $2254 €1936 Still life of haddock on plate (42x48cm-17x19in) s.d.26. 19-Nov-3 Grev Wedels Plass, Oslo #76/R est:10000-12000 (N.KR 15500)

KAAN, Simon (20th C) New Zealander
£725 $1167 €1059 He Kawau (76x106cm-30x42in) s.d.01. 20-Aug-3 Dunbar Sloane, Auckland #90/R est:2000-4000 (NZ.D 2000)

KAAN-ALBEST, Julius von (1874-1942) German
£500 $880 €730 Grodner-tal, with Alps beyond (48x56cm-19x22in) s.i.d.1931 board. 19-May-4 Christie's, Kensington #673/R

KABAKOV, Ilya (1933-) Russian
£71856 $120000 €104910 List of what I was supposed to do before March of 1961 (260x190cm-102x75in) enamel on masonite pants shirt exec 1989 prov. 12-Nov-3 Christie's, Rockefeller NY #640/R est:60000-80000
Works on paper
£1923 $3500 €2808 Fly (10x24cm-4x9in) s.d.97 W/C pencil prov. 29-Jun-4 Sotheby's, New York #626/R est:2000-3000

KABANOV, Viktor (1928-) Russian
£313 $509 €450 Woman (89x69cm-35x27in) painted 1951. 24-Sep-3 Cambi, Genoa #1392

KABELL, Ludwig (1853-1902) Danish
£354 $556 €517 Sunset (25x40cm-10x16in) s. plywood. 30-Aug-3 Rasmussen, Havnen #2241 (D.KR 3800)
£671 $1229 €980 Garden with elderberry flowers (45x59cm-18x23in) s. exhib. 9-Jun-4 Rasmussen, Copenhagen #1923/R (D.KR 7500)
£888 $1403 €1288 Wide landscape from Kallundborg area (65x100cm-26x39in) s.d.1894 exhib. 2-Sep-3 Rasmussen, Copenhagen #1951/R (D.KR 9500)
£1264 $2363 €1845 Road through hilly landscape with sheep grazing, Lonstrup. s.d.1899-1900 exhib. 25-Feb-4 Museumsbygningen, Copenhagen #117/R est:6000-8000 (D.KR 14000)
£6616 $11843 €9659 Landscape from Mons Klit with rainbow, cow and milkmaid (91x148cm-36x58in) s. 12-Jan-4 Rasmussen, Vejle #86/R est:15000 (D.KR 70000)

KABER, G Frederick (20th C) American
Works on paper
£1842 $3334 €2800 Elegante se promenant dans une voiture (32x37cm-13x15in) s. 19-Apr-4 Horta, Bruxelles #160 est:3000-4000

KABOTIE, Fred (1900-1985) American
Works on paper
£4076 $7500 €5951 Broadface Ogre Kachina (45x37cm-18x15in) gouache prov. 24-Jun-4 Sotheby's, New York #174/R est:3000-5000
£4891 $9000 €7141 Mastof K (49x39cm-19x15in) gouache. 24-Jun-4 Sotheby's, New York #175/R est:4000-6000

KABREGU, Enzo Domestico (1906-1971) South American
£793 $1300 €1158 Village in Lungro (53x70cm-21x28in) s. prov. 3-Jun-3 Galeria y Remates, Montevideo #97
£899 $1700 €1313 Woman reading (69x59cm-27x23in) s. 22-Feb-4 Galeria y Remates, Montevideo #74/R est:2000
£1033 $1900 €1508 In the park (60x69cm-24x27in) s. 22-Jun-4 Galeria y Remates, Montevideo #67/R est:2000-3000

KACERE, John (1920-) American
£11409 $20423 €17000 Dara (101x152cm-40x60in) s.i.d.89 verso prov.lit. 27-May-4 Sotheby's, Paris #265/R est:10000-15000
£26846 $48054 €40000 Lorena (101x152cm-40x60in) s.i.d.91 verso prov. 27-May-4 Sotheby's, Paris #280/R est:8000-12000

KACZ, Endre Komaromi (1880-1969) Hungarian
£298 $545 €450 River landscape with goosemaid (33x43cm-13x17in) s. board. 8-Apr-4 Dorotheum, Vienna #13/R

KADAR, Bela (1877-1955) Hungarian
£382 $638 €550 Men and dos (16x21cm-6x8in) s. Indian ink brush. 24-Oct-3 Ketterer, Hamburg #854/R
£1154 $2100 €1685 Arrangement of hollyhocks (81x61cm-32x24in) s. 8-Feb-4 William Jenack, New York #111 est:2100
£1268 $2269 €1800 Four women drying themselves under a tree after bathing (45x58cm-18x23in) s. lit. 8-Jan-4 Allgauer, Kempten #2429/R est:1800
£1493 $2479 €2180 Blond girl in white blouse (29x21cm-11x8in) s. tempera paper. 4-Oct-3 Kieselbach, Budapest #195/R (H.F 550000)
£1566 $2709 €2286 Scene (28x45cm-11x18in) s. tempera paper. 12-Dec-3 Kieselbach, Budapest #68/R (H.F 600000)
£1827 $3161 €2667 Still life (43x28cm-17x11in) s. tempera paper. 12-Dec-3 Kieselbach, Budapest #26/R (H.F 700000)
£2088 $3612 €3048 Church garden in Szolnok (64x50cm-25x20in) s. cardboard. 12-Dec-3 Kieselbach, Budapest #179/R (H.F 800000)
£3448 $5759 €5000 Composition au verre de fin et des fruits (68x48cm-27x19in) s. oil paper. 17-Nov-3 Claude Boisgirard, Paris #41/R est:5000-6000
£3474 $6149 €5072 Young couple (50x39cm-20x15in) s. tempera paper. 28-Apr-4 Kieselbach, Budapest #153/R (H.F 1300000)
£4344 $7211 €6342 Still life of fruit with flowers (60x42cm-24x17in) s. tempera. 4-Oct-3 Kieselbach, Budapest #34/R (H.F 1600000)
£5879 $10406 €8583 Still life with fruit (50x35cm-20x14in) s. tempera paper. 28-Apr-4 Kieselbach, Budapest #133/R (H.F 2200000)
£6323 $11445 €9232 Friends (83x97cm-33x38in) tempera paper on card. 16-Apr-4 Mu Terem Galeria, Budapest #123/R (H.F 2400000)
£13050 $22577 €19053 Girl with coral necklace with a bird (70x50cm-28x20in) s. tempera paper. 12-Dec-3 Kieselbach, Budapest #49/R (H.F 5000000)
£21718 $36053 €31708 Woman in veil with fruit bowl (70x50cm-28x20in) s. tempera paper. 4-Oct-3 Kieselbach, Budapest #184/R (H.F 8000000)
Works on paper
£267 $477 €400 Femme (28x20cm-11x8in) s. ink wash. 17-May-4 Chayette & Cheval, Paris #111
£280 $468 €409 Composition (23x29cm-9x11in) s. ink. 22-Oct-3 Bonhams, New Bond Street #59/R
£316 $500 €461 Horse and rider (22x15cm-9x6in) s. ink gouache. 27-Jul-3 Bonhams & Butterfields, Los Angeles #7037/R
£350 $637 €511 Decorative designs (23x34cm-9x13in) s. pencil gouache double-sided. 15-Jun-4 Bonhams, Knightsbridge #192
£353 $600 €515 Untitled (18x23cm-7x9in) W/C. 9-Nov-3 Wright, Chicago #177
£355 $592 €500 Sketch A90/150 (7x28cm-3x11in) s. Indian ink gouache. 16-Oct-3 Dorotheum, Salzburg #831/R
£417 $696 €600 Composition with figure and tree (28x20cm-11x8in) s. Indian ink. 24-Oct-3 Ketterer, Hamburg #853/R
£455 $782 €650 Kneeling female nude (23x29cm-9x11in) s. W/C. 4-Dec-3 Van Ham, Cologne #257
£464 $850 €677 Figures and horses (40x57cm-16x22in) s. ink. 1-Feb-4 Ben-Ami, Tel Aviv #4578/R
£471 $800 €688 Untitled (18x23cm-7x9in) s. W/C. 9-Nov-3 Wright, Chicago #176
£471 $800 €688 Untitled (18x23cm-7x9in) s. W/C. 9-Nov-3 Wright, Chicago #178
£537 $988 €800 Napozok - sunbathers (15x23cm-6x9in) mono. Indian ink brush. 26-Mar-4 Ketterer, Hamburg #489/R
£540 $988 €788 Dream city (18x23cm-7x9in) s. bodycol prov. 8-Jul-4 Duke & Son, Dorchester #62/R
£633 $1077 €924 Untitled (30x23cm-12x9in) s. i.verso ink prov. 22-Nov-3 Burkhard, Luzern #88/R (S.FR 1400)
£741 $1200 €1074 Landschaft (43x34cm-17x13in) s. gouache prov. 8-Aug-3 Barridorf, Portland #37/R est:1200-1800
£769 $1308 €1123 Landscape with coach (17x25cm-7x10in) wash chl prov. 25-Nov-3 Germann, Zurich #127/R est:1800-2200 (S.FR 1700)
£979 $1664 €1400 Couple in the street with dog (35x25cm-14x10in) chk. 26-Nov-3 Lempertz, Koln #743/R
£1122 $1987 €1638 City nude (29x32cm-11x13in) s. mixed media. 28-Apr-4 Kieselbach, Budapest #4/R (H.F 420000)
£1181 $1972 €1700 Bird metamorphosis (33x47cm-13x19in) s. d. verso Indian ink brush W/C. 24-Oct-3 Ketterer, Hamburg #416/R est:1800-2400
£1198 $2000 €1749 Peasant table (20x24cm-8x9in) s. ink W/C. 7-Oct-3 Sotheby's, New York #270 est:2000-3000
£1201 $2077 €1753 Circus (29x45cm-11x18in) mixed media. 12-Dec-3 Kieselbach, Budapest #151/R (H.F 460000)
£1300 $2379 €1898 Study of a figure in a doorway with a horse (43x30cm-17x12in) s. bodycol. 8-Jul-4 Duke & Son, Dorchester #65/R est:100-200
£1317 $2384 €1923 After awakening (45x29cm-18x11in) s. ink. 16-Apr-4 Mu Terem Galeria, Budapest #111/R (H.F 500000)
£1448 $2462 €2114 Untitled (29x22cm-11x9in) s. pastel W/C chl prov. 22-Nov-3 Burkhard, Luzern #89/R est:2500-3000 (S.FR 3200)
£1497 $2500 €2186 Profile and potteries (47x31cm-19x12in) s. i.d.verso crayon exec.c.1924. 7-Oct-3 Sotheby's, New York #268 est:3000-5000
£1500 $2505 €2190 Still life with flowers and pears (49x36cm-19x14in) s. gouache paper on card. 22-Oct-3 Bonhams, New Bond Street #30/R est:2000-3000
£1514 $2603 €2210 Man with horse (30x23cm-12x9in) s. gouache W/C. 2-Dec-3 Koller, Zurich #3077/R est:3500-8000 (S.FR 3360)
£1600 $2544 €2320 Deux clowns (80x57cm-31x22in) s. gouache. 11-Sep-3 Christie's, Kensington #73/R est:2000-3000
£1799 $2950 €2500 La couple. gouache. 6-Jun-3 Chochon-Barre & Allardi, Paris #58a
£2449 $4506 €3576 Woman and blue horse (33x55cm-13x22in) s. W/C. 29-Mar-4 Goodman, Sydney #122/R est:6000-8000 (A.D 6000)
£2489 $4231 €3634 Lovers with two dogs (35x25cm-14x10in) s. gouache prov.exhib. 25-Nov-3 Germann, Zurich #27/R est:6000-8000 (S.FR 5500)
£2727 $4636 €3900 Nature morte (50x40cm-20x16in) s. gouache. 27-Nov-3 Millon & Associes, Paris #79/R est:1500-2000
£2857 $5257 €4171 Rider (48x35cm-19x14in) s. W/C gouache. 29-Mar-4 Goodman, Sydney #124/R est:7000-10000 (A.D 7000)
£3000 $5010 €4380 Geometric design (27x21cm-11x8in) i.verso chl exec c.1920 prov. 22-Oct-3 Sotheby's, Olympia #136/R est:1000-1500
£3132 $5418 €4573 Still life of fruit with colour draperies (64x44cm-25x17in) s. gouache. 12-Dec-3 Kieselbach, Budapest #101/R (H.F 1200000)
£3200 $5344 €4672 Vue d'une place (42x57cm-17x22in) s. gouache exec c.1930-40. 22-Oct-3 Sotheby's, Olympia #183/R est:2000-3000
£3243 $6000 €4735 Country Woman (58x43cm-23x17in) s. gouache paper on board. 12-Feb-4 Sotheby's, New York #68/R est:4000-6000
£3258 $5408 €4757 Scene with horses (57x66cm-22x26in) s.d.1912 pastel paper on cardboard. 4-Oct-3 Kieselbach, Budapest #49/R (H.F 1200000)
£3333 $6133 €5000 Lovers (45x29cm-18x11in) s. W/C. 11-Jun-4 Villa Grisebach, Berlin #1581/R est:2000-3000
£3467 $6379 €5200 Female nude with cats (47x299cm-19x118in) s. gouache. 11-Jun-4 Villa Grisebach, Berlin #1582/R est:1500-2000
£4106 $7473 €6200 Bouquet et fruits (63x41cm-25x16in) s. gouache. 15-Jun-4 Rossini, Paris #141/R est:5000-7000
£4600 $8464 €6716 Nature morte (48x38cm-19x15in) s. gouache. 24-Mar-4 Sotheby's, Olympia #125/R est:3500-4500
£4698 $8128 €6859 Music (47x30cm-19x12in) s. mixed media. 12-Dec-3 Kieselbach, Budapest #129/R (H.F 1800000)
£4790 $8000 €6993 Diners (61x75cm-24x30in) s. gouache exec.c.1925. 7-Oct-3 Sotheby's, New York #269 est:6000-8000
£5000 $9100 €7300 The baptism (60x78cm-24x31in) s. mixed media. 15-Jun-4 Sotheby's, London #82/R est:7000-10000
£5080 $9500 €7417 The Holy Family (51x62cm-20x24in) s. gouache board. 25-Feb-4 Christie's, Rockefeller NY #91/R est:6000-8000
£5215 $8500 €7614 Deux nus (85x58cm-33x23in) s. gouache paper on board. 25-Sep-3 Christie's, Rockefeller NY #620/R est:4000-6000
£5500 $10010 €8030 Maternity (88x56cm-35x22in) s. mixed media. 15-Jun-4 Sotheby's, London #83/R est:5000-7000

£8500 $15470 €12410 Nude, erotic scene (81x56cm-32x22in) W/C prov. 21-Jun-4 Bonhams, New Bond Street #43/R est:5000-7000
£8589 $14000 €12540 Femme avec chat (101x73cm-40x29in) s. gouache paper on board. 25-Sep-3 Christie's, Rockefeller NY #619/R est:5000-7000

KADAR, Geza (1878-1952) Hungarian
£2480 $4290 €3621 Thawing in Nagybanya (70x70cm-28x28in) s.d.1919. 12-Dec-3 Kieselbach, Budapest #12/R (H.F 950000)
£3162 $5723 €4617 In the autumn sunshine (68x55cm-27x22in) s. 16-Apr-4 Mu Terem Galeria, Budapest #31/R (H.F 1200000)
£5006 $9061 €7309 Sparkling water (81x90cm-32x35in) s. 16-Apr-4 Mu Terem Galeria, Budapest #65/R (H.F 1900000)
£5270 $9538 €7694 Winter forest (60x69cm-24x27in) s. 16-Apr-4 Mu Terem Galeria, Budapest #146/R (H.F 2000000)

KADISHMAN, Menashe (1932-) Israeli
£656 $1200 €958 Sheep's head (80x60cm-31x24in) s. s.verso acrylic. 1-Jun-4 Ben-Ami, Tel Aviv #4885/R est:1500-2000
£791 $1400 €1155 Sheep's head (80x60cm-31x24in) s. s.verso acrylic. 1-May-4 Ben-Ami, Tel Aviv #4826/R est:1500-2000
£824 $1400 €1203 Sheep's head (80x60cm-31x24in) s. acrylic. 1-Dec-3 Ben-Ami, Tel Aviv #4319/R est:1500-2000
£1366 $2500 €1994 Sheep's head (100x100cm-39x39in) s. s.verso acrylic. 1-Jun-4 Ben-Ami, Tel Aviv #4913/R est:3000-4000
£1500 $2385 €2175 Head (100x73cm-39x29in) s.d.85 acrylic paper on lithographic base on canvas. 11-Sep-3 Christie's, Kensington #224/R est:1500-2000
£1949 $3450 €2846 Lovers (110x110cm-43x43in) s. s.d.verso. 1-May-4 Ben-Ami, Tel Aviv #4825/R est:4000-6000
£2288 $4050 €3340 Sheep's head (110x110cm-43x43in) s.d.1992 verso acrylic. 1-May-4 Ben-Ami, Tel Aviv #4824/R est:4500-6000
£3147 $5350 €4500 Mouton (80x60cm-31x24in) s.i.verso. 27-Nov-3 Calmels Cohen, Paris #65/R est:3000-4000
Sculpture
£1016 $1900 €1483 Donkey in a landscape (35cm-14in) s.verso cut iron. 1-Mar-4 Ben-Ami, Tel Aviv #4709/R est:2400-3000
£1506 $2500 €2199 Standing triangle (29x28x28cm-11x11x11in) s. aluminium. 2-Oct-3 Christie's, Tel Aviv #104/R est:3000-5000
£1506 $2500 €2199 Double arches (39x33x13cm-15x13x5in) s. num.4/10 aluminium. 2-Oct-3 Christie's, Tel Aviv #106/R est:3000-5000

KAEHRLING, Suzanne Blanche (1902-1985) French
£897 $1659 €1300 L'enfant aux jouets (65x54cm-26x21in) s. 17-Jan-4 Rossini, Paris #11/R
Works on paper
£275 $506 €410 Garden party (48x63cm-19x25in) s. pastel. 27-Mar-4 Dannenberg, Berlin #575/R
£276 $510 €400 Tournesols et fleurs des champs (70x57cm-28x22in) s. pastel. 17-Jan-4 Rossini, Paris #12
£276 $510 €400 La place du grand lac (49x64cm-19x25in) s. pastel. 17-Jan-4 Rossini, Paris #25/R
£290 $536 €420 La fenetre (60x45cm-24x18in) s. pastel. 17-Jan-4 Rossini, Paris #14/R
£302 $561 €450 Bouquet de fleurs devant la fenetre (60x47cm-24x19in) s. pastel. 3-Mar-4 Tajan, Paris #109
£310 $574 €450 Anemones en harmonie (44x36cm-17x14in) s. pastel. 17-Jan-4 Rossini, Paris #34/R
£331 $612 €480 Dejeuner sur la mer (47x62cm-19x24in) s. pastel. 17-Jan-4 Rossini, Paris #29/R
£331 $612 €480 Tulipes en eclats (58x44cm-23x17in) s. pastel. 17-Jan-4 Rossini, Paris #50/R
£331 $612 €480 La terrasse (49x60cm-19x24in) s. pastel. 17-Jan-4 Rossini, Paris #52/R
£345 $638 €500 La lecture (57x43cm-22x17in) s. pastel. 17-Jan-4 Rossini, Paris #9/R
£345 $638 €500 Les fleurs du jardin (54x36cm-21x14in) s. pastel. 17-Jan-4 Rossini, Paris #56/R
£379 $702 €550 Les jonquilles (54x45cm-21x18in) s. pastel. 17-Jan-4 Rossini, Paris #31/R
£379 $702 €550 Au jardin ensoleille (62x47cm-24x19in) s. pastel. 17-Jan-4 Rossini, Paris #35/R
£379 $702 €550 Belles de jour roses (63x47cm-25x19in) s. pastel. 17-Jan-4 Rossini, Paris #40/R
£386 $714 €560 Nu au bain (62x47cm-24x19in) s. pastel. 17-Jan-4 Rossini, Paris #43/R
£414 $766 €600 Les amies (37x45cm-15x18in) s. pastel. 17-Jan-4 Rossini, Paris #62/R
£428 $791 €620 Les anemones (59x45cm-23x18in) s. pastel. 17-Jan-4 Rossini, Paris #21
£483 $893 €700 Le dejeuner au bord de Marne (59x72cm-23x28in) s. pastel. 17-Jan-4 Rossini, Paris #55/R
£503 $936 €750 Bouquet de fleurs sur le Gueridon (74x62cm-29x24in) s. pastel. 3-Mar-4 Tajan, Paris #107
£517 $957 €750 La lecture (49x64cm-19x25in) s. pastel. 17-Jan-4 Rossini, Paris #49/R
£517 $957 €750 Francoise reveuse (62x47cm-24x19in) s. pastel. 17-Jan-4 Rossini, Paris #17/R
£517 $957 €750 Le banc vert (46x61cm-18x24in) s. pastel. 17-Jan-4 Rossini, Paris #32/R
£586 $1084 €850 Repos au jardin (43x52cm-17x20in) s. pastel. 17-Jan-4 Rossini, Paris #6/R
£586 $1084 €850 Les deux amies au jardin (49x60cm-19x24in) s. pastel. 17-Jan-4 Rossini, Paris #58/R
£621 $1148 €900 Jeunes filles (59x71cm-23x28in) s. pastel. 17-Jan-4 Rossini, Paris #61/R
£690 $1276 €1000 Le vase bleu (49x60cm-19x24in) s. pastel. 17-Jan-4 Rossini, Paris #47/R
£1034 $1914 €1500 La table devant la mer (59x44cm-23x17in) s. pastel. 17-Jan-4 Rossini, Paris #59/R est:350-500

KAELIN, Charles Salis (1858-1929) American
Works on paper
£1006 $1800 €1469 Rocky coast (40x44cm-16x17in) s. i.verso pastel. 14-May-4 Skinner, Boston #287/R est:600-700

KAEMMERER, Frederik Hendrik (1839-1902) Dutch
£822 $1397 €1200 Girl on the edge of the water (31x23cm-12x9in) s. panel. 5-Nov-3 Vendue Huis, Gravenhage #89
£822 $1397 €1200 Lady as a harlequin (31x23cm-12x9in) s. panel. 5-Nov-3 Vendue Huis, Gravenhage #90/R
£1111 $1756 €1600 Preparing for the music lesson (26x17cm-10x7in) s. canvas on paper. 2-Sep-3 Christie's, Amsterdam #191 est:1400-1800
£2246 $3750 €3279 Market woman (36x27cm-14x11in) s. prov. 7-Oct-3 Sotheby's, New York #144 est:3000-4000
£2800 $5152 €4088 Springtime promenade (25x15cm-10x6in) s. 25-Mar-4 Christie's, Kensington #63/R est:3000-5000
£13889 $23194 €20000 Flirtation (37x24cm-15x9in) s. 21-Oct-3 Sotheby's, Amsterdam #28/R est:10000-15000
£33333 $60000 €48666 Wedding procession (99x160cm-39x63in) s. canvas on masonite. 23-Apr-4 Sotheby's, New York #124/R est:70000-100000
£38000 $65360 €55480 Proud moment (110x75cm-43x30in) s. 3-Dec-3 Christie's, London #7/R est:40000-60000
Works on paper
£1600 $2864 €2400 Worshipper (33x22cm-13x9in) s. W/C. 11-May-4 Vendu Notarishuis, Rotterdam #247/R est:1800-2200

KAEMMERER, Frederik Hendrik (attrib) (1839-1902) Dutch
Works on paper
£351 $586 €512 Villageoise avec seau (30x16cm-12x6in) s. W/C. 16-Nov-3 Koller, Geneva #1289 (S.FR 800)

KAEMMERER, Johan Hendrik (1894-1970) Dutch
£420 $701 €600 Interior scene with mother and child (61x51cm-24x20in) s. 30-Jun-3 Sotheby's, Amsterdam #374/R
£625 $987 €900 Farm by a river (50x90cm-20x35in) s. 2-Sep-3 Christie's, Amsterdam #238

KAESBACH, Rudolph (1873-?) German
Sculpture
£1800 $2988 €2628 Fighting athlete (56cm-22in) s. green brown pat bronze incl marble base Cast f.Pastille. 30-Sep-3 Sotheby's, London #290/R est:1000-1500

KAESELAU, Charles Anton (1889-1972) American
£552 $900 €806 Ship at sea (76x102cm-30x40in) s. 19-Jul-3 Outer Cape Auctions, Provincetown #63/R
Works on paper
£255 $400 €372 Three masted schooner (43x30cm-17x12in) s. W/C. 20-Apr-3 Outer Cape Auctions, Provincetown #87/R

KAESLIN, Reto (1945-) Swiss
Works on paper
£371 $631 €542 Summer idyll (42x57cm-17x22in) s. w/C. 19-Nov-3 Fischer, Luzern #2639/R (S.FR 820)
£500 $830 €725 Mistery of Spring (60x44cm-24x17in) s.d. w/C. 13-Jun-3 Zofingen, Switzerland #2900/R (S.FR 1100)

KAFKA, Cestmir (1922-1988) Czechoslovakian
Works on paper
£1793 $3155 €2690 Abstract composition (53x46cm-21x18in) s.d.61 mixed media. 22-May-4 Dorotheum, Prague #175/R est:60000-90000 (C.KR 85000)

KAFRI (1959-) Austrian
£667 $1200 €1000 Untitled (156x128cm-61x50in) s.i.d.82 verso acrylic masonite. 21-Apr-4 Dorotheum, Vienna #269/R

KAGAN, Larry (20th C) American
Sculpture
£237 $425 €346 Flag (3x30cm-1x12in) prov. 16-May-4 Wright, Chicago #394/R
£363 $650 €530 Flag (3x33cm-1x13in) prov. 16-May-4 Wright, Chicago #389/R

KAGER, Johann Matthias (1575-1634) German
£1793 $2994 €2600 Madonna with child and Infant St John (14x11cm-6x4in) s.d.1606 verso copper. 15-Nov-3 Lempertz, Koln #1073/R est:2800

KAGER, Johann Matthias (style) (1575-1634) German
£5570 $10250 €8300 Joseph and his brothers (180x277cm-71x109in) 25-Mar-4 Dr Fritz Nagel, Stuttgart #662/R est:7500

KAHAN, Louis (1905-2002) Australian
Works on paper
£289 $535 €422 Magic mantle (48x32cm-19x13in) s.d.66 W/C chl paper on board. 10-Mar-4 Deutscher-Menzies, Melbourne #541/R est:1000-2000 (A.D 700)
£328 $518 €479 Flute player and friend (56x38cm-22x15in) s. W/C pen prov. 2-Sep-3 Deutscher-Menzies, Melbourne #387 (A.D 800)
£537 $994 €784 Girl with guitar (49x35cm-19x14in) s.d.76 pen ink. 10-Mar-4 Deutscher-Menzies, Melbourne #511/R est:1000-1500 (A.D 1300)
£723 $1230 €1056 Reclining figures (34x50cm-13x20in) s. W/C. 26-Nov-3 Deutscher-Menzies, Melbourne #153/R est:800-1200 (A.D 1700)
£840 $1528 €1226 Jardin du Palais Royale, Paris (28x38cm-11x15in) s.i.d.1946 W/C ink wash. 16-Jun-4 Deutscher-Menzies, Melbourne #613 est:800-1200 (A.D 2200)

£992 $1806 €1448 Figure group (38x55cm-15x22in) s. ink wash. 16-Jun-4 Deutscher-Menzies, Melbourne #563/R est:1000-2000 (A.D 2600)
£1012 $1630 €1478 Cecilia (73x54cm-29x21in) s.i.d.66 mixed media. 13-Oct-3 Joel, Victoria #375 est:2500-3500 (A.D 2500)
£1053 $1695 €1537 Bali scene, the artist and his model (55x74cm-22x29in) s.i.d.1973 pencil col chk ink wash. 13-Oct-3 Joel, Victoria #335 est:1500-2000 (A.D 2600)

KAHILL, Joseph B (1882-1957) American
£341 $550 €498 Mr and Mrs Nathan A Cushman (69x56cm-27x22in) s. pair. 20-Aug-3 James Julia, Fairfield #852/R
Works on paper
£256 $400 €374 Child picking flowers (69x56cm-27x22in) s.d.1917 pastel on board. 12-Apr-3 Auctions by the Bay, Alameda #246/R

KAHLER, Carl (1855-?) Austrian
£793 $1300 €1150 White Persian cat (61x51cm-24x20in) s. canvas on board. 4-Jun-3 Alderfer's, Hatfield #271
£1453 $2600 €2121 White kitten (35x25cm-14x10in) s. 14-May-4 Skinner, Boston #330/R est:3000-5000
£3693 $6500 €5392 Proud mother (86x97cm-34x38in) s.d.94. 18-May-4 Bonhams & Butterfields, San Francisco #102/R est:10000-15000
£4341 $7250 €6338 Lost in thought (63x76cm-25x30in) s. 7-Oct-3 Sotheby's, New York #126 est:8000-12000

KAHLER, Eugen von (1882-1911) Czechoslovakian
£420 $713 €600 Still life of flowers with books (70x50cm-28x20in) mono. board double-sided. 20-Nov-3 Weidler, Nurnberg #4500

KAHLHAMER, Brad (1956-) American?
£4790 $8000 €6993 American eagles, USA (213x152cm-84x60in) d.i.d.1999 verso prov.exhib. 14-Nov-3 Phillips, New York #102/R est:12000-18000
£8383 $14000 €12239 Ugh Jr. and Missy, American Eagles US (213x305cm-84x120in) s.i.d.1999 verso prov.exhib. 12-Nov-3 Christie's, Rockefeller NY #515/R est:18000-22000
Works on paper
£2235 $4000 €3263 2 Javelinas - car crash Highway 80 (57x75cm-22x30in) s.d.99 W/C ink prov. 13-May-4 Sotheby's, New York #372/R est:4000-6000

KAHLO, Frida (1907-1954) Mexican
£705882 $1200000 €1030588 Self portrait with curly hair (18x14cm-7x6in) oil on tin painted 1935 sketch of self portrait verso prov.lit. 18-Nov-3 Christie's, Rockefeller NY #25/R est:1500000-2000000
Prints
£46667 $85867 €70000 Frida and the miscarriage (31x24cm-12x9in) i. lithograph exec.1932 prov.exhib.lit. 10-Jun-4 Christie's, Paris #1/R est:48000-65000

KAHN, Leo (1893-1983) Israeli
£647 $1100 €945 Landscape of the Sharon Valley (49x69cm-19x27in) s. painted 1940's. 1-Dec-3 Ben-Ami, Tel Aviv #4278/R est:1000-1500

KAHN, Susan B (1924-) American
£466 $750 €680 Reading (51x41cm-20x16in) s.d.1964. 22-Feb-3 Bunte, Elgin #1208
£1111 $2000 €1622 Rausnitz girls (91x76cm-36x30in) s.d.75 prov. 23-Jan-4 Freeman, Philadelphia #179/R est:500-800

KAHN, Wolf (1927-) American
£4545 $8000 €6636 Farm pond (58x112cm-23x44in) s. 23-May-4 Hindman, Chicago #997/R est:800-12000
£5163 $9500 €7538 Great meadows of the Connecticut (71x86cm-28x34in) s. 11-Jun-4 David Rago, Lambertville #263/R est:9000-12000
£5946 $11000 €8681 Guilford Center Grange (51x81cm-20x32in) s. prov. 11-Mar-4 Christie's, Rockefeller NY #106/R est:8000-12000
£6630 $12000 €9680 Autumn landscape (41x76cm-16x30in) prov. 31-Mar-4 Sotheby's, New York #155/R est:6000-8000
£7558 $13000 €11035 Tre alberi (44x89cm-17x35in) painted 1964 prov.exhib. 3-Dec-3 Doyle, New York #89/R est:4000-6000
£9581 $16000 €13988 Young elms and maples (102x133cm-40x52in) s. prov. 9-Oct-3 Christie's, Rockefeller NY #106/R est:15000-25000
£11377 $19000 €16610 Homer Johnson's studio (81x132cm-32x52in) s. prov. 9-Oct-3 Christie's, Rockefeller NY #93/R est:2000-30000
Works on paper
£815 $1500 €1190 Seen between Troy and Bennington (30x46cm-12x18in) s. pastel. 11-Jun-4 David Rago, Lambertville #261/R est:1800-2500
£815 $1500 €1190 Barn with open gates (30x46cm-12x18in) s. pastel. 11-Jun-4 David Rago, Lambertville #262/R est:1800-2500
£930 $1600 €1358 A tree (23x30cm-9x12in) s.d.53 pastel prov. 6-Dec-3 Neal Auction Company, New Orleans #1359/R est:1000-1500
£978 $1800 €1428 Moores farm, west Brattleboro, Vermont (30x46cm-12x18in) s. pastel. 11-Jun-4 David Rago, Lambertville #264/R est:1800-2500
£1159 $1900 €1681 Landscape with grove of trees (28x36cm-11x14in) s. pastel prov. 31-May-3 Brunk, Ashville #152/R est:1500-2500
£1351 $2500 €1972 Landscape (28x35cm-11x14in) s. pastel. 12-Feb-4 Sotheby's, New York #157/R est:2000-2500
£1957 $3600 €2857 Promenade (30x41cm-12x16in) s.d.1979 col pastel. 10-Jun-4 Swann Galleries, New York #126/R est:2000-3000

KAHRER, Max (1878-1937) Rumanian
£333 $600 €500 House with garden (42x53cm-17x21in) s. 21-Apr-4 Dorotheum, Vienna #18/R
£667 $1200 €1000 Hadersfeld (23x30cm-9x12in) s.i.d.1916 verso. 21-Apr-4 Dorotheum, Vienna #20/R

KAHUKIWA, Robyn (20th C) New Zealander
£1038 $1858 €1515 Untitled family scene (56x69cm-22x27in) s.d.75 board. 12-May-4 Dunbar Sloane, Wellington #15/R est:6000-12000 (NZ.D 3000)
£1974 $3355 €2882 Guitar player (112x69cm-44x27in) s. board. 26-Nov-3 Dunbar Sloane, Wellington #113/R est:4000-6000 (NZ.D 5250)
£2182 $3425 €3164 Where to now (59x72cm-23x28in) s.d.1974 board. 27-Aug-3 Dunbar Sloane, Wellington #46/R est:4000-6000 (NZ.D 6000)
£9455 $14844 €13710 Immigrants (70x86cm-28x34in) s.d.1973 board. 27-Aug-3 Dunbar Sloane, Wellington #19/R est:12000-20000 (NZ.D 26000)
Works on paper
£451 $767 €658 Reclining woman (40x43cm-16x17in) s.d.1975 pastel. 26-Nov-3 Dunbar Sloane, Wellington #114 est:1500-2500 (NZ.D 1200)
£1455 $2284 €2110 Ko Hikurangi Te Maunga (151x100cm-59x39in) s.i.d.1994 mixed media canvas panel two. 27-Aug-3 Dunbar Sloane, Wellington #42/R est:7000-13000 (NZ.D 4000)

KAIGORODOV, Anatole Dmitrevich (1878-1945) Russian
£1118 $2058 €1700 Wild gees in flight (60x81cm-24x32in) s.d.34. 25-Jun-4 Millon & Associes, Paris #113/R est:2000-3000
£20000 $34000 €29200 Ryabinushka (68x85cm-27x33in) s. 19-Nov-3 Sotheby's, London #132/R est:6000-8000

KAIJALA, Ilmari (?) Finnish
£296 $473 €420 Klosterbacken in Aabo (37x45cm-15x18in) s. 18-Sep-3 Hagelstam, Helsinki #875

KAINDL, Franz (1932-) Austrian
£493 $863 €700 January sky, March field (56x70cm-22x28in) s.i.d.83 masonite. 19-Dec-3 Dorotheum, Vienna #342/R
£3289 $6053 €5000 Leiser Berg (65x65cm-26x26in) s.d.1959 i.verso chipboard. 22-Jun-4 Wiener Kunst Auktionen, Vienna #352/R est:4000

KAINEN, Jacob (1909-2001) American
£694 $1200 €1013 Argosy II (137x122cm-54x48in) s.i.verso. 15-Dec-3 Hindman, Chicago #111/R

KAIOKU, Nukina (1778-1863) Japanese
Works on paper
£870 $1600 €1270 Saikan yuban - accompanying a friend in winter (29x129cm-11x51in) s. ink hanging scroll. 23-Mar-4 Christie's, Rockefeller NY #106/R est:2000-3000

KAIRA, Alice (1913-) Finnish
£1419 $2540 €2100 The kiss (38x48cm-15x19in) s.d.77. 8-May-4 Bukowskis, Helsinki #264/R est:1200-1500
£1486 $2661 €2200 Self-portrait (63x47cm-25x19in) s.d.1972-77. 8-May-4 Bukowskis, Helsinki #251/R est:1500-2000

KAISEKI NORO (1747-1828) Japanese
Works on paper
£882 $1500 €1288 Landscape with narrow river gorge, crossed by a log bridge (312x66cm-123x26in) s.i.d.1797 ink col hanging scroll sold with wooden tomobako. 4-Nov-3 Bonhams & Butterfields, San Francisco #3071/R est:2000-3000

KAISER, Charles (1893-?) American
Works on paper
£838 $1500 €1223 Still life of boy's toys (38x38cm-15x15in) s. W/C lit. 15-May-4 Illustration House, New York #48/R est:1500-2000

KAISER, Friedrich (1815-1889) German
£900 $1494 €1314 Collecting hay (63x63cm-25x25in) s. 1-Oct-3 Sotheby's, Olympia #204/R
£1597 $2603 €2300 Prussian cavalry near Koniggratz (43x60cm-17x24in) s. 24-Sep-3 Neumeister, Munich #461/R est:3000
£2400 $4344 €3600 Prussian cavalry on the march in the dunes (29x40cm-11x16in) s. 1-Apr-4 Van Ham, Cologne #1462/R est:3700
£65972 $112153 €95000 Battle of Balaklawa at the Sapoune Heights on the Crim-25th October 1854 (153x218cm-60x86in) s. prov. 28-Oct-3 Christie's, Amsterdam #204/R est:20000-30000
Works on paper
£326 $535 €450 Cavalry battle (53x93cm-21x37in) mono. pen brush wash. 30-May-3 Bassenge, Berlin #7876

KAISER, Josef Maria (1824-1893) Austrian
Works on paper
£433 $776 €650 Interior (23x33cm-9x13in) s.d.868 mixed media. 13-May-4 Dorotheum, Linz #547/R

KAISER, Raffi (1931-) Israeli
£564 $975 €800 Pont (116x89cm-46x35in) s.d.71. 9-Dec-3 Artcurial Briest, Paris #329

KAISER, Richard (1868-1941) German
£315 $526 €450 Trees by stream (63x80cm-25x31in) i. 11-Oct-3 Dr Fritz Nagel, Leipzig #3949/R
£333 $610 €500 Summer landcape with pond (79x99cm-31x39in) s.i.d.1904. 5-Jun-4 Arnold, Frankfurt #619/R
£385 $654 €562 Country road on summer's day (62x99cm-24x39in) s.i.d.1910. 28-Nov-3 Zofingen, Switzerland #2611/R (S.FR 850)
£486 $812 €700 Frank landscape (65x100cm-26x39in) s.i.d. 24-Oct-3 Ketterer, Hamburg #186/R
£662 $1205 €1000 River landscape (65x80cm-26x31in) s. 16-Jun-4 Hugo Ruef, Munich #995

£1135 $1895 €1600 Woodland pond (41x50cm-16x20in) s.d.1909 i. stretcher. 17-Oct-3 Behringer, Furth #1511/R est:1100
£2667 $4853 €4000 Landscape with trees by river (170x210cm-67x83in) s.i.d.1902. 30-Jun-4 Neumeister, Munich #584/R est:3000

KAISER-HERBST, Carl (1858-1940) Austrian
£347 $566 €500 Cornwall (63x90cm-25x35in) s.d.904. 23-Sep-3 Wiener Kunst Auktionen, Vienna #115/R
£426 $711 €600 Wienerwald (27x21cm-11x8in) s. s.i. verso board. 14-Oct-3 Dorotheum, Vienna #55/R
£933 $1717 €1400 Corfu terrace Ybso, view towards Albania (31x47cm-12x19in) s.d.1894 i.d. verso board. 9-Jun-4 Dorotheum, Salzburg #598/R
£2013 $3604 €3000 Garden (35x43cm-14x17in) s. board. 25-May-4 Dorotheum, Vienna #153/R est:3000-3600

KAISIN, Lucien (1901-1963) Belgian
£382 $600 €550 Port de peche (60x70cm-24x28in) s. 26-Aug-3 Galerie Moderne, Brussels #276
£400 $736 €600 Vue du port de peche (40x50cm-16x20in) s. 14-Jun-4 Horta, Bruxelles #280

KAIVANTO, Kimmo (1932-) Finnish
Works on paper
£574 $1028 €850 Arabesque (84x61cm-33x24in) s.d.24.II.84 gouache. 8-May-4 Bukowskis, Helsinki #259/R
£1056 $1827 €1500 Flag in evening (37x45cm-15x18in) s.d.1974 gouache. 13-Dec-3 Hagelstam, Helsinki #194/R est:1000

KAIWE, Stephen (20th C) Australian
£823 $1490 €1202 Mand woman, New Guinea (76x57cm-30x22in) s. oil paper pair. 31-Mar-4 Goodman, Sydney #478/R (A.D 2000)

KAKAYAK, Jimmy (1917-) North American
Sculpture
£1396 $2374 €2038 Inuit hunter with seal over his shoulder, carrying a harpoon (28cm-11in) i. mottled grey soapstone ivory. 3-Nov-3 Waddingtons, Toronto #37/R est:2000-3000 (C.D 3100)

KAKS, Olle (1941-) Swedish
Works on paper
£290 $522 €423 Untitled (52x37cm-20x15in) s.d.77 mixed media collage prov. 26-Apr-4 Bukowskis, Stockholm #491/R (S.KR 4000)

KALAEF, Alexei (1902-) Russian
£1192 $2170 €1800 Le chantier (59x81cm-23x32in) s.d.1931. 16-Jun-4 Claude Boisgirard, Paris #81/R est:1500-2000

KALB, Edmund (1900-1952) Austrian
Works on paper
£1974 $3632 €3000 Portrait of a man (57x43cm-22x17in) mono.i.d.25 chl. 22-Jun-4 Wiener Kunst Auktionen, Vienna #140/R est:2800

KALB, Friedrich Wilhelm (1889-?) German
£280 $467 €400 Garden in bloom with campanula (70x50cm-28x20in) mono. panel. 28-Jun-3 Bolland & Marotz, Bremen #774

KALB, John (1968-) Dutch
£1645 $3026 €2500 Great spotted woodpecker (44x59cm-17x23in) s.d.92 s.i.d.verso. 22-Jun-4 Christie's, Amsterdam #594/R est:1500-2000

KALB, Rudolf (19/20th C) German
£268 $494 €400 Wayside cross in winter landscape (70x100cm-28x39in) s. 24-Mar-4 Hugo Ruef, Munich #101

KALBAK, Annelise (1940-) Danish
£587 $1079 €857 Five theatre palms (200x130cm-79x51in) s.d.83 prov. 29-Mar-4 Rasmussen, Copenhagen #355/R (D.KR 6500)

KALCHER, Raimund (1889-1959) Austrian
£448 $820 €650 Villach (175x305cm-69x120in) s.d.1928 oil tempera prov. 27-Jan-4 Dorotheum, Vienna #43/R
£559 $951 €800 Bridge building site in Unterdrauburg (85x110cm-33x43in) s.d.42. 27-Nov-3 Dorotheum, Linz #462/R
£1329 $2259 €1900 Ossiachersee (115x180cm-45x71in) s.d.1940. 27-Nov-3 Dorotheum, Linz #461/R est:2400-2800

KALCKREUTH, Patrick von (1892-1970) German
£333 $613 €500 Four-master on the high seas (80x120cm-31x47in) s. 11-Jun-4 Wendl, Rudolstadt #4103/R
£347 $573 €500 Surf (60x90cm-24x35in) s. 3-Jul-3 Van Ham, Cologne #1285
£347 $549 €500 Waves breaking on beach (60x90cm-24x35in) s. 19-Sep-3 Schloss Ahlden, Ahlden #1572/R
£350 $584 €500 Surf on rocky coast (60x90cm-24x35in) s. 28-Jun-3 Bolland & Marotz, Bremen #777/R
£420 $701 €600 Surf (60x90cm-24x35in) s. 28-Jun-3 Bolland & Marotz, Bremen #776/R
£433 $789 €650 Coastal scene with breakers (60x90cm-24x35in) s. 1-Jul-4 Van Ham, Cologne #1440
£436 $798 €650 Breakers in the sea (60x90cm-24x35in) s. lit. 8-Jul-4 Allgauer, Kempten #2125/R
£455 $773 €650 Waves (61x90cm-24x35in) s. 20-Nov-3 Van Ham, Cologne #1673
£490 $832 €700 Turbulent seas (60x90cm-24x35in) s. 28-Nov-3 Wendl, Rudolstadt #4025/R
£503 $841 €720 Waves (70x100cm-28x39in) s. 26-Jun-3 Weidler, Nurnberg #7054/R
£524 $902 €750 Sea surf on the rocky coast (60x80cm-24x31in) s. 5-Dec-3 Bolland & Marotz, Bremen #726/R
£530 $991 €800 Stormy breakers (68x98cm-27x39in) s. 23-Jul-4 Altus, Berlin #588/R
£537 $988 €800 Ship on the high seas (70x100cm-28x39in) s. 26-Mar-4 Bolland & Marotz, Bremen #629/R
£562 $876 €820 High sea waves (59x78cm-23x31in) s. 10-Apr-3 Weidler, Nurnberg #4403/R
£667 $1207 €1000 Waves (61x90cm-24x35in) s. 1-Apr-4 Van Ham, Cologne #1463
£680 $1238 €1000 Sunrise over the sea (60x90cm-24x35in) s. 3-Feb-4 Christie's, Amsterdam #239/R est:1000-1500
£733 $1327 €1100 Breaking waves in morning light (61x80cm-24x31in) s. 1-Apr-4 Van Ham, Cologne #1464
£769 $1308 €1100 Fishing boats on the open sea (80x120cm-31x47in) s. 28-Nov-3 Schloss Ahlden, Ahlden #1494/R
£811 $1265 €1200 Four master under full sail (83x111cm-33x44in) s. 31-Mar-3 Bloss, Merzhausen #1569/R
£865 $1573 €1263 Sailing ship at sea (70x100cm-28x39in) s. 20-Jun-4 Agra, Warsaw #17/R (P.Z 6000)
£892 $1373 €1400 Waves breaking on beach in evening (60x88cm-24x35in) s. 4-Sep-2 Schopman, Hamburg #256/R
£903 $1472 €1300 Waves at sunset (61x90cm-24x35in) 26-Sep-3 Bolland & Marotz, Bremen #660/R
£1020 $1827 €1500 Stormy sea (61x90cm-24x35in) s. 17-Mar-4 Neumeister, Munich #494/R est:1000
£1274 $1962 €2000 North Sea in evening (62x90cm-24x35in) s. 4-Sep-2 Schopman, Hamburg #257/R est:1400
£1538 $2646 €2200 Rolling seas (69x120cm-27x47in) s. 5-Dec-3 Bolland & Marotz, Bremen #725/R est:940

KALCKREUTH, Stanislas von (1821-1894) German
£306 $504 €440 Konigssee (20x27cm-8x11in) s. 3-Jul-3 Neumeister, Munich #2857/R
£1034 $1728 €1500 Konigsee with Watzmann (20x27cm-8x11in) s. prov. 15-Nov-3 Lempertz, Koln #1635/R est:1500
£1667 $2750 €2400 Mountain landscape in evening light (38x63cm-15x25in) s.d.59. 2-Jul-3 Neumeister, Munich #676/R est:1500

KALF, Willem (1619-1693) Dutch
£6291 $11450 €9500 Still life with vase, fruit and pocket watch (93x77cm-37x30in) 18-Jun-4 Bolland & Marotz, Bremen #505/R est:7500

KALF, Willem (circle) (1619-1693) Dutch
£6293 $10510 €9000 Still life with silver jug and pewter plate on a draped table (48x60cm-19x24in) 30-Jun-3 Sotheby's, Amsterdam #28/R
£31042 $55565 €45321 Still life of food and a nautical cup (88x100cm-35x39in) prov. 28-May-4 Uppsala Auktionskammare, Uppsala #13/R est:250000-300000 (S.KR 420000)

KALFAS, Christos (1955-) Greek
Works on paper
£1100 $1969 €1606 Dispute entre sourds et muets (90x83cm-35x33in) s.d.1998 s.i.d.verso mixed media collage electric light sound. 10-May-4 Sotheby's, Olympia #103/R est:1000-1500

KALIMA, Veli (20th C) Finnish
£268 $494 €400 Child playing on beach (50x61cm-20x24in) s.d.1955. 25-Mar-4 Hagelstam, Helsinki #1034/R

KALIN, Victor (1919-) American
Works on paper
£2416 $4325 €3600 En observation (48x34cm-19x13in) s. gouache crayon ink. 27-May-4 Sotheby's, Paris #115/R est:800-1200

KALINOWSKI, Horst Egon (1924-) German
Works on paper
£467 $859 €700 L'ultime rayon du couchant (38x53cm-15x21in) s.i.d. collage. 11-Jun-4 Hauswedell & Nolte, Hamburg #1372/R

KALISCHER, Clemens (1921-) German
Photographs
£2536 $4159 €3500 India- Banglaore, scaffolds (35x28cm-14x11in) s.i.d. verso vintage silver gelatin. 30-May-3 Villa Grisebach, Berlin #1218/R est:1400-1600

KALKAR, Isidor (19/20th C) ?
£549 $1000 €802 Interior scene with young woman in front of mirror (23x27cm-9x11in) init.d.1876. 7-Feb-4 Rasmussen, Havnen #2253/R (D.KR 6000)

KALLENBERG, Anders (1834-1902) Swedish
£1256 $2249 €1834 Paddle-steamer on fire by rocky cliffs, moonlit night (45x64cm-18x25in) s. after Marcus Larson. 26-May-4 AB Stockholms Auktionsverk #2164/R est:10000-12000 (S.KR 17000)

KALLERT, August (1882-1958) German
Works on paper
£933 $1671 €1400 Artistes (40x27cm-16x11in) s. W/C over pencil prov. 14-May-4 Ketterer, Munich #36/R est:800-1200

KALLIGAS, Pavlos (1884-1942) Greek
£700 $1253 €1022 Church in Santorini (12x22cm-5x9in) init. panel painted 1933. 11-May-4 Bonhams, New Bond Street #73/R

KALLMANN, Hans Jurgen (1908-1991) German
£2734 $4483 €3800 Country doctor outside village (121x121cm-48x48in) s. 4-Jun-3 Ketterer, Hamburg #539/R est:4000-5000
Works on paper
£743 $1330 €1100 Owl (10x14cm-4x6in) s.d.21/6/56 pencil. 7-May-4 Paul Kieffer, Pforzhiem #7821
£743 $1330 €1100 Owl and dove (62x86cm-24x34in) s. pastel. 7-May-4 Paul Kieffer, Pforzhiem #7822
£1667 $2783 €2400 Storm (98x66cm-39x26in) s. pastel. 24-Oct-3 Ketterer, Hamburg #417/R est:2800-3200
£1727 $2832 €2400 Woodland path (98x66cm-39x26in) s. pastel. 4-Jun-3 Ketterer, Hamburg #540/R est:3000-3500

KALLMORGEN, Friedrich (1856-1924) German
£473 $832 €700 Couple in front of houses on grey day (46x48cm-18x19in) s.i. verso board lit. 21-May-4 Mehlis, Plauen #15128/R
£1438 $2445 €2100 Early dusk (43x38cm-17x15in) s.d.95 prov. 8-Nov-3 Hans Stahl, Toestorf #90/R est:2500
£1600 $2864 €2400 Harvesting (31x44cm-12x17in) mono. lit. 14-May-4 Schloss Ahlden, Ahlden #2946/R est:800
£2482 $4145 €3500 Gathering dusk (43x38cm-17x15in) s.d.95 prov. 21-Jun-3 Hans Stahl, Hamburg #96/R est:4000
£2778 $4639 €4000 Dampfer mit Schlepper - the harbour of Hamburg (37x52cm-15x20in) s.i.on stretcher. 21-Oct-3 Sotheby's, Amsterdam #72/R est:4000-6000
£2797 $4755 €4000 Grotzingen landscape (53x59cm-21x23in) s. 29-Nov-3 Villa Grisebach, Berlin #127/R est:250-3500
£3472 $5521 €5000 Gleaner (42x26cm-17x10in) mono.d.1887 canvas on board. 13-Sep-3 Quittenbaum, Hamburg #20/R est:4000

KALLOS, Paul (1928-2002) French
£347 $580 €500 Composition (56x46cm-22x18in) s.d.1960. 21-Oct-3 Artcurial Briest, Paris #658
£733 $1320 €1100 Composition (104x74cm-41x29in) s.d.1956. 24-Apr-4 Cornette de St.Cyr, Paris #578/R
£833 $1392 €1200 Composition abstraite (128x97cm-50x38in) s.d.58. 21-Oct-3 Artcurial Briest, Paris #659/R
£987 $1816 €1500 Composition (81x116cm-32x46in) s.d.1957. 27-Jun-4 Versailles Encheres #46/R est:1500-1800
£987 $1816 €1500 Composition (65x54cm-26x21in) s.d.1958 prov. 27-Jun-4 Versailles Encheres #44/R est:1600-1800
£1467 $2640 €2200 Paysage aux grands arbres (100x73cm-39x29in) s.d.1956 s.d.verso prov.lit. 24-Apr-4 Cornette de St.Cyr, Paris #576 est:1500-2000

KALLSTENIUS, Gottfried (1861-1943) Swedish
£278 $464 €400 Sunset (74x100cm-29x39in) s.d.1930. 23-Oct-3 Hagelstam, Helsinki #900
£480 $860 €701 Landscape (65x43cm-26x17in) s.i.d.1901. 28-May-4 Uppsala Auktionskammare, Uppsala #223 (S.KR 6500)
£591 $1058 €863 Evening landscape towards Vaestervik (50x84cm-20x33in) s.i.d.1911. 28-May-4 Uppsala Auktionskammare, Uppsala #224 (S.KR 8000)
£653 $1175 €980 Oland 's Palace ruins (54x44cm-21x17in) s. 25-Apr-4 Goteborg Auktionsverk, Sweden #172/R (S.KR 9000)
£702 $1257 €1025 Summer evening (54x72cm-21x28in) s.d.1904. 28-May-4 Uppsala Auktionskammare, Uppsala #226/R (S.KR 9500)
£808 $1389 €1180 Autumn day in Grez (36x44cm-14x17in) s.i. panel exhib.prov. 2-Dec-3 Bukowskis, Stockholm #163a/R (S.KR 10500)
£887 $1588 €1295 Coastal landscape - evening glow (70x90cm-28x35in) s.d.33 panel. 26-May-4 AB Stockholms Auktionsverk #2110/R (S.KR 12000)
£903 $1563 €1318 Coastal landscape with pines in sunshine (110x130cm-43x51in) s. 15-Dec-3 Lilla Bukowskis, Stockholm #25 (S.KR 11500)
£923 $1588 €1348 Cloudy summer's day, Brittany (32x54cm-13x21in) s.d.1891. 3-Dec-3 AB Stockholms Auktionsverk #2313/R (S.KR 12000)
£961 $1720 €1403 Archipelago with pines in sunshine (100x130cm-39x51in) s.d.21. 28-May-4 Uppsala Auktionskammare, Uppsala #222/R (S.KR 13000)
£1139 $1971 €1663 Panoramic coastal landscape (30x99cm-12x39in) s.d.35. 15-Dec-3 Lilla Bukowskis, Stockholm #56 (S.KR 14500)
£1147 $1846 €1675 Coastal landscape with vessel (85x83cm-33x33in) s. 25-Aug-3 Lilla Bukowskis, Stockholm #495 est:15000-20000 (S.KR 15000)
£1385 $2382 €2022 Cliffs in the skerries at sunset (64x80cm-25x31in) s.d.32. 7-Dec-3 Uppsala Auktionskammare, Uppsala #193/R est:8000-10000 (S.KR 18000)

KALMAKOFF, Nicolas (1873-1955) Russian
£8352 $14449 €12194 Pharao (55x55cm-22x22in) init.d.1927 panel. 12-Dec-3 Kieselbach, Budapest #183/R (H.F 3200000)
£15000 $26850 €21900 Pharaoh (54x54cm-21x21in) s.d.1927 tempera on panel. 26-May-4 Sotheby's, London #115/R est:15000-20000
£19004 $31546 €27746 Wonder, der (46x58cm-18x23in) cardboard. 4-Oct-3 Kieselbach, Budapest #105 (H.F 7000000)
£41760 $72245 €60970 Forerunner of Our Lord - Saint John - Self Portrait (69x62cm-27x24in) init.d.1921 cardboard. 12-Dec-3 Kieselbach, Budapest #113/R (H.F 16000000)
Works on paper
£5220 $9031 €7621 Seahorses (26x20cm-10x8in) init.d.1947 W/C. 12-Dec-3 Kieselbach, Budapest #62/R (H.F 2000000)
£7308 $12643 €10670 Bedroom (41x39cm-16x15in) init.d.1914 mixed media. 12-Dec-3 Kieselbach, Budapest #60/R (H.F 2800000)
£8352 $14449 €12194 Red Birds (71x72cm-28x28in) mixed media. 12-Dec-3 Kieselbach, Budapest #169/R (H.F 3200000)
£18000 $30600 €26280 Horrors of War (68x92cm-27x36in) s.d.1917 pastel card. 19-Nov-3 Sotheby's, London #188/R est:20000-30000
£65000 $110500 €94900 Salome (103x83cm-41x33in) s.d.1918 mixed media card. 19-Nov-3 Sotheby's, London #189/R est:40000-60000

KALMAN, Peter (1877-1948) Hungarian
£287 $493 €410 Girl with lute (27x23cm-11x9in) s. panel. 4-Dec-3 Neumeister, Munich #2779
£769 $1323 €1100 Two women making music at home (64x53cm-25x21in) s.d.1925 board. 4-Dec-3 Neumeister, Munich #2778/R
£979 $1684 €1400 Five young women sitting together around a table singing (83x74cm-33x29in) s.d.1932 board. 3-Dec-3 Neumeister, Munich #608/R

KALMENOFF, Matthew (1905-) American
£484 $900 €707 Harbour scene with fishing boats (61x76cm-24x30in) s. i.verso. 3-Mar-4 Alderfer's, Hatfield #372/R est:500-700

KALMUS, Leo (1904-1986) Austrian
£862 $1543 €1259 Peasants harvesting in the fields (40x68cm-16x27in) s.d.44. 14-May-4 Dobiaschofsky, Bern #132/R est:2800 (S.FR 2000)

KALMYKOFF, Ivan Leondovich (1866-1925) Russian
Works on paper
£2378 $4042 €3400 Temple (50x65cm-20x26in) s.d.1918 W/C. 27-Nov-3 Millon & Associes, Paris #20a est:450-600

KALMYKOV, Nickolai Pavlovich (1924-1994) Russian
£320 $582 €467 Still life with apples and pears (48x70cm-19x28in) s. board painted 1953. 20-Jun-4 Lots Road Auctions, London #350/R
£380 $692 €555 Still life with apples (28x35cm-11x14in) s. board painted 1956. 20-Jun-4 Lots Road Auctions, London #365/R

KALOGEROPOULOS, Leon (1928-) Greek
£1900 $3401 €2774 Helle, flagship of the Greek Navy (80x120cm-31x47in) s. 11-May-4 Bonhams, New Bond Street #57/R est:1500-2000
£1900 $3401 €2774 Full sail ahead (30x40cm-12x16in) both s. pair exhib. 10-May-4 Sotheby's, Olympia #146/R est:1000-1500

KALTENMOSER, Karl (1853-1923) German
£1127 $1870 €1600 Summer landscape with fields of corn (60x90cm-24x35in) s. board. 16-Jun-3 Dorotheum, Vienna #81/R est:1600-1800

KALTENMOSER, Kaspar (1806-1867) German
£1818 $3127 €2600 The haircut (33x27cm-13x11in) s.i.d.1840. 3-Dec-3 Neumeister, Munich #609/R est:2600
£4861 $7924 €7000 Southern mother with child (29x23cm-11x9in) s.d.1865 panel. 25-Sep-3 Dr Fritz Nagel, Stuttgart #1359/R est:9500

KALUCKI, Jerzy (1931-) Polish
£1379 $2303 €2000 White construction (72x74cm-28x29in) s.i.d.1962 verso oil collage. 16-Nov-3 Agra, Warsaw #21/R est:1000

KALURAQ, Francis (1931-1990) North American
Sculpture
£946 $1608 €1381 Head of an Inuk (5cm-2in) dark soapstone. 3-Nov-3 Waddingtons, Toronto #172/R est:400-600 (C.D 2100)

KALVODA, Alois (1875-1934) Czechoslovakian
£438 $727 €639 Landscape with water surface (23x28cm-9x11in) s. panel. 4-Oct-3 Dorotheum, Prague #53/R est:20000-30000 (C.KR 20000)
£1204 $1998 €1758 Mountain landscape with buildings (57x95cm-22x37in) s. 4-Oct-3 Dorotheum, Prague #71/R est:50000-75000 (C.KR 55000)
£3951 $6716 €5768 Winter in a forest (98x68cm-39x27in) s. cardboard. 29-Nov-3 Dorotheum, Prague #73/R est:80000-120000 (C.KR 180000)

KAMARRE, Maggie (c.1950-) Australian
Works on paper
£1157 $2141 €1689 Untitled (126x347cm-50x137in) synthetic polymer painted 1995. 15-Mar-4 Sotheby's, Melbourne #25/R est:2500-3500 (A.D 2800)
£2479 $4587 €3619 Kurrajong bore (125x366cm-49x144in) synthetic polymer. 15-Mar-4 Sotheby's, Melbourne #24 est:3000-5000 (A.D 6000)

KAMEKE, Otto von (1826-1899) German
£1611 $2964 €2400 High alpine valley with waterfall and chapel (135x95cm-53x37in) s. 26-Mar-4 Bolland & Marotz, Bremen #541/R est:1600

KAMINSKI, Alexander Stephanovitch (1829-1897) Russian
Works on paper
£1000 $1810 €1500 Sketch for orthodox church (46x36cm-18x14in) s.d.1892 Indian ink W/C. 1-Apr-4 Van Ham, Cologne #1465 est:1300

KAMINSKI, Max G (1938-) German
£1034 $1728 €1500 Window picture with trees (110x130cm-43x51in) s.d.1970. 13-Nov-3 Neumeister, Munich #566/R est:2000-2200

KAMINSKI, Stan (1952-) British
£650 $1183 €949 Salute, every morning (53x52cm-21x20in) s. board. 1-Jul-4 Christie's, Kensington #275/R
Works on paper
£300 $555 €438 Salute at sunrise (30x30cm-12x12in) s. pencil W/C. 11-Mar-4 Christie's, Kensington #290/R

£320 $582 €467 St Mark's Square, Venice (34x49cm-13x19in) s. pencil W/C. 1-Jul-4 Christie's, Kensington #277/R
£380 $703 €555 Towards Tower Bridge, London (32x48cm-13x19in) s. pencil W/C. 11-Mar-4 Christie's, Kensington #292/R
£380 $692 €555 Santa Maria della Salute, Venice (53x23cm-21x9in) s. pencil W/C. 1-Jul-4 Christie's, Kensington #278/R

KAMINSKY, Alexander Valentinovich (1822-1886) Russian
£10500 $17850 €15330 Begging for alms (130x102cm-51x40in) s.d.1846. 19-Nov-3 Sotheby's, London #15/R est:12000-18000

KAMIR-KAUFMAN, Léon (1872-1933) Polish
Works on paper
£2609 $4774 €3809 Colombine (96x70cm-38x28in) s.i.d.1916 pastel cardboard. 5-Jun-4 Galerie du Rhone, Sion #548/R est:7000-9000 (S.FR 6000)

KAMKE, Ivar (1882-1936) Swedish
£1536 $2504 €2243 Reclining female nude (81x98cm-32x39in) s.d.1918. 29-Sep-3 Lilla Bukowskis, Stockholm #276 est:15000-18000 (S.KR 20000)

KAMLANDER, Franz (1920-) Austrian
Works on paper
£333 $600 €500 Cow (14x20cm-6x8in) s. pencil. 21-Apr-4 Dorotheum, Vienna #249/R

KAMM, John Daniel (1702-?) British
Miniatures
£5500 $9845 €8030 Prince Charles Edward Stuart (6x7cm-2x3in) vellum rectangular frame prov. 25-May-4 Christie's, London #63/R est:3000-5000

KAMMERER, Paul (1868-1950) German
£867 $1551 €1300 Allegory for summer (55x83cm-22x33in) mono. panel lit. 14-May-4 Schloss Ahlden, Ahlden #2943/R

KAMOCKI, Stanislaw (1875-1944) Polish
£781 $1305 €1140 Landscape of Woli Radziszowskiej (36x50cm-14x20in) s.d.1933 cardboard. 19-Oct-3 Agra, Warsaw #60/R (P.Z 5000)
£908 $1570 €1326 The rectory (51x71cm-20x28in) s. cardboard painted c.1920. 14-Dec-3 Agra, Warsaw #53/R est:6000 (P.Z 6000)

KAMP, F (19th C) Dutch
£4819 $8000 €7036 Scullery maid and her child in a kitchen interior (46x65cm-18x26in) indis.sig.d.1638 panel. 30-Sep-3 Christie's, Rockefeller NY #418/R est:8000-12000

KAMP, Louise M (1867-1959) American
£2374 $4250 €3466 Woodstock garden (112x76cm-44x30in) bears sig. 26-May-4 Doyle, New York #72a/R est:4000-6000

KAMPF, Arthur (1864-1950) German
£379 $702 €550 Woodland path (23x35cm-9x14in) mono. i. verso panel. 14-Feb-4 Hans Stahl, Hamburg #45/R
£629 $1083 €900 Young woman with guitar (69x49cm-27x19in) s. board. 5-Dec-3 Bolland & Marotz, Bremen #580/R
Works on paper
£280 $515 €420 Man's head (35x28cm-14x11in) s.d.1899 pencil. 10-Jun-4 Hauswedell & Nolte, Hamburg #311/R

KAMPF, Eugen (1861-1933) German
£433 $789 €650 Coastal landscape with sand dunes near Knokke (46x53cm-18x21in) s. board. 1-Jul-4 Van Ham, Cologne #1441
£591 $1045 €880 Steamer in stormy seas (42x52cm-17x20in) s. 28-Apr-4 Schopman, Hamburg #671/R
£604 $1111 €900 Thatched farmstead with tree (50x60cm-20x24in) s. board lit. 25-Mar-4 Karlheinz Kaupp, Staufen #2532/R
£872 $1544 €1300 Savoy landscape near Trelechamp (38x45cm-15x18in) s. board. 28-Apr-4 Schopman, Hamburg #488/R
£1200 $2172 €1800 Flanders village (61x80cm-24x31in) s. 1-Apr-4 Van Ham, Cologne #1467/R est:2000
£1200 $2184 €1800 Farmer woman standing in front of a farmhouse (45x55cm-18x22in) s. panel. 1-Jul-4 Van Ham, Cologne #1442/R est:1400
£1389 $2292 €2000 Farmstead in Flanders (44x55cm-17x22in) s. 3-Jul-3 Van Ham, Cologne #1291/R est:2800
£2639 $4169 €3800 Last rays of the sun (30x49cm-12x19in) s. board lit. 19-Sep-3 Schloss Ahlden, Ahlden #1576/R est:2200

KAMPF, Karl (1902-1987) German
£278 $439 €400 Extensive heathland (61x100cm-24x39in) s. 19-Sep-3 Schloss Ahlden, Ahlden #1518/R

KAMPF, Max (1912-1982) Swiss
£498 $846 €727 Houses (27x35cm-11x14in) double-sided. 28-Nov-3 Zofingen, Switzerland #3037 (S.FR 1100)
£819 $1466 €1196 In the studio (49x39cm-19x15in) s.d.38 board. 14-May-4 Dobiaschofsky, Bern #188/R est:2600 (S.FR 1900)

KAMPH, A (19th C) ?
£284 $455 €412 Southern mountain lake (41x62cm-16x24in) s. 17-Sep-3 Kunsthallen, Copenhagen #459 (D.KR 3000)

KAMPHUIS, Gerrit (fl.1761-1772) Dutch
Miniatures
£2000 $3600 €2920 Villiam V Batavus, Prince of Orange-Nassau (6cm-2in) s.d.1764 gilt metal frame rec. prov.exhib. 22-Apr-4 Bonhams, New Bond Street #27/R est:1500-2500

KAMPMAN, Jack (1914-1989) Danish
£271 $500 €396 Farm and fields (33x42cm-13x17in) s. 15-Mar-4 Rasmussen, Vejle #639/R (D.KR 3000)
£282 $470 €412 Rural district at Faroe Islands with view of the sea (46x65cm-18x26in) s. 7-Oct-3 Rasmussen, Copenhagen #363 (D.KR 3000)
£307 $574 €448 Houses by fjord, Faroe Islands (36x49cm-14x19in) s. 25-Feb-4 Kunsthallen, Copenhagen #219 (D.KR 3400)
£376 $677 €549 Houses with sea in background, Faroe Islands (62x75cm-24x30in) s. 24-Apr-4 Rasmussen, Havnen #4112/R (D.KR 4200)
£470 $800 €686 Landscape from Faroe Islands (46x55cm-18x22in) s. 29-Nov-3 Rasmussen, Havnen #4136/R (D.KR 5000)
£489 $832 €714 Field landscape with farms (65x85cm-26x33in) s.d.56. 29-Nov-3 Rasmussen, Havnen #4183/R (D.KR 5200)
£523 $968 €764 Figures and houses (27x35cm-11x14in) s. 15-Mar-4 Rasmussen, Vejle #662/R (D.KR 5800)
£587 $1079 €857 Coastal landscape, Faroe Islands (60x81cm-24x32in) s. 29-Mar-4 Rasmussen, Copenhagen #257 (D.KR 6500)
£633 $1134 €924 Houses by the sea (34x42cm-13x17in) s. 10-May-4 Rasmussen, Vejle #669/R (D.KR 7000)
£670 $1085 €972 Landscape with houses (54x65cm-21x26in) s. 4-Aug-3 Rasmussen, Vejle #594/R (D.KR 7000)

KAMPMANN, Gustav (1859-1917) German
£367 $675 €550 On the banks of the river (20x31cm-8x12in) s. tempera gouache. 11-Jun-4 Wendl, Rudolstadt #4104/R
Works on paper
£270 $489 €405 Odilienberg (36x28cm-14x11in) mono.i.d.9 April 1899 htd white chl. 2-Apr-4 Winterberg, Heidelberg #440

KAMPPURI, Vaino (1891-1972) Finnish
£486 $812 €700 Landscape (35x44cm-14x17in) s. 23-Oct-3 Hagelstam, Helsinki #993
£533 $981 €800 Winter landscape (29x38cm-11x15in) s.d.22. 9-Jun-4 Bukowskis, Helsinki #420/R
£599 $958 €850 Still life (38x50cm-15x20in) s/. 18-Sep-3 Hagelstam, Helsinki #763
£1127 $1803 €1600 Farm (37x45cm-15x18in) s. 18-Sep-3 Hagelstam, Helsinki #791/R est:2000
£1133 $2029 €1700 Mill (50x60cm-20x24in) s. board. 15-May-4 Hagelstam, Helsinki #165/R est:2000
£1268 $2193 €1800 Landscape (37x45cm-15x18in) s. board. 13-Dec-3 Hagelstam, Helsinki #137/R est:2000
£1399 $2378 €2000 Beach huts (50x40cm-20x16in) s.d.32. 29-Nov-3 Bukowskis, Helsinki #22/R est:1700-2000
£1736 $2899 €2500 Landscape (45x56cm-18x22in) s. 23-Oct-3 Hagelstam, Helsinki #1003/R est:2000
£1748 $2972 €2500 Vihavuoksi mill (45x54cm-18x21in) s. 29-Nov-3 Bukowskis, Helsinki #163/R est:2500-3000
£1824 $3266 €2700 Reflections (43x35cm-17x14in) s. board. 8-May-4 Bukowskis, Helsinki #139/R est:1500-2000
£1959 $3507 €2900 Sunny day in February (48x60cm-19x24in) s.d.1946. 8-May-4 Bukowskis, Helsinki #152/R est:2800-3200

KAMPS, Jean (1938-) Dutch
£347 $552 €500 La peche miraculeuse (82x70cm-32x28in) s.d.86. 15-Sep-3 Horta, Bruxelles #178

KAMZOLKIN, Eugen (19/20th C) Russian
£1617 $3008 €2361 In the young forest (44x75cm-17x30in) s.d.1918 prov. 2-Mar-4 Rasmussen, Copenhagen #1329/R est:15000-20000 (D.KR 18000)

KANAGA, Consuelo (1894-1978) American?
Photographs
£1695 $3000 €2475 Alice Rohrer (25x19cm-10x7in) s. gelatin silver print executed c.1930. 27-Apr-4 Christie's, Rockefeller NY #98/R est:4000-6000
£4671 $7800 €6820 She is the tree of life to them, Florida (24x17cm-9x7in) st.sig.verso gelatin silver print exec.1950 lit. 17-Oct-3 Phillips, New York #65/R est:7000-10000

KANAS, Antonis (1915-) Greek
£800 $1432 €1168 Still life of flowers (44x60cm-17x24in) s. board. 10-May-4 Sotheby's, Olympia #168/R
£2400 $4296 €3504 Harbour view (55x81cm-22x32in) s. 10-May-4 Sotheby's, Olympia #23/R est:1500-2000
£3000 $5370 €4380 Mykonos (50x70cm-20x28in) s. 10-May-4 Sotheby's, Olympia #24/R est:3000-5000

KAND, Helmut (1946-) Austrian
Works on paper
£500 $900 €750 Electric meadow (70x70cm-28x28in) s.d.85 mixed media gold canvas. 22-Apr-4 Dorotheum, Graz #98

KANDELIN, Ole (1920-1947) Finnish
Works on paper
£704 $1127 €1000 Bird's-eye view (32x21cm-13x8in) s.d.46 W/C. 21-Sep-3 Bukowskis, Helsinki #367/R
£839 $1427 €1200 Elements of the sea (23x30cm-9x12in) s.d.46 mixed media. 29-Nov-3 Bukowskis, Helsinki #290/R
£839 $1427 €1200 Meeting with the troll artist (23x30cm-9x12in) s.d.46 mixed media. 29-Nov-3 Bukowskis, Helsinki #296/R

KANDINSKY, Wassily (1866-1944) Russian

£135294	$230000	€197529	Murnau coastline II (33x41cm-13x16in) board painted 1908 prov.exhib.lit. 6-Nov-3 Sotheby's, New York #220/R est:250000-350000
£300000	$552000	€438000	Flachen und Linien - Lines and spaces (49x69cm-19x27in) mono.d.30 cardboard prov.exhib.lit. 23-Jun-4 Christie's, London #252/R est:220000-280000
£647059	$1100000	€944706	Launischer strich (70x49cm-28x19in) mono.d.24 board prov.exhib.lit. 4-Nov-3 Christie's, Rockefeller NY #36/R est:600000-800000
£2700000	$4968000	€3942000	Mountainous landscape (33x45cm-13x18in) s.d.1909 s.d.verso board prov.exhib.lit. 22-Jun-4 Christie's, London #24/R est:1400000-1800000

Prints

£1935	$3600	€2825	Kleine Welten VII (27x23cm-11x9in) s. woodcut. 2-Mar-4 Swann Galleries, New York #297/R est:4000-6000
£2013	$3765	€3000	Small worlds VI (27x23cm-11x9in) s.mono. woodcut. 28-Feb-4 Quittenbaum, Hamburg #74/R est:5800
£2500	$4550	€3650	Kleine Welten X (24x19cm-9x7in) s. drypoint. 30-Jun-4 Christie's, London #240/R est:2000-2500
£2516	$4000	€3673	Small world XII (23x16cm-9x6in) s. drypoint. 12-Sep-3 Skinner, Boston #93/R
£2523	$4213	€3658	Second etching for Cahiers d'Art. s. drypoint. 19-Jun-3 Kornfeld, Bern #514 est:7500 (S.FR 5500)
£2644	$4494	€3860	Lithographie Blau (21x15cm-8x6in) s. one of 100 col lithograph pasted on board lit. 5-Nov-3 AB Stockholms Auktionsverk #1243/R est:30000-40000 (S.KR 35000)
£2941	$5000	€4294	Kleine welten VI (27x23cm-11x9in) s. woodcut edition of 200. 6-Nov-3 Swann Galleries, New York #583/R est:5000-8000
£3000	$5160	€4380	Kleine Welten IX (24x19cm-9x7in) s. drypoint prov. 2-Dec-3 Christie's, London #166/R est:3000-5000
£3172	$5298	€4600	Ganymed (15x20cm-6x8in) s. xilograph prov.lit. 13-Nov-3 Finarte Semenzato, Rome #56/R est:4800-5500
£3200	$5504	€4672	Kleine Welten XII (24x19cm-9x7in) s. drypoint prov. 2-Dec-3 Christie's, London #169/R est:2500-3500
£3500	$6020	€5110	Kleine Welten XI (23x19cm-9x7in) s. drypoint prov. 2-Dec-3 Christie's, London #168/R est:3000-5000
£3581	$6517	€5228	Blue. s.i. col lithograph. 17-Jun-4 Kornfeld, Bern #455/R est:10000 (S.FR 8200)
£3672	$6500	€5361	Kleine Welten X (24x20cm-9x8in) s. drypoint. 30-Apr-4 Sotheby's, New York #113/R est:4000-6000
£3800	$6916	€5548	Kleine Welten VIII (27x23cm-11x9in) s. woodcut prov. 30-Jun-4 Christie's, London #239/R est:2500-3500
£3955	$7000	€5774	Kleine Welten VI (36x31cm-14x12in) s. woodcut. 30-Apr-4 Sotheby's, New York #110/R est:7000-9000
£4000	$6880	€5840	Kleine Welten VI (27x23cm-11x9in) s. woodcut prov. 2-Dec-3 Christie's, London #163/R est:4000-6000
£4237	$7500	€6186	Kleine Welten XII (30x27cm-12x11in) s. drypoint. 30-Apr-4 Sotheby's, New York #114/R est:4000-6000
£4491	$7500	€6557	Kleine welten. s. col lithograph edition of 200. 21-Oct-3 Bonhams & Butterfields, San Francisco #1187/R
£4520	$8000	€6599	Kleine welten III (28x23cm-11x9in) s. col lithograph edition of 200. 28-Apr-4 Christie's, Rockefeller NY #56/R est:8000-10000
£4520	$8000	€6599	Kleine Welten IX (31x27cm-12x11in) s. drypoint. 30-Apr-4 Sotheby's, New York #112/R est:5000-7000
£5511	$9920	€8046	Kleine welten III (28x23cm-11x9in) s. col lithograph one of 230 lit. 26-Apr-4 Bukowskis, Stockholm #360/R est:80000-100000 (S.KR 76000)
£7000	$12040	€10220	Kleine Welten II (25x21cm-10x8in) s. col lithograph. 2-Dec-3 Christie's, London #159/R est:7000-10000
£7000	$12040	€10220	Kleine Welten V (27x22cm-11x9in) s. col lithograph prov. 2-Dec-3 Christie's, London #162/R est:7000-10000
£7059	$12000	€10306	Small world I (35x28cm-14x11in) s. col lithograph exec.1922. 31-Oct-3 Sotheby's, New York #295
£7059	$12000	€10306	Radierung 1916, no II (12x8cm-5x3in) s.i.d.1916 num.II brown ink drypoint. 6-Nov-3 Swann Galleries, New York #582/R est:15000-20000
£7345	$13000	€10724	Kleine Welten V (35x27cm-14x11in) s. col woodcut lithograph. 30-Apr-4 Sotheby's, New York #109/R est:12000-15000
£8000	$13760	€11680	Kleine Welten IV (27x26cm-11x10in) s. col lithograph prov. 2-Dec-3 Christie's, London #161/R est:8000-12000
£8475	$15000	€12374	Kleine Welten II (35x28cm-14x11in) s. col lithograph. 30-Apr-4 Sotheby's, New York #106/R est:12000-15000
£10169	$18000	€14847	Kleine Welten III (36x28cm-14x11in) s. col lithograph. 30-Apr-4 Sotheby's, New York #107/R est:14000-18000
£10734	$19000	€15672	Kleine Welten VII (36x28cm-14x11in) s. col woodcut lithograph. 30-Apr-4 Sotheby's, New York #111/R est:12000-15000
£11000	$18920	€16060	Kleine Welten VII (27x23cm-11x9in) s. col woodcut prov. 2-Dec-3 Christie's, London #164/R est:8000-12000
£12994	$23000	€18971	Kleine Welten IV (34x29cm-13x11in) s. col lithograph. 30-Apr-4 Sotheby's, New York #108/R est:12000-15000
£13000	$22360	€18980	Kleine Welten III (28x23cm-11x9in) s. col lithograph prov. 2-Dec-3 Christie's, London #160/R est:10000-15000
£15254	$27000	€22271	Kleine welten I (36x28cm-14x11in) s. col lithograph. 30-Apr-4 Sotheby's, New York #105/R est:14000-18000
£15284	$27817	€22315	Poem without words (32x25cm-13x10in) s. wood cut album of 16 conceived 1903 exec.1904. 18-Jun-4 Kornfeld, Bern #63/R est:35000 (S.FR 35000)
£17000	$29240	€24820	Kleine Welten I (25x22cm-10x9in) s. col lithograph prov. 2-Dec-3 Christie's, London #158/R est:10000-15000
£27972	$47552	€40000	Blue rider (29x22cm-11x9in) col woodcuts exec.with other artists prov.exhib.lit. 26-Nov-3 Lempertz, Koln #820/R est:42000-45000
£39161	$67357	€56000	Woman with fan (24x15cm-9x6in) col woodcut. 2-Dec-3 Hauswedell & Nolte, Hamburg #288/R est:35000

Works on paper

£10227	$18000	€14931	Composition (18x28cm-7x11in) init.d.1933 ink prov. 22-May-4 Selkirks, St. Louis #785/R est:12500-15000
£11888	$20447	€17000	Composition (15x24cm-6x9in) mono.d.33 Chinese ink prov.exhib.lit. 8-Dec-3 Artcurial Briest, Paris #42/R est:20000-30000
£12353	$21000	€18035	Untitled (30x15cm-12x6in) mono.d.25 pen India ink paper on card. 6-Nov-3 Sotheby's, New York #217/R est:12000-18000
£22000	$36740	€32120	Untitled (35x23cm-14x9in) mono.d.29 pen ink prov.exhib. 21-Oct-3 Sotheby's, London #46/R est:20000-30000
£26000	$47320	€37960	Composition (31x24cm-12x9in) mono.d.34 pen ink paper on card prov. 4-Feb-4 Sotheby's, London #489/R est:25000-35000
£26816	$48000	€39151	Untitled (20x28cm-8x11in) gouache W/C pen blk ink exec 1920-21 prov.exhib.lit. 5-May-4 Christie's, Rockefeller NY #138/R est:35000-45000
£42667	$78080	€64000	Tendances tranquilles (35x23cm-14x9in) mono.d.34 W/C Indian ink W/C oil prov.lit. 5-Jun-4 Lempertz, Koln #775/R est:50000-60000
£67000	$121940	€97820	Oui (31x48cm-12x19in) i.verso col crayon card exec.1937 prov.lit. 4-Feb-4 Sotheby's, London #490/R est:70000-100000
£70588	$120000	€103058	Concentric (35x23cm-14x9in) mono.d.24 W/C pen ink prov.exhib.lit. 6-Nov-3 Sotheby's, New York #214/R est:70000-90000
£90000	$165600	€131400	Au-dessus (34x50cm-13x20in) init.d.38 gouache prov.exhib.lit. 22-Jun-4 Sotheby's, London #480/R est:60000-80000
£94972	$170000	€138659	Untitled (19x30cm-7x12in) d.19 W/C India ink prov.exhib.lit. 6-May-4 Sotheby's, New York #108/R est:150000-200000
£106145	$190000	€154972	Ascent (48x28cm-19x11in) mono.d.29 init.i.d.verso W/C India ink prov.exhib.lit. 6-May-4 Sotheby's, New York #443/R est:150000-200000
£173184	$310000	€252849	Untitled (36x25cm-14x10in) mono.d.23 gouache W/C India ink prov.lit. 6-May-4 Sotheby's, New York #112/R est:200000-300000
£420000	$764400	€613200	Aquarell for Poul Bjerre - watercolour for Poul Bjerre (23x34cm-9x13in) W/C pen brush ink executed March 1916 prov.exhib.lit. 3-Feb-4 Sotheby's, London #11/R est:300000-400000

KANDLER, Ludwig (1856-1927) German

£235	$400	€343	Apostle Saint Mathias (81x66cm-32x26in) s.d.1883. 22-Nov-3 Jackson's, Cedar Falls #34/R

KANDLER, Wilhelm (1816-1896) Czechoslovakian

£1389	$2361	€2000	Julia's Forum (37x54cm-15x21in) s.i. verso paper on canvas one of pair. 28-Oct-3 Dorotheum, Vienna #178/R est:2400-3000
£1389	$2361	€2000	Temple of Minerva (37x54cm-15x21in) s. paper on canvas one of pair. 28-Oct-3 Dorotheum, Vienna #179/R est:2400-3000

KANDYLIS, Michalis (1909-) Greek

£1100	$1969	€1606	Ships in Drapetsona, Piraeus (51x63cm-20x25in) s. panel. 11-May-4 Bonhams, New Bond Street #58/R est:1000-1500
£1400	$2450	€2044	Port of Piraeus (60x80cm-24x31in) s. s.i.verso. 16-Dec-3 Bonhams, New Bond Street #107/R est:1200-1800

KANE, Art (1925-1995) American

Photographs

£2933	$5250	€4282	Great day in Harlem (99x99cm-39x39in) s.verso gelatin silver print. 7-May-4 Sloans & Kenyon, Bethesda #1636/R est:1000-1500

KANE, John (1860-1934) American

£368	$600	€537	Commercial Street, East End (20x25cm-8x10in) s. 19-Jul-3 Outer Cape Auctions, Provincetown #183/R
£4063	$6500	€5932	Bathers (25x36cm-10x14in) s. painted c.1928. 17-May-3 Bunte, Elgin #1281 est:4000-6000

KANE, Michael (20th C) Irish?

£1972	$3155	€2800	Blue figure (122x76cm-48x30in) s.d.1990 oil acrylic. 16-Sep-3 Whyte's, Dublin #132/R est:3000-4000

Works on paper

£361	$567	€520	Female nude (22x33cm-9x13in) s.d.63 pen ink. 26-Aug-3 James Adam, Dublin #26/R

KANECKE, W V (19/20th C) ?

£2500	$4550	€3650	Portrait of a lady, possibly Lady Violet Nevill (76x55cm-30x22in) s.d.1907. 21-Jun-4 Christie's, London #194/R est:300-500

KANELBA, Raymond (1897-1960) Polish

£1300	$2301	€1898	Portrait of a woman in a blue dress (91x71cm-36x28in) s. 27-Apr-4 Bonhams, Knightsbridge #135/R est:500-700
£2087	$3464	€3047	Flowers (45x31cm-18x12in) s. painted c.1945. 15-Jun-3 Agra, Warsaw #19/R est:10000 (P.Z 13000)
£3960	$6970	€5782	Woman (61x46cm-24x18in) s. 23-May-4 Agra, Warsaw #14/R (P.Z 28000)

Works on paper

£417	$696	€600	Femme au voile (73x46cm-29x18in) s. W/C gouache. 21-Oct-3 Artcurial Briest, Paris #252

KANELLIS, Orestis (1910-1979) Greek

£8500	$14450	€12410	Girls in interior (73x100cm-29x39in) s. 18-Nov-3 Sotheby's, London #139/R est:3000-5000

KANERVA, Aino (1909-1991) Finnish

£507	$847	€730	The gaze (53x42cm-21x17in) s.d.41. 26-Oct-3 Bukowskis, Helsinki #381/R
£800	$1432	€1200	Portrait of Helge Dahlman (63x48cm-25x19in) s.d.1960 cardboard. 15-May-4 Hagelstam, Helsinki #192/R

Works on paper

£479	$800	€690	Mountain landscape (35x54cm-14x21in) s.d.51 W/C. 26-Oct-3 Bukowskis, Helsinki #379/R
£493	$789	€700	Samos (40x62cm-16x24in) s.d.18.4.87 W/C. 18-Sep-3 Hagelstam, Helsinki #1027
£493	$883	€730	River landscape (48x63cm-19x25in) s.d.64 W/C. 8-May-4 Bukowskis, Helsinki #124/R
£559	$951	€800	Barns in landscape, Impilax (31x40cm-12x16in) s.d.38 W/C. 29-Nov-3 Bukowskis, Helsinki #46/R
£585	$935	€830	Mountain landscape (46x59cm-18x23in) s.d.60 W/C. 21-Sep-3 Bukowskis, Helsinki #368/R
£709	$1270	€1050	Pine trees (62x50cm-24x20in) s.d.66 W/C. 8-May-4 Bukowskis, Helsinki #82/R
£946	$1693	€1400	Branch of rowanberries (50x65cm-20x26in) s.d.19.8.77 W/C. 8-May-4 Bukowskis, Helsinki #51/R
£1224	$2080	€1750	Trees on sandy beach, Helsingfors (21x41cm-8x16in) s.d.49 W/C. 29-Nov-3 Bukowskis, Helsinki #73/R est:500-700
£1486	$2661	€2200	Summer flowers (51x67cm-20x26in) s.d.72 W/C. 8-May-4 Bukowskis, Helsinki #53/R est:700-1000

KANGXI (fl.1662-1722) Chinese

Works on paper

£21337	$38407	€31152	Landscape after the Mi style (24x131cm-9x52in) i. handscroll ink. 26-Apr-4 Christie's, Hong Kong #934/R est:60000-80000 (HK.D 300000)

KANGYO, Sumiyoshi (attrib) (1809-1892) Japanese
Works on paper
£280 $481 €400 Lovers, representation of Shunga (21x33cm-8x13in) ink col gold silk. 5-Dec-3 Lempertz, Koln #805/R

KANN, Frederick (c.1886-1965) American
Works on paper
£1765 $3000 €2577 Aerial grid (18x20cm-7x8in) W/C. 9-Nov-3 Wright, Chicago #249 est:2500-3500

KANNEMANS, Christian Cornelis (1812-1884) Dutch
£4667 $8400 €7000 Two-master approaching a harbour on choppy waters (55x75cm-22x30in) s.d.1850 panel. 21-Apr-4 Christie's, Amsterdam #66/R est:7000-9000
£11348 $18950 €16000 Ships in a strong breeze. Ships on calm sea (60x85cm-24x33in) s. panel two. 20-Oct-3 Glerum, Amsterdam #15/R est:10000-15000

KANNIK, Frans (1949-) Danish
£853 $1365 €1237 Figure composition (120x90cm-47x35in) s.d.2002. 17-Sep-3 Kunsthallen, Copenhagen #148/R (D.KR 9000)
Works on paper
£1218 $2242 €1778 Erotic figure composition (140x75cm-55x30in) s.d.1991 mixed media corrugated card. 29-Mar-4 Rasmussen, Copenhagen #397/R est:12000 (D.KR 13500)

KANO SCHOOL (17th C) Japanese
Works on paper
£4469 $8000 €6525 Autumn plants and grasses (173x244cm-68x96in) ink gold paper folding screen. 10-May-4 Bonhams & Butterfields, San Francisco #4139/R est:9000-12000
£10870 $20000 €15870 Scenes from the Tale of Genji (148x328cm-58x129in) ink gold leaf six panel screen. 23-Mar-4 Christie's, Rockefeller NY #69/R est:20000-30000

KANO SCHOOL (19th C) Japanese
Works on paper
£7059 $12000 €10306 Birds and flowers (434x457cm-171x180in) ink col gold two panel screens pair. 4-Nov-3 Bonhams & Butterfields, San Francisco #3080/R est:15000-25000

KANOLDT, Alexander (1881-1939) German
Works on paper
£467 $835 €700 In conversation (13x9cm-5x4in) s. pencil. 15-May-4 Bassenge, Berlin #6928
£1867 $3341 €2800 Bridge in Besigheim (26x42cm-10x17in) s.i.d. gouache paper on board. 15-May-4 Bassenge, Berlin #6927/R est:750
£3020 $5557 €4500 Winter landscape in Chiemsee (47x62cm-19x24in) s. W/C. 26-Mar-4 Ketterer, Hamburg #492/R est:4500-4800

KANOLDT, Edmund (1845-1904) German
£451 $745 €650 Nervi beach (29x50cm-11x20in) s. i.d.1888 verso panel. 3-Jul-3 Neumeister, Munich #2858
£3200 $5792 €4800 Iphigenia as Artemis priestess (129x95cm-51x37in) s. lit. 1-Apr-4 Frank Peege, Freiburg #1149/R est:4800

KANOLDT, Edmund (attrib) (1845-1904) German
£9091 $15455 €13000 Young Russian girl wearing red headscarf (57x136cm-22x54in) mono. 21-Nov-3 Reiss & Sohn, Konigstein #20/R est:1000

KANONY, Marie (20th C) French
£5556 $9278 €8000 Composition (130x97cm-51x38in) s. s.d.1974 verso. 25-Oct-3 Cornette de St.Cyr, Paris #714/R est:8000-10000

KANOVITZ, Howard (1929-) American
Works on paper
£3352 $6000 €4894 New sky with Andre (203x151cm-80x59in) s.i.d.1972 verso liquitex polymer acrylic canvas prov.exhib. 14-May-4 Phillips, New York #295/R est:8000-12000

KANTAROFF, Maryon (1933-) ?
Sculpture
£1280 $2342 €1869 Abstract (66cm-26in) bronze. 1-Jun-4 Joyner Waddington, Toronto #338/R est:1500-2000 (C.D 3200)
£1696 $2918 €2476 Evolution (29cm-11in) s.d.74 num.4/6 base bronze. 2-Dec-3 Joyner Waddington, Toronto #305/R est:1000-1500 (C.D 3800)

KANTERS, Hans (1947-) ?
£3667 $6747 €5500 Art dealer (44x53cm-17x21in) s. panel prov. 8-Jun-4 Sotheby's, Amsterdam #29/R est:6000-8000
£7333 $13493 €11000 Erotic landscape (57x36cm-22x14in) s.d.1974 panel triptych prov. 9-Jun-4 Christie's, Amsterdam #109/R est:6000-8000

KANTILLA, Kitty (c.1928-2003) Australian
Sculpture
£1138 $1798 €1650 Bird (38cm-15in) earth pigments ironwood exec.c.1988 prov. 28-Jul-3 Sotheby's, Paddington #360 est:1000-1500 (A.D 2800)
£4688 $8766 €7032 Untitled, bird (72cm-28in) earth pigments ironwood exec.c.1988 prov. 26-Jul-4 Sotheby's, Melbourne #52/R est:5000-8000 (A.D 12000)
£9756 $15415 €14146 Purukaparli and Bimi (86x75cm-34x30in) earth pigments feathers ironwood pair prov. 28-Jul-3 Sotheby's, Paddington #86/R est:12000-18000 (A.D 24000)
Works on paper
£2500 $4675 €3750 Untitled (76x57cm-30x22in) pigment prov.exhib. 21-Jul-4 Shapiro, Sydney #2/R est:7000-10000 (A.D 6400)
£3659 $5780 €5306 Untitled (70x50cm-28x20in) earth pigments eucalyptus bark binder prov. 28-Jul-3 Sotheby's, Paddington #359/R est:6000-8000 (A.D 9000)
£4297 $8035 €6446 Untitled (76x57cm-30x22in) pigment prov.exhib. 21-Jul-4 Shapiro, Sydney #4/R est:7000-10000 (A.D 11000)
£10156 $18992 €15234 Untitled (71x78cm-28x31in) name.d.August 1997 verso earth pigment bush gum canvas prov. 26-Jul-4 Sotheby's, Melbourne #223/R est:25000-35000 (A.D 26000)
£13281 $24836 €19922 Untitled (91x68cm-36x27in) earth pigments synthetic binder linen prov.exhib. 26-Jul-4 Sotheby's, Melbourne #50/R est:40000-60000 (A.D 34000)
£19531 $36523 €29297 Untitled (96x71cm-38x28in) bears name.verso earth pigments synthetic binder linen prov. 26-Jul-4 Sotheby's, Melbourne #62/R est:50000-70000 (A.D 50000)
£23171 $36610 €33598 Untitled (96x86cm-38x34in) i.verso earth pigments canvas exec.c.1928 prov. 28-Jul-3 Sotheby's, Paddington #87/R est:25000-35000 (A.D 57000)

KANTOR, Tadeus (1915-1990) Polish
£5164 $8624 €7539 Composition (70x87cm-28x34in) s.d.62 s.d.1962 verso. 7-Oct-3 Rasmussen, Copenhagen #78/R est:40000-60000 (D.KR 55000)
£5172 $8638 €7500 Composition (67x96cm-26x38in) s. oil gouache board. 16-Nov-3 Agra, Warsaw #49/R est:2000
£5913 $10584 €8633 Composition (80x100cm-31x39in) s.d.1961 s.i.verso. 28-May-4 Uppsala Auktionskammare, Uppsala #332/R est:30000-40000 (S.KR 80000)
£6430 $11510 €9388 Composition (80x100cm-31x39in) s. s.i.verso. 28-May-4 Uppsala Auktionskammare, Uppsala #330/R est:40000-50000 (S.KR 87000)
£6504 $11642 €9496 Figure with umbrellas (95x67cm-37x26in) 28-May-4 Uppsala Auktionskammare, Uppsala #335/R est:10000-12000 (S.KR 88000)
£7021 $12568 €10251 Postacie i przedmioty - cgtopic z parasolam (68x69cm-27x27in) s. s.i.d.5.1.1972 verso. 28-May-4 Uppsala Auktionskammare, Uppsala #333/R est:15000-20000 (S.KR 95000)
£7391 $13230 €10791 Postac (93x68cm-37x27in) s.i.d.5.1972 verso. 28-May-4 Uppsala Auktionskammare, Uppsala #334/R est:15000-20000 (S.KR 100000)
£8123 $14946 €11860 Peinture (140x130cm-55x51in) s.verso exhib. 29-Mar-4 Rasmussen, Copenhagen #168/R est:80000-100000 (D.KR 90000)
Works on paper
£403 $734 €588 Sketch of three figures in Napoleon dress (17x21cm-7x8in) s.d.1980 mixed media pastel gouache. 20-Jun-4 Agra, Warsaw #19/R (P.Z 2800)
£425 $761 €621 Study (21x30cm-8x12in) mixed media pastel. 6-May-4 Agra, Warsaw #70/R (P.Z 3000)
£612 $1015 €894 Characters (19x14cm-7x6in) pencil exec. 1968. 2-Oct-3 Agra, Warsaw #3/R (P.Z 4000)
£621 $1037 €900 Sketch of three men in a room (21x29cm-8x11in) s. pastel. 16-Nov-3 Agra, Warsaw #36/R
£1153 $2098 €1683 Person with a hat (19x30cm-7x12in) s. gouache pastel mixed media. 20-Jun-4 Agra, Warsaw #18/R (P.Z 8000)
£4276 $7141 €6200 Multipart (110x120cm-43x47in) s. s.d.1972 verso collage acrylic canvas. 16-Nov-3 Agra, Warsaw #66/R est:3000
£5026 $8996 €7338 Emballage (60x70cm-24x28in) s.d.1966. 28-May-4 Uppsala Auktionskammare, Uppsala #331/R est:30000-40000 (S.KR 68000)
£5172 $9466 €7500 Composition (81x100cm-32x39in) s. s.i.d.20 VI 1961 verso mixed media. 27-Jan-4 Dorotheum, Vienna #163/R est:4000-6000
£6874 $12304 €10036 Composition (99x81cm-39x32in) s.i.d.1962 verso. 28-May-4 Uppsala Auktionskammare, Uppsala #128/R est:40000-50000 (S.KR 93000)
£7021 $12568 €10251 Peinture (80x100cm-31x39in) s.d.1963 verso mixed media exhib. 28-May-4 Uppsala Auktionskammare, Uppsala #329/R est:40000-50000 (S.KR 95000)

KANTOROWICZ, Serge (1942-) French?
£322 $593 €480 Six dernieres tomates du Palace Hotel (146x89cm-57x35in) s.i.d.1985-1986 verso prov. 24-Mar-4 Joron-Derem, Paris #167

KANTSEROV, Alexander Grigorievitch (1877-?) Russian
Works on paper
£662 $1205 €1000 Les chalets dans la foret (42x54cm-17x21in) s. W/C cardboard. 16-Jun-4 Claude Boisgirard, Paris #83/R

KAPELL, Paul (1876-1943) German
£1486 $2661 €2200 On the terrace (40x50cm-16x20in) s. lit. 8-May-4 Schloss Ahlden, Ahlden #814/R est:2400
£10069 $15910 €14500 Concert in the park (62x76cm-24x30in) s. lit. 19-Sep-3 Schloss Ahlden, Ahlden #1646/R est:6800

KAPELLER, Joseph Anton (1761-1806) Austrian
Works on paper
£861 $1567 €1300 Vue de chateau Saint-Ange et de l'eglise Saint Pierre de Rome (37x51cm-15x20in) s.d.1769 wash black crayon. 16-Jun-4 Piasa, Paris #144

KAPLAN, Hubert (1940-) German
£1141 $2019 €1700 Children watching over a small flock of sheep, a village in the background (10x13cm-4x5in) s. cardboard lit. 30-Apr-4 Auktionhaus Georg Rehm, Augsburg #7514/R est:2400
£2000 $3700 €3000 Winter landscape with skaters and horse-drawn vehicles (19x39cm-7x15in) s. panel. 16-Jul-4 Weidler, Nurnberg #8718/R

KAPOOR, Anish (1954-) British/Indian
Sculpture
£13000 $23660 €18980 Echo. one s.d.1993 num.20/30 metal bronze painted wood five prov. 6-Feb-4 Sotheby's, London #122/R est:6000-8000
£67039 $120000 €97877 Untitled (74x74x63cm-29x29x25in) gesso wood aluminium red pigment exec 1984 prov.exhib. 13-May-4 Sotheby's, New York #348/R est:40000-60000
£200000 $368000 €292000 Untitled - from the Voltera series (217x82x40cm-85x32x16in) alabaster on wood base prov.exhib.lit. 24-Jun-4 Christie's, London #16/R est:150000-200000

KAPP, Gary (1942-) American
£2174 $3500 €3152 Last days of summer (53x69cm-21x27in) 22-Aug-3 Altermann Galleries, Santa Fe #37

£3529 $6000 €5152 Wapiti hunters (76x102cm-30x40in) 1-Nov-3 Altermann Galleries, Santa Fe #8
£4469 $8000 €6525 Return to camp (76x102cm-30x40in) 15-May-4 Altermann Galleries, Santa Fe #27/R

KAPPE, van (19th C) ?
£355 $635 €518 Landscape with figures by castle (50x67cm-20x26in) s. 28-May-4 Uppsala Auktionskammare, Uppsala #137 (S.KR 4800)

KAPPIS, Albert (1836-1914) German
£1056 $1690 €1500 Trees (51x37cm-20x15in) s. 18-Sep-3 Rieber, Stuttgart #791/R est:3980
£1745 $3263 €2600 Riva degli Schiavoni, Venice (17x28cm-7x11in) s. i.d.1874 verso paper on panel. 28-Feb-4 Bolland & Marotz, Bremen #292/R est:1300
£2394 $4142 €3400 Ducks on village pond (26x38cm-10x15in) s. board prov. 13-Dec-3 Lempertz, Koln #224/R est:2000
£2766 $4619 €3900 Lake landscape with boats and far off mountains (44x67cm-17x26in) s. 21-Jun-3 Hans Stahl, Hamburg #4/R est:4500
£2937 $4993 €4200 Clouds. Ivy covered wall. Lake shore. Plant (24x34cm-9x13in) st.sig. canvas on board studies four. 20-Nov-3 Van Ham, Cologne #1675/R est:700
£3741 $6810 €5500 Unloading the catch (61x96cm-24x38in) s. 3-Feb-4 Christie's, Amsterdam #238/R est:3500-5000
£5944 $10105 €8500 Harvesting (27x43cm-11x17in) s. 20-Nov-3 Dorotheum, Salzburg #172/R est:3000-4000
£6944 $11458 €10000 Grape harvest possibly in Neckar Valley (24x32cm-9x13in) s.d.76. 2-Jul-3 Neumeister, Munich #677/R est:6000

KAPPL, Franko (1962-) Austrian
£1184 $2179 €1800 White heat (70x100cm-28x39in) paper. 22-Jun-4 Wiener Kunst Auktionen, Vienna #407/R est:2000
£1549 $2711 €2200 Bullet soup (163x142cm-64x56in) s.i.d.1991 verso acrylic chl collage. 19-Dec-3 Dorotheum, Vienna #399/R est:3000-4500

KAPPSTEIN, Carl (1869-1933) German
£307 $500 €448 Cows in a meadow (42x55cm-17x22in) s. board. 28-Sep-3 Bonhams & Butterfields, Los Angeles #7033

KAPRIELIAN, Yetvart (1959-) French
£258 $475 €377 Ruelle Sans Ombrage (56x46cm-22x18in) s. s.i.verso. 23-Jun-4 Doyle, New York #5048/R
£279 $500 €407 Moret sur Loing, bord du canal (33x41cm-13x16in) s. i.s.verso studio st. 8-Jan-4 Doyle, New York #27/R
£326 $600 €476 Village de Ramatuelle, Provence (33x41cm-13x16in) s. s.i.verso. 23-Jun-4 Doyle, New York #5047/R
£382 $650 €558 Foret sur loing (53x66cm-21x26in) s. 5-Nov-3 Doyle, New York #36/R
£408 $750 €596 Port de Sanary (23x28cm-9x11in) s. s.i.verso. 25-Mar-4 Doyle, New York #35/R

KAPUSTIN, Grigory (1865-1925) Russian
£1736 $2951 €2500 Shipwreck (23x16cm-9x6in) s.cyrillic i. board. 28-Oct-3 Dorotheum, Vienna #87/R est:2500-2800
£2394 $4142 €3400 Night and day views of Black Sea coast (17x58cm-7x23in) s. cyrillic panel two. 10-Dec-3 Dorotheum, Vienna #57/R est:3000-3200

KARAS, E (20th C) American
£1667 $3050 €2500 Jeune fille a la guirlande (79x58cm-31x23in) s. 3-Jun-4 Tajan, Paris #285/R est:3000-3500

KARAS, Michael B (20th C) American
£597 $950 €872 Autumn reflections (28x36cm-11x14in) s. 10-Sep-3 Alderfer's, Hatfield #346

KARASEK, Rudolf (1895-?) Czechoslovakian
£702 $1194 €1025 Self portrait. Portrait of a man (51x41cm-20x16in) s.d.1921 double-sided. 29-Nov-3 Dorotheum, Prague #55/R est:20000-30000 (C.KR 32000)

KARASIN, Nikolai (1842-1908) Russian
Works on paper
£882 $1500 €1288 Troika on the Volga (28x48cm-11x19in) s. W/C gouache. 22-Nov-3 Jackson's, Cedar Falls #41/R est:1000-2000
£1078 $2005 €1574 Russian winter landscape with two hunters and horse-drawn sleigh (18x25cm-7x10in) s.d.88 gouache W/C. 2-Mar-4 Rasmussen, Copenhagen #1319/R est:6000-8000 (D.KR 12000)
£2400 $4296 €3504 Cossack on horseback (28x38cm-11x15in) s.i.d.28 Ok 1895 ink wash. 26-May-4 Sotheby's, Olympia #369/R est:1500-2000
£6500 $11635 €9490 Medieval Russian scene (19x16cm-7x6in) s.d.1884 wash W/C. 26-May-4 Sotheby's, Olympia #443/R est:1500-2000
£8000 $14320 €11680 Troika by the river (29x48cm-11x19in) s.d.900 W/C over pencil htd gouache. 26-May-4 Sotheby's, London #87/R est:3500-4500

KARBERG, Bruno (1896-1967) German
£590 $933 €850 Blue foal (64x74cm-25x29in) s. 6-Sep-3 Schopman, Hamburg #800/R

KARBOWSKY, Adrien (1855-?) French
£1538 $2646 €2200 Portrait presume de Louise Breslau (44x32cm-17x13in) s. prov. 8-Dec-3 Rossini, Paris #98/R est:1200-1500

KARDAMATIS, Ioannis (1916-) Greek
Works on paper
£1100 $1969 €1606 Goldon doors (215x83cm-85x33in) wood plastic plaster two. 10-May-4 Sotheby's, Olympia #64/R est:600-800

KARDORFF, Konrad von (1877-1945) German
Works on paper
£1067 $1931 €1600 Children playing on summer's day (41x49cm-16x19in) s.d.15 pastel. 1-Apr-4 Van Ham, Cologne #1468/R est:1800
£1189 $2021 €1700 On the Landwehrkanal (22x29cm-9x11in) s.d.12 pastel. 29-Nov-3 Villa Grisebach, Berlin #588/R est:1500-2000

KAREDADA, Lily (c.1937-) Australian
Works on paper
£293 $548 €440 Wandjina (57x38cm-22x15in) pigment exec. c.1998 prov. 21-Jul-4 Shapiro, Sydney #28/R (A.D 750)
£313 $584 €468 Wandjina (57x38cm-22x15in) pigment exec. c.1996 prov. 21-Jul-4 Shapiro, Sydney #30/R (A.D 800)
£353 $632 €515 Wadjina (56x17cm-22x7in) natural earth pigments bark exec 2002. 25-May-4 Lawson Menzies, Sydney #166/R (A.D 900)
£373 $667 €545 Wadjina (52x16cm-20x6in) natural earth pigments bark exec 2002. 25-May-4 Lawson Menzies, Sydney #167/R (A.D 950)
£469 $877 €704 Untitled (33x89cm-13x35in) earth pigments eucalyptus bark exec.c.1975. 26-Jul-4 Sotheby's, Melbourne #455 (A.D 1200)

KARELLA, Marina (1940-) American
Sculpture
£1000 $1790 €1460 Untitled (226x136cm-89x54in) bronze relief. 10-May-4 Sotheby's, Olympia #91/R est:1000-1500

KARER, F (19th C) German
£1331 $2183 €1850 Romantic river landscape with washerwomen and cows (51x64cm-20x25in) s.d.1876. 3-Jun-3 Sigalas, Stuttgart #423/R est:1950

KARFIOL, Bernard (1886-1952) American
£391 $700 €571 Two women (28x56cm-11x22in) s.d.1917. 8-Jan-4 James Julia, Fairfield #1037/R
£939 $1700 €1371 Seated nude (56x46cm-22x18in) s. 16-Apr-4 James Julia, Fairfield #803/R est:800-1000
£966 $1700 €1410 World War II lovers (30x41cm-12x16in) s. prov. 3-Jan-4 Collins, Maine #18/R est:1000-1500
£1364 $2400 €1991 Maine farmhouse (46x69cm-18x27in) s. prov. 3-Jan-4 Collins, Maine #17/R est:1200-1600
£2963 $4800 €4296 Young bathers (36x51cm-14x20in) 8-Aug-3 Barridorf, Portland #191/R est:2000-3000
£3704 $6000 €5371 After a swim, Ogunquit Beach (99x63cm-39x25in) prov. 8-Aug-3 Barridorf, Portland #187/R est:4000-6000

KARFVE, Fritz (1880-1967) Swedish
£887 $1588 €1295 Still life of flowers in jugs and vases (92x76cm-36x30in) s.d.35. 28-May-4 Uppsala Auktionskammare, Uppsala #268/R (S.KR 12000)

KARGEL, Axel (1896-1971) Swedish
£1335 $2310 €1949 Arcadic landscape (30x44cm-12x17in) s.i.d.1955 panel exhib. 15-Dec-3 Lilla Bukowskis, Stockholm #545 est:6000-8000 (S.KR 17000)

KARGER, Karl (attrib) (1848-1913) Austrian
£333 $600 €500 Girl at school (24x39cm-9x15in) 26-Apr-4 Rieber, Stuttgart #1174/R

KARGER, Richard (attrib) (20th C) ?
£300 $552 €450 Female nude (75x60cm-30x24in) i. 11-Jun-4 Wendl, Rudolstadt #4105/R

KARIMO, Aarno (1886-1952) Finnish
£282 $451 €400 Famine year (23x26cm-9x10in) s.d.1931. 18-Sep-3 Hagelstam, Helsinki #793/R

KARINGER, Anton (1829-1870) Austrian
£1700 $3043 €2482 Tuareglager (31x40cm-12x16in) s.d.1869 paper on panel. 28-May-4 Uppsala Auktionskammare, Uppsala #121/R est:5000-6000 (S.KR 23000)

KARLOVSKY, Bertalan de (1858-c.1938) Austrian
£1159 $2098 €1692 Female nude (54x34cm-21x13in) s. oil on wood. 16-Apr-4 Mu Terem Galeria, Budapest #163/R (H.F 440000)
£4072 $6760 €5945 Female portrait (70x51cm-28x20in) s. panel. 4-Oct-3 Kieselbach, Budapest #66/R (H.F 1500000)
Works on paper
£501 $906 €731 Loving (24x17cm-9x7in) s. mixed media. 16-Apr-4 Mu Terem Galeria, Budapest #41/R (H.F 190000)

KARLOWSKA, Stanislawa (1876-1952) Polish
£550 $974 €803 Town on the banks of a river (32x27cm-13x11in) s. board. 27-Apr-4 Bonhams, Knightsbridge #72/R
£600 $1032 €876 Houses along the shore (32x27cm-13x11in) s. board. 3-Dec-3 Christie's, Kensington #695/R
£3000 $5550 €4380 Mydlow (43x53cm-17x21in) s. 11-Mar-4 Christie's, Kensington #77 est:1500-2000

KARLSON, Fritz (?) Swedish
£426 $711 €600 Caleche en Siberie (160x214cm-63x84in) s. 17-Jun-3 Vanderkindere, Brussels #6

KARLSSON, C Goran (1944-) Swedish
£680 $1156 €993 Composition (77x57cm-30x22in) init.d.89 tempera. 5-Nov-3 AB Stockholms Auktionsverk #831/R (S.KR 9000)
£1245 $2204 €1818 Horrods ballet (80x60cm-31x24in) init.d.88 tempera panel. 27-Apr-4 AB Stockholms Auktionsverk #1146/R est:10000-12000 (S.KR 17000)
Works on paper
£319 $574 €466 Untitled (38x29cm-15x11in) init.d.96 gouache. 26-Apr-4 Bukowskis, Stockholm #514/R (S.KR 4400)
£403 $713 €588 Figure marching (38x14cm-15x6in) init.d.95 gouache. 27-Apr-4 AB Stockholms Auktionsverk #1136/R (S.KR 5500)

KARLSSON-STIG, Ante (1885-1967) Swedish
£1346 $2315 €1965 Northern landscape in spring (59x75cm-23x30in) s.d.17. 3-Dec-3 AB Stockholms Auktionsverk #2529/R est:10000-15000 (S.KR 17500)

KARNEC, J E (1875-1934) Austrian
£1118 $2058 €1700 Marine (33x41cm-13x16in) s. panel on isorel. 24-Jun-4 Claude Boisgirard, Paris #17/R est:900-1000
Works on paper
£397 $743 €600 Voilier au port (18x28cm-7x11in) mono. W/C gouache. 24-Jul-4 Thierry & Lannon, Brest #63

KARNEC, Jean Etienne (1875-1934) Austrian
£867 $1577 €1300 Vue du port (19x28cm-7x11in) s. panel. 5-Jul-4 Le Mouel, Paris #22/R
£921 $1667 €1400 Vue sur Rouen (22x27cm-9x11in) s. 19-Apr-4 Boscher, Cherbourg #862/R

KAROLDT, Alexander (?) ?
£397 $723 €600 Still life with vases (66x48cm-26x19in) 21-Jun-4 Pandolfini, Florence #104

KAROLY, Gerna (1867-1944) Hungarian
£417 $688 €600 Scene de rue Orientaliste (60x78cm-24x31in) s.i. 3-Jul-3 Claude Aguttes, Neuilly #112b
£417 $688 €600 Scene de rue Orientaliste (80x60cm-31x24in) s.i. 3-Jul-3 Claude Aguttes, Neuilly #112a
£1333 $2427 €2000 Caravan (76x126cm-30x50in) s. 3-Jul-4 Badum, Bamberg #258/R est:4000

KARPATHY, Eugène (1871-1950) French?
£680 $1218 €1000 Dreve animee (65x70cm-26x28in) s. 17-Mar-4 Hotel des Ventes Mosan, Brussels #106

KARPATHY, Jeno (1871-?) Hungarian
£400 $668 €584 Boat trip to market (61x79cm-24x31in) s. 8-Oct-3 Christie's, Kensington #907
£706 $1172 €1031 Sea (80x132cm-31x52in) s. 4-Oct-3 Kieselbach, Budapest #197/R (H.F 260000)
£1057 $1797 €1543 Faraglioni rocks (80x132cm-31x52in) s.i. 5-Nov-3 Dobiaschofsky, Bern #706/R est:1700 (S.FR 2400)
£1342 $2510 €2000 Southern village street (100x74cm-39x29in) s. 24-Feb-4 Dorotheum, Vienna #187/R est:2400-3000

KARPATHY, Laszlo (20th C) Hungarian
£629 $1051 €900 Winter landscape (60x80cm-24x31in) 10-Oct-3 Stadion, Trieste #82/R

KARPELES, Andree (1885-?) French
£1497 $2679 €2200 Dans la foret srilankaise (60x81cm-24x32in) s.i.d.1912 lit. 21-Mar-4 St-Germain-en-Laye Encheres #118/R est:2000-2500

KARPFF, Jean Jacques (1770-1829) French
Works on paper
£884 $1583 €1300 Portrait de Gottlieb Konrad Pfeffel en buste (16x11cm-6x4in) i. black chk estompe oval. 18-Mar-4 Christie's, Paris #211/R

KARPINSKI, Alfons (1875-1961) Polish
£969 $1648 €1415 Still life with yellow roses in porcelain vase (32x42cm-13x17in) s. board. 5-Nov-3 Dobiaschofsky, Bern #707/R (S.FR 2200)
£990 $1743 €1445 Still life of flowers (35x49cm-14x19in) s. board. 23-May-4 Agra, Warsaw #36/R (P.Z 7000)
£1081 $1967 €1578 Jug of roses (35x50cm-14x20in) s. paper board. 20-Jun-4 Agra, Warsaw #21/R (P.Z 7500)
£1176 $1834 €1717 Pink roses (25x42cm-10x17in) s.d.944 cardboard. 30-Mar-3 Agra, Warsaw #41/R est:7000 (P.Z 7500)
£2017 $3671 €2945 Still life with flowers, bottle and plate (48x58cm-19x23in) s.d.1946 paper board. 20-Jun-4 Agra, Warsaw #20/R (P.Z 14000)
£32000 $58240 €46720 Au cafe concert (113x197cm-44x78in) s.d.1907 prov. 15-Jun-4 Sotheby's, London #55/R est:30000-50000

KARPOFF, Ivan (1898-1970) Russian
£468 $767 €650 Mountains (50x70cm-20x28in) s. i.verso. 10-Jun-3 Pandolfini, Florence #343/R
£600 $1074 €900 Winter landscape (50x70cm-20x28in) s. 12-May-4 Stadion, Trieste #659/R
£800 $1432 €1200 Fishermen in Venice (62x85cm-24x33in) s. 12-May-4 Stadion, Trieste #639/R
£845 $1479 €1200 Salt tower in Milan (40x29cm-16x11in) board. 17-Dec-3 Finarte Semenzato, Milan #249/R
£940 $1682 €1400 Seascape (40x75cm-16x30in) s. 25-May-4 Finarte Semenzato, Milan #42/R est:800-1000
£1690 $2958 €2400 Snowfall (70x100cm-28x39in) s. board. 17-Dec-3 Il Ponte, Milan #580/R est:2500-3000

KARPOV, E (19th C) Russian
Sculpture
£13000 $23270 €18980 Merchant couple being driven on a troika (38x80cm-15x31in) bronze st.f.Chopin. 26-May-4 Sotheby's, London #464/R est:5000-7000

KARPPANEN, Matti (1873-1953) Finnish
£845 $1352 €1200 Duck (35x47cm-14x19in) s. 21-Sep-3 Bukowskis, Helsinki #369/R
£1267 $2267 €1900 Stone crushers - birds on branch with berries (40x40cm-16x16in) s.d.1933. 15-May-4 Hagelstam, Helsinki #124/R est:2500
£1333 $2387 €2000 Wild geese (46x62cm-18x24in) s.d.1947. 15-May-4 Hagelstam, Helsinki #121/R est:3000
£1600 $2864 €2400 Snowbunting (17x22cm-7x9in) s. panel. 15-May-4 Hagelstam, Helsinki #126/R est:1500
£1667 $2983 €2500 Marsh harriers (55x39cm-22x15in) s.d.1927. 15-May-4 Hagelstam, Helsinki #125/R est:3500
£1892 $3386 €2800 Redstarts on branch in Haminanlax (17x24cm-7x9in) s.d.1903 board. 8-May-4 Bukowskis, Helsinki #144/R est:3000-3500
£2000 $3580 €3000 Crested larks (36x38cm-14x15in) s.d.1935. 15-May-4 Hagelstam, Helsinki #123/R est:2500
£2349 $4322 €3500 Black grouse (61x58cm-24x23in) s.d.1952. 25-Mar-4 Hagelstam, Helsinki #970/R est:3500
£6294 $10699 €9000 Capercaillies on branch (75x92cm-30x36in) s.d.1926. 29-Nov-3 Bukowskis, Helsinki #189/R est:7000-8000

KARRUWARA, Wattie (c.1910-1983) Australian
Sculpture
£1138 $1798 €1650 Untitled, didjeridu with prawn and other creatures (157cm-62in) earth pigments synthetic polymer paint hardwood exec.c.1965. 28-Jul-3 Sotheby's, Paddington #55/R est:3000-5000 (A.D 2800)
£1789 $2826 €2594 Untitled, didjeridu with sea creatures and figure (157cm-62in) earth pigments synthetic polymer paint hardwood exec.c.1965. 28-Jul-3 Sotheby's, Paddington #54/R est:4000-6000 (A.D 4400)
£1870 $2954 €2712 Untitled, shield with figures (69cm-27in) synthetic polymer paint softwood exec.c.1965. 28-Jul-3 Sotheby's, Paddington #41/R est:4000-6000 (A.D 4600)
£2033 $3211 €2948 Untitled, coolamon with face and landscape (64cm-25in) earth pigment synthetic polymer paint hardwood exec.c.1965. 28-Jul-3 Sotheby's, Paddington #33/R est:5000-8000 (A.D 5000)
£2642 $4175 €3831 Untitled, shield (85cm-33in) synthetic polymer paint hardwood exec.c.1965. 28-Jul-3 Sotheby's, Paddington #42/R est:4000-6000 (A.D 6500)
£3862 $6102 €5600 Untitled, coolamon with head, torso and landscape (66cm-26in) earth pigments synthetic polymer paint hardwood exec.c.1965. 28-Jul-3 Sotheby's, Paddington #34/R est:5000-8000 (A.D 9500)
£4065 $6423 €5894 Untitled, coolamon with face and animals (67cm-26in) earth pigments synthetic polymer paint hardwood exec.c.1965. 28-Jul-3 Sotheby's, Paddington #32/R est:7000-10000 (A.D 10000)
£4065 $6423 €5894 Untitled, coolamon with figures and animals (61cm-24in) earth pigments hardwood exec.c.1965. 28-Jul-3 Sotheby's, Paddington #35/R est:7000-10000 (A.D 10000)
£5285 $8350 €7663 Untitled, coolamon with Wanjina, a spirit and animals in a landscape (63cm-25in) earth pigments synthetic polymer paint hardwood exec.c.1965. 28-Jul-3 Sotheby's, Paddington #31/R est:7000-10000 (A.D 13000)
Works on paper
£2439 $3854 €3537 Wanjina (41x23cm-16x9in) earth pigments eucalyptus bark exec.c.1962 prov. 28-Jul-3 Sotheby's, Paddington #72/R est:12000-18000 (A.D 6000)
£2846 $4496 €4127 Untitled, cliffs, burnt hinterland and the sea with creatures (57x78cm-22x31in) W/C exec.c.1965. 28-Jul-3 Sotheby's, Paddington #28/R est:7000-10000 (A.D 7000)
£3659 $5780 €5306 Untitled, Bunjunni Island in St George Basin (56x76cm-22x30in) W/C exec.c.1965. 28-Jul-3 Sotheby's, Paddington #22/R est:8000-12000 (A.D 9000)
£4065 $6423 €5894 Untitled, skinks beneath a mountain range (57x76cm-22x30in) W/C exec.c.1965. 28-Jul-3 Sotheby's, Paddington #29/R est:10000-15000 (A.D 10000)
£5894 $9313 €8546 Untitled, burnt country fringing the tidal flats and sea (57x78cm-22x31in) W/C exec.c.1965. 28-Jul-3 Sotheby's, Paddington #20/R est:8000-12000 (A.D 14500)
£6098 $9634 €8842 Untitled, variety of birds (56x77cm-22x30in) W/C exec.c.1965. 28-Jul-3 Sotheby's, Paddington #6/R est:15000-25000 (A.D 15000)
£6098 $9634 €8842 Untitled, landscape with emus, snakes, wallabies and an ibis (56x78cm-22x31in) W/C exec.c.1965. 28-Jul-3 Sotheby's, Paddington #8/R est:10000-15000 (A.D 15000)
£6098 $9634 €8842 Untitled, Ngayangkanen, Mount Trafalgar with animals (57x78cm-22x31in) W/C exec.c.1965. 28-Jul-3 Sotheby's, Paddington #16/R est:15000-25000 (A.D 15000)
£6098 $9634 €8842 Untitled, sea filled with fish, turtle and crocodile (57x76cm-22x30in) W/C exec.c.1965. 28-Jul-3 Sotheby's, Paddington #23/R est:15000-25000 (A.D 15000)
£6504 $10276 €9431 Untitled, after the fire (56x76cm-22x30in) W/C exec.c.1965. 28-Jul-3 Sotheby's, Paddington #4/R est:15000-25000 (A.D 16000)
£6504 $10276 €9431 Untitled, rock face (57x77cm-22x30in) W/C exec.c.1965. 28-Jul-3 Sotheby's, Paddington #14/R est:8000-10000 (A.D 16000)
£7317 $11561 €10610 Untitled, landscape with birds and wallabies (56x76cm-22x30in) W/C exec.c.1965. 28-Jul-3 Sotheby's, Paddington #2/R est:15000-25000 (A.D 18000)
£7724 $12203 €11200 Untitled, serpents and birds (56x76cm-22x30in) W/C exec.c.1965. 28-Jul-3 Sotheby's, Paddington #10/R est:20000-30000 (A.D 19000)
£7724 $12203 €11200 Untitled, rocky outcrops with animals (56x76cm-22x30in) W/C exec.c.1965. 28-Jul-3 Sotheby's, Paddington #25/R est:20000-30000 (A.D 19000)
£8130 $12846 €11789 Untitled, emu and wallabies feeding in the scrub (57x76cm-22x30in) W/C exec.c.1965. 28-Jul-3 Sotheby's, Paddington #1/R est:20000-30000 (A.D 20000)
£8130 $12846 €11789 Untitled, emus, wallabies and pair of eagles (56x76cm-22x30in) W/C exec.c.1965. 28-Jul-3 Sotheby's, Paddington #7/R est:20000-30000 (A.D 20000)
£8130 $12846 €11789 Untitled, wallabies and birds (57x76cm-22x30in) W/C exec.c.1965. 28-Jul-3 Sotheby's, Paddington #13/R est:20000-30000 (A.D 20000)
£8130 $12846 €11789 Untitled, landscape with kurrajongs, acacias and boabs (56x76cm-22x30in) W/C exec.c.1965. 28-Jul-3 Sotheby's, Paddington #24/R est:20000-30000 (A.D 20000)
£8537 $13488 €12379 Untitled, sea eagles on an outcrop (77x57cm-30x22in) W/C exec.c.1965. 28-Jul-3 Sotheby's, Paddington #21/R est:25000-35000 (A.D 21000)
£8594 $16070 €12891 Wanjina (78x31cm-31x12in) earth pigments eucalyptus bark prov. 26-Jul-4 Sotheby's, Melbourne #16/R est:15000-20000 (A.D 22000)

£8943	$14130	€12967	Untitled, landscape with birds, emus and jabiru (56x76cm-22x30in) W/C exec.c.1965. 28-Jul-3 Sotheby's, Paddington #5/R est:15000-25000 (A.D 22000)
£9756	$15415	€14146	Untitled, emus and wallabies in acacia scrub (56x76cm-22x30in) W/C exec.c.1965. 28-Jul-3 Sotheby's, Paddington #3/R est:20000-30000 (A.D 24000)
£10163	$16057	€14736	Untitled, grassland, and marshland, with birds (56x76cm-22x30in) W/C exec.c.1965. 28-Jul-3 Sotheby's, Paddington #11/R est:20000-30000 (A.D 25000)
£12195	$19268	€17683	Untitled, spirit beings and animals (56x76cm-22x30in) W/C exec.c.1965. 28-Jul-3 Sotheby's, Paddington #15/R est:30000-40000 (A.D 30000)
£13821	$21837	€20040	Untitled, landscape with animals (56x76cm-22x30in) W/C exec.c.1965. 28-Jul-3 Sotheby's, Paddington #9/R est:25000-35000 (A.D 34000)

KARS, Georges (1882-1945) Czechoslovakian

£3636	$6073	€5200	Odalisque (46x33cm-18x13in) s. d.45 verso. 25-Jun-3 Rabourdin & Choppin de Janvry, Paris #43/R est:5000-5500
£5986	$10356	€8500	Modele nu assis (46x55cm-18x22in) s.d.1933. 14-Dec-3 Eric Pillon, Calais #127/R

Works on paper

£272	$487	€400	Etude de nu (48x63cm-19x25in) s. chl col crayon. 22-Mar-4 Digard, Paris #114g

KARSEN, Jan Eduard (1860-1941) Dutch

£987	$1816	€1500	Pampus by moonlight (38x48cm-15x19in) s. 28-Jun-4 Sotheby's, Amsterdam #62/R est:1500-2000
£1389	$2194	€2000	Achter eene boerderij (17x27cm-7x11in) s. panel exhib. 2-Sep-3 Christie's, Amsterdam #225/R est:2500-3500

KARSEN, Kaspar (1810-1896) Dutch

£3125	$5313	€4500	View of a town by a river in Germany (14x19cm-6x7in) s. panel. 28-Oct-3 Christie's, Amsterdam #5/R est:3000-5000
£3333	$5567	€4800	View of Scheveningen (26x35cm-10x14in) s.d.1885 panel. 21-Oct-3 Sotheby's, Amsterdam #62/R est:5000-7000
£5333	$9600	€8000	Figures on a frozen city canal at dusk (21x27cm-8x11in) s.d.1880 panel. 21-Apr-4 Christie's, Amsterdam #29/R est:3000-5000
£8333	$13917	€12000	Town on the waterfront (22x32cm-9x13in) s. panel. 21-Oct-3 Sotheby's, Amsterdam #40/R est:10000-15000

KARSENTY, Daniele (1933-) French

Works on paper

£268	$497	€400	Composition (48x61cm-19x24in) s. gouache. 14-Mar-4 Eric Pillon, Calais #255/R

KARSH, Yousuf (1908-) Armenian

Photographs

£1657	$3000	€2419	George Bernard Shaw (50x41cm-20x16in) s. gelatin silver print 1943/printed later. 19-Apr-4 Bonhams & Butterfields, San Francisco #421/R est:3000-4000
£1693	$3200	€2472	Pablo Casals (49x39cm-19x15in) s. gelatin silver print executed 1954. 17-Feb-4 Christie's, Rockefeller NY #78/R est:2500-3500
£1705	$3000	€2489	Winston Churchill (27x22cm-11x9in) with sig. silver print. 20-May-4 Swann Galleries, New York #394/R est:4000-6000
£1916	$3200	€2797	Winston Churchill (21x17cm-8x7in) s. gelatin silver print exec.1941 printed later lit. 20-Oct-3 Christie's, Rockefeller NY #68/R est:4000-6000
£2096	$3500	€3060	Georgia O'Keeffe (50x41cm-20x16in) s. i.verso gelatin silver print exec.1956. 21-Oct-3 Bonhams & Butterfields, San Francisco #1543/R
£2874	$4800	€4196	Georgia O'Keefe (50x40cm-20x16in) s. i.d.1956 verso gelatin silver print lit. 20-Oct-3 Christie's, Rockefeller NY #58/R est:7000-9000
£4237	$7500	€6186	Georgia O'Keeffe (50x40cm-20x16in) st.verso photo printed c.1963 exhib. 28-Apr-4 Sotheby's, New York #213/R est:5000-7000
£4520	$8000	€6599	Georgia O'Keeffe (50x40cm-20x16in) s. i.d.1956 verso gelatin silver print lit. 27-Apr-4 Christie's, Rockefeller NY #12/R est:8000-10000
£5988	$10000	€8742	Winston Churchill (34x27cm-13x11in) s.i. gelatin silver print. 20-Oct-3 Christie's, Rockefeller NY #70/R est:7000-9000
£20359	$34000	€29724	Portraits. s.num.58/100 photos 15 portfolio prov. 17-Oct-3 Sotheby's, New York #127/R est:40000-60000

KARSKAYA, Ida (1905-1990) French

Works on paper

£278	$506	€420	Visage (32x24cm-13x9in) s. gouache. 15-Jun-4 Blanchet, Paris #254
£300	$540	€450	Composition (46x27cm-18x11in) s. mixed media on canvas. 24-Apr-4 Cornette de St.Cyr, Paris #580/R
£317	$510	€450	Untitled (30x23cm-12x9in) s. gouache. 11-May-3 Versailles Encheres #204
£352	$567	€500	Tete (50x34cm-20x13in) s. mixed media collage. 11-May-3 Versailles Encheres #207
£387	$624	€550	Untitled (42x35cm-17x14in) s. gouache collage. 11-May-3 Versailles Encheres #202

KARSTEN, Ludvig (1876-1926) Norwegian

£58070	$96977	€84782	Helge Rode (208x85cm-82x33in) s.d.19 prov.exhib.lit. 13-Oct-3 Blomqvist, Oslo #289/R est:200000-300000 (N.KR 680000)
£65041	$119024	€94960	Resting in bed - the artist's sister Rikke (81x104cm-32x41in) s.d.16 prov.exhib.lit. 7-Jun-4 Blomqvist, Oslo #386/R est:1000000 (N.KR 800000)

KASEBIER, Gertrude (1852-1934) American

Photographs

£5072	$8319	€7000	Edward Steichen, Munich (10x16cm-4x6in) i.d. i. verso vintage gum print lit. 30-May-3 Villa Grisebach, Berlin #1222/R est:7000-9000
£16949	$30000	€24746	Untitled - billiard game (19x24cm-7x9in) platinum print. 27-Apr-4 Christie's, Rockefeller NY #25/R est:3000-5000

KASIEWICZ, Marcin (1834-1898) Polish

£1879	$3495	€2800	Making music. Dancing (32x17cm-13x7in) s. pair. 5-Mar-4 Wendl, Rudolstadt #3728/R est:3200

KASIMIR, Luigi (1881-1962) Austrian

Works on paper

£972	$1585	€1400	Memorial tablet (19x12cm-7x5in) s.i.d.1932 pencil col pencil. 23-Sep-3 Wiener Kunst Auktionen, Vienna #42/R

KASKAS, Ivar (1841-1898) Finnish

£2517	$4280	€3600	The young gate keepers (75x101cm-30x40in) s.d.1866. 29-Nov-3 Bukowskis, Helsinki #208/R est:3000-5000

KASPAR, Paul (1891-1953) Austrian

Works on paper

£280	$476	€400	Horse and carriage in front of Burgtheater in Vienna (10x13cm-4x5in) s.d.1922 W/C. 27-Nov-3 Dorotheum, Linz #577/R
£474	$849	€692	Karntnerstrasse in Vienna (14x20cm-6x8in) s.d.1926 W/C. 12-May-4 Dobiaschofsky, Bern #681/R (S.FR 1100)
£486	$792	€700	Opera House (15x15cm-6x6in) s. W/C. 23-Sep-3 Wiener Kunst Auktionen, Vienna #40/R
£537	$988	€800	Karlskirche in blue (27x22cm-11x9in) s.d.1926 W/C. 26-Mar-4 Dorotheum, Vienna #262/R
£556	$906	€800	Stephansdom (20x14cm-8x6in) s. 23-Sep-3 Wiener Kunst Auktionen, Vienna #36/R
£805	$1482	€1200	Opera, Vienna (9x12cm-4x5in) s. W/C. 26-Mar-4 Dorotheum, Vienna #283/R
£1208	$2223	€1800	Technical University with Karlskirche (26x21cm-10x8in) s. W/C. 26-Mar-4 Dorotheum, Vienna #261/R est:1400-1500

KASPARIDES, Edouard (1858-1926) Austrian

£2448	$4210	€3500	Villach-Bad (56x69cm-22x27in) s.i.d.1909. 4-Dec-3 Van Ham, Cologne #258/R est:3000
£2797	$4755	€4000	Sunset (83x108cm-33x43in) s. board. 28-Nov-3 Wiener Kunst Auktionen, Vienna #454/R est:4000-12000
£3691	$6607	€5500	Sun on lake (97x110cm-38x43in) s.d.19 board. 25-May-4 Dorotheum, Vienna #152/R est:7000-12000
£4861	$8264	€7000	Evening (87x12cm-34x5in) s.d.1920 board. 28-Oct-3 Wiener Kunst Auktionen, Vienna #58/R est:7000-12000
£5034	$8909	€7500	Blooming wisteria (89x112cm-35x44in) s.d.1922 i. verso board. 28-Apr-4 Wiener Kunst Auktionen, Vienna #40/R est:7500-10000
£5594	$9510	€8000	Melk (86x100cm-34x39in) s.d.08. 26-Nov-3 Dorotheum, Vienna #119/R est:8000-11000
£12000	$21480	€17520	Portrait of a lady (121x82cm-48x32in) s.d.889. 11-May-4 Bonhams, New Bond Street #24/R est:12000-18000

KASPER, Arnaud (?) ?

Sculpture

£1933	$3499	€2900	L'etalon pur race (42x50cm-17x20in) s. num.4/8 brown blk pat bronze Cast Serraleiro cire perdue. 2-Apr-4 Coutau Begarie, Paris #211/R est:3000-4000

KASS, Deborah (20th C) American

Prints

£1850	$3200	€2701	Six Barbras, the Jewish Jackie series (76x61cm-30x24in) s.i.d.1992 silkscreen prov. 10-Dec-3 Phillips, New York #550/R est:2000-3000

KASSAK, Lajos (1887-1967) Hungarian

£2941	$5000	€4294	Sordino (62x55cm-24x22in) s.i.d.1962 i. stretcher. 25-Nov-3 Germann, Zurich #116/R est:5000-8000 (S.FR 6500)

Works on paper

£420	$713	€600	Composition aux triangles (14x25cm-6x10in) mono. gouache W/C prov. 23-Nov-3 Cornette de St.Cyr, Paris #163
£559	$962	€800	Composition (23x19cm-9x7in) s.d.1953 W/C. 2-Dec-3 Hauswedell & Nolte, Hamburg #292/R
£643	$1107	€920	Composition (21x18cm-8x7in) W/C. 2-Dec-3 Hauswedell & Nolte, Hamburg #293/R
£1295	$2124	€1800	Composition abstraite (30x23cm-12x9in) s. Indian ink. 6-Jun-3 Chochon-Barre & Allardi, Paris #59/R est:2000-2200
£1629	$2769	€2378	Architectural composition (24x15cm-9x6in) mono. s.d.1922 verso ink W/C pencil lit. 22-Nov-3 Burkhard, Luzern #181/R est:2400-2800 (S.FR 3600)
£3200	$5344	€4672	Composition (51x34cm-20x13in) init. s.i.d.1959 verso gouache board prov. 22-Oct-3 Sotheby's, Olympia #148/R est:1000-1500
£5000	$8350	€7200	Composition geometrique. s.d.1927 ink gouache prov. 25-Oct-3 Cornette de St.Cyr, Paris #517 est:1500-2000
£6294	$10699	€9000	Composition sur fond orange (35x23cm-14x9in) mono.d.1922 gouache prov. 23-Nov-3 Cornette de St.Cyr, Paris #164/R est:600-800

KASTEELE, Johanna Margaretha van de (1858-1951) Dutch

£699	$1168	€1000	Flower still life with roses (45x30cm-18x12in) s.d.1888. 30-Jun-3 Sotheby's, Amsterdam #465

KASYN, John (1926-) Canadian

£813	$1455	€1187	Hey, Mister, paint my picture (30x25cm-12x10in) s. i.verso oil lucite masonite prov. 6-May-4 Heffel, Vancouver #78/R est:1200-1500 (C.D 2000)
£1071	$1843	€1564	Parliament St., Toronto (25x20cm-10x8in) s. board. 2-Dec-3 Joyner Waddington, Toronto #229/R est:1500-1800 (C.D 2400)
£1464	$2489	€2137	Mutual at Shuter St., Toronto (30x25cm-12x10in) s.d.1978 s.i.d.verso oil lucite prov. 27-Nov-3 Heffel, Vancouver #42 est:2000-3000 (C.D 3250)
£1524	$2728	€2225	Narrow lane off Ontario Street (30x22cm-12x9in) s.d.1970 s.i.d.verso oil lucite board prov. 27-May-4 Heffel, Vancouver #178/R est:1800-2200 (C.D 3750)
£1889	$3135	€2758	After the snow, Parkdale (41x30cm-16x12in) s. hard board. 5-Oct-3 Levis, Calgary #56/R est:5000-6000 (C.D 4250)
£2455	$4223	€3584	On a winter afternoon, Lansdowne Ave (30x50cm-12x20in) s. board. 2-Dec-3 Joyner Waddington, Toronto #206/R est:5000-7000 (C.D 5500)
£2846	$5093	€4155	Back yard on Nepean Street, Ottawa (50x40cm-20x16in) s. s.i.verso oil lucite board painted 1974. 27-May-4 Heffel, Vancouver #177/R est:7000-9000 (C.D 7000)
£3281	$5479	€4790	Entrance to de grassi St Yards (40x55cm-16x22in) s.i. panel. 17-Nov-3 Hodgins, Calgary #405/R est:7500-9000 (C.D 7250)
£3348	$5692	€4888	After the snow (41x56cm-16x22in) s. s.i.verso masonite prov. 6-Nov-3 Heffel, Vancouver #70/R est:8000-10000 (C.D 7500)

£3778	$6271	€5516	Red house near Baldwin St (61x46cm-24x18in) s. s.i.verso hard board. 5-Oct-3 Levis, Calgary #55/R est:10000-12000 (C.D 8500)
£4400	$8052	€6424	Laneway to Bleeker St (60x75cm-24x30in) s.d.69 board. 1-Jun-4 Joyner Waddington, Toronto #283/R est:10000-15000 (C.D 11000)
£7207	$12252	€10522	Behind the pawn shop, Queen Street West (76x61cm-30x24in) s. s.i.verso masonite lucite prov. 18-Nov-3 Sotheby's, Toronto #178/R est:18000-20000 (C.D 16000)
£7207	$12252	€10522	In late December, Toronto (76x61cm-30x24in) s. s.i.verso board. 27-Nov-3 Heffel, Vancouver #40/R est:16000-18000 (C.D 16000)
£10268	$17661	€14991	Behind Grand Ave - Toronto (70x90cm-28x35in) s. board. 2-Dec-3 Joyner Waddington, Toronto #116/R est:25000-30000 (C.D 23000)
Works on paper			
£428	$728	€625	Backyard with wire fence, Spruce St. (17x27cm-7x11in) s.d.1976 i.verso W/C. 27-Nov-3 Heffel, Vancouver #41 (C.D 950)
£520	$952	€759	Row of houses (14x34cm-6x13in) s.d.65 W/C. 1-Jun-4 Joyner Waddington, Toronto #346/R (C.D 1300)
£732	$1310	€1069	Dundas Street West (14x21cm-6x8in) s.d.1976 W/C prov. 6-May-4 Heffel, Vancouver #77/R (C.D 1800)
£813	$1455	€1187	Path to back door, Henry Street (17x27cm-7x11in) s.d.1970 W/C prov. 6-May-4 Heffel, Vancouver #79/R est:1500-2000 (C.D 2000)

KAT, Anne-Pierre de (1881-1968) Belgian

£608	$1149	€900	Degel sur l'etang (50x60cm-20x24in) s.d.1926 cardboard. 17-Feb-4 Vanderkindere, Brussels #15
£709	$1184	€1000	La descente vers la foret (60x50cm-24x20in) s.d.1940. 17-Jun-3 Vanderkindere, Brussels #116
£1382	$2501	€2100	Etang en automne (50x60cm-20x24in) s. 19-Apr-4 Horta, Bruxelles #44 est:1500-2000
£2000	$3680	€3000	Street scene (49x59cm-19x23in) s. board. 8-Jun-4 Sotheby's, Amsterdam #192/R est:3000-4000
£2013	$3725	€3000	Descente vers la foret (60x50cm-24x20in) s.d.1940 i.verso exhib. 13-Mar-4 De Vuyst, Lokeren #97/R est:2000-2400
£3007	$5172	€4300	Bezon (39x47cm-15x19in) s. i.verso exhib. 2-Dec-3 Sotheby's, Amsterdam #54/R est:4000-6000
£3217	$5372	€4600	Portrait d'homme, fauvisme (60x48cm-24x19in) s. 13-Oct-3 Horta, Bruxelles #197/R est:3500-5000
Works on paper			
£263	$484	€400	Femme a la robe verte (26x15cm-10x6in) s.d.1924 chl W/C. 22-Jun-4 Palais de Beaux Arts, Brussels #220

KAT, Otto Boudewijn de (1907-1995) Dutch

£658	$1211	€1000	French landscape (50x60cm-20x24in) s.d.75. 22-Jun-4 Christie's, Amsterdam #564/R
£658	$1211	€1000	In the country (50x65cm-20x26in) st.mono. s.d.91 verso. 22-Jun-4 Christie's, Amsterdam #567/R
£2098	$3566	€3000	Still life with apples in a bowl (20x40cm-8x16in) s.d.88. 25-Nov-3 Christie's, Amsterdam #14/R est:1800-2200
£4406	$7490	€6300	Round table (100x150cm-39x59in) s.d.37 prov.exhib. 25-Nov-3 Christie's, Amsterdam #192/R est:7000-9000
Works on paper			
£625	$1018	€900	View of a landscape, France (26x36cm-10x14in) s.d.71 pastel. 29-Sep-3 Sotheby's, Amsterdam #312/R

KATCHADOURIAN, Sarkis (20th C) Iranian

£399	$650	€583	Ararat (36x46cm-14x18in) s. s.i.verso. 24-Sep-3 Doyle, New York #54
Works on paper			
£460	$750	€672	Arakatz, Erivan (30x58cm-12x23in) s. i.d.1919 verso W/C gouache pastel paperboard prov.exhib. 24-Sep-3 Doyle, New York #53/R

KATEI, Taki (1830-1901) Japanese

Works on paper			
£408	$750	€596	Peacocks and parrot (161x71cm-63x28in) s. col ink gold silk hanging scroll. 23-Mar-4 Christie's, Rockefeller NY #126/R

KATH, Ludwig (1886-?) German

£510	$785	€800	Helgoland (30x35cm-12x14in) s. 4-Sep-2 Schopman, Hamburg #258/R

KATHY, Roger (1934-1979) Belgian

£679	$1154	€991	Winter in Fricktal (54x65cm-21x26in) s. 25-Nov-3 Germann, Zurich #819 est:1800-2200 (S.FR 1500)

KATO, Kentaro (1889-1926) American

£4942	$8500	€7215	New York snow storm (50x40cm-20x16in) s. prov. 3-Dec-3 Doyle, New York #259/R est:3000-5000

KATTEN, F (20th C) British?

£1400	$2324	€2044	Pan (90x70cm-35x28in) s.d.34. 30-Sep-3 Sotheby's, London #255/R est:1000-1500

KATZ, Alex (1927-) American

£2297	$4250	€3354	West Palm Beach (30x40cm-12x16in) s.d.97 panel. 12-Feb-4 Sotheby's, New York #344/R est:6000-8000
£5500	$10120	€8030	Green couch (30x41cm-12x16in) s. masonite painted 1970. 25-Jun-4 Christie's, London #197/R est:8000-12000
£6593	$12000	€9626	Green trees (23x30cm-9x12in) s.d.81 masonite. 29-Jun-4 Sotheby's, New York #551/R est:4000-6000
£9100	$15197	€13286	Summer trio (45x61cm-18x24in) s.d.93 panel prov. 22-Oct-3 Christie's, London #88/R est:10000-15000
£13473	$22500	€19671	Anne (41x30cm-16x12in) s.d. 13-Nov-3 Sotheby's, New York #294/R est:12000-18000
£13473	$22500	€19671	Ivonne and green (30x40cm-12x16in) s.d. prov. 13-Nov-3 Sotheby's, New York #295/R est:10000-15000
£17000	$31280	€24820	Ada in orange straw hat (41x29cm-16x11in) s.d.90 board prov. 24-Jun-4 Sotheby's, London #272/R est:7000-10000
£29940	$50000	€43712	10 Pm - Portrait Lit from the Back (86x122cm-34x48in) s.d.77 prov. 12-Nov-3 Christie's, Rockefeller NY #379/R est:50000-70000
£41899	$75000	€61173	Forsythia (198x122cm-78x48in) painted 1997 prov. 12-May-4 Christie's, Rockefeller NY #185/R est:35000-45000
£77844	$130000	€113652	Birthday Party (183x198cm-72x78in) painted 1990 prov.exhib. 12-Nov-3 Christie's, Rockefeller NY #398/R est:120000-180000
£131737	$220000	€192336	Nine A.M. (244x305cm-96x120in) painted 1999 prov.exhib. 11-Nov-3 Christie's, Rockefeller NY #67/R est:180000-220000
Prints			
£1963	$3200	€2866	Orange band (102x72cm-40x28in) s. num.PP 1/2 col screenprint on Arches exec 1979. 24-Sep-3 Christie's, Rockefeller NY #269/R est:1500-2000
£2206	$3750	€3221	Ada and Alex (76x92cm-30x36in) s. col screenprint. 31-Oct-3 Sotheby's, New York #617/R
£2945	$4800	€4300	Samantha (168x73cm-66x29in) s. num.PP 1/3 col screenprint wove paper exec 1987. 24-Sep-3 Christie's, Rockefeller NY #270/R est:4000-6000
£4520	$8000	€6599	Red cap (53x177cm-21x70in) s.num.22/60 col aquatint. 28-Apr-4 Christie's, Rockefeller NY #335/R est:4000-6000
Works on paper			
£1957	$3600	€2857	Self portrait (28x20cm-11x8in) s.d.1965 ball point pen ink. 10-Jun-4 Swann Galleries, New York #127/R est:3000-5000
£5000	$9100	€7300	Barbara (76x57cm-30x22in) s.d.1971 pencil prov. 4-Feb-4 Sotheby's, Olympia #23/R est:2500-3500

KATZENSTEIN, Uri (1951-) Israeli

Sculpture			
£2793	$5000	€4078	Figure, from the series Home (65cm-26in) cast painted bronze clothes exhib. 18-Mar-4 Sotheby's, New York #88/R est:5000-7000
£2793	$5000	€4078	Figure, from the series Home (65cm-26in) cast painted bronze clothes exhib. 18-Mar-4 Sotheby's, New York #89/R est:5000-7000

KATZMAN, Herbert (1923-) ?

£318	$550	€464	Still life with crabs (99x64cm-39x25in) s.d.51 prov. 15-Dec-3 Hindman, Chicago #13/R

KAUBA, C (1865-1922) Austrian/American

Sculpture			
£1356	$2400	€1980	Horse and Indian with eagle (18x15cm-7x6in) s.num.1485 polychrome bronze marble base st.f.Bergman. 2-May-4 William Jenack, New York #111 est:2500-3500

KAUBA, Carl (1865-1922) Austrian/American

Sculpture			
£1344	$2500	€1962	Smoking elk (8x25cm-3x10in) s. polychrome bronze. 7-Mar-4 William Jenack, New York #341 est:4000-5000
£1667	$2717	€2400	Mare with foal (38cm-15in) s. brown dark pat.bronze. 25-Sep-3 Dr Fritz Nagel, Stuttgart #1571/R est:2200
£1818	$3200	€2654	Indian chief (33cm-13in) cold painted bronze marble plinth. 22-May-4 Pook & Pook, Downington #499/R est:2000-3000
£1882	$3500	€2748	Indian running (28cm-11in) s. polychrome bronze. 7-Mar-4 William Jenack, New York #268 est:4000-5000
£1935	$3600	€2825	Running warrior (28cm-11in) s. polychrome bronze. 7-Mar-4 William Jenack, New York #248 est:4000-5000
£1988	$3200	€2902	Indian warrior (46cm-18in) green brown pat.bronze. 20-Aug-3 James Julia, Fairfield #1426/R est:4000-6000
£2067	$3700	€3018	Indian warrior with rifle (28cm-11in) s. bronze agate base. 11-Jan-4 William Jenack, New York #175 est:2500-3500
£2067	$3741	€3100	Chef indien a cheval (33x34cm-13x13in) s.i. brown red pat bronze. 2-Apr-4 Coutau Begarie, Paris #212 est:2700-3500
£2151	$4000	€3140	Clear shot (20cm-8in) s. polychrome ba. 7-Mar-4 William Jenack, New York #316 est:2500-3000
£2446	$4500	€3571	Indians on horseback (26x25cm-10x10in) i. golden brown pat bronze wood base sold with similar companion. 27-Jun-4 Freeman, Philadelphia #92/R est:2500-3500
£2626	$4700	€3834	Indian brave (30cm-12in) s. bronze agate base. 11-Jan-4 William Jenack, New York #275 est:2500-3000
£2867	$5275	€4186	Indian stepping into a canoe (34x67cm-13x26in) i. bronze. 27-Jun-4 Freeman, Philadelphia #91/R est:8000-12000
£3873	$6430	€5500	Group of horseman taking care of his horse (25cm-10in) brown pat. bronze. 11-Jun-3 Sotheby's, Amsterdam #358/R est:6000-7000
£10215	$19000	€14914	A friend in need (56cm-22in) s. bronze polychrome. 7-Mar-4 William Jenack, New York #221/R est:20000-25000
£10452	$18500	€15260	For death or for glory (69cm-27in) s. bronze agate base. 2-May-4 William Jenack, New York #294 est:20000-25000

KAUFFER, Edward McKnight (1890-1954) American

Works on paper			
£550	$875	€803	Aladdin paraffin (45x57cm-18x22in) s.d.33 d.14 Nov 1933 verso gouache. 10-Sep-3 Sotheby's, Olympia #52/R
£750	$1193	€1095	Sailor pulling a rope. Sailor hauling on chain (44x28cm-17x11in) init. ink gouache pair. 10-Sep-3 Sotheby's, Olympia #46/R
£950	$1511	€1387	Shell lubricating oil stays on the job (46x61cm-18x24in) s.d.39 gouache board sold with another by the same hand. 10-Sep-3 Sotheby's, Olympia #50/R
£1200	$1908	€1752	Lubrication by Shell must be rather good (28x58cm-11x23in) s. d.1 Oct 1936 verso gouache board sold with 2 others. 10-Sep-3 Sotheby's, Olympia #59/R est:300-500
£1400	$2226	€2044	Mechanical man (30x38cm-12x15in) init. pen ink. 10-Sep-3 Sotheby's, Olympia #58/R est:400-600
£1600	$2544	€2336	Double shell (45x61cm-18x24in) s. d.6 Feb 1934 verso gouache. 10-Sep-3 Sotheby's, Olympia #51/R est:400-600
£1600	$2544	€2336	Stronger and stronger Shell (30x45cm-12x18in) s.d.39 d.14 Aug 1939 verso gouache sold with 2 others. 10-Sep-3 Sotheby's, Olympia #60/R est:600-800
£1600	$2544	€2336	Pain in the neck (27x20cm-11x8in) init.i. pen ink sold with 5 similar by the same hand. 10-Sep-3 Sotheby's, Olympia #94/R est:300-500
£2400	$3816	€3504	New Shell lubricating oils (38x60cm-15x24in) s.d.37 gouache sold with another by the same hand lit. 10-Sep-3 Sotheby's, Olympia #53/R est:800-1200

£2400	$3816	€3504	BP Plus, plus a little something that some others haven't got (54x89cm-21x35in) s.d.32 d.12 Dec 1932 verso gouache. 10-Sep-3 Sotheby's, Olympia #56/R est:500-700
£2400	$3816	€3504	Musicians prefer Shell (46x61cm-18x24in) s. d.14 Aug 1934 verso gouache. 10-Sep-3 Sotheby's, Olympia #73/R est:300-500
£2800	$4452	€4088	Merchants prefer Shell (45x57cm-18x22in) s.d.33 d.22 Dec 1933 verso gouache. 10-Sep-3 Sotheby's, Olympia #75 est:400-600
£3400	$5406	€4964	Llanfair (19x25cm-7x10in) init. pen ink sold with 5 similar by the same hand. 10-Sep-3 Sotheby's, Olympia #96/R est:700-900
£3800	$6042	€5548	BP ethyl controls horse-power (55x78cm-22x31in) s. d.14 Jul 1933 verso gouache collage sold with 2 others. 10-Sep-3 Sotheby's, Olympia #55/R est:300-500
£3800	$6042	€5548	Alice and giraffe (23x29cm-9x11in) init. pen ink sold with 6 similar by the same hand. 10-Sep-3 Sotheby's, Olympia #95/R est:500-700
£4000	$6360	€5840	Henley on Thames but Shell in the tank (13x18cm-5x7in) pen ink sold with 7 similar by the same hand. 10-Sep-3 Sotheby's, Olympia #97/R est:500-700

KAUFFMANN, Angelica (1741-1807) Swiss

£498	$831	€727	Harmony (24x29cm-9x11in) copper oval. 17-Nov-3 Waddingtons, Toronto #300/R (C.D 1100)
£13423	$24698	€20000	Odysseus discovering Achilles among daughters of Lycomedes (20x25cm-8x10in) paper on canvas exhib.lit.prov. 24-Mar-4 Dorotheum, Vienna #242/R est:20000-30000
£24828	$41214	€36000	Ariadne and Theseus at the entrance of labyrinth (95x80cm-37x31in) s. 1-Oct-3 Dorotheum, Vienna #220/R est:30000-50000
£27933	$50000	€40782	Portrait of lady (92x72cm-36x28in) prov. 27-May-4 Sotheby's, New York #245/R est:60000-80000
£50279	$90000	€73407	Portrait of Lady Louisa Dorothea Holroyd (79x65cm-31x26in) prov.lit. 27-May-4 Sotheby's, New York #262/R est:40000-60000
Prints			
£3147	$5350	€4500	Holy Family (25x19cm-10x7in) etching. 27-Nov-3 Bassenge, Berlin #5188 est:3000
Works on paper			
£387	$700	€580	Achilles' mourning the death of Patroklos (30x39cm-12x15in) W/C. 2-Apr-4 Winterberg, Heidelberg #319
£656	$1036	€958	Classical sacrifice 18th C (31x47cm-12x19in) chk W/C prov. 2-Sep-3 Deutscher-Menzies, Melbourne #446/R est:2000-3000 (A.D 1600)
£1600	$2928	€2336	Mirtillo leaving for the hunt. Mirtillo and Ergasto returning from the hunt (224x23cm-88x9in) i. pen ink wash two. 6-Jul-4 Christie's, London #185/R est:1500-2000

KAUFFMANN, Angelica (after) (1741-1807) Swiss

£14000	$25620	€20440	Venus appearing to Aeneas (89x71cm-35x28in) 9-Jul-4 Christie's, Kensington #120/R est:4000-6000

KAUFFMANN, Angelica (attrib) (1741-1807) Swiss

Works on paper			
£940	$1729	€1400	Sacrifice to Cupid (30x39cm-12x15in) wash Indian ink. 26-Mar-4 Ketterer, Hamburg #191/R

KAUFFMANN, H (19/20th C) German

Works on paper			
£340	$609	€500	Village (20x14cm-8x6in) s.d.60 W/C over pencil htd white. 18-Mar-4 Neumeister, Munich #2508/R

KAUFFMANN, Hermann (elder) (1808-1889) German

£2917	$4608	€4200	Horses pulling log waggon in snow storm (54x79cm-21x31in) s.d.1876. 6-Sep-3 Arnold, Frankfurt #590/R est:3200
£4200	$7560	€6132	Snow storm (56x80cm-22x31in) 21-Jan-4 Sotheby's, Olympia #416/R est:2000-3000
£4206	$6645	€6099	Gentleman being helped onboard a horse carriage in front of stable in rain (33x44cm-13x17in) s. 2-Sep-3 Rasmussen, Copenhagen #1694/R est:15000-20000 (D.KR 45000)
£6643	$11427	€9500	Transporting hay in the snowdrifts (41x62cm-16x24in) s. 6-Dec-3 Hans Stahl, Toestorf #118/R est:9500
Works on paper			
£245	$450	€358	Horsecart (20x28cm-8x11in) s. W/C. 25-Mar-4 Doyle, New York #37/R

KAUFFMANN, Hermann (elder-attrib) (1808-1889) German

£458	$792	€650	Young man with beard (11x8cm-4x3in) panel. 10-Dec-3 Hugo Ruef, Munich #2443

KAUFFMANN, Hermann (younger) (1873-?) German

£2448	$4161	€3500	Old traveller on country lane (10x7cm-4x3in) s. panel. 20-Nov-3 Van Ham, Cologne #1676 est:450

KAUFFMANN, Hugo Wilhelm (1844-1915) German

£395	$608	€620	Bearded old man (33x21cm-13x8in) board. 4-Sep-2 Schopman, Hamburg #21/R
£1458	$2377	€2100	End of work (20x14cm-8x6in) s.d.89 panel. 24-Sep-3 Neumeister, Munich #463/R est:3000
£2667	$4853	€4000	Peasant girl by window with dachshund (11x8cm-4x3in) s.d.05 panel. 30-Jun-4 Neumeister, Munich #586/R est:4000
£2676	$4630	€3800	Man teasing girl in tavern (12x10cm-5x4in) s.d.96 i. verso. 11-Dec-3 Dr Fritz Nagel, Stuttgart #527/R est:4200
£2800	$5152	€4088	Rest on the hunt. Returning home (13x9cm-5x4in) s.d.68 panel pair. 25-Mar-4 Christie's, Kensington #207/R est:3000-5000
£2819	$5187	€4200	Man reading newspaper (12x10cm-5x4in) s.d.7 panel. 26-Mar-4 Ketterer, Hamburg #192/R est:2000-2400
£5172	$9259	€7551	Two peasants at beer table (12x16cm-5x6in) s.d.84 panel. 13-May-4 Stuker, Bern #211/R est:7000-9000 (S.FR 12000)
£5319	$8617	€7500	Barber at work in tavern (25x36cm-10x14in) s.d.67 lit. 23-May-3 Karlheinz Kaupp, Staufen #1757/R est:500
£12500	$22375	€18250	Man talking to young girl in tavern (17x13cm-7x5in) s.d.84 panel. 13-May-4 Stuker, Bern #210/R est:7000-9000 (S.FR 29000)

KAUFMANN, A (1848-1916) Austrian

£2200	$4158	€3212	Haywain on a riverside track (63x102cm-25x40in) s. 19-Feb-4 Christie's, Kensington #135/R est:800-1200
£2400	$4368	€3600	Landscape (35x90cm-14x35in) s. 1-Jul-4 Weidler, Nurnberg #317/R est:600

KAUFMANN, Adolf (1848-1916) Austrian

£688	$1079	€990	Lively Dutch harbour with fishing boats and windmills (53x42cm-21x17in) s. panel. 30-Aug-3 Hans Stahl, Toestorf #11/R
£1259	$2140	€1800	Mountain river (79x106cm-31x42in) s. 20-Nov-3 Van Ham, Cologne #1678/R est:2000
£1338	$2315	€1900	Birch forest with fishpond and figure (54x65cm-21x26in) 10-Dec-3 Dorotheum, Vienna #256/R est:1600-1800
£1900	$3173	€2774	Wooded landscape, near Lyon. Haycart in a wooded clearing, near Nancy (58x37cm-23x15in) s.i. panel pair. 11-Nov-3 Bonhams, Knightsbridge #173/R est:1200-1800
£2416	$4325	€3600	Winter forest with woodcutters (74x47cm-29x19in) s. panel. 27-May-4 Dorotheum, Vienna #32/R est:3800-4200
£2416	$4325	€3600	Spring landscape (45x70cm-18x28in) s. 27-May-4 Dorotheum, Vienna #91/R est:3800-4500
£2448	$4161	€3500	Ducks by pond behind village (65x75cm-26x30in) s. 20-Nov-3 Van Ham, Cologne #1677/R est:1800
£2500	$4550	€3650	Troppau, Bohemia (108x99cm-43x39in) s.d.1913. 16-Jun-4 Christie's, Kensington #186/R est:3000-5000
£2503	$4530	€3654	Brushwood collector (80x60cm-31x24in) s. 16-Apr-4 Mu Terem Galeria, Budapest #95/R (H.F 950000)
£2980	$5454	€4500	St Denis, France (68x47cm-27x19in) s.i. panel. 8-Apr-4 Dorotheum, Vienna #46/R est:3000-3600
£3000	$5160	€4380	Fishing boats moored in a harbour (76x113cm-30x44in) s. 4-Dec-3 Christie's, Kensington #190/R est:3000-4000
£3147	$5350	€4500	Faggot gatherer in winter (63x41cm-25x16in) s. board. 24-Nov-3 Dorotheum, Vienna #197/R est:3800-4200
£3147	$5350	€4500	Still life with plates, jugs and lobster (42x147cm-17x58in) s.d.1898. 24-Nov-3 Dorotheum, Vienna #223/R est:3400-4000
£4545	$7727	€6500	Fishing boats in harbour (130x90cm-51x35in) s.d.1884. 24-Nov-3 Dorotheum, Vienna #116/R est:5500-6500
£7692	$13077	€11000	Woman gathering sticks in snowy wood (97x141cm-38x56in) s. 20-Nov-3 Dorotheum, Salzburg #116/R est:5000-7000
£10067	$18020	€15000	Winter evening (160x247cm-63x97in) s.d.1909. 27-May-4 Dorotheum, Vienna #82/R est:10000-12000
Works on paper			
£483	$801	€700	Steppensee with boat (57x42cm-22x17in) s. mixed media. 30-Sep-3 Dorotheum, Vienna #338/R

KAUFMANN, Adolf (attrib) (1848-1916) Austrian

£2000	$3620	€3000	Woman gathering wood in forest clearing (82x129cm-32x51in) s. 1-Apr-4 Van Ham, Cologne #1470/R est:1300
£2148	$4016	€3200	Woman gathering wood in autumn (74x101cm-29x40in) 24-Feb-4 Dorotheum, Vienna #117/R est:2800-3400

KAUFMANN, Ferdinand (1864-1942) German/American

£647	$1100	€945	Bearskin dock, Rockport harbour (18x25cm-7x10in) s. i.verso canvas on board. 18-Nov-3 John Moran, Pasadena #21a
£2500	$4250	€3650	Flint Ridge, west of Rose Bowl, Pasadena (38x41cm-15x16in) s. board prov. 18-Nov-3 John Moran, Pasadena #12 est:3000-5000

KAUFMANN, Hans (20th C) ?

£1342	$2510	€2000	Roses. Irises (70x30cm-28x12in) s. two. 24-Feb-4 Dorotheum, Vienna #173/R est:2200-2600

KAUFMANN, Hugo (attrib) (1868-1919) German

£1087	$2000	€1587	Learning from the master (38x51cm-15x20in) 9-Jun-4 Doyle, New York #3050 est:1500-2500
£2951	$4750	€4308	Untitled (15x20cm-6x8in) s.d.1903 wood panel. 22-Feb-3 Bunte, Elgin #1268c est:3000-5000

KAUFMANN, Isidor (1853-1921) Austrian

£12667	$22800	€19000	Those funny little ads (34x28cm-13x11in) s. panel. 20-Apr-4 Sotheby's, Amsterdam #55/R est:5000-7000
£19553	$35000	€28547	Lady in an interior, the artist's wife (16x12cm-6x5in) s. panel prov. 18-Mar-4 Sotheby's, New York #256/R est:35000-45000
£33520	$60000	€48939	Portrait of a Rabbi (20x15cm-8x6in) s. panel. 18-Mar-4 Sotheby's, New York #258/R est:50000-70000
£100559	$180000	€146816	Portrait of Yeshiva boy wearing a streimen, in front of torah ark curtain (35x26cm-14x10in) s. panel prov. 18-Mar-4 Sotheby's, New York #254/R est:180000-220000
£122222	$220000	€178444	Commercial instruction (39x31cm-15x12in) s. panel prov.exhib.lit. 22-Apr-4 Christie's, Rockefeller NY #30/R est:150000-200000
£125698	$225000	€183519	Portrait of a Rabbi wearing a kittel and tallith (37x30cm-15x12in) s. panel. 18-Mar-4 Sotheby's, New York #255/R est:180000-220000

KAUFMANN, Joseph Clemens (1867-1925) Swiss

£325	$581	€475	Heuet on the Allmend, Lucern (19x30cm-7x12in) s. canvas on board. 22-Mar-4 Philippe Schuler, Zurich #4339 (S.FR 750)
£480	$874	€701	A mother's love (114x140cm-45x55in) s.d.1919 exhib. 16-Jun-4 Fischer, Luzern #2234/R (S.FR 1100)

KAUFMANN, Karl (1843-1901) Austrian

£333	$610	€500	Steam boat and fishing boat on choppy seas before harbour entrance (52x75cm-20x30in) s. canvas on canvas. 5-Jun-4 Arnold, Frankfurt #622/R
£350	$584	€500	Norwegian fjord in evening sun (47x69cm-19x27in) s.pseudonym J Holmstedt. 28-Jun-3 Bolland & Marotz, Bremen #681/R
£350	$584	€500	Autumn (47x69cm-19x27in) s.pseudonym B Lambert. 28-Jun-3 Bolland & Marotz, Bremen #682/R
£352	$585	€500	Fishing boats in harbour (21x31cm-8x12in) s.pseudonym Leo Perla. 12-Jun-3 Dorotheum, Graz #29/R

£436 $803 €650 Dutch harbour town (70x100cm-28x39in) s.pseudonym. 27-Mar-4 L & B, Essen #132/R
£486 $792 €700 Norwegian fjord (75x100cm-30x39in) s.pseudonym. 26-Sep-3 Bolland & Marotz, Bremen #559/R
£490 $817 €700 Winter wood (31x47cm-12x19in) s.pseudonym B Lambert i. verso panel. 28-Jun-3 Bolland & Marotz, Bremen #683/R
£490 $842 €700 Norwegian fjord landscape (74x100cm-29x39in) s. 5-Dec-3 Bolland & Marotz, Bremen #583/R
£507 $892 €750 Fjord landscape with fishing boats (56x77cm-22x30in) s. 21-May-4 Mehlis, Plauen #15129/R
£513 $934 €770 Coastal scene with town (33x53cm-13x21in) s. lit. 3-Jul-4 Badum, Bamberg #126/R
£513 $934 €770 Southern coastal town (31x59cm-12x23in) s. lit. 3-Jul-4 Badum, Bamberg #127/R
£533 $971 €800 Harbour scene at twilight (41x64cm-16x25in) s. 1-Jul-4 Van Ham, Cologne #1447
£540 $950 €810 Inside the mosque courtyard (30x20cm-12x8in) s. panel. 23-May-4 William Jenack, New York #255
£544 $974 €800 Rococo Linderhof (40x52cm-16x20in) s.pseudonym panel lit. 20-Mar-4 Bergmann, Erlangen #1088
£600 $1074 €876 On the lagoon, Venice at, dusk. Figures on a quay by an Italian lake (31x52cm-12x20in) s. pair. 18-Mar-4 Christie's, Kensington #633
£604 $1111 €900 Oriental city with market stalls and figures (31x19cm-12x7in) s. lit. 25-Mar-4 Karlheinz Kaupp, Staufen #2377/R
£634 $1052 €900 Fjord landscape (68x105cm-27x41in) s.pseudonym J Holmstedt. 16-Jun-3 Dorotheum, Vienna #195/R
£800 $1440 €1200 Venice, St Maria della Salute and Grand Canal (50x82cm-20x32in) s. 26-Apr-4 Rieber, Stuttgart #1145/R
£845 $1462 €1200 Fjord landscape (68x105cm-27x41in) s. 10-Dec-3 Dorotheum, Vienna #242/R
£862 $1586 €1259 English bridge (26x39cm-10x15in) s. panel. 26-Mar-4 Koller, Zurich #3118/R est:2000-3000 (S.FR 2000)
£867 $1560 €1300 Venice, sailing ships before Doges Palace (50x39cm-20x15in) s.pseudonym Ch. Erkan. 26-Apr-4 Rieber, Stuttgart #12222/R
£927 $1724 €1353 View of Rome with Angel Castle (18x31cm-7x12in) s.pseudonyn H Carniar panel. 6-Mar-4 Dorotheum, Prague #18/R est:40000-60000 (C.KR 45000)
£940 $1729 €1400 View over the water to Venice (18x31cm-7x12in) lit. 25-Mar-4 Karlheinz Kaupp, Staufen #2378/R
£1000 $1820 €1460 Oriental view (47x68cm-19x27in) s. 16-Jun-4 Christie's, Kensington #273/R est:1000-1500
£1042 $1719 €1500 Shore of upper italian lake (74x100cm-29x39in) s. two. 3-Jul-3 Van Ham, Cologne #1295/R est:1200
£1059 $1832 €1546 Norwegian fjord scene (74x100cm-29x39in) s. painted c.1900. 14-Dec-3 Agra, Warsaw #44/R est:7000 (P.Z 7000)
£1267 $2305 €1900 Sailing boat at anchor in an Italian harbour (51x77cm-20x30in) s. 1-Jul-4 Van Ham, Cologne #1446/R est:1900
£1389 $2361 €2000 River landscape (82x50cm-32x20in) s.pseudonym J Rollin. 28-Oct-3 Dorotheum, Vienna #266/R est:2000-2500
£1413 $2600 €2063 Venetian canal scene (18x30cm-7x12in) s. 26-Jun-4 Sloans & Kenyon, Bethesda #1063/R est:1800-2200
£1457 $2652 €2200 Venice in the evening (50x82cm-20x32in) s. 19-Jun-4 Bergmann, Erlangen #800 est:1800
£1477 $2761 €2200 Florence (36x50cm-14x20in) s.pseudonym Fr Gilbert i. i. verso one of pair. 24-Feb-4 Dorotheum, Vienna #15/R est:1400-1600
£1667 $2833 €2400 Southern harbour (31x47cm-12x19in) s.d.1898 panel one of pair. 28-Oct-3 Dorotheum, Vienna #77/R est:3000-3500
£1690 $2924 €2400 Canal in Amsterdam (74x100cm-29x39in) s. 10-Dec-3 Dorotheum, Vienna #117/R est:2800-3200
£1745 $3263 €2600 Torbole, Italy (36x50cm-14x20in) s.pseudonym Fr. Gilbert i. i. verso one of pair. 24-Feb-4 Dorotheum, Vienna #16/R est:1400-1600
£1879 $3477 €2800 View of Amsterdam (53x80cm-21x31in) s. 15-Mar-4 Sotheby's, Amsterdam #116/R est:1600-1800
£1900 $3040 €2755 Venetian back water (47x30cm-19x12in) s. panel. 18-Sep-3 Christie's, Kensington #78/R est:1500-2000
£1972 $3411 €2800 Old city port with fishing boats (71x98cm-28x39in) s. board. 10-Dec-3 Dorotheum, Vienna #42/R est:3600-4000
£2096 $3815 €3060 Rome. Venice (18x31cm-7x12in) s. panel pair. 16-Jun-4 Fischer, Luzern #1218/R est:5000-7000 (S.FR 4800)
£2270 $3790 €3200 Venetian harbour (32x52cm-13x20in) s.d.1889. 17-Oct-3 Berlinghof, Heidelberg #1049/R est:3400
£2292 $3735 €3300 Doges Palace/ Maria della Salute (52x31cm-20x12in) 29-Sep-3 Dr Fritz Nagel, Stuttgart #7051/R est:300
£2517 $4280 €3600 Hallstatt in Salzkammergut (69x105cm-27x41in) s. 20-Nov-3 Dorotheum, Salzburg #169/R est:3000-4000
£3500 $5600 €5075 Doge's Palace, Venice (68x106cm-27x42in) bears another sig. 18-Sep-3 Christie's, Kensington #76/R est:3500-4500
£3691 $6607 €5500 Venice (50x82cm-20x32in) s.d.1894. 27-May-4 Dorotheum, Graz #27/R est:1100
£3991 $7144 €5827 Canale Grande, Venedig (53x80cm-21x31in) s. 28-May-4 Uppsala Auktionskammare, Uppsala #128/R est:15000-18000 (S.KR 54000)
£4362 $7809 €6500 View of S Maria della Salute (52x31cm-20x12in) s. panel. 27-May-4 Dorotheum, Vienna #57/R est:4000-6000
£4700 $7991 €6862 Venetian canal scene with figures (70x105cm-28x41in) s.d.1891. 10-Nov-3 Rasmussen, Vejle #21/R est:30000-40000 (D.KR 51000)
£5034 $9010 €7500 View from the Riva degi Schiavoni of Markusbecken and Santa Maria della Salute (98x143cm-39x56in) s. 27-May-4 Dorotheum, Vienna #204/R est:7000-9000

KAUFMANN, Massimo (1963-) Italian
£2667 $4907 €4000 Now that I see you (120x100cm-47x39in) s.i.d.1993 verso mixed media on canvas. 8-Jun-4 Finarte Semenzato, Milan #389/R est:4000-5000

KAUFMANN, Robert D (1913-1959) American
£272 $500 €397 Still life (46x53cm-18x21in) s. masonite. 27-Jun-4 Hindman, Chicago #905/R

KAUFMANN, Wilhelm (1895-1975) Austrian
£347 $566 €500 Mountain lake (49x38cm-19x15in) s. masonite. 23-Sep-3 Wiener Kunst Auktionen, Vienna #118/R
£369 $683 €550 Jesus, John and angel (51x82cm-20x32in) s. masonite. 9-Mar-4 Dorotheum, Vienna #88/R
£387 $678 €550 Still life with fruit (25x36cm-10x14in) s. 19-Dec-3 Dorotheum, Vienna #191/R
£544 $974 €800 Roses in blue vase (60x80cm-24x31in) s. 17-Mar-4 Dorotheum, Vienna #2
£690 $1262 €1000 In front of the mirror (74x69cm-29x27in) s. 27-Jan-4 Dorotheum, Vienna #139/R
£738 $1366 €1100 Stillupp, Tyrol (40x50cm-16x20in) s. masonite. 9-Mar-4 Dorotheum, Vienna #130/R
£867 $1560 €1300 Dolomites, hay harvest (60x80cm-24x31in) s. masonite. 21-Apr-4 Dorotheum, Vienna #96/R
£1000 $1790 €1500 Nude with red high heels (49x38cm-19x15in) s. panel. 13-May-4 Dorotheum, Linz #481/R est:2000-2400
£1007 $1862 €1500 Heiligenblut (49x70cm-19x28in) s. i. verso masonite. 9-Mar-4 Dorotheum, Vienna #116/R est:1800-2400
£1056 $1849 €1500 Venice (50x65cm-20x26in) s. cardboard. 19-Dec-3 Dorotheum, Vienna #147/R est:1500-2000
£2267 $4080 €3400 Village in winter (53x68cm-21x27in) s. board. 21-Apr-4 Dorotheum, Vienna #97/R est:2800-3800
£3092 $5689 €4700 Houses on the left side of Vienna (73x93cm-29x37in) s. board. 22-Jun-4 Wiener Kunst Auktionen, Vienna #70/R est:3000
Works on paper
£567 $948 €800 Still water (48x63cm-19x25in) s. W/C gouache. 14-Oct-3 Dorotheum, Vienna #161/R
£586 $1073 €850 Faakersee (49x65cm-19x26in) s. mixed media. 27-Jan-4 Dorotheum, Vienna #96/R
£600 $1080 €900 Still life with flowers and pears (48x46cm-19x18in) s. W/C. 21-Apr-4 Dorotheum, Vienna #168/R

KAUL, August (1873-1949) German
£269 $487 €393 Buildings beyond a garden (78x99cm-31x39in) s. canvas on board. 30-Mar-4 Stephan Welz, Johannesburg #412 est:3500-5000 (SA.R 3200)

KAULA, Lee Lufkin (1865-1957) American
£944 $1500 €1378 Amsterdam (18x24cm-7x9in) s. i.d.1904 verso panel. 12-Sep-3 Skinner, Boston #467/R
£5814 $10000 €8488 Portrait of a woman in an interior (89x64cm-35x25in) s. painted c.1920. 7-Dec-3 Treadway Gallery, Cincinnati #521/R est:12000-17000

KAULA, William J (1871-1952) American
£615 $1100 €898 Woodland stream (25x30cm-10x12in) canvas on board prov. 26-May-4 Doyle, New York #39/R
£1069 $1700 €1561 Distant farm (38x46cm-15x18in) s. 12-Sep-3 Skinner, Boston #409/R
£3911 $7000 €5710 September skies (61x74cm-24x29in) s. prov. 6-May-4 Shannon's, Milford #7/R est:5000-7000
£3971 $6750 €5798 Landscape with trees and clouds scattered sky (46x56cm-18x22in) s. 21-Nov-3 Eldred, East Dennis #832/R est:4000-5000
Works on paper
£469 $750 €685 River landscape with town in the distance (94x79cm-37x31in) s. W/C. 18-May-3 Auctions by the Bay, Alameda #1048/R
£750 $1200 €1095 Summer clouds (43x53cm-17x21in) s.d.1901 W/C. 21-Sep-3 Grogan, Boston #56/R

KAULBACH, Anton (1864-1930) German
Works on paper
£358 $641 €530 Portrait of Spanish dancer (69x54cm-27x21in) s. pastel. 6-May-4 Michael Zeller, Lindau #719/R

KAULBACH, Friedrich (1822-1903) German
Works on paper
£395 $726 €600 Portrait of bearded man (58x52cm-23x20in) s. chl paper board. 24-Jun-4 Dr Fritz Nagel, Stuttgart #524/R

KAULBACH, Friedrich August von (1850-1920) German
£1013 $1722 €1479 Dachsund begging (73x43cm-29x17in) mono.d.31. Marz 1906 panel. 5-Nov-3 Dobiaschofsky, Bern #713/R est:1500 (S.FR 2300)
£3667 $6673 €5500 Mother and child (82x42cm-32x17in) s. panel. 30-Jun-4 Neumeister, Munich #587/R est:5000
£3846 $6538 €5500 Portrait of Frieda von Kaulbach nee Scotta (135x95cm-53x37in) mono. lit. 28-Nov-3 Schloss Ahlden, Ahlden #1556/R est:5800
£4333 $7843 €6500 Allegorical scene (102x72cm-40x28in) s.d.1905 panel. 1-Apr-4 Van Ham, Cologne #1475/R est:6800
£4362 $8027 €6500 Clara von Watjen (136x104cm-54x41in) s. prov. 26-Mar-4 Ketterer, Hamburg #193/R est:7000-9000
£21000 $38220 €30660 Cherries (101x77cm-40x30in) s.d.1903 prov. 15-Jun-4 Sotheby's, London #41/R est:6000-8000

KAULBACH, Georg (1866-1945) German
£276 $510 €400 Country road (24x40cm-9x16in) s.d.1890 i. verso canvasboard. 14-Feb-4 Hans Stahl, Hamburg #46
£276 $510 €400 September day in Prussian Lithuania (24x40cm-9x16in) s. i.d.1890 verso board. 14-Feb-4 Hans Stahl, Hamburg #47

KAULBACH, Hermann (1846-1909) German
£833 $1358 €1200 Study of door with steps (31x24cm-12x9in) mono. paper on panel. 24-Sep-3 Neumeister, Munich #465/R
£2000 $3640 €3000 Soldner children receiving bread from St Elisabeth (78x61cm-31x24in) s.d.1878 grisaille. 30-Jun-4 Neumeister, Munich #588/R est:4000
£2993 $5358 €4400 Little boy holding flowers (24x15cm-9x6in) s. panel. 17-Mar-4 Neumeister, Munich #496/R est:7000
£3401 $6088 €5000 Dwarf with toothache (45x33cm-18x13in) s. panel. 17-Mar-4 Neumeister, Munich #497/R est:5000

KAUS, Max (1891-1977) German
£3147 $5350 €4500 Still life of flowers (76x57cm-30x22in) s.d.76 tempera dispersion W/C. 29-Nov-3 Villa Grisebach, Berlin #252/R est:4000-6000
£3667 $6747 €5500 Amaryllis on a red background (75x60cm-30x24in) s.d.75 i.verso canvas on board prov. 12-Jun-4 Villa Grisebach, Berlin #324/R est:6000-8000
£5282 $9137 €7500 Tulips (90x74cm-35x29in) s.d.29 i. verso. 13-Dec-3 Lempertz, Koln #159/R est:8000-10000
£10490 $17832 €15000 Passau - Inn shore II (95x118cm-37x46in) s. s.i.d.28 verso canvas on paper prov. 29-Nov-3 Villa Grisebach, Berlin #216/R est:15000-20000

£13333 $24400 €20000 Bathers in mountain stream (80x100cm-31x39in) s.d.25 s.i.d. verso prov. 5-Jun-4 Lempertz, Koln #778/R est:20000-25000
Prints
£1958 $3329 €2800 Nudes by the sea (30x25cm-12x10in) s.i. aquatint drypoint. 29-Nov-3 Villa Grisebach, Berlin #589/R est:1800-2400
£3000 $5520 €4500 Turu sleeping (48x65cm-19x26in) s.d.1922 lithograph. 12-Jun-4 Villa Grisebach, Berlin #254/R est:3500-4500
Works on paper
£667 $1227 €1000 Coastal landscape (53x68cm-21x27in) s.d.1942 W/C. 12-Jun-4 Villa Grisebach, Berlin #580/R
£809 $1400 €1181 Marsh landscape (51x67cm-20x26in) s.i.d.45 W/C ink. 13-Dec-3 Weschler, Washington #524
£1200 $2208 €1800 Still life of lemons (43x68cm-17x27in) s.d.1950 s.i.d.verso gouache ink chk. 12-Jun-4 Villa Grisebach, Berlin #579/R est:2000-3000
£1208 $2223 €1800 City in the Campagna II (49x67cm-19x26in) s.d. gouache oil prov. 26-Mar-4 Ketterer, Hamburg #493/R est:2500-2600
£1250 $2088 €1800 Reclining female nude (15x28cm-6x11in) s. chl. 24-Oct-3 Ketterer, Hamburg #421/R est:2000-2500
£1667 $3067 €2500 Landscape (52x68cm-20x27in) s.i. W/C chl cardboard. 12-Jun-4 Villa Grisebach, Berlin #3316/R est:2500-3500
£2431 $4059 €3500 Three horses by lake (53x68cm-21x27in) s.d. gouache. 24-Oct-3 Ketterer, Hamburg #419/R est:3500-4000
£2778 $4639 €4000 Two horses in meadow (52x68cm-20x27in) s.d. W/C gouache. 24-Oct-3 Ketterer, Hamburg #420/R est:4000-5000
£2939 $4996 €4200 Still life of flowers with candle holder (48x67cm-19x26in) s.d.49 gouache. 29-Nov-3 Villa Grisebach, Berlin #256/R est:3000-4000
£5944 $10224 €8500 Small harbour (53x68cm-21x27in) s.i.d.1942 mixed media. 2-Dec-3 Hauswedell & Nolte, Hamburg #295/R est:6000
£12000 $22080 €18000 Reclining lady (46x63cm-18x25in) s.d.22 W/C ink chk prov. 11-Jun-4 Villa Grisebach, Berlin #1574/R est:15000-20000

KAUTZKY, Ted (?-1953) American/Hungarian
Works on paper
£465 $800 €679 New England harbour, no 12 (25x23cm-10x9in) s. pencil board exec.c.1930. 7-Dec-3 Treadway Gallery, Cincinnati #604/R

KAUZMANN, Paul (1874-1951) German
£2550 $4667 €3800 View over the old bridge over the Danube near Leipheim (40x98cm-16x39in) s.d.1919 lit. 8-Jul-4 Allgauer, Kempten #2128/R est:3800
£2603 $4425 €3800 Wooded river shore (66x83cm-26x33in) s.d.1928 lit. 6-Nov-3 Allgauer, Kempten #3464/R est:3800
£2676 $4790 €3800 View through the trees of the English gardens (80x75cm-31x30in) s. lit. 8-Jan-4 Allgauer, Kempten #2432/R est:4000
£3200 $5760 €4800 In the church tower (107x76cm-42x30in) s.d.1919 lit. 22-Apr-4 Allgauer, Kempten #3599/R est:4800

KAUZMANN, Paul (attrib) (1874-1951) German
£1200 $2160 €1800 Inner courtyard of Fussen castle (63x44cm-25x17in) i.d.1909 verso. 22-Apr-4 Allgauer, Kempten #3600/R est:900

KAVAN, Frantisek (1866-1941) Czechoslovakian
£569 $945 €831 Daffodils (45x55cm-18x22in) panel. 4-Oct-3 Dorotheum, Prague #57/R est:26000-40000 (C.KR 26000)
£613 $1017 €895 Landscape with building (24x35cm-9x14in) s.i. board. 4-Oct-3 Dorotheum, Prague #56/R est:20000-30000 (C.KR 28000)
£618 $1149 €902 Winter landscape under Kumburk (24x37cm-9x15in) s.i. board. 6-Mar-4 Dorotheum, Prague #93 est:30000-45000 (C.KR 30000)
£657 $1090 €959 On the railway turning at Jivany (40x52cm-16x20in) s.i. board. 4-Oct-3 Dorotheum, Prague #55/R est:30000-45000 (C.KR 30000)
£658 $1119 €961 Avenue (40x49cm-16x19in) s. cardboard. 29-Nov-3 Dorotheum, Prague #70/R est:26000-42000 (C.KR 30000)
£746 $1269 €1089 Landscape with trees and a church (25x34cm-10x13in) cardboard. 29-Nov-3 Dorotheum, Prague #68/R est:34000 50000 (C.KR 34000)
£878 $1493 €1282 Winter landscape (36x44cm-14x17in) s. cardboard. 29-Nov-3 Dorotheum, Prague #71/R est:30000-45000 (C.KR 40000)
£949 $1671 €1424 Summer landscape (24x35cm-9x14in) s.i. cardboard. 22-May-4 Dorotheum, Prague #70/R est:30000-45000 (C.KR 45000)
£1055 $1856 €1583 Early evening (20x28cm-8x11in) s.i. cardboard. 22-May-4 Dorotheum, Prague #62/R est:40000-60000 (C.KR 50000)
£1207 $2052 €1762 Forest stream (25x37cm-10x15in) cardboard. 29-Nov-3 Dorotheum, Prague #72/R est:30000-45000 (C.KR 55000)
£1532 $2543 €2237 Kumburk viewed from Podlevin (26x37cm-10x15in) s. board. 4-Oct-3 Dorotheum, Prague #73/R est:36000-50000 (C.KR 70000)
£1544 $2873 €2254 Landscape with Trosky Castle (48x64cm-19x25in) s.i. board. 6-Mar-4 Dorotheum, Prague #91/R est:38000-60000 (C.KR 75000)
£2085 $3545 €3044 Winter in Vitanov (40x50cm-16x20in) s. cardboard. 29-Nov-3 Dorotheum, Prague #67/R est:30000-45000 (C.KR 95000)
£3064 $5086 €4473 Spring in Krkonose Mountains (25x36cm-10x14in) s. board. 4-Oct-3 Dorotheum, Prague #74/R est:36000-54000 (C.KR 140000)

KAVANAGH, J M (19th C) Irish
£800 $1448 €1200 Poachers (48x60cm-19x24in) s. canvas on board. 30-Mar-4 De Veres Art Auctions, Dublin #214/R

KAVANAGH, Joseph Malachy (1856-1918) Irish
£800 $1464 €1168 Girl praying (50x40cm-20x16in) s. board. 2-Jun-4 John Ross, Belfast #25
£2222 $3622 €3200 Sheep grazing under trees in landscape (24x34cm-9x13in) s.d.1904 board. 24-Sep-3 James Adam, Dublin #128/R est:2000-3000
£2797 $4755 €4000 Stately elm, Rathfarnham Park (35x25cm-14x10in) s.i.d.July 1903 panel. 25-Nov-3 De Veres Art Auctions, Dublin #100/R est:4000-6000
£3611 $5886 €5200 In the Baskin Fields, Fingal (24x34cm-9x13in) s.i.verso d.1903 board. 24-Sep-3 James Adam, Dublin #72/R est:5000-7000

KAVIK, John (1897-1993) North American
Sculpture
£1081 $1838 €1578 Musk ox with horns (27cm-11in) s. mottled grey soapstone. 3-Nov-3 Waddingtons, Toronto #228/R est:2000-3000 (C.D 2400)
£1441 $2450 €2104 Inuit woman (20cm-8in) s. mottled dark soapstone. 3-Nov-3 Waddingtons, Toronto #231/R est:2000-3000 (C.D 3200)
£1622 $2757 €2368 Standing Inuk (28cm-11in) s. mottled dark soapstone. 3-Nov-3 Waddingtons, Toronto #229/R est:2500-3500 (C.D 3600)
£1982 $3369 €2894 Inuit mother with a child in her amaut (30cm-12in) mottled green soapstone. 3-Nov-3 Waddingtons, Toronto #220/R est:2500-3500 (C.D 4400)
£2252 $3829 €3288 Inuit mother and child (38cm-15in) mottled grey soapstone. 3-Nov-3 Waddingtons, Toronto #224/R est:5000-7000 (C.D 5000)
Works on paper
£541 $919 €790 Untitled, Inuit couple (24x32cm-9x13in) pencil crayon. 3-Nov-3 Waddingtons, Toronto #218/R (C.D 1200)
£946 $1608 €1381 Untitled (30x46cm-12x18in) s. col pencil. 3-Nov-3 Waddingtons, Toronto #202/R est:700-1000 (C.D 2100)

KAVLI, Arne Texnes (1878-1970) Norwegian
£1278 $2300 €1866 Harbour scene at dusk (66x60cm-26x24in) s. 24-Apr-4 Weschler, Washington #567/R est:2000-3000
£3454 $5734 €5008 Summer landscape, Sorlandet (57x78cm-22x31in) s. 16-Jun-3 Blomqvist, Lysaker #1096 est:60000-80000 (N.KR 40000)
£3589 $6424 €5240 Still life of flowers in vase (76x65cm-30x26in) s.d.1920. 25-May-4 Grev Wedels Plass, Oslo #82/R est:50000-70000 (N.KR 44000)
£3740 $6844 €5460 Gathering in the garden at Ronnes (18x23cm-7x9in) s. panel. 7-Jun-4 Blomqvist, Oslo #380/R est:25000-30000 (N.KR 46000)
£5285 $9671 €7716 Flying the flag (57x67cm-22x26in) s. 7-Jun-4 Blomqvist, Oslo #389/R est:80000-90000 (N.KR 65000)
£7000 $12740 €10220 By the sea (65x76cm-26x30in) init. 15-Jun-4 Sotheby's, London #324a/R est:8000-12000
£17109 $29085 €24979 Woman with coffee pot and two cups on garden steps (80x89cm-31x35in) s. 19-Nov-3 Grev Wedels Plass, Oslo #72/R est:200000-300000 (N.KR 200000)
£24470 $43801 €35726 Dronningen restaurant by Oslo fjord (95x76cm-37x30in) init. exhib. 25-May-4 Grev Wedels Plass, Oslo #100/R est:200000-300000 (N.KR 300000)
£33442 $59861 €48825 Woman at table (68x67cm-27x26in) s.d.09 canvas on panel. 25-May-4 Grev Wedels Plass, Oslo #76/R est:150000-200000 (N.KR 410000)

KAWARA, On (1933-) Japanese
Works on paper
£22754 $38000 €33221 Monday Sept 6 1999 - today series no.34 (34x44cm-13x17in) s.verso liquitex canvas on cardboard box newspaper clipping. 14-Nov-3 Phillips, New York #130/R est:25000-35000
£31285 $56000 €45676 Thursday November 19, 1981, Today series no 43 (33x43cm-13x17in) liquitex canvas cardboard box newspaper clipping prov.lit. 14-May-4 Phillips, New York #244/R est:25000-35000

KAWASHIMA, Takeshi (1930-) Japanese
£529 $900 €772 Untitled (61x61cm-24x24in) s.d.1966 acrylic varnish. 9-Nov-3 Wright, Chicago #404
£2235 $4000 €3263 Untitled (119x119cm-47x47in) prov. 16-May-4 Wright, Chicago #291/R est:2000-3000

KAWIAK, Tomek (1943-) French
Sculpture
£1724 $2879 €2500 Elle enleve le jean (47cm-19in) bronze exec. 1993. 16-Nov-3 Agra, Warsaw #38/R est:3000
Works on paper
£336 $558 €491 Twofold portrait (107x75cm-42x30in) gouache mixed media exec.1989. 2-Oct-3 Agra, Warsaw #36/R (P.Z 2200)
£425 $761 €621 Untitled (95x60cm-37x24in) collage on canvas exec.2003. 6-May-4 Agra, Warsaw #17/R (P.Z 3000)

KAY, Alan (1917-2003) British
£280 $476 €409 Close-ny-Mona, Lezayre (41x61cm-16x24in) s.verso. 31-Oct-3 Chrystals Auctions, Isle of Man #424
£310 $527 €453 Maughold church (41x56cm-16x22in) s.verso. 31-Oct-3 Chrystals Auctions, Isle of Man #434
£320 $544 €467 Corner of Orrisdale (41x56cm-16x22in) s.verso board. 31-Oct-3 Chrystals Auctions, Isle of Man #421
£320 $544 €467 Bride church (51x76cm-20x30in) s.verso. 31-Oct-3 Chrystals Auctions, Isle of Man #427

KAY, Alexander (18/19th C) British
Works on paper
£550 $919 €803 Burgh of Comrie (33x49cm-13x19in) s.d.1818 pen ink W/C. 16-Oct-3 Lyon & Turnbull, Edinburgh #77

KAY, Archibald (1860-1935) British
£500 $860 €730 Cattle grazing (40x60cm-16x24in) s. 7-Dec-3 Uppsala Auktionskammare, Uppsala #187/R (S.KR 6500)
£700 $1127 €1015 Harvesting (24x34cm-9x13in) s. panel. 21-Aug-3 Bonhams, Edinburgh #1012/R
£700 $1302 €1022 Houses on a moor (30x40cm-12x16in) s. canvas on board. 4-Mar-4 Christie's, Kensington #186/R
£780 $1326 €1139 Waves breaking on the shore (32x42cm-13x17in) s.i. 5-Nov-3 Rupert Toovey, Partridge Green #157/R
£800 $1336 €1168 Autumn river scene (25x36cm-10x14in) s. 16-Oct-3 Bonhams, Edinburgh #203
£924 $1700 €1349 Harvest landscape (41x61cm-16x24in) a.s.1893 panel. 11-Jun-4 David Rago, Lambertville #305/R est:1000-1500
£2200 $3454 €3190 Silver river, pass of lows (30x41cm-12x16in) s. i.verso board prov. 27-Aug-3 Sotheby's, London #1123/R est:1500-2000
£3000 $5370 €4380 On the leny (87x112cm-34x44in) s. 28-May-4 Lyon & Turnbull, Edinburgh #17 est:2000-3000
£3800 $5966 €5510 Autumn sunset (76x102cm-30x40in) s. 27-Aug-3 Sotheby's, London #1117/R est:3000-4000

Works on paper
£2000 $3140 €2900 Coming from church (54x39cm-21x15in) s. W/C prov. 27-Aug-3 Sotheby's, London #1141/R est:2000-3000

KAY, Dorothy (1886-1964) South African/Irish
£1268 $2193 €1800 Bit of glamour (71x60cm-28x24in) s.d.1950 prov.exhib.lit. 10-Dec-3 Bonhams & James Adam, Dublin #134/R est:1200-1600
£1552 $2591 €2266 Salt shovellers (72x70cm-28x28in) s.d.1940. 20-Oct-3 Stephan Welz, Johannesburg #271/R est:15000-20000 (SA.R 18000)

KAY, Hermann (1839-1902) German
£828 $1382 €1200 Looking out on the world (28x19cm-11x7in) s. lit. 10-Jul-3 Allgauer, Kempten #2551/R

KAY, James (1858-1942) British
£700 $1281 €1022 Beach on the Clyde Riviera (17x24cm-7x9in) s. board. 8-Apr-4 Bonhams, Edinburgh #87
£1000 $1570 €1450 Shore of the loch (30x46cm-12x18in) s. 27-Aug-3 Sotheby's, London #1083/R est:1000-1500
£1400 $2604 €2044 Figures on the shore (17x39cm-7x15in) indis sig. panel. 4-Mar-4 Christie's, Kensington #129/R est:1000-1500
£1400 $2604 €2044 Woodland scene Loch Long (25x35cm-10x14in) s. indis d. board. 4-Mar-4 Christie's, Kensington #138/R est:800-1200
£2600 $4420 €3796 Shipyard on the Clyde (66x86cm-26x34in) s. buff paper. 30-Oct-3 Christie's, London #135/R est:2500-3500
£3000 $5160 €4380 Mafarka, Majorca (54x79cm-21x31in) s. board. 4-Dec-3 Bonhams, Edinburgh #102a est:2500-3000
£3000 $5190 €4380 Cathedral interior (75x62cm-30x24in) s. board. 11-Dec-3 Lyon & Turnbull, Edinburgh #69/R est:3000-4000
£4100 $6437 €5945 Outward bound (30x66cm-12x26in) s. prov. 27-Aug-3 Sotheby's, London #1101/R est:2500-3500
£4600 $7820 €6716 Steam launch on the river (49x60cm-19x24in) s. panel sold with an oil on panel by same hand two. 30-Oct-3 Christie's, London #138/R est:3000-5000
£8500 $13345 €12325 Street scene in Majorca (53x63cm-21x25in) s. board. 27-Aug-3 Sotheby's, London #1073/R est:8000-12000
£15000 $23550 €21750 La grosse horlodge, Rouen (77x63cm-30x25in) s. prov.exhib. 27-Aug-3 Sotheby's, London #1139/R est:15000-20000
£22000 $34540 €31900 Rue Saint Romain, Rouen (91x71cm-36x28in) s.d. exhib. 27-Aug-3 Sotheby's, London #1140/R est:22000-28000
Works on paper
£580 $1079 €847 Bustling coastal scene (24x35cm-9x14in) s.i. pastel col chk. 4-Mar-4 Christie's, Kensington #130/R
£1600 $2912 €2336 A paddle tug on an industrial river. The ferry crossing (16x24cm-6x9in) one s.i. pencil W/C htd white one s. col chk pair. 1-Jul-4 Christie's, Kensington #428/R est:800-1200
£2000 $3620 €2920 Return of the fishing fleet (47x59cm-19x23in) s. W/C prov. 19-Apr-4 Sotheby's, London #108/R est:2000-3000

KAY, Pamela (1939-) British
£640 $1005 €928 Breakfast still life with hyacinths (35x30cm-14x12in) init. i.verso board. 28-Aug-3 Christie's, Kensington #296/R

KAYE, Otis (1885-1974) American
£10795 $19000 €15761 Washington and the half-dollar (15x20cm-6x8in) s. panel prov. 19-May-4 Sotheby's, New York #72/R est:20000-30000
£11364 $20000 €16591 Fool and his money (15x23cm-6x9in) s. panel prov. 19-May-4 Sotheby's, New York #71/R est:20000-30000
£26163 $45000 €38198 Two to win (27x32cm-11x13in) s.i. panel prov. 3-Dec-3 Sotheby's, New York #114/R est:40000-60000
Prints
£2429 $4250 €3546 Rembrant's etching of The Goldsmith with 10 dollar eagle note (10x8cm-4x3in) s. etching oil prov. 19-Dec-3 Sotheby's, New York #1011/R est:4000-6000

KAYSER, Conrad (1880-?) German
£986 $1577 €1400 Black Forest in the Rhineland (55x40cm-22x16in) s.d.1948. 18-Sep-3 Rieber, Stuttgart #1233/R

KAYSER-EICHBERG, Carl (1873-1964) German
£268 $497 €400 Extensive landscape (125x161cm-49x63in) s.d.04 lit. 12-Mar-4 Zadick, Uberlingen #4056
£280 $467 €400 Mill in the Mark region (45x60cm-18x24in) s.d.32 i. verso board. 28-Jun-3 Bolland & Marotz, Bremen #684
£336 $624 €500 Shepherd (90x120cm-35x47in) s. 7-Mar-4 Bukowskis, Helsinki #494/R

KAYYALI, Louai (1934-1978) Syrian
£8000 $14160 €11680 Portrait (58x37cm-23x15in) s.d.64 oil htd chl. 29-Apr-4 Bonhams, New Bond Street #570/R est:8000-10000

KAZAKIEWICZ, Anton (?) ?
£3125 $5000 €4563 Garden Scene (43x36cm-17x14in) panel. 19-Sep-3 Du Mouchelle, Detroit #2057/R est:5000-6000

KAZOVSZKIJ, El (1950-) Hungarian
£992 $1716 €1448 Chimaera leaving (80x60cm-31x24in) s. 12-Dec-3 Kieselbach, Budapest #148/R (H.F 380000)

KAZUO, Udagawa (fl.1900-1910) Japanese
Sculpture
£10490 $18042 €15000 Mother sitting on a bench feeding her child (57cm-22in) s. bronze wood. 5-Dec-3 Lempertz, Koln #832/R est:15000

KCHO (1970-) Cuban
Sculpture
£4790 $8000 €6993 Refrigeration boat (284x114x56cm-112x45x22in) copper tubing refrigeration unit hosing prov. 13-Nov-3 Sotheby's, New York #472/R est:10000-15000
£6176 $10500 €9017 Sin titulo (109x63x39cm-43x25x15in) mixed media bronze prov. 19-Nov-3 Sotheby's, New York #151/R est:10000-15000
Works on paper
£10000 $17000 €14600 La isla de mis suenos I and II - The island of my dreams (150x305cm-59x120in) s.i.d.96 chl diptych prov. 18-Nov-3 Christie's, Rockefeller NY #10/R est:20000-30000

KEABLE, Robert (18th C) British
£360 $673 €526 Half length portrait of a gentleman in a white cravat (70x62cm-28x24in) s.d.1736. 26-Feb-4 Locke & England, Leamington Spa #111

KEAN, Michael (c.1761-1823) British
Miniatures
£5800 $10440 €8468 John Hayes St Leger (4cm-2in) i.verso gold frame oval prov.exhib.lit. 22-Apr-4 Bonhams, New Bond Street #38/R est:2500-3500

KEANE, Margaret (1927-) American
£2174 $3500 €3174 Wind-sand-oil (76x58cm-30x23in) s. i. stretcher prov. 20-Aug-3 James Julia, Fairfield #1594/R est:1000-2000

KEARSE, Mary (fl.1794-1830) British
Works on paper
£3500 $5845 €5110 Glories of the garden (65x53cm-26x21in) s.d.1799 gouache. 16-Oct-3 Lawrence, Crewkerne #628/R est:1500-2500

KEATING, Sean (1889-1978) Irish
£8000 $14320 €11680 Man standing by a column (56x69cm-22x27in) s. 14-May-4 Christie's, London #188/R est:5000-8000
£34965 $59441 €50000 Aran turf boat (76x91cm-30x36in) s.i. i.verso board prov. 25-Nov-3 De Veres Art Auctions, Dublin #52/R est:50000-70000
£40845 $65352 €58000 Patrick Lynch's boat (53x66cm-21x26in) s. prov. 16-Sep-3 Whyte's, Dublin #71/R est:50000-70000
£85000 $152150 €124100 An Roinnet; the share out (107x122cm-42x48in) s. s. in gaelic verso board. 13-May-4 Sotheby's, London #61/R est:60000-80000
£114094 $204228 €170000 Self portrait - man of Aran (91x70cm-36x28in) s. prov.lit. 26-May-4 James Adam, Dublin #50/R est:50000-80000
Works on paper
£800 $1432 €1168 Study of a girl (34x26cm-13x10in) s. pastel. 14-May-4 Christie's, Kensington #314/R
£1181 $1924 €1700 The imp (33x25cm-13x10in) s. i.verso chl. 24-Sep-3 James Adam, Dublin #135/R est:800-1200
£1351 $2554 €2000 Head of an actress (38x30cm-15x12in) s. chl pastel. 17-Feb-4 Whyte's, Dublin #50/R est:1200-1500
£1600 $2896 €2400 Female portrait study (41x33cm-16x13in) s. col chk oval. 30-Mar-4 De Veres Art Auctions, Dublin #177 est:2000-3000
£1745 $3089 €2600 Head of a woman (36x27cm-14x11in) s. pastel. 27-Apr-4 Whyte's, Dublin #109/R est:2000-3000
£1800 $3294 €2628 After orpen (38x28cm-15x11in) s. chl. 2-Jun-4 John Ross, Belfast #135 est:1500-2000
£2448 $4161 €3500 Portrait of a young girl (34x25cm-13x10in) s. pastel. 18-Nov-3 Whyte's, Dublin #230/R est:2500-3000
£2535 $4056 €3600 Man of Aran (74x51cm-29x20in) s. chl prov. 16-Sep-3 Whyte's, Dublin #76/R est:3000-4000
£2657 $4517 €3800 Dail Land Court sitting in Westport, County Mayo (15x41cm-6x16in) s. chl. 18-Nov-3 Whyte's, Dublin #123/R est:3000-5000
£2797 $4755 €4000 Portrait of Eamon de Valera (46x36cm-18x14in) s. chl htd white prov. 18-Nov-3 Whyte's, Dublin #122/R est:3500-4500
£2937 $4993 €4200 Movita (27x29cm-11x11in) s. chl pastel. 18-Nov-3 Whyte's, Dublin #128/R est:1500-1800
£2958 $4732 €4200 Galway hooker (38x48cm-15x19in) s. chl prov. 16-Sep-3 Whyte's, Dublin #74/R est:3000-4000
£3169 $5070 €4500 Self portrait (44x38cm-17x15in) s. pastel prov. 16-Sep-3 Whyte's, Dublin #73/R est:4000-5000
£4014 $6423 €5700 King of Aran (41x33cm-16x13in) s. chl. 16-Sep-3 Whyte's, Dublin #75/R est:3000-4000
£4577 $7324 €6500 Portrait of a young girl (34x27cm-13x11in) s. pastel. 16-Sep-3 Whyte's, Dublin #77/R est:1500-2000
£5369 $9503 €8000 Conversation piece (51x71cm-20x28in) s. black sanguine conte crayon. 27-Apr-4 Whyte's, Dublin #108/R est:6000-8000
£6081 $11493 €9000 Siobhan McKenna in the Playboy of the western world (55x34cm-22x13in) s. chl bodycol. 17-Feb-4 Whyte's, Dublin #49/R est:6000-8000
£9060 $16037 €13500 Self portrait in Bainin hat (48x38cm-19x15in) s. pastel prov. 27-Apr-4 Whyte's, Dublin #22/R est:8000-10000
£11972 $19155 €17000 Head of the turf gatherer (50x41cm-20x16in) s. pastel prov. 16-Sep-3 Whyte's, Dublin #72/R est:6000-8000

KEATS, Charles James (19/20th C) British
Works on paper
£250 $465 €365 Orleans, French street scene (48x30cm-19x12in) s. 5-Mar-4 Dee Atkinson & Harrison, Driffield #685
£500 $850 €730 Ghent with figures and market stalls (31x49cm-12x19in) s.i. W/C pair. 26-Nov-3 Peter Wilson, Nantwich #118

KECIR, Bohomil (1904-1987) Austrian
£546 $1000 €797 Still life with flowers (48x38cm-19x15in) s. board painted c.1937. 5-Jun-4 Treadway Gallery, Cincinnati #729/R est:2000-3000
£546 $1000 €797 Still life with fruit (38x48cm-15x19in) s. board painted c.1937. 5-Jun-4 Treadway Gallery, Cincinnati #733/R est:2000-3000
£1379 $2524 €2000 Still life (56x41cm-22x16in) s. board. 27-Jan-4 Dorotheum, Vienna #92/R est:2600-3500

£2207 $4039 €3200 Still life (60x45cm-24x18in) s. board. 27-Jan-4 Dorotheum, Vienna #91/R est:4000-4500

KECK, H (19/20th C) ?
Sculpture
£2418 $4400 €3530 Dancing woman. s. polychrome bronze ivory. 8-Feb-4 William Jenack, New York #175 est:4400

KECK, Paul (1904-1973) German
£1329 $2219 €1900 Nagelfluh mountains with Mittagsspitze (46x61cm-18x24in) s.d.1944. 9-Oct-3 Michael Zeller, Lindau #623/R est:1900

KECK, William (20th C) American?
£250 $425 €365 Untitled (36x53cm-14x21in) s. oil on paper. 9-Nov-3 Wright, Chicago #447

KEDL, Rudolf (1928-1991) Austrian?
Sculpture
£2685 $4752 €4000 Knospe (65cm-26in) s.d. green pat.bronze. 28-Apr-4 Wiener Kunst Auktionen, Vienna #256/R est:3500-5000
£3020 $5406 €4500 Reclining figure (23x47x28cm-9x19x11in) s. black brown pat.bronze. 25-May-4 Dorotheum, Vienna #353/R est:5000-7000

KEEGAN, Marie (1941-) American
£333 $600 €486 Under the big top (89x104cm-35x41in) acrylic painted c.1980 prov.exhib. 24-Apr-4 Slotin Folk Art, Buford #263/R

KEELEY, John (1849-1930) British
Works on paper
£280 $448 €409 Bont Newydd, N Wales (22x33cm-9x13in) s. W/C. 16-Sep-3 Bonhams, Knowle #64
£360 $612 €526 Sunday evening (47x62cm-19x24in) s. pencil W/C. 19-Nov-3 Tennants, Leyburn #986

KEELHOFF, Alice (19th C) Belgian
Works on paper
£426 $711 €600 Ballade en voilier (28x41cm-11x16in) s.d.juillet 1883 W/C. 17-Jun-3 Vanderkindere, Brussels #224

KEELHOFF, Frans (1820-1893) Belgian
£651 $1106 €950 Chaumiere (47x66cm-19x26in) s.d.1869. 10-Nov-3 Horta, Bruxelles #377
£655 $1212 €950 Conduite du troupeau (32x55cm-13x22in) s. 19-Jan-4 Horta, Bruxelles #465
£2133 $3840 €3200 Woodview with pond and shepherdess (100x70cm-39x28in) s.d.1858. 26-Apr-4 Bernaerts, Antwerp #61/R est:2000-3000

KEELING, David (1951-) Australian
£345 $542 €500 Buona vista (30x5cm-12x2in) board. 27-Aug-3 Christie's, Sydney #687 (A.D 850)
£407 $638 €590 Gate (25x20cm-10x8in) prov. 27-Aug-3 Christie's, Sydney #599 (A.D 1000)
£1138 $1787 €1650 Isthmus (91x121cm-36x48in) s.d.94 oil wax prov.exhib. 27-Aug-3 Christie's, Sydney #616/R est:4000-6000 (A.D 2800)
£2254 $3562 €3291 Threshold (50x81cm-20x32in) s.d.94 diptych linen exhib. 2-Sep-3 Deutscher-Menzies, Melbourne #3/R est:5000-7000 (A.D 5500)
£2273 $3864 €3319 Monumental landscape (102x110cm-40x43in) s.d.87. 29-Oct-3 Lawson Menzies, Sydney #7/R est:7000-10000 (A.D 5500)
£2273 $4205 €3319 Cave (175x170cm-69x67in) s.d.91 exhib. 15-Mar-4 Sotheby's, Melbourne #20/R est:5000-8000 (A.D 5500)
£2614 $4366 €3921 Fox on the table (76x91cm-30x36in) s.d.94. 27-Oct-3 Goodman, Sydney #34/R est:4000-6000 (A.D 6300)
£4339 $8027 €6335 Spread (141x160cm-56x63in) s. oil on linen prov. 10-Mar-4 Deutscher-Menzies, Melbourne #189/R est:12000-18000 (A.D 10500)
Works on paper
£3099 $5733 €4525 Ground still life (137x137cm-54x54in) s.d.87-88 prov. 15-Mar-4 Sotheby's, Melbourne #21/R est:5000-8000 (A.D 7500)

KEELING, William Knight (1807-1886) British
£294 $550 €429 Portrait of a girl (28x20cm-11x8in) s. 24-Feb-4 Peter Webb, Auckland #202/R (NZ.D 800)

KEEN, M (?) ?
£939 $1700 €1371 Industrial scene with two men hoisting an anchor (41x53cm-16x21in) masonite. 3-Apr-4 David Rago, Lambertville #99/R est:800-1200

KEENE, Alfred John (1863-1930) British
Works on paper
£270 $494 €394 Willow Row, Derby - street scene with figures and children at play (26x38cm-10x15in) W/C bodycol htd white. 10-Jun-4 Neales, Nottingham #559

KEENE, Charles Samuel (1823-1891) British
Works on paper
£800 $1480 €1168 Portrait of a young woman (12x8cm-5x3in) d.1857 pencil W/C pencil sketch verso double-sided. 10-Mar-4 Sotheby's, Olympia #89/R

KEENE, Paul F (1920-) American
£281 $450 €410 Untitled (23x15cm-9x6in) s. indis d.57 oil on paper. 19-Sep-3 Freeman, Philadelphia #64
Works on paper
£266 $425 €388 Nude (25x20cm-10x8in) s. ink. 19-Sep-3 Freeman, Philadelphia #2/R

KEETMAN, Peter (1916-) German
Photographs
£1867 $3435 €2800 City morning (29x23cm-11x9in) s.i.d. verso silver gelatin le. 10-Jun-4 Villa Grisebach, Berlin #1144/R est:2000-2500
£2027 $3628 €3000 Pendulum swinging (30x23cm-12x9in) s.i.d. verso silver gelatin. 8-May-4 Lempertz, Koln #142/R est:3200
£2098 $3566 €3000 Munich: View from the Neuen Post (23x30cm-9x12in) i.d. silver gelatin. 27-Nov-3 Villa Grisebach, Berlin #1242/R est:2500-3000
£2395 $4000 €3497 Eichheim Schnee - Snow in Eichheim (31x24cm-12x9in) s.i.d.1960 verso gelatin silver print prov. 17-Oct-3 Phillips, New York #270/R est:4000-6000
£2533 $4661 €3800 Rainy station (23x17cm-9x7in) s.i.d. verso silver gelatin lit.exhib. 10-Jun-4 Villa Grisebach, Berlin #1146/R est:2000-2500
£2536 $4159 €3500 Untitled (23x17cm-9x7in) s.d. vintage bromide silver gelatin. 30-May-3 Villa Grisebach, Berlin #1224/R est:2500-3000
£2667 $4907 €4000 Ice rink (40x50cm-16x20in) s.i.d. verso silver gelatin lit.exhib. 10-Jun-4 Villa Grisebach, Berlin #1147/R est:4000-5000
£2899 $4754 €4000 Landscape (22x30cm-9x12in) s.i.d. verso vintage silver gelatin. 30-May-3 Villa Grisebach, Berlin #1223/R est:3000-4000
£3497 $5944 €5000 1001 faces (50x41cm-20x16in) s.i.d. verso silver gelatin lit.exhib. 27-Nov-3 Villa Grisebach, Berlin #1245/R est:4000-5000

KEFFER, Frances (1881-1953) American
£741 $1400 €1082 Garden flowers (41x41cm-16x16in) s. s.i. verso board prov. 17-Feb-4 John Moran, Pasadena #111/R est:1000-1500

KEGHEL, Desire de (1839-1901) Belgian
£1733 $3189 €2600 Jetee de roses jaunes (71x43cm-28x17in) s. 14-Jun-4 Horta, Bruxelles #76 est:2000-3000

KEHOE, John (20th C) Irish?
£278 $436 €400 Figures in extensive landscape (82x115cm-32x45in) s. board. 26-Aug-3 James Adam, Dublin #9/R

KEHOE, Patrice (1952-) American
Works on paper
£330 $600 €482 Catawba (112x140cm-44x55in) chl pastel. 7-Feb-4 Harvey Clar, Oakland #1496

KEHR, Karl (1866-1919) German
£629 $1083 €900 Walking in the countryside after the rain (62x49cm-24x19in) s.i. 3-Dec-3 Neumeister, Munich #613/R

KEIBUN, Matsumura (1779-1843) Japanese
Works on paper
£1033 $1900 €1508 Rabbit and bamboo (98x29cm-39x11in) s. ink hanging scroll. 23-Mar-4 Christie's, Rockefeller NY #107/R est:1500-2000
£1507 $2562 €2200 Mushroom. Mussel (34x46cm-13x18in) s. Indian ink col hanging scrolls pair. 8-Nov-3 Dr Fritz Nagel, Stuttgart #1780/R est:1900

KEIGHTLEY, May (20th C) British
£280 $496 €409 Spanish landscape (61x51cm-24x20in) 27-Apr-4 Bonhams, Knowle #129

KEIJERT, Rienk (1709-1775) Dutch
£1900 $3154 €2774 Portrait of a lady wearing a yellow dress, red cloak and pearl necklace (40x34cm-16x13in) s.d.1742. 30-Sep-3 Sotheby's, London #336/R est:1200-1800

KEIL, Bernhard (1624-1687) Danish
£11000 $20021 €16500 Joueur de flute (49x39cm-19x15in) 30-Jun-4 Pierre Berge, Paris #43/R est:10000-12000
£21434 $38367 €31294 Three children (70x94cm-28x37in) 26-May-4 AB Stockholms Auktionsverk #2516/R est:100000-125000 (S.KR 290000)
£32000 $55360 €46720 Boy seated holding a red pot with his left hand (96x72cm-38x28in) lit. 10-Dec-3 Christie's, London #47/R est:20000-30000
£42000 $72660 €61320 Young man with a pot of roses (96x72cm-38x28in) prov.lit. 10-Dec-3 Christie's, London #46/R est:30000-40000

KEIL, Edouard (20th C) French
£1448 $2418 €2114 Rococo interior with figures. Gentleman courting. Ladies and gentlemen conversing (31x21cm-12x8in) s. three. 17-Nov-3 Waddingtons, Toronto #188/R (C.D 3200)

KEIL, Franz Friedrich (1813-1875) German
£352 $609 €500 Portrait of grey haired man in black suit (68x59cm-27x23in) s.d.1845. 11-Dec-3 Dr Fritz Nagel, Stuttgart #525/R

KEIL, Peter (1943-) German
£400 $736 €600 Portrait (67x47cm-26x19in) s.d.87 acrylic masonite. 9-Jun-4 Dorotheum, Salzburg #687/R
£414 $757 €600 Untitled (100x70cm-39x28in) s. acrylic. 27-Jan-4 Dorotheum, Vienna #211/R
£455 $800 €664 Abstract woman (66x51cm-26x20in) s. board painted c.1980. 23-May-4 Treadway Gallery, Cincinnati #761/R
£470 $869 €700 Bridge over the Spree (75x100cm-30x39in) s. s.i. verso acrylic. 9-Mar-4 Dorotheum, Vienna #218/R

£486	$812	€700	Brunnenstrasse on Humboldthain (50x61cm-20x24in) s.d. i.d. verso acrylic masonite. 24-Oct-3 Ketterer, Hamburg #862/R
£486	$812	€700	City indian from Berlin (100x100cm-39x39in) s.d. s.i.d. stretcher acrylic cotton damask. 24-Oct-3 Ketterer, Hamburg #863/R
£561	$920	€780	Belly dance club (100x69cm-39x27in) s. s.i. verso acrylic. 4-Jun-3 Ketterer, Hamburg #549/R
£586	$1073	€850	Untitled (100x70cm-39x28in) s. acrylic. 27-Jan-4 Dorotheum, Vienna #210/R

Works on paper

£1208	$2235	€1800	Paris Bar Berlin (80x68cm-31x27in) s.i.d.1959 verso mixed media panel. 9-Mar-4 Dorotheum, Vienna #226 est:800-1200

KEIL, Robert (1905-1989) Austrian

£2817	$4930	€4000	Shapes in yellow (134x100cm-53x39in) s.i.d.57. 19-Dec-3 Dorotheum, Vienna #198/R est:4000-6000

KEIME, Jean (20th C) French

£472	$750	€689	Pont et canal, lumiere du soir (53x46cm-21x18in) s. 14-Sep-3 Susanin's, Chicago #6091/R

KEIMEL, Hermann (1889-1948) German

£865	$1573	€1263	At the front of the house (41x54cm-16x21in) s. 20-Jun-4 Agra, Warsaw #22/R (P.Z 6000)

KEINANEN, Sigfrid August (1841-1914) Finnish

£1259	$2140	€1800	Hut in the woods (45x31cm-18x12in) s. 29-Nov-3 Bukowskis, Helsinki #75/R est:2000-2500
£1408	$2254	€2000	Landscape (39x95cm-15x37in) s. 18-Sep-3 Hagelstam, Helsinki #966/R est:2500
£2308	$3923	€3300	View of Larsmo Vicarage (27x38cm-11x15in) i. verso board. 29-Nov-3 Bukowskis, Helsinki #110/R est:1800-2000
£3636	$6182	€5200	The bay near home (40x96cm-16x38in) s. 29-Nov-3 Bukowskis, Helsinki #155/R est:4000-5000
£5315	$9035	€7600	Street scene in Brahestad (27x36cm-11x14in) s.d.1881. 29-Nov-3 Bukowskis, Helsinki #112/R est:2500-3000

KEIRINCX, Alexander (1600-1652) Flemish

£12000	$21600	€17520	Wooded landscape with the hunt of Diana (78x121cm-31x48in) panel. 21-Apr-4 Christie's, London #8/R est:12000-16000

KEIRINCX, Alexander (circle) (1600-1652) Flemish

£5172	$9517	€7551	Paradise (58x90cm-23x35in) panel prov.lit. 26-Mar-4 Koller, Zurich #3039/R est:12000-18000 (S.FR 12000)

KEIRSBILCK, Jules van (1833-1896) Belgian

£1611	$2980	€2400	Jeune mendiant souriant (90x60cm-35x24in) s. 15-Mar-4 Horta, Bruxelles #442 est:1500-2000

KEISER, Joseph (1859-?) Swiss

£326	$597	€476	Winter landscape with a farm (48x64cm-19x25in) s. i.verso. 4-Jun-4 Zofingen, Switzerland #2858 (S.FR 750)

KEISERMANN, Franz (1765-1833) Swiss

Works on paper

£3221	$5154	€4703	Tivoli waterfall (38x54cm-15x21in) s. i. verso W/C. 19-Sep-3 Koller, Zurich #3067/R est:7000-12000 (S.FR 7120)
£5200	$8840	€7592	Rome, a view of the arch of Constantine (51x69cm-20x27in) bears sig pen ink W/C. 30-Oct-3 Sotheby's, Olympia #182/R est:2500-4500
£5200	$8840	€7592	Rome, view of the Forum, with the arch of Septimus Severus (51x69cm-20x27in) bears sig pen ink W/C. 30-Oct-3 Sotheby's, Olympia #183/R est:2500-4500
£6000	$10740	€9000	Paestum temples. View of Castel Sant'Angelo (29x41cm-11x16in) s. ink W/C dr pair. 17-May-4 Finarte Semenzato, Rome #17/R est:10000-12000
£9444	$17000	€13788	View of the ruins at Tivoli (76x54cm-30x21in) s. W/C over pen ink. 21-Jan-4 Sotheby's, New York #122/R est:10000-15000
£10204	$18265	€15000	La Grotte de Neptune a Tivoli, un pecheur au premier plan (66x102cm-26x40in) s. i.verso graphite pen brown ink W/C prov. 18-Mar-4 Christie's, Paris #206/R est:8000-12000
£14966	$26789	€22000	L'Arc de Constantin a Rome, des personnages au premier plan (66x102cm-26x40in) s. s.i.d.1816 verso graphite pen brown ink wash W/C prov. 18-Mar-4 Christie's, Paris #205/R est:12000-16000

KEISERMANN, Franz (attrib) (1765-1833) Swiss

Works on paper

£6849	$11644	€10000	Paysages suisses (59x90cm-23x35in) W/C over crayon pair. 6-Nov-3 Tajan, Paris #110/R est:10000-12000

KEISERMANN, Franz (circle) (1765-1833) Swiss

Works on paper

£5600	$10416	€8176	Tivoli with artist sketching (81x64cm-32x25in) W/C. 2-Mar-4 Bearnes, Exeter #348/R est:600-800

KEISTER, Roy (1886-?) American

£216	$400	€315	At the fiesta (61x76cm-24x30in) s. 19-Jan-4 O'Gallerie, Oregon #154/R
£373	$600	€545	Young Navajo drilling turquoise with a hand drill (61x76cm-24x30in) s. 24-Feb-3 O'Gallerie, Oregon #194/R

KEITA, Seydou (1921-2001) African

Photographs

£1808	$3200	€2640	Elegant young man holding a flower, 1958 (52x40cm-20x16in) s.d. gelatin silver print lit. 27-Apr-4 Christie's, Rockefeller NY #349/R est:4000-6000
£2000	$3640	€2920	Untitled (50x60cm-20x24in) s.d.52 A 56 1998 blk white photo. 4-Feb-4 Sotheby's, Olympia #74/R est:2000-3000
£2111	$3800	€3082	Young couple and their friend (53x38cm-21x15in) s.d. gelatin silver print prov.lit. 23-Apr-4 Phillips, New York #192/R est:3000-5000
£2395	$4000	€3497	Woman in loose dress with triple puff sleeves (51x37cm-20x15in) s.d.1957-1958 gelatin silver print lit. 20-Oct-3 Christie's, Rockefeller NY #222/R est:5000-7000
£2395	$4000	€3497	Young mother with her baby (39x55cm-15x22in) s.d.1952-1955 gelatin silver print lit. 20-Oct-3 Christie's, Rockefeller NY #224/R est:5000-7000
£2500	$4500	€3650	Father and child (54x39cm-21x15in) s. gelatin silver print prov.lit. 23-Apr-4 Phillips, New York #187/R est:3000-5000
£2515	$4200	€3672	Twins in European dress (39x55cm-15x22in) s.d.1952-1955 gelatin silver print lit. 20-Oct-3 Christie's, Rockefeller NY #223/R est:5000-7000
£2778	$5000	€4056	Two young women posing as twins (38x55cm-15x22in) s.d.1952-55 gelatin silver print prov.lit. 23-Apr-4 Phillips, New York #172/R est:3000-5000

KEITH, William (1839-1911) American

£1216	$2250	€1775	Italian peasant woman knitting (86x76cm-34x30in) s.d.1885. 15-Jul-4 Doyle, New York #51/R est:2000-3000
£1344	$2500	€1962	Pastoral landscape (46x66cm-18x26in) s. 6-Mar-4 Harvey Clar, Oakland #1577
£1589	$2750	€2320	Figure at the edge of a clearing (51x71cm-20x28in) s. prov. 10-Dec-3 Bonhams & Butterfields, San Francisco #6150/R est:3000-5000
£2038	$3750	€2975	Cows in a clearing (46x76cm-18x30in) s. 8-Jun-4 Bonhams & Butterfields, San Francisco #4172/R est:3000-5000
£2174	$4000	€3174	Clearing at dusk (63x76cm-25x30in) s. prov. 8-Jun-4 Bonhams & Butterfields, San Francisco #4173/R est:5000-7000
£2174	$4000	€3174	Wooded landscape with cattle watering at a lake (55x71cm-22x28in) s.i. prov. 8-Jun-4 Bonhams & Butterfields, San Francisco #4175/R est:3000-5000
£2857	$5000	€4171	Misty morning in May (59x86cm-23x34in) s.indis.d. prov. 19-Dec-3 Sotheby's, New York #1084/R est:3000-5000
£2890	$5000	€4219	Cattle grazing by a stream (36x74cm-14x29in) s.i. 10-Dec-3 Bonhams & Butterfields, San Francisco #6152/R est:7000-10000
£2969	$4750	€4335	The meadow. s. sold with signed book. 20-Sep-3 Harvey Clar, Oakland #1532a
£3022	$5500	€4412	Pond in wooded forest (66x41cm-26x16in) s. board on masonite prov. 15-Jun-4 John Moran, Pasadena #76 est:4000-6000
£3175	$6000	€4636	Landscape - evening in Berkeley Hills (43x58cm-17x23in) s.d.1906 prov. 17-Feb-4 John Moran, Pasadena #67/R est:4500-6500
£3846	$7000	€5615	View of Mount Diablo. s.i. 7-Feb-4 Harvey Clar, Oakland #1582
£3846	$7000	€5615	Palo Alto Oaks at Stanford, California (76x117cm-30x46in) s. 7-Feb-4 Neal Auction Company, New Orleans #452/R est:6000-8000
£4348	$8000	€6348	Cowboy herding cattle with Mount Hood in the distance (25x45cm-10x18in) s. paper prov. 8-Jun-4 Bonhams & Butterfields, San Francisco #4161/R est:3000-5000
£4670	$8500	€6818	Figures in an oak glade (43x64cm-17x25in) s. prov. 15-Jun-4 John Moran, Pasadena #60 est:9000-12000
£5202	$9000	€7595	Path to a distant lake (51x76cm-20x30in) s.i. 10-Dec-3 Bonhams & Butterfields, San Francisco #6151/R est:7000-10000
£8671	$15000	€12660	Clearing among the oaks, Alameda, California (61x91cm-24x36in) s. prov. 10-Dec-3 Bonhams & Butterfields, San Francisco #6146/R est:20000-30000
£13006	$22500	€18989	Cattle watering at a pond with a shepherd nearby (51x77cm-20x30in) s.i. prov. 10-Dec-3 Bonhams & Butterfields, San Francisco #6145/R est:15000-20000
£19022	$35000	€27772	View of Donner lake (116x76cm-46x30in) s.i. prov. 8-Jun-4 Bonhams & Butterfields, San Francisco #4170/R est:40000-60000
£24457	$45000	€35707	Riders cresting a Sierra pass (61x91cm-24x36in) s.i. prov. 8-Jun-4 Bonhams & Butterfields, San Francisco #4177/R est:30000-50000

KEITH, William (attrib) (1839-1911) American

£1347	$2250	€1967	Shepherd with his sheep in a glen (51x76cm-20x30in) bears sig.i. 26-Oct-3 Bonhams & Butterfields, San Francisco #6482/R
£5307	$9500	€7961	Country landscape with trees (46x56cm-18x22in) s. 16-May-4 Abell, Los Angeles #426

KEITH, William Castle (1864-1927) American

£638	$1066	€900	The Mills of Leidschendam (41x51cm-16x20in) s.i. 20-Oct-3 Glerum, Amsterdam #65/R
£699	$1300	€1021	Drying laundry Holland (36x48cm-14x19in) s. 7-Mar-4 William Jenack, New York #182 est:1200-1600

KEIZO, Morishita (1944-) Japanese

£282	$468	€400	Acripelago (50x70cm-20x28in) s. d.1982 verso acrylic tempera board. 14-Jun-3 Meeting Art, Vercelli #573
£476	$852	€700	Geography (89x116cm-35x46in) s.i.d.1969 verso acrylic. 16-Mar-4 Finarte Semenzato, Milan #145/R

KELDER, Toon (1894-1973) Dutch

£625	$1018	€900	Figures in a street at night (46x38cm-18x15in) s.i. canvas on board. 29-Sep-3 Sotheby's, Amsterdam #255
£789	$1453	€1200	Female nude (54x44cm-21x17in) s.d.1927. 28-Jun-4 Sotheby's, Amsterdam #168/R
£979	$1684	€1400	Lonely landscape with covered wagon (30x45cm-12x18in) s. 8-Dec-3 Glerum, Amsterdam #59/R
£1200	$2196	€1800	Don Quixote (46x67cm-18x26in) s. 7-Jun-4 Glerum, Amsterdam #54/R est:1800-2000
£1399	$2378	€2000	Nudes in a forest (52x42cm-20x17in) s. 25-Nov-3 Christie's, Amsterdam #7/R est:2000-3000
£1579	$2905	€2400	Breakers (24x35cm-9x14in) s. 28-Jun-4 Sotheby's, Amsterdam #170/R est:800-1200
£3333	$6133	€5000	Standing nude (55x38cm-22x15in) 8-Jun-4 Sotheby's, Amsterdam #188/R est:5000-7000
£4000	$7360	€6000	Nude (52x36cm-20x14in) s. 9-Jun-4 Christie's, Amsterdam #4/R est:3000-5000
£4545	$7727	€6500	Female nude with rider and cellists in the background (34x55cm-13x22in) s. 24-Nov-3 Glerum, Amsterdam #109/R est:3000-4000
£4667	$8587	€7000	Reclining nude (29x49cm-11x19in) s.d.31. 8-Jun-4 Sotheby's, Amsterdam #2/R est:7000-10000
£6159	$10101	€8500	Landscape with musical party (32x39cm-13x15in) s. prov. 27-May-3 Sotheby's, Amsterdam #477/R est:2000-3000
£12587	$21650	€18000	Untitled (106x140cm-42x55in) s.d.50. 2-Dec-3 Sotheby's, Amsterdam #118/R est:8000-12000

Works on paper
£769 $1308 €1100 Female nude standing (49x38cm-19x15in) s.i.d.1932 pastel pencil. 24-Nov-3 Glerum, Amsterdam #105/R
£2899 $4754 €4000 Portrait of Mina (71x55cm-28x22in) s. ink W/C. 27-May-3 Sotheby's, Amsterdam #327/R est:4000-5000

KELETI, Gusztav (1834-1902) Hungarian
£426 $711 €600 Landscape with water (45x32cm-18x13in) s.d.87 board. 17-Oct-3 Behringer, Furth #1673/R
£1054 $1908 €1539 Grazing (16x26cm-6x10in) s. oil on wood. 16-Apr-4 Mu Terem Galeria, Budapest #105/R (H.F 400000)

KELETY, Alexander (20th C) French
Sculpture
£1448 $2404 €2100 L'athlete aux quatre chiens (28x20x105cm-11x8x41in) s. green pat bronze exec. c.1925-1930. 5-Oct-3 Lombrail & Teucquam, Paris #421
£1517 $2534 €2200 La reverence (20cm-8in) s.d.1932 bronze ivory. 16-Nov-3 Muizon & Le Coent, Paris #117/R
£1700 $2890 €2482 Genie (27cm-11in) s. bronze. 25-Nov-3 Sotheby's, Olympia #150/R est:700-1000
£2000 $3660 €2920 Young boy (29cm-11in) i. bronze ivory. 3-Jun-4 Sotheby's, Olympia #244/R est:2000-2500
£3352 $6000 €4894 Figure with a spear (43x74cm-17x29in) bronze. 14-May-4 Du Mouchelle, Detroit #2009/R est:1500-1800
£18667 $33413 €28000 Danseuse a la culotte bouffante (54cm-21in) s. pat bronze. 17-May-4 Sotheby's, Paris #80/R est:20000-30000

KELLER (?) ?
£216 $387 €315 Southern coast with fortified town and figures (52x69cm-20x27in) s.d. 22-Mar-4 Philippe Schuler, Zurich #6025 (S.FR 500)

KELLER, A (?) ?
£1100 $2079 €1606 Travelers on a track by a woodland shrine (47x69cm-19x27in) s. 19-Feb-4 Christie's, Kensington #142/R est:600-800

KELLER, Adolphe (20th C) Belgian
£612 $1096 €900 Cour de ferme Flamande animee (75x110cm-30x43in) s.d.1936. 16-Mar-4 Vanderkindere, Brussels #151
£1126 $2049 €1700 Stokel (85x120cm-33x47in) s. 15-Jun-4 Galerie Moderne, Brussels #403/R est:300-500
£1972 $3411 €2800 Le port de Cassis (74x92cm-29x36in) s.d.1938. 10-Dec-3 Hotel des Ventes Mosan, Brussels #249 est:2200-2800
£2308 $3854 €3300 Le port de Saint Tropez (73x92cm-29x36in) s.d.31. 11-Oct-3 De Vuyst, Lokeren #204/R est:2800-3600
£7285 $13258 €11000 Sous-bois ensoleille (85x100cm-33x39in) s. 15-Jun-4 Galerie Moderne, Brussels #375/R est:1200-1600

KELLER, Albert von (1844-1920) Swiss
£620 $1128 €930 Mary, female nude (24x18cm-9x7in) s.i.d.1914 board. 1-Jul-4 Van Ham, Cologne #1450
£961 $1748 €1403 Young girl wearing a choker (66x45cm-26x18in) s. 16-Jun-4 Fischer, Luzern #2235/R (S.FR 2200)
£1200 $2184 €1800 Portrait of a stylishly dressed lady wearing a black hat (87x61cm-34x24in) s. 1-Jul-4 Van Ham, Cologne #1449/R est:2500
£1267 $2280 €1900 Wife of the artist (88x71cm-35x28in) s. 26-Apr-4 Rieber, Stuttgart #1188/R est:2400
£1300 $2431 €1950 Portrait of Negsa Cheyne (48x66cm-19x26in) sold with a book. 21-Jul-4 Anthemion, Cardiff #601/R est:300-500
£1310 $2384 €1913 In the boudoir (24x19cm-9x7in) mono. panel. 16-Jun-4 Fischer, Luzern #2236/R est:600-800 (S.FR 3000)
£5208 $8594 €7500 Music in the house (121x83cm-48x33in) s.d.1871. 2-Jul-3 Neumeister, Munich #680/R est:6000

KELLER, Albert von (attrib) (1844-1920) Swiss
£738 $1358 €1100 Young woman with umbrella in park (52x23cm-20x9in) s. panel. 25-Mar-4 Dr Fritz Nagel, Stuttgart #721/R
Works on paper
£336 $561 €480 Path with small bridge by wood (16x23cm-6x9in) i. verso wash pen over pencil. 10-Oct-3 Winterberg, Heidelberg #613

KELLER, Arthur I (1866-1925) American
Works on paper
£2235 $4000 €3263 Adulteress and child on display in town square (46x23cm-18x9in) s. gouache. 15-May-4 Illustration House, New York #51/R est:3000-5000

KELLER, Carl Urban (1772-1844) German
£1053 $1937 €1600 Extensive idealistic landscape under summer blue sky (69x52cm-27x20in) s.d.1842. 28-Jun-4 Bloss, Merzhausen #1264/R
Works on paper
£490 $817 €700 Cestisu Gaius pyramid and Porta S Paolo (11x19cm-4x7in) s.i.d. wash pen over pencil. 10-Oct-3 Winterberg, Heidelberg #614/R

KELLER, Clyde Leon (1872-1962) American
£209 $375 €305 Autumn on the Columbia (41x30cm-16x12in) s. s.i.d.1951 verso canvasboard. 16-Mar-4 Matthew's, Oregon #78/R
£230 $425 €336 Sunny field (46x61cm-18x24in) s. board. 19-Jan-4 O'Gallerie, Oregon #48/R
£251 $475 €366 Rogue River (51x66cm-20x26in) s. s.verso panel. 23-Feb-4 O'Gallerie, Oregon #667/R
£258 $475 €377 Oregon seascape (51x41cm-20x16in) s. i.d.1960 verso academy board. 29-Mar-4 O'Gallerie, Oregon #69/R
£259 $425 €378 Eagle Creek, Oregon (46x61cm-18x24in) s. i.verso panel. 9-Jun-3 O'Gallerie, Oregon #23/R
£279 $500 €407 Happy hunting grounds (30x46cm-12x18in) s.d.1942 canvasboard. 16-Mar-4 Matthew's, Oregon #105/R
£280 $450 €409 Happy hunting grounds (25x36cm-10x14in) s.i.d.1944 panel. 18-Aug-3 O'Gallerie, Oregon #109/R
£335 $600 €489 Autumn gold, Sauvie's Island, Oregon (51x41cm-20x16in) s. s.i.d.1950 verso canvasboard. 16-Mar-4 Matthew's, Oregon #77/R
£377 $600 €550 Defiance, near Pirates's Cove on the Oregon coast (41x51cm-16x20in) s. s.i.d.1947 verso panel. 5-May-3 O'Gallerie, Oregon #831
£397 $750 €580 End of day (51x66cm-20x26in) s. s.i.d.1953 verso panel. 23-Feb-4 O'Gallerie, Oregon #712/R
£459 $850 €670 Impressionistic landscape, dawn (33x33cm-13x13in) s. i.verso board. 19-Jan-4 O'Gallerie, Oregon #691/R
£595 $1100 €869 Autumn in the Zig Zags (46x61cm-18x24in) s. i.d.1949 verso. 19-Jan-4 O'Gallerie, Oregon #740/R est:1000-1400
£1497 $2500 €2186 Landscape at sunset (30x41cm-12x16in) s. board. 27-Oct-3 O'Gallerie, Oregon #793/R est:1000-1500

KELLER, Ferdinand (1842-1922) German
£1056 $1690 €1500 Nymph (27x17cm-11x7in) canvas on board. 19-Sep-3 Sigalas, Stuttgart #386/R est:1500
£6993 $11888 €10000 Forest stream (100x80cm-39x31in) mono.d.1902 lit. 28-Nov-3 Schloss Ahlden, Ahlden #1569/R est:11000
£8000 $14560 €12000 The Ceres festival (203x146cm-80x57in) mono.i.d.1874 lit. 1-Jul-4 Van Ham, Cologne #1451/R est:10000
Works on paper
£2767 $4953 €4040 Study of a woman's head (43x43cm-17x17in) s.d.1897 pastel tinted paper prov. 15-May-4 Christie's, Sydney #375/R est:3000-5000 (A.D 7000)

KELLER, Ferdinand (attrib) (1842-1922) German
£604 $1111 €900 Female nude (59x17cm-23x7in) mono. board. 25-Mar-4 Dr Fritz Nagel, Stuttgart #726/R

KELLER, Friedrich von (1840-1914) German
£1121 $2006 €1637 Blacksmiths at work (32x40cm-13x16in) s.d.1908. 12-May-4 Dobiaschofsky, Bern #690/R est:3500 (S.FR 2600)
£1972 $3155 €2800 Hammer mill (35x45cm-14x18in) s. 18-Sep-3 Rieber, Stuttgart #825/R est:4500
£3020 $5557 €4500 Quarryman with wheelbarrow (31x23cm-12x9in) s. 25-Mar-4 Dr Fritz Nagel, Stuttgart #728/R est:3900
£3873 $6197 €5500 Four stonemasons pulling stone (70x107cm-28x42in) s. 18-Sep-3 Rieber, Stuttgart #1270 est:9800
£4085 $6535 €5800 Reading the newspaper (24x17cm-9x7in) s.i.d.1887. 18-Sep-3 Rieber, Stuttgart #1271/R est:3500

KELLER, Gottfried (attrib) (1819-1890) Swiss
Works on paper
£550 $919 €803 Tree, roots and rocks by stream bed (19x24cm-7x9in) W/C. 23-Jun-3 Philippe Schuler, Zurich #3906/R (S.FR 1200)

KELLER, Heinrich (1778-1862) Swiss
Works on paper
£862 $1586 €1259 Landscape with town (20x42cm-8x17in) i. W/C sepia pen. 26-Mar-4 Koller, Zurich #3349/R est:1800-2200 (S.FR 2000)

KELLER, Henry George (1870-1949) American
£595 $1100 €869 Floral still life (102x89cm-40x35in) s. 13-Mar-4 DeFina, Austinburg #794/R
£833 $1392 €1200 Mountain landscape (40x49cm-16x19in) s. bears i. 24-Oct-3 Ketterer, Hamburg #422/R
£1377 $2300 €2010 White horse at sand pit (33x28cm-13x11in) mono. tempera cardboard painted 1913 exhib. 25-Oct-3 Rachel Davis, Shaker Heights #194/R
Works on paper
£220 $400 €321 John Barrymore (64x46cm-25x18in) s. pastel. 19-Jun-4 Rachel Davis, Shaker Heights #196
£257 $475 €375 Red tipped sunflowers (66x48cm-26x19in) s. W/C exhib. 13-Mar-4 DeFina, Austinburg #795
£299 $500 €437 Elephants (48x36cm-19x14in) s. W/C exhib. 25-Oct-3 Rachel Davis, Shaker Heights #195/R
£412 $750 €602 In the big tent (76x102cm-30x40in) s. pastel exhib. 19-Jun-4 Rachel Davis, Shaker Heights #192

KELLER, Johann Sigmund (18th C) German
£1500 $2550 €2190 Rocky coastline with a shipwreck in stormy seas (51x69cm-20x27in) s.d.1789. 29-Oct-3 Bonhams, New Bond Street #129/R est:2000-3000

KELLER, Willi (1942-) Swiss
£173 $310 €253 Alpine pasture near Kaser (22x33cm-9x13in) s.d. masonite. 22-Mar-4 Philippe Schuler, Zurich #6071 (S.FR 400)
£433 $775 €632 Dance on the alpine pasture (35x47cm-14x19in) s.d. masonite. 22-Mar-4 Philippe Schuler, Zurich #6069 (S.FR 1000)
£476 $852 €695 Winter landscape in Santis (33x48cm-13x19in) s.d. masonite. 22-Mar-4 Philippe Schuler, Zurich #6070 (S.FR 1100)

KELLER-REUTLINGEN, Paul Wilhelm (1854-1920) German
£1338 $2395 €1900 Summer landscape with trees and cloudy skies (28x37cm-11x15in) s. canvas on board lit. 8-Jan-4 Allgauer, Kempten #2437/R est:1900
£2500 $4075 €3600 Dachau landscape (43x65cm-17x26in) s. 24-Sep-3 Neumeister, Munich #467/R est:5500
£3819 $6302 €5500 Young goose girl with flock by water (64x86cm-25x34in) s. 3-Jul-3 Dr Fritz Nagel, Stuttgart #498/R est:9800
£4861 $7924 €7000 Girl with geese on track to farmstead (39x60cm-15x24in) s. 25-Sep-3 Dr Fritz Nagel, Stuttgart #1366/R est:5000

KELLER-VENTON, Edwin (1930-1990) Swiss
£345 $617 €504 Charettes (96x145cm-38x57in) s.d.61 i. verso. 12-May-4 Dobiaschofsky, Bern #691 (S.FR 800)

KELLERTHALER, Johann (younger-attrib) (c.1560-1637) German
Works on paper
£986 $1706 €1400 Sainte Cecile (26x21cm-10x8in) pen brown ink black crayon sanguine brown wash. 12-Dec-3 Renaud, Paris #113/R

KELLETT, Dennis (20th C) American
£355 $650 €533 Morning in desert (91x94cm-36x37in) 10-Jul-4 Hindman, Chicago #260/R

KELLEY, Mike (1954-) American
£2577 $4200 €3762 Garbage drawing no 14 (33x81cm-13x32in) acrylic prov.exhib. 23-Sep-3 Christie's, Rockefeller NY #81/R est:3000-5000
£14000 $25760 €21000 Study for blood and soil (137x96cm-54x38in) acrylic col crayon paper painted 1989 prov. 8-Jun-4 Artcurial Briest, Paris #284/R est:12000-15000
£32934 $55000 €48084 Hierarchical Figure (240x122cm-94x48in) acrylic on four panels ribbon painted 1989 prov.exhib.lit. 12-Nov-3 Christie's, Rockefeller NY #510/R est:40000-60000
£83799 $150000 €122347 Head's the same as between the legs symmetrical sets round eye, straight line of mouth (127x96cm-50x38in) acrylic on paper triptych prov.exhib.lit. 13-May-4 Phillips, New York #53/R est:40000-60000
Photographs
£3352 $6000 €4894 Psychic waveforms, Gerome Kamrowski's sculpture garden, Ann Arbor MI (59x216cm-23x85in) gelatin silver print edition of 5 prov. 14-May-4 Phillips, New York #149/R est:8000-12000
£10778 $18000 €15736 Nostalgic manipulating man-produced, idealized objects (24x16cm-9x6in) black white print edition 9 of 10 prov.exhib.lit. 13-Nov-3 Sotheby's, New York #412/R est:12000-18000
Prints
£11173 $20000 €16313 Pansy metal, clovered hoof (133x95cm-52x37in) s.d.1989 num. of 40 silkscreen silk ten prov.exhib. 14-May-4 Phillips, New York #146/R est:25000-35000
£22754 $38000 €33221 Pansy metal/clovered hoof (133x95cm-52x37in) s.d,1989 num.40 silkscreen on silk set of 10 prov.exhib.lit. 14-Nov-3 Phillips, New York #133/R est:20000-30000
Sculpture
£49102 $82000 €71689 Memory ware flat no.30 (178x117x10cm-70x46x4in) s.i.d.2001 verso plastic glass wooden beads on panel prov.exhib. 14-Nov-3 Phillips, New York #119/R est:40000-60000
£69832 $125000 €101955 Memory ware flat num 20 (179x117x10cm-70x46x4in) s.i.verso pulp tile grout acrylic beads jewelry panel prov. 14-May-4 Phillips, New York #123/R est:50000-70000
£97826 $180000 €142826 Memory ware flat no 10 (216x155x18cm-85x61x7in) s.i.verso mixed media synthetic resin wood panel prov. 10-Jun-4 Phillips, New York #430/R est:30000-40000
Works on paper
£8939 $16000 €13051 Uniforms (66x51cm-26x20in) s.i.d.1997 verso pencil col pencil W/C prov. 13-May-4 Sotheby's, New York #475/R est:10000-15000

KELLEY, Mike and McCARTHY, Paul (20th C) American
Photographs
£2283 $4200 €3425 Untitled, Heidi series (41x51cm-16x20in) s.d.1992-1993 num.10 verso cibachrome paperboard prov. 10-Jun-4 Phillips, New York #431/R est:4000-6000

KELLEY, Ramon (1939-) American
£497 $800 €721 El Caballo Rojo (28x36cm-11x14in) oil wash. 22-Aug-3 Altermann Galleries, Santa Fe #21
£1024 $1700 €1495 Sea shells (36x46cm-14x18in) s.i. board prov. 4-Oct-3 Neal Auction Company, New Orleans #605/R est:1500-2500
£1553 $2500 €2252 Vignette nude (25x30cm-10x12in) 22-Aug-3 Altermann Galleries, Santa Fe #187
£2259 $3750 €3298 Antiques and oranges (61x76cm-24x30in) s. s.i.verso prov. 4-Oct-3 Neal Auction Company, New Orleans #604/R est:3000-5000
£3209 $6000 €4685 Navajo portrait (41x30cm-16x12in) s.d.1971 canvas on board prov. 24-Jul-4 Coeur d'Alene, Hayden #278/R est:2000-4000
Works on paper
£346 $550 €505 Little Amalia (34x26cm-13x10in) s.d.71 pastel. 12-Sep-3 Skinner, Boston #319/R
£497 $800 €721 Spanish hat (41x30cm-16x12in) conte crayon. 22-Aug-3 Altermann Galleries, Santa Fe #182
£2360 $3800 €3422 Felicity (43x53cm-17x21in) pastel. 22-Aug-3 Altermann Galleries, Santa Fe #186

KELLEY, Tom (1914-) American
Photographs
£8571 $15000 €12514 Marilyn Monroe (93x75cm-37x30in) init. num.195/300 cibachrome exec 1953 lit. 17-Dec-3 Christie's, Rockefeller NY #2/R est:8000-10000

KELLIN, Nicolas Joseph (1788-1858) French
Works on paper
£750 $1275 €1095 Head of the caravan (16x32cm-6x13in) s.d.1847 W/C bodycol. 4-Nov-3 Bonhams, New Bond Street #99/R

KELLNER, Carl Philipp (1886-1953) German
£633 $1140 €950 Ossinger (78x59cm-31x23in) s.d.1927. 22-Apr-4 Weidler, Nurnberg #7006/R

KELLNER, Charles H (1890-?) American
£407 $700 €594 Artist's model (91x91cm-36x36in) s.i. painted c.1930. 7-Dec-3 Treadway Gallery, Cincinnati #549/R

KELLY, Annie Elizabeth (1877-1946) New Zealander
£372 $639 €543 Woman in blue gown (60x45cm-24x18in) 7-Dec-3 International Art Centre, Auckland #417 (NZ.D 1000)
£625 $1131 €913 Oxford terrace (34x44cm-13x17in) s. 4-Apr-4 International Art Centre, Auckland #228/R (NZ.D 1750)
Works on paper
£347 $552 €507 Lake Bruner, westland (24x34cm-9x13in) s. W/C. 1-May-3 Dunbar Sloane, Wellington #108 est:1500-2500 (NZ.D 1000)

KELLY, Annie Elizabeth (attrib) (1877-1946) New Zealander
£659 $1219 €962 Tranquil waters (39x27cm-15x11in) s. board. 9-Mar-4 Watson's, Christchurch #71 est:1800-2800 (NZ.D 1800)

KELLY, Cecil (1879-1954) New Zealander
£297 $512 €434 Streets in Cornwall (45x33cm-18x13in) canvasboard. 7-Dec-3 International Art Centre, Auckland #412 (NZ.D 800)
£536 $970 €783 The Dome, Torlusse Range (29x40cm-11x16in) s. 4-Apr-4 International Art Centre, Auckland #233/R (NZ.D 1500)
£643 $1164 €939 Street scene (30x40cm-12x16in) s. canvas on board. 30-Mar-4 Peter Webb, Auckland #172/R est:2000-3000 (NZ.D 1800)

KELLY, Ellsworth (1923-) American
£185629 $310000 €271018 Yellow Curve (109x84cm-43x33in) s.d.62 prov.exhib. 11-Nov-3 Christie's, Rockefeller NY #10/R est:300000-500000
£290000 $533600 €423400 Red orange white - rogue (86x96cm-34x38in) init. painted 1956 prov.exhib.lit. 24-Jun-4 Christie's, London #22/R est:170000-240000
£446927 $800000 €652513 White black (262x357cm-103x141in) s.i.overlap two attached panels painted 1988 prov. 11-May-4 Christie's, Rockefeller NY #37/R est:600000-800000
£1452514 $2600000 €2120670 Chatham XIII - yellow red (244x207cm-96x81in) init.d.1971 overlap two parts prov.exhib. 12-May-4 Sotheby's, New York #14/R est:1200000-1800000
Prints
£1359 $2500 €1984 Blue, white, red (108x76cm-43x30in) col lithograph edition of 54 prov. 10-Jun-4 Phillips, New York #602/R est:1800-2500
£1707 $2800 €2475 Flower (86x61cm-34x24in) s.num.19/75 black white lithograph. 2-Jun-3 Grogan, Boston #686b/R
£1765 $3000 €2577 Wild grape (70x63cm-28x25in) s. lithograph. 31-Oct-3 Sotheby's, New York #625/R
£1765 $3000 €2577 EK (65x239cm-26x94in) s. col lithograph exec.1990. 4-Nov-3 Christie's, Rockefeller NY #288/R est:3500-4500
£1840 $3000 €2686 Concorde III (105x75cm-41x30in) s. num.APVII/X etching aquatint Arches exec 1981-2. 24-Sep-3 Christie's, Rockefeller NY #274/R est:1500-2500
£1882 $3200 €2748 Blue-green (100x96cm-39x38in) s. col lithograph. 4-Nov-3 Christie's, Rockefeller NY #283/R est:2000-3000
£1912 $3250 €2792 Green curve with radius of 20 (61x61cm-24x24in) s. col lithograph. 31-Oct-3 Sotheby's, New York #620/R
£1977 $3500 €2886 Concorde (40x32cm-16x13in) s.i. etching aquatint. 30-Apr-4 Sotheby's, New York #366/R est:3000-4000
£2119 $3750 €3094 Untitled (129x117cm-51x46in) s. num.18/18 purple lithograph. 30-Apr-4 Sotheby's, New York #367/R est:3000-4000
£2147 $3800 €3135 Leaf IX (44x93cm-17x37in) s.i.num.14/20 lithograph. 28-Apr-4 Christie's, Rockefeller NY #340/R est:1500-2500
£2197 $3800 €3208 Untitled (91x88cm-36x35in) s. num.75 prov. 10-Dec-3 Phillips, New York #677/R est:2000-3000
£2206 $3750 €3221 Yellow with dark blue (89x60cm-35x24in) s. col lithograph. 31-Oct-3 Sotheby's, New York #618/R
£2260 $4000 €3300 Wild grape leaf (70x63cm-28x25in) s. num.33/50 lithograph. 30-Apr-4 Sotheby's, New York #365/R est:2500-3500
£2353 $4000 €3435 Red over yellow (89x59cm-35x23in) s. col lithograph. 31-Oct-3 Sotheby's, New York #619/R
£2353 $4000 €3435 Dracena (109x80cm-43x31in) s. transfer lithograph. 4-Nov-3 Christie's, Rockefeller NY #286/R est:4000-5000
£2542 $4500 €3711 Blue, yellow and red squares (61x183cm-24x72in) s.num.VIII col screenprint. 28-Apr-4 Christie's, Rockefeller NY #337/R est:4000-6000
£2542 $4500 €3711 Untitled (118x115cm-46x45in) s. num.18/18 orange lithograph. 30-Apr-4 Sotheby's, New York #368/R est:3000-4000
£2712 $4800 €3960 Ailanthus leaves II (93x43cm-37x17in) s.num.14/50 lithograph. 28-Apr-4 Christie's, Rockefeller NY #336/R est:4000-6000
£2712 $4800 €3960 Untitled, purple (107x94cm-42x37in) s.num.18/18 col lithograph. 28-Apr-4 Christie's, Rockefeller NY #342/R est:2500-3500
£3390 $6000 €4949 Daffodil (99x72cm-39x28in) s.num.33/50 lithograph. 30-Apr-4 Sotheby's, New York #364/R est:3000-4000
£3529 $6000 €5152 Wall (41x35cm-16x14in) s. etching aquatint. 31-Oct-3 Sotheby's, New York #624/R
£4118 $7000 €6012 Coloured paper image XVIII (81x78cm-32x31in) s. pressed paper pulp. 31-Oct-3 Sotheby's, New York #623/R
£4294 $7000 €6269 Grape leaves (121x81cm-48x32in) s. num.AP VII lithograph on Arches exec 1973-4. 24-Sep-3 Christie's, Rockefeller NY #272/R est:1800-2200
£5000 $8500 €7300 Nine squares (103x103cm-41x41in) s. col screenprint offset lithograph. 4-Nov-3 Christie's, Rockefeller NY #285/R est:10000-15000
£5988 $10000 €8742 Coloured paper image VII (117x81cm-46x32in) s.num.12/20 hand col print. 11-Nov-3 Doyle, New York #284/R est:7000-9000
£6215 $11000 €9074 Blue curve (65x183cm-26x72in) s.num.4/5 blue lithograph. 28-Apr-4 Christie's, Rockefeller NY #341/R est:6000-8000
£6471 $11000 €9448 Blue curve (95x213cm-37x84in) s. num.16/25 lithograph. 4-Nov-3 Christie's, Rockefeller NY #287/R est:8000-12000
£6587 $11000 €9617 Coloured paper image X (117x81cm-46x32in) s.num.10/20 hand col print. 11-Nov-3 Doyle, New York #285/R est:7000-9000
£8235 $14000 €12023 Coloured paper image I (117x81cm-46x32in) s. col pressed paper pulp. 31-Oct-3 Sotheby's, New York #622/R
£9605 $17000 €14023 Nine squares (102x102cm-40x40in) s.num.38/44 col screenprint offset lithograph. 28-Apr-4 Christie's, Rockefeller NY #339/R est:15000-25000
£22059 $37500 €32206 Colours on grid (102x102cm-40x40in) s. col screenprint. 31-Oct-3 Sotheby's, New York #621/R
£25424 $45000 €37119 Purple, red, grey and orange (121x573cm-48x226in) s. num.18/18 col lithograph. 30-Apr-4 Sotheby's, New York #370/R est:30000-40000
Sculpture
£22346 $40000 €32625 Untitled (63x76cm-25x30in) s.i.d.1986 num.9/9 wall relief steel prov. 12-May-4 Christie's, Rockefeller NY #204/R est:24000-35000
Works on paper
£3571 $6500 €5214 Self portrait (46x36cm-18x14in) s. pencil executed c.1951 prov. 29-Jun-4 Sotheby's, New York #456/R est:8000-12000

£28443 $47500 €41527 Wire (57x72cm-22x28in) s.d.9 March 1963 verso pencil prov. 13-Nov-3 Sotheby's, New York #116/R est:12000-18000

KELLY, Felix (1916-1994) New Zealander
£900 $1665 €1314 Act II duel of angels, Old Vic (26x37cm-10x15in) s.i.d.1961 tempera on board. 11-Mar-4 Christie's, Kensington #6/R
£980 $1823 €1431 A day by the sea (19x25cm-7x10in) s. board sold with two similar by the same hand. 2-Mar-4 Bristol Auction Rooms #320/R

KELLY, Frances (fl.1929-1937) Irish
£1081 $2043 €1600 Still life with lilies and Staffordshire figurine (64x76cm-25x30in) prov. 17-Feb-4 Whyte's, Dublin #45/R est:3000-4000

KELLY, John (20th C) Irish
Works on paper
£986 $1577 €1400 Self portrait (53x71cm-21x28in) s.d.1987 W/C pastel prov. 16-Sep-3 Whyte's, Dublin #139/R

KELLY, John (1965-) Australian
£2734 $5113 €4101 Dobell's cow XI (9x18cm-4x7in) s.d.93 canvas on board prov.exhib. 21-Jul-4 Shapiro, Sydney #164/R est:8000-12000 (A.D 7000)
£4580 $8336 €6687 Study for man wearing a cow's head (50x25cm-20x10in) s.d.94 i.d.verso prov. 16-Jun-4 Deutscher-Menzies, Melbourne #148/R est:12000-16000 (A.D 12000)
£4858 $7822 €7093 Aerial landscape (25x25cm-10x10in) s.d.95 prov.exhib. 25-Aug-3 Sotheby's, Paddington #119/R est:12000-15000 (A.D 12000)
£5102 $9388 €7449 The game (33x55cm-13x22in) s.d.02 exhib. 29-Mar-4 Goodman, Sydney #86a/R est:12000-15000 (A.D 12500)
£5263 $8474 €7684 Sunday Painting (76x91cm-30x36in) s.d.99 s.i.d.7 Nov 1999 verso. 25-Aug-3 Sotheby's, Paddington #194/R est:12000-18000 (A.D 13000)
£5372 $9938 €7843 Umpire's decision (83x55cm-33x22in) i.verso prov. 15-Mar-4 Sotheby's, Melbourne #47/R est:8000-12000 (A.D 13000)
£5579 $10320 €8145 Bowled (86x121cm-34x48in) init.d.89 i.verso prov. 15-Mar-4 Sotheby's, Melbourne #7/R est:15000-25000 (A.D 13500)
£5579 $10320 €8145 Cow with figure (46x61cm-18x24in) board painted 1992 prov. 10-Mar-4 Deutscher-Menzies, Melbourne #83a/R est:15000-20000 (A.D 13500)
£5745 $9766 €8388 Dobell's cow 14 (26x39cm-10x15in) s.d.93 i.verso linen prov. 25-Nov-3 Christie's, Melbourne #1/R est:12000-15000 (A.D 13500)
£7438 $13760 €10859 Head 1994 (61x76cm-24x30in) i.d.1994 prov. 10-Mar-4 Deutscher-Menzies, Melbourne #6/R est:25000-35000 (A.D 18000)
£9426 $15270 €13762 Cricket match (152x168cm-60x66in) init.d.90 s.i.d.verso prov. 30-Jul-3 Goodman, Sydney #35/R est:25000-35000 (A.D 23000)
£18182 $33636 €26546 Head and backbone (50x152cm-20x60in) s.d.94 i.verso prov.exhib. 15-Mar-4 Sotheby's, Melbourne #15/R est:28000-38000 (A.D 44000)
£20243 $32591 €29555 Unpainted cows (91x137cm-36x54in) s.d.95 i.d.verso prov. 25-Aug-3 Sotheby's, Paddington #106/R est:50000-70000 (A.D 50000)
£20492 $32377 €29918 Two rear ends (91x136cm-36x54in) s.d.95 i.d.1994/95 verso. 2-Sep-3 Deutscher-Menzies, Melbourne #47/R est:55000-75000 (A.D 50000)
£24390 $38293 €35609 Painted cows (121x121cm-48x48in) s.d.95 i.d.verso prov. 26-Aug-3 Christie's, Sydney #14/R est:60000-80000 (A.D 60000)
£25424 $43220 €37119 Camouflage cow on trestles (122x183cm-48x72in) s.d.96 i.d.verso linen canvas prov.exhib. 24-Nov-3 Sotheby's, Melbourne #4/R est:60000-80000 (A.D 60000)
Prints
£2066 $3822 €3016 Head (20x25cm-8x10in) s.d.1996 etching. 10-Mar-4 Deutscher-Menzies, Melbourne #390/R est:3000-4000 (A.D 5000)
Sculpture
£4959 $9174 €7240 Head in a landscape (45x62cm-18x24in) s.d.02 num.8/9 lasercut steel prov. 10-Mar-4 Deutscher-Menzies, Melbourne #7/R est:12000-15000 (A.D 12000)
£6489 $11809 €9474 Upside down cow 1996 (23x18x33cm-9x7x13in) s.d.96 painted bronze. 16-Jun-4 Deutscher-Menzies, Melbourne #3/R est:12000-16000 (A.D 17000)
£10638 $18085 €15531 Cow up a tree (57x40x62cm-22x16x24in) st.base num.9/.9 painted bronze exec 1999. 26-Nov-3 Deutscher-Menzies, Melbourne #5/R est:16000-20000 (A.D 25000)
£10656 $16836 €15558 Four cows stacked (13x22x16cm-5x9x6in) painted bronze. 2-Sep-3 Deutscher-Menzies, Melbourne #5/R est:9000-12000 (A.D 26000)
£36735 $67592 €53633 Blot on the landscape. s.num.5/6 painted bronze stainless steel base prov. 29-Mar-4 Goodman, Sydney #92/R est:90000-110000 (A.D 90000)
Works on paper
£1787 $3038 €2609 The cricketers (50x74cm-20x29in) s.d.90 W/C ink gouache. 25-Nov-3 Christie's, Melbourne #98/R est:4000-8000 (A.D 4200)
£2439 $3829 €3561 Cow head and grid (21x28cm-8x11in) s.d.01 W/C gouache pencil prov. 26-Aug-3 Christie's, Sydney #272/R est:6000-8000 (A.D 6000)
£6301 $9892 €9199 Head I. Head II (16x17cm-6x7in) s.i.d.94 W/C pair prov. 26-Aug-3 Christie's, Sydney #261/R est:10000-15000 (A.D 15500)
£7025 $12996 €10257 Cow heads (25x43cm-10x17in) s.d.94 W/C pastel prov. 10-Mar-4 Deutscher-Menzies, Melbourne #188/R est:8000-12000 (A.D 17000)

KELLY, John (1932-) Irish
£507 $932 €770 Figure in interior (27x18cm-11x7in) s. 22-Jun-4 De Veres Art Auctions, Dublin #210/R
£674 $1058 €970 Figures with still life (40x20cm-16x8in) s. oil crayon on paper prov. 26-Aug-3 James Adam, Dublin #68/R
Works on paper
£336 $601 €500 Figure in a landscape (34x24cm-13x9in) s. W/C. 31-May-4 Hamilton Osborne King, Dublin #60/R
£514 $807 €740 Female figure (57x36cm-22x14in) s. W/C. 26-Aug-3 Thomas Adams, Dublin #4

KELLY, Julia (1953-) American
£216 $400 €315 My garden (41x56cm-16x22in) s. 15-Feb-4 Outer Cape Auctions, Provincetown #11/R

KELLY, Leon (1901-1982) American
£246 $425 €359 Page of fruit (25x33cm-10x13in) s.i.verso. 10-Dec-3 Alderfer's, Hatfield #488
£1163 $2000 €1698 Disenchantment of love (97x56cm-38x22in) s.d.1959 i.d.verso. 7-Dec-3 Freeman, Philadelphia #182 est:1000-1500
Works on paper
£217 $400 €317 Spring landscape (36x46cm-14x18in) s. W/C. 25-Jun-4 Freeman, Philadelphia #20/R
£3593 $6000 €5246 Mountain village (36x51cm-14x20in) s.d.1920 pastel prov. 23-Oct-3 Shannon's, Milford #163/R est:6000-8000

KELLY, Pat M (20th C) American
£688 $1300 €1004 Cowboy saddling a horse (33x41cm-13x16in) s. canvasboard. 17-Feb-4 John Moran, Pasadena #125a/R

KELLY, Paul (1968-) Irish
£387 $620 €550 Still life with fish (25x30cm-10x12in) s.d.1991. 16-Sep-3 Whyte's, Dublin #181/R
£671 $1201 €1000 Rush beach (24x35cm-9x14in) s. board. 26-May-4 James Adam, Dublin #89/R est:1200-1800
£738 $1321 €1100 Lilly pond, the garden of remembrance, Island Bridge (27x37cm-11x15in) s. board. 26-May-4 James Adam, Dublin #85/R est:1500-2000
£1074 $1922 €1600 Circus, Skerries (30x35cm-12x14in) s. board. 26-May-4 James Adam, Dublin #81/R est:1500-2500
£1141 $2042 €1700 Summer's evening, Skerries Strand (29x36cm-11x14in) s.d.97 panel. 26-May-4 James Adam, Dublin #82/R est:1400-1800
£1242 $2222 €1850 Fruit and vegetable stall, Dublin Market (25x30cm-10x12in) s. 26-May-4 James Adam, Dublin #90/R est:1200-1800

KELLY, Philip (1950-) Irish
£320 $534 €467 Parque, Mexico (90x70cm-35x28in) s.i.d.Sept 89 verso. 11-Nov-3 Rosebery Fine Art, London #987

KELLY, Robert George Talbot (1861-1934) British
Works on paper
£1500 $2505 €2190 Extensive river landscape (53x91cm-21x36in) s.d.86. 17-Oct-3 Keys, Aylsham #585/R est:1500
£2200 $3740 €3212 View of the Temple of Hatshepsut, Deir El Bahri, Egypt (41x57cm-16x22in) s. pencil W/C. 20-Nov-3 Christie's, London #126a/R est:2500-3500

KELLY, Sir Gerald (1879-1972) British
£600 $1074 €876 View of Ramonceto (31x39cm-12x15in) canvasboard. 14-May-4 Christie's, Kensington #365/R
£680 $1258 €993 Yein pure dancers, Nyangu (26x34cm-10x13in) d.16th Febry 1909 verso panel. 16-Feb-4 Bonhams, Bath #59
£850 $1522 €1241 Rural landscape (27x34cm-11x13in) board. 14-May-4 Christie's, Kensington #361/R
£900 $1638 €1314 Olive groves as Clarissa (101x76cm-40x30in) exhib. 1-Jul-4 Christie's, Kensington #188/R
£1050 $1659 €1523 Portrait of Mrs E B Innes (71x59cm-28x23in) 2-Sep-3 Bonhams, Oxford #71 est:1000-1500
£1500 $2685 €2190 Waterbearers (21x27cm-8x11in) panel. 16-Mar-4 Bonhams, New Bond Street #31/R est:1000-1500
£1900 $3363 €2774 Standing female nude (65x40cm-26x16in) prov. 27-Apr-4 Bonhams, Knightsbridge #218/R est:600-1000
£2200 $3938 €3212 Pagoda, twilight, Myanmar (22x27cm-9x11in) i.d.Jan Feb 1909 verso board. 14-May-4 Christie's, Kensington #362/R est:400-600
£2600 $4654 €3796 White pagoda seen against the sunset, Magwe (22x27cm-9x11in) panel. 14-May-4 Christie's, Kensington #363/R est:400-600
£2676 $4630 €3800 Khieuvan dancing (63x45cm-25x18in) 10-Dec-3 Bonhams & James Adam, Dublin #114/R est:4000-6000
£3500 $6265 €5110 Taungdwingyi, Myanmar (15x18cm-6x7in) i.verso board. 14-May-4 Christie's, Kensington #364/R est:400-600
£3800 $6802 €5548 Portrait of Mrs Boardman (203x92cm-80x36in) s.verso prov.exhib. 14-May-4 Christie's, Kensington #362a est:2000-3000
£4900 $8330 €7154 On the beach (40x33cm-16x13in) init. panel. 1-Dec-3 Bonhams, Bath #41/R est:2000-3000

KELLY, Walt (1913-1973) American
Works on paper
£241 $450 €352 Fox realizes that the secret ingredients is gold, or rather brass (10x41cm-4x16in) s. pen ink blue pencil. 26-Feb-4 Illustration House, New York #98

KELPE, Paul (1902-) German
£8475 $15000 €12374 Composition 509 (72x49cm-28x19in) s.i.verso masonite painted c.1935 prov. 2-May-4 Bonhams & Butterfields, Los Angeles #3026/R est:8000-10000
Works on paper
£9040 $16000 €13198 Composition (28x36cm-11x14in) s.d.1935 W/C prov. 2-May-4 Bonhams & Butterfields, Los Angeles #3027/R est:3000-4000

KELSEY, Arthur (19/20th C) British
£400 $716 €584 Portrait of a wire haired terrier in a stable (23x30cm-9x12in) s.d.1899. 7-May-4 Mallams, Oxford #318

KELSEY, Frank (fl.1887-1923) British
Works on paper
£280 $515 €409 Ghosting into the harbour at dusk (24x34cm-9x13in) s. pncil W/C. 25-Mar-4 Christie's, Kensington #196
£350 $595 €511 Sailing ship entering harbour with fishing smacks nearby (24x34cm-9x13in) s. W/C. 6-Nov-3 Hobbs Parker, Ashford #673
£550 $1029 €803 Fishing boats at anchor (14x20cm-6x8in) W/C. 26-Feb-4 Lane, Penzance #61

KELSEY, Richmond Irwin (1905-1987) American
£284 $475 €415 California oaks (23x31cm-9x12in) s.d.1930. 26-Oct-3 Bonhams & Butterfields, San Francisco #6539/R
£1099 $2000 €1605 Panoramic landscape (51x76cm-20x30in) s. i.verso. 15-Jun-4 John Moran, Pasadena #181 est:1500-2000

KEMARRE, Gladdy (c.1950-) Australian
Works on paper
£588 $1053 €858 Alkwa - Bush plum (60x60cm-24x24in) i. verso synthetic polymer paint canvas diptych prov. 25-May-4 Lawson Menzies, Sydney #4/R (A.D 1500)

KEMARRE, Josie Petrick (1953-) Australian
Works on paper
£1563 $2922 €2345 Bush tomato country (152x91cm-60x36in) bears name.verso synthetic polymer paint linen prov. 26-Jul-4 Sotheby's, Melbourne #471/R est:3000-5000 (A.D 4000)

KEMBLE, Kenneth (1912-) Argentinian
£2186 $4000 €3192 Multiples (35x50cm-14x20in) acrylic. 1-Jun-4 Arroyo, Buenos Aires #5

KEMENEDY, Jeno (1860-1925) Hungarian
£949 $1717 €1386 Theatrical scene (52x34cm-20x13in) s. oil on card. 16-Apr-4 Mu Terem Galeria, Budapest #26/R (H.F 360000)

KEMENY, Zoltan (1907-1965) Swiss
Sculpture
£13974 $25712 €20402 Jonction de la pensee et du reel (94x106x320cm-37x42x126in) i. verso brass relief prov.exhib.lit. 8-Jun-4 Germann, Zurich #14/R est:30000-40000 (S.FR 32000)

KEMERRE, Josie Petrick (1953-) Australian
£610 $1092 €891 Sunset dreaming (105x173cm-41x68in) i. verso acrylic. 10-May-4 Joel, Victoria #396 est:1500-2500 (A.D 1500)
£1098 $1965 €1603 Bush tucker dreaming (128x198cm-50x78in) acrylic. 10-May-4 Joel, Victoria #216 est:1500-2500 (A.D 2700)

KEMM, Robert (fl.1874-1885) British
£1627 $2635 €2359 Coastal landscapes with figures, England (66x55cm-26x22in) s. d.1891 verso pair. 4-Aug-3 Rasmussen, Vejle #193/R est:15000-20000 (D.KR 17000)

KEMM, Robert (attrib) (fl.1874-1885) British
£1615 $2778 €2358 Young Indian girls dressed for party (77x55cm-30x22in) 7-Dec-3 Uppsala Auktionskammare, Uppsala #117/R est:12000-15000 (S.KR 21000)

KEMP, Gyrinthe (19th C) Danish
£1797 $3342 €2624 Dandelions (32x26cm-13x10in) s.verso. 2-Mar-4 Rasmussen, Copenhagen #1534/R est:5000 (D.KR 20000)

KEMP, Muriel (20th C) British
£320 $573 €467 View Faraglioni, Capri (66x97cm-26x38in) s.d.1962 canvas on board. 11-May-4 Bonhams, Knightsbridge #54/R

KEMP, Roger (1908-1987) Australian
£1362 $2356 €1989 Untitled (70x53cm-28x21in) s. board. 10-Dec-3 Shapiro, Sydney #24/R est:4000-6000 (A.D 3200)
£5410 $8548 €7899 Untitled (78x117cm-31x46in) s. board prov. 2-Sep-3 Deutscher-Menzies, Melbourne #154/R est:10000-15000 (A.D 13200)
£6173 $11173 €9013 No.5 (154x208cm-61x82in) 30-Mar-4 Lawson Menzies, Sydney #150/R est:12000-18000 (A.D 15000)
£12977 $23618 €18946 Untitled (150x234cm-59x92in) prov. 16-Jun-4 Deutscher-Menzies, Melbourne #27/R est:20000-30000 (A.D 34000)
Works on paper
£370 $670 €540 Note in space (35x49cm-14x19in) synthetic polymer executed c.1978. 30-Mar-4 Lawson Menzies, Sydney #109/R est:1000-1500 (A.D 900)
£10569 $18919 €15431 Untitled (154x150cm-61x59in) synthetic polymer paper on canvas prov. 4-May-4 Sotheby's, Melbourne #97/R est:12000-15000 (A.D 26000)
£10687 $19450 €15603 Untitled (152x303cm-60x119in) synthetic polymer paper on linen prov.exhib. 16-Jun-4 Deutscher-Menzies, Melbourne #28/R est:20000-30000 (A.D 28000)

KEMP-WELCH, Lucy (1869-1958) British
£4000 $7280 €5840 Horse carts beneath the end of the pier at St. Ives, low tide (30x45cm-12x18in) s.i. board. 21-Jun-4 Bonhams, Bath #457/R est:3000-4000
Works on paper
£1050 $1932 €1533 Study of a horse's head (45x50cm-18x20in) chk. 23-Jun-4 Bonhams, Bury St Edmunds #323 est:400-600
£2000 $3580 €2920 Study of a dog, the joy of life (20x16cm-8x6in) chl prov. 22-Mar-4 Bonhams & Brooks, Norfolk #119/R est:300-500
£2800 $5152 €4088 Circus horse (47x56cm-19x22in) s. pastel. 10-Jun-4 Christie's, Kensington #169/R est:3000-5000
£3000 $5160 €4380 Brick cart (29x20cm-11x8in) s.d.1915 W/C htd bodycol over pencil lit. 2-Dec-3 Bonhams, New Bond Street #22/R est:3500-4500
£5500 $9460 €8030 Down! (30x20cm-12x8in) init.d.1915 W/C gouache htd white. 2-Dec-3 Bonhams, New Bond Street #21/R est:6000-8000
£5500 $9460 €8030 Handsome pair (36x26cm-14x10in) init.d.1915 W/C gouache htd white over pencil lit. 2-Dec-3 Bonhams, New Bond Street #23/R est:6000-8000
£6000 $10320 €8760 I'll drive you straight to the hospital (38x26cm-15x10in) init.d.1916 W/C gouache htd white pencil lit. 2-Dec-3 Bonhams, New Bond Street #20/R est:7000-9000

KEMP-WELCH, Lucy (attrib) (1869-1958) British
£1500 $2775 €2190 Mare and foal at a water butt at eventide (89x70cm-35x28in) 14-Jan-4 Lawrence, Crewkerne #1435 est:300-500

KEMPE, Roland (1907-1991) Swedish
£1330 $2381 €1942 Lucretzia Fiorentina (96x130cm-38x51in) s.d.1965. 28-May-4 Uppsala Auktionskammare, Uppsala #338/R est:6000-8000 (S.KR 18000)

KEMPER, Charles Jean (1913-1986) Dutch
£345 $576 €500 Polder landscape (38x58cm-15x23in) s. 11-Nov-3 Vendu Notarishuis, Rotterdam #152
Works on paper
£290 $484 €420 Beach amusement (28x38cm-11x15in) s. W/C. 11-Nov-3 Vendu Notarishuis, Rotterdam #57/R
£548 $932 €800 Square near Kurhaus in the rain (51x71cm-20x28in) s. W/C. 5-Nov-3 Vendue Huis, Gravenhage #511/R

KEMPF, Franz Moishe (1926-) Australian
£1215 $1955 €1774 Interior with figure (30x30cm-12x12in) s.d.68 prov. 25-Aug-3 Sotheby's, Paddington #266/R est:2000-2500 (A.D 3000)
£1220 $2183 €1781 Interior (128x99cm-50x39in) s.d.71 i. verso. 10-May-4 Joel, Victoria #206 est:3000-5000 (A.D 3000)

KEMPSTER, Ruth (1904-?) American
£317 $600 €463 Cactus in bloom (51x41cm-20x16in) s. panel. 22-Feb-4 Bonhams & Butterfields, Los Angeles #7000

KEMPTER, Ernst (1891-1958) Swiss
£498 $846 €727 Still life with flowers (42x27cm-17x11in) s. 18-Nov-3 Hans Widmer, St Gallen #1110 (S.FR 1100)

KENAN, Avi (1951-) Israeli
Sculpture
£1333 $2453 €2000 Dancing couple (80cm-31in) s. num.1/1 bronze unique prov. 9-Jun-4 Christie's, Amsterdam #269/R est:1200-1600

KENATH, Jorg (20th C) ?
£310 $574 €450 Two soldiers pursuing fleeing figures (36x48cm-14x19in) s.d.1929 board. 12-Feb-4 Weidler, Nurnberg #6670

KENDALL, Marie B (1885-1953) American
£375 $600 €548 View to the valley through the trees (130x104cm-51x41in) init. 18-May-3 Auctions by the Bay, Alameda #1174/R

KENDALL, William Sergeant (1869-1938) American
£599 $1000 €875 Little Dutch girl (43x36cm-17x14in) s. s.i.d.1908 verso. 20-Jun-3 Freeman, Philadelphia #262/R
£9249 $16000 €13504 Two Brittany girls (76x56cm-30x22in) s.i.d.18. 13-Dec-3 Sloans & Kenyon, Bethesda #818/R est:5000-7000

KENDE, Geza (1889-1952) American
£811 $1500 €1184 Reclining nude (89x114cm-35x45in) s.d.1941. 18-Jul-4 Bonhams & Butterfields, Los Angeles #7047/R est:2000-3000

KENDRICK, Mel (1949-) American
Sculpture
£1757 $3250 €2565 N0.11181 Untitled (197x10x42cm-78x4x17in) s.d.1982 painted wood incl metal stand prov. 12-Feb-4 Sotheby's, New York #222/R est:4000-6000

KENDRICK, Sydney (1874-1955) British
£650 $1034 €949 Portrait of an airforce officer (75x56cm-30x22in) 12-Sep-3 Bracketts, Tunbridge Wells #943/R
£750 $1193 €1095 Portrait of Mrs Winter (75x60cm-30x24in) painted c.1940. 12-Sep-3 Bracketts, Tunbridge Wells #944/R
£2400 $3888 €3480 In front of a fire (107x79cm-42x31in) s. 30-Jul-3 Hamptons Fine Art, Godalming #237/R est:2500-3500
£4200 $7140 €6132 Woodland walk (61x46cm-24x18in) s. 19-Nov-3 Bonhams, New Bond Street #62/R est:4000-6000

KENES, Marcel (1898-1960) Belgian
£338 $639 €500 Nature morte au bouquet (53x40cm-21x16in) s. panel. 17-Feb-4 Galerie Moderne, Brussels #262/R

KENNA, Michael (1953-) ?
Photographs
£3293 $5500 €4808 Eiffel Tower, study 3, Paris, France (44x39cm-17x15in) s.d.1987 num.16/25 s.i.num.verso gelatin silver print lit. 20-Oct-3 Christie's, Rockefeller NY #110/R est:3000-5000

KENNAWAY, Charles G (1860-1925) British
Works on paper
£360 $612 €526 Oyster beds, Cancale (22x28cm-9x11in) s. i. gouache. 29-Oct-3 Bonhams, Chester #452

KENNEDY, Cecil (1905-1997) British
£320 $598 €467 Still life with flowers in a wicker basket (49x59cm-19x23in) s. 26-Feb-4 Locke & England, Leamington Spa #106
£750 $1253 €1095 Visit to the country cousin (51x41cm-20x16in) s. prov. 8-Oct-3 Christie's, Kensington #973/R
£960 $1747 €1402 Red, white and yellow chrysanthemums in a blue and white vase (61x51cm-24x20in) s.d.1929. 29-Jun-4 Bonhams, Knowle #108
£3200 $5056 €4672 Pink roses in a glass vase (35x25cm-14x10in) s. 6-Sep-3 Shapes, Edinburgh #320/R est:1000-1500
£4500 $7965 €6570 Still life of summer flowers in a green vase (61x51cm-24x20in) s.d.1928. 1-May-4 Shapes, Edinburgh #451/R est:4000-6000

£6800 $11696 €9928 Spring (25x19cm-10x7in) s. prov. 3-Dec-3 Christie's, Kensington #537/R est:2000-3000
£7000 $11130 €10220 White roses (40x30cm-16x12in) prov. 10-Sep-3 Sotheby's, Olympia #229/R est:3000-5000
£7500 $13875 €10950 Madame Butterfly Roses (51x41cm-20x16in) s. prov. 11-Mar-4 Christie's, Kensington #117/R est:6000-8000
£8000 $13360 €11680 Summer (25x20cm-10x8in) s. prov. 16-Oct-3 Christie's, Kensington #362/R est:2000-3000
£8000 $14640 €11680 Anemones (56x46cm-22x18in) s. 4-Jun-4 Christie's, London #102/R est:8000-12000
£8000 $14640 €11680 Still life of pink roses in a wine glass (36x25cm-14x10in) s. 7-Jul-4 George Kidner, Lymington #160/R est:2500-3500
£8099 $14173 €11500 Bouquet d'anemones (50x40cm-20x16in) s. prov. 16-Dec-3 Claude Aguttes, Neuilly #24/R est:6000-8000
£16000 $26720 €23360 Summer flowers (75x62cm-30x24in) s. prov. 16-Oct-3 Lawrence, Crewkerne #762/R
£16000 $29120 €23360 Still life with romneya in a vase (51x41cm-20x16in) s. prov. 1-Jul-4 Christie's, Kensington #144/R est:7000-10000
£20000 $37000 €29200 Flowers in a glass vase (51x41cm-20x16in) s. prov. 11-Feb-4 Sotheby's, Olympia #121/R est:8000-12000
£21557 $36000 €31473 Still life of flowers (66x51cm-26x20in) 17-Oct-3 Du Mouchelle, Detroit #2038/R est:7000-10000
£28000 $50960 €40880 Summer (50x41cm-20x16in) s. prov. 15-Jun-4 Bonhams, New Bond Street #11/R est:6000-9000
£30000 $51000 €43800 Still life of peonies, roses and other flowers (61x51cm-24x20in) s. prov. 19-Nov-3 Tennants, Leyburn #1227/R est:8000-12000
£58000 $99760 €84680 Still life of summer flowers. s. prov.exhib. 2-Dec-3 Bonhams, New Bond Street #1/R est:25000-35000

KENNEDY, Charles Napier (1852-1898) British
£1150 $2151 €1725 Portraits of William Boyd, his wife Charlotte and their son John Dopping (120x90cm-47x35in) s.d.1896 i.verso one oval three. 26-Jul-4 Bonhams, Bath #51/R est:1000-1500
£1923 $3308 €2808 Elegant visitor at the artist's studio (61x46cm-24x18in) s.d.1879. 2-Dec-3 Bukowskis, Stockholm #282/R est:30000-35000 (S.KR 25000)

KENNEDY, Grant (1963-) Zimbabwean
£550 $1018 €803 Gorilla (25x20cm-10x8in) s.i.d.1997 verso. 15-Jan-4 Christie's, Kensington #1037/R
£700 $1295 €1022 Coyote II (150x130cm-59x51in) s.i.d.1995 verso. 11-Mar-4 Christie's, Kensington #165/R
£1300 $2171 €1898 Two figures (150x130cm-59x51in) s.i.d.1998 verso. 16-Oct-3 Christie's, Kensington #596/R est:1000-1500

KENNEDY, Peter (1945-) Australian
£1301 $2042 €1899 Untitled, everything that is built here to be torn down (136x156cm-54x61in) init.d.20.10.1987 s.verso prov. 27-Aug-3 Christie's, Sydney #618/R est:2000-4000 (A.D 3200)
£1707 $2680 €2492 Melbourne, dusk (122x213cm-48x84in) init.s.d.1991 i.verso triptych. 27-Aug-3 Christie's, Sydney #590/R est:2000-4000 (A.D 4200)

KENNEDY, Scott (20th C) American
£1078 $1800 €1574 Keeping watch (30x89cm-12x35in) s.d. 11-Oct-3 Nadeau, Windsor #138/R est:2500-5000
Works on paper
£329 $550 €480 Aurora Borealis (58x36cm-23x14in) s.d. W/C. 11-Oct-3 Nadeau, Windsor #139/R
£389 $650 €568 After dinner music (30x91cm-12x36in) s.d. W/C. 11-Oct-3 Nadeau, Windsor #137/R
£2540 $4750 €3708 Snowshoes (25x66cm-10x26in) s. W/C. 24-Jul-4 Coeur d'Alene, Hayden #10/R est:4000-8000

KENNEDY, William (1860-1918) British
£1500 $2355 €2175 An Arab camp (28x34cm-11x13in) i.verso panel exhib. 27-Aug-3 Sotheby's, London #1026/R est:1500-2000
£1500 $2355 €2175 Milking time (51x61cm-20x24in) s. prov. 27-Aug-3 Sotheby's, London #1027/R est:2000-3000
£1500 $2685 €2190 Outside the farm (40x51cm-16x20in) s. 26-May-4 Sotheby's, Olympia #111/R est:800-1200
£4000 $6280 €5800 News from the front (29x38cm-11x15in) s. panel. 27-Aug-3 Sotheby's, London #1032/R est:1500-2000
£75676 $140000 €110487 Little girl with her black cat (81x56cm-32x22in) painted c.1840. 16-Jan-4 Sotheby's, New York #3/R est:30000-50000

KENNEDY, William W (1818-1871) American
£1111 $1800 €1611 Portraits of Mr and Mrs E peace (56x48cm-22x19in) i.verso. 10-Aug-3 Skinner, Bolton #131/R est:2500-3500

KENNEDY, William W (attrib) (1818-1871) American
£39683 $75000 €57937 Portrait of girl in red dress (56x43cm-22x17in) board prov. 22-Feb-4 Skinner, Boston #73/R est:15000-25000

KENNELL, W H (fl.1872-1890) British
Works on paper
£320 $518 €467 Still life of grapes and apples on a ledge (25x36cm-10x14in) init.d.1889 W/C. 25-May-3 Desmond Judd, Cranbrook #1037

KENNETHSON, George (1910-1993) British
Sculpture
£3200 $5888 €4672 Untitled (30cm-12in) alabaster sold with base. 24-Jun-4 Sotheby's, Olympia #515/R est:2000-3000

KENNEY, John Theodore Eardley (1911-1972) British
£1650 $3086 €2409 Fernie hunt at wood (51x77cm-20x30in) s.d.69 prov. 24-Feb-4 Bonhams, Knowle #119/R est:1500-2000

KENNINGTON, Eric (1888-1960) British
Works on paper
£550 $1001 €803 Head of an Evzone (37x27cm-15x11in) s.d.36 indis.i. pastel. 1-Jul-4 Christie's, Kensington #21/R
£2800 $4760 €4088 Alice (37x29cm-15x11in) s.d.20 pastel W/C buff paper. 20-Nov-3 Christie's, London #178/R est:3000-5000

KENNINGTON, Thomas Benjamin (1856-1916) British
£300 $555 €438 Portrait of medieval lady in art and crafts style (33x25cm-13x10in) gold leaf. 10-Feb-4 David Lay, Penzance #591
£500 $795 €725 Robin Hood's bay (24x35cm-9x14in) i.d.1892 board prov. 9-Sep-3 David Duggleby, Scarborough #287/R
£4800 $8640 €7008 Figurative subject with two young girls seated on stone steps (88x62cm-35x24in) s.d.89. 21-Apr-4 Tennants, Leyburn #1215/R est:5000-5500
£13000 $23920 €18980 Glory of womanhood (153x100cm-60x39in) s.i.d. 11-Jun-4 Christie's, London #188/R est:8000-12000

KENNIS, Ignace Jacques Lucien (1888-1973) Belgian
£284 $474 €400 Na de school (100x75cm-39x30in) s. 20-Oct-3 Bernaerts, Antwerp #295

KENNY, Alan (?) Irish
£694 $1090 €1000 Near Clifden, Connemara (46x61cm-18x24in) s. 26-Aug-3 James Adam, Dublin #233/R est:800-1200

KENNY, Desmond (fl.1934-40) British
£634 $1109 €900 Moore Street (66x82cm-26x32in) i.d.03 verso canvas on board. 16-Dec-3 James Adam, Dublin #164/R
£662 $1158 €940 Moore Street (63x85cm-25x33in) i.d.03 verso canvas on board. 16-Dec-3 James Adam, Dublin #163/R

KENNY, Michael (1941-2000) British
Works on paper
£450 $765 €657 Corpus - Study V (37x53cm-15x21in) s.i.d.96 chl drawing prov. 18-Nov-3 Bonhams, Knightsbridge #129/R
£500 $850 €730 Alone II (57x77cm-22x30in) s.i.d.92 chl drawing. 18-Nov-3 Bonhams, Knightsbridge #131/R
£500 $850 €730 Alone I (57x77cm-22x30in) s.i.d.92 chl drawing. 18-Nov-3 Bonhams, Knightsbridge #133/R
£500 $925 €730 Aphrodisias (37x27cm-15x11in) s. i.d.91 chl pencil pastel. 13-Jul-4 Bonhams, Knightsbridge #92/R
£750 $1275 €1095 Sculpture in a landscape IV (57x77cm-22x30in) s.i.d.90 pastel chl drawing prov. 18-Nov-3 Bonhams, Knightsbridge #140/R
£800 $1480 €1168 Baby love - Don't your eyes get tired VII (78x112cm-31x44in) s.i.d.92 chl pastel. 13-Jul-4 Bonhams, Knightsbridge #95/R

KENSETT, John Frederick (1816-1872) American
£2329 $3750 €3400 Figure by fence (38x25cm-15x10in) s. board. 20-Aug-3 James Julia, Fairfield #669/R est:2000-3000
£90909 $160000 €132727 Bash Bish Falls (56x46cm-22x18in) painted c.1855-60 prov.lit. 18-May-4 Christie's, Rockefeller NY #17/R est:200000-300000
£116279 $200000 €169767 Study on Long Island Sound (39x70cm-15x28in) painted 1872 prov.exhib.lit. 4-Dec-3 Christie's, Rockefeller NY #9/R
£153409 $270000 €223977 Landscape - Mount Chocorua from Conway (53x74cm-21x29in) mono.d.54 prov. 19-May-4 Sotheby's, New York #69/R est:60000-80000
£232558 $400000 €339535 Waterfall in the woods with Indians (43x61cm-17x24in) init.d.50 prov.exhib.lit. 4-Dec-3 Christie's, Rockefeller NY #17/R
£426136 $750000 €622159 View of Mount Washington (76x114cm-30x45in) init.d.52 prov.exhib. 18-May-4 Christie's, Rockefeller NY #14/R est:800000-1200000
£497159 $875000 €725852 On the coast Beverley Shore, Massachusetts (46x76cm-18x30in) mono.d.72 prov.exhib. 19-May-4 Sotheby's, New York #61/R est:700000-900000

KENSINGTON, C (?) ?
£1150 $2116 €1679 SS City of Cambridge (58x91cm-23x36in) s.i. 12-Jun-4 Dickins, Middle Claydon #13

KENSLEY, Marie (?) British
Works on paper
£290 $499 €423 Anemones on mossy bank (23x41cm-9x16in) s.d.1898 W/C. 3-Dec-3 Andrew Hartley, Ilkley #1097

KENT, Leslie (1890-1980) British
£430 $770 €628 Newton Ferrers (36x46cm-14x18in) s. 26-May-4 Christie's, Kensington #750/R

KENT, Nigel (1933-) Australian
£280 $476 €400 Number 6 (60x60cm-24x24in) s.i.d.1992 verso acrylic. 24-Nov-3 Glerum, Amsterdam #250/R

KENT, Rockwell (1882-1971) American
£56818 $100000 €82954 Ice, sea and rock (66x119cm-26x47in) s. painted c.1932-33 prov.exhib. 19-May-4 Sotheby's, New York #116/R est:100000-150000
£116279 $200000 €169767 Blue day, Greenland (86x113cm-34x44in) s.i.d.1935-37 prov.exhib.lit. 3-Dec-3 Sotheby's, New York #68/R est:200000-300000
Prints
£3059 $5200 €4466 Lovers (17x26cm-7x10in) s. wood engraving. 6-Nov-3 Swann Galleries, New York #583a/R est:2000-3000
Works on paper
£615 $1100 €898 Parry harbour, looking south (8x15cm-3x6in) s.i. pencil. 8-Jan-4 James Julia, Fairfield #928/R

£870 $1600 €1270 Don Juan (23x15cm-9x6in) i. pen black ink card. 10-Jun-4 Swann Galleries, New York #129/R est:1000-1500
£1205 $2000 €1747 Wilderness scene (8x15cm-3x6in) s. pen ink exec.c.1940. 14-Jun-3 Rachel Davis, Shaker Heights #323/R est:1500-2000
£1564 $2800 €2283 Group of people in car, about to drive off cliff (23x38cm-9x15in) s. pen ink. 15-May-4 Illustration House, New York #149/R est:3000-5000
£1617 $2700 €2361 People approaching moonlit cabin, occupants asleep (25x43cm-10x17in) s. pen ink exec.c.1929. 15-Nov-3 Illustration House, New York #26/R est:3000-5000
£1728 $2800 €2506 Men of Greenland (25x18cm-10x7in) dr. 8-Aug-3 Barridorf, Portland #304/R est:1500-2500
£1815 $3250 €2650 Wedgewood Mountain (43x33cm-17x13in) s.i.d.1936 chl graphite. 20-Mar-4 Rachel Davis, Shaker Heights #197/R est:3500-4000
£4261 $7500 €6221 Dan Ward's cottage, Donegal, Ireland (25x36cm-10x14in) s.d.1927 W/C. 3-Jan-4 Collins, Maine #44/R est:5000-7000
£10227 $18000 €14931 Amercia's Steel Industry (33x46cm-13x18in) s. brush pen ink lithographic crayon exec c.1945 prov.lit. 19-May-4 Sotheby's, New York #115/R est:18000-24000

KENTRIDGE, William (1955-) South African?
£26816 $48000 €39151 Bicycle man (161x110cm-63x43in) gouache chk chl paper on paper prov.lit. 14-May-4 Phillips, New York #145/R est:40000-60000
Works on paper
£8982 $15000 €13114 Collage procession (29x82cm-11x32in) cut paper collage col pencil executed 2000. 14-Nov-3 Phillips, New York #228/R est:10000-15000
£14864 $26606 €21701 Iris (65x52cm-26x20in) s.d.91 mixed media collage. 31-May-4 Stephan Welz, Johannesburg #517/R est:60000-80000 (SA.R 180000)
£25140 $45000 €36704 Man with microphone (207x108cm-81x43in) W/C chl gouache chk prov.exhib.lit. 12-May-4 Christie's, Rockefeller NY #329/R est:50000-70000

KENWORTHY, Jonathan (1943-) British
Sculpture
£8176 $13000 €11937 Cheetah (39cm-15in) s.d.67 num.1/3 bronze. 12-Sep-3 Skinner, Boston #316a/R est:18000

KENYON, Henry Rodman (1861-1926) American
£5233 $9000 €7640 River shed with lobster traps (35x50cm-14x20in) s. prov. 3-Dec-3 Doyle, New York #207/R est:10000-15000

KENZLER, Carl (20th C) German
£420 $713 €600 Rocky coast in the evening (70x100cm-28x39in) s. 20-Nov-3 Van Ham, Cologne #1678a
£927 $1687 €1400 Rocky coast in evening light (70x100cm-28x39in) s. 21-Jun-4 Dorotheum, Vienna #307/R

KEOWN, Mary Therese (20th C) Irish?
£2267 $4103 €3400 Virginnia's walk (65x110cm-26x43in) s. i.verso. 30-Mar-4 De Veres Art Auctions, Dublin #68a/R est:3500-4500
£3067 $5551 €4600 The mother (65x110cm-26x43in) s.i. s.verso. 30-Mar-4 De Veres Art Auctions, Dublin #71a est:3500-4500
£3217 $5469 €4600 Exporter (77x127cm-30x50in) s. i.verso. 25-Nov-3 De Veres Art Auctions, Dublin #168/R est:4500-5500

KEPES, Gyorgy (1906-2001) American/Hungarian
£233 $400 €340 Stone acrobats (102x102cm-40x40in) s.i.d.1964 verso. 7-Dec-3 Grogan, Boston #120a
£670 $1200 €978 Untitled (30x15cm-12x6in) s.i.d.1977 oil sand prov. 16-May-4 Wright, Chicago #258/R est:1500-2000
Photographs
£1867 $3435 €2800 Untitled (25x20cm-10x8in) i. verso silver gelatin prov. 10-Jun-4 Villa Grisebach, Berlin #1151/R est:2000-2500
£2133 $3925 €3200 Untitled (25x20cm-10x8in) s.d. verso photogram silver gelatin prov. 10-Jun-4 Villa Grisebach, Berlin #1150/R est:2000-2500
£2174 $3565 €3000 Untitled (50x40cm-20x16in) s.i.d. verso vintage silver gelatin prov. 30-May-3 Villa Grisebach, Berlin #1230/R est:2000-2500
£2667 $4907 €4000 Waterforms (24x19cm-9x7in) s.i.d. verso silver gelatin prov.lit.exhib. 10-Jun-4 Villa Grisebach, Berlin #1149/R est:2000-2500
Works on paper
£2654 $4750 €3875 Loose fabric (124x124cm-49x49in) loose fabric oil sand canvas prov.exhib. 16-May-4 Wright, Chicago #385/R est:1000-1500

KEPPENS, Jules (1910-1992) Belgian
£315 $536 €460 Vue de Bruges (50x60cm-20x24in) s. 4-Nov-3 Servarts Themis, Bruxelles #585

KEPPIE, Jessie (1868-1951) British
Works on paper
£350 $662 €511 Gathering firewood (44x31cm-17x12in) s. W/C. 19-Feb-4 Lyon & Turnbull, Edinburgh #121

KEPPIE, W (?) British?
£3000 $5430 €4380 Highland cottages (35x50cm-14x20in) s. 3-Apr-4 Shapes, Edinburgh #438 est:200-300

KERELS, Henri (1896-1956) Belgian
£400 $720 €600 Mouvement lyrique (100x80cm-39x31in) s.d.55 verso. 26-Apr-4 Bernaerts, Antwerp #557/R
£714 $1279 €1050 Musongi Kasai (35x27cm-14x11in) s.d.1931 panel lit. 21-Mar-4 St-Germain-en-Laye Encheres #93/R

KERINEC, Roger (1917-1997) French
£704 $1232 €1000 Douarnenz vu des Plomarch (42x30cm-17x12in) s. gouache. 21-Dec-3 Thierry & Lannon, Brest #396
£1467 $2625 €2200 Paysage aux chaumieres et a la barque rouge (80x210cm-31x83in) s.d.65. 16-May-4 Thierry & Lannon, Brest #216/R est:2200-2400
Works on paper
£1056 $1849 €1500 Douarnenez chalutiers a quai (63x48cm-25x19in) s.d.79 gouache. 21-Dec-3 Thierry & Lannon, Brest #398/R est:1500-1800

KERKAM, Earl C (1890-1965) American
£216 $400 €315 Roslyn (76x62cm-30x24in) s. 18-Jan-4 Bonhams & Butterfields, Los Angeles #7043/R

KERKHOFF, Daniel Johannes Torman (1766-1831) Dutch
Works on paper
£1311 $2400 €1914 Wooded landscape with a canal (57x48cm-22x19in) s.i.d.1812 verso W/C. 29-Jan-4 Swann Galleries, New York #194/R est:3000-5000

KERKOVIUS, Ida (1879-1970) German
£699 $1203 €1000 Composition (10x15cm-4x6in) mono. oil chk. 2-Dec-3 Hauswedell & Nolte, Hamburg #296/R
£1208 $2138 €1800 Small format (25x35cm-10x14in) mono. board. 30-Apr-4 Dr Fritz Nagel, Stuttgart #854/R est:1800
£2000 $3600 €3000 Interior (58x40cm-23x16in) mono. tempera board. 24-Apr-4 Dr Lehr, Berlin #213/R est:4000
£2083 $3479 €3000 Composition, mother with child (31x21cm-12x8in) mono.d. oil chk pencil prov. 24-Oct-3 Ketterer, Hamburg #424/R est:3000-4000
£2416 $4277 €3600 Yellow house with figures (24x26cm-9x10in) mono. prov. 30-Apr-4 Dr Fritz Nagel, Stuttgart #851/R est:3000
£2703 $4838 €4000 Colour composition (50x40cm-20x16in) mono. lit. 8-May-4 Schloss Ahlden, Ahlden #845/R est:3800
£6250 $10438 €9000 Brittany landscape (38x45cm-15x18in) mono. board on masonite prov. 24-Oct-3 Ketterer, Hamburg #423/R est:10000-15000
£6667 $11933 €10000 Figural (33x46cm-13x18in) mono. i.d.verso board prov.lit. 14-May-4 Ketterer, Munich #216/R est:10000-15000
£7692 $13077 €11000 Composition (62x67cm-24x26in) s.d.48 s.i. verso prov. 29-Nov-3 Villa Grisebach, Berlin #199/R est:14000-18000
£8333 $13583 €12000 St Angelo (51x67cm-20x26in) mono.d.1954 prov. 27-Sep-3 Dr Fritz Nagel, Stuttgart #9568/R est:15000
Works on paper
£267 $480 €400 In garden house (15x10cm-6x4in) pencil. 24-Apr-4 Reiss & Sohn, Konigstein #5650/R
£390 $616 €550 Scene with four figures (15x16cm-6x6in) mono. chl. 22-Jul-3 Sigalas, Stuttgart #308
£503 $891 €750 Quarry (15x20cm-6x8in) mono. pastel. 30-Apr-4 Dr Fritz Nagel, Stuttgart #852/R
£533 $976 €800 Small format 276 (15x21cm-6x8in) i. verso chk graphite. 5-Jun-4 Lempertz, Koln #780/R
£629 $1083 €900 Modern composition (61x45cm-24x18in) mixed media. 5-Dec-3 Michael Zeller, Lindau #884/R
£800 $1472 €1200 Children playing (10x13cm-4x5in) mono. W/C on pencil. 10-Jun-4 Hauswedell & Nolte, Hamburg #317/R
£872 $1544 €1300 Composition with curved forms (19x28cm-7x11in) s. W/C board. 30-Apr-4 Dr Fritz Nagel, Stuttgart #855/R
£1007 $1782 €1500 House in the vineyards (20x29cm-8x11in) mono. W/C prov. 30-Apr-4 Dr Fritz Nagel, Stuttgart #853/R est:2000
£1119 $1924 €1600 Three figures (17x25cm-7x10in) mono. i.verso pastel exec. c.1965. 6-Dec-3 Hans Stahl, Toestorf #387 est:900
£1690 $2704 €2400 Composition with houses (48x33cm-19x13in) mono. W/C. 19-Sep-3 Sigalas, Stuttgart #322/R est:2500
£1933 $3557 €2900 Yellow head (32x25cm-13x10in) mono. pastel. 12-Jun-4 Villa Grisebach, Berlin #587/R est:2500-3000
£2098 $3566 €3000 Loving couple (13x17cm-5x7in) s. pastel chk prov.exhib. 26-Nov-3 Lempertz, Koln #755/R est:3000
£2797 $4755 €4000 Bodensee (50x70cm-20x28in) mono. pastel paper on board. 29-Nov-3 Villa Grisebach, Berlin #227/R est:3500-4500
£3067 $5612 €4600 Vase and flowers (40x37cm-16x15in) mono. pastel prov. 5-Jun-4 Lempertz, Koln #781/R est:3000
£7333 $13493 €11000 Self portrait (32x22cm-13x9in) mono. gouache W/C card exec. c.1923 prov. 12-Jun-4 Villa Grisebach, Berlin #270/R est:9000-12000

KERL, Hermann (1813-1912) French?
£816 $1298 €1200 Le vegetable seller (47x31cm-19x12in) s. panel. 23-Mar-3 Mercier & Cie, Lille #218

KERLING, Anna (1862-1955) Dutch
Works on paper
£1161 $1996 €1695 Summer, girl seated in a field (61x51cm-24x20in) s.i. W/C paper on board exhib. 2-Dec-3 Ritchie, Toronto #119/R est:1200-1800 (C.D 2600)

KERMADEC, Eugène Nestor le (1899-1976) French
£469 $778 €680 Petit noeud rouge (56x46cm-22x18in) s. 1-Oct-3 Millon & Associes, Paris #147/R
£8054 $14416 €12000 Pyjama rouge contre nature morte (73x50cm-29x20in) s. s.i.on stretcher. 26-May-4 Christie's, Paris #48/R est:2500-3500
Works on paper
£290 $522 €423 Composition (23x30cm-9x12in) s. W/C. 26-Apr-4 Bukowskis, Stockholm #243/R (S.KR 4000)

KERMARREC, Joel (1939-) French
£634 $1096 €900 Sans titre (130x130cm-51x51in) s.i.d.1969 verso acrylic. 14-Dec-3 Versailles Encheres #168
£660 $1102 €950 Composition rose (130x130cm-51x51in) s.d.1964 verso. 25-Oct-3 Cornette de St.Cyr, Paris #716
£811 $1427 €1200 Untitled (116x89cm-46x35in) s.d.1969 acrylic prov. 18-May-4 Tajan, Paris #157/R est:1200-1500
Works on paper
£278 $464 €400 Ardoise (27x19cm-11x7in) s.d.1973 verso collage gouache oil slate. 25-Oct-3 Cornette de St.Cyr, Paris #721

KERN, Anton (1710-1747) German

£3158	$5811	€4800	La visitation (36x31cm-14x12in) 23-Jun-4 Millon & Associes, Paris #31/R est:3000-4000

KERN, Anton (attrib) (1710-1747) German

£3453	$5663	€4800	Le frappement de rocher (54x92cm-21x36in) pair. 6-Jun-3 Drouot Estimations, Paris #34/R est:12000-15000

KERN, Benedikt (1704-?) German

£2113	$3655	€3000	Moon-lit Mediterranean harbour view with fishermen and travellers (93x130cm-37x51in) s. 10-Dec-3 Christie's, Amsterdam #805/R est:3000-5000

KERN, Hermann (1839-1912) Hungarian

£550	$995	€803	Drinker and smokers in interiors (46x30cm-18x12in) s. pair. 16-Apr-4 Keys, Aylsham #703/R
£1358	$2200	€1983	Brewmaster in cellar (69x48cm-27x19in) s. 7-Aug-3 Eldred, East Dennis #138/R est:3000-5000
£2000	$3640	€2920	Welcome refreshment (51x39cm-20x15in) s. s.i.verso. 16-Jun-4 Christie's, Kensington #214/R est:2000-3000
£2013	$3604	€3000	A good mouthful (31x25cm-12x10in) s. panel. 27-May-4 Dorotheum, Vienna #171/R est:3000-3800
£2027	$3628	€3000	Favourite corner (47x31cm-19x12in) s. i. verso panel. 6-May-4 Michael Zeller, Lindau #722/R est:1000
£2028	$3488	€2900	Old man feeding his bird in a cage (48x32cm-19x13in) i. 3-Dec-3 Neumeister, Munich #621 est:3000
£2098	$3608	€3000	Old man with his caged bird (42x53cm-17x21in) s.d.1909. 3-Dec-3 Neumeister, Munich #620 est:3000
£2098	$3608	€3000	Household servant (68x47cm-27x19in) s. panel. 3-Dec-3 Neumeister, Munich #614 est:3000
£2238	$3849	€3200	The botanist (47x31cm-19x12in) s.d.1909. 3-Dec-3 Neumeister, Munich #622/R est:3000
£2308	$3969	€3300	Monk reading a newspaper in his cell (47x32cm-19x13in) s. panel. 3-Dec-3 Neumeister, Munich #615/R est:3000
£2416	$4325	€3600	A good pipe (31x25cm-12x10in) s. panel. 27-May-4 Dorotheum, Vienna #120/R est:3000-3800
£2448	$4210	€3500	Old man feeding his little bird (46x30cm-18x12in) s. panel. 3-Dec-3 Neumeister, Munich #617/R est:3000
£2550	$4565	€3800	The spirit of the music (74x62cm-29x24in) st.sig.verso. 27-May-4 Dorotheum, Vienna #169/R est:4000-5000
£2557	$4500	€3733	Clockmaker (48x30cm-19x12in) s. panel. 18-May-4 Bonhams & Butterfields, San Francisco #104/R est:3000-5000
£2667	$4800	€4000	Thirsty reader (47x31cm-19x12in) s. panel. 20-Apr-4 Sotheby's, Amsterdam #54/R est:4000-6000
£3207	$5676	€4682	Tasting wine (47x31cm-19x12in) s.d.1909. 28-Apr-4 Kieselbach, Budapest #80/R (H.F 1200000)
£3211	$5362	€4656	Fruit seller (47x31cm-19x12in) s. panel. 23-Jun-3 Philippe Schuler, Zurich #3532/R est:4000-6000 (S.FR 7000)
£3333	$6033	€5000	Old man in wine cellar lighting lantern (48x32cm-19x13in) s.d.1905. 1-Apr-4 Van Ham, Cologne #1478/R est:4000
£3497	$5944	€5000	Vegetable seller (48x32cm-19x13in) s.d.1907. 24-Nov-3 Dorotheum, Vienna #97/R est:5000-5500
£3500	$5530	€5075	Mending the net (46x30cm-18x12in) s. panel. 4-Sep-3 Christie's, Kensington #292/R est:1000-1500
£3620	$5792	€5285	Well-wisher (47x31cm-19x12in) s.d.1905 panel. 19-Sep-3 Koller, Zurich #3115/R est:4000-6000 (S.FR 8000)
£4545	$7727	€6500	Thirsty fiddler (46x31cm-18x12in) s. i. verso panel. 24-Nov-3 Dorotheum, Vienna #96/R est:5000-5500
£5705	$10211	€8500	News of the day (43x53cm-17x21in) s. 27-May-4 Dorotheum, Vienna #200/R est:7500-8500
£6376	$11413	€9500	A tricky card group (58x80cm-23x31in) s.d.1903 i.verso. 27-May-4 Dorotheum, Vienna #127/R est:6000-8000

KERN, Josef (20th C) ?

£221	$400	€323	Waiting for the train (58x79cm-23x31in) s. 16-Apr-4 James Julia, Fairfield #1004/R
£671	$1242	€1000	Dream (110x70cm-43x28in) s.d.1983 acrylic. 9-Mar-4 Dorotheum, Vienna #223/R
£1067	$1963	€1600	Large pumpkin on African stool (87x71cm-34x28in) s.d.1993 verso acrylic oil. 9-Jun-4 Dorotheum, Salzburg #746/R est:2400-2800

KERN, Leonhard (attrib) (1588-1662) German

Sculpture

£46000	$79580	€67160	Reclining woman (4x23x10cm-2x9x4in) ivory prov.lit. 12-Dec-3 Sotheby's, London #167/R est:20000-30000

KERNEKAMP, F W (19th C) German

£1197	$2071	€1700	View of Heidelberg (64x84cm-25x33in) s.d.1891. 12-Dec-3 Berlinghof, Heidelberg #1067/R est:330

KERNN-LARSEN, Rita (1904-1998) Danish

£496	$917	€724	Surrealistic landscape with sun (80x110cm-31x43in) init. 15-Mar-4 Rasmussen, Vejle #523/R (D.KR 5500)
£611	$1040	€892	View from the artist's studio (41x33cm-16x13in) s. 29-Nov-3 Rasmussen, Havnen #4303/R (D.KR 6500)
£798	$1333	€1165	Landscape from South of France (38x56cm-15x22in) s. 7-Oct-3 Rasmussen, Copenhagen #333/R (D.KR 8500)
£986	$1646	€1440	Future happenings (35x46cm-14x18in) s.i. exhib. 7-Oct-3 Rasmussen, Copenhagen #188/R (D.KR 10500)
£2611	$4699	€3812	Nature morte II (98x75cm-39x30in) init. painted c.1933-34. 26-Apr-4 Bukowskis, Stockholm #255/R est:20000-25000 (S.KR 36000)

Works on paper

£267	$485	€401	Young woman in Paris (28x24cm-11x9in) init. W/C Indian ink pencil exec.c.1934. 19-Jun-4 Rasmussen, Havnen #4212/R (D.KR 3000)
£271	$498	€396	Bathing girl with red spotted sunhat (29x24cm-11x9in) init. W/C Indian ink pencil. 29-Mar-4 Rasmussen, Copenhagen #543 (D.KR 3000)
£406	$747	€593	Young woman wearing brown jacket with trees and clouds (28x23cm-11x9in) init. W/C Indian ink. 29-Mar-4 Rasmussen, Copenhagen #542/R (D.KR 4500)
£406	$747	€593	Autumn - elegant lady with hat (28x23cm-11x9in) init. W/C lit. 29-Mar-4 Rasmussen, Copenhagen #545/R (D.KR 4500)
£751	$1254	€1096	Visiting the exhibition (28x22cm-11x9in) init. gouache. 7-Oct-3 Rasmussen, Copenhagen #193/R (D.KR 8000)
£845	$1411	€1234	Sur la mer (21x32cm-8x13in) init. gouache. 7-Oct-3 Rasmussen, Copenhagen #196/R (D.KR 9000)
£2160	$3607	€3154	Seated around the stove, outdoor cafe in Paris, Aux deux Magots (41x33cm-16x13in) init.d.31 W/C Indian ink pencil. 7-Oct-3 Rasmussen, Copenhagen #205/R est:10000 (D.KR 23000)

KERNOFF, Harry Aaron (1900-1974) British

£1259	$2140	€1800	Irish eyes (21x16cm-8x6in) s.d.1968 oil pastel card. 18-Nov-3 Whyte's, Dublin #127/R est:2000-3000
£1892	$3576	€2800	Study of a lady (34x24cm-13x9in) s. board. 17-Feb-4 Whyte's, Dublin #244/R est:1500-2000
£3067	$5551	€4600	Study of a young boy (31x26cm-12x10in) s. board. 30-Mar-4 De Veres Art Auctions, Dublin #66/R est:3000-5000
£3154	$5583	€4700	Trade unionist (43x30cm-17x12in) s. 27-Apr-4 Whyte's, Dublin #40/R est:3000-4000
£3356	$6007	€5000	Owl and the leprechaun (39x30cm-15x12in) s. board. 26-May-4 James Adam, Dublin #69/R est:5000-8000
£5035	$8559	€7200	Phoenix Park, Dublin (31x40cm-12x16in) s. board. 25-Nov-3 De Veres Art Auctions, Dublin #16/R est:7000-10000
£5263	$9684	€8000	Floating cubes (50x53cm-20x21in) s. 22-Jun-4 De Veres Art Auctions, Dublin #128/R est:8000-10000
£6294	$10699	€9000	Portrait of Liam O'Flaherty on the Aran Islands (49x38cm-19x15in) s.d.1936 board. 25-Nov-3 De Veres Art Auctions, Dublin #96/R est:7000-10000
£19737	$36316	€30000	Balascadden Bay, Howth (37x50cm-15x20in) s.i.d.1936 board. 22-Jun-4 De Veres Art Auctions, Dublin #59/R est:20000-30000
£20139	$32826	€29000	Summer day in St Stephen's Green, Dublin (30x40cm-12x16in) s.d.1936 board. 24-Sep-3 James Adam, Dublin #69/R est:12000-18000
£24161	$42765	€36000	Autumn day at Island-Bridge, Dublin (61x91cm-24x36in) s.d.1934 i.verso panel prov. 27-Apr-4 Whyte's, Dublin #34/R est:40000-50000
£34211	$62947	€52000	Misery Hill, Dublin (66x97cm-26x38in) s.d.43 i.verso board prov. 22-Jun-4 De Veres Art Auctions, Dublin #23/R est:35000-50000

Works on paper

£1258	$2290	€1900	Bust length portrait of a gentleman (51x39cm-20x15in) s. chl. 15-Jun-4 James Adam, Dublin #136/R est:1000-1500
£1469	$2497	€2100	Richard Hayward (51x38cm-20x15in) s.i. chl htd white. 18-Nov-3 Whyte's, Dublin #125/R est:1500-2000
£1812	$3244	€2700	Fiddler of Dooney (20x15cm-8x6in) s. pen ink. 26-May-4 James Adam, Dublin #163/R est:2500-3500
£2676	$4282	€3800	Crock of gold (30x19cm-12x7in) init.i.d.1925 W/C pen ink exhib.lit. 16-Sep-3 Whyte's, Dublin #61/R est:3500-4500
£2800	$5068	€4200	Fishing boats, west of Ireland (27x36cm-11x14in) s.d.33 W/C prov. 30-Mar-4 De Veres Art Auctions, Dublin #111/R est:3500-5000
£3667	$6637	€5500	Galloping on the Curragh (28x38cm-11x15in) s.d.55 pastel. 30-Mar-4 De Veres Art Auctions, Dublin #153/R est:3000-4000
£4027	$7208	€6000	Old Skerries windmill (40x30cm-16x12in) s. mixed media panel exec 1942. 31-May-4 Hamilton Osborne King, Dublin #108/R est:6000-10000
£5263	$9684	€8000	Portmarnock summer (30x40cm-12x16in) s.i.verso pastel bodycol exec. 1928 prov. 22-Jun-4 De Veres Art Auctions, Dublin #92/R est:8000-12000
£6000	$10980	€8760	James Joyce (18x14cm-7x6in) s. pen ink dr. 8-Apr-4 Christie's, London #702/R est:3000-5000
£6434	$10937	€9200	Labour meeting (24x23cm-9x9in) s.d.54 W/C. 25-Nov-3 De Veres Art Auctions, Dublin #5/R est:3000-4000
£8054	$14255	€12000	Funeral in Mayo (43x56cm-17x22in) s.d.1947 W/C pencil. 27-Apr-4 Whyte's, Dublin #41/R est:8000-10000
£8451	$14620	€12000	Currachs in from the sea, Renvyle, Connemara (24x30cm-9x12in) s.d.34 s.i.verso W/C. 10-Dec-3 Bonhams & James Adam, Dublin #187/R est:4000-5000
£11333	$20513	€17000	St Stephens Green, Dublin, summer (25x31cm-10x12in) s. W/C. 31-Mar-4 James Adam, Dublin #43/R est:12000-15000
£12000	$21480	€17520	Study for 'in Davy's Parlour Snug: self portrait with Davy Byrne and Martin Murphy (23x33cm-9x13in) s. W/C pencil. 13-May-4 Sotheby's, London #84/R est:12000-18000

KERNOFF, Harry Aaron (attrib) (1900-1974) British

Works on paper

£1700	$3043	€2482	Farmyard with white horse (24x34cm-9x13in) s. W/C. 17-Mar-4 James Thompson, Kirby Lonsdale #305

KERNSTOCK, Karoly (1873-1940) Hungarian

£950	$1577	€1387	Towage on the river Danube by Nagymaros (56x71cm-22x28in) s. cardboard. 4-Oct-3 Kieselbach, Budapest #22/R (H.F 350000)
£1265	$2289	€1847	Resting in the shadow (40x50cm-16x20in) s. oil on wood. 16-Apr-4 Mu Terem Galeria, Budapest #125/R (H.F 480000)
£3132	$5418	€4573	Autumn landscape in Nagymaros (56x72cm-22x28in) s. 12-Dec-3 Kieselbach, Budapest #178/R (H.F 1200000)
£3529	$5859	€5152	In the vineyard (92x75cm-36x30in) s. 4-Oct-3 Kieselbach, Budapest #79/R (H.F 1300000)
£10440	$18061	€15242	Afternoon rest - sitting in the park (42x51cm-17x20in) s. 12-Dec-3 Kieselbach, Budapest #110/R (H.F 4000000)

KERPEL, Lipot (1818-1880) Hungarian

£3448	$5759	€5000	Mountain village with view of Albanian mountains (30x59cm-12x23in) s.i.d.1845. 9-Jul-3 Hugo Ruef, Munich #116/R est:1200

KERR, Adma Green (1879-1949) American

£444	$800	€648	Long's Peak and Autumn Willows, Gates Park, Colo (89x99cm-35x39in) s. s.i.d.1936 verso board. 26-Apr-4 Schrager Galleries, Milwaukee #1065/R

KERR, David Ord (1952-) British

£647	$1080	€945	Still life of a brace of pheasants (74x59cm-29x23in) s. 20-Oct-3 Stephan Welz, Johannesburg #211/R est:9000-12000 (SA.R 7500)

KERR, Estelle Muriel (1897-1971) Canadian

£803	$1494	€1172	Bathing in surf (25x35cm-10x14in) s. board. 2-Mar-4 Ritchie, Toronto #70/R est:2000-2500 (C.D 2000)

KERR, George Cochrane (c.1825-1907) British

Works on paper

£300	$519	€438	Fishing fleet off shore on a stormy day. W/C. 13-Dec-3 Nigel Ward, Hereford #1418/R

KERR, Henry Wright (1857-1936) British

£380	$635	€555	James Sidey in a landscape (127x92cm-50x36in) s. 19-Jun-3 Bonhams, Edinburgh #345

Works on paper

£300	$552	€438	Study of an elderly gentleman (16x12cm-6x5in) init. W/C. 22-Jun-4 Bonhams, Knightsbridge #67
£380	$635	€555	Boy with a donkey (31x23cm-12x9in) init. W/C. 16-Oct-3 Bonhams, Edinburgh #138
£726	$1335	€1060	Portrait of a man. Portrait of a lady (37x27cm-15x11in) s.d.1909 W/C pair. 14-Jun-4 Waddingtons, Toronto #177/R est:800-1000 (C.D 1800)
£900	$1611	€1314	Irish donkey (23x28cm-9x11in) s. W/C. 26-May-4 Sotheby's, Olympia #229/R est:1000-1500
£1000	$1840	€1460	Man in red cap. s. W/C. 25-Mar-4 Bonhams, Edinburgh #364/R est:400-600
£1200	$2208	€1752	Cleric (33x23cm-13x9in) W/C. 28-Jun-4 British Auctioneer #372/R
£2600	$4706	€3796	Old shepherd (30x23cm-12x9in) s. W/C. 19-Apr-4 British Auctioneer #492/R

KERR, Illingsworth Holey (1905-1988) Canadian

£320	$586	€467	Wolf listening (40x30cm-16x12in) s.i.d.1958 board. 1-Jun-4 Hodgins, Calgary #34/R (C.D 800)
£560	$1025	€818	Mud road I (30x40cm-12x16in) s.i.d.1980 board. 1-Jun-4 Hodgins, Calgary #261/R (C.D 1400)
£661	$1197	€965	White rock and fireweed, Storm Mountain (30x41cm-12x16in) mono. s.i.d.1987 verso canvasboard prov. 18-Apr-4 Levis, Calgary #54/R est:1200-1500 (C.D 1600)
£680	$1244	€993	In the Windermere (30x40cm-12x16in) s.i. board. 1-Jun-4 Hodgins, Calgary #168/R (C.D 1700)
£685	$1261	€1000	First snow, foothills (29x40cm-11x16in) mono. i.verso board. 9-Jun-4 Walker's, Ottawa #11/R (C.D 1700)
£811	$1378	€1184	Sumac and stumps (30x41cm-12x16in) mono. s.i.d.1967 verso board prov. 23-Nov-3 Levis, Calgary #55a/R est:2000-2500 (C.D 1800)
£905	$1511	€1321	Alberta roadside (45x60cm-18x24in) mono.i.d.1982. 17-Nov-3 Hodgins, Calgary #329/R est:2500-3000 (C.D 2000)
£960	$1757	€1402	Hills south of Red Deer Lake, September 1979 (40x50cm-16x20in) mono. canvasboard painted 1979. 1-Jun-4 Joyner Waddington, Toronto #138/R est:3000-4000 (C.D 2400)
£1014	$1723	€1480	Journey (76x61cm-30x24in) init. s.i.verso. 27-Nov-3 Heffel, Vancouver #201/R est:1200-1600 (C.D 2250)
£1071	$1843	€1564	Once upon a time (30x40cm-12x16in) mono. canvasboard painted 1985. 2-Dec-3 Joyner Waddington, Toronto #124/R est:2000-3000 (C.D 2400)
£1176	$1965	€1717	October evening, Qu' Appelle Valley (30x40cm-12x16in) mono.i.d.1974 board. 17-Nov-3 Hodgins, Calgary #281/R est:2000-2500 (C.D 2600)
£1216	$2068	€1775	Beaver Flats, Elbow River Forest Reserve (46x61cm-18x24in) mono. s.i.d.1973 verso canvasboard prov. 23-Nov-3 Levis, Calgary #54a/R est:3000-3500 (C.D 2700)
£1464	$2489	€2137	Eagle Ridge, Bancroft, Ontario (45x61cm-18x24in) init. s.i.d.1978 verso board. 27-Nov-3 Heffel, Vancouver #181/R est:1200-1600 (C.D 3250)
£1810	$3023	€2643	Before the combine (55x70cm-22x28in) mono.i.d.1982. 17-Nov-3 Hodgins, Calgary #349/R est:3500-4500 (C.D 4000)
£3571	$6143	€5214	Passing rain, Autumn 1975 (90x120cm-35x47in) mono. painted 1975 prov. 2-Dec-3 Joyner Waddington, Toronto #14/R est:8000-10000 (C.D 8000)
£4072	$6801	€5945	Rangeland nocture (60x90cm-24x35in) mono.i.d.1983. 17-Nov-3 Hodgins, Calgary #73/R est:7000-9000 (C.D 9000)

KERR, Paul (20th C) Irish?

£369	$661	€550	An awkward child (120x40cm-47x16in) s. 31-May-4 Hamilton Osborne King, Dublin #11

KERR, Tiko (1953-) Canadian?

£897	$1480	€1301	Red gondolas (91x183cm-36x72in) i.verso acrylic. 3-Jul-3 Heffel, Vancouver #19/R est:2500-3500 (C.D 2000)

KERR, Tom (1925-) Irish

Works on paper

£240	$446	€350	Misty day, Strangford (33x43cm-13x17in) s. W/C. 3-Mar-4 John Ross, Belfast #189
£450	$774	€657	Out for a walk (23x23cm-9x9in) s. W/C. 3-Dec-3 John Ross, Belfast #176
£480	$797	€701	Winter in the park (25x20cm-10x8in) s. W/C. 1-Oct-3 John Ross, Belfast #65

KERR-LAWSON, James (1865-1939) British

£360	$623	€526	Study of a young girl playing the violin (34x46cm-13x18in) s. 9-Dec-3 Bonhams, Oxford #126
£1600	$2768	€2336	Piazzetta with San Giogio Maggiore, Venice (168x117cm-66x46in) 10-Dec-3 Bonhams, Bury St Edmunds #572/R est:1800-2500

KERSEBOOM, Johann (attrib) (17/18th C) British

£1000	$1790	€1460	Portrait of Hester in brown satin robe with her dog (76x63cm-30x25in) 22-Mar-4 Bonhams & Brooks, Norfolk #197/R est:2000-3000

KERSEY, Laurie (20th C) American

£2168	$3750	€3165	Orchid study (51x41cm-20x16in) s. i.d.2003 stretcher. 10-Dec-3 Bonhams & Butterfields, San Francisco #6343/R est:3000-4000

KERSTING, Georg Friedrich (1785-1847) Danish

£35810	$65533	€52283	Park landscape with spring water (40x33cm-16x13in) init.d.1808 prov. 9-Jun-4 Rasmussen, Copenhagen #1422/R est:500000 (D.KR 400000)

KERTESZ, Andre (1894-1985) American/Hungarian

£3067	$5489	€4600	Untitled (33x49cm-13x19in) s.d.1963 silver print. 13-May-4 Le Mouel, Paris #213/R est:3500-4000

Photographs

£1647	$2750	€2405	Distortion no 40 (9x11cm-4x4in) s. num.PP040-8 verso gelatin silver print exec.1933/1980 lit. 21-Oct-3 Bonhams & Butterfields, San Francisco #1533/R
£1796	$3000	€2622	Distortion no.72 (7x5cm-3x2in) with sig.i.d.1933 verso silver print. 21-Oct-3 Swann Galleries, New York #150/R est:3500-4500
£1808	$3200	€2640	Place du Carrousel, Paris, 1929 (25x19cm-10x7in) d. gelatin silver print. 27-Apr-4 Christie's, Rockefeller NY #269/R est:3000-5000
£1977	$3500	€2886	Washington Square, February, 1966 (25x16cm-10x6in) s.i.d. gelatin silver print. 27-Apr-4 Christie's, Rockefeller NY #270/R est:4000-6000
£2096	$3500	€3060	Armonk (34x26cm-13x10in) s.d.1959 verso gelatin silver print prov.lit. 17-Oct-3 Phillips, New York #267/R est:4000-6000
£2116	$4000	€3089	Bocskay ter, Budapest (19x25cm-7x10in) s.verso gelatin silver print. 17-Feb-4 Christie's, Rockefeller NY #139/R est:3000-5000
£2210	$4000	€3227	The fork, Paris (28x35cm-11x14in) s.d.verso gelatin silver print 1928/printed later prov. 19-Apr-4 Bonhams & Butterfields, San Francisco #427/R est:5000-7000
£2222	$4200	€3244	The Daisy Bar, Montmartre (25x18cm-10x7in) s. verso silver print. 17-Feb-4 Swann Galleries, New York #50/R est:3500-4500
£2222	$4000	€3244	6th Ave (8x10cm-3x4in) s. silver gelatin emulsion print. 24-Apr-4 David Rago, Lambertville #552/R est:1000-2000
£2386	$4200	€3484	Underwater swimmer, Esztergom, Hungary (18x25cm-7x10in) with sig.i.d.1917 verso silver print. 20-May-4 Swann Galleries, New York #297/R est:2500-3500
£2400	$4080	€3504	Carrefour, Blois (20x25cm-8x10in) s.d.verso silver print exec.1930 printed later lit. 19-Nov-3 Sotheby's, Olympia #127/R est:2000-3000
£2515	$4200	€3672	Satiric dancer (35x27cm-14x11in) s.d.1926 verso gelatin silver print printed later prov.lit. 20-Oct-3 Christie's, Rockefeller NY #43/R est:4000-6000
£2733	$4893	€4100	Roof tops (9x10cm-4x4in) mono. mono.d.1947 verso silver print. 13-May-4 Le Mouel, Paris #166/R est:4200-4800
£3000	$5100	€4380	Fork, Paris (28x35cm-11x14in) s.i.d.verso silver print exec.1928 printed later lit. 19-Nov-3 Sotheby's, Olympia #126/R est:3000-5000
£3293	$5500	€4808	Magda Forstner in the doorway of Etienne Beothy's Studio (9x5cm-4x2in) i.d.1926 verso gelatin silver print prov.lit. 20-Oct-3 Christie's, Rockefeller NY #170/R est:7000-9000
£3295	$5800	€4811	Chez mondrian (25x18cm-10x7in) with sig.d.1926 silver print. 20-May-4 Swann Galleries, New York #313/R est:5000-7500
£3500	$5950	€5110	Chez Mondrian, Paris (35x28cm-14x11in) s.d.verso silver print exec.1926 printed later lit. 19-Nov-3 Sotheby's, Olympia #125/R est:2000-3000
£4192	$7000	€6120	Martinique (41x50cm-16x20in) s.i.d.1972 verso gelatin silver print prov.lit. 21-Oct-3 Bonhams & Butterfields, San Francisco #1554
£4336	$7371	€6200	Winter garden, New York (18x25cm-7x10in) s.d. verso silver gelatin lit.exhib. 27-Nov-3 Villa Grisebach, Berlin #1249/R est:3000-3500
£4491	$7500	€6557	New York (24x18cm-9x7in) s. i.d.1962 verso gelatin silver print printed later prov.lit. 20-Oct-3 Christie's, Rockefeller NY #219/R est:3000-5000
£5988	$10000	€8742	Chez Mondrian, Paris (50x37cm-20x15in) s.d.1926/1980s verso gelatin silver print. 20-Oct-3 Christie's, Rockefeller NY #44/R est:8000-10000
£11976	$20000	€17485	Distortion (32x24cm-13x9in) st.sig.i. verso gelatin silver print exec.1933 lit. 17-Oct-3 Phillips, New York #83/R est:20000-30000
£14444	$26000	€21088	Bibliotheque, Paris (27x17cm-11x7in) s.d.1928 gelatin silver print lit. 23-Apr-4 Phillips, New York #72/R est:30000-40000

Prints

£1503	$2600	€2194	Pont des Arts, Paris (36x28cm-14x11in) s.i.verso gelatin silver print. 15-Dec-3 Hindman, Chicago #10/R est:2500-3000

KERTON, Sudjana (1922-1994) Indonesian

£13900	$23212	€20294	Hujan hujanan - fun in the rain (87x70cm-34x28in) s. lit. 26-Oct-3 Christie's, Hong Kong #90/R est:180000-280000 (HK.D 180000)
£15686	$28392	€22902	Fish seller (70x90cm-28x35in) s.d.74 canvas on board. 3-Apr-4 Glerum, Singapore #66/R est:40000-50000 (S.D 48000)
£16340	$29575	€23856	Lahang - palm wine drinker (128x148cm-50x58in) s.d.77 lit. 4-Apr-4 Sotheby's, Singapore #150/R est:40000-60000 (S.D 50000)
£23938	$39977	€34949	Pagi di kampung - village morning (96x69cm-38x27in) s.d.1983 i.verso. 26-Oct-3 Christie's, Hong Kong #91/R est:200000-300000 (HK.D 310000)
£31250	$52187	€45625	Makan Siang (65x95cm-26x37in) s.d.82 prov. 12-Oct-3 Sotheby's, Singapore #149/R est:70000-90000 (S.D 90000)
£67568	$121622	€98649	Kuda lumping - flat horse trance dance (110x140cm-43x55in) s.d.90 exhib.lit. 25-Apr-4 Christie's, Hong Kong #580/R est:380000-550000 (HK.D 950000)
£114379	$207026	€166993	Sisingaan (128x150cm-50x59in) s.d.90 lit. 4-Apr-4 Sotheby's, Singapore #148/R est:80000-120000 (S.D 350000)

KERTON, Sudjana (attrib) (1922-1994) Indonesian

£6950	$11606	€10147	Mambaca buku - girl reading a book (99x70cm-39x28in) s. board. 26-Oct-3 Christie's, Hong Kong #70/R est:110000-180000 (HK.D 90000)

KESSANLIS, Nikos (1930-) Greek

£5000	$8750	€7300	Mur (65x100cm-26x39in) s. s.i.d.1961 verso oil mixed media. 16-Dec-3 Bonhams, New Bond Street #145/R est:4500-6000

KESSEL, Ferdinand van (1648-1696) Flemish

£8453	$14793	€12000	Singerie, scene de corps de garde (21x30cm-8x12in) panel. 18-Dec-3 Tajan, Paris #30/R est:6000-8000

KESSEL, Ferdinand van (attrib) (1648-1696) Flemish

£2956	$5292	€4316	Allegory of school (35x30cm-14x12in) 26-May-4 AB Stockholms Auktionsverk #2506/R est:40000-60000 (S.KR 40000)

KESSEL, Ferdinand van (studio) (1648-1696) Flemish

£9396	$17476	€14000	Singes jouant au backgammon (35x43cm-14x17in) panel. 8-Mar-4 Artcurial Briest, Paris #21/R est:5000

KESSEL, Ferdinand van (style) (1648-1696) Flemish

£6000	$11040	€9000	Singes jouant au jacquet (11x16cm-4x6in) copper on panel. 14-Jun-4 Horta, Bruxelles #172/R est:5000-7000

KESSEL, Jan van (attrib) (17th C) Flemish

£7383	$13584	€11000	Virgin and Child surrounded by flowers (106x90cm-42x35in) prov. 24-Mar-4 Dorotheum, Vienna #363/R est:12000-16000

KESSEL, Jan van (circle) (17th C) Flemish
£7955 $14000 €11614 Monkey feast (27x36cm-11x14in) copper. 19-May-4 Doyle, New York #6065/R est:8000-12000

KESSEL, Jan van (studio) (17th C) Flemish
£11409 $20423 €17000 Dogs and monkey (24x31cm-9x12in) copper. 26-May-4 Porro, Milan #8/R est:12000-15000

KESSEL, Jan van I (1626-1679) Flemish
£24828 $41214 €36000 Landscape with birds (28x33cm-11x13in) 30-Sep-3 Ansorena, Madrid #57/R est:30000
£428571 $681429 €630000 Butterflies and insects (16x23cm-6x9in) s.d.1659 copper. 23-Mar-3 Mercier & Cie, Lille #147/R est:30000-45000
Works on paper
£30000 $50100 €43800 Grasshopper, moths, butterflies, insects, larva (10x23cm-4x9in) s.d.1664 gouache on vellum prov. 18-Jun-3 John Nicholson, Haslemere #603/R est:5000-10000

KESSEL, Jan van I (attrib) (1626-1679) Flemish
£26846 $48054 €40000 Table with fish and vegetables. Basket with grapes and peaches (15x21cm-6x8in) copper pair. 26-May-4 Porro, Milan #6/R est:50000-60000

KESSEL, Jan van I (style) (1626-1679) Flemish
£5822 $9897 €8500 Still life with fruit, and nuts on plates, a knife and jug on a ledge (12x18cm-5x7in) copper. 4-Nov-3 Sotheby's, Amsterdam #97/R est:8000-12000

KESSEL, Jan van II (1654-1708) Flemish
£1197 $2071 €1700 Vierge a l'enfant entre saint Gregoire et sainte Catherine (64x48cm-25x19in) panel. 10-Dec-3 Neret-Minet, Paris #69 est:3000-4000
£13158 $24211 €20000 Still life with bowl of fruit and little monkey (23x28cm-9x11in) panel octagonal. 25-Jun-4 Piasa, Paris #13/R est:20000-30000
£20134 $37450 €30000 Still life of fruit (12x18cm-5x7in) s. copper. 2-Mar-4 Ansorena, Madrid #281/R est:30000
£21769 $34612 €32000 Two cats playing with fish. Dog, cat and lobster (23x31cm-9x12in) copper pair prov. 23-Mar-3 Mercier & Cie, Lille #187/R est:38000-40000
Works on paper
£5634 $9859 €8000 Allegorie de l'Eau (19x25cm-7x10in) s. gouache prov. 17-Dec-3 Piasa, Paris #35/R est:8000-10000

KESSEL, Jan van II (attrib) (1654-1708) Flemish
£1197 $2071 €1700 Vierge a l'enfant entre Saint Gregoire et Sainte Catherine (64x48cm-25x19in) panel. 10-Dec-3 Remi Ader, Paris #69 est:3000-4000
£13889 $23194 €20000 Still lives of vegetables (21x30cm-8x12in) copper pair. 22-Oct-3 Finarte Semenzato, Milan #40/R
£21528 $35951 €31000 Still life with flowers and hens (21x30cm-8x12in) copper. 22-Oct-3 Finarte Semenzato, Milan #39/R

KESSEL, Jan van II (studio) (1654-1708) Flemish
£28000 $48440 €40880 Monkey with a melon, artichoke and other fruit and vegetable, dog nearby (16x22cm-6x9in) copper. 10-Dec-3 Bonhams, New Bond Street #31/R est:10000-15000

KESSELL, J E (1915-1978) British
£700 $1260 €1022 Harbour with fishing boats and church tower beyond (85x91cm-33x36in) s.d.59. 22-Apr-4 Locke & England, Leamington Spa #115/R

KESSLER, A (20th C) German
£4392 $7730 €6500 Landscape in the Hegau region (50x75cm-20x30in) s.d.1947 board. 22-May-4 Sigalas, Stuttgart #434/R est:150

KESSLER, August (1826-1906) German
£921 $1695 €1400 Shady wood (34x47cm-13x19in) s.d.1855. 24-Jun-4 Dr Fritz Nagel, Stuttgart #721/R
£1408 $2254 €2000 Romantic wooded landscape (34x47cm-13x19in) s.d.1872. 19-Sep-3 Sigalas, Stuttgart #387/R est:2500

KESSLER, Carl (1876-1968) German
Works on paper
£442 $791 €650 Winter morning near Kitzbuhl (53x73cm-21x29in) s. w/C. 17-Mar-4 Neumeister, Munich #298/R
£800 $1448 €1200 Hospitz Saint Christoph (68x98cm-27x39in) s.i. W/C. 30-Mar-4 Gioffredo, Nice #377
£972 $1585 €1400 Hospice St Christoph am Arlberg in winter (34x48cm-13x19in) s.i. W/C. 24-Sep-3 Neumeister, Munich #282
£1067 $1941 €1600 Kitzbuhl with Salve (36x50cm-14x20in) s.i. i. verso W/C. 30-Jun-4 Neumeister, Munich #417/R est:1500
£1769 $3166 €2600 Early spring in Kitbuhl (36x51cm-14x20in) s.i. i. verso W/C over pencil. 17-Mar-4 Neumeister, Munich #296/R est:2500

KESSLER, Jon (1957-) American
Sculpture
£1892 $3500 €2762 X-Ray (51x37x32cm-20x15x13in) s.d.1987 num.5/6 verso metal various objects. 12-Feb-4 Sotheby's, New York #307/R est:2500-3500

KESSLER, Joseph (1826-1887) Austrian
Works on paper
£1457 $2666 €2200 Young Italian woman at fountain (41x25cm-16x10in) s.d.6 Jan 1864 W/C. 8-Apr-4 Dorotheum, Vienna #163/R est:1000-1200

KESSLER, Max (1897-?) Swiss
£295 $490 €428 Solothurn (54x78cm-21x31in) s.d.1936. 13-Jun-3 Zofingen, Switzerland #2904 (S.FR 650)
£814 $1385 €1188 Fete a Paris - trois musiciens (29x23cm-11x9in) s.i.d.1921. 28-Nov-3 Zofingen, Switzerland #3038/R est:1000 (S.FR 1800)

KESSLER, Stephan (1622-1700) Austrian
£21477 $39517 €32000 Heliodor being driven out of Temple (162x227cm-64x89in) 24-Mar-4 Dorotheum, Vienna #218/R est:15000-20000

KESSLY, Istvan (19/20th C) Hungarian
£582 $990 €850 Bather by woodland lake (120x160cm-47x63in) s. 5-Nov-3 Hugo Ruef, Munich #1036

KESTER, Lenard (1917-1997) American
£345 $650 €504 East point (83x108cm-33x43in) s. board. 22-Feb-4 Bonhams & Butterfields, Los Angeles #7009

KESTING, Edmund (1892-1970) German
£3333 $5967 €5000 Houses (16x16cm-6x6in) s.d. tempera W/C over pencil board prov. 14-May-4 Ketterer, Munich #37/R est:5000-7000
£22378 $38042 €32000 Composition in black (72x70cm-28x28in) s.d.22 s.i. stretcher oil tempera hessian prov.exhib. 26-Nov-3 Lempertz, Koln #758/R est:35000-45000
Works on paper
£375 $626 €540 Dalmatian fisher woman (46x24cm-18x9in) s.d. s. verso W/C over pencil. 25-Oct-3 Dr Lehr, Berlin #264/R
£660 $1102 €950 Untitled - woodland path in autumn (39x55cm-15x22in) s. mixed media transparent paper on board. 25-Oct-3 Dr Lehr, Berlin #267/R
£694 $1160 €1000 Polish landscape (51x72cm-20x28in) s. i.d. verso gouache board. 25-Oct-3 Dr Lehr, Berlin #265/R

KESZEBI, S L (19/20th C) Hungarian
£1000 $1850 €1460 Bathers (120x160cm-47x63in) s. 14-Jul-4 Christie's, Kensington #1125/R est:1000-1500

KET, Dick (1902-1940) Dutch
£486 $812 €700 Still life with coffee cup (30x40cm-12x16in) s.d.1931. 21-Oct-3 Campo & Campo, Antwerp #558

KETCHAM, Susan Merrill (1841-1930) American
£1081 $2000 €1578 Impressionist river landscape leading to a village (64x76cm-25x30in) s. 24-Jan-4 Jeffery Burchard, Florida #104/R

KETHULLE, Eugene de la (fl.1846) French
£5517 $10207 €8000 La conduite du troupeau sur fond de paysage avec cascade et montagne (71x94cm-28x37in) s. i.verso. 16-Feb-4 Horta, Bruxelles #173/R est:8500-12000

KETTEMANN, Erwin (1897-1971) German
£247 $450 €361 Alpine winter landscape (99x69cm-39x27in) s. 19-Jun-4 Jackson's, Cedar Falls #59/R
£306 $498 €440 Early spring near Berchtesgaden with Watzmann and Hochkalter (60x80cm-24x31in) s.i. i. verso. 25-Sep-3 Neumeister, Munich #2805/R
£324 $518 €460 Winter evening in Wiessee with Wallberg (60x80cm-24x31in) s. 18-Sep-3 Rieber, Stuttgart #1324/R
£336 $617 €500 Summer in Valstal (80x100cm-31x39in) s. i. verso. 24-Mar-4 Hugo Ruef, Munich #1012
£340 $619 €500 Winter evening near Oberstdorf, Spielmannsau (80x101cm-31x40in) s.i. i. verso. 4-Feb-4 Neumeister, Munich #710/R
£350 $594 €500 Gross Glockner from the Franz Joseph Hut (80x90cm-31x35in) s.i. 22-Nov-3 Arnold, Frankfurt #563/R
£350 $601 €500 Early spring in Spielmannsau near Oberstdorf (60x80cm-24x31in) s.i. i. verso. 4-Dec-3 Neumeister, Munich #2782
£367 $660 €550 Winter evening in Ehrwald/Tir with Wetterstein (61x80cm-24x31in) s.i. 22-Apr-4 Allgauer, Kempten #3604/R
£379 $702 €550 Winter evening near St Moritz (69x98cm-27x39in) s. 12-Feb-4 Weidler, Nurnberg #352/R
£414 $691 €600 Early spring near Wallgau with Karwendel (80x100cm-31x39in) s. 9-Jul-3 Hugo Ruef, Munich #117
£436 $803 €650 Chiemsee fishing (11x15cm-4x6in) s. panel. 24-Mar-4 Hugo Ruef, Munich #1013
£490 $832 €700 Stream in snowy Alps near Cortina, Dolomites (70x100cm-28x39in) s. 20-Nov-3 Van Ham, Cologne #1680
£590 $962 €850 Winter evening near Bischofswiesen with Hohem Goll (60x80cm-24x31in) s.i. i. verso. 25-Sep-3 Neumeister, Munich #2804
£600 $1080 €900 Early spring in Spielmannsau b/Oberstdorf (60x80cm-24x31in) s.i. i. verso lit. 22-Apr-4 Allgauer, Kempten #3603/R
£699 $1203 €1000 Winter evening in the Ramsau with Hohem Goll (68x100cm-27x39in) s. 4-Dec-3 Schopman, Hamburg #630/R
£775 $1356 €1100 Winter evening in Fraisertal near Kufstein (89x108cm-35x43in) s.i.verso. 19-Dec-3 Dorotheum, Vienna #93/R
£839 $1427 €1200 Winter morning looking towards the Hochkalter (71x100cm-28x39in) s.i. 29-Nov-3 Sigalas, Stuttgart #285/R
£867 $1560 €1300 Winter evening near Lermoos (80x110cm-31x43in) s.i. i. verso. 21-Apr-4 Neumeister, Munich #2663/R
£933 $1708 €1400 Winter evening in Valstal (80x97cm-31x38in) s.i. i.verso. 5-Jun-4 Arnold, Frankfurt #624/R
£1067 $1920 €1600 Winter morning in Lofer - Austria (70x100cm-28x39in) s.i. verso. 21-Apr-4 Dorotheum, Vienna #98/R est:1600-2000
£1197 $2095 €1700 Kitzbuhel-Kaiser mountains (71x100cm-28x39in) s. 19-Dec-3 Dorotheum, Vienna #74/R est:1500-2500
£1197 $2095 €1700 Reiter near Kitzbuhel with Kaiser mountains (60x80cm-24x31in) s.i.verso. 19-Dec-3 Dorotheum, Vienna #84/R est:1600-2000
£1408 $2437 €2000 View of Zugspitze from Murnauer Moor (79x120cm-31x47in) s.i.verso. 10-Dec-3 Dorotheum, Vienna #254/R est:2000-2400
£1667 $2783 €2400 Winter evening near Cortina (95x125cm-37x49in) s.i. i. verso. 22-Oct-3 Neumeister, Munich #719/R est:1000

KETTER, Clay (1961-) Swedish
£2103 $3785 €3070 Trace study (48x49cm-19x19in) s.d.1998 verso house paint on laminate chipboard prov.exhib.lit. 26-Apr-4 Bukowskis, Stockholm #466/R est:15000-20000 (S.KR 29000)

KETTLE, Tilly (1735-1786) British
£5278 $9500 €7706 Portrait of gentleman in India (129x103cm-51x41in) 23-Jan-4 Christie's, Rockefeller NY #136/R est:8000-12000
£18000 $33120 €26280 Self portrait wearing blue coat with gold buttons (74x62cm-29x24in) s. prov.lit. 26-Mar-4 Sotheby's, London #19/R est:7000-10000

KEUDELL, Marie von (1836-1918) German
£2676 $4630 €3800 Gardasee (39x67cm-15x26in) i.verso. 10-Dec-3 Dorotheum, Vienna #1/R est:4500-5000

KEULEMANS, Johannes Gerardus (1842-1912) Dutch
Works on paper
£280 $468 €406 Pigeons in a parkland setting (48x62cm-19x24in) mono. W/C. 14-Jul-3 Trembath Welch, Great Dunmow #551
£320 $586 €467 Sparrow hawk (25x20cm-10x8in) s. W/C htd bodycol. 27-Jan-4 Bonhams, Knightsbridge #123

KEULEYAN-LAFON, Jean (1886-1973) French
£297 $550 €434 Bay (38x46cm-15x18in) s. 13-Mar-4 Susanin's, Chicago #6116/R
£300 $477 €438 The boat (50x99cm-20x39in) s. prov. 12-Sep-3 Jacobs & Hunt, Petersfield #298/R
£407 $700 €594 Seascape (20x25cm-8x10in) s. d.1955 verso board. 7-Dec-3 Treadway Gallery, Cincinnati #617/R

KEULLER, Vital (1866-1945) Belgian
£280 $476 €400 Le jardin de la ferme (40x60cm-16x24in) s. panel. 18-Nov-3 Vanderkindere, Brussels #206
£302 $562 €450 Flowery bush (40x60cm-16x24in) s.d.40. 8-Mar-4 Bernaerts, Antwerp #754
£336 $621 €500 Le mat de charge de la ferme (40x60cm-16x24in) s.d.32 panel. 15-Mar-4 Horta, Bruxelles #276
£385 $642 €550 View of forest (80x100cm-31x39in) s.d.41. 11-Oct-3 De Vuyst, Lokeren #205/R
£517 $957 €750 Pont sur le Semois (60x80cm-24x31in) s.d.36. 19-Jan-4 Horta, Bruxelles #449
£620 $1035 €905 Woodland study (74x48cm-29x19in) s.d. board. 26-Oct-3 Tayler & Fletcher, Cheltenham #3

KEUN, Hendrik (1738-1788) Dutch
£4730 $8324 €7000 Haaelem, view from the south east (33x36cm-13x14in) s. panel. 18-May-4 Sotheby's, Amsterdam #119/R est:8000-12000
£9247 $15719 €13500 View of the Weerdpoort with the Domtorne beyond (49x65cm-19x26in) s. 4-Nov-3 Sotheby's, Amsterdam #105/R est:10000-15000

KEUNEN, Alexis (1921-1990) Belgian
£490 $832 €700 Les amants (27x19cm-11x7in) s.d.IX 59 s.i.d.verso. 23-Nov-3 Cornette de St.Cyr, Paris #171/R

KEUS, Adriaan (1875-1955) Dutch
£342 $582 €500 Meadow land with trees (45x37cm-18x15in) s. 5-Nov-3 Vendue Huis, Gravenhage #152/R

KEVER, Gerard (1956-) German
£1867 $3416 €2800 Heart attack III (172x145cm-68x57in) s.d.Okt. 80 verso acrylic cotton prov. 4-Jun-4 Lempertz, Koln #236/R est:1500

KEVER, Jacob Simon Hendrik (1854-1922) Dutch
£467 $849 €700 Yellow flower in a vase (61x51cm-24x20in) s. 1-Jul-4 Christie's, Amsterdam #448/R
£592 $1089 €900 A colourful bouquet (44x40cm-17x16in) s. 22-Jun-4 Christie's, Amsterdam #173/R
£822 $1397 €1200 Mother and child in a basket (10x14cm-4x6in) s. panel. 5-Nov-3 Vendue Huis, Gravenhage #112/R
£1398 $2600 €2041 Reading the news (79x63cm-31x25in) s. 5-Mar-4 Skinner, Boston #233/R est:3000-5000
£1579 $2905 €2400 Children reading in an interior (45x56cm-18x22in) s. 22-Jun-4 Christie's, Amsterdam #274/R est:1800-2200
£2041 $3714 €3000 Teatime in a rural interior (46x56cm-18x22in) s.d.79 prov. 3-Feb-4 Christie's, Amsterdam #188/R est:3000-5000
£2329 $3959 €3400 Interior of farmhouse (41x53cm-16x21in) s. prov. 5-Nov-3 Vendue Huis, Gravenhage #113/R est:3000-4000
£4000 $7200 €6000 Careful sip (106x78cm-42x31in) s. 21-Apr-4 Christie's, Amsterdam #154/R est:6000-8000

KEVORKIAN, Jean (1933-) French?
£1268 $2193 €1800 Paysage de Vendee (73x92cm-29x36in) s. 14-Dec-3 Eric Pillon, Calais #195/R

KEWILL, D H M (19th C) ?
Works on paper
£867 $1577 €1300 Calzano, Lake Iseo (28x65cm-11x26in) s.d.1867 W/C. 12-Jul-4 Il Ponte, Milan #437

KEWLEY, Brian David (1933-) Australian
£697 $1101 €1018 South Melbourne beach (60x75cm-24x30in) s.d.78 board. 2-Sep-3 Deutscher-Menzies, Melbourne #383/R est:200-300 (A.D 1700)
£732 $1310 €1069 St Kilda Beach (59x74cm-23x29in) s. board. 10-May-4 Joel, Victoria #361 est:1800-2200 (A.D 1800)
£1220 $1915 €1781 City and bay (120x135cm-47x53in) s.d.78. 27-Aug-3 Christie's, Sydney #676/R est:3000-5000 (A.D 3000)

KEY, Adriaen Thomasz (1544-1590) Flemish
£8621 $15862 €12587 Portrait of man in black jacket (46x34cm-18x13in) d.1568 panel prov.exhib.lit. 26-Mar-4 Koller, Zurich #3015/R est:20000-30000 (S.FR 20000)
£15000 $25500 €21900 Portrait of a lady wearing a black coat and white ruff, holding a book (104x74cm-41x29in) mono. panel. 30-Oct-3 Sotheby's, Olympia #96/R est:5000-7000

KEY, Geoffrey (1946-) British
£1800 $3294 €2628 Albert Square - Manchester (66x46cm-26x18in) s.d.72 board. 6-Apr-4 Capes Dunn, Manchester #839/R
Works on paper
£360 $666 €526 Evening trees (15x22cm-6x9in) s.d.82 mixed media. 14-Jul-4 Bonhams, Chester #368
£360 $666 €526 Head and hands (25x18cm-10x7in) indis.s. d.82 pen ink bodycol. 14-Jul-4 Bonhams, Chester #370

KEY, Henry E (19th C) British?
£600 $1074 €876 Going fishing (51x77cm-20x30in) prov. 27-May-4 Christie's, Kensington #158/R

KEY, John Ross (1837-1920) American
£924 $1700 €1349 Sylan landscape with figure boating on river, figure in woods (28x46cm-11x18in) s. 9-Jun-4 Alderfer's, Hatfield #378 est:1500-2000
£3784 $7000 €5525 Blue Ridge Mountains (61x76cm-24x30in) s. 13-Mar-4 DeFina, Austinburg #864/R est:3000-5000
£11050 $20000 €16133 Washington DC, from Arlington, Virginia (91x152cm-36x60in) s.i. 31-Mar-4 Sotheby's, New York #73/R est:10000-15000
£18824 $32000 €27483 Sierra Falls (60x103cm-24x41in) s.d.74. 29-Oct-3 Christie's, Los Angeles #34/R est:20000-30000

KEY, Willem (1520-1568) Flemish
£83333 $150000 €121666 Venus and Cupid (94x129cm-37x51in) panel prov.lit. 22-Jan-4 Sotheby's, New York #34/R est:150000-250000

KEY, Willem (circle) (1520-1568) Flemish
£6000 $10380 €8760 Portrait of a lady wearing a black dress with a white collar and headdress (79x59cm-31x23in) d.1560 panel prov. 9-Dec-3 Sotheby's, Olympia #330/R est:6000-8000

KEYES, Bernard M (1898-1973) American
£391 $700 €571 Connoisseru (62x51cm-24x20in) 18-Mar-4 Skinner, Bolton #773/R

KEYL, Friedrich Wilhelm (attrib) (1823-1871) German
£900 $1530 €1314 Portraits of William Pierce Hayward and his daughter, Jane Pierce Hayward (46x60cm-18x24in) 28-Oct-3 Henry Adams, Chichester #435/R

KEYMEULEN, Émile (1840-1882) Belgian
£367 $656 €550 Nature morte aux fleurs (30x40cm-12x16in) s. wood. 16-May-4 MonsAntic, Maisieres #433
£959 $1630 €1400 Landscape with shepherd and flock (59x49cm-23x19in) s. panel. 5-Nov-3 Vendue Huis, Gravenhage #44/R

KEYSER, Albert de (1829-1890) Belgian
£276 $500 €420 Anvers (25x38cm-10x15in) s.i. i.verso panel. 19-Apr-4 Glerum, Amsterdam #100
£2200 $3938 €3300 Vue d'Anvers du cote de l'Escaut (68x93cm-27x37in) s. s.i.verso. 15-May-4 De Vuyst, Lokeren #428/R est:3000-3600

KEYSER, Auguste Paul de (19th C) Belgian
£367 $664 €550 Bonheur familial (67x53cm-26x21in) s. panel. 30-Mar-4 Campo, Vlaamse Kaai #33

KEYSER, Elisabeth (1851-1898) Swedish
£729 $1341 €1094 Cleaning the nets (54x65cm-21x26in) s. 14-Jun-4 Lilla Bukowskis, Stockholm #87 (S.KR 10000)
£776 $1389 €1133 Still life of summer flowers (55x38cm-22x15in) init.d.1894. 26-May-4 AB Stockholms Auktionsverk #2285/R (S.KR 10500)

KEYSER, Emil (1846-1923) Swiss
£2848 $5183 €4300 Cockchafer collecting from a mountain summit (85x65cm-33x26in) s. canvas on canvas. 19-Jun-4 Bergmann, Erlangen #785 est:1900

KEYSER, Ephraim (1850-1937) American
Sculpture
£4032 $7500 €5887 Boy with Mandolin (137cm-54in) s.d.96 num.20/6 base dark brown pat bronze. 3-Mar-4 Christie's, Rockefeller NY #1/R est:4000-6000
£5650 $10000 €8249 Figure of a cavalier (52cm-20in) s. copper pat bronze Cast Nelli Roma. 2-May-4 Bonhams & Butterfields, San Francisco #1525/R est:4000-6000

KEYSER, Jef de (?) Belgian
Sculpture
£1241 $2297 €1800 Joueur de cithare (74x127x62cm-29x50x24in) s. brown pat bronze. 16-Feb-4 Horta, Bruxelles #60 est:1800-2000

KEYSER, N de (1813-1887) Flemish
£2721 $4871 €4000 Dame au tambourin (63x48cm-25x19in) 22-Mar-4 Amberes, Antwerp #188/R

KEYSER, Nicaise de (1813-1887) Flemish
£1399 $2378 €2000 Sapho et son modele (28x22cm-11x9in) mono.i. 18-Nov-3 Vanderkindere, Brussels #172 est:1500-2500

KEYSER, Raoul de (1933-) Belgian
£14667 $26253 €22000 Visp (120x90cm-47x35in) s.i.d.1968 verso. 15-May-4 De Vuyst, Lokeren #494/R est:10000-12500

KEYSER, Robert G (1924-) American
£269 $450 €393 Forms by a green sea (53x66cm-21x26in) s.d.55 s.on stretcher exhib. 15-Nov-3 Sloans & Kenyon, Bethesda #100/R

KEYSER, Thomas de (1596-1667) Dutch
£14474 $26632 €22000 Portrait of man in black suit with white collar and cuffs holding hat (63x47cm-25x19in) i. 24-Jun-4 Dr Fritz Nagel, Stuttgart #600/R est:30000

KEYT, George (1901-1993) Indian
£2582 $4750 €3770 Sunbather (60x96cm-24x38in) s.d.63 prov. 24-Mar-4 Sotheby's, New York #162/R est:5000-7000
£7000 $11690 €10220 Landscape with a house (75x67cm-30x26in) s. 14-Oct-3 Sotheby's, London #129/R est:6000-8000
£7000 $11690 €10220 Portrait of Russell's soul in the guise of a Kandyan peasant (32x44cm-13x17in) s. s.verso. 14-Oct-3 Sotheby's, London #131/R est:4000-6000
£8000 $13360 €11680 Nayika (61x48cm-24x19in) s. 14-Oct-3 Sotheby's, London #132/R est:6000-8000
£9000 $15030 €13140 Nayika III (69x47cm-27x19in) s. 14-Oct-3 Sotheby's, London #130/R est:6000-8000

KHAIMOV, Iakov (1914-1991) Russian
£4000 $6800 €5840 Pigeons on the windowsill (79x99cm-31x39in) s.d.1950. 19-Nov-3 Sotheby's, London #236/R est:4000-6000

KHAKKAR, Bhupen (1934-) Indian
£2989 $5500 €4364 In Rishikesh (48x67cm-19x26in) s.d. acrylic. 25-Mar-4 Christie's, Rockefeller NY #233/R est:6000-8000
Works on paper
£4620 $8500 €6745 Pichwai (105x96cm-41x38in) s.d. W/C pencil. 25-Mar-4 Christie's, Rockefeller NY #230/R est:7000-9000
£4620 $8500 €6745 Three figures (101x99cm-40x39in) s.d. W/C pencil. 25-Mar-4 Christie's, Rockefeller NY #232/R est:7000-9000

KHANINE, Alexandre (1955-) Russian
£333 $607 €500 Apres la soiree (81x65cm-32x26in) s. painted 2002. 5-Jul-4 Millon & Associes, Paris #281
£347 $631 €520 Aurore (70x110cm-28x43in) s. painted 2004. 5-Jul-4 Millon & Associes, Paris #280
£400 $720 €600 Sweet apples (80x120cm-31x47in) s. 26-Apr-4 Millon & Associes, Paris #246/R
£467 $849 €700 Soir tiede (100x100cm-39x39in) s. painted 2003. 5-Jul-4 Millon & Associes, Paris #276
£500 $910 €750 Pastoral scene (108x101cm-43x40in) s. painted 2004. 5-Jul-4 Millon & Associes, Paris #277
£520 $946 €780 Sauna (102x112cm-40x44in) s. painted 2004. 5-Jul-4 Millon & Associes, Paris #279/R
£700 $1260 €1050 After the rain (65x120cm-26x47in) s. s.d.1999 verso. 26-Apr-4 Millon & Associes, Paris #244/R

KHANNA, Krishen (1925-) Indian
£5978 $11000 €8728 La carelle (61x46cm-24x18in) s.i.d.11th Aug 1981 verso. 25-Mar-4 Christie's, Rockefeller NY #213/R est:6000-8000
£21739 $40000 €31739 Pieta (131x212cm-52x83in) s.i.verso acrylic. 25-Mar-4 Christie's, Rockefeller NY #211/R est:25000-30000

KHARITONOV, Nikolai Vasilievich (1880-1944) Russian
£7000 $12530 €10220 Portrait of a gypsy girl (76x54cm-30x21in) s. 26-May-4 Sotheby's, London #304/R est:7500-9000

KHARLAMOV, Alexei (1842-c.1920) Russian
Works on paper
£6500 $11635 €9490 Portrait of a young lady (48x40cm-19x16in) s. chl. 26-May-4 Sotheby's, Olympia #362/R est:2000-3000

KHIMOUNE, Rachid (1953-) Algerian
Sculpture
£1879 $3439 €2800 Adonis (170x134cm-67x53in) bas-relief in polyester resin. 7-Jul-4 Artcurial Briest, Paris #290 est:3000-3500

KHLOMOV, Nestor (1928-1988) Russian
£288 $530 €420 Sketch (25x26cm-10x10in) cardboard painted 1950's. 27-Mar-4 Shishkin Gallery, Moscow #63/R
£299 $550 €437 Nothern country (35x50cm-14x20in) cardboard painted 1960's. 27-Mar-4 Shishkin Gallery, Moscow #61/R
£435 $800 €635 In the north country (99x74cm-39x29in) tempera paper painted 1950's. 27-Mar-4 Shishkin Gallery, Moscow #62/R
£543 $1000 €793 Old Moscow (26x32cm-10x13in) painted 1960's. 27-Mar-4 Shishkin Gallery, Moscow #64/R
Works on paper
£326 $600 €476 Moscow river (53x66cm-21x26in) W/C marker painted 1950's. 27-Mar-4 Shishkin Gallery, Moscow #58/R
£598 $1100 €873 In the Moscow of the XVIII century (49x29cm-19x11in) mixed media painted 1950's. 27-Mar-4 Shishkin Gallery, Moscow #65/R

KHMELEVA, Elena (20th C) Russian
£340 $619 €500 Terrasse en Crimee. s. 8-Feb-4 Lesieur & Le Bars, Le Havre #54
£442 $805 €650 Les barsois. s. 8-Feb-4 Lesieur & Le Bars, Le Havre #53
£503 $916 €740 Les cavaliers. s. 8-Feb-4 Lesieur & Le Bars, Le Havre #55
£544 $990 €800 Les goelands. s. 8-Feb-4 Lesieur & Le Bars, Le Havre #56

KHMELUK, Vassyl (1903-) Russian
£360 $601 €526 Russian still life (51x64cm-20x25in) 21-Oct-3 Gorringes, Lewes #2114
£374 $670 €550 Bouquet de fleurs (41x33cm-16x13in) s.d.66. 19-Mar-4 Millon & Associes, Paris #104
£374 $670 €550 Petite fille. s. panel. 19-Mar-4 Millon & Associes, Paris #106/R
£403 $745 €600 Grand nu couche (60x119cm-24x47in) s. isorel. 15-Mar-4 Claude Boisgirard, Paris #64

KHNOPFF, Fernand (1858-1921) Belgian
Sculpture
£32000 $58240 €46720 Hypnos (21cm-8in) dark brown pat bronze marble plinth prov.lit. 17-Jun-4 Christie's, London #64/R est:20000-30000
Works on paper
£8725 $15443 €13000 Etude de femme (12x10cm-5x4in) s. dr. 27-Apr-4 Campo, Vlaamse Kaai #475/R est:15000-20000
£20000 $36400 €29200 Study for L'idee de Justice (19x15cm-7x6in) s. pencil crayon. 17-Jun-4 Christie's, London #17/R est:20000-30000
£67000 $123280 €97820 Portrait de femme (12x7cm-5x3in) mono. col crayon chk paper on card prov.lit. 22-Jun-4 Sotheby's, London #416/R est:30000-40000

KHOA PHAM (20th C) ?
£472 $789 €680 Sans titre (114x149cm-45x59in) s.d.1988 verso acrylic collage prov. 25-Oct-3 Cornette de St.Cyr, Paris #447

KHODASEVICH, Valentina (1894-1970) Russian
Works on paper
£2083 $3479 €3000 Projet de costume d'arlequin pour Arlequin Squelette (33x23cm-13x9in) s.i.d.1921 W/C lead pencil. 21-Oct-3 Artcurial Briest, Paris #78/R est:3000-4000

KHOURY, Michael (?) Canadian?
£335 $576 €489 Still life with iris, roses and fruit (35x27cm-14x11in) s. prov. 2-Dec-3 Joyner Waddington, Toronto #271/R (C.D 750)
£400 $732 €584 Still life with fruits and roses (40x50cm-16x20in) s. prov. 1-Jun-4 Joyner Waddington, Toronto #294/R (C.D 1000)

KHRUTSKY, Ivan (1810-1885) Russian
£17361 $28299 €25000 Still life with flowers and citrus fruit (47x73cm-19x29in) s.d.1839. 24-Sep-3 Neumeister, Munich #405/R est:15000

KIAERSKOU, F (1805-1891) Danish
£284 $508 €415 Hilly landscape with country road (23x32cm-9x13in) panel. 12-Jan-4 Rasmussen, Vejle #77 (D.KR 3000)
£331 $572 €483 Windy weather (34x48cm-13x19in) 9-Dec-3 Rasmussen, Copenhagen #1700/R (D.KR 3500)
£356 $581 €520 Landscape from Kalovig (39x49cm-15x19in) init. 27-Sep-3 Rasmussen, Havnen #2142/R (D.KR 3800)
£359 $643 €524 Evening landscape with figures chatting (24x32cm-9x13in) init. 12-Jan-4 Rasmussen, Vejle #83 (D.KR 3800)
£375 $645 €548 Hintern-See in Tyrol (32x39cm-13x15in) s.d.1878. 3-Dec-3 Museumsbygningen, Copenhagen #186 (D.KR 4000)
£424 $721 €619 Mountain landscape with figures and cabin (24x31cm-9x12in) panel. 10-Nov-3 Rasmussen, Vejle #358/R (D.KR 4600)
£425 $761 €621 Landscape from Kalovig with figures (39x49cm-15x19in) mono. 12-Jan-4 Rasmussen, Vejle #84 (D.KR 4500)
£493 $887 €720 Mountain landscape with waterfall (30x24cm-12x9in) s. panel. 24-Apr-4 Rasmussen, Havnen #2315/R (D.KR 5500)
£561 $1004 €819 Landscape from southern Bavaria (36x49cm-14x19in) s.d.1874. 10-May-4 Rasmussen, Vejle #211/R (D.KR 6200)
£608 $1034 €888 Landscape with view of fjord, Nibe (22x29cm-9x11in) init. 10-Nov-3 Rasmussen, Vejle #59/R (D.KR 6600)
£962 $1750 €1405 Summer's day in the country with horse and figures (65x83cm-26x33in) 7-Feb-4 Rasmussen, Havnen #2283/R (D.KR 10500)
£1164 $2130 €1699 Coastal landscape in summer with boats (20x28cm-8x11in) init.d.1880. 7-Jun-4 Museumsbygningen, Copenhagen #4 est:4000 (D.KR 13000)
£1890 $3384 €2759 Coastal landscape with trees and woman walking, Denmark (99x144cm-39x57in) s.d.1872. 12-Jan-4 Rasmussen, Vejle #79/R est:25000 (D.KR 20000)

KIAERSKOU, Frederik (1805-1891) Danish
£548 $932 €800 Landscape with mountain lake and trees (59x85cm-23x33in) s. 5-Nov-3 Vendue Huis, Gravenhage #351/R
£738 $1381 €1100 Ziller valley (26x35cm-10x14in) d.1873 verso panel. 24-Feb-4 Dorotheum, Vienna #132/R
£1067 $1931 €1600 Burg Stolzenfels (33x45cm-13x18in) s.d.1852. 1-Apr-4 Van Ham, Cologne #1480/R est:1500
£1121 $1772 €1625 View across Rosenborg Garden (21x29cm-8x11in) s.d.1854 panel prov. 2-Sep-3 Rasmussen, Copenhagen #1883/R est:5000 (D.KR 12000)
£1197 $2071 €1700 Extensive landscape with lake (25x32cm-10x13in) s.d.1849 board. 11-Dec-3 Dr Fritz Nagel, Stuttgart #528/R est:1400

£2069 $3704 €3021 View from the coast at old Humlebeck towards Helsingborg (36x48cm-14x19in) s.d.1854. 26-May-4 AB Stockholms Auktionsverk #2406/R est:30000-35000 (S.KR 28000)
£3925 $6202 €5691 Hilly landscape with lake in foreground, Jylland (140x198cm-55x78in) s.d.1868. 2-Sep-3 Rasmussen, Copenhagen #1680/R est:30000-40000 (D.KR 42000)

KIAKSHUK (1886-1966) North American
Works on paper
£1351 $2297 €1972 Ancient meeting (63x48cm-25x19in) stencil. 3-Nov-3 Waddingtons, Toronto #266/R est:1500-2000 (C.D 3000)
£1577 $2680 €2302 Driving moulting geese into stone pens (48x61cm-19x24in) sealskin stencil. 3-Nov-3 Waddingtons, Toronto #282/R est:2500-3500 (C.D 3500)
£2117 $3599 €3091 Eskimo wrestling two spirits (46x57cm-18x22in) stencil. 3-Nov-3 Waddingtons, Toronto #265/R est:1500-2000 (C.D 4700)

KIBEL, Jeremy (1972-) Australian?
£340 $579 €496 Untitled (43x39cm-17x15in) init.d.93 composition board. 26-Nov-3 Deutscher-Menzies, Melbourne #206/R (A.D 800)
Works on paper
£413 $764 €603 Eclipse - black sun (128x29cm-50x11in) s.i.d.93 synthetic polymer chl on cloth. 10-Mar-4 Deutscher-Menzies, Melbourne #244a/R est:1200-1800 (A.D 1000)

KIBEL, Wolf (1903-1938) Polish
£2890 $5173 €4219 Flowers in a vase (60x47cm-24x19in) s. pastel paper on board. 31-May-4 Stephan Welz, Johannesburg #514/R est:15000-20000 (SA.R 35000)
Works on paper
£1197 $2034 €1748 Flowers in a vase (60x47cm-24x19in) s. pastel paper on board. 4-Nov-3 Stephan Welz, Johannesburg #713/R est:8000-12000 (SA.R 14000)

KIBIGER, Julius (1903-) German
£352 $563 €500 Composition (40x60cm-16x24in) s. i.d.1976 verso panel lit. 19-Sep-3 Karlheinz Kaupp, Staufen #2035

KIBWANGA, Mwenze (?) ?
£759 $1366 €1100 Combat d'animaux (49x69cm-19x27in) s. oil paper laid down. 20-Jan-4 Galerie Moderne, Brussels #271

KICCO (1969-) Italian
£352 $585 €500 Paradiso artificiale (40x40cm-16x16in) s.i.d.2002 verso paint silicone photo plastic panel. 14-Jun-3 Meeting Art, Vercelli #343

KICK, Cornelis (attrib) (1635-1681) Dutch
£53333 $98133 €80000 Bouquet de fleurs dans un vase sur un entablement (62x46cm-24x18in) 11-Jun-4 Maigret, Paris #43/R est:30000-40000

KICK, Simon (1603-1652) Dutch
£12329 $20959 €18000 Soldiers in a barn playing cards (75x105cm-30x41in) panel prov.lit. 4-Nov-3 Sotheby's, Amsterdam #13/R est:20000-30000
£28017 $51552 €40905 Gendarme and party (91x75cm-36x30in) panel prov.exhib.lit. 26-Mar-4 Koller, Zurich #3052/R est:15000-20000 (S.FR 65000)

KIDD, Joseph Bartholomew (1806-1889) British
£14535 $25000 €21221 Baltimore oriole (66x52cm-26x20in) painted c.1831-33 after John James Audobon. 3-Dec-3 Sotheby's, New York #126/R est:40000-60000

KIDD, Steven R (1911-1987) American
£234 $375 €342 Advertising piece created for Abbott Labs in the 40s (53x46cm-21x18in) s.d.1952 verso tempera board. 20-Sep-3 Susanin's, Chicago #5007/R

KIDD, William (attrib) (1790-1863) British
£1171 $1991 €1710 The cut finger (30x41cm-12x16in) bears name.i.d.1840 verso panel. 23-Nov-3 Levis, Calgary #205/R est:1400-1600 (C.D 2600)

KIDDER, Harvey (1918-) American
Works on paper
£254 $425 €371 View in the Adirondacks (58x84cm-23x33in) s. W/C. 29-Jun-3 William Jenack, New York #247

KIDERLIN, Johanna (20th C) German
£374 $670 €550 Summer view of Fussen (49x60cm-19x24in) s. board lit. 20-Mar-4 Bergmann, Erlangen #1163

KIEDERICH, Ludwig (1885-?) German
£294 $532 €429 Wagon in a rural landscape (58x79cm-23x31in) s. 30-Mar-4 Stephan Welz, Johannesburg #414 est:3500-5000 (SA.R 3500)

KIEFER, Anselm (1945-) German
£27933 $50000 €40782 Des Malers atelier (50x61cm-20x24in) acrylic W/C gouache painted c.1980-81 prov. 12-May-4 Christie's, Rockefeller NY #478/R est:50000-70000
£50000 $91000 €73000 Johannis Nacht, midsummer night (100x140cm-39x55in) acrylic emulsion fern shellac cardboard lead prov.exhib. 6-Feb-4 Sotheby's, London #136/R est:60000-80000
£81006 $145000 €118269 Weichsel, weichsel, weisse weichsel ach was trauerst du so sehr (130x160cm-51x63in) i. oil sand wood shavings chl prov.exhib.lit. 14-May-4 Phillips, New York #208/R est:100000-150000
£131737 $220000 €192336 Ygdrasil (146x118cm-57x46in) i. prov. 13-Nov-3 Sotheby's, New York #546/R est:100000-150000
£206704 $370000 €301788 Palette (290x400cm-114x157in) acrylic oil coarsely woven canvas painted 1981 prov.exhib.lit. 13-May-4 Phillips, New York #32/R est:250000-350000
Photographs
£65868 $110000 €96167 Elisabeth von Oesterreich (172x132cm-68x52in) s.d.1977/91 verso resin on gelatin silver print prov. 12-Nov-3 Christie's, Rockefeller NY #590/R est:60000-80000
£85000 $141950 €124100 Yggdrasil (211x102cm-83x40in) i. black white photo branch chl lead board prov. 22-Oct-3 Christie's, London #95/R est:80000-120000
Sculpture
£22455 $37500 €32784 Dein goldenes haar, margarete (58x82cm-23x32in) i. gouache straw pencil glue photo prov. 13-Nov-3 Sotheby's, New York #151/R est:28000-35000
£59880 $100000 €87425 Katarina (175x206x173cm-69x81x68in) steel plaster fabric terracotta shellac pigment prov.lit. 12-Nov-3 Christie's, Rockefeller NY #588/R est:120000-180000
Works on paper
£3297 $6000 €4814 Aufstrebender vogel - soaring bird (49x29cm-19x11in) W/C newsprint executed 1985 prov. 29-Jun-4 Sotheby's, New York #566/R est:5000-7000
£7186 $12000 €10492 Die donauquelle (29x20cm-11x8in) mixed media oil sand burlap canvas on book edition of 25 prov. 13-Nov-3 Sotheby's, New York #553/R est:12000-18000
£20423 $35331 €29000 Portrait (58x76cm-23x30in) i. s.d.81 verso mixed media over photograph prov. 9-Dec-3 Artcurial Briest, Paris #435/R est:20000-25000
£72000 $132480 €105120 Der Eingergorene (101x72cm-40x28in) s.i.d.91 verso dried foliage roses photo on lead prov.exhib. 24-Jun-4 Sotheby's, London #279/R est:60000-80000

KIEFF, Grediaga Antonio (1936-) Spanish
Sculpture
£949 $1500 €1386 Evaluation (43cm-17in) s.num.3/5 bronze marble plinth. 27-Jul-3 Simpson's, Houston #330

KIEFHABER, Christoph (20th C) Austrian
Works on paper
£308 $524 €450 Habban/Jemen (55x68cm-22x27in) s.d W/C oil chk. 5-Nov-3 Dorotheum, Vienna #45/R

KIEFT, Jan (1798-1870) Dutch
£699 $1168 €1000 Mother and child (59x48cm-23x19in) s.indis.d. panel. 30-Jun-3 Sotheby's, Amsterdam #156

KIELDRUP, A E (1826-1869) Danish
£332 $531 €485 Coastal landscape, Vierwaldstatter See 7 sep.63 (27x38cm-11x15in) init. 22-Sep-3 Rasmussen, Vejle #287/R (D.KR 3500)
£403 $737 €588 Norwegian landscape with houses (19x31cm-7x12in) s. verso prov. 9-Jun-4 Rasmussen, Copenhagen #1691/R (D.KR 4500)
£507 $922 €761 Summer landscape with mill, Denmark (30x42cm-12x17in) init.d.47. 19-Jun-4 Rasmussen, Havnen #2293 (D.KR 5700)
£667 $1213 €1001 Mother and daughter picking berries (48x58cm-19x23in) mono.d.58. 19-Jun-4 Rasmussen, Havnen #2245/R (D.KR 7500)
£1258 $2340 €1837 Marienborg at sunset (52x78cm-20x31in) mono.d.62. 2-Mar-4 Rasmussen, Copenhagen #1385/R est:15000 (D.KR 14000)

KIELDRUP, Anton Edvard (1826-1869) Danish
£2056 $3249 €2981 Houses and industry in a Norwegian village (31x42cm-12x17in) init. 2-Sep-3 Rasmussen, Copenhagen #1611/R est:15000 (D.KR 22000)
£3300 $5478 €4818 Sunset (80x118cm-31x46in) mono. 1-Oct-3 Sotheby's, Olympia #261/R est:3000-4000
£3925 $6202 €5691 Wooded landscape with footbridge across river (105x140cm-41x55in) s.d.1862. 2-Sep-3 Rasmussen, Copenhagen #1773/R est:30000-40000 (D.KR 42000)
£7188 $13369 €10494 Sunlit country road in Trorod (118x158cm-46x62in) s. 2-Mar-4 Rasmussen, Copenhagen #1338/R est:20000-30000 (D.KR 80000)

KIELHOLZ, Heiner (20th C) Swiss?
Works on paper
£452 $769 €660 Art of the pocket calculator (31x23cm-12x9in) s.i.d.1975 W/C prov.exhib. 25-Nov-3 Germann, Zurich #820 (S.FR 1000)

KIELLAND, Kirstine (1882-1979) Norwegian
£332 $531 €485 View of Paris, seen from Notre Dame (54x88cm-21x35in) s. 22-Sep-3 Rasmussen, Vejle #124 (D.KR 3500)

KIELLAND, Kitty (1843-1914) Norwegian
£11976 $20359 €17485 Landscape (63x103cm-25x41in) s. 19-Nov-3 Grev Wedels Plass, Oslo #41/R est:200000 (N.KR 140000)
£21386 $36356 €31224 Landscape with peat bog (51x96cm-20x38in) s.d.1911. 19-Nov-3 Grev Wedels Plass, Oslo #40/R est:200000 (N.KR 250000)
£46114 $77011 €67326 Summer night in Sandviken (101x151cm-40x59in) s.d.1891 i.verso lit. 13-Oct-3 Blomqvist, Oslo #270/R est:600000-800000 (N.KR 540000)

KIELLERUP, Theodor Julius (1818-1850) Danish
£1896 $3033 €2768 Nature morte with duck, pheasant and hare (76x106cm-30x42in) s. 22-Sep-3 Rasmussen, Vejle #95/R est:20000-25000 (D.KR 20000)

KIELWEIN, Ernst (1864-1902) German
£1154 $1927 €1650 Midday meal (50x60cm-20x24in) s. 10-Oct-3 Winterberg, Heidelberg #617/R est:2400

KIEN, Josef (1903-) German
£4138 $6910 €6000 Scenery (70x110cm-28x43in) s. s.i.verso. 13-Nov-3 Neumeister, Munich #567/R est:6000-6500

KIENBUSCH, William (1914-1980) American
Works on paper
£1734 $3000 €2532 Fog, Oceanville Quarry (69x89cm-27x35in) s.d.55 casein paper on board prov. 15-Dec-3 Hindman, Chicago #18/R est:1000-1500

KIENER, Robert (1866-1945) Swiss
£259 $463 €378 Gurnigel (46x55cm-18x22in) s. i. verso board. 12-May-4 Dobiaschofsky, Bern #693/R (S.FR 600)

KIENERK, Giorgio (1869-1948) Italian
£2254 $3899 €3200 Filicchi Garden, Fauglia (18x26cm-7x10in) s.d.31 i.verso board. 9-Dec-3 Pandolfini, Florence #109/R est:2500-3000
Works on paper
£1987 $3616 €3000 Portrait of Pio Gatteschi (46x27cm-18x11in) s.d.1901 pastel exhib. 21-Jun-4 Pandolfini, Florence #217/R est:3200-3500

KIENHOLZ, Edward (1927-1994) American
Sculpture
£1200 $2208 €1800 Econo-can (30x22x24cm-12x9x9in) s.i. num.52/53 radio jerrican prov. 9-Jun-4 Artcurial Briest, Paris #493/R est:2000-2500
£4500 $8190 €6570 Reliefs (60x60cm-24x24in) s.verso mixed media melamine three parts exec.1969-73 prov.exhib. 4-Feb-4 Sotheby's, Olympia #155/R est:5000-7000
£26946 $45000 €39341 Spit in the ocean (97x184x43cm-38x72x17in) s.i.d.1984 verso mixed media assemblage prov.exhib. 13-Nov-3 Sotheby's, New York #287/R est:30000-40000
Works on paper
£1000 $1810 €1460 Untitled - for dollar 151.00 (31x41cm-12x16in) s.d.70 W/C pencil ink stamp. 1-Apr-4 Christie's, Kensington #283/R est:1000-1500
£1259 $2140 €1800 For 185 dollars (29x39cm-11x15in) s.d.70 stamp on W/C. 27-Nov-3 Lempertz, Koln #208/R est:2000

KIENHOLZ, Edward and Nancy (20th C) American
Sculpture
£1538 $2800 €2245 Double cross (53x33x37cm-21x13x15in) s. mixed media plexiglass. 29-Jun-4 Sotheby's, New York #464/R est:3000-4000
£1923 $3500 €2808 Same old shoe (27x24x42cm-11x9x17in) sig. num.33 mixed media. 29-Jun-4 Sotheby's, New York #465/R est:4000-6000

KIENMAYER, Franz (20th C) German
£385 $662 €550 Rider in the Andes (69x54cm-27x21in) s. i.verso. 5-Dec-3 Bolland & Marotz, Bremen #729/R
£2536 $3931 €3703 By the river (100x130cm-39x51in) s. 6-Oct-2 Sotheby's, Singapore #29/R est:7000-9000 (S.D 7000)

KIERS, George Laurens (1838-1916) Dutch
£1293 $2159 €1888 Shipping in port (62x85cm-24x33in) s. 20-Oct-3 Stephan Welz, Johannesburg #186/R est:7000-10000 (SA.R 15000)
£2500 $4475 €3650 Preparing to set sail (64x84cm-25x33in) s. 26-May-4 Christie's, Kensington #660/R est:3000-5000
£8667 $15600 €13000 View of the Oosterdok, Amsterdam (44x50cm-17x20in) s. 20-Apr-4 Sotheby's, Amsterdam #46a/R est:8000-12000

KIERZKOWSKI, Bronislaw (1924-1993) Polish
Works on paper
£2232 $3839 €3259 Composition 30 (81x65cm-32x26in) s.d.1963 collage oil canvas. 4-Dec-3 Agra, Warsaw #30/R est:5000 (P.Z 15000)

KIES, Helmut (1933-) Austrian
£400 $736 €600 Lansdcape with tree (21x10cm-8x4in) s.i.d.79 canvas on panel. 9-Jun-4 Dorotheum, Salzburg #712/R

KIESEL, Conrad (1846-1921) German
£878 $1572 €1300 Woman with fan (39x24cm-15x9in) s.i.d.March 25th 1896 lit. 8-May-4 Schloss Ahlden, Ahlden #716/R
£1736 $2743 €2500 Yellow dress (60x78cm-24x31in) s. 2-Sep-3 Christie's, Amsterdam #179/R est:3000-5000
£1765 $3000 €2577 Grafin Marie Donhoff, later Furstin Bulow (27x20cm-11x8in) s.i. panel i. exhib. 28-Nov-3 Zofingen, Switzerland #2617/R est:3500 (S.FR 3900)
£5114 $9000 €7466 Portrait of a lady, thought to be the artist's wife (54x43cm-21x17in) s. 18-May-4 Bonhams & Butterfields, San Francisco #103/R est:10000-15000
£90000 $154800 €131400 Mandolin player (106x134cm-42x53in) s. 3-Dec-3 Christie's, London #79/R est:100000-120000

KIESEL, Conrad (attrib) (1846-1921) German
£802 $1475 €1203 Woman in profile (47x37cm-19x15in) s. 14-Jun-4 Lilla Bukowskis, Stockholm #508 (S.KR 11000)

KIESEWETTER, Johan Willem (attrib) (1883-1951) Dutch
£234 $425 €351 Peasants repairing a boat near a farmhouse with windmill (51x71cm-20x28in) indis sig. 19-Jun-4 Harvey Clar, Oakland #2180

KIESLER, Frederic (1896-?) American
Sculpture
£8649 $16000 €12628 Bird (74x76x76cm-29x30x30in) green pat bronze wood 4 parts exec c.1960 prov. 12-Feb-4 Sotheby's, New York #205/R est:1800-2200

KIESS, Emil (1930-) German
£867 $1551 €1300 27/37 (26x36cm-10x14in) s.d.58 verso canvas on board. 15-May-4 Van Ham, Cologne #713/R est:1000

KIESSLING, Heinz (1915-) German
£355 $592 €500 Cow in barn (37x48cm-15x19in) s. canvas on panel. 21-Jun-3 Hans Stahl, Hamburg #69

KIETAIBL-HOFFMANN, Anna (1877-?) Austrian
£467 $840 €700 In the garden (50x60cm-20x24in) s. 21-Apr-4 Dorotheum, Vienna #102/R

KIETZ, Ernst Benedikt (1815-1892) German
Works on paper
£972 $1585 €1400 Portrait of princes and princesses from Saxony (35x38cm-14x15in) s.d.94 chk htd white. 25-Sep-3 Dr Fritz Nagel, Stuttgart #1316/R

KIFF, Ken (1935-2001) British
Works on paper
£3600 $6444 €5256 Two people walking separately (31x26cm-12x10in) s. W/C gouache prov. 16-Mar-4 Bonhams, New Bond Street #96/R est:2000-3000

KIGHT, Louis (?) ?
£320 $592 €467 River landscape at sunset (27x18cm-11x7in) s. board. 13-Jan-4 Bonhams, Knightsbridge #21

KIHLE, Harald (1905-1997) Norwegian
£400 $669 €584 Rider (16x22cm-6x9in) s. panel. 17-Nov-3 Blomqvist, Lysaker #1161/R (N.KR 4800)
£447 $823 €653 To the Big boy (24x19cm-9x7in) init.d.43 i. verso study. 10-Jun-4 Grev Wedels Plass, Oslo #198/R (N.KR 5500)
£515 $901 €752 Deciduous thicket, Vaa in Rauland (26x32cm-10x13in) s. s.i.d.1942 verso panel. 16-Dec-3 Grev Wedels Plass, Oslo #184/R (N.KR 6000)
£515 $901 €752 Summer landscape, Vaa in Rauland (28x35cm-11x14in) s.d.44 s.i.d. verso panel. 16-Dec-3 Grev Wedels Plass, Oslo #187/R (N.KR 6000)
£584 $975 €853 Botn valley (16x20cm-6x8in) s. panel painted c.1955. 17-Nov-3 Blomqvist, Lysaker #1160/R (N.KR 7000)
£601 $1052 €877 Hazy sunshine, Holsbu (38x46cm-15x18in) s.d.47 s.i.d.Easter 1947 verso panel. 16-Dec-3 Grev Wedels Plass, Oslo #185/R (N.KR 7000)
£987 $1727 €1441 Lake landscape, Totakvatn (25x32cm-10x13in) init. s.i.d.43 verso. 16-Dec-3 Grev Wedels Plass, Oslo #186/R (N.KR 11500)
£1030 $1803 €1504 Old farmyard in Mo in Telemark (26x32cm-10x13in) s.d.68 s.i.d.verso panel. 16-Dec-3 Grev Wedels Plass, Oslo #356/R est:20000-30000 (N.KR 12000)
£1220 $2232 €1781 Dark overcast weather (28x35cm-11x14in) mono.d.46 s.i.d.1946 verso panel. 7-Jun-4 Blomqvist, Oslo #423/R est:16000-18000 (N.KR 15000)
£1789 $3077 €2612 Rain showers in Setesdalheiene (55x46cm-22x18in) s. panel. 8-Dec-3 Blomqvist, Oslo #508/R est:20000-25000 (N.KR 21000)
£1967 $3345 €2872 At the horsefield at Dalen in Telemark (28x35cm-11x14in) s. s.i.d.60 verso panel. 19-Nov-3 Grev Wedels Plass, Oslo #85/R est:20000-30000 (N.KR 23000)
£2129 $3663 €3108 Summer in Setesdalsheiene (38x46cm-15x18in) s. panel. 8-Dec-3 Blomqvist, Oslo #509/R est:18000-20000 (N.KR 25000)
£2555 $4395 €3730 Winter landscape, Raasjoen, Hakadal (26x32cm-10x13in) s.i.d.Mars 1953 panel. 8-Dec-3 Blomqvist, Oslo #534/R est:25000-28000 (N.KR 30000)

KIITSU, Suzuki (1796-1858) Japanese
Works on paper
£400 $668 €584 Grapevine (121x27cm-48x11in) s. ink. 12-Nov-3 Christie's, London #24

KIITSU, Suzuki (attrib) (1796-1858) Japanese
Works on paper
£1196 $2200 €1746 Shuttle and plum branch (27x40cm-11x16in) s. ink hanging scroll sold with a scroll after Hakuin Ekaku. 23-Mar-4 Christie's, Rockefeller NY #113 est:1500-2000

KIJNO, Ladislas (1921-) French
£319 $533 €450 Composition (29x15cm-11x6in) s. crumpled paper. 20-Jun-3 Drouot Estimations, Paris #218
£369 $687 €550 Icone pour un voyant (61x50cm-24x20in) s. s.i.d.1978 verso acrylic. 3-Mar-4 Artcurial Briest, Paris #464
£369 $687 €550 Icone pour un voyant (61x50cm-24x20in) s. s.i.d.1978 acrylic. 3-Mar-4 Artcurial Briest, Paris #465
£403 $749 €600 Untitled (66x52cm-26x20in) s.d.1959 paper. 3-Mar-4 Tajan, Paris #217
£521 $870 €750 Sans titre (27x45cm-11x18in) s.d.1956 peinture panel double-sided. 25-Oct-3 Cornette de St.Cyr, Paris #727
£537 $999 €800 Icone pour un voyant (65x54cm-26x21in) s. s.i.d.1978 verso acrylic. 3-Mar-4 Artcurial Briest, Paris #463
£541 $952 €800 Untitled (29x23cm-11x9in) s. crumpled paper prov. 18-May-4 Tajan, Paris #48/R
£604 $1069 €900 Composition (61x38cm-24x15in) s.d.57 s.i.d.verso crumpled paper on canvas prov. 28-Apr-4 Artcurial Briest, Paris #283
£629 $1051 €900 Composition (78x60cm-31x24in) s. paint. 25-Jun-3 Blanchet, Paris #139/R
£629 $1083 €900 Composition (39x39cm-15x15in) s. acrylic cardboard. 4-Dec-3 Piasa, Paris #93/R
£667 $1200 €1000 Serie de miroirs (42x33cm-17x13in) s. s.i.d.1973 verso prov. 25-Apr-4 Versailles Encheres #40
£872 $1623 €1300 L'Art d'Aimer d'Ovide (100x80cm-39x31in) s. i.d.1982 verso acrylic. 3-Mar-4 Tajan, Paris #234 est:1000-1500
£872 $1544 €1300 Composition (90x63cm-35x25in) s. acrylic glycerol paint crumpled paper. 28-Apr-4 Artcurial Briest, Paris #286a est:1500-2000
£957 $1599 €1350 Composition (39x81cm-15x32in) s.d.1956. 20-Jun-3 Drouot Estimations, Paris #217
£1007 $1782 €1500 Stele (86x44cm-34x17in) s.d.65 glycerol paint. 28-Apr-4 Artcurial Briest, Paris #285/R est:1500-2000
£1074 $1901 €1600 Untitled (66x80cm-26x31in) s. acrylic crumpled paper prov. 28-Apr-4 Artcurial Briest, Paris #284 est:1500-2000
£1074 $1901 €1600 Composition (76x64cm-30x25in) s. acrylic glycerol paint crumpled paper painted c.1980. 28-Apr-4 Artcurial Briest, Paris #286 est:1500-2000

£1200	$2160	€1800	Composition (118x90cm-46x35in) s.d.1970. 26-Apr-4 Tajan, Paris #214 est:2000-2500
£1200	$2160	€1800	Composition rouge, blanc et noir (131x99cm-52x39in) s. s.i.d.1970 verso. 26-Apr-4 Tajan, Paris #215 est:2000-2500
£1200	$2160	€1800	Composition (93x134cm-37x53in) s. prov. 25-Apr-4 Versailles Encheres #11 est:1500-1800
£1216	$2299	€1800	Retour de chine (130x96cm-51x38in) s. 21-Feb-4 Cornette de St.Cyr, Paris #316/R est:4000-5000
£1250	$2088	€1800	Composition (59x47cm-23x19in) s. acrylic creased paper. 21-Oct-3 Artcurial Briest, Paris #411 est:1200-1500
£1275	$2334	€1900	Composition pour Igor Stravinsky (114x80cm-45x31in) s. s.i.d.87 verso acrylic paper on canvas prov. 7-Jul-4 Artcurial Briest, Paris #291 est:2000-3000
£1316	$2197	€1895	Retour de Chine, Serie des - Cavaliers eclabousses (129x97cm-51x38in) s. i.d.1984 verso acrylic. 21-Oct-3 Artcurial Briest, Paris #410/R est:2000-2500
£1329	$2219	€1900	Image pour Isadora Duncan (116x89cm-46x35in) s. s.i.d.1975 verso. 25-Jun-3 Blanchet, Paris #137/R
£1333	$2400	€2000	Hommage a la mere d'Andrei Roublev (131x97cm-52x38in) s. s.i.verso acrylic. 24-Apr-4 Cornette de St.Cyr, Paris #589/R est:2000
£1333	$2400	€2000	Composition (81x65cm-32x26in) s.d.1958 paper on canvas prov. 25-Apr-4 Versailles Encheres #41 est:1500-1800
£1419	$2497	€2100	Composition (131x90cm-52x35in) s. s.d.1962 verso prov. 18-May-4 Tajan, Paris #47/R est:2500-3000
£1466	$2698	€2200	Untitled (100x73cm-39x29in) s.d.1967 verso acrylic crumpled paper prov. 9-Jun-4 Artcurial Briest, Paris #471 est:1500-2000
£2416	$4446	€3600	Variations sur le jazz (116x89cm-46x35in) s.d.1960. 24-Mar-4 Joron-Derem, Paris #178/R est:4000-5000
£4895	$8322	€7000	Les elements mecaniques d'apres Leger (196x154cm-77x61in) s. s.i.d.1969 verso prov.exhib.lit. 25-Nov-3 Tajan, Paris #20/R est:5000-6000
£9524	$15143	€14000	Hommage to Roublev (81x64cm-32x25in) s. i.d.73 verso. 23-Mar-3 Mercier & Cie, Lille #290 est:2000-2500
Works on paper			
£347	$580	€500	Composition (36x27cm-14x11in) glycerol spray crumpled paper. 21-Oct-3 Artcurial Briest, Paris #662
£352	$609	€500	Composition (20x13cm-8x5in) s. mixed media crumpled paper. 14-Dec-3 Versailles Encheres #4
£372	$665	€550	Untitled (32x21cm-13x8in) s. mixed media paper on canvas. 4-May-4 Calmels Cohen, Paris #257
£395	$726	€600	Miroirs et blasons (55x46cm-22x18in) mixed media on canvas. 22-Jun-4 Chassaing Rivet, Toulouse #304
£403	$749	€600	Composition (36x21cm-14x8in) s.d.60 W/C gouache ink. 3-Mar-4 Artcurial Briest, Paris #466
£414	$757	€600	Hommage a Andrei Roublev (28x20cm-11x8in) s.d.73 crumpled paper. 1-Feb-4 Feletin, Province #141
£414	$757	€600	Hommage a Andrei Roublev (28x20cm-11x8in) s.d.1973 verso mixed media crumpled paper. 1-Feb-4 Feletin, Province #142
£493	$863	€700	Neroda (108x68cm-43x27in) s. crumpled paper. 16-Dec-3 Claude Aguttes, Neuilly #44/R
£556	$878	€800	Composition (62x54cm-24x21in) s. mixed media. 27-Apr-3 Versailles Encheres #16
£667	$1227	€1000	Composition abstraite (87x65cm-34x26in) s. 10-Jun-4 Camard, Paris #92
£667	$1227	€1000	Composition sur fond jaune, bleu, rouge et vert (45x35cm-18x14in) s. 10-Jun-4 Camard, Paris #93
£667	$1227	€1000	Composition abstraite (41x33cm-16x13in) s. mixed media. 10-Jun-4 Camard, Paris #94
£667	$1227	€1000	Composition sur fond mastic et mauve (83x61cm-33x24in) s. 10-Jun-4 Camard, Paris #96/R
£700	$1288	€1050	Composition (53x39cm-21x15in) s. 10-Jun-4 Camard, Paris #97/R
£719	$1223	€1050	Composition (47x44cm-19x17in) s. mixed media. 9-Nov-3 Eric Pillon, Calais #260/R
£800	$1472	€1200	Interferences des figuiers (50x65cm-20x26in) s.d.58 W/C crumpled paper on canvas prov.lit. 9-Jun-4 Artcurial Briest, Paris #472
£805	$1498	€1200	Untitled. s. mixed media. 8-Mar-4 Rieunier, Paris #180/R
£909	$1564	€1300	Untitled (102x76cm-40x30in) s. mixed media on torn paper. 2-Dec-3 Calmels Cohen, Paris #95/R
£921	$1695	€1400	Composition (109x83cm-43x33in) s. mixed media prov. 27-Jun-4 Versailles Encheres #36/R
£967	$1740	€1450	Composition (55x65cm-22x26in) s.d.1958 mixed media paper on canvas. 25-Apr-4 Versailles Encheres #10
£1027	$1747	€1500	Composition (70x55cm-28x22in) s. mixed media. 8-Nov-3 Gerard, Besancon #18
£1733	$3189	€2600	Composition (154x194cm-61x76in) s. mixed media canvas on panel. 10-Jun-4 Camard, Paris #95/R est:2500-3000
£2148	$3802	€3200	Untitled (113x82cm-44x32in) s. mixed media paper on canvas. 28-Apr-4 Artcurial Briest, Paris #282/R est:3500-4000
£6000	$11040	€9000	Composition (130x162cm-51x64in) s.d.1962 mixed media canvas prov.lit. 9-Jun-4 Artcurial Briest, Paris #470/R est:6000-8000

KIKOINE, Michel (1892-1968) Russian

£1793	$3228	€2600	Portrait of Monsieur Barrey (61x50cm-24x20in) s. painted c.1930 lit. 25-Jan-4 Chayette & Cheval, Paris #175/R est:2000-3000
£1947	$3621	€2900	Paysage au maisons (26x46cm-10x18in) s. cardboard on panel lit. 2-Mar-4 Artcurial Briest, Paris #176/R est:3000-4000
£2069	$3828	€3000	Maison dans la foret (80x60cm-31x24in) s. 11-Feb-4 Beaussant & Lefèvre, Paris #200/R est:3500-4000
£2098	$3566	€3000	Bouquet de fleurs (62x46cm-24x18in) s. 23-Nov-3 Cornette de St.Cyr, Paris #610/R est:5000-6000
£2282	$4039	€3400	Paysage aux toits rouges (38x46cm-15x18in) s. painted c.1950. 27-Apr-4 Artcurial Briest, Paris #152/R est:3000-4000
£2797	$4671	€4000	Vase de fleurs (65x46cm-26x18in) s. 29-Jun-3 Eric Pillon, Calais #260/R
£3087	$5526	€4600	Fruits et fleurs (80x65cm-31x26in) s. prov.lit. 25-May-4 Chambelland & Giafferi, Paris #70/R est:3000-4000
£4966	$8292	€7200	Vue sur la vallee (65x54cm-26x21in) s. 17-Nov-3 Claude Boisgirard, Paris #45/R est:5000-6000
£5035	$8408	€7200	Landscape (50x61cm-20x24in) s. 29-Jun-3 Eric Pillon, Calais #257/R
£5517	$9931	€8000	Bouquet of flowers in an interior (81x65cm-32x26in) s. lit. 25-Jan-4 Chayette & Cheval, Paris #161/R est:8000-10000
£9718	$16813	€13800	Trois baigneuses (81x65cm-32x26in) s. prov.lit. 15-Dec-3 Marc Kohn, Paris #103/R est:14000-18000
Works on paper			
£298	$545	€450	Sentier en bordure d'un village (25x37cm-10x15in) s. W/C. 7-Apr-4 Piasa, Paris #152
£329	$605	€500	Paysage aux vaches (27x39cm-11x15in) s.s.verso W/C graphite. 25-Jun-4 Millon & Associes, Paris #186
£390	$651	€550	Scene de village (28x36cm-11x14in) s. gouache chl graphite pen. 14-Oct-3 Millon & Associes, Paris #88/R
£537	$983	€800	Paysage de bord de mer (31x45cm-12x18in) s. gouache. 7-Jul-4 Artcurial Briest, Paris #105
£867	$1577	€1300	Maisons au bord de chemin (26x36cm-10x14in) s. W/C. 4-Jul-4 Eric Pillon, Calais #126/R

KILBERT, Robert P (20th C) American

£234	$425	€342	Farm pond with ducks (25x20cm-10x8in) s. board. 19-Jun-4 Jackson's, Cedar Falls #35/R
£549	$1000	€802	Forest interior with stream (46x56cm-18x22in) s. board. 19-Jun-4 Jackson's, Cedar Falls #23/R

KILBOURNE, Samuel A (1836-1881) American

£426	$750	€622	Landscape with sluice (30x20cm-12x8in) s. 23-May-4 William Jenack, New York #374

KILBURN, Joyce (1884-?) British

£600	$1020	€876	Portrait of a young lady, Dolly (41x31cm-16x12in) s.d.21 i.verso. 19-Nov-3 Tennants, Leyburn #1170 est:300-500

KILBURN, William Edward (19th C) British

Photographs			
£6500	$11440	€9490	Sir Joseph Dalton Hooker. daguerrotype prov. 19-May-4 Christie's, London #6/R est:6000-8000

KILBURNE, George Goodwin (1839-1924) British

£6000	$10320	€8760	Recital. Welcome advances (24x16cm-9x6in) s. panel pair. 4-Dec-3 Bonhams, Edinburgh #10/R est:1200-1800
£9500	$17100	€13870	To crown the feast (60x90cm-24x35in) prov. 21-Apr-4 Cheffins, Cambridge #489/R est:10000-15000
£14000	$26040	€20440	Her first appearance (81x112cm-32x44in) s. prov. 4-Mar-4 Christie's, Kensington #611/R est:7000-10000
£18000	$33120	€26280	Hopeless case (77x117cm-30x46in) s. prov. 11-Jun-4 Christie's, London #182/R est:8000-12000
Works on paper			
£350	$557	€511	Portrait of a maid reading a book, next to an open bookcase (18x10cm-7x4in) s. W/C. 9-Sep-3 Peter Francis, Wales #60/R
£440	$788	€642	A cavalier (22x13cm-9x5in) s.d.1874 W/C bodycol. 25-May-4 Bonhams, Knightsbridge #203/R
£480	$782	€696	Puritan's daughter (17x14cm-7x6in) init. W/C. 23-Sep-3 Bonhams, Knightsbridge #62/R
£521	$828	€761	Glass of milk (19x15cm-7x6in) s. W/C. 1-May-3 Dunbar Sloane, Wellington #72a/R est:1500-2500 (NZ.D 1500)
£600	$942	€870	Afternoon tea (36x62cm-14x24in) s. pencil W/C htd white. 28-Aug-3 Christie's, Kensington #465/R
£600	$1038	€876	Two eastern ladies eating fruit on a shaded terrace (8x14cm-3x6in) s. W/C. 9-Dec-3 Bonhams, Oxford #49/R
£900	$1548	€1314	Attending to her ladyship (25x36cm-10x14in) s. pencil W/C. 3-Dec-3 Christie's, Kensington #74/R
£900	$1530	€1314	Interior scene with two ladies (13x16cm-5x6in) s. W/C. 28-Oct-3 Henry Adams, Chichester #375/R
£1049	$1700	€1532	Portrait of a woman in fur trimmed coat on sofa with book (25x36cm-10x14in) s. W/C. 3-Aug-3 North East Auctions, Portsmouth #2120/R
£1300	$2054	€1898	Toilet interior scene maid attending to her mistress hair (18x23cm-7x9in) s. W/C. 4-Sep-3 Amersham Auction Rooms, UK #295
£1463	$2620	€2136	Three o'clock (26x35cm-10x14in) s. W/C exec c.1910. 10-May-4 Joel, Victoria #374 est:2500-3500 (A.D 3600)
£1650	$2805	€2409	Interior scene depicting lady seated on a chaise long greeting three gentlemen (16x33cm-6x13in) s. W/C. 28-Oct-3 Henry Adams, Chichester #374/R est:1000-1500
£1700	$2890	€2482	Woman and dog before a cottage (22x16cm-9x6in) s. W/C. 29-Oct-3 Bonhams, Chester #409/R est:1800-2500
£1800	$2844	€2628	Reading lesson, mother seated with her two girls (18x23cm-7x9in) s. W/C. 4-Sep-3 Amersham Auction Rooms, UK #294
£1900	$3230	€2774	An interruption (26x36cm-10x14in) s. W/C. 4-Nov-3 Bonhams, New Bond Street #142/R est:1500-2200
£1900	$3401	€2774	Mother and child (26x20cm-10x8in) s. W/C. 26-May-4 Sotheby's, Olympia #172/R est:1000-1500
£1900	$3458	€2774	Hush a bye. Convalescent (17x13cm-7x5in) both s. W/C htd bodycol two. 1-Jul-4 Sotheby's, London #255/R est:2000-3000
£2100	$3570	€3066	Difficult question (22x28cm-9x11in) s. W/C over pencil. 1-Dec-3 Bonhams, Bath #62/R est:2000-3000
£2300	$3910	€3358	Waiting for mother (22x17cm-9x7in) s. W/C. 25-Nov-3 Bonhams, Knowle #167/R est:400-600
£2400	$4440	€3504	Serving the tea (36x52cm-14x20in) s. W/C. 9-Mar-4 Bonhams, New Bond Street #125/R est:2000-3000
£2500	$4250	€3650	Dear mother (30x21cm-12x8in) s. W/C. 18-Nov-3 Bonhams, Leeds #109/R est:2500-3000
£2500	$4625	€3650	At the tavern (36x51cm-14x20in) s. W/C. 9-Mar-4 Bonhams, New Bond Street #126/R est:2000-3000
£2600	$4784	€3796	Post bag (36x53cm-14x21in) s. pencil W/C. 25-Mar-4 Christie's, Kensington #237/R est:1500-2500
£2700	$4860	€3942	Lady reading (24x34cm-9x13in) s. W/C. 21-Jan-4 Sotheby's, Olympia #193/R est:3000-5000
£3000	$5550	€4380	Music room (25x34cm-10x13in) s. W/C. 14-Jul-4 Sotheby's, Olympia #105/R est:2000-3000
£3200	$5760	€4672	Messenger (26x36cm-10x14in) s. pencil W/C htd white. 22-Apr-4 Mellors & Kirk, Nottingham #1033/R est:1500-2000
£3400	$5678	€4964	Good catch (35x30cm-14x12in) s. pencil W/C prov. 16-Oct-3 Christie's, Kensington #98/R est:1500-2000
£3600	$6480	€5256	New gown (23x32cm-9x13in) s. pencil W/C htd white. 22-Apr-4 Mellors & Kirk, Nottingham #1034/R est:1000-1500
£3900	$6630	€5694	Tying on the bait (21x32cm-8x13in) s.d.1866 W/C bodycol. 25-Nov-3 Bonhams, Knowle #194/R est:700-1000
£4000	$7480	€5840	Young lady and two children presenting flowers to a seated lady, interior scene (35x51cm-14x20in) s. pencil W/C htd white prov. 22-Jul-4 Tennants, Leyburn #719/R est:4000-6000
£5500	$9350	€8030	Mother and child at the cottage door (31x48cm-12x19in) s. W/C. 4-Nov-3 Bonhams, New Bond Street #141/R est:4000-6000
£5600	$9520	€8176	Affectionate pets (38x27cm-15x11in) s. pencil W/C. 19-Nov-3 Tennants, Leyburn #941/R est:3000-3500

KILGOUR, Andrew Wilkie (1868-1930) Canadian
£400 $732 €584 North River, St Andrews (27x37cm-11x15in) s.d.1913 board prov. 1-Jun-4 Joyner Waddington, Toronto #477 (C.D 1000)

KILIAN, Hannes (1909-1999) German
Photographs
£1800 $3312 €2700 Dragonfly wing (27x24cm-11x9in) i.d. i. verso silver gelatin. 10-Jun-4 Villa Grisebach, Berlin #1154/R est:1000-1500
£1818 $3091 €2600 Guggenheim, New York (29x23cm-11x9in) i.d. verso silver gelatin. 27-Nov-3 Villa Grisebach, Berlin #1252/R est:1200-1500

KILIAN, Lukas (1579-1637) German
Works on paper
£625 $1100 €913 Allegorical figure of fame (14x10cm-6x4in) pen brown ink brown wash prov. 19-May-4 Doyle, New York #6012

KILIAN, Philip Andreas (1714-1759) German
Works on paper
£545 $927 €780 Man and two female figures (15x9cm-6x4in) Indian ink. 21-Nov-3 Reiss & Sohn, Konigstein #91/R

KILIMNICK, Karen (1962-) American
£5000 $9050 €7300 Pond (13x18cm-5x7in) s. i.d.March 11 99 verso prov. 1-Apr-4 Christie's, Kensington #242/R est:5000-7000
Sculpture
£17877 $32000 €26100 Swan lake (215x550x700cm-85x217x276in) five curtains aluminum rods ballet dresses various items prov. 14-May-4 Phillips, New York #144/R est:20000-30000
Works on paper
£3500 $5845 €5110 Richard at the Anvil (105x66cm-41x26in) i.d.January 7'95 pencil gouache prov. 22-Oct-3 Christie's, London #174/R est:4000-6000
£17877 $32000 €26100 Blizzard, Siberia (61x46cm-24x18in) s.i.d.September 28 '01 verso water soluble oil prov. 12-May-4 Christie's, Rockefeller NY #351/R est:20000-30000

KILLALY, Alicia (1836-1916) Canadian
Works on paper
£1629 $2802 €2378 View of the Horseshoe Falls, winter (30x46cm-12x18in) s. W/C. 2-Dec-3 Joyner Waddington, Toronto #254/R est:1500-2000 (C.D 3650)

KILLEEN, Richard (1946-) New Zealander
£1083 $1765 €1581 In formation (121x61cm-48x24in) s. i.d.April 1973 verso board. 23-Sep-3 Peter Webb, Auckland #116/R est:3000-5000 (NZ.D 3000)
£1268 $2042 €1851 Attack through time (80x61cm-31x24in) s. board. 20-Aug-3 Dunbar Sloane, Auckland #87 est:4000-6000 (NZ.D 3500)
£6993 $12727 €10210 18 objects (69x69cm-27x27in) i. board. 29-Jun-4 Peter Webb, Auckland #24/R est:15000-25000 (NZ.D 20000)
£16071 $29089 €23464 Structures and references no.2 (250x250cm-98x98in) s.i.d.May 1983 verso alkyd on aluminium 16 pieces prov. 30-Mar-4 Peter Webb, Auckland #25/R est:30000-40000 (NZ.D 45000)
Works on paper
£979 $1782 €1429 Back from the dead (35x50cm-14x20in) s.i.d.1995 W/C. 29-Jun-4 Peter Webb, Auckland #6/R est:1500-3000 (NZ.D 2800)
£1178 $1896 €1720 Scientific woman (76x58cm-30x23in) s.d.84 W/C. 20-Aug-3 Dunbar Sloane, Auckland #59/R est:3000-5000 (NZ.D 3250)
£1264 $2060 €1845 Stack - months and days (38x58cm-15x23in) s.i.d.November 16 1989 mixed media. 23-Sep-3 Peter Webb, Auckland #8/R est:3500-4500 (NZ.D 3500)

KILLGORE, Charles P (20th C) American
£1324 $2250 €1933 Arroyo landscape (41x51cm-16x20in) s. masonite prov. 18-Nov-3 John Moran, Pasadena #165 est:1000-2000

KILPACK, Sarah Louise (fl.1880-1909) British
£270 $451 €394 Fishing boats at low-tide (44x33cm-17x13in) s. 16-Oct-3 Lawrence, Crewkerne #744
£310 $484 €450 Fishing smack passing a merchantman in choppy seas (36x51cm-14x20in) s.d.1894. 20-Oct-2 Desmond Judd, Cranbrook #823
£350 $616 €511 Figures on a cliff top (26x20cm-10x8in) s. board. 19-May-4 John Bellman, Billingshurst #1767/R
£360 $673 €526 Chepstow Castle, Wales (19x21cm-7x8in) s. paper. 22-Jul-4 Martel Maides, Guernsey #195/R
£420 $697 €613 Fisherman's quarter (20x15cm-8x6in) s. i.stretcher. 3-Oct-3 Mallams, Oxford #247/R
£420 $722 €613 Figure beside a river (18x13cm-7x5in) s. board. 2-Dec-3 Gorringes, Lewes #2290
£500 $920 €730 Figures on a cliff path (12x18cm-5x7in) s. board. 29-Mar-4 Bonhams, Bath #79/R
£520 $832 €759 French canal scene (12x18cm-5x7in) s. card. 17-Sep-3 Bonhams, Brooks & Langlois, Jersey #82/R
£620 $992 €905 Cliffs in rough seas (14x10cm-6x4in) s. card. 17-Sep-3 Bonhams, Brooks & Langlois, Jersey #79/R
£680 $1088 €993 Castle and rough seas (10x13cm-4x5in) s. card. 17-Sep-3 Bonhams, Brooks & Langlois, Jersey #76/R
£780 $1248 €1139 Wolf Rock Lighthouse (7x10cm-3x4in) card. 17-Sep-3 Bonhams, Brooks & Langlois, Jersey #77/R
£800 $1360 €1168 Coming home safely (11x19cm-4x7in) s. board. 19-Nov-3 Christie's, Kensington #545/R
£950 $1520 €1387 Figures and sheep on cliffs at sunset (14x10cm-6x4in) s. card. 17-Sep-3 Bonhams, Brooks & Langlois, Jersey #78/R
£950 $1520 €1387 Ship near cliffs (14x10cm-6x4in) s. card. 17-Sep-3 Bonhams, Brooks & Langlois, Jersey #80/R
£1000 $1670 €1460 Salvaging the wreck (36x66cm-14x26in) s. 8-Oct-3 Christie's, Kensington #739/R est:1000-1500
£1100 $1892 €1606 Fishermen's wives sorting the catch (25x36cm-10x14in) s. board. 2-Dec-3 Gorringes, Lewes #2277/R est:400-600
£1100 $1991 €1606 Sunrise over a harbour, with ship and figures (23x23cm-9x9in) s. card. 1-Apr-4 Martel Maides, Guernsey #240/R est:500-700
£1250 $2263 €1825 Approaching storm (23x18cm-9x7in) s. 1-Apr-4 Martel Maides, Guernsey #222/R est:600-800
£1400 $2534 €2044 Salvaging the wreck. The Peastacks, Guernsey (21x30cm-8x12in) one s. board pair. 1-Apr-4 Martel Maides, Guernsey #253/R est:800-1000
£1500 $2400 €2190 North coast of Jersey. The Cup and Cover Fort, Guernsey (11x14cm-4x6in) card pair. 17-Sep-3 Bonhams, Brooks & Langlois, Jersey #81/R

KILPATRICK, Aaron Edward (1872-1953) American
£209 $350 €305 Harbour inlet, Morrow bay (31x40cm-12x16in) s. board. 19-Oct-3 Bonhams & Butterfields, Los Angeles #7006
£284 $475 €415 Old adobe, San Luis Obispo (30x41cm-12x16in) s. board. 19-Oct-3 Bonhams & Butterfields, Los Angeles #7007
£419 $700 €612 Autumn landscape (41x51cm-16x20in) s. 19-Oct-3 Bonhams & Butterfields, Los Angeles #7005

KILPIN, Legh Mulhall (1853-1919) British
Works on paper
£351 $636 €512 Untitled - summer rains (47x65cm-19x26in) s.d.1904 W/C. 18-Apr-4 Levis, Calgary #487/R (C.D 850)

KILVERT, B Cory (1881-1946) American
Works on paper
£559 $1000 €816 Bumblebee attracted to young girl's cereal bowl (43x38cm-17x15in) s. gouache W/C. 15-May-4 Illustration House, New York #76/R est:1800-2400

KILVINGTON, Patrick (1922-1990) Australian
£267 $486 €390 Now listen mate (40x30cm-16x12in) s.i.verso prov. 16-Jun-4 Deutscher-Menzies, Melbourne #611/R (A.D 700)
£535 $969 €781 Right mean beast (25x30cm-10x12in) s. 31-Mar-4 Goodman, Sydney #390 (A.D 1300)

KIM JONG HAK (1937-) Chinese?
£2000 $3580 €2920 Spring (53x33cm-21x13in) s.verso. 6-May-4 Sotheby's, London #100/R est:2200-2500
£3200 $5728 €4672 Spring (33x53cm-13x21in) s. 6-May-4 Sotheby's, London #99/R est:2200-2500

KIM, Galina (20th C) New Zealander?
£426 $787 €622 Chardonnay (92x30cm-36x12in) s.d.2004. 13-Jul-4 Watson's, Christchurch #17/R est:1500-2500 (NZ.D 1200)
£507 $807 €740 Love to three oranges, music series (44x58cm-17x23in) s.d.2003 acrylic after Prokoviev. 9-Sep-3 Watson's, Christchurch #66 (NZ.D 1400)

KIM, Tschang Yeul (1929-) Korean
£1267 $2331 €1900 Waterdrop (23x19cm-9x7in) mono.d. 11-Jun-4 Hauswedell & Nolte, Hamburg #1378/R est:2000

KIMHI, Avi (1945-) Israeli
Sculpture
£1399 $2378 €2000 L'homme assis (30x11x7cm-12x4x3in) 27-Nov-3 Calmels Cohen, Paris #92/R est:1000-1200

KIML, Vaclav (1928-) Czechoslovakian
£744 $1235 €1086 Capuchins (41x48cm-16x19in) s.d.73 canvas on board. 4-Oct-3 Dorotheum, Prague #130/R est:20000-30000 (C.KR 34000)

KIMLER, Wesley (1953-) American
£973 $1800 €1421 Dark Sleeper (192x395cm-76x156in) s.d.1986 i.verso two parts prov. 12-Feb-4 Sotheby's, New York #295/R est:2500-3500
Works on paper
£254 $425 €371 Untitled (97x127cm-38x50in) s. chl rag. 19-Oct-3 Bonhams & Butterfields, Los Angeles #7088
£578 $1000 €844 Eight miles high (97x127cm-38x50in) chl. 15-Dec-3 Hindman, Chicago #133/R

KIMMEL, Cornelis (1804-1877) British
£930 $1600 €1358 Frozen waterway with skaters and villagers gathering around a koek en zopie (20x25cm-8x10in) s. panel. 3-Dec-3 Doyle, New York #105/R est:3000-5000

KIMMEL, Lu (1908-1973) American
£2890 $5000 €4219 Winter's joy (71x89cm-28x35in) 12-Dec-3 Du Mouchelle, Detroit #2045/R est:5000-8000

KIMMELMAN, Harold (20th C) American
Sculpture
£1078 $1800 €1574 Fence walkers (91x147cm-36x58in) bronze steel wood. 20-Jun-3 Freeman, Philadelphia #88/R est:300-500

KIMMICH, Wilhelm (1897-?) German
£1867 $3379 €2800 Portrait of young girl (38x30cm-15x12in) s.d.1925 lit. 1-Apr-4 Frank Peege, Freiburg #1216/R est:200

KIMPE, Reimond (1885-1970) Belgian
£900 $1440 €1305 Abstract composition (55x36cm-22x14in) s.d.35 board. 16-Sep-3 Bonhams, Knightsbridge #198/R

£2333 $4293 €3500 Untitled (40x36cm-16x14in) s. board. 8-Jun-4 Sotheby's, Amsterdam #240/R est:2000-3000
£2333 $4293 €3500 Drummer (65x60cm-26x24in) s. i.stretcher. 8-Jun-4 Sotheby's, Amsterdam #245/R est:3000-5000
£2897 $5359 €4200 Le pecheur (69x52cm-27x20in) s.d.46. 16-Feb-4 Horta, Bruxelles #276 est:400-600
£3034 $5614 €4400 La femme au cactus (55x50cm-22x20in) s. 16-Feb-4 Horta, Bruxelles #199/R est:3500-4500
£4000 $7360 €6000 Untitled (65x50cm-26x20in) s. 8-Jun-4 Sotheby's, Amsterdam #246/R est:4500-5500
£4082 $7429 €6000 Village street (86x94cm-34x37in) s.d.36. 3-Feb-4 Christie's, Amsterdam #479/R est:5000-7000
£4082 $7429 €6000 Two mannequins (65x50cm-26x20in) s. 3-Feb-4 Christie's, Amsterdam #537 est:6000-8000
£4333 $7930 €6500 Farm in the snow (80x90cm-31x35in) s.d.31. 7-Jun-4 Glerum, Amsterdam #120/R est:7000-9000
£4545 $7818 €6500 Boerinnetje (38x33cm-15x13in) s.d.36 i.verso panel. 2-Dec-3 Sotheby's, Amsterdam #4/R est:2500-3500
Works on paper
£302 $556 €450 Au theatre (34x22cm-13x9in) s. ink gouache. 23-Mar-4 Galerie Moderne, Brussels #302
£652 $1200 €952 Musicians (36x28cm-14x11in) s. gouache pair. 23-Mar-4 Arthur James, Florida #13/R est:1000-1500

KINCH, Agnete Helvig (1872-1956) Danish
£356 $594 €520 Horses (100x140cm-39x55in) init.d.1902. 25-Oct-3 Rasmussen, Havnen #2149 (D.KR 3800)
£549 $1000 €802 Working horses grazing, grey day, early spring (128x98cm-50x39in) init.d.1902. 7-Feb-4 Rasmussen, Havnen #2160 (D.KR 6000)

KINCH, Hayter (19th C) British
£850 $1573 €1241 Huntsmen and hounds on hillside, Salt Hill. The Chase, Salt Hill, Sussex (32x42cm-13x17in) one s.d.1839 pair. 11-Feb-4 Cheffins, Cambridge #438/R

KINDBORG, Johan (1861-1907) Swedish
£517 $926 €755 Wooded landscape at dusk (91x71cm-36x28in) s.d.95. 26-May-4 AB Stockholms Auktionsverk #2214/R (S.KR 7000)
£615 $1058 €898 House and figure by lake (24x33cm-9x13in) s.d.83. 3-Dec-3 AB Stockholms Auktionsverk #2374/R (S.KR 8000)
£671 $1248 €1000 Moonlit landscape (77x63cm-30x25in) 7-Mar-4 Bukowskis, Helsinki #495/R
£1923 $3308 €2808 Girl on country road (23x18cm-9x7in) s.d.85. 3-Dec-3 AB Stockholms Auktionsverk #2310/R est:15000-18000 (S.KR 25000)

KINDER, Hans (1900-1986) German
Works on paper
£362 $666 €550 Still life with guitar, jug, bottle and male bust (86x101cm-34x40in) mixed media exec. 1960's. 26-Jun-4 C & K, Leipzig #750/R

KINDER, John (1819-1903) New Zealander
Works on paper
£692 $1239 €1010 Wangaroa Harbour (9x44cm-4x17in) i.d.Dec 29 1859 pen W/C pencil. 12-May-4 Dunbar Sloane, Wellington #123/R est:2000-4000 (NZ.D 2000)
£1042 $1656 €1521 Pohaturoa from near Waimahana (9x27cm-4x11in) s.i.d.January 1862 W/C. 1-May-3 Dunbar Sloane, Wellington #49 est:3000-5000 (NZ.D 3000)
£1812 $2917 €2646 St. John's College from the west (24x18cm-9x7in) s. W/C. 20-Aug-3 Dunbar Sloane, Auckland #67 est:5000-7000 (NZ.D 5000)

KINDERMANN, Adolf (1823-1892) German
£1350 $2133 €1958 Mother and her three children in an elegant interior (56x46cm-22x18in) s. 17-Nov-2 Desmond Judd, Cranbrook #811

KINDLER, Albert (1833-1876) German
£298 $498 €432 Footbath (33x24cm-13x9in) s.d.1856. 23-Jun-3 Philippe Schuler, Zurich #8610a (S.FR 650)

KINDLEY, Lance E (20th C) American
Works on paper
£250 $450 €365 Pair of Canadian geese in the water (53x71cm-21x28in) s.d.1980 W/C. 26-Apr-4 Schrager Galleries, Milwaukee #1397/R

KING CARL XV OF SWEDEN (1826-1872) Swedish
£9796 $16848 €14302 Norwegian landscape (120x164cm-47x65in) init.i.d.65 prov. 8-Dec-3 Blomqvist, Oslo #457/R est:120000-150000 (N.KR 115000)

KING, Albert F (1854-1945) American
£3911 $7000 €5710 Apples (36x51cm-14x20in) s. painted c.1895 prov. 26-May-4 Doyle, New York #8/R est:10000-15000
£8750 $14000 €12775 Still life with spilled basket of flowers, raspberries and pitcher of water (66x53cm-26x21in) s.d.87. 20-Sep-3 Pook & Pook, Downington #447/R est:4000-6000

KING, Andrew (1956-) British
£250 $463 €365 Sunlit Square (24x34cm-9x13in) s.d.87 board. 13-Feb-4 Sworder & Son, Bishops Stortford #80/R

KING, Cecil (1921-1986) Irish
£613 $1110 €920 Untitled (18x18cm-7x7in) card. 30-Mar-4 De Veres Art Auctions, Dublin #140/R
£1159 $2109 €1750 Landscape (23x15cm-9x6in) s. board. 15-Jun-4 James Adam, Dublin #188/R est:1000-1500
£1600 $2896 €2400 Suspended (76x50cm-30x20in) prov. 31-Mar-4 James Adam, Dublin #67/R est:1500-2000
£1608 $2734 €2300 Nexus (38x28cm-15x11in) s. board prov.exhib. 18-Nov-3 Whyte's, Dublin #158/R est:1500-2000
£1933 $3499 €2900 Two (53x91cm-21x36in) s.verso prov. 31-Mar-4 James Adam, Dublin #64/R est:1000-2000
£2282 $4039 €3400 Thrust (38x52cm-15x20in) s. one i. two i.verso one oil paper one W/C one silkscreen 3 prov. 27-Apr-4 Whyte's, Dublin #89/R est:2000-2500
£2400 $4344 €3600 King (64x54cm-25x21in) prov.exhib. 31-Mar-4 James Adam, Dublin #65/R est:2000-3000
£2667 $4827 €4000 Wasteland (37x41cm-15x16in) prov. 30-Mar-4 De Veres Art Auctions, Dublin #150/R est:4000-5000
£2800 $5068 €4200 Within (43x55cm-17x22in) s.i.d.1974 verso prov. 31-Mar-4 James Adam, Dublin #63/R est:1500-2000
Works on paper
£667 $1207 €1000 Early one morning (24x20cm-9x8in) s. pastel. 31-Mar-4 James Adam, Dublin #68/R
£799 $1254 €1150 Pastel 1962 (25x19cm-10x7in) s. pastel. 26-Aug-3 James Adam, Dublin #133/R est:750-1000
£1000 $1810 €1500 Trapeze (35x25cm-14x10in) s. mixed media prov. 30-Mar-4 De Veres Art Auctions, Dublin #4/R est:900-1200
£1197 $2095 €1700 Abstract (34x24cm-13x9in) s. pastel. 16-Dec-3 James Adam, Dublin #236/R est:800-1200

KING, Dorothy (fl.1937-1940) British
£300 $528 €438 Vase of yellow, red and white roses (50x40cm-20x16in) s. canvasboard. 18-May-4 Bonhams, Knightsbridge #25

KING, Edith Louise Mary (1870-1962) South African
Works on paper
£414 $691 €604 Aloe in winter grass (30x28cm-12x11in) s. W/C. 20-Oct-3 Stephan Welz, Johannesburg #358 est:5000-7000 (SA.R 4800)
£414 $691 €604 Rock pool (36x28cm-14x11in) s. W/C. 20-Oct-3 Stephan Welz, Johannesburg #360 est:5000-7000 (SA.R 4800)
£431 $720 €629 Cascade (26x27cm-10x11in) s. W/C. 20-Oct-3 Stephan Welz, Johannesburg #357 est:5000-7000 (SA.R 5000)

KING, Edward (1863-?) British
£950 $1501 €1378 Cattle grazing in rural southern landscape (51x97cm-20x38in) s. 27-Apr-3 Desmond Judd, Cranbrook #1045

KING, Edward R (fl.1884-1904) British
£3200 $5856 €4672 Frolic, children in a tug of war, St Ives harbour (60x75cm-24x30in) s.d.1894 prov. 3-Jun-4 Lane, Penzance #145/R est:3000-5000

KING, Emma B (20th C) American
£265 $475 €387 On the river bank (38x55cm-15x22in) s. 14-May-4 Skinner, Boston #165/R

KING, Ethel Slade (attrib) (19th C) British
Works on paper
£290 $452 €421 Mixed summer flowers in a vase (20x30cm-8x12in) mono. W/C. 22-Sep-2 Desmond Judd, Cranbrook #891

KING, Frank L (19th C) British
£380 $695 €555 Young girl seated on a sofa holding a doll (71x91cm-28x36in) s.i.verso. 7-Apr-4 Gardiner & Houlgate, Bath #346/R

KING, George W (1836-1922) American
£1006 $1800 €1469 L. WITH COWS (43x30cm-17x12in) S. B. 7-May-4 Sloans & Kenyon, Bethesda #1687/R est:1200-1500

KING, Gordon (?) British
Works on paper
£360 $612 €526 Panier of fresh flowers (53x69cm-21x27in) s. W/C. 25-Nov-3 Bonhams, Knowle #191
£400 $708 €584 Samantha and Georgina (37x26cm-15x10in) s. W/C. 27-Apr-4 Bonhams, Knightsbridge #79/R
£420 $794 €613 Two urchins seated on fishing baskets (27x37cm-11x15in) s. W/C. 17-Feb-4 Fellows & Sons, Birmingham #132/R
£460 $782 €672 Daydreams (47x68cm-19x27in) s. W/C. 25-Nov-3 Bonhams, Knowle #179
£500 $885 €730 Black lace (48x69cm-19x27in) s. W/C. 27-Apr-4 Bonhams, Knightsbridge #12/R
£550 $974 €803 Flower girl (35x53cm-14x21in) s. W/C. 27-Apr-4 Bonhams, Knightsbridge #9/R
£750 $1343 €1095 Flower seller (54x35cm-21x14in) s. W/C. 20-Mar-4 Lacy Scott, Bury St.Edmunds #473
£800 $1264 €1168 Two half-naked girls reclining on a bed (46x71cm-18x28in) s. red chk. 2-Sep-3 Gildings, Market Harborough #386/R
£950 $1796 €1387 Nudes (50x71cm-20x28in) s. red chk. 23-Feb-4 David Duggleby, Scarborough #651/R

KING, H (?) ?
£2600 $4654 €3796 Young woman seated in a country cottage preparing vegetables from a cane basket (60x50cm-24x20in) s.d.1876. 26-May-4 Outhwaite & Litherland, Liverpool #305/R

KING, Haynes (1831-1904) British
£346 $595 €505 On the look-out - girl waiting for her fiancee (31x25cm-12x10in) s.d.61 panel. 7-Dec-3 Uppsala Auktionskammare, Uppsala #84/R (S.KR 4500)
£560 $1030 €818 Portrait study of a seated pheasant girl (18x13cm-7x5in) s. panel. 8-Jun-4 Lawrences, Bletchingley #1387
£726 $1335 €1060 Highland fisher girl (32x20cm-13x8in) s.d.1883 panel. 14-Jun-4 Waddingtons, Toronto #133/R est:1500-2500 (C.D 1800)

£1700 $3111 €2482 Reflection (35x30cm-14x12in) s.d.1875. 6-Jul-4 Bearnes, Exeter #471/R est:1200-1800
£2400 $4296 €3504 Oyster gatherer (25x20cm-10x8in) s. 26-May-4 Sotheby's, Olympia #142/R est:1500-2000
£2900 $5278 €4234 Taking it easy (30x25cm-12x10in) s. panel. 29-Jun-4 Bonhams, Knowle #100 est:2000-3000
£4000 $7360 €5840 Reading the news (36x31cm-14x12in) s. 23-Mar-4 Bonhams, New Bond Street #70/R est:2000-3000

KING, Henry John Yeend (1855-1924) British

£460 $851 €672 River landscape with figure on a bridge at dusk (26x22cm-10x9in) s. board. 13-Jan-4 Bonhams, Knightsbridge #88/R
£552 $1000 €806 Pastoral Sussex (51x76cm-20x30in) s. 3-Apr-4 Nadeau, Windsor #77/R est:2000-4000
£580 $1038 €847 Old mill (19x29cm-7x11in) s. board. 18-Mar-4 Neales, Nottingham #766/R
£650 $1034 €943 Highland river landscape with deer (44x34cm-17x13in) s. panel. 9-Sep-3 Bonhams, Knightsbridge #221/R
£725 $1305 €1088 Ruins in garden (36x50cm-14x20in) s. 25-Apr-4 Goteborg Auktionsverk, Sweden #214/R (S.KR 10000)
£1000 $1830 €1460 River scene with woman and child on a bridge (39x29cm-15x11in) board. 6-Jul-4 John Taylors, Louth #367
£1100 $1837 €1606 Birch wood (52x35cm-20x14in) s.i. 16-Oct-3 Lawrence, Crewkerne #743/R
£1200 $2220 €1752 Mill on the Calne (45x60cm-18x24in) s. board. 13-Jan-4 Bonhams, Knightsbridge #312/R est:1000-1500
£1316 $2237 €1921 Summer evening walk (55x45cm-22x18in) s. 26-Nov-3 Dunbar Sloane, Wellington #59/R est:4000-7000 (NZ.D 3500)
£1350 $2390 €1971 Feeding the pigeons (39x30cm-15x12in) 29-Apr-4 Christie's, Kensington #181/R est:1500-2000
£1400 $2506 €2044 Frittleworth Common, Sussex (35x51cm-14x20in) s. board. 18-Mar-4 Neales, Nottingham #768
£1528 $2750 €2231 Winding the whirl (51x41cm-20x16in) s. 21-Jan-4 Sotheby's, New York #208/R est:4000-6000
£1810 $3023 €2643 The Lych Gate, Welford (40x30cm-16x12in) s. s.i.verso canvasboard. 17-Nov-3 Waddingtons, Toronto #117/R est:4000-6000 (C.D 4000)
£2200 $4070 €3212 Little angler (46x34cm-18x13in) s. panel. 14-Jul-4 Sotheby's, Olympia #119/R est:2500-3500
£2308 $3969 €3370 By the river (61x92cm-24x36in) s. 3-Dec-3 AB Stockholms Auktionsverk #2616/R est:35000-40000 (S.KR 30000)
£2400 $4296 €3504 River bank (36x52cm-14x20in) s. board. 26-May-4 Sotheby's, Olympia #153/R est:2000-3000
£2483 $4594 €3700 Peaceful stretch of the river (35x52cm-14x20in) s. panel prov. 10-Mar-4 James Adam, Dublin #30/R est:3000-4000
£3695 $6615 €5395 Pastoral landscape with sheep grazing (101x76cm-40x30in) s. 26-May-4 AB Stockholms Auktionsverk #2396/R est:50000-60000 (S.KR 50000)
£4600 $8510 €6716 View of timbered thatched cottage with a mother and child by a pond (51x36cm-20x14in) s.d.1892 panel. 13-Jan-4 Bonhams, Knightsbridge #191/R est:2500-3500
£4800 $8928 €7008 Gathering water from summer stream (59x89cm-23x35in) s. 2-Mar-4 Bearnes, Exeter #416/R est:2000-3000
£5090 $8500 €7431 Love letter (61x91cm-24x36in) s. 7-Oct-3 Sotheby's, New York #82/R est:4000-6000
£5500 $9130 €8030 End of the village (61x45cm-24x18in) s. 1-Oct-3 Sotheby's, Olympia #85/R est:3000-5000
£6000 $10200 €8760 At the village pond (61x91cm-24x36in) s. 27-Nov-3 Sotheby's, London #414/R est:6000-8000
£18000 $30600 €26280 Day's at the well (92x72cm-36x28in) s. 27-Nov-3 Sotheby's, London #416/R est:10000-15000

Works on paper

£440 $801 €642 Landscape with river and a figure by a gate (34x26cm-13x10in) s. W/C. 16-Jun-4 Rupert Toovey, Partridge Green #66/R
£480 $883 €701 Woman plucking a chicken in a cottage doorway (53x35cm-21x14in) s. W/C. 23-Jun-4 Cheffins, Cambridge #462/R
£495 $842 €723 Castle ruins (38x76cm-15x30in) s. W/C. 21-Nov-3 Walker's, Ottawa #265/R (C.D 1100)
£868 $1380 €1267 Cottage near Wareham (26x44cm-10x17in) s. W/C. 1-May-3 Dunbar Sloane, Wellington #73 est:3000-7000 (NZ.D 2500)
£1200 $2208 €1752 View of the south coast. Thatched cottage (16x23cm-6x9in) s. W/C pair. 22-Jun-4 Bonhams, Knightsbridge #162a/R est:800-1200

KING, Inge (1918-) Australian

Sculpture

£1034 $1614 €1499 Lovers (54cm-21in) init. bronze. 1-Aug-2 Joel, Victoria #223 est:3500-4500 (A.D 3000)
£1215 $1955 €1774 Untitled (133cm-52in) init. welded painted steel. 13-Oct-3 Joel, Victoria #381/R est:3000-4000 (A.D 3000)
£1653 $2926 €2413 Untitled (39cm-15in) welded steel prov. 3-May-4 Christie's, Melbourne #361/R est:4000-6000 (A.D 4000)

KING, Jessie M (1875-1949) British

Works on paper

£500 $900 €730 Puffer at Corrie (19x28cm-7x11in) W/C. 21-Apr-4 Lyon & Turnbull, Edinburgh #249/R
£550 $990 €803 Puffer at Corrie (22x27cm-9x11in) s. W/C exhib. 21-Apr-4 Lyon & Turnbull, Edinburgh #250/R
£900 $1620 €1314 Suggestion for waitress costume (30x18cm-12x7in) pencil W/C prov. 21-Apr-4 Lyon & Turnbull, Edinburgh #247/R
£950 $1739 €1387 King of the Castle (19x35cm-7x14in) W/C ink vellum. 28-Jan-4 Dreweatt Neate, Newbury #19/R
£1600 $2880 €2336 Puffer at Corrie (22x28cm-9x11in) s. W/C. 21-Apr-4 Lyon & Turnbull, Edinburgh #248/R est:300-500
£1700 $3060 €2482 Suggestion for tea room costume (29x18cm-11x7in) pencil W/C prov. 21-Apr-4 Lyon & Turnbull, Edinburgh #253/R est:200-300
£1900 $3420 €2774 Fisherman finds the mermaid in his net (28x21cm-11x8in) s.i. pen ink wash vellum on board prov. 21-Apr-4 Lyon & Turnbull, Edinburgh #254/R est:800-1200
£2000 $3440 €2920 House in the Trongate (23x9cm-9x4in) s.i. black ink vellum lit. 3-Dec-3 Christie's, Kensington #259/R est:1500-2500
£2200 $3454 €3190 Pont Neuf, Paris (18x16cm-7x6in) s. i.verso pen ink on vellum prov. 27-Aug-3 Sotheby's, London #1062/R est:1000-1500
£3800 $6840 €5548 Flying a kite (34x43cm-13x17in) s. ink W/C prov. 21-Apr-4 Lyon & Turnbull, Edinburgh #252/R est:1500-2000
£4400 $6908 €6380 March (28x20cm-11x8in) s.i. pen ink W/C on vellum. 27-Aug-3 Sotheby's, London #1063/R est:2000-3000
£5400 $9720 €7884 Town by the river (18x20cm-7x8in) s.i. ink vellum prov. 21-Apr-4 Lyon & Turnbull, Edinburgh #251/R est:3000-4000

KING, John Baragwanath (1864-1939) British

Works on paper

£360 $619 €526 White Wings, the Safari and Astra (29x45cm-11x18in) s. W/C gouache. 2-Dec-3 Sotheby's, London #126/R

KING, John Gregory (1929-) British

Works on paper

£350 $585 €511 Hunting scene (37x53cm-15x21in) s. 9-Oct-3 Greenslade Hunt, Taunton #468/R
£500 $850 €730 Grand National, 1965 (37x48cm-15x19in) s.i.d.1965 pencil W/C htd white. 27-Nov-3 Christie's, Kensington #187/R

KING, Marcus (1891-1985) New Zealander

£297 $512 €434 Waikanae river (32x40cm-13x16in) s.d.1975 board. 7-Dec-3 International Art Centre, Auckland #329/R (NZ.D 800)
£316 $543 €461 Swimming in the river (44x57cm-17x22in) s. board. 7-Dec-3 International Art Centre, Auckland #298/R (NZ.D 850)
£346 $619 €505 Cattle grazing (31x39cm-12x15in) s. board. 11-May-4 Watson's, Christchurch #13/R (NZ.D 1000)
£362 $583 €529 Dominion Monarch (30x46cm-12x18in) board. 20-Aug-3 Dunbar Sloane, Auckland #86/R est:600-1000 (NZ.D 1000)

KING, Michel (1930-) French

£340 $622 €496 Temps gris a Lesconil (46x64cm-18x25in) s.i.verso. 7-Apr-4 Woolley & Wallis, Salisbury #198/R
£480 $878 €701 Saint Guerole (54x72cm-21x28in) s.i.verso. 7-Apr-4 Woolley & Wallis, Salisbury #197/R
£517 $864 €750 Regate (22x27cm-9x11in) s. 11-Nov-3 Lesieur & Le Bars, Le Havre #134
£979 $1684 €1400 Les trois cabines bleues (30x61cm-12x24in) s. 7-Dec-3 Lesieur & Le Bars, Le Havre #222

KING, Paul (1867-1947) American

£245 $450 €358 Midsummer, Adirondacks (20x25cm-8x10in) s.i. panel. 25-Jun-4 Freeman, Philadelphia #187/R
£1571 $2750 €2294 Spring landscape (56x46cm-22x18in) s. 19-Dec-3 Sotheby's, New York #1133/R est:3000-5000
£1571 $2750 €2294 Still life with flowers and Asian statue (41x51cm-16x20in) s. canvasboard. 19-Dec-3 Sotheby's, New York #1116/R est:3000-5000
£1676 $3000 €2447 Ships in a harbour (76x61cm-30x24in) s. 6-May-4 Shannon's, Milford #255/R est:3000-5000
£3488 $6000 €5092 Hunting season (56x71cm-22x28in) s. i.d.1917 verso. 7-Dec-3 Freeman, Philadelphia #131 est:6000-9000

KING, Robert (1936-) British

£700 $1204 €1022 Normandy (28x38cm-11x15in) s. 5-Dec-3 Keys, Aylsham #626/R

KING, W Gunning (1859-1940) British

£720 $1224 €1051 On the way home (43x51cm-17x20in) s.d.1929. 6-Nov-3 Christie's, Kensington #805/R
£1500 $2655 €2190 Milking time, shorthorn dairy cow (43x47cm-17x19in) s.d.1918 i.verso. 28-Apr-4 Peter Wilson, Nantwich #70 est:1500-2000

Works on paper

£820 $1509 €1197 Motherless (28x23cm-11x9in) s. monochrome wash drawing. 11-Jun-4 Halls, Shrewsbury #737

KING, William Dickey (1925-) American

Sculpture

£3571 $6500 €5214 Evening (129cm-51in) mono. black pat. bronze prov.exhib.lit. 29-Jun-4 Sotheby's, New York #510/R est:4000-6000

KING, William J (1857-?) British

£520 $962 €759 Landscape with figures on a stone bridge (15x23cm-6x9in) s. board. 9-Mar-4 Gorringes, Lewes #2132
£750 $1373 €1095 Old Harbour, Pwllheli (36x46cm-14x18in) s.d.1917. 27-Jan-4 Gorringes, Lewes #1553/R

KING-HARMAN, Ann Stafford (1919-1979) Irish

£464 $844 €700 Clare Island (25x45cm-10x18in) s. board. 15-Jun-4 James Adam, Dublin #113/R
£526 $968 €800 Soller, Majorca (41x51cm-16x20in) s. board. 22-Jun-4 De Veres Art Auctions, Dublin #220/R

Works on paper

£420 $713 €600 Mayo farm (36x46cm-14x18in) s. gouache. 25-Nov-3 De Veres Art Auctions, Dublin #28/R
£704 $1127 €1000 Westport harbour, County Mayo (28x15cm-11x6in) s. i.verso gouache prov. 16-Sep-3 Whyte's, Dublin #19/R
£769 $1308 €1100 Cottages and hay stacks with rain clouds approaching (41x51cm-16x20in) s. gouache board. 18-Nov-3 Whyte's, Dublin #137/R

KING-SMITH, Leah (1957-) Australian

Photographs

£1860 $3440 €2716 Untitled no.3 from the patterns of connection series (115x117cm-45x46in) cibachrome photograph executed 1991 prov. 15-Mar-4 Sotheby's, Melbourne #32 est:5000-8000 (A.D 4500)
£1957 $3327 €2857 Untitled no. (101x102cm-40x40in) cibachrome photograph. 26-Nov-3 Deutscher-Menzies, Melbourne #100/R est:3000-4000 (A.D 4600)

£2766 $4702 €4038 Untitled (101x102cm-40x40in) cibachrome photograph exhib. 26-Nov-3 Deutscher-Menzies, Melbourne #99/R est:3000-4000 (A.D 6500)
£3404 $5787 €4970 Untitled no.5 (101x102cm-40x40in) cibachrome photograph exhib. 26-Nov-3 Deutscher-Menzies, Melbourne #98/R est:3000-4000 (A.D 8000)

KINGCOME, Catherine (20th C) Irish?
£3691 $6607 €5500 Frankie Gavin in Corcomroe Abbey (150x110cm-59x43in) s. 26-May-4 James Adam, Dublin #147/R est:1500-2500

KINGERLEE, John (1936-) Irish?
£320 $534 €467 Abstract. s. linen. 15-Nov-3 Nigel Ward, Hereford #1429/R
£600 $1086 €900 Untitled (51x76cm-20x30in) s.d.67 canvas on board. 30-Mar-4 De Veres Art Auctions, Dublin #242/R
£650 $1079 €949 Night at the opera (35x25cm-14x10in) mono.88 board. 1-Oct-3 John Ross, Belfast #126
£933 $1689 €1400 Untitled (22x26cm-9x10in) mono. board. 30-Mar-4 De Veres Art Auctions, Dublin #117/R
£987 $1816 €1500 Untitled (31x56cm-12x22in) mono. canvasboard. 22-Jun-4 De Veres Art Auctions, Dublin #253 est:1500-2000
£1200 $2172 €1800 Untitled (43x28cm-17x11in) mono.d.90 acrylic. 30-Mar-4 De Veres Art Auctions, Dublin #132/R est:1400-1800
£1200 $2172 €1800 Untitled (36x26cm-14x10in) mono.d.86. 30-Mar-4 De Veres Art Auctions, Dublin #232/R est:2000-3000
£1267 $2293 €1900 Untitled (26x31cm-10x12in) mono. board. 30-Mar-4 De Veres Art Auctions, Dublin #116/R est:1400-1800
£1316 $2421 €2000 Watching, waiting (45x40cm-18x16in) mono.d.86 s.i.d.verso acrylic. 22-Jun-4 De Veres Art Auctions, Dublin #120/R est:1500-2000
£1500 $2580 €2190 Composition, abstract with bird (40x50cm-16x20in) board. 3-Dec-3 John Ross, Belfast #175a est:1500-1800
£1748 $2972 €2500 Young traveller (59x47cm-23x19in) mono. i.verso board. 25-Nov-3 De Veres Art Auctions, Dublin #143/R est:2500-3000
£1748 $2972 €2500 Untitled (59x47cm-23x19in) mono. i.verso board. 25-Nov-3 De Veres Art Auctions, Dublin #144/R est:2500-3000
£1818 $3091 €2600 Dancing on the shore (25x33cm-10x13in) mono.d.1990 prov.exhib. 18-Nov-3 Whyte's, Dublin #70/R est:1200-1500
£6643 $11294 €9500 Faces in the bog (41x52cm-16x20in) mono. board. 25-Nov-3 De Veres Art Auctions, Dublin #58/R est:4000-6000
£14500 $25955 €21170 Lingham, the whisper (68x94cm-27x37in) mono.d.86 mono.i.d.1986 verso. 14-May-4 Christie's, Kensington #455/R est:5000-8000
Works on paper
£300 $498 €438 Ancient ones (25x33cm-10x13in) mono.d.80 verso mixed media. 1-Oct-3 John Ross, Belfast #232
£347 $566 €500 Every mother's child (23x15cm-9x6in) mono.d.96 mixed media. 23-Sep-3 De Veres Art Auctions, Dublin #225
£361 $589 €520 Mindful (23x15cm-9x6in) mono.d.96 mixed media. 23-Sep-3 De Veres Art Auctions, Dublin #224
£451 $736 €650 Heads above water (21x14cm-8x6in) mono. mixed media. 23-Sep-3 De Veres Art Auctions, Dublin #223/R
£3200 $5728 €4672 Twitter, twitter, twitter (30x46cm-12x18in) mono.d.91 s.i.d.1991 verso mixed media board. 13-May-4 Sotheby's, London #112/R est:2000-3000

KINGHAN, Charles R (1895-1984) American
Works on paper
£228 $425 €333 Fisherman on the rocks (36x53cm-14x21in) s. W/C. 7-Mar-4 William Jenack, New York #218

KINGMAN, Dong (1911-2000) American
Works on paper
£909 $1700 €1327 View of San Francisco (43x63cm-17x25in) s. W/C. 29-Feb-4 Bonhams & Butterfields, San Francisco #4579 est:1000-1500
£1125 $1800 €1643 San Francisco (102x74cm-40x29in) s.d.Jan 72 collage. 18-May-3 Auctions by the Bay, Alameda #1176/R
£1173 $2100 €1713 Still life of fruit with wood bowl (36x51cm-14x20in) s.d.77 W/C. 8-Jan-4 James Julia, Fairfield #110/R est:1000-2000
£1511 $2750 €2206 Mission Street, San Francisco (53x36cm-21x14in) s. W/C. 7-Feb-4 Auctions by the Bay, Alameda #1571/R
£4571 $8000 €6674 Boat in Malaya (40x56cm-16x22in) s.d.55 i.verso W/C prov. 19-Dec-3 Sotheby's, New York #1146/R est:2000-3000
£5233 $9000 €7640 Junks under the Brooklyn Bridge (47x72cm-19x28in) W/C htd white board. 3-Dec-3 Doyle, New York #271/R est:3000-5000

KINGMAN, Eduardo (1913-1997) Ecuadorian
£4706 $8000 €6871 Unity (140x70cm-55x28in) s.d.1989. 25-Nov-3 Galeria y Remates, Montevideo #182/R

KINGSBURY, Alan (1960-) British
£800 $1416 €1168 Divertimento nel acqua (25x35cm-10x14in) s. board. 27-Apr-4 Bonhams, Knightsbridge #185/R

KINGSBURY, Edward R (1879-1940) American
£267 $425 €390 Crane beach, Barbados (41x50cm-16x20in) s. i.verso panel. 12-Sep-3 Skinner, Boston #522/R

KINGSBURY, Henry (18th C) British
Works on paper
£320 $582 €467 St Nicholas' Church, Newcastle-on-Tyne (28x37cm-11x15in) W/C. 29-Jun-4 Anderson & Garland, Newcastle #197/R

KINGSFORD, Florence (fl.1899-1901) British
Works on paper
£320 $592 €467 Young lady reading from a book (36x25cm-14x10in) s.d.1901 W/C. 13-Feb-4 Keys, Aylsham #503

KINGSTON, Jennifer (20th C) Irish
£800 $1448 €1200 Rockpool (74x62cm-29x24in) s. board prov. 30-Mar-4 De Veres Art Auctions, Dublin #14/R

KINGSTON, Richard (1922-2003) British
£921 $1695 €1400 Farm land (17x28cm-7x11in) s. board. 22-Jun-4 De Veres Art Auctions, Dublin #62/R
£1184 $2179 €1800 Mature apples (29x24cm-11x9in) s.i. board. 22-Jun-4 De Veres Art Auctions, Dublin #61/R est:2000-3000
£1538 $2615 €2200 Crumbling cottage (28x35cm-11x14in) s. board prov. 25-Nov-3 De Veres Art Auctions, Dublin #131/R est:800-1200
£1667 $3017 €2500 Nuts in rusks (21x26cm-8x10in) s. board prov. 30-Mar-4 De Veres Art Auctions, Dublin #109/R est:2500-3000
£1761 $3046 €2500 Hill fire (41x61cm-16x24in) s. i.verso prov. 10-Dec-3 Bonhams & James Adam, Dublin #174/R est:2500-3500
£1958 $3329 €2800 Third hour (76x30cm-30x12in) s. i.verso canvas on board. 18-Nov-3 Whyte's, Dublin #80/R est:2000-3000
£4000 $7240 €6000 Back of sand dunes, Brittas Bay (39x71cm-15x28in) s. i.d.1981 verso canvasboard. 30-Mar-4 De Veres Art Auctions, Dublin #127/R est:4000-6000
£4014 $6423 €5700 Slaky, cats in a garden (86x56cm-34x22in) s.i.d.1980 board. 16-Sep-3 Whyte's, Dublin #136/R est:6000-8000
£6338 $10141 €9000 Elements of Port Salon (76x99cm-30x39in) s. i.verso board. 16-Sep-3 Whyte's, Dublin #56/R est:8000-10000
£10417 $16979 €15000 Waterhen Pool, Blessington, Co Wicklow (76x121cm-30x48in) s. board. 24-Sep-3 James Adam, Dublin #86/R est:15000-20000
£11333 $20513 €17000 Timeless burren (124x147cm-49x58in) s. i.verso board. 30-Mar-4 De Veres Art Auctions, Dublin #53a/R est:10000-15000
Works on paper
£307 $552 €460 Imprisoned spirit (28x20cm-11x8in) s. W/C. 20-Apr-4 James Adam, Dublin #59/R
£633 $1140 €950 Killarney, plein air (10x12cm-4x5in) s. W/C. 20-Apr-4 James Adam, Dublin #60/R
£667 $1207 €1000 Still life (33x28cm-13x11in) s.d.88 mixed media. 30-Mar-4 De Veres Art Auctions, Dublin #89/R
£764 $1245 €1100 Supper time, Irish Tinkers, Connemara (19x24cm-7x9in) s. gouache prov. 24-Sep-3 James Adam, Dublin #124/R est:1200-1800
£1477 $2613 €2200 Flooded quarry (43x58cm-17x23in) s. i.d.1983 verso W/C exhib. 27-Apr-4 Whyte's, Dublin #148/R est:2000-3000
£1622 $3065 €2400 Dodder view from Ballsbridge, prospect of St. Mary's Church Simmonscourt Road (24x29cm-9x11in) s.i.d.1996 W/C. 17-Feb-4 Whyte's, Dublin #22/R est:1500-1800
£1745 $3089 €2600 Leaves, Wellington Road (30x20cm-12x8in) s. W/C pastel. 27-Apr-4 Whyte's, Dublin #87/R est:1800-2200

KINGSTONE, Ian (20th C) New Zealander
£260 $448 €380 The usual suspects (45x45cm-18x18in) s. 7-Dec-3 International Art Centre, Auckland #205/R (NZ.D 700)
£362 $587 €525 White lilies (65x44cm-26x17in) s. board. 31-Jul-3 International Art Centre, Auckland #141/R est:1200-1400 (NZ.D 1000)
£414 $703 €604 Broken butterflies (45x45cm-18x18in) s. 27-Nov-3 International Art Centre, Auckland #166/R (NZ.D 1100)

KINGWELL, Mabel A (fl.1914-1923) British
Works on paper
£750 $1403 €1095 Farmer with three shire horses ploughing a field (17x35cm-7x14in) s.d.1916 pencil W/C htd white. 22-Jul-4 Tennants, Leyburn #752

KINIEUES, Elio (19/20th C) ?
£1950 $3315 €2847 Moltrasio. Washing the laundry in the lake (16x24cm-6x9in) s.i.d.May 1903 panel two. 4-Nov-3 Dreweatt Neate, Newbury #146/R est:400-500

KINIGSTEIN, Jonah (1923-) American
£217 $375 €317 Equestrian (38x91cm-15x36in) s. board prov. 15-Dec-3 Hindman, Chicago #31/R
£407 $650 €594 Manipulator (89x152cm-35x60in) masonite board. 20-Sep-3 Bunte, Elgin #339

KININGER, Vincenz Georg (1767-1851) German
Works on paper
£300 $543 €450 Hungarian peasants (18x24cm-7x9in) i. Indian ink pen brush htd red. 2-Apr-4 Winterberg, Heidelberg #441/R

KININMONTH, Caroline (1907-1978) British
£1300 $2171 €1898 Still life (75x62cm-30x24in) s. 16-Oct-3 Bonhams, Edinburgh #53/R est:800-1200

KINKEAD, Alice S (fl.1897-1926) British
£320 $509 €464 Fishing fleet in harbour (55x68cm-22x27in) s.d.1901. 9-Sep-3 David Duggleby, Scarborough #283
£420 $701 €613 Fishing fleet (51x64cm-20x25in) s.d.1904. 17-Oct-3 Keys, Aylsham #697

KINKOKU, Yokoi (1761-1832) Japanese
Works on paper
£850 $1420 €1241 Mountainous landscapes (132x11cm-52x4in) s. ink col pair. 12-Nov-3 Christie's, London #18/R
£2600 $4342 €3796 Spring landscape. Winter landscape (115x41cm-45x16in) s.i. ink col silk pair. 12-Nov-3 Christie's, London #48/R est:3000-5000

KINLEY, Peter (1926-1988) British
£1200 $2148 €1752 Studio interior (25x20cm-10x8in) s. oil paper prov. 14-May-4 Christie's, Kensington #632/R est:1200-1800
£1300 $2405 €1898 Study for studio interior (25x20cm-10x8in) s. board exhib. 11-Mar-4 Christie's, Kensington #306/R est:600-800

£2300 $3841 €3358 Vase of flowers (76x63cm-30x25in) 16-Oct-3 Lawrence, Crewkerne #755
Works on paper
£800 $1432 €1168 Standing figure, Monika (23x13cm-9x5in) pencil oil. 14-May-4 Christie's, Kensington #561a/R

KINNAIRD, Frederick Gerald (19th C) British
£318 $569 €464 Landscape (40x65cm-16x26in) s. 28-May-4 Uppsala Auktionskammare, Uppsala #133 (S.KR 4300)

KINNAIRD, Henry J (fl.1880-1908) British
£1400 $2562 €2044 Cornstalks in a field, extensive landscape beyond (46x81cm-18x32in) s. 27-Jan-4 Gorringes, Lewes #1602/R est:800-1200
£1900 $3173 €2774 Haymaking scene (39x60cm-15x24in) s.i. 16-Oct-3 Lawrence, Crewkerne #745
Works on paper
£350 $571 €511 Shepherd and his flock, Lancing Church, Sussex (34x25cm-13x10in) s.i. W/C. 24-Sep-3 Dreweatt Neate, Newbury #2/R
£350 $644 €511 Near Henley on Thames (23x32cm-9x13in) s.i. pencil W/C. 25-Mar-4 Christie's, Kensington #208
£520 $848 €759 Thames near Pangbourne (20x39cm-8x15in) s.i. W/C htd white. 24-Sep-3 Dreweatt Neate, Newbury #46
£580 $998 €847 Sussex cornfield (34x51cm-13x20in) s.i. W/C. 3-Dec-3 Cheffins, Cambridge #567
£580 $1038 €847 River landscape (31x50cm-12x20in) s. W/C. 25-May-4 Bonhams, Knightsbridge #282/R
£583 $916 €840 Thames at Pangbourne (34x52cm-13x20in) s.i. W/C lit. 30-Aug-3 Hans Stahl, Toestorf #50/R
£720 $1296 €1051 On the Thames near Stoke (19x40cm-7x16in) s.i. W/C. 21-Jan-4 Sotheby's, Olympia #179/R
£800 $1448 €1168 Sussex Downs, shepherd and sheep beside a cottage (18x28cm-7x11in) s. W/C. 31-Mar-4 Brightwells, Leominster #895
£850 $1522 €1241 Thames, near Abingdon, figure in a punt and cattle at the waters edge (18x28cm-7x11in) s.i. 17-Mar-4 John Nicholson, Haslemere #682
£944 $1500 €1378 Cows watering (34x51cm-13x20in) s.i. W/C gouache. 12-Sep-3 Skinner, Boston #246/R
£1300 $2236 €1898 Sussex lane (35x53cm-14x21in) s.i. pencil W/C bodycol. 3-Dec-3 Christie's, Kensington #125/R est:800-1200
£1300 $2236 €1898 Harvesters before Salisbury Cathedral. Autumn lane (33x23cm-13x9in) s.i. W/C pair. 3-Dec-3 Christie's, Kensington #137/R est:600-800
£1300 $2080 €1898 Cooksbridge (48x36cm-19x14in) s.i. W/C. 16-Sep-3 Capes Dunn, Manchester #837/R
£1750 $2975 €2555 Haymakers in a landscape (33x53cm-13x21in) s.i. W/C. 28-Oct-3 Lawrences, Bletchingley #1846 est:1000-1500
£2100 $3696 €3066 Near Pulborough, Sussex (52x34cm-20x13in) s.i. W/C. 18-May-4 Fellows & Sons, Birmingham #176/R est:850-1250

KINNAIRD, Henry J (attrib) (fl.1880-1908) British
£279 $500 €407 Landscape (48x71cm-19x28in) board. 8-May-4 Susanin's, Chicago #6030/R

KINNAIRD, Wiggs (1875-1915) British
Works on paper
£380 $623 €555 The Derwent, near Ashford (34x50cm-13x20in) s.i. W/C. 3-Jun-3 Fellows & Sons, Birmingham #121/R
£580 $1061 €847 Wangford, Suffolk. River Nene at Irchester (34x49cm-13x19in) s. W/C pair. 7-Apr-4 Bonhams, Bury St Edmunds #390

KINNEAR, James (fl.1880-1917) British
£206 $375 €301 Glen Groe (25x36cm-10x14in) s. i.verso oil paper on wood panel. 19-Jun-4 Jackson's, Cedar Falls #54b/R
£290 $499 €423 Children at play in the forest (48x35cm-19x14in) s. 2-Dec-3 Ritchie, Toronto #52/R (C.D 650)
£12000 $18840 €17400 Links at St. Andrews (30x42cm-12x17in) s. i.verso board. 27-Aug-3 Sotheby's, London #914/R est:2000-3000
Works on paper
£202 $371 €295 Mountain and flood (75x54cm-30x21in) s.d.1903 i.verso W/C. 9-Jun-4 Walker's, Ottawa #361/R (C.D 500)
£300 $552 €438 Cannes from Mont-Chevalier (33x51cm-13x20in) s.i. pencil W/C htd white. 25-Mar-4 Christie's, Kensington #89/R
£300 $543 €438 Figure on a lakeside path (50x75cm-20x30in) s. W/C. 30-Mar-4 Sworder & Son, Bishops Stortford #554/R
£350 $613 €511 Woman and young girl on a roadway leading from a farm (20x33cm-8x13in) s. W/C. 18-Dec-3 John Nicholson, Haslemere #1038
£360 $659 €526 Rural setting (51x75cm-20x30in) s.d.1900 W/C htd bodycol. 27-Jan-4 Bonhams, Knightsbridge #220/R
£447 $800 €653 St Mary's Loch, Selkirkshire, Scotland (43x60cm-17x24in) i.verso W/C. 4-May-4 Ritchie, Toronto #3/R est:800-1000 (C.D 1100)
£700 $1106 €1022 Tummel Pitlochry (48x74cm-19x29in) s.d.1909 W/C. 2-Sep-3 Gildings, Market Harborough #417

KINNEY, Charlie (20th C) American
£222 $400 €324 Bear eating ants (56x71cm-22x28in) oil maker on posterboard. 24-Apr-4 Slotin Folk Art, Buford #525/R
£254 $425 €371 Pole cat (56x74cm-22x29in) paint poster. 15-Nov-3 Slotin Folk Art, Buford #371/R
Works on paper
£299 $500 €437 Cow going dry (56x71cm-22x28in) W/C pencil poster. 15-Nov-3 Slotin Folk Art, Buford #370/R

KINSBOURG, C (?) French
Sculpture
£1333 $2440 €2000 Jeune femme noire assise tenant un enfant accroupi sur ses jambes (19x18x8cm-7x7x3in) s. pat bronze Cast Susse. 3-Jun-4 E & Eve, Paris #50/R est:2000-2500

KINSBOURG, Levy (?) French
Sculpture
£2000 $3660 €3000 Jeune femme noire tenant un enfant sur son dos (33x11x9cm-13x4x4in) pat bronze Cast Susse. 3-Jun-4 E & Eve, Paris #49/R est:3000-3500

KINSELLA, James (attrib) (1857-1923) American
£645 $1200 €942 Ploughing at sunset (47x73cm-19x29in) 5-Mar-4 Skinner, Boston #283/R

KINSEN, M (1888-1959) Japanese
£1569 $2839 €2291 View of a lake (60x95cm-24x37in) s. 4-Apr-4 Sotheby's, Singapore #27/R est:4000-6000 (S.D 4800)

KINSEY, Alberta (1875-1955) American
£326 $600 €476 French Quarter Courtyard (30x23cm-12x9in) s. board. 27-Mar-4 New Orleans Auction, New Orleans #827
£659 $1200 €962 French Quarter Courtyard (38x30cm-15x12in) s. board. 7-Feb-4 Neal Auction Company, New Orleans #1113
£941 $1600 €1374 Vieux Carre courtyard with fountain (46x36cm-18x14in) s. canvasboard. 22-Nov-3 New Orleans Auction, New Orleans #1076/R est:1500-2500
£1420 $2300 €2073 French quarter courtyard (41x30cm-16x12in) s. canvasboard. 2-Aug-3 Neal Auction Company, New Orleans #402/R est:1500-2500
£1705 $3000 €2489 French Quarter, New Orleans (58x76cm-23x30in) s. canvas on board painted c.1940. 23-May-4 Treadway Gallery, Cincinnati #728/R est:1500-2500

KINSEY, Alberta (attrib) (1875-1955) American
£243 $450 €355 Landscape with boat and Spanish moss (46x61cm-18x24in) indis sig. 12-Mar-4 Jackson's, Cedar Falls #770/R

KINSLEY, Edgar L (19th C) American
£223 $400 €326 Echo Bridge (51x66cm-20x26in) s.d.1878. 16-May-4 CRN Auctions, Cambridge #21/R

KINSLEY, Nelson Gray (1863-1945) German
£486 $768 €700 Altkonig in summer (17x27cm-7x11in) s. 6-Sep-3 Arnold, Frankfurt #594/R
£567 $1031 €850 Landscape (23x37cm-9x15in) s.d.1941. 1-Jul-4 Van Ham, Cologne #1453
£872 $1623 €1300 Autumn moorland by moonlight (26x22cm-10x9in) s. 6-Mar-4 Arnold, Frankfurt #756/R
£1800 $3276 €2700 Landscape with trees (52x62cm-20x24in) s. 1-Jul-4 Van Ham, Cologne #1454/R est:3100
Works on paper
£268 $499 €400 Taunus in summer (18x22cm-7x9in) s. W/C. 6-Mar-4 Arnold, Frankfurt #757/R

KINSON, François Joseph (1771-1839) Flemish
£12587 $21650 €18000 Portrait de femme en robe bleue (190x126cm-75x50in) s. 2-Dec-3 Sotheby's, Paris #27/R est:20000-30000

KINZEL, Josef (1852-1925) Austrian
£950 $1511 €1378 Elegant lady (27x23cm-11x9in) s. panel. 9-Sep-3 Bonhams, Knightsbridge #163/R

KIOERBOE, Carl Fredrik (1799-1876) Swedish
£465 $838 €679 Landscape with cattle (52x46cm-20x18in) s.indis.d. 26-Jan-4 Lilla Bukowskis, Stockholm #203 (S.KR 6200)
£532 $953 €777 Chasseur - gundog in landscape (27x35cm-11x14in) s. 26-May-4 AB Stockholms Auktionsverk #2217/R (S.KR 7200)
£658 $1211 €1000 Lionceaux (73x92cm-29x36in) s. 28-Jun-4 Joron-Derem, Paris #107/R
£1056 $1827 €1500 Foxes (82x100cm-32x39in) s. 11-Dec-3 Christie's, Rome #138 est:1500-2000
£1405 $2600 €2051 Head of bassett hound (64x53cm-25x21in) s. i. verso. 10-Feb-4 Doyle, New York #161/R est:1500-2500

KIPNISS, Robert (1931-) American
£1384 $2200 €2021 Landscape in green (63x76cm-25x30in) s. 12-Sep-3 Skinner, Boston #398/R
£1509 $2400 €2203 Mid afternoon (122x102cm-48x40in) s. acrylic. 14-Sep-3 Susanin's, Chicago #6010/R est:700-900

KIPPENBERGER, Martin (1953-1997) German
£3667 $6710 €5500 Social pasta (28x21cm-11x8in) mono.i.d.92 oil chk hotel letterhead. 4-Jun-4 Lempertz, Koln #248/R est:3500
£8333 $15250 €12500 Untitled (65x81cm-26x32in) s.d.87 verso on tablecloth. 4-Jun-4 Lempertz, Koln #242/R est:12000-15000
£14000 $25760 €20440 Anschaung (60x51cm-24x20in) s.d.90 verso prov. 25-Jun-4 Christie's, London #212/R est:10000-15000
£14336 $24371 €20500 Olblomov 2 (90x75cm-35x30in) s.i. verso oil latex prov. 27-Nov-3 Lempertz, Koln #216/R est:12000-15000
£26000 $47320 €37960 Copacabana Palace (65x92cm-26x36in) i. oil paint coins prov. 6-Feb-4 Sotheby's, London #112/R est:25000-35000
£37000 $68080 €54020 Untitled (90x75cm-35x30in) s.d.91/92 verso. 24-Jun-4 Sotheby's, London #286/R est:25000-35000
£46000 $83720 €67160 Einsam (120x100cm-47x39in) i. s.d.83 verso oil spraypaint prov. 6-Feb-4 Sotheby's, London #242/R est:25000-35000
£48951 $83217 €70000 Girl mixes up pattex with her pills (90x75cm-35x30in) oil collage newspaper cutting prov.exhib. 27-Nov-3 Lempertz, Koln #213/R est:28000-32000
£50000 $92000 €73000 Untitled - Ricki (100x120cm-39x47in) oil spraypaint on canvas prov. 25-Jun-4 Christie's, London #217/R est:25000-35000
£72626 $130000 €106034 Untitled (120x100cm-47x39in) init.d.96 verso. 13-May-4 Phillips, New York #49/R est:100000-150000

£110000	$202400	€160600	Entwurf fur die Verbesserung des Ruckenschwimmens in Rio II (177x150cm-70x59in) init.d.1984 acrylic silicone sand plaster linen canvas towelling. 25-Jun-4 Christie's, London #211/R est:60000-80000
£251397	$450000	€367040	Self with Michel Wurthle (160x185cm-63x73in) four parts painted 1992 prov.exhib. 12-May-4 Sotheby's, New York #6/R est:200000-300000
£346369	$620000	€505699	Wie komme ich in kriegszeiten mit knoch enbruch und futurismus klar (222x178cm-87x70in) d.12/84 verso oil metallic paint six panels prov.lit. 14-May-4 Phillips, New York #207/R est:60000-80000
Photographs			
£2333	$4177	€3500	Untitled (60x50cm-24x20in) mono.d.86 verso C print. 15-May-4 Van Ham, Cologne #714/R est:3500
Sculpture			
£3352	$6000	€4894	Kippenseltzer (29x28x4cm-11x11x2in) s.verso wood prov.exhib.lit. 14-May-4 Phillips, New York #319/R est:6000-8000
£15035	$25559	€21500	Neonbabies (10x60x5cm-4x24x2in) neon light strip bronze plastic varnish wood lit. 27-Nov-3 Lempertz, Koln #211/R est:8500
£20979	$35664	€30000	Family hunger (78x48x19cm-31x19x7in) mono.d.84 verso col styropor plaster gauze exhib.lit. 27-Nov-3 Lempertz, Koln #210/R est:20000
£40268	$72081	€60000	Mary Wigmann (189x52x50cm-74x20x20in) mirrors wood prov. 25-May-4 Dorotheum, Vienna #102/R est:60000-80000
£170000	$283900	€248200	Kellner Des (200x240x19cm-79x94x7in) wall-lights oil canvas on panel prov.lit. 21-Oct-3 Sotheby's, London #363/R est:100000-150000
Works on paper			
£1100	$2002	€1606	Three views (24x19cm-9x7in) init.i.d.88 pencil three prov. 4-Feb-4 Sotheby's, Olympia #3/R est:1000-1500
£3000	$5010	€4380	Stigenberger, Berlin (30x21cm-12x8in) pen ink graphite hotel stationary exec.c.1988 prov. 22-Oct-3 Christie's, London #173/R est:5000-7000
£3478	$5704	€4800	Untitled (22x16cm-9x6in) s.d.85/86 gouache collage ink three. 27-May-3 Sotheby's, Amsterdam #449/R est:2000-3000
£5000	$9200	€7300	Tanzflache fur huhner (29x20cm-11x8in) init.i.d.88 pencil col ballpoint pen gouache printed paper. 24-Jun-4 Sotheby's, Olympia #435/R est:4000-6000
£5000	$9200	€7300	Hotel drawings (61x46cm-24x18in) graphite pen ink col pencil felt tip pen two works prov. 10-Jun-4 Phillips, New York #652/R est:4000-6000
£5667	$10427	€8500	Untitled (33x20cm-13x8in) pencil blue crayon W/C prov. 12-Jun-4 Villa Grisebach, Berlin #443/R est:4000-6000
£6000	$11040	€9000	Untitled (33x20cm-13x8in) pencil blue crayon biro W/C prov. 12-Jun-4 Villa Grisebach, Berlin #442/R est:3500-4500
£6333	$11590	€9500	Individual (30x21cm-12x8in) mono.d.92 pencil col pen hotel letterhead. 4-Jun-4 Lempertz, Koln #247/R est:3500
£6643	$11294	€9500	Untitled - Argumentos caros. Una sonata en verde (65x64cm-26x25in) i. stretcher collage material plexiglas silicon nylon prov. 27-Nov-3 Lempertz, Koln #212/R est:6000
£9667	$17690	€14500	Untitled (69x98cm-27x39in) mono.d.89 collage silkscreen transparent foil prov. 4-Jun-4 Lempertz, Koln #243/R est:12000-15000
£11173	$20000	€16313	We don't have problems with KG when we are high (32x23cm-13x9in) init.d.86 col pencil graphite W/C paper collage prov. 14-May-4 Phillips, New York #151/R est:12000-15000
£11377	$19000	€16610	Untitled - Heartbreak Hotel. init.i.d.95 graphite col pencil prov.exhib. 14-Nov-3 Phillips, New York #192/R est:8000-12000
£16304	$30000	€23804	Hotel drawings. graphite pen ink col pencil four parts prov. 10-Jun-4 Phillips, New York #443/R est:8000-12000
£17333	$31720	€26000	Untitled - 1889 souvenir (42x56cm-17x22in) mono.i.d.91 W/C Indian ink pencil lit. 4-Jun-4 Lempertz, Koln #246/R est:10000-15000
£20667	$37820	€31000	Now I'm going into the wood (42x56cm-17x22in) mono.i.d.91 W/C Indian ink pencil lit. 4-Jun-4 Lempertz, Koln #245/R est:10000-15000
£26816	$48000	€39151	Hotel drawings (29x21cm-11x8in) graphite pen ink col pencil felt tip pen four prov. 14-May-4 Phillips, New York #206/R est:15000-20000
£48000	$87840	€72000	Untitled - self portrait (35x50cm-14x20in) mono.d.88 brio W/C gouache. 4-Jun-4 Lempertz, Koln #244/R est:15000-20000

KIPS, Erich (1869-?) German

£1678	$2887	€2400	View of Malcesine at Gardasee (101x152cm-40x60in) s. 5-Dec-3 Bolland & Marotz, Bremen #585/R est:1500

KIRALL, Emmerich (20th C) Austrian

Works on paper			
£268	$494	€400	Old Vienna, Gumpendorf street, Windmill street (11x9cm-4x4in) s.i.d.1927 W/C. 26-Mar-4 Dorotheum, Vienna #285/R

KIRBERG, Otto (1850-1926) German

£1429	$2557	€2100	Friesian peasant family building model ship (43x54cm-17x21in) s.i. 18-Mar-4 Neumeister, Munich #2699/R est:200
£10884	$17306	€16000	Flemish interior (105x123cm-41x48in) s. trace d. 23-Mar-3 Mercier & Cie, Lille #210/R est:12000-15000

KIRCHBACH, Frank (1859-1912) German

£669	$1070	€950	Kaiser Friedrich III (24x18cm-9x7in) 18-Sep-3 Rieber, Stuttgart #813/R
£2333	$4223	€3500	Scene mythologique (115x87cm-45x34in) s.d.1881. 3-Apr-4 Gerard, Besancon #56

KIRCHER, Alexandre (1867-?) German

£449	$836	€656	Fishing boat on fjord at sunset (80x120cm-31x47in) s. 2-Mar-4 Rasmussen, Copenhagen #1353/R (D.KR 5000)
£699	$1189	€1000	Sea in the evening (70x10cm-28x4in) s. 20-Nov-3 Van Ham, Cologne #1683
£1200	$2148	€1752	German liner Bremen outward bound for New York (63x93cm-25x37in) 26-May-4 Christie's, Kensington #739/R est:800-1200

KIRCHGRABER, Bruno (20th C) ?

£271	$462	€396	Berneck in Rhine valley (51x75cm-20x30in) s.d.69 i. verso. 18-Nov-3 Hans Widmer, St Gallen #1112 (S.FR 600)

KIRCHMAIR, Joseph (1806-1846) German

£986	$1706	€1400	Hunters by river (41x64cm-16x25in) s.d.40. 11-Dec-3 Dr Fritz Nagel, Stuttgart #531/R

KIRCHMAYR, Cherubino (1848-?) Italian

Works on paper			
£280	$442	€406	Portrait of a young girl in a lace collar (47x35cm-19x14in) s.i.d.94 s. verso w/. 2-Sep-3 Bonhams, Oxford #61/R
£800	$1480	€1168	Elsie, Blanche, Evelyn, Frances, Haite (43x33cm-17x13in) s.i.d.1894 W/C. 10-Mar-4 Sotheby's, Olympia #301/R

KIRCHNER, Ernst Ludwig (1880-1938) German

£6944	$11597	€10000	Still life of flowers (38x49cm-15x19in) s.d. i. verso W/C over pencil. 25-Oct-3 Dr Lehr, Berlin #270/R est:12000
£20000	$36800	€30000	Bathing scene through trees (43x40cm-17x16in) woodcut. 10-Jun-4 Hauswedell & Nolte, Hamburg #327/R est:28000
£20979	$36084	€30000	Sea with boat (24x33cm-9x13in) gouache oil over pencil cardboard prov. 5-Dec-3 Ketterer, Munich #48/R est:20000-30000
£81448	$138462	€180000	Woman with cat (64x48cm-25x19in) s. painted 1930-32. 25-Nov-3 Pierre Berge, Paris #15/R est:120000-150000
£100000	$184000	€146000	Cantatrice au piano (121x150cm-48x59in) s.i.d.29 prov.exhib.lit. 23-Jun-4 Christie's, London #176/R est:120000-180000
£123333	$220767	€185000	Reclining female nude on divan (43x34cm-17x13in) col chk board prov. 14-May-4 Ketterer, Munich #136/R est:60000-80000
£180000	$327600	€262800	Ice hockey players (86x70cm-31x28in) s.d.34 prov.exhib.lit. 3-Feb-4 Sotheby's, London #28/R est:180000-250000
Photographs			
£5046	$8427	€7317	Photograph of the oil painting 'English dancing couple' (21x17cm-8x7in) bears s.i. photo. 19-Jun-3 Kornfeld, Bern #552 est:2000 (S.FR 11000)
Prints			
£1733	$3189	€2600	Female nude with long hair (32x41cm-13x16in) lithograph. 11-Jun-4 Villa Grisebach, Berlin #1532/R est:3000-4000
£2200	$3938	€3300	Nudes with deer (18x18cm-7x7in) s.i. drypoint etching. 15-May-4 Bassenge, Berlin #6938/R est:3500
£2542	$4500	€3711	Knaben Im Zimmer (25x20cm-10x8in) etching. 28-Apr-4 Christie's, Rockefeller NY #57/R est:5000-7000
£2797	$4671	€4000	Ruth seated (26x32cm-10x13in) lithograph. 10-Oct-3 Winterberg, Heidelberg #1507/R est:5600
£2800	$5152	€4200	Alp scene with horses (25x30cm-10x12in) s.i. etching drypoint exec. 1922. 11-Jun-4 Villa Grisebach, Berlin #1539/R est:5000-7000
£2953	$5434	€4400	Elisabeth shore (20x23cm-8x9in) i. woodcut lit. 27-Mar-4 Auktionhaus Herr, Cologne #196/R est:2200
£3125	$5219	€4500	Seated woman wearing light coloured blouse (17x15cm-7x6in) s.i. i. verso drypoint etching. 24-Oct-3 Ketterer, Hamburg #428/R est:4500-5500
£3211	$5362	€4656	Midday meal. s.i. woodcut. 19-Jun-3 Kornfeld, Bern #540 est:10000 (S.FR 7000)
£3356	$5940	€5000	Herdsman (64x42cm-25x17in) s.i. woodcut. 30-Apr-4 Dr Fritz Nagel, Stuttgart #864/R est:9800
£3529	$6000	€5152	Liegender madchenkopf (25x24cm-10x9in) s.i.d.1917 blue ink drypoint. 6-Nov-3 Swann Galleries, New York #587/R est:8000-12000
£4056	$6976	€5800	Female nude standing (12x3cm-5x1in) woodcut prov. 5-Dec-3 Ketterer, Munich #42/R est:6000-8000
£4333	$7973	€6500	Rapperswil (50x35cm-20x14in) woodcut. 10-Jun-4 Hauswedell & Nolte, Hamburg #329/R est:7500
£4412	$7500	€6442	Fingerspiel (15x9cm-6x4in) s.num.handdruck i.verso woodcut. 6-Nov-3 Swann Galleries, New York #585/R est:10000-15000
£4895	$8322	€7000	Nude figures in wood (31x25cm-12x10in) s.i.d. etching board. 29-Nov-3 Villa Grisebach, Berlin #170/R est:7000-9000
£5240	$9537	€7650	Among the larches. s.d.18 etching. 17-Jun-4 Kornfeld, Bern #463 est:12500 (S.FR 12000)
£5594	$9622	€8000	Figure standing up (41x33cm-16x13in) s. lithograph. 2-Dec-3 Hauswedell & Nolte, Hamburg #302/R est:6000
£5594	$9510	€8000	Two men bathing (25x19cm-10x7in) s. etching board. 29-Nov-3 Villa Grisebach, Berlin #172/R est:7000-9000
£5652	$10343	€8252	Slender girl in front of open door (34x25cm-13x10in) s.i. woodcut prov.lit. 7-Jun-4 Christie's, Zurich #99/R est:15000-25000 (S.FR 13000)
£6294	$10699	€9000	Reclining nude (29x19cm-11x7in) woodcut. 29-Nov-3 Villa Grisebach, Berlin #150/R est:5000-7000
£6294	$10699	€9000	Bathers in hut (31x25cm-12x10in) s.i.d.23 etching board. 29-Nov-3 Villa Grisebach, Berlin #171/R est:9000-11000
£6667	$12267	€10000	Blossoming tree (34x24cm-13x9in) s.i. woodcut exec. 1909. 12-Jun-4 Villa Grisebach, Berlin #203/R est:10000-15000
£6881	$11491	€9977	Botanical garden in Jea. woodcut. 19-Jun-3 Kornfeld, Bern #535/R est:17500 (S.FR 15000)
£7667	$14107	€11500	Head of Robert Binswanger (38x26cm-15x10in) s.i. woodcut. 10-Jun-4 Hauswedell & Nolte, Hamburg #328/R est:15000
£8000	$14720	€12000	Girls walking in woodland (31x25cm-12x10in) s.i. etching. 10-Jun-4 Hauswedell & Nolte, Hamburg #326/R est:10000
£8297	$15100	€12114	Dodo playing with her fingers. s.i. lithograph. 17-Jun-4 Kornfeld, Bern #464/R est:15000 (S.FR 19000)
£8734	$15895	€12752	Portrait of Hans Mardersteig (61x51cm-24x20in) s.i. col lithograph exec. 1920. 18-Jun-4 Kornfeld, Bern #74/R est:20000 (S.FR 20000)
£9174	$15321	€13302	Chopping wood. s.i. woodcut. 19-Jun-3 Kornfeld, Bern #537/R est:22500 (S.FR 20000)
£9333	$17173	€14000	Peasant couple dancing (59x50cm-23x20in) s.i. lithograph exec. 1920. 11-Jun-4 Villa Grisebach, Berlin #1540/R est:18000-24000
£9655	$16124	€14000	Indian dancer (38x28cm-15x11in) s.i. lithograph. 13-Nov-3 Neumeister, Munich #358/R est:12000-15000
£9667	$17787	€14500	Girls doing themselves up (38x32cm-15x13in) i.verso lithograph exec. 1910 one of three. 11-Jun-4 Villa Grisebach, Berlin #1534/R est:15000-20000
£11354	$20664	€16577	Three bathers on Fehmarn beach (31x42cm-12x17in) s. lithograph exec. 1913. 18-Jun-4 Kornfeld, Bern #67/R est:30000 (S.FR 26000)
£15000	$25800	€21900	Aus der apokalypse (22x21cm-9x8in) s.i.d.1920 col woodcut. 4-Dec-3 Sotheby's, London #154/R est:15000-18000
£20000	$35800	€30000	Reclining nude (20x28cm-8x11in) s.i. woodcut. 15-May-4 Dr Sturies, Dusseldorf #103/R
£20000	$36800	€30000	Melancholic girl, self portrait with Erna (70x40cm-28x16in) s.i.indis.d. woodcut prov. 11-Jun-4 Villa Grisebach, Berlin #26/R est:35000-45000
£22707	$41328	€33152	Still life with a wooden figure (40x31cm-16x12in) i.verso col woodcut exec. 1919. 18-Jun-4 Kornfeld, Bern #70/R est:50000 (S.FR 52000)
£25333	$46613	€38000	Pedestrians and tram (25x20cm-10x8in) s. drypoint etching prov. 11-Jun-4 Villa Grisebach, Berlin #24/R est:30000-40000
£38667	$69213	€58000	Three nudes in water (33x38cm-13x15in) s.i. lithograph. 15-May-4 Dr Sturies, Dusseldorf #105/R
£50000	$89500	€75000	Three cocottes at night (25x17cm-10x7in) s. etching. 15-May-4 Dr Sturies, Dusseldorf #104/R

£50218	$91397	€73318	Blond woman and dark haired woman (69x40cm-27x16in) s.i.d.22 woodcut. 18-Jun-4 Kornfeld, Bern #73/R est:100000 (S.FR 115000)
£54585	$99345	€79694	The sale of the shadows (32x22cm-13x9in) s. col woodcut exec. 1915 lit. 18-Jun-4 Kornfeld, Bern #68/R est:150000 (S.FR 125000)
£85315	$146741	€122000	Battles - torment of love - self portrait (33x22cm-13x9in) s. col woodcut. 2-Dec-3 Hauswedell & Nolte, Hamburg #304/R est:80000
£200000	$364000	€292000	Wettertannen (67x402cm-26x158in) s.i. col woodcut from three blocks. 1-Jul-4 Sotheby's, London #190/R est:60000-80000

Works on paper

£688	$1149	€998	Quartet (19x16cm-7x6in) Indian ink sold with another. 19-Jun-3 Kornfeld, Bern #525 (S.FR 1500)
£1067	$1920	€1600	Chansonette (21x16cm-8x6in) i.d. verso graphite. 24-Apr-4 Dr Lehr, Berlin #216/R est:1600
£1100	$1837	€1606	Tanzerin im Glockenrock (21x17cm-8x7in) graphite prov. 22-Oct-3 Bonhams, New Bond Street #40/R est:1500-2000
£1101	$1839	€1596	Three women at round table (13x15cm-5x6in) ink. 19-Jun-3 Kornfeld, Bern #532 est:2000 (S.FR 2400)
£1189	$2045	€1700	Girl on stage (15x20cm-6x8in) pencil. 2-Dec-3 Hauswedell & Nolte, Hamburg #297/R est:2000
£1259	$2140	€1800	Dancer (12x9cm-5x4in) Indian ink prov. exhib. 29-Nov-3 Villa Grisebach, Berlin #596/R est:1800-2400
£1364	$2400	€1991	Wooded landscape of Davos (10x18cm-4x7in) s. ink pencil executed c.1916 prov. 22-May-4 New Orleans Auction, New Orleans #127 est:2500-4000
£1376	$2298	€1995	Two girls and two men (28x22cm-11x9in) pencil. 19-Jun-3 Kornfeld, Bern #526 est:1500 (S.FR 3000)
£1400	$2338	€2044	Landschaft agyptische grabmalerei (21x28cm-8x11in) i.verso graphite. 22-Oct-3 Bonhams, New Bond Street #42/R est:1500-2000
£1533	$2821	€2300	Female nude with child (21x18cm-8x7in) pencil. 10-Jun-4 Hauswedell & Nolte, Hamburg #318/R est:3000
£1651	$2758	€2394	Group of five figures (15x15cm-6x6in) s.d.1915 Indian ink over pencil. 19-Jun-3 Kornfeld, Bern #529 est:2000 (S.FR 3600)
£1667	$3067	€2500	Ballet scene (22x17cm-9x7in) bears sig. pencil W/C exec. c.1915 prov. 12-Jun-4 Villa Grisebach, Berlin #199/R est:3000-4000
£2661	$4443	€3858	Two girls wearing hats (16x21cm-6x8in) s. Indian ink. 19-Jun-3 Kornfeld, Bern #524/R est:2500 (S.FR 5800)
£2667	$4907	€4000	Female nude, rear view (44x33cm-17x13in) black chk wash exec. c.1909-10 prov. 12-Jun-4 Villa Grisebach, Berlin #198/R est:4000-6000
£2685	$4752	€4000	Kneeling female nude (52x35cm-20x14in) col chk wash board. 30-Apr-4 Dr Fritz Nagel, Stuttgart #863/R est:1800
£2715	$4697	€3964	Group of people (15x15cm-6x6in) s.d.1915 pencil ink. 9-Dec-3 Sotheby's, Zurich #47/R est:5500-8500 (S.FR 6000)
£2797	$4755	€4000	River - Hamburg (19x13cm-7x5in) pen col chk. 29-Nov-3 Bassenge, Berlin #6818/R est:6000
£3211	$5362	€4656	Nude in room (20x14cm-8x6in) s. Indian ink. 19-Jun-3 Kornfeld, Bern #530/R est:4000 (S.FR 7000)
£3303	$5516	€4789	Girl (28x22cm-11x9in) pen brush Indian ink. 19-Jun-3 Kornfeld, Bern #523 est:5000 (S.FR 7200)
£3706	$6375	€5300	Nude female strutting and wooing (49x33cm-19x13in) s. i.verso black chk double-sided prov.exhib. 5-Dec-3 Ketterer, Munich #51/R est:5000-7000
£3977	$7000	€5806	Two bathers on the beach (25x20cm-10x8in) s.d.25 i.verso ink pencil. 22-May-4 New Orleans Auction, New Orleans #134/R est:3500-5000
£4103	$7262	€5990	Figuren im Staffelalp - Tobel (16x26cm-6x10in) W/C ink prov. 27-Apr-4 AB Stockholms Auktionsverk #1216/R est:25000-30000 (S.KR 56000)
£4533	$8115	€6800	Two nudes in Dresden studio (33x26cm-13x10in) s.d.05 i.d. verso pen Indian ink wash prov.exhib. 14-May-4 Ketterer, Munich #148/R est:8000-10000
£4679	$7814	€6785	Dance couple (16x21cm-6x8in) s.d.08 W/C brush Indian ink over pencil. 19-Jun-3 Kornfeld, Bern #519 est:3000 (S.FR 10200)
£5000	$9100	€7300	Komposition - Composition (34x49cm-13x19in) s. W/C pastel. 4-Feb-4 Sotheby's, London #477/R est:3500-4500
£5034	$9262	€7500	Meadow flowers (34x30cm-13x12in) W/C col chk prov. 27-Mar-4 Geble, Radolfzell #785/R est:4000
£5594	$9510	€8000	Girl with hat (34x27cm-13x11in) s. pencil. 29-Nov-3 Bassenge, Berlin #6819/R est:4500
£5667	$10427	€8500	River landscape (32x42cm-13x17in) s. chl chk. 10-Jun-4 Hauswedell & Nolte, Hamburg #319/R est:6000
£6193	$10342	€8980	Two naked girls on sofa (30x45cm-12x18in) pencil. 19-Jun-3 Kornfeld, Bern #520/R est:12500 (S.FR 13500)
£6294	$10699	€9000	Seated female nude (50x39cm-20x15in) s.d.27 chk prov. 29-Nov-3 Villa Grisebach, Berlin #174/R est:7000-9000
£6294	$10825	€9000	Village street (42x34cm-17x13in) pencil exec.1908/09 prov. 5-Dec-3 Ketterer, Munich #46/R est:9000-12000
£6667	$12267	€10000	Two girls (12x15cm-5x6in) W/C pencil black chk exec. c.1910 prov.lit. 12-Jun-4 Villa Grisebach, Berlin #202/R est:5000-7000
£6957	$12730	€10157	Mountain lake (32x51cm-13x20in) s. chl. 7-Jun-4 Christie's, Zurich #101/R est:15000-20000 (S.FR 16000)
£7333	$13127	€11000	Dancing girls in coloured stripes (52x35cm-20x14in) pen col chk transparent paper prov. 14-May-4 Ketterer, Munich #190/R est:9000-12000
£7667	$14030	€11500	Three nudes in the dunes (46x30cm-18x12in) i. verso W/C on pencil. 5-Jun-4 Lempertz, Koln #782/R est:12000-14000
£7692	$13231	€11000	Children playing. Black cat (47x38cm-19x15in) blue black chk double-sided exec.1924-26. 5-Dec-3 Ketterer, Munich #49/R est:11000-13000
£8000	$14720	€11680	Nudes (35x45cm-14x18in) crayon exec.1910 prov. 22-Jun-4 Sotheby's, London #497/R est:8000-12000
£8297	$15100	€12114	Group of houses, Dresden (22x33cm-9x13in) W/C pencil exec. c.1910. 18-Jun-4 Kornfeld, Bern #66/R est:20000 (S.FR 19000)
£8667	$15947	€13000	Landscape near Dresden (17x23cm-7x9in) col chk. 12-Jun-4 Villa Grisebach, Berlin #179/R est:12000-15000
£8734	$15895	€12752	Sawmill in Taunus (38x53cm-15x21in) pen ink exec. 1916. 18-Jun-4 Kornfeld, Bern #65/R est:25000 (S.FR 20000)
£9174	$15321	€13302	Nude on bed (33x44cm-13x17in) col chks pencil. 19-Jun-3 Kornfeld, Bern #521/R est:25000 (S.FR 20000)
£9633	$16087	€13968	Dodo nude (43x34cm-17x13in) chk. 19-Jun-3 Kornfeld, Bern #522 est:25000 (S.FR 21000)
£10000	$18200	€14600	Street scene (20x16cm-8x6in) pencil col crayon prov. 4-Feb-4 Sotheby's, London #433/R est:10000-20000
£10000	$18400	€15000	House under the trees (45x58cm-18x23in) chk exec. c.1913. 12-Jun-4 Villa Grisebach, Berlin #204/R est:15000-20000
£11000	$20240	€16060	Female nudes playing in the woods (49x35cm-19x14in) col crayon exhib. 22-Jun-4 Sotheby's, London #499/R est:12000-15000
£11189	$19021	€16000	Figures round table (67x41cm-26x16in) col chks. 29-Nov-3 Bassenge, Berlin #6817/R est:7500
£11333	$20740	€17000	Nude woman seated by tree in forest (39x43cm-15x17in) i. col chk on W/C. 5-Jun-4 Lempertz, Koln #784/R est:15000-20000
£11888	$20448	€17000	Three female nudes (57x46cm-22x18in) chl cardboard prov. 5-Dec-3 Ketterer, Munich #52/R est:17000-19000
£12587	$21399	€18000	Two girls in Sertig valley (51x39cm-20x15in) i. verso col chk prov.exhib. 26-Nov-3 Lempertz, Koln #760/R est:18000
£13333	$23867	€20000	Spring - three peasants (51x36cm-20x14in) W/C on pencil prov. 14-May-4 Ketterer, Munich #170/R est:20000-25000
£15284	$27817	€22315	Dodo from in front, hands folded (55x36cm-22x14in) pencil. 17-Jun-4 Kornfeld, Bern #460/R est:30000 (S.FR 35000)
£16197	$28021	€23000	Three peasants in field (40x55cm-16x22in) W/C gouache graphite board. 13-Dec-3 Lempertz, Koln #160/R est:25000-30000
£18667	$34347	€28000	Standing female nude (49x32cm-19x13in) W/C pencil prov. 12-Jun-4 Villa Grisebach, Berlin #210/R est:18000-24000
£18881	$32476	€27000	Hilly landscape with sea in front (51x35cm-20x14in) W/C over pencil cardboard exec.1933-35 prov.exhib. 5-Dec-3 Ketterer, Munich #55/R est:14000-18000
£19333	$35573	€29000	Seated nude woman (53x39cm-21x15in) pencil. 10-Jun-4 Hauswedell & Nolte, Hamburg #321/R est:30000
£21678	$36853	€31000	Trees by lake - Bohmen (27x35cm-11x14in) i. verso W/C pencil prov.exhib. 26-Nov-3 Lempertz, Koln #759/R est:25000
£23333	$41767	€35000	Alpine scene (23x27cm-9x11in) s.mono. W/C chk prov. 14-May-4 Ketterer, Munich #166/R est:8000-12000
£24476	$41608	€35000	Bathers on each in Fehmarn (46x59cm-18x23in) s.d.12 pen Indian in ink prov. 28-Nov-3 Villa Grisebach, Berlin #27/R est:40000-50000
£29333	$53973	€44000	Models in the Dresden studio (49x60cm-19x24in) i.verso ink exec. 1910-11 prov.lit. 11-Jun-4 Villa Grisebach, Berlin #1535/R est:30000-40000
£40667	$74827	€61000	Landscape with a figure near Davos (38x50cm-15x20in) s.d.19 gouache pencil card prov. 12-Jun-4 Villa Grisebach, Berlin #211/R est:25000-35000

KIRCHNER, Eugen (1865-?) German

Works on paper

£733	$1349	€1100	La sortie des Nonnes (25x45cm-10x18in) s. pastel gouache. 11-Jun-4 Claude Aguttes, Neuilly #81/R

KIRCHNER, Heinrich (1902-1984) German

Sculpture

£2215	$4053	€3300	Motorbike with sidecar (44x37x32cm-17x15x13in) brown pat. bronze. 9-Jul-4 Dawo, Saarbrucken #128/R est:3600
£2819	$5158	€4200	The walker (48cm-19in) gold brown pat. bronze. 9-Jul-4 Dawo, Saarbrucken #127/R est:2800

KIRCHNER, Otto (1887-1960) German

£265	$482	€400	Elderly bookkeeper (12x9cm-5x4in) s. panel. 18-Jun-4 Bolland & Marotz, Bremen #816
£296	$545	€450	Elderly gentleman reading a letter (18x14cm-7x6in) 28-Jun-4 Dr Fritz Nagel, Stuttgart #7170/R
£333	$607	€500	Enjoying a glass of wine (24x18cm-9x7in) s. panel. 1-Jul-4 Van Ham, Cologne #1455
£336	$621	€500	Old man smoking a pipe (24x18cm-9x7in) s.i. panel. 15-Mar-4 Sotheby's, Amsterdam #68/R
£417	$658	€600	Man reading (24x18cm-9x7in) s.i. panel lit. 19-Sep-3 Schloss Ahlden, Ahlden #1595/R
£467	$845	€700	Peasant reading newspaper (24x18cm-9x7in) s. panel. 1-Apr-4 Van Ham, Cologne #1483
£681	$1178	€994	Glass of good wine (24x18cm-9x7in) s. panel. 14-Dec-3 Agra, Warsaw #57/R (P.Z 4500)
£1259	$2165	€1800	Four art lovers from the Rococo period poring over pictures together (60x50cm-24x20in) s.i. panel. 3-Dec-3 Neumeister, Munich #625/R est:800

KIRCHNER, Raphael (1867-1917) Austrian

Works on paper

£987	$1816	€1500	I have got the key (40x19cm-16x7in) s. W/C gouache. 25-Jun-4 Millon & Associes, Paris #147 est:700-800
£1513	$2784	€2300	Lulu (40x19cm-16x7in) s. crayon gouache. 25-Jun-4 Millon & Associes, Paris #146/R est:800-1200
£1748	$2920	€2500	Nu a la jarretiere (47x25cm-19x10in) W/C gouache. 24-Jun-3 Millon & Associes, Paris #3/R est:2500-3000

KIRCHOFFER, Henry (1781-1860) British

Miniatures

£1300	$2210	€1898	Thomas Henry Gray (8cm-3in) s.d.1804 gold frame oval. 18-Nov-3 Bonhams, New Bond Street #80/R est:600-800

KIRCHSBERG, Ernestine von (1857-1924) Austrian

£300	$540	€450	Leonhard Church in Graz (37x31cm-15x12in) s. canvas on board. 22-Apr-4 Dorotheum, Graz #14
£633	$1140	€950	Hilly landscape in the Steier (21x27cm-8x11in) s. board. 22-Apr-4 Dorotheum, Graz #12/R
£667	$1200	€1000	Stream (44x35cm-17x14in) s. canvas on board. 22-Apr-4 Dorotheum, Graz #15/R
£733	$1320	€1100	Old Posthof in southern Tyrol (44x35cm-17x14in) s. board. 22-Apr-4 Dorotheum, Graz #22
£733	$1320	€1100	Kottubinsky garden (37x28cm-15x11in) s. W/C. 22-Apr-4 Dorotheum, Graz #60/R
£800	$1440	€1200	Barenschutz (27x38cm-11x15in) s. canvas on board. 22-Apr-4 Dorotheum, Graz #16/R
£805	$1442	€1200	Farmstead (29x38cm-11x15in) s. i. verso canvas on board. 27-May-4 Dorotheum, Graz #31/R
£805	$1442	€1200	Mulhviertel courtyard (60x47cm-24x19in) s. canvas on board. 27-May-4 Dorotheum, Graz #34/R
£1208	$2162	€1800	Old courtyard (50x38cm-20x15in) s. 27-May-4 Dorotheum, Graz #32/R est:1800
£1342	$2403	€2000	Coastal landscape with ruins (38x61cm-15x24in) s. canvas on board. 27-May-4 Dorotheum, Graz #33/R est:1100
£1477	$2643	€2200	Meran in southern Tyrol (35x54cm-14x21in) s. canvas on board. 27-May-4 Dorotheum, Graz #36/R est:1300
£1745	$3123	€2600	In the summer freshness (20x27cm-8x11in) s. i. verso canvas on board. 27-May-4 Dorotheum, Graz #30/R est:700
£1879	$3364	€2800	Canal near Chioggia (39x45cm-15x18in) s. canvas on board. 27-May-4 Dorotheum, Graz #28/R est:1599
£1879	$3364	€2800	Southern coast (44x61cm-17x24in) s. 27-May-4 Dorotheum, Graz #35/R est:900
£2013	$3604	€3000	Flowers at edge of wood (53x43cm-21x17in) s. i. verso. 27-May-4 Dorotheum, Graz #29/R est:1100
£2533	$4560	€3800	In the country (50x41cm-20x16in) s. canvas on board. 22-Apr-4 Dorotheum, Graz #13/R est:900

Works on paper

£300	$540	€450	Graz from Schlossberg (27x37cm-11x15in) s. W/C heightened bodycol. 22-Apr-4 Dorotheum, Graz #53/R
£300	$540	€450	Sailing boats on the Attersee (27x39cm-11x15in) s. W/C. 22-Apr-4 Dorotheum, Graz #56
£300	$540	€450	Landscape (18x26cm-7x10in) s. pencil W/C. 22-Apr-4 Dorotheum, Graz #59/R
£333	$600	€500	Sawmill in Gurk/Karnten (35x47cm-14x19in) s. W/C paper on panel. 22-Apr-4 Dorotheum, Graz #54
£333	$600	€500	Church on the Attersee (25x37cm-10x15in) i. verso W/C. 22-Apr-4 Dorotheum, Graz #58
£400	$720	€600	Flowers in front garden (16x12cm-6x5in) s. W/c. 22-Apr-4 Dorotheum, Graz #51
£403	$721	€600	Mur to the north (40x53cm-16x21in) s. gouache. 27-May-4 Dorotheum, Graz #176/R
£433	$780	€650	Mill (33x41cm-13x16in) s. W/C paper on board. 22-Apr-4 Dorotheum, Graz #50
£433	$780	€650	Barn in Preding (37x46cm-15x18in) s. W/C. 22-Apr-4 Dorotheum, Graz #52
£800	$1440	€1200	Schloss Eggenberg with view of Graz (27x37cm-11x15in) s. W/C. 22-Apr-4 Dorotheum, Graz #57/R

KIRILI, Alain (1946-) French

£563	$975	€800	Untitled (100x100cm-39x39in) s.d.1946 verso acrylic prov. 15-Dec-3 Charbonneaux, Paris #245
Sculpture			
£2027	$3750	€2959	Laocoon II (249x18x15cm-98x7x6in) forged iron exec 1978 prov. 12-Feb-4 Sotheby's, New York #204/R est:2000-2500

KIRK, David S R (20th C) British

£320	$522	€464	Sleep (35x91cm-14x36in) s.d.89. 17-Jul-3 Tennants, Leyburn #932

KIRK, Eve (1900-) British

£480	$864	€701	Guidecca, Venice (40x60cm-16x24in) prov. 20-Jan-4 Bonhams, Knightsbridge #192/R
£600	$1032	€876	Corinth from Loutraki, overlooking the Gulf of Corinth, Greece (51x75cm-20x30in) 3-Dec-3 Christie's, Kensington #479

KIRK, Frank C (1889-1963) American

£412	$750	€602	East Glocester (25x30cm-10x12in) s. i.verso canvasboard. 19-Jun-4 Jackson's, Cedar Falls #25/R
£467	$850	€682	Lands End (25x30cm-10x12in) s. i.verso canvasboard. 19-Jun-4 Jackson's, Cedar Falls #26/R
£1087	$2000	€1587	Japanesque (55x46cm-22x18in) s. s. verso exhib. 27-Jun-4 Freeman, Philadelphia #127/R est:2000-3000

KIRKEBY, Per (1938-) Danish

£9859	$16465	€14394	Composition (122x92cm-48x36in) init.d.1970-71 verso masonite lit. 7-Oct-3 Rasmussen, Copenhagen #106/R est:75000 (D.KR 105000)
£13000	$23530	€18980	Untitled (116x95cm-46x37in) s.d.1983 verso acrylic prov. 1-Apr-4 Christie's, Kensington #261/R est:8000-12000
£18957	$30332	€27488	Composition in green (116x95cm-46x37in) s.d.1986 verso lit. 17-Sep-3 Kunsthallen, Copenhagen #13/R est:225000 (D.KR 200000)
£23000	$42320	€33580	Untitled (200x130cm-79x51in) s.d.1979 verso prov.exhib. 24-Jun-4 Sotheby's, London #288/R est:15000-20000
£23518	$39981	€34336	Salzburg 7 (100x120cm-39x47in) s.d.1984 verso prov.lit. 26-Nov-3 Kunsthallen, Copenhagen #13/R est:225000 (D.KR 250000)
£25271	$46498	€36896	Composition (122x122cm-48x48in) s.d.1978 verso masonite exhib. 29-Mar-4 Rasmussen, Copenhagen #134/R est:225000-275000 (D.KR 280000)
£26667	$48800	€40000	Untitled (145x135cm-57x53in) s.d.1989 prov. 4-Jun-4 Lempertz, Koln #253/R est:40000-45000
£34667	$63440	€52000	With Absalon (200x130cm-79x51in) s.i.d.1988 verso prov.exhib. 4-Jun-4 Lempertz, Koln #252/R est:50000-55000
£40000	$72800	€58400	Smaland (150x200cm-59x79in) s.i.d.1984 verso prov. 5-Feb-4 Christie's, London #194/R est:40000-60000
Works on paper			
£1450	$2611	€2117	Interior scene with model (29x42cm-11x17in) s.d.1964 mixed media W/C. 26-Apr-4 Bukowskis, Stockholm #510a/R est:12000-15000 (S.KR 20000)
£1958	$3329	€2800	Untitled (59x42cm-23x17in) mono.d.86 Indian ink W/C chk. 27-Nov-3 Lempertz, Koln #218/R est:2800-3000
£2133	$3904	€3200	Untitled (39x29cm-15x11in) mono.d.80 W/C col chks. 4-Jun-4 Lempertz, Koln #254/R est:2500
£2133	$3904	€3200	Untitled (39x29cm-15x11in) mono.d.80 W/C col chks. 4-Jun-4 Lempertz, Koln #256/R est:2500
£2267	$4148	€3400	Untitled (48x36cm-19x14in) mono.d.83 gouache Indian ink pastel chk. 4-Jun-4 Lempertz, Koln #257/R est:3600-3800
£3733	$6832	€5600	Laeso (42x59cm-17x23in) mono.i.d.83 Indian ink chl. 4-Jun-4 Lempertz, Koln #258/R est:3600

KIRKEGAARD, Anders (1946-) Danish

£542	$996	€791	Portrait of Dantes and Kirkegaards and Luthers and Kirkegaards workroom (122x122cm-48x48in) mono.d.September 1970 Marts 1971 verso. 29-Mar-4 Rasmussen, Copenhagen #331/R (D.KR 6000)
£812	$1519	€1186	Conversation with George Orwell anno 1985 (54x65cm-21x26in) s.d.70 verso. 25-Feb-4 Kunsthallen, Copenhagen #27/R (D.KR 9000)
£1043	$1668	€1512	Portrait of a wise man holding back his wisdom (94x114cm-37x45in) s.d.71 panel. 17-Sep-3 Kunsthallen, Copenhagen #76/R (D.KR 11000)

KIRKHAM, Norman (1936-) British

£320	$534	€467	Portrait study as Father Christmas (60x45cm-24x18in) s.d.77 board. 16-Oct-3 Lyon & Turnbull, Edinburgh #58

KIRKHAM, R (19th C) American

£2188	$3500	€3194	Landscape (69x102cm-27x40in) 19-Sep-3 Du Mouchelle, Detroit #2122/R est:2000-4000

KIRKMAN, Jay Boyd (1958-) British

£5000	$9200	€7300	First fence (61x91cm-24x36in) s.d.1987 prov. 10-Jun-4 Christie's, Kensington #219/R est:4000-6000
Works on paper			
£2700	$4968	€3942	Horse on lead rein (67x25cm-26x10in) s.d.92 pastel. 10-Jun-4 Christie's, Kensington #218/R est:2000-3000
£6000	$11040	€8760	On the gallops (53x88cm-21x35in) s. pastel. 10-Jun-4 Christie's, Kensington #220/R est:4000-6000

KIRKPATRICK, Alan (1929-) British

Works on paper			
£380	$673	€555	Westminster Reach (48x63cm-19x25in) s. W/C. 28-Apr-4 Peter Wilson, Nantwich #168
£450	$752	€657	George Basin, Liverpool (49x66cm-19x26in) s. W/C. 9-Jul-3 Peter Wilson, Nantwich #81
£600	$1020	€876	Caernarvon Castle with fishing boats drawn up onto the sands (48x63cm-19x25in) s. W/C. 26-Nov-3 Peter Wilson, Nantwich #132/R

KIRKPATRICK, Ethel (fl.1891-1941) British

£5800	$10614	€8468	Cornish floral dance (50x78cm-20x31in) s. 7-Apr-4 Bonhams, Bury St Edmunds #463/R est:800-1000

KIRKPATRICK, Joseph (1872-c.1930) British

Works on paper			
£800	$1472	€1168	Walking amongst the haystack (20x37cm-8x15in) s.d.1902 W/C. 8-Jun-4 Bonhams, Knightsbridge #69/R
£800	$1456	€1168	Goose Girl (32x24cm-13x9in) s. W/C. 29-Jun-4 Anderson & Garland, Newcastle #172/R
£1000	$1720	€1460	Lady by herbaceous borders (33x23cm-13x9in) s. W/C. 3-Dec-3 Andrew Hartley, Ilkley #1030 est:1000-1200
£1200	$2040	€1752	Farm girl attending to the chickens (34x49cm-13x19in) s. W/C. 18-Nov-3 Bonhams, Leeds #66/R est:1200-1800
£1312	$2191	€1916	In the orchard (35x25cm-14x10in) s. i.verso W/C. 17-Nov-3 Waddingtons, Toronto #68/R est:1500-2000 (C.D 2900)
£1800	$2952	€2628	Gloucestershire lane, a young girl carrying a basket of flowers (33x23cm-13x9in) s. W/C bodycol htd white. 29-May-3 Neales, Nottingham #735/R est:1500-2000

KIRKWOOD, H W (1854-1925) New Zealander

£952	$1762	€1390	Dusky sound (29x44cm-11x17in) s. board. 9-Mar-4 Watson's, Christchurch #68 est:2600-3600 (NZ.D 2600)

KIRKWOOD, Henry William (1854-1925) New Zealander

£308	$496	€450	Mt Egmont (14x21cm-6x8in) init. board. 12-Aug-3 Peter Webb, Auckland #151/R (NZ.D 850)
£380	$616	€551	Dusky Sounds (23x14cm-9x6in) s. board. 31-Jul-3 International Art Centre, Auckland #188 est:1000-2000 (NZ.D 1050)
£436	$685	€637	Paritutu, New Plymouth (22x45cm-9x18in) init. 27-Aug-3 Dunbar Sloane, Wellington #155/R (NZ.D 1200)
£471	$763	€683	River landscape (15x30cm-6x12in) s. board. 31-Jul-3 International Art Centre, Auckland #187 est:1000-2000 (NZ.D 1300)
£507	$817	€740	Fiordland (28x45cm-11x18in) init. board. 12-Aug-3 Peter Webb, Auckland #150/R (NZ.D 1400)
£520	$895	€759	Southern lake shore (15x30cm-6x12in) s. board. 7-Dec-3 International Art Centre, Auckland #276/R (NZ.D 1400)
£564	$959	€823	Nelson landscape (16x23cm-6x9in) s. board. 27-Nov-3 International Art Centre, Auckland #162/R (NZ.D 1500)
£865	$1470	€1263	Mt Egmont (24x16cm-9x6in) s. board. 27-Nov-3 International Art Centre, Auckland #161/R (NZ.D 2300)

KIRMSE, Marguerite (1885-1954) American/British

Works on paper			
£389	$700	€568	Song without words (25x18cm-10x7in) s.i. pencil. 23-Jan-4 Freeman, Philadelphia #47/R

KIRNIG, Alois (1840-1911) Austrian

£350	$651	€511	Willows at stream (26x36cm-10x14in) s.d.1896 canvas on board. 6-Mar-4 Dorotheum, Prague #23 est:10000-15000 (C.KR 17000)

KIROUAC, Louise Lecor (1939-) Canadian

£360	$659	€526	Ferme pres de Degelis, Temis, QC (40x50cm-16x20in) s.i. acrylic. 1-Jun-4 Hodgins, Calgary #139/R (C.D 900)
£360	$659	€526	Magnifique village de Severin, Beauce, Quebec (50x60cm-20x24in) s.i. acrylic. 1-Jun-4 Hodgins, Calgary #408/R (C.D 900)
£413	$748	€603	Evasion, Charlevoix (51x61cm-20x24in) s. s.i.verso acrylic. 18-Apr-4 Levis, Calgary #56/R est:1000-1250 (C.D 1000)
£536	$921	€783	Sortie Printaniere, Laurentides, Quebec (50x60cm-20x24in) s. 2-Dec-3 Joyner Waddington, Toronto #313/R (C.D 1200)
£640	$1171	€934	Ste Marie de Beauce (60x75cm-24x30in) s.i. acrylic. 1-Jun-4 Hodgins, Calgary #16/R (C.D 1600)
£714	$1229	€1042	St Tite-des-Caps, Charlevoix, Quebec (60x75cm-24x30in) s. 2-Dec-3 Joyner Waddington, Toronto #351/R (C.D 1600)

KIRSCH, Johanna (1856-?) German

£355	$592	€500	Vache et chevres au pre (31x39cm-12x15in) s. panel. 14-Oct-3 Vanderkindere, Brussels #45
£3333	$6033	€5000	Vue d'interieur (65x82cm-26x32in) s. 30-Mar-4 Campo & Campo, Antwerp #150 est:800-1000

KIRSCH, Max E (20th C) ?

£1020	$1857	€1500	Boulevard katwijk aan zee (37x53cm-15x21in) s.i.d.1913 board. 3-Feb-4 Christie's, Amsterdam #389a est:700-900

KIRSCHL, Wilfried (1930-) Austrian
£2667 $4907 €4000 Patmos-chor (65x85cm-26x33in) mono.d.74. 9-Jun-4 Dorotheum, Salzburg #713/R est:1600-2000
Works on paper
£897 $1641 €1300 Roofs (20x16cm-8x6in) mono.d.78 s.i.d.78 verso pastel. 27-Jan-4 Dorotheum, Vienna #206/R

KIRSOP, Joseph Henry (1886-1981) British
£360 $572 €526 Staithes, Yorkshire (33x40cm-13x16in) s.i.d.1911. 18-Mar-3 Anderson & Garland, Newcastle #229/R

KIRTON, Douglas (1955-) Canadian
£2365 $4021 €3453 Toxic pool group, 8 (91x203cm-36x80in) s.i.d.1987 verso panel prov. 18-Nov-3 Sotheby's, Toronto #132/R est:5000-8000 (C.D 5250)

KISCHKA, Isis (1908-1974) French
£464 $844 €700 Bouquet de bleuets (46x38cm-18x15in) s. 16-Jun-4 Claude Boisgirard, Paris #88/R

KISELYOV, Sergei (1974-) Russian
£268 $481 €400 Harem (55x38cm-22x15in) 25-May-4 Durán, Madrid #718/R
£300 $489 €438 On the terrace (55x38cm-22x15in) s. after Sir Lawrence Alma-Tadema. 28-Sep-3 John Nicholson, Haslemere #146
£450 $734 €657 Gold fishes (55x38cm-22x15in) s. 28-Sep-3 John Nicholson, Haslemere #65
£537 $961 €800 Kiss (46x28cm-18x11in) 25-May-4 Durán, Madrid #717/R

KISLAKOV, Sergei (1897-1980) Russian
£620 $1097 €905 Villefranche sur mer with figures on the quay side (40x32cm-16x13in) i.d.1953 verso board. 28-Apr-4 Peter Wilson, Nantwich #33

KISLING, Moise (1891-1953) French
£6000 $10860 €9000 Nature morte au lievre (33x55cm-13x22in) s.i. 1-Apr-4 Credit Municipal, Paris #66 est:1000-1200
£7500 $12525 €10950 Paysage de Provence (33x41cm-13x16in) s. painted 1932 prov.lit. 21-Oct-3 Sotheby's, London #152/R est:8000-12000
£9091 $15455 €13000 Arbuste fleuri dans un vase (41x27cm-16x11in) s. 1-Dec-3 Palais de Beaux Arts, Brussels #359/R est:12000-15000
£10000 $17000 €14600 Bateau et Grue a la Seyne (41x33cm-16x13in) s.i.d.1935 prov.lit. 6-Nov-3 Sotheby's, New York #322/R est:18000-25000
£11921 $21695 €18000 Tete de jeune femme rousse (27x19cm-11x7in) s. 15-Jun-4 Rossini, Paris #88/R est:12000-18000
£13000 $23660 €18980 Couple se promenant dans une foret (73x60cm-29x24in) s. painted 1916 prov. 3-Feb-4 Christie's, London #268/R est:12000-18000
£14261 $26240 €21390 Jeune fille au corsage rouge (41x33cm-16x13in) s. prov. 9-Jun-4 Tajan, Paris #47/R est:25000-35000
£15294 $26000 €22329 Dahlias (47x34cm-19x13in) s.d.1917 prov.lit. 6-Nov-3 Sotheby's, New York #195/R est:25000-35000
£16760 $30000 €24470 Nu allonge (33x4cm-13x2in) s. prov.lit. 18-Mar-4 Sotheby's, New York #97/R est:30000-40000
£17450 $31235 €26000 Portrait de femme (41x33cm-16x13in) s. painted 1934 prov. 26-May-4 Christie's, Paris #31/R est:20000-30000
£17483 $29720 €25000 Paysage de Sanary (21x26cm-8x10in) s. 27-Nov-3 Calmels Cohen, Paris #41/R est:15000-20000
£17606 $30810 €25000 Nue allongee dans l'herbe (21x27cm-8x11in) s. prov.lit. 18-Dec-3 Tajan, Paris #45/R est:25000-30000
£20588 $35000 €30058 Paysage du Midi (46x55cm-18x22in) s. painted c.1917 prov. 5-Nov-3 Christie's, Rockefeller NY #248/R est:30000-40000
£20629 $35483 €29500 Le col de dentelle (41x33cm-16x13in) s. 3-Dec-3 Beaussant & Lefèvre, Paris #44/R est:20000 22000
£20690 $34345 €30000 Paysage de Sanary (55x46cm-22x18in) s.i.d.1948. 2-Oct-3 Sotheby's, Paris #162/R est:40000
£20980 $35036 €30000 Provence, lavandiere devant la mer (54x65cm-21x26in) s.d.1917 lit. 30-Jun-3 Artcurial Briest, Paris #733/R est:25000-30000
£22028 $37888 €31500 Bouquet de bleuets (53x37cm-21x15in) s. 5-Dec-3 Gros & Delettrez, Paris #92a est:30000-40000
£23490 $42047 €35000 Fleurs (41x33cm-16x13in) s. painted 1947 prov.lit. 26-May-4 Christie's, Paris #35/R est:35000-40000
£23529 $40000 €34352 Marguerites (73x54cm-29x21in) s. painted 1943 prov.lit. 5-Nov-3 Christie's, Rockefeller NY #289/R est:50000-70000
£25000 $42500 €36500 Buste de jeune fille (59x46cm-23x18in) s. painted c.1951 prov.lit. 6-Nov-3 Sotheby's, New York #365/R est:25000-35000
£26471 $45000 €38648 Renee Kisling (100x73cm-39x29in) s. painted 1928 prov.exhib.lit. 6-Nov-3 Sotheby's, New York #341/R est:60000-80000
£28000 $51520 €40880 Still life (54x65cm-21x26in) s.d.1917 prov. 22-Jun-4 Sotheby's, London #165/R est:30000-40000
£29412 $50000 €42942 Roses dans un vase (73x60cm-29x24in) s.d.1947 prov. 6-Nov-3 Sotheby's, New York #287/R est:60000-80000
£29412 $50000 €42942 Catherine (81x60cm-32x24in) s. prov.exhib.lit. 6-Nov-3 Sotheby's, New York #339/R est:60000-80000
£30000 $55200 €43800 Oeillets de poete (55x38cm-22x15in) s.d.1952 prov.lit. 22-Jun-4 Sotheby's, London #250/R est:35000-45000
£31544 $56463 €47000 Portrait de Renee Kisling (65x50cm-26x20in) s. painted 1918 lit. 30-May-4 Eric Pillon, Calais #31/R
£34667 $63787 €52000 Still life with flowers in a vase (73x60cm-29x24in) s. prov.exhib. 9-Jun-4 Christie's, Amsterdam #217/R est:30000-50000
£36913 $67919 €55000 Buste nu (55x38cm-22x15in) s. prov.lit. 28-Mar-4 Anaf, Lyon #167/R est:55000-65000
£41899 $75000 €61173 La fille au chale verte (81x65cm-32x26in) s.d.1919 prov. 18-Mar-4 Sotheby's, New York #98/R est:50000-70000
£51205 $85000 €74759 Mimosas (55x46cm-22x18in) s.i.d.1948 lit. 2-Oct-3 Christie's, Tel Aviv #32/R est:90000-120000
£55944 $96224 €80000 Fleurs blanches (108x80cm-43x31in) s.i.d.45. 5-Dec-3 Chochon-Barre & Allardi, Paris #114/R est:50000-80000
£70000 $128800 €102200 Coquelicots (73x54cm-29x21in) s. painted 1950 prov.exhib.lit. 22-Jun-4 Sotheby's, London #254/R est:35000-45000
Prints
£1765 $3000 €2577 Nu au turban (57x42cm-22x17in) s.num.7/100 col aquatint etching. 6-Nov-3 Swann Galleries, New York #588/R est:2000-3000

KISLING, Philipp Heinrich (1713-1788) German
£1667 $2717 €2400 Portrait of a lady dressed as widow (144x110cm-57x43in) i. verso. 25-Sep-3 Dr Fritz Nagel, Stuttgart #1246/R est:2500

KISS, Paul (?) ?
Sculpture
£5000 $9150 €7500 Untitled (162x207cm-64x81in) s. wrought iron. 3-Jun-4 E & Eve, Paris #48/R est:6000-8000

KISSELEOV, Alexandre Alexandrovitch (1838-1911) Russian
£55000 $98450 €80300 Dacha by the river (66x92cm-26x36in) s.d.1889. 26-May-4 Sotheby's, London #31/R est:15000-20000
£80000 $143200 €116800 Boys by a steam (82x108cm-32x43in) s.d.1887. 26-May-4 Sotheby's, London #30/R est:18000-22000

KITAJ, R B (1932-) American
£5500 $9955 €8030 Louis Jouvet as Anne (30x25cm-12x10in) s. exhib. 1-Apr-4 Christie's, Kensington #297/R est:4000-6000
£220000 $400400 €321200 Value, Price and Profit (153x153cm-60x60in) exec 1963. 5-Feb-4 Sotheby's, London #27/R est:230000-280000
Works on paper
£1500 $2715 €2190 Babyface (49x40cm-19x16in) s.i. pencil chl oil canvas on board. 1-Apr-4 Christie's, Kensington #296/R est:2000-3000

KITCHELL, Hudson Mindell (1862-1944) American
£538 $1000 €785 As the sun sets (41x30cm-16x12in) s. 5-Mar-4 Skinner, Boston #298/R
£628 $1125 €917 Woodland sunset (20x28cm-8x11in) s.d.1918. 19-Mar-4 Aspire, Cleveland #15 est:800-1200
£698 $1200 €1019 Landscape (64x76cm-25x30in) s. 7-Dec-3 Susanin's, Chicago #6009/R
£1076 $1700 €1571 Landscape with two figures in a clearing (46x61cm-18x24in) s. 6-Sep-3 Brunk, Ashville #866
£1098 $1800 €1592 Autumn woods (25x30cm-10x12in) s. painted c.1900. 7-Jun-3 Treadway Gallery, Cincinnati #1332 est:1500-2500
£1456 $2300 €2126 Autumn landscape (46x61cm-18x24in) s. 7-Sep-3 Treadway Gallery, Cincinnati #568/R est:2000-3000

KITE, Joseph Milner (1862-1946) British
£250 $453 €365 Harbour scene with moored fishing boats and figures (36x54cm-14x21in) s. 2-Apr-4 Moore Allen & Innocent, Cirencester #401/R
£280 $501 €409 Portrait of a maid (80x63cm-31x25in) s.d.1891. 16-Mar-4 Bonhams, Leeds #630
£629 $1170 €918 Young dark haired girl wearing green dress (92x74cm-36x29in) i.verso. 2-Mar-4 Rasmussen, Copenhagen #1623/R (D.KR 7000)
£1972 $3451 €2800 Jeune fille allongee (55x13cm-22x5in) s. 16-Dec-3 Claude Aguttes, Neuilly #25/R est:2000-3000

KITO, Akira (1925-) Japanese
£704 $1218 €1000 Source noire (22x27cm-9x11in) s. s.i.d.1961 verso. 14-Dec-3 Versailles Encheres #31/R
£1467 $2699 €2200 Promenade au coucher du soleil (61x59cm-24x23in) s. s.i.d.1965 verso. 9-Jun-4 Christie's, Amsterdam #182/R est:2000-3000

KITSELL, T Rogers (1864-?) British
Works on paper
£280 $496 €409 Museum and art gallery and Free Library Plymouth (28x88cm-11x35in) s.d.1907 W/C. 27-Apr-4 Bonhams, Knowle #152/R

KITT, Ferdinand (1897-1962) Austrian
Works on paper
£1333 $2453 €2000 Winter landscape (44x60cm-17x24in) s. W/C. 9-Jun-4 Dorotheum, Salzburg #844/R est:1400-2000
£1560 $2606 €2200 Salzkammergut (40x57cm-16x22in) s. W/C. 14-Oct-3 Dorotheum, Vienna #143/R est:1400-1800

KITTELSEN, Theodor (1857-1914) Norwegian
£16260 $29756 €23740 Summer's day, Laulia in Eggedal (46x68cm-18x27in) s.d.1899 i.verso exhib.lit. 7-Jun-4 Blomqvist, Oslo #326/R est:225000-275000 (N.KR 200000)
£56459 $95979 €82430 Woodland tarn (68x91cm-27x36in) s.d.1897 s.i.d.verso. 19-Nov-3 Grev Wedels Plass, Oslo #38/R est:400000-600000 (N.KR 660000)
Works on paper
£3080 $5235 €4497 Woodland troll (22x14cm-9x6in) init. pencil pen. 19-Nov-3 Grev Wedels Plass, Oslo #70/R est:20000-25000 (N.KR 36000)
£3165 $5381 €4621 Troll carrying huge bag of stones (17x14cm-7x6in) init. pen wash. 19-Nov-3 Grev Wedels Plass, Oslo #69/R est:20000-25000 (N.KR 37000)

KITZ, Marcin (1891-1943) Polish
£4288 $7932 €6260 Busy street with horse-drawn carriages (50x70cm-20x28in) 14-Mar-4 Agra, Warsaw #53/R (P.Z 31000)

KITZIS, W (19/20th C) ?
£1600 $2528 €2336 Empress of Ireland (69x102cm-27x40in) s. sold with a book. 23-Jul-3 Hampton & Littlewood, Exeter #442/R est:500-700

KIVITS, Jos (1945-) Australian
£429 $789 €626 Resting shepherd (58x74cm-23x29in) s. board. 25-Mar-4 International Art Centre, Auckland #143/R (NZ.D 1200)

£1268 $2054 €1839 Classic arrangement (55x59cm-22x23in) s. board. 31-Jul-3 International Art Centre, Auckland #88/R est:5000-7000 (NZ.D 3500)

KIYOHIRO, Torii (fl.1736-1776) Japanese
Prints
£9500 $17480 €13870 Onoe Kikugora as Issun Tokubei (39x17cm-15x7in) s.i. print exec. 1760. 8-Jun-4 Sotheby's, London #52/R est:2000-3000

KIYOMASU, Torii I (fl.1696-1716) Japanese
Prints
£2000 $3680 €2920 Kumagai Naozane at the battle of Ichi-No-Tani (59x31cm-23x12in) s. print lit. 8-Jun-4 Sotheby's, London #9/R est:2000-3000
£8500 $15640 €12410 Osome and Hisamatsu (58x32cm-23x13in) pront lit. exec. mid 1710's. 8-Jun-4 Sotheby's, London #12/R est:4000-5000
£10000 $18400 €14600 The actor Fujimura Handaya II as Oiso No Tora (64x31cm-25x12in) s. print exec. 1715 one of three lit. 8-Jun-4 Sotheby's, London #10/R est:10000-15000
£30000 $55200 €43800 Ichikawa Danjuro I as Yamagami Gennai Saemon and Yamanaka Heikuro as Suzuka No Oji (63x32cm-25x13in) s. print exec. 1701 lit. 8-Jun-4 Sotheby's, London #11/R est:3000-5000

KIYOMASU, Torii II (1706-1763) Japanese
Prints
£3400 $6256 €4964 Saimyoji Tsuneyo Setchu No Hachinoki (33x47cm-13x19in) print. 8-Jun-4 Sotheby's, London #28/R est:1800-2200

KIYOMINE, Torii II (1787-1868) Japanese
Prints
£10000 $18400 €14600 Woman arranging her coiffure (38x25cm-15x10in) s. print prov.lit. 8-Jun-4 Sotheby's, London #268/R est:5000-7000

KIYOMITSU, Torii (1735-1785) Japanese
Prints
£2400 $4416 €3504 Onoe Matsusuke I as Bijo Gozen (31x14cm-12x6in) s.i. print. 8-Jun-4 Sotheby's, London #54/R est:1500-2000
£3000 $5520 €4380 Ichimura Uzaemon IX as Kajiwara Genta (31x14cm-12x6in) s. print exec. 1764 prov. 8-Jun-4 Sotheby's, London #55/R est:2000-3000
£6000 $11040 €8760 Soap bubbles as the autumn evening moon (31x43cm-12x17in) s.i. print exec. c.1760's lit. 8-Jun-4 Sotheby's, London #58/R est:6000-8000
£8000 $14720 €11680 Mitate of Ono No Tofu (36x24cm-14x9in) s. print exec. c.1760's. 8-Jun-4 Sotheby's, London #57/R est:3000-4000

KIYONAGA (18th C) Japanese
Prints
£3000 $5520 €4500 Two women. s. print. 11-Jun-4 Tajan, Paris #117/R est:4500-5000

KIYONAGA, Torii (1752-1815) Japanese
Prints
£6993 $11888 €10000 Loisirs (36x24cm-14x9in) col print prov.lit. 25-Nov-3 Sotheby's, Paris #106/R est:9000-12000
£8696 $16000 €12696 Jittai e-fuzoku - Young woman seated on a bamboo bench (39x27cm-15x11in) s. print prov.exhib. 23-Mar-4 Christie's, Rockefeller NY #11/R est:18000-22000
Works on paper
£1049 $1783 €1500 Untitled (38x27cm-15x11in) ink pair. 25-Nov-3 Sotheby's, Paris #207/R est:700-900

KIYONOBU, Torii I (1664-1729) Japanese
Prints
£2200 $4048 €3212 Falcon on pine tree (55x31cm-22x12in) s. print. 8-Jun-4 Sotheby's, London #7/R est:900-1200
£4800 $8832 €7008 The actor Sanagawa Mangiku I (22x30cm-9x12in) s. print. 8-Jun-4 Sotheby's, London #6/R est:3000-4000

KIYOOKA, Roy Kenzie (1926-1994) Canadian
£203 $344 €296 Girl in green and red (51x41cm-20x16in) s.i.verso enamel board prov. 23-Nov-3 Levis, Calgary #308/R (C.D 450)
£631 $1072 €921 Circus (61x46cm-24x18in) canvasboard prov. 23-Nov-3 Levis, Calgary #307/R (C.D 1400)

KJAER, Anders (1940-) Norwegian
£2135 $3565 €3117 The inland summer (146x110cm-57x43in) s. s.i.d.1996 stretcher. 13-Oct-3 Blomqvist, Oslo #329/R est:35000-45000 (N.KR 25000)
£2726 $4688 €3980 Untitled - XXXXIX (190x135cm-75x53in) s. s.i.d.verso exhib.lit. 8-Dec-3 Blomqvist, Oslo #567/R est:25000-30000 (N.KR 32000)

KJAER, Harald (1876-1948) Danish
£307 $567 €448 Summer landscape with milkmaid and cows (33x45cm-13x18in) s. 15-Mar-4 Rasmussen, Vejle #418 (D.KR 3400)

KJAERSGAARD, Soren (1935-) Danish
£316 $581 €461 Figure composition (130x160cm-51x63in) s.d.1975 verso. 29-Mar-4 Rasmussen, Copenhagen #356 (D.KR 3500)

KJARVAL, Johannes (1885-1972) Icelandic
£2817 $4704 €4113 Composition with female head (56x66cm-22x26in) s. 7-Oct-3 Rasmussen, Copenhagen #137/R est:30000 (D.KR 30000)
£4964 $9282 €7247 Figures in landscape, Iceland (50x95cm-20x37in) s. 25-Feb-4 Kunsthallen, Copenhagen #207/R est:60000 (D.KR 55000)
£6498 $11957 €9487 Mountain landscape, Iceland (105x150cm-41x59in) s. 29-Mar-4 Rasmussen, Copenhagen #243/R est:80000 (D.KR 72000)
Works on paper
£496 $913 €724 Roof tops, Copenhagen with Vognmagergade (17x24cm-7x9in) s.d.27/1 1913 W/C lit. 29-Mar-4 Rasmussen, Copenhagen #246/R (D.KR 5500)
£1354 $2491 €1977 Landscape, Thinkvellir (86x112cm-34x44in) s.d.1946 Indian ink exhib.prov. 29-Mar-4 Rasmussen, Copenhagen #238/R est:20000-25000 (D.KR 15000)

KJELDBAEK, Bentemarie (1952-) Danish
£451 $753 €658 Bull fighting scene (96x95cm-38x37in) s.d.1999 verso. 7-Oct-3 Rasmussen, Copenhagen #286 (D.KR 4800)

KJERNER, Esther (1873-1952) Swedish
£314 $544 €458 Still life of amaryllis (43x35cm-17x14in) s.d.45 canvas on panel prov. 15-Dec-3 Lilla Bukowskis, Stockholm #860 (S.KR 4000)
£456 $788 €666 Pear on pewter dish (32x48cm-13x19in) s.d.1944 prov. 15-Dec-3 Lilla Bukowskis, Stockholm #861 (S.KR 5800)
£550 $951 €803 Drottningholm (37x27cm-15x11in) s. panel. 15-Dec-3 Lilla Bukowskis, Stockholm #536 (S.KR 7000)
£554 $1019 €831 Lake landscape (37x45cm-15x18in) s.d.1941 panel. 14-Jun-4 Lilla Bukowskis, Stockholm #234 (S.KR 7600)
£612 $985 €894 Still life of flowers (46x40cm-18x16in) s.d.1946. 25-Aug-3 Lilla Bukowskis, Stockholm #764 (S.KR 8000)
£882 $1623 €1323 Roses (35x24cm-14x9in) s. panel prov. 14-Jun-4 Lilla Bukowskis, Stockholm #242 (S.KR 12100)
£1035 $1852 €1511 Still life of punch bowl, jug and vegetables (50x60cm-20x24in) s. canvas on panel. 28-May-4 Uppsala Auktionskammare, Uppsala #186/R est:12000-15000 (S.KR 14000)
£1077 $1852 €1572 Still life of peonies (40x32cm-16x13in) s.d.46 canvas on panel. 2-Dec-3 Bukowskis, Stockholm #57/R (S.KR 14000)
£1185 $1908 €1730 Tulips and willow (46x37cm-18x15in) s.d.1940 lit. 25-Aug-3 Lilla Bukowskis, Stockholm #734 est:10000-12000 (S.KR 15500)
£1256 $2249 €1834 Farm yard (66x55cm-26x22in) s.d.1920. 26-May-4 AB Stockholms Auktionsverk #2320/R est:20000-25000 (S.KR 17000)
£1308 $2249 €1910 Still life of tulips in black vase (27x35cm-11x14in) s. panel. 3-Dec-3 AB Stockholms Auktionsverk #2273/R est:15000-18000 (S.KR 17000)
£1330 $2381 €1942 Red tulips (46x38cm-18x15in) s.d.1943 panel prov. 25-May-4 Bukowskis, Stockholm #48/R est:12000-15000 (S.KR 18000)
£1478 $2646 €2158 Still life of teapot, lemons and grapes (60x73cm-24x29in) s.d.1941. 26-May-4 AB Stockholms Auktionsverk #2197/R est:20000-25000 (S.KR 20000)
£1626 $2911 €2374 Still life of lily-of-the-valley (27x22cm-11x9in) s. panel prov. 26-May-4 AB Stockholms Auktionsverk #2286/R est:25000-30000 (S.KR 22000)
£2077 $3572 €3032 Still life of roses (29x30cm-11x12in) s. canvas on board. 2-Dec-3 Bukowskis, Stockholm #59/R est:12000-15000 (S.KR 27000)
£2217 $3969 €3237 Still life of fruit (46x54cm-18x21in) s.d.1930 panel. 26-May-4 AB Stockholms Auktionsverk #2233/R est:30000-35000 (S.KR 30000)
£2882 $5160 €4208 Still life of white roses (35x37cm-14x15in) s.d.1932 panel. 25-May-4 Bukowskis, Stockholm #48a/R est:20000-25000 (S.KR 39000)
£4769 $8203 €6963 Peonies and honeysuckle in blue-white bowl (63x51cm-25x20in) s.d.1925 prov. 2-Dec-3 Bukowskis, Stockholm #148/R est:20000-25000 (S.KR 62000)

KLACH, J (18th C) German
£2735 $4895 €3993 Offering to the God Pan (49x66cm-19x26in) s. 26-May-4 AB Stockholms Auktionsverk #2584/R est:20000-30000 (S.KR 37000)

KLAIBERG, Fritz (1921-) German
£800 $1336 €1168 Grand Canal, Venice (61x79cm-24x31in) s. 8-Oct-3 Christie's, Kensington #794/R

KLAPHECK, Konrad (1935-) German
£12587 $21399 €18000 Sad mama (62x40cm-24x16in) s. verso s.i. stretcher prov.exhib. 27-Nov-3 Lempertz, Koln #219/R est:12000
£21678 $37287 €31000 Pretentius spouse (100x80cm-39x31in) s.d.1968 verso i. on stretcher prov. 5-Dec-3 Ketterer, Munich #161/R est:20000-30000
£28671 $48741 €41000 Strong mother (40x89cm-16x35in) s. verso i. stretcher prov.exhib. 27-Nov-3 Lempertz, Koln #220/R est:20000-24000

KLAPISH, Liliane (1933-) Israeli
£3614 $6000 €5276 Files in disorder (73x50cm-29x20in) s.d.77 exhib. 2-Oct-3 Christie's, Tel Aviv #115/R est:6000-8000
£7263 $13000 €10604 Interior (116x81cm-46x32in) s. 18-Mar-4 Sotheby's, New York #55/R est:12000-15000
Works on paper
£927 $1687 €1400 Untitled (59x29cm-23x11in) s. mixed media on canvas. 15-Jun-4 Rossini, Paris #184/R

KLAPSTE, Jaroslav (1923-1999) Czechoslovakian
£702 $1194 €1025 Factory (50x73cm-20x29in) s. 29-Nov-3 Dorotheum, Prague #97/R est:8000-12000 (C.KR 32000)

KLAR, Otto (1908-1994) South African
£372 $665 €543 Mountain peaks capped with snow (57x78cm-22x31in) s. board. 31-May-4 Stephan Welz, Johannesburg #531 (SA.R 4500)
£442 $813 €645 Basothos with huts (19x44cm-7x17in) board. 8-Jun-4 Dales, Durban #10 (SA.R 5250)
£495 $887 €723 Farm cottage (28x32cm-11x13in) s. board. 31-May-4 Stephan Welz, Johannesburg #116 (SA.R 6000)
£537 $961 €784 Cape cottage (21x29cm-8x11in) s.d.1948 board. 31-May-4 Stephan Welz, Johannesburg #161 (SA.R 6500)
£862 $1440 €1259 Bushveld landscape (32x61cm-13x24in) s. board. 20-Oct-3 Stephan Welz, Johannesburg #240/R est:10000-16000 (SA.R 10000)
£1026 $1744 €1498 Bushveld landscape (24x79cm-9x31in) s. board. 4-Nov-3 Stephan Welz, Johannesburg #623/R est:6000-9000 (SA.R 12000)
£2241 $3743 €3272 Bushveld scene (46x57cm-18x22in) s. board. 20-Oct-3 Stephan Welz, Johannesburg #241/R est:15000-20000 (SA.R 26000)

Works on paper
£289 $517 €422 Cottage in a landscape (18x31cm-7x12in) s. brown conte. 31-May-4 Stephan Welz, Johannesburg #266 (SA.R 3500)
£513 $872 €749 Mountain landscape (15x41cm-6x16in) s. pastel W/C. 4-Nov-3 Stephan Welz, Johannesburg #605 est:2500-4000 (SA.R 6000)
£769 $1308 €1123 Landscape near Victoria West (19x32cm-7x13in) s. pastel W/C. 4-Nov-3 Stephan Welz, Johannesburg #616 est:2500-4000 (SA.R 9000)

KLARL, Joseph (1909-1986) German
£769 $1323 €1100 Concert at home (60x50cm-24x20in) s. 5-Dec-3 Michael Zeller, Lindau #665/R
£884 $1583 €1300 Skiers in the Alps (79x69cm-31x27in) bears sig. board. 18-Mar-4 Neumeister, Munich #2700/R
£1049 $1804 €1500 Garden cafe on Worthersee (70x60cm-28x24in) s. i. verso. 5-Dec-3 Michael Zeller, Lindau #666/R est:1000

KLASEN, Peter (1935-) German
£839 $1401 €1200 Camion bache rouge gris (41x33cm-16x13in) s. i.verso acrylic. 29-Jun-3 Versailles Encheres #165/R
£839 $1443 €1200 Danger (49x64cm-19x25in) s. acrylic cardboard. 3-Dec-3 Tajan, Paris #491/R est:800-1000
£1042 $1719 €1500 Camion bache rouge et bleu (47x40cm-19x16in) s.i.verso acrylic. 2-Jul-3 Cornette de St.Cyr, Paris #140/R est:2000-2500
£1067 $1920 €1600 MM75 (56x42cm-22x17in) s.i. acrylic cardboard prov.exhib. 25-Apr-4 Versailles Encheres #143 est:1500-2000
£1389 $2292 €2000 Bouche fond rouge et noir (57x47cm-22x19in) s.i.verso acrylic. 2-Jul-3 Cornette de St.Cyr, Paris #142/R est:2500-3000
£1528 $2551 €2200 Camion bache rouge-gris (55x44cm-22x17in) s.i.d.1986 verso. 25-Oct-3 Cornette de St.Cyr, Paris #730 est:2200-2500
£1543 $2732 €2300 Cadran noir/auf-zu/fond vert (63x49cm-25x19in) s.i. acrylic collage board. 28-Apr-4 Artcurial Briest, Paris #419/R est:2500-3000
£1667 $3066 €2500 Haute tension auf/zu bleu (65x49cm-26x19in) s.i.d.90 acrylic collage board prov.lit. 9-Jun-4 Artcurial Briest, Paris #511/R est:2500-3000
£1689 $3193 €2500 Oeil/HB-inflammable (42x32cm-17x13in) s.i.d.1999 acrylic collage. 21-Feb-4 Cornette de St.Cyr, Paris #319/R est:2500-3000
£1879 $3326 €2800 Manette G49 radioactif III (81x65cm-32x26in) s.i.d.1994 verso acrylic. 28-Apr-4 Artcurial Briest, Paris #416/R est:3000-4000
£2134 $3840 €3200 Camion SITA jaune (130x97cm-51x38in) s.i.d.1985 verso acrylic. 26-Apr-4 Tajan, Paris #249 est:3500-4000
£2500 $4725 €3700 Iron lady (61x50cm-24x20in) s.i.d.2000 verso aerosol paint aluminium neon. 21-Feb-4 Cornette de St.Cyr, Paris #321/R est:2000-3000
£2797 $4671 €4000 Untitled (104x74cm-41x29in) s. acrylic cardboard prov. 29-Jun-3 Versailles Encheres #167/R
£3021 $5045 €4350 Wagon rouge (100x81cm-39x32in) s.i.d.1984 verso. 25-Oct-3 Cornette de St.Cyr, Paris #732/R est:5000-6000
£3067 $5520 €4600 Camion bache (65x53cm-26x21in) s.i.d.1986 verso acrylic. 24-Apr-4 Cornette de St.Cyr, Paris #594 est:5000
£3846 $6423 €5500 Great nude and metre (100x81cm-39x32in) s.i.d.1974 verso acrylic prov. 29-Jun-3 Versailles Encheres #166/R
£4196 $7007 €6000 Clap, verrou sur fond gris (114x146cm-45x57in) s.d.1991-1992 verso prov. 11-Oct-3 Cornette de St.Cyr, Paris #27/R est:5000-7000
£4306 $7104 €6200 Camion bache (89x116cm-35x46in) s.i.d.1976 verso acrylic. 2-Jul-3 Cornette de St.Cyr, Paris #128/R est:7000-8000
£4362 $7983 €6500 Camion SI.T.A. detail C 46 (81x65cm-32x26in) s.i. verso acrylic. 7-Jul-4 Artcurial Briest, Paris #293/R est:2000-3000
£4698 $8644 €7000 Verrou wagon SNCF, produits inflammables (105x75cm-41x30in) s. s.i.verso acrylic cardboard laid down prov. 28-Mar-4 Anaf, Lyon #169/R est:7000-8000
£5208 $8698 €7500 Manette/fond bleu (146x114cm-57x45in) s.i.d.1986 verso acrylic prov. 21-Oct-3 Artcurial Briest, Paris #558/R est:8000-12000
£6667 $12133 €10000 Fond jaune (116x89cm-46x35in) s.i.d.1990 acrylic lit. 29-Jun-4 Cornette de St.Cyr, Paris #102/R est:10000-12000
£6690 $11574 €9500 Disjoncteur bleu 1 (100x73cm-39x29in) s.i.d.1972 verso acrylic thermometer. 14-Dec-3 Versailles Encheres #163/R est:6000-8000
£6757 $12095 €10000 Prise male plus bouche (65x81cm-26x32in) s.i.d.1969 verso acrylic. 4-May-4 Calmels Cohen, Paris #216/R est:10000-12000
£7394 $12940 €10500 Poignee and face no.2 (80x116cm-31x46in) s.i.d.1971 verso acrylic. 18-Dec-3 Cornette de St.Cyr, Paris #122/R est:10000-12000
£7447 $12436 €10500 Camion citerne bache TK ASM (97x130cm-38x51in) s.i.d.1985 verso acrylic prov.exhib. 19-Oct-3 Anaf, Lyon #175/R est:10000-12000
£8389 $15436 €12500 Prise Male No 2 (92x65cm-36x26in) s.i.d.1968 verso prov. 29-Mar-4 Cornette de St.Cyr, Paris #74/R est:12000-15000
£8741 $14598 €12500 Sans titre (40x32cm-16x13in) s.d.1965 acrylic cardboard prov.lit. 11-Oct-3 Cornette de St.Cyr, Paris #92/R est:10000-12000
£9859 $17056 €14000 Tilt (161x114cm-63x45in) s.i.d.1967 verso acrylic prov. 9-Dec-3 Artcurial Briest, Paris #377/R est:15000-20000
£9859 $17056 €14000 Interior (161x130cm-63x51in) s.i.d.1967 acrylic prov.exhib. 9-Dec-3 Artcurial Briest, Paris #378/R est:15000-20000
£10067 $18020 €15000 Nu de face et grille (130x98cm-51x39in) s.i.d.1971 verso oil canvas metal grill prov. 27-May-4 Sotheby's, Paris #271/R est:8000-12000
£10333 $19013 €15500 Explosifs Composition81 fond rouge (145x85cm-57x33in) s.i.d.1989 verso acrylic various objects prov.exhib.lit. 8-Jun-4 Artcurial Briest, Paris #264/R est:15000-20000
£12667 $23053 €19000 Oxygenateur (162x130cm-64x51in) s.i.d.1974 verso acrylic prov.lit. 29-Jun-4 Cornette de St.Cyr, Paris #83/R est:15000-20000
£13380 $23148 €19000 Fauteuil dentaire (200x190cm-79x75in) s.i.verso acrylic prov.lit. 9-Dec-3 Artcurial Briest, Paris #379/R est:20000-25000
Sculpture
£972 $1624 €1400 Prise electrique (50x65x19cm-20x26x7in) s.d.71 resin polyester paint edition of 25. 21-Oct-3 Artcurial Briest, Paris #500/R est:2000-2500
£972 $1624 €1400 Prise electrique (45x60x19cm-18x24x7in) resin polyester paint edition 8/25. 21-Oct-3 Artcurial Briest, Paris #501/R est:2000-2500
Works on paper
£336 $594 €500 Whirlpool (79x53cm-31x21in) s.d.1997 collage col serigraph. 28-Apr-4 Artcurial Briest, Paris #425
£1389 $2319 €2000 Ficelle-fond brun (45x32cm-18x13in) s.d.1988 i. gouache collage cardboard. 25-Oct-3 Cornette de St.Cyr, Paris #729/R est:2000-2200
£2098 $3566 €3000 Frein controle/cadran bleu (49x39cm-19x15in) s.i. mixed media collage. 30-Nov-3 Anaf, Lyon #121/R est:3000-3500
£3497 $5945 €5000 Projet pour la mairie de lille (64x202cm-25x80in) s.i. gouache cardboard prov. 25-Nov-3 Tajan, Paris #59/R est:5000-6000
£3873 $6701 €5500 Camion bache bleu (98x130cm-39x51in) s.i.d.1978 verso mixed media. 10-Dec-3 Rossini, Paris #83/R
£4698 $8644 €7000 Electricite (75x53cm-30x21in) s. mixed media collage exec.c.1965. 28-Mar-4 Anaf, Lyon #168/R est:7000-8000

KLASHORST, Peter (1957-) Dutch?
£400 $732 €600 Under world, over world (70x75cm-28x30in) s.d.83 acrylic prov.exhib.lit. 7-Jun-4 Glerum, Amsterdam #298/R
£467 $854 €700 Female nude for Albert Heijn (94x61cm-37x24in) s.d.99 verso panel. 7-Jun-4 Glerum, Amsterdam #210/R
£500 $915 €750 Gambia (140x150cm-55x59in) s. 7-Jun-4 Glerum, Amsterdam #291/R
£909 $1518 €1300 Figures (200x180cm-79x71in) s. paper. 30-Jun-3 Sotheby's, Amsterdam #495
Works on paper
£629 $1070 €900 Two figures (210x260cm-83x102in) s. mixed media. 24-Nov-3 Glerum, Amsterdam #259/R

KLASS, Friedrich Christian (1752-1827) German
Works on paper
£537 $988 €800 Lovers under tree (22x18cm-9x7in) s. wash pen. 26-Mar-4 Dorotheum, Vienna #81/R

KLAUCK, Ernst A (20th C) German
£440 $796 €660 Bathers (78x78cm-31x31in) s.d.67 i. verso board. 3-Apr-4 Hans Stahl, Hamburg #50/R
£480 $869 €720 Nehrung fishermen near Nidden (63x72cm-25x28in) i.d.18/9/52 verso board. 3-Apr-4 Hans Stahl, Hamburg #51/R
£587 $1062 €880 In the cafe (78x78cm-31x31in) s. board. 3-Apr-4 Hans Stahl, Hamburg #52/R

KLAUKE, Jurgen (1943-) German
Photographs
£2600 $4784 €3796 Kunstlerpech (60x50cm-24x20in) s.i.d.1980 num.1/3 verso gelatin silver print. 24-Jun-4 Sotheby's, Olympia #615/R est:2500-3500
£9028 $15347 €13000 Home game (180x125cm-71x49in) gelatin silver prov.lit. 31-Oct-3 Lempertz, Koln #384/R est:12000-15000
Works on paper
£333 $613 €500 Untitled (29x21cm-11x8in) d.1975 ink pen brush exhib. 12-Jun-4 Villa Grisebach, Berlin #776/R
£600 $1074 €900 Untitled (42x56cm-17x22in) s.d. W/C. 15-May-4 Dr Sturies, Dusseldorf #108/R
£704 $1169 €1000 Composition (41x55cm-16x22in) s.d.1994 W/C. 13-Jun-3 Hauswedell & Nolte, Hamburg #738/R
£917 $1532 €1330 Double axle (41x29cm-16x11in) W/C. 19-Jun-3 Kornfeld, Bern #556 est:2000 (S.FR 2000)

KLAUS, Joseph (19th C) Belgian
£662 $1205 €1000 Roses (60x90cm-24x35in) s. 15-Jun-4 Galerie Moderne, Brussels #151
£1000 $1790 €1500 Bouquet de fleurs (109x83cm-43x33in) s. 11-May-4 Christie's, Paris #209/R est:1500-2000

KLAUS, Reinhold (1881-1963) Austrian
Works on paper
£604 $1117 €900 View from window of Waidhofen an der Ybbs (49x68cm-19x27in) s.d.1931 col pen. 9-Mar-4 Dorotheum, Vienna #52/R
£704 $1232 €1000 Monument in the Graben in Vienna (32x24cm-13x9in) s.d.1925 mixed media. 19-Dec-3 Dorotheum, Vienna #67/R

KLAUSNER, R (?) ?
£680 $1265 €993 Two cardinals at a table drinking hock and with still life of fruit (33x43cm-13x17in) s. board. 4-Mar-4 Mitchells, Cockermouth #795

KLAUSNER, Ruth (?) ?
£3400 $5678 €4964 New acquisition (50x61cm-20x24in) s. panel. 12-Nov-3 Sotheby's, Olympia #226/R est:2000-3000

KLEE, Paul (1879-1940) Swiss
£57647 $98000 €84165 Ein Strassenmusiker (34x22cm-13x9in) s.i.d.1940 mount tempera paper on board prov.exhib.lit. 5-Nov-3 Christie's, Rockefeller NY #130/R est:35000-45000
£60000 $110400 €90000 Your ancestor? (59x43cm-23x17in) s. i.d.1933 on support tempera paper on cardboard prov.exhib.lit. 11-Jun-4 Villa Grisebach, Berlin #51/R est:70000-90000
£112676 $197183 €160000 Frucht der kuste (35x43cm-14x17in) i.d.1933 oil wax paper prov.exhib.lit. 18-Dec-3 Tajan, Paris #37/R est:180000-200000
£227074 $413275 €331528 Landscape (20x26cm-8x10in) s.d.1919 cardboard prov.exhib.lit. 18-Jun-4 Kornfeld, Bern #81/R est:600000 (S.FR 520000)
Prints
£2183 $3974 €3187 Small world. s.i. etching. 17-Jun-4 Kornfeld, Bern #472/R est:6000 (S.FR 5000)
£2657 $4571 €3800 Head - bearded man (22x15cm-9x6in) s.i.d.1925 lithograph. 2-Dec-3 Hauswedell & Nolte, Hamburg #305/R est:3000
£2982 $4979 €4324 Small world. s.i. etching. 19-Jun-3 Kornfeld, Bern #558 est:7500 (S.FR 6500)
£3067 $5643 €4600 Bird comedy (42x20cm-17x8in) s.mono. lithograph. 10-Jun-4 Hauswedell & Nolte, Hamburg #334/R est:4000
£4128 $6894 €5986 Witch with comb. s. lithograph. 19-Jun-3 Kornfeld, Bern #559/R est:10000 (S.FR 9000)
£4200 $7644 €6132 Der verliebte (34x25cm-13x10in) s. col lithograph. 1-Jul-4 Sotheby's, London #192/R est:3000-4000
£4698 $8644 €7000 What's happening? (23x29cm-9x11in) s. etching. 26-Mar-4 Ketterer, Hamburg #498/R est:7000-9000
£5333 $9813 €8000 Calculating old man (29x23cm-11x9in) s. etching exec. 1929 one of 130. 12-Jun-4 Villa Grisebach, Berlin #232/R est:9000-12000
£5650 $10000 €8249 Gestrupp (14x10cm-6x4in) s.i.d.1928 num.11.12 etching. 30-Apr-4 Sotheby's, New York #116/R est:15000-20000
£5895 $10729 €8607 Unending. s.i. etching. 17-Jun-4 Kornfeld, Bern #474/R est:12500 (S.FR 13500)

£6780	$12000	€9899	Hoffmanneske Szene (31x22cm-12x9in) s.i.d.1921 col lithograph. 30-Apr-4 Sotheby's, New York #115/R est:7000-10000
£6993	$11888	€10000	Composition (24x30cm-9x12in) s. etching zinc on paper. 29-Nov-3 Bassenge, Berlin #6821/R est:12000
£8734	$15895	€12752	Donkey (24x14cm-9x6in) s.i. lithograph exec. 1925 lit. 18-Jun-4 Kornfeld, Bern #92/R est:25000 (S.FR 20000)
£10000	$18400	€15000	Composition (24x30cm-9x12in) s. etching. 10-Jun-4 Hauswedell & Nolte, Hamburg #333/R est:12000
£10490	$17832	€15000	Tightrope walker (44x27cm-17x11in) s.i.d. lithograph. 29-Nov-3 Bassenge, Berlin #6824/R est:15000
£15721	$28611	€22953	Narretei (19x15cm-7x6in) s.i. lithograph exec. 1922 lit. 18-Jun-4 Kornfeld, Bern #90/R est:40000 (S.FR 36000)
£17467	$31790	€25502	Reflection in a window (15x11cm-6x4in) s.i.d.1915 etching lit. 18-Jun-4 Kornfeld, Bern #89/R est:50000 (S.FR 40000)
£20000	$36800	€30000	Contemplation - self portrait (24x16cm-9x6in) s.i.d.1919 W/C lithograph. 10-Jun-4 Hauswedell & Nolte, Hamburg #335/R est:6000
£21834	$39738	€31878	Thistle, the clown (29x24cm-11x9in) s.i.d.1931 etching lit. 18-Jun-4 Kornfeld, Bern #93/R est:60000 (S.FR 50000)
£22667	$41480	€34000	Tightrope walker (44x27cm-17x11in) s.i.d.1923 col lithograph. 5-Jun-4 Lempertz, Koln #787/R est:20000-25000
£24017	$43712	€35065	Station (14x19cm-6x7in) s.i.d.1911 drypoint celluloid lit. 18-Jun-4 Kornfeld, Bern #88/R est:50000 (S.FR 55000)
£25328	$46096	€36979	Stepping out (29x19cm-11x7in) mono.i.d.1923 col lithograph lit. 18-Jun-4 Kornfeld, Bern #91/R est:50000 (S.FR 58000)
£26201	$47686	€38253	Perseus, invention 8 (12x14cm-5x6in) s.i. etching exec.December 1904 lit. 18-Jun-4 Kornfeld, Bern #86/R est:75000 (S.FR 60000)
£56769	$103319	€82883	Venerable phoenix, invention 9 (27x19cm-11x7in) s.i.d.1905 etching lit. 18-Jun-4 Kornfeld, Bern #87/R est:125000 (S.FR 130000)
£117904	$214585	€172140	Woman and animal, invention I (20x22cm-8x9in) s.i.d.1904 etching lit. 18-Jun-4 Kornfeld, Bern #85/R est:175000 (S.FR 270000)
Works on paper			
£4525	$7557	€6607	Animal fairytale (15x29cm-6x11in) s.i. ink letter paper on board prov.lit. 24-Jun-3 Germann, Zurich #89/R est:10000-14000 (S.FR 10000)
£4698	$8644	€7000	Donkey (20x13cm-8x5in) s.d.25 pen W/C paper on board prov.lit. 26-Mar-4 Ketterer, Hamburg #496/R est:5000-7000
£6000	$11040	€8760	Composition (20x27cm-8x11in) s.verso pencil prov. 24-Mar-4 Sotheby's, Olympia #37/R est:6000-8000
£9500	$17480	€13870	Blutgericht - blood court (13x21cm-5x8in) s. pen ink executed 1933 lit. 24-Mar-4 Sotheby's, Olympia #38/R est:7000-9000
£10056	$18000	€14682	Verhexte Landschaft (27x36cm-11x14in) s.i.d.1923 pencil paper on paper on board prov.exhib.lit. 5-May-4 Christie's, Rockefeller NY #123/R est:15000-20000
£12000	$22080	€18000	Revolution in the Lowlands (20x30cm-8x12in) s.i.d.1932 pen card prov.exhib.lit. 12-Jun-4 Villa Grisebach, Berlin #261/R est:14000-18000
£12227	$22253	€17851	Dynamoradiolaren 2 (32x18cm-13x7in) i. pencil ink exec. 1926 prov.exhib.lit. 18-Jun-4 Kornfeld, Bern #82/R est:30000 (S.FR 28000)
£13333	$24533	€20000	Rising pathways (47x30cm-19x12in) s.i.d.1930 pen lit.prov. 10-Jun-4 Hauswedell & Nolte, Hamburg #332/R est:14000
£15284	$27817	€22315	St Beatenburg, Birrenfluh (26x22cm-10x9in) s.i.d.1909 pen ink exhib.lit. 18-Jun-4 Kornfeld, Bern #79/R est:40000 (S.FR 35000)
£17647	$30000	€25765	Ein Busser (35x22cm-14x9in) s.i.d.1925 pencil paper on board prov.lit. 5-Nov-3 Christie's, Rockefeller NY #114/R est:20000-30000
£18000	$32760	€26280	Das arme Sunderglocklein (18x25cm-7x10in) s.i.d.1913 pen ink paper on artist mount prov.exhib.lit. 5-Feb-4 Christie's, London #366/R est:10000-15000
£18667	$34347	€28000	Stromgeist (10x29cm-4x11in) s.i.d.1920 Indian ink. 10-Jun-4 Hauswedell & Nolte, Hamburg #330/R est:25000
£19333	$35573	€29000	Bazaar still life (19x23cm-7x9in) s.i.d.1924 pen. 10-Jun-4 Hauswedell & Nolte, Hamburg #331/R est:35000
£26000	$47320	€37960	Die Rolle (54x63cm-21x25in) s.i. W/C paper on artist mount exec 1930 prov.lit. 5-Feb-4 Christie's, London #371/R est:15000-20000
£26574	$45707	€38000	Regentag (36x50cm-14x20in) s.i.d.1935 gouache col crayon prov.lit. 8-Dec-3 Artcurial Briest, Paris #46/R est:28000-35000
£27933	$50000	€40782	Idols (28x24cm-11x9in) s. d.1913 i.mount pen ink paper on card prov.exhib.lit. 6-May-4 Sotheby's, New York #320/R est:25000-35000
£30303	$54242	€44242	In der Opernloge (26x21cm-10x8in) s. gouache paper on cardboard painted 1938 exhib.prov. 28-May-4 Uppsala Auktionskammare, Uppsala #273/R est:250000-300000 (S.KR 410000)
£32353	$55000	€47235	Zum Goedenkblatt fur Lieschen (22x28cm-9x11in) s.i.d.1921 pen ink paper on board prov.exhib.lit. 5-Nov-3 Christie's, Rockefeller NY #123/R est:40000-60000
£35000	$63700	€51100	Auferstehende - Rising from the dead (27x21cm-11x8in) s. i.d.1938 on mount casein gouache pencil prov.exhib.lit. 4-Feb-4 Sotheby's, London #535/R est:40000-50000
£35808	$65170	€52280	Pathos I (65x47cm-26x19in) s.i.d.1937 chl col paste lit. 18-Jun-4 Kornfeld, Bern #84/R est:40000 (S.FR 82000)
£45852	$83450	€66944	Bern (13x26cm-5x10in) s.i.d.1909 pen ink exhib.lit. 18-Jun-4 Kornfeld, Bern #80/R est:80000 (S.FR 105000)
£62000	$112840	€90520	Nachts, grun Indischrot, duster - At night, green Indian red, gloomy (15x22cm-6x9in) s. W/C paper on card exec.1921 prov.lit. 4-Feb-4 Sotheby's, London #470/R est:50000-70000
£70588	$120000	€103058	Pferd und Mann (23x19cm-9x7in) s.i.d.1923 gouache W/C pen blk ink paper on paper prov.exhib.lit. 5-Nov-3 Christie's, Rockefeller NY #122/R est:100000-150000
£73427	$124825	€105000	The horse (14x21cm-6x8in) s.i. W/C paper on board prov.exhib. 28-Nov-3 Villa Grisebach, Berlin #57/R est:80000-120000
£100000	$182000	€146000	Sonnen Untergang (40x60cm-16x24in) s.i.d.1937 W/C chl paper on artist mount prov.exhib.lit. 5-Feb-4 Christie's, London #364/R est:70000-100000
£100437	$182795	€146638	Rock in the darkness (48x31cm-19x12in) s.i.d.1927 W/C pen ink paper on cardboard exhib.lit. 18-Jun-4 Kornfeld, Bern #83/R est:250000 (S.FR 230000)
£150000	$276000	€219000	Rotes Madchen mit gelbem Topfhut (32x25cm-13x10in) s.d.1919-224 W/C over oil-transfer drawing prov.exhib.lit. 24-Jun-4 Christie's, London #386/R est:90000-120000
£200000	$366000	€300000	Physiognomy of planting (26x25cm-10x10in) s. W/C board prov. 5-Jun-4 Lempertz, Koln #788/R est:250000-300000
£205882	$350000	€300588	Harmony of southern flora (31x41cm-12x16in) s. i.d.1927 mount W/C pen ink paper on board prov.lit. 6-Nov-3 Sotheby's, New York #216/R est:80000-120000
£280000	$515200	€408800	Nacht-Eindruck einer sudliechen Stadt (30x23cm-12x9in) s.d.1925 pen ink ink wash exec 1925 prov.exhib.lit. 24-Jun-4 Christie's, London #337/R est:100000-150000

KLEEHAAS, Theodor (1854-1929) German

£533	$971	€800	Young girl playing the guitar in a mountainous landscape (71x56cm-28x22in) s. 1-Jul-4 Van Ham, Cologne #1456/R
£979	$1684	€1400	Two children playing together (81x66cm-32x26in) s.i.d.89. 3-Dec-3 Neumeister, Munich #626/R

KLEH, Janos (19th C) ?

£2271	$4020	€3316	Garden with roses in Szolnok (52x62cm-20x24in) s. 28-Apr-4 Kieselbach, Budapest #32/R (H.F 850000)

KLEIBER, Hans (1887-1967) American

£2540	$4750	€3708	Wyoming landscape (23x30cm-9x12in) s. board prov. 24-Jul-4 Coeur d'Alene, Hayden #212/R est:3000-5000

KLEIMER, Axel Bernhard (1881-1945) Swedish

£347	$590	€500	Landscape near Kvidinge (40x60cm-16x24in) s.d. 1-Nov-3 Meeting Art, Vercelli #356

KLEIN VON DIEPOLD (19/20th C) German

£545	$856	€796	Stags (79x98cm-31x39in) s. 27-Aug-3 Dunbar Sloane, Wellington #78/R (NZ.D 1500)

KLEIN VON DIEPOLD, Julian (1868-1947) German

£2450	$4460	€3700	Landscape with windmill (40x50cm-16x20in) s. board. 18-Jun-4 Bolland & Marotz, Bremen #659/R est:1300

KLEIN, B (19/20th C) Dutch

£2699	$4750	€3941	Interior with family (91x122cm-36x48in) s. painted c.1910. 23-May-4 Treadway Gallery, Cincinnati #516/R est:4000-6000

KLEIN, Bernhard (1888-?) German

£1445	$2500	€2110	Dutch genre scene (89x119cm-35x47in) painted c.1925. 12-Dec-3 Du Mouchelle, Detroit #2032/R est:3500-4500

KLEIN, Cesar (1876-1954) German

£4667	$8587	€7000	Still life with a vase of flowers and fruit bowl (50x40cm-20x16in) s.d.1908 prov. 12-Jun-4 Villa Grisebach, Berlin #169/R est:7000-9000
£9396	$17289	€14000	Fishing boats on southern coast (70x80cm-28x31in) s. 24-Mar-4 Hugo Ruef, Munich #1239/R est:8000
£10000	$18400	€15000	Still life with flower pots and jug. Portrait of a woman wearing a hat (50x62cm-20x24in) s.d.1911 double-sided prov. 12-Jun-4 Villa Grisebach, Berlin #222/R est:12000-14000
Works on paper			
£594	$993	€850	Evening thought (22x33cm-9x13in) i.d. verso gouache. 28-Jun-3 Bolland & Marotz, Bremen #853/R
£2980	$5424	€4500	Woman reading (33x42cm-13x17in) s.d.1925 gouache. 18-Jun-4 Bolland & Marotz, Bremen #909/R est:6000
£4545	$7818	€6500	Song of the Sibyls (69x79cm-27x31in) s.d.1946 s.i. verso. 2-Dec-3 Hauswedell & Nolte, Hamburg #306/R est:5000

KLEIN, Friedrich Franz (1898-1990) Dutch

£993	$1658	€1400	La Loge (61x50cm-24x20in) s.d.1932. 20-Jun-3 Drouot Estimations, Paris #176
£1678	$2887	€2400	Garden scene (17x38cm-7x15in) s. canvas on board. 2-Dec-3 Sotheby's, Amsterdam #234/R est:1800-2200
£1905	$3467	€2800	On the beach (47x33cm-19x13in) s. board. 3-Feb-4 Christie's, Amsterdam #541 est:2800-3200
£2517	$4580	€3800	Autoportrait (60x50cm-24x20in) s.d.1923 verso. 16-Jun-4 Claude Boisgirard, Paris #89/R est:1500-2000
£2800	$5152	€4200	Three horses between trees with a setting sun (65x81cm-26x32in) s. exhib. 8-Jun-4 Sotheby's, Amsterdam #210/R est:3000-4000
Works on paper			
£500	$915	€750	Houses in Spain (32x40cm-13x16in) s. pastel. 7-Jun-4 Glerum, Amsterdam #90/R
£537	$993	€800	Flower market (40x31cm-16x12in) s. pastel. 15-Mar-4 Sotheby's, Amsterdam #205/R
£660	$1076	€950	Horses (23x32cm-9x13in) s. gouache. 29-Sep-3 Sotheby's, Amsterdam #378/R

KLEIN, Georges Andre (1901-1992) French

£322	$537	€460	Nature morte a la coupe de poires et au melon. s. masonite. 30-Jun-3 Bailly Pommery, Paris #110/R

KLEIN, Jan (?) ?

£280	$445	€406	Dutch windmill scene (50x40cm-20x16in) s. 9-Sep-3 Bonhams, Knightsbridge #175b

KLEIN, Johann Adam (1792-1875) German

£3179	$5785	€4800	Ponte Agiore in Tivoli (17x23cm-7x9in) i.d.24 July 1821 cardboard. 16-Jun-4 Hugo Ruef, Munich #997/R est:1800
£5944	$9927	€8500	Resting outside village in Frank area. s.d.1842 panel. 26-Jun-3 Weidler, Nurnberg #7023/R est:12000
£6207	$10366	€9000	Resting outside the city (74x94cm-29x37in) s.d.1834 lit. 12-Jul-3 Bergmann, Erlangen #712/R est:6500
£13974	$25432	€20402	Crashed beer transport coach (32x42cm-13x17in) s.d.1864. 16-Jun-4 Fischer, Luzern #1188/R est:4000-5000 (S.FR 32000)
Works on paper			
£455	$759	€650	Soldiers resting (12x16cm-5x6in) W/C drawing. 26-Jun-3 Weidler, Nurnberg #7008/R

KLEIN, Jozsef (1896-1945) Hungarian?

£4479	$8107	€6539	Baia mare knolls (55x68cm-22x27in) s. 16-Apr-4 Mu Terem Galeria, Budapest #30/R (H.F 1700000)

KLEIN, L (19th C) German

£1019	$1569	€1600	Wild boar by stream in winter at sunset (70x98cm-28x39in) s. 4-Sep-2 Schopman, Hamburg #95/R est:950

KLEIN, Medard P (1905-2000) American

£559 $1000 €816 Untitled (33x53cm-13x21in) acrylic gouache board prov. 16-May-4 Wright, Chicago #228/R
Works on paper
£199 $350 €291 Untitled (23x30cm-9x12in) s. pencil. 23-May-4 Hindman, Chicago #1048/R
£199 $350 €291 Untitled (23x30cm-9x12in) s. pencil. 23-May-4 Hindman, Chicago #1049/R
£279 $475 €407 Untitled (20x30cm-8x12in) s. pencil. 9-Nov-3 Wright, Chicago #277
£294 $500 €429 Untitled (20x30cm-8x12in) s. pencil. 9-Nov-3 Wright, Chicago #275
£2059 $3500 €3006 Arrangement 50 (76x56cm-30x22in) s.d.1943 casein on board exhib. 9-Nov-3 Wright, Chicago #274 est:3000-4000

KLEIN, Micha (1964-) Dutch

Photographs
£9090 $15635 €13000 The temple (180x180cm-71x71in) s.i.d.2000 num.3/12 verso col print. 3-Dec-3 Sotheby's, Amsterdam #493/R est:10000-15000
£10000 $18400 €15000 Break of dawn (300x165cm-118x65in) s.i.d.1998 num.2/3 verso colour print. 8-Jun-4 Sotheby's, Amsterdam #150/R est:15000-20000
Prints
£4348 $7130 €6000 Artificial beauty series: hope (75x74cm-30x29in) s.i.d.98 num.1/5 verso col print prov. 27-May-3 Sotheby's, Amsterdam #470/R est:4000-5000

KLEIN, Paul (1909-1993) French

£267 $477 €400 Deux personnages (60x30cm-24x12in) s. d.1971 verso. 11-May-4 Vanderkindere, Brussels #99
£270 $511 €400 Nu assis (33x22cm-13x9in) s. panel. 17-Feb-4 Galerie Moderne, Brussels #233/R
£278 $464 €400 Voiliers (24x30cm-9x12in) s. d.1969 verso. 21-Oct-3 Campo, Vlaamse Kaai #892
£315 $535 €450 Plat pays de Flandre (40x80cm-16x31in) s. 18-Nov-3 Galerie Moderne, Brussels #682
£333 $597 €500 Plat pays a Oost-Kerk (60x80cm-24x31in) s. panel. 11-May-4 Vanderkindere, Brussels #41
£350 $594 €500 Les musiciens (35x27cm-14x11in) s. 18-Nov-3 Galerie Moderne, Brussels #694
£455 $773 €650 Modern jazz quartet (40x80cm-16x31in) s.d.59 i.verso. 18-Nov-3 Vanderkindere, Brussels #153
£559 $951 €800 L'orchestre (38x46cm-15x18in) s. panel. 18-Nov-3 Galerie Moderne, Brussels #658
£780 $1303 €1100 Orgue de barbarie (41x33cm-16x13in) s. d.1951 verso panel. 14-Oct-3 Vanderkindere, Brussels #557
£868 $1380 €1250 Clowns (92x60cm-36x24in) s. 9-Sep-3 Vanderkindere, Brussels #56
£972 $1546 €1400 Le vol d'Oies (120x150cm-47x59in) s.d.75 s.i.d.verso. 15-Sep-3 Horta, Bruxelles #351

KLEIN, Philipp (1871-1907) German

£278 $458 €400 Visiting the blacksmith (38x30cm-15x12in) s.i.d.93 board. 3-Jul-3 Neumeister, Munich #2860
£1053 $1937 €1600 Two girls playing summer landscape (31x46cm-12x18in) s.i.d.98. 24-Jun-4 Dr Fritz Nagel, Stuttgart #725/R est:1900

KLEIN, William (1926-) American

Photographs
£1916 $3200 €2797 Modern dance ceremony (27x40cm-11x16in) i.verso gelatin silver print lit. 16-Oct-3 Phillips, New York #156/R est:8000-12000
£2333 $4177 €3500 Man under El, New York (45x33cm-18x13in) s.i.d.1955 verso silver print lit. 13-May-4 Le Mouel, Paris #195/R est:2500 3000
£4790 $8000 €6993 End of the day dance (28x39cm-11x15in) i. gelatin silver print lit. 16-Oct-3 Phillips, New York #152/R est:10000-15000
£13986 $23776 €20000 Car under El, New York (35x28cm-14x11in) s.i.d. verso silver gelatin lit.exhib. 27-Nov-3 Villa Grisebach, Berlin #1256/R est:10000-15000

KLEIN, Yves (1928-1962) French

£29371 $50517 €42000 Monochrome blanc (15x32cm-6x13in) s.i.d.57 paint paper on cardboard prov. 4-Dec-3 Piasa, Paris #80/R est:12000-15000
£188811 $324755 €270000 Monochrome bleu IKB 113 (46x55cm-18x22in) s.d.9 Fevrier 1959 verso paint canvas on panel exhib. 4-Dec-3 Piasa, Paris #22/R est:300000-400000
£202797 $348811 €290000 Peinture de feu, F 125 (57x200cm-22x79in) s.i.d.61 verso asbestos cardboard diptych prov.exhib. 4-Dec-3 Piasa, Paris #84/R est:60000-80000
Sculpture
£2153 $3595 €3100 Petite venus bleue (12x8x7cm-5x3x3in) num.380/500 bronze blue pigment plexiglas box gold leaf. 25-Oct-3 Cornette de St.Cyr, Paris #232/R est:3500-4000
£2467 $4440 €3700 Petite Venus bleue (12x5x7cm-5x2x3in) bronze pigment plexiglas. 24-Apr-4 Cornette de St.Cyr, Paris #596/R est:3500-4000
£5028 $9000 €7341 Table bleue (37x125x100cm-15x49x39in) s. num.99 blue pigment in Plexiglas table. 13-May-4 Sotheby's, New York #209/R est:8000-12000
£6294 $10699 €9000 Table bleue (36x124x100cm-14x49x39in) glass aluminium pigment. 24-Nov-3 Christie's, Milan #152/R est:9000-12000
£6419 $11298 €9500 Blue table (125x100x37cm-49x39x15in) blue pigment under plexiglass table. 18-May-4 Tajan, Paris #80/R est:10000-12000
£6500 $11830 €9490 La terre bleue (36cm-14in) i.star num.263/300 pigment resin plaster cast prov.lit. 6-Feb-4 Sotheby's, London #227/R est:5000-7000
£7042 $12324 €10000 La terre bleue RP 7 (36cm-14in) blue pigment resin on plaster lit. 18-Dec-3 Cornette de St.Cyr, Paris #112/R est:10000-12000
£7200 $13104 €10512 Blue table (37x125x100cm-15x49x39in) pigment plexiglas table. 6-Feb-4 Sotheby's, London #223/R est:6000-8000
£7500 $13800 €10950 Terre bleue (36cm-14in) num.195/300 pigment synthetic resin plaster cast prov.lit. 24-Jun-4 Sotheby's, London #262/R est:5000-7000
£8108 $14271 €12000 Table doree (125x100x37cm-49x39x15in) gold leaves under plexiglas table. 18-May-4 Tajan, Paris #79/R est:10000-12000
£9000 $16560 €13140 Table bleue (36x124x100cm-14x49x39in) glass plexiglas blue pigment. 25-Jun-4 Christie's, London #136/R est:6000-8000
£9000 $16560 €13140 Blue table (37x125x100cm-15x49x39in) s. num.97 A1121 pigment in plexiglass table prov. 24-Jun-4 Sotheby's, London #161/R est:6000-8000
£10000 $18500 €15000 Table rose (37x125x100cm-15x49x39in) s. num.4114 pigment plexiglas. 18-Jul-4 Sotheby's, Paris #193/R est:8000-12000
£10778 $18000 €15736 Victory of Samothrace (52cm-20in) IKB pigment plaster cast mounted on stone executed 1962 prov.lit. 14-Nov-3 Phillips, New York #149/R est:35000-45000
£12667 $23433 €19000 Table bleue (37x125x100cm-15x49x39in) s. num.AI9010 pigment plexiglas. 18-Jul-4 Sotheby's, Paris #203/R est:10000-15000
£13000 $21710 €18980 S20, l'esclave mourant d'apres Michel-Ange (57cm-22in) s.num.239/300 blue pigment resin plaster prov.lit. 22-Oct-3 Christie's, London #20/R est:10000-15000
£13415 $22000 €19586 Eponge se 267 (8x7x4cm-3x3x2in) pigment synthetic resin sponge metal base. 28-May-3 Sotheby's, Amsterdam #105/R est:15000-18000
£15942 $26145 €22000 Blue table (36x124x100cm-14x49x39in) plexiglass pigment one of 300 exhib.lit. 29-May-3 Galleria Pace, Milan #139/R est:32000
£20000 $37125 €30000 Table or (37x125x100cm-15x49x39in) s. num.96AII10 gold leaf plexiglas. 18-Jul-4 Sotheby's, Paris #221/R est:12000-18000
£22000 $36740 €32120 Venus bleue (69x30x20cm-27x12x8in) num.HC IV/L pigment synthetic resin plaster case prov.lit. 21-Oct-3 Sotheby's, London #345/R est:20000-30000
£26000 $47320 €37960 SE 221 (14x12x6cm-6x5x2in) pigment resin sponge plexiglas base exec.c.1960 prov. 6-Feb-4 Sotheby's, London #127/R est:20000-30000
£27933 $50000 €40782 Victoire de Samothrace (50x25x36cm-20x10x14in) dry blue pigment on synthetic resin on plaster exec.1973 prov. 13-May-4 Sotheby's, New York #211/R est:30000-40000
£30000 $54600 €43800 Venus d'Alexandrie (68cm-27in) st. num.34/300 blue pigment in synthetic resin plaster prov.lit. 5-Feb-4 Christie's, London #156/R est:20000-30000
£35000 $63700 €51100 Venus (69x30x20cm-27x12x8in) i.star num.48/50 pigment resin plaster cast prov.lit. 6-Feb-4 Sotheby's, London #232/R est:18000-25000
£65101 $119785 €97000 Se 40 (6x18x16cm-2x7x6in) pigment synthetic resin sponge marble base exec c.1960 prov.lit. 29-Mar-4 Cornette de St.Cyr, Paris #69/R est:100000-120000
£100000 $182000 €146000 SE 191 (28x18x11cm-11x7x4in) s.d.59 pigment synthetic resin sponge iron stone prov.exhib.lit. 5-Feb-4 Sotheby's, London #10/R est:70000-100000
£131469 $226126 €188000 SE 206, rose (38cm-15in) s.d.59 rose pigment sponge metal rod quartz socle lit. 4-Dec-3 Piasa, Paris #29/R est:50000-60000
Works on paper
£20000 $37000 €30000 Monochrome rouge (17x39cm-7x15in) s.d.57 pigment paper on panel prov.exhib. 18-Jul-4 Sotheby's, Paris #252/R est:25000-35000
£27439 $45000 €40061 KB 242 A (21x18cm-8x7in) i.verso blue pigment prov.exhib. 28-May-3 Sotheby's, Amsterdam #49/R est:28000-35000
£28169 $49296 €40000 Monochrome orange (22x16cm-9x6in) s.verso pigment canvas on panel prov.exhib.lit. 18-Dec-3 Cornette de St.Cyr, Paris #111/R est:30000-40000
£180000 $331200 €262800 Rp. 2 Grenoble (41x65cm-16x26in) s.d.1961 i.verso pigment synthetic resin on card prov.lit. 23-Jun-4 Sotheby's, London #11/R est:140000-180000
£950000 $1748000 €1387000 Re 29 blue sponge relief (100x100cm-39x39in) pigment synthetic resin sponges on canvas executed 1957 prov.lit. 24-Jun-4 Christie's, London #37/R est:800000-1200000

KLEINBARDT-WEGER, Maria (1882-1980) German

£385 $642 €550 Rococco woman in evening landscape (99x80cm-39x31in) s. 28-Jun-3 Bolland & Marotz, Bremen #779

KLEINEH, Oskar (1846-1919) Finnish

£1467 $2625 €2200 Landscape from the Alps (10x15cm-4x6in) s. painted c.1867-70. 15-May-4 Hagelstam, Helsinki #85/R est:2800
£1667 $2633 €2400 Boats at night (46x55cm-18x22in) s. 6-Sep-3 Schopman, Hamburg #852/R est:1800
£1879 $3458 €2800 House in Vitre, Brittany (36x22cm-14x9in) s.d.1869. 25-Mar-4 Hagelstam, Helsinki #925 est:3000
£6338 $10965 €9000 From the French coast (23x35cm-9x14in) s. mahogany panel. 13-Dec-3 Hagelstam, Helsinki #124/R est:7000
£9790 $16643 €14000 Seascape with vessel at night (29x45cm-11x18in) s. 29-Nov-3 Bukowskis, Helsinki #151/R est:12000-15000
£12937 $21993 €18500 Calm day at sea (60x36cm-24x14in) s. 29-Nov-3 Bukowskis, Helsinki #167/R est:16000-20000
£16892 $30236 €25000 Sailing at moonlight (63x48cm-25x19in) s. i.verso. 8-May-4 Bukowskis, Helsinki #179/R est:20000-25000
£17568 $31446 €26000 Vessel in moonlight (60x48cm-24x19in) s. 8-May-4 Bukowskis, Helsinki #169/R est:22000-25000
£21622 $38703 €32000 Sailing in the skerries off Helsingfors (51x75cm-20x30in) s. 8-May-4 Bukowskis, Helsinki #147/R est:30000-40000
£33566 $57063 €48000 Sunny summer Sunday in the skerries (38x61cm-15x24in) s.i.d.1883. 29-Nov-3 Bukowskis, Helsinki #87/R est:25000-35000
£75676 $135459 €112000 Fisherman's croft (90x144cm-35x57in) s.i. 8-May-4 Bukowskis, Helsinki #109/R est:100000-150000

KLEINEH, Oskar (attrib) (1846-1919) Finnish

£1408 $2254 €2000 Archipelago (12x16cm-5x6in) oil sketch. 18-Sep-3 Hagelstam, Helsinki #1051 est:2000

KLEINER, Ilia (?) ?

£279 $500 €407 Tree of life. s.i. 13-May-4 Dallas Auction Gallery, Dallas #194b/R
£419 $750 €612 Jewish wedding. s.i. verso. 13-May-4 Dallas Auction Gallery, Dallas #170b/R

KLEINERT, Hans (1884-1972) ?

Works on paper
£839 $1427 €1200 Karntner Rauchkuchl (37x48cm-15x19in) s. W/C paper on board. 19-Nov-3 Dorotheum, Klagenfurt #52

KLEINHOLZ, Frank (1901-?) American

£260 $450 €380 Teacher's pet (3x13cm-1x5in) s. board prov. 15-Dec-3 Hindman, Chicago #29/R

KLEINMANN, Alain (1953-) French

Works on paper
£1678 $2853 €2400 Souvenir d'enfance (60x73cm-24x29in) s. mixed media. 27-Nov-3 Calmels Cohen, Paris #69/R est:2500-3000

KLEINSCHMIDT, Paul (1883-1949) German

£7263 $13000 €10604 Landscape (70x90cm-28x35in) init.d.27 prov. 6-May-4 Sotheby's, New York #437/R est:15000-20000
£8380 $15000 €12235 Still life (90x70cm-35x28in) init.d.34. 6-May-4 Sotheby's, New York #321/R est:18000-25000
£22667 $41707 €34000 Woman applying her make-up (90x72cm-35x28in) s.d.30 Jun 33 prov.exhib. 11-Jun-4 Villa Grisebach, Berlin #1569/R est:20000-30000
£24000 $44160 €36000 Barmaid (154x84cm-61x33in) mono.d.40 canvas on canvas prov.exhib. 11-Jun-4 Villa Grisebach, Berlin #46/R est:40000-50000

Works on paper

£420 $713 €600 Hyena (28x22cm-11x9in) mono.d.23 W/C. 29-Nov-3 Villa Grisebach, Berlin #600/R
£493 $789 €700 Two seated women (33x26cm-13x10in) mono.i.d.30.X.28 wash Indian ink lit. 19-Sep-3 Karlheinz Kaupp, Staufen #2181/R
£503 $891 €750 Women's group (32x21cm-13x8in) d.4.II.47 Indian ink. 30-Apr-4 Dr Fritz Nagel, Stuttgart #286/R
£537 $950 €800 Women's group (33x22cm-13x9in) s.d.3 February 47 Indian ink. 30-Apr-4 Dr Fritz Nagel, Stuttgart #285/R
£537 $950 €800 Women's group (32x21cm-13x8in) Indian ink. 30-Apr-4 Dr Fritz Nagel, Stuttgart #287/R
£1433 $2637 €2150 Trees in landscape (44x48cm-17x19in) mono.d.1929 W/C on pencil. 10-Jun-4 Hauswedell & Nolte, Hamburg #336/R est:1500
£2667 $4773 €4000 Still life with lemons and cakes (50x36cm-20x14in) mono.d. W/C board. 15-May-4 Bassenge, Berlin #6940/R est:5000

KLEINTJES, Jan (1872-1955) Dutch

£2778 $4528 €4000 De Breiles (102x81cm-40x32in) s. 29-Sep-3 Sotheby's, Amsterdam #167/R
£4422 $8048 €6500 Daydreaming (175x89cm-69x35in) s.d.1915. 3-Feb-4 Christie's, Amsterdam #254/R est:3500-4500

KLEISS-HERZIG, Yvonne (1895-1968) French

Works on paper

£2914 $5332 €4400 Les potiers kabyles (30x45cm-12x18in) s. gouache cardboard. 9-Apr-4 Claude Aguttes, Neuilly #125/R est:300

KLEITSCH, Joseph (1885-1931) American

£6145 $11000 €9218 Cottage amongst trees (18x23cm-7x9in) s. board. 16-May-4 Abell, Los Angeles #169/R
£9730 $18000 €14206 Still life of fruit (56x36cm-22x14in) 12-Mar-4 Du Mouchelle, Detroit #2081/R est:3000-4000
£13587 $25000 €19837 Le Pont Napoleon (45x53cm-18x21in) s. s.i. stretcher prov. 8-Jun-4 Bonhams & Butterfields, San Francisco #4298/R est:30000-50000
£16176 $27500 €23617 Woman sewing (53x43cm-21x17in) s.i. canvas on canvas painted c.1926. 18-Nov-3 John Moran, Pasadena #37 est:10000-15000
£17341 $30000 €25318 Park Road (53x46cm-21x18in) init. 10-Dec-3 Bonhams & Butterfields, San Francisco #6240/R est:30000-50000

KLEIVA, Per (1933-) Norwegian

£2358 $4315 €3443 America's butterflies (96x72cm-38x28in) s.i.d.70 col silkscreen lit. 7-Jun-4 Blomqvist, Oslo #465/R est:28000-32000 (N.KR 29000)

KLEMCZYNSKI, Pierre (1910-) French?

£493 $818 €700 Route des peupliers (23x34cm-9x13in) 11-Jun-3 Delorme & Bocage, Paris #62/R

KLEMENS, J Bozetech (19th C) Hungarian

£1570 $2669 €2292 Portrait of Zsofia Berzeviczy de Berzevicze seated at her writing desk (72x56cm-28x22in) s.d.1845. 29-Oct-3 Lawson Menzies, Sydney #274/R est:3000-4000 (A.D 3800)

KLEMENT, Alfons (1930-2000) Dutch

£525 $876 €750 La table bleu (80x80cm-31x31in) s.d.87 acrylic. 30-Jun-3 Sotheby's, Amsterdam #446

KLEMM, Ernst (19th C) Austrian

£1729 $3198 €2524 Table top still life with elegant objects (29x23cm-11x9in) 14-Mar-4 Agra, Warsaw #54/R (P.Z 12500)

KLEMM, Fritz (1902-) German

Works on paper

£333 $603 €500 Table (15x14cm-6x6in) s.i.d. collage. 2-Apr-4 Winterberg, Heidelberg #1195

KLEMME, August (1830-1870) German

£1020 $1827 €1500 Frau Henriette von Selslick (90x65cm-35x26in) s.d.1872 i. verso lit. 20-Mar-4 Bergmann, Erlangen #1086 est:1500

KLENE, Bernardus Henricus (1870-1930) Dutch

£898 $1500 €1311 Bord de la Seine (53x64cm-21x25in) s. 16-Nov-3 Simpson's, Houston #299/R

KLENGEL, Johan Christian (1751-1824) German

£4392 $7730 €6500 Mountain landscape with hunter (36x46cm-14x18in) s. 22-May-4 Lempertz, Koln #1085/R est:4000

Works on paper

£699 $1272 €1021 Hay workers, four figures (32x47cm-13x19in) s. black chk brush ink wash htd white prov. 17-Jun-4 Kornfeld, Bern #22/R (S.FR 1600)
£1141 $2042 €1700 Landscape with figures and ruins (21x30cm-8x12in) s.d.1770 pen wash. 25-May-4 Karl & Faber, Munich #36/R est:1800

KLENGEL, Johan Christian (attrib) (1751-1824) German

£500 $815 €720 Landscape with cows and herders (34x26cm-13x10in) paper on canvas. 26-Sep-3 Bolland & Marotz, Bremen #474

Works on paper

£263 $484 €400 Cattle in meadow (14x18cm-6x7in) pen wash. 24-Jun-4 Dr Fritz Nagel, Stuttgart #522/R

KLENKE, H (19th C) German

£274 $466 €400 Ambush (44x67cm-17x26in) s. canvas on panel. 8-Nov-3 Geble, Radolfzell #783/R

KLEPINSKI, Johann (1872-?) Polish

£567 $919 €800 Lake with boys swimming (55x65cm-22x26in) s. lit. 23-May-3 Karlheinz Kaupp, Staufen #1844

KLEPPER, Frank (1890-1955) American

£1138 $1900 €1661 Untitled (41x51cm-16x20in) estate st.verso. 18-Oct-3 David Dike, Dallas #313/R est:500-1000
£10778 $18000 €15736 Morning gossip (56x71cm-22x28in) 18-Oct-3 David Dike, Dallas #190/R est:8000-12000

KLERK, Willem de (1800-1876) Dutch

£2533 $4535 €3800 Rocky landscape with castle and waterfall (45x42cm-18x17in) s. panel. 15-May-4 De Vuyst, Lokeren #528/R est:3800-4000
£2639 $4301 €3800 Mountain in landscape in evening sunshine with a waterfall in background. s. panel. 29-Sep-3 Sotheby's, Amsterdam #32/R
£4667 $8400 €7000 Sunlit clearing in a forest (70x99cm-28x39in) s. 21-Apr-4 Christie's, Amsterdam #214/R est:6000-8000
£7800 $14040 €11388 Cows watering (64x89cm-25x35in) s.i. panel. 21-Jan-4 Sotheby's, Olympia #393/R est:5000-6000

KLETT, Walter (1897-1966) American

Works on paper

£326 $600 €476 Composition 60, butterflies (23x28cm-9x11in) s. i.verso W/C exec. c.1959. 10-Jun-4 Swann Galleries, New York #131/R

KLEUDGEN, Fritz von (1846-?) German

£3819 $6226 €5500 Ligurian coast (53x80cm-21x31in) s. s. verso. 26-Sep-3 Bolland & Marotz, Bremen #560/R est:3300

KLEUEZ, Julius V (19/20th C) German

£2800 $4676 €4088 Woodland pond (80x101cm-31x40in) s.d.1906. 14-Oct-3 Rosebery Fine Art, London #588 est:400-600

KLEVER, Julius Sergius von (1850-1924) Russian

£1615 $2778 €2358 Forest landscape at sunset (21x18cm-8x7in) s.d.1924 panel. 7-Dec-3 Uppsala Auktionskammare, Uppsala #145/R est:10000-12000 (S.KR 21000)
£1678 $3087 €2500 Abandoned bathing hut (54x71cm-21x28in) s.cyrillic d.1908. 26-Mar-4 Bolland & Marotz, Bremen #544/R est:2700
£2817 $4676 €4000 Winter woodland scene with sledge (30x48cm-12x19in) s.cyrillic d.1899 board. 16-Jun-3 Dorotheum, Vienna #145/R est:2200-2900
£13380 $21408 €19000 Brown bear in wood (72x90cm-28x35in) lit. 19-Sep-3 Karlheinz Kaupp, Staufen #2119/R est:2500
£25000 $45000 €36500 Forest clearing (54x70cm-21x28in) s.d.1905 canvas on masonite prov. 23-Apr-4 Sotheby's, New York #26/R est:25000-35000
£30537 $56493 €45500 La foret (81x100cm-32x39in) s. 15-Mar-4 Claude Boisgirard, Paris #65/R est:12000-15000
£35000 $62650 €51100 Winter landscape (49x75cm-19x30in) s.d.1894. 26-May-4 Sotheby's, London #29/R est:14000-18000
£40000 $68000 €58400 Forest landscape (163x125cm-64x49in) s.d.1896. 19-Nov-3 Sotheby's, London #30/R est:40000-60000
£44444 $80000 €64888 Through the woods (66x84cm-26x33in) s.d.1911 prov. 23-Apr-4 Sotheby's, New York #27/R est:35000-45000
£48000 $85920 €70080 Winter landscape (85x59cm-33x23in) s.d.1918. 26-May-4 Sotheby's, London #27/R est:15000-20000
£52000 $89440 €75920 Lake in Pavlovsk Park, St Petersburg (80x100cm-31x39in) s.d.1906. 4-Dec-3 Christie's, Kensington #219/R est:10000-15000
£61111 $110000 €89222 Forest in winter (133x89cm-52x35in) s.d.1919. 23-Apr-4 Sotheby's, New York #30/R est:40000-50000

KLEVER, Julius Sergius von (attrib) (1850-1924) Russian

£6471 $11000 €9448 Wooded landscape at sunset (41x27cm-16x11in) bears sig.d.1910 canvas on board. 19-Nov-3 Bonhams & Butterfields, San Francisco #91/R

KLEVER, Julius Sergius von (school) (1850-1924) Russian

£6000 $10860 €9000 Herder with cattle on forest path by stream (98x117cm-39x46in) 1-Apr-4 Van Ham, Cologne #1484/R est:11000

KLEVER, Julius Sergius von (style) (1850-1924) Russian

£7500 $13425 €10950 Winter landscape (57x98cm-22x39in) bears sig. 26-May-4 Sotheby's, Olympia #383/R est:800-1200

KLEY, Heinrich (1863-1945) German

Works on paper

£294 $490 €420 Sting in the tail (21x27cm-8x11in) s.i. col pen Indian ink. 10-Oct-3 Winterberg, Heidelberg #853
£414 $691 €600 Procession (30x49cm-12x19in) s.i. pencil W/C htd white board. 15-Nov-3 Von Zezschwitz, Munich #35/R
£433 $797 €650 Schlossbrucke Berlin (22x26cm-9x10in) s. W/C. 12-Jun-4 Villa Grisebach, Berlin #588/R
£586 $979 €850 Industrial landscape (40x67cm-16x26in) s. W/C chk over pencil. 13-Nov-3 Neumeister, Munich #359/R

£604 $1081 €900 Hijacking (32x25cm-13x10in) s. Indian ink. 25-May-4 Karl & Faber, Munich #368
£856 $1600 €1250 Louis XVI on throne, approached by commoners (25x30cm-10x12in) s. pen ink. 26-Feb-4 Illustration House, New York #100 est:1200-1800

KLEYN, Lodewyk Johannes (1817-1897) Dutch
£1049 $1752 €1500 Hunters with dog in high mountain winter landscape (45x61cm-18x24in) s. 9-Oct-3 Michael Zeller, Lindau #632/R est:1250
£2482 $4145 €3500 Summer landscape with mill (34x52cm-13x20in) s. panel. 20-Oct-3 Glerum, Amsterdam #54/R est:3500-4500
£3947 $7263 €6000 Panoramic river landscape with figures on an embankment and town in distance (40x55cm-16x22in) s. indis.i.verso panel prov. 22-Jun-4 Christie's, Amsterdam #31/R est:7000-9000
£4000 $7200 €6000 Figures on a frozen river by a windmill (53x74cm-21x29in) s. 21-Apr-4 Christie's, Amsterdam #73/R est:5000-7000
£4422 $8048 €6500 Skaters on the ice by a koek en zopie, windmill in the distance (34x52cm-13x20in) s. panel. 3-Feb-4 Christie's, Amsterdam #78/R est:3000-4000
£5333 $9600 €8000 An idyllic summer landscape (45x70cm-18x28in) s. panel. 21-Apr-4 Christie's, Amsterdam #231/R est:12000-16000
£6944 $10972 €10000 Skaters on the ice by a church, a koek and zopie and sunlit town in the distance (35x42cm-14x17in) with sig. panel. 2-Sep-3 Christie's, Amsterdam #160/R est:5000-7000
£6944 $11597 €10000 Peasants in a winter landscape (33x44cm-13x17in) s. panel. 21-Oct-3 Sotheby's, Amsterdam #60/R est:6000-8000
£7639 $12757 €11000 Figures in a summer landscape (44x63cm-17x25in) s. panel prov. 21-Oct-3 Sotheby's, Amsterdam #69/R est:7000-10000
£8333 $14167 €12000 Figures on a frozen waterway with windmills on the river bank (26x35cm-10x14in) s. panel. 28-Oct-3 Christie's, Amsterdam #52/R est:6000-8000
£10000 $18000 €15000 Moored vessels on the Vliet, The Hague beyond (28x40cm-11x16in) s. panel. 21-Apr-4 Christie's, Amsterdam #240/R est:12000-16000
£10000 $18000 €15000 Figures on a frozen waterway by a windmill (25x37cm-10x15in) s. panel. 20-Apr-4 Sotheby's, Amsterdam #29/R est:8000-12000
£10067 $18020 €15000 Dutch river landscape with fishermen (60x80cm-24x31in) s. canvas on panel. 27-May-4 Dorotheum, Vienna #17/R est:10000-14000
£20000 $36000 €30000 Summer landscape with figures along a waterway (37x50cm-15x20in) s. panel. 20-Apr-4 Sotheby's, Amsterdam #182/R est:30000-50000
£28000 $50400 €42000 Summer landscape with figure on a riverbank. Winter landscape with skaters on a frozen waterway (36x47cm-14x19in) one s. panel pair. 20-Apr-4 Sotheby's, Amsterdam #160/R est:30000-50000

Works on paper
£933 $1699 €1400 Figures on a sledge on a frozen river in winter (37x29cm-15x11in) s.verso W/C. 1-Jul-4 Van Ham, Cologne #1457/R
£1293 $2352 €1900 View of Haarlem across the Spaarne with the St. Bavo church in the distance (17x25cm-7x10in) s. pencil W/C. 3-Feb-4 Christie's, Amsterdam #316/R est:1500-2000

KLEYNE, David (attrib) (1754-1805) Dutch
£1333 $2413 €2000 Sailing boats (18x24cm-7x9in) i. panel. 2-Apr-4 Dr Fritz Nagel, Leipzig #3962/R est:500

KLEYNE, David (circle) (1754-1805) Dutch
£5556 $8778 €8000 Shipping off the coast of Zuyder Zee, a states yacht raising its sails (25x33cm-10x13in) init. panel prov. 2-Sep-3 Christie's, Amsterdam #107/R est:2500-3500

KLIE, Zoltan (1897-?) Swiss?
£1195 $1983 €1745 Reading woman in a Bhaus armchair (40x30cm-16x12in) s.d.1943 verso. 4-Oct-3 Kieselbach, Budapest #196/R (H.F 440000)
£1265 $2289 €1847 Village detail (49x60cm-19x24in) s. oil on wood-fibre. 16-Apr-4 Mu Terem Galeria, Budapest #127/R (H.F 480000)
£4933 $9028 €7400 Woman with flower (100x80cm-39x31in) s.d.9.31. 5-Jun-4 Lempertz, Koln #790/R est:3000

KLIEN, Erika Giovanna (1900-1957) German
£18056 $30694 €26000 Flight rhythm (51x40cm-20x16in) mono.d.1951. 28-Oct-3 Wiener Kunst Auktionen, Vienna #103/R est:18000-50000

Works on paper
£2685 $4752 €4000 Rhythms of Growth (62x48cm-24x19in) s.i.d.1932 chk lit. 28-Apr-4 Wiener Kunst Auktionen, Vienna #119/R est:4000-8000
£5369 $9503 €8000 Grass in wind wave (48x62cm-19x24in) mono.i.d.1945 chk lit. 28-Apr-4 Wiener Kunst Auktionen, Vienna #122/R est:7000-12000
£6250 $10625 €9000 Gulls - waves - fog (42x60cm-17x24in) s.d.1929 chl. 28-Oct-3 Wiener Kunst Auktionen, Vienna #102/R est:8000-15000
£7692 $13077 €11000 The female dancer (50x34cm-20x13in) black chk. 28-Nov-3 Wiener Kunst Auktionen, Vienna #533/R est:4000-10000
£12081 $21383 €18000 Conversation (35x50cm-14x20in) mono.d.1951 W/C lit. 28-Apr-4 Wiener Kunst Auktionen, Vienna #121/R est:7000-14000

KLIMA, Heinz (1924-) Austrian
£1316 $2421 €2000 Untitled (171x81cm-67x32in) 22-Jun-4 Wiener Kunst Auktionen, Vienna #446/R est:2000

KLIMEK, Ludwig (1912-1992) Polish
£360 $637 €526 Les Oliviers (39x46cm-15x18in) s. 27-Apr-4 Bonhams, Knightsbridge #231/R
£400 $736 €600 Two friends (74x54cm-29x21in) i.verso. 8-Jun-4 Livinec, Gaudcheau & Jezequel, Rennes #157
£437 $795 €660 Bouquet de fleurs (55x46cm-22x18in) s. 16-Jun-4 Claude Boisgirard, Paris #90/R

Works on paper
£260 $460 €380 Two seated woman (50x35cm-20x14in) s.d.16 X II.57 black pen. 27-Apr-4 Bonhams, Knightsbridge #177
£1837 $3343 €2700 Acteon (65x92cm-26x36in) s. gouache varnish paper on canvas. 8-Feb-4 Anaf, Lyon #199/R est:1500-1600

KLIMSCH, Eugen (1839-1896) German

Works on paper
£503 $841 €720 Girl and cat playing (27x21cm-11x8in) s. htd white W/C over pencil. 10-Oct-3 Winterberg, Heidelberg #621/R

KLIMSCH, Ferdinand Carl (1812-1890) German

Works on paper
£280 $476 €400 French prisoners at Frankfurt station (25x37cm-10x15in) Indian ink brush over pencil htd bocycol. 21-Nov-3 Reiss & Sohn, Konigstein #228/R

KLIMSCH, Fritz (1870-1960) German

Sculpture
£1399 $2378 €2000 Looking at the sun (41cm-16in) mono. terracotta wooden socle lit. 26-Nov-3 Lempertz, Koln #766/R est:1500
£1469 $2497 €2100 Seated woman (30cm-12in) mono. terracotta exhib.lit. 26-Nov-3 Lempertz, Koln #764/R est:2500
£1724 $2879 €2500 Siesta (24cm-9in) mono. brown pat bronze st.f.Strassacker. 13-Nov-3 Neumeister, Munich #360/R est:3000-3500
£1818 $3127 €2600 Paul von Hindenburg (43cm-17in) i. bronze black marble base exec. 1916 st.f. Noack. 4-Dec-3 Van Ham, Cologne #272/R est:2500
£6993 $12028 €10000 Small gazer (48x33x55cm-19x13x22in) mono. st.f.Noack brown pat bronze prov.exhib.lit. 5-Dec-3 Ketterer, Munich #82/R est:12000-15000
£8392 $14266 €12000 Grace - standing girl (62cm-24in) mono. bronze Cast.H.Noack Berlin exhib.lit. 26-Nov-3 Lempertz, Koln #765/R est:12000-15000
£12081 $22228 €18000 Bather (63x39cm-25x15in) i. pat.bronze Cast.H. Noack Berlin Friedenau. 26-Mar-4 Bolland & Marotz, Bremen #739/R est:13000
£14583 $23771 €21000 Thoughtful (74cm-29in) mono. dark pat.bronze Cast.H Noack prov.exhib. 27-Sep-3 Dr Fritz Nagel, Stuttgart #9575/R est:26000
£14667 $26253 €22000 Storm (77x34x41cm-30x13x16in) s. brown green pat.bronze Cast.H.Noack Berlin prov.exhib.lit. 15-May-4 Van Ham, Cologne #718/R est:23000
£19580 $33678 €28000 Lost in thought (74x62x43cm-29x24x17in) mono. dark brown pat bronze exec. 1931 st.f. Noak prov.lit. 4-Dec-3 Van Ham, Cologne #271/R est:18000
£22378 $38042 €32000 In wind and sun (147cm-58in) mono. dark brown pat.bronze Cast.H.Noack Berlin. 29-Nov-3 Villa Grisebach, Berlin #247/R est:20000-30000
£26573 $45175 €38000 Meditation (183x78x47cm-72x31x19in) s. marble prov.lit. 20-Nov-3 Van Ham, Cologne #1268/R est:35000

KLIMSCH, Karl (1867-?) German
£355 $574 €500 Two women in park (55x71cm-22x28in) s. 23-May-3 Altus, Berlin #543/R
£3077 $5138 €4400 Women in park (54x71cm-21x28in) s. 11-Oct-3 Hans Stahl, Hamburg #22/R est:5500

KLIMT, Gustav (1862-1918) Austrian
£25140 $45000 €36704 Mannliche akstudie - nude male. i. 13-May-4 Dallas Auction Gallery, Dallas #312/R est:50000-80000
£1800000 $3276000 €2628000 Farmhouse with birch trees (80x80cm-31x31in) s. painted 1900 prov.exhib.lit. 21-Jun-4 Sotheby's, London #37/R est:2000000-3000000
£15294118 $26000000 €22329412 Landhaus am Attersee (110x110cm-43x43in) s. painted c.1914 prov.exhib.lit. 5-Nov-3 Sotheby's, New York #25a/R est:18000000-25000000

Works on paper
£2797 $4755 €4000 Girl's head (29x34cm-11x13in) pencil prov. 26-Nov-3 Dorotheum, Vienna #15/R est:5000-7000
£3497 $5944 €5000 Old man with beard and cap (42x31cm-17x12in) s. chk htd white prov. 26-Nov-3 Dorotheum, Vienna #111/R est:5000-7000
£4324 $8000 €6313 Woman in profile (49x35cm-19x14in) pencil exec.c.1904-05. 11-Feb-4 Sotheby's, New York #45/R est:8000-12000
£4972 $8750 €7259 Study for potrait of Adele Bloch-Bauer (43x33cm-17x13in) s. pencil executed c.1906. 22-May-4 New Orleans Auction, New Orleans #135/R est:10000-15000
£5000 $9200 €7300 Mada Primavesi (55x37cm-22x15in) pencil Japan paper drawn c.1912 prov.lit. 24-Jun-4 Christie's, London #325/R est:8000-12000
£5369 $9611 €8000 Seated nude (56x36cm-22x14in) pencil prov. 25-May-4 Dorotheum, Vienna #17/R est:9000-12000
£6028 $10067 €8500 Seated old woman (45x31cm-18x12in) i. pencil htd white paper on board. 14-Oct-3 Dorotheum, Vienna #1/R est:7000-10000
£6294 $10699 €9000 Seated female nude (45x31cm-18x12in) pencil prov. 26-Nov-3 Dorotheum, Vienna #13/R est:8000-13000
£6667 $12267 €10000 Head and shoulders portrait of a lady glancing upwards (42x27cm-17x11in) s.d.1880 i.verso black chk htd white prov. 12-Jun-4 Villa Grisebach, Berlin #120/R est:3000-4000
£6704 $12000 €9788 Seated lady from the front - study for the portrait of Marie Henneberg (43x32cm-17x13in) s.i. artist's sister chk exec c.1901-02 prov.lit. 6-May-4 Sotheby's, New York #313/R est:8000-12000
£6704 $12000 €9788 Whole figure head and chest. Seated nude in front of a mirror (57x37cm-22x15in) pencil double-sided exec.1916 lit. 6-May-4 Sotheby's, New York #303/R est:15000-20000
£6993 $11888 €10000 Seated female nude with head in hands (44x31cm-17x12in) pencil prov. 26-Nov-3 Dorotheum, Vienna #8/R est:13000-18000
£6993 $11888 €10000 Three sketches of a child and nude back of a man (48x31cm-19x12in) i. chk double-sided prov.lit. 25-Nov-3 Hassfurther, Vienna #45/R est:10000-12000
£7000 $12880 €10220 Mann und Frau einander gegenubergestellt (37x56cm-15x22in) i. pencil Japan paper exec 1907-1908 prov. 24-Jun-4 Christie's, London #326/R est:10000-15000
£8054 $14416 €12000 Portrait of Magda Mautner-Markhof (55x35cm-22x14in) chk. 25-May-4 Dorotheum, Vienna #16/R est:13000-17000
£9000 $16560 €13140 Nude turned to the left (57x37cm-22x15in) i. pencil prov.exhib.lit. 22-Jun-4 Sotheby's, London #496/R est:10000-15000
£9091 $15455 €13000 Reclining figure (31x45cm-12x18in) pencil htd white prov. 26-Nov-3 Dorotheum, Vienna #3/R est:15000-20000
£9333 $17173 €14000 Seated female nude, turned to the right (55x34cm-22x13in) pencil exec. 1911-12. 11-Jun-4 Villa Grisebach, Berlin #1530/R est:10000-12000
£9396 $16819 €14000 Reclining nude facing left (37x57cm-15x22in) pencil lit. 27-May-4 Hassfurther, Vienna #13/R est:12000-14000
£10000 $18200 €14600 Stehend etwas nach links - Portrait of Margaret Stonborough-Wittgenstein (55x34cm-22x13in) pencil exec.1904-05 prov.lit. 4-Feb-4 Sotheby's, London #473/R est:12000-15000
£10000 $18400 €15000 Lovers (37x56cm-15x22in) pencil exec. c.1913. 11-Jun-4 Villa Grisebach, Berlin #1529/R est:7000-9000
£10056 $18000 €14682 Nude female figure (44x31cm-17x12in) s.i. chl exec 1901-02 prov.exhib. 6-May-4 Sotheby's, New York #310/R est:15000-20000

£10667 $19627 €16000 Female nude bent over (56x37cm-22x15in) blue crayon exec. c.1907 prov. 12-Jun-4 Villa Grisebach, Berlin #125/R est:14000-18000
£11409 $20423 €17000 Dancer (56x36cm-22x14in) pencil. 25-May-4 Dorotheum, Vienna #13/R est:15000-19000
£11888 $20210 €17000 Nude lying on stomach, from the right (31x45cm-12x18in) i. chk. 25-Nov-3 Hassfurther, Vienna #46/R est:10000-12000
£12000 $22080 €18000 Reclining female nude (36x54cm-14x21in) pencil exec. 1914 prov.exhib. 11-Jun-4 Villa Grisebach, Berlin #1531/R est:7000-9000
£12291 $22000 €17945 Standing nude with her face covered by her long hair (56x37cm-22x15in) pencil exec c.1907 lit. 6-May-4 Sotheby's, New York #308/R est:20000-30000
£12587 $21399 €18000 Woman slouched in armchair (45x32cm-18x13in) col pen prov. 26-Nov-3 Dorotheum, Vienna #9/R est:18000-26000
£12587 $21399 €18000 Reclining figure (37x56cm-15x22in) pencil htd white prov. 26-Nov-3 Dorotheum, Vienna #16/R est:20000-26000
£13000 $23660 €18980 Athlete in profile facing right, female nude seen from the front (56x37cm-22x15in) pencil exec.1917-18 prov.lit. 4-Feb-4 Sotheby's, London #425/R est:12000-15000
£14765 $26430 €22000 Lovers (56x37cm-22x15in) pencil. 25-May-4 Dorotheum, Vienna #14/R est:12000-18000
£15721 $28611 €22953 Young nude with long, open hair (55x37cm-22x15in) pencil exec. 1905-1907. 18-Jun-4 Kornfeld, Bern #95/R est:40000 (S.FR 36000)
£16760 $30000 €24470 Auf gestutzt liegender Halbakt nacht rechts (37x56cm-15x22in) st.s. blue pencil buff paper exec 1907 prov.lit. 5-May-4 Christie's, Rockefeller NY #125/R est:30000-40000
£17450 $31235 €26000 Seated woman with long hair (56x37cm-22x15in) pencil prov. 25-May-4 Dorotheum, Vienna #15/R est:22000-28000
£18182 $30909 €26000 Reclining female nude (37x56cm-15x22in) pencil prov. 26-Nov-3 Dorotheum, Vienna #10/R est:22000-26000
£18182 $30909 €26000 Friends (55x35cm-22x14in) pencil prov. 26-Nov-3 Dorotheum, Vienna #11/R est:14000-18000
£18182 $30909 €26000 Seated female nude (31x45cm-12x18in) black chk prov. 26-Nov-3 Dorotheum, Vienna #12/R est:10000-14000
£18341 $33380 €26778 Seated nude turned to the right (57x37cm-22x15in) pencil exec. 1916. 18-Jun-4 Kornfeld, Bern #94/R est:40000 (S.FR 42000)
£21141 $37842 €31500 Reclining nude with baby (37x56cm-15x22in) blue col pencil double-sided prov.lit. 27-May-4 Hassfurther, Vienna #11/R est:20000-25000
£23776 $40420 €34000 Reclining figure (37x56cm-15x22in) pencil prov. 26-Nov-3 Dorotheum, Vienna #7/R est:22000-28000
£24832 $44450 €37000 Reclining female nude facing right (36x56cm-14x22in) pencil. 27-May-4 Hassfurther, Vienna #12/R est:20000-25000
£25000 $45500 €36500 Stehend nach links - Standing turned to the left, sketch of collar from reverse (44x31cm-17x12in) black crayon exec.1903-04 prov.exhib.lit. 4-Feb-4 Sotheby's, London #474/R est:25000-35000
£25140 $45000 €36704 Portrait bust three quarter profile facing left (57x37cm-22x15in) pencil exec 1916-17 prov.lit. 6-May-4 Sotheby's, New York #309/R est:35000-45000
£32000 $53440 €46720 Brustbild einer jungen frau mit nach links geneigtem kopf - girl with her head turned left (44x32cm-17x13in) pencil white chk executed c.1895 prov.exhib.lit. 21-Oct-3 Sotheby's, London #100/R est:10000-15000
£45455 $77273 €65000 Woman in armchair (31x45cm-12x18in) col pen prov. 26-Nov-3 Dorotheum, Vienna #5/R est:34000-50000
£110000 $202400 €160600 Reclining female nude (37x57cm-15x22in) s. pencil exec.c.1914-15 prov. 22-Jun-4 Sotheby's, London #494/R est:60000-80000
£160000 $291200 €233600 Girl with long hair in profile (55x37cm-22x15in) s. pastel executed c.1898-99 p. 3-Feb-4 Sotheby's, London #1/R est:80000-120000

KLIN, Leo (1887-?) British
£320 $509 €467 Horse in the wind (36x47cm-14x19in) s.d.1953 board. 10-Sep-3 Cheffins, Cambridge #547/R

KLINCKOWSTROM, Harald (1897-1973) Swedish
£1038 $1786 €1515 Mergansers in flight, Lofoten (71x121cm-28x48in) s.d.18 prov.lit. 3-Dec-3 AB Stockholms Auktionsverk #2262/R (S.KR 13500)

KLINE, Franz (1910-1962) American
£8791 $16000 €12835 Sheridan Square, New York (41x30cm-16x12in) s.d.40 s.i.verso canvasboard prov. 29-Jun-4 Sotheby's, New York #457/R est:5000-7000
£13761 $22982 €19953 Untitled (21x27cm-8x11in) s. oil on bodycol paper on canvas. 19-Jun-3 Kornfeld, Bern #565/R est:30000 (S.FR 30000)
£17857 $32500 €26071 Untitled (28x21cm-11x8in) oil pastel executed c.1952 prov. 29-Jun-4 Sotheby's, New York #462/R est:12000-18000
£28743 $48000 €41965 Untitled 1 (27x25cm-11x10in) board painted c.1961 prov. 12-Nov-3 Christie's, Rockefeller NY #315/R est:35000-45000
£31250 $51562 €45000 Zinc, yellows and grey (56x48cm-22x19in) s.d.1958 i.verso cardboard prov. 2-Jul-3 Cornette de St.Cyr, Paris #10/R est:50000-70000
£1017964 $1700000 €1486227 Four Square (198x122cm-78x48in) s.i.verso painted 1953 prov.exhib.lit. 11-Nov-3 Christie's, Rockefeller NY #20/R est:1500000-2000000
£1197605 $2000000 €1748503 Rue (259x201cm-102x79in) s.d.59 verso prov.exhib. 11-Nov-3 Christie's, Rockefeller NY #34/R est:3500000-4500000
Works on paper
£1963 $3200 €2866 Nude self portrait (30x22cm-12x9in) init. ink graphite exec.c.1938-39 prov.exhib. 23-Sep-3 Christie's, Rockefeller NY #16/R est:4000-6000
£2577 $4200 €3762 Untitled (23x21cm-9x8in) init. ink prov. 23-Sep-3 Christie's, Rockefeller NY #15/R est:4000-6000
£11173 $20000 €16313 Untitled (22x22cm-9x9in) s.verso ink telephone book paper on cardboard exec c.1950 prov. 13-May-4 Sotheby's, New York #116/R est:15000-20000
£18310 $32042 €26000 Composition (34x34cm-13x13in) ink W/C prov. 16-Dec-3 Porro, Milan #34/R est:20000-25000
£24865 $46000 €37298 Untitled (25x23cm-10x9in) s. ink prov.exhib. 14-Jul-4 American Auctioneer #490249/R est:25000-35000
£30726 $55000 €44860 Untitled (15x13cm-6x5in) ink prov. 13-May-4 Sotheby's, New York #135/R est:18000-22000
£33742 $55000 €49263 Untitled (35x27cm-14x11in) ink oil prov.exhib. 23-Sep-3 Christie's, Rockefeller NY #31/R est:30000-40000
£54749 $98000 €79934 Untitled (30x26cm-12x10in) s. ink exec 1954 prov. 12-May-4 Christie's, Rockefeller NY #107/R est:50000-70000
£77844 $130000 €113652 Study for White forms (26x18cm-10x7in) s. s.i.d.58 backboard prov.exhib. 11-Nov-3 Christie's, Rockefeller NY #21/R est:40000-60000

KLINE, Harriet (20th C) American
£301 $550 €439 Louis Armstrong (58x74cm-23x29in) s.d.1958 s.verso. 5-Jun-4 Neal Auction Company, New Orleans #722

KLINEK, Edward (20th C) American
£267 $425 €390 Boy with apple (71x53cm-28x21in) s.d.1939. 14-Sep-3 Susanin's, Chicago #6104/R

KLINGBEIL, Fritz (1936-) German
£302 $514 €441 387 (34x34cm-13x13in) s.d.1981 verso canvas on panel. 5-Nov-3 AB Stockholms Auktionsverk #949/R (S.KR 4000)

KLINGER, Ernst (1900-) German
£724 $1332 €1100 Midday Sunday in the park (95x72cm-37x28in) s. acrylic. 25-Jun-4 Von Zezschwitz, Munich #336/R

KLINGER, H (19/20th C) ?
£1268 $2193 €1800 The newest report (58x45cm-23x18in) s. 10-Dec-3 Dorotheum, Vienna #197/R est:1600-1800

KLINGER, Karl (20th C) Austrian
£2448 $4087 €3500 Roses with insects and grapes (61x46cm-24x18in) s. canvas on panel. 9-Oct-3 Michael Zeller, Lindau #634/R est:2500
£3642 $6666 €5500 Still life with flowers (76x74cm-30x29in) s. canvas on panel. 8-Apr-4 Dorotheum, Vienna #285/R est:1300-1500

KLINGER, Max (1857-1920) German
£769 $1308 €1100 Bow sitting on chair (44x30cm-17x12in) canvas on board. 27-Nov-3 Bassenge, Berlin #5605
£7500 $12975 €10950 Woman in a landscape (93x136cm-37x54in) init.d.12. 11-Dec-3 Christie's, Kensington #1/R est:4000-6000
Sculpture
£3077 $5231 €4400 Portrait of Friedrich Nietzsche (39cm-15in) s.i. bronze Cast.Gladenbeck Berlin Friedrichshagen lit. 26-Nov-3 Lempertz, Koln #768/R est:4000
Works on paper
£544 $974 €800 Portrait de femme portant une coiffe (14x12cm-6x5in) s. pen black ink grey wash black pencil. 19-Mar-4 Piasa, Paris #210
£935 $1534 €1300 Female nude (27x36cm-11x14in) mono. chl. 4-Jun-3 Ketterer, Hamburg #559/R
£3667 $6747 €5500 Female nude (43x37cm-17x15in) mono.d.8.Febr. 15.10.FEbr. 15 chk htd bodycol. 10-Jun-4 Hauswedell & Nolte, Hamburg #340/R est:5000

KLINGER, Max (attrib) (1857-1920) German
£839 $1427 €1200 Female nude with arms raised by sea (42x26cm-17x10in) board. 21-Nov-3 Reiss & Sohn, Konigstein #229/R est:800

KLINGSBOGL, Rudolf (1881-?) Austrian
£403 $753 €600 Stift Geras (80x58cm-31x23in) s.d.1913. 24-Feb-4 Dorotheum, Vienna #40/R
£671 $1255 €1000 Roses in Stift Geras (69x48cm-27x19in) s. bears d.1911. 24-Feb-4 Dorotheum, Vienna #247/R

KLINKAN, Alfred (1950-) Austrian
£1958 $3329 €2800 The blue world (100x70cm-39x28in) s.i.d.1982. 28-Nov-3 Wiener Kunst Auktionen, Vienna #675/R est:2000-3000
£4861 $8264 €7000 Atalanta fugios - birth (207x164cm-81x65in) s.i.d.1987 verso. 28-Oct-3 Wiener Kunst Auktionen, Vienna #278/R est:8700-13000
£6711 $11879 €10000 Untitled (200x135cm-79x53in) 28-Apr-4 Wiener Kunst Auktionen, Vienna #262/R est:7000-13000

KLINKENBERG, Johannes Christiaan Karel (1852-1924) Dutch
£959 $1630 €1400 Canal anime en Hollande (51x69cm-20x27in) s. 10-Nov-3 Horta, Bruxelles #443
£11111 $18556 €16000 Street in a Dutch town (33x24cm-13x9in) s. panel. 21-Oct-3 Sotheby's, Amsterdam #154/R est:6000-8000
£13333 $24000 €20000 Busy quay in Rotterdam (24x31cm-9x12in) s. panel. 20-Apr-4 Sotheby's, Amsterdam #162/R est:20000-30000
£27000 $49140 €39420 A view of Amsterdam (41x52cm-16x20in) s. 15-Jun-4 Sotheby's, London #158/R est:20000-30000
£43972 $73433 €62000 View of the Coolvest of Rotterdam with the mill, De Hoop (39x52cm-15x20in) s. 20-Oct-3 Glerum, Amsterdam #14/R est:28000-34000
£104167 $173958 €150000 View of the Montelbaanstoren, Amsterdam (80x100cm-31x39in) s. prov. 21-Oct-3 Sotheby's, Amsterdam #236/R est:100000-150000
Works on paper
£2431 $4132 €3500 Weighing house, Alkmaar (51x36cm-20x14in) s. W/C pencil htd white. 28-Oct-3 Christie's, Amsterdam #97/R est:4000-6000

KLINT, Hilma af (1862-1944) Swedish
£631 $1135 €921 Coastal landscape with cliffs (22x51cm-9x20in) s.d.92. 26-Jan-4 Lilla Bukowskis, Stockholm #333 (S.KR 8400)

KLIOUNE (19/20th C) Russian
Works on paper
£11486 $20216 €17000 Composition aux trois centres (42x30cm-17x12in) W/C gouache exec.c.1919. 19-May-4 Camard, Paris #82 est:15000-20000

KLIPPEL, Robert (1920-2001) Australian
Sculpture
£1532 $2604 €2237 No 908 (23x45x8cm-9x18x3in) init.d.98 base painted wood prov.exhib. 26-Nov-3 Deutscher-Menzies, Melbourne #73/R est:3000-5000 (A.D 3600)
£1695 $2881 €2475 No 905 (42x21x8cm-17x8x3in) init.d.1998 i.base mixed media construction prov. 24-Nov-3 Sotheby's, Melbourne #215/R est:4000-6000 (A.D 4000)
£2254 $3562 €3291 No 411 (16x5x4cm-6x2x2in) s.d.81 bronze prov.exhib. 2-Sep-3 Deutscher-Menzies, Melbourne #213/R est:3000-5000 (A.D 5500)

£3252 $5821 €4748 No. 829 (33x49x43cm-13x19x17in) init. num.d.828.89 painted wood. 4-May-4 Sotheby's, Melbourne #215/R est:8000-12000 (A.D 8000)
£4122 $7502 €6018 RK 446 (87cm-34in) init.i.d. num.3/6 bronze. 16-Jun-4 Deutscher-Menzies, Melbourne #114/R est:14000-18000 (A.D 10800)
£4918 $7770 €7180 No 443 (85x23x12cm-33x9x5in) init.i.d.82 bronze prov. 2-Sep-3 Deutscher-Menzies, Melbourne #130/R est:14000-18000 (A.D 12000)
£4918 $7770 €7180 Parmelia - No 731 (10x12x4cm-4x5x2in) s.i.d.88 prov. gold. 2-Sep-3 Deutscher-Menzies, Melbourne #131/R est:14000-18000 (A.D 12000)
£6147 $9713 €8975 No 433 (80cm-31in) init.i.d.82 bronze prov. 2-Sep-3 Deutscher-Menzies, Melbourne #57/R est:16000-20000 (A.D 15000)
£8264 $15289 €12065 No.453 (104x15x20cm-41x6x8in) init.d.1982 bronze prov.exhib. 10-Mar-4 Deutscher-Menzies, Melbourne #148/R est:32000-38000 (A.D 20000)
£10569 $18919 €15431 No 454 (113cm-44in) s.d.82 num.base edn 3/6 bronze prov. 4-May-4 Sotheby's, Melbourne #34/R est:18000-25000 (A.D 26000)
£16598 $27718 €24897 Untitled (199x83x21cm-78x33x8in) i. bronze Cast Meridian prov. 27-Oct-3 Goodman, Sydney #33/R est:40000-60000 (A.D 40000)
Works on paper
£412 $745 €602 Untitled (35x49cm-14x19in) init.d.5/78 collage W/C. 31-Mar-4 Goodman, Sydney #485 (A.D 1000)
£466 $792 €680 Untitled (22x32cm-9x13in) s.d.89 mixed media collage prov. 24-Nov-3 Sotheby's, Melbourne #189 (A.D 1100)
£488 $766 €708 Untitled (14x24cm-6x9in) s.d.18/7/63 torn paper ink W/C silver foil prov. 26-Aug-3 Christie's, Sydney #247 (A.D 1200)
£738 $1165 €1077 Untitled (41x59cm-16x23in) s.d.1986 pastel W/C. 2-Sep-3 Deutscher-Menzies, Melbourne #220/R est:1000-1500 (A.D 1800)
£813 $1276 €1179 Untitled (35x22cm-14x9in) s.d.2/49 gouache prov. 26-Aug-3 Christie's, Sydney #291/R est:2000-3000 (A.D 2000)
£1475 $2331 €2154 Untitled (76x101cm-30x40in) s. pastel chl prov. 2-Sep-3 Deutscher-Menzies, Melbourne #192/R est:3500-5500 (A.D 3600)
£1545 $2425 €2240 Untitled (34x24cm-13x9in) s.d.9/49 ink gouache prov. 26-Aug-3 Christie's, Sydney #286/R est:2500-3500 (A.D 3800)
£1967 $3187 €2872 LS102 (28x39cm-11x15in) i. pencil gouache collage sold with book exhib.lit. 30-Jul-3 Goodman, Sydney #63/R est:2000-2500 (A.D 4800)
£2290 $4168 €3343 LS102 (28x39cm-11x15in) init.d.6/78 gouache pencil collage prov.exhib. 16-Jun-4 Deutscher-Menzies, Melbourne #111/R est:4000-6000 (A.D 6000)

KLITSCH, Peter (1934-) Austrian
£3147 $5350 €4500 Transformation of MK (60x50cm-24x20in) s. masonite prov. 26-Nov-3 Dorotheum, Vienna #281/R est:4500-5500

KLITZ, Anthony Robert (1917-) British
£500 $895 €730 View of Westminster (30x51cm-12x20in) s. 14-May-4 Christie's, Kensington #335
£650 $1164 €949 Banks of the Liffey (47x36cm-19x14in) s. 14-May-4 Christie's, Kensington #422/R
£1000 $1590 €1460 Dublin (50x60cm-20x24in) 30-Apr-3 Peter Wilson, Nantwich #70/R est:400-450

KLITZ, Tony (1917-2000) Irish/British
£563 $986 €800 Sailing boats (40x30cm-16x12in) s. 16-Dec-3 James Adam, Dublin #107/R
£563 $986 €800 Gentle view of Dublin Bay (30x40cm-12x16in) s. 16-Dec-3 James Adam, Dublin #105/R
£600 $1080 €900 Dublin castle (45x35cm-18x14in) s. 20-Apr-4 James Adam, Dublin #106/R
£667 $1207 €1000 London view (36x61cm-14x24in) s. canvasboard. 30-Mar-4 De Veres Art Auctions, Dublin #228/R
£694 $1132 €1000 View of cathedral with figures in park (60x49cm-24x19in) s. 24-Sep-3 James Adam, Dublin #132/R est:1000-1500
£800 $1440 €1200 Couple strolling in Phoenix Park (45x34cm-18x13in) s. 20-Apr-4 James Adam, Dublin #107/R
£1000 $1800 €1500 Figures and cars in Phoenix Park (38x75cm-15x30in) s. 20-Apr-4 James Adam, Dublin #108/R est:1200-1500
£1538 $2615 €2200 Yachts on the water (51x102cm-20x40in) s. d.1978 verso. 18-Nov-3 Whyte's, Dublin #198/R est:1500-2000
£2027 $3831 €3000 Views towards Trinity Collage from Grafton Street (46x36cm-18x14in) s.d.1978 verso. 17-Feb-4 Whyte's, Dublin #219 est:1200-1500

KLIUN, Ivan (1873-1943) Russian
Works on paper
£363 $650 €530 Untitled (13x18cm-5x7in) pencil. 13-May-4 Dallas Auction Gallery, Dallas #421/R
£4942 $8500 €7215 Composition (15x13cm-6x5in) s.d.1918 verso W/C pencil. 7-Dec-3 Treadway Gallery, Cincinnati #645/R est:10000-15000
£40000 $72800 €58400 Study for Landscape rushing by (16x15cm-6x6in) i. brush ink exec c.1914-15 prov.exhib.lit. 5-Feb-4 Christie's, London #346/R est:40000-60000

KLODIC, Paolo (1887-1961) Italian
£867 $1551 €1300 Capos Sounion (35x49cm-14x19in) s. cardboard. 12-May-4 Stadion, Trieste #759/R est:600-800
Works on paper
£909 $1518 €1300 Sailing boats in high seas (60x50cm-24x20in) s. col pastel. 10-Oct-3 Stadion, Trieste #15/R

KLODT, Pjotr (1815-1897) ?
£7200 $13104 €10800 Rowing boat moored on the lakeside (46x82cm-18x32in) s.d.1889. 3-Jul-4 Geble, Radolfzell #406/R est:6500

KLOMBEEK, Johann Bernard (1815-1893) Dutch
£18056 $30694 €26000 Travellers on a sandy track in a storm (39x54cm-15x21in) s.d.1847 panel. 28-Oct-3 Christie's, Amsterdam #236/R est:25000-35000
£23611 $42500 €34472 Forest and river landscape in winter with skaters and villagers on a path (103x121cm-41x48in) s.d.1864 prov. 23-Apr-4 Sotheby's, New York #35/R est:40000-60000

KLOMBEEK, Johann Bernard and VERBOECKHOVEN, Eugène (19th C) Dutch
£10204 $18571 €15000 Return of the cattle (68x87cm-27x34in) s.d.1875 prov.lit. 3-Feb-4 Christie's, Amsterdam #114/R est:10000-15000
£13423 $24027 €20000 Shepherd with his herd on the way home (92x126cm-36x50in) s. 27-May-4 Dorotheum, Vienna #16/R est:30000-40000

KLOMP, Aelbert (1618-1688) Dutch
£2400 $4320 €3504 River landscape with cattle and sheep before farm buildings (81x102cm-32x40in) s. 20-Apr-4 Sotheby's, Olympia #282/R est:2000-4000

KLOMP, Aelbert (attrib) (1618-1685) Dutch
£1310 $2410 €1913 Landscape with herder and animals (74x91cm-29x36in) 14-Jun-4 Philippe Schuler, Zurich #4308/R est:4000-6000 (S.FR 3000)

KLOOS, Cornelis (1895-1976) Dutch
£3221 $5960 €4800 Het witte vosje (81x50cm-32x20in) s.d.1933 s.i.verso. 15-Mar-4 Sotheby's, Amsterdam #221/R est:1500-2000

KLOSE, Paul (20th C) German
£578 $1040 €844 Rayu how double (141x193cm-56x76in) s. painted 1968. 25-Apr-4 Subastas Odalys, Caracas #28
£679 $1250 €1019 Untitled (110x175cm-43x69in) s.verso acrylic painted 1982. 27-Jun-4 Subastas Odalys, Caracas #134
£1985 $3375 €2898 Phoennyx (107x157cm-42x62in) s. painted 1969. 23-Nov-3 Subastas Odalys, Caracas #163/R est:3000

KLOSS, Friedrich Theodore (1802-1876) German
£1053 $1917 €1537 Seascape with vessels off Gibraltar (31x41cm-12x16in) with sig. d.1843 verso panel. 7-Feb-4 Rasmussen, Havnen #2219/R (D.KR 11500)

KLOSS, Gene (1903-) American
£6593 $12000 €9626 October snow (61x66cm-24x26in) s. 20-Jun-4 Charlton Hall, Columbia #562/R est:10000-15000
Prints
£1618 $2750 €2362 Old road to Taos (38x30cm-15x12in) s.i. drypoint prov.lit. 1-Nov-3 Santa Fe Art, Santa Fe #207/R est:2500-3500
£1630 $3000 €2380 Rio Grande footbridge (48x40cm-19x16in) print. 24-Jun-4 Sotheby's, New York #165/R est:2500-3500
£1766 $3250 €2578 Song of creation (56x45cm-22x18in) print. 24-Jun-4 Sotheby's, New York #162/R est:3000-5000
£3591 $6500 €5243 Penitente fires (28x36cm-11x14in) s.i. drypoint aquatint edition of 50. 19-Apr-4 Bonhams & Butterfields, San Francisco #32/R est:2000-3000
Works on paper
£4190 $7500 €6117 October in the mountains. s. W/C. 13-May-4 Dallas Auction Gallery, Dallas #331/R est:2000-4000
£5588 $9500 €8158 Blue peaks (71x51cm-28x20in) s. W/C prov.lit. 1-Nov-3 Santa Fe Art, Santa Fe #147/R est:15000-20000

KLOSSOWSKI, Pierre (1905-2001) French
Sculpture
£26667 $49333 €40000 Mr de Max et Mlle glissant dans les roles de Diane et Acteone (245x170x120cm-96x67x47in) s. pat bronze Cast Bocquel exec.1991-92 prov.exhib. 18-Jul-4 Sotheby's, Paris #166/R est:40000-60000
Works on paper
£2323 $4019 €3300 Portrait de Balthus (21x16cm-8x6in) i. crayon dr. 9-Dec-3 Artcurial Briest, Paris #185/R est:3000-4000
£14667 $27133 €22000 Roberte face au miroir (195x90cm-77x35in) col crayon exec.1984 prov.exhib.lit. 18-Jul-4 Sotheby's, Paris #272/R est:15000-20000
£18667 $33973 €28000 Belle Versaillaise (221x147cm-87x58in) s.d.1981 col crayon prov.lit. 29-Jun-4 Cornette de St.Cyr, Paris #9/R est:15000-20000

KLOTZ, Lenz (1925-) Swiss
£4148 $7633 €6056 I saw what was missing (125x145cm-49x57in) s.d.1990 d. verso acrylic Indian ink print prov.exhib.lit. 8-Jun-4 Germann, Zurich #80/R est:8000-12000 (S.FR 9500)

KLOTZ, Simon Petrus (1776-1824) German
£897 $1497 €1300 Classical buildings in trees (45x54cm-18x21in) W/C prov. 15-Nov-3 Lempertz, Koln #1339/R
£2192 $3726 €3200 Mountainous landscape with waterfall (53x42cm-21x17in) s. 5-Nov-3 Hugo Ruef, Munich #1042/R est:2800

KLUCIS, Gustav (1895-1944) Russian?
Photographs
£2899 $4754 €4000 Untitled (17x12cm-7x5in) i. verso vintage silver gelatin photo montage. 30-May-3 Villa Grisebach, Berlin #1242/R est:4000-6000

KLUGE, Constantine (1912-) French
£267 $491 €400 Fleurs dans un jardin (61x50cm-24x20in) s. 9-Jun-4 Le Roux & Morel, Paris #51
£430 $774 €628 Chinese landscape with bridge across river (46x66cm-18x26in) s. 24-Apr-4 Rasmussen, Havnen #2363/R (D.KR 4800)
£1176 $2200 €1717 Flowering peonies (119x61cm-47x24in) s. s.i.d.1980 verso. 24-Feb-4 Arthur James, Florida #273
£2000 $3460 €2920 La Seine, Paris (60x81cm-24x32in) s. prov. 11-Dec-3 Christie's, Kensington #44/R est:2000-3000
£2222 $4000 €3244 Notre-Dame de Paris (81x81cm-32x32in) s.i. prov. 20-Jan-4 Arthur James, Florida #149
£2273 $4250 €3319 Paris park scene (66x81cm-26x32in) s. 24-Feb-4 Arthur James, Florida #127
£2374 $4250 €3466 View from the Seine (73x73cm-29x29in) s. 14-May-4 Skinner, Boston #306/R est:1500-3000

£2540 $4750 €3708 Paris winter scene (81x102cm-32x40in) s. prov. 24-Feb-4 Arthur James, Florida #274
£2557 $4500 €3733 Les Cafe du Trocadero (81x66cm-32x26in) s. 18-May-4 Bonhams & Butterfields, San Francisco #196/R est:3000-5000
£3049 $5457 €4452 Porte St. Denis (61x91cm-24x36in) s. prov. 4-May-4 Ritchie, Toronto #85/R est:2000-4000 (C.D 7500)
£3056 $5500 €4462 Paris street scene (74x91cm-29x36in) s. prov. 20-Jan-4 Arthur James, Florida #150
£3153 $4950 €4603 Bridge over river (66x91cm-26x36in) s. 1-Sep-3 William A Smith, Plainfield #5/R

KLUGE, Harry (1879-1963) Danish
£269 $484 €393 Farm yard (63x43cm-25x17in) s.d.1929. 24-Apr-4 Rasmussen, Havnen #2176 (D.KR 3000)
£1791 $3277 €2615 Danish men-o-war disappearing in the haze (73x97cm-29x38in) s.d.1924. 9-Jun-4 Rasmussen, Copenhagen #1816/R est:20000 (D.KR 20000)

KLUGE, Kurt (1886-1940) German
Sculpture
£2667 $4773 €4000 Standing female nude with hand on hip (39cm-15in) s.d. yellow brown pat.bronze. 15-May-4 Bassenge, Berlin #6942/R est:1500

KLUGE, Thomas (1969-) Danish
£4964 $9134 €7247 Grown up's game II - Portrait of childhood friend N C Waldau with playmobile dolls (73x90cm-29x35in) s.i.d.20/4 1993 verso acrylic exhib.prov. 29-Mar-4 Rasmussen, Copenhagen #183/R est:60000-75000 (D.KR 55000)

KLUM, Ottone (19/20th C) Italian
£497 $904 €750 Fear (80x66cm-31x26in) s. 18-Jun-4 Stadion, Trieste #374/R

KLUMPP, Gustav (1902-1980) American
£16111 $29000 €23522 Nude in the woods (46x56cm-18x22in) 24-Apr-4 Slotin Folk Art, Buford #294/R est:4000-6000

KLUSKA, Johann (1904-c.1973) German
£267 $480 €400 Flagellation of Christ (115x94cm-45x37in) 26-Apr-4 Rieber, Stuttgart #1094/R
£282 $451 €400 Dante allegory (50x30cm-20x12in) s. panel. 19-Sep-3 Sigalas, Stuttgart #388/R
£300 $540 €450 Christ carrying the cross (115x94cm-45x37in) 26-Apr-4 Rieber, Stuttgart #1096/R
£333 $600 €500 Nailing Christ to the cross (115x94cm-45x37in) 26-Apr-4 Rieber, Stuttgart #1098/R
£367 $660 €550 Crucifixion (240x95cm-94x37in) s.d.1935. 26-Apr-4 Rieber, Stuttgart #1099/R
£408 $654 €580 Boy playing flute (80x60cm-31x24in) mono. 18-Sep-3 Rieber, Stuttgart #1100/R
£480 $864 €720 Ecce homo (115x94cm-45x37in) 26-Apr-4 Rieber, Stuttgart #1101/R
£563 $901 €800 Scene from Dantes Inferno XXV (93x55cm-37x22in) s.d.1970. 18-Sep-3 Rieber, Stuttgart #1268/R
£1056 $1690 €1500 Female nude wearing mask (160x110cm-63x43in) s.d.1946 board. 18-Sep-3 Rieber, Stuttgart #1103/R est:1800
£2533 $4560 €3800 The damned from Dante, Comedy, Purgatory (105x321cm-41x126in) s.d.1937. 26-Apr-4 Rieber, Stuttgart #1100/R est:2200
£3427 $5722 €4900 Naked bodies (233x146cm-92x57in) s.d1941 panel. 26-Jun-3 Weidler, Nurnberg #4529/R est:400

KLUYVER, Pieter Lodewijk Francisco (1816-1900) Dutch
£329 $595 €500 Polder landscape with a woman and her dog on a sandy path (14x30cm-6x12in) s. panel. 19-Apr-4 Glerum, Amsterdam #46/R
£633 $1153 €950 Extensive summer landscape (39x50cm-15x20in) s.d.39 canvas on board. 1-Jul-4 Van Ham, Cologne #1460
£991 $1775 €1447 Winter scene with frozen lake (17x23cm-7x9in) bears sig. pael. 12-May-4 Dobiaschofsky, Bern #696/R est:3300 (S.FR 2300)
£1181 $1972 €1700 Figures by a forest stream (34x24cm-13x9in) s. panel. 21-Oct-3 Sotheby's, Amsterdam #43/R est:1500-2000
£1208 $2223 €1800 Frozen Dutch river with horse drawn cart and windmill (16x24cm-6x9in) s. panel lit. 25-Mar-4 Karlheinz Kaupp, Staufen #2546/R est:1400
£1233 $2096 €1800 Hunter on country path (29x21cm-11x8in) s. panel. 5-Nov-3 Vendue Huis, Gravenhage #48/R est:2000-3000
£3125 $5094 €4500 Landscape with sheep and water (47x59cm-19x23in) s. panel. 25-Sep-3 Dr Fritz Nagel, Stuttgart #1365/R est:5600
£5263 $9526 €8000 Wood gatherers on the ice, a mill in the distance (76x73cm-30x29in) s. 19-Apr-4 Glerum, Amsterdam #60/R est:4000-6000

KLYN, Hendrik Albertus (1860-1929) Dutch
£259 $432 €378 Deer in a forest (72x57cm-28x22in) s.d.Dec 88. 20-Oct-3 Stephan Welz, Johannesburg #463 est:2500-3500 (SA.R 3000)

KMELUCK, Wassyl (1903-) ?
£440 $810 €642 Evelin, seated (60x37cm-24x15in) s.d.1953. 23-Mar-4 Rosebery Fine Art, London #928
£621 $1117 €900 Bouquet of lilies (55x37cm-22x15in) s.d.1954 panel. 25-Jan-4 Chayette & Cheval, Paris #173

KMETTY, Janos (1889-1975) Hungarian
£1697 $2935 €2478 Szentendre (25x35cm-10x14in) s. cardboard. 12-Dec-3 Kieselbach, Budapest #8/R (H.F 650000)
£3207 $5676 €4682 Houses in Szentendre (24x32cm-9x13in) s. cardboard. 28-Apr-4 Kieselbach, Budapest #90/R (H.F 1200000)
£4887 $8112 €7135 Autumn landscape (56x69cm-22x27in) s. painted c.1910. 4-Oct-3 Kieselbach, Budapest #114/R (H.F 1800000)
£5077 $8987 €7412 A summer day (56x69cm-22x27in) s. 28-Apr-4 Kieselbach, Budapest #174b (H.F 1900000)
£9396 $16255 €13718 Blue still life (59x54cm-23x21in) s.d.1924 cardboard on news. 12-Dec-3 Kieselbach, Budapest #24/R (H.F 3600000)
£25386 $44933 €37064 Still life with fruit (60x80cm-24x31in) s. painted c.1930. 28-Apr-4 Kieselbach, Budapest #52/R (H.F 9500000)
£71139 $128761 €103863 Still life with the Kut magazine (75x47cm-30x19in) s. 16-Apr-4 Mu Terem Galeria, Budapest #69/R (H.F 27000000)
Works on paper
£783 $1355 €1143 Szamarhegy in Szentendre with the Danube in the background (25x33cm-10x13in) s. pastel. 12-Dec-3 Kieselbach, Budapest #51/R (H.F 300000)
£802 $1419 €1171 Szentendre (24x31cm-9x12in) s. pastel. 28-Apr-4 Kieselbach, Budapest #34/R (H.F 300000)
£855 $1514 €1248 Lakeside landscape (24x31cm-9x12in) s. pastel. 28-Apr-4 Kieselbach, Budapest #42/R (H.F 320000)
£923 $1532 €1348 On the main square of Nagybanya (27x37cm-11x15in) s. W/C. 4-Oct-3 Kieselbach, Budapest #7/R (H.F 340000)
£923 $1532 €1348 Still life (22x29cm-9x11in) s. W/C. 4-Oct-3 Kieselbach, Budapest #42/R (H.F 340000)

KMIT, Michael (1910-1981) Russian
£356 $655 €520 Harbour at night (25x19cm-10x7in) s. board. 28-Jun-4 Australian Art Auctions, Sydney #93 (A.D 950)
£681 $1157 €994 Head of young woman (29x22cm-11x9in) s.d.1970 acrylic gouache ink board. 25-Nov-3 Christie's, Melbourne #301 (A.D 1600)
£688 $1108 €1004 Actress (48x38cm-19x15in) s.d.48 s.i.verso. 13-Oct-3 Joel, Victoria #430 est:1000-2000 (A.D 1700)
£994 $1829 €1451 Sisters (43x34cm-17x13in) s.i.verso board. 29-Mar-4 Goodman, Sydney #189/R (A.D 2435)
£3512 $6498 €5128 Girl with a flower (122x81cm-48x32in) s.d.65 s.i.d.verso board prov. 10-Mar-4 Deutscher-Menzies, Melbourne #55/R est:8000-12000 (A.D 8500)
£3644 $5866 €5320 Proprietress (64x54cm-25x21in) s.d.62 s.i.d.1963 verso composition board. 25-Aug-3 Sotheby's, Paddington #313/R est:8000-10000 (A.D 9000)
Works on paper
£758 $1228 €1107 Head of a woman (34x19cm-13x7in) s.d.69 mixed media. 30-Jul-3 Goodman, Sydney #69/R (A.D 1850)

KNAB, F (1834-1902) German
£1342 $2403 €2000 Vue de parc au crepuscule (120x100cm-47x39in) s. 25-May-4 Palais de Beaux Arts, Brussels #371/R est:2000-3000

KNAB, Ferdinand (1834-1902) German
£298 $550 €435 Ruins by the shore (58x81cm-23x32in) s. 17-Jul-4 New Orleans Auction, New Orleans #175/R
£1060 $1928 €1600 Southern landscape with a lake, ruins and a deer (85x65cm-33x26in) s.d.1896. 17-Jun-4 Frank Peege, Freiburg #1186/R est:1800
£1538 $2615 €2200 Coastal landscape with temple ruins (45x35cm-18x14in) s.d.1892 lit. 28-Nov-3 Schloss Ahlden, Ahlden #1414/R est:2400
£1678 $2853 €2400 Fountain in a park landscape (50x40cm-20x16in) s.d.1900 lit. 28-Nov-3 Schloss Ahlden, Ahlden #1413/R est:2400

KNAFLEWSKI, Leszek (1960-) Polish
Works on paper
£494 $895 €721 Composition (173x53cm-68x21in) s.d.1996 collage. 4-Apr-4 Agra, Warsaw #91/R (P.Z 3500)

KNAP, Gerrit Willem (1873-?) Dutch
£855 $1574 €1300 View of Amsterdam (65x100cm-26x39in) s. 28-Jun-4 Sotheby's, Amsterdam #127/R

KNAP, Jan (1949-) Czechoslovakian?
£13333 $24400 €20000 Water washes skin, love the heart (190x285cm-75x112in) s.d.85 i. verso exhib. 4-Jun-4 Lempertz, Koln #260/R est:7000-8000
Works on paper
£347 $621 €520 Holy Family (28x26cm-11x10in) s.d. W/C Indian ink. 15-May-4 Dr Sturies, Dusseldorf #110/R
£1056 $1849 €1500 Boy with book (49x60cm-19x24in) s. pastel exec.1995 prov. 16-Dec-3 Finarte Semenzato, Milan #348/R est:1500-1800

KNAP, Joseph D (1875-?) American
Works on paper
£320 $550 €467 Hazy weather-red heads (38x53cm-15x21in) s. W/C. 7-Dec-3 Grogan, Boston #75/R

KNAPP, Charles W (1822-1900) American
£988 $1700 €1442 Autumn landscape (23x33cm-9x13in) init. board. 7-Dec-3 Freeman, Philadelphia #115 est:1000-1500
£1220 $2000 €1769 Pastoral landscape with cows and boy with fishing pole (41x71cm-16x28in) s. 4-Jun-3 Alderfer's, Hatfield #413/R est:2500-3000
£1243 $2300 €1865 Pastoral landscape with farmhouse and cattle (69x112cm-27x44in) s. 14-Jul-4 American Auctioneer #490297/R est:3000-5000
£1744 $3000 €2546 Figures by a house in a winter landscape (69x56cm-27x22in) s. 7-Dec-3 Freeman, Philadelphia #116 est:4000-6000
£6051 $9500 €8834 Pastoral landscape, possibly Delaware water gap, scene with mountains (51x91cm-20x36in) s. 30-Aug-3 Fallon, Copake #21 est:5000-6000
£6790 $11000 €9846 Autumn river landscape (76x117cm-30x46in) s. 8-Aug-3 Barridorf, Portland #136/R est:5000-7000

KNAPP, George Kasson (1833-1910) American
£363 $650 €610 Still life with grapes, butterfly and glass (48x38cm-19x15in) s. 20-Mar-4 Pook & Pook, Downington #346

KNAPP, Stephan (1921-) British
£1374 $2500 €2006 Red Eclipse (196x104cm-77x41in) enamel steel panel. 19-Jun-4 Skinner, Boston #22/R est:400-600
£1429 $2600 €2086 Red Eclipse (196x104cm-77x41in) enamel steel panel. 19-Jun-4 Skinner, Boston #21/R est:400-600

KNAPPE, Prof Karl (1884-1970) German

Sculpture

£2000	$3580	€3000	Beggar (40x19x12cm-16x7x5in) s.d. polished dark brown pat.bronze prov. 14-May-4 Ketterer, Munich #39/R est:2500-3500

KNAPTON, George (1698-1778) British

£2000	$3680	€2920	Portrait of a gentleman of the Broughton Adderley family (91x71cm-36x28in) s.d.1731. 23-Jun-4 Bonhams, Bury St Edmunds #404/R est:2000-3000
£4500	$7650	€6570	Portrait of a lady wearing a blue dress (75x62cm-30x24in) painted oval. 27-Nov-3 Sotheby's, London #155/R est:3000-5000
£26000	$44200	€37960	Portrait of Mrs Neate, of Donnington, Hampshire, seated at a table with a spaniel trying to sit on h (102x127cm-40x50in) prov. 25-Nov-3 Christie's, London #28/R est:15000-20000

KNAPTON, George (attrib) (1698-1778) British

£2600	$4420	€3796	Portrait of Ann Wolojlife in a pink dress, her apron filled with flowers (127x104cm-50x41in) prov. 25-Nov-3 Christie's, London #23/R est:3000-5000

KNATHS, Karl (1891-1971) American

£230	$375	€336	Untitled (18x5cm-7x2in) oil on paper. 19-Jul-3 Outer Cape Auctions, Provincetown #158/R
£429	$700	€626	Island imagery (23x28cm-9x11in) s. oil on paper. 19-Jul-3 Outer Cape Auctions, Provincetown #111/R
£459	$850	€670	Nude portrait (51x41cm-20x16in) s. 17-Jul-4 Outer Cape Auctions, Provincetown #13/R
£2907	$5000	€4244	Duck decoy, Provincetown (77x92cm-30x36in) s. s.i.d.1970 on stretcher prov. 3-Dec-3 Doyle, New York #5/R est:3000-5000
£3529	$6000	€5152	Dancers (107x66cm-42x26in) s. i.verso painted c.1952. 9-Nov-3 Outer Cape Auctions, Provincetown #70/R
£10180	$17000	€14863	Clock (69x91cm-27x36in) s. s.i.d.1951 stretcher prov.exhib.lit. 7-Oct-3 Sotheby's, New York #232 est:3000-5000
£10615	$19000	€15498	Red clock (102x76cm-40x30in) s. prov.exhib. 6-May-4 Doyle, New York #114/R est:6000-8000
£14110	$23000	€20601	Portrait of Agnes Weinrich (102x76cm-40x30in) s. 19-Jul-3 Outer Cape Auctions, Provincetown #85/R

Works on paper

£652	$1200	€952	The brook (30x46cm-12x18in) s. W/C double-sided. 10-Jun-4 Swann Galleries, New York #133/R
£767	$1250	€1120	Pay day (18x23cm-7x9in) W/C. 19-Jul-3 Outer Cape Auctions, Provincetown #64/R

KNAUS, Ludwig (1829-1910) German

£1389	$2319	€2000	Young soldier (25x15cm-10x6in) mono.d. paper on board. 24-Oct-3 Ketterer, Hamburg #430/R est:2000-2400
£1818	$3091	€2600	Satyr and nymphs (29x20cm-11x8in) s.d.1866. 24-Nov-3 Dorotheum, Vienna #19/R est:3000-4000
£2400	$4344	€3600	Wilhellm Adolf von Carstanjen as mountaineer (95x38cm-37x15in) s.d.1874 prov.lit. 1-Apr-4 Van Ham, Cologne #1485/R est:2400
£28409	$50000	€41477	Springtime (51x66cm-20x26in) painted 1868 prov. 23-May-4 Hindman, Chicago #20/R est:3000-6000

KNAUTH, Arnold (1918-) American

£299	$550	€437	Harbour scene (56x81cm-22x32in) s. board. 25-Jun-4 Freeman, Philadelphia #271/R

KNEALE, Bryan (1930-) British

£600	$1092	€876	Portrait of a Spanish lady (76x63cm-30x25in) s.d.1957 sold with another portrait by the same hand. 15-Jun-4 Rosebery Fine Art, London #558/R
£650	$1183	€949	Portrait of Mizoumi Mouari (121x91cm-48x36in) s.d.1958 prov. 15-Jun-4 Rosebery Fine Art, London #556/R
£950	$1729	€1387	Portrait of a man holding an animal skull (91x71cm-36x28in) s.d.1957 prov. 15-Jun-4 Rosebery Fine Art, London #557

Works on paper

£580	$1073	€847	Bird on head (48x32cm-19x13in) s. pen ink exhib. 11-Mar-4 Christie's, Kensington #232
£600	$1110	€876	Goat I (49x33cm-19x13in) s.d.60 pen brush ink exhib. 11-Mar-4 Christie's, Kensington #221/R
£600	$1110	€876	Bird form (43x53cm-17x21in) s.d.1960 pencil gouache exhib. 11-Mar-4 Christie's, Kensington #223/R
£750	$1388	€1095	Goat II (49x32cm-19x13in) s.d.1958 pen brush ink exhib. 11-Mar-4 Christie's, Kensington #225/R

KNEBEL, Franz (jnr) (1809-1877) Swiss

£8000	$14720	€12000	Vue de Florence (52x94cm-20x37in) 11-Jun-4 Claude Aguttes, Neuilly #6/R est:12000-15000

Works on paper

£3394	$5871	€4955	Vue du temple de la SYbille a Tivoli (32x43cm-13x17in) s.i.d.1855 W/C prov. 12-Dec-3 Galerie du Rhone, Sion #626/R est:8000-10000 (S.FR 7500)

KNEBEL, Franz (jnr-attrib) (1809-1877) Swiss

£1810	$3241	€2643	Ruins by Italian lake (48x57cm-19x22in) i. stretcher. 12-May-4 Dobiaschofsky, Bern #698/R est:2900 (S.FR 4200)

KNEBEL, Wilhelm (19th C) German

£420	$722	€600	Fishing boat in stormy seas (21x29cm-8x11in) s. 5-Dec-3 Bolland & Marotz, Bremen #588/R

KNECHT, Hermann (19th C) ?

£628	$1048	€917	Rhine landscape (26x35cm-10x14in) s. i. verso panel. 24-Oct-3 Hans Widmer, St Gallen #145/R (S.FR 1400)

KNEFFEL, Karin (1957-) German

£7343	$12483	€10500	Untitled - animal heads (100x100cm-39x39in) s.d.1992-1993 verso nine mounted as one prov.exhib. 27-Nov-3 Lempertz, Koln #227/R est:8000

KNELL, Adolphus (fl.1860-1890) British

£280	$468	€409	Highland cattle (17x25cm-7x10in) s. board. 16-Oct-3 Lawrence, Crewkerne #747
£500	$860	€730	Hay barge and other shipping along the coast (15x23cm-6x9in) s. 2-Dec-3 Gorringes, Lewes #2433
£600	$1020	€876	Hay barges (18x23cm-7x9in) s.indis.d. 19-Nov-3 Christie's, Kensington #567/R
£600	$1110	€876	Moonlit seascape (11x31cm-4x12in) s. board. 10-Feb-4 Bonhams, Knightsbridge #147/R
£621	$1148	€900	Shipping in moonlight (28x22cm-11x9in) 11-Feb-4 Woodwards, Cork #12/R
£625	$994	€900	Trois-mats au crepuscule (15x25cm-6x10in) s. cardboard. 15-Sep-3 Horta, Bruxelles #380
£650	$1118	€949	Fishing boats off the coast (20x25cm-8x10in) s. 2-Dec-3 Gorringes, Lewes #2431/R
£750	$1290	€1095	Shipping at anchor (178x25cm-70x10in) s. 2-Dec-3 Gorringes, Lewes #2434
£850	$1522	€1241	Shipping in coastal waters by moonlight (30x58cm-12x23in) s. board. 26-May-4 Christie's, Kensington #647/R
£900	$1530	€1314	Figures and fishing boats on a beach at low tide (15x30cm-6x12in) s. board. 19-Nov-3 Tennants, Leyburn #1017
£980	$1793	€1431	Sunset and moonlight, coastal shipping scenes (14x22cm-6x9in) s. board pair. 6-Apr-4 Bristol Auction Rooms #492/R
£1100	$2035	€1606	Southampton water under moonlight (20x38cm-8x15in) 9-Mar-4 Gorringes, Lewes #2028 est:1000-1500
£1200	$1908	€1752	Sailing boats and a rowing boat in choppy seas (33x43cm-13x17in) s. 12-Sep-3 Gardiner & Houlgate, Bath #181/R est:500-750
£1300	$2236	€1898	Shipping in harbour at sunset (178x25cm-70x10in) s. 2-Dec-3 Gorringes, Lewes #2432/R est:800-1200
£1350	$2255	€1971	Coastal scene (7x24cm-3x9in) s. board. 16-Oct-3 Lawrence, Crewkerne #748
£1400	$2618	€2044	Shipping off the south west (13x30cm-5x12in) s. board. 26-Feb-4 Lane, Penzance #302 est:1250-1500
£1478	$2646	€2158	Seascape with sailing vessel at sunset (34x54cm-13x21in) 25-May-4 Bukowskis, Stockholm #364/R est:18000-20000 (S.KR 20000)
£1750	$2923	€2555	Tall ships at anchor at twilight. s.d.1876. 19-Oct-3 Desmond Judd, Cranbrook #1097
£1848	$3307	€2698	Seascape with sailing vessels and steam ship (30x46cm-12x18in) s. panel. 26-May-4 AB Stockholms Auktionsverk #2388/R est:15000-20000 (S.KR 25000)
£2400	$3840	€3504	Shipping by moonlight (16x23cm-6x9in) s. board pair. 16-Sep-3 Bonhams, New Bond Street #51/R est:1200-1800
£2500	$4725	€3650	Shipping by sunrise. Shipping by moonlight (15x23cm-6x9in) both board pair. 17-Feb-4 Bonhams, New Bond Street #22/R est:1200-1800
£2800	$4760	€4088	Three-decker in busy anchorage (26x35cm-10x14in) s. 19-Nov-3 Christie's, Kensington #554/R

Works on paper

£420	$714	€613	Frigates (22x34cm-9x13in) s.i. pencil W/C gum arabic. 19-Nov-3 Christie's, Kensington #340/R
£800	$1448	€1168	Marine with fishermen in rowing boat (18x41cm-7x16in) s. W/C. 16-Apr-4 Keys, Aylsham #516/R

KNELL, William Adolphus (1805-1875) British

£297	$550	€434	Marine landscape (58x71cm-23x28in) board. 13-Feb-4 Du Mouchelle, Detroit #2321/R
£550	$935	€803	Clear night (30x26cm-12x10in) s. 19-Nov-3 Christie's, Kensington #553/R
£694	$1160	€1000	Ships at sea at night (30x59cm-12x23in) s. board lit. 25-Oct-3 Bergmann, Erlangen #953/R
£919	$1700	€1342	Shipping at sunset. Early morning mist (15x23cm-6x9in) s. board pair. 10-Mar-4 Doyle, New York #37/R est:1500-2500
£950	$1700	€1387	Early morning shipping (13x30cm-5x12in) s. i.verso panel. 6-May-4 Doyle, New York #20/R est:1000-1500
£1000	$1660	€1460	Putting out the nets (22x31cm-9x12in) s. board. 1-Oct-3 Bonhams, Knightsbridge #168/R est:1000-1500
£1000	$1670	€1460	Shipping in Channel off Seven Sisters (44x59cm-17x23in) s. board. 11-Nov-3 Bonhams, Knightsbridge #179/R est:1200-1800
£1000	$1860	€1460	Sunset. Sunrise (9x30cm-4x12in) mono. board pair. 4-Mar-4 Christie's, Kensington #556/R est:800-1200
£1150	$2082	€1679	Moonlit seascape with boats and figures (23x36cm-9x14in) s. 16-Apr-4 Keys, Aylsham #776/R est:550-700
£1300	$2405	€1898	Careening the hulls. Waiting the tide (20x35cm-8x14in) s. pair. 10-Mar-4 Sotheby's, Olympia #195/R est:800-1200
£1600	$2960	€2336	Shipping at sunset. Fishing in rough seas (29x46cm-11x18in) s. board pair. 10-Mar-4 Sotheby's, Olympia #191/R est:1500-2000
£1700	$3145	€2482	Shipwreck (22x14cm-9x6in) s. board sold with three seascapes by same hand four. 10-Mar-4 Sotheby's, Olympia #192/R est:1200-1800
£1900	$3515	€2774	Evening seascapes (14x22cm-6x9in) s. board three. 10-Mar-4 Sotheby's, Olympia #194/R est:800-1200
£2200	$4070	€3212	Fishing in the moonlight. Stormy seas (29x46cm-11x18in) each s. board pair. 10-Mar-4 Sotheby's, Olympia #193/R est:1500-2000
£2600	$4316	€3796	Shipping at dawn. Returning home at dusk (18x30cm-7x12in) s. board pair. 1-Oct-3 Bonhams, Knightsbridge #167/R est:1200-1800
£2600	$4472	€3796	Shipping at sunset (46x76cm-18x30in) s.d.59. 2-Dec-3 Gorringes, Lewes #2496/R est:700-1000
£4800	$8592	€7008	East Indiaman reefed down and riding out a gale (75x104cm-30x41in) prov. 26-May-4 Christie's, Kensington #683/R est:4000-6000

Works on paper

£900	$1620	€1314	Shipping in a rough sea (15x23cm-6x9in) s. W/C over pencil. 21-Jan-4 Sotheby's, Olympia #242/R est:1000-5000

KNELL, William Adolphus (attrib) (1805-1875) British

£355	$561	€515	Mountain landscape with highland cattle by river (23x30cm-9x12in) s. 2-Sep-3 Rasmussen, Copenhagen #1911 (D.KR 3800)

KNELL, William Callcott (19th C) British

£440	$788	€642	Shipping off the coast at sunset (24x35cm-9x14in) s.d.59. 11-May-4 Dreweatt Neate, Newbury #492/R
£450	$837	€657	St. Omer, Strasbourg (41x30cm-16x12in) s.d.1871 i.verso. 4-Mar-4 Christie's, Kensington #570/R
£905	$1620	€1321	Fishing boats off the French coast (46x85cm-18x33in) s.d.1877. 10-May-4 Rasmussen, Vejle #389/R (D.KR 10000)

£944	$1700	€1378	Summer's afternoon of Whitby (21x41cm-8x16in) s.d.1876 s.i.verso. 21-Jan-4 Doyle, New York #133/R est:2000-3000
£1200	$2040	€1752	Shipping off the entrance to Portsmouth harbour (46x81cm-18x32in) s.indis.d. 19-Nov-3 Christie's, Kensington #522/R
£1259	$2102	€1800	Lug sail fishing boat making for wreck (45x81cm-18x32in) s.d.1868 i. verso canvas on panel. 28-Jun-3 Bolland & Marotz, Bremen #687/R est:2000
£1400	$2590	€2044	Shipping off a coastline (28x54cm-11x21in) s. 13-Jan-4 Bonhams, Knightsbridge #105/R est:1500-2000
£1600	$2960	€2336	Fishing boats in a calm sea off a harbour. Coastal scene (25x44cm-10x17in) s. pastel pair. 13-Feb-4 Bracketts, Tunbridge Wells #705/R est:1800-2000
£3000	$4890	€4380	Seascape at sunset, a windmill upon the shoreline (66x106cm-26x42in) s. indis.d.1865. 24-Sep-3 Dreweatt Neate, Newbury #134/R est:1200-1500
Works on paper			
£1931	$3572	€2800	Sailing barges in calm estuaries (19x35cm-7x14in) s.d.1866 W/C pair. 11-Feb-4 Woodwards, Cork #19/R est:3000-4000

KNELL, William Callcott (attrib) (19th C) British

£399	$718	€599	Seascape with sailing vessel (38x66cm-15x26in) 25-Apr-4 Goteborg Auktionsverk, Sweden #205/R (S.KR 5500)

KNELLER, Sir Godfrey (1646-1723) British

£2000	$3720	€2920	Portrait of a lady in a grey dress and blue mantle (76x63cm-30x25in) oval painted with studio prov. 4-Mar-4 Christie's, Kensington #327/R est:2500-3500
£3000	$5490	€4380	Portrait of Lady Dianna Feilding, in a white chemise and a green wrap (75x62cm-30x24in) i.verso oval. 7-Jul-4 Bonhams, New Bond Street #109/R est:3000-5000
£3800	$6460	€5548	Portrait of Sir John Wedderburn (127x102cm-50x40in) s.i. 27-Nov-3 Sotheby's, London #122/R est:2500-4000
£4500	$7470	€6570	Portrait of Count Henry of Nassau Auverquerque, Marshal D'Auverquerque (121x102cm-48x40in) i. 30-Sep-3 Sotheby's, London #11/R est:5000-7000
£5500	$10285	€8030	Portrait of a gentleman (126x100cm-50x39in) s.d.1688. 22-Jul-4 Sotheby's, Olympia #393/R est:6000-8000
£10227	$18000	€14931	Portrait of Sir John Rushout (127x102cm-50x40in) s.d.1716 prov. 18-May-4 Bonhams & Butterfields, San Francisco #45/R est:15000-20000
£11173	$20000	€16313	Portrait of Robert, Lord Willoughby (112x89cm-44x35in) prov. 27-May-4 Sotheby's, New York #217/R est:20000-30000
£16000	$29440	€23360	Portrait of Admiral James Berkeley, 3rd Earl of Berkeley (127x102cm-50x40in) i. prov. 26-Mar-4 Sotheby's, London #7/R est:8000-12000
£23743	$42500	€34665	Portrait of Meliora Fitch (127x102cm-50x40in) lit. 27-May-4 Sotheby's, New York #216/R est:20000-30000

KNELLER, Sir Godfrey (after) (1646-1723) British

£7500	$13800	€10950	Portrait of George I, wearing state robes (239x145cm-94x57in) 26-Mar-4 Sotheby's, London #9/R est:4000-6000

KNELLER, Sir Godfrey (attrib) (1646-1723) British

£1508	$2700	€2202	Portrait of Thomas Knipe (76x64cm-30x25in) oval. 7-May-4 Sloans & Kenyon, Bethesda #1659/R est:3000-5000
£2545	$3996	€3690	Portrait of a lady (122x97cm-48x38in) 27-Aug-3 Dunbar Sloane, Wellington #77/R est:10000-15000 (NZ.D 7000)
£2793	$5000	€4190	Portrait of woman with bouquet (127x102cm-50x40in) 16-May-4 Abell, Los Angeles #414/R
£4000	$6920	€5840	Portrait of Lady Lucy Leake, seated three-quarter (124x99cm-49x39in) prov. 11-Dec-3 Neales, Nottingham #649/R est:4000-6000

KNELLER, Sir Godfrey (circle) (1646-1723) British

£4200	$7770	€6132	Portrait of Rebecca Hillhouse, Daughter of Colonel James Lennox (124x100cm-49x39in) prov. 10-Mar-4 Sotheby's, Olympia #1/R est:2000-3000
£5689	$9500	€8306	Portrait of Charles Montagu, 1st Earl of Halifax (125x100cm-49x39in) i. 7-Oct-3 Sotheby's, New York #25/R est:6000-8000

KNELLER, Sir Godfrey (studio) (1646-1723) British

£9000	$16380	€13500	Portrait of 1st Duke of Dorset (126x103cm-50x41in) 20-Jun-4 Wilkinson, Doncaster #348 est:14000-18000

KNELLER, Sir Godfrey (style) (1646-1723) British

£3977	$7000	€5806	Portrait of a Peer of the Realm with Parliamentary robes (91x74cm-36x29in) 19-May-4 Doyle, New York #6087/R est:3000-5000
£5000	$9300	€7300	Portrait of Charles II in ceremonial robes (76x63cm-30x25in) feigned oval. 4-Mar-4 Christie's, Kensington #282/R est:2000-3000
£5100	$8670	€7446	Portrait of Sir Wadham Wyndham, seated three quarter length (125x100cm-49x39in) bears i.d.1665. 29-Oct-3 Hampton & Littlewood, Exeter #555/R est:2000-3000
£8840	$16000	€12906	Portraits of a lady and gentleman. i.verso pair. 3-Apr-4 Neal Auction Company, New Orleans #826/R est:1500-2500

KNGWARREYE, Emily (c.1916-1996) Australian

£5602	$9355	€8403	Wild flower (121x90cm-48x35in) i.verso acrylic. 27-Oct-3 Goodman, Sydney #53/R est:12000-15000 (A.D 13500)
£5799	$10671	€8467	Wild potato (120x90cm-47x35in) acrylic prov. 29-Mar-4 Goodman, Sydney #170/R est:18000-22000 (A.D 14210)
£9375	$17531	€14063	Untitled (121x90cm-48x35in) bears name.d.1989 verso synthetic polymer paint canvas prov.exhib. 26-Jul-4 Sotheby's, Melbourne #212/R est:30000-50000 (A.D 24000)
Works on paper			
£1240	$2107	€1810	Untitled 1994 (80x76cm-31x30in) synthetic polymer paint on paper. 29-Oct-3 Lawson Menzies, Sydney #68/R est:4000-6000 (A.D 3000)
£1653	$3058	€2413	Karma seeds - yam dreaming (66x56cm-26x22in) synthetic polymer linen on canvas executed 1995 prov. 15-Mar-4 Sotheby's, Melbourne #48 est:4000-6000 (A.D 4000)
£1859	$3291	€2714	Yam dreaming (91x63cm-36x25in) s.verso synthetic polymer paint canvas. 3-May-4 Christie's, Melbourne #325/R est:5000-8000 (A.D 4500)
£2033	$3211	€2948	My mother's country (71x126cm-28x50in) s.d.27/9/94 verso synthetic polymer paint linen. 28-Jul-3 Sotheby's, Paddington #504/R est:5000-7000 (A.D 5000)
£2213	$3828	€3231	Untitled (69x56cm-27x22in) synthetic polymer paint canvas prov. 10-Dec-3 Shapiro, Sydney #195/R est:6000-8000 (A.D 5200)
£2459	$3984	€3590	Untitled (53x83cm-21x33in) synthetic polymer canvas prov. 30-Jul-3 Goodman, Sydney #135/R est:6000-8000 (A.D 6000)
£2637	$4931	€3956	Body paint (76x56cm-30x22in) synthetic polymer paint prov. 26-Jul-4 Sotheby's, Melbourne #480/R est:6000-8000 (A.D 6750)
£2642	$4175	€3831	Untitled, alhakere (91x61cm-36x24in) i.verso synthetic polymer paint linen prov. 28-Jul-3 Sotheby's, Paddington #371/R est:4000-6000 (A.D 6500)
£2745	$4914	€4008	Yam dreaming (63x93cm-25x37in) synthetic polymer paint linen exec 1995 prov. 25-May-4 Lawson Menzies, Sydney #25/R est:8000-10000 (A.D 7000)
£2893	$4917	€4224	Bush yam 1994 (59x40cm-23x16in) synthetic polymer paint on canvas prov. 29-Oct-3 Lawson Menzies, Sydney #66/R est:8000-10000 (A.D 7000)
£3036	$4889	€4433	Brown, white and black stripes (121x90cm-48x35in) synthetic polymer paint canvas exhib. 25-Aug-3 Sotheby's, Paddington #287/R est:5000-8000 (A.D 7500)
£3125	$5844	€4688	Merne everything (121x91cm-48x36in) bears name.verso synthetic polymer paint linen prov. 26-Jul-4 Sotheby's, Melbourne #483/R est:8000-12000 (A.D 8000)
£3137	$5616	€4580	My Country body paint (91x121cm-36x48in) synthetic polymer paint linen exec 1994. 25-May-4 Lawson Menzies, Sydney #223/R est:18000-20000 (A.D 8000)
£3294	$5896	€4809	Arlatyete wildflower dreaming (96x139cm-38x55in) s. verso synthetic polymer paint canvas exec 1996 prov. 25-May-4 Lawson Menzies, Sydney #214/R est:15000-20000 (A.D 8400)
£3319	$5742	€4846	Bush yam awelye (60x55cm-24x22in) i.verso synthetic polymer paint canvas prov. 10-Dec-3 Shapiro, Sydney #217/R est:6000-9000 (A.D 7800)
£3711	$6939	€5567	Awelye (90x60cm-35x24in) s.verso synthetic polymer paint linen prov. 26-Jul-4 Sotheby's, Melbourne #246/R est:10000-15000 (A.D 9500)
£3926	$6674	€5732	Wild potato dreaming 1995 (120x90cm-47x35in) synthetic polymer paint on canvas prov. 29-Oct-3 Lawson Menzies, Sydney #69/R est:7000-9000 (A.D 9500)
£4065	$6423	€5894	My country (84x91cm-33x36in) synthetic polymer paint linen prov. 28-Jul-3 Sotheby's, Paddington #503/R est:5000-7000 (A.D 10000)
£4102	$7670	€6153	Awelye (91x61cm-36x24in) bears name.verso synthetic polymer paint linen prov. 26-Jul-4 Sotheby's, Melbourne #247/R est:12000-18000 (A.D 10500)
£4472	$7065	€6484	My country (90x121cm-35x48in) i.verso synthetic polymer paint linen prov.exhib.lit. 28-Jul-3 Sotheby's, Paddington #370/R est:12000-18000 (A.D 11000)
£4492	$8400	€6738	Untitled, awelye (119x119cm-47x47in) s.i.verso synthetic polymer paint canvas prov. 26-Jul-4 Sotheby's, Melbourne #479/R est:12000-18000 (A.D 11500)
£4959	$8430	€7240	Merne anooralya 1993 (121x92cm-48x36in) i.verso synthetic polymer paint on canvas prov. 29-Oct-3 Lawson Menzies, Sydney #70/R est:12000-15000 (A.D 12000)
£4961	$9277	€7427	Wildflower dreaming (122x93cm-48x37in) synthetic polymer linen exec. 1994 prov. 21-Jul-4 Shapiro, Sydney #114/R est:14000-18000 (A.D 12700)
£5328	$8631	€7779	Earths creation (91x122cm-36x48in) synthetic polymer canvas prov. 30-Jul-3 Goodman, Sydney #39/R est:8000-12000 (A.D 13000)
£5532	$9570	€8077	Bush yam awelye (131x65cm-52x26in) i.verso synthetic polymer paint canvas prov. 10-Dec-3 Shapiro, Sydney #216/R est:15000-25000 (A.D 13000)
£5957	$10306	€8697	Emu (60x90cm-24x35in) i.verso synthetic polymer paint linen. 10-Dec-3 Shapiro, Sydney #159/R est:15000-25000 (A.D 14000)
£6641	$12418	€9962	Untitled (151x121cm-59x48in) bears name.verso synthetic polymer paint canvas prov.exhib.lit. 26-Jul-4 Sotheby's, Melbourne #214/R est:20000-30000 (A.D 17000)
£9375	$17531	€14063	Yam story 1 (92x122cm-36x48in) bears name.verso synthetic polymer paint linen prov. 26-Jul-4 Sotheby's, Melbourne #88/R est:25000-35000 (A.D 24000)
£9375	$17531	€14063	Yam dreaming (151x91cm-59x36in) bears name.verso synthetic polymer paint linen prov. 26-Jul-4 Sotheby's, Melbourne #244/R est:25000-35000 (A.D 24000)
£9375	$17531	€14063	Dried desert flowers (151x90cm-59x35in) synthetic polymer paint canvas prov. 26-Jul-4 Sotheby's, Melbourne #477/R est:18000-25000 (A.D 24000)
£9375	$17531	€14063	Untitled (152x91cm-60x36in) s.verso synthetic polymer paint canvas prov.exhib.lit. 26-Jul-4 Sotheby's, Melbourne #481/R est:20000-30000 (A.D 24000)
£10156	$18992	€15234	Alalgura, my country (121x90cm-48x35in) s. synthetic polymer paint canvas prov. 26-Jul-4 Sotheby's, Melbourne #248/R est:30000-40000 (A.D 26000)
£10163	$16057	€14736	Anooralya (151x121cm-59x48in) i.verso synthetic polymer paint linen prov.exhib.lit. 28-Jul-3 Sotheby's, Paddington #211/R est:25000-35000 (A.D 25000)
£10163	$16057	€14736	Desert flowers (151x121cm-59x48in) s.verso synthetic polymer paint linen prov.exhib.lit. 28-Jul-3 Sotheby's, Paddington #212/R est:30000-50000 (A.D 25000)
£10196	$18251	€14886	Alagura - My country (60x90cm-24x35in) synthetic polymer paint canvas exec 1989 prov. 25-May-4 Lawson Menzies, Sydney #44/R est:30000-40000 (A.D 26000)
£10569	$16699	€15325	Alatji bush tucker (152x121cm-60x48in) i.verso synthetic polymer paint linen prov.exhib. 28-Jul-3 Sotheby's, Paddington #207/R est:22000-28000 (A.D 26000)
£10569	$16699	€15325	Untitled, body paint (94x69cm-37x27in) i.d.29-9-95 verso synthetic polymer paint linen 2 prov.exhib.lit. 28-Jul-3 Sotheby's, Paddington #213/R est:20000-30000 (A.D 26000)
£10938	$20453	€16407	Yam story (120x91cm-47x36in) s.verso synthetic polymer paint canvas pair exhib.lit. 26-Jul-4 Sotheby's, Melbourne #211/R est:40000-60000 (A.D 28000)
£11066	$17926	€16156	Awelye (124x116cm-49x46in) i.verso synthetic polymer canvas prov. 30-Jul-3 Goodman, Sydney #41/R est:25000-35000 (A.D 27000)
£11382	$17984	€16504	Untitled (121x92cm-48x36in) i.verso synthetic polymer paint linen prov. 28-Jul-3 Sotheby's, Paddington #129/R est:20000-30000 (A.D 28000)
£11885	$19254	€17352	Yam dreaming (120x90cm-47x35in) i.verso synthetic polymer canvas prov. 30-Jul-3 Goodman, Sydney #37/R est:30000-40000 (A.D 29000)
£13281	$24836	€19922	Emu country (151x121cm-59x48in) bears name.verso synthetic polymer paint canvas prov.exhib.lit. 26-Jul-4 Sotheby's, Melbourne #213/R est:40000-60000 (A.D 34000)
£13333	$23867	€19466	Alalgura - May Contry - Muna, Everything (151x91cm-59x36in) synthetic polymer paint canvas exec 1993 prov. 25-May-4 Lawson Menzies, Sydney #35/R est:40000-60000 (A.D 34000)
£14063	$26297	€21095	Untitled, body paint (152x73cm-60x29in) bears name.d.1995 verso synthetic polymer paint canvas prov. 26-Jul-4 Sotheby's, Melbourne #116/R est:35000-45000 (A.D 36000)
£15625	$29219	€23438	Awelye (114x95cm-45x37in) bears name.d.1995 verso synthetic polymer paint polyester prov. 26-Jul-4 Sotheby's, Melbourne #117/R est:40000-60000 (A.D 40000)
£15625	$29219	€23438	Anoorlya awelye (122x92cm-48x36in) s.verso synthetic polymer paint linen prov. 26-Jul-4 Sotheby's, Melbourne #249/R est:40000-60000 (A.D 40000)
£16406	$30680	€24609	Winter exposition (204x122cm-80x48in) bears name.verso synthetic polymer paint linen prov. 26-Jul-4 Sotheby's, Melbourne #245/R est:50000-70000 (A.D 42000)
£18039	$32290	€26337	All the Country - It's whole lot everything (182x105cm-72x41in) synthetic polymer paint canvas exec 1996 prov. 25-May-4 Lawson Menzies, Sydney #40/R est:80000-100000 (A.D 46000)
£19141	$35793	€28712	Kame colour (152x91cm-60x36in) bears name.verso synthetic polymer paint canvas prov.exhib.lit. 26-Jul-4 Sotheby's, Melbourne #482/R est:50000-60000 (A.D 49000)
£21484	$40176	€32226	Untitled, yam (152x122cm-60x48in) synthetic polymer paint linen prov. 26-Jul-4 Sotheby's, Melbourne #186/R est:70000-100000 (A.D 55000)
£21777	$40724	€32666	Bush yam awelye (171x140cm-67x55in) i.verso synthetic polymer canvas exec. 1995-96 prov. 21-Jul-4 Shapiro, Sydney #43/R est:55000-75000 (A.D 55750)

£22461 $42002 €33692 Anooralya awelye (151x90cm-59x35in) synthetic polymer paint linen prov. 26-Jul-4 Sotheby's, Melbourne #250/R est:55000-75000 (A.D 57500)
£25203 $39569 €36544 My country, body paint (182x122cm-72x48in) i. synthetic polymer paint canvas prov. 26-Aug-3 Christie's, Sydney #108/R est:55000-75000 (A.D 62000)
£25391 $47480 €38087 Awelye (151x90cm-59x35in) bears name.verso synthetic polymer paint linen prov.exhib.lit. 26-Jul-4 Sotheby's, Melbourne #187/R est:80000-120000 (A.D 65000)
£26423 $41748 €38313 Anooralya yam (122x213cm-48x84in) synthetic polymer paint linen prov.exhib. 28-Jul-3 Sotheby's, Paddington #132/R est:60000-80000 (A.D 65000)
£26563 $49672 €39845 Kame colour (150x121cm-59x48in) bears name.verso synthetic polymer paint canvas prov.exhib.lit. 26-Jul-4 Sotheby's, Melbourne #215/R est:60000-80000 (A.D 68000)
£32422 $60629 €48633 Yam country (228x148cm-90x58in) synthetic polymer paint linen prov. 26-Jul-4 Sotheby's, Melbourne #118/R est:100000-150000 (A.D 83000)
£37109 $69395 €55664 Anooralya awelye (151x90cm-59x35in) bears name.verso synthetic polymer paint canvas prov.lit. 26-Jul-4 Sotheby's, Melbourne #89/R est:100000-150000 (A.D 95000)
£42683 $67439 €61890 Yam awelye (153x92cm-60x36in) s.verso synthetic polymer paint linen prov. 28-Jul-3 Sotheby's, Paddington #368/R est:10000-15000 (A.D 105000)
£48780 $77073 €70731 Awelye (152x121cm-60x48in) synthetic polymer paint linen prov. 28-Jul-3 Sotheby's, Paddington #130/R est:90000-120000 (A.D 120000)
£93750 $175313 €140625 Untitled (230x131cm-91x52in) bears name.verso synthetic polymer paint canvas prov. 26-Jul-4 Sotheby's, Melbourne #90/R est:150000-250000 (A.D 240000)
£162602 $256911 €235773 Untitled, spring celebration (130x230cm-51x91in) i.verso synthetic polymer paint linen prov.exhib. 28-Jul-3 Sotheby's, Paddington #131/R est:150000-200000 (A.D 400000)

KNGWARREYE, Lily (1937-2002) Australian
£1362 $2315 €1989 Untitled (137x183cm-54x72in) s.i.verso synthetic polymer paint canvas. 25-Nov-3 Christie's, Melbourne #192/R est:3000-5000 (A.D 3200)
Works on paper
£1406 $2630 €2109 Bush medicine leaves (125x83cm-49x33in) i.verso synthetic polymer linen exec. 2000 prov. 21-Jul-4 Shapiro, Sydney #85/R est:4000-6000 (A.D 3600)

KNIE, Rolf (jnr) (1949-) Swiss
Works on paper
£1379 $2469 €2013 Circus number with seals (29x34cm-11x13in) s.d.94 mixed media tent canvas. 14-May-4 Dobiaschofsky, Bern #260/R est:3500 (S.FR 3200)

KNIEP, Christoph Heinrich (1755-1825) German
Works on paper
£2303 $4237 €3500 Homage to Karl Theodor Korner (48x33cm-19x13in) i. pencil prov.exhib. 22-Jun-4 Sotheby's, Milan #68/R est:3500-4000

KNIGHT, A Roland (19th C) British
£400 $636 €580 Caught by a fly (36x56cm-14x22in) s. 9-Sep-3 Bonhams, Knightsbridge #154/R
£520 $931 €759 Salmon fishing - The gaff (40x61cm-16x24in) s. i.verso. 17-Mar-4 Bonhams, Chester #393
£600 $954 €870 Brown trout on a riverbank (35x52cm-14x20in) s. 9-Sep-3 Bonhams, Knightsbridge #147/R
£600 $954 €870 Still life of pike, brown trout and other fish on a river bank (41x61cm-16x24in) s. 9-Sep-3 Bonhams, Knightsbridge #148/R
£700 $1239 €1022 Two brown trout on a riverbank (45x100cm-18x39in) s. 27-Apr-4 Henry Adams, Chichester #768/R
£716 $1311 €1045 Group of dogs trying to get a dead otter (76x84cm-30x33in) s. 9-Jun-4 Rasmussen, Copenhagen #1694/R (D.KR 8000)
£800 $1272 €1160 Taking the bait. Netting a trout (35x56cm-14x22in) s. pair. 9-Sep-3 Bonhams, Knightsbridge #143/R
£1200 $1908 €1740 2 to 1 bar - pike and roach (46x82cm-18x32in) s. 9-Sep-3 Bonhams, Knightsbridge #152/R est:1200-1800
£1700 $2703 €2465 On the banks of the Tweed, salmon and trout (46x81cm-18x32in) s.i.verso. 9-Sep-3 Bonhams, Knightsbridge #151/R est:1500-2000
£1800 $3060 €2628 Still life of salmon, pike and other fish with fishing tackle (76x127cm-30x50in) s. 19-Nov-3 Tennants, Leyburn #1210/R est:1800-2200
£1900 $3021 €2755 Jack's breakfast. Twixt life and death. Nemesis or bitter end (41x61cm-16x24in) s.i.verso set of three. 9-Sep-3 Bonhams, Knightsbridge #146/R est:1500-2000
£8000 $14720 €11680 Perch. Salmon and trout. Roach. Pike. Barbel and Chubb. Trout the fist leap (13x22cm-5x9in) five s. one init. board set of six. 10-Jun-4 Christie's, Kensington #232/R est:4000-6000

KNIGHT, Adah (fl.1887-1928) British
£1150 $2128 €1679 Ecce Ancilla Dominci (71x40cm-28x16in) i. stretcher after Rossetti. 16-Feb-4 Bonhams, Bath #74 est:150-250

KNIGHT, Adah (attrib) (fl.1887-1928) British
£820 $1509 €1197 Needlework (75x55cm-30x22in) s.d.1908. 29-Mar-4 Bonhams, Bath #102/R

KNIGHT, Adam (1855-1931) British
Works on paper
£250 $398 €363 Home from the sea (28x37cm-11x15in) s. W/C. 14-Sep-3 Lots Road Auctions, London #338

KNIGHT, Charles (19/20th C) British
£500 $920 €730 Greenhouses behind Marlborough buildings, Bath (47x36cm-19x14in) canvasboard prov. 14-Jun-4 Bonhams, Bath #199
Works on paper
£350 $616 €511 On the Wye (24x34cm-9x13in) i. W/C. 18-May-4 Bonhams, Knightsbridge #116/R

KNIGHT, Charles Parsons (1829-1897) British
£950 $1501 €1387 Sailing ships in heavy seas off-shore (13x20cm-5x8in) s. board pair. 23-Jul-3 Grant, Worcester #493

KNIGHT, Dame Laura (1877-1970) British
£320 $534 €467 Study of clowns (36x25cm-14x10in) 21-Oct-3 Gorringes, Lewes #2138/R
£6200 $11098 €9052 Bathing Gilderoy (37x46cm-15x18in) s. panel prov. 16-Mar-4 Bonhams, New Bond Street #40/R est:5000-7000
£7200 $12384 €10512 His only home (63x76cm-25x30in) s. 2-Dec-3 Bonhams, New Bond Street #13/R est:8000-12000
£10460 $18933 €15272 The maiden (61x50cm-24x20in) s.i. prov.exhib.lit. 1-Apr-4 Heffel, Vancouver #63/R est:13000-16000 (C.D 25000)
£16000 $29280 €23360 Ice hockey (63x76cm-25x30in) s. prov. 2-Jun-4 Sotheby's, London #39/R est:15000-20000
£17000 $30600 €24820 Cottage interior with young girl seated beside a fire toasting bread (34x40cm-13x16in) s. 21-Apr-4 Tennants, Leyburn #1270/R est:8000-10000
£80000 $146400 €116800 Sennen Cove (51x61cm-20x24in) s. prov. 2-Jun-4 Sotheby's, London #16/R est:80000-120000
Works on paper
£250 $418 €365 Portrait of a clown (23x28cm-9x11in) s. black chk. 8-Oct-3 Andrew Hartley, Ilkley #1013/R
£250 $418 €365 Harem (23x18cm-9x7in) s.i. pencil sketch. 26-Oct-3 Tayler & Fletcher, Cheltenham #1
£260 $416 €380 Sketch of a group of standing figures (16x27cm-6x11in) s. pencil prov. 16-Sep-3 Rosebery Fine Art, London #537
£290 $481 €423 Dancer (35x20cm-14x8in) s. ink. 2-Oct-3 Lane, Penzance #194
£300 $510 €438 Pavlova, practice at the bar (29x20cm-11x8in) s.i. pencil. 4-Nov-3 Rowley Fine Art, Newmarket #378
£320 $534 €467 Doey (10x14cm-4x6in) s.i.d.1941 pencil prov. 16-Oct-3 Christie's, Kensington #243
£320 $592 €467 Circus elephant (23x18cm-9x7in) s. pencil. 12-Feb-4 Andrew Hartley, Ilkley #750
£350 $637 €511 Chinese acrobat (25x41cm-10x16in) s.i. pencil. 16-Jun-4 Andrew Hartley, Ilkley #955/R
£390 $686 €569 Study of a circus elephant (14x18cm-6x7in) s. pencil sketch. 18-May-4 Fellows & Sons, Birmingham #298/R
£400 $728 €584 Chinese boy (30x20cm-12x8in) s.d.1921 pencil chl. 15-Jun-4 David Lay, Penzance #17
£440 $823 €642 Recumbent black and white cat licking its paw. init.i. pencil. 24-Feb-4 Wotton Auction Rooms, Wotton #792
£450 $833 €657 Portrait of Dame Edith Evans (23x21cm-9x8in) s. pencil pen brush ink. 11-Mar-4 Christie's, Kensington #3/R
£480 $878 €720 Ballerina dancing (20x23cm-8x9in) s. pencil prov. 30-Jul-4 Bigwood, Stratford on Avon #352
£500 $835 €730 Circus ring (26x34cm-10x13in) s. pencil. 21-Oct-3 Bonhams, Knightsbridge #10/R
£500 $915 €730 Ring master (27x18cm-11x7in) s. pencil. 3-Jun-4 Lane, Penzance #51
£550 $1012 €803 Studies of a horse (25x35cm-10x14in) s. pencil pair. 29-Mar-4 Bonhams, Bath #42
£600 $1002 €876 Photographs in the theatre (24x30cm-9x12in) init. conte. 21-Oct-3 Bonhams, Knightsbridge #5/R
£600 $1092 €876 Ballet dancer (30x21cm-12x8in) s. pencil. 1-Jul-4 Christie's, Kensington #4/R
£620 $1029 €905 Seated figure of a girl (25x20cm-10x8in) s. chl prov. 2-Oct-3 Lane, Penzance #109
£700 $1169 €1022 Arabesque (38x50cm-15x20in) s.i. pencil chl. 16-Oct-3 Christie's, Kensington #241
£700 $1295 €1022 Ballerina (29x21cm-11x8in) s. prov. 10-Mar-4 British Auctioneer #504/R
£700 $1274 €1022 Behind the scenes at the Old Vic (35x25cm-14x10in) s.i. chl. 1-Jul-4 Mellors & Kirk, Nottingham #707/R
£750 $1193 €1095 Hans (37x26cm-15x10in) s.i. pencil. 10-Sep-3 Sotheby's, Olympia #139/R
£750 $1365 €1095 Study of a man seated at a table (25x18cm-10x7in) s. pencil chk W/C prov. 1-Jul-4 Christie's, Kensington #7/R
£750 $1373 €1095 Circus elephant (33x25cm-13x10in) s. chl. 8-Jul-4 Duke & Son, Dorchester #67/R
£780 $1225 €1139 Human serpent (8x11cm-3x4in) chl. 31-Aug-3 Paul Beighton, Rotherham #534/R
£800 $1456 €1168 Circus elephants (28x20cm-11x8in) s. pencil. 15-Jun-4 David Lay, Penzance #89/R
£1050 $1754 €1533 Old Vic (35x25cm-14x10in) s.i.d.47 chl. 16-Oct-3 Christie's, Kensington #250/R est:800-1200
£1250 $1988 €1825 Quiet read (25x20cm-10x8in) s. W/C crayon. 12-Sep-3 Gardiner & Houlgate, Bath #70/R est:800-1200
£2200 $3784 €3212 Ballerina (34x25cm-13x10in) s. pencil. 3-Dec-3 Christie's, Kensington #423/R est:700-1000
£2200 $3740 €3212 Orchestra (36x26cm-14x10in) s.i. chl prov. 20-Nov-3 Christie's, London #187/R est:1500-2000
£2300 $4209 €3358 The ringmaster (36x26cm-14x10in) s.i. chl. 28-Jan-4 Hampton & Littlewood, Exeter #371/R est:1500-2000
£2400 $3816 €3504 Clown (33x23cm-13x9in) init.i.d.1920 crayon. 10-Sep-3 Sotheby's, Olympia #138/R est:1500-2000
£2400 $4128 €3504 Ballerina in her dressing room (43x35cm-17x14in) s. conte prov. 2-Dec-3 Bonhams, New Bond Street #44/R est:800-1200
£2500 $4025 €3625 Como's circus, Southsea (18x13cm-7x5in) s.d.October 1929 W/C pastel. 15-Aug-3 Keys, Aylsham #585/R est:2500-3000
£2600 $4862 €3900 Rainbow and storm over a rural landscape (72x81cm-28x32in) s.d.1950 W/C possibly exhib. 26-Jul-4 Bonhams, Bath #29/R est:2500-3500
£3200 $5440 €4672 Goliath the Clown (35x25cm-14x10in) s. chl col chks prov. 20-Nov-3 Christie's, London #190/R est:2500-3500
£3500 $6405 €5110 Fair at night (34x25cm-13x10in) s. i. verso blk ink W/C. 3-Jun-4 Christie's, London #198/R est:3000-5000
£4000 $7400 €5840 Seated clown (36x25cm-14x10in) s. chl. 10-Feb-4 David Lay, Penzance #528/R est:4000-5000
£4800 $8880 €7008 Clowns (36x25cm-14x10in) s. W/C. 10-Feb-4 David Lay, Penzance #527/R est:4000-5000
£5000 $9150 €7300 Ready for entrance (26x36cm-10x14in) s. s.i.verso pencil chl W/C prov. 3-Jun-4 Christie's, London #197/R est:5000-8000
£5200 $8840 €7592 Major Atherley (46x52cm-18x20in) s.d.1932 chk W/C. 1-Dec-3 Bonhams, Bath #54/R est:4000-6000
£5200 $9724 €7800 Ploughing (38x28cm-15x11in) s. col chl prov.lit. 21-Jul-4 John Nicholson, Haslemere #163/R est:2000-4000

KNIGHT, Daniel Ridgway (1839-1924) American

£2989	$5500	€4364	Punts on a river (45x75cm-18x30in) s. 27-Jun-4 Freeman, Philadelphia #79/R est:5000-8000
£3593	$6000	€5246	Peasant girl, Picardy (56x47cm-22x19in) s.i.d.1917 stretcher prov. 7-Oct-3 Sotheby's, New York #182 est:8000-12000
£39773	$70000	€58069	Returning home (56x46cm-22x18in) s.i. prov. 18-May-4 Christie's, Rockefeller NY #30/R est:30000-50000
£44118	$75000	€64412	La Seine a Vernon (66x82cm-26x32in) s.i. prov. 29-Oct-3 Christie's, Rockefeller NY #145/R est:80000-120000
£49419	$85000	€72152	Young girl holding puppy (118x91cm-46x36in) s.i. 4-Dec-3 Christie's, Rockefeller NY #57/R est:100000-150000
£56604	$90000	€82642	In her garden (82x66cm-32x26in) s.i. 12-Sep-3 Skinner, Boston #349/R est:100000-150000
£83333	$150000	€121666	Far away thoughts (117x84cm-46x33in) s.i. 22-Apr-4 Christie's, Rockefeller NY #136/R est:100000-150000
£94118	$160000	€137412	La flaneuse (198x130cm-78x51in) s.d.1893 prov.exhib. 29-Oct-3 Christie's, Rockefeller NY #152/R est:180000-220000
£111111	$185556	€160000	Deux jeunes filles sur les bords de la Seine (73x92cm-29x36in) s.i. 22-Oct-3 Ribeyre & Baron, Paris #33/R est:60000-90000
£233333	$420000	€340666	Gathering lilacs (118x91cm-46x36in) s.i. prov. 22-Apr-4 Christie's, Rockefeller NY #139/R est:300000-400000
Works on paper			
£509	$850	€743	Seascape (25x36cm-10x14in) s. W/C. 16-Nov-3 Bonhams & Butterfields, Los Angeles #7025/R
£2300	$4071	€3358	Awaiting the return (27x37cm-11x15in) s. W/C. 27-Apr-4 Bonhams, New Bond Street #111/R est:2000-3000
£3600	$6588	€5256	Figures drinking outside a woodland cottage (43x58cm-17x23in) s.d.1881 W/C bodycol. 8-Jul-4 Duke & Son, Dorchester #75/R est:3000-4000

KNIGHT, Edwin (?) British?

£581	$1000	€848	Off Blackwall (30x61cm-12x24in) s. 7-Dec-3 Grogan, Boston #51/R

KNIGHT, Ernest (20th C) British?

£600	$1074	€876	Mandraki harbour, Rhodes (41x51cm-16x20in) s.d.73. 18-Mar-4 Christie's, Kensington #641/R

KNIGHT, George (19th C) British

£260	$468	€380	Fishing boats off a coastline (25x35cm-10x14in) s. 21-Apr-4 Tennants, Leyburn #1104
£420	$769	€613	Fishing vessels off the coast (30x61cm-12x24in) s.d.68. 7-Apr-4 Bonhams, Bury St Edmunds #447
£450	$792	€657	Shipping off the coastline (40x61cm-16x24in) s. 19-May-4 Christie's, Kensington #579/R
£600	$1002	€876	Fishing boats off a coastline (50x76cm-20x30in) s. 11-Nov-3 Bonhams, Knightsbridge #223/R
£650	$1164	€949	Fishing fleet off the harbour mouth (41x61cm-16x24in) s. 26-May-4 Christie's, Kensington #698/R
£700	$1113	€1015	Off the coast (51x76cm-20x30in) s. 9-Sep-3 David Duggleby, Scarborough #383
£900	$1503	€1314	Fishing boats (28x58cm-11x23in) s. prov. 17-Oct-3 Keys, Aylsham #707
£2200	$3674	€3212	Fishing fleet heading out. Fishing fleet running into harbour (25x46cm-10x18in) one indis.sig. pair. 8-Oct-3 Christie's, Kensington #736/R est:600-800
£3200	$5856	€4672	Barges in heavy swell off the coast (76x128cm-30x50in) one s.d.92 pair. 6-Apr-4 Bonhams, Knightsbridge #190/R est:1000-1500

KNIGHT, Gwen (19/20th C) New Zealander

£313	$497	€457	Road to Whitlanga (39x48cm-15x19in) s. 1-May-3 Dunbar Sloane, Wellington #388 (NZ.D 900)
£347	$552	€507	Spring landscape (34x42cm-13x17in) s. board. 1-May-3 Dunbar Sloane, Wellington #469 est:300-500 (NZ.D 1000)
£602	$1023	€879	Tree lined river bank (36x47cm-14x19in) prov. 26-Nov-3 Dunbar Sloane, Wellington #94 est:1200-1800 (NZ.D 1600)
£606	$1084	€885	Riverbank with willows (44x54cm-17x21in) s. board. 12-May-4 Dunbar Sloane, Wellington #185/R est:2000-4000 (NZ.D 1750)
£761	$1363	€1111	Golden Harbour view through trees (37x90cm-15x35in) s. board. 12-May-4 Dunbar Sloane, Wellington #184 est:2000-4000 (NZ.D 2200)

KNIGHT, Harold (1874-1961) British

£780	$1412	€1139	Lady seated reading a book (46x58cm-18x23in) s. 16-Apr-4 Keys, Aylsham #823
£1500	$2385	€2190	Portrait of a lady, said to be Laura Knight's mother (51x41cm-20x16in) s. i.verso. 10-Sep-3 Sotheby's, Olympia #158/R est:1500-2000
£1800	$2862	€2628	Bride (76x63cm-30x25in) 10-Sep-3 Sotheby's, Olympia #201/R est:1000-1500
£8000	$14400	€11680	Study of young Dutch girl seated beside window (35x25cm-14x10in) s. canvasboard. 21-Apr-4 Tennants, Leyburn #1269/R est:4000-5000
£95000	$161500	€138700	Morning sun (77x64cm-30x25in) s.i. prov.exhib.lit. 21-Nov-3 Christie's, London #39/R est:80000-120000

KNIGHT, John Buxton (1843-1908) British

£950	$1767	€1387	Harbour at low tide (30x41cm-12x16in) s. 4-Mar-4 Christie's, Kensington #488/R
Works on paper			
£400	$688	€584	Old breakwater near Ventnor, Isle of Wight (24x41cm-9x16in) s. W/C gouache. 2-Dec-3 Sotheby's, London #115/R

KNIGHT, Joseph (1837-1909) British

£260	$413	€380	Sandy road (28x39cm-11x15in) s.d.1895. 18-Mar-3 Anderson & Garland, Newcastle #358
£400	$668	€584	Morning mist (36x43cm-14x17in) s.d.79 board. 13-Nov-3 Christie's, Kensington #132/R
Works on paper			
£650	$1216	€949	Autumn (22x18cm-9x7in) s.d.1884 W/C. 25-Feb-4 Mallams, Oxford #204/R

KNIGHT, Ken (1956-) Australian

£830	$1386	€1245	Above Chinamen's Beach (23x84cm-9x33in) s. board. 27-Oct-3 Goodman, Sydney #239/R (A.D 2000)

KNIGHT, Louis Aston (1873-1948) American

£531	$850	€775	Neo-classical building (33x25cm-13x10in) s. board. 16-Sep-3 Lincoln, Orange #96
£703	$1300	€1026	Autumn landscape (69x56cm-27x22in) s. 18-Jul-4 William Jenack, New York #139 est:2000-3000
£867	$1500	€1266	Flowers on the riverbank (25x18cm-10x7in) s. i.verso board. 13-Dec-3 Sloans & Kenyon, Bethesda #805/R est:1200-1500
£1944	$3130	€2838	Sunset over river (13x36cm-5x14in) s. panel. 20-Aug-3 James Julia, Fairfield #1275/R est:3500-4000
£3631	$6500	€5301	Cottage in Normandy (28x36cm-11x14in) s.i. panel. 20-Mar-4 Selkirks, St. Louis #159/R est:7000-9000
£4078	$7300	€5954	Cottage in Rancon (28x36cm-11x14in) s.i. panel. 20-Mar-4 Selkirks, St. Louis #158/R est:7500-9500
£4396	$8000	€6418	Warson House, Oldwick New Jersey (91x81cm-36x32in) s.i. 29-Jun-4 Sotheby's, New York #214/R est:6000-8000
£6471	$11000	€9448	French street scene, with gothic spires (56x46cm-22x18in) s. i.verso. 8-Nov-3 Van Blarcom, South Natick #132/R est:2000-3000
£8108	$15000	€11838	On the river (65x81cm-26x32in) s.i. painted c.1920-1930 prov. 11-Mar-4 Christie's, Rockefeller NY #38/R est:15000-25000
£10270	$19000	€14994	View of Rouen (65x81cm-26x32in) s.i. painted c.1920-1930 prov. 11-Mar-4 Christie's, Rockefeller NY #35/R est:20000-30000
£17442	$30000	€25465	Above the mill (65x81cm-26x32in) s. 3-Dec-3 Sotheby's, New York #15/R est:15000-20000
Works on paper			
£795	$1486	€1200	La roseraie (27x46cm-11x18in) s. pastel. 24-Jul-4 Thierry & Lannon, Brest #103/R

KNIGHT, Robert T (1827-?) American

£495	$900	€723	Hudson River Valley landscape (28x20cm-11x8in) mono. board. 7-Feb-4 Neal Auction Company, New Orleans #778

KNIGHT, Roland (?) British?

£820	$1443	€1197	A naval engagement, a pike taking a mallard (39x61cm-15x24in) s.i.verso. 18-May-4 Woolley & Wallis, Salisbury #138/R

KNIGHT, Sophie (1965-) British

£520	$868	€759	Pulpit (190x120cm-75x47in) 21-Oct-3 Bonhams, Knightsbridge #83/R

KNIKKER, Aris (1887-1962) Dutch

£284	$474	€400	In the kitchen garden (30x40cm-12x16in) s. 20-Oct-3 Glerum, Amsterdam #139/R
£300	$546	€450	Polder landscape with farm (20x33cm-8x13in) s. 30-Jun-4 Vendue Huis, Gravenhage #150
£315	$541	€450	Peep through (29x23cm-11x9in) s. 8-Dec-3 Glerum, Amsterdam #90/R
£382	$603	€550	Canal landscape with fishermen (30x43cm-12x17in) s. 6-Sep-3 Arnold, Frankfurt #599/R
£548	$932	€800	Polder landscape with mill (38x58cm-15x23in) s. 5-Nov-3 Vendue Huis, Gravenhage #154
£616	$1048	€900	Woman and child on village lane (68x58cm-27x23in) s. 5-Nov-3 Vendue Huis, Gravenhage #155/R
£709	$1184	€1000	Bord de riviere (30x51cm-12x20in) s. panel. 15-Oct-3 Hotel des Ventes Mosan, Brussels #230
£759	$1267	€1100	Fisherman at the forest brook (89x59cm-35x23in) s. 11-Nov-3 Vendu Notarishuis, Rotterdam #6
£816	$1486	€1200	Punter at work in a polder landscape (56x96cm-22x38in) s. indis d. 3-Feb-4 Christie's, Amsterdam #258/R est:1500-2000
£855	$1574	€1300	By a bridge (30x40cm-12x16in) s. 22-Jun-4 Christie's, Amsterdam #249/R
£1027	$1747	€1500	Farmer in rowing boat (78x58cm-31x23in) s. 5-Nov-3 Vendue Huis, Gravenhage #153/R est:1500-2000

KNIKKER, Jan (jnr) (1911-1990) Dutch

£280	$467	€400	Moored boats in a polder landscape (35x51cm-14x20in) s. 30-Jun-3 Sotheby's, Amsterdam #280/R
£300	$546	€450	Dutch village on the water's edge (28x38cm-11x15in) s. 30-Jun-4 Vendue Huis, Gravenhage #165
£307	$513	€440	Roses in a vase (24x30cm-9x12in) s. 30-Jun-3 Sotheby's, Amsterdam #406
£400	$728	€600	Maas lock (28x38cm-11x15in) s. 30-Jun-4 Vendue Huis, Gravenhage #313/R
£461	$834	€700	Polder landscape with a footbridge over a canal, possibly Giethoorn (58x78cm-23x31in) s. 19-Apr-4 Glerum, Amsterdam #235/R
£600	$1092	€876	Ships and tugs in the harbour (51x69cm-20x27in) s. 16-Jun-4 John Nicholson, Haslemere #756
£724	$1310	€1100	View of the Singel and Munt Tower with flower sellers in the foreground (34x44cm-13x17in) s. prov. 19-Apr-4 Glerum, Amsterdam #185/R
£1049	$1804	€1500	View of Leidschendam (50x70cm-20x28in) s. 7-Dec-3 Sotheby's, Amsterdam #652/R
£1361	$2435	€2000	Flower market in Amsterdam (51x70cm-20x28in) 17-Mar-4 De Zwann, Amsterdam #4593/R est:2000-3000

KNIKKER, Jan (snr) (1889-1957) Dutch

£319	$533	€450	Stately lake view (40x80cm-16x31in) s. 20-Oct-3 Glerum, Amsterdam #163
£342	$629	€520	Polder landscape (31x45cm-12x18in) s. 28-Jun-4 Sotheby's, Amsterdam #156/R
£342	$629	€520	Farmhouse in a Polder landscape (30x40cm-12x16in) s. 28-Jun-4 Sotheby's, Amsterdam #157/R
£454	$759	€650	View of a polder landscape (30x40cm-12x16in) s. 30-Jun-3 Sotheby's, Amsterdam #201/R
£461	$834	€700	Landscape with farmer ploughing (45x61cm-18x24in) s. 19-Apr-4 Glerum, Amsterdam #196
£658	$1211	€1000	Lunschoten near Montvoort (30x40cm-12x16in) s. 22-Jun-4 Christie's, Amsterdam #251/R
£1020	$1857	€1500	By the windmill (41x61cm-16x24in) s. 3-Feb-4 Christie's, Amsterdam #185/R est:1200-1600

£1497 $2724 €2200 Panoramic landscape with cows along a river (60x100cm-24x39in) s. 3-Feb-4 Christie's, Amsterdam #267/R est:2500-3500

KNIP, August (1819-?) Dutch
£1259 $2102 €1800 Poultry yard (50x42cm-20x17in) s. oval. 9-Oct-3 Michael Zeller, Lindau #636/R est:1500

KNIP, August (attrib) (1819-?) Dutch
£4054 $7135 €6000 Wooded hilly landscape with a shepherd resting in a grotto (46x56cm-18x22in) 18-May-4 Sotheby's, Amsterdam #118/R est:6000-8000

KNIP, H G (1783-1842) Dutch
£1103 $1843 €1600 Nature morte aux fleurs (53x40cm-21x16in) mono. 17-Nov-3 Bernaerts, Antwerp #139/R est:1250-1500

KNIP, Henri (1819-1897) Dutch
£512 $958 €748 By the farm (50x72cm-20x28in) s.d.1836. 29-Feb-4 Uppsala Auktionskammare, Uppsala #364 (S.KR 7000)
Works on paper
£559 $934 €800 Peasant woman and her livestock crossing a bridge (19x24cm-7x9in) W/C. 30-Jun-3 Sotheby's, Amsterdam #119/R
£658 $1211 €1000 Shepherdess with her flock in a mountainous landscape (49x74cm-19x29in) s. W/C gouache. 28-Jun-4 Sotheby's, Amsterdam #2/R
£1333 $2400 €2000 Mountainous landscape (49x57cm-19x22in) s. W/C gouache. 20-Apr-4 Sotheby's, Amsterdam #17/R est:2000-3000
£3087 $5681 €4600 View of Helmond Castle. View of Hedel Church (48x71cm-19x28in) s. gouache two. 29-Mar-4 Glerum, Amsterdam #156 est:2200-2500

KNIP, Josephus Augustus (1777-1847) Dutch
£364 $663 €550 Paysage avec riviere, pecheurs et ruines (15x19cm-6x7in) copper. 15-Jun-4 Galerie Moderne, Brussels #158/R
£2639 $4169 €3800 Oxen resting by the lakeside, Italy (57x63cm-22x25in) s.d.1815. 2-Sep-3 Christie's, Amsterdam #152/R est:2500-3500
Works on paper
£1944 $3500 €2838 Confluence of the rivers Talfer and Eisak at Bolzano (36x54cm-14x21in) i.verso bodycol pen. 22-Jan-4 Christie's, Rockefeller NY #223/R est:4000-6000
£2397 $4075 €3500 Extensive landscape with peasants and a priest by a fountain (56x43cm-22x17in) black chk bodycol. 5-Nov-3 Christie's, Amsterdam #138/R est:4000-6000
£2397 $4075 €3500 Extensive landscape with travellers at a roadside shrine, steep gorge b eyond (73x56cm-29x22in) black chk bodycol. 5-Nov-3 Christie's, Amsterdam #139/R est:4000-6000
£3041 $5351 €4500 Studies of monks and clerics, including Carthusians and Franciscans (35x24cm-14x9in) bears i.verso pen grey ink W/C black chk exhib.lit. 19-May-4 Sotheby's, Amsterdam #326/R est:1500-2000
£4795 $8151 €7000 Ruined chapel with a pig sty, poultry and peacock (52x63cm-20x25in) black chk bodycol. 5-Nov-3 Christie's, Amsterdam #135/R est:4000-6000
£5743 $10108 €8500 Farm buildings by a woodland path (40x58cm-16x23in) W/C gouache prov. 19-May-4 Sotheby's, Amsterdam #278/R est:5000-7000
£10811 $19027 €16000 Landscape near Galloro, with traveller on a wooded road and a fountain (28x44cm-11x17in) i. grey wash W/C black chk prov.exhib.lit. 19-May-4 Sotheby's, Amsterdam #327/R est:3500-4500
£23649 $41622 €35000 Palace of the Caesars, Rome (36x50cm-14x20in) i. brush grey ink W/C black chk prov.exhib.lit. 19-May-4 Sotheby's, Amsterdam #324/R est:12000-18000
£23649 $41622 €35000 Aqueduct of Nero, Rome (36x51cm-14x20in) i. W/C black chk prov.exhib.lit. 19-May-4 Sotheby's, Amsterdam #325/R est:9000-12000
£37162 $65405 €55000 Basilica of Constantine and Maxentius, Rome (35x51cm-14x20in) i. pen grey ink W/C black chk prov.exhib. 19-May-4 Sotheby's, Amsterdam #333/R est:7500-9000
£74324 $130811 €110000 Temple of Minerva Medica, Rome (44x59cm-17x23in) i. W/C black lead black chk prov.exhib.lit. 19-May-4 Sotheby's, Amsterdam #323/R est:18000-22000

KNIP, Matthys Dirk (1785-1845) Dutch
Works on paper
£1769 $3166 €2600 Un parc avec un jet d'eau dans un bassin entoure de figures et animaux (29x36cm-11x14in) pen brown ink W/C gouache. 18-Mar-4 Christie's, Paris #198/R est:2000-3000
£2113 $3697 €3000 Vue de Coblence (50x71cm-20x28in) s. gouache. 18-Dec-3 Tajan, Paris #134/R est:3000-4000
£4500 $8235 €6570 Mountainous river landscape with sailing boats. Ships on choppy sea by lighthouse (51x72cm-20x28in) s. W/C bodycol pair. 6-Jul-4 Christie's, London #191/R est:5000-7000

KNIP, Willem (1883-1967) Dutch
£451 $736 €650 Shepherd with his flock (40x60cm-16x24in) s. 29-Sep-3 Sotheby's, Amsterdam #124/R
£625 $987 €900 In de haven van Concarneau, France (29x38cm-11x15in) s. s.i.verso plywood. 2-Sep-3 Christie's, Amsterdam #311
£685 $1164 €1000 Fishing smack near Veere (22x30cm-9x12in) s. 5-Nov-3 Vendue Huis, Gravenhage #266
£855 $1574 €1300 A view in Paris (40x50cm-16x20in) s. 22-Jun-4 Christie's, Amsterdam #199/R
£1164 $1979 €1700 Prince Henry quay , Amsterdam (39x49cm-15x19in) s. 5-Nov-3 Vendue Huis, Gravenhage #268/R est:1000-1400
£1208 $2235 €1800 View of Pont Neuf (54x65cm-21x26in) s. 15-Mar-4 Sotheby's, Amsterdam #114/R est:800-1200
£1316 $2421 €2000 View of San Marco, Venice (52x41cm-20x16in) s. 28-Jun-4 Sotheby's, Amsterdam #129/R est:2000-3000
£1842 $3389 €2800 Shipping on the Ij, Amsterdam (38x80cm-15x31in) s. 22-Jun-4 Christie's, Amsterdam #236/R est:2000-3000

KNIP, Willem (attrib) (1883-1967) Dutch
£699 $1168 €1000 City view of Paris (50x60cm-20x24in) s. 10-Oct-3 Vendue Huis, Gravenhage #818

KNIZEK, Emanuel (1889-?) Czechoslovakian
£422 $742 €633 Prague (60x80cm-24x31in) s. hardboard. 22-May-4 Dorotheum, Prague #110/R est:20000-30000 (C.KR 20000)

KNOBLOCH, Josef Rolf (1891-1964) Czechoslovakian
£267 $491 €400 Porto Finare (34x46cm-13x18in) s.i.d.56 masonite. 9-Jun-4 Dorotheum, Salzburg #612/R
£267 $485 €400 Landscape with lake, horse wagon and mountains in distance (60x80cm-24x31in) s. 1-Jul-4 Weidler, Nurnberg #320/R
£272 $495 €400 Grain harvest (25x30cm-10x12in) s.i.d.63 panel. 4-Feb-4 Neumeister, Munich #716/R
£276 $461 €400 Dinkelsbuhl (25x29cm-10x11in) s. board. 9-Jul-3 Hugo Ruef, Munich #119
£310 $518 €450 Normannen-Kastell Majori (50x34cm-20x13in) s.i. board. 9-Jul-3 Hugo Ruef, Munich #122
£367 $675 €550 Women gathering wood in forest clearing (38x58cm-15x23in) s.i. board. 9-Jun-4 Dorotheum, Salzburg #617/R
£625 $1031 €900 Moor in pre alpine landscape (70x100cm-28x39in) s. i. verso. 3-Jul-3 Neumeister, Munich #2865
£1361 $2435 €2000 Storm gathering over Kloster Reutberg (50x80cm-20x31in) s.i. panel. 17-Mar-4 Neumeister, Munich #502/R est:2000

KNOEBEL, Imi (1940-) German
£1259 $2140 €1800 Untitled (54x38cm-21x15in) s.d. verso acrylic board. 27-Nov-3 Lempertz, Koln #230/R est:1800
£2267 $4057 €3400 Untitled (99x70cm-39x28in) s.d. collage. 15-May-4 Dr Sturies, Dusseldorf #111/R
£3333 $6100 €5000 Untitled (119x100cm-47x39in) s.d.89 acrylic varnish bord transparent foil. 4-Jun-4 Lempertz, Koln #262/R est:5000
£3472 $5799 €5000 Untitled (99x70cm-39x28in) s.mono.d. acrylic paper on board prov. 24-Oct-3 Ketterer, Hamburg #431/R est:5500-6000
£3774 $6113 €5510 Untitled (100x70cm-39x28in) s.d.1980 acrylic board prov. 24-May-3 Burkhard, Luzern #169/R est:8000-12000 (S.FR 8000)
£4545 $7727 €6500 Untitled (104x75cm-41x30in) s.d.90 verso acrylic scratching panel. 27-Nov-3 Lempertz, Koln #229/R est:7000
£5000 $9100 €7300 Untitled (140x100cm-55x39in) s.d.90 acrylic plastic film card blk tape collage cardboard prov. 5-Feb-4 Christie's, London #192/R est:6000-8000
£10778 $18000 €15736 Figurenbild (237x170cm-93x67in) s.d.89 acrylic on wood prov. 14-Nov-3 Phillips, New York #152/R est:20000-30000
£13473 $22500 €19671 Constellation B (331x327cm-130x129in) init.d.87 verso panel four parts prov. 13-Nov-3 Sotheby's, New York #578/R est:12000-18000
£14000 $23380 €20440 39A, 39B, 39C, 39D (170x249cm-67x98in) init.i.d.86 acrylic four attached wood panels prov. 22-Oct-3 Christie's, London #98/R est:18000-22000
£17333 $31027 €26000 Untitled (200x150cm-79x59in) s.i.d. verso varnish hardfibre prov.lit. 14-May-4 Ketterer, Munich #265/R est:26000-32000
Sculpture
£14525 $26000 €21207 Kammerstuck (325x250x125cm-128x98x49in) cabinet metal rod prov.exhib.lit. 14-May-4 Phillips, New York #276/R est:10000-15000
Works on paper
£2793 $5000 €4078 Untitled, messerschnitt (99x56cm-39x22in) s.d.77 cut paper collage two works prov. 14-May-4 Phillips, New York #277/R est:6000-8000

KNOEBEL, Robert (1874-1924) Czechoslovakian
£268 $494 €400 Boys playing in summer landscape (56x81cm-22x32in) s.d.49. 27-Mar-4 L & B, Essen #136/R
£331 $603 €500 Portrait of a young lady with bare shoulders (50x40cm-20x16in) s. 18-Jun-4 Bolland & Marotz, Bremen #660/R

KNOEPFLER, Alphonse (19/20th C) ?
£313 $500 €457 Place of theatre Francais on Paris (65x81cm-26x32in) mono. 20-Sep-3 Harvey Clar, Oakland #1710

KNOFF, Johan (1935-) Norwegian
£278 $481 €406 Woman wearing red dress (115x155cm-45x61in) s. 13-Dec-3 Blomqvist, Lysaker #1208 (N.KR 3200)
£301 $503 €439 Woman wearing red dress (115x155cm-45x61in) s. 20-Oct-3 Blomqvist, Lysaker #1170/R (N.KR 3500)
£489 $876 €714 Mean Street 1978 (96x121cm-38x48in) s.d.78 i.stretcher. 25-May-4 Grev Wedels Plass, Oslo #113/R (N.KR 6000)
£674 $1240 €984 Memories of summer (90x120cm-35x47in) s. painted c.1992/93. 29-Mar-4 Blomqvist, Lysaker #1164 (N.KR 8500)

KNOLL, Waldemar (1839-1909) German
£3357 $5606 €4800 Roaring river in the Caucasus (76x111cm-30x44in) s. 9-Oct-3 Michael Zeller, Lindau #637/R est:4800

KNOLLER, Martin (1725-1804) Austrian
£6897 $11517 €10000 Education of Maria (81x61cm-32x24in) s.d. prov. 15-Nov-3 Lempertz, Koln #1076/R est:12000

KNOOP, August (1856-1900) German
£347 $566 €500 Geographer (27x20cm-11x8in) s. panel. 26-Sep-3 Bolland & Marotz, Bremen #561/R
£412 $750 €618 Portrait of seated cavalier drinking wine (30x23cm-12x9in) s. 16-Jun-4 Wolf's, New York #486747/R
£420 $713 €600 Gentleman playing chess (22x15cm-9x6in) s. panel. 28-Nov-3 Wendl, Rudolstadt #4031/R
£923 $1588 €1348 Cardinal studying Crucifixion scene (25x35cm-10x14in) s. panel. 3-Dec-3 AB Stockholms Auktionsverk #2622/R (S.KR 12000)
£1259 $2165 €1800 Elegant cavalier in 18th century dress (25x18cm-10x7in) s.d.1902 panel. 5-Dec-3 Michael Zeller, Lindau #669/R est:1800
£1284 $2298 €1900 Men in 18th C costume reading contract (32x44cm-13x17in) s. panel. 6-May-4 Michael Zeller, Lindau #726/R est:1900
£1379 $2303 €2000 At the art dealer's (67x56cm-26x22in) s. prov. 15-Nov-3 Lempertz, Koln #1641/R est:1500
£2568 $4263 €3749 Game of chess (27x35cm-11x14in) s. painted c.1900. 15-Jun-3 Agra, Warsaw #13/R est:14000 (P.Z 16000)
£2568 $4263 €3749 Game of cards (27x35cm-11x14in) s. painted c.1900. 15-Jun-3 Agra, Warsaw #15/R (P.Z 16000)

KNOOP, Guiton (20th C) French?
Sculpture
£987 $1816 €1500 Composition (57x46x16cm-22x18x6in) s.d.1966 num.3/6 verso bronze. 28-Jun-4 Joron-Derem, Paris #153/R est:1500-2000

KNOP, Naum (20th C) Argentinian
Sculpture
£13408 $24000 €19576 Tragic woman (114cm-45in) pat bronze exec.c.1960 granite base. 4-May-4 Arroyo, Buenos Aires #33/R est:18000

KNOPPEL, Arvid (1893-1970) Swedish
Sculpture
£1154 $1985 €1685 Seated bear (31cm-12in) s. dark pat.bronze Cast Bergman. 2-Dec-3 Bukowskis, Stockholm #243/R est:10000-12000 (S.KR 15000)
£1848 $3307 €2698 Girl on shell (57cm-22in) s.d.26 dark pat.bronze cast Otto Meyers. 25-May-4 Bukowskis, Stockholm #303/R est:20000-25000 (S.KR 25000)

KNORR, Hugo (1834-1904) German
£2500 $4175 €3650 View over a Norwegian fjord (49x85cm-19x33in) s. 19-Oct-3 Agra, Warsaw #24/R est:16000 (P.Z 16000)

KNOTEL, Richard (1857-1914) German?
Works on paper
£667 $1213 €1000 After battle. s. gouache. 30-Jun-4 Neumeister, Munich #418/R

KNOWLER, Brian (20th C) British
£270 $475 €394 Red tanker II (26x37cm-10x15in) s. acrylic. 18-May-4 Woolley & Wallis, Salisbury #285/R
£740 $1302 €1080 Hayling Island beach huts (45x61cm-18x24in) s. board. 18-May-4 Woolley & Wallis, Salisbury #64/R
Works on paper
£680 $1197 €993 Red umbrella. Sailboards (18x26cm-7x10in) s. W/C htd white gouache. 18-May-4 Woolley & Wallis, Salisbury #297/R

KNOWLES, David (20th C) New Zealander
£382 $607 €558 Overview (99x120cm-39x47in) s.d.1983 acrylic on board. 1-May-3 Dunbar Sloane, Wellington #513 est:400-900 (NZ.D 1100)

KNOWLES, Davidson (fl.1879-1902) British
£800 $1360 €1168 Drawing room interior with lady playing a piano, a gentleman nearby (35x46cm-14x18in) s. panel. 19-Nov-3 Tennants, Leyburn #1234
£1300 $2418 €1898 Sonnet (91x71cm-36x28in) i.verso. 4-Mar-4 Christie's, Kensington #621 est:1500-2000

KNOWLES, Dorothy (1927-) Canadian
Works on paper
£200 $366 €292 Pasture (19x28cm-7x11in) s.i.d.1982 W/C prov. 1-Jun-4 Hodgins, Calgary #145/R (C.D 500)
£305 $546 €445 Spring thaw (37x54cm-15x21in) s.d.1971 W/C. 6-May-4 Heffel, Vancouver #81/R (C.D 750)
£407 $680 €594 Campground (26x36cm-10x14in) s.d.1978 W/C. 17-Nov-3 Hodgins, Calgary #197/R (C.D 900)
£446 $768 €651 Little blue weeds (55x75cm-22x30in) s.d.80 W/C. 2-Dec-3 Joyner Waddington, Toronto #426 (C.D 1000)
£454 $844 €663 Landscape (24x53cm-9x21in) s.d.47 W/C. 2-Mar-4 Ritchie, Toronto #136/R (C.D 1130)
£520 $952 €759 Trees in a row (55x75cm-22x30in) s.i.d.1978 W/C prov. 1-Jun-4 Hodgins, Calgary #100/R (C.D 1300)
£537 $972 €784 Untitled - Qu Appelle Valley (56x76cm-22x30in) s.d.1980 W/C. 18-Apr-4 Levis, Calgary #58/R est:1500-2000 (C.D 1300)
£661 $1197 €965 Untitled - cottage country (56x76cm-22x30in) s.d.1978 W/C prov. 18-Apr-4 Levis, Calgary #57/R est:1500-2000 (C.D 1600)

KNOWLES, Elizabeth McGillivray (1886-1929) Canadian
£536 $921 €783 Unwelcome visitors (22x30cm-9x12in) canvas on board. 2-Dec-3 Joyner Waddington, Toronto #414 (C.D 1200)
£848 $1459 €1238 Edge of the Forest, sunset (52x35cm-20x14in) s.d.1898 canvas on board. 2-Dec-3 Joyner Waddington, Toronto #371/R est:2500-3000 (C.D 1900)

KNOWLES, Farquhar McGillivray (1859-1932) Canadian
£640 $1171 €934 Summer landscape (30x40cm-12x16in) s. board. 1-Jun-4 Joyner Waddington, Toronto #250/R (C.D 1600)
£893 $1536 €1304 Harbour scene (19x29cm-7x11in) s.d.94 canvas on board. 2-Dec-3 Joyner Waddington, Toronto #518 est:800-1200 (C.D 2000)
£6098 $10915 €8903 East Coast fisherman (66x91cm-26x36in) s. 27-May-4 Heffel, Vancouver #65/R est:6000-8000 (C.D 15000)

KNOWLES, Fred J (1874-?) British
£1056 $1700 €1542 Love's messenger (53x41cm-21x16in) s.d.1913. 14-Jan-4 Christie's, Rockefeller NY #76/R est:1000-1500
Works on paper
£212 $390 €310 Banks of the Rye (35x53cm-14x21in) s. W/C. 14-Jun-4 Waddingtons, Toronto #63/R (C.D 525)
£262 $482 €383 Fording the river (40x30cm-16x12in) s. W/C. 14-Jun-4 Waddingtons, Toronto #64/R (C.D 650)
£280 $445 €409 Barge on the river (33x46cm-13x18in) s. W/C. 12-Sep-3 Gardiner & Houlgate, Bath #65/R
£500 $895 €730 Shepherd and his flock, Bridlepath (19x28cm-7x11in) s. W/C pair. 26-May-4 Sotheby's, Olympia #93/R
£600 $1074 €876 Rest along the way (24x35cm-9x14in) s. W/C. 17-Mar-4 Bonhams, Chester #244
£800 $1432 €1168 Forest Clearing (24x35cm-9x14in) s. W/C. 17-Mar-4 Bonhams, Chester #249

KNOWLES, George Sheridan (1863-1931) British
£450 $806 €657 Scotsman in a rowing boat before a country house (41x61cm-16x24in) s. 18-Mar-4 Christie's, Kensington #594/R
£6471 $11000 €9448 If music be the food of love (91x70cm-36x28in) s.d.1915. 19-Nov-3 Bonhams & Butterfields, San Francisco #140/R
£9444 $17000 €13788 Red parasol (92x61cm-36x24in) s. panelr. 22-Apr-4 Christie's, Rockefeller NY #69/R est:15000-20000
£18100 $30226 €26426 Eventide (91x61cm-36x24in) s. i. verso. 17-Nov-3 Waddingtons, Toronto #134/R est:25000-35000 (C.D 40000)
Works on paper
£329 $588 €480 Windsor Castle (26x35cm-10x14in) s. W/C. 11-May-4 Watson's, Christchurch #30/R (NZ.D 950)
£560 $952 €818 Little red riding hood (33x25cm-13x10in) s.d.83 W/C. 29-Oct-3 Bonhams, Chester #504
£1245 $2079 €1868 Bedtime stories (74x49cm-29x19in) s.d.1907 W/C. 27-Oct-3 Goodman, Sydney #227a/R est:2500-5000 (A.D 3000)
£2700 $4995 €3942 Bedtime story (71x47cm-28x19in) s.d.1907 W/C. 9-Mar-4 Bonhams, New Bond Street #110/R est:3000-5000

KNOWLES, Lila Caroline McGillivray (?) Canadian
£200 $366 €292 Autumn afternoon (25x30cm-10x12in) s. board. 1-Jun-4 Hodgins, Calgary #315/R (C.D 500)

KNOX, Archibald (1864-1933) British
Works on paper
£440 $704 €642 Stylized landscape with clouds (43x56cm-17x22in) W/C. 18-Sep-3 Scarborough Perry Fine Arts, Hove #616

KNOX, George James (1810-1897) British
Works on paper
£260 $450 €380 Figures before cottages in a winter landscape (22x30cm-9x12in) s. W/C. 11-Dec-3 Lane, Penzance #33
£300 $510 €438 Dutch harbour scene in winter (29x44cm-11x17in) s.d.59 W/C. 29-Oct-3 Edgar Horn, Eastbourne #352

KNOX, Jack (1936-) British
Works on paper
£380 $635 €555 Cockerel (58x44cm-23x17in) s. chl exhib. 16-Oct-3 Lyon & Turnbull, Edinburgh #56

KNOX, John (1778-1845) British
£17000 $28900 €24820 The Clyde at Govan, with figures and a boat in the foreground (56x76cm-22x30in) prov. 30-Oct-3 Christie's, London #1/R est:10000-15000

KNOX, Peter (?) British?
£1050 $1859 €1533 Barque - the Tweed entrance (25x48cm-10x19in) s.i. board. 28-Apr-4 Peter Wilson, Nantwich #81 est:600-800

KNOX, Susan Ricker (1875-1959) American
£1497 $2500 €2186 Nancy (51x41cm-20x16in) s. 7-Oct-3 Sotheby's, New York #201 est:2500-3500
£1824 $3100 €2663 In the garden (35x41cm-14x16in) s. prov. 21-Nov-3 Skinner, Boston #382/R est:1500-2500

KNOX, W D (1880-1945) Australian
£763 $1389 €1114 Homestead (34x44cm-13x17in) s. i.verso canvas on board. 16-Jun-4 Deutscher-Menzies, Melbourne #345/R est:2000-3000 (A.D 2000)
£936 $1591 €1367 Little Dock (25x33cm-10x13in) s. oil composition board painted 1910 prov. 26-Nov-3 Deutscher-Menzies, Melbourne #168/R (A.D 2200)

KNOX, Wilfred (1884-1966) British
Works on paper
£480 $850 €701 Sailing boats in the Venetian Lagoon (30x46cm-12x18in) s. W/C htd. bodycol. 28-Apr-4 Halls, Shrewsbury #454

KNOX, William (1862-1925) British
Works on paper
£260 $465 €380 Shore scene with figures unloading fishing boats (27x36cm-11x14in) s. W/C. 17-Mar-4 Bonhams, Chester #337
£280 $512 €409 An evening on the Venetian Lagoon (25x36cm-10x14in) bodycol. 27-Jan-4 Bonhams, Knightsbridge #40/R
£300 $498 €438 Venice (26x36cm-10x14in) s. W/C. 1-Oct-3 Woolley & Wallis, Salisbury #138/R
£380 $695 €555 Gondolas on the Venice lagoon (26x36cm-10x14in) s. W/C. 27-Jan-4 Bonhams, Knightsbridge #25/R
£460 $823 €672 Resting in Venice (25x37cm-10x15in) s.d.1916 W/C. 25-May-4 Gildings, Market Harborough #423/R
£520 $822 €754 Scenes of Venice from the canal, with barges and gondola (25x36cm-10x14in) s. W/C pair. 2-Sep-3 Bonhams, Oxford #52/R
£650 $1183 €949 Bustling activity on the Lagoon, Venice (25x37cm-10x15in) s. pencil W/C htd white. 1-Jul-4 Christie's, Kensington #349/R
£1200 $2220 €1752 Entrance to the Grand Canal, Venice. View of Venice (25x37cm-10x15in) s. W/C bodycol pair. 9-Mar-4 Bonhams, Knightsbridge #77/R est:1200-1800

KNOX, William Dunn (1880-1945) Australian

£1301	$2328	€1899	Mentone (19x28cm-7x11in) s. paper. 4-May-4 Sotheby's, Melbourne #119 est:2000-4000 (A.D 3200)
£1465	$2286	€2124	Panorama from Arthur's Seat (44x54cm-17x21in) S. 1-Aug-2 Joel, Victoria #140 est:2500-3500 (A.D 4250)
£2033	$3191	€2948	Towards the dandenongs (44x65cm-17x26in) s. 26-Aug-3 Christie's, Sydney #353/R est:5000-8000 (A.D 5000)
£2236	$4002	€3265	Little duck (33x43cm-13x17in) s. board. 10-May-4 Joel, Victoria #350/R est:6000-8000 (A.D 5500)
£2979	$5064	€4349	Tasmanian schooner (34x44cm-13x17in) s. i.verso canvasboard prov. 25-Nov-3 Christie's, Melbourne #263/R est:7000-10000 (A.D 7000)
£4472	$8004	€6529	Fisherman's beach Mornington (22x31cm-9x12in) s. bears i.verso artist board prov. 4-May-4 Sotheby's, Melbourne #238/R est:6000-8000 (A.D 11000)

KNUDSEN, Borge L (1911-1994) Danish

£344	$558	€499	Composition with guitar (65x85cm-26x33in) s.d.37. 4-Aug-3 Rasmussen, Vejle #606/R (D.KR 3600)

KNUDSEN, Gerda (1899-1945) Scandinavian

£2722	$4873	€3974	Cutting the corn (130x100cm-51x39in) s.d.40 exhib.lit. 22-Mar-4 Blomqvist, Oslo #398/R est:15000-18000 (N.KR 34000)

KNUDSEN, Peder (1868-1944) Danish

£281	$458	€410	Evening by the fjord (40x51cm-16x20in) s.d.1942. 27-Sep-3 Rasmussen, Havnen #2108 (D.KR 3000)
£300	$489	€438	Landscape from Bornholm with cliffs (73x54cm-29x21in) s.d.1920. 27-Sep-3 Rasmussen, Havnen #2076 (D.KR 3200)
£325	$527	€471	Coastal landscape with cliffs, Bornholm (65x80cm-26x31in) s. 4-Aug-3 Rasmussen, Vejle #403 (D.KR 3400)
£468	$782	€683	Coastal landscape (74x96cm-29x38in) s. 25-Oct-3 Rasmussen, Havnen #2006/R (D.KR 5000)
£662	$1184	€967	Norwegian landscape with cabins (75x100cm-30x39in) s. 12-Jan-4 Rasmussen, Vejle #114/R (D.KR 7000)
£737	$1253	€1076	Breakers and rocky coast (104x134cm-41x53in) s. 10-Nov-3 Rasmussen, Vejle #70 (D.KR 8000)
£775	$1387	€1132	Snow covered mountains, Norway (101x130cm-40x51in) s. 12-Jan-4 Rasmussen, Vejle #113/R (D.KR 8200)
£1078	$2005	€1574	Waves breaking on the rocky coast at Bornholm (100x136cm-39x54in) s. 2-Mar-4 Rasmussen, Copenhagen #1393/R est:8000 (D.KR 12000)
£1086	$1944	€1586	Coastal landscape with cliffs (74x96cm-29x38in) s. 10-May-4 Rasmussen, Vejle #388/R est:4000 (D.KR 12000)

KNUPFER, Benes (1848-1910) Czechoslovakian

£1646	$2799	€2403	The sea (43x107cm-17x42in) s. 29-Nov-3 Dorotheum, Prague #33/R est:60000-90000 (C.KR 75000)
£1751	$2907	€2556	Muse (46x36cm-18x14in) s.i. 4-Oct-3 Dorotheum, Prague #10/R est:70000-100000 (C.KR 80000)
£2000	$3340	€2920	Dolphins (82x144cm-32x57in) s.i. 12-Nov-3 Sotheby's, Olympia #208/R est:3000-4000
£5705	$10211	€8500	Dolphins (82x144cm-32x57in) s.i. 27-May-4 Dorotheum, Vienna #167/R est:7000-9000

KNUPFER, Nicolaus (1603-1660) German

£1923	$3308	€2808	Figures outside a building (35x42cm-14x17in) indis.sig. panel. 3-Dec-3 AB Stockholms Auktionsverk #2678/R est:30000-35000 (S.KR 25000)

KNUTSON, Johan (1816-1899) Finnish

£1549	$2680	€2200	Archipelago (23x35cm-9x14in) s. board. 13-Dec-3 Hagelstam, Helsinki #126/R est:2500
£1761	$2817	€2500	Coastal landscape with fishermen (24x36cm-9x14in) s. 18-Sep-3 Hagelstam, Helsinki #861/R est:2000
£1892	$3386	€2800	Summer evening (17x37cm-7x15in) s. board. 8-May-4 Bukowskis, Helsinki #28/R est:1700-2000
£2533	$4535	€3800	Archipelago (23x32cm-9x13in) s. canvas on board. 15-May-4 Hagelstam, Helsinki #78/R est:2500
£4054	$7257	€6000	Every day chores on the mountain farm (89x128cm-35x50in) s.d.1878. 8-May-4 Bukowskis, Helsinki #199/R est:6000-8000
£6757	$12095	€10000	Summer Sunday in the garden (70x99cm-28x39in) s. 8-May-4 Bukowskis, Helsinki #193/R est:10000-15000

KNUTSON, Johan (attrib) (1816-1899) Finnish

£1127	$1803	€1600	Woodland marsh (42x66cm-17x26in) painted c.1850 prov. 18-Sep-3 Hagelstam, Helsinki #787/R est:800

KNUTTEL, Graham (1954-) Irish

£493	$908	€750	Still life (36x23cm-14x9in) 22-Jun-4 De Veres Art Auctions, Dublin #268
£500	$830	€730	Punch (35x25cm-14x10in) s. 1-Oct-3 John Ross, Belfast #259
£739	$1294	€1050	Portrait of a woman (30x25cm-12x10in) s. 16-Dec-3 James Adam, Dublin #75/R
£1184	$2179	€1800	Punch and Judy (59x49cm-23x19in) s. 22-Jun-4 De Veres Art Auctions, Dublin #146/R est:2000-3000
£1316	$2421	€2000	The bottom of the sea (59x49cm-23x19in) s. 22-Jun-4 De Veres Art Auctions, Dublin #147/R est:2000-3000
£1316	$2421	€2000	Cat (29x23cm-11x9in) s. 22-Jun-4 De Veres Art Auctions, Dublin #200/R est:1000-1500
£1600	$2896	€2400	Still life (61x51cm-24x20in) s. 30-Mar-4 De Veres Art Auctions, Dublin #36/R est:1500-2000
£1690	$2958	€2400	Chefs in a kitchen interior (40x45cm-16x18in) s. 16-Dec-3 James Adam, Dublin #11/R est:1200-1500
£2042	$3574	€2900	Smoking, non smoking (122x93cm-48x37in) s. prov. 16-Dec-3 James Adam, Dublin #212/R est:3000-5000
£2098	$3566	€3000	Still life with peaches (41x30cm-16x12in) s. 18-Nov-3 Whyte's, Dublin #213/R est:1800-2200
£2105	$3874	€3200	Red bird (40x45cm-16x18in) s. 22-Jun-4 De Veres Art Auctions, Dublin #258 est:1500-2000
£2550	$4565	€3800	Two felines (60x50cm-24x20in) s. 31-May-4 Hamilton Osborne King, Dublin #213/R est:2000-3000
£2569	$4034	€3700	Still life in open window (106x76cm-42x30in) s. 26-Aug-3 James Adam, Dublin #188/R est:3500-4000
£2770	$5236	€4100	Aubergines (61x61cm-24x24in) s. 17-Feb-4 Whyte's, Dublin #192/R est:3000-4000
£2797	$4755	€4000	Still life before a window (91x91cm-36x36in) s. 18-Nov-3 Whyte's, Dublin #212/R est:4000-6000
£2800	$4648	€4088	Bird of paradise (86x114cm-34x45in) s. 1-Oct-3 John Ross, Belfast #122 est:3000-4000
£3087	$5464	€4600	Tropical fish (91x91cm-36x36in) s. 27-Apr-4 Whyte's, Dublin #183/R est:4000-6000
£3147	$5350	€4500	The proposal (91x91cm-36x36in) s. 18-Nov-3 Whyte's, Dublin #211/R est:5000-7000
£4500	$7470	€6570	Off the coast at Calabar (137x236cm-54x93in) s. 1-Oct-3 John Ross, Belfast #117 est:6000-8000
£4698	$8315	€7000	Man and woman seated before a window (122x91cm-48x36in) s. board. 27-Apr-4 Whyte's, Dublin #182/R est:7000-9000
£5282	$8451	€7500	Four hustlers (91x72cm-36x28in) s. prov. 16-Sep-3 Whyte's, Dublin #220/R est:6000-8000
£7500	$13425	€10950	Cordon Bleu (122x91cm-48x36in) s. 13-May-4 Sotheby's, London #116/R est:5000-7000
£7746	$12394	€11000	Artist and muse (122x91cm-48x36in) s. 16-Sep-3 Whyte's, Dublin #135/R est:6000-8000
Works on paper			
£993	$1808	€1500	Wolf (86x66cm-34x26in) s.d.87 crayon. 15-Jun-4 James Adam, Dublin #51/R est:1500-2000
£1275	$2283	€1900	Self portrait (53x49cm-21x19in) s. mixed media. 31-May-4 Hamilton Osborne King, Dublin #30/R est:2000-3000

KNYFF, Chevalier Alfred de (1819-1885) Belgian

£483	$806	€700	Les lavandieres (56x46cm-22x18in) mono. 17-Nov-3 Tajan, Paris #49
£1200	$2172	€1800	Deux cavaliers sous l'orage (15x20cm-6x8in) mono.d.46 i.verso cardboard. 30-Mar-4 Rossini, Paris #1017/R est:400-700
£3380	$5848	€4800	River view (70x124cm-28x49in) s. 13-Dec-3 De Vuyst, Lokeren #536/R est:5000-6000

KNYFF, Jacob (attrib) (1638-1681) Dutch

£3311	$6026	€5000	Coastal landscape with ships lying at anchor on a calm sea (46x65cm-18x26in) panel. 16-Jun-4 Dorotheum, Vienna #38/R est:6000-9000

KNYFF, Wouter (1607-1693) Dutch

£4769	$8203	€6963	Coastal landscape with castle and boats (47x69cm-19x27in) panel. 2-Dec-3 Bukowskis, Stockholm #391/R est:40000-50000 (S.KR 62000)

KO, Young-Hoon (1952-) Japanese?

£13408	$24000	€19576	Untitled (84x121cm-33x48in) s.d.1996 acrylic W/C paper collage linen on panel prov. 13-May-4 Sotheby's, New York #464/R est:12000-18000

KOBEL, Georg (1807-1894) German

£1034	$1728	€1500	Mill in summer landscape (35x43cm-14x17in) s.d.1847. 9-Jul-3 Hugo Ruef, Munich #126/R est:900
£2778	$4583	€4000	Italian landscape (81x123cm-32x48in) s. 2-Jul-3 Neumeister, Munich #686/R est:2500

KOBELL, Ferdinand (1740-1799) German

£2817	$4873	€4000	Waterfall in rocky landscape (24x51cm-9x20in) 13-Dec-3 Lempertz, Koln #27/R est:4000
Works on paper			
£487	$881	€730	Two peasants talking (11x8cm-4x3in) Indian ink 1. 2-Apr-4 Winterberg, Heidelberg #322
£656	$1200	€958	Landscape with travellers resting (22x29cm-9x11in) s.d.1775 pencil. 29-Jan-4 Swann Galleries, New York #306/R
£800	$1432	€1200	River landscape with boys on shore (23x31cm-9x12in) brush on pencil. 13-May-4 Bassenge, Berlin #5414/R

KOBELL, Ferdinand (attrib) (1740-1799) German

£6000	$10920	€8760	Wooded landscapes (46x37cm-18x15in) one bears sig.d.1819 two prov. 15-Jun-4 Sotheby's, London #51/R est:6000-8000
Works on paper			
£333	$600	€500	Farmstead by wooded lake (10x13cm-4x5in) Indian ink. 24-Apr-4 Reiss & Sohn, Konigstein #5412/R

KOBELL, Franz (1749-1822) German

Works on paper			
£311	$556	€460	Temple square (14x21cm-6x8in) pen wash. 4-May-4 Hartung & Hartung, Munich #4047/R
£439	$786	€650	Building surrounded by trees (17x21cm-7x8in) brush. 4-May-4 Hartung & Hartung, Munich #4050
£473	$847	€700	Rocky landscape with trees (13x21cm-5x8in) pen wash. 4-May-4 Hartung & Hartung, Munich #4048/R
£733	$1313	€1100	Rocky coast (16x20cm-6x8in) brush. 13-May-4 Bassenge, Berlin #5415
£1200	$2172	€1800	Rocky landscape with classical ruins and small waterfall (20x27cm-8x11in) W/C Indian ink. 2-Apr-4 Winterberg, Heidelberg #325/R est:2400
£2162	$3805	€3200	Landscapes (17x21cm-7x8in) brush brown ink wash red chk two sold with an album prov. 19-May-4 Sotheby's, Amsterdam #316/R est:600-800
£3243	$5708	€4800	Mountainous landscape with bathers near a pool. Wooded landscape (16x20cm-6x8in) one s.d.1819 verso pen brown ink two sold with an album prov. 19-May-4 Sotheby's, Amsterdam #315/R est:800-1000
£5405	$9514	€8000	Landscapes, including wooded scenes and waterfalls (17x21cm-7x8in) brush brown ink wash six prov.exhib. 19-May-4 Sotheby's, Amsterdam #314/R est:1200-1800
£5743	$10108	€8500	Wooded landscapes (17x21cm-7x8in) brush brown ink wash six prov.exhib. 19-May-4 Sotheby's, Amsterdam #312/R est:1200-1800
£7432	$13081	€11000	Landscapes (17x21cm-7x8in) brush brown ink wash six prov. 19-May-4 Sotheby's, Amsterdam #313/R est:1200-1800

KOBELL, Hendrik (1751-1779) Dutch
Works on paper
£1467 $2625 €2200 Sailing ship off Dutch coast (11x16cm-4x6in) s.d.1777 pen wash. 13-May-4 Bassenge, Berlin #5419 est:1500

KOBELL, Jan (1756-1833) Dutch
£1042 $1740 €1500 Cows by lake (49x63cm-19x25in) s.d. panel. 24-Oct-3 Ketterer, Hamburg #82/R est:2000-3000
Works on paper
£467 $845 €700 Paysage anime (14x19cm-6x7in) s. pen brown ink wash. 30-Mar-4 Rossini, Paris #25

KOBELL, Jan Baptist (1778-1814) Dutch
£1875 $2963 €2700 Coastal landscape with cows and goat (34x29cm-13x11in) mono. panel lit. 19-Sep-3 Schloss Ahlden, Ahlden #1425/R est:2900

KOBELL, Jan Baptist (attrib) (1778-1814) Dutch
£2448 $4210 €3500 Shepherds fishing (32x40cm-13x16in) panel. 4-Dec-3 Vendue Huis, Gravenhage #1027
£2448 $4210 €3500 Shepherds fishing (32x40cm-13x16in) panel. 3-Dec-3 Auction Maastricht #1027/R est:4000-5000

KOBELL, Jan III (1800-1838) Dutch
£1842 $3389 €2800 Cows by a pond in summer (29x34cm-11x13in) s. panel. 22-Jun-4 Christie's, Amsterdam #38/R est:2000-3000

KOBELL, Wilhelm von (1766-1855) German
£10667 $19413 €16000 Herdsman with cows in lower mountain landscape (37x46cm-15x18in) s. 30-Jun-4 Neumeister, Munich #590/R est:16000
Works on paper
£1259 $2140 €1800 Wolfratshausen on the Loisach (19x24cm-7x9in) W/C on pen pencil. 27-Nov-3 Bassenge, Berlin #5461 est:1800

KOBERLING, Bernd (1938-) German
£699 $1189 €1000 Untitled (100x70cm-39x28in) s.d.87 acrylic. 27-Nov-3 Lempertz, Koln #231/R
Works on paper
£280 $481 €400 Composition (20x14cm-8x6in) s.d. W/C. 3-Dec-3 Hauswedell & Nolte, Hamburg #904/R

KOBERSTEIN, Hans (1864-?) German
£559 $951 €800 Fairytale scene with a king and a princess (50x70cm-20x28in) s.d.1922 lit. 28-Nov-3 Schloss Ahlden, Ahlden #1575/R
Works on paper
£315 $525 €450 Mythological scene (57x111cm-22x44in) s. gouache. 30-Jun-3 Sotheby's, Amsterdam #367/R

KOBINGER, Hans (1892-1974) Austrian
Works on paper
£367 $675 €550 Still life with teddy bear and toys (48x51cm-19x20in) s.d.1956 mixed media. 9-Jun-4 Dorotheum, Salzburg #641/R
£426 $711 €600 Woodland stream (48x50cm-19x20in) s.d.1939 Indian ink W/C. 16-Oct-3 Dorotheum, Salzburg #898/R

KOBKE, Christen (1810-1848) Danish
£47259 $81758 €68998 Sophie Krohn, artist's sister standing by window in the family home, Kastellet (31x21cm-12x8in) painted c.1830 exhib.prov. 9-Dec-3 Rasmussen, Copenhagen #1229/R est:500000 (D.KR 500000)
£368620 $637713 €538185 Coastal landscape from southern Capri, clear day, large waves (122x173cm-48x68in) init.d.1841 exhib.prov. 9-Dec-3 Rasmussen, Copenhagen #1242/R est:4000000-6000000 (D.KR 3900000)
Works on paper
£607 $960 €880 Allegory of spring in shape of young woman with flowers (28x11cm-11x4in) s. pencil. 2-Sep-3 Rasmussen, Copenhagen #2014/R (D.KR 6500)
£1354 $2532 €1977 Mister Krohn wearing high hat and coat (20x11cm-8x4in) pencil. 25-Feb-4 Museumsbygningen, Copenhagen #131/R est:15000-20000 (D.KR 15000)
£3592 $6214 €5244 Estate-owner Niels Schryth (21x15cm-8x6in) i. pencil. 9-Dec-3 Rasmussen, Copenhagen #17117/R est:25000-30000 (D.KR 38000)

KOBZDEJ, Aleksander (1920-1972) Polish
£5791 $10482 €8455 Composition (100x91cm-39x36in) s.d.1967 oil mixed media. 4-Apr-4 Agra, Warsaw #8/R (P.Z 41000)
Works on paper
£282 $511 €412 Untitled (40x30cm-16x12in) s.d.1966 Indian ink W/C gouache paper on paper board. 4-Apr-4 Agra, Warsaw #47/R (P.Z 2000)

KOCH, Eleanore (20th C) British?
£250 $417 €365 Still life of red flowers (92x66cm-36x26in) s. 14-Oct-3 Sotheby's, London #546
£400 $668 €584 Kettle (117x89cm-46x35in) s. 14-Oct-3 Sotheby's, London #543/R
£500 $835 €730 Pier (119x160cm-47x63in) s.d.7.73. 14-Oct-3 Sotheby's, London #544/R

KOCH, François (19/20th C) Austrian
£3230 $5200 €4684 Elephant (51x79cm-20x31in) 22-Aug-3 Altermann Galleries, Santa Fe #221
£21390 $40000 €31229 Golden flow, Yosemite (91x127cm-36x50in) s. 24-Jul-4 Coeur d'Alene, Hayden #190/R est:15000-25000

KOCH, Georg (1857-1926) German
£2759 $5103 €4000 Horses in meadow (66x100cm-26x39in) s. 14-Feb-4 Hans Stahl, Hamburg #49/R est:5500
Works on paper
£660 $1042 €950 Officials at the races (23x17cm-9x7in) s. W/C htd white. 5-Sep-3 Wendl, Rudolstadt #3457/R

KOCH, George Joseph (1885-1951) American
£2514 $4500 €3670 Nudes in an inlet (64x76cm-25x30in) s.d.1944 masonite prov. 6-May-4 Shannon's, Milford #46/R est:3000-5000

KOCH, Heinrich (1806-1893) German
£340 $626 €496 Pope Gregory VII with an open bible (84x68cm-33x27in) s. i.verso panel. 14-Jun-4 Bonhams, Bath #3

KOCH, Hermann (1856-1894) German
£262 $461 €383 Ferry trip (22x36cm-9x14in) s.i. board. 22-May-4 Galerie Gloggner, Luzern #64/R (S.FR 600)
£280 $481 €400 Fruit still life with grapes, peach and plum (18x25cm-7x10in) s. canvas on panel. 6-Dec-3 Dannenberg, Berlin #801/R
£667 $1213 €1000 Still lifes with fruit (26x39cm-10x15in) s. panel pair. 1-Jul-4 Weidler, Nurnberg #4503/R
£2568 $4263 €3749 Still life with fruit and goblet (36x50cm-14x20in) s. cardboard painted c.1900. 15-Jun-3 Agra, Warsaw #14/R est:9000 (P.Z 16000)

KOCH, Jakob (fl.1900-1920) ?
Works on paper
£1734 $3000 €2532 Along the stream. Morning Enchantment (32x48cm-13x19in) s. W/C pair prov. 10-Dec-3 Bonhams & Butterfields, San Francisco #6160/R est:3000-5000

KOCH, John (1909-1978) American
£1297 $2400 €1894 Still life with flowers (36x28cm-14x11in) s.d.1953. 17-Jan-4 New Orleans Auction, New Orleans #519/R est:2500-4000
£7568 $14000 €11049 Young boy sleeping (41x51cm-16x20in) prov. 11-Mar-4 Christie's, Rockefeller NY #71/R est:5000-7000
£8140 $14000 €11884 Sleeping boy (51x41cm-20x16in) s. 3-Dec-3 Doyle, New York #309/R est:8000-12000
£8242 $15000 €12033 Afternoon labors (127x152cm-50x60in) s.d.36 prov. 29-Jun-4 Sotheby's, New York #263/R est:12000-18000
Works on paper
£656 $1200 €958 Study of a woman in a chair (18x13cm-7x5in) s. pencil htd white. 3-Jun-4 Christie's, Rockefeller NY #1300/R est:400-600
£1676 $3000 €2447 Study of a standing young man (46x28cm-18x11in) s. pencil. 26-May-4 Doyle, New York #152/R est:1500-2500

KOCH, Julius (1882-1952) German
£524 $876 €750 Interior (71x61cm-28x24in) s.d.17. 30-Jun-3 Bloss, Merzhausen #1916/R

KOCH, Karl Georg (1857-1936) German
£6630 $12000 €9680 Hunt scene with stag (119x201cm-47x79in) s. 3-Apr-4 Neal Auction Company, New Orleans #378/R est:8000-12000

KOCH, Ludwig (1866-1934) Austrian
£313 $538 €457 Grooms bathing horses in the river (35x50cm-14x20in) s.d.1932 i.verso W/C board. 2-Dec-3 Ritchie, Toronto #130/R (C.D 700)
£1000 $1840 €1500 Horses drinking (66x91cm-26x36in) s.d.1928. 9-Jun-4 Dorotheum, Salzburg #538/R est:3000-4000
£4545 $7727 €6500 Procession of mounted soldiers in Vienna (60x86cm-24x34in) s.d.1929. 26-Nov-3 Dorotheum, Vienna #136/R est:5000-7000
£4545 $7727 €6500 Horse drawn coach in the rain (62x106cm-24x42in) s.d.1923. 20-Nov-3 Dorotheum, Salzburg #162/R est:3000-4000
Works on paper
£397 $727 €600 Soldiers in snowstorm (35x22cm-14x9in) s.d.1915 W/C bodycol. 8-Apr-4 Dorotheum, Vienna #171/R
£537 $950 €800 Kaiser Franz Joseph I with entourage (35x25cm-14x10in) s. pencil. 29-Apr-4 Dorotheum, Vienna #99/R
£780 $1303 €1100 Hussars with horses (27x49cm-11x19in) s.d.1924 pencil htd white two. 14-Oct-3 Dorotheum, Vienna #43/R
£1277 $2132 €1800 King's Troop riding out (27x39cm-11x15in) s.d.1924 pen Indian ink sepia W/C gouache. 14-Oct-3 Dorotheum, Vienna #42/R est:1500-2000
£1560 $2606 €2200 Soldiers on horseback (27x39cm-11x15in) s.d.1924 pen Indian ink sepia W/C gouache. 14-Oct-3 Dorotheum, Vienna #41/R est:1500-2000

KOCH, Maggie (1880-1964) German?
Works on paper
£324 $581 €480 Meersburg am Bodensee (44x34cm-17x13in) W/C i.verso. 7-May-4 Paul Kieffer, Pforzhiem #6677/R

KOCH, Martin (20th C) American
£269 $487 €393 Near Elsenberg (49x59cm-19x23in) s.d.76. 30-Mar-4 Stephan Welz, Johannesburg #450 est:3000-5000 (SA.R 3200)
£403 $730 €588 An old Cape farmhouse (50x60cm-20x24in) s.d.74 canvasboard. 30-Mar-4 Stephan Welz, Johannesburg #449 est:3000-5000 (SA.R 4800)
£437 $791 €638 Stellenbosch Valley (49x75cm-19x30in) s.d.84 canvasboard. 30-Mar-4 Stephan Welz, Johannesburg #448 est:3000-5000 (SA.R 5200)
£1744 $3000 €2546 Kalahari gemscock (60x31cm-24x12in) s.d.74. 5-Dec-3 Christie's, Rockefeller NY #101/R est:4000-6000

£8140	$14000	€11884	Elephants (108x184cm-43x72in) s.d.72 panel. 5-Dec-3 Christie's, Rockefeller NY #102/R est:8000-12000

KOCH, Michael (?) German

£1049	$1783	€1500	Inner courtyard of Heidelberg Castle (50x65cm-20x26in) s. 22-Nov-3 Arnold, Frankfurt #570/R est:1000

KOCH, Peter (1874-1956) German

£428	$736	€625	Girl with puppy and toys (101x76cm-40x30in) s.d.1907. 8-Dec-3 Philippe Schuler, Zurich #5860 (S.FR 950)
£940	$1738	€1400	Girl in high chair (101x76cm-40x30in) s.d.1907 lit. 12-Mar-4 Zadick, Uberlingen #4031/R

KOCH, Pyke (1901-1991) Dutch

£73427	$126294	€105000	Rustende slaapwandelaarster I (18x35cm-7x14in) s.d.59 prov.lit. 2-Dec-3 Sotheby's, Amsterdam #30/R est:50000-70000

KOCH, Walther (1875-1915) German

£2609	$4774	€3809	Spring landscape with clouds (56x52cm-22x20in) s.d.1912 canvas on board. 4-Jun-4 Zofingen, Switzerland #2477/R est:3000 (S.FR 6000)

KOCH-ZEUTHEN, Reinhold (1889-1949) German

£347	$545	€500	The Loire and Orleans in summer (60x80cm-24x31in) s.i.d.1942. 30-Aug-3 Hans Stahl, Toestorf #37/R

KOCHANOWSKY, Roman (1856-1945) Polish

£451	$745	€650	Horse and cart in Dachauer Moos (13x18cm-5x7in) s. panel. 2-Jul-3 Neumeister, Munich #685
£517	$864	€750	Farmstead (14x12cm-6x5in) s. panel. 9-Jul-3 Hugo Ruef, Munich #125/R
£612	$1096	€900	Cows grazing in landscape with trees (16x20cm-6x8in) s. canvas on panel. 17-Mar-4 Neumeister, Munich #503
£612	$1096	€900	Peasant woman in wood (21x14cm-8x6in) s. board. 17-Mar-4 Neumeister, Munich #504
£990	$1743	€1445	River landscape (18x13cm-7x5in) s. 23-May-4 Agra, Warsaw #32/R (P.Z 7000)
£1081	$1967	€1578	Wooded landscape with figure (21x13cm-8x5in) s. paper on board. 20-Jun-4 Agra, Warsaw #23/R (P.Z 7500)
£1176	$2175	€1717	Village street scene with figure (16x20cm-6x8in) 14-Mar-4 Agra, Warsaw #9/R (P.Z 8500)
£1362	$2356	€1989	Moon rising over a country landscape (34x25cm-13x10in) s. painted c.1900. 14-Dec-3 Agra, Warsaw #35/R est:8000 (P.Z 9000)
£1839	$3236	€2685	River landscape (22x14cm-9x6in) s. panel. 23-May-4 Agra, Warsaw #20/R (P.Z 13000)
£2344	$3914	€3422	Collecting kindling wood (45x26cm-18x10in) s.d.1872. 19-Oct-3 Agra, Warsaw #26/R est:10000 (P.Z 15000)
£2368	$4358	€3600	At the farm. Winter landscape (12x20cm-5x8in) s. panel two. 22-Jun-4 Wiener Kunst Auktionen, Vienna #193/R est:2000
£4426	$8188	€6462	Landscape with a figure (37x54cm-15x21in) 14-Mar-4 Agra, Warsaw #8/R (P.Z 32000)
Works on paper			
£1528	$2521	€2200	Woman gathering sticks in moorland (45x26cm-18x10in) s.d.1892 gouache. 2-Jul-3 Neumeister, Munich #473/R est:1700

KOCHERSCHEIDT, Kurt (1943-1992) Austrian

£7292	$12396	€10500	Untitled (65x80cm-26x31in) s.d.79. 28-Oct-3 Wiener Kunst Auktionen, Vienna #257/R est:10000-15000
£9028	$15347	€13000	Untitled (45x34cm-18x13in) mono.d.89 two parts. 28-Oct-3 Wiener Kunst Auktionen, Vienna #253/R est:8000-14000
£33557	$59396	€50000	The song (180x340cm-71x134in) mono. triptych lit. 28-Apr-4 Wiener Kunst Auktionen, Vienna #263/R est:50000-65000
Works on paper			
£1399	$2378	€2000	Abandoned warehouse (35x50cm-14x20in) s.i.d.1972 mixed media. 28-Nov-3 Wiener Kunst Auktionen, Vienna #657/R est:1200-2500
£1879	$3364	€2800	Death of Cleopatra (49x40cm-19x16in) s.i.d.67 mixed media. 25-May-4 Dorotheum, Vienna #360/R est:1800-2200
£3020	$5346	€4500	Glass jar (49x64cm-19x25in) s.d.76 mixed media. 28-Apr-4 Wiener Kunst Auktionen, Vienna #264/R est:4500-6000

KOCK, Franz (1886-1975) German

£336	$601	€500	Ice rink in winter landscape (38x50cm-15x20in) s. board. 27-May-4 Dorotheum, Graz #39/R
£764	$1245	€1100	Mountain landscape (70x90cm-28x35in) s. 25-Sep-3 Dorotheum, Graz #17

KOCKERT, Julius (1827-1918) German

£13986	$25455	€20420	After the harvest (84x155cm-33x61in) s.i. prov. 29-Jun-4 Peter Webb, Auckland #99/R est:45000-60000 (NZ.D 40000)

KODERA, Craig (20th C) American

£240	$400	€350	Hitting the Kwai (30x61cm-12x24in) s. 11-Oct-3 Nadeau, Windsor #181/R
£299	$500	€437	Jimmy and the Gee Bee (33x61cm-13x24in) s. 11-Oct-3 Nadeau, Windsor #182/R
£1437	$2400	€2098	Enola Gay (64x114cm-25x45in) s. 11-Oct-3 Nadeau, Windsor #183/R est:2500-4000

KODRA, Ibrahim (1918-) Middle Eastern

£483	$806	€700	Figure (50x35cm-20x14in) s. board. 13-Nov-3 Galleria Pace, Milan #89/R
£552	$921	€800	Mater (40x30cm-16x12in) s. s.i.verso. 13-Nov-3 Galleria Pace, Milan #27/R
£940	$1738	€1400	Untitled (75x58cm-30x23in) s.i.d.1974 tempera paper. 11-Mar-4 Galleria Pace, Milan #125/R est:1700-2500
Works on paper			
£1007	$1862	€1500	Floral homage (70x50cm-28x20in) s. mixed media cardboard on canvas. 13-Mar-4 Meeting Art, Vercelli #508 est:1500
£1164	$1816	€1700	Mother (100x80cm-39x31in) s. s.i.d.verso mixed media. 8-Apr-3 Il Ponte, Milan #1000

KOECHLIN, Daniel Jules Camille (1845-1914) French

£367	$671	€550	Hunting with hounds (53x74cm-21x29in) s.i. 5-Jun-4 Arnold, Frankfurt #628/R

KOEDIJK, Isaak (c.1616-c.1668) Dutch

£70000	$126000	€102200	Interior of a Dutch house with a seated cavalier holding an upturned glass (66x55cm-26x22in) d.1648 panel prov.lit. 22-Apr-4 Sotheby's, London #37/R est:60000-80000

KOEFOED, Hans Christian (1849-1921) Danish

£1715	$3207	€2504	Girl seated writing a letter, two women watching (63x87cm-25x34in) mono.d.1889. 25-Feb-4 Museumsbygningen, Copenhagen #108/R est:6000 (D.KR 19000)

KOEHLER, Henry (1927-) American

£1453	$2500	€2121	Farrier filing (24x34cm-9x13in) s. oil on paper painted 1993. 5-Dec-3 Christie's, Rockefeller NY #128/R est:2500-3500
£1512	$2600	€2208	Farrier shoeing (24x34cm-9x13in) s. oil on paper painted 1993. 5-Dec-3 Christie's, Rockefeller NY #127/R est:2500-3500
£2500	$4600	€3650	Windsor starters (61x102cm-24x40in) s. s.i.d.1973 verso. 10-Jun-4 Christie's, Kensington #217/R est:3000-4000
£2907	$5000	€4244	Hunting whip hook (38x28cm-15x11in) s. i.verso painted 1999. 5-Dec-3 Christie's, Rockefeller NY #125/R est:6000-8000
£4651	$8000	€6790	Stag hunting saddles (33x24cm-13x9in) s. canvas on panel painted 1995. 5-Dec-3 Christie's, Rockefeller NY #126/R est:7000-10000
£5233	$9000	€7640	Three jockey studies in blue (25x100cm-10x39in) s. painted 1987. 5-Dec-3 Christie's, Rockefeller NY #123/R est:10000-15000
£5233	$9000	€7640	Deauville start (54x73cm-21x29in) s. painted 1987. 5-Dec-3 Christie's, Rockefeller NY #124/R est:10000-15000
£6395	$11000	€9337	Jockeys in yellow, below (48x41cm-19x16in) s. oil on paper painted 1993. 5-Dec-3 Christie's, Rockefeller NY #122/R est:8000-12000
Works on paper			
£300	$546	€438	Groom, Phoenix Park (28x44cm-11x17in) s. chl prov. 30-Jun-4 Mervyn Carey, Tenterden #147/R
£556	$872	€800	Etudes de jockeys (28x45cm-11x18in) s. pastel. 29-Aug-3 Deauville, France #56/R

KOEHLER, Paul R (c.1866-1909) American

Works on paper			
£335	$600	€489	Country landscape with grazing cattle (51x76cm-20x30in) s. pastel board. 14-May-4 Skinner, Boston #94/R
£699	$1300	€1021	Landscape with a man fishing in a rowboat (41x61cm-16x24in) s. pastel. 3-Mar-4 Alderfer's, Hatfield #301/R est:800-1200

KOEK-KOEK, Stephen Roberto (1887-1934) Argentinian

£1923	$3500	€2808	Bright corner (32x42cm-13x17in) s. board. 5-Jul-4 Arroyo, Buenos Aires #46/R est:3500
£3315	$6000	€4840	Harbour (23x28cm-9x11in) board. 30-Mar-4 Arroyo, Buenos Aires #60
£3352	$6000	€4894	Procession (8x10cm-3x4in) s. copper. 4-May-4 Arroyo, Buenos Aires #58/R est:1700
£3407	$6200	€4974	Mills (24x33cm-9x13in) s. cardboard. 29-Jun-4 Arroyo, Buenos Aires #1/R est:3800
£3631	$6500	€5301	Ocaso (27x35cm-11x14in) s. cardboard. 4-May-4 Arroyo, Buenos Aires #8/R est:4500
£3644	$5940	€5320	Boats (50x60cm-20x24in) s. board. 17-Jul-3 Naón & Cia, Buenos Aires #81/R
£3846	$7000	€5615	Factory entrance (52x62cm-20x24in) s.d.1925. 29-Jun-4 Arroyo, Buenos Aires #28/R est:6800
£4396	$8000	€6418	Boats at dusk (56x70cm-22x28in) s. 29-Jun-4 Arroyo, Buenos Aires #94/R est:8000
£4860	$8700	€7096	Dusk in the ranch (39x51cm-15x20in) board. 11-May-4 Arroyo, Buenos Aires #53
£5191	$9500	€7579	Entering the harbour (26x37cm-10x15in) board. 1-Jun-4 Arroyo, Buenos Aires #75
£5525	$10000	€8067	Landscape in Spain (28x50cm-11x20in) board. 30-Mar-4 Arroyo, Buenos Aires #110
£6044	$11000	€8824	Cardinal (29x33cm-11x13in) s. board. 29-Jun-4 Arroyo, Buenos Aires #12/R est:4000
£6108	$10200	€8918	Red roofs (92x122cm-36x48in) s. 7-Oct-3 Galeria y Remates, Montevideo #23/R est:10000
£6425	$11500	€9381	Market (38x46cm-15x18in) s. cardboard. 4-May-4 Arroyo, Buenos Aires #29/R est:9500
£6557	$12000	€9573	Lonely (46x50cm-18x20in) board. 1-Jun-4 Arroyo, Buenos Aires #98
£6630	$12000	€9680	Mill (61x51cm-24x20in) 30-Mar-4 Arroyo, Buenos Aires #32
£9777	$17500	€14274	Procession (50x60cm-20x24in) s. cardboard. 4-May-4 Arroyo, Buenos Aires #86/R est:10000
£10056	$18000	€14682	Cardinal (30x40cm-12x16in) s. board. 4-May-4 Arroyo, Buenos Aires #91/R est:4000
£11264	$20500	€16445	Last lights (57x67cm-22x26in) s. 29-Jun-4 Arroyo, Buenos Aires #83/R est:8000
£13260	$24000	€19360	Procession (45x94cm-18x37in) canvas on board. 30-Mar-4 Arroyo, Buenos Aires #77
£18033	$33000	€26328	Out of the boat (22x50cm-9x20in) board. 1-Jun-4 Arroyo, Buenos Aires #95
£19553	$35000	€28547	In the temple (97x120cm-38x47in) s. 4-May-4 Arroyo, Buenos Aires #85/R est:28000

KOEKKOEK (19/20th C) Dutch

£6993	$12028	€10000	Bergers et troupeau dans un paysage boise avec riviere (84x109cm-33x43in) s. 3-Dec-3 Palais de Beaux Arts, Brussels #1283/R est:10000-12500

KOEKKOEK, Barend Cornelis (1803-1862) Dutch

£6200	$10354	€9052	A winter landscape with a castle in centre and figures on frozen lake (25x36cm-10x14in) s.indis.d.18. panel prov. 18-Jun-3 John Nicholson, Haslemere #745/R est:5000-8000
£66667	$120000	€100000	Summer landscape with travellers on a path (61x73cm-24x29in) s.d.1826 prov. 20-Apr-4 Sotheby's, Amsterdam #183/R est:100000-150000
£220000	$396000	€330000	Wooded landscape with figures along a stream (82x106cm-32x42in) s.d.1846. 20-Apr-4 Sotheby's, Amsterdam #173/R est:300000-500000
£230000	$391000	€335800	Cattle drivers in landscape (111x141cm-44x56in) s.d.1839 panel exhib.lit. 18-Nov-3 Sotheby's, London #324/R
Works on paper			
£811	$1427	€1200	Shepherdess (21x17cm-8x7in) s. black lead prov.exhib. 19-May-4 Sotheby's, Amsterdam #339/R

KOEKKOEK, Barend Cornelis (attrib) (1803-1862) Dutch

£6918	$11000	€10100	Port (41x55cm-16x22in) panel. 12-Sep-3 Skinner, Boston #308/R

KOEKKOEK, Gerard (1871-1956) Dutch

Works on paper			
£329	$595	€500	River landscape with mills and ships, a town in the background (41x61cm-16x24in) s. W/C. 19-Apr-4 Glerum, Amsterdam #16/R

KOEKKOEK, Hendrik Barend (1849-1909) Dutch

£2431	$4059	€3500	Woodgatherers in a winter forest (98x65cm-39x26in) s. 21-Oct-3 Sotheby's, Amsterdam #14/R est:3000-5000
£3333	$6067	€5000	Farmers bringing in the hay (60x80cm-24x31in) s. 1-Jul-4 Van Ham, Cologne #1463/R est:8000
£5347	$8395	€7700	Shepherdess with flock and dog in winter wood (76x63cm-30x25in) s. lit. 30-Aug-3 Hans Stahl, Toestorf #51/R est:7000

KOEKKOEK, Hendrik Pieter (1843-1890) Dutch

£340	$629	€496	Extensive landscape (26x35cm-10x14in) s. 13-Jan-4 Bonhams, Knightsbridge #66/R
£405	$714	€600	Lady walking through the woods with a dog (61x51cm-24x20in) i. 22-May-4 Sigalas, Stuttgart #438/R
£1316	$2421	€2000	Wooded landscape with a deer nearby a river (66x54cm-26x21in) s. 28-Jun-4 Sotheby's, Amsterdam #7/R est:1500-2000
£1933	$3480	€2900	Figures on a country road (42x62cm-17x24in) s.d.1868. 20-Apr-4 Sotheby's, Amsterdam #40/R est:3000-5000
£4645	$8500	€6782	Forest landscape with travellers (102x127cm-40x50in) s. 5-Jun-4 Neal Auction Company, New Orleans #483/R est:8000-12000

KOEKKOEK, Hermanus (1815-1882) Dutch

£2500	$4425	€3650	Beached fishing boats on a rocky shore. Dutch fishing boats in a calm (13x18cm-5x7in) s. panel pair. 28-Apr-4 Halls, Shrewsbury #501/R est:4000-6000
£3313	$5500	€4837	Boats on a Dutch canal (46x61cm-18x24in) bears another sig. 30-Sep-3 Christie's, Rockefeller NY #436/R est:5000-7000
£3472	$5729	€5000	Sailing ship in stormy sea (27x34cm-11x13in) mono.i. panel. 2-Jul-3 Neumeister, Munich #687/R est:3800
£4200	$7770	€6132	An estuary scene with a hay barge (25x38cm-10x15in) mono.d.1862 panel prov. 11-Mar-4 Duke & Son, Dorchester #209/R est:5000-10000
£9500	$17385	€13870	Shipping in an estuary with figures pushing a rowing boat into the surf (46x58cm-18x23in) mono.d.1858. 8-Jul-4 Duke & Son, Dorchester #168/R
£10667	$19200	€16000	Bringing in the catch (62x84cm-24x33in) s. indis d.1845 prov. 20-Apr-4 Sotheby's, Amsterdam #170/R est:12000-18000
£10690	$17852	€15500	Ships in choppy seas off coast (30x40cm-12x16in) s. prov. 15-Nov-3 Lempertz, Koln #1642/R est:12000
£12500	$20875	€18000	Fishing boats at low tide (24x34cm-9x13in) s.d.1849. 21-Oct-3 Sotheby's, Amsterdam #31/R est:8000-12000
£13673	$24475	€19963	Sailing in rough seas (26x35cm-10x14in) s.d.64. 25-May-4 Bukowskis, Stockholm #369/R est:20000-25000 (S.KR 185000)
£14000	$25900	€20440	Estuary with sailing boats, with a view of a city beyond, probably Amsterdam (36x58cm-14x23in) s. prov. 11-Mar-4 Duke & Son, Dorchester #227/R est:5000-10000
£26000	$47840	€37960	On the Scheldt (36x55cm-14x22in) s.d.1853. 23-Mar-4 Bonhams, New Bond Street #14/R est:20000-30000
£26000	$47320	€37960	Gathering in the nets in stormy seas (67x100cm-26x39in) s. 17-Jun-4 Christie's, London #3/R est:20000-30000
£31250	$53125	€45000	Calm - the barge De Vrouw preparing for departure (50x69cm-20x27in) s. panel. 28-Oct-3 Christie's, Amsterdam #246/R est:45000-60000

KOEKKOEK, Hermanus (attrib) (19th C) Dutch

£1000	$1720	€1460	Dutch shipping off the coast (20x26cm-8x10in) bears init. panel. 2-Dec-3 Sotheby's, London #36/R est:800-1200
£2083	$3312	€3000	Grand voilier (99x135cm-39x53in) 9-Sep-3 Vanderkindere, Brussels #8

KOEKKOEK, Hermanus (jnr) (1836-1909) Dutch

£671	$1242	€1000	Windmill in a polder landscape (46x36cm-18x14in) s.verso. 15-Mar-4 Sotheby's, Amsterdam #81/R est:800-1200
£2105	$3874	€3200	A village by a stream in spring (51x77cm-20x30in) s. 22-Jun-4 Christie's, Amsterdam #186/R est:2500-3500
£2174	$3500	€3174	Amsterdam (76x102cm-30x40in) s.J. van Couver. 20-Aug-3 James Julia, Fairfield #960/R est:2500-3000
£3766	$6816	€5498	The Old Harbour, Flushing, Holland (74x100cm-29x39in) s. i.verso. 1-Apr-4 Heffel, Vancouver #64/R est:8000-10000 (C.D 9000)
£9000	$16110	€13140	Calm water with fishing boats at the river near Amsterdam (42x66cm-17x26in) s. s.i. panel. 26-May-4 Christie's, Kensington #654/R est:5000-7000

KOEKKOEK, Hermanus Willem (1867-1929) Dutch

£1361	$2476	€2000	French infantry on reconnaissance (32x24cm-13x9in) s. panel. 3-Feb-4 Christie's, Amsterdam #74/R est:2000-3000
£6944	$11597	€10000	Battle scene from the French Prussian war (56x66cm-22x26in) s. 21-Oct-3 Sotheby's, Amsterdam #57/R est:10000-15000
£21333	$38400	€32000	Trumpeteer of the Third Regiment Hussars (45x60cm-18x24in) s. 21-Apr-4 Christie's, Amsterdam #222/R est:6000-8000

KOEKKOEK, J (?) Dutch

£3200	$5216	€4672	Man stood on a hump-back bridge over a stream, lake and mountains beyond (67x98cm-26x39in) 28-Sep-3 Wilkinson, Doncaster #270/R

KOEKKOEK, J H (1778-1851) Dutch

£2703	$5000	€3946	Landscape with waterfalls (58x71cm-23x28in) canvas on board. 13-Feb-4 Du Mouchelle, Detroit #2246/R est:5000-7000

KOEKKOEK, Jan Hermanus (1778-1851) Dutch

£1233	$2096	€1800	Shipping disaster in front of Zeeuwse coast (25x33cm-10x13in) s.i. panel. 5-Nov-3 Vendue Huis, Gravenhage #30/R est:1500-2000
£2800	$4480	€4088	At the harbour mouth (63x85cm-25x33in) s.d.1838 panel. 16-Sep-3 Bonhams, New Bond Street #52/R est:3000-5000
£4500	$7740	€6570	Rescue (77x103cm-30x41in) s. indis d. 2-Dec-3 Sotheby's, London #10/R est:5000-7000
£5500	$9460	€8030	Meeting on the beach (14x20cm-6x8in) s. i.d.1882 verso panel. 4-Dec-3 Christie's, Kensington #194/R est:3000-5000
£6000	$10800	€9000	Shipping by a coast in a brisk wind (21x27cm-8x11in) s. panel. 21-Apr-4 Christie's, Amsterdam #211/R est:10000-15000
Works on paper			
£320	$579	€480	Dutch coast with castle (14x18cm-6x7in) mono. wash Indian ink brush. 2-Apr-4 Winterberg, Heidelberg #454/R
£767	$1435	€1120	Seascape with paddle steamer in rough seas (22x31cm-9x12in) s. W/C pen. 25-Feb-4 Museumsbygningen, Copenhagen #126 (D.KR 8500)
£878	$1546	€1300	Fortress on water's edge (24x35cm-9x14in) s. pen Indian ink brush. 22-May-4 Lempertz, Koln #1428/R

KOEKKOEK, Jan Hermanus Barend (1840-1912) Dutch

£658	$1211	€1000	Cows in a landscape (16x24cm-6x9in) s. panel. 28-Jun-4 Sotheby's, Amsterdam #12/R
£1020	$1857	€1500	Sewing on the doorstep (29x36cm-11x14in) s. oil paper on panel. 3-Feb-4 Christie's, Amsterdam #117/R est:1500-2000
£1259	$2102	€1800	Fishermen on the beach (27x36cm-11x14in) s. panel. 30-Jun-3 Sotheby's, Amsterdam #139
£2200	$3740	€3212	Barges moored (22x30cm-9x12in) s. 19-Nov-3 Christie's, Kensington #536/R
£4133	$7605	€6200	River landscape with anglers in boat (23x40cm-9x16in) s. panel. 11-Jun-4 Hauswedell & Nolte, Hamburg #1043/R est:4000
£4167	$7083	€6000	Fishermen near a ruin on a riverbank (33x51cm-13x20in) s. prov. 28-Oct-3 Christie's, Amsterdam #18/R est:8000-12000
£5556	$9278	€8000	Peasants and his dog on a path (38x50cm-15x20in) s.d.1898 panel prov. 21-Oct-3 Sotheby's, Amsterdam #33/R est:8000-12000
£6250	$10438	€9000	Coastal scene (18x27cm-7x11in) s.d.1888 panel. 21-Oct-3 Sotheby's, Amsterdam #24/R est:3000-5000
£6800	$10812	€9860	Coastal scene, possibly off the Needles (81x132cm-32x52in) s. indis i. 9-Sep-3 Bonhams, Knightsbridge #305/R est:1500-2000
£6944	$11597	€10000	Shipping in a calm (37x54cm-15x21in) s.d.1860. 21-Oct-3 Sotheby's, Amsterdam #38/R est:6000-8000
£9028	$15076	€13000	Shipping in a calm (41x64cm-16x25in) s.d.67 panel. 21-Oct-3 Sotheby's, Amsterdam #196/R est:9000-12000
£9667	$17400	€14500	Unloading the catch (14x19cm-6x7in) s. panel. 20-Apr-4 Sotheby's, Amsterdam #19/R est:8000-12000
£11888	$20210	€17000	Fishing boat and rowing boat at harbour entrance (70x115cm-28x45in) s.d.1878. 22-Nov-3 Arnold, Frankfurt #571/R est:8000
£14667	$26400	€22000	Shipping in a calm (37x55cm-15x22in) s.d.60 panel. 20-Apr-4 Sotheby's, Amsterdam #1/R est:8000-12000
Works on paper			
£1000	$1600	€1460	Figures on shore watching shipping (20x33cm-8x13in) s.d.1865 W/C. 21-Sep-3 William Jenack, New York #284 est:3000-5000

KOEKKOEK, Johannes (1811-1831) Dutch

£10000	$18000	€15000	Shipping in a stiff breeze off the Dutch coast (21x27cm-8x11in) s. panel lit. 21-Apr-4 Christie's, Amsterdam #235/R est:14000-18000

KOEKKOEK, Marinus Adrianus I (1807-1870) Dutch

£1379	$2552	€2000	Wooded landscape with thatched cottage, logs and man with axe (21x32cm-8x13in) s. 11-Feb-4 Woodwards, Cork #15/R est:3000-5000
£2013	$3745	€3000	Extensive landscape with church and figures in the distance (34x45cm-13x18in) s.d.1845. 5-Mar-4 Wendl, Rudolstadt #3738/R est:2400
£2667	$4827	€4000	Paysage fluvial ensoleille avec vaches au paturage (49x73cm-19x29in) s. 30-Mar-4 Palais de Beaux Arts, Brussels #627/R est:4500-6000
£2917	$4871	€4200	Summer landscape with figures by a farm (46x62cm-18x24in) s. indis d. 21-Oct-3 Sotheby's, Amsterdam #67/R est:5000-7000
£4196	$7133	€6000	Berger et moutons dans un paysage rocheux (49x73cm-19x29in) s. 1-Dec-3 Palais de Beaux Arts, Brussels #367/R est:5000-7000
£5594	$9510	€8000	River landscape (34x41cm-13x16in) s. panel. 22-Nov-3 Arnold, Frankfurt #572/R est:1200
£6250	$10438	€9000	Extensive river landscape (39x45cm-15x18in) s.d.1840 prov. 21-Oct-3 Sotheby's, Amsterdam #44/R est:10000-15000
£8000	$14320	€12000	Lively mountain landscape (48x65cm-19x26in) d.1847 s.d.47 verso panel. 15-May-4 De Vuyst, Lokeren #416/R est:11000-13000
£19595	$34486	€29000	Mountain landscape with horse drawn cart (61x80cm-24x31in) s.d.1862. 22-May-4 Lempertz, Koln #1540/R est:20000-25000
£25333	$46613	€38000	Dutch landscape (74x100cm-29x39in) s.d.1845. 12-Jun-4 Villa Grisebach, Berlin #104/R est:9000-12000

KOEKKOEK, Marinus Adrianus I (attrib) (1807-1870) Dutch

£3311	$6026	€5000	Encounter in a mountain landscape (35x45cm-14x18in) panel. 21-Jun-4 Dorotheum, Vienna #130/R est:3600-4500

KOEKKOEK, Marinus Adrianus II (1873-1944) Dutch

£496	$829	€700	Ducks at the edge of the water (28x37cm-11x15in) s. 20-Oct-3 Glerum, Amsterdam #144/R
£2657	$4517	€3800	Patineurs en Hollande (37x60cm-15x24in) s. panel. 18-Nov-3 Vanderkindere, Brussels #11 est:2000-3000

KOEKKOEK, Willem (1839-1895) Dutch
£15000 $26850 €21900 Figures in a busy street (38x51cm-15x20in) s. 28-May-4 Lyon & Turnbull, Edinburgh #47/R est:15000-20000

KOELLA, Johann (1740-1778) Swiss
£10738 $19758 €16000 Portrait of Johann Caspar Lavater (18x13cm-7x5in) panel. 24-Mar-4 Dorotheum, Vienna #270/R est:9000-12000

KOELMAN, R (1847-1920) Italian
£1141 $2020 €1700 Echoppe dans une vieille rue a Rome (79x60cm-31x24in) s.i.d.1878. 30-Apr-4 Tajan, Paris #202/R est:1200-1500

KOEMAN, Kees (1895-1954) Dutch
£385 $654 €550 Still life (53x42cm-21x17in) s.d.23 i.verso board. 24-Nov-3 Glerum, Amsterdam #22/R

KOEMPOEL (1912-1987) Indonesian
£1290 $2065 €1883 Riverscene (30x40cm-12x16in) s. 18-May-3 Sotheby's, Singapore #169/R est:2000-3000 (S.D 3600)
£1376 $2202 €2009 Dodol manuk (30x40cm-12x16in) s.d.66 lit. 18-May-3 Sotheby's, Singapore #167/R est:2000-3000 (S.D 3840)
£1458 $2435 €2129 Flower seller (60x85cm-24x33in) s. 12-Oct-3 Sotheby's, Singapore #169/R est:3000-4000 (S.D 4200)
£1812 $2808 €2646 Cockfight (40x60cm-16x24in) s. 6-Oct-2 Sotheby's, Singapore #167/R est:2000-3000 (S.D 5000)
£2151 $3441 €3140 Pasar sudut kota (60x90cm-24x35in) s. 18-May-3 Sotheby's, Singapore #168/R est:4000-6000 (S.D 6000)

KOEMPOEL, Sujantno (20th C) Indonesian
£1088 $1948 €1600 Country road with ox-cart (60x120cm-24x47in) s. 16-Mar-4 Christie's, Amsterdam #58 est:700-900

KOEN, Irma René (?-1974) American
£1509 $2700 €2203 Wharf view (41x51cm-16x20in) s. prov. 14-May-4 Skinner, Boston #263/R est:1000-1500
£2514 $4500 €3670 Evening light, Rockport (31x31cm-12x12in) s. board prov. 14-May-4 Skinner, Boston #265/R est:1800-2200

KOEN, Niwayama (1870-1942) Japanese
Works on paper
£455 $782 €650 Mount Fuji reflected in the water near Tagonoura (113x29cm-44x11in) s.i.d.1910 ink col hanging scroll. 5-Dec-3 Lempertz, Koln #785/R

KOENIG, Anton Friedrich (elder) (1722-1787) German
Miniatures
£5000 $8650 €7300 Frederick William II, King of Prussia (9x7cm-4x3in) wood frame. 9-Dec-3 Christie's, London #27/R est:5000-7000
£6000 $10380 €8760 Frederick the Great, King of Prussia (8x7cm-3x3in) gilt-metal frame. 9-Dec-3 Christie's, London #24/R est:6000-8000

KOENIG, Dezso (1902-1972) South African
£413 $739 €603 Next to factory (38x49cm-15x19in) s. canvas on board. 31-May-4 Stephan Welz, Johannesburg #261 (SA.R 5000)

KOENIG, Ike (20th C) American
£335 $550 €489 Landscape with bluebonnets, hills and cabin in the distance (30x41cm-12x16in) s. prov. 31-May-3 Brunk, Ashville #429/R

KOENIG, John Franklin (1924-) American
£299 $500 €437 Untitled (89x89cm-35x35in) s.d.1958. 25-Oct-3 Rachel Davis, Shaker Heights #582/R
£299 $500 €437 S.F. an V (81x64cm-32x25in) s.i.d.1965 verso acrylic oil. 25-Oct-3 Rachel Davis, Shaker Heights #583/R
£1277 $2132 €1800 Carvoys (182x94cm-72x37in) s.i.d.1972 verso lit. 19-Oct-3 Charbonneaux, Paris #149/R est:1200
Works on paper
£296 $545 €450 Composition (36x48cm-14x19in) s.d.1954 mixed media. 28-Jun-4 Joron-Derem, Paris #221
£329 $605 €500 Composition (33x51cm-13x20in) s.d.1955 mixed media paper on canvas. 28-Jun-4 Joron-Derem, Paris #222
£336 $628 €500 Praya (66x35cm-26x14in) s.i.d.1996 collage. 29-Feb-4 Versailles Encheres #256/R
£336 $628 €500 Sans titre (65x44cm-26x17in) s.d.1983 mixed media collage. 29-Feb-4 Versailles Encheres #257
£369 $690 €550 Arriere-regard (50x40cm-20x16in) s.i.d.1988 mixed media collage cardboard. 29-Feb-4 Versailles Encheres #258

KOENIG, Jules Raymond (1872-?) French
£333 $597 €500 Village breton en bord de mer (50x65cm-20x26in) s. 16-May-4 Thierry & Lannon, Brest #325
Works on paper
£662 $1238 €1000 Bord de mer en Bretagne (52x79cm-20x31in) pastel. 24-Jul-4 Thierry & Lannon, Brest #104

KOENIGER, Walter (1881-1945) American
£549 $900 €796 Wooded landscape (41x53cm-16x21in) s. indis.i.verso. 4-Jun-3 Alderfer's, Hatfield #275/R
£1353 $2300 €1975 Woodland cottages, winter (51x61cm-20x24in) s. 21-Nov-3 Skinner, Boston #488/R est:1200-1800
£1477 $2600 €2156 Summer Woodstock, New York (43x56cm-17x22in) prov. 23-May-4 Hindman, Chicago #149/R est:2000-4000
£1648 $2950 €2406 Incoming sea, Monhegan Island, Maine (64x76cm-25x30in) s.d.27. 8-Jan-4 James Julia, Fairfield #571/R est:3000-4000
£1734 $3000 €2532 Silvered stream (61x91cm-24x36in) i. 10-Dec-3 Alderfer's, Hatfield #339/R est:3000-4000
£1772 $2800 €2587 Spring landscape with lake (81x81cm-32x32in) s. 7-Sep-3 Treadway Gallery, Cincinnati #590/R est:2500-4500
£2258 $4200 €3297 Winter afternoon (36x36cm-14x14in) s. canvasboard. 3-Mar-4 Christie's, Rockefeller NY #31/R est:2500-3500
£2258 $4200 €3297 Landscape with a stream, late winter (51x61cm-20x24in) s. 3-Mar-4 Christie's, Rockefeller NY #32/R est:3000-5000
£2374 $4250 €3466 By a brook in winter (64x76cm-25x30in) s. prov. 6-May-4 Shannon's, Milford #38/R est:4000-6000
£3824 $6500 €5583 Snow clad hills (76x76cm-30x30in) s. i.on stretcher. 29-Oct-3 Christie's, Los Angeles #68/R est:7000-9000
£4790 $8000 €6993 Winter Glow (51x61cm-20x24in) s. i.verso canvas on panel. 23-Oct-3 Shannon's, Milford #28/R est:4000-6000
Works on paper
£1196 $2200 €1746 Manhattan skyline (61x97cm-24x38in) col pastel exec. c.1940. 10-Jun-4 Swann Galleries, New York #135/R est:3000-5000

KOEPKE, Robert (1893-1968) German
£397 $723 €600 Landscape with the river Wumme (26x33cm-10x13in) s. board. 18-Jun-4 Bolland & Marotz, Bremen #357/R
£439 $786 €650 Two masted schooner in Arnis harbour on the Schlei (29x39cm-11x15in) s. i. verso board. 8-May-4 Hans Stahl, Toestorf #70
£570 $1050 €850 Blossoming trees in Worpswede (35x45cm-14x18in) s. board. 26-Mar-4 Bolland & Marotz, Bremen #341/R

KOERLE, Pancraz (1823-1875) German
£1597 $2635 €2300 Love token (56x47cm-22x19in) s.d.67 lit. 3-Jul-3 Van Ham, Cologne #1310/R est:3800

KOERNER, Ernst Karl Eugen (1846-1927) German
£278 $453 €400 Kom Ombo on the Nile (28x50cm-11x20in) mono.i.d.10/2 1905 canvas on board. 27-Sep-3 Dannenberg, Berlin #569/R
£600 $966 €870 Rough sea lashing against cliffs (81x122cm-32x48in) s.d.1926. 20-Aug-3 Brightwells, Leominster #892/R
£800 $1432 €1200 On the River Mole (24x39cm-9x15in) s.d.68 lit. 14-May-4 Schloss Ahlden, Ahlden #2836/R
£959 $1630 €1400 Nile landscape (35x51cm-14x20in) s.d.1921. 8-Nov-3 Geble, Radolfzell #784/R
£3000 $5370 €4380 View of Baalbeck, Lebanon (35x51cm-14x20in) s.d.1921. 26-May-4 Sotheby's, Olympia #306/R est:3000-5000
£4500 $7515 €6570 Sunset over the Pyramids (50x75cm-20x30in) s.d.1924 prov. 14-Oct-3 Sotheby's, London #74/R est:2000-3000
£28000 $46760 €40880 View inside the temple of Philae, Egypt (100x150cm-39x59in) s.d.1910 prov. 14-Oct-3 Sotheby's, London #62/R est:15000-20000

KOERNER, W H D (1878-1938) American
£2206 $3750 €3221 When a rope was the law (76x43cm-30x17in) init. board prov.lit. 1-Nov-3 Santa Fe Art, Santa Fe #107/R est:6000-8000
£5882 $10000 €8588 Long rifle, Senorita (66x84cm-26x33in) init. board prov.lit. 1-Nov-3 Santa Fe Art, Santa Fe #109/R est:20000-30000
£8235 $14000 €12023 The law must act (91x71cm-36x28in) s.d.1921 prov.lit. 1-Nov-3 Santa Fe Art, Santa Fe #233/R est:30000-40000

KOERNER, William Henry Dethlef (1878-1938) American
£2727 $4800 €3981 Western scene (91x41cm-36x16in) s. 21-May-4 Pook & Pook, Downington #230/R est:4000-5000
Works on paper
£621 $1000 €900 Steve Davis, sheriff (33x25cm-13x10in) chl. 22-Aug-3 Altermann Galleries, Santa Fe #82

KOESTER, Alexander (1864-1932) German
£3056 $5042 €4400 Portrait of Alois Konrad Schweizler from Gossensass (83x65cm-33x26in) i. i. verso. 2-Jul-3 Neumeister, Munich #688/R est:3000
£3267 $5847 €4900 Ducks by lakeshore (44x61cm-17x24in) prov.lit. 14-May-4 Schloss Ahlden, Ahlden #2918/R est:2800
£6711 $12349 €10000 Winter landscape (98x33cm-39x13in) s. 25-Mar-4 Dr Fritz Nagel, Stuttgart #729/R est:10000
£7692 $13231 €11000 By the side of a pond (55x78cm-22x31in) s. 3-Dec-3 Neumeister, Munich #633/R est:6500
£7862 $13130 €11400 Faggot gatherer in autumn wood (79x124cm-31x49in) s. lit. 10-Jul-3 Allgauer, Kempten #2558/R est:9500
£23490 $41577 €35000 Ducks resting (56x76cm-22x30in) prov. 28-Apr-4 Wiener Kunst Auktionen, Vienna #90/R est:35000-70000
£23529 $40000 €34352 Five ducks in a pond (42x60cm-17x24in) s. 28-Oct-3 Sotheby's, New York #170/R est:40000-60000
£35000 $59500 €51100 Ducks in a pond (61x80cm-24x31in) s. prov. 18-Nov-3 Sotheby's, London #351/R
£37500 $60000 €54750 Ducks along riverbank (64x89cm-25x35in) s. 20-Sep-3 Sloans & Kenyon, Bethesda #1183/R est:35000-40000
£46980 $84094 €70000 Ducks in the reeds (53x81cm-21x32in) s. lit. 27-May-4 Hassfurther, Vienna #55/R est:70000-80000
£52083 $84896 €75000 Five white ducks in reedy water (70x100cm-28x39in) s. lit. 24-Sep-3 Neumeister, Munich #472/R est:95000
£63333 $115267 €95000 Ducks on jetty and in water (77x127cm-30x50in) s. 30-Jun-4 Neumeister, Munich #591/R est:65000
Works on paper
£313 $522 €450 Six ducks on shore with clouds (13x17cm-5x7in) pencil paper on board. 24-Oct-3 Ketterer, Hamburg #875/R
£347 $580 €500 Five ducks in reeds (9x16cm-4x6in) pencil. 24-Oct-3 Ketterer, Hamburg #874/R
£1053 $1937 €1600 Six ducks in the reeds at the lakeshore (14x22cm-6x9in) W/C pencil. 26-Jun-4 Karrenbauer, Konstanz #1739/R est:800
£1250 $2088 €1800 Ducks on pond (22x33cm-9x13in) chl. 24-Oct-3 Ketterer, Hamburg #433/R est:1800-2000
£1316 $2421 €2000 Ten ducks swimming in the sunlight (12x17cm-5x7in) s. mixed media oil tempera cardboard. 26-Jun-4 Karrenbauer, Konstanz #1738/R est:1200

KOETS, Roelof (younger) (1655-1725) Dutch

£1078 $1800 €1574 Portrait (43x36cm-17x14in) 19-Oct-3 Susanin's, Chicago #6024/R est:2000-4000

KOFOED, Herman (1743-1815) Danish

£595 $1083 €869 Portrait of the actress Miss Marie Schmidt as Dyveke (74x59cm-29x23in) 7-Feb-4 Rasmussen, Havnen #2004/R (D.KR 6500)

KOGAN, Moissey (1879-1942) Russian

Sculpture

£2667 $4907 €4000 Seated female nude by plant (37x27x3cm-15x11x1in) mono. bronze relief. 10-Jun-4 Hauswedell & Nolte, Hamburg #345/R est:2000

£3813 $6253 €5300 Bather (29x38x3cm-11x15x1in) bears i. verso terracotta. 4-Jun-3 Ketterer, Hamburg #572/R est:2500-3000

Works on paper

£300 $540 €450 Reclining female nude (32x50cm-13x20in) chl. 24-Apr-4 Dr Lehr, Berlin #220/R

KOGAN, Nina (1887-1942) Russian

£34667 $63440 €52000 Suprematist composition (56x50cm-22x20in) prov. 5-Jun-4 Lempertz, Koln #794/R est:40000-50000

Works on paper

£812 $1495 €1186 Composition (27x20cm-11x8in) s. gouache. 29-Mar-4 Rasmussen, Copenhagen #436/R (D.KR 9000)

£2125 $3760 €3103 Untitled (20x21cm-8x8in) init. verso W/C exhib. 27-Apr-4 AB Stockholms Auktionsverk #1200/R est:6000-8000 (S.KR 29000)

£3971 $7307 €5798 Surrealistic composition (30x23cm-12x9in) s.in Russian verso gouache Indian ink pencil. 29-Mar-4 Rasmussen, Copenhagen #437/R est:6000 (D.KR 44000)

KOGANOWSKY, Jakob (1874-1926) Austrian

£780 $1303 €1100 Village street in spring (90x100cm-35x39in) s. 14-Oct-3 Dorotheum, Vienna #18/R

£1900 $3401 €2774 Roman ruin in Schonbrunn, Vienna (125x156cm-49x61in) s.i.d.1912. 26-May-4 Sotheby's, Olympia #321/R est:1000-1500

KOGELNIK, Kiki (1935-1997) Austrian

£27778 $47222 €40000 Beautiful but sad (200x140cm-79x55in) s.d.73 oil acrylic exhib.lit. 28-Oct-3 Wiener Kunst Auktionen, Vienna #275/R est:35000-70000

Prints

£2400 $4296 €3600 Split magenta (50x40cm-20x16in) s.i.d.96 etching diamond dust. 13-May-4 Dorotheum, Linz #644/R est:2400-2800

Sculpture

£3497 $5944 €5000 Female clones (35x27x27cm-14x11x11in) mono.verso pat bronze marble base. 28-Nov-3 Wiener Kunst Auktionen, Vienna #693/R est:5000-8000

Works on paper

£1560 $2606 €2200 Outer space head (80x60cm-31x24in) s.i.d.92 mixed media. 14-Oct-3 Dorotheum, Vienna #306/R est:1500-1600

KOGEVINAS, Lykourgos (1887-1940) Greek

£3200 $5728 €4672 View of Constantinople from Peran (33x41cm-13x16in) s. canvas on cardboard. 11-May-4 Bonhams, New Bond Street #78/R est:2000-3000

£8000 $14320 €11680 View of Corfu (70x100cm-28x39in) s. exhib. 11-May-4 Bonhams, New Bond Street #32/R est:6000-8000

KOGL, Benedict (1892-1969) German

£310 $518 €450 Cat (24x18cm-9x7in) s. panel. 9-Jul-3 Hugo Ruef, Munich #127/R

£430 $688 €628 Four young cats (14x18cm-6x7in) s. panel. 16-Sep-3 Philippe Schuler, Zurich #3366 (S.FR 950)

£517 $864 €750 Two cats with snail (12x17cm-5x7in) s. panel. 9-Jul-3 Hugo Ruef, Munich #128

£550 $1007 €803 Heartfelt plea (7x6cm-3x2in) s. board. 8-Apr-4 Christie's, Kensington #142/R

£671 $1235 €1000 Four kittens watching butterfly (18x24cm-7x9in) s. 25-Mar-4 Dr Fritz Nagel, Stuttgart #743/R

£909 $1545 €1300 Three kittens in garden looking at butterfly (18x24cm-7x9in) s. 20-Nov-3 Van Ham, Cologne #1686/R

£1034 $1914 €1500 Five kittens playing (23x18cm-9x7in) s. 12-Feb-4 Weidler, Nurnberg #303/R est:1500

£1119 $1902 €1600 Four kittnes (18x24cm-7x9in) s. panel. 20-Nov-3 Van Ham, Cologne #1687 est:900

£1310 $2188 €1900 Interior with cat family (28x42cm-11x17in) s. lit. 10-Jul-3 Allgauer, Kempten #2559/R

KOGLER, Harry (1921-1999) German

Works on paper

£600 $1074 €900 Abstract composition (29x45cm-11x18in) s.d. bodycol. 15-May-4 Bassenge, Berlin #6943/R

KOGLER, Karl (1838-1923) German

£3356 $6242 €5000 Allegorical portrayal of childhood (129x217cm-51x85in) s.d.1892. 6-Mar-4 Arnold, Frankfurt #760/R est:1200

KOGLER, Peter (1959-) Austrian

£1259 $2140 €1800 Alf (180x120cm-71x47in) s.d.88 verso acrylic silkscreen exhib. 27-Nov-3 Lempertz, Koln #228/R est:2000

KOHL, Ludwig (1746-1821) Austrian

£8437 $14849 €12656 Interior of a church (65x87cm-26x34in) s. panel. 22-May-4 Dorotheum, Prague #3/R est:260000-400000 (C.KR 400000)

KOHL, Pierre-Ernest (1897-1987) French

£315 $526 €450 Paris, la Seine au Louvre (33x47cm-13x19in) s. 7-Oct-3 Livinec, Gaudcheau & Jezequel, Rennes #107

£629 $1051 €900 Portrait de femme (41x33cm-16x13in) s.d.31. 7-Oct-3 Livinec, Gaudcheau & Jezequel, Rennes #115

£699 $1168 €1000 Ballerine (61x50cm-24x20in) s. 7-Oct-3 Livinec, Gaudcheau & Jezequel, Rennes #114/R

£867 $1560 €1300 Collier rouge a la robe verte (66x50cm-26x20in) s. 26-Apr-4 Tajan, Paris #191 est:1200-1500

£1189 $1985 €1700 Jeune femme aux fleurs (73x50cm-29x20in) s.d.1927 prov. 7-Oct-3 Livinec, Gaudcheau & Jezequel, Rennes #113/R

£1259 $2102 €1800 Nu au sofa (46x49cm-18x19in) s.d. 7-Oct-3 Livinec, Gaudcheau & Jezequel, Rennes #108

£1818 $3036 €2600 Femme au bonnet (65x50cm-26x20in) s.d.28. 7-Oct-3 Livinec, Gaudcheau & Jezequel, Rennes #106/R

£3636 $6073 €5200 Chapeau de paille (65x46cm-26x18in) s.d.26. 7-Oct-3 Livinec, Gaudcheau & Jezequel, Rennes #112/R

£3846 $6423 €5500 Femme au voile (116x81cm-46x32in) s.d.1930. 7-Oct-3 Livinec, Gaudcheau & Jezequel, Rennes #111/R

£9650 $16116 €13800 Salome (116x81cm-46x32in) s.d.1925 exhib. 7-Oct-3 Livinec, Gaudcheau & Jezequel, Rennes #110/R

Works on paper

£392 $654 €560 Nu allonge (31x43cm-12x17in) s.d.32 crayon stump dr. 7-Oct-3 Livinec, Gaudcheau & Jezequel, Rennes #116

KOHL, Robert (1891-1944) German

£9396 $16819 €14000 Jug with flowers in front of blue cupboard (70x56cm-28x22in) s. 25-May-4 Dorotheum, Vienna #193/R est:8000-12000

Works on paper

£526 $968 €800 Woodland landscape (37x47cm-15x19in) s.i.d.1922 W/C. 25-Jun-4 Michael Zeller, Lindau #604/R

KOHL, Thomas (1960-) German

£280 $476 €400 Marseilles (51x73cm-20x29in) s.d.1990 verso board exhib. 27-Nov-3 Lempertz, Koln #232/R

£350 $594 €500 Loren (50x70cm-20x28in) s.i.d.1993 verso exhib. 27-Nov-3 Lempertz, Koln #233/R

KOHLER, Edgar (?) British?

£350 $648 €511 Study of blossom in a blue vase (48cm-19in circular) 13-Feb-4 Keys, Aylsham #262a

KOHLER, Fritz (1887-1971) German

£433 $793 €650 Summer at Niederrhein (61x81cm-24x32in) s.i. 5-Jun-4 Arnold, Frankfurt #630/R

£524 $876 €750 Snowy garden (40x50cm-16x20in) s. i. verso board. 28-Jun-3 Bolland & Marotz, Bremen #688/R

£699 $1189 €1000 Lower Rhine at Kaiserswerth (60x80cm-24x31in) s. 20-Nov-3 Van Ham, Cologne #1688

£1467 $2655 €2200 Baltic coast near Arenshoop (260x190cm-102x75in) s. 1-Apr-4 Van Ham, Cologne #1488/R est:2000

KOHLER, Giampaolo (20th C) ?

£671 $1242 €1000 Nativity on Mount Fuji (35x150cm-14x59in) s.i.d.2004 acrylic in 3 pieces. 13-Mar-4 Meeting Art, Vercelli #73

KOHLER, Gustav (1859-?) German

£1955 $3500 €2854 Portraits of a mand and a woman (18x13cm-7x5in) s. oil paper pair. 7-May-4 Sloans & Kenyon, Bethesda #1650/R est:4000-6000

KOHLER, Maxim (1908-1959) German

£278 $453 €400 Coastal landscape (66x82cm-26x32in) s. 27-Sep-3 Dr Fritz Nagel, Stuttgart #9237/R

£2128 $3553 €3000 Woman sitting in armchair (65x80cm-26x31in) s. bears d. 16-Oct-3 Dorotheum, Salzburg #683/R est:2800-3500

KOHLER, Mela (attrib) (1885-1960) Austrian

Works on paper

£470 $869 €700 Spanish Madonna with child (6x5cm-2x2in) gouache W/C silver. 9-Mar-4 Dorotheum, Vienna #25/R

KOHLHOFF, Walter (1906-1981) German

£267 $480 €400 Industrial landscape, Berlin (50x70cm-20x28in) s.d. egg tempera panel. 24-Apr-4 Dr Lehr, Berlin #221/R

£417 $696 €600 Berlin street (49x70cm-19x28in) s.d. egg tempera panel. 25-Oct-3 Dr Lehr, Berlin #277/R

Works on paper

£313 $494 €450 Mountain landscape (40x57cm-16x22in) s.d.52 W/C lit. 19-Sep-3 Schloss Ahlden, Ahlden #1666/R

KOHLHOFF, Wilhelm (1893-1971) German

£10490 $17832 €15000 Light night sky over mountain village (63x51cm-25x20in) exhib. 29-Nov-3 Villa Grisebach, Berlin #229/R est:15000-20000

Works on paper

£1000 $1790 €1500 Girl nude (43x22cm-17x9in) s.d.Marz 27 pencil oil chk. 14-May-4 Ketterer, Munich #40/R est:1800-2200

KOHLMANN, Ejnar (1888-1968) Finnish

£272 $495 €400 Winter landscape (30x38cm-12x15in) s. 8-Feb-4 Bukowskis, Helsinki #376/R

£302	$562	€450	Pine trees by the shore (60x80cm-24x31in) s,. 7-Mar-4 Bukowskis, Helsinki #356/R
£306	$510	€440	Cranes in flight (50x61cm-20x24in) s. 26-Oct-3 Bukowskis, Helsinki #389/R
£324	$518	€460	Capercaillies in pine tree (68x56cm-27x22in) s. 21-Sep-3 Bukowskis, Helsinki #372/R
£333	$613	€500	Autumn landscape (56x76cm-22x30in) s.d.1951. 9-Jun-4 Bukowskis, Helsinki #432/R
£362	$674	€540	Capercaillie in birch wood (50x61cm-20x24in) s. 7-Mar-4 Bukowskis, Helsinki #353/R
£376	$699	€560	Pheasants (63x83cm-25x33in) s. 7-Mar-4 Bukowskis, Helsinki #352/R
£382	$638	€550	Ducks (70x86cm-28x34in) s. 23-Oct-3 Hagelstam, Helsinki #823
£387	$620	€550	Mallards (45x75cm-18x30in) s. 21-Sep-3 Bukowskis, Helsinki #371/R
£423	$676	€600	Marshes (73x45cm-29x18in) s. 18-Sep-3 Hagelstam, Helsinki #1004/R
£533	$981	€800	Capercaillie crooning (61x50cm-24x20in) s.d.65. 9-Jun-4 Bukowskis, Helsinki #431/R
£691	$1243	€1009	Capercaillies crooning (64x91cm-25x36in) s.d.1956. 26-Jan-4 Lilla Bukowskis, Stockholm #25 (S.KR 9200)
£1745	$3246	€2600	Winter landscape with capercaillies (100x134cm-39x53in) s.d.1954. 7-Mar-4 Bukowskis, Helsinki #354/R est:1500
£2973	$5322	€4400	Geese in early spring landscape (84x113cm-33x44in) s.d.1948. 8-May-4 Bukowskis, Helsinki #83/R est:2000-2300

KOHLMANN, Hermann (1907-) German?

£284	$443	€420	Portrait of peasant woman (107x75cm-42x30in) s.d.1939. 28-Mar-3 Altus, Berlin #544/R

KOHLMEYER, Ida (1912-1997) American

£1000	$1840	€1500	Adrift (23x19cm-9x7in) s. canvas on masonite. 11-Jun-4 Hauswedell & Nolte, Hamburg #1381/R est:1500
£1111	$1800	€1622	Cloth with fruit (36x46cm-14x18in) s.i.verso. 2-Aug-3 Neal Auction Company, New Orleans #397/R est:1500-2500
£1163	$2000	€1698	Abstract squares (10x23cm-4x9in) s.d.1977. 6-Dec-3 Neal Auction Company, New Orleans #614/R est:2000-3000
£1412	$2400	€2062	Mimbus (84x53cm-33x21in) s. prov. 22-Nov-3 New Orleans Auction, New Orleans #1244/R est:2500-4000
£1765	$3000	€2577	Cluster 2-16 (91x117cm-36x46in) s.d.1977 oil oilstick prov. 9-Nov-3 Bonhams & Butterfields, Los Angeles #4089/R est:6000-8000
£2439	$3829	€3537	Circus series num 18 (126x123cm-50x48in) s.d.78 oil pastel. 27-Aug-3 Christie's, Sydney #573/R est:12000-15000 (A.D 6000)
£3039	$5500	€4437	Cluster A-87 (81x86cm-32x34in) s.d.1987 oil stick acrylic. 3-Apr-4 Neal Auction Company, New Orleans #561/R est:7000-10000
£6044	$11000	€8824	Cluster 2-16 (91x117cm-36x46in) s.d.1977 i.verso. 7-Feb-4 Neal Auction Company, New Orleans #496/R est:8000-12000

KOHLSTADT, Fritz (1921-) German

Works on paper

£268	$475	€400	Old aqueduct in Andalusia (29x33cm-11x13in) s.d. gouache col chk. 30-Apr-4 Dr Fritz Nagel, Stuttgart #297/R
£336	$594	€500	Finca in Andalusia (24x32cm-9x13in) s.i.d. gouache col chk paper on board. 30-Apr-4 Dr Fritz Nagel, Stuttgart #296/R

KOHN, Jay (20th C) American

£546	$1000	€819	Rosey green wall (246x300cm-97x118in) 10-Jul-4 Hindman, Chicago #275/R est:1000-1500

KOHNHOLZ, Johann Wilhelm Julius (1839-1925) German

£940	$1748	€1400	Mountain scene with lake and approaching storms (109x137cm-43x54in) s. 5-Mar-4 Wendl, Rudolstadt #3737/R
£1528	$2521	€2200	Schloss Starnberg (115x82cm-45x32in) s. 3-Jul-3 Van Ham, Cologne #1308/R est:2500
£1538	$2615	€2200	Early morning on the Schliersee (55x81cm-22x32in) s. 20-Nov-3 Van Ham, Cologne #1689/R est:2500

KOHRL, Ludwig (1858-1927) German

£467	$845	€700	Girl with goldfish in bowl (38x30cm-15x12in) s. 1-Apr-4 Van Ham, Cologne #1494

KOISTINEN, Unto (1917-1994) Finnish

£972	$1624	€1400	Two oaks (62x50cm-24x20in) s.d.1962. 23-Oct-3 Hagelstam, Helsinki #906/R
£1149	$2056	€1700	Mountain landscape (34x46cm-13x18in) s.d.1959 board. 8-May-4 Bukowskis, Helsinki #146/R est:2000-2500
£1408	$2437	€2000	Couple (23x19cm-9x7in) s.d.1970 board. 13-Dec-3 Hagelstam, Helsinki #167/R est:2500
£1538	$2615	€2200	Model in the studio (30x23cm-12x9in) s. board. 29-Nov-3 Bukowskis, Helsinki #129/R est:2500-2800
£1678	$3121	€2500	Nude (18x17cm-7x7in) s.d.1978. 7-Mar-4 Bukowskis, Helsinki #357/R est:2500
£1689	$3024	€2500	A beauty (22x18cm-9x7in) s.d.1978. 8-May-4 Bukowskis, Helsinki #71/R est:2500-3000
£1745	$3211	€2600	Nude (19x22cm-7x9in) s.d.1982. 25-Mar-4 Hagelstam, Helsinki #942/R est:2500
£1888	$3210	€2700	Model resting (28x40cm-11x16in) s.d.1960 board. 29-Nov-3 Bukowskis, Helsinki #171/R est:3000-3500
£1946	$3620	€2900	Seated female nude (21x18cm-8x7in) s.d.1977. 7-Mar-4 Bukowskis, Helsinki #359/R est:3000
£1946	$3620	€2900	Standing female nude (22x17cm-9x7in) s.d.1977. 7-Mar-4 Bukowskis, Helsinki #361/R est:3000
£1946	$3620	€2900	The back of a female nude (21x17cm-8x7in) s.d.1977. 7-Mar-4 Bukowskis, Helsinki #362/R est:3000
£2162	$3870	€3200	Mother's love (22x18cm-9x7in) s.d.1977 board. 8-May-4 Bukowskis, Helsinki #127/R est:3000-3500
£2183	$3777	€3100	Grieving Tanja (19x23cm-7x9in) s.d.1984 board. 13-Dec-3 Hagelstam, Helsinki #168/R est:2500
£2308	$3923	€3300	Model (40x28cm-16x11in) s.d.1961 board. 29-Nov-3 Bukowskis, Helsinki #128/R est:3000-3500
£2333	$4177	€3500	Two female nudes (27x33cm-11x13in) s.d.1976 board. 15-May-4 Hagelstam, Helsinki #177/R est:4000
£2400	$4296	€3600	Woman's back (27x33cm-11x13in) s.d.1979 board. 15-May-4 Hagelstam, Helsinki #178/R est:4000
£2667	$4773	€4000	Nude (36x31cm-14x12in) s.d.1972 board. 15-May-4 Hagelstam, Helsinki #180/R est:4000
£2667	$4773	€4000	Nude (38x33cm-15x13in) s.d.1973 board. 15-May-4 Hagelstam, Helsinki #181/R est:4000
£2685	$4993	€4000	Female nude (60x73cm-24x29in) s.d.50 exhib. 7-Mar-4 Bukowskis, Helsinki #358/R est:5000
£2703	$4838	€4000	Seated woman (35x31cm-14x12in) s.d.1971 board. 8-May-4 Bukowskis, Helsinki #128/R est:5000-5500
£3378	$6047	€5000	Anja (93x73cm-37x29in) s. board. 8-May-4 Bukowskis, Helsinki #69/R est:6000-8000
£3378	$6047	€5000	Tanja (37x29cm-15x11in) s.d.1979 board. 8-May-4 Bukowskis, Helsinki #125/R est:5000-6000
£3691	$6866	€5500	Coastal landscape (73x92cm-29x36in) s.d.1950 exhib. 7-Mar-4 Bukowskis, Helsinki #360/R est:3500
£4000	$7160	€6000	Woman (92x74cm-36x29in) s.d.1963. 15-May-4 Hagelstam, Helsinki #176/R est:6000
£4196	$7133	€6000	Seated female nude (65x50cm-26x20in) s.d.1965 board. 29-Nov-3 Bukowskis, Helsinki #127/R est:6000-7000

Works on paper

£660	$1102	€950	Head (45x36cm-18x14in) s. wash. 23-Oct-3 Hagelstam, Helsinki #1016

KOIVIKKO, Pentti (1944-) Finnish

£437	$699	€620	Snowball fight, Naadendal (90x60cm-35x24in) s.d.2001. 21-Sep-3 Bukowskis, Helsinki #377/R

KOIVU, Rudolf (1890-1946) Finnish

£604	$1111	€900	Landscape (40x50cm-16x20in) s. 25-Mar-4 Hagelstam, Helsinki #824
£2400	$4296	€3600	Early spring sunshine (73x48cm-29x19in) s.d.1917. 15-May-4 Hagelstam, Helsinki #141/R est:1200

KOJVANEC, Vladim (19/20th C) ?

£734	$1248	€1050	Summer's day (70x100cm-28x39in) s. 28-Nov-3 Schloss Ahlden, Ahlden #721/R

KOKAIA, Badri (20th C) ?

Works on paper

£1034	$1914	€1500	Untitled (195x195cm-77x77in) s.d.1997 mixed media on canvas. 14-Jan-4 Castellana, Madrid #241/R est:1500

KOKAN, Shiba (attrib) (1747-1818) Japanese

Works on paper

£1600	$2672	€2336	Ferry (31x31cm-12x12in) s. ink col. 12-Nov-3 Christie's, London #59/R est:2000-3000

KOKEN, Gustav (1850-1910) German

£1250	$1975	€1800	Farmstead in summer landscape (46x54cm-18x21in) mono. paper on canvas lit. 19-Sep-3 Schloss Ahlden, Ahlden #1695/R est:1800

KOKEN, Paul (1853-?) German

£1338	$2154	€1900	Old town in summer with river and stone bridge (107x78cm-42x31in) s.d. 22-Aug-3 Altus, Berlin #527/R est:850
£2200	$3982	€3300	North German city (106x79cm-42x31in) s. 1-Apr-4 Van Ham, Cologne #1495/R est:4000

KOKINE, Mikhail (1921-) Russian

£336	$601	€500	Still life in the garden (65x46cm-26x18in) s. 25-May-4 Durán, Madrid #719/R
£451	$736	€650	Spring day (65x65cm-26x26in) s. 23-Sep-3 Durán, Madrid #664/R

KOKKA, Astrid (1938-) ?

£600	$1092	€876	White (161x126cm-63x50in) s.verso. 4-Feb-4 Sotheby's, Olympia #231/R

KOKKEN, Henry (1860-1941) Belgian

£372	$654	€550	Violets (40x50cm-16x20in) s. 24-May-4 Bernaerts, Antwerp #476/R
£372	$665	€550	Portrait d'homme (100x85cm-39x33in) 10-May-4 Amberes, Antwerp #277
£738	$1373	€1100	Still life with fruit and flowers (33x51cm-13x20in) s. panel. 8-Mar-4 Bernaerts, Antwerp #6/R
£1241	$2061	€1800	Still life with roses (74x49cm-29x19in) 6-Oct-3 Amberes, Antwerp #233

KOKKINIDIS, Dimosthenis (1929-) Greek

Works on paper

£1300	$2327	€1898	Composition (55x55cm-22x22in) s.d.65 gouache cardboard. 11-May-4 Bonhams, New Bond Street #124/R est:500-700

KOKLIOUCHKINE, Georgi (1926-) Russian

£272	$495	€400	Au champ des courses. s. 8-Feb-4 Lesieur & Le Bars, Le Havre #25

KOKO, Demeter (1891-1929) Austrian

£3846	$6538	€5500	Steinerne Mill (67x94cm-26x37in) s. board. 27-Nov-3 Dorotheum, Linz #452/R est:9000-12000

KOKO-MICOLETZKY, Friedrich (1887-1981) Austrian

£297	$475	€434	Sunrise over snow covered peaks (61x81cm-24x32in) s. 20-Sep-3 Sloans & Kenyon, Bethesda #147/R
£650	$1086	€949	Sunlit alpine landscape (51x65cm-20x26in) s.i. 8-Oct-3 Christie's, Kensington #762/R
£664	$1143	€950	Snowy winter landscape in evening light (50x75cm-20x30in) s. 5-Dec-3 Michael Zeller, Lindau #672/R
£900	$1611	€1314	New dawn in the Alps (50x70cm-20x28in) s. 18-Mar-4 Christie's, Kensington #509/R
£1268	$2218	€1800	Innsbruck as seen from Isel mountains (69x94cm-27x37in) s.i.verso prov. 19-Dec-3 Dorotheum, Vienna #96/R est:1000-1500

KOKOSCHKA, Oskar (1886-1980) Austrian

£26846	$48054	€40000	Portrait of a girl (41x28cm-16x11in) mono. canvas on masonite. 27-May-4 Hassfurther, Vienna #5/R est:30000-40000
£41176	$70000	€60117	Still life with fruit and jug (60x93cm-24x37in) init. painted 1931 prov.lit. 6-Nov-3 Sotheby's, New York #231/R est:80000-120000
£70470	$126141	€105000	Self portrait (44x32cm-17x13in) mono. chl lit. 27-May-4 Hassfurther, Vienna #1/R est:40000-70000
£500000	$850000	€730000	London, Richmond Terrace (89x130cm-35x51in) init. painted 1926 prov.exhib.lit. 5-Nov-3 Sotheby's, New York #21/R est:700000-900000
Prints			
£2657	$4438	€3800	Portrait of working woman (44x32cm-17x13in) s. lithograph. 10-Oct-3 Winterberg, Heidelberg #1540/R est:4800
£2800	$5152	€4200	Ruth II - Ruth Landshoff (31x23cm-12x9in) s. lithograph. 10-Jun-4 Hauswedell & Nolte, Hamburg #358/R est:2500
£3667	$6747	€5500	Self portrait (96x59cm-38x23in) s. col lithograph. 10-Jun-4 Hauswedell & Nolte, Hamburg #361/R est:6000
£5944	$9927	€8500	Working woman wearing blue scarf (34x25cm-13x10in) col lithograph. 10-Oct-3 Winterberg, Heidelberg #1541/R est:4800
£20979	$35664	€30000	Woman picking cotton (94x38cm-37x15in) mono. col lithograph. 26-Nov-3 Dorotheum, Vienna #22/R est:17000-24000
Works on paper			
£1398	$2600	€2041	Mannerakt (28x21cm-11x8in) init. pen ink. 2-Mar-4 Swann Galleries, New York #316/R est:2500-3500
£1800	$3114	€2628	Flasche und Trauben (27x35cm-11x14in) init.i.d.46 pencil col crayon. 11-Dec-3 Christie's, Kensington #174/R est:2000-3000
£1899	$3000	€2773	Battle of Thermopolis (64x56cm-25x22in) mono. W/C. 27-Jul-3 William Jenack, New York #60 est:2000-3000
£2000	$3680	€2920	Landschaft mit Hauschen. Springende Lachsforelle (19x28cm-7x11in) i. col crayon double-sided exec c.1943 prov. 24-Jun-4 Christie's, London #383/R est:3000-4000
£2400	$4296	€3504	Nude woman (33x24cm-13x9in) s.i. col crayon prov. 11-May-4 Sotheby's, Olympia #622/R est:3000-4000
£3200	$5536	€4672	Konstanze Isepp II (27x35cm-11x14in) s.i.d.46 col crayon prov. 11-Dec-3 Christie's, Kensington #171/R est:3000-4000
£4027	$7208	€6000	Wine leaves (27x37cm-11x15in) s.d.47 col pen prov. 25-May-4 Dorotheum, Vienna #219/R est:7000-9000
£4200	$7602	€6132	Portrat von Jacqueline Borowski (71x51cm-28x20in) s.i.d.59 chl. 1-Apr-4 Christie's, Kensington #45/R est:3000-4000
£4333	$7973	€6500	Ullapool mountain stream (24x35cm-9x14in) mono.i. col pencil. 9-Jun-4 Dorotheum, Salzburg #529/R est:10000-16000
£5000	$9200	€7500	Woman's portrait (68x48cm-27x19in) s. chk. 10-Jun-4 Hauswedell & Nolte, Hamburg #349/R est:8000
£5000	$9200	€7500	Trudl (48x35cm-19x14in) s. pencil. 10-Jun-4 Hauswedell & Nolte, Hamburg #350/R est:8000
£7692	$13077	€11000	Minonna (38x37cm-15x15in) s.d.1944 col pen prov. 26-Nov-3 Dorotheum, Vienna #50/R est:12000-18000
£14000	$25480	€20440	Blumen in einer vase - Flowers in a vase (45x60cm-18x24in) init.i. W/C prov. 4-Feb-4 Sotheby's, London #546/R est:15000-20000
£14000	$25760	€21000	Portrait of Ludwig Renn (43x38cm-17x15in) mono.i.d.1939 chk. 10-Jun-4 Hauswedell & Nolte, Hamburg #351/R est:28000
£18500	$34040	€27010	Yellow and purple irises (66x48cm-26x19in) s.d.1965 W/C prov.exhib. 24-Mar-4 Sotheby's, Olympia #28/R est:12000-18000
£24476	$41608	€35000	Summer blooms including zinnia and carnations (62x59cm-24x23in) s.d.67 W/C. 26-Nov-3 Lempertz, Koln #770/R est:35000-37000
£25175	$42797	€36000	Spring flowers in vase (66x48cm-26x19in) s.d.2.1.1965 W/C sketch verso. 26-Nov-3 Lempertz, Koln #769/R est:35000-38000
£27074	$49275	€39528	Bouquet of flowers (65x47cm-26x19in) s.d.1970 W/C. 18-Jun-4 Kornfeld, Bern #96/R est:20000 (S.FR 62000)
£40268	$72081	€60000	Amor and psyche (90x34cm-35x13in) s.i.d.1955 mixed media board lit. 27-May-4 Hassfurther, Vienna #6/R est:70000-80000
£53691	$96107	€80000	Nude boy standing with right arm in the air (41x22cm-16x9in) mono. black chk W/C lit. 27-May-4 Hassfurther, Vienna #4/R est:70000-100000
£120805	$216242	€180000	Girl in exotic landscape (33x20cm-13x8in) pen brush ink over pencil lit. 27-May-4 Hassfurther, Vienna #3/R est:100000-160000
£221477	$396443	€330000	Runner (24x17cm-9x7in) mono. pen brush ink W/C tempera htd white over pencil double-side. 27-May-4 Hassfurther, Vienna #2/R

KOLAR, Jiri (1914-2002) Czechoslovakian

Sculpture			
£1000	$1840	€1500	Chinese sideboard (14x25x7cm-6x10x3in) chiasmage. 11-Jun-4 Hauswedell & Nolte, Hamburg #1387/R est:1500
Works on paper			
£300	$540	€450	Self-portrait (24x34cm-9x13in) mono.d.1979 exhib.lit. 25-Apr-4 Versailles Encheres #170
£340	$609	€500	Untitled (24x17cm-9x7in) mono.d.87 collage. 21-Mar-4 Calmels Cohen, Paris #101
£367	$660	€550	Voiture, froissage (36x25cm-14x10in) mono.d.1979 paper on cardboard exhib.lit. 25-Apr-4 Versailles Encheres #185
£433	$797	€650	Small butterflies (31x25cm-12x10in) s.d.1970 collage. 12-Jun-4 Villa Grisebach, Berlin #780/R
£436	$807	€650	Untitled (25x19cm-10x7in) init.d.1992 collage. 13-Mar-4 Meeting Art, Vercelli #18
£547	$979	€820	Untitled (30x21cm-12x8in) mono.d. collage. 15-May-4 Dr Sturies, Dusseldorf #113/R
£559	$951	€800	Untitled (22x30cm-9x12in) s.d.79 crumblage board. 27-Nov-3 Lempertz, Koln #237/R
£563	$900	€822	Untitled (79x58cm-31x23in) mixed media. 20-Sep-3 Bunte, Elgin #3851
£569	$945	€831	Sleeping paradise (28x43cm-11x17in) mono.d.6 collage. 4-Oct-3 Dorotheum, Prague #324/R est:24000-36000 (C.KR 26000)
£600	$1080	€900	Homage to Otaka Brezina (45x33cm-18x13in) collage cardboard lit. 25-Apr-4 Versailles Encheres #169
£600	$1098	€900	Untitled (23x23cm-9x9in) col paper collage board. 4-Jun-4 Lempertz, Koln #267/R
£610	$1000	€891	Portrait Carl Laszlo number 1 (29x20cm-11x8in) mono.d.71 s.d.81 verso paper collage on card prov. 28-May-3 Sotheby's, Amsterdam #133/R
£629	$1070	€900	Untitled - Maya (26x26cm-10x10in) mono. paper collage on board. 27-Nov-3 Lempertz, Koln #235/R
£979	$1664	€1400	Untitled - Laguna (28x54cm-11x21in) mono. paper collage board. 27-Nov-3 Lempertz, Koln #236/R
£1200	$2160	€1800	Images et mots decoupes (50x65cm-20x26in) s.i.d.1965 verso collage panel. 24-Apr-4 Cornette de St.Cyr, Paris #597 est:2500
£1225	$2192	€1800	Nez prisel lev (30x40cm-12x16in) mono.d.1989 s.i.d.verso collage panel prov. 21-Mar-4 Calmels Cohen, Paris #100/R est:800-1200
£1379	$2303	€2000	May love (29x21cm-11x8in) s.d.1961 verso collage cardboard. 13-Nov-3 Galleria Pace, Milan #94/R est:2800
£2276	$3641	€3300	Composition (45x33cm-18x13in) s.d.1965 mixed media. 13-Mar-3 Galleria Pace, Milan #33/R est:4000-5200
£2533	$4535	€3800	Sample book III/Temptation of St Anthony (99x70cm-39x28in) mono.d. collage. 15-May-4 Dr Sturies, Dusseldorf #112/R

KOLARE, Nils (1930-) Swedish

£378	$642	€552	Untitled (35x45cm-14x18in) s. acrylic panel. 5-Nov-3 AB Stockholms Auktionsverk #787/R (S.KR 5000)

KOLB, Alois (1875-1942) Austrian

Works on paper			
£490	$832	€700	Male and female nudes (61x42cm-24x17in) pencil. 21-Nov-3 Reiss & Sohn, Konigstein #433/R

KOLBE, Carl Wilhelm (elder-attrib) (1757-1835) German

Works on paper			
£656	$1200	€958	Old oak and a farm house in a wooded landscape (53x43cm-21x17in) i. brush col wash pen black ink. 29-Jan-4 Swann Galleries, New York #314/R

KOLBE, Ernst (1876-1945) German

£979	$1684	€1400	Fishing houses at Ahrenshoop (80x100cm-31x39in) s. 5-Dec-3 Bolland & Marotz, Bremen #590/R

KOLBE, Georg (1877-1947) German

Sculpture			
£1588	$2700	€2318	Female portrait bust (36cm-14in) mono. st.f.Noack bronze. 7-Nov-3 Selkirks, St. Louis #632/R est:2000-3000
£13000	$23920	€18980	Kneeling woman I (30cm-12in) mono. bronze conceived 1923 prov.lit. 22-Jun-4 Sotheby's, London #292/R est:8000-12000
£13986	$23776	€20000	Standing girl (120cm-47in) mono. green pat.bronze Cast.H.Noack Berling Friedenau prov.lit. 29-Nov-3 Villa Grisebach, Berlin #232/R est:24000-28000
£18881	$32098	€27000	Kneeling figure (54cm-21in) mono. yellow brown pat.bronze Cast.H.Noack Berlin. 29-Nov-3 Villa Grisebach, Berlin #196/R est:28000-32000
£32353	$55000	€47235	Tanzerin (69cm-27in) init. brown pat bronze st.f.H NOACK conceived 1922 lit. 5-Nov-3 Christie's, Rockefeller NY #295/R est:50000-70000
Works on paper			
£1000	$1790	€1500	Standing nude (48x34cm-19x13in) mono.i. wash pencil. 13-May-4 Neumeister, Munich #399/R est:1200-1400
£2133	$3840	€3200	Untitled - female nude (36x48cm-14x19in) mono. brush sepai wash over pencil. 24-Apr-4 Dr Lehr, Berlin #222/R est:3800
£2448	$4161	€3500	Movement study (36x28cm-14x11in) mono. Indian ink pen brush. 29-Nov-3 Villa Grisebach, Berlin #195/R est:2500-4000
£6434	$10937	€9200	Seated nude (34x45cm-13x18in) mono. Indian ink pen brush prov. 29-Nov-3 Villa Grisebach, Berlin #194/R est:4000-5000

KOLBE, Heinrich Christoph (1771-1836) German

£352	$609	€500	Portrait d'une dame de qualite (65x54cm-26x21in) s.d.1820 prov. 9-Dec-3 Vanderkindere, Brussels #329

KOLBE, Jean Paul (fl.1776) German?

Works on paper			
£1200	$2160	€1752	Compositions, possibly a collection of snuff boxes (26x42cm-10x17in) s.i.d.1776 pen col ink wash black chk. 20-Apr-4 Sotheby's, Olympia #177/R est:1500-2000

KOLESNIKOFF, Stepan (1879-1955) Russian

£3500	$5950	€5250	Winter landscape (18x23cm-7x9in) s. card. 25-Nov-3 Christie's, London #178/R est:3500-4500
£7000	$11900	€10220	Repairing the net (96x125cm-38x49in) s. 19-Nov-3 Sotheby's, London #72/R est:8000-12000
£13174	$22000	€19234	Church scene (67x86cm-26x34in) s. 21-Oct-3 Christie's, Rockefeller NY #110 est:7000-9000
£53215	$95255	€77694	Elderly Bedouin on horseback in mountain landscape (109x142cm-43x56in) s.d.1918. 28-May-4 Uppsala Auktionskammare, Uppsala #119/R est:200000-250000 (S.KR 720000)
Works on paper			
£2800	$5012	€4088	Washerwoman at the river (23x29cm-9x11in) s. gouache. 26-May-4 Sotheby's, Olympia #482/R est:1000-1500
£4800	$8160	€7200	Washerwoman at lakeside (24x29cm-9x11in) s. gouache card. 25-Nov-3 Christie's, London #177/R est:3500-4500
£5389	$9000	€7868	Winter scene (22x27cm-9x11in) s. i.verso gouache cardboard sold with an oil by the same hand. 21-Oct-3 Christie's, Rockefeller NY #90 est:5000-7000
£10000	$17000	€15000	Gathering at church. gouache cardboard. 25-Nov-3 Christie's, London #176/R est:6000-8000
£10000	$17000	€15000	Feast (34x44cm-13x17in) s. gouache cardboard oval. 25-Nov-3 Christie's, London #175/R est:7000-9000

KOLIG, Anton (1886-1950) Austrian
Works on paper
£1250 $2037 €1800 Two young men asleep (40x54cm-16x21in) mono. chk transparent paper. 26-Sep-3 Venator & Hansten, Koln #1498 est:2500
£1399 $2378 €2000 Nude man (44x35cm-17x14in) i. pencil. 25-Nov-3 Hassfurther, Vienna #54/R est:2000-3000
£1818 $3091 €2600 Nude man (41x32cm-16x13in) pencil. 25-Nov-3 Hassfurther, Vienna #55/R est:2500-3000
£1958 $3329 €2800 Nude man (44x34cm-17x13in) i. pencil. 25-Nov-3 Hassfurther, Vienna #50/R est:3000-3500
£2238 $3804 €3200 Nude man (45x35cm-18x14in) s.d.1941 chl. 25-Nov-3 Hassfurther, Vienna #49/R est:2000-2500
£3020 $5406 €4500 Male nude standing (60x45cm-24x18in) s.i.d.1925 chl. 27-May-4 Hassfurther, Vienna #15/R est:3000-4000
£15436 $27631 €23000 The woman (215x175cm-85x69in) black chl lit. 27-May-4 Hassfurther, Vienna #14/R est:18000-22000

KOLIG, Anton (attrib) (1886-1950) Austrian
Works on paper
£524 $892 €750 Two reclining male nudes (50x70cm-20x28in) pencil. 19-Nov-3 Dorotheum, Klagenfurt #94
£839 $1427 €1200 Two reclining male nudes (45x32cm-18x13in) pencil transparent paper two. 19-Nov-3 Dorotheum, Klagenfurt #96
£1049 $1783 €1500 Two reclining male nudes (49x34cm-19x13in) pencil transparent paper two. 19-Nov-3 Dorotheum, Klagenfurt #95/R est:1000

KOLIG, Cornelius (1942-) Austrian?
Works on paper
£592 $1089 €900 Vom Ursprung der Musik - About the origin of the music (21x30cm-8x12in) mono.i.d.1996 mixed media. 22-Jun-4 Wiener Kunst Auktionen, Vienna #430/R

KOLK, Douglas (1963-) German
Works on paper
£1133 $2085 €1700 We're ruined Toni (101x66cm-40x26in) s.i.d.96 verso col felt-tip W/C pair. 12-Jun-4 Villa Grisebach, Berlin #781/R est:1500-2000

KOLKO, Berenice (1905-1970) American
Photographs
£2111 $3800 €3082 Frida Kahlo (25x20cm-10x8in) i.d.1953 gelatin silver print prov.lit. 23-Apr-4 Phillips, New York #188/R est:3000-5000

KOLLAR, Francois (1904-1979) American?
Photographs
£1889 $3400 €2758 Smoke stacks (28x22cm-11x9in) i.verso gelatin silver print lit. 22-Apr-4 Phillips, New York #206/R est:4000-6000

KOLLAR, Wilhelm (20th C) Austrian
£274 $466 €400 Camillia woman (90x120cm-35x47in) tempera. 5-Nov-3 Dorotheum, Vienna #68/R

KOLLE, C A (1827-1872) Danish
£543 $972 €793 Seascape with mountains near Tenerife (35x57cm-14x22in) s. d.1852 verso. 10-May-4 Rasmussen, Vejle #384/R (D.KR 6000)
£561 $886 €813 Landscape with winding river (39x63cm-15x25in) init. 2-Sep-3 Rasmussen, Copenhagen #1896/R (D.KR 6000)
£664 $1128 €969 View from Langelinie towards Trekroner (15x22cm-6x9in) s.d.49. 10-Nov-3 Rasmussen, Vejle #296/R (D.KR 7200)
£1254 $2258 €1831 Country road with flowers (19x21cm-7x8in) init.d.1848 panel. 24-Apr-4 Rasmussen, Havnen #2355 est:1500-2000 (D.KR 14000)

KOLLE, Helmut (1899-1931) German
£14483 $24186 €21000 Young man in a red chair (99x81cm-39x32in) s. prov.lit. 13-Nov-3 Neumeister, Munich #362/R est:8000-10000
Prints
£2374 $3894 €3300 City city (45x64cm-18x25in) s.i.d. col serigraph. 4-Jun-3 Ketterer, Hamburg #501/R est:3000-4000

KOLLER, Ben-Ami (1948-) French?
Works on paper
£333 $603 €500 Sans titre (47x47cm-19x19in) s. pigment pierre noire dry pastel. 3-Apr-4 Neret-Minet, Paris #132/R
£350 $594 €500 Sans titre (45x64cm-18x25in) s. pastel pierre noire. 27-Nov-3 Calmels Cohen, Paris #116/R

KOLLER, G (19th C) ?
£1042 $1656 €1500 Deux elegantes dans un interieur (30x22cm-12x9in) s. panel. 9-Sep-3 Palais de Beaux Arts, Brussels #244/R est:1600-2400

KOLLER, Johann Jakob (1746-1805) Swiss
£15068 $25616 €22000 View of the Spui, Amsterdam (42x56cm-17x22in) s.d.1778. 4-Nov-3 Sotheby's, Amsterdam #104/R est:8000-12000

KOLLER, Konrad (1916-2001) Austrian
£676 $1189 €1000 Houses with goods waggon (33x39cm-13x15in) board. 19-May-4 Dorotheum, Klagenfurt #14/R
£1216 $2141 €1800 Shore with tower (38x37cm-15x15in) board double-sided. 19-May-4 Dorotheum, Klagenfurt #13 est:1400

KOLLER, Oskar (20th C) German?
£300 $537 €450 Untitled (28x38cm-11x15in) s.d.79 oil collage. 15-May-4 Van Ham, Cologne #739/R
£556 $906 €800 Look through (130x100cm-51x39in) s.d.1973 acrylic. 27-Sep-3 Dr Fritz Nagel, Stuttgart #9245/R
£1469 $2497 €2100 House (71x98cm-28x39in) s. panel. 20-Nov-3 Weidler, Nurnberg #7008/R
Works on paper
£278 $442 €400 Southern village - house with tree (28x38cm-11x15in) s.d.1978. 11-Sep-3 Weidler, Nurnberg #7044
£280 $501 €420 Red flowers (22x15cm-9x6in) s.i.d.87. 14-May-4 Behringer, Furth #2130/R
£300 $537 €450 Untitled (38x27cm-15x11in) s.d. W/C. 15-May-4 Van Ham, Cologne #730/R
£347 $566 €500 Landscape in Persia (57x82cm-22x32in) s.d. 1975 W/C tempera. 27-Sep-3 Dr Fritz Nagel, Stuttgart #9240/R

KOLLER, Rudolf (1828-1905) Swiss
£280 $502 €409 Landscape with foundling (39x55cm-15x22in) mono. chl htd wash. 12-May-4 Dobiaschofsky, Bern #1143/R (S.FR 650)
£606 $1085 €885 Study of peasant woman (54x33cm-21x13in) chl htd white prov. 22-Mar-4 Philippe Schuler, Zurich #4341 (S.FR 1400)
£1239 $2068 €1797 Hay waggon (80x100cm-31x39in) mono.d. 23-Jun-3 Philippe Schuler, Zurich #3401 est:3000-5000 (S.FR 2700)
£1645 $2945 €2402 Wooded landscape with stream, cows and sheep (70x102cm-28x40in) s. 22-Mar-4 Philippe Schuler, Zurich #4340 est:2000-2600 (S.FR 3800)
£2203 $3744 €3216 Haycart on the Furth (80x100cm-31x39in) mono.d.55 prov.exhib. 7-Nov-3 Dobiaschofsky, Bern #42/R est:5800 (S.FR 5000)
£2203 $3744 €3216 Girl and boy with cows and sheep (55x75cm-22x30in) mono.d.63. 7-Nov-3 Dobiaschofsky, Bern #43/R est:7000 (S.FR 5000)
£2358 $4292 €3443 Cows in a country landscape (81x100cm-32x39in) mono.d.67. 16-Jun-4 Fischer, Luzern #1278/R est:6000-8000 (S.FR 5400)
£6087 $11139 €8887 Reclining calf (30x39cm-12x15in) mono.d.59. 7-Jun-4 Christie's, Zurich #17/R est:9000-12000 (S.FR 14000)
£6335 $10959 €9249 Bull in the meadow (60x73cm-24x29in) s. 9-Dec-3 Sotheby's, Zurich #23/R est:7000-9000 (S.FR 14000)
£6987 $12507 €10201 Anni at the spring (60x50cm-24x20in) s.d.1861. 26-May-4 Sotheby's, Zurich #17/R est:10000-15000 (S.FR 16000)
£8696 $15913 €12696 Homecoming from the Alps in moonlight (80x74cm-31x29in) mono.d.54. 7-Jun-4 Christie's, Zurich #18/R est:20000-30000 (S.FR 20000)
£24017 $42991 €35065 Sowing (72x104cm-28x41in) s.d.1882. 26-May-4 Sotheby's, Zurich #14/R est:15000-20000 (S.FR 55000)
£33621 $60181 €49087 Little shepherdess knitting (57x57cm-22x22in) s.d.1859 lit. 17-May-4 Beurret, Zurich #16/R est:20000-30000 (S.FR 78000)
Works on paper
£294 $491 €429 Cows grazing (24x30cm-9x12in) s.d.1876 pencil. 24-Jun-3 Germann, Zurich #990 (S.FR 650)
£611 $1113 €892 Two cows in a stable (31x41cm-12x16in) s.d.Nov 1842 ink. 16-Jun-4 Fischer, Luzern #2785/R (S.FR 1400)
£1310 $2345 €1913 Cow watering (25x37cm-10x15in) s.d.1859 chl egg-white prov.exhib. 26-May-4 Sotheby's, Zurich #9/R est:3000-5000 (S.FR 3000)

KOLLER-PINELL, Broncia (1863-1934) Austrian
£2282 $4221 €3400 Etka (29x29cm-11x11in) s. 9-Mar-4 Dorotheum, Vienna #12/R est:2200-3000

KOLLMANN, Carl Ivanovich (1788-1846) Russian
Works on paper
£1600 $2720 €2400 Russian country fair (24x32cm-9x13in) s.d.1812 pencil W/C. 25-Nov-3 Christie's, London #94/R est:800-1200
£1600 $2720 €2400 Russian baptism (24x32cm-9x13in) s. pencil W/C. 25-Nov-3 Christie's, London #96/R est:800-1200
£1700 $2890 €2550 Russian peasant with sledge (24x32cm-9x13in) s.d.1812 pencil W/C. 25-Nov-3 Christie's, London #97/R est:800-1200
£1700 $2890 €2550 Russian peasant selling fish (24x32cm-9x13in) s.d.1812 pencil W/C. 25-Nov-3 Christie's, London #95/R est:800-1200
£2000 $3400 €2920 Coachmen outside Cathedral of the Mother of God of Kazan, St Petersburg (15x21cm-6x8in) s.d.1820 W/C over pencil. 19-Nov-3 Sotheby's, London #5/R est:800-1000

KOLLMANN, Renzo (1922-) Italian
£2238 $3737 €3200 Fantastic Trieste (150x200cm-59x79in) s.d.51 cardboard. 10-Oct-3 Stadion, Trieste #730/R est:1500-2000
Works on paper
£400 $716 €600 Jugglers (67x48cm-26x19in) s. mixed media cardboard. 12-May-4 Stadion, Trieste #827/R
£733 $1313 €1100 Circus (62x85cm-24x33in) s. mixed media cardboard. 12-May-4 Stadion, Trieste #829/R

KOLLORSZ, Richard Franz (1900-1983) American
£2581 $4750 €3768 Figures on Laguna Beach with the pier beyond (50x61cm-20x24in) i.verso prov. 8-Jun-4 Bonhams & Butterfields, San Francisco #4361/R est:4000-6000

KOLLREIDER, Oswald (1922-) Austrian
£867 $1595 €1300 Peasant woman carrying bundle of hay (70x50cm-28x20in) mono.d.91 board. 9-Jun-4 Dorotheum, Salzburg #651/R
£1000 $1840 €1500 Mountain village (50x70cm-20x28in) mono. panel. 9-Jun-4 Dorotheum, Salzburg #650/R est:800-1100
£1007 $1862 €1500 Drummer (99x69cm-39x27in) mono.d.61 tempera. 9-Mar-4 Dorotheum, Vienna #134/R est:1500-2000

KOLLWITZ, Kathe (1867-1945) German
Prints
£1732 $3100 €2529 Working class woman (52x39cm-20x15in) s.i. chk brush lithograph lit. 22-Mar-4 Philippe Schuler, Zurich #4023/R est:3300-4600 (S.FR 4000)

£2000	$3440	€2920	Besuch I, Krankenhaus (28x36cm-11x14in) s. woodcut. 2-Dec-3 Christie's, London #175/R est:2000-3000
£2000	$3580	€3000	Self portrait with hand on forehead (16x13cm-6x5in) s. etching board. 15-May-4 Bassenge, Berlin #6964/R est:1800
£2000	$3580	€3000	Seated worker (33x35cm-13x14in) s. lithograph. 15-May-4 Bassenge, Berlin #6967/R est:3500
£2098	$3608	€3000	Bread! (35x28cm-14x11in) s.i. lithograph. 2-Dec-3 Hauswedell & Nolte, Hamburg #344/R est:4000
£2300	$4209	€3358	Mutter (45x59cm-18x23in) s. lithograph edition of 300. 3-Jun-4 Christie's, Kensington #228/R est:1500-2500
£2353	$4000	€3435	Death (53x43cm-21x17in) s. lithograph lit. 31-Oct-3 Sotheby's, New York #297/R
£2517	$4330	€3600	Mary and Elisabeth (36x34cm-14x13in) s. woodcut. 2-Dec-3 Hauswedell & Nolte, Hamburg #348/R est:4000
£2533	$4535	€3800	Parents with child (21x31cm-8x12in) lithograph prov. 14-May-4 Ketterer, Munich #182/R est:3000-4000
£2533	$4661	€3800	Inspiration (56x29cm-22x11in) s. etching drypoint vernis mou. 10-Jun-4 Hauswedell & Nolte, Hamburg #379/R est:2200
£2620	$4769	€3825	Sick woman with children. s. lithograph. 17-Jun-4 Kornfeld, Bern #487/R est:7500 (S.FR 6000)
£2639	$4301	€3800	Mother with boy (50x38cm-20x15in) s.i. lithograph. 27-Sep-3 Dr Fritz Nagel, Stuttgart #9574/R est:3400
£2657	$4571	€3800	Self-portrait (21x19cm-8x7in) s. lithograph. 2-Dec-3 Hauswedell & Nolte, Hamburg #349/R est:5000
£2667	$4773	€4000	Two women chattering with two children (50x36cm-20x14in) s. lithograph. 15-May-4 Bassenge, Berlin #6970 est:4500
£2682	$4800	€3916	Mutter mit jungen (36x22cm-14x9in) s. lithograph. 6-May-4 Swann Galleries, New York #474a/R est:4000-6000
£2797	$4811	€4000	Self portrait in profile (32x30cm-13x12in) s.d.1927 lithograph. 5-Dec-3 Ketterer, Munich #62/R est:3000-4000
£2800	$5124	€4088	Frau mit totem Kind (42x49cm-17x19in) s.num.24/50 etching drypoint. 3-Jun-4 Christie's, Kensington #223/R est:2000-3000
£2819	$5187	€4200	Mother with young boy (36x21cm-14x8in) s. lithograph. 26-Mar-4 Ketterer, Hamburg #517/R est:3500-4000
£3231	$5881	€4717	Mother. s. woodcut. 17-Jun-4 Kornfeld, Bern #489 est:7500 (S.FR 7400)
£3319	$6040	€4846	Prisoner, listening to music. s. lithograph. 17-Jun-4 Kornfeld, Bern #493/R est:7500 (S.FR 7600)
£3557	$6545	€5300	Call of death (38x38cm-15x15in) s.i. lithograph. 26-Mar-4 Ketterer, Hamburg #520/R est:2000-2500
£3636	$6255	€5200	Death and woman (45x45cm-18x18in) s.d.1910 etching. 2-Dec-3 Hauswedell & Nolte, Hamburg #334/R est:4000
£3670	$6128	€5322	Working woman with blue scarf. s. col lithograph. 19-Jun-3 Kornfeld, Bern #574 est:10000 (S.FR 8000)
£3800	$6916	€5548	Brustbild einer arbeiterfrau mit blauem tuch (36x24cm-14x9in) s. col lithograph. 30-Jun-4 Christie's, London #241/R est:3000-5000
£3824	$6500	€5583	Schlafende mit kind (30x36cm-12x14in) s. woodcut. 6-Nov-3 Swann Galleries, New York #595/R est:6000-9000
£3867	$6921	€5800	Mother (34x40cm-13x16in) s.i. woodcut. 15-May-4 Bassenge, Berlin #6953/R est:6000
£4196	$7217	€6000	Woman with dead child (42x48cm-17x19in) num.21/50 etching vernis mou print. 5-Dec-3 Ketterer, Munich #63/R est:6000-8000
£4667	$8587	€7000	Self portrait (32x29cm-13x11in) s.d.1927 lithograph. 10-Jun-4 Hauswedell & Nolte, Hamburg #399/R est:7000
£4817	$8044	€6985	Mother and Child. s. lithograph. 19-Jun-3 Kornfeld, Bern #579/R est:12500 (S.FR 10500)
£5333	$9813	€8000	Honing (29x29cm-11x11in) s. etching. 10-Jun-4 Hauswedell & Nolte, Hamburg #380/R est:5500
£5734	$9863	€8200	Germany's children are hungry (41x29cm-16x11in) s. lithograph. 2-Dec-3 Hauswedell & Nolte, Hamburg #342/R est:10000
£5963	$9959	€8646	Self portrait. s.i. woodcut. 19-Jun-3 Kornfeld, Bern #578/R est:12500 (S.FR 13000)
£6000	$10800	€9000	Mother and child (27x22cm-11x9in) s.i. chk lithograph. 24-Apr-4 Reiss & Sohn, Konigstein #5657/R est:10000
£6711	$12349	€10000	Woman with arms crossed (55x42cm-22x17in) s. col lithograph. 26-Mar-4 Ketterer, Hamburg #516/R est:10000-15000
£7424	$13511	€10839	Mary and Elizabeth. s.i. woodcut. 17-Jun-4 Kornfeld, Bern #494/R est:17500 (S.FR 17000)
£8734	$15895	€12752	Young child drinking from a cup (36x33cm-14x13in) lithograph pencil exec. c.1926 prov.exhib. 18-Jun-4 Kornfeld, Bern #103/R est:25000 (S.FR 20000)
£10000	$18400	€15000	Head of working woman (30x24cm-12x9in) s. lithograph. 10-Jun-4 Hauswedell & Nolte, Hamburg #377/R est:18000
£12227	$22253	€17851	Slaughterfield (40x52cm-16x20in) s.i. line etching drypoint aquatint emery vernis mou prov.exhib. 18-Jun-4 Kornfeld, Bern #101/R est:20000 (S.FR 28000)
£14847	$27022	€21677	Death, a woman and a child (40x41cm-16x16in) s.i. line etching drypoint emery vernis mou chk ink prov. 18-Jun-4 Kornfeld, Bern #100/R est:35000 (S.FR 34000)
£22707	$41328	€33152	March cemetery (45x37cm-18x15in) s. col lithograph W/C exec. 1913 prov.exhib. 18-Jun-4 Kornfeld, Bern #102/R est:40000 (S.FR 52000)

Sculpture

£6993	$12028	€10000	Farewell (17x11x9cm-7x4x4in) bronze. 2-Dec-3 Hauswedell & Nolte, Hamburg #330/R est:12000
£8000	$14320	€12000	Brothers and sisters (17x6x7cm-7x2x3in) s. brown pat.bronze Cast.H.Noack Berlin. 15-May-4 Bassenge, Berlin #6951/R est:12000
£19553	$35000	€28547	Pieta (38cm-15in) s.st.f.H.Noack brown pat bronze conceived 1937 prov.lit. 5-May-4 Christie's, Rockefeller NY #308/R est:35000-45000
£26573	$45706	€38000	Pieta (38x27x39cm-15x11x15in) bronze. 2-Dec-3 Hauswedell & Nolte, Hamburg #328/R est:40000

Works on paper

£1500	$2595	€2190	Mutter mit kind (41x27cm-16x11in) s. chl prov. 11-Dec-3 Christie's, Kensington #71/R est:500-700
£4000	$6920	€5840	Junger Arbeiter (61x47cm-24x19in) s. chl exec.c.1920 prov. 11-Dec-3 Christie's, Kensington #73/R est:4000-6000
£4362	$8027	€6500	Head of young woman (25x21cm-10x8in) s.d.92 ochre. 27-Mar-4 L & B, Essen #273/R est:5000
£6500	$11635	€9490	Family (54x36cm-21x14in) s. black chk. 11-May-4 Sotheby's, Olympia #600/R est:3000-4000
£6993	$12028	€10000	Battlefield (39x37cm-15x15in) s. chl chk. 2-Dec-3 Hauswedell & Nolte, Hamburg #331/R est:12000
£9091	$15182	€13000	Woman with child in arms (59x47cm-23x19in) s. chl sketch. 10-Oct-3 Winterberg, Heidelberg #1535/R est:9800
£11354	$20664	€16577	Woman digging (38x25cm-15x10in) chl exec. 1903 prov.exhib.lit. 18-Jun-4 Kornfeld, Bern #98/R est:25000 (S.FR 26000)
£16667	$30667	€25000	Woman sitting with eyes closed, head in her right hand (64x48cm-25x19in) s. i.verso chl exhib.lit. 11-Jun-4 Villa Grisebach, Berlin #35/R est:25000-30000
£16667	$30667	€25000	Pregnant woman , drowning herself (58x48cm-23x19in) s. chl grey paper on paper lit. 11-Jun-4 Villa Grisebach, Berlin #36/R est:25000-30000
£25000	$41750	€36500	Losbruch - outbreak (60x63cm-24x25in) s.d.1901 chl white chk prov.lit. 21-Oct-3 Sotheby's, London #110/R est:12000-15000

KOLNER, August (1812-1906) American

Works on paper

£435	$800	€635	Near falls of Schuykill, Phila (25x30cm-10x12in) s.d.Nov 1878 W/C. 9-Jun-4 Alderfer's, Hatfield #379
£1494	$2750	€2181	Maiden Creek Valley, Berks (28x33cm-11x13in) s.d.1868 W/C. 9-Jun-4 Alderfer's, Hatfield #380 est:300-500

KOLNIK, Arthur (1890-1972) Israeli

£241	$434	€350	Manege (26x21cm-10x8in) s. paper. 21-Jan-4 Tajan, Paris #101
£414	$691	€600	Collioure (38x46cm-15x18in) s. panel. 17-Nov-3 Claude Boisgirard, Paris #47/R

KOLOSOV, Alexei Alexandrovich (1892-1972) Russian

£9500	$17005	€13870	Crimean street scene (69x79cm-27x31in) indis sig. verso. 26-May-4 Sotheby's, London #193/R est:5000-7000

KOLOSVARY, Sigismund (1899-1983) Hungarian

£336	$621	€500	Interruption (73x60cm-29x24in) s.d.1973 s.i.d.verso. 15-Mar-4 Blanchet, Paris #164
£362	$605	€529	Untitled (50x40cm-20x16in) s.d.1956. 24-Jun-3 Germann, Zurich #991 (S.FR 800)
£962	$1703	€1405	Composition (73x92cm-29x36in) s.d.1959. 28-Apr-4 Kieselbach, Budapest #131/R (H.F 360000)
£1737	$3074	€2536	Tornado (118x59cm-46x23in) s.d.1957. 28-Apr-4 Kieselbach, Budapest #132/R (H.F 650000)

KOLOTOVAS, Stephen (20th C) ?

Works on paper

£680	$1218	€1000	Panoramique de la cote de Tamatave (11x74cm-4x29in) s.i.d.1910 W/C. 21-Mar-4 St-Germain-en-Laye Encheres #102/R

KOLOUPAIEV, Dimitri A (1883-1954) Russian

£355	$560	€500	Rider on bridge (41x71cm-16x28in) s.d.1939. 24-Jul-3 Claude Boisgirard, Paris #43/R

Works on paper

£355	$560	€500	Dog waltz (24x57cm-9x22in) s.d.1918 gouache W/C. 24-Jul-3 Claude Boisgirard, Paris #29/R

KOLSTO, Frederik (1860-1945) Norwegian

£1253	$2294	€1829	Hazy winter's day (57x67cm-22x26in) s. 9-Jun-4 Rasmussen, Copenhagen #1759/R est:15000-20000 (D.KR 14000)
£1652	$2858	€2412	Evening on the fjord (74x53cm-29x21in) s. 13-Dec-3 Blomqvist, Lysaker #1209/R est:20000-25000 (N.KR 19000)
£4259	$7325	€6218	Waiting by the coast, winter (80x137cm-31x54in) s. 8-Dec-3 Blomqvist, Oslo #412/R est:30000-40000 (N.KR 50000)

Works on paper

£407	$744	€594	Man with sou'wester in rowing boat (26x27cm-10x11in) init.d.93 pencil. 7-Jun-4 Blomqvist, Oslo #258/R (N.KR 5000)

KOLTHOFF, Mark (1901-) Dutch

£738	$1366	€1100	Untitled (49x65cm-19x26in) s.d.38 exhib. 15-Mar-4 Sotheby's, Amsterdam #241/R est:800-1200

Works on paper

£403	$745	€600	Still life with banjo (20x30cm-8x12in) s.d.43 gouache exhib. 15-Mar-4 Sotheby's, Amsterdam #245
£570	$1055	€850	Still life with letters (24x29cm-9x11in) s.d.43 gouache. 15-Mar-4 Sotheby's, Amsterdam #291 est:750-900
£671	$1242	€1000	Still life (21x28cm-8x11in) s. gouache exhib. 15-Mar-4 Sotheby's, Amsterdam #242/R est:750-900

KOLTMANN, F (?) ?

£479	$815	€699	Fjord landscape with vessels at moonlight (66x94cm-26x37in) s. 10-Nov-3 Rasmussen, Vejle #351/R (D.KR 5200)

KOLTSOV, S V (1892-1951) Russian

£2179	$3900	€3181	Autumn (46x38cm-18x15in) painted 1939. 29-May-4 Shishkin Gallery, Moscow #11/R est:2000-3000
£2514	$4500	€3670	French workers by the lottery circle (54x46cm-21x18in) painted 1930. 29-May-4 Shishkin Gallery, Moscow #10/R est:10000-15000

Works on paper

£447	$800	€653	Parisian woman (25x21cm-10x8in) sepia exec. 1928-31. 29-May-4 Shishkin Gallery, Moscow #6/R
£475	$850	€694	So-called sandwiches (63x48cm-25x19in) W/C paper on cardboard exec. 1929. 29-May-4 Shishkin Gallery, Moscow #7/R
£503	$900	€734	The seller of patented goods (63x48cm-25x19in) W/C paper on cardboard exec. 1928-30. 29-May-4 Shishkin Gallery, Moscow #8/R
£670	$1200	€978	Family of workers in intensely cold weather (63x47cm-25x19in) W/C paper on cardboard exec. 1928-29. 29-May-4 Shishkin Gallery, Moscow #9/R

KOMAREK, Vladimir (1928-2002) Czechoslovakian

£700	$1163	€1022	Trinity (65x90cm-26x35in) s. 4-Oct-3 Dorotheum, Prague #147 est:20000-30000 (C.KR 32000)

KOMAROV, Anatoliy (1949-) Russian

£403	$713	€600	Still life by the window (65x46cm-26x18in) s. 27-Apr-4 Durán, Madrid #717/R

KOMPOCZY, Paulina H (?) ?
£769 $1285 €1100 Flowers (60x80cm-24x31in) 10-Oct-3 Stadion, Trieste #78

KONARSKI, Jan (?) Polish?
£3918 $6113 €5720 Soldiers on horseback (57x44cm-22x17in) s. 30-Mar-3 Agra, Warsaw #15/R est:25000 (P.Z 25000)

KONCHALOVSKY, Piotr Petrovich (1876-1956) Russian
£733 $1327 €1100 Portrait d'un peintre (61x50cm-24x20in) 5-Apr-4 Marie & Robert, Paris #83/R
£26000 $46540 €37960 Still life with lilacs (68x54cm-27x21in) s.i.verso. 26-May-4 Sotheby's, Olympia #438/R est:10000-15000
£45000 $76500 €65700 Apple trees in blossom (60x88cm-24x35in) s. s.d.1939 verso. 19-Nov-3 Sotheby's, London #205/R est:35000-45000
£45000 $80550 €65700 Forest clearing (58x49cm-23x19in) s. s.d.1932 verso. 26-May-4 Sotheby's, London #254/R est:35000-45000
£180000 $306000 €262800 Bathing at Midday (69x90cm-27x35in) s. s.i.d.1923 verso lit. 19-Nov-3 Sotheby's, London #207/R est:50000-70000
£290000 $519100 €423400 Flowers on pink (89x108cm-35x43in) s. i.verso exhib.lit. 26-May-4 Sotheby's, London #245/R est:80000-120000

KONDOR, Bela (1931-1972) Hungarian
£25030 $45305 €36544 Bluebeard prince (52x35cm-20x14in) s. oil on wood. 16-Apr-4 Mu Terem Galeria, Budapest #79/R (H.F 9500000)

KONDRATENKO, Gavril (1854-1924) Russian
£7500 $13425 €10950 Old stone bridge (28x21cm-11x8in) s. 26-May-4 Sotheby's, London #39/R est:5000-7000
£18000 $32220 €26280 Ruin by the coast (34x46cm-13x18in) s. panel. 26-May-4 Sotheby's, London #26/R est:10000-15000
£90000 $161100 €131400 Fishermen (185x145cm-73x57in) s.d.89. 26-May-4 Sotheby's, London #40/R est:30000-40000

KONECNY, Josef (1907-) Czechoslovakian
£1027 $1747 €1500 Still life of flowers (69x52cm-27x20in) s. panel. 5-Nov-3 Hugo Ruef, Munich #1048/R est:1500
£1399 $2406 €2000 Still life with flowers (91x62cm-36x24in) s. 3-Dec-3 Neumeister, Munich #634/R est:1800
£2098 $3566 €3000 Spring flowers in glass vase (48x30cm-19x12in) s. panel. 24-Nov-3 Dorotheum, Vienna #195/R est:3000-3600
£4000 $6400 €5800 Large bouquet of summer flowers (140x105cm-55x41in) s. 18-Sep-3 Christie's, Kensington #36/R est:3500-4500

KONER, Sophie (1855-1929) British
£287 $493 €410 Half-portrait of fisherman with binoculars (90x68cm-35x27in) s.d.1891. 6-Dec-3 Dannenberg, Berlin #802/R

KONGSRUD, Anders (1866-1938) Norwegian
£555 $1021 €810 Winter landscape with small birds (25x28cm-10x11in) s. 29-Mar-4 Blomqvist, Lysaker #1168/R (N.KR 7000)
£634 $1167 €926 Pair of chaffinches on pine branch (35x45cm-14x18in) s. panel. 29-Mar-4 Blomqvist, Lysaker #1167/R (N.KR 8000)
£793 $1459 €1158 Driving timber in winter woods (62x42cm-24x17in) s. panel. 29-Mar-4 Blomqvist, Lysaker #1166/R (N.KR 10000)
£2555 $4395 €3730 Sparrows in sheaf of oats (66x51cm-26x20in) s. 8-Dec-3 Blomqvist, Oslo #444/R est:20000-25000 (N.KR 30000)
£3066 $5274 €4476 Winter landscape with birds on sheaf of corn and houses (70x55cm-28x22in) s.d.26. 8-Dec-3 Blomqvist, Oslo #406/R est:25000-30000 (N.KR 36000)

KONIG, Franz Niklaus (1765-1832) Swiss
Works on paper
£517 $926 €755 Bacchanale (23x25cm-9x10in) wash pen. 13-May-4 Stuker, Bern #9176/R (S.FR 1200)

KONIG, Friedrich (1857-1941) Austrian
£5034 $8909 €7500 Knight, dragon and girl (120x81cm-47x32in) s. 28-Apr-4 Wiener Kunst Auktionen, Vienna #38/R est:5500-8000

KONIG, Fritz (1924-) German
Sculpture
£1890 $3250 €2759 Gondolas (20x9x24cm-8x4x9in) s.d.58 mottled green pat. bronze prov. 3-Dec-3 Doyle, New York #71/R est:1500-2500
£2448 $4210 €3500 Disc picture (15x15cm-6x6in) mono. num.2/5 gold brown pat bronze round exhib. 5-Dec-3 Ketterer, Munich #140/R est:4000-5000
£6993 $12028 €10000 Sphere - Kugelkaryatide (10x7x7cm-4x3x3in) mono. bronze. 3-Dec-3 Hauswedell & Nolte, Hamburg #906/R est:12000
£9091 $15455 €13000 Wall of despair (71cm-28in) s. brown pat.bronze prov. 29-Nov-3 Villa Grisebach, Berlin #349/R est:1000-15000
£10000 $18200 €14600 Herd (7x50x31cm-3x20x12in) s. bronze prov.exhib.lit. 6-Feb-4 Sotheby's, London #195/R est:6500-9000
£10140 $17441 €14500 Golgatha (23x23x12cm-9x9x5in) bronze. 3-Dec-3 Hauswedell & Nolte, Hamburg #905/R est:2000
£11189 $19021 €16000 Small rider (45cm-18in) mono. prov. 29-Nov-3 Villa Grisebach, Berlin #351/R est:8000-10000
£13986 $24056 €20000 Small quadriga (25x39x6cm-10x15x2in) s. goldbrown pat bronze one of 5 prov. 5-Dec-3 Ketterer, Munich #141/R est:15000-20000
£14000 $25060 €21000 Derby I (31x57x65cm-12x22x26in) s.i. blackish brown pat.bronze prov. 14-May-4 Ketterer, Munich #237/R est:14000-16000

KONIG, G (20th C) German
£993 $1658 €1400 Working in wood with horses (40x60cm-16x24in) s. 17-Oct-3 Behringer, Furth #1622/R est:1500

KONIG, Hein (1891-1971) German
£1286 $2225 €1878 Group of elderly men poring over a newspaper (75x61cm-30x24in) s. painted c.1930. 14-Dec-3 Agra, Warsaw #2/R est:5000 (P.Z 8500)

KONIG, Heinrich-Justus (1862-?) German
£528 $845 €750 Classical scene (71x100cm-28x39in) s.d.1907 board. 18-Sep-3 Rieber, Stuttgart #1004/R

KONIG, Johann (1586-1642) German
£3667 $6563 €5500 Suzanna in a landscape with a peacock, pheasant and dog (25x34cm-10x13in) panel prov. 17-May-4 Glerum, Amsterdam #10/R est:5000-7000

KONIG, Leo von (1871-1944) German
£76923 $130769 €110000 Ernst Barlach - II (92x78cm-36x31in) s.i.d.1937 prov.exhib. 28-Nov-3 Villa Grisebach, Berlin #69/R est:70000-90000

KONIG-INGENHEIM, Marie (1849-?) Austrian
£2778 $4722 €4000 Still pond (79x120cm-31x47in) s. 28-Oct-3 Dorotheum, Vienna #274/R est:2800-3200

KONIGSBRUNN, Hermann von (1823-1907) Austrian
£2517 $4330 €3600 Kaleuiganga River in Ceylon (80x120cm-31x47in) mono.d.903 s.i.verso. 4-Dec-3 Dorotheum, Graz #32/R est:1800

KONIJNENBURG, Willem A van (1868-1943) Dutch
£367 $671 €550 Farm (43x30cm-17x12in) mono. panel. 7-Jun-4 Glerum, Amsterdam #29/R
£476 $867 €700 Figures in a landscape (45x31cm-18x12in) mono. panel. 3-Feb-4 Christie's, Amsterdam #525
£544 $990 €800 Peasants on a farmyard in Limburg (31x39cm-12x15in) panel. 3-Feb-4 Christie's, Amsterdam #495
Works on paper
£1096 $1863 €1600 Boy with cow (106x90cm-42x35in) init. chl brown chk exhib. 5-Nov-3 Vendue Huis, Gravenhage #338/R est:700-1000

KONINCK, Daniel de (1668-?) Dutch
£7200 $12456 €10512 Portrait of a man wearing a turban and chain of office over a brown cloak (63x46cm-25x18in) panel prov. 9-Dec-3 Sotheby's, Olympia #328/R est:5000-7000

KONINCK, Kerstiaen de (elder) (fl.1580-1630) Flemish
£8333 $15000 €12166 Theseus on the road to Athens (27x41cm-11x16in) s. panel prov. 22-Jan-4 Sotheby's, New York #37/R est:20000-30000

KONINCK, Philips de (1619-1688) Dutch
£44828 $74414 €65000 Landscape with pond and large tree (86x85cm-34x33in) lit.prov. 1-Oct-3 Dorotheum, Vienna #90/R est:70000-100000
Works on paper
£4054 $7135 €6000 Interior scene, with standing and seated figures (13x15cm-5x6in) bears sig. pen brown ink wash prov.exhib.lit. 19-May-4 Sotheby's, Amsterdam #73/R est:9000-12000
£23611 $42500 €34472 Panoramic landscape with the mouth of a river (13x27cm-5x11in) bear i.verso W/C gouache htd red chk prov.lit. 21-Jan-4 Sotheby's, New York #63/R est:40000-60000
£55556 $100000 €81112 Extensive landscape with a lake, distant mill and town (10x25cm-4x10in) pen brown ink wash prov. 22-Jan-4 Christie's, Rockefeller NY #120/R est:20000-30000

KONINCK, Philips de (attrib) (1619-1688) Dutch
Works on paper
£430 $783 €650 Le Christ apparaissant a Marie-Madeleine (16x21cm-6x8in) pen ink. 16-Jun-4 Piasa, Paris #51

KONING, Arnold Hendrik (1860-1945) Dutch
£2098 $3503 €3000 Peasant with cattle in a landscape with a church in the background (70x113cm-28x44in) s. 30-Jun-3 Sotheby's, Amsterdam #205

KONING, Edzard (1869-1954) Dutch
£461 $847 €700 Huntsmen on the heath (40x60cm-16x24in) s. 22-Jun-4 Christie's, Amsterdam #279/R
£1053 $1937 €1600 Gathering wood in the forest (146x70cm-57x28in) s. 22-Jun-4 Christie's, Amsterdam #107/R est:1200-1600

KONING, Elisabeth Johanna (1816-1888) Dutch
£3357 $5773 €4800 Still life of grapes, a peach and a butterfly on a table (38x28cm-15x11in) s.d.1830 panel. 7-Dec-3 Sotheby's, Amsterdam #576/R
£3667 $6600 €5500 Flowers in a basket with shells on a ledge (22x29cm-9x11in) s.d.1843 panel. 21-Apr-4 Christie's, Amsterdam #3/R est:3000-5000

KONING, Roeland (1898-1985) Dutch
£1189 $2044 €1700 Corn bundles (51x71cm-20x28in) s.d.1919 i.verso board prov. 7-Dec-3 Sotheby's, Amsterdam #698/R

KONINGH, Leendert de (elder) (1777-1849) Dutch
£1944 $3072 €2800 Washer woman at a riverbank, a castle beyond (33x43cm-13x17in) s. panel. 2-Sep-3 Christie's, Amsterdam #158/R est:1200-1600

KONINGH, Leendert de (elder-attrib) (1777-1849) Dutch
£1500 $2580 €2190 Firewood gatherers by a frozen river in a Dutch hamlet (51x61cm-20x24in) s. 4-Dec-3 Christie's, Kensington #186/R est:1200-1800

KONINGH, Leonard de (younger) (1810-1887) Dutch
£658 $1211 €1000 A peaceful moment during the harvest (62x50cm-24x20in) s. panel. 22-Jun-4 Christie's, Amsterdam #70a/R

KONINGSBRUGGEN, Rob van (1948-) Dutch?
£2133 $3819 €3200 Circle (45x45cm-18x18in) s.d.1965 verso. 11-May-4 Vendu Notarishuis, Rotterdam #28/R est:500-700
£6294 $10825 €9000 Untitled (110x110cm-43x43in) s.d.1988 on overlap. 2-Dec-3 Sotheby's, Amsterdam #184/R est:10000-15000
£6667 $12267 €10000 Untitled (60x60cm-24x24in) s.d.1976 verso two separate sheets prov. 8-Jun-4 Sotheby's, Amsterdam #143/R est:10000-15000
£10145 $16638 €14000 Untitled (140x140cm-55x55in) s.verso painted 1972 exhib. 27-May-3 Sotheby's, Amsterdam #460/R est:15000-20000
Works on paper
£333 $610 €500 Abstract composition (70x50cm-28x20in) s.d.89 mixed media. 7-Jun-4 Glerum, Amsterdam #312/R

KONO, Micao (1900-1979) Japanese
£2270 $3790 €3200 Femme allongee (55x45cm-22x18in) s.d.32. 20-Jun-3 Drouot Estimations, Paris #172 est:1000-1200
£2766 $4619 €3900 Femme au chat (55x36cm-22x14in) s.d.35. 20-Jun-3 Drouot Estimations, Paris #171 est:800-900
£2778 $4639 €4000 Nature morte aux pivoines (54x65cm-21x26in) s.d.1940. 23-Oct-3 Credit Municipal, Paris #63/R est:3000-3500
£5208 $8698 €7500 Deux amies (60x73cm-24x29in) s.d.XXX. 21-Oct-3 Artcurial Briest, Paris #205/R est:7000-9000
£7692 $13077 €11000 Jeune femme endormie (50x92cm-20x36in) s. 27-Nov-3 Millon & Associes, Paris #176/R est:12000-15000

KONOK, Tamas (1930-) Hungarian
£905 $1538 €1321 The construction (49x64cm-19x25in) s.d.1974 s.d. verso acrylic. 25-Nov-3 Germann, Zurich #821 est:300-500 (S.FR 2000)
£905 $1538 €1321 Composition (70x93cm-28x37in) s.d.1975 s.d. verso. 25-Nov-3 Germann, Zurich #822 est:500-700 (S.FR 2000)
Works on paper
£1069 $1892 €1561 Still life by a window (50x70cm-20x28in) s. pastel. 28-Apr-4 Kieselbach, Budapest #197/R (H.F 400000)

KONOW, Jurgen von (1915-1959) Swedish
£793 $1348 €1158 Summer morning, Strandvagen (55x46cm-22x18in) s. panel. 5-Nov-3 AB Stockholms Auktionsverk #864/R (S.KR 10500)
£1245 $2204 €1818 Stromsborg with seagulls - Stockholm (65x54cm-26x21in) s. panel. 27-Apr-4 AB Stockholms Auktionsverk #892/R est:12000-15000 (S.KR 17000)

KONOW, Karl (1865-1928) Norwegian
£285 $524 €416 Winter landscape with smallholding in evening (53x70cm-21x28in) s.inid.d.1895. 10-Jun-4 Grev Wedels Plass, Oslo #199/R (N.KR 3500)

KONRAD, Adolf (20th C) American
£569 $950 €831 Nie ventilators (76x61cm-30x24in) s.i.d.39. 29-Jun-3 William Jenack, New York #119

KONTIO, Pekka (1933-1976) Finnish
Sculpture
£2297 $4112 €3400 Female nude (78cm-31in) s.d.68 exhib. 8-May-4 Bukowskis, Helsinki #219/R est:2000-2500

KOOGH, Adrianus van der (1796-1831) Dutch
£8333 $14167 €12000 Extensive rolling landscape with travellers on a sandy track by a watermill (73x101cm-29x40in) s. painted c.1820 exhib.lit. 28-Oct-3 Christie's, Amsterdam #41/R est:12000-16000

KOOL, Sipke (1836-1902) Dutch
£959 $1630 €1400 Interior of fisherman's house (40x51cm-16x20in) 5-Nov-3 Vendue Huis, Gravenhage #59/R

KOONING, Elaine de (1920-1989) American
£5978 $11000 €8728 Redondo (46x61cm-18x24in) s.d.1960 stretcher verso acrylic masonite. 27-Jun-4 Freeman, Philadelphia #130/R est:3000-5000
£11538 $21000 €16845 Portrait of JFK (79x56cm-31x22in) i.overlap prov. 29-Jun-4 Sotheby's, New York #460/R est:3000-5000

KOONING, Willem de (1904-1997) American/Dutch
£14970 $25000 €21856 Untitled (48x61cm-19x24in) oil paper painted c.1968 prov. 13-Nov-3 Sotheby's, New York #172/R est:25000-35000
£17000 $30940 €24820 Untitled (63x41cm-25x16in) s. oil newspaper on canvas exec c.1967 prov. 5-Feb-4 Christie's, London #170/R est:18000-22000
£18000 $33120 €26280 Untitled (38x54cm-15x21in) s. on newspaper painted c.1964 prov.exhib. 24-Jun-4 Sotheby's, London #252/R est:20000-25000
£25449 $42500 €37156 Untitled (48x61cm-19x24in) oil paper painted c.1968 prov. 13-Nov-3 Sotheby's, New York #173/R est:35000-45000
£26174 $48160 €39000 Untitled (58x74cm-23x29in) newspaper on canvas painted c.1978 prov. 29-Mar-4 Cornette de St.Cyr, Paris #43/R est:40000-60000
£29167 $48125 €42000 Sans titre (58x75cm-23x30in) s. oil newspaper on canvas. 2-Jul-3 Cornette de St.Cyr, Paris #27/R est:40000-50000
£29940 $50000 €43712 Untitled (58x74cm-23x29in) oil newsprint painted c.1965 prov. 13-Nov-3 Sotheby's, New York #166/R est:60000-80000
£78212 $140000 €114190 Black and white - Rome (99x70cm-39x28in) s.d.60 oil paper assemblage prov. 13-May-4 Sotheby's, New York #117/R est:70000-90000
£111732 $200000 €163129 Oil painting on Paper VI (54x71cm-21x28in) s. paper on canvas painted 1958 prov.exhib.lit. 12-May-4 Christie's, Rockefeller NY #112/R est:200000-300000
£145251 $260000 €212066 East Hampton XXI (103x67cm-41x26in) s. s.i.backing board paper on canvas painted 1968 prov.exhib. 12-May-4 Christie's, Rockefeller NY #143/R est:250000-350000
£173184 $310000 €252849 East Hampton X (93x75cm-37x30in) s. paper on canvas painted 1968 prov.exhib.lit. 13-May-4 Sotheby's, New York #130/R est:300000-400000
£508982 $850000 €743114 Untitled XLVIII (223x196cm-88x77in) painted 1983 prov.exhib. 12-Nov-3 Sotheby's, New York #23/R est:700000-900000
£837989 $1500000 €1223464 Untitled XXI (178x203cm-70x80in) s. stretcher painted 1985 prov.exhib. 11-May-4 Christie's, Rockefeller NY #38/R est:1500000-2500000
£1284916 $2300000 €1875977 Porch in a landscape (151x140cm-59x55in) painted 1977 prov.exhib.lit. 11-May-4 Christie's, Rockefeller NY #30/R est:1900000-2400000
£1976048 $3300000 €2885030 Untitled XVII (203x178cm-80x70in) s. stretcher painted 1984 prov.exhib.lit. 11-Nov-3 Christie's, Rockefeller NY #32/R est:1500000-2000000
£5988024 $10000000 €8742515 Spike's folly I (200x174cm-79x69in) s. painted 1959. 12-Nov-3 Sotheby's, New York #15/R est:10000000-15000000
Prints
£1630 $3000 €2380 Figure at Gerard Beach (84x60cm-33x24in) s.d.70 num.28/32 lithograph. 8-Jun-4 Auctions by the Bay, Alameda #1154/R
£1765 $3000 €2577 Clam digger (43x57cm-17x22in) s.i. lithograph. 21-Nov-3 Swann Galleries, New York #100/R est:2500-3500
£1836 $3250 €2681 Souvenir of montauk (110x88cm-43x35in) s.d.1971 num.13/43 lithograph. 30-Apr-4 Sotheby's, New York #372/R est:2500-3000
£1912 $3250 €2792 Man and the big blond (54x69cm-21x27in) s. offset lithograph. 31-Oct-3 Sotheby's, New York #631
£1935 $3600 €2825 Clam digger (43x57cm-17x22in) s.num.24/100 lithograph. 2-Mar-4 Swann Galleries, New York #320/R est:2500-3500
£2059 $3500 €3006 Love to Wakako (114x72cm-45x28in) s. lithograph. 31-Oct-3 Sotheby's, New York #629/R
£2147 $3800 €3135 Weekend at Mr and Mrs Krisher (127x89cm-50x35in) s.i.d.70 num.28/75 lithograph on foam core. 28-Apr-4 Christie's, Rockefeller NY #344/R est:3000-4000
£2417 $4109 €3529 Love to Wakako (104x65cm-41x26in) s.d.70 num.36/58 lithograph lit. 5-Nov-3 AB Stockholms Auktionsverk #1245/R est:18000-20000 (S.KR 32000)
£2647 $4500 €3865 Woman with corset (94x76cm-37x30in) s.d.70 lithograph. 31-Oct-3 Sotheby's, New York #627/R
£2647 $4500 €3865 Landscape at Stanton Station (65x48cm-26x19in) s. lithograph. 31-Oct-3 Sotheby's, New York #630/R
£3824 $6500 €5583 Reflections (127x88cm-50x35in) s. lithograph. 31-Oct-3 Sotheby's, New York #628/R
£4469 $8000 €6525 Marshes (103x72cm-41x28in) s.d.1971 num.4/20 lithograph. 6-May-4 Swann Galleries, New York #475/R est:6000-9000
£4802 $8500 €7011 Reflections (116x81cm-46x32in) s.d.70 num.4/28 lithograph on foam core. 28-Apr-4 Christie's, Rockefeller NY #345/R est:4000-6000
£5367 $9500 €7836 Untitled (61x91cm-24x36in) s.num.62/75 screenprint exec.c.1972. 28-Apr-4 Christie's, Rockefeller NY #346/R est:3000-4000
£5449 $9100 €7956 Untitled (71x61cm-28x24in) s.d. col lithograph prov. 23-Oct-3 Shannon's, Milford #164/R est:10000-15000
Sculpture
£1731844 $3100000 €2528492 Standing figure (376x641x203cm-148x252x80in) s.d.1969-84 num.2/2 brown pat bronze prov.exhib.lit. 11-May-4 Christie's, Rockefeller NY #22/R est:2000000-3000000
Works on paper
£7500 $12000 €10950 Figure study (26x21cm-10x8in) s.i. chl exec.c.1965. 18-Sep-3 Swann Galleries, New York #341/R est:8000-12000
£13174 $22000 €19234 Untitled (61x46cm-24x18in) s. chl paper on paper exec 1969 prov.exhib. 12-Nov-3 Christie's, Rockefeller NY #413/R est:25000-35000
£41899 $75000 €61173 Untitled - woman (50x38cm-20x15in) s.d.June 9 1955 pencil prov. 13-May-4 Sotheby's, New York #114/R est:35000-45000
£117318 $210000 €171284 Untitled - Artist's sketch book (36x28cm-14x11in) s.d.verso pencil 18 drawings 12 sheets exec c.1975 prov. 13-May-4 Sotheby's, New York #115/R est:120000-180000
£137725 $230000 €201079 Woman (189x94cm-74x37in) s.d.65 chl paper collage paper on paperboard on masonite prov. 13-Nov-3 Sotheby's, New York #179/R est:80000-120000

KOONS, Jeff (1955-) American
£56886 $95000 €83054 Hennessy, The Civilized Way to Lay Down the Law (114x152cm-45x60in) oil inks painted 1986 prov.exhib.lit. 12-Nov-3 Christie's, Rockefeller NY #518/R est:60000-80000
£268156 $480000 €391508 Ponies (229x152cm-90x60in) s.d.91 overlap oil inks silkscreened on canvas prov.exhib.lit. 11-May-4 Christie's, Rockefeller NY #6/R est:200000-300000
£837989 $1500000 €1223464 Saint Benedict (279x204cm-110x80in) painted 2000 prov.exhib. 11-May-4 Christie's, Rockefeller NY #47/R est:550000-650000
Photographs
£4237 $7500 €6186 Everybody I love you (78x70cm-31x28in) cibachrome photo. 28-Apr-4 Christie's, Rockefeller NY #348/R est:7000-10000
Prints
£10169 $18000 €14847 Art magazine ads (96x75cm-38x30in) s.d.89 num.10/10 col photo lithographs set of four album. 28-Apr-4 Christie's, Rockefeller NY #347/R est:6000-9000
Sculpture
£1000 $1820 €1460 Bread with egg (4x15cm-2x6in) d.95 num.162/250 painted plaster. 4-Feb-4 Sotheby's, Olympia #150/R est:1000-1500
£1049 $1783 €1500 Puppie (45cm-18in) s.num.870/3000 white porcelain. 25-Nov-3 Tajan, Paris #65/R est:900-1200
£1399 $2378 €2000 Puppy. s.num.1056/3000. 27-Nov-3 Calmels Cohen, Paris #96/R est:1200-1400
£15642 $28000 €22837 Donkey (61x46x2cm-24x18x1in) s.d.1997 num. of ten verso stainless steel prov. 14-May-4 Phillips, New York #192/R est:20000-30000
£28443 $47500 €41527 Donkey (61x46x1cm-24x18x0in) s.d.1997 num.19/50 verso polished stainless steel prov. 13-Nov-3 Sotheby's, New York #468/R est:25000-35000
£95808 $160000 €139880 Jim beam baggage car (21x41x16cm-8x16x6in) stainless steel executed 1986 prov.exhib.lit. 13-Nov-3 Phillips, New York #37/R est:100000-150000
£149701 $250000 €218563 Toaster (69x23x33cm-27x9x13in) toaster acrylic fluorescent lights exec 1979 prov.lit. 11-Nov-3 Christie's, Rockefeller NY #48/R est:150000-250000
£212291 $380000 €309945 Encased five rows (203x172x45cm-80x68x18in) 24 basketballs six soccer balls glass metal display case prov. 13-May-4 Phillips, New York #18/R est:150000-200000

£335329 $560000 €489580 New hover deluxe shampoo polisher (142x60x36cm-56x24x14in) two hover deluxe fluorescent lights plexiglas vitrine executed 80. 13-Nov-3 Phillips, New York #16/R est:400000-600000
£449102 $750000 €655689 Vase of Flowers (184x135x2cm-72x53x1in) mirror exec 1988 prov.exhib.lit. 11-Nov-3 Christie's, Rockefeller NY #53/R est:450000-550000
£1077844 $1800000 €1573652 Lifeboat (30x203x152cm-12x80x60in) bronze exec 1985 prov.exhib.lit. 11-Nov-3 Christie's, Rockefeller NY #46/R est:1600000-1900000
£2737430 $4900000 €3996648 Jim Beam JB Turner train (28x289x16cm-11x114x6in) stainless steel bourbon edn 1/3 exec 1986 prov.exhib.lit. 11-May-4 Christie's, Rockefeller NY #32/R est:2000000-3000000
Works on paper
£1449 $2377 €2000 Composition (70x60cm-28x24in) s.d.1993 felt-tip pen dr on poster. 27-May-3 Il Ponte, Milan #564

KOOP, Wanda (1951-) Canadian
£301 $560 €439 Untitled (55x76cm-22x30in) acrylic paper painted c.1984 prov.exhib. 4-Mar-4 Heffel, Vancouver #24/R (C.D 750)

KOOPER, Ary Cornelis (1855-1921) Dutch
£1180 $1924 €1700 Cattle in landscape (42x64cm-17x25in) s. panel. 29-Sep-3 Sotheby's, Amsterdam #70/R

KOOPMAN, Augustus (1869-1914) American
£599 $1000 €875 Sea at dawn (61x46cm-24x18in) s.d.96. 20-Jun-3 Freeman, Philadelphia #186/R
£1268 $2193 €1800 Paysage cotier sous la tempete (73x92cm-29x36in) s. 10-Dec-3 Millon & Associes, Paris #67/R est:1800-2000

KOPAC, Slavko (1913-) Yugoslavian
Works on paper
£467 $859 €700 Untitled (16x12cm-6x5in) s.d.66 mixed media on felt on wood. 9-Jun-4 Artcurial Briest, Paris #361

KOPCKE, Arthur (1928-1977) Danish
£271 $486 €396 Composition (34x29cm-13x11in) 10-May-4 Rasmussen, Vejle #713/R (D.KR 3000)
£627 $1129 €915 Composition (97x69cm-38x27in) s.d.feb.60 verso panel. 24-Apr-4 Rasmussen, Havnen #4194/R (D.KR 7000)
Works on paper
£316 $581 €461 Concert at T H Lang's Gymnasium (20x39cm-8x15in) s. collage crayon Indian ink exhib.prov. 29-Mar-4 Rasmussen, Copenhagen #367 (D.KR 3500)
£722 $1350 €1054 Go into the painting - Juke Box and Mertz (50x65cm-20x26in) s. collage crayon Indian ink. 25-Feb-4 Kunsthallen, Copenhagen #158/R (D.KR 8000)
£756 $1353 €1104 Composition (43x60cm-17x24in) s.i. collage. 12-Jan-4 Rasmussen, Vejle #648/R (D.KR 8000)
£1119 $1924 €1600 Nature cannot deal with such brightness (50x64cm-20x25in) s.i. s.i. verso W/C fibretip oil chk collage. 3-Dec-3 Hauswedell & Nolte, Hamburg #909/R est:2000

KOPECKY, John (20th C) American
£301 $550 €452 Summer morning (122x152cm-48x60in) acrylic. 10-Jul-4 Hindman, Chicago #276/R

KOPF, Josef (1873-1953) Austrian
£414 $757 €600 Peonies (32x23cm-13x9in) panel. 27-Jan-4 Dorotheum, Vienna #82/R
Sculpture
£12941 $22000 €18894 Beauty holding a flower basket (196cm-77in) s.d.1869 white marble incl. base. 29-Oct-3 Christie's, Rockefeller NY #40/R est:18000-25000

KOPMAN, Benjamin (1887-1965) American
£497 $800 €726 Old woman (89x71cm-35x28in) s.d.1959. 22-Feb-3 Bunte, Elgin #1169
£1714 $3000 €2502 Summer landscape, midday (71x89cm-28x35in) s. 19-Dec-3 Sotheby's, New York #1055/R est:1500-2000

KOPONEN, Erkki (1899-1996) Finnish
£839 $1427 €1200 Vertical element (117x117cm-46x46in) s. 29-Nov-3 Bukowskis, Helsinki #282/R
£878 $1572 €1300 Composition (102x125cm-40x49in) s.d.1985 exhib. 8-May-4 Bukowskis, Helsinki #308/R
£1119 $1902 €1600 Parisian woman (46x38cm-18x15in) s.d.49 board exhib. 29-Nov-3 Bukowskis, Helsinki #260/R est:500-700

KOPP, Dieter (1939-) German
£667 $1200 €1000 Paros (26x41cm-10x16in) s.i.d.1972-73 verso board. 22-Apr-4 Finarte Semenzato, Rome #174/R

KOPPAY, Joszi Arpad Baron von Dretoma (1859-?) Hungarian
£3571 $6500 €5214 Portrait of a young girl and her dog (154x86cm-61x34in) s. indis d.1902. 29-Jun-4 Sotheby's, New York #114/R est:6000-8000
Works on paper
£738 $1307 €1100 Erzherzogin Elisabeth (70x46cm-28x18in) s. pastel board. 29-Apr-4 Dorotheum, Vienna #175

KOPPELAAR, Frans (1943-) Dutch
£748 $1362 €1100 Bij de stallen, Duindigt (50x60cm-20x24in) s. i.d.1996 stretcher. 3-Feb-4 Christie's, Amsterdam #384 est:1000-1500
£816 $1486 €1200 Haarlemmerpleins, winter (50x70cm-20x28in) s. 3-Feb-4 Christie's, Amsterdam #326/R est:1200-1600
£1156 $2105 €1700 Kalverstraat by night (50x40cm-20x16in) s. 3-Feb-4 Christie's, Amsterdam #329/R est:1000-1500

KOPPEN, Theodor (1828-1903) German
£350 $601 €500 Extensive river valley (19x32cm-7x13in) canvas on board. 4-Dec-3 Neumeister, Munich #2786

KOPPENOL, C (1865-1946) Dutch
£1088 $1981 €1600 Minding the geese (24x32cm-9x13in) s. panel. 3-Feb-4 Christie's, Amsterdam #224 est:1200-1600
£1528 $2414 €2200 Feeding the geese (30x41cm-12x16in) s. 2-Sep-3 Christie's, Amsterdam #233 est:1000-1500

KOPPENOL, Cornelis (1865-1946) Dutch
£420 $685 €613 Young woman sewing (21x15cm-8x6in) s. indis d. canvas on panel. 23-Sep-3 Bonhams, Chester #964
£738 $1373 €1100 Woman standing on the beach with a toy boat at her feet (24x18cm-9x7in) s. i. stretcher panel. 5-Mar-4 Wendl, Rudolstadt #3747/R
£1528 $2490 €2200 Picnic in the dunes (27x49cm-11x19in) s. 29-Sep-3 Sotheby's, Amsterdam #75/R
£2466 $4192 €3600 Two children with geese (29x39cm-11x15in) s. 5-Nov-3 Vendue Huis, Gravenhage #142/R est:3000-4000

KOPPI (20th C) American?
£1676 $3000 €2447 Seated by the window (36x28cm-14x11in) s. board sold with another by same hand. 8-May-4 Susanin's, Chicago #6090/R est:1200-1600

KOPPITZ, Rudolf (1884-1936) German
Photographs
£17956 $32500 €26216 Movement study (30x30cm-12x12in) s. brown toned bromoil print lit. 19-Apr-4 Bonhams & Butterfields, San Francisco #433/R est:40000-60000
£50898 $85000 €74311 Study of movement (28x21cm-11x8in) s. gelatin silver print prov.lit. 20-Oct-3 Christie's, Rockefeller NY #37/R est:70000-90000

KOR, Paul (1926-) French
£813 $1276 €1179 La toilette (64x49cm-25x19in) s. 26-Aug-3 Christie's, Sydney #380 est:2000-3000 (A.D 2000)

KORAB, Karl (1937-) Austrian
£4500 $8280 €6570 Stilleben (110x130cm-43x51in) s.d.73 i.d.1973 stretcher prov. 24-Jun-4 Sotheby's, Olympia #517/R est:5000-7000
Works on paper
£833 $1358 €1200 Houses (19x26cm-7x10in) s.d.70 gouache. 23-Sep-3 Wiener Kunst Auktionen, Vienna #140/R
£855 $1574 €1300 Landscape (21x16cm-8x6in) s.d.75 gouache. 22-Jun-4 Wiener Kunst Auktionen, Vienna #316/R
£855 $1574 €1300 Landscape (21x15cm-8x6in) s.d.75 gouache. 22-Jun-4 Wiener Kunst Auktionen, Vienna #317/R
£987 $1816 €1500 The red thing (22x16cm-9x6in) s.d.75 i.d.verso gouache. 22-Jun-4 Wiener Kunst Auktionen, Vienna #315/R est:1300
£993 $1658 €1400 Kellerkasse (35x48cm-14x19in) s.d.96 gouache. 14-Oct-3 Dorotheum, Vienna #295/R
£2685 $4805 €4000 Der einsiedler (57x40cm-22x16in) s. s.i.d.1972 verso. 26-May-4 Christie's, Paris #45/R est:300-400

KORAN, Yanagawa and SEIGAN, Yanagawa (19th C) Japanese
Works on paper
£1000 $1670 €1450 Flowering plum branch with poem (135x31cm-53x12in) s.i. ink hanging scroll. 18-Jun-3 Christie's, London #291/R est:1500-2000

KORBEL, Mario Joseph (1882-1954) American
Sculpture
£1123 $2100 €1640 Female nude (74x15x18cm-29x6x7in) s.num.4/12 brown pat bronze st.f.Roman Bronze. 25-Feb-4 Dallas Auction Gallery, Dallas #120/R

KORBER, Wilhelm (1902-1990) German
£347 $580 €500 Girl plaiting hair (60x44cm-24x17in) mono. mono.i.d.1958 verso after Albert Anker lit. 25-Oct-3 Bergmann, Erlangen #978/R

KORCHAN (19/20th C) Russian
£9000 $15300 €13140 Crimean landscape (74x101cm-29x40in) s.d.1909. 19-Nov-3 Sotheby's, London #22/R est:10000-15000

KORD, Victor (1935-) American
£833 $1350 €1216 Abstract composition (274x274cm-108x108in) s.d.1972 acrylic. 2-Aug-3 Neal Auction Company, New Orleans #387/R est:2000-3000

KORECKI, Victor (1890-1980) Polish
£260 $476 €380 Lake at sunset (51x61cm-20x24in) s. 27-Jan-4 Gorringes, Lewes #1655
£537 $988 €800 Snowy river landscape in evening sun (50x79cm-20x31in) s. 26-Mar-4 Bolland & Marotz, Bremen #632/R
£781 $1305 €1140 Winter landscape with cabin. cardboard painted c.1945. 19-Oct-3 Agra, Warsaw #61/R (P.Z 5000)
£830 $1535 €1212 Winter landscape (45x54cm-18x21in) 14-Mar-4 Agra, Warsaw #41/R (P.Z 6000)
£908 $1570 €1326 Night-time winter landscape with cottage (40x60cm-16x24in) s. board painted after 1950. 14-Dec-3 Agra, Warsaw #29/R est:5000 (P.Z 6000)
£990 $1743 €1445 Landscape covered in snow (50x79cm-20x31in) s. 23-May-4 Agra, Warsaw #34/R (P.Z 7000)
£1059 $1832 €1546 Winter landscape with two cottages (39x60cm-15x24in) s. board painted after 1950. 14-Dec-3 Agra, Warsaw #28/R est:5000 (P.Z 7000)

£1094	$1827	€1597	Winter landscape with stream (37x45cm-15x18in) s. cardboard. 19-Oct-3 Agra, Warsaw #49/R est:5000 (P.Z 7000)
£1254	$1956	€1831	Winter forest scene (39x60cm-15x24in) s. painted c.1945. 30-Mar-3 Agra, Warsaw #40/R est:5000 (P.Z 8000)
£1445	$2398	€2110	Forest path in winter (51x69cm-20x27in) s. painted c.1945. 15-Jun-3 Agra, Warsaw #26/R est:7000 (P.Z 9000)
£1724	$2690	€2517	Pinetrees in the sunlight (49x80cm-19x31in) s. painted c.1945. 30-Mar-3 Agra, Warsaw #31/R est:7000 (P.Z 11000)

KORELEVSKY, A K (19/20th C) Russian?

£4225	$7310	€6000	Wolves chasing carriage with horses (80x130cm-31x51in) indis.s. 10-Dec-3 Dorotheum, Vienna #77/R est:2800-3200

KORETSKY, Viktor Borisowitch (1909-) Russian

Photographs

£2000	$3580	€3000	Down with Hitler (35x23cm-14x9in) photomontage gouache. 12-May-4 Millon & Associes, Paris #309/R est:1000-1200

KORIN, Aleksei Mikhailovich (1865-1923) Russian

£10000	$18000	€14600	Leaving church (38x39cm-15x15in) s.d.1921 board. 23-Apr-4 Sotheby's, New York #18/R est:10000-15000

KORMENDI-FRIM, Ervin (1885-1939) Hungarian

£1470	$2601	€2146	Corner of the studio with a nude (100x120cm-39x47in) s. 28-Apr-4 Kieselbach, Budapest #65/R (H.F 550000)

KORN, Johan Philip (1728-1796) Swedish

£1308	$2249	€1910	Landscape with figures (34x52cm-13x20in) panel. 3-Dec-3 AB Stockholms Auktionsverk #2462/R est:12000-15000 (S.KR 17000)
£1577	$2712	€2302	Pastoral landscapes with figures (13x20cm-5x8in) s.verso panel pair. 3-Dec-3 AB Stockholms Auktionsverk #2467/R est:15000-18000 (S.KR 20500)

KORN, Johann Robert (1873-1921) German

Sculpture

£1329	$2259	€1900	Reindeer with calf (20cm-8in) s. bronze marble base. 29-Nov-3 Bukowskis, Helsinki #352/R est:1800-2000
£1712	$2911	€2500	Chimpanzee (36cm-14in) i. verso. 8-Nov-3 Quittenbaum, Munich #476/R est:1800

KORNBECK, Julius (1839-1920) German

£327	$594	€480	Late summer landscape (24x42cm-9x17in) s. board. 3-Feb-4 Sigalas, Stuttgart #502/R
£979	$1664	€1400	Shepherd with flock by river (42x61cm-17x24in) s. 20-Nov-3 Dorotheum, Salzburg #170/R
£986	$1577	€1400	Cows watering (40x39cm-16x15in) s. 18-Sep-3 Rieber, Stuttgart #774
£1127	$1803	€1600	Shepherd (71x97cm-28x38in) s. 18-Sep-3 Rieber, Stuttgart #771

KORNBECK, Peter (1837-1894) Danish

£1025	$1610	€1497	Italian street scene with figures (42x28cm-17x11in) s.d.1875. 30-Aug-3 Rasmussen, Havnen #2116/R (D.KR 11000)
£1418	$2453	€2070	Young girl on balcony (47x36cm-19x14in) init. i.verso. 9-Dec-3 Rasmussen, Copenhagen #1663/R est:15000-20000 (D.KR 15000)
£1867	$3397	€2801	Street scene in Padova (37x30cm-15x12in) s.d.1885 exhib. 19-Jun-4 Rasmussen, Havnen #2265/R est:10000-15000 (D.KR 21000)
£2222	$4044	€3333	Town scene with archway with market in Spoleto (45x30cm-18x12in) s.d.1873. 19-Jun-4 Rasmussen, Havnen #2266/R est:10000-15000 (D.KR 25000)
£24823	$41454	€35000	Rue animee au Caire (123x83cm-48x33in) s.d.1889. 16-Jun-3 Gros & Delettrez, Paris #146/R est:20000-30000

KORNER, Erich (1866-?) German

£993	$1808	€1500	Portrait of a military leader (92x73cm-36x29in) i.verso after a painting y Anthonis van Dyck. 16-Jun-4 Dorotheum, Vienna #419/R est:1500-2000

KORNERUP, Jacob (1825-1913) Danish

£703	$1209	€1026	Mountain landscape from Alhambra, Granada (31x46cm-12x18in) init.d.1860. 3-Dec-3 Museumsbygningen, Copenhagen #197/R (D.KR 7500)

KORNHAS, Walter (1887-?) German

£3408	$5691	€4976	Peasant with four cows in front of Engadin Alps (90x111cm-35x44in) i. stretcher. 24-Oct-3 Hans Widmer, St Gallen #23/R est:12000 (S.FR 7600)

KORNIG, Hans (1905-1989) German

£3333	$5567	€4800	Untitled (36x37cm-14x15in) s.d.1936. 25-Oct-3 Dr Lehr, Berlin #283/R est:4500

KORNISS, Dezso (1908-1984) Hungarian

£3529	$5859	€5152	Kalligraph (24x128cm-9x50in) enamel paint. 4-Oct-3 Kieselbach, Budapest #174/R (H.F 1300000)

KORNMEIER, Carl (20th C) German?

£268	$494	€400	Weinheim a d Bergatz (48x87cm-19x34in) s. 25-Mar-4 Karlheinz Kaupp, Staufen #2554

KOROCHANSKY, Michel (1866-1925) Russian

£468	$748	€650	Shepherds and cattle in landscape (36x28cm-14x11in) s. 18-May-3 Salle des ventes Pillet, Lyon la Foret #76
£504	$806	€700	Washerwoman by river (36x28cm-14x11in) s. 18-May-3 Salle des ventes Pillet, Lyon la Foret #75
£537	$1004	€800	Paysage couche de soleil (38x55cm-15x22in) s. 29-Feb-4 Osenat, Fontainebleau #218
£669	$1084	€950	Shepherd and his sheep in a wooded landscape (36x28cm-14x11in) s. 11-Aug-3 Boscher, Cherbourg #762/R
£1042	$1740	€1500	Bergers et moutons (65x81cm-26x32in) s. 25-Oct-3 Dianous, Marseille #385
£2042	$3533	€2900	Petite ferme derriere les arbres (46x25cm-18x10in) s. 14-Dec-3 Eric Pillon, Calais #56/R
£2333	$4293	€3500	La mare aux canards (33x46cm-13x18in) s. 11-Jun-4 Claude Aguttes, Neuilly #52/R est:3000-4000
£2686	$4915	€3922	Landscape with cabins at sunset (38x56cm-15x22in) s. 9-Jun-4 Rasmussen, Copenhagen #1619/R est:30000 (D.KR 30000)

KOROSFOI-KRIESCH, Aladar (1863-1920) Hungarian

£4437	$7676	€6478	Young girl with a rose - Portrait of Klotild Abt (60x50cm-24x20in) s.d.87. 12-Dec-3 Kieselbach, Budapest #70/R (H.F 1700000)

Works on paper

£2240	$4054	€3270	Reflection. Palacepark (41x34cm-16x13in) s. gouache pair. 16-Apr-4 Mu Terem Galeria, Budapest #22/R (H.F 850000)

KOROVIAKOV, Alexandre (1912-) Russian

£671	$1242	€1000	Paysage de neige (53x49cm-21x19in) s.verso panel. 14-Mar-4 Eric Pillon, Calais #172/R

KOROVINE, Alexis (fl.1920s) Russian

Works on paper

£1622	$2854	€2400	Lilas (40x56cm-16x22in) s.d.1940 gouache. 19-May-4 Camard, Paris #106 est:3000-4000

KOROVINE, Constantin (1861-1939) Russian

£420	$668	€613	Horse-drawn sleigh passing a village (53x64cm-21x25in) s. 10-Sep-3 Cheffins, Cambridge #548
£3716	$6652	€5500	Winter's day (14x18cm-6x7in) s. panel. 8-May-4 Bukowskis, Helsinki #468/R est:6000-8000
£5615	$9658	€8198	Landscape with snow covered trees (33x41cm-13x16in) s.i.d.1914 panel. 7-Dec-3 Uppsala Auktionskammare, Uppsala #144/R est:40000-50000 (S.KR 73000)
£6000	$10740	€8760	Paris at night (15x31cm-6x12in) s.i. panel. 26-May-4 Sotheby's, London #198/R est:6000-8000
£6081	$10703	€9000	Paris (22x18cm-9x7in) s.d.1924. 19-May-4 Camard, Paris #45 est:1500-2000
£6500	$11635	€9490	Stage design for the opera Russalka (29x41cm-11x16in) s.i. board prov. 26-May-4 Sotheby's, London #210/R est:7000-9000
£6507	$11062	€9500	Troika dans un village russe (33x40cm-13x16in) s. panel. 9-Nov-3 Eric Pillon, Calais #102/R
£8000	$14320	€11680	Rue du Moulin des pres (33x40cm-13x16in) s.i. panel. 26-May-4 Sotheby's, London #141/R est:8000-12000
£8000	$14320	€11680	By the station (33x40cm-13x16in) s.d.1933 i.verso. 26-May-4 Sotheby's, London #144/R est:8000-12000
£8974	$14000	€	Paris by night (26x39cm-10x15in) s.d.1880 board. 11-Apr-3 Christie's, Rockefeller NY #30/R est:6000-8000
£9272	$16874	€14000	Ballade en traineaux (32x40cm-13x16in) s. cardboard. 16-Jun-4 Claude Boisgirard, Paris #92/R est:12000-13000
£10000	$18000	€14600	Side street on the place pigalle, Montmartre (33x41cm-13x16in) s.i. board. 23-Apr-4 Sotheby's, New York #68/R est:12000-18000
£10345	$17276	€15000	Une rue a Montmartre (34x41cm-13x16in) s. cardboard. 17-Nov-3 Claude Boisgirard, Paris #49/R est:20000-25000
£12000	$20400	€17520	Dacha by the river (33x41cm-13x16in) s.i. 19-Nov-3 Sotheby's, London #125/R est:3000-4000
£13000	$23270	€18980	View of Russia (30x40cm-12x16in) s.i.board. 26-May-4 Sotheby's, London #197/R est:10000-15000
£13514	$25000	€19730	Paris street scene (41x33cm-16x13in) s. board. 12-Mar-4 Jackson's, Cedar Falls #778/R est:3000-5000
£13889	$25000	€20278	Riding through the village, sunset (33x41cm-13x16in) s.i. board. 23-Apr-4 Sotheby's, New York #71/R est:12000-18000
£15000	$26850	€21900	View of the Rue de Venise, Paris (38x31cm-15x12in) s.i. board. 26-May-4 Sotheby's, London #140/R est:15000-20000
£16000	$28640	€23360	Tour Saint Jacques, Paris (32x25cm-13x10in) s. i.verso oil paper on board. 26-May-4 Sotheby's, London #139/R est:8000-12000
£16667	$30000	€24334	Paris at night (19x27cm-7x11in) s.i. s.i.d.1927 verso board. 23-Apr-4 Sotheby's, New York #69/R est:6000-8000
£16667	$30000	€24334	Racing troika (33x41cm-13x16in) s.i. board. 23-Apr-4 Sotheby's, New York #73/R est:12000-18000
£17219	$31510	€26000	Une porte a Paris (33x41cm-13x16in) s. panel. 7-Apr-4 Piasa, Paris #138/R est:5000-6000
£18056	$32500	€26362	Riding through the village (33x41cm-13x16in) s.i. board. 23-Apr-4 Sotheby's, New York #74/R est:12000-18000
£19444	$35000	€28388	Racing troika (41x34cm-16x13in) s.i. board. 23-Apr-4 Sotheby's, New York #72/R est:15000-20000
£19868	$36159	€30000	Place a Vichy (23x31cm-9x12in) s.d.1902. 16-Jun-4 Claude Boisgirard, Paris #91/R est:10000-12000
£20000	$34000	€29200	Racing Troika, Tverskaya Gubernai (40x31cm-16x12in) s.i. studio st.verso. 19-Nov-3 Sotheby's, London #84/R est:5000-7000
£20000	$34000	€30000	Statue in a park (34x45cm-13x18in) s. paper on cardboard. 25-Nov-3 Christie's, London #224/R est:15000-25000
£22222	$40000	€32444	La coupole, Paris (33x41cm-13x16in) s.i. board. 23-Apr-4 Sotheby's, New York #67/R est:25000-35000
£22308	$38369	€32570	Palace interior (67x87cm-26x34in) s. prov. 7-Dec-3 Uppsala Auktionskammare, Uppsala #142/R est:200000-250000 (S.KR 290000)
£24000	$42960	€35040	Paris street scene with tram and red car (25x32cm-10x13in) s.i. oil gouache on card. 26-May-4 Sotheby's, London #142/R est:10000-15000
£25000	$42500	€36500	Songs around the campfire (34x41cm-13x16in) s.i. board. 19-Nov-3 Sotheby's, London #133/R est:5000-7000
£25000	$45000	€36500	Cafe des Sport, Paris (33x41cm-13x16in) s.i. board. 23-Apr-4 Sotheby's, New York #70/R est:40000-60000
£25517	$42614	€37000	Place blanche (46x55cm-18x22in) s. 17-Nov-3 Claude Boisgirard, Paris #51 est:30000-35000
£26000	$44200	€37960	Gypsies by the river, Yaroslavl Gubernia, Russia (28x37cm-11x15in) s. i. studio st.verso board. 19-Nov-3 Sotheby's, London #134/R est:4000-6000
£26000	$46540	€37960	Street scene in the suburbs of Paris (78x110cm-31x43in) bears sig board. 26-May-4 Sotheby's, Olympia #418/R est:4000-6000
£28086	$50273	€41006	Parisian street scene (38x46cm-15x18in) s. 28-May-4 Uppsala Auktionskammare, Uppsala #184/R est:150000-200000 (S.KR 380000)
£28873	$49951	€41000	Sur les grands boulevards (45x60cm-18x24in) s.i. panel. 12-Dec-3 Piasa, Paris #112/R est:4000-6000

£30000 $53700 €43800 Portrait of Fedor Chaliapin (71x96cm-28x38in) s.d.1938. 26-May-4 Sotheby's, London #137/R est:30000-50000
£30000 $53700 €43800 Parisian night life (54x73cm-21x29in) prov. 26-May-4 Sotheby's, London #148/R est:25000-35000
£30556 $55000 €44612 Moulin rouge (31x40cm-12x16in) s. board. 23-Apr-4 Sotheby's, New York #66/R est:25000-35000
£31788 $57854 €48000 Paris, terrasse de cafe (16x6cm-6x2in) s. paper. 15-Jun-4 Rossini, Paris #51/R est:2500-3500
£32000 $58880 €48000 Bouquet de roses et coupe de fruits (63x41cm-25x16in) s. 11-Jun-4 Claude Aguttes, Neuilly #46/R est:40000-60000
£35000 $59500 €51100 Paris by night (33x41cm-13x16in) s.i. board. 19-Nov-3 Sotheby's, London #135/R est:12000-15000
£40000 $71600 €58400 Nice (65x50cm-26x20in) s. 26-May-4 Sotheby's, London #149/R est:40000-60000
£45033 $81960 €68000 Boulevards a Paris (46x61cm-18x24in) s. 15-Jun-4 Rossini, Paris #52/R est:12000-18000
£45085 $80702 €65824 Parisian boulevard with men about town (38x46cm-15x18in) s.i. cardboard prov. 25-May-4 Bukowskis, Stockholm #384/R est:150000-175000 (S.KR 610000)
£50000 $86000 €73000 Landscape with tent and figures by camp fire (73x92cm-29x36in) s.d.1913. 7-Dec-3 Uppsala Auktionskammare, Uppsala #141/R est:300000-400000 (S.KR 650000)
£53947 $99263 €82000 Caucase (81x114cm-32x45in) s.i.d.1930. 28-Jun-4 Joron-Derem, Paris #126/R est:40000-45000
£61589 $112093 €93000 Voitures et boulevards illumines, Paris (65x54cm-26x21in) s.i.d.1923. 15-Jun-4 Rossini, Paris #50/R est:12000-18000
£90000 $153000 €135000 View of Parisian street corner (50x61cm-20x24in) s.i. 25-Nov-3 Christie's, London #186/R est:20000-30000
£120000 $204000 €175200 View of the boulevard Haussman, Paris (65x82cm-26x32in) s.i. 19-Nov-3 Sotheby's, London #136/R est:30000-50000
£155000 $277450 €226300 Parisian street scene (71x90cm-28x35in) s.i. 26-May-4 Sotheby's, London #147/R est:60000-80000

Works on paper
£2397 $4075 €3500 Eglise sous la neige (33x24cm-13x9in) s.d.1895 W/C. 9-Nov-3 Eric Pillon, Calais #101/R
£2797 $4755 €4000 Paris, la nuit (27x19cm-11x7in) s.d.1897 pastel gouache. 27-Nov-3 Millon & Associes, Paris #12/R est:1500-2000
£3593 $6000 €5246 Stage design with wooded landscape by the sea (33x44cm-13x17in) s.i.d.1911 W/C. 21-Oct-3 Christie's, Rockefeller NY #91 est:4000-6000
£5000 $8950 €7300 By the campfire (25x30cm-10x12in) indis sig. gouache ink on card. 26-May-4 Sotheby's, London #145/R est:5000-7000
£6376 $11795 €9500 Village russe sous la neige (32x40cm-13x16in) s. gouache. 14-Mar-4 Eric Pillon, Calais #171/R
£8503 $15221 €12500 Paysage de neige (31x36cm-12x14in) s.d.1919 gouache. 19-Mar-4 Ribeyre & Baron, Paris #82/R est:1500-2000
£16000 $28640 €23360 Sketch of Prais by night with promenading couple (31x40cm-12x16in) s.i. gouache on card. 26-May-4 Sotheby's, London #143/R est:8000-10000

KORSCHMANN, Charles (1872-?) Czechoslovakian
Sculpture
£2747 $5000 €4011 Art Nouveau beauty within a vase (43cm-17in) s.st.f. gilt bronze. 19-Jun-4 Jackson's, Cedar Falls #114/R est:5000-8000
£3425 $5822 €5000 Buste de femme (37cm-15in) gilt pat bronze. 5-Nov-3 Tajan, Paris #33/R

KORTE, Hennie de (1941-) Dutch
£338 $541 €480 Still life of flowers and medicine bottles on table (60x70cm-24x28in) s. 18-Sep-3 Rieber, Stuttgart #868

KORTHALS, Johannes (1916-) Dutch
£278 $453 €400 Harbour scene, South of France (50x60cm-20x24in) s. 29-Sep-3 Sotheby's, Amsterdam #333
£822 $1397 €1200 Street in Elburg (59x49cm-23x19in) s. 5-Nov-3 Vendue Huis, Gravenhage #254

KORTLANDER, William (1925-) American
£314 $500 €458 Meadow's edge (122x137cm-48x54in) 14-Sep-3 Susanin's, Chicago #6031/R

KORTOKRAKS, Rudolf (1923-) German
Works on paper
£333 $613 €500 Tulips (66x48cm-26x19in) s. pastel chk. 9-Jun-4 Dorotheum, Salzburg #826/R

KORTRIGHT, Guy (1877-?) British
£1900 $3021 €2774 Mediterranean landscape (64x76cm-25x30in) s. 10-Sep-3 Sotheby's, Olympia #170/R est:800-1200

KORWAN, Franz (1865-?) German
£486 $768 €700 Sailing boat pulled up on the beach (26x36cm-10x14in) s. board. 5-Sep-3 Wendl, Rudolstadt #3468/R
£486 $768 €700 Coastal landscape with rowing boat pulled up onto the beach (21x32cm-8x13in) s. board. 5-Sep-3 Wendl, Rudolstadt #3469/R
£667 $1207 €1000 Cows grazing - Sylt 1929 (37x49cm-15x19in) s. i. verso panel. 3-Apr-4 Hans Stahl, Hamburg #54/R

KORYUSAI, Isoda (fl.c.1766-1788) Japanese
Prints
£2000 $3680 €2920 The departure (69x12cm-27x5in) s. print lit. 8-Jun-4 Sotheby's, London #105/R est:2000-2500
£2000 $3680 €2920 Courtesan Handayu seated with a brush in her hand before a low table (38x26cm-15x10in) s. print exec. c.1776 prov.lit. 8-Jun-4 Sotheby's, London #116/R est:1000-1500
£2500 $4600 €3650 A giant and a beauty (69x12cm-27x5in) s.i. print lit. 8-Jun-4 Sotheby's, London #110/R est:800-1200
£5000 $9200 €7300 Courtesan Kasugano parading in her finery (39x26cm-15x10in) s. print exec. c.1778-80 prov.lit. 8-Jun-4 Sotheby's, London #120/R est:1800-2200
£8000 $14720 €11680 Parrot and cockatoo perched on a wooden bar above a brocade Kicho (28x20cm-11x8in) s. print lit. 8-Jun-4 Sotheby's, London #127/R est:1500-2000

KORYUSAI, Isoda (attrib) (1725-1785) Japanese
Prints
£4200 $7728 €6132 Willow blown by the fresh wind (26x19cm-10x7in) print exec. c.1773-75 prov.lit. 8-Jun-4 Sotheby's, London #129/R est:2500-3000

KORZOUKHIN, Alexei Ivanovich (1835-1894) Russian
£4500 $7650 €6570 Portrait of an Officer (30x23cm-12x9in) 19-Nov-3 Sotheby's, London #20/R est:4000-6000

KOSA, Emil (jnr) (1903-1968) American
£1630 $3000 €2380 Pink mums (76x61cm-30x24in) s. 8-Jun-4 Bonhams & Butterfields, San Francisco #4374/R est:4000-6000
£1923 $3500 €2808 Standing woman in white dress (76x56cm-30x22in) s. i.verso board. 15-Jun-4 John Moran, Pasadena #111 est:4000-6000
£2989 $5500 €4364 Landscape (50x76cm-20x30in) s. i. stretcher prov. 8-Jun-4 Bonhams & Butterfields, San Francisco #4330/R est:6000-8000
£6936 $12000 €10127 Lasting happiness (66x96cm-26x38in) s. masonite. 10-Dec-3 Bonhams & Butterfields, San Francisco #6246/R est:8000-12000
£7453 $12000 €10807 Silver and gold (61x91cm-24x36in) 22-Aug-3 Altermann Galleries, Santa Fe #172
£12363 $22500 €18050 Porto Fino 2 (58x79cm-23x31in) s. i.verso prov. 15-Jun-4 John Moran, Pasadena #99 est:12000-18000
£20588 $35000 €30058 Circus scene, big top (61x71cm-24x28in) s. i.verso. 18-Nov-3 John Moran, Pasadena #67 est:10000-15000

Works on paper
£495 $900 €723 Study of a seated nude (71x46cm-28x18in) s. chl wash. 15-Jun-4 John Moran, Pasadena #79b
£1984 $3750 €2897 Favourite spot (51x71cm-20x28in) s. i. verso W/C prov. 17-Feb-4 John Moran, Pasadena #83a/R est:3000-5000
£2910 $5500 €4249 Early spring storm (43x58cm-17x23in) s. i.d.1937 verso W/C exhib.prov. 17-Feb-4 John Moran, Pasadena #83/R est:5000-7000
£4412 $7500 €6442 Taxco (56x74cm-22x29in) s. W/C prov. 18-Nov-3 John Moran, Pasadena #88 est:3000-4500
£4412 $7500 €6442 Figures in winter mountain landscape (51x71cm-20x28in) s. W/C prov. 18-Nov-3 John Moran, Pasadena #130 est:3000-4000
£4497 $8500 €6566 Rural landscape probably Salinas, Calif (46x64cm-18x25in) s. W/C prov. 17-Feb-4 John Moran, Pasadena #86/R est:7000-9000
£5495 $10000 €8023 Bunker Hill (51x71cm-20x28in) i.verso W/C prov. 15-Jun-4 John Moran, Pasadena #83 est:5000-7000
£21978 $40000 €32088 Bunker Hill, Downtown Los Angeles (53x74cm-21x29in) s. W/C. 15-Jun-4 John Moran, Pasadena #82a est:8000-10000

KOSA, Emil (jnr-attrib) (1903-1968) American
Works on paper
£2206 $3750 €3221 Cabin in mountain landscape (22x28cm-9x11in) W/C prov. 18-Nov-3 John Moran, Pasadena #125 est:2000-3000

KOSA, Emil (snr) (1876-1955) American
£882 $1500 €1288 Floral still life (66x79cm-26x31in) s. 18-Nov-3 John Moran, Pasadena #170 est:2500-3500
£1324 $2250 €1933 Landscape (30x41cm-12x16in) s. board prov. 18-Nov-3 John Moran, Pasadena #97b est:1000-2000
£1563 $2500 €2282 Still life of chrysanthemums (165x201cm-65x79in) s. 18-May-3 Auctions by the Bay, Alameda #1100/R
£2601 $4500 €3797 Floral still life with chrysanthemums (114x89cm-45x35in) s. 10-Dec-3 Bonhams & Butterfields, San Francisco #6269/R est:3000-5000
£5202 $9000 €7595 Malibu Coast (71x86cm-28x34in) s. board. 10-Dec-3 Bonhams & Butterfields, San Francisco #6208/R est:6000-8000

KOSAK, F V (20th C) ?
Works on paper
£336 $621 €500 Girl sitting on chair (144x88cm-57x35in) s. pastel board. 9-Mar-4 Dorotheum, Vienna #39/R

KOSCIANSKI, Leonard (1952-) American?
Works on paper
£412 $750 €602 Pop-top (74x102cm-29x40in) s.d.1971 pastel. 19-Jun-4 Harvey Clar, Oakland #2366

KOSENG YOO-ZOO KWAN (18th C) Korean
Works on paper
£1536 $2750 €2243 The goat herder (163x41cm-64x16in) i. ink paper on fabric. 8-May-4 Auctions by the Bay, Alameda #564/R

KOSHELEV, Nikolaij Andreevitch (1840-1918) Russian
£12162 $21770 €18000 The rowing trip (32x50cm-13x20in) s.d.1886 exhib. 8-May-4 Bukowskis, Helsinki #467/R est:6000-10000

KOSHLAND, Phyllis (1949-) Australian
Sculpture
£1532 $2650 €2237 Unfurling (26x71x26cm-10x28x10in) s.d.1988 num.2/5 bronze prov. 10-Dec-3 Shapiro, Sydney #90/R est:2000-4000 (A.D 3600)

KOSICE, Gyula (1924-) Argentinian

Sculpture
£1899 $3400 €2773 Air stone (44cm-17in) s. plexiglas. 4-May-4 Arroyo, Buenos Aires #30/R est:2800
£2486 $4500 €3630 Untitled (39cm-15in) plexiglas water. 30-Mar-4 Arroyo, Buenos Aires #22
£4396 $8000 €6418 Untitled (60cm-24in) s. plexiglas. 29-Jun-4 Arroyo, Buenos Aires #32/R est:7500

KOSINSKI, Joseph (1753-1821) Polish

Miniatures
£1500 $2595 €2190 Young gentleman holding left hand to chest and wearing black hat (6x5cm-2x2in) s.d.1800 silver-gilt frame ocatgonal. 9-Dec-3 Christie's, London #89/R est:1500-2500

KOSKULL, Anders Gustaf (1831-1904) Swedish

£703 $1132 €1026 Three generations (71x61cm-28x24in) s. 25-Aug-3 Lilla Bukowskis, Stockholm #481 (S.KR 9200)
£2310 $3926 €3373 Church interior with woman, girl and boy (72x61cm-28x24in) s. s.i.stretcher lit. 19-Nov-3 Grev Wedels Plass, Oslo #11/R est:30000-40000 (N.KR 27000)

KOSLOFF, Abraham (20th C) Russian

£331 $603 €500 Village path (45x54cm-18x21in) s.d.1929. 19-Jun-4 Quittenbaum, Hamburg #86/R

KOSMADOPOULOS, Georgios (1895-1967) Greek

£3000 $5250 €4380 Views of Myconos (21x32cm-8x13in) s. hardboard pair. 16-Dec-3 Bonhams, New Bond Street #51/R est:3000-5000

KOSNICK-KLOSS, Jeanne (1892-1955) German

£805 $1498 €1200 Composition (33x24cm-13x9in) mono. panel. 3-Mar-4 Artcurial Briest, Paris #473
Works on paper
£364 $663 €550 Composition (31x24cm-12x9in) mono.d.1927 pastel. 18-Jun-4 Charbonneaux, Paris #96

KOSONEN, Erkki (1902-1966) Finnish

£604 $1111 €900 Vessel at Aura river (40x55cm-16x22in) s.d.1963. 25-Mar-4 Hagelstam, Helsinki #1053

KOSSAK, Jerzy (1890-1963) Polish

£246 $450 €359 Returning with the flock (23x33cm-9x13in) s.d.1933 board. 5-Jun-4 Treadway Gallery, Cincinnati #569/R
£500 $915 €730 Tracker (30x38cm-12x15in) s.d.1933 panel. 8-Apr-4 Christie's, Kensington #198/R
£832 $1439 €1215 Captivity (37x49cm-15x19in) s.d.27 cardboard. 14-Dec-3 Agra, Warsaw #21/R (P.Z 5500)
£861 $1567 €1300 Summer forest landscape with Kosak chase (38x49cm-15x19in) s.d.1929 board. 19-Jun-4 Bergmann, Erlangen #780
£1342 $2470 €2000 Battle scene in winter (36x47cm-14x19in) s.d.1929 board. 27-Mar-4 Dannenberg, Berlin #579/R est:2000
£4389 $6846 €6408 Soldier with two horses (47x58cm-19x23in) s. panel painted c.1920. 30-Mar-3 Agra, Warsaw #12/R est:28000 (P.Z 28000)

KOSSAK, Woiciech von (1857-1942) Polish

£1333 $2400 €2000 Portrait of Maria Kossakowa (64x74cm-25x29in) s.d.1941. 21-Apr-4 Dorotheum, Vienna #110/R est:2000-2800
£1411 $2201 €2060 Arabian horses (39x49cm-15x19in) s. painted c.1920. 30-Mar-3 Agra, Warsaw #35/R est:9000 (P.Z 9000)
£1528 $2551 €2200 Soldier (31x39cm-12x15in) s.d.1876 i. verso lit. 25-Oct-3 Bergmann, Erlangen #958/R est:1200
£1567 $2445 €2288 Signaling to the other ships (51x40cm-20x16in) s.d.1935. 30-Mar-3 Agra, Warsaw #33/R est:9000 (P.Z 10000)
£1620 $2802 €2300 Kaiser Wilhelm II and the manoeuvre of the king in the year 1901 (50x40cm-20x16in) s.i.verso panel. 10-Dec-3 Dorotheum, Vienna #114/R est:4500-5500
£2688 $4382 €3924 Uhlander playing (53x79cm-21x31in) s.d.1924. 29-Sep-3 Lilla Bukowskis, Stockholm #676 est:15000-18000 (S.KR 35000)
£8000 $14400 €12000 Polish lancers of the French Imperial Guard (77x59cm-30x23in) s.d.1907. 21-Apr-4 Christie's, Amsterdam #174/R est:8000-12000

KOSSOFF, Léon (1926-) British

£10305 $18756 €15045 Reclining nude (32x47cm-13x19in) prov.exhib. 16-Jun-4 Deutscher-Menzies, Melbourne #89/R est:34000-45000 (A.D 27000)
£26000 $43420 €37960 Fidelma No.1 (49x61cm-19x24in) board painted 1984 prov.exhib. 21-Oct-3 Sotheby's, London #413/R est:25000-35000
£150000 $276000 €219000 Here comes the diesel, early summer (137x122cm-54x48in) board painted 1987 exhib.lit. 23-Jun-4 Sotheby's, London #7/R est:120000-180000
Works on paper
£900 $1548 €1314 Study of a face of a woman (25x18cm-10x7in) chl chk. 3-Dec-3 Christie's, Kensington #649/R
£4200 $7518 €6132 Swimming Pool (34x50cm-13x20in) s. chl. 16-Mar-4 Bonhams, Knightsbridge #110/R est:1000-1500
£10000 $18300 €14600 School building, Willesden III (60x84cm-24x33in) chl col chk executed 1979 prov. 4-Jun-4 Christie's, London #95/R est:4000-6000

KOSSONOGI, Joseph (1908-1981) ?

£382 $650 €558 The orchestra (10x25cm-4x10in) s. cardboard on board. 1-Dec-3 Ben-Ami, Tel Aviv #4321/R
Works on paper
£410 $750 €599 Urban landscape (46x31cm-18x12in) s. W/C. 1-Feb-4 Ben-Ami, Tel Aviv #4656/R
£588 $1100 €858 Landscape of Zaffed (34x49cm-13x19in) s. W/C exec.c.1942. 1-Mar-4 Ben-Ami, Tel Aviv #4695/R
£706 $1200 €1031 Landscape of the Yarkon River (32x45cm-13x18in) s.d.1945 W/C. 1-Dec-3 Ben-Ami, Tel Aviv #4363/R

KOSSOWSKI, Henryk (19/20th C) Belgian

Sculpture
£1000 $1670 €1460 Le fleurs (65cm-26in) s. reddish brown pat. bronze. 14-Oct-3 Sotheby's, Olympia #62/R est:1200-1800

KOST, Frederick W (1861-1923) American

£647 $1100 €945 Mill at Smithtown, Long Island (69x61cm-27x24in) s. 5-Nov-3 Doyle, New York #37/R est:2000-3000
£1098 $1800 €1592 Landscape with rustic wooden bridge and distant tree (41x61cm-16x24in) s. prov. 31-May-3 Brunk, Ashville #542/R est:500-1000
£2095 $3750 €3059 Road to the beach (38x56cm-15x22in) s. s.i.d.1890 verso prov. 6-May-4 Shannon's, Milford #249/R est:2500-3500

KOSTA, Alex (1925-) Swiss?

Sculpture
£938 $1744 €1400 Man at the wheel (78x56cm-31x22in) s.i.d.1967 collage paint cardboard relief box. 3-Mar-4 Artcurial Briest, Paris #481 est:1200-1800
£1074 $1997 €1600 Man with a hat no 72 (99x61cm-39x24in) s.i.d.1966 collage paint cardboard relief box. 3-Mar-4 Artcurial Briest, Paris #478/R est:1800-2200
£1208 $2247 €1800 Une femme en or (69x69cm-27x27in) s.i.d.1969 collage paint cardboard relief box. 3-Mar-4 Artcurial Briest, Paris #477 est:600-800
£2551 $4744 €3800 Gilbert (57x83cm-22x33in) s.i.d.1969 collage paint cardboard relief box. 3-Mar-4 Artcurial Briest, Paris #476 est:1800-2500
£3020 $5618 €4500 Right hand in a green frame (67x52cm-26x20in) s.i.d.1965 polychrome wood relief. 3-Mar-4 Artcurial Briest, Paris #475 est:2000-2500

KOSTABI, Mark (1961-) American

£417 $750 €609 Ammnition for anger (23x17cm-9x7in) s.d.1984 acrylic paper. 24-Apr-4 David Rago, Lambertville #513/R
£528 $877 €750 Evidence of analysis (76x66cm-30x26in) s. s.i.d.1997 verso acrylic paper. 14-Jun-3 Meeting Art, Vercelli #223/R
£563 $1025 €850 My love (25x20cm-10x8in) s.d.2001 s.i.d.verso. 17-Jun-4 Galleria Pananti, Florence #429/R
£662 $1205 €1000 Quiet garden (30cm-12in circular) s.d.2002 acrylic. 17-Jun-4 Galleria Pananti, Florence #428/R
£828 $1324 €1200 Attention getter (25x20cm-10x8in) s.d.2001 s.i.d.verso. 13-Mar-3 Galleria Pace, Milan #56/R est:1600-2000
£833 $1358 €1200 Diver (60x171cm-24x67in) s.d.1985/86. 27-Sep-3 Dr Fritz Nagel, Stuttgart #9571/R
£897 $1434 €1300 Protection (25x30cm-10x12in) s.i.verso painted 2002. 13-Mar-3 Galleria Pace, Milan #109/R est:1350-1550
£1000 $1840 €1500 Changing the sound (45x30cm-18x12in) s.d.2002 oval. 12-Jun-4 Meeting Art, Vercelli #265/R est:1500
£1042 $1646 €1500 Whittier's autumn (46x30cm-18x12in) oval. 6-Sep-3 Meeting Art, Vercelli #325 est:1500
£1042 $1646 €1500 Advantage (28x28cm-11x11in) painted 2002. 6-Sep-3 Meeting Art, Vercelli #3480 est:1500
£1067 $1963 €1600 Hijiki (122x75cm-48x30in) s.d.1997 acrylic cardboard. 12-Jun-4 Meeting Art, Vercelli #305/R est:1500
£1127 $1870 €1600 Onement (25x30cm-10x12in) s.d.2002 s.i.d.verso. 14-Jun-3 Meeting Art, Vercelli #187/R est:1000
£1133 $2085 €1700 Surreal aerobics (61x41cm-24x16in) s.d.1993. 11-Jun-4 Farsetti, Prato #175/R est:1500-1800
£1141 $2111 €1700 Second thoughts (45x30cm-18x12in) s.i.d.2002 verso oval. 13-Mar-4 Meeting Art, Vercelli #378 est:1500
£1172 $1876 €1700 Smolder (cm-12in circular) s.d.2002 s.i.d.verso. 13-Mar-3 Galleria Pace, Milan #97/R est:1800-2400
£1241 $2073 €1800 Spell (25x30cm-10x12in) s.d.2003. 13-Nov-3 Galleria Pace, Milan #149/R est:2400
£1310 $2097 €1900 Way split (61x46cm-24x18in) s.d.1997 s.i.d.verso. 13-Mar-3 Galleria Pace, Milan #57/R est:2200-3000
£1319 $2085 €1900 Caffeine dreams (61x46cm-24x18in) painted 2002. 6-Sep-3 Meeting Art, Vercelli #560 est:1500
£1333 $2453 €2000 Facing the truth (65x45cm-26x18in) s.d.2002 s.i.d.verso. 10-Jun-4 Galleria Pace, Milan #123/R est:3000
£1342 $2483 €2000 Utopy (45x30cm-18x12in) s. s.i.d.2002 verso oval. 13-Mar-4 Meeting Art, Vercelli #112 est:1500
£1377 $2258 €1900 Only yesterday (61x46cm-24x18in) s.d.2000. 29-May-3 Galleria Pace, Milan #127/R
£1517 $2534 €2200 Light source (76x35cm-30x14in) s.d.2000. 13-Nov-3 Galleria Pace, Milan #146/R est:3500
£1544 $2763 €2300 Cellist (101x76cm-40x30in) s.d.1997 s.i.d.verso. 28-May-4 Farsetti, Prato #1/R est:1900-2200
£1611 $2980 €2400 Clutch (61x46cm-24x18in) s.d.2000 s.i.d.verso. 11-Mar-4 Galleria Pace, Milan #52/R est:2750-3500
£1678 $3104 €2500 Balancing act (76x61cm-30x24in) s.d.1996. 13-Mar-4 Meeting Art, Vercelli #125 est:2500
£1733 $3189 €2600 Way split (61x46cm-24x18in) s.d.1997. 12-Jun-4 Meeting Art, Vercelli #727/R est:2000
£1745 $3089 €2600 Pianist (121x191cm-48x75in) 30-Apr-4 Dr Fritz Nagel, Stuttgart #860/R est:2200
£1793 $2869 €2600 Approach (61x46cm-24x18in) s.d.2001 s.i.d.verso. 13-Mar-3 Galleria Pace, Milan #13/R est:3200-4200
£1793 $2994 €2600 Sustain (60cm-24in circular) s.d.2002. 13-Nov-3 Galleria Pace, Milan #31/R est:3000-3300
£1875 $2963 €2700 Toehold on reality (76x61cm-30x24in) 6-Sep-3 Meeting Art, Vercelli #356 est:2500
£1958 $3329 €2800 Unlimited (61x45cm-24x18in) painted 2001. 19-Nov-3 Cambi, Genoa #482/R est:2500-3000
£2000 $3680 €3000 Cat flowers (76x102cm-30x40in) s.d.1991 s.i.d.verso. 12-Jun-4 Meeting Art, Vercelli #999/R est:3000
£2029 $3328 €2800 L (6x75cm-2x30in) s.d.2001 ac. 29-May-3 Galleria Pace, Milan #147/R est:4000
£2174 $3565 €3000 Flight of memory (62x45cm-24x18in) s.i.d.2000 verso acrylic. 29-May-3 Galleria Pace, Milan #30/R est:3800
£2238 $3804 €3200 A la merci du rouge (123x91cm-48x36in) s.d.1991. 28-Nov-3 Farsetti, Prato #206/R est:3200-3700
£2333 $4200 €3500 Binary system (76x111cm-30x44in) s. s.d.1997 verso. 22-Apr-4 Finarte Semenzato, Rome #284/R est:3500-3800

£2394 $3975 €3400 Necessary evil (99x81cm-39x32in) s.d.1999 s.i.d.verso exhib.lit. 13-Jun-3 Farsetti, Prato #125/R
£2550 $4565 €3800 Wayward dimensions (106x90cm-42x35in) s.d.1987. 28-May-4 Farsetti, Prato #208/R est:2600-2900
£2685 $4966 €4000 Women's mystery (71x106cm-28x42in) s.d.2001 s.i.verso. 13-Mar-4 Meeting Art, Vercelli #402 est:4000
£2759 $4414 €4000 Losing myself (102x76cm-40x30in) s.d.1999 s.i.d.verso. 13-Mar-3 Galleria Pace, Milan #25/R est:4200-5400
£2778 $4389 €4000 Shadows of the present (90x90cm-35x35in) painted 1998. 6-Sep-3 Meeting Art, Vercelli #587 est:4000
£2784 $4927 €4065 Untitled (178x122cm-70x48in) s.d.1984-85 verso prov. 27-Apr-4 AB Stockholms Auktionsverk #1000/R est:20000-25000 (S.KR 38000)
£2819 $5215 €4200 Fire starter (100x100cm-39x39in) s.d.2003 acrylic. 11-Mar-4 Galleria Pace, Milan #75/R est:4500-6000
£2953 $5286 €4400 Multiculturalism (76x102cm-30x40in) s.d.1997 lit. 30-May-4 Meeting Art, Vercelli #20 est:4000
£3099 $5144 €4400 Entwined (90x122cm-35x48in) s.d.1994 s.i.d.verso. 14-Jun-3 Meeting Art, Vercelli #691/R est:4000
£3733 $6869 €5600 Rigged (76x101cm-30x40in) s.d.2001. 12-Jun-4 Meeting Art, Vercelli #589/R est:4000

Prints

£2391 $3922 €3300 On the edge (117x91cm-46x36in) s.d.1988-2002 serigraph felt-tip pen. 30-May-3 Farsetti, Prato #50/R

Works on paper

£278 $453 €400 Untitled (70x50cm-28x20in) s.d.1996 mixed media metal foil. 27-Sep-3 Dr Fritz Nagel, Stuttgart #9250/R
£845 $1479 €1200 Untitled (21x24cm-8x9in) s.d.1991 pencil set of 4. 16-Dec-3 Finarte Semenzato, Milan #138/R est:1200-1500

KOSTABI, Paul (1962-) American

£313 $577 €470 Dij Jery (50x50cm-20x20in) s. oil acrylic painted 2000. 12-Jun-4 Meeting Art, Vercelli #76

KOSTANDI, Kiriak (1853-1921) Russian

Works on paper

£743 $1330 €1100 Moonlight (21x29cm-8x11in) s. gouache. 8-May-4 Bukowskis, Helsinki #453/R

KOSTER, Antonie L (1859-1937) Dutch

£17105 $31474 €26000 A beautiful day in a tulip field (51x75cm-20x30in) s. 22-Jun-4 Christie's, Amsterdam #323/R est:7000-9000

KOSTER, Antonius Henricus (1913-1990) Dutch

£276 $461 €400 View of the Seine in Paris (47x58cm-19x23in) s. board. 11-Nov-3 Vendu Notarishuis, Rotterdam #26/R
£278 $453 €400 View of a landscape (50x75cm-20x30in) s. 29-Sep-3 Sotheby's, Amsterdam #331

KOSTER, E (19th C) Dutch

£1831 $3204 €2600 Bateau a maree basse (20x36cm-8x14in) s. panel. 16-Dec-3 Galerie Moderne, Brussels #772/R est:400-600

KOSTER, Everhardus (1817-1892) Dutch

£1447 $2620 €2200 Three-mast ship of the seventeenth century welcoming a yacht (39x50cm-15x20in) s. panel. 19-Apr-4 Glerum, Amsterdam #14/R est:1400-1600
£1724 $2879 €2500 Old Dutch city square with figures by the water (51x41cm-20x16in) s. 11-Nov-3 Vendu Notarishuis, Rotterdam #154/R est:2500-3000
£6944 $11597 €10000 Shipping on the IJ, Amsterdam (55x76cm-22x30in) s. indis d. 21-Oct-3 Sotheby's, Amsterdam #184/R est:10000-15000

Works on paper

£1310 $2384 €1913 Dutch trading house on the edge of canal (35x44cm-14x17in) s.d.1845 brush bistre ink over pencil. 17-Jun-4 Kornfeld, Bern #26/R est:3000 (S.FR 3000)

KOSTER, Heinrich (1878-1909) German

£638 $1129 €950 Countryside (90x75cm-35x30in) s.d.09. 28-Apr-4 Schopman, Hamburg #630/R

KOSTER, Jo (1869-1944) Dutch

£382 $623 €550 Portrait of a baby (31x24cm-12x9in) s.d.1921 canvas on board. 29-Sep-3 Sotheby's, Amsterdam #178
£638 $1180 €950 Portrait of a bearded man smoking a pipe (25x17cm-10x7in) s. canvas on board. 15-Mar-4 Sotheby's, Amsterdam #190/R est:800-1200
£1678 $2853 €2400 Still life with anemones, a bottle and pewter plates (65x90cm-26x35in) s.d.1923. 25-Nov-3 Christie's, Amsterdam #16/R est:2500-3500

KOSTER, Karl Georg (1812-1893) German

£268 $494 €400 Landscape near Bremen (24x35cm-9x14in) s. board. 26-Mar-4 Bolland & Marotz, Bremen #546/R
£805 $1482 €1200 Winter landscape with peasants returning home in the evening (32x38cm-13x15in) s. panel. 26-Mar-4 Bolland & Marotz, Bremen #545a/R
£839 $1401 €1200 Pasture with stream in Tyrolean Alps (41x54cm-16x21in) s. canvas on panel. 28-Jun-3 Bolland & Marotz, Bremen #690/R

Works on paper

£405 $726 €600 City with figures (19x28cm-7x11in) s. pencil. 6-May-4 Michael Zeller, Lindau #729/R

KOSTER, Paul (1855-1946) German

£667 $1207 €1000 Steamer at quayside (27x35cm-11x14in) panel. 2-Apr-4 Dr Fritz Nagel, Leipzig #3967/R

KOSTER, Walter (20th C) German

£282 $504 €400 Winter landscape with village (46x54cm-18x21in) s.d.41 board. 8-Jan-4 Allgauer, Kempten #2443/R

KOSTKA, Joseph (1846-1927) Polish

£1611 $2851 €2400 Still life with flowers and fruit. s.d.1915. 28-Apr-4 Schopman, Hamburg #489/R est:1200

KOSUTH, Joseph (1945-) American

Prints

£14000 $25760 €20440 Art as idea as idea (115x115cm-45x45in) photostat board exec 1966 prov. 24-Jun-4 Sotheby's, London #147/R est:6000-8000
£19461 $32500 €28413 Titled, art as idea as idea (122x122cm-48x48in) s.i.d.1967 photostat board prov. 13-Nov-3 Sotheby's, New York #574/R est:15000-20000

Sculpture

£2917 $4813 €4200 Wittgenstein's color (38x17cm-15x7in) neon electric. 2-Jul-3 Cornette de St.Cyr, Paris #225/R est:4500-5000
£7821 $14000 €11419 Omission without submissions is found in the following example (193x11cm-76x4in) neon transfer text prov. 14-May-4 Phillips, New York #250/R est:15000-20000
£11189 $19021 €16000 I return now to our topic (220x13cm-87x5in) neon prov. 25-Nov-3 Tajan, Paris #55/R est:20000-30000
£73333 $135667 €110000 Self-described and self-defined (10x220cm-4x87in) red neon light exec.1965 prov. 18-Jul-4 Sotheby's, Paris #222/R est:75000-100000

Works on paper

£6159 $10101 €8500 Material (97x97cm-38x38in) mixed media photostat on board exec.1969-70. 27-May-3 Sotheby's, Amsterdam #454a/R est:6000-8000
£6159 $10101 €8500 Water (97x97cm-38x38in) mixed media photostat on board exec.1969-70. 27-May-3 Sotheby's, Amsterdam #454b/R est:6000-8000
£7246 $11884 €10000 Translate (97x97cm-38x38in) mixed media photostat on board exec.1969-70. 27-May-3 Sotheby's, Amsterdam #454/R est:6000-8000

KOSVANEC, Vlastimil (1887-1961) Czechoslovakian

£548 $965 €822 Diana (90x70cm-35x28in) s. 22-May-4 Dorotheum, Prague #107/R est:20000-30000 (C.KR 26000)
£988 $1679 €1442 Summer afternoon (68x88cm-27x35in) s. cardboard. 29-Nov-3 Dorotheum, Prague #62/R est:20000-30000 (C.KR 45000)
£1055 $1856 €1583 Summer (70x100cm-28x39in) s. 22-May-4 Dorotheum, Prague #127 est:36000-50000 (C.KR 50000)
£1133 $2107 €1654 A rest (69x100cm-27x39in) s. 6-Mar-4 Dorotheum, Prague #53 est:30000-45000 (C.KR 55000)
£1236 $2298 €1805 Vintage (70x100cm-28x39in) s. 6-Mar-4 Dorotheum, Prague #141/R est:30000-45000 (C.KR 60000)
£1646 $2799 €2403 Hoppers (72x100cm-28x39in) s. 29-Nov-3 Dorotheum, Prague #65/R est:26000-38000 (C.KR 75000)

KOSZKOL, Jeno (1868-1935) Hungarian

Works on paper

£1253 $2167 €1829 Children by the Easel (76x55cm-30x22in) s. mixed media. 12-Dec-3 Kieselbach, Budapest #180/R (H.F 480000)

KOSZTA, Jozsef (1864-1949) Hungarian

£6264 $10837 €9145 Isolated farm (36x52cm-14x20in) s. cardboard. 12-Dec-3 Kieselbach, Budapest #225/R (H.F 2400000)
£6850 $12399 €10001 Flowers in jug (46x34cm-18x13in) s. oil on card. 16-Apr-4 Mu Terem Galeria, Budapest #53/R (H.F 2600000)
£16033 $28379 €23408 Geranium (50x40cm-20x16in) s. 28-Apr-4 Kieselbach, Budapest #45/R (H.F 6000000)

KOSZTOLANYI, Gyula (1868-1945) Hungarian

£949 $1717 €1386 View of the provincial church (38x48cm-15x19in) s. oil on card. 16-Apr-4 Mu Terem Galeria, Budapest #124/R (H.F 360000)

KOTARBINSKI, Wilhelm Aleksandrovich (1849-1921) Polish

£24000 $42960 €35040 Roman feast (46x91cm-18x36in) s. 26-May-4 Sotheby's, London #20/R est:6000-8000
£38000 $64600 €55480 Playing chess (73x101cm-29x40in) s.i.d.79. 19-Nov-3 Sotheby's, London #24/R est:10000-15000
£80000 $143200 €116800 Carrying the urn (67x52cm-26x20in) s.i. 26-May-4 Sotheby's, London #22/R est:20000-30000

KOTHE, Fritz (1916-) German

£430 $783 €650 Number 8 (30x35cm-12x14in) mono.d.1989 s.i.d.verso stretcher. 19-Jun-4 Quittenbaum, Hamburg #126/R
£728 $1326 €1100 Auto portrait with Eda (90x69cm-35x27in) s.d.1945 tempera oil. 19-Jun-4 Quittenbaum, Hamburg #119/R
£1060 $1928 €1600 Calypso (64x70cm-25x28in) mono.d.1951 s.i.d.verso tempera oil. 19-Jun-4 Quittenbaum, Hamburg #122/R est:1300
£1192 $2170 €1800 Dunlop (100x75cm-39x30in) s.d.1984 s.i.d.verso stretcher. 19-Jun-4 Quittenbaum, Hamburg #125/R est:1200
£1457 $2652 €2200 Reyno (70x100cm-28x39in) s.d.1965 tempera oil. 19-Jun-4 Quittenbaum, Hamburg #123/R est:1500
£1457 $2652 €2200 The pink scarf (75x103cm-30x41in) mono.d.1979 s.i.d.verso stretcher tempera oil. 19-Jun-4 Quittenbaum, Hamburg #124/R est:1600
£2958 $5117 €4200 Pall Mall (90x70cm-35x28in) mono.d.1974 i. stretcher. 13-Dec-3 Lempertz, Koln #162/R est:3000
£3239 $5604 €4600 Amba (91x70cm-36x28in) mono.d.1965. 13-Dec-3 Lempertz, Koln #161/R est:3000

Works on paper

£350 $584 €500 Epilectics (46x60cm-18x24in) s.d.70 gouache study verso. 28-Jun-3 Dannenberg, Berlin #717/R
£430 $783 €650 Arai (24x30cm-9x12in) s.i.d.1985 W/C. 19-Jun-4 Quittenbaum, Hamburg #130/R

KOTIK, Pravoslav (1889-1970) Czechoslovakian

£391 $728 €571 After bath (24x17cm-9x7in) mono. tempera. 6-Mar-4 Dorotheum, Prague #209/R est:10000-15000 (C.KR 19000)
£659 $1226 €962 Couple (27x35cm-11x14in) s.d.48 board. 6-Mar-4 Dorotheum, Prague #143/R est:32000-50000 (C.KR 32000)

£748 $1339 €1100 Personnages allonges au panier (34x41cm-13x16in) mono. panel. 16-Mar-4 Chochon-Barre & Allardi, Paris #108
£782 $1400 €1150 Femmes a la bougie (60x49cm-24x19in) s. cardboard. 16-Mar-4 Chochon-Barre & Allardi, Paris #107/R
£952 $1705 €1400 Profil de femme (33x45cm-13x18in) s. panel. 16-Mar-4 Chochon-Barre & Allardi, Paris #143
£1156 $2070 €1700 L'acrobate (57x35cm-22x14in) s. panel. 16-Mar-4 Chochon-Barre & Allardi, Paris #142 est:3000-4000
£1701 $3044 €2500 Jeunes filles et les vaches (65x81cm-26x32in) s. 16-Mar-4 Chochon-Barre & Allardi, Paris #128/R est:800-1000
£2041 $3653 €3000 Au bord de la mer (40x50cm-16x20in) s. 16-Mar-4 Chochon-Barre & Allardi, Paris #136/R est:2500-3000
£2685 $4966 €4000 Couple having a drink (45x41cm-18x16in) s.d.28 canvasboard. 15-Mar-4 Sotheby's, Amsterdam #150/R est:2500-3500
£2789 $4993 €4100 Nu sur fond bleu (61x50cm-24x20in) s. 16-Mar-4 Chochon-Barre & Allardi, Paris #126/R est:5000-6000
£3064 $5086 €4473 Dialogue (46x33cm-18x13in) s.d.29 board. 4-Oct-3 Dorotheum, Prague #100/R est:80000-120000 (C.KR 140000)
£3401 $6088 €5000 Personnages debout (43x40cm-17x16in) s. panel. 16-Mar-4 Chochon-Barre & Allardi, Paris #109/R est:5000
£7746 $13556 €11000 Social group talking (71x97cm-28x38in) s.d.30 i.d.30 verso plywood. 19-Dec-3 Dorotheum, Vienna #71/R est:18000-22000
Works on paper
£268 $498 €391 In theatre (14x31cm-6x12in) s. W/C. 6-Mar-4 Dorotheum, Prague #208/R est:8000-12000 (C.KR 13000)
£306 $548 €450 Conversation (31x22cm-12x9in) s. Indian ink wash. 16-Mar-4 Chochon-Barre & Allardi, Paris #98
£329 $613 €480 In garden (13x17cm-5x7in) mono pencil W/C. 6-Mar-4 Dorotheum, Prague #211/R est:10000-15000 (C.KR 16000)
£340 $609 €500 L'heure de la pause (27x36cm-11x14in) s. W/C. 16-Mar-4 Chochon-Barre & Allardi, Paris #122
£340 $609 €500 Detente sur la plage (30x43cm-12x17in) s. gouache. 16-Mar-4 Chochon-Barre & Allardi, Paris #124
£340 $609 €500 La jeune fille a la chevre (31x28cm-12x11in) s. W/C. 16-Mar-4 Chochon-Barre & Allardi, Paris #135
£340 $609 €500 Nu aux chevaux (28x40cm-11x16in) mono. W/C graphite. 16-Mar-4 Chochon-Barre & Allardi, Paris #147
£371 $689 €542 Reader (14x20cm-6x8in) mono. pencil W/C. 6-Mar-4 Dorotheum, Prague #210/R est:8000-12000 (C.KR 18000)
£408 $731 €600 Nu dans la foret (41x32cm-16x13in) s. W/C. 16-Mar-4 Chochon-Barre & Allardi, Paris #120
£442 $791 €650 Trois femmes (30x41cm-12x16in) s. W/C. 16-Mar-4 Chochon-Barre & Allardi, Paris #138
£476 $852 €700 Cavalier (30x40cm-12x16in) s. W/C. 16-Mar-4 Chochon-Barre & Allardi, Paris #113
£476 $852 €700 Jeux de plein air (44x59cm-17x23in) s. W/C. 16-Mar-4 Chochon-Barre & Allardi, Paris #130/R
£544 $974 €800 Jeux de ballon II (43x58cm-17x23in) s. W/C. 16-Mar-4 Chochon-Barre & Allardi, Paris #103
£544 $974 €800 Jeunes femmes aux seins blance (35x48cm-14x19in) s. W/C. 16-Mar-4 Chochon-Barre & Allardi, Paris #106
£544 $974 €800 Le saltimbanque au singe (30x22cm-12x9in) s. W/C. 16-Mar-4 Chochon-Barre & Allardi, Paris #114/R
£544 $974 €800 La danse (43x58cm-17x23in) s. W/C. 16-Mar-4 Chochon-Barre & Allardi, Paris #132
£544 $974 €800 L'etendage (17x15cm-7x6in) mono. W/C. 16-Mar-4 Chochon-Barre & Allardi, Paris #149
£680 $1218 €1000 Les ramasseuses de pommes de terre (34x47cm-13x19in) s. W/C. 16-Mar-4 Chochon-Barre & Allardi, Paris #105
£816 $1461 €1200 Jeunes filles aux chapeaux (34x49cm-13x19in) s. sanguine cardboard. 16-Mar-4 Chochon-Barre & Allardi, Paris #102/R
£816 $1461 €1200 Jeune fille a la cravate (47x37cm-19x15in) s. W/C. 16-Mar-4 Chochon-Barre & Allardi, Paris #104/R
£816 $1461 €1200 La fille de joie (26x19cm-10x7in) s. W/C. 16-Mar-4 Chochon-Barre & Allardi, Paris #111/R
£884 $1583 €1300 Au cabaret (65x76cm-26x30in) s. gouache comte crayon. 16-Mar-4 Chochon-Barre & Allardi, Paris #133/R
£1020 $1827 €1500 Fermiere au soleil couchant (44x30cm-17x12in) s. gouache. 16-Mar-4 Chochon-Barre & Allardi, Paris #112/R est:1500-1700
£1293 $2314 €1900 Nature morte aux livres (33x25cm-13x10in) s.i. W/C. 16-Mar-4 Chochon-Barre & Allardi, Paris #144/R est:1500-1800
£1497 $2679 €2200 Scene de bar (26x33cm-10x13in) s. W/C. 16-Mar-4 Chochon-Barre & Allardi, Paris #116/R est:1500-1800

KOTOKU, Yukie (1890-1933) Japanese
£1200 $2148 €1752 River (65x81cm-26x32in) s. 6-May-4 Sotheby's, London #64/R est:1500-2500

KOTOV, N G (1889-1968) Russian
£556 $1000 €812 In Kuzbass (23x16cm-9x6in) oil on cardboard. 24-Apr-4 Shishkin Gallery, Moscow #20/R est:1500-2000
£667 $1200 €974 Behind the lake (26x36cm-10x14in) oil on cardboard. 24-Apr-4 Shishkin Gallery, Moscow #22/R est:3000-4000
£1667 $3000 €2434 Novosibirsk state farm wheat (30x40cm-12x16in) oil cardboard. 24-Apr-4 Shishkin Gallery, Moscow #21/R est:2000-3000
£1850 $3330 €2701 Vehicle (30x40cm-12x16in) oil cardboard. 24-Apr-4 Shishkin Gallery, Moscow #19/R est:4000-5000

KOTSCHENREITER, Hugo (1854-1908) German
£389 $650 €568 Portrait of man with a pipe (48x41cm-19x16in) s.d.05. 14-Nov-3 Aspire, Cleveland #37
£900 $1665 €1314 Portrait of a man with a pipe (34x27cm-13x11in) s.d.98 prov. 14-Jul-4 Christie's, Kensington #872/R

KOTSIS, Alexandre (1836-1877) Polish
£11755 $18339 €17162 At the kitchen stove (41x50cm-16x20in) canvas on canvasboard painted c.1870. 30-Mar-3 Agra, Warsaw #5/R est:65000 (P.Z 75000)
Works on paper
£484 $896 €707 Portrait of a gentleman (14x19cm-6x7in) pencil. 14-Mar-4 Agra, Warsaw #45/R (P.Z 3500)

KOTTIS, Yannis (20th C) ?
£11000 $19690 €16060 Tree (162x130cm-64x51in) s.d.99 acrylic prov. 10-May-4 Sotheby's, Olympia #54/R est:4000-6000

KOTULA, Jo (1910-1998) American
Works on paper
£642 $1200 €937 World War II dogfight, aircraft carrier and escorts below (41x33cm-16x13in) s. W/C gouache. 26-Feb-4 Illustration House, New York #102

KOTVALD, Ferdinand (1898-?) Czechoslovakian
£461 $847 €700 Southern lakeside town (31x47cm-12x19in) 25-Jun-4 Michael Zeller, Lindau #613/R
£675 $1188 €1013 Petrin Hill in spring II (42x28cm-17x11in) oil tempers cardboard. 22-May-4 Dorotheum, Prague #165/R est:10000-15000 (C.KR 32000)

KOTZ, Daniel (1848-1933) American
Works on paper
£192 $350 €280 Forest brook (46x64cm-18x25in) s. pastel. 19-Jun-4 Jackson's, Cedar Falls #33/R

KOUDELKA, Zora (20th C) Czechoslovakian?
£1014 $1814 €1500 Woman with greyhound in park (70x90cm-28x35in) s.d.1911. 8-May-4 Dawo, Saarbrucken #91/R est:1800

KOUKAS, Stefanos (1944-) Greek
£2900 $5075 €4234 View of Hydra (61x160cm-24x63in) s.d.81 acrylic diptych lit. 16-Dec-3 Bonhams, New Bond Street #140/R est:2000-3000

KOULICHE, Michael (1922-) French
£938 $1500 €1369 Montmartre (76x102cm-30x40in) s.i. s.d.1987 verso. 20-Sep-3 Sloans & Kenyon, Bethesda #1169/R est:1500-1750

KOUNELAKIS, Nicholaos (1829-1869) Greek
£25000 $44750 €36500 Zoe Cabbani (26x23cm-10x9in) prov.lit. 11-May-4 Bonhams, New Bond Street #11/R est:25000-35000

KOUNELLIS, Jannis (1936-) Greek
£900 $1629 €1314 Untitled (23x30cm-9x12in) s.d.98 oilstick on paper prov. 1-Apr-4 Christie's, Kensington #233/R est:1000-1500
£10563 $18486 €15000 Untitled (70x100cm-28x39in) s.verso tempera card prov. 16-Dec-3 Porro, Milan #47/R est:15000-18000
£11620 $19289 €16500 Untitled (71x101cm-28x40in) s.d.1964 verso acrylic paper. 11-Jun-3 Finarte Semenzato, Milan #599/R
£11842 $21789 €18000 Untitled (70x100cm-28x39in) s. tempera board. 22-Jun-4 Wiener Kunst Auktionen, Vienna #384/R est:18000
£12667 $22800 €19000 Untitled (70x100cm-28x39in) tempera paper prov. 22-Apr-4 Finarte Semenzato, Rome #273/R est:18000-20000
£14371 $24000 €20982 Untitled (70x100cm-28x39in) oil gouache newsprint on paper exec 1961 prov.exhib.lit. 12-Nov-3 Christie's, Rockefeller NY #605/R est:20000-30000
£14789 $25880 €21000 Untitled (70x100cm-28x39in) tempera paper painted 1963 prov. 16-Dec-3 Finarte Semenzato, Milan #294/R est:19000-21000
£17333 $31547 €26000 Untitled (100x70cm-39x28in) oil lead wire paper painted 1997 prov. 29-Jun-4 Cornette de St.Cyr, Paris #131/R est:20000-30000
£17931 $29945 €26000 Untitled (70x100cm-28x39in) tempera paper prov. 13-Nov-3 Finarte Semenzato, Rome #425/R est:18000-20000
Sculpture
£3067 $5643 €4600 Leaf (89x68cm-35x27in) s.i. plastic on paper. 10-Jun-4 Galleria Pace, Milan #133/R est:7000
£3636 $6182 €5200 Knives (47x39x10cm-19x15x4in) s.d.verso num.13/25 knives box serigraph. 20-Nov-3 Finarte Semenzato, Milan #115/R est:5200-5500
Works on paper
£861 $1567 €1300 Figure (23x32cm-9x13in) s.d.1992 Chinese ink. 17-Jun-4 Galleria Pananti, Florence #548/R
£3448 $5517 €5000 Leaf (85x68cm-33x27in) s.i. cut plastic on paper. 13-Mar-3 Galleria Pace, Milan #79/R est:6000-8000
£10490 $17832 €15000 Untitled (54x70cm-21x28in) s.d.1960 Chinese ink paper on canvas prov. 25-Nov-3 Sotheby's, Milan #240/R est:15000-20000
£11409 $20423 €17000 Untitled (69x99cm-27x39in) s.d.1960 ink. 25-May-4 Sotheby's, Milan #317/R est:18000-22000
£26000 $43420 €37960 Senza titolo (69x88cm-27x35in) ink prov.exhib. 21-Oct-3 Christie's, London #54/R est:12000-18000
£50725 $83188 €70000 Rose (196x123cm-77x48in) painted 1967 prov. 27-May-3 Sotheby's, Milan #291/R est:70000-90000

KOUPETZIAN, Aram (1928-) Russian
£345 $572 €500 Expromt (49x69cm-19x27in) s. s.verso. 1-Oct-3 Millon & Associes, Paris #274/R
£520 $936 €780 Violins (40x30cm-16x12in) s.verso masonite. 26-Apr-4 Millon & Associes, Paris #153/R
£590 $962 €850 Chiaro (65x50cm-26x20in) s. 16-Jul-3 Durán, Madrid #647/R
£604 $1081 €900 Shapes and music (90x52cm-35x20in) s. 25-May-4 Durán, Madrid #720/R
£633 $1140 €950 Musique de chambre (61x50cm-24x20in) s.d.02. 26-Apr-4 Millon & Associes, Paris #152/R
£638 $1129 €950 Composition with violin (60x53cm-24x21in) s. 27-Apr-4 Durán, Madrid #718/R
£667 $1200 €1000 Music (50x61cm-20x24in) s.d.verso. 26-Apr-4 Millon & Associes, Paris #154/R
£671 $1255 €1000 Music sheets (49x57cm-19x22in) s. s.d.98 verso. 24-Feb-4 Durán, Madrid #728/R
£680 $1218 €1000 Violin (62x68cm-24x27in) s.d.68. 22-Mar-4 Durán, Madrid #697/R
£780 $1303 €1100 Composition with music (50x65cm-20x26in) s. 20-Oct-3 Durán, Madrid #710/R
£816 $1461 €1200 Melody (65x44cm-26x17in) s. 22-Mar-4 Durán, Madrid #698/R

£845 $1479 €1200 Composition with violin (50x61cm-20x24in) s. 16-Dec-3 Durán, Madrid #709/R
£884 $1610 €1300 Violino. s. 8-Feb-4 Lesieur & Le Bars, Le Havre #71
£903 $1435 €1300 Composition (48x58cm-19x23in) s. 29-Apr-3 Durán, Madrid #805/R
£922 $1540 €1300 Musical composition (50x61cm-20x24in) s. 20-Oct-3 Durán, Madrid #711/R
£1449 $2377 €2000 Musical composition (51x78cm-20x31in) s. 27-May-3 Durán, Madrid #771/R est:1200

KOURA, Bernard (1923-) French
£272 $433 €400 Vue de saint-Cenery dans l'Orne (62x96cm-24x38in) s. 21-Mar-3 Bailly Pommery, Paris #141

KOUSENS, Lou (1899-1997) American
£193 $350 €282 Chicago river locks (51x61cm-20x24in) s. 18-Apr-4 Bonhams & Butterfields, Los Angeles #7073

KOUSNETZOFF, Constantin (1863-1936) Russian
£1842 $3389 €2800 Paysage Breton (81x99cm-32x39in) s.d.1912 s.i. verso. 28-Jun-4 Joron-Derem, Paris #125/R est:1500-2000
£3082 $5240 €4500 Portrait de Galina Brailovskaya (55x44cm-22x17in) s. 9-Nov-3 Eric Pillon, Calais #97/R
£3262 $5155 €4600 Untitled (140x200cm-55x79in) s. 24-Jul-3 Claude Boisgirard, Paris #54/R
£3333 $6033 €5000 Petit pont (65x81cm-26x32in) s. 1-Apr-4 Credit Municipal, Paris #50 est:500-600
£4667 $8353 €7000 Les javelles a Pleneuf (81x100cm-32x39in) s. 16-May-4 Thierry & Lannon, Brest #144/R est:2200-2500
£5000 $8500 €7300 Women with wild boar and turkey (140x200cm-55x79in) s. 19-Nov-3 Sotheby's, London #153/R est:5000-7000

KOUTACHY, Joseph (1907-) French/Yugoslavian
£217 $400 €317 Lady among tall trees (56x46cm-22x18in) s. 26-Jun-4 Sloans & Kenyon, Bethesda #259/R

KOUWENBERGH, Philips van (1671-1729) Dutch
£27397 $46575 €40000 Still lifes of flowers, birds, butterfly, lizards, snail and squirrel (51x59cm-20x23in) mono. pair prov. 4-Nov-3 Sotheby's, Amsterdam #24/R est:40000-60000

KOVACIC, Mijo (1935-) Yugoslavian
£1200 $2076 €1752 Village (53x41cm-21x16in) s. glass sold with another by Ivan Lackovic Croata. 11-Dec-3 Christie's, Kensington #183/R est:800-1200

KOVACS, Mihaly (1818-1892) Hungarian
£1944 $3306 €2800 Alms (47x36cm-19x14in) s.d.1848. 28-Oct-3 Dorotheum, Vienna #119/R est:2000-2600

KOVACS, Peter (1943-) Hungarian
£302 $535 €450 Lonesome rider (40x40cm-16x16in) mono. 30-Apr-4 Auktionhaus Georg Rehm, Augsburg #7608
Works on paper
£336 $594 €500 Lonesome rider (36x33cm-14x13in) mixed media. 30-Apr-4 Auktionhaus Georg Rehm, Augsburg #7609

KOVALENKO, I A (1931-) Russian
£556 $1000 €812 Still life with spring flowers (88x69cm-35x27in) 24-Apr-4 Shishkin Gallery, Moscow #70/R est:3000-4000
£598 $1100 €873 Still life with guitar and violin (105x88cm-41x35in) painted 1982. 27-Mar-4 Shishkin Gallery, Moscow #27/R
£833 $1500 €1216 Summer day (100x100cm-39x39in) 24-Apr-4 Shishkin Gallery, Moscow #71/R est:4000-5000
£978 $1800 €1428 Still life with a willow branch (60x80cm-24x31in) painted 1985. 27-Mar-4 Shishkin Gallery, Moscow #24/R est:2000-2500
£1222 $2200 €1784 Fishermen's nets (80x100cm-31x39in) 24-Apr-4 Shishkin Gallery, Moscow #72/R est:3000-4000
£1630 $3000 €2380 Platan Avenue (65x87cm-26x34in) painted 1969. 27-Mar-4 Shishkin Gallery, Moscow #28/R est:6000-7000
£1667 $3000 €2434 Still life with peony (79x123cm-31x48in) 24-Apr-4 Shishkin Gallery, Moscow #69/R est:4000-5000
£1957 $3600 €2857 In the port (64x88cm-25x35in) painted 1968. 27-Mar-4 Shishkin Gallery, Moscow #29/R est:3000-4000

KOVATS, Z (19/20th C) ?
Sculpture
£1259 $2140 €1800 Nu assis (50x40x21cm-20x16x8in) s. pat bronze marble base. 25-Nov-3 Millon & Associes, Paris #39/R

KOVNER, Saul (1904-1982) American
Works on paper
£2059 $3500 €3006 Snow over Crotona Park (53x74cm-21x29in) s.d.40 W/C exhib. 18-Nov-3 John Moran, Pasadena #90 est:1000-2000

KOW, Alexis (20th C) ?
Works on paper
£352 $584 €500 Panhard, stabilite, securite (43x34cm-17x13in) s. gouache Indian ink lit. 15-Jun-3 Artcurial Briest, Paris #101/R

KOWALCZEWSKI, Paul Ludwig (1865-1910) German
Sculpture
£1014 $1814 €1500 Standing beauty (63cm-25in) s. marble socle. 8-May-4 Sebok, Bamberg #4907/R
£1229 $2200 €1794 Untitled (12cm-5in) bronze marble pair exec c.1900. 9-Jan-4 Du Mouchelle, Detroit #1027/R est:1200-1800
£1660 $2972 €2424 Seduction of Danae (27cm-11in) s.i. bronze marble base prov. 15-May-4 Christie's, Sydney #149/R est:5000-8000 (A.D 4200)

KOWALEWSKY, Pawel Ossipovitch (1843-1903) Russian
£10000 $18400 €14600 Frolocking in the meadow (24x43cm-9x17in) s. prov. 25-Mar-4 Christie's, Kensington #186/R est:2000-3000
£38732 $67007 €55000 Soldiers resting in camp (25x50cm-10x20in) s.d.1896 s.cyrillic. 11-Dec-3 Dr Fritz Nagel, Stuttgart #530/R est:3500

KOWALEWSKY, Pawel Ossipovitch (attrib) (1843-1903) Russian
£7047 $12966 €10500 Busy farmstead (58x88cm-23x35in) s.cyrillic. 25-Mar-4 Dr Fritz Nagel, Stuttgart #732/R est:4500

KOWALSKI, A W (19th C) Polish
£2308 $3923 €3300 Two horse-drawn coaches (17x24cm-7x9in) s. panel painted c.1900. 28-Nov-3 Wendl, Rudolstadt #4041/R

KOWALSKI, Antoni (1957-) Polish
£759 $1267 €1100 This moment belongs to no-one (60x40cm-24x16in) s.d.87 s.i.d.verso. 16-Nov-3 Agra, Warsaw #63/R

KOWALSKI, Arthur (1893-1958) American
£324 $600 €473 Gooseneck Creek (51x61cm-20x24in) s. exhib. 24-Jan-4 Jeffery Burchard, Florida #52a/R

KOWALSKI, Ludwig Peter (1891-1967) German
Works on paper
£400 $720 €600 Girl wearing hat (78x45cm-31x18in) mono.d. s.d. verso mixed media board. 24-Apr-4 Dr Lehr, Berlin #228/R

KOWALSKI, Piotr (1927-) ?
Sculpture
£903 $1507 €1300 Cube no 7 (56x56x13cm-22x22x5in) mono.d.1967 num.23/30 inox plexiglas rose fluo exhib. 21-Oct-3 Artcurial Briest, Paris #509/R est:300-500
£1149 $2171 €1700 Sans titre (58x58x15cm-23x23x6in) mono.num.22/30 metal plexiglas. 21-Feb-4 Cornette de St.Cyr, Paris #329/R est:800-1200

KOWALSKY, Leopold Franz (1856-1931) Russian/French
£395 $726 €600 Sous - bois (27x35cm-11x14in) st.mono. board. 28-Jun-4 Joron-Derem, Paris #134
£3448 $6172 €5034 Two young women picking meadow flowers (90x116cm-35x46in) s. 13-May-4 Stuker, Bern #218/R est:8000-12000 (S.FR 8000)
£8333 $15000 €12166 Picking wild flowers (52x65cm-20x26in) s. 22-Apr-4 Christie's, Rockefeller NY #46/R est:15000-20000

KOWNATZKI, Hans (1886-1947) German
£1284 $2259 €1900 Armed Germania (122x222cm-48x87in) s.d.1910. 21-May-4 Mehlis, Plauen #15136/R est:400

KOYANAGUI, Sei (1896-?) Japanese
£769 $1308 €1100 Couple de bazelles dans le brousse (73x54cm-29x21in) s. canvas laid down. 20-Nov-3 Millon & Associes, Paris #98/R
£800 $1336 €1168 Deux biches (41x33cm-16x13in) s. 22-Oct-3 Sotheby's, Olympia #197/R
£800 $1432 €1168 Farmyard (55x66cm-22x26in) s. 6-May-4 Sotheby's, London #65/R

KOZAK, Vaclav (1889-?) Czechoslovakian
£329 $613 €480 Church of St John (36x45cm-14x18in) s. board. 6-Mar-4 Dorotheum, Prague #64 est:6000-9000 (C.KR 16000)

KOZAKIEWICZ, Anton (1841-1929) Polish
£2098 $3503 €3000 Peasant couple. s. panel. 28-Jun-3 Bolland & Marotz, Bremen #692/R est:3900
£9952 $16520 €14530 Gypsy girl (81x54cm-32x21in) s.d.1909. 15-Jun-3 Agra, Warsaw #8/R est:55000 (P.Z 62000)
£15129 $26172 €22088 Travelling theatre (35x48cm-14x19in) s. panel exec.1881 exhib. 14-Dec-3 Agra, Warsaw #17/R est:100000 (P.Z 100000)
£23511 $36677 €34326 Street scene (42x58cm-17x23in) s. panel. 30-Mar-3 Agra, Warsaw #1/R est:70000 (P.Z 150000)

KOZAN, Matsumoto (attrib) (1784-1866) Japanese
Works on paper
£275 $500 €402 Geisha (38x13cm-15x5in) s. ink col silk. 7-Feb-4 Sloans & Kenyon, Bethesda #1126/R

KOZLOFF, Joyce (1942-) American
Works on paper
£235 $425 €343 Study for home savings of America (102x51cm-40x20in) s.d.1989 mixed media. 18-Apr-4 Bonhams & Butterfields, Los Angeles #7097

KOZMAN, Myron (1916-2002) American
£228 $425 €333 Variation (30x36cm-12x14in) s. tempera on paper painted c.1940. 7-Mar-4 Treadway Gallery, Cincinnati #753/R
£276 $475 €403 Composition (20x38cm-8x15in) s.d.1960 verso board prov. 7-Dec-3 Treadway Gallery, Cincinnati #710/R

£316 $500 €461 Composition (36x30cm-14x12in) s. d.1960 verso board. 7-Sep-3 Treadway Gallery, Cincinnati #752/R
£443 $700 €647 Composition (36x30cm-14x12in) s. d.1960 verso board. 7-Sep-3 Treadway Gallery, Cincinnati #694/R
£579 $950 €840 Portrait, variation (48x38cm-19x15in) s. tempera painted c.1940. 7-Jun-3 Treadway Gallery, Cincinnati #1507

KPACYNUM, B (?) ?
£1141 $2099 €1700 Vue de Saint-Petersbourg (57x67cm-22x26in) s. 23-Mar-4 Galerie Moderne, Brussels #353/R est:1400-1600

KRAAYER, Juul (1970-) Dutch
Works on paper
£2133 $3925 €3200 Untitled (208x74cm-82x29in) pastel exec 1997. 8-Jun-4 Sotheby's, Amsterdam #161/R est:2000-3000
£3333 $6133 €5000 Untitled (146x46cm-57x18in) pastel exec 1997. 8-Jun-4 Sotheby's, Amsterdam #160/R est:2000-3000

KRABBE, Hendrik Maarten (1868-1931) Dutch
£570 $1055 €850 Reclining nude (16x43cm-6x17in) s. board. 15-Mar-4 Sotheby's, Amsterdam #103a est:750-850
Works on paper
£1096 $1863 €1600 Little sister reading by the window (64x46cm-25x18in) s. W/C prov. 5-Nov-3 Vendue Huis, Gravenhage #337/R est:2000-2500

KRABBES, Hermann (1840-1920) German
Works on paper
£651 $1106 €950 Townhall at Rothenburg (49x37cm-19x15in) s.i. black chk ink W/C. 5-Nov-3 Christie's, Amsterdam #136/R

KRACHKOVSKY, Iosef Evstafevich (1854-1899) Russian
£9500 $17005 €13870 Reeds by the river (34x26cm-13x10in) s.i.d.1882. 26-May-4 Sotheby's, London #32/R est:6000-8000
£18000 $32220 €26280 Young shepherd girl watching her sheep (83x58cm-33x23in) init. 26-May-4 Sotheby's, London #33/R est:8000-10000

KRAEMER, Dieter (1937-) German
£350 $601 €500 Camping with a Volkswagen (40x60cm-16x24in) s.i.d.1969 verso. 4-Dec-3 Van Ham, Cologne #286/R

KRAEMER, Hermann (19th C) German
£685 $1164 €1000 Farmstead in the southern Tyrol (43x31cm-17x12in) s.i. 5-Nov-3 Hugo Ruef, Munich #1052/R
£1061 $1867 €1549 Landscape at dusk (37x56cm-15x22in) s. 23-May-4 Agra, Warsaw #29/R (P.Z 7500)

KRAEMER, Peter (jnr) (1857-1941) German
Works on paper
£385 $642 €550 Newspaper seller (23x19cm-9x7in) s.i. W/C. 28-Jun-3 Dannenberg, Berlin #718/R
£2200 $4004 €3300 Hunter (24x19cm-9x7in) s.i. W/C htd white. 30-Jun-4 Neumeister, Munich #420 est:1200
£2333 $4247 €3500 Peasant sneezing (17x14cm-7x6in) s.i. W/C htd white. 30-Jun-4 Neumeister, Munich #419/R est:2000

KRAEMER, Peter (19/20th C) German
£347 $573 €500 Peasant drinking (23x20cm-9x8in) 7-Jul-3 Dr Fritz Nagel, Stuttgart #7006/R
Works on paper
£510 $913 €750 Newspaper seller (21x17cm-8x7in) s.i. W/C. 18-Mar-4 Neumeister, Munich #2512/R
£828 $1374 €1200 Sour Vienna (23x20cm-9x8in) s. W/C. 30-Sep-3 Dorotheum, Vienna #386/R
£833 $1358 €1200 Portrait of Bavarian woodcutter (24x20cm-9x8in) s.i. W/C bodycol over pencil. 25-Sep-3 Dr Fritz Nagel, Stuttgart #1367/R
£903 $1472 €1300 Peasant tasting wine (15x12cm-6x5in) s.i. W/C htd white. 24-Sep-3 Neumeister, Munich #283
£1049 $1804 €1500 Two peasants playing cards in the living room (24x19cm-9x7in) s.i. W/C htd white. 3-Dec-3 Neumeister, Munich #408 est:850
£1818 $3127 €2600 Farmer with pipe. Farmer with rifle (23x17cm-9x7in) s.i. W/C htd white pair. 3-Dec-3 Neumeister, Munich #407/R est:1600

KRAFFT, Carl R (1884-1938) American
£1136 $2000 €1659 Moonrise (25x28cm-10x11in) s. d.1934 verso canvasboard. 28-May-4 Aspire, Cleveland #28/R est:2000-3000
£1505 $2800 €2197 From the hilltop (56x97cm-22x38in) s. board. 7-Mar-4 Treadway Gallery, Cincinnati #536/R est:4000-6000
£1747 $3250 €2551 Turkey Creek (46x51cm-18x20in) s. masonite painted c.1920. 7-Mar-4 Treadway Gallery, Cincinnati #544/R est:2000-3000
£1788 $3200 €3002 Sunset landscape (79x107cm-31x42in) s. 20-Mar-4 Pook & Pook, Downington #567/R est:2000-3000
£2500 $4250 €3650 Across and beyond (30x30cm-12x12in) s. board prov. 18-Nov-3 John Moran, Pasadena #141b est:1000-2000
£2616 $4500 €3819 Early snow (46x51cm-18x20in) s. painted c.1920. 7-Dec-3 Treadway Gallery, Cincinnati #540/R est:4000-6000
£2717 $5000 €3967 Across and beyond (30x32cm-12x13in) s. i. verso board. 27-Jun-4 Freeman, Philadelphia #118/R est:3000-5000
£5063 $8000 €7392 Snow symphony (56x76cm-22x30in) s. 7-Sep-3 Treadway Gallery, Cincinnati #597/R est:6000-8000
£5882 $10000 €8588 Edge of the woods (97x102cm-38x40in) s. prov. 18-Nov-3 John Moran, Pasadena #141a est:4000-6000
£7692 $14000 €11230 Cabin and figure in winter landscape (61x76cm-24x30in) s. masonite prov. 15-Jun-4 John Moran, Pasadena #146 est:6000-8000
£10000 $17000 €14600 In the garden (61x69cm-24x27in) s. exhib. 18-Nov-3 John Moran, Pasadena #141 est:3000-5000

KRAFFT, David von (1655-1724) Swedish
£2882 $5160 €4208 Portrait of Baroness Margareta Horn of Aaminne (84x68cm-33x27in) i.verso oval prov. 26-May-4 AB Stockholms Auktionsverk #2250/R est:15000-18000 (S.KR 39000)

KRAFFT, David von (attrib) (1655-1724) Swedish
Works on paper
£628 $1125 €917 Musicians on balustrade (20x24cm-8x9in) i.verso brown black ink wash prov. 26-May-4 AB Stockholms Auktionsverk #2261/R (S.KR 8500)

KRAFFT, David von (studio) (1655-1724) Swedish
£10717 $19183 €15647 Portrait of Duke Karl Frederik of Holstein-Gottorp (195x124cm-77x49in) prov.lit. 25-May-4 Bukowskis, Stockholm #403/R est:100000-125000 (S.KR 145000)

KRAFFT, Elton G (20th C) American
£395 $700 €577 Autumn fields, Elroy (76x102cm-30x40in) s. 1-May-4 Harvey Clar, Oakland #1239

KRAFFT, Joseph (1787-1828) German
Works on paper
£2416 $4446 €3600 Kaiser Franz I in uniform (7x6cm-3x2in) s. W/C ivory oval. 26-Mar-4 Dorotheum, Vienna #364/R est:1400-1600

KRAFT, Frederik (1823-1854) Danish
£8953 $16383 €13071 September evening by Dyrehaven (110x157cm-43x62in) s.d.1854 exhib.prov. 9-Jun-4 Rasmussen, Copenhagen #1655/R est:100000-150000 (D.KR 100000)

KRAGH, Ejnar R (1903-1981) Danish
£275 $500 €402 Summer landscape (97x145cm-38x57in) s.d.44. 7-Feb-4 Rasmussen, Havnen #4105 (D.KR 3000)

KRAGH, Johannes (1870-1946) Danish
£2804 $4430 €4066 The Judgement of Paris (95x121cm-37x48in) s.d.1925-28 panel. 2-Sep-3 Rasmussen, Copenhagen #1704/R est:30000 (D.KR 30000)

KRAGH-HANSEN, Viggo (1910-) Danish
£474 $758 €692 Nybol Watermill - the white house (48x60cm-19x24in) s.d.1983. 22-Sep-3 Rasmussen, Vejle #606/R (D.KR 5000)

KRAHL, Joseph von (19/20th C) Austrian
£222 $408 €324 Arab singing (27x11cm-11x4in) s. panel. 14-Jun-4 Waddingtons, Toronto #26/R (C.D 550)

KRAJCBERG, Frans (1921-) Brazilian/Polish
£495 $900 €723 Abstract (64x51cm-25x20in) s.d.1963. 1-Jul-4 Dan Ripley, Indianapolis #117
£495 $900 €723 Abstract (64x51cm-25x20in) s.d.1963. 1-Jul-4 Dan Ripley, Indianapolis #119
£549 $1000 €802 Abstract (66x51cm-26x20in) s.d.1963. 1-Jul-4 Dan Ripley, Indianapolis #107
£577 $1050 €842 Abstract (51x64cm-20x25in) s.d.1963. 1-Jul-4 Dan Ripley, Indianapolis #109
£577 $1050 €842 Abstract (97x51cm-38x20in) s.d.1963 verso. 1-Jul-4 Dan Ripley, Indianapolis #111
£1319 $2400 €1926 Abstract (109x64cm-43x25in) s.verso. 1-Jul-4 Dan Ripley, Indianapolis #115
£1923 $3500 €2808 Abstract (102x64cm-40x25in) s. s.d.1963 verso. 1-Jul-4 Dan Ripley, Indianapolis #113
Sculpture
£30220 $53489 €45330 Roots (190x184cm-75x72in) s.d.1970 verso painted wood. 27-Apr-4 Bolsa de Arte, Rio de Janeiro #128/R (B.R 165000)

KRAJEWSKI, Alex (fl.1890s) German
Photographs
£4000 $7360 €6000 Otto Lilienthal flying one of his gliding planes near Berlin (15x21cm-6x8in) vintage collodion. 11-Jun-4 Bassenge, Berlin #4055/R est:5000

KRAL, Jaroslav (1883-1942) Czechoslovakian
£5766 $10725 €8418 Mother with child (74x67cm-29x26in) s.d.1926. 6-Mar-4 Dorotheum, Prague #125/R est:280000-450000 (C.KR 280000)

KRAMER, Jacob (1892-1962) British
£300 $501 €438 Profile portrait of a gentleman (30x23cm-12x9in) 21-Oct-3 Gorringes, Lewes #2111
£820 $1394 €1197 Nude study with the model (25x27cm-10x11in) s. board two. 18-Nov-3 Bonhams, Leeds #119
Works on paper
£300 $549 €438 Portrait of Mrs Redman King (25x20cm-10x8in) s.d.1922. 27-Jan-4 Gorringes, Lewes #1512
£300 $555 €438 Portrait of a female (20x25cm-8x10in) s. 12-Feb-4 Andrew Hartley, Ilkley #789
£300 $546 €438 Head study of a bearded gentleman (49x36cm-19x14in) s.indis.d.1920 W/C chk. 15-Jun-4 Bonhams, Leeds #55/R
£350 $641 €511 Portrait of a woman (30x23cm-12x9in) s. pencil. 7-Apr-4 Andrew Hartley, Ilkley #1130/R
£380 $684 €555 Caricature study of a large gentleman at a bar with a pipe and a glass of ale (27x19cm-11x7in) s.d.1947 pen ink brush. 21-Apr-4 Tennants, Leyburn #1005/R

£500 $860 €730 Portrait of Sarah (46x32cm-18x13in) s.d.1956 chl blue chk. 3-Dec-3 Christie's, Kensington #740

£720 $1224 €1051 Study of a female model, seated (61x39cm-24x15in) s. chl pastel. 18-Nov-3 Bonhams, Leeds #118

£1850 $3145 €2701 Portrait of a bohemian lady (54x43cm-21x17in) s.d.1919 pastel chl. 18-Nov-3 Bonhams, Leeds #121 est:300-500

£2200 $4070 €3212 Portrait of a lady (61x47cm-24x19in) s.d.1927 pastel sold with another by same hand. 11-Feb-4 Sotheby's, Olympia #135/R est:1000-1500

KRAMER, James (1927-) American

Works on paper

£1863 $3000 €2701 Autumn in the Plaza of Sanctuario de Potrero (51x71cm-20x28in) W/C. 22-Aug-3 Altermann Galleries, Santa Fe #152

£1863 $3000 €2701 Market in the Plaza, Santa Fe (41x61cm-16x24in) W/C. 22-Aug-3 Altermann Galleries, Santa Fe #193

KRAMER, Johann Victor (1861-1949) Austrian

£3162 $5723 €4617 Spring (200x81cm-79x32in) s. oil pastel. 16-Apr-4 Mu Terem Galeria, Budapest #164/R (H.F 1200000)

KRAMER, Josef von (attrib) (?) ?

£1414 $2446 €2064 Girl with pheasant on a dish (135x70cm-53x28in) 15-Dec-3 Lilla Bukowskis, Stockholm #606/R est:20000-25000 (S.KR 18000)

KRAMM, Willibald (1891-1969) German

£265 $482 €400 Berlin in winter (70x83cm-28x33in) s. panel. 19-Jun-4 Dannenberg, Berlin #582/R

KRAMPE, Fritz (1913-1966) German

Works on paper

£311 $563 €454 Lion (22x43cm-9x17in) fibre tip pen. 30-Mar-4 Stephan Welz, Johannesburg #239 est:2000-3000 (SA.R 3700)

KRANENBURG, Hendrik Cornelis (jnr) (1917-) Dutch

£329 $605 €500 View of the Schrierstoren and St Nicholas church, Amsterdam (50x70cm-20x28in) s. 22-Jun-4 Christie's, Amsterdam #453/R

£833 $1358 €1200 Town view (40x60cm-16x24in) s. 29-Sep-3 Sotheby's, Amsterdam #171/R

KRANEWITTER, Josef (attrib) (1756-1825) German

£1033 $1881 €1550 Jesus heals the sick. Jesus blesses the children (62x49cm-24x19in) i.d.1821 verso canvas on canvas pair. 1-Jul-4 Neumeister, Munich #2737 est:1000

KRANS, Louis (1875-1932) Dutch

£780 $1303 €1100 Cooking still life (38x48cm-15x19in) s. board on panel. 20-Oct-3 Glerum, Amsterdam #221/R

KRANTZ, Charles Frederick (1881-1959) American

£270 $475 €394 Chain of lakes, Golden Gate Park, San Francisco (53x64cm-21x25in) s. i.verso. 22-May-4 Harvey Clar, Oakland #2232

KRANZ, Kurt (1910-1997) German

Works on paper

£800 $1472 €1200 Composition (39x57cm-15x22in) s.d. W/C bodycol. 11-Jun-4 Hauswedell & Nolte, Hamburg #1395/R

KRARUP, Theodora (1860-1941) Danish

£9000 $15300 €13500 Portrait of Rasputin (100x77cm-39x30in) s.d.1916 prov.lit. 25-Nov-3 Christie's, London #164/R est:10000-15000

KRASILNIKOV, Viktor (1964-) Russian

£350 $585 €511 On the Protva river (39x68cm-15x27in) s. 13-Jul-3 John Nicholson, Haslemere #111/R

KRASNER, Lee (1908-1984) American

£72626 $130000 €106034 Image surfacing (69x51cm-27x20in) s.d.1944 verso prov.exhib.lit. 12-May-4 Christie's, Rockefeller NY #105/R est:90000-120000

£83799 $150000 €122347 Peacock (208x208cm-82x82in) s.d.73 s.i.d.stretcher prov.exhib.lit. 12-May-4 Christie's, Rockefeller NY #179/R est:200000-300000

£131737 $220000 €192336 Majuscule (175x209cm-69x82in) s.d.71 s.i.stretcher prov.exhib.lit. 13-Nov-3 Sotheby's, New York #189/R est:80000-120000

£305389 $510000 €445868 The city (122x91cm-48x36in) s.i.d.1953 verso oil paper collage masonite prov.exhib.lit. 13-Nov-3 Sotheby's, New York #174/R est:120000-180000

£430168 $770000 €628045 Double Helix (179x158cm-70x62in) s.d.61 s.stretcher prov.exhib.lit. 12-May-4 Christie's, Rockefeller NY #131/R est:250000-350000

£1017964 $1700000 €1486227 Celebration (234x469cm-92x185in) s.d.60 prov.exhib.lit. 11-Nov-3 Christie's, Rockefeller NY #27/R est:300000-400000

KRASNOPEVTSEV, Dimitri (1925-) Russian

£13500 $24165 €19710 Pitcher and bowls (45x48cm-18x19in) init.d.60 board. 26-May-4 Sotheby's, London #316/R est:15000-20000

£28000 $47600 €40880 Composition with flowers in a vase (40x47cm-16x19in) i.verso board prov. 19-Nov-3 Sotheby's, London #243/R est:8000-12000

KRASNY, Yuri (1925-) Russian

Works on paper

£2432 $4354 €3600 Our boyfriend (35x56cm-14x22in) s.d.78 gouache. 8-May-4 Bukowskis, Helsinki #432/R est:2500-2700

KRASSOULINE, Valery (1949-) Russian

£355 $592 €500 Dunes (21x26cm-8x10in) s. 20-Oct-3 Durán, Madrid #712/R

£1020 $1857 €1500 Soir a St Petersbourg. s. 8-Feb-4 Lesieur & Le Bars, Le Havre #91

KRASULIN, Valery (1950-) Russian

£604 $1130 €900 Flower market (50x61cm-20x24in) s. 24-Feb-4 Durán, Madrid #730

KRASULIN, Victor (1950-) Russian

£278 $453 €400 Mercado de Paris (50x61cm-20x24in) s. 16-Jul-3 Durán, Madrid #648/R

KRASZEWSKA, Otolia (1859-?) German

£1231 $2117 €1797 Child in flower meadow (77x52cm-30x20in) s. 7-Dec-3 Uppsala Auktionskammare, Uppsala #171/R est:20000-25000 (S.KR 16000)

£1674 $2846 €2444 Two elegant women in salon (34x51cm-13x20in) s. panel. 5-Nov-3 Dobiaschofsky, Bern #725/R est:3600 (S.FR 3800)

KRATKE, Charles Louis (1848-1921) French

£1563 $2750 €2282 Genre scene of man and woman dining in a garden (25x20cm-10x8in) s.d.1878 panel. 21-May-4 North East Auctions, Portsmouth #471/R

KRATSCHOWSKI, Jossif (1854-1914) Russian

£1724 $2879 €2500 Chateau au bord du lac (39x46cm-15x18in) s. 17-Nov-3 Claude Boisgirard, Paris #52 est:2500-3000

£3800 $6802 €5548 Haystacks (25x46cm-10x18in) s.i.d.83. 26-May-4 Sotheby's, Olympia #378/R est:2000-3000

£35811 $64101 €53000 Autumn by the river (59x72cm-23x28in) s.d.1904. 8-May-4 Bukowskis, Helsinki #460/R est:35000-40000

£51748 $87972 €74000 Landscape from the Crimean coast (75x112cm-30x44in) s.d.1903. 29-Nov-3 Bukowskis, Helsinki #418/R est:40000-50000

KRAUEL, Bruno (1911-) German

£268 $475 €400 Haymaking (10x20cm-4x8in) s. panel. 30-Apr-4 Auktionhaus Georg Rehm, Augsburg #7516

KRAUGERUD, Ragnar (1909-1987) Norwegian

£2802 $5016 €4091 House in the woods (87x118cm-34x46in) init. 22-Mar-4 Blomqvist, Oslo #613/R est:25000-30000 (N.KR 35000)

KRAUPE, Janina (1954-) Polish

Works on paper

£317 $577 €463 Snopy (64x47cm-25x19in) s.d.1991 W/C pastel. 20-Jun-4 Agra, Warsaw #24/R (P.Z 2200)

KRAUS, August (1868-1934) German

Sculpture

£3000 $5520 €4500 Heinrich Zille (48cm-19in) s.st.f. Martin and Piltzing black pat bronze. 12-Jun-4 Villa Grisebach, Berlin #134/R est:5000-7000

KRAUS, Georg Melchior (1737-1806) German

Works on paper

£6987 $12716 €10201 Fruit market in a small town (19x26cm-7x10in) s. W/C over pencil bistre prov. 17-Jun-4 Kornfeld, Bern #27/R est:10000 (S.FR 16000)

KRAUS, Georg Melchior (attrib) (1737-1806) German

Works on paper

£574 $1011 €850 Young man seated at table (30x22cm-12x9in) chk wash. 22-May-4 Lempertz, Koln #1306

KRAUS, Rudolf (19/20th C) ?

£556 $944 €800 Still life with porcelain (20x31cm-8x12in) s. panel. 28-Oct-3 Dorotheum, Vienna #205/R

KRAUSE WICHMANN, Eduard (1864-?) German

£490 $817 €700 Baltic fishing harbour (46x65cm-18x26in) s. 28-Jun-3 Bolland & Marotz, Bremen #693/R

KRAUSE, Bernhard (19th C) German

£1042 $1698 €1500 Tyrolean castle by river in evening (74x104cm-29x41in) s.d.1869. 25-Sep-3 Dr Fritz Nagel, Stuttgart #1364/R est:1700

KRAUSE, Ellen (20th C) Danish

£395 $672 €577 Still life of jug, flowers in vase and fruit (60x74cm-24x29in) s. s.d.1964 verso. 26-Nov-3 Kunsthallen, Copenhagen #343 (D.KR 4200)

KRAUSE, Emil (1871-1945) Danish

£609 $1097 €889 Portrait of young woman (40x33cm-16x13in) mono. panel. 24-Apr-4 Rasmussen, Havnen #2337 (D.KR 6800)

KRAUSE, Emil A (fl.1891-1914) British

Works on paper

£280 $507 €409 On Loch Striven, a small craft moored at the water's edge (23x33cm-9x13in) s.i. W/C. 1-Apr-4 Amersham Auction Rooms, UK #314

£550 $919 €803 Falcon Crag, Derwentwater. Grasmere (35x25cm-14x10in) s.i. W/C pair. 16-Oct-3 Lyon & Turnbull, Edinburgh #12
£980 $1695 €1431 Rydalwater and Thirlmere Lake (35x53cm-14x21in) s.i. W/C pair. 9-Dec-3 Anderson & Garland, Newcastle #206/R
£1100 $2024 €1606 On Thirlmere (33x50cm-13x20in) s.i. W/C. 23-Mar-4 Anderson & Garland, Newcastle #257/R est:200-300

KRAUSE, Franz Emil (1836-1900) German
£664 $1129 €950 Romantic landscape (53x74cm-21x29in) s. 28-Nov-3 Wendl, Rudolstadt #4043/R
£1600 $2928 €2400 Southern coastal landscape (32x42cm-13x17in) s. pair. 5-Jun-4 Arnold, Frankfurt #636/R est:1600

KRAUSE, Hans (1864-?) German
£2200 $4158 €3212 Lion and lioness on a rocky hillside (66x81cm-26x32in) s.d.1922. 19-Feb-4 Christie's, Kensington #363/R est:1000-1500

KRAUSE, Heinrich (1885-1985) Austrian
£537 $993 €800 Narcissi and tulips (62x52cm-24x20in) s. 9-Mar-4 Dorotheum, Vienna #59/R
£563 $986 €800 Still life with flowers (43x55cm-17x22in) s. 19-Dec-3 Dorotheum, Vienna #151/R
£897 $1641 €1300 Still life with wine glasses and pot plant (47x60cm-19x24in) s. 27-Jan-4 Dorotheum, Vienna #81/R
£1549 $2711 €2200 Still life with cacti (45x54cm-18x21in) s. oil tempera paper. 19-Dec-3 Dorotheum, Vienna #152/R est:1000-1300
£2254 $3944 €3200 Harbour (47x67cm-19x26in) s. oil tempera paper. 19-Dec-3 Dorotheum, Vienna #188/R est:1200-1500
£2394 $4190 €3400 Red roofs in green landscape (62x53cm-24x21in) s. 19-Dec-3 Dorotheum, Vienna #149/R est:2000-2800
£4698 $8409 €7000 Still life with chopping board, potatoes, eggs and blue salt bag (60x79cm-24x31in) s. panel prov. 25-May-4 Dorotheum, Vienna #203/R est:3800-5500
Works on paper
£1056 $1849 €1500 Vase with flowers (55x44cm-22x17in) s. mixed media. 19-Dec-3 Dorotheum, Vienna #150/R est:1000-1300

KRAUSE, Karl Heinz (1924-) German
Sculpture
£1067 $1963 €1600 Daphne (81cm-32in) mono.d.85 st.f. Lotito bronze. 12-Jun-4 Villa Grisebach, Berlin #783/R est:1400-1800
£1479 $2558 €2100 Ozeanide (23x34cm-9x13in) mono.i.d.57 bronze lit. 13-Dec-3 Lempertz, Koln #325/R est:1000
£1600 $2928 €2400 Seated youth (30cm-12in) mono. pat.bronze. 5-Jun-4 Lempertz, Koln #809/R est:1400
£2133 $3904 €3200 Seated youth (45cm-18in) mono.i.d.1980 pat.bronze. 5-Jun-4 Lempertz, Koln #808/R est:2800

KRAUSE, Lina (1857-?) German
£1217 $2239 €1850 Bouquets de fleurs dans un vase (32x28cm-13x11in) s. panel pair. 24-Jun-4 Claude Boisgirard, Paris #9/R est:1500-2000

KRAUSE, Max (jnr) (19th C) British
£1900 $3515 €2774 Near Middleton, Manchester (61x51cm-24x20in) s.d.1880. 15-Jan-4 Christie's, Kensington #911/R est:1000-1500

KRAUSE, Rolf (1908-1982) German
£300 $540 €450 Still life (46x65cm-18x26in) board. 24-Apr-4 Dr Lehr, Berlin #230/R

KRAUSE, Wilhelm August (1803-1864) German
£987 $1816 €1500 Extensive valley in summer with figures (96x108cm-38x43in) s.d.1848 i. verso. 24-Jun-4 Dr Fritz Nagel, Stuttgart #720/R est:3000
£1200 $2148 €1800 Fishing boats on coast (26x43cm-10x17in) s.d.1836 panel lit. 14-May-4 Schloss Ahlden, Ahlden #2854/R est:450
£1573 $2628 €2250 Fishing boats off rocky coast (27x37cm-11x15in) s. board. 28-Jun-3 Dannenberg, Berlin #719/R est:800

KRAUSE-KIEDERLING, Max (1892-1962) German
£600 $1080 €900 Dresden market (47x61cm-19x24in) s.d. 24-Apr-4 Dr Lehr, Berlin #231/R

KRAUSKOPF, Bruno (1892-1960) German
£600 $1074 €900 Still life of flowers (42x32cm-17x13in) s. 13-May-4 Neumeister, Munich #403/R
£903 $1472 €1300 Flowers in glass vase (75x55cm-30x22in) s. oil tempera. 26-Sep-3 Bolland & Marotz, Bremen #778/R
£1189 $2021 €1700 The garden (40x50cm-16x20in) s. chipboard lit. 28-Nov-3 Schloss Ahlden, Ahlden #1604/R est:1800
£1379 $2303 €2000 Landscape with figure and horses (55x66cm-22x26in) s.d.1926. 13-Nov-3 Neumeister, Munich #368/R est:2300-2800
£1486 $2750 €2170 Chestnut Vendor (52x70cm-20x28in) s. board prov. 12-Feb-4 Sotheby's, New York #60/R est:2500-3500
£1800 $3222 €2700 Village with a church (20x26cm-8x10in) s. board. 14-May-4 Behringer, Furth #1718/R est:3000
£1892 $3500 €2762 New Jersey Nudist beach (50x64cm-20x25in) s. masonite prov. 12-Feb-4 Sotheby's, New York #61/R est:2500-3500
£2333 $4177 €3500 Self portrait (61x50cm-24x20in) s. fibreboard prov. 14-May-4 Ketterer, Munich #196/R est:4000-4500
£2703 $5000 €3946 Outdoor Cafe Scene (76x100cm-30x39in) s. prov. 12-Feb-4 Sotheby's, New York #51/R est:7000-10000
£2797 $4755 €4000 Still life with flowers (41x48cm-16x19in) s.d.1921 board. 29-Nov-3 Villa Grisebach, Berlin #249/R est:4000-6000
£3453 $5663 €4800 Three torreros (70x90cm-28x35in) mono. 4-Jun-3 Ketterer, Hamburg #587/R est:5000-6000
Works on paper
£403 $741 €600 Kamasutra (21x14cm-8x6in) s.d. gouache Indian ink. 26-Mar-4 Ketterer, Hamburg #991/R
£467 $835 €700 Sleeping figure (44x58cm-17x23in) s. 13-May-4 Neumeister, Munich #404/R
£867 $1551 €1300 North African scene (42x51cm-17x20in) s. W/C Indian ink chl board. 15-May-4 Van Ham, Cologne #742/R
£972 $1585 €1400 On deck (65x50cm-26x20in) s.d.1933 gouache. 27-Sep-3 Dr Fritz Nagel, Stuttgart #9564/R

KRAUSS, Max (1902-?) German
£587 $1056 €880 Men playing chess (69x98cm-27x39in) s. 22-Apr-4 Weidler, Nurnberg #4561

KRAUSS-PABST, Amelie (1805-1883) German
£500 $895 €730 Pianist (15x23cm-6x9in) panel. 7-May-4 Mallams, Oxford #301/R

KRAUT, Susan (20th C) American
£260 $475 €390 Ox box still life (69x107cm-27x42in) 10-Jul-4 Hindman, Chicago #281a/R

KRAVTCHENKO, Alexei Illiitch (1889-1940) Russian
£5608 $10039 €8300 Russian village in winter (49x64cm-19x25in) s. board. 8-May-4 Bukowskis, Helsinki #472/R est:1100-1500

KRAWAGNER, Peter (1937-) German
Works on paper
£1103 $2019 €1600 Untitled (47x60cm-19x24in) s.d.74 pencil W/C prov. 27-Jan-4 Dorotheum, Vienna #226/R est:800-1200

KRAWIEC, Harriet (1894-1968) American
£335 $600 €489 Still life with flowers (64x71cm-25x28in) s. 8-May-4 Susanin's, Chicago #6106/R
£430 $800 €628 Still life (81x76cm-32x30in) s. painted c.1935. 7-Mar-4 Treadway Gallery, Cincinnati #547/R
£563 $900 €822 Still life with flowers (81x76cm-32x30in) s. painted c.1945. 17-May-3 Bunte, Elgin #1229 est:800-1200

KRAWIEC, Walter (1889-?) American
£471 $800 €688 Zebras (38x48cm-15x19in) s. 9-Nov-3 Wright, Chicago #220
£706 $1200 €1031 Untitled - circus horse stable (43x58cm-17x23in) s. board. 9-Nov-3 Wright, Chicago #219 est:1500-2000
£870 $1400 €1270 Watering horses (51x46cm-20x18in) s. wood panel painted c.1935. 22-Feb-3 Bunte, Elgin #1218 est:400-600

KRAY, N W (19th C) German?
£2685 $5020 €4000 Water nymphs (74x121cm-29x48in) 24-Feb-4 Dorotheum, Vienna #130/R est:4500-5000

KRAY, Wilhelm (1828-1889) German
£1100 $2002 €1606 Mother and children on the coast with a basket of grapes, Capri beyond (38x69cm-15x27in) s.i.d.1873. 3-Feb-4 Gorringes, Bexhill #1012/R est:1000-1500

KRAY, Wilhelm (attrib) (1828-1889) German
£2361 $4014 €3400 Fisherman's dream (131x90cm-52x35in) 28-Oct-3 Dorotheum, Vienna #47/R est:2400-2800

KREBS, Fritz (1914-1995) Swiss
£450 $775 €657 Female nude (46x38cm-18x15in) s. 8-Dec-3 Philippe Schuler, Zurich #5937 (S.FR 1000)
Works on paper
£270 $465 €394 Untitled (49x33cm-19x13in) s.d.1967 mixed media. 8-Dec-3 Philippe Schuler, Zurich #3205 (S.FR 600)

KREBS, Walter (1900-1965) Swiss
£280 $502 €409 Gypsy family (45x55cm-18x22in) s. panel. 13-May-4 Stuker, Bern #222 (S.FR 650)
£281 $504 €410 Spruce in mountains (72x64cm-28x25in) s.d. tempera gouache. 22-Mar-4 Philippe Schuler, Zurich #4179 (S.FR 650)
£308 $524 €450 Evening landscape with peasant woman and child (64x73cm-25x29in) s.d.1949 bodycol paper on panel. 5-Nov-3 Dobiaschofsky, Bern #3538 (S.FR 700)
£776 $1389 €1133 Appearance of Jesus by the lake (54x70cm-21x28in) s.d.57. 13-May-4 Stuker, Bern #220 est:2000-2500 (S.FR 1800)
Works on paper
£344 $575 €499 Rocky mountain landscape (83x72cm-33x28in) s.d. W/C. 23-Jun-3 Philippe Schuler, Zurich #3256 (S.FR 750)
£819 $1466 €1196 Jesus preaching in house of God (62x35cm-24x14in) s. i. verso mixed media panel on masonite. 13-May-4 Stuker, Bern #221 est:1700-2500 (S.FR 1900)

KREGAR, Stane (1905-?) Yugoslavian
£369 $650 €539 Trumpeter of horror (117x89cm-46x35in) s.d.1956 oil linen exhib. 22-May-4 Selkirks, St. Louis #787/R

KREGCZY, Edmund (1855-?) Austrian
£294 $490 €420 Summer beach near Grado (25x36cm-10x14in) s.i.d.1901 panel. 10-Oct-3 Winterberg, Heidelberg #643

KREGTEN, Fedor van (1871-1937) Dutch
£514 $873 €750 Arabs with donkeys near mountain village (58x79cm-23x31in) s. 5-Nov-3 Vendue Huis, Gravenhage #253/R

£884 $1610 €1300 Cows in a sunlit polder landscape (40x60cm-16x24in) s. 3-Feb-4 Christie's, Amsterdam #249 est:800-1200
£2148 $3973 €3200 Cows in a meadow (60x80cm-24x31in) s. 15-Mar-4 Sotheby's, Amsterdam #118/R est:1000-1500

KREHBIEL, Albert H (20th C) American
£559 $1000 €816 Snowy landscape (56x76cm-22x30in) s. 21-Mar-4 Hindman, Chicago #846/R est:1000-2000

KREHL, Gosta (1860-1899) Swedish
£258 $451 €377 Still life of flowers in vase (35x27cm-14x11in) s.d.1899. 16-Dec-3 Grev Wedels Plass, Oslo #160/R (N.KR 3000)

KREHM, William P (1901-1968) American
£270 $475 €394 Mountain lake (41x51cm-16x20in) s. board painted c.1930. 23-May-4 Treadway Gallery, Cincinnati #556/R

KREIDOLF, Ernst Konrad Theophil (1863-1956) Swiss
£325 $581 €475 Mountain landscape in autumn with deer (36x48cm-14x19in) s. exhib. 22-Mar-4 Philippe Schuler, Zurich #4342 (S.FR 750)
£436 $803 €650 Hubertus I (62x83cm-24x33in) s.d.1912 s.i. verso lit. 25-Mar-4 Karlheinz Kaupp, Staufen #2556/R
Works on paper
£733 $1312 €1070 Boy by water source (27x19cm-11x7in) s.i.mono. Indian ink W/C. 12-May-4 Dobiaschofsky, Bern #1750/R est:1400 (S.FR 1700)

KREIENBUHL, Jurg (1932-) Swiss
£1048 $1876 €1530 Theo Gerber in studio (45x39cm-18x15in) s.d.1967 dispersion pavatex. 26-May-4 Sotheby's, Zurich #69/R est:4000-5000 (S.FR 2400)

KREISEL, Paul (1891-1982) Polish?
£938 $1566 €1369 Gdansk, view from a window (80x60cm-31x24in) s. painted c.1930. 19-Oct-3 Agra, Warsaw #55/R est:6000 (P.Z 6000)

KREITZ, Willy (1903-1982) Belgian
Sculpture
£1325 $2411 €2000 Standing female nude (40cm-16in) bronze stone base. 15-Jun-4 Christie's, Amsterdam #350/R est:1500-2500
£1589 $2893 €2400 Standing female nude (36cm-14in) pat bronze stone base. 15-Jun-4 Christie's, Amsterdam #349/R est:1500-2500
£5694 $9054 €8200 Standing female nude (177cm-70in) s. galvanized metal green pat stand. 15-Sep-3 Bernaerts, Antwerp #777/R est:2000-3000

KREJCAR, Anton (1923-) Austrian
£1389 $2264 €2000 The spider (50x41cm-20x16in) s.d.1955 fibreboard. 23-Sep-3 Wiener Kunst Auktionen, Vienna #141/R est:2000-3500
Works on paper
£352 $616 €500 The onion polyp (24x27cm-9x11in) s.d.1956 mixed media. 19-Dec-3 Dorotheum, Vienna #276/R

KREMEGNE, Pinchus (1890-1981) Russian
£1056 $1827 €1500 Deux personnages au parapluie (55x33cm-22x13in) s. 12-Dec-3 Piasa, Paris #170 est:1800-2200
£1333 $2387 €2000 Les capucins a Ceret (35x48cm-14x19in) s. isorel. 16-May-4 Lombrail & Teucquam, Paris #266/R
£1338 $2315 €1900 Petite place (55x33cm-22x13in) s. 12-Dec-3 Piasa, Paris #169/R est:1800-2200
£1399 $2406 €2000 Nature morte aux courgettes (46x65cm-18x26in) s. 3-Dec-3 Beaussant & Lefèvre, Paris #42/R est:2000-2500
£1406 $2348 €2053 Anemones in a vase (50x60cm-20x24in) s. 19-Oct-3 Agra, Warsaw #40/R est:9000 (P.Z 9000)
£1689 $3023 €2500 Nature morte aux peches et au sucrier (33x41cm-13x16in) s. 4-May-4 Calmels Cohen, Paris #151/R est:2500-3000
£2013 $3604 €3000 Paysage de Ceret (46x55cm-18x22in) s. 25-May-4 Chambelland & Giafferi, Paris #71/R est:3000-4000
£2123 $3610 €3100 Still life with fruit (27x35cm-11x14in) s. 9-Nov-3 Eric Pillon, Calais #164/R
£2162 $3871 €3200 Paysage (54x72cm-21x28in) s. 4-May-4 Calmels Cohen, Paris #150/R est:2500-3000
£2552 $4593 €3700 Still life (46x55cm-18x22in) s. painted c.1955. 25-Jan-4 Chayette & Cheval, Paris #178/R est:4000-5000
£2617 $4685 €3900 Landscape (54x65cm-21x26in) s. 26-May-4 Christie's, Paris #29/R est:4000-6000
£2685 $4913 €4000 Paysage (54x65cm-21x26in) s. 7-Jul-4 Artcurial Briest, Paris #129/R est:4000-5000
£3297 $6000 €4814 Landscape with trees (66x81cm-26x32in) s. 29-Jun-4 Sotheby's, New York #344/R est:6000-8000
£3793 $6828 €5500 Paysage a Annay sur Serein, Yonneq (49x61cm-19x24in) s. 25-Jan-4 Chayette & Cheval, Paris #171/R est:5000-6000
£4636 $8437 €7000 Paysage a la Tourelle (54x65cm-21x26in) s. exhib. 15-Jun-4 Rossini, Paris #85/R est:7000-10000
£7000 $12530 €10220 Couple walking their dog. Townscape (55x33cm-22x13in) s. two. 26-May-4 Sotheby's, London #287/R est:7000-9000
£15363 $27500 €22430 Landscape in Ceret (37x129cm-15x51in) s. painted c.1916 exhib. 18-Mar-4 Sotheby's, New York #100/R est:25000-35000
Works on paper
£694 $1159 €1000 Composition surrealiste (33x25cm-13x10in) s. W/C lead pencil. 21-Oct-3 Artcurial Briest, Paris #258/R

KREMER, Nicolaus (attrib) (?-1553) German
£4483 $7486 €6500 Portrait of bearded man wearing beret (57x43cm-22x17in) d.1530 panel. 15-Nov-3 Lempertz, Koln #1080/R est:7000

KREMER, Petrus (1801-1888) Flemish
£921 $1667 €1400 Jeune femme et son enfant au jardin (49x39cm-19x15in) s. panel. 19-Apr-4 Horta, Bruxelles #25
£1103 $2041 €1600 Jeune femme et son enfant au jardin (49x39cm-19x15in) s. panel. 19-Jan-4 Horta, Bruxelles #231 est:1800-2200
£2517 $4580 €3800 La rose et le verre de vin (80x67cm-31x26in) s. 15-Jun-4 Galerie Moderne, Brussels #256/R est:3800-4200

KREMLICKA, Rudolf (1886-1932) Czechoslovakian
Works on paper
£372 $618 €543 Forest (28x42cm-11x17in) s.d.1925 ink wash. 4-Oct-3 Dorotheum, Prague #250/R est:12000-18000 (C.KR 17000)

KREMP, Erminio (20th C) Italian
£556 $928 €800 In the harem (143x94cm-56x37in) s.i.d.08. 22-Oct-3 Neumeister, Munich #725/R
£1611 $2996 €2400 Italian coast with horse cart and fishing boats (58x94cm-23x37in) s.d.1912. 6-Mar-4 Arnold, Frankfurt #761/R est:600

KRENN, Edmund (1846-1902) Austrian
Works on paper
£530 $970 €800 Klosterneuburg (31x46cm-12x18in) s.d.1861 W/C. 8-Apr-4 Dorotheum, Vienna #161/R

KRENN, Hans (1932-) German
Works on paper
£390 $697 €569 How well you play (31x23cm-12x9in) s.i.d. W/C over sepia Indian ink. 22-Mar-4 Philippe Schuler, Zurich #4025/R (S.FR 900)

KRENZ, Alfred (1899-1980) South African
£470 $799 €686 Herdsmen and their flock (74x94cm-29x37in) s.d.60 board. 4-Nov-3 Stephan Welz, Johannesburg #664 est:6000-9000 (SA.R 5500)
£619 $1109 €904 Magnolias in a brown vase (60x76cm-24x30in) s. board. 31-May-4 Stephan Welz, Johannesburg #176 (SA.R 7500)
Works on paper
£325 $552 €475 Western Cape landscape (22x31cm-9x12in) s.d.1971 pastel. 4-Nov-3 Stephan Welz, Johannesburg #609 est:3500-5000 (SA.R 3800)

KRESS, Annick (20th C) French
£300 $543 €450 Sans titre (80x80cm-31x31in) s. acrylic. 3-Apr-4 Neret-Minet, Paris #77/R
£333 $603 €500 Sans titre (60x60cm-24x24in) s. acrylic. 3-Apr-4 Neret-Minet, Paris #127a

KRESSEL, Diether (1925-) German
Works on paper
£493 $818 €700 Lobster (33x50cm-13x20in) s.d.1987 col chk W/C. 13-Jun-3 Hauswedell & Nolte, Hamburg #743/R

KRESTIN, Lazar (1868-1938) Russian
£2195 $3731 €3205 Portrait of a Rabbi (26x21cm-10x8in) s. 29-Nov-3 Dorotheum, Prague #19/R est:80000-120000 (C.KR 100000)
£3911 $7000 €5710 Man from Jerusalem (53x43cm-21x17in) s.i. 18-Mar-4 Sotheby's, New York #270/R est:4000-6000

KRETZ, Leopold (1907-) French
£302 $553 €450 Self portrait (50x39cm-20x15in) s. 7-Jul-4 Artcurial Briest, Paris #122
£503 $921 €750 Nude in front of a mirror (46x22cm-18x9in) s. board on isorel panel. 7-Jul-4 Artcurial Briest, Paris #120
£503 $921 €750 Femme a sa toilette (65x54cm-26x21in) s.d.1973 board. 7-Jul-4 Artcurial Briest, Paris #124
Sculpture
£1958 $3270 €2800 Nu debout (52cm-20in) s. pat bronze. 7-Oct-3 Livinec, Gaudcheau & Jezequel, Rennes #164/R

KRETZMAN, Max (20th C) ?
£8054 $14416 €12000 Untitled (128x220cm-50x87in) s.d.1985 verso. 27-May-4 Sotheby's, Paris #275/R est:12000-15000

KRETZSCHMAR, Bernhard (1889-1972) German
£8333 $13917 €12000 Resting on the Flight (54x70cm-21x28in) mono.d. double-sided. 25-Oct-3 Dr Lehr, Berlin #289/R est:15000

KRETZSCHMER, Johann Hermann (1811-1890) German
£972 $1604 €1400 Standing girl wearing headscarf and carrying book (35x27cm-14x11in) s.i.d.1871. 3-Jul-3 Dr Fritz Nagel, Stuttgart #499/R

KREUGER, Nils (1858-1930) Swedish
£370 $661 €540 The carpenter (19x14cm-7x6in) panel. 26-May-4 AB Stockholms Auktionsverk #2325/R (S.KR 5000)
£1231 $2117 €1797 Trees by road (24x34cm-9x13in) s.d.1919 panel exhib.lit. 3-Dec-3 AB Stockholms Auktionsverk #2526/R est:12000-15000 (S.KR 16000)
£3538 $6086 €5165 Horses by Borgholm's ruins (85x111cm-33x44in) s.d.1919. 2-Dec-3 Bukowskis, Stockholm #91/R est:50000-55000 (S.KR 46000)
£4615 $7938 €6738 On the outskirts of Bourg-la-Reine (27x40cm-11x16in) s.i.d.1886 canvas on panel prov.lit. 2-Dec-3 Bukowskis, Stockholm #265/R est:30000-35000 (S.KR 60000)
£5077 $8732 €7412 Bay horse in landscape (76x107cm-30x42in) s.d.1919 panel exhib.lit. 2-Dec-3 Bukowskis, Stockholm #189/R est:40000-50000 (S.KR 66000)
£5174 $9261 €7554 Approaching storm (96x65cm-38x26in) s.d.1927 prov.lit. 25-May-4 Bukowskis, Stockholm #16/R est:100000-125000 (S.KR 70000)

£5538 $9526 €8085 Garden in Grez (13x24cm-5x9in) mono.d.83 panel lit. 3-Dec-3 AB Stockholms Auktionsverk #2257/R est:50000-60000 (S.KR 72000)
£6154 $10585 €8985 Panorama landscape from Borgholm (60x195cm-24x77in) s.d.1911 lit. 2-Dec-3 Bukowskis, Stockholm #94/R est:100000-150000 (S.KR 80000)
£7538 $12966 €11005 Landscape from Hallandsaas near Baastad (52x97cm-20x38in) s.d.1907 prov.lit. 2-Dec-3 Bukowskis, Stockholm #93/R est:60000-80000 (S.KR 98000)
£13462 $23154 €19655 Horse-drawn taxies outside the Opera, Stockholm (78x100cm-31x39in) s.d.1903 exhib.lit. 2-Dec-3 Bukowskis, Stockholm #183/R est:175000-200000 (S.KR 175000)
Works on paper
£437 $805 €656 Untitled (26x50cm-10x20in) s.d.1922 chk W/C. 14-Jun-4 Lilla Bukowskis, Stockholm #321 (S.KR 6000)
£2033 $3638 €2968 Old beam-tree (50x61cm-20x24in) s.d.sept 1915 gouache panel. 25-May-4 Bukowskis, Stockholm #14/R est:15000-20000 (S.KR 27500)

KREUL, Johann Friedrich Karl (attrib) (1804-1867) German
£281 $484 €410 Landscape with couple wearing German national costumes (21x18cm-8x7in) s. metal. 3-Dec-3 Museumsbygningen, Copenhagen #154/R (D.KR 3000)

KREUTZ, Heinz (1923-) German
£1399 $2378 €2000 Small pagoda (34x11cm-13x4in) s.d.59 s.i.d.1959 verso panel prov. 27-Nov-3 Lempertz, Koln #243/R est:1600
£1399 $2378 €2000 Untitled (33x13cm-13x5in) s.d.59 i. stretcher board on panel prov. 27-Nov-3 Lempertz, Koln #242/R est:1600
£1733 $3189 €2600 Composition (18x20cm-7x8in) s.d. 11-Jun-4 Hauswedell & Nolte, Hamburg #1397/R est:800
£2098 $3566 €3000 Untitled (25x35cm-10x14in) s.d.56 verso prov. 27-Nov-3 Lempertz, Koln #241/R est:3000
£2238 $3804 €3200 Before Rosa (26x35cm-10x14in) s.d. s.i.d. verso. 21-Nov-3 Reiss & Sohn, Konigstein #593/R est:2000
£2267 $4171 €3400 Composition (50x70cm-20x28in) s.d. s.i.d.December verso. 11-Jun-4 Hauswedell & Nolte, Hamburg #1396/R est:1500
£4667 $8353 €7000 Untitled (65x81cm-26x32in) s.d. s.i.d1969 Aug-Okt prov. 14-May-4 Ketterer, Munich #278/R est:7000-9000
Works on paper
£524 $892 €750 Composition in quarters (40x80cm-16x31in) s.d.5.12.68 collage. 29-Nov-3 Arnold, Frankfurt #337
£559 $951 €800 Seven colour figures (38x53cm-15x21in) s.i.d.75 co pen. 27-Nov-3 Lempertz, Koln #245/R

KREUTZER, A (19th C) German
£1200 $2172 €1800 Moonlight on boats (94x77cm-37x30in) s. 1-Apr-4 Van Ham, Cologne #1498/R est:1600

KREUTZER, Felix (1835-1876) German
£1103 $1832 €1600 Evening wood (90x118cm-35x46in) s. 6-Oct-3 Bloss, Merzhausen #1210/R est:1000

KREUZER, Vinzenz (1809-1888) Austrian
£1250 $2088 €1800 Extensive evening landscape with burning house (29x37cm-11x15in) s.d.1881 board on panel lit. 25-Oct-3 Bergmann, Erlangen #919/R est:1700

KREUZHAGE, Werner (1904-) German
£1892 $3386 €2800 Untitled (43x55cm-17x22in) board on panel. 6-May-4 Michael Zeller, Lindau #1026/R est:2800

KREVASZ, Krzysztof (20th C) Polish
£237 $425 €346 Still life of apples, white tureen and bread (51x64cm-20x25in) s.d.1985 s.i.verso. 7-May-4 Sloans & Kenyon, Bethesda #1155/R

KREYDER, Alexis (1839-1912) French
£2133 $3925 €3200 Coupe de raisins (50x61cm-20x24in) s. 9-Jun-4 Beaussant & Lefèvre, Paris #173/R est:1500-2000
£28000 $51240 €42000 Roses dans un pot japonais (133x79cm-52x31in) s. 4-Jun-4 Pierre Berge, Paris #67/R est:5000-6000

KREYFELT, Julius van (1863-?) German
Works on paper
£280 $515 €420 Old mill on the banks of the river (25x35cm-10x14in) s. W/C. 11-Jun-4 Wendl, Rudolstadt #4127/R

KRICHELDORF, Carl (1863-?) German
£417 $679 €600 Young woman sitting at window writing letter (60x45cm-24x18in) s. 27-Sep-3 Dannenberg, Berlin #570/R
£903 $1426 €1300 Female nude reclining on the beach (24x35cm-9x14in) s. panel. 5-Sep-3 Wendl, Rudolstadt #3471/R

KRICHELDORF, Hermann (1867-1949) German
£1188 $1900 €1734 Still life with lobster and cheese (58x81cm-23x32in) s.d.1903 verso. 17-May-3 Bunte, Elgin #1261 est:2000-3000

KRICKE, Norbert (1922-1984) German
Sculpture
£6000 $10980 €9000 Untitled (27x58x6cm-11x23x2in) s.i.d.29.01.65 steel prov. 4-Jun-4 Lempertz, Koln #279/R est:10000-12000
£28873 $49951 €41000 Object (32cm-13in) s.d.57 wire. 13-Dec-3 Lempertz, Koln #328/R est:7000
Works on paper
£634 $1096 €900 Untitled (43x61cm-17x24in) mono.d.68 s.i.d.1980 verso Indian ink board. 13-Dec-3 Lempertz, Koln #329/R

KRIEGER, Wilhelm (1877-?) German
Sculpture
£1644 $2795 €2400 Rabbits (24cm-9in) s. pat.bronze. 5-Nov-3 Hugo Ruef, Munich #2160/R est:800

KRIEGHOFF, Cornelius (1815-1872) Canadian
£10135 $17230 €14797 Indian Head Rock (51x41cm-20x16in) s. i.verso on frame prov. 18-Nov-3 Sotheby's, Toronto #170/R est:25000-30000 (C.D 22500)
£12195 $21829 €17805 Indian hunter with toboggan greeting a native woman and child (21x28cm-8x11in) s. board painted c.1855 prov.lit. 27-May-4 Heffel, Vancouver #68/R est:25000-35000 (C.D 30000)
£14400 $26352 €21024 Indians crossing the lake, Autumn (21x32cm-8x13in) s. prov. 1-Jun-4 Joyner Waddington, Toronto #29/R est:25000-30000 (C.D 36000)
£14640 $24887 €21374 Old habitant (28x23cm-11x9in) s. prov. 18-Nov-3 Sotheby's, Toronto #120/R est:12000-15000 (C.D 32500)
£26000 $47580 €37960 Indians shooting the rapids (31x43cm-12x17in) s.d.1861 prov. 1-Jun-4 Joyner Waddington, Toronto #56/R est:40000-50000 (C.D 65000)
£30000 $54900 €43800 White Horse Tavern (19x21cm-7x8in) s.d.1845 board prov.lit. 1-Jun-4 Joyner Waddington, Toronto #44/R est:40000-60000 (C.D 75000)
£38000 $61940 €55480 Wrecked raft (36x61cm-14x24in) s. prov. 25-Sep-3 Christie's, London #446/R est:18000-24000
£38000 $61940 €55480 Deer hunters in a winter landscape (40x66cm-16x26in) s. prov. 25-Sep-3 Christie's, London #445/R est:20000-30000
£65041 $116423 €94960 Leisure moments at Big Rock (40x64cm-16x25in) s. painted c.1853 prov.lit. 27-May-4 Heffel, Vancouver #66/R est:125000-175000 (C.D 160000)

KRIEGHOFF, Cornelius (attrib) (1815-1872) Canadian
£6504 $11642 €9496 Indian basket seller (30x22cm-12x9in) bears sig prov. 31-May-4 Sotheby's, Toronto #144/R est:4000-6000 (C.D 16000)
Works on paper
£2642 $4730 €3857 Bilking the toll gate (13x20cm-5x8in) s.d.1863 W/C gouache prov. 27-May-4 Heffel, Vancouver #69/R est:4000-6000 (C.D 6500)

KRIEGHOFF, William G (1875-1930) American
£190 $350 €277 The Great Philadelphia Fire (51x41cm-20x16in) s.d.23. 25-Jun-4 Freeman, Philadelphia #158/R

KRIEHUBER, Fritz (1836-1871) Austrian
£1660 $2972 €2424 Portrait of a young boy (44x34cm-17x13in) prov. 15-May-4 Christie's, Sydney #119/R est:4000-6000 (A.D 4200)

KRIEHUBER, Josef (1800-1876) Austrian
£780 $1248 €1139 Portrait of Arthur Russell, seated half-length holding a book (23x15cm-9x6in) board lit. 16-Sep-3 Gorringes, Bexhill #1554/R
Works on paper
£759 $1259 €1100 Portrait of Johanna Grafin Erdody in brown silk dress (25x19cm-10x7in) s.d.856 w/C. 30-Sep-3 Dorotheum, Vienna #399/R
£2013 $3705 €3000 Portrait of red haired boy (21x16cm-8x6in) s.d.868 W/C. 26-Mar-4 Dorotheum, Vienna #359/R est:2000-2200
£5921 $10895 €9000 Princesses of Lichtenstein (25x20cm-10x8in) s.d.835 W/C. 22-Jun-4 Wiener Kunst Auktionen, Vienna #14/R est:7000

KRIGE, François (1913-1994) South African
£1293 $2159 €1888 Bunches of freesias (30x43cm-12x17in) s.d.62. 20-Oct-3 Stephan Welz, Johannesburg #268/R est:12000-16000 (SA.R 15000)
£1638 $2735 €2391 Tree in a gorge (65x39cm-26x15in) s. board. 20-Oct-3 Stephan Welz, Johannesburg #317/R est:12000-18000 (SA.R 19000)
£1724 $2879 €2517 San woman (50x39cm-20x15in) s.d.85. 20-Oct-3 Stephan Welz, Johannesburg #321/R est:15000-20000 (SA.R 20000)
£2312 $4139 €3376 View of Cairo from the Continental Savoy Hotel (39x49cm-15x19in) s. canvasboard. 31-May-4 Stephan Welz, Johannesburg #555/R est:12000-16000 (SA.R 28000)
£2477 $4434 €3616 Roses in a blue bowl (60x49cm-24x19in) 31-May-4 Stephan Welz, Johannesburg #516/R est:30000-40000 (SA.R 30000)
£3448 $5759 €5034 Goat herder (66x43cm-26x17in) s. board. 20-Oct-3 Stephan Welz, Johannesburg #320/R est:15000-20000 (SA.R 40000)
£4310 $7198 €6293 Still life of proteas in a brown jug (61x51cm-24x20in) s.d.87. 20-Oct-3 Stephan Welz, Johannesburg #277/R est:30000-40000 (SA.R 50000)
£7563 $13689 €11042 Constantia Valley (55x62cm-22x24in) s. 30-Mar-4 Stephan Welz, Johannesburg #461/R est:70000-90000 (SA.R 90000)
Works on paper
£252 $456 €368 Seascape with sea birds (26x37cm-10x15in) s. pastel. 30-Mar-4 Stephan Welz, Johannesburg #181 est:1800-2400 (SA.R 3000)
£294 $532 €429 Cottage, Swellendam (35x50cm-14x20in) s.i. chl. 30-Mar-4 Stephan Welz, Johannesburg #197 est:1500-2000 (SA.R 3500)
£420 $761 €613 Migrant worker (65x35cm-26x14in) s.d.71 chl. 30-Mar-4 Stephan Welz, Johannesburg #231 est:2500-3500 (SA.R 5000)
£1073 $1922 €1567 Washerwoman (29x45cm-11x18in) s. gouache. 31-May-4 Stephan Welz, Johannesburg #579/R (SA.R 13000)

KRIKHAAR, Herman (1930-) Dutch
£3067 $5612 €4600 Olive trees in a Mediterranean landscape (112x144cm-44x57in) init. 7-Jun-4 Glerum, Amsterdam #208/R est:4000-6000

KRIKI (1965-) French
£366 $634 €520 Le 45 tour (69x115cm-27x45in) s.d.1991 acrylic canvas decoupee. 10-Dec-3 Millon & Associes, Paris #125/R
£867 $1560 €1300 Martiens (129x116cm-51x46in) s.d.1988 acrylic panel. 24-Apr-4 Cornette de St.Cyr, Paris #605
£946 $1788 €1400 Foule (100x100cm-39x39in) s. acrylic laser discs cut canvas. 21-Feb-4 Cornette de St.Cyr, Paris #332
£1892 $3576 €2800 Fuzz et tous ses amis (150x160cm-59x63in) s.d.1989 acrylic cut canvas. 21-Feb-4 Cornette de St.Cyr, Paris #330/R est:2500-3500
£2013 $3604 €3000 Les enfants du rock (162x130cm-64x51in) mono.d.90 acrylic prov. 27-May-4 Sotheby's, Paris #277/R est:3000-4000

£2083 $3479 €3000 Duel (200x200cm-79x79in) s. acrylic cut canvas. 25-Oct-3 Cornette de St.Cyr, Paris #734 est:3000-5000
£2431 $4010 €3500 La dentelliere (100x73cm-39x29in) s.d. s.i.d.1986 verso acrylic. 2-Jul-3 Cornette de St.Cyr, Paris #148/R est:3000-4000
Sculpture
£1333 $2400 €2000 Pas net (100x51x97cm-39x20x38in) s.i.d.1989 acrylic glass. 24-Apr-4 Cornette de St.Cyr, Paris #602/R est:1500-2000

KRILLE, Jean (20th C) ?
£352 $616 €500 Still life of flowers (70x50cm-28x20in) s. acrylic panel. 19-Dec-3 Dorotheum, Vienna #315/R
£423 $739 €600 Winter landscape (60x73cm-24x29in) s.d.88 acrylic panel. 19-Dec-3 Dorotheum, Vienna #341/R
£563 $986 €800 Autumn landscape (80x100cm-31x39in) s. acrylic panel. 19-Dec-3 Dorotheum, Vienna #345/R
£634 $1109 €900 Flowers (50x60cm-20x24in) s. s.d.1983 verso panel. 19-Dec-3 Dorotheum, Vienna #347/R

KRILOV, Boris (1891-1977) Russian
£322 $516 €470 Still life of lilacs in vase (60x71cm-24x28in) s. 22-Sep-3 Rasmussen, Vejle #100 (D.KR 3400)
Works on paper
£321 $583 €469 Outskirts of a Russian town (30x37cm-12x15in) s. W/C. 7-Feb-4 Rasmussen, Havnen #2059 (D.KR 3500)
£2200 $3938 €3212 Russian peasants enjoying summer (29x23cm-11x9in) s. one d.1935 W/C pair. 26-May-4 Sotheby's, Olympia #449/R est:1000-1500

KRINNER, Michaela (1915-) German
£1200 $2208 €1800 Woman in red (51x42cm-20x17in) s.d.66 masonite lit. 9-Jun-4 Dorotheum, Salzburg #682/R est:2800-3500
£1277 $2132 €1800 Spanish man (54x43cm-21x17in) s.d.58 masonite. 16-Oct-3 Dorotheum, Salzburg #677/R est:2400-3000
£1408 $2338 €2000 Kala (64x41cm-25x16in) s. masonite. 12-Jun-3 Dorotheum, Graz #32/R est:2000

KRIPPENDORF, William (1910-) American
£297 $550 €434 Zinnias (79x66cm-31x26in) 12-Mar-4 Du Mouchelle, Detroit #2231/R

KRISANAMIS, Udomsak (1966-) American?
Works on paper
£7362 $12000 €10749 Scottish lassie (162x117cm-64x46in) i.verso collage acrylic polycotton prov.exhib. 23-Sep-3 Christie's, Rockefeller NY #59/R est:6000-8000
£19461 $32500 €28413 Alice (122x122cm-48x48in) black marker paper collage on canvas prov. 13-Nov-3 Sotheby's, New York #529/R est:10000-18000

KRISCHKE, Franz (1885-1960) Austrian
£839 $1427 €1200 Still life with clock, flowers and cup and saucer (40x32cm-16x13in) s. 28-Nov-3 Wendl, Rudolstadt #4045/R

KRISTENMACHER, Charles E (20th C) American
£809 $1400 €1181 Yellow aspen (61x76cm-24x30in) s. 13-Dec-3 Charlton Hall, Columbia #531/R est:500-800

KRISTENSEN, Johannes V (20th C) Danish
£356 $594 €520 Evening landscape from Nymindegab (97x98cm-38x39in) s.d.1921. 25-Oct-3 Rasmussen, Havnen #2101/R (D.KR 3800)

KRISTIANSEN, Joannis (1918-1988) Danish
£993 $1827 €1450 Skarvanes, houses by the sea (53x74cm-21x29in) s.d.69. 29-Mar-4 Rasmussen, Copenhagen #269 (D.KR 11000)

KRISTO, Bela de (1920-) ?
£1958 $3368 €2800 Nature morte sur fond gris (75x100cm-30x39in) s. 5-Dec-3 Chochon-Barre & Allardi, Paris #116/R est:3000-3500
£2086 $3422 €2900 Composition a la chandelle inspiratrice (80x63cm-31x25in) s. panel painted c.1970. 6-Jun-3 Chochon-Barre & Allardi, Paris #60/R est:2500-2800

KRIUKOV, Lev Dmitrievitch (1773-1843) Russian
Works on paper
£2800 $5012 €4088 Portrait of a lady in pink scarf (15x13cm-6x5in) s. W/C. 26-May-4 Sotheby's, London #16 est:3000-4000

KRIZEK, Jan (attrib) (1919-1985) Czechoslovakian
£2278 $3554 €3600 Still life (13x43cm-5x17in) s. paper on panel. 18-Oct-2 Von Zezschwitz, Munich #74/R est:4800

KRIZSAN, Janos (1866-1948) Hungarian
£790 $1431 €1153 Brother of the painter at the Zazar (56x69cm-22x27in) s. 16-Apr-4 Mu Terem Galeria, Budapest #145/R (H.F 300000)
£887 $1535 €1295 Banks of the Zazar in Nagybanya, Reformed Church in the background (70x79cm-28x31in) s.d.1912. 12-Dec-3 Kieselbach, Budapest #6/R (H.F 340000)

KROCK, Hendrik (1671-1738) German
£756 $1308 €1104 The Acts of the Apostles (73x51cm-29x20in) prov. 9-Dec-3 Rasmussen, Copenhagen #1603/R (D.KR 8000)
£1418 $2453 €2070 The Finding of Moses (57x70cm-22x28in) prov. 9-Dec-3 Rasmussen, Copenhagen #1604/R est:25000-30000 (D.KR 15000)

KROCKER, Anna (19th C) German
£2000 $3200 €2920 Imitating her sister (81x65cm-32x26in) s. 18-Sep-3 Christie's, Kensington #152/R est:2000-3000

KROEGER, Carole (20th C) American
£324 $550 €473 Gray Summitt, MO (117x163cm-46x64in) s. s.i.d.1991 verso. 7-Nov-3 Selkirks, St. Louis #490/R
£471 $800 €688 Osborne County Co-op, Kansas (130x99cm-51x39in) s.i.d.1990 verso. 7-Nov-3 Selkirks, St. Louis #489

KROES, Nol (1918-1976) Dutch
£1301 $2212 €1900 Petrouchka. s.d.68. 5-Nov-3 Vendue Huis, Gravenhage #450/R est:800-1200
Works on paper
£350 $601 €500 Composition (31x47cm-12x19in) s.d.63 black chk. 8-Dec-3 Glerum, Amsterdam #177/R
£350 $601 €500 Horse ride, Petrouchka (41x41cm-16x16in) s.d.72 ink. 8-Dec-3 Glerum, Amsterdam #332/R
£548 $932 €800 Copulating butterfly (70x50cm-28x20in) s.d.64 mixed media. 5-Nov-3 Vendue Huis, Gravenhage #451/R

KROETER, Jimmie (1911-) American
£597 $950 €872 Cloudy winter afternoon (76x91cm-30x36in) s. 10-Sep-3 Alderfer's, Hatfield #291/R

KROGH, Charlotte Sofie von (1827-1914) Danish
£486 $768 €700 Christmas Eve in Danish village (23x33cm-9x13in) s. 6-Sep-3 Schopman, Hamburg #673/R

KROGSTAD, Bjorn (1943-) Norwegian
£2733 $4564 €3990 Figures with mask (100x200cm-39x79in) s. 13-Oct-3 Blomqvist, Oslo #327/R est:15000-18000 (N.KR 32000)

KROHG, Christian (1852-1925) Norwegian
£1130 $1956 €1650 Portrait of Dr Jorgen Christian Aall Sandberg (68x50cm-27x20in) s. 13-Dec-3 Blomqvist, Lysaker #1221/R est:15000-18000 (N.KR 13000)
£1222 $2114 €1784 Self portrait (86x56cm-34x22in) s. 9-Dec-3 Maynards, Vancouver #151 est:3000-5000 (C.D 2750)
£1382 $2543 €2073 Small boy by window (18x14cm-7x6in) s. panel. 14-Jun-4 Blomqvist, Lysaker #1212/R est:16000-18000 (N.KR 17000)
£1595 $2872 €2393 The pilot (73x53cm-29x21in) s. 25-Apr-4 Goteborg Auktionsverk, Sweden #165/R est:25000 (S.KR 22000)
£1601 $2866 €2337 Old woman (41x34cm-16x13in) s. i. verso panel. 22-Mar-4 Blomqvist, Oslo #351/R est:20000-25000 (N.KR 20000)
£1626 $2976 €2374 Eye witnesses (35x62cm-14x24in) s. panel lit. 7-Jun-4 Blomqvist, Oslo #284/R est:25000-35000 (N.KR 20000)
£1707 $3141 €2561 Woman on jetty (50x58cm-20x23in) s. panel. 14-Jun-4 Blomqvist, Lysaker #1211 est:10000-12000 (N.KR 21000)
£2114 $3868 €3086 On the bridge (47x69cm-19x27in) s. 7-Jun-4 Blomqvist, Oslo #293/R est:30000-40000 (N.KR 26000)
£2418 $4014 €3506 Overboard (45x53cm-18x21in) s. panel. 16-Jun-3 Blomqvist, Lysaker #1339/R est:20000-25000 (N.KR 28000)
£2802 $5016 €4091 Woman by birch tree (55x46cm-22x18in) s. 22-Mar-4 Blomqvist, Oslo #312/R est:40000-50000 (N.KR 35000)
£3252 $5951 €4748 Sailor on a jetty, Dieppe (38x46cm-15x18in) s. lit. 7-Jun-4 Blomqvist, Oslo #367/R est:50000-70000 (N.KR 40000)
£4323 $7739 €6312 Rowing in heavy seas (50x60cm-20x24in) s. 22-Mar-4 Blomqvist, Oslo #329/R est:60000-80000 (N.KR 54000)
£4878 $8927 €7122 Interior scene with woman in a fisherman's cottage at Skagen (36x32cm-14x13in) s. lit. 7-Jun-4 Blomqvist, Oslo #328/R est:35000-45000 (N.KR 60000)
£4964 $8886 €7247 Small girl wearing red coat and hat (32x33cm-13x13in) s. panel. 22-Mar-4 Blomqvist, Oslo #324/R est:50000-60000 (N.KR 62000)
£5235 $9632 €7643 Interior, possibly the artist's home (52x33cm-20x13in) s. painted c.1915. 29-Mar-4 Rasmussen, Copenhagen #217/R est:50000 (D.KR 58000)
£5383 $9636 €7859 Self-portrait (55x40cm-22x16in) s. 25-May-4 Grev Wedels Plass, Oslo #40/R est:50000-70000 (N.KR 66000)
£5988 $10180 €8742 Pilot at the helm (40x52cm-16x20in) s. lit. 19-Nov-3 Grev Wedels Plass, Oslo #63/R est:40000-60000 (N.KR 70000)
£18760 $33581 €27390 A distress signal (94x101cm-37x40in) s. lit. 25-May-4 Grev Wedels Plass, Oslo #41/R est:200000-300000 (N.KR 230000)
£34217 $58169 €49957 The pilot boat going out (93x120cm-37x47in) s. 19-Nov-3 Grev Wedels Plass, Oslo #64/R est:250000 (N.KR 400000)

KROHG, Guy (1917-2002) Norwegian
£238 $438 €347 Chopping logs (46x55cm-18x22in) s. panel. 29-Mar-4 Blomqvist, Lysaker #1181/R (N.KR 3000)
£604 $1003 €876 Theatre, a rehearsal (75x48cm-30x19in) s. enamel panel. 16-Jun-3 Blomqvist, Lysaker #1112 (N.KR 7000)

KROHG, Per (1889-1965) Norwegian
£278 $481 €406 Portrait of a nobleman (77x61cm-30x24in) 13-Dec-3 Blomqvist, Lysaker #1224 (N.KR 3200)
£281 $515 €410 Portrait of Veronika (38x23cm-15x9in) s. panel. 2-Feb-4 Blomqvist, Lysaker #1157/R (N.KR 3500)
£476 $875 €695 Landscape (46x55cm-18x22in) s. panel. 29-Mar-4 Blomqvist, Lysaker #1182/R (N.KR 6000)
£528 $972 €792 Landscape from Nyhellesund (43x51cm-17x20in) indis.init. panel. 14-Jun-4 Blomqvist, Lysaker #1214/R (N.KR 6500)
£577 $928 €842 Norwegian landscape (33x41cm-13x16in) s. panel. 25-Aug-3 Blomqvist, Lysaker #1160/R (N.KR 6700)
£775 $1293 €1132 Magpies (51x61cm-20x24in) s. panel. 20-Oct-3 Blomqvist, Lysaker #1184/R (N.KR 9000)
£1110 $1854 €1621 Stormy weather - couple in small boat (55x65cm-22x26in) s.d.1950 i.stretcher. 13-Oct-3 Blomqvist, Oslo #304/R est:12000-15000 (N.KR 13000)
£1193 $1992 €1730 Fireman saving young woman from the flames (50x37cm-20x15in) s.d.26 panel. 23-Jun-3 Philippe Schuler, Zurich #3566 est:2000-2500 (S.FR 2600)
£1196 $1997 €1746 Washing clothes in the backyard (60x73cm-24x29in) s.d.1951 panel. 13-Oct-3 Blomqvist, Oslo #309/R est:20000-25000 (N.KR 14000)
£1240 $2109 €1810 Flowers in vase (42x34cm-17x13in) s.d.1953 s.i.verso panel. 19-Nov-3 Grev Wedels Plass, Oslo #81/R est:15000-20000 (N.KR 14500)

£1463 $2678 €2136 Three women at the water pump (46x55cm-18x22in) s. panel. 7-Jun-4 Blomqvist, Oslo #381/R est:25000-30000 (N.KR 18000)
£1721 $2874 €2513 Peace - the Krohg family (185x132cm-73x52in) s. verso sketch. 20-Oct-3 Blomqvist, Lysaker #1185/R est:50000 (N.KR 20000)
£2802 $5016 €4091 Lucy wearing brown (93x65cm-37x26in) s.d.25 lit. 22-Mar-4 Blomqvist, Oslo #389/R est:45000-55000 (N.KR 35000)
£3018 $5402 €4406 Landscape from Hvaler (81x100cm-32x39in) s.d.1944 panel. 25-May-4 Grev Wedels Plass, Oslo #80/R est:30000-40000 (N.KR 37000)
£3066 $5274 €4476 Kitchen interior with boy (79x66cm-31x26in) s.d.43. 8-Dec-3 Blomqvist, Oslo #520/R est:40000-60000 (N.KR 36000)
£4611 $7701 €6732 From the terrace (82x100cm-32x39in) s.d.1949 exhib. 13-Oct-3 Blomqvist, Oslo #315/R est:60000-80000 (N.KR 54000)

KROHN, Xan (1882-1959) Norwegian
£285 $525 €416 Landscape (88x116cm-35x46in) s. 29-Mar-4 Blomqvist, Lysaker #1186 (N.KR 3600)
£293 $489 €428 Apostle (66x50cm-26x20in) s. 20-Oct-3 Blomqvist, Lysaker #1193 (N.KR 3400)
£349 $642 €510 Portrait of woman (58x44cm-23x17in) s. 29-Mar-4 Blomqvist, Lysaker #1187 (N.KR 4400)
£430 $719 €628 Flowering cactus (100x76cm-39x30in) s. 20-Oct-3 Blomqvist, Lysaker #1194/R (N.KR 5000)
£539 $992 €787 Winter landscape (48x67cm-19x26in) s. 29-Mar-4 Blomqvist, Lysaker #1188/R (N.KR 6800)

KROJER, Tom (1942-) Danish
£380 $680 €555 Performance Art - composition (75x102cm-30x40in) s.d.97. 10-May-4 Rasmussen, Vejle #772/R (D.KR 4200)
£1221 $2038 €1783 Composition (130x97cm-51x38in) s.d.1991. 7-Oct-3 Rasmussen, Copenhagen #235/R est:10000-12000 (D.KR 13000)
Works on paper
£469 $784 €685 Figure composition (100x90cm-39x35in) s.d.1977 mixed media with offset print. 7-Oct-3 Rasmussen, Copenhagen #237/R (D.KR 5000)

KROKFORS, Kristian (1952-) Finnish
£839 $1427 €1200 Blue smoke (127x91cm-50x36in) s.d.88. 29-Nov-3 Bukowskis, Helsinki #279/R

KROLIKOWSKI, Jozef Auguste (1811-1879) German
£638 $1180 €950 La source (67x56cm-26x22in) s. 13-Mar-4 De Vuyst, Lokeren #203

KROLL, Leon (1884-1974) American
£543 $1000 €793 Lake scene with canoe (20x25cm-8x10in) s. board. 11-Jun-4 David Rago, Lambertville #257/R est:500-750
£559 $1000 €816 Portrait of a gentleman, in a tuxedo (102x84cm-40x33in) s.d.1920. 8-Jan-4 James Julia, Fairfield #906/R
£1850 $3200 €2701 Autumn landscape (33x41cm-13x16in) s.i. panel. 13-Dec-3 Charlton Hall, Columbia #573/R est:3000-5000
£2056 $3700 €3002 Portrait of Theresa Rogers (38x47cm-15x19in) s. prov. 24-Apr-4 Weschler, Washington #638/R est:3000-5000
£2285 $4250 €3336 Seated female nude (45x38cm-18x15in) s. board. 5-Mar-4 Skinner, Boston #398/R est:5000-7000
Works on paper
£706 $1200 €1031 Study of a woman wearing a hat (36x28cm-14x11in) chl prov. 9-Nov-3 Wright, Chicago #113 est:1500-2000
£706 $1200 €1031 Nude reclining on an upholstered chair (33x51cm-13x20in) sanquin conte prov. 9-Nov-3 Wright, Chicago #115 est:1500-2000

KROMANN, Albert (19th C) Scandinavian
£595 $1083 €869 Seascape with sailing vessel in Copenhagen Harbour (93x139cm-37x55in) s.i.d.1893. 7-Feb-4 Rasmussen, Havnen #2126/R (D.KR 6500)
£968 $1645 €1413 Seascape with sailing ship (29x42cm-11x17in) s.d.92. 10-Nov-3 Rasmussen, Vejle #300/R (D.KR 10500)

KROMJONG, Paul (1903-) Dutch
£570 $1061 €850 Fisherman on the Maas near Slavante Maastricht (48x60cm-19x24in) s. 4-Mar-4 Auction Maastricht #1112/R

KROMKA, Frederico (19/20th C) ?
Works on paper
£315 $535 €450 Composition aux triangles (23x33cm-9x13in) s.d.1925 Indian ink wash prov. 23-Nov-3 Cornette de St.Cyr, Paris #175
£420 $713 €600 Composition mecanique (20x29cm-8x11in) s.d.1923 Indian ink gouache prov. 23-Nov-3 Cornette de St.Cyr, Paris #176
£420 $713 €600 Symbole azteque (23x18cm-9x7in) s.i.d.1931 gouache prov. 23-Nov-3 Cornette de St.Cyr, Paris #178
£1399 $2378 €2000 Mouvement mecanique (38x30cm-15x12in) s.i.d.1919 gouache W/C ink prov. 23-Nov-3 Cornette de St.Cyr, Paris #177/R est:100-150

KRON, Paul (1869-1936) French
£374 $637 €546 Market day (60x73cm-24x29in) s. 5-Nov-3 Dobiaschofsky, Bern #726/R (S.FR 850)

KRONBERG, Julius (1850-1921) Swedish
£1404 $2514 €2050 Girl with brown curly hair (44x32cm-17x13in) s.d.79. 25-May-4 Bukowskis, Stockholm #19/R est:18000-20000 (S.KR 19000)
£2365 $4234 €3453 Woman playing the harp (41x32cm-16x13in) s.d.1916 panel. 26-May-4 AB Stockholms Auktionsverk #2268/R est:20000-25000 (S.KR 32000)
£39172 $70118 €57191 Girl with cupid (135x73cm-53x29in) s.i.d.1882 lit. 25-May-4 Bukowskis, Stockholm #51/R est:150000-175000 (S.KR 530000)

KRONBERG, Louis (1872-1965) American
£659 $1100 €962 Ballet dancer (46x25cm-18x10in) s.d.1905. 19-Oct-3 Bonhams & Butterfields, Los Angeles #7055
£1934 $3500 €2824 Ballerina (61x46cm-24x18in) s. i.stretcher prov. 31-Mar-4 Sotheby's, New York #168/R est:2500-3500
£3073 $5500 €4487 Guitarista (64x89cm-25x35in) s.i.d.1936. 7-May-4 Sloans & Kenyon, Bethesda #1726/R est:6000-8000
Works on paper
£202 $375 €295 Seville, a fan design (41x63cm-16x25in) init.i. pastel. 5-Mar-4 Skinner, Boston #383/R
£254 $425 €371 Blue ballerina (71x58cm-28x23in) init. pastel. 19-Oct-3 Susanin's, Chicago #6046/R
£749 $1400 €1094 Curtain call (56x71cm-22x28in) s. pastel board. 24-Feb-4 Arthur James, Florida #72

KRONBERGER, Carl (1841-1921) Austrian
£1389 $2292 €2000 Ruins beneath stormy skies (31x20cm-12x8in) s. panel. 2-Jul-3 Neumeister, Munich #690/R est:1400
£2200 $4004 €3300 Peasant with cigar (18x13cm-7x5in) s. panel. 30-Jun-4 Neumeister, Munich #596/R est:3000

KRONDORF, William (20th C) American
Works on paper
£344 $550 €502 Landscape of St Augustine, Florida (25x36cm-10x14in) s.i.d.1945 W/C. 20-Sep-3 Jeffery Burchard, Florida #65a/R

KRONER, Christian (1838-1911) German
£467 $845 €700 Woodland path (25x35cm-10x14in) s.d.7/866 panel. 1-Apr-4 Van Ham, Cologne #1500/R
£524 $892 €750 Forest clearing (41x30cm-16x12in) s. canvas on board. 20-Nov-3 Van Ham, Cologne #1700
£1655 $2764 €2400 Deer resting in landscape (30x23cm-12x9in) s. lit. 12-Jul-3 Bergmann, Erlangen #695/R est:2200

KROPFF, Joop (1892-1979) Dutch
£385 $662 €550 Landscape with cows (40x50cm-16x20in) s. 8-Dec-3 Glerum, Amsterdam #207/R
£395 $726 €600 Free composition (64x76cm-25x30in) s. i. on stretcher prov. 22-Jun-4 Christie's, Amsterdam #374/R
£395 $726 €600 Moored boats (54x65cm-21x26in) s. 28-Jun-4 Sotheby's, Amsterdam #176/R
£454 $782 €650 Town view (30x24cm-12x9in) s. triplex. 7-Dec-3 Sotheby's, Amsterdam #687/R
£490 $842 €700 Breakwater (50x60cm-20x24in) s. 8-Dec-3 Glerum, Amsterdam #227/R
£514 $873 €750 Breakwater (38x50cm-15x20in) s. 5-Nov-3 Vendue Huis, Gravenhage #401/R
£594 $1022 €850 Market scene (35x30cm-14x12in) s. 7-Dec-3 Sotheby's, Amsterdam #688/R
£839 $1443 €1200 Reclining nude (19x37cm-7x15in) s. board. 8-Dec-3 Glerum, Amsterdam #239/R
£1958 $3270 €2800 Schevening boulevard (46x55cm-18x22in) s. 30-Jun-3 Sotheby's, Amsterdam #269/R
£2148 $3973 €3200 View of the Lange Voorhout, The Hague (35x40cm-14x16in) s. 15-Mar-4 Sotheby's, Amsterdam #117/R est:750-800

KROTOV, Youri (1964-) Russian
£461 $847 €700 Rose bush in the garden (55x46cm-22x18in) s. 22-Jun-4 Durán, Madrid #703/R
£738 $1321 €1100 Autumn (61x50cm-24x20in) s. 25-May-4 Durán, Madrid #722/R
£1449 $2377 €2000 Summer on the beach (46x61cm-18x24in) s. 27-May-3 Durán, Madrid #772/R est:2000
£2400 $4296 €3504 Nude young boy on the rocks (49x60cm-19x24in) s. 5-May-4 John Nicholson, Haslemere #203/R
£3618 $6549 €5500 Deux enfants en promenade sur un ane (50x65cm-20x26in) s. 19-Apr-4 Horta, Bruxelles #152 est:3500-4500
£3750 $6788 €5700 Dejeuner a la terrasse (73x100cm-29x39in) s. 19-Apr-4 Horta, Bruxelles #151 est:5500-7500

KROUTHEN, Johan (1858-1932) Swedish
£355 $635 €518 Portrait of Anna Euphrosyne Barnekow (101x76cm-40x30in) s.d.1903. 28-May-4 Uppsala Auktionskammare, Uppsala #207 (S.KR 4800)
£1109 $1984 €1619 River landscape with Svaraan from Svia (48x67cm-19x26in) s.d.1902. 28-May-4 Uppsala Auktionskammare, Uppsala #210/R est:18000-20000 (S.KR 15000)
£1308 $2249 €1910 Birch grove at sunset (75x49cm-30x19in) s.d.1918. 7-Dec-3 Uppsala Auktionskammare, Uppsala #176/R est:18000-20000 (S.KR 17000)
£1692 $2911 €2470 Summer landscape with cottage and apple tree in blossom (30x40cm-12x16in) s. panel. 3-Dec-3 AB Stockholms Auktionsverk #2474/R est:25000-30000 (S.KR 22000)
£1968 $3621 €2952 Autumn landscape (71x104cm-28x41in) s.d.1912. 14-Jun-4 Lilla Bukowskis, Stockholm #958 est:30000-35000 (S.KR 27000)
£2000 $3440 €2920 Still watercourse with waterlilies (55x79cm-22x31in) s. 7-Dec-3 Uppsala Auktionskammare, Uppsala #179/R est:20000-25000 (S.KR 26000)
£2143 $3837 €3129 Cattle grazing in summer meadow (100x150cm-39x59in) s.d.1916. 25-May-4 Bukowskis, Stockholm #204/R est:40000-50000 (S.KR 29000)
£2308 $3969 €3370 Cottage with trees in blossom in sunshine (50x75cm-20x30in) s. 7-Dec-3 Uppsala Auktionskammare, Uppsala #177/R est:30000-35000 (S.KR 30000)
£2769 $4763 €4043 Chickens on road in autumn (50x76cm-20x30in) s.d.1922. 2-Dec-3 Bukowskis, Stockholm #133/R est:35000-40000 (S.KR 36000)
£3252 $5821 €4748 Summer landscape (71x101cm-28x40in) s.d.1927. 25-May-4 Bukowskis, Stockholm #203/R est:40000-50000 (S.KR 44000)
£3695 $6615 €5395 Summer landscape with farm by lake (72x103cm-28x41in) s.d.1914. 26-May-4 AB Stockholms Auktionsverk #2106/R est:50000-60000 (S.KR 50000)
£4213 $7541 €6151 Summer landscape with apple-tree in blossom (50x75cm-20x30in) s. 26-May-4 AB Stockholms Auktionsverk #2107/R est:35000-40000 (S.KR 57000)
£4615 $7938 €6738 Summer idyll with boy and chickens (40x64cm-16x25in) s.d.1909. 2-Dec-3 Bukowskis, Stockholm #62a/R est:50000-55000 (S.KR 60000)
£4692 $8071 €6850 Underneath the apple-tree (80x110cm-31x43in) s.d.1916. 2-Dec-3 Bukowskis, Stockholm #131/R est:50000-55000 (S.KR 61000)
£4692 $8071 €6850 Summer landscape (70x100cm-28x39in) s. 2-Dec-3 Bukowskis, Stockholm #132/R est:40000-50000 (S.KR 61000)
£8130 $14553 €11870 Picnic in the meadow (93x65cm-37x26in) s.d.1911. 25-May-4 Bukowskis, Stockholm #205/R est:60000-70000 (S.KR 110000)

£11086 $19845 €16186 Rainbow at end of road (137x199cm-54x78in) s.d.1895 exhib. 26-May-4 AB Stockholms Auktionsverk #2321/R est:300000-350000 (S.KR 150000)

KROYER, Marie (1867-1940) Danish

£22462 $41779 €32795 Woman at the loom (45x57cm-18x22in) 2-Mar-4 Rasmussen, Copenhagen #1264/R est:300000-400000 (D.KR 250000)

KROYER, Peder Severin (1851-1909) Danish

£2686 $4915 €3922 Villa in moonlight, lights on indoors (27x37cm-11x15in) s.d.1872. 9-Jun-4 Rasmussen, Copenhagen #1805/R est:25000 (D.KR 30000)
£3551 $5611 €5149 A duet - study (21x18cm-8x7in) init. painted c.1887. 2-Sep-3 Rasmussen, Copenhagen #1507/R est:25000 (D.KR 38000)
£5000 $9200 €7300 View from Castle St Valentin in the Tyrol (29x69cm-11x27in) init.i.d.1901. 23-Mar-4 Bonhams, New Bond Street #24/R est:6000-8000
£6000 $11040 €8760 View of the Antique theatre in Taormina (33x64cm-13x25in) s.i.d.1901 panel. 23-Mar-4 Bonhams, New Bond Street #23/R est:6000-8000
£6542 $10336 €9486 View from Christianshavn towards Nicolai Tower (16x20cm-6x8in) init. exec.c.1868. 3-Sep-3 Museumsbygningen, Copenhagen #248/R est:40000-60000 (D.KR 70000)
£9400 $17202 €13724 Portrait of the artist's foster father, professor Henrik Nicolai Kroyer (76x63cm-30x25in) s.d.1872 exhib.prov. 9-Jun-4 Rasmussen, Copenhagen #1515/R est:75000-100000 (D.KR 105000)
£12981 $23756 €18952 Autumn landscape, view from Schloss St Valentin in Tyrol (30x70cm-12x28in) init.i.d.Nobr.1901 prov. 9-Jun-4 Rasmussen, Copenhagen #1470/R est:150000 (D.KR 145000)
£13575 $24299 €19820 Sunshine through trees in Skagen Plantation (34x43cm-13x17in) init.d.86. 10-May-4 Rasmussen, Vejle #18/R est:200000-300000 (D.KR 150000)
£14019 $22150 €20328 Young girl on the beach at Hornbaek (35x26cm-14x10in) s.i.d.73 prov. 2-Sep-3 Rasmussen, Copenhagen #1510/R est:100000 (D.KR 150000)
£17905 $32766 €26141 A blond boy - Portrait of Jens Drachmann (44x32cm-17x13in) s.i.d.Aug.83 panel prov. 9-Jun-4 Rasmussen, Copenhagen #1503/R est:200000-250000 (D.KR 200000)
£33243 $61833 €48535 Fisherman seen from the right handside at Skagen Strand (64x38cm-25x15in) mono.d.83 exhib.prov. 2-Mar-4 Rasmussen, Copenhagen #1232/R est:150000 (D.KR 370000)
£226843 $392439 €331191 Mrs Marie Kroyer in the garden at Skagen (22x32cm-9x13in) init.d.22 Juni 92 panel prov. 9-Dec-3 Rasmussen, Copenhagen #1264/R est:1200000-1500000 (D.KR 2400000)

Works on paper
£1348 $2507 €1968 Italian boy (17x10cm-7x4in) mono.d.1880 Indian ink pencil. 2-Mar-4 Rasmussen, Copenhagen #1685/R est:10000-12000 (D.KR 15000)
£1375 $2378 €2008 Woman sleeping (23x29cm-9x11in) s.i.d.23 mars 90 pencil. 15-Dec-3 Lilla Bukowskis, Stockholm #258 est:5000 (S.KR 17500)
£1887 $3509 €2755 The artist Johan Ericson (20x14cm-8x6in) s.i.d.5 Oktober 79 pencil exhib. 2-Mar-4 Rasmussen, Copenhagen #1683/R est:10000-15000 (D.KR 21000)
£2254 $4170 €3291 Dinner party in Wiesbaden with two ladies and two gentlemen (11x16cm-4x6in) init.i.d.31 oktober 1904 chl pastel. 15-Mar-4 Rasmussen, Vejle #435/R est:20000 (D.KR 25000)
£13477 $25067 €19676 Maria Kroyer asleep (23x29cm-9x11in) init.i.d.23 mars 90 chl. 2-Mar-4 Rasmussen, Copenhagen #1263/R est:30000 (D.KR 150000)

KROYER, Peder Severin (attrib) (1851-1909) Danish

£541 $849 €790 Study of seated fisherman (28x22cm-11x9in) init.i. pencil. 30-Aug-3 Rasmussen, Havnen #2155/R (D.KR 5800)
£574 $930 €832 Portrait of small girl with hat (40x30cm-16x12in) pen crayon. 4-Aug-3 Rasmussen, Vejle #387/R (D.KR 6000)
£15123 $26163 €22080 The artist's self portrait (24x18cm-9x7in) 9-Dec-3 Rasmussen, Copenhagen #1538/R est:20000-25000 (D.KR 160000)

Works on paper
£379 $709 €553 Portrait of a child (22x18cm-9x7in) s.d.16 Febr.1872 pencil. 25-Feb-4 Museumsbygningen, Copenhagen #158 (D.KR 4200)
£485 $761 €708 Pulling in the nets, study of a fisherman (32x22cm-13x9in) init.i.d.26 oktober 76 pencil. 30-Aug-3 Rasmussen, Havnen #2154/R (D.KR 5200)
£629 $1170 €918 Profile portrait of Edvard Hornemann (25x19cm-10x7in) s.i.d.14 Aug 1875 i.verso pencil. 2-Mar-4 Rasmussen, Copenhagen #1684/R (D.KR 7000)
£679 $1215 €991 Dinner party (11x17cm-4x7in) pen. 10-May-4 Rasmussen, Vejle #413/R (D.KR 7500)
£701 $1107 €1016 Alma Pfaff (26x20cm-10x8in) chl prov. 2-Sep-3 Rasmussen, Copenhagen #2009/R (D.KR 7500)

KRUCHEN, Julius (1845-1912) German

£839 $1443 €1200 Moonlit landscape with pond (27x41cm-11x16in) s. panel. 5-Dec-3 Michael Zeller, Lindau #677/R
£1200 $2184 €1800 Spring landscape (65x95cm-26x37in) s. 30-Jun-4 Neumeister, Munich #597/R est:1500

KRUG, Carl Heinz (1915-) German

Works on paper
£284 $474 €400 Composition (50x60cm-20x24in) mono. W/C mixed media. 16-Oct-3 Dorotheum, Salzburg #895/R

KRUGER, Barbara (1945-) American

Photographs
£53892 $90000 €78682 Untitled, money can buy you love (252x223cm-99x88in) s. verso gelatin silver print prov.exhib.lit. 13-Nov-3 Sotheby's, New York #404/R est:40000-60000

Prints
£10588 $18000 €15458 Untitled (52x52cm-20x20in) s col lithograph album. 31-Oct-3 Sotheby's, New York #633/R
£10615 $19000 €15498 Untitled, fight like us (140x140cm-55x55in) silkscreen ink plexiglas prov.lit. 12-May-4 Christie's, Rockefeller NY #364/R est:10000-15000

KRUGER, Franz (1797-1857) German

Works on paper
£655 $1192 €956 Study for portrait of Field Marshall von Woronbzoff, bust-length (44x28cm-17x11in) black chk prov. 17-Jun-4 Kornfeld, Bern #30/R (S.FR 1500)
£1310 $2384 €1913 Woman from Hollman, bust-length (22x18cm-9x7in) black chk htd white brown paper prov.exhib. 17-Jun-4 Kornfeld, Bern #28/R est:4000 (S.FR 3000)

KRUGER, Franz (attrib) (1797-1857) German

Works on paper
£596 $1085 €900 Portrait of Christian Heinrich Stobwasser (24x19cm-9x7in) i.verso chk. 16-Jun-4 Hugo Ruef, Munich #1129

KRUGER, L (20th C) German?

£1733 $3103 €2600 Ducks (45x71cm-18x28in) s. board. 14-May-4 Schloss Ahlden, Ahlden #2919/R est:350

KRUGER, Richard (1880-?) American

£323 $600 €472 Desert landscape (71x91cm-28x36in) s. 7-Mar-4 Treadway Gallery, Cincinnati #580/R
£353 $600 €515 Evening marshscape (30x46cm-12x18in) s. 22-Nov-3 Jackson's, Cedar Falls #101/R

KRUININGEN, Harry van (1906-1996) Dutch

Works on paper
£382 $603 €550 Horse in a landscape (19x26cm-7x10in) s. gouache W/C. 2-Sep-3 Christie's, Amsterdam #442

KRULL, Germaine (1897-1985) Czechoslovakian

Photographs
£1958 $3270 €2800 Empilement de caisses (8x11cm-3x4in) silver print. 10-Oct-3 Tajan, Paris #234/R
£2994 $5000 €4371 Les amies (16x22cm-6x9in) gelatin silver print exec.1924 prov.lit. 17-Oct-3 Phillips, New York #207/R est:5000-7000
£5245 $8759 €7500 Forme nue (8x12cm-3x5in) silver print exhib. 10-Oct-3 Tajan, Paris #233/R
£18000 $33120 €27000 Friends (16x21cm-6x8in) silver gelatin lit.exhib. 10-Jun-4 Villa Grisebach, Berlin #1168/R est:12000-15000

KRULLAARS, William John (1878-?) American

£261 $425 €381 Winter along the river town (64x76cm-25x30in) s. 24-Sep-3 Jackson's, Cedar Falls #785/R

KRUMLINDE, Olof (1856-1945) Swedish

£355 $635 €518 By woodland glade (58x43cm-23x17in) s. 28-May-4 Uppsala Auktionskammare, Uppsala #176 (S.KR 4800)
£595 $1070 €893 Spring landscape (38x52cm-15x20in) s. 25-Apr-4 Goteborg Auktionsverk, Sweden #181/R (S.KR 8200)
£1183 $2117 €1727 Coastal landscape (26x38cm-10x15in) s.i.d.82. 25-May-4 Bukowskis, Stockholm #59/R est:20000-25000 (S.KR 16000)
£1478 $2646 €2158 Country road - landscape from Skaane (48x74cm-19x29in) s. 26-May-4 AB Stockholms Auktionsverk #2186/R est:20000-25000 (S.KR 20000)

KRUMMACHER, Karl (1867-1955) German

£979 $1664 €1400 Landscape with pond, house and two people walking on a path (40x55cm-16x22in) s. lit. 28-Nov-3 Schloss Ahlden, Ahlden #709/R
£1477 $2717 €2200 Early spring (48x68cm-19x27in) s.panel. 26-Mar-4 Bolland & Marotz, Bremen #344/R est:3200
£2119 $3857 €3200 Forest path (46x63cm-18x25in) s. board. 18-Jun-4 Bolland & Marotz, Bremen #358/R est:2000
£2431 $3962 €3500 Moorland canal in early autumn (44x66cm-17x26in) s. board panel. 26-Sep-3 Bolland & Marotz, Bremen #340/R est:3200
£2953 $5434 €4400 Spring landscape (64x81cm-25x32in) 26-Mar-4 Bolland & Marotz, Bremen #343/R est:4400

KRUPA-KRUPINSKY, Emil (1872-1924) German

£1096 $1863 €1600 Night of the full moon - six naked women dancing round fire (52x65cm-20x26in) s.d.1922 lit. 6-Nov-3 Allgauer, Kempten #3473/R est:1600

KRUSE, Carl Benjamin (attrib) (1782-1870) German

Works on paper
£1389 $2264 €2000 How to go the fastest (46x59cm-18x23in) i.d.Feb. 1823 W/C bodycol. 25-Sep-3 Dr Fritz Nagel, Stuttgart #1155/R est:2300

KRUSE, Max (attrib) (1854-1942) German

Sculpture
£1117 $2000 €1631 Lovers (58cm-23in) s. brown pat bronze. 20-Mar-4 Freeman, Philadelphia #770/R est:1000-1500

KRUSE, Ole Waldemar (1868-1948) Danish

£544 $979 €816 Old town scene (42x150cm-17x59in) mono.d.1905-1906 canvas on panel. 25-Apr-4 Goteborg Auktionsverk, Sweden #180/R (S.KR 7500)

KRUSEMAN, Cornelis (1797-1857) Dutch

£560 $936 €818 Winter landscape with figures and cows in a road (21x41cm-8x16in) s. panel. 20-Oct-3 Stephan Welz, Johannesburg #445 est:1500-2000 (SA.R 6500)
£4000 $7200 €6000 At rest (98x84cm-39x33in) s. 20-Apr-4 Sotheby's, Amsterdam #22/R est:5000-7000

KRUSEMAN, Cornelis (attrib) (1797-1857) Dutch
£592 $1089 €900 Portrait of a student (23x16cm-9x6in) canvas on panel. 28-Jun-4 Sotheby's, Amsterdam #8/R

KRUSEMAN, F M (1817-1882) Dutch
£1172 $1958 €1700 Winter landscape with amusement on the ice (66x98cm-26x39in) 11-Nov-3 Vendu Notarishuis, Rotterdam #172 est:2000-2500

KRUSEMAN, Frederik Marianus (1817-1882) Dutch
£13986 $23776 €20000 Winter river landscape (45x62cm-18x24in) s. panel. 20-Nov-3 Van Ham, Cologne #1702/R est:22000
£19444 $33056 €28000 Cattle passing a ford in a wooded landscape in summer (65x94cm-26x37in) s.d.1872. 28-Oct-3 Christie's, Amsterdam #231/R est:20000-30000
£43056 $73194 €62000 Winterfun at sunset by a mansion (22x31cm-9x12in) s.d.1875 s.i.d.verso panel. 28-Oct-3 Christie's, Amsterdam #247/R est:20000-30000
£100000 $182000 €146000 Castle in a winter landscape and skaters on a frozen river (48x63cm-19x25in) s.d.1855 panel prov.lit. 16-Jun-4 Bonhams, New Bond Street #16/R est:60000-80000

KRUSEMAN, Jan Adam (1804-1862) Dutch
£1200 $2244 €1800 River landscape at a ford (36x55cm-14x22in) s.d.49 panel. 26-Jul-4 Bonhams, Bath #53/R est:1200-1800

KRUSHENICK, Nicholas (1929-) American
£1718 $2800 €2508 Black satin (127x102cm-50x40in) s.d.1970 verso acrylic prov. 23-Sep-3 Christie's, Rockefeller NY #110/R est:2000-3000

KRUSI, Hans (1920-1995) Swiss
£628 $1048 €917 Two figures with tent in wood (50x70cm-20x28in) mono. acrylic board. 24-Oct-3 Hans Widmer, St Gallen #114/R (S.FR 1400)
£673 $1123 €983 Meeting (15x62cm-6x24in) s.d.1984 acrylic. 24-Oct-3 Hans Widmer, St Gallen #147/R est:1500-2800 (S.FR 1500)
Works on paper
£181 $308 €264 Red figures (21x30cm-8x12in) s.mono. mono. verso feltpen acrylic. 18-Nov-3 Hans Widmer, St Gallen #1249 (S.FR 400)
£271 $462 €396 Bracken (30x42cm-12x17in) s. mixed media. 18-Nov-3 Hans Widmer, St Gallen #1247 (S.FR 600)
£294 $500 €429 Serviette picture (25x33cm-10x13in) mono.d.1977 mixed media collage. 25-Nov-3 Germann, Zurich #824 (S.FR 650)
£362 $615 €529 Figures with cow (23x25cm-9x10in) s. feltpen. 18-Nov-3 Hans Widmer, St Gallen #1244 (S.FR 800)
£431 $772 €629 Untitled (20x37cm-8x15in) mono.i.d.1981 collage. 14-May-4 Dobiaschofsky, Bern #262/R (S.FR 1000)
£452 $756 €660 Napkin picture (32x32cm-13x13in) mono. feltpen. 24-Jun-3 Germann, Zurich #994 (S.FR 1000)
£517 $926 €755 Herdsman with small cow (20x28cm-8x11in) mono. collage. 12-May-4 Dobiaschofsky, Bern #706/R (S.FR 1200)
£905 $1538 €1321 Cows, bird, figures and cats (14x66cm-6x26in) s.d.1980 collage mixed media. 18-Nov-3 Hans Widmer, St Gallen #1248 est:1400-2500 (S.FR 2000)
£952 $1705 €1390 Going up to the alpine pastures (25x35cm-10x14in) mono.d. mixed media. 22-Mar-4 Philippe Schuler, Zurich #4181/R (S.FR 2200)
£1509 $2700 €2203 Taking the animals up to the alpine pastures (44x55cm-17x22in) mono.d.1980 mixed media. 14-May-4 Dobiaschofsky, Bern #263/R est:2400 (S.FR 3500)
£2371 $4244 €3462 Figures with animals (51x91cm-20x36in) mono.d.1977-78 collage. 14-May-4 Dobiaschofsky, Bern #261/R est:4500 (S.FR 5500)

KRUSNYAK, Karoly (1889-?) Hungarian
£241 $450 €352 Veiled thoughts (33x25cm-13x10in) s.d.1923 canvas on board laid on masonite. 25-Feb-4 Doyle, New York #75/R

KRUUSE, Hans (1893-1964) Danish
£694 $1130 €1013 Town scene with street orchestra marching, Copenhagen (88x147cm-35x58in) s. 28-Sep-3 Hindemae, Ullerslev #99/R (D.KR 7400)

KRUYDER, Herman (1881-1935) Dutch
Works on paper
£4133 $7605 €6200 Tak van een zee-den (65x48cm-26x19in) s. blk chk W/C exec. c.1917-18 prov.exhib. 9-Jun-4 Christie's, Amsterdam #200/R est:7000-9000
£4196 $7217 €6000 De ruiter (95x80cm-37x31in) s. black chk executed 1933. 2-Dec-3 Sotheby's, Amsterdam #5/R est:7000-10000

KRUYS, Cornelis (?-1702) Dutch
£55172 $91586 €80000 Decorative still life (91x120cm-36x47in) 1-Oct-3 Dorotheum, Vienna #118/R est:80000-120000

KRUYSEN, A (1898-1977) Dutch
£403 $749 €600 Flowers in vase (55x45cm-22x18in) s. 4-Mar-4 Auction Maastricht #1032/R
£403 $749 €600 Holy cross in Limburgs landscape (50x60cm-20x24in) s. 4-Mar-4 Auction Maastricht #1159/R

KRUYSEN, Antoon (1898-1977) Dutch
£360 $590 €500 Bouquet de fleurs (46x32cm-18x13in) s.d.68. 3-Jun-3 Livinec, Gaudcheau & Jezequel, Rennes #90
£360 $590 €500 Paysage au village (54x65cm-21x26in) s.d.71. 3-Jun-3 Livinec, Gaudcheau & Jezequel, Rennes #91
£432 $708 €600 Coq (50x61cm-20x24in) s.d.56. 3-Jun-3 Livinec, Gaudcheau & Jezequel, Rennes #87
£432 $708 €600 Bouquet de fleurs (61x50cm-24x20in) s. 3-Jun-3 Livinec, Gaudcheau & Jezequel, Rennes #85
£633 $1159 €950 Still life of flowers (39x49cm-15x19in) s. 7-Jun-4 Glerum, Amsterdam #8/R
£680 $1238 €1000 Going to church (60x70cm-24x28in) s. 3-Feb-4 Christie's, Amsterdam #519 est:1000-1500
£719 $1180 €1000 Pont sur le village (61x46cm-24x18in) s. 3-Jun-3 Livinec, Gaudcheau & Jezequel, Rennes #86
£719 $1180 €1000 Paysage de la Beauce (64x50cm-25x20in) s.d.63. 3-Jun-3 Livinec, Gaudcheau & Jezequel, Rennes #93
£791 $1298 €1100 Bouquet de fleurs (46x33cm-18x13in) s.d.60. 3-Jun-3 Livinec, Gaudcheau & Jezequel, Rennes #83
£1189 $1985 €1700 Booksellers along the Seine in Paris (50x60cm-20x24in) s. d.1936 verso. 10-Oct-3 Vendue Huis, Gravenhage #819
£1189 $1985 €1700 Booksellers along the Seine (50x60cm-20x24in) s. d.1936 verso. 10-Oct-3 Auction Maastricht #819

KRUYSEN, Johannes (1874-1938) Dutch
£629 $1051 €900 Farm in landscape (42x56cm-17x22in) s. panel. 10-Oct-3 Auction Maastricht #816/R
£629 $1051 €900 Farm in a landscape of Brabant (42x56cm-17x22in) s. panel. 10-Oct-3 Vendue Huis, Gravenhage #816

KRUZWICKI, Hans (1885-?) German
£300 $546 €450 Floods in Boppard in 1920 (60x71cm-24x28in) s. 1-Jul-4 Van Ham, Cologne #1470

KRYCEVSKY, Nicolai Vassilievitch (1898-1961) Russian
£1489 $2353 €2100 Cliff (61x50cm-24x20in) s.d.1925. 24-Jul-3 Claude Boisgirard, Paris #24/R est:600-700

KRYMOV, Nikolai Petrovich (1884-1958) Russian
£1500 $2685 €2190 Study of reeds (20x26cm-8x10in) s.d.1916 board exhib. 26-May-4 Sotheby's, Olympia #396/R est:2500-3500

KRYSTALLIS, Andreas (1901-1951) Greek
£1207 $2160 €1762 Piraeus harbour (13x17cm-5x7in) s. panel. 12-May-4 Dobiaschofsky, Bern #707/R est:2000 (S.FR 2800)
£2000 $3580 €2920 Scenes from the port of Piraeus (19x13cm-7x5in) panel three. 11-May-4 Bonhams, New Bond Street #43/R est:1200-1800
£5000 $8750 €7300 Mikrolimano, Piraeus (66x80cm-26x31in) s. 16-Dec-3 Bonhams, New Bond Street #45/R est:4000-6000
Works on paper
£3600 $6444 €5256 At the potter's (49x36cm-19x14in) s. gouache. 10-May-4 Sotheby's, Olympia #129/R est:4000-6000

KRYSTUFEK, Elke (1970-) Austrian
£2717 $5000 €3967 2001 nights (70x70cm-28x28in) s.i.d.2000 overlap acrylic prov. 10-Jun-4 Phillips, New York #478/R est:2500-3500

KRYZANOVSKY, Roman (20th C) American
£1033 $1900 €1508 Flowers (46x56cm-18x22in) 11-Jun-4 Du Mouchelle, Detroit #2025/R est:2000-3000

KRYZHITSKY, Constantin (1858-1911) Russian
£900 $1611 €1350 The ocean (24x33cm-9x13in) s. cardboard. 15-May-4 Hagelstam, Helsinki #39/R
Works on paper
£1350 $2295 €1971 Mountain scenes (10x14cm-4x6in) both s.d.98 W/C over pencil pair. 19-Nov-3 Sotheby's, London #66/R est:100-1500
£3800 $6460 €5700 Farmhouse landscape (44x55cm-17x22in) s.d.1901 W/C paper on board. 25-Nov-3 Christie's, London #117/R est:4000-5000
£8000 $13600 €11680 Lake at sunset (48x68cm-19x27in) s.d.1902 W/C gouache. 19-Nov-3 Sotheby's, London #80/R est:6000-8000

KRYZYSZTOFIAK, Hilary (1926-1979) Polish
Works on paper
£311 $562 €467 Composition (42x30cm-17x12in) s.d.64 Indian ink. 4-Apr-4 Agra, Warsaw #63/R (P.Z 2200)

KRZYSTON, Sue (1948-) American
£706 $1250 €1031 From people of the earth (17x23cm-7x9in) s.d.92. 1-May-4 Dan Ripley, Indianapolis #566

KUAPIL (20th C) ?
£1831 $3039 €2600 Bouquet de fleurs, violon et chaise (65x91cm-26x36in) s. isorel. 16-Jun-3 E & Eve, Paris #99
£2746 $4559 €3900 Glaieuls et fleurs jaune dans un vase devant un jardin (84x91cm-33x36in) s.d. 16-Jun-3 E & Eve, Paris #98/R

KUBA, Ludvik (1863-1956) Czechoslovakian
£1751 $2907 €2556 Slovak cradle (51x43cm-20x17in) s. canvas on board. 4-Oct-3 Dorotheum, Prague #33/R est:80000-120000 (C.KR 80000)

KUBACH, Wolfgang and WILMSEN, Anna-Maria (20th C) German
Sculpture
£8000 $14320 €12000 Stone books (132x29x22cm-52x11x9in) marble. 13-May-4 Neumeister, Munich #678/R est:7000-9000

KUBANYI, Lajos (1855-1912) Hungarian
£993 $1808 €1500 Hunting with hounds (82x138cm-32x54in) s.d.1890. 21-Jun-4 Dorotheum, Vienna #127/R est:1400-1600

KUBARKKU, Mick (c.1922-) Australian

Works on paper

£366	$578	€534	Djen, freshwater fishes (38x77cm-15x30in) i.verso earth pigments eucalyptus bark exec.c.1980 prov. 28-Jul-3 Sotheby's, Paddington #535 (A.D 900)
£371	$694	€557	Untitled (22x63cm-9x25in) earth pigments eucalyptus bark prov. 26-Jul-4 Sotheby's, Melbourne #290/R (A.D 950)
£586	$1096	€879	Crocodile ancestor (55x21cm-22x8in) bears name.verso earth pigments eucalyptus bark exec.c.1973 prov. 26-Jul-4 Sotheby's, Melbourne #546/R (A.D 1500)
£630	$996	€920	Rainbow serpent and kangaroo (66x47cm-26x19in) earth pigments eucalyptus bark exec.c.1990 prov. 28-Jul-3 Sotheby's, Paddington #457/R est:1000-2000 (A.D 1550)
£1707	$2698	€2492	Three saltwater crocodiles, one barramundi (83x60cm-33x24in) earth pigments eucalyptus bark exec.c.1972 prov.exhib. 28-Jul-3 Sotheby's, Paddington #353/R est:3000-4000 (A.D 4200)
£2236	$3533	€3265	Salt water crocodile (148x64cm-58x25in) i.verso earth pigments eucalyptus bark exec.c.1982 prov. 28-Jul-3 Sotheby's, Paddington #354/R est:3000-5000 (A.D 5500)
£2642	$4175	€3857	Five freshwater crocodiles (86x71cm-34x28in) earth pigments eucalyptus bark exec.c.1970 prov. 28-Jul-3 Sotheby's, Paddington #351/R est:4000-6000 (A.D 6500)
£2813	$5259	€4220	Yawk yawk water (97x53cm-38x21in) earth pigments eucalyptus bark exec.c.1975 prov. 26-Jul-4 Sotheby's, Melbourne #285/R est:8000-12000 (A.D 7200)

KUBICEK, Juro (1906-1970) German

£833	$1392	€1200	Black sun (50x125cm-20x49in) mono.d. s.i.d. verso. 25-Oct-3 Dr Lehr, Berlin #293/R

KUBIERSCHKY, Erich (1854-1944) German

Works on paper

£517	$940	€780	Spring evening (28x42cm-11x17in) s.d.1893 gouache. 18-Jun-4 Bolland & Marotz, Bremen #666/R
£728	$1326	€1100	Spring landscape (32x45cm-13x18in) s.d.1893 gouache. 18-Jun-4 Bolland & Marotz, Bremen #665/R

KUBIN, Alfred (1877-1959) Austrian

£5046	$8427	€7317	Tower (18x26cm-7x10in) s.i. W/C over Indian ink. 19-Jun-3 Kornfeld, Bern #585/R est:12500 (S.FR 11000)

Works on paper

£261	$477	€381	Man with a dog (19x13cm-7x5in) s. pen wash. 4-Jun-4 Zofingen, Switzerland #2478 (S.FR 600)
£315	$535	€450	Kidnapping of girl (28x21cm-11x8in) pencil. 27-Nov-3 Dorotheum, Linz #624/R
£385	$654	€550	Figural representation (23x30cm-9x12in) s. pencil. 27-Nov-3 Dorotheum, Linz #617/R
£447	$822	€670	Man in hat (19x14cm-7x6in) s. Indian ink. 10-Jun-4 Hauswedell & Nolte, Hamburg #409/R
£455	$773	€650	Old mill (21x36cm-8x14in) s. 27-Nov-3 Dorotheum, Linz #616/R
£524	$892	€750	Representation of fable (31x23cm-12x9in) mono. pencil. 27-Nov-3 Dorotheum, Linz #621/R
£556	$906	€800	The cripple (30x21cm-12x8in) mono.i. pencil. 26-Sep-3 Venator & Hansten, Koln #1510
£559	$951	€800	Figural representation (29x23cm-11x9in) mono. pencil. 27-Nov-3 Dorotheum, Linz #623/R
£638	$1066	€900	Entrance of priest's school, Passau (14x18cm-6x7in) i. pencil Indian ink. 14-Oct-3 Dorotheum, Vienna #137/R
£667	$1227	€1000	Audience with Pharoah (17x34cm-7x13in) mono. Indian ink. 10-Jun-4 Hauswedell & Nolte, Hamburg #406/R
£733	$1313	€1100	The packet (11x14cm-4x6in) mono. i. verso W/C Indian ink. 13-May-4 Neumeister, Munich #406/R
£800	$1432	€1200	The drowned (11x14cm-4x6in) s.i. pen. 13-May-4 Dorotheum, Linz #616/R
£800	$1472	€1200	Ruebezahl - sketch (39x25cm-15x10in) s.i.d.16/XI.49 pencil. 9-Jun-4 Dorotheum, Salzburg #799/R
£826	$1379	€1198	Cow (21x17cm-8x7in) Indian ink wash brush. 19-Jun-3 Kornfeld, Bern #590 (S.FR 1800)
£839	$1427	€1200	In front of plain nude (13x13cm-5x5in) mono. ink. 27-Nov-3 Dorotheum, Linz #614/R
£1000	$1820	€1460	Buchstabei I, Prophet Daniel - Letter I, Prophet Daniel (9x12cm-4x5in) i.verso pen brush ink W/C exec.c.1918. 4-Feb-4 Sotheby's, London #481/R est:1500-2000
£1007	$1802	€1500	Women working the fields of Flanders (40x31cm-16x12in) s.i.d.26 Indian ink. 25-May-4 Dorotheum, Vienna #175/R est:1500-2200
£1049	$1783	€1500	Goat herder and landscape (29x23cm-11x9in) s. pencil. 27-Nov-3 Dorotheum, Linz #622/R est:1500-1700
£1049	$1783	€1500	Figural representation (29x22cm-11x9in) s. pencil. 27-Nov-3 Dorotheum, Linz #625/R est:1200-1500
£1103	$1843	€1600	In the workhouse (13x16cm-5x6in) pen ink. 13-Nov-3 Neumeister, Munich #372/R est:2000-2500
£1189	$2021	€1700	Street musician (21x34cm-8x13in) s. pencil. 27-Nov-3 Dorotheum, Linz #615/R est:1600-1800
£1208	$2223	€1800	River landscape (37x28cm-15x11in) s. i. verso Indian ink prov. 26-Mar-4 Ketterer, Hamburg #525/R est:2000-3000
£1267	$2267	€1900	Trio - musicians on a cliff (24x18cm-9x7in) s.i. Indian ink. 13-May-4 Neumeister, Munich #405/R est:2000-2500
£1333	$2453	€2000	Figure resting - humid day (24x26cm-9x10in) s. Indian ink. 10-Jun-4 Hauswedell & Nolte, Hamburg #408/R est:2500
£1376	$2298	€1995	Human animal (29x38cm-11x15in) mono.i. pencil. 19-Jun-3 Kornfeld, Bern #588 est:3000 (S.FR 3000)
£1399	$2378	€2000	Landscape (36x30cm-14x12in) s.d.26 ink. 28-Nov-3 Wiener Kunst Auktionen, Vienna #501/R est:2000-5000
£1400	$2548	€2044	Verhullte Leiche - Covered corpse (20x31cm-8x12in) s. pen ink exec.c.1912-15. 4-Feb-4 Sotheby's, London #482/R est:2000-3000
£1560	$2605	€2262	Salome dancing with tambourine (14x9cm-6x4in) s.i. verso. W/C over Indian ink. 19-Jun-3 Kornfeld, Bern #583 est:3000 (S.FR 3400)
£1611	$2883	€2400	The shot (21x34cm-8x13in) s. pencil prov. 25-May-4 Dorotheum, Vienna #174/R est:1900-2600
£1733	$3172	€2600	Pirate ship (25x10cm-10x4in) s. verso Indian ink prov. 5-Jun-4 Lempertz, Koln #810/R est:2000
£1835	$3064	€2661	Moose hunter (13x30cm-5x12in) s. W/C over Indian ink. 19-Jun-3 Kornfeld, Bern #586/R est:5000 (S.FR 4000)
£1835	$3064	€2661	Fakir (31x24cm-12x9in) s.i. pen brush Indian ink. 19-Jun-3 Kornfeld, Bern #589 est:5000 (S.FR 4000)
£1842	$3389	€2800	Dusk (39x31cm-15x12in) s.i. ink. 22-Jun-4 Wiener Kunst Auktionen, Vienna #154/R est:1500
£1927	$3217	€2794	Frozen (39x30cm-15x12in) s.i. Indian ink W/C. 19-Jun-3 Kornfeld, Bern #587 est:5000 (S.FR 4200)
£2018	$3371	€2926	House in garden (25x27cm-10x11in) s.i. W/C over Indian ink. 19-Jun-3 Kornfeld, Bern #591/R est:5000 (S.FR 4400)
£2098	$3566	€3000	Bull and horse (20x32cm-8x13in) s.i. ink W/C. 28-Nov-3 Wiener Kunst Auktionen, Vienna #500/R est:3000-7000
£2448	$4161	€3500	Dead horse (25x34cm-10x13in) s. W/C over Indian ink. 29-Nov-3 Bassenge, Berlin #6852 est:4500
£2550	$4718	€3800	Castle (25x17cm-10x7in) Indian ink W/C. 9-Mar-4 Dorotheum, Vienna #77/R est:3000-4000
£3020	$5406	€4500	Victor (32x23cm-13x9in) s.i. Indian ink W/C. 25-May-4 Dorotheum, Vienna #172/R est:4000-6000
£3087	$5526	€4600	Shadows (18x16cm-7x6in) mono. ink seven lit. 27-May-4 Hassfurther, Vienna #58/R est:4000-6000
£3217	$5533	€4600	Heads (22x16cm-9x6in) mono. Indian ink ten. 2-Dec-3 Hauswedell & Nolte, Hamburg #354/R est:5500
£3333	$6133	€5000	Portrait of a gentleman wearing a powdered wig (34x26cm-13x10in) s. ink W/C exec. c.1920. 11-Jun-4 Villa Grisebach, Berlin #1551/R est:4000-6000
£4196	$7133	€6000	Rich girl (28x21cm-11x8in) s.i. sprayed ink board. 21-Nov-3 Reiss & Sohn, Konigstein #435/R est:6000
£6897	$11517	€10000	Visit from a witch (30x27cm-12x11in) s. W/C pen ink. 13-Nov-3 Neumeister, Munich #373/R est:7000-8000
£6987	$12716	€10201	Forests spirits leaving their destroyed wood (24x13cm-9x5in) s.i. pen ink W/C exec. c.1915-1920. 18-Jun-4 Kornfeld, Bern #106/R est:20000 (S.FR 16000)
£8392	$14434	€12000	The three coffins (28x30cm-11x12in) s.i. W/C Indian ink. 2-Dec-3 Hauswedell & Nolte, Hamburg #353/R est:10000
£8734	$15895	€12752	The frog (23x28cm-9x11in) s. pen ink wash htd white exec. c.1905. 18-Jun-4 Kornfeld, Bern #104/R est:17500 (S.FR 20000)
£9091	$15455	€13000	Wake (24x35cm-9x14in) s. pen W/C. 25-Nov-3 Hassfurther, Vienna #56/R est:8000-10000
£20000	$36400	€29200	Am Abgrund liegendes nacktes Madchen - Reclining nude by a cliff (10x11cm-4x4in) s. i.verso pen brush ink wash exec.c.1900-01 prov. 4-Feb-4 Sotheby's, London #480/R est:18000-25000
£20000	$36800	€29200	Der Mann im Mond (27x22cm-11x9in) s. blk ink wash Spritzechnik exec 1903-4 prov. 24-Jun-4 Christie's, London #404/R est:15000-20000
£30000	$54600	€43800	Indian prince leaning on a panther (34x25cm-13x10in) s. g. ink executed 1904. 3-Feb-4 Sotheby's, London #2/R est:35000-55000
£56769	$103319	€82883	The fat and the thin people (16x39cm-6x15in) s. pen ink wash exec. c.1900 exhib. 18-Jun-4 Kornfeld, Bern #105/R est:40000 (S.FR 130000)
£90000	$163800	€131400	Aug um aug - eye for an eye (38x30cm-15x12in) s.i. pen brush ink executed c.1905-10. 3-Feb-4 Sotheby's, London #4/R est:90000-120000

KUBLER, Ludwig (19th C) Austrian

£1250	$2125	€1800	Horse in stable (55x68cm-22x27in) mono. 28-Oct-3 Dorotheum, Vienna #273/R est:1800-2200

KUBOVSKY, Peter (1930-) Austrian?

Works on paper

£276	$461	€400	Venice (43x60cm-17x24in) s.i. Indian ink. 11-Nov-3 Dorotheum, Vienna #133/R

KUBRYN, Genevieve (20th C) Canadian

£362	$605	€529	Tulip spectacular (50x60cm-20x24in) s. 17-Nov-3 Hodgins, Calgary #139/R (C.D 800)
£720	$1318	€1051	Beginning of spring (60x75cm-24x30in) s.i. 1-Jun-4 Hodgins, Calgary #188/R (C.D 1800)
£760	$1391	€1110	Sunfaces (60x75cm-24x30in) s.i. 1-Jun-4 Hodgins, Calgary #369/R (C.D 1900)

KUCHARSKI, Alexander (1741-1819) Polish

Works on paper

£2000	$3460	€2920	Portrait of Madame Antoine Seguier, nee Vastal (62x51cm-24x20in) pastel oval. 12-Dec-3 Christie's, Kensington #467/R est:2500-3500

KUCHENMEISTER, Rainer (1926-) German

Works on paper

£278	$453	€400	Untitled (48x36cm-19x14in) mono.d.X.69 W/C Indian ink collage. 27-Sep-3 Dr Fritz Nagel, Stuttgart #9252/R
£278	$453	€400	Untitled (39x29cm-15x11in) mono.d.17.V.1973 W/C Indian ink. 27-Sep-3 Dr Fritz Nagel, Stuttgart #9253/R
£313	$509	€450	Untitled (48x36cm-19x14in) mono.d.XII.73 W/C Indian ink prov. 27-Sep-3 Dr Fritz Nagel, Stuttgart #9254/R
£3267	$5847	€4900	Pegasus (110x92cm-43x36in) s.i. verso mixed media panel. 13-May-4 Neumeister, Munich #679/R est:4000-4500

KUCHLER, Albert (1803-1886) Danish

£1432	$2621	€2091	Portrait of young Italian girl (40x32cm-16x13in) s.d.1838 verso. 7-Jun-4 Museumsbygningen, Copenhagen #23/R est:10000-15000 (D.KR 16000)
£6144	$10629	€8970	Grandmother dressing small boy while mother getting ready in front of mirror (73x63cm-29x25in) s. exhib.prov. 9-Dec-3 Rasmussen, Copenhagen #1238/R est:75000-100000 (D.KR 65000)

KUCHLER, Karl (20th C) Austrian

£496	$829	€700	Rock and ice (70x98cm-28x39in) s.d.1924. 14-Oct-3 Dorotheum, Vienna #45/R

KUCHLIN, Jacob (1820-1885) Swiss

£498	$846	€727	Rheinfall near Schaffhausen by moonlight (19x27cm-7x11in) s.d.1883. 28-Nov-3 Zofingen, Switzerland #2471 (S.FR 1100)

KUCHUMOV, Vasili Nikitich (1888-1959) Russian
£4895 $8322 €7000 View over the Neva from the canal of the Winter Palace (43x48cm-17x19in) s. board. 29-Nov-3 Bukowskis, Helsinki #408/R est:1800-2000
Works on paper
£3000 $5370 €4380 Two interior of Gatchina Palace, St. Petersburg (18x24cm-7x9in) s. one d.1922 W/C pair. 26-May-4 Sotheby's, London #6/R est:4000-6000

KUCKEI, Peter (1938-) German
£4196 $7133 €6000 Untitled - Nr 211 (138x138cm-54x54in) s.i.d.1982/83 verso. 27-Nov-3 Lempertz, Koln #246/R est:8000-10000

KUDDGI (20th C) Australian
£1138 $1798 €1650 Emu dreaming (152x92cm-60x36in) acrylic. 22-Jul-3 Lawson Menzies, Sydney #68/R est:3500-5000 (A.D 2800)

KUDDITJI (20th C) Australian
£741 $1341 €1082 Caama 8-288 (62x92cm-24x36in) s.i.verso acrylic. 30-Mar-4 Lawson Menzies, Sydney #270/R est:2000-3000 (A.D 1800)

KUDLOTEYA (20th C) North American
Sculpture
£946 $1608 €1381 Inuit couple (25cm-10in) s. marbled green soapstone base exec.c.1950. 3-Nov-3 Waddingtons, Toronto #58/R est:2500-3500 (C.D 2100)

KUDLUK, Thomassie (1910-1989) North American
Sculpture
£868 $1562 €1302 Shaman with an owl perched on his head (15cm-6in) s. grey soapstone. 26-Apr-4 Waddingtons, Toronto #82/R est:500-700 (C.D 2100)
£950 $1711 €1425 Polar bear standing on the ice. Two Inuit figures (14cm-6in) grey soapstone two. 26-Apr-4 Waddingtons, Toronto #83/R est:300-500 (C.D 2300)

KUDO, Tetsumi (1935-) Japanese
Sculpture
£13333 $24667 €20000 Vie confortable (47x50x37cm-19x20x15in) s.d.1972-73 cage metal mixed media prov.exhib.lit. 18-Jul-4 Sotheby's, Paris #287/R est:4000-6000

KUDRIASHEV, Ivan (1896-1972) Russian
Works on paper
£405 $714 €600 Still life (29x24cm-11x9in) s. W/C exec.c.1925. 19-May-4 Camard, Paris #14
£8966 $14972 €13000 Watercolour 27 (20x23cm-8x9in) s.d.1924 W/C exhib.lit. 17-Nov-3 Sant Agostino, Torino #296/R est:13000-16000

KUEHL, Gotthardt Johann (1850-1915) German
£2069 $3455 €3000 Drinking coffee (30x23cm-12x9in) s. panel prov.lit. 15-Nov-3 Lempertz, Koln #1648/R est:3000
£8054 $15060 €12000 Mother with child in chair (47x35cm-19x14in) s. 28-Feb-4 Bolland & Marotz, Bremen #294/R est:5500
£17450 $32631 €26000 Woman at window reading newspaper (52x37cm-20x15in) s. panel sketch verso. 28-Feb-4 Bolland & Marotz, Bremen #293/R est:8700
Works on paper
£1458 $2304 €2100 Workshop interior (48x32cm-19x13in) s. pencil gouache board lit. 19-Sep-3 Schloss Ahlden, Ahlden #1631/R est:2800
£2098 $3566 €3000 Monk praying in church (62x50cm-24x20in) s. W/C bodycol on chl board. 27-Nov-3 Bassenge, Berlin #5609/R est:3500

KUEHNE, Max (1880-c.1968) American
£187 $350 €273 San Lorenzo at dusk (61x76cm-24x30in) prov. 29-Feb-4 Grogan, Boston #71/R
£269 $500 €393 Autumn (30x40cm-12x16in) panel. 5-Mar-4 Skinner, Boston #473/R
£279 $500 €407 Villa by the beach (28x38cm-11x15in) s. masonite. 10-Jan-4 Pook & Pook, Downington #563/R
£346 $550 €505 Whitecaps mid-ocean (61x73cm-24x29in) s. prov. 13-Sep-3 Weschler, Washington #780/R
£346 $550 €505 Path to the beach (27x35cm-11x14in) st.sig. masonite prov. 13-Sep-3 Weschler, Washington #781/R
£347 $600 €507 Rocky coastline (66x79cm-26x31in) estate st. prov. 13-Dec-3 Weschler, Washington #588
£347 $600 €507 European village with white tower (79x91cm-31x36in) estate st. prov. 13-Dec-3 Weschler, Washington #589
£359 $600 €524 Gate San Martin (66x81cm-26x32in) s.indis.d. prov. 19-Oct-3 William Jenack, New York #412
£396 $650 €574 Roses in a vase (46x38cm-18x15in) s. 2-Jun-3 Grogan, Boston #641g
£457 $850 €667 Still life with peonies (68x55cm-27x22in) st.sig. panel prov. 5-Mar-4 Skinner, Boston #411/R
£457 $850 €667 Coastal view (50x60cm-20x24in) st.sig. panel prov. 5-Mar-4 Skinner, Boston #547/R
£469 $750 €685 Coastal scene with cliffs (64x76cm-25x30in) s.d.28. 20-Sep-3 Pook & Pook, Downington #127
£497 $800 €726 Fall flower still life (30x23cm-12x9in) s. board. 20-Aug-3 James Julia, Fairfield #1650/R
£503 $900 €734 Cove at Prouts Neck, Maine (46x61cm-18x24in) s. exhib. 8-Jan-4 James Julia, Fairfield #818/R
£503 $900 €734 Cove at Prouts Neck, Maine (46x61cm-18x24in) st.sig. exhib. 8-Jan-4 James Julia, Fairfield #818/R
£570 $900 €832 Crashing surf (38x46cm-15x18in) s. masonite prov. 27-Jul-3 William Jenack, New York #339
£739 $1300 €1079 Spanish town (71x112cm-28x44in) s. masonite. 22-May-4 Selkirks, St. Louis #584/R est:1000-1500
£754 $1350 €1101 Big wave (61x76cm-24x30in) st.sig. masonite. 8-Jan-4 James Julia, Fairfield #817/R est:1500-2500
£814 $1400 €1188 Spanish town (71x76cm-28x30in) estate st. painted c.1925. 7-Dec-3 Treadway Gallery, Cincinnati #619/R
£1160 $2100 €1694 Bridge of Alcantara Spain (51x71cm-20x28in) s. oil on wood. 16-Apr-4 James Julia, Fairfield #680/R est:3000-5000
£1221 $2100 €1783 Coastal scene (64x76cm-25x30in) s. painted c.1925. 7-Dec-3 Treadway Gallery, Cincinnati #518/R est:2500-4500
£1630 $3000 €2380 House in the snow (20x29cm-8x11in) s. s.indis.i. verso board. 27-Jun-4 Freeman, Philadelphia #117/R est:3000-5000
£2095 $3750 €3059 View of Gloucester (18x23cm-7x9in) estate st. panel prov. 6-May-4 Shannon's, Milford #181/R est:3000-5000
£2235 $4000 €3263 Rockport Harbour (18x23cm-7x9in) estate st. panel prov. 6-May-4 Shannon's, Milford #84/R est:4000-6000
£2581 $4800 €3768 Open window near the shore (51x38cm-20x15in) s. panel prov. 3-Mar-4 Christie's, Rockefeller NY #52/R est:4000-6000
£6704 $12000 €9788 Floral bouquet (81x66cm-32x26in) s. prov. 6-May-4 Shannon's, Milford #155/R est:8000-12000
Works on paper
£259 $425 €376 Studio still life (48x38cm-19x15in) s. W/C prov. 2-Jun-3 Grogan, Boston #694
£328 $600 €479 View from the rocks (38x51cm-15x20in) s. W/C executed c.1925. 5-Jun-4 Treadway Gallery, Cincinnati #644/R
£349 $600 €510 View from the rocks (38x51cm-15x20in) s. W/C exec.c.1925. 7-Dec-3 Treadway Gallery, Cincinnati #553/R
£870 $1600 €1270 New Hope - Lambertville, River Bank (35x49cm-14x19in) st.sig. s.i.d.1927 verso W/C prov. 27-Jun-4 Freeman, Philadelphia #170/R est:1500-2500
£978 $1800 €1428 View of a church (38x48cm-15x19in) s. W/C. 10-Jun-4 Swann Galleries, New York #130/R est:2000-3000

KUERNER, Karl J III (1957-) American
£649 $1200 €974 Turning the soil (61x122cm-24x48in) s. acrylic on board. 15-Jul-4 Doyle, New York #53/R est:400-600
£919 $1700 €1379 Brandywine wildflowers (61x91cm-24x36in) s. i.d.Sep 86 verso acrylic on board prov. 15-Jul-4 Doyle, New York #52/R est:400-600

KUGACH, Y P (1917-) Russian
£652 $1200 €952 Evening (23x37cm-9x15in) plywood painted 1996. 27-Mar-4 Shishkin Gallery, Moscow #21/R
£870 $1600 €1270 In winter (29x25cm-11x10in) cardboard painted 1963. 27-Mar-4 Shishkin Gallery, Moscow #22/R est:1400-1600
£1005 $1850 €1467 Melting road (46x37cm-18x15in) cardboard painted 1973. 27-Mar-4 Shishkin Gallery, Moscow #20/R est:2500-3000
£1848 $3400 €2698 New month birth (47x63cm-19x25in) cardboard painted 1985. 27-Mar-4 Shishkin Gallery, Moscow #23/R est:4000-5000

KUGELGEN, Gerhard von (1772-1820) German
Miniatures
£2000 $3600 €2920 Theresa von Thurn und Taxis, nee Mecklenburg-Strelitz (6cm-2in) i.verso gilt metal mount oval exhib.lit. 22-Apr-4 Bonhams, New Bond Street #149/R est:2000-3000
£29000 $52200 €42340 Empress Maria Feodorovna wearing a chain and cross (7cm-3in) gilt mount tortoiseshell octagon leather wallet oval prov.exhib. 22-Apr-4 Bonhams, New Bond Street #81/R est:5000-7000
Works on paper
£4000 $6800 €6000 Portrait of Tsar Alexander I (28x22cm-11x9in) init. pencil chl htd white. 25-Nov-3 Christie's, London #99/R est:2000-3000

KUGELGEN, Wilhelm von (1802-1867) German
£537 $988 €800 Jesus by bed of young woman (27x17cm-11x7in) board prov. 27-Mar-4 Geble, Radolfzell #731/R
Works on paper
£267 $477 €400 Expulsion from Paradise (21x19cm-8x7in) bears sig. verso pen. 13-May-4 Bassenge, Berlin #5601/R

KUGELGEN, Wilhelm von (attrib) (1802-1867) German
£1342 $2470 €2000 Portrait of silk trader, Johann Carl Gottlob Schneider (63x51cm-25x20in) 24-Mar-4 Hugo Ruef, Munich #1020/R est:2000

KUGHLER, Francis Vandeveer (1901-) American
£329 $550 €480 Martini (76x61cm-30x24in) s. 19-Oct-3 Susanin's, Chicago #6073/R
£419 $750 €612 Lobster fisherman. i.verso. 8-Jan-4 James Julia, Fairfield #979/R
£449 $750 €656 Sleeping woman (76x61cm-30x24in) s. 19-Oct-3 Susanin's, Chicago #6072/R
£833 $1500 €1216 Coastal cottage with boat (61x76cm-24x30in) s. masonite. 20-Apr-4 Arthur James, Florida #48/R est:1500-2500
£2639 $4750 €3853 New York skyline (61x76cm-24x30in) one s. masonite two. 20-Apr-4 Arthur James, Florida #49/R est:3000-5000

KUGLER, August (fl.1890-1910) Austrian
£1389 $2361 €2000 Feeding the goat (58x76cm-23x30in) s. 28-Oct-3 Dorotheum, Vienna #5/R est:2200-2500

KUGLER, Heinrich (?) German
£336 $617 €500 Roses in front of park landscape (80x108cm-31x43in) s. 24-Mar-4 Hugo Ruef, Munich #1022

KUGLER, Josef (19/20th C) ?
£307 $558 €460 View of Lake Garda at sunrise (90x130cm-35x51in) s. 1-Jul-4 Neumeister, Munich #2741

KUGLER, Rudolf (1921-) German
£1200 $2208 €1800 Composition (50x50cm-20x20in) s. i.stretcher. 11-Jun-4 Hauswedell & Nolte, Hamburg #1400/R est:2500

KUHBERGER, Martin (attrib) (20th C) German
£1420 $2500 €2073 Scene with three urchins at dice (122x102cm-48x40in) s. 1-Jan-4 Nadeau, Windsor #256 est:2000-3000

KUHFELD, Peter (1952-) British
£1000 $1850 €1460 At the National Gallery (52x48cm-20x19in) board prov. 11-Mar-4 Christie's, Kensington #216/R est:1000-1500
£1100 $1980 €1606 In the garden, summer (34x52cm-13x20in) s. board. 20-Jan-4 Bonhams, Knightsbridge #92
£1300 $2288 €1898 River entrance to Case Brigida (56x41cm-22x16in) board. 19-May-4 Sotheby's, Olympia #221/R est:1000-1500

KUHFUSS, Paul (1883-1960) German
£367 $660 €550 Woodland path (61x78cm-24x31in) tempera board. 24-Apr-4 Dr Lehr, Berlin #237/R
£417 $696 €600 Fasano street (52x70cm-20x28in) s.d. tempera board. 25-Oct-3 Dr Lehr, Berlin #296/R
£559 $934 €800 Path home (34x46cm-13x18in) s. i.d.1936 verso panel lit. 11-Oct-3 Hans Stahl, Hamburg #74/R
£2222 $3711 €3200 On the balcony (76x90cm-30x35in) s. i. verso panel. 25-Oct-3 Dr Lehr, Berlin #295/R est:2400
Works on paper
£347 $566 €500 Gardener in garden (47x61cm-19x24in) s. gouache. 27-Sep-3 Dannenberg, Berlin #571/R
£347 $580 €500 Gondolas before Santa Maria della Salute, Venice (60x75cm-24x30in) s. chk. 25-Oct-3 Dr Lehr, Berlin #298/R
£556 $906 €800 Cathedral in Berlin (51x67cm-20x26in) s. i.d.1931 verso. 27-Sep-3 Dannenberg, Berlin #572/R
£733 $1320 €1100 German cathedral on Gendarmenmarkt Berlin (51x67cm-20x26in) s. i.d. verso W/C tempera on chk board. 24-Apr-4 Dr Lehr, Berlin #236/R
£769 $1308 €1100 Neukolln am Wasser, Spree (44x60cm-17x24in) s.i. W/C. 29-Nov-3 Bassenge, Berlin #7244
£811 $1451 €1200 Harbour (55x73cm-22x29in) s. W/C lit. 8-May-4 Schloss Ahlden, Ahlden #831/R
£1333 $2387 €2000 View into the Krogel (42x62cm-17x24in) W/C. 15-May-4 Bassenge, Berlin #6982/R est:2400

KUHLES, August (1859-1926) German
£761 $1407 €1111 Street scene (101x62cm-40x24in) 14-Mar-4 Agra, Warsaw #62/R (P.Z 5500)

KUHLING, Wilhelm (1823-1886) German
£1319 $2177 €1900 Little herdress with cattle (57x72cm-22x28in) s.d.57. 2-Jul-3 Neumeister, Munich #691/R est:2000
£1408 $2437 €2000 Cows grazing in extensive landscape (26x42cm-10x17in) s.d.78. 11-Dec-3 Dr Fritz Nagel, Stuttgart #529/R est:1600

KUHLMANN-REHER, Emil (1876-1957) German
£347 $580 €500 Wine drinker (30x25cm-12x10in) s.i. 22-Oct-3 Neumeister, Munich #726
£805 $1498 €1200 In the tavern (80x100cm-31x39in) s.i. 6-Mar-4 Arnold, Frankfurt #763/R
£1037 $1919 €1514 Gentleman drinking in an interior, smoking a pipe (40x35cm-16x14in) 14-Mar-4 Agra, Warsaw #39/R (P.Z 7500)

KUHLSTRUNK, Franz (1861-1944) Austrian
£658 $1211 €1000 Salzach Ursprung (20x34cm-8x13in) s. 22-Jun-4 Wiener Kunst Auktionen, Vienna #180/R
Works on paper
£355 $592 €500 Augustinerbrau with Mullner Church, view of Gaisberg and Nockstein (18x28cm-7x11in) s. pencil Indian ink W/C. 16-Oct-3 Dorotheum, Salzburg #899/R

KUHN, Albin (1843-1911) German
£599 $958 €850 Landscape with river and viaduct (33x49cm-13x19in) s.d.1987 W/C. 18-Sep-3 Rieber, Stuttgart #790/R
Works on paper
£486 $812 €700 Louis Philippe interior (28x41cm-11x16in) s.i.d.1889 W/C lit. 25-Oct-3 Bergmann, Erlangen #988/R

KUHN, Bob (1920-) American
£16043 $30000 €23423 View from the parapets (61x76cm-24x30in) s. acrylic on board. 24-Jul-4 Coeur d'Alene, Hayden #48/R est:30000-50000

KUHN, Friedrich (1926-1972) Swiss
Works on paper
£524 $964 €765 Studio (60x46cm-24x18in) s.d.1960 pencil. 8-Jun-4 Germann, Zurich #826 (S.FR 1200)
£588 $1000 €858 Women's right to vote (41x42cm-16x17in) s.d.1967 mixed media. 25-Nov-3 Germann, Zurich #825 (S.FR 1300)
£724 $1231 €1057 Untitled (36x33cm-14x13in) s. mixed media. 25-Nov-3 Germann, Zurich #52/R est:1500-2000 (S.FR 1600)
£913 $1671 €1333 Interior scene with figures (37x50cm-15x20in) s.d.1959 mixed media prov. 4-Jun-4 Zofingen, Switzerland #2867/R (S.FR 2100)
£1629 $2720 €2378 Untitled (98x68cm-39x27in) s. mixed media collage paper on board. 24-Jun-3 Germann, Zurich #175/R est:4000-6000 (S.FR 3600)
£2183 $4017 €3187 Untitled (102x72cm-40x28in) s.d.1971 mixed media. 8-Jun-4 Germann, Zurich #143/R est:5000-7000 (S.FR 5000)

KUHN, Hans (1905-1992) German
£3333 $6133 €5000 Portrait of Werner Gilles (53x68cm-21x27in) s. painted 1931 lit. 12-Jun-4 Villa Grisebach, Berlin #308/R est:5000-7000

KUHN, Heinrich (1866-1944) German
Photographs
£2246 $3750 €3279 The reaper (28x21cm-11x8in) s.d. bromoil print tissue exec.c.1930 prov. 17-Oct-3 Sotheby's, New York #156/R est:3000-4000
£2517 $4280 €3600 Miss Mary (29x23cm-11x9in) s.i.d. verso rubber print. 27-Nov-3 Villa Grisebach, Berlin #1270/R est:3000-4000
£2667 $4907 €4000 Walter and Hanns Kuhn (23x17cm-9x7in) vintage gum bicrhomate platinum i. verso le. 11-Jun-4 Bassenge, Berlin #4231/R est:4500
£2844 $4750 €4152 Hay harvest (28x21cm-11x8in) s. bromoil print tissue prov. 17-Oct-3 Sotheby's, New York #158/R est:3000-4000
£3611 $6139 €5200 Summer (39x29cm-15x11in) rubber print lit. 31-Oct-3 Lempertz, Koln #197/R est:4500
£4196 $7133 €6000 Edeltrude and Hanns Kuhn (24x30cm-9x12in) i. verso pigment. 28-Nov-3 Bassenge, Berlin #4299/R est:4000
£4545 $7727 €6500 Hans and Lotte (23x29cm-9x11in) s.d. i. verso. 27-Nov-3 Villa Grisebach, Berlin #1271/R est:3000-4000
£6081 $10885 €9000 Emma Kuhn, the photographer's wife, reading (73x54cm-29x21in) s.d. rubber print. 8-May-4 Lempertz, Koln #181/R est:10000-12000
£9444 $17000 €13788 Miss Mary bei der Morgentoilette (29x23cm-11x9in) s. s.i.verso gum bichromate print. 22-Apr-4 Phillips, New York #192/R est:10000-15000

KUHN, Rosina (1940-) Swiss
Works on paper
£543 $923 €793 Mussels (70x100cm-28x39in) s.i.d.1986 pastel gouache double-sided. 25-Nov-3 Germann, Zurich #114/R (S.FR 1200)

KUHN, Walt (1877-1949) American
£446 $825 €651 Winter landscape (46x36cm-18x14in) s. canvasboard. 16-Jan-4 Aspire, Cleveland #72/R
£3243 $6000 €4735 Portrait of a clown (36x30cm-14x12in) s. board. 14-Jan-4 Dallas Auction Gallery, Dallas #87/R est:6000-8000
£3704 $6000 €5371 Cubist still life (15x21cm-6x8in) prov. 8-Aug-3 Barridorf, Portland #280/R est:6000-9000
£5000 $8750 €7300 Hunter's cabin (30x38cm-12x15in) s.d.1919 prov. 19-Dec-3 Sotheby's, New York #1033/R est:10000-15000
£5556 $9000 €8056 Circus performer (46x30cm-18x12in) board prov. 8-Aug-3 Barridorf, Portland #279/R est:9000-12000
£8824 $15000 €12883 Head of a young girl (33x25cm-13x10in) s.d.1921 prov.exhib.lit. 29-Oct-3 Christie's, Los Angeles #71/R est:20000-30000
£10857 $19000 €15851 Three apples (21x25cm-8x10in) s.d.1933 prov. 19-Dec-3 Sotheby's, New York #1031/R est:10000-15000
£23256 $40000 €33954 Hedda in green bodice (61x51cm-24x20in) s.d.1943 prov. 4-Dec-3 Christie's, Rockefeller NY #94/R est:40000-60000
£62500 $110000 €91250 Basket of green apples (63x76cm-25x30in) s.d.1943 prov. 18-May-4 Christie's, Rockefeller NY #113/R est:50000-70000
Works on paper
£258 $475 €377 Clown head (13x13cm-5x5in) ink. 25-Jun-4 Freeman, Philadelphia #45/R
£343 $600 €501 Reclining woman (28x36cm-11x14in) s.d.28 black ink paper on board prov. 19-Dec-3 Sotheby's, New York #1009/R
£543 $1000 €793 Still life with shallots and squash (28x41cm-11x16in) s. W/C. 10-Jun-4 Swann Galleries, New York #137/R
£591 $1100 €863 Portrait of woman (25x46cm-10x18in) s.d.29 chl. 3-Mar-4 Alderfer's, Hatfield #344/R est:2000-3000
£598 $950 €873 Three acrobats (20x14cm-8x6in) s.d.June 37 sepia ink prov. 13-Sep-3 Weschler, Washington #788/R
£611 $1100 €892 Haying (18x20cm-7x8in) init.i. ink prov. 23-Jan-4 Freeman, Philadelphia #55/R
£699 $1300 €1021 Reclining nude on couch (25x35cm-10x14in) s. pen ink. 2-Mar-4 Swann Galleries, New York #324/R est:1500-2500
£1074 $1750 €1568 Reclining woman in robe, asleep (25x46cm-10x18in) s.d.1939 ink. 27-Sep-3 Thomaston Place, Thomaston #266
£1278 $2300 €1866 Portrait of a lady with necklace (30x20cm-12x8in) s.d.28 ink. 23-Jan-4 Freeman, Philadelphia #54/R est:500-800
£5163 $9500 €7538 Seated girl in a white pierrot costume (58x42cm-23x17in) s.d.1919 W/C prov. 27-Jun-4 Freeman, Philadelphia #126/R est:9000-12000
£6704 $12000 €9788 Lavender plumes (48x33cm-19x13in) W/C prov.exhib. 26-May-4 Doyle, New York #99/R est:15000-25000

KUHNEN, Pieter Lodewyk (1812-1877) Belgian
£1700 $3094 €2482 Sheep before a farmhouse in a wooded river landscape (37x34cm-15x13in) s. panel. 16-Jun-4 Christie's, Kensington #175/R est:2000-3000
£4276 $7868 €6500 Figures by a ruin in an extensive wooded landscape (57x80cm-22x31in) s. panel. 22-Jun-4 Christie's, Amsterdam #5/R est:4000-6000

KUHNERT, Wilhelm (1865-1926) German
£2083 $3437 €3000 Oil study of a lion (20x28cm-8x11in) i. canvas on board. 3-Jul-3 Van Ham, Cologne #1319 est:1400
£2752 $5063 €4100 Woodland (40x61cm-16x24in) s.d.28.9.16 canvas on board. 26-Mar-4 Bolland & Marotz, Bremen #549/R est:3400
£3733 $6757 €5600 Kisigo (37x63cm-15x25in) s.d.29.1.12 canvas on board lit. 3-Apr-4 Badum, Bamberg #153/R est:7500
£9459 $16932 €14000 Elephant in African bush (32x47cm-13x19in) s.i.d.25.6.02 canvas on board lit. 8-May-4 Schloss Ahlden, Ahlden #755/R est:12500
£9790 $16350 €14000 Slim pickings (33x72cm-13x28in) s. s.i. verso. 28-Jun-3 Bolland & Marotz, Bremen #694/R est:17000
£18000 $30600 €26280 Watchful tiger (27x46cm-11x18in) s. panel prov. 19-Nov-3 Bonhams, New Bond Street #35/R est:20000-30000
Works on paper
£420 $713 €600 Rats in cellar (21x31cm-8x12in) s. chk bodycol wash. 27-Nov-3 Bassenge, Berlin #5610
£704 $1127 €1000 Lion lying down (21x29cm-8x11in) s. Indian ink. 19-Sep-3 Altus, Berlin #492/R

KUHNERT, Wilhelm (attrib) (1865-1926) German
£467 $840 €700 Sleeping lioness (41x29cm-16x11in) d.7.VIII.03 canvas on board lit. 22-Apr-4 Allgauer, Kempten #3610/R

KUHSTOSS, Paul (1870-1898) Belgian
£676 $1277 €1000 Pecheur aux pieds du moulin a vent (55x38cm-22x15in) s. 17-Feb-4 Vanderkindere, Brussels #25
£1972 $3411 €2800 L'arrivee des pecheurs (60x73cm-24x29in) s. 9-Dec-3 Campo, Vlaamse Kaai #342/R est:3000-3500

KUIPER, Jan (1928-) Dutch
£521 $823 €750 Green power station (22x39cm-9x15in) s.d.1995 acrylic. 26-Apr-3 Auction Maastricht #70/R
£1111 $1756 €1600 Eye contact (50x50cm-20x20in) s.d.2000 acrylic. 26-Apr-3 Auction Maastricht #157/R

KUITCA, Guillermo (1961-) Argentinian
£5405 $9514 €8000 Untitled (98x68cm-39x27in) s. s.d.1991 verso acrylic prov. 24-May-4 Christie's, Milan #198/R est:10000-15000
£27933 $50000 €40782 Untitled (127x160cm-50x63in) s.i.d.1996 verso acrylic prov. 13-May-4 Sotheby's, New York #377/R est:20000-30000
£29940 $50000 €43712 Coming (140x100cm-55x39in) s.i.d.1988 verso acrylic prov.exhib. 12-Nov-3 Christie's, Rockefeller NY #592/R est:50000-70000
£32432 $60000 €47351 Untitled (105x198cm-41x78in) s. s.d.1987 verso prov.lit. 12-Feb-4 Sotheby's, New York #262/R est:40000-60000
£34667 $63787 €52000 Red theatre (142x188cm-56x74in) acrylic oil painted 1995 prov. 10-Jun-4 Christie's, Paris #92/R est:55000-75000
£36000 $66240 €52560 Untitled (123x142cm-48x56in) s.i.d.1987 verso acrylic prov. 24-Jun-4 Sotheby's, London #130/R est:30000-40000
£51676 $92500 €75447 Sacramento (189x91cm-74x36in) s.i.d.1990 verso 11 parts prov. 13-May-4 Sotheby's, New York #375/R est:40000-60000
Works on paper
£17000 $31280 €24820 Untitled (100x177cm-39x70in) s.i.d.1994 verso graphite acrylic prov. 24-Jun-4 Sotheby's, London #132/R est:15000-20000

KUJASALO, Matti (1946-) Finnish
£278 $464 €400 Composition (36x36cm-14x14in) s.d.76 acrylic. 26-Oct-3 Bukowskis, Helsinki #391/R
£352 $609 €500 Construction (120x39cm-47x15in) s.d.1979 acrylic mixed media. 13-Dec-3 Hagelstam, Helsinki #195/R
£541 $968 €800 Composition (80x30cm-31x12in) s.d.80 verso canvas on board. 8-May-4 Bukowskis, Helsinki #299/R
£563 $975 €800 Chinese painting (25x125cm-10x49in) s. d.1986 verso acrylic mixed media board. 13-Dec-3 Hagelstam, Helsinki #196/R
£906 $1541 €1323 Walking square (228x60cm-90x24in) s.d.77 verso acrylic prov. 5-Nov-3 AB Stockholms Auktionsverk #984/R (S.KR 12000)
£1119 $1902 €1600 Untitled (118x21cm-46x8in) s.d.86 verso acrylic plastic. 29-Nov-3 Bukowskis, Helsinki #294/R est:700-1000
£1351 $2419 €2000 As you please (170x90cm-67x35in) s.d.71. 8-May-4 Bukowskis, Helsinki #270/R est:2500-3000
£1399 $2378 €2000 Untitled (152x152cm-60x60in) s.d.86 verso acrylic canvas on board. 29-Nov-3 Bukowskis, Helsinki #275/R est:2500-3000
£2162 $3870 €3200 Untitled composition (200x72cm-79x28in) s.d.1978-80 verso canvas on board exhib. 8-May-4 Bukowskis, Helsinki #282/R est:2000-2500

KUKRYNISKY (20th C) Russian
Works on paper
£2217 $3969 €3237 Caricature pictures - one being of Hitler (49x42cm-19x17in) s. W/C four. 28-May-4 Uppsala Auktionskammare, Uppsala #282/R est:8000-10000 (S.KR 30000)

KUKUK, Willy (1875-1943) German
£1224 $2192 €1800 Pond (85x100cm-33x39in) s. 22-Mar-4 Sant Agostino, Torino #180/R est:1400

KULESZA, Jozef (20th C) Polish
£245 $406 €358 Flowers (97x97cm-38x38in) acrylic. 2-Oct-3 Agra, Warsaw #55/R (P.Z 1600)

KULICKE, Robert (1924-) American
£462 $800 €675 Still life of apples. Still life of fruit and a white vase (13x18cm-5x7in) one s. canvasboard one W/C two. 13-Dec-3 Weschler, Washington #582
£549 $950 €802 Geometric still lifes (36x51cm-14x20in) one s.d.56 board one s.d.1950 canvasboard two. 13-Dec-3 Weschler, Washington #583
£867 $1500 €1266 Floral still life. Still life of tulips (15x13cm-6x5in) one s.d.59 board one s.i.d.64 gouache two. 13-Dec-3 Weschler, Washington #581 est:500-700

KULIKOFF, Ivan (1875-1941) Russian
£13000 $22100 €18980 Young girl in blue headscarf (43x32cm-17x13in) s. 19-Nov-3 Sotheby's, London #61/R est:2500-3500
Works on paper
£6000 $10740 €8760 Russian peasant girl (43x32cm-17x13in) s.d.1912 W/C. 26-May-4 Sotheby's, London #97/R est:3000-5000

KULISIEWICZ, Tadeusz (1899-1900) Polish
Works on paper
£283 $507 €413 Landscape at night (29x42cm-11x17in) wash paper on cardboard. 6-May-4 Agra, Warsaw #57/R (P.Z 2000)
£446 $768 €651 Portrait of a woman (43x33cm-17x13in) s.i.d.76 ink pen. 4-Dec-3 Agra, Warsaw #40/R (P.Z 3000)

KULKARNI, Krishna Shamrao (1916-1996) Indian
£838 $1500 €1223 Storyteller (45x86cm-18x34in) s. 10-May-4 Bonhams & Butterfields, San Francisco #4161/R est:1000-1500
£2095 $3750 €3059 Mahatma Gandhi (75x54cm-30x21in) s. 10-May-4 Bonhams & Butterfields, San Francisco #4159/R est:2000-3000
Works on paper
£949 $1700 €1386 Figures (54x32cm-21x13in) s. ink pastel two. 10-May-4 Bonhams & Butterfields, San Francisco #4160/R est:1200-1800

KULLE, Axel (1846-1908) Swedish
£993 $1808 €1500 Interior scene with young girl sewing (59x42cm-23x17in) s. 17-Jun-4 Frank Peege, Freiburg #1122/R est:800
£1500 $2505 €2190 Still life with fan and Oriental vase (69x58cm-27x23in) s.d.75. 12-Nov-3 Sotheby's, Olympia #215/R est:1500-2000

KULOVESI, Erkki (1895-1971) Finnish
£417 $696 €600 Flowers (46x38cm-18x15in) s.d.1952. 23-Oct-3 Hagelstam, Helsinki #1005

KULPRATI (attrib) (c.1955-) Australian
Sculpture
£1953 $3652 €2930 Dugong (12x42cm-5x17in) earth pigments hardwood exec.c.1955 prov. 26-Jul-4 Sotheby's, Melbourne #37/R est:2000-3000 (A.D 5000)

KUMALO, Sidney (1935-) South African
Sculpture
£2414 $4031 €3524 Trojan toy horse (25cm-10in) s.num.3/10 brown pat. bronze. 20-Oct-3 Stephan Welz, Johannesburg #401/R est:12000-16000 (SA.R 28000)
£3468 $6208 €5063 Horse and rider (41cm-16in) s. num.1/5 bronze. 31-May-4 Stephan Welz, Johannesburg #541/R est:18000-24000 (SA.R 42000)
£3716 $6652 €5425 Whistle-man (89cm-35in) s. num.4/7 bronze. 31-May-4 Stephan Welz, Johannesburg #595/R est:35000-50000 (SA.R 45000)

KUMAR, Ram (1924-) Indian
£13587 $25000 €19837 Untitled (178x76cm-70x30in) s.d. 24-Mar-4 Sotheby's, New York #172/R est:10000-15000
£14130 $26000 €20630 Untitled (102x83cm-40x33in) s.i.d.1976 verso. 25-Mar-4 Christie's, Rockefeller NY #220/R est:15000-20000
£15217 $28000 €22217 Ladakh (84x153cm-33x60in) s. s.i.d.93 verso exhib.lit. 25-Mar-4 Christie's, Rockefeller NY #219/R est:22000-28000
£21337 $38407 €31152 Untitled (82x151cm-32x59in) s.i.d.94. 25-Apr-4 Christie's, Hong Kong #608/R est:170000-200000 (HK.D 300000)
£32609 $60000 €47609 Untitled (91x63cm-36x25in) s. board. 25-Mar-4 Christie's, Rockefeller NY #215/R est:60000-80000
Works on paper
£4076 $7500 €5951 Khemkaran waterfront (58x74cm-23x29in) s.d. lit. 24-Mar-4 Sotheby's, New York #173/R est:7000-10000

KUMMER, Karl Robert (1810-1889) German
£909 $1545 €1300 Winterberg (38x50cm-15x20in) board. 22-Nov-3 Arnold, Frankfurt #575/R est:2000
£1149 $2022 €1700 Mediterranean plant study (30x26cm-12x10in) paper. 22-May-4 Lempertz, Koln #1431 est:800
£1732 $3100 €2529 European mountain and lake scene (23x18cm-9x7in) s. board. 8-Jan-4 James Julia, Fairfield #675/R est:1000-2000

KUMMER, Karl Robert (attrib) (1810-1889) German
£292 $461 €420 Landscape with Lake Chiem (26x43cm-10x17in) i.verso paper on panel. 5-Sep-3 Wendl, Rudolstadt #3477/R
£979 $1664 €1400 High mountains with river (21x31cm-8x12in) panel. 22-Nov-3 Arnold, Frankfurt #576/R est:1200

KUMPF, Gottfried (1930-) Austrian
£11409 $20423 €17000 Salzburg, Mirabel garden with fortress (50x64cm-20x25in) s.d.67 masonite. 25-May-4 Dorotheum, Vienna #265/R est:20000-28000
Sculpture
£1268 $2218 €1800 Elephant (16cm-6in) s. num.41/200 brown gold pat bronze. 19-Dec-3 Dorotheum, Vienna #409/R est:1300-1800
£4225 $7394 €6000 Antisocial (23cm-9in) s.i. dark light pat bronze Cast Venturi Arte. 19-Dec-3 Dorotheum, Vienna #407/R est:2800-3800

KUNC, Milan (1944-) Czechoslovakian
£1310 $2410 €1913 Tenerife (127x101cm-50x40in) s.d.1986 prov. 8-Jun-4 Germann, Zurich #117/R est:2000-5000 (S.FR 3000)

KUNCAN (1612-c.1674) Chinese
Works on paper
£9266 $15475 €13528 Boating amongst hills and streams (136x51cm-54x20in) s.i. ink col. 26-Oct-3 Christie's, Hong Kong #477/R (HK.D 120000)

KUNCAN (style) (1612-c.1674) Chinese
Works on paper
£7722 $12896 €11274 Landscape (258x103cm-102x41in) s.i. ink col. 26-Oct-3 Christie's, Hong Kong #466/R est:40000-50000 (HK.D 100000)

KUNCEVICH, Michael (20th C) American
£281 $450 €410 Man and three horses (46x61cm-18x24in) s. 19-Sep-3 Freeman, Philadelphia #147/R

KUNDE, Eric (1969-) American
£1135 $2100 €1657 Open, orchids on a branch in bloom (102x127cm-40x50in) s.verso. 16-Jan-4 Aspire, Cleveland #80/R est:2750-3500

KUNDIG, Reinhold (1888-1984) Swiss

£260 $465 €380 Winter landscape with trees (27x22cm-11x9in) s. 22-Mar-4 Philippe Schuler, Zurich #6029 (S.FR 600)
£315 $542 €460 Snowy landscape (20x26cm-8x10in) s. painted 1952. 8-Dec-3 Philippe Schuler, Zurich #3342 (S.FR 700)
£679 $1154 €991 Composition (54x64cm-21x25in) s. 25-Nov-3 Germann, Zurich #828 est:1500-2000 (S.FR 1500)
£749 $1273 €1094 Winter landscape (50x61cm-20x24in) s. 7-Nov-3 Dobiaschofsky, Bern #190/R (S.FR 1700)
£779 $1395 €1137 Summer landscape with stream and flowers (61x50cm-24x20in) s. 22-Mar-4 Philippe Schuler, Zurich #4345 (S.FR 1800)
£1222 $2077 €1784 Children by water (54x65cm-21x26in) s. 19-Nov-3 Fischer, Luzern #1289/R est:2000-2500 (S.FR 2700)
£1293 $2315 €1888 Autumn landscape with hills (72x100cm-28x39in) s. 14-May-4 Dobiaschofsky, Bern #199/R est:4000 (S.FR 3000)
£1422 $2375 €2062 Autumn landscape near Hirzel (81x100cm-32x39in) s. 23-Jun-3 Philippe Schuler, Zurich #3404 est:4000-6000 (S.FR 3100)
£1493 $2538 €2180 Fextal (81x100cm-32x39in) s. 19-Nov-3 Fischer, Luzern #1290/R est:2500-3500 (S.FR 3300)
£1515 $2712 €2212 Sunny winter's day with sea of cloud (50x61cm-20x24in) s.d. 22-Mar-4 Philippe Schuler, Zurich #4344/R est:1300-1700 (S.FR 3500)
£1719 $2923 €2510 Garden (65x80cm-26x31in) s. 25-Nov-3 Germann, Zurich #45/R est:3500-4500 (S.FR 3800)
£1810 $3131 €2643 Winter sun and cloud (50x61cm-20x24in) s. exhib. 9-Dec-3 Sotheby's, Zurich #102/R est:4000-6000 (S.FR 4000)
£2018 $3370 €2946 View from Horgenberg over Zurichsee to alps (71x90cm-28x35in) s. 24-Oct-3 Hans Widmer, St Gallen #6/R est:3500-6000 (S.FR 4500)
£2064 $3447 €2993 Autumn landscape near Hirzel (79x100cm-31x39in) s/. 23-Jun-3 Philippe Schuler, Zurich #3402/R est:6000-8000 (S.FR 4500)
£3947 $7263 €5763 Garden (81x100cm-32x39in) s.d.1978 prov. 23-Jun-4 Koller, Zurich #3012/R est:9000-14000 (S.FR 9000)
Works on paper
£271 $462 €396 Still life with apples (35x47cm-14x19in) s. W/C. 25-Nov-3 Germann, Zurich #827 (S.FR 600)

KUNG, Walter (1912-) Swiss

£690 $1234 €1007 Vierwaldstattersee in the evening (42x101cm-17x40in) s.d.1963 canvas on panel. 12-May-4 Dobiaschofsky, Bern #710/R est:1500 (S.FR 1600)
£1965 $3576 €2869 Summer (70x55cm-28x22in) s.d.1943. 16-Jun-4 Fischer, Luzern #1325/R est:5000-7000 (S.FR 4500)

KUNIMASA, Utagawa (1773-1810) Japanese

Prints
£2238 $3805 €3200 Portrait d'acteur en okibi-e. s. print. 25-Nov-3 Tajan, Paris #391/R est:3500-3800
£18021 $30636 €25770 Portrait d'acteur (38x26cm-15x10in) col print exhib.lit. 25-Nov-3 Sotheby's, Paris #110/R est:30000-40000

KUNINGBAL, Crusoe (1922-1984) Australian

Works on paper
£894 $1413 €1296 Narmankol, the silver barramundi (37x85cm-15x33in) earth pigments eucalyptus bark exec.c.1977 prov. 28-Jul-3 Sotheby's, Paddington #346/R est:2000-3000 (A.D 2200)

KUNINTJI, Rita (c.1936-) Australian

Works on paper
£1172 $2191 €1758 Yapalirra (100x76cm-39x30in) bears name.verso synthetic polymer paint canvas prov.lit. 26-Jul-4 Sotheby's, Melbourne #432/R est:3000-5000 (A.D 3000)

KUNISADA, Utagawa (1786-1864) Japanese

Works on paper
£734 $1248 €1050 Actors. Portrait study (30x23cm-12x9in) ink pair. 25-Nov-3 Sotheby's, Paris #208/R

KUNIYOSHI, Ichiyusai (1797-1861) Japanese

Prints
£3636 $6182 €5200 Femmes cueillant algues a Omori (24x34cm-9x13in) s. col print lit. 25-Nov-3 Sotheby's, Paris #109/R est:6000-7000
Works on paper
£1250 $2000 €1825 Yoshitsune at one of the sea battles of 1184-85 against the Taira Clan. ink. 20-Sep-3 Sloans & Kenyon, Bethesda #1263/R est:500-700

KUNIYOSHI, Yasuo (1893-1953) American

Prints
£1899 $3400 €2773 Girl in feathered hat (19x15cm-7x6in) s.d.1928 num.16/26 lithograph. 6-May-4 Swann Galleries, New York #476/R est:3500-5000
Works on paper
£2874 $4800 €4196 Weathervane, horse and fruit (43x33cm-17x13in) s. chl ink wash prov. 11-Nov-3 Christie's, Rockefeller NY #142/R est:8000-12000
£8602 $16000 €12559 Reclining female model (22x30cm-9x12in) s. W/C gouache over pencil. 2-Mar-4 Swann Galleries, New York #326/R est:10000-15000
£25926 $42000 €37593 At a cafe (36x41cm-14x16in) mixed media prov. 8-Aug-3 Barridorf, Portland #158/R est:15000-25000

KUNKEL, George (20th C) American

£432 $700 €626 Waves (46x76cm-18x30in) s. acrylic collage. 8-Aug-3 Barridorf, Portland #310/R

KUNST, Berend (1794-1881) Dutch

Works on paper
£308 $529 €440 Bust portrait of a young woman (49x39cm-19x15in) s.d.1842 pastel. 5-Dec-3 Bolland & Marotz, Bremen #591

KUNSTLER, Mort (1931-) American

£6145 $11000 €8972 Vanishing American (58x76cm-23x30in) board. 15-May-4 Altermann Galleries, Santa Fe #112/R

KUNTZ, Carl (1770-1830) German

£307 $555 €460 Young bull (31x42cm-12x17in) i. panel lit. 3-Apr-4 Badum, Bamberg #58/R
£2676 $4630 €3800 Landscape with cattle and herdsman (42x50cm-17x20in) s.d.1821 panel. 13-Dec-3 Lempertz, Koln #227/R est:3000
£9396 $16819 €14000 Meadow scene (46x61cm-18x24in) s.i.d.1822 panel. 27-May-4 Dorotheum, Vienna #190/R est:3500-4000

KUNZ, Ludwig Adam (1857-1929) Austrian

£861 $1575 €1300 Bacchus with Ceres and Cupid (28x24cm-11x9in) s. canvas on board. 8-Apr-4 Dorotheum, Vienna #229/R
£952 $1705 €1400 Still life of fruit (61x72cm-24x28in) s.d.1904. 17-Mar-4 Neumeister, Munich #507/R
£2797 $4755 €4000 Still life with grapes, silver vase, pear and glass (83x106cm-33x42in) s. 24-Nov-3 Dorotheum, Vienna #224/R est:3200-3800
£3642 $6629 €5500 Still life with grapes and quince (137x94cm-54x37in) s.d.1900 panel. 16-Jun-4 Hugo Ruef, Munich #1006/R est:2800

KUNZE, Alfred (1866-1943) German

£1233 $2096 €1800 Johannisplatz in Chemnitz (67x80cm-26x31in) s. i.d.1925 verso. 5-Nov-3 Hugo Ruef, Munich #1053 est:450

KUNZLI, David (20th C) ?

Works on paper
£338 $639 €500 La geisha (49x42cm-19x17in) mono. chl mixed media linen. 21-Feb-4 Cornette de St.Cyr, Paris #333

KUPCZYNSKI, Zbigniew (1930-) Canadian?

£356 $583 €520 King and his children (91x122cm-36x48in) s. 28-May-3 Maynards, Vancouver #118 (C.D 800)

KUPER, Yuri (1940-) ?

£1020 $1825 €1489 The nail - The Nale (50x50cm-20x20in) s.d.80 indis.i. verso. 25-May-4 Grev Wedels Plass, Oslo #120/R est:20000-30000 (N.KR 12500)
£1467 $2640 €2200 Draw (116x158cm-46x62in) s.d.1989 oil collage panel. 24-Apr-4 Cornette de St.Cyr, Paris #610 est:2000
£3000 $5400 €4500 Baket (200x200cm-79x79in) s.d.1989 s.d.verso. 24-Apr-4 Cornette de St.Cyr, Paris #608/R est:3000
£3514 $6500 €5130 Untitled (250x190cm-98x75in) oil chk leather canvas on canvas. 12-Feb-4 Sotheby's, New York #281/R est:4000-6000
£4000 $7200 €6000 Brash (200x200cm-79x79in) s.d.1989 s.d.verso. 24-Apr-4 Cornette de St.Cyr, Paris #609 est:3000
Works on paper
£420 $713 €600 Le pinceau (24x35cm-9x14in) s. mixed media. 28-Nov-3 Blanchet, Paris #230/R
£1333 $2400 €2000 Plume sergent Major (114x157cm-45x62in) s.d.1989 mixed media. 24-Apr-4 Cornette de St.Cyr, Paris #607 est:2000

KUPETZKI, Johann (1667-1740) German

£2431 $3840 €3500 Portrait of royal chamber musician (67x55cm-26x22in) mono. lit. 19-Sep-3 Schloss Ahlden, Ahlden #1442/R est:3800

KUPETZKI, Johann (attrib) (1667-1740) German

£738 $1373 €1100 Portrait d'hommes (29x21cm-11x8in) bears sig.verso panel pair. 7-Mar-4 Livinec, Gaudcheau & Jezequel, Rennes #49
£1974 $3632 €3000 Husar officer smoking pipe (119x92cm-47x36in) 24-Jun-4 Dr Fritz Nagel, Stuttgart #662/R est:3000
£2817 $4873 €4000 Officer of the Hussars smoking pipe (119x92cm-47x36in) 11-Dec-3 Dr Fritz Nagel, Stuttgart #435/R est:6000

KUPETZKI, Johann (circle) (1667-1740) German

£6897 $11448 €10000 Portrait of Prince Eugene (30x22cm-12x9in) metal oval prov. 1-Oct-3 Dorotheum, Vienna #209/R est:8000-12000
£8725 $16054 €13000 Portrait of Prince Eugene of Savoie (30x24cm-12x9in) metal oval convex prov. 24-Mar-4 Dorotheum, Vienna #236/R est:8000-12000

KUPFER, Johann Michael (1859-1917) Austrian

£1458 $2682 €2187 Pan (180x80cm-71x31in) s. 14-Jun-4 Lilla Bukowskis, Stockholm #566/R est:20000-25000 (S.KR 20000)

KUPFERMAN, David (20th C) American

£403 $750 €588 Landscape views (59x88cm-23x35in) s. acrylic paper two. 5-Mar-4 Skinner, Boston #481/R
£403 $750 €588 Cape Beach. Landscape (67x97cm-26x38in) s. acrylic paper two. 5-Mar-4 Skinner, Boston #572/R

KUPFERMAN, Lawrence Edward (1909-1982) American

Works on paper
£250 $400 €365 Roofs, New York. s.d.1945 mixed media. 20-Sep-3 Bunte, Elgin #385b
£462 $850 €675 Gnarled trunk (53x53cm-21x21in) s.d.1945 i.verso W/C pen ink paper on card. 10-Jun-4 Swann Galleries, New York #138/R
£806 $1500 €1177 Tomorrow? (61x46cm-24x18in) s. s.i.d.1946 verso W/C wash pen ink. 2-Mar-4 Swann Galleries, New York #328/R est:2000-3000

KUPFERMAN, Moshe (1926-2003) Israeli

£1049	$1783	€1500	Composition (50x55cm-20x22in) s. 27-Nov-3 Calmels Cohen, Paris #104/R est:2000-3000
£1417	$2650	€2069	Abstract (76x106cm-30x42in) s.d.1996 oil graphite. 1-Mar-4 Ben-Ami, Tel Aviv #4680/R est:3000-4000
£1676	$3000	€2447	Untitled (46x46cm-18x18in) s.d.1980 verso. 18-Mar-4 Sotheby's, New York #53/R est:4000-6000
£2596	$4750	€3790	Abstract (114x130cm-45x51in) s.d.1983. 1-Jun-4 Ben-Ami, Tel Aviv #4860/R est:6000-8000
£3073	$5500	€4487	Untitled (44x44cm-17x17in) s.d.79. 18-Mar-4 Sotheby's, New York #52/R est:4000-6000
£7263	$13000	€10604	Untitled (130x190cm-51x75in) s.d.1983 verso. 18-Mar-4 Sotheby's, New York #42/R est:18000-22000
£8735	$14500	€12753	Composition (130x195cm-51x77in) s.d.85. 2-Oct-3 Christie's, Tel Aviv #99/R est:12000-16000
Works on paper			
£495	$900	€723	Untitled (46x76cm-18x30in) s.d.87 mixed media. 29-Jun-4 Sotheby's, New York #577/R
£522	$950	€762	Untitled (35x50cm-14x20in) s.d.72 pencil two. 29-Jun-4 Sotheby's, New York #539/R est:1000-1500
£549	$1000	€802	Untitled (70x99cm-28x39in) s.d.86 mixed media. 29-Jun-4 Sotheby's, New York #538/R est:1200-1800

KUPHAL, Walter (1890-?) German

£350	$601	€500	Church tower and factory houses in Neuruppin (75x65cm-30x26in) s. panel. 5-Dec-3 Bolland & Marotz, Bremen #734
£462	$785	€660	Landscape with stream (48x58cm-19x23in) s. board. 20-Nov-3 Weidler, Nurnberg #342

KUPKA, Frank (1871-1957) Czechoslovakian

£26573	$45175	€38000	Portrait de femme (45x31cm-18x12in) s.d.1906 cardboard prov. 23-Nov-3 Cornette de St.Cyr, Paris #195/R est:200-300
Works on paper			
£490	$832	€700	Femme debout (11x6cm-4x2in) s. graphite prov. 23-Nov-3 Cornette de St.Cyr, Paris #194
£524	$892	€750	Gust of wind (20x16cm-8x6in) s. pencil. 29-Nov-3 Bassenge, Berlin #6857/R
£629	$1070	€900	Silhouettes (15x20cm-6x8in) s. crayon prov. 23-Nov-3 Cornette de St.Cyr, Paris #197
£699	$1189	€1000	Six etudes (26x21cm-10x8in) st. crayon prov. 23-Nov-3 Cornette de St.Cyr, Paris #196
£909	$1545	€1300	Hermes (18x20cm-7x8in) st.sig. black crayon prov. 23-Nov-3 Cornette de St.Cyr, Paris #180/R
£909	$1545	€1300	Etudes de tetes de femme et de bras (22x32cm-9x13in) st.sig. graphite prov.lit. 23-Nov-3 Cornette de St.Cyr, Paris #181/R
£909	$1545	€1300	Composition abstraite (20x20cm-8x8in) studio st. black crayon prov. 23-Nov-3 Cornette de St.Cyr, Paris #190/R
£979	$1664	€1400	Composition mecanique (8x8cm-3x3in) st. col crayon prov. 23-Nov-3 Cornette de St.Cyr, Paris #186
£1049	$1783	€1500	L'entremetteur sans la savoir (21x12cm-8x5in) s. wax crayon pastel prov. 23-Nov-3 Cornette de St.Cyr, Paris #185 est:200-300
£1119	$1902	€1600	Composition (11x16cm-4x6in) crayon W/C gouache prov. 23-Nov-3 Cornette de St.Cyr, Paris #188 est:300-400
£1259	$2102	€1800	Composition geometrique (38x27cm-15x11in) s.d.34 Indian ink. 13-Oct-3 Horta, Bruxelles #100 est:1500-2500
£1294	$2199	€1850	Composition erotique (15x12cm-6x5in) studio st. crayon prov. 23-Nov-3 Cornette de St.Cyr, Paris #193 est:100
£1333	$2453	€2000	Composition en noir (21x13cm-8x5in) bears studio st. gouache. 14-Jun-4 Tajan, Paris #136 est:2000-3000
£1538	$2615	€2200	Contrastes gothiques (10x26cm-4x10in) studio st. crayon W/C prov. 23-Nov-3 Cornette de St.Cyr, Paris #199 est:250-300
£1608	$2686	€2300	Lisystrata (11x32cm-4x13in) s. gouache ch. lit. 29-Jun-3 Versailles Encheres #45/R
£1748	$2972	€2500	Cercles et verticales (11x15cm-4x6in) st. chl exec.c.1910-1911 prov. 23-Nov-3 Cornette de St.Cyr, Paris #189/R est:200-300
£1892	$3386	€2800	Composition (20x20cm-8x8in) i. gouache Chinese ink over photograph. 10-May-4 Giraudeau, Tours #56
£1958	$3329	€2800	Composition abstraite (6x8cm-2x3in) s. W/C prov. 23-Nov-3 Cornette de St.Cyr, Paris #191/R est:200-300
£2098	$3566	€3000	La chanson de Roland. pseudonym sig. W/C. 23-Nov-3 Cornette de St.Cyr, Paris #400/R est:300-400
£2168	$3685	€3100	Etude pour ensemble convexe (11x15cm-4x6in) st.sig. crayon W/C prov.lit. 23-Nov-3 Cornette de St.Cyr, Paris #183/R est:200-300
£2238	$3804	€3200	Blanc et noir, printemps cosmique (12x20cm-5x8in) s. ink gouache prov.lit. 23-Nov-3 Cornette de St.Cyr, Paris #184/R est:150-200
£2446	$4158	€3571	Composition (32x32cm-13x13in) s. gouache on stencil print exec.c.1935. 26-Nov-3 Kunsthallen, Copenhagen #89a/R est:30000 (D.KR 26000)
£2685	$4913	€4000	Mouvement (20x22cm-8x9in) s. W/C gouache. 7-Jul-4 Artcurial Briest, Paris #68/R est:3000-4000
£3846	$6538	€5500	Perpendiculaires (15x11cm-6x4in) st.sig. crayon gouache W/C prov.lit. 23-Nov-3 Cornette de St.Cyr, Paris #182/R est:400-500
£4336	$7371	€6200	Verticales et cercles (17x10cm-7x4in) studio st. gouache prov. 23-Nov-3 Cornette de St.Cyr, Paris #198/R est:400-500
£4545	$7727	€6500	Le berger (19x14cm-7x6in) s. W/C exec.c.1905 prov. 23-Nov-3 Cornette de St.Cyr, Paris #192/R est:200-300
£4577	$8194	€6500	Va petit mousse ou le vent te pousse (38x57cm-15x22in) s. Indian ink htd white blue. 11-Jan-4 Rouillac, Vendome #62
£4685	$7824	€6700	Danseuse (45x41cm-18x16in) s. W/C gouache Chinese ink. 29-Jun-3 Eric Pillon, Calais #69/R
£4730	$8324	€7000	Etude (21x17cm-8x7in) s. gouache. 19-May-4 Camard, Paris #111/R est:6500-7500
£5245	$8916	€7500	L'arbre enchante (22x17cm-9x7in) st.sig. col ink prov. 23-Nov-3 Cornette de St.Cyr, Paris #187/R est:400-500
£7000	$12670	€10220	Etude pour Le miroir ovale (26x20cm-10x8in) s. pastel exec.c.1910. 1-Apr-4 Christie's, Kensington #67/R est:7000-9000
£7973	$14032	€11800	Etude (25x25cm-10x10in) s. gouache. 19-May-4 Camard, Paris #112/R est:7500-8500
£12000	$22080	€17520	Portrait of a woman (65x48cm-26x19in) s. chl pastel pencil exec 1907-1909 prov. 24-Jun-4 Christie's, London #384/R est:8000-12000
£13000	$23660	€18980	Etude pour la localisation des mobiles graphiques (33x31cm-13x12in) st.sig. studio st.verso pastel exec 1911-1913 prov. 5-Feb-4 Christie's, London #352/R est:12000-16000
£13000	$23920	€18980	Tregastel (22x29cm-9x11in) s. gouache W/C. 22-Jun-4 Sotheby's, London #473/R est:8000-12000
£13158	$24211	€20000	Theatre des marionnettes (42x37cm-17x15in) s. pen Chinese ink chk W/C prov. 25-Jun-4 Millon & Associes, Paris #122/R est:20000-25000
£14000	$25480	€20440	Sans titre (31x32cm-12x13in) s. gouache chl exec.c.1911-12 prov. 4-Feb-4 Sotheby's, London #488/R est:12000-15000
£15000	$27600	€21900	Contrastes (32x31cm-13x12in) s. W/C gouache pencil exec c.1947 prov. 24-Jun-4 Christie's, London #393/R est:12000-16000
£22000	$40040	€32120	Plans minuscules (34x29cm-13x11in) s. gouache W/C pencil prov. 5-Feb-4 Christie's, London #353/R est:15000-20000
£22378	$38042	€32000	Composition symbolique (61x46cm-24x18in) s.d.1911 gouache prov. 23-Nov-3 Cornette de St.Cyr, Paris #179/R est:500-600

KUPPERS, Leo (1884-?) Dutch

£251	$450	€366	Chess game (61x71cm-24x28in) s. prov. 21-Mar-4 Hindman, Chicago #786/R
£272	$500	€397	Chess game (61x71cm-24x28in) s. prov. 27-Jun-4 Hindman, Chicago #845a/R
£500	$895	€750	Still life with cactus (40x30cm-16x12in) mono. board. 15-May-4 Van Ham, Cologne #744

KURAHARA, Ted (20th C) American

£906	$1632	€1323	Untitled (91x90cm-36x35in) s. d.1983-84 verso paper on panel diptych prov. 26-Apr-4 Bukowskis, Stockholm #623/R (S.KR 12500)

KURELEK, William (1927-1977) Canadian

£8559	$14550	€12496	Winter's last fling, Manitoba (63x20cm-25x8in) init.d.1970 i.verso board lit. 27-Nov-3 Heffel, Vancouver #144/R est:10000-15000 (C.D 19000)
£15244	$27287	€22256	Winter road in Alberta (34x76cm-13x30in) init. i.d.1966 verso board prov.lit. 27-May-4 Heffel, Vancouver #180/R est:10000-15000 (C.D 37500)
£22523	$38288	€32884	First snow from the south (71x51cm-28x20in) masonite prov.lit. 18-Nov-3 Sotheby's, Toronto #23/R est:35000-45000 (C.D 50000)
Works on paper			
£364	$593	€531	Abandoned house (25x21cm-10x8in) ink wash. 23-Sep-3 Ritchie, Toronto #156/R (C.D 800)
£450	$766	€657	Scarecrow (53x37cm-21x15in) i. Cyrillic blue ink. 21-Nov-3 Walker's, Ottawa #39/R (C.D 1000)
£909	$1482	€1327	Chicken man (25x20cm-10x8in) ink wash. 23-Sep-3 Ritchie, Toronto #162/R est:700-900 (C.D 2000)
£968	$1781	€1413	Prairie landscape (37x59cm-15x23in) mono.i.d.77 mixed media. 9-Jun-4 Walker's, Ottawa #45/R est:3000-4000 (C.D 2400)
£3600	$6588	€5256	Winter in dad's pond (20x30cm-8x12in) init.d.74 mixed media board prov.lit. 1-Jun-4 Joyner Waddington, Toronto #99/R est:5000-7000 (C.D 9000)
£4878	$8732	€7122	Hail cloud (37x22cm-15x9in) s.d.73 i.verso mixed media on masonite prov. 31-May-4 Sotheby's, Toronto #172/R est:6000-7000 (C.D 12000)
£5357	$9214	€7821	BC seen through sunglasses (32x79cm-13x31in) init. mixed media board exec 1973 prov.lit. 2-Dec-3 Joyner Waddington, Toronto #103/R est:12000-15000 (C.D 12000)
£5691	$10187	€8309	Temptation in the desert, hiding head in the sand (50x38cm-20x15in) s.d.75 i.d.verso mixed media on masonite prov. 31-May-4 Sotheby's, Toronto #174/R est:12000-15000 (C.D 14000)
£6504	$11642	€9496	Trompe l'oeil with scissors (36x27cm-14x11in) s.i.d.1960 verso gouache ink paper on plywood prov.lit. 31-May-4 Sotheby's, Toronto #173/R est:9000-11000 (C.D 16000)
£6757	$11486	€9865	Abandoned goulettes (51x71cm-20x28in) mono. mixed media masonite two prov.exhib. 18-Nov-3 Sotheby's, Toronto #89/R est:15000-20000 (C.D 15000)
£10163	$18191	€14838	Hell - the worm that dies not (157x49cm-62x19in) s.d.62 i.verso mixed media on masonite prov. 31-May-4 Sotheby's, Toronto #90/R est:4000-6000 (C.D 25000)
£11712	$19910	€17100	Three surveyors (46x51cm-18x20in) i.verso on stretcher mixed media board prov. 18-Nov-3 Sotheby's, Toronto #159/R est:20000-25000 (C.D 26000)
£12946	$22268	€18901	Indian summer on the Humber (60x120cm-24x47in) init.d.72 mixed media prov.exhib.lit. 2-Dec-3 Joyner Waddington, Toronto #68/R est:30000-40000 (C.D 29000)
£14228	$25467	€20773	Plane watching at Malton (121x119cm-48x47in) s.d.72 i.verso mixed media on masonite prov.exhib.lit. 31-May-4 Sotheby's, Toronto #59/R est:40000-60000 (C.D 35000)
£14400	$26352	€21024	Fishing (41x50cm-16x20in) s.d.1961 mixed media board prov.lit. 1-Jun-4 Joyner Waddington, Toronto #26/R est:2000-25000 (C.D 36000)

KURON, Herbert (1888-?) German

£313	$497	€450	Mer se fracassant sur les rochers (49x69cm-19x27in) s. cardboard. 9-Sep-3 Vanderkindere, Brussels #81
£313	$494	€450	View of Wornitz in summer (68x80cm-27x31in) s. painted c.1910. 5-Sep-3 Wendl, Rudolstadt #3479/R
£400	$728	€600	View of the the Wannsee, Berlin (50x60cm-20x24in) s. 1-Jul-4 Van Ham, Cologne #1473
£1189	$2021	€1700	Summer's day on the Wannsee (69x100cm-27x39in) s. board. 29-Nov-3 Bassenge, Berlin #7247/R est:1500

KURPERSHOEK, Theo (1914-1998) Dutch

£2721	$4952	€4000	Haven van Ancona, snachts - harbour of Acona by night (54x62cm-21x24in) s.d.73 s.i.verso. 3-Feb-4 Christie's, Amsterdam #543/R est:3000-5000

KURSCHNER, Henning (1941-) German

£368	$615	€530	Untitled (100x120cm-39x47in) s.d. verso acrylic. 24-Oct-3 Ketterer, Hamburg #903/R

KURTH, Damian (20th C) New Zealander

£435	$704	€631	Two thirty 2002 (46x40cm-18x16in) s.verso. 31-Jul-3 International Art Centre, Auckland #92/R est:1400-1600 (NZ.D 1200)
£435	$704	€631	One thirty 2002 (62x42cm-24x17in) s.verso. 31-Jul-3 International Art Centre, Auckland #93/R est:1000-1500 (NZ.D 1200)

KURTZ, Arthur (1860-1917) Swiss

£1972	$3411	€2800	Portrait of horses (84x127cm-33x50in) s.d.895. 10-Dec-3 Dorotheum, Vienna #214/R est:1500-2000

KURTZ, Carl von (1817-1887) Italian

£1867 $3360 €2800 Peasant girls by fountain (102x76cm-40x30in) s.i.d.1839. 26-Apr-4 Rieber, Stuttgart #1280/R est:2800

KURZ, Albrecht (1858-1928) German

£420 $722 €600 Norwegian fjord landscape with steamship (50x70cm-20x28in) s. 5-Dec-3 Bolland & Marotz, Bremen #592/R

Works on paper

£400 $728 €600 French town scene (62x50cm-24x20in) s. W/C. 1-Jul-4 Van Ham, Cologne #1474

KURZ, Louis (1835-1921) American

£424 $750 €619 Naive folk art (15x23cm-6x9in) s.indis.d. 1-May-4 Dan Ripley, Indianapolis #559

KURZAWA, Antoni (1842-1898) Polish

Sculpture

£6051 $10469 €8834 Mickiewicz waking up the genius of poetry (49cm-19in) s.d.1891 pat bronze. 14-Dec-3 Agra, Warsaw #14/R est:30000 (P.Z 40000)

KURZAWSKI, Andrzej (1928-) Polish

£872 $1447 €1273 Village landscape (60x81cm-24x32in) painted1979. 2-Oct-3 Agra, Warsaw #23/R (P.Z 5700)

KURZBAUER, Eduard (1840-1879) Austrian

£775 $1340 €1100 Young girl (15x12cm-6x5in) s. canvas on board. 10-Dec-3 Dorotheum, Vienna #261/R

KURZWEIL, Maximilian (1867-1916) Austrian

£8333 $14167 €12000 River in Pont Aven Brittany (52x63cm-20x25in) 28-Oct-3 Wiener Kunst Auktionen, Vienna #90/R est:12000-25000

£8725 $15617 €13000 On the coast at Concarneau (99x100cm-39x39in) s. prov.exhib. 25-May-4 Dorotheum, Vienna #130/R est:13000-20000

KUSAMA, Yayoi (1929-) Japanese

£2050 $3772 €2993 Nets (41x32cm-16x13in) s.i.d.1997 verso acrylic. 24-Jun-4 Sotheby's, Olympia #492/R est:2000-3000

£2060 $3750 €3008 Sea at night (65x80cm-26x31in) s.d.1978 s.d.verso acrylic. 29-Jun-4 Sotheby's, New York #503/R est:6000-8000

£2703 $5000 €3946 Ocean in the Morning (80x65cm-31x26in) s.d.1978 s.i.d.verso. 12-Feb-4 Sotheby's, New York #340/R est:8000-12000

£2747 $5000 €4011 Flower (80x65cm-31x26in) s.d.1978 s.d.verso acrylic. 29-Jun-4 Sotheby's, New York #502/R est:8000-12000

£6000 $10920 €8760 Pumpkin (45x38cm-18x15in) s.d.1991 verso acrylic. 4-Feb-4 Sotheby's, Olympia #31/R est:3000-4000

£11000 $20020 €16060 Nets (73x61cm-29x24in) s.i.d.1999 verso acrylic prov.exhib. 6-Feb-4 Sotheby's, London #123/R est:10000-15000

£29940 $50000 €43712 Sea of Night (194x131cm-76x52in) s.i.d.1985 stretcher acrylic prov.exhib. 12-Nov-3 Christie's, Rockefeller NY #426/R est:40000-60000

£38922 $65000 €56826 Infinity nets (90x100cm-35x39in) s.i.d.1960 verso acrylic prov. 13-Nov-3 Sotheby's, New York #191/R est:30000-40000

£44693 $80000 €65252 Infinity nets (100x90cm-39x35in) s.i.d.1960 verso. 13-May-4 Sotheby's, New York #133/R est:40000-60000

Sculpture

£973 $1800 €1421 Silver Shoe (20x24cm-8x9in) s.d.1976 num.7/30 painted silver bronze. 12-Feb-4 Sotheby's, New York #342/R est:3000-5000

£1800 $3312 €2628 Sprout (20x27cm-8x11in) s.i.d.1999 acrylic wood. 24-Jun-4 Sotheby's, Olympia #488/R est:2000-3000

£2500 $4600 €3650 Box, cherry (11x33x27cm-4x13x11in) s.i.d.1999 verso mixed media painted box. 24-Jun-4 Sotheby's, Olympia #493/R est:3000-4000

£3049 $5000 €4452 Shoe with phallic forms (15x9x22cm-6x4x9in) s.d.1966 gold paint shoe stuffed fabric prov. 28-May-3 Sotheby's, Amsterdam #70/R est:5000-7000

£3659 $6000 €5342 Shoe with phallic forms (15x9x22cm-6x4x9in) s.d.1966 gold paint shoe stuffed fabric leather on board prov. 28-May-3 Sotheby's, Amsterdam #69/R est:5000-7000

£4000 $7280 €5840 Shoes (21x21x8cm-8x8x3in) s.d.1999 two painted shoes with stuffed fabric prov. two. 4-Feb-4 Sotheby's, Olympia #27/R est:2000-3000

£4324 $8000 €6313 Gold Shoes (23x25cm-9x10in) each s.d.1999 soles shoes fabric spray paint. 12-Feb-4 Sotheby's, New York #343/R est:4000-6000

£8000 $14560 €11680 In the woods (60x37x16cm-24x15x6in) s.i.d.1983 acrylic fabric wood plastic piping. 4-Feb-4 Sotheby's, Olympia #29/R est:5000-7000

£9000 $16380 €13140 Dots (52x52x12cm-20x20x5in) s.i.d.1999 verso mixed media prov. 4-Feb-4 Sotheby's, Olympia #30/R est:2000-3000

Works on paper

£1117 $2000 €1631 Flower bloomin in melancholy (27x24cm-11x9in) s.d.1978 s.i.d.1978 verso silver paint gouache calligraphy board. 14-May-4 Phillips, New York #348/R est:3000-5000

£1300 $2366 €1898 Untitled (64x49cm-25x19in) s.d.1983 mixed media collage. 4-Feb-4 Sotheby's, Olympia #28/R est:1000-1500

£3846 $6538 €5500 Rain on yellow river (27x24cm-11x9in) s.d.1978 s.i.d.verso W/C card prov. 25-Nov-3 Sotheby's, Milan #107/R est:2500-3000

£6704 $12000 €9788 Flower O W E (37x32cm-15x13in) s.i.d.19852 verso gouache prov. 12-May-4 Christie's, Rockefeller NY #118/R est:15000-20000

£6704 $12000 €9788 Untitled (35x26cm-14x10in) s.d.1952 gouache prov. 12-May-4 Christie's, Rockefeller NY #119/R est:15000-20000

£16000 $29120 €23360 The ground. Flower petal 2. The moon (25x19cm-10x7in) one s.i.d.1952 verso two s.i.d.1954 verso gouache three prov. 6-Feb-4 Sotheby's, London #121/R est:7000-10000

£33520 $60000 €48939 Group of four drawings (38x27cm-15x11in) s.d.1951 1952 ink coloured paper Japanese paper four prov.exhib. 13-May-4 Sotheby's, New York #132/R est:35000-45000

KUSCOWSKY, D (?) ?

£579 $950 €845 Still life with flowers, fruit and peppers on table (64x53cm-25x21in) s. prov. 31-May-3 Brunk, Ashville #147/R

KUSHNER, Dorothy B (1909-) American

£241 $450 €362 Reflections (39x49cm-15x19in) s. 25-Jul-4 Bonhams & Butterfields, San Francisco #6132/R

KUSNADI (1921-) Indonesian

£1993 $3089 €2910 Two girls (62x87cm-24x34in) s.d.60 exhib. 6-Oct-2 Sotheby's, Singapore #118/R est:4000-6000 (S.D 5500)

KUSTER, Frederick (attrib) (fl.1811-1822) American

Works on paper

£3293 $5500 €4808 Geburts und taufschein (29x39cm-11x15in) W/C ink lit. 11-Nov-3 Christie's, Rockefeller NY #210/R est:4000-6000

KUSTER, Johann Kaspar (1747-1818) Swiss

£452 $769 €660 Shepherd boy resting (36x44cm-14x17in) 28-Nov-3 Zofingen, Switzerland #2470 (S.FR 1000)

KUSTNER, Carl (1861-1934) German

£268 $494 €400 Waterside village (32x34cm-13x13in) s. board. 24-Mar-4 Hugo Ruef, Munich #1021

£333 $607 €500 Grazing at the water (50x65cm-20x26in) s. 1-Jul-4 Neumeister, Munich #2739

£433 $789 €650 Corn-poppy field (38x29cm-15x11in) s.d.92 verso board. 1-Jul-4 Neumeister, Munich #2740

KUSTODIEV, Boris (1878-1927) Russian

Works on paper

£1923 $3000 € Landscape (24x36cm-9x14in) s.cyrillic d.1920 col pencil card. 11-Apr-3 Christie's, Rockefeller NY #42/R est:2000-3000

£4000 $6800 €5840 Costume design for Dasha, the Merchant's Wife (33x21cm-13x8in) s.i.d.1919 W/C over pencil prov. 19-Nov-3 Sotheby's, London #159/R est:3000-5000

£6000 $10200 €8760 Costume design for Pyotr with cane (33x21cm-13x8in) s.i.d.1919 W/C over pencil prov. 19-Nov-3 Sotheby's, London #160/R est:5000-7000

£10000 $17000 €14600 On the way to the fair (21x33cm-8x13in) s.i.d.1919 W/C over pencil prov. 19-Nov-3 Sotheby's, London #158/R est:6000-8000

KUSUMI RYUEN (18th C) Japanese

Works on paper

£1507 $2562 €2200 Pheasant beneath flowers (111x48cm-44x19in) s. seal Indian ink col gold hanging scroll. 8-Nov-3 Dr Fritz Nagel, Stuttgart #1869/R est:1800

KUTSCHA, Paul (1872-?) Czechoslovakian

£647 $1157 €945 Vierwaldstattersee with Urirotstock (60x79cm-24x31in) S. 12-May-4 Dobiaschofsky, Bern #711/R est:1200 (S.FR 1500)

£1589 $2909 €2400 Malaga harbour (60x81cm-24x32in) s.d.93. 8-Apr-4 Dorotheum, Vienna #139/R est:1800-2000

KUTTERER, August (1898-1954) German

£699 $1168 €1000 Summer interior (69x59cm-27x23in) s. 30-Jun-3 Bloss, Merzhausen #1936/R

£1399 $2336 €2000 Snowy Bernau (70x84cm-28x33in) s. board. 30-Jun-3 Bloss, Merzhausen #1934/R est:500

Works on paper

£280 $467 €400 Bodensee (53x68cm-21x27in) s. W/C. 30-Jun-3 Bloss, Merzhausen #1935/R

KUWASSEG, Charles Euphrasie (1838-1904) French

£1061 $1900 €1549 Port scene with townsfolk (38x46cm-15x18in) s. 7-May-4 Sloans & Kenyon, Bethesda #1665/R est:1500-2500

£1467 $2625 €2200 Rocky landscape with mountain village and waterfall (33x24cm-13x9in) s. 15-May-4 De Vuyst, Lokeren #174/R est:2200-2600

£1678 $3087 €2500 River landscape with village (27x46cm-11x18in) s. panel. 24-Mar-4 Hugo Ruef, Munich #1023/R est:2500

£1800 $3222 €2628 An alpine village above a gorge with waterfall (64x53cm-25x21in) s. 25-May-4 Sworder & Son, Bishops Stortford #409/R est:1000-1500

£1900 $2983 €2755 Fishing vessels in a French harbour before a fish market (70x94cm-28x37in) s. 28-Aug-3 Christie's, Kensington #213/R est:1200-1800

£2133 $3861 €3200 Place de village (13x9cm-5x4in) s. panel. 5-Apr-4 Deburaux, Boulogne #102 est:1600-1800

£2533 $4585 €3800 Quai anime a Amsterdam (22x16cm-9x6in) s.d.1872. 5-Apr-4 Deburaux, Boulogne #101/R est:2000-2500

£2533 $4585 €3800 Rouen (13x9cm-5x4in) s. panel. 5-Apr-4 Deburaux, Boulogne #103/R est:1800-2000

£2657 $4571 €3800 Village Normand, Bernay dans l'Eure (22x41cm-9x16in) s. i.verso panel. 7-Dec-3 Osenat, Fontainebleau #172 est:2500-3000

£2676 $4683 €3800 Les lavandieres (32x24cm-13x9in) s. panel. 16-Dec-3 Claude Aguttes, Neuilly #106/R est:3000-5000

£3000 $5460 €4380 Vessels at their moorings under moonlight (32x47cm-13x19in) s.d.1867. 16-Jun-4 Christie's, Kensington #42/R est:1500-2000

£3357 $5773 €4800 Ville fluviale (38x46cm-15x18in) s.d.56. 8-Dec-3 Horta, Bruxelles #112 est:5000-7000

£3533 $6500 €5158 Busy port (25x33cm-10x13in) s.d. 27-Jun-4 Freeman, Philadelphia #24/R est:3000-5000

£4054 $7662 €6000 Bord de mer anime en Bretagne (24x32cm-9x13in) s. 17-Feb-4 Vanderkindere, Brussels #128 est:625-875

£5594 $9622 €8000 Canal a Venise au coucher de soleil (56x100cm-22x39in) s. 3-Dec-3 Palais de Beaux Arts, Brussels #625/R est:8000-12000

£6250 $11313 €9500 Bateau a roue (33x67cm-13x26in) s.d.1856 panel. 19-Apr-4 Boscher, Cherbourg #818/R est:8000-10000

£7692 $13077 €11000 Le bateau a roue reliant Honfleur a Trouville (33x67cm-13x26in) s.d.1856 panel. 24-Nov-3 Boscher, Cherbourg #728/R est:8000-10000

£22000 $35200 €31900 Venice (57x101cm-22x40in) s.d.1869 prov. 18-Sep-3 Christie's, Kensington #74/R est:15000-20000

KUWASSEG, Charles Euphrasie (attrib) (1838-1904) French
£600 $1020 €876 French seaside town (21x41cm-8x16in) panel. 19-Nov-3 Christie's, Kensington #563/R

KUWASSEG, Karl-Josef (1802-1877) French
£1700 $2890 €2482 Mounted figures in a ravine (92x73cm-36x29in) s. 2-Nov-3 Lots Road Auctions, London #355
£2676 $4442 €3800 Resting under the trees (46x38cm-18x15in) s. 15-Jun-3 Peron, Melun #173
£10000 $18000 €14600 Path along the Mediterranean coast (74x93cm-29x37in) s.i.d.1871 prov. 23-Apr-4 Sotheby's, New York #207/R est:8000-12000

KUYCK, Jean Louis van (1821-1871) Flemish
£567 $1014 €850 Interieur de la grange (33x45cm-13x18in) s. panel. 11-May-4 Vanderkindere, Brussels #101
£1342 $2483 €2000 Harnessing the horse (31x38cm-12x15in) s.d.1857. 13-Mar-4 De Vuyst, Lokeren #356/R est:800-1200

KUYPERS, Adrianus (1862-1945) Dutch
£469 $877 €704 Iceskating (31x61cm-12x24in) indis.sig. i.d.1892 verso. 20-Jul-4 Goodman, Sydney #88/R (A.D 1200)

KUYPERS, Cornelis (1864-1932) Dutch
£329 $605 €500 A farmer at work, The Veluwe (34x48cm-13x19in) s. canvas on plywood. 22-Jun-4 Christie's, Amsterdam #302/R
£526 $953 €800 Farmer on his land behind his farm (24x38cm-9x15in) s. canvas on panel. 19-Apr-4 Glerum, Amsterdam #208
£671 $1201 €1000 Bucherons dans un paysage (52x128cm-20x50in) s. 25-May-4 Campo & Campo, Antwerp #139
£805 $1490 €1200 Peasant woman near a windmill (41x29cm-16x11in) s. canvas on panel. 15-Mar-4 Sotheby's, Amsterdam #94/R est:1500-2500
£884 $1610 €1300 Peat diggers at work (23x48cm-9x19in) s. canvas on board. 3-Feb-4 Christie's, Amsterdam #209 est:800-1200
£1400 $2520 €2044 Dutch river scene (68x46cm-27x18in) s. 21-Jan-4 Sotheby's, Olympia #397/R est:1000-2000
£1900 $3002 €2755 Boats off the riverbank (91x84cm-36x33in) s. 3-Sep-3 Bonhams, Bury St Edmunds #425/R est:2000-3000
£2667 $4800 €4000 Summer landscape with boats on a waterway (92x84cm-36x33in) s. prov. 20-Apr-4 Sotheby's, Amsterdam #97/R est:2000-3000

KUYPERS, Dirk (attrib) (1733-1796) Dutch
Works on paper
£338 $595 €500 Moated castle, with elegant figures and fisherman in the foreground (13x19cm-5x7in) pen grey ink wash. 19-May-4 Sotheby's, Amsterdam #252/R

KUYPERS, Theo (20th C) ?
Works on paper
£1867 $3435 €2800 Icelandic tales, Stroomgebied Gullfoss (216x123cm-85x48in) s.i.d.97 gouache cardboard. 9-Jun-4 Christie's, Amsterdam #388/R est:2000-3000

KUYTEN, Harrie (1883-1952) Dutch
£300 $549 €450 Landscape with corn bales (18x33cm-7x13in) s. canvas on panel. 7-Jun-4 Glerum, Amsterdam #111/R
£694 $1132 €1000 Flower still life with roses (55x40cm-22x16in) s. 29-Sep-3 Sotheby's, Amsterdam #212
£769 $1284 €1100 View of a village, Bergen (45x59cm-18x23in) s. black chk. 30-Jun-3 Sotheby's, Amsterdam #402/R
£1067 $1952 €1600 Still life with dried flowers in a green pot (89x51cm-35x20in) s.d.1914. 7-Jun-4 Glerum, Amsterdam #103/R est:1800-2200
£1224 $2229 €1800 Boats on a lake in Friesland (32x38cm-13x15in) s. 3-Feb-4 Christie's, Amsterdam #446/R est:1500-2000
£2632 $4842 €4000 Landscape of Loenen (66x55cm-26x22in) s. s.i. on stretcher. 22-Jun-4 Christie's, Amsterdam #554/R est:2500-3500
£2961 $5447 €4500 Sailing boats on a lake (55x40cm-22x16in) s.d.47. 22-Jun-4 Christie's, Amsterdam #461/R est:1500-2000
£5902 $9621 €8500 Paris model (65x50cm-26x20in) s. prov.exhib. 29-Sep-3 Sotheby's, Amsterdam #197/R
£6944 $11318 €10000 View of the Herengracht (65x80cm-26x31in) s. prov. 29-Sep-3 Sotheby's, Amsterdam #193/R
£7638 $12450 €11000 Village by canal (61x71cm-24x28in) s. prov. 29-Sep-3 Sotheby's, Amsterdam #196/R
£10667 $19627 €16000 At the beach (45x55cm-18x22in) s. prov. 9-Jun-4 Christie's, Amsterdam #39/R est:5000-7000
Works on paper
£455 $773 €650 Street scene in Amsterdam (21x26cm-8x10in) init. pencil. 24-Nov-3 Glerum, Amsterdam #14/R
£764 $1245 €1100 Cross bearer (80x54cm-31x21in) s.i.verso gouache prov. 29-Sep-3 Sotheby's, Amsterdam #203/R

KUYTENBROUWER, Martinus Antonius (attrib) (18/19th C) Dutch
£805 $1426 €1200 Quatre chevaliers au soleil levant (61x83cm-24x33in) bears sig panel. 30-Apr-4 Tajan, Paris #225/R

KUZAN, Vadin (20th C) Russian
£402 $651 €583 Market scene with many figures (84x116cm-33x46in) 4-Aug-3 Rasmussen, Vejle #418/R (D.KR 4200)

KUZMA, Stephen (1933-) American
£235 $400 €343 Yellow field by the edge of a wood (51x81cm-20x32in) s.d.68. 5-Nov-3 Doyle, New York #40/R

KUZNETSOV, Pavel (1878-1968) Russian
£18121 $33523 €27000 Les Chameaux dans la Steppe (50x59cm-20x23in) s.d.1912. 15-Mar-4 Claude Boisgirard, Paris #66/R est:28000-30000
Works on paper
£1677 $2800 €2448 Landscape (33x28cm-13x11in) s.d.1925 pencil W/C. 21-Oct-3 Christie's, Rockefeller NY #116 est:2500-3500

KVALSTAD, Louis (20th C) Norwegian
£370 $618 €540 Woodland path (36x32cm-14x13in) s, panel. 20-Oct-3 Blomqvist, Lysaker #1195 (N.KR 4300)

KVAPIL, Charles (1884-1958) Belgian
£315 $536 €460 Nu endormi (40x50cm-16x20in) s. 10-Nov-3 Horta, Bruxelles #8
£385 $654 €550 Le soldat (80x95cm-31x37in) s. 18-Nov-3 Galerie Moderne, Brussels #644
£567 $1043 €850 Nu a la toilette (35x27cm-14x11in) panel. 11-Jun-4 Pierre Berge, Paris #179
£661 $1123 €965 Lock cottage (26x35cm-10x14in) s.d.1925 panel. 5-Nov-3 Dobiaschofsky, Bern #728/R (S.FR 1500)
£665 $1030 €971 Untitled (33x41cm-13x16in) s. 29-Sep-2 Subastas Odalys, Caracas #55/R
£764 $1276 €1100 Corbeille de fleurs (55x81cm-22x32in) s.d.1936. 21-Oct-3 Artcurial Briest, Paris #192
£865 $1600 €1263 Deux nus (25x23cm-10x9in) s. 10-Mar-4 Doyle, New York #58a/R est:900-1200
£986 $1706 €1400 Nu au parasol (16x27cm-6x11in) s. i.verso canvas on panel. 9-Dec-3 Artcurial Briest, Paris #220 est:1200-1600
£1056 $1828 €1500 Sur la plage (33x24cm-13x9in) s. panel. 9-Dec-3 Artcurial Briest, Paris #219/R est:1800-2200
£1080 $1933 €1620 Maison et eglise a Carnac (27x35cm-11x14in) s.d.1926 panel. 16-May-4 Thierry & Lannon, Brest #145/R est:1500-2000
£1200 $2004 €1752 Femme allongee (24x33cm-9x13in) s. 22-Oct-3 Sotheby's, Olympia #108/R est:1500-2000
£1275 $2283 €1900 Vase de glaieuls (60x73cm-24x29in) s.d.1939. 25-May-4 Chambelland & Giafferi, Paris #105/R est:2000-2500
£1325 $2411 €2000 Nature morte aux fleurs et aux fruits (46x38cm-18x15in) s. isorel. 15-Jun-4 Blanchet, Paris #223/R est:1500-2000
£1409 $2437 €2000 Jeune femme au bouquet (46x38cm-18x15in) 9-Dec-3 Artcurial Briest, Paris #215/R est:2500-3500
£1409 $2437 €2000 Roses rouges (46x38cm-18x15in) s. s.i.verso. 9-Dec-3 Artcurial Briest, Paris #217 est:2000-3000
£1409 $2437 €2000 Baignade (32x40cm-13x16in) s. cardboard. 9-Dec-3 Artcurial Briest, Paris #216 est:2000-3000
£1469 $2497 €2100 Bouquet de fleurs (81x60cm-32x24in) s.d.1942. 18-Nov-3 Pierre Berge, Paris #69/R est:2000-2500
£1477 $2643 €2200 Nu devant la fenetre (41x33cm-16x13in) s.d.1972. 30-May-4 Eric Pillon, Calais #59/R
£1565 $2801 €2300 Bouquet de dahlias orange sur une table (54x73cm-21x29in) s.d.1934. 21-Mar-4 Muizon & Le Coent, Paris #52/R
£1678 $2970 €2500 Fillette a la poupee (74x60cm-29x24in) s. panel. 29-Apr-4 David Kahn, Paris #215/R est:2800-3000
£1760 $3046 €2500 Roses et poires (46x55cm-18x22in) s.d.1932 s.i.d.verso. 9-Dec-3 Artcurial Briest, Paris #221/R est:2500-3000
£1879 $3439 €2800 Baigneuse dans un paysage (90x116cm-35x46in) s.d.1936. 7-Jul-4 Artcurial Briest, Paris #86/R est:1500-2000
£1905 $3410 €2800 Nu allonge (18x28cm-7x11in) s.d.1925 bears i.verso panel. 19-Mar-4 Millon & Associes, Paris #78/R est:1000-1500
£2013 $3745 €3000 Nu alangui (46x65cm-18x26in) s. 2-Mar-4 Artcurial Briest, Paris #208/R est:3000-4000
£2013 $3725 €3000 Deux baigneuses (33x55cm-13x22in) s.d.1925. 15-Mar-4 Blanchet, Paris #112/R est:2500-3000
£2177 $3897 €3200 La toilette (60x73cm-24x29in) s. 19-Mar-4 Millon & Associes, Paris #79/R est:3000-4000
£2582 $4390 €3770 Nude (38x55cm-15x22in) s. painted 1925. 23-Nov-3 Subastas Odalys, Caracas #67 est:4000
£3662 $6335 €5200 Baigneuses en plein air (60x81cm-24x32in) s. 13-Dec-3 Martinot & Savignat, Pontoise #131/R est:4000-5000
£3873 $6701 €5500 Bouquets de fleurs sur entablement (73x116cm-29x46in) s.d.1939. 9-Dec-3 Artcurial Briest, Paris #218/R est:6000-10000
£4161 $7740 €6200 Femme nue (64x98cm-25x39in) s.d.1928. 3-Mar-4 Tajan, Paris #61/R est:2500-3000

KVIUM, Michael (1955-) Danish
£845 $1411 €1234 Reality (30x38cm-12x15in) s.d.90 verso. 7-Oct-3 Rasmussen, Copenhagen #199/R (D.KR 9000)
£1033 $1725 €1508 Gnom (25x28cm-10x11in) s.d.1986-87 verso. 7-Oct-3 Rasmussen, Copenhagen #245/R (D.KR 11000)
£2437 $4557 €3558 Fatass (65x148cm-26x58in) s.d.99 verso. 25-Feb-4 Kunsthallen, Copenhagen #90/R est:30000 (D.KR 27000)
£2978 $5569 €4348 Composition U.T. (130x120cm-51x47in) s.d.99 verso. 25-Feb-4 Kunsthallen, Copenhagen #37/R est:35000 (D.KR 33000)
£4225 $7056 €6169 Naive picture (82x100cm-32x39in) s.d.93 prov. 7-Oct-3 Rasmussen, Copenhagen #82/R est:50000 (D.KR 45000)
Works on paper
£329 $549 €480 Organic composition (33x25cm-13x10in) s.d.88 W/C Indian ink pencil. 7-Oct-3 Rasmussen, Copenhagen #202/R (D.KR 3500)
£357 $596 €521 Organic composition (33x24cm-13x9in) s.d.88 W/C. 7-Oct-3 Rasmussen, Copenhagen #246 (D.KR 3800)
£473 $846 €691 Composition (17x27cm-7x11in) s.d.92 W/C. 12-Jan-4 Rasmussen, Vejle #685 (D.KR 5000)

KYHN, Knud (1880-1967) Danish
£275 $500 €402 Winter landscape with two pheasants. Snowy landscape with hare (73x71cm-29x28in) s. double-sided. 7-Feb-4 Rasmussen, Havnen #4081/R (D.KR 3000)
£373 $679 €560 Winter landscape with swans in flight and geese by the coast (121x151cm-48x59in) mono.d.1955. 19-Jun-4 Rasmussen, Havnen #4104/R (D.KR 4200)
£389 $622 €568 View towards the sea with many oyster catchers (124x158cm-49x62in) mono.d.1936. 22-Sep-3 Rasmussen, Vejle #586/R (D.KR 4100)
£403 $726 €588 Horses underneath old hawthorn (85x100cm-33x39in) mono.d.1940. 24-Apr-4 Rasmussen, Havnen #4235/R (D.KR 4500)
£514 $951 €750 Seagulls by large stone at water's edge (143x183cm-56x72in) mono.d.1923. 15-Mar-4 Rasmussen, Vejle #672/R (D.KR 5700)
£578 $925 €844 Birds by the sea (132x143cm-52x56in) mono.d.1926. 22-Sep-3 Rasmussen, Vejle #585/R (D.KR 6100)
£595 $1083 €869 Coastal landscape with horses and seagulls (145x160cm-57x63in) mono.d.1942. 7-Feb-4 Rasmussen, Havnen #4169 (D.KR 6500)

KYHN, Vilhelm (1819-1903) Danish

£289	$540	€422	Sunset (21x29cm-8x11in) panel. 25-Feb-4 Kunsthallen, Copenhagen #493 (D.KR 3200)
£375	$625	€548	Heath landscape (19x29cm-7x11in) init. 25-Oct-3 Rasmussen, Havnen #2185 (D.KR 4000)
£449	$836	€656	Farm in evening light, late summer (37x50cm-15x20in) 2-Mar-4 Rasmussen, Copenhagen #1368/R (D.KR 5000)
£537	$983	€784	Landscape with lake and tall trees (41x51cm-16x20in) init. 9-Jun-4 Rasmussen, Copenhagen #1710/R (D.KR 6000)
£614	$1100	€896	Coastal landscape with cliffs, Bornholm (30x44cm-12x17in) mono. 12-Jan-4 Rasmussen, Vejle #90/R (D.KR 6500)
£627	$1147	€915	Snow blowing over houses and path in outskirts of wood (39x52cm-15x20in) s.d.1892 exhib. 9-Jun-4 Rasmussen, Copenhagen #1758/R (D.KR 7000)
£645	$1097	€942	View across roof tops, winter (41x36cm-16x14in) s. i.stretcher. 10-Nov-3 Rasmussen, Vejle #25/R (D.KR 7000)
£709	$1269	€1035	Danish summer landscape with figures and houses (30x38cm-12x15in) mono. 12-Jan-4 Rasmussen, Vejle #66/R (D.KR 7500)
£800	$1456	€1200	Landscape from Ellekrat in Rold Wood (40x53cm-16x21in) 19-Jun-4 Rasmussen, Havnen #2079/R (D.KR 9000)
£809	$1504	€1181	Landscape from Isefjord (77x108cm-30x43in) 2-Mar-4 Rasmussen, Copenhagen #1634/R (D.KR 9000)
£922	$1567	€1346	Beach scene, Capri (22x25cm-9x10in) mono.i.d.15/4-51. 10-Nov-3 Rasmussen, Vejle #76/R (D.KR 10000)
£992	$1776	€1448	Danish summer evening (109x163cm-43x64in) s.d.1888. 12-Jan-4 Rasmussen, Vejle #81/R (D.KR 10500)
£1075	$1935	€1570	Landscape from Roskilde fjord (30x47cm-12x19in) s. 24-Apr-4 Rasmussen, Havnen #2141/R est:8000-12000 (D.KR 12000)
£1165	$2097	€1701	Summer's day by the fjord (32x48cm-13x19in) i.verso. 24-Apr-4 Rasmussen, Havnen #2144/R est:6000-8000 (D.KR 13000)
£1244	$2115	€1816	Summer landscape with figures by lake, Denmark (33x45cm-13x18in) init.d.1878 i.verso. 10-Nov-3 Rasmussen, Vejle #29/R est:10000-12000 (D.KR 13500)
£1254	$2258	€1831	Seascape with sailing vessels in a calm (21x32cm-8x13in) i.verso cardboard on canvas. 24-Apr-4 Rasmussen, Havnen #2136/R est:8000-10000 (D.KR 14000)
£1343	$2457	€1961	Woodland lake in summer (33x25cm-13x10in) init.d.44. 7-Jun-4 Museumsbygningen, Copenhagen #17/R est:12000-15000 (D.KR 15000)
£1611	$2949	€2352	Dog roses by waterway (47x59cm-19x23in) mono. prov. 9-Jun-4 Rasmussen, Copenhagen #1654/R est:20000-25000 (D.KR 18000)
£1797	$3342	€2624	Bird on branch in snow covered woods (37x50cm-15x20in) s.d.1919. 2-Mar-4 Rasmussen, Copenhagen #1374/R est:20000 (D.KR 20000)
£3308	$5723	€4830	Coastal landscape, Falster (34x46cm-13x18in) mono.d.22/6/59 exhib.prov. 9-Dec-3 Rasmussen, Copenhagen #1210/R est:30000-40000 (D.KR 35000)
£3308	$5723	€4830	Sailing at Sundet (88x124cm-35x49in) s.d.1897. 9-Dec-3 Rasmussen, Copenhagen #1486/R est:50000 (D.KR 35000)
£5771	$10676	€8426	Landscape from Aadal (64x84cm-25x33in) s.d.1872. 15-Mar-4 Rasmussen, Vejle #19/R est:35000-40000 (D.KR 64000)
£7240	$12959	€10570	Summer landscape from the east coast of Jylland with girls picking flowers (73x110cm-29x43in) s. exhib. 10-May-4 Rasmussen, Vejle #43/R est:100000 (D.KR 80000)

KYLBERG, Carl (1878-1952) Swedish

£1435	$2440	€2095	Coastal landscape (26x36cm-10x14in) 4-Nov-3 Bukowskis, Stockholm #199/R est:20000-25000 (S.KR 19000)
£2190	$3724	€3197	Man in red (66x54cm-26x21in) 4-Nov-3 Bukowskis, Stockholm #195/R est:40000-50000 (S.KR 29000)
£2344	$4149	€3422	Woman with red hair (63x44cm-25x17in) panel. 27-Apr-4 AB Stockholms Auktionsverk #877/R est:40000-50000 (S.KR 32000)
£3021	$5136	€4411	Evening's light and dark (39x47cm-15x19in) init. exhib.lit. 5-Nov-3 AB Stockholms Auktionsverk #893/R est:50000-60000 (S.KR 40000)
£3771	$6788	€5506	Britta (69x57cm-27x22in) init. verso painted c.1930 exhib. 26-Apr-4 Bukowskis, Stockholm #134/R est:30000-35000 (S.KR 52000)
£4810	$8851	€7215	In the field (44x46cm-17x18in) init. 14-Jun-4 Lilla Bukowskis, Stockholm #698/R est:30000-40000 (S.KR 66000)
£5136	$8731	€7499	Ruth (59x42cm-23x17in) init. exhib.prov. 4-Nov-3 Bukowskis, Stockholm #195a/R est:80000-90000 (S.KR 68000)
£5231	$8997	€7637	Landscape (48x55cm-19x22in) mono. s.d.23/4 1937 verso. 7-Dec-3 Uppsala Auktionskammare, Uppsala #232/R est:40000-50000 (S.KR 68000)
£5366	$9659	€7834	Coastal landscape, by Vasterhavet (48x61cm-19x24in) exhib. 26-Apr-4 Bukowskis, Stockholm #140/R est:60000-70000 (S.KR 74000)
£12085	$20544	€17644	Meditation - study (49x56cm-19x22in) init. lit. 5-Nov-3 AB Stockholms Auktionsverk #860/R est:140000-160000 (S.KR 160000)
£33988	$57779	€49622	Night I I (91x110cm-36x43in) init. painted c.1936-37 exhib. 4-Nov-3 Bukowskis, Stockholm #159/R est:500000-600000 (S.KR 450000)
£36258	$65265	€52937	Meditation (89x99cm-35x39in) init. painted 1925 prov.exhib.lit. 26-Apr-4 Bukowskis, Stockholm #143/R est:500000-600000 (S.KR 500000)
£79768	$143582	€116461	Morning in the harbour (100x82cm-39x32in) s. painted c.1939 prov. 26-Apr-4 Bukowskis, Stockholm #49/R est:700000-800000 (S.KR 1100000)
Works on paper			
£566	$963	€826	The monkey and the chicken - from Leo the Lion (31x17cm-12x7in) W/C pencil. 4-Nov-3 Bukowskis, Stockholm #200/R (S.KR 7500)
£691	$1243	€1009	Meditation (17x19cm-7x7in) s. study lit. 26-Jan-4 Lilla Bukowskis, Stockholm #12 (S.KR 9200)
£1577	$2838	€2302	Figure scene with the artist's self portrait (70x141cm-28x56in) chk. 26-Jan-4 Lilla Bukowskis, Stockholm #628 est:15000-18000 (S.KR 21000)
£1652	$2973	€2412	Figure scene with old woman smoking pipe (95x186cm-37x73in) chk. 26-Jan-4 Lilla Bukowskis, Stockholm #623 est:20000-25000 (S.KR 22000)
£1652	$2973	€2412	Figure scene with policeman and man smoking cigar (70x150cm-28x59in) chk. 26-Jan-4 Lilla Bukowskis, Stockholm #626 est:15000-18000 (S.KR 22000)
£1727	$3108	€2521	Figure scene with figures dancing (69x97cm-27x38in) chk. 26-Jan-4 Lilla Bukowskis, Stockholm #630 est:10000-12000 (S.KR 23000)
£2477	$4459	€3616	Figure scene with man playing concertina (95x191cm-37x75in) chk. 26-Jan-4 Lilla Bukowskis, Stockholm #624 est:20000-25000 (S.KR 33000)

KYLE, Georgina Moutray (1865-1950) British

£1000	$1660	€1460	Female study (33x22cm-13x9in) s. board. 1-Oct-3 John Ross, Belfast #17 est:600-800

KYODEN, Santo (1761-1816) Japanese

Prints			
£2800	$5012	€4088	Untitled (37x50cm-15x20in) col print. 13-May-4 Christie's, Kensington #290/R est:2500-4000

KYOSAI, Kawanabe (1831-1899) Japanese

Works on paper			
£588	$1000	€858	Amorous men and women posed together (38x930cm-15x366in) s. ink col sketches eleven on one handscroll. 4-Nov-3 Bonhams & Butterfields, San Francisco #3074/R est:2000-3000

KYOSHO, Tachihara (1785-1840) Japanese

Works on paper			
£815	$1500	€1190	Recluses fishing on a river in autumn (130x49cm-51x19in) s. col ink hanging scroll. 23-Mar-4 Christie's, Rockefeller NY #112/R est:3000-4000

KYOSHO, Tachihara and SUIKEN, Tachihara (18/19th C) Japanese

Works on paper			
£1300	$2171	€1885	Willow tree with scholar crossing a bridge (92x27cm-36x11in) s.i.d.1806 ink hanging scroll silk. 18-Jun-3 Christie's, London #277/R est:1500-2000

KYUZAN, Kano (1655-1724) Japanese

Works on paper			
£1096	$1863	€1600	Landscape (30x491cm-12x193in) s. seal Indian ink col handscroll prov. 8-Nov-3 Dr Fritz Nagel, Stuttgart #2004/R est:400

KYYHKYNEN, Juho (1875-1909) Finnish

£2313	$4210	€3400	Laplander's tent in winter (41x29cm-16x11in) s.d.1908. 8-Feb-4 Bukowskis, Helsinki #384/R est:1500
£3200	$5728	€4800	Laplander and reindeer in winter (25x48cm-10x19in) s.d.1907 canvas on board. 15-May-4 Hagelstam, Helsinki #138/R est:1500
£8108	$14514	€12000	In Lapland (63x61cm-25x24in) s. 8-May-4 Bukowskis, Helsinki #97/R est:3500-4000

LAABS, Hans (1915-) Polish

£315	$535	€450	Abstract portrait in orange, purple and blue (29x38cm-11x15in) s.d.96 s. verso acrylic paper. 29-Nov-3 Arnold, Frankfurt #345/R
£503	$926	€750	Coastal landscape (35x46cm-14x18in) s.d.85 s.i.d.1985 verso. 27-Mar-4 Dannenberg, Berlin #582/R

LAAGE, Wilhelm (1868-1930) German

£2098	$3566	€3000	Cornfield (65x80cm-26x31in) mono. i. verso. 21-Nov-3 Reiss & Sohn, Konigstein #452/R est:3500

LAAN, Gerard van der (1844-1915) Dutch

£1111	$1811	€1600	Boats sailing on the sea (39x28cm-15x11in) s. canvas on panel. 29-Sep-3 Sotheby's, Amsterdam #154/R
Works on paper			
£448	$749	€654	Sailing boats on a choppy sea (46x69cm-18x27in) s. W/C. 20-Oct-3 Stephan Welz, Johannesburg #461 est:1800-2400 (SA.R 5200)

LAAN, Jan Zeeuw van der (1832-1892) Dutch

£724	$1310	€1100	Back of a farm (50x72cm-20x28in) s.d.1879 panel. 19-Apr-4 Glerum, Amsterdam #42/R

LAANEN, Jasper van der (attrib) (1592-1626) Flemish

£2500	$4600	€3800	Peasants on path by river (16x19cm-6x7in) panel. 25-Jun-4 Piasa, Paris #86 est:2500-3000

LAAR, Bartol Wilhelm van (1818-1901) Dutch

£490	$842	€700	Fishing boats on misty morning (27x44cm-11x17in) s. panel. 5-Dec-3 Michael Zeller, Lindau #682/R
£1633	$2971	€2400	Steamer on a stormy sea. Shipping on a calm (34x51cm-13x20in) s. panel pair. 3-Feb-4 Christie's, Amsterdam #94/R est:800-1200

LAAR, Pieter Jacobsz van (c.1582-c.1642) Dutch

Works on paper			
£2397	$4075	€3500	View of the Aqua Condotto, Rome (19x30cm-7x12in) bears sig.i. pen brown ink wash. 4-Nov-3 Sotheby's, Amsterdam #98/R est:6000-8000

LAAR, Pieter Jacobsz van (attrib) (c.1582-c.1642) Dutch

£2649	$4821	€4000	Rider resting by camp (30x38cm-12x15in) prov. 16-Jun-4 Christie's, Rome #287/R est:4000-5000
£3077	$5292	€4492	Harbour scene with figures (91x94cm-36x37in) 3-Dec-3 AB Stockholms Auktionsverk #2692/R est:40000-50000 (S.KR 40000)
£7383	$13584	€11000	Acqua Acetosa near Rome (66x50cm-26x20in) i. prov. 25-Mar-4 Dr Fritz Nagel, Stuttgart #619/R est:7000

LAASIO, Mikko (1913-1997) Finnish

£400	$736	€600	Still life of lemons and oranges (40x47cm-16x19in) s.d.72. 9-Jun-4 Bukowskis, Helsinki #450/R
£775	$1340	€1100	Still life of flowers (43x55cm-17x22in) s.d.1969. 13-Dec-3 Hagelstam, Helsinki #159/R
£775	$1340	€1100	Landscape in winter (50x73cm-20x29in) s.d.1961. 13-Dec-3 Hagelstam, Helsinki #160/R
£845	$1352	€1200	Summer landscape from Lapland (66x76cm-26x30in) s.d.69. 21-Sep-3 Bukowskis, Helsinki #380/R
£972	$1624	€1400	Wet winter's day (46x61cm-18x24in) s.d.69 exhib. 26-Oct-3 Bukowskis, Helsinki #392/R

LABARRE, Charles (?-1906) French?

£775	$1340	€1100	Jeune femme et son enfant passant le gue (46x33cm-18x13in) s. 14-Dec-3 Eric Pillon, Calais #28/R

LABAT, Achille (attrib) (1889-?) French
Works on paper
£340 $609 €500 Marine (21x26cm-8x10in) s.d.1903 W/C black pencil. 19-Mar-4 Piasa, Paris #207

LABBE, Jean (20th C) French
Works on paper
£634 $1027 €900 Port of Cherbourg (26x48cm-10x19in) s.i.d.1942 W/C. 11-Aug-3 Boscher, Cherbourg #866/R

LABILLE-GUIARD, Madame Adelaide (1749-1803) French
Works on paper
£12245 $21918 €18000 La Princesse de Montlear (80x64cm-31x25in) pastel oval prov.lit. 18-Mar-4 Christie's, Paris #144/R est:10000-15000

LABIOS, Agapito (1898-1996) Mexican
£455 $850 €664 Young girl in blue on a terrace (61x46cm-24x18in) s. 25-Feb-4 Doyle, New York #83/R
£3804 $7000 €5554 Ninas mejicanas (56x41cm-22x16in) s. five. 10-Jun-4 Sotheby's, New York #123/R est:3000-5000

LABISSE, Felix (1905-1982) French
£452 $719 €660 Woman (57x69cm-22x27in) s. 29-Apr-3 Louis Morton, Mexico #116 (M.P 7500)
£1119 $1902 €1600 Dansons la trompeuse (73x60cm-29x24in) s. prov. 23-Nov-3 Cornette de St.Cyr, Paris #200/R est:800-1000
£1224 $2192 €1800 Oilette (33x24cm-13x9in) s. s.i.d.1974 verso. 19-Mar-4 Millon & Associes, Paris #163/R est:1000-1200
£2041 $3653 €3000 L'Imprudence (35x27cm-14x11in) s. s.i.d.1941 verso exhib. 21-Mar-4 Calmels Cohen, Paris #37/R est:3000-4000
£2083 $3479 €3000 Rupex (55x46cm-22x18in) s.d.1960. 21-Oct-3 Campo, Vlaamse Kaai #463 est:4000-4500
£3000 $5400 €4500 Iphianasses (65x54cm-26x21in) s. i.d.1980 verso exhib. 24-Apr-4 Cornette de St.Cyr, Paris #375/R est:7000
£5245 $9021 €7500 La visiteuse (81x65cm-32x26in) s. s.i.d.44 verso. 2-Dec-3 Sotheby's, Amsterdam #76/R est:4500-5500
£6597 $11017 €9500 Ils attendent Captain Crook (151x165cm-59x65in) s. d.1953 verso. 21-Oct-3 Campo & Campo, Antwerp #167/R est:5000-8000
Works on paper
£268 $499 €400 Costume pour Johanne (36x18cm-14x7in) s.i. gouache pencil. 2-Mar-4 Artcurial Briest, Paris #78
£451 $754 €650 Water nymphs (19x27cm-7x11in) s. gouache. 21-Oct-3 Campo & Campo, Antwerp #168/R
£533 $981 €800 Le temps (47x27cm-19x11in) s.i. gouache. 11-Jun-4 Pierre Berge, Paris #111/R
£1020 $1857 €1500 La nuit verte - green night (52x35cm-20x14in) s. s.i.d.1969 verso gouache. 3-Feb-4 Christie's, Amsterdam #566/R est:1500-2000
£1300 $2171 €1898 African scene (56x74cm-22x29in) s. gouache prov. 22-Oct-3 Sotheby's, Olympia #182/R est:1500-2000

LABITTE, Eugène-Leon (1858-1937) French
£1127 $1972 €1600 Fenaison en Bretagne (33x41cm-13x16in) s. panel. 21-Dec-3 Thierry & Lannon, Brest #170/R est:800-1000
£1972 $3530 €2800 Couple pres de la fontaine (111x115cm-44x45in) s. 11-Jan-4 Rouillac, Vendome #355

LABO, Savinio (1899-1976) Italian
£467 $859 €700 Landscape in Anticoli (30x40cm-12x16in) s. s.i.verso. 10-Jun-4 Galleria Pace, Milan #17/R
£493 $853 €700 View of village (45x35cm-18x14in) s. cardboard. 11-Dec-3 Christie's, Rome #102
£503 $931 €750 White socks (40x30cm-16x12in) s. s.i.verso. 11-Mar-4 Galleria Pace, Milan #35/R
£805 $1490 €1200 Landscape on the Elba (40x50cm-16x20in) s. s.i.verso. 13-Mar-4 Meeting Art, Vercelli #492
£870 $1426 €1200 Little nude (65x50cm-26x20in) s. prov. 29-May-3 Galleria Pace, Milan #35
£1408 $2338 €2000 Still life (60x45cm-24x18in) s.d.1950. 11-Jun-3 Finarte Semenzato, Milan #719

LABOMBARDA, Eduardo (20th C) Venezuelan?
£1985 $3375 €2898 Untitled (80x120cm-31x47in) painted 2002. 23-Nov-3 Subastas Odalys, Caracas #82 est:3500

LABORDE, Chas (1886-1941) French
Works on paper
£1075 $2000 €1570 American soldiers (34x26cm-13x10in) s.d.1919 pen ink W/C. 2-Mar-4 Swann Galleries, New York #329/R est:2500-3500

LABORDE, Emile (19th C) French?
£1399 $2378 €2000 L'entree de la messe (38x27cm-15x11in) s.d.1869. 30-Nov-3 Anaf, Lyon #122 est:2000-3000

LABORNE, Edme Émile (1837-1913) French
£350 $594 €500 La chapelle du chateau royal d'Amboise (41x32cm-16x13in) panel. 28-Nov-3 Doutrebente, Paris #35
£1469 $2497 €2100 Bord de Loire (55x76cm-22x30in) s. 28-Nov-3 Doutrebente, Paris #32/R est:1500-2000
£1645 $2977 €2500 Fete champetre (24x35cm-9x14in) s. 19-Apr-4 Boscher, Cherbourg #810/R
£1748 $2972 €2500 Les bucherons (130x98cm-51x39in) s. 28-Nov-3 Doutrebente, Paris #33/R est:3000-3500
£3385 $5822 €4942 Still life of flowers (100x74cm-39x29in) s. 2-Dec-3 Bukowskis, Stockholm #281/R est:60000-80000 (S.KR 44000)
£3916 $6657 €5600 Riviere en Touraine (130x98cm-51x39in) s. 28-Nov-3 Doutrebente, Paris #34/R est:2000-3000
£4167 $7500 €6084 Country landscape (133x97cm-52x38in) s. 22-Apr-4 Christie's, Rockefeller NY #117/R est:8000-12000
£7133 $12126 €10200 Bordeaux, le port, a gauche la place des Quinconces (71x100cm-28x39in) s.i.d.1871. 28-Nov-3 Doutrebente, Paris #31/R est:4000-5000
Works on paper
£280 $476 €400 Bord de fleuve (25x27cm-10x11in) s. W/C. 28-Nov-3 Doutrebente, Paris #19/R
£385 $654 €550 Cour de ferme a Coulanges, Loir-et-Cher (34x41cm-13x16in) s. pastel. 28-Nov-3 Doutrebente, Paris #23/R
£528 $850 €771 Canotage sur la seine, Argenteuil (25x40cm-10x16in) s.i. W/C bodycol. 14-Jan-4 Christie's, Rockefeller NY #37/R
£839 $1427 €1200 Paris, le bassin des Tuileries (32x43cm-13x17in) s. W/C. 28-Nov-3 Doutrebente, Paris #18/R

LABORNE, Marguerite (?) French?
£455 $773 €650 Maree basse (4x24cm-2x9in) s. oil paper. 28-Nov-3 Doutrebente, Paris #37/R

LABOULAYE, Paul de (19th C) French
£1275 $2359 €1900 Diane chasseresse (115x115cm-45x45in) s. 15-Mar-4 Horta, Bruxelles #244 est:2000-3000

LABOUREUR, Jean Émile (1877-1943) French
Prints
£2800 $4816 €4088 Lassitude (24x27cm-9x11in) s.num.24/35 col woodcut. 2-Dec-3 Christie's, London #176/R est:3000-5000
Works on paper
£364 $667 €550 Scene des Iles (32x25cm-13x10in) Indian ink wash prov. 7-Apr-4 Piasa, Paris #210/R
£775 $1356 €1100 Peche a la crevette (22x14cm-9x6in) s. pen drawing. 21-Dec-3 Thierry & Lannon, Brest #113
£2238 $3804 €3200 Jeune femme devant la baie (29x20cm-11x8in) s. crayon dr. 28-Nov-3 Drouot Estimations, Paris #138 est:250-400

LABOURN, Colley (?) ?
£500 $820 €730 Young sportsman tending injured bird (28x23cm-11x9in) s. 6-Jun-3 Biddle & Webb, Birmingham #212

LABRA, Jose Maria de (1925-) Spanish
Works on paper
£336 $601 €500 Nude (123x70cm-48x28in) s.i.d.57 dr. 25-May-4 Durán, Madrid #628/R

LABRADOR, Adelina (20th C) Spanish
£660 $1122 €950 Segovia (70x80cm-28x31in) s. s.i.verso. 28-Oct-3 Segre, Madrid #92/R

LABRANCHE, Gilles (1947-) Canadian
£280 $512 €409 Parfum d'ete, Porte St Louis, Quebec (50x40cm-20x16in) s.i.d.1997 acrylic. 1-Jun-4 Hodgins, Calgary #71/R (C.D 700)

LABROUCHE, Pierre (fl.1905-1921) French
£2069 $3434 €3000 View of Sepulveda (75x100cm-30x39in) s. 30-Sep-3 Ansorena, Madrid #96/R est:3000

LABRUZZI, Carlo (1748-1818) Italian
Works on paper
£4000 $7360 €6000 Scenes in Rome (37x52cm-15x20in) one s. ink W/C set of 6. 10-Jun-4 Christie's, Rome #91/R est:6000-8000

LABRUZZI, Carlo (circle) (1748-1818) Italian
£5000 $8500 €7300 Rocky river landscape with a figure in a boat, hilltop ruin and a view to a village beyond (86x120cm-34x47in) 29-Oct-3 Bonhams, New Bond Street #128/R est:3000-5000

LABY, Auguste François (1784-1860) French
£8054 $14819 €12000 Portrait du Comte de Narcillac. Portrait de la Comtesse de Narcillac (92x73cm-36x29in) s.d.1825 pair. 26-Mar-4 Daguerre, Paris #59/R est:12000-15000

LACALLE, Abraham (1968-) Spanish
£3401 $6190 €5000 Interior (95x83cm-37x33in) s.d.1992 prov. 3-Feb-4 Segre, Madrid #371/R est:3500

LACAMERA, Fortunato (1887-1951) Argentinian
£7967 $14500 €11632 Composition with grapes (35x50cm-14x20in) s. cardboard. 29-Jun-4 Arroyo, Buenos Aires #76/R est:14500
£9392 $17000 €13712 Still life (43x50cm-17x20in) cardboard. 30-Mar-4 Arroyo, Buenos Aires #75

LACASSE, Joseph (1894-1975) Belgian
£256 $409 €371 Composition (24x18cm-9x7in) panel. 22-Sep-3 Blomqvist, Lysaker #1194/R (N.KR 3000)
£403 $713 €600 Composition (23x19cm-9x7in) mono.d.1936 oil collage paper on canvas. 27-Apr-4 Artcurial Briest, Paris #117
£2400 $4248 €3504 Abstract in yellow and green (32x40cm-13x16in) s.i.d.1948. 27-Apr-4 Bonhams, Knightsbridge #37/R est:1500-2500

£4865 $9000 €7103 Composition (81x99cm-32x39in) s.d.1959. 13-Jul-4 Christie's, Rockefeller NY #68/R est:6000-8000
£6803 $12177 €10000 Tournoi (100x81cm-39x32in) s.d.1913-14 s.i.d.verso. 19-Mar-4 Millon & Associes, Paris #83/R est:2000-3000
£7823 $14003 €11500 Nature morte cubiste au pichet (40x50cm-16x20in) s.d.1912. 19-Mar-4 Millon & Associes, Paris #84 est:1200-1500

LACAZE, Germaine (1908-1994) French
£629 $1070 €900 Les abatilles sur la dune (55x46cm-22x18in) s. lit. 27-Nov-3 Millon & Associes, Paris #221
£769 $1308 €1100 Bouquet de fiancailles (65x46cm-26x18in) s.d.22-3-70 lit. 27-Nov-3 Millon & Associes, Paris #216/R
£769 $1308 €1100 Les poupees (60x73cm-24x29in) s. lit. 27-Nov-3 Millon & Associes, Paris #219
£1761 $3046 €2500 A l'atelier, le chien de porcelaine (146x89cm-57x35in) s. i.d.1956 verso lit. 10-Dec-3 Millon & Associes, Paris #107a est:3000-4000

LACCETTI, Valerico (1836-1909) Italian
£528 $877 €750 Pecore lungo il torrente (18x31cm-7x12in) s. panel. 11-Jun-3 Christie's, Rome #20
£1400 $2590 €2044 Barn interior with bull and figures (86x74cm-34x29in) s. 14-Jul-4 Bonhams, Chester #400/R est:1500-2000

LACCETTI, Valerico (attrib) (1836-1909) Italian
£333 $613 €500 Cows at pasture (64x77cm-25x30in) bears sig. 10-Jun-4 Christie's, Rome #8

LACH, Andreas (1817-1882) Austrian
£1538 $2646 €2200 Still life with roses (30x37cm-12x15in) s. 3-Dec-3 Neumeister, Munich #641/R est:1500
£1944 $3306 €2800 Alpine flowers with landscape beyond (44x36cm-17x14in) s.d.1854. 28-Oct-3 Dorotheum, Vienna #211/R est:3000-3600
£2000 $3700 €2920 Still life of game (60x50cm-24x20in) s. 14-Jul-4 Sotheby's, Olympia #222/R est:2000-3000

LACH, Fritz (1868-1933) Austrian
Works on paper
£680 $1272 €993 Stein a Donau (37x48cm-15x19in) s.d.1902 W/C. 20-Jul-4 Sworder & Son, Bishops Stortford #676/R
£1275 $2346 €1900 Theben on the Donau (22x17cm-9x7in) s.i.d.07 W/C. 26-Mar-4 Dorotheum, Vienna #298/R est:1400-1500
£2013 $3705 €3000 Allerheiligen, Murztal (25x40cm-10x16in) s.i.d.09 w/C. 26-Mar-4 Dorotheum, Vienna #235/R est:2000-2500

LACHAISE, Gaston (1882-1935) American/French
Works on paper
£599 $1000 €875 Two women dancing (48x30cm-19x12in) s. black ink pencil prov. 7-Oct-3 Sotheby's, New York #210
£1081 $2000 €1578 Female figure (61x48cm-24x19in) init. blk ink double-sided prov. 15-Jul-4 Sotheby's, New York #85 est:700-1200
£1890 $3250 €2759 Female Nude (43x30cm-17x12in) s. pencil. 7-Dec-3 Freeman, Philadelphia #146 est:3000-5000
£2072 $3750 €3025 Female nude (24x18cm-9x7in) s. pencil. 31-Mar-4 Sotheby's, New York #150/R est:1500-2500
£2571 $4500 €3754 Female nude (48x30cm-19x12in) s. pencil prov. 19-Dec-3 Sotheby's, New York #1050/R est:2500-3500
£3039 $5500 €4437 Nude torso with drapery (35x25cm-14x10in) s. pencil prov. 31-Mar-4 Sotheby's, New York #149/R est:3000-5000

LACHER, Max (1905-) German
£1074 $1922 €1600 Nude woman, surrounded by animals, lying on sofa (35x50cm-14x20in) s. behind glass. 25-May-4 Karl & Faber, Munich #375/R est:1200

LACHEVRE, Bernard (1885-1950) French
£347 $580 €500 Paquebot sur mer formee (60x78cm-24x31in) s. cardboard. 26-Oct-3 Lesieur & Le Bars, Le Havre #37

LACHIEZE-REY, Henri (1927-1974) French
£2013 $3685 €3000 Marche (41x19cm-16x7in) s. s.i.d.1968 verso. 7-Jul-4 Artcurial Briest, Paris #168 est:1500-1800

LACHMAN, Fran (1911-1980) American
£559 $1000 €816 Symphony in red (91x130cm-36x51in) s. 7-May-4 Sloans & Kenyon, Bethesda #1740/R

LACHMAN, Harry (1886-1974) American/French
£483 $850 €705 Ruins in Northern France (61x51cm-24x20in) s. 23-May-4 Hindman, Chicago #42/R
£2174 $4000 €3174 Sun-dappled garden (56x71cm-22x28in) s.d.37 prov. 8-Jun-4 Bonhams & Butterfields, San Francisco #4070/R est:4000-6000
£2174 $4000 €3174 Automne, St Paul (54x45cm-21x18in) s. i. stretcher prov. 8-Jun-4 Bonhams & Butterfields, San Francisco #4071/R est:4000-6000

LACHNIT, Wilhelm (1899-1962) German
£6533 $11695 €9800 Still life (70x120cm-28x47in) s.d.44. 15-May-4 Van Ham, Cologne #746/R est:6000

LACHTROPIUS, Nicolaes (17th C) Dutch
£30000 $54900 €43800 Roses, tulip, carnation and other flowers in a gilt bronze bowl, butterfly on a ledge (43x32cm-17x13in) 7-Jul-4 Bonhams, New Bond Street #30/R est:15000-20000

LACK, Stephen (fl.1970) Canadian
£830 $1527 €1212 Soldiers in the snow (137x155cm-54x61in) s.d.1986 verso acrylic prov. 8-Jun-4 Germann, Zurich #827/R (S.FR 1900)

LACOMBE, Georges (1868-1916) French
Works on paper
£360 $644 €540 Orchidees (50x32cm-20x13in) i. black crayon ink. 16-May-4 Thierry & Lannon, Brest #400/R
£486 $812 €700 Brindille de hetre (20x26cm-8x10in) st.mono.i. ink graphite. 25-Oct-3 Cornette de St.Cyr, Paris #518
£577 $1033 €860 Sylvie prenant son repas (49x32cm-19x13in) mono. black crayon. 25-May-4 Thierry & Lannon, Brest #287/R

LACOMBLEZ, Jacques (1934-) Belgian
£403 $713 €600 Tombeau pour Anton. mono. s.d.1974 verso. 27-Apr-4 Campo, Vlaamse Kaai #479

LACON, J (18th C) ?
Miniatures
£1400 $2380 €2044 Gentleman wearing blue coat, red waistcoat, white lace cravat and stock (4cm-2in) gold frame oval. 18-Nov-3 Bonhams, New Bond Street #65/R est:1400-1600

LACOSTE, Charles (1870-1959) French
£430 $788 €650 Paysage (24x32cm-9x13in) s. cardboard. 9-Apr-4 Claude Aguttes, Neuilly #12
£2098 $3608 €3000 Les amandiers ou Avril dans la brume (46x65cm-18x26in) s.d.1921. 3-Dec-3 Beaussant & Lefèvre, Paris #47/R est:3000-3200
£2267 $4103 €3400 Les arbres (54x65cm-21x26in) s. 5-Apr-4 Marie & Robert, Paris #43 est:4000-5000

LACOSTE, Eugène (19th C) French
Works on paper
£340 $541 €500 Projet pour Polyeucte (23x13cm-9x5in) W/C. 21-Mar-3 Bailly Pommery, Paris #103
£476 $757 €700 Projet pour Polyeucte (23x13cm-9x5in) W/C. 21-Mar-3 Bailly Pommery, Paris #104

LACOUR, Pierre (18/19th C) French
Works on paper
£872 $1632 €1300 Homme assis vu de profil (34x26cm-13x10in) i. black crayon white chk. 29-Feb-4 Osenat, Fontainebleau #228

LACROIX DE MARSEILLE (attrib) (18/19th C) French
£3217 $5469 €4600 Pecheurs sur les bords d'un rivage agite (68x84cm-27x33in) prov. 1-Dec-3 Millon & Associes, Paris #43/R est:4000-6000

LACROIX DE MARSEILLE, Charles François (1720-c.1782) French
£2395 $4000 €3497 Figures along the shore (61x83cm-24x33in) prov.exhib. 22-Oct-3 Doyle, New York #106 est:2000-3000
£10526 $19368 €16000 Danse au bord de l'eau au soleil couchant (26x38cm-10x15in) s.d.1764 panel prov.exhib.lit. 24-Jun-4 Christie's, Paris #128/R est:8000-12000
£16000 $27680 €23360 Mediterranean harbour scene with figures on the shore and fisherman (25x32cm-10x13in) bears sig. prov. 11-Dec-3 Sotheby's, London #233/R est:10000-15000
£23684 $43579 €36000 Pecheurs au bord de la mer au soleil couchant (23x34cm-9x13in) s.d.1769. 24-Jun-4 Christie's, Paris #113/R est:15000-20000
£105263 $193684 €160000 Paysage avec temple de Vesta (112x168cm-44x66in) s.d.1766. 24-Jun-4 Christie's, Paris #86/R est:160000-200000
£181208 $333423 €270000 Vue d'un port Mediterraneen imaginaire (60x113cm-24x44in) s.i.d.1750. 29-Mar-4 Rieunier, Paris #15/R est:80000-100000

LACROIX DE MARSEILLE, Charles François (attrib) (1720-c.1782) French
£2361 $4250 €3447 Port scene (33x99cm-13x39in) 21-Jan-4 Doyle, New York #53/R est:4000-6000
£2649 $4821 €4000 Scene de port mediterraneen (19x28cm-7x11in) panel. 21-Jun-4 Tajan, Paris #118 est:4000-6000
£2841 $5000 €4148 Busy harbour scene (41x65cm-16x26in) 19-May-4 Doyle, New York #6078/R est:6000-8000

LACROIX DE MARSEILLE, Charles François (style) (1720-c.1782) French
£6011 $11000 €8776 Mediterranean port with a lighthouse and an English man-o-war (102x128cm-40x50in) 3-Jun-4 Christie's, Rockefeller NY #1163/R est:1500-2500

LACROIX, Clemence (1849-1925) French
£510 $913 €750 Canal a Gand (65x81cm-26x32in) s. 16-Mar-4 Vanderkindere, Brussels #273

LACROIX, Gaspard Jean (1810-1878) French
£340 $569 €480 Scene de campagne animee (31x43cm-12x17in) studio st. 15-Oct-3 Hotel des Ventes Mosan, Brussels #116
£2536 $4159 €3500 Scene champetre (65x82cm-26x32in) s.d.1862. 11-May-3 Osenat, Fontainebleau #205/R est:3800-4000

LACROIX, L (?) French?
Works on paper
£1736 $2830 €2500 Chevaux au relais (68x90cm-27x35in) W/C. 29-Sep-3 Coutau Begarie, Paris #273/R est:2500-3000

LACROIX, Tristan (19th C) French
£1722 $3220 €2600 Bergers et moutons. 20-Jul-4 other European Auctioneer #124
£4942 $8500 €7215 On the scent (73x92cm-29x36in) s.d.95. 5-Dec-3 Christie's, Rockefeller NY #74/R est:10000-15000

LACY, Charles J de (1860-1936) British
£277 $510 €416 Seascape (20x30cm-8x12in) s.d.1883. 14-Jun-4 Lilla Bukowskis, Stockholm #663 (S.KR 3800)
£370 $677 €540 Winter's night on the river (32x46cm-13x18in) s. board. 8-Jul-4 Lawrence, Crewkerne #1644
£500 $835 €730 Hulk on a beach at dusk (19x48cm-7x19in) s.d.1896. 13-Nov-3 Christie's, Kensington #348/R
£600 $1104 €876 Beach scene at sunset (17x23cm-7x9in) s. board pair. 23-Jun-4 Bonhams, Bury St Edmunds #434
£1750 $3238 €2555 Shipping on the Thames at dusk, Tower of London in the background (52x76cm-20x30in) s.d.1883. 9-Mar-4 Bonhams, Knightsbridge #171/R est:1000-1500
£1875 $3000 €2738 Shipping offshore (20x30cm-8x12in) s.d.19 pair. 21-Sep-3 Bonhams & Butterfields, San Francisco #2799/R est:1500-2000
Works on paper
£400 $668 €584 On the Thames (36x52cm-14x20in) s. W/C. 14-Oct-3 Bonhams, Knightsbridge #6/R
£460 $727 €667 Thames barges near Waterloo bridge (36x52cm-14x20in) s. W/C over pencil. 24-Jul-3 Lawrence, Crewkerne #867/R

LADA, Josef (1887-1957) Czechoslovakian
Works on paper
£391 $728 €571 Village fair goose (13x25cm-5x10in) s. ink white lead. 6-Mar-4 Dorotheum, Prague #212/R est:10000-15000 (C.KR 19000)
£439 $746 €641 Dissatisfied guest (13x24cm-5x9in) mono. ink white lead. 29-Nov-3 Dorotheum, Prague #161/R est:10000-15000 (C.KR 20000)
£482 $799 €704 Professor (15x12cm-6x5in) s. ink W/C. 4-Oct-3 Dorotheum, Prague #309/R est:15000-25000 (C.KR 22000)
£482 $799 €704 Polite officer (12x24cm-5x9in) mono. ink white lead. 4-Oct-3 Dorotheum, Prague #310/R est:15000-25000 (C.KR 22000)
£702 $1194 €1025 Chandler (14x21cm-6x8in) s. ink W/C. 29-Nov-3 Dorotheum, Prague #162/R est:20000-30000 (C.KR 32000)
£1860 $3088 €2716 Cow will not catch the hare (25x35cm-10x14in) s.d.36 ink W/C. 4-Oct-3 Dorotheum, Prague #307/R est:55000-80000 (C.KR 85000)
£2408 $3996 €3516 Boar hunt (33x24cm-13x9in) s. ink W/C. 4-Oct-3 Dorotheum, Prague #308/R est:60000-100000 (C.KR 110000)
£5691 $9446 €8309 Raising snow man (17x28cm-7x11in) s.d.46 ink W/C gouache. 4-Oct-3 Dorotheum, Prague #311/R est:180000-280000 (C.KR 260000)
£8015 $14107 €12023 Building a snowman (25x38cm-10x15in) s.d.49 gouache. 22-May-4 Dorotheum, Prague #237/R est:180000-280000 (C.KR 380000)

LADBROOKE, E B (19th C) British
£1100 $1980 €1606 Horse and groom (63x76cm-25x30in) s.i.d.1866. 21-Jan-4 Sotheby's, Olympia #322/R est:800-1200

LADBROOKE, Henry (1800-1870) British
£7000 $12530 €10220 Near Falmouth (101x127cm-40x50in) 22-Mar-4 Bonhams & Brooks, Norfolk #233/R est:5000-8000

LADBROOKE, Robert (1770-1842) British
£1227 $2000 €1779 Portrait of Robert Dixon, landscape painter (61x43cm-24x17in) i.verso. 19-Jul-3 New Orleans Auction, New Orleans #216/R est:2000-4000
£1497 $2500 €2186 View near Cromer (63x76cm-25x30in) 7-Oct-3 Sotheby's, New York #81/R est:4000-6000

LADD, Anna Coleman (1878-1939) American
Sculpture
£1747 $3250 €2551 Charles Lindberg (55cm-22in) s. bronze. 5-Mar-4 Skinner, Boston #407/R est:1400-1600

LADELL, Edward (1821-1886) British
£1268 $2193 €1800 Festive meal of fresh mallard (30x35cm-12x14in) mono.d.1876 prov. 10-Dec-3 Christie's, Amsterdam #842/R est:2000-3000
£7000 $11620 €10220 Still life of prawns, peeled lemon, plums, and glass on a table ledge (28x23cm-11x9in) mono. 3-Oct-3 Mallams, Oxford #232/R est:3000-5000
£11000 $17380 €15950 Grapes, peaches and other fruit and a basket. Grapes, plums and other fruit on a mossy bank (24x29cm-9x11in) mono. pair prov. 4-Sep-3 Christie's, Kensington #327/R est:7000-9000
£11000 $20240 €16060 Still life with plums in a silver tazza, peach, black and white grapes in a basket on a marble ledge (46x36cm-18x14in) 11-Jun-4 Christie's, London #94/R est:8000-12000
£12000 $22080 €17520 Still life with assorted fruit, jug and glass of wine on a ledge (36x31cm-14x12in) mono. 23-Mar-4 Bonhams, New Bond Street #67/R est:12000-18000
£32000 $58240 €46720 Still life with fruit, hazelnuts and a wine glass and a casket (46x35cm-18x14in) mono. prov. 1-Jul-4 Sotheby's, London #310/R est:25000-35000
£34000 $61880 €49640 Still life with fruit, hazelnuts and a wine glass (43x35cm-17x14in) mono. prov. 1-Jul-4 Sotheby's, London #311/R est:30000-40000

LADELL, Ellen (fl.1886-1898) British
£950 $1634 €1387 Still life study of mixed fruit on a ledge by a window (20x28cm-8x11in) prov. 5-Dec-3 Keys, Aylsham #685/R
£3500 $5810 €5110 Still life with exotic birds and fruit (45x35cm-18x14in) s. canvas on board. 1-Oct-3 Sotheby's, Olympia #59/R est:3500-4500
£12000 $22080 €17520 Still life with pears, apples and grapes, bird's nest and a jug (40x40cm-16x16in) s. 26-Mar-4 Sotheby's, London #74/R est:7000-9000

LADERMAN, Gabriel (1929-) American
£283 $450 €413 Still life IV. init. 14-Sep-3 Susanin's, Chicago #6030/R

LADEVEZE-CAUCHOIS, Louise de (1860-?) French
£1118 $2024 €1700 Avenue of flowers near a house (42x60cm-17x24in) s. 19-Apr-4 Glerum, Amsterdam #184/R est:1000-1200

LAELY, Christen (1913-) Swiss
£560 $1003 €818 Morning (69x112cm-27x44in) mono.d.37 s.i.d1936/37 verso. 14-May-4 Dobiaschofsky, Bern #286/R (S.FR 1300)
£688 $1149 €998 Peterli, the cat, in landscape (83x45cm-33x18in) i.d. verso. 19-Jun-3 Kornfeld, Bern #596 (S.FR 1500)

LAEMMLE, Cheryl (20th C) American?
£432 $800 €631 Wooden Monkey (142x298cm-56x117in) s.d.1982 verso oil canvas shaped panels 3 parts prov. 12-Feb-4 Sotheby's, New York #277/R

LAENDER, Paulo (20th C) Brazilian?
Sculpture
£2143 $3793 €3215 Guardian (203cm-80in) s.d.1992 wood. 27-Apr-4 Bolsa de Arte, Rio de Janeiro #85/R (B.R 11700)

LAENDLER (?) ?
£4500 $7200 €6525 Nude servant girl. s.d.1929. 18-Sep-3 Christie's, Kensington #187/R est:5000-7000

LAENEN, Gerard (1899-1980) Belgian
£537 $988 €800 Echopes dans Rangoon (37x45cm-15x18in) s. cardboard. 23-Mar-4 Galerie Moderne, Brussels #208
£3475 $5803 €5074 Chinese temple (80x70cm-31x28in) s.d.1932. 26-Oct-3 Christie's, Hong Kong #13/R est:38000-45000 (HK.D 45000)

LAENEN, Jean (19/20th C) Dutch?
£290 $536 €420 Fumeur de pipe (28x22cm-11x9in) s. 19-Jan-4 Horta, Bruxelles #502

LAER, Alexander T van (1857-1920) American
£1018 $1700 €1486 Meadow (20x30cm-8x12in) s. indis.i.stretcher exhib. 18-Jun-3 Doyle, New York #79/R est:1000-1500

LAERMANS, Eugène (1864-1940) Belgian
£5667 $10143 €8500 Mother and children (60x40cm-24x16in) s. lit. 15-May-4 De Vuyst, Lokeren #546/R est:8500-9500
£6643 $11094 €9500 Amour (138x70cm-54x28in) 11-Oct-3 De Vuyst, Lokeren #518/R est:10000-14000
£9790 $16839 €14000 Paysant avec deux enfants se promenant dans un champ (75x100cm-30x39in) s.d.1917 i.stretcher lit. 2-Dec-3 Sotheby's, Amsterdam #61/R est:15000-20000
£9790 $16350 €14000 Back from the fields (58x105cm-23x41in) s. 26-Jun-3 Sant Agostino, Torino #295/R est:10000-14000
£16107 $29799 €24000 Le fermier (76x100cm-30x39in) s.d.1917 lit. 13-Mar-4 De Vuyst, Lokeren #426/R
Works on paper
£1958 $3270 €2800 Pan (63x48cm-25x19in) s. gouache W/C lit. 11-Oct-3 De Vuyst, Lokeren #210/R est:2800-3600
£8000 $14320 €12000 Le semeur (76x55cm-30x22in) s.d.1900 chl W/C prov.exhib.lit. 15-May-4 De Vuyst, Lokeren #443/R est:12500-15000

LAESECKE, F (19th C) ?
£1111 $1811 €1600 River shore with fishing boats and windmills before storm (40x55cm-16x22in) 26-Sep-3 Bolland & Marotz, Bremen #567/R est:1900

LAESSLE, Albert (after) (1877-1954) American
Sculpture
£10811 $20000 €15784 Upturned tortoise (20cm-8in) i.d.1906 black brown pat bronze rouge marble base st.f.Hebrard. 10-Feb-4 Sotheby's, New York #215/R est:2000-3000

LAESSOE, Augusta (1851-1926) Danish?
£622 $1132 €933 Still life of roses in vase (32x26cm-13x10in) s. 19-Jun-4 Rasmussen, Havnen #2071/R (D.KR 7000)
£4297 $7864 €6274 From Ponte Mill, Italy (21x30cm-8x12in) mono.d.11 Nov 1845. 7-Jun-4 Museumsbygningen, Copenhagen #102/R est:20000-25000 (D.KR 48000)

LAESSOE, Thorald (1816-1878) Danish
£284 $508 €415 Mountain landscape (53x67cm-21x26in) s.d.1860. 12-Jan-4 Rasmussen, Vejle #395/R (D.KR 3000)
£449 $836 €656 Landscape with sunset, lake and mountains in background (18x25cm-7x10in) mono. 2-Mar-4 Rasmussen, Copenhagen #1348 (D.KR 5000)
£609 $1016 €889 Entrance from Collosseum. Cottage interior (23x20cm-9x8in) cardboard two prov. 25-Oct-3 Rasmussen, Havnen #2036/R (D.KR 6500)
£1217 $2033 €1777 Thistles in woodland, fjord landscape. two mono.d.1838 and 1870 three prov. 25-Oct-3 Rasmussen, Havnen #2012/R est:5000 (D.KR 13000)
£1895 $3544 €2767 Landscape from Terslose (18x30cm-7x12in) s. verso paper on cardboard prov. 25-Feb-4 Museumsbygningen, Copenhagen #155/R est:12000-15000 (D.KR 21000)
£2527 $4726 €3689 Vesuvius erupting, seen from Castellamare (24x30cm-9x12in) i.verso. 25-Feb-4 Museumsbygningen, Copenhagen #167/R est:10000-15000 (D.KR 28000)
£3178 $5021 €4608 The fort and monastery Grottaferrata on the Roman Campagna (22x30cm-9x12in) s.d.1850 panel. 2-Sep-3 Rasmussen, Copenhagen #1520/R est:35000-40000 (D.KR 34000)
£3611 $5958 €5200 Prague (30x21cm-12x8in) s.d.1843. 2-Jul-3 Neumeister, Munich #695/R est:3500
£3695 $6615 €5395 The Bay of Naples with Vesuvius (40x61cm-16x24in) s/. 25-May-4 Bukowskis, Stockholm #317a/R est:60000-80000 (S.KR 50000)
£3791 $7088 €5535 View of an Italian town, mountains in background (22x30cm-9x12in) paper on canvas prov. 25-Feb-4 Museumsbygningen, Copenhagen #162/R est:20000-25000 (D.KR 42000)
£4655 $8519 €6796 Rocky coastal landscape, Italy with large clouds (19x28cm-7x11in) prov. 7-Jun-4 Museumsbygningen, Copenhagen #101/R est:10000-12000 (D.KR 52000)

£5144 $9620 €7510 Landscape from Terrecina, mountains in background (23x30cm-9x12in) i.verso paper on canvas. 25-Feb-4 Museumsbygningen, Copenhagen #166/R est:15000-20000 (D.KR 57000)
£6983 $12779 €10195 From Villa Borghese with fountains and large trees (19x27cm-7x11in) with sig.i.d.c.1845 verso prov. 7-Jun-4 Museumsbygningen, Copenhagen #95/R est:20000-25000 (D.KR 78000)
£7341 $13434 €10718 Villa Broghese with fountain and garden wall (26x35cm-10x14in) s. prov. 7-Jun-4 Museumsbygningen, Copenhagen #97/R est:20000-25000 (D.KR 82000)
£16129 $27419 €23548 Landscape from Rome from the heights off Porta del Popolo (104x147cm-41x58in) s.d.1874. 10-Nov-3 Rasmussen, Vejle #1/R est:100000 (D.KR 175000)
£41588 $71947 €60718 Rome seen from Monte Mario (133x192cm-52x76in) s.d.1861 exhib. 9-Dec-3 Rasmussen, Copenhagen #1251/R est:300000-400000 (D.KR 440000)
Works on paper
£515 $887 €752 Interior scene with table and chair, Valloe Palace 1838 (14x12cm-6x5in) mono. pencil prov. 3-Dec-3 Museumsbygningen, Copenhagen #141/R (D.KR 5500)

LAET, Alois de (1869-1949) Belgian
£1267 $2318 €1900 Berger et troupeau dans la brume (77x101cm-30x40in) s. 7-Jun-4 Palais de Beaux Arts, Brussels #235/R est:2000-3000

LAEUGER, Max (20th C) German?
£759 $1185 €1200 Female nude hand on head (82x45cm-32x18in) linen. 18-Oct-2 Von Zezschwitz, Munich #54/R
Works on paper
£310 $518 €450 Woman under tree (15x7cm-6x3in) s. i. verso Indian ink. 14-Nov-3 Von Zezschwitz, Munich #262/R
£552 $921 €800 Nude with raised arms (49x38cm-19x15in) s. i. verso pencil gouache W/C board. 14-Nov-3 Von Zezschwitz, Munich #261/R

LAEVERENZ, Gustav (1851-1909) German
£701 $1079 €1100 Ambush (23x34cm-9x13in) s.d.1879 panel. 4-Sep-2 Schopman, Hamburg #22/R

LAEZZA, Giuseppe (?-1905) Italian
£2245 $4018 €3300 Bay of Naples (20x39cm-8x15in) s. 17-Mar-4 Neumeister, Munich #508/R est:1400
£2533 $4661 €3800 Back from the market (40x66cm-16x26in) s. 10-Jun-4 Christie's, Rome #153/R est:3800-4500
£4500 $8100 €6570 Bay of Naples (35x63cm-14x25in) s. 21-Jan-4 Sotheby's, Olympia #417/R est:2000-3000

LAFAGE, Raymond (1656-1690) French
£1000 $1670 €1460 Narcissus looking at his reflection (17x22cm-7x9in) s. indis.d. grisaille sold with small collection of drawings. 16-Oct-3 Lyon & Turnbull, Edinburgh #156 est:400-600
Works on paper
£294 $490 €420 Les nymphes et les satyres au bain. pen. 10-Oct-3 Winterberg, Heidelberg #328
£733 $1313 €1100 Moses and snake (54x44cm-21x17in) pen wash. 13-May-4 Bassenge, Berlin #5198
£1633 $2922 €2400 Personnages conversant a l'ombre d'un arbre (34x25cm-13x10in) i. pen brown ink crayon prov. 17-Mar-4 Maigret, Paris #41/R est:800-1200
£1667 $3000 €2434 Last judgment (30x22cm-12x9in) i. pen ink wash black chk prov. 21-Jan-4 Sotheby's, New York #123/R est:3000-4000
£1761 $3081 €2500 Un paysage avec une riviere pres d'une ville (11x15cm-4x6in) pen brown ink W/C vellum prov. 17-Dec-3 Christie's, Paris #45/R est:1000-1500
£1867 $3435 €2800 Loth et ses filles (28x21cm-11x8in) i. pen brown ink. 11-Jun-4 Maigret, Paris #14/R est:300-400
£1888 $3153 €2700 Etude d'homme etendu (17x25cm-7x10in) i. pen. 30-Jun-3 Bailly Pommery, Paris #11

LAFAGE, Raymond (attrib) (1656-1690) French
Works on paper
£700 $1260 €1022 Moses drawing water from the rock (52x41cm-20x16in) pen brown ink black chk prov. 20-Apr-4 Sotheby's, Olympia #59/R

LAFARGE, John (1835-1910) American
Works on paper
£241 $450 €352 Castle (8x15cm-3x6in) s. W/C. 28-Feb-4 Thomaston Place, Thomaston #81/R
£2486 $4500 €3630 Village huts at Matakula Devil Country, Figi (10x16cm-4x6in) i. graphite pastel prov.exhib. 31-Mar-4 Sotheby's, New York #41/R est:2000-4000
£7186 $12000 €10492 Harpist (25x15cm-10x6in) s.d.84 W/C gouache prov.exhib.lit. 23-Oct-3 Shannon's, Milford #96/R est:12000-18000
£11364 $20000 €16591 Gladiolus (15x10cm-6x4in) mono.i. gouache exec c.1865 prov.exhib.lit. 19-May-4 Sotheby's, New York #36/R est:25000-35000
£69892 $130000 €102042 Water lily (22x24cm-9x9in) i.verso W/C prov. 5-Mar-4 Skinner, Boston #355/R est:30000-50000

LAFARGUE VAN NIEUWLAND, Isaac Lodewyk de (1734-1805) Dutch
Works on paper
£2000 $3340 €2900 Interior with people (49x36cm-19x14in) W/C. 11-Nov-3 Vendu Notarishuis, Rotterdam #81/R est:1500-2000

LAFAYE, Jacques (1921-1994) French
Works on paper
£1067 $1963 €1600 Recreation (50x53cm-20x21in) mono.d.76 glycerol gouache ink varnish. 9-Jun-4 Artcurial Briest, Paris #343/R est:1600-1800

LAFFERT, Carl Friedrich (1783-1825) German
Works on paper
£7042 $12324 €10000 Finance Minister of Britain (20x20cm-8x8in) s.i. on porcelain. 17-Dec-3 Finarte Semenzato, Milan #248/R est:4000-4500

LAFFITTE, Theodore (1816-?) French
£496 $829 €700 Horses in stable (27x22cm-11x9in) s. 17-Oct-3 Berlinghof, Heidelberg #1063/R
£1517 $2534 €2200 Portrait de Tom (41x28cm-16x11in) s. 17-Nov-3 Tajan, Paris #54/R est:2000-3000

LAFFON, Carmen (1934-) Spanish
£18116 $29710 €25000 Landscape (26x35cm-10x14in) s.d.1976 verso exhib. 27-May-3 Durán, Madrid #298/R est:20000
Sculpture
£2133 $3861 €3200 Still life (32x19x13cm-13x7x5in) s. bronze one of 30. 30-Mar-4 Segre, Madrid #127/R est:2700

LAFITE, Carl (1830-1900) Austrian
£467 $840 €700 River landscape with sailing boats (51x37cm-20x15in) s. 26-Apr-4 Rieber, Stuttgart #1180/R
£743 $1308 €1100 Landscape (29x36cm-11x14in) s. panel. 19-May-4 Dorotheum, Klagenfurt #15/R
£915 $1584 €1300 Portrait of young woman in national costume (53x45cm-21x18in) s. 10-Dec-3 Dorotheum, Vienna #200/R
Works on paper
£333 $597 €500 Back yard with church tower (19x28cm-7x11in) s. W/C. 13-May-4 Dorotheum, Linz #537/R

LAFITE, Ernst (1826-1885) Austrian
£503 $941 €750 Portrait of woman in blue dress (64x47cm-25x19in) s. 24-Feb-4 Dorotheum, Vienna #121

LAFLAMME, Roger (1925-) Canadian
£558 $932 €809 L'encan (84x66cm-33x26in) s.d.49. 17-Jun-3 Pinneys, Montreal #166 est:700-900 (C.D 1250)

LAFON, François (19th C) French
£1467 $2669 €2200 Portrait of a young Italian girl (57x37cm-22x15in) s. lit. 3-Jul-4 Badum, Bamberg #87/R est:2650

LAFONT, Emile René (1853-1917) French
£1060 $1928 €1600 Les Boulevards (15x23cm-6x9in) s. wood. 16-Jun-4 Renaud, Paris #43 est:2800-3000

LAFONTAINE, Ludolf Ernst Andreas (1704-1774) German
£3704 $6704 €5408 Portrait of a gentleman, wearing armour and a wig (80x65cm-31x26in) i. 30-Mar-4 Christie's, Melbourne #381/R est:4000-6000 (A.D 9000)

LAFORCADE, Isabelle (20th C) French
£1761 $3046 €2500 Toscane (73x100cm-29x39in) s. 9-Dec-3 Chambelland & Giafferi, Paris #83/R est:2500-3000
Works on paper
£352 $609 €500 Composition (26x20cm-10x8in) s. mixed media. 9-Dec-3 Chambelland & Giafferi, Paris #84/R

LAFOSSE, Cecile (attrib) (19th C) French
£1049 $1804 €1500 De ontdekking (40x28cm-16x11in) s.d.1865. 2-Dec-3 Campo & Campo, Antwerp #201/R est:1600-1800

LAFOSSE, Charles de (1636-1716) French
£6292 $11451 €9500 Sainte Marie-Madeleine (44x33cm-17x13in) oval. 21-Jun-4 Tajan, Paris #87/R est:7000-9000
Works on paper
£4828 $8062 €7000 Etudes de mains (19x21cm-7x8in) pierre noire sanguine prov. 17-Nov-3 Delorme & Bocage, Paris #64/R est:4500-6000
£11111 $20000 €16222 Reclining allegorical figure of Architecture with a reclining nude (28x40cm-11x16in) i. red white chk prov. 22-Jan-4 Christie's, Rockefeller NY #87/R est:7000-10000

LAFOSSE, Charles de (studio) (1636-1716) French
£8333 $15000 €12166 God the Father with the symbols of the four Evangelists (82x66cm-32x26in) 23-Jan-4 Christie's, Rockefeller NY #191/R est:15000-20000

LAFOURCADE, Leon (19/20th C) French
£526 $968 €800 The au Ritz (73x60cm-29x24in) s. s.i.d.1913 verso. 28-Jun-4 Joron-Derem, Paris #127
£987 $1816 €1500 Bord de mer (70x70cm-28x28in) s. 28-Jun-4 Joron-Derem, Paris #128 est:800-1000

LAFRENSEN, Nicolas (younger) (1737-1807) Swedish
£1560 $2605 €2200 La visite a la nourrice (38x46cm-15x18in) 17-Oct-3 Tajan, Paris #110/R est:3000-5000
Miniatures
£2500 $4250 €3650 Gentleman (4cm-2in) s.verso oval. 18-Nov-3 Bonhams, New Bond Street #45/R est:2500-3500
£10000 $18000 €14600 Lady, traditionally called Princesse de Vaudemont-Lorraine (18cm-7in) gilt metal frame rec. exhib. 22-Apr-4 Bonhams, New Bond Street #86/R est:12000-18000

Works on paper
£650 $1086 €949 Young woman with her dog in a garden (210x165cm-83x65in) black red chk. 14-Oct-3 Bonhams, Knightsbridge #204/R

LAFUENTE, Ramiro (19th C) Spanish
£369 $687 €550 Lake landscape with trees (75x40cm-30x16in) s. 2-Mar-4 Ansorena, Madrid #157/R

LAGAGE, Pierre (1911-1977) French
£600 $954 €870 Composition (65x49cm-26x19in) s.d.68 oil on card sold with another by same hand. 11-Sep-3 Christie's, Kensington #203/R
£600 $1038 €876 Composition (65x49cm-26x19in) s.d.68 card sold with another by the same artist. 11-Dec-3 Christie's, Kensington #225/R
£600 $1038 €876 Composition (65x49cm-26x19in) s.d.69 card sold with another by the same artist. 11-Dec-3 Christie's, Kensington #227/R
£600 $1038 €876 Composition (65x49cm-26x19in) s.d.67 card sold with another by the same artist. 11-Dec-3 Christie's, Kensington #236/R

LAGAR, Celso (1891-1966) Spanish
£3500 $5565 €5075 La masquerade (28x22cm-11x9in) s. oil paper on board prov. 11-Sep-3 Christie's, Kensington #161/R est:2000-3000
£3600 $6012 €5256 Still life (30x40cm-12x16in) s. 22-Oct-3 Sotheby's, Olympia #92/R est:2000-3000
£3800 $6992 €5548 Nature morte (47x55cm-19x22in) s. 24-Mar-4 Sotheby's, Olympia #69/R est:2000-3000
£4895 $8419 €7000 L'ecuyere de cirque (24x27cm-9x11in) s. cardboard on wood. 3-Dec-3 Tajan, Paris #396/R est:4000-6000
£6291 $11450 €9500 Beach in Normandy with figures (24x33cm-9x13in) s. 20-Jun-4 Imberdis, Pont Audemer #15
£6738 $10915 €9500 Marina (33x40cm-13x16in) s. canvas on panel. 20-May-3 Ansorena, Madrid #151/R est:9500
£7241 $12093 €10500 La Cathedrale de Rouen (72x58cm-28x23in) s. cardboard. 16-Nov-3 Muizon & Le Coent, Paris #50/R
£7383 $13732 €11000 Harbour (33x41cm-13x16in) s. canvas on board. 2-Mar-4 Ansorena, Madrid #75/R est:8000
£9000 $16560 €13140 Nature morte (33x55cm-13x22in) s. 24-Mar-4 Sotheby's, Olympia #71/R est:4000-6000
£11000 $18370 €16060 Paysage a Blanes (60x82cm-24x32in) s. painted 1915 prov.exhib. 22-Oct-3 Sotheby's, Olympia #38/R est:4000-6000
£12517 $22780 €18900 Acrobats on la Bouille (38x46cm-15x18in) s. 20-Jun-4 Imberdis, Pont Audemer #14
£16667 $30667 €25000 Scene de flamenco (45x55cm-18x22in) s. isorel prov. 8-Jun-4 Artcurial Briest, Paris #166/R est:28000-32000
£18000 $32760 €27000 Village Portuaire (60x81cm-24x32in) s. painted c.1923-4. 30-Jun-4 Calmels Cohen, Paris #6/R est:8000-12000
Works on paper
£280 $481 €400 Peniche sur la riviere (30x46cm-12x18in) bears studio st. W/C. 3-Dec-3 Tajan, Paris #141
£361 $650 €527 Nude seated (25x15cm-10x6in) pencil. 24-Apr-4 Du Mouchelle, Detroit #3154/R
£417 $750 €609 Nude (20x38cm-8x15in) W/C. 24-Apr-4 Du Mouchelle, Detroit #3151/R
£503 $936 €750 Female nude (33x22cm-13x9in) s. pencil dr. 2-Mar-4 Ansorena, Madrid #325/R
£517 $859 €750 Inn (30x43cm-12x17in) s. chl dr. 1-Oct-3 Ansorena, Madrid #475/R
£537 $961 €800 Female nude (37x26cm-15x10in) ink dr. 25-May-4 Durán, Madrid #606/R
£629 $1083 €900 Le chat (20x21cm-8x8in) s. ink W/C. 5-Dec-3 Chochon-Barre & Allardi, Paris #117/R
£699 $1202 €1000 Bateau a quai (20x27cm-8x11in) s. W/C. 3-Dec-3 Tajan, Paris #140
£1609 $2767 €2300 Le clown (25x38cm-10x15in) W/C. 3-Dec-3 Tajan, Paris #142/R est:1000-1500
£1611 $2996 €2400 Composition with Lucienne Boyer (23x22cm-9x9in) s.i.d.1932 verso mixed media. 2-Mar-4 Ansorena, Madrid #868/R est:2400
£1678 $3087 €2500 Artistes on stage (22x26cm-9x10in) s. W/C gouache pen. 26-Mar-4 Venator & Hansten, Koln #1774 est:750
£3684 $6779 €5600 Saltimbanque et son singe (55x38cm-22x15in) s.i. chl W/C. 25-Jun-4 Millon & Associes, Paris #144/R est:5000-6000

LAGARTO, Luis (1556-?) Mexican
Works on paper
£12222 $22000 €17844 Holy Family with St Anne and St John the Evangalist, God the Father above (23x18cm-9x7in) s.d.1616 pen brown ink bodycol gold vellum. 22-Jan-4 Christie's, Rockefeller NY #29/R est:2500-3500

LAGATTA, John (1894-1977) American
£1676 $3000 €2447 Dressing woman seated by French doors (76x66cm-30x26in) s. 15-May-4 Illustration House, New York #121/R est:3500-5000
£3631 $6500 €5301 Couple relaxing (91x53cm-36x21in) s. 15-May-4 Illustration House, New York #93/R est:5000-8000
Works on paper
£1796 $3000 €2622 It's toasted (43x79cm-17x31in) s. chl exec.c.1933 sold with a photocopy. 15-Nov-3 Illustration House, New York #123/R est:2000-4000
£2514 $4500 €3670 Elegant lounging couple lighting up at the beach (56x61cm-22x24in) s. chl. 15-May-4 Illustration House, New York #5/R est:2000-4000

LAGE, Julie von der (1841-?) German
£458 $792 €650 Emblematic flower arrangement (81x62cm-32x24in) s. 12-Dec-3 Berlinghof, Heidelberg #1147/R

LAGERHOLM, Wilhelmina (1826-1917) Swedish
£2979 $4974 €4200 Interior (83x98cm-33x39in) s. 14-Oct-3 Finarte Semenzato, Milan #72/R est:1500-2000

LAGERSTAM, Berndt (1868-1930) Finnish
£556 $928 €800 Winter landscape (49x51cm-19x20in) s.i. 23-Oct-3 Hagelstam, Helsinki #828/R

LAGIER, Erica (1830-?) British
Works on paper
£380 $692 €555 Child asleep with a doll (65x78cm-26x31in) s.d.1867 pastel oval. 15-Jun-4 Bonhams, Oxford #34

LAGLENNE, Jean Francis (1899-1962) French
£403 $749 €600 Composition abstraite (60x81cm-24x32in) s. 3-Mar-4 Ferri, Paris #29

LAGNEAU, Nicolas (16/17th C) French
Works on paper
£710 $1300 €1037 Portrait of an old woman (30x21cm-12x8in) col chk. 29-Jan-4 Swann Galleries, New York #204/R
£2177 $3897 €3200 Portrait de femme un buste portant une coiffe (30x22cm-12x9in) i. black red chk oval. 18-Mar-4 Christie's, Paris #243/R est:2000-3000
£3716 $6541 €5500 Head of an old man (33x24cm-13x9in) black red chk stumping prov.exhib.lit. 19-May-4 Sotheby's, Amsterdam #141/R est:2500-3500
£8000 $14640 €11680 Bearded man (42x29cm-17x11in) coloured chk prov.exhib.lit. 6-Jul-4 Christie's, London #117/R est:8000-12000

LAGO RIVERA, Antonio (1916-1990) Spanish
£780 $1303 €1100 Landscape (31x26cm-12x10in) s. board. 20-Oct-3 Durán, Madrid #1199/R
£800 $1456 €1200 Parisian landscape (19x24cm-7x9in) s.d.1946 s.verso. 29-Jun-4 Segre, Madrid #98/R
£1701 $3044 €2500 Still life (50x61cm-20x24in) s.d.1977. 22-Mar-4 Durán, Madrid #169/R est:2500
£2449 $4457 €3600 Nude and two heads (61x50cm-24x20in) s.d.1982. 3-Feb-4 Segre, Madrid #175/R est:3000

LAGOOR, Jan van (17th C) Dutch
£1133 $2029 €1700 Wood (55x44cm-22x17in) board. 12-May-4 Finarte Semenzato, Milan #80/R est:1500-2000
£1600 $2864 €2400 Wood and lake (34x44cm-13x17in) init. 12-May-4 Finarte Semenzato, Milan #81/R est:1000-1500

LAGORIO, Lev Feliksovich (1827-1905) Russian
£7095 $12699 €10500 Coastal cliffs (34x51cm-13x20in) s.d.1884. 8-May-4 Bukowskis, Helsinki #463/R est:2000-4000
£16216 $29027 €24000 House on the cliff (69x32cm-27x13in) s. 8-May-4 Bukowskis, Helsinki #431/R est:4000-6000
£24000 $42960 €35040 Cattle by a stream (47x68cm-19x27in) s.d.1905. 26-May-4 Sotheby's, London #38/R est:10000-15000
£30000 $51000 €43800 Travellers in a landscape (44x72cm-17x28in) s.d.1886. 19-Nov-3 Sotheby's, London #27/R est:12000-18000
£32000 $57280 €46720 Caucasian landscape (54x71cm-21x28in) s.d.1903. 26-May-4 Sotheby's, London #25/R est:15000-20000
£32000 $54400 €48000 Watchers on the Crimean coast (45x64cm-18x25in) s.d.1897. 25-Nov-3 Christie's, London #166/R est:10000-12000
£40217 $74000 €58717 Two ships in a harbour (58x89cm-23x35in) s.d.1900 prov. 26-Jun-4 Sloans & Kenyon, Bethesda #1096a/R est:9000-12000
£48000 $85920 €70080 Steamship Olga (49x39cm-19x15in) s.d.1891. 26-May-4 Sotheby's, London #68/R est:15000-20000
£75000 $134250 €109500 Imperial yacht, Derzhava (62x50cm-24x20in) s.d.1886 canvas on board. 26-May-4 Sotheby's, London #69/R est:35000-45000

LAGORIO, Lev Feliksovich (attrib) (1827-1905) Russian
£861 $1567 €1300 Moonlight coastal scene on the Black Sea (19x32cm-7x13in) indis.s. panel. 19-Jun-4 Hans Stahl, Hamburg #65/R

LAGOS, Ibelice (?) Venezuelan?
Sculpture
£997 $1625 €1456 Nap (79x49x84cm-31x19x33in) s. bronze. 20-Jul-3 Subastas Odalys, Caracas #109

LAGRANGE, Andre (1889-?) French
£7639 $12986 €11000 Bathers (130x97cm-51x38in) s. painted 1930 prov. 28-Oct-3 Il Ponte, Milan #280/R

LAGRANGE, Jacques (1917-1995) French
£322 $602 €480 Sans titre (61x50cm-24x20in) s. 29-Feb-4 Versailles Encheres #155/R
£1678 $2853 €2400 Jardin exotique (54x64cm-21x25in) s. s.i.d.1958 verso. 28-Nov-3 Drouot Estimations, Paris #221/R est:1000-1200

LAGRENEE, Jean Jacques (1739-1821) French
Works on paper
£733 $1327 €1100 Agar et Ismael (15x20cm-6x8in) i.d.1785 verso pen black ink grey wash. 30-Mar-4 Rossini, Paris #4/R

LAGRENEE, Jean Jacques (attrib) (1739-1821) French
£2667 $4827 €4000 La joueuse de harpe (61x89cm-24x35in) oval prov. 2-Apr-4 Rossini, Paris #42/R est:4000-6000
Works on paper
£345 $576 €500 Phryne before judges (17x19cm-7x7in) W/C htd white over pen prov. 15-Nov-3 Lempertz, Koln #1345/R

LAGRENEE, Louis Jean François (1725-1805) French

£15385 $26462 €22462 Diana and the sleeping Endymion (88x110cm-35x43in) 2-Dec-3 Bukowskis, Stockholm #427/R est:60000-80000 (S.KR 200000)
£17105 $31474 €26000 Holy Family (56x37cm-22x15in) s.d.1767 panel. 24-Jun-4 Tajan, Paris #55/R est:5000-7000
£22000 $40260 €33000 Madonna and Child with Saint John (66x82cm-26x32in) oval. 4-Jun-4 Pierre Berge, Paris #195/R est:10000-12000
£22346 $40000 €32625 Galatee se jouant sur les eaux avec les tritons (112x135cm-44x53in) s.d.1757 prov.exhib.lit. 27-May-4 Sotheby's, New York #47/R est:50000-70000
£25352 $44366 €36000 Baigneuses (27x22cm-11x9in) s. copper pair. 17-Dec-3 Piasa, Paris #98/R est:10000-12000
£36185 $66580 €55000 Jupiter et Junon sur le Mont Ida (121x97cm-48x38in) bears sig.d.1774 oval. 24-Jun-4 Tajan, Paris #56/R est:60000-80000

Works on paper

£664 $1109 €950 Christ crucifie (14x16cm-6x6in) s.d. ink dr. 29-Jun-3 St-Germain-en-Laye Encheres #1/R
£1103 $1843 €1600 Jeune fille endormie (23x31cm-9x12in) i. pierre noire sanguine prov. 17-Nov-3 Delorme & Bocage, Paris #65/R est:900-1200
£1190 $2131 €1750 Diverses etudes d'objets antiques (20x42cm-8x17in) pen black ink brown wash htd gouache. 19-Mar-4 Piasa, Paris #102 est:1000-1200

LAGRENEE, Louis Jean François (attrib) (1725-1805) French

£7092 $11844 €10000 Allegorie de la poesie (78x89cm-31x35in) bears sig. 17-Oct-3 Tajan, Paris #107/R est:6000-8000

Works on paper

£646 $1157 €950 Cadmus et le dragon (39x55cm-15x22in) black chk pen brown ink wash. 18-Mar-4 Christie's, Paris #273/R

LAGRENEE, Louis Jean François (circle) (1725-1805) French

£9091 $15636 €13000 Venus and putto (72x91cm-28x36in) 2-Dec-3 Sotheby's, Milan #87/R est:7000-10000

LAGRENEE, Lucy (1873-?) French

£300 $546 €450 Fleurs de printemps (32x40cm-13x16in) s. panel. 29-Jun-4 Chenu & Scrive, Lyon #109/R

LAGRUE, Jean Pierre (1939-) French

£352 $630 €500 Le Bistrot Mazarin (54x65cm-21x26in) s. 11-Jan-4 Rouillac, Vendome #358
£667 $1220 €1000 Dimanche apres-midi (60x73cm-24x29in) s. 6-Jun-4 Rouillac, Vendome #43

LAGUZZI, Atilio (1945-2001) Argentinian

Works on paper

£1312 $2126 €1850 Siento cerca una sombra (79x59cm-31x23in) s.d.85 pencil chl. 20-May-3 Ansorena, Madrid #422/R est:1450

LAGYE, Victor (1825-1896) Belgian

£3289 $5954 €5000 Le verre de vin offert au menestrel (62x67cm-24x26in) s.i.d.1866 panel. 19-Apr-4 Horta, Bruxelles #109/R est:4000-6000

LAHALLE, Charles Dominique Oscar (1832-1909) French

£10000 $18400 €15000 Jour d'ete, les permissionnaires en pique-nique (74x101cm-29x40in) s. 9-Jun-4 Beaussant & Lefèvre, Paris #179/R est:12000-15000

LAHARRAGUE, Carlos (1936-) Spanish

£855 $1548 €1300 Hydrangeas (38x46cm-15x18in) 14-Apr-4 Ansorena, Madrid #81/R

Works on paper

£267 $485 €400 La Gran Via, Madrid (24x19cm-9x7in) s.d.1972 pastel. 29-Jun-4 Segre, Madrid #312/R

LAHAUT, Pierre (1931-) Belgian

£1042 $1740 €1500 Figuration abstraite (146x196cm-57x77in) 21-Oct-3 Campo & Campo, Antwerp #170 est:1600-1800

LAHEY, Frances Vida (1882-1968) Australian

£6911 $10850 €10021 Anzac Square, Brisbane (29x34cm-11x13in) s. canvas on board painted c.1931. 26-Aug-3 Christie's, Sydney #335/R est:3500-5500 (A.D 17000)

Works on paper

£992 $1806 €1448 Beach (33x22cm-13x9in) s.d.56 W/C. 16-Jun-4 Deutscher-Menzies, Melbourne #592/R est:800-1200 (A.D 2600)

LAHEY, Richard Francis (1893-1979) American

Works on paper

£380 $700 €555 Still life with yellow straw hat (51x36cm-20x14in) s. s.i.d.1945 verso W/C gouache. 10-Jun-4 Swann Galleries, New York #139/R

LAHNER, Émile (1893-1980) French

£556 $928 €800 Paysage de bord de mer (46x54cm-18x21in) s. 21-Oct-3 Artcurial Briest, Paris #338

Works on paper

£324 $531 €450 Composition abstraite (42x31cm-17x12in) s. gouache. 6-Jun-3 Chochon-Barre & Allardi, Paris #65
£396 $649 €550 Etude sur fond noir (33x21cm-13x8in) s. gouache. 6-Jun-3 Chochon-Barre & Allardi, Paris #66
£1007 $1652 €1400 Composition abstraite (31x22cm-12x9in) s. gouache. 6-Jun-3 Chochon-Barre & Allardi, Paris #68

LAHOTAN, Robert L (1927-) American

£1006 $1800 €1469 Still life, white carnations. s.i. 13-May-4 Dallas Auction Gallery, Dallas #231/R est:1500-2500

LAHS, Curt (1893-1958) German

£400 $720 €600 Jugs by window (14x33cm-6x13in) board. 24-Apr-4 Dr Lehr, Berlin #248/R
£1119 $1902 €1600 Abstract composition (24x32cm-9x13in) s.d.1930 canvas on board. 26-Nov-3 Lempertz, Koln #784/R est:1500

LAHUERTA, Genaro (1905-1985) Spanish

£1268 $2193 €1800 Sailing boats (14x24cm-6x9in) s. 15-Dec-3 Ansorena, Madrid #280/R est:900
£3521 $6092 €5000 Nude (61x48cm-24x19in) s. 10-Dec-3 Castellana, Madrid #160/R est:5500

Works on paper

£276 $497 €400 Four figures (47x64cm-19x25in) s. dr. 26-Jan-4 Durán, Madrid #1163
£317 $527 €460 Portrait of woman with fan (22x18cm-9x7in) s. pencil dr. 1-Oct-3 Ansorena, Madrid #490/R
£580 $951 €800 Marineros (44x48cm-17x19in) s.d.1956 wax crayon. 27-May-3 Durán, Madrid #4/R
£897 $1614 €1300 The Seine in Paris (22x31cm-9x12in) s. W/C. 26-Jan-4 Ansorena, Madrid #305/R

LAI FONG (attrib) (fl.1890-1910) Chinese

£1400 $2506 €2044 French barque in the company of a deep water junk (46x59cm-18x23in) 26-May-4 Christie's, Kensington #636/R est:1500-2000

LAI ZHAO (19th C) Chinese

Works on paper

£616 $1048 €900 Beggar (88x28cm-35x11in) i. seals Indian ink col hanging scroll prov. 7-Nov-3 Dr Fritz Nagel, Stuttgart #854/R
£616 $1048 €900 Scholar and beggar (89x28cm-35x11in) i. seals Indian ink col hanging scroll prov. 7-Nov-3 Dr Fritz Nagel, Stuttgart #855/R

LAIB, Wolfgang (1950-) German

Sculpture

£10180 $17000 €14863 Milkstone (5x46x35cm-2x18x14in) s.d.81 Carrara marble milk lit. 13-Nov-3 Sotheby's, New York #510/R est:10000-15000

Works on paper

£915 $1602 €1300 Chambre de certitudes (21x30cm-8x12in) s.i.d.1996 crayon pastel. 18-Dec-3 Cornette de St.Cyr, Paris #33/R
£1162 $2033 €1650 Nicht hier (21x30cm-8x12in) s.i.d.1996 crayon pastel. 18-Dec-3 Cornette de St.Cyr, Paris #36/R est:1000-1500
£1197 $2095 €1700 Nicht hier (21x30cm-8x12in) s.i.d.1996 crayon pastel. 18-Dec-3 Cornette de St.Cyr, Paris #34/R est:1000-1500
£1197 $2095 €1700 Nicht hier (21x30cm-8x12in) s.i.d.1996 crayon pastel. 18-Dec-3 Cornette de St.Cyr, Paris #35/R est:1000-1500

LAIBLE, Otto (1898-1962) German

Works on paper

£313 $509 €450 Woman wearing hat sitting on sofa (50x32cm-20x13in) s.i.d.1933 W/C pencil tempera. 27-Sep-3 Dr Fritz Nagel, Stuttgart #9256/R

LAIDLAY, William James (1846-1912) British

£300 $501 €438 Arrival of the ferry (30x40cm-12x16in) s. 16-Oct-3 Lyon & Turnbull, Edinburgh #154
£620 $1073 €905 Boat at Sea, Ballantine with the Argyllshire hills in the distance (29x37cm-11x15in) s.d.1907 verso board. 9-Dec-3 Bonhams, Oxford #99
£2600 $4862 €3796 Morning in the Channel (51x71cm-20x28in) s. 22-Jul-4 Tennants, Leyburn #803/R est:1500-2000

LAINE, Olavi (1922-) Finnish

£267 $491 €400 Girl with dark hair (73x54cm-29x21in) s. 9-Jun-4 Bukowskis, Helsinki #451/R
£268 $494 €400 Fisherman (73x60cm-29x24in) s. 25-Mar-4 Hagelstam, Helsinki #803
£282 $451 €400 Man with hat (73x60cm-29x24in) s/. 21-Sep-3 Bukowskis, Helsinki #382/R
£352 $563 €500 Music (92x73cm-36x29in) s. 18-Sep-3 Hagelstam, Helsinki #951
£387 $620 €550 Early spring (66x54cm-26x21in) s. 21-Sep-3 Bukowskis, Helsinki #383/R
£387 $620 €550 Woman wearing red (81x55cm-32x22in) s. 21-Sep-3 Bukowskis, Helsinki #384/R
£431 $719 €620 The white hat (61x50cm-24x20in) s. 26-Oct-3 Bukowskis, Helsinki #395/R
£537 $988 €800 Town (73x60cm-29x24in) s. 25-Mar-4 Hagelstam, Helsinki #810
£638 $1173 €950 Fishing harbour (50x65cm-20x26in) s. 25-Mar-4 Hagelstam, Helsinki #806/R
£638 $1173 €950 Landscape, cypresses (60x50cm-24x20in) s.d.1957. 25-Mar-4 Hagelstam, Helsinki #986
£671 $1235 €1000 Winter (73x93cm-29x37in) s. 25-Mar-4 Hagelstam, Helsinki #1025
£775 $1239 €1100 Southern town scene (53x44cm-21x17in) s. 18-Sep-3 Hagelstam, Helsinki #1019

LAINE, Victor (1830-?) French

£2133 $3861 €3200 Les devotes, auvergnates en costume traditionnel (160x100cm-63x39in) s. 30-Mar-4 Gioffredo, Nice #116/R

LAING, Annie Rose (1869-1946) British
£25000 $43000 €36500 Afternoon (61x50cm-24x20in) s. 4-Dec-3 Bonhams, Edinburgh #86/R est:5000-8000

LAING, Georgina (fl.1898-1901) British
Works on paper
£700 $1253 €1022 Game keeper's cottage, Woodley, near Sonning on Thames (23x33cm-9x13in) s. W/C. 5-May-4 John Nicholson, Haslemere #414/R

LAING, James Garden (1852-1915) British
Works on paper
£280 $468 €409 Chelsea (24x17cm-9x7in) s. W/C. 16-Oct-3 Bonhams, Edinburgh #197
£280 $448 €409 Norwich (17x24cm-7x9in) s.i. W/C. 15-May-3 Bonhams, Edinburgh #342
£329 $550 €480 Market place (25x18cm-10x7in) s. W/C. 27-Oct-3 O'Gallerie, Oregon #806/R
£340 $629 €496 East Hartlepool (18x25cm-7x10in) s. 9-Mar-4 Gorringes, Lewes #2064
£600 $1134 €876 Unloading the catch (18x26cm-7x10in) s. W/C. 19-Feb-4 Lyon & Turnbull, Edinburgh #37
£800 $1440 €1200 Rochester sea harbour (30x40cm-12x16in) s. W/C. 26-Apr-4 Rieber, Stuttgart #1214/R

LAING, Tomson (fl.1890-1904) British
£440 $774 €642 Sheep in a farm landscape (21x34cm-8x13in) s. panel. 20-May-4 Bonhams, Edinburgh #307
£450 $824 €657 On the shore, Ballantrae (33x51cm-13x20in) s.i. 8-Jul-4 Duke & Son, Dorchester #260
£500 $835 €730 Watering the plough team (20x34cm-8x13in) s. 16-Oct-3 Bonhams, Edinburgh #202
£600 $1098 €876 Kelp gatherers on the seashore (36x56cm-14x22in) s. 8-Jul-4 Duke & Son, Dorchester #261
£750 $1418 €1095 Highland cattle in a snow covered landscape (60x45cm-24x18in) s. 19-Feb-4 Lyon & Turnbull, Edinburgh #112
£950 $1739 €1387 Gathering wrack (50x95cm-20x37in) s. 8-Apr-4 Bonhams, Edinburgh #96

LAIRESSE, Gerard de (1641-1711) Flemish
£33333 $60000 €48666 Allegory with infant surrounded by women (152cm-60in circular) 22-Jan-4 Sotheby's, New York #119/R est:70000-90000
Works on paper
£1149 $2022 €1700 King David (19x13cm-7x5in) pen grey ink wash exhib. 19-May-4 Sotheby's, Amsterdam #112/R est:1500-2000

LAIRESSE, Gerard de (attrib) (1641-1711) Flemish
£31469 $53497 €45000 Scene de massacre (103x120cm-41x47in) 21-Nov-3 Coutau Begarie, Paris #127/R est:45000-55000
Works on paper
£340 $609 €500 Saul et la magicienne d'Endor (20x27cm-8x11in) i.verso pen brown ink prov. 18-Mar-4 Christie's, Paris #82
£2200 $4026 €3212 Figure walking to the right in a strong gale (30x20cm-12x8in) red chk pen ink prov. 6-Jul-4 Christie's, London #183/R est:2500-3500

LAISHLEY, Rev Richard (1816-1897) New Zealander
£10714 $19714 €15642 Fruit season pickers New Zealand (93x70cm-37x28in) s. i.verso. 25-Mar-4 International Art Centre, Auckland #74/R est:25000-35000 (NZ.D 30000)

LAITILA, Atte (1893-1972) Finnish
£336 $624 €500 The rescuers (60x72cm-24x28in) s. 7-Mar-4 Bukowskis, Helsinki #366/R
£336 $624 €500 Silkes-Sara (46x26cm-18x10in) s. 7-Mar-4 Bukowskis, Helsinki #367/R

LAITY, David (1958-) Australian
£2290 $4168 €3343 Pony club (100x145cm-39x57in) s. oil on hessian. 16-Jun-4 Deutscher-Menzies, Melbourne #367/R est:4000-6000 (A.D 6000)
£3862 $6913 €5639 Flirt (140x140cm-55x55in) s.d.2003 i.verso hessian canvas. 4-May-4 Sotheby's, Melbourne #94/R est:7000-10000 (A.D 9500)

LAJOUE, Jacques de (1687-1761) French
£4667 $8447 €7000 La danse dans le parc dit aussi l'Escalier de pierre (58x73cm-23x29in) prov.lit. 2-Apr-4 Rossini, Paris #27/R est:7500-8500
£6944 $11597 €10000 Paysage d'escalier avec cinq personnages pres d'une fontaine (56x80cm-22x31in) 22-Oct-3 Ribeyre & Baron, Paris #6/R est:10000-15000
Works on paper
£6111 $11000 €8922 Rocaille fantasy with a garden decorated with rococo trellis (54x32cm-21x13in) pen ink wash htd white. 21-Jan-4 Sotheby's, New York #111/R est:7000-9000

LAJOUE, Jacques de (attrib) (1687-1761) French
Works on paper
£2550 $4743 €3800 Caprice a l'escalier (27x41cm-11x16in) pen grey wash. 8-Mar-4 Artcurial Briest, Paris #8 est:1200

LAKHOVSKY, Arnold Borisovich (1880-1937) Russian
£2200 $4070 €3212 At the edge of the lake (60x73cm-24x29in) s. board. 15-Jan-4 Christie's, Kensington #994/R est:600-800
£2300 $4255 €3358 Riverside town (51x65cm-20x26in) s. 15-Jan-4 Christie's, Kensington #993/R est:600-800
£4305 $7834 €6500 Troika (23x29cm-9x11in) s. paint paper on cardboard. 15-Jun-4 Rossini, Paris #64/R est:1500-2500
£5026 $8996 €7338 Elderly man on the quay (68x52cm-27x20in) s. 28-May-4 Uppsala Auktionskammare, Uppsala #178/R est:50000-60000 (S.KR 68000)
£5500 $9350 €8030 French village by the sea (49x65cm-19x26in) s. s.i.verso card. 19-Nov-3 Sotheby's, London #104/R est:3000-4000
£5667 $10313 €8500 Village on winter's day (60x73cm-24x29in) s.d.31 i. verso. 30-Jun-4 Neumeister, Munich #599/R est:1500
£6111 $11000 €8922 La fenetre ouverte (61x48cm-24x19in) s.d.30 i.verso. 23-Apr-4 Sotheby's, New York #60/R est:10000-15000
£8000 $13600 €11680 View of Venice (61x50cm-24x20in) s. s.i.verso. 19-Nov-3 Sotheby's, London #101/R est:3000-4000
£9500 $17005 €13870 After rain, Pskov (60x73cm-24x29in) s.i.verso exhib. 26-May-4 Sotheby's, London #264/R est:10000-15000
£10000 $17900 €14600 Russian winter (72x89cm-28x35in) s. 26-May-4 Sotheby's, London #262/R est:5000-7000
£10000 $17900 €14600 Landscape with cows (50x61cm-20x24in) s. exhib. 26-May-4 Sotheby's, London #263/R est:8000-12000
£16667 $30000 €24334 At the flea market (56x33cm-22x13in) s.d.1911. 23-Apr-4 Sotheby's, New York #53/R est:20000-30000

LALANNE, Claude (1927-) French
Sculpture
£2667 $4907 €4000 Pomme bouche. copper round prov. 11-Jun-4 Pierre Berge, Paris #106/R est:4000-5000
£43114 $72000 €62946 Camel Couches (117x213x165cm-46x84x65in) wool soft leather aluminium on foam rubber wood pair prov. 12-Nov-3 Christie's, Rockefeller NY #341/R est:50000-70000

LALANNE, François-Xavier (1924-) French
Sculpture
£1067 $1931 €1600 Carpe doree (31x56x12cm-12x22x5in) s. num.151/250 gilded resin. 1-Apr-4 Credit Municipal, Paris #92 est:1000-1200
£1701 $3044 €2500 Tortue (13cm-5in) st.d.1973 num.26/100 red copper. 19-Mar-4 Millon & Associes, Paris #160/R est:1200-1500
£2267 $4193 €3400 Seau (28x19cm-11x7in) st.mono. white porcelain exec.1973 prov. 18-Jul-4 Sotheby's, Paris #191/R est:1000-1500
£2857 $5114 €4200 Tortue (13cm-5in) st.d.1973 num.4/100 polished brass. 19-Mar-4 Millon & Associes, Paris #161/R est:1200-1500
£3521 $6162 €5000 Gorille de pierre (60x80x32cm-24x31x13in) reconstituted stone exec 1970-1974. 18-Dec-3 Cornette de St.Cyr, Paris #158/R est:5000-6000
£3521 $6162 €5000 Gorille de pierre (60x80x32cm-24x31x13in) reconstituted stone exec 1970-1974. 18-Dec-3 Cornette de St.Cyr, Paris #159/R est:5000-6000
£6667 $11933 €10000 Sheep (87x94x40cm-34x37x16in) mono.st.sig. num.9/60 bronze stone. 15-May-4 De Vuyst, Lokeren #521/R est:7500-10000
£6667 $11933 €10000 Sheep (90x100x35cm-35x39x14in) mono.st.sig. num.26/250 bronze stone. 15-May-4 De Vuyst, Lokeren #522/R est:7500-10000
£7000 $12530 €10500 Sheep (90x100x35cm-35x39x14in) mono.st.sig. num.41/250 bronze stone. 15-May-4 De Vuyst, Lokeren #520/R est:7500-10000
£9091 $15455 €13000 Mouton (90x102x34cm-35x40x13in) s.num.96/250 stone bronze prov. 25-Nov-3 Tajan, Paris #58/R est:12000-15000

LALANNE, Maxime (1827-1886) French
Works on paper
£233 $400 €340 Extensive wooded landscape (56x42cm-22x17in) s. chl. 2-Dec-3 Christie's, Rockefeller NY #154b/R
£274 $465 €400 Paysage avec escalier (32x49cm-13x19in) s. chl stump. 6-Nov-3 Tajan, Paris #220

LALARA, Admiral (20th C) Australian
Works on paper
£447 $702 €653 Untitled (42x77cm-17x30in) natural pigments bark. 27-Aug-3 Christie's, Sydney #764 (A.D 1100)

LALARA, Nadjuwa (?-1960) Australian
Works on paper
£407 $638 €590 Untitled (73x42cm-29x17in) natural pigments bark. 27-Aug-3 Christie's, Sydney #770 (A.D 1000)
£528 $829 €766 Untitled (38x60cm-15x24in) natural pigments bark. 27-Aug-3 Christie's, Sydney #774 est:500-800 (A.D 1300)
£650 $1021 €943 Untitled (45x66cm-18x26in) natural pigments bark. 27-Aug-3 Christie's, Sydney #776 est:500-800 (A.D 1600)

LALAUZE, Alphonse (1872-?) French
£867 $1551 €1300 Chasseurs a cheval (65x54cm-26x21in) s.d.1932. 11-May-4 Vanderkindere, Brussels #216

LALIBERTE, Alfred (1878-1953) Canadian
£311 $538 €454 Portrait de jeune femme (43x33cm-17x13in) board painted c.1940. 15-Dec-3 Iegor de Saint Hippolyte, Montreal #27 (C.D 700)
£711 $1230 €1038 Femme nue et chat blanc (61x44cm-24x17in) s. board. 15-Dec-3 Iegor de Saint Hippolyte, Montreal #28 (C.D 1600)
£1333 $2307 €1946 Nu masculin au bouclier (106x71cm-42x28in) 15-Dec-3 Iegor de Saint Hippolyte, Montreal #29 (C.D 3000)
Sculpture
£714 $1214 €1042 Le Semeur (21x15x9cm-8x6x4in) bronze. 6-Nov-3 Heffel, Vancouver #072a/R est:1500-2000 (C.D 1600)
£889 $1538 €1298 Alarme (33cm-13in) s. num.2/6 bronze. 15-Dec-3 Iegor de Saint Hippolyte, Montreal #26 (C.D 2000)
£1126 $1914 €1644 Separating the wheat (14cm-6in) s. brown pat bronze. 21-Nov-3 Walker's, Ottawa #60/R est:2000-2500 (C.D 2500)
£2016 $3710 €2943 L'epuchette (17cm-7in) s.i. num.16 green pat bronze Cast Andro prov. 9-Jun-4 Walker's, Ottawa #61/R est:3500-4500 (C.D 5000)
£2679 $4607 €3911 Poule Noir (46cm-18in) s. bronze. 2-Dec-3 Joyner Waddington, Toronto #113/R est:3000-4000 (C.D 6000)
£8889 $15378 €12978 Poesie (46x66x32cm-18x26x13in) s.i. white marble. 15-Dec-3 Iegor de Saint Hippolyte, Montreal #25 (C.D 20000)

LALIQUE, René J (1860-1945) French
Works on paper
£596 $1091 €900 Coraux (28x22cm-11x9in) Chinese ink gouache. 7-Apr-4 Maigret, Paris #19/R
£728 $1333 €1100 Glycine (28x22cm-11x9in) Chinese ink gouache. 7-Apr-4 Maigret, Paris #18/R
£993 $1818 €1500 Montre-chatelaine (28x22cm-11x9in) gouache. 7-Apr-4 Maigret, Paris #12/R est:750-900
£993 $1818 €1500 Pendentif (28x22cm-11x9in) Chinese ink W/C gouache. 7-Apr-4 Maigret, Paris #23/R est:750-900
£1325 $2424 €2000 Deux libellules accolees (28x22cm-11x9in) Chinese ink gouache. 7-Apr-4 Maigret, Paris #16/R est:1500-1800
£1457 $2666 €2200 Quatre libellules (28x22cm-11x9in) Chinese ink gouache. 7-Apr-4 Maigret, Paris #17/R est:1500-1800
£1656 $3030 €2500 Joueuse de flute (28x22cm-11x9in) Chinese ink gouache. 7-Apr-4 Maigret, Paris #15/R
£1722 $3151 €2600 Sauterelles (28x22cm-11x9in) gouache W/C. 7-Apr-4 Maigret, Paris #13/R est:3000-3300
£1722 $3151 €2600 Pendentif (28x22cm-11x9in) Chinese ink gouache W/C. 7-Apr-4 Maigret, Paris #22/R est:2700-3000
£1788 $3272 €2700 Crabe (28x22cm-11x9in) Chinese ink gouache. 7-Apr-4 Maigret, Paris #20 est:1400-1500
£1788 $3272 €2700 Peigne (28x22cm-11x9in) Chinese ink W/C lit. 7-Apr-4 Maigret, Paris #26/R est:1200-1500
£1921 $3515 €2900 Femme libellule (28x22cm-11x9in) Chinese ink gouache. 7-Apr-4 Maigret, Paris #14/R est:3300-3500
£2119 $3878 €3200 Peigne (28x22cm-11x9in) crayon gouache W/C. 7-Apr-4 Maigret, Paris #25/R est:750-900
£2384 $4363 €3600 Dragon (28x22cm-11x9in) Chinese ink gouache. 7-Apr-4 Maigret, Paris #21/R est:1000-1200
£2649 $4848 €4000 Pendentif (28x22cm-11x9in) Chinese ink gouache W/C. 7-Apr-4 Maigret, Paris #24/R est:3800-4600

LALIQUE, Rene J and RIVIERE, Theodore (20th C) French
Sculpture
£13333 $24533 €20000 Brodeuse Tunisienne (32x22x25cm-13x9x10in) marble bronze ivory wood emaux plomb socle exhib. 14-Jun-4 Gros & Delettrez, Paris #103/R est:20000-30000

LALIQUE, Suzanne (1899-?) French
£616 $1048 €900 Ami du peuple (65x54cm-26x21in) s.d.1930. 10-Nov-3 Horta, Bruxelles #512
£2800 $4452 €4088 Petits fours (31x39cm-12x15in) s.d.1932. 9-Sep-3 Sotheby's, Olympia #300/R est:3000-4000

LALL, Oscar de (1903-1971) Canadian
£223 $373 €323 Breaking waves along the shore (51x66cm-20x26in) s. 17-Jun-3 Pinneys, Montreal #186 (C.D 500)
£311 $538 €454 Spring break up - Laurentians, Quebec (41x51cm-16x20in) s. 9-Dec-3 Pinneys, Montreal #15 (C.D 700)
£385 $700 €562 Mountain landscape (20x26cm-8x10in) s. 7-Feb-4 Sloans & Kenyon, Bethesda #894/R

LALLEMAND, Adele (attrib) (1807-?) French
£2292 $3735 €3300 Still life of flowers (40x32cm-16x13in) s.i.d.1849 mixed media. 25-Sep-3 Dr Fritz Nagel, Stuttgart #1159/R est:3000

LALLEMAND, Henri (1810-?) Belgian
£1200 $2172 €1800 Vue de ville (42x69cm-17x27in) s.d.1872. 30-Mar-4 Campo & Campo, Antwerp #152/R est:2000-4000

LALLEMAND, Jean Baptiste (1710-1805) French
£6667 $12067 €10000 Le tombeau de Neron sous l'orage (210x136cm-83x54in) 30-Mar-4 Rossini, Paris #51/R est:10000-15000
£8939 $16000 €13051 Quack doctor in a village (66x82cm-26x32in) s. prov. 27-May-4 Sotheby's, New York #46/R est:12000-16000
£16549 $27472 €23500 Scenes de paysages Mediterraneens (47x62cm-19x24in) s.d.1764 pair prov. 13-Jun-3 Ferri, Paris #58/R est:25000-30000
£22069 $36855 €32000 Rome, the Quirinale (35x52cm-14x20in) tempera paper prov. 12-Nov-3 Sotheby's, Milan #168/R est:15000-20000
Works on paper
£1769 $3166 €2600 Une ville Italienne avec les ruines d'une temple corinthien (25x38cm-10x15in) i. pen col ink grey wash. 18-Mar-4 Christie's, Paris #126/R est:1500-2000
£2158 $3540 €3000 Vue de port avec ruines (20x29cm-8x11in) s. gouache. 6-Jun-3 Drouot Estimations, Paris #14/R est:2200-2500
£2238 $3804 €3200 Scene de genre (15x22cm-6x9in) s.indis.d. gouache pair. 24-Nov-3 Boscher, Cherbourg #725/R est:1200-1500
£2400 $4392 €3504 Port scene with figures in the foreground working (19x36cm-7x14in) s. gouache. 7-Jul-4 Bonhams, Knightsbridge #2/R est:1500-2000
£4491 $7500 €6557 Untitled (30cm-12in circular) one s. gouache pair prov. 20-Oct-3 Sotheby's, New York #442/R est:1500-2500
£5238 $9376 €7700 Paysage italien avec temple (27x40cm-11x16in) pen ink W/C. 17-Mar-4 Maigret, Paris #88/R est:1200-1500
£6593 $12000 €9626 Figures among Roman ruins (36x49cm-14x19in) gouache pair. 29-Jun-4 Sotheby's, New York #3/R est:6000-8000
£6623 $12053 €10000 Vue de temple de Diane a Baia. Vue du temple de Venus a Baia (36x53cm-14x21in) one i. gouache. 16-Jun-4 Piasa, Paris #111/R est:10000-12000
£7237 $13316 €11000 Paysages de la cote mediterraneenne (33x49cm-13x19in) s.i. gouache pair. 24-Jun-4 Tajan, Paris #71/R est:10000-12000

LALLEMAND, Jean Baptiste (attrib) (1710-1805) French
£3467 $6275 €5200 Le soir, villageoises a la riviere. Le matin, deux jeunes femmes se baignant. (32x56cm-13x22in) pair. 2-Apr-4 Rossini, Paris #28/R est:4500-5500

LALLEMAND, Jean Baptiste (circle) (1710-1805) French
£5822 $9897 €8500 Figure in Mercury temple and ruins (55x70cm-22x28in) board prov. 4-Nov-3 Ansorena, Madrid #361/R est:8500

L'ALLEMAND, Siegmund (1840-1910) Austrian
£1189 $2045 €1700 Horse rider with hound in the forest (18x14cm-7x6in) s.d.1874 cardboard. 3-Dec-3 Neumeister, Munich #525 est:1000

LALLI, A Corsi (19/20th C) ?
£7500 $13800 €10950 Gentle music of a byegone day (19x15cm-7x6in) s.i.d.1893 oil on ivorine. 11-Jun-4 Christie's, London #100/R est:8000-12000

LALLICH, Giuseppe (1867-1950) Italian
£667 $1193 €1000 Boats in Ragusa harbour (24x35cm-9x14in) s. i.verso cardboard. 13-May-4 Babuino, Rome #496

LALOUCHI, L (19th C) ?
£1657 $3000 €2419 Shore scene (66x94cm-26x37in) s. 3-Apr-4 Charlton Hall, Columbia #119/R est:800-1200

LALOY, Yves (1920-1999) French
£333 $617 €500 Le port de Cancale (37x55cm-15x22in) s. 14-Jul-4 Livinec, Gaudcheau & Jezequel, Rennes #232
£9333 $17173 €14000 Ouah-Ouah (107x210cm-42x83in) s.d.1960 verso prov. 9-Jun-4 Artcurial Briest, Paris #415/R est:15000-20000

LALUMIA, Frank (1948-) American
£3235 $5500 €4723 Shalako (76x102cm-30x40in) 1-Nov-3 Altermann Galleries, Santa Fe #93

LAM, Wilfredo (1902-1982) Cuban
£10056 $18000 €14682 Untitled, abstract figure (35x25cm-14x10in) s.d.1975 lit. 26-May-4 Sotheby's, New York #101/R est:10000-15000
£10067 $18624 €15000 Untitled (30x40cm-12x16in) s. painted 1973. 13-Mar-4 Meeting Art, Vercelli #401 est:12000
£21127 $36972 €30000 Personnage (46x38cm-18x15in) s. s.d.1972 verso lit. 18-Dec-3 Cornette de St.Cyr, Paris #68/R est:15000-20000
£32667 $59453 €49000 Untitled (71x100cm-28x39in) s.d.1974 s.d.verso prov.lit. 29-Jun-4 Cornette de St.Cyr, Paris #36/R est:50000-60000
£36313 $65000 €53017 Mere et enfant (103x84cm-41x33in) s.d.43 chl pastel paper on board prov.exhib. 26-May-4 Sotheby's, New York #82/R est:18000-22000
£44118 $75000 €64412 Totem (80x60cm-31x24in) s.d.1972 s.d.verso prov.exhib.lit. 19-Nov-3 Sotheby's, New York #121/R est:80000-100000
£79020 $135915 €113000 Untitled (92x76cm-36x30in) s.d.1942 tempera gouache paper on canvas prov.lit. 8-Dec-3 Artcurial Briest, Paris #57/R est:95000-120000
£89385 $160000 €130502 Surrealistic (89x67cm-35x26in) s.d.1947 paper prov.exhib.lit. 26-May-4 Sotheby's, New York #8/R est:125000-175000
£120000 $220800 €180000 Quatre mains pour un etre (92x73cm-36x29in) s.d.1967 prov.exhib.lit. 10-Jun-4 Christie's, Paris #47/R est:200000-240000
£173184 $310000 €252849 Grande composition (130x161cm-51x63in) oil chl painted 1966 prov.exhib.lit. 26-May-4 Sotheby's, New York #23/R est:180000-200000
£205882 $350000 €300588 Sans titre, la pareja - Untitled, the couple (105x84cm-41x33in) oil chl painted c.1942 prov.exhib.lit. 18-Nov-3 Christie's, Rockefeller NY #30/R est:280000-320000
£206667 $380267 €310000 Untitled (79x81cm-31x32in) s.d.1947 prov.exhib.lit. 10-Jun-4 Christie's, Paris #38/R est:325000-365000
£300000 $510000 €438000 Femme cheval (124x108cm-49x43in) s.d.1955 prov.exhib.lit. 19-Nov-3 Sotheby's, New York #8/R est:300000-400000
Sculpture
£1000 $1820 €1500 Bird. s. num.348/500 pat bronze. 12-Jul-4 Il Ponte, Milan #1060 est:1600-1800
£1135 $1838 €1600 Figuraje surrealista (27cm-11in) s. num.478/500 metal. 20-May-3 Ansorena, Madrid #811/R est:1200
£1352 $2419 €2000 Oiseau de feu. Oiseau de fer (26cm-10in) s. tin pair. 4-May-4 Calmels Cohen, Paris #195 est:2000-2500
£1500 $2715 €2190 L'oiseau zombie (27cm-11in) incised sig.d.1977 num.19/50 verso bronze prov. 1-Apr-4 Christie's, Kensington #246/R est:1500-2000
£1832 $3242 €2675 Mask (47x47cm-19x19in) s. green pat.bronze tondo one of 100. 27-Apr-4 AB Stockholms Auktionsverk #1161/R est:25000-30000 (S.KR 25000)
£3235 $5500 €4723 Sin titulo - Untitled (35x35cm-14x14in) s.d.1962 i. num.41/200 verso green pat. bronze prov. 18-Nov-3 Christie's, Rockefeller NY #114/R est:7000-9000
£8000 $14560 €12000 Mayimbe (85x63x12cm-33x25x5in) s.d.1977 num2/8 pat bronze lit. 29-Jun-4 Cornette de St.Cyr, Paris #39/R est:8000-10000
£15000 $27600 €21900 Untitled (87x87cm-34x34in) s.d.1962 glazed ceramic prov. 24-Jun-4 Sotheby's, London #206/R est:15000-20000
Works on paper
£438 $727 €639 Bird (24x18cm-9x7in) s.d. pencil col crayon. 4-Oct-3 Dorotheum, Prague #323/R est:20000-30000 (C.KR 20000)
£621 $1037 €900 Untitled (21x19cm-8x7in) s.d.1978 mixed media. 14-Nov-3 Farsetti, Prato #52
£805 $1482 €1200 Figure (42x27cm-17x11in) s. collage paper on board. 24-Mar-4 Joron-Derem, Paris #104
£1645 $3026 €2500 Untitled (47x66cm-19x26in) s.i.d.1970 pen dr. 27-Jun-4 Versailles Encheres #145 est:2500-3000
£2819 $5046 €4200 Untitled (36x48cm-14x19in) s.d.1969 pen pastel prov. 25-May-4 Sotheby's, Milan #5/R est:3000
£4696 $8500 €6856 Woman (32x21cm-13x8in) W/C. 30-Mar-4 Arroyo, Buenos Aires #53
£6463 $11569 €9500 Untitled (34x46cm-13x18in) s.i.d.1960 col ink col crayon prov.exhib. 21-Mar-4 Calmels Cohen, Paris #35/R est:10000-12000
£6711 $12013 €10000 Totem (61x51cm-24x20in) s.d.1969 pastel paper on canvas. 30-May-4 Meeting Art, Vercelli #33 est:10000
£7647 $13000 €11165 Sans titre (50x65cm-20x26in) s.i. crayon col pencil executed 1959 prov. 19-Nov-3 Sotheby's, New York #119/R est:18000-22000
£8242 $15000 €12033 Sana titre (76x57cm-30x22in) s.d.1970 s.verso pastel chl. 29-Jun-4 Sotheby's, New York #415/R est:4000-6000
£9000 $16380 €13500 Untitled (49x69cm-19x27in) s. pastel chl. 29-Jun-4 Cornette de St.Cyr, Paris #33/R est:15000-20000
£13966 $25000 €20390 Three figures (76x56cm-30x22in) s.d.1969 chl pastel prov. 26-May-4 Sotheby's, New York #175/R est:20000-25000
£14094 $25933 €21000 Untitled (76x56cm-30x22in) s.d.1964 pastel chl prov. 29-Mar-4 Cornette de St.Cyr, Paris #46/R est:20000-25000
£14493 $23768 €20000 Untitled (63x45cm-25x18in) s.d.1975 pastel prov. 27-May-3 Sotheby's, Amsterdam #388/R est:12000-15000
£16760 $30000 €24470 Figures (50x40cm-20x16in) s.d.1975 prov.lit. 26-May-4 Sotheby's, New York #121/R est:25000-35000

£18000 $32760 €27000 Femme cheval (68x47cm-27x19in) s.d.1969 pastel chl. 29-Jun-4 Cornette de St.Cyr, Paris #35/R est:20000-30000
£18182 $30364 €26000 Sans titre (61x47cm-24x19in) s.d.1958 W/C chl. 11-Oct-3 Cornette de St.Cyr, Paris #70/R est:20000-25000
£64706 $110000 €94471 Desnudo en el balcon - Nude on balcony (89x69cm-35x27in) gouache paper on canvas exec. c.1938 prov.lit. 18-Nov-3 Christie's, Rockefeller NY #40/R est:120000-160000
£83799 $150000 €122347 Letter II (100x71cm-39x28in) s.d.1938 gouache paper on canvas prov.exhib.lit. 26-May-4 Sotheby's, New York #6/R est:150000-200000

LAMA, Giovanni Battista (1673-c.1748) Italian
£4577 $8011 €6500 Venus (50x75cm-20x30in) 17-Dec-3 Christie's, Rome #422/R est:3000-4000
£5282 $9243 €7500 Diana and Acteone (50x75cm-20x30in) 17-Dec-3 Christie's, Rome #421/R est:3000-4000

LAMA, Giulia (1681-1747) Italian
£10000 $16600 €14600 The Standard bearer (43x33cm-17x13in) 3-Oct-3 Mallams, Oxford #214/R est:3000-4000

LAMANTIA, James (1923-) American
£401 $650 €585 Mississippi Gulf Coast (41x51cm-16x20in) s.d.65 masonite. 2-Aug-3 Neal Auction Company, New Orleans #555
Works on paper
£262 $425 €383 Oak alley (36x51cm-14x20in) s.d.48 W/C. 2-Aug-3 Neal Auction Company, New Orleans #562

LAMAS, Menchu (1954-) Spanish
£2535 $4437 €3600 Moon-fish (81x100cm-32x39in) s.i.d.1986 verso. 16-Dec-3 Durán, Madrid #96/R est:1800
£4930 $7887 €7000 Arp player (230x150cm-91x59in) s.d.1983 verso prov.exhib. 16-Sep-3 Segre, Madrid #142/R est:5000
£5944 $9927 €8500 Untitled (196x132cm-77x52in) s.d.1984 prov. 24-Jun-3 Segre, Madrid #140/R est:4000
£6122 $11143 €9000 Untitled (240x200cm-94x79in) s.d.1985 prov. 3-Feb-4 Segre, Madrid #212/R est:6000
£6944 $11458 €10000 Fish and men (280x200cm-110x79in) 2-Jul-3 Ansorena, Madrid #858d/R est:10000

LAMASURE, Edwin (jnr) (1866-1916) American
Works on paper
£220 $350 €321 Grey day (30x50cm-12x20in) s. W/C. 12-Sep-3 Skinner, Boston #285/R
£265 $475 €387 Seaside path (24x51cm-9x20in) s. W/C. 14-May-4 Skinner, Boston #76/R
£366 $600 €531 House by the stream (33x64cm-13x25in) s. W/C exec.c.1900. 7-Jun-3 Treadway Gallery, Cincinnati #1348
£377 $600 €550 Mill (44x80cm-17x31in) s. W/C. 12-Sep-3 Skinner, Boston #280/R

LAMB, Charles Vincent (1893-1965) Irish
£417 $679 €600 Cottages at Keel (30x38cm-12x15in) s. i.verso canvasboard. 23-Sep-3 De Veres Art Auctions, Dublin #143
£690 $1276 €1000 West of Ireland landscapes with grazing sheep (30x40cm-12x16in) s. double-sided. 11-Feb-4 Woodwards, Cork #17/R
£1958 $3329 €2800 View at Carraroe (25x34cm-10x13in) s. board. 25-Nov-3 De Veres Art Auctions, Dublin #108/R est:3000-4000
£2027 $3831 €3000 Green roofed cottage and farm buildings (27x36cm-11x14in) s. board prov. 17-Feb-4 Whyte's, Dublin #67/R est:3000-4000
£2300 $4209 €3358 Landscape with figures walking along a track (27x36cm-11x14in) s. board. 28-Jan-4 Dreweatt Neate, Newbury #48/R est:1200-1500
£2819 $4989 €4200 Cottages, Carraroe, County Galway (27x36cm-11x14in) s. board exhib. 27-Apr-4 Whyte's, Dublin #25/R est:4000-6000
£3333 $6033 €5000 Chapel lake (27x35cm-11x14in) s. board. 31-Mar-4 James Adam, Dublin #41/R est:4000-6000
£3380 $5848 €4800 Sketch near Ramelton looking to Slieve Snaght (23x30cm-9x12in) s. panel. 10-Dec-3 Bonhams & James Adam, Dublin #196/R est:3000-4000
£3667 $6637 €5500 Landscape with a woman on a roadway (27x36cm-11x14in) s. board. 30-Mar-4 De Veres Art Auctions, Dublin #53/R est:3500-5000
£3800 $6232 €5548 Bachelors Walk, Portadown (45x56cm-18x22in) s. 4-Jun-3 John Ross, Belfast #207
£3986 $6776 €5700 West of Ireland cottage with woman carrying turf (26x36cm-10x14in) s. board. 25-Nov-3 De Veres Art Auctions, Dublin #34/R est:4000-6000
£4500 $7380 €6570 Evening on the Bann (40x50cm-16x20in) s. board. 4-Jun-3 John Ross, Belfast #74 est:7000
£4832 $8650 €7200 Mountain landscape with estuary and white cottages (32x40cm-13x16in) s. board. 26-May-4 James Adam, Dublin #52/R est:4000-6000
£5000 $8200 €7300 Carlingford Lough (50x61cm-20x24in) s. 4-Jun-3 John Ross, Belfast #155
£5034 $8909 €7500 River scene (27x36cm-11x14in) s. panel painted c.1934 prov.exhib. 27-Apr-4 Whyte's, Dublin #19/R est:4000-6000
£5282 $8451 €7500 Evening on the Old Bann, Portadown (41x51cm-16x20in) s. i.verso board exhib. 16-Sep-3 Whyte's, Dublin #114/R est:8000-10000
£7292 $11885 €10500 Bean na nGeabha - Woman with geese outside a cottage (32x40cm-13x16in) s. board. 24-Sep-3 James Adam, Dublin #36/R est:6000-8000
£8000 $13760 €11680 View of Carlingford Lough (46x56cm-18x22in) s. prov. 3-Dec-3 Sotheby's, London #22/R est:8000-12000
£8000 $14320 €11680 Coilin, head of Connemara boy (40x33cm-16x13in) s. prov. 13-May-4 Sotheby's, London #79/R est:5000-7000
£25503 $45651 €38000 Study for Quaint couple (33x42cm-13x17in) canvas on board. 26-May-4 James Adam, Dublin #49/R est:15000-20000

LAMB, Chloe (20th C) British
£620 $1091 €905 Castries Market, St Lucia (61x76cm-24x30in) s.d.98. 18-May-4 Woolley & Wallis, Salisbury #30/R

LAMB, F Mortimer (1861-1936) American
£1509 $2700 €2203 Arab horseman (61x107cm-24x42in) s.i.d.1907 prov. 14-May-4 Skinner, Boston #145/R est:2000-4000
Works on paper
£1156 $2000 €1688 I'm his sweetheart (23x33cm-9x13in) s.d.97 W/C. 13-Dec-3 Charlton Hall, Columbia #529/R est:1500-2500

LAMB, Florence E (fl.1880s-1899) British
£480 $816 €701 Interior scene with naval officer's seated around table (55x90cm-22x35in) s. indis d. 29-Oct-3 Bonhams, Chester #509

LAMB, Frederick Stymetz (1863-?) American
£1074 $1750 €1568 Ramapo river (41x51cm-16x20in) painted c.1900. 27-Sep-3 Thomaston Place, Thomaston #262

LAMB, Henry (1883-1960) British
£550 $935 €803 Children in summer landscape (29x40cm-11x16in) board prov. 26-Nov-3 Sotheby's, Olympia #58/R
£600 $1080 €876 Fallen tree (31x23cm-12x9in) s.d.27 canvasboard prov.exhib. 20-Apr-4 Rosebery Fine Art, London #489
£1000 $1850 €1460 Ruined church (49x39cm-19x15in) s.d.47 canvasboard prov. 11-Feb-4 Sotheby's, Olympia #132/R est:1000-1500
£1800 $3330 €2628 Portrait of Henrietta Phipps, the artist's daughter (61x51cm-24x20in) prov. 11-Feb-4 Sotheby's, Olympia #125/R est:2000-3000
£2200 $3498 €3212 Portrait of a girl (29x39cm-11x15in) s. board. 10-Sep-3 Sotheby's, Olympia #177/R est:1800-2500
£2200 $3740 €3212 Scene (38x45cm-15x18in) s.d.38 board. 26-Nov-3 Sotheby's, Olympia #54/R est:1000-1500
£3800 $6802 €5548 The conversation, boys, some with bicycles standing around (53x74cm-21x29in) s.d.51. 5-May-4 John Nicholson, Haslemere #447/R est:2000-3000
£5200 $9620 €7592 Still life with yellow flowers (48x38cm-19x15in) s.d.39 prov. 11-Feb-4 Sotheby's, Olympia #128/R est:2000-3000
£5500 $10175 €8030 Artist's wife and child reading (50x32cm-20x13in) s.d.34 prov. 11-Feb-4 Sotheby's, Olympia #126/R est:3000-4000
£8000 $14800 €11680 Artist's children Henrietta and Felicia with their nanny (40x44cm-16x17in) s.d.40 board prov. 11-Feb-4 Sotheby's, Olympia #130/R est:3000-5000
£8000 $14800 €11680 Under the tank (35x50cm-14x20in) s.d.42 canvasboard prov. 11-Feb-4 Sotheby's, Olympia #133/R est:4000-6000
Works on paper
£750 $1320 €1095 Under the tank (15x25cm-6x10in) W/C pencil. 19-May-4 Sotheby's, Olympia #72/R
£2800 $4928 €4088 Portrait of Euphemia Lamb (30x23cm-12x9in) s.d.1906 pencil exhib. 19-May-4 Sotheby's, Olympia #75/R est:2000-3000
£3800 $6802 €5548 Portrait of a lady, Ottoline Morrell (46x30cm-18x12in) pencil W/C. 16-Mar-4 Bonhams, New Bond Street #36/R est:2000-3000
£9500 $16340 €13870 Portrait of Lady Ottoline Morrell (28x23cm-11x9in) s. blk chk exec 1913 prov. 3-Dec-3 Sotheby's, London #7/R est:4000-6000

LAMB, Matt (20th C) American
£389 $650 €568 Couple (61x61cm-24x24in) board prov. 15-Nov-3 Slotin Folk Art, Buford #474/R

LAMB, Oscar Hermann (1876-1947) Austrian
£2763 $5084 €4200 Portrait of a young woman (105x90cm-41x35in) s.d.1911. 22-Jun-4 Wiener Kunst Auktionen, Vienna #73/R est:3000
Works on paper
£1200 $2148 €1800 Moonlight (45x63cm-18x25in) s.d.1924 W/C. 12-May-4 Stadion, Trieste #744/R est:800-1200

LAMBA, Jacqueline and TANGUY, Yves (20th C) American/French
Photographs
£2448 $4210 €3500 Yves Tanguy et Jacqueline Lamba devant la celebre porte de la galerie Gradiva (11x13cm-4x5in) photo. 6-Dec-3 Renaud, Paris #120

LAMBDIN, George Cochran (1830-1896) American
£2688 $5000 €3924 Woman with roses (76x51cm-30x20in) s. prov. 3-Mar-4 Christie's, Rockefeller NY #10/R est:6000-8000
£3704 $6000 €5371 Still life with straw hat (62x51cm-24x20in) s. 8-Aug-3 Barridorf, Portland #181/R est:6000-9000
£7014 $11011 €10240 Roses et pois de senteur (30x51cm-12x20in) s.d.1875 board. 26-Aug-3 Iegor de Saint Hippolyte, Montreal #95 (C.D 15500)
Works on paper
£3056 $5500 €4462 Wildflowers (36x25cm-14x10in) s. W/C sold with another by the same hand. 23-Jan-4 Freeman, Philadelphia #82/R est:2000-3000

LAMBDIN, Robert (1886-1981) American
Works on paper
£486 $900 €710 Perilous swap crossing (38x48cm-15x19in) s. chl. 15-Jul-4 Doyle, New York #54/R

LAMBEAUX, Jef (1852-1908) Belgian
Sculpture
£1027 $1747 €1500 Deux femmes nues et un enfant (67cm-26in) s. pat bronze. 10-Nov-3 Horta, Bruxelles #58
£1184 $2179 €1800 Lutteurs (71cm-28in) pat bronze. 22-Jun-4 Palais de Beaux Arts, Brussels #64 est:3000-5000
£1300 $2366 €1898 Reclining nude (22x59cm-9x23in) s.i. brown pat bronze. 15-Jun-4 Sotheby's, Olympia #104/R est:1500-2000
£1342 $2483 €2000 Bust of a young woman (177x45cm-70x18in) s. green pat bronze incl marble bronze base lit. 13-Mar-4 De Vuyst, Lokeren #211/R est:2000-3000
£1722 $3134 €2600 Le baiser (56cm-22in) s. green pat bronze. 15-Jun-4 Vanderkindere, Brussels #205/R est:1200-1800
£2069 $3434 €3000 Tete d'homme (55cm-22in) s. marble base. 2-Oct-3 Sotheby's, Paris #149/R
£2361 $3943 €3400 Nu couche (22x58x22cm-9x23x9in) s. bronze marble base. 21-Oct-3 Campo, Vlaamse Kaai #464a/R est:3500-4000

£3200 $5792 €4800 Femme couchee avec enfant (62x90x27cm-24x35x11in) bronze. 30-Mar-4 Campo & Campo, Antwerp #154/R est:5000-6000
£5333 $9600 €8000 Le chasseur de lionne (125cm-49in) s.st.f.Bronzes de Bruxelles green pat bronze. 20-Apr-4 Galerie Moderne, Brussels #1521/R est:5000-7000

LAMBERT, Andre Eugene (?) French?
Works on paper
£263 $415 €410 Aux postes de manoeuvre (44x60cm-17x24in) s. W/C. 12-Nov-2 Adjug'art, Brest #67/R

LAMBERT, B (19th C) ?
£1133 $2051 €1700 Wood in early autumn (58x36cm-23x14in) s. panel. 1-Apr-4 Van Ham, Cologne #1503/R est:900
£1200 $2172 €1800 Summer wood (58x36cm-23x14in) s. panel. 1-Apr-4 Van Ham, Cologne #1504 est:900

LAMBERT, Bradford (?) ?
£550 $1012 €803 River landscape at dusk (35x67cm-14x26in) s. 8-Jun-4 Bonhams, Knightsbridge #291/R

LAMBERT, Camille Nicholas (1876-?) Belgian
£733 $1313 €1100 Plage animee (29x26cm-11x10in) s. panel. 11-May-4 Vanderkindere, Brussels #78
£845 $1596 €1250 Plage animee (28x33cm-11x13in) s. panel. 17-Feb-4 Vanderkindere, Brussels #68
£2759 $5103 €4000 Cabines a la mer du Nord (30x22cm-12x9in) s. panel. 16-Feb-4 Horta, Bruxelles #485 est:700-900
£3169 $5482 €4500 Au bal masque (18x33cm-7x13in) s. panel. 13-Dec-3 De Vuyst, Lokeren #451/R est:4500-5500
£5921 $10895 €9000 Journee d'ete (60x73cm-24x29in) s. 22-Jun-4 Palais de Beaux Arts, Brussels #266/R est:6000-8000

LAMBERT, Edwin J (fl.1877-1904) British
£600 $1002 €876 Old toll bridge, Putney (34x61cm-13x24in) s. 13-Nov-3 Christie's, Kensington #146/R

LAMBERT, Eugène (1825-1900) French
£1159 $2167 €1750 Chien et chats (62x45cm-24x18in) 20-Jul-4 other European Auctioneer #120
£1631 $2643 €2300 Still life of flowers (46x32cm-18x13in) s.i.d.1868-1893 lit. 23-May-3 Karlheinz Kaupp, Staufen #1928/R est:1200
£2000 $3600 €2920 Family of cats (65x49cm-26x19in) s. 21-Jan-4 Sotheby's, Olympia #446/R est:2000-3000
Works on paper
£526 $968 €800 Trois chatons (22x27cm-9x11in) s. W/C. 22-Jun-4 Chassaing Rivet, Toulouse #307

LAMBERT, Eugène (attrib) (1825-1900) French
£1389 $2361 €2000 Still life with spring flowers (41x33cm-16x13in) s.d.12 Fevrier 1896. 28-Oct-3 Dorotheum, Vienna #59/R est:2400-2800

LAMBERT, George (1700-1765) British
£7143 $13000 €10429 View of Dover Castle and bay (63x119cm-25x47in) s.d.1737 prov.lit. 29-Jun-4 Sotheby's, New York #33/R est:8000-12000

LAMBERT, George Washington (1873-1930) Australian
£2024 $3259 €2955 River with boats (22x31cm-9x12in) init. board. 13-Oct-3 Joel, Victoria #396/R (A.D 5000)
£16170 $27489 €23608 Miss Alison Preston (213x106cm-84x42in) s. exhib.lit. 25-Nov-3 Christie's, Melbourne #81/R est:40000-60000 (A.D 38000)

LAMBERT, Georges (1919-) French
£330 $600 €482 Broc D'Etain (46x61cm-18x24in) s.d.1958 s.i.verso. 7-Feb-4 Neal Auction Company, New Orleans #650

LAMBERT, Gertrude A (1885-?) American
£814 $1400 €1188 Figures by a church (36x25cm-14x10in) s. oil pencil. 7-Dec-3 Freeman, Philadelphia #174

LAMBERT, James (snr) (1725-1788) British
£3300 $5511 €4818 Pastoral scenes with sheep (30x42cm-12x17in) s.d.1771 pair. 21-Oct-3 Bruton Knowles, Cheltenham #453/R est:2500-3000
£4500 $8190 €6570 Italianate landscape with drovers crossing a bridge and figures by a camp fire (158x264cm-62x104in) indis.s. 1-Jul-4 Sotheby's, London #143/R est:5000-7000

LAMBERT, Kurt (1908-) German
£345 $638 €500 Signal mast (53x37cm-21x15in) s. i. verso board. 14-Feb-4 Hans Stahl, Hamburg #157/R

LAMBERT, Marcel (?) ?
Works on paper
£1224 $2192 €1800 Buffet d'eau a Trianon (49x78cm-19x31in) s. pen W/C. 19-Mar-4 Beaussant & Lefèvre, Paris #32/R est:800-1000

LAMBERT, Maurice (1901-) French
Sculpture
£1100 $1749 €1606 J B Priestly (33cm-13in) mono.num.1/6 terracotta. 10-Sep-3 Sotheby's, Olympia #185/R est:600-800
£1500 $2385 €2190 Dame Margot Fonteyn (53cm-21in) mono. brown pat bronze base. 10-Sep-3 Sotheby's, Olympia #189/R est:1000-1500
£2800 $4452 €4088 Icarus (71cm-28in) mono.num.2/6 green pat bronze base. 10-Sep-3 Sotheby's, Olympia #186/R est:3000-5000
£4500 $7155 €6570 Aengus and the birds (119cm-47in) mono.num.1/6 bronze base. 10-Sep-3 Sotheby's, Olympia #187/R est:5000-7000
£6800 $10812 €9928 William Walton (30x18cm-12x7in) mono.num.4/6 green pat bronze. 10-Sep-3 Sotheby's, Olympia #184/R est:3000-5000

LAMBERT, Philippe (20th C) Belgian
£288 $489 €420 Jeu de chatons (51x71cm-20x28in) s. 10-Nov-3 Horta, Bruxelles #9

LAMBERT, Ronald (1923-1995) Australian
£412 $745 €602 Buckaneering Ploy (61x92cm-24x36in) s. i.d.1985 verso. 30-Mar-4 Lawson Menzies, Sydney #16 est:1000-1500 (A.D 1000)
£579 $1070 €845 Calligraph (91x101cm-36x40in) s.d.1990 i.verso prov. 15-Mar-4 Sotheby's, Melbourne #90 est:1000-1500 (A.D 1400)
£905 $1639 €1321 No.5 (73x209cm-29x82in) s.d.1984-85. 30-Mar-4 Lawson Menzies, Sydney #70/R est:1500-3000 (A.D 2200)

LAMBERT, Ted R (1905-1960) American
£10989 $20000 €16044 Mt McKinley 20,300 feet from the Susitna River (41x51cm-16x20in) s.d.1940 s.i.verso masonite prov. 15-Jun-4 John Moran, Pasadena #98 est:10000-15000

LAMBERT-RUCKI, Jean (1888-1967) French
£1888 $3153 €2700 Figures dans la ville (19x27cm-7x11in) s.d.1923 panel. 29-Jun-3 Eric Pillon, Calais #266/R
£1946 $3601 €2900 Vue sur le jardin (33x24cm-13x9in) s.d.1923 panel. 14-Mar-4 Eric Pillon, Calais #233/R
£2310 $4250 €3373 Scenes de la vie parisienne (9x6cm-4x2in) s. panel on board set of 3 prov.lit. 10-Jun-4 Phillips, New York #54/R est:6000-8000
£2721 $4327 €4000 Profils dans la ville (40x50cm-16x20in) s.d.1922 cardboard. 21-Mar-3 Bailly Pommery, Paris #118/R
£4000 $7280 €6000 Deux figures (75x51cm-30x20in) s. cardboard. 29-Jun-4 Sotheby's, Paris #21/R est:6000-8000
£7483 $12496 €10700 Couple (72x60cm-28x24in) s.d.1926 panel. 29-Jun-3 Eric Pillon, Calais #265/R
£10067 $18624 €15000 Jardin public (73x100cm-29x39in) s.d.1923 panel. 14-Mar-4 Eric Pillon, Calais #219/R
Sculpture
£1333 $2453 €2000 Vierge a l'enfant (67cm-26in) s. num.3/8 brown pat. bronze Cast Bernart. 10-Jun-4 Camard, Paris #118/R est:2000-2200
£1972 $3194 €2800 Les danseurs (16x4x3cm-6x2x1in) s.num.IV/IV black pat bronze socle st.f. 5-Aug-3 Tajan, Paris #35/R est:1500-2000
£2817 $4563 €4000 Groupe a l'accordeoniste (19x8x6cm-7x3x2in) s.num.IV/IV black pat bronze socle st.f. 5-Aug-3 Tajan, Paris #34/R est:3000-5000
£3521 $5705 €5000 L'homme de fer (51x9cm-20x4in) s.d.num.III/IV polychrome pat bronze socle exec.c.1945 st.f. 5-Aug-3 Tajan, Paris #32/R est:6000-8000
£3784 $7000 €5525 Couple au chapeau gibus (55cm-22in) bronze num.3/8. 11-Mar-4 Sotheby's, New York #273/R est:5000-7000
£10204 $18266 €15000 Totem (285cm-112in) painted wood. 17-Mar-4 Tajan, Paris #19/R est:15000-18000
Works on paper
£513 $873 €750 Tete de femme au bonnet (47x35cm-19x14in) s.d.1930 Chinese ink dr. 5-Nov-3 Tajan, Paris #12/R
£629 $1051 €900 Deux figures fantastiques (32x24cm-13x9in) s.i.d.37 crayon stump. 25-Jun-3 Blanchet, Paris #32

LAMBERTI, Lamberto (1925-2003) Italian
£268 $497 €400 Artichokes (50x70cm-20x28in) s. s.i.verso. 13-Mar-4 Meeting Art, Vercelli #486
£312 $516 €450 Flowers in a vase (70x50cm-28x20in) s. masonite. 1-Jul-3 Il Ponte, Milan #819
£317 $526 €450 Le colline (100x120cm-39x47in) s. s.i.verso. 14-Jun-3 Meeting Art, Vercelli #197
£333 $613 €500 Flowers (70x90cm-28x35in) s. masonite. 12-Jun-4 Meeting Art, Vercelli #690/R
£333 $613 €500 Beach (49x60cm-19x24in) s. s.i.d.1964 verso. 12-Jun-4 Meeting Art, Vercelli #934
£336 $621 €500 Flowers in blue background (80x60cm-31x24in) s. s.i.verso. 13-Mar-4 Meeting Art, Vercelli #194
£336 $621 €500 Bananas (80x60cm-31x24in) s. s.i.d.1988 verso. 13-Mar-4 Meeting Art, Vercelli #450
£352 $585 €500 Le amiche (100x150cm-39x59in) s. s.i.verso. 14-Jun-3 Meeting Art, Vercelli #490/R
£387 $643 €550 Still life with regatta tent (80x60cm-31x24in) s. s.i.d. 14-Jun-3 Meeting Art, Vercelli #215/R
£400 $736 €600 Bamboo (80x120cm-31x47in) s. s.i.verso painted 1989. 12-Jun-4 Meeting Art, Vercelli #674/R
£600 $1092 €900 Venice (58x80cm-23x31in) s. 12-Jul-4 Il Ponte, Milan #1040
£667 $1227 €1000 Still life (120x120cm-47x47in) s. 12-Jun-4 Meeting Art, Vercelli #613/R
£867 $1595 €1300 Isle of Ponza (90x150cm-35x59in) s. s.i.verso. 12-Jun-4 Meeting Art, Vercelli #989/R
£1000 $1840 €1500 Sun in Ischia (150x200cm-59x79in) s. painted 1990 lit. 12-Jun-4 Meeting Art, Vercelli #245/R est:1500

LAMBILLOTTE, George (1915-) Belgian
£300 $540 €450 Le debardage (46x56cm-18x22in) s. 20-Apr-4 Galerie Moderne, Brussels #261

LAMBINET, Émile (1815-1877) French
£867 $1586 €1300 River landscape in summer (34x47cm-13x19in) s.d.1867. 5-Jun-4 Arnold, Frankfurt #644/R
£1538 $2646 €2200 Forest landscape (39x39cm-15x15in) s.d.1847 panel round. 2-Dec-3 Christie's, Paris #358/R est:2000-3000
£1781 $3027 €2600 Petite ferme en Normandie (23x46cm-9x18in) s. panel. 5-Nov-3 Rabourdin & Choppin de Janvry, Paris #43/R est:2500-3000
£2202 $3677 €3193 Stream landscape with farmstead and cow herdress (30x49cm-12x19in) s.d.65. 23-Jun-3 Philippe Schuler, Zurich #3533/R est:2000-2500 (S.FR 4800)

£2469	$4000	€3580	Fishing pond (27x37cm-11x15in) s.d.1848 panel. 8-Aug-3 Barridorf, Portland #51/R est:5000-7000
£2600	$4082	€3770	Pres de la ferme, Normandie (30x46cm-12x18in) s.d.71 s.i.d.verso panel. 28-Aug-3 Christie's, Kensington #226/R est:500-700
£2600	$4758	€3900	Promenade champetre (27x40cm-11x16in) s. panel. 6-Jun-4 Osenat, Fontainebleau #68/R est:3500-4000
£2733	$5002	€4100	Bord de mer (42x64cm-17x25in) s. 6-Jun-4 Osenat, Fontainebleau #67/R est:4000-4500
£3712	$6830	€5420	Cows and peasants by water (35x66cm-14x26in) s.d.1856. 14-Jun-4 Philippe Schuler, Zurich #4309/R est:2500-3000 (S.FR 8500)
£4577	$7599	€6500	Bord de riviere anime (24x33cm-9x13in) s. panel. 15-Jun-3 Peron, Melun #171
£5208	$8594	€7500	Le chemin vert (73x120cm-29x47in) s.d.1870. 3-Jul-3 Van Ham, Cologne #1323/R est:4000

LAMBINET, Emile (attrib) (1815-1877) French

Works on paper

£374	$670	€550	Vue des etangs de Montbaron (24x17cm-9x7in) i.verso graphite. 18-Mar-4 Christie's, Paris #247

LAMBIRIS, N I (19th C) Greek

£5000	$8750	€7300	Erechtheum (75x56cm-30x22in) s. 16-Dec-3 Bonhams, New Bond Street #10/R est:4000-5000

LAMBOURNE, Alfred (attrib) (1850-1926) American

£852	$1500	€1244	Among the geysers in their old ages (41x61cm-16x24in) s. i.d.verso. 22-May-4 Harvey Clar, Oakland #2228

LAMBRE, Sylvain (1889-1958) Belgian

£367	$667	€550	Vue de reu nocturne (66x77cm-26x30in) s. 4-Jul-4 MonsAntic, Maisieres #448
Works on paper			
£342	$582	€500	Scandal (47x57cm-19x22in) s.d.1933 mixed media. 10-Nov-3 Horta, Bruxelles #450

LAMBRECHT, Constant (1915-1993) Belgian

£451	$754	€650	Composition (85x60cm-33x24in) s. panel. 21-Oct-3 Campo, Vlaamse Kaai #913

LAMBRECHTS, Jan Baptist (1680-1731) Flemish

£2128	$3553	€3000	Une scene d'interieur de cuisine (56x47cm-22x19in) 17-Oct-3 Tajan, Paris #71/R est:4000-6000
£3067	$5612	€4600	Interior of kitchen (21x17cm-8x7in) panel. 3-Jun-4 E & Eve, Paris #43 est:4500-5000
£3311	$6026	€5000	Scene de fetes galantes (60x50cm-24x20in) pair. 16-Jun-4 Hotel des Ventes Mosan, Brussels #136/R est:6000-6500

LAMBRECHTS, Jan Baptist (attrib) (1680-1731) Flemish

£972	$1546	€1400	Interior of inn with figures (51x41cm-20x16in) pair. 9-Sep-3 Vanderkindere, Brussels #542
£1048	$1928	€1530	Young couple in kitchen (28x22cm-11x9in) panel. 14-Jun-4 Philippe Schuler, Zurich #4310/R est:3000-4000 (S.FR 2400)
£1597	$2603	€2300	Pipe smoking man at table in tavern (37x31cm-15x12in) i. stretcher pair. 25-Sep-3 Dr Fritz Nagel, Stuttgart #1256/R est:4500
£2105	$3874	€3200	Figures round tavern table (37x31cm-15x12in) one i. stretcher pair. 24-Jun-4 Dr Fritz Nagel, Stuttgart #603/R est:3000

LAMBRICHS, Edmond Alfonse Charles (1830-1887) Belgian

£496	$829	€700	Jeune femme aux lilas (59x43cm-23x17in) s.d.84. 17-Jun-3 Vanderkindere, Brussels #124/R
£738	$1373	€1100	Young woman with mirror (70x50cm-28x20in) s. 8-Mar-4 Bernaerts, Antwerp #273/R

LAMEE, L (?) French?

£1892	$3386	€2800	Naufrages devant la cote (41x52cm-16x20in) panel. 10-May-4 Amberes, Antwerp #286/R
£5405	$9676	€8000	Bac dans un paysage fluvial (40x53cm-16x21in) panel. 10-May-4 Amberes, Antwerp #285/R

LAMEN, Christoffel Jacobsz van der (c.1606-1651) Flemish

£3378	$6047	€5000	Figures at dance (48x65cm-19x26in) panel lit. 8-May-4 Schloss Ahlden, Ahlden #674/R est:6500
£3691	$6607	€5500	Compagnie elegante dans un interieur (40x51cm-16x20in) panel. 25-May-4 Palais de Beaux Arts, Brussels #88/R est:8000-12000
£5200	$8840	€7592	Elegant company eating and drinking in an interior (46x67cm-18x26in) mono. panel. 29-Oct-3 Bonhams, New Bond Street #65/R est:3000-5000

LAMEN, Christoffel Jacobsz van der (attrib) (c.1606-1651) Flemish

£608	$1070	€900	Elegant company (60x50cm-24x20in) lit. 21-May-4 Mehlis, Plauen #15138/R
£2416	$4325	€3600	Personnages dans un interieur jouant le jeu de la main chaude (53x87cm-21x34in) panel. 25-May-4 Palais de Beaux Arts, Brussels #87/R est:3500-4500

LAMEN, van der (17th C) Flemish

£5634	$9746	€8000	Scene de Tabagie dans un interieur Hollandais (43x56cm-17x22in) panel. 14-Dec-3 St-Germain-en-Laye Encheres #10/R est:5000-7000

LAMERS, Kiki (1964-) Dutch

£2754	$4516	€3800	Couple in orange room (220x145cm-87x57in) s.d.1993 verso exhib. 27-May-3 Sotheby's, Amsterdam #465/R est:4000-6000
£3200	$5888	€4800	Nippel (50x45cm-20x18in) s.d.1998 verso. 8-Jun-4 Sotheby's, Amsterdam #151/R est:2000-3000
£7246	$11884	€10000	Doll's head (200x200cm-79x79in) s.d.1998 verso prov.exhib. 27-May-3 Sotheby's, Amsterdam #464/R est:6000-8000

LAMESI, Temistocle A (1870-1957) Italian

£1316	$2421	€2000	Femme de dos assise sur son lit (35x19cm-14x7in) s. panel. 25-Jun-4 Daguerre, Paris #132/R est:2000-2500

LAMI, Eugène Louis (1800-1890) French

Works on paper

£709	$1149	€1000	Postillon galopant dans la campagne (12x18cm-5x7in) s. W/C black crayon. 21-May-3 Daguerre, Paris #95
£769	$1323	€1100	La visite a l'hopital (12x9cm-5x4in) s.d.1867 lead pencil W/C gouache. 2-Dec-3 Christie's, Paris #672/R
£1088	$1948	€1600	Une scene de Manon Lescaut. Illustration pour la chronique de Charles IX (17x19cm-7x7in) s.d.1878 graphite W/C gouache pair. 18-Mar-4 Christie's, Paris #295/R est:2500-3500
£1127	$1949	€1600	Garde imperiale (19x29cm-7x11in) mono. W/C. 10-Dec-3 Piasa, Paris #118/R est:1500-2000
£1300	$2379	€1898	Standing elegant dressed gentleman (47x39cm-19x15in) s.d.1885 W/C over pencil. 7-Jul-4 Bonhams, Knightsbridge #38/R est:800-1200
£1329	$2285	€1900	Concert. Retour au foyer (13x10cm-5x4in) lead pencil W/C gouache pair prov. 2-Dec-3 Christie's, Paris #673/R est:1200-1600
£1361	$2436	€2000	Cuirassier a cheval (24x19cm-9x7in) s. black crayon W/C. 17-Mar-4 Tajan, Paris #85/R est:1500-1800
£1500	$2745	€2190	Two mounted offices surveying a battle (30x48cm-12x19in) s.d.42 W/C gouache pen ink over pencil. 7-Jul-4 Bonhams, Knightsbridge #76a/R est:1500-2000
£1712	$2911	€2500	Vue du Pont de la Concorde (12x19cm-5x7in) s. W/C gouache. 6-Nov-3 Tajan, Paris #112/R
£1748	$3007	€2500	L'Etourdi, d'apres Moliere - Acte 1, Scene VI, Lemoisne no 1339 (19x14cm-7x6in) s. lead pencil W/C gouache. 2-Dec-3 Christie's, Paris #638/R est:2000-3000
£1748	$3007	€2500	Quatre ecossais dans un camp (11x15cm-4x6in) s. lead pencil W/C gouache prov. 2-Dec-3 Christie's, Paris #677/R est:1500-2000
£2042	$3533	€2900	Etude de grand escalier (43x29cm-17x11in) s. W/C gouache htd gold. 10-Dec-3 Maigret, Paris #18 est:1500-2000
£2098	$3608	€3000	Les facheux, d'apres Miliere - Acte 1, Scene V (20x14cm-8x6in) s. lead pencil W/C gouache. 2-Dec-3 Christie's, Paris #642/R est:2000-3000
£2238	$3849	€3200	Le depit Amoureux, d'apres Moliere - Acte IV Scene III, Lemoisne, no 1340 (19x14cm-7x6in) lead pencil W/C gouache. 2-Dec-3 Christie's, Paris #639/R est:2000-3000
£2238	$3849	€3200	Hussard a cheval, tourne vers la gauche (14x12cm-6x5in) s. lead pencil W/C gouache. 2-Dec-3 Christie's, Paris #674/R est:800-1200
£2448	$4210	€3500	Sganarelle, d'apres Moliere - Acte 1, Scene VI (19x15cm-7x6in) lead pencil W/C gouache. 2-Dec-3 Christie's, Paris #641/R est:2000-3000
£2657	$4571	€3800	Comtesse d'Escarbagnas (20x14cm-8x6in) s. lead pencil W/C gouache. 2-Dec-3 Christie's, Paris #664/R est:2000-3000
£2657	$4571	€3800	Trois hommes fumant assis dans des fauteuils (12x22cm-5x9in) s.d.1836 pencil W/C gouache with 4 drawings 2 aquatints seven. 2-Dec-3 Christie's, Paris #681/R est:1200-1600
£2797	$4811	€4000	Les Precieuses redicules, d'apres Moliere - Acte 1, Scene III (20x14cm-8x6in) lead pencil W/C gouache. 2-Dec-3 Christie's, Paris #640/R est:2000-3000
£2797	$4811	€4000	Doom Garcie de Navarre, d'apres Moliere 0 Acte II, Scene VI (20x14cm-8x6in) s. lead pencil W/C gouache. 2-Dec-3 Christie's, Paris #643/R est:2000-3000
£2797	$4811	€4000	Officer assis a une table pres d'un hussard debout tenant un verre de vin (15x21cm-6x8in) s. lead pencil W/C gouache. 2-Dec-3 Christie's, Paris #670/R est:800-1200
£2797	$4811	€4000	Elle aime a rire, elle aime a boire (19x15cm-7x6in) s.d.1869 lead pencil W/C gouache prov. 2-Dec-3 Christie's, Paris #678/R est:1200-1600
£2937	$5052	€4200	Psychee (19x14cm-7x6in) s. lead pencil W/C gouache. 2-Dec-3 Christie's, Paris #663/R est:2000-3000
£3147	$5413	€4500	L'Ecole des Maris (19x14cm-7x6in) s. lead pencil W/C gouache. 2-Dec-3 Christie's, Paris #644/R est:2000-3000
£3147	$5413	€4500	L'Amour Medecin (19x14cm-7x6in) s. lead pencil W/C gouache. 2-Dec-3 Christie's, Paris #651/R est:2000-3000
£3147	$5413	€4500	Amphityron (19x14cm-7x6in) s. lead pencil W/C gouache. 2-Dec-3 Christie's, Paris #657/R est:2000-3000
£3357	$5773	€4800	La Princesse d'Elide (19x14cm-7x6in) s. lead pencil W/C gouache. 2-Dec-3 Christie's, Paris #649/R est:2000-3000
£3357	$5773	€4800	Le Medecin malgre lui (19x14cm-7x6in) s. lead pencil W/C gouache. 2-Dec-3 Christie's, Paris #653/R est:2000-3000
£3357	$5773	€4800	Melicerte (19x14cm-7x6in) s. lead pencil W/C gouache. 2-Dec-3 Christie's, Paris #654/R est:2000-3000
£3357	$5773	€4800	Le Sicilien ou L'Amour peintre (20x14cm-8x6in) s. lead pencil W/C gouache. 2-Dec-3 Christie's, Paris #655/R est:2000-3000
£3357	$5773	€4800	Monsieur de Pourceaugnac (20x14cm-8x6in) s. lead pencil W/C gouache. 2-Dec-3 Christie's, Paris #660/R est:2000-3000
£3357	$5773	€4800	L'Ecole des femmes (20x14cm-8x6in) s. lead pencil W/C gouache. 2-Dec-3 Christie's, Paris #645/R est:2000-3000
£3497	$6014	€5000	Georges Dandin (20x14cm-8x6in) s. lead pencil W/C gouache. 2-Dec-3 Christie's, Paris #658/R est:2000-3000
£3497	$6014	€5000	L'Avare (19x14cm-7x6in) s. lead pencil W/C gouache. 2-Dec-3 Christie's, Paris #659/R est:2000-3000
£3636	$6255	€5200	Don Juan (19x14cm-7x6in) s. lead pencil W/C gouache. 2-Dec-3 Christie's, Paris #650/R est:2000-3000
£3636	$6255	€5200	Le Tartuffe (20x14cm-8x6in) s. lead pencil W/C gouache. 2-Dec-3 Christie's, Paris #656/R est:2000-3000
£3636	$6255	€5200	Fourberies de Scapin (20x14cm-8x6in) s. lead pencil W/C gouache. 2-Dec-3 Christie's, Paris #665/R est:2000-3000
£3846	$6615	€5500	La critique de l'ecole des femmes (19x14cm-7x6in) s. lead pencil W/C gouache. 2-Dec-3 Christie's, Paris #646/R est:2000-3000
£3846	$6615	€5500	L'Impromptu de Versailles (19x14cm-7x6in) s. lead pencil W/C gouache. 2-Dec-3 Christie's, Paris #647/R est:2000-3000
£3846	$6615	€5500	Femmes Savantes (10x14cm-4x6in) s. lead pencil W/C gouache. 2-Dec-3 Christie's, Paris #666/R est:2000-3000
£3846	$6615	€5500	Elegants dans un interieur, un homme conversant avec une jeune femme (22x31cm-9x12in) pen grey ink W/C htd white sold with three other drawings prov. 2-Dec-3 Christie's, Paris #679 est:1500-2000
£3889	$7000	€5678	Great exhibition in London (38x53cm-15x21in) s.d.1852 W/C gouache. 21-Jan-4 Sotheby's, New York #207/R est:10000-15000
£4056	$6976	€5800	Plaisirs de l'Ille Enchantee (20x14cm-8x6in) s. lead pencil W/C gouache. 2-Dec-3 Christie's, Paris #648/R est:2000-3000
£4056	$6976	€5800	Les Amants Magnifiques (20x14cm-8x6in) s. lead pencil W/C gouache. 2-Dec-3 Christie's, Paris #661/R est:2000-3000
£4056	$6976	€5800	Le Bourgeois Gentilhomme (20x14cm-8x6in) s. lead pencil W/C gouache. 2-Dec-3 Christie's, Paris #662/R est:2000-3000

£4196	$7217	€6000	Le Misanthrope (19x14cm-7x6in) s. lead pencil W/C gouache. 2-Dec-3 Christie's, Paris #652/R est:2000-3000
£4196	$7217	€6000	Salut des etendards (21x20cm-8x8in) s.d.1871 blk chk W/C gouache prov. 2-Dec-3 Christie's, Paris #680/R est:2000-3000
£4755	$8179	€6800	Malade imaginaire (20x14cm-8x6in) s. lead pencil W/C gouache. 2-Dec-3 Christie's, Paris #667/R est:2000-3000
£5245	$9021	€7500	Cheval dans un paysage, tourne vers la droite (19x27cm-7x11in) s. lead pencil W/C gouache prov. 2-Dec-3 Christie's, Paris #669/R est:1000-1500
£5455	$9382	€7800	Officier hussard a cheval pointant vers la droite. Un dragon a cheval (19x15cm-7x6in) s.d.1886 s.d.1854 lead pencil W/C gouache pair. 2-Dec-3 Christie's, Paris #675/R est:1500-2000
£6993	$12028	€10000	Mameluck tenant un cheval arnache de profil a gauche (12x19cm-5x7in) s.d.1837 lead pencil W/C gouache prov. 2-Dec-3 Christie's, Paris #671/R est:700-1000
£7133	$12269	€10200	L'arrivee de Louis XIV au chateau de Fontainebleau (19x33cm-7x13in) s.d.1863 lead pencil W/C gouache. 2-Dec-3 Christie's, Paris #668/R est:3000-5000
£7343	$12629	€10500	Les Amants surpris (33x25cm-13x10in) s.d.1870 lead pencil W/C gouache prov. 2-Dec-3 Christie's, Paris #676/R est:3000-5000
£15101	$27785	€22500	Portrait du Comte de Ganay en tenue de chasse de l'equipage l'Aigle (28x19cm-11x7in) s.d.1862 W/C rounded top lit. 26-Mar-4 Pierre Berge, Paris #44/R est:10000-12000

LAMI, Rene (19/20th C) French?

£2200	$4158	€3212	Cattle grazing on a hillside (117x185cm-46x73in) s. 19-Feb-4 Christie's, Kensington #202/R est:1500-2000

LAMI, Stanislas (1858-1944) French

Sculpture

£1976	$3538	€2885	Bust of Rembrandt (56cm-22in) bronze. 15-May-4 Christie's, Sydney #264/R est:4000-6000 (A.D 5000)

LAMIEL, Jose (1924-) Spanish

£470	$879	€700	Nude (24x19cm-9x7in) s. s.i.d.2003 verso. 24-Feb-4 Durán, Madrid #33/R

LAMMERHIRT, Otto (1867-?) German

£769	$1323	€1100	Hiddensee, Ostsee (50x75cm-20x30in) s.d.1934 i.verso. 5-Dec-3 Bolland & Marotz, Bremen #593

LAMMERVO, Marko (1970-) Finnish

£289	$537	€430	Partridges (46x58cm-18x23in) s. 7-Mar-4 Bukowskis, Helsinki #368/R
£437	$731	€630	Bullfinches on sheaf of corn (61x50cm-24x20in) s.d.99. 26-Oct-3 Bukowskis, Helsinki #396/R
£850	$1548	€1250	Wolves (60x80cm-24x31in) s. 8-Feb-4 Bukowskis, Helsinki #387/R

LAMMI, Ilkka (1976-2000) Finnish

£2667	$4773	€4000	Gate in the wall (52x47cm-20x19in) s.d.1998 board. 15-May-4 Hagelstam, Helsinki #209/R est:4000
£3636	$6182	€5200	May she live a hundred years (74x52cm-29x20in) s.d.99 board. 29-Nov-3 Bukowskis, Helsinki #302/R est:2500-3500
£3649	$6531	€5400	Tree trunks (85x54cm-33x21in) s.d.99. 8-May-4 Bukowskis, Helsinki #316/R est:5000-6000
£26573	$45175	€38000	Dream (130x110cm-51x43in) s.d.99. 29-Nov-3 Bukowskis, Helsinki #292/R est:25000-35000

LAMOINE, Corinne (20th C) French

£385	$654	€550	Mitific hotel (100x81cm-39x32in) s. acrylic. 29-Nov-3 Neret-Minet, Paris #157

LAMOND, William B (1857-1924) British

£300	$567	€438	Young fisher girl (35x24cm-14x9in) s. 19-Feb-4 Lyon & Turnbull, Edinburgh #38
£900	$1548	€1314	Fisherfolk, Angus (36x53cm-14x21in) s. 4-Dec-3 Bonhams, Edinburgh #34/R
£900	$1503	€1314	Shepherd and his flock (25x30cm-10x12in) s. 23-Oct-3 Bonhams, Edinburgh #325
£1200	$2064	€1752	Cattle in woodland (36x46cm-14x18in) s. 2-Dec-3 Gorringes, Lewes #2538/R est:1000-1500
£1500	$2444	€2190	Autumn scene with potato pickers (42x53cm-17x21in) s. panel. 27-Sep-3 Rasmussen, Havnen #2215/R est:4000-6000 (D.KR 16000)
£1500	$2790	€2190	Midday rest (16x23cm-6x9in) s. canvasboard. 4-Mar-4 Christie's, Kensington #650/R est:1200-1800
£1600	$2752	€2336	Plough horses beside woodland (36x46cm-14x18in) s. 2-Dec-3 Gorringes, Lewes #2539/R est:1000-1500
£1774	$3175	€2590	Landscape with sheep (51x76cm-20x30in) init. prov. 26-May-4 AB Stockholms Auktionsverk #2432/R est:15000-18000 (S.KR 24000)
£2500	$4525	€3650	Gathering potatoes, Menzieshill (35x46cm-14x18in) s. board. 19-Apr-4 Sotheby's, London #111/R est:2500-3000
£3400	$6154	€4964	Good day's catch (35x53cm-14x21in) s.d.98 prov. 19-Apr-4 Sotheby's, London #113/R est:3000-4000
£5500	$9955	€8030	Shaded grazing. Moment at rest (35x46cm-14x18in) s. two. 19-Apr-4 Sotheby's, London #112/R est:4000-6000

LAMONT, Joseph (20th C) French

£592	$958	€840	Marine. Plage (12x16cm-5x6in) s. two. 11-Aug-3 Boscher, Cherbourg #776

Works on paper

£270	$511	€400	Marine (10x15cm-4x6in) s. W/C. 21-Feb-4 Livinec, Gaudcheau & Jezequel, Rennes #77

LAMONT, Thomas Reynolds (1826-1898) British

Works on paper

£600	$1104	€876	At the opera (35x25cm-14x10in) s.d.1857 pencil W/C bodycol prov. 25-Mar-4 Christie's, Kensington #241/R

LAMORA, Maya (20th C) French?

Works on paper

£400	$724	€600	Insensee (50x100cm-20x39in) s. mixed media. 3-Apr-4 Neret-Minet, Paris #97/R
£685	$1165	€980	Reverie (100x50cm-39x20in) s. mixed media canvas. 29-Nov-3 Neret-Minet, Paris #91/R

LAMORINIERE, Jean Pierre François (1828-1911) Belgian

£340	$609	€500	Vue de village (37x43cm-15x17in) s. oil paper. 16-Mar-4 Vanderkindere, Brussels #376
£1074	$1965	€1600	Vue de bruyere a Kalmthout (23x40cm-9x16in) s. panel. 8-Jul-4 Campo, Vlaamse Kaai #158 est:1000-1200
£2133	$3840	€3200	Panoramic view of a lake at sunset (30x48cm-12x19in) s.d.95. 21-Apr-4 Christie's, Amsterdam #199/R est:3500-4500
£2254	$3899	€3200	Le berger et son troupeau (60x84cm-24x33in) s. 9-Dec-3 Campo, Vlaamse Kaai #343/R est:2000-2200
£3500	$5950	€5110	Walk beside a river (59x81cm-23x32in) s.d.1855 panel. 19-Nov-3 Bonhams, New Bond Street #3/R est:3000-5000

LAMOTTE, Bernard (1903-1983) French

£568	$1000	€829	Harbour scene (38x46cm-15x18in) s. board painted c.1950. 23-May-4 Treadway Gallery, Cincinnati #638/R

LAMOTTE, Emmanuel (?) French

Works on paper

£276	$461	€400	Soleil rouge (48x64cm-19x25in) s. gouache. 11-Nov-3 Lesieur & Le Bars, Le Havre #67

LAMPER, Pol de (1878-?) Belgian?

£1138	$1900	€1650	L'aurore (200x300cm-79x118in) s.d.1930. 17-Nov-3 Bernaerts, Antwerp #350/R est:1000-1500

LAMPI, Johann Baptist (elder) (1751-1830) Italian

£5000	$9200	€7500	Portrait d'un officier polonais (68x52cm-27x20in) 11-Jun-4 Maigret, Paris #60/R est:8000-12000
£11409	$20993	€17000	Alleged juvenile portrait of Empress Maria Ludovica (79x63cm-31x25in) 24-Mar-4 Dorotheum, Vienna #273/R est:15000-25000
£12414	$20607	€18000	Portrait of Emperor Leopold II (77x60cm-30x24in) 1-Oct-3 Dorotheum, Vienna #211/R est:15000-20000

LAMPI, Johann Baptist (younger) (1775-1837) Italian

£2649	$4821	€4000	Portrait of a young lady with a golden headband (56x43cm-22x17in) prov. 16-Jun-4 Dorotheum, Vienna #150/R est:4000-5000

LAMPLE, Ronald (20th C) ?

£253	$400	€369	French country side (64x84cm-25x33in) s. 27-Jul-3 Simpson's, Houston #335

LAMPLOUGH, Augustus Osborne (1877-1930) British

Works on paper

£250	$450	€365	Fishing boat on the Lagoon, Venice (27x49cm-11x19in) s. W/C. 21-Jan-4 John Bellman, Billingshurst #1769
£280	$510	€409	Arab scene with flower seller (28x18cm-11x7in) s.i. 3-Feb-4 Gorringes, Bexhill #1072
£320	$544	€467	Suez Canal, near Ismalia (34x51cm-13x20in) s. W/C. 29-Oct-3 Bonhams, Chester #408
£345	$576	€500	Bedouin village in the desert (25x37cm-10x15in) s.d.1913 W/C. 9-Jul-3 Hugo Ruef, Munich #280/R
£350	$564	€508	On the upper Nile (23x61cm-9x24in) W/C. 20-Aug-3 Brightwells, Leominster #861
£360	$659	€526	Worshippers at a mosque in the desert (18x51cm-7x20in) s. W/C htd white. 27-Jan-4 Bonhams, Knightsbridge #23/R
£380	$692	€555	An oasis in the desert (34x48cm-13x19in) s.d.1909 pencil W/C. 1-Jul-4 Christie's, Kensington #340/R
£383	$651	€559	Egyptian Bedouin gathering (24x36cm-9x14in) s.d.1904 W/C. 21-Nov-3 Walker's, Ottawa #272/R (C.D 850)
£400	$736	€584	Feluccaas on the Nile (23x62cm-9x24in) s.indis.d. W/C. 25-Mar-4 Christie's, Kensington #66/R
£400	$720	€584	Arab village near Cairo (39x59cm-15x23in) s.i. W/C htd white. 22-Apr-4 Mellors & Kirk, Nottingham #1052/R
£480	$878	€701	Nile, afterglow (21x58cm-8x23in) s.i. W/C. 27-Jan-4 Bonhams, Knightsbridge #24/R
£493	$853	€700	Pyramids seen from the Nile (23x60cm-9x24in) s. W/C. 15-Dec-3 Gros & Delettrez, Paris #457
£500	$915	€730	Isle of Philae (35x52cm-14x20in) s.i.indis.d. W/C. 28-Jan-4 Dreweatt Neate, Newbury #43/R
£524	$965	€765	Caravan in the desert (23x61cm-9x24in) s.d.1917 W/C. 14-Jun-4 Waddingtons, Toronto #89/R est:700-900 (C.D 1300)
£560	$1036	€818	Young women gathering water (34x24cm-13x9in) s. W/C. 9-Mar-4 Bonhams, Knightsbridge #1/R
£570	$1077	€832	Nile scenes (61x23cm-24x9in) W/C pair. 21-Feb-4 Nigel Ward, Hereford #1457/R
£600	$1098	€876	Valley of Death. On the Nile (24x62cm-9x24in) s.i. W/C pair. 27-Jan-4 Bonhams, Knightsbridge #22/R
£700	$1260	€1022	Evening in the Valley of the Kings (55x38cm-22x15in) s. W/C. 21-Jan-4 Sotheby's, Olympia #218/R
£700	$1239	€1022	Dhow on the Nile (50x86cm-20x34in) s.d.1912 W/C. 27-Apr-4 Bonhams, New Bond Street #60/R
£700	$1281	€1022	Desert Nomads. The pyramids from the desert (14x22cm-6x9in) both s. latter i. W/C pair. 8-Jul-4 Lawrence, Crewkerne #1525/R
£800	$1360	€1168	On the Upper Nile (21x60cm-8x24in) s. W/C. 4-Nov-3 Bonhams, New Bond Street #103/R
£850	$1445	€1241	Sunset on the Nile (24x62cm-9x24in) s. W/C. 4-Nov-3 Bonhams, New Bond Street #102/R

£850	$1445	€1241	Dhows by the banks of the Nile (34x50cm-13x20in) s. W/C. 4-Nov-3 Bonhams, New Bond Street #105/R
£852	$1500	€1244	An Arab village scene near Luxor (42x60cm-17x24in) s.i. pencil W/C htd white. 18-May-4 Bonhams & Butterfields, San Francisco #183/R est:2000-3000
£900	$1413	€1305	Market boat at Kous. Ruins at Wady Kardass, Nubia (23x58cm-9x23in) s.i. pencil W/C bodycol pair. 28-Aug-3 Christie's, Kensington #413/R
£991	$1705	€1447	Temple ruins on the banks of the Nile (65x98cm-26x39in) s.d.1919 W/C. 8-Dec-3 Philippe Schuler, Zurich #4213 (S.FR 2200)
£1100	$1738	€1606	Desert scenes with Bedouin on camels (23x61cm-9x24in) s. W/C pair. 22-Jul-3 Peter Francis, Wales #42/R est:250-350
£1100	$1947	€1606	Pyramids at dusk (51x74cm-20x29in) s. W/C. 27-Apr-4 Bonhams, New Bond Street #65a est:1000-1500
£1171	$2014	€1710	Sunset over Cairo (50x73cm-20x29in) s. W/C. 8-Dec-3 Philippe Schuler, Zurich #4212/R est:1400-1800 (S.FR 2600)
£1400	$2338	€2044	Sheikh's tomb in the desert. Arabs in the desert. Boats on the Nile (25x63cm-10x25in) s. one i. W/C over pencil htd bodycol three. 14-Oct-3 Sotheby's, London #87/R est:1500-2000
£1400	$2576	€2044	Sheiks Tomb and other North African scenes (24x62cm-9x24in) s.i. three. 23-Mar-4 Anderson & Garland, Newcastle #127/R est:300-450
£1500	$2700	€2190	Skies yet blushing with departed light, Luxor (51x74cm-20x29in) s. W/C. 21-Jan-4 Sotheby's, Olympia #216/R est:1000-1500
£1900	$3420	€2774	Thebian Hills, Luxor. Rosy dawn (24x62cm-9x24in) s. W/C pair sold with another attrib to the artist. 21-Jan-4 Sotheby's, Olympia #213/R est:1000-2000
£2400	$4320	€3504	Evening in the Valley of the Kings, Luxor (51x73cm-20x29in) s. W/C. 21-Jan-4 Sotheby's, Olympia #217/R est:1000-1500
£2600	$4680	€3796	Egyptian silhouette. Cairo-Citadel from the desert (23x61cm-9x24in) s. W/C pair. 21-Jan-4 Sotheby's, Olympia #214/R est:1000-2000
£3000	$5400	€4380	Moonlight at Luxor. On the Nile, near Aswan (35x51cm-14x20in) s. W/C pair. 21-Jan-4 Sotheby's, Olympia #215/R est:1500-2500
£8000	$13360	€11680	Valley of the Kings - Temple of Hatshepsut (46x74cm-18x29in) s. W/C over pencil. 14-Oct-3 Sotheby's, London #84/R est:6000-8000

LAMPLOUGH, Augustus Osborne (attrib) (1877-1930) British

£276	$461	€400	Bedouin riders in the desert (24x37cm-9x15in) W/C. 9-Jul-3 Hugo Ruef, Munich #281

LAMPRECHT, Anton (1901-1984) German

£374	$681	€550	Moor landscape (75x100cm-30x39in) s. 4-Feb-4 Neumeister, Munich #725
£450	$792	€657	Harvest (60x81cm-24x32in) s. 19-May-4 Christie's, Kensington #740/R

LAMPUGNANI, Giovanni Battista (fl.1619-1644) Italian

Works on paper

£5000	$9000	€7300	Standing and kneeling figures for an assumption (20x28cm-8x11in) brush pen ink or possibly by Giovanni Francesco prov.lit. 21-Jan-4 Sotheby's, New York #26/R est:5000-7000

LAMR, Ales (1943-) Czechoslovakian

£1313	$2180	€1917	Island of Joy (95x95cm-37x37in) s.d.74. 4-Oct-3 Dorotheum, Prague #142/R est:60000-90000 (C.KR 60000)

LAMSWEERDE, Inez van (1963-) Dutch?

Photographs

£5587	$10000	€8157	KirSTEN STAR (99x75cm-39x30in) s.num.of ten verso with V Matadin c-print prov. 14-May-4 Phillips, New York #162/R est:12000-18000
£7000	$11690	€10220	Kirsten's war face (100x75cm-39x30in) cibachrome printed mounted on aluminium exec 1996 prov. 21-Oct-3 Sotheby's, London #454/R est:7000-10000

LAMURI, Louis (19th C) ?

£1275	$2359	€1900	Vegetable seller (74x104cm-29x41in) s.d.1902. 13-Mar-4 De Vuyst, Lokeren #213/R est:1500-2000

LAMY, Aline (1862-?) French

£566	$900	€821	Flowers (74x56cm-29x22in) s. pencil W/C board. 12-Sep-3 Aspire, Cleveland #173

LAMY, Eugene (?) ?

Works on paper

£313	$516	€450	Le passage du Gue (16x12cm-6x5in) init. gouache. 3-Jul-3 Claude Aguttes, Neuilly #115

LAMY, G (19th C) French

£352	$563	€500	Still life of flowers (55x46cm-22x18in) s. 21-Sep-3 Bukowskis, Helsinki #512/R

LAMY, Jacques (1946-) French

£419	$750	€612	Untitled. s. 13-May-4 Dallas Auction Gallery, Dallas #272/R
£950	$1700	€1387	Abstract. s. 13-May-4 Dallas Auction Gallery, Dallas #226/R est:1800-2800

LAN MENG (17th C) Chinese

Works on paper

£6757	$12162	€9865	Landscape (159x44cm-63x17in) s.i. ink col hanging scroll silk. 25-Apr-4 Christie's, Hong Kong #363/R est:30000-40000 (HK.D 95000)

LAN YINDING (1903-1979) Chinese

Works on paper

£301	$500	€439	Walking to a Mountain Temple (27x19cm-11x7in) ink. 30-Sep-3 Bonhams & Butterfields, San Francisco #4260/R
£1300	$2171	€1898	Harbour scene (14x31cm-6x12in) s. W/C. 14-Nov-3 Christie's, Kensington #276/R est:1000-1500
£3235	$5500	€4723	Landscape (81x61cm-32x24in) s. W/C. 4-Nov-3 Bonhams & Butterfields, San Francisco #3454/R est:3000-5000
£5587	$10000	€8157	Mountain landscape with bridge (42x67cm-17x26in) s.i.d.1959 ink hanging scroll. 10-May-4 Bonhams & Butterfields, San Francisco #4407/R est:10000-15000
£5587	$10000	€8157	Mountain village at sunset (67x42cm-26x17in) s.i.d.1960 ink. 10-May-4 Bonhams & Butterfields, San Francisco #4409/R est:10000-15000
£20000	$34000	€29200	Resting along a mountain gorge (188x137cm-74x54in) s. W/C. 4-Nov-3 Bonhams & Butterfields, San Francisco #3455/R est:6000-8000
£24893	$44808	€36344	Bliss (75x56cm-30x22in) s.d.1974 W/C. 25-Apr-4 Christie's, Hong Kong #714/R est:350000-450000 (HK.D 350000)

LAN YING (1585-1664) Chinese

Works on paper

£5690	$10242	€8307	Landscape (183x98cm-72x39in) s.i.d.1635 ink col hanging scroll ink after Wang Wei prov. 25-Apr-4 Christie's, Hong Kong #347/R est:80000-120000 (HK.D 80000)
£5792	$9672	€8456	Landscape (122x55cm-48x22in) s.i. ink col after WANG MENG. 26-Oct-3 Christie's, Hong Kong #479/R (HK.D 75000)
£21337	$38407	€31152	Travelling in the autumn hills (130x46cm-51x18in) s.i.d.1658 ink col hanging scroll silk. 25-Apr-4 Christie's, Hong Kong #356/R est:60000-80000 (HK.D 300000)

LAN-BAR, David (1912-1987) Israeli

£420	$713	€600	Portrait (65x50cm-26x20in) s. s.d.55 verso. 27-Nov-3 Calmels Cohen, Paris #56
£759	$1366	€1100	Composition (33x24cm-13x9in) s. s.d.1964 verso. 25-Jan-4 Chayette & Cheval, Paris #185/R

Works on paper

£310	$559	€450	Composition (75x54cm-30x21in) s. gouache exec 1975. 25-Jan-4 Chayette & Cheval, Paris #193
£345	$621	€500	Composition (73x52cm-29x20in) s.d.1962 gouache. 25-Jan-4 Chayette & Cheval, Paris #192
£483	$869	€700	Composition (106x74cm-42x29in) s. gouache exec 1967. 25-Jan-4 Chayette & Cheval, Paris #191

LANCASTER, Mark (1938-) British

£378	$700	€552	Chock Full O' Nuts (122x91cm-48x36in) s.d.75 verso prov. 13-Jul-4 Christie's, Rockefeller NY #136/R

LANCASTER, Osbert (1908-1986) British

Works on paper

£250	$448	€365	Astronauts down (24x13cm-9x5in) s. pen ink crayon. 25-May-4 Bonhams, Knightsbridge #202/R
£400	$736	€584	The legal Mafia (24x32cm-9x13in) i. W/C pen. 22-Jun-4 Bonhams, Knightsbridge #50/R
£600	$1092	€876	Cheer up, Darling. But I promise you, Auntie (25x14cm-10x6in) one.s. pencil black ink blue crayon pair. 1-Jul-4 Christie's, Kensington #514/R

LANCASTER, Paul (?) American?

£778	$1300	€1136	Landscape with family (79x91cm-31x36in) acrylic prov. 15-Nov-3 Slotin Folk Art, Buford #236/R

LANCASTER, Percy (1878-1951) British

£600	$1074	€876	Timber wagon (43x52cm-17x20in) board. 17-Mar-4 James Thompson, Kirby Lonsdale #85/R
£1500	$2730	€2190	Hayfield (68x101cm-27x40in) s. prov. 15-Jun-4 Bonhams, Leeds #158 est:1000-1400

Works on paper

£300	$531	€438	Country landscape with cows (26x47cm-10x19in) s. W/C. 27-Apr-4 Bonhams, Knightsbridge #188/R
£340	$612	€496	Moorland (21x33cm-8x13in) s. W/C. 20-Jan-4 Bonhams, Knightsbridge #40
£360	$648	€526	Church at Addingham (34x49cm-13x19in) s.d.20 W/C. 20-Jan-4 Bonhams, Knightsbridge #13/R
£400	$728	€584	Rochdale from the river (33x48cm-13x19in) s.i. W/C. 16-Jun-4 Andrew Hartley, Ilkley #1005
£400	$728	€584	Bend of the Duddon (33x48cm-13x19in) W/C. 29-Jun-4 Beeston Castle Salerooms, Tarporley #398/R
£400	$732	€584	The old shop door (23x30cm-9x12in) mono. W/C. 28-Jul-4 Mallams, Oxford #152/R
£500	$850	€730	Little farmstead. Cattle beside a river with meadows beyond (23x32cm-9x13in) s. pencil W/C pair. 19-Nov-3 Tennants, Leyburn #995
£550	$990	€803	Figures looking out to sea (23x33cm-9x13in) s. W/C. 20-Jan-4 Bonhams, Knightsbridge #10/R
£600	$1002	€876	Fisherwomen sorting the catch on a blustery day (34x49cm-13x19in) s. pencil W/C. 16-Oct-3 Christie's, Kensington #145/R
£650	$1086	€949	Seaweed gatherers (23x30cm-9x12in) s. pencil W/C. 16-Oct-3 Christie's, Kensington #199
£720	$1332	€1051	Harvest field, evening (34x50cm-13x20in) s.d.1927 W/C. 14-Jul-4 Bonhams, Chester #341
£1100	$1837	€1606	Idle gossip (23x29cm-9x11in) mono. pencil W/C. 16-Oct-3 Christie's, Kensington #146/R est:600-800

LANCASTER, Richard Hume (1773-1853) British

£2055	$3493	€3000	Shipping off Dover (46x61cm-18x24in) mono. 7-Nov-3 David Kahn, Paris #65/R est:4000-6000

LANCE, George (1802-1864) British

£1100	$1749	€1595	Still life of fruit in a basket (40x51cm-16x20in) 9-Sep-3 Bonhams, Knightsbridge #29 est:1200-1800
£2800	$4592	€4088	Still life with pomegranate, peaches, other fruits on white cloth in silver dish (28x38cm-11x15in) s.d.1837 panel. 29-May-3 Neales, Nottingham #784/R est:2500-3000

£6500 $12090 €9490 Grapes, cherries and other fruit silver platter with bejeweled cup on ledge (61x61cm-24x24in) s.d.1853. 4-Mar-4 Christie's, Kensington #668/R est:4000-6000

LANCE, George (attrib) (1802-1864) British
£399 $678 €583 Study of grapes with castle in the distance (45x38cm-18x15in) panel oval. 4-Nov-3 Peter Webb, Auckland #229/R est:600-1200 (NZ.D 1100)
£420 $735 €613 Apple, strawberry and grapes (15x19cm-6x7in) board. 18-Dec-3 Bonhams, Edinburgh #373
£480 $787 €701 Head and shoulders portrait of G Lance (31x42cm-12x17in) i.verso. 3-Jun-3 Fellows & Sons, Birmingham #60/R

LANCELEY, Colin (1938-) Australian
£1653 $2810 €2413 Land sea sky - morning, noon, and evening (57x44cm-22x17in) i. oil ink crayon on paper triptych. 29-Oct-3 Lawson Menzies, Sydney #178/R est:4500-6500 (A.D 4000)
£1860 $3161 €2716 Gentleman's gym (100x81cm-39x32in) s. i.d.1991 verso. 29-Oct-3 Lawson Menzies, Sydney #177/R est:5000-10000 (A.D 4500)
Works on paper
£826 $1529 €1206 End of the pier (70x105cm-28x41in) s.i.d.76 W/C pastel pen ink prov. 10-Mar-4 Deutscher-Menzies, Melbourne #288/R est:3000-4000 (A.D 2000)

LANCERAY, Eugène Alexandro (1848-1886) Russian
Sculpture
£1117 $2000 €1631 Cossack cavalry (53cm-21in) i. brown pat bronze. 20-Mar-4 Freeman, Philadelphia #593/R est:1500-2000
£1757 $3250 €2565 Farewell kiss 1 (41x33x15cm-16x13x6in) s. gilt pat bronze. 13-Mar-4 DeFina, Austinburg #809/R est:1200-1800
£2200 $3872 €3212 An equestrian falconer (32cm-13in) bronze. 18-May-4 Woolley & Wallis, Salisbury #373/R est:300-500
£2533 $4661 €3800 Cavalier maure (34x25cm-13x10in) s.i. brown pat. bronze. 14-Jun-4 Horta, Bruxelles #249 est:2500-3000
£2654 $4750 €3875 Cossack on horseback (28cm-11in) s. bronze. 20-Mar-4 Freeman, Philadelphia #603/R est:4000-6000
£2781 $5062 €4200 Eclaireur a cheval (32cm-13in) s.d.1882 pat bronze. 16-Jun-4 Beaussant & Lefèvre, Paris #135/R est:2000-2500
£3000 $5490 €4500 Combattant cosaque a cheval (29cm-11in) i. brown pat. bronze Cast Braunlick and Langlotz. 3-Jun-4 Tajan, Paris #220/R est:2300-2600
£3310 $5329 €4700 Les deux meres (30x32cm-12x13in) s.d.1884 brown pat bronze Cast Susse. 6-May-3 Coutau Begarie, Paris #74 est:4500-5000
£4247 $7219 €6200 Cosaque (38x40x15cm-15x16x6in) pat bronze lit. 5-Nov-3 Beaussant & Lefèvre, Paris #194/R
£4790 $8000 €6993 Tcherkess, Caucasian on horseback (27cm-11in) d.1870 bronze naturalistic base st.f.F. Chopin. 21-Oct-3 Christie's, Rockefeller NY #1 est:2000-3000
£5090 $8500 €7431 Bachkir, tartar on horseback (27cm-11in) d.1870 bronze naturalistic base st.f.F. Chopin. 21-Oct-3 Christie's, Rockefeller NY #2 est:2000-3000
£11000 $19910 €16500 Prise du cheval sauvage (44x63cm-17x25in) s.base brown pat bronze Cast Chopin. 2-Apr-4 Coutau Begarie, Paris #214 est:12000-15000
£18000 $32220 €26280 After battle (61cm-24in) s. bronze st.f.N.Shtanger. 26-May-4 Sotheby's, London #460/R est:6000-9000
£26000 $46540 €37960 After battle (69cm-27in) bronze st.f.F Chopin. 26-May-4 Sotheby's, London #462/R est:10000-15000

LANCERAY, Yevgeni (1875-1946) Russian
Works on paper
£3077 $4800 € View of an abandoned church (45x58cm-18x23in) s.d.1920 W/C white chk pencil. 11-Apr-3 Christie's, Rockefeller NY #41/R est:2000-3000
£11000 $19690 €16060 Dagestanis in the mountains (35x53cm-14x21in) s.d.1926 gouache. 26-May-4 Sotheby's, London #231/R est:4000-6000
£16000 $28640 €23360 Cossacks (63x46cm-25x18in) s.i.d.1918 gouache exhib.lit. 26-May-4 Sotheby's, London #228/R est:8000-12000

LANCEROTTO, Egisto (1848-1916) Italian
£46980 $84094 €70000 Bingo (115x174cm-45x69in) s. 25-May-4 Finarte Semenzato, Milan #205/R est:80000-90000

LANCKOW, Ludwig (19th C) German
£267 $485 €400 View of Reifferscheid (35x55cm-14x22in) s. 1-Jul-4 Van Ham, Cologne #1477
£403 $741 €600 Hay harvest (25x42cm-10x17in) s. panel. 27-Mar-4 L & B, Essen #142/R

LANCON, Auguste Andre (1836-1887) French
Works on paper
£915 $1584 €1300 Etude de tigre couche (15x23cm-6x9in) mono. W/C gouache. 10-Dec-3 Piasa, Paris #84 est:600

LANCRET, Nicolas (1690-1743) French
£111111 $200000 €162222 Fete galante, an elegant lady dancing with Pulcinella in a wooded landscape (28x23cm-11x9in) panel prov.exhib. 23-Jan-4 Christie's, Rockefeller NY #65/R est:200000-300000
Works on paper
£1389 $2500 €2028 Young man standing holding a hat (19x10cm-7x4in) red chk prov. 21-Jan-4 Sotheby's, New York #110/R est:4000-6000
£2381 $4262 €3500 Couple galant assist. Couple galant (22x13cm-9x5in) sanguine two exhib. 17-Mar-4 Tajan, Paris #50/R est:4500

LANCRET, Nicolas (after) (1690-1743) French
£7800 $14040 €11388 Elegant company celebrating the festival of Saint Jacques (126x132cm-50x52in) 21-Apr-4 Bonhams, New Bond Street #82/R est:7000-10000

LANCRET, Nicolas (attrib) (1690-1743) French
£6667 $12000 €9734 L'Eau (64x53cm-25x21in) prov.lit. 23-Jan-4 Christie's, Rockefeller NY #100/R est:1000-1500

LANCRET, Nicolas (style) (1690-1743) French
£4217 $7000 €6157 Elegant figures in a garden (75x86cm-30x34in) prov. 30-Sep-3 Christie's, Rockefeller NY #392/R est:7000-12000

LAND, Ernest Albert (20th C) American
£552 $1000 €806 Trompe l'oeil cabinet (76x48cm-30x19in) board. 16-Apr-4 American Auctioneer #232/R
£1272 $2200 €1857 Violin (81x43cm-32x17in) s.d.1972 panel trompe l'oeil. 13-Dec-3 Weschler, Washington #603 est:800-1200
£1734 $3000 €2532 Passing by (79x140cm-31x55in) s.d.1969 board. 13-Dec-3 Weschler, Washington #602 est:1000-1500

LANDAU, Sigalit (1969-) Israeli
Sculpture
£12849 $23000 €18760 Rose bleed (50cm-20in) s.d.2003 num.1/5 bronze exhib. 18-Mar-4 Sotheby's, New York #85/R est:18000-24000

LANDAU, Zygmunt (1898-1962) Polish
£1773 $2961 €2500 Nature morte a la banane (42x75cm-17x30in) s. 19-Jun-3 Millon & Associes, Paris #214/R est:1000-1500
£3087 $5711 €4600 Femmes a la lecture (73x51cm-29x20in) s. 15-Mar-4 Claude Boisgirard, Paris #68/R est:2000-3000
Works on paper
£703 $1174 €1026 Portrait of a lady (69x48cm-27x19in) s.d.1959 W/C. 19-Oct-3 Agra, Warsaw #63/R (P.Z 4500)

LANDEAU, Ergy (1896-1967) ?
Photographs
£2676 $4630 €3800 Nu au squelette (20x14cm-8x6in) s. photograph. 10-Dec-3 Artcurial Briest, Paris #14/R est:2000-3000

LANDEGHEM, Gaston van (19/20th C) Belgian
£1528 $2551 €2200 Village sous la neige (100x130cm-39x51in) s. 21-Oct-3 Campo & Campo, Antwerp #326/R est:2000-3000

LANDELLE, Charles Zacharie (1812-1908) French
£800 $1448 €1200 Le Sphinx, Egypte (13x23cm-5x9in) s. cardboard. 30-Mar-4 Rossini, Paris #295/R
£2700 $4914 €3942 An Arab beauty (45x30cm-18x12in) s. 16-Jun-4 Bonhams, New Bond Street #93/R est:3000-5000
£2907 $5000 €4244 Portrait of an oriental beauty (56x46cm-22x18in) s.d.1847 oval. 7-Dec-3 Freeman, Philadelphia #28 est:5000-8000
£3546 $5922 €5000 Odalisque (37x46cm-15x18in) s. 17-Jun-3 Christie's, Paris #1/R est:5000-7000

LANDENBERGER, Christian (1862-1927) German
£3557 $6545 €5300 Lakeside (40x37cm-16x15in) s. i. verso. 25-Mar-4 Dr Fritz Nagel, Stuttgart #740/R est:3800
£5563 $8901 €7900 Lakeside benches (63x71cm-25x28in) 18-Sep-3 Rieber, Stuttgart #1051/R est:6800

LANDER, Henry Longley (fl.1864-1887) British
£310 $564 €453 In the Lledr Valley, North Wales (24x34cm-9x13in) s.d.1868. 21-Jun-4 Bonhams, Bath #338

LANDER, John St Helier (1869-1944) British
£1900 $3097 €2774 Portrait of a lady wearing an ermine edged cape (130x95cm-51x37in) s.d.1914 panel. 25-Sep-3 Clevedon Sale Rooms #161/R est:3000-4500

LANDER, Mark (1955-) New Zealander
£336 $528 €491 Pauatahanui rainclouds (150x120cm-59x47in) s.d.75 acrylic. 27-Aug-3 Dunbar Sloane, Wellington #317 (NZ.D 925)

LANDERS, Sean (1962-) German
£14371 $24000 €20982 Untitled (213x310cm-84x122in) painted c.1994 prov. 14-Nov-3 Phillips, New York #215/R est:12000-18000

LANDEZIO, E (19th C) ?
£5697 $9855 €8318 Entry to the farm (28x42cm-11x17in) s.d.1834. 9-Dec-3 Louis Morton, Mexico #389/R est:120000-130000 (M.P 110000)

LANDFORS, Kjell (1933-) Scandinavian
£529 $899 €772 Inuit (162x103cm-64x41in) s.d.1987 verso exhib.prov. 4-Nov-3 Bukowskis, Stockholm #654/R (S.KR 7000)

LANDI, Bruno (1941-) Italian
£282 $468 €400 Ragazza con mela (50x40cm-20x16in) s. 14-Jun-3 Meeting Art, Vercelli #210
£300 $552 €450 Serenade (29x20cm-11x8in) s. cardboard painted 2002. 12-Jun-4 Meeting Art, Vercelli #199
£300 $552 €450 Waiting (29x20cm-11x8in) s. cardboard painted 2002. 12-Jun-4 Meeting Art, Vercelli #282
£302 $559 €450 Lovers (26x36cm-10x14in) s. canvas on cardboard. 13-Mar-4 Meeting Art, Vercelli #259
£302 $559 €450 Little nude (26x36cm-10x14in) s. canvas on cardboard painted 2003 lit. 13-Mar-4 Meeting Art, Vercelli #554
£333 $613 €500 Storyteller (43x27cm-17x11in) s. cardboard painted 2002. 12-Jun-4 Meeting Art, Vercelli #370/R

£367	$675	€550	Gladiators (25x20cm-10x8in) s. s.i.verso cardboard painted 2002 lit. 12-Jun-4 Meeting Art, Vercelli #931/R
£369	$683	€550	First meeting's emotions (36x26cm-14x10in) s. canvas on cardboard painted 2003. 13-Mar-4 Meeting Art, Vercelli #418
£387	$643	€550	La venere (60x30cm-24x12in) s. s.i.verso. 14-Jun-3 Meeting Art, Vercelli #220/R
£423	$701	€600	Donna con fiori (60x30cm-24x12in) s. s.i.verso painted 2001. 14-Jun-3 Meeting Art, Vercelli #670
£470	$869	€700	Venus (56x40cm-26x16in) s. card painted 2003. 13-Mar-4 Meeting Art, Vercelli #146
£503	$931	€750	Horse and rider (70x50cm-28x20in) s. 13-Mar-4 Meeting Art, Vercelli #218
£537	$993	€800	Surprise (36x26cm-14x10in) s. canvas on cardboard lit. 13-Mar-4 Meeting Art, Vercelli #539
£604	$1117	€900	Surprise (70x70cm-28x28in) s. painted 2003. 13-Mar-4 Meeting Art, Vercelli #188
£667	$1227	€1000	Horse and rider (60x120cm-24x47in) s. s.verso. 12-Jun-4 Meeting Art, Vercelli #349/R
£900	$1656	€1350	Woman and vase (80x60cm-31x24in) s. s.i.verso painted 2004 lit. 12-Jun-4 Meeting Art, Vercelli #591/R
£1000	$1840	€1500	Woman with necklace (80x60cm-31x24in) s. s.verso painted 2004. 12-Jun-4 Meeting Art, Vercelli #267/R est:750
£1275	$2359	€1900	Still life (100x120cm-39x47in) s. painted 2003. 13-Mar-4 Meeting Art, Vercelli #179 est:1000
£1333	$2453	€2000	Woman with guitar and ancient bust (120x100cm-47x39in) s. s.i.verso painted 2004 lit. 12-Jun-4 Meeting Art, Vercelli #957/R est:1150
£1409	$2523	€2100	Still life (100x120cm-39x47in) s. painted 2003 lit. 30-May-4 Meeting Art, Vercelli #80 est:1000
£3356	$6208	€5000	Great battle (150x200cm-59x79in) s. painted 2003. 13-Mar-4 Meeting Art, Vercelli #280 est:5000

LANDI, Ricardo Verdugo (1871-1930) Spanish

£537	$950	€800	Seascape (14x9cm-6x4in) s. cardboard. 27-Apr-4 Durán, Madrid #667/R
£1074	$1922	€1600	Seascape (14x30cm-6x12in) s. board. 25-May-4 Durán, Madrid #154/R est:1000
£3239	$5604	€4600	Choppy sea (25x49cm-10x19in) s. board. 15-Dec-3 Ansorena, Madrid #308/R est:4200
Works on paper			
£851	$1379	€1200	Batalla naval de la I Guerra Mundial (36x65cm-14x26in) s. gouache W/C. 20-May-3 Ansorena, Madrid #214/R

LANDIN, Bengt (1933-) Swedish

£1342	$2415	€1959	The favourite place (100x70cm-39x28in) s. 26-Apr-4 Bukowskis, Stockholm #588/R est:15000-18000 (S.KR 18500)

LANDINI, Andrea (1847-1912) Italian

£26000	$44200	€37960	His favourite pet (46x38cm-18x15in) s. prov.exhib. 18-Nov-3 Sotheby's, London #332/R
£48000	$79680	€70080	Chacun son metier (78x64cm-31x25in) s.i.d.1921 s.i.stretcher. 1-Oct-3 Sotheby's, Olympia #251/R est:20000-30000

LANDINI, Jacopo (1297-1358) Italian

£211268	$350704	€300000	Archangel Gabriel. Annunciation. Crucifixion (56x13cm-22x5in) tempera gold board in two parts lit. 11-Jun-3 Semenzato, Florence #17/R est:320000-350000

LANDIS, John (attrib) (1805-1851) American

Works on paper			
£2813	$4500	€4107	Religious drawings depicting Joseph from Genesis (20x30cm-8x12in) W/C pen three. 20-Sep-3 Pook & Pook, Downington #438/R est:1500-2500

LANDKROON, Piet (1907-) Dutch

£476	$867	€700	Plough teams in a hilly landscape (70x99cm-28x39in) s. 3-Feb-4 Christie's, Amsterdam #460

LANDOLT, Karl (1925-) Swiss

£430	$731	€628	Cherries (25x31cm-10x12in) s. i. verso pavatex on board. 18-Nov-3 Hans Widmer, St Gallen #1115 (S.FR 950)
£647	$1157	€945	Lattenberg in March 1972 (80x80cm-31x31in) mono. s.i.d.1972 verso. 12-May-4 Dobiaschofsky, Bern #718/R est:1600 (S.FR 1500)
£807	$1348	€1178	Rotterdam harbour (100x81cm-39x32in) i. verso. 24-Oct-3 Hans Widmer, St Gallen #60/R est:1400-3500 (S.FR 1800)
£917	$1669	€1339	Lattenberg, near Stafa (50x81cm-20x32in) mono. painted 1977. 16-Jun-4 Fischer, Luzern #2243/R (S.FR 2100)

LANDON, Charles Paul (1760-1826) French

£4605	$8474	€7000	Portrait de Victoire-Josephine Delaunay nee Brayer (65x54cm-26x21in) s. prov. 25-Jun-4 Piasa, Paris #120/R est:5000-7000

LANDON, Edward August (1911-1984) American

£652	$1200	€952	Figures in abstract composition. Stop, don't go (61x41cm-24x16in) s. one i. masonite two. 10-Jun-4 Swann Galleries, New York #142/R
Works on paper			
£815	$1500	€1190	Abstract composition with triangles (36x51cm-14x20in) s. pen ink W/C exec. c.1935. 10-Jun-4 Swann Galleries, New York #141/R est:1000-1500

LANDOWSKI, Paul Maximilien (1875-1961) French

Sculpture			
£1119	$1902	€1600	Tete d'homme Barbu (53x43x47cm-21x17x19in) rose granite. 1-Dec-3 Rieunier, Paris #14 est:3000-4000
£1502	$2689	€2193	Head of woman (35x23cm-14x9in) s. marble. 15-May-4 Christie's, Sydney #89/R est:2500-3500 (A.D 3800)
£2695	$4366	€3800	Monument a Wilbur Wright (81x18cm-32x7in) s.st.f.Barbedienne green pat bronze exec.c.1922. 24-May-3 Martinot & Savignat, Pontoise #128/R est:3800-4200
£2759	$4579	€4000	Icare (82cm-32in) s.st.f.Barbedienne green pat bronze. 2-Oct-3 Sotheby's, Paris #38/R
£2867	$5275	€4300	Homme bras leve (80x18x14cm-31x7x6in) st.f.Barbedienne pat bronze. 14-Jun-4 Cornette de St.Cyr, Paris #87/R est:3000-4000
£3953	$7075	€5771	Reclining female figure (58x33cm-23x13in) s.d. marble. 15-May-4 Christie's, Sydney #593/R est:3000-5000 (A.D 10000)
£4138	$7572	€6000	Sisyphe (80cm-31in) s.st.f.F. Barbedienne black pat bronze. 28-Jan-4 Piasa, Paris #28/R est:5000-6000
£5683	$9321	€7900	La bayadere (68cm-27in) bronze exec.c.1903. 6-Jun-3 Chochon-Barre & Allardi, Paris #17b
£6376	$10265	€9500	Le fils de Cain, buste (53cm-21in) s.d.1994 num.III/VIII green pat bronze st.f.Landowski. 23-Feb-3 St-Germain-en-Laye Encheres #125/R est:9000-10000
£6667	$12267	€10000	Femme a l'enfant (74cm-29in) stone. 10-Jun-4 Camard, Paris #60/R est:6000-8000

LANDQVIST, Lennart (1925-) Swedish

£508	$914	€762	Composition (70x95cm-28x37in) s. acrylic. 25-Apr-4 Goteborg Auktionsverk, Sweden #343/R (S.KR 7000)

LANDSEER, Sir Edwin (1802-1873) British

£1366	$2500	€1994	Terrier confronting a hedge hog (18x23cm-7x9in) s. prov. 10-Apr-4 Cobbs, Peterborough #108/R
£1800	$3294	€2628	A J Coleridge with dog (25x38cm-10x15in) painted with Thomas Landseer. 30-Jan-4 Tring Auctions, Tring #339/R est:1000-1500
£5800	$9628	€8468	Dear study (13x18cm-5x7in) init.d.60 canvas on board. 3-Oct-3 Mallams, Oxford #209/R est:1000-1500
£6200	$11098	€9052	Mountainous landscape with a figure by a cottage and sheep in the foreground (14x21cm-6x8in) i. board prov. 27-May-4 Christie's, Kensington #182/R est:1500-2000
£32000	$54400	€46720	Reflection, the monkey and the looking glass (35x43cm-14x17in) i. prov. 27-Nov-3 Sotheby's, London #193/R est:6000-8000
Works on paper			
£284	$475	€412	Head of a cow (23x30cm-9x12in) s. graphite dr. 22-Jun-3 Simpson's, Houston #60
£550	$919	€803	Study of Henry Drummond, MP (18x11cm-7x4in) init.i.d.1858 pen brown ink wash prov. 16-Oct-3 Christie's, Kensington #172/R

LANDSEER, Sir Edwin (after) (1802-1873) British

£25140	$45000	€36704	Eos (90x107cm-35x42in) 27-May-4 Sotheby's, New York #207/R est:8000-12000

LANDSEER, Sir Edwin (attrib) (1802-1873) British

£5500	$10120	€8030	Study of two dogs (24x30cm-9x12in) panel prov. 11-Jun-4 Christie's, London #52/R est:2000-3000
Works on paper			
£260	$411	€380	Vegetable seller (12x8cm-5x3in) pencil. 23-Jul-3 Hampton & Littlewood, Exeter #388/R
£400	$704	€584	Cart horse and ostler (10x16cm-4x6in) pen ink. 19-May-4 Dreweatt Neate, Newbury #3

LANDSEER, Sir Edwin (circle) (1802-1873) British

£16575	$30000	€24200	Two brown and white spaniles beside a velvet covered box (71x91cm-28x36in) 30-Mar-4 Bonhams & Butterfields, San Francisco #48/R est:30000-40000

LANDT, Frants (1885-1976) Danish

£301	$512	€439	Seascape with many vessels (64x93cm-25x37in) s.d.1929. 29-Nov-3 Rasmussen, Havnen #2110 (D.KR 3200)
£317	$567	€463	The steam ship Gudrun of Esbjerg (70x107cm-28x42in) s. 10-May-4 Rasmussen, Vejle #354/R (D.KR 3500)
£375	$625	€548	Seascape with sailing vessels (70x100cm-28x39in) s. 25-Oct-3 Rasmussen, Havnen #2527 (D.KR 4000)
£379	$701	€553	Vessel Flottbek of Hamburg in collision with iceberg (49x68cm-19x27in) s.d.1961. 15-Mar-4 Rasmussen, Vejle #152/R (D.KR 4200)
£407	$748	€611	Sailing vessel by the Danish coast (46x68cm-18x27in) s. 14-Jun-4 Blomqvist, Lysaker #1220/R (N.KR 5000)
£427	$682	€623	Seascape with Danish man-o-war (64x87cm-25x34in) s.d.1936. 22-Sep-3 Rasmussen, Vejle #269 (D.KR 4500)
£537	$983	€784	Seascape with vessels (41x58cm-16x23in) s.d.1944. 9-Jun-4 Rasmussen, Copenhagen #1810/R (D.KR 6000)
£611	$1100	€892	Ship in full sail (53x76cm-21x30in) s. 24-Apr-4 Weschler, Washington #568/R
£885	$1522	€1292	Seascape with sailing vessel (55x83cm-22x33in) s.indis.d.1923. 3-Dec-3 AB Stockholms Auktionsverk #2580/R (S.KR 11500)
£1141	$2019	€1700	Danish ship in Sund (50x85cm-20x33in) s.d.1917. 28-Apr-4 Schopman, Hamburg #672/R est:1200

LANDUYT, Charles Joseph van (1854-1934) Belgian

£400	$728	€600	Nu, Appels Bloemen (42x31cm-17x12in) s. 4-Jul-4 MonsAntic, Maisieres #488
£517	$957	€750	Chemin enneige (56x82cm-22x32in) s. 16-Feb-4 Horta, Bruxelles #488
£6000	$10740	€9000	Jeu de quilles (111x146cm-44x57in) s. painted c.1890. 17-May-4 Chayette & Cheval, Paris #170/R est:10000-12000

LANDUYT, Octave (1922-) Belgian

£559	$1000	€816	Projection (25x28cm-10x11in) s.d.62. 21-Mar-4 Jeffery Burchard, Florida #48/R
Works on paper			
£600	$1098	€900	Grenouille (61x45cm-24x18in) s. mixed media. 7-Jun-4 Palais de Beaux Arts, Brussels #370/R
£699	$1168	€1000	Inside this life (30x44cm-12x17in) s. i.verso pencil dr. 11-Oct-3 De Vuyst, Lokeren #215
£1818	$3036	€2600	Pour un voyage au long cours (50x70cm-20x28in) s. pastel panel prov.exhib.lit. 11-Oct-3 De Vuyst, Lokeren #214/R est:3000-3600
£2416	$4470	€3600	L'oiseau (64x98cm-25x39in) s. mixed media. 15-Mar-4 Horta, Bruxelles #186/R est:4000-6000

LANE, Abigail (1967-) British
Photographs
£3000 $5520 €4380 You know who you are (126x72cm-50x28in) colour photograph exec 2000 edn 8/10 prov.exhib. 24-Jun-4 Sotheby's, London #307/R est:3000-4000

LANE, Christopher (1937-) American
Works on paper
£243 $450 €355 Paint Tube (15x19cm-6x7in) s.d.1967 pastel. 13-Jul-4 Christie's, Rockefeller NY #24/R

LANE, Fitz Hugh (1804-1865) American
£167614 $295000 €244716 Mary Ann (48x70cm-19x28in) s.d.1846. 18-May-4 Christie's, Rockefeller NY #20/R est:80000-120000
Prints
£1852 $3000 €2685 View of Boston harbour. hand col lithograph exec.c.1855. 26-Jul-3 Thomaston Place, Thomaston #53/R

LANE, John J (19th C) British
£326 $600 €476 Flowers in an urn (69x84cm-27x33in) 25-Jun-4 Freeman, Philadelphia #233/R

LANE, Katharine Ward (1899-1989) American
Sculpture
£7547 $12000 €11019 Elephant (26cm-10in) s.verso bronze. 12-Sep-3 Skinner, Boston #364/R est:4000-6000

LANE, Leonard C (c.1910-1978) Canadian?
£373 $600 €545 Lighthouse at Peggy's Cove, Nova Scotia (30x41cm-12x16in) s. masonite. 20-Aug-3 James Julia, Fairfield #816/R
£435 $700 €635 Early moonrise (30x41cm-12x16in) s. s.i. verso masonite. 20-Aug-3 James Julia, Fairfield #815/R
£1056 $1700 €1542 End of a foggy day (56x71cm-22x28in) s. board. 20-Aug-3 James Julia, Fairfield #814/R est:1500-2500

LANE, Lina (20th C) American
Works on paper
£465 $800 €679 Floral still life (61x46cm-24x18in) s. W/C gouache. 7-Dec-3 Grogan, Boston #80/R

LANE, Samuel (1780-1859) British
£360 $644 €526 Portrait of William Turner, seated at a writing table (16x12cm-6x5in) d.1827 board. 22-Mar-4 Bonhams & Brooks, Norfolk #56/R
£8000 $14880 €11680 Portrait of Major Garnham in uniform (240x147cm-94x58in) i. prov.exhib.lit. 4-Mar-4 Christie's, Kensington #369/R est:5000-8000

LANE, Theodore (attrib) (1800-1828) British
£1200 $2040 €1752 Sporting student (40x49cm-16x19in) 18-Nov-3 Bonhams, Leeds #173/R est:1200-1800

LANE, Thomas (19th C) British
£1400 $2534 €2044 Portrait of Thomas Farmer of Bridnorth with hid dogs, in Farley Hall (44x61cm-17x24in) indis sig.i.d.1827 verso. 31-Mar-4 Bonhams, Knightsbridge #37/R est:1500-2000

LANE, Tony (1949-) New Zealander
£1455 $2284 €2110 Cross, night (52x52cm-20x20in) s.i.d.1996 oil gold leaf gesso panel. 27-Aug-3 Dunbar Sloane, Wellington #28/R est:3000-5000 (NZ.D 4000)
£3430 $5590 €5008 Hand (80x80cm-31x31in) init.d.1997 oil silver leaf gesso panel. 23-Sep-3 Peter Webb, Auckland #89/R est:7000-9000 (NZ.D 9500)
£4255 $7532 €6212 Landscape with wounds (84x140cm-33x55in) init. oil gold leaf gesso panel. 28-Apr-4 Dunbar Sloane, Auckland #27/R est:16000-22000 (NZ.D 12000)
Works on paper
£364 $571 €528 Phosphorescence (48x62cm-19x24in) pastel. 27-Aug-3 Dunbar Sloane, Wellington #117 (NZ.D 1000)

LANFANT DE METZ, François Louis (1814-1892) French
£660 $1089 €950 Enfant (10x6cm-4x2in) s. panel. 3-Jul-3 Claude Aguttes, Neuilly #115a
£966 $1612 €1400 Gladiateur (17x7cm-7x3in) s. panel. 11-Nov-3 Lesieur & Le Bars, Le Havre #68
£1233 $2096 €1800 Le jeune enfant (10x6cm-4x2in) s. panel. 9-Nov-3 Eric Pillon, Calais #5/R
£1333 $2427 €2000 Wedding party in boat. Wedding party with musicians (12x20cm-5x8in) s. panel pair. 30-Jun-4 Neumeister, Munich #600/R est:2000
£1507 $2562 €2200 Dans la laitiere (13x8cm-5x3in) s. panel. 9-Nov-3 Eric Pillon, Calais #3/R
£1879 $3326 €2800 Petite collation (27x21cm-11x8in) s. panel. 30-Apr-4 Tajan, Paris #86/R est:2000-3000
£1973 $3137 €2900 Enfant jouant avec des poissons rouges (22x16cm-9x6in) s. 21-Mar-3 Bailly Pommery, Paris #91 est:2500
£2013 $3705 €3000 Three children playing with wheelbarrow (48x60cm-19x24in) s. 25-Mar-4 Dr Fritz Nagel, Stuttgart #731/R est:2100
£2585 $4110 €3800 Young boy and his dog. Little girl with flowers (10x7cm-4x3in) both s. panel two. 23-Mar-3 Mercier & Cie, Lille #235/R est:3000-4000
£3221 $5928 €4800 Peasant woman with three children (39x23cm-15x9in) s. 25-Mar-4 Dr Fritz Nagel, Stuttgart #730/R est:2800
£3960 $7365 €5900 La peche miraculeuse (13x18cm-5x7in) s. cardboard. 7-Mar-4 Lesieur & Le Bars, Le Havre #73/R
£4133 $7481 €6200 Le tambour et les enfants (39x23cm-15x9in) s. panel pair. 5-Apr-4 Deburaux, Boulogne #91/R est:5000-5500

LANFANT DE METZ, François Louis (attrib) (1814-1892) French
£1308 $2067 €1897 Fishergirl surprised by the sea (49x38cm-19x15in) with sig. panel. 2-Sep-3 Rasmussen, Copenhagen #1801/R est:15000 (D.KR 14000)

LANFRANCO, Giovanni (1582-1647) Italian
£60403 $106913 €90000 David's triumph (55x165cm-22x65in) board. 27-Apr-4 Porro, Milan #321/R est:100000
£255034 $456510 €380000 Rinaldo's farewelll to Armida (109x178cm-43x70in) s.d.1614. 26-May-4 Porro, Milan #40/R
£492414 $822331 €714000 Crucifixion (298x177cm-117x70in) prov.exhib.lit. 15-Nov-3 Porro, Milan #256/R est:620000
Works on paper
£3611 $6500 €5272 Putto reclining on a cloud, with a head study (21x27cm-8x11in) black white chk. 22-Jan-4 Christie's, Rockefeller NY #43/R est:3000-5000
£3800 $6954 €5548 Head of a boy turned to the left (19x17cm-7x7in) i. black white chk. 6-Jul-4 Christie's, London #47/R est:3000-5000
£3889 $7000 €5678 Bearded prophet attended by a bishop and another figure (29x23cm-11x9in) black chk pen brown ink. 22-Jan-4 Christie's, Rockefeller NY #44/R est:3000-5000

LANFRANCO, Giovanni (style) (1582-1647) Italian
£16000 $29280 €23360 Departure of the Prodigal Son. Return of the Prodigal Son (206x281cm-81x111in) pair. 9-Jul-4 Christie's, Kensington #169/R est:4000-6000

LANG SHINING (1688-1766) Chinese/Italian
£22148 $39644 €33000 Chinese man seated under tree (43x27cm-17x11in) s. paint ink. 27-May-4 Beaussant & Lefèvre, Paris #263/R est:15000-20000
Works on paper
£189723 $339605 €284585 An Imperial procession to Luan Yang (53x684cm-21x269in) s.i. ink col silk handscroll brocade case. 17-May-4 Sotheby's, Melbourne #317/R est:15000-20000 (A.D 480000)

LANG, A (19th C) German
£940 $1598 €1372 Mountain landscape with figures and cabins by foaming river, Southern Germany (73x100cm-29x39in) s.d.869. 10-Nov-3 Rasmussen, Vejle #349/R (D.KR 10200)

LANG, Albert (1847-1933) German
£1936 $3582 €2827 River landscape (52x84cm-20x33in) 14-Mar-4 Agra, Warsaw #57/R (P.Z 14000)
£2585 $4627 €3800 Bathers (88x66cm-35x26in) s.d.1927. 17-Mar-4 Neumeister, Munich #511/R est:2200
Works on paper
£371 $619 €530 Small village on Maloja Pass, Engadin (31x48cm-12x19in) s.i.d.August 1913 htd white W/C Indian ink. 10-Oct-3 Winterberg, Heidelberg #679

LANG, C L (19th C) ?
£412 $750 €602 Seascape with boats in rough seas (31x49cm-12x19in) mono. 7-Feb-4 Rasmussen, Havnen #2220/R (D.KR 4500)

LANG, Fritz (1877-1961) German
£738 $1307 €1100 Moonlit Barensee (100x150cm-39x59in) mono.d. panel. 30-Apr-4 Dr Fritz Nagel, Stuttgart #872/R
£1007 $1782 €1500 Papaya tree with pelicans (109x87cm-43x34in) mono. panel. 30-Apr-4 Dr Fritz Nagel, Stuttgart #874/R est:1500
£1033 $1860 €1550 Shepherd by pine wood (135x90cm-53x35in) s.d.1923. 26-Apr-4 Rieber, Stuttgart #1133/R est:1800

LANG, George Ernest (1907-) South African
£353 $639 €515 Ship and a tugboat (35x50cm-14x20in) s. canvasboard. 30-Mar-4 Stephan Welz, Johannesburg #184 est:1600-2000 (SA.R 4200)

LANG, Hans (1898-1971) Austrian
£347 $552 €507 Alpine valley, Southern German/Austrian border (34x43cm-13x17in) i. i.verso board. 1-May-3 Dunbar Sloane, Wellington #71 est:500-1000 (NZ.D 1000)

LANG, Louis (1814-1893) German
£1415 $2250 €2066 Three girls with flowers (51x41cm-20x16in) s. board. 10-Sep-3 Alderfer's, Hatfield #263 est:500-700
£5556 $9167 €8000 Roman carnival (75x63cm-30x25in) s.i.d.184. 2-Jul-3 Neumeister, Munich #696/R est:4000

LANG, Nikolaus (1941-) German
Works on paper
£2800 $5124 €4200 Childhood memories (162x107cm-64x42in) animal bones earth stones nails string prov.exhib. 4-Jun-4 Lempertz, Koln #280/R est:3000

LANG, Steven (1944-) American
£5587 $10000 €8157 Kiowa Dutch (76x94cm-30x37in) 15-May-4 Altermann Galleries, Santa Fe #49/R
£6471 $11000 €9448 Sunset at Medicine bow (76x152cm-30x60in) 1-Nov-3 Altermann Galleries, Santa Fe #107

LANGASKENS, Maurice (1884-1946) Belgian
£483 $893 €700 Prisonnier lisant (16x25cm-6x10in) s. 19-Jan-4 Horta, Bruxelles #158
£521 $828 €750 Pause des soldats (35x70cm-14x28in) s.d. canvas on panel. 9-Sep-3 Vanderkindere, Brussels #4/R
£839 $1401 €1200 L'etude de l'insecte (30x34cm-12x13in) s. panel. 13-Oct-3 Horta, Bruxelles #339

£1000 $1840 €1500 La chapelle en hiver (49x49cm-19x19in) s. panel. 9-Jun-4 Christie's, Amsterdam #102/R est:1500-2000
£1259 $2165 €1800 Un conte de Noel (37x49cm-15x19in) s. panel. 8-Dec-3 Horta, Bruxelles #68 est:2000-3000
£1517 $2807 €2200 Semeur (46x58cm-18x23in) s. panel. 19-Jan-4 Horta, Bruxelles #157 est:2000-3000
Works on paper
£486 $792 €700 Serenade aux secours divers (56x32cm-22x13in) s.i.d.1941 W/C pencil. 29-Sep-3 Sotheby's, Amsterdam #148/R
£986 $1706 €1400 La fin (62x47cm-24x19in) s.i.d.1914-15-16 W/C. 13-Dec-3 De Vuyst, Lokeren #196

LANGE, Dorothea (1895-1965) American
Photographs
£2000 $3520 €2920 Ireland, group of men (25x16cm-10x6in) vintage gelatin silver print. 18-May-4 Bonhams, New Bond Street #395/R est:2500-3000
£2395 $4000 €3497 Abandoned tenant cabin in the Mississippi Delta (26x33cm-10x13in) gelatin silver print board exec.1937 prov.lit. 17-Oct-3 Phillips, New York #170/R est:4000-6000
£3704 $7000 €5408 Crossroads store, Alabama (17x24cm-7x9in) gelatin silver print. 17-Feb-4 Christie's, Rockefeller NY #192/R est:3000-4000
£3892 $6500 €5682 Black Maria, Oakland (28x26cm-11x10in) i.verso gelatin silver print exec.1957 prov.lit. 17-Oct-3 Phillips, New York #132/R est:5000-7000
£4233 $8000 €6180 Street demonstration, Chinatown, San Francisco, CA (34x26cm-13x10in) gelatin silver print. 17-Feb-4 Christie's, Rockefeller NY #190/R est:5000-7000
£5111 $9200 €7462 Newspaper headline, 3000 plane armada devastated Germany, 1942 (18x23cm-7x9in) num.42112 gelatin silver print lit. 23-Apr-4 Phillips, New York #81/R est:6000-9000
£7222 $13000 €10544 Untitled (12x32cm-5x13in) i.verso gelatin silver print prov. 23-Apr-4 Phillips, New York #34/R est:6000-8000
£7407 $14000 €10814 Funeral cortege, end of an era in a small valley town (41x39cm-16x15in) gelatin silver print. 17-Feb-4 Christie's, Rockefeller NY #191/R est:6000-8000
£9040 $16000 €13198 Torso, San Francisco (34x27cm-13x11in) gelatin silver print executed c.1965 lit. 27-Apr-4 Christie's, Rockefeller NY #88/R est:18000-24000
£30000 $54000 €43800 White angel bread line (50x40cm-20x16in) gelatin silver print prov.lit. 23-Apr-4 Phillips, New York #37/R est:30000-50000
£32934 $55000 €48084 Damaged child, shacktown, Elm Grove, Oklahoma (23x19cm-9x7in) s.i. gelatin silver print board exec.1936 prov.exhib.lit. 17-Oct-3 Phillips, New York #67/R est:60000-90000

LANGE, Evaline (?) British?
Works on paper
£380 $688 €555 Young boy and girl with puppy and kitten (23x15cm-9x6in) init. i.verso W/C. 1-Apr-4 Biddle & Webb, Birmingham #981

LANGE, Fritz (1851-1922) German
£1824 $3211 €2700 Poultry (18x24cm-7x9in) s.d.1900 panel two. 22-May-4 Lempertz, Koln #1544/R est:1500

LANGE, Johann Gustav (1811-1887) German
£671 $1235 €1000 Village in winter landscape (94x76cm-37x30in) s. 24-Mar-4 Hugo Ruef, Munich #1026/R
£1399 $2378 €2000 Snowy winter landscape with traveller (37x52cm-15x20in) s. 20-Nov-3 Van Ham, Cologne #1706/R est:1800
£2215 $4119 €3300 Playing on the ice by moonlight (109x125cm-43x49in) s. 6-Mar-4 Arnold, Frankfurt #767/R est:1200

LANGE, Johann Gustav (attrib) (1811-1887) German
£667 $1213 €1000 Farming couple in a path through the field in front of farm cottage (65x96cm-26x38in) s. 1-Jul-4 Neumeister, Munich #2743

LANGE, Julius (1817-1878) German
£634 $1096 €900 River landscape with angler (22x16cm-9x6in) s. panel. 13-Dec-3 Lempertz, Koln #228

LANGE, Ludwig (1808-1868) German
Works on paper
£2345 $3916 €3400 Mykene (21x21cm-8x8in) i. verso gouache. 15-Nov-3 Lempertz, Koln #1516/R est:1700

LANGE, Niels Erik (1890-1919) Danish
£860 $1359 €1247 Circus in town, Faelledeb (34x38cm-13x15in) init.indis.d. canvas on plywood. 3-Sep-3 Museumsbygningen, Copenhagen #28 (D.KR 9200)

LANGE, Otto (1879-1944) German
£347 $580 €500 Fjord landscape in winter (32x39cm-13x15in) s. i. verso board. 25-Oct-3 Dr Lehr, Berlin #308/R
Works on paper
£533 $976 €800 Masks (45x34cm-18x13in) s. W/C bodycol. 5-Jun-4 Lempertz, Koln #815/R
£2667 $4773 €4000 Winter landscape (37x52cm-15x20in) s. W/C double-sided prov. 14-May-4 Ketterer, Munich #49/R est:4000-6000

LANGE, Soren Laessoe (1760-1828) Danish
£722 $1300 €1054 Portrait of a gentleman (69x50cm-27x20in) i. oval. 21-Jan-4 Doyle, New York #135/R est:1500-2500

LANGE, Thomas (20th C) German
£2000 $3680 €3000 Red head (120x150cm-47x59in) mono.d.86. 12-Jun-4 Villa Grisebach, Berlin #413/R est:3000-4000

LANGEN, Hendrikus Johannes van (1874-1964) Dutch
£250 $400 €365 Tending the fire. s. 20-Sep-3 Harvey Clar, Oakland #1228
£469 $750 €685 Needlework. s. 20-Sep-3 Harvey Clar, Oakland #1230
£625 $1150 €950 Little donkeys on the beach (35x50cm-14x20in) s. 28-Jun-4 Sotheby's, Amsterdam #120/R

LANGENDOERFFER, Johanne (19th C) Austrian?
Works on paper
£440 $800 €642 Portrait of two sisters (66x56cm-26x22in) s.d.1835 pastel. 7-Feb-4 Auctions by the Bay, Alameda #1523/R

LANGENDYK, Dirk (1748-1805) Dutch
Works on paper
£440 $800 €642 Cavalry attack (24x33cm-9x13in) pen ink wash prov. 29-Jun-4 Sotheby's, New York #1/R
£500 $865 €730 Elaborate cartouche with three battle scenes (10x17cm-4x7in) pen col ink grey wash. 12-Dec-3 Christie's, Kensington #538
£692 $1191 €1010 Landscapes with soldiers, farmers and cattle (24x36cm-9x14in) s.one d.1799 W/C pair. 2-Dec-3 Bukowskis, Stockholm #449/R (S.KR 9000)
£850 $1530 €1241 Landscape with classical ruins and shepherd with his herd (25x24cm-10x9in) s.d.1783 pen black ink brown wash black chk. 20-Apr-4 Sotheby's, Olympia #175/R
£1667 $3000 €2434 Cavalry battle (36x52cm-14x20in) s.d.1785 pen black ink grey wash. 22-Jan-4 Christie's, Rockefeller NY #252 est:2000-4000
£2740 $4658 €4000 Explosion on a battle field (31x55cm-12x22in) s.d.1801 pen brown ink col wash. 4-Nov-3 Sotheby's, Amsterdam #134/R est:4000-6000

LANGENDYK, Dirk (attrib) (1748-1805) Dutch
Works on paper
£2000 $3620 €3000 Accueil triomphale de Napoleon (31x40cm-12x16in) W/C pen. 4-Apr-4 St-Germain-en-Laye Encheres #5/R est:1000-1500

LANGENDYK, Jan Anthonie (1780-1818) Dutch
Works on paper
£6849 $11644 €10000 Interior with figures listening to music played by children. Street scene (19x27cm-7x11in) s.d.1805 pen brown ink W/C over black chk pair. 4-Nov-3 Sotheby's, Amsterdam #137/R est:3500-4500

LANGER, Jorg (?) ?
£315 $541 €450 Narrative composition (33x33cm-13x13in) s.d.2003 oil linocut. 4-Dec-3 Schopman, Hamburg #686/R

LANGER, Karel (1878-1947) Czechoslovakian
£657 $1090 €959 Stream (50x66cm-20x26in) s. board. 4-Oct-3 Dorotheum, Prague #65/R est:30000-50000 (C.KR 30000)

LANGER, Viggo (1860-1942) Danish
£289 $534 €422 Snow-covered landscape with windblown trees (38x58cm-15x23in) s. 15-Mar-4 Rasmussen, Vejle #427 (D.KR 3200)
£311 $566 €467 Summer landscape with waterway in forest (24x32cm-9x13in) s.d.1849. 19-Jun-4 Rasmussen, Havnen #2294 (D.KR 3500)
£321 $583 €469 Spring day in the wood (47x64cm-19x25in) s.d.1925. 7-Feb-4 Rasmussen, Havnen #2290 (D.KR 3500)
£328 $547 €479 Summer's day on country road (41x53cm-16x21in) s.d.1933. 25-Oct-3 Rasmussen, Havnen #2118 (D.KR 3500)
£379 $709 €553 The flower market in Menton (46x59cm-18x23in) s.d.1930. 25-Feb-4 Kunsthallen, Copenhagen #222 (D.KR 4200)
£564 $960 €823 Wooded landscape with anemones (64x75cm-25x30in) s.d.1917. 29-Nov-3 Rasmussen, Havnen #2182 (D.KR 6000)
£582 $1048 €850 Summer's day in the wood (74x95cm-29x37in) s.d.1898. 24-Apr-4 Rasmussen, Havnen #2215/R (D.KR 6500)
£714 $1300 €1042 Garden from Aalsgaarde. View of a mill (39x49cm-15x19in) s. two. 7-Feb-4 Rasmussen, Havnen #2029/R (D.KR 7800)
£719 $1337 €1050 White lilies by a fountain in Italy (140x100cm-55x39in) s.d.1918. 2-Mar-4 Rasmussen, Copenhagen #1357/R (D.KR 8000)
£851 $1472 €1242 River landscape at sunset (37x57cm-15x22in) s. 9-Dec-3 Rasmussen, Copenhagen #1699/R (D.KR 9000)
£945 $1635 €1380 Woodland lake with yellow house in background (62x84cm-24x33in) s.d.1893. 9-Dec-3 Rasmussen, Copenhagen #1680/R (D.KR 10000)
£1134 $2030 €1656 Wooded landscape with lake (64x76cm-25x30in) s.d.1917. 12-Jan-4 Rasmussen, Vejle #91/R est:12000 (D.KR 12000)
£1168 $2173 €1705 Summer landscape with cows outside woods, Lejre (55x74cm-22x29in) s. 2-Mar-4 Rasmussen, Copenhagen #1370/R est:10000 (D.KR 13000)
£1935 $3290 €2825 Wooded landscape with bird by lake, Denmark (95x139cm-37x55in) s.d.1928 i.stretcher. 10-Nov-3 Rasmussen, Vejle #95/R est:6000 (D.KR 21000)

LANGEROCK, Henri (1830-1915) Belgian
£1361 $2435 €2000 Jeune femme a l'eventail dans une barque fleurie (45x37cm-18x15in) s. panel. 21-Mar-4 Muizon & Le Coent, Paris #30/R
Works on paper
£322 $599 €480 Villa Orientaliste animee (27x44cm-11x17in) s. gouache. 7-Mar-4 Livinec, Gaudcheau & Jezequel, Rennes #19
£338 $595 €500 Mediterranean landscape with figures on stairs of villa (28x45cm-11x18in) s. W/C. 24-May-4 Bernaerts, Antwerp #464/R
£2198 $3890 €3297 Sailing boat (29x44cm-11x17in) i. gouache. 27-Apr-4 Bolsa de Arte, Rio de Janeiro #11/R (B.R 12000)
£2198 $3890 €3297 Sailing boat (29x44cm-11x17in) s. gouache. 27-Apr-4 Bolsa de Arte, Rio de Janeiro #12/R (B.R 12000)

LANGETTI, Giovanni Battista (attrib) (1625-1676) Italian
£6294 $10699 €9000 Bound fawn (130x96cm-51x38in) 20-Nov-3 Van Ham, Cologne #1372/R est:10000

LANGETTI, Giovanni Battista (circle) (1625-1676) Italian
£24828 $41214 €36000 Jacob Wrestling with angel (108x139cm-43x55in) prov. 1-Oct-3 Dorotheum, Vienna #300/R est:5000-7000

LANGEVELD, Frans (1877-1939) Dutch
£750 $1178 €1088 Leading cows into pasture (41x50cm-16x20in) s. 28-Aug-3 Christie's, Kensington #87/R
£1020 $1857 €1500 Cows in a meadow, with woman on a path (41x63cm-16x25in) s. panel painted with T.Offermans, W.Roelofs and E.Gerardus. 3-Feb-4 Christie's, Amsterdam #196/R est:1500-2000
£1806 $3015 €2600 Windmills along a waterway (71x61cm-28x24in) s. prov. 21-Oct-3 Sotheby's, Amsterdam #103/R est:4000-6000

LANGEVELDT, Rutger van (1635-1695) Dutch
£7343 $12483 €10500 Scene de campement (48x71cm-19x28in) bears sig. panel. 1-Dec-3 Rieunier, Paris #8 est:8000-10000

LANGEVIN, Claude (1942-) Canadian
£383 $651 €559 Farmstead in winter (41x51cm-16x20in) s. i.verso prov. 21-Nov-3 Walker's, Ottawa #13/R (C.D 850)
£386 $691 €564 St Hilarion, Charlevoix (25x30cm-10x12in) s. s.i.verso prov. 6-May-4 Heffel, Vancouver #85/R (C.D 950)
£440 $805 €642 Colour automnal (20x40cm-8x16in) s.i. 1-Jun-4 Hodgins, Calgary #137/R (C.D 1100)
£520 $952 €759 Neige fondante (40x30cm-16x12in) s.i. 1-Jun-4 Hodgins, Calgary #15/R (C.D 1300)
£528 $946 €771 Coming back home, Laurentide (50x61cm-20x24in) s. i.verso prov. 6-May-4 Heffel, Vancouver #84/R (C.D 1300)
£600 $1098 €876 Sous bois (40x30cm-16x12in) s.i. 1-Jun-4 Hodgins, Calgary #275/R est:1250-1500 (C.D 1500)
£622 $1076 €908 Autumn snow (51x61cm-20x24in) s.i. 9-Dec-3 Maynards, Vancouver #234 est:600-800 (C.D 1400)
£631 $1072 €921 Farm in the Laurentians (41x51cm-16x20in) s. s.i.verso. 21-Nov-3 Walker's, Ottawa #40/R (C.D 1400)
£640 $1171 €934 Fin d'apres-midi, Laurentides (30x40cm-12x16in) s. 1-Jun-4 Joyner Waddington, Toronto #363/R (C.D 1600)
£714 $1229 €1042 Drifting snow (60x90cm-24x35in) s.d.76. 2-Dec-3 Joyner Waddington, Toronto #221/R est:2000-2500 (C.D 1600)
£889 $1476 €1298 Maison ancestrale (61x76cm-24x30in) s. s.i.verso. 5-Oct-3 Levis, Calgary #61a/R est:2500-3000 (C.D 2000)
£893 $1536 €1304 Triumvirat (50x60cm-20x24in) s. 2-Dec-3 Joyner Waddington, Toronto #510 est:1500-2000 (C.D 2000)
£995 $1662 €1453 Sur les hauteurs (75x100cm-30x39in) s.i. 17-Nov-3 Hodgins, Calgary #269/R est:3000-4000 (C.D 2200)
£1040 $1903 €1518 Avec Grand-Papa (60x75cm-24x30in) s. 1-Jun-4 Joyner Waddington, Toronto #179/R est:2800-3200 (C.D 2600)
£1074 $1945 €1568 Pres du lac (61x76cm-24x30in) s. s.i.verso. 18-Apr-4 Levis, Calgary #62/R est:2500-3000 (C.D 2600)
£1118 $2001 €1632 Premiere neige (61x76cm-24x30in) s. s.i.verso. 27-May-4 Heffel, Vancouver #200/R est:2000-3000 (C.D 2750)
£1161 $1996 €1695 Docteur (60x75cm-24x30in) s. 2-Dec-3 Joyner Waddington, Toronto #264/R est:2000-2500 (C.D 2600)
£1403 $2343 €2048 La premiee neige (50x60cm-20x24in) s.i. 17-Nov-3 Hodgins, Calgary #180 est:2250-2750 (C.D 3100)
£1563 $2688 €2282 Travail du matin (40x50cm-16x20in) s. 2-Dec-3 Joyner Waddington, Toronto #272/R est:1000-1500 (C.D 3500)
£1600 $2624 €2336 Fin de journey (61x76cm-24x30in) s. 28-May-3 Maynards, Vancouver #154/R est:1200-1400 (C.D 3600)
£1760 $3221 €2570 Fonte des Glaces (75x100cm-30x39in) s. 1-Jun-4 Joyner Waddington, Toronto #218/R est:2000-2500 (C.D 4400)
£1802 $3063 €2631 Back from the village (76x101cm-30x40in) s. i.verso acrylic. 27-Nov-3 Heffel, Vancouver #197/R est:3500-4500 (C.D 4000)

LANGEVIN, David (1959-) Canadian
£360 $659 €526 Two weekends in a row (60x40cm-24x16in) s.i.d.2003 acrylic board. 1-Jun-4 Hodgins, Calgary #277/R (C.D 900)

LANGEWEG, Ger (1891-1970) Dutch
£699 $1189 €1000 Three Graces (65x50cm-26x20in) s. 24-Nov-3 Glerum, Amsterdam #121/R
£1316 $2421 €2000 At the crack of doom (54x73cm-21x29in) s. s.i.verso panel exhib. 22-Jun-4 Christie's, Amsterdam #600/R est:2000-3000

LANGFELDT, Kjeld (1890-?) Norwegian
£275 $460 €402 Lamholmen, Svolvaer (50x62cm-20x24in) s. 20-Oct-3 Blomqvist, Lysaker #1197 (N.KR 3200)

LANGHAMMER, Carl (1868-?) German
£265 $482 €400 Summer evening (33x25cm-13x10in) s.d.91. 18-Jun-4 Bolland & Marotz, Bremen #673
£403 $741 €600 Mountain slope in summer with goats (54x42cm-21x17in) s. 27-Mar-4 Dannenberg, Berlin #585
£417 $679 €600 Jungfrau (72x168cm-28x66in) s. s. stretcher. 27-Sep-3 Dannenberg, Berlin #574/R
£903 $1426 €1300 Sheep in northern German landscape (50x37cm-20x15in) s. board. 6-Sep-3 Schopman, Hamburg #805/R
Works on paper
£397 $723 €600 Stone steps in a park landscape (45x31cm-18x12in) s.d.90 gouache. 18-Jun-4 Bolland & Marotz, Bremen #672/R

LANGHEINRICH, Josef (19th C) German
£699 $1189 €1000 Still life with fruit, vegetables and zinc jug (70x91cm-28x36in) s.i.d.90. 22-Nov-3 Arnold, Frankfurt #580/R

LANGHORST, Carl (1867-1950) German?
£629 $1000 €918 Portrait of a young man (137x74cm-54x29in) s.d.1916. 23-Mar-3 Auctions by the Bay, Alameda #834/R

LANGKER, Sir Erik (1898-1982) Australian
£309 $558 €451 Burragorang Valley (50x39cm-20x15in) s.d.Aub 1946 i.verso composition board. 31-Mar-4 Goodman, Sydney #474 (A.D 750)
£897 $1399 €1301 Towards twilight (58x73cm-23x29in) s. 1-Aug-2 Joel, Victoria #294 est:2000-2500 (A.D 2600)

LANGKO, Dietrich (1819-1896) German
£2098 $3608 €3000 Summer landscape with village and gathering rain clouds (17x31cm-7x12in) mono.d.1886 paper on panel prov. 5-Dec-3 Ketterer, Munich #5/R est:2000-3000
£2639 $4486 €3800 Chiemsee landscape (35x66cm-14x26in) s.d.1854 panel. 28-Oct-3 Dorotheum, Vienna #189/R est:1400-1800

LANGL, Josef (1843-1920) Austrian
£839 $1427 €1200 The Zwinger in Dresden (76x56cm-30x22in) s.d.94. 24-Nov-3 Dorotheum, Vienna #212/R
£845 $1403 €1200 San Vigilio on Lake Garda (31x39cm-12x15in) s.i.d.1915 verso board. 16-Jun-3 Dorotheum, Vienna #3/R
£1060 $1939 €1600 Cloister (44x59cm-17x23in) s. 8-Apr-4 Dorotheum, Vienna #61/R est:1600-2000
£1224 $2192 €1800 Burgos Cathedral (75x56cm-30x22in) s.d.1892 lit. 20-Mar-4 Bergmann, Erlangen #1079 est:1800
£1571 $2514 €2278 Worthersee (37x53cm-15x21in) s.d.93 canvas on board. 15-May-3 Stuker, Bern #1344/R est:2000-2500 (S.FR 3300)

LANGLAIS, Bernard (1921-1977) American
£3704 $6000 €5371 Fish (76x69cm-30x27in) painted on wood. 8-Aug-3 Barridorf, Portland #218/R est:6000-9000
£7407 $12000 €10740 Lion (84x122cm-33x48in) s.i. i.verso painted on wood prov. 8-Aug-3 Barridorf, Portland #214/R est:12000-18000
Sculpture
£1111 $1800 €1611 Seagull (30x107cm-12x42in) s. wood prov. 8-Aug-3 Barridorf, Portland #204/R est:2000-3000
£1728 $2800 €2506 Horse (211x81cm-83x32in) s. wood construction. 8-Aug-3 Barridorf, Portland #205/R est:3000-5000
£4938 $8000 €7160 Buffalo (171x137cm-67x54in) wood construction prov. 8-Aug-3 Barridorf, Portland #203/R est:12000-18000

LANGLANDS and BELL (20th C) British
Sculpture
£1800 $3312 €2628 UN Food and Agriculture Organization, Rome (69x62x21cm-27x24x8in) s.i.d.1991 verso fibre-board rohacell paint glass cellulose prov. 24-Jun-4 Sotheby's, Olympia #421/R est:1500-2000

LANGLEY, Nina Scott (fl.1928) British
Works on paper
£400 $664 €584 Did you say something? (38x25cm-15x10in) s.d.1930 W/C. 2-Oct-3 Neales, Nottingham #614

LANGLEY, W (19/20th C) British
Works on paper
£7800 $14742 €11388 At evening time it shall be light (23x33cm-9x13in) s. W/C. 19-Feb-4 Grant, Worcester #412/R est:400-600

LANGLEY, Walter (1852-1922) British
£1418 $2453 €2070 Children playing roulette (77x64cm-30x25in) s. 9-Dec-3 Rasmussen, Copenhagen #1650/R est:15000-20000 (D.KR 15000)
£130000 $221000 €189800 When the boats are away (137x107cm-54x42in) s.d.1903 prov.exhib.lit. 26-Nov-3 Christie's, London #36/R est:150000-250000
Works on paper
£450 $752 €657 Church in a landscape (20x30cm-8x12in) mono. W/C. 14-Oct-3 David Lay, Penzance #367
£950 $1577 €1387 A chip off the old block (21x18cm-8x7in) chl chk study exec. 1905 prov. 2-Oct-3 Lane, Penzance #260/R
£1000 $1830 €1460 Mounts Bay in a calm (12x17cm-5x7in) s. W/C. 7-Apr-4 Woolley & Wallis, Salisbury #168/R est:200-300
£2400 $4080 €3504 Chelsea pensioner (16x10cm-6x4in) s.i.d.1891 W/C. 4-Nov-3 Bristol Auction Rooms #498/R est:200-400
£3000 $5190 €4380 Half portrait of a Dutch girl in national costume (24x15cm-9x6in) s. W/C. 11-Dec-3 Lane, Penzance #185/R est:2800-3500
£4200 $7014 €6132 Village gossip (39x49cm-15x19in) s. W/C pencil htd white prov. 16-Oct-3 Lawrence, Crewkerne #662/R
£10000 $18300 €14600 Old harbour wall (49x71cm-19x28in) s. W/C en grisaille. 2-Jun-4 Sotheby's, London #9/R est:10000-15000
£11000 $20130 €16060 Carrying the catch (35x46cm-14x18in) s. pencil W/C htd bodycol scratching out prov. 3-Jun-4 Christie's, London #194/R est:7000-10000
£11154 $19185 €16285 Domestic duties (56x60cm-22x24in) s. W/C. 2-Dec-3 Bukowskis, Stockholm #291/R est:30000-40000 (S.KR 145000)

LANGLEY, William (1852-1922) British
£260 $434 €380 Cattle watering (41x53cm-16x21in) s. 17-Oct-3 Keys, Aylsham #696
£260 $486 €380 Tambourine player (15x7cm-6x3in) s. 25-Feb-4 Mallams, Oxford #398
£260 $478 €380 Cattle taking water (49x75cm-19x30in) 8-Jun-4 Bonhams, Knightsbridge #115
£280 $518 €409 Cattle watering at a stream with building in distance (43x64cm-17x25in) s. 13-Feb-4 Keys, Aylsham #714

£280	$515	€409	Cattle watering in an extensive Highland river landscape (43x61cm-17x24in) s. 11-Jun-4 Halls, Shrewsbury #726
£280	$510	€409	Sandy shoreline (39x59cm-15x23in) s. 4-Jul-4 Lots Road Auctions, London #372
£320	$544	€467	Shore scene with sand dunes and seagulls (38x58cm-15x23in) s. 5-Nov-3 Brightwells, Leominster #1094/R
£320	$566	€467	Young girl selling grapes (61x30cm-24x12in) s. 27-Apr-4 Bonhams, Knowle #87
£320	$586	€480	Village and river landscape (50x75cm-20x30in) s. 27-Jul-4 Henry Adams, Chichester #470/R
£320	$598	€480	Highland landscape with cattle watering (41x61cm-16x24in) s. 22-Jul-4 Gorringes, Lewes #1965
£350	$585	€511	Extensive landscape with figures (38x53cm-15x21in) s. 17-Oct-3 Keys, Aylsham #733
£380	$619	€555	Highland loch scene with a cattle drover in foreground (29x49cm-11x19in) s. 23-Sep-3 Anderson & Garland, Newcastle #367/R
£390	$718	€569	Figures and cattle by a wooded lake (50x76cm-20x30in) s. 8-Jun-4 Bonhams, Knowle #337
£420	$701	€613	Highland cattle watering at a loch (41x61cm-16x24in) s. 8-Oct-3 Christie's, Kensington #717/R
£420	$714	€613	Highland cattle watering by a loch (30x51cm-12x20in) s. 25-Nov-3 Bonhams, Knowle #199
£420	$769	€613	River landscape with figures on the far bank. Cattle watering (41x61cm-16x24in) s. pair. 8-Jul-4 Duke & Son, Dorchester #195
£450	$824	€657	Loch landscape with highland cattle watering (49x74cm-19x29in) s. 6-Jul-4 Bonhams, Knightsbridge #237/R
£500	$930	€730	Cattle watering at sunset (41x58cm-16x23in) s. 4-Mar-4 Mitchells, Cockermouth #763
£750	$1193	€1088	Sheep by a moorland steam (51x76cm-20x30in) s. 9-Sep-3 Bonhams, Knightsbridge #256/R
£833	$1500	€1216	Highland landscape (50x76cm-20x30in) s. 25-Apr-4 Bonhams & Butterfields, San Francisco #5488/R est:2000-3000
£1300	$2249	€1898	Highland cattle on the banks of a loch. Highland cattle on a track (30x51cm-12x20in) pair. 12-Dec-3 Halls, Shrewsbury #599 est:700-1000
£1350	$2471	€1971	Highland cattle watering. Sheep in a glen (50x75cm-20x30in) s. pair. 8-Apr-4 Bonhams, Edinburgh #113 est:1000-1500
£1700	$2822	€2482	Returning home with the catch (76x50cm-30x20in) s. 2-Oct-3 Lane, Penzance #280/R est:1500-1750

LANGLOIS, Chris (1969-) Australian

£3053	$5557	€4457	Dawn (168x168cm-66x66in) s. i.d.2002 verso prov. 16-Jun-4 Deutscher-Menzies, Melbourne #199/R est:8000-12000 (A.D 8000)
£3239	$5215	€4729	Study for sky - white grey and green no.1 (122x198cm-48x78in) s.d.2000 i.verso prov. 25-Aug-3 Sotheby's, Paddington #230/R est:8000-12000 (A.D 8000)
£3252	$5106	€4715	Ocean no 11 (153x167cm-60x66in) s.i.d.1997 verso prov. 26-Aug-3 Christie's, Sydney #15/R est:8000-12000 (A.D 8000)

LANGLOIS, J (19th C) British

£1081	$2000	€1578	Keeping watch (18x25cm-7x10in) board. 10-Feb-4 Doyle, New York #191/R est:2000-3000

LANGLOIS, L A (19th C) ?

Works on paper

£1103	$2041	€1600	Paysages (21x27cm-8x11in) painted 1813 two. 19-Jan-4 Horta, Bruxelles #462 est:1000-1500

LANGLOIS, Mark W (fl.1862-1873) British

£231	$425	€337	Going to school (53x43cm-21x17in) s. s.i.stretcher. 9-Jun-4 Doyle, New York #3051
£262	$482	€383	The west wind (53x43cm-21x17in) s. 9-Jun-4 Walker's, Ottawa #339/R (C.D 650)
£300	$555	€438	Terriers examining a trap (25x30cm-10x12in) s. 13-Jan-4 Bonhams, Knightsbridge #251
£300	$552	€438	Girl and a boy seated on a bench in a landscape (63x49cm-25x19in) s. 8-Jun-4 Holloways, Banbury #297/R
£343	$630	€501	Feeding the rabbit (53x43cm-21x17in) s. 9-Jun-4 Walker's, Ottawa #338/R (C.D 850)
£550	$1018	€803	Truant (30x25cm-12x10in) s. 14-Jul-4 Christie's, Kensington #869/R
£675	$1080	€986	Young boy and girl with birds nest (51x41cm-20x16in) s. 8-Jan-3 Biddle & Webb, Birmingham #906
£850	$1522	€1241	Method of correction (31x25cm-12x10in) init. s.i.stretcher. 18-Mar-4 Christie's, Kensington #491/R
£2800	$5012	€4088	Toy vendor (76x63cm-30x25in) s. 27-May-4 Christie's, Kensington #282/R est:2500-3500

LANGLOIS, Mark W (attrib) (fl.1862-1873) British

£880	$1461	€1285	At the Fair (31x26cm-12x10in) indis.s. 31. 1-Oct-3 Sotheby's, Olympia #55/R

LANGLOIS, Paul (1858-1906) French

£1047	$1800	€1529	Rouen street view with vegetable market (38x46cm-15x18in) s. board. 6-Dec-3 Neal Auction Company, New Orleans #442/R est:2000-3000

LANGLOIS, Paul (1946-) French

£347	$641	€520	Bord de mer (22x40cm-9x16in) s. panel. 14-Jul-4 Livinec, Gaudcheau & Jezequel, Rennes #187

LANGLOIS, T (?) ?

£1150	$2093	€1679	Wooded landscape with three terriers chasing a fox (76x127cm-30x50in) s. 15-Jun-4 Bonhams, Oxford #90 est:250-350

LANGMAID, Rowland (1897-1956) British

Works on paper

£4800	$8496	€7008	HMS Victory in dry dock in Portsmouth (27x20cm-11x8in) s. W/C. 27-Apr-4 Henry Adams, Chichester #643/R est:1000-1500

LANGMAID, Rowland (attrib) (1897-1956) British

£320	$506	€467	Battle scene with galleons (64x130cm-25x51in) 4-Sep-3 Amersham Auction Rooms, UK #298

LANGTON, Albert (?) British?

£400	$708	€584	Children in a cottage interior (51x38cm-20x15in) s. 29-Apr-4 Gorringes, Lewes #2521

LANGUM, Runi (20th C) Norwegian

Works on paper

£409	$707	€597	Woman moving (70x56cm-28x22in) s. mixed media. 13-Dec-3 Blomqvist, Lysaker #1228/R (N.KR 4700)

LANGWORTHY, William H (19th C) American

£447	$800	€653	Mountainous landscape with river and fisherman (56x91cm-22x36in) s.d.1871. 10-Jan-4 Pook & Pook, Downington #159/R

LANKOW, L (19th C) ?

£1678	$2887	€2400	Evening winter landscape (47x65cm-19x26in) s. one of pair. 5-Dec-3 Michael Zeller, Lindau #685/R est:900

LANMAN, Charles (1819-1895) American

£391	$700	€571	Figures on rocky coast (28x38cm-11x15in) board. 7-May-4 Sloans & Kenyon, Bethesda #1969/R
£475	$850	€694	Fisherman on rocks by stream (38x28cm-15x11in) s.d.1880 board. 7-May-4 Sloans & Kenyon, Bethesda #1695/R

LANNAY, Ady de (20th C) Belgian?

£272	$487	€400	La femme au livre (92x73cm-36x29in) s. painted c.1925-1935. 16-Mar-4 Vanderkindere, Brussels #292
£284	$474	€400	Nature morte aux masques et a la mandoline (60x73cm-24x29in) s.d.1927. 17-Jun-3 Vanderkindere, Brussels #72
£284	$474	€400	Le violonniste Japonais (73x54cm-29x21in) studio st. 17-Jun-3 Vanderkindere, Brussels #85
£355	$592	€500	La lecture (92x73cm-36x29in) s. 17-Jun-3 Vanderkindere, Brussels #62
£674	$1125	€950	A table (90x116cm-35x46in) s. 17-Jun-3 Vanderkindere, Brussels #52
£674	$1125	€950	Nature morte a la guitare (146x114cm-57x45in) s. 17-Jun-3 Vanderkindere, Brussels #65
£2482	$4145	€3500	La loge des artistes de cirque (100x140cm-39x55in) s. exhib. 17-Jun-3 Vanderkindere, Brussels #78/R est:1250-1750

LANNES, Mario (1900-1983) Italian

£629	$1051	€900	Girl in red background (90x80cm-35x31in) s. 10-Oct-3 Stadion, Trieste #673/R
£2308	$3969	€3300	Landscape in Tunisia (59x79cm-23x31in) s.i. 3-Dec-3 Stadion, Trieste #1071/R est:700-1000

LANOE, Alphonse (1926-) Swiss

£517	$926	€755	La vague (27x46cm-11x18in) s.d.83 i. stretcher. 12-May-4 Dobiaschofsky, Bern #719/R (S.FR 1200)
£1131	$1923	€1651	Summer landscape (33x55cm-13x22in) s. pavatex. 19-Nov-3 Fischer, Luzern #1112/R est:2800-3200 (S.FR 2500)

Works on paper

£345	$617	€504	Orage de printemps (22x34cm-9x13in) s. i. verso gouache. 12-May-4 Dobiaschofsky, Bern #720/R (S.FR 800)

LANOE-JUNGI, Margrit (1931-) Swiss

Works on paper

£1000	$1660	€1450	Blooming peasant garden (14x22cm-6x9in) s.d.1982 W/C. 13-Jun-3 Zofingen, Switzerland #2914/R est:400 (S.FR 2200)

LANOEL, Juan Alejandro (1919-1985) Argentinian

Works on paper

£279	$500	€407	Cowboy riding (31x23cm-12x9in) W/C. 11-May-4 Arroyo, Buenos Aires #54

LANOUE, Terence (1940-) American

Works on paper

£408	$750	€596	Vartieties of coral (99x86cm-39x34in) s.d.85 mixed media. 26-Jun-4 Susanin's, Chicago #6106/R
£1511	$2750	€2206	Castle of the wind, series I (165x147cm-65x58in) s.d.88 collage prov. 29-Jun-4 Sotheby's, New York #598/R est:4000-6000
£2335	$4250	€3409	Book of Hercules (135x262cm-53x103in) s.d.1988-89 i.verso mixed media. 29-Jun-4 Sotheby's, New York #595/R est:6000-8000

LANPHEAR, Lavinia (19th C) American?

Works on paper

£398	$700	€581	Untitled (18x28cm-7x11in) s. pencil. 1-Jan-4 Fallon, Copake #215/R

LANSDOWNE, James Fenwick (1937-) Canadian

Works on paper

£311	$538	€454	Study for buffalo head (25x20cm-10x8in) s.d. pencil. 9-Dec-3 Maynards, Vancouver #232 (C.D 700)
£1556	$2691	€2272	Surf scooter, male and female (64x56cm-25x22in) s.d.1972 W/C sold with a dr. prov. 9-Dec-3 Maynards, Vancouver #219 est:3000-4000 (C.D 3500)

£1667	$2883	€2434	Horned grebe (43x38cm-17x15in) s.d.1973 W/C sold with dr. prov. 9-Dec-3 Maynards, Vancouver #220 est:4000-6000 (C.D 3750)
£1931	$3456	€2819	Icterus Galbula, northern oriole (50x40cm-20x16in) s.i.d.1969 W/C prov. 27-May-4 Heffel, Vancouver #194/R est:2500-3500 (C.D 4750)
£2033	$3638	€2968	Robin (55x45cm-22x18in) s.d.1982 s.i.d.verso W/C prov. 27-May-4 Heffel, Vancouver #197/R est:2000-3000 (C.D 5000)
£5405	$9189	€7891	Trumpeter swan (132x110cm-52x43in) s.d.1975 gouache canvas. 27-Nov-3 Heffel, Vancouver #53/R est:4000-6000 (C.D 12000)

LANSERE, E (19th C) Russian?

Sculpture

£4297	$7864	€6274	Cossack on horseback (39x38cm-15x15in) s.d.1873 pat.bronze Cast.Shopan. 2-Jun-4 Rasmussen, Copenhagen #1307/R est:25000 (D.KR 48000)

LANSIL, Walter Franklin (1846-1925) American

£670	$1200	€978	New Brunswick fishing boats (51x61cm-20x24in) s. s.d.1883 verso. 10-Jan-4 CRN Auctions, Cambridge #15/R
£2267	$4240	€3310	Venice (56x91cm-22x36in) s. 29-Feb-4 Grogan, Boston #16/R

LANSKOY, Andre (1902-1976) French/Russian

£670	$1200	€978	Still life (23x33cm-9x13in) s. s.verso. 16-May-4 CRN Auctions, Cambridge #4/R
£1053	$1937	€1600	Personnages attbales (22x28cm-9x11in) s. 25-Jun-4 Millon & Associes, Paris #195/R est:800-1000
£1250	$2300	€1900	Personnages dans un salon (22x27cm-9x11in) init. cardboard. 25-Jun-4 Millon & Associes, Paris #196/R est:800-1000
£2254	$3741	€3200	Bouquet de fleurs a la carafe (81x44cm-32x17in) s. 11-Jun-3 Delorme & Bocage, Paris #27/R est:2000-2500
£2961	$5447	€4500	Famille (54x65cm-21x26in) s. 25-Jun-4 Millon & Associes, Paris #198/R est:2500-3000
£3125	$5000	€4563	Nature morte avec fruits et poissons (54x66cm-21x26in) s. painted c.1935-40. 18-Sep-3 Swann Galleries, New York #358/R est:7000-10000
£3147	$5413	€4500	Legumes et poisson (24x46cm-9x18in) s. 4-Dec-3 Piasa, Paris #105/R est:600-800
£3421	$6295	€5200	Heure du the (54x65cm-21x26in) s. 25-Jun-4 Millon & Associes, Paris #197/R est:2000-3000
£3974	$7232	€6000	Nature morte au raisin (33x53cm-13x21in) s. 16-Jun-4 Claude Boisgirard, Paris #96/R est:6000-7000
£4333	$7973	€6500	Family in an interior (60x80cm-24x31in) s. painted c.1924. 9-Jun-4 Christie's, Amsterdam #41/R est:5000-7000
£4500	$7785	€6570	Portrait de Nathalie (57x32cm-22x13in) s.d.25 panel prov. 11-Dec-3 Christie's, Kensington #80/R est:2000-3000
£5034	$9312	€7500	Nature morte aux huitres (46x55cm-18x22in) s. painted c.1925. 15-Mar-4 Claude Boisgirard, Paris #70/R est:6000-7000
£5369	$9933	€8000	Nature morte au gateau (46x61cm-18x24in) s. painted c.1925. 15-Mar-4 Claude Boisgirard, Paris #69/R est:5000-6000
£5495	$10000	€8023	Portrait of a peasant woman (92x73cm-36x29in) s. painted c.1925-27. 29-Jun-4 Sotheby's, New York #507/R est:1500-2000
£5960	$10848	€9000	Personnages sur un escalier (64x54cm-25x21in) s. 16-Jun-4 Claude Boisgirard, Paris #97/R est:9000-10000
£6000	$10200	€8760	Boy wearing red braces (55x46cm-22x18in) s.d.25. 19-Nov-3 Sotheby's, London #234/R est:6000-8000
£6040	$11235	€9000	Le penseur (65x46cm-26x18in) s. 2-Mar-4 Artcurial Briest, Paris #180/R est:7000-8000
£6579	$11908	€10000	La table servie (54x64cm-21x25in) s. 16-Apr-4 Pierre Berge, Paris #8/R est:3000-3500
£6643	$11294	€9500	Still life with fruits and flowers (60x80cm-24x31in) s. 25-Nov-3 Christie's, Amsterdam #195/R est:5000-7000
£6944	$11458	€10000	Composition (92x73cm-36x29in) s. painted c.1960. 2-Jul-3 Cornette de St.Cyr, Paris #46/R est:10000-15000
£7552	$12839	€10800	Le temps d'un poeme (92x65cm-36x26in) s. i.d.1961 verso. 28-Nov-3 Blanchet, Paris #209/R est:12000-15000
£7692	$13231	€11000	Composition (50x61cm-20x24in) s. 5-Dec-3 Chochon-Barre & Allardi, Paris #118/R est:15000-17000
£7914	$12978	€11000	Composition (61x50cm-24x20in) s. 6-Jun-3 David Kahn, Paris #38 est:9000-11000
£7947	$14464	€12000	Nature morte aux fleurs et a la statuette (73x54cm-29x21in) s. 16-Jun-4 Claude Boisgirard, Paris #95/R est:10000-12000
£8500	$14450	€12410	Still life with vase of flowers (46x55cm-18x22in) s. 19-Nov-3 Sotheby's, London #118/R est:6000-8000
£9050	$15113	€13213	Composition (100x65cm-39x26in) s. s.i. verso prov. 24-Jun-3 Germann, Zurich #46/R est:25000-30000 (S.FR 20000)
£9091	$15182	€13000	Berger des etoiles (73x60cm-29x24in) s. s.i.d.1963 verso. 25-Jun-3 Blanchet, Paris #133/R est:12000
£10069	$15910	€14500	Soeur de la violette (60x73cm-24x29in) s. i.verso prov. 27-Apr-3 Versailles Encheres #37
£10135	$17838	€15000	Taquinerie chinoise (73x59cm-29x23in) s. i.d.1950. 19-May-4 Camard, Paris #42 est:3000-4000
£10227	$18000	€14931	Russian ballet (58x71cm-23x28in) s. 22-May-4 Selkirks, St. Louis #790 est:400-600
£10490	$18042	€15000	Untitled (61x46cm-24x18in) s. prov. 2-Dec-3 Sotheby's, Amsterdam #117/R est:10000-15000
£11000	$19030	€16060	Composition (70x80cm-28x31in) s. 11-Dec-3 Christie's, Kensington #234/R est:7000-10000
£11111	$18333	€16000	Les herbes et le foin (81x100cm-32x39in) s. i.d.1967 verso. 2-Jul-3 Cornette de St.Cyr, Paris #3/R est:15000-20000
£11268	$19493	€16000	Eclair qui sonne (73x60cm-29x24in) s. i.d.1962 verso. 9-Dec-3 Artcurial Briest, Paris #415/R est:15000-18000
£11486	$20216	€17000	Untitled (54x81cm-21x32in) s. painted c.1955 prov.exhib. 18-May-4 Tajan, Paris #49/R est:12000-15000
£11589	$21209	€17500	La bizarre chose (81x60cm-32x24in) s. d.67 verso. 9-Apr-4 Claude Aguttes, Neuilly #98/R est:10000-12000
£11888	$20210	€17000	Le nuage dore (81x65cm-32x26in) s. i.d.1965 verso prov. 25-Nov-3 Tajan, Paris #5/R est:10000-12000
£12081	$21624	€18000	Untitled (92x72cm-36x28in) s. s.verso. 30-May-4 Meeting Art, Vercelli #32 est:10000
£12270	$20000	€17914	Untitled (61x72cm-24x28in) s. 23-Sep-3 Christie's, Rockefeller NY #8/R est:8000-12000
£12587	$21650	€18000	Nature morte (59x71cm-23x28in) s. prov. 2-Dec-3 Sotheby's, Amsterdam #99/R est:10000-15000
£13000	$23660	€18980	Composition (97x130cm-38x51in) s. painted c.1959-60 prov. 5-Feb-4 Christie's, London #128/R est:15000-20000
£14085	$24366	€20000	Composition abstraite (54x73cm-21x29in) s. 12-Dec-3 Piasa, Paris #50/R est:10000-15000
£14685	$24965	€21000	Exclamation sombre (73x100cm-29x39in) s.d.59 verso prov. 1-Dec-3 Palais de Beaux Arts, Brussels #168/R est:20000-30000
£14728	$25038	€21503	Clair vertical (100x73cm-39x29in) s. prov. 5-Nov-3 AB Stockholms Auktionsverk #1081/R est:80000-100000 (S.KR 195000)
£15000	$27300	€21900	Vagabondage (146x89cm-57x35in) s.d.64 i.d.verso prov. 5-Feb-4 Christie's, London #105/R est:15000-20000
£16000	$28800	€24000	Situations dangereuses (146x97cm-57x38in) s. s.i.d.1966 verso prov.exhib. 25-Apr-4 Versailles Encheres #110 est:25000-30000
£18000	$32760	€26280	L'odeur des fruits (60x73cm-24x29in) s. prov. 6-Feb-4 Sotheby's, London #163/R est:8000-12000
£18000	$33120	€26280	Untitled (79x63cm-31x25in) s.d.67. 24-Jun-4 Sotheby's, London #182/R est:10000-12000
£18667	$34160	€28000	Le recit d'un mauvais baiser (100x73cm-39x29in) s.d.57 verso. 7-Jun-4 Palais de Beaux Arts, Brussels #180/R est:15000-20000
£19000	$34960	€27740	Les herbes et le foin (73x100cm-29x39in) s.d.67 i.verso prov. 25-Jun-4 Christie's, London #106/R est:15000-20000
£19728	$35313	€29000	Vent convoyeur (97x146cm-38x57in) i.d.58 verso prov. 19-Mar-4 Millon & Associes, Paris #171/R est:18000-25000
£21834	$40175	€31878	Composition (152x67cm-60x26in) s. prov. 8-Jun-4 Germann, Zurich #78/R est:30000-40000 (S.FR 50000)
£22000	$40480	€32120	Le nuage dore (81x65cm-32x26in) s.i.d.63 verso. 25-Jun-4 Christie's, London #105/R est:10000-15000
£22000	$40480	€33000	L'eau fraiche (60x73cm-24x29in) s. painted 1955 prov. 8-Jun-4 Artcurial Briest, Paris #209/R est:25000-30000
£26816	$48000	€39151	Lumiere blanche (100x73cm-39x29in) s. i.d.Aout 55 verso prov.exhib. 12-May-4 Christie's, Rockefeller NY #126/R est:40000-60000
£27083	$44688	€39000	Composition (196x98cm-77x39in) s. painted c.1958. 2-Jul-3 Cornette de St.Cyr, Paris #28/R est:45000-50000
£27815	$50623	€42000	Meli-melo endiable (81x65cm-32x26in) s. i.d.1964 verso. 15-Jun-4 Blanchet, Paris #267/R est:12000-15000
£28000	$50960	€40880	Les joies des autres (98x147cm-39x58in) s.i.d.60 prov. 5-Feb-4 Christie's, London #114/R est:25000-35000
£32000	$53440	€46720	Untitled (194x96cm-76x38in) s. painted c.1970. 21-Oct-3 Sotheby's, London #401/R est:20000-30000
£32000	$58880	€48000	L'enfant du miracle (115x160cm-45x63in) s.i.d.60 prov. 8-Jun-4 Artcurial Briest, Paris #206/R est:35000-45000
£33334	$60668	€50000	Untitled (146x97cm-57x38in) s. painted c.1960. 30-Jun-4 Calmels Cohen, Paris #61/R est:50000-60000
£36810	$60000	€53743	Le combat sand rancune (96x296cm-38x117in) s. i.verso prov. 23-Sep-3 Christie's, Rockefeller NY #6/R est:15000-20000
£40000	$73600	€58400	Reponse de l'ambassadeur (97x146cm-38x57in) s. prov. 24-Jun-4 Sotheby's, London #173/R est:20000-30000
£44000	$80960	€64240	Untitled (128x87cm-50x34in) s. exec c.1955 prov. 24-Jun-4 Sotheby's, London #187/R est:15000-20000

Works on paper

£1408	$2437	€2000	Composition (24x31cm-9x12in) s. gouache. 13-Dec-3 De Vuyst, Lokeren #197/R est:1500-2000
£1538	$2646	€2200	Composition florale (54x39cm-21x15in) s. gouache. 8-Dec-3 Horta, Bruxelles #115 est:2500-3500
£1689	$2973	€2500	Composition sur fond vert (53x39cm-21x15in) s. gouache. 19-May-4 Camard, Paris #105 est:2500-3000
£1757	$3250	€2565	Untitled (25x63cm-10x25in) i. gouache over pencil. 12-Feb-4 Sotheby's, New York #134/R est:1400-1800
£1933	$3518	€2900	Untitled (24x31cm-9x12in) s. gouache. 30-Jun-4 Calmels Cohen, Paris #19/R est:3000-4000
£1958	$3328	€2800	Composition (68x35cm-27x14in) s. gouache prov. 25-Nov-3 Tajan, Paris #6/R est:3000-4000
£2000	$3639	€3000	Untitled (24x31cm-9x12in) s. gouache. 30-Jun-4 Calmels Cohen, Paris #20/R est:3000-4000
£2013	$3725	€3000	Composition (64x49cm-25x19in) s. collage gouache prov. 13-Mar-4 De Vuyst, Lokeren #214/R est:3300-3800
£2013	$3725	€3000	Composition (63x48cm-25x19in) s. collage gouache prov. 13-Mar-4 De Vuyst, Lokeren #215/R est:3300-3800
£2162	$4086	€3200	Composition sur fond noir (24x32cm-9x13in) s. gouache. 21-Feb-4 Cornette de St.Cyr, Paris #340/R est:3500-4000
£2238	$3804	€3200	Composition (65x49cm-26x19in) s. gouache. 1-Dec-3 Palais de Beaux Arts, Brussels #164/R est:2700-3200
£2344	$4149	€3422	Sans titre (64x49cm-25x19in) s. gouache. 27-Apr-4 AB Stockholms Auktionsverk #1233/R est:40000-45000 (S.KR 32000)
£2517	$4330	€3600	Composition abstraite (49x64cm-19x25in) s. gouache. 8-Dec-3 Horta, Bruxelles #114 est:2500-3500
£2800	$5152	€4200	Composition fond noir (65x50cm-26x20in) s.d.70 gouache prov. 9-Jun-4 Artcurial Briest, Paris #456/R est:5000-6000
£2817	$4873	€4000	Composition (64x50cm-25x20in) s. gouache prov. 14-Dec-3 Versailles Encheres #76/R est:4000-4500
£2979	$4974	€4200	Sans titre (53x79cm-21x31in) s. gouache collage. 19-Oct-3 Anaf, Lyon #195/R est:3000-4000
£3087	$5526	€4600	Composition (65x50cm-26x20in) s. gouache. 25-May-4 Chambelland & Giafferi, Paris #69/R est:6000-8000
£3691	$6829	€5500	Composition (107x72cm-42x28in) s. collage gouache prov. 13-Mar-4 De Vuyst, Lokeren #482/R est:5000-6000
£3793	$7017	€5500	Composition abstraite (64x50cm-25x20in) s. gouache exec.c.1960. 13-Feb-4 Charbonneaux, Paris #56/R est:3000-5000
£3893	$6968	€5800	Composition (64x49cm-25x19in) s. gouache. 26-May-4 Christie's, Paris #65/R est:4000-5000
£4000	$6680	€5840	Untitled (108x75cm-43x30in) s. chl crayon exec c.1950. 21-Oct-3 Sotheby's, London #397/R est:4000-6000
£4167	$6583	€6000	Composition (49x62cm-19x24in) s. gouache. 27-Apr-3 Versailles Encheres #19
£4595	$8087	€6800	Composition (120x83cm-47x33in) s. collage prov. 18-May-4 Tajan, Paris #50/R est:6000-8000
£18310	$31676	€26000	Foire nocturne (73x100cm-29x39in) s. i.d.1956 verso prov. 11-Dec-3 Binoche, Paris #4/R est:20000-30000

LANSKOY, Andre (attrib) (1902-1976) French/Russian

£1457	$2652	€2200	Composition with figures (51x41cm-20x16in) s. 19-Jun-4 Bergmann, Erlangen #887

LANSON, Charles (fl.1880-1907) British

£750	$1253	€1095	Estaury (64x102cm-25x40in) s. 12-Nov-3 Sotheby's, Olympia #114/R

LANTARA, Simon Mathurin (1729-1778) French

Works on paper

£563	$975	€800	Riviere dans un paysage (15x24cm-6x9in) d.1762 blk crayon. 10-Dec-3 Piasa, Paris #52

LANTEIGNE, Danielle (1959-) Canadian
£1200 $2196 €1752 Marguerites aux mapperon (150x150cm-59x59in) s.i.d.2000 oil acrylic. 1-Jun-4 Hodgins, Calgary #421/R est:3500-4500 (C.D 3000)

LANTHIN, Georges (?) French?
£403 $749 €600 Leopold III as a boy on a horse (58x47cm-23x19in) s. 8-Mar-4 Bernaerts, Antwerp #753/R

LANTOINE, Fernand (1876-c.1955) French
£428 $774 €650 Castellone de Ampuries (54x60cm-21x24in) s. 19-Apr-4 Horta, Bruxelles #174
£594 $1022 €850 Lac en Suisse. Bord de Meuse enneige (37x45cm-15x18in) s. pair. 8-Dec-3 Horta, Bruxelles #276
£927 $1687 €1400 Village africain (50x65cm-20x26in) s. panel. 16-Jun-4 Hotel des Ventes Mosan, Brussels #220
£1333 $2440 €2000 Paysage mediterraneen avec eglise (60x82cm-24x32in) s.d.1913. 7-Jun-4 Palais de Beaux Arts, Brussels #73/R est:2000-3000
£1678 $2803 €2400 Port de plaisance en Mediterranee (58x80cm-23x31in) s. 13-Oct-3 Horta, Bruxelles #50 est:3000-4000
£2797 $4755 €4000 Paysage cotier (80x100cm-31x39in) s. 1-Dec-3 Palais de Beaux Arts, Brussels #89/R est:4000-6000
£2961 $5359 €4500 Trois mats dans un port Oriental (70x80cm-28x31in) s.d.1921 verso. 19-Apr-4 Horta, Bruxelles #173 est:5000-6000
£4514 $7358 €6500 Printemps en Scandinavie (130x130cm-51x51in) s. 23-Sep-3 Galerie Moderne, Brussels #854/R
Works on paper
£1733 $3103 €2600 Vue de Bizerte anime (47x61cm-19x24in) s.d.1923 pastel exhib. 11-May-4 Vanderkindere, Brussels #249 est:400-600

LANTOINE-NEVEUX, Germaine (1892-?) French
£270 $511 €400 Vue de la Cote d'Azur (38x46cm-15x18in) s. 17-Feb-4 Vanderkindere, Brussels #402

LANTU, Georges (?) French?
£674 $1125 €950 Neige en suisse, le sapin (81x100cm-32x39in) s. 19-Oct-3 Peron, Melun #353e

LANYON, Ellen (1926-) American
£419 $750 €612 Pianist. s. 13-May-4 Dallas Auction Gallery, Dallas #65/R
Works on paper
£301 $550 €439 Favorite postcard II (51x66cm-20x26in) col pencil. 10-Jul-4 Hindman, Chicago #290/R

LANYON, Peter (1918-1964) British
£1100 $1837 €1606 Portrait of Jimmy Limpots (36x25cm-14x10in) indis sig.verso. 14-Oct-3 David Lay, Penzance #582/R est:1000-2000
£4000 $7280 €5840 Harbour, St. Ives (8x23cm-3x9in) i.verso collage postcards. 15-Jun-4 David Lay, Penzance #578/R est:3500-4500
£5800 $10382 €8468 Red roof and yellow foreground. Study (33x40cm-13x16in) s. s.i.d.1948 verso double-sided panel prov. 16-Mar-4 Bonhams, New Bond Street #78/R est:5000-7000
£230000 $420900 €335800 Headwind (122x198cm-48x78in) s.d.61 s.i.d.verso prov.exhib.lit. 4-Jun-4 Christie's, London #120/R est:70000-100000
Works on paper
£2800 $5124 €4088 Clevedon study no II (39x49cm-15x19in) st.sig. pencil executed 1964 prov.exhib. 4-Jun-4 Christie's, London #119/R est:3000-5000
£3200 $5728 €4672 Clevedon study no 5 (39x50cm-15x20in) s.d.1964 backboard conte prov.exhib. 16-Mar-4 Bonhams, New Bond Street #79/R est:1200-1800

LANZA, Giovanni (1827-1889) Italian
Works on paper
£700 $1253 €1022 Temple of Olympeus Zeus with the Acropolis beyond (25x18cm-10x7in) s. W/C pen ink. 10-May-4 Sotheby's, Olympia #143/R
£704 $1169 €1000 Villa sul Golfo di Napoli (23x33cm-9x13in) s. W/C cardboard. 11-Jun-3 Christie's, Rome #34
£704 $1218 €1000 Amalfi (36x23cm-14x9in) s. W/C. 9-Dec-3 Finarte Semenzato, Milan #107/R
£2661 $4763 €3885 Cattle grazing near Poseidon Temple, Paestum (42x74cm-17x29in) s. W/C. 28-May-4 Uppsala Auktionskammare, Uppsala #125/R est:15000-18000 (S.KR 36000)
£2800 $4480 €4060 Riverside village, Waterfall in the gorge (68x50cm-27x20in) s. W/C pair. 18-Sep-3 Christie's, Kensington #89/R est:3000-5000
£2817 $4873 €4000 Peasants and buffalos in Paestum (43x75cm-17x30in) s. W/C card. 11-Dec-3 Christie's, Rome #43/R est:3000-3500

LANZA, Stefano (19/20th C) Italian
Works on paper
£1376 $2600 €2009 Olympeion (23x36cm-9x14in) s. W/C paper on card. 21-Feb-4 Brunk, Ashville #605/R est:500-1000
£1500 $2685 €2190 Hadrian's Gate, Athens (21x14cm-8x6in) s. W/C. 11-May-4 Bonhams, New Bond Street #3/R est:600-800

LANZA, Vicenzo (1822-1902) Italian
Works on paper
£15000 $25500 €21900 House of Parliament (35x55cm-14x22in) s. W/C prov. 18-Nov-3 Sotheby's, London #4/R est:15000-20000

LANZANI, Polidoro (circle) (1515-1565) Italian
£9732 $17225 €14500 Annunciation (57x67cm-22x26in) tempera board lit. 2-May-4 Finarte, Venice #58/R est:18000-20000

LANZIROTI, A G (1839-?) Italian
Sculpture
£2000 $3620 €3000 Buste de satyre. Buste de faunesse (70cm-28in) pat bronze two st.f.Martin. 30-Mar-4 Palais de Beaux Arts, Brussels #1135/R est:2400-4000

LAPA, Manuel (1914-1979) Portuguese
£671 $1201 €1000 Landscape with trees (35x50cm-14x20in) s.d.1936 cardboard. 31-May-4 Cabral Moncada Leiloes, Lisbon #237

LAPADY (19/20th C) Hungarian
£7000 $12040 €10220 Forbidden fruit (119x177cm-47x70in) indis.sig. 4-Dec-3 Christie's, Kensington #237/R est:7000-10000

LAPAYESE BRUNA, Jose (1899-1982) Spanish
£500 $905 €750 Aerial view (49x65cm-19x26in) s. leather on panel. 30-Mar-4 Segre, Madrid #332/R
Works on paper
£638 $1034 €900 Untitled (148x195cm-58x77in) s. pencil sanguinne. 20-May-3 Ansorena, Madrid #346/R
£655 $1179 €950 Composition (155x200cm-61x79in) s. s.i.verso pencil sanguine. 26-Jan-4 Ansorena, Madrid #917/R

LAPAYESE DEL RIO, Jose (1926-2000) Spanish
£780 $1303 €1100 Molinos (55x38cm-22x15in) s. s.i.verso. 23-Jun-3 Durán, Madrid #59/R
£1118 $2024 €1700 Avila (66x93cm-26x37in) s. s.d.1993. 14-Apr-4 Ansorena, Madrid #285/R est:1500
Sculpture
£1184 $2143 €1800 Saint Cecily (105cm-41in) s. wood. 14-Apr-4 Ansorena, Madrid #899/R est:1800
Works on paper
£282 $493 €400 Old arcades (21x26cm-8x10in) s. mixed media board. 16-Dec-3 Durán, Madrid #3/R

LAPCHINE, Georges (1885-1951) Russian
£1458 $2406 €2100 Neige en sous-bois (81x100cm-32x39in) s. 3-Jul-3 Claude Aguttes, Neuilly #116 est:3000
£1500 $2685 €2190 Winter sun (19x24cm-7x9in) s. board. 26-May-4 Sotheby's, Olympia #380/R est:1500-2000
£1579 $2905 €2400 Maison en foret (24x35cm-9x14in) s. board. 28-Jun-4 Joron-Derem, Paris #174/R est:1200-1500
£3500 $6265 €5110 View of Martigues (22x15cm-9x6in) s. board. 26-May-4 Sotheby's, Olympia #420/R est:1800-2500
£3776 $6420 €5400 Terrasse a Capri (27x35cm-11x14in) s. 24-Nov-3 Boscher, Cherbourg #701/R est:100-150
£3916 $6540 €5600 Bateaux aux Martigues (42x64cm-17x25in) s. panel. 29-Jun-3 Eric Pillon, Calais #216/R
£5000 $8950 €7300 Sunset in the forest (81x100cm-32x39in) s. 26-May-4 Sotheby's, London #106/R est:5000-7000
£7000 $12530 €10220 Provincial riverside view (49x63cm-19x25in) 26-May-4 Sotheby's, London #170/R est:5000-7000
£8000 $13600 €11680 Spring thaw (33x46cm-13x18in) s. board. 19-Nov-3 Sotheby's, London #106/R est:2000-3000
£13862 $23150 €20100 Vue de Venise (60x12cm-24x5in) s. 17-Nov-3 Claude Boisgirard, Paris #55/R est:7500-8500
£14000 $25060 €20440 Italian lake (59x91cm-23x36in) s.verso. 26-May-4 Sotheby's, London #187/R est:5000-6000
£20000 $35800 €29200 Cap d'antibes (50x100cm-20x39in) s. 26-May-4 Sotheby's, London #176/R est:10000-15000
£32000 $54400 €46720 Russian Church in a winter landscape (100x155cm-39x61in) s. 19-Nov-3 Sotheby's, London #107/R est:5000-7000

LAPERRIERE, Gaston de (1848-?) French
£1184 $2179 €1800 Jeune femme pechant a la ligne (27x34cm-11x13in) s. 28-Jun-4 Joron-Derem, Paris #131 est:800-1000

LAPEYRE, Lucien (19th C) French
£909 $1545 €1300 Caravan in the desert (48x64cm-19x25in) s. 1-Dec-3 Camard, Paris #43/R est:500-600
£909 $1545 €1300 Halte pres des pyramides (49x64cm-19x25in) s.d.05. 1-Dec-3 Camard, Paris #44/R

LAPICCOLA, Nicolo (1730-1790) Italian
Works on paper
£32787 $60000 €47869 Life of Psyche (35x66cm-14x26in) s. pen ink W/C bodycol set of 10 after Raphael. 3-Jun-4 Christie's, Rockefeller NY #863/R est:15000-20000

LAPICQUE, Charles (1898-1988) French
£533 $960 €800 Untitled (10x36cm-4x14in) s. paper on canvas. 25-Apr-4 Versailles Encheres #126
£600 $1080 €900 Untitled (27x22cm-11x9in) s. paper on canvas. 25-Apr-4 Versailles Encheres #117
£704 $1218 €1000 Campagne bretonne (60x81cm-24x32in) s.d.34 lit. 9-Dec-3 Artcurial Briest, Paris #332
£1342 $2470 €2000 Ruines Romaines (24x32cm-9x13in) s. 24-Mar-4 Binoche, Paris #109 est:2000-3000
£1678 $3121 €2500 Funerailles de Leclerc (61x47cm-24x19in) s. i.d.1974 verso. 2-Mar-4 Artcurial Briest, Paris #261 est:3000-3500
£1678 $3121 €2500 L'exode (38x54cm-15x21in) s. acrylic. 2-Mar-4 Artcurial Briest, Paris #262 est:2500-3000
£1850 $3145 €2701 Paysage grec (22x22cm-9x9in) s. i.d.1964 verso prov. 5-Nov-3 Dobiaschofsky, Bern #731/R est:4000 (S.FR 4200)
£1958 $3270 €2800 Untitled (48x64cm-19x25in) s. acrylic paper. 29-Jun-3 Versailles Encheres #146/R
£2333 $4247 €3500 Joseph et la femme de Putiphar (54x73cm-21x29in) s.d.1972 s.i.d.verso. 5-Jul-4 Neret-Minet, Paris #46/R est:3000-4000

£2483 $4619 €3700 Nature morte aux chocolats (46x65cm-18x26in) s.d.63 i.d.1963 verso. 2-Mar-4 Artcurial Briest, Paris #260/R est:4000-5000
£2685 $4805 €4000 Desert (24x35cm-9x14in) s.d.62 s.i.d.verso prov. 26-May-4 Christie's, Paris #82/R est:5000-7000
£2685 $4805 €4000 Ruine romaine (24x33cm-9x13in) s. s.i.d.1972 verso. 30-May-4 Eric Pillon, Calais #135/R
£3289 $6053 €5000 Ermite (27x25cm-11x10in) s.d.60 paper on canvas. 25-Jun-4 Millon & Associes, Paris #243/R
£3380 $5848 €4800 Temple Grec (50x31cm-20x12in) s.d.1954 acrylic paper on canvas. 14-Dec-3 St-Germain-en-Laye Encheres #84/R est:5000-6000
£3497 $6014 €5000 Mere et enfant (55x33cm-22x13in) s.d.1947 s.i.d.1947 verso prov.exhib. 5-Dec-3 Ketterer, Munich #143/R est:6000-7000
£3667 $6600 €5500 Rochers a Brehat (45x31cm-18x12in) s.d.1956 paper on canvas prov. 25-Apr-4 Versailles Encheres #116 est:6000-7000
£3667 $6747 €5500 Chocolat et dragees (60x73cm-24x29in) s.d.1963 s.i.d.verso prov.lit. 11-Jun-4 Pierre Berge, Paris #102/R est:6000-8000
£4225 $7310 €6000 Tigre buvant (32x26cm-13x10in) s.d.1961 oil paper on canvas. 14-Dec-3 Versailles Encheres #142/R est:6000-7000
£4310 $7716 €6293 Saul cherchant les anesses (100x81cm-39x32in) s.d.73 i. verso. 12-May-4 Dobiaschofsky, Bern #721/R est:12000 (S.FR 10000)
£4545 $7591 €6500 Bords du Trieux (21x34cm-8x13in) s. i.d.1961 verso paper on cardboard. 25-Jun-3 Blanchet, Paris #113/R
£8121 $15186 €12100 Force huit (60x81cm-24x32in) s. i.verso painted c.1980 prov. 29-Feb-4 Versailles Encheres #261/R est:12000-15000
£8224 $15132 €12500 Force 8 (89x116cm-35x46in) s.d.1984 prov. 27-Jun-4 Versailles Encheres #123/R est:15000-18000
£10695 $20000 €15615 Paysage (73x99cm-29x39in) s.d.57 acrylic. 25-Feb-4 Christie's, Rockefeller NY #2/R est:15000-20000
£11189 $18685 €16000 Nuit sur la lagune (46x55cm-18x22in) s.d.1955. 29-Jun-3 Eric Pillon, Calais #271/R
£13816 $25421 €21000 Semaphore de Pleubian (54x65cm-21x26in) s.d.1953 s.i.d.verso prov. 27-Jun-4 Versailles Encheres #114/R est:22000-25000
£15333 $27600 €23000 Derniers conseils (92x65cm-36x26in) s.d.1950 prov. 25-Apr-4 Versailles Encheres #127 est:25000-30000
£21472 $35000 €31349 Moulin a Lanmodez (74x100cm-29x39in) s.d.47 s.i.d.1947 verso prov.lit. 25-Sep-3 Christie's, Rockefeller NY #562/R est:35000-45000

Works on paper
£302 $561 €450 Le chatelain (33x18cm-13x7in) s.d.74 W/C cut up paper. 2-Mar-4 Artcurial Briest, Paris #99
£302 $534 €450 Regates (44x56cm-17x22in) s.d.52 Indian ink brush. 27-Apr-4 Artcurial Briest, Paris #97
£350 $602 €500 Composition (38x24cm-15x9in) s.d.71 Indian ink W/C. 3-Dec-3 Tajan, Paris #99
£367 $667 €550 Untitled (30x20cm-12x8in) s.d.79 dr. 29-Jun-4 Chenu & Scrive, Lyon #112/R
£417 $696 €600 Personnage (27x21cm-11x8in) s.d.57 crayon drawing. 21-Oct-3 Artcurial Briest, Paris #322
£500 $900 €750 Brehat (39x29cm-15x11in) s.i.d. mixed media. 25-Apr-4 Versailles Encheres #135
£559 $934 €800 Untitled (31x48cm-12x19in) s.d.49 ink. 29-Jun-3 Versailles Encheres #147
£604 $1124 €900 Marine (33x49cm-13x19in) s.d.50 W/C pastel lit. 2-Mar-4 Artcurial Briest, Paris #98
£604 $1105 €900 Paysage au moulin (23x32cm-9x13in) s.d.74 W/C. 7-Jul-4 Artcurial Briest, Paris #59
£704 $1218 €1000 En regate (45x55cm-18x22in) s.d.52 brush Chinese ink lit. 9-Dec-3 Artcurial Briest, Paris #331
£805 $1498 €1200 La serenade (61x47cm-24x19in) s.d.73 W/C. 2-Mar-4 Artcurial Briest, Paris #103/R
£909 $1545 €1300 Composition (40x30cm-16x12in) s. felt. 27-Nov-3 Calmels Cohen, Paris #42/R
£1479 $2559 €2100 Rencontre a Paris (50x65cm-20x26in) s.d.45 crayon pastel lit. 9-Dec-3 Artcurial Briest, Paris #333/R est:1200-1500
£3472 $5486 €5000 Henri III (63x37cm-25x15in) s.d.1954 gouache oil prov. 27-Apr-3 Versailles Encheres #60

LAPIERRE-RENOUARD, Paul Marie (1854-?) French
£1944 $3306 €2800 Sunflowers in vase (81x65cm 32x26in) s. 28 Oct 3 Dorotheum, Vienna #264/R est:2800 3200

LAPINE, Andreas Christian Gottfried (1868-1952) Canadian
£252 $463 €368 Late afternoon, New Lowell (34x26cm-13x10in) s. s.i.verso panel. 9-Jun-4 Walker's, Ottawa #143/R (C.D 625)
£261 $486 €381 Sunset Lake Superior (30x41cm-12x16in) s. canvasboard prov. 2-Mar-4 Ritchie, Toronto #41/R (C.D 650)
£340 $622 €496 Horses and wagon (41x50cm-16x20in) s. 1-Jun-4 Joyner Waddington, Toronto #470 (C.D 850)
£360 $659 €526 Daybreak (40x50cm-16x20in) s. board. 1-Jun-4 Joyner Waddington, Toronto #286/R (C.D 900)
£1577 $2680 €2302 Round Lake, Peterborough. The pioneers (35x27cm-14x11in) one s. one panel one canvas two prov.exhib. 18-Nov-3 Sotheby's, Toronto #26/R est:4000-6000 (C.D 3500)

LAPINI, Cesare (1848-?) Italian
Sculpture
£2267 $4103 €3400 Femme voilee (67cm-26in) s. alabaster. 30-Mar-4 Rossini, Paris #659 est:2000-3000
£4412 $7500 €6442 Bather (77cm-30in) s. marble. 28-Oct-3 Christie's, Rockefeller NY #139/R
£5200 $9308 €7592 Young girl seated on a chair (58cm-23in) s. alabaster. 25-May-4 Sotheby's, Billingshurst #367/R est:2500-3500
£6111 $11000 €8922 Volere e potere, figure of a seated girl (56cm-22in) s.i. white marble. 23-Apr-4 Christie's, Rockefeller NY #100/R est:6000-8000
£11000 $18700 €16060 Fior del pensiero (191cm-75in) s.d.1892 marble lit. 28-Oct-3 Sotheby's, London #188/R

LAPIRA (?) Italian
Works on paper
£7606 $13158 €10800 Vue de la baie de Naples (42x63cm-17x25in) s.i.verso gouache. 10-Dec-3 Maigret, Paris #16/R est:6000-7000

LAPITO, Louis Auguste (1803-1874) French
£537 $951 €800 Foret de Fontainebleau (33x41cm-13x16in) s. panel. 30-Apr-4 Tajan, Paris #106
£2013 $3725 €3000 Vallee du Tesson (46x38cm-18x15in) s. 14-Mar-4 Eric Pillon, Calais #6/R
Works on paper
£800 $1384 €1168 Tree on a sloping ground at Fontainebleau. Tree tops in a forest (33x44cm-13x17in) s. one i.d.1852 black chk pair. 12-Dec-3 Christie's, Kensington #489/R

LAPITO, Louis Auguste (attrib) (1803-1874) French
Works on paper
£733 $1327 €1100 Peintres et promeneurs en foret de Fontainebleau (24x34cm-9x13in) i. W/C exhib. 30-Mar-4 Rossini, Paris #1020

LAPLACE, Jacques (1890-1955) French
£300 $546 €450 Nature morte (55x56cm-22x22in) s.d.1920. 29-Jun-4 Chenu & Scrive, Lyon #113/R
Works on paper
£320 $582 €480 Bord de Saone a Lyon (24x31cm-9x12in) s.i.d.1927 W/C. 29-Jun-4 Chenu & Scrive, Lyon #114/R
£347 $631 €520 Ile Barbe (31x24cm-12x9in) s.i.d.29 W/C. 29-Jun-4 Chenu & Scrive, Lyon #115/R

LAPLANTE, Charles (?-1903) French
£1000 $1630 €1460 French street in Autumn (55x81cm-22x32in) s.d.1883. 24-Sep-3 Dreweatt Neate, Newbury #164 est:1000-1500

LAPORTA Y VALOR, Francisco (1850-1914) Spanish
£805 $1426 €1200 Knight with armour (80x70cm-31x28in) s. 27-Apr-4 Durán, Madrid #698/R

LAPORTE, Domingo (1855-1928) Uruguayan
£412 $700 €602 Coastal view (46x66cm-18x26in) s. 25-Nov-3 Galeria y Remates, Montevideo #15/R

LAPORTE, Emile (1858-1907) French
Sculpture
£1034 $1728 €1500 Acteon (83cm-33in) s.i. brown pat bronze. 16-Nov-3 Muizon & Le Coent, Paris #114/R
£1788 $3200 €2610 Le metal, muscular standing male figure (84cm-33in) brown pat. bronze prov. 20-Mar-4 Selkirks, St. Louis #570/R est:3500-4500

LAPORTE, Émile Henri (1841-1919) French
Sculpture
£1141 $2042 €1700 Viking et son fils (60cm-24in) pat bronze Cast Siot. 25-May-4 Palais de Beaux Arts, Brussels #99/R est:2000-2600

LAPORTE, George Henry (1799-1873) German
£310 $533 €453 Stabled horse with groom (82x62cm-32x24in) 4-Dec-3 Bonhams, Cornwall #441
£3800 $6992 €5548 Sam, a racehorse with jockey up (51x87cm-20x34in) s.i.d.1825 oil paper on canvas. 10-Jun-4 Christie's, Kensington #15/R est:3000-4000
Works on paper
£274 $450 €397 Hunt scene (23x30cm-9x12in) s.indis.d.18 W/C prov. 31-May-3 Brunk, Ashville #425/R

LAPORTE, George Henry (attrib) (1799-1873) German
£5800 $9860 €8468 The 1825 Derby (76x127cm-30x50in) bears sig.d.1825. 19-Nov-3 Sotheby's, Olympia #24/R est:3000-5000

LAPORTE, Georges (1926-2000) French
£258 $475 €377 Snow in Burgundy (13x23cm-5x9in) s. prov. 25-Jun-4 Freeman, Philadelphia #228/R
£284 $474 €400 Barques noires (26x37cm-10x15in) s. 20-Jun-3 Drouot Estimations, Paris #199
£362 $615 €529 Sailing boat by shore (32x50cm-13x20in) s.d.65 pavatex. 18-Nov-3 Hans Widmer, St Gallen #1116 (S.FR 800)
£671 $1201 €1000 Barques a maree basse (27x35cm-11x14in) s. 30-May-4 Eric Pillon, Calais #140/R
£733 $1320 €1100 Maree basse verte (73x101cm-29x40in) s. 24-Apr-4 Cornette de St.Cyr, Paris #611
£833 $1392 €1200 Maree basse en Bretagne (46x55cm-18x22in) s. 23-Oct-3 Credit Municipal, Paris #101
£1141 $2122 €1700 Maree basse (27x41cm-11x16in) s. 7-Mar-4 Lesieur & Le Bars, Le Havre #74
£4505 $7748 €6577 Landscape (60x80cm-24x31in) s. 2-Dec-3 Koller, Zurich #3116/R est:10000-150000 (S.FR 10000)

LAPORTE, John (1761-1839) British
Works on paper
£700 $1260 €1022 Killarney Lake from Lord Kenmares Park (34x51cm-13x20in) W/C. 21-Jan-4 John Bellman, Billingshurst #1881
£828 $1531 €1200 Paysage de la campagne Anglaise a la cascade avec un patre et moutons (31x37cm-12x15in) s.d.1802 W/C prov. 13-Feb-4 Rossini, Paris #4/R

LAPORTE-BLAIRSY, Leo (1865-1923) French
Sculpture
£7667 $13723 €11500 Voie lactee (42cm-17in) s.st.f.Susse pat bronze lit. 17-May-4 Sotheby's, Paris #68/R est:7000-9000

LAPOSTOLET, Charles (1824-1890) French

£1133	$2051	€1700	Paysage d'Ile de France (20x31cm-8x12in) d.2 Juin 1867 oil paper on canvas. 30-Mar-4 Rossini, Paris #1021/R est:700-1000
£2800	$4564	€4060	Boats moored on a river with town beyond (39x55cm-15x22in) s. prov. 17-Jul-3 Tennants, Leyburn #814/R est:2000-3000
£3007	$5172	€4300	Rue de village dans le Midi (55x46cm-22x18in) i. 7-Dec-3 Osenat, Fontainebleau #207 est:4500-5000
£3497	$6014	€5000	Voiliers ancres pres de la ville (38x55cm-15x22in) s. 7-Dec-3 Osenat, Fontainebleau #189 est:6000-7000
£4733	$8662	€7100	Port de peche (38x55cm-15x22in) s. 6-Jun-4 Osenat, Fontainebleau #178/R est:8000-9000

LAPOSTOLET, Charles (attrib) (1824-1890) French

£800	$1472	€1168	Village in northern France (33x45cm-13x18in) 25-Mar-4 Christie's, Kensington #1/R

LAPRADE, Pierre (1875-1932) French

£272	$487	€400	Paysage (43cm-17in) cardboard oval. 21-Mar-4 Teitgen, Nancy #61
£524	$876	€750	Pierrot et Colombine (32x42cm-13x17in) s.d.1909. 25-Jun-3 Blanchet, Paris #19/R
£814	$1385	€1188	Boat in the reeds (65x81cm-26x32in) s. 1-Dec-3 Koller, Zurich #6559 est:1800-2800 (S.FR 1800)
£1056	$1827	€1500	Vue d'Avignon (54x65cm-21x26in) s. 12-Dec-3 Piasa, Paris #98/R est:1500-2000
£2128	$3447	€3000	Vase de fleurs (73x54cm-29x21in) s. 23-May-3 Sotheby's, Paris #60/R est:2000-3000
Works on paper			
£336	$625	€500	L'Arlequin au singe (24x17cm-9x7in) s. W/C. 3-Mar-4 Tajan, Paris #75/R
£352	$609	€500	Paysage (17x15cm-7x6in) s. W/C prov. 12-Dec-3 Piasa, Paris #129

LAQUY, Willem Joseph (1738-1798) German

£6667	$12000	€9734	Scullery maid preparing a chicken (48x39cm-19x15in) s. 22-Jan-4 Sotheby's, New York #288/R est:10000-15000
Works on paper			
£1600	$2944	€2336	At the tea merchants (38x32cm-15x13in) s.i. pencil W/C. 25-Mar-4 Christie's, Kensington #215/R est:1500-2000
£1700	$3128	€2482	Spinner sitting beside an open window (38x32cm-15x13in) s. pencil W/C. 25-Mar-4 Christie's, Kensington #211/R est:1500-2000

LARA, Clever (1952-) ?

£706	$1200	€1031	Doll (51x61cm-20x24in) s.d.91 acrylic. 25-Nov-3 Galeria y Remates, Montevideo #86/R
£952	$1800	€1390	Doll (70x70cm-28x28in) s. 22-Feb-4 Galeria y Remates, Montevideo #129/R est:1700-2000
£1588	$2700	€2318	Interior with doll (114x146cm-45x57in) s.d.89. 25-Nov-3 Galeria y Remates, Montevideo #85/R

LARA, Edwina (19th C) British

£1006	$1800	€1688	Harbour scene (46x81cm-18x32in) s. i.verso. 20-Mar-4 Pook & Pook, Downington #397 est:1500-2500

LARA, Georgina (fl.1862-1871) British

£1300	$2054	€1885	Village lane (25x36cm-10x14in) pair. 4-Sep-3 Christie's, Kensington #166/R est:600-800
£1700	$3128	€2482	Busy village scene (51x76cm-20x30in) 23-Jun-4 Bonhams, Bury St Edmunds #366/R est:1500-2000
£1750	$2765	€2538	Figures and animals by rural hamlet (15x20cm-6x8in) s. painted c.1860. 27-Apr-3 Desmond Judd, Cranbrook #1036
£3300	$5709	€4818	Figures, a hay cart and animals outside a farmhouse (24x34cm-9x13in) sold with companion piece pair. 9-Dec-3 Bonhams, Oxford #125/R est:2000-3000
£3400	$5678	€4964	Rustic farm (22x34cm-9x13in) s.i. 8-Oct-3 Rupert Toovey, Partridge Green #55/R est:1000-1500

LARA, Georgina (attrib) (fl.1862-1871) British

£410	$664	€599	Figures on a country track (19x37cm-7x15in) 27-Jan-3 Bristol Auction Rooms #547
£2095	$3750	€3143	Village inn, Sussex (51x76cm-20x30in) 16-May-4 Abell, Los Angeles #24/R
£5800	$10382	€8468	Figures before a cottages (23x33cm-9x13in) pair. 22-Mar-4 Bonhams & Brooks, Norfolk #238/R est:2000-3000

LARA, William (19th C) British

£470	$799	€686	Fishing on the estate. s. 27-Nov-3 International Art Centre, Auckland #188 (NZ.D 1250)
£1600	$2672	€2336	Figures before a barn (22x36cm-9x14in) 13-Nov-3 Christie's, Kensington #223/R est:1000-1500

LARBAUD, Valery (1881-1957) French

Works on paper			
£367	$675	€550	Vue d'un chateau et de ses douves (15x23cm-6x9in) s.d.1890 W/C. 9-Jun-4 Piasa, Paris #127

LARCHE, Raoul (1860-1912) French

Sculpture			
£987	$1816	€1500	Buste de jeune fille (39x40x26cm-15x16x10in) pat bronze Cast Siot. 22-Jun-4 Palais de Beaux Arts, Brussels #62/R est:1000-1200
£1250	$2300	€1900	Buste de jeune fille (38x40x25cm-15x16x10in) pat bronze. 22-Jun-4 Palais de Beaux Arts, Brussels #619/R est:2500-3500
£1321	$2365	€1929	Vingt ans (89cm-35in) incised sig. dark brown pat. bronze. 4-May-4 Ritchie, Toronto #111/R est:3000-5000 (C.D 3250)
£1500	$2550	€2190	Joan of Arc (54cm-21in) s.st.f.Decauville pat bronze. 28-Oct-3 Sotheby's, London #172/R
£1500	$2715	€2250	Tobie retirant la poisson de l'eau (52x31x32cm-20x12x13in) s. num.7 brown green pat bronze Cast Susse Freres. 1-Apr-4 Credit Municipal, Paris #91/R est:5000-6000
£1600	$2720	€2336	Christ (36cm-14in) s.st.f.Siot-Decauville pat bronze. 28-Oct-3 Sotheby's, London #195/R
£2695	$4501	€3800	La seve ou metamorphose de Daphnee (32cm-13in) s.i. gilt pat bronze sold with alabaster socle st.f.Siot. 19-Oct-3 Peron, Melun #378
£3546	$5922	€5000	Petit roi (37cm-15in) s.st.f.Siot gilt pat bronze marble socle. 19-Oct-3 Peron, Melun #356
£3784	$7000	€5525	Table lamp (33cm-13in) num.0836 gilt bronze exec.c.1900 st.f.Siot. 9-Mar-4 Christie's, Rockefeller NY #12/R est:8000-12000
£22000	$38060	€32120	Amphitrite on a dolphin (86cm-34in) s. white marble gild bronze base lit. 12-Dec-3 Sotheby's, London #249/R est:15000-25000

LARCHE, Raoul (after) (1860-1912) French

Sculpture			
£5000	$9000	€7300	Tobacco jar decorated with small female heads amidst tobacco leaves (21cm-8in) s.i. st.f.Siot gilt bronze. 21-Apr-4 Christie's, Kensington #243/R est:5000-7000
£6395	$11000	€9337	Figural lamp, woman in flowing gown (43cm-17in) s. st.f.Siot-Decauville bronze. 6-Dec-3 Selkirks, St. Louis #682/R est:2000-3000
£7115	$12735	€10388	Dancer - table lamp (32cm-13in) s. st.f.Siot de Decquville gilt bronze. 15-May-4 Christie's, Sydney #230/R est:8000-10000 (A.D 18000)
£11462	$20518	€16735	Dancer with swirling costume - table lamp (44cm-17in) s. st.f.Siot De Decquville gilt bronze after R Larche. 15-May-4 Christie's, Sydney #332/R est:15000-25000 (A.D 29000)
£12752	$22570	€19000	Untitled (46cm-18in) st.f.Siot-Decauville pat bronze. 30-Apr-4 Drouot Estimations, Paris #7/R est:7000-8000

LARCHET, Nancy (20th C) Irish?

Works on paper			
£306	$480	€440	Shadows on the pool deck (37x26cm-15x10in) s. pastel. 26-Aug-3 James Adam, Dublin #249/R

LARCHEVEQUE, Pierre Hubert (1721-1778) French

Works on paper			
£680	$1218	€1000	Projet de fontaine (53x38cm-21x15in) ink grey wash. 17-Mar-4 Maigret, Paris #69

LARCO, Jorge (1897-1967) Argentinian

Works on paper			
£495	$900	€723	Dancer Irina Borowsky (46x30cm-18x12in) s. W/C exec.c.1953. 5-Jul-4 Arroyo, Buenos Aires #95/R
£838	$1500	€1223	Landscape (61x46cm-24x18in) W/C. 11-May-4 Arroyo, Buenos Aires #56

LARDERA, Berto (1911-) French

Sculpture			
£5315	$9141	€7600	Composition (43x31x13cm-17x12x5in) steel. 3-Dec-3 Hauswedell & Nolte, Hamburg #919/R est:4000
£9790	$16643	€14000	Sculpture I (54x61x49cm-21x24x19in) welded iron prov.exhib.lit. 24-Nov-3 Christie's, Milan #260/R est:14000-18000
Works on paper			
£2800	$5152	€4200	Composition (74x53cm-29x21in) s.d.1953 collage gouache prov. 9-Jun-4 Artcurial Briest, Paris #435/R est:2000-2500
£4000	$7360	€6000	Sculpture Murale No 3 (38x32cm-15x13in) iron cut painted panel prov.exhib.lit. 9-Jun-4 Artcurial Briest, Paris #434/R est:3000-4000

LARGE, George (1936-) British

Works on paper			
£300	$555	€438	Cage birds (45x70cm-18x28in) s.d.91 W/C prov. 13-Jul-4 Rosebery Fine Art, London #661

LARGILLIERE, Nicolas de (1656-1746) French

£2747	$5000	€4011	Portrait of Elisabeth Marguerite, the artist daughter (74x93cm-29x37in) prov.exhib.lit. 29-Jun-4 Sotheby's, New York #20/R est:8000-12000
£4934	$9079	€7500	Portrait de Pierre Grassin (27x22cm-11x9in) 24-Jun-4 Christie's, Paris #123/R est:1000-2000
£5500	$9130	€8030	Portrait of a gentleman, wearing a red cape and a white shirt (72x62cm-28x24in) painted oval. 30-Sep-3 Sotheby's, London #165/R est:6000-8000
£5986	$9937	€8500	Portrait de gentilhomme (80x50cm-31x20in) s.d.169 verso. 13-Jun-3 Ferri, Paris #55/R est:10000-12000
£8500	$14705	€12410	Portrait of an Echevin, half length wearing the order of the Saint-Esprit (79x64cm-31x25in) 11-Dec-3 Sotheby's, London #215/R est:8000-12000
£13245	$24106	€20000	Portrait of Charles Gobinet (65x54cm-26x21in) prov. 15-Jun-4 Artcurial Briest, Paris #214/R est:20000-25000
£15000	$25950	€21900	Vanitas still life with skull, rose and pocket watch all on a draped table (51x43cm-20x17in) bears sig. 11-Dec-3 Sotheby's, London #210/R est:10000-15000
£19737	$36316	€30000	Portrait d'Angelique d'Hautefort (82x64cm-32x25in) s.i.d.1696 oval. 24-Jun-4 Christie's, Paris #35/R est:12000-18000
£20000	$36000	€29200	Portrait of a gentleman in blue and gold purple coat, in a landscape (82x68cm-32x27in) 21-Apr-4 Christie's, London #63/R est:20000-30000
£32895	$60526	€50000	Portrait de dame (83x66cm-33x26in) s.d.1713 prov. 24-Jun-4 Christie's, Paris #91/R est:50000-70000
£302632	$556842	€460000	Self-portrait (92x73cm-36x29in) s.d.1707 prov. 24-Jun-4 Christie's, Paris #88/R est:300000-500000

LARGILLIERE, Nicolas de (attrib) (1656-1746) French

£1916	$3200	€2797	Portrait (89x71cm-35x28in) 19-Oct-3 Susanin's, Chicago #6025/R est:4000-6000
£2586	$4629	€3776	Portraits of Marquise Athenaise de Montespan and Duchesse de Bourgogne (42x37cm-17x15in) two. 12-May-4 Dobiaschofsky, Bern #725/R est:12000 (S.FR 6000)

£8451 $14620 €12000 Portrait of gentleman (73x59cm-29x23in) oval. 15-Dec-3 Ansorena, Madrid #115/R est:12000
£11364 $20000 €16591 Still life with roses and other flowers in an oriental bowl with pomegranates and grapes (107x138cm-42x54in) 18-May-4 Bonhams & Butterfields, San Francisco #44/R est:20000-30000

LARI, P (?) ?
£1786 $3250 €2608 Young beauty descending steps (74x46cm-29x18in) s. 7-Feb-4 Neal Auction Company, New Orleans #92/R est:2500-3500

LARIONOV, Mikhail (1881-1964) Russian
£16000 $27680 €23360 Boulevard Venus (36x26cm-14x10in) card prov. 11-Dec-3 Christie's, Kensington #72/R est:5000-7000
£25000 $45000 €36500 Still life with roses (24x34cm-9x13in) init. 23-Apr-4 Sotheby's, New York #47/R est:30000-40000
£190000 $340100 €277400 Through the nets, bathers (49x61cm-19x24in) init. canvas on board prov.exhib. 26-May-4 Sotheby's, London #248/R est:200000-300000
£233333 $420000 €340666 Reclining nude (97x73cm-38x29in) s.d.1900. 23-Apr-4 Sotheby's, New York #45/R est:100000-150000
Works on paper
£405 $714 €600 Man (29x18cm-11x7in) mono. crayon dr. 19-May-4 Camard, Paris #13
£800 $1448 €1168 Femme assise (13x11cm-5x4in) init. pen black ink. 1-Apr-4 Christie's, Kensington #60/R
£839 $1427 €1200 La marchande de poisson (28x22cm-11x9in) s.i. graphite prov. 23-Nov-3 Cornette de St.Cyr, Paris #208
£1119 $1902 €1600 Portrait de Gontcharova (24x19cm-9x7in) s.i.d.1913 black crayon prov. 23-Nov-3 Cornette de St.Cyr, Paris #204 est:100
£1329 $2259 €1900 Portrait presume de Nicolas Gogol (14x10cm-6x4in) s.i. ink prov. 23-Nov-3 Cornette de St.Cyr, Paris #207 est:100
£1469 $2497 €2100 Portrait de N Gontcharova (21x13cm-8x5in) s.i.d.1913 crayon prov. 23-Nov-3 Cornette de St.Cyr, Paris #205 est:100
£1469 $2497 €2100 Silhouette de femme (33x21cm-13x8in) init.d.1907 gouache prov. 23-Nov-3 Cornette de St.Cyr, Paris #206
£1701 $3044 €2500 Etude de poele pour le ballet Kikimora (37x18cm-15x7in) mono.i. W/C. 17-Mar-4 Maigret, Paris #106/R est:600-800
£3352 $6000 €4894 Abstraction (23x15cm-9x6in) s. gouache. 16-May-4 Wright, Chicago #138/R est:3000-4000
£3500 $6265 €5110 Apollinaire and Diaghilev watching a rehearsal (26x20cm-10x8in) init. pencil pen Indian ink. 11-May-4 Sotheby's, Olympia #543/R est:4000-6000
£4500 $8190 €6570 Composition rayonniste (23x22cm-9x9in) init. pencil W/C gouache wax crayon exec.c.1915 prov. 21-Jun-4 Bonhams, New Bond Street #20/R est:5000-7000
£22000 $40480 €32120 Rayonist composition (34x24cm-13x9in) init. gouache W/C tracing paper exec c.1911 prov.exhib. 24-Jun-4 Christie's, London #365/R est:10000-15000

LARIONOV, Mikhail (attrib) (1881-1964) Russian
Works on paper
£3378 $5946 €5000 Cock (24x15cm-9x6in) s.d.1917 pierre noire dr. 19-May-4 Camard, Paris #81/R est:7000-8000

LARIVA-MUNOZ, Maria Luisa de (1859-1926) Spanish
Works on paper
£1500 $2775 €2190 Still life of grapes in a basket (46x55cm-18x22in) s. pastel. 13-Feb-4 Bracketts, Tunbridge Wells #690/R est:200-300

LARIVE-GODEFROY, Pierre Louis de (1735-1817) Swiss
£9050 $15385 €13213 Idyllic landscape with park entrance and herders resting in with cattle (55x69cm-22x27in) s.d.1795 panel prov. 19-Nov-3 Fischer, Luzern #1229/R est:20000-24000 (S.FR 20000)
Works on paper
£1086 $1846 €1586 Mountain landscape with ruined fortress, waterall, cows and figures (40x51cm-16x20in) s.d.1793 sepia W/C. 19-Nov-3 Fischer, Luzern #2608/R est:1900-2200 (S.FR 2400)

LARIVIERE, Charles Philippe Auguste de (1798-1876) French
£1722 $3151 €2600 Portrait de Nicolas du Roux, colonel de la Garde Nationale de Paris (122x90cm-48x35in) s. 7-Apr-4 Libert, Castor, Paris #49/R est:5000-7000
£33557 $61745 €50000 Aristaeus (216x143cm-85x56in) 24-Mar-4 Dorotheum, Vienna #284/R est:50000-70000

LARK, Raymond (1939-) American
Works on paper
£976 $1600 €1415 Boy with daisies (71x56cm-28x22in) s. pastel exec.c.1960. 7-Jun-3 Treadway Gallery, Cincinnati #1513 est:500-700

LARKEN, Diarmud (1918-1989) Irish
£389 $611 €560 Coastal landscape with trees (18x24cm-7x9in) s. board. 26-Aug-3 James Adam, Dublin #242/R

LARKIN, William (circle) (17th C) British
£12000 $21840 €17520 Portrait of a Nobleman said to be Robert, Earl of Essex (63x50cm-25x20in) i. painted oval prov. 1-Jul-4 Sotheby's, London #107 est:12000-18000
£45000 $74700 €65700 Portrait of Elizabeth Honeywood wearing embroidered dress holding a fan (91x71cm-36x28in) i.d.1617 prov. 30-Sep-3 Sotheby's, London #64/R est:30000-40000

LARKING, Patrick (1907-1981) British
£700 $1274 €1022 Wallflower (34x45cm-13x18in) canvasboard exhib. 15-Jun-4 Bonhams, Knightsbridge #231/R

LAROCHE, Ernesto (1879-1940) Uruguayan
£353 $600 €515 Dusk (13x18cm-5x7in) s. board. 25-Nov-3 Galeria y Remates, Montevideo #22
£471 $800 €688 Mountainous landscape (13x18cm-5x7in) s. board. 25-Nov-3 Galeria y Remates, Montevideo #23/R
£529 $1000 €772 Native song (25x30cm-10x12in) s. board. 22-Feb-4 Galeria y Remates, Montevideo #7/R
£1412 $2400 €2062 Landscape (95x95cm-37x37in) s. 25-Nov-3 Galeria y Remates, Montevideo #37/R
£1529 $2600 €2232 Landscape (74x93cm-29x37in) s. 25-Nov-3 Galeria y Remates, Montevideo #36
£2439 $4000 €3561 Cerro Arisco (86x112cm-34x44in) s. 3-Jun-3 Galeria y Remates, Montevideo #90
£3409 $6000 €4977 Dusk (73x100cm-29x39in) s. board. 5-Jan-4 Galeria y Remates, Montevideo #75/R est:8000-10000
£6471 $11000 €9448 Chacra (73x106cm-29x42in) s. 25-Nov-3 Galeria y Remates, Montevideo #144/R
£8824 $15000 €12883 Landscape (72x80cm-28x31in) s.d.1911. 25-Nov-3 Galeria y Remates, Montevideo #145/R
£12059 $20500 €17606 Landscape with river (100x100cm-39x39in) s. 25-Nov-3 Galeria y Remates, Montevideo #143/R

LAROCHE, Fernando (1870-1938) ?
£706 $1200 €1031 Paseo (47x57cm-19x22in) s.d.1911 cardboard. 20-Nov-3 Galeria y Remates, Montevideo #195/R
£1059 $1800 €1546 Fair (37x46cm-15x18in) s.d.1914 cardboard. 25-Nov-3 Galeria y Remates, Montevideo #191/R
£1529 $2600 €2232 Grand Canal, Venice (50x60cm-20x24in) s.d.1920 cardboard. 25-Nov-3 Galeria y Remates, Montevideo #190/R

LAROCK, Evert (1865-1901) Belgian
£700 $1169 €1022 Seated woman knitting (40x32cm-16x13in) board. 11-Nov-3 Bonhams, Knightsbridge #242/R

LAROON, Marcellus (jnr) (1679-1774) British
£1300 $2327 €1898 Portrait of James Macardell (59x40cm-23x16in) prov. 27-May-4 Christie's, Kensington #49/R est:1500-2000

LAROSE, Ludger (1868-1915) Canadian
£2321 $3993 €3389 Plat de noix piguees (24x32cm-9x13in) s.d.1900 panel prov. 2-Dec-3 Joyner Waddington, Toronto #106/R est:5000-6000 (C.D 5200)

LAROT, Dina (1943-) Austrian
Works on paper
£400 $736 €600 Two nude girls reclining (33x58cm-13x23in) s.d.1980 ochre W/C. 9-Jun-4 Dorotheum, Vienna #270

LARRAMENDI, Juan (1917-) Spanish
Works on paper
£625 $1131 €950 Landscape (27x35cm-11x14in) s. mixed media. 14-Apr-4 Ansorena, Madrid #28/R

LARRANAGA, Enrique de (1900-1956) Argentinian
£5495 $10000 €8023 Estuary (42x50cm-17x20in) s. cardboard. 29-Jun-4 Arroyo, Buenos Aires #74/R est:4500
£9341 $17000 €13638 Gran Via, Madrid (69x76cm-27x30in) s.d.1927 canvas on board. 29-Jun-4 Arroyo, Buenos Aires #95/R est:15000

LARRAVIDE, Manuel (1871-1910) Uruguayan
£586 $950 €850 Vapor (39x70cm-15x28in) s. 29-Jul-3 Galeria y Remates, Montevideo #99/R
£1118 $1900 €1632 Seascape (70x120cm-28x47in) s. 25-Nov-3 Galeria y Remates, Montevideo #166/R
£1176 $2000 €1717 Seascape (60x100cm-24x39in) s. 25-Nov-3 Galeria y Remates, Montevideo #167/R
£3297 $6000 €4814 Buenos Aires harbour (25x47cm-10x19in) s.d.97. 29-Jun-4 Arroyo, Buenos Aires #51/R est:5500

LARRAZ, Julio (1944-) Cuban
£11173 $20000 €16313 Study for the poet KIng (61x91cm-24x36in) s. 26-May-4 Sotheby's, New York #142/R est:25000-30000
£16760 $30000 €24470 Little bell (56x71cm-22x28in) s.i.d.1991 verso. 26-May-4 Sotheby's, New York #160/R est:30000-40000
£19118 $32500 €27912 Study for the landing (91x91cm-36x36in) s. painted 1986 prov. 19-Nov-3 Sotheby's, New York #134/R est:25000-30000
£33333 $61333 €50000 Total eclypse (183x132cm-72x52in) s. painted 1998 prov. 10-Jun-4 Christie's, Paris #77/R est:65000-80000
£55866 $100000 €81564 View of the Gulfstream (151x181cm-59x71in) s. painted 1982 prov. 26-May-4 Sotheby's, New York #21/R est:70000-90000
£55882 $95000 €81588 Numbers (176x207cm-69x81in) s. painted 1996. 19-Nov-3 Sotheby's, New York #130/R est:80000-100000

LARREGIEU, Fulbert Pierre (?-1886) French
Sculpture
£2500 $4250 €3650 Blood hound scratching his ear (19x28cm-7x11in) s. pat bronze. 28-Oct-3 Sotheby's, London #116/R est:2500-3500

LARRIEU, Gaston (1908-) French
£539 $900 €787 Landscape with buildings (65x92cm-26x36in) s. lit. 7-Oct-3 Sotheby's, New York #321

LARROUX, Antonin (1859-1913) French
Sculpture
£2819 $4989 €4200 Moissons (52x41x41cm-20x16x16in) st.f.Siot pat bronze. 30-Apr-4 Tajan, Paris #61/R est:5000-6000
£2958 $5176 €4200 Les bles (53cm-21in) s.d.1895 pewter Cast Siot-Decauville lit. 16-Dec-3 Artcurial Briest, Paris #37/R est:4500-6000

LARSEN, Adolph (1856-1942) Danish
£290 $518 €423 Landscape with thatched farm and chickens (37x49cm-15x19in) s.d.1891. 10-May-4 Rasmussen, Vejle #86/R (D.KR 3200)
£459 $744 €666 Landscape with rowing boat by riverbank (24x35cm-9x14in) s.d.1918. 4-Aug-3 Rasmussen, Vejle #306/R (D.KR 4800)
£937 $1528 €1368 Girl feeding cat (29x33cm-11x13in) init.d.1886 sold with print. 27-Sep-3 Rasmussen, Havnen #2231 (D.KR 10000)

LARSEN, Alfred (1860-1946) Danish
£289 $540 €422 Evening landscape with hill and trees (29x46cm-11x18in) 25-Feb-4 Museumsbygningen, Copenhagen #17 (D.KR 3200)
£1385 $2382 €2022 Mother and daughter in landscape at dusk (98x121cm-39x48in) s.d.87. 2-Dec-3 Bukowskis, Stockholm #255/R est:18000-20000 (S.KR 18000)

LARSEN, Emanuel (1823-1859) Danish
£1701 $2943 €2483 Study for The coast off Humlebaek (14x24cm-6x9in) s.d.1848 exhib.prov. 9-Dec-3 Rasmussen, Copenhagen #1483/R est:6000-8000 (D.KR 18000)
£3581 $6553 €5228 Windy day by the sea (67x100cm-26x39in) s.d.1852. 9-Jun-4 Rasmussen, Copenhagen #1846/R est:50000 (D.KR 40000)

LARSEN, Gerhard Lucas (1911-1965) German
£452 $810 €660 Coastal landscape with breakers (41x81cm-16x32in) s. 10-May-4 Rasmussen, Vejle #386/R (D.KR 5000)

LARSEN, Hugo Valdemar (1875-1950) Danish
£302 $502 €438 Woman at table (67x82cm-26x32in) s. 16-Jun-3 Blomqvist, Lysaker #1120 (N.KR 3500)
£347 $596 €507 Landscape (37x53cm-15x21in) s.i.d.1921. 2-Dec-3 Kunsthallen, Copenhagen #538 (D.KR 3700)
£701 $1107 €1016 Smiling young lady seated at laden table (67x72cm-26x28in) s.d.1913 exhib. 2-Sep-3 Rasmussen, Copenhagen #1954/R (D.KR 7500)

LARSEN, Johannes (1867-1961) Danish
£709 $1226 €1035 A teal (22x27cm-9x11in) mono.indis.d. 9-Dec-3 Rasmussen, Copenhagen #1402 (D.KR 7500)
£851 $1523 €1242 Night bird (33x42cm-13x17in) mono.d.28. 12-Jan-4 Rasmussen, Vejle #668 (D.KR 9000)
£936 $1564 €1367 Garden scene, leaves have fallen (70x86cm-28x34in) mono.d.37 exhib. 25-Oct-3 Rasmussen, Havnen #4150/R (D.KR 10000)
£1082 $2002 €1580 Ducks in flight over meadows (62x68cm-24x27in) mono.d.32. 15-Mar-4 Rasmussen, Vejle #656/R est:10000-12000 (D.KR 12000)
£1164 $2130 €1699 Bird on sandy beach (32x42cm-13x17in) mono.d.18. 9-Jun-4 Rasmussen, Copenhagen #1646/R est:6000-8000 (D.KR 13000)
£1229 $2126 €1794 A lark (35x48cm-14x19in) mono.d.1910. 9-Dec-3 Rasmussen, Copenhagen #1405/R est:10000 (D.KR 13000)
£1438 $2674 €2099 Duck on a lawn (39x48cm-15x19in) mono.d.17. 2-Mar-4 Rasmussen, Copenhagen #1242/R est:8000-12000 (D.KR 16000)
£1887 $3509 €2755 Stag and female deer on the outskirts of wood (90x136cm-35x54in) mono.d.1918. 2-Mar-4 Rasmussen, Copenhagen #1585/R est:20000-25000 (D.KR 21000)
£2705 $5005 €3949 Coastal landscape with houses (80x95cm-31x37in) mono.d.1904. 15-Mar-4 Rasmussen, Vejle #655/R est:20000-30000 (D.KR 30000)
£2715 $4860 €3964 Bird in flight over the sea (48x63cm-19x25in) mono.d.1915. 10-May-4 Rasmussen, Vejle #552/R est:30000 (D.KR 30000)
£2728 $4638 €3983 Ducks in landscape (50x60cm-20x24in) mono.d.1918. 26-Nov-3 Kunsthallen, Copenhagen #307/R est:40000 (D.KR 29000)
£3055 $5682 €4460 View of Kerteminde in snow, from the artist's garden room (57x70cm-22x28in) mono.d.37. 2-Mar-4 Rasmussen, Copenhagen #1211/R est:10000-15000 (D.KR 34000)
£3055 $5682 €4460 Summer landscape with large birds, Denmark (70x86cm-28x34in) mono.d.1941. 2-Mar-4 Rasmussen, Copenhagen #1583/R est:30000 (D.KR 34000)
Works on paper
£422 $725 €616 Three ducks in flight over water (31x41cm-12x16in) crayon pencil W/C prov. 3-Dec-3 Museumsbygningen, Copenhagen #40/R (D.KR 4500)
£466 $732 €680 Bird in flight over field landscape (51x64cm-20x25in) mono.d.38 W/C. 30-Aug-3 Rasmussen, Havnen #4396 (D.KR 5000)
£488 $791 €708 Coastal landscape with many mallards (24x39cm-9x15in) init.d.99 pen W/C. 4-Aug-3 Rasmussen, Vejle #666/R (D.KR 5100)
£588 $940 €853 Sparrows in winter landscape (23x39cm-9x15in) mono. W/C. 17-Sep-3 Kunsthallen, Copenhagen #269 (D.KR 6200)
£1432 $2621 €2091 Ducks (53x68cm-21x27in) mono.d.2-23 pen W/C. 9-Jun-4 Rasmussen, Copenhagen #1647/R est:10000-15000 (D.KR 16000)

LARSEN, Jorn (1926-) Danish
Works on paper
£664 $1062 €963 Composition (81x73cm-32x29in) s.d.IV 1977 pencil pen parchment. 17-Sep-3 Kunsthallen, Copenhagen #82/R (D.KR 7000)

LARSEN, Karl (1897-1977) Danish
£275 $500 €402 Still life of fruit, jug and books (100x126cm-39x50in) init. 7-Feb-4 Rasmussen, Havnen #4093 (D.KR 3000)
£298 $468 €435 Still life (55x65cm-22x26in) s.d.1957. 30-Aug-3 Rasmussen, Havnen #4064 (D.KR 3200)
£303 $485 €442 Still life of apples (34x42cm-13x17in) init.d.38. 22-Sep-3 Rasmussen, Vejle #555 (D.KR 3200)
£469 $764 €685 The Lord's Supper (41x65cm-16x26in) 27-Sep-3 Rasmussen, Havnen #4152 (D.KR 5000)
£469 $806 €685 Still life of onion, apple and vase on table (34x49cm-13x19in) s.d.1943 study verso. 3-Dec-3 Museumsbygningen, Copenhagen #41/R (D.KR 5000)

LARSEN, Knud (1865-1922) Danish
£284 $455 €415 Christ and Nikodemus (33x23cm-13x9in) mono. s.i.verso. 22-Sep-3 Rasmussen, Vejle #424/R (D.KR 3000)
£287 $516 €419 Interior scene with figures at table (31x43cm-12x17in) init. 24-Apr-4 Rasmussen, Havnen #2284/R (D.KR 3200)
£357 $608 €521 Woman picking berries on the heath (35x28cm-14x11in) init. 29-Nov-3 Rasmussen, Havnen #2013 (D.KR 3800)
£481 $900 €702 Sand dunes at shore (48x66cm-19x26in) init.d.1902. 28-Feb-4 Thomaston Place, Thomaston #68/R
£4942 $9191 €7215 Small girl by fence in a Danish summer landscape (57x79cm-22x31in) s.d.1917. 2-Mar-4 Rasmussen, Copenhagen #1274/R est:50000 (D.KR 55000)

LARSEN, Lars (1876-1955) Norwegian
£310 $499 €453 Farm in the mountains, Vaagen (58x81cm-23x32in) s. 25-Aug-3 Blomqvist, Lysaker #1162 (N.KR 3600)

LARSEN, Mike (1945-) American
£1914 $3100 €2775 Black hat with feather (122x91cm-48x36in) 23-May-3 Altermann Galleries, Santa Fe #140
£4136 $6700 €5997 Dancers with hoops (122x91cm-48x36in) 23-May-3 Altermann Galleries, Santa Fe #141

LARSEN, Ole (20th C) American
£313 $500 €457 Hunters with dogs (64x76cm-25x30in) s. painted c.1960. 20-Sep-3 Bunte, Elgin #1481

LARSEN, Oscar (1882-1972) Austrian
£532 $888 €750 Scene from Thirty Year War (60x80cm-24x31in) s.d.1934. 14-Oct-3 Dorotheum, Vienna #83
Works on paper
£270 $484 €400 Taking Christ down from the cross (33x47cm-13x19in) s.d.1919 mixed media. 6-May-4 Michael Zeller, Lindau #747/R
£284 $474 €400 Bacchanal (34x49cm-13x19in) s. mixed media board. 14-Oct-3 Dorotheum, Vienna #87/R
£333 $613 €500 Christ (75x53cm-30x21in) s.d.1965 mixed media. 9-Jun-4 Dorotheum, Salzburg #625/R
£333 $613 €500 Dreamer (58x38cm-23x15in) s.d.1926 pastel. 9-Jun-4 Dorotheum, Vienna #271
£338 $605 €500 Lot and his daughter (46x33cm-18x13in) s. W/C mixed media. 6-May-4 Michael Zeller, Lindau #751/R
£475 $760 €694 Outdoor feast (70x99cm-28x39in) s.d. mixed media. 16-Sep-3 Philippe Schuler, Zurich #5016a (S.FR 1050)
£604 $1117 €900 Evening song (99x73cm-39x29in) s.d.1920 mixed media board. 9-Mar-4 Dorotheum, Vienna #19/R
£867 $1595 €1300 Loving couples and mother in park landscape (73x98cm-29x39in) s.d.1921 mixed media. 9-Jun-4 Dorotheum, Salzburg #583/R
£867 $1595 €1300 Flight to Egypt (72x102cm-28x40in) s.d.1921 mixed media. 9-Jun-4 Dorotheum, Salzburg #649/R

LARSEN, Thorvald (1881-1947) Scandinavian
£507 $958 €750 Canal in Venice (63x63cm-25x25in) s. s.d.1936 verso. 20-Feb-4 Stadion, Trieste #464

LARSEN-SAERSLOV, Fredrik (1870-1942) Danish
£2617 $4135 €3795 Young girl picking poppies in a garden (85x112cm-33x44in) s.d.1899. 2-Sep-3 Rasmussen, Copenhagen #1532/R est:30000 (D.KR 28000)

LARSON, Ed (20th C) American
£1006 $1600 €1469 Boxing match. s.d.1963. 14-Sep-3 Susanin's, Chicago #6097/R est:400-600

LARSSEN, Johan (1853-1920) Norwegian
£900 $1584 €1314 Norwegian fjord (59x99cm-23x39in) s. i.verso. 19-May-4 Christie's, Kensington #667/R
£948 $1517 €1384 Seascape with boats on a calm summer's day (65x54cm-26x21in) s.d.81. 22-Sep-3 Rasmussen, Vejle #279/R (D.KR 10000)

LARSSON, Bo (1945-) Swedish
£1465 $2593 €2139 Landscape from Smedsudden, Stockholm (56x73cm-22x29in) init.d.81 s.d.81 verso. 27-Apr-4 AB Stockholms Auktionsverk #801/R est:25000-30000 (S.KR 20000)

LARSSON, Carl (1853-1919) Swedish
£24615 $42338 €35938 The sculptor Johan Tobias Sergel in his studio with Carl Michael Bellman (117x68cm-46x27in) sketch painted autumn 1895 lit. 3-Dec-3 AB Stockholms Auktionsverk #2351/R est:200000-250000 (S.KR 320000)
Works on paper
£290 $522 €435 Self-portrait (26x21cm-10x8in) s.d.1893 Indian ink on photo. 25-Apr-4 Goteborg Auktionsverk, Sweden #228/R (S.KR 4000)
£2217 $3969 €3237 Three ages of women (46x30cm-18x12in) init. Indian ink two pieces of paper. 25-May-4 Bukowskis, Stockholm #184/R est:30000-40000 (S.KR 30000)
£2615 $4498 €3818 Nude woman resting (52x40cm-20x16in) mono.i.d.febr.1915 mixed media. 7-Dec-3 Uppsala Auktionskammare, Uppsala #153/R est:20000-25000 (S.KR 34000)
£4582 $8203 €6690 Annunciation (54x37cm-21x15in) W/C after Fra Angelico painted 1888 prov.exhib.lit. 25-May-4 Bukowskis, Stockholm #140/R est:50000-60000 (S.KR 62000)
£6061 $10848 €8849 Saints Birgitta and Mathias (54x33cm-21x13in) init. mixed media rounded top lit. 25-May-4 Bukowskis, Stockholm #139/R est:75000-80000 (S.KR 82000)
£10000 $18200 €14600 The bridge (67x56cm-26x22in) init. pastel exec. 1909 exhib.lit. 15-Jun-4 Sotheby's, London #315/R est:15000-20000
£10000 $18200 €14600 The log cabin (67x56cm-26x22in) init. pastel exec. 1909 exhib.lit. 15-Jun-4 Sotheby's, London #315a/R est:15000-20000
£11000 $20240 €16060 Siri Anders Carlsson (46x31cm-18x12in) init. gouache W/C pen ink exec 1897 prov.lit. 24-Jun-4 Christie's, London #323/R est:8000-12000
£11456 $20506 €16726 Rabbits in Barbizon (32x15cm-13x6in) init.i.d.1881 W/C prov.exhib.lit. 25-May-4 Bukowskis, Stockholm #25/R est:200000-250000 (S.KR 155000)

£31538	$54246	€46045	Founder of art collection C G Tessin, showing his treasures to Lovisa Ulrika (117x68cm-46x27in) sketch painted autumn 1895 lit. 3-Dec-3 AB Stockholms Auktionsverk #2350/R est:250000-300000 (S.KR 410000)
£37694	$67472	€55033	Garden with lots of flowers (52x35cm-20x14in) s. W/C painted c.1878-1882. 25-May-4 Bukowskis, Stockholm #106/R est:200000-250000 (S.KR 510000)
£43077	$74092	€62892	My kitchen and my farm foreman (51x74cm-20x29in) init.d.1912 W/C lit. 3-Dec-3 AB Stockholms Auktionsverk #2408/R est:600000-800000 (S.KR 560000)
£81301	$145528	€118699	In Bergmansstugan - Interior scene with Kersti and Erik Kvarnberg and their daughter (53x75cm-21x30in) init.i.d.1914 W/C paper on canvas prov.exhib.lit. 25-May-4 Bukowskis, Stockholm #141/R est:1200000-1500000 (S.KR 1100000)
£110000	$200200	€160600	The old room (51x73cm-20x29in) mono.d.1909 pencil pen ink W/C htd gouache exhib.lit. 15-Jun-4 Sotheby's, London #314/R est:70000-100000
£176923	$304308	€258308	Hilda - 16 years old in interior (67x101cm-26x40in) init.d.1911 W/C paper on canvas exhib.lit. 2-Dec-3 Bukowskis, Stockholm #56/R est:1500000-1800000 (S.KR 2300000)
£188470	$337361	€275166	Brita reading (50x71cm-20x28in) init.d.1908 W/C prov.exhib.lit. 25-May-4 Bukowskis, Stockholm #148/R est:1400000-1500000 (S.KR 2550000)
£192308	$330769	€280770	Birgit (64x46cm-25x18in) init.d.Nov.1897 W/C exhib.lit. 3-Dec-3 AB Stockholms Auktionsverk #2421/R est:2500000-3000000 (S.KR 2500000)

LARSSON, Gerhard (1910-) Swedish

£544	$990	€800	Flowers in vase (65x55cm-26x22in) s.d.46. 8-Feb-4 Bukowskis, Helsinki #499/R

LARSSON, Marcus (1825-1864) Swedish

£650	$1105	€949	Swedish and Danish frigates (34x53cm-13x21in) mono.i. 19-Nov-3 Christie's, Kensington #497/R
£1070	$1723	€1562	Seascape with sailing vessel (25x36cm-10x14in) s.d.1850. 25-Aug-3 Lilla Bukowskis, Stockholm #477 (S.KR 14000)
£1923	$3308	€2808	Landscape with waterfall in hazy sunshine (58x74cm-23x29in) s.d.1857. 7-Dec-3 Uppsala Auktionskammare, Uppsala #103/R est:20000-25000 (S.KR 25000)
£2100	$3864	€3066	Moonlight in the harbour, Calais France (60x90cm-24x35in) mono.i.verso. 29-Mar-4 Bonhams, Bath #68/R est:1500-2500
£3169	$5482	€4500	Stormy sea (50x73cm-20x29in) s. 13-Dec-3 Hagelstam, Helsinki #44/R est:5000
£5617	$10055	€8201	Steam ship on fire (63x101cm-25x40in) s.d.1857. 25-May-4 Bukowskis, Stockholm #213/R est:50000-60000 (S.KR 76000)
£11923	$20508	€17408	View of Kronborg Palace (110x168cm-43x66in) s.d.1863. 2-Dec-3 Bukowskis, Stockholm #102/R est:130000-150000 (S.KR 155000)

LARSSON, Ola (1863-1939) Swedish

£517	$926	€755	Coastal landscape with girl holding parasol on jetty (37x48cm-15x19in) s.d.1900. 26-May-4 AB Stockholms Auktionsverk #2153/R (S.KR 7000)

LARTER, Pat (1936-1996) Australian

Works on paper

£340	$589	€496	Rainbow image (122x91cm-48x36in) s.i.d.July 1994 verso mixed media holograms board prov. 10-Dec-3 Shapiro, Sydney #112 (A.D 800)

LARTER, Richard (1929-) Australian

£1065	$1683	€1555	Untitled - head (66x40cm-26x16in) init.d.61 s.d.May 1961 verso enamel oil board prov. 2-Sep-3 Deutscher-Menzies, Melbourne #195/R est:2500-4000 (A.D 2600)
£1069	$1945	€1561	Montezuma (179x103cm-70x41in) init.d.1986 s.i.d.verso prov. 16-Jun-4 Deutscher-Menzies, Melbourne #241/R est:4500-6500 (A.D 2800)
£1069	$1945	€1561	Montezuma II (179x103cm-70x41in) init.d.1986 prov. 16-Jun-4 Deutscher-Menzies, Melbourne #242/R est:4500-6500 (A.D 2800)
£1446	$2459	€2111	Weak winter sun (180x104cm-71x41in) init.d.27.6.94 chrome acrylic paint gesso on canvas. 29-Oct-3 Lawson Menzies, Sydney #152/R est:6000-8000 (A.D 3500)
£1475	$2331	€2154	Port workings (61x91cm-24x36in) init. s.i. verso board exhib. 2-Sep-3 Deutscher-Menzies, Melbourne #209/R est:4000-6000 (A.D 3600)
£1653	$2926	€2413	Stickerci (175x132cm-69x52in) init.d.1984 acrylic prov. 3-May-4 Christie's, Melbourne #213 est:4000-6000 (A.D 4000)
£2869	$4533	€4189	Untitled (171x106cm-67x42in) init.d.2.1983 synthetic polymer prov. 2-Sep-3 Deutscher-Menzies, Melbourne #157/R est:7000-10000 (A.D 7000)
£3512	$6217	€5128	Scatter shift (184x160cm-72x63in) init.d.12.80 acrylic prov. 3-May-4 Christie's, Melbourne #262/R est:7000-12000 (A.D 8500)
£4527	$8193	€6609	Untitled (180x120cm-71x47in) init.d.9.79 exhib. 30-Mar-4 Lawson Menzies, Sydney #152/R est:7000-10000 (A.D 11000)
£4962	$9031	€7245	Roses tattoo (184x135cm-72x53in) s.d.1978 s.stretcher. 16-Jun-4 Deutscher-Menzies, Melbourne #198/R est:14000-18000 (A.D 13000)
£5488	$8616	€7958	Abstract (181x158cm-71x62in) init.d.9.79 s.i.d.1979 stretcher acrylic prov. 27-Aug-3 Christie's, Sydney #526/R est:7000-10000 (A.D 13500)

Works on paper

£533	$842	€778	Untitled (76x56cm-30x22in) s.d.20.2./58 pastel card. 2-Sep-3 Deutscher-Menzies, Melbourne #256/R est:1800-2600 (A.D 1300)
£851	$1447	€1242	Nude (36x52cm-14x20in) init.d.1990 pastel. 26-Nov-3 Deutscher-Menzies, Melbourne #200/R (A.D 2000)
£851	$1447	€1242	Seated Nude (52x36cm-20x14in) init.d.24-3-90 pastel pencil. 26-Nov-3 Deutscher-Menzies, Melbourne #201/R (A.D 2000)
£932	$1585	€1361	Portrait of Pat (54x37cm-21x15in) s.d.1986 pastel. 24-Nov-3 Sotheby's, Melbourne #216/R est:1000-1500 (A.D 2200)
£2869	$4533	€4189	The light that is was (176x130cm-69x51in) s.d.1972 s.i.d.March 1982 verso synthetic polymer prov. 2-Sep-3 Deutscher-Menzies, Melbourne #193/R est:9000-12000 (A.D 7000)
£2893	$5351	€4224	Scansion No.1 (176x110cm-69x43in) init.d.18.2.88 s.i.verso synthetic polymer on canvas prov. 15-Mar-4 Sotheby's, Melbourne #68/R est:7000-10000 (A.D 7000)
£2893	$5351	€4224	Scansion No.3 (176x113cm-69x44in) init.d.22.2.88 s.i.verso synthetic polymer on canvas. 15-Mar-4 Sotheby's, Melbourne #70/R est:7000-10000 (A.D 7000)
£2893	$5351	€4224	Scansion No.5 (176x113cm-69x44in) init.d.24.2.88 s.i.verso synthetic polymer. 15-Mar-4 Sotheby's, Melbourne #76/R est:7000-10000 (A.D 7000)
£2893	$5351	€4224	Scansion No.6 (176x112cm-69x44in) init.d.25.2.88 s.i.verso synthetic polymer. 15-Mar-4 Sotheby's, Melbourne #77/R est:7000-10000 (A.D 7000)
£2996	$5542	€4374	Scansion No.2 (176x122cm-69x48in) init.d.19.2.88 s.i.verso synthetic polymer on canvas. 15-Mar-4 Sotheby's, Melbourne #69/R est:7000-10000 (A.D 7250)
£3099	$5733	€4525	Scansion No.4 (176x113cm-69x44in) init.d.23.2.88 s.i.verso synthetic polymer. 15-Mar-4 Sotheby's, Melbourne #75/R est:7000-10000 (A.D 7500)

LARTIGUE, Dany (1921-) French

£268	$499	€400	Dielette, enfant au coq (60x72cm-24x28in) s. painted 1961. 3-Mar-4 Ferri, Paris #91/R
£302	$562	€450	La plage (106x256cm-42x101in) s.d.58. 3-Mar-4 Ferri, Paris #97/R
£436	$811	€650	La bravade I (200x81cm-79x32in) s.d.juillet 62. 3-Mar-4 Ferri, Paris #99/R

Works on paper

£789	$1453	€1200	Vue du port de Saint Tropez (54x65cm-21x26in) s. mixed media paper on canvas. 28-Jun-4 Joron-Derem, Paris #245

LARTIGUE, Jacques Henri (1894-1986) French

£4000	$7360	€6000	Palmeraie a Marrakech (97x130cm-38x51in) s. 14-Jun-4 Gros & Delettrez, Paris #199/R est:5000-7000

Photographs

£1556	$2800	€2272	Etude de mains (17x10cm-7x4in) gelatin silver print executed c.1932. 22-Apr-4 Phillips, New York #203/R est:3000-5000
£1587	$3000	€2317	Grand prix (24x27cm-9x11in) s.i. gelatin silver print. 17-Feb-4 Christie's, Rockefeller NY #107/R est:2000-3000
£1916	$3200	€2797	M Folletete and Tupy (24x27cm-9x11in) s. gelatin silver print exec.1912 printed later lit. 20-Oct-3 Christie's, Rockefeller NY #171/R est:4000-6000
£2133	$3925	€3200	Chambre d'amour, Biarritz (8x19cm-3x7in) silver gelatin prov. 10-Jun-4 Villa Grisebach, Berlin #1177/R est:2000-2500
£2200	$3740	€3212	Anna la Pradvina avec ses chiens Cogo et Chichi (30x41cm-12x16in) s. silver print exec.1911 printed later prov. 19-Nov-3 Sotheby's, Olympia #123/R est:1200-1800
£2260	$4000	€3300	Renee (38x53cm-15x21in) s.num.5/25 photo printed later. 28-Apr-4 Sotheby's, New York #179/R est:5000-7000
£2260	$4000	€3300	Carriage day at the races at Auteuil, Paris (41x54cm-16x21in) mono.num.6/25 photo printed later. 28-Apr-4 Sotheby's, New York #180/R est:5000-7000
£2994	$5000	€4371	Bibi a Marseille (19x34cm-7x13in) s. i.d.1928 verso gelatin silver print lit. 17-Oct-3 Phillips, New York #184/R est:2000-3000
£3427	$5825	€4900	Renee Perle in satin pantsuit and silver bangles (13x22cm-5x9in) gelatin silver lit. 28-Nov-3 Bassenge, Berlin #4306/R est:5500
£3497	$5840	€5000	Ombre chinoise (8x14cm-3x6in) silver print prov. 10-Oct-3 Tajan, Paris #240/R
£3800	$6460	€5548	Grand Prix de L'A C F, automobile delage, 26 Juin 1912 (31x41cm-12x16in) s. silver print exec.1912 printed later prov. 19-Nov-3 Sotheby's, Olympia #120/R est:2000-3000
£4790	$8000	€6993	ACF Grand Prix, Automobile Delage (35x54cm-14x21in) s.num.17/25 gelatin silver print exec.1912 printed later prov.lit. 20-Oct-3 Christie's, Rockefeller NY #49/R est:7000-9000
£13333	$23867	€20000	Avenue du Bois de Boulogne (7x5cm-3x2in) s.i.d.juin 1910 verso gelatin silver print prov. 12-May-4 Millon & Associes, Paris #110/R
£16000	$29600	€24000	Lacoste et Borotra gagnant du double (30x40cm-12x16in) s. gelatin silver print exec.1926 prov. 18-Jul-4 Sotheby's, Paris #293/R est:5000-8000
£26667	$47733	€40000	Championnat de bobsleigh, St Morits (8x11cm-3x4in) i.verso silver gelatin print exec. c.1913 prov. 12-May-4 Millon & Associes, Paris #111/R

LARTIGUE, Jacques Henri (attrib) (1894-1986) French

£724	$1310	€1100	Palmeraie (97x130cm-38x51in) s.d.1938. 18-Apr-4 Rouillac, Vendome #154

LARUE, Andre Léon (1785-1834) French

Miniatures

£1133	$2062	€1700	Monsieur Boulanger (13x10cm-5x4in) s.d.1821 oval. 30-Jun-4 Pierre Berge, Paris #97 est:1200-1800
£2800	$4844	€4088	Young gentleman (13cm-5in) s.d.1819 oval. 9-Dec-3 Christie's, London #225/R est:1500-2500

LARUE, Andre Léon (attrib) (1785-1834) French

£333	$550	€480	Portrait of woman in empire style dress (8x6cm-3x2in) i. ivory oval. 3-Jul-3 Van Ham, Cologne #1345

LARUE, John M (1920-) American

£320	$550	€467	Still life with flowers and fruit (48x61cm-19x24in) s. 6-Dec-3 Selkirks, St. Louis #200

LARUE, Lucien de (1925-) French

£625	$1000	€913	Landscape with houses (61x51cm-24x20in) s. painted c.1960. 17-May-3 Bunte, Elgin #1287 est:1000-1500
£838	$1500	€1223	Montmartre, Paris. s.i. 13-May-4 Dallas Auction Gallery, Dallas #114/R est:1000-2000

LARUS, Eliane (1944-) French

£507	$958	€750	Enfant dans un jardin (100x65cm-39x26in) s. s.i.d.1989 verso acrylic cardboard. 21-Feb-4 Cornette de St.Cyr, Paris #342
£1867	$3379	€2800	Dans la cuisine (100x81cm-39x32in) s. acrylic wood. 3-Apr-4 Neret-Minet, Paris #103/R est:2550-2850
£2168	$3685	€3100	Le tagger (100x100cm-39x39in) s. acrylic panel painted 1992. 29-Nov-3 Neret-Minet, Paris #102/R est:2550-2850

Works on paper

£315	$535	€450	A las cinco de la tarde - 5pm (22x17cm-9x7in) s. ink W/C exec. 1991. 29-Nov-3 Neret-Minet, Paris #166/R
£455	$773	€650	Jour d'hiver (40x30cm-16x12in) s. china ink pastel bark. 29-Nov-3 Neret-Minet, Paris #57/R

LARWILL, David (1956-) Australian

£1728	$3128	€2523	Lion 1983 (31x29cm-12x11in) acrylic on paper exhib. 30-Mar-4 Lawson Menzies, Sydney #75/R est:800-1000 (A.D 4200)
£3099	$5733	€4525	Hill near Rainbow Valley (152x182cm-60x72in) s.d.1991 i.verso prov. 15-Mar-4 Sotheby's, Melbourne #117/R est:5000-7000 (A.D 7500)
£4132	$7314	€6033	Reconcile now (60x80cm-24x31in) init.d.97 s.i.d.1997 verso prov. 3-May-4 Christie's, Melbourne #83/R est:10000-15000 (A.D 10000)

£4198 $7641 €6129 Untitled (126x178cm-50x70in) prov. 16-Jun-4 Deutscher-Menzies, Melbourne #91a/R est:14000-18000 (A.D 11000)
£4898 $9012 €7151 The fall (91x108cm-36x43in) init.d.03 s.i.d.verso acrylic linen prov. 29-Mar-4 Goodman, Sydney #68/R est:12000-18000 (A.D 12000)
£7257 $13353 €10595 Please explain (152x122cm-60x48in) s. s.i.d.2003 verso acrylic linen prov. 29-Mar-4 Goodman, Sydney #80/R est:20000-25000 (A.D 17780)
£7787 $12303 €11369 Seated woman (99x90cm-39x35in) s.i.d.1985 verso prov. 2-Sep-3 Deutscher-Menzies, Melbourne #67/R est:12000-18000 (A.D 19000)
£8907 $14340 €13004 Beast master No. 2 (185x155cm-73x61in) prov. 25-Aug-3 Sotheby's, Paddington #282/R est:18000-22000 (A.D 22000)
£12295 $19426 €17951 On the street (292x184cm-115x72in) s.i.d.August 1984 verso diptych prov. 2-Sep-3 Deutscher-Menzies, Melbourne #24/R est:30000-40000 (A.D 30000)
£26718 $48626 €39008 Skate borders (213x304cm-84x120in) init. s.i.d.15.6.88 verso diptych prov. 16-Jun-4 Deutscher-Menzies, Melbourne #84/R est:55000-75000 (A.D 70000)
Works on paper
£267 $486 €390 Untitled (20x28cm-8x11in) d.20.4.93 pencil. 16-Jun-4 Deutscher-Menzies, Melbourne #585/R (A.D 700)
£382 $695 €558 Untitled (37x26cm-15x10in) s.d.1988 gouache ink pastel. 16-Jun-4 Deutscher-Menzies, Melbourne #586/R est:1500-2500 (A.D 1000)
£725 $1320 €1059 What was had and what was got (27x46cm-11x18in) s.i. synthetic polymer. 16-Jun-4 Deutscher-Menzies, Melbourne #528/R est:2000-3000 (A.D 1900)
£729 $1173 €1064 Nightmare (54x72cm-21x28in) s.i.d.1993 mixed media. 13-Oct-3 Joel, Victoria #243 est:1000-1500 (A.D 1800)
£1069 $1945 €1561 Untitled - mother and child (70x49cm-28x19in) synthetic polymer. 16-Jun-4 Deutscher-Menzies, Melbourne #368/R est:3000-5000 (A.D 2800)
£1221 $2223 €1783 Discourse - mining mob- usual way (51x71cm-20x28in) s.i.d.1998 synthetic polymer. 16-Jun-4 Deutscher-Menzies, Melbourne #272/R est:3500-5500 (A.D 3200)
£1271 $2161 €1856 Figure (41x32cm-16x13in) s.d.1988 W/C gouache prov. 24-Nov-3 Sotheby's, Melbourne #84/R est:3000-4000 (A.D 3000)
£1728 $3128 €2523 Untitled (46x46cm-18x18in) s.d.84 verso gouache. 30-Mar-4 Lawson Menzies, Sydney #4/R est:1500-2500 (A.D 4200)
£2099 $3821 €3065 De traps (54x72cm-21x28in) s.i.d.1999 synthetic polymer gouache. 16-Jun-4 Deutscher-Menzies, Melbourne #91b/R est:4500-6500 (A.D 5500)
£3252 $5106 €4715 Tribal thing (71x49cm-28x19in) s.i.d.1997 W/C gouache. 26-Aug-3 Christie's, Sydney #203/R est:8000-10000 (A.D 8000)
£3284 $5583 €4795 Yardwork (65x42cm-26x17in) s.i.d.1989 gouache prov. 24-Nov-3 Sotheby's, Melbourne #71/R est:5000-7000 (A.D 7750)

LARY, Roland (1855-1933) Dutch
£500 $895 €750 Female worker, sleeping (24x31cm-9x12in) mono. panel. 11-May-4 Vendu Notarishuis, Rotterdam #237

LARY, Roland (attrib) (1855-1933) Dutch
Works on paper
£214 $400 €321 Girl with a tambourine (46x27cm-18x11in) indis.sig. pencil W/C paper laid down prov. 25-Jul-4 Bonhams & Butterfields, San Francisco #6056/R

LARZELERE, Charles Laverne (1883-1937) American
£370 $700 €540 California foothill landscape (41x51cm-16x20in) s. masonite prov. 17-Feb-4 John Moran, Pasadena #198/R

LASALLE, Charles (1894-1958) American
£889 $1600 €1298 Nightwatch (76x101cm-30x40in) s.i. prov. 25-Apr-4 Bonhams & Butterfields, San Francisco #5532/R est:2500-3500
Works on paper
£889 $1600 €1298 Catching up with the news (63x76cm-25x30in) s. chl. 25-Apr-4 Bonhams & Butterfields, San Francisco #5531/R est:1200-1600

LASAR, Charles (1856-1936) American
£838 $1500 €1223 Night-time landscape with shepherd and his flock of sheep (43x58cm-17x23in) s. 20-Mar-4 Pook & Pook, Downington #371 est:800-1200
£2260 $4000 €3300 Lady artist (91x64cm-36x25in) s.i.d.86 prov. 27-Apr-4 Doyle, New York #16/R est:2000-3000

LASARTE, Mercedes (20th C) Spanish
£3289 $6053 €5000 Painter (178x81cm-70x32in) s. 22-Jun-4 Durán, Madrid #185/R est:3000

LASCANO, Juan (1947-) Argentinian
£1732 $3100 €2529 Bust (34x26cm-13x10in) 11-May-4 Arroyo, Buenos Aires #57

LASCAUX, Elie (1888-1969) French
£241 $383 €352 Lake (61x49cm-24x19in) s.d.1953. 29-Apr-3 Louis Morton, Mexico #136/R (M.P 4000)
£363 $668 €530 Village de Liancous (54x73cm-21x29in) s.d.56 i.verso prov. 9-Jun-4 Walker's, Ottawa #323/R (C.D 900)

LASCHKE, August (20th C) German
£2200 $4048 €3300 The brig Johanna von Schubert von Wolgast on the high seas (50x76cm-20x30in) s.i.d.74. 11-Jun-4 Wendl, Rudolstadt #4138/R est:250

LASELLAZ, Gustave François (19th C) French
£2600 $4784 €3796 Elegantes aux bord de la mer (21x16cm-8x6in) s. pair. 25-Mar-4 Christie's, Kensington #62/R est:3000-4000

LASKARIDOU, Sophia (1882-1965) Greek?
£7900 $13825 €11534 Tea on the veranda (80x66cm-31x26in) s. exhib. 16-Dec-3 Bonhams, New Bond Street #43/R est:4000-6000

LASKE, Oskar (1874-1951) Austrian
Works on paper
£250 $415 €365 Buildings in moonlight (28x23cm-11x9in) mono.d.1902 col chk htd white on board. 4-Oct-3 Finan Watkins & Co, Mere #144
£369 $683 €550 Museum, Vienna (15x10cm-6x4in) s.i. Indian ink W/C. 9-Mar-4 Dorotheum, Vienna #55
£379 $694 €550 Donau near Simmering (15x10cm-6x4in) mono.i. pencil W/C. 27-Jan-4 Dorotheum, Vienna #129
£455 $773 €650 Frightening dual (13x22cm-5x9in) mono. i.verso ink W/C. 28-Nov-3 Wiener Kunst Auktionen, Vienna #359/R
£690 $1262 €1000 Autumn (20x15cm-8x6in) mono.i. pencil W/C. 27-Jan-4 Dorotheum, Vienna #128
£1049 $1783 €1500 White ware shop (12x21cm-5x8in) mono.d.16 i.verso ink W/C. 28-Nov-3 Wiener Kunst Auktionen, Vienna #540/R est:500-1500
£1064 $1777 €1500 Vase of carnations (31x23cm-12x9in) s. gouache. 14-Oct-3 Dorotheum, Vienna #131/R
£2098 $3566 €3000 Examination (25x40cm-10x16in) i.d.1939 verso W/C. 28-Nov-3 Wiener Kunst Auktionen, Vienna #541/R est:3000-6000
£2416 $4470 €3600 Blue house with garden (29x45cm-11x18in) s.d.1948 gouache W/C. 9-Mar-4 Dorotheum, Vienna #113/R est:3800-5000
£2937 $4993 €4200 Self portrait scene (30x42cm-12x17in) s. mixed media prov. 28-Nov-3 Wiener Kunst Auktionen, Vienna #534/R est:1000-3000
£3000 $5520 €4500 Neapel, via Tasso (41x50cm-16x20in) s.i. W/C gouache paper on paper. 8-Jun-4 Sotheby's, Amsterdam #208/R est:3000-5000
£3472 $5660 €5000 Market place in Czernowitz (30x42cm-12x17in) s.i. gouache. 23-Sep-3 Wiener Kunst Auktionen, Vienna #96/R est:5000-8000
£3497 $5944 €5000 Amusement park (50x48cm-20x19in) s. mixed media prov. 28-Nov-3 Wiener Kunst Auktionen, Vienna #538/R est:5000-12000
£3521 $6162 €5000 Puchenstuben (33x47cm-13x19in) s.i.d.1920 W/C gouache. 19-Dec-3 Dorotheum, Vienna #58/R est:5000-8000
£3636 $6182 €5200 Tunis (40x50cm-16x20in) s.i. W/C. 25-Nov-3 Hassfurther, Vienna #57/R est:4000-6000
£4167 $7083 €6000 Still life of flowers (44x35cm-17x14in) s.i.d.1943 mixed media prov. 28-Oct-3 Wiener Kunst Auktionen, Vienna #95/R est:3000-7000
£5594 $9510 €8000 Venice (41x43cm-16x17in) s. mixed media prov. 28-Nov-3 Wiener Kunst Auktionen, Vienna #535/R est:4000-12000
£6294 $10699 €9000 Food market (48x41cm-19x16in) s.i. mixed media prov. 28-Nov-3 Wiener Kunst Auktionen, Vienna #537/R est:6000-15000
£6944 $11806 €10000 Traunkirchen (38x48cm-15x19in) s.i. W/C prov. 28-Oct-3 Wiener Kunst Auktionen, Vienna #97/R est:5000-15000
£6944 $11806 €10000 Salzburg (39x45cm-15x18in) s.d.30/40 gouache. 28-Oct-3 Wiener Kunst Auktionen, Vienna #96/R est:8000-16000

LASKER, Jonathan (1948-) American
£6667 $12267 €10000 Oasis (145x208cm-57x82in) s.i.d. verso. 11-Jun-4 Hauswedell & Nolte, Hamburg #1403/R est:20000
£12291 $22000 €17945 Strawberry fields (61x51cm-24x20in) s.i.d.83 verso acrylic prov. 12-May-4 Christie's, Rockefeller NY #476/R est:18000-22000
£14000 $25340 €20440 To manufacture transcendence (76x61cm-30x24in) s.i.d.1987 s.d.on overlap prov. 1-Apr-4 Christie's, Kensington #277/R est:8000-12000
£33520 $60000 €48939 Ascension (147x183cm-58x72in) s.i.d.1983 verso prov.exhib. 12-May-4 Christie's, Rockefeller NY #474/R est:30000-40000
Works on paper
£436 $772 €650 Untitled (66x50cm-26x20in) s.d. pencil chl. 30-Apr-4 Dr Fritz Nagel, Stuttgart #316/R

LASKER, Joseph Leon (1919-) American
£1243 $2250 €1865 Interior (102x127cm-40x50in) 16-Apr-4 American Auctioneer #241/R
£2060 $3750 €3008 Brown and yellow house (76x86cm-30x34in) s. painted 1978 prov.exhib. 29-Jun-4 Sotheby's, New York #496/R est:2000-3000
Works on paper
£1243 $2250 €1865 Study for slanting light (20x25cm-8x10in) pencil. 16-Apr-4 American Auctioneer #240/R

LASKY, L (19th C) French
£972 $1624 €1400 Cossacks in winter (50x82cm-20x32in) s. 24-Oct-3 Ketterer, Hamburg #84/R
£2649 $4821 €4000 Cossacks in winter (51x81cm-20x32in) s. 21-Jun-4 Dorotheum, Vienna #92/R est:3000-3200

LASOCKI, Kazimierz (1871-1952) Polish
£486 $792 €700 Cows getting out of river (60x80cm-24x31in) s.d.1936 panel. 27-Sep-3 Dannenberg, Berlin #575/R

LASSALLE, Emile (1813-1871) French
£2802 $5015 €4091 Children with goat (26x21cm-10x8in) s. panel. 17-May-4 Beurret, Zurich #18/R est:4000-6000 (S.FR 6500)

LASSAW, Ibram (1913-) American/Egyptian
£529 $900 €772 Untitled (28x33cm-11x13in) s.d.1985 acrylic on paper. 9-Nov-3 Wright, Chicago #464
Sculpture
£5946 $11000 €8681 Untitled (42x48x26cm-17x19x10in) metal alloy. 12-Feb-4 Sotheby's, New York #180/R est:3500-4500

LASSEN, Hans August (1857-1938) German
£304 $535 €450 Two men enjoying lobster supper (24x36cm-9x14in) s.d.1914. 22-May-4 Lempertz, Koln #1545
£1049 $1783 €1500 In the wine cellar (41x31cm-16x12in) s.i.d.1900 panel lit. 28-Nov-3 Schloss Ahlden, Ahlden #1416/R est:1800
£1333 $2413 €2000 Two men with punch (24x36cm-9x14in) s.d.1902. 1-Apr-4 Van Ham, Cologne #1507 est:400
£2667 $4853 €4000 Two men drinking punch (23x35cm-9x14in) s. panel. 30-Jun-4 Neumeister, Munich #601/R est:3500

LASSIEUR, Berth (1882-1919) ?
£2620 $4690 €3825 L'automne (88x110cm-35x43in) s. 26-May-4 Sotheby's, Zurich #42/R est:6000-9000 (S.FR 6000)

LASSINI, J (18th C) Italian
£2160 $3737 €3154 Madonna and Child with Saint John (103x82cm-41x32in) s.i. 9-Dec-3 Sotheby's, Olympia #396/R est:1200-1800

LASSNIG, Maria (1919-) Austrian
£92105 $169474 €140000 Science fiction (192x128cm-76x50in) s.d.1963 lit.exhib. 22-Jun-4 Wiener Kunst Auktionen, Vienna #411/R est:110000
Works on paper
£634 $1052 €900 Smoke drawing (19x31cm-7x12in) s.i.d.1997 pencil. 13-Jun-3 Hauswedell & Nolte, Hamburg #744/R
£1208 $2162 €1800 Self portrait (20x15cm-8x6in) s. pencil W/C. 25-May-4 Dorotheum, Vienna #124/R est:2000-2600
£1208 $2162 €1800 Self portrait (20x15cm-8x6in) s.d.2000 pencil W/C. 25-May-4 Dorotheum, Vienna #125/R est:2000-2600
£4698 $8315 €7000 Birth of ego (43x30cm-17x12in) i.d.1948 pencil. 28-Apr-4 Wiener Kunst Auktionen, Vienna #215/R est:5000-10000
£5944 $10105 €8500 Self portrait (57x42cm-22x17in) s.d.1970 W/C. 26-Nov-3 Dorotheum, Vienna #84/R est:6000-7000
£6550 $12052 €9563 Family Fly von Beutelstroke family tree (61x43cm-24x17in) i.d.1979 W/C pencil prov.exhib. 8-Jun-4 Germann, Zurich #17/R est:8000-12000 (S.FR 15000)
£6711 $11879 €10000 Self portrait (44x63cm-17x25in) s.i.d. W/C. 28-Apr-4 Wiener Kunst Auktionen, Vienna #281/R est:10000-20000

LASTRA, Ramon (?) Spanish
Works on paper
£616 $1010 €850 Santiago in the snow (68x96cm-27x38in) s.i. W/C. 27-May-3 Durán, Madrid #45/R

LASZLO DE LOMBOS, Philip Alexius de (1869-1937) British
£1111 $1889 €1600 Portrait of man with moustache (87x68cm-34x27in) s.d.904. 28-Oct-3 Dorotheum, Vienna #130/R est:1800-2400
£3022 $5500 €4412 Portrait of a lady (93x74cm-37x29in) s.d.1926. 29-Jun-4 Sotheby's, New York #77/R est:3000-5000
£14000 $25620 €20440 Portrait of Sir Robert Gresley (96x71cm-38x28in) s.i.d.1924 prov. 2-Jun-4 Sotheby's, London #41/R est:6000-8000
£20000 $36600 €29200 Portrait of Lady Frances Gresley (98x72cm-39x28in) s.i.d.1924 prov. 2-Jun-4 Sotheby's, London #42/R est:14000-18000

LASZLO, Fulop (20th C) Hungarian
£1283 $2270 €1873 Man with a moustache (73x54cm-29x21in) s.i.d.1911 cardboard. 28-Apr-4 Kieselbach, Budapest #20/R (H.F 480000)

LASZLO, Phillip (1892-1968) American?
£894 $1600 €1305 Impressionist landscape (58x79cm-23x31in) s.d.1937. 8-May-4 Susanin's, Chicago #6060/R est:800-1200

LATAPIE, Louis (1891-1972) French
£490 $832 €700 Oiseau (17x52cm-7x20in) s. oil paper on canvas prov. 23-Nov-3 Cornette de St.Cyr, Paris #213
£503 $856 €720 Nu assi (38x40cm-15x16in) s. 20-Nov-3 Claude Aguttes, Neuilly #222
£559 $951 €800 Nu assis au chapeau (65x54cm-26x21in) s. 20-Nov-3 Claude Aguttes, Neuilly #210
£629 $1070 €900 Baigneuse (14x51cm-6x20in) s. oil W/C prov. 23-Nov-3 Cornette de St.Cyr, Paris #210/R
£629 $1070 €900 Baigneuse dans un paysage (18x62cm-7x24in) s. panel. 28-Nov-3 Blanchet, Paris #176
£764 $1276 €1100 Autoportrait (50x51cm-20x20in) s. panel. 21-Oct-3 Artcurial Briest, Paris #352
£839 $1427 €1200 Bouquet de fleurs (62x47cm-24x19in) s. oil paper on canvas. 23-Nov-3 Cornette de St.Cyr, Paris #611
£909 $1545 €1300 Poisson (50x65cm-20x26in) s. oil paper on canvas prov. 23-Nov-3 Cornette de St.Cyr, Paris #211/R
£1342 $2376 €2000 Modele dans l'atelier (79x56cm-31x22in) s.d.1938. 29-Apr-4 Claude Aguttes, Neuilly #70 est:1300-1500
£1399 $2406 €2000 Reclining nude (36x50cm-14x20in) s. s.d.28 verso board prov. 2-Dec-3 Sotheby's, Amsterdam #218/R est:2000-3000
£1400 $2520 €2100 Deux amies (32x44cm-13x17in) s. panel. 24-Apr-4 Cornette de St.Cyr, Paris #378/R est:2000
£1867 $3435 €2800 Femme nue (108x72cm-43x28in) s. s.d.1944 verso. 10-Jun-4 Camard, Paris #187/R est:3000-4000
£3333 $6133 €5000 Hommage a Matisse (116x130cm-46x51in) s. 10-Jun-4 Camard, Paris #186/R est:5000-7000
£3401 $6088 €5000 Nu allonge (50x65cm-20x26in) s. 19-Mar-4 Millon & Associes, Paris #86/R est:4000-5000
£4897 $8128 €7100 Creole (46x65cm-18x26in) s. 1-Oct-3 Millon & Associes, Paris #97/R
Works on paper
£278 $464 €400 Visage de femme (26x20cm-10x8in) s. gouache prov. 25-Oct-3 Cornette de St.Cyr, Paris #521
£300 $543 €450 Jardin (21x50cm-8x20in) s. W/C lead pencil. 1-Apr-4 Credit Municipal, Paris #83
£387 $670 €550 Projet de fontaine (20x17cm-8x7in) mono. black ink gouache exec.c.1960. 13-Dec-3 Martinot & Savignat, Pontoise #24/R
£524 $892 €750 Voilier jaune (51x22cm-20x9in) s. W/C paper on canvas prov. 23-Nov-3 Cornette de St.Cyr, Paris #212
£571 $1061 €850 Visage de femme (35x25cm-14x10in) s. W/C gouache Indian ink. 2-Mar-4 Artcurial Briest, Paris #91
£863 $1416 €1200 Composition (48x64cm-19x25in) s. mixed media. 6-Jun-3 David Kahn, Paris #48
£1192 $2181 €1800 Nature morte au couteau (49x32cm-19x13in) W/C gouache varnish laid on canvas. 7-Apr-4 Piasa, Paris #183 est:1800-2000
£1241 $2234 €1800 Nu debout sur fond de bateaux (54x41cm-21x16in) s. W/C ink paper on canvas. 25-Jan-4 Chayette & Cheval, Paris #274 est:600-800

LATASTER, Ger (1920-) Dutch
£1000 $1840 €1500 De laatste dronk (90x110cm-35x43in) s.d.95 s.i.d.verso. 9-Jun-4 Christie's, Amsterdam #395/R est:1500-2000
£2098 $3566 €3000 Portugees interieur (180x200cm-71x79in) s.d.79 i.stretcher oil acrylic spray can paint. 25-Nov-3 Christie's, Amsterdam #74/R est:4500-6500
£2098 $3608 €3000 Untitled (80x100cm-31x39in) s.d.73 oil plastic prov. 2-Dec-3 Sotheby's, Amsterdam #320/R est:3000-5000
£2533 $4661 €3800 Dubbelportret - double portrait (140x90cm-55x35in) s.i.d.88 verso prov.exhib. 9-Jun-4 Christie's, Amsterdam #174/R est:3500-5000
£4196 $7217 €6000 Verduisterd strand (120x110cm-47x43in) s.d.59 prov. 2-Dec-3 Sotheby's, Amsterdam #316/R est:6000-8000
£4545 $7727 €6500 Brule (115x110cm-45x43in) s.d.59 s.d.8 juin 1959 verso exhib. 28-Nov-3 Blanchet, Paris #227/R est:6000-8000
Works on paper
£302 $561 €450 Femmes en Larmes II (100x69cm-39x27in) s.d.1985 wax crayon prov. 3-Mar-4 Tajan, Paris #244
£302 $561 €450 Autoportrait avec lunettes (69x98cm-27x39in) s.d.1984 wax crayon W/C prov. 3-Mar-4 Tajan, Paris #246
£369 $687 €550 Vulcanus 2 (98x69cm-39x27in) s.d.1985 wax crayon prov. 3-Mar-4 Tajan, Paris #245
£420 $713 €600 Two figures (29x41cm-11x16in) s.d.11/83 pencil col crayons. 25-Nov-3 Christie's, Amsterdam #121/R
£420 $722 €600 Untitled (54x75cm-21x30in) s.d.1982 W/C prov. 7-Dec-3 Sotheby's, Amsterdam #730/R
£559 $951 €800 Het brood - the bread (45x58cm-18x23in) s.d.83 pastel W/C. 25-Nov-3 Christie's, Amsterdam #115/R
£3566 $6063 €5100 Triple explosion (100x100cm-39x39in) s.d.1972 mixed media canvas plexiglass frame prov. 28-Nov-3 Blanchet, Paris #229/R est:4000-5000

LATHAM, John (1921-) British
Works on paper
£3200 $5504 €4672 Belief system (122x96cm-48x38in) mixed media. 2-Dec-3 Bonhams, New Bond Street #175/R est:1500-2500

LATHAM, Molly M (c.1900-1987) British
Works on paper
£400 $720 €584 E A Merckel and the hunt at Chailey, Sussex (51x69cm-20x27in) s.d.1932 W/C htd white. 20-Apr-4 Rowley Fine Art, Newmarket #430/R
£500 $935 €730 Huntsman (43x61cm-17x24in) s.d.1933 W/C. 24-Feb-4 Tayler & Fletcher, Cheltenham #4

LATHANGUE, Henry Herbert (1859-1929) British
£35000 $64050 €51100 Ligurian olives (76x81cm-30x32in) s. s.i.stretcher prov.exhib. 4-Jun-4 Christie's, London #131/R est:35000-45000
£243902 $436585 €356097 The first meal - girl feeding calves from bucket (107x96cm-42x38in) s. prov. 26-May-4 AB Stockholms Auktionsverk #2436/R est:800000-1000000 (S.KR 3300000)
£440000 $748000 €642400 Winter in Liguria (106x89cm-42x35in) s. painted 1906 prov.exhib.lit. 26-Nov-3 Christie's, London #37/R est:400000-600000
£470000 $799000 €686200 In the Dauphine (239x159cm-94x63in) painted 1885 prov.exhib.lit. 26-Nov-3 Christie's, London #26/R est:200000-300000
Works on paper
£8500 $15470 €12410 Woodsmen (51x36cm-20x14in) init. conte. 15-Jun-4 Bonhams, New Bond Street #5/R est:3000-5000

LATHROP, Gertrude Katherine (20th C) American
Sculpture
£2654 $4750 €3875 Seated pup (29cm-11in) s.i.d.1926 bronze st.f.Kunst. 14-May-4 Skinner, Boston #325/R est:800-1200

LATHROP, Ida Pulis (1859-1937) American
£1511 $2750 €2206 Young girl putting teddy to bed (41x28cm-16x11in) s. 15-Jun-4 John Moran, Pasadena #102 est:3000-5000

LATHROP, Sobrina P (20th C) American
£569 $950 €831 Shepherdess (51x76cm-20x30in) s. i.d.1915 verso. 14-Nov-3 Aspire, Cleveland #67 est:1000-2000

LATHROP, William Langson (1859-1938) American
£4491 $7500 €6557 Montauk (41x46cm-16x18in) s.i.d.1938 masonite. 23-Oct-3 Shannon's, Milford #69/R est:7000-9000
£10000 $17000 €14600 Keyport (64x76cm-25x30in) s.i. prov. 30-Oct-3 Phillips, New York #62/R est:15000-25000
£21739 $40000 €31739 Sunlight and shadow (55x63cm-22x25in) s. prov. 8-Jun-4 Bonhams & Butterfields, San Francisco #4036/R est:3000-5000

LATIL, Eugenie (1808-1879) French
£3171 $5549 €4500 Romeo et Juliette (65x81cm-26x32in) s.d.1843. 18-Dec-3 Tajan, Paris #51/R est:4000-6000

LATIMER, Lorenzo Palmer (1857-1941) American
£1902 $3500 €2777 Lyon Ranch, October (55x68cm-22x27in) s. i.d.1930 verso exhib. 8-Jun-4 Bonhams & Butterfields, San Francisco #4191/R est:4000-7000
£2446 $4500 €3571 Glimpse of Washoe Lake, Nevada (55x68cm-22x27in) s. i.d.1936 verso exhib. 8-Jun-4 Bonhams & Butterfields, San Francisco #4192/R est:5000-7000
Works on paper
£472 $850 €689 California Redwoods (36x20cm-14x8in) s. W/C pencil. 24-Apr-4 Weschler, Washington #611/R
£539 $900 €787 Tree in a landscape (20x13cm-8x5in) s.d.1901 W/C. 26-Oct-3 Bonhams & Butterfields, San Francisco #6501/R
£1477 $2600 €2156 Felta Creek near Healdsburg, California (36x25cm-14x10in) s.d.1914 W/C. 23-May-4 Treadway Gallery, Cincinnati #497/R est:3000-4000
£1879 $3250 €2743 Forest stream (61x36cm-24x14in) s.d.1901 W/C paper on board prov. 10-Dec-3 Bonhams & Butterfields, San Francisco #6163/R est:3000-5000
£2168 $3750 €3165 Lone Oak (26x20cm-10x8in) s.d.1911 pencil W/C. 10-Dec-3 Bonhams & Butterfields, San Francisco #6161/R est:2000-3000

LATINIS, Georges (1885-1963) Belgian
£306 $548 €450 La ferme au ruisseau (73x92cm-29x36in) s. 16-Mar-4 Vanderkindere, Brussels #237

LATOIX, Gaspard (fl.1882-1903) British
£245 $400 €358 Riding horse by a country house (51x76cm-20x30in) s. 28-Sep-3 Bonhams & Butterfields, Los Angeles #7035
£3235 $5500 €4723 Indian rider (33x43cm-13x17in) s. canvas on board prov. 1-Nov-3 Santa Fe Art, Santa Fe #82/R est:5000-7000

LATORRE VIEDMA, Rafael (1872-1960) Spanish
£347 $552 €500 Don Quijote y Sancho (115x57cm-45x22in) s. 29-Apr-3 Durán, Madrid #745/R

LATOUCHE, Gaston de (1854-1913) French
£705 $1247 €1050 Souper de gala (36x26cm-14x10in) s. 29-Apr-4 David Kahn, Paris #217
£818 $1300 €1194 Pont de St Cloud. Canal a Caen (15x15cm-6x6in) one s. panel pair. 13-Sep-3 Weschler, Washington #678/R
£1868 $3400 €2727 Quiet moment with a friend (41x33cm-16x13in) s. panel. 7-Feb-4 Neal Auction Company, New Orleans #148/R est:2500-3500
£5000 $9200 €7500 Le jour de l'audience (76x80cm-30x31in) s. prov.exhib. 9-Jun-4 Beaussant & Lefèvre, Paris #180/R est:8000-10000
£5588 $9500 €8158 Leda and the swan at Versailles (57x45cm-22x18in) s.d.1887 panel. 29-Oct-3 Christie's, Rockefeller NY #167/R est:12000-18000
£5687 $9100 €8303 L'acouchee - interior with new mother resting, old nanny with baby (97x130cm-38x51in) s.d.1883 exhib. 22-Sep-3 Rasmussen, Vejle #237/R est:60000-80000 (D.KR 60000)
£16552 $27641 €24000 Le ballet (77x56cm-30x22in) s. panel lit. 16-Nov-3 Muizon & Le Coent, Paris #40/R
£32000 $55040 €46720 Ancient air (114x77cm-45x30in) s. panel prov.exhib.lit. 3-Dec-3 Christie's, London #36/R est:30000-50000
£44118 $75000 €64412 The rescue (173x208cm-68x82in) s. 29-Oct-3 Christie's, Rockefeller NY #144/R est:50000-70000
Works on paper
£2027 $3831 €3000 Femme nue endormie (77x55cm-30x22in) s. W/C. 17-Feb-4 Vanderkindere, Brussels #19/R est:3000-4000

LATOUR, Eugene (?) ?
£400 $728 €600 Gathering flowers in the mountains (38x48cm-15x19in) s. 30-Jun-4 Vendue Huis, Gravenhage #70

LATOUR, Georges de (1593-1652) French
£125000 $230000 €190000 Tete de femme, fragment (39x31cm-15x12in) prov.exhib.lit. 24-Jun-4 Christie's, Paris #48/R est:150000-200000

LATOUR, Georges de (circle) (1593-1652) French
£9050 $14480 €13213 Christ and Nikodemus (123x128cm-48x50in) 19-Sep-3 Koller, Zurich #3014/R est:30000-50000 (S.FR 20000)

LATOUR, Jean (1719-1782) Flemish
£2095 $3750 €3059 Beauty reading letter (56x38cm-22x15in) s. 7-May-4 Sloans & Kenyon, Bethesda #1654/R est:5000-7000

LATOUR, Joseph Pierre Tancrede (1807-1865) French
£3200 $5120 €4640 La lettre (47x38cm-19x15in) mono. prov. 18-Sep-3 Christie's, Kensington #172/R est:2000-3000

LATOUR, Marie Elizabeth de (1750-1834) Flemish
£2517 $4580 €3800 Le Concert galant (30x27cm-12x11in) s.d.1827 panel. 20-Jun-4 Versailles Encheres #13/R est:1000-1500

LATOUR, Maurice Quentin de (1704-1788) French
Works on paper
£3448 $5759 €5000 Portrait du Marechal de Saxe (38x30cm-15x12in) pierre noire pastel prov.lit. 17-Nov-3 Delorme & Bocage, Paris #66/R est:3000-4500
£188889 $340000 €275778 Portrait of Charles Louis Auguste Fouquet (59x50cm-23x20in) pastel paper on linen prov.exhib.lit. 23-Jan-4 Christie's, Rockefeller NY #63/R est:350000-450000

LATOUR, Maurice Quentin de (studio) (1704-1788) French
Works on paper
£22069 $36855 €32000 Portrait of Madame de Pompadour. Portrait of Louis de France (64x54cm-25x21in) pastel pair. 12-Nov-3 Sotheby's, Milan #124/R est:12000-16000

LATOUR, Tony de (20th C) New Zealander
£614 $1000 €896 There are no words (24x34cm-9x13in) s.d.1997 canvas on board. 23-Sep-3 Peter Webb, Auckland #119/R (NZ.D 1700)

LATTEY, Edward B (20th C) New Zealander
£277 $496 €404 Autumn morning, Taringamotu Valley (66x89cm-26x35in) s.d.1957. 11-May-4 Peter Webb, Auckland #185/R (NZ.D 800)

LATTKE, Fritz (1895-?) German?
£400 $736 €600 Fisherman on a pond in a rowing boat (17x25cm-7x10in) s. i.d.1968 verso board. 11-Jun-4 Wendl, Rudolstadt #4139/R

LATTRY, Michel (1875-1941) French/Russian
Works on paper
£403 $745 €600 Parc aux cygnes (28x20cm-11x8in) s. W/C. 15-Mar-4 Claude Boisgirard, Paris #72
£671 $1242 €1000 Cueillette de champignons (32x25cm-13x10in) s. gouache. 15-Mar-4 Claude Boisgirard, Paris #71/R est:1000-12000
£1267 $2331 €1900 Paysage au paon (35x27cm-14x11in) s. gouache. 11-Jun-4 Claude Aguttes, Neuilly #40/R est:1500-2000
£1333 $2453 €2000 Paysage aux cygnes et aux flamants roses (25x29cm-10x11in) s. W/C. 11-Jun-4 Claude Aguttes, Neuilly #39/R est:1500-2000
£1342 $2483 €2000 Paysage aux animaux (31x24cm-12x9in) s. gouache. 15-Mar-4 Claude Boisgirard, Paris #73/R est:1000-1200

LAU, Mathias Josephus (1889-1958) Dutch
£408 $743 €600 Schoorl (39x52cm-15x20in) 3-Feb-4 Christie's, Amsterdam #346/R

LAUBE, Otto (?) Dutch?
Sculpture
£1379 $2207 €2000 Rearing horse (38cm-15in) bronze marble foot. 12-Mar-3 Auction Maastricht #64/R est:1000-1200

LAUBER, Joseph (19/20th C) American?
Works on paper
£2703 $5000 €3946 Study for a four panel window (28x44cm-11x17in) s. W/C paperboard exec.c.1910 for Tiffany Studios. 9-Mar-4 Christie's, Rockefeller NY #55/R est:6000-8000

LAUBIES, René (1924-) French
£347 $580 €500 Composition abstraite (46x55cm-18x22in) s.d.72 paper on canvas. 21-Oct-3 Artcurial Briest, Paris #665
£493 $908 €750 Composition (11x37cm-4x15in) s.d.1959 paper on panel prov. 28-Jun-4 Joron-Derem, Paris #216
£1119 $1869 €1600 Composition (92x56cm-36x22in) s.d.1960 verso paper on canvas. 29-Jun-3 Versailles Encheres #9
£1513 $2784 €2300 Composition (67x51cm-26x20in) s. paper on canvas. 28-Jun-4 Joron-Derem, Paris #215/R est:1200-1500
Works on paper
£280 $467 €400 Composition (22x33cm-9x13in) s.d.1965 W/C. 29-Jun-3 Versailles Encheres #11

L'AUBINIERE, Georgina M de (1848-1930) British
£1889 $3250 €2758 Willow tree (61x91cm-24x36in) s. 6-Dec-3 Neal Auction Company, New Orleans #619/R est:2500-3500

LAUBSCHER, Erik (1927-) South African
£299 $509 €437 Noordhoek wrak (88x115cm-35x45in) s.i.d.1973 i.verso. 4-Nov-3 Stephan Welz, Johannesburg #600 est:2500-4000 (SA.R 3500)
£359 $610 €524 Red rocks, Bokkeveld (73x92cm-29x36in) s. s.i.verso. 4-Nov-3 Stephan Welz, Johannesburg #610 est:4000-6000 (SA.R 4200)
£756 $1369 €1104 Strandfontein cliffs (62x91cm-24x36in) s.d.73 s.i.d.verso canvas on panel. 30-Mar-4 Stephan Welz, Johannesburg #430 est:5000-8000 (SA.R 9000)

LAUBSER, Maggie (1886-1973) South African
£1073 $1922 €1567 Still life of king proteas (49x45cm-19x18in) canvas on board sold with poem by same artist two. 31-May-4 Stephan Welz, Johannesburg #512/R (SA.R 13000)
£4138 $6910 €6041 Woman with a pink kopdoek (44x35cm-17x14in) s.d.30 board. 20-Oct-3 Stephan Welz, Johannesburg #309/R est:40000-60000 (SA.R 48000)
£4741 $7918 €6922 Sailing boats and bird (50x42cm-20x17in) s. board. 20-Oct-3 Stephan Welz, Johannesburg #294/R est:25000-35000 (SA.R 55000)
£4741 $7918 €6922 Sword lily and nasturtiums in a blue green vase (51x38cm-20x15in) s. board. 20-Oct-3 Stephan Welz, Johannesburg #310/R est:40000-50000 (SA.R 55000)
£5042 $9126 €7361 Still life of hibiscus and irises in a vase (49x40cm-19x16in) s. board exhib. 30-Mar-4 Stephan Welz, Johannesburg #537/R est:40000-60000 (SA.R 60000)
£5128 $8718 €7487 Bird and lambs in an extensive landscape (45x40cm-18x16in) s. board. 4-Nov-3 Stephan Welz, Johannesburg #663/R est:50000-80000 (SA.R 60000)
£8621 $14397 €12587 Woman harvesting in a landscape (45x39cm-18x15in) s. canvasboard. 20-Oct-3 Stephan Welz, Johannesburg #311/R est:40000-60000 (SA.R 100000)
£10084 $18252 €14723 Cape homestead amongst trees (40x34cm-16x13in) s.d.24 panel. 30-Mar-4 Stephan Welz, Johannesburg #460/R est:50000-70000 (SA.R 120000)
Works on paper
£264 $473 €385 Three women meeting (10x18cm-4x7in) s.d.30 pencil col crayon. 31-May-4 Stephan Welz, Johannesburg #351 (SA.R 3200)
£495 $887 €723 Head of a woman (40x31cm-16x12in) s.d.60 pencil. 31-May-4 Stephan Welz, Johannesburg #310 (SA.R 6000)
£578 $1035 €844 Shepherd tending a flock (12x16cm-5x6in) pencil W/C. 31-May-4 Stephan Welz, Johannesburg #365 (SA.R 7000)

LAUCHERT, Richard (1823-1869) German
Works on paper
£1197 $1915 €1700 Portraits of Princes and Princess of Hohenzollern (45x36cm-18x14in) s.d.1849 two i.verso pastel ovals three prov. 22-Sep-3 Sotheby's, Amsterdam #4/R est:1500-2500

LAUDER, Charles James (1841-1920) British
£1700 $2669 €2465 At Leith Docks (40x61cm-16x24in) s.i. 27-Aug-3 Sotheby's, London #1109/R est:1000-1500
Works on paper
£440 $818 €642 Boating on the river (15x21cm-6x8in) s. W/C htd white. 4-Mar-4 Christie's, Kensington #114
£560 $1003 €818 Houses of Parliament in London (44x29cm-17x11in) s. W/C on pencil. 12-May-4 Dobiaschofsky, Bern #727/R (S.FR 1300)
£620 $1073 €905 Bruges (62x47cm-24x19in) s. W/C. 11-Dec-3 Lyon & Turnbull, Edinburgh #106/R

LAUDER, James Eckford (1811-1869) British
£512 $830 €748 The Adoration of the Magi (47x70cm-19x28in) after Bonifazio. 9-Aug-3 Hindemae, Ullerslev #161/R (D.KR 5400)

LAUDER, Robert Scott (1803-1869) British
£900 $1674 €1314 Portrait of Lord Charles Thynne wearing a burgundy waistcoat (41x30cm-16x12in) init. 4-Mar-4 Christie's, Kensington #9
£950 $1492 €1387 Portrait of a young gentleman (11x9cm-4x4in) 31-Aug-3 Paul Beighton, Rotherham #506

LAUDERBACK, Frances (20th C) American
£952 $1800 €1390 Genre scenes (20x15cm-8x6in) one s. verso prov. three. 17-Feb-4 John Moran, Pasadena #154/R est:2000-3000

LAUDY, Jacques (20th C) Belgian
£694 $1132 €1000 Nature morte aux fleurs et aux pommes (80x75cm-31x30in) s. 23-Sep-3 Galerie Moderne, Brussels #912/R

LAUDY, Jean (1877-1956) Belgian
£500 $900 €750 Still life with chicken (60x73cm-24x29in) s. 26-Apr-4 Bernaerts, Antwerp #413/R
£596 $1085 €900 Bouquet de fleurs (70x56cm-28x22in) s. 15-Jun-4 Vanderkindere, Brussels #132
£759 $1403 €1100 Table fleurie (35x47cm-14x19in) s. panel. 16-Feb-4 Horta, Bruxelles #463
£1049 $1783 €1500 Vase de roses (60x80cm-24x31in) s. 1-Dec-3 Palais de Beaux Arts, Brussels #88/R est:1600-2400
£1119 $1869 €1600 Vase fleuri de roses sur fond de paysage (60x80cm-24x31in) s. 13-Oct-3 Horta, Bruxelles #225 est:1500-2000
£2113 $3655 €3000 Vase de roses (73x92cm-29x36in) s. 9-Dec-3 Vanderkindere, Brussels #30/R est:2500-3500
£3667 $6637 €5500 Still life with roses (59x80cm-23x31in) s. 1-Apr-4 Van Ham, Cologne #1508/R est:8500
£3691 $6534 €5500 Nu assis (90x119cm-35x47in) s.d.1918. 27-Apr-4 Campo & Campo, Antwerp #142/R est:4000-5000
Works on paper
£436 $772 €650 Nu (45x36cm-18x14in) s. mixed media. 27-Apr-4 Campo & Campo, Antwerp #143/R

LAUER, Josef (1818-1881) Austrian
£2551 $4515 €3800 Roses dans un panier (32x39cm-13x15in) s. 30-Apr-4 Tajan, Paris #120/R est:4000-6000
£3654 $6321 €5335 Autumn - a glass of red wine (40x32cm-16x13in) s. 12-Dec-3 Kieselbach, Budapest #126/R (H.F 1400000)
£8437 $14849 €12656 Autumn still life (63x76cm-25x30in) s. 22-May-4 Dorotheum, Prague #39/R est:400000-600000 (C.KR 400000)
£12587 $21399 €18000 Madonna statue in niche with flowers and ivy (90x74cm-35x29in) s.i.d.1851. 24-Nov-3 Dorotheum, Vienna #68/R est:17000-20000
£13889 $23611 €20000 Still life with flowers and bird (31x38cm-12x15in) s. 28-Oct-3 Wiener Kunst Auktionen, Vienna #29/R est:10000-25000
£18182 $30909 €26000 Roses in basket by stream (50x63cm-20x25in) s. 24-Nov-3 Dorotheum, Vienna #34/R est:25000-30000

LAUERSEN, Harald V (20th C) Danish
£709 $1269 €1035 Confirmand (110x103cm-43x41in) 12-Jan-4 Rasmussen, Vejle #601/R (D.KR 7500)

LAUFFER, Erwin (20th C) American
£881 $1400 €1286 Landscape with houses and rolling hills (46x56cm-18x22in) s. 10-Sep-3 Alderfer's, Hatfield #340a/R est:800-1200

LAUFMAN, Sidney (1891-1985) American
£419 $750 €612 Path to the pasture, Bluffton, South Carolina (48x64cm-19x25in) s. i. stretcher exhib. 8-Jan-4 Doyle, New York #29/R

LAUGE, Achille (1861-1944) French
£1301 $2212 €1900 Vase with flowers (50x39cm-20x15in) s. 5-Nov-3 Vendue Huis, Gravenhage #308/R est:1500-2000
£3020 $5618 €4500 Vase de fleurs (50x40cm-20x16in) s. prov. 2-Mar-4 Artcurial Briest, Paris #132/R est:3500-4500
£11667 $21467 €17500 Notre-Dame des Pres, Cailhau (73x50cm-29x20in) s. i.verso panel. 11-Jun-4 Pierre Berge, Paris #252/R est:20000-25000
£14189 $26818 €21000 Paysage (50x73cm-20x29in) s.d.1922. 21-Feb-4 Cornette de St.Cyr, Paris #213/R est:15000-18000
£23529 $40000 €34352 Route de Cailhauvers Cailhavel (53x73cm-21x29in) s.d.10. 6-Nov-3 Sotheby's, New York #148/R est:30000-40000
£24333 $44043 €36500 L'allee des saules a Cailhau (48x61cm-19x24in) s. painted 1896. 1-Apr-4 Credit Municipal, Paris #62/R est:30000-40000
Works on paper
£5333 $9653 €8000 L'allee aux environs de Cailhau (30x52cm-12x20in) s. pastel canvas. 1-Apr-4 Credit Municipal, Paris #65/R est:8000-10000

LAUGEE, Desire (1823-1896) French
£26471 $45000 €38648 Au printemps de la vie (127x93cm-50x37in) s.d.1890 prov.exhib. 28-Oct-3 Sotheby's, New York #131/R est:20000-30000

LAUGEE, Georges (1853-?) French
£845 $1403 €1200 Paysanne pendant la fenaison (21x15cm-8x6in) s. panel. 15-Jun-3 Peron, Melun #153
Works on paper
£1127 $1870 €1600 Repas du moissonneur (38x48cm-15x19in) s. pastel cardboard. 15-Jun-3 Peron, Melun #185

LAUGHLIN, Clarence John (1905-1985) American
Photographs
£2889 $5200 €4218 Dream of American power (34x26cm-13x10in) i.num.verso gelatin silver print. 22-Apr-4 Phillips, New York #228/R est:4000-6000
Works on paper
£588 $1000 €858 Secret place (33x48cm-13x19in) s. W/C. 22-Nov-3 New Orleans Auction, New Orleans #1082/R est:1200-1800

LAUNOIS, Jean (1898-1942) French
Works on paper
£2270 $3790 €3200 Pierre Deval et sa famille (45x58cm-18x23in) s. gouache exhib. 19-Oct-3 Rabourdin & Choppin de Janvry, Paris #151/R est:2500-3000
£3497 $6014 €5000 Sur la plage (46x61cm-18x24in) s. gouache prov. 3-Dec-3 Beaussant & Lefèvre, Paris #46/R est:600-800

LAUPHEIMER, Anton (1848-1927) German
£2245 $4018 €3300 Interior of Marienmunster in Diessen am Ammersee (71x49cm-28x19in) s.d.83. 17-Mar-4 Neumeister, Munich #515/R est:1500

LAUR, Marie Yvonne (1879-1943) French
£829 $1500 €1210 Cat, kittens and blue fan (46x38cm-18x15in) s. 16-Apr-4 James Julia, Fairfield #656/R est:3000-5000
£2500 $4625 €3650 Three kittens (49x65cm-19x26in) s. 14-Jul-4 Sotheby's, Olympia #236/R est:2500-3500
£2775 $4718 €4052 Cats playing (60x73cm-24x29in) s. 5-Nov-3 Dobiaschofsky, Bern #733/R est:8000 (S.FR 6300)
£5500 $10175 €8030 Playtime (60x74cm-24x29in) s. 14-Jul-4 Sotheby's, Olympia #235/R est:3000-4000
£7092 $11844 €10000 Chaos dans la cuisine (60x73cm-24x29in) s. 17-Jun-3 Christie's, Paris #155/R est:7000-10000

LAURE, Jean Francois Hyacinthe Jules (1806-1861) French
£780 $1427 €1139 Portrait d'homme (74x60cm-29x24in) s. 8-Apr-4 Christie's, Kensington #44/R

LAUREL, Pierre (?) French
Sculpture
£2600 $4576 €3796 Seated naked child. Seated Satyr (18cm-7in) i. bronze two. 20-May-4 David Lay, Penzance #81/R est:2500-3000

LAURENCE (?) ?
Works on paper
£278 $464 €400 Woman (78x62cm-31x24in) pastel. 23-Oct-3 Hagelstam, Helsinki #829

LAURENCE, Charles (18/19th C) American?
£3056 $5500 €4462 Portrait of Charles Laurence (76x64cm-30x25in) s.d.1812. 20-Apr-4 Bunch, West Chester #397/R est:3000-5000

LAURENCE, Janet Lister (1949-) Australian
Works on paper
£1653 $3058 €2413 Pacific iosis suite (76x56cm-30x22in) init.d.90 mixed media on canvas six panel. 15-Mar-4 Sotheby's, Melbourne #49 est:3000-5000 (A.D 4000)

LAURENCE, Sydney Mortimer (1865-1940) American
£389 $650 €568 Alaska (8x13cm-3x5in) s. board. 19-Jun-3 Shelley, Hendersonville #874
£1183 $2200 €1727 Shorebreak (23x40cm-9x16in) s. panel. 3-Mar-4 Christie's, Rockefeller NY #23/R est:3000-5000
£5348 $10000 €7808 Cabbages and kings (25x20cm-10x8in) s. canvas on board prov. 24-Jul-4 Coeur d'Alene, Hayden #149/R est:5000-8000
£7609 $14000 €11109 Mount McKinley, Alaska (40x30cm-16x12in) s. canvas on masonite. 8-Jun-4 Bonhams & Butterfields, San Francisco #4118/R est:12000-16000
£7692 $14000 €11230 Evening light, Mount McKinley, Alaska (41x51cm-16x20in) s. prov. 29-Jun-4 Sotheby's, New York #248/R est:12000-18000
£8021 $15000 €11711 Mt. Mckinley (25x20cm-10x8in) s. board prov. 24-Jul-4 Coeur d'Alene, Hayden #29/R est:8000-12000
£9091 $17000 €13273 Cache (25x20cm-10x8in) s. canvas on board prov. 24-Jul-4 Coeur d'Alene, Hayden #30/R est:8000-12000
£9091 $17000 €13273 Mt. McKinley (36x25cm-14x10in) s. board prov. 24-Jul-4 Coeur d'Alene, Hayden #182/R est:10000-15000
£12032 $22500 €17567 Mt. McKinley (51x41cm-20x16in) s. canvas on board prov. 24-Jul-4 Coeur d'Alene, Hayden #32/R est:15000-25000
£12032 $22500 €17567 Northern lights with cabin (41x51cm-16x20in) s. board prov. 24-Jul-4 Coeur d'Alene, Hayden #183/R est:15000-25000
£12032 $22500 €17567 Chi pot (25x20cm-10x8in) canvas on board prov. 24-Jul-4 Coeur d'Alene, Hayden #184/R est:8000-12000
£13369 $25000 €19519 Alaska trail (41x51cm-16x20in) s. prov. 24-Jul-4 Coeur d'Alene, Hayden #233/R est:15000-25000
£13587 $25000 €19837 Rapids of the Tokositna River (55x71cm-22x28in) s. painted 1925 prov. 8-Jun-4 Bonhams & Butterfields, San Francisco #4120/R est:25000-35000
£14706 $27500 €21471 Night's fuel (36x51cm-14x20in) s. prov.exhib.lit. 24-Jul-4 Coeur d'Alene, Hayden #28/R est:15000-25000
£16043 $30000 €23423 Mt. McKinley (71x56cm-28x22in) s. prov. 24-Jul-4 Coeur d'Alene, Hayden #27/R est:30000-50000
£20053 $37500 €29277 Dawn, Mt. McKinley (61x81cm-24x32in) s. prov. 24-Jul-4 Coeur d'Alene, Hayden #187/R est:30000-50000
£20231 $35000 €29537 Mount McKinley from the headwaters of the Tokachutna river (51x38cm-20x15in) painted 1920 prov. 10-Dec-3 Bonhams & Butterfields, San Francisco #6116/R est:30000-50000
£22727 $42500 €33181 Golden north (41x51cm-16x20in) s. canvas on board prov.lit. 24-Jul-4 Coeur d'Alene, Hayden #186/R est:15000-25000

£23121	$40000	€33757	Boat rounding Fire Island (41x51cm-16x20in) s. prov. 10-Dec-3 Bonhams & Butterfields, San Francisco #6115/R est:30000-50000
£29412	$55000	€42942	Mt. KcKinley (61x51cm-24x20in) s. prov.exhib. 24-Jul-4 Coeur d'Alene, Hayden #234/R est:25000-35000

Works on paper

£380	$707	€555	Venetian bridge with gondolas (66x30cm-26x12in) s. W/C. 4-Mar-4 Mitchells, Cockermouth #845
£400	$744	€584	Venetian Palace with canal to the front (61x43cm-24x17in) s. W/C. 4-Mar-4 Mitchells, Cockermouth #844

LAURENCIN, Marie (1885-1956) French

£8099	$14011	€11500	Paysage (21x26cm-8x10in) s. painted c.1940 prov.exhib.lit. 13-Dec-3 Martinot & Savignat, Pontoise #244/R est:12000-15000
£9341	$17000	€13638	Jeune femme au chapeau (27x22cm-11x9in) s. board prov.lit. 29-Jun-4 Sotheby's, New York #329/R est:10000-15000
£12752	$23718	€19000	Portrait d'Elizabeth Baudry (46x38cm-18x15in) s. prov.exhib. 2-Mar-4 Artcurial Briest, Paris #206/R est:20000-25000
£15351	$28246	€22412	Portrait of a girl (33x24cm-13x9in) s. i.verso panel lit. 23-Jun-4 Koller, Zurich #3027/R est:30000-45000 (S.FR 35000)
£16000	$29440	€23360	Bouquet of flowers (54x65cm-21x26in) s. prov. 22-Jun-4 Sotheby's, London #286/R est:18000-25000
£18235	$31000	€26623	Melancolie (46x38cm-18x15in) s.d.1921 prov.exhib.lit. 5-Nov-3 Christie's, Rockefeller NY #278/R est:40000-60000
£18824	$32000	€27483	Femme a la robe verte (41x33cm-16x13in) s.d.1933 prov.lit. 5-Nov-3 Christie's, Rockefeller NY #298/R est:30000-40000
£20588	$35000	€30058	Tete de femme aux perles (34x27cm-13x11in) s. prov. 5-Nov-3 Christie's, Rockefeller NY #269/R est:40000-60000
£22000	$40480	€32120	Tete de femme (27x21cm-11x8in) s. panel painted c.1909 prov.lit. 22-Jun-4 Sotheby's, London #278/R est:12000-15000
£23529	$40000	€34352	Brigitte Sourdel (61x50cm-24x20in) s. painted c.1923 prov.lit. 6-Nov-3 Sotheby's, New York #327/R est:30000-40000
£27933	$50000	€40782	Two women (38x47cm-15x19in) s. 5-May-4 Christie's, Rockefeller NY #335/R est:50000-70000
£30000	$55200	€43800	La lecture (34x26cm-13x10in) s. painted c.1950 prov.lit. 23-Jun-4 Christie's, London #192/R est:30000-40000
£37417	$68099	€56500	Mere et enfant (46x38cm-18x15in) s. prov. 18-Jun-4 Piasa, Paris #33/R est:55000-60000
£39106	$70000	€57095	Deux jeunes filles (41x33cm-16x13in) s. prov. 6-May-4 Sotheby's, New York #472/R est:50000-70000
£41176	$70000	€60117	Portrait d'Agathe (54x46cm-21x18in) s. prov. 6-Nov-3 Sotheby's, New York #332/R est:40000-60000
£42000	$77280	€61320	Nicole Groult (41x33cm-16x13in) s.d.1931 prov.exhib.lit. 22-Jun-4 Sotheby's, London #281/R est:40000-60000
£47486	$85000	€69330	Trois femmes et deux chiens (46x55cm-18x22in) s. painted 1943 prov. 6-May-4 Sotheby's, New York #448/R est:70000-90000
£52001	$95682	€78000	Jeune fille aux cheveux noues d'un ruban rouge (55x46cm-22x18in) s. prov. 9-Jun-4 Tajan, Paris #51/R est:60000-80000
£58000	$105560	€84680	Deux filles (41x33cm-16x13in) s. i.stretcher prov. 4-Feb-4 Sotheby's, London #312/R est:30000-40000
£58000	$106720	€84680	Jeune fille a la chevlure fleurie (64x53cm-25x21in) s. painted c.1937. 23-Jun-4 Christie's, London #230/R est:60000-80000
£130000	$236600	€189800	Trois femmes avec fleurs (46x38cm-18x15in) s. painted 1949 prov.lit. 3-Feb-4 Christie's, London #264/R est:100000-150000
£230000	$418600	€335800	La poetesse Marguerite Gillot (81x64cm-32x25in) painted 1912 prov.exhib.lit. 3-Feb-4 Christie's, London #219/R est:120000-160000

Prints

£1724	$2879	€2500	Biches (20x26cm-8x10in) s. num.60/70 eau forte lit. 13-Nov-3 Finarte Semenzato, Rome #102/R est:2500-3000
£2000	$3680	€3000	Portrait d'Alice (19x23cm-7x9in) lithograph exec.1930. 10-Jun-4 Piasa, Paris #154
£2394	$4142	€3400	La premiere voiture Renault (34x29cm-13x11in) s. col lithograph vellum. 11-Dec-3 Piasa, Paris #75/R

Works on paper

£268	$499	€400	Jeune fille assise (18x13cm-7x5in) st.init. graphite prov. 2-Mar-4 Artcurial Briest, Paris #37
£294	$499	€420	Toujours fidele (12x9cm-5x4in) init.i. i.verso graphite col crayon. 27-Nov-3 Millon & Associes, Paris #39
£315	$535	€450	Petit chien (15x10cm-6x4in) init. graphite. 27-Nov-3 Millon & Associes, Paris #38
£350	$594	€500	Femme de profil (12x8cm-5x3in) blue ink. 27-Nov-3 Millon & Associes, Paris #36
£350	$594	€500	Chien et chat (13x9cm-5x4in) init. felt pen. 27-Nov-3 Millon & Associes, Paris #42
£385	$654	€550	Femme de trois quart (10x14cm-4x6in) felt pen ink. 27-Nov-3 Millon & Associes, Paris #48
£490	$832	€700	Visage de femme (9x14cm-4x6in) i. felt pen. 27-Nov-3 Millon & Associes, Paris #34
£734	$1248	€1050	Jeune femme de profil (15x10cm-6x4in) graphite col crayon. 27-Nov-3 Millon & Associes, Paris #50
£769	$1308	€1100	Portrait de femme (10x14cm-4x6in) ink felt pen sold with another similar. 27-Nov-3 Millon & Associes, Paris #53
£1049	$1783	€1500	Portrait de femme (15x10cm-6x4in) init. graphite col crayon. 27-Nov-3 Millon & Associes, Paris #23/R est:800-1000
£1119	$1902	€1600	Profil de femme au chapeau (12x9cm-5x4in) graphite col crayon. 27-Nov-3 Millon & Associes, Paris #25/R est:800-1000
£1119	$1902	€1600	La femme au chale bleu (12x9cm-5x4in) W/C graphite col crayon. 27-Nov-3 Millon & Associes, Paris #27 est:800-1000
£1250	$2300	€1900	Jeune fille a la lecture (26x21cm-10x8in) s. graphite. 28-Jun-4 Rossini, Paris #75/R est:1500-2000
£1259	$2140	€1800	Portrait de jeune homme (15x10cm-6x4in) init.i. graphite. 27-Nov-3 Millon & Associes, Paris #30 est:400-500
£1329	$2259	€1900	Profil de jeune fille (29x24cm-11x9in) col crayon graphite. 27-Nov-3 Millon & Associes, Paris #55 est:1000-1500
£1397	$2500	€2040	Tete de jeune fille avec un noeud papillon rose (17x13cm-7x5in) s. pencil col pencil prov. 6-May-4 Doyle, New York #113/R est:1500-2500
£1399	$2378	€2000	Ange. Etude de chiens (11x11cm-4x4in) init. graphite col crayon pair. 27-Nov-3 Millon & Associes, Paris #56a est:400-600
£1469	$2497	€2100	Portrait de femme (12x8cm-5x3in) i.d.7 fevrier ink sold with another similar. 27-Nov-3 Millon & Associes, Paris #46 est:800-1000
£1538	$2615	€2200	Visage de femme (12x8cm-5x3in) init.i. graphite col crayon. 27-Nov-3 Millon & Associes, Paris #28 est:600-800
£1538	$2615	€2200	Portrait de femme (12x9cm-5x4in) init.i. graphite col crayon. 27-Nov-3 Millon & Associes, Paris #29 est:500-600
£1608	$2734	€2300	Le chat sauvage. Un oiseau qui se tait (12x9cm-5x4in) init.i. graphite col crayon pair. 27-Nov-3 Millon & Associes, Paris #44/R est:1000-1500
£1700	$2941	€2482	Jeune fille au chapeau (24x19cm-9x7in) st.init.d.19 Juillet 1953 pencil col ink prov.exhib. 11-Dec-3 Christie's, Kensington #60/R est:1000-1500
£1828	$3400	€2669	Les deux Espagnoles (10x7cm-4x3in) s.d.1915 W/C pencil cardstock. 2-Mar-4 Swann Galleries, New York #341/R est:1500-2500
£1888	$3210	€2700	La petite fille (15x10cm-6x4in) init.i. graphite col crayon. 27-Nov-3 Millon & Associes, Paris #24/R est:800-1000
£1888	$3210	€2700	Portrait de femme (17x12cm-7x5in) i. graphite col crayon. 27-Nov-3 Millon & Associes, Paris #43 est:800-1000
£1958	$3329	€2800	Portrait de jeune femme (11x8cm-4x3in) init. graphite col crayon. 27-Nov-3 Millon & Associes, Paris #26/R est:800-1000
£2013	$3725	€3000	Fillette et petit chien (12x9cm-5x4in) W/C. 14-Mar-4 Eric Pillon, Calais #95/R
£2168	$3685	€3100	Portrait de jeune femme (8x10cm-3x4in) init. W/C ink graphite. 27-Nov-3 Millon & Associes, Paris #33/R est:1000-1200
£2300	$4232	€3358	Portrait (14x12cm-6x5in) init. pencil col crayons. 24-Mar-4 Sotheby's, Olympia #142/R est:2000-3000
£2448	$4161	€3500	Portrait de jeune fille. s. chl col crayon. 28-Nov-3 Blanchet, Paris #99/R est:4000-5000
£2517	$4280	€3600	Les deux amies (29x24cm-11x9in) i.d.49 col crayon. 27-Nov-3 Millon & Associes, Paris #56 est:1000-1500
£2535	$4386	€3600	Jeune fille assise (12x9cm-5x4in) W/C. 14-Dec-3 Eric Pillon, Calais #137/R
£2596	$4700	€3790	Portrait of girl (43x36cm-17x14in) s. gouache. 16-Apr-4 James Julia, Fairfield #973/R est:300-500
£2603	$4425	€3800	Portrait de femme au collier de perles (12x10cm-5x4in) W/C. 9-Nov-3 Eric Pillon, Calais #82/R
£2603	$4425	€3800	Portrait de jeune fille aux tresses rouges (12x9cm-5x4in) W/C. 9-Nov-3 Eric Pillon, Calais #81/R
£3000	$5010	€4380	Head of a young girl (31x23cm-12x9in) s. pencil col crayon prov.exhib. 22-Oct-3 Sotheby's, Olympia #18/R est:3000-5000
£4196	$7133	€6000	Portrait de jeune fille (15x9cm-6x4in) s.d.1953 W/C. 18-Nov-3 Sotheby's, Paris #14/R est:7000-10000
£5689	$9500	€8306	Woman with yellow drape (30x25cm-12x10in) s. W/C. 7-Oct-3 Sotheby's, New York #259 est:10000-15000
£6333	$11463	€9500	Jeune femme au chapeau (24x16cm-9x6in) s. W/C prov. 4-Apr-4 St-Germain-en-Laye Encheres #15/R est:7000-7500
£6667	$12200	€10000	Jeune fille au chapeau (31x24cm-12x9in) s. i. verso W/C on pencil prov. 5-Jun-4 Lempertz, Koln #816/R est:10000
£6704	$12000	€9788	Jeune fille a la guitare (34x25cm-13x10in) s.i. W/C over pencil. 5-May-4 Christie's, Rockefeller NY #144/R est:12000-16000
£8000	$14720	€11680	Jeune fille rousse en bleu (24x19cm-9x7in) s. W/C over pencil prov.lit. 22-Jun-4 Sotheby's, London #433/R est:8000-12000
£8021	$15000	€11711	Femme accoudee (18x14cm-7x6in) s. W/C over pencil prov. 25-Feb-4 Christie's, Rockefeller NY #75/R est:5000-7000
£8500	$15640	€12410	Three young girls (33x25cm-13x10in) s. W/C pencil prov.exhib. 24-Jun-4 Christie's, London #351/R est:8000-12000
£8939	$16000	€13051	Jeune fille aux lauriers (34x25cm-13x10in) s. W/C prov. 6-May-4 Sotheby's, New York #467/R est:15000-20000
£9000	$16560	€13140	L'Espagnole a l'eventail (24x19cm-9x7in) s. gouache pen ink prov. 24-Jun-4 Christie's, London #350/R est:8000-12000
£9155	$15838	€13000	Portrait de jeune fille (29x25cm-11x10in) s. W/C. 14-Dec-3 Eric Pillon, Calais #101/R
£9730	$18000	€14206	Femme a la mantille (30x25cm-12x10in) s. W/C prov. 11-Feb-4 Sotheby's, New York #61/R est:8000-12000
£10056	$18000	€14682	Trois femmes (25x34cm-10x13in) s. W/C pencil. 6-May-4 Sotheby's, New York #466/R est:15000-20000
£10596	$19285	€16000	Jeune fille a la guitare (35x27cm-14x11in) s. W/C. 18-Jun-4 Piasa, Paris #28/R est:15000-20000
£11404	$20982	€16650	Jeune fille au voile bleu (37x28cm-15x11in) s. prov.lit. 23-Jun-4 Koller, Zurich #3026/R est:20000-30000 (S.FR 26000)
£11987	$21816	€18100	Jeune femme et jeune fille aupres d'un rideau rose (28x37cm-11x15in) s. W/C paper on cardboard prov.lit. 18-Jun-4 Piasa, Paris #29/R est:10000-12000
£13500	$24570	€19710	Odalisque aux perles et son amie (26x34cm-10x13in) s. W/C pencil prov.lit. 4-Feb-4 Sotheby's, London #448/R est:15000-20000
£14000	$25760	€20440	Princesse et sa suivante dans la foret (38x28cm-15x11in) s. W/C pen ink over pencil prov.lit. 22-Jun-4 Sotheby's, London #520/R est:15000-20000

LAURENDEAU, A (20th C) ?

£1061	$1900	€1592	Nature morte of game bird's in landscape (74x46cm-29x18in) s. 29-May-4 Brunk, Ashville #564/R

LAURENS, Camille Adolphe (1870-1934) French

£2128	$3553	€3000	Dans le parc (46x38cm-18x15in) s. 16-Jun-3 Gros & Delettrez, Paris #528/R est:2500-3000

LAURENS, Hedwig von (1872-?) German

Works on paper

£2238	$3804	€3200	Femme allongee (15x22cm-6x9in) s.i. Indian ink exec.c.1950 prov. 23-Nov-3 Cornette de St.Cyr, Paris #214/R est:100-150

LAURENS, Henri (1885-1954) French

£65000	$108550	€94900	Tete de boxeur (25x25cm-10x10in) i.verso painted terracotta tile prov.exhib.lit. 21-Oct-3 Sotheby's, London #48/R est:40000-60000

Sculpture

£17877	$32000	€26100	Femme couchee (39cm-15in) num.6/8 verso brown pat bronze relief conceived 1921 prov.lit. 5-May-4 Christie's, Rockefeller NY #284/R est:30000-40000
£18000	$32760	€26280	Femme drapee (48cm-19in) mono. num.HL4 terracotta conceived 1924 lit. 3-Feb-4 Christie's, London #205/R est:18000-24000
£19737	$36316	€30000	Petite baigneuse (31cm-12in) st.f.Valsuani pat bronze lit. 25-Jun-4 Millon & Associes, Paris #240/R est:30000-40000
£20000	$35800	€30000	Reclining girl with arms raised (11x10x27cm-4x4x11in) mono. bronze Cast.C.Valsuani prov.lit. 15-May-4 Van Ham, Cologne #748/R est:35000
£23205	$41769	€33879	The sleeping woman (13x27cm-5x11in) init.num.5 terracotta. 26-Apr-4 Bukowskis, Stockholm #262/R est:150000-175000 (S.KR 320000)
£24615	$42338	€35938	Femme nue a la mandoline (15x19cm-6x7in) terracotta prov.exhib.lit. exec.c.1919. 2-Dec-3 Bukowskis, Stockholm #240a/R est:175000-200000 (S.KR 320000)
£26106	$46991	€38115	Le compotier (38x35cm-15x14in) num.1/7 terracotta relief. 26-Apr-4 Bukowskis, Stockholm #263/R est:150000-175000 (S.KR 360000)
£27556	$49601	€40232	Deux femmes (20x24cm-8x9in) init.num.8/8 terracotta prov.lit. 26-Apr-4 Bukowskis, Stockholm #265/R est:400000-425000 (S.KR 380000)
£30211	$51360	€44108	Femme debout au miroir (28cm-11in) init.num.2/6 pat.bronze prov.exhib.lit. 5-Nov-3 AB Stockholms Auktionsverk #1086/R est:500000-600000 (S.KR 400000)
£31469	$54126	€45000	Femme accroupie (21x16x12cm-8x6x5in) terracotta one of 6 prov.exhib.lit. 8-Dec-3 Artcurial Briest, Paris #21/R est:50000-80000

£38235 $65000 €55823 Femme debout (45cm-18in) init. num.1/6 terracotta conceived 1930. 6-Nov-3 Sotheby's, New York #207/R est:50000-70000
£40667 $74826 €61000 Femme debout au miroir (28cm-11in) mono. num.2/6 black pat bronze prov.lit. 8-Jun-4 Artcurial Briest, Paris #178/R est:40000-50000
Works on paper
£2416 $4325 €3600 Femme allongee (12x16cm-5x6in) mono. pencil. 25-May-4 Dorotheum, Vienna #44/R est:3600-5000
£2500 $4600 €3650 Nu allonge (14x22cm-6x9in) s.i. pen ink. 24-Mar-4 Sotheby's, Olympia #133/R est:3000-4000
£18000 $30060 €26280 Instruments de musique (18x23cm-7x9in) s.d.17 W/C pen ink pencil prov.exhib. 21-Oct-3 Sotheby's, London #53/R est:20000-30000
£35294 $60000 €51529 Nature morte a la Mandoline (25x20cm-10x8in) s.d.18 blk crayon col paper collage prov. 6-Nov-3 Sotheby's, New York #209/R est:35000-45000
£54931 $96128 €78000 Homme a la pipe. init.d.1919 gouache crayon prov. 18-Dec-3 Tajan, Paris #28/R est:80000-100000
£88235 $150000 €195000 Composition (22x24cm-9x9in) s.d.18 gouache W/C lit. 25-Nov-3 Pierre Berge, Paris #10/R est:80000-100000

LAURENS, Jean Joseph Bonaventure (1801-1890) French
Works on paper
£252 $403 €350 Woman in a landscape scene (25x18cm-10x7in) s. blk crayon W/C gouache beige paper. 16-May-3 Tajan, Paris #157
£533 $965 €800 Le Gardon et le Pont du Gard (9x29cm-4x11in) mono.i.d.1871 W/C lit. 30-Mar-4 Rossini, Paris #1022/R

LAURENS, Jean Joseph Bonaventure (attrib) (1801-1890) French
Works on paper
£250 $460 €365 Figures by a triumphal arch (16x24cm-6x9in) s.d.1837 pencil W/C. 25-Mar-4 Christie's, Kensington #11

LAURENS, Jean Pierre (1875-1932) French
£552 $921 €800 Portrait de jeune fille (35x27cm-14x11in) mono. panel. 11-Nov-3 Lesieur & Le Bars, Le Havre #145

LAURENS, Jules Joseph Augustin (1825-1901) French
£20000 $33400 €29200 Meeting house in Teheran (73x91cm-29x36in) s.d.1863. 14-Oct-3 Sotheby's, London #44/R est:20000-30000
Works on paper
£367 $664 €550 Teheran, Doulab-Capou (21x31cm-8x12in) s.i.d.29 mars 1948 graphite brown wash exhib. 30-Mar-4 Rossini, Paris #1023

LAURENT, Bruno Émile (1928-) French
£530 $964 €800 Le lapin agile (54x65cm-21x26in) s. 18-Jun-4 Charbonneaux, Paris #174
Works on paper
£278 $506 €420 Montmartre, rue du Chevalier de la Barre (50x60cm-20x24in) s. gouache. 18-Jun-4 Charbonneaux, Paris #102
£310 $518 €450 Le lapin agile a Montmartre (45x59cm-18x23in) s. gouache paper on cardboard. 17-Nov-3 Charbonneaux, Paris #143

LAURENT, E (?) ?
Sculpture
£921 $1500 €1345 Figure of a young girl (67x20x20cm-26x8x8in) s. bronze. 28-Sep-3 Bonhams & Butterfields, Los Angeles #7577 est:1800-2250

LAURENT, Ernest Joseph (1859-1929) French
£1007 $1652 €1400 Paysage Mediterraneen (24x35cm-9x14in) s.i.d.1919 panel. 3-Jun-3 Livinec, Gaudcheau & Jezequel, Rennes #51/R
£2551 $4515 €3800 Age d'or (68x123cm-27x48in) mono. en grisaille. 30-Apr-4 Tajan, Paris #173/R est:3000-4000
Works on paper
£385 $642 €550 Etude de figure (42x32cm-17x13in) studio st. chl dr. 7-Oct-3 Livinec, Gaudcheau & Jezequel, Rennes #127

LAURENT, François-Nicolas (?-1828) French
£4000 $6800 €5840 Still life of grapes, peaches and flowers hanging from a rope (55x46cm-22x18in) s. 30-Oct-3 Sotheby's, Olympia #178/R est:4000-6000

LAURENT, Georges H (20th C) French
Sculpture
£2400 $4392 €3600 Leaping stag (49x58cm-19x23in) i. bronze black marble base. 3-Jun-4 Sotheby's, Olympia #246/R est:1800-2500

LAURENT, Jean (1906-) French
£324 $581 €480 Seascape with sailing boats and village church on shore (24x49cm-9x19in) s. panel. 6-May-4 Michael Zeller, Lindau #753
£403 $749 €600 Seascape with yacht near stockade (30x40cm-12x16in) s. panel. 8-Mar-4 Bernaerts, Antwerp #262/R
£460 $731 €667 Shipping off the coast (40x50cm-16x20in) s. panel. 9-Sep-3 David Duggleby, Scarborough #344
£704 $1218 €1000 Quais de Rabat (33x45cm-13x18in) s. canvas on cardboard. 15-Dec-3 Gros & Delettrez, Paris #45
£1900 $3420 €2774 Dutch ships off the coast (30x40cm-12x16in) s. set of three panel. 21-Jan-4 Sotheby's, Olympia #370/R est:1000-1500
£2600 $4680 €3796 Merchant ships off the coast (40x56cm-16x22in) s. set of three. 21-Jan-4 Sotheby's, Olympia #369/R est:1500-2000

LAURENT, Jean Antoine (1763-1832) French
£600 $1080 €900 La mariee (14x10cm-6x4in) s. panel. 20-Apr-4 Galerie Moderne, Brussels #378/R
Miniatures
£1300 $2327 €1898 Marquis de Chieza in blue coat (6cm-2in circular) s. gilt metal mount. 25-May-4 Christie's, London #212/R est:800-1200
£2270 $3791 €3200 Portrait de femme tenant un livre (14x14cm-6x6in) s. gilt frame. 23-Jun-3 Tajan, Paris #127 est:1500-2000
£4600 $7820 €6716 Sir Charles Hugh Lowther (14cm-6in) s.verso. 18-Nov-3 Bonhams, New Bond Street #157/R est:3000-5000

LAURENT, John Louis (1921-) American
£1852 $3000 €2685 Laurent farm (36x81cm-14x32in) s. board prov. 8-Aug-3 Barridorf, Portland #236/R est:3000-5000

LAURENT, P (?) ?
£1793 $3317 €2600 Bouc et moutons dans un paysage (75x100cm-30x39in) s.d.1864. 19-Jan-4 Horta, Bruxelles #226 est:1800-2200

LAURENT, Robert (1890-1970) American
Sculpture
£2703 $5000 €3946 Female nude (26cm-10in) s. parcel gilt pat bronze black marble base. 11-Mar-4 Christie's, Rockefeller NY #101/R est:6000-8000

LAURENT-GSELL, Lucien (1860-1944) French
£1067 $1909 €1600 Paysage avec maison. s. 15-May-4 other European Auctioneer #60

LAURENTI, Cesare (1854-1937) Italian
£3779 $6500 €5517 Flirting by the canal (224x170cm-88x67in) s. board. 2-Dec-3 Christie's, Rockefeller NY #50/R est:7000-9000
£8939 $16000 €13051 Peasant family at home (107x77cm-42x30in) s. 6-May-4 Doyle, New York #49/R est:15000-25000

LAURENTI, Nicola (1873-1943) Italian
£268 $475 €400 Landscape in Lombardy (35x50cm-14x20in) s.d.1931 board. 1-May-4 Meeting Art, Vercelli #289
£490 $817 €700 Boats on the lake (25x31cm-10x12in) s. board. 26-Jun-3 Sant Agostino, Torino #87/R

LAURER, Johann (1892-1949) Austrian
£347 $566 €500 Still life (59x69cm-23x27in) tempera board. 23-Sep-3 Wiener Kunst Auktionen, Vienna #95/R

LAURET, Emmanuel Joseph (1809-1882) French
£464 $848 €700 Portrait de dame (103x84cm-41x33in) s.d.1854. 9-Apr-4 Claude Aguttes, Neuilly #129
£1060 $1939 €1600 Village Oriental (19x26cm-7x10in) s. cardboard. 9-Apr-4 Claude Aguttes, Neuilly #128/R est:1200-1500
£1268 $2218 €1800 Jeune garcon aux anes (26x19cm-10x7in) s.d.1857 cardboard prov. 16-Dec-3 Claude Aguttes, Neuilly #48/R est:2000-3000
£1667 $2750 €2400 Cavaliers Arabes (18x24cm-7x9in) s.i. one d.1851 cardboard pair. 3-Jul-3 Claude Aguttes, Neuilly #118 est:3000-4000
£2817 $4930 €4000 Jeune danseuse Oriental et jeune Oriental sur la terrasse (30x20cm-12x8in) s. cardboard pair prov. 16-Dec-3 Claude Aguttes, Neuilly #53/R est:4000-5000
£2837 $4738 €4000 Jeune femme dans un interieur (24x19cm-9x7in) s.d.1851 cardboard. 16-Jun-3 Gros & Delettrez, Paris #112/R est:2200-4000

LAUREUS, Alexander (1783-1823) Swedish
£3462 $5954 €5055 Figures by open fire on the beach (60x80cm-24x31in) 2-Dec-3 Bukowskis, Stockholm #429/R est:50000-60000 (S.KR 45000)

LAUREYS, Armand (1867-?) Belgian
£270 $511 €400 Jeune femme devant son chevalet (35x26cm-14x10in) s. cardboard. 17-Feb-4 Vanderkindere, Brussels #21

LAURI, Filippo (1623-1694) Italian
£3000 $5490 €4380 King Midas judging the musical contest between Apollo and Pan (13x21cm-5x8in) copper oval. 6-Jul-4 Sotheby's, Olympia #520/R est:3000-4000
£6500 $11700 €9490 Madonna and Child appearing to Saint Francis of Assisi (13x17cm-5x7in) copper. 21-Apr-4 Christie's, London #73/R est:6000-8000

LAURI, Filippo (attrib) (1623-1694) Italian
£4605 $8474 €7000 Martyrdom of Saint Catherine. Fall of the rebellious angels (15x11cm-6x4in) copper oval pair prov. 24-Jun-4 Christie's, Paris #60/R est:7000-10000

LAURI, Filippo (circle) (1623-1694) Italian
£5000 $8650 €7300 Venus and Cupid surprised by a satyr (29cm-11in circular) canvas on panel. 10-Dec-3 Bonhams, New Bond Street #57/R est:4000-6000

LAURIE, Hamish (?) British
£260 $442 €380 Cliffs and surf (36x46cm-14x18in) s. board. 10-Nov-3 Thomson Roddick & Medcalf, Edinburgh #217
£520 $957 €759 Flowers at Kirkapol, Isle of Tiree (50x60cm-20x24in) s. board. 29-Mar-4 Thomson Roddick & Medcalf, Edinburgh #224/R

LAURIE, Hamish (attrib) (?) British
£350 $595 €511 Vase of flowers. board. 10-Nov-3 Thomson Roddick & Medcalf, Edinburgh #218

LAURIOZ, Patrice (1959-) French
£775 $1340 €1100 Marche de Ouargla (61x120cm-24x47in) s. i.verso. 15-Dec-3 Gros & Delettrez, Paris #419/R

£780 $1303 €1100 Troupeau dans le Sud de l'Atlas, Maroc (60x81cm-24x32in) s. s.i.verso panel. 16-Jun-3 Gros & Delettrez, Paris #329/R
£1489 $2487 €2100 Vue de Fes (61x81cm-24x32in) s.i. s.verso panel. 16-Jun-3 Gros & Delettrez, Paris #328/R est:1500-2300
£1844 $3079 €2600 Menace d'orage sur le Djebel Sarhro, region d'El Kelaa M'Gouma, Maroc (60x73cm-24x29in) s. 16-Jun-3 Gros & Delettrez, Paris #339/R est:2300-3000
£2837 $4738 €4000 Personnages devant les remparts de Fes (50x62cm-20x24in) s. i.verso. 16-Jun-3 Gros & Delettrez, Paris #340/R est:2000-3000
£3262 $5448 €4600 Place du marche a Ouargla (96x114cm-38x45in) s. s.i.verso. 16-Jun-3 Gros & Delettrez, Paris #331/R est:3000-4500

LAURITZ, Paul (1889-1975) American
£441 $750 €644 Virginia barn (61x86cm-24x34in) s. prov.exhib. 29-Oct-3 Christie's, Los Angeles #28/R
£471 $800 €688 Laguna tide pools (61x76cm-24x30in) s. i.verso wood panel prov. 18-Nov-3 John Moran, Pasadena #171
£735 $1250 €1073 Fjord in Norway (61x91cm-24x36in) s. board prov. 18-Nov-3 John Moran, Pasadena #134
£1099 $2000 €1605 Mojave Desert landscape (36x41cm-14x16in) s. canvasboard prov. 15-Jun-4 John Moran, Pasadena #16 est:3000-4000
£1471 $2500 €2148 After the storm (56x71cm-22x28in) s. i.verso canvas on canvas. 18-Nov-3 John Moran, Pasadena #105a est:2000-3000
£1648 $3000 €2406 High Sierras landscape (64x76cm-25x30in) s. prov. 15-Jun-4 John Moran, Pasadena #154 est:2500-3500
£1734 $3000 €2532 Kingman Mountains, Arizona (31x38cm-12x15in) canvasboard. 10-Dec-3 Bonhams & Butterfields, San Francisco #6320/R est:3000-5000
£1879 $3250 €2743 Verdant Hills (61x86cm-24x34in) s. prov. 10-Dec-3 Bonhams & Butterfields, San Francisco #6321/R est:4000-6000
£2023 $3500 €2954 Oak Creek Canyon, Arizona (61x86cm-24x34in) s. i.stretcher prov. 10-Dec-3 Bonhams & Butterfields, San Francisco #6322/R est:4000-6000
£2116 $4000 €3089 Desert clouds (46x51cm-18x20in) s. board prov. 17-Feb-4 John Moran, Pasadena #103/R est:4000-5000
£2941 $5000 €4294 Morning light, Grand Canyon, Arizona (61x86cm-24x34in) s. i.verso prov. 18-Nov-3 John Moran, Pasadena #132 est:4000-6000
£4706 $8000 €6871 River landscape (51x61cm-20x24in) s. 18-Nov-3 John Moran, Pasadena #94 est:5000-7000
£4762 $9000 €6953 Landscape High Sierras (61x66cm-24x26in) s. prov. 17-Feb-4 John Moran, Pasadena #64/R est:7000-9000
£10582 $20000 €15450 Houses in landscape (81x91cm-32x36in) s.i. verso prov. 17-Feb-4 John Moran, Pasadena #57/R est:12000-18000
Works on paper
£375 $600 €548 Stormy seascape (84x130cm-33x51in) s. W/C. 18-May-3 Auctions by the Bay, Alameda #1106/R
£1059 $1800 €1546 Atmospheric landscape (51x66cm-20x26in) s. W/C prov. 18-Nov-3 John Moran, Pasadena #174 est:1000-2000

LAUTERBURG, Martin (1891-1960) Swiss
£345 $617 €504 Landscape with large farmstead (51x75cm-20x30in) s.d.51. 12-May-4 Dobiaschofsky, Bern #728/R (S.FR 800)
£529 $899 €772 Studio still life (110x180cm-43x71in) 5-Nov-3 Dobiaschofsky, Bern #3552 (S.FR 1200)

LAUTERS, Guillaume (19/20th C) Belgian
£433 $776 €650 Paysage (60x40cm-24x16in) s. 11-May-4 Vanderkindere, Brussels #586

LAUTERS, Paul (1806-1876) Belgian
£1034 $1914 €1500 Pecheur en barque (60x80cm-24x31in) s. 13-Jan-4 Vanderkindere, Brussels #21 est:1250-1750

LAUTERS, Paul and MADOU, Jean Baptiste (19th C) Belgian
£6207 $11483 €9000 La diseuse de bonne aventure (76x68cm-30x27in) s. panel. 16-Feb-4 Horta, Bruxelles #192/R est:10000-12000

LAUTOUR, Tony de (20th C) New Zealander
£420 $764 €613 Crawl (20x30cm-8x12in) s.i.d.1997. 29-Jun-4 Peter Webb, Auckland #7/R est:1200-1800 (NZ.D 1200)
£484 $867 €707 Hearts, crosses, stars and skulls (30x44cm-12x17in) init.d.1995 prov. 12-May-4 Dunbar Sloane, Wellington #4/R est:2000-3000 (NZ.D 1400)
£603 $1115 €880 Three lions (45x35cm-18x14in) s.d.2000. 13-Jul-4 Watson's, Christchurch #38/R est:1800-3500 (NZ.D 1700)
£1250 $2263 €1825 Double cross (100x70cm-39x28in) i. s.d.1987 verso. 30-Mar-4 Peter Webb, Auckland #127/R est:3500-5000 (NZ.D 3500)
£1453 $2601 €2121 Sweet white dreams (123x105cm-48x41in) s.d.1994 verso. 11-May-4 Watson's, Christchurch #18/R est:4000-6000 (NZ.D 4200)
£5594 $10182 €8167 X (120x120cm-47x47in) s.d.2003 exhib. 29-Jun-4 Peter Webb, Auckland #47/R est:16000-19000 (NZ.D 16000)
Works on paper
£347 $552 €507 Hunter of hunted (88cm-35in) mixed media gun shaped. 1-May-3 Dunbar Sloane, Wellington #19a/R est:2000-3000 (NZ.D 1000)

LAUTOUR, Tony de and ROBINSON, Peter (20th C) New Zealander
£2799 $4841 €4087 Hate (60x120cm-24x47in) s. acrylic board. 9-Dec-3 Peter Webb, Auckland #73/R est:7000-9000 (NZ.D 7500)
Works on paper
£1119 $2036 €1634 Kiwi pecking bone (21x45cm-8x18in) i. s.d.1993 verso mixed media on board. 29-Jun-4 Peter Webb, Auckland #141/R est:3500-4500 (NZ.D 3200)

LAUVRAY, Abel (1870-1950) French
£493 $853 €700 Bouquet (27x34cm-11x13in) s. oil paper on canvas. 10-Dec-3 Rossini, Paris #86/R
£528 $914 €750 Paysage (26x41cm-10x16in) s. panel. 13-Dec-3 Touati, Paris #134/R
£563 $975 €800 Arbre en fleurs (27x34cm-11x13in) s. panel. 10-Dec-3 Rossini, Paris #85

LAUWERS, Jacobus Johannes (1753-1800) Belgian
£8000 $14400 €12000 Maid grinding coffee (31x24cm-12x9in) s. panel. 20-Apr-4 Sotheby's, Amsterdam #209/R est:7000-10000

LAUX, August (1847-1921) American
£1075 $2000 €1570 Passing time (46x61cm-18x24in) s. 3-Mar-4 Christie's, Rockefeller NY #16/R est:3000-5000
£1272 $2200 €1857 Leader of the pack (25x38cm-10x15in) s. 13-Dec-3 Sloans & Kenyon, Bethesda #812/R est:2000-3000
£1676 $3000 €2447 Still life with fruit and fly (20x25cm-8x10in) init.d.1888 prov. 6-May-4 Shannon's, Milford #168/R est:3000-5000
£2096 $3500 €3060 Gooseberries on a ledge (25x36cm-10x14in) s. prov. 23-Oct-3 Shannon's, Milford #78/R est:3000-5000

LAVAGNA, Francesco (18th C) Italian
£7383 $13584 €11000 Still life in a garden (75x50cm-30x20in) 27-Mar-4 Farsetti, Prato #327/R est:13000
£15000 $25500 €21900 Roses, narcissi and other flowers in an urn with flower garlands draped on a stone pedestal (178x161cm-70x63in) 29-Oct-3 Christie's, London #64/R est:15000-25000

LAVAGNA, Francesco (attrib) (18th C) Italian
£1000 $1670 €1460 Still life with flowers (34x23cm-13x9in) 7-Oct-3 Bonhams, Knightsbridge #266/R est:1000-1500

LAVAGNA, Francesco (circle) (18th C) Italian
£5500 $10285 €8030 Sliced watermelon, pomegranates and flowers near a stone wall (71x95cm-28x37in) 27-Feb-4 Christie's, Kensington #194/R est:2000-3000
£9220 $15397 €13000 Nature morte au perroquet (97x145cm-38x57in) 23-Jun-3 Ribeyre & Baron, Paris #34/R est:8000-10000

LAVAGNA, Giuseppe (1684-1724) Italian
£6500 $11895 €9490 Carnations, tulips, peonies and other flowers in an urn with other flowers (49x74cm-19x29in) 7-Jul-4 Bonhams, New Bond Street #9/R est:7000-10000
£8453 $14793 €12000 Jetes de roses, pasteque dans un parc (73x93cm-29x37in) 18-Dec-3 Tajan, Paris #9/R est:10000-12000

LAVAGNINO, Pier Luigi (1933-1999) Italian
£1600 $2944 €2400 Forms on golden ground (81x100cm-32x39in) s.d.72 s.i.d.verso prov. 8-Jun-4 Finarte Semenzato, Milan #163/R est:250-300

LAVAL, Fernand (1886-1966) French
£364 $667 €550 Les Puces (73x100cm-29x39in) s. 7-Apr-4 Piasa, Paris #120
£1000 $1820 €1500 Lieutenance a Honfleur (60x73cm-24x29in) s. 4-Jul-4 Eric Pillon, Calais #227/R

LAVALLE, Giovanni (1887-1964) Italian
£586 $973 €850 Still life of fruit (29x49cm-11x19in) s. 1-Oct-3 Della Rocca, Turin #314/R

LAVALLEE, Geeraert de (17th C) Flemish
£3158 $5811 €4800 Eliezer and Rebecca (21x38cm-8x15in) copper. 25-Jun-4 Piasa, Paris #74/R est:6000-8000
£6164 $10479 €9000 Christ and the centurion (92x117cm-36x46in) 4-Nov-3 Sotheby's, Amsterdam #46/R est:10000-15000

LAVALLEE, Geeraert de (attrib) (17th C) Flemish
£4636 $8437 €7000 Appel de Saint-Pierre (23x33cm-9x13in) copper. 15-Jun-4 Claude Aguttes, Neuilly #27/R est:4000-6000

LAVALLEN, Julio (20th C) South American
£704 $1127 €1000 Woman with hat (130x195cm-51x77in) s.d.1989 s.i.d.verso prov. 16-Sep-3 Segre, Madrid #181/R

LAVARENNE, Pierre (?) Canadian?
Works on paper
£1689 $2973 €2500 Pierrot (56x33cm-22x13in) s. pastel col chk exhib. 19-May-4 Sotheby's, Amsterdam #387/R est:1200-1800

LAVAULT, Albert Tibule Furcy de (19th C) French
£6319 $11500 €9226 Still life with roses and a blue fan (124x91cm-49x36in) s.d.1879. 7-Feb-4 Neal Auction Company, New Orleans #395/R est:12000-18000

LAVENSON, Alma R (1897-1989) American
Photographs
£3107 $5500 €4536 Self portrait, hands (17x23cm-7x9in) s. photo printed 1986 prov.lit. 28-Apr-4 Sotheby's, New York #176/R est:6000-8000

LAVENY, J (19th C) British
£1250 $2150 €1825 Wooded landscape with figure before an old cottage (43x58cm-17x23in) s. 5-Dec-3 Keys, Aylsham #614/R est:1500-2000

LAVER, John H (fl.1938) British
£260 $473 €380 Derbyshire farm and landscape (39x54cm-15x21in) s.verso. 15-Jun-4 Bonhams, Leeds #77

LAVERY, Sir John (1856-1941) British
£500 $925 €730 Portrait of Lady Beattie Beaumont (15x13cm-6x5in) 15-Jul-4 Mitchells, Cockermouth #614/R

£11748 $19972 €17152 Portrait of Mrs Rothasay Stuart Wortley (61x51cm-24x20in) s. s.i.d.1930 verso canvasboard prov.lit. 21-Nov-3 Walker's, Ottawa #236/R est:30000-40000 (C.D 26080)
£13500 $24165 €19710 A Moorish Garden, Tangier (25x36cm-10x14in) s. s.i.d.1911 verso canvasboard. 14-May-4 Christie's, London #170/R est:15000-20000
£19014 $32894 €27000 Sketch for unsaddling the Derby winner, 1925 (61x64cm-24x25in) s.i. prov. 10-Dec-3 Bonhams & James Adam, Dublin #133/R est:15000-20000
£23611 $38486 €34000 Miss Pike and Miss Pilkington (50x59cm-20x23in) s. s.i.d.1931 verso board. 24-Sep-3 James Adam, Dublin #53/R est:15000-20000
£25676 $48527 €38000 House tops, Tangier (25x36cm-10x14in) s. i.d.1912 verso board prov. 17-Feb-4 Whyte's, Dublin #57/R est:40000-50000
£27972 $47552 €40000 Angler (25x35cm-10x14in) s.i.d.1911 verso board. 25-Nov-3 De Veres Art Auctions, Dublin #45/R est:40000-60000
£28000 $50120 €40880 A Moorish Madonna (76x63cm-30x25in) s.i.d.1920. 13-May-4 Sotheby's, London #28/R est:30000-40000
£35000 $62650 €51100 Madonna Trinita dei Monti, Rome (35x25cm-14x10in) s.i. s.i.verso canvasboard prov. 13-May-4 Sotheby's, London #23/R est:15000-20000
£38000 $68020 €55480 The Bathing Pool, North Berwick (46x58cm-18x23in) s. s.i.d.1919 verso panel prov. 14-May-4 Christie's, London #38/R est:40000-60000
£46000 $82340 €67160 Portrait of Madame Robert de Billy (76x63cm-30x25in) s.d.1911 s.i.verso exhib.lit. 13-May-4 Sotheby's, London #20/R est:30000-50000
£55944 $95105 €80000 Maison Louis XIV, St Jean de Luz (64x76cm-25x30in) s.i. s.i.d.1917 verso board. 25-Nov-3 De Veres Art Auctions, Dublin #27/R est:60000-80000
£63380 $109648 €90000 St Patrick's purgatory, Lough Derg (50x60cm-20x24in) s. canvasboard exhib. 10-Dec-3 Bonhams & James Adam, Dublin #132/R est:90000-120000
£69930 $118881 €100000 Yellow room (77x64cm-30x25in) s. 25-Nov-3 De Veres Art Auctions, Dublin #70/R est:100000-150000
£70000 $125300 €102200 Portrait of Mrs James v Rank (92x71cm-36x28in) s. s.i.d.1930 verso. 13-May-4 Sotheby's, London #40/R est:40000-60000
£95070 $164472 €135000 Moorish courtyard with figures (51x61cm-20x24in) s. 10-Dec-3 Bonhams & James Adam, Dublin #97/R est:100000-150000
£103521 $179092 €147000 Housetop, evening (56x122cm-22x48in) s. s.i.d.1914 verso exhib.lit. 10-Dec-3 Bonhams & James Adam, Dublin #96/R est:130000-180000
£167598 $300000 €244693 Weighing in at Sandown Park (46x69cm-18x27in) s. prov.exhib. 5-May-4 Sotheby's, New York #34/R est:300000-500000
£260000 $465400 €379600 Sketch of a summer afternoon (29x34cm-11x13in) s.i.d.1884 panel exhib. 13-May-4 Sotheby's, London #13/R est:150000-200000
£320000 $572800 €467200 Lady in red, portrait of Constance Bridges (183x92cm-72x36in) s. s.d.1924 verso. 13-May-4 Sotheby's, London #62/R est:120000-180000
£530000 $948700 €773800 Finale (86x112cm-34x44in) s. 13-May-4 Sotheby's, London #16/R est:400000-600000

Prints
£6040 $10691 €9000 Arthur Griffith. Michael Collins (51x41cm-20x16in) s. by artist and sitter lithograph pair. 27-Apr-4 Whyte's, Dublin #110/R est:3000-4000

Works on paper
£44000 $78760 €64240 Her Sunday best (44x34cm-17x13in) s. W/C bodycol. 14-May-4 Christie's, London #164/R est:30000-50000

LAVERY, Sir John (attrib) (1856-1941) British
£340 $537 €493 Lake scene with hills at sunset (30x38cm-12x15in) canvas on board. 24-Jul-3 Lawrence, Crewkerne #969

LAVES, Werner (1903-1972) German
£833 $1392 €1200 Flats and caravans (70x90cm-28x35in) i. verso panel. 25-Oct-3 Dr Lehr, Berlin #312/R

Works on paper
£430 $671 €680 Still life (47x54cm-19x21in) s. chl chk. 18-Oct-2 Von Zezschwitz, Munich #87/R

LAVIE, Raffi (1937-) Israeli
£2793 $5000 €4078 Untitled (100x81cm-39x32in) s.d.67 oil graphite. 18-Mar-4 Sotheby's, New York #40/R est:5000-7000

LAVIEILLE, Eugène (1820-1889) French
£464 $844 €700 Paysage au crepuscule (27x40cm-11x16in) s. paper on canvas. 18-Jun-4 Piasa, Paris #55
£1485 $2732 €2168 Extensive landscape with village (46x85cm-18x33in) s. 14-Jun-4 Philippe Schuler, Zurich #4311/R est:4000-5000 (S.FR 3400)
£2098 $3608 €3000 La gardeuse d'oies (27x40cm-11x16in) s.d.1874 panel. 7-Dec-3 Osenat, Fontainebleau #55 est:3000-3200
£2174 $3565 €3000 Le plateau de la Mare aux Fees (22x42cm-9x17in) s.d.1845 cardboard. 11-May-3 Osenat, Fontainebleau #24/R est:3200-3500
£3562 $6055 €5200 Vaches en foret de Fontainebleau (82x92cm-32x36in) s. i.verso. 9-Nov-3 Eric Pillon, Calais #48/R

LAVIEILLE, Marie (19th C) French
£282 $504 €400 Femme agenouillee en priere (46x55cm-18x22in) s. 11-Jan-4 Rouillac, Vendome #363

LAVIEILLE, Marie (attrib) (19th C) French
£493 $882 €700 Decor d'interieur (41x32cm-16x13in) 11-Jan-4 Rouillac, Vendome #362

LAVIER, Bertrand (1949-) French
£483 $869 €700 Sans titre (18x11cm-7x4in) s.d.2002 verso acrylic sold with print. 25-Jan-4 Cornette de St.Cyr, Paris #384
£6667 $12133 €10000 Composition 8 (60cm-24in circular) s.d.1986 verso acrylic panel prov.exhib. 29-Jun-4 Cornette de St.Cyr, Paris #132/R est:8000-10000
£8667 $15773 €13000 Whistler (70x50cm-28x20in) s.d.1996 acrylic on mirror prov. 29-Jun-4 Cornette de St.Cyr, Paris #133/R est:15000-18000
£13333 $24667 €20000 Miroir (113x143cm-44x56in) s.verso painted mirror exec.1984 prov.exhib. 18-Jul-4 Sotheby's, Paris #265/R est:15000-20000

LAVIK, Olav (1897-1968) Norwegian
£452 $832 €660 Landscape from Sandviken (67x83cm-26x33in) s. 29-Mar-4 Blomqvist, Lysaker #1194/R (N.KR 5700)

LAVILLE, Joy (1923-) British
£676 $1216 €987 Toreador (46x57cm-18x22in) s. panel. 26-Jan-4 Lilla Bukowskis, Stockholm #290 (S.KR 9000)

LAVOIE, Alain (1961-) Canadian
£225 $383 €329 Histoire d'amour (91x61cm-36x24in) s. s.i.verso acrylic prov. 23-Nov-3 Levis, Calgary #494/R (C.D 500)

LAVOINE, L P Robert (1916-1999) French
£405 $726 €600 Notre-Dame de Paris (54x73cm-21x29in) s.d.1943. 5-May-4 Coutau Begarie, Paris #65
£563 $907 €800 Rouen, le port (66x87cm-26x34in) s.i. s.i.verso. 11-May-3 Versailles Encheres #126

Works on paper
£336 $624 €500 Paris, le Pont Neuf (23x31cm-9x12in) s.i.d.1952 W/C. 7-Mar-4 Lesieur & Le Bars, Le Havre #76
£690 $1152 €1000 Le havre, bateaux (48x63cm-19x25in) s.i. gouache. 11-Nov-3 Lesieur & Le Bars, Le Havre #69

LAVONEN, Ahti (1928-1970) Finnish
£3497 $5944 €5000 Sensation black and yellow (48x100cm-19x39in) s.d.62. 29-Nov-3 Bukowskis, Helsinki #263/R est:4000-4500

LAVRILLIER, Gaston Andre (1885-1987) French
Sculpture
£987 $1816 €1500 Leda (34x20cm-13x8in) s.i.d.1921 gilded bronze bas-relief on wood. 25-Jun-4 Tajan, Paris #25/R est:1500-1800

LAVROFF, G (1895-?) Russian
Sculpture
£2766 $4619 €3900 Lionne a l'affut (61cm-24in) s. pat bronze marble base. 16-Oct-3 Camard, Paris #106 est:500-600

LAVROFF, Georges (1895-?) Russian
Sculpture
£1111 $1856 €1600 Faisans sur berge (78cm-31in) s.st.f.Chardon pat bronze. 21-Oct-3 Galerie Moderne, Brussels #1508/R
£2000 $3580 €2920 Lioness and her cub (63cm-25in) s. pat bronze. 13-May-4 Christie's, Kensington #323/R est:2500-3500
£2000 $3660 €2920 Walking tiger (51cm-20in) s. bronze black marble base. 3-Jun-4 Sotheby's, Olympia #259/R est:1200-1500
£3200 $5856 €4672 Song birds, bookends (20cm-8in) s. bronze. 3-Jun-4 Sotheby's, Olympia #260/R est:800-1200

LAW, Andrew (fl.1895-1940) British
£950 $1520 €1387 Chrysanthemums (64x54cm-25x21in) s. 18-Sep-3 Bonhams, Edinburgh #363/R
£1500 $2745 €2190 Portrait of a lady seated, wearing a black dress (106x90cm-42x35in) s. 6-Jul-4 Bonhams, Knightsbridge #173/R est:1500-2000
£3000 $4710 €4350 Still life with summer flowers (76x63cm-30x25in) s. s.verso. 27-Aug-3 Sotheby's, London #1059/R est:3000-4000
£3400 $6222 €4964 Tabletop still life (56x66cm-22x26in) s. 8-Apr-4 Bonhams, Edinburgh #103/R est:1000-1500

LAW, Charles Anthony (1916-1996) Canadian
£191 $352 €279 Winter in Baie St Paul, Quebec (23x30cm-9x12in) s. board. 9-Jun-4 Walker's, Ottawa #22 (C.D 475)
£191 $352 €279 The Saguenay River (50x63cm-20x25in) s. board. 9-Jun-4 Walker's, Ottawa #44/R (C.D 475)
£300 $469 €435 Mountain stream (34x39cm-13x15in) s.d.1949. 26-Mar-3 Walker's, Ottawa #405/R (C.D 700)
£320 $586 €467 Side Road (34x39cm-13x15in) s. board. 1-Jun-4 Joyner Waddington, Toronto #491 (C.D 800)
£360 $613 €526 The side road (33x40cm-13x16in) s. i.verso panel. 21-Nov-3 Walker's, Ottawa #62/R (C.D 800)

LAW, David (1831-1901) British
Works on paper
£300 $510 €438 Venetian canal scene (39x24cm-15x9in) s. pencil W/C. 19-Nov-3 Tennants, Leyburn #899
£380 $619 €551 Fishing on a Highland river (39x59cm-15x23in) s.d.76 W/C. 23-Sep-3 Bonhams, Knightsbridge #67/R
£420 $777 €613 Hereford - river landscape with anglers on a bank, the cathedral visible (29x44cm-11x17in) s. s.i. backing board W/C. 14-Jul-4 Bonhams, Chester #410

LAW, Denys (1907-1981) British
£250 $440 €365 Overlooking Larmona Cove (48x58cm-19x23in) s. board. 31-Dec-3 Lambrays, Wadebridge #644
£500 $910 €730 April morning (51x61cm-20x24in) s. board. 1-Jul-4 Christie's, Kensington #151
£520 $863 €759 French crabber under sail off the coast (31x39cm-12x15in) s. board. 2-Oct-3 Lane, Penzance #48
£600 $1092 €876 Lamorna stream (20x23cm-8x9in) s. board. 15-Jun-4 David Lay, Penzance #376
£950 $1587 €1387 Moorland stream (41x51cm-16x20in) s. board. 14-Oct-3 David Lay, Penzance #27

Works on paper
£380 $631 €555 Boleigh farm near Land's End (24x35cm-9x14in) s. W/C. 2-Oct-3 Lane, Penzance #135/R

LAWES, Harold (fl.1890`s) British

Works on paper

£181	$302	€264	Doonie Valley (24x54cm-9x21in) s.i. W/C. 17-Nov-3 Waddingtons, Toronto #41/R (C.D 400)
£226	$378	€330	Sidenham Bucks (64x94cm-25x37in) s.i. W/C. 17-Nov-3 Waddingtons, Toronto #42/R (C.D 500)
£250	$430	€365	Sutton near Oxford (23x36cm-9x14in) s.i. W/C. 5-Dec-3 Keys, Aylsham #216/R
£310	$564	€453	Cattle resting by a river (19x49cm-7x19in) s.d.1899 W/C over traces pencil. 29-Jun-4 Bonhams, Knowle #61
£350	$648	€511	Landscape with cattle watering (36x51cm-14x20in) W/C. 15-Jul-4 Mitchells, Cockermouth #516
£500	$810	€725	Angler fishing by Dedham Church (15x36cm-6x14in) s. W/C exec.c.1870-1880. 25-May-3 Desmond Judd, Cranbrook #1046
£550	$1018	€803	Poughill, Cornwall (33x51cm-13x20in) s. W/C. 13-Feb-4 Keys, Aylsham #479/R

LAWES-WITTERONGE, Charles Bennet (1843-1911) British

Sculpture

£17000	$30430	€25500	Figure of a naked woman (173cm-68in) s. white marble pedestal. 25-May-4 Sotheby's, Billingshurst #360/R est:8000-12000

LAWLER, Louise (1947-) American

Photographs

£1667	$3000	€2434	Lost at sea (58x43cm-23x17in) num,1/5 cibachrome print. 23-Apr-4 Phillips, New York #214/R est:5000-7000
£2400	$4008	€3504	Untitled (61x51cm-24x20in) s.d.1991 num.2/5 cibachrome print prov. 21-Oct-3 Sotheby's, London #319/R est:3000-4000
£3000	$5520	€4380	Painting and wall - grey (59x42cm-23x17in) cibachrome print exec 1989 prov. 24-Jun-4 Sotheby's, London #319/R est:4000-6000
£3500	$5950	€5110	Arranged by Claire Vencent at the Metropolitan Museum of art, New York (70x80cm-28x31in) s.d.1982 num.1/5 gelatin silver print. 18-Nov-3 Christie's, Kensington #241/R est:4000-6000
£6587	$11000	€9617	Scene (121x179cm-48x70in) s.num.d.1990 cibachrome printed on Cintra prov. 12-Nov-3 Christie's, Rockefeller NY #528/R est:10000-15000
£7263	$13000	€10604	Positioned together, tous les deux, ensemble, New York (48x61cm-19x24in) s.d.1986 num.1/5 verso cibachrome print prov. 13-May-4 Sotheby's, New York #389/R est:6000-8000
£8380	$15000	€12235	Bedroom with fireplace arranged by Mr and Mrs Burton Tremaine NY City (80x63cm-31x25in) s.i.num.1/5 backing blk white photo printed mat exec 1984-89 prov. 13-May-4 Sotheby's, New York #401/R est:4000-6000
£8982	$15000	€13114	What else could I do (61x61cm-24x24in) s.d.1994 num.1/5 verso c-print panel prov. 13-Nov-3 Sotheby's, New York #482/R est:15000-20000
£10000	$18200	€14600	CS num.204 (97x134cm-38x53in) s.d.1990 num.4/5 verso cibachrome print prov.lit. 6-Feb-4 Sotheby's, London #283/R est:10000-15000
£25150	$42000	€36719	Detail (100x135cm-39x53in) s.d.1990 num.5 cibachrome prov.exhib. 14-Nov-3 Phillips, New York #111/R est:20000-30000

LAWLESS, Carl (1894-1934) American

£2844	$4750	€4152	Mountainside in Winter (56x56cm-22x22in) s. 23-Oct-3 Shannon's, Milford #182/R est:3000-5000

LAWLESS, Matthew James (1837-1864) Irish

£9155	$15838	€13000	Sailor awaiting embarkation (20x15cm-8x6in) s.d.1859. 10-Dec-3 Bonhams & James Adam, Dublin #19/R est:5000-8000

LAWLEY, Douglas (1906-1971) Canadian

£360	$659	€526	Fishing boats (45x59cm-18x23in) s. canvas on board. 1-Jun-4 Joyner Waddington, Toronto #272/R (C.D 900)
£625	$1075	€913	Circus, Gloucester, Mass (16x21cm-6x8in) s. canvasboard. 2-Dec-3 Joyner Waddington, Toronto #236/R (C.D 1400)
£720	$1318	€1051	Low tide, Gloucester, Mass (50x60cm-20x24in) s. board. 1-Jun-4 Joyner Waddington, Toronto #399/R est:800-1200 (C.D 1800)

LAWMAN, Jasper Holman (1825-1906) American

£1963	$3200	€2866	Mr and Mrs Henry B Cole (61x74cm-24x29in) d.1869 verso pair. 26-Sep-3 York Town, York #818 est:3200

LAWRENCE, Bringhurst B (fl.1881-1889) British

£1100	$2024	€1606	Terrier puppy (51x41cm-20x16in) s.d.1895. 10-Jun-4 Christie's, Kensington #362/R est:600-800

LAWRENCE, Edith Mary (1890-1973) British

£600	$1110	€900	Noonday rest (48x73cm-19x29in) indis.sig. 14-Jul-4 Sotheby's, Olympia #84/R

LAWRENCE, George Feather (1901-1981) Australian

£522	$872	€757	The Strand, London (39x54cm-15x21in) s. board. 30-Jun-3 Australian Art Auctions, Sydney #104 (A.D 1300)
£531	$977	€775	Boatshed (25x33cm-10x13in) s. board. 29-Mar-4 Goodman, Sydney #182/R (A.D 1300)
£553	$1007	€807	Man in the street (30x25cm-12x10in) s. board prov. 16-Jun-4 Deutscher-Menzies, Melbourne #565/R est:1000-2000 (A.D 1450)
£567	$913	€828	Road to the coast (40x55cm-16x22in) s. board. 13-Oct-3 Joel, Victoria #273 est:1250-1500 (A.D 1400)
£602	$1006	€873	Harbour at Looe (55x76cm-22x30in) s. board. 30-Jun-3 Australian Art Auctions, Sydney #121 (A.D 1500)
£691	$1085	€1002	Waterfront, Wooloomooloo (25x33cm-10x13in) s.d.55 board. 26-Aug-3 Christie's, Sydney #265 (A.D 1700)
£725	$1320	€1059	Interior, Northwood - artist's living room (35x45cm-14x18in) s.d.49 canvas on board. 16-Jun-4 Deutscher-Menzies, Melbourne #566/R est:2000-3000 (A.D 1900)
£813	$1276	€1179	Untitled - street scene (39x54cm-15x21in) s. board. 26-Aug-3 Lawson Menzies, Sydney #366 est:3000-4000 (A.D 2000)
£820	$1328	€1197	Landscape and quarry (39x49cm-15x19in) s.d.60 board. 30-Jul-3 Goodman, Sydney #113/R (A.D 2000)
£977	$1826	€1466	Figures in a Laneway Balmain (50x40cm-20x16in) s. board. 20-Jul-4 Goodman, Sydney #105/R (A.D 2500)
£1229	$1942	€1794	Laneway, Surrey Hills (61x76cm-24x30in) s.d.67 board. 2-Sep-3 Deutscher-Menzies, Melbourne #286/R est:3000-4000 (A.D 3000)
£1450	$2640	€2117	Bombo Beach (61x76cm-24x30in) s.d.64 board. 16-Jun-4 Deutscher-Menzies, Melbourne #320/R est:4000-6000 (A.D 3800)
£1619	$2607	€2364	Rozelle Bay (49x75cm-19x30in) s. i.verso composition board prov. 25-Aug-3 Sotheby's, Paddington #259/R est:4000-6000 (A.D 4000)
£2149	$4018	€3224	Elizabeth St (70x90cm-28x35in) s.d.57 board. 20-Jul-4 Goodman, Sydney #11/R est:6000-8000 (A.D 5500)
£2656	$4967	€3984	Dusk, city street (61x50cm-24x20in) s.d.56 board. 20-Jul-4 Goodman, Sydney #109/R est:5000-7000 (A.D 6800)

LAWRENCE, Jacob (1917-2000) American

£31977	$55000	€46686	After the snow (46x61cm-18x24in) s.d.53 tempera on board prov. 3-Dec-3 Sotheby's, New York #70/R est:25000-35000

Prints

£2011	$3600	€2936	Windows (45x56cm-18x22in) s.i.d.1977 num.64/300 offset lithograph. 6-May-4 Swann Galleries, New York #484/R est:3000-5000
£2118	$3600	€3092	Builders three (76x55cm-30x22in) s.i.d.1991 num.54/90 col lithograph. 6-Nov-3 Swann Galleries, New York #600/R est:3000-5000
£3529	$6000	€5152	The 1920's, the migrants arrive and cast their ballots (81x62cm-32x24in) s.i.d.1974 num.20/125 col screenprint. 6-Nov-3 Swann Galleries, New York #599/R est:2500-3500

Works on paper

£81395	$140000	€118837	Rain (72x51cm-28x20in) s.d.38 s.i.verso gouache on board prov. 3-Dec-3 Sotheby's, New York #69/R est:60000-80000

LAWRENCE, Sir Thomas (1769-1830) British

£7000	$11060	€10150	Portrait of Sir Robert Wigram, 1st Bt. seated in an interior (254x145cm-100x57in) prov.exhib.lit. 4-Sep-3 Christie's, Kensington #51/R est:7000-10000
£13000	$23920	€18980	Portrait of Henry Bathurst, 3rd Earl Bathurst, wearing a white stockinqs (57x48cm-22x19in) framed as oval. 26-Mar-4 Sotheby's, London #33/R est:8000-12000
£20833	$37500	€30416	Portrait of an officer of the 11th Light Dragoons (92x72cm-36x28in) prov. painted with studio. 21-Jan-4 Doyle, New York #128/R est:10000-15000
£25000	$45000	€36500	Portrait of Anne, lady Lethbridge (76x63cm-30x25in) prov.lit. 23-Jan-4 Christie's, Rockefeller NY #80/R est:50000-70000
£25140	$45000	€36704	Portrait of lady, said to be Mrs Finch (76x63cm-30x25in) prov.exhib.lit. 27-May-4 Sotheby's, New York #284/R est:20000-30000
£32000	$54400	€46720	Portrait of Elizabeth Williams of Gwersylt Park, Denbighshire (73x61cm-29x24in) prov.exhib.lit. 27-Nov-3 Sotheby's, London #169/R est:25000-35000
£32000	$59840	€46720	Half length portrait of Sir George Cornewall 2nd Bt (75x62cm-30x24in) prov.lit. 21-Jul-4 Lyon & Turnbull, Edinburgh #141/R est:20000-30000
£50279	$90000	€73407	Portrait of Lady Georgina North (76x63cm-30x25in) prov.lit. 27-May-4 Sotheby's, New York #278/R est:60000-80000
£60000	$109200	€87600	Portrait of Anne Perry (90x70cm-35x28in) prov.exhib.lit. 1-Jul-4 Sotheby's, London #13/R est:60000-80000

Works on paper

£1176	$2000	€1717	Portrait of Harriet Bowdler in a blue and white dress (29x24cm-11x9in) pastel. 20-Nov-3 Auctions by the Bay, Alameda #1005/R
£1500	$2550	€2190	Portrait of Countess Georgina Bathurst, bust length (17x14cm-7x6in) i.d.1823 pencil red chk. sold with companion by another hand two. 20-Nov-3 Christie's, London #20/R est:1000-1500
£2232	$3839	€3259	Robert Morris dressed as an officer for the 59th Nottinghamshire Regiment (30x25cm-12x10in) i. on paper in same frame col chk pastel sold with letter prov. 2-Dec-3 Ritchie, Toronto #3/R est:5000-7000 (C.D 5000)

LAWRENCE, Sir Thomas (attrib) (1769-1830) British

£1500	$2445	€2190	Portrait of a young girl sat with a picture book on her lap (53x43cm-21x17in) 28-Sep-3 Wilkinson, Doncaster #290/R
£7616	$13937	€11500	Portrait de jeune femme en robe blanche, Mrs Canby Skipton (68x62cm-27x24in) painted c.1800. 7-Apr-4 Libert, Castor, Paris #26/R est:4000-5000

LAWRENCE, Sir Thomas (circle) (1769-1830) British

£7059	$12000	€10306	Portrait of Francis Humberston Mackenzie (93x72cm-37x28in) prov. 25-Nov-3 Christie's, Rockefeller NY #490/R est:2000-3000
£13115	$24000	€19148	Portrait of a young girl (51x43cm-20x17in) painted oval prov. 3-Jun-4 Christie's, Rockefeller NY #266/R est:7000-10000

LAWRENCE, T (?) British

£3198	$5500	€4669	To the Casbah, Sais waiting (97x71cm-38x28in) s. 7-Dec-3 Hindman, Chicago #736/R est:2000-3000

LAWRENCE, William Goadby (?) ?

£2038	$3750	€2975	Marlin rising (50x76cm-20x30in) s. i.verso. 8-Jun-4 Bonhams & Butterfields, San Francisco #4146/R est:3000-5000

LAWRENSON, Edward Louis (1868-1940) British

Works on paper

£270	$464	€394	Kerry bog with peat diggers (28x38cm-11x15in) s.d.1929 verso W/C. 5-Dec-3 Keys, Aylsham #314/R

LAWRIE, Hamish (1919-1987) British

£300	$549	€438	Yachts (17x21cm-7x8in) s. board sold with W/C by same hand. 8-Apr-4 Bonhams, Edinburgh #36
£480	$802	€701	Skyline, Mound, Edinburgh (34x44cm-13x17in) s. board. 16-Oct-3 Bonhams, Edinburgh #45
£600	$1002	€876	Highland landscape (30x39cm-12x15in) s. board. 16-Oct-3 Bonhams, Edinburgh #46
£1000	$1830	€1460	Continental town scene (65x90cm-26x35in) s. board. 8-Apr-4 Bonhams, Edinburgh #22 est:500-800

Works on paper
£360 $659 €526 Dean Village - Evening (25x19cm-10x7in) s. mixed media. 31-Jan-4 Shapes, Edinburgh #376

LAWSON, Cecil Gordon (1851-1882) British
£5028 $9000 €7341 Hop gardens of England (154x213cm-61x84in) s. prov. 6-May-4 Doyle, New York #22/R est:10000-15000

LAWSON, Cecil Gordon (attrib) (1851-1882) British
£1500 $2745 €2190 Covenantors (41x66cm-16x26in) 8-Jul-4 Duke & Son, Dorchester #233/R est:1500-2500

LAWSON, Ernest (1873-1939) American
£7186 $12000 €10492 The Lock (46x81cm-18x32in) s. prov.exhib.lit. 9-Oct-3 Christie's, Rockefeller NY #71/R est:15000-25000
£8383 $14000 €12239 Lighthouse at Peggy's Cove, Nova Scotia (35x48cm-14x19in) s. panel prov.exhib. 9-Oct-3 Christie's, Rockefeller NY #69/R est:12000-18000
£10778 $18000 €15736 Seagulls by the coast (38x48cm-15x19in) s. prov. 23-Oct-3 Shannon's, Milford #139/R est:25000-35000
£11173 $20000 €16313 Summer landscape (36x46cm-14x18in) s. board. 8-May-4 Susanin's, Chicago #6050/R est:15000-20000
£14535 $25000 €21221 View of Segovia (30x41cm-12x16in) s. prov. 3-Dec-3 Sotheby's, New York #60/R est:15000-20000
£16766 $28000 €24478 Biltmore Hotel, Coral Gables, Florida (51x54cm-20x21in) s. prov. 9-Oct-3 Christie's, Rockefeller NY #57/R est:20000-30000
£19886 $35000 €29034 Haystacks on the farm (46x58cm-18x23in) s. prov. 19-May-4 Sotheby's, New York #112/R est:30000-50000
£22346 $40000 €32625 Horse and cart, autumn (51x61cm-20x24in) s. board. 26-May-4 Doyle, New York #88/R est:30000-50000
£25157 $40000 €36729 Quiet river (41x51cm-16x20in) s. 12-Sep-3 Skinner, Boston #404/R est:25000
£40698 $70000 €59419 Winter landscape (41x51cm-16x20in) s. 4-Dec-3 Christie's, Rockefeller NY #77/R est:50000-70000
£85227 $150000 €124431 Suburban Road (51x62cm-20x24in) s. painted c.1916-18 prov.exhib. 18-May-4 Christie's, Rockefeller NY #79/R est:120000-180000
Works on paper
£1630 $3000 €2380 Sailboat at night (31x25cm-12x10in) s.d.13 pencil gouache prov. 8-Jun-4 Bonhams & Butterfields, San Francisco #4048/R est:3000-5000

LAWSON, Fred (1888-1968) British
Works on paper
£270 $459 €394 Bolton Castle (24x33cm-9x13in) s. W/C. 18-Nov-3 Bonhams, Leeds #88
£300 $531 €438 Glasson Dock Morecambe Lancashire (27x37cm-11x15in) s.d.1921 i.verso W/C. 28-Apr-4 Peter Wilson, Nantwich #163
£300 $561 €438 Penhill, Wensleydale (36x55cm-14x22in) s. pencil W/C. 22-Jul-4 Tennants, Leyburn #774
£328 $547 €479 European city scene with figures crossing a bridge (48x59cm-19x23in) s.d.1913 W/C. 20-Oct-3 Stephan Welz, Johannesburg #456 est:2500-3500 (SA.R 3800)
£380 $684 €555 Leyburn, October fair (22x29cm-9x11in) s.i.d.October 9th 1959 pen ink dr. 21-Apr-4 Tennants, Leyburn #963
£400 $680 €584 Cart and figures on a wooded path (32x39cm-13x15in) s. W/C. 18-Nov-3 Bonhams, Leeds #87
£400 $680 €584 Barn interior with grain, barrels and other implements (25x34cm-10x13in) s.i.d.March 28th 1949 black white pen ink. 19-Nov-3 Tennants, Leyburn #951
£400 $680 €584 Figures and dog beside trees, walls of a fortified town beyond (25x25cm-10x10in) s. pencil W/C. 19-Nov-3 Tennants, Leyburn #952
£420 $756 €613 Castle Bolton, with chickens in the foreground (23x32cm-9x13in) s. pencil W/C. 21-Apr-4 Tennants, Leyburn #1016
£700 $1260 €1022 Dales farm with buildings amongst trees (27x44cm-11x17in) s.d.1916 pencil W/C htd white. 21-Apr-4 Tennants, Leyburn #1014
£900 $1530 €1314 Edge of the wood (44x56cm-17x22in) s.d.1916 i.d.verso pencil W/C. 19-Nov-3 Tennants, Leyburn #950/R
£1100 $1870 €1606 Figure beside a fairground on a village green, possibly Reeth or Leyburn (23x30cm-9x12in) s. pencil W/C. 19-Nov-3 Tennants, Leyburn #979 est:500-600
£1200 $2160 €1752 Gypsy caravan and a vehicle on a village green in the Dales (24x31cm-9x12in) s. pen ink W/C sold with book. 21-Apr-4 Tennants, Leyburn #1013 est:600-800

LAWSON, Fred (attrib) (1888-1968) British
Works on paper
£380 $684 €555 View of Bootham Bar, York, with figures in foreground (25x18cm-10x7in) bears sig. pencil W/C. 21-Apr-4 Tennants, Leyburn #1019

LAWSON, George Anderson (1832-1904) British
Sculpture
£7200 $11592 €10440 Robert Burns (98cm-39in) bronze st.f.J Moore. 21-Aug-3 Bonhams, Edinburgh #894/R est:2000-3000

LAWSON, Louisa Napaltjarri (c.1926-) Australian
Works on paper
£2734 $5113 €4101 Mala, wallaby story (166x154cm-65x61in) bears name.i.d.June 1990 synthetic polymer paint canvas prov. 26-Jul-4 Sotheby's, Melbourne #270/R est:7000-10000 (A.D 7000)

LAWSON, Mehl (1942-) American
Sculpture
£1176 $2000 €1717 Cow boss (36cm-14in) bronze. 1-Nov-3 Altermann Galleries, Santa Fe #23
£1242 $2000 €1813 Montana cowboy (14x17cm-6x7in) bronze edition of 35. 22-Aug-3 Altermann Galleries, Santa Fe #117
£1796 $3000 €2622 Breakin' daylight (56x89x48cm-22x35x19in) num.1/25 bronze. 11-Oct-3 Nadeau, Windsor #43/R est:4000-7000
£4022 $7200 €5872 Mystic trail (64cm-25in) bronze edn of 25. 15-May-4 Altermann Galleries, Santa Fe #48/R

LAWSON, Sonia (1934-) British
£1350 $2295 €1971 Rubbish dump (61x60cm-24x24in) init. canvas on board. 18-Nov-3 Bonhams, Leeds #146/R est:700-900

LAWSON, William (fl.1819-1864) British
£270 $494 €394 An early lesson in knitting (32x28cm-13x11in) s.d.1856 panel. 8-Jul-4 Lawrence, Crewkerne #1631

LAY, Cecil Howard (1885-1956) British
£450 $806 €657 August dawn (38x48cm-15x19in) s. panel. 22-Mar-4 Bonhams & Brooks, Norfolk #335/R

LAY, Edward (?) ?
£424 $734 €619 River landscape (46x60cm-18x24in) s. 15-Dec-3 Lilla Bukowskis, Stockholm #552 (S.KR 5400)

LAYCOCK, Brent R (1947-) Canadian
£222 $384 €324 Rising above the lake (81x122cm-32x48in) s. acrylic prov. 9-Dec-3 Maynards, Vancouver #250 (C.D 500)
Works on paper
£317 $529 €463 Untitled - road in the foothills (61x86cm-24x34in) s.d. W/C. 17-Nov-3 Hodgins, Calgary #316/R (C.D 700)

LAYCOCK, Donald (1931-) Australian
£1220 $1915 €1769 Flower, peach (119x147cm-47x58in) init.d.68 s.i.verso exhib.lit. 27-Aug-3 Christie's, Sydney #674/R est:2000-4000 (A.D 3000)

LAYCOX, Jack (20th C) American
Works on paper
£307 $550 €448 California Street. s. W/C. 10-Jan-4 Harvey Clar, Oakland #1204
£363 $650 €530 Mason at Columbus. s. 10-Jan-4 Harvey Clar, Oakland #1205

LAYNAUD, Ernest (1830-?) French
£15278 $27500 €22306 L' ile Saint Louis a Paris (117x89cm-46x35in) s.d.96. 23-Apr-4 Sotheby's, New York #139/R est:12000-15000

LAYS, Jean Pierre (1825-1887) French
£15333 $27447 €23000 Vigne au buste et au bas-relief (120x81cm-47x32in) i. 16-May-4 Joron-Derem, Paris #183/R est:20000-25000

LAYS, Jean Pierre (attrib) (1825-1887) French
£5369 $9879 €8000 Still life of flowers and fruit (100x81cm-39x32in) 25-Mar-4 Dr Fritz Nagel, Stuttgart #733/R est:1500

LAZARE-LEVY (1867-1933) ?
£483 $806 €700 Sur la banc public (46x61cm-18x24in) s. 17-Nov-3 Claude Boisgirard, Paris #56

LAZAREFF, Alexandra de (?) ?
Sculpture
£1325 $2424 €2000 Rhinoceros (63cm-25in) s. num.8/8 pat bronze Cast f.M Italy. 7-Apr-4 Piasa, Paris #214 est:1600-1800
£1408 $2437 €2000 Le martin-pecheur (69cm-27in) s.st.f. Fonderia M num.1/8 pat bronze. 12-Dec-3 Piasa, Paris #204 est:2000-3000
£2113 $3655 €3000 L'effet boeuf (58x60cm-23x24in) s.st.f. Arte Bronzo num.1/8 pat bronze. 12-Dec-3 Piasa, Paris #202/R est:2000-3000

LAZAREV, Pavel (20th C) ?
£250 $418 €365 Evening, country landscape (59x70cm-23x28in) s. s.i.d.1997 verso. 9-Jul-3 Peter Wilson, Nantwich #43

LAZEREV, Pavel (20th C) ?
£270 $440 €394 First snow (58x68cm-23x27in) s. s.i.d.1996 verso. 24-Sep-3 Peter Wilson, Nantwich #55

LAZERGES, Jean Raymond Hippolyte (1817-1887) French
£629 $1083 €900 Scene religieuse (61x38cm-24x15in) s. 5-Dec-3 Chochon-Barre & Allardi, Paris #119
Works on paper
£3878 $6941 €5700 Christ en croix entre l'eglise et la foi (58x48cm-23x19in) mono.d.1866 1868 black crayon white chk triptych. 17-Mar-4 Tajan, Paris #127/R est:2000

LAZERGES, Paul Jean Baptiste (1845-1902) French
£900 $1647 €1314 Portrait of a lady seated, wearing a feather hat (22x17cm-9x7in) s.d.1880 board. 8-Apr-4 Christie's, Kensington #36/R est:800-1200
£6667 $12267 €10000 Jeune femme a la fontaine (61x47cm-24x19in) s.d.1888 panel. 14-Jun-4 Gros & Delettrez, Paris #410/R est:10000-15000
£10588 $18000 €15458 Arab caravan (81x100cm-32x39in) s.d.1895. 29-Oct-3 Christie's, Rockefeller NY #161/R est:10000-15000
£31333 $57653 €47000 Caravane traversant un oued (81x100cm-32x39in) s.d.1895. 14-Jun-4 Gros & Delettrez, Paris #63/R est:35000-45000
Sculpture
£2105 $3874 €3200 Arab and his camel (70cm-28in) s. brown pat. bronze exec. c.1900. 22-Jun-4 Sotheby's, Amsterdam #156/R est:2000-3000

LAZO, Antonio (1943-) Venezuelan
Works on paper
£1985 $3375 €2898 Smell (196x140cm-77x55in) s. mixed media on canvas exec.1988. 23-Nov-3 Subastas Odalys, Caracas #16/R

LAZZARI, Alfredo (1871-1949) Argentinian
£1421 $2600 €2075 Ranch (25x35cm-10x14in) cardboard. 1-Jun-4 Arroyo, Buenos Aires #49

LAZZARI, Bice (1900-1981) Italian
£2800 $5152 €4200 Vase with arum lilies (70x80cm-28x31in) s. panel. 10-Jun-4 Christie's, Rome #219/R est:1800-2500

LAZZARI, Sebastiano (attrib) (18th C) Italian
£18056 $30153 €26000 Trompe l'oeil with table and bird (77x99cm-30x39in) 22-Oct-3 Finarte Semenzato, Milan #46/R est:25000-35000

LAZZARINI, Elisabetta (attrib) (1662-1729) Italian
£1631 $2643 €2300 Cristo deriso (47x30cm-19x12in) 22-May-3 Stadion, Trieste #648/R est:3500-4500

LAZZELL, Blanche (1878-1956) American
Prints
£1796 $3000 €2622 My Provincetown studio (28x20cm-11x8in) s.i.d.1933 woodcut. 11-Nov-3 Doyle, New York #301/R est:2000-3000
Works on paper
£778 $1300 €1136 Landscape with house (30x36cm-12x14in) s. pastel. 25-Oct-3 Rachel Davis, Shaker Heights #216/R
£1667 $3100 €2434 Abstract projet (46x86cm-18x34in) s.d. casein masonite. 7-Mar-4 William Jenack, New York #310 est:800-1200

LAZZINI, Paolo (1953-) Italian
£464 $844 €700 Venice (30x60cm-12x24in) s. s.i.verso board. 17-Jun-4 Galleria Pananti, Florence #138/R

LAZZOLO, Vasco (20th C) ?
£500 $915 €730 Women in an interior (51x76cm-20x30in) s. 8-Jul-4 Duke & Son, Dorchester #197/R

LE BA DANG (1922-) Vietnamese
£818 $1300 €1194 Abstract expression (81x66cm-32x26in) 10-Sep-3 Alderfer's, Hatfield #304/R

LE PHO (1907-2001) Vietnamese
£1375 $2200 €2008 Fleurs des champs (30x23cm-12x9in) s. 20-Sep-3 Bunte, Elgin #1300f est:300-500
£1800 $3006 €2628 Les anemones (46x27cm-18x11in) s. silk on masonite prov. 22-Oct-3 Sotheby's, Olympia #40/R est:2000-3000
£2119 $3963 €3200 Roses tremieres et dahlias (46x26cm-18x10in) s. 20-Jul-4 Gioffredo, Nice #13/R
£2174 $3370 €3174 Fleurs (46x33cm-18x13in) s. prov. 6-Oct-2 Sotheby's, Singapore #93/R est:4500-6500 (S.D 6000)
£2361 $4250 €3447 La couture (41x23cm-16x9in) s. canvasboard prov. 20-Jan-4 Arthur James, Florida #170
£2431 $4059 €3549 Les poppies (61x38cm-24x15in) s. prov. 12-Oct-3 Sotheby's, Singapore #106/R est:7000-9000 (S.D 7000)
£2431 $4059 €3549 Fleurs (27x35cm-11x14in) s. 12-Oct-3 Sotheby's, Singapore #109/R est:7000-9000 (S.D 7000)
£3333 $6133 €5000 La maternite au bouquet jaune (14x22cm-6x9in) s. silk on cardboard painted c.1950 prov. 11-Jun-4 Pierre Berge, Paris #229/R est:5000-6000
£3333 $6133 €5000 La maternite (14x22cm-6x9in) s. i.verso silk on cardboard painted c.1950 prov. 11-Jun-4 Pierre Berge, Paris #232/R est:5000-6000
£3421 $6295 €5200 Giroflees et gentes (46x27cm-18x11in) s. silk on cardboard. 25-Jun-4 Millon & Associes, Paris #183/R est:3000-4000
£3441 $5505 €5024 Fleurs (65x46cm-26x18in) s.d. prov. 18-May-3 Sotheby's, Singapore #127/R est:7000-9000 (S.D 9600)
£3459 $5500 €5050 Les deux fleurs (51x61cm-20x24in) s. i.on stretcher prov. 9-Sep-3 Arthur James, Florida #103
£3467 $6379 €5200 Still life of a vase of flowers (35x22cm-14x9in) s. canvasboard. 9-Jun-4 Le Roux & Morel, Paris #57/R est:2000-2500
£3774 $6000 €5510 Two girls in a garden (51x61cm-20x24in) s. prov. 9-Sep-3 Arthur James, Florida #104
£3779 $6500 €5517 Renunculas (46x38cm-18x15in) s. i.stretcher prov. 3-Dec-3 Doyle, New York #154/R est:4000-6000
£4360 $7500 €6366 Young woman with flowers (41x33cm-16x13in) s. prov. 3-Dec-3 Doyle, New York #155/R est:4000-6000
£4545 $8000 €6636 Les pivoines, peonies in a vase (99x81cm-39x32in) s. 21-May-4 North East Auctions, Portsmouth #877/R est:6000-9000
£4575 $8281 €6680 Fleurs (61x45cm-24x18in) s. silk on board painted 1960. 4-Apr-4 Sotheby's, Singapore #59/R est:6500-8500 (S.D 14000)
£4575 $8281 €6680 Still life with fruits and seashell (33x46cm-13x18in) s. silk on board painted c.1956. 4-Apr-4 Sotheby's, Singapore #87/R est:12000-18000 (S.D 14000)
£4839 $9000 €7065 Mere et enfant (48x35cm-19x14in) s. 5-Mar-4 Skinner, Boston #392/R est:3000-5000
£5517 $9931 €8000 La jeune fille en mauve (61x38cm-24x15in) i.verso canvas on silk exhib. 26-Jan-4 Gros & Delettrez, Paris #41/R est:7500-12000
£5556 $10056 €8112 La jeune fille en mauve (61x38cm-24x15in) s. silk on cardboard painted c.1958 prov. 4-Apr-4 Sotheby's, Singapore #70/R est:18000-25000 (S.D 17000)
£5797 $8986 €8464 Fleurs. Fleurs (46x33cm-18x13in) s. two prov. 6-Oct-2 Sotheby's, Singapore #94/R est:9000-12000 (S.D 16000)
£5903 $9858 €8618 Fleurs (100x73cm-39x29in) s. prov. 12-Oct-3 Sotheby's, Singapore #108/R est:15000-20000 (S.D 17000)
£6159 $9547 €8992 Les pivones (46x58cm-18x23in) s. silk on board. 6-Oct-2 Sotheby's, Singapore #104/R est:8000-12000 (S.D 17000)
£6250 $11500 €9500 Tet (46x27cm-18x11in) s. silk on cardboard. 25-Jun-4 Millon & Associes, Paris #182/R est:4500-6000
£6536 $11830 €9543 Girl in the garden (50x61cm-20x24in) s. painted c.1970. 4-Apr-4 Sotheby's, Singapore #56/R est:20000-25000 (S.D 20000)
£6536 $11830 €9543 Les poppies (60x92cm-24x36in) s. silk on board painted c.1955. 4-Apr-4 Sotheby's, Singapore #58/R est:8000-12000 (S.D 20000)
£6711 $11879 €10000 Jeune femme au bouquet (81x60cm-32x24in) s. 27-Apr-4 Artcurial Briest, Paris #246/R est:15000-20000
£6989 $13000 €10204 Composition (92x66cm-36x26in) s. 5-Mar-4 Skinner, Boston #394/R est:6000-8000
£7246 $11232 €10579 Les tulipes jaunes (92x65cm-36x26in) s. silk on board prov. 6-Oct-2 Sotheby's, Singapore #105/R est:10000-15000 (S.D 20000)
£7263 $13000 €10604 Le jeune fille aux fleurs (65x46cm-26x18in) s. i.verso oil silk on board prov. 6-May-4 Doyle, New York #76/R est:5000-7000
£7895 $14526 €12000 Tasse de the (45x26cm-18x10in) s. 24-Jun-4 Credit Municipal, Paris #48/R est:10000-12000
£8000 $14720 €12000 Portrait de jeune femme dans un decor floral (50x37cm-20x15in) s. isorel panel. 9-Jun-4 Le Roux & Morel, Paris #58/R est:3000-4000
£8380 $15000 €12235 Floral still life (92x57cm-36x22in) s. i.verso oil silk on masonite prov. 6-May-4 Doyle, New York #77/R est:6000-8000
£9058 $14040 €13225 Mother and child (60x48cm-24x19in) s. silk prov. 6-Oct-2 Sotheby's, Singapore #98/R est:15000-18000 (S.D 25000)
£9804 $17745 €14314 Vietnamese woman at a table (92x60cm-36x24in) s. s.verso silk on board painted c.1963. 4-Apr-4 Sotheby's, Singapore #57/R est:12000-15000 (S.D 30000)
£10056 $18000 €14682 Vase of flowers (73x54cm-29x21in) s. prov. 6-May-4 Sotheby's, New York #421/R est:12000-16000
£10753 $17204 €15699 Fleurs (130x89cm-51x35in) s. 18-May-3 Sotheby's, Singapore #128/R est:20000-25000 (S.D 30000)
£12883 $21000 €18809 Fleurs (98x130cm-39x51in) s. prov. 25-Sep-3 Christie's, Rockefeller NY #556/R est:14000-18000
£13072 $23660 €19085 Serenity of companionship (82x64cm-32x25in) s.i. oil gouache silk. 3-Apr-4 Glerum, Singapore #90/R est:45000-55000 (S.D 40000)
£14444 $26000 €21088 Le te (89x150cm-35x59in) s. prov. 20-Apr-4 Arthur James, Florida #132/R est:20000-30000
£15647 $28165 €22845 Jeune fille au bouquet - young girl with a bouquet of flowers (65x91cm-26x36in) s. oil silk on board. 25-Apr-4 Christie's, Hong Kong #529/R est:65000-95000 (HK.D 220000)
£15698 $27000 €22919 La couture (88x116cm-35x46in) s.i. oil silk on masonite prov. 3-Dec-3 Doyle, New York #153/R est:8000-12000
£16216 $27081 €23675 Dans le jardin - in the garden (130x162cm-51x64in) s. 26-Oct-3 Christie's, Hong Kong #46/R est:180000-280000 (HK.D 210000)
£18533 $30950 €27058 Le bain de la mer - bath at the sea (90x58cm-35x23in) s. i.verso silk on paper. 26-Oct-3 Christie's, Hong Kong #45/R est:250000-350000 (HK.D 240000)
£19203 $34566 €28036 Nature morte aux fleurs et pommes - still life with flowers and apples (92x60cm-36x24in) s. oil silk on board prov. 25-Apr-4 Christie's, Hong Kong #528/R est:160000-200000 (HK.D 270000)
£21337 $38407 €31152 Filles dans jardin - girl in the garden (117x178cm-46x70in) s. prov. 25-Apr-4 Christie's, Hong Kong #526/R est:320000-450000 (HK.D 300000)
£28289 $52053 €43000 Femme allongee (90x180cm-35x71in) s.i.d.1931. 25-Jun-4 Millon & Associes, Paris #184/R est:30000-40000
Sculpture
£16993 $30758 €24810 Vietnamese landscape (46x24x8cm-18x9x3in) lacquer box prov.exhib.lit. 4-Apr-4 Sotheby's, Singapore #80/R est:30000-40000 (S.D 52000)
Works on paper
£1935 $3097 €2825 Wise Vietnamese (28x20cm-11x8in) s.i. prov. 18-May-3 Sotheby's, Singapore #118/R est:5000-7000 (S.D 5400)
£3595 $6507 €5249 Bouquet of lilies (35x54cm-14x21in) s. ink gouache silk on cardboard painted c.1938. 4-Apr-4 Sotheby's, Singapore #61/R est:10000-15000 (S.D 11000)
£4196 $7217 €6000 Head and shoulders portrait of a seated young woman (31x24cm-12x9in) s. ink silk on cardboard. 5-Dec-3 Lempertz, Koln #270/R est:5000
£11111 $18556 €16222 Mother and child (65x49cm-26x19in) s. ink gouache silk. 12-Oct-3 Sotheby's, Singapore #102/R est:28000-35000 (S.D 32000)
£28873 $49951 €41000 La reverie (58x47cm-23x19in) s. i.verso W/C silk on paper. 10-Dec-3 Rossini, Paris #21/R
£34409 $55054 €50237 Ladies by the balcony (64x42cm-25x17in) s. ink silk on paper. 18-May-3 Sotheby's, Singapore #97/R est:45000-65000 (S.D 96000)
£83333 $139167 €121666 Mother and child (72x52cm-28x20in) s. ink gouache silk on paper exec c.1938. 12-Oct-3 Sotheby's, Singapore #99/R est:120000-150000 (S.D 240000)

LE THI LUU (1911-1988) Vietnamese
£1517 $2534 €2200 Enfant dans un champ de fleurs (26x19cm-10x7in) bears sig silk. 14-Nov-3 Piasa, Paris #301/R est:2200-2500
Works on paper
£1935 $3097 €2825 Maternity (66x42cm-26x17in) s.d.1946 gouache ink silk on panel. 18-May-3 Sotheby's, Singapore #103/R est:5000-7000 (S.D 5400)

LE VUONG (1952-) Vietnamese
£1505 $2409 €2197 Still life (60x60cm-24x24in) s.d.98. 18-May-3 Sotheby's, Singapore #132/R est:3500-4500 (S.D 4200)
£2604 $4349 €3802 Still life (68x79cm-27x31in) s.d.2002. 12-Oct-3 Sotheby's, Singapore #117/R est:5500-6800 (S.D 7500)

LEA, Tom (1907-2001) American
£67066 $112000 €97916 Dry December (71x91cm-28x36in) 18-Oct-3 David Dike, Dallas #181/R est:110000-125000
Works on paper
£3593 $6000 €5246 Chungking (23x18cm-9x7in) mixed media. 18-Oct-3 David Dike, Dallas #273/R est:6000-8000
£15569 $26000 €22731 Dalmatia coast, Yugoslavia (43x64cm-17x25in) pastel. 18-Oct-3 David Dike, Dallas #189/R est:24000-30000

LEACH, M W (?) British
Works on paper
£400 $668 €584 Douglas Harbour (25x23cm-10x9in) init. W/C. 20-Jun-3 Chrystals Auctions, Isle of Man #240e

LEACH-JONES, Alun (1937-) Australian
£1951 $3063 €2829 Noumenon XXXIX Yantra (137x203cm-54x80in) s.i.stretcher acrylic exhib. 27-Aug-3 Christie's, Sydney #575/R est:4000-6000 (A.D 4800)

LEADER, B W (1831-1923) British

£3200	$5760	€4672	At Bettwys Coed, North Wales (51x76cm-20x30in) s.d.1896. 21-Apr-4 Brightwells, Leominster #758/R est:4000-6000

LEADER, Benjamin Williams (1831-1923) British

£500	$835	€730	Claines church, Warwickshire (30x40cm-12x16in) s. 11-Nov-3 Bonhams, Knightsbridge #225/R
£700	$1169	€1022	Old parish church of Albury (55x87cm-22x34in) s. 12-Nov-3 Sotheby's, Olympia #41/R
£800	$1488	€1168	Village church, Shere, Surrey (30x41cm-12x16in) s. 4-Mar-4 Christie's, Kensington #521/R
£1000	$1660	€1460	River landscape (32x43cm-13x17in) s.d.1910 board. 1-Oct-3 Sotheby's, Olympia #145/R est:1200-1800
£1255	$2272	€1832	The last load (30x50cm-12x20in) s.d.1906 prov. 1-Apr-4 Heffel, Vancouver #67/R est:4000-6000 (C.D 3000)
£1400	$2576	€2044	On Ullswater (22x35cm-9x14in) s. i.verso. 23-Mar-4 Anderson & Garland, Newcastle #425/R est:600-900
£1500	$2370	€2175	On the Thames at Shillingford (32x43cm-13x17in) s.d.1907 i.verso board. 4-Sep-3 Christie's, Kensington #128/R est:2000-3000
£2500	$4250	€3650	River landscape with figure beside rocks in the foreground (46x81cm-18x32in) s.d.84 prov. 19-Nov-3 Tennants, Leyburn #1113/R est:2500-3000
£3000	$5520	€4380	Ben Vorlic (22x36cm-9x14in) s.d.1858 board prov. 11-Jun-4 Christie's, London #103/R est:3000-5000
£3200	$5216	€4672	Llyn Llydaw (38x58cm-15x23in) s.i.d.1871 board. 27-Sep-3 Rogers Jones, Clwyd #102/R
£5000	$9100	€7300	Willy Lott's house, the subject of Constable's Hay Wain (30x46cm-12x18in) s.d.1901 s.i. verso prov.lit. 1-Jul-4 Sotheby's, London #359/R est:4000-6000
£5500	$9845	€8030	Stream from the hills (61x92cm-24x36in) s.d.1922 i.verso exhib. 27-May-4 Christie's, Kensington #176/R est:5000-8000
£5500	$10120	€8030	Ullswater (23x36cm-9x14in) s. s.i.verso board prov.lit. 11-Jun-4 Christie's, London #104/R est:4000-6000
£6000	$11040	€8760	Stokesay Castle, Shropshire (36x46cm-14x18in) s.d.1872 s.i.d.verso board prov.lit. 11-Jun-4 Christie's, London #105/R est:5000-8000
£7317	$13098	€10683	Slugwy, below Capel Curig (92x60cm-36x24in) s.d.1875 prov.exhib. 4-May-4 Ritchie, Toronto #34a/R est:20000-30000 (C.D 18000)
£7500	$12750	€10950	Retiring home (53x81cm-21x32in) s.d.1897. 25-Nov-3 Christie's, London #132/R est:7000-10000
£8000	$14640	€11680	Weald of Surrey from Burrow's Cross (59x90cm-23x35in) s.d.1918 prov.exhib. 6-Jul-4 Peter Wilson, Nantwich #30/R est:8000-12000
£9000	$16560	€13140	River Llugwy, Bettws-y-coed, North Wales (49x89cm-19x35in) s.d.1863 s.i.verso prov.lit. 11-Jun-4 Christie's, London #144/R est:10000-15000
£9500	$17005	€13870	Figures by a river, thought to be Llugwy, North Wales (42x62cm-17x24in) s.d.1865 board. 27-May-4 Christie's, Kensington #175/R est:7000-10000
£11000	$18700	€16060	Betws-y-coed church, on the Conway (61x91cm-24x36in) s.d.1864 prov. 19-Nov-3 Bonhams, New Bond Street #65/R est:10000-15000
£11500	$21160	€16790	Evening on the Severn (46x77cm-18x30in) s.d.1894 prov.lit. 11-Jun-4 Christie's, London #143/R est:10000-15000
£11800	$20060	€17228	Llugwy, autumn (41x61cm-16x24in) s.d.1880 panel. 25-Nov-3 Christie's, London #131/R est:8000-12000
£12000	$20400	€17520	Derwentwater, Cumberland, figures beside a river and cattle nearby (51x76cm-20x30in) s.d.1869 prov. 19-Nov-3 Tennants, Leyburn #1114/R est:10000-15000
£12500	$23000	€18250	Stream from the hills, North Wales (91x76cm-36x30in) s.d.1903 prov.exhib.lit. 11-Jun-4 Christie's, London #178/R est:8000-12000
£20000	$36400	€29200	On the Sout near Flatford Mill, Suffolk (51x76cm-20x30in) s.d.1901 s.i. stretcher prov.exhib. 1-Jul-4 Sotheby's, London #360/R est:15000-20000
£24000	$44160	€35040	Sunny stream - Beardon, Dartmoor (143x107cm-56x42in) s.d.1883 s.i.d.verso prov.lit. 11-Jun-4 Christie's, London #117/R est:15000-20000
£26000	$47840	€37960	English country churchyard, autumn (81x136cm-32x54in) s.d.63 prov.exhib.lit. 11-Jun-4 Christie's, London #119/R est:30000-50000
£39000	$71760	€56940	Lonely grange (92x154cm-36x61in) s.d.1902 s.i.verso prov.exhib.lit. 11-Jun-4 Christie's, London #145/R est:20000-30000
£43000	$79120	€62780	Summer time, through the hayfields, Worcestershire (70x120cm-28x47in) s.d.1866 prov.lit. 11-Jun-4 Christie's, London #118/R est:20000-25000
£145000	$246500	€211700	Summer's day - when the south wind congregates in crowds, floating mountains (127x216cm-50x85in) s.d.1888 prov.exhib.lit. 27-Nov-3 Sotheby's, London #24/R est:80000-120000

LEADER, Benjamin Williams (attrib) (1831-1923) British

£380	$703	€555	An angler in river and mountain landscape (13x33cm-5x13in) init.d. 13-Feb-4 Keys, Aylsham #690/R
£860	$1462	€1256	The Wetter Horn (35x25cm-14x10in) bears sig. 27-Nov-3 Greenslade Hunt, Taunton #1005/R
£2100	$3276	€3045	Tranquil river landscape, mountains beyond (51x76cm-20x30in) indis.sig. 20-Oct-2 Desmond Judd, Cranbrook #817

LEADER, Charles (19th C) British

£640	$1165	€934	Mountain river landscape. River landscape (30x41cm-12x16in) s. pair. 29-Jun-4 Bonhams, Knowle #83
£1400	$2590	€2044	River landscape with cottages beyond (61x91cm-24x36in) s. 10-Feb-4 Bonhams, Knightsbridge #180/R est:1200-1800
£3000	$5100	€4380	Highland landscape (61x91cm-24x36in) s. pair. 29-Oct-3 Bonhams, Chester #431/R est:3000-4000

LEADER, Walton (1877-1966) American

£1218	$1900	€1778	Bluebonnets (41x51cm-16x20in) s.verso. 12-Apr-3 Auctions by the Bay, Alameda #247/R
£1618	$2800	€2362	Wash through the hills (41x51cm-16x20in) s. i.verso. 13-Dec-3 Weschler, Washington #566 est:1000-1500
£1850	$3200	€2701	Bluebonnet valley (41x51cm-16x20in) s. i.verso. 13-Dec-3 Weschler, Washington #567 est:1000-1500

LEAF, June (1929-) American

£1765	$3000	€2577	Untitled (56x74cm-22x29in) s.d.1962 oil pastel collage. 9-Nov-3 Wright, Chicago #417 est:3000-4000

Works on paper

£958	$1600	€1399	Murder in the Bronx (117x102cm-46x40in) s. mixed media board. 19-Oct-3 Bonhams & Butterfields, Los Angeles #7072 est:500-700

LEAKE, Gerald (1885-1975) American

£1143	$2000	€1669	Leaving for war (76x89cm-30x35in) s. 19-Dec-3 Sotheby's, New York #1140/R est:2500-3500

LEAKEY, James (1775-1865) British

£4000	$6800	€5840	Reading the local news (37x34cm-15x13in) s.d.1820 panel. 25-Nov-3 Christie's, London #51/R est:4000-6000

LEAL, Pedro Paulo (1894-?) Brazilian

£3480	$6159	€5220	Landscape (77x90cm-30x35in) s. 27-Apr-4 Bolsa de Arte, Rio de Janeiro #79/R (B.R 19000)

LEANDRE, Charles (1862-1930) French

£704	$1141	€1000	Trou de memoire ou les pommes cuites (57x43cm-22x17in) s. chl htd chalk. 11-Aug-3 Boscher, Cherbourg #728

Works on paper

£350	$584	€500	Boxeur (66x46cm-26x18in) s. crayon dr. 29-Jun-3 St-Germain-en-Laye Encheres #12/R
£400	$720	€600	Sur le banc (22x15cm-9x6in) s.d.1890 W/C gouache crayon. 26-Apr-4 Tajan, Paris #2
£3944	$6823	€5600	Chemin en bord de chateau (74x93cm-29x37in) s.d.1904 pastel canvas. 12-Dec-3 Piasa, Paris #100/R est:1500-2000

LEAPER, Tom (?) British

Works on paper

£1200	$1992	€1752	The Abbey Gardens, Tresco (67x96cm-26x38in) s. pastel. 2-Oct-3 Lane, Penzance #305 est:1000-1200

LEAR, Edward (1812-1888) British

£22000	$40480	€32120	View of the Citadel, Corfu, with orange grove (48x76cm-19x30in) s. 11-Jun-4 Christie's, London #146/R est:20000-30000

Prints

£1728	$3128	€2523	Leadbeater's cockatoo (49x33cm-19x13in) hand col lithograph. 30-Mar-4 Christie's, Melbourne #359/R est:3500-4000 (A.D 4200)

Works on paper

£280	$501	€409	Study of pine trees (28x20cm-11x8in) i. pencil. 25-May-4 Bonhams, Knightsbridge #178/R
£450	$806	€657	The Roman campagnia (13x18cm-5x7in) s.i. pen ink. 25-May-4 Bonhams, Knightsbridge #76/R
£652	$1200	€952	Head of a Turk (13x10cm-5x4in) W/C pencil. 25-Jun-4 Freeman, Philadelphia #36/R
£750	$1275	€1095	Italian landscape (24x37cm-9x15in) s.d.1840 pencil prov. 4-Nov-3 Bonhams, New Bond Street #44/R
£800	$1456	€1168	Kom Ombos (7x15cm-3x6in) i.d.1867 brown ink W/C. 1-Jul-4 Christie's, Kensington #182
£900	$1620	€1314	Flowing like a crystal river, Platania, Crete (31x52cm-12x20in) i. pen brown ink wash over pencil prov. 21-Jan-4 Sotheby's, Olympia #144/R est:1000-1500
£900	$1638	€1314	Cannes (11x26cm-4x10in) i.d.1865 pencil ink W/C prov. sold with another by different hand. 1-Jul-4 Christie's, Kensington #388
£950	$1615	€1387	Ruined tower in a river landscape (22x36cm-9x14in) pencil pen brown ink brown wash. 20-Nov-3 Christie's, London #131/R
£1000	$1830	€1460	Viosa, Albania (12x18cm-5x7in) i.d.16 April 1857 W/C over pen pencil prov. 7-Apr-4 Bonhams, Bury St Edmunds #419/R est:800-1200
£1050	$1754	€1533	Middle Eastern lake (10x25cm-4x10in) i. pencil W/C dr. 17-Oct-3 Keys, Aylsham #501
£1300	$2392	€1898	Thebes, Valley of the Tombs of the Kings (27x42cm-11x17in) i.d.21 Feby 1854 pencil brown ink W/C exhib. 25-Mar-4 Christie's, Kensington #45/R est:800-1200
£1350	$2430	€1971	Mandello (25x35cm-10x14in) i.d.13 October 1837 pencil htd white. 22-Apr-4 Lawrence, Crewkerne #752/R est:800-1200
£1400	$2380	€2044	Rio Nero, Italy (28x46cm-11x18in) i.d.1847 pencil pen brown ink prov.exhib. 20-Nov-3 Christie's, London #130/R est:1500-2000
£1500	$2760	€2190	Rio Nero, Italy (28x46cm-11x18in) i.d.27 Spet 1847 pencil brown ink prov.exhib. 25-Mar-4 Christie's, Kensington #47/R est:1500-2000
£1500	$2760	€2190	Gibeah (49x16cm-19x6in) indis.i.d.9 May 1838 pencil brown ink W/C prov. 25-Mar-4 Christie's, Kensington #48/R est:800-1200
£1550	$2573	€2263	Nice (8x13cm-3x5in) pen ink wash. 3-Oct-3 Mallams, Oxford #122/R est:800-1200
£1600	$2960	€2336	Lago Maggiore, Italy (10x22cm-4x9in) i.d.May 29 1867 W/C. 9-Mar-4 Bonhams, New Bond Street #52/R est:1000-1500
£1800	$3060	€2628	Civita Castellana (17x25cm-7x10in) s.i.d.1843 pencil pen brown ink brown wash htd white. 20-Nov-3 Christie's, London #129/R est:2000-3000
£1800	$3294	€2628	Lonely valley of Zebbug, Malta (16x25cm-6x10in) i.d.1866 pencil brown ink W/C. 3-Jun-4 Christie's, London #167/R est:2000-3000
£2100	$3822	€3066	Lago d'Idro and Rocca D'Anfo (10x22cm-4x9in) i. pen brown ink blue lilac grey washes. 29-Jun-4 Anderson & Garland, Newcastle #243/R est:2000-3000
£2200	$3894	€3212	Temple of Horus, Edfu, Egypt (24x42cm-9x17in) s.i. W/C pen ink. 27-Apr-4 Bonhams, New Bond Street #63/R est:2500-3500
£2300	$4186	€3358	Lago d'Idro (10x22cm-4x9in) i. pen brown ink blue ochre reddish wash. 29-Jun-4 Anderson & Garland, Newcastle #241/R est:2000-3500
£2400	$4392	€3504	Landscape scene, probably Ascensio, Corfu (33x51cm-13x20in) bears i.d.1856 verso pen brown ink over pencil. 8-Jul-4 Lawrence, Crewkerne #1522/R est:1500-2500
£2600	$4420	€3796	Near Thebes, Egypt (9x18cm-4x7in) mono.i.d.1884 W/C htd white prov. 20-Nov-3 Christie's, London #126/R est:1000-1500
£2800	$4676	€4088	Beer suez (14x22cm-6x9in) i. pen brown ink W/C over pencil prov. 14-Oct-3 Sotheby's, London #114/R est:3000-4000
£2800	$5152	€4088	Assiout, Egypt (13x30cm-5x12in) i.d.1867 verso pen ink W/C prov. 8-Jun-4 Bonhams, New Bond Street #58/R est:2000-2500
£2800	$5236	€4200	Desert landscape (15x23cm-6x9in) i.d.August 1856 April 1857 pencil wash. 20-Jul-4 Peter Francis, Wales #72 est:3000-3500
£3000	$5100	€4380	Bocche di Cattaro, Montenegro (33x48cm-13x19in) i. pen ink wash over pencil. 27-Nov-3 Sotheby's, London #302/R est:3000-4000
£3000	$5520	€4380	Corfu from Viro, Greece (32x50cm-13x20in) pencil lit. 8-Jun-4 Bonhams, New Bond Street #59/R est:1500-2000
£3200	$5312	€4672	View of Palaiokhora (20x33cm-8x13in) d.29 April 1864 pen ink wash. 3-Oct-3 Mallams, Oxford #121/R est:3000-5000
£3200	$5824	€4672	St Erenzo and Lerici from Palmaria (12x35cm-5x14in) i.d.1860 pen brown ink blue lilac grey washes. 29-Jun-4 Anderson & Garland, Newcastle #242/R est:2500-4000
£3500	$5845	€5110	View at Wadi Halfa, Egypt (15x23cm-6x9in) i. pen brown ink over pencil. 14-Oct-3 Sotheby's, London #115/R est:3000-4000

£3500	$6020	€5110	Cervera, on the Roman campagna (10x20cm-4x8in) init.i. pencil W/C prov.exhib. 3-Dec-3 Christie's, Kensington #25/R est:3000-5000
£3800	$6460	€5548	Honiston Crag, near Buttermere, Cumbria (18x26cm-7x10in) i.d.1836 pencil W/C htd white prov. 20-Nov-3 Christie's, London #54/R est:1500-2500
£3800	$6954	€5548	View of Interlaken, Switzerland (28x46cm-11x18in) i. pencil blue brown ink grey blue wash prov.exhib. 3-Jun-4 Christie's, London #166/R est:3000-5000
£5000	$8500	€7300	Ithaca, the fountain of Arethusa (30x22cm-12x9in) i.d.May 1848 pencil pen brown ink W/C htd bodycol prov. 20-Nov-3 Christie's, London #56/R est:3000-5000
£5000	$9200	€7300	Distant view of Nice from the hills (15x23cm-6x9in) pen ink W/C over pencil htd bodycol gum arabic. 26-Mar-4 Sotheby's, London #131/R est:3000-5000
£5200	$9568	€7592	Feluccas on the Nile near Abu-Simbel (8x17cm-3x7in) mono.d.1884 W/C over pencil htd bodycol. 26-Mar-4 Sotheby's, London #134/R est:3000-5000
£6000	$10200	€8760	Greek figures and mules on a rocky track, Crete (16x26cm-6x10in) i. pencil pen brown ink W/C htd white prov. 20-Nov-3 Christie's, London #55/R est:5000-8000
£6000	$11040	€8760	Denderah on the Nile (17x36cm-7x14in) mono.i. W/C over pencil htd bodycol prov. 26-Mar-4 Sotheby's, London #133/R est:4000-6000
£6500	$11895	€9490	Palaiukhora, Crete (22x35cm-9x14in) i.d.1864 brown ink W/C htd white. 3-Jun-4 Christie's, London #165/R est:3000-5000
£6800	$12172	€9928	Edfoo - sunrise (32x51cm-13x20in) d.12 Feb 1854 on ink W/C. 25-May-4 Sworder & Son, Bishops Stortford #339/R est:3000-4000
£7000	$11900	€10220	Sunrise at Erment, Egypt (30x50cm-12x20in) i.d.1854 pencil pen brown ink W/C htd white. 20-Nov-3 Christie's, London #127/R est:8000-12000
£7000	$11900	€10220	Monastery of Baarlam (16x28cm-6x10in) mono. W/C over pencil htd bodycol. 18-Nov-3 Sotheby's, London #1/R est:7000-10000
£7500	$12750	€10950	Ain Gedi and the Dead Sea, Israel (34x49cm-13x19in) i.d.19 April 1858 pencil pen red brown ink W/C prov. 20-Nov-3 Christie's, London #57/R est:8000-12000
£7800	$14196	€11388	Gozo, Malta (16x25cm-6x10in) mono.i.d.1866 W/C htd bodycol. 1-Jul-4 Sotheby's, London #211/R est:3000-5000
£8500	$14450	€12410	Windermere from Lowwood,Cumbria (17x26cm-7x10in) i.d.1836 pencil grey blue paper prov. 20-Nov-3 Christie's, London #53/R est:3000-5000
£8500	$15640	€12410	View of the Ducal Palace, Massa, Northern Italy (16x25cm-6x10in) mono. W/C over pencil bodycol. 26-Mar-4 Sotheby's, London #132/R est:4000-6000
£11000	$19470	€16060	Matahleb, Malta (36x53cm-14x21in) i.d.11 Feby 1866 W/C bodycol prov. 27-Apr-4 Bonhams, New Bond Street #77/R est:12000-18000
£12000	$19560	€17520	View of the Ghats at Benares from the river Ganges (23x38cm-9x15in) mono.d.1875 i.verso pencil W/C touches bodycol prov. 24-Sep-3 Christie's, London #48/R est:7000-10000
£13000	$23660	€18980	Ramesseum, Thebes (29x49cm-11x19in) i.d.1854 pen brown ink W/C over pencil. 1-Jul-4 Sotheby's, London #236/R est:10000-15000
£16000	$27200	€23360	Varied Lorikeet, illustration for Sir W Jardine's 'The Naturalist's Library' (17x11cm-7x4in) s.i. pencil pen brown in, W/C gum arabic prov.exhib.lit. 20-Nov-3 Christie's, London #74/R est:10000-15000
£16000	$27200	€23360	Great Green Macaw, an illustration for Sir W. Jardine's The Naturalist Library' (18x11cm-7x4in) s.i. pencil pen brown ink W/C htd gum arabic prov.exhib.lit. 20-Nov-3 Christie's, London #75/R est:10000-15000
£17000	$28900	€24820	Distant view of Athens (25x48cm-10x19in) s.i.d.1854 pen ink W/C over pencil htd bodycol prov. 18-Nov-3 Sotheby's, London #2/R est:15000-20000
£18000	$30600	€26280	Derwentwater and six other sketches of the Lake District (16x25cm-6x10in) i.d.1836 pencil htd white grey blue paper seven prov. 20-Nov-3 Christie's, London #77/R est:12000-18000
£27000	$49140	€39420	Cedars of Lebanon (17x25cm-7x10in) mono.d.1858/1862 W/C over pencil htd bodycol buff paper. 1-Jul-4 Sotheby's, London #212/R est:7000-10000

LEAR, Edward (attrib) (1812-1888) British

Works on paper

£300	$540	€450	Continental landscape with figures (17x36cm-7x14in) mono.d. W/C. 21-Apr-4 Wingetts, Wrexham #270

LEAR, John (20th C) American

£236	$425	€345	In suspense (33x18cm-13x7in) prov. 23-Jan-4 Freeman, Philadelphia #240/R
£472	$850	€689	Landing (30x23cm-12x9in) s. board. 23-Jan-4 Freeman, Philadelphia #143/R
£667	$1200	€974	Patchwork fragment (25x36cm-10x14in) s. canvasboard. 23-Jan-4 Freeman, Philadelphia #174/R
£750	$1350	€1095	Landscape (41x30cm-16x12in) s. board exhib. 25-Apr-4 Locati, Maple Glen #470202/R
£1557	$2600	€2273	Tattered patches (20x25cm-8x10in) s. board. 20-Jun-3 Freeman, Philadelphia #223/R est:400-600

Works on paper

£472	$850	€689	Figures (48x64cm-19x25in) s.d.87 W/C. 23-Jan-4 Freeman, Philadelphia #60/R
£520	$900	€759	New mandella (43x53cm-17x21in) s.d.97 W/C. 10-Dec-3 Alderfer's, Hatfield #445/R est:1500-2000
£983	$1700	€1435	Nude male reclining in foreground looking at woman in white (46x69cm-18x27in) s. W/C. 10-Dec-3 Alderfer's, Hatfield #444/R est:1500-2000
£1006	$1600	€1469	Two nude and partially nude men standing on rocks lifting weights (20x28cm-8x11in) s. W/C. 10-Sep-3 Alderfer's, Hatfield #313/R est:800-1000

LEARY, Elizabeth W (20th C) American

£250	$425	€365	Wild grapes (10x18cm-4x7in) s.i.d.1996 panel. 21-Nov-3 Skinner, Boston #279/R

LEASON, Percival Alexander (1889-1959) Australian

£680	$1251	€993	Still life stocks (45x35cm-18x14in) s. 29-Mar-4 Thomson Roddick & Medcalf, Edinburgh #267

Works on paper

£345	$538	€500	Unusual encounter (21x9cm-8x4in) s. W/C. 1-Aug-2 Joel, Victoria #227 est:1000-1500 (A.D 1000)

LEATHAM, William J (fl.1840-1855) British

Works on paper

£600	$1098	€876	Keeling through a squall (64x99cm-25x39in) s.d.44 W/C. 27-Jan-4 Bonhams, Knightsbridge #30/R

LEAVER, Charles (19th C) British

£600	$1020	€876	Winter landscape with huntsman and his dog before cottages (20cm-8in circular) s.d.1879. 29-Oct-3 Bonhams, Chester #482
£820	$1369	€1189	Deer in a wooded parkland (30x38cm-12x15in) s.d.1865. 22-Jun-3 Desmond Judd, Cranbrook #1081
£850	$1420	€1241	Forest track (61x92cm-24x36in) s.d.1872. 13-Nov-3 Christie's, Kensington #133/R
£1400	$2296	€2044	Near Lyndhurst, Hampshire, wooded landscape with figure and cottage (74x49cm-29x19in) s.d.1867 i.d. stretcher. 3-Jun-3 Fellows & Sons, Birmingham #79/R est:1500-2500
£1600	$2768	€2336	Ratherarns Oak-Farm amid snow covered woods (76x127cm-30x50in) s. 10-Dec-3 Bonhams, Bury St Edmunds #574a est:1500-2000
£2200	$4114	€3212	Winter landscape with mother and child approaching Nassington (51x76cm-20x30in) s. 22-Jul-4 Tennants, Leyburn #829/R est:1000-1200

LEAVER, Charles (attrib) (19th C) British

£2000	$3400	€2920	Winter landscape with figure on a path and hens beside a barn nearby (43x54cm-17x21in) prov. 19-Nov-3 Tennants, Leyburn #1082/R est:700-9000

LEAVER, Noel Harry (1889-1951) British

Works on paper

£420	$756	€613	Norfolk landscape with figures beside a pond, cottages and a church (25x35cm-10x14in) s. pencil W/C. 21-Apr-4 Tennants, Leyburn #968
£420	$752	€613	Fingest Church, Buckinghamshire (37x26cm-15x10in) s. bears i.verso W/C. 17-Mar-4 Bonhams, Chester #281
£420	$785	€613	The little flower shop (30x28cm-12x11in) s.i. pencil W/C htd white. 22-Jul-4 Tennants, Leyburn #710
£450	$765	€657	Robin Hodd Bay (25x35cm-10x14in) s. W/C. 18-Nov-3 Sotheby's, Olympia #31/R
£540	$886	€788	Continental street scene with figures promenading in the sunlight (35x24cm-14x9in) s. W/C. 30-May-3 Bigwood, Stratford on Avon #301
£580	$1044	€847	Eastern archway (25x35cm-10x14in) s.i. pencil W/C prov. 21-Apr-4 Tennants, Leyburn #967
£719	$1200	€1050	Scene in York (51x36cm-20x14in) s. W/C. 20-Jun-3 Freeman, Philadelphia #21/R est:400-600
£820	$1517	€1197	Distant Appenines (36x26cm-14x10in) s. W/C. 14-Jul-4 Bonhams, Chester #334
£919	$1700	€1342	Castle city scene (46x33cm-18x13in) W/C. 13-Feb-4 Du Mouchelle, Detroit #2175/R est:1500-2000
£1000	$1730	€1460	Old watermill (38x51cm-15x20in) s. W/C. 11-Dec-3 Lyon & Turnbull, Edinburgh #73/R est:1000-1500
£1000	$1850	€1460	Continental street scene. W/C. 14-Jan-4 Brightwells, Leominster #779 est:150-200
£1008	$1855	€1472	Wells Cathedral (37x27cm-15x11in) s. W/C. 14-Jun-4 Waddingtons, Toronto #88/R est:1500-2500 (C.D 2500)
£1042	$1656	€1521	British castle and river (24x36cm-9x14in) s. W/C. 1-May-3 Dunbar Sloane, Wellington #382 est:400-800 (NZ.D 3000)
£1042	$1656	€1521	Green lawns of Oxford (34x24cm-13x9in) s. W/C. 1-May-3 Dunbar Sloane, Wellington #383 est:400-800 (NZ.D 3000)
£1210	$2226	€1767	Street in Tunis (37x27cm-15x11in) s. W/C. 14-Jun-4 Waddingtons, Toronto #90/R est:1500-2500 (C.D 3000)
£1300	$2405	€1898	River landscape with a church (25x36cm-10x14in) s. W/C. 14-Jan-4 Brightwells, Leominster #778 est:150-200
£1400	$2296	€2044	Riverside scene with moored sailing vessels and a pleasure yacht (37x27cm-15x11in) s. W/C. 30-May-3 Bigwood, Stratford on Avon #305
£1400	$2506	€2044	Street in North Africa (16x25cm-6x10in) s. W/C bodycol. 25-May-4 Bonhams, Knightsbridge #59/R est:1500-2000
£1400	$2548	€2044	Westminster from the Embankment (18x25cm-7x10in) s. pencil W/C htd white. 1-Jul-4 Christie's, Kensington #450/R est:600-800
£1500	$2505	€2190	Church of St. Pierre Coutances (26x36cm-10x14in) s.i. W/C. 7-Oct-3 Fellows & Sons, Birmingham #460/R est:500-800
£1500	$2805	€2190	English cathedral seen from an ancient wall with cottages nearby (25x35cm-10x14in) s. pencil W/C. 22-Jul-4 Tennants, Leyburn #655/R est:1200-1500
£1600	$2944	€2336	Robin Hood's Bay (25x36cm-10x14in) s. W/C. 24-Mar-4 Hamptons Fine Art, Godalming #258/R
£1700	$3043	€2482	Lincoln cathedral (34x52cm-13x20in) s. W/C. 25-May-4 Bonhams, Knightsbridge #61/R est:1000-1500
£1700	$3111	€2550	Market Cross, Chichester (52x37cm-20x15in) s. W/C. 27-Jul-4 Henry Adams, Chichester #376/R est:2000-3000
£1950	$3315	€2847	Dutch canal (37x26cm-15x10in) s. W/C. 18-Nov-3 Bonhams, Leeds #68/R est:1000-1500
£2200	$3938	€3212	Arched entrance to a North African town (36x51cm-14x20in) s. W/C. 25-May-4 Bonhams, Knightsbridge #60/R est:2500-3000
£2250	$4095	€3285	North African town scene with mosque in the background (27x37cm-11x15in) s. W/C. 3-Feb-4 Sworder & Son, Bishops Stortford #288/R est:1000-1500
£2400	$4080	€3504	Sunlit eastern gateway with figures (35x51cm-14x20in) s. pencil W/C. 19-Nov-3 Tennants, Leyburn #888/R est:1800-2500
£2600	$4680	€3796	Still life of anemones and other flowers in a vase with book nearby (35x51cm-14x20in) s. pencil W/C gouache. 21-Apr-4 Tennants, Leyburn #969/R est:700-900
£3000	$5400	€4380	Whitby harbour with figures on quayside and boats in foreground (28x36cm-11x14in) s. pencil W/C gouache htd white prov. 21-Apr-4 Tennants, Leyburn #970/R est:1400-1600
£3200	$5888	€4672	At the mosque (25x36cm-10x14in) s. W/C bodycol pair. 8-Jun-4 Bonhams, New Bond Street #134/R est:1000-1500
£3307	$6250	€4828	On Tunisian shores (36x51cm-14x20in) s. i.verso W/C board. 21-Feb-4 Jeffery Burchard, Florida #36a/R

LEAVITT, Edward C (1842-1904) American

£645	$1200	€942	Pink roses (19x25cm-7x10in) s.d.1894. 5-Mar-4 Skinner, Boston #264/R
£703	$1300	€1026	Still life with grapes (20x30cm-8x12in) s. 13-Mar-4 Susanin's, Chicago #6193/R
£761	$1400	€1111	Still life with urn and roses (61x30cm-24x12in) s. canvasboard. 11-Jun-4 David Rago, Lambertville #289/R est:600-900
£854	$1400	€1238	Still life with grapes (15x30cm-6x12in) s.d.1900. 2-Jun-3 Grogan, Boston #642/R
£1215	$2200	€1774	Still life of roses spilling from a basket beside a glass of water (51x81cm-20x32in) s. 2-Apr-4 Eldred, East Dennis #879/R est:2000-3000
£2374	$4250	€3466	Still life with fruit (51x56cm-20x22in) s.d.1891. 16-May-4 CRN Auctions, Cambridge #7/R
£2395	$4000	€3497	Still life with gladiolas (53x38cm-21x15in) s. painted c.1890. 9-Oct-3 Christie's, Rockefeller NY #25/R est:5000-7000
£2907	$5000	€4244	Still life with raspberries (20x40cm-8x16in) s.d.1900. 3-Dec-3 Doyle, New York #174/R est:3000-5000

£2907 $5000 €4244 Still life with yellow pears (25x40cm-10x16in) s.d.1899. 3-Dec-3 Doyle, New York #175/R est:3000-5000

LEBADANG (1922-) French/Vietnamese
£621 $1000 €907 Abandoned garden (71x91cm-28x36in) 20-Aug-3 James Julia, Fairfield #958/R

LEBAS, Gabriel-Hippolyte (1812-1880) French
£1329 $2259 €1900 Marine au clair de lune (64x100cm-25x39in) s.d.1876. 27-Nov-3 Millon & Associes, Paris #189/R est:1500-2000

LEBAS, Leonie (19th C) French
£529 $1000 €772 Paris street scene (25x34cm-10x13in) s. 22-Feb-4 Bonhams & Butterfields, Los Angeles #7037 est:1500-2000

LEBASQUE, Henri (1865-1937) French
£5973 $11050 €8900 Bord de riviere (14x21cm-6x8in) st.sig. panel. 14-Mar-4 Eric Pillon, Calais #117/R
£6376 $11860 €9500 Les bords de la Marne a Pomponne (23x33cm-9x13in) s. cardboard painted c.1906-1907 lit. 2-Mar-4 Artcurial Briest, Paris #129/R est:8000-10000
£6500 $10335 €9425 Vase de fleurs (41x27cm-16x11in) s. 11-Sep-3 Christie's, Kensington #18/R est:8000-12000
£6875 $11000 €10038 Nature morte a la theiere et aux fruits (41x51cm-16x20in) s. masonite. 18-Sep-3 Swann Galleries, New York #359/R est:10000-15000
£10417 $17396 €15000 Roses dans un pichet (46x55cm-18x22in) s.d.1912. 21-Oct-3 Fraysse & Associes, Paris #17/R
£12000 $21601 €18000 Jeune garcon au balcon en bord de mer (52x44cm-20x17in) s. 26-Apr-4 Tajan, Paris #112/R est:15000-25000
£14803 $27237 €22500 Jeune fille a la mandoline (46x38cm-18x15in) s. 24-Jun-4 Credit Municipal, Paris #50/R est:20000-25000
£15000 $27600 €21900 Paysage (46x61cm-18x24in) s. prov. 22-Jun-4 Sotheby's, London #236/R est:18000-25000
£16000 $28801 €24000 Pichet de fleurs sur une table (73x60cm-29x24in) s. 26-Apr-4 Tajan, Paris #113/R est:10000-12000
£17647 $30000 €25765 Nu au fauteuil (46x56cm-18x22in) s. prov. 5-Nov-3 Christie's, Rockefeller NY #245/R est:35000-45000
£18000 $33120 €26280 Nu a la fenetre (55x37cm-22x15in) s. prov. 22-Jun-4 Sotheby's, London #146/R est:20000-30000
£20724 $38132 €31500 Homme balayant la neige dans une cour (46x55cm-18x22in) s. 22-Jun-4 Ribeyre & Baron, Paris #49/R est:20000-30000
£20979 $36084 €30000 Le canet (46x55cm-18x22in) s. 2-Dec-3 Calmels Cohen, Paris #60/R est:30000-40000
£22000 $40480 €32120 Femme a sa coiffure assise dans un fauteuil (55x46cm-22x18in) s. 22-Jun-4 Sotheby's, London #149/R est:25000-35000
£22346 $40000 €32625 Roses dans un pichet (46x55cm-18x22in) st.sig. prov. 6-May-4 Sotheby's, New York #433/R est:25000-35000
£40000 $72800 €58400 La place a Monterrain (60x72cm-24x28in) s. painted c.1895 prov. 3-Feb-4 Christie's, London #150/R est:40000-60000
£41958 $71329 €60000 Le repos (92x119cm-36x47in) s. 27-Nov-3 Millon & Associes, Paris #199/R est:60000-80000
£42000 $77280 €61320 La partie de peche (38x46cm-15x18in) s. painted c.1920 prov. 23-Jun-4 Christie's, London #132/R est:30000-40000
£44118 $75000 €64412 Villa Demiere, St Tropez (74x92cm-29x36in) s. prov. 5-Nov-3 Christie's, Rockefeller NY #259/R est:80000-100000
£47059 $80000 €68706 Paris, remorqueur sur la Seine (54x65cm-21x26in) s.d.04 prov. 5-Nov-3 Christie's, Rockefeller NY #223/R est:80000-120000
£47486 $85000 €69330 Lecture au jardin (44x36cm-17x14in) s. prov. 6-May-4 Sotheby's, New York #252/R est:30000-40000
£55866 $100000 €81564 Nu au cannet (74x58cm-29x23in) s. painted 1926 prov. 6-May-4 Sotheby's, New York #255/R est:100000-150000
£64706 $110000 €94471 Jeune peintre (81x66cm-32x26in) painted c.1904-05 prov. 6-Nov-3 Sotheby's, New York #145/R est:120000-180000
£65000 $119600 €94900 Nu sur le lit (73x54cm-29x21in) s. painted c.1927-28 prov. 22-Jun-4 Sotheby's, London #145/R est:70000-100000
£80000 $145600 €116800 Nu sur une peau de panthere (60x92cm-24x36in) st.sig. painted c.1932. 4-Feb-4 Sotheby's, London #240/R est:80000-120000
£106145 $190000 €154972 Pierrefonds, la promenade en foret (73x60cm-29x24in) s. painted c.1907 prov. 5-May-4 Christie's, Rockefeller NY #274/R est:150000-200000
£106145 $190000 €154972 Femme nue allongee (73x100cm-29x39in) s. prov. 6-May-4 Sotheby's, New York #256/R est:150000-200000
£113333 $207400 €170000 Nono, fillette de l'artiste (54x45cm-21x18in) s. prov. 6-Jun-4 Rouillac, Vendome #45

Works on paper
£312 $521 €450 Sculpteur ou etude pour mon fils (27x17cm-11x7in) s. lead pencil prov. 21-Oct-3 Artcurial Briest, Paris #2
£329 $516 €480 Soldat au repos (14x19cm-6x7in) s. W/C. 20-Apr-3 Deauville, France #9
£329 $516 €480 Soldat au repos (14x19cm-6x7in) s. W/C. 20-Apr-3 Deauville, France #10
£356 $559 €520 Soldat au repos (14x19cm-6x7in) s. W/C. 20-Apr-3 Deauville, France #11
£403 $745 €600 Jeune femme a la coiffe orientale (27x22cm-11x9in) s. graphite dr. 14-Mar-4 Eric Pillon, Calais #98/R
£420 $722 €600 Le bain de mer (26x33cm-10x13in) crayon. 3-Dec-3 Tajan, Paris #128/R
£455 $800 €664 Young woman bathing (10x23cm-4x9in) s. W/C hand study verso double-sided. 23-May-4 Hindman, Chicago #51/R
£510 $913 €750 Baigneuses (15x25cm-6x10in) W/C black pencil. 19-Mar-4 Piasa, Paris #212
£600 $1038 €876 Seated woman with long earrings (30x24cm-12x9in) s. black chk. 12-Dec-3 Christie's, Kensington #512/R
£670 $1200 €978 Standing model (48x30cm-19x12in) s. ink ink wash. 7-May-4 Sloans & Kenyon, Bethesda #1641/R
£750 $1253 €1095 Rosena in traditional dress (60x40cm-24x16in) s.verso W/C bodycol prov. 21-Oct-3 Bonhams, Knightsbridge #42/R
£800 $1472 €1168 Femme s'habillant (23x16cm-9x6in) s. W/C pencil. 24-Mar-4 Sotheby's, Olympia #26/R
£1000 $1840 €1460 Vase de fleurs (42x24cm-17x9in) s. W/C gouache over pencil prov. 24-Mar-4 Sotheby's, Olympia #27/R est:800-1200
£1067 $1952 €1600 Les grands arbres (28x20cm-11x8in) s. W/C graphite. 6-Jun-4 Anaf, Lyon #397/R est:1600-1800
£1608 $2734 €2300 Port de Bretagne (29x43cm-11x17in) s. W/C chl. 18-Nov-3 Pierre Berge, Paris #91/R est:1700-1800
£1748 $2972 €2500 Femme assise a la terasse (30x38cm-12x15in) s. W/C. 18-Nov-3 Vanderkindere, Brussels #156 est:2500-3500
£1905 $3410 €2800 Femme au chale assise (19x14cm-7x6in) s. gouache lead pencil. 19-Mar-4 Millon & Associes, Paris #76/R est:1000-1200
£2162 $4000 €3157 Nu allonge (42x55cm-17x22in) s. gouache W/C over chl. 12-Feb-4 Sotheby's, New York #7/R est:2500-3500
£2260 $3549 €3300 Bords de Seine a Vezillon (40x35cm-16x14in) s. W/C gouache exec.c.1913. 20-Apr-3 Deauville, France #8/R est:3000-3500
£2606 $4508 €3700 Prefailles, sur la terrasse (26x28cm-10x11in) bears sig. W/C. 13-Dec-3 Touati, Paris #136/R est:4000-4500
£2752 $5063 €4100 La plage du Canet (20x26cm-8x10in) s. W/C chl. 26-Mar-4 Neret-Minet, Paris #6/R est:3000
£2778 $4639 €4000 Nu a la fenetre (27x17cm-11x7in) s. W/C lead pencil paper on board prov. 21-Oct-3 Artcurial Briest, Paris #1/R est:4000-5000
£2800 $5152 €4088 Sur la plage (17x23cm-7x9in) s. W/C pencil pen ink. 24-Mar-4 Sotheby's, Olympia #4/R est:1500-2000
£2819 $5215 €4200 Jeune femme assise (59x40cm-23x16in) st.sig. W/C gouache lit. 14-Mar-4 Eric Pillon, Calais #102/R
£3893 $7240 €5800 Femme des Iles (29x23cm-11x9in) s. W/C chl. 3-Mar-4 Tajan, Paris #66/R est:2000-3000
£4500 $7515 €6570 Femme au jardin (38x51cm-15x20in) s. gouache W/C over chl. 21-Oct-3 Sotheby's, London #151/R est:5000-7000
£4800 $8832 €7008 La Barque au port (29x43cm-11x17in) s. pencil W/C. 24-Mar-4 Sotheby's, Olympia #3/R est:2500-3500
£4895 $8419 €7000 La sortie de bain (27x21cm-11x8in) s. W/C. 3-Dec-3 Tajan, Paris #127/R est:5000-7000
£5500 $9185 €8030 Sur la plage (30x37cm-12x15in) s. W/C gouache chl. 22-Oct-3 Sotheby's, Olympia #54/R est:4000-5000
£8000 $14720 €11680 Point St Gildas, scene de plage (28x42cm-11x17in) s. W/C pencil exec 1922 prov. 24-Jun-4 Christie's, London #318/R est:10000-15000
£9000 $16560 €13500 Femme dans un paysage a Sanary (47x30cm-19x12in) s. W/C exec. c.1911. 8-Jun-4 Artcurial Briest, Paris #120/R est:5000-6000

LEBDUSKA, Lawrence (1894-1966) American
£252 $400 €368 Deer in a landscape (30x41cm-12x16in) indis.sig. canvas on board. 10-Sep-3 Sotheby's, New York #169/R
£736 $1200 €1075 Crucifixion (76x61cm-30x24in) s.d.May 45. 25-Sep-3 Christie's, Rockefeller NY #638/R est:2000-3000
£983 $1700 €1435 Rhinoceri and hippopotamus in a stream. s.d.1943 masonite. 13-Dec-3 Sloans & Kenyon, Bethesda #808/R est:1000-1250

LEBEDA, Otakar (1877-1901) Czechoslovakian
£7002 $13023 €10223 From Okor Castle (53x39cm-21x15in) s.d.97 board. 6-Mar-4 Dorotheum, Prague #90/R est:80000-120000 (C.KR 340000)

LEBEDEV, Mikhail (19th C) Russian
Works on paper
£700 $1253 €1022 Tsar Nicholas I and his sons (16x12cm-6x5in) s.i.d.1833 pencil. 26-May-4 Sotheby's, Olympia #364/R

LEBEDEV, Vladimir (attrib) (1911-1989) Russian
£645 $1187 €942 Soccer players (37x58cm-15x23in) 14-Jun-4 Waddingtons, Toronto #351/R est:1500-2500 (C.D 1600)

LEBEDEV, Vladimir V (1891-1967) Russian
£516 $950 €753 Tug boats off Manhattan (23x30cm-9x12in) s. one s.i.d.1958 verso one board one masonite two. 10-Jun-4 Swann Galleries, New York #143/R

Prints
£2207 $3686 €3200 Dancing pair (28x16cm-11x6in) stencil print gouache pencil pen ink. 13-Nov-3 Neumeister, Munich #382/R est:1000-1200

Works on paper
£226 $385 €330 Man walking barefoot (34x25cm-13x10in) Indian ink W/C template prov. 18-Nov-3 Hans Widmer, St Gallen #1119 (S.FR 500)
£249 $431 €364 Personnage (18x14cm-7x6in) ink pochoir W/C. 12-Dec-3 Galerie du Rhone, Sion #123 (S.FR 550)
£271 $470 €396 Soiree arrosee (22x16cm-9x6in) ink pochoir W/C. 12-Dec-3 Galerie du Rhone, Sion #124 (S.FR 600)
£280 $502 €409 Labourer (31x21cm-12x8in) Indian ink pochoir. 12-May-4 Dobiaschofsky, Bern #1767/R (S.FR 650)
£304 $557 €444 Femme opulente (31x21cm-12x8in) ink pochoir W/C exec. c.1925. 5-Jun-4 Galerie du Rhone, Sion #502 (S.FR 700)
£304 $557 €444 L'architecte (31x21cm-12x8in) ink pochoir W/C exec. c.1925. 5-Jun-4 Galerie du Rhone, Sion #503 (S.FR 700)
£304 $557 €444 Paysan a la fourche (31x21cm-12x8in) ink pochoir W/C exec. c.1925. 5-Jun-4 Galerie du Rhone, Sion #504 (S.FR 700)
£304 $557 €444 Travail a l'etabli (31x21cm-12x8in) ink pochoir W/C exec. c.1925. 5-Jun-4 Galerie du Rhone, Sion #505 (S.FR 700)
£317 $548 €463 Sur banc public (22x22cm-9x9in) ink pochoir W/C. 12-Dec-3 Galerie du Rhone, Sion #125 (S.FR 700)
£317 $548 €463 En retard (34x24cm-13x9in) ink pochoir W/C. 12-Dec-3 Galerie du Rhone, Sion #122 (S.FR 700)
£330 $562 €482 Traffic policeman (34x24cm-13x9in) Indian ink W/C stencil prov. 18-Nov-3 Hans Widmer, St Gallen #1118 (S.FR 730)
£413 $689 €599 Le knout (22x14cm-9x6in) ink pochoir W/C exec.c.1925. 21-Jun-3 Galerie du Rhone, Sion #114/R (S.FR 900)
£413 $689 €599 Les grands nettoyages (23x17cm-9x7in) ink pochoir W/C exec.c.1925. 21-Jun-3 Galerie du Rhone, Sion #115/R (S.FR 900)
£459 $766 €666 Balakaika au ruban (29x20cm-11x8in) ink pochoir W/C exec.c.1925. 21-Jun-3 Galerie du Rhone, Sion #111/R (S.FR 1000)
£459 $766 €666 La decouverte (21x15cm-8x6in) ink pochoir W/C exec.c.1925. 21-Jun-3 Galerie du Rhone, Sion #113/R (S.FR 1000)
£505 $843 €732 Matriarcat (22x14cm-9x6in) ink pochoir W/C exec.c.1925. 21-Jun-3 Galerie du Rhone, Sion #117/R (S.FR 1100)
£505 $843 €732 Philosophie de trottoir (22x16cm-9x6in) ink pochoir W/C exec.c.1925. 21-Jun-3 Galerie du Rhone, Sion #118/R (S.FR 1100)
£550 $919 €798 Dans le tramway (22x14cm-9x6in) ink pochoir W/C exec.c.1925. 21-Jun-3 Galerie du Rhone, Sion #112/R (S.FR 1200)
£596 $996 €864 Les patineurs (26x21cm-10x8in) ink pochoir W/C exec.c.1925. 21-Jun-3 Galerie du Rhone, Sion #116/R (S.FR 1300)
£671 $1248 €1000 Stripper with revolver (25x15cm-10x6in) gouache Indian ink pencil. 6-Mar-4 Arnold, Frankfurt #769/R
£826 $1379 €1198 Travail a l'etabil (27x21cm-11x8in) ink pochoir W/C exec.c.1925. 21-Jun-3 Galerie du Rhone, Sion #119/R (S.FR 1800)

£1193 $1992 €1730 A la poursuite nu nez (24x23cm-9x9in) ink pochoir W/C exec.c.1925. 21-Jun-3 Galerie du Rhone, Sion #110/R est:900-1200 (S.FR 2600)

LEBEDEV, Vladimir V (attrib) (1891-1967) Russian
Works on paper
£302 $540 €441 Policeman (31x21cm-12x8in) Indian ink pochoir. 12-May-4 Dobiaschofsky, Bern #1766 (S.FR 700)

LEBEDJEV, Klawdij (1852-1916) Russian
£15278 $27500 €22306 Bear baiting (27x36cm-11x14in) s.d.1907 board. 23-Apr-4 Sotheby's, New York #3/R est:15000-20000
Works on paper
£1300 $2327 €1898 Resting peasant (34x27cm-13x11in) s.i. W/C. 26-May-4 Sotheby's, Olympia #374/R est:1200-1800
£2200 $3740 €3300 Head of bear (24x31cm-9x12in) s.d.1911 W/C bodycol. 25-Nov-3 Christie's, London #128/R est:2500-3500

LEBEL, C (18/19th C) French
Miniatures
£1127 $1870 €1600 Autoportrait presume de l'artiste avec sa femme (9x8cm-4x3in) s. oval. 11-Jun-3 Delorme & Bocage, Paris #13/R est:1200-1500

LEBEL, Edmond (1834-1909) French
£6291 $11450 €9500 Scene religieuse (31x39cm-12x15in) s. panel. 20-Jun-4 Salle des ventes Pillet, Lyon la Foret #25/R est:2200-2500

LEBEL, Jean Jacques (1936-) French
£2000 $3680 €3000 Untitled (80x40cm-31x16in) s.d.56. 9-Jun-4 Christie's, Amsterdam #123/R est:3000-5000
£2349 $4370 €3500 La vie quotidienne au japon (91x59cm-36x23in) mono. s.d.57 verso. 3-Mar-4 Artcurial Briest, Paris #488 est:4000-6000
Works on paper
£749 $1340 €1100 Portrait of Katchina (32x23cm-13x9in) mono.i.d.1981 verso mixed media collage double-sided prov. 21-Mar-4 Calmels Cohen, Paris #1324/R

LEBEL, Maurice (1898-1963) Canadian
Works on paper
£313 $522 €454 La vieille ferme (40x55cm-16x22in) s.d.1950 W/C prov. 17-Jun-3 Pinneys, Montreal #174 (C.D 700)

LEBENSTEIN, Jan (1930-1999) Polish/French
£1412 $2556 €2062 La Quete (60x38cm-24x15in) s.d.67. 4-Apr-4 Agra, Warsaw #94/R (P.Z 10000)
£5650 $10226 €8249 L'apogee (81x64cm-32x25in) s.d.69 oval. 4-Apr-4 Agra, Warsaw #92/R (P.Z 40000)
£6207 $10366 €9000 Woman with cat (123x74cm-48x29in) painted before 1958. 16-Nov-3 Agra, Warsaw #13/R est:4000
£6579 $12105 €10000 Enlevement d'Europe (81x130cm-32x51in) s.d.32. 25-Jun-4 Millon & Associes, Paris #248/R est:800-1000
£10738 $19866 €16000 Figure hieratique (97x65cm-38x26in) s.d.1956 s.i.d.verso prov.exhib.lit. 15-Mar-4 Claude Boisgirard, Paris #76/R est:16000-18000
Works on paper
£263 $484 €400 Femme sur les coudes (40x29cm-16x11in) s.d.62 pen. 25-Jun-4 Millon & Associes, Paris #246
£275 $457 €402 Figures on a bench (35x57cm-14x22in) ink pen wash exec.1957. 2-Oct-3 Agra, Warsaw #9/R (P.Z 1800)
£276 $461 €400 Female nude (36x25cm-14x10in) s.d.55 ink pen pencil. 16-Nov-3 Agra, Warsaw #27/R
£276 $508 €420 Peau d'ane (23x30cm-9x12in) s.d.62 felt-tip pen. 25-Jun-4 Millon & Associes, Paris #245
£282 $511 €412 Composition (57x37cm-22x15in) s. d.1957 or 1958 Indian ink pen squared paper. 4-Apr-4 Agra, Warsaw #74/R (P.Z 2000)
£296 $545 €450 Femme sur la table (40x29cm-16x11in) s.d.62 pen. 25-Jun-4 Millon & Associes, Paris #247
£339 $614 €495 Composition (35x26cm-14x10in) s.d.68 Indian ink pen pastel. 4-Apr-4 Agra, Warsaw #56/R (P.Z 2400)
£362 $666 €550 Personnage sur la plage (40x29cm-16x11in) s.d.63 W/C collage pen. 25-Jun-4 Millon & Associes, Paris #250
£389 $708 €568 Composition (57x36cm-22x14in) s. India ink pen exec c.1958-59. 20-Jun-4 Agra, Warsaw #25/R (P.Z 2700)
£491 $845 €717 Guru V (42x30cm-17x12in) s. ink pen exec.1965. 4-Dec-3 Agra, Warsaw #37/R (P.Z 3300)
£596 $990 €870 Abstract forms (56x37cm-22x15in) ink pen wash exec. c.1956. 2-Oct-3 Agra, Warsaw #27/R (P.Z 3900)
£655 $1094 €950 Poids lourds (30x42cm-12x17in) s.i.d.66 ink pen wash. 16-Nov-3 Agra, Warsaw #2/R
£2828 $4722 €4100 Adam and Eve (69x49cm-27x19in) s.d.88 pastel ink pen gouache. 16-Nov-3 Agra, Warsaw #61/R est:2000
£3058 $5076 €4465 Abstract figure (135x100cm-53x39in) ink chk exec.1961. 2-Oct-3 Agra, Warsaw #16/R est:5000 (P.Z 20000)
£3824 $6500 €5583 Figure axiale 53 (130x97cm-51x38in) s.d.1960 s.i.d.verso encaustic on canvas. 9-Nov-3 Wright, Chicago #411 est:1000-1500

LEBLANC, Gustave (19th C) French
£1552 $2778 €2266 Cat family (54x65cm-21x26in) s. 12-May-4 Dobiaschofsky, Bern #731/R est:3000 (S.FR 3600)

LEBLANC, Marie de Hoa (1874-?) American
£311 $500 €454 Texas landscape (56x71cm-22x28in) s. 17-Aug-3 Jeffery Burchard, Florida #38

LEBLANC, Roger (?) French
£428 $787 €650 Paysage Provencal - Route de Rousset (41x33cm-16x13in) s. s.i. verso wood. 28-Jun-4 Joron-Derem, Paris #140

LEBLANC, Walter (1932-1986) Belgian
£1127 $1949 €1600 Torsions PF 0117 (28x28cm-11x11in) s.verso polyvinyl exhib.lit. 13-Dec-3 De Vuyst, Lokeren #200/R est:1600-2000
£2744 $4500 €4006 The 25F X819 (81x65cm-32x26in) s.i. verso oil cotton thread on canvas exec.c.1960/64 prov.exhib. 28-May-3 Sotheby's, Amsterdam #122/R est:4500-5500
£4667 $8540 €7000 Composition (81x65cm-32x26in) painted 1962 prov. 7-Jun-4 Palais de Beaux Arts, Brussels #135/R est:5000-7000
Sculpture
£1267 $2116 €1850 Torsions LB 180 (66x56cm-26x22in) s.i. verso plastic on pavatex. 24-Jun-3 Germann, Zurich #998 est:800-1000 (S.FR 2800)

LEBLING, Max Ludwig (1851-?) German
£591 $1058 €863 Donkey and rams in stable (50x70cm-20x28in) s.d.06 prov. 26-May-4 AB Stockholms Auktionsverk #2433/R (S.KR 8000)

LEBON, Charles (1906-1957) Belgian
£464 $844 €700 Paysage hivernal (80x150cm-31x59in) s. 16-Jun-4 Hotel des Ventes Mosan, Brussels #255
£759 $1403 €1100 Dreve a Overijssche (152x184cm-60x72in) s.d.1925. 13-Jan-4 Vanderkindere, Brussels #170

LEBOUR, Alexandre Xavier (attrib) (1801-?) French
£1200 $2172 €1800 Gerard de Nerval (146x113cm-57x44in) exhib.lit. 30-Mar-4 Rossini, Paris #253/R est:1500-2000

LEBOURG, Albert (1849-1928) French
£1067 $1920 €1600 Beach (26x22cm-10x9in) s. panel. 22-Apr-4 Weidler, Nurnberg #6504/R est:1000
£2318 $4219 €3500 La Seine a Elbeuf (35x65cm-14x26in) s.i.d.1892. 20-Jun-4 Salle des ventes Pillet, Lyon la Foret #26/R est:10000-12000
£2679 $4473 €3885 Ville de Clermont-Ferrand (61x38cm-24x15in) s. i.verso painted c.1895. 17-Jun-3 Pinneys, Montreal #47 est:7000-9000 (C.D 6000)
£2797 $4811 €4000 La rue des Bouchers a Alger (46x30cm-18x12in) s.i. cardboard on canvas. 3-Dec-3 Tajan, Paris #348/R est:4600-6000
£3000 $5310 €4380 La vallee de la Seine (46x55cm-18x22in) s. 29-Apr-4 Christie's, Kensington #177/R est:2000-3000
£4110 $6986 €6000 La Seine a Charenton (40x73cm-16x29in) s. 5-Nov-3 Rabourdin & Choppin de Janvry, Paris #44/R est:6500-7000
£4577 $7370 €6500 Paris, Pont-Neuf (14x24cm-6x9in) s. panel lit. 22-Aug-3 Deauville, France #53/R
£4895 $8420 €7000 Autumn (46x76cm-18x30in) s. 5-Dec-3 Maigret, Paris #15/R est:8000-10000
£5135 $9500 €7497 Chemin montant le long de voie ferree (50x65cm-20x26in) s. prov.lit. 11-Feb-4 Sotheby's, New York #7/R est:10000-15000
£5166 $9401 €7800 Bords de Seine avec cavalier (40x65cm-16x26in) s. 16-Jun-4 Renaud, Paris #42/R est:4500-5000
£5334 $9601 €8000 Vue du bas de Meudon (39x64cm-15x25in) s. 26-Apr-4 Tajan, Paris #100/R est:6000-8000
£5594 $9622 €8000 Vue de Notre Dame et des quais (33x40cm-13x16in) s. panel. 2-Dec-3 Calmels Cohen, Paris #42/R est:8000-12000
£5594 $9510 €8000 Mondouville (46x65cm-18x26in) s.i. 27-Nov-3 Millon & Associes, Paris #198/R est:4000-5000
£5867 $10560 €8800 Bras de riviere en automne (34x56cm-13x22in) s. 26-Apr-4 Tajan, Paris #99/R est:9000-12000
£6486 $12000 €9470 Patineurs sur le canal de la villette (49x65cm-19x26in) s. prov.lit. 11-Feb-4 Sotheby's, New York #9/R est:15000-20000
£6711 $12483 €10000 Le bas de Meudon, vue de Bellevue, effet de soleil derriere les nuages (44x61cm-17x24in) s. exhib.lit. 2-Mar-4 Artcurial Briest, Paris #116/R est:10000-15000
£6993 $11678 €10000 Village de Montort-sur-Risle (46x55cm-18x22in) s. lit. 29-Jun-3 Eric Pillon, Calais #85/R
£7047 $12474 €10500 Embarcation sur la Seine (40x66cm-16x26in) s. prov. 30-Apr-4 Tajan, Paris #148/R est:12000-15000
£7383 $11886 €11000 Les bords de Seine aux alentours de Rouen (46x73cm-18x29in) s.i. 23-Feb-3 St-Germain-en-Laye Encheres #75/R est:6000-8000
£7500 $13800 €10950 Soleil couchant aux environs de Rouen (50x64cm-20x25in) s. 24-Mar-4 Sotheby's, Olympia #44/R est:8000-12000
£8500 $15640 €12410 Au bas-meudon (40x54cm-16x21in) s. 24-Mar-4 Sotheby's, Olympia #43/R est:7000-9000
£8562 $14555 €12500 Bord de Seine pres de Rouen (46x73cm-18x29in) s. 9-Nov-3 Eric Pillon, Calais #75/R
£9061 $16037 €13500 Paysage (36x65cm-14x26in) s. prov. 30-Apr-4 Tajan, Paris #149/R est:12000-15000
£10563 $18486 €15000 La Seine aux environs de Rouen (65x81cm-26x32in) s. painted c.1900-1905. 19-Dec-3 Delvaux, Paris #21/R est:15000-20000
£10738 $19973 €16000 Paysage au ruisseau (50x65cm-20x26in) s. 7-Mar-4 Lesieur & Le Bars, Le Havre #77
£11268 $19493 €16000 Paris, peniche en bord de Seine (40x65cm-16x26in) s. 14-Dec-3 Eric Pillon, Calais #70/R
£11268 $19493 €16000 La Seine a Triel (50x73cm-20x29in) s.i. 12-Dec-3 Piasa, Paris #9/R est:15000-20000
£12667 $23180 €19000 Vue de Hollande (46x61cm-18x24in) s.d.1896 lit. 7-Jun-4 Artcurial Briest, Paris #21/R est:20000-25000
£13000 $23920 €18980 Seine en hiver (46x73cm-18x29in) s.d.1899 prov. 22-Jun-4 Sotheby's, London #237/R est:15000-20000
£14027 $24267 €20479 Environs de Rouen (50x73cm-20x29in) s.d.1902 prov.exhib.lit. 12-Dec-3 Galerie du Rhone, Sion #193/R est:20000-30000 (S.FR 31000)
£16000 $29120 €23360 Port de Bercy en hiver (46x85cm-18x33in) s.i. prov.lit. 3-Feb-4 Christie's, London #123/R est:12000-18000
£17483 $30070 €25000 Voiliers a La Rochelle (50x73cm-20x29in) s. prov.exhib. 8-Dec-3 Artcurial Briest, Paris #7/R est:15000-20000
£21831 $35148 €31000 Garage a bateaux (54x81cm-21x32in) s. lit. 22-Aug-3 Deauville, France #52/R est:30000-40000
£22148 $41196 €33000 Les quais de Paris, en ete, soleil couchant (68x100cm-27x39in) s.d.1907 lit. 2-Mar-4 Artcurial Briest, Paris #117/R est:25000-30000
Works on paper
£280 $481 €400 Mosquee pres de la mer a Alger (28x45cm-11x18in) i. chl. 2-Dec-3 Claude Aguttes, Neuilly #60
£282 $487 €400 Petit port aux environs de Rouen (16x30cm-6x12in) s. chl dr. 9-Dec-3 Artcurial Briest, Paris #125
£302 $562 €450 Notre-Dame. s. chl. 3-Mar-4 Ferri, Paris #339

£367 $675 €550 La Seine a Rouen (32x50cm-13x20in) s.i. chl. 14-Jun-4 Tajan, Paris #41
£423 $731 €600 Cheval de trait (13x30cm-5x12in) W/C. 9-Dec-3 Chambelland & Giafferi, Paris #88/R
£669 $1157 €950 Bord d'etang (30x45cm-12x18in) mono.i. graphite. 9-Dec-3 Chambelland & Giafferi, Paris #87/R
£754 $1281 €1100 Environs deRouen (18x26cm-7x10in) s.i. W/C over crayon. 6-Nov-3 Tajan, Paris #230
£816 $1461 €1200 Etude d'anes et de dromadaire. Tente kabyle dans un paysage (28x45cm-11x18in) s.i.d.1873 chl white chk. 19-Mar-4 Piasa, Paris #128
£1056 $1827 €1500 Vue de la Rochelle (30x46cm-12x18in) s.i. brown wash W/C black crayon. 12-Dec-3 Renaud, Paris #81/R est:1200-1500
£1620 $2802 €2300 Promeneur en bord de riviere a Neuville (37x54cm-15x21in) s. W/C gouache. 14-Dec-3 Eric Pillon, Calais #55/R
£1667 $2783 €2400 Paysage de compagne, Hondouville-sur-Iton (32x48cm-13x19in) s.i. W/C chl col chk exhib. 21-Oct-3 Christie's, Paris #92/R est:2000-3000
£1667 $3033 €2500 Moulin pres de Rotterdam (36x51cm-14x20in) s.i. W/C. 4-Jul-4 Eric Pillon, Calais #117/R
£1844 $3079 €2600 Paysage anime (51x63cm-20x25in) s.i.d.1848 W/C. 19-Oct-3 Anaf, Lyon #197/R est:2500-3000
£2267 $4057 €3400 Port de Rotterdam (30x47cm-12x19in) s.i. W/C lit. 17-May-4 Chayette & Cheval, Paris #175/R est:4000-5000
£4110 $6452 €6000 Paris, pont Saint-Michel (30x47cm-12x19in) s.i. W/C. 20-Apr-3 Deauville, France #101/R est:6000-7000
£10780 $18003 €15200 Femme a l'ouvrage (30x46cm-12x18in) s. estompe exhib. 12-Oct-3 St-Germain-en-Laye Encheres #11/R est:300-400

LEBOURG, Charles Auguste (1829-1906) French
Sculpture
£1711 $3147 €2600 Jeune fille (54x40cm-21x16in) s.d.83 terracotta marble base. 23-Jun-4 Rieunier, Paris #39 est:1000-1200

LEBRECHT, Ise (1881-?) Italian
£2318 $4219 €3500 Verona, Erbe Square (35x50cm-14x20in) s. cardboard. 18-Jun-4 Stadion, Trieste #184/R est:1000-1500

LEBRET, Frans (1820-1909) Dutch
£1041 $1697 €1500 Little boy with a horse (24x28cm-9x11in) s. panel. 29-Sep-3 Sotheby's, Amsterdam #51/R
£1275 $2359 €1900 Tavern interior (36x45cm-14x18in) s. panel. 15-Mar-4 Sotheby's, Amsterdam #88/R est:1000-1500

LEBRET, Frans and PORTIELJE, Gerard (19th C) Dutch
£4605 $8336 €7000 Shepherdess and her flock (55x73cm-22x29in) s. 19-Apr-4 Glerum, Amsterdam #66/R est:2700-3200

LEBRET, Paul (19th C) French
Works on paper
£1136 $2000 €1659 Project for a munumental staircase in a park (43x49cm-17x19in) s.i. pencil W/C exhib. 19-May-4 Doyle, New York #6030/R est:2500-3500

LEBRETON, Constant (1895-1985) French
£749 $1400 €1094 Bateau Hollandais, le Pointe Bouchemaine (53x66cm-21x26in) s. i.stretcher. 25-Feb-4 Doyle, New York #114/R
£1399 $2378 €2000 Barques en bord de Loire (50x65cm-20x26in) s.d.76. 21-Nov-3 Coutau Begarie, Paris #58/R est:2000-3500

LEBRON, Robert (1928-) American
£361 $600 €523 Central Park (61x91cm-24x36in) 13-Jun-3 Du Mouchelle, Detroit #2456/R

LEBRUN, Andre Jean (1737-1811) French
Works on paper
£1267 $2267 €1900 Youth being torn from the arms of girl by Chronos (45x36cm-18x14in) s. pen over pencil wash. 13-May-4 Bassenge, Berlin #5426/R est:900

LEBRUN, Charles (after) (1619-1690) French
£5500 $9900 €8030 Defeat of Porus (122x205cm-48x81in) 23-Apr-4 Christie's, Kensington #171/R est:6000-8000

LEBRUN, Charles (attrib) (1619-1690) French
£44218 $79150 €65000 Portrait de Louis XIV (115x89cm-45x35in) 19-Mar-4 Oger, Dumont, Paris #35/R est:90000-100000
Works on paper
£11790 $21459 €17213 Half length female nude, right profile (14x18cm-6x7in) i. chl prov. 16-Jun-4 Fischer, Luzern #2531 est:200-300 (S.FR 27000)

LEBRUN, Charles (style) (1619-1690) French
£7000 $12600 €10220 Portrait of Louis XIV wearing a Roman Imperial costume (79x64cm-31x25in) painted cartouche. 20-Apr-4 Sotheby's, Olympia #347/R est:3000-5000

LEBRUN, Christopher (1951-) British
£900 $1620 €1314 Sleep (180x130cm-71x51in) s.i.verso prov. 20-Jan-4 Bonhams, Knightsbridge #267/R

LEBRUN, Rico (1900-1964) American/Italian
Works on paper
£408 $750 €596 Massacre of the Innocents (41x51cm-16x20in) s.d.1948 chl htd white chk board. 10-Jun-4 Swann Galleries, New York #144/R

LECCIA, Ange (1952-) French
Works on paper
£1133 $2063 €1700 SPNPMDF (92x73cm-36x29in) s.d.1984 verso ink collage paper on canvas. 29-Jun-4 Cornette de St.Cyr, Paris #129/R est:1500-2000

LECHAY, James (1907-2001) American
Works on paper
£1307 $2300 €1908 Railroad crossing (36x53cm-14x21in) s. W/C. 3-Jan-4 Outer Cape Auctions, Provincetown #50/R

LECHESNE, Auguste Jean Baptiste (c.1815-1888) French
Sculpture
£10000 $18000 €14600 Wild boar hunt (32x53cm-13x21in) s.d.1853 brown pat bronze st.f.F de Eck et Durand. 21-Apr-4 Sotheby's, London #72/R est:8000-12000

LECHNER, Ferdinand (1855-?) German
£313 $494 €450 Kitchen interior (56x79cm-22x31in) s.i. tempera canvas panel. 25-Apr-3 Altus, Berlin #534/R

LECHNER, Karl Max (1890-1974) German
£428 $787 €650 Still life with flowering cactus (78x59cm-31x23in) s. 25-Jun-4 Michael Zeller, Lindau #563/R

LECHUGA, David (1950-) Spanish
Sculpture
£1049 $1752 €1500 Fumadora de opio (155x65x40cm-61x26x16in) s.d.1986 iron wood oil paint. 24-Jun-3 Segre, Madrid #188/R est:1500
£1467 $2655 €2200 English couple (170x85x60cm-67x33x24in) s. iron wood exec.1988 exhib.lit. 30-Mar-4 Segre, Madrid #333/R est:2000
£2113 $3697 €3000 Fandango standing (117x17x15cm-46x7x6in) painted wood prov. 16-Dec-3 Segre, Madrid #182/R est:1500

LECK, Bart van der (1876-1958) Dutch
Works on paper
£2000 $3680 €3000 Ontwerp Tegeltableau, Vara Studio, Hilversum (24x31cm-9x12in) i. verso gouache pencil exec 1958 prov. 8-Jun-4 Sotheby's, Amsterdam #212/R est:3000-4000
£3333 $6133 €5000 Four studios for Vlas (18x15cm-7x6in) pencil W/C exec.1952 lit. 9-Jun-4 Christie's, Amsterdam #54/R est:5000-7000

LECKWIJCK, Edith van (1899-1987) Belgian
£2878 $4719 €4000 Trebeurden, Brittany (50x65cm-20x26in) s. i. stretcher prov. 4-Jun-3 Ketterer, Hamburg #233/R est:5000-6000

LECLAIRE, Victor (1830-1885) French
£667 $1200 €1000 Pintade et dindon, aupres d'un pommier (50x65cm-20x26in) s.i.d.1874. 26-Apr-4 Tajan, Paris #86

LECLERC DES GOBELINS, Sebastian (1734-1785) French
£5944 $10224 €8500 Apollon et Daphne. Pan et Syrinx (33x41cm-13x16in) pair. 8-Dec-3 Christie's, Paris #50/R est:5000-7000

LECLERC, Henry (1905-1970) French
£353 $650 €515 Port de Bretagne (38x46cm-15x18in) s. 25-Mar-4 Doyle, New York #39/R

LECLERC, Jakob Friedrich (1717-?) German/British
Works on paper
£541 $951 €800 Still life with dead pheasant on a ledge (11x11cm-4x4in) s.d.1768 gouache prov.exhib. 19-May-4 Sotheby's, Amsterdam #181/R

LECLERC, Sebastien (elder) (1637-1714) French
Works on paper
£1549 $2680 €2200 Sac d'une bibliotheque (13x20cm-5x8in) sanguine sanguine wash. 12-Dec-3 Libert, Castor, Paris #8/R est:2000-3000

LECLERC, Sebastien (elder-attrib) (1637-1714) French
Works on paper
£544 $974 €800 Ceremonie religieuse (14x21cm-6x8in) sanguine. 19-Mar-4 Piasa, Paris #30/R
£4828 $8062 €7000 Ceremonie faite a Madrid a l'occasion de la proclamation du duc d'Anjou (24x24cm-9x9in) pen Indian ink grey wash. 17-Nov-3 Delorme & Bocage, Paris #61/R est:900-1200

LECLERCQ, Emile Carolus (1827-1907) French
£479 $815 €700 Two ladies and a child (70x57cm-28x22in) s.d.1858. 5-Nov-3 Vendue Huis, Gravenhage #136

LECLERCQ, Guy (1940-) Belgian
Works on paper
£533 $976 €800 Op de drempel (103x85cm-41x33in) s. pastel. 7-Jun-4 Palais de Beaux Arts, Brussels #181

LECLERCQ, Lucien (1895-1955) Belgian

£3099	$5361	€4400	Un village (60x81cm-24x32in) s. 10-Dec-3 Rossini, Paris #87/R

LECLERCQ, M (19/20th C) ?

£2267	$4103	€3400	L'attente (127x98cm-50x39in) s.d.1864. 30-Mar-4 Palais de Beaux Arts, Brussels #636/R est:2500-3500

LECLERCQ, Victor (1896-1944) Belgian

£1678	$2853	€2400	Maisons sous la neige (58x54cm-23x21in) s. 1-Dec-3 Palais de Beaux Arts, Brussels #93/R est:1000-1250
£2797	$4755	€4000	Coupe de fruits, coquillage et partitions sur une table (50x55cm-20x22in) s. 1-Dec-3 Palais de Beaux Arts, Brussels #90/R est:1250-1750

LECOMTE (?) French

£1489	$2413	€2100	Pirates Algerienes enlevant une bergere des environs de Naples (40x52cm-16x20in) s. 24-May-3 Martinot & Savignat, Pontoise #197

LECOMTE, Adolphe (1850-1921) Dutch

£1500	$2580	€2190	Winter landscape possibly near Dordrecht (89x128cm-35x50in) s. 4-Dec-3 Christie's, Kensington #188/R est:2000-3000

LECOMTE, Émile (1866-1938) Belgian

£592	$1089	€900	Vue de ville avec figures (62x62cm-24x24in) s.d.1934 panel. 22-Jun-4 Palais de Beaux Arts, Brussels #271

LECOMTE, Hippolyte (1781-1857) French

£3000	$5400	€4380	Kidnap (40x52cm-16x20in) s.d.1827. 21-Jan-4 Sotheby's, Olympia #415/R est:3000-4000

LECOMTE, L E (19th C) French

Miniatures			
£10135	$17838	€15000	Lady with harp (33cm-13in) s. gilt bronze frame. 18-May-4 Sotheby's, Milan #536/R est:2500-3500

LECOMTE, Louis (19/20th C) French

£4667	$8540	€7000	Magie et theatre de Tabarin (54x73cm-21x29in) s.d.1890. 5-Jun-4 Gros & Delettrez, Paris #63/R est:5000-6000

LECOMTE, Michel (1935-) French

Works on paper			
£658	$1210	€1000	Perspective (50x65cm-20x26in) s.d.1991 col ink lit. 28-Jun-4 Artcurial Briest, Paris #64
£1316	$2421	€2000	Symphonie inachevee (86x69cm-34x27in) s.d.94 col ink. 28-Jun-4 Artcurial Briest, Paris #65/R est:700-900

LECOMTE, Paul (1842-1920) French

£353	$650	€515	Washerwoman by a stream (33x46cm-13x18in) s. 25-Mar-4 Doyle, New York #40/R
£646	$1028	€950	Portes du port (23x14cm-9x6in) s. panel. 23-Mar-3 St-Germain-en-Laye Encheres #64/R
£897	$1498	€1310	Waterside wood and boat harbour (32x41cm-13x16in) s. 24-Oct-3 Hans Widmer, St Gallen #97/R est:1200-2500 (S.FR 2000)
£1267	$2305	€1900	Rivage de Bretagne (32x46cm-13x18in) s. 4-Jul-4 Eric Pillon, Calais #68/R
£1293	$2379	€1888	Rider and fishermen on shore (31x38cm-12x15in) s. 26-Mar-4 Koller, Zurich #3126/R est:2500-3500 (S.FR 3000)
£1377	$2300	€2010	Ships in harbour, Nantes (53x79cm-21x31in) s.i. 20-Jun-3 Freeman, Philadelphia #237/R est:700-1000
£1944	$3072	€2800	Encounter on a village road (38x55cm-15x22in) s. 2-Sep-3 Christie's, Amsterdam #234/R est:2500-3000
Works on paper			
£450	$828	€657	Promenade (18x27cm-7x11in) s. W/C. 8-Jun-4 Bonhams, Knightsbridge #74/R
£524	$964	€765	Canal St Martin (17x25cm-7x10in) s. i. verso W/C. 14-Jun-4 Philippe Schuler, Zurich #4440 (S.FR 1200)
£662	$1238	€1000	Vue de village (27x38cm-11x15in) s. W/C two. 24-Jul-4 Thierry & Lannon, Brest #243b

LECOMTE, Paul Émile (1877-1950) French

£451	$736	€650	Peniches sur la Seine (26x36cm-10x14in) st.sig. W/C. 29-Sep-3 Charbonneaux, Paris #243
£458	$801	€650	Personnages sur un chemin (21x27cm-8x11in) s. panel. 21-Dec-3 Thierry & Lannon, Brest #171
£699	$1189	€1000	Port dans le midi (30x40cm-12x16in) s. panel. 1-Dec-3 Camard, Paris #45
£700	$1253	€1022	Market day (55x66cm-22x26in) s. 16-Mar-4 Bonhams, Leeds #580/R
£852	$1500	€1278	Le port de Joinville (61x81cm-24x32in) s. painted c.1920. 23-May-4 William Jenack, New York #261 est:2000-3000
£909	$1564	€1300	Dejeuner devant la villa (38x45cm-15x18in) s. panel. 5-Dec-3 Chochon-Barre & Allardi, Paris #121/R
£1200	$2184	€1800	Rue de village anime (24x33cm-9x13in) s. 4-Jul-4 Eric Pillon, Calais #63/R
£1972	$3411	€2800	Sur la place du village (24x33cm-9x13in) s. 10-Dec-3 Millon & Associes, Paris #52/R est:1800-2200
£2333	$4270	€3500	Marche au soleil (24x33cm-9x13in) s. 6-Jun-4 Osenat, Fontainebleau #275/R est:4000-4500
£4000	$7280	€5840	Marche a melon. L'Ile d'yeu (38x46cm-15x18in) s. pair. 16-Jun-4 Christie's, Kensington #36/R est:4000-6000
£6993	$11678	€10000	Canotage sur la riviere (50x73cm-20x29in) s. 29-Jun-3 Eric Pillon, Calais #94/R
Works on paper			
£350	$594	€500	Chantilly (11x14cm-4x6in) s.i. W/C. 24-Nov-3 E & Eve, Paris #171
£500	$800	€730	View of Mevagisey harbour. W/C. 16-Sep-3 Lawrences, Bletchingley #1966
£570	$1055	€850	Roseraie dans le parc (27x37cm-11x15in) s. W/C. 14-Mar-4 Eric Pillon, Calais #70/R
£662	$1238	€1000	Marche anime, la carriole (23x32cm-9x13in) s. W/C. 24-Jul-4 Thierry & Lannon, Brest #66/R
£795	$1446	€1200	Vue d'un port mediterraneen (33x40cm-13x16in) s. W/C htd black crayon. 16-Jun-4 Piasa, Paris #188/R
£900	$1656	€1314	Bustling activity on th banks of the Seine, Paris (46x53cm-18x21in) s. pencil W/C black ink. 25-Mar-4 Christie's, Kensington #247/R

LECOMTE-VERNET, Charles Émile (1821-1900) French

£1650	$2953	€2409	An Oriental beauty (60x39cm-24x15in) s.d.1877. 26-May-4 Sotheby's, Olympia #315/R est:1500-2000
£2431	$3962	€3500	Oriental woman carrying water (60x39cm-24x15in) s.d.1877. 24-Sep-3 Neumeister, Munich #476/R est:2000

LECOQ, R (20th C) French?

Sculpture			
£989	$1800	€1484	Usher trumpeting the movie Desire (33cm-13in) bronze. 16-Jun-4 Wolf's, New York #487268/R est:1500-2500

LECOQUE, Alois (1891-1981) Czechoslovakian

£265	$475	€387	Full sail at sea (36x48cm-14x19in) s. i.d.1939 verso prov. 20-Mar-4 Sloans & Kenyon, Bethesda #1169/R
£294	$500	€429	Parisian street scene (41x48cm-16x19in) s. canvasboard. 7-Nov-3 Selkirks, St. Louis #625
£317	$600	€463	Church (68x88cm-27x35in) s. board. 22-Feb-4 Bonhams & Butterfields, Los Angeles #7079
£335	$600	€489	Sailboat on shore (30x41cm-12x16in) s. board prov. 20-Mar-4 Sloans & Kenyon, Bethesda #1170/R
£353	$600	€515	Place du Tertre (41x51cm-16x20in) s. s.i.verso board. 7-Nov-3 Selkirks, St. Louis #626
£735	$1250	€1073	Sacre Coeur au Montmartre (61x81cm-24x32in) s. 7-Nov-3 Selkirks, St. Louis #627/R
£2147	$3500	€3135	Marine (61x81cm-24x32in) s.d.1965. 25-Sep-3 Christie's, Rockefeller NY #633/R est:2000-4000

LECOR, Paul Tex (1930-) Canadian

£290	$485	€421	Jeune fille (51x41cm-20x16in) s. 17-Jun-3 Pinneys, Montreal #152 (C.D 650)

LECOSTY, J (fl.1890s) Belgian

£1333	$2400	€2000	Still life with flowers and Delft vase (80x98cm-31x39in) s.d.1891. 26-Apr-4 Bernaerts, Antwerp #241/R est:2000-2500

LECOULTRE, Jean (1930-) Swiss

£2018	$3371	€2926	Personnage accoude (72x59cm-28x23in) s.d. init.verso prov. 21-Jun-3 Galerie du Rhone, Sion #484/R est:5000-7000 (S.FR 4400)

LECOURT, Elisabeth (20th C) British?

Works on paper			
£700	$1295	€1022	Lost in the Museum II. s.d.2003 mixed media. 13-Feb-4 Sworder & Son, Bishops Stortford #106/R

LECOURT, Raymond (1882-1946) French

£828	$1382	€1200	Au bord de la Truyere (50x73cm-20x29in) s. d.35 verso. 11-Nov-3 Lesieur & Le Bars, Le Havre #75
£1007	$1872	€1500	Au bord du gave de Gavarnie (50x73cm-20x29in) s.d.35 verso canvas on panel. 7-Mar-4 Lesieur & Le Bars, Le Havre #79
£1034	$1728	€1500	Jument et poulain (54x65cm-21x26in) s.d.1923. 11-Nov-3 Lesieur & Le Bars, Le Havre #76
£1074	$1997	€1600	Les labours (30x50cm-12x20in) s.i.d.1922 verso. 7-Mar-4 Lesieur & Le Bars, Le Havre #78
£1241	$2073	€1800	Chevaux pres de riviere (51x73cm-20x29in) s. 11-Nov-3 Lesieur & Le Bars, Le Havre #74
£1310	$2188	€1900	Chevaux a l'herbage (53x73cm-21x29in) s. panel. 11-Nov-3 Lesieur & Le Bars, Le Havre #71
£1310	$2188	€1900	Vaches sous pommier (50x73cm-20x29in) s. 11-Nov-3 Lesieur & Le Bars, Le Havre #72
£1544	$2840	€2300	French peasant ploughing (80x117cm-31x46in) s.d.23 aout 1901. 26-Mar-4 Bolland & Marotz, Bremen #633/R est:2200
£2766	$4619	€3900	Jument et son poulain sous un arbre (79x58cm-31x23in) s. 19-Oct-3 Imberdis, Pont Audemer #47
£3709	$6750	€5600	Vachere et troupeau (130x97cm-51x38in) s. 20-Jun-4 Imberdis, Pont Audemer #44

LECOURTIER, E (20th C) French

Sculpture			
£1810	$3241	€2643	Roman chariot with shying horses (60cm-24in) s.d.1904 pat.bronze. 13-May-4 Stuker, Bern #6754/R est:3000-4000 (S.FR 4200)

LECOURTIER, Prosper (1855-1924) French

Sculpture			
£769	$1400	€1123	Striding rooster (48x20x20cm-19x8x8in) cast sig. num.105 base gilt bronze marble octagonal plinth. 7-Feb-4 Neal Auction Company, New Orleans #404 est:500-700
£1000	$1700	€1460	King Charles spaniel (5x17cm-2x7in) s. pat bronze. 28-Oct-3 Sotheby's, London #149/R
£2467	$4415	€3700	Les bassets au terrier (29x33cm-11x13in) brown pat bronze. 12-May-4 Coutau Begarie, Paris #246/R est:4000-4500

LECOURTIER, Prosper and MOREAU, Hippolite (19th C) French
Sculpture
£3421 $6295 €5200 Le Piqueux sonnant de la trompe (84cm-33in) s. pat bronze black marble base Cast Societe des Bronzes de Paris. 25-Jun-4 Rossini, Paris #156/R est:4000-5000

LECUONA MONTEVERDE, Elena (1944-) Spanish
£797 $1307 €1100 View of Toledo (81x100cm-32x39in) s. 27-May-3 Durán, Madrid #61/R

LECURIEUX, Jacques Joseph (1801-1867) French
£3600 $6228 €5256 Portrait of Charles de Bourbon (6x54cm-2x21in) i.verso prov. 9-Dec-3 Sotheby's, Olympia #412/R est:800-1200

LEDA, Jean van (1926-) Belgian
£282 $487 €400 Vue sur les toits de la ville (46x36cm-18x14in) s.d.1954. 9-Dec-3 Campo, Vlaamse Kaai #459
£500 $915 €750 Les facades (73x60cm-29x24in) s.d.1953. 7-Jun-4 Palais de Beaux Arts, Brussels #313

LEDELI, Moritz (1856-1920) Czechoslovakian
Works on paper
£1074 $1901 €1600 King Edward VII of Great Britain and Ireland (62x42cm-24x17in) s. W/C. 29-Apr-4 Dorotheum, Vienna #252/R est:1200-1600

LEDERER, Bruno (20th C) German
£315 $535 €450 Still life with pot plant (80x98cm-31x39in) s.d.1933 panel. 28-Nov-3 Wendl, Rudolstadt #4058/R

LEDERER, Hugo (1871-?) German
Sculpture
£2095 $3750 €3059 Man with sword (94cm-37in) s. brown pat bronze marble base. 20-Mar-4 Freeman, Philadelphia #774/R est:1500-2000

LEDERER, Mia (1921-) Danish
£764 $1276 €1100 A piece of glass (70x50cm-28x20in) mono. s.i. verso. 25-Oct-3 Dr Lehr, Berlin #313/R

LEDGER, Mildred Mai (fl.1901-1937) British
Works on paper
£1200 $2148 €1752 Evelyn (54x38cm-21x15in) s. pencil W/C htd bodycol prov. 14-May-4 Christie's, London #84/R est:1000-1500

LEDIEU, Philippe (19th C) French
£1192 $2181 €1800 Chasseur et chiens a l'arret (30x48cm-12x19in) s. 9-Apr-4 Bailly Pommery, Paris #35 est:1200-1800

LEDOUX, Jeanne Philiberte (attrib) (1767-1840) French
£2128 $3553 €3000 Une jeune paysanne au fichu blanc (54x46cm-21x18in) 17-Oct-3 Tajan, Paris #115 est:1200-1500

LEDRAY, Charles (1960-) American
Sculpture
£11043 $18000 €16123 Untitled, sailor (32x30x2cm 13x12x1in) fabric hanger prov.exhib. 23-Sep-3 Christie's, Rockefeller NY #78/R est:15000-20000
£11656 $19000 €17018 Untitled, black suit (52x40x4cm-20x16x2in) i.d.1993 fabric hanger prov.exhib. 23-Sep-3 Christie's, Rockefeller NY #79/R est:15000-20000

LEDRU, Auguste (1860-1902) French
Sculpture
£1409 $2593 €2100 Sirenes et poissons (34cm-13in) s.st.f.Susse pat bronze. 23-Mar-4 Piasa, Paris #12/R

LEDUC, Charles (1831-1911) French
£993 $1609 €1400 La peche au filet (54x99cm-21x39in) s. 21-May-3 Daguerre, Paris #59

LEDUC, Ozias (1864-1955) Canadian
Works on paper
£442 $822 €645 Epiphany (12x16cm-5x6in) init. graphite prov. 2-Mar-4 Ritchie, Toronto #91/R (C.D 1100)

LEDUC, Paul (1876-1943) Belgian
£1049 $1752 €1500 Vieux moulin a Uccle (36x44cm-14x17in) s.d.1911. 13-Oct-3 Horta, Bruxelles #217 est:2500-3500
£1081 $2043 €1600 Statues a l'Antique dans les Jardins de Versailles (45x60cm-18x24in) s. 17-Feb-4 Galerie Moderne, Brussels #180/R est:1500-2000
£1100 $1969 €1650 Route Provencale (31x24cm-12x9in) s. canvas on panel. 11-May-4 Vanderkindere, Brussels #223 est:1250-1750
£1733 $3172 €2600 Pinede a Saint Tropez (24x32cm-9x13in) s. canvas on panel. 6-Jun-4 Anaf, Lyon #416 est:1500-2000
£1867 $3341 €2800 The Mediterranean (35x45cm-14x18in) s. 15-May-4 De Vuyst, Lokeren #178 est:1350-1600
£2083 $3312 €3000 Fermette au printemps (60x80cm-24x31in) s.d.1905. 15-Sep-3 Horta, Bruxelles #155 est:2000-2500
£2400 $4392 €3600 Saint Tropez (24x32cm-9x13in) s. canvas on panel. 6-Jun-4 Anaf, Lyon #414/R est:1500-2000
£3497 $6014 €5000 View on Notre Dame, Paris (60x73cm-24x29in) s. 2-Dec-3 Sotheby's, Amsterdam #53/R est:5000-7000
£3667 $6710 €5500 Voiliers dans le port de Saint Tropez (35x45cm-14x18in) s. 6-Jun-4 Anaf, Lyon #415/R est:2000-2200
£8054 $14255 €12000 Vue de Martigues. s. 27-Apr-4 Campo & Campo, Antwerp #146/R est:14000-18000

LEE DOYOUNG (1884-1933) Korean
Works on paper
£1087 $2000 €1587 Orchids and bamboo with poems, plum and rock (120x31cm-47x12in) s. ink six panel screen some by another artist. 23-Mar-4 Christie's, Rockefeller NY #322/R est:4000-6000

LEE JIN (1958-) Chinese
Works on paper
£7112 $12802 €10384 Balcony with flowers, breeding fish and beauties II. s. col inkwash three pieces. 25-Apr-4 Christie's, Hong Kong #769/R est:100000-120000 (HK.D 100000)

LEE MAN FONG (1913-1988) Chinese
£5556 $10056 €8112 Goldfish (35x48cm-14x19in) s. board. 4-Apr-4 Sotheby's, Singapore #139/R est:8000-12000 (S.D 17000)
£5882 $10647 €8588 Goldfish (104x50cm-41x20in) st.seal i. board. 3-Apr-4 Glerum, Singapore #17/R est:20000-25000 (S.D 18000)
£6250 $10438 €9125 Goldfish (122x61cm-48x24in) s.i.d.1980 panel. 12-Oct-3 Sotheby's, Singapore #139/R est:12000-18000 (S.D 18000)
£6250 $10438 €9125 Orchids (104x50cm-25x20in) s. 12-Oct-3 Sotheby's, Singapore #167/R est:18000-25000 (S.D 18000)
£7190 $13013 €10497 Year of the rooster (103x50cm-41x20in) st.seal i.d.1981 hardboard. 3-Apr-4 Glerum, Singapore #71/R est:20000-30000 (S.D 22000)
£8497 $15379 €12406 Doves (103x49cm-41x19in) s. board. 4-Apr-4 Sotheby's, Singapore #143/R est:18000-25000 (S.D 26000)
£9804 $17745 €14314 Summer (102x49cm-40x19in) st.seal i.d.1981 board. 3-Apr-4 Glerum, Singapore #18/R est:20000-30000 (S.D 30000)
£10039 $16764 €14657 Two parrots (122x59cm-48x23in) s.i.d.July 1982 board. 26-Oct-3 Christie's, Hong Kong #60/R est:90000-140000 (HK.D 130000)
£10323 $16516 €15072 Rabbits (120x60cm-47x24in) s.d.1977 board. 18-May-3 Sotheby's, Singapore #147/R est:12000-15000 (S.D 28800)
£12418 $22477 €18130 Rooster and hen (120x60cm-47x24in) s.d.1980 board. 4-Apr-4 Sotheby's, Singapore #142/R est:25000-35000 (S.D 38000)
£12802 $23044 €18691 Two doves (113x50cm-44x20in) s. board. 25-Apr-4 Christie's, Hong Kong #577/R est:100000-200000 (HK.D 180000)
£16988 $28371 €24802 Tigers (102x48cm-40x19in) s.i.d.1976 board lit. 26-Oct-3 Christie's, Hong Kong #84/R est:90000-140000 (HK.D 220000)
£17070 $30725 €24922 Cowherd playing flute with two buffaloes (103x50cm-41x20in) s. board. 25-Apr-4 Christie's, Hong Kong #578/R est:110000-160000 (HK.D 240000)
£17204 $27527 €25118 Riverscene (103x50cm-41x20in) s. board. 18-May-3 Sotheby's, Singapore #146/R est:22000-28000 (S.D 48000)
£22876 $41405 €33399 Doves (91x152cm-36x60in) s. board. 4-Apr-4 Sotheby's, Singapore #147/R est:68000-88000 (S.D 70000)
£34139 $61451 €49843 Pair of doves (120x39cm-47x15in) s.i.d.1935 board prov. 25-Apr-4 Christie's, Hong Kong #576/R est:200000-300000 (HK.D 480000)
£34409 $55054 €50237 Goldfish (79x119cm-31x47in) S. B. 18-May-3 Sotheby's, Singapore #148/R est:50000-70000 (S.D 96000)
£34749 $58031 €50734 Forgotten (90x59cm-35x23in) s. board lit. 26-Oct-3 Christie's, Hong Kong #80/R est:140000-180000 (HK.D 450000)
£35948 $65065 €52484 Stay seller (102x50cm-40x20in) s. board. 4-Apr-4 Sotheby's, Singapore #146/R est:60000-80000 (S.D 110000)
£39118 $70413 €57112 Rojak seller (103x50cm-41x20in) s. board. 25-Apr-4 Christie's, Hong Kong #579/R est:130000-200000 (HK.D 550000)
£39382 $65768 €57498 Grooming the hair (122x60cm-48x24in) s. board. 26-Oct-3 Christie's, Hong Kong #61/R est:110000-160000 (HK.D 510000)
£41667 $69583 €60834 Goldfish (91x153cm-36x60in) s. panel. 12-Oct-3 Sotheby's, Singapore #142/R est:90000-150000 (S.D 120000)
£42471 $70927 €62008 Satay seller (103x50cm-41x20in) s. board prov. 26-Oct-3 Christie's, Hong Kong #81/R est:200000-250000 (HK.D 550000)
£67568 $121622 €98649 Satay seller (103x49cm-41x19in) s.d.1958 board. 25-Apr-4 Christie's, Hong Kong #575/R est:280000-350000 (HK.D 950000)
£71895 $130131 €104967 Horses (60x80cm-24x31in) s. board. 4-Apr-4 Sotheby's, Singapore #145/R est:60000-80000 (S.D 220000)
Works on paper
£915 $1656 €1336 Balinese girl weaving (54x39cm-21x15in) s.d.1953 ink. 3-Apr-4 Glerum, Singapore #3/R est:3000-4000 (S.D 2800)
£1961 $3549 €2863 Indian woman (35x24cm-14x9in) s. chl col chk. 4-Apr-4 Sotheby's, Singapore #166/R est:6000-8000 (S.D 6000)
£6882 $11011 €10048 Kedaton, Bali (59x46cm-23x18in) s.i.d.July 1954 pastel paperboard. 18-May-3 Sotheby's, Singapore #150/R est:16000-22000 (S.D 19200)

LEE SANG BOM (1897-1972) Korean
Works on paper
£3823 $6500 €5582 Winter landscape (71x183cm-28x72in) s. ink col. 4-Nov-3 Bonhams & Butterfields, San Francisco #3183/R est:7000-10000
£7692 $14000 €11230 Autumn colours on Puktam river in the Diamond Mountains (12x50cm-5x20in) s. ink W/C prov. 7-Feb-4 Sloans & Kenyon, Bethesda #1130/R est:15000-20000

LEE TIEFU (1869-1952) Chinese
£32006 $57610 €46729 Still life (63x76cm-25x30in) s. painted c.1947 prov. 25-Apr-4 Christie's, Hong Kong #709/R est:500000-700000 (HK.D 450000)

LEE UNG NO (1904-1989) Korean
Works on paper
£5500 $9845 €8030 Men in white (67x38cm-26x15in) s.d.1967 ink colour on Korean paper. 6-May-4 Sotheby's, London #91/R est:6000-7000
£5500 $9845 €8030 Informal (69x38cm-27x15in) s.d.1967 ink colour on Korean paper. 6-May-4 Sotheby's, London #92/R est:6000-7000

LEE, Ann K (20th C) American

£299	$500	€437	San Francisco Bay seascape under stormy skies (91x122cm-36x48in) s. prov. 14-Jul-3 O'Gallerie, Oregon #840/R

LEE, Bertha Stringer (1873-1937) American

£320	$550	€467	By the lake (23x30cm-9x12in) s. board. 6-Dec-3 Neal Auction Company, New Orleans #630/R
£629	$1000	€918	California seascape (36x41cm-14x16in) s. 5-May-3 O'Gallerie, Oregon #118/R
£745	$1200	€1088	Amidst the lupines (46x36cm-18x14in) s. 20-Jan-3 O'Gallerie, Oregon #789/R
£1604	$3000	€2342	Monterey seascape (77x86cm-30x34in) s. board prov. 29-Feb-4 Bonhams & Butterfields, San Francisco #4545 est:1000-1500

LEE, Catherine (1950-) American

Works on paper			
£1572	$2893	€2295	Planar Quits (47x31cm-19x12in) s.i.d.1990 encaustic wax pigment panel prov. 8-Jun-4 Germann, Zurich #88/R est:2000-3000 (S.FR 3600)

LEE, Charles (attrib) (19th C) British

£800	$1472	€1168	Young Roscius, Master Betty (28x23cm-11x9in) 8-Jun-4 Bonhams, Knightsbridge #341/R

LEE, Dick (1923-2001) British

£500	$815	€730	Catch 22 (122x216cm-48x85in) 13 panels in one frame. 23-Sep-3 John Nicholson, Haslemere #159/R

LEE, Doris (1905-1983) American

£539	$900	€787	Still life of strawberries (13x18cm-5x7in) s. board. 12-Jul-3 Auctions by the Bay, Alameda #429/R
£559	$900	€816	The raven (13x15cm-5x6in) s. 20-Aug-3 James Julia, Fairfield #1835/R
£2429	$4250	€3546	Zodiac (114x112cm-45x44in) s. s.i.verso. 19-Dec-3 Sotheby's, New York #1149/R est:6000-8000
£2647	$4500	€3865	Cathedral (76x97cm-30x38in) s. 9-Nov-3 Wright, Chicago #213 est:6000-8000
£3235	$5500	€4723	Bather in red suit (43x30cm-17x12in) s. canvasboard. 9-Nov-3 Wright, Chicago #214 est:3000-5000

LEE, Frederick Richard (1798-1879) British

£284	$474	€400	Le pont au-dessus du ruisseau (37x31cm-15x12in) s. canvas on cardboard. 19-Jun-3 Millon & Associes, Paris #137/R
£356	$615	€520	Landscape and stream (53x71cm-21x28in) s. 9-Dec-3 Maynards, Vancouver #133 (C.D 800)
£3500	$6265	€5110	Trout stream (44x53cm-17x21in) s. board prov. 27-May-4 Christie's, Kensington #150/R est:4000-6000
£6800	$10812	€9928	Pont Du Gard (113x182cm-44x72in) 18-Mar-3 Anderson & Garland, Newcastle #544/R est:8000-12000
£11000	$20240	€16060	Estuary scene with figures unloading a ferry (79x114cm-31x45in) s.d.1834. 11-Jun-4 Christie's, London #61/R est:8000-12000

LEE, H (19th C) ?

£2800	$4648	€4088	Flood (70x90cm-28x35in) s. 30-Sep-3 Sotheby's, London #305/R est:3000-4000

LEE, Jake (1915-1992) American

Works on paper			
£3439	$6500	€5021	View of San Francisco (36x53cm-14x21in) s. W/C. 17-Feb-4 John Moran, Pasadena #90/R est:1000-2000

LEE, Lindy (1954-) Australian

£3252	$5106	€4715	Untitled (214x160cm-84x63in) s.d.1988 verso oil wax prov.exhib. 26-Aug-3 Christie's, Sydney #413 est:6500-8500 (A.D 8000)

LEE, Nikki S (1970-) American

Photographs			
£1796	$3000	€2622	Untitled, no 17 from the Hispanic project (60x72cm-24x28in) c-print edition 1 of 5 prov.lit. 13-Nov-3 Sotheby's, New York #437/R est:3000-4000

LEE, Owen R (20th C) New Zealander

£284	$502	€415	Waiau gorge (61x90cm-24x35in) s. board. 28-Apr-4 Dunbar Sloane, Auckland #233/R (NZ.D 800)
£290	$461	€423	Farm buildings Otahuna, Christchurch (43x57cm-17x22in) s. board. 9-Sep-3 Watson's, Christchurch #96 (NZ.D 800)
£294	$526	€429	Morning light, Tauranga waterfront (43x54cm-17x21in) s. canvas on board. 12-May-4 Dunbar Sloane, Wellington #320/R (NZ.D 850)
£297	$512	€434	Repair works, Lyttelton (30x50cm-12x20in) s. board. 7-Dec-3 International Art Centre, Auckland #364/R (NZ.D 800)
£364	$571	€528	Coastal shipping Tauranga (44x57cm-17x22in) s.d.96. 27-Aug-3 Dunbar Sloane, Wellington #202/R (NZ.D 1000)
£372	$639	€543	Rocky Crags, Waiau river (61x75cm-24x30in) s.d.1994 board. 7-Dec-3 International Art Centre, Auckland #254 (NZ.D 1000)
£390	$671	€569	Canterbury Nor'wester, Prebbleton (51x61cm-20x24in) s. board. 7-Dec-3 International Art Centre, Auckland #333/R (NZ.D 1050)
£471	$758	€688	Still life with cauliflower (73x86cm-29x34in) s.d.36 board. 20-Aug-3 Dunbar Sloane, Auckland #128 est:2000-3000 (NZ.D 1300)
£507	$817	€740	Colourful shipping, Auckland waterfront (54x69cm-21x27in) s.verso board. 20-Aug-3 Dunbar Sloane, Auckland #129/R est:1500-2500 (NZ.D 1400)
£543	$875	€793	Coastal scene (41x51cm-16x20in) s. board. 20-Aug-3 Dunbar Sloane, Auckland #131 est:900-1500 (NZ.D 1500)
£727	$1142	€1054	Morning haze, Lyytelton (58x75cm-23x30in) s.d.96. 27-Aug-3 Dunbar Sloane, Wellington #201/R (NZ.D 2000)
£772	$1444	€1127	Reclining nude (58x85cm-23x33in) s.d.1938. 24-Feb-4 Peter Webb, Auckland #115/R (NZ.D 2100)
£1522	$2450	€2222	Stillwater heads (69x88cm-27x35in) board. 20-Aug-3 Peter Webb, Auckland #2046 est:800-1200 (NZ.D 4200)

LEE, Richard (20th C) British

Works on paper			
£280	$524	€409	Fakenham races (22x16cm-9x6in) s. pencil W/C chk. 24-Feb-4 Rowley Fine Art, Newmarket #421

LEE, Robert (20th C) Australian

£288	$521	€420	Untitled (207x289cm-81x114in) 30-Mar-4 Lawson Menzies, Sydney #183a/R (A.D 700)

LEE, Robert E (1899-?) American

£1337	$2500	€1952	Native American greeting sun (91x76cm-36x30in) s. painted c.1935. 26-Feb-4 Illustration House, New York #105 est:3000-5000

LEE, Rosie (1935-) British

£800	$1432	€1168	Over the maze (122x122cm-48x48in) 18-Mar-4 Christie's, Kensington #699/R
£979	$1684	€1400	Child in the garden (106x106cm-42x42in) s. 4-Dec-3 Schopman, Hamburg #688/R

LEE, Thomas Stirling (1856-1916) British

Sculpture			
£4800	$8832	€7008	Child (40cm-16in) black pat. green marble socle prov. 11-Jun-4 Christie's, London #81/R est:2000-3000

LEE-HANKEY, William (1869-1952) British

£250	$460	€365	View of a farm (25x34cm-10x13in) init. board. 23-Mar-4 Rosebery Fine Art, London #920
£820	$1394	€1197	Corcarneau (35x43cm-14x17in) s.d.08. 25-Nov-3 Bonhams, Knowle #223/R
£950	$1587	€1387	Continental village square (36x27cm-14x11in) s. board. 16-Oct-3 Christie's, Kensington #408/R
£2700	$5103	€3942	Girl in church interior (61x46cm-24x18in) s. 19-Feb-4 Lyon & Turnbull, Edinburgh #147 est:600-800
£3000	$5160	€4380	Affection (26x21cm-10x8in) panel prov. 2-Dec-3 Bonhams, New Bond Street #12/R est:3000-5000
£3200	$5344	€4672	Figures in a north African market (63x76cm-25x30in) s. 16-Oct-3 Christie's, Kensington #409/R est:3000-5000
£3500	$6020	€5110	View at Dieppe (51x61cm-20x24in) s. 2-Dec-3 Bonhams, New Bond Street #9/R est:4000-6000
£3571	$6464	€5214	Woman in the garden (50x60cm-20x24in) s. 30-Mar-4 Peter Webb, Auckland #116/R est:8000-10000 (NZ.D 10000)
£4751	$7934	€6936	On the Brittany coast (63x76cm-25x30in) s. i. stretcher prov. 17-Nov-3 Waddingtons, Toronto #124/R est:5000-7000 (C.D 10500)
£5500	$8745	€8030	Place Nationale, Dieppe (63x76cm-25x30in) s. s.i.d.1927 overlap. 10-Sep-3 Sotheby's, Olympia #157/R est:3000-5000
£5500	$9350	€8030	Crockery stall, Menton (63x76cm-25x30in) s. s.i.verso. 21-Nov-3 Christie's, London #48/R est:6000-8000
£8500	$14450	€12410	Harbour at Concarneau (63x76cm-25x30in) s. 21-Nov-3 Christie's, London #47/R est:7000-10000
Works on paper			
£650	$1027	€943	Anxious moment (30x26cm-12x10in) s. s.i.verso W/C. 3-Sep-3 Bonhams, Bury St Edmunds #344
£1600	$2544	€2320	Blue Sonata lady playing piano (34x43cm-13x17in) s. W/C. 9-Sep-3 David Duggleby, Scarborough #169/R est:700-1000
£1700	$3060	€2482	The stile (35x24cm-14x9in) s. W/C prov. 21-Jan-4 Sotheby's, Olympia #253/R est:1200-1800
£1700	$3060	€2482	Granada Cathedral, figures with a donkey cart in foreground (38x35cm-15x14in) s. pencil W/C. 21-Apr-4 Tennants, Leyburn #950/R est:600-800
£2385	$4102	€3482	Mother and children (31x30cm-12x12in) s. W/C. 2-Dec-3 Bukowskis, Stockholm #292/R est:15000-20000 (S.KR 31000)
£2717	$4402	€3940	Lady on the steps (30x40cm-12x16in) s. W/C. 31-Jul-3 International Art Centre, Auckland #56/R est:4000-6000 (NZ.D 7500)
£2800	$5152	€4200	In the orchard (30x50cm-12x20in) s. gouache. 11-Jun-4 Villa Grisebach, Berlin #1525/R est:1000-1500

LEE-HANKEY, William (attrib) (1869-1952) British

£615	$1100	€898	Cottage in Normandy (79x58cm-31x23in) 14-May-4 Skinner, Boston #301/R
Works on paper			
£420	$752	€613	Woman praying in Lady chapel (64x23cm-25x9in) W/C. 7-May-4 Mallams, Oxford #283/R

LEE-JOHNSON, Eric (1908-1993) New Zealander

£290	$467	€423	Trees in a landscape (33x39cm-13x15in) s.d.1969. 12-Aug-3 Peter Webb, Auckland #186 (NZ.D 800)
£1573	$2864	€2297	Abstract mountain range (37x122cm-15x48in) s. cardboard. 29-Jun-4 Peter Webb, Auckland #140/R est:5000-6000 (NZ.D 4500)
Works on paper			
£1730	$3097	€2526	Portrait of Charles Brash (41x25cm-16x10in) i. pastel ink. 12-May-4 Dunbar Sloane, Wellington #52/R est:5000-7000 (NZ.D 5000)

LEE-SMITH, Hughie (1915-1999) American

£13812	$25000	€20166	On the rooftop (40x91cm-16x36in) s.d.54 masonite. 31-Mar-4 Sotheby's, New York #132/R est:12000-18000
Works on paper			
£479	$800	€699	Female nude (41x20cm-16x8in) gouache pencil. 17-Oct-3 Du Mouchelle, Detroit #2213/R
£1788	$3200	€2610	Portrait of a Negro boy (30x41cm-12x16in) s. pastel. 8-May-4 Susanin's, Chicago #6065/R est:800-1200
£4375	$7000	€6388	Beach scene (33x43cm-13x17in) W/C exec 1956. 19-Sep-3 Du Mouchelle, Detroit #2023/R est:2000-3000

LEECH, John (1817-1864) British

£400	$720	€584	Good little boy, child in a bathing machine (36x46cm-14x18in) 20-Apr-4 Rowley Fine Art, Newmarket #403/R

LEECH, Raymond (20th C) ?

£750	$1358	€1095	Clearing storm, River Orwell (36x48cm-14x19in) s. 16-Apr-4 Keys, Aylsham #667
£750	$1358	€1095	Near Burg St. Peter Waveney Valley (36x48cm-14x19in) s. 16-Apr-4 Keys, Aylsham #668/R
£800	$1336	€1168	After a shower, South Beach, Lowestoft (46x69cm-18x27in) s. 17-Oct-3 Keys, Aylsham #685
£880	$1593	€1285	Old mill, Oulton (43x53cm-17x21in) s. 16-Apr-4 Keys, Aylsham #671
£980	$1774	€1431	Broadland, Thurne Mill (43x51cm-17x20in) s. 16-Apr-4 Keys, Aylsham #670/R

LEECH, William John (1881-1968) Irish

£5000	$8950	€7300	The rowing boat (25x30cm-10x12in) s. panel. 14-May-4 Christie's, London #173/R est:7000-10000
£6294	$10699	€9000	Reflections Queen Mary's Garden (27x36cm-11x14in) s. board prov. 25-Nov-3 De Veres Art Auctions, Dublin #121/R est:9000-12000
£6338	$10965	€9000	Little cottage and little girl (35x45cm-14x18in) i.verso. 10-Dec-3 Bonhams & James Adam, Dublin #100/R est:6000-9000
£25000	$44750	€36500	View towards Ireland's Eye and Howth from Portmarnock (15x42cm-6x17in) s. diptych board prov. 13-May-4 Sotheby's, London #19/R est:10000-15000
£35211	$56338	€50000	Painting in a garden (69x53cm-27x21in) s. prov.exhib. 16-Sep-3 Whyte's, Dublin #87/R est:60000-80000
£36364	$61818	€52000	London arches (36x46cm-14x18in) s. s.i.verso board. 25-Nov-3 De Veres Art Auctions, Dublin #33/R est:30000-40000
£40000	$71600	€58400	Concarneau (41x33cm-16x13in) s. prov. 13-May-4 Sotheby's, London #21/R est:40000-60000
Works on paper			
£1972	$3155	€2800	Study of a young girl in a pensive mood (61x48cm-24x19in) s. conte crayon lit. 16-Sep-3 Whyte's, Dublin #80/R est:2500-3500
£4000	$7160	€5840	The Pool of London (38x56cm-15x22in) s. W/C gouache prov. 13-May-4 Sotheby's, London #100/R est:3000-5000

LEEF, Frans de (1949-) Dutch

Works on paper			
£278	$439	€400	Torenstraat (60x65cm-24x26in) s.d.2000 W/C. 26-Apr-3 Auction Maastricht #54/R

LEEKE, Ferdinand (1859-1923) German

£333	$597	€500	House in the wood (51x35cm-20x14in) s. paper. 13-May-4 Neumeister, Munich #415/R
£556	$878	€800	Amazonian warrior (90x54cm-35x21in) s.i.d.1906. 2-Sep-3 Christie's, Amsterdam #188/R
£655	$1212	€950	Fortress in southern Tyrol (21x31cm-8x12in) s. panel. 14-Feb-4 Hans Stahl, Hamburg #57/R
£704	$1218	€1000	Siegfried (31x21cm-12x8in) mono.d.10 i.verso panel. 10-Dec-3 Dorotheum, Vienna #150/R
£1736	$2743	€2500	Young women talking in tavern (118x149cm-46x59in) s. 6-Sep-3 Schopman, Hamburg #806/R est:3000
£2035	$3459	€2910	Valkyrie (118x150cm-46x59in) s.d.1907. 20-Nov-3 Van Ham, Cologne #1709/R est:3800
£6000	$10320	€8760	Mermaids (95x124cm-37x49in) s.i.d.1921. 3-Dec-3 Christie's, London #70/R est:10000-15000

LEEMANS, E F (1812-1886) Dutch

£1916	$3200	€2797	Still lifes of fruit and flowers (25x23cm-10x9in) s. panel pair. 16-Nov-3 CRN Auctions, Cambridge #44/R

LEEMPOELS, Jef (1867-1935) Belgian

£759	$1403	€1100	Arbres de la Cote d'Azur (45x61cm-18x24in) s s.i.verso. 19-Jan-4 Horta, Bruxelles #26
£1477	$2732	€2200	Grande ferme Flamande (75x95cm-30x37in) s. s.i.verso. 13-Mar-4 De Vuyst, Lokeren #217/R est:2200-2600
£3200	$5792	€4800	Homme assis devant un mur decore de gravures et de dessins (100x65cm-39x26in) s.d.1890. 30-Mar-4 Palais de Beaux Arts, Brussels #638/R est:3000-5000
£4667	$8353	€7000	Ouvriers revenant du travail (101x120cm-40x47in) s. 15-May-4 De Vuyst, Lokeren #446/R est:6500-8500

LEEMPUTTEN, Cornelis van (1841-1902) Belgian

£570	$1055	€850	Sheep and hen in the meadow (16x25cm-6x10in) s. panel. 13-Mar-4 De Vuyst, Lokeren #357
£669	$1157	€950	L'homme a la pioche (27x15cm-11x6in) s. 9-Dec-3 Vanderkindere, Brussels #59
£699	$1203	€1000	Young shepherd with his sheep (17x23cm-7x9in) s. panel. 3-Dec-3 Neumeister, Munich #645
£761	$1393	€1111	Landscapes with sheep resting (11x14cm-4x6in) i.verso panel pair. 9-Jun-4 Rasmussen, Copenhagen #1640/R (D.KR 8500)
£830	$1510	€1212	Ducks by a pond (22x33cm-9x13in) s. panel. 16-Jun-4 Fischer, Luzern #1115/R (S.FR 1900)
£1105	$1900	€1613	Sheep and hen in barnyard (31x20cm-12x8in) s. panel. 2-Dec-3 Christie's, Rockefeller NY #42/R est:4000-6000
£1118	$2024	€1700	Coq et poules dans un paysage (17x24cm-7x9in) s. panel. 19-Apr-4 Horta, Bruxelles #43 est:1500-2000
£1332	$2158	€1945	Life in the barn (68x56cm-27x22in) s. 30-Jul-3 Goodman, Sydney #201/R est:5000-8000 (A.D 3250)
£1348	$2250	€1900	Poules, coq et canards dans le pre (18x24cm-7x9in) s. panel. 17-Jun-3 Vanderkindere, Brussels #19 est:1250-1750
£2083	$3542	€3000	Interieur d'etable avec moutons (22x31cm-9x12in) s. panel. 28-Oct-3 Christie's, Amsterdam #44/R est:3000-5000
£2200	$3586	€3212	Poultry in a landscape. Landscape with sheep and goats (17x23cm-7x9in) one s.d.1865 panel pair. 25-Sep-3 Mellors & Kirk, Nottingham #789/R est:2000-3000
£5307	$9500	€7748	Shepherd with sheep (71x97cm-28x38in) s. i.verso. 6-May-4 Doyle, New York #42/R est:6000-8000

LEEMPUTTEN, Frans van (1850-1914) Belgian

£600	$1110	€876	Road home (27x41cm-11x16in) s. panel. 15-Jan-4 Christie's, Kensington #830/R
£800	$1456	€1200	On the way to the fields (50x30cm-20x12in) s.d.1889. 1-Jul-4 Van Ham, Cologne #1479/R
£1408	$2437	€2000	La recolte (19x37cm-7x15in) s. panel. 10-Dec-3 Hotel des Ventes Mosan, Brussels #151 est:500-600
£2000	$3580	€3000	Farmer ploughing (35x51cm-14x20in) s. 15-May-4 De Vuyst, Lokeren #359/R est:1700-2000
Works on paper			
£270	$476	€400	Shepherds and flock at edge of wood (86x56cm-34x22in) s. pencil. 24-May-4 Bernaerts, Antwerp #547/R

LEEMPUTTEN, J L van (19th C) Belgian

£1400	$2240	€2030	Poultry in a field (24x39cm-9x15in) s.d.1869 panel. 18-Sep-3 Christie's, Kensington #48/R est:1000-1500
£1700	$2839	€2482	Sheep and ducks. Sheep and chicken (24x35cm-9x14in) s.d.1873 panel pair. 12-Nov-3 Sotheby's, Olympia #196/R est:2000-3000
£1769	$3166	€2600	Bergere dans un paysage avec des chevres, des moutons et des chevaux (89x128cm-35x50in) 22-Mar-4 Amberes, Antwerp #261/R

LEEMPUTTEN, J van (?) Belgian

£1225	$2242	€1850	A la ferme, poules, poussins, moutons, poules aux champs (24x36cm-9x14in) s. set of four. 9-Apr-4 Claude Aguttes, Neuilly #3/R est:1500-1800

LEEMPUTTEN, Jan van (19th C) Belgian

£1700	$2720	€2465	Shepherd and his flock (25x35cm-10x14in) s.d.1867 panel. 18-Sep-3 Christie's, Kensington #47/R est:1000-1500

LEEMPUTTEN, Jean Baptiste Leopold van (1831-1924) Belgian

£315	$541	€450	Bergere et moutons dans un paysage (12x17cm-5x7in) s. panel. 2-Dec-3 Campo & Campo, Antwerp #385
£433	$784	€650	Poussins et raisins (25x36cm-10x14in) s. 30-Mar-4 Campo & Campo, Antwerp #312/R

LEEMPUTTEN, Jef Louis van (1865-1948) Belgian

£284	$474	€400	Shepherd with sheep near the stable (25x36cm-10x14in) s. 20-Oct-3 Bernaerts, Antwerp #45
£426	$711	€600	Sheep and chicken at the stable (38x51cm-15x20in) s. 20-Oct-3 Bernaerts, Antwerp #45a/R
£466	$750	€680	Sheep grazing in a landscape (24x34cm-9x13in) s.d.1876 panel. 14-Jan-4 Christie's, Rockefeller NY #19/R
£574	$1085	€850	Coq et poules au pre (25x35cm-10x14in) s. panel. 17-Feb-4 Vanderkindere, Brussels #469
£600	$1086	€900	Poules a la basse-court (24x36cm-9x14in) s. 30-Mar-4 Campo & Campo, Antwerp #315
£608	$1089	€900	Visite de la Sainte-Vierge (124x95cm-49x37in) 10-May-4 Amberes, Antwerp #339
£616	$1048	€900	Moutons au paturage (24x36cm-9x14in) s. pair. 4-Nov-3 Servarts Themis, Bruxelles #637
£671	$1235	€1000	Couple de fermiers en carriole (70x100cm-28x39in) s. 23-Mar-4 Galerie Moderne, Brussels #305/R
£671	$1201	€1000	Chicks (23x25cm-9x10in) s. 27-May-4 Dorotheum, Graz #69/R
£733	$1320	€1100	Hilly landscape with sheep at sunset (38x50cm-15x20in) s. 26-Apr-4 Bernaerts, Antwerp #314/R
£1092	$1987	€1594	Chicken pen with a coastal landscape in the distance (32x47cm-13x19in) s. panel. 16-Jun-4 Fischer, Luzern #1114/R est:2500-3000 (S.FR 2500)
£1399	$2336	€2000	Coq et poules (24x35cm-9x14in) s. 29-Jun-3 Eric Pillon, Calais #56/R
£1399	$2336	€2000	Coq et poules (24x35cm-9x14in) s. 29-Jun-3 Eric Pillon, Calais #55/R
£1550	$2899	€2263	Sheep and chickens in a meadow (14x19cm-6x7in) s. 26-Feb-4 Lane, Penzance #145/R est:700-1000
Works on paper			
£867	$1551	€1300	In front of the King, God and fatherland (75x109cm-30x43in) s.i.d.1916 W/C gouache pencil. 15-May-4 De Vuyst, Lokeren #360/R est:1250-1500

LEEN, Willem van (1753-1825) Dutch

£7000	$12110	€10220	Still life of grapes and other fruits, flowers and vines upon a table top (47x37cm-19x15in) s. prov. 11-Dec-3 Sotheby's, London #166/R est:7000-12000
Miniatures			
£22000	$39380	€32120	Still life in a stone vase sculpted with Amorini, goldfinches in a bird's nest (9cm-4in) s. gilt metal frame. 25-May-4 Christie's, London #95/R est:8000-12000
Works on paper			
£3378	$5946	€5000	Two green parakeets on a branch (36x24cm-14x9in) s.verso W/C gouache grey wash prov.exhib.lit. 19-May-4 Sotheby's, Amsterdam #228/R est:4000-6000

LEENE, Jules van de (1887-1962) Belgian

£629	$1051	€900	Les anemones (81x70cm-32x28in) s. 13-Oct-3 Horta, Bruxelles #341
£642	$1149	€950	Vase fleuri d'arums (90x80cm-35x31in) s. 10-May-4 Horta, Bruxelles #306
£1223	$2225	€1786	Anemones et coloquintes (80x90cm-31x35in) s.d.1927. 16-Jun-4 Fischer, Luzern #1126/R est:2000-2500 (S.FR 2800)
£1773	$2961	€2500	Nature morte aux bouquets (120x110cm-47x43in) s. 14-Oct-3 Vanderkindere, Brussels #130/R
Works on paper			
£411	$699	€600	La ramasseuse de bois mort (100x68cm-39x27in) s. gouache. 4-Nov-3 Servarts Themis, Bruxelles #636
£611	$1113	€892	Fishermen checking their nets on the beach (52x65cm-20x26in) s.i. mixed media. 16-Jun-4 Fischer, Luzern #2247 (S.FR 1400)
£733	$1313	€1100	Rozenhoed quay and the Belfort of Bruges under snow (98x67cm-39x26in) s. gouache. 15-May-4 De Vuyst, Lokeren #338

LEENERS, Jef (20th C) Belgian
£559 $951 €800 Vase d'oeillets (69x50cm-27x20in) s. 18-Nov-3 Vanderkindere, Brussels #42

LEENHOUWERS, Carl (20th C) ?
£400 $708 €584 White shore (41x51cm-16x20in) init. i.d.2003 verso board. 28-Apr-4 Halls, Shrewsbury #520/R

LEES, Derwent (1885-1931) British
£4000 $7160 €5840 Lyndra at Aldbourne, the red jacket (39x51cm-15x20in) s. panel prov.exhib. 16-Mar-4 Bonhams, New Bond Street #12/R est:1500-2500
£8200 $15006 €11972 The Blue Pool (32x40cm-13x16in) s. panel exhib. 7-Apr-4 Woolley & Wallis, Salisbury #292/R est:1500-2500
£9500 $17385 €13870 Landscape 3 (32x41cm-13x16in) s.d.14 panel prov.exhib. 2-Jun-4 Sotheby's, London #26/R est:10000-15000
Works on paper
£800 $1456 €1200 Portrait of Lyndra the artist's wife (47x30cm-19x12in) s. i.d.1926 verso W/C pencil pen ink. 2-Jul-4 Bloomsbury, London #184/R

LEES, Derwent (attrib) (1885-1931) British
£480 $778 €696 Straw hat (41x33cm-16x13in) panel. 30-Jul-3 Hamptons Fine Art, Godalming #168

LEES, John (1943-) American
Works on paper
£231 $400 €337 Mountain (113x141cm-44x56in) mixed media prov. 10-Dec-3 Phillips, New York #553/R

LEES, Michael (20th C) British
£1350 $2484 €1971 Bideford Bridge (45x58cm-18x23in) s.d.1990 board. 25-Mar-4 Bonhams, West Country #819

LEESE, Spencer (fl.1882-1892) British
£300 $516 €438 River landscape with horse drawn barge (76x122cm-30x48in) s. exhib. 2-Dec-3 Peter Francis, Wales #56/R

LEEUW, Alexis de (fl.1848-1883) Belgian
£488 $873 €712 Shepherdess with flock on a winter path (102x76cm-40x30in) s. 4-May-4 Ritchie, Toronto #83/R est:800-1000 (C.D 1200)
£1400 $2380 €2044 Timber wagon (76x127cm-30x50in) indis.sig. 19-Nov-3 Tennants, Leyburn #1087 est:1500-2000
£1500 $2505 €2190 Snowscene with log cart (58x89cm-23x35in) s. 8-Oct-3 Andrew Hartley, Ilkley #1138/R est:1200-1800
£1750 $2923 €2555 Winter landscape with figures conversing and skating on frozen river (36x46cm-14x18in) s.d.1854. 16-Nov-3 Desmond Judd, Cranbrook #1022
£2200 $3938 €3212 Horsemen by a stream (61x91cm-24x36in) s. 27-May-4 Christie's, Kensington #170/R est:1200-1800

LEEUW, Alexis de (attrib) (fl.1848-1883) Belgian
£1100 $2035 €1606 Country folk with cattle and sheep at a woodland pool (69x100cm-27x39in) 14-Jan-4 Lawrence, Crewkerne #1414 est:600-900

LEEUW, Bert de (1926-) Belgian
£1111 $1856 €1600 Composition abstraite (140x100cm-55x39in) s. s.verso. 21-Oct-3 Campo & Campo, Antwerp #68 est:800-1000

LEEUW, Franciscus Theodorus Gysbertus van der (1881-1930) Dutch
£308 $524 €450 Nude sitting on blue cloth (20x15cm-8x6in) s. panel. 5-Nov-3 Vendue Huis, Gravenhage #303

LEEUW, Gerard de (1912-1985) ?
Sculpture
£1293 $2159 €1888 Witch doctor with impundulu (91cm-36in) s. bronze. 20-Oct-3 Stephan Welz, Johannesburg #351/R est:10000-15000 (SA.R 15000)

LEEUW, Pieter van de (1647-1679) Dutch
£828 $1531 €1200 Landscape with peasant woman, sheep and horse (31x46cm-12x18in) mono. panel. 14-Feb-4 Hans Stahl, Hamburg #180/R

LEEUWEN, Henk van (1890-1972) Dutch
£338 $605 €500 Pond with punts and farmstead (60x100cm-24x39in) s. 6-May-4 Michael Zeller, Lindau #757/R
£340 $619 €500 Ploughing the field (40x50cm-16x20in) s. 3-Feb-4 Christie's, Amsterdam #219
£616 $1048 €900 Small farm (38x48cm-15x19in) s. 5-Nov-3 Vendue Huis, Gravenhage #164/R
£664 $1143 €950 Farmer ploughing (38x51cm-15x20in) s. panel. 8-Dec-3 Glerum, Amsterdam #255/R
£987 $1816 €1500 Het werkhuis, Leiden (50x70cm-20x28in) s.i. 28-Jun-4 Sotheby's, Amsterdam #150/R est:1500-2000

LEEWENS, Will (1923-1987) Dutch
£524 $902 €750 Composition (60x80cm-24x31in) 8-Dec-3 Glerum, Amsterdam #167/R
£1678 $2887 €2400 Petite parade (72x91cm-28x36in) s.d.85 acrylic. 8-Dec-3 Glerum, Amsterdam #197/R est:2500-3500
£1818 $3127 €2600 Composition (47x68cm-19x27in) s. 8-Dec-3 Glerum, Amsterdam #163/R est:3000-5000

LEFEBRE, Wilhelm (1873-1974) German
£267 $480 €400 Woodland (33x41cm-13x16in) s. 24-Apr-4 Reiss & Sohn, Konigstein #5361/R
£400 $732 €600 Horses in the riding-school (11x18cm-4x7in) s. i.d.1901 verso. 5-Jun-4 Arnold, Frankfurt #648/R

LEFEBRE, Wilhelm (attrib) (1873-1974) German
£268 $499 €400 Lovers by birch trees (75x43cm-30x17in) 6-Mar-4 Arnold, Frankfurt #772/R

LEFEBVRE, Charles (?) French
£460 $782 €672 Shepherd, his dog and cattle beside a lake (53x89cm-21x35in) s. 18-Nov-3 Bonhams, Leeds #225

LEFEBVRE, Charles Amable (1827-?) French
£1867 $3435 €2800 Marche a Tanger (24x35cm-9x14in) s. panel. 11-Jun-4 Claude Aguttes, Neuilly #123/R est:2500-3000

LEFEBVRE, Charles Victor (1805-1882) French
£634 $1096 €900 Vue du Chateau Saint-Ange (35x52cm-14x20in) s. 15-Dec-3 Bailly Pommery, Paris #99/R
Works on paper
£262 $450 €383 View of the countryside with figures looking into distance (23x29cm-9x11in) s.d.1850 pencil pen ink htd white W/C. 2-Dec-3 Christie's, Rockefeller NY #154a/R

LEFEBVRE, Jules Joseph (1836-1911) French
£1064 $1723 €1500 Nu feminin, etude pour Chloe (29x16cm-11x6in) bears sig. panel. 23-May-3 Sotheby's, Paris #33/R est:1500-2000
£3593 $6000 €5246 Lady Godiva (51x43cm-20x17in) 14-Nov-3 Du Mouchelle, Detroit #2018/R est:6000-8000
£23529 $40000 €34352 Clemence Isaure (67x55cm-26x22in) s.i. 28-Oct-3 Sotheby's, New York #52/R est:18000-25000

LEFEBVRE, Valentin (c.1642-1680) Flemish
Works on paper
£426 $711 €600 Scene de l'histoire antique. i. sanguine wash prov. 15-Oct-3 Sotheby's, Paris #95/R
£467 $845 €700 Christ entoure d'anges et Saint-Esprit (26x30cm-10x12in) pen ink wash over crayon. 4-Apr-4 St-Germain-en-Laye Encheres #1/R
£1497 $2679 €2200 La Naissance de Saint Jean Baptiste (38x19cm-15x7in) black chk pen brown ink wash prov.exhib.lit. 18-Mar-4 Christie's, Paris #28/R est:1500-2000

LEFEBVRE, Valentin (attrib) (c.1642-1680) Flemish
Works on paper
£1500 $2700 €2190 Diana and Acteon (32x20cm-13x8in) d.1656 mount pen brown ink wash black chk prov. 20-Apr-4 Sotheby's, Olympia #37/R est:600-800

LEFEBVRE, W (19/20th C) French
Works on paper
£852 $1500 €1244 Homecoming (25x23cm-10x9in) s.d.1900 mixed media. 23-May-4 Treadway Gallery, Cincinnati #496/R est:600-800

LEFEUBURE, Karl (1847-1911) German
£352 $599 €514 Angler by sawmill (12x26cm-5x10in) s. panel. 5-Nov-3 Dobiaschofsky, Bern #741/R (S.FR 800)
£2100 $3864 €3066 Artist's studio (73x60cm-29x24in) s. prov. 23-Jun-4 Cheffins, Cambridge #522/R est:1200-1800
£3333 $5433 €4800 Farmstead by pond (76x112cm-30x44in) s. 24-Sep-3 Neumeister, Munich #477/R est:4000

LEFEUVRE, Arsene M (19/20th C) French
£6667 $12000 €9734 An interesting story (80x100cm-31x39in) s.d.1892. 23-Apr-4 Sotheby's, New York #159/R est:12000-15000

LEFEVRE, Robert Jacques François (1755-1830) French
£7692 $13077 €11000 Portrait de Charles Francois le Brun, duc de Plaisance (82x65cm-32x26in) s.d.1808 prov.lit. 1-Dec-3 Coutau Begarie, Paris #314/R est:10000-15000
£31469 $53497 €45000 L'amour aiguisant ses fleches (64x54cm-25x21in) s.d.1795 exhib. 1-Dec-3 Coutau Begarie, Paris #282/R est:60000-80000
£52632 $96842 €80000 Portrait presume de la comedienne Sophie de Gevaudan (96x74cm-38x29in) s.d.1796 prov. 23-Jun-4 Sotheby's, Paris #50/R est:80000-120000

LEFEVRE, Robert Jacques François (attrib) (1755-1830) French
£2133 $3861 €3200 Portrait de femme en blanc (81x65cm-32x26in) bears mono.d.1813. 30-Mar-4 Rossini, Paris #61/R est:3000-5000
Works on paper
£476 $852 €700 Portrait de Francois Charles Joseph Bonaparte, Roi de Rome (36x26cm-14x10in) black white chk pastel. 18-Mar-4 Christie's, Paris #304/R

LEFFEL, David (1931-) American
£2310 $4250 €3373 Grapes and eggs (33x37cm-13x15in) s.d.68 canvas laid down prov. 27-Jun-4 Freeman, Philadelphia #136/R est:2000-3000

LEFKOVITZ, Sylvia (1924-) Canadian
£240 $439 €350 Woman on beach (20x64cm-8x25in) s.d.73. 1-Jun-4 Joyner Waddington, Toronto #423 (C.D 600)
Sculpture
£833 $1492 €1216 Zephir (20x43cm-8x17in) s.d.61 white marble prov. 22-Mar-4 Waddingtons, Toronto #623/R est:2000-3000 (C.D 2000)

LEFORT, Agnes (1891-1973) Canadian
£226 $355 €330 Arbres (30x40cm-12x16in) s.d.42 i.verso. 26-Aug-3 Iegor de Saint Hippolyte, Montreal #99 (C.D 500)

LEFORT, Jean (1875-1954) French
£620 $1141 €905 Eglise St. Rue, et la rue St. Denis, Paris (54x37cm-21x15in) s.i. 29-Mar-4 Bonhams, Bath #39
£700 $1113 €1015 Tuilleries Gardens (26x35cm-10x14in) s. board. 9-Sep-3 Bonhams, Knightsbridge #37/R

LEFRANC, Jules (1887-1972) French
£1678 $2887 €2400 Le Chateau de Josselin (46x69cm-18x27in) s. s.i.verso prov.exhib.lit. 3-Dec-3 Tajan, Paris #291/R est:2000-2400
£1958 $3368 €2800 Alain Gerbault, Saint Malo (57x40cm-22x16in) s. cardboard. 3-Dec-3 Tajan, Paris #213/R est:3000-4000
£2238 $3849 €3200 Paysage Basco-Bearnais (61x33cm-24x13in) s. isorel. 3-Dec-3 Tajan, Paris #217/R est:2000-2500
£2238 $3849 €3200 La riviere dans l'ile de France (61x33cm-24x13in) s.i. i.verso board prov. 2-Dec-3 Sotheby's, Amsterdam #200/R est:1800-2500
£2658 $4571 €3800 L'amer (55x33cm-22x13in) s. s.i.verso. 3-Dec-3 Tajan, Paris #214/R est:4000-5000
£2717 $5000 €3967 St. Malo. Le Mole, Les Ramparts (20x25cm-8x10in) s. s.i.verso panel. 10-Jun-4 Sotheby's, New York #488/R est:700-900
£3200 $5760 €4800 Le phare (36x49cm-14x19in) s. cardboard. 26-Apr-4 Tajan, Paris #370/R est:5000-6000
Works on paper
£1259 $2165 €1800 Camping, Porquerolles (32x49cm-13x19in) s. gouache varnish prov. 3-Dec-3 Tajan, Paris #218 est:1800-2000

LEFRANC, Roland (1931-2000) French
£940 $1748 €1400 Les chalutiers (22x27cm-9x11in) s. 7-Mar-4 Lesieur & Le Bars, Le Havre #81
£986 $1597 €1400 La palanguee (73x54cm-29x21in) s. i.verso. 11-Aug-3 Boscher, Cherbourg #748
£1358 $2539 €2050 Les marchandes de poisson (46x55cm-18x22in) s. 25-Jul-4 Feletin, Province #88
£1517 $2534 €2200 Paysage a Reviers (65x81cm-26x32in) s. d.74 verso. 11-Nov-3 Lesieur & Le Bars, Le Havre #77

LEFRANCQ, Marcel (20th C) Belgian
Works on paper
£1333 $2387 €2000 Archipel de memoire (34x51cm-13x20in) s. collage exec.1972. 15-May-4 Renaud, Paris #132/R

LEFT, Ron (fl.1980s) New Zealander
£729 $1159 €1064 Tondo 5 (119cm-47in circular) s.i.d.1975 verso. 1-May-3 Dunbar Sloane, Wellington #100/R est:2000-3000 (NZ.D 2100)

LEFTON, Carl (?) American
£230 $375 €336 Harbour scene (56x71cm-22x28in) s. 19-Jul-3 Outer Cape Auctions, Provincetown #68/R
£257 $475 €375 West end home, John Dowd's (46x61cm-18x24in) s. 17-Jul-4 Outer Cape Auctions, Provincetown #89/R
£297 $550 €434 Old reliable Alley (74x41cm-29x16in) s. 15-Feb-4 Outer Cape Auctions, Provincetown #29/R
£324 $600 €473 East end cottage (41x51cm-16x20in) s. 15-Feb-4 Outer Cape Auctions, Provincetown #96a/R
£331 $600 €483 William Maynard's home (46x36cm-18x14in) s. 3-Apr-4 Outer Cape Auctions, Provincetown #43/R

LEFUR, Joe (1920) French
£667 $1193 €1000 Marais salants a Batz (55x73cm-22x29in) s. 16-May-4 Thierry & Lannon, Brest #327

LEGA, Achille (1899-1934) Italian
£2721 $4871 €4000 Old woman (31x31cm-12x12in) cardboard. 22-Mar-4 Sant Agostino, Torino #213/R est:5000

LEGA, Giovanni (attrib) (19th C) Italian
£1519 $2750 €2218 Natura morta (43x64cm-17x25in) s.d.verso. 3-Apr-4 Harvey Clar, Oakland #1536

LEGA, Silvestro (1826-1895) Italian
£38406 $62986 €53000 Countryside with woman (26x35cm-10x14in) s. board lit. 27-May-3 Finarte Semenzato, Milan #75/R est:38000-44000
£180000 $331200 €270000 Gabbrigiana (38x29cm-15x11in) s. board painted 1888 prov.exhib.lit. 11-Jun-4 Farsetti, Prato #556/R est:230000-260000
£186667 $343467 €280000 Innocence dreaming (96x59cm-38x23in) s. prov.exhib.lit. 10-Jun-4 Christie's, Rome #190/R est:230000-280000

LEGAE, Ezrom (1938-1999) South African
Sculpture
£2586 $4319 €3776 Head (51cm-20in) init.num.III/X bronze. 20-Oct-3 Stephan Welz, Johannesburg #385/R est:25000-35000 (SA.R 30000)

LEGANGER, Nicolay Tysland (1832-1894) American
£1235 $2000 €1791 Afternoon at Tamworth (53x43cm-21x17in) s.i.verso. 8-Aug-3 Barridorf, Portland #295/R est:3000-5000
£1573 $2500 €2297 After the storm (46x76cm-18x30in) s.i.d.1890 verso. 12-Sep-3 Skinner, Boston #286/R

LEGARES, Josep Olivet (1885-1956) Spanish
£296 $536 €450 Lake (14x21cm-6x8in) s. cardboard. 14-Apr-4 Ansorena, Madrid #245/R

LEGAT, Léon (1829-?) French
£21127 $35070 €30000 Visite du marchand ambulant (90x117cm-35x46in) s. 15-Jun-3 Peron, Melun #108

LEGENDRE, Léon (19th C) French
£467 $845 €700 Scene de rue au Caire (55x46cm-22x18in) s.d.188.. 1-Apr-4 Credit Municipal, Paris #72

LEGER, Fernand (1881-1955) French
£18182 $30909 €26000 David triomphant (16x18cm-6x7in) tempera pencil paper. 29-Nov-3 Farsetti, Prato #422/R est:25000-30000
£73333 $134200 €110000 La vache (164x200cm-65x79in) mono. panel painted c.1950 prov. lit. 7-Jun-4 Artcurial Briest, Paris #61/R est:150000-200000
£93333 $170800 €140000 La grande parade (131x167cm-52x66in) mono. stained glass painted c.1961-1962 prov. 7-Jun-4 Artcurial Briest, Paris #63/R est:200000-300000
£130000 $239200 €189800 Composition (64x49cm-25x19in) s.d.37 prov.lit. 23-Jun-4 Christie's, London #257/R est:130000-190000
£164706 $280000 €240471 Paysage (74x91cm-29x36in) s.d.41-42 prov. 5-Nov-3 Christie's, Rockefeller NY #351/R est:200000-300000
£180000 $331200 €262800 Composition I (65x50cm-26x20in) s.d.38 s.i.d.verso prov.lit. 23-Jun-4 Christie's, London #246/R est:150000-200000
£189944 $340000 €277318 Composition a la toupie (65x46cm-26x18in) s.d.29 s.i.d.verso prov.exhib.lit. 5-May-4 Christie's, Rockefeller NY #297/R est:200000-300000
£212291 $380000 €309945 Composition avec vase (50x65cm-20x26in) s.d.38 s.i.d.verso prov.exhib.lit. 6-May-4 Sotheby's, New York #137/R est:250000-350000
£250000 $455000 €365000 Composition circulaire (60x73cm-24x29in) s.d.47 i.verso prov.exhib.lit. 3-Feb-4 Sotheby's, London #50/R est:250000-350000
£282353 $480000 €412235 Joie de vivre (91x73cm-36x29in) s.d.53 prov.lit. 5-Nov-3 Sotheby's, New York #56/R est:500000-700000
£302115 $513595 €441088 Nature morte (65x46cm-26x18in) s.d.28 s.d. verso prov.exhib.lit. 4-Nov-3 Bukowskis, Stockholm #141/R est:3000000-4000000 (S.KR 4000000)
£305882 $520000 €446588 Esquisse pour - La partie de campagne (60x92cm-24x36in) s.d.53-54 s.i.d.verso prov. 5-Nov-3 Christie's, Rockefeller NY #305/R est:400000-600000
£402235 $720000 €587263 Nature morte aux fruits sur fond bleu (130x89cm-51x35in) s.d.39 s.i.d.verso prov.exhib.lit. 6-May-4 Sotheby's, New York #150/R est:700000-900000
£460000 $837200 €671600 Le quatorze Juillet a Vernon (24x33cm-9x13in) init. painted 1918 prov.lit. 3-Feb-4 Sotheby's, London #44/R est:400000-600000
£470588 $800000 €687058 Composition au feuillage (92x60cm-36x24in) s.d.26 prov.exhib.lit. 4-Nov-3 Christie's, Rockefeller NY #39/R est:600000-800000
£474860 $850000 €693296 Composition aux deux papillons (73x92cm-29x36in) s.d.43 s.i.d.verso prov.exhib.lit. 6-May-4 Sotheby's, New York #140/R est:600000-800000
£550000 $1006500 €803000 Araignee bleue (92x65cm-36x26in) s.d.38 s.i.d.verso prov.exhib.lit. 2-Feb-4 Christie's, London #36/R est:500000-700000
£754190 $1350000 €1101117 Nature morte (65x50cm-26x20in) s.i.d.23 verso prov.exhib.lit. 4-May-4 Christie's, Rockefeller NY #28/R est:600000-800000
£1229050 $2200000 €1794413 Deux femmes a l'enfant (63x46cm-25x18in) s.d.19 s.i.d.verso prov.lit. 4-May-4 Christie's, Rockefeller NY #25/R est:2000000-3000000
£11764707 $20000000 €17176472 La femme en rouge et vert (101x80cm-40x31in) s. i.d.14 verso prov.exhib. 4-Nov-3 Christie's, Rockefeller NY #32/R est:10000000-15000000
Prints
£1808 $3200 €2640 L'Echafaudage au soleil (34x45cm-13x18in) s.num.28/75 col lithograph. 28-Apr-4 Christie's, Rockefeller NY #61/R est:4000-6000
£1867 $3435 €2800 Le tournesol (40x33cm-16x13in) s. col lithograph one of 130. 12-Jun-4 Villa Grisebach, Berlin #784/R est:1800-2400
£1933 $3500 €2822 Les constructeurs (50x63cm-20x25in) s. col lithograph. 19-Apr-4 Bonhams & Butterfields, San Francisco #164/R est:3500-4500
£2011 $3600 €2936 Nadia Leger (33x25cm-13x10in) s. col lithograph. 8-May-4 Susanin's, Chicago #6096/R est:2600-3200
£2098 $3566 €3000 Paysage (43x36cm-17x14in) col lithograph exec.1948. 28-Nov-3 Tajan, Paris #295/R est:2000-2500
£2235 $4000 €3263 Les constructeurs (43x59cm-17x23in) s.num.187/260 color lithograph. 6-May-4 Swann Galleries, New York #487/R est:4000-6000
£2321 $4177 €3389 La lecture (43x55cm-17x22in) s.num.109/350 col lithograph lit. 26-Apr-4 Bukowskis, Stockholm #368/R est:20000-25000 (S.KR 32000)
£2795 $4751 €4081 La femme et la fleur (57x52cm-22x20in) s.num.14/75 col lithograph lit. 5-Nov-3 AB Stockholms Auktionsverk #1246/R est:30000-40000 (S.KR 37000)
£3200 $5888 €4800 Les danseuses (56x46cm-22x18in) s. col lithograph exec. 1954 one of 75. 12-Jun-4 Villa Grisebach, Berlin #380/R est:3000-4000
£3712 $6755 €5420 La chaise. s.i. col lithograph. 17-Jun-4 Kornfeld, Bern #5617 est:10000 (S.FR 8500)
£3955 $7000 €5774 La femme et la fleur (57x52cm-22x20in) s.num.68/75 col lithograph. 28-Apr-4 Christie's, Rockefeller NY #62/R est:4000-6000
£6471 $11000 €9448 Femmes au perroquet (50x65cm-20x26in) s. col lithograph exec.1952. 4-Nov-3 Christie's, Rockefeller NY #103/R est:7000-9000
£9040 $16000 €13198 Cirque, Teriade, Les Editions Verve (42x33cm-17x13in) col lithograph 34 black lithograph 29 with decorations album. 28-Apr-4 Christie's, Rockefeller NY #60/R est:14000-18000
Sculpture
£2349 $4370 €3500 Sans titre, deux pointes (28x35cm-11x14in) s.verso white stone emaillee. 2-Mar-4 Artcurial Briest, Paris #155/R est:3000-4000
£6333 $11653 €9500 Composition au buste blanc et noir (28x37x3cm-11x15x1in) st.sig. num.16 polychrome enamel. 10-Jun-4 Camard, Paris #112/R est:10000-12000
£6376 $11413 €9500 Nature morte aux fruits (30x25cm-12x10in) i. num.56 plaster lit. 30-May-4 Eric Pillon, Calais #217/R
£15000 $27600 €21900 Composition (64x39cm-25x15in) i. num.2/8 bronze relief st.f.C Valsuani cast 1960 prov.lit. 22-Jun-4 Sotheby's, London #302/R est:18000-25000
£17000 $31280 €24820 Visage aux deux mains (46x33cm-18x13in) i. num.3/8 bronze relief st.f.C Valsuani conceived 1940. 22-Jun-4 Sotheby's, London #305/R est:18000-25000
£20000 $36400 €29200 La fleur qui marche (65cm-26in) s.d.52 glazed ceramic conceived 1952 prov. 3-Feb-4 Christie's, London #201/R est:12000-16000
£22667 $41480 €34000 Le tournesol ou soleil (120cm-47in) ceramic enamel exec. c.1970 Cast Brice prov.lit. 7-Jun-4 Artcurial Briest, Paris #67/R est:35000-45000
£34000 $62560 €49640 Branche musee (67cm-26in) i. num.6/8 painted ceramic exec c.1952 lit. 22-Jun-4 Sotheby's, London #303/R est:20000-30000
£38235 $65000 €55823 Femmes au perroquet (82x120cm-32x47in) i. num.III/VIII painted bronze st.f.Tesconi prov. 6-Nov-3 Sotheby's, New York #272/R est:30000-40000
£54000 $98280 €78840 Femme et perroquet (82x121cm-32x48in) i.num.6/8 bronze conceived c.1950-52 prov.exhb. 4-Feb-4 Sotheby's, London #281/R est:30000-40000

£111732	$200000	€163129	Femmes aux perroquets (95x82x200cm-37x32x79in) s.d.52 partially glazed ceramic four sections exec 1952 prov. 6-May-4 Sotheby's, New York #382a/R est:120000-180000
£203333	$372100	€305000	La fleur qui marche (315cm-124in) polychrome ceramic exec. 1987 one of four prov.lit. 7-Jun-4 Artcurial Briest, Paris #62/R est:300000-400000

Works on paper

£769	$1308	€1100	Composition (14x11cm-6x4in) mono.d.34 pen drawing. 1-Dec-3 Camard, Paris #61
£1200	$2208	€1800	Etude pour un portrait (21x14cm-8x6in) pencil. 10-Jun-4 Hauswedell & Nolte, Hamburg #424/R est:2400
£2000	$3340	€2920	Projet de costume creation du monde (31x24cm-12x9in) init.i. gouache over pencil executed c.1923 prov.exhib. 21-Oct-3 Sotheby's, London #66/R est:2000-3000
£3916	$6540	€5600	Projet pour la creation du monde (30x23cm-12x9in) gouache prov. 29-Jun-3 Eric Pillon, Calais #256/R
£4000	$6680	€5840	New York (13x18cm-5x7in) s.i. pen ink gouache pencil on card executed c.1940-41 prov. 21-Oct-3 Sotheby's, London #73/R est:4000-6000
£4000	$7280	€5840	Portrait de Flechtheim (32x26cm-13x10in) s.i. pen ink exec 1928 prov.lit. 5-Feb-4 Christie's, London #376/R est:3000-5000
£6620	$11452	€9400	Etude pour les constructeurs (31x38cm-12x15in) s.i.d.1948/50 ink. 9-Dec-3 Chambelland & Giafferi, Paris #94/R est:12000-15000
£7000	$12880	€10220	Projet de costume (22x17cm-9x7in) s. W/C brush ink pencil prov.exhib. 22-Jun-4 Sotheby's, London #471/R est:7000-9000
£7000	$12880	€10220	Composition abstraite (33x22cm-13x9in) s.i.verso W/C prov. 22-Jun-4 Sotheby's, London #523/R est:5000-7000
£7500	$13800	€10950	Femme au chat (33x25cm-13x10in) s.d.46 pen ink over pencil prov. 22-Jun-4 Sotheby's, London #519/R est:5000-7000
£7500	$13800	€10950	Illumination (33x25cm-13x10in) s.d.48 W/C pen brush ink prov. 22-Jun-4 Sotheby's, London #522/R est:7000-9000
£8696	$15913	€12696	Composition abstraite en bleu et blanc (53x37cm-21x15in) mono.d.26 gouache prov.exhib. 5-Jun-4 Galerie du Rhone, Sion #574/R est:25000-35000 (S.FR 20000)
£9732	$17906	€14500	Portrait de Rimbaud (26x21cm-10x8in) mono.i.d. gouache Indian ink. 26-Mar-4 Ketterer, Hamburg #527/R est:5000-6000
£10056	$18000	€14682	Queue de comete (308x150cm-121x59in) woven sig. woven tapestry. 6-May-4 Sotheby's, New York #407/R est:15000-20000
£10465	$18000	€15279	Clarinettiste (30x23cm-12x9in) init.d.1948 ink W/C prov. 7-Dec-3 Freeman, Philadelphia #67 est:18000-25000
£10588	$18000	€15458	Composition with fruits (25x31cm-10x12in) init.d.6.38 gouache brush India ink prov. 5-Nov-3 Christie's, Rockefeller NY #133/R est:22000-28000
£11628	$20000	€16977	Composition with bird, head and sun (33x25cm-13x10in) init. ink W/C exec 1948 prov. 7-Dec-3 Freeman, Philadelphia #66 est:20000-30000
£12454	$22044	€18183	Composition (30x40cm-12x16in) init.i.d.32 Indian ink prov. 27-Apr-4 AB Stockholms Auktionsverk #1220/R est:100000-125000 (S.KR 170000)
£12570	$22500	€18352	Cirque (43x32cm-17x13in) init.i.d.1950 W/C brush ink prov. 6-May-4 Doyle, New York #108/R est:14000-18000
£12658	$20000	€18481	Etude pour les plongeurs (30x46cm-12x18in) s.i. ink W/C. 7-Sep-3 Treadway Gallery, Cincinnati #705/R est:50000-70000
£12667	$23180	€19000	Composition (29x29cm-11x11in) st.init. gouache prov. 7-Jun-4 Artcurial Briest, Paris #56/R est:12000-15000
£12844	$21450	€18624	La sacoche (40x32cm-16x13in) mono.d.49 Indian ink brush over pencil. 19-Jun-3 Kornfeld, Bern #614/R est:30000 (S.FR 28000)
£13333	$24533	€20000	Transport des forces (15x29cm-6x11in) s.i. gouache prov. 9-Jun-4 Tajan, Paris #42/R est:15000-20000
£13500	$24570	€19710	Composition a la chaise (42x33cm-17x13in) init. pencil ink over pencil exec.c.1930 prov. 4-Feb-4 Sotheby's, London #466/R est:14000-18000
£13500	$24840	€19710	Composition (28x36cm-11x14in) s.i.d.1936 gouache over pencil prov. 22-Jun-4 Sotheby's, London #472/R est:15000-20000
£14118	$24000	€20612	Still life with fruit (32x24cm-13x9in) gouache W/C brush India ink pencil prov. 5-Nov-3 Christie's, Rockefeller NY #132/R est:30000-40000
£15294	$26000	€22329	Composition avec des lunettes (31x23cm-12x9in) init.d.31 pencil paper on board. 5-Nov-3 Christie's, Rockefeller NY #126/R est:12000-16000
£15385	$27231	€22462	Les Clefs (26x20cm-10x8in) init.i.d.28 pencil writing-paper prov. 27-Apr-4 AB Stockholms Auktionsverk #1219/R est:100000-125000 (S.KR 210000)
£16667	$26333	€24000	Etude pour sculpture (49x32cm-19x13in) mono. ink gouache. 27-Apr-3 Versailles Encheres #44
£18000	$30060	€26280	L'avion dans les nuages (14x27cm-6x11in) init.d.39 gouache pencil prov. 21-Oct-3 Sotheby's, London #64/R est:20000-30000
£18000	$32760	€26280	Rechaud, Gaz de France (16x21cm-6x8in) init. gouache brush ink over pencil paper on canvas prov.exhib. 4-Feb-4 Sotheby's, London #518/R est:10000-15000
£18667	$34160	€28000	Tournesol (46x37cm-18x15in) mono.i.d.53 gouache prov.exhib. 7-Jun-4 Artcurial Briest, Paris #59/R est:25000-30000
£18794	$30447	€26500	Profil d'homme sur une junk piles (17x25cm-7x10in) mono.i.d.43 W/C gouache prov. 24-May-3 Martinot & Savignat, Pontoise #48/R est:14000-15000
£19000	$34960	€27740	Dessin de mains et de baton (32x49cm-13x19in) s. pencil brush ink wash prov. 22-Jun-4 Sotheby's, London #455/R est:20000-30000
£25000	$42500	€36500	Tete de femme et fleurs (32x25cm-13x10in) init.d.49 gouache prov.exhib. 9-Nov-3 Bonhams & Butterfields, Los Angeles #4013/R
£26573	$45175	€38000	Etude pour la composition a la femme en bleu (33x40cm-13x16in) init.d.6.3 gouache htd W/C exec.c.1937. 27-Nov-3 Millon & Associes, Paris #81/R est:40000-60000
£27000	$49680	€39420	Partie de campagne (34x44cm-13x17in) s. brush ink over pencil prov.exhib. 22-Jun-4 Sotheby's, London #461/R est:30000-40000
£27149	$46154	€60000	Joueurs de balons (18x23cm-7x9in) mono.d.1938 gouache lit. 25-Nov-3 Pierre Berge, Paris #9/R est:50000-70000
£29000	$52780	€42340	Les plongeurs (56x43cm-22x17in) s. gouache over black crayon exec.c.1942 prov. 4-Feb-4 Sotheby's, London #516/R est:30000-40000
£33333	$61000	€50000	La femme a la fleur (38x26cm-15x10in) gouache crayon exec. 1952 prov. 7-Jun-4 Artcurial Briest, Paris #60/R est:40000-60000
£34000	$62560	€49640	Acrobate et cheval (32x50cm-13x20in) s.d.53 gouache brush ink prov.exhib. 22-Jun-4 Sotheby's, London #463/R est:30000-40000
£34014	$60885	€50000	Femme au miroir. L'homme et les disques (28x22cm-11x9in) mono.d.20 indian ink cardboard double-sided prov.exhib.lit. 21-Mar-4 Calmels Cohen, Paris #166/R est:60000-80000
£36000	$66240	€52560	Etude pour le mosaique monumentale du Musee de Biot (15x84cm-6x33in) gouache paper on board exec.1954 prov. 22-Jun-4 Sotheby's, London #469/R est:35000-45000
£40000	$73600	€58400	Etude pour les acrobates (48x63cm-19x25in) s.d.39 pen ink paper on canvas prov. 22-Jun-4 Sotheby's, London #459/R est:50000-70000
£46667	$85400	€70000	Femme a la rose (55x43cm-22x17in) st.init. gouache prov. 7-Jun-4 Artcurial Briest, Paris #58/R est:70000-90000
£50000	$91000	€73000	Women and the vase (37x34cm-15x13in) st.init. brush ink exec c.1952 prov. 5-Feb-4 Christie's, London #434/R est:50000-70000
£55882	$95000	€81588	Grande Parade (239x319cm-94x126in) woven sig. d.53 wool tapestry prov. 6-Nov-3 Sotheby's, New York #276/R est:70000-90000
£60000	$109200	€87600	Acrobates (49x32cm-19x13in) gouache W/C brush ink exec c.1953 prov.exhib. 5-Feb-4 Christie's, London #435/R est:50000-70000
£70000	$128100	€105000	Les oiseaux sur l'echelle (26x44cm-10x17in) mono.d.43 gouache prov. 7-Jun-4 Artcurial Briest, Paris #55/R est:80000-100000
£72072	$123964	€105225	Femme au bouquet (32x24cm-13x9in) mono.d.21 W/C prov. 2-Dec-3 Koller, Zurich #3051/R est:50000-65000 (S.FR 160000)
£80000	$145600	€116800	Les amoureux (76x51cm-30x20in) s.i.d.55 gouache W/C brush ink prov. 4-Feb-4 Sotheby's, London #519/R est:60000-80000
£95238	$170476	€140000	Femmes a la toilette (44x36cm-17x14in) mono.d.20 W/C prov.exhib. 21-Mar-4 Calmels Cohen, Paris #169/R est:150000-200000
£300000	$552000	€450000	Oiseaux blancs, fond bleu (211x143cm-83x56in) s. gouache paper on canvas exhib. 9-Jun-4 Tajan, Paris #41/R est:300000-350000

LEGER, Fernand (after) (1881-1955) French

Prints

£3955	$7000	€5774	La lecture (43x55cm-17x22in) s.num.245/350 col lithograph. 28-Apr-4 Christie's, Rockefeller NY #63/R est:5000-7000

LEGGE, Arthur J (1859-1942) British

£460	$846	€672	Woman gathering sticks by a woodland cottage (77x64cm-30x25in) s. 23-Jun-4 Bonhams, Bury St Edmunds #355

LEGGE, Jasper (20th C) Australian

£413	$702	€603	Polycrest (120x150cm-47x59in) s. i.d.2002 verso acrylic prov. 29-Oct-3 Lawson Menzies, Sydney #139/R est:1500-2000 (A.D 1000)

LEGGETT, Alexander (19th C) British

£500	$920	€730	The auld shepherd. A Turk (15x13cm-6x5in) s. s.i.verso board pair. 10-Jun-4 Lyon & Turnbull, Edinburgh #115
£581	$1000	€848	Cottage door (30x23cm-12x9in) s. s.i.verso board. 6-Dec-3 Neal Auction Company, New Orleans #348/R
£1000	$1670	€1460	Fishermen's return (70x105cm-28x41in) s.d.1862. 16-Oct-3 Lyon & Turnbull, Edinburgh #48 est:500-700
£2800	$4424	€4060	Saved from the wreck (71x76cm-28x30in) mono.d.1861 i.verso. 4-Sep-3 Christie's, Kensington #295/R est:3000-5000

LEGHORN, Luigi Renault (19th C) British?

£1900	$3021	€2774	Ships portrait sail and steam vessel (56x97cm-22x38in) s.d.1885. 9-Sep-3 David Duggleby, Scarborough #291/R

LEGI, Giacomo (style) (?-1640) Flemish

£12000	$21960	€17520	Still life with cabbages, asparagus, basket of chestnuts, celery, mushrooms and other vegetables (106x154cm-42x61in) 8-Jul-4 Sotheby's, London #320/R est:12000-18000

LEGILLON, Jean François (1739-1797) Flemish

Works on paper

£1800	$3294	€2628	River landscape with a ruined mill. Landscape with a watermill (20x26cm-8x10in) s. black chk pair. 7-Jul-4 Bonhams, Knightsbridge #26/R est:2000-3000

LEGLER, Wilhelm (1875-1951) Italian

£1399	$2378	€2000	Peaceful fairy-tale landscape (64x80cm-25x31in) s. 28-Nov-3 Wiener Kunst Auktionen, Vienna #464/R est:2500-5000

LEGNANI, Stefano Maria (attrib) (1660-1715) Italian

£5000	$8650	€7300	Bishop Saint with an Angel holding the Bible (88x66cm-35x26in) 10-Dec-3 Bonhams, New Bond Street #120/R est:5000-7000

LEGORA, Giovanni Cappa (1887-1970) Italian

£1304	$2139	€1800	Mountain cottage (34x44cm-13x17in) s. 27-May-3 Finarte Semenzato, Milan #23/R
£1667	$2833	€2400	Yard (35x45cm-14x18in) s. s.i.d.1965 verso cardboard on canvas. 1-Nov-3 Meeting Art, Vercelli #192/R est:2000
£2685	$4752	€4000	Courmayeur (46x60cm-18x24in) s.i.d.1932. 1-May-4 Meeting Art, Vercelli #110 est:4000

LEGOUT-GERARD, Fernand (1856-1924) French

£927	$1734	€1400	Retour de peche (12cm-5in circular) s. board. 24-Jul-4 Thierry & Lannon, Brest #187/R
£1921	$3591	€2900	Femme a la lecture. s. 24-Jul-4 Thierry & Lannon, Brest #442
£2000	$3320	€2920	Home with the catch (33x54cm-13x21in) s. 1-Oct-3 Sotheby's, Olympia #286/R est:2000-3000
£2282	$4039	€3400	Retour de peche (15x17cm-6x7in) s. panel. 30-Apr-4 Tajan, Paris #216/R est:1800-2000
£2733	$4893	€4100	Marine, Concarneau (22x27cm-9x11in) s. panel painted c.1890/95. 16-May-4 Thierry & Lannon, Brest #148/R est:3000-4000
£2800	$5180	€4088	Market at Concarneau (21x27cm-8x11in) s. panel. 14-Jul-4 Sotheby's, Olympia #208/R est:3000-4000
£3194	$5750	€4663	Market at Concareau (22x27cm-9x11in) s. panel. 21-Jan-4 Sotheby's, New York #192/R est:5000-7000
£3889	$7000	€5678	Fishmarket at Concarneau (22x27cm-9x11in) s. panel. 21-Jan-4 Sotheby's, New York #191/R est:5000-7000
£4444	$8000	€6488	Port scene in Brittany (33x46cm-13x18in) s. prov. 23-Apr-4 Sotheby's, New York #171/R est:8000-12000
£4545	$7545	€6590	Barques de peches et riche personnage dans un port breton (3x46cm-1x18in) s. 13-Jun-3 Zofingen, Switzerland #2480/R est:6500 (S.FR 10000)
£5000	$9000	€7300	Port of Concarneau (74x60cm-29x24in) s. 21-Jan-4 Sotheby's, Olympia #524/R est:4000-6000
£5455	$9273	€7800	Scene de marche (22x27cm-9x11in) s. panel. 24-Nov-3 Boscher, Cherbourg #802 est:6000-7000
£5500	$9900	€8030	Marche en Bretagne (21x26cm-8x10in) s. panel. 21-Jan-4 Sotheby's, Olympia #512/R est:3500-4500
£6225	$11641	€9400	Montee a l'eglise de Plogonnec (35x43cm-14x17in) s. 24-Jul-4 Thierry & Lannon, Brest #189/R est:8000-9000
£8609	$16099	€13000	Scene de marche en Bretagne (45x54cm-18x21in) s. 24-Jul-4 Thierry & Lannon, Brest #188/R est:12000-14000

Works on paper			
£300	$474	€435	Continental town with boats on the river (25x39cm-10x15in) s.d.05 W/C. 2-Sep-3 Bonhams, Oxford #50/R
£300	$474	€435	French town with busy street before a cathedral (40x25cm-16x10in) s.d.05 W/C htd white. 2-Sep-3 Bonhams, Oxford #56/R
£2781	$5090	€4200	Retour des pecheurs (39x59cm-15x23in) s. pastel. 7-Apr-4 Piasa, Paris #29/R est:2000-3000
£3867	$6921	€5800	Concarneau, le retour des pecheurs (36x51cm-14x20in) s.d.99 pastel. 16-May-4 Thierry & Lannon, Brest #88/R est:5500-6000

LEGRAND, Louis Auguste Mathieu (1863-1951) French

£406	$650	€593	Bergere avec moutons (23x31cm-9x12in) s. black chk blue gouache card. 18-Sep-3 Swann Galleries, New York #369/R
Works on paper			
£320	$512	€467	Reclining woman in a wood (61x49cm-24x19in) init.i. col chk. 16-Sep-3 Rosebery Fine Art, London #545
£1056	$1827	€1500	Paysanne courbee dans un champ (21x33cm-8x13in) s. i.verso black crayon gouache wood. 12-Dec-3 Renaud, Paris #103/R est:1200-1500
£11921	$21815	€18000	Portrait (62x47cm-24x19in) pastel gouache. 9-Apr-4 Claude Aguttes, Neuilly #65/R est:18000-22000

LEGRAND, Marie Mathilde (19th C) French

£274	$466	€400	Paysage (14x21cm-6x8in) s.d.1877 cardboard. 5-Nov-3 Beaussant & Lefèvre, Paris #30

LEGRAS, Auguste J F (1864-1915) Dutch

£284	$474	€400	Thaw entering (30x90cm-12x35in) s.d.1904. 20-Oct-3 Glerum, Amsterdam #68/R

LEGROS, Alphonse (1837-1911) French

Works on paper			
£1000	$1820	€1500	Fisherman (37x54cm-15x21in) s. W/C pen ink. 2-Jul-4 Bloomsbury, London #9/R est:1000-1500
£2600	$4784	€3796	Portrait of Lucian Legros (14x10cm-6x4in) i. pencil. 8-Jun-4 Bonhams, Knightsbridge #44/R est:300-400

LEGROS, Pierre (elder-attrib) (1629-1714) French

Works on paper			
£608	$1070	€900	Two classical soldiers (22x13cm-9x5in) pen prov. double-sided. 22-May-4 Lempertz, Koln #1309

LEGUA IBANEZ, Francisco (?-1926) Spanish

£387	$678	€550	Harbour scene (23x32cm-9x13in) s. board. 16-Dec-3 Segre, Madrid #23/R

LEGUAY, Charles Étienne (1762-1846) French

Miniatures			
£15000	$26850	€21900	Young gentleman standing with his left hand raised (18cm-7in) s. porcelain rectangular fame. 25-May-4 Christie's, London #47/R est:3000-5000
Works on paper			
£5594	$9622	€8000	Portrait de jeune garcon en buste portant un chapeau a plume (49x37cm-19x15in) blk white red blue chk stumping out. 2-Dec-3 Christie's, Paris #509/R est:2000-3000

LEGUEULT, Raymond (1898-1971) French

£260	$413	€380	Still life with flowers (18x28cm-7x11in) s. board. 1-May-3 John Nicholson, Haslemere #686
£625	$1044	€900	Portrait de femme nue (41x33cm-16x13in) s.d.28 prov. exhib. 21-Oct-3 Christie's, Paris #140/R
£1806	$3015	€2600	La Loue a Mouthier (73x100cm-29x39in) s.d.47 s.i.d.verso exhib. 21-Oct-3 Christie's, Paris #152/R est:3000-5000
£2917	$4871	€4200	Garrigues en feu, Eygalieres (73x92cm-29x36in) s.d.50. 21-Oct-3 Christie's, Paris #150/R est:700-900
£3333	$5567	€4800	Noemie au turban (92x73cm-36x29in) s.d.29 exhib. 21-Oct-3 Christie's, Paris #139/R est:1000-1500
£3497	$6014	€5000	Vue de Campeaux (60x80cm-24x31in) s. i.d.mai 1943 verso. 5-Dec-3 Gros & Delettrez, Paris #88/R est:5000-6000
£3819	$6378	€5500	Le parc au soleil (82x101cm-32x40in) s.d.57 s.i.d.verso prov.exhib. 21-Oct-3 Christie's, Paris #149/R est:3000-5000
£4028	$6726	€5800	Le dahlia rouge (81x100cm-32x39in) s.d.64 s.i.d.verso. 21-Oct-3 Christie's, Paris #160/R est:3000-5000
£4967	$9040	€7500	Endormie a la robe puce (92x73cm-36x29in) s.d.1948. 15-Jun-4 Rossini, Paris #169/R est:10000
£5417	$9046	€7800	Emilienne a la robe grise (92x74cm-36x29in) s.d.57 s.i.verso peinture a l'essence prov. 21-Oct-3 Christie's, Paris #151/R est:5000-7000
£5694	$9510	€8200	La vie en rose (73x92cm-29x36in) s.d.50 s.i.d.verso oil peinture a l'essence exhib.lit. 21-Oct-3 Christie's, Paris #148/R est:5000-7000
£5903	$9858	€8500	Emilienne a la campagne (81x100cm-32x39in) s.d.60 s.i.d.verso peinture a l'essence exhib. 21-Oct-3 Christie's, Paris #164/R est:6000-8000
£6111	$10206	€8800	Les pins de Porquerolles (81x100cm-32x39in) s.d.54 s.i.d.verso exhib.lit. 21-Oct-3 Christie's, Paris #147/R est:4000-6000
£6250	$10438	€9000	Le chapeau a plumes (73x100cm-29x39in) s. painted c.1945 exhib.lit. 21-Oct-3 Christie's, Paris #159/R est:5000-7000
£8333	$13917	€12000	Dans l'ile de Porquerolles (73x92cm-29x36in) s.i.d.1954 peinture a l'essence prov.exhib. 21-Oct-3 Christie's, Paris #158/R est:5000-7000
Works on paper			
£268	$499	€400	Baigneuse sur la plage (48x55cm-19x22in) s. black crayon. 3-Mar-4 Ferri, Paris #337
£278	$464	€400	Compotier (32x42cm-13x17in) s.d.60 i.d.verso chl prov. 21-Oct-3 Christie's, Paris #135/R
£284	$474	€400	Vases de fleurs sur un gueridon (33x26cm-13x10in) st.sig. pencil. 12-Oct-3 St-Germain-en-Laye Encheres #211
£347	$580	€500	Nu allonge au collier (42x54cm-17x21in) studio st. pencil. 21-Oct-3 Christie's, Paris #132/R
£382	$638	€550	Jeune femme pensive (42x31cm-17x12in) s. chl. 21-Oct-3 Christie's, Paris #130/R
£382	$638	€550	Composition abstraite (32x42cm-13x17in) studio st. W/C. 21-Oct-3 Christie's, Paris #154/R
£417	$696	€600	Emilienne dans le petit salon des Sorbiers (42x54cm-17x21in) init.i. s.i.d.1958 verso chl prov. 21-Oct-3 Christie's, Paris #131/R
£417	$696	€600	Le jardin de Madame Moreux a Malet (34x41cm-13x16in) s.d.1951 s.i.d.verso chl prov. 21-Oct-3 Christie's, Paris #136/R
£451	$754	€650	Jeune fille allongee sur la plage, ile de Porquerolles (33x42cm-13x17in) s.i.d.1954 chl. 21-Oct-3 Christie's, Paris #134/R
£451	$754	€650	Nature morte (42x54cm-17x21in) s.i. chl prov. 21-Oct-3 Christie's, Paris #137/R
£590	$986	€850	Dans l'ile (49x55cm-19x22in) s.d.66 s.i.d.verso W/C pencil prov. 21-Oct-3 Christie's, Paris #156/R
£903	$1508	€1300	Deux femmes a la plage (42x54cm-17x21in) s.d.56 W/C pencil. 21-Oct-3 Christie's, Paris #145/R
£1042	$1740	€1500	Deux femmes au transat (42x54cm-17x21in) s. W/C pencil. 21-Oct-3 Christie's, Paris #153/R est:1500-2000
£1111	$1856	€1600	Jeune femme a la robe grise dans un interieur (54x42cm-21x17in) s. W/C pencil. 21-Oct-3 Christie's, Paris #141/R est:1500-2000
£1141	$2122	€1700	Deux femmes se parant les cheveux (40x52cm-16x20in) s. W/C. 3-Mar-4 Ferri, Paris #336 est:1500-1800
£1181	$1972	€1700	Le grand divan devant la mer (49x65cm-19x26in) s.d.66 W/C pencil. 21-Oct-3 Christie's, Paris #146/R est:1800-2400
£1334	$2454	€2000	Les baigneuses de Porquerolle (42x54cm-17x21in) s.d.62 W/C crayon exhib. 8-Jun-4 Artcurial Briest, Paris #129/R est:800-1000
£1528	$2551	€2200	Deux femmes assoupies (42x54cm-17x21in) s.d.54 W/C pencil. 21-Oct-3 Christie's, Paris #155/R est:1800-2200
£1667	$2783	€2400	Jeune femme accoudee a une table (50x39cm-20x15in) s.i.d.1950 chl prov. 21-Oct-3 Christie's, Paris #129/R est:800-1200
£1736	$2899	€2500	Au bord de la plage (43x54cm-17x21in) s.d.54 W/C pencil. 21-Oct-3 Christie's, Paris #157/R est:1800-2200
£2222	$3711	€3200	Emilienne (31x41cm-12x16in) s.i.d.1943 W/C gouache pencil prov.exhib. 21-Oct-3 Christie's, Paris #161/R est:1500-1800

LEHERB, Helmut (1933-1997) Austrian

£272	$487	€400	Night music (45x36cm-18x14in) s. W/C exec.1971 exhib. 22-Mar-4 Sant Agostino, Torino #313/R

LEHMAN, Anne (20th C) American

£215	$400	€314	Sunnyside up (76x61cm-30x24in) init. executed c.1950. 7-Mar-4 Treadway Gallery, Cincinnati #730/R
£269	$500	€393	Abstract composition (102x76cm-40x30in) init. painted c.1950. 7-Mar-4 Treadway Gallery, Cincinnati #739/R

LEHMAN, Carl Peter (1794-1876) Swedish

£692	$1191	€1010	Portrait of gentleman Portrait of lady (58x51cm-23x20in) pair. 3-Dec-3 AB Stockholms Auktionsverk #2464/R (S.KR 9000)

LEHMANN, Alfred (1899-1979) German

Works on paper			
£278	$453	€400	Figure composition (16x11cm-6x4in) s. col chk pencil. 27-Sep-3 Dr Fritz Nagel, Stuttgart #9247/R

LEHMANN, Edvard (1815-1892) Danish

£629	$1170	€918	Susannah in the bath (20x14cm-8x6in) init. 2-Mar-4 Rasmussen, Copenhagen #1495/R (D.KR 7000)
£898	$1671	€1311	Early morning in the carnival time at Paris Boulevard (41x32cm-16x13in) init. study exhib. 2-Mar-4 Rasmussen, Copenhagen #1354/R (D.KR 10000)

LEHMANN, Henri (1814-1882) French

£1277	$2068	€1800	Deux tetes d'anges (35x27cm-14x11in) one mono.i.d.1839 one mono.d.1842 pair. 23-May-3 Sotheby's, Paris #6/R est:2000-3000
£1517	$2807	€2200	Mountain valley with river and houses (127x152cm-50x60in) 12-Feb-4 Weidler, Nurnberg #6510/R est:1850
£59289	$106126	€86562	Portrait of Leo Faustine (100x81cm-39x32in) s.i.d.1842 prov. 15-May-4 Christie's, Sydney #81/R est:120000-150000 (A.D 150000)
Works on paper			
£323	$518	€450	Spring (62x38cm-24x15in) chl white chk. 16-May-3 Tajan, Paris #155

LEHMANN, Henri (attrib) (1814-1882) French

£1067	$1931	€1600	Tete de femme (38x31cm-15x12in) 30-Mar-4 Rossini, Paris #820/R est:700-1000

LEHMANN, Rudolf (1819-1905) German

£300	$555	€438	Portrait of a gentleman, quarter-length in a black jacket and red bow tie (66x55cm-26x22in) s.d.1819 feigned oval. 14-Jul-4 Christie's, Kensington #853/R
£1100	$2013	€1606	Portraits, believed to be of Frederica Lehmann and her husband (65x53cm-26x21in) one s. pair oval. 6-Apr-4 Bonhams, Knightsbridge #174/R est:1000-1500

LEHMANN, Wilhelm Ludwig (1861-1932) Swiss

£385	$654	€562	River landscape in lower Alps (90x130cm-35x51in) s. 18-Nov-3 Hans Widmer, St Gallen #1120 (S.FR 850)
£631	$1085	€921	Lenzerheide (54x72cm-21x28in) s.i.d.1902. 8-Dec-3 Philippe Schuler, Zurich #3344/R (S.FR 1400)
£905	$1448	€1321	Snowy landscape with small lake (91x130cm-36x51in) s. prov. 16-Sep-3 Philippe Schuler, Zurich #3242/R est:1800-2400 (S.FR 2000)

LEHMANN-BRAUNS, Paul (1885-?) German

£350	$584	€500	Reimersfleet in Hamburg (70x60cm-28x24in) s. i. verso. 28-Jun-3 Bolland & Marotz, Bremen #782/R

LEHMANN-FAHRWASSER, Georg (1887-) German
£265 $482 €400 Schloss Charlottenburg park (59x69cm-23x27in) s. panel double-sided. 19-Jun-4 Dannenberg, Berlin #584/R

LEHMBRUCK, Wilhelm (1881-1919) German
Prints
£2238 $3804 €3200 Reclining nude (13x18cm-5x7in) s.i. drypoint etching. 29-Nov-3 Bassenge, Berlin #6867/R est:3000
£2752 $4596 €3990 Young girl. s. drypoint. 19-Jun-3 Kornfeld, Bern #621/R est:5000 (S.FR 6000)
Sculpture
£9091 $15455 €13000 Girl bathing (41cm-16in) s.i. bronze prov. 26-Nov-3 Lempertz, Koln #787/R est:7000
£38462 $65385 €55000 Girls head (41cm-16in) i. verso burnt pat.terracotta prov. 26-Nov-3 Lempertz, Koln #788/R est:80000-90000
£60000 $109200 €87600 Hagener torso, small female torso (70cm-28in) i. cast stone conceived c.1911 prov.exhib.lit. 3-Feb-4 Sotheby's, London #14/R est:80000-120000
£90000 $165600 €131400 Small female torso (70cm-28in) i. stone conceived c.1911 prov.exhib.lit. 22-Jun-4 Sotheby's, London #179/R est:100000-150000
£120000 $220800 €175200 Bust of the kneeling woman (50cm-20in) i. stone conceived c.1911 prov.exhib.lit. 22-Jun-4 Sotheby's, London #171/R est:120000-150000
Works on paper
£3670 $6128 €5322 Seated nude (35x21cm-14x8in) s. pencil. 19-Jun-3 Kornfeld, Bern #620 est:7500 (S.FR 8000)
£4895 $8420 €7000 Standing female nude (64x23cm-25x9in) s. ochre lit. 2-Dec-3 Hauswedell & Nolte, Hamburg #363/R est:6000

LEHNER, Fritz (?) ?
Works on paper
£417 $663 €600 Oriental city view with figures (37x50cm-15x20in) s. W/C. 15-Sep-3 Bernaerts, Antwerp #730/R

LEHR, Adam (1853-1924) American
£299 $550 €437 Landscape with house on a hill (30x51cm-12x20in) s. 25-Jun-4 Freeman, Philadelphia #128/R
£667 $1200 €974 Still life of plums and a pitcher (25x34cm-10x13in) s.d.1903 panel. 24-Apr-4 Weschler, Washington #594/R

LEHR, Paul (1930-1998) American
£267 $500 €390 Standing man in landscape, other figures, many with prehensile tails (38x25cm-15x10in) s. masonite. 26-Feb-4 Illustration House, New York #107
£1337 $2500 €1952 Speeding spacecraft against burgundy sky (38x41cm-15x16in) s. masonite. 26-Feb-4 Illustration House, New York #108 est:500-800

LEHRE, Wanda (20th C) German
£405 $726 €600 Still life (64x85cm-25x33in) s. oval. 6-May-4 Michael Zeller, Lindau #758

LEHTINEN, Kauko (1925-) Finnish
Works on paper
£933 $1671 €1400 Dream picture (48x72cm-19x28in) s.d.1969 mixed media. 15-May-4 Hagelstam, Helsinki #212/R
£1678 $2853 €2400 Dream (40x52cm-16x20in) s.d.69 mixed media exhib. 29-Nov-3 Bukowskis, Helsinki #267/R est:2500-3000

LEHTO, Nikolai (1905-1994) Finnish
£268 $494 €400 Girl (20x20cm-8x8in) s.d.1981. 25-Mar-4 Hagelstam, Helsinki #862
£272 $495 €400 Curious inspection (15x15cm-6x6in) s. 8-Feb-4 Bukowskis, Helsinki #395/R
£347 $580 €500 Mothering Sunday (30x16cm-12x6in) s.d.74. 26-Oct-3 Bukowskis, Helsinki #404/R
£354 $644 €520 Stones on beach (42x34cm-17x13in) s.d.59. 8-Feb-4 Bukowskis, Helsinki #394/R
£375 $626 €540 The world (31x24cm-12x9in) s.d.1974. 23-Oct-3 Hagelstam, Helsinki #1017
£395 $718 €580 Angels on telephone cables (25x30cm-10x12in) s.d.84. 8-Feb-4 Bukowskis, Helsinki #391/R
£517 $941 €760 The family (24x22cm-9x9in) s.d.81. 8-Feb-4 Bukowskis, Helsinki #393/R
£556 $928 €800 Red cottage (39x45cm-15x18in) s.d.1945. 23-Oct-3 Hagelstam, Helsinki #956
£625 $1044 €900 The couple (27x22cm-11x9in) s.d.81. 26-Oct-3 Bukowskis, Helsinki #403/R
£933 $1671 €1400 Robbers on path to house (39x45cm-15x18in) s.d.1959 canvas on board. 15-May-4 Hagelstam, Helsinki #195/R
Works on paper
£634 $1096 €900 Rasputin (33x24cm-13x9in) s.d.1977 mixed media. 13-Dec-3 Hagelstam, Helsinki #186/R

LEI LI (attrib) (?) Chinese
Works on paper
£1243 $2250 €1815 Windswept palace (152x99cm-60x39in) bears sig. i. ink wash silk. 6-Apr-4 Bonhams & Butterfields, San Francisco #6209/R est:800-1200

LEIBER, Otto Ferdinand (1878-1958) German
£284 $460 €400 Amoltern on sunny autumn day (34x52cm-13x20in) s.i.d.46 board lit. 23-May-3 Karlheinz Kaupp, Staufen #1895

LEIBL, Wilhelm (1844-1900) German
£7000 $12740 €10220 Portrait of the painter Johann Herterich (69x49cm-27x19in) painted 1868 prov. 15-Jun-4 Sotheby's, London #35/R est:8000-12000
Works on paper
£769 $1323 €1100 Portrait of a bearded man (43x34cm-17x13in) i.d.1869 black chk grey wash. 3-Dec-3 Neumeister, Munich #414/R

LEIBOVITZ, Annie (1949-) American
Photographs
£1795 $3250 €2621 Whoopi Goldberg, Berkeley, California (36x36cm-14x14in) s.i.d.1984 num.13/40 cibachrome print. 19-Apr-4 Bonhams & Butterfields, San Francisco #437/R est:3000-5000
£1808 $3200 €2640 Milhail Baryshnikov and Linda Dowdell, White Oak, Florida (40x33cm-16x13in) s.i.d.1990 num.19/25 gelatin silver print prov.lit. 27-Apr-4 Christie's, Rockefeller NY #324/R est:3500-4500
£2600 $4758 €3796 Cindy Crawford, Brookville, New York (50x41cm-20x16in) s.i.d.1993 silver print edition 27/40. 8-Jul-4 Sotheby's, London #492/R est:2500-3500
£2624 $4750 €3831 Steve Martin, Beverly Hills (37x37cm-15x15in) s.i.d.1981 num.35/40 cibachrome print. 19-Apr-4 Bonhams & Butterfields, San Francisco #436/R est:4000-6000
£3179 $5500 €4641 Mikhail Baryshikov and Linda Dowdell, white oak dance project (42x34cm-17x13in) s.i.d.1990 num.10 gelatin silver print. 12-Dec-3 Sotheby's, New York #305/R est:3000-5000
£3968 $7500 €5793 John Lennon and Yoko Ono, New York (30x30cm-12x12in) s.i.d.1980 num27/40 dye destruction print. 17-Feb-4 Christie's, Rockefeller NY #270/R est:5000-7000
£4233 $8000 €6180 Whoopie Goldberg, Berkeley, California (35x34cm-14x13in) s.i.d.1984 num.23/40 dye destruction print. 17-Feb-4 Christie's, Rockefeller NY #272/R est:8000-10000
£5000 $9000 €7300 Juliew Worden, dancer Mark Morris Dance Group (83x111cm-33x44in) s.i.num.16/25 digital inkjet print. 23-Apr-4 Phillips, New York #135/R est:7000-9000
£5714 $10000 €8342 Jerry Hall (39x39cm-15x15in) dye transfer print exec 1985. 17-Dec-3 Christie's, Rockefeller NY #276/R est:1000-1500
£6349 $12000 €9270 Keith Haring (24x30cm-9x12in) s.i.d.1986 num.39/40 dye destruction print. 17-Feb-4 Christie's, Rockefeller NY #271/R est:8000-12000

LEIBOWITZ, Cary (1963-) American
£236 $431 €350 I love Sherrie Levine (31x41cm-12x16in) mono.d.89 verso panel prov. 7-Jul-4 Artcurial Briest, Paris #301
£236 $431 €350 I love Joseph Beuys (30x41cm-12x16in) mono.d.1989 verso panel prov. 7-Jul-4 Artcurial Briest, Paris #301b

LEIBSCHER, Adolf (19/20th C) German
£1099 $2000 €1649 First steps (25x33cm-10x13in) s.d.1906 board. 19-Jun-4 Charlton Hall, Columbia #127/R est:2000-2500

LEICKERT, Charles (1818-1907) Belgian
£2313 $4140 €3400 Paysage hivernal aux patineurs (9x14cm-4x6in) s. panel. 16-Mar-4 Vanderkindere, Brussels #24 est:1500-2000
£2381 $4333 €3500 Winter evening (9x11cm-4x4in) init. panel. 3-Feb-4 Christie's, Amsterdam #53/R est:4000-6000
£2500 $4250 €3650 Winter landscape with skaters on a river and town beyond (21x33cm-8x13in) s. canvas on board. 19-Nov-3 Bonhams & Butterfields, San Francisco #58/R
£2632 $4763 €4000 City view with activity on a canal (21x14cm-8x6in) s. panel prov. 19-Apr-4 Glerum, Amsterdam #36/R est:3000-5000
£2673 $4250 €3903 River scene with windmill and boaters (23x33cm-9x13in) s. panel. 13-Sep-3 Selkirks, St. Louis #489/R est:1500-2000
£2685 $4752 €4000 Dutch winter landscape (30x46cm-12x18in) s. 28-Apr-4 Wiener Kunst Auktionen, Vienna #11/R est:4000-7000
£2802 $5015 €4091 River in Holland (15x25cm-6x10in) mono. panel. 12-May-4 Dobiaschofsky, Bern #738/R est:2600 (S.FR 6500)
£3591 $6500 €5243 Dutch landscape with windmill, figures in foreground (36x53cm-14x21in) s. 3-Apr-4 Nadeau, Windsor #216/R est:10000-15000
£4027 $7409 €6000 Busy market in old town (43x55cm-17x22in) s.d.1888. 25-Mar-4 Dr Fritz Nagel, Stuttgart #735/R est:7500
£4397 $7343 €6200 Paysage hollandais enneige aux patineurs (31x42cm-12x17in) s.d.69 panel. 14-Oct-3 Vanderkindere, Brussels #18 est:4500-6500
£4667 $8400 €7000 Frozen winter landscape (11x16cm-4x6in) init. panel. 21-Apr-4 Christie's, Amsterdam #70/R est:7000-9000
£5556 $9278 €8000 Town by a river at dusk (15x21cm-6x8in) s. panel prov. 21-Oct-3 Sotheby's, Amsterdam #12/R est:8000-12000
£6000 $10020 €8760 Path to the sea (19x28cm-7x11in) s.d.66 panel. 12-Nov-3 Sotheby's, Olympia #165/R est:2000-3000
£6597 $11215 €9500 Figures on a street in winter (27x19cm-11x7in) s. panel prov. 28-Oct-3 Christie's, Amsterdam #20/R est:7000-9000
£7333 $13200 €11000 Summer landscape with boats on a river (17x27cm-7x11in) s. panel. 20-Apr-4 Sotheby's, Amsterdam #171/R est:10000-15000
£7500 $13800 €10950 Coast scene near Scheveningen, Holland (23x34cm-9x13in) s. board. 25-Mar-4 Christie's, Kensington #162/R est:5000-8000
£7586 $12669 €11000 Dutch landscape in winter (62x100cm-24x39in) s. prov. 15-Nov-3 Lempertz, Koln #1650/R est:13000
£8156 $13621 €11500 Une ville animee en Hollande (38x55cm-15x22in) s. canvas laid down. 19-Oct-3 St-Germain-en-Laye Encheres #15/R est:12000-15000
£9184 $16439 €13500 Ice scene. Figures by water edge (17x22cm-7x9in) panel two. 17-Mar-4 De Zwann, Amsterdam #4548a/R est:8000-12000
£9375 $15656 €13500 Winter landscape with figures on the ice (42x61cm-17x24in) s. 21-Oct-3 Sotheby's, Amsterdam #203/R est:15000-20000
£9722 $16528 €14000 Figures on the ice by a Dutch town (17x25cm-7x10in) s. panel. 28-Oct-3 Christie's, Amsterdam #8/R est:8000-12000
£10417 $17396 €15000 View of a Dutch town with figures by a vegetable stall (78x104cm-31x41in) s. 21-Oct-3 Sotheby's, Amsterdam #191/R est:20000-30000
£11111 $18889 €16000 Summer - a ferry crossing on a windy day (25x36cm-10x14in) s. panel. 28-Oct-3 Christie's, Amsterdam #225/R est:15000-20000
£12500 $21250 €18000 Figures and a koek en zopie on the ice by a windmill (42x65cm-17x26in) s. 28-Oct-3 Christie's, Amsterdam #217/R est:20000-30000
£13194 $22431 €19000 Winter - figures on the ice by a windmill (24x29cm-9x11in) s. panel. 28-Oct-3 Christie's, Amsterdam #1/R est:10000-15000
£13194 $22035 €19000 Summer landscape with figures walking along a waterway (34x43cm-13x17in) s. panel. 21-Oct-3 Sotheby's, Amsterdam #182/R est:15000-20000
£14667 $26400 €22000 Daily activities on a quay in a Dutch town (16x23cm-6x9in) s. panel. 21-Apr-4 Christie's, Amsterdam #210/R est:18000-22000
£14865 $26608 €22000 Paysage fluvial (64x99cm-25x39in) 10-May-4 Amberes, Antwerp #289/R

£15000 $27300 €21900 Skaters in a winter landscape (61x101cm-24x40in) s.i.d.80. 17-Jun-4 Christie's, London #1/R est:20000-30000
£15278 $23986 €22000 Lively Dutch town on winter afternoon (32x26cm-13x10in) s. panel prov.lit. 30-Aug-3 Hans Stahl, Toestorf #27/R est:17000
£18182 $30364 €26000 Vue de ville (30x22cm-12x9in) s. panel. 26-Jun-3 Artcurial Briest, Paris #528 est:8000-10000
£18667 $33600 €28000 River landscape with figures in rowing boats, town beyond (39x53cm-15x21in) s. panel. 20-Apr-4 Sotheby's, Amsterdam #168/R est:30000-35000
£20833 $34792 €30000 Skating in the late afternoon (59x95cm-23x37in) s. canvas on board. 21-Oct-3 Sotheby's, Amsterdam #177/R est:25000-35000
£20833 $34792 €30000 Skaters on a frozen waterway (70x101cm-28x40in) s. 21-Oct-3 Sotheby's, Amsterdam #209/R est:25000-30000
£27778 $47222 €40000 Figures on the ice by a koek en zopie, a road leading to a town in the distance (27x39cm-11x15in) s. panel. 28-Oct-3 Christie's, Amsterdam #245/R est:40000-60000
£30000 $54000 €45000 Figures on the ice by a Dutch town (60x71cm-24x28in) s. 20-Apr-4 Sotheby's, Amsterdam #172/R est:40000-60000
£31250 $53125 €45000 View of a canal in a Dutch town (25x21cm-10x8in) s.d.51 panel. 28-Oct-3 Christie's, Amsterdam #228/R est:25000-35000
£40000 $72000 €60000 Figures loading a horse drawn cart on the ice (80x114cm-31x45in) s. 20-Apr-4 Sotheby's, Amsterdam #194/R est:70000-90000
Works on paper
£839 $1443 €1200 Skating scene (27x39cm-11x15in) s. W/C gouache. 7-Dec-3 Sotheby's, Amsterdam #586/R
£1611 $2980 €2400 Winter landscape with skaters on the ice (28x42cm-11x17in) s. W/C. 15-Mar-4 Sotheby's, Amsterdam #74 est:2000-3000
£1745 $3246 €2600 Windmills by frozen canal (35x50cm-14x20in) s.d.95 W/C bodycol. 6-Mar-4 Arnold, Frankfurt #775/R est:600
£2400 $4320 €3600 Figures in the streets of Scheveningen (38x31cm-15x12in) s. W/C htd white. 20-Apr-4 Sotheby's, Amsterdam #49/R est:2500-3500

LEICKERT, Charles (attrib) (1818-1907) Belgian
£419 $750 €612 Villagers on street (25x30cm-10x12in) s. paper on panel. 20-Mar-4 Sloans & Kenyon, Bethesda #1175/R
£1745 $3211 €2600 Winter landscape with windmill by frozen lake (21x24cm-8x9in) bears sig. panel. 25-Mar-4 Dr Fritz Nagel, Stuttgart #734/R est:2700
£2083 $3396 €3000 Winter landscape with windmill by frozen lake (21x24cm-8x9in) bears sig. panel. 25-Sep-3 Dr Fritz Nagel, Stuttgart #1368/R est:4500

LEIGH, Conrad (?) British?
£556 $944 €812 Sound advice (49x59cm-19x23in) s. 4-Nov-3 Stephan Welz, Johannesburg #569 est:5000-8000 (SA.R 6500)

LEIGH, William R (1866-1955) American
£5294 $9000 €7729 Northern Waso Nyiro (30x41cm-12x16in) canvas on board prov.lit. 1-Nov-3 Santa Fe Art, Santa Fe #113/R est:20000-30000
£9626 $18000 €14054 Swirling clouds (23x30cm-9x12in) s.d.1911 board prov. 24-Jul-4 Coeur d'Alene, Hayden #119/R est:8000-12000
£17380 $32500 €25375 Moonlight in the badlands (18x20cm-7x8in) s. canvas on board prov. 24-Jul-4 Coeur d'Alene, Hayden #59/R est:20000-30000
£22727 $42500 €33181 Indian pottery (20x25cm-8x10in) s. prov. 24-Jul-4 Coeur d'Alene, Hayden #25/R est:30000-40000
£29070 $50000 €42442 Campfire (41x53cm-16x21in) s.d.1912 prov. 4-Dec-3 Christie's, Rockefeller NY #67/R
£63953 $110000 €93371 Bucking the load (26x44cm-10x17in) s. prov. 4-Dec-3 Christie's, Rockefeller NY #66/R est:50000-70000
£68182 $120000 €99546 Sand painter (64x76cm-25x30in) s.d.1951 s.i.d.stretcher prov.exhib. 19-May-4 Sotheby's, New York #208/R est:100000-150000
£141176 $240000 €206117 Scout (76x102cm-30x40in) s. prov. 29-Oct-3 Christie's, Los Angeles #25/R est:250000-350000
Works on paper
£346 $550 €505 Mount Kenya (20x30cm-8x12in) s.i.d.May 10th 1926 pencil prov. 9-Mar-3 William Jenack, New York #212

LEIGH-PEMBERTON, John (1911-) British
£800 $1472 €1168 Coaches leaving St. James Palace (76x102cm-30x40in) s.d.57. 8-Jun-4 Gorringes, Lewes #2233
£6500 $12025 €9490 Scenes of different eras with figures (42x52cm-17x20in) s.d.49 or 50 board nine. 13-Jan-4 Bonhams, Knightsbridge #242/R est:6000-8000

LEIGHTON, Alfred Crocker (1901-1965) British
£1471 $2456 €2148 Moraine lake (48x63cm-19x25in) i. 17-Nov-3 Hodgins, Calgary #92/R est:4500-6500 (C.D 3250)
Works on paper
£280 $512 €409 The open gate, over the moor to Widdecombe (18x24cm-7x9in) s. W/C prov. 1-Jun-4 Hodgins, Calgary #341/R (C.D 700)
£331 $598 €483 Untitled - city square (18x24cm-7x9in) s.i. W/C. 18-Apr-4 Levis, Calgary #63/R (C.D 800)
£407 $680 €594 Rochester, the Medway (30x38cm-12x15in) s. W/C. 17-Nov-3 Hodgins, Calgary #154/R (C.D 900)
£1810 $3023 €2643 Cathedral mountain from the Yoho (38x48cm-15x19in) s.i. W/C. 17-Nov-3 Hodgins, Calgary #377/R est:3000-4000 (C.D 4000)

LEIGHTON, Edmund Blair (1853-1922) British
£9500 $16340 €13870 Happy thoughts (25x36cm-10x14in) s.d.1908 panel. 2-Dec-3 Gorringes, Lewes #2502/R est:10000-15000
£13673 $24475 €19963 Picking daffodils (115x84cm-45x33in) s.d.90. 25-May-4 Bukowskis, Stockholm #357/R est:175000-200000 (S.KR 185000)
£15556 $28000 €22712 Sally (35x25cm-14x10in) init.d.95 panel prov. 22-Apr-4 Christie's, Rockefeller NY #71/R est:30000-40000
£20588 $35000 €30058 Piano lesson (32x44cm-13x17in) init.d.96 prov. 29-Oct-3 Christie's, Rockefeller NY #60/R est:35000-45000
£150000 $255000 €219000 Hostage (112x150cm-44x59in) s.d.1912 prov.exhib.lit. 27-Nov-3 Sotheby's, London #33/R est:150000-200000

LEIGHTON, Kathryn Woodman (1876-1952) American
£466 $750 €680 Homes on a hillside (61x71cm-24x28in) 17-Aug-3 Bonhams & Butterfields, San Francisco #5804
£590 $950 €861 Coastal valley (46x60cm-18x24in) s. board. 17-Aug-3 Bonhams & Butterfields, San Francisco #5803
£1374 $2500 €2006 Landscape (30x41cm-12x16in) s. i.verso canvas on masonite prov. 15-Jun-4 John Moran, Pasadena #128c est:1000-1500
£10695 $20000 €15615 Little Bison (61x46cm-24x18in) s. 24-Jul-4 Coeur d'Alene, Hayden #70/R est:5000-8000

LEIGHTON, Lord Frederic (1830-1896) British
£16000 $29440 €23360 Portrait of Dr Frederic Septimus Leighton, artist's father (61x46cm-24x18in) prov.exhib.lit. 9-Jun-4 Christie's, London #27/R est:20000-30000
£19000 $34960 €27740 Head of a girl, thought to be from Capri (22x17cm-9x7in) exhib. 11-Jun-4 Christie's, London #158/R est:15000-20000
£38000 $69920 €55480 Vittoria (23x18cm-9x7in) s.i. prov.exhib.lit. 9-Jun-4 Christie's, London #29/R est:30000-50000
Sculpture
£13295 $23000 €19411 Sluggard (53cm-21in) with sig.i. bronze. 11-Dec-3 Sotheby's, New York #165/R est:20000-30000
£15000 $27600 €21900 Needless alarms (48cm-19in) green brown pat. bronze marble plinth prov.exhib.lit. 11-Jun-4 Christie's, London #74/R est:8000-12000
Works on paper
£369 $650 €539 Study of Proserpine (28x36cm-11x14in) s. graphite. 23-May-4 William Jenack, New York #208
£800 $1360 €1168 Studies of cloaked figures (20x27cm-8x11in) black chk htd white prov. 4-Nov-3 Bonhams, New Bond Street #96/R
£960 $1517 €1392 Figure groups. studio st. black white crayon two framed as one prov. 24-Jul-3 Lawrence, Crewkerne #844/R
£2800 $4760 €4088 Study for weaving the wreath (26x17cm-10x7in) black white chk. 27-Nov-3 Sotheby's, London #314/R est:1000-1500

LEIGHTON, Lord Frederic (after) (1830-1896) British
£8500 $15555 €12410 Captain Sir Richard Burton (38x30cm-15x12in) 7-Apr-4 Christie's, London #214/R est:3000-5000

LEIGHTON, Lord Frederic (attrib) (1830-1896) British
£1810 $3023 €2643 The rendezvous (69x50cm-27x20in) init.d.1874. 17-Nov-3 Waddingtons, Toronto #118/R est:4000-6000 (C.D 4000)

LEIGHTON, Scott (1849-1898) American
£209 $350 €303 Ducks in a shady brook (23x18cm-9x7in) s. 13-Jul-3 Butterfields, San Francisco #2024/R
£419 $700 €608 Country farm beside a lazy river (18x23cm-7x9in) s. 13-Jul-3 Butterfields, San Francisco #2025/R
£1129 $2100 €1648 Mare and foal (76x61cm-30x24in) s. exhib. 7-Mar-4 William Jenack, New York #105 est:3000-5000
£1369 $2450 €1999 Farmyard family (30x41cm-12x16in) s. prov. 8-Jan-4 James Julia, Fairfield #804/R est:1500-2500

LEIHE, Yesgondi (attrib) (?) ?
£360 $601 €526 Cattle grazing in an autumnal setting (56x76cm-22x30in) s. i.verso. 16-Oct-3 Mallams, Cheltenham #205/R

LEIMANIS, Andris (1938-) Canadian
£600 $1098 €876 Melting snow, a spring time view of St Paul St corner Saint Gabriel St. (50x75cm-20x30in) s. painted 1982. 1-Jun-4 Joyner Waddington, Toronto #359/R (C.D 1500)
£880 $1610 €1285 Golden Hour - Romantic view of Montreal skyline (75x100cm-30x39in) s. 1-Jun-4 Joyner Waddington, Toronto #203/R est:2000-2500 (C.D 2200)

LEINBERGER, Christian (attrib) (1706-1770) Dutch
Works on paper
£345 $572 €500 Mythological scene (23x35cm-9x14in) s. pen. 30-Sep-3 Dorotheum, Vienna #23

LEINONEN, Paavo (1894-1964) Finnish
£349 $649 €520 Still life of fruit and jug (46x62cm-18x24in) s.d.59. 7-Mar-4 Bukowskis, Helsinki #370/R
£537 $999 €800 Old jetty (46x61cm-18x24in) s.d.63. 7-Mar-4 Bukowskis, Helsinki #371/R

LEINWEBER, Anton Robert (1845-1921) Czechoslovakian
£2703 $4757 €4000 Street in Tunis (37x58cm-15x23in) s. panel. 22-May-4 Lempertz, Koln #1549/R est:4000-6000

LEINWEBER, Heinrich (1836-1908) German
£5500 $9350 €8030 Ein gluckliches Parchen (63x52cm-25x20in) s.d.1867 exhib.lit. 19-Nov-3 Bonhams, New Bond Street #32/R est:3000-5000

LEINWEBER, Hermanus (1824-?) German
£265 $482 €400 Still life with flowers (27x22cm-11x9in) s.d.1870 panel. 16-Jun-4 Hugo Ruef, Munich #1021

LEIPOLD, Karl (1864-1943) German
£604 $1130 €900 Windmill on the Elbe marshes (80x70cm-31x28in) i. verso. 28-Feb-4 Quittenbaum, Hamburg #56/R
£671 $1255 €1000 Hagia Sophia (70x103cm-28x41in) s. board on panel. 28-Feb-4 Quittenbaum, Hamburg #57/R
£1528 $2399 €2200 Watermill (80x118cm-31x46in) s. 30-Aug-3 Hans Stahl, Toestorf #81/R est:3900

LEIRNER, Jac (1961-) Brazilian
Sculpture
£5333 $9813 €8000 Nice to meet you 2 (10x243cm-4x96in) business cards pins plexiglas aluminium wood exec.1995 exhib. 10-Jun-4 Christie's, Paris #89/R est:6500-8000

Works on paper
£6000 $11040 €9000 Untitled (74x72cm-29x28in) banknotes on fabric exec.1992 prov.exhib. 10-Jun-4 Christie's, Paris #87/R est:5000-7000

LEIRO, Francisco (1957-) Spanish
£1549 $2479 €2200 Untitled (37x23cm-15x9in) s.d.1985 board. 16-Sep-3 Segre, Madrid #148/R
Sculpture
£15278 $25208 €22000 Icon (320cm-126in) s.d.84 wood lit. 2-Jul-3 Ansorena, Madrid #876d/R est:15000

LEIST, Frederick William (1878-1945) Australian
£2697 $4504 €4046 Summer scene (51x61cm-20x24in) 27-Oct-3 Goodman, Sydney #178/R est:7000-9000 (A.D 6500)
£10000 $18500 €15000 Early editions (93x71cm-37x28in) s.d.10 exhib. 14-Jul-4 Sotheby's, Olympia #138/R est:10000-15000
Works on paper
£936 $1591 €1367 Lovers (27x34cm-11x13in) s.d.06 W/C. 26-Nov-3 Deutscher-Menzies, Melbourne #282/R (A.D 2200)

LEISTEN, Jacobus (1844-1918) German
£1690 $2924 €2400 Farewell (32x25cm-13x10in) s.d.73 panel. 13-Dec-3 Lempertz, Koln #29/R est:2000

LEISTIKOW, Walter (1865-1908) Russian
£10000 $18400 €15000 Family at the lakeside with a rowing boat, sailing boats in the distance (41x56cm-16x22in) s.d.88 prov. 12-Jun-4 Villa Grisebach, Berlin #114/R est:15000-20000
Works on paper
£262 $477 €383 Village church (45x31cm-18x12in) s.indis.i. W/C. 16-Jun-4 Fischer, Luzern #2590 (S.FR 600)
£500 $895 €750 Dune landscape (9x14cm-4x6in) chl. 15-May-4 Bassenge, Berlin #6990
£1189 $2021 €1700 Hessen town (33x51cm-13x20in) s.d.1939 i. verso W/C Indian ink. 26-Nov-3 Lempertz, Koln #793/R est:1800
£5245 $8916 €7500 Summer landscape (34x54cm-13x21in) s. gouache paper on board prov. 26-Nov-3 Lempertz, Koln #791/R est:8000

LEISZ, M B (?) ?
£943 $1500 €1377 Autumn landscape with lake and rolling hills (81x102cm-32x40in) s.d.1926. 10-Sep-3 Alderfer's, Hatfield #404/R est:600-800
£1415 $2250 €2066 Spring landscape depicting lake and rolling hills with buildings (30x56cm-12x22in) s.d.1928. 10-Sep-3 Alderfer's, Hatfield #405 est:600-800

LEITCH, William Leighton (1804-1883) British
£667 $1200 €974 Rocky road (31x46cm-12x18in) mono. 21-Jan-4 Sotheby's, New York #214/R est:1500-2500
Works on paper
£300 $501 €438 Figures on a track in a mountainous landscape (16x24cm-6x9in) init.d.1845 pencil W/C. 16-Oct-3 Christie's, Kensington #213
£320 $544 €467 River landscape with castle, possibly on the river Wharfe (25x37cm-10x15in) i. W/C. 19-Nov-3 Tennants, Leyburn #979
£400 $736 €584 Italian terrace (16x23cm-6x9in) mono. W/C. 23-Mar-4 Bonhams, Knightsbridge #50/R
£460 $727 €667 Castle on a hill (8x12cm-3x5in) s. W/C. 2-Sep-3 Bonhams, Oxford #40
£600 $1098 €876 Figures by a stream (29x44cm-11x17in) s.d.1835 W/C. 27-Jan-4 Bonhams, Knightsbridge #375/R
£600 $1092 €876 Evening light, the Italian Campagna (15x23cm-6x9in) pencil W/C prov. 1-Jul-4 Christie's, Kensington #72/R
£698 $1200 €1019 Fairlight, landscape and windmill (28x46cm-11x18in) mono.i.d.1859 W/C gouache. 6-Dec-3 Neal Auction Company, New Orleans #286
£1224 $2227 €1787 Isola Bella (31x43cm-12x17in) s.d.1868 W/C. 29-Jun-4 Peter Webb, Auckland #100/R est:4000-6000 (NZ.D 3500)
£1400 $2380 €2044 Italianate landscape with figures beside a lake and a tower and mountains beyond (18x33cm-7x13in) mono.d.1860 W/C bodycol. 30-Oct-3 Duke & Son, Dorchester #77 est:200-400
£1800 $3330 €2628 Italian lake scene (18x33cm-7x13in) mono.d.1850 W/C. 9-Mar-4 Bonhams, New Bond Street #80/R est:2000-3000
£1800 $3240 €2628 Harbour scene at Salerno (18x27cm-7x11in) s.d.1872 pencil W/C. 21-Apr-4 Tennants, Leyburn #922 est:1200-1400
£3000 $5190 €4380 Mr Muir's house on Gareloch, Argyll (60x100cm-24x39in) W/C. 11-Dec-3 Lyon & Turnbull, Edinburgh #26/R est:3000-5000

LEITE, Jose (1873-1939) Portuguese
£1007 $1802 €1500 Landscape with stream (26x34cm-10x13in) s. canvas on cardboard. 31-May-4 Cabral Moncada Leiloes, Lisbon #76/R est:1500-2250

LEITE, Osvaldo (?) South American
£462 $850 €675 Bridge (46x55cm-18x22in) s.d.75. 22-Jun-4 Galeria y Remates, Montevideo #155/R
£976 $1600 €1425 Story teller (81x65cm-32x26in) s.d.86 s.i.d.86-88 verso. 3-Jun-3 Galeria y Remates, Montevideo #106

LEITER, Saul (1923-) American
Photographs
£2174 $3565 €3000 Untitled (33x15cm-13x6in) s. verso vintage silver gelatin. 30-May-3 Villa Grisebach, Berlin #1260/R est:4000-5000

LEITGEB, Franz (19th C) Austrian
£430 $800 €628 Portrait of a bearded man with pipe (26x20cm-10x8in) s. board. 5-Mar-4 Skinner, Boston #234/R

LEITGEB, Franz (1911-1997) Austrian
£272 $500 €397 Still life with flowers and grapes (38x33cm-15x13in) s. panel. 25-Jun-4 Freeman, Philadelphia #300/R
£300 $531 €438 Red roses with a butterfly (30x25cm-12x10in) panel. 29-Apr-4 Christie's, Kensington #294

LEITH, Jacob (attrib) (1812-?) American
Works on paper
£223 $400 €326 Tulips in elaborate pot (15x10cm-6x4in) d.1820 W/C ink sold with another. 20-Mar-4 Pook & Pook, Downington #140/R
£1006 $1800 €1469 Spread winged eagle with heart shaped body holding flowers (8x10cm-3x4in) i. W/C ink. 20-Mar-4 Pook & Pook, Downington #137/R est:1000-1500
£1117 $2000 €1631 Bird perched on flowering tulip branch (10x8cm-4x3in) i. W/C ink. 20-Mar-4 Pook & Pook, Downington #141/R est:300-500
£1453 $2600 €2121 Bird perched on an urn with flowering branches (10x8cm-4x3in) i. W/C ink. 20-Mar-4 Pook & Pook, Downington #145/R est:500-800
£3631 $6500 €5301 Flowers, birds and face arising from an urn (13x8cm-5x3in) W/C ink. 20-Mar-4 Pook & Pook, Downington #143/R est:1500-2500
£5587 $10000 €8157 Red and yellow bird perched on a branch (10x8cm-4x3in) i.d.1818 W/C ink. 20-Mar-4 Pook & Pook, Downington #138/R est:400-800
£11173 $20000 €16313 Dog in elaborate border (8x8cm-3x3in) i.d.1822 W/C ink. 20-Mar-4 Pook & Pook, Downington #144/R est:1200-1500
£14525 $26000 €21207 Heart with birds, tulips, flowers and angel (20x10cm-8x4in) d.1824 W/C ink 2 panels. 20-Mar-4 Pook & Pook, Downington #139/R est:4000-6000
£15642 $28000 €22837 Soldier in elaborate uniform with raised sword on horseback (10x8cm-4x3in) i.d.1821 W/C ink. 20-Mar-4 Pook & Pook, Downington #142/R est:3000-5000

LEITH-ROSS, Harry (1886-1973) American
£2844 $4750 €4152 Nova Scotia Harbour (20x25cm-8x10in) canvas on board prov. 23-Oct-3 Shannon's, Milford #64/R est:3000-5000
£5814 $10000 €8488 Spring House, Diabase Farm, New Hope, Pennsylvania (30x41cm-12x16in) s. i.verso canvas on masonite prov. 7-Dec-3 Freeman, Philadelphia #156 est:8000-12000
£17663 $32500 €25788 Lambertville - view from the canal (30x41cm-12x16in) s. board. 11-Jun-4 David Rago, Lambertville #345/R est:6000-9000
£52326 $90000 €76396 Bridge at New Hope (41x51cm-16x20in) s. s.i.stretcher prov. 7-Dec-3 Freeman, Philadelphia #157 est:10000-15000
£65340 $115000 €95396 Bucks county landscape (76x102cm-30x40in) s. 21-May-4 Pook & Pook, Downington #321/R est:18000-25000
Works on paper
£856 $1600 €1250 View of a lake with trees in the foreground (48x66cm-19x26in) s. W/C. 29-Feb-4 Bonhams & Butterfields, San Francisco #4578 est:1000-1500
£898 $1500 €1311 Maine harbour view (23x38cm-9x15in) s. W/C. 16-Nov-3 CRN Auctions, Cambridge #28/R
£1796 $3000 €2622 Yellow Sail (25x36cm-10x14in) s. W/C prov. 23-Oct-3 Shannon's, Milford #67/R est:3000-5000

LEITHAUSER, Mark Alan (1950-) American
£860 $1600 €1256 Cotan fan (20x25cm-8x10in) s.d.1995 panel prov. 5-Mar-4 Skinner, Boston #594/R est:1500-2000

LEITNER, Heinrich (1842-1913) Austrian
£800 $1360 €1168 Frigate in open waters (62x90cm-24x35in) s.d.1881 board. 19-Nov-3 Christie's, Kensington #501/R

LEITNER, Thomas (1876-1948) Austrian
£385 $700 €562 Cave hideway (89x61cm-35x24in) s.d.1905 board. 19-Jun-4 Jackson's, Cedar Falls #61/R
£414 $757 €600 Valley view (65x60cm-26x24in) bears d.1920. 27-Jan-4 Dorotheum, Vienna #47/R
£1702 $2843 €2400 On the Donau (39x49cm-15x19in) s.d.1940 masonite. 14-Oct-3 Dorotheum, Vienna #117/R est:1500-2000
£2270 $3790 €3200 Wooden bridge near Waidhofen a d Thaya (47x63cm-19x25in) s.d.1920 board exhib. 14-Oct-3 Dorotheum, Vienna #60/R est:1800-2200
£2411 $4027 €3400 Summer landscape with cornstooks (68x90cm-27x35in) s.d.1910. 14-Oct-3 Dorotheum, Vienna #32/R est:1900-3000
£4698 $8409 €7000 On the Hochschwab (70x100cm-28x39in) s.d.1921 board. 25-May-4 Dorotheum, Vienna #156/R est:3200-4000

LEJEUNE, Adolphe Frederic (fl.1879-1912) French
£377 $600 €547 Paysage (74x58cm-29x23in) s. 12-Sep-3 Aspire, Cleveland #54

LEJEUNE, Emile (1885-1964) Swiss
£215 $400 €314 Les oellets au picher d'etain (69x43cm-27x17in) s.d.1939 board. 7-Mar-4 Treadway Gallery, Cincinnati #617/R

LEJEUNE, Frans (1879-1963) Belgian
£872 $1544 €1300 Paysage enneige au ruisseau (60x70cm-24x28in) s. d.1928 verso. 27-Apr-4 Campo & Campo, Antwerp #148/R

LEJEUNE, Geo (?) Belgian?
£532 $888 €750 Les mimosas (85x120cm-33x47in) s. 17-Jun-3 Galerie Moderne, Brussels #242

LEJEUNE, Louis (19th C) French
£285 $464 €410 Trees on riverbank (68x85cm-27x33in) s. 27-Sep-3 Dannenberg, Berlin #576/R
£294 $471 €429 Calm pond (42x52cm-17x20in) s. s.i. verso. 16-Sep-3 Philippe Schuler, Zurich #5458 (S.FR 650)

LEKAKIS, Michael (1907-1998) American
Works on paper
£353 $600 €515 Untitled (56x79cm-22x31in) s. gouache. 9-Nov-3 Wright, Chicago #332

LEKEGIAN, Gabriel (fl.1883-1885) British
Works on paper
£500 $835 €730 Cairo, street scenes with market stall, figures and camel (46x30cm-18x12in) s.i. W/C pair. 9-Jul-3 Peter Wilson, Nantwich #65

LEKGOTHO, Simon (1929-1985) South African
£1404 $2513 €2050 Still life with calabashes (54x44cm-21x17in) s.d.66 canvas on board. 31-May-4 Stephan Welz, Johannesburg #519 est:6000-8000 (SA.R 17000)
£3303 $5912 €4822 Still life with sangomas's bones and other objects (59x74cm-23x29in) s.d.1964 canvas on board. 31-May-4 Stephan Welz, Johannesburg #520/R est:12000-18000 (SA.R 40000)

LELE, Ouka (1957-) Spanish
Photographs
£2027 $3568 €3000 Pink banana (49x39cm-19x15in) s. painted photograph exec.1981 exhib.lit. 18-May-4 Segre, Madrid #154/R est:3000

LELEUX-GIRAUD, Louise-Emilie (1824-1885) Swiss
£617 $1048 €901 Tarot reading (51x40cm-20x16in) s. panel. 5-Nov-3 Dobiaschofsky, Bern #744/R (S.FR 1400)

LELIE, Adriaen de (1755-1820) Dutch
£21053 $38737 €32000 Back from the market (59x48cm-23x19in) s.d.1795 panel prov. 23-Jun-4 Sotheby's, Paris #47/R est:15000-20000

LELIENBERGH, Cornelis van (1626-c.1676) Dutch
£2459 $4500 €3590 Still life and game catch (92x80cm-36x31in) 1-Feb-4 Ben-Ami, Tel Aviv #4658/R est:6000-9000

LELIENBERGH, Cornelis van (attrib) (1626-c.1676) Dutch
£1333 $2387 €2000 Still life of cabbages and pots (26x35cm-10x14in) panel. 15-May-4 Hagelstam, Helsinki #36/R est:3000

LELLOUCHE, Jules (1903-1963) French
£805 $1425 €1200 Goulette, le canal et le fort (24x33cm-9x13in) s. board. 27-Apr-4 Artcurial Briest, Paris #190
£903 $1507 €1300 Bateaux dans le port de Tunis (38x46cm-15x18in) panel. 21-Oct-3 Artcurial Briest, Paris #267 est:1200-1500
£1250 $2088 €1800 Minaret a Tozeur (50x62cm-20x24in) s.i.d.1943. 21-Oct-3 Artcurial Briest, Paris #265 est:1500-2000
£1319 $2203 €1900 Voiliers dans le port de Sfax (38x46cm-15x18in) s.i. panel. 21-Oct-3 Artcurial Briest, Paris #259/R est:1200-1500
£1389 $2320 €2000 Port de Tunis (50x61cm-20x24in) s.d.48 i.verso. 21-Oct-3 Artcurial Briest, Paris #264 est:1500-1800
£1389 $2320 €2000 Monastir, La Falaise (50x61cm-20x24in) s. 21-Oct-3 Artcurial Briest, Paris #260 est:1800-2200
£1528 $2551 €2200 Hammamet (50x61cm-20x24in) s.i.d.42. 21-Oct-3 Artcurial Briest, Paris #266/R est:1500-1800
£2014 $3364 €2900 Monastir, la mosquee (61x50cm-24x20in) s. 21-Oct-3 Artcurial Briest, Paris #261/R est:1800-2200
£2083 $3479 €3000 Port de la Goulette (54x65cm-21x26in) s. s.i.verso. 21-Oct-3 Artcurial Briest, Paris #262/R est:2700-3500
£2083 $3479 €3000 Plage et palmiers a Djerba (54x65cm-21x26in) s. 21-Oct-3 Artcurial Briest, Paris #263/R est:2300-2600
£2517 $4280 €3600 La goulette (41x33cm-16x13in) cardboard. 27-Nov-3 Calmels Cohen, Paris #57/R est:2000-2500

LELOIR, Alexandre Louis (1843-1884) French
£904 $1500 €1311 Gentleman admiring Venus de Milo (30x20cm-12x8in) wood panel. 13-Jun-3 Du Mouchelle, Detroit #2223/R est:1000-2000

LELOIR, Maurice (1853-1940) French
£2414 $4031 €3500 Young woman with flowers sitting by tree (70x60cm-28x24in) s. lit. 10-Jul-3 Allgauer, Kempten #2587/R est:5500
£3293 $5500 €4808 Montagnes d'aubergene and paysans landais (38x21cm-15x8in) s. panel pair. 7-Oct-3 Sotheby's, New York #80/R est:6000-8000
£8667 $15513 €13000 Au ble (168x124cm-66x49in) s.d.1883. 17-May-4 Chayette & Cheval, Paris #170a/R est:6000-8000
Works on paper
£1000 $1790 €1500 Elegante devant le pavillon de l'Exposition Universelle (30x23cm-12x9in) s. gouache W/C. 17-May-4 Chayette & Cheval, Paris #173/R est:2400-2600
£2000 $3440 €2920 Le rendezvous (55x43cm-22x17in) s. W/C. 4-Dec-3 Christie's, Kensington #134/R est:3000-5000

LELONG (17/19th C) French
Works on paper
£1549 $2572 €2200 Nature morte a la guitare et aux poissons rouges (9x7cm-4x3in) gouache. 13-Jun-3 Ferri, Paris #35/R est:1800-2000

LELONG, Corinne (20th C) French
Works on paper
£420 $713 €600 La taille III (90x90cm-35x35in) mono. mixed media canvas. 29-Nov-3 Neret-Minet, Paris #110/R
£600 $1086 €900 Champs (73x116cm-29x46in) mono. mixed media canvas. 3-Apr-4 Neret-Minet, Paris #129

LELONG, Paul (19th C) French
Works on paper
£1447 $2663 €2200 Still life with parrot, dish of fruit and vase of flowers (14x20cm-6x8in) gouache. 22-Jun-4 Sotheby's, Milan #105/R est:1200-1800

LELONG, Pierre (?-1645) French
Works on paper
£4645 $8500 €6782 Still life with flowers, fruit and items on stone ledge (16x22cm-6x9in) bodycol paper on board set of six. 3-Jun-4 Christie's, Rockefeller NY #1288/R est:4000-6000

LELU, Pierre (1741-1810) French
Works on paper
£578 $1035 €850 Bergers tirant le lait de leurs chevres (22x41cm-9x16in) pen brown ink wash. 19-Mar-4 Piasa, Paris #85
£1500 $2745 €2190 Two women dancing with a comedian in a landscape (16x21cm-6x8in) s. black chk pen ink. 6-Jul-4 Christie's, London #124/R est:1000-1500

LELY, Sir Peter (1618-1680) British
£867 $1551 €1300 Portrait of a lady (83x77cm-33x30in) 17-May-4 Glerum, Amsterdam #46/R
£5556 $10000 €8112 Portrait of Mrs Charles Bertie (127x101cm-50x40in) 22-Jan-4 Sotheby's, New York #248a/R est:30000-50000
£5556 $10000 €8112 Portrait of the Hon Charles Bertie of Uffington (127x101cm-50x40in) 22-Jan-4 Sotheby's, New York #248b/R est:25000-35000

LELY, Sir Peter (after) (1618-1680) British
£5800 $10788 €8468 Portrait of King Charles II wearing breast plate and lace cravat (86x68cm-34x27in) feigned oval prov.exhib. 4-Mar-4 Christie's, Kensington #283/R est:1000-1500

LELY, Sir Peter (attrib) (1618-1680) British
£3691 $6792 €5500 Portrait of Lady Anne Hyde (42x32cm-17x13in) panel prov. 24-Mar-4 Dorotheum, Vienna #318/R est:5000-7000
£4196 $7133 €6000 Portrait of young woman in white dress (73x58cm-29x23in) 20-Nov-3 Van Ham, Cologne #1374/R est:6500

LELY, Sir Peter (circle) (1618-1680) British
£5200 $9568 €7592 Henrietta Maria (70x57cm-28x22in) 29-Mar-4 Bonhams, Bath #51/R est:2500-3500
£5700 $9690 €8322 Portrait of Sir Hugh Briggs, standing full length wearing a blue dress (125x100cm-49x39in) bears i. d.1687. 29-Oct-3 Hampton & Littlewood, Exeter #561/R est:4000-6000
£8500 $15215 €12410 Portrait of a lady in a white silk dress and pearls (109x93cm-43x37in) oval. 27-May-4 Christie's, Kensington #20/R est:6000-8000
£12000 $20400 €17520 Portrait of a lady, identified as Mary, Lady Tichborne in a golden dress and blue wrap (127x102cm-50x40in) 25-Nov-3 Christie's, London #10/R est:7000-10000

LELY, Sir Peter (studio) (1618-1680) British
£6000 $10920 €9000 Portrait of the Duchess of Cleveland (126x101cm-50x40in) prov. 1-Jul-4 Van Ham, Cologne #1129/R est:9000
£6500 $11050 €9490 Portrait of a lady, holding a flower, a landscape beyond (127x102cm-50x40in) 19-Nov-3 Tennants, Leyburn #1142/R est:4000-5000
£8500 $14705 €12410 Portrait of Barbara Villiers, Duchess of Cleveland (75x73cm-30x29in) 10-Dec-3 Bonhams, New Bond Street #19/R est:5000-7000
£11600 $21692 €16936 Three quarter length portrait of Louise de Kerouaille (122x99cm-48x39in) 29-Feb-4 Wilkinson, Doncaster #284/R
£13000 $23660 €18980 Portrait of Diana Countess of Ailesbury (127x98cm-50x39in) i. prov. 1-Jul-4 Sotheby's, London #108 est:8000-12000
£23000 $42320 €33580 Portrait of Lady Elizabeth Jones, later Countess of Kildare (125x99cm-49x39in) 26-Mar-4 Sotheby's, London #1/R est:6000-8000

LELY, Sir Peter (style) (1618-1680) British
£2778 $5000 €4056 Portrait of a boy (40x30cm-16x12in) panel prov. 23-Jan-4 Christie's, Rockefeller NY #116/R est:1000-1500
£17486 $32000 €25530 Portrait of a lady, seated in a gold dress with blue shawl in a landscape (124x99cm-49x39in) prov. 3-Jun-4 Christie's, Rockefeller NY #429/R est:10000-15000

LEMAIRE, Louis Marie (1824-1910) French
£400 $724 €600 Vaches en bord d'etang (48x74cm-19x29in) s. 2-Apr-4 Rossini, Paris #59/R
£650 $1203 €949 Farmyard scene (30x23cm-12x9in) s. panel. 13-Jan-4 Bonhams, Knightsbridge #254/R
£650 $1203 €949 Chickens in a farmyard (19x14cm-7x6in) s. panel. 10-Feb-4 Bonhams, Knightsbridge #291/R
£950 $1758 €1387 Country landscape with various fowl by a tree trunk (28x38cm-11x15in) s. 10-Feb-4 Bonhams, Knightsbridge #158/R

LEMAIRE, Madeleine (1845-1928) French
£1126 $2060 €1700 Coupe de roses (54x36cm-21x14in) s. W/C. 9-Apr-4 Bailly Pommery, Paris #58 est:500-600
£5467 $9895 €8200 Portrait de Colette Dumas, fille d'Alexandre Dumas fils (80x55cm-31x22in) s. lit. 31-Mar-4 Sotheby's, Paris #93/R est:9000-12000
Works on paper
£403 $713 €600 Roses dans un pichet (56x40cm-22x16in) s. W/C. 30-Apr-4 Tajan, Paris #122
£596 $1091 €900 Roses dans un vase de faience (54x37cm-21x15in) s. W/C. 9-Apr-4 Bailly Pommery, Paris #49
£596 $1091 €900 Iris et roses (54x37cm-21x15in) s. W/C. 9-Apr-4 Bailly Pommery, Paris #50/R
£634 $1052 €900 Elegantes (50x31cm-20x12in) s. W/C chl. 15-Jun-3 Peron, Melun #119
£728 $1333 €1100 Corbeille de roses (45x57cm-18x22in) s. W/C. 9-Apr-4 Bailly Pommery, Paris #61
£728 $1333 €1100 Peches, noix et raisins (37x54cm-15x21in) s. W/C. 9-Apr-4 Bailly Pommery, Paris #63
£828 $1515 €1250 Jetee de roses (17x25cm-7x10in) s. W/C. 9-Apr-4 Bailly Pommery, Paris #56
£851 $1379 €1200 Bouquet de roses (72x53cm-28x21in) s. W/C. 21-May-3 Daguerre, Paris #23/R

£861 $1575 €1300 Peches, raisins et pichet bleu (40x55cm-16x22in) s. pastel. 9-Apr-4 Bailly Pommery, Paris #55/R
£861 $1575 €1300 Roses (75x55cm-30x22in) s. W/C. 9-Apr-4 Bailly Pommery, Paris #60
£927 $1697 €1400 Oeillets dans un vase de faience (39x24cm-15x9in) s. W/C. 9-Apr-4 Bailly Pommery, Paris #46
£960 $1796 €1450 Nature morte aux citrons et anemones (36x53cm-14x21in) s. W/C. 24-Jul-4 Thierry & Lannon, Brest #67/R
£993 $1818 €1500 Trois elegantes au salon (53x35cm-21x14in) s. W/C. 9-Apr-4 Bailly Pommery, Paris #44/R est:2000-3000
£993 $1818 €1500 Pavots et coquelicots (36x53cm-14x21in) s. W/C. 9-Apr-4 Bailly Pommery, Paris #51 est:500-600
£993 $1818 €1500 Roses (37x26cm-15x10in) s. W/C. 9-Apr-4 Bailly Pommery, Paris #67 est:400-600
£1000 $1830 €1500 Bouquet de roses (55x38cm-22x15in) s. W/C. 6-Jun-4 Osenat, Fontainebleau #73/R est:2000-2500
£1060 $1939 €1600 Giroflees dans un vase (34x26cm-13x10in) s. W/C. 9-Apr-4 Bailly Pommery, Paris #45 est:600-800
£1107 $1982 €1650 Fleurs des champs (38x28cm-15x11in) s. W/C. 26-May-4 Blanchet, Paris #192/R est:1500-1800
£1192 $2181 €1800 Roses (28x37cm-11x15in) s. W/C pair. 9-Apr-4 Bailly Pommery, Paris #48 est:600-800
£1192 $2181 €1800 Panier de roses (35x49cm-14x19in) s. W/C. 9-Apr-4 Bailly Pommery, Paris #59 est:500-600
£1258 $2303 €1900 Corbeille d'oeillets (36x51cm-14x20in) s. W/C. 9-Apr-4 Bailly Pommery, Paris #62/R est:800-1100
£1391 $2545 €2100 Roses, lilas et chevrefeuille (38x53cm-15x21in) s. W/C. 9-Apr-4 Bailly Pommery, Paris #54 est:600-800
£1457 $2666 €2200 Primeveres, iris et roses (18x26cm-7x10in) s. W/C pair. 9-Apr-4 Bailly Pommery, Paris #52 est:600-800
£1457 $2666 €2200 Camelias doubles et collier de perles (40x28cm-16x11in) s. W/C. 9-Apr-4 Bailly Pommery, Paris #65 est:400-600
£1589 $2909 €2400 Bouquet de roses (36x52cm-14x20in) s. W/C. 9-Apr-4 Bailly Pommery, Paris #57 est:400-600
£1656 $3030 €2500 Panier de framboises (26x35cm-10x14in) s. W/C. 9-Apr-4 Bailly Pommery, Paris #64 est:600-800
£1788 $3272 €2700 Hortensias (36x52cm-14x20in) s. W/C. 9-Apr-4 Bailly Pommery, Paris #53 est:400-600
£2517 $4605 €3800 Roses tremieres (138x63cm-54x25in) s. pastel. 9-Apr-4 Bailly Pommery, Paris #47 est:2500-3000
£2848 $5211 €4300 Brassee de lilas (51x72cm-20x28in) s. W/C. 9-Apr-4 Bailly Pommery, Paris #66/R est:2000-3000

LEMAITRE, Albert (1886-1975) Belgian
£638 $1066 €900 Les chevaux de St Marc, Venice (25x35cm-10x14in) s. i.verso panel. 15-Oct-3 Hotel des Ventes Mosan, Brussels #161
£2119 $3857 €3200 Port de St-Tropez (88x75cm-35x30in) s.d.1920. 16-Jun-4 Hotel des Ventes Mosan, Brussels #217/R est:2800-3200

LEMAITRE, Andre (1909-1995) French
£450 $752 €657 Nature morte (46x55cm-18x22in) s. i.d.64 verso. 8-Oct-3 Christie's, Kensington #962/R
£1465 $2667 €2139 Still life of cherries, potted plants and hat on table (59x64cm-23x25in) s. s.d.1970 verso. 7-Feb-4 Rasmussen, Havnen #4140/R est:15000 (D.KR 16000)

LEMAITRE, Eduard Charles (19th C) French
£647 $1062 €900 Village et troupeau dans des paysages de marais (46x65cm-18x26in) s. pair. 3-Jun-3 Livinec, Gaudcheau & Jezequel, Rennes #55

LEMAITRE, J (?) ?
£1042 $1740 €1500 Landscape (56x92cm-22x36in) s. 23-Oct-3 Hagelstam, Helsinki #863 est:1000

LEMAITRE, Maurice (1926-) French
£434 $750 €634 Coastal village (48x61cm-19x24in) s. 10-Dec-3 Alderfer's, Hatfield #310
£1656 $3013 €2500 Calendrier rituel (100x81cm-39x32in) s.d.1966 i.d.verso. 18-Jun-4 Charbonneaux, Paris #149/R est:2500-3000

LEMAITRE, Maurice (1929-) French
£385 $662 €550 Bord de Marne a Vaires (22x33cm-9x13in) s. panel. 5-Dec-3 Maigret, Paris #113
£782 $1400 €1142 Punts along a river (23x28cm-9x11in) s. 7-May-4 Sloans & Kenyon, Bethesda #1663/R
£800 $1456 €1200 Peniches a Saint-Mammes (27x35cm-11x14in) s. 4-Jul-4 Eric Pillon, Calais #239/R
£973 $1810 €1450 Peche dans l'Herault (46x61cm-18x24in) s. 7-Mar-4 Lesieur & Le Bars, Le Havre #83
£1000 $1820 €1500 Pecheur a Clairmarais (38x55cm-15x22in) s. 4-Jul-4 Eric Pillon, Calais #240/R
£1007 $1872 €1500 Printemps a Maisoncelles en Brie (46x61cm-18x24in) s.d.89 verso. 7-Mar-4 Lesieur & Le Bars, Le Havre #84

LEMAITRE, Nathanael (1831-1897) French
£565 $1034 €825 Au bord du lac (35x28cm-14x11in) s. 4-Jun-4 Zofingen, Switzerland #2353 (S.FR 1300)
£1034 $1852 €1510 Shepherd with sheep (39x58cm-15x23in) s. 13-May-4 Stuker, Bern #230/R est:2000-3000 (S.FR 2400)

LEMAITRE, Vincent (20th C) French?
Works on paper
£533 $960 €800 Composition (61x61cm-24x24in) s.d.2003 verso torn posters panel. 25-Apr-4 Versailles Encheres #205
£633 $1140 €950 Composition (87x81cm-34x32in) s.d.2003 verso torn posters panel. 25-Apr-4 Versailles Encheres #195

LEMAR, Marcel (1892-1941) French
Sculpture
£1867 $3341 €2800 Babouin nourrissant son petit (27cm-11in) s. num.1 pat bronze wooden base. 17-May-4 Sotheby's, Paris #75/R est:3000-4000

LEMBECK, Jack (1942-) American
£243 $450 €355 Capital Custom (71x91cm-28x36in) s. s.i.d.1988 verso acrylic prov. 13-Jul-4 Christie's, Rockefeller NY #122/R

LEMCKE, Dietmar (1930-) German
£2000 $3680 €3000 Still life with alarm clock in red (50x81cm-20x32in) s.d.1958 lit. 12-Jun-4 Villa Grisebach, Berlin #323/R est:2500-3500

LEME, Bella Paes (20th C) Brazilian
£724 $1332 €1100 Paysage de Bresil (29x48cm-11x19in) s.d.60 panel. 22-Jun-4 Calmels Cohen, Paris #34a

LEMET, Louis (19th C) American
Works on paper
£4706 $8000 €6871 Portrait of Charles Graff of Philadelphia (48x36cm-19x14in) black white chk prov.exhib.lit. 31-Oct-3 North East Auctions, Portsmouth #1653 est:8000-12000

LEMEUNIER, Basile (1852-?) French
£804 $1343 €1150 Nature morte avec diner paysan (12x16cm-5x6in) s. 29-Jun-3 Eric Pillon, Calais #26/R
£4126 $7097 €5900 Elegantes sur la plage a Deauville (41x61cm-16x24in) s. cardboard. 7-Dec-3 Osenat, Fontainebleau #215 est:3000-3500
£6000 $11040 €8760 Nourriture pour les petits oiseaux (46x32cm-18x13in) s.i.d.1901. 25-Mar-4 Christie's, Kensington #31/R est:6000-8000

LEMIEUX, Clement (1946-) Canadian
Sculpture
£1700 $3111 €2482 L'enfant de notre amour (181cm-71in) painted wood granite base. 1-Jun-4 Joyner Waddington, Toronto #230/R est:5000-7000 (C.D 4250)
£11607 $19964 €16946 Les yeux dans les yeux (174cm-69in) painted wood granite base. 2-Dec-3 Joyner Waddington, Toronto #231/R est:3500-4000 (C.D 26000)

LEMIEUX, Jean Paul (1904-1990) Canadian
£3455 $6185 €5044 Enfants sur la plage (25x30cm-10x12in) s. i.verso lit. 27-May-4 Heffel, Vancouver #112/R est:5500-6500 (C.D 8500)
£4878 $8732 €7122 La procession (20x25cm-8x10in) s. i.verso painted 1985 prov. 27-May-4 Heffel, Vancouver #113/R est:8000-10000 (C.D 12000)
£8036 $13821 €11733 Urbain (60x50cm-24x20in) s. painted c.1989 exhib.lit. 2-Dec-3 Joyner Waddington, Toronto #90/R est:20000-30000 (C.D 18000)
£8130 $14553 €11870 Beach scene (38x45cm-15x18in) s. board. 27-May-4 Heffel, Vancouver #59/R est:20000-25000 (C.D 20000)
£8130 $14553 €11870 Le nuage (27x35cm-11x14in) s. i.verso lit. 27-May-4 Heffel, Vancouver #111/R est:14000-16000 (C.D 20000)
£9009 $15315 €13153 Jeune fille aux tresses (60x28cm-24x11in) s. board painted c.1951 prov.lit. 27-Nov-3 Heffel, Vancouver #120/R est:25000-30000 (C.D 20000)
£13393 $23036 €19554 Portrait of Yvon Bouchard (72x60cm-28x24in) s.d.7. 2-Dec-3 Joyner Waddington, Toronto #98/R est:35000-45000 (C.D 30000)
£14228 $25467 €20773 Le bouquet (61x91cm-24x36in) s. i.verso. 27-May-4 Heffel, Vancouver #108/R est:35000-45000 (C.D 35000)
£24775 $42117 €36172 Two sisters (41x30cm-16x12in) s.d.1967 diptych prov.exhib. 18-Nov-3 Sotheby's, Toronto #14/R est:35000-40000 (C.D 55000)
£26423 $47297 €38578 Paysage (30x110cm-12x43in) s. painted 1966 prov.exhib.lit. 27-May-4 Heffel, Vancouver #107/R est:65000-85000 (C.D 65000)
£27027 $45946 €39459 Port-au-Persil (72x87cm-28x34in) s. 18-Nov-3 Sotheby's, Toronto #52/R est:20000-30000 (C.D 60000)
£34553 $61850 €50447 Chemin d'hiver (122x152cm-48x60in) s.i.d.1984 prov.lit. 31-May-4 Sotheby's, Toronto #156/R est:120000-150000 (C.D 85000)
£56000 $102480 €81760 Monde de Donate (60x82cm-24x32in) s.d.61 prov. 1-Jun-4 Joyner Waddington, Toronto #53/R est:100000-125000 (C.D 140000)
Works on paper
£200 $366 €292 Portrait of Ron Everson, New Smurna beach (40x33cm-16x13in) s.d.72 pencil. 1-Jun-4 Joyner Waddington, Toronto #442 (C.D 500)
£2232 $3839 €3259 Visiteur (50x65cm-20x26in) s.i.d.73 col felt pens. 2-Dec-3 Joyner Waddington, Toronto #142/R est:10000-15000 (C.D 5000)
£5357 $9214 €7821 Le petit garcon (64x49cm-25x19in) s.d.74 col felt pen. 2-Dec-3 Joyner Waddington, Toronto #184/R est:12000-15000 (C.D 12000)
£7317 $13098 €10683 Peche sur glace (21x23cm-8x9in) s. W/C exec. c.1935 prov. 27-May-4 Heffel, Vancouver #70/R est:5000-7000 (C.D 18000)

LEMIRE, Charles (elder) (18/19th C) French
Works on paper
£1294 $2200 €1889 Young gentleman (56x46cm-22x18in) s.d.1814 graphite chl. 22-Nov-3 New Orleans Auction, New Orleans #480/R est:800-1200

LEMIRE, Charles Gabriel (1741-1827) French
Works on paper
£1511 $2750 €2206 Portrait of a woman (41x34cm-16x13in) s. graphite. 29-Jun-4 Sotheby's, New York #100/R est:4000-6000

LEMIRE, Madeleine (20th C) Canadian
£610 $1110 €915 La rengaine des narcisses (102x76cm-40x30in) s. s.i.verso. 1-Jul-4 Heffel, Vancouver #18/R est:1800-2200 (C.D 1500)

LEMKE, Johann Philip (1631-1711) German
£1996 $3572 €2914 Battle scene (35x58cm-14x23in) prov. 25-May-4 Bukowskis, Stockholm #402/R est:20000-25000 (S.KR 27000)

LEMMEN, Georges (1865-1916) Belgian

£667	$1193	€1000	Study of a puss (31x20cm-12x8in) st.mono.d.90 lit. 15-May-4 De Vuyst, Lokeren #184
£1000	$1790	€1500	L'artiste peintre devant son chevalet (30x22cm-12x9in) s. panel lit. 15-May-4 De Vuyst, Lokeren #180/R est:1500-2000
£1399	$2406	€2000	Project for painting (36x51cm-14x20in) oil on cardboard prov. 2-Dec-3 Sotheby's, Amsterdam #46/R est:4000-6000
£2113	$3655	€3000	Bouquet de fleurs (46x30cm-18x12in) s.d.1898. 14-Dec-3 Eric Pillon, Calais #94/R
£4054	$7500	€5919	Jeune fille assise au chapeau bleu (58x47cm-23x19in) init.d.1908 paper on board prov. 11-Feb-4 Sotheby's, New York #8/R est:15000-20000
£5245	$8916	€7500	Jeune femme au bouquet de fleurs (32x36cm-13x14in) cardboard. 1-Dec-3 Palais de Beaux Arts, Brussels #94/R est:7500-10000
£5369	$9933	€8000	Three bathers (37x51cm-15x20in) board lit. 13-Mar-4 De Vuyst, Lokeren #425/R est:4000-5000
£5500	$9185	€8030	La source (46x55cm-18x22in) board. 22-Oct-3 Bonhams, New Bond Street #10/R est:3000-4000
£5594	$9343	€8000	Still life of roses (34x44cm-13x17in) s.d.1915 board lit. 11-Oct-3 De Vuyst, Lokeren #435/R est:5000-7000
£7718	$14201	€11500	Lise (44x32cm-17x13in) oil paper on cardboard painted c.1907 prov. 24-Mar-4 Binoche, Paris #78/R est:10000-12000
£44000	$78760	€66000	Portrait of the artist's wife (33x40cm-13x16in) s.d.1901 cardboard. 15-May-4 Hagelstam, Helsinki #45/R est:30000
£150000	$276000	€219000	Modiste (35x42cm-14x17in) mono.d.1901 oil gouache pastel board prov. 22-Jun-4 Christie's, London #1/R est:60000-80000
Works on paper			
£317	$573	€475	Bulletin meteo (10x16cm-4x6in) Studio st. india ink W/C. 30-Mar-4 Palais de Beaux Arts, Brussels #639/R
£349	$600	€510	Woman sewing in interior (25x35cm-10x14in) init.d.1900 chl. 2-Dec-3 Christie's, Rockefeller NY #154d/R
£385	$642	€550	Cheval dans une ecurie (38x39cm-15x15in) mono. chl chk prov.lit. 11-Oct-3 De Vuyst, Lokeren #223
£490	$817	€700	Etude de femme (23x30cm-9x12in) st.sig.d.septembre 22/90 wax crayon. 13-Oct-3 Horta, Bruxelles #306
£671	$1188	€1000	Yachts, maree Montante (31x23cm-12x9in) studio st. blk wax crayon col crayons. 27-Apr-4 Artcurial Briest, Paris #12
£685	$1164	€1000	Fillette (28x24cm-11x9in) studio st. mixed media. 10-Nov-3 Horta, Bruxelles #394
£724	$1332	€1100	Nu de dos (62x49cm-24x19in) studio st. pastel. 22-Jun-4 Palais de Beaux Arts, Brussels #273/R
£753	$1281	€1100	Bebe endormi (22x35cm-9x14in) st.sig. chl dr. 10-Nov-3 Horta, Bruxelles #393
£855	$1574	€1300	Deux baigneuses (64x44cm-25x17in) mono.d.1909 pastel. 22-Jun-4 Palais de Beaux Arts, Brussels #272
£872	$1544	€1300	Bateaux sur l'escaut, Anvers (31x23cm-12x9in) studio st. blk wax crayon col crayons. 27-Apr-4 Artcurial Briest, Paris #8 est:1200-1500
£1352	$2419	€2000	Interior scene (20x25cm-8x10in) d.1905 ink. 4-May-4 Calmels Cohen, Paris #125/R est:2000-2500
£1824	$3448	€2700	Femme a la lecture. Femme a la couture (20x13cm-8x5in) one bears studio st.d.8 mars 1910 one d.10 mars 1910 ink W/C pair. 17-Feb-4 Vanderkindere, Brussels #2 est:1000-1500
£2027	$3628	€3000	Reclining female nude (17x24cm-7x9in) ink wash W/C. 4-May-4 Calmels Cohen, Paris #126/R est:1500-2000
£11765	$20000	€17177	Snowy evening (75x105cm-30x41in) s.d.1910 pastel paper on canvas. 28-Oct-3 Sotheby's, New York #100/R est:10000-15000

LEMMENS, Theophile Victor Émile (1821-1867) French

£1958	$3368	€2800	Barque au bord de la riviere (27x38cm-11x15in) s. 7-Dec-3 Osenat, Fontainebleau #171 est:2500-3000

LEMMENS, Theophile Victor Emile (attrib) (1821-1867) French

£1528	$2521	€2200	Oriental mountain landscape (27x40cm-11x16in) s. bears i. 3-Jul-3 Dr Fritz Nagel, Stuttgart #505/R est:1200

LEMMER SANDORIA (?) Belgian?

Sculpture			
£1088	$1948	€1600	Buste (70cm-28in) s. bronze marble socle. 16-Mar-4 Vanderkindere, Brussels #148 est:400-600

LEMMERS, Georges (1871-1944) Belgian

£317	$548	€450	Maisons rouges a Vale de Rita (34x44cm-13x17in) s. 9-Dec-3 Vanderkindere, Brussels #103
£497	$904	€750	Le Chenal (35x45cm-14x18in) s. 15-Jun-4 Galerie Moderne, Brussels #372/R
£563	$986	€800	Village, les Contamines (44x57cm-17x22in) s. 16-Dec-3 Galerie Moderne, Brussels #805/R
£769	$1285	€1100	Village au bord d'un cours d'eau (34x44cm-13x17in) s. 13-Oct-3 Horta, Bruxelles #149/R
£769	$1308	€1100	Vue d'un port au Portugal (63x82cm-25x32in) 1-Dec-3 Amberes, Antwerp #322
£2483	$4469	€3600	Elegante dans un interieur (40x32cm-16x13in) s. panel. 20-Jan-4 Galerie Moderne, Brussels #286/R est:2000-3000
£26471	$45000	€38648	The love letter (119x147cm-47x58in) s.d.1903. 29-Oct-3 Christie's, Rockefeller NY #170/R est:25000-35000
Works on paper			
£733	$1320	€1100	Portrait of a girl at the park (86x64cm-34x25in) s.d.1917 pastel oval. 26-Apr-4 Bernaerts, Antwerp #434/R

LEMMERZ, Christian (1959-) German

Sculpture			
£2160	$3607	€3154	Wrapped up horse (24cm-9in) init.num.2/3 bronze prov. 7-Oct-3 Rasmussen, Copenhagen #86/R est:25000-30000 (D.KR 23000)

LEMMI, Angiolo (19/20th C) Italian

£658	$1211	€1000	In a Roman courtyard (44x34cm-17x13in) s. 22-Jun-4 Christie's, Amsterdam #65/R

LEMMING, J B (20th C) American

£898	$1500	€1311	Number 12 (61x91cm-24x36in) s. paint wood double-sided prov. 15-Nov-3 Slotin Folk Art, Buford #300/R est:800-1200
£898	$1500	€1311	Bulls eye man Number 13 (61x71cm-24x28in) paint wood double-sided prov. 15-Nov-3 Slotin Folk Art, Buford #302/R est:800-1200
£958	$1600	€1399	Number 14 (61x94cm-24x37in) paint wood double-sided prov. 15-Nov-3 Slotin Folk Art, Buford #301/R est:800-1200

LEMOINE, Jacques (1751-1824) French

Miniatures			
£2667	$4853	€4000	Portrait de Madame Baguenaut (6cm-2in circular) s.d.1795 lit. 30-Jun-4 Pierre Berge, Paris #106/R est:4000-5000
Works on paper			
£646	$1157	€950	Scene de la vie paysanne de la region de Rouen (40x55cm-16x22in) bears sig. grey wash. 17-Mar-4 Maigret, Paris #33/R

LEMOINE, Marie Victoire (attrib) (1754-1820) French

£4333	$7843	€6500	Portrait de jeune femme au chapeau fleuri (65x54cm-26x21in) oval lit. 30-Mar-4 Rossini, Paris #50/R est:6000-8000

LEMOKH, Kirill Vikentevich (1841-1910) Russian

£40000	$68000	€58400	Two young peasant girls (83x57cm-33x22in) s.d.1892. 19-Nov-3 Sotheby's, London #62/R est:50000-70000

LEMON, Arthur (1850-1912) British

£900	$1665	€1314	Ploughing team (54x105cm-21x41in) s. 10-Mar-4 Sotheby's, Olympia #215/R est:1000-2000

LEMONNIER, Anicet Charles Gabriel (1743-1824) French

Works on paper			
£300	$519	€438	Mountainous landscape with a ruined tower in the foreground (24x15cm-9x6in) i. col chk. 12-Dec-3 Christie's, Kensington #464

LEMONNIER, Eugene (19th C) French?

Works on paper			
£979	$1635	€1400	Femme et enfant pleurant (109x75cm-43x30in) s.d.1877 pastel. 26-Jun-3 Artcurial Briest, Paris #516 est:2000-2500

LEMORDANT, Jean Julien (1882-1968) French

£1117	$2000	€1631	Brittany seacoast (81x99cm-32x39in) s. 21-Mar-4 Hindman, Chicago #850/R est:2500-5000
£2817	$4930	€4000	Scene de pardon au pays bigouden (50x60cm-20x24in) board. 21-Dec-3 Thierry & Lannon, Brest #333/R est:4000-5000
Works on paper			
£336	$624	€500	Bateaux (30x40cm-12x16in) s.i. blue ink wash. 7-Mar-4 Livinec, Gaudcheau & Jezequel, Rennes #38a
£430	$805	€650	Danse bretonne (22x36cm-9x14in) chl. 24-Jul-4 Thierry & Lannon, Brest #41
£460	$842	€672	Danse Breton (25x47cm-10x19in) W/C. 7-Apr-4 Woolley & Wallis, Salisbury #132/R

LEMOS, Luis (1954-) French?

Works on paper			
£280	$476	€400	L'envol (80x65cm-31x26in) s. mixed media canvas. 20-Nov-3 Claude Aguttes, Neuilly #185

LEMOYNE, François (attrib) (1688-1737) French

£2671	$4541	€3900	Bather (55x38cm-22x15in) i.verso. 9-Nov-3 Finarte, Venice #14/R est:3000-4000
Sculpture			
£2778	$4639	€4000	Jeanne d'Arc (76cm-30in) st.f.Compagnie des Bronzes de Paris pat bronze ivory. 21-Oct-3 Galerie Moderne, Brussels #1518/R
Works on paper			
£483	$806	€700	Mythological scene (27x44cm-11x17in) i. chk prov. double-sided. 15-Nov-3 Lempertz, Koln #1350/R

LEMOYNE, Jean Baptiste (younger-attrib) (1704-1778) French

Sculpture			
£13158	$24211	€20000	Tete de femme lauree (51cm-20in) pat terracotta prov.lit. 23-Jun-4 Sotheby's, Paris #64/R est:20000-30000

LEMPEREUR-HAUT, Marcel (1898-1986) Belgian

£3243	$5806	€4800	Bouquet d'etoiles (115x50cm-45x20in) s.d.1950 s.i.d.verso panel exhib. 4-May-4 Calmels Cohen, Paris #187/R est:1500-2000

LEMPICKA, Tamara de (1898-1980) Polish

£13497	$22000	€19706	Rose (35x27cm-14x11in) s. painted c.1930. 25-Sep-3 Christie's, Rockefeller NY #618/R est:15000-20000
£14865	$27500	€21703	Pot de fuschias (49x34cm-19x13in) s. board painted c.1922 prov.lit. 11-Feb-4 Sotheby's, New York #33/R est:12000-15000
£223529	$380000	€326352	Polonaise (35x27cm-14x11in) s. panel painted 1933 prov.exhib.lit. 6-Nov-3 Sotheby's, New York #233/R est:150000-200000
£2290503	$4100000	€3344134	Portrait de Mrs Bush (122x66cm-48x26in) s. painted 1929 prov.lit. 4-May-4 Christie's, Rockefeller NY #36/R est:1200000-1600000

Prints
£1765 $3000 €2577 Femme au turban rouge (33x26cm-13x10in) s.num.117/200 col aquatint. 6-Nov-3 Swann Galleries, New York #604/R est:4000-6000
£8667 $15947 €13000 La musicienne (57x36cm-22x14in) s. col engraving etching one of 100 exec. c.1930. 12-Jun-4 Villa Grisebach, Berlin #280/R est:3000-4000
Works on paper
£6000 $10380 €8760 Madagascan girls II (25x16cm-10x6in) st.sig. pencil lit. 11-Dec-3 Christie's, Kensington #86/R est:4000-6000

LEMPICKA, Tamara de (after) (1898-1980) Polish
Prints
£7027 $13000 €10259 La femme bleue a la guitare (58x35cm-23x14in) s.num.75/100 etching aquatint. 11-Mar-4 Sotheby's, New York #199/R est:4000-6000

LENAGHAN, Brenda (1941-) British
£700 $1288 €1022 Girl with black tights and shoes (50x50cm-20x20in) s. board. 10-Jun-4 Lyon & Turnbull, Edinburgh #49
Works on paper
£500 $915 €730 In the garden (50x51cm-20x20in) s.d.1982 W/C. 8-Apr-4 Bonhams, Edinburgh #39

LENAIL, Marie Joseph Ernest (19th C) French
£467 $835 €700 Bergere et promenade (40x54cm-16x21in) 16-May-4 other European Auctioneer #40a

LENAIN, A (1588-1648) French
£1299 $2325 €1897 Still life of flowers (65x54cm-26x21in) s. 22-Mar-4 Philippe Schuler, Zurich #4415/R est:2000-2500 (S.FR 3000)

LENAIN, Mathieu (attrib) (1607-1677) French
£2207 $4039 €3200 Dutch tavern interior (21x26cm-8x10in) sheet copper. 30-Jan-4 Altus, Berlin #588/R est:2900

LENAIN, Mathieu (circle) (1607-1677) French
£6111 $11000 €8922 Bird catcher (97x77cm-38x30in) 23-Jan-4 Christie's, Rockefeller NY #108/R est:6000-8000
£11000 $20130 €16060 Portrait of man, head and shoulders, said to be the philosopher Renee Descartes (46x35cm-18x14in) exhib.lit. 8-Jul-4 Sotheby's, London #212/R est:5000-7000

LENBACH, Franz von (1836-1904) German
£1259 $2165 €1800 Portrait of a man (66x55cm-26x22in) s. canvas on board. 3-Dec-3 Neumeister, Munich #649/R est:2000
£1656 $3013 €2500 Portrait of Karl Maximilian Heyl zu Herrnsheim (116x87cm-46x34in) s.d.81. 16-Jun-4 Hugo Ruef, Munich #1022/R est:2500
£2013 $3705 €3000 Portrait of elegant woman (56x51cm-22x20in) s.d.1896 board. 25-Mar-4 Dr Fritz Nagel, Stuttgart #737/R est:6000
£2361 $4250 €3447 Portrait of two young girls said to be the artist's daughters (73x62cm-29x24in) oil pencil on board oval prov. 21-Jan-4 Sotheby's, New York #254/R est:3500-5500
£2867 $5131 €4300 Women's portrait (82x62cm-32x24in) s. prov. 14-May-4 Ketterer, Munich #108/R est:4000-5000
£3497 $5944 €5000 Woman's portrait (78x70cm-31x28in) s.d.1898 board. 29-Nov-3 Villa Grisebach, Berlin #100/R est:5000-7000
£3521 $6092 €5000 Portrait of Bismarck (86x71cm-34x28in) s.d.1894. 11-Dec-3 Dr Fritz Nagel, Stuttgart #533/R est:6800
£3618 $6658 €5500 Portrait of Gabriele von Lang-Buchhof (205x116cm-81x46in) 24-Jun-4 Dr Fritz Nagel, Stuttgart #727/R est:6000
£9333 $17173 €14000 Portrait of Otto, Count of Bismarck (121x87cm-48x34in) s. prov. 12-Jun-4 Villa Grisebach, Berlin #116/R est:14000-18000
Works on paper
£306 $550 €447 Portrait of a woman profile (47x38cm-19x15in) s. conte crayon brown paper. 24-Apr-4 Weschler, Washington #571/R
£348 $550 €508 Self portrait of Franz Liszt, seated (38x28cm-15x11in) s. W/C. 6-Sep-3 Brunk, Ashville #454
£1197 $2071 €1700 Portrait of Cara von Goldammer (73x60cm-29x24in) bears i. verso pastel htd white pencil board. 11-Dec-3 Dr Fritz Nagel, Stuttgart #532/R est:2500
£1552 $2778 €2266 Portrait of the actress, Eleonora Duse (56x49cm-22x19in) s.d.1902 i. verso W/C gouache board. 13-May-4 Stuker, Bern #233/R est:4000-6000 (S.FR 3600)
£1667 $3017 €2500 Portrait of young woman (49x34cm-19x13in) s.d.1890 pastel board. 1-Apr-4 Van Ham, Cologne #1509/R est:3200
£2431 $4010 €3500 Young woman (76x63cm-30x25in) s. pastel. 2-Jul-3 Neumeister, Munich #478/R est:1100

LENBACH, Franz von (attrib) (1836-1904) German
£1351 $2378 €2000 Landscape study (43x36cm-17x14in) prov. 22-May-4 Lempertz, Koln #1550/R est:1500

LENCI, Marino (1874-1939) Italian
£355 $592 €500 Sparrow in its nest (29x19cm-11x7in) s. board. 17-Jun-3 Finarte Semenzato, Milan #372

LENCKER, Christoph (1556-?) German
Sculpture
£250000 $432500 €365000 Figure of King David (18cm-7in) parcel-gilt. 12-Dec-3 Sotheby's, London #45/R est:250000-350000

LENEPVEU, Jules Eugène (1819-1898) French
£1053 $1937 €1600 Portraits des musiciens Halevy et Auber (43cm-17in circular) pair. 25-Jun-4 Piasa, Paris #118 est:1500-2000
£9220 $15397 €13000 Le projet du cycle de la vie de Jeanne d'Arc au Pantheon (102x143cm-40x56in) painted c.1886. 17-Jun-3 Christie's, Paris #61/R est:8000-12000
Works on paper
£629 $1083 €900 Vue de la galerie Mollien au Louvre (31x27cm-12x11in) s. W/C black crayon. 8-Dec-3 Piasa, Paris #41

LENFESTEY, Giffard Hocart (1872-1943) British
Works on paper
£420 $752 €613 Noon at the Rectory garden, Langparish (27x37cm-11x15in) s. W/C. 25-May-4 Bonhams, Knightsbridge #41/R

LENG MEI (18th C) Chinese
Works on paper
£11957 $22000 €17457 Family portrait with boating ladies (273x56cm-107x22in) ink on silk. 23-Mar-4 Sotheby's, New York #556/R est:6000-8000

LENGELLE, Paul (20th C) French
Works on paper
£414 $757 €600 Batiment de la marine Francaise faisant route en ligne de file (51x103cm-20x41in) s. gouache. 31-Jan-4 Neret-Minet, Paris #146/R
£517 $947 €750 Caravelles (58x98cm-23x39in) s. gouache. 31-Jan-4 Neret-Minet, Paris #155/R
£709 $1121 €1000 Pointe du raz (50x60cm-20x24in) s.i. gouache. 24-Jul-3 Adjug'art, Brest #243/R

L'ENGLE, Lucy Brown (1889-1978) American
Works on paper
£243 $450 €355 Still life (61x56cm-24x22in) s. W/C. 17-Jul-4 Outer Cape Auctions, Provincetown #15a/R

L'ENGLE, William (1884-1957) American
Works on paper
£324 $550 €473 Wrestlers (25x43cm-10x17in) s. W/C. 9-Nov-3 Outer Cape Auctions, Provincetown #49/R

LENGO Y MARTINEZ, Horacio (1840-1890) Spanish
£946 $1665 €1400 Garden (33x24cm-13x9in) s. board. 18-May-4 Segre, Madrid #46/R
£11333 $20513 €17000 Love (57x46cm-22x18in) s.i. 30-Mar-4 Segre, Madrid #98/R est:10000

LENGYEL-RHEINFUSS, Ede (1873-1942) Hungarian
£594 $1100 €867 The winter march (84x129cm-33x51in) s. 18-Jan-4 Bonhams & Butterfields, Los Angeles #7024/R

LENICA, Alfred (1899-1977) Polish
£777 $1406 €1134 Untitled (38x46cm-15x18in) s.d.1975. 4-Apr-4 Agra, Warsaw #77/R (P.Z 5500)
£828 $1382 €1200 Myth (33x44cm-13x17in) s. s.i.d.1968 verso tempera paper. 16-Nov-3 Agra, Warsaw #31/R
£2825 $5113 €4125 Composition (54x73cm-21x29in) s.d.1968. 4-Apr-4 Agra, Warsaw #64/R (P.Z 20000)
Works on paper
£287 $497 €419 Abstract (29x39cm-11x15in) s. gouache ink. 10-Dec-3 Agra, Warsaw #24/R (P.Z 1900)
£379 $633 €550 Abstract (41x28cm-16x11in) s. gouache exec. 1960's. 16-Nov-3 Agra, Warsaw #82/R
£517 $864 €750 Autoportrait (41x29cm-16x11in) s. chk W/C. 16-Nov-3 Agra, Warsaw #77/R
£565 $1023 €825 Abstract (29x41cm-11x16in) s. gouache. 4-Apr-4 Agra, Warsaw #45/R (P.Z 4000)
£637 $1141 €930 Autumn landscape (39x57cm-15x22in) W/C wash pastel exec.1964. 6-May-4 Agra, Warsaw #37/R (P.Z 4500)

LENK, Franz (1898-1968) German
£2349 $4322 €3500 Bodensee (30x40cm-12x16in) mono.d.1954 oil tempera board. 27-Mar-4 Geble, Radolfzell #737/R est:3500
£2667 $4853 €4000 Italian landscape (46x38cm-18x15in) mono.d.1949 oil tempera cardboard lit. 3-Jul-4 Geble, Radolfzell #407/R est:4000
£4000 $7360 €6000 Landscape (34x57cm-13x22in) s.d.1932 i.verso oil tempera canvas on panel prov.lit. 12-Jun-4 Villa Grisebach, Berlin #245/R est:7000-9000
£4247 $7219 €6200 Bodensee landscape near Friedrichshafen (50x74cm-20x29in) mono.d.1952 oil egg tempera canvas on panel. 8-Nov-3 Geble, Radolfzell #789/R est:6200
Works on paper
£805 $1426 €1200 Swabian landscape (26x42cm-10x17in) s.d. W/C board. 30-Apr-4 Dr Fritz Nagel, Stuttgart #319/R
£1049 $1783 €1500 Bodensee landscape (41x65cm-16x26in) mono.d.1954 W/C brush pen. 29-Nov-3 Villa Grisebach, Berlin #614/R est:1500-2000
£1329 $2259 €1900 Kehlstein against Goll (45x66cm-18x26in) s.d.1939 i. verso W/C Indian ink. 26-Nov-3 Lempertz, Koln #792/R est:2000
£1370 $2329 €2000 Mountain landscape (20x36cm-8x14in) mono.d.1948 W/C lit. 8-Nov-3 Geble, Radolfzell #832/R est:2000
£1370 $2329 €2000 Tree (40x23cm-16x9in) mono.d.1949 mixed media lit. 8-Nov-3 Geble, Radolfzell #833/R est:2000
£1600 $2928 €2400 Leichtenburg with Saale valley (46x65cm-18x26in) s.d.1939 i. verso W/C Indian ink. 5-Jun-4 Lempertz, Koln #826/R est:3000
£1611 $2964 €2400 Bodensee (30x48cm-12x19in) s.d.1933 W/C. 27-Mar-4 Geble, Radolfzell #787/R est:2400

LENKIEWICZ (1941-2002) British/Jewish
£15000 $27750 €21900 Portrait of Myriam Romeg on a brass bed (85x60cm-33x24in) s. 15-Feb-4 Robin Fenner, Tavistock #351/R est:16500-18000

Works on paper

£1500	$2505	€2190	Diogenes with mask and model (28x32cm-11x13in) s. pen ink sketch. 27-Oct-3 Robin Fenner, Tavistock #1146 est:800-1200

LENKIEWICZ, R O (1941-2002) British/Jewish

£2000	$3700	€2920	Portrait of Harry Simons (122x91cm-48x36in) s.i.verso. 15-Feb-4 Robin Fenner, Tavistock #325/R est:2200-2700
£2500	$4525	€3650	Child in need (71x51cm-28x20in) board. 15-Apr-4 Rendalls, Ashburton #2028/R
£3800	$7030	€5548	Painter with Lisa (50x25cm-20x10in) s.i.verso. 11-Feb-4 Sotheby's, Olympia #235/R est:2000-3000
£3800	$7030	€5548	Karen Ciambriello (76x60cm-30x24in) s.i.verso. 15-Feb-4 Robin Fenner, Tavistock #334/R est:4000-6000
£4000	$7400	€5840	Sketch belle pecorini in blue shawl (48x23cm-19x9in) s.i.verso. 15-Feb-4 Robin Fenner, Tavistock #319/R est:4000-5000
£4000	$7240	€5840	Study of Monica (46x36cm-18x14in) board. 15-Apr-4 Rendalls, Ashburton #2037/R
£4000	$6680	€5840	Study of Elaine Armstrong in starry vest (50x24cm-20x9in) s.verso. 27-Oct-3 Robin Fenner, Tavistock #1163/R est:4000-5000
£4250	$7098	€6205	Self portrait with Elaine (41x30cm-16x12in) s.verso board. 27-Oct-3 Robin Fenner, Tavistock #1158/R est:3000-4000
£4500	$8145	€6570	Study of Gemma in red top (25x20cm-10x8in) s. board. 15-Apr-4 Rendalls, Ashburton #2031/R
£5000	$9250	€7300	Candle, cloth and cup, still life (305x280cm-120x110in) s. 15-Feb-4 Robin Fenner, Tavistock #332/R est:5500-6500
£5000	$9250	€7300	French girl in red jacket (48x23cm-19x9in) s. 15-Feb-4 Robin Fenner, Tavistock #321a est:5000-7000
£5000	$8000	€7300	Anna Navas at the house, Lower Compton (48x23cm-19x9in) s.verso. 18-Sep-3 Rendalls, Ashburton #1963
£5000	$9050	€7300	Self portrait (20x15cm-8x6in) s.verso. 15-Apr-4 Rendalls, Ashburton #2047/R
£5200	$9412	€7592	Redhead in lilac dress (48x23cm-19x9in) s. 15-Apr-4 Rendalls, Ashburton #2039/R
£5500	$10175	€8030	Girl in pink (50x23cm-20x9in) s.verso. 15-Feb-4 Robin Fenner, Tavistock #316a est:6000-7000
£6000	$10020	€8760	Study of Lisa Stokes the painter (49x24cm-19x9in) s.verso. 27-Oct-3 Robin Fenner, Tavistock #1164/R est:5000-6000
£6100	$11041	€8906	Painter at easel (25x20cm-10x8in) s.verso. 15-Apr-4 Rendalls, Ashburton #2050/R
£6800	$12308	€9928	Anna with large tea cup (41x28cm-16x11in) s. board. 15-Apr-4 Rendalls, Ashburton #2035/R
£7250	$12108	€10585	Self portrait at easel in private studio 5 (48x48cm-19x19in) s.i.verso. 13-Nov-3 Rendalls, Ashburton #2000
£7500	$12525	€10950	Painter with Jane Rowan (60x53cm-24x21in) s.i.verso. 27-Oct-3 Robin Fenner, Tavistock #1170/R est:8000-12000
£7500	$12525	€10950	Study of Bella in pink (61x61cm-24x24in) s.verso. 27-Oct-3 Robin Fenner, Tavistock #1169/R est:8000-12000
£7750	$12943	€11315	Self portrait in private studio (49x24cm-19x9in) s.verso. 27-Oct-3 Robin Fenner, Tavistock #1165/R est:5000-6000
£7800	$14118	€11388	Study of French girl with scarf (48x23cm-19x9in) s. 15-Apr-4 Rendalls, Ashburton #2036/R
£8200	$14842	€11972	Elaine Armstrong in Indian top (58x58cm-23x23in) s.i.verso. 15-Apr-4 Rendalls, Ashburton #2042/R
£8250	$15263	€12045	Painter with Anna Mendham (57x34cm-22x13in) s.verso board. 15-Feb-4 Robin Fenner, Tavistock #316/R est:6500-7500
£8800	$14696	€12848	Fiorella Ciani with Portugese shawl (58x58cm-23x23in) s.i.verso. 16-Oct-3 Rendalls, Ashburton #1658
£9000	$16650	€13140	Study of the painter with Jay (87x67cm-34x26in) s.verso. 15-Feb-4 Robin Fenner, Tavistock #327/R est:9500-10500
£9500	$15295	€13870	Alisa with a Chinese shawl (91x58cm-36x23in) s. i.verso. 14-Aug-3 Rendalls, Ashburton #1653
£10000	$18100	€14600	Study of vagrant (81x61cm-32x24in) 15-Apr-4 Rendalls, Ashburton #2045/R
£11000	$20350	€16060	Painter with woman (93x120cm-37x47in) s.verso. 15-Feb-4 Robin Fenner, Tavistock #320a est:8000-12000
£14000	$25340	€20440	Self portrait in private studio (48x48cm-19x19in) s.verso. 15-Apr-4 Rendalls, Ashburton #2051/R
£15000	$27750	€21900	Portrait of Karen Ciambriello in brown coat (100x79cm-39x31in) s.verso. 15-Feb-4 Robin Fenner, Tavistock #350/R est:13000-15000
£15000	$25050	€21900	Study of Anna Navas at the Compton studio (127x127cm-50x50in) s.verso. 27-Oct-3 Robin Fenner, Tavistock #1168/R est:16000-20000
£18000	$30060	€26280	Self portrait with Karen Ciambriello (175x155cm-69x61in) s.verso. 27-Oct-3 Robin Fenner, Tavistock #1167/R est:18000-22000
£18500	$30895	€27010	Lisa on floor (57x74cm-22x29in) s.i.verso board. 27-Oct-3 Robin Fenner, Tavistock #1173/R est:23000-26000
£19000	$35150	€27740	Study of Patti Avery (154x91cm-61x36in) s.verso. 15-Feb-4 Robin Fenner, Tavistock #349/R est:20000-30000
£20000	$37000	€29200	Esther in white daemon series (120x92cm-47x36in) s. 15-Feb-4 Robin Fenner, Tavistock #341/R est:15000-20000

Prints

£2400	$4440	€3504	Anna with black shawl (70x34cm-28x13in) s. print. 15-Feb-4 Robin Fenner, Tavistock #188/R est:1500-2000

Works on paper

£400	$720	€584	Retriever. s. pencil. 22-Jan-4 Rendalls, Ashburton #1911
£460	$768	€672	Portrait of a young girl (35x27cm-14x11in) s. pencil sketch. 27-Oct-3 Robin Fenner, Tavistock #1140
£550	$1018	€803	Portrait of a young boy (27x22cm-11x9in) s. pencil. 15-Feb-4 Robin Fenner, Tavistock #177/R
£600	$1110	€876	Flying figure (7x15cm-3x6in) pen ink prov. 15-Feb-4 Robin Fenner, Tavistock #298/R
£800	$1480	€1168	Head studies (36x23cm-14x9in) pencil prov. 15-Feb-4 Robin Fenner, Tavistock #281/R
£900	$1665	€1314	Study of a Elizabethan lady's costume (24x23cm-9x9in) i. Indian ink prov. 15-Feb-4 Robin Fenner, Tavistock #270/R
£900	$1665	€1314	Study of cavalry horse (26x37cm-10x15in) pencil prov. 15-Feb-4 Robin Fenner, Tavistock #296/R
£1000	$1850	€1460	Sketch for running group (28x30cm-11x12in) i. pencil. 15-Feb-4 Robin Fenner, Tavistock #262/R est:1200-1500
£1000	$1850	€1460	Study for dancing figure (32x27cm-13x11in) pencil prov. 15-Feb-4 Robin Fenner, Tavistock #288/R est:1200-1500
£1000	$1850	€1460	Unity of Christmas, Jewish and Muslim religions (24x15cm-9x6in) i. Indian ink prov. 15-Feb-4 Robin Fenner, Tavistock #295/R est:1200-1500
£1200	$2220	€1752	View of Smeaton's Tower on Plymouth Hoe (30x38cm-12x15in) s.d.70 W/C. 15-Feb-4 Robin Fenner, Tavistock #255/R est:1000-1200
£1200	$2220	€1752	Francis Bacon (40x29cm-16x11in) i. pen ink prov. 15-Feb-4 Robin Fenner, Tavistock #263/R est:1500-1800
£1500	$2775	€2190	Terry Goldstone as Simon Forman, Lambeth astrologer (29x22cm-11x9in) pencil prov. 15-Feb-4 Robin Fenner, Tavistock #286/R est:1800-2000
£1600	$2960	€2336	Sketch for Inigo Jones (35x26cm-14x10in) i. pencil prov. 15-Feb-4 Robin Fenner, Tavistock #279/R est:1800-2500
£1600	$2672	€2336	Study of Zenobie (36x26cm-14x10in) s.i. W/C. 27-Oct-3 Robin Fenner, Tavistock #1048a est:1200-1500
£1800	$3330	€2628	Sketch of self (47x26cm-19x10in) s. pencil. 15-Feb-4 Robin Fenner, Tavistock #242/R est:2000-2500
£1800	$3330	€2628	Shakespeare (38x24cm-15x9in) i. Indian ink W/C prov. 15-Feb-4 Robin Fenner, Tavistock #309/R est:2000-2500
£2000	$3620	€2920	Study of boy physically disadvantaged, project 3 (30x30cm-12x12in) s. W/C. 15-Apr-4 Rendalls, Ashburton #2020/R
£2100	$3801	€3066	Study of David Helingre cleaning studio windows (38x30cm-15x12in) W/C gouache. 15-Apr-4 Rendalls, Ashburton #2121/R
£2400	$4440	€3504	Sketch of Raleigh (38x24cm-15x9in) i.verso Indian ink W/C prov. 15-Feb-4 Robin Fenner, Tavistock #308/R est:2000-2500
£2400	$4440	€3504	Early study of mouse (27x23cm-11x9in) s. mixed media on board. 15-Feb-4 Robin Fenner, Tavistock #339/R est:2000-2500
£2400	$4008	€3504	Portrait of Sir Walter Raleigh (20x21cm-8x8in) bears sig pencil. 27-Oct-3 Robin Fenner, Tavistock #1147/R est:2000-2500
£2600	$4810	€3796	Study - Lisa Stokes (38x28cm-15x11in) s. W/C. 15-Feb-4 Robin Fenner, Tavistock #257 est:1500-2000
£2600	$4706	€3796	Esther on the settle (36x28cm-14x11in) s. W/C. 15-Apr-4 Rendalls, Ashburton #2023/R
£2800	$5180	€4088	16th century minstrel (30x19cm-12x7in) s. pen ink W/C gouache. 15-Feb-4 Robin Fenner, Tavistock #252/R est:2000-3000
£2800	$5180	€4088	16th century minstrel (35x20cm-14x8in) s. pen ink W/C gouache. 15-Feb-4 Robin Fenner, Tavistock #256/R est:2000-3000
£3000	$5430	€4380	Study of Diogenes (41x25cm-16x10in) s. W/C. 15-Apr-4 Rendalls, Ashburton #2024/R
£3800	$6346	€5548	Blue candle in the garden (28x40cm-11x16in) s. W/C. 27-Oct-3 Robin Fenner, Tavistock #1141/R est:2500-3000

LENKIEWICZ, Robert O (1941-2002) British/Jewish

£435	$800	€635	Study of young woman seated with an old man seated in background (39x49cm-15x19in) s.d.71. 24-Mar-4 Eldred, East Dennis #93
£707	$1300	€1032	Study of a young woman (56x45cm-22x18in) 24-Mar-4 Eldred, East Dennis #92
£750	$1200	€1095	Seated man (81x61cm-32x24in) s. 18-Sep-3 Sotheby's, Olympia #27/R
£780	$1451	€1139	Tower of Babel (44x38cm-17x15in) i. paper. 2-Mar-4 Bearnes, Exeter #426/R
£950	$1520	€1387	Wally Carter with his son Martin John (121x91cm-48x36in) 18-Sep-3 Sotheby's, Olympia #34/R
£960	$1517	€1402	Portrait of a girl with blue eyes (34x38cm-13x15in) s. 4-Sep-3 Bonhams, Cornwall #473/R
£1000	$1600	€1460	Young man with long dark hair (66x46cm-26x18in) 18-Sep-3 Sotheby's, Olympia #12/R est:1000-1500
£1000	$1600	€1460	Woman with restricted growth syndrome (131x91cm-52x36in) 18-Sep-3 Sotheby's, Olympia #31/R est:1000-1500
£1000	$1670	€1460	Diogenes (51x61cm-20x24in) 14-Oct-3 David Lay, Penzance #553 est:1500-2000
£1200	$1920	€1752	Monca (57x37cm-22x15in) 18-Sep-3 Sotheby's, Olympia #2/R est:2000-3000
£1500	$2400	€2190	Portrait of a bearded man (57x49cm-22x19in) 18-Sep-3 Sotheby's, Olympia #14/R est:800-1200
£1500	$2400	€2190	Transvestite in blonde wig (148x92cm-58x36in) 18-Sep-3 Sotheby's, Olympia #134/R est:1200-1800
£1600	$2560	€2336	Portrait of a man in a green jacket (63x40cm-25x16in) 18-Sep-3 Sotheby's, Olympia #15/R est:2000-3000
£1600	$2560	€2336	Lisa, rear view (51x25cm-20x10in) 18-Sep-3 Sotheby's, Olympia #60/R est:600-800
£1700	$2720	€2482	Mother and her two children (113x127cm-44x50in) 18-Sep-3 Sotheby's, Olympia #29/R est:1200-1800
£1700	$2720	€2482	Portrait of Mr Wilkinson and his son Nicki (113x135cm-44x53in) 18-Sep-3 Sotheby's, Olympia #30/R est:1000-1500
£1700	$2720	€2482	Child with cerebral palsy (122x91cm-48x36in) i. 18-Sep-3 Sotheby's, Olympia #33/R est:800-1200
£1700	$2720	€2482	Family group (90x79cm-35x31in) 18-Sep-3 Sotheby's, Olympia #120/R est:1500-2000
£1800	$2880	€2628	Artist with Meg (64x64cm-25x25in) i.verso. 18-Sep-3 Sotheby's, Olympia #91/R est:1500-2000
£1850	$3386	€2701	Girl in an orange dress lying on a couch (69x100cm-27x39in) board. 3-Jun-4 Lane, Penzance #318 est:2000-3000
£1900	$3040	€2774	Mark with dreadlocks (61x76cm-24x30in) 18-Sep-3 Sotheby's, Olympia #127/R est:800-1200
£1900	$3040	€2774	Nuka Wondrausch in purple sweater (122x91cm-48x36in) 18-Sep-3 Sotheby's, Olympia #131/R est:800-1200
£2200	$3520	€3212	Jonathan, known as flower pot (52x39cm-20x15in) s.i. canvas on board. 18-Sep-3 Sotheby's, Olympia #13/R est:800-1200
£2200	$3520	€3212	Pregnant woman reclining (127x124cm-50x49in) 18-Sep-3 Sotheby's, Olympia #58/R est:2000-3000
£2200	$3520	€3212	Skinhead in Union Jack (160x81cm-63x32in) 18-Sep-3 Sotheby's, Olympia #118/R est:1500-2000
£2200	$3520	€3212	Ian and Devon (137x79cm-54x31in) 18-Sep-3 Sotheby's, Olympia #135/R est:800-1200
£2200	$3520	€3212	Mark with dreadlocks looking sideways (76x61cm-30x24in) 18-Sep-3 Sotheby's, Olympia #128/R est:600-800
£2400	$3840	€3504	Study of Monca Quirk (55x53cm-22x21in) s.d.68/74 i.verso board. 18-Sep-3 Sotheby's, Olympia #3/R est:1200-1800
£2400	$3840	€3504	Portrait of Sharon Leslie Rogers (88x28cm-35x11in) d.22 September 1965 board exhib. 18-Sep-3 Sotheby's, Olympia #17/R est:2000-3000
£2400	$3840	€3504	Belle seated (31x27cm-12x11in) board. 18-Sep-3 Sotheby's, Olympia #47/R est:1000-1500
£2400	$3840	€3504	Esther sucking her thumb (61x61cm-24x24in) board. 18-Sep-3 Sotheby's, Olympia #66/R est:700-1000
£2400	$3840	€3504	Punk seated, fragment from the fight (127x80cm-50x31in) 18-Sep-3 Sotheby's, Olympia #117/R est:1000-1500
£2400	$3840	€3504	Nahen Shoa (121x121cm-48x48in) i. 18-Sep-3 Sotheby's, Olympia #138/R est:800-1200
£2400	$3840	€3504	Terry Waite (137x137cm-54x54in) 18-Sep-3 Sotheby's, Olympia #140/R est:2000-3000
£2400	$4008	€3504	Study of Ailsa (61x51cm-24x20in) s. board. 14-Oct-3 David Lay, Penzance #554 est:1500-2000
£2600	$4160	€3796	Study of Belle Pecorini in the kitchen, Priory Road (27x22cm-11x9in) s.i. board. 18-Sep-3 Sotheby's, Olympia #46/R est:800-1200
£2600	$4160	€3796	Painter with Lisa (41x30cm-16x12in) 18-Sep-3 Sotheby's, Olympia #87/R est:700-1000

£2600	$4160	€3796	Prefect from the fight (193x81cm-76x32in) 18-Sep-3 Sotheby's, Olympia #113/R est:3000-5000
£2600	$4160	€3796	Group of druids (227x171cm-89x67in) 18-Sep-3 Sotheby's, Olympia #136/R est:2000-3000
£2600	$4160	€3796	Self portrait as a teenager (174x99cm-69x39in) 18-Sep-3 Sotheby's, Olympia #147/R est:1500-2000
£2600	$4160	€3796	Painter's son, Wolfe, with girl (125x96cm-49x38in) 18-Sep-3 Sotheby's, Olympia #152/R est:800-1200
£2800	$4480	€4088	Monca Quirk, just out of the asylum (65x46cm-26x18in) s.i.verso board. 18-Sep-3 Sotheby's, Olympia #4/R est:2500-3500
£2800	$4480	€4088	Mr Sam Decent, sailor (61x49cm-24x19in) 18-Sep-3 Sotheby's, Olympia #10/R est:2000-3000
£2800	$4480	€4088	Study of Kevin Gasson (101x101cm-40x40in) s.i.d.1985. 18-Sep-3 Sotheby's, Olympia #32/R est:3000-5000
£2800	$4480	€4088	Esther with legs folded (79x105cm-31x41in) 18-Sep-3 Sotheby's, Olympia #67/R est:800-1200
£2800	$4480	€4088	Gipsy woman (51x42cm-20x17in) s.i.d.1974/5 verso s.stretcher. 18-Sep-3 Sotheby's, Olympia #112/R est:2000-3000
£2800	$4480	€4088	Young actor in blue (122x91cm-48x36in) 18-Sep-3 Sotheby's, Olympia #130/R est:800-1200
£2800	$4480	€4088	Paul Abbot, head and shoulders (30x40cm-12x16in) 18-Sep-3 Sotheby's, Olympia #137/R est:800-1200
£2800	$4480	€4088	Self portrait, aged 18 (19x19cm-7x7in) board. 18-Sep-3 Sotheby's, Olympia #146/R est:1500-2000
£2800	$4480	€4088	Self portrait at foot of stairs (151x91cm-59x36in) s.i. 18-Sep-3 Sotheby's, Olympia #148/R est:3000-5000
£2800	$4480	€4088	Life class (102x102cm-40x40in) card. 18-Sep-3 Sotheby's, Olympia #151/R est:1000-1500
£3000	$4800	€4380	Mary kneeling (124x80cm-49x31in) s. 18-Sep-3 Sotheby's, Olympia #41/R est:3000-5000
£3000	$4800	€4380	Joanne (122x93cm-48x37in) 18-Sep-3 Sotheby's, Olympia #73/R est:1200-1800
£3000	$4800	€4380	Painter with woman (40x33cm-16x13in) 18-Sep-3 Sotheby's, Olympia #93/R est:800-1200
£3000	$5460	€4380	Self portrait breast feeding (61x41cm-24x16in) board. 15-Jun-4 Bonhams, Knightsbridge #221/R est:3000-5000
£3200	$5120	€4672	Painter with Yana (78x62cm-31x24in) 18-Sep-3 Sotheby's, Olympia #48/R est:1200-1800
£3200	$5120	€4672	Portrait of Yana (86x42cm-34x17in) board. 18-Sep-3 Sotheby's, Olympia #49/R est:2000-3000
£3200	$5120	€4672	Painter with Ria Ney Hoch (145x90cm-57x35in) s.i.d.88. 18-Sep-3 Sotheby's, Olympia #56/R est:2000-3000
£3200	$5120	€4672	Painter with Julie (122x95cm-48x37in) s.i.d.88 i.verso. 18-Sep-3 Sotheby's, Olympia #92/R est:2000-3000
£3200	$5120	€4672	Painter with Monca (131x94cm-52x37in) s. i.verso. 18-Sep-3 Sotheby's, Olympia #96/R est:2000-3000
£3200	$5120	€4672	Man and woman (38x38cm-15x15in) s. oil paper on board. 18-Sep-3 Sotheby's, Olympia #103/R est:300-500
£3200	$5120	€4672	Across Trefusis valley from painter's house (77x117cm-30x46in) s.i.d.1968 i.verso board. 18-Sep-3 Sotheby's, Olympia #104/R est:1500-2000
£3200	$5120	€4672	Two punks (40x79cm-16x31in) 18-Sep-3 Sotheby's, Olympia #115/R est:500-700
£3200	$5120	€4672	Two girls (30x51cm-12x20in) 18-Sep-3 Sotheby's, Olympia #116/R est:400-600
£3200	$5120	€4672	Nathan Bolt (121x121cm-48x48in) 18-Sep-3 Sotheby's, Olympia #125/R est:3000-5000
£3200	$5120	€4672	Toby in straw had (122x122cm-48x48in) 18-Sep-3 Sotheby's, Olympia #139/R est:1500-2000
£3200	$5120	€4672	Wolfe painting at an easel (101x76cm-40x30in) 18-Sep-3 Sotheby's, Olympia #153/R est:3000-5000
£3200	$5920	€4672	Painter with Jenny Gitson (76x33cm-30x13in) s.i. verso. 11-Feb-4 Sotheby's, Olympia #240/R est:1500-2000
£3400	$5440	€4964	Annie with Rembrant as Father Christmas peering through the window (33x43cm-13x17in) s.i.verso board. 18-Sep-3 Sotheby's, Olympia #18/R est:2500-3500
£3400	$5440	€4964	Painter with Mary (107x87cm-42x34in) board. 18-Sep-3 Sotheby's, Olympia #100/R est:1000-1500
£3400	$5440	€4964	Chef and owner of Pilgrims' Rest Cafe (45x42cm-18x17in) s.i. board. 18-Sep-3 Sotheby's, Olympia #111/R est:1500-2000
£3400	$5440	€4964	Charles in leather and chains (122x122cm-48x48in) 18-Sep-3 Sotheby's, Olympia #129/R est:2000-3000
£3400	$5678	€4964	Portrait of a girl (130x66cm-51x26in) s. 14-Oct-3 David Lay, Penzance #552/R est:4000-5000
£3400	$5678	€4964	Portrait of a gentleman (76x58cm-30x23in) s. 16-Oct-3 Rendalls, Ashburton #1651 est:3000-4000
£3500	$5600	€5110	Michael Rhodes with saxophone (115x87cm-45x34in) 18-Sep-3 Sotheby's, Olympia #132/R est:2000-3000
£3600	$5760	€5256	Mary, naked with sheet (121x91cm-48x36in) 18-Sep-3 Sotheby's, Olympia #42/R est:3000-5000
£3600	$5760	€5256	Patti Avery in orange dress (69x102cm-27x40in) board. 18-Sep-3 Sotheby's, Olympia #52/R est:2000-3000
£3600	$5760	€5256	Ria as Janus (138x60cm-54x24in) 18-Sep-3 Sotheby's, Olympia #55/R est:2500-3500
£3600	$5760	€5256	Painter with Amelie (61x76cm-24x30in) 18-Sep-3 Sotheby's, Olympia #80/R est:2000-3000
£3600	$5760	€5256	Girl with pink ribbon (60x60cm-24x24in) board. 18-Sep-3 Sotheby's, Olympia #121/R est:1000-1500
£3600	$6120	€5256	Vagrants (51x76cm-20x30in) s. 26-Nov-3 Sotheby's, Olympia #100/R est:3000-5000
£3800	$6080	€5548	Painter with Bianca (183x157cm-72x62in) 18-Sep-3 Sotheby's, Olympia #81/R est:3000-5000
£3800	$6080	€5548	Painter with Lisa (91x91cm-36x36in) 18-Sep-3 Sotheby's, Olympia #88/R est:1500-2000
£3800	$6080	€5548	Reclining woman (76x128cm-30x50in) 18-Sep-3 Sotheby's, Olympia #90/R est:1500-2000
£3800	$6080	€5548	Painter with naked woman (60x50cm-24x20in) s.i. board. 18-Sep-3 Sotheby's, Olympia #94/R est:800-1200
£3800	$6080	€5548	Self portrait (32x16cm-13x6in) board. 18-Sep-3 Sotheby's, Olympia #145/R est:1000-1500
£3800	$7030	€5548	Go away, nearer (139x82cm-55x32in) s.i.verso sold with four photos prov. 11-Feb-4 Sotheby's, Olympia #238/R est:3000-5000
£4000	$6400	€5840	Self portrait as a young man (59x48cm-23x19in) s.d.1958 Sept board. 18-Sep-3 Sotheby's, Olympia #1/R est:4000-6000
£4000	$6400	€5840	Louise Courtnell (121x121cm-48x48in) 18-Sep-3 Sotheby's, Olympia #83/R est:1000-1500
£4000	$6400	€5840	Graveyard (74x95cm-29x37in) s.verso board. 18-Sep-3 Sotheby's, Olympia #105/R est:2000-3000
£4200	$6720	€6132	Man in flying jacket (74x60cm-29x24in) s. board exhib. 18-Sep-3 Sotheby's, Olympia #28/R est:3000-5000
£4200	$6720	€6132	Myriam in red poncho seated on the floor (79x58cm-31x23in) s. board. 18-Sep-3 Sotheby's, Olympia #50/R est:3000-5000
£4200	$6720	€6132	Rachel in red (51x25cm-20x10in) 18-Sep-3 Sotheby's, Olympia #61/R est:600-800
£4200	$6720	€6132	Lady with long red hair (61x61cm-24x24in) 18-Sep-3 Sotheby's, Olympia #84/R est:1200-1800
£4200	$6720	€6132	Woman and ghost (74x25cm-29x10in) board. 18-Sep-3 Sotheby's, Olympia #102/R est:2000-3000
£4200	$6720	€6132	Scott Dann (122x122cm-48x48in) 18-Sep-3 Sotheby's, Olympia #122/R est:1000-1500
£4200	$6720	€6132	Ben and rat (121x91cm-48x36in) 18-Sep-3 Sotheby's, Olympia #124/R est:2000-3000
£4400	$7040	€6424	Danielle with pink and purple scarf (91x61cm-36x24in) indis.i. 18-Sep-3 Sotheby's, Olympia #85/R est:1200-1800
£4500	$7200	€6570	The Bishop at St Andrew's Cross (102x75cm-40x30in) s. 18-Sep-3 Sotheby's, Olympia #23/R est:4000-6000
£4500	$7200	€6570	Patti Avery in blue dress (142x76cm-56x30in) 18-Sep-3 Sotheby's, Olympia #53/R est:3000-5000
£4500	$7200	€6570	Portrait of Lisa (61x61cm-24x24in) 18-Sep-3 Sotheby's, Olympia #64/R est:800-1200
£4500	$7200	€6570	Esther in brown skirt (183x121cm-72x48in) 18-Sep-3 Sotheby's, Olympia #78/R est:1500-2500
£4500	$7200	€6570	Girl with doll (91x61cm-36x24in) i. 18-Sep-3 Sotheby's, Olympia #86/R est:1200-1800
£4500	$7200	€6570	Painter with Jackie (61x31cm-24x12in) 18-Sep-3 Sotheby's, Olympia #89/R est:2500-3500
£4500	$7200	€6570	Painter with Eliza (61x101cm-24x40in) s.i.verso. 18-Sep-3 Sotheby's, Olympia #95/R est:4000-6000
£4500	$7200	€6570	Fishermen on the Barbican (141x214cm-56x84in) 18-Sep-3 Sotheby's, Olympia #108/R est:4000-6000
£4500	$7785	€6570	Study of a girl with blonde hair (48x22cm-19x9in) s.i.verso. 11-Dec-3 Lane, Penzance #25/R est:5000-6000
£4800	$7680	€7008	Lisa in blue dress (162x51cm-64x20in) 18-Sep-3 Sotheby's, Olympia #63/R est:2000-3000
£4800	$7680	€7008	Lisa in blue, seated (122x91cm-48x36in) 18-Sep-3 Sotheby's, Olympia #65/R est:2500-3500
£4800	$8880	€7008	Painter with Esther Dallaway (76x33cm-30x13in) s.i. verso. 11-Feb-4 Sotheby's, Olympia #239/R est:2000-3000
£5000	$8000	€7300	Vagrants in the street lights. s. 18-Sep-3 Sotheby's, Olympia #22/R est:2000-3000
£5000	$8000	€7300	Elaine reclining (91x122cm-36x48in) 18-Sep-3 Sotheby's, Olympia #69/R est:1000-1500
£5000	$8000	€7300	Frederick Hutchings, oldest practising fisherman on the Barbican (31x40cm-12x16in) s.d.1979 i.verso. 18-Sep-3 Sotheby's, Olympia #110/R est:2000-3000
£5000	$8000	€7300	Union Jack skinhead (71x66cm-28x26in) 18-Sep-3 Sotheby's, Olympia #114/R est:700-1000
£5000	$8000	€7300	Painter with Monca and Reuben (157x161cm-62x63in) 18-Sep-3 Sotheby's, Olympia #149/R est:6000-8000
£5000	$8300	€7300	Painter with Billy (40x33cm-16x13in) 2-Oct-3 Lane, Penzance #380 est:5000-6000
£5500	$8800	€8030	Study, painter with Ria Ney Hoch (37x32cm-15x13in) s.i. 18-Sep-3 Sotheby's, Olympia #57/R est:3000-5000
£6000	$9600	€8760	Myriam in red dress (86x60cm-34x24in) s. panel. 18-Sep-3 Sotheby's, Olympia #51/R est:5000-7000
£6000	$9600	€8760	Anna (152x152cm-60x60in) 18-Sep-3 Sotheby's, Olympia #79/R est:2000-3000
£6000	$9600	€8760	Punk family (170x120cm-67x47in) hessian. 18-Sep-3 Sotheby's, Olympia #119/R est:3000-5000
£6000	$9600	€8760	Desmond Horton (122x122cm-48x48in) 18-Sep-3 Sotheby's, Olympia #123/R est:2000-3000
£6000	$9960	€8760	Red haired girl with blue cap (48x22cm-19x9in) s.i.verso. 2-Oct-3 Lane, Penzance #45/R est:4000-5000
£6500	$10400	€9490	Lelya, seated in a Windsor chair (101x76cm-40x30in) 18-Sep-3 Sotheby's, Olympia #16/R est:3000-5000
£6500	$10400	€9490	Romney in a green coat (91x61cm-36x24in) 18-Sep-3 Sotheby's, Olympia #75/R est:2000-3000
£7000	$12740	€10220	The painter with Lucy Walsh (100x103cm-39x41in) s.i. 15-Jun-4 Bonhams, New Bond Street #129/R est:7000-10000
£7400	$11840	€10804	Painter with Lucinda (45x30cm-18x12in) board. 18-Sep-3 Sotheby's, Olympia #74/R est:2500-3500
£7500	$12000	€10950	Painter with Elaine and the devil (122x76cm-48x30in) 18-Sep-3 Sotheby's, Olympia #70/R est:1500-2000
£7500	$12000	€10950	Painter with Greenie (132x94cm-52x37in) 18-Sep-3 Sotheby's, Olympia #72/R est:1500-2000
£7500	$12000	€10950	Gemma in purple (91x76cm-36x30in) 18-Sep-3 Sotheby's, Olympia #76/R est:2000-3000
£7500	$12000	€10950	Karen reclining (121x121cm-48x48in) 18-Sep-3 Sotheby's, Olympia #97/R est:1500-2000
£8000	$12800	€11680	Group at Eton Avenue Studio (219x287cm-86x113in) painted c.1960 lit. 18-Sep-3 Sotheby's, Olympia #8/R est:10000-15000
£8000	$12800	€11680	Reclining female nude (83x150cm-33x59in) 18-Sep-3 Sotheby's, Olympia #71/R est:3000-5000
£8000	$12800	€11680	Portrait of Ali (102x76cm-40x30in) 18-Sep-3 Sotheby's, Olympia #82/R est:2000-3000
£8000	$12800	€11680	Billy Connolly (51x51cm-20x20in) 18-Sep-3 Sotheby's, Olympia #141/R est:3000-5000
£8000	$14080	€11680	Self portrait with Yana (94x131cm-37x52in) s. i.verso. 19-May-4 Sotheby's, Olympia #258/R est:8000-12000
£8200	$15006	€11972	Anna navas reading - Lower Compton Studio (58x58cm-23x23in) s.i. verso. 6-Jul-4 Bearnes, Exeter #504/R est:8000-10000
£8500	$13600	€12410	Charlotte seated (51x25cm-20x10in) 18-Sep-3 Sotheby's, Olympia #62/R est:1000-1500
£8500	$13600	€12410	Karen, Thais and Khaya reclining (122x122cm-48x48in) 18-Sep-3 Sotheby's, Olympia #14/R est:2000-3000
£9000	$14400	€13140	Painter with Patti Avery (156x124cm-61x49in) 18-Sep-3 Sotheby's, Olympia #54/R est:10000-15000
£9000	$14400	€13140	Jack the burglar in checked shirt (121x91cm-48x36in) 18-Sep-3 Sotheby's, Olympia #133/R est:10000-15000
£9500	$15200	€13870	Study of Karen Cambriello, pregnant with Thais (212x127cm-83x50in) s.i.verso. 18-Sep-3 Sotheby's, Olympia #144/R est:8000-12000
£10000	$16000	€14600	Richard with Bentwood chair (152x122cm-60x48in) 18-Sep-3 Sotheby's, Olympia #126/R est:6000-8000
£11000	$17600	€16060	Cider Ryder, pram factory (97x145cm-38x57in) s.i.verso. 18-Sep-3 Sotheby's, Olympia #24/R est:6000-8000
£11000	$17600	€16060	Painter with Esther (152x122cm-60x48in) 18-Sep-3 Sotheby's, Olympia #68/R est:6000-8000
£11000	$17600	€16060	Markie (122x122cm-48x48in) 18-Sep-3 Sotheby's, Olympia #107/R est:2500-3500
£11000	$17600	€16060	Painter and the dead painter (55x40cm-22x16in) s.i.verso board exhib. 18-Sep-3 Sotheby's, Olympia #154/R est:3000-5000
£12000	$19200	€17520	Portrait of Jeny Lelya Bremer (121x90cm-48x35in) s. 18-Sep-3 Sotheby's, Olympia #11/R est:5000-7000

£13000 $20800 €18980 Rachel in red (92x92cm-36x36in) 18-Sep-3 Sotheby's, Olympia #77/R est:3000-5000
£15000 $24000 €21900 Painter with Wolfe and Reuben (145x98cm-57x39in) exhib. 18-Sep-3 Sotheby's, Olympia #150/R est:6000-8000
£18000 $33300 €26280 Painter with Anna Navas (127x75cm-50x30in) s. i.verso. 11-Feb-4 Sotheby's, Olympia #237/R est:6000-8000
£22000 $35200 €32120 The Bishop and the painter dancing to Mahler (218x300cm-86x118in) i.verso oil sail cloth. 18-Sep-3 Sotheby's, Olympia #26/R est:10000-15000
£24000 $38400 €35040 Self portrait (61x61cm-24x24in) 18-Sep-3 Sotheby's, Olympia #155/R est:2500-3500

Works on paper
£280 $510 €409 Portrait of Rachel (38x28cm-15x11in) s. pencil chk. 15-Jun-4 Bonhams, Knightsbridge #206
£340 $612 €496 Study of Marnie Doble (37x29cm-15x11in) s. pencil. 23-Apr-4 Charterhouse, Sherborne #679/R
£500 $850 €730 Portrait of Janet Tregale (32x22cm-13x9in) s. pencil exhib.1973. 18-Nov-3 Bearnes, Exeter #568
£700 $1120 €1022 Mouse and baby (25x25cm-10x10in) pen ink sold with another similar. 18-Sep-3 Sotheby's, Olympia #6/R
£850 $1360 €1241 Yana Bernadette Travail (31x21cm-12x8in) ink W/C. 18-Sep-3 Sotheby's, Olympia #39/R
£1100 $1837 €1606 Sixteenth century minstrels (35x20cm-14x8in) s. pen ink W/C gouache pair. 24-Jun-3 Bonhams, Chester #850 est:200-300
£1200 $1920 €1752 Diogene's bed (33x101cm-13x40in) i. pencil two in one frame. 18-Sep-3 Sotheby's, Olympia #20/R est:400-600
£1300 $2080 €1898 Mouse reading. Mouse playing cards (23x27cm-9x11in) pen ink two in one frame. 18-Sep-3 Sotheby's, Olympia #5/R est:300-500
£1400 $2240 €2044 Harmonica Jim and Diogenes (40x25cm-16x10in) pencil. 18-Sep-3 Sotheby's, Olympia #19/R est:400-600
£1600 $2560 €2336 Death stares himself out as he waits for signs of fidelity (13x30cm-5x12in) i. pen ink. 18-Sep-3 Sotheby's, Olympia #35/R est:300-500
£1700 $2720 €2482 Vagrant in a floppy hat (30x23cm-12x9in) pencil. 18-Sep-3 Sotheby's, Olympia #21/R est:400-600
£1800 $2880 €2628 Study, Karen Ciambriello (35x21cm-14x8in) s.i. ink gouache W/C. 18-Sep-3 Sotheby's, Olympia #38/R est:400-600
£2000 $3200 €2920 Come in, I can't be threatened by shadows in the dark (28x19cm-11x7in) i. W/C gouache. 18-Sep-3 Sotheby's, Olympia #36/R est:600-800
£2200 $3520 €3212 Circus horses (74x109cm-29x43in) s. ink W/C gouache. 18-Sep-3 Sotheby's, Olympia #7/R est:600-800
£2600 $4160 €3796 Blue and black figures (53x68cm-21x27in) i. mixed media exhib. 18-Sep-3 Sotheby's, Olympia #43/R est:300-500
£2800 $4480 €4088 Patti Avery (36x32cm-14x13in) ink gouache W/C. 18-Sep-3 Sotheby's, Olympia #37/R est:500-700
£2800 $4480 €4088 Barbican fishermen (38x46cm-15x18in) W/C gouache. 18-Sep-3 Sotheby's, Olympia #109/R est:700-1000
£3000 $4800 €4380 Gender reversal (48x39cm-19x15in) ink W/C gouache. 18-Sep-3 Sotheby's, Olympia #101/R est:500-700
£3500 $6475 €5110 Diogenes as death and the maiden (35x27cm-14x11in) s. ink W/C gouache. 11-Feb-4 Sotheby's, Olympia #236/R est:800-1200
£3600 $5760 €5256 Painter with Mary (41x55cm-16x22in) i. mixed media exhib. 18-Sep-3 Sotheby's, Olympia #45/R est:600-800
£4000 $6400 €5840 Study, Karen Ciambriello (33x27cm-13x11in) s.i. ink gouache W/C. 18-Sep-3 Sotheby's, Olympia #40/R est:600-800
£4500 $7200 €6570 Lovers' meeting (42x55cm-17x22in) i. mixed media exhib.lit. 18-Sep-3 Sotheby's, Olympia #44/R est:300-500

LENKIEWICZ, Robert O (attrib) (1941-2002) British/Jewish
£900 $1665 €1314 Portrait of a bearded gentleman (36x29cm-14x11in) acrylic paper on board. 15-Feb-4 Robin Fenner, Tavistock #318/R
£3000 $5010 €4380 Portrait of a seated woman (66x61cm-26x24in) canvas on board. 16-Oct-3 Rendalls, Ashburton #1652
£4750 $7933 €6935 Portrait of Holly and Gemma (63x76cm-25x30in) panel. 27-Oct-3 Robin Fenner, Tavistock #1157/R est:5000-6000
£5750 $9603 €8395 Charles in leather and chains (122x122cm-48x48in) 27-Oct-3 Robin Fenner, Tavistock #1160 est:5000-7000

Works on paper
£800 $1512 €1168 Young girl (38x28cm-15x11in) pencil. 19-Feb-4 Rendalls, Ashburton #1596

LENNON, Bernard (20th C) American
£272 $500 €397 Stonington boats (18x28cm-7x11in) s. s.i.verso masonite. 25-Jun-4 Freeman, Philadelphia #231/R

LENNON, David (20th C) British?
£250 $458 €365 Still life (40x43cm-16x17in) s. board. 2-Jun-4 John Ross, Belfast #177
£350 $641 €511 Still life, tulips (48x40cm-19x16in) s. board. 2-Jun-4 John Ross, Belfast #52
£380 $654 €555 At Ballymacormack Point (25x30cm-10x12in) mono.d.96 verso board. 3-Dec-3 John Ross, Belfast #142

LENNON, John (1940-1980) British
Sculpture
£1087 $1750 €1587 Neon cat (25x39cm-10x15in) s. neon two dimensional. 20-Aug-3 Dunbar Sloane, Auckland #121/R est:3000-4000 (NZ.D 3000)

LENNON, Paddy (1955-) Irish
£387 $678 €550 Beach (14x23cm-6x9in) s. board. 16-Dec-3 James Adam, Dublin #113/R

Works on paper
£855 $1574 €1300 Female nude study (107x76cm-42x30in) s. chl. 22-Jun-4 De Veres Art Auctions, Dublin #130/R
£1053 $1937 €1600 Study of a horse's head (79x55cm-31x22in) s. chl. 22-Jun-4 De Veres Art Auctions, Dublin #118/R est:1400-1800

LENOIR, Charles Amable (1861-1940) French
£2139 $4000 €3123 Woman with dove (41x20cm-16x8in) s. panel. 25-Feb-4 Doyle, New York #35/R est:4000-6000
£8380 $15000 €12570 Morning swim (132x71cm-52x28in) s. 16-May-4 Abell, Los Angeles #461/R
£12941 $22000 €18894 Spinner by the sea (116x73cm-46x29in) s. 28-Oct-3 Sotheby's, New York #41/R est:30000-40000
£25000 $45000 €36500 Reve d'Orient (57x76cm-22x30in) s.d.1912. 22-Apr-4 Christie's, Rockefeller NY #127/R est:40000-60000

LENOIR, Simon Bernard (1729-1791) French
Works on paper
£906 $1604 €1350 Portrait de jeune femme en robe bleue, de profil (57x46cm-22x18in) i.d.1762 pastel. 29-Apr-4 David Kahn, Paris #171
£2000 $3680 €3000 Portrait presume de Francoise Beguyer (64x53cm-25x21in) s.d.1783 pastel. 11-Jun-4 Maigret, Paris #27/R est:2000-2500
£2781 $5090 €4200 Portrait d'homme a la cravatte de dentelle (52x44cm-20x17in) pastel oval. 7-Apr-4 Libert, Castor, Paris #35/R est:2000-3000
£3667 $6747 €5500 Portrait presume de Louis de Brillemont. Portrait presume de Anne Marie Beguyer (64x53cm-25x21in) s.d.1783 pastel pair. 11-Jun-4 Maigret, Paris #26/R est:5000-7000

LENORDEZ, Pierre (19th C) French
Sculpture
£1027 $1747 €1500 Two jockeys (23cm-9in) s. pat.bronze gilt. 5-Nov-3 Hugo Ruef, Munich #2161/R est:1200
£1067 $1941 €1600 Gallop (22x36cm-9x14in) s. pat bronze. 29-Jun-4 Gioffredo, Nice #83/R
£1888 $3153 €2700 Cheval de course monte au galop (34x50cm-13x20in) s. brown pat bronze. 13-Oct-3 Horta, Bruxelles #138 est:3000-4000
£1947 $3445 €2900 Trois chevaux (24x41x12cm-9x16x5in) s. pat bronze. 30-Apr-4 Tajan, Paris #32/R est:3000-5000
£2039 $3691 €3100 Jument et son poulain (22x38cm-9x15in) s. brown pat bronze. 19-Apr-4 Horta, Bruxelles #126 est:1500-2000
£3000 $4740 €4350 Best of friends (38x23cm-15x9in) s. bronze exec.c.1850-1870. 27-Jul-3 Desmond Judd, Cranbrook #534
£3333 $5233 €4800 Fitz gladiator (21x30x9cm-8x12x4in) s.i. pat bronze. 29-Aug-3 Deauville, France #201 est:6000-8000
£4000 $7320 €5840 Seconde Croisade (33x36cm-13x14in) s.i. pat bronze. 9-Jul-4 Sotheby's, London #132/R est:4000-6000
£8500 $14450 €12410 Angelo (40x48cm-16x19in) s. pat bronze. 28-Oct-3 Sotheby's, London #127/R

LENS, Andries (1739-1822) Flemish
£2778 $4639 €4000 Flore et Cupidon (103x89cm-41x35in) s.d.1783. 21-Oct-3 Galerie Moderne, Brussels #363

LENS, Bernard (17/18th C) British
Miniatures
£865 $1600 €1263 Portrait of a gentleman (8x3cm-3x1in) exec.c.1710-20 oval. 12-Mar-4 Du Mouchelle, Detroit #2052/R est:1000-2000

LENS, Bernard III (1682-1740) British
Miniatures
£4800 $8640 €7008 John Wooton (8cm-3in) mono. i.verso wood frame oval exhib.lit. 22-Apr-4 Bonhams, New Bond Street #23/R est:2500-3500

LENS, Bob (1939-) Dutch
£699 $1203 €1000 Route 8 in Alexander Street in The Hague (34x45cm-13x18in) s.d.1975. 8-Dec-3 Glerum, Amsterdam #157/R

LENSON, Michael (1903-1971) American
£323 $600 €472 Surrealist landscape (45x60cm-18x24in) s. canvasboard. 5-Mar-4 Skinner, Boston #611/R
£2654 $4750 €3875 Kite fliers (61x41cm-24x16in) s. i.verso masonite. 16-May-4 Wright, Chicago #144/R est:4000-6000

LENT, Harlan Luther (attrib) (?) American?
£1836 $3250 €2681 Two children in a landscape (69x86cm-27x34in) init. 27-Apr-4 Doyle, New York #17/R est:2500-3500

LENTEMAN, Hans (20th C) Dutch
£329 $550 €480 Floral still life. s. 18-Oct-3 Harvey Clar, Oakland #1193

LENTREIN, Charlotte (19th C) ?
£570 $1021 €850 Eplucheuse de pommes de terre et son enfant (24x29cm-9x11in) s.d.1874 panel. 25-May-4 Campo & Campo, Antwerp #148/R

LENTREIN, Jules (1875-1943) Belgian
£753 $1281 €1100 Barques au coucher de soleil (28x36cm-11x14in) s. cardboard. 10-Nov-3 Horta, Bruxelles #402

Works on paper
£699 $1168 €1000 Elegante se mirant. Composition (48x63cm-19x25in) s. mixed media pair. 13-Oct-3 Horta, Bruxelles #264
£800 $1448 €1200 Vases de fleurs sur une table (49x62cm-19x24in) s. W/C. 30-Mar-4 Palais de Beaux Arts, Brussels #640

LENZ, Maximilien (1860-1948) Austrian
£2797 $4755 €4000 Way through, Lunz on the Lake (91x101cm-36x40in) s.d.1920 i.verso. 28-Nov-3 Wiener Kunst Auktionen, Vienna #466/R est:4000-7000

LEO, Mario de (1944-) Italian

Works on paper

£342	$582	€500	Maze (36x71cm-14x28in) s.verso mixed media board. 7-Nov-3 Galleria Rosenberg, Milan #144/R

LEON (?) ?

£7905	$14150	€11541	Palazzo Pitti, with famous artists throughout the ages (81x109cm-32x43in) mono. painted c.1890 prov. 15-May-4 Christie's, Sydney #232/R est:18000-25000 (A.D 20000)

Works on paper

£37762	$64196	€54000	Oriental dancer (62x44cm-24x17in) s. W/C brush over pencil ochre prov. 26-Nov-3 Lempertz, Koln #558/R est:20000-25000

LEON Y ESCOSURA, Ignacio de (1834-1901) Spanish

£2748	$4480	€4012	View of stable (27x29cm-11x11in) s.d.1879 board. 17-Jul-3 Naón & Cia, Buenos Aires #21/R
£3472	$5660	€5000	Music lesson (18x12cm-7x5in) s. board. 23-Sep-3 Durán, Madrid #198/R est:3250
£6711	$12013	€10000	Mosquetaire with hound (40x30cm-16x12in) s.d.1887. 25-May-4 Durán, Madrid #199/R est:10000
£7821	$14000	€11419	Bird man (46x36cm-18x14in) s. panel. 20-Mar-4 Selkirks, St. Louis #527/R est:15000-20000
£10500	$19110	€15330	Card party (31x40cm-12x16in) s.d.1868 panel. 16-Jun-4 Christie's, Kensington #149/R est:5000-8000
£19606	$33330	€28625	Studio of Velasquez (296x237cm-117x93in) s.d.1869 prov. 28-Oct-3 Sotheby's, New York #91/R est:50000-70000
£28523	$51057	€42500	Velazquez' study (307x236cm-121x93in) s.d.1869 prov. 25-May-4 Durán, Madrid #216/R est:42500

LEON, Carlos (1948-) Spanish

£280	$467	€400	Untitled (70x91cm-28x36in) s.d.1990 card. 24-Jun-3 Segre, Madrid #158/R
£336	$561	€480	Untitled (70x100cm-28x39in) s.d.1991 card. 24-Jun-3 Segre, Madrid #157/R

LEON, Ernesto (1956-) Venezuelan

£459	$720	€670	Still life (61x66cm-24x26in) s. panel. 23-Nov-2 Subastas Odalys, Caracas #1/R

LEON, Geronimo de (fl.1911) Mexican

£4706	$8000	€6871	Ex votos (25x36cm-10x14in) with sig.i.d.1912 oil copper sheet pair. 19-Nov-3 Sotheby's, New York #72/R est:10000-15000

LEON, Jose de (1958-) Spanish?

£800	$1448	€1200	Turkey at night (99x100cm-39x39in) s.d.1995 s.i.d.verso. 30-Mar-4 Segre, Madrid #277/R

LEON, Maurits (1838-1865) Dutch

£1042	$1719	€1500	Still life painter in studio (56x71cm-22x28in) s.d.59. 3-Jul-3 Van Ham, Cologne #1328 est:600

LEON, Omar de (20th C) South American

£599	$1000	€875	Three musicians (71x91cm-28x36in) s.i. 25-Oct-3 David Rago, Lambertville #1016

LEONARD, Agathan (1841-1923) French

Sculpture

£1042	$1771	€1500	Becasse (21x22cm-8x9in) brown pat bronze. 28-Oct-3 Rabourdin & Choppin de Janvry, Paris #88/R est:1550-1750
£2483	$4146	€3600	Angelot au carquois (47x38x31cm-19x15x12in) Carrara marble. 11-Jul-3 Rabourdin & Choppin de Janvry, Paris #147/R
£2980	$5424	€4500	Jeune femme se coiffant avec des fleurs (62x36x30cm-24x14x12in) s. marble. 19-Jun-4 St-Germain-en-Laye Encheres #90/R est:3000
£5556	$8833	€8000	Jeune femme au tambourin (57cm-22in) s. pat bronze. 9-Sep-3 Vanderkindere, Brussels #200/R
£8333	$15333	€12500	Femme chantant (55cm-22in) s. gold pat bronze st.f. Susse lit. 9-Jun-4 Beaussant & Lefèvre, Paris #271/R est:5000-7000
£8392	$14266	€12000	Danseuse a la sandale (53cm-21in) s.st.f.Susse pat bronze. 21-Nov-3 Lombrail & Teucquam, Paris #76/R est:4500-5000
£8667	$15947	€13000	Femme au cothurne (53cm-21in) s. gold pat bronze st.f. Susse lit. 9-Jun-4 Beaussant & Lefèvre, Paris #272/R est:5000-7000
£9500	$17765	€13870	Scarf dancer (29cm-11in) s.st.f.Susse gilt bronze lamp exec.c.1900. 24-Feb-4 Sotheby's, Olympia #76/R est:8500-9500
£11000	$17490	€16060	Scarf dancer (35cm-14in) s. bronze ivory. 9-Sep-3 Sotheby's, Olympia #180/R est:12000-15000

LEONARD, Alexandre (1821-1877) French?

Sculpture

£2128	$3553	€3000	Mehariste (25x23cm-10x9in) s. pat bronze marble socle. 19-Oct-3 Rabourdin & Choppin de Janvry, Paris #21/R est:4200-4500

LEONARD, Charly (1894-1953) Belgian

£333	$600	€500	Interieur au poele (50x60cm-20x24in) 20-Apr-4 Galerie Moderne, Brussels #371/R

LEONARD, J H (?) ?

Works on paper

£650	$1086	€949	English landscape, figures on a horse drawn cart by a lake (41x74cm-16x29in) s. W/C. 18-Jun-3 John Nicholson, Haslemere #606

LEONARD, Jules (1827-1897) Belgian

£533	$981	€800	Deux enfants au pigeonnier (98x128cm-39x50in) s. 14-Jun-4 Horta, Bruxelles #215
£887	$1480	€1250	Vendange (46x37cm-18x15in) s.d.1881. 17-Jun-3 Vanderkindere, Brussels #44

LEONARD, Maurice (1899-1971) French

£268	$481	€400	Bord de lisiere sur la mer (46x55cm-18x22in) s. painted 1936. 25-May-4 Thierry & Lannon, Brest #126/R
£268	$481	€400	Composition florale (46x55cm-18x22in) s. oil paper painted 1956. 25-May-4 Thierry & Lannon, Brest #128
£268	$481	€400	Le pichet bleu (46x55cm-18x22in) s. painted 1939. 25-May-4 Thierry & Lannon, Brest #134
£268	$481	€400	Les deux promeneurs (38x55cm-15x22in) s. painted 1939. 25-May-4 Thierry & Lannon, Brest #139
£268	$481	€400	Le plan d'eau (54x65cm-21x26in) s. oil paper painted 1955. 25-May-4 Thierry & Lannon, Brest #153
£268	$481	€400	Sur le pont (50x65cm-20x26in) s. oil paper painted 1957. 25-May-4 Thierry & Lannon, Brest #163
£268	$481	€400	Les pommes (81x65cm-32x26in) s. painted 1960. 25-May-4 Thierry & Lannon, Brest #181
£268	$481	€400	La maison du garde (81x100cm-32x39in) s. painted 1964. 25-May-4 Thierry & Lannon, Brest #193
£268	$481	€400	Le chemin enneige (81x100cm-32x39in) s. painted 1951. 25-May-4 Thierry & Lannon, Brest #197
£268	$481	€400	L'arbre (81x100cm-32x39in) s. 25-May-4 Thierry & Lannon, Brest #200
£268	$481	€400	Sous les arbres (146x114cm-57x45in) s. painted 1956. 25-May-4 Thierry & Lannon, Brest #204
£284	$474	€400	Pommes et fleurs (65x54cm-26x21in) 23-Jun-3 Lombrail & Teucquam, Paris #139
£298	$497	€420	Brune au bord de la mer (73x76cm-29x30in) 23-Jun-3 Lombrail & Teucquam, Paris #134
£298	$497	€420	Belleville sous la neige (38x46cm-15x18in) panel. 23-Jun-3 Lombrail & Teucquam, Paris #150
£302	$541	€450	Barques sur le sable (24x35cm-9x14in) s. isorel. 25-May-4 Thierry & Lannon, Brest #109
£302	$541	€450	Nature morte au pigeon (46x55cm-18x22in) painted 1948. 25-May-4 Thierry & Lannon, Brest #130
£302	$541	€450	Le pique-nique (55x46cm-22x18in) s. cardboard painted 1934. 25-May-4 Thierry & Lannon, Brest #136
£302	$541	€450	Le souk (33x55cm-13x22in) s. cardboard painted 1952. 25-May-4 Thierry & Lannon, Brest #140
£302	$541	€450	Vue sur le rivage (32x49cm-13x19in) s. cardboard painted 1953. 25-May-4 Thierry & Lannon, Brest #215
£309	$553	€460	Les deux baigneuses (54x73cm-21x29in) s. oil paper painted 1956. 25-May-4 Thierry & Lannon, Brest #174
£309	$553	€460	Le chemin botanique (50x73cm-20x29in) s. painted 1946. 25-May-4 Thierry & Lannon, Brest #211
£310	$515	€450	Retour de peche. 5-Oct-3 Lombrail & Teucquam, Paris #330
£322	$577	€480	Les bords de Seine (50x65cm-20x26in) s. oil paper painted 1929. 25-May-4 Thierry & Lannon, Brest #165/R
£333	$597	€500	Le casse-croute (50x61cm-20x24in) s. painted c.1934. 16-May-4 Thierry & Lannon, Brest #336
£336	$601	€500	Le manege (33x46cm-13x18in) s. oil paper painted 1953. 25-May-4 Thierry & Lannon, Brest #120/R
£336	$601	€500	Chemin dans les dunes (50x61cm-20x24in) s. painted 1954. 25-May-4 Thierry & Lannon, Brest #145
£336	$601	€500	La jetee bretonne (50x65cm-20x26in) s. oil mixed media paper painted 1958. 25-May-4 Thierry & Lannon, Brest #160
£336	$601	€500	Promeneurs sur la plage (54x73cm-21x29in) s. oil paper painted 1955. 25-May-4 Thierry & Lannon, Brest #178/R
£336	$601	€500	Jeune femme a la lecture (81x100cm-32x39in) s. painted 1969. 25-May-4 Thierry & Lannon, Brest #190
£336	$601	€500	La tombee du jour (81x100cm-32x39in) s. painted 1954. 25-May-4 Thierry & Lannon, Brest #192
£336	$601	€500	L'arbre dans la clairiere (81x100cm-32x39in) s. painted 1953. 25-May-4 Thierry & Lannon, Brest #198
£336	$601	€500	Le ramasseur de bois (146x97cm-57x38in) s. painted 1955. 25-May-4 Thierry & Lannon, Brest #208
£336	$601	€500	La guitariste (170x100cm-67x39in) s. painted 1956. 25-May-4 Thierry & Lannon, Brest #213
£336	$601	€500	Voilier en Bretagne (32x49cm-13x19in) s. cardboard painted 1948. 25-May-4 Thierry & Lannon, Brest #217
£340	$569	€480	En calle seche (33x41cm-13x16in) panel isorel. 23-Jun-3 Lombrail & Teucquam, Paris #154
£342	$613	€510	Paysage de Bretagne (32x49cm-13x19in) painted 1948. 25-May-4 Thierry & Lannon, Brest #216
£355	$592	€500	Le dolmen (46x55cm-18x22in) panel isorel. 23-Jun-3 Lombrail & Teucquam, Paris #144
£367	$656	€550	La poule, ses poussins et les deux lapins (54x73cm-21x29in) s. panel. 16-May-4 Thierry & Lannon, Brest #337
£369	$661	€550	La baie bretonne (32x49cm-13x19in) s. cardboard painted 1948. 25-May-4 Thierry & Lannon, Brest #219
£376	$673	€560	La brodeuse (60x73cm-24x29in) s. painted 1964. 25-May-4 Thierry & Lannon, Brest #172
£389	$697	€580	Canal Saint Martin (32x49cm-13x19in) s. cardboard painted 1925. 25-May-4 Thierry & Lannon, Brest #223
£397	$743	€600	Vue sur la crique (33x46cm-13x18in) s. isorel. 24-Jul-4 Thierry & Lannon, Brest #190
£397	$743	€600	La grande falaise (54x65cm-21x26in) s. paper painted 1958. 24-Jul-4 Thierry & Lannon, Brest #392
£400	$716	€600	Quatorze juillet en Bretagne (46x38cm-18x15in) s. paper painted c.1954. 16-May-4 Thierry & Lannon, Brest #149/R
£403	$721	€600	La butee (38x46cm-15x18in) s. 25-May-4 Thierry & Lannon, Brest #115
£403	$721	€600	Le vallon (33x46cm-13x18in) cardboard painted 1948. 25-May-4 Thierry & Lannon, Brest #119
£403	$721	€600	La grande corniche (46x55cm-18x22in) s. painted 1960. 25-May-4 Thierry & Lannon, Brest #124
£403	$721	€600	Les bateaux charbonniers (50x65cm-20x26in) s. oil paper painted 1929. 25-May-4 Thierry & Lannon, Brest #164
£403	$721	€600	La foret en ete (81x100cm-32x39in) s. painted 1963. 25-May-4 Thierry & Lannon, Brest #196
£416	$745	€620	Le chemin vers la plage (46x55cm-18x22in) s. painted 1940. 25-May-4 Thierry & Lannon, Brest #131

£416	$745	€620	Le port d'Orient (33x55cm-13x22in) s. cardboard painted 1952. 25-May-4 Thierry & Lannon, Brest #142/R
£426	$711	€600	Le poupon (60x73cm-24x29in) 23-Jun-3 Lombrail & Teucquam, Paris #133
£430	$769	€640	La besace bretonne (54x73cm-21x29in) s. oil paper painted 1934. 25-May-4 Thierry & Lannon, Brest #177/R
£430	$805	€650	Le cirque en Bretagne (33x46cm-13x18in) paper painted c.54. 24-Jul-4 Thierry & Lannon, Brest #191
£430	$805	€650	Les poissons rieurs, les maquereaux (38x46cm-15x18in) s. isorel painted c.1953. 24-Jul-4 Thierry & Lannon, Brest #391/R
£436	$781	€650	Paysage maritime (33x46cm-13x18in) s. isorel painted 1945. 25-May-4 Thierry & Lannon, Brest #121
£456	$817	€680	La baigneuse (60x73cm-24x29in) s. painted 1954. 25-May-4 Thierry & Lannon, Brest #169
£456	$817	€680	Les chataigniers (73x92cm-29x36in) s. painted 1956. 25-May-4 Thierry & Lannon, Brest #187
£464	$867	€700	Les roches noires, Bretagne (46x55cm-18x22in) s. isorel painted c.1929. 24-Jul-4 Thierry & Lannon, Brest #390
£470	$841	€700	La ferme dans la montagne (46x55cm-18x22in) s. painted 1968. 25-May-4 Thierry & Lannon, Brest #133
£470	$841	€700	Les falaises (38x55cm-15x22in) s. painted 1928. 25-May-4 Thierry & Lannon, Brest #137
£470	$841	€700	Campagne bretonne (60x73cm-24x29in) s. painted 1958. 25-May-4 Thierry & Lannon, Brest #166
£470	$841	€700	Le bain de soleil (60x73cm-24x29in) s. painted 1954. 25-May-4 Thierry & Lannon, Brest #171
£470	$841	€700	Scene de ferme (65x81cm-26x32in) s. painted 1956. 25-May-4 Thierry & Lannon, Brest #184/R
£477	$853	€710	Les champignons dans l'herbe (81x100cm-32x39in) s. painted 1945. 25-May-4 Thierry & Lannon, Brest #189
£483	$865	€720	Le canape rouge (54x73cm-21x29in) s. oil paper painted 1957. 25-May-4 Thierry & Lannon, Brest #175
£503	$901	€750	Le cabanon abandonne (38x46cm-15x18in) s. 25-May-4 Thierry & Lannon, Brest #116
£523	$937	€780	La chaumiere bretonne (46x55cm-18x22in) s. painted 1932. 25-May-4 Thierry & Lannon, Brest #125/R
£533	$955	€800	Vue d'un port breton (60x73cm-24x29in) s. i.d.1961 verso. 16-May-4 Thierry & Lannon, Brest #150/R
£537	$961	€800	La pause repas (50x65cm-20x26in) painted 1940 oil paper. 25-May-4 Thierry & Lannon, Brest #159/R
£544	$973	€810	La chaumiere bretonne (60x73cm-24x29in) s. painted 1945. 25-May-4 Thierry & Lannon, Brest #167
£557	$997	€830	Par dela la foret (130x98cm-51x39in) s. painted 1954. 25-May-4 Thierry & Lannon, Brest #201/R
£658	$1177	€980	La riviere sous le pont (73x92cm-29x36in) s. painted 1959. 25-May-4 Thierry & Lannon, Brest #186
£671	$1201	€1000	Les bateaux dans la crique (50x61cm-20x24in) s. painted 1959. 25-May-4 Thierry & Lannon, Brest #148/R
£671	$1201	€1000	Le salon de jardin (100x81cm-39x32in) painted 1963. 25-May-4 Thierry & Lannon, Brest #199
£674	$1125	€950	Les citrons (65x81cm-26x32in) 23-Jun-3 Lombrail & Teucquam, Paris #125
£695	$1300	€1050	La liseuse (50x61cm-20x24in) s. painted 1960. 24-Jul-4 Thierry & Lannon, Brest #192/R est:600-800
£728	$1362	€1100	Les barques (54x73cm-21x29in) s. painted 1954. 24-Jul-4 Thierry & Lannon, Brest #193/R
£733	$1313	€1100	Voiliers en mer (46x55cm-18x22in) s. painted c.1936. 16-May-4 Thierry & Lannon, Brest #334
£767	$1372	€1150	Bateaux en cale seche (54x65cm-21x26in) s. panel painted c.1950. 16-May-4 Thierry & Lannon, Brest #331/R
£800	$1432	€1200	Bord de cote en Bretagne (50x61cm-20x24in) s. cardboard painted c.1930. 16-May-4 Thierry & Lannon, Brest #335/R
£805	$1442	€1200	Le marche oriental (50x61cm-20x24in) s. oil paper painted 1952. 25-May-4 Thierry & Lannon, Brest #144/R
£805	$1442	€1200	Le nu (54x65cm-21x26in) s. panel painted 1953. 25-May-4 Thierry & Lannon, Brest #156/R
£805	$1442	€1200	Plage sur l'Orient (54x73cm-21x29in) s. oil paper. 25-May-4 Thierry & Lannon, Brest #179/R
£833	$1492	€1250	Marins dans le port (50x65cm-20x26in) s. panel painted c.1926. 16-May-4 Thierry & Lannon, Brest #151/R
£839	$1502	€1250	Les lingeres (46x55cm-18x22in) s. painted 1950. 25-May-4 Thierry & Lannon, Brest #127/R
£867	$1551	€1300	Le port breton, les casiers (54x73cm-21x29in) s. 16-May-4 Thierry & Lannon, Brest #330/R
£872	$1562	€1300	Les roches dominant la mer (54x65cm-21x26in) s. painted 1953. 25-May-4 Thierry & Lannon, Brest #157/R
£872	$1562	€1300	Le port de peche (81x100cm-32x39in) s. painted 1964. 25-May-4 Thierry & Lannon, Brest #195/R
£906	$1622	€1350	La sieste (146x97cm-57x38in) s. painted 1956. 25-May-4 Thierry & Lannon, Brest #207
£973	$1742	€1450	Le souk (46x55cm-18x22in) s. painted 1953. 25-May-4 Thierry & Lannon, Brest #129/R
£1107	$1982	€1650	Fenaison (146x97cm-57x38in) s. painted 1948. 25-May-4 Thierry & Lannon, Brest #209b/R est:1000-1200
£1133	$2029	€1700	La baie de Yaudet en Bretagne (73x92cm-29x36in) s. painted c.1964. 16-May-4 Thierry & Lannon, Brest #152 est:1000-1200
£1170	$1954	€1650	Le port (54x65cm-21x26in) 23-Jun-3 Lombrail & Teucquam, Paris #124
£1200	$2148	€1800	Le village de pecheurs (81x60cm-32x24in) s. painted c.1956. 16-May-4 Thierry & Lannon, Brest #333 est:800-1000
£1309	$2343	€1950	La lecture (146x114cm-57x45in) painted 1958. 25-May-4 Thierry & Lannon, Brest #205 est:800-1000
£1333	$2387	€2000	Le pecheur breton (46x55cm-18x22in) s. 16-May-4 Thierry & Lannon, Brest #332/R est:450-600
£1644	$2943	€2450	La fete foraine (171x101cm-67x40in) s. painted 1958. 25-May-4 Thierry & Lannon, Brest #214/R est:1000-1200
£1745	$3123	€2600	Les marins bretons pres du port (146x97cm-57x38in) s. painted 1955. 25-May-4 Thierry & Lannon, Brest #209/R est:1000-1200

Works on paper

£278	$520	€420	Le phare breton, les filets rouges (20x42cm-8x17in) s.d.1955 pastel crayon. 24-Jul-4 Thierry & Lannon, Brest #330
£280	$501	€420	Les voiliers, la mer bleue (45x59cm-18x23in) s. W/C wash. 16-May-4 Thierry & Lannon, Brest #58
£282	$527	€420	Fumeur de pipe depart pour la peche (26x36cm-10x14in) s. W/C gouache. 24-Feb-4 Thierry & Lannon, Brest #139
£282	$527	€420	Sur les docks Bretons (28x38cm-11x15in) s. W/C gouache. 24-Feb-4 Thierry & Lannon, Brest #141
£282	$505	€420	Bigoudene devant la voile bleue (28x38cm-11x15in) s. W/C wash. 25-May-4 Thierry & Lannon, Brest #11/R
£282	$505	€420	Ruelle orientale en bleu (27x17cm-11x7in) s. W/C. 25-May-4 Thierry & Lannon, Brest #55/R
£289	$517	€430	Le souk a la porte de la cite (21x28cm-8x11in) s. W/C. 25-May-4 Thierry & Lannon, Brest #58/R
£300	$537	€450	Deux marins au cafe (27x38cm-11x15in) s. gouache W/C. 16-May-4 Thierry & Lannon, Brest #261
£300	$537	€450	Nu de dos (31x44cm-12x17in) s. W/C. 16-May-4 Thierry & Lannon, Brest #340
£302	$541	€450	Cinq marins, l'ancre et les filets (28x38cm-11x15in) s. W/C. 25-May-4 Thierry & Lannon, Brest #15
£302	$541	€450	L'entree du souk, la porte rouge (26x18cm-10x7in) s. W/C. 25-May-4 Thierry & Lannon, Brest #62/R
£317	$527	€460	Bateaux au port. W/C. 5-Oct-3 Lombrail & Teucquam, Paris #327
£317	$527	€460	Les voiles. pastel. 5-Oct-3 Lombrail & Teucquam, Paris #328
£317	$527	€460	Etude de bretonnes (27x37cm-11x15in) s. gouache dr. 5-Oct-3 Lombrail & Teucquam, Paris #166
£317	$555	€450	Procession (28x38cm-11x15in) W/C gouache chl exec c.1948-50. 21-Dec-3 Thierry & Lannon, Brest #237
£336	$628	€500	Treize marins en diverses attitudes (26x38cm-10x15in) s. gouache. 24-Feb-4 Thierry & Lannon, Brest #132
£336	$601	€500	Pecheurs et bretonnes pres de la barque (34x26cm-13x10in) s. pastel. 25-May-4 Thierry & Lannon, Brest #77
£336	$601	€500	Deux pecheurs, trois chalutiers (26x34cm-10x13in) s. W/C. 25-May-4 Thierry & Lannon, Brest #89/R
£349	$653	€520	Huit marins mains dans les poches (28x39cm-11x15in) s. W/C gouache. 24-Feb-4 Thierry & Lannon, Brest #137/R
£349	$625	€520	Deux pecheurs, le panier et la barque (18x33cm-7x13in) s. pastel. 25-May-4 Thierry & Lannon, Brest #78/R
£369	$690	€550	Bolee des quatre mains (25x37cm-10x15in) s. pastel. 24-Feb-4 Thierry & Lannon, Brest #134/R
£369	$690	€550	Cinq marins en conversation (29x39cm-11x15in) s. W/C. 24-Feb-4 Thierry & Lannon, Brest #135/R
£376	$673	€560	Vareuse orange et voiles blanches (28x38cm-11x15in) s. pastel. 25-May-4 Thierry & Lannon, Brest #81/R
£389	$697	€580	Les marins, les sardines et le panier de peche (28x38cm-11x15in) s. W/C. 25-May-4 Thierry & Lannon, Brest #9
£400	$716	€600	Les deux berets blancs, les marins (30x40cm-12x16in) s. W/C gouache chl. 16-May-4 Thierry & Lannon, Brest #59
£400	$716	€600	Les trois marins (24x32cm-9x13in) s. pastel. 16-May-4 Thierry & Lannon, Brest #89
£400	$716	€600	Les Bretonnes au port en discussion (30x40cm-12x16in) s. gouache mixed media. 16-May-4 Thierry & Lannon, Brest #90
£400	$716	€600	Les marins bretons, les barques et l'enfant (28x38cm-11x15in) s. W/C exec. 1949. 16-May-4 Thierry & Lannon, Brest #262
£403	$721	€600	Les marins, tonneaux et bassine (28x38cm-11x15in) W/C. 25-May-4 Thierry & Lannon, Brest #22
£409	$733	€610	Les marins, quatre berets blancs (28x38cm-11x15in) s. W/C. 25-May-4 Thierry & Lannon, Brest #14
£411	$768	€620	Douze marins et deux barques (26x35cm-10x14in) s. W/C chl. 24-Jul-4 Thierry & Lannon, Brest #70
£420	$752	€630	Les marins bretons, le cire jaune (30x39cm-12x15in) s. W/C chl. 16-May-4 Thierry & Lannon, Brest #259
£423	$757	€630	Dechargement de la peche (19x26cm-7x10in) s. pastel. 25-May-4 Thierry & Lannon, Brest #71/R
£430	$769	€640	Dix marins et bretonnes (30x40cm-12x16in) W/C gouache. 25-May-4 Thierry & Lannon, Brest #21
£436	$781	€650	Trois pecheurs pres de la barque (18x33cm-7x13in) s. pastel. 25-May-4 Thierry & Lannon, Brest #87/R
£463	$829	€690	Les marins et la barque a deux mats (28x38cm-11x15in) s. W/C. 25-May-4 Thierry & Lannon, Brest #48/R
£493	$863	€700	Marins au bistrot (27x37cm-11x15in) W/C chl. 21-Dec-3 Thierry & Lannon, Brest #60/R
£503	$901	€750	Marins a la veste orange et la barque (25x37cm-10x15in) pastel. 25-May-4 Thierry & Lannon, Brest #30/R
£510	$954	€760	Retour de peche l'attente des femmes sur les quais (34x43cm-13x17in) s. pastel. 24-Feb-4 Thierry & Lannon, Brest #133/R
£523	$979	€780	Quai anime en Bretagne (29x39cm-11x15in) s. W/C gouache. 24-Feb-4 Thierry & Lannon, Brest #136/R
£567	$1014	€850	Le village de pecheurs, conversation sur la cale (61x42cm-24x17in) s. mixed media. 16-May-4 Thierry & Lannon, Brest #260
£599	$1048	€850	Les marins en diverses attitudes (28x38cm-11x15in) studio st. gouache chl. 21-Dec-3 Thierry & Lannon, Brest #61/R
£599	$1048	€850	Marins bretons a la barque (27x38cm-11x15in) s. W/C gouache chl exec c.1948-50. 21-Dec-3 Thierry & Lannon, Brest #235
£634	$1109	€900	Marins en conversation (28x38cm-11x15in) exec c.1948-50. 21-Dec-3 Thierry & Lannon, Brest #2236/R
£671	$1255	€1000	Attroupement de marins (26x31cm-10x12in) s. pastel. 24-Feb-4 Thierry & Lannon, Brest #131/R
£775	$1356	€1100	Marins en conversation (36x26cm-14x10in) s. W/C gouache chl exec c.1948-50. 21-Dec-3 Thierry & Lannon, Brest #59
£845	$1479	€1200	Marins et leurs casiers (47x35cm-19x14in) s. pastel chl exec c.1948-50. 21-Dec-3 Thierry & Lannon, Brest #254/R

LEONARD, Michael (1933-) British

£2800	$4648	€4088	Five pomegranates (43x47cm-17x19in) mono.d.96 i.verso alkyd oil masonite prov. 30-Sep-3 Sotheby's, London #209/R est:1000-1500
£8000	$13280	€11680	Bather's knee (55x60cm-22x24in) mono.d.96 i.verso alkyd oil masonite. 30-Sep-3 Sotheby's, London #325 est:600-800
£11500	$19090	€16790	Boy with pomegranates (96x79cm-38x31in) s.d.95 alkyd oil masonite. 30-Sep-3 Sotheby's, London #326/R est:1000-1500

LEONARD, Patrick (1918-) British

£700	$1204	€1022	Connolly station platform A, Dublin (50x40cm-20x16in) s.d.3/6/85 verso board. 3-Dec-3 John Ross, Belfast #130
£789	$1453	€1200	Corfu (21x26cm-8x10in) s. board. 22-Jun-4 De Veres Art Auctions, Dublin #171/R
£1014	$1916	€1500	Homeward bound, Skerries evening (48x38cm-19x15in) s.i.d.17 May 1981 board. 17-Feb-4 Whyte's, Dublin #243/R est:2000-3000
£1184	$2179	€1800	Dassia, Corfu (31x38cm-12x15in) s.i.d. June 83 verso canvasboard. 22-Jun-4 De Veres Art Auctions, Dublin #91/R est:900-1200
£1250	$2037	€1800	Evening (40x50cm-16x20in) s. board. 24-Sep-3 James Adam, Dublin #109/R est:1000-1500
£1342	$2376	€2000	Railway workers, Skerries (50x32cm-20x13in) s.i.d.11 March 1986 s.verso panel. 27-Apr-4 Whyte's, Dublin #103/R est:2000-2500
£1408	$2254	€2000	Tablecloth and lace seller, Costa del Sol (37x28cm-15x11in) s. s.i.d.4 June 1986 verso board. 16-Sep-3 Whyte's, Dublin #207/R est:2000-3000

£1892 $3576 €2800 Red Island 1978 (41x51cm-16x20in) s. i.verso board. 17-Feb-4 Whyte's, Dublin #6/R est:2500-3500
£2098 $3566 €3000 Mother and child in coastal landscape (51x61cm-20x24in) s. board. 25-Nov-3 De Veres Art Auctions, Dublin #214b/R est:3000-4000
£4577 $7324 €6500 Girls at village pump (61x51cm-24x20in) s. board. 16-Sep-3 Whyte's, Dublin #57/R est:4000-5000
£5369 $9611 €8000 Harbour at Skerries (62x70cm-24x28in) 31-May-4 Hamilton Osborne King, Dublin #157/R est:8000-12000

LEONARDI, Achille (19th C) Italian
£1438 $2300 €2099 Holy Family in stable with cherubs looking over head (58x46cm-23x18in) s. 17-May-3 Bunte, Elgin #1232 est:3000-5000

LEONARDO DA PISTOIA (fl.1516-1540) Italian
£30000 $51900 €43800 Holy Family with Saint Elizabeth and Saint John the Baptist (117x95cm-46x37in) panel. 11-Dec-3 Sotheby's, London #174/R est:8000-12000

LEONARDO DA VINCI (style) (1452-1519) Italian
£54000 $98820 €78840 Leda (24x24cm-9x9in) panel prov.exhib.lit. 6-Jul-4 Sotheby's, Olympia #412/R est:5000-7000

LEONCILLO (1915-1968) Italian
£1333 $2400 €2000 Little concert (44x55cm-17x22in) board. 22-Apr-4 Finarte Semenzato, Rome #96/R est:1800-2400
Sculpture
£2838 $4995 €4200 Cat (28cm-11in) painted ceramic. 24-May-4 Christie's, Milan #16/R est:4000-5000
£3667 $6747 €5500 Horse (30x32x11cm-12x13x4in) s. terracotta. 12-Jun-4 Meeting Art, Vercelli #95/R est:5000
£4333 $7800 €6500 Dance (41cm-16in) s. ceramic. 22-Apr-4 Finarte Semenzato, Rome #361/R est:3500-4000
£5333 $9600 €8000 Paper seller. Blacksmith (27cm-11in) s. ceramic two. 22-Apr-4 Finarte Semenzato, Rome #359/R est:5000-5500
£8000 $14400 €12000 Tree (44cm-17in) s. ceramic. 22-Apr-4 Finarte Semenzato, Rome #360/R est:5000-5500
£10490 $17832 €15000 Saint Sebastian (62cm-24in) gres enamel prov. 20-Nov-3 Finarte Semenzato, Milan #138/R est:15000-18000
£15035 $25559 €21500 Call centre (113x64x32cm-44x25x13in) terracotta prov. 20-Nov-3 Finarte Semenzato, Milan #172/R est:23000-28000
£16084 $27343 €23000 Typist (116x65x30cm-46x26x12in) painted terracotta. 20-Nov-3 Finarte Semenzato, Milan #171/R est:23000-28000
Works on paper
£433 $784 €650 Untitled (70x50cm-28x20in) gouache. 2-Apr-4 Farsetti, Prato #291/R
£966 $1612 €1400 Cut (69x50cm-27x20in) mixed media paper on card. 14-Nov-3 Farsetti, Prato #304/R

LEONE, Romolo (19th C) French
£324 $571 €480 Farm with figures (21x25cm-8x10in) s.i. cardboard. 19-May-4 Il Ponte, Milan #526
£370 $676 €540 Animated square in Naples (33x44cm-13x17in) s.i. board. 4-Jun-4 Zofingen, Switzerland #2479 (S.FR 850)
£423 $731 €600 Landscape (19x28cm-7x11in) s. cardboard. 10-Dec-3 Finarte Semenzato, Rome #253/R
£520 $962 €759 View of Sorrento (23x36cm-9x14in) s. 16-Feb-4 Bonhams, Bath #151
£591 $981 €857 Fishing boats in Bay of Naples (24x18cm-9x7in) s.i. verso panel. 13-Jun-3 Zofingen, Switzerland #2482/R (S.FR 1300)
£1056 $1827 €1500 Cloth designer (16x14cm-6x6in) s. board. 10-Dec-3 Finarte Semenzato, Rome #245/R est:650-750

LEONELLI DA CREVALCORE, Antonio (attrib) (fl.1478-1515) Italian
£35000 $60550 €51100 Madonna and Child with Saint John the Baptist and another Saint (69x60cm-27x24in) indis i. tempera linen on panel. 10-Dec-3 Christie's, London #96/R est:20000-30000

LEONESSA, Enrico della (1865-1921) Italian
£23611 $42500 €34472 Fiore e frutta - Flower and fruit (114x78cm-45x31in) s.d.1907 exhib. 23-Apr-4 Sotheby's, New York #82/R est:25000-35000
£41667 $75000 €60834 Al caffe concerto - Cafe concert (129x119cm-51x47in) s.d.1911 prov.exhib.lit. 23-Apr-4 Sotheby's, New York #83/R est:30000-50000

LEONHARDI, August (19/20th C) German
£690 $1152 €1000 Summer evening (52x71cm-20x28in) 15-Nov-3 Von Zezschwitz, Munich #12/R

LEONI, Ippolito (1616-1694) Italian
Works on paper
£750 $1418 €1095 Portrait of Settimia Manenti of Salerno (21x14cm-8x6in) black red chk corners made up. 19-Feb-4 Christie's, Kensington #15/R

LEONI, Ottavio (1587-1630) Italian
Works on paper
£1667 $3000 €2434 Portrait of a young lady wearing a high collar (21x14cm-8x6in) black white chk. 22-Jan-4 Christie's, Rockefeller NY #33/R est:3000-5000
£3100 $5642 €4526 Portrait of a gentleman, quarter length (21x15cm-8x6in) d.1608 black white chk. 3-Feb-4 Sworder & Son, Bishops Stortford #246/R est:1000-2000
£5918 $10594 €8700 Portrait de l'abee Gaetano (23x17cm-9x7in) i.d.1628 i.verso col chk prov. 18-Mar-4 Christie's, Paris #18/R est:8000-12000
£8333 $15000 €12166 Portrait of Principessa Saponara (22x16cm-9x6in) i.d.i54/i620 i.verso col chk prov.lit. 22-Jan-4 Christie's, Rockefeller NY #32/R est:6000-8000

LEONI, Ottavio (attrib) (1587-1630) Italian
£10333 $18910 €15500 Portrait de femme en buste (67x49cm-26x19in) 6-Jun-4 Rouillac, Vendome #30/R

LEONI, Ottavio (circle) (1587-1630) Italian
£5000 $9000 €7300 Portrait of a gentleman in a brown coat and white collar (8x6cm-3x2in) copper oval. 21-Apr-4 Christie's, London #74/R est:5000-7000

LEONTINA, Maria (20th C) Brazilian?
£2381 $4214 €3572 Untitled (73x60cm-29x24in) s. 27-Apr-4 Bolsa de Arte, Rio de Janeiro #115/R (B.R 13000)
£16850 $29824 €25275 Untitled (38x61cm-15x24in) s.d.1956-1958 verso. 27-Apr-4 Bolsa de Arte, Rio de Janeiro #121/R (B.R 92000)
Works on paper
£1832 $3242 €2748 Untitled (22x28cm-9x11in) s. pastel. 27-Apr-4 Bolsa de Arte, Rio de Janeiro #103/R (B.R 10000)

LEONTUS, Adam (1928-) Haitian
£341 $600 €498 Surrealist scene with two headed goat and figural tree (61x51cm-24x20in) s. board. 1-Jan-4 Quinn's, Falls Church #29/R

LEOPOLD-LEVY (1882-1966) French
£333 $597 €500 Quais de Seine (54x45cm-21x18in) s. 12-May-4 Brissoneau, France #100/R
£336 $625 €500 Paysage du Midi (22x33cm-9x13in) s. 2-Mar-4 Artcurial Briest, Paris #184
£403 $749 €600 Paysage de Saint-Cyr (27x41cm-11x16in) s. 2-Mar-4 Artcurial Briest, Paris #186
£403 $737 €600 Still life with fruit (38x46cm-15x18in) s.d.28. 7-Jul-4 Artcurial Briest, Paris #118
£470 $874 €700 La ciotat (24x35cm-9x14in) s. 2-Mar-4 Artcurial Briest, Paris #185
£604 $1124 €900 Paysage a la ciotat (27x41cm-11x16in) s. 2-Mar-4 Artcurial Briest, Paris #187
£671 $1248 €1000 La ciotat (33x46cm-13x18in) s. 2-Mar-4 Artcurial Briest, Paris #188
£805 $1498 €1200 Dieppe (33x41cm-13x16in) s. 2-Mar-4 Artcurial Briest, Paris #183
£1074 $1965 €1600 Paysage (54x65cm-21x26in) s.d.28. 7-Jul-4 Artcurial Briest, Paris #117 est:1500-1800
£1476 $2746 €2200 Nature morte a la cruche (50x73cm-20x29in) s. 2-Mar-4 Artcurial Briest, Paris #182 est:500-600

LEPAGE, Celine (1882-1928) French
Sculpture
£34965 $59441 €50000 Chevaux cambres (72x85cm-28x33in) s.d.1924 num.2 gold leaf lead pair exhib.lit. 24-Nov-3 Tajan, Paris #92/R est:80000-100000

LEPAGE, Pierre (1906-1983) French
£350 $594 €500 Notre Dame vue des quais de la Seine (50x61cm-20x24in) s. 23-Nov-3 Cornette de St.Cyr, Paris #613/R

LEPAPE, George (1887-1971) French
Works on paper
£379 $630 €550 Etude (33x28cm-13x11in) s. gouache. 6-Oct-3 Blanchet, Paris #206
£414 $687 €600 Etude (33x38cm-13x15in) d.1920 gouache. 6-Oct-3 Blanchet, Paris #204/R
£448 $744 €650 Clown (33x28cm-13x11in) gouache. 6-Oct-3 Blanchet, Paris #205

LEPAULLE, François Gabriel (1804-1886) French
£32353 $55000 €47235 Colonel George Fergusson Henry, Honorary Bey at the Sultan's court (84x63cm-33x25in) s.d.1846. 29-Oct-3 Christie's, Rockefeller NY #165/R est:40000-60000

LEPCKE, Ferdinand (1866-1909) German
Sculpture
£1712 $2911 €2500 Amazone (99cm-39in) s. pat.bronze Cast.Lauchhammer. 5-Nov-3 Hugo Ruef, Munich #2162/R est:1200
£3026 $5234 €4418 The kiss (63cm-25in) s. pat bronze exec. c.1895. 14-Dec-3 Agra, Warsaw #6/R est:11000 (P.Z 20000)

LEPEC, Charles (1830-?) French
£1364 $2400 €1991 Scene of young girl holding a dove (20x13cm-8x5in) s. enamel panel. 23-May-4 Hindman, Chicago #84/R est:1500-2000

LEPEINTRE, Charles (1735-1803) French
£1761 $3081 €2500 Deux jeunes files et leur grand-mere (73x54cm-29x21in) i.verso. 17-Dec-3 Piasa, Paris #108/R est:3000-4000

LEPERE, Auguste (1849-1918) French
£3404 $5685 €4800 La Place de l'Abreuvoir a Montmartre (61x38cm-24x15in) s.d.75 lit. 12-Oct-3 St-Germain-en-Laye Encheres #61/R est:2500-3000
Works on paper
£265 $482 €400 Paysage fluvial (12x16cm-5x6in) i. W/C pen ink. 16-Jun-4 Piasa, Paris #213
£379 $702 €550 Saint Severin (20x11cm-8x4in) s.i. W/C. 16-Feb-4 Giraudeau, Tours #24

LEPICIE, Michel Nicolas Bernard (1735-1784) French
£10855 $19974 €16500 Petit indigent. Petite indigente (11x8cm-4x3in) one s. one s.d.1784 panel pair prov.exhib.lit. 25-Jun-4 Piasa, Paris #48/R est:15000-20000

Works on paper

£1053 $1937 €1600 Homme nu (45x38cm-18x15in) s. sanguine. 23-Jun-4 Sotheby's, Paris #13/R est:2000-3000
£2254 $3741 €3200 Le depart du braconnier (31x24cm-12x9in) s. grey wash black crayon. 10-Jun-3 Renaud, Paris #3/R est:3000
£2817 $4676 €4000 La paysanne revenant du bois (31x24cm-12x9in) s. grey wash black crayon. 10-Jun-3 Renaud, Paris #4/R est:2000-2500
£4000 $7320 €5840 Heads of a bearded man, child and a woman and two studies of hands (41x26cm-16x10in) s. i.verso black white red chk. 6-Jul-4 Christie's, London #137/R est:4000-6000

LEPIE, Ferdinand (1824-1883) Czechoslovakian

£650 $1034 €943 Alpine stream (86x56cm-34x22in) s.d.1886. 9-Sep-3 Bonhams, Knightsbridge #46/R
£986 $1706 €1400 View of Melk (28x34cm-11x13in) s. 10-Dec-3 Dorotheum, Vienna #4/R
£1009 $1836 €1473 Mountainous landscape (27x52cm-11x20in) s. 20-Jun-4 Agra, Warsaw #26/R (P.Z 7000)
£1325 $2424 €2000 Hallstadt in Salzkammergut (37x76cm-15x30in) s. canvas on board. 7-Apr-4 Dorotheum, Salzburg #116/R est:2200-3000
£1325 $2424 €2000 Gmunden with Schloss Orth and Traunstein (36x77cm-14x30in) s.d.1871 canvas on board. 7-Apr-4 Dorotheum, Salzburg #117/R est:2200-3000
£1690 $2924 €2400 View of Hallstatt (76x92cm-30x36in) s.d.1889. 10-Dec-3 Dorotheum, Vienna #5/R est:2600-3000
£2649 $4821 €4000 View of Marcus Basin, Venice (90x150cm-35x59in) s. 21-Jun-4 Dorotheum, Vienna #207/R est:4000-5000
£2657 $4517 €3800 Gmunden (56x68cm-22x27in) s. 24-Nov-3 Dorotheum, Vienna #17/R est:3000-3500

LEPIE, Ferdinand (attrib) (1824-1883) Czechoslovakian

£1690 $2924 €2400 View of Gmunden (55x79cm-22x31in) 10-Dec-3 Dorotheum, Vienna #195/R est:2400-2600

LEPINARD, Paul (20th C) Swiss

£286 $457 €415 St Saphorin (28x23cm-11x9in) s.d.43 board. 15-May-3 Stuker, Bern #1357 (S.FR 600)
£696 $1273 €1016 Le Leman vu de Lavaux (52x74cm-20x29in) s.d.1925. 5-Jun-4 Galerie du Rhone, Sion #355 (S.FR 1600)
£1357 $2348 €1981 Au Lac Leman, Corniche (46x60cm-18x24in) s.d.1940. 9-Dec-3 Sotheby's, Zurich #92/R est:3000-5000 (S.FR 3000)

LEPINE, Joseph Louis Francois (1867-1943) French

£1467 $2699 €2200 Pres de Cavalaire - Var (58x70cm-23x28in) s. board. 10-Jun-4 Hauswedell & Nolte, Hamburg #430/R est:2000
£3467 $6275 €5200 Rue animee a Vannes (70x60cm-28x24in) s. panel. 5-Apr-4 Marie & Robert, Paris #46/R est:5000-6000
£3500 $6475 €5110 Still life (61x104cm-24x41in) 14-Jul-4 Sotheby's, Olympia #217/R est:3000-4000

LEPINE, Stanislas (1835-1892) French

£3636 $6036 €5272 Marche a Paris (35x27cm-14x11in) s. 13-Jun-3 Zofingen, Switzerland #2367/R est:10000 (S.FR 8000)
£6500 $11960 €9490 Bords de Seine en Aval de Paris (24x38cm-9x15in) s. painted c.1878-1882 prov.exhib.lit. 22-Jun-4 Sotheby's, London #211/R est:7000-9000
£8392 $14434 €12000 Bord de riviere, la Marne (34x22cm-13x9in) s.i. 7-Dec-3 Osenat, Fontainebleau #187
£9790 $16839 €14000 Les coteaux de Sannois et Argenteuil (14x23cm-6x9in) s. panel. 7-Dec-3 Osenat, Fontainebleau #188
£12766 $20681 €18000 Le quai du Louvre au pont des Saints-Peres (15x24cm-6x9in) s. panel lit. 21-May-3 Daguerre, Paris #67/R est:10000-12000
£17483 $30070 €25000 Bords de Seine en aval de Paris (27x45cm-11x18in) s.d.78 panel exhib.lit. 8-Dec-3 Artcurial Briest, Paris #5/R est:30000-35000
£21127 $36549 €30000 La Seine a Rouen (33x46cm-13x18in) s. prov.exhib. 11-Dec-3 Binoche, Paris #20/R est:30000-40000
£28000 $51520 €40880 Bords de la Marne (50x80cm-20x31in) s. painted c.1878-82 prov.exhib.lit. 22-Jun-4 Sotheby's, London #104/R est:30000-40000

LEPINE, Stanislas (attrib) (1835-1892) French

£734 $1226 €1064 La neige a St Denis (19x34cm-7x13in) panel. 23-Jun-3 Philippe Schuler, Zurich #8615 (S.FR 1600)
£1216 $2092 €1775 Summer landscape (15x23cm-6x9in) s. panel. 8-Dec-3 Philippe Schuler, Zurich #3419/R est:3000-3500 (S.FR 2700)

L'EPLATTENIER, Charles (1874-1946) Swiss

£280 $502 €409 Seated nude woman (61x44cm-24x17in) s. chl chk. 12-May-4 Dobiaschofsky, Bern #1759/R (S.FR 650)
£647 $1157 €945 Mme D (120x86cm-47x34in) s.d1937 i. verso board. 12-May-4 Dobiaschofsky, Bern #712/R est:2200 (S.FR 1500)
£1293 $2315 €1888 Les mosses (54x46cm-21x18in) s.i.d.oct 1908. 14-May-4 Dobiaschofsky, Bern #114/R est:3600 (S.FR 3000)
£1542 $2621 €2251 Jura nuageux (46x61cm-18x24in) s. i.d.1939 verso. 7-Nov-3 Dobiaschofsky, Bern #102/R est:4500 (S.FR 3500)
£2371 $4244 €3462 Vue des Alpes - coup de soleil (49x61cm-19x24in) s.d.1939 i. verso canvas on board. 14-May-4 Dobiaschofsky, Bern #95/R est:5500 (S.FR 5500)
£3084 $5242 €4503 Soir d'hiver (73x92cm-29x36in) s.d.1944 i.d.1945 verso. 7-Nov-3 Dobiaschofsky, Bern #101/R est:10000 (S.FR 7000)
£10480 $18760 €15301 Nu a la marguerite (96x142cm-38x56in) s.d.1936. 26-May-4 Sotheby's, Zurich #57/R est:25000-30000 (S.FR 24000)
£14655 $26233 €21396 Paysage du Jura (95x140cm-37x55in) s.d.1918. 14-May-4 Dobiaschofsky, Bern #94/R est:21000 (S.FR 34000)

Works on paper

£396 $674 €578 Portrait of bearded man (62x48cm-24x19in) s.d.1941 col chk. 7-Nov-3 Dobiaschofsky, Bern #85/R (S.FR 900)
£776 $1389 €1133 Summer river landscape in the Jura (27x42cm-11x17in) s.d.1923 pastel. 14-May-4 Dobiaschofsky, Bern #97/R est:2600 (S.FR 1800)

LEPOITTEVIN, Eugène (1806-1870) French

£1224 $1947 €1800 Young fishermen (24x32cm-9x13in) mono. 23-Mar-3 Mercier & Cie, Lille #247/R est:2000-3000
£1259 $2140 €1800 La pose du pecheur (55x46cm-22x18in) bears sig. 18-Nov-3 Vanderkindere, Brussels #139/R est:625-875
£1300 $2353 €1950 Enfant dans une cour de ferme (19x30cm-7x12in) oil paper on cardboard. 4-Apr-4 Salle des ventes Pillet, Lyon la Foret #40/R est:2200-2500
£2324 $4020 €3300 Sailor's wife - woman with children looking out to sea (47x55cm-19x22in) s. 11-Dec-3 Dr Fritz Nagel, Stuttgart #526/R est:3600
£4733 $8567 €7100 Portraits d'homme et de femme. Falaises d'Etretat (46x38cm-18x15in) mono.i. one d.1861 one d.1866 pair one double-sided. 4-Apr-4 Salle des ventes Pillet, Lyon la Foret #39/R est:5000-6000

LEPOITTEVIN, Louis (1847-1909) French

£1987 $3636 €3000 Summer river landscape (46x65cm-18x26in) s. 8-Apr-4 Dorotheum, Vienna #293/R est:3800-4200

LEPPANEN, Lauri (1895-1977) Finnish

Sculpture

£1419 $2540 €2100 The hunter (52cm-20in) s. bronze. 8-May-4 Bukowskis, Helsinki #6/R

LEPPIEN, Jean (1910-1991) German

£759 $1267 €1100 Untitled (55x46cm-22x18in) mono.i.d.64 verso. 13-Nov-3 Neumeister, Munich #573/R
£759 $1267 €1100 Untitled (92x60cm-36x24in) s. mono.i.d.67 verso. 13-Nov-3 Neumeister, Munich #574/R
£759 $1267 €1100 UFO (64x54cm-25x21in) s. mono.i.d.67 verso. 13-Nov-3 Neumeister, Munich #575/R
£759 $1267 €1100 UFO (81x64cm-32x25in) s. mono.i.d.70 verso. 13-Nov-3 Neumeister, Munich #576/R
£759 $1267 €1100 Untitled (65x54cm-26x21in) mono.i.d.71 verso. 13-Nov-3 Neumeister, Munich #577/R
£1748 $2972 €2500 Composition au cercle rouge (35x28cm-14x11in) s. i.d.7/68 verso. 23-Nov-3 Cornette de St.Cyr, Paris #218/R est:300-400
£3533 $6360 €5300 Composition LXI (55x47cm-22x19in) s. s.i.d.60 verso prov. 25-Apr-4 Versailles Encheres #29 est:3000-4000

Works on paper

£709 $1269 €1050 LXVIII (42x31cm-17x12in) s.d.52 s.i.d.verso pastel exhib. 4-May-4 Calmels Cohen, Paris #184
£709 $1269 €1050 XXIV (42x30cm-17x12in) s.d.50 pastel. 4-May-4 Calmels Cohen, Paris #180/R

LEPRI, Stanislao (1905-1980) Italian

Works on paper

£1399 $2378 €2000 Libro maestro (35x59cm-14x23in) s.d. gouache prov. 23-Nov-3 Cornette de St.Cyr, Paris #221/R

LEPRIN, Marcel (1891-1933) French

£838 $1500 €1223 View of a cathedral (61x51cm-24x20in) s. 20-Mar-4 Selkirks, St. Louis #531/R est:1800-2500
£9000 $16380 €13500 Lieutenance a Honfleur (47x56cm-19x22in) s. 4-Jul-4 Eric Pillon, Calais #138/R

Works on paper

£625 $1150 €950 Lavoir sur la place animee (33x46cm-13x18in) s. gouache. 22-Jun-4 Chassaing Rivet, Toulouse #308

LEPRINCE, Auguste Xavier (attrib) (1799-1826) French

£600 $1086 €900 Le port de Honfleur (46x32cm-18x13in) exhib. 30-Mar-4 Rossini, Paris #1026/R

LEPRINCE, Jean Baptiste (1734-1781) French

£5500 $9515 €8030 Portrait of a bearded man, head and shoulders, dressed in Oriental costume (60x49cm-24x19in) oval prov. 11-Dec-3 Sotheby's, London #217/R est:6000-8000

Works on paper

£380 $700 €555 Russian Girl (20x15cm-8x6in) ink wash prov. 26-Jun-4 Sloans & Kenyon, Bethesda #1021/R
£437 $800 €638 Two women in Russian costume (21x17cm-8x7in) pen brown ink. 29-Jan-4 Swann Galleries, New York #233/R
£900 $1557 €1314 Chinese presenting a potted plant to two Chinese girls (18x35cm-7x14in) red chk brown ink wash arched. 12-Dec-3 Christie's, Kensington #452/R
£986 $1766 €1450 Tete de vieillard barbu (36x27cm-14x11in) chl htd white. 17-Mar-4 Maigret, Paris #71/R
£1879 $3458 €2800 Renaud et armide (20x24cm-8x9in) s.d.1761 pen grey wash prov. 24-Mar-4 Claude Boisgirard, Paris #15/R est:3000
£2292 $3735 €3300 Children in park (34x48cm-13x19in) pen wash. 25-Sep-3 Dr Fritz Nagel, Stuttgart #1161/R est:2900

LEPRINCE, Jean Baptiste (attrib) (1734-1781) French

£11111 $20000 €16222 Chinoiserie with man smoking pipe (45x38cm-18x15in) prov. 22-Jan-4 Sotheby's, New York #97/R est:20000-30000
£14043 $25137 €20503 Temple interior with figures in front to the Goddess Minerva (45x54cm-18x21in) brown oil prov. 25-May-4 Bukowskis, Stockholm #503/R est:20000-25000 (S.KR 190000)

Works on paper

£320 $589 €480 Joueur de mandoline et cosaque du Don (15x22cm-6x9in) bears sig. mono.i. graphite W/C. 11-Jun-4 Maigret, Paris #23/R
£612 $1096 €900 Cosque du don et guitariste Russe (15x23cm-6x9in) i. bears mono. black crayon grey wash W/C. 17-Mar-4 Tajan, Paris #68
£1034 $1717 €1500 Figures assises pres de riviere (15x22cm-6x9in) graphite chk. 30-Sep-3 Christie's, Paris #6/R est:1500-2000

LEPRINCE, Robert Leopold (1800-1847) French

£2000 $3620 €3000 Wedding. First Communion (33x41cm-13x16in) s.d.1825 pair. 1-Apr-4 Van Ham, Cologne #1510/R est:2200

£4800 $8688 €7200 Jetee du Havre (22x30cm-9x12in) s.i.d.1823 verso oil paper on cardboard exhib.lit. 30-Mar-4 Rossini, Paris #262/R est:1500-2500
£10000 $18400 €15000 Paysage au moulin (41x65cm-16x26in) s. 11-Jun-4 Claude Aguttes, Neuilly #5/R est:10000-12000
Works on paper
£510 $913 €750 Scene d'interieur (21x27cm-8x11in) s. W/C gouache black pencil grattages. 19-Mar-4 Piasa, Paris #144

LEPROHON, Gisele Leclerc (1931-) Canadian
£1208 $2163 €1764 Visages (124x272cm-49x107in) s.d.76. 22-Mar-4 Waddingtons, Toronto #635/R est:300-500 (C.D 2900)

LEQUESNE, Eugène L (1815-1887) French
Sculpture
£2400 $4080 €3504 Faune dansant (48cm-19in) s.i. pat bronze. 28-Oct-3 Sotheby's, London #96/R

LERAY, Léon (1901-1976) French
£280 $507 €420 Beloning (36x30cm-14x12in) studio st. panel. 30-Mar-4 Campo & Campo, Antwerp #160/R

LERAY, Prudent Louis (1820-1879) French
£1348 $2250 €1900 Public house with officer reading (32x40cm-13x16in) s. panel. 20-Oct-3 Glerum, Amsterdam #36/R est:3000-5000

LERBERGHE, Karel van (1899-1953) Dutch
£333 $557 €480 Mill in landscape (55x65cm-22x26in) s. 21-Oct-3 Campo & Campo, Antwerp #329

LERCHE, Freddie A (1937-) Danish
£371 $664 €542 Blue No.1 (61x95cm-24x37in) s.d.78 verso. 10-May-4 Rasmussen, Vejle #528/R (D.KR 4100)
£1792 $3226 €2616 Interior I (118x90cm-46x35in) s.d.62 exhib. 24-Apr-4 Rasmussen, Havnen #4073 est:6000 (D.KR 20000)

LERCHE, Vincent Stoltenberg (1837-1892) Norwegian
£426 $681 €618 Monk in archway (18x21cm-7x8in) s. 22-Sep-3 Blomqvist, Lysaker #1195/R (N.KR 5000)
£470 $864 €700 In the chapel (29x22cm-11x9in) s. panel. 27-Mar-4 L & B, Essen #147/R
£650 $1197 €975 Monastery interior (40x30cm-16x12in) s. panel. 14-Jun-4 Blomqvist, Lysaker #1226/R (N.KR 8000)
Works on paper
£402 $736 €587 From a monastery, Venice (41x27cm-16x11in) W/C. 2-Feb-4 Blomqvist, Lysaker #1169 (N.KR 5000)

LERDAL, Thoralf (1888-1961) Norwegian
£273 $500 €399 Hans (60x50cm-24x20in) s. 2-Feb-4 Blomqvist, Lysaker #1170 (N.KR 3400)

LERE, Mark (1950-) American
Works on paper
£649 $1200 €948 Bird in Palm (135x107cm-53x42in) indis.s.i. pencil W/C on herculene drafting film exec 1986 prov. 12-Feb-4 Sotheby's, New York #318/R

LERFELDT, Hans Henrik (1946-1990) Danish
£722 $1329 €1054 Long haired woman with green drapery (30x22cm-12x9in) s.d.1976 verso prov.lit. 29-Mar-4 Rasmussen, Copenhagen #283/R (D.KR 8000)
£857 $1578 €1251 Composition with man in sofa (35x25cm-14x10in) s.d.1974 board exhib.prov. 29-Mar-4 Rasmussen, Copenhagen #289/R (D.KR 9500)
£903 $1661 €1318 Through the letterbox (6x27cm-2x11in) s.d.1972 canvas on panel exhib.prov. 29-Mar-4 Rasmussen, Copenhagen #300/R (D.KR 10000)
£1083 $1993 €1581 Sphinx Boulevard, 1930 - Kurt Weill (17x12cm-7x5in) s.d.78 verso board exhib.prov. 29-Mar-4 Rasmussen, Copenhagen #301/R (D.KR 12000)
£1264 $2325 €1845 Sphinx Boulevard - black gloves on woman (17x12cm-7x5in) s.d.1978 verso board prov.exhib.lit. 29-Mar-4 Rasmussen, Copenhagen #296/R est:20000 (D.KR 14000)
£1354 $2491 €1977 Museum of the night (30x22cm-12x9in) s.d.18/12 1976 verso board exhib.prov. 29-Mar-4 Rasmussen, Copenhagen #287/R est:20000 (D.KR 15000)
£1354 $2491 €1977 Sphinx Boulevard, 1936 - Diana Mitford (17x12cm-7x5in) s.d.1978 verso board exhib.prov. 29-Mar-4 Rasmussen, Copenhagen #302/R est:20000 (D.KR 15000)
£1354 $2532 €1977 Self-portrait (33x23cm-13x9in) s.d.24.8.1988 verso. 25-Feb-4 Kunsthallen, Copenhagen #15/R est:15000 (D.KR 15000)
£1444 $2657 €2108 Siegfried's death (40x30cm-16x12in) s.d.1973 verso board exhib.prov. 29-Mar-4 Rasmussen, Copenhagen #306/R est:20000 (D.KR 16000)
£1534 $2823 €2240 Long haired woman with brown drapery (30x22cm-12x9in) s/d/1976 verso board prov.lit. 29-Mar-4 Rasmussen, Copenhagen #309/R est:8000-12000 (D.KR 17000)
£2166 $3986 €3162 Sphinx Boulevard, Edgar Quinet 1939 (17x12cm-7x5in) s.d.1978 verso board exhib.prov. 29-Mar-4 Rasmussen, Copenhagen #299/R est:20000 (D.KR 24000)
£2166 $3986 €3162 Magic meeting (65x54cm-26x21in) s.d.1975 verso exhib.prov. 29-Mar-4 Rasmussen, Copenhagen #305/R est:30000 (D.KR 24000)
£2437 $4484 €3558 Sphinx Boulevard, Freddie 1938 (17x12cm-7x5in) s.d.78 board exhib.prov. 29-Mar-4 Rasmussen, Copenhagen #298/R est:20000 (D.KR 27000)
£2798 $5148 €4085 Hotel la Potiniere (73x60cm-29x24in) s.d.76 verso prov. 29-Mar-4 Rasmussen, Copenhagen #297/R est:30000-40000 (D.KR 31000)
£5596 $10296 €8170 Nature waking after the rain (100x81cm-39x32in) s.d.sep-nov 1974 verso prov.exhib.lit. 29-Mar-4 Rasmussen, Copenhagen #307/R est:60000-80000 (D.KR 62000)
£6318 $11625 €9224 Black innocence (100x81cm-39x32in) s.d.1977-78 verso prov.exhib.lit. 29-Mar-4 Rasmussen, Copenhagen #284/R est:80000-100000 (D.KR 70000)
£6385 $10663 €9322 Seated young woman (45x35cm-18x14in) s.d.1978 verso canvasboard exhib.prov. 7-Oct-3 Rasmussen, Copenhagen #109/R est:50000 (D.KR 68000)
Works on paper
£280 $515 €409 Kneeling model (31x23cm-12x9in) s.d.84 Indian ink prov. 29-Mar-4 Rasmussen, Copenhagen #288 (D.KR 3100)
£289 $531 €422 Figure composition (31x25cm-12x10in) s.d.1973 W/C chk prov. 29-Mar-4 Rasmussen, Copenhagen #294 (D.KR 3200)
£438 $688 €639 Composition with figures by coast (13x18cm-5x7in) s. s.i.d.1975 verso W/C Indian ink. 30-Aug-3 Rasmussen, Havnen #4411 (D.KR 4700)
£451 $830 €658 Sleeping girl and grasshopper (19x23cm-7x9in) s.d.80 W/C Indian ink pencil. 29-Mar-4 Rasmussen, Copenhagen #329 (D.KR 5000)
£496 $913 €724 Standing model stripped to the waist (31x23cm-12x9in) s.d.84 Indian ink prov. 29-Mar-4 Rasmussen, Copenhagen #290 (D.KR 5500)
£542 $996 €791 Nude woman (31x23cm-12x9in) s.d.1984 Indian ink pr. 29-Mar-4 Rasmussen, Copenhagen #292 (D.KR 6000)
£632 $1162 €923 Self-portrait with sunglasses (31x23cm-12x9in) Indian ink htd white prov. 29-Mar-4 Rasmussen, Copenhagen #281/R (D.KR 7000)
£1173 $2159 €1713 Self-portrait with painting in background (46x35cm-18x14in) s.d.82 Indian ink prov. 29-Mar-4 Rasmussen, Copenhagen #308/R est:10000 (D.KR 13000)
£1218 $2278 €1778 Making love (19x25cm-7x10in) s.d.80 W/C lit. 25-Feb-4 Kunsthallen, Copenhagen #38/R est:8000 (D.KR 13500)
£1443 $2669 €2107 Erotic scenes (30x23cm-12x9in) s.d.76 crayon pencil W/C pair. 15-Mar-4 Rasmussen, Vejle #578/R est:12000-15000 (D.KR 16000)
£1878 $3136 €2742 Erotic figure composition (36x50cm-14x20in) s. W/C prov. 7-Oct-3 Rasmussen, Copenhagen #197/R est:20000-25000 (D.KR 20000)
£2076 $3882 €3031 Street scene, Berlin (35x49cm-14x19in) s.d.88 W/C exhib. 25-Feb-4 Kunsthallen, Copenhagen #79/R est:25000 (D.KR 23000)
£2347 $3920 €3427 Double image (30x22cm-12x9in) s.d.81 gouache airbrush lit. 7-Oct-3 Rasmussen, Copenhagen #81/R est:25000 (D.KR 25000)
£2708 $4982 €3954 Rainbow ends (60x44cm-24x17in) s.d.1975 W/C in yellow prov.exhib.lit. 29-Mar-4 Rasmussen, Copenhagen #282/R est:40000 (D.KR 30000)
£2708 $5063 €3954 Model (62x44cm-24x17in) s.d.88 W/C. 25-Feb-4 Kunsthallen, Copenhagen #30/R est:30000 (D.KR 30000)
£2888 $5314 €4216 Double image (49x35cm-19x14in) s.d.80-81 air brush W/C. 29-Mar-4 Rasmussen, Copenhagen #280/R est:30000 (D.KR 32000)
£3286 $5488 €4798 Poor Cinderella (30x22cm-12x9in) s. gouache airbrush lit.exhib. 7-Oct-3 Rasmussen, Copenhagen #80/R est:35000 (D.KR 35000)
£3610 $6643 €5271 Wonders of the unseen world - erotic scene with woman and grasshopper (61x45cm-24x18in) s.d.81 W/C air brush prov.exhib.lit. 29-Mar-4 Rasmussen, Copenhagen #286/R est:50000 (D.KR 40000)
£3763 $6397 €5494 Sweet reason (32x26cm-13x10in) s.d.80 W/C exhib.lit. 26-Nov-3 Kunsthallen, Copenhagen #96/R est:25000 (D.KR 40000)
£4964 $9134 €7247 L'univers bleu (47x33cm-19x13in) s.d.86 col pencil exhib.prov. 29-Mar-4 Rasmussen, Copenhagen #285/R est:30000-40000 (D.KR 55000)
£5235 $9632 €7643 L'univers bleu (60x44cm-24x17in) s.d.86 W/C in blue exhib.prov. 29-Mar-4 Rasmussen, Copenhagen #310/R est:40000 (D.KR 58000)
£8303 $15278 €12122 Vanitas picture - woman and veil and fly (46x31cm-18x12in) s. W/C air brush prov.exhib.lit. 29-Mar-4 Rasmussen, Copenhagen #303/R est:40000 (D.KR 92000)
£9657 $17769 €14099 The key of dreams - Vanitas picture (50x36cm-20x14in) s.d.1980 W/C air brush prov.lit. 29-Mar-4 Rasmussen, Copenhagen #304/R est:40000 (D.KR 107000)

LERGAARD, Niels (1893-1982) Danish
£3249 $5978 €4744 Woman and man by the sea (60x80cm-24x31in) init.d.52 prov. 29-Mar-4 Rasmussen, Copenhagen #203/R est:30000 (D.KR 36000)
£8123 $14946 €11860 Interior scene with two women (93x105cm-37x41in) s. painted c.1955 prov. 29-Mar-4 Rasmussen, Copenhagen #201/R est:100000 (D.KR 90000)

LERIUS, Joseph Henri François van (1823-1876) Belgian
£7500 $13650 €10950 Jeune fille de la paroisse de rittvik dans dalarne (114x77cm-45x30in) s.d.1862 i.stretcher. 16-Jun-4 Bonhams, New Bond Street #6/R est:8000-12000

LERNER, Arthur (1929-) American
Works on paper
£429 $750 €626 Red beans and ricely yours (34x20cm-13x8in) ink two attached pieces of paper on board exec 1955 lit. 17-Dec-3 Christie's, Rockefeller NY #14/R

LERNER, Nathan (1913-1997) American?
Photographs
£2275 $3800 €3322 Eye and nails (34x27cm-13x11in) s.i.d.40 gelatin silver print lit. 16-Oct-3 Phillips, New York #133/R est:1200-1800

LERNOUT, Ward (1931-) Belgian
£274 $466 €400 Jeune femme de face (33x25cm-13x10in) s. panel. 10-Nov-3 Horta, Bruxelles #265

LERO, T (?) ?
£898 $1500 €1311 Portrait. s. enamel. 18-Oct-3 Harvey Clar, Oakland #1570

LEROUX COMENDADOR, M (19/20th C) Italian
£709 $1149 €1000 Roma vista dal Pincio (35x45cm-14x18in) s. 22-May-3 Stadion, Trieste #377/R

LEROUX, Andre (1911-) French
£1300 $2353 €1950 Nature morte a l'encrier et maquet de bateaux (46x38cm-18x15in) s.d.1935. 4-Apr-4 Salle des ventes Pillet, Lyon la Foret #41/R est:2000-2500
Works on paper
£347 $566 €500 La lande Bretonne (52x87cm-20x34in) mono. gouache. 21-Jul-3 Lesieur & Le Bars, Le Havre #70

LEROUX, Auguste (1871-1954) French
£667 $1200 €974 Le Mont St Victor. Scene Voisin Fontainebleau (30x41cm-12x16in) first canvas second board painted c.1889 two. 22-Jan-4 Swann Galleries, New York #73
£979 $1664 €1400 Nu devant le miroir (80x64cm-31x25in) s. 1-Dec-3 Palais de Beaux Arts, Brussels #361
£1348 $2507 €1968 Lady with parasol and wearing white dress on the beach at St.Brieue (19x24cm-7x9in) s. 2-Mar-4 Rasmussen, Copenhagen #1619/R est:15000 (D.KR 15000)

LEROUX, Gaston (1854-1942) French
Sculpture
£1325 $2424 €2000 Young Oriental couple at a well (69cm-27in) s. cols painted spelter. 6-Apr-4 Sotheby's, Amsterdam #390/R est:3000-5000
£2535 $4208 €3600 La lecture de Coran - seated Arab (65cm-26in) s. brown pat. bronze. 11-Jun-3 Sotheby's, Amsterdam #329/R est:4000-6000
£2649 $4821 €4000 Seated Arab smoking (88cm-35in) i. pat bronze. 18-Jun-4 Bolland & Marotz, Bremen #1049/R est:2700
£4546 $7819 €6500 Lecture du Coran (68cm-27in) i.base pat bronze. 8-Dec-3 Tajan, Paris #297/R est:6000-7000

LEROUX, Georges (1877-1957) French
£563 $975 €800 Marechal-ferrand dans un village (27x35cm-11x14in) s. panel. 14-Dec-3 Eric Pillon, Calais #114/R
Works on paper
£349 $600 €510 Grazing horses near a mill (25x46cm-10x18in) s.d.1918 conte crayon. 7-Dec-3 Treadway Gallery, Cincinnati #479/R

LEROUX, Henri (1872-1942) Belgian
£270 $476 €400 Estacade de Newport (33x41cm-13x16in) s. 18-May-4 Galerie Moderne, Brussels #130/R
£426 $711 €600 Borinage (80x101cm-31x40in) s. i.verso. 15-Oct-3 Hotel des Ventes Mosan, Brussels #172

LEROUX, Le Roux Smith (1914-1963) South African
£661 $1182 €965 Figure with two horses (80x94cm-31x37in) s.d.44. 31-May-4 Stephan Welz, Johannesburg #540 (SA.R 8000)

LEROUX, Louis Hector (1829-1900) French
£1736 $2743 €2500 Poetess Sappho in contemplation (65x34cm-26x13in) s. 2-Sep-3 Christie's, Amsterdam #183/R est:2000-3000

LEROY, Camille (1905-1995) French?
£800 $1472 €1200 Le Chenoua pres d'Alger (46x55cm-18x22in) s. 14-Jun-4 Gros & Delettrez, Paris #215/R

LEROY, Eugène (1910-2000) French
£7075 $12664 €10400 Nu allonge (65x100cm-26x39in) s. 19-Mar-4 Millon & Associes, Paris #189/R est:7000-8000
£8163 $14612 €12000 Visage (81x54cm-32x21in) s. 19-Mar-4 Millon & Associes, Paris #187/R est:6000-8000
£8503 $15221 €12500 Paysage (195x130cm-77x51in) s. prov. 19-Mar-4 Millon & Associes, Paris #188/R est:12000-15000
£10204 $18265 €15000 Personnages (195x130cm-77x51in) s. indis.d. s.verso prov. 19-Mar-4 Millon & Associes, Paris #186/R est:12000-15000
£10564 $18275 €15000 Juif errant (150x74cm-59x29in) s.i.d.1968 verso prov.exhib. 9-Dec-3 Artcurial Briest, Paris #401/R est:15000-20000
£13986 $23776 €20000 Figure (130x130cm-51x51in) s. fabric on canvas prov. 1-Dec-3 Palais de Beaux Arts, Brussels #173/R est:20000-30000
Works on paper
£1321 $2140 €1929 Les trois graces (63x48cm-25x19in) s.d.1961 pencil. 24-May-3 Burkhard, Luzern #137/R est:2800-3400 (S.FR 2800)
£2254 $3899 €3200 Untitled (49x64cm-19x25in) s.d.82 chl gouache prov. 9-Dec-3 Artcurial Briest, Paris #488/R est:2000-2500

LEROY, George B (19th C) ?
£699 $1168 €1000 Brittany (50x100cm-20x39in) s. 30-Jun-3 Ansorena, Madrid #247/R

LEROY, Henri (1851-?) French
Works on paper
£967 $1769 €1450 Chatte et chatons (35x45cm-14x18in) s. pastel cardboard. 6-Jun-4 Osenat, Fontainebleau #244/R

LEROY, Jean Francois (20th C) French?
Sculpture
£5417 $9208 €7800 La horde (19x99cm-7x39in) num.I/IV brown pat bronze Cast Bronze Lauragaise. 28-Oct-3 Rabourdin & Choppin de Janvry, Paris #79/R est:10000-11000

LEROY, Jules (1833-1865) French
£1197 $2071 €1700 Still life with roses (28x37cm-11x15in) s.d.1858 panel. 13-Dec-3 Lempertz, Koln #230/R est:1500

LEROY, Jules (1856-1921) French
£444 $800 €648 Little tiger (22x16cm-9x6in) s. init.i.verso. 21-Jan-4 Sotheby's, New York #259/R
£667 $1227 €1000 Chatons devant leur assiette (21x27cm-8x11in) s. panel. 9-Jun-4 Le Roux & Morel, Paris #35/R
£839 $1427 €1200 Chaton au cigare (30cm-12in circular) s. panel. 1-Dec-3 Palais de Beaux Arts, Brussels #370/R
£900 $1656 €1350 Chaton termine l'assiette (35x27cm-14x11in) s. 14-Jun-4 Cornette de St.Cyr, Paris #80/R
£1250 $2000 €1825 Kitten with a timepiece (30x25cm-12x10in) s. 19-Sep-3 Freeman, Philadelphia #95/R est:1500-2500
£1377 $2300 €2010 Cat and kittens (86x76cm-34x30in) s. 14-Nov-3 Aspire, Cleveland #39 est:3000-4000
£1457 $2652 €2200 Les chats (41x33cm-16x13in) s. 16-Jun-4 Renaud, Paris #34/R est:800-1000
£1797 $3342 €2624 Three cats playing in a smart interior (65x54cm-26x21in) s. 2-Mar-4 Rasmussen, Copenhagen #1605/R est:20000 (D.KR 20000)
£1818 $3091 €2600 L'assiette de lait (27x35cm-11x14in) s. 28-Nov-3 Doutrebente, Paris #39/R est:3000-4000
£4196 $7217 €6000 Chatons devant une bonne assiette. Chatons a la pelote de laine. Chatons a la rose. s. panel five one frame. 8-Dec-3 Cornette de St.Cyr, Paris #67/R est:6000-8000

LEROY, Louis Joseph (1812-1885) French
£6667 $12067 €10000 Chats jouant dans une grange (127x159cm-50x63in) s.d.1839 prov.exhib.lit. 31-Mar-4 Sotheby's, Paris #89/R est:10000-15000

LEROY, Patrick (1948-) French
£385 $642 €550 Promenade au bord de lac (71x59cm-28x23in) s. panel. 29-Jun-3 Eric Pillon, Calais #275/R
£470 $841 €700 Composition a l'as de coeur (61x52cm-24x20in) s. panel. 30-May-4 Eric Pillon, Calais #281/R
£537 $961 €800 Composition (85x68cm-33x27in) s. panel. 30-May-4 Eric Pillon, Calais #280/R
£582 $990 €850 Promenade en bord de riviere (71x58cm-28x23in) s. panel. 9-Nov-3 Eric Pillon, Calais #248/R
£867 $1577 €1300 Petite riviere traversant le village medieval (65x55cm-26x22in) s.panel. 4-Jul-4 Eric Pillon, Calais #251/R
£872 $1614 €1300 Village (89x71cm-35x28in) s. panel. 14-Mar-4 Eric Pillon, Calais #267/R

LEROY, Paul Alexandre Alfred (1860-1942) French
£3191 $5330 €4500 Cavalier dans l'oasis de Biskra (46x33cm-18x13in) s.i.d.1908. 16-Jun-3 Gros & Delettrez, Paris #419/R est:2300-3000

LERRY, William (fl.1860-1870) British
£750 $1245 €1095 Snowy landscape (33x43cm-13x17in) s. 1-Oct-3 Sotheby's, Olympia #138/R

LERSY, Roger (1920-) French
£380 $695 €555 Trotteur (44x53cm-17x21in) s.d.58 exhib. 8-Jul-4 Lawrence, Crewkerne #1625
£490 $842 €700 Composition a la voile (116x81cm-46x32in) s.d.1960. 3-Dec-3 Fraysse & Associes, Paris #104

LESAGE, Augustin (1876-1954) French
£3867 $6960 €5800 Untitled (58x45cm-23x18in) s. 26-Apr-4 Tajan, Paris #392/R est:2500-3000
£4225 $7310 €6000 Scene religieuse (100x73cm-39x29in) s.d.1940. 9-Dec-3 Artcurial Briest, Paris #470/R est:3800-4200
£4334 $7801 €6500 Composition symbolique (58x45cm-23x18in) s.i. 26-Apr-4 Tajan, Paris #394/R est:2500-3000

LESAGRE, Julia (attrib) (19th C) ?
Works on paper
£569 $950 €831 European square with bronze statue of a horse and rider (36x51cm-14x20in) s. W/C. 27-Oct-3 O'Gallerie, Oregon #809/R

LESIEUR, Pierre (1922-) French
£367 $660 €550 La Seine et l'Institut (22x27cm-9x11in) s.d.1941. 22-Apr-4 Christie's, Paris #247
£581 $1000 €848 La petite plage (100x100cm-39x39in) s.d.65 prov. 3-Dec-3 Doyle, New York #43/R est:2000-3000
£594 $993 €850 Paysage (22x33cm-9x13in) s.d.84. 25-Jun-3 Blanchet, Paris #88/R
£660 $1102 €950 Composition (50x61cm-20x24in) s.d.1962. 25-Oct-3 Cornette de St.Cyr, Paris #524
£733 $1320 €1100 Timbale de violettes (24x19cm-9x7in) s.d.1941. 22-Apr-4 Christie's, Paris #248/R
£2282 $4176 €3400 Composition (81x76cm-32x30in) s.d.57. 7-Jul-4 Artcurial Briest, Paris #302 est:1000-1500
£5594 $9343 €8000 Interieur au pot vert (100x100cm-39x39in) s.d. prov. 7-Oct-3 Livinec, Gaudcheau & Jezequel, Rennes #154/R

LESKI, Soloman (1928-) ?
£600 $1020 €876 Indoor pursuits (61x51cm-24x20in) s. 6-Nov-3 Christie's, Kensington #833/R

LESKOSCHEK, Axel (1889-1976) Austrian
£259 $480 €389 Rural scene (58x38cm-23x15in) init.d.52 masonite. 14-Jul-4 American Auctioneer #490409/R
Works on paper
£467 $840 €700 Brazilian landscape (25x35cm-10x14in) mono.d.40 pencil W/C. 22-Apr-4 Dorotheum, Graz #63/R

LESLIE (?) British
£1189 $2200 €1736 Figures by a mountain lake (30x61cm-12x24in) 12-Mar-4 Du Mouchelle, Detroit #2140/R est:1500-2000

LESLIE, Alfred (1927-) American
Works on paper
£378 $700 €552 Untitled (100x75cm-39x30in) s.d.1972 pencil prov. 12-Feb-4 Sotheby's, New York #191/R
£2703 $5000 €3946 Second drawing for Act and Portrait (70x87cm-28x34in) s.i.d.1970 pencil prov. 12-Feb-4 Sotheby's, New York #196/R est:800-1200

LESLIE, Charles (1835-1890) British
£380 $680 €555 Gynant, in North Wales (74x112cm-29x44in) s.d.1876. 6-Jan-4 Gildings, Market Harborough #423/R
£400 $716 €584 Moonlight in the Highlands (28x51cm-11x20in) s.d.1876. 6-Jan-4 Gildings, Market Harborough #424/R
£500 $835 €730 Primitive harvest scene (49x75cm-19x30in) 21-Oct-3 Bruton Knowles, Cheltenham #481

£500 $935 €730 Helwellyn (30x61cm-12x24in) s.d.1881. 20-Jul-4 Sworder & Son, Bishops Stortford #763/R
£520 $900 €759 Pit Head (36x72cm-14x28in) s.d.1875. 10-Dec-3 Bonhams, Bury St Edmunds #596/R
£652 $1200 €952 Landscape with lake and mountain vista (41x61cm-16x24in) s. 27-Jun-4 Hindman, Chicago #789/R est:1000-2000
£680 $1272 €1020 Anglers in a Highland river (60x95cm-24x37in) s. 26-Jul-4 Bonhams, Bath #70/R
£700 $1092 €1022 Mountainous lake scene with shepherd and flock (28x58cm-11x23in) s. 25-Mar-3 Andrew Smith, Winchester #123
£780 $1459 €1139 On the Aber, North Wales (11x23cm-4x9in) s.d.1881 i.stretcher. 25-Feb-4 Mallams, Oxford #207/R
£800 $1336 €1168 Llyn Taly-Llyn, Wales (46x81cm-18x32in) s.d.1884 i.verso. 13-Nov-3 Christie's, Kensington #190/R
£800 $1496 €1168 Loch Lindsay, Scotland (12x23cm-5x9in) s.d.1881 i.stretcher. 25-Feb-4 Mallams, Oxford #136/R
£820 $1337 €1197 Moonrise over a mountain lake (44x76cm-17x30in) s.d.1881 mono.verso. 25-Sep-3 Mellors & Kirk, Nottingham #753/R
£950 $1501 €1378 On the Thames, Wargrave. Evening near Medmenham (51x76cm-20x30in) pair. 3-Sep-3 Bonhams, Bury St Edmunds #420
£1100 $1837 €1606 Hoel Siabod, north Wales (30x61cm-12x24in) 13-Nov-3 Christie's, Kensington #186 est:400-600
£1700 $2941 €2482 Callandar Brig from the River Vennachar an extensive landscape with figures (46x89cm-18x35in) 11-Dec-3 Neales, Nottingham #646/R est:500-700
£1900 $3534 €2774 Evening, Lyn Nant. Highland landscape (30x61cm-12x24in) s.d.1878-79 pair. 4-Mar-4 Christie's, Kensington #515/R est:2000-3000
£2100 $3507 €3066 Cattle watering in a Welsh landscape. Anglers by a lake (30x25cm-12x10in) indis.i.stretcher pair. 13-Nov-3 Christie's, Kensington #191/R est:1500-2000

LESLIE, Charles Robert (1794-1859) British
£1200 $2160 €1752 Katherine of Aragon in her bed chamber at Kimbolton Castle (39x53cm-15x21in) s. 21-Jan-4 Sotheby's, Olympia #282/R est:800-1200
£11000 $18700 €16060 Ben Lawers from Ben Ledi, looking across Loch Tay (97x154cm-38x61in) s.d.1874. 30-Oct-3 Christie's, London #69/R est:4000-6000
Works on paper
£17000 $29920 €24820 Head and shoulders portrait of the poet S T Coleridge (31x27cm-12x11in) i. pencil chl white chk blue/grey paper prov. 19-May-4 Rupert Toovey, Partridge Green #3/R est:3000-5000

LESLIE, George Dunlop (1835-1921) British
£3600 $6552 €5256 Riverside, Wallingford, Berks (130x94cm-51x37in) 17-Jun-4 Gorringes, Worthing #682/R est:4000-6000

LESLIE, Robert Charles (attrib) (fl.1843-1887) British
£699 $1189 €1000 Scottish Highlands (30x61cm-12x24in) s.d.1879. 20-Nov-3 Van Ham, Cologne #1713

LESNIEWICZ, Horst (1926-) German
£280 $481 €400 Kino (57x67cm-22x26in) i.d.1981 verso. 5-Dec-3 Bolland & Marotz, Bremen #841

LESREL, Adolphe Alexandre (1839-1929) French
£2600 $4784 €3796 Cavalier (25x20cm-10x8in) s.d.1879. 25-Mar-4 Christie's, Kensington #191/R est:3000-5000
£2900 $4582 €4205 Cavalier reading at a table (15x11cm-6x4in) s.d.1895 board. 24-Jul-3 Dominic Winter, Swindon #106/R est:1000-1500
£2937 $5052 €4200 Le bon verre (35x25cm-14x10in) s.d.1907 panel. 2-Dec-3 Campo & Campo, Antwerp #209/R est:4000-5000
£4514 $7132 €6500 The surprise (65x51cm-26x20in) s.d.1891 lit. 19-Sep-3 Schloss Ahlden, Ahlden #1474/R est:6800
£6800 $12172 €9928 Good vintage (35x25cm-14x10in) s.d.1907 panel. 26-May-4 Sotheby's, Olympia #257/R est:4000-6000
£15882 $27000 €23188 Collectors (58x48cm-23x19in) s.d.1896 panel. 28-Oct-3 Sotheby's, New York #156/R est:20000-25000
£35000 $63700 €51100 Music party (58x48cm-23x19in) s.d.1894 panel prov. 16-Jun-4 Bonhams, New Bond Street #96/R est:35000-45000
£41667 $65833 €60000 Morning hour (140x100cm-55x39in) s. lit. 19-Sep-3 Schloss Ahlden, Ahlden #1537/R est:65000

LESSI, Giovanni (1852-1922) Italian
£1033 $1850 €1550 Riding (24x33cm-9x13in) s. 12-May-4 Stadion, Trieste #643/R est:500-700

LESSI, Tito (1858-1917) Italian
Works on paper
£282 $487 €400 Study (33x15cm-13x6in) s. W/C paper on card. 9-Dec-3 Pandolfini, Florence #71/R

LESSIEUX, Ernest Louis (1848-1925) French
£7447 $12436 €10500 Les marchands de fruits sur la plage (81x117cm-32x46in) s.i.d.1913. 16-Jun-3 Gros & Delettrez, Paris #34/R est:8000-10000
Works on paper
£282 $519 €412 Mediterranean coastal scene (15x28cm-6x11in) s. W/C prov. 9-Jun-4 Walker's, Ottawa #320/R (C.D 700)
£300 $510 €438 Toledo (44x27cm-17x11in) s. W/C. 25-Nov-3 Bonhams, Knightsbridge #42/R
£413 $756 €603 Chemin sur la Cote d'Azur (28x46cm-11x18in) s. W/C. 5-Jun-4 Galerie du Rhone, Sion #207 (S.FR 950)
£440 $717 €638 Evening on Cape Martin, the French Riviera (27x46cm-11x18in) s. W/C. 23-Sep-3 Bonhams, Knightsbridge #28/R
£533 $981 €800 Pergola au bord de la mer (32x48cm-13x19in) s.i.d.aout 1924 gouache. 14-Jun-4 Tajan, Paris #23
£645 $1187 €942 Italian coastal village (28x47cm-11x19in) s. W/C prov. 9-Jun-4 Walker's, Ottawa #321 (C.D 1600)
£867 $1577 €1300 Fez, marchand de lampes (47x29cm-19x11in) s.i. W/C. 4-Jul-4 Eric Pillon, Calais #23/R
£1000 $1840 €1460 Exotic blooms by the church steps. Bridge above a viaduct (43x29cm-17x11in) s. pencil W/C pair. 25-Mar-4 Christie's, Kensington #116/R est:1000-1500

LESSING, Karl Friedrich (1808-1880) German
£667 $1207 €1000 Battle scene at besieged town (32x34cm-13x13in) mono. panel. 1-Apr-4 Van Ham, Cologne #1512
£6294 $10510 €9000 Hunter resting in wood (45x67cm-18x26in) mono.d.1839 panel. 10-Oct-3 Winterberg, Heidelberg #685/R est:4800
Works on paper
£400 $716 €600 Woodland source (18x23cm-7x9in) mono. pen. 13-May-4 Bassenge, Berlin #5064

LESSING, Konrad Ludwig (1852-1916) German
£331 $603 €500 Konigssee with St Bartholoma (77x96cm-30x38in) s.d.06. 19-Jun-4 Dannenberg, Berlin #590/R
£733 $1327 €1100 Eifel landscape (68x83cm-27x33in) s. board. 1-Apr-4 Van Ham, Cologne #1511/R
£1745 $3211 €2600 Walkenried in southern Harz (87x132cm-34x52in) s.i. 24-Mar-4 Hugo Ruef, Munich #1029/R est:2600
£2083 $3396 €3000 Rocky landscape with sheep (135x180cm-53x71in) s.i.d.1889. 24-Sep-3 Neumeister, Munich #478/R est:2400
£3691 $6607 €5500 On the way to church (68x118cm-27x46in) s. canvas on board. 27-May-4 Dorotheum, Vienna #218/R est:6500-7500

LESSORE, Émile (1805-1876) French
£2270 $3700 €3314 Flower girls (30x46cm-12x18in) s. prov. 19-Jul-3 Skinner, Boston #33 est:1000-1500

LESSORE, Jules (1849-1892) French/British
£1600 $2944 €2336 French harbour scene (60x89cm-24x35in) s. 8-Jun-4 Bonhams, Knightsbridge #241/R est:500-800
Works on paper
£300 $555 €438 Beached sailing boat (49x34cm-19x13in) s. W/C. 16-Feb-4 Bonhams, Bath #185
£500 $895 €730 Crowded Clyde (26x48cm-10x19in) s. pencil W/C htd white. 26-May-4 Christie's, Kensington #457/R

LESSORE, Therese (1884-1945) French
£420 $672 €609 Recital (91x91cm-36x36in) 16-Sep-3 Bonhams, Knightsbridge #73/R
£1800 $3096 €2628 Assembly rooms, Bath (61x86cm-24x34in) s.d.40 exhib. 3-Dec-3 Christie's, Kensington #453/R est:1500-2000
Works on paper
£320 $550 €467 Seated girl (38x28cm-15x11in) s. pencil W/C chl red crayon. 3-Dec-3 Christie's, Kensington #419/R

LESTER, Adrienne (19/20th C) British
£462 $800 €675 Portrait of a Newfoundland dog (69x58cm-27x23in) s. 10-Dec-3 Alderfer's, Hatfield #312
£1049 $1900 €1532 Old English sheepdogs (51x68cm-20x27in) s. 30-Mar-4 Bonhams & Butterfields, San Francisco #118/R est:1800-2800
£1100 $2024 €1606 We two (23x33cm-9x13in) s. 10-Jun-4 Christie's, Kensington #442/R est:700-900

LESTER, Leonard (1876-?) American/British
£3235 $5500 €4723 Sunlight and shadow (48x76cm-19x30in) s.d.1900. 29-Oct-3 Christie's, Los Angeles #6/R est:5000-7000

LESTER, William Lewis (1910-1991) American
£1856 $3100 €2710 The joke (76x61cm-30x24in) board. 18-Oct-3 David Dike, Dallas #126/R est:3500-4500
Works on paper
£240 $400 €350 Untitled (28x36cm-11x14in) W/C. 18-Oct-3 David Dike, Dallas #102/R

LESUEUR, Catherine (20th C) French
£2013 $3564 €3000 Planete (100x100cm-39x39in) s. acrylic. 29-Apr-4 Claude Aguttes, Neuilly #259 est:3000-3200
Sculpture
£1007 $1782 €1500 Aurore (30cm-12in) s. terracotta. 29-Apr-4 Claude Aguttes, Neuilly #81/R est:1600-1800

LESUR, Henri Victor (1863-1900) French
£3750 $6000 €5475 Market scene (53x43cm-21x17in) s. prov. 20-Sep-3 Pook & Pook, Downington #185/R est:3000-5000
£4969 $8000 €7255 Morning promenade (55x44cm-22x17in) s. panel. 14-Jan-4 Christie's, Rockefeller NY #15/R est:10000-15000
£7386 $13000 €10784 Lover's dalliance (41x32cm-16x13in) s. panel. 18-May-4 Bonhams & Butterfields, San Francisco #123/R est:4000-6000
£8667 $15600 €13000 Visit to the florist (61x50cm-24x20in) s. panel. 20-Apr-4 Sotheby's, Amsterdam #78/R est:8000-12000

LESY, Desire (1806-1859) Belgian
£541 $1022 €800 Paysage romantique anime (35x47cm-14x19in) s. 17-Feb-4 Vanderkindere, Brussels #100

LETELLIER, Pierre (1928-2000) French
£282 $487 €400 Saglier (89x116cm-35x46in) s.d.1972. 10-Dec-3 Rossini, Paris #92

LETENDRE, Rita (1928-) Canadian
£800 $1464 €1168 Field (120x180cm-47x71in) s.i.d.1974 verso acrylic. 1-Jun-4 Joyner Waddington, Toronto #214/R est:2000-2500 (C.D 2000)
£909 $1482 €1327 Naskapi (76x274cm-30x108in) i.d.75 on stretcher acrylic. 23-Sep-3 Ritchie, Toronto #184/R est:2000-2500 (C.D 2000)
£1321 $2365 €1929 Echo (76x122cm-30x48in) s.i.d.81 verso prov. 31-May-4 Sotheby's, Toronto #93/R est:2500-3500 (C.D 3250)
£1577 $2680 €2302 Untitled (45x50cm-18x20in) s.d.1963 prov. 27-Nov-3 Heffel, Vancouver #121 est:3000-4000 (C.D 3500)
£1778 $3076 €2596 Saugeen (92x183cm-36x72in) s.i.d.78 verso acrylic. 15-Dec-3 Iegor de Saint Hippolyte, Montreal #33 (C.D 4000)
£14400 $26352 €21024 Antares (179x200cm-70x79in) s.d.62 prov.lit. 1-Jun-4 Joyner Waddington, Toronto #153/R est:6000-8000 (C.D 36000)
Works on paper
£772 $1383 €1127 Untitled (31x39cm-12x15in) s. gouache prov. 27-May-4 Heffel, Vancouver #127/R est:1400-1600 (C.D 1900)

LETERRA, Maxime (20th C) French
Sculpture
£1027 $1747 €1500 Nu assis (24cm-9in) s. num.4/8 pat bronze. 9-Nov-3 Eric Pillon, Calais #200/R

LETERREUX, Gervaix (1930-2003) French
£302 $562 €450 Maree basse a Cancale (38x46cm-15x18in) s. 7-Mar-4 Lesieur & Le Bars, Le Havre #164

LETH, Harald (1899-1986) Danish
£541 $1001 €790 Sun - fjord landscape (56x50cm-22x20in) mono. prov. 15-Mar-4 Rasmussen, Vejle #613 (D.KR 6000)
£993 $1827 €1450 Harvesters, Lonkolt Olden (33x53cm-13x21in) s.d.1961 stretcher. 29-Mar-4 Rasmussen, Copenhagen #482/R (D.KR 11000)

LETH, Hendrik de (younger) (1703-c.1766) Dutch
Works on paper
£2740 $4658 €4000 Views of Kestert (18x28cm-7x11in) i. black lead pen ink W/C framing lines set of seven. 5-Nov-3 Christie's, Amsterdam #128/R est:3000-4000

LETH, Jan (20th C) Danish
Sculpture
£3430 $6310 €5008 Freedom knight (207cm-81in) bronze incl. socle. 29-Mar-4 Rasmussen, Copenhagen #176/R est:40000-50000 (D.KR 38000)

LETHBRIDGE, Walter Stephens (1771-1831) British
Miniatures
£1000 $1730 €1460 Young lady (7cm-3in) gilt-metal frame oval. 9-Dec-3 Christie's, London #237 est:1000-1500
£1000 $1840 €1460 Young child, wearing smock, leaning on a rocking horse (13cm-5in) wood frame rec. 24-Jun-4 Bonhams, New Bond Street #144/R est:1000-1500
£1900 $3496 €2774 Captain Augustus Donaldson R.N (8cm-3in) s.i. papier mache frame. 24-Jun-4 Bonhams, New Bond Street #124/R est:600-800

LETHEN, J B (fl.1883-1887) ?
Works on paper
£750 $1223 €1095 Farmyard scene with ducks and donkey feeding (25x36cm-10x14in) s. W/C. 24-Sep-3 Peter Wilson, Nantwich #113
£1450 $2364 €2117 Toy (34x25cm-13x10in) s. W/C. 24-Sep-3 Peter Wilson, Nantwich #112

LETHIERE, Guillaume-Guillon (attrib) (1760-1832) French
Works on paper
£567 $1026 €850 La coupe d'etat du 18 brumaire (27x38cm-11x15in) pen brown ink black crayon brown wash. 30-Mar-4 Rossini, Paris #28/R

LETIN, Jacques Ninet de (1597-1661) French
£40845 $71479 €58000 Judith et sa servante (106x103cm-42x41in) prov. 19-Dec-3 Pierre Berge, Paris #47/R est:40000-60000

LETO, Antonino (1844-1913) Italian
£1333 $2427 €2000 Playing on the seashore (13x20cm-5x8in) s. board. 12-Jul-4 Il Ponte, Milan #495 est:2000-2200
£2153 $3660 €3100 Amalfi coast (10x18cm-4x7in) s. board. 1-Nov-3 Meeting Art, Vercelli #181/R est:2500
£8882 $16342 €13500 View of Capri (26x42cm-10x17in) s.i. panel. 24-Jun-4 Christie's, Paris #148/R est:5500-7500
£22667 $41707 €34000 Square in Paris (106x150cm-42x59in) s. exhib.lit. 8-Jun-4 Sotheby's, Milan #91/R est:20000-30000

LETO, Antonino (attrib) (1844-1913) Italian
£1164 $1816 €1700 Rue Royal, Paris (20x25cm-8x10in) s. board. 8-Apr-3 Il Ponte, Milan #612

LETOURNEAU, Edouard (1851-1907) French
£4000 $7360 €6000 La detente (21x27cm-8x11in) s. panel. 14-Jun-4 Gros & Delettrez, Paris #95/R est:6000-7500

LETRONNE, Louis René (1790-1842) French
Works on paper
£1168 $2173 €1705 Portrait of Comtesse Roselie Rzewuska and Comtesse Appony (20x15cm-8x6in) s.i.d.1814 chk pencil pair prov. 2-Mar-4 Rasmussen, Copenhagen #1676/R est:6000-8000 (D.KR 13000)

LETSCH, Louis (1856-?) German
£671 $1235 €1000 Chrysanthemums in basket (60x80cm-24x31in) s. lit. 25-Mar-4 Karlheinz Kaupp, Staufen #2586/R

LETSIA, Louis (19/20th C) ?
£961 $1748 €1403 Meadow flowers (71x49cm-28x19in) s. painted 1918. 16-Jun-4 Fischer, Luzern #2251/R (S.FR 2200)

LETT, Barry (20th C) New Zealander
Works on paper
£846 $1581 €1235 Portrait of Tony Fomison (35x38cm-14x15in) s.d.1978 comte. 24-Feb-4 Peter Webb, Auckland #140/R (NZ.D 2300)

LETTAZZI, E (20th C) Italian?
£2349 $4393 €3500 Young women bathing (125x100cm-49x39in) panel. 26-Feb-4 Cambi, Genoa #594 est:800-1200

LETTNER, Franz (1909-1998) Austrian
£638 $1066 €900 Small island (60x80cm-24x31in) acrylic. 16-Oct-3 Dorotheum, Salzburg #704/R
£1135 $1895 €1600 The crossing (42x56cm-17x22in) s. panel. 16-Oct-3 Dorotheum, Salzburg #703/R est:800-1200
£1206 $2013 €1700 Sunday by the city (40x60cm-16x24in) s.d.88 acrylic. 16-Oct-3 Dorotheum, Salzburg #702/R est:800
£2000 $3680 €3000 Tyrolean area (56x80cm-22x31in) s.d.74 i. verso. 9-Jun-4 Dorotheum, Salzburg #664/R est:1200-1600
Works on paper
£390 $651 €550 Small island (23x31cm-9x12in) s.d.83 mixed media. 16-Oct-3 Dorotheum, Salzburg #701/R
£390 $651 €550 Pilgrim (27x29cm-11x11in) s.d.78 W/C mixed media board. 16-Oct-3 Dorotheum, Salzburg #705/R
£1067 $1963 €1600 Landscape (40x48cm-16x19in) s.d.79 mixed media board. 9-Jun-4 Dorotheum, Salzburg #665/R est:480-700
£1867 $3435 €2800 Waterside castle (58x79cm-23x31in) s.d.79 W/C mixed media. 9-Jun-4 Dorotheum, Salzburg #666/R est:800-1100

LEU, August Wilhelm (1819-1897) German
£568 $1000 €829 Landscape of a woodland scene with people walking down a road beside a river (79x112cm-31x44in) b,. 3-Jan-4 Cobbs, Peterborough #12/R
£1049 $1804 €1500 Hintersee in Bavaria (50x71cm-20x28in) s.d.1881. 6-Dec-3 Dannenberg, Berlin #810/R est:1000
£3497 $5944 €5000 Capri (50x71cm-20x28in) s.d.1874. 20-Nov-3 Van Ham, Cologne #1714/R est:2800
£23500 $40420 €34310 View of the Amalfi coast (107x145cm-42x57in) s.d.1871. 3-Dec-3 Christie's, London #62/R est:15000-25000

LEU, Fritz (1906-) Swiss
£345 $617 €504 Boy playing (150x92cm-59x36in) s. pavatex. 13-May-4 Stuker, Bern #236/R (S.FR 800)

LEU, Oscar (1864-1942) German
£282 $451 €400 Mountain landscape with stream (70x80cm-28x31in) s. lit. 19-Sep-3 Karlheinz Kaupp, Staufen #1999/R
£294 $499 €420 Mountain landscape (50x41cm-20x16in) s. cardboard. 28-Nov-3 Wendl, Rudolstadt #4060/R
£345 $576 €500 Pre-alpine landscape (47x73cm-19x29in) s. panel. 9-Jul-3 Hugo Ruef, Munich #134
£350 $594 €500 Morning in the valley (43x42cm-17x17in) i. board. 28-Nov-3 Wendl, Rudolstadt #4061/R
£352 $563 €500 Southern coast landscape (51x65cm-20x26in) s.d.1902 board. 18-Sep-3 Rieber, Stuttgart #1017/R
£612 $1096 €900 Woodland stream (68x52cm-27x20in) s. 17-Mar-4 Neumeister, Munich #519
£646 $1157 €950 Portofino shore (27x21cm-11x8in) s. panel. 17-Mar-4 Neumeister, Munich #520/R

LEU, Otto (1855-1922) German
£567 $1020 €850 Mediterranean coast (51x65cm-20x26in) s.d.1902 board. 26-Apr-4 Rieber, Stuttgart #952/R
£667 $1220 €1000 Sea coast near Nervi (100x85cm-39x33in) s.d.1910 i.verso. 5-Jun-4 Arnold, Frankfurt #650/R
£811 $1451 €1200 Dent du Midi (61x42cm-24x17in) s.i.d.1907. 6-May-4 Michael Zeller, Lindau #759/R

LEU, Otto (attrib) (1855-1922) German
£441 $749 €644 Mountain landscape with lake (72x94cm-28x37in) s.i. 5-Nov-3 Dobiaschofsky, Bern #748/R (S.FR 1000)

LEUCHS, Isaac Francis (20th C) New Zealander
£638 $1181 €957 Sally Woods (112x100cm-44x39in) s.verso. 13-Jul-4 Watson's, Christchurch #61/R est:2000-3000 (NZ.D 1800)

LEUENBERGER, Ernst Otto (1856-1937) Swiss
£478 $875 €698 Country house in a winter Black Forest scene (100x78cm-39x31in) s. i.verso prov. 4-Jun-4 Zofingen, Switzerland #2870 (S.FR 1100)
£3664 $6558 €5349 Avalanche on the St Bernhard (197x149cm-78x59in) s.d.1916. 14-May-4 Dobiaschofsky, Bern #71/R est:6000 (S.FR 8500)

LEUERS, Jeanette (20th C) ?
£800 $1440 €1168 Summertime (19x24cm-7x9in) s. board. 22-Apr-4 Mellors & Kirk, Nottingham #1079

LEULLIER, Louis Felix (attrib) (1811-1882) French
£814 $1303 €1188 Fishing boats in the Lagoon, Venice (49x72cm-19x28in) s. 16-Sep-3 Philippe Schuler, Zurich #3339/R est:2000-2500 (S.FR 1800)

LEUPIN, Hans W (1920-) Swiss
£862 $1543 €1259 St Paul de Vence (38x55cm-15x22in) mono. s.i.d.78 verso. 14-May-4 Dobiaschofsky, Bern #233/R est:2600 (S.FR 2000)

LEUPPI, Leo Peter (1893-1972) Swiss
£1316 $2421 €1921 Pieta (76x50cm-30x20in) s.d.27 i.verso. 23-Jun-4 Koller, Zurich #3120/R est:3000-4000 (S.FR 3000)
£2579 $4385 €3765 Change (88x62cm-35x24in) s.d.1950 s.i.d.verso prov. 22-Nov-3 Burkhard, Luzern #185/R est:6000-8000 (S.FR 5700)
£3275 $5961 €4782 Composition (76x54cm-30x21in) s.d.46 masonite exhib. 16-Jun-4 Fischer, Luzern #1336/R est:6000-8000 (S.FR 7500)
£7424 $13288 €10839 Composition (75x112cm-30x44in) s.d.1960. 26-May-4 Sotheby's, Zurich #156/R est:8000-12000 (S.FR 17000)
Works on paper
£303 $542 €442 Untitled (33x24cm-13x9in) d.V.49 collage. 22-Mar-4 Philippe Schuler, Zurich #5862 (S.FR 700)
£413 $756 €603 Growing (42x30cm-17x12in) s.d.IX/49 collage gouache. 4-Jun-4 Zofingen, Switzerland #2871/R (S.FR 950)
£452 $783 €660 Shell-bird (41x29cm-16x11in) s.i.d.1948 collage. 9-Dec-3 Sotheby's, Zurich #126/R (S.FR 1000)
£679 $1174 €991 Exotic carpet (39x58cm-15x23in) s.i. collage. 9-Dec-3 Sotheby's, Zurich #125/R (S.FR 1500)
£1719 $2871 €2510 Abstract composition (48x68cm-19x27in) s.d.1952 gouache. 24-Jun-3 Germann, Zurich #2/R est:3000-4000 (S.FR 3800)
£1834 $3338 €2678 Collage I. Collage II (20x12cm-8x5in) s.d.65 verso collage two. 17-Jun-4 Kornfeld, Bern #525 est:5000 (S.FR 4200)
£6335 $10136 €9249 Untitled (63x51cm-25x20in) s.d.1930 mixed media board. 16-Sep-3 Philippe Schuler, Zurich #3158 est:2000-3000 (S.FR 14000)

LEURS, Hendrik Johannes (1890-1956) Dutch
£1277 $2132 €1800 Flat bottom boats in the wind on the Zuiderzee (60x80cm-24x31in) s. 20-Oct-3 Glerum, Amsterdam #118/R est:800-1200

LEURS, Johannes Karel (1865-1938) Dutch
£578 $1052 €850 Ducks on the waterside (27x39cm-11x15in) s. canvas on panel. 3-Feb-4 Christie's, Amsterdam #193
£922 $1540 €1300 Polder landscape with cattle and farm (34x51cm-13x20in) s. 20-Oct-3 Glerum, Amsterdam #156/R
£1206 $2013 €1700 Cattle watering (47x68cm-19x27in) s. 20-Oct-3 Glerum, Amsterdam #160/R est:800-1200

LEURS, Jos (1947-) Dutch
£537 $988 €800 Magnolia (80x100cm-31x39in) s. i. verso. 25-Mar-4 Karlheinz Kaupp, Staufen #2587/R

LEUTENEZ, Richard (1884-1963) Belgian
£483 $893 €700 Vue panoramique de Bruxelles (84x107cm-33x42in) s.d.21. 19-Jan-4 Horta, Bruxelles #482

LEUTERITZ, Franz Wilhelm (1817-1902) German
£816 $1461 €1200 Romantic alpine lake landscape (61x81cm-24x32in) s.d.1889 lit. 20-Mar-4 Bergmann, Erlangen #1099

LEUTZE, Emanuel Gottlieb (1816-1868) American/German
£227273 $400000 €331819 General Ulysses S Grant in his tent (127x102cm-50x40in) s.d.66 prov.lit. 19-May-4 Sotheby's, New York #77/R est:400000-600000

LEUTZGEN, Johannes (18th C) German
£1350 $2147 €1971 Nobleman and his wife (76x61cm-30x24in) s.d.1776 verso trompe l'oeil oval pair. 12-Sep-3 Gardiner & Houlgate, Bath #135/R est:1200-1500

LEUUS, Jesus (1931-) Mexican
£988 $1700 €1442 Pareja d'enamorados (68x41cm-27x16in) s.d.1964 board prov. 3-Dec-3 Doyle, New York #16/R est:1500-2500
£1130 $2000 €1650 Violin player (49x39cm-19x15in) s.i.d.69 masonite prov. 2-May-4 Bonhams & Butterfields, Los Angeles #3117/R est:1000-1500
£3497 $5944 €5000 Tenderness (59x40cm-23x16in) s.d.93 oil mixed media board. 29-Nov-3 Bukowskis, Helsinki #331/R est:4000-5000
Works on paper
£1017 $1800 €1485 Familia (30x23cm-12x9in) s.d.80 mixed media masonite. 2-May-4 Bonhams & Butterfields, Los Angeles #3118/R est:1000-1500

LEUZE-HIRSCHFELD, Emmy (1884-?) Austrian
£384 $718 €580 Manege forain a Concarneau (22x27cm-9x11in) s. 24-Jul-4 Thierry & Lannon, Brest #381
£861 $1610 €1300 Locronan (50x61cm-20x24in) s. 24-Jul-4 Thierry & Lannon, Brest #179/R
Works on paper
£600 $1098 €900 Danseur negre, Marrakech (58x41cm-23x16in) s.i.d.1927 gouache. 3-Jun-4 Tajan, Paris #280/R

LEV, Verkman (20th C) ?
£278 $453 €400 Reclining female nude (40x50cm-16x20in) painted 1950. 24-Sep-3 Cambi, Genoa #1391

LEVASSEUR, Henri (1853-1934) French
Sculpture
£1061 $1900 €1549 Ture (53cm-21in) bronze. 14-May-4 Du Mouchelle, Detroit #2008/R est:1500-2000

LEVASTI, Filli (1883-1966) Italian
£3333 $6133 €5000 Still life (47x64cm-19x25in) s. 11-Jun-4 Farsetti, Prato #576/R est:5000-6000
Works on paper
£497 $904 €750 Circus (24x33cm-9x13in) pencil. 17-Jun-4 Galleria Pananti, Florence #92/R

LEVEDAG, Fritz (1899-1951) German
£1119 $1902 €1600 Nr 1472 (24x17cm-9x7in) s.mono.i.d.1950 tempera. 26-Nov-3 Lempertz, Koln #794/R est:1000
£1517 $2534 €2200 Geometric composition (14x20cm-6x8in) s.verso paper on fibreboard. 13-Nov-3 Neumeister, Munich #385/R est:800-1200

LEVEE, John (1924-) American
£670 $1200 €978 Abstraction (81x99cm-32x39in) s.d.1959 prov. 16-May-4 Wright, Chicago #260/R
£757 $1400 €1105 September IV (81x100cm-32x39in) s.d.58 s.i.verso prov. 12-Feb-4 Sotheby's, New York #97/R est:2000-3000
£1042 $1646 €1500 Composition (195x195cm-77x77in) s.d.1959. 27-Apr-3 Versailles Encheres #20
£1081 $2000 €1578 September III (72x100cm-28x39in) s.d.60 s.i.d.verso prov. 12-Feb-4 Sotheby's, New York #95/R est:1500-2000
£1209 $2200 €1765 October 2, 1955 (70x140cm-28x55in) s.d.55 prov.exhib. 29-Jun-4 Sotheby's, New York #451/R est:2000-3000
£1508 $2700 €2202 April VIII 1957 (38x46cm-15x18in) s.d.1957 s.i.verso prov.lit. 16-May-4 Wright, Chicago #261/R est:1000-2000
£3243 $6000 €4735 September (99x99cm-39x39in) s.d.58 s.i.verso prov. 12-Feb-4 Sotheby's, New York #96/R est:2000-3000
£3297 $6000 €4814 February I (213x174cm-84x69in) s.d.58 s.i.d.verso prov. 29-Jun-4 Sotheby's, New York #446/R est:7000-9000
Works on paper
£595 $1100 €869 Gouache No XV (76x56cm-30x22in) s.d.59 gouache prov. 15-Jul-4 Sotheby's, New York #102/R

LEVEILLE, Andre (1880-1963) French
£563 $986 €800 Le pont de village (61x50cm-24x20in) s. 19-Dec-3 Delvaux, Paris #43

LEVELT, Heinrich Jacob (1808-1889) Dutch
£3000 $5460 €4500 Daily activities on the Dam, Amsterdam (34x48cm-13x19in) s.d.1860 panel. 1-Jul-4 Christie's, Amsterdam #704/R est:2000-3000

LEVENE, Ben (1938-) British
£430 $731 €628 Cold spell (51x56cm-20x22in) mono. s.i.verso. 25-Nov-3 Bonhams, Knowle #205
£880 $1549 €1285 Still life of anemones. Still life of fruit (52x40cm-20x16in) board two. 18-May-4 Woolley & Wallis, Salisbury #272/R
£1800 $3060 €2628 Still life with begonia (76x63cm-30x25in) init. s.verso. 26-Nov-3 Sotheby's, Olympia #89/R est:2000-3000
£2400 $4440 €3504 View from the artist's house (60x56cm-24x22in) init. s.i.d.81 verso board. 11-Feb-4 Sotheby's, Olympia #226/R est:800-1200
£2800 $5180 €4088 Still life with camellia Tomorrow's Dawn (122x101cm-48x40in) init. s.i.d.Oct 87 verso board prov. 11-Feb-4 Sotheby's, Olympia #185/R est:3000-5000

LEVEQUE, Auguste (1866-1921) Belgian
£1200 $2064 €1752 Artist's model (70x40cm-28x16in) s. 4-Dec-3 Christie's, Kensington #165/R est:1500-2000

LEVEQUE, Henri (1769-1832) Swiss
Miniatures
£3800 $6802 €5548 Gentleman, standing in a street with building beyond (8cm-3in) enamel on copper. 25-May-4 Christie's, London #36/R est:800-1200

LEVER, Richard Hayley (1876-1958) American
£285 $510 €416 Seascape (24x31cm-9x12in) s. board. 10-May-4 Joel, Victoria #210 (A.D 700)
£324 $550 €473 Old English cottage, Devon (15x23cm-6x9in) s. i.verso. 5-Nov-3 Doyle, New York #52/R
£347 $639 €507 Boats (14x22cm-6x9in) s. wood panel prov. 29-Mar-4 Goodman, Sydney #101/R (A.D 850)
£447 $800 €653 Davison home, Peacock Point, Locust Valley (23x28cm-9x11in) s. board. 8-Jan-4 James Julia, Fairfield #816/R
£480 $768 €701 Winter street scene (38x48cm-15x19in) s. 8-Jan-3 Biddle & Webb, Birmingham #953
£588 $1000 €858 Train station (19x24cm-7x9in) board. 21-Nov-3 Skinner, Boston #591/R est:800-1200
£706 $1200 €1031 Autumn landscape (25x35cm-10x14in) s. canvasboard. 21-Nov-3 Skinner, Boston #438/R est:800-1200
£706 $1200 €1031 Railroad tracks (19x25cm-7x10in) panel. 21-Nov-3 Skinner, Boston #588/R est:800-1200
£706 $1200 €1031 Hills and clouds (23x43cm-9x17in) board. 5-Nov-3 Doyle, New York #47/R est:800-1200
£706 $1200 €1031 Island off a rocky coast (20x25cm-8x10in) s.d.41 canvas on board. 5-Nov-3 Doyle, New York #53/R est:1200-1800
£973 $1800 €1421 City scene (30x41cm-12x16in) s. board. 18-Jan-4 Carlsen Gallery, Greenville #404/R
£988 $1700 €1442 Boathouses (41x46cm-16x18in) canvas on board prov. 7-Dec-3 Freeman, Philadelphia #128 est:1500-2500

£1050	$1900	€1533	Peacock Point, Locust Valley (20x25cm-8x10in) board. 3-Apr-4 South Bay, Long Island #116
£1176	$2000	€1717	Stowe, Vermont (25x30cm-10x12in) s. s.i.verso board. 5-Nov-3 Doyle, New York #44/R est:1000-1500
£1294	$2200	€1889	Sunbathing by the pier (30x41cm-12x16in) canvas on masonite. 5-Nov-3 Doyle, New York #45/R est:2000-3000
£1294	$2200	€1889	Brookdale, Mt. Vernon (15x20cm-6x8in) i.verso panel. 5-Nov-3 Doyle, New York #51/R est:1000-1500
£1453	$2500	€2121	Tarrytown, New York (26x45cm-10x18in) i.d.1950 s.verso board. 3-Dec-3 Doyle, New York #244/R est:2000-3000
£1497	$2500	€2186	Queensboro Bridge and New York from Astoria (25x36cm-10x14in) s. prov. 23-Oct-3 Shannon's, Milford #179/R est:2500-3500
£1591	$2800	€2323	Rock by the sea (36x46cm-14x18in) s. prov. 23-May-4 Hindman, Chicago #153/R est:3000-5000
£1713	$3100	€2501	Autumn near Stowe (46x56cm-18x22in) prov. 3-Apr-4 South Bay, Long Island #117
£1714	$3000	€2502	Sailboats (35x46cm-14x18in) s. canvas on board. 19-Dec-3 Sotheby's, New York #1154a/R est:4000-8000
£1765	$3000	€2577	Ferry boat. Sailing boats in an inlet (10x15cm-4x6in) s. one on board one on panel. 5-Nov-3 Doyle, New York #43/R est:1500-2500
£1816	$3250	€2651	River scene (30x58cm-12x23in) s. board prov. 26-May-4 Doyle, New York #116/R est:4000-6000
£1852	$3000	€2685	At Bronxville, Bronx (30x41cm-12x16in) s.d.1935 board. 8-Aug-3 Barridorf, Portland #363/R est:5000-7000
£2077	$3800	€3032	Presidential yacht Mayflower (47x53cm-19x21in) init. paper. 29-Jul-4 Christie's, Rockefeller NY #289/R est:4000-6000
£2162	$4000	€3157	Quay (15x23cm-6x9in) s. board. 18-Jan-4 Carlsen Gallery, Greenville #536/R
£2168	$3750	€3165	Spring, Caldwell, New Jersey (41x51cm-16x20in) s. i.stretcher prov. 10-Dec-3 Bonhams & Butterfields, San Francisco #6040/R est:3000-5000
£2400	$4008	€3504	American fishing boats at sea. 21-Oct-3 Gorringes, Lewes #2012/R est:2000-3000
£2616	$4500	€3819	42nd Street looking east from 8th Avenue, New York City (25x30cm-10x12in) s. i.verso canvas on board. 3-Dec-3 Doyle, New York #258/R est:3000-5000
£2695	$4500	€3935	East River, New York (48x64cm-19x25in) s. prov. 23-Oct-3 Shannon's, Milford #180/R est:5000-7000
£2794	$4750	€4079	Sunset. Rowboat. Mill (13x15cm-5x6in) two s. panel set of three. 5-Nov-3 Doyle, New York #54/R est:1800-2200
£2907	$5000	€4244	Marblehead, Massachusetts (20x25cm-8x10in) s. canvas on board. 3-Dec-3 Doyle, New York #206/R est:3000-5000
£3000	$5100	€4380	The harbour, St Ives (15x23cm-6x9in) s. bears i. verso pair. 27-Nov-3 Greenslade Hunt, Taunton #1034/R est:600-800
£3400	$5678	€4964	American fishing boats in St Ives harbour (36x46cm-14x18in) 21-Oct-3 Gorringes, Lewes #2011 est:3000-4000
£3593	$6000	€5246	Farm scene, west Caldwell (61x76cm-24x30in) s. prov. 9-Oct-3 Christie's, Rockefeller NY #42/R est:5000-7000
£3867	$7000	€5646	View of Gloucester from Rockport (33x41cm-13x16in) s.d.1928. 31-Mar-4 Sotheby's, New York #26/R est:4000-6000
£3892	$6500	€5682	Fishing Boats, St Ives, Cornwall Pier. By the Coast (15x23cm-6x9in) s. one i.verso prov. pair. 23-Oct-3 Shannon's, Milford #141/R est:5000-7000
£3911	$7000	€5710	Fish nets, Gloucester, Mass. Fishing boats, Gloucester, Mass (15x23cm-6x9in) s. pair. 6-May-4 Shannon's, Milford #90/R est:5000-7000
£4070	$7000	€5942	St. Ives harbour at sunset (35x45cm-14x18in) s. 3-Dec-3 Doyle, New York #205/R est:5000-7000
£4360	$7500	€6366	St. Ives Cornwall (25x32cm-10x13in) s.i. canvas on board. 3-Dec-3 Doyle, New York #190/R est:3000-4000
£4469	$8000	€6525	Boat cove, Gloucester. Nantucket, Massachusetts. Sorting the catch (10x12cm-4x5in) s. prov. three. 6-May-4 Shannon's, Milford #141/R est:6000-8000
£4749	$8500	€6934	Entrance to the harbour, Cornwall, England. Fish house, Nantucket (10x12cm-4x5in) s. pair prov. 6-May-4 Shannon's, Milford #140/R est:6000-8000
£6395	$11000	€9337	Dock Scene (33x41cm-13x16in) s. board prov. 7-Dec-3 Freeman, Philadelphia #127 est:5000-8000
£6704	$12000	€9788	Signac Bridge, Pasaic, NJ (41x51cm-16x20in) s. s.i.d.1932 verso board. 6-May-4 Shannon's, Milford #78/R est:6000-8000
£8380	$15000	€12235	Boats in the bay, Marblehead, Mass. Out to the boats, Marblehead, Mass (25x30cm-10x12in) s. pair. 6-May-4 Shannon's, Milford #91/R est:6000-8000
£9659	$17000	€14102	Gloucester (39x48cm-15x19in) s. indis.d. canvasboard prov. 18-May-4 Christie's, Rockefeller NY #103/R est:10000-15000
£12784	$22500	€18665	Sea mist, Gloucester (61x76cm-24x30in) s. s.i.verso. 19-May-4 Sotheby's, New York #47/R est:15000-20000
£23256	$40000	€33954	Impression of London Bridge (45x60cm-18x24in) s.i. 3-Dec-3 Doyle, New York #189/R est:20000-30000
£34884	$60000	€50931	Gloucester Harbour (61x76cm-24x30in) s. prov. 3-Dec-3 Sotheby's, New York #61/R est:20000-30000
£55866	$100000	€81564	Marblehead harbour (61x91cm-24x36in) s. panel painted c.1915. 6-May-4 Shannon's, Milford #43/R est:30000-50000

Works on paper

£328	$600	€492	Floral still life with beach plums (28x43cm-11x17in) s.d.1929 W/C. 2-Aug-4 Grogan, Boston #144
£382	$650	€558	Houses in winter (41x56cm-16x22in) init. W/C. 5-Nov-3 Doyle, New York #49/R
£412	$700	€602	Edge of the wood, New Jersey (38x56cm-15x22in) s.i. W/C. 5-Nov-3 Doyle, New York #48/R
£454	$850	€663	Barn on the road, Stowe, Vermont (36x53cm-14x21in) s.d.1935 i.verso W/C. 29-Feb-4 Grogan, Boston #77/R
£475	$850	€694	Gloucester (42x52cm-17x20in) s.i. W/C. 14-May-4 Skinner, Boston #231/R
£479	$800	€699	Washington, DC (38x56cm-15x22in) s.i. W/C over chl. 18-Jun-3 Doyle, New York #49/R
£726	$1300	€1060	Connecticut (41x51cm-16x20in) s.i. casein ground. 8-Jan-4 James Julia, Fairfield #815/R
£765	$1300	€1117	Route 22 (38x56cm-15x22in) s. indis d. W/C. 5-Nov-3 Doyle, New York #50/R est:1000-1500

LEVERD, René (1872-1938) French

Works on paper

£769	$1323	€1100	La place de la Concorde (12x19cm-5x7in) s.d.1918 W/C. 5-Dec-3 Chochon-Barre & Allardi, Paris #124/R
£1486	$2661	€2200	La tentation de Saint Antoine (75x155cm-30x61in) s.d.09 W/C gouache paper on canvas. 7-May-4 Millon & Associes, Paris #61/R est:2000-2500

LEVERSBY, Dag (1952-) Norwegian

Works on paper

£1025	$1711	€1497	Magnolia Cross (75x58cm-30x23in) s.d.91 W/C pair. 13-Oct-3 Blomqvist, Oslo #382/R (N.KR 12000)

LEVESQUE, Lise (19th C) French

Works on paper

£1093	$2000	€1596	Death of Hippolytus (62x89cm-24x35in) s. black chk chl stumped. 29-Jan-4 Swann Galleries, New York #262/R est:3000-5000

LEVI, Angelo Adolfo (1812-1883) Italian

£3000	$5460	€4380	Self portraits in the artist's studio (162x117cm-64x46in) 16-Jun-4 Christie's, Kensington #218/R est:4000-6000

LEVI, Basil (1878-1954) Russian

£473	$847	€700	Mountain road (64x80cm-25x31in) s. board. 8-May-4 Bukowskis, Helsinki #474/R

LEVI, Carlo (1902-1975) Italian

£1133	$2085	€1700	Tree lined path (22x16cm-9x6in) s. cardboard prov. 14-Jun-4 Sant Agostino, Torino #345/R est:1200-1600
£1538	$2615	€2200	Portrait of sister (60x49cm-24x19in) s. s.i.verso. 26-Nov-3 Pandolfini, Florence #90/R est:1000-1100
£1733	$3103	€2600	Lovers (50x70cm-20x28in) prov. 12-May-4 Stadion, Trieste #762/R est:2000-3000
£2000	$3600	€3000	Trunk (70x50cm-28x20in) s.verso painted 1971. 22-Apr-4 Finarte Semenzato, Rome #260/R est:2800-3500
£2013	$3604	€3000	Still life (38x46cm-15x18in) s. s.i.verso. 29-May-4 Farsetti, Prato #546/R est:3000-4000
£2067	$3803	€3100	Landscape (50x70cm-20x28in) s. painted 1970. 12-Jun-4 Meeting Art, Vercelli #386/R est:2500
£2113	$3507	€3000	Flowers (50x70cm-20x28in) s. s.verso. 11-Jun-3 Finarte Semenzato, Milan #702/R
£2133	$3840	€3200	Portrait in red (32x24cm-13x9in) 22-Apr-4 Finarte Semenzato, Rome #267/R est:2300-2800
£2448	$4161	€3500	Seascape (70x50cm-28x20in) s.d.1947 verso. 24-Nov-3 Christie's, Milan #162/R est:5000-7000
£2448	$4161	€3500	Wood (73x92cm-29x36in) s.verso. 25-Nov-3 Sotheby's, Milan #30/R est:2000-3000
£2667	$4800	€4000	Patio (45x60cm-18x24in) board painted 1960. 22-Apr-4 Finarte Semenzato, Rome #161/R est:3800-4200
£2721	$4871	€4000	Peasants from Lucca (65x50cm-26x20in) s. s.d.70 verso. 22-Mar-4 Sant Agostino, Torino #514/R est:4500
£3356	$6007	€5000	Trinita' dei Monti, Rome (20x25cm-8x10in) s. painted 1947. 30-May-4 Meeting Art, Vercelli #90 est:5000
£3586	$5953	€5200	Still life with shells (69x73cm-27x29in) s. 1-Oct-3 Della Rocca, Turin #53/R
£5594	$9343	€8000	Flower (61x50cm-24x20in) s. painted 1930. 26-Jun-3 Sant Agostino, Torino #244/R est:5000-6000
£6122	$10959	€9000	Nude (65x115cm-26x45in) s.i.d.1958 verso. 22-Mar-4 Sant Agostino, Torino #516/R est:14000
£14483	$24186	€21000	Pink nude (89x68cm-35x27in) painted c.1930. 17-Nov-3 Sant Agostino, Torino #208/R est:16000-20000

Works on paper

£800	$1440	€1200	Cutlery and crockery (30x21cm-12x8in) d.1921 pencil exhib.lit. 22-Apr-4 Finarte Semenzato, Rome #82
£1133	$2040	€1700	Winged victory (34x24cm-13x9in) s. Chinese ink. 22-Apr-4 Finarte Semenzato, Rome #72/R est:1400-1800

LEVI, Clemente Pugliese (1855-1936) Italian

£1319	$2243	€1900	Landscape (27x40cm-11x16in) s. board. 1-Nov-3 Meeting Art, Vercelli #144/R est:1500

LEVI, Julian E (1900-1982) American

£1946	$3250	€2841	Driftwood (51x76cm-20x30in) s. painted c.1939 prov.exhib.lit. 7-Oct-3 Sotheby's, New York #224 est:2000-4000
£5233	$9000	€7640	Figures in a landscape (71x86cm-28x34in) s.d.1923. 7-Dec-3 Freeman, Philadelphia #215 est:2000-3000

LEVIANT, Isia (?) ?

£1200	$2196	€1800	One dollar (90x210cm-35x83in) s. 6-Jun-4 Anaf, Lyon #418/R est:1500-2000

LEVIDO, Brad (1953-) Australian

£329	$596	€480	Behind the fence (77x110cm-30x43in) s. s.i.d.1988 verso. 30-Mar-4 Lawson Menzies, Sydney #82/R (A.D 800)

LEVIER, Adolfo (1873-1953) Italian

£2400	$4296	€3600	Trieste (49x69cm-19x27in) s. cardboard exhib. 12-May-4 Stadion, Trieste #714/R est:3000-4000
£2800	$5012	€4200	Entrance to the villa (70x58cm-28x23in) s. 12-May-4 Stadion, Trieste #748/R est:2500-3500

LEVIER, Charles (1920-) French

£242	$450	€353	Harbour view (50x60cm-20x24in) s. 5-Mar-4 Skinner, Boston #519/R
£245	$450	€358	Moored sailboats (76x102cm-30x40in) s. 23-Jun-4 Doyle, New York #5049/R
£315	$500	€460	Cityscape (38x76cm-15x30in) s. 12-Sep-3 Skinner, Boston #475/R
£382	$650	€558	Le chat (76x61cm-30x24in) s. s.i.d.1955 verso. 7-Nov-3 Selkirks, St. Louis #628
£419	$700	€612	Three boats in a harbour (51x61cm-20x24in) s. 7-Oct-3 Sotheby's, New York #326
£598	$1100	€873	After the show (51x61cm-20x24in) s. s.i.verso. 25-Mar-4 Doyle, New York #41/R est:800-1200
£598	$1100	€873	Woman seated at a table (102x76cm-40x30in) s. 25-Jun-4 Freeman, Philadelphia #299/R
£598	$1100	€873	Le table rouge (51x122cm-20x48in) s. 9-Jun-4 Doyle, New York #3052

£610 $1000 €885 Dans un cafe (76x61cm-30x24in) s. i.verso painted c.1965. 7-Jun-3 Treadway Gallery, Cincinnati #1519
£670 $1200 €978 Women (76x38cm-30x15in) s. 16-May-4 Wright, Chicago #305/R
£1118 $1800 €1632 French street scene (61x91cm-24x36in) s. 20-Aug-3 James Julia, Fairfield #1735/R est:1500-2000
£2162 $4000 €3157 Notre Dame, Paris (51x127cm-20x50in) s. s.i. verso prov. 15-Jul-4 Sotheby's, New York #95/R est:2000-3000

LEVIEUX, Reynaud (attrib) (c.1625-1690) French
£1678 $3087 €2500 La Vierge a l'Enfant (82x54cm-32x21in) 26-Mar-4 Piasa, Paris #53 est:3000-4000
£1748 $3007 €2500 La visitation (64x53cm-25x21in) 5-Dec-3 Chochon-Barre & Allardi, Paris #8/R est:3000-3500

LEVIGNE, H (20th C) French?
£309 $574 €460 Spring landscape in Southern Limburg (50x40cm-20x16in) s. 4-Mar-4 Auction Maastricht #1113/R

LEVIGNE, Theodore (1848-1912) French
£367 $675 €550 Portrait de femme a la mantille (27x21cm-11x8in) s. 9-Jun-4 Beaussant & Lefèvre, Paris #176/R
£862 $1543 €1259 Au Lac d'Annecy (46x65cm-18x26in) s. 12-May-4 Dobiaschofsky, Bern #745/R est:3000 (S.FR 2000)
£950 $1501 €1387 Portrait of a hunting dog in landscape (62x81cm-24x32in) 27-Apr-3 Wilkinson, Doncaster #279/R
£1067 $1920 €1600 Paysage de montagne avec heron cendre au bord du lac (27x41cm-11x16in) s. 20-Apr-4 Chenu & Scrive, Lyon #115/R est:1000-1200
£1382 $2542 €2100 Paysage (50x65cm-20x26in) 27-Jun-4 Teitgen, Nancy #75
£1400 $2562 €2044 Courtship (46x63cm-18x25in) s. 6-Jul-4 Bonhams, Knightsbridge #186/R est:1500-2000
£1842 $3389 €2800 Ascension de la Meige (46x35cm-18x14in) s. 25-Jun-4 Millon & Associes, Paris #108 est:3000-4000
£2207 $3686 €3200 Bergere et son troupeau (103x143cm-41x56in) s. 17-Nov-3 Tajan, Paris #58 est:2500-3000
£3333 $5967 €5000 Hunting the lion (124x200cm-49x79in) s.d.1889. 17-May-4 Finarte Semenzato, Rome #80/R est:5000-6000
£3537 $6438 €5200 Gendarmes a cheval avec un garde forestier dans un hameau sous la neige (60x92cm-24x36in) s.d.1877. 8-Feb-4 Anaf, Lyon #224/R est:3000-3500

LEVILLAIN, F (1837-1905) French
Sculpture
£2100 $3885 €3066 Empire figure of a lady holding a aloft an urn. bronze. 14-Jan-4 Brightwells, Leominster #682/R est:400-600

LEVILLE, A G (19th C) French
£2000 $3700 €3000 Vue des remparts de Saint Malo sous un temps menacant (33x53cm-13x21in) s.d.1882. 14-Jul-4 Livinec, Gaudcheau & Jezequel, Rennes #197

LEVIN, Joseph (1894-1979) Russian
£490 $817 €700 Composition multicolore (81x62cm-32x24in) s. 25-Jun-3 Rabourdin & Choppin de Janvry, Paris #116/R
£559 $934 €800 Composition sur fond bleu (65x81cm-26x32in) s. 25-Jun-3 Rabourdin & Choppin de Janvry, Paris #109/R

LEVIN, Julo (1901-1943) ?
£2083 $3479 €3000 Deux vaches dans un paysage (101x72cm-40x28in) isorel panel. 21-Oct-3 Artcurial Briest, Paris #229/R est:2000-3000

LEVINE, David (20th C) American
£1047 $1800 €1529 Baker's Field, New York (40x50cm-16x20in) s.d.59 hardboard prov. 3-Dec-3 Doyle, New York #272/R est:2500-3500
£1196 $2200 €1746 The fashion model. init. board sold with another. 10-Jun-4 Swann Galleries, New York #147/R est:1000-1500
Works on paper
£838 $1400 €1223 Lucy Vincent pond (28x36cm-11x14in) s.d.79 W/C over pencil prov. 18-Jun-3 Doyle, New York #52/R

LEVINE, Jack (1915-) American
£3409 $6000 €4977 Horse and cart (51x61cm-20x24in) s. prov.exhib. 18-May-4 Sotheby's, New York #211/R est:10000-15000
£4790 $8000 €6993 Aileen (61x53cm-24x21in) init. 9-Oct-3 Christie's, Rockefeller NY #102/R est:8000-12000
£8982 $15000 €13114 Lady with opera glasses (36x30cm-14x12in) init. prov.exhib.lit. 9-Oct-3 Christie's, Rockefeller NY #103/R est:10000-15000
Works on paper
£380 $700 €555 Tokyo waitress (41x30cm-16x12in) init.i. pencil W/C gouache. 10-Jun-4 Swann Galleries, New York #148/R
£435 $800 €635 Head of a man. Head of a man with cigarette (46x28cm-18x11in) s. india ink. 10-Jun-4 Swann Galleries, New York #149/R
£1105 $2000 €1613 Roman girl (44x30cm-17x12in) s. canvasboard prov. 31-Mar-4 Sotheby's, New York #160/R est:3000-5000

LEVINE, Sherrie (1947-) American
£7784 $13000 €11365 Untitled, golden knots 2 (159x128cm-63x50in) oil plywood prov.exhib. 13-Nov-3 Sotheby's, New York #487/R est:15000-20000
£13174 $22000 €19234 White Knot no. 1 (78x61cm-31x24in) s.d.1986 caesin plywood prov. 12-Nov-3 Christie's, Rockefeller NY #529/R est:10000-15000
Photographs
£2395 $4000 €3497 After Walker Evans (7x11cm-3x4in) s.i.d.1981 verso gelatin silver print prov. 17-Oct-3 Phillips, New York #172/R est:4000-6000
£10778 $18000 €15736 President profile I. Untitled. Untitled woman's head (25x20cm-10x8in) s.d.num.14/30 verso gelatin silver print 3 multiple artists prov. 13-Nov-3 Sotheby's, New York #533/R est:20000-30000
Works on paper
£22346 $40000 €32625 Check no 1 (61x51cm-24x20in) casein wax mahogany exec 1985 prov. 13-May-4 Sotheby's, New York #461/R est:10000-15000

LEVINSEN, Sophus (1869-1943) French
£267 $491 €400 Canal anime (26x41cm-10x16in) s. panel. 14-Jun-4 Horta, Bruxelles #394
£313 $522 €450 Berger et son troupeau en bordure de mer en Afrique du Nord (41x57cm-16x22in) s. panel. 25-Oct-3 Binoche, Orleans #41
£521 $828 €750 Vue de Venise animee (27x35cm-11x14in) s. cardboard. 9-Sep-3 Vanderkindere, Brussels #41
£900 $1620 €1314 Continental market town (26x33cm-10x13in) s. board. 23-Apr-4 Charterhouse, Sherborne #649/R

LEVINSON, Mon (1926-) American
£353 $600 €515 Tondo VI. composition board. 9-Nov-3 Wright, Chicago #389

LEVINSTEIN, Leon (1913-1988) ?
Photographs
£1796 $3000 €2622 Untitled (32x26cm-13x10in) gelatin silver print exec.1960s. 17-Oct-3 Phillips, New York #103/R est:3000-4000
£2036 $3400 €2973 Untitled - family in the park (28x49cm-11x19in) silver print. 21-Oct-3 Swann Galleries, New York #240/R est:3000-4000

LEVINTHAL, David (1949-) American?
Photographs
£1693 $3200 €2472 Untitled from the wild west series (55x62cm-22x24in) s.d.1994 num.1/5 polaroid print. 17-Feb-4 Christie's, Rockefeller NY #171/R est:2000-3000
£4790 $8000 €6993 Untitled, cowboy with lasso and white horse (60x51cm-24x20in) polaroid print edition 8 of 10 prov. 13-Nov-3 Sotheby's, New York #530/R est:4000-6000

LEVIS, Giuseppe Augusto (1873-1926) Italian
£592 $1089 €900 Landscape with peasants (48x34cm-19x13in) s.d.1911 board. 23-Jun-4 Finarte Semenzato, Rome #44
£592 $1089 €900 Landscape (30x44cm-12x17in) s.d.1912 board. 23-Jun-4 Finarte Semenzato, Rome #88/R
£921 $1695 €1400 Village in the mountains (46x33cm-18x13in) s.d.1925 board. 23-Jun-4 Finarte Semenzato, Rome #96/R est:800-900
£1118 $2058 €1700 Winter landscapes (30x44cm-12x17in) s. board pair. 23-Jun-4 Finarte Semenzato, Rome #89/R est:1000-1200
£1342 $2376 €2000 Stream (34x48cm-13x19in) s.d.1912 board. 1-May-4 Meeting Art, Vercelli #404 est:1500

LEVIS, Maurice (1860-1940) French
£764 $1245 €1100 Pont-en-Royen, Isere (23x33cm-9x13in) s. i.d.18 Sept 1907 verso panel. 24-Sep-3 Neumeister, Munich #479/R
£887 $1632 €1295 Punt nearing shore (42x34cm-17x13in) s. panel. 14-Jun-4 Waddingtons, Toronto #285/R est:3000-4000 (C.D 2200)
£1000 $1790 €1460 Le chateau de clisson (35x42cm-14x17in) s. s.i.stretcher. 26-May-4 Sotheby's, Olympia #274/R est:1200-1800
£1174 $2149 €1750 Tour d'angle du Chateau de Josselin (55x42cm-22x17in) s.i. verso cardboard. 9-Jul-4 Dawo, Saarbrucken #18/R est:1400
£1224 $2192 €1800 La Seine en amont d'Herblay (32x46cm-13x18in) s. peinture. 20-Mar-4 Binoche, Orleans #47 est:600-750
£1293 $2352 €1900 Etang de valfleur (38x55cm-15x22in) s.d.91 s.i.on stretcher. 3-Feb-4 Christie's, Amsterdam #234/R est:1800-2200
£1863 $3000 €2701 River scene (46x65cm-18x26in) s. 24-Aug-3 Bonhams & Butterfields, Los Angeles #7029 est:1500-2000
£1955 $3500 €2854 Morning at Boutigny (39x30cm-15x12in) s. prov. 6-May-4 Doyle, New York #39/R est:3000-5000
£2041 $3245 €3000 Bord de riviere anime au printemps (36x65cm-14x26in) s. 23-Mar-3 St-Germain-en-Laye Encheres #54/R
£2483 $4569 €3700 Paysage au chateau (40x53cm-16x21in) s. panel. 29-Mar-4 Lombrail & Teucquam, Paris #58/R
£2600 $4342 €3796 On the Loire, landscape with cottages (21x31cm-8x12in) s.d.94 panel. 8-Oct-3 Rupert Toovey, Partridge Green #25/R est:1000-1500
£2800 $4480 €4060 French river landscape (23x33cm-9x13in) s. panel. 18-Sep-3 Christie's, Kensington #3/R est:1500-2000
£2800 $5152 €4088 Women washing clothes (16x24cm-6x9in) s. panel. 25-Mar-4 Christie's, Kensington #38/R est:2000-3000
£2837 $4738 €4000 La berge a St Mammes (21x26cm-8x10in) s.d.32 panel. 15-Oct-3 Claude Aguttes, Neuilly #17/R est:4000-5000
£3400 $5440 €4964 La ferme au bord du Ruisseau (15x23cm-6x9in) 16-Sep-3 Gorringes, Bexhill #1529 est:3000-4000
£4196 $7217 €6000 Fishermen preparing to push off from the beach in their boat (26x35cm-10x14in) s. i.verso panel. 3-Dec-3 Neumeister, Munich #650/R est:3000
£7000 $12740 €10220 Lavandieres au bord de la riviere. Couple sur le chemin de compagne (23x27cm-9x11in) s. pair. 15-Jun-4 Sotheby's, London #172/R est:7000-10000
£8000 $14720 €11680 Gypsy encampment. Boats on a river (13x18cm-5x7in) s. board panel pair. 25-Mar-4 Christie's, Kensington #37/R est:8000-12000
Works on paper
£403 $741 €600 Passeur sur une barque, au fond une ville (27x35cm-11x14in) s. W/C gouache chl. 29-Mar-4 Rieunier, Paris #61/R
£987 $1786 €1500 Etang de Madrelle (29x45cm-11x18in) s.i.d.19 W/C. 19-Apr-4 Boscher, Cherbourg #772/R est:1800

LEVITAN, Isaac Ilyitch (1860-1900) Russian
£19444 $35000 €28388 Landscape (11x14cm-4x6in) s.i.d.1897 board. 23-Apr-4 Sotheby's, New York #8/R est:30000-40000
£20000 $34000 €30000 Lane through village (20x31cm-8x12in) 25-Nov-3 Christie's, London #179/R est:20000-25000
£51282 $80000 € Landscape at dawn (56x73cm-22x29in) i. 11-Apr-3 Christie's, Rockefeller NY #23/R est:75000-95000
£51282 $80000 € Golden autumn by the river (58x89cm-23x35in) s.cyrillic d.1896. 11-Apr-3 Christie's, Rockefeller NY #35/R est:80000-120000
£75000 $134250 €109500 Birch grove (31x22cm-12x9in) s.i. prov.lit. 26-May-4 Sotheby's, London #48/R est:20000-30000

Works on paper

£4000	$6800	€6000	View of house in Crimea (27x15cm-11x6in) s.i.d.85 pencil W/C. 25-Nov-3 Christie's, London #180/R est:5000-7000
£6579	$12105	€10000	Landscape in spring (41x38cm-16x15in) s. pastel. 25-Jun-4 Millon & Associes, Paris #112/R est:8000-10000

LEVITT, Helen (1918-) American
Photographs

£1667	$3000	€2434	New York (36x24cm-14x9in) s.i.d.1993 dye transfer print prov.lit. 23-Apr-4 Phillips, New York #186/R est:2500-3500
£1695	$3000	€2475	N.Y.C (18x25cm-7x10in) s.i.d. gelatin silver print executed c.1940. 27-Apr-4 Christie's, Rockefeller NY #206/R est:3500-4500
£2000	$3520	€2920	New York sidewalk scene (27x21cm-11x8in) i. gelatin silver print exhib. 19-May-4 Christie's, London #191/R est:3000-5000
£2395	$4000	€3497	Untitled (18x23cm-7x9in) s.i. gelatin silver print on board. 16-Oct-3 Phillips, New York #108/R est:8000-12000
£3390	$6000	€4949	NYC, boys with guns (20x13cm-8x5in) s.i.d.1938 verso photo exhib. 28-Apr-4 Sotheby's, New York #198/R est:8000-12000
£3390	$6000	€4949	NY, children in hydrant spray (16x23cm-6x9in) s.i.d.1945 verso photo. 28-Apr-4 Sotheby's, New York #199/R est:8000-12000
£4192	$7000	€6120	New York City (11x17cm-4x7in) s.i.d.verso gelatin silver print lit. 16-Oct-3 Phillips, New York #107/R est:10000-15000
£4790	$8000	€6993	Girl with lily (17x25cm-7x10in) s.i.d.verso gelatin silver print exec.c.1942 lit. 16-Oct-3 Phillips, New York #103/R est:18000-22000
£5988	$10000	€8742	New York City (11x16cm-4x6in) s.i.d.verso gelatin silver print set of 3 lit. 16-Oct-3 Phillips, New York #100 est:30000-40000
£7186	$12000	€10492	New York City (20x15cm-8x6in) s.i.d.verso gelatin silver print set of 3. 16-Oct-3 Phillips, New York #101/R est:30000-40000
£8383	$14000	€12239	New York City (18x20cm-7x8in) s.i.d. gelatin silver print on board lit. 16-Oct-3 Phillips, New York #102/R est:20000-25000
£9581	$16000	€13988	New York City (16x21cm-6x8in) s.verso gelatin silver print on board set of 3 lit. 16-Oct-3 Phillips, New York #99/R est:30000-40000
£25150	$42000	€36719	Untitled (11x16cm-4x6in) s.i.gelatin silver print on board. 16-Oct-3 Phillips, New York #104/R est:15000-20000

LEVITT, Joel J (1875-1937) American/Russian

£281	$450	€410	Landscape (25x36cm-10x14in) s. board. 21-Sep-3 Grogan, Boston #65e/R

LEVITTE, A G (19th C) ?

£1078	$1800	€1520	St Malo (35x55cm-14x22in) 19-Oct-3 Daniel Herry, Beaune #9

LEVRAC-TOURNIERES, Robert (attrib) (1667-1752) French

£2958	$5176	€4200	Portrait de gentilhomme (81x64cm-32x25in) 19-Dec-3 Delvaux, Paris #107/R est:4500-6000

LEVY, Alexander (1881-1947) American

£228	$425	€333	Landscape. board. 6-Mar-4 Page, Batavia #53
£231	$430	€337	Duck pond. double-sided. 6-Mar-4 Page, Batavia #52
£269	$500	€393	Circus time. 6-Mar-4 Page, Batavia #57
£591	$1100	€863	Levy at piano (28x28cm-11x11in) board. 6-Mar-4 Page, Batavia #144
£1075	$2000	€1570	Negro spiritual (76x76cm-30x30in) board. 6-Mar-4 Page, Batavia #136

LEVY, Beatrice S (1892-1974) American

£217	$350	€317	Midwestern farmyard (64x76cm-25x30in) s. 20-Aug-3 James Julia, Fairfield #1767/R

LEVY, Charles (19th C) French
Sculpture

£2908	$4856	€4100	Judith (83cm-33in) s. brown pat bronze. 12-Oct-3 St-Germain-en-Laye Encheres #56/R est:4200-4500

LEVY, Edgar (1907-1975) American

£10227	$18000	€14931	Still life - African Mask (71x91cm-28x36in) s.d.Aug 34 verso prov. 19-May-4 Sotheby's, New York #120/R est:18000-24000

LEVY, Émile (1826-1890) French

£4422	$7031	€6500	La declaration d'amour. s. 22-Mar-3 Dubee & Berron, Vernou en Sologne #19

Works on paper

£1974	$3632	€3000	Portrait de dame en bleu (110x76cm-43x30in) s.d.1885 pastel. 22-Jun-4 Ribeyre & Baron, Paris #41/R est:4000-6000

LEVY, Emmanuel (1900-) British

£250	$448	€365	Rabbis (65x50cm-26x20in) 14-May-4 Christie's, Kensington #616
£300	$525	€438	Portrait of the artists father (76x64cm-30x25in) s.d.25. 16-Dec-3 Capes Dunn, Manchester #707/R
£380	$695	€555	Still life of vase of flowers (61x51cm-24x20in) s. 6-Apr-4 Capes Dunn, Manchester #844/R
£450	$792	€657	Mandrill (122x94cm-48x37in) s. board. 18-May-4 Bonhams, Knightsbridge #79/R
£1900	$3420	€2774	Crucifixion (102x80cm-40x31in) s.d.1942 exhib. 20-Jan-4 Bonhams, Knightsbridge #138/R est:1000-1500

LEVY, Henri (?) French?

£655	$1094	€950	Woman's portrait (35x26cm-14x10in) s. panel. 9-Jul-3 Hugo Ruef, Munich #135/R

Works on paper

£533	$965	€800	L'appel au combat (24x16cm-9x6in) s. wash white gouache. 4-Apr-4 Salle des ventes Pillet, Lyon la Foret #42

LEVY, Henri Leopold (1840-1904) French

£2482	$4145	€3500	Dalila (59x39cm-23x15in) s. 19-Jun-3 Millon & Associes, Paris #121/R est:4000-5000
£3901	$6514	€5500	Etude preparatoire pour Samson et Dalila (37x29cm-15x11in) s. panel. 19-Jun-3 Millon & Associes, Paris #122/R est:4500-5000

LEVY, Julien (20th C) American
Photographs

£2222	$4200	€3244	Untitled (17x12cm-7x5in) silver print photomontage pen. 17-Feb-4 Swann Galleries, New York #42/R est:2000-3000

LEVY, Lazar (20th C) French

£1600	$2928	€2400	Repos sous le vieil arbre (45x52cm-18x20in) s. 3-Jun-4 Tajan, Paris #281 est:1000-1200

LEVY, Moses (1885-1968) Italian

£2057	$3435	€2900	Nature morte aux poissons (23x33cm-9x13in) s. oil gouache cardboard. 19-Oct-3 Rabourdin & Choppin de Janvry, Paris #137/R est:3000-3500
£2533	$4661	€3800	Parasols on the beach (21x26cm-8x10in) s. board. 8-Jun-4 Sotheby's, Milan #73/R est:3000-5000
£3973	$6197	€5800	Bather (38x46cm-15x18in) s. board. 8-Apr-3 Il Ponte, Milan #598/R est:3000
£5667	$10427	€8500	Viareggio (13x19cm-5x7in) s. s.i.d.1919 verso. 8-Jun-4 Sotheby's, Milan #74/R est:2000-3000

Works on paper

£552	$921	€800	Bathers on the beach (13x21cm-5x8in) s.d.1957 ink col crayon. 14-Nov-3 Farsetti, Prato #131
£2482	$4145	€3500	Parasols bleus (20x32cm-8x13in) s. W/C gouache. 19-Oct-3 Rabourdin & Choppin de Janvry, Paris #136/R est:3000-3500

LEVY, Nat (1896-1984) American
Works on paper

£240	$400	€350	Loggers at work (38x38cm-15x15in) s. W/C paperboard. 11-Oct-3 Auctions by the Bay, Alameda #1704/R
£241	$450	€352	Landscape with golden hills (37x51cm-15x20in) s. pencil W/C. 29-Feb-4 Bonhams & Butterfields, San Francisco #4550
£321	$600	€469	Old barn by the sea (42x55cm-17x22in) s. pencil W/C. 29-Feb-4 Bonhams & Butterfields, San Francisco #4551
£520	$900	€759	Waterfall (14x21cm-6x8in) s. W/C. 13-Dec-3 Auctions by the Bay, Alameda #1825/R
£879	$1600	€1283	Barn in a landscape (36x51cm-14x20in) s. i.v W/C prov. 15-Jun-4 John Moran, Pasadena #137a est:1000-1500
£1511	$2750	€2206	Barn and corral in a landscape (33x48cm-13x19in) s. i.verso W/C. 15-Jun-4 John Moran, Pasadena #137b est:1000-1500

LEVY, Ra'anan (1954-) Israeli
Works on paper

£749	$1400	€1094	Urban landscape (48x63cm-19x25in) init.d.1999 pastel. 1-Mar-4 Ben-Ami, Tel Aviv #4663/R est:1500-2000

LEVY, Rudolf (1875-1943) German

£6294	$10699	€9000	Portrait of the artist Kurt Craemer (81x61cm-32x24in) prov.exhib. 26-Nov-3 Lempertz, Koln #795/R est:6000
£6993	$11678	€10000	Landscape in Provence (60x73cm-24x29in) s.d.1926. 26-Jun-3 Sant Agostino, Torino #298/R est:8000-9000
£14667	$26253	€22000	Narcissi in ceramic jug (64x46cm-25x18in) prov. 14-May-4 Ketterer, Munich #52/R est:6000-8000

LEVY-DHURMER, Lucien (1865-1953) French

£1867	$3435	€2800	Neige au chevet de Notre Dame (72x53cm-28x21in) s. i. stretcher prov.exhib. 9-Jun-4 Christie's, Amsterdam #37/R est:2500-3500
£8144	$13520	€11890	Composition (92x65cm-36x26in) 4-Oct-3 Kieselbach, Budapest #150/R (H.F 3000000)
£60000	$110400	€90000	Grenade (46x61cm-18x24in) s. painted c.1900. 11-Jun-4 Claude Aguttes, Neuilly #74/R est:100000-120000

Works on paper

£800	$1472	€1200	Nature morte aux ceramiques a lustre metallique (62x46cm-24x18in) s. pastel. 9-Jun-4 Beaussant & Lefèvre, Paris #181/R
£1133	$2063	€1700	Orientale au tapis (50x40cm-20x16in) pastel prov. 5-Jul-4 Neret-Minet, Paris #36/R est:1500-1800
£1538	$2615	€2200	Le nu bleu, etude (56x39cm-22x15in) pastel. 27-Nov-3 Millon & Associes, Paris #151/R est:1200-2000
£2000	$3680	€3000	Nude (75x48cm-30x19in) pastel prov. 9-Jun-4 Christie's, Amsterdam #38/R est:2000-3000
£2657	$4517	€3800	Portrait de Camille Mauclair (48x34cm-19x13in) s.d.97 pastel. 27-Nov-3 Millon & Associes, Paris #170/R est:1500-2000
£3310	$5528	€4800	Profil de femme (46x32cm-18x13in) s.d.99 pastel. 17-Nov-3 Tajan, Paris #118/R est:1500-2000
£3916	$6657	€5600	Projet pour nocturne (21x19cm-8x7in) s. chl. 27-Nov-3 Millon & Associes, Paris #174/R est:6000-8000
£4196	$7133	€6000	Portrait de l'academicien Rene Boysleve (90x63cm-35x25in) s. pastel. 27-Nov-3 Millon & Associes, Paris #173/R est:6000-8000
£4287	$7673	€6259	White chalk cliffs (67x85cm-26x33in) s. pastel. 25-May-4 Bukowskis, Stockholm #380/R est:20000-25000 (S.KR 58000)
£29371	$49930	€42000	Femme devant le bois sacre (46x36cm-18x14in) s.d.98 pastel lit. 27-Nov-3 Millon & Associes, Paris #171/R est:40000-60000
£33566	$57063	€48000	Les chardons bleus (73x36cm-29x14in) s.d.96 pastel htd gold prov.exhib. 27-Nov-3 Millon & Associes, Paris #172/R est:60000-80000
£40780	$68103	€57500	La bourrasque (37x44cm-15x17in) s.d.97 pastel. 19-Jun-3 Millon & Associes, Paris #160/R

LEW, Frederic (20th C) ?
£400 $724 €600 Judaica (120x80cm-47x31in) s. 30-Mar-4 Gioffredo, Nice #127/R

LEWANDOWSKI, Edmund D (1914-1998) American
Works on paper
£412 $700 €602 Venice no.6 (38x51cm-15x20in) s.d.1956 prov. 9-Nov-3 Wright, Chicago #307
£588 $1000 €858 Employers insurance of Wausau (86x36cm-34x14in) s. s.i.d.1967 verso gouache on board. 9-Nov-3 Wright, Chicago #313 est:1500-2000
£1176 $2000 €1717 Pompidou Centre scaffolding (51x69cm-20x27in) s.d.1995 gouache. 9-Nov-3 Wright, Chicago #158 est:2000-3000

LEWANDOWSKI, Slawomir J (20th C) American
£523 $900 €764 Spring landscape, along the Delaware, Carversville, Pa (58x74cm-23x29in) s.d.54 i.verso. 6-Dec-3 Pook & Pook, Downington #96/R

LEWCZUK, Margrit (1952-) American
Works on paper
£306 $550 €447 Drawing for T (28x21cm-11x8in) chl pastel. 24-Apr-4 David Rago, Lambertville #253/R

LEWEN, Si (20th C) American
£326 $600 €476 Evening procession (69x99cm-27x39in) s. 10-Jun-4 Swann Galleries, New York #150/R

LEWERS, Margo (1908-1978) Australian
£492 $797 €718 From the past (58x34cm-23x13in) s. i.verso board prov. 30-Jul-3 Goodman, Sydney #60/R (A.D 1200)
£1322 $2446 €1930 Circles with red and blue (75x50cm-30x20in) s. s.i.verso oil paper on board prov. 10-Mar-4 Deutscher-Menzies, Melbourne #262/R est:3000-5000 (A.D 3200)
£1475 $2390 €2154 Night and day (57x91cm-22x36in) s. i.verso board. 30-Jul-3 Goodman, Sydney #62/R est:1500-2000 (A.D 3600)
£3306 $6116 €4827 Movement with res (137x167cm-54x66in) i.stretcher prov. 10-Mar-4 Deutscher-Menzies, Melbourne #261/R est:7000-12000 (A.D 8000)
Works on paper
£1653 $3058 €2413 Above (81x45cm-32x18in) s. i.verso synthetic polymer on board prov. 10-Mar-4 Deutscher-Menzies, Melbourne #263/R est:3000-5000 (A.D 4000)

LEWIN, C L (19th C) ?
£486 $900 €710 Portrait of a seated gentleman with patterned mustard coloured vest (89x71cm-35x28in) s. 19-Jan-4 Winter Associates, Plainville #56/R

LEWIN, John William (1770-1819) British
Works on paper
£7000 $11410 €10220 Studies of a fish (22x56cm-9x22in) i. black wash W/C prov. 25-Sep-3 Christie's, London #477/R est:7000-10000
£18000 $29340 €26280 Nightjar (28x48cm-11x19in) indis.i. W/C prov. 25-Sep-3 Christie's, London #476/R est:12000-16000
£30000 $46500 €43800 Gymea lily - Doryanthes excelsa (55x41cm-22x16in) s.i.d.1807 W/C prov. 26-Sep-2 Christie's, London #67/R est:30000-50000

LEWIN, Stephen (fl.1890-1910) British
£950 $1615 €1387 Sleeping fisherman (63x46cm-25x18in) s.d.1902. 19-Nov-3 Tennants, Leyburn #1253/R
£1700 $3145 €2482 Performers (36x47cm-14x19in) s. indis.d. 14-Jul-4 Bonhams, Chester #427/R est:1500-2000
£3500 $6265 €5110 An apt pupil (60x81cm-24x32in) s.d.1903. 26-May-4 Sotheby's, Olympia #82/R est:1800-2500

LEWIS, Charles (attrib) (1753-1795) British
£1200 $2232 €1752 Peaches, grapes and greengages in a basket (30x35cm-12x14in) 4-Mar-4 Christie's, Kensington #659/R est:600-1000

LEWIS, Charles George (19th C) British
Prints
£6500 $10595 €9490 Relief of Lucknow and triumphant meeting of Havelock (64x122cm-25x48in) mixed method engraving after Thomas Jones Barker. 24-Sep-3 Christie's, London #97/R est:4000-6000

LEWIS, Charles James (1830-1892) British
£360 $619 €526 Figures gathering flowers (19x30cm-7x12in) indis.s. board. 5-Dec-3 Honiton Galleries, Honiton #13
£370 $629 €540 Farmyard scene (41x60cm-16x24in) init.indis.i.d.1867. 25-Nov-3 Bonhams, Knowle #235
£700 $1169 €1022 Feeding the ducks (36x25cm-14x10in) s.d.1880 board. 8-Oct-3 Christie's, Kensington #859/R
£750 $1350 €1095 Farmyard scene, breakfast time at Olford (40x59cm-16x23in) init.i. 22-Apr-4 Lawrence, Crewkerne #910/R
£880 $1443 €1285 Rural landscape with rocky stream and mountains in distance (67x44cm-26x17in) s. 3-Jun-3 Fellows & Sons, Birmingham #80/R
£994 $1800 €1451 Two young girls with their King Charles Spaniel (30x25cm-12x10in) s. canvas on panel. 3-Apr-4 Neal Auction Company, New Orleans #601/R est:2000-3000
£1117 $2000 €1631 Richmond bridge (41x61cm-16x24in) s. prov. 21-Mar-4 Hindman, Chicago #839/R est:2000-4000
£1150 $1817 €1679 Waiting in a Country Churchyard (13x12cm-5x5in) i.verso panel. 2-Sep-3 Gildings, Market Harborough #422/R est:200-300
£1500 $2700 €2190 Birds nesting (15x20cm-6x8in) s.d.1857 i.verso panel. 20-Apr-4 Clarke Gammon, Guildford #7/R est:800-1200
£2200 $3740 €3212 Little hay girl (20x13cm-8x5in) s.d.1863 panel. 19-Nov-3 Bonhams, New Bond Street #50/R est:1200-1800

LEWIS, David (20th C) British
Works on paper
£1100 $1749 €1606 Summer shell (57x76cm-22x30in) s. gouache board. 10-Sep-3 Sotheby's, Olympia #61/R est:300-500

LEWIS, Don (20th C) American
Works on paper
£1829 $3200 €2670 Bunny in stockings (72x56cm-28x22in) s. acrylic gouache W/C board exec Nov 1968. 17-Dec-3 Christie's, Rockefeller NY #123/R est:2000-3000
£2743 $4800 €4005 Bunny in water (69x53cm-27x21in) s. gouache board exec c.1964. 17-Dec-3 Christie's, Rockefeller NY #124/R est:2000-3000
£2857 $5000 €4171 Bunny (40x20cm-16x8in) s. gouache W/C exec c.1967. 17-Dec-3 Christie's, Rockefeller NY #122/R est:2000-3000
£3143 $5500 €4589 Bunny (56x38cm-22x15in) s. gouache board lit. 17-Dec-3 Christie's, Rockefeller NY #125/R est:2000-3000

LEWIS, Edmund Darch (1835-1910) American
£718 $1300 €1048 Mountainous landscape with watering cows (18x25cm-7x10in) s. 3-Apr-4 Nadeau, Windsor #230 est:800-1200
£1000 $1700 €1460 Coastal rocks (36x46cm-14x18in) s.d.1887. 21-Nov-3 Skinner, Boston #307/R est:2500-3500
£1375 $2200 €2008 Harbour scene (20x30cm-8x12in) s.d.1870. 20-Sep-3 Pook & Pook, Downington #489 est:500-1000
£2095 $3750 €3059 By the pond in autumn (28x48cm-11x19in) s.d.1873 prov. 6-May-4 Shannon's, Milford #25/R est:2500-3500
£2471 $4250 €3608 Trees by a river (28x48cm-11x19in) s.d.1866. 7-Dec-3 Freeman, Philadelphia #160 est:1000-1500
£3125 $5500 €4563 Harbour view (41x69cm-16x27in) s.d.1869 prov. 21-May-4 North East Auctions, Portsmouth #671/R est:5000-8000
£3352 $6000 €5628 Mountain landscape, autumn (28x48cm-11x19in) s.d.1884. 20-Mar-4 Pook & Pook, Downington #112/R est:3000-4000
£3443 $5750 €5027 Cattle watering (56x91cm-22x36in) s.d.1884 prov. 23-Oct-3 Shannon's, Milford #265/R est:5000-7000
£3593 $6000 €5246 Cows watering by the Old Mill (76x127cm-30x50in) s.d.1921 prov. 23-Oct-3 Shannon's, Milford #114/R est:6000-8000
£4032 $7500 €5887 Mountainous landscape with lake and fishermen (89x152cm-35x60in) s.d.1871. 6-Mar-4 North East Auctions, Portsmouth #1133/R est:6000-9000
£4076 $7500 €5951 Sailing boat by a waterfall (76x127cm-30x50in) s.d.189. 27-Jun-4 Freeman, Philadelphia #78/R est:8000-12000
£4853 $8250 €7085 Hudson River view with boatman (51x91cm-20x36in) s.d.1871. 21-Nov-3 Eldred, East Dennis #831/R est:7000-8000
£5389 $9000 €7868 Fishing by the Mill (51x76cm-20x30in) s.d.1875. 23-Oct-3 Shannon's, Milford #263/R est:6000-8000
£15642 $28000 €22837 Stroll by the riverside (127x102cm-50x40in) s.d.1877 prov. 6-May-4 Shannon's, Milford #151/R est:12000-18000
Works on paper
£202 $375 €295 Waves and distant coastline (49x74cm-19x29in) s.d.1908 W/C gouache. 5-Mar-4 Skinner, Boston #308/R
£229 $410 €334 Untitled (25x53cm-10x21in) s.d.1889 W/C exhib. 19-Mar-4 Aspire, Cleveland #125
£233 $400 €340 Mountain landscape with figures (43x46cm-17x18in) s.d.1857 W/C board. 7-Dec-3 Treadway Gallery, Cincinnati #481/R
£240 $400 €350 Boats along a shoreline (22x48cm-9x19in) s.d.1857 W/C gouache. 19-Oct-3 Bonhams & Butterfields, Los Angeles #7001
£246 $425 €359 Shoreline landscape (23x51cm-9x20in) s.d.1891 W/C. 10-Dec-3 Alderfer's, Hatfield #494
£313 $500 €457 Sailboats on the river (46x66cm-18x26in) s.d.1877 W/C gouache. 19-Sep-3 Freeman, Philadelphia #23/R
£313 $500 €457 Summer landscape (33x64cm-13x25in) s.d.1887 W/C. 20-Sep-3 Pook & Pook, Downington #159
£353 $600 €515 Man walking riverside, distant city (30x66cm-12x26in) s.d.1888 W/C. 28-Nov-3 Thomaston Place, Thomaston #817
£378 $650 €552 Cottage by the bay (51x76cm-20x30in) s.d.1901 W/C board. 7-Dec-3 Treadway Gallery, Cincinnati #484/R
£391 $700 €657 River landscape with sailboat and buildings (51x74cm-20x29in) W/C gouache. 20-Mar-4 Pook & Pook, Downington #549
£422 $700 €616 Returning to harbour (23x51cm-9x20in) s.d.00 W/C. 4-Oct-3 Neal Auction Company, New Orleans #366/R
£441 $700 €644 Coast (22x51cm-9x20in) s.d.88 W/C gouache. 12-Sep-3 Skinner, Boston #299/R
£475 $850 €797 Coastal landscape (30x61cm-12x24in) s.d.1889 W/C. 20-Mar-4 Pook & Pook, Downington #115/R
£479 $800 €699 Cows watering (23x51cm-9x20in) s.d.1886 W/C. 20-Jun-3 Freeman, Philadelphia #83/R
£503 $900 €844 Coastal scene (25x51cm-10x20in) s.d.1899 W/C. 20-Mar-4 Pook & Pook, Downington #109/R
£503 $900 €844 Coastal scene (23x48cm-9x19in) s.d.1893 W/C. 20-Mar-4 Pook & Pook, Downington #111/R
£615 $1100 €1032 Coastal scene (51x61cm-20x24in) s.d.1902 W/C. 20-Mar-4 Pook & Pook, Downington #110/R
£688 $1100 €1004 The Blue Zebra Inn (5x84cm-2x33in) s.d.1909 W/C gouache. 20-Sep-3 Pook & Pook, Downington #197a/R
£688 $1100 €1004 Coastal scene with sailboats (20x51cm-8x20in) s.d.1888 W/C gouache. 20-Sep-3 Pook & Pook, Downington #392
£719 $1200 €1050 Cape May (23x51cm-9x20in) s.d.1894 W/C gouache. 20-Jun-3 Freeman, Philadelphia #1/R est:1000-1500
£782 $1400 €1313 Coastal scene with sailboats (53x66cm-21x26in) W/C gouache. 20-Mar-4 Pook & Pook, Downington #548 est:1200-1500
£815 $1500 €1190 Seascape with coastal rocks in foreground (23x51cm-9x20in) s.d.1888 W/C. 9-Jun-4 Alderfer's, Hatfield #480/R est:3000-5000
£1040 $1800 €1518 Landscape with figures on a road (48x51cm-19x20in) s.d.1897 W/C. 10-Dec-3 Alderfer's, Hatfield #459 est:700-900
£1180 $1900 €1723 Coastal sailing (48x71cm-19x28in) s. W/C gouache. 20-Aug-3 James Julia, Fairfield #936/R est:1000-2000
£1229 $2200 €2063 Coastal scene with sailboat and lighthouse (23x51cm-9x20in) s.d.1898 W/C. 20-Mar-4 Pook & Pook, Downington #550/R est:700-1000
£1536 $2750 €2243 Flower garden, Narragansett (23x51cm-9x20in) s.indis.d. W/C prov. 6-May-4 Shannon's, Milford #189/R est:3000-5000

LEWIS, Edward Morland (1903-1943) British
£1900 $3344 €2774 September, Ferryside (19x27cm-7x11in) board prov.exhib. 19-May-4 Sotheby's, Olympia #186/R est:800-1200

£3800 $6042 €5548 Harbour scene (30x39cm-12x15in) board exhib. 10-Sep-3 Sotheby's, Olympia #183/R est:1000-1500

LEWIS, Frederick (19/20th C) British
£700 $1190 €1022 Autumn in the pasture, Epsom (33x48cm-13x19in) mono.d.1887 i.verso. 27-Nov-3 Christie's, Kensington #146/R
£1400 $2324 €2044 Inarticulate sympathy, portraits of Baronet and Rex (43x53cm-17x21in) s.i.d.1892 verso. 1-Oct-3 Sotheby's, Olympia #133/R est:1000-1500

LEWIS, Geoffrey (20th C) American
£305 $550 €445 The swan (19x19cm-7x7in) board. 25-Apr-4 Bonhams & Butterfields, San Francisco #5539/R
£348 $650 €508 River scene (20x25cm-8x10in) s. board. 25-Feb-4 Dallas Auction Gallery, Dallas #532/R

LEWIS, George Robert (1782-1871) British
£9000 $15840 €13140 Gentleman with shooting dogs and the day's bag (76x65cm-30x26in) s.d.1828 panel prov.exhib. 21-May-4 Christie's, London #75/R est:10000-15000
Works on paper
£222 $400 €324 View of the cathedral at Angers (8x13cm-3x5in) W/C. 21-Jan-4 Doyle, New York #19
£800 $1440 €1168 Ayez pitie du pauvre aveugle (26x18cm-10x7in) s.d.1828 W/C over pencil bodycol prov.lit. 21-Jan-4 Sotheby's, Olympia #127/R

LEWIS, Hank (20th C) American
Works on paper
£963 $1800 €1406 Outdoor cafe seen from above (33x25cm-13x10in) ink gouache. 26-Feb-4 Illustration House, New York #109 est:1500-2500

LEWIS, Harry Emerson (1892-1958) American
£882 $1500 €1288 Old barn (61x76cm-24x30in) s. board prov. 18-Nov-3 John Moran, Pasadena #69 est:1500-2500
£1000 $1800 €1460 Desert Walls, Utah (50x61cm-20x24in) s. 25-Apr-4 Bonhams & Butterfields, San Francisco #5527/R est:1500-1800

LEWIS, Henry (1819-1904) German
£2353 $4000 €3435 Alpine landscape with waterfall and lake (48x71cm-19x28in) s.i.d.1874. 31-Oct-3 North East Auctions, Portsmouth #1211 est:4000-6000

LEWIS, J (?) ?
£949 $1700 €1386 His Majesty's frigate - Blonde - leaving Portsmouth (46x66cm-18x26in) s. indis.d. 16-Mar-4 Bonhams & Butterfields, San Francisco #6127/R est:1000-1500

LEWIS, James (20th C) American
£443 $700 €647 Still life of fruit (36x51cm-14x20in) s.d.1888 canvas on board. 27-Jul-3 William Jenack, New York #118
£696 $1100 €1016 Still life of fruit (36x51cm-14x20in) s.d.1888. 27-Jul-3 William Jenack, New York #272

LEWIS, Jeannie Napurrula (20th C) Australian
Works on paper
£413 $702 €603 Warna jukurra - snake dreaming (140x90cm-55x35in) synthetic polymer paint on canvas. 29-Oct-3 Lawson Menzies, Sydney #62/R est:1500-2000 (A.D 1000)

LEWIS, John (18th C) British
£1800 $3294 €2628 Portrait of a lady waering a gold dress with white lace neck and blue bows (77x64cm-30x25in) s.d.17-4. 7-Apr-4 Bonhams, Bury St Edmunds #485/R est:1800-2500
£4027 $7450 €6000 Portrait of a lady (73x58cm-29x23in) s.d.1759 painted oval sold with an associated portrait. 10-Mar-4 James Adam, Dublin #10/R est:4000-6000
£8523 $15257 €12700 Portrait of a lady in a gold dress with lace collar (75x62cm-30x24in) s.d.1753 painted oval. 26-May-4 James Adam, Dublin #6/R est:12500-18500
Works on paper
£640 $1024 €934 Old gamekeeper Bowden, at Mr Butler, Lyneham Devon (36x46cm-14x18in) 16-Sep-3 Capes Dunn, Manchester #866/R

LEWIS, John (attrib) (18th C) British
£3200 $5888 €4672 Portrait of a lady and her child, in a landscape (126x101cm-50x40in) prov. 26-Mar-4 Sotheby's, London #16/R est:4000-6000

LEWIS, John Frederick (1805-1876) British
Works on paper
£260 $447 €380 San Lorenzo de El Escorial, Spain (13x19cm-5x7in) i.d.Aug 27/Dec 1845 pencil. 3-Dec-3 Christie's, Kensington #35/R
£320 $544 €467 Monastery garden (13x10cm-5x4in) d.Dec 5 pen ink chk. 25-Nov-3 Bonhams, Knightsbridge #16/R
£1100 $1870 €1606 Vine-covered pergola, by a rustic house, Ronda, Spain (26x35cm-10x14in) i. pencil htd white prov. 20-Nov-3 Christie's, London #128/R est:1200-1800
£8000 $14400 €11680 Marie folliglie, Val d'Aosta, Italy (36x28cm-14x11in) i. W/C pencil. 22-Apr-4 Lawrence, Crewkerne #756/R est:2000-3000

LEWIS, John Frederick (attrib) (1805-1876) British
Works on paper
£300 $510 €438 Portrait head and shoulders of a pretty girl (15x8cm-6x3in) s. 5-Nov-3 John Nicholson, Haslemere #474

LEWIS, John Hardwicke (1840-1927) British
Works on paper
£550 $1007 €803 Eiger Monch (14x20cm-6x8in) mono. W/C sold with another by same hand. 27-Jan-4 Bonhams, Knightsbridge #374

LEWIS, Martin (1881-1962) American
Prints
£2018 $3250 €2946 Giant shadow (25x18cm-10x7in) s. drypoint prov. 20-Aug-3 James Julia, Fairfield #1216/R est:2000-4000
£2206 $3750 €3221 Under the street lamp (38x24cm-15x9in) s. etching exec.1928. 31-Oct-3 Sotheby's, New York #189/R
£2374 $4250 €3466 Under the street lamp (38x23cm-15x9in) etching. 14-May-4 Du Mouchelle, Detroit #2119/R est:3000-3500
£2489 $4156 €3634 Great shadow (25x17cm-10x7in) s.i. drypoint edition of 100 prov. 16-Oct-3 Waddingtons, Toronto #19/R est:4000-6000 (C.D 5500)
£3239 $5215 €4729 New York (31x44cm-12x17in) s.i. etching. 13-Oct-3 Joel, Victoria #329 est:1000-1500 (A.D 8000)
£3261 $5250 €4761 Chance meeting (25x18cm-10x7in) s. dyrpoint prov. 20-Aug-3 James Julia, Fairfield #1217/R est:2000-4000
£3495 $6500 €5103 Corner shadows (22x23cm-9x9in) s. drypoint. 2-Mar-4 Swann Galleries, New York #259/R est:6000-9000
£3614 $6000 €5240 Corner shadows (20x23cm-8x9in) s.d. drypoint edition of 232. 14-Jun-3 Rachel Davis, Shaker Heights #366/R est:4000-6000
£4237 $7500 €6186 Little penthouse (30x23cm-12x9in) s.num.20 drypoint. 30-Apr-4 Sotheby's, New York #21/R est:5000-7000
£4706 $8000 €6871 Bay windows (30x20cm-12x8in) s. drypoint. 31-Oct-3 Sotheby's, New York #190/R
£4706 $8000 €6871 Big freighter (31x45cm-12x18in) s.i. brown etching aquatint. 6-Nov-3 Swann Galleries, New York #605/R est:8000-12000
£4802 $8500 €7011 Chance meeting (26x19cm-10x7in) s. drypoint. 30-Apr-4 Sotheby's, New York #22/R est:7000-9000
£5882 $10000 €8588 Two A M (23x38cm-9x15in) s. drypoint. 6-Nov-3 Swann Galleries, New York #606/R est:8000-12000
£6704 $12000 €9788 Chance meeting (26x18cm-10x7in) s. drypoint. 6-May-4 Swann Galleries, New York #493/R est:7000-10000
£7821 $14000 €11419 Rainy day, Queens (27x30cm-11x12in) s. drypoint edition of 70. 4-May-4 Doyle, New York #208/R est:8000-10000
£9877 $16000 €14322 Stoops in snow (25x37cm-10x15in) s. drypoint prov. 8-Aug-3 Barridorf, Portland #44/R est:2000-3000
£11176 $19000 €16317 Snow on the El (35x23cm-14x9in) s. drypoint exec.1931. 31-Oct-3 Sotheby's, New York #191/R
£13580 $22000 €19691 Snow on the El (35x22cm-14x9in) s. drypoint prov. 8-Aug-3 Barridorf, Portland #43/R est:6000-9000

LEWIS, Mary Amanda (1872-1953) American
£1000 $1700 €1460 Indian woman with basket in a landscape (20x33cm-8x13in) s. board prov. 18-Nov-3 John Moran, Pasadena #98 est:1000-1500

LEWIS, Maud (1903-1970) Canadian
£1200 $1968 €1752 Village scene with train (30x36cm-12x14in) s. panel. 28-May-3 Maynards, Vancouver #7 est:3000-4000 (C.D 2700)
£1200 $2196 €1752 Covered bridge in winter (30x40cm-12x16in) s. board. 1-Jun-4 Joyner Waddington, Toronto #228/R est:1800-2200 (C.D 3000)
£1220 $2183 €1781 Sleigh ride in winter (30x35cm-12x14in) s. board prov. 31-May-4 Sotheby's, Toronto #45/R est:3000-4000 (C.D 3000)
£1220 $2183 €1781 Team of oxen in winter (29x35cm-11x14in) s. board on panel prov. 31-May-4 Sotheby's, Toronto #46/R est:3000-5000 (C.D 3000)
£1423 $2547 €2078 Fishing schooner in the Bay of Fundy (30x35cm-12x14in) s. board prov. 31-May-4 Sotheby's, Toronto #47/R est:4000-6000 (C.D 3500)
£1525 $2729 €2227 Winter sleigh ride (32x35cm-13x14in) s. board prov. 31-May-4 Sotheby's, Toronto #170/R est:3000-4000 (C.D 3750)
£1810 $3023 €2643 Untitled - oxen and logging wagon (25x35cm-10x14in) s. board. 17-Nov-3 Hodgins, Calgary #45/R est:3500-4500 (C.D 4000)
£1829 $3274 €2670 Covered bridge in winter (27x33cm-11x13in) s. board prov. 27-May-4 Heffel, Vancouver #214/R est:4000-5000 (C.D 4500)
£1829 $3274 €2670 Waiting oxen (30x30cm-12x12in) s. board. 31-May-4 Sotheby's, Toronto #169/R est:3000-5000 (C.D 4500)
£2027 $3446 €2959 Winter country scene with oxen (30x36cm-12x14in) s. board prov. 18-Nov-3 Sotheby's, Toronto #21/R est:3000-4000 (C.D 4500)
£2236 $4002 €3265 Horse and sleigh (27x33cm-11x13in) s. board prov. 27-May-4 Heffel, Vancouver #215/R est:4000-5000 (C.D 5500)
£2846 $5093 €4155 Three black kittens (29x29cm-11x11in) s. board prov. 27-May-4 Heffel, Vancouver #217/R est:4000-5000 (C.D 7000)
£4065 $7276 €5935 Grazing (30x30cm-12x12in) s. board on panel. 31-May-4 Sotheby's, Toronto #171/R est:3000-5000 (C.D 10000)
Works on paper
£455 $741 €664 Harbour scene. Landscape (9x14cm-4x6in) s. W/C pair sold with a letter. 23-Sep-3 Ritchie, Toronto #157/R est:700-900 (C.D 1000)
£588 $982 €858 Untitled - ships at sunset (7x11cm-3x4in) s. W/C gouache. 17-Nov-3 Hodgins, Calgary #257 est:1200-1500 (C.D 1300)
£633 $1058 €924 Untitled - water reflections (7x11cm-3x4in) s. W/C gouache. 17-Nov-3 Hodgins, Calgary #322 est:1200-1500 (C.D 1400)

LEWIS, Neville (1895-1972) South African
£672 $1217 €981 Young African man (34x24cm-13x9in) s. 30-Mar-4 Stephan Welz, Johannesburg #486 est:3000-5000 (SA.R 8000)
£1724 $2879 €2517 Young man with an orange blanket (60x50cm-24x20in) s. 20-Oct-3 Stephan Welz, Johannesburg #257/R est:10000-15000 (SA.R 20000)
Works on paper
£940 $1598 €1372 Pondo girl with a red blanket (67x51cm-26x20in) 4-Nov-3 Stephan Welz, Johannesburg #657/R est:12000-16000 (SA.R 11000)

LEWIS, Shelton (fl.1875-1880) British
Works on paper
£961 $1720 €1403 Cottage garden (45x76cm-18x30in) s.d.1877 W/C. 28-May-4 Uppsala Auktionskammare, Uppsala #109/R est:5000-6000 (S.KR 13000)

LEWIS, Thomas E (1909-1979) American
£331 $600 €483 Tulips (58x36cm-23x14in) s. 18-Apr-4 Bonhams & Butterfields, Los Angeles #7077

LEWIS, Thomas L (1907-1978) American
£272 $500 €397 Water oaks, autumn landscape with stream (61x76cm-24x30in) s. 29-Mar-4 O'Gallerie, Oregon #784/R
£312 $550 €456 Desert landscape, Taos (61x77cm-24x30in) s. 23-May-4 Bonhams & Butterfields, Los Angeles #7063a/R
£514 $950 €750 Tranquil waters (71x91cm-28x36in) s.i. 14-Jan-4 Dallas Auction Gallery, Dallas #432/R

LEWIS-BROWN, John (1829-1890) British
Works on paper
£1594 $2614 €2200 L'attelage dans la cour (21x19cm-8x7in) W/C. 28-May-3 Coutau Begarie, Paris #312/R est:2200-2500

LEWITSKA, Sophie (1882-1937) Polish?
Works on paper
£1060 $1928 €1600 Parc. Fete foraine (24x32cm-9x13in) one s. W/C pair. 15-Jun-4 Rossini, Paris #156 est:300-400

LEWITT, Sol (1928-) American
£1342 $2470 €2000 Napoli (34x41cm-13x16in) s.i.d.1995 painted torn paper prov. 24-Mar-4 Joron-Derem, Paris #186/R est:2000-2500
£80000 $145600 €116800 1 2 3 4 5 Half Off (197x272cm-78x107in) baked enamel aluminium exec 1968 prov. 5-Feb-4 Sotheby's, London #43/R est:40000-60000
Prints
£1912 $3250 €2792 Fifteen equal arcs (93x47cm-37x19in) s. col etching aquatint. 31-Oct-3 Sotheby's, New York #636/R
£2054 $3800 €2999 Untitled, bands of colour in four directions (73x25cm-29x10in) s.num.16/45 col woodcut exec.c.1995. 12-Feb-4 Christie's, Rockefeller NY #127/R est:1500-2500
£2667 $4907 €4000 Double composite (86x60cm-34x24in) s.i. col serigraph. 11-Jun-4 Hauswedell & Nolte, Hamburg #1405/R est:4500
£4237 $7500 €6186 Stars - 8 pointed (137x137cm-54x54in) s.num.3/15 verso col relief prints 36 in one frame. 28-Apr-4 Christie's, Rockefeller NY #349/R est:5000-7000
Sculpture
£5780 $10000 €8439 Untitled (76x75x15cm-30x30x6in) painted steel with base prov. 10-Dec-3 Phillips, New York #419/R est:3000-4000
£14054 $26000 €20519 Serial Project no. 1 A-7 (24x22x22cm-9x9x9in) white grey baked enamel steel prov. 12-Feb-4 Sotheby's, New York #99/R est:6000-8000
£18156 $32500 €26508 Incomplete open cube 10 / 4 (20x20x20cm-8x8x8in) s.d.1975 underside painted white wood exec 1974 prov. 13-May-4 Sotheby's, New York #174/R est:12000-18000
£41916 $70000 €61197 Column with geometric figures within square (289x98x98cm-114x39x39in) painted wood executed 1984 prov. 13-Nov-3 Phillips, New York #30/R est:80000-120000
£47904 $80000 €69940 A 8 (35x35x35cm-14x14x14in) baked enamel aluminum. 13-Nov-3 Sotheby's, New York #127/R est:10000-15000
£65868 $110000 €96167 Incomplete open cube no 8-12 (102x102x102cm-40x40x40in) baked enamel aluminum prov.exhib. 13-Nov-3 Sotheby's, New York #119/R est:50000-70000
£83832 $140000 €122395 Incomplete open cube no 7-31 (102x102x102cm-40x40x40in) baked enamel aluminum prov.exhib. 13-Nov-3 Sotheby's, New York #118/R est:50000-70000
£125749 $210000 €183594 A 6 (206x206x206cm-81x81x81in) baked enamel aluminum prov.exhib.lit. 13-Nov-3 Sotheby's, New York #124/R est:120000-160000
£150838 $270000 €220223 Serial Project 1 ABCD 6 (50x145x145cm-20x57x57in) baked enamel on steel exec 1968 prov.exhib.lit. 12-May-4 Sotheby's, New York #15/R est:120000-180000
£178771 $320000 €261006 Untitled (244x70x70cm-96x28x28in) enamel steel prov.exhib. 12-May-4 Christie's, Rockefeller NY #415/R est:150000-200000
Works on paper
£769 $1323 €1100 Untitled (28x18cm-11x7in) s.d.91 W/C prov. 2-Dec-3 Sotheby's, Amsterdam #338/R est:1200-1500
£833 $1392 €1200 Composition in yellow, red and blue (13x9cm-5x4in) s.i.d. gouache board. 24-Oct-3 Ketterer, Hamburg #444/R
£1000 $1840 €1460 Untitled (15x10cm-6x4in) s.indis.i.d.88 gouache prov. 24-Jun-4 Sotheby's, Olympia #475/R est:1000-1500
£1733 $3120 €2600 Small pyramid 2 (17x25cm-7x10in) s.d.1985 W/C prov. 25-Apr-4 Versailles Encheres #198 est:1500-2000
£1800 $3240 €2700 Small pyramid (17x25cm-7x10in) s.d.1985 W/C prov. 25-Apr-4 Versailles Encheres #200 est:1500-2000
£1818 $3127 €2600 Untitled (29x41cm-11x16in) s. folded paper. 2-Dec-3 Sotheby's, Amsterdam #342/R est:1000-1500
£2200 $3498 €3190 Vertical lines, not straight, not touching (75x44cm-30x17in) s.i.d.1990 pencil gouache. 11-Sep-3 Christie's, Kensington #243/R est:1500-2000
£2266 $3852 €3308 Untitled (53x48cm-21x19in) s.d.90 gouache. 5-Nov-3 AB Stockholms Auktionsverk #1073/R est:30000-35000 (S.KR 30000)
£2400 $3816 €3480 Vertical lines, not straight, not touching (75x44cm-30x17in) s.i.d.1990 pencil gouache prov. 11-Sep-3 Christie's, Kensington #246/R est:1500-2000
£2400 $3816 €3480 Vertical lines, not straight, not touching (75x44cm-30x17in) s.i.d.1990 pencil W/C prov. 11-Sep-3 Christie's, Kensington #247/R est:1500-2000
£2434 $4479 €3700 Small pyramid 7 (17x24cm-7x9in) s.d.1985 gouache prov. 27-Jun-4 Versailles Encheres #159/R est:2500-3000
£2500 $3975 €3625 Vertical lines, not straight, not touching (75x44cm-30x17in) s.i.d.1990 pencil gouache prov. 11-Sep-3 Christie's, Kensington #248/R est:1500-2000
£2533 $4661 €3800 Black gouache (35x27cm-14x11in) s.d.92 blk gouache exhib. 9-Jun-4 Artcurial Briest, Paris #550/R est:4000-5000
£2600 $4784 €3900 Striped composition (28x19cm-11x7in) s.d.1994 gouache board. 12-Jun-4 Villa Grisebach, Berlin #787/R est:1800-2400
£3000 $5010 €4380 Untitled (27x27cm-11x11in) s.d.93 gouache prov. 22-Oct-3 Bonhams, New Bond Street #99/R est:2000-3000
£3200 $5856 €4800 Untitled (35x29cm-14x11in) s.d.92 gouache board. 4-Jun-4 Lempertz, Koln #271/R est:2000
£3380 $5611 €4800 Octogon (50x69cm-20x27in) s.d.1986 W/C. 13-Jun-3 Hauswedell & Nolte, Hamburg #745/R est:5000
£3400 $5678 €4964 Untitled (28x38cm-11x15in) s.d.1994 gouache prov. 22-Oct-3 Bonhams, New Bond Street #98/R est:2000-3000
£3927 $6677 €5733 Lines in four directions (14x37cm-6x15in) s.d.5/10-71 mixed media exhib. 4-Nov-3 Bukowskis, Stockholm #556/R est:20000-25000 (S.KR 52000)
£4333 $7800 €6500 Untitled (55x75cm-22x30in) s.d.1986 gouache prov. 25-Apr-4 Versailles Encheres #199 est:3500-4500
£4698 $8645 €7000 Lucky strike (56x75cm-22x30in) s.d.1989 gouache. 29-Mar-4 Cornette de St.Cyr, Paris #38/R est:3000-4000
£4800 $8784 €7200 Diagonal yellow lines (35x29cm-14x11in) s.i.d.Sept.2, 1971 col pen board. 4-Jun-4 Lempertz, Koln #270/R est:2500
£5000 $9100 €7300 Untitled (27x19cm-11x7in) s.d.93 gouache card prov. 4-Feb-4 Sotheby's, Olympia #7/R est:200-3000
£5263 $9684 €8000 Untitled (39x58cm-15x23in) s.d.1987 gouache prov. 27-Jun-4 Versailles Encheres #161/R est:4500-5000
£5500 $9955 €8030 Irregular horizontal bands of equal width starting at bottom (56x75cm-22x30in) s.d.91 gouache prov.exhib. 1-Apr-4 Christie's, Kensington #273/R est:5000-7000
£5705 $10211 €8500 Horizonta bands (29x76cm-11x30in) s.d.03 gouache. 26-May-4 Christie's, Paris #114/R est:4000-6000
£7000 $12740 €10220 Untitled (48x48cm-19x19in) s.d.84 gouache pencil card prov. 4-Feb-4 Sotheby's, Olympia #8/R est:4000-6000
£7222 $13000 €10544 Four colour line drawing with progressively wider spaces between (10x8cm-4x3in) s.i.d.1972 col pencil prov. 24-Apr-4 David Rago, Lambertville #153/R est:1000-2000
£7263 $13000 €10604 Untitled (56x56cm-22x22in) s.i.d.1984/85 gouache prov. 13-May-4 Sotheby's, New York #185/R est:5000-7000
£8000 $13360 €11680 Irregular form (153x166cm-60x65in) s.d.1997 gouache prov. 22-Oct-3 Bonhams, New Bond Street #100/R est:8000-12000
£9497 $17000 €13866 Straight pencil lines from the top and left side (36x36cm-14x14in) s.i.d.July 6 1972 graphite prov. 14-May-4 Phillips, New York #247/R est:10000-15000
£9500 $17480 €13870 Untitled (38x57cm-15x22in) s.d.87 gouache pencil prov.exhib. 24-Jun-4 Sotheby's, London #144/R est:5000-7000
£11173 $20000 €16313 Irregular grid (88x65cm-35x26in) s.d.01 gouache prov. 13-May-4 Sotheby's, New York #184/R est:8000-10000
£14595 $27000 €21309 Red grid, yellow circles, blue and black arcs (33x33cm-13x13in) s.i.d.3/24/72 col inks pencil cardboard prov.exhib. 12-Feb-4 Sotheby's, New York #98/R est:8000-12000
£17450 $31235 €26000 Composition (36x36cm-14x14in) s.d.1970 col ink prov. 26-May-4 Christie's, Paris #91/R est:5000-8000
£18000 $33120 €26280 Untitled (110x151cm-43x59in) col ink wash pencil on four sheets. 25-Jun-4 Christie's, London #181/R est:15000-20000
£28000 $46760 €40880 Wall drawing number 451. col ink wash prov. 22-Oct-3 Christie's, London #68/R est:15000-20000
£35928 $60000 €52455 Wavy brushstrokes, vertical (156x154cm-61x61in) gouache prov. 13-Nov-3 Sotheby's, New York #581/R est:30000-40000
£38922 $65000 €56826 Wall drawing no 560, symmetrical pyramid. col ink wash prov.lit. 13-Nov-3 Sotheby's, New York #120/R est:18000-22000
£56886 $95000 €83054 Wall drawing no 99, arcs from the midpoints of four sides. black pencil prov.exhib.lit. 13-Nov-3 Sotheby's, New York #121/R est:25000-35000

LEWY, Kurt (1898-1963) Belgian
£800 $1464 €1200 Composition (9x11cm-4x4in) mono.d.59 enamel. 7-Jun-4 Palais de Beaux Arts, Brussels #373

LEXOW, Borghild Berge (1898-1976) Norwegian
£407 $748 €611 Villeneuf-les-Avignon (51x61cm-20x24in) s. 14-Jun-4 Blomqvist, Lysaker #1227 (N.KR 5000)

LEYBOLD, Eduard Friedrich (1798-1847) German
£4167 $6792 €6000 Portrait of Johann Fritz and wife (131x108cm-52x43in) s.d.1838. 25-Sep-3 Dr Fritz Nagel, Stuttgart #1373/R est:8900

LEYBOLD, Karl Jakob Theodor (1786-1844) German
Works on paper
£503 $866 €720 View of the bridge Rheinstein (18x25cm-7x10in) gouache. 7-Dec-3 Sotheby's, Amsterdam #646/R

LEYDE, Kurt (1881-?) German
£664 $1129 €950 Cala San Vicente (80x100cm-31x39in) s.d.1940 i.verso. 28-Nov-3 Wendl, Rudolstadt #4064/R
£1879 $3458 €2800 Frolicking bacchanten (78x100cm-31x39in) s. 26-Mar-4 Bolland & Marotz, Bremen #633a/R est:5500
£2083 $3437 €3000 Fisherman taking siesta on spanish coast (65x81cm-26x32in) s.d.1933. 3-Jul-3 Van Ham, Cologne #1330/R est:2600
£4698 $8785 €7000 Spring in Palma de Mallorca (81x90cm-32x35in) s. 24-Feb-4 Dorotheum, Vienna #286/R est:2800-3200

LEYDE, Otto (1835-1897) German
£1405 $2600 €2051 Volpino Italiano (46x30cm-18x12in) s.d.75 prov. 10-Feb-4 Doyle, New York #129/R est:2500-3500
Works on paper
£780 $1412 €1139 Portrait of two young sisters holding a book (74x56cm-29x22in) s. W/C. 16-Apr-4 Keys, Aylsham #528/R
£2200 $3542 €3190 Highland house (34x42cm-13x17in) s. W/C htd white. 21-Aug-3 Bonhams, Edinburgh #1126/R est:1000-1500
£3200 $5792 €4672 Young girl seated in a chair holding a cat (74x48cm-29x19in) s. W/C. 16-Apr-4 Keys, Aylsham #529 est:800-1200

LEYDEN, Ernest van (1892-1969) Dutch
£2431 $3840 €3500 Still life with flowers and an oil lamp (92x63cm-36x25in) s.d.22. 2-Sep-3 Christie's, Amsterdam #434 est:1800-2200
Works on paper
£223 $400 €326 La Bardelle (41x48cm-16x19in) s.d.1960 mixed media collage masonite. 16-May-4 Wright, Chicago #267/R

LEYDEN, Jan van (17th C) Dutch
£4895 $8174 €7000 Sea battle scene between Dutch an English Men o' War (73x116cm-29x46in) bears sig. panel prov. 30-Jun-3 Sotheby's, Amsterdam #60/R

LEYDEN, Louise Hannon (?) American?
£313 $500 €457 Gateway to Saddleback, Mission Viejo. s. board. 20-Sep-3 Harvey Clar, Oakland #1318

LEYDEN, Lucas van (1494-1538) Dutch

Prints

£1882	$3200	€2748	Fall of man (12x7cm-5x3in) engraving. 6-Nov-3 Swann Galleries, New York #175/R est:1500-2500
£2098	$3566	€3000	Couple playing musical instruments (12x7cm-5x3in) copperplate. 27-Nov-3 Bassenge, Berlin #5252/R est:1800
£2353	$4000	€3435	Young man with a skull (18x14cm-7x6in) engraving executed c.1519. 6-Nov-3 Swann Galleries, New York #20/R est:4000-6000

LEYDEN, Lucas van (style) (1494-1538) Dutch

£5500	$9900	€8030	Triumph of David (33x46cm-13x18in) panel. 20-Apr-4 Sotheby's, Olympia #243/R est:6000-8000

LEYDENFROST, Alexander (1888-1961) American?

Works on paper

£535	$1000	€781	Industrial landscape with giant spoon of sugar (41x48cm-16x19in) s. Wolff pencil gouache en grisaille exec.c.1930. 26-Feb-4 Illustration House, New York #110

LEYENDECKER, Frank Xavier (1877-1924) American

£2310	$4250	€3373	Man wearing overalls stretching a sock above his head (25x20cm-10x8in) i. 9-Jun-4 Alderfer's, Hatfield #447/R est:500-700

Works on paper

£294	$550	€429	Couple with binoculars (13x10cm-5x4in) init. gouache W/C. 26-Feb-4 Illustration House, New York #111

LEYENDECKER, Joseph C (1874-1951) American

£23952	$40000	€34970	New year's baby sprinkling salt on dove (53x43cm-21x17in) mono. 15-Nov-3 Illustration House, New York #98/R est:20000-30000
£78378	$145000	€114432	Parade (71x53cm-28x21in) pair prov. 11-Mar-4 Christie's, Rockefeller NY #89/R est:10000-15000
£97297	$180000	€142054	Football scrimmage (56x56cm-22x22in) one mono. pair prov. 11-Mar-4 Christie's, Rockefeller NY #88/R est:12000-118000

LEYENDECKER, Paul Joseph (1842-?) French

£932	$1500	€1361	Man reading (23x15cm-9x6in) panel. 15-Aug-3 Du Mouchelle, Detroit #2014/R est:1500-2000

LEYINE, Jack (20th C) ?

£550	$1012	€803	Gone to ground (68x89cm-27x35in) s. canvasboard. 10-Jun-4 Christie's, Kensington #197/R
£600	$1104	€876	Clearing the ditch (58x88cm-23x35in) s. canvasboard. 10-Jun-4 Christie's, Kensington #199/R

LEYMAN, A (1856-1933) British

Works on paper

£1200	$1908	€1752	Gittisham, near Honiton (36x53cm-14x21in) s. W/C. 9-Sep-3 Gorringes, Lewes #1884 est:400-600

LEYMAN, Alfred (1856-1933) British

£600	$1002	€876	St Ives (53x36cm-21x14in) s. 14-Oct-3 Bearnes, Exeter #331
£600	$1002	€876	Road to up Ottery (36x52cm-14x20in) s.d.1904. 14-Oct-3 Bearnes, Exeter #332

Works on paper

£260	$476	€380	Clovelly (26x42cm-10x17in) s. W/C. 6-Apr-4 Bearnes, Exeter #606
£280	$462	€409	Waving hello from a cottage at Gittisham (38x31cm-15x12in) s. W/C. 4-Jul-3 Honiton Galleries, Honiton #57/R
£400	$748	€600	West country village scene (36x53cm-14x21in) s. W/C. 21-Jul-4 John Nicholson, Haslemere #92
£460	$782	€672	Exeter Guildhall (75x53cm-30x21in) s. w/. 18-Nov-3 Bearnes, Exeter #546
£700	$1169	€1022	Clovelly (54x37cm-21x15in) s. W/C. 14-Oct-3 Bearnes, Exeter #330/R
£800	$1440	€1168	Scenes of Clovelly, north Devon (54x36cm-21x14in) s. W/C pair. 21-Jan-4 Sotheby's, Olympia #250/R
£920	$1711	€1343	Dartmouth. Figures in cobbled street (53x36cm-21x14in) s. W/C pair. 2-Mar-4 Bearnes, Exeter #397
£1000	$1750	€1460	Axmouth village and church, Devon (20x53cm-8x21in) W/C sold with another W/C. 16-Dec-3 Gorringes, Bexhill #1167 est:100-150

LEYPOLD, Karl Julius von (1806-1874) German

£3846	$6538	€5500	Seashore in winter (22x34cm-9x13in) s. board. 20-Nov-3 Van Ham, Cologne #1716/R est:6000

LEYRITZ, Léon Albert Marie de (1888-1976) French

Works on paper

£300	$537	€450	Jeunes femmes sur la plage de La Baule (26x17cm-10x7in) s. W/C. 16-May-4 Thierry & Lannon, Brest #264

LEYS, Baron H (1815-1869) Belgian

£265	$482	€400	La discussion (26x31cm-10x12in) indis.sig. panel. 15-Jun-4 Vanderkindere, Brussels #146

LEYS, Baron Hendrik (1815-1869) Belgian

£308	$514	€440	Interieur de cuisine avec femme devant l'atre (18x22cm-7x9in) s.i.d.1860 verso panel. 7-Oct-3 Palais de Beaux Arts, Brussels #570
£380	$703	€555	Man crossing a bridge (30x40cm-12x16in) st.sig. board. 10-Feb-4 Bonhams, Knightsbridge #57/R
£420	$722	€600	Scene de famille dans un interieur (38x29cm-15x11in) s. canvas on panel. 2-Dec-3 Campo & Campo, Antwerp #211
£671	$1201	€1000	Autoportrait (24x19cm-9x7in) mono. panel. 25-May-4 Campo & Campo, Antwerp #150/R
£927	$1687	€1400	Jeune fille en priere (22x15cm-9x6in) s. panel. 21-Jun-4 Bernaerts, Antwerp #161/R
£1127	$1949	€1600	Three interiors (24x55cm-9x22in) one mono. canvas on panel three. 13-Dec-3 De Vuyst, Lokeren #208 est:1000-1250
£1733	$3103	€2600	Homme de science dans son cabinet (20x16cm-8x6in) s.d.1845. 11-May-4 Vanderkindere, Brussels #777 est:800-1200
£2267	$4103	€3400	Autoportrait (24x19cm-9x7in) mono. panel. 30-Mar-4 Campo & Campo, Antwerp #161/R est:2000-4000
£2979	$4974	€4200	La priere (45x36cm-18x14in) s.d.1857. 17-Jun-3 Galerie Moderne, Brussels #248/R est:4000-6000

LHARDY Y GARRIGUES, Agustin (1848-1918) Spanish

£738	$1321	€1100	Landscape at dusk (33x47cm-13x19in) s. paper. 25-May-4 Durán, Madrid #157/R
£1585	$2773	€2250	View of the Castle (30x44cm-12x17in) s. cardboard. 16-Dec-3 Durán, Madrid #134/R est:2250

LHERMITTE (?) ?

Works on paper

£1187	$1947	€1650	Villageoises (51x37cm-20x15in) s.i. chl. 6-Jun-3 David Kahn, Paris #49 est:1800-2200

LHERMITTE, Georges (20th C) French?

£397	$743	€600	Thoniers sous voiles (46x38cm-18x15in) s. panel. 24-Jul-4 Thierry & Lannon, Brest #393

LHERMITTE, Léon (1844-1925) French

£11806	$18653	€17000	Woman carrying sheaves of corn (55x30cm-22x12in) s. lit. 19-Sep-3 Schloss Ahlden, Ahlden #1640/R est:8500
£35000	$63700	€51100	Gouter (39x55cm-15x22in) s. painted 1917 prov.lit. 17-Jun-4 Christie's, London #20/R est:40000-60000
£38235	$65000	€55823	Dejeuner du bucheron (56x42cm-22x17in) s.d.1918 prov.lit. 28-Oct-3 Sotheby's, New York #27/R est:40000-60000
£66667	$120000	€97334	La Marne (142x203cm-56x80in) s.d.1903 prov.exhib.lit. 23-Apr-4 Sotheby's, New York #19/R est:70000-90000

Works on paper

£260	$450	€380	Interior scene with flat cupboard and basket (33x25cm-13x10in) s. chl. 10-Dec-3 Alderfer's, Hatfield #290/R
£310	$574	€450	Etude pour la Cathedrale de Rouen (55x44cm-22x17in) st.init. black crayon exec.c.1883. 11-Feb-4 Beaussant & Lefèvre, Paris #50/R
£483	$893	€700	Etude d'homme pour le pressoir (15x12cm-6x5in) st.init. chl estompe lit. 11-Feb-4 Beaussant & Lefèvre, Paris #30/R
£546	$1000	€797	Street scene (20x25cm-8x10in) s. pen ink. 5-Jun-4 Neal Auction Company, New Orleans #100 est:1200-1800
£724	$1340	€1050	Academie d'homme (44x29cm-17x11in) st.init.i. chl estompe lit. 11-Feb-4 Beaussant & Lefèvre, Paris #31/R
£759	$1403	€1100	Portrait d'homme assis (30x46cm-12x18in) st.init. black crayon tracing paper pair lit. 11-Feb-4 Beaussant & Lefèvre, Paris #37
£1034	$1914	€1500	Etude pour La veillee (27x47cm-11x19in) st.init. chl estompe el. 11-Feb-4 Beaussant & Lefèvre, Paris #32/R est:300
£1034	$1914	€1500	La veillee (28x29cm-11x11in) st.init. chl estompe lit. 11-Feb-4 Beaussant & Lefèvre, Paris #33/R est:500
£1172	$2169	€1700	Etude de faucheuse (30x44cm-12x17in) st.init. black crayon estompe. 11-Feb-4 Beaussant & Lefèvre, Paris #45/R est:1000
£1423	$2461	€2020	Paysage (40x46cm-16x18in) s. pastel. 13-Dec-3 Martinot & Savignat, Pontoise #211/R est:1400-1500
£1946	$3581	€2900	Fumees de grasse (23x32cm-9x13in) mono. pastel. 24-Mar-4 Joron-Derem, Paris #47/R est:4500-5000
£2980	$5454	€4500	Mare pres de Mezy (25x33cm-10x13in) s. i.verso pastel. 9-Apr-4 Bailly Pommery, Paris #81/R est:4000-6000
£3618	$6658	€5500	Paysanne endormie (26x61cm-10x24in) s. chl lit. 23-Jun-4 Sotheby's, Paris #93/R est:6000-8000
£4722	$8500	€6894	Farmyard (22x30cm-9x12in) s. pastel. 23-Apr-4 Sotheby's, New York #147/R est:8000-12000
£6599	$11812	€9700	Faucheur au champ (44x53cm-17x21in) s. pastel. 22-Mar-4 Digard, Paris #125/R est:8000-10000
£7000	$11900	€10220	Marche, Senlis (44x35cm-17x14in) s. pastel chl prov.exhib.lit. 19-Nov-3 Bonhams, New Bond Street #129/R est:7000-10000
£8333	$15000	€12166	Les gerbes de bles (28x44cm-11x17in) s. pastel prov. 23-Apr-4 Sotheby's, New York #148/R est:15000-20000
£8824	$15000	€12883	Fontaine a Chatelguyon (48x51cm-19x20in) s. chl exec.1906 prov.exhib.lit. 29-Oct-3 Christie's, Rockefeller NY #87/R est:15000-20000
£8824	$15000	€12883	Femmes a la fontaine (38x48cm-15x19in) pastel paper on canvas exec.1903 prov.lit. 29-Oct-3 Christie's, Rockefeller NY #105/R est:18000-25000
£9091	$15455	€13000	Lavandieres (42x53cm-17x21in) s.d.1925 pastel lit. 21-Nov-3 Lombrail & Teucquam, Paris #103/R est:3000-3500
£22059	$37500	€32206	Laveuses a la Marne, le matin (72x94cm-28x37in) s.d.1921 pastel paper on canvas prov.lit. 28-Oct-3 Sotheby's, New York #28/R est:25000-35000
£38000	$69160	€55480	Soleil dans les herbes (60x560cm 24x220in) s. pastel paper on canvas exec 1885 exhib.lit. 17-Jun-4 Christie's, London #19/R est:40000-60000

LHERMITTE, Léon (attrib) (1844-1925) French

Works on paper

£629	$1145	€950	Village landscape (25x33cm-10x13in) s. pastel. 19-Jun-4 Bergmann, Erlangen #844

LHOTA, Albin (1847-1889) Czechoslovakian

£535	$996	€781	Winter landscape (13x22cm-5x9in) s. panel. 6-Mar-4 Dorotheum, Prague #61 est:12000-18000 (C.KR 26000)

LHOTAK, Kamil (1912-1990) Czechoslovakian

£3375	$5940	€5063	Landscape with a plane (50x40cm-20x16in) s.d.1957. 22-May-4 Dorotheum, Prague #166/R est:150000-230000 (C.KR 160000)

Works on paper

£285	$472	€416	Sport car (6x11cm-2x4in) mono.d.34 col ink. 4-Oct-3 Dorotheum, Prague #314/R est:10000-15000 (C.KR 13000)
£372	$618	€543	Cars in front of Trion Hotel (9x19cm-4x7in) s.d.1967 ink wash. 4-Oct-3 Dorotheum, Prague #321/R est:12000-18000 (C.KR 17000)
£416	$690	€607	Yellow airship (14x22cm-6x9in) s.d.81 col ink. 4-Oct-3 Dorotheum, Prague #317/R est:12000-18000 (C.KR 19000)
£416	$690	€607	Yellow airplane (8x14cm-3x6in) s.d.81 col ink. 4-Oct-3 Dorotheum, Prague #316/R est:10000-15000 (C.KR 19000)
£438	$727	€639	Racing car (5x12cm-2x5in) s.d.44 col ink. 4-Oct-3 Dorotheum, Prague #315/R est:10000-15000 (C.KR 20000)
£464	$817	€696	From Paris (22x30cm-9x12in) init. pencil W/C. 22-May-4 Dorotheum, Prague #260/R est:20000-30000 (C.KR 22000)
£482	$799	€704	Blue car (14x22cm-6x9in) s.d.81 ink W/C. 4-Oct-3 Dorotheum, Prague #319/R est:12000-18000 (C.KR 22000)
£875	$1453	€1278	French flag (29x31cm-11x12in) s.d.79 col ink. 4-Oct-3 Dorotheum, Prague #320/R est:20000-30000 (C.KR 40000)

LHOTE, Andre (1885-1962) French

£1611	$2851	€2400	Nu assis cubiste (34x24cm-13x9in) s.i. cardboard on panel. 27-Apr-4 Campo & Campo, Antwerp #149/R est:1800-2000
£2973	$5352	€4341	In the kitchen (24x16cm-9x6in) s. 26-Apr-4 Bukowskis, Stockholm #248/R est:30000-35000 (S.KR 41000)
£3889	$7000	€5678	Scene de port (38x53cm-15x21in) 24-Apr-4 Du Mouchelle, Detroit #3158/R est:2000-4000
£4698	$8409	€7000	Ceremonie officielle au Pantheon (54x73cm-21x29in) s. painted 1933 prov. 26-May-4 Christie's, Paris #56/R est:8000-12000
£4861	$8118	€7000	Paysage de Mirmande (38x46cm-15x18in) s. paper on canvas. 21-Oct-3 Artcurial Briest, Paris #216/R est:8000-12000
£6000	$9540	€8700	L'aperitif apres le bain (16x22cm-6x9in) init. board painted 1933. 11-Sep-3 Christie's, Kensington #63/R est:6000-8000
£6040	$10692	€9000	Tolede (24x42cm-9x17in) panel painted c.1923. 27-Apr-4 Artcurial Briest, Paris #184/R est:8000-10000
£6338	$10204	€9000	Untitled (49x63cm-19x25in) s. paper on canvas prov. 11-May-3 Versailles Encheres #132/R
£7500	$12525	€10950	Nu (33x22cm-13x9in) s. s.d.1954 verso. 22-Oct-3 Sotheby's, Olympia #120/R est:4000-5000
£8000	$14640	€12000	Portrait de femme (42x37cm-17x15in) s. stretcher prov. 5-Jun-4 Lempertz, Koln #827/R est:14000-16000
£8392	$14014	€12000	Le pin (65x86cm-26x34in) s. 30-Jun-3 Artcurial Briest, Paris #752/R est:12000-15000
£9608	$17199	€14028	Still life of flowers in a vase (60x75cm-24x30in) s. cardboard on canvas. 28-May-4 Uppsala Auktionskammare, Uppsala #272/R est:60000-80000 (S.KR 130000)
£11628	$20000	€16977	La cadiere, village et foret (73x92cm-29x36in) s. i.d.1960 on stretcher exhib. 3-Dec-3 Doyle, New York #10/R est:15000-25000
£13000	$21710	€18980	Palmiers a thebes (89x116cm-35x46in) s.d.52 prov.exhib. 21-Oct-3 Sotheby's, London #54/R est:15000-20000
£14584	$24355	€21000	Theme pour la decoration du Palais de la decouverte - Les Acieries (50x61cm-20x24in) s. prov.lit. 21-Oct-3 Artcurial Briest, Paris #231/R est:20000-30000
£14667	$26694	€22000	Port of Bordeaux (36x54cm-14x21in) s. board painted c.1930. 30-Jun-4 Calmels Cohen, Paris #8/R est:15000-18000
£16000	$29440	€23360	Baigneurs (54x81cm-21x32in) s. 24-Mar-4 Sotheby's, Olympia #128/R est:12000-15000
£18000	$32760	€26280	Paysage (54x46cm-21x18in) s. prov. 4-Feb-4 Sotheby's, London #256/R est:20000-30000
£18000	$32760	€26280	Portrait d'Anne a la robe rouge (92x60cm-36x24in) s. painted c.1926. 3-Feb-4 Christie's, London #241/R est:18000-25000
£19333	$34607	€29000	Paysage fauve (53x70cm-21x28in) d.1907. 16-May-4 Osenat, Fontainebleau #88/R est:30000-40000
£20588	$35000	€30058	Ferme au Cypres (82x116cm-32x46in) s.d.32 paper on canvas prov.exhib.lit. 6-Nov-3 Sotheby's, New York #178/R est:40000-60000
£23743	$42500	€34665	Cadiere, village et foret (72x92cm-28x36in) s. painted 1960 exhib. 6-May-4 Sotheby's, New York #409/R est:30000-40000
£28000	$50960	€40880	Neuilly, la fete a neuneu (116x81cm-46x32in) s. oil paper on canvas prov. 4-Feb-4 Sotheby's, London #259/R est:30000-40000
£28169	$48732	€40000	Port de Marseille (38x55cm-15x22in) s. painted 1936 prov.exhib. 10-Dec-3 Ferri, Paris #66/R est:35000-40000
£33334	$55667	€48000	Nature morte (54x66cm-21x26in) s. exhib.lit. 21-Oct-3 Artcurial Briest, Paris #218/R est:25000-30000
£73426	$126293	€105000	Port de Bordeaux (45x55cm-18x22in) s. s.d.1912 verso prov.exhib.lit. 8-Dec-3 Artcurial Briest, Paris #36/R est:90000-110000

Works on paper

£267	$491	€400	Modele nu assis (26x20cm-10x8in) s. ink. 9-Jun-4 Beaussant & Lefèvre, Paris #186
£349	$646	€520	Femme accroupie, un bras leve (32x18cm-13x7in) s. chl two joined sheets. 15-Mar-4 Blanchet, Paris #94
£497	$900	€726	Cubist head of a woman (23x18cm-9x7in) pencil. 16-Apr-4 Du Mouchelle, Detroit #2129/R
£517	$957	€750	Paysage (19x27cm-7x11in) s. ink. 13-Jan-4 Vanderkindere, Brussels #61
£559	$951	€800	Nude study (26x19cm-10x7in) s. ink drawing. 1-Dec-3 Camard, Paris #71
£564	$975	€800	Nu assis (26x35cm-10x14in) s. crayon dr. 9-Dec-3 Artcurial Briest, Paris #202
£600	$1074	€900	Nu allonge (24x36cm-9x14in) s. crayon. 11-May-4 Vanderkindere, Brussels #154
£629	$1083	€900	Paysage (18x31cm-7x12in) s. ballpoint pen. 3-Dec-3 Beaussant & Lefèvre, Paris #43/R
£634	$1097	€900	Femme assise (21x30cm-8x12in) s. crayon dr. 9-Dec-3 Artcurial Briest, Paris #201
£769	$1308	€1100	Buste de jeune femme (49x31cm-19x12in) mono.i. pastel prov. 23-Nov-3 Cornette de St.Cyr, Paris #222
£833	$1392	€1200	Nu (34x20cm-13x8in) graphite. 25-Oct-3 Cornette de St.Cyr, Paris #525
£833	$1500	€1216	Landscape (28x38cm-11x15in) W/C. 24-Apr-4 Du Mouchelle, Detroit #3157/R est:1000-1500
£839	$1427	€1200	Acieries (51x61cm-20x24in) st.sig. ink wash. 21-Nov-3 Coutau Begarie, Paris #66/R
£882	$1500	€1288	Landscape (29x39cm-11x15in) s. gouache pencil. 9-Nov-3 Bonhams & Butterfields, Los Angeles #4022/R
£993	$1808	€1500	Femme aux porte-jarretelles (24x12cm-9x5in) s. graphite dr. 19-Jun-4 St-Germain-en-Laye Encheres #180/R est:1800
£1000	$1840	€1500	Femme allongee (23x32cm-9x13in) s. W/C dr. 11-Jun-4 Pierre Berge, Paris #190/R est:1500-2000
£1007	$1852	€1500	Cathedrale (53x35cm-21x14in) studio st. gouache. 24-Mar-4 Joron-Derem, Paris #66/R est:2000-2500
£1119	$1902	€1600	Paysage (24x35cm-9x14in) mono. graphite prov. 23-Nov-3 Cornette de St.Cyr, Paris #224 est:200-300
£1267	$2267	€1900	Paysage au pont (52x36cm-20x14in) s. W/C. 11-May-4 Vanderkindere, Brussels #145/R est:1000-1500
£1450	$2611	€2175	Le Piquey (56x38cm-22x15in) s.d.1917 i.verso W/C. 25-Apr-4 Goteborg Auktionsverk, Sweden #316/R est:15000 (S.KR 20000)
£1457	$2652	€2200	Le Caire (28x38cm-11x15in) s. W/C exec. c.1951. 18-Jun-4 Piasa, Paris #156 est:1000-1200
£1467	$2699	€2200	Paysage de la Drome (38x28cm-15x11in) gouache exec. 1935. 9-Jun-4 Beaussant & Lefèvre, Paris #185/R est:800-1000
£1469	$2497	€2100	Sous la tonnelle (39x29cm-15x11in) s. W/C exec.c.1920 prov.exhib. 23-Nov-3 Cornette de St.Cyr, Paris #223/R est:300-400
£1538	$2615	€2200	Village au pied du Chateau (37x57cm-15x22in) s. W/C. 28-Nov-3 Doutrebente, Paris #20/R est:2000-3000
£1544	$2872	€2300	Paysage (28x40cm-11x16in) s. W/C. 3-Mar-4 Tajan, Paris #160 est:2500-3000
£1552	$2778	€2266	Landscape with tree by jetty (38x57cm-15x22in) s. W/C. 28-May-4 Uppsala Auktionskammare, Uppsala #270/R est:12000-15000 (S.KR 21000)
£1748	$2972	€2500	Still life with flowers (42x28cm-17x11in) s. gouache lit. 28-Nov-3 Schloss Ahlden, Ahlden #1629/R est:2800
£1760	$3046	€2500	Nu assis (22x14cm-9x6in) s. W/C. 9-Dec-3 Artcurial Briest, Paris #211/R est:1300-1800
£1958	$3329	€2800	Petit pont dans le village (38x58cm-15x23in) s. W/C. 1-Dec-3 Camard, Paris #70/R est:3000-4000
£2000	$3680	€3000	Reclining female nude (24x35cm-9x14in) s. pencil paper on cardboard. 11-Jun-4 Villa Grisebach, Berlin #1584/R est:1500-2000
£2013	$3705	€3000	Venise (25x32cm-10x13in) studio st. pastel. 24-Mar-4 Joron-Derem, Paris #67/R est:3000-3500
£2113	$3655	€3000	Paysage (29x39cm-11x15in) s. W/C. 11-Dec-3 Binoche, Paris #3 est:1800-2000
£2113	$3655	€3000	Paysage (29x39cm-11x15in) s. W/C. 11-Dec-3 Binoche, Paris #2 est:1800-2200
£2200	$3938	€3300	Village de provence (39x28cm-15x11in) s. W/C. 16-May-4 Osenat, Fontainebleau #36/R est:2000-3000
£2397	$4075	€3500	Maisons dans les arbres (29x46cm-11x18in) s. W/C. 9-Nov-3 Eric Pillon, Calais #184/R
£2400	$4416	€3600	Nu cubiste (21x30cm-8x12in) s. ink exec. c.1920 prov. 11-Jun-4 Pierre Berge, Paris #183/R est:600-800
£2500	$3975	€3625	Rue de Mirmande (31x25cm-12x10in) s. pastel. 11-Sep-3 Christie's, Kensington #84/R est:2500-3500
£2533	$4535	€3800	Paysage du midi (27x37cm-11x15in) s. gouache. 11-May-4 Vanderkindere, Brussels #150 est:1250-1750
£2653	$4749	€3900	Le village (29x38cm-11x15in) s. W/C. 19-Mar-4 Millon & Associes, Paris #82/R est:4000-5000
£2958	$4732	€4200	Lady in an interior (21x28cm-8x11in) s. gouache board prov. 16-Sep-3 Whyte's, Dublin #23/R est:4000-6000
£3691	$6607	€5500	Canal a Venise (38x55cm-15x22in) s. W/C. 30-May-4 Eric Pillon, Calais #185/R
£3974	$7232	€6000	Baigneuse au paysage (44x55cm-17x22in) s. W/C gouache. 15-Jun-4 Rossini, Paris #163/R est:4000-7000
£5034	$9010	€7500	Femme a la rose (24x31cm-9x12in) s.i.d.31 W/C graphite prov. 26-May-4 Christie's, Paris #38/R est:3000-5000
£5665	$9630	€8271	Arlequin et Colombine (26x21cm-10x8in) s. gouache prov. 5-Nov-3 AB Stockholms Auktionsverk #1106/R est:30000-35000 (S.KR 75000)
£6301	$10712	€9200	Nu assis au miroir (27x20cm-11x8in) s. gouache exec.1946. 9-Nov-3 Eric Pillon, Calais #166/R
£7500	$13800	€10950	Composition fantastique (60x47cm-24x19in) s.d.1917 W/C pencil brush ink. 24-Mar-4 Sotheby's, Olympia #121/R est:5000-7000
£9091	$15455	€13000	Tete d'expression (34x26cm-13x10in) s. W/C prov.lit. 26-Nov-3 Lempertz, Koln #797/R est:16000-18000
£24000	$43680	€35040	Maisons en campagne (39x38cm-15x15in) s. gouache W/C pencil prov. 5-Feb-4 Christie's, London #357/R est:10000-15000

LI HUAYI (1948-) Chinese

Works on paper

£19915	$35846	€29076	Landscape (138x68cm-54x27in) s. ink col. 26-Apr-4 Sotheby's, Hong Kong #534/R est:160000-200000 (HK.D 280000)

LI JIAN (18/19th C) Chinese

Works on paper

£3707	$6190	€5412	Landscapes of Luofu (29x22cm-11x9in) s.i. ink col on silk set of 11. 26-Oct-3 Christie's, Hong Kong #480/R (HK.D 48000)

LI KERAN (1907-1989) Chinese

Works on paper

£4795	$8151	€7000	Returning home with the cattle (69x45cm-27x18in) s.i. Indian ink col. 7-Nov-3 Dr Fritz Nagel, Stuttgart #956/R est:3300
£7112	$12802	€10384	Buffalo (67x45cm-26x18in) s. ink col. 26-Apr-4 Sotheby's, Hong Kong #643/R est:100000-120000 (HK.D 100000)
£8494	$14185	€12401	Buffaloes (46x68cm-18x27in) s.i.d.1988 ink col scroll. 26-Oct-3 Christie's, Hong Kong #234/R est:100000-150000 (HK.D 110000)
£10039	$16764	€14657	Cowherds (58x42cm-23x17in) s. ink col hanging scroll. 26-Oct-3 Christie's, Hong Kong #237/R est:80000-100000 (HK.D 130000)
£11380	$20484	€16615	Herdboy with flute (75x48cm-30x19in) s.i.d.1979 ink col prov. 26-Apr-4 Sotheby's, Hong Kong #635/R est:80000-100000 (HK.D 160000)
£12091	$21764	€17653	Herdboy on a buffalo (76x49cm-30x19in) s.i.d.1960 ink col hanging scroll. 26-Apr-4 Sotheby's, Hong Kong #636/R est:80000-100000 (HK.D 170000)
£12802	$23044	€18691	Landscape (95x42cm-37x17in) s.i.d.1984 ink col hanging scroll. 25-Apr-4 Christie's, Hong Kong #128/R est:200000-300000 (HK.D 180000)
£15444	$25792	€22548	Scholar beneath a tree (71x34cm-28x13in) s. ink col hanging scroll exhib. 27-Oct-3 Sotheby's, Hong Kong #281/R est:80000-100000 (HK.D 200000)
£21337	$38407	€31152	Herdboys with birds (33x35cm-13x14in) s. ink col. 26-Apr-4 Sotheby's, Hong Kong #642/R est:60000-80000 (HK.D 300000)
£29344	$49004	€42842	Mount Shu in rain (80x49cm-31x19in) s.i.d.1966 ink col hanging scroll lit. 26-Oct-3 Christie's, Hong Kong #238/R est:250000-300000 (HK.D 380000)
£38610	$64479	€56371	Mount Jiuhua (76x47cm-30x19in) s.i.d.1979 ink col hanging scroll. 26-Oct-3 Christie's, Hong Kong #235/R est:350000-450000 (HK.D 500000)
£54054	$90270	€78919	Landscape inspired by Chairman Mao's verses (60x84cm-24x33in) s.i. ink col scroll lit. 26-Oct-3 Christie's, Hong Kong #236/R est:500000-600000 (HK.D 700000)

LI KUCHAN (1898-1983) Chinese

Works on paper

£1486 $2616 €2200 Cormorant (68x43cm-27x17in) s. seal Indian ink col. 21-May-4 Dr Fritz Nagel, Stuttgart #1104/R est:700

£1575 $2678 €2300 Crane beneath banana leaves (82x49cm-32x19in) s. sea. Indian ink col hanging scroll. 7-Nov-3 Dr Fritz Nagel, Stuttgart #947/R est:350

£2703 $4757 €4000 Birds on shore (68x45cm-27x18in) s. seal Indian ink col. 21-May-4 Dr Fritz Nagel, Stuttgart #1134/R est:700

£3200 $5728 €4672 Lotus and bamboo (134x67cm-53x26in) s. ink hanging scroll. 6-May-4 Sotheby's, London #110/R est:800-1200

LI LIUFANG (1575-1629) Chinese

Works on paper

£3861 $6448 €5637 Trees (93x42cm-37x17in) s.i. ink. 26-Oct-3 Christie's, Hong Kong #436/R (HK.D 50000)

LI MOULIN (20th C) Chinese?

Works on paper

£1100 $1969 €1606 Cicada on a flowering branch (105x33cm-41x13in) s. ink W/C hanging scroll. 6-May-4 Sotheby's, London #104/R est:800-1000

LI QIANG (20th C) Chinese?

£237 $425 €346 Chines peasant (43x53cm-17x21in) s.d.Dec 1987. 8-May-4 Susanin's, Chicago #6080/R

LI QIONGHUA (19th C) Chinese

Works on paper

£616 $1048 €900 Woman playing flute (73x38cm-29x15in) Indian ink col silk hanging scroll prov. 7-Nov-3 Dr Fritz Nagel, Stuttgart #852/R

LI SHAN (1686-1756) Chinese

Works on paper

£14225 $25605 €20769 Five pines (179x96cm-70x38in) s.i.d.1744 ink hanging scroll. 25-Apr-4 Christie's, Hong Kong #418/R est:150000-200000 (HK.D 200000)

LI SHIZHUO (1687-c.1765) Chinese

Works on paper

£3556 $6401 €5192 Landscape (97x31cm-38x12in) s.mink col hanging scroll. 25-Apr-4 Christie's, Hong Kong #415/R est:30000-40000 (HK.D 50000)

LI SHUANG (20th C) Chinese?

£903 $1508 €1300 Dame de cour (100x73cm-39x29in) oil collage. 25-Oct-3 Cornette de St.Cyr, Paris #811

LI XIAO (1969-) Oriental

£1797 $3253 €2624 Warrior no 16 (150x150cm-59x59in) s.d.2003. 3-Apr-4 Glerum, Singapore #55/R est:7000-9000 (S.D 5500)

LI XIONGCAI (1912-) Chinese

Works on paper

£1622 $2854 €2400 Landscape with waterfall (102x54cm-40x21in) s.i. Indian ink col hanging scroll. 21-May-4 Dr Fritz Nagel, Stuttgart #1100/R est:1500

£3243 $5416 €4735 Monkeys in the forest (94x41cm-37x16in) s.d.1960 ink col scroll. 26-Oct-3 Christie's, Hong Kong #255/R est:20000 30000 (HK.D 42000)

LI YING (1934-) Chinese

Works on paper

£274 $466 €400 Huang mountains (68x34cm-27x13in) s.d.1978 seal hanging scroll. 7-Nov-3 Dr Fritz Nagel, Stuttgart #964/R

LI ZHONGLIANG (1944-) Chinese

Works on paper

£2151 $4000 €3140 Horseman (97x99cm-38x39in) s. W/C gouache handmade rice paper. 7-Mar-4 William Jenack, New York #209 est:2000-3000

LI ZICHANG (19/20th C) Chinese

Works on paper

£308 $524 €450 Landscape (122x47cm-48x19in) d.1915 Indian ink handscroll prov. 7-Nov-3 Dr Fritz Nagel, Stuttgart #833/R

LIAN, Laura (1952-) British

Sculpture

£5000 $9300 €7300 Buddha (47x20cm-19x8in) bronze. 8-Mar-4 Christie's, London #3

LIAO CHI-CHUN (1902-1976) Chinese

£193050 $322394 €281853 Fish (65x80cm-26x31in) s. painted c.1960 lit. 26-Oct-3 Christie's, Hong Kong #123/R est:2500000-2800000 (HK.D 2500000)

£213371 $384068 €311522 View of Kwan Yin Shan (72x60cm-28x24in) s.d.1962.5. 25-Apr-4 Christie's, Hong Kong #702/R est:1200000-1400000 (HK.D 3000000)

£227596 $409673 €332290 Street scene (72x60cm-28x24in) s.d.1962.5. 25-Apr-4 Christie's, Hong Kong #703/R est:1000000-1500000 (HK.D 3200000)

£298720 $537696 €436131 Still life in green (80x65cm-31x26in) s.d.1962.5. 25-Apr-4 Christie's, Hong Kong #701/R est:1400000-1600000 (HK.D 4200000)

LIARDO, Filippo (1840-1917) Italian

£2105 $3874 €3200 Truffle seeker with five pigs (35x57cm-14x22in) s. panel. 23-Jun-4 Rieunier, Paris #38/R est:2000-3000

LIBAL, Frantisek (1896-1974) Czechoslovakian

£288 $536 €420 Rainy day birches (42x52cm-17x20in) s.d.1944 canvas on board. 6-Mar-4 Dorotheum, Prague #101 est:14000-22000 (C.KR 14000)

£455 $773 €650 View of Nurnberg (95x80cm-37x31in) s.d.1921. 28-Nov-3 Wendl, Rudolstadt #4067/R

LIBERA, Giovanni Battista della (1826-1886) Italian

£3691 $6607 €5500 Vegetable seller in Venice (63x51cm-25x20in) s.d.1858. 27-May-4 Dorotheum, Vienna #60/R est:3200-4000

LIBERALE DA VERONA (1445-1526) Italian

£11207 $20060 €16362 Madonna with Child holding songbird (43x38cm-17x15in) bears init. tempera panel. 12-May-4 Dobiaschofsky, Bern #747/R est:26000 (S.FR 26000)

LIBERATORE, Fausto Maria (1923-) Italian

£232 $422 €350 Faces of women (69x29cm-27x11in) s. board. 21-Jun-4 Pandolfini, Florence #351

£265 $482 €400 Female nude (69x48cm-27x19in) s. 21-Jun-4 Pandolfini, Florence #470/R

£397 $723 €600 Masks (29x39cm-11x15in) s. s.i.verso. 21-Jun-4 Pandolfini, Florence #350/R

£430 $783 €650 Nude (82x52cm-32x20in) s.d.1961 cardboard. 17-Jun-4 Galleria Pananti, Florence #558/R

Works on paper

£839 $1427 €1200 Study of nude (69x97cm-27x38in) s.d.1973 chl pastel. 20-Nov-3 Finarte Semenzato, Milan #63/R

LIBERI, Marco (1640-1687) Italian

£28000 $48440 €40880 Allegory of Filial Advice (95x79cm-37x31in) i. prov. 10-Dec-3 Christie's, London #109/R est:15000-20000

LIBERI, Pietro (attrib) (1614-1687) Italian

£6250 $10188 €9000 Venus and Cupid (50x63cm-20x25in) 25-Sep-3 Dr Fritz Nagel, Stuttgart #1212/R est:9000

Works on paper

£273 $492 €410 Holy Family and dove of the Holy Ghost (22x16cm-9x6in) i. Indian ink on pencil prov. 24-Apr-4 Reiss & Sohn, Konigstein #5416/R

£887 $1588 €1295 Figure scene with Diana, Goddess of Hunting (18x41cm-7x16in) red chk. 25-May-4 Bukowskis, Stockholm #551/R (S.KR 12000)

LIBERI, Pietro (circle) (1614-1687) Italian

£6154 $10585 €8985 L'hymen et l'Amour (255x180cm-100x71in) 3-Dec-3 AB Stockholms Auktionsverk #2719/R est:125000-150000 (S.KR 80000)

£6643 $11094 €9500 Madonna and Child and Saint Filippo Neri (101x82cm-40x32in) 7-Oct-3 Pandolfini, Florence #538/R est:10000-12000

LIBERICH, Nicolai Ivanovich (1828-1883) Russian

Sculpture

£6667 $12133 €10000 Wolf hunt (26x55x24cm-10x22x9in) s. brown pat.bronze lit. 30-Jun-4 Neumeister, Munich #279/R est:2000

£14000 $25060 €20440 Wolf hunt (32cm-13in) s. bronze marble base. 26-May-4 Sotheby's, London #461/R est:8000-12000

LIBERMAN, Alexander (1912-) American

£757 $1400 €1105 Untitled B (76x56cm-30x22in) s.d.76 acrylic paper prov.exhib. 12-Feb-4 Sotheby's, New York #124/R est:2000-3000

Sculpture

£865 $1600 €1263 Untitled (33x21x21cm-13x8x8in) init.d.1976 num.9-30 aluminium st.f.Krieitel-Gratz Co. 12-Feb-4 Sotheby's, New York #287/R est:2000-3000

£1761 $2800 €2571 Sacred precinct (71x76x38cm-28x30x15in) bronze edition of 3. 14-Sep-3 Susanin's, Chicago #6013/R est:700-900

£3571 $6500 €5214 Allegory (35x30x30cm-14x12x12in) init. painted steel raised on base prov. 29-Jun-4 Sotheby's, New York #515/R est:2000-3000

Works on paper

£310 $500 €453 Untitled - abstract (102x63cm-40x25in) s. gouache. 17-Aug-3 Bonhams & Butterfields, San Francisco #5830

LIBERT, Betzy Marie Petrea (attrib) (1859-?) Danish

£387 $658 €565 Still life of Japanese parasol, flowers books and palette (80x61cm-31x24in) 10-Nov-3 Rasmussen, Vejle #402/R (D.KR 4200)

LIBERT, Georg Emil (1820-1908) Danish

£271 $500 €396 Coastal landscape with fishermen pulling net (36x52cm-14x20in) s. 15-Mar-4 Rasmussen, Vejle #83/R (D.KR 3000)

£341 $613 €498 Seascape with steamer off rocky coast (27x36cm-11x14in) s.d.1901. 24-Apr-4 Rasmussen, Havnen #2324 (D.KR 3800)

£397 $711 €580 Sailing vessel in moonlight (51x77cm-20x30in) s. 12-Jan-4 Rasmussen, Vejle #29/R (D.KR 4200)

£406 $751 €593 From the Norwegian skerries (36x51cm-14x20in) s.d.90. 15-Mar-4 Rasmussen, Vejle #87/R (D.KR 4500)

£466 $732 €680 Shepherd boy and sheep at Helligdomsgarden, Bornholm (40x55cm-16x22in) s.d.71. 30-Aug-3 Rasmussen, Havnen #2103/R (D.KR 5000)

£650 $1164 €949 Hardanger Fjord, Norway (40x58cm-16x23in) init.d.83. 18-Mar-4 Christie's, Kensington #503/R

£841 $1329 €1219 Sorfjorden near Odde in Hardanger, Norway (45x64cm-18x25in) s. 2-Sep-3 Rasmussen, Copenhagen #1671/R (D.KR 9000)
£992 $1835 €1448 Mountain landscape in moonlight with figures by rapids (87x63cm-34x25in) s. 15-Mar-4 Rasmussen, Vejle #80/R (D.KR 11000)
£1014 $1724 €1480 Coastal cliffs at moonlight (36x52cm-14x20in) s. 10-Nov-3 Rasmussen, Vejle #297/R (D.KR 11000)
£1121 $1772 €1625 Heidelberg's Palace and ruins on hillside (50x42cm-20x17in) s. 2-Sep-3 Rasmussen, Copenhagen #1798/R est:12000 (D.KR 12000)
£1164 $2130 €1699 Coastal landscape from Moens Klint with Sommerspiret and full moon (26x36cm-10x14in) 9-Jun-4 Rasmussen, Copenhagen #1665/R est:5000 (D.KR 13000)
£1418 $2453 €2070 Fishing village, North Sjaelland (40x60cm-16x24in) s.d.1858. 9-Dec-3 Rasmussen, Copenhagen #1543/R est:8000-12000 (D.KR 15000)
£1682 $2658 €2439 Winter landscape with sunrise, North Sjaelland (83x117cm-33x46in) s.d.79 exhib. 2-Sep-3 Rasmussen, Copenhagen #1535/R est:25000 (D.KR 18000)
£1890 $3270 €2759 Landscape with large trees by lake (105x80cm-41x31in) s.indis.d.18. 9-Dec-3 Rasmussen, Copenhagen #1397/R est:15000-20000 (D.KR 20000)
£2896 $5184 €4228 Summer landscape from the Norwegian skerries (95x132cm-37x52in) s. 10-May-4 Rasmussen, Vejle #159/R est:40000 (D.KR 32000)

LIBERT, Georg Emil (attrib) (1820-1908) Danish
£880 $1408 €1250 Rocky sea coast with figures (26x37cm-10x15in) i. verso. 19-Sep-3 Sigalas, Stuttgart #398/R

LIBERTE, Jean (1896-1965) American/Italian
£235 $400 €343 Untitled, wharf scene (28x46cm-11x18in) s. board. 9-Nov-3 Outer Cape Auctions, Provincetown #152/R
£270 $500 €394 Mountain village (41x61cm-16x24in) s. board. 17-Jul-4 New Orleans Auction, New Orleans #869/R

LIBERTS, Ludolfs (1895-1945) Russian
£838 $1500 €1223 Fishing fleet (61x51cm-24x20in) s. sold with a book. 8-Jan-4 James Julia, Fairfield #732/R est:900-1200

LIBERTS, Ludolfs (attrib) (1895-1945) Russian
£845 $1462 €1200 Picnic in the park (60x75cm-24x30in) s. 10-Dec-3 Hugo Ruef, Munich #2449

LIBESKI, Robert (1892-1988) German
£1745 $3228 €2600 Two female nudes (104x134cm-41x53in) s.d.56 oil col chk biro masonite. 9-Mar-4 Dorotheum, Vienna #118/R est:2000-2800

LIBOUR, Esprit Aime (1784-1845) French
£2716 $4400 €3965 Portrait of a handsome gentleman in black suit with red lapel ribbon (61x48cm-24x19in) s.d.1829. 2-Aug-3 Neal Auction Company, New Orleans #175/R est:5000-7000

LIBUDA, Walter (1950-) German
£1389 $2319 €2000 Over winter (182x71cm-72x28in) s.d. s.i.d. verso mixed media collage board. 25-Oct-3 Dr Lehr, Berlin #316/R est:3000
£2222 $3711 €3200 Composition - three points (182x62cm-72x24in) s.d. s.i.d. verso mixed media collage board. 25-Oct-3 Dr Lehr, Berlin #315/R est:3000

LIBUM, C (19th C) ?
£3349 $5426 €4856 Coastal landscape with cliffs, figures and ruins (45x59cm-18x23in) s. 4-Aug-3 Rasmussen, Vejle #277/R est:40000 (D.KR 35000)

LICATA, Riccardo (1929-) Italian
£503 $931 €750 Egyptian 4 (20x24cm-8x9in) s. painted terracotta acrylic exec.2003. 13-Mar-4 Meeting Art, Vercelli #439
£552 $883 €800 Untitled (29x19cm-11x7in) s.d.1995 tempera card. 13-Mar-3 Galleria Pace, Milan #112/R
£595 $1011 €850 Composition (33x23cm-13x9in) s.d.80 tempera paper on canvas. 26-Nov-3 Pandolfini, Florence #149
£667 $1227 €1000 RMMRBR (24x17cm-9x7in) s.d.2003 painted on brass exhib.lit. 12-Jun-4 Meeting Art, Vercelli #458/R
£690 $1103 €1000 Untitled (35x25cm-14x10in) s.d.1995 tempera paper. 13-Mar-3 Galleria Pace, Milan #69/R
£694 $1097 €1000 Plaisir d'amour (24x10cm-9x4in) panel painted 2000. 6-Sep-3 Meeting Art, Vercelli #531
£797 $1307 €1100 Untitled (29x19cm-11x7in) s.d.1995 tempera card. 29-May-3 Galleria Pace, Milan #26/R
£845 $1403 €1200 Untitled (33x41cm-13x16in) s.d.2002. 14-Jun-3 Meeting Art, Vercelli #52/R
£878 $1546 €1300 Composition (37x37cm-15x15in) tempera masonite painted 1962. 19-May-4 Il Ponte, Milan #1101 est:1300-1500
£1333 $2453 €2000 Copper XLI (50x70cm-20x28in) s.d.96 copper oval lit. 10-Jun-4 Galleria Pace, Milan #35/R est:3500
£1408 $2338 €2000 Untitled (58x76cm-23x30in) s. oil pastel paper. 14-Jun-3 Meeting Art, Vercelli #296/R est:2000
£1837 $3288 €2700 Untitled (46x39cm-18x15in) s.d.78. 16-Mar-4 Finarte Semenzato, Milan #355/R est:3000
£2041 $3653 €3000 Composition (37x45cm-15x18in) s.d.1960. 16-Mar-4 Finarte Semenzato, Milan #154/R est:1700
£2069 $3455 €3000 Composition (55x46cm-22x18in) s.d.2002. 13-Nov-3 Galleria Pace, Milan #141/R est:4500
£2500 $3950 €3600 Untitled (60x72cm-24x28in) painted 1982. 6-Sep-3 Meeting Art, Vercelli #574 est:3600
£2819 $5046 €4200 Untitled (92x73cm-36x29in) s.d.1996. 30-May-4 Meeting Art, Vercelli #37 est:3000
£2828 $4722 €4100 Composition (43x27cm-17x11in) s.d.1984. 13-Nov-3 Galleria Pace, Milan #72/R est:4800
£4552 $7601 €6600 Composition (64x64cm-25x25in) s.d.57. 14-Nov-3 Farsetti, Prato #288/R est:5500-6500
£4698 $8691 €7000 Untitled (65x200cm-26x79in) s.d.1995. 11-Mar-4 Galleria Pace, Milan #141/R est:8000-11000
£4759 $7947 €6900 Composition (64x94cm-25x37in) s.d.57. 14-Nov-3 Farsetti, Prato #287/R est:5500-6500
Sculpture
£694 $1097 €1000 Tifeo (171x17cm-67x7in) painted wood. 6-Sep-3 Meeting Art, Vercelli #302
£1042 $1646 €1500 Licaone (71x28cm-28x11in) wood. 6-Sep-3 Meeting Art, Vercelli #534 est:1500
Works on paper
£352 $585 €500 Giudizio universale (24x22cm-9x9in) s. W/C pastel. 14-Jun-3 Meeting Art, Vercelli #20
£464 $844 €700 Dream tree (25x35cm-10x14in) s.d.1965 gouache paper on board. 17-Jun-4 Galleria Pananti, Florence #242/R
£470 $869 €700 Spatial (10x17cm-4x7in) pastel paper on canvas. 11-Mar-4 Galleria Pace, Milan #20/R
£694 $1097 €1000 Composition (35x24cm-14x9in) mixed media. 6-Sep-3 Meeting Art, Vercelli #307
£1342 $2403 €2000 Composition (41x33cm-16x13in) s.d.72 hydropaint on canvas. 28-May-4 Farsetti, Prato #108/R est:1600-1900

LICHISLOVSKY, Leonide (?) ?
£514 $920 €750 Boudoir scene (24x19cm-9x7in) s. wood panel. 15-May-4 Christie's, Sydney #389 (A.D 1300)

LICHT, Hans (1876-1935) German
£295 $543 €440 Farmsteads by water lit by setting sun (46x98cm-18x39in) s.d.1900 lit. 25-Mar-4 Karlheinz Kaupp, Staufen #2588/R
£349 $649 €520 Street scene with houses on either side (70x58cm-28x23in) s. cardboard. 5-Mar-4 Wendl, Rudolstadt #3765/R
£490 $842 €700 Winter's evening (47x58cm-19x23in) s. i.verso board. 4-Dec-3 Van Ham, Cologne #294/R
£764 $1207 €1100 Village (57x68cm-22x27in) s. i. verso board. 6-Sep-3 Schopman, Hamburg #807/R

LICHTENAUER, Joseph Mortimer (1876-?) American
£369 $650 €539 Swords into plow shares (18x25cm-7x10in) s. board prov. 3-Jan-4 Collins, Maine #19/R

LICHTENBERG, Manes (1920-) American
£276 $500 €403 Cadeques, Spain (36x58cm-14x23in) 16-Apr-4 American Auctioneer #249/R
£442 $800 €645 La voiture (36x58cm-14x23in) 16-Apr-4 American Auctioneer #248/R

LICHTENBERGER, Hans Reinhold (1876-1941) German
£540 $885 €750 Bathers (49x63cm-19x25in) 4-Jun-3 Ketterer, Hamburg #602/R

LICHTENSTEIN, Roy (1923-1997) American
£26536 $47500 €38743 Littoral (55x66cm-22x26in) s.d.1965 verso plastic aluminium magna board prov. 13-May-4 Sotheby's, New York #165/R est:30000-40000
£33520 $60000 €48939 Water lilies with cloud (166x114cm-65x45in) s.d.92 verso screenprinted enamel stainless steel prov.lit. 12-May-4 Christie's, Rockefeller NY #203/R est:35000-45000
£50279 $90000 €73407 Water Lily pond with reflections (147x215cm-58x85in) s.d.92 verso screenprinted enamel stainless steel prov.lit. 12-May-4 Christie's, Rockefeller NY #186/R est:40000-60000
£234637 $420000 €342570 Two paintings - Alien (127x178cm-50x70in) s.d.83 verso oil magna prov.exhib. 12-May-4 Sotheby's, New York #55/R est:500000-700000
£311377 $520000 €454610 Modern painting with yellow interweave (142x122cm-56x48in) s.d.67 verso oil magna prov.exhib.lit. 13-Nov-3 Sotheby's, New York #194/R est:250000-350000
£650000 $1196000 €949000 Modern painting (92x92cm-36x36in) s.verso oil magna on canvas triptych in three parts prov. 23-Jun-4 Sotheby's, London #13/R est:500000-700000
£670391 $1200000 €978771 Stretcher frame with vertical bars (91x173cm-36x68in) s.d.68 verso oil magna prov.exhib.lit. 12-May-4 Sotheby's, New York #43/R est:1500000-2000000
£2541900 $4550000 €3711174 Step-on can with leg (81x132cm-32x52in) s.d.61 verso two parts prov.exhib.lit. 12-May-4 Sotheby's, New York #31/R est:4000000-5000000
Prints
£1657 $3000 €2419 Bull I (69x89cm-27x35in) s.d.1973 num.28/100 line-cut. 19-Apr-4 Bonhams & Butterfields, San Francisco #276/R est:3500-4500
£1730 $3200 €2526 Knight on horseback III (28x20cm-11x8in) s.i.d.1950 num.6/25 etching aquatint engraving. 12-Feb-4 Christie's, Rockefeller NY #129/R est:2500-3500
£1734 $3000 €2532 Haystacks number 5 (52x78cm-20x31in) s.d.69 lithograph screenprint one of 100 prov. 10-Dec-3 Phillips, New York #421/R est:1500-2000
£1766 $3250 €2578 The Solomon R Guggenheim Museum poster (71x71cm-28x28in) s.d.69 num.216/250 col silkscreen. 8-Jun-4 Auctions by the Bay, Alameda #1155/R
£1769 $3166 €2600 Glass and lemon (105x80cm-41x31in) s. col serigraph exec.1974. 16-Mar-4 Finarte Semenzato, Milan #402/R est:2400
£1796 $3000 €2622 Real estate (33x81cm-13x32in) s.i.d.1969 lithograph. 11-Nov-3 Doyle, New York #312/R est:1500-2000
£1840 $3000 €2686 Untitled shirt (76x91cm-30x36in) s.d.1979 num.41/1000 col screenprint. 24-Sep-3 Christie's, Rockefeller NY #287/R est:1800-2500
£1840 $3000 €2686 Apple and Lemon (80x107cm-31x42in) s.d.1983 num.AP 10/14 col woodcut handmade Japan paper. 24-Sep-3 Christie's, Rockefeller NY #290/R est:3000-5000
£1882 $3200 €2748 Modern print (79x78cm-31x31in) s.d.1971 lithograph col screenprint. 4-Nov-3 Christie's, Rockefeller NY #295/R est:4000-6000
£1902 $3500 €2777 American Indian theme I (83x81cm-33x32in) col woodcut edition of 50 prov. 10-Jun-4 Phillips, New York #598/R est:4000-6000
£1923 $3500 €2808 Mirror (51cm-20in circular) num.75/80 color silkscreen. 19-Jun-4 Du Mouchelle, Detroit #3120/R est:1200-2200
£1946 $3250 €2841 Morton A Mort (59x83cm-23x33in) s.d.1980 num.8/50 col woodcut. 21-Oct-3 Bonhams & Butterfields, San Francisco #1354/R
£1974 $3632 €3000 Bicentennial print (76x57cm-30x22in) s.d.75 num.75/200 lithograph serigraphie lit. 22-Jun-4 Wiener Kunst Auktionen, Vienna #373/R est:2000
£1977 $3500 €2886 Entablature VIII (56x97cm-22x38in) s.d.1976 num.11/30 screenprint collage. 28-Apr-4 Christie's, Rockefeller NY #356/R est:2000-3000
£1991 $3325 €2907 Explosion (56x43cm-22x17in) s.num.85/100 col lithograph. 16-Oct-3 Waddingtons, Toronto #38 est:3000-4000 (C.D 4400)
£2060 $3750 €3008 Mirror (53cm-21in circular) num.4/75 lithograph. 19-Jun-4 Du Mouchelle, Detroit #3121/R est:1200-2200
£2060 $3750 €3008 Mirror (86x61cm-34x24in) num.5/75 color silkscreen. 19-Jun-4 Du Mouchelle, Detroit #3125/R est:1200-2200
£2105 $3874 €3200 Composition III (56x69cm-22x27in) s.d.95 num.87/120 col serigraph. 22-Jun-4 Wiener Kunst Auktionen, Vienna #374/R est:2500

£2118	$3600	€3092	Foot and hand (42x53cm-17x21in) s.d.1964 num.151/300 offset col lithograph. 21-Nov-3 Swann Galleries, New York #109/R est:3500-5000
£2133	$3819	€3200	Landscape 4 (28x45cm-11x18in) s.i.d. verso col silkscreen. 15-May-4 Dr Sturies, Dusseldorf #118/R
£2147	$3800	€3135	Turkey shopping bag (19x22cm-7x9in) s. col screenprint shopping bag handles. 28-Apr-4 Christie's, Rockefeller NY #352/R est:2000-3000
£2200	$4004	€3212	Knock knock (66x48cm-26x19in) s.d.1975 offset lithograph. 30-Jun-4 Christie's, Kensington #55/R est:1000-1500
£2207	$3686	€3200	M-Maybe he became ill and couldn't leave the studio (84x85cm-33x33in) s. col serigraph board. 13-Nov-3 Neumeister, Munich #578/R est:2000-2500
£2270	$4200	€3314	Solomon R Guggenheim Museum poster (59x59cm-23x23in) s.d.1969 num.128/250 col screenprint. 12-Feb-4 Christie's, Rockefeller NY #133/R est:3000-4000
£2283	$4200	€3333	American Indian theme vI (96x128cm-38x50in) col woodcut edition of 50 prov. 10-Jun-4 Phillips, New York #597/R est:5000-7000
£2312	$4000	€3376	Bicentennial print, from the America, the third century portfolio (63x46cm-25x18in) s.d.75 col lithograph silkscreen one of 200 prov. 10-Dec-3 Phillips, New York #423/R est:5000-7000
£2333	$4177	€3500	Still life from The Metropolitan Scene (86x86cm-34x34in) s.d. silkscreen aluminium. 15-May-4 Van Ham, Cologne #764/R est:3000
£2353	$4000	€3435	Mirror I (53cm-21in circular) s. col screenprint. 31-Oct-3 Sotheby's, New York #646/R
£2353	$4000	€3435	Composition (56x69cm-22x27in) s.d.1995 col screenprint. 4-Nov-3 Christie's, Rockefeller NY #303/R est:3500-4500
£2374	$3894	€3300	Inaugural print (41x66cm-16x26in) s.i.d. col serigraph. 4-Jun-3 Ketterer, Hamburg #605/R est:2800-3400
£2395	$4000	€3497	Modern head no 5 (71x49cm-28x19in) s.d.1970 num.81/100 embossed graphite die-cut paper. 21-Oct-3 Bonhams & Butterfields, San Francisco #1350/R
£2401	$4250	€3505	American Indian theme I (62x61cm-24x24in) s.d.1980 num.42/50 col woodcut. 30-Apr-4 Sotheby's, New York #384/R est:3000-4000
£2448	$4161	€3500	Figures (60x39cm-24x15in) s.d. col lithograph board. 29-Nov-3 Villa Grisebach, Berlin #333/R est:4000-6000
£2473	$4500	€3611	Mirror no.6 (81x56cm-32x22in) num.24/80 color silkscreen. 19-Jun-4 Du Mouchelle, Detroit #3126/R est:1200-2200
£2500	$4150	€3650	Seascape II (34x63cm-13x25in) silkscreen die-cut collage rowlux prov. 6-Oct-3 Sotheby's, London #261/R est:2500-3500
£2500	$4150	€3650	Sunrise (4x59cm-2x23in) s. offset col lithograph. 6-Oct-3 Sotheby's, London #264/R est:2000-3000
£2542	$4500	€3711	Still life with red jar (38x33cm-15x13in) s.d.1994 num.141/250 col screenprint. 30-Apr-4 Sotheby's, New York #391/R est:3500-4500
£2577	$4200	€3762	Modern Head Relief (71x49cm-28x19in) s.d.1970 num.32/100 embossing die-cut collage wove paper. 24-Sep-3 Christie's, Rockefeller NY #286/R est:2000-3000
£2695	$4500	€3935	Modern head no 1 (51x32cm-20x13in) s.d.1970 num.81/100 col woodcut. 21-Oct-3 Bonhams & Butterfields, San Francisco #1349/R
£2703	$4838	€4000	Against apartheid (85x60cm-33x24in) s.d.1983 col lithograph. 4-May-4 Calmels Cohen, Paris #114/R est:2500-3000
£2761	$4500	€4031	Foot and Hand (44x55cm-17x22in) s.d.1964 offset col lithograph edition of 300. 24-Sep-3 Christie's, Rockefeller NY #285/R est:2000-4000
£2763	$5084	€4200	Still life with glass and lemon (103x81cm-41x32in) s.d.74 num.13/100 lithograph serigraph lit. 22-Jun-4 Wiener Kunst Auktionen, Vienna #372/R est:2700
£2794	$4750	€4079	Bicentennial (63x46cm-25x18in) s. col lithograph screenprint. 31-Oct-3 Sotheby's, New York #650/R
£2794	$4750	€4079	Red lamp (40x47cm-16x19in) s. col lithograph. 31-Oct-3 Sotheby's, New York #659/R
£2800	$5096	€4088	Foot and hand (44x54cm-17x21in) s. col offset lithograph. 30-Jun-4 Christie's, Kensington #52/R est:2000-3000
£2800	$5096	€4088	Red barn (37x44cm-15x17in) s.d.1969 num.166/250 col screenprint. 30-Jun-4 Christie's, Kensington #53/R est:2500-3500
£2901	$5221	€4235	Before the mirror (89x63cm-35x25in) s.num.25/100 col lithograph screenprint lit. 26-Apr-4 Bukowskis, Stockholm #370/R est:40000-50000 (S.KR 40000)
£3000	$4980	€4380	Moonscape (51x61cm-20x24in) s.d.1965 num.XVIII verso col silkscreen rowlux. 6-Oct-3 Sotheby's, London #265/R est:3000-3500
£3022	$4955	€4200	Apple with grey background (64x68cm-25x27in) s.i.d. col woodcut. 4-Jun-3 Ketterer, Hamburg #604/R est:5500-6500
£3067	$5643	€4600	Haystack (36x43cm-14x17in) s.d.1969 col serigraph one of 250. 12-Jun-4 Villa Grisebach, Berlin #395/R est:4000-6000
£3073	$5500	€4487	As I opened fire. s.i. lithograph three separate. 13-May-4 Dallas Auction Gallery, Dallas #275/R est:1500-2500
£3107	$5500	€4536	Red apple and yellow apple (71x95cm-28x37in) s.d.1983 num.58/60 col woodcut. 30-Apr-4 Sotheby's, New York #385/R est:4000-6000
£3200	$5312	€4672	Aspen winter jazz poster (102x66cm-40x26in) s.num.283/300 col silkscreen gloss paper. 6 Oct-3 Sotheby's, London #270/R est:1200-1800
£3235	$5500	€4723	Mirror VI (81x56cm-32x22in) s. col lithograph screenprint. 31-Oct-3 Sotheby's, New York #647/R
£3235	$5500	€4723	Figures with rope (39x55cm-15x22in) s. col lithograph. 31-Oct-3 Sotheby's, New York #651/R
£3235	$5500	€4723	Still life with windmill (74x97cm-29x38in) s. col screenprint lithograph. 31-Oct-3 Sotheby's, New York #649/R
£3293	$5500	€4808	Oval office (76x99cm-30x39in) s.d.1992 num.126/175 col screenprint. 11-Nov-3 Doyle, New York #313/R est:2500-3500
£3356	$6208	€5000	Cow going abstract (66x234cm-26x92in) s. num.90/150 col serigraph exec.1982. 11-Mar-4 Galleria Pace, Milan #87/R est:4000-5200
£3390	$6000	€4949	Brushstrokes (55x76cm-22x30in) s. num.277/300 col screenprint. 30-Apr-4 Sotheby's, New York #377/R est:6000-8000
£3500	$6370	€5110	Untitled, still life with lemon and glass (83x61cm-33x24in) s.d.1974 num.18/100 col lithograph screenprint. 1-Jul-4 Sotheby's, London #420/R est:3000-4000
£3500	$6370	€5110	Hommage to Max Ernst (40x54cm-16x21in) s.d.1975 num.XXII/XII col screenprint. 30-Jun-4 Christie's, Kensington #57/R est:3500-4000
£3672	$6500	€5361	Entableture V. Entablature VIII (74x114cm-29x45in) s.d.1976 num.30/30 col screenprint two. 30-Apr-4 Sotheby's, New York #381 est:3500-4500
£3672	$6500	€5361	Green face (149x104cm-59x41in) s.d.1989 num.18/60 lithograph woodcut. 30-Apr-4 Sotheby's, New York #388/R est:7000-9000
£3728	$6860	€5443	Homage to Max Ernst (53x40cm-21x16in) s.d.75 num.33/100 serigraph. 23-Jun-4 Koller, Zurich #3255/R est:4200-5500 (S.FR 8500)
£3824	$6500	€5583	Red barn (48x66cm-19x26in) s.d.1969 col screenprint. 4-Nov-3 Christie's, Rockefeller NY #293/R est:5000-7000
£3988	$6500	€5822	Best buddies (91x81cm-36x32in) s.d.1991 num.6/100 col screenprint wove paper. 24-Sep-3 Christie's, Rockefeller NY #293/R est:4000-5000
£4000	$6640	€5840	Still life with lobster (82x79cm-32x31in) s.d.1974 num.59/100 col silkscreen. 6-Oct-3 Sotheby's, London #272/R est:4000-5000
£4000	$7320	€5840	Musical notes (33x49cm-13x19in) s.d.1995 num.71/120 col screenprint. 3-Jun-4 Christie's, Kensington #433/R est:2500-3000
£4118	$7000	€6012	Modern head I (51x32cm-20x13in) s. col woodcut. 31-Oct-3 Sotheby's, New York #644/R
£4118	$7000	€6012	Study of hands (80x83cm-31x33in) s. col screenprint lithograph. 31-Oct-3 Sotheby's, New York #653/R
£4118	$7000	€6012	At the beach (66x107cm-26x42in) s.d.1978 col lithograph. 4-Nov-3 Christie's, Rockefeller NY #296/R est:5000-7000
£4118	$7000	€6012	Haystack (48x66cm-19x26in) s.d.1969 col screenprint. 4-Nov-3 Christie's, Rockefeller NY #292/R est:4000-6000
£4118	$7000	€6012	Painting (117x91cm-46x36in) s.d.1984 woodcut lithograph col screenprint. 4-Nov-3 Christie's, Rockefeller NY #298/R est:4000-6000
£4143	$7500	€6049	Pyramids (29x88cm-11x35in) s.d.1969 num.33/101 col lithograph. 19-Apr-4 Bonhams & Butterfields, San Francisco #275/R est:5000-7000
£4200	$7224	€6132	Still life with pitcher and flowers (77x115cm-30x45in) s.d.1974 num.74/100 col silkscreen. 4-Dec-3 Sotheby's, London #247/R est:4000-5000
£4237	$7500	€6186	Brushstrokes (55x76cm-22x30in) s.num.12/300 col screenprint. 28-Apr-4 Christie's, Rockefeller NY #353/R est:4000-6000
£4237	$7500	€6186	Still life with portrait (119x95cm-47x37in) s.d.1974 num.91/100 col lithograph screenprint. 30-Apr-4 Sotheby's, New York #380/R est:3000-5000
£4412	$7500	€6442	Titled (61x83cm-24x33in) s. col screenprint. 31-Oct-3 Sotheby's, New York #663/R
£4412	$7500	€6442	Brushstroke (58x74cm-23x29in) s. num.109/280 col screenprint exec.1965. 4-Nov-3 Christie's, Rockefeller NY #290/R est:7000-10000
£4412	$7500	€6442	Imperfect (161x226cm-63x89in) s.d.1988 woodcut col screenprint. 4-Nov-3 Christie's, Rockefeller NY #301/R est:9000-11000
£4491	$7500	€6557	Crak (47x69cm-19x27in) s.d.1964 num.263/300 col offset lithograph. 21-Oct-3 Bonhams & Butterfields, San Francisco #1348/R
£4500	$8190	€6570	Still life with Picasso (72x53cm-28x21in) s.i.d.1973 col screenprint prov. 30-Jun-4 Christie's, Kensington #58/R est:5000-7000
£4532	$7704	€6617	Peace through chemistry IV (64x114cm-25x45in) s.num.6/56 col lithograph lit. 4-Nov-3 Bukowskis, Stockholm #394/R est:60000-80000 (S.KR 60000)
£4706	$8000	€6871	Crak ! (49x70cm-19x28in) s.d.1963 offset lithograph. 4-Nov-3 Christie's, Rockefeller NY #289/R est:7000-9000
£4706	$8000	€6871	Modern Art II (123x97cm-48x38in) s.d.1996 col screenprint. 4-Nov-3 Christie's, Rockefeller NY #305/R est:10000-15000
£4802	$8500	€7011	Composition II (72x96cm-28x38in) s.d.1996 num.34/50 col screenprint. 28-Apr-4 Christie's, Rockefeller NY #367/R est:5000-7000
£4802	$8500	€7011	Modern art II (123x97cm-48x38in) s.d.1996 num.16/50 col screenprint. 30-Apr-4 Sotheby's, New York #393/R est:8000-10000
£5000	$9100	€7300	Composition III (109x77cm-43x30in) s.i.num.36/36 col silkscreen. 1-Jul-4 Sotheby's, London #419/R est:4000-6000
£5085	$9000	€7424	Haystack (36x44cm-14x17in) s.d.1969 num.52/250 yello black screenprint. 30-Apr-4 Sotheby's, New York #378/R est:4000-6000
£5200	$8632	€7592	Huh (101x71cm-40x28in) s.d.1976 num.35/100 col silkscreen. 6-Oct-3 Sotheby's, London #258/R est:4000-6000
£5245	$8916	€7500	Wallpaper with blue floor interior (260x380cm-102x150in) s.d. col serigraph. 27-Nov-3 Lempertz, Koln #249/R est:6000
£5294	$9000	€7729	On (15x11cm-6x4in) s. etching. 31-Oct-3 Sotheby's, New York #641/R
£5369	$9503	€8000	Crak! (50x70cm-20x28in) s.i.d. col offset lithograph board. 30-Apr-4 Dr Fritz Nagel, Stuttgart #878/R est:5800
£5588	$9500	€8158	Reflections on hair (126x99cm-50x39in) s. col screenprint woodcut lithograph collage embossing. 31-Oct-3 Sotheby's, New York #657/R
£5588	$9500	€8158	Imperfect (170x203cm-67x80in) s.d.1988 woodcut col screenprint collage. 4-Nov-3 Christie's, Rockefeller NY #299/R est:8000-10000
£6000	$10020	€8760	Modern room - interior series (143x205cm-56x81in) s.d.90 num.37/40 lithograph woodcut screenprint lit. 22-Oct-3 Bonhams, New Bond Street #113/R est:6000-8000
£6000	$10020	€8760	Red lamps - interior series (146x20cm-57x8in) s.d.90 num.37/60 lithograph woodcut screenprint lit. 22-Oct-3 Bonhams, New Bond Street #116/R est:6000-8000
£6000	$10020	€8760	Blue floor - interior series (147x212cm-58x83in) s.d.90 num.37/60 lithograph woodcut screenprint lit. 22-Oct-3 Bonhams, New Bond Street #118/R est:6000-8000
£6114	$11249	€8926	The student from the series 'Expressionist Woodcut' (89x77cm-35x30in) s.d.1980 col woodcut lit. 8-Jun-4 Germann, Zurich #499/R est:10000-14000 (S.FR 14000)
£6294	$10699	€9000	Green lamp (90x127cm-35x50in) num.47/60 lithograph serigraph collage lit. 24-Nov-3 Christie's, Milan #7/R est:5000-7000
£6452	$12000	€9420	Crak! (50x68cm-20x27in) s. offset col lithograph. 2-Mar-4 Swann Galleries, New York #363/R est:6000-9000
£6471	$11000	€9448	Modern Art I (130x96cm-51x38in) s.d.1996 col screenprint. 4-Nov-3 Christie's, Rockefeller NY #304/R est:9000-12000
£6757	$12500	€9865	Crak (47x39cm-19x15in) s.d.1963-4 num.62/300 offset col lithograph. 12-Feb-4 Christie's, Rockefeller NY #130/R est:8000-10000
£6780	$12000	€9899	Imperfect 63 3/8 88 7/8 (147x208cm-58x82in) s.d.1988 num.24/45 col woodcut screenprint. 28-Apr-4 Christie's, Rockefeller NY #360/R est:9000-11000
£6780	$12000	€9899	Blonde (75x68cm-30x27in) s.i.d.1978 col lithograph. 30-Apr-4 Sotheby's, New York #383/R est:6000-8000
£7000	$11620	€10220	Crying girl (44x59cm-17x23in) s. offset col lithograph. 6-Oct-3 Sotheby's, London #260/R est:7000-9000
£7000	$11620	€10220	Peace through chemistry III (96x161cm-38x63in) s.i.d.1970 lithograph prov. 6-Oct-3 Sotheby's, London #269/R est:7000-9000
£7200	$11952	€10512	On (15x11cm-6x4in) s.d.1962 num.6/60 etching. 6-Oct-3 Sotheby's, London #257/R est:3000-4000
£7345	$13000	€10724	Modern art (130x96cm-51x38in) s.d.1996 num.15/50 col screenprint. 30-Apr-4 Sotheby's, New York #392/R est:9000-12000
£7500	$13650	€10950	Shipboard girl (69x51cm-27x20in) s. col offset lithograph. 1-Jul-4 Sotheby's, London #418/R est:6000-8000
£7647	$13000	€11165	Reflections on conversation (120x154cm-47x61in) s. col lithograph screenprint collage embossing. 31-Oct-3 Sotheby's, New York #656/R
£7647	$13000	€11165	Wallpaper (259x381cm-102x150in) s.d.1992 col screenprint. 4-Nov-3 Christie's, Rockefeller NY #302/R est:4000-6000
£7800	$14196	€11388	Crying girl (44x58cm-17x23in) s. col offset lithograph. 1-Jul-4 Sotheby's, London #415/R est:5000-7000
£8824	$15000	€12883	Two nudes (105x89cm-41x35in) s. col relief print. 31-Oct-3 Sotheby's, New York #660/R
£8824	$15000	€12883	Imperfect (172x232cm-68x91in) s.d.1988 woodcut col screenprint. 4-Nov-3 Christie's, Rockefeller NY #300/R est:8000-12000
£9000	$15480	€13140	Shipboard girl (69x51cm-27x20in) s. offset col lithograph. 4-Dec-3 Sotheby's, London #248/R est:5000-7000
£9040	$16000	€13198	Crak (47x69cm-19x27in) s.i.d.1963-4 num.242/300 col offset lithograph. 28-Apr-4 Christie's, Rockefeller NY #351/R est:8000-10000
£9040	$16000	€13198	Imperfect 67 5/8 9 1/2 (479x218cm-189x86in) s.d.1988 num.6/14 col woodcut screenprint collage. 28-Apr-4 Christie's, Rockefeller NY #359/R est:8000-12000
£10169	$18000	€14847	Reflections on soda fountain (72x77cm-28x30in) s.d.1991 num.28/85 col screenprint. 28-Apr-4 Christie's, Rockefeller NY #366/R est:14000-18000
£10169	$18000	€14847	Modern art I (111x78cm-44x31in) s.d.1996 num.27/50 col screenprint. 28-Apr-4 Christie's, Rockefeller NY #368/R est:12000-18000
£10169	$18000	€14847	Reflection on conversation (119x154cm-47x61in) s.i.d.1990 num.5/16 lithograph screenprint. 30-Apr-4 Sotheby's, New York #389/R est:15000-20000
£10588	$18000	€15458	Seascape (95x133cm-37x52in) s. col lithograph screenprint woodcut. 31-Oct-3 Sotheby's, New York #654/R
£10588	$18000	€15458	Nude reading (61x77cm-24x30in) s. col print relief. 31-Oct-3 Sotheby's, New York #661/R
£10734	$19000	€15672	Crying girl (44x59cm-17x23in) s. col offset lithograph. 28-Apr-4 Christie's, Rockefeller NY #350/R est:18000-25000
£10734	$19000	€15672	I love liberty (82x54cm-32x21in) s.d.1982 num.225/250 col screenprint. 28-Apr-4 Christie's, Rockefeller NY #358/R est:12000-16000
£11000	$18260	€16060	Crying girl (44x59cm-17x23in) s. offset col lithograph. 6-Oct-3 Sotheby's, London #259/R est:8000-10000

£11000	$18260	€16060	Shipboard girl (69x52cm-27x20in) s. offset col lithograph. 6-Oct-3 Sotheby's, London #256/R est:6000-7000
£11000	$20020	€16060	Whaam (63x147cm-25x58in) s. col offset lithograph two sheets edition of 3000. 30-Jun-4 Christie's, Kensington #56/R est:2500-3500
£11176	$19000	€16317	Crying girl (44x59cm-17x23in) s. offset lithograph. 31-Oct-3 Sotheby's, New York #640/R
£11176	$19000	€16317	Reflections on girl (98x124cm-39x49in) s. lithograph screenprint collage embossing. 31-Oct-3 Sotheby's, New York #658/R
£11299	$20000	€16497	La sortie (135x173cm-53x68in) s.d.90 num.26/60 col woodcut. 28-Apr-4 Christie's, Rockefeller NY #364/R est:20000-30000
£11299	$20000	€16497	Seascape (102x104cm-40x41in) s.d.1985 num.5/60 lithograph woodcut. 30-Apr-4 Sotheby's, New York #387/R est:18000-22000
£12429	$22000	€18146	Reflection on girl (98x124cm-39x49in) s.d.1990 num.61/68 col lithograph screenprint relief collage. 28-Apr-4 Christie's, Rockefeller NY #363/R est:20000-30000
£12712	$22500	€18560	La sortie (134x190cm-53x75in) s.i.d.1990 num.3/6 col woodcut. 30-Apr-4 Sotheby's, New York #390/R est:15000-20000
£12941	$22000	€18894	I love liberty (97x69cm-38x27in) s.d.1982 col screenprint. 4-Nov-3 Christie's, Rockefeller NY #297/R est:10000-15000
£13529	$23000	€19752	Thinking nude (89x141cm-35x56in) s. col relief print. 31-Oct-3 Sotheby's, New York #662/R
£14000	$23240	€20440	Wallpaper with blue floor interior (259x381cm-102x150in) s.d.1992 num.204/300 col silkscreen set of five. 6-Oct-3 Sotheby's, London #271/R est:6000-8000
£14000	$24080	€20440	Two nudes state (106x89cm-42x35in) s.d.1994 num.12/12 col relief print. 4-Dec-3 Sotheby's, London #249/R est:8000-10000
£14706	$25000	€21471	Sweet dreams baby ! (90x65cm-35x26in) s. col screenprint. 31-Oct-3 Sotheby's, New York #643/R
£14728	$25038	€21503	Sweet dreams baby - pop artists portfolio Volume III (91x65cm-36x26in) s.num.21/200 col silkscreen prov.lit. 4-Nov-3 Bukowskis, Stockholm #393/R est:180000-200000 (S.KR 195000)
£15000	$24900	€21900	Roommates (147x115cm-58x45in) s.d.1994 num.36/40 col relief print. 6-Oct-3 Sotheby's, London #275/R est:10000-12000
£15000	$24900	€21900	Two nudes (106x89cm-42x35in) s.d.1994 num.35/40 col relief print. 6-Oct-3 Sotheby's, London #276/R est:8000-10000
£15254	$27000	€22271	Landscape with poet (21x76cm-8x30in) s.d.1996 num.26/60 col lithograph screenprint. 30-Apr-4 Sotheby's, New York #394/R est:20000-25000
£15537	$27500	€22684	Reverie (68x58cm-27x23in) s. num.73/200 col screenprint. 30-Apr-4 Sotheby's, New York #374/R est:25000-35000
£15819	$28000	€23096	Tel Aviv museum (65x131cm-26x52in) s.d.1989 num.20/20 col lithograph. 28-Apr-4 Christie's, Rockefeller NY #361/R est:18000-25000
£16000	$26560	€23360	Reflections on girl (96x124cm-38x49in) s.d.1990 num.14/16 col silkscreen lithograph woodcut collage. 6-Oct-3 Sotheby's, London #274/R est:12000-18000
£16000	$29120	€23360	Modern room (143x21cm-56x8in) s.d.1990 num.37/60 col lithograph woodcut screenprint. 1-Jul-4 Sotheby's, London #422/R est:10000-12000
£16176	$27500	€23617	Reflections on crash (135x175cm-53x69in) s. lithograph screenprint collage embossing. 31-Oct-3 Sotheby's, New York #655/R
£18079	$32000	€26395	Peace through chemistry I (81x146cm-32x57in) s.d.1970 num.22/32 col lithograph screenprint. 28-Apr-4 Christie's, Rockefeller NY #354/R est:20000-30000
£18079	$32000	€26395	Relections on crash (135x185cm-53x73in) s.d.1990 num.61/68 col lithograph screenprint relief collage. 28-Apr-4 Christie's, Rockefeller NY #362/R est:25000-35000
£19000	$31540	€27740	Reflections on the scream (108x150cm-43x59in) s.d.1990 num.43/68 col silkscreen lithograph woodcut collage. 6-Oct-3 Sotheby's, London #273/R est:15000-18000
£19118	$32500	€27912	Reverie (69x58cm-27x23in) s. col screenprint. 31-Oct-3 Sotheby's, New York #642/R
£20904	$37000	€30520	Ten landscapes (37x45cm-15x18in) s. num.19/100 col screenprints set of ten. 30-Apr-4 Sotheby's, New York #376/R est:35000-45000
£26347	$44000	€38467	Bull profile series. s.num.89/100 col lithograph silkscreen line-cut 6. 21-Oct-3 Bonhams & Butterfields, San Francisco #1352/R
£28235	$48000	€41223	Reverie (76x61cm-30x24in) s. num.128/200 col screenprint exec.1965. 4-Nov-3 Christie's, Rockefeller NY #291/R est:35000-45000
£32353	$55000	€47235	Bull profile (69x89cm-27x35in) media print album. 31-Oct-3 Sotheby's, New York #648/R
£36723	$65000	€53616	Bull profile series (69x89cm-27x35in) s.d.1973 num.15/100 col lithograph screenprint linocut set of six. 28-Apr-4 Christie's, Rockefeller NY #355/R est:40000-60000
£38000	$69160	€55480	Ten landscapes (46x59cm-18x23in) s.d.1967 num.27/100 col screenprint die cut collage set of 10. 1-Jul-4 Sotheby's, London #423/R est:15000-20000
£46000	$83720	€67160	Reverie (77x61cm-30x24in) s.num.136 col screenprint edition of 250. 1-Jul-4 Sotheby's, London #417/R est:25000-35000
Sculpture			
£5588	$9500	€8158	Modern head (61x45cm-24x18in) st.sig.d.1970 brass relief. 4-Nov-3 Christie's, Rockefeller NY #294/R est:12000-18000
£6115	$10215	€8928	Modern head relief (61x45cm-24x18in) s.d.1970 num.81/100 brass relief. 21-Oct-3 Bonhams & Butterfields, San Francisco #1351/R
£7059	$12000	€10306	Modern head (61x45x2cm-24x18x1in) st.sig. brass relief. 31-Oct-3 Sotheby's, New York #645/R
£9605	$17000	€14023	Modern head relief (61x45x2cm-24x18x1in) incised sig.d.1970 brass relief. 30-Apr-4 Sotheby's, New York #379/R est:14000-18000
£18156	$32500	€26508	Brush Stroke I (52x16x18cm-20x6x7in) s.i.verso acrylic lacquer acrylic resin cherrywood prov.lit. 13-May-4 Sotheby's, New York #213/R est:30000-40000
£83832	$140000	€122395	Suspended mobile (129x192x10cm-51x76x4in) s.d.90 num.9/19 verso col silkscreen fabric prov.lit. 13-Nov-3 Sotheby's, New York #266/R est:35000-45000
£335196	$600000	€489386	Brushstroke Head (211x61x61cm-83x24x24in) s.d.94 num.1/6 base enamel nickel plated bronze prov.lit. 12-May-4 Christie's, Rockefeller NY #194/R est:400000-600000
£949721	$1700000	€1386593	Three brushstrokes (307x81x117cm-121x32x46in) i.sig. d.84 num.1/2 fabricated painted aluminium prov. 12-May-4 Sotheby's, New York #46/R est:2000000-3000000
£1137725	$1900000	€1661079	Woman, sunlight, moonlight (101x64x3cm-40x25x1in) s.d.96 num.4/6 painted bronze prov.exhib.lit. 12-Nov-3 Sotheby's, New York #31/R est:1500000-2000000
Works on paper			
£4118	$7000	€6012	Sunrise (17x23cm-7x9in) s. blue pencil. 21-Nov-3 Swann Galleries, New York #111/R est:8000-12000
£7333	$13127	€11000	Shipboard girl (66x49cm-26x19in) s. col offset lithograph. 15-May-4 Dr Sturies, Dusseldorf #117/R
£9040	$16000	€13198	Blue floor (131x197cm-52x78in) s.d.1991 num.18/60 col lithograph woodcut screenprint. 28-Apr-4 Christie's, Rockefeller NY #365/R est:10000-15000
£18666	$34346	€28000	Study for night seascape banner (47x31cm-19x12in) s.i.d.1988 felt pen wax crayon tracing paper. 8-Jun-4 Artcurial Briest, Paris #230/R est:24000-30000
£22455	$37500	€32784	House with grey roof (20x22cm-8x9in) s.d.97 verso col pencil pencil prov.exhib. 13-Nov-3 Sotheby's, New York #265/R est:35000-45000

LICHTENSTEIN, Roy (after) (1923-1997) American

Prints			
£5500	$9130	€8030	Whaam, poster (63x74cm-25x29in) complimentary sig. offset col lithograph two sheets. 6-Oct-3 Sotheby's, London #268/R est:3000-5000

LICHTFUS, Yvette (1925-) Belgian

£203	$344	€296	Les Saules (72x79cm-28x31in) s. i.verso. 21-Nov-3 Walker's, Ottawa #217/R (C.D 450)
£403	$741	€600	Saint-Pierre de Maille pres de Chatellerault (50x65cm-20x26in) s. 23-Mar-4 Galerie Moderne, Brussels #207

LICINI, Osvaldo (1894-1958) Italian

£9122	$16054	€13500	Seascape (32x47cm-13x19in) paper on canvas painted 1922 lit. 24-May-4 Christie's, Milan #168/R est:7000-10000
£47651	$85295	€71000	Study (22x28cm-9x11in) oil tempera collage prov.lit. 25-May-4 Sotheby's, Milan #289/R est:60000-80000
Works on paper			
£1538	$2615	€2200	Untitled (18x27cm-7x11in) pencil prov. 24-Nov-3 Christie's, Milan #39/R est:1500-2000
£3147	$5350	€4500	Amalassunta (20x29cm-8x11in) pencil lead exec.1945. 25-Nov-3 Sotheby's, Milan #139/R est:4000-5000
£3497	$5944	€5000	Rebel angel (25x34cm-10x13in) pencil. 24-Nov-3 Christie's, Milan #37/R est:4500-6500
£3986	$6536	€5500	Flower (18x26cm-7x10in) pencil graphite pen double-sided prov. 27-May-3 Sotheby's, Milan #81/R est:6000-8000

LICINIO, Bernardino (1489-1565) Italian

£66901	$115739	€95000	Madonna and Child (266x202cm-105x80in) s. painted with Carlo Cozza. 14-Dec-3 Finarte, Venice #100/R est:140000-155000

LIDDELL, John Davison (1859-1942) British

£447	$800	€653	Topsail schooner running into the sunset (36x56cm-14x22in) s. 16-Mar-4 Bonhams & Butterfields, San Francisco #6161/R

LIDDELL, T Hodgson (1860-1925) British

£300	$555	€438	Extensive river landscape (151x90cm-59x35in) s. 9-Mar-4 Bonhams, Knightsbridge #336/R
Works on paper			
£2400	$4008	€3504	Peking, Lama Temple (52x74cm-20x29in) s. W/C over pencil htd bodycol. 14-Oct-3 Sotheby's, London #163/R est:2000-3000

LIDDELL, William F (19/20th C) British

Works on paper			
£850	$1521	€1241	Westminster Abbey (24x35cm-9x14in) s.d.1909 W/C. 26-May-4 Sotheby's, Olympia #156/R est:500-700

LIDDERDALE, Charles Sillem (1831-1895) British

£700	$1099	€1015	At the well (81x61cm-32x24in) s.d.1870. 28-Aug-3 Christie's, Kensington #157/R
£1000	$1670	€1460	Country girl (61x51cm-24x20in) mono.d.1880. 13-Nov-3 Christie's, Kensington #252/R est:1000-1500
£1200	$2196	€1752	Portrait of a girl (53x43cm-21x17in) mono. 7-Apr-4 Gardiner & Houlgate, Bath #228/R est:2000-3000
£1450	$2668	€2117	Portrait of a young girl wearing a red cloak (53x43cm-21x17in) mono.d.83. 23-Jun-4 Bonhams, Bury St Edmunds #401/R est:1500-2000
£1700	$2890	€2482	Young fisher girl with net over her shoulder (41x30cm-16x12in) mono. board. 30-Oct-3 Duke & Son, Dorchester #245/R est:800-1600
£1800	$3276	€2628	Country girl (53x43cm-21x17in) mono. 16-Jun-4 Bonhams, New Bond Street #45/R est:2000-3000
£2033	$3191	€2968	Untitled, gypsy girl resting on a fence post (92x71cm-36x28in) monod.82. 1-Sep-3 Shapiro, Sydney #347/R est:5000-7000 (A.D 5000)
£2500	$4650	€3650	Fisher girl (39x29cm-15x11in) mono.d.65 panel prov. 4-Mar-4 Christie's, Kensington #581/R est:3000-5000
£3167	$5290	€4624	Young beauty by a fence (45x33cm-18x13in) mono.d.79. 17-Nov-3 Waddingtons, Toronto #112/R est:3000-5000 (C.D 7000)
£4000	$6680	€5840	Day dreaming (81x56cm-32x22in) mono.d.80. 14-Oct-3 Canterbury Auctions, UK #89/R est:4500-6000
£4514	$7674	€6500	Young beauty (54x44cm-21x17in) mono.d.78. 28-Oct-3 Christie's, Amsterdam #95/R est:7000-9000
£5000	$8500	€7300	Knitting (47x34cm-19x13in) mono.d.80 panel. 25-Nov-3 Christie's, London #199/R est:3000-5000
£14000	$23800	€20440	In hiding after Culloden (73x114cm-29x45in) mono.d.1869 exhib.lit. 30-Oct-3 Christie's, London #121a/R est:15000-20000
Works on paper			
£350	$627	€511	Rejection, study of a young girl (39x31cm-15x12in) init.d.78 W/C bodycol. 18-Mar-4 Neales, Nottingham #744
£1100	$1947	€1606	A dark beauty (43x33cm-17x13in) mono.d.74 W/C. 1-May-4 Hamptons Fine Art, Godalming #54

LIDDERDALE, Charles Sillem (attrib) (1831-1895) British

£693	$1240	€1012	The blond (61x50cm-24x20in) mono.d.75 i. verso. 22-Mar-4 Philippe Schuler, Zurich #6163 (S.FR 1600)

LIDDY, Pat (20th C) Irish

£403	$721	€600	Obelisk at Killiney Hill (90x60cm-35x24in) s. 31-May-4 Hamilton Osborne King, Dublin #41/R

LIDMAN, Torsten (20th C) Swedish

£1100	$1870	€1606	Figures in tradition costume, St Marks Square, Venice (91x122cm-36x48in) s. board. 6-Nov-3 Christie's, Kensington #853/R est:800-1200

LIE, Edvarda (1910-1983) Norwegian
£571 $1051 €834 Woman with bowl of fruit (46x35cm-18x14in) s. 29-Mar-4 Blomqvist, Lysaker #1195/R (N.KR 7200)
£688 $1108 €1004 Woman with bouquet of flowers (100x81cm-39x32in) s. panel. 25-Aug-3 Blomqvist, Lysaker #1041 (N.KR 8000)
£1401 $2508 €2045 Woman and birds in garden (71x78cm-28x31in) init.d.47. 22-Mar-4 Blomqvist, Oslo #661/R est:25000-30000 (N.KR 17500)

LIE, Jonas (1880-1940) American
£4624 $8000 €6751 Sailboats gathered in a harbour at dusk (89x107cm-35x42in) s. prov. 13-Dec-3 Weschler, Washington #552 est:15000-25000

LIEBER, Max (1851-1918) German
£556 $928 €800 Low tide (70x101cm-28x40in) mono. 24-Oct-3 Ketterer, Hamburg #18/R

LIEBER, Tom (20th C) American
£2119 $3750 €3094 Twilight breeder (168x244cm-66x96in) s.i.d.1981 verso acrylic. 2-May-4 Bonhams & Butterfields, Los Angeles #3084/R est:1500-2500
Works on paper
£273 $500 €399 Untitled (53x58cm-21x23in) mixed media on rhoplex. 10-Jul-4 Hindman, Chicago #300/R

LIEBERMANN, Ernst (1869-1960) German
£284 $460 €400 Ostersee area (32x42cm-13x17in) s. board lit. 23-May-3 Karlheinz Kaupp, Staufen #2002
£590 $962 €850 Blue interior (70x57cm-28x22in) s.i.d.1912 i. stretcher. 24-Sep-3 Neumeister, Munich #482/R
£738 $1358 €1100 Peasant (70x60cm-28x24in) s.i. i. stretcher. 26-Mar-4 Ketterer, Hamburg #250/R
£903 $1472 €1300 Dinkelsbuhl (46x58cm-18x23in) s.i. board. 24-Sep-3 Neumeister, Munich #481/R
£1389 $2264 €2000 Snowy city (100x120cm-39x47in) s.i.d.1928 i. stretcher. 24-Sep-3 Neumeister, Munich #480/R est:2400
£1532 $2482 €2160 Black haired woman (73x59cm-29x23in) s. s.i. verso lit. 23-May-3 Karlheinz Kaupp, Staufen #1785/R est:2500
£1600 $2944 €2400 Portrait of a young girl (76x66cm-30x26in) s.d.1921. 11-Jun-4 Wendl, Rudolstadt #4144/R est:2400

LIEBERMANN, Ferdinand (1883-1941) German
Sculpture
£2198 $4000 €3209 Woman astride an ostrich (55x60cm-22x24in) i.d.08 dark brown pat. bronze prov. 29-Jun-4 Sotheby's, New York #131/R est:5000-7000
£2400 $4296 €3600 Philosophical dispute, faun and heron (22x45x12cm-9x18x5in) s.d. 06 black pat bronze Cast.A Brandstetter lit. 14-May-4 Von Zezschwitz, Munich #58/R est:3000

LIEBERMANN, Max (1847-1935) German
£600 $1110 €876 Seated female nude (75x65cm-30x26in) s.i.d.1918. 10-Feb-4 Bonhams, Knightsbridge #90/R
£2900 $5220 €4234 Portrait of an unknown gentleman (55x47cm-22x19in) s. prov. 20-Jan-4 Bonhams, Knightsbridge #309/R est:4000-6000
£4196 $7007 €6000 At work (20x15cm-8x6in) s.d.73 panel prov. 11-Oct-3 Hans Stahl, Hamburg #75/R est:6000
£4545 $7818 €6500 Portrait d'un ami intellectuel (70x49cm-28x19in) s. prov. 5-Dec-3 Chochon-Barre & Allardi, Paris #125/R est:8000-10000
£6711 $12013 €10000 Portrait of a man (91x70cm-36x28in) s.d.1920 prov.exhib. 25-May-4 Dorotheum, Vienna #27/R est:12000-18000
£10000 $18400 €15000 Monte Olivieto, Florence (30x40cm-12x16in) s. pastel paper on cardboard prov.exhib.lit. 11-Jun-4 Villa Grisebach, Berlin #6/R est:12000-15000
£18440 $30794 €26000 Sunny avenue with figures, horses and coaches (15x32cm-6x13in) s. canvas on board. 21-Jun-3 Hans Stahl, Hamburg #56/R est:25000
£19580 $33287 €28000 Haman before Ahasver and Esther (39x50cm-15x20in) s. panel prov.exhib. 29-Nov-3 Villa Grisebach, Berlin #138/R est:18000-24000
£22000 $40480 €32120 Der Jager in den Dunen - Hunter in the sand dunes (82x66cm-32x26in) s.d.14 lit. 23-Jun-4 Christie's, London #166/R est:15000-20000
£22378 $38490 €32000 Rider on beach (31x24cm-12x9in) s. 2-Dec-3 Hauswedell & Nolte, Hamburg #367/R est:12000
£24000 $44160 €36000 Dutch farm below trees (24x32cm-9x13in) s.d.98 panel prov. 11-Jun-4 Villa Grisebach, Berlin #2/R est:15000-20000
£25000 $45500 €36500 Spinnerin (73x42cm-29x17in) s.d.84 board. 3-Feb-4 Christie's, London #178/R est:25000-35000
£25175 $42797 €36000 Girl with windlass (78x55cm-31x22in) board prov.exhib.lit. 26-Nov-3 Lempertz, Koln #799/R est:35000-40000
£28000 $51520 €40880 Selbstbildnis - Self portrait (75x49cm-30x19in) s.d.1916 board. 23-Jun-4 Christie's, London #167/R est:15000-20000
£33937 $57692 €49548 Sisters - Hertha and Hilde Bohm (75x94cm-30x37in) s.d.1918 i. verso prov.exhib.lit. 25-Nov-3 Germann, Zurich #40/R est:70000-90000 (S.FR 75000)
£36667 $67467 €55000 Self portrait sitting in front of easel, to the right (31x25cm-12x10in) s. panel prov. 11-Jun-4 Villa Grisebach, Berlin #10/R est:35000-45000
£84507 $146197 €120000 Tiergarten (42x64cm-17x25in) s. 13-Dec-3 Lempertz, Koln #164/R est:120000-140000
£153333 $282133 €230000 Woman with cradle, mother with child in farmhouse (59x65cm-23x26in) s.d.89 paintboard on wood prov.exhib.lit. 11-Jun-4 Villa Grisebach, Berlin #4/R est:200000-300000
£241228 $443860 €352193 Oude Vink (66x80cm-26x31in) s.d.1911 prov.exhib.lit. 23-Jun-4 Koller, Zurich #3024/R est:350000-500000 (S.FR 550000)
£292793 $503604 €427478 Wannsee garden (54x75cm-21x30in) s. prov. 2-Dec-3 Koller, Zurich #3048/R est:380000-500000 (S.FR 650000)
Prints
£3636 $6182 €5200 Girl reading (30x24cm-12x9in) s. col lithograph. 29-Nov-3 Bassenge, Berlin #6873/R est:3000
Works on paper
£389 $650 €568 Two seated women (23x16cm-9x6in) s. chl double-sided. 7-Oct-3 Sotheby's, New York #139
£433 $797 €650 Man and dog and porter. In boat (29x22cm-11x9in) chk two. 12-Jun-4 Villa Grisebach, Berlin #601/R
£500 $835 €730 Dunenlandschaft mit weiblicher figur (10x16cm-4x6in) s. chl executed c.1895. 22-Oct-3 Bonhams, New Bond Street #5/R
£533 $981 €800 Boys bathing. Four figures in a landscape (10x15cm-4x6in) chk two. 12-Jun-4 Villa Grisebach, Berlin #600/R
£568 $1045 €829 Studies (11x14cm-4x6in) s. verso pencil two. 14-Jun-4 Philippe Schuler, Zurich #4014 (S.FR 1300)
£733 $1349 €1100 Twig collecting (28x22cm-11x9in) s. pen brush. 12-Jun-4 Villa Grisebach, Berlin #603/R
£750 $1358 €1095 Waschtag. Umbiegende Frau (16x10cm-6x4in) s. pencil double-sided exec.c.1885. 1-Apr-4 Christie's, Kensington #15/R
£900 $1629 €1314 Am Tisch (15x19cm-6x7in) s. pencil. 1-Apr-4 Christie's, Kensington #17/R
£1000 $1730 €1460 Pferdebandiger (44x35cm-17x14in) init. chl prov. 11-Dec-3 Christie's, Kensington #6/R est:1000-1500
£1000 $1820 €1460 Netzflickerinnen (35x23cm-14x9in) s. chl buff paper prov. 5-Feb-4 Christie's, London #308/R est:3000-4000
£1138 $1900 €1661 Interior (23x30cm-9x12in) s. W/C gouache. 7-Oct-3 Sotheby's, New York #140 est:2500-3500
£1193 $1992 €1730 Study for beer garden in Brannenburg (11x18cm-4x7in) s. chk double-sided. 19-Jun-3 Kornfeld, Bern #628 est:3000 (S.FR 2600)
£1223 $2225 €1786 Girl with long hair (36x24cm-14x9in) s. chl. 17-Jun-4 Kornfeld, Bern #528 est:5000 (S.FR 2800)
£1259 $2140 €1800 Dune landscape with two figures (12x16cm-5x6in) s. chl prov. 26-Nov-3 Lempertz, Koln #802/R est:1200
£1276 $2131 €1850 Children playing under a tree (18x20cm-7x8in) s. black chk. 13-Nov-3 Neumeister, Munich #386/R est:1500-1800
£1284 $2145 €1862 Woman in vegetable garden (11x17cm-4x7in) mono. chk. 19-Jun-3 Kornfeld, Bern #627 est:3000 (S.FR 2800)
£1467 $2699 €2200 Peasant and small child (17x20cm-7x8in) s. pencil double-sided. 12-Jun-4 Villa Grisebach, Berlin #602/R est:400-500
£1600 $2672 €2336 Stevenstift in Leiden, Juli 1900 (11x19cm-4x7in) s. chl. 22-Oct-3 Bonhams, New Bond Street #4/R est:800-1200
£1600 $2896 €2336 Dunenlandschaft mit zwei figuren (11x18cm-4x7in) s. pen black ink exec.c.1985. 1-Apr-4 Christie's, Kensington #12/R est:1200-1800
£1678 $2887 €2400 Self portrait (29x20cm-11x8in) s.d.1925 chl. 2-Dec-3 Hauswedell & Nolte, Hamburg #369/R est:2000
£1799 $2950 €2500 Dunes (27x36cm-11x14in) s. i.d.1896 verso chk exhib. 4-Jun-3 Ketterer, Hamburg #606/R est:2500-2800
£1800 $3222 €2700 Weaving in Laren (11x16cm-4x6in) s. chl. 15-May-4 Bassenge, Berlin #6996/R est:4000
£1965 $3576 €2869 Martha Liebermann with daughter Kathe sitting at table (19x27cm-7x11in) s. chl sketch verso. 17-Jun-4 Kornfeld, Bern #529 est:6000 (S.FR 4500)
£2000 $3580 €3000 In the dunes near Katwijk (13x18cm-5x7in) s. chk htd white. 15-May-4 Bassenge, Berlin #6995/R est:3500
£2156 $3600 €3126 Woodland path near lake (11x18cm-4x7in) s. chl. 19-Jun-3 Kornfeld, Bern #630 est:4000 (S.FR 4700)
£2238 $3849 €3200 Landscape with fence (27x37cm-11x15in) s. chl chk. 2-Dec-3 Hauswedell & Nolte, Hamburg #370/R est:2500
£2342 $3653 €3700 Dutch landscape (23x32cm-9x13in) s. chl htd white board. 18-Oct-2 Von Zezschwitz, Munich #21/R est:4200
£2400 $3816 €3480 Madchen im profil (13x10cm-5x4in) st.sig. pen ink wash. 11-Sep-3 Christie's, Kensington #11/R est:1500-2000
£2667 $4773 €4000 Cart in the dunes (188x25cm-74x10in) mono. chk. 15-May-4 Bassenge, Berlin #6994/R est:5000
£2982 $4979 €4324 Girl from Laren (53x36cm-21x14in) s. chl wash htd white. 19-Jun-3 Kornfeld, Bern #626/R est:7500 (S.FR 6500)
£3463 $6199 €5056 Sailing boat on shore (23x34cm-9x13in) s. bears i. verso pastel chk. 22-Mar-4 Philippe Schuler, Zurich #4030/R est:4600-5900 (S.FR 8000)
£9500 $15105 €13775 Gattin des kunstlers, Martha (30x23cm-12x9in) s. indis i.d.85 pencil W/C. 11-Sep-3 Christie's, Kensington #35/R est:5000-7000
£11000 $20020 €16060 Landschaft - landscape (20x30cm-8x12in) s. pastel exec.1925. 4-Feb-4 Sotheby's, London #476/R est:4000-6000
£11189 $19021 €16000 Extensive beach landscape with figures (13x18cm-5x7in) s. pastel. 29-Nov-3 Bassenge, Berlin #6869/R est:6000
£11712 $20144 €17100 Eva (20x14cm-8x6in) s. chk htd white prov. 2-Dec-3 Koller, Zurich #3044/R est:20000-30000 (S.FR 26000)
£12937 $21993 €18500 Beach shelters (12x20cm-5x8in) pastel prov. 26-Nov-3 Lempertz, Koln #803/R est:15000-20000
£13986 $23776 €20000 Boys bathing (46x60cm-18x24in) s. chl htd white crayon double-sided prov. 28-Nov-3 Villa Grisebach, Berlin #11/R est:20000-30000
£18667 $34347 €28000 Garden party on the lakeside (19x28cm-7x11in) s. pastel prov. 12-Jun-4 Villa Grisebach, Berlin #152/R est:20000-30000
£26573 $45175 €38000 Artist's garden by Wannsee (25x30cm-10x12in) s. pastel prov. 28-Nov-3 Villa Grisebach, Berlin #15/R est:20000-25000
£29333 $53973 €44000 Portrait of Walther Rathenau (44x28cm-17x11in) s. chk over blue crayon prov.exhib.lit. 11-Jun-4 Villa Grisebach, Berlin #12/R est:24000-28000
£30000 $55200 €43800 Garten am Wannsee (19x24cm-7x9in) s. pastel pencil exec c.1918 prov. 24-Jun-4 Christie's, London #315/R est:15000-20000

LIEBICH, Curt (1868-?) German
£3333 $5567 €4800 Girl in Black Forest house (53x46cm-21x18in) s. 22-Oct-3 Neumeister, Munich #733 est:600

LIEBKNECHT, Robert (1903-1994) German
£1107 $1960 €1650 View from window, Berlin (75x100cm-30x39in) s. board. 28-Apr-4 Schopman, Hamburg #560/R est:1650

LIEBMANN, Gerhardt (1928-1989) American
£221 $400 €323 View looking out window (152x122cm-60x48in) masonite. 16-Apr-4 American Auctioneer #251/R
Works on paper
£318 $550 €464 Parking (43x33cm-17x13in) s.d.1964 casein board. 13-Dec-3 Weschler, Washington #610

LIEDER, Friedrich (younger) (1807-1884) Austrian
Works on paper
£300 $546 €450 Portrait of a young lady (16x11cm-6x4in) s. W/C mixed media cardboard. 3-Jul-4 Geble, Radolfzell #446/R

LIEDTKE, Alfred (1877-1914) German
£451 $754 €650 Hamburg harbour with St Paulo jetty (44x63cm-17x25in) s. board. 24-Oct-3 Ketterer, Hamburg #19/R

LIEGI, Ulvi (1860-1939) Italian

£5000 $9200 €7500 Landscape with figures (12x22cm-5x9in) s. cardboard prov. 10-Jun-4 Christie's, Rome #176/R est:3000-5000
£5634 $9746 €8000 Livorno, lights and colours (20x22cm-8x9in) s.d.21 board. 11-Dec-3 Christie's, Rome #167/R est:7000-10000
£8725 $16315 €13000 Street in Viareggio (29x25cm-11x10in) s.d.1910 cardboard on canvas prov.exhib.lit. 25-Feb-4 Porro, Milan #17/R est:9000-11000
£10000 $18400 €15000 Cottages in Valsugana (28x38cm-11x15in) s. prov. 10-Jun-4 Christie's, Rome #175/R est:7000-9000
£12500 $21250 €18000 Painter's study (38x20cm-15x8in) s.d.1897 board. 1-Nov-3 Meeting Art, Vercelli #110/R est:15000
£13669 $22417 €19000 Centostelle Street (21x32cm-8x13in) s.i.d.37 board double-sided. 10-Jun-3 Pandolfini, Florence #272/R est:22000-24000
£26000 $47060 €39000 Ponte Vecchio, Florence (35x50cm-14x20in) s. s.i.d.1901 verso cardboard exhib.lit. 2-Apr-4 Farsetti, Prato #593/R est:35000-45000

Works on paper
£671 $1235 €1000 Back home (45x60cm-18x24in) s. pencil dr. 24-Mar-4 Il Ponte, Milan #521/R

LIENARD, E (19th C) French

Sculpture
£1700 $2686 €2482 Dog retrieving a pheasant (37x48cm-15x19in) golden brown pat bronze on naturalistic base. 27-Apr-3 Wilkinson, Doncaster #6/R

LIENARD, Jacques (19th C) French

Miniatures
£5867 $10678 €8800 Napoleon (13x10cm-5x4in) s. on porcelain oval lit. 30-Jun-4 Pierre Berge, Paris #110/R est:3000-4000

LIENARD, Jean Auguste Edouard (1779-1848) French

Miniatures
£2150 $3956 €3139 Madame Elisabeth Philippine Marie Helen of France (13cm-5in) s.i.verso ormolu frame. 24-Jun-4 Bonhams, New Bond Street #165/R est:600-800

LIENARD, Jean Baptiste (18/19th C) French

Works on paper
£2800 $5124 €4088 Picturesque landscape with a watermill and classical ruins (20x30cm-8x12in) indis sig.i.d.1777 brush brown ash black chk pair. 7-Jul-4 Bonhams, Knightsbridge #9/R est:2000-3000

LIENARD, Sophie (19th C) French

Miniatures
£10500 $18795 €15330 Marie Amelie, French Queen (13cm-5in) s. porcelain gilt bronze easel frame. 25-May-4 Christie's, London #46/R est:3000-5000

LIENDER, Jacobus van (1696-1759) Flemish

Works on paper
£576 $921 €800 Country landscape (24x35cm-9x14in) s. W/C pen blk ink. 16-May-3 Tajan, Paris #73

LIENDER, Paul van (1731-1797) Dutch

Works on paper
£400 $716 €600 River landscape with ruined bridge and castle (26x34cm-10x13in) bears sig. verso pen brush. 13-May-4 Bassenge, Berlin #5429/R
£959 $1630 €1400 Tree by the gateway to a castle. Extensive landscape beyond (13x19cm-5x7in) s.d.1776 black chk W/C pen ink framing lines two. 5-Nov-3 Christie's, Amsterdam #131/R est:600-800
£1351 $2378 €2000 Set design for De Nieuwe Tuin (19x35cm-7x14in) pen grey ink wash black chk exhib. 19-May-4 Sotheby's, Amsterdam #246/R est:3000-4000
£1781 $3027 €2600 Small town of Heemstede (20x42cm-8x17in) wash. 5-Nov-3 Vendue Huis, Gravenhage #25/R est:1000-1200

LIENDER, Pieter Jan van (1727-1779) Dutch

£2192 $3726 €3200 Wooded landscape with travellers, and wagon resting near a tavern (45x66cm-18x26in) s.d.1766 canvas on board prov. 4-Nov-3 Sotheby's, Amsterdam #100/R est:4000-6000

LIER, Adolf (1826-1882) German

£738 $1351 €1100 Forest path with shrine (23x19cm-9x7in) s. canvas on board lit. 8-Jul-4 Allgauer, Kempten #2154/R
£1477 $2717 €2200 Upper Bavarian landscape (24x35cm-9x14in) s. 25-Mar-4 Dr Fritz Nagel, Stuttgart #736/R est:1800
£1528 $2521 €2200 Air study (26x44cm-10x17in) prov.lit. 2-Jul-3 Neumeister, Munich #700/R est:2500
£2113 $3655 €3000 Landscape with herder and cattle (40x66cm-16x26in) 13-Dec-3 Lempertz, Koln #30/R est:2500
£2292 $3781 €3300 Summer landscape in the evening (13x26cm-5x10in) s. panel. 2-Jul-3 Neumeister, Munich #701/R est:1800
£13889 $22639 €20000 Moonlit Chiemsee (46x100cm-18x39in) s. 24-Sep-3 Neumeister, Munich #483/R est:7500
£23077 $39692 €33000 Wedding procession in Oberbayern (80x112cm-31x44in) s.d.1857 lit. 3-Dec-3 Neumeister, Munich #651/R est:30000

LIERNUR, Martinus Wilhelmus (1833-1901) Dutch

£362 $655 €550 Rider with a laden donkey near a house (22x28cm-9x11in) s.d.1874 panel. 19-Apr-4 Glerum, Amsterdam #70/R

LIES, Jozef H (1821-1865) Belgian

£1500 $2505 €2190 Blacksmith (47x38cm-19x15in) s. board. 12-Nov-3 Sotheby's, Olympia #152/R est:800-1200
£5594 $9343 €8000 The beloved (62x77cm-24x30in) s. panel. 11-Oct-3 De Vuyst, Lokeren #412/R est:7500-8500

LIESEGANG, Helmut (1858-1945) German

£475 $850 €694 Flower field (51x71cm-20x28in) s. panel on board prov. 21-Mar-4 Hindman, Chicago #788/R est:1500-3000
£604 $1111 €900 Flock of sheep in lower Rhine landscape (37x27cm-15x11in) s. 27-Mar-4 L & B, Essen #149/R
£972 $1536 €1400 By the stream (60x50cm-24x20in) s. lit. 19-Sep-3 Schloss Ahlden, Ahlden #1610/R
£1014 $1784 €1500 Winter on the lower Rhine (34x43cm-13x17in) s. 22-May-4 Lempertz, Koln #1553/R est:1500
£1049 $1783 €1500 Windmill by canal (41x51cm-16x20in) s. 20-Nov-3 Van Ham, Cologne #1717/R est:2200
£1329 $2259 €1900 Going home (33x43cm-13x17in) s. 20-Nov-3 Van Ham, Cologne #1718/R est:1500
£1389 $2292 €2000 Lower Rhine (17x26cm-7x10in) s. panel. 3-Jul-3 Van Ham, Cologne #1334/R est:2200
£1793 $3317 €2600 Canal with boats, figures windmill and small town (40x50cm-16x20in) s. 14-Feb-4 Hans Stahl, Hamburg #58/R est:2700
£2432 $4354 €3600 Dutch town (40x50cm-16x20in) s. 8-May-4 Dawo, Saarbrucken #47/R est:1200

LIESHOUT, Joep van (1963-) ?

Sculpture
£1677 $2800 €2448 Sink - bathroom furniture series (30x50x25cm-12x20x10in) painted polyester resin chrome plated plumbing fixture prov. 14-Nov-3 Phillips, New York #291/R est:3000-4000
£1748 $3007 €2500 Orgone helmet (75cm-30in) polyester helmet with hook executed 1996. 2-Dec-3 Sotheby's, Amsterdam #194/R est:1600-1800

LIESTE, Cornelis (1817-1861) Dutch

£1701 $3095 €2500 Sunset over heathland (70x95cm-28x37in) s. 3-Feb-4 Christie's, Amsterdam #121/R est:3500-5000
£10667 $19307 €16000 Heathland near Oosterbeek (70x95cm-28x37in) s. panel. 1-Apr-4 Van Ham, Cologne #1516/R est:4500

LIETZMANN, Hans (1872-?) German

Works on paper
£345 $576 €500 Fishermen mending nets on southern coast (50x64cm-20x25in) s.d.1925 mixed media. 9-Jul-3 Hugo Ruef, Munich #283

LIEVENS, Jan (1607-1674) Dutch

£524138 $870069 €760000 Portrait of young man (83x49cm-33x19in) panel prov. 1-Oct-3 Dorotheum, Vienna #85/R est:20000-30000
£1016484 $1850000 €1484067 Portrait of a boy in Persian dress (67x52cm-26x20in) panel prov.exhib.lit. 17-Jun-4 Christie's, Rockefeller NY #72/R est:1000000-1500000
£1650000 $3019500 €2409000 Tronie (58x47cm-23x19in) panel prov.exhib.lit. 7-Jul-4 Sotheby's, London #7/R est:200000-300000

Prints
£3007 $5112 €4300 Head of old man (8x7cm-3x3in) etching. 27-Nov-3 Bassenge, Berlin #5168/R est:1800

LIEVIN, Jacques (1850-?) French

£2210 $4000 €3227 Paris boulevard with snow (37x48cm-15x19in) s. board prov. 30-Mar-4 Christie's, Rockefeller NY #105/R est:4000-6000
£2550 $4718 €3800 Entree du village (41x40cm-16x16in) s. 14-Mar-4 Eric Pillon, Calais #90/R
£3867 $7000 €5646 Boulevard St. Germain (30x46cm-12x18in) s.i. 30-Mar-4 Christie's, Rockefeller NY #106/R est:3000-5000

Works on paper
£2000 $3660 €3000 Paris, les fortifications (18x30cm-7x12in) s. gouache. 6-Jun-4 Anaf, Lyon #420 est:3000-4000

LIEVRE, Peter le (attrib) (?) ?

Works on paper
£300 $543 €438 Character study sketches (38x51cm-15x20in) pencil. 1-Apr-4 Martel Maides, Guernsey #226

LIEZEN-MAYER, Alexander von (1839-1898) Austrian

£528 $945 €750 Portrait of a lady (63x53cm-25x21in) s. lit. 8-Jan-4 Allgauer, Kempten #2451/R

LIFAZ, Serge (20th C) ?

£671 $1248 €1000 Lys Blancs (72x59cm-28x23in) s.i.d.2002. 3-Mar-4 Tajan, Paris #262

LIFSHITZ, Uri (1936-) Israeli

£1176 $2000 €1717 Figures (89x116cm-35x46in) s. painted 1970's. 1-Dec-3 Ben-Ami, Tel Aviv #4330/R est:3000-4000

LIGARE, David (1945-) American

£1648 $3000 €2406 Delphi IV (82x122cm-32x48in) s.i.d.1972 verso acrylic prov. 29-Jun-4 Sotheby's, New York #487/R est:3000-5000

LIGARI, Pietro (1686-1752) Italian
Works on paper
£765 $1400 €1117 Bishop seated in a niche with a staff and bell (23x17cm-9x7in) pen brown ink wash gouache. 29-Jan-4 Swann Galleries, New York #104/R

LIGER-HIDALGO, T (20th C) Spanish
£1800 $3060 €2628 Moorish palace courtyard (45x33cm-18x13in) s.i. 18-Nov-3 Sotheby's, London #263/R est:2000-3000
£5000 $8500 €7300 Fountain in Moorish courtyard (91x68cm-36x27in) s.i. 18-Nov-3 Sotheby's, London #252/R est:5000-7000

LIGETI, Antal (1823-1890) Hungarian
£3425 $6200 €5001 Castle on the top of hill (56x70cm-22x28in) s. 16-Apr-4 Mu Terem Galeria, Budapest #49/R (H.F 1300000)
£23490 $40638 €34295 Sunset by the castle of Szigliget (80x118cm-31x46in) s.d.1885. 12-Dec-3 Kieselbach, Budapest #215/R (H.F 9000000)

LIGNIS, Pierre de (attrib) (?-1627) Flemish
£8000 $14400 €11680 Adoration of the Magi (66x51cm-26x20in) copper. 23-Apr-4 Christie's, Kensington #12/R est:5000-8000

LIGNON, Bernard (1928-) French
£315 $526 €450 Paris, place animee (60x73cm-24x29in) s. 29-Jun-3 Eric Pillon, Calais #218/R
£364 $681 €550 Clown a la cage (73x50cm-29x20in) s. 20-Jul-4 Gioffredo, Nice #15/R
£667 $1193 €1000 Nature morte aux fleurs et aux poires (72x49cm-28x19in) s. 16-May-4 Thierry & Lannon, Brest #345
£1350 $2200 €1971 La baranade de St Tropez (110x163cm-43x64in) s. prov. 25-Sep-3 Christie's, Rockefeller NY #530/R est:2000-3000

LIGON, Glenn (1960-) American
£1470 $2500 €2146 Invisible man no.3 (51x41cm-20x16in) oilstick on paper prov. 9-Nov-3 Bonhams & Butterfields, Los Angeles #4085/R est:3000-5000
£1618 $2750 €2362 Invisible man no.1 (51x41cm-20x16in) oilstick on paper prov. 9-Nov-3 Bonhams & Butterfields, Los Angeles #4084/R est:3000-5000
£1765 $3000 €2577 Invisible man no.4 (51x41cm-20x16in) oilstick on paper prov. 9-Nov-3 Bonhams & Butterfields, Los Angeles #4083/R est:3000-5000
£4790 $8000 €6993 Untitled, study for Stranger in the Village series (77x57cm-30x22in) s.d.1999 verso gesso acrylic coal dust glitter paper on canvas pr. 13-Nov-3 Sotheby's, New York #528/R est:8000-12000
£16467 $27500 €24042 Prologue series invisible man, small version (61x40cm-24x16in) s.i.d.1991 verso oilstick prov. 13-Nov-3 Sotheby's, New York #146/R est:14000-18000
£43413 $72500 €63383 Walt Whitman no 1 (203x73cm-80x29in) s.i.d.1991 verso oil wood prov. 13-Nov-3 Sotheby's, New York #462/R est:50000-70000

LIGORIO, Pirro (1513-1583) Italian
Works on paper
£10556 $19000 €15412 Two princes of the House of Guelph, Duke William VII and Duke Philip VI (22x11cm-9x4in) i. black chk pen brown ink wash two joined sheets. 22-Jan-4 Christie's, Rockefeller NY #3/R est:5000-7000

LIGOZZI, Bartolomeo (1630-1695) Italian
£26846 $50201 €40000 Still life of fruit with grapes and peaches and vase of flowers (40x51cm-16x20in) 25-Feb-4 Porro, Milan #81/R est:40000

LIGOZZI, Jacopo (attrib) (1547-1632) Italian
£9955 $16923 €14534 Christ in the entrance to hell (41x31cm-16x12in) gold panel prov. 19-Nov-3 Fischer, Luzern #1008/R est:3000-4000 (S.FR 22000)

LIIPOLA, Yrjo (1881-1971) Finnish
Sculpture
£1533 $2745 €2300 Woman and bird (42cm-17in) s.d.1925 bronze. 15-May-4 Hagelstam, Helsinki #14/R est:1800

LIJN, Liliane (1939-) American
Sculpture
£2200 $4004 €3212 Inner light (200cm-79in) marble exec 1996. 4-Feb-4 Sotheby's, Olympia #105c/R est:1000-1500

LIL, Joseph van (19th C) Dutch?
£643 $1150 €939 Boy with horn (51x61cm-20x24in) s.d.1872. 8-Jan-4 James Julia, Fairfield #983/R

LILANGA DI NYAMA, Georges (1944-) African
£700 $1288 €1050 Untitled (50cm-20in circular) s. acrylic masonite lit. 12-Jun-4 Meeting Art, Vercelli #485/R

LILIO, Andrea (1555-1610) Italian
Works on paper
£306 $548 €450 La Vierge a l'Enfant couronnee par des anges avec St Francois (24x17cm-9x7in) black chk brown wash prov. 18-Mar-4 Christie's, Paris #81
£680 $1218 €1000 Trois papes autour d'une globe entoures d'anges avec St Pierre (27x19cm-11x7in) red chk pen brown ink wash prov. 18-Mar-4 Christie's, Paris #76/R
£680 $1218 €1000 La Vierge sur un trone entouree d'apotres lui tenant un livre (28x21cm-11x8in) red chk prov. 18-Mar-4 Christie's, Paris #79/R
£816 $1461 €1200 St Antoine entoure de deux anges. Un sainte eveque sur un trone (23x17cm-9x7in) red chk pen brown ink wash pair prov. 18-Mar-4 Christie's, Paris #77/R
£1156 $2070 €1700 L'Assomption de la Vierge (27x20cm-11x8in) red chk pen brown ink grey wash prov. 18-Mar-4 Christie's, Paris #74/R est:2000-3000
£1633 $2922 €2400 St Jerome et St Francois (23x23cm-9x9in) black chk pen brown ink prov. 18-Mar-4 Christie's, Paris #72/R est:2500-3500
£1769 $3166 €2600 L'Adoration des Bergers (26x20cm-10x8in) red chk pen brown ink prov. 18-Mar-4 Christie's, Paris #75/R est:3000-5000
£2041 $3653 €3000 St Charles Borromee, St Jerome et St Francois dans un paysage (23x27cm-9x11in) black chk pen brown ink wash prov. 18-Mar-4 Christie's, Paris #71/R est:3000-5000
£3401 $6088 €5000 Saint Francois-de-Paule prenant une braise dans ses mains (26x18cm-10x7in) i. col chk pen brown ink col wash prov. 18-Mar-4 Christie's, Paris #6/R est:1000-1500

LILIO, Andrea (attrib) (1555-1610) Italian
Works on paper
£2303 $4237 €3500 Saint Anthony of Padua (29x15cm-11x6in) sanguine. 22-Jun-4 Sotheby's, Milan #27/R est:3500-4000

LILJEFORS, Bruno (1860-1939) Swedish
£673 $1083 €983 Gransnaar (32x42cm-13x17in) s. panel prov. 25-Aug-3 Lilla Bukowskis, Stockholm #449 (S.KR 8800)
£739 $1323 €1079 Cliffs by the sea (17x32cm-7x13in) init. panel. 26-May-4 AB Stockholms Auktionsverk #2306/R (S.KR 10000)
£923 $1588 €1348 Snipes (21x16cm-8x6in) init.d.84 cardboard. 2-Dec-3 Bukowskis, Stockholm #52/R (S.KR 12000)
£1057 $1945 €1586 Landscape with church (31x48cm-12x19in) s. i.verso painted c.1878-79. 14-Jun-4 Lilla Bukowskis, Stockholm #1033 est:10000 (S.KR 14500)
£1577 $2838 €2302 Swans in flight (12x24cm-5x9in) panel. 26-Jan-4 Lilla Bukowskis, Stockholm #550 est:10000-12000 (S.KR 21000)
£1682 $2708 €2456 Coastal landscape (24x36cm-9x14in) s. panel. 25-Aug-3 Lilla Bukowskis, Stockholm #119 est:20000-25000 (S.KR 22000)
£1846 $3175 €2695 Study in the air - swans in flight (23x28cm-9x11in) mono. panel. 7-Dec-3 Uppsala Auktionskammare, Uppsala #201/R est:20000-25000 (S.KR 24000)
£2308 $3969 €3370 Study of a fox (41x47cm-16x19in) 3-Dec-3 AB Stockholms Auktionsverk #2367/R est:30000-40000 (S.KR 30000)
£2385 $4102 €3482 Peregrine falcon having caught a duck (43x55cm-17x22in) mono. canvas on panel exhib. 7-Dec-3 Uppsala Auktionskammare, Uppsala #200/R est:30000-40000 (S.KR 31000)
£2915 $5364 €4373 Woodcock (45x64cm-18x25in) s.d.1904. 14-Jun-4 Lilla Bukowskis, Stockholm #919/R est:50000-60000 (S.KR 40000)
£3030 $5424 €4424 Woodland glade with grouse (29x149cm-11x59in) init. 26-May-4 AB Stockholms Auktionsverk #2353/R est:20000-25000 (S.KR 41000)
£3077 $5292 €4492 Autumn landscape with elk (60x80cm-24x31in) 3-Dec-3 AB Stockholms Auktionsverk #2321/R est:50000-60000 (S.KR 40000)
£5765 $10319 €8417 Winter landscape with hare by fence (35x50cm-14x20in) s. 25-May-4 Bukowskis, Stockholm #173/R est:60000-80000 (S.KR 78000)
£6538 $11246 €9545 Winter landscape with fox (56x55cm-22x22in) s.d.1917. 2-Dec-3 Bukowskis, Stockholm #47/R est:80000-100000 (S.KR 85000)
£7021 $12568 €10251 Winter landscape with fox (70x90cm-28x35in) s. 25-May-4 Bukowskis, Stockholm #229/R est:120000-140000 (S.KR 95000)
£7391 $13230 €10791 Ducks in flight at dusk (42x63cm-17x25in) init. 26-May-4 AB Stockholms Auktionsverk #2319/R est:60000-80000 (S.KR 100000)
£8077 $13892 €11792 Swans landing (35x50cm-14x20in) s. 2-Dec-3 Bukowskis, Stockholm #137/R est:80000-100000 (S.KR 105000)
£8130 $14553 €11870 Dogs by fence (75x145cm-30x57in) s.d.1904. 25-May-4 Bukowskis, Stockholm #178/R est:100000-125000 (S.KR 110000)
£8462 $14554 €12355 Winter landscape with hare (32x42cm-13x17in) s.i.d.1923 panel. 3-Dec-3 AB Stockholms Auktionsverk #2264/R est:80000-100000 (S.KR 110000)
£8846 $15215 €12915 Winter landscape with hare (35x51cm-14x20in) s. prov. 2-Dec-3 Bukowskis, Stockholm #51/R est:80000-100000 (S.KR 115000)
£9231 $15877 €13477 Winter landscape with fox and magpies (35x50cm-14x20in) s. 3-Dec-3 AB Stockholms Auktionsverk #2265/R est:100000-125000 (S.KR 120000)
£9239 $16537 €13489 Winter landscape with fox (70x100cm-28x39in) s.d.1922. 26-May-4 AB Stockholms Auktionsverk #2180/R est:125000-150000 (S.KR 125000)
£9615 $16538 €14038 Still life of flowers in vase (46x37cm-18x15in) s.i.d.1879. 3-Dec-3 AB Stockholms Auktionsverk #2523/R est:125000-150000 (S.KR 125000)
£9978 $17860 €14568 Wild geese in winter landscape (52x75cm-20x30in) s.d.1930. 25-May-4 Bukowskis, Stockholm #230/R est:150000-175000 (S.KR 135000)
£10200 $18257 €14892 Duck and ducklings at water's edge (60x80cm-24x31in) s.d.1917. 28-May-4 Uppsala Auktionskammare, Uppsala #240/R est:120000-150000 (S.KR 138000)
£10385 $17862 €15162 Pair of foxes on cliff at dusk (15x22cm-6x9in) s.d.89 panel. 2-Dec-3 Bukowskis, Stockholm #46a/R est:100000-125000 (S.KR 135000)
£10769 $18523 €15723 Winter landscape with fox being hunted by dogs (80x100cm-31x39in) s.d.1917. 7-Dec-3 Uppsala Auktionskammare, Uppsala #199/R est:120000-150000 (S.KR 140000)
£11538 $19846 €16845 Winter landscape with hare in snow (60x85cm-24x33in) s.d.1930. 2-Dec-3 Bukowskis, Stockholm #135/R est:120000-140000 (S.KR 150000)
£11826 $21168 €17266 Hare among tufts of grass in winter (75x100cm-30x39in) s.d.1906. 25-May-4 Bukowskis, Stockholm #34/R est:200000-225000 (S.KR 160000)
£13304 $23814 €19424 Fox and duck in flight (115x163cm-45x64in) s.d.1914. 25-May-4 Bukowskis, Stockholm #182/R est:175000-200000 (S.KR 180000)
£18000 $32760 €26280 Fox in a winter landscape (52x75cm-20x30in) s.d.1930 prov.exhib. 17-Jun-4 Christie's, London #47/R est:20000-30000
£18077 $31092 €26392 Winter landscape with black grouse in bushes (70x100cm-28x39in) s.d.1910. 3-Dec-3 AB Stockholms Auktionsverk #2286/R est:175000-200000 (S.KR 235000)
£18477 $33075 €26976 Marshy landscape with geese (70x100cm-28x39in) s.d.1917. 26-May-4 AB Stockholms Auktionsverk #2290/R est:250000-300000 (S.KR 250000)
£18846 $32415 €27515 Crows (19x24cm-7x9in) s.d.82 cardboard. 2-Dec-3 Bukowskis, Stockholm #142/R est:275000-300000 (S.KR 245000)
£20000 $34400 €29200 Black-cock's crooning (105x160cm-41x63in) s.d.1928. 3-Dec-3 AB Stockholms Auktionsverk #2425/R est:300000-400000 (S.KR 260000)
£20385 $35062 €29762 Winter landscape with wild geese (64x105cm-25x41in) s.d.1927. 2-Dec-3 Bukowskis, Stockholm #55/R est:150000-175000 (S.KR 265000)
£24390 $43659 €35609 Sparrows in the snow (24x33cm-9x13in) s.d.91 panel exhib. 26-May-4 AB Stockholms Auktionsverk #2150/R est:275000-300000 (S.KR 330000)
£26154 $44985 €38185 Great tit and two sparrows in winter (44x29cm-17x11in) s.d.1881. 2-Dec-3 Bukowskis, Stockholm #46/R est:300000-400000 (S.KR 340000)
£26977 $48289 €39386 Capercaillies displaying (100x130cm-39x51in) s.d.1908. 25-May-4 Bukowskis, Stockholm #177/R est:300000-350000 (S.KR 365000)
£29564 $52919 €43163 Golden eagle and hare (109x164cm-43x65in) s.d.1924. 25-May-4 Bukowskis, Stockholm #30/R est:275000-300000 (S.KR 400000)
£33784 $60473 €50000 Wild geese resting (62x86cm-24x34in) s.d.1929. 8-May-4 Bukowskis, Helsinki #389/R est:22000-25000

£49231 $84677 €71877 Hunds on foxhunt (75x107cm-30x42in) s.d.94. 2-Dec-3 Bukowskis, Stockholm #184/R est:600000-800000 (S.KR 640000)
£153363 $274520 €223910 Cat sneaking (47x96cm-19x38in) s.d.92. 25-May-4 Bukowskis, Stockholm #107/R est:1500000-1800000 (S.KR 2075000)
£326923 $562308 €477308 The cat called Jeppe basking in the sun (75x62cm-30x24in) s.d.84 exhib.prov. 2-Dec-3 Bukowskis, Stockholm #134/R (S.KR 4250000)
Sculpture
£1183 $2117 €1727 Athlete (10cm-4in) s.d.1900 silver Cast H Bergman. 25-May-4 Bukowskis, Stockholm #290/R est:15000-20000 (S.KR 16000)
Works on paper
£407 $728 €594 Geese at water's edge (10x16cm-4x6in) Indian ink pencil prov. 28-May-4 Uppsala Auktionskammare, Uppsala #249 (S.KR 5500)
£437 $805 €656 The artist John Kindborg in his studio (31x20cm-12x8in) s.i. Indian ink. 14-Jun-4 Lilla Bukowskis, Stockholm #688 (S.KR 6000)
£3991 $7144 €5827 Winter with bullfinches in bushes (14x12cm-6x5in) i.verso W/C. 26-May-4 AB Stockholms Auktionsverk #2149/R est:20000-25000 (S.KR 54000)
£5913 $10584 €8633 Birds on branch (30x23cm-12x9in) s. W/C. 25-May-4 Bukowskis, Stockholm #31/R est:100000-125000 (S.KR 80000)

LILJEFORS, Lindorm (1909-1985) Swedish
£430 $701 €628 Winter landscape with deer (33x41cm-13x16in) s.d.56 panel. 29-Sep-3 Lilla Bukowskis, Stockholm #576 (S.KR 5600)
£462 $794 €675 Winter landscape with fox running (54x64cm-21x25in) s. panel. 3-Dec-3 AB Stockholms Auktionsverk #2319/R (S.KR 6000)
£571 $1027 €834 Fox on snowy country road (45x54cm-18x21in) s/d/51 panel. 26-Jan-4 Lilla Bukowskis, Stockholm #703 (S.KR 7600)
£577 $992 €842 Winter landscape with fox at dusk (38x46cm-15x18in) s.d.64 panel. 3-Dec-3 AB Stockholms Auktionsverk #2365/R (S.KR 7500)
£591 $1058 €863 Elks in landscape (41x56cm-16x22in) s.d.71 panel. 28-May-4 Uppsala Auktionskammare, Uppsala #253/R (S.KR 8000)
£596 $960 €870 Winter landscape with fox (31x45cm-12x18in) s.d.56 panel. 25-Aug-3 Lilla Bukowskis, Stockholm #156 (S.KR 7800)
£598 $1100 €897 Landscape with hunters and dog (44x65cm-17x26in) s.d.67. 14-Jun-4 Lilla Bukowskis, Stockholm #220 (S.KR 8200)
£615 $1058 €898 Woodland glade with black grouse (55x46cm-22x18in) s.d.61 panel. 3-Dec-3 AB Stockholms Auktionsverk #2368/R (S.KR 8000)
£654 $1125 €955 Spring landscape with ducks in flight (41x56cm-16x22in) s.d.64 panel. 3-Dec-3 AB Stockholms Auktionsverk #2380/R (S.KR 8500)
£702 $1257 €1025 Ducks in early spring landscape (47x55cm-19x22in) s.d.53. 28-May-4 Uppsala Auktionskammare, Uppsala #245/R (S.KR 9500)
£813 $1455 €1187 Wood-pigeons (66x89cm-26x35in) s.d.75. 28-May-4 Uppsala Auktionskammare, Uppsala #252/R (S.KR 11000)
£846 $1455 €1235 Crows on frozen water (40x63cm-16x25in) s.d.65 panel. 7-Dec-3 Uppsala Auktionskammare, Uppsala #211/R (S.KR 11000)
£1035 $1852 €1511 Wooded landscape with deer (60x73cm-24x29in) s.d.45 panel. 28-May-4 Uppsala Auktionskammare, Uppsala #243/R est:10000-12000 (S.KR 14000)
£1183 $2117 €1727 Autumn landscape with waxwings (63x73cm-25x29in) s.d.46 panel. 28-May-4 Uppsala Auktionskammare, Uppsala #244/R est:10000-12000 (S.KR 16000)
£1257 $2174 €1835 Cranes landing (60x93cm-24x37in) s.d.69. 15-Dec-3 Lilla Bukowskis, Stockholm #18 est:20000-25000 (S.KR 16000)
£1848 $3307 €2698 Winter landscape with fox (70x100cm-28x39in) s.d.47. 28-May-4 Uppsala Auktionskammare, Uppsala #251/R est:15000-18000 (S.KR 25000)
£2000 $3440 €2920 Horses grazing (45x54cm-18x21in) s.d.39 panel. 7-Dec-3 Uppsala Auktionskammare, Uppsala #210/R est:8000-10000 (S.KR 26000)
£4582 $8203 €6690 Autumn landscape with elks and elkhound (100x150cm-39x59in) s.d.40. 28-May-4 Uppsala Auktionskammare, Uppsala #242/R est:50000-60000 (S.KR 62000)
£5499 $9513 €8029 Winter landscape with fox and crows (35x50cm-14x20in) s.d.1939 exhib. 15-Dec-3 Lilla Bukowskis, Stockholm #363 est:80000-100000 (S.KR 70000)
Works on paper
£462 $794 €675 Winter landscape birds in flight (38x49cm-15x19in) s.d.55 panel. 7-Dec-3 Uppsala Auktionskammare, Uppsala #209 (S.KR 6000)

LILJELUND, Arvid (1844-1899) Finnish
£3776 $6420 €5400 Girl from Loko (29x22cm-11x9in) s. exhib. 29-Nov-3 Bukowskis, Helsinki #153/R est:2500-3000
£22000 $39380 €33000 A tangled muddle (85x69cm-33x27in) s. painted c.1882 exhib.lit. 15-May-4 Hagelstam, Helsinki #103/R est:35000
£34965 $59441 €50000 Visiting Grandma and Grandad (74x94cm-29x37in) s.d.1876 exhib.lit. 29-Nov-3 Bukowskis, Helsinki #103/R est:50000-60000

LILJESTROM, Gustave (1882-1958) American
£1455 $2750 €2124 Seascape (51x76cm-20x30in) s. prov. 17-Feb-4 John Moran, Pasadena #96/R est:2000-3000

LILLIE, John (1867-?) American
£222 $400 €324 Landscape with approaching storm (51x76cm-20x30in) s. 23-Apr-4 Weschler, Washington #112/R

LILLIENDAHL, Alfred Harry (1909-) Danish
Works on paper
£271 $506 €396 Botany (33x24cm-13x9in) s.d.48 crayon. 25-Feb-4 Kunsthallen, Copenhagen #46 (D.KR 3000)

LILLIS, Richard (20th C) American
£1564 $2800 €2283 Gunfight on western street (66x46cm-26x18in) painted c.1930. 15-May-4 Illustration House, New York #33/R est:3000-4000

LILLONI, Umberto (1898-1980) Italian
£1884 $3090 €2600 Untitled (64x89cm-25x35in) s.i.d.53 verso oil mixed media board. 27-May-3 Sotheby's, Milan #105 est:800-1000
£2042 $3390 €2900 Arianna (25x35cm-10x14in) s. 11-Jun-3 Finarte Semenzato, Milan #648/R
£2432 $4281 €3600 Madonna of Burano (42x30cm-17x12in) s. 22-May-4 Galleria Pananti, Florence #444/R est:3800-4200
£2958 $5176 €4200 Cinquale (21x31cm-8x12in) s. s.i.verso board. 17-Dec-3 Il Ponte, Milan #1106/R est:2500-3000
£3691 $6607 €5500 Path in the green (30x40cm-12x16in) s. painted 1967 prov. 25-May-4 Sotheby's, Milan #47/R est:6000
£3873 $6430 €5500 Lake landscape (30x40cm-12x16in) s. s.i.d.verso. 11-Jun-3 Finarte Semenzato, Milan #535/R
£4000 $7360 €6000 Beeches on the Generoso (30x40cm-12x16in) s. s.i.d.1969 verso lit. 12-Jun-4 Meeting Art, Vercelli #276/R est:5000
£4072 $6923 €5945 L'uomo rustico (103x82cm-41x32in) s.d. s.i.d.1927 verso exhib. 25-Nov-3 Germann, Zurich #131/R est:10000-12000 (S.FR 9000)
£4295 $7989 €6400 River bending (40x50cm-16x20in) s. painted 1977. 4-Mar-4 Babuino, Rome #144 est:1500-2000
£4483 $7486 €6500 Landscape in Brianza (30x40cm-12x16in) s. painted 1963. 13-Nov-3 Galleria Pace, Milan #77/R est:9500
£4861 $7681 €7000 Mountains near Bergamo (27x35cm-11x14in) painted 1966. 6-Sep-3 Meeting Art, Vercelli #492 est:7000
£4895 $8322 €7000 Wood in Bardonecchia (38x50cm-15x20in) s. s.i.d.1960 verso lit. 20-Nov-3 Finarte Semenzato, Milan #199/R est:6000-7000
£5369 $9611 €8000 Spring (40x50cm-16x20in) s. s.i.d.1969 verso. 29-May-4 Farsetti, Prato #553/R est:5000-6000
£5435 $8913 €7500 Path to Gondrio (50x65cm-20x26in) s. painted 1945. 29-May-3 Galleria Pace, Milan #107/R est:10000
£5556 $9444 €8000 Boats (50x80cm-20x31in) s.i.d.1953 prov. 28-Oct-3 Il Ponte, Milan #274/R
£5594 $9510 €8000 Wood (40x50cm-16x20in) s. s.i.d.1963 verso lit. 20-Nov-3 Finarte Semenzato, Milan #197/R est:6000-7000
£5594 $9510 €8000 Dry flowers (41x52cm-16x20in) s. s.i.d.1944 verso prov.lit. 20-Nov-3 Finarte Semenzato, Milan #198/R est:7000-8000
£6597 $11215 €9500 Wood (50x65cm-20x26in) s. prov. 28-Oct-3 Il Ponte, Milan #272/R
£7241 $12093 €10500 Landscape in Lombardy (50x73cm-20x29in) s. s.i.d.1965 verso lit. 17-Nov-3 Sant Agostino, Torino #266/R est:7000-9000
£7246 $11884 €10000 Garafani e margherite (75x55cm-30x22in) s.d.55 lit. 31-May-3 Farsetti, Prato #751/R est:5000-6000
£7246 $11884 €10000 Landscape with vineyards (50x65cm-20x26in) s. painted 1946 prov. 27-May-3 Sotheby's, Milan #82/R est:5000-6000
£7383 $13215 €11000 Cliffs in Levanto (35x45cm-14x18in) s.d.1948 s.i.d.verso lit. 30-May-4 Meeting Art, Vercelli #91 est:10000
£7483 $13395 €11000 Carnations in crystal vase (70x60cm-28x24in) s.d.58 lit. 16-Mar-4 Finarte Semenzato, Milan #451/R est:10000
£7639 $12986 €11000 Landscape (50x72cm-20x28in) s.d.1953 prov. 28-Oct-3 Il Ponte, Milan #275/R
£7692 $13077 €11000 Dams at stream (75x90cm-30x35in) s. 24-Nov-3 Christie's, Milan #255/R est:12000-16000
£7718 $14279 €11500 Varigotti (50x80cm-20x31in) s.i.d.1953. 13-Mar-4 Meeting Art, Vercelli #279 est:10000
£8276 $13241 €12000 Railway crossing (50x65cm-20x26in) s. painted 1936. 13-Mar-3 Galleria Pace, Milan #128/R est:14000-18000
Works on paper
£933 $1717 €1400 My trees (55x42cm-22x17in) s. pencil. 10-Jun-4 Galleria Pace, Milan #31/R est:2200
£2013 $3725 €3000 Flowers in Chinese vase (63x48cm-25x19in) s. pastel. 11-Mar-4 Galleria Pace, Milan #117/R est:4000-5000

LILLY, James (18/19th C) American?
Works on paper
£222 $400 €324 Penmanship drawing (18x30cm-7x12in) 20-Apr-4 Bunch, West Chester #253/R

LILLY, Ken (?) British
Works on paper
£300 $474 €438 Moorhen chicks (40x58cm-16x23in) s. W/C. 5-Sep-3 Honiton Galleries, Honiton #24/R

LIM WA SIM (1929-) Javanese
£1720 $2753 €2511 Still life (80x60cm-31x24in) s. s.d.1989 verso. 18-May-3 Sotheby's, Singapore #157/R est:4000-6000 (S.D 4800)

LIM, H H (1954-) ?
£1538 $2615 €2200 Interior at night (94x42cm-37x17in) s.i.d.1999 verso resin on board. 24-Nov-3 Christie's, Milan #87/R est:2000-3000
Works on paper
£1000 $1800 €1500 Today (46x56cm-18x22in) s.i.d.2001 verso mixed media board. 22-Apr-4 Finarte Semenzato, Rome #312/R est:1500-1800

LIMA, Fausto de (1926-) Spanish
£278 $458 €400 Hooded (54x38cm-21x15in) s. 2-Jul-3 Ansorena, Madrid #984/R
£292 $481 €420 Travelling clowns (54x38cm-21x15in) s. 2-Jul-3 Ansorena, Madrid #983/R

LIMA, Manolo (1919-1990) Uruguayan
£251 $420 €366 Urban landscape (60x45cm-24x18in) s.d.74 s.i.d.verso. 7-Oct-3 Galeria y Remates, Montevideo #85

LIMAN, V (20th C) ?
£1600 $2960 €2336 Good old tune (64x92cm-25x36in) s. 15-Jan-4 Christie's, Kensington #805/R est:800-1200

LIMBRICK, Frank (20th C) British?
£250 $393 €363 Roses, acorns, fruits and vase of summer flowers on a plinth (76x63cm-30x25in) s.verso exhib. 28-Aug-3 Christie's, Kensington #274

LIMMER, Emil (1854-?) German
Works on paper
£333 $600 €500 Naples with view of Ischia. s.i.d.1904 W/C. 26-Apr-4 Rieber, Stuttgart #1309/R

LIMOSIN, Leonard (c.1505-c.1575) French

£17450 $32457 €26000 La mort du Christ entoure des deux larrons et de multiples personnages (27x20cm-11x8in) s. enamel copper painted c.1560-1565. 5-Mar-4 Tajan, Paris #236/R est:10000-15000

LIMOUSE, Roger (1894-1990) French

£483 $894 €720 Femme assis dans un interieur (55x46cm-22x18in) s.d.33. 15-Mar-4 Blanchet, Paris #79
£748 $1190 €1100 Livre (50x62cm-20x24in) s. s.i.verso. 23-Mar-3 St-Germain-en-Laye Encheres #70/R
£805 $1482 €1200 Nature morte a cruche rouge (58x48cm-23x19in) s. cardboard double-sided. 28-Mar-4 MonsAntic, Maisieres #410
£1534 $2760 €2300 Pichet de fleurs et assiette de fruits (62x46cm-24x18in) s. 26-Apr-4 Tajan, Paris #161/R est:600-900
£1921 $3591 €2900 Mayotte (47x55cm-19x22in) s. oil paper laid down. 20-Jul-4 Gioffredo, Nice #33
£2133 $3904 €3200 Le gueridon rose (55x46cm-22x18in) s. 6-Jun-4 Anaf, Lyon #421/R est:3000-3500
£2303 $4237 €3500 Nature morte (60x73cm-24x29in) s. 22-Jun-4 Ribeyre & Baron, Paris #63/R est:1000-1200
£2482 $4145 €3500 Cabaret marocain (33x41cm-13x16in) s. cardboard. 16-Jun-3 Gros & Delettrez, Paris #37/R est:2500-3000
£2533 $4661 €3800 Jeune femme dans un interieur. Vue de Venise (73x54cm-29x21in) s.d.39 double-sided. 14-Jun-4 Gros & Delettrez, Paris #401/R est:4000-6000
£5298 $9695 €8000 Scene de marche Marocin (4x123cm-2x48in) s. paper on canvas. 7-Apr-4 Piasa, Paris #154/R est:8000-10000

LIMPERT, Heinrich (1858-1938) German

£467 $854 €700 Cows in the storm (32x44cm-13x17in) s. canvas on canvas. 5-Jun-4 Arnold, Frankfurt #652
£2400 $4392 €3600 Beach at Capri (55x127cm-22x50in) s. lit. 5-Jun-4 Arnold, Frankfurt #651/R est:1600

LIN FENGMIAN (1900-1991) Chinese

£142248 $256046 €207682 Farewell my concubine (58x46cm-23x18in) s. canvas on board painted c.1959-1960. 25-Apr-4 Christie's, Hong Kong #704/R est:1000000-1500000 (HK.D 2000000)
£199147 $358464 €290755 Madame snake white (58x46cm-23x18in) s. canvas on board painted c.1959-1960. 25-Apr-4 Christie's, Hong Kong #705/R est:1000000-1500000 (HK.D 2800000)

Works on paper

£1158 $1934 €1691 Sailing boat (22x23cm-9x9in) s. ink col scroll. 26-Oct-3 Christie's, Hong Kong #241/R est:18000-22000 (HK.D 15000)
£2013 $3725 €3000 Grues et arbre (45x44cm-18x17in) 12-Mar-4 Piasa, Paris #309/R est:1200-1500
£2317 $3869 €3383 Village (32x32cm-13x13in) s. ink col scroll. 26-Oct-3 Christie's, Hong Kong #242/R est:35000-45000 (HK.D 30000)
£2317 $3869 €3383 Old man admiring bamboo (32x33cm-13x13in) s. ink col scroll. 26-Oct-3 Christie's, Hong Kong #310/R est:22000-28000 (HK.D 30000)
£2703 $4514 €3946 Pavilion (38x47cm-15x19in) s. ink col scroll. 26-Oct-3 Christie's, Hong Kong #243/R est:40000-50000 (HK.D 35000)
£2703 $4514 €3946 Opera figure (34x22cm-13x9in) s. ink col scroll. 26-Oct-3 Christie's, Hong Kong #309/R est:30000-45000 (HK.D 35000)
£3861 $6448 €5637 Lady (45x32cm-18x13in) artist seal ink col scroll. 26-Oct-3 Christie's, Hong Kong #341/R est:40000-60000 (HK.D 50000)
£3861 $6448 €5637 Bird (39x28cm-15x11in) s. ink col scroll. 26-Oct-3 Christie's, Hong Kong #346/R est:30000-50000 (HK.D 50000)
£4362 $7809 €6500 Landscape (65x65cm-26x26in) s. W/C. 27-May-4 Beaussant & Lefèvre, Paris #280/R est:6000-7000
£5019 $8382 €7328 Lady in a garden (50x41cm-20x16in) s. ink col scroll. 26-Oct-3 Christie's, Hong Kong #342/R est:50000-70000 (HK.D 65000)
£5690 $10242 €8307 Fisherman (34x34cm-13x13in) s. ink col. 26-Apr-4 Sotheby's, Hong Kong #540/R est:80000-100000 (HK.D 80000)
£5690 $10242 €8307 Two ladies (33x22cm-13x9in) s. ink col two. 26-Apr-4 Sotheby's, Hong Kong #542/R est:50000-70000 (HK.D 80000)
£5792 $9672 €8456 Opera figure (38x41cm-15x16in) s. ink col scroll. 26-Oct-3 Christie's, Hong Kong #343/R est:40000-60000 (HK.D 75000)
£5792 $9672 €8456 Portrait of a lady (32x33cm-13x13in) s. ink col. 27-Oct-3 Sotheby's, Hong Kong #357/R est:50000-70000 (HK.D 75000)
£6711 $12013 €10000 Untitled (61x74cm-24x29in) s. W/C. 27-May-4 Beaussant & Lefèvre, Paris #281/R est:6000-7000
£6950 $11606 €10147 Houses in the wood (55x66cm-22x26in) s. ink col scroll. 26-Oct-3 Christie's, Hong Kong #240/R est:100000-120000 (HK.D 90000)
£8054 $14416 €12000 Landscape (64x64cm-25x25in) s. W/C. 27-May-4 Beaussant & Lefèvre, Paris #279/R est:6000-7000
£8494 $14185 €12401 Lady playing guitar (70x65cm-28x26in) s. ink col scroll. 26-Oct-3 Christie's, Hong Kong #344/R est:100000-150000 (HK.D 110000)
£8535 $15363 €12461 Landscapes, cranes (22x26cm-9x10in) s. ink col scroll set of three prov. 25-Apr-4 Christie's, Hong Kong #45/R est:20000-40000 (HK.D 120000)
£8535 $15363 €12461 Birds amidst willow (69x44cm-27x17in) s. ink col. 26-Apr-4 Sotheby's, Hong Kong #543/R est:120000-150000 (HK.D 120000)
£9266 $15475 €13528 Autumn (64x65cm-25x26in) s. ink col scroll. 26-Oct-3 Christie's, Hong Kong #313/R est:150000-200000 (HK.D 120000)
£12091 $21764 €17653 Egrets (41x81cm-16x32in) s.d.1932 ink col scroll silk. 25-Apr-4 Christie's, Hong Kong #132/R est:200000-250000 (HK.D 170000)
£12091 $21764 €17653 Resting egret (97x43cm-38x17in) s. ink col prov. 26-Apr-4 Sotheby's, Hong Kong #545/R est:55000-70000 (HK.D 170000)
£12355 $20633 €18038 Opera figures (63x64cm-25x25in) s. ink col scroll. 26-Oct-3 Christie's, Hong Kong #246/R est:180000-220000 (HK.D 160000)
£12355 $20633 €18038 Ladies in opera costumes (34x33cm-13x13in) s. ink col scrolls set of four. 26-Oct-3 Christie's, Hong Kong #308/R est:100000-120000 (HK.D 160000)
£12355 $20633 €18038 Reeds (65x66cm-26x26in) s. ink col scroll. 26-Oct-3 Christie's, Hong Kong #311/R est:60000-80000 (HK.D 160000)
£12355 $20633 €18038 Lady (70x67cm-28x26in) s. ink col scroll. 26-Oct-3 Christie's, Hong Kong #345/R est:100000-150000 (HK.D 160000)
£12802 $23044 €18691 Ladies (33x22cm-13x9in) s. ink col scroll set of three prov. 25-Apr-4 Christie's, Hong Kong #43/R est:40000-60000 (HK.D 180000)
£12802 $23044 €18691 Egrets and reed (34x34cm-13x13in) s. ink col scroll lit. 25-Apr-4 Christie's, Hong Kong #136/R est:70000-90000 (HK.D 180000)
£13900 $23212 €20294 Clouds amongst hills (66x66cm-26x26in) s. ink col scroll. 26-Oct-3 Christie's, Hong Kong #244/R est:200000-250000 (HK.D 180000)
£13900 $23212 €20294 Houses amongst trees (66x67cm-26x26in) s. ink col scroll. 26-Oct-3 Christie's, Hong Kong #314/R est:150000-200000 (HK.D 180000)
£13900 $23212 €20294 Wisteria (53x46cm-21x18in) s. ink col exhib. 27-Oct-3 Sotheby's, Hong Kong #358/R est:120000-150000 (HK.D 180000)
£14225 $25605 €20769 Leisure pastime (33x22cm-13x9in) s. ink col two. 26-Apr-4 Sotheby's, Hong Kong #539/R est:50000-70000 (HK.D 200000)
£15444 $25792 €22548 Ladies (33x33cm-13x13in) s. ink col scrolls set of five. 26-Oct-3 Christie's, Hong Kong #312/R est:100000-120000 (HK.D 200000)
£15647 $28165 €22845 Egret (97x43cm-38x17in) s. ink col prov. 26-Apr-4 Sotheby's, Hong Kong #546/R est:60000-80000 (HK.D 220000)
£17070 $30725 €24922 Landscape, figures (43x40cm-17x16in) s. ink col scroll set of three prov. 25-Apr-4 Christie's, Hong Kong #139/R est:100000-120000 (HK.D 240000)
£19915 $35846 €29076 Still life (35x35cm-14x14in) s. ink col scroll lit. 25-Apr-4 Christie's, Hong Kong #134/R est:150000-200000 (HK.D 280000)
£19915 $35846 €29076 Autumn forest (68x66cm-27x26in) s. ink col scroll. 25-Apr-4 Christie's, Hong Kong #135/R est:300000-350000 (HK.D 280000)
£20077 $33529 €29312 Swordsmen (50x41cm-20x16in) s. ink col. 27-Oct-3 Sotheby's, Hong Kong #354/R est:120000-180000 (HK.D 260000)
£21337 $38407 €31152 Ladies (33x22cm-13x9in) s. ink col scroll set of four prov. 25-Apr-4 Christie's, Hong Kong #138/R est:80000-100000 (HK.D 300000)
£21622 $36108 €31568 Seascape (66x66cm-26x26in) s. ink col hanging scroll title slip. 27-Oct-3 Sotheby's, Hong Kong #294/R est:280000-350000 (HK.D 280000)
£24893 $44808 €36344 Figures (33x34cm-13x13in) s. ink col scroll pair prov. 25-Apr-4 Christie's, Hong Kong #46/R est:40000-60000 (HK.D 350000)
£25605 $46088 €37383 Ladies, landscape (31x33cm-12x13in) s. ink col scroll set of three prov. 25-Apr-4 Christie's, Hong Kong #44/R est:60000-80000 (HK.D 360000)
£27799 $46425 €40587 Flowers (67x69cm-26x27in) s. ink col. 27-Oct-3 Sotheby's, Hong Kong #360/R est:150000-200000 (HK.D 360000)
£31294 $56330 €45689 Landscapes (29x28cm-11x11in) s. ink col scroll set of four prov. 25-Apr-4 Christie's, Hong Kong #137/R est:100000-120000 (HK.D 440000)
£39118 $70413 €57112 Chrysanthemum (69x66cm-27x26in) s. ink col scroll. 25-Apr-4 Christie's, Hong Kong #47/R est:200000-250000 (HK.D 550000)
£39118 $70413 €57112 Houses in the forest (68x69cm-27x27in) s. ink col scroll. 25-Apr-4 Christie's, Hong Kong #48/R est:200000-250000 (HK.D 550000)
£44097 $79374 €64382 Dahlias (69x69cm-27x27in) s.d.1977 ink col scroll. 25-Apr-4 Christie's, Hong Kong #133/R est:250000-280000 (HK.D 620000)
£46332 $77375 €67645 Autumn (68x65cm-27x26in) s. ink col hanging scroll title slip. 27-Oct-3 Sotheby's, Hong Kong #293/R est:350000-500000 (HK.D 600000)
£46332 $77375 €67645 Lotus pond (66x67cm-26x26in) s. ink col. 27-Oct-3 Sotheby's, Hong Kong #361/R est:180000-250000 (HK.D 600000)
£56899 $102418 €83073 Crucifixion (49x40cm-19x16in) s. i.verso ink col prov.exhib.lit. 26-Apr-4 Sotheby's, Hong Kong #544/R est:120000-150000 (HK.D 800000)
£99573 $179232 €145377 Maple wood (68x67cm-27x26in) s. ink col prov.exhib.lit. 26-Apr-4 Sotheby's, Hong Kong #541/R est:350000-450000 (HK.D 1400000)
£156472 $281650 €228449 Dressing up (67x66cm-26x26in) s. ink col prov.exhib.lit. 26-Apr-4 Sotheby's, Hong Kong #547/R est:280000-350000 (HK.D 2200000)

LIN HUKUI (1945-) Chinese

Works on paper

£4247 $7093 €6201 Lotus (70x100cm-28x39in) s.i.d.2002 ink col goldboard. 26-Oct-3 Christie's, Hong Kong #269/R est:60000-80000 (HK.D 55000)
£4267 $7681 €6230 Two monkeys (124x63cm-49x25in) s. ink col scroll. 25-Apr-4 Christie's, Hong Kong #26/R est:60000-80000 (HK.D 60000)

LIN XIMING (1926-) Chinese

Works on paper

£507 $892 €750 River landscape with sailing ships (61x68cm-24x27in) s. seal Indian ink col hanging scroll. 21-May-4 Dr Fritz Nagel, Stuttgart #1108/R

LIN, Maya (1959-) American

Sculpture

£2703 $5000 €3946 Twitch (115x10x9cm-45x4x4in) lead beeswax exec 1990 prov.exhib. 12-Feb-4 Sotheby's, New York #244/R est:1800-2200
£7263 $13000 €10604 Nervous (8x140x7cm-3x55x3in) aluminium broken green glass assemblage exec 1988 exhib. 13-May-4 Sotheby's, New York #347/R est:6000-8000

LIN, Richard (1933-) British

£1923 $3500 €2808 Painting 1964-66 (64x76cm-25x30in) prov. 29-Jun-4 Sotheby's, New York #434/R est:3000-5000
£2793 $5000 €4078 Painting relief (127x91cm-50x36in) s.i.d.1962 verso oil perspex prov.exhib. 16-May-4 Wright, Chicago #269/R est:5000-7000
£3667 $6563 €5500 Painting relief (127x127cm-50x50in) s.d.1961 verso oil metal diptych. 15-May-4 De Vuyst, Lokeren #489/R est:4000-5500
£3691 $6829 €5500 Painting relief (127x101cm-50x40in) s.d.1961 verso oil mixed media on canvas. 13-Mar-4 De Vuyst, Lokeren #567/R est:3000-5000
£5588 $9500 €8158 Painting relief (127x102cm-50x40in) s.i.d.1962 verso acrylic canvas plexiglass aluminum. 9-Nov-3 Wright, Chicago #384 est:500-700

Sculpture

£3179 $5500 €4641 Painting relief (91x102cm-36x40in) aluminium perspex oil canvas prov. 15-Dec-3 Hindman, Chicago #90/R est:5000-7000

Works on paper

£264 $473 €385 Drawing B (55x70cm-22x28in) s. ink oil prov. 31-May-4 Stephan Welz, Johannesburg #45 (SA.R 3200)
£6046 $10882 €8827 Painting relief (127x102cm-50x40in) mixed media canvas. 25-Apr-4 Christie's, Hong Kong #718/R est:100000-150000 (HK.D 85000)

LINA, Louis (1855-1936) French

£667 $1200 €1000 L'arriere-pays provencal (38x55cm-15x22in) s. 26-Apr-4 Tajan, Paris #153
£734 $1320 €1100 La cote aux environs de Marseille (38x55cm-15x22in) s. 26-Apr-4 Tajan, Paris #155

LINAAE, Paul (1791-1866) Norwegian

Works on paper

£292 $476 €426 From the park at Safstaholm with Oxenstierna family (39x31cm-15x12in) i.verso W/C. 29-Sep-3 Lilla Bukowskis, Stockholm #854 (S.KR 3800)

LINARD, Jacques (1600-1645) French

£47368 $87158 €72000 Nature morte aux fraises, citrons, roses et grenades (27x36cm-11x14in) s.i. panel. 23-Jun-4 Rieunier, Paris #26/R est:70000-90000

LINARD, Jacques (attrib) (1600-1645) French

£19444 $35000 €28388 Still life of a plate of plums and a loaf of bread (32x45cm-13x18in) prov.exhib. 22-Jan-4 Sotheby's, New York #215/R est:35000-45000

£88000 $152240 €128480 Still life of shells in a wooded box surrounded by other shells (25x34cm-10x13in) panel prov. 10-Dec-3 Bonhams, New Bond Street #46/R est:15000-20000

LINARI, Giacomo (1912-1993) Italian

£604 $1081 €900 Coast in Liguria (53x41cm-21x16in) board. 25-May-4 Finarte Semenzato, Milan #168/R

LINCE, Marcel de (1886-?) Belgian

£603 $1007 €850 Pecheurs au bord de l'Ourthe (50x60cm-20x24in) s.d.1926. 17-Jun-3 Vanderkindere, Brussels #188

LINCK, Jean Antoine (1766-1843) Swiss

Prints

£5000 $8850 €7300 Mountain landscapes (39x48cm-15x19in) i.verso hand col etching pair. 29-Apr-4 Christie's, Kensington #216/R est:1000-1500

Works on paper

£4000 $7080 €5840 Vue du Mont Blanc du Glacier de la Brenua (42x55cm-17x22in) s. black white chk. 29-Apr-4 Christie's, Kensington #219/R est:800-1200

£7500 $13275 €10950 Vue de la sommite du Rocher du Couverele (28x40cm-11x16in) s. i.verso pencil W/C bodycol. 29-Apr-4 Christie's, Kensington #220/R est:3000-4000

£12000 $21240 €17520 View of the Vallee of Chamonix with la Mer de Glace (42x55cm-17x22in) s. pencil W/C bodycol two sections. 29-Apr-4 Christie's, Kensington #221/R est:10000-15000

LINCK, Walter (1903-1975) Swiss

Sculpture

£8257 $13789 €11973 Balance (27x47x11cm-11x19x4in) iron steel. 19-Jun-3 Kornfeld, Bern #634/R est:15000 (S.FR 18000)

£15721 $28140 €22953 Fenetre vers le ciel (91x62x15cm-36x24x6in) mono. num.4/4 iron steel prov.exhib.lit. 26-May-4 Sotheby's, Zurich #155/R est:18000-25000 (S.FR 36000)

LINCOLN, Kevin (1941-) Australian

£1967 $3108 €2872 LF4 (96x106cm-38x42in) s. i.d.2-9-85 verso. 2-Sep-3 Deutscher-Menzies, Melbourne #332/R est:2500-3500 (A.D 4800)

Works on paper

£246 $388 €359 Self portrait with mask (49x75cm-19x30in) s.i.d.75 pastel chl pen wash. 2-Sep-3 Deutscher-Menzies, Melbourne #390 (A.D 600)

LIND, Andreas (1815-1885) Norwegian

£6525 $11680 €9527 Ship's portrait of Hovding (61x91cm-24x36in) s.i.d.1849. 25-May-4 Grev Wedels Plass, Oslo #29/R est:40000-60000 (N.KR 80000)

Works on paper

£1448 $2592 €2114 Ship's portrait of Ydun of Svendborg (41x61cm-16x24in) s.d.1877 gouache. 10-May-4 Rasmussen, Vejle #338/R est:10000-15000 (D.KR 16000)

£1626 $2976 €2374 Ship's portrait of Solon af Tonsberg (49x76cm-19x30in) s.i.d.1873 mixed media lit. 7-Jun-4 Blomqvist, Oslo #291/R est:25000-35000 (N.KR 20000)

LIND, Axel (1907-) Danish

£271 $500 €396 Coastal landscape with swans in flight (131x197cm-52x78in) s. 15-Mar-4 Rasmussen, Vejle #652 (D.KR 3000)

LIND, Folke (1931-) Swedish

£377 $679 €566 Summer night, Lofoten (80x80cm-31x31in) s.d.85. 25-Apr-4 Goteborg Auktionsverk, Sweden #423/R (S.KR 5200)

LIND, Wilgot (1915-1996) Swedish

£290 $522 €435 Circus people (68x61cm-27x24in) s. panel. 25-Apr-4 Goteborg Auktionsverk, Sweden #329/R (S.KR 4000)

£334 $600 €501 Still life (46x55cm-18x22in) s. panel. 25-Apr-4 Goteborg Auktionsverk, Sweden #330/R (S.KR 4600)

£384 $692 €576 On the way forward (69x99cm-27x39in) s. acrylic. 25-Apr-4 Goteborg Auktionsverk, Sweden #331/R (S.KR 5300)

LIND, Yrsa (1948-) Danish

£902 $1668 €1317 Figure composition (206x120cm-81x47in) s.d.92. 15-Mar-4 Rasmussen, Vejle #535/R (D.KR 10000)

£902 $1668 €1317 Clowns (206x120cm-81x47in) s.d.92. 15-Mar-4 Rasmussen, Vejle #536/R (D.KR 10000)

LINDAU, Uwe (1950-) German

Works on paper

£300 $543 €450 Sans pitie (27x26cm-11x10in) s.i. mixed media on offset. 2-Apr-4 Winterberg, Heidelberg #1275

LINDAUR, Bohumir (19th C) ?

£1042 $1698 €1500 Portrait of young woman in traditional costume with roses (80x66cm-31x26in) s.i.d.1862. 25-Sep-3 Neumeister, Munich #2819/R est:700

LINDBERG DE GEER, Marianne (1946-) Swedish

Works on paper

£1958 $3524 €2859 Rabbit tales - study in postcoital depression (66x86cm-26x34in) s.verso crayon prov. 26-Apr-4 Bukowskis, Stockholm #498/R est:8000-10000 (S.KR 27000)

LINDBERG, Alf (1905-1990) Swedish

£338 $608 €493 Landscape (66x80cm-26x31in) s. 26-Jan-4 Lilla Bukowskis, Stockholm #654 (S.KR 4500)

£384 $692 €576 Composition (60x70cm-24x28in) s. 25-Apr-4 Goteborg Auktionsverk, Sweden #303/R (S.KR 5300)

£415 $676 €606 The steps (58x42cm-23x17in) s. canvas on panel. 29-Sep-3 Lilla Bukowskis, Stockholm #668 (S.KR 5400)

£435 $783 €653 Green landscape (55x66cm-22x26in) s. 25-Apr-4 Goteborg Auktionsverk, Sweden #302/R (S.KR 6000)

£604 $1027 €882 Self-portrait (100x73cm-39x29in) s. exhib. 4-Nov-3 Bukowskis, Stockholm #196/R (S.KR 8000)

£691 $1127 €1009 Colourful landscape (77x64cm-30x25in) s. 29-Sep-3 Lilla Bukowskis, Stockholm #664 (S.KR 9000)

£1832 $3242 €2675 The family (90x123cm-35x48in) s. prov. 27-Apr-4 AB Stockholms Auktionsverk #802/R est:30000-40000 (S.KR 25000)

LINDBERG, Harald (1901-1976) Swedish

£352 $566 €514 Svarkobbens lighthouse (38x46cm-15x18in) s. panel. 25-Aug-3 Lilla Bukowskis, Stockholm #977 (S.KR 4600)

£399 $651 €583 The skerry (30x53cm-12x21in) s.d.1970 canvas on panel. 29-Sep-3 Lilla Bukowskis, Stockholm #540 (S.KR 5200)

£541 $973 €790 The pilot goes in front (41x61cm-16x24in) s. panel. 26-Jan-4 Lilla Bukowskis, Stockholm #646 (S.KR 7200)

LINDBERG, Maria (1958-) Swedish

Works on paper

£435 $783 €635 Sock on the hand (51x38cm-20x15in) Indian ink prov. 26-Apr-4 Bukowskis, Stockholm #499/R (S.KR 6000)

LINDBERG, Niels (1886-1974) Danish

£496 $917 €724 Cutting wood - father and son with logs (101x101cm-40x40in) s.d.32. 15-Mar-4 Rasmussen, Vejle #680/R (D.KR 5500)

LINDBERG, Stig (1916-1982) Swedish

Works on paper

£305 $548 €445 Blue agitation (47x60cm-19x24in) s. W/C panel varnished. 26-Apr-4 Bukowskis, Stockholm #1012/R (S.KR 4200)

£377 $679 €550 Woman with fish on her head (25x17cm-10x7in) s. Indian ink. 26-Apr-4 Bukowskis, Stockholm #1013/R (S.KR 5200)

£377 $679 €550 Girl with blue bird (31x22cm-12x9in) s.d.78 W/C Indian ink. 26-Apr-4 Bukowskis, Stockholm #1014/R (S.KR 5200)

£464 $835 €677 Southern landscape with herder (41x31cm-16x12in) s.d.41 masonite. 26-Apr-4 Bukowskis, Stockholm #1011/R (S.KR 6400)

LINDBERGH, Peter (1944-) ?

Photographs

£3356 $6007 €5000 Naomi Campbell allongee (39x48cm-15x19in) cibachrome. 26-May-4 Christie's, Paris #185/R est:1000-1500

£6215 $11000 €9074 Berri Smither, Harper's Bazaar, El Mirage, California (56x38cm-22x15in) s.i.d.1993 num.12/25 gelatin silver print. 27-Apr-4 Christie's, Rockefeller NY #321/R est:12000-18000

£6294 $10699 €9000 Tatjana Patitz, Deauville (52x35cm-20x14in) s.i.d. verso silver gelatin lit.exhib. 27-Nov-3 Villa Grisebach, Berlin #1292/R est:10000-12000

£7222 $13000 €10544 Catherine Deneuve (56x39cm-22x15in) s.i.d.1989 gelatin silver print prov. 23-Apr-4 Phillips, New York #141/R est:8000-12000

£7246 $11884 €10000 Kristen Mc Menamy and Tom Dey, El Mirage/Dry Lake, Pirelli (52x35cm-20x14in) s.i.d. verso silver gelatin. 30-May-3 Villa Grisebach, Berlin #1264/R est:10000-12000

£7609 $12478 €10500 Christy Turlington, Los Angeles, Alberto Aspesi (52x35cm-20x14in) s.i.d. verso silver gelatin. 30-May-3 Villa Grisebach, Berlin #1263/R est:10000-12000

£8383 $14000 €12239 Amber Valletta, Harper's Bazaar, New York (60x50cm-24x20in) s.i.d.1993 num.6/25 verso gelatin silver print. 20-Oct-3 Christie's, Rockefeller NY #162/R est:10000-15000

£17778 $32000 €25956 Mathilde on Eiffel Tower (157x124cm-62x49in) s.i.d.1989 num.17/25 gelatin silver print prov.lit. 23-Apr-4 Phillips, New York #28/R est:20000-30000

LINDE, Jan van der (1864-1945) Dutch

£292 $476 €420 Sailing vessel at sea (30x40cm-12x16in) s. 29-Sep-3 Sotheby's, Amsterdam #244a

£526 $968 €800 Haybarges on a calm (50x40cm-20x16in) s. 22-Jun-4 Christie's, Amsterdam #106/R

£540 $950 €788 Peasant woman on a forest road (51x41cm-20x16in) s. 22-May-4 Harvey Clar, Oakland #2219

£694 $1132 €1000 Dutch landscape with windmills in evening (64x99cm-25x39in) s. 25-Sep-3 Neumeister, Munich #2820

LINDE-WALTHER, Heinrich Eduard (1868-1939) German

£909 $1518 €1300 Washerwomen in Brittany (27x35cm-11x14in) canvas on board. 10-Oct-3 Winterberg, Heidelberg #1610

LINDELL, Lage (1920-1980) Swedish

£656 $1207 €984 Still life (48x67cm-19x26in) init. 14-Jun-4 Lilla Bukowskis, Stockholm #966 (S.KR 9000)

£1057 $1798 €1543 Tree and stones (20x57cm-8x22in) init. canvas on panel. 4-Nov-3 Bukowskis, Stockholm #232/R est:10000-12000 (S.KR 14000)

£1435 $2440 €2095 Figure composition (37x45cm-15x18in) s. paper exhib. 4-Nov-3 Bukowskis, Stockholm #235/R est:15000-18000 (S.KR 19000)

£1813 $3082 €2647 Untitled (25x25cm-10x10in) init. canvas on panel prov. 4-Nov-3 Bukowskis, Stockholm #233/R est:22000-25000 (S.KR 24000)

£1888 $3210 €2756 Landscape from Ven (70x100cm-28x39in) s.verso. 5-Nov-3 AB Stockholms Auktionsverk #778/R est:25000-30000 (S.KR 25000)
£2344 $4149 €3422 Landscape by the ocean I (66x78cm-26x31in) init. exhib. 27-Apr-4 AB Stockholms Auktionsverk #770/R est:40000-50000 (S.KR 32000)
£2756 $4960 €4024 Landscape from Gotland (68x94cm-27x37in) init. 26-Apr-4 Bukowskis, Stockholm #222/R est:45000-50000 (S.KR 38000)
£3550 $6035 €5183 Landscape, Herrvik (55x71cm-22x28in) init. cop. 4-Nov-3 Bukowskis, Stockholm #236/R est:25000-30000 (S.KR 47000)
£4683 $7961 €6837 Landscape (49x70cm-19x28in) init. 4-Nov-3 Bukowskis, Stockholm #237/R est:20000-25000 (S.KR 62000)
£5275 $9336 €7702 Spanish street (49x60cm-19x24in) init. painted 1947 exhib.prov. 27-Apr-4 AB Stockholms Auktionsverk #771/R est:35000-40000 (S.KR 72000)
Works on paper
£366 $648 €534 Figure on the move (13x18cm-5x7in) s. mixed media. 27-Apr-4 AB Stockholms Auktionsverk #765/R (S.KR 5000)
£505 $812 €737 Composition in blue, yellow, red and black (16x18cm-6x7in) s. gouache. 25-Aug-3 Lilla Bukowskis, Stockholm #922 (S.KR 6600)
£619 $1053 €904 Untitled (38x47cm-15x19in) s. mixed media. 4-Nov-3 Bukowskis, Stockholm #233b/R (S.KR 8200)
£831 $1412 €1213 Untitled (38x46cm-15x18in) s. mixed media. 4-Nov-3 Bukowskis, Stockholm #233a/R (S.KR 11000)
£1586 $2696 €2316 Composition (19x30cm-7x12in) s. gouache pencil. 4-Nov-3 Bukowskis, Stockholm #234/R est:18000-20000 (S.KR 21000)
£2051 $3631 €2994 Figures on the move (37x46cm-15x18in) s. gouache. 27-Apr-4 AB Stockholms Auktionsverk #768/R est:18000-20000 (S.KR 28000)

LINDEMAN, Emil (1864-c.1945) Polish
£833 $1317 €1200 Evening landscape (50x72cm-20x28in) s. 5-Sep-3 Wendl, Rudolstadt #3486/R

LINDEMANN, Kai (1931-) Danish
£269 $484 €393 Unknown landscape (60x80cm-24x31in) s.d.65 verso. 24-Apr-4 Rasmussen, Havnen #4123 (D.KR 3000)
£535 $894 €781 Landscape (73x88cm-29x35in) s. d.88 verso. 7-Oct-3 Rasmussen, Copenhagen #220/R (D.KR 5700)
£1317 $2239 €1923 Model seen from behind (130x97cm-51x38in) s. 26-Nov-3 Kunsthallen, Copenhagen #138/R est:18000 (D.KR 14000)
£1670 $3072 €2438 Composition (114x146cm-45x57in) s.d.62 verso. 29-Mar-4 Rasmussen, Copenhagen #415/R est:20000-25000 (D.KR 18500)
£1737 $2901 €2536 Landscape from Vence (80x100cm-31x39in) s. s.i.d.98 verso. 7-Oct-3 Rasmussen, Copenhagen #299/R est:15000 (D.KR 18500)

LINDEMANN-FROMMEL, Karl (1819-1891) German
£2083 $3437 €3000 Black Forest valley in evening sun (107x83cm-42x33in) s.i.d.85. 3-Jul-3 Dr Fritz Nagel, Stuttgart #489/R est:3800

LINDEN, Carl (1869-1942) American
£1975 $3200 €2864 Moonlight (46x61cm-18x24in) s. 8-Aug-3 Barridorf, Portland #190/R est:1500-2500

LINDEN, Frederic van der (1852-1926) Belgian
£582 $1100 €850 Artist studio (65x77cm-26x30in) s. board. 22-Feb-4 Bonhams & Butterfields, Los Angeles #7036 est:1000-1500

LINDENAU, Martin (20th C) French
£1773 $2961 €2500 Saint Tropez (66x92cm-26x36in) s. 19-Oct-3 Anaf, Lyon #199/R est:3000-4000

LINDENBAUM-SHARON, Or (20th C) ?
Works on paper
£839 $1427 €1200 Michali (80x200cm-31x79in) s.verso W/C. 27-Nov-3 Calmels Cohen, Paris #87/R

LINDENMUTH, Arlington N (1867-?) American
£326 $600 €476 Landscape with trees in field (41x56cm-16x22in) s. 9-Jun-4 Alderfer's, Hatfield #481

LINDENMUTH, Tod (1885-1976) American
£506 $800 €739 Sand dunes and cloudy sky (56x81cm-22x32in) s. 6-Sep-3 Brunk, Ashville #258
£529 $900 €772 Untitled, sea/townscape, Provincetown (30x41cm-12x16in) s. board. 9-Nov-3 Outer Cape Auctions, Provincetown #42/R
£1006 $1600 €1469 Rough seas (49x59cm-19x23in) s. board. 12-Sep-3 Skinner, Boston #499/R
£1136 $2000 €1659 Dune scape (56x81cm-22x32in) s. 3-Jan-4 Outer Cape Auctions, Provincetown #80/R
£1912 $3250 €2792 Path of the moon (56x71cm-22x28in) s. s.i.verso masonite. 21-Nov-3 Skinner, Boston #574/R est:1500-2500
£2270 $3700 €3314 Ships at sea (64x76cm-25x30in) s. 19-Jul-3 Outer Cape Auctions, Provincetown #71
£3588 $6100 €5238 Fog bound harbour (53x86cm-21x34in) s. 9-Nov-3 Outer Cape Auctions, Provincetown #91/R

LINDER, Alf (1944-) Swedish
£2039 $3467 €2977 The climbing clowns (58x102cm-23x40in) s.d.1987 verso triptych. 5-Nov-3 AB Stockholms Auktionsverk #929/R est:15000-18000 (S.KR 27000)

LINDER, Philippe Jacques (19th C) French
£694 $1132 €1000 Going out for a walk (30x23cm-12x9in) s. 24-Sep-3 Neumeister, Munich #484

LINDEROS, Bengt Arne (1929-1989) Swedish
£348 $627 €522 Landscape (70x80cm-28x31in) init. acrylic. 25-Apr-4 Goteborg Auktionsverk, Sweden #375/R (S.KR 4800)

LINDFORS, Kent (1938-) Swedish
Works on paper
£769 $1362 €1123 Double river (92x60cm-36x24in) s.d.1988 mixed media panel prov. 27-Apr-4 AB Stockholms Auktionsverk #945/R (S.KR 10500)

LINDGREN, Emil (1866-1940) Swedish
£349 $639 €510 Young peasant girl with orange lantern (89x67cm-35x26in) s.d.1927. 9-Jun-4 Rasmussen, Copenhagen #1950/R (D.KR 3900)
£433 $801 €632 Fishergirl on beach at Brittany (68x100cm-27x39in) s.d.1926. 15-Mar-4 Rasmussen, Vejle #72 (D.KR 4800)
£462 $794 €675 Drying the nets (70x100cm-28x39in) s.i.d.1915. 7-Dec-3 Uppsala Auktionskammare, Uppsala #194 (S.KR 6000)

LINDH, Bror (1877-1941) Swedish
£477 $820 €696 Winter landscape at dusk (32x38cm-13x15in) s. canvas on panel. 7-Dec-3 Uppsala Auktionskammare, Uppsala #140/R (S.KR 6200)
£2735 $4895 €3993 Snow-covered landscape in moonlight (133x116cm-52x46in) s. 25-May-4 Bukowskis, Stockholm #194/R est:50000-60000 (S.KR 37000)

LINDHBERG, Per (attrib) (1785-1868) Swedish
Works on paper
£600 $1074 €900 Girl in blue dress, Augusta Ahlberg (26x20cm-10x8in) s.d.1842 pastel gouache. 15-May-4 Hagelstam, Helsinki #50/R

LINDHE, Ivan (1875-1954) Swedish
£813 $1455 €1187 The white outfit - portrait of girl seated (118x81cm-46x32in) s.d.1917. 26-May-4 AB Stockholms Auktionsverk #2220/R (S.KR 11000)

LINDHOLM, Berndt (1841-1914) Finnish
£570 $1061 €850 Woodland hill (13x13cm-5x5in) s. prov. 7-Mar-4 Bukowskis, Helsinki #373/R
£2215 $4119 €3300 Sailing in the evening (27x52cm-11x20in) s.d.1896. 7-Mar-4 Bukowskis, Helsinki #372/R est:4000
£3099 $4958 €4400 Mountain slope (28x35cm-11x14in) s. 18-Sep-3 Hagelstam, Helsinki #786 est:6500
£3691 $6866 €5500 Coastal breakers (26x40cm-10x16in) s. 7-Mar-4 Bukowskis, Helsinki #376/R est:5000
£4085 $7066 €5800 Coastal landscape (38x47cm-15x19in) s. 13-Dec-3 Hagelstam, Helsinki #79/R est:6000
£4225 $7310 €6000 Coastal cliff (26x45cm-10x18in) s. panel. 13-Dec-3 Hagelstam, Helsinki #78/R est:6000
£4667 $8353 €7000 Wooded landscape (48x67cm-19x26in) s.d.1891. 15-May-4 Hagelstam, Helsinki #86/R est:12000
£5231 $8997 €7637 Vessels in harbour, winter (32x52cm-13x20in) s.d.1875. 2-Dec-3 Bukowskis, Stockholm #268/R est:40000-50000 (S.KR 68000)
£7769 $13363 €11343 Summer landscape with waterway and figure (37x58cm-15x23in) init.d.1874. 3-Dec-3 AB Stockholms Auktionsverk #2556/R est:125000-150000 (S.KR 101000)
£8099 $14011 €11500 Two boys on stony beach (24x36cm-9x14in) s. panel. 13-Dec-3 Hagelstam, Helsinki #77/R est:8000
£8451 $14620 €12000 Seascape with sailing boats by the coast (47x68cm-19x27in) s.d.1890. 13-Dec-3 Hagelstam, Helsinki #76/R est:10000
£8500 $15214 €12410 Coastal landscape with cliffs (50x80cm-20x31in) s.d.1895. 25-May-4 Bukowskis, Stockholm #339/R est:80000-100000 (S.KR 115000)
£8784 $15723 €13000 At sea (42x70cm-17x28in) s.d.1901. 8-May-4 Bukowskis, Helsinki #134/R est:10000-14000
£8846 $15215 €12915 Wooded landscape with woman (50x80cm-20x31in) s. 2-Dec-3 Bukowskis, Stockholm #271/R est:140000-150000 (S.KR 115000)
£10811 $19351 €16000 Light in the forest (30x47cm-12x19in) s. 8-May-4 Bukowskis, Helsinki #113/R est:12000-15000
£11189 $19021 €16000 Sailing in autumn - rocky coastal landscape (41x57cm-16x22in) s.d.98. 29-Nov-3 Bukowskis, Helsinki #219/R est:15000-18000
£13176 $23584 €19500 Walking in the woods (30x41cm-12x16in) s. 8-May-4 Bukowskis, Helsinki #92/R est:15000-17000
£17568 $31446 €26000 Summer afternoon (47x65cm-19x26in) s.d.1892. 8-May-4 Bukowskis, Helsinki #49/R est:20000-25000

LINDIN, Carl Olof Eric (1869-1942) American/Swedish
£1852 $3500 €2704 Moonlight (20x25cm-8x10in) board prov. 17-Feb-4 John Moran, Pasadena #21/R est:1000-2000

LINDKVIST, Jonas (1889-1955) Swedish
£450 $751 €657 Fyris river with view towards Uppsala Palace (62x92cm-24x36in) s.d.46 panel. 12-Oct-3 Uppsala Auktionskammare, Uppsala #579 (S.KR 5800)

LINDLAR, Johann Wilhelm (1816-1896) German
£1200 $2196 €1752 Alpine scene, with snow covered mountains (108x134cm-43x53in) s. 6-Jul-4 Bonhams, Knightsbridge #216/R est:1200-1800
£3704 $7000 €5408 View of Lago Maggiore, with figures in a rowboat and distant village (69x122cm-27x48in) s.d.1892. 21-Feb-4 Brunk, Ashville #147/R est:3000-6000

LINDLAR, Johann Wilhelm (attrib) (1816-1896) German
£396 $674 €578 Sunlit mountain landscape (34x51cm-13x20in) i. canvas on panel. 5-Nov-3 Dobiaschofsky, Bern #751/R (S.FR 900)

LINDLEY, Brian (20th C) British
Works on paper
£600 $1056 €876 Gondalas, Venice (3x47cm-1x19in) pastel. 18-May-4 Woolley & Wallis, Salisbury #278/R
£620 $1091 €905 The pink jacket (18x23cm-7x9in) pastel. 18-May-4 Woolley & Wallis, Salisbury #292/R
£650 $1144 €949 The National Gallery and St Martins in the Fields. The Carousel, Montmartre (21x20cm-8x8in) s. pastel two. 18-May-4 Woolley & Wallis, Salisbury #289/R

LINDLEY, Frank (20th C) British?
£1399 $2378 €2000 Paysage avec ferme et vaches (81x117cm-32x46in) s. 18-Nov-3 Vanderkindere, Brussels #72 est:1000-1500

LINDMAN, Axel (1848-1930) Swedish
£421 $682 €610 Landscape with cattle (26x35cm-10x14in) s.i.d.79. 4-Aug-3 Rasmussen, Vejle #128/R (D.KR 4400)
£538 $926 €785 Capri - Grande Marina (42x60cm-17x24in) s.d.1891. 3-Dec-3 AB Stockholms Auktionsverk #2254/R (S.KR 7000)
£692 $1191 €1010 The town wall, Visby (27x18cm-11x7in) s.i.d.1882 panel. 2-Dec-3 Bukowskis, Stockholm #82/R (S.KR 9000)
£1147 $1846 €1675 Winter landscape (55x73cm-22x29in) s. 25-Aug-3 Lilla Bukowskis, Stockholm #599 est:12000-15000 (S.KR 15000)
£1183 $2117 €1727 River landscape from the outskirts of Paris (21x33cm-8x13in) i. cardboard. 25-May-4 Bukowskis, Stockholm #5/R est:20000-25000 (S.KR 16000)
£1923 $3308 €2808 Winter landscape in afternoon light, possibly Kilsbergen, Narke (73x100cm-29x39in) s. 2-Dec-3 Bukowskis, Stockholm #121/R est:20000-25000 (S.KR 25000)
£2587 $4630 €3777 Coastal landscape with sailing boats (36x55cm-14x22in) s. 25-May-4 Bukowskis, Stockholm #159/R est:15000-20000 (S.KR 35000)

LINDNER, Degen (1943-) Canadian
£280 $512 €409 Forest tangle (50x70cm-20x28in) s.i.d.2001 paper. 1-Jun-4 Hodgins, Calgary #319/R (C.D 700)

LINDNER, Ernest (1897-1988) Canadian
£3400 $6222 €4964 Young model (64x40cm-25x16in) painted c.1930. 1-Jun-4 Hodgins, Calgary #112/R est:3000-5000 (C.D 8500)
Works on paper
£240 $439 €350 Portrait of Degen (26x19cm-10x7in) s.d.1959 pencil. 1-Jun-4 Hodgins, Calgary #350/R (C.D 600)
£249 $416 €364 Untitled - Bodil (29x23cm-11x9in) pencil. 17-Nov-3 Hodgins, Calgary #332/R (C.D 550)
£339 $567 €495 Untitled - woman with braid (30x23cm-12x9in) s.d.1936 pencil. 17-Nov-3 Hodgins, Calgary #93/R (C.D 750)
£1493 $2494 €2180 Untitled - young mother (36x34cm-14x13in) s.i. pencil. 17-Nov-3 Hodgins, Calgary #94/R est:700-1000 (C.D 3300)

LINDNER, Friedrich Paul (18th C) German
£1351 $2108 €2000 Landscape with horses and figures (19x15cm-7x6in) s.d.1719. 28-Mar-3 Behringer, Furth #1113/R est:400

LINDNER, J (19th C) Austrian
£1268 $2104 €1800 Beautiful women resting surrounded by roses (42x80cm-17x31in) s. 16-Jun-3 Dorotheum, Vienna #185/R est:1400-1600

LINDNER, Michael (20th C) Dutch?
£553 $996 €830 Going to church (59x48cm-23x19in) s.d.1935 lit. 22-Apr-4 Weidler, Nurnberg #4503/R

LINDNER, Peter Moffat (1854-1949) British
£250 $403 €365 Arundel Castle (48x74cm-19x29in) s.d.1885. 15-Aug-3 Keys, Aylsham #428
£267 $425 €390 Coastal view with sailing ships on the horizon (30x61cm-12x24in) mono. 9-Mar-3 William Jenack, New York #309
£370 $670 €540 Castle in the mist (48x74cm-19x29in) s.d.1895. 16-Apr-4 Keys, Aylsham #295/R
£950 $1739 €1387 Twilight calm (51x73cm-20x29in) s.d.1885. 3-Jun-4 Lane, Penzance #222
Works on paper
£420 $769 €613 Fishing vessels in the Grand Canal (33x51cm-13x20in) s. W/C. 7-Apr-4 Woolley & Wallis, Salisbury #39/R
£800 $1416 €1168 Venice from the lagoon. Fishing boats on a calm sea (46x58cm-18x23in) s. W/C two. 29-Apr-4 Gorringes, Lewes #2544

LINDNER, Richard (1901-1978) American/German
Works on paper
£11377 $19000 €16610 Hit (60x49cm-24x19in) W/C paper on mylar prov.exhib.lit. 13-Nov-3 Sotheby's, New York #162/R est:18000-22000
£13500 $24840 €19710 Lady in a hat (62x52cm-24x20in) s.i.d.1969 W/C pencil. 25-Jun-4 Christie's, London #194/R est:10000-15000
£15493 $26803 €22000 Pink pussycat (53x34cm-21x13in) s.i. W/C crayon prov.exhib.lit. 9-Dec-3 Artcurial Briest, Paris #394/R est:12000-15000

LINDNER, Wilhelm (1881-?) German?
£849 $1494 €1274 Farm interior (80x70cm-31x28in) s. 23-May-4 Agra, Warsaw #41/R (P.Z 6000)

LINDOE, Luke (1913-2001) Canadian
£317 $529 €463 Wood cutting in burnt timber (24x31cm-9x12in) s.i. board. 17-Nov-3 Hodgins, Calgary #357/R (C.D 700)

LINDQUIST, Rurik (1870-1950) Finnish
£268 $494 €400 In the garden (41x49cm-16x19in) s. 25-Mar-4 Hagelstam, Helsinki #891

LINDQVIST, Herman (1868-1923) Swedish
£922 $1502 €1346 Molin's fountain (100x138cm-39x54in) s.d.1917. 29-Sep-3 Lilla Bukowskis, Stockholm #342 (S.KR 12000)
£1000 $1720 €1460 Early spring, Tegerlunden, Stockholm (41x44cm-16x17in) s.d.1921. 2-Dec-3 Bukowskis, Stockholm #23/R (S.KR 13000)
£1035 $1852 €1511 Skeppsholms Church in Stockholm, winter (62x52cm-24x20in) s.d.08. 25-May-4 Bukowskis, Stockholm #13/R (S.KR 14000)
£3538 $6086 €5165 Winter scene with figures walking by Johannes Church, Stockholm (105x140cm-41x55in) s.d.1893. 2-Dec-3 Bukowskis, Stockholm #24/R est:20000-25000 (S.KR 46000)
£4231 $7277 €6177 Girl by corn field (45x35cm-18x14in) s.d.98. 3-Dec-3 AB Stockholms Auktionsverk #2233/R est:12000-15000 (S.KR 55000)

LINDSAY, H C (20th C) American
£1512 $2600 €2208 Rural landscape with houses (64x76cm-25x30in) s. 7-Dec-3 Freeman, Philadelphia #155 est:1000-1500

LINDSAY, Norman Alfred Williams (1879-1969) Australian
£288 $521 €420 Untitled. 1-Apr-4 Joel, Victoria #17 (A.D 700)
£3239 $5215 €4729 Old Robbie (34x29cm-13x11in) s. prov.exhib.lit. 25-Aug-3 Sotheby's, Paddington #225/R est:8000-12000 (A.D 8000)
£3805 $5974 €5555 Untitled (56x46cm-22x18in) s. 1-Sep-3 Shapiro, Sydney #328/R est:15000-20000 (A.D 9360)
£4198 $7641 €6129 Bathers (11x22cm-4x9in) s. board prov. 16-Jun-4 Deutscher-Menzies, Melbourne #126/R est:10000-15000 (A.D 11000)
£6356 $10805 €9280 Sultan's pleasure (34x24cm-13x9in) s. canvasboard prov. 24-Nov-3 Sotheby's, Melbourne #47/R est:15000-20000 (A.D 15000)
£8907 $14340 €13004 The Fan (30x26cm-12x10in) s. prov. 25-Aug-3 Sotheby's, Paddington #136/R est:20000-25000 (A.D 22000)
£10204 $18776 €14898 Portrait (35x30cm-14x12in) s. prov. 29-Mar-4 Goodman, Sydney #19/R est:25000-30000 (A.D 25000)
£10526 $16947 €15368 Imperia (30x24cm-12x9in) s. prov.exhib. 25-Aug-3 Sotheby's, Paddington #159/R est:25000-35000 (A.D 26000)
£11915 $20255 €17396 Sea nymphs (40x29cm-16x11in) canvas on board prov. 25-Nov-3 Christie's, Melbourne #15/R est:28000-35000 (A.D 28000)
£12988 $20391 €18962 In the woods (62x48cm-24x19in) s. 1-Sep-3 Shapiro, Sydney #327/R est:50000-70000 (A.D 31950)
£13636 $25227 €19909 Nude and curtain (35x40cm-14x16in) s. canvas on board. 10-Mar-4 Deutscher-Menzies, Melbourne #167/R est:25000-35000 (A.D 33000)
£14575 $23466 €21280 Conquerors (34x40cm-13x16in) s. canvas on board prov. 25-Aug-3 Sotheby's, Paddington #117/R est:25000-35000 (A.D 36000)
£16194 $26073 €23643 Threat (64x52cm-25x20in) bears i.verso lit. 25-Aug-3 Sotheby's, Paddington #185/R est:40000-60000 (A.D 40000)
£18293 $28720 €26525 Blue shawl, portrait of Miss Morgan (57x47cm-22x19in) s. canvas on board prov. 26-Aug-3 Christie's, Sydney #153/R est:25000-35000 (A.D 45000)
£26271 $44661 €38356 Introduction (69x94cm-27x37in) s. canvas on board prov. 24-Nov-3 Sotheby's, Melbourne #9/R est:60000-80000 (A.D 62000)
£28723 $48830 €41936 Portrait of Rita (41x45cm-16x18in) s. prov. 26-Nov-3 Deutscher-Menzies, Melbourne #40/R est:60000-80000 (A.D 67500)
£36260 $65992 €52940 Dignity (59x49cm-23x19in) s. canvas on board prov. 16-Jun-4 Deutscher-Menzies, Melbourne #70/R est:80000-100000 (A.D 95000)
£42373 $72034 €61865 Rita (51x41cm-20x16in) s. canvas on board prov. 24-Nov-3 Sotheby's, Melbourne #18/R est:100000-150000 (A.D 100000)
£60729 $97773 €88664 Revellers (85x93cm-33x37in) s. prov.exhib. 25-Aug-3 Sotheby's, Paddington #130/R est:150000-180000 (A.D 150000)
£97166 $156437 €141862 Rita (75x60cm-30x24in) s.d.1938 prov. 25-Aug-3 Sotheby's, Paddington #146/R est:240000-280000 (A.D 240000)
Prints
£1758 $3287 €2637 Love on earth (35x29cm-14x11in) s.d.1925 num.39/55 etching. 20-Jul-4 Goodman, Sydney #6/R est:4000-6000 (A.D 4500)
£1837 $3380 €2682 Apex of life (37x30cm-15x12in) s.d.1926 num.19/55 etching prov.lit. 29-Mar-4 Goodman, Sydney #21/R est:2000-3000 (A.D 4500)
£1931 $3456 €2819 To the refined spirit (24x30cm-9x12in) s.i.d.1926 drypoint etching engraving. 10-May-4 Joel, Victoria #222 est:5000-6000 (A.D 4750)
£2041 $3755 €2980 The audience (24x17cm-9x7in) s.d.1925 num.5/38 etching prov.lit. 29-Mar-4 Goodman, Sydney #23/R est:2500-4500 (A.D 5000)
£2273 $4205 €3319 Toilet (16x14cm-6x6in) s.i. num.19/45 aquatint etching engraving. 10-Mar-4 Deutscher-Menzies, Melbourne #443/R est:2500-3500 (A.D 5500)
£2377 $3851 €3470 Escapade (30x25cm-12x10in) num.23/40 etching aquatint stipple prov. 30-Jul-3 Goodman, Sydney #84/R est:5000-6000 (A.D 5800)
£2449 $4506 €3576 Summer day Andante (33x38cm-13x15in) s.d.1925 num.7/55 etching prov.lit. 29-Mar-4 Goodman, Sydney #22/R est:4000-6000 (A.D 6000)
£2857 $5257 €4171 Unmasked (35x30cm-14x12in) s. num.2 etching lit. 29-Mar-4 Goodman, Sydney #29/R est:4000-6000 (A.D 7000)
£3061 $5633 €4469 C-sharp minor quartet (37x30cm-15x12in) s.d.1927 num.14/55 etching prov.lit. 29-Mar-4 Goodman, Sydney #30/R est:5000-7000 (A.D 7500)
£5306 $9763 €7747 Enter the magicians (30x35cm-12x14in) s.num.42/55 etching prov.lit. 29-Mar-4 Goodman, Sydney #24/R est:10000-15000 (A.D 13000)
Sculpture
£1220 $2183 €1781 Sphinx, hood ornament (20cm-8in) init. bronze edn 88/200 st.f.National Trust. 4-May-4 Sotheby's, Melbourne #235/R est:3000-5000 (A.D 3000)
£6055 $11323 €9083 Diana (44x28x12cm-17x11x5in) s.num.10/10 bronze Cast Copperfield. 20-Jul-4 Goodman, Sydney #10/R est:10000-15000 (A.D 15500)
Works on paper
£468 $796 €683 Dream (30x23cm-12x9in) pencil pen ink exec c.1908. 26-Nov-3 Deutscher-Menzies, Melbourne #276/R (A.D 1100)
£473 $856 €691 Francis (16x15cm-6x6in) init. pencil. 31-Mar-4 Goodman, Sydney #350 (A.D 1150)
£496 $903 €724 Casanova (22x25cm-9x10in) init. pencil. 16-Jun-4 Deutscher-Menzies, Melbourne #357/R est:1500-2500 (A.D 1300)
£679 $1133 €991 Untitled - reclining nude (28x24cm-11x9in) init. pencil. 17-Nov-3 Hodgins, Calgary #96/R est:1500-1800 (C.D 1500)
£720 $1303 €1051 Rita (20x25cm-8x10in) init. pencil. 31-Mar-4 Goodman, Sydney #505 (A.D 1750)
£840 $1528 €1226 Preliminary sketch for your dream (24x21cm-9x8in) pencil. 16-Jun-4 Deutscher-Menzies, Melbourne #355/R est:2500-4500 (A.D 2200)
£840 $1528 €1226 Exotic nude (21x16cm-8x6in) pencil. 16-Jun-4 Deutscher-Menzies, Melbourne #435/R est:1500-2500 (A.D 2200)
£992 $1835 €1448 Faun and the maiden (13x23cm-5x9in) s. pen ink. 10-Mar-4 Deutscher-Menzies, Melbourne #281/R est:1000-1500 (A.D 2400)
£1000 $1850 €1460 Betty (22x17cm-9x7in) s.i.d.16.10.20 pen black ink sold with another by the same hand. 13-Jul-4 Rosebery Fine Art, London #549
£1016 $1819 €1483 Blue Gum Billy (15x10cm-6x4in) s. pen ink. 10-May-4 Joel, Victoria #395/R est:2200-3200 (A.D 2500)
£1029 $1862 €1502 In spite of Hitler (18x22cm-7x9in) init. ink. 31-Mar-4 Goodman, Sydney #453 (A.D 2500)
£1031 $1876 €1505 Time to be good (36x36cm-14x14in) s.i.verso pen ink. 16-Jun-4 Deutscher-Menzies, Melbourne #353/R est:3500-5000 (A.D 2700)
£1145 $2084 €1672 Nude (33x19cm-13x7in) init. pencil. 16-Jun-4 Deutscher-Menzies, Melbourne #356/R est:2000-3000 (A.D 3000)

£1149	$1988	€1678	Study from the model (25x19cm-10x7in) init. pencil. 10-Dec-3 Shapiro, Sydney #67/R est:2000-3000 (A.D 2700)
£1527	$2779	€2229	Reclining nude (19x26cm-7x10in) init. pencil. 16-Jun-4 Deutscher-Menzies, Melbourne #359/R est:4000-6000 (A.D 4000)
£1603	$2918	€2340	Mona (36x15cm-14x6in) init. pencil. 16-Jun-4 Deutscher-Menzies, Melbourne #354/R est:3000-4000 (A.D 4200)
£1837	$3380	€2682	Nude (35x51cm-14x20in) s. pencil prov. 29-Mar-4 Goodman, Sydney #16/R est:1500-2500 (A.D 4500)
£1908	$3473	€2786	Lips to lips (36x27cm-14x11in) s. ink pencil. 16-Jun-4 Deutscher-Menzies, Melbourne #358/R est:4000-6000 (A.D 5000)
£2041	$3755	€2980	Nude (34x10cm-13x4in) s. pencil prov. 29-Mar-4 Goodman, Sydney #17/R est:1500-2500 (A.D 5000)
£2273	$3864	€3319	Nude study (29x34cm-11x13in) s. pencil prov. 29-Oct-3 Lawson Menzies, Sydney #96/R est:2000-3000 (A.D 5500)
£2341	$3979	€3418	Surprised (39x15cm-15x6in) s. pencil. 26-Nov-3 Deutscher-Menzies, Melbourne #275/R est:4000-6000 (A.D 5500)
£2439	$3829	€3537	The game (36x25cm-14x10in) s. W/C. 26-Aug-3 Christie's, Sydney #359/R est:5000-7000 (A.D 6000)
£2592	$4769	€3784	Nude (35x20cm-14x8in) s. pencil prov. 29-Mar-4 Goodman, Sydney #18/R est:1800-2500 (A.D 6350)
£2686	$4566	€3922	Chase (28x40cm-11x16in) ink. 29-Oct-3 Lawson Menzies, Sydney #97/R est:5000-7000 (A.D 6500)
£2834	$4563	€4138	Study for 'Out of the Dawn' (45x43cm-18x17in) pencil prov. 25-Aug-3 Sotheby's, Paddington #138/R est:12000-18000 (A.D 7000)
£2846	$5093	€4155	Running water (23x17cm-9x7in) s.d.1917 W/C prov. 4-May-4 Sotheby's, Melbourne #324/R est:8000-10000 (A.D 7000)
£3239	$5215	€4729	Chase (37x30cm-15x12in) s. ink wash pencil. 25-Aug-3 Sotheby's, Paddington #485/R est:8000-12000 (A.D 8000)
£3252	$5821	€4748	Study for the Last Ride (44x41cm-17x16in) init. pencil prov.lit. 4-May-4 Sotheby's, Melbourne #11/R est:8000-12000 (A.D 8000)
£3265	$6008	€4767	The diadem (45x45cm-18x18in) init. pencil prov. 29-Mar-4 Goodman, Sydney #26/R est:4000-6000 (A.D 8000)
£3404	$5787	€4970	Britannia Arises (45x32cm-18x13in) s. ink gouache exec c.1918 prov. 26-Nov-3 Deutscher-Menzies, Melbourne #38/R est:9000-14000 (A.D 8000)
£4237	$7203	€6186	Arabella (24x15cm-9x6in) init. W/C exhib. 24-Nov-3 Sotheby's, Melbourne #155/R est:6000-8000 (A.D 10000)
£4297	$8035	€6446	The ballet (39x31cm-15x12in) s. i.verso W/C. 21-Jul-4 Shapiro, Sydney #150/R est:4000-6000 (A.D 11000)
£4942	$8500	€7215	Good fellows (43x36cm-17x14in) s.i. pen ink. 7-Dec-3 Freeman, Philadelphia #52 est:2000-3000
£5178	$9527	€7560	Pirate welcome (46x56cm-18x22in) init. dr prov. 29-Mar-4 Goodman, Sydney #25/R est:6500-8500 (A.D 12685)
£5372	$9938	€7843	Four continents (46x36cm-18x14in) pencil executed c.1934. 10-Mar-4 Deutscher-Menzies, Melbourne #168/R est:14000-18000 (A.D 13000)
£5668	$9126	€8275	Who wins (30x28cm-12x11in) s. bears i.verso prov. 25-Aug-3 Sotheby's, Paddington #224/R est:14000-18000 (A.D 14000)
£5870	$9451	€8570	Age of Consent (39x30cm-15x12in) s.i. ink wash pencil. 25-Aug-3 Sotheby's, Paddington #486/R est:8000-12000 (A.D 14500)
£6504	$11642	€9496	Odalisque in all her glory (34x27cm-13x11in) s. W/C prov. 10-May-4 Joel, Victoria #285 est:16000-20000 (A.D 16000)
£7644	$13531	€11160	Blue shawl (33x24cm-13x9in) s.d.1918 W/C prov. 3-May-4 Christie's, Melbourne #108/R est:12000-14000 (A.D 18500)
£9570	$17897	€14355	Untitled (28x22cm-11x9in) s. W/C. 20-Jul-4 Goodman, Sydney #15/R est:8000-12000 (A.D 24500)
£9756	$17463	€14244	Last Ride (46x41cm-18x16in) s. W/C prov.lit. 4-May-4 Sotheby's, Melbourne #10/R est:25000-35000 (A.D 24000)
£9756	$17463	€14244	Seated nude (27x27cm-11x11in) s. W/C prov. 4-May-4 Sotheby's, Melbourne #90/R est:28000-38000 (A.D 24000)
£10169	$17288	€14847	Princess and Slave (34x27cm-13x11in) s.d.1919 W/C. 24-Nov-3 Sotheby's, Melbourne #8/R est:15000-20000 (A.D 24000)
£10569	$18919	€15431	Water nymphs (35x28cm-14x11in) s. W/C. 10-May-4 Joel, Victoria #386/R est:6000-8000 (A.D 26000)
£12955	$20858	€18914	Warrior Queen (66x90cm-26x35in) s.indis.i. pencil wash paper on board prov. 25-Aug-3 Sotheby's, Paddington #163/R est:15000-20000 (A.D 32000)
£13223	$22479	€19306	Youthful adoration (42x31cm-17x12in) s. W/C prov. 29-Oct-3 Lawson Menzies, Sydney #90/R est:20000-30000 (A.D 32000)
£13740	$25008	€20060	To the Indies (46x57cm-18x22in) s. W/C prov. 16-Jun-4 Deutscher-Menzies, Melbourne #128/R est:40000-60000 (A.D 36000)
£14170	$22814	€20688	Party (42x34cm-17x13in) s. W/C. 25-Aug-3 Sotheby's, Paddington #164/R est:20000-30000 (A.D 35000)
£15698	$27000	€22919	Premiere danseuse (36x41cm-14x16in) s.d.1930 W/C. 7-Dec-3 Freeman, Philadelphia #51 est:10000-15000
£16194	$26073	€23643	Courting (56x39cm-22x15in) s.d.1930 W/C prov. 25-Aug-3 Sotheby's, Paddington #103/R est:40000-60000 (A.D 40000)
£17814	$28680	€26008	Picnic - Bacchanalia (30x36cm-12x14in) s. W/C. 25-Aug-3 Sotheby's, Paddington #102/R est:20000-30000 (A.D 44000)
£19672	$31082	€28721	Siren (55x46cm-22x18in) s. W/C prov. 2-Sep-3 Deutscher-Menzies, Melbourne #70/R est:50000-70000 (A.D 48000)
£21053	$33895	€30737	Showgirl (38x38cm-15x15in) s.d.1950 W/C prov. 25-Aug-3 Sotheby's, Paddington #107/R est:35000-45000 (A.D 52000)
£24291	$39109	€35465	Temple Party (54x42cm-21x17in) s. W/C. 25-Aug-3 Sotheby's, Paddington #118/R est:60000-80000 (A.D 60000)
£24793	$45868	€36198	Four continents (52x38cm-20x15in) s. i.verso W/C executed c.1934 exhib. 10-Mar-4 Deutscher-Menzies, Melbourne #46/R est:65000-85000 (A.D 60000)
£25424	$43220	€37119	Ball (58x46cm-23x18in) s.d.1929 W/C. 24-Nov-3 Sotheby's, Melbourne #6/R est:60000-80000 (A.D 60000)
£28926	$49174	€42232	That maid (48x44cm-19x17in) s.d.1930 W/C prov. 29-Oct-3 Lawson Menzies, Sydney #29/R est:70000-90000 (A.D 70000)
£28926	$49174	€42232	Dolly sisters (48x38cm-19x15in) s. W/C prov. 29-Oct-3 Lawson Menzies, Sydney #35/R est:70000-90000 (A.D 70000)
£36437	$58664	€53198	Out of the Dawn (60x50cm-24x20in) s.d.1933 W/C prov.lit. 25-Aug-3 Sotheby's, Paddington #108/R est:60000-80000 (A.D 90000)

LINDSAY, Percy (1870-1952) Australian

£816	$1502	€1191	Road to the homestead (23x30cm-9x12in) s. canvas on cardboard prov. 29-Mar-4 Goodman, Sydney #108/R (A.D 2000)
£898	$1652	€1311	Landscape with trees (21x28cm-8x11in) s. canvas on cardboard prov. 29-Mar-4 Goodman, Sydney #106/R (A.D 2200)
£1061	$1953	€1549	Riverscene (18x23cm-7x9in) canvas on cardboard prov. 29-Mar-4 Goodman, Sydney #99/R est:1500-2500 (A.D 2600)
£1224	$2253	€1787	Sydney harbour (28x33cm-11x13in) s. canvas on board prov. 29-Mar-4 Goodman, Sydney #111/R est:3000-5000 (A.D 3000)
£1660	$2772	€2490	Moored boats (19x26cm-7x10in) s. board. 27-Oct-3 Goodman, Sydney #169/R est:5000-7000 (A.D 4000)
£1878	$3455	€2742	Pastoral (38x47cm-15x19in) s. prov. 29-Mar-4 Goodman, Sydney #107/R est:2000-3000 (A.D 4600)
£2033	$3191	€2948	Young child with goose and ducks (64x49cm-25x19in) s. canvas on board. 26-Aug-3 Christie's, Sydney #323/R est:7000-9000 (A.D 5000)
Works on paper			
£255	$434	€372	Yes, let him go (29x20cm-11x8in) s. pen ink. 26-Nov-3 Deutscher-Menzies, Melbourne #278/R (A.D 600)
£410	$767	€615	Yes let him go (29x21cm-11x8in) s. pen. 21-Jul-4 Goodman, Sydney #205 (A.D 1050)

LINDSAY, Raymond (1904-1960) Australian

£244	$383	€356	Untitled, pirates (56x46cm-22x18in) s. board. 1-Sep-3 Shapiro, Sydney #384 (A.D 600)

LINDSAY, Robert Henry (1868-1938) Canadian

£244	$401	€356	Still life (10x15cm-4x6in) s.d.1924 panel. 28-May-3 Maynards, Vancouver #111 (C.D 550)
£269	$450	€393	Autumn (25x30cm-10x12in) s.d.23 board. 20-Jun-3 Freeman, Philadelphia #183/R

LINDSAY, Sir Daryl Ernest (1889-1976) Australian

£2893	$5351	€4224	Mulberry Hill (62x77cm-24x30in) s. prov.exhib. 10-Mar-4 Deutscher-Menzies, Melbourne #57/R est:2000-4000 (A.D 7000)

LINDSAY, Sir Lionel (1874-1961) Australian

Works on paper			
£332	$621	€498	Landscape with farmsheds (24x33cm-9x13in) s. W/C. 21-Jul-4 Goodman, Sydney #173 (A.D 850)
£405	$652	€591	Spanish church (22x28cm-9x11in) s. W/C. 13-Oct-3 Joel, Victoria #259 est:1000-1500 (A.D 1000)
£569	$1019	€831	Courtyard in Capri, Italy (24x34cm-9x13in) s. W/C. 10-May-4 Joel, Victoria #292 est:800-1000 (A.D 1400)
£700	$1267	€1022	The dance (52x36cm-20x14in) s. W/C. 31-Mar-4 Goodman, Sydney #420/R (A.D 1700)
£859	$1607	€1289	Gate at Jaipour (38x56cm-15x22in) s.i. W/C. 21-Jul-4 Goodman, Sydney #225 (A.D 2200)

LINDSAY, Thomas (c.1793-1861) British

Works on paper			
£1700	$3043	€2482	Strand Road near Sandymount, Dublin (17x26cm-7x10in) i.d.58 verso pencil W/C prov. 14-May-4 Christie's, London #58/R est:1000-1500

LINDSAY, Thomas Corwin (1845-1907) American

£1829	$3000	€2652	Covered bridge in winter (18x28cm-7x11in) init. painted c.1890. 7-Jun-3 Treadway Gallery, Cincinnati #1446 est:2000-3000
£2298	$3700	€3355	Autumn forest (107x91cm-42x36in) s. 20-Aug-3 James Julia, Fairfield #1711/R est:1000-2000
£4595	$8500	€6709	Afternoon in the marsh (91x107cm-36x42in) s. 17-Jan-4 New Orleans Auction, New Orleans #737/R est:3000-5000

LINDSELL, Violet Thorpe (fl.1912-1927) British

Works on paper			
£350	$571	€511	Cottage garden (25x35cm-10x14in) s. pencil htd white. 25-Sep-3 Mellors & Kirk, Nottingham #693
£480	$850	€701	Long Compton. Cotswold village street (36x49cm-14x19in) s. W/C over pencil htd white two. 27-Apr-4 Bonhams, Knowle #56

LINDSTRAND, Vicke (1904-1983) Swedish

£1538	$2723	€2245	Still life of white lilies (61x50cm-24x20in) s. 27-Apr-4 AB Stockholms Auktionsverk #442/R est:20000-25000 (S.KR 21000)
Works on paper			
£330	$584	€482	I Kongostatens Tjaenst (45x30cm-18x12in) mixed media original for book cover. 27-Apr-4 AB Stockholms Auktionsverk #443/R (S.KR 4500)

LINDSTROM, Arvid Mauritz (1849-1923) Swedish

£577	$992	€842	Winter landscape (122x74cm-48x29in) s.d.1917. 7-Dec-3 Uppsala Auktionskammare, Uppsala #184/R (S.KR 7500)
£923	$1588	€1348	Farm in winter (36x73cm-14x29in) s.i. 3-Dec-3 AB Stockholms Auktionsverk #2312/R (S.KR 12000)
£1200	$2040	€1752	Swedish woodland scene in autumn, with pond in the foreground (110x190cm-43x75in) s.indis.d.23. 19-Nov-3 Tennants, Leyburn #1119/R est:1200-1500
£1700	$3145	€2482	Wooded landscape (109x193cm-43x76in) s.d.1880. 15-Jan-4 Christie's, Kensington #791/R est:1500-2000
£1769	$3043	€2583	Wooded landscape with waterway, winter (76x126cm-30x50in) s. 3-Dec-3 AB Stockholms Auktionsverk #2422/R est:12000-15000 (S.KR 23000)
£2154	$3705	€3145	Lake landscape in spring (118x67cm-46x26in) s. 3-Dec-3 AB Stockholms Auktionsverk #2282/R est:18000-20000 (S.KR 28000)
£2692	$4631	€3930	Landscape with trees by waterway, autumn colours (77x127cm-30x50in) s. 3-Dec-3 AB Stockholms Auktionsverk #2395/R est:30000-35000 (S.KR 35000)
£3231	$5557	€4717	Summer landscape (128x78cm-50x31in) s. 2-Dec-3 Bukowskis, Stockholm #127/R est:20000-25000 (S.KR 42000)

LINDSTROM, Bengt (1925-) Swedish

£417	$696	€600	Nu allonge (43x55cm-17x22in) s. oil paper painted c.1950. 25-Oct-3 Cornette de St.Cyr, Paris #744
£556	$928	€800	Tete (91x63cm-36x25in) s. acrylic paper. 21-Oct-3 Campo, Vlaamse Kaai #467
£769	$1323	€1100	Sans titre (74x54cm-29x21in) s. acrylic. 3-Dec-3 Tajan, Paris #475
£1089	$1959	€1590	Sunrise over the mountains (27x46cm-11x18in) s. 26-Jan-4 Lilla Bukowskis, Stockholm #520 (S.KR 14500)
£1256	$2249	€1834	Composition with head (88x90cm-35x35in) s. acrylic. 28-May-4 Uppsala Auktionskammare, Uppsala #324/R est:12000-15000 (S.KR 17000)
£1376	$2216	€2009	Composition with figure (46x38cm-18x15in) s. 25-Aug-3 Lilla Bukowskis, Stockholm #687 est:12000-15000 (S.KR 18000)
£1389	$2319	€2000	Figure (121x80cm-48x31in) s. acrylic paper. 21-Oct-3 Campo, Vlaamse Kaai #468/R est:1200-1500
£1419	$2682	€2100	Trois visages (56x75cm-22x30in) s. acrylic. 21-Feb-4 Cornette de St.Cyr, Paris #345/R est:2500-3000

£1465	$2593	€2139	The meeting (41x33cm-16x13in) s. 27-Apr-4 AB Stockholms Auktionsverk #839/R est:18000-20000 (S.KR 20000)
£1478	$2646	€2158	Composition of head (46x38cm-18x15in) s. canvas on panel. 28-May-4 Uppsala Auktionskammare, Uppsala #319/R est:20000-25000 (S.KR 20000)
£1491	$2400	€2177	Demon (46x38cm-18x15in) s. 25-Aug-3 Lilla Bukowskis, Stockholm #269 est:12000-15000 (S.KR 19500)
£1493	$2582	€2180	Le jongleur (46x38cm-18x15in) s. 15-Dec-3 Lilla Bukowskis, Stockholm #40 est:12000-15000 (S.KR 19000)
£1529	$2462	€2232	Composition with two figures (46x38cm-18x15in) s. 25-Aug-3 Lilla Bukowskis, Stockholm #689 est:12000-15000 (S.KR 20000)
£1606	$2585	€2345	Composition with figures (46x38cm-18x15in) s. 25-Aug-3 Lilla Bukowskis, Stockholm #962 est:12000-15000 (S.KR 21000)
£1667	$2983	€2500	Portrait (106x71cm-42x28in) s. acrylic painted c.1988. 16-May-4 Thierry & Lannon, Brest #219 est:2500-3000
£1848	$3307	€2698	Composition of head (46x38cm-18x15in) s. 28-May-4 Uppsala Auktionskammare, Uppsala #318/R est:20000-25000 (S.KR 25000)
£1888	$3210	€2700	Paysage (50x50cm-20x20in) s. panel. 20-Nov-3 Claude Aguttes, Neuilly #249/R est:2450-2700
£1905	$3371	€2781	Confrontation (61x50cm-24x20in) s. 27-Apr-4 AB Stockholms Auktionsverk #837/R est:25000-30000 (S.KR 26000)
£1989	$3581	€2904	Wild heads (46x38cm-18x15in) s. 26-Jan-4 Lilla Bukowskis, Stockholm #510 est:15000-18000 (S.KR 26500)
£2039	$3467	€2977	Confrontation (35x27cm-14x11in) s. 5-Nov-3 AB Stockholms Auktionsverk #829/R est:18000-20000 (S.KR 27000)
£2039	$3467	€2977	Figure composition in green (55x65cm-22x26in) s. 4-Nov-3 Bukowskis, Stockholm #223/R est:25000-30000 (S.KR 27000)
£2053	$3736	€3100	Visage (55x46cm-22x18in) s. 18-Jun-4 Piasa, Paris #233/R est:1500-2000
£2098	$3566	€3000	Abstract Composition (61x50cm-24x20in) s. 25-Nov-3 Christie's, Amsterdam #71/R est:3000-5000
£2098	$3608	€3000	Personnages (32x23cm-13x9in) s. painted 1973 prov. 2-Dec-3 Sotheby's, Amsterdam #226/R est:3000-4000
£2153	$3595	€3100	L'oracle (46x38cm-18x15in) s. 25-Oct-3 Cornette de St.Cyr, Paris #743/R est:2000-3000
£2308	$3923	€3300	Blue head (60x60cm-24x24in) s. painted 1968. 28-Nov-3 Farsetti, Prato #145/R est:3200-3700
£2321	$4177	€3389	Meeting in the mountains (46x38cm-18x15in) s. 26-Apr-4 Bukowskis, Stockholm #206/R est:18000-20000 (S.KR 32000)
£2341	$3980	€3418	Deux personages (92x73cm-36x29in) s. 5-Nov-3 AB Stockholms Auktionsverk #821/R est:30000-35000 (S.KR 31000)
£2368	$4358	€3600	Untitled (38x46cm-15x18in) s. prov. 27-Jun-4 Versailles Encheres #111/R est:3000-3500
£2417	$4109	€3529	The embrace (55x46cm-22x18in) s. 5-Nov-3 AB Stockholms Auktionsverk #819/R est:20000-25000 (S.KR 32000)
£2417	$4109	€3529	Yellow happiness (56x47cm-22x19in) s. 4-Nov-3 Bukowskis, Stockholm #221/R est:15000-20000 (S.KR 32000)
£2465	$4313	€3500	Untitled (75x56cm-30x22in) s. acrylic cardboard prov. 16-Dec-3 Finarte Semenzato, Milan #304/R est:2200-2800
£2492	$4237	€3638	Figures embracing (100x81cm-39x32in) s. 5-Nov-3 AB Stockholms Auktionsverk #820/R est:30000-35000 (S.KR 33000)
£2500	$4175	€3600	L'envie (101x70cm-40x28in) s. oil paper on canvas. 25-Oct-3 Cornette de St.Cyr, Paris #746 est:4000-5000
£2568	$4366	€3749	The cogitator (73x100cm-29x39in) s. 5-Nov-3 AB Stockholms Auktionsverk #742/R est:25000-30000 (S.KR 34000)
£2611	$4699	€3812	Twilight (54x65cm-21x26in) s. 26-Apr-4 Bukowskis, Stockholm #205/R est:20000-25000 (S.KR 36000)
£2639	$4407	€3800	Le cyclope (65x54cm-26x21in) s. 25-Oct-3 Cornette de St.Cyr, Paris #742/R est:3000-4000
£2711	$4798	€3958	The observer (46x38cm-18x15in) s. 27-Apr-4 AB Stockholms Auktionsverk #838/R est:20000-25000 (S.KR 37000)
£2756	$4960	€4024	Man with pipes (60x60cm-24x24in) s. 26-Apr-4 Bukowskis, Stockholm #207/R est:20000-25000 (S.KR 38000)
£2819	$5187	€4200	Tete (61x50cm-24x20in) s. acrylic. 29-Mar-4 Cornette de St.Cyr, Paris #17/R est:4000-5000
£3356	$6007	€5000	Unreal figure (65x54cm-26x21in) s. 30-May-4 Meeting Art, Vercelli #34 est:5000
£3370	$5965	€4920	Friends in the north (81x65cm-32x26in) s. 27-Apr-4 AB Stockholms Auktionsverk #836/R est:25000-30000 (S.KR 46000)
£3399	$5778	€4963	Soleil dans les yeux (130x54cm-51x21in) s. d.61 verso. 4-Nov-3 Bukowskis, Stockholm #219/R est:35000-40000 (S.KR 45000)
£3626	$6526	€5294	Figure (82x65cm-32x26in) s. d.1966 verso. 26-Apr-4 Bukowskis, Stockholm #208/R est:25000-30000 (S.KR 50000)
£4000	$7200	€6000	Deux profils (66x81cm-26x32in) s. 24-Apr-4 Cornette de St.Cyr, Paris #617/R est:4000
£4079	$6934	€5955	Queen Cristina (131x90cm-52x35in) s. 4-Nov-3 Bukowskis, Stockholm #222/R est:40000-50000 (S.KR 54000)
£4267	$7808	€6400	Figure (160x130cm-63x51in) s. prov. 7-Jun-4 Palais de Beaux Arts, Brussels #338/R est:5000-7000
£4496	$8093	€6564	Portrait de Balzac (91x71cm-36x28in) s. painted 1966 exhib. 26-Apr-4 Bukowskis, Stockholm #210/R est:40000-50000 (S.KR 62000)
£5034	$9363	€7500	Visage (61x50cm-24x20in) s. i.verso. 3-Mar-4 Artcurial Briest, Paris #492 est:3000-4000
£5164	$8624	€7539	Figure composition (145x113cm-57x44in) s. 7-Oct-3 Rasmussen, Copenhagen #73/R est:50000-75000 (D.KR 55000)
£5245	$8916	€7500	Untitled (73x92cm-29x36in) s. 28-Nov-3 Farsetti, Prato #312/R est:7500-8500
£5282	$8768	€7500	Figure (80x100cm-31x39in) s. 11-Jun-3 Finarte Semenzato, Milan #591/R
£5282	$9137	€7500	Heads (116x89cm-46x35in) s. prov. 13-Dec-3 De Vuyst, Lokeren #515/R est:9000-11000
£5903	$9740	€8500	Tete (81x65cm-32x26in) s. 2-Jul-3 Cornette de St.Cyr, Paris #49/R est:2500-3000
£6803	$12177	€10000	Poupee magique (146x89cm-57x35in) s. prov. 19-Mar-4 Millon & Associes, Paris #169/R est:10000-15000
£7382	$13067	€11000	Roi Lear (147x114cm-58x45in) s. painted 1983 prov. 28-Apr-4 Artcurial Briest, Paris #322/R est:10000-15000
£7383	$13658	€11000	La panique (162x130cm-64x51in) s. prov. 13-Mar-4 De Vuyst, Lokeren #503/R est:14000-16000
£8308	$14124	€12130	Le partage de Midi (146x114cm-57x45in) s. 5-Nov-3 AB Stockholms Auktionsverk #823/R est:60000-80000 (S.KR 110000)
£10067	$18725	€15000	Wolves (190x200cm-75x79in) s. 3-Mar-4 Artcurial Briest, Paris #491/R est:10000-12000
£10952	$18618	€15990	Menage a Trois (195x180cm-77x71in) s. 5-Nov-3 AB Stockholms Auktionsverk #822/R est:80000-100000 (S.KR 145000)

Works on paper

£556	$928	€800	Paysage anime (43x54cm-17x21in) s. gouache exec.c.1950. 25-Oct-3 Cornette de St.Cyr, Paris #745
£863	$1554	€1260	Blue head (75x55cm-30x22in) s.i. gouache. 26-Jan-4 Lilla Bukowskis, Stockholm #341 (S.KR 11500)
£1141	$2111	€1700	Reclining female nude (44x56cm-17x22in) s. mixed media card on cardboard. 13-Mar-4 Meeting Art, Vercelli #337 est:1500
£1268	$2193	€1800	Sans titre (56x75cm-22x30in) s. gouache. 14-Dec-3 Versailles Encheres #145/R est:1500-2000
£1389	$2319	€2000	Roda figurer (56x75cm-22x30in) s. gouache paper on canvas. 23-Oct-3 Credit Municipal, Paris #75 est:1500-2000
£2733	$4975	€4100	Untitled (106x76cm-42x30in) s. gouache paper on panel exec 1985. 29-Jun-4 Segre, Madrid #151/R est:3500

LINDSTROM, Fritz (1874-1962) Swedish

£443	$794	€647	View from Djurgarden towards Kastellholmen (24x33cm-9x13in) s.d.13/8 99 paper on panel. 28-May-4 Uppsala Auktionskammare, Uppsala #197 (S.KR 6000)

LINDSTROM, Rikard (1882-1943) Swedish

£355	$635	€518	Nude women in landscape by waterway (67x80cm-26x31in) s. panel. 28-May-4 Uppsala Auktionskammare, Uppsala #232 (S.KR 4800)
£367	$591	€536	View from the artist's window (22x22cm-9x9in) panel prov. 25-Aug-3 Lilla Bukowskis, Stockholm #1079 (S.KR 4800)
£730	$1189	€1066	By Mariehamn's quay (64x56cm-25x22in) s.d.1939 panel. 29-Sep-3 Lilla Bukowskis, Stockholm #665 (S.KR 9500)
£883	$1440	€1289	The flight (27x22cm-11x9in) s. 29-Sep-3 Lilla Bukowskis, Stockholm #681 (S.KR 11500)
£911	$1676	€1367	Sailing boat in the harbour (84x109cm-33x43in) s.d.1926. 14-Jun-4 Lilla Bukowskis, Stockholm #659 (S.KR 12500)

LINDT, John William (1845-1926) Australian

Photographs

£45000	$79200	€67500	Aboringinal scenes (20x15cm-8x6in) albumen prints album of 31. 18-May-4 Bonhams, New Bond Street #46/R est:45000-62000

LINEN, George (1802-1888) American

£2374	$4250	€3466	Portrait of Miss Catherine Swan. Portrait of Mrs Smith Culter (23x18cm-9x7in) panel pair. 20-Mar-4 Sloans & Kenyon, Bethesda #1203/R est:2500-3500

LINER, Carl (1914-1997) Swiss

£498	$846	€727	Trees on Corsica (22x30cm-9x12in) s.i.d.52 gouache. 18-Nov-3 Hans Widmer, St Gallen #1129 (S.FR 1100)
£543	$923	€793	Composition in yellow-white-black on green (46x38cm-18x15in) s.d.57. 18-Nov-3 Hans Widmer, St Gallen #1123 (S.FR 1200)
£642	$1072	€931	Composition (73x51cm-29x20in) s.d.1968 masonite. 23-Jun-3 Philippe Schuler, Zurich #3406 (S.FR 1400)
£814	$1385	€1188	Cafe in Corsica (33x49cm-13x19in) s. tempera. 18-Nov-3 Hans Widmer, St Gallen #1127 est:900-1800 (S.FR 1800)
£927	$1687	€1400	Composition (71x49cm-28x19in) s.d.70 paper. 18-Jun-4 Charbonneaux, Paris #151
£940	$1719	€1400	Composition (72x51cm-28x20in) s.d.70 paper. 7-Jul-4 Artcurial Briest, Paris #304 est:1500-1800
£1147	$1915	€1663	Summer in Corsica (49x57cm-19x22in) s. masonite. 23-Jun-3 Philippe Schuler, Zurich #3405/R est:3000-3500 (S.FR 2500)
£1256	$2097	€1834	Composition in orange and blue (45x36cm-18x14in) s.d.50 board. 24-Oct-3 Hans Widmer, St Gallen #53/R est:2500-4500 (S.FR 2800)
£1310	$2410	€1913	Composition (92x73cm-36x29in) s.d.1958. 8-Jun-4 Germann, Zurich #94/R est:4000-5000 (S.FR 3000)
£1357	$2308	€1981	Composition on light green (61x38cm-24x15in) s.d.69. 18-Nov-3 Hans Widmer, St Gallen #1126 est:3000-6000 (S.FR 3000)
£1441	$2652	€2104	Morning in Alpstein (50x67cm-20x26in) s.d. 14-Jun-4 Philippe Schuler, Zurich #4218/R est:5000-6000 (S.FR 3300)
£1525	$2546	€2227	High winter moorland (34x49cm-13x19in) s.d.47 tempera. 24-Oct-3 Hans Widmer, St Gallen #102/R est:2000-3600 (S.FR 3400)
£1584	$2692	€2313	Landscape (50x70cm-20x28in) s.d.1950. 25-Nov-3 Germann, Zurich #98/R est:5000-7000 (S.FR 3500)
£1879	$3326	€2800	Composition (145x113cm-57x44in) s.d.1973. 28-Apr-4 Charbonneaux, Paris #193 est:3500-4500
£1897	$3395	€2770	Pond in wood (46x65cm-18x26in) s.d.1958. 14-May-4 Dobiaschofsky, Bern #197/R est:5500 (S.FR 4400)
£2036	$3400	€2973	Composition (100x81cm-39x32in) s.d.1962. 24-Jun-3 Germann, Zurich #94/R est:5000-7000 (S.FR 4500)
£2036	$3462	€2973	Marwees (50x65cm-20x26in) s. 18-Nov-3 Hans Widmer, St Gallen #1136/R est:4000-7000 (S.FR 4500)
£2261	$4137	€3301	Seascape (24x33cm-9x13in) s.d.48 paper on masonite. 7-Jun-4 Christie's, Zurich #122/R est:3500-4500 (S.FR 5200)
£2287	$3819	€3339	Composition in grey, light blue, brown (61x36cm-24x14in) s.d.58. 24-Oct-3 Hans Widmer, St Gallen #99/R est:3000-5500 (S.FR 5100)
£2691	$4493	€3929	Appenzell landscape with tree by stream (60x81cm-24x32in) s. 24-Oct-3 Hans Widmer, St Gallen #37/R est:6000-11000 (S.FR 6000)
£2703	$4649	€3946	Summer in Schwende (60x81cm-24x32in) s. 8-Dec-3 Philippe Schuler, Zurich #3347/R est:5000-7000 (S.FR 6000)
£2826	$5172	€4126	Toscana (63x48cm-25x19in) s.d.49 chipboard. 7-Jun-4 Christie's, Zurich #121/R est:6000-8000 (S.FR 6500)
£2941	$5000	€4294	Landscape with grazing cows near Unterrain (50x73cm-20x29in) s. 18-Nov-3 Hans Widmer, St Gallen #1135/R est:4000-7000 (S.FR 6500)
£3153	$5423	€4603	Winter landscape (54x73cm-21x29in) s. 8-Dec-3 Philippe Schuler, Zurich #3348 est:4000-5000 (S.FR 7000)
£3167	$5385	€4624	Composition (91x125cm-36x49in) s.d.68 board. 22-Nov-3 Burkhard, Luzern #83/R est:8000-12000 (S.FR 7000)
£3303	$5615	€4822	Composition (104x76cm-41x30in) s.d.64 board. 22-Nov-3 Burkhard, Luzern #82/R est:8000-12000 (S.FR 7300)
£3409	$5659	€4943	Provencal landscape in summer (65x92cm-26x36in) s. exhib. 13-Jun-3 Zofingen, Switzerland #2921/R est:7500 (S.FR 7500)
£3448	$6172	€5034	Woman by well (88x116cm-35x46in) s.d.57. 14-May-4 Dobiaschofsky, Bern #195/R est:10000 (S.FR 8000)
£3587	$5991	€5237	Schwende valley and Alpstein (65x92cm-26x36in) s. 24-Oct-3 Hans Widmer, St Gallen #34/R est:8000-14000 (S.FR 8000)
£3587	$5991	€5237	Composition in brown, black, grey (162x97cm-64x38in) s.d.60. 24-Oct-3 Hans Widmer, St Gallen #36/R est:7000-12000 (S.FR 8000)
£3620	$6154	€5285	Composition (130x97cm-51x38in) s.d.65. 22-Nov-3 Burkhard, Luzern #75/R est:8000-12000 (S.FR 8000)
£3665	$6231	€5351	Woman carrying water (100x76cm-39x30in) s.d.48. 18-Nov-3 Hans Widmer, St Gallen #1122/R est:7000-12000 (S.FR 8100)
£3812	$6365	€5566	Rhine harbour, Basle (72x100cm-28x39in) s.d.55. 24-Oct-3 Hans Widmer, St Gallen #100/R est:8500-12000 (S.FR 8500)
£3846	$6423	€5615	Composition (65x50cm-26x20in) s.d.1971 panel. 24-Jun-3 Germann, Zurich #173/R est:4000-7000 (S.FR 8500)

£4072 $6923 €5945 Forest pool (80x117cm-31x46in) s.d.50. 22-Nov-3 Burkhard, Luzern #73/R est:10000-14000 (S.FR 9000)
£4505 $7748 €6577 Figures walking near Appenzell with Hoher Kasten and Kamor (73x92cm-29x36in) s. prov. 2-Dec-3 Koller, Zurich #3020/R est:8000-12000 (S.FR 10000)

Works on paper

£226 $385 €330 Compostiion in light red-black-brown-blue (29x21cm-11x8in) s.d.71 gouache. 18-Nov-3 Hans Widmer, St Gallen #1125 (S.FR 500)
£271 $462 €396 Seated female nude (60x40cm-24x16in) s. pastel chk study. 18-Nov-3 Hans Widmer, St Gallen #1128 (S.FR 600)
£317 $538 €463 Portrait of young woman (47x40cm-19x16in) s.d.1934 pastel chk. 18-Nov-3 Hans Widmer, St Gallen #1132 (S.FR 700)
£348 $637 €508 Abstract composition (24x32cm-9x13in) mixed media. 4-Jun-4 Zofingen, Switzerland #2872 (S.FR 800)
£362 $615 €529 Olive trees on Corsica (24x31cm-9x12in) s.d.51 gouache. 18-Nov-3 Hans Widmer, St Gallen #1124 (S.FR 800)
£431 $772 €629 Untitled (36x25cm-14x10in) s.d.70 gouache. 12-May-4 Dobiaschofsky, Bern #749/R (S.FR 1000)
£495 $852 €723 Untitled (30x44cm-12x17in) s.d.1950 mixed media. 8-Dec-3 Philippe Schuler, Zurich #3208/R (S.FR 1100)
£500 $830 €725 Sunlit Moorish city (15x24cm-6x9in) s.d.1949 gouache. 13-Jun-3 Zofingen, Switzerland #2919 (S.FR 1100)
£500 $830 €725 Market in Taragona (32x47cm-13x19in) s.d.1954 W/C. 13-Jun-3 Zofingen, Switzerland #2920/R (S.FR 1100)
£606 $1085 €885 Walled city by sea (22x30cm-9x12in) s.d. w/C. 22-Mar-4 Philippe Schuler, Zurich #4187 (S.FR 1400)
£633 $1077 €924 Mountain landscape (23x29cm-9x11in) s. gouache exec. 1950's. 22-Nov-3 Burkhard, Luzern #74/R (S.FR 1400)
£679 $1154 €991 Houses in southern landscape with water (23x32cm-9x13in) s.d.54 W/C on chl. 18-Nov-3 Hans Widmer, St Gallen #1130 est:1000-2000 (S.FR 1500)
£783 $1432 €1143 Toscana (24x34cm-9x13in) s.d.49 W/C. 7-Jun-4 Christie's, Zurich #119/R est:2000-3000 (S.FR 1800)
£870 $1591 €1270 Toscana (32x48cm-13x19in) s.d.48 gouache. 7-Jun-4 Christie's, Zurich #118/R est:2500-3500 (S.FR 2000)
£905 $1538 €1321 Harbour scene (24x32cm-9x13in) s.d.54 gouache. 22-Nov-3 Burkhard, Luzern #72/R (S.FR 2000)
£1048 $1928 €1530 On Corsica (32x52cm-13x20in) s. gouache. 14-Jun-4 Philippe Schuler, Zurich #4150/R est:2000-2500 (S.FR 2400)
£1345 $2247 €1964 Portrait of young girl from Appenzell wearing hat (50x32cm-20x13in) s.d.34 pastel chk. 24-Oct-3 Hans Widmer, St Gallen #38/R est:1500-3000 (S.FR 3000)
£1614 $2696 €2356 Egyptian girl (48x32cm-19x13in) s.d.36 pastel chk. 24-Oct-3 Hans Widmer, St Gallen #35/R est:1800-3000 (S.FR 3600)
£2000 $3660 €2920 Southern France (72x52cm-28x20in) s. W/C. 7-Jun-4 Christie's, Zurich #120/R est:2000-3000 (S.FR 4600)

LINER, Carl August (1871-1946) Swiss

£226 $385 €330 Portrait of artist's father on death bed (38x46cm-15x18in) s. 18-Nov-3 Hans Widmer, St Gallen #1144 (S.FR 500)
£317 $538 €463 Portrait of artist's mother (40x40cm-16x16in) s. 18-Nov-3 Hans Widmer, St Gallen #1142 (S.FR 700)
£317 $538 €463 Portrait of young woman (71x51cm-28x20in) s. 18-Nov-3 Hans Widmer, St Gallen #1143 (S.FR 700)
£1233 $2097 €1800 Young man playing accordion (40x36cm-16x14in) s.d.21. 7-Nov-3 Dobiaschofsky, Bern #187/R est:5000 (S.FR 2800)
£1538 $2615 €2245 Appenzell peasant mowing (24x33cm-9x13in) s.d.29 canvas on board. 18-Nov-3 Hans Widmer, St Gallen #1140/R est:1400-4000 (S.FR 3400)
£1704 $2846 €2488 Portrait of young Italian woman (51x40cm-20x16in) s. 24-Oct-3 Hans Widmer, St Gallen #13/R est:2000-5000 (S.FR 3800)
£1878 $3455 €2742 Children's festival (38x47cm-15x19in) st.sig. canvas on masonite. 14-Jun-4 Philippe Schuler, Zurich #4217/R est:6000-8000 (S.FR 4300)
£1973 $3295 €2881 Italian street (33x44cm-13x17in) s. 24-Oct-3 Hans Widmer, St Gallen #127/R est:1000-2500 (S.FR 4400)
£3677 $6141 €5368 Portrait of his son, Carl Liner jnr (30x29cm-12x11in) s. 24-Oct-3 Hans Widmer, St Gallen #10/R est:6000-12000 (S.FR 8200)
£6726 $11233 €9820 Self portrait with brush and palette (68x48cm-27x19in) s. 24-Oct-3 Hans Widmer, St Gallen #11/R est:14000-24000 (S.FR 15000)
£8597 $14615 €12552 Interior of farmstead in Schwende, Appenzell (49x64cm-19x25in) s.d.1896 board prov.lit. 25-Nov-3 Germann, Zurich #56/R est:10000-15000 (S.FR 19000)
£9417 $15726 €13749 Midday on the Nile (40x50cm-16x20in) s.i.d.1934. 24-Oct-3 Hans Widmer, St Gallen #12/R est:14000-24000 (S.FR 21000)
£13453 $22466 €19641 Eggerstander Moos (51x70cm-20x28in) s.d.24. 24-Oct-3 Hans Widmer, St Gallen #30/R est:30000-45000 (S.FR 30000)

Prints

£3409 $5659 €4943 Appenzell procession (21x63cm-8x25in) s.i. col lithograph. 13-Jun-3 Zofingen, Switzerland #2705/R est:1200 (S.FR 7500)

Works on paper

£633 $1077 €924 Portrait of young woman (48x32cm-19x13in) s. chl pastel chk. 18-Nov-3 Hans Widmer, St Gallen #1141 (S.FR 1400)
£717 $1198 €1047 Young woman reading letter (29x22cm-11x9in) s. pencil. 24-Oct-3 Hans Widmer, St Gallen #1/R est:800-1800 (S.FR 1600)
£769 $1308 €1123 St Galler children's festival (9x14cm-4x6in) mono.i. W/C. 18-Nov-3 Hans Widmer, St Gallen #1139 est:800-1800 (S.FR 1700)
£897 $1498 €1310 Boy writing (23x29cm-9x11in) s.d.29. Marz 1922 chl. 24-Oct-3 Hans Widmer, St Gallen #104/R est:1400-2600 (S.FR 2000)
£1031 $1722 €1505 Portrait of Carl Liner jnr (31x25cm-12x10in) pastel chk. 24-Oct-3 Hans Widmer, St Gallen #106/R est:3000-5500 (S.FR 2300)
£1076 $1797 €1571 Self portrait (24x16cm-9x6in) s.d.22 Marz 1895 pencil bodycol. 24-Oct-3 Hans Widmer, St Gallen #31/R est:1500-3000 (S.FR 2400)
£1166 $1947 €1702 Reclining female nude (33x48cm-13x19in) s. chl pastel chk. 24-Oct-3 Hans Widmer, St Gallen #81/R est:2000-4500 (S.FR 2600)
£1267 $2192 €1850 View of Santis and Altmann (16x22cm-6x9in) s. pencil W/C. 9-Dec-3 Sotheby's, Zurich #85/R est:3000-4000 (S.FR 2800)
£1345 $2247 €1964 Portrait of Carl Liner jnr (26x18cm-10x7in) s.i.d.25. Marz 1922 col pen. 24-Oct-3 Hans Widmer, St Gallen #33/R est:1000-2500 (S.FR 3000)
£1525 $2546 €2227 Portrait of girl wearing headscarf (33x24cm-13x9in) s.d.98 W/C. 24-Oct-3 Hans Widmer, St Gallen #75/R est:2800-5500 (S.FR 3400)
£2242 $3744 €3273 Innerrhoden interior (30x40cm-12x16in) s.i. chl pencil Indian ink. 24-Oct-3 Hans Widmer, St Gallen #29/R est:2500-3800 (S.FR 5000)
£2332 $3894 €3405 Appenzell peasant dancing with woman in traditional costume (50x40cm-20x16in) s. pastel chk board study verso. 24-Oct-3 Hans Widmer, St Gallen #77/R est:4500-8500 (S.FR 5200)
£2402 $4299 €3507 In the church courtyard (9x14cm-4x6in) mono. pencil W/C. 26-May-4 Sotheby's, Zurich #83/R est:2000-3000 (S.FR 5500)
£3498 $5841 €5107 Terracina (25x33cm-10x13in) s.i.d.98 W/C over pen. 24-Oct-3 Hans Widmer, St Gallen #14/R est:3500-8000 (S.FR 7800)

LINES, Frederick Thomas (19th C) British

Works on paper

£290 $537 €423 Fanny Delavan Goddard and Caroline Elizabeth Goddard as girls (34x39cm-13x15in) s. pencil W/C. 16-Feb-4 Bonhams, Bath #180

LINES, Henry H (1800-1889) British

£380 $646 €555 Landscape with a figure on a path, a farm and hills nearby (22x30cm-9x12in) s. board. 19-Nov-3 Tennants, Leyburn #1096
£400 $720 €584 Wooded landscape with figures beside a river (18x23cm-7x9in) s. i.verso board. 21-Apr-4 Tennants, Leyburn #1159

LINFORD, Charles (1846-1897) American

£1056 $1900 €1542 Autumn landscape (30x43cm-12x17in) s. 23-Jan-4 Freeman, Philadelphia #196/R est:1500-2500

LING JIAN (1963-) Chinese

£4267 $7681 €6230 Zha Zha (125cm-49in circular) oil acrylic. 25-Apr-4 Christie's, Hong Kong #740/R est:60000-80000 (HK.D 60000)
£4623 $8321 €6750 New Buddha Ming (137cm-54in circular) oil acrylic. 25-Apr-4 Christie's, Hong Kong #739/R est:65000-85000 (HK.D 65000)

LINGELBACH, Johannes (1622-1674) Dutch

£2032 $3250 €2967 Traveller's greeting (41x61cm-16x24in) s. 21-Sep-3 Grogan, Boston #4/R
£19956 $35721 €29136 Mediterranean harbour scene with figures and Oriental trader (53x65cm-21x26in) s. 25-May-4 Bukowskis, Stockholm #459/R est:60000-80000 (S.KR 270000)

LINGELBACH, Johannes (attrib) (1622-1674) Dutch

£6500 $11700 €9490 Merchant with stevedores on a quayside with moored shipping beyond (30x41cm-12x16in) 21-Apr-4 Bonhams, New Bond Street #115/R est:5000-8000

LINGELBACH, Johannes and VERBOOM, Adriaen (17th C) Dutch

£12000 $20760 €17520 Wooded landscape with hunters on a path (87x112cm-34x44in) prov. 12-Dec-3 Christie's, Kensington #45/R est:12000-18000

LINGEMAN, Lambertus (1829-1894) Dutch

£1560 $2606 €2200 Le prisonnier (35x44cm-14x17in) s.d.1859 panel. 17-Jun-3 Galerie Moderne, Brussels #245/R est:500-800
£2667 $4800 €4000 Soldiers preparing for departure (46x60cm-18x24in) s.d.78 panel. 21-Apr-4 Christie's, Amsterdam #36/R est:4000-6000

LINGENFELDER, Eugen (1862-?) German

£599 $1036 €850 Farmer. Farmer's wife (20x15cm-8x6in) panel pair. 10-Dec-3 Hugo Ruef, Munich #2450/R
£1107 $2047 €1616 Portrait of a early lady. Portrait of a early gentleman smoking a pipe (21x16cm-8x6in) pair. 14-Mar-4 Agra, Warsaw #38/R (P.Z 8000)
£2978 $4646 €4348 Portraits of a man and a woman (21x16cm-8x6in) s. panel pair. 30-Mar-3 Agra, Warsaw #18/R est:5000 (P.Z 19000)

LINGER, Helene von (1856-?) German

£800 $1448 €1200 Castle park in Charlottenburg (64x83cm-25x33in) s. 1-Apr-4 Van Ham, Cologne #1517

LINGNER, Otto (1856-?) German

£1197 $2071 €1700 Spring (100x67cm-39x26in) s. 13-Dec-3 De Vuyst, Lokeren #209/R est:1000-1400
£9396 $16819 €14000 Reclining female nude (82x135cm-32x53in) s.i. exhib. 27-May-4 Dorotheum, Vienna #96/R est:14000-16000

LINK, O Winston (1914-2001) American

Photographs

£1695 $3000 €2475 NW8, J W Dalhouse Stares eye-to-eye at a K2a 127 engine (39x49cm-15x19in) s.d.1955 gelatin silver print. 27-Apr-4 Christie's, Rockefeller NY #266/R est:3000-5000
£2000 $3680 €3000 Norfolk and Western (38x49cm-15x19in) silver print. 10-Jun-4 Artcurial Briest, Paris #234/R est:3000-4000
£2395 $4000 €3497 Maud bows to the Virginia Creeper, Green Cove, Virginia (33x46cm-13x18in) s. num.NW39K verso col coupler print exec.1956 printed later lit. 20-Oct-3 Christie's, Rockefeller NY #215/R est:3000-5000
£2400 $4224 €3504 Hotshot (39x49cm-15x19in) s. gelatin silver print lit. 19-May-4 Christie's, London #192/R est:3000-4000
£3439 $6500 €5021 Hotshot, eastbount, lager, West Virginia (39x49cm-15x19in) s.d.1986 gelatin silver print. 17-Feb-4 Christie's, Rockefeller NY #108/R est:4000-6000
£3800 $6460 €5548 Hot shot (39x49cm-15x19in) s.d.verso gelatin silver print. 18-Nov-3 Christie's, Kensington #210/R est:3000-5000
£4311 $7200 €6294 Hot shot eastbound, West Virginia (39x49cm-15x19in) s. gelatin silver print exec. c.1956 lit. 17-Oct-3 Phillips, New York #190/R est:3000-5000
£4491 $7500 €6557 Hot shot eastbound, lager, West Virginia (39x49cm-15x19in) s.d.1957 st.verso photo. 17-Oct-3 Sotheby's, New York #257/R est:6000-9000
£4802 $8500 €7011 Hot shot eastbound, lager, West Virginia (39x49cm-15x19in) s.i.d.1957 num.NW1103 verso photo printed 1996. 28-Apr-4 Sotheby's, New York #215/R est:6000-9000

LINK, R L (?) ?

Sculpture

£973 $1800 €1421 Child with turtle (13cm-5in) s. bronze. 13-Mar-4 DeFina, Austinburg #756/R

LINKE, J Conrad (1892-1995) American
£283 $450 €413 Man with spaniel (66x99cm-26x39in) s. 10-Sep-3 Alderfer's, Hatfield #334

LINKE, Paul Rudolf (1844-1917) German
£990 $1743 €1445 Mountainous landscape (23x31cm-9x12in) s. board. 23-May-4 Agra, Warsaw #35/R (P.Z 7000)

LINKLATER, Barrie (1931-) British
Works on paper
£500 $915 €730 Study of a jockey on a grey (35x26cm-14x10in) s. pastel. 7-Apr-4 Woolley & Wallis, Salisbury #81/R

LINN, Warren (1946-) American
Works on paper
£457 $800 €667 Hugh Hefner (51x46cm-20x18in) s. pastel board exec c.1970. 17-Dec-3 Christie's, Rockefeller NY #260/R

LINNELL, James Thomas (1826-1905) British
£9500 $17100 €13870 Shepherd's repose and extensive landscape (101x157cm-40x62in) s.d.1869. 20-Apr-4 Hutchinson, Boroughbridge #323/R
£14000 $25760 €20440 Afternoon (80x123cm-31x48in) s.i. prov. 11-Jun-4 Christie's, London #120/R est:15000-20000
£14000 $25760 €20440 Cottager and tramps (80x123cm-31x48in) s.d.1884 prov.exhib. 11-Jun-4 Christie's, London #121/R est:15000-20000

LINNELL, James Thomas (attrib) (1826-1905) British
£450 $765 €657 Drover and animals on heathland (33x60cm-13x24in) s.d.1868. 26-Nov-3 Hamptons Fine Art, Godalming #194

LINNELL, John (1792-1882) British
£800 $1336 €1168 Shepherd and flock in a coastal landscape (19x24cm-7x9in) s. panel. 14-Oct-3 Bearnes, Exeter #374/R
£1400 $2506 €2044 Portrait of Reverend Edward Daniell (16x12cm-6x5in) init.d.1840 panel. 22-Mar-4 Bonhams & Brooks, Norfolk #276/R est:600-800
£1400 $2534 €2044 Near Redbrook, Kent (30x38cm-12x15in) s.d.1870. 16-Apr-4 Keys, Aylsham #744/R est:1500-2000
£1420 $2500 €2073 Rest on the flight to Egypt (28x42cm-11x17in) i.verso oil on paper. 18-May-4 Bonhams & Butterfields, San Francisco #155/R est:3000-5000
£2642 $4200 €3857 North Hazelmere, Surrey (41x70cm-16x28in) s. 13-Sep-3 Weschler, Washington #670/R est:6000-8000
£3600 $6552 €5256 Young brood, children with a hen and chicks in a landscape (53x68cm-21x27in) s.d.1846 panel. 15-Jun-4 Bonhams, Oxford #73/R est:4000-6000
£8400 $14280 €12264 Portrait of E Sterling Esq, standing three quarter length (49x36cm-19x14in) s.d.1834 panel. 29-Oct-3 Hampton & Littlewood, Exeter #580/R est:4000-6000
Works on paper
£400 $728 €584 Twickenham (16x25cm-6x10in) s.i. pencil white chk. 1-Jul-4 Christie's, Kensington #119
£700 $1281 €1022 View of Lymington (11x17cm-4x7in) s.i.d.1815 pencil prov. 3-Jun-4 Christie's, London #76/R
£1800 $3330 €2628 Fisherfolk on the beach (17x28cm-7x11in) s.d.1819 W/C prov. 9-Mar-4 Bonhams, New Bond Street #42/R est:800-1200
£2700 $4995 €3942 Edge of the field (33x23cm-13x9in) s. indis d. W/C. 10-Feb-4 David Lay, Penzance #135/R est:400-600
£4600 $7314 €6670 Barley harvest, near Witley, Surrey (21x34cm-8x13in) s.d.1863 W/C bodycol. 11-Sep-3 Morphets, Harrogate #293 est:4500-5500
£8600 $15652 €12556 Study of a punt moored at Twickenham. River landscape (16x25cm-6x10in) one s. verso millboard two prov. 1-Jul-4 Sotheby's, London #176/R est:2000-3000

LINNELL, William (attrib) (1826-1910) British
£250 $425 €365 Autumnal river landscape (49x75cm-19x30in) bears sig. 31-Oct-3 Moore Allen & Innocent, Cirencester #654/R

LINNIG, Ben (1860-1929) Belgian
£733 $1327 €1100 De bibliofiel (74x57cm-29x22in) s. panel. 30-Mar-4 Campo & Campo, Antwerp #162/R

LINNIG, Egidius (1821-1860) Belgian
£559 $951 €800 Marine (25x18cm-10x7in) s. panel. 18-Nov-3 Vanderkindere, Brussels #214
£1958 $3368 €2800 Vue sur l'Escaut (26x35cm-10x14in) s.d.1856 panel. 2-Dec-3 Campo & Campo, Antwerp #215/R est:2000-3000
£4577 $7919 €6500 Marine (35x52cm-14x20in) s. panel. 9-Dec-3 Campo, Vlaamse Kaai #349/R est:7000-8000
£9722 $15361 €14000 The Vierge Marie (54x70cm-21x28in) panel lit. 19-Sep-3 Schloss Ahlden, Ahlden #1565/R est:14000

LINNIG, Willem (19th C) Belgian
£3600 $6012 €5256 Letter. s.d.1850 panel. 7-Oct-3 Bonhams, Knightsbridge #285/R est:2000-3000
Works on paper
£331 $612 €480 Venus (54x45cm-21x18in) s.d.1887 Indian ink paper on board. 19-Jan-4 Horta, Bruxelles #320

LINNOVAARA, Juhani (1934-) Finnish
£2133 $3819 €3200 The red spot (52x133cm-20x52in) s.d.1965. 15-May-4 Hagelstam, Helsinki #213/R est:3000
£9790 $16643 €14000 Woman and trembling landscape (42x52cm-17x20in) s.d.66. 29-Nov-3 Bukowskis, Helsinki #270/R est:7000-8000
£18919 $33865 €28000 The Sun Cathedral (170x150cm-67x59in) s.d.67-68 exhib. 8-May-4 Bukowskis, Helsinki #277/R est:20000-25000
Works on paper
£845 $1462 €1200 Landscape (48x60cm-19x24in) s.d.1962 W/C. 13-Dec-3 Hagelstam, Helsinki #166/R
£946 $1693 €1400 Landscape from Fuengirola (46x60cm-18x24in) s.d.57 W/C. 8-May-4 Bukowskis, Helsinki #309/R
£2587 $4399 €3700 Blue beam (35x25cm-14x10in) s. gouache. 29-Nov-3 Bukowskis, Helsinki #287/R est:2000-2500

LINNQVIST, Hilding (1891-1984) Swedish
£2344 $4149 €3422 Woman with black-cock (62x49cm-24x19in) s. painted c.1915 exhib. 27-Apr-4 AB Stockholms Auktionsverk #843/R est:20000-25000 (S.KR 32000)
£2901 $5221 €4235 Campanil, Venice (55x66cm-22x26in) mono.i. 26-Apr-4 Bukowskis, Stockholm #108b/R est:30000-35000 (S.KR 40000)
£4029 $7132 €5882 Group of horses (63x81cm-25x32in) mono. panel exhib. 27-Apr-4 AB Stockholms Auktionsverk #842/R est:60000-80000 (S.KR 55000)
£6420 $10914 €9373 Still life of lilies (135x68cm-53x27in) init. 5-Nov-3 AB Stockholms Auktionsverk #681/R est:100000-125000 (S.KR 85000)
Works on paper
£369 $601 €539 Egyptian scene (20x27cm-8x11in) s. W/C exec.c.1946-47 exhib. 29-Sep-3 Lilla Bukowskis, Stockholm #366 (S.KR 4800)
£510 $939 €765 Still life of flowers (36x29cm-14x11in) init. W/C. 14-Jun-4 Lilla Bukowskis, Stockholm #334 (S.KR 7000)
£535 $862 €781 Cabaret audience (47x61cm-19x24in) s. W/C paper in two parts. 25-Aug-3 Lilla Bukowskis, Stockholm #789 (S.KR 7000)
£1088 $1958 €1588 The market in Chinon (42x58cm-17x23in) pencil. 26-Apr-4 Bukowskis, Stockholm #18/R est:20000-25000 (S.KR 15000)
£1099 $1945 €1605 Girl washing herself (104x76cm-41x30in) s.d.1917 W/C exhib.lit. 27-Apr-4 AB Stockholms Auktionsverk #868/R est:25000-30000 (S.KR 15000)
£1978 $3501 €2888 Traders at Kornhams market, Stockholm (35x25cm-14x10in) init. W/C pencil. 27-Apr-4 AB Stockholms Auktionsverk #841/R est:18000-20000 (S.KR 27000)
£2321 $4177 €3389 Horses and sleighs (21x37cm-8x15in) s.d.1917 mixed media. 26-Apr-4 Bukowskis, Stockholm #130/R est:40000-50000 (S.KR 32000)

LINO, Gustave (1893-1961) ?
£1135 $1895 €1600 Portrait d'un Juif Tunisien (60x50cm-24x20in) s. 20-Jun-3 Drouot Estimations, Paris #38 est:650-800
£1867 $3341 €2800 Mauresques le soir sur la terrasse, Alger (24x30cm-9x12in) s. i.verso cardboard. 16-May-4 Thierry & Lannon, Brest #155/R est:600-800
£3893 $7201 €5800 Alger, le port (38x55cm-15x22in) s. 15-Mar-4 Gros & Delettrez, Paris #211/R est:4000-6000
£6690 $11574 €9500 Marche aux moutons (59x90cm-23x35in) s. 14-Dec-3 St-Germain-en-Laye Encheres #66 est:10000-12000

LINO, Maria (1945-) ?
£278 $506 €420 Striped towel (50x60cm-20x24in) s.d.1985. 17-Jun-4 Frank Peege, Freiburg #1205/R

LINO, Silva (1911-1984) Portuguese
£2416 $4325 €3600 Convent of the Jeronimos (56x70cm-22x28in) s. board. 31-May-4 Cabral Moncada Leiloes, Lisbon #230/R est:3000-4500

LINS, Adolf (1856-1927) German
£874 $1486 €1250 Summer landscape with stream (49x37cm-19x15in) s. board. 20-Nov-3 Van Ham, Cologne #1719/R
£1268 $2028 €1800 Ducks by stream (46x28cm-18x11in) s. board. 18-Sep-3 Rieber, Stuttgart #1339/R est:1680
£2000 $3620 €3000 Behind the farmstead (21x35cm-8x14in) s. board. 1-Apr-4 Van Ham, Cologne #1518/R est:2000
£2000 $3640 €3000 Springtime (65x50cm-26x20in) s.d.91. 1-Jul-4 Van Ham, Cologne #1483/R est:1400
£2083 $3479 €3000 Ducks at edge of stream (56x73cm-22x29in) s. prov. 24-Oct-3 Ketterer, Hamburg #85/R est:3500-4000
£5882 $10000 €8588 Goose girl (66x86cm-26x34in) s.d.98. 29-Oct-3 Christie's, Rockefeller NY #54/R est:10000-15000

LINSENMAIER, Walter (1917-) German
Works on paper
£271 $462 €396 Ophrys fucifeora (26x19cm-10x7in) s.d.1947 gouache. 25-Nov-3 Germann, Zurich #832 (S.FR 600)

LINSON, Corwin Knapp (1864-1934) American
Works on paper
£246 $425 €359 By the sea of Galilee (20x30cm-8x12in) s.i. W/C gouache. 13-Dec-3 Sloans & Kenyon, Bethesda #519

LINT, Giacomo van (1723-1790) Italian
£26000 $44980 €37960 Rome, a view of the Ponte Rotto with the Basilica of Saint Peter's in distance (28x45cm-11x18in) 11-Dec-3 Sotheby's, London #231/R est:8000-12000
£68966 $115172 €100000 Rome, view of San Pietro (31x46cm-12x18in) lit. 12-Nov-3 Sotheby's, Milan #161/R est:50000-70000

LINT, Hendrik van (1684-1763) Flemish
£17241 $28793 €25000 View of promontory (23x34cm-9x13in) lit. 12-Nov-3 Sotheby's, Milan #160/R est:25000-35000
£26207 $43766 €38000 Village on the Mediterranean coast (23x34cm-9x13in) lit. 12-Nov-3 Sotheby's, Milan #159/R est:30000-40000
£33333 $60000 €48666 View of the Colosseum and Arch of Constantine, Rome (46x72cm-18x28in) s.i.indis.d. 22-Jan-4 Sotheby's, New York #64/R est:30000-50000
£35000 $64050 €51100 Extensive Italianate river landscape with huntsmen (35x44cm-14x17in) pair. 7-Jul-4 Christie's, London #105/R est:30000-40000
£50279 $90000 €73407 Saint Mark's Square, Venice (48x73cm-19x29in) s.indis.d. prov.lit. 27-May-4 Sotheby's, New York #112/R est:100000-150000
£128492 $230000 €187598 Piazza del Popolo, Rome (48x73cm-19x29in) s.i.d.1750 prov.lit. 27-May-4 Sotheby's, New York #111/R est:200000-300000

LINT, Hendrik van (attrib) (1684-1763) Flemish

£3056	$5500	€4462	View of Rome along the Tiber (52x63cm-20x25in) 21-Jan-4 Doyle, New York #112/R est:5000-7000

LINT, Louis van (1909-1986) Belgian

£497	$904	€750	Nature morte aux cartes et a la bouteille de vin (50x40cm-20x16in) s. 15-Jun-4 Galerie Moderne, Brussels #407/R
£1000	$1830	€1500	Vue de village (60x50cm-24x20in) s. 7-Jun-4 Palais de Beaux Arts, Brussels #390/R est:1200-1500
£1342	$2376	€2000	Composition (48x63cm-19x25in) s. paper. 27-Apr-4 Campo & Campo, Antwerp #244 est:800-1200
£1467	$2684	€2200	Vue sur le jardin (65x54cm-26x21in) s. 7-Jun-4 Palais de Beaux Arts, Brussels #199/R est:1500-2000
£1986	$3316	€2800	Abstraction (50x65cm-20x26in) s. 17-Jun-3 Vanderkindere, Brussels #133 est:3000-5000
£2400	$4296	€3600	Lumiere hivernale (100x80cm-39x31in) s.d.63 i.d.1964 verso lit. 15-May-4 De Vuyst, Lokeren #497/R est:5000-6000
£3077	$5138	€4400	Ma mere (60x50cm-24x20in) s.d.45 i.verso prov.lit. 11-Oct-3 De Vuyst, Lokeren #463/R est:3500-4000
Works on paper			
£2349	$4158	€3500	Abstraction (50x68cm-20x27in) s. W/C. 27-Apr-4 Campo & Campo, Antwerp #243/R est:2500-3500

LINT, Peter van (1609-1690) Flemish

£2837	$4738	€4000	Le Christ et la femme adultere (74x90cm-29x35in) copper. 19-Oct-3 Anaf, Lyon #200 est:4000-5000
£3000	$5400	€4380	Christ and the Adulterous (74x90cm-29x35in) copper. 20-Apr-4 Sotheby's, Olympia #260/R est:3000-4000
£6667	$12200	€10000	Marie Madeleine (54x40cm-21x16in) panel. 3-Jun-4 E & Eve, Paris #27/R est:8000-12000

LINT, Peter van (attrib) (1609-1690) Flemish

Works on paper			
£4397	$7343	€6200	Etude pur une statue de Neptune (32x19cm-13x7in) sanguine black crayon htd white gouache. 19-Oct-3 St-Germain-en-Laye Encheres #5/R est:3000-4000

LINT, Peter van (style) (1609-1690) Flemish

£7000	$11900	€10220	Adoration of the shepheards (69x87cm-27x34in) copper. 30-Oct-3 Sotheby's, Olympia #47/R est:3000-5000

LINTHORST, Jacobus (1745-1815) Dutch

£28889	$52000	€42178	Pineapple, plums, grapes and other fruit and flowers in a basket on marble ledge (58x44cm-23x17in) s.d.1810 panel. 23-Jan-4 Christie's, Rockefeller NY #35/R est:25000-35000

LINTON, Sir James Dromgole (1840-1916) British

£2400	$4416	€3504	View of a Swiss mountain village (45x83cm-18x33in) 11-Jun-4 Christie's, London #176/R est:2000-3000
Works on paper			
£650	$1040	€949	Interior scene with young lady looking into a hand mirror (46x33cm-18x13in) init.d.88 W/C. 8-Jan-3 Biddle & Webb, Birmingham #903
£920	$1527	€1343	Music that on the spirit lies, gentlier on tired eye-lids (36x40cm-14x16in) s. W/C prov. 1-Oct-3 Sotheby's, Olympia #176/R

LINTON, W (1791-1876) British

£1600	$2896	€2336	Views of Cheronoed and Napoli di Romania (13x18cm-5x7in) init. oil on card pair. 31-Mar-4 Brightwells, Leominster #959 est:2000-3000

LINTON, William (1791-1876) British

£550	$880	€803	Cheronoed. Napoli di Romania (11x16cm-4x6in) init. board pair. 16-Sep-3 Rosebery Fine Art, London #606
£860	$1539	€1256	Figures by a cottage. Cottage in a landscape (17x22cm-7x9in) mono. board pair. 27-May-4 Christie's, Kensington #189/R
£4469	$8000	€6525	View of the Tiber from Monte Mario (24x34cm-9x13in) s.i.d.1829 paper on canvas prov. 27-May-4 Sotheby's, New York #222/R est:4000-6000

LINTON, William (attrib) (1791-1876) British

£500	$930	€730	Ruined temple in an Italianate landscape (13x18cm-5x7in) oil on paper. 4-Mar-4 Christie's, Kensington #566/R

LINTON, William Evans (1878-?) British

£270	$500	€394	Camels near an oasis (25x32cm-10x13in) s. board. 16-Feb-4 Bonhams, Bath #78

LINTON, William Evans (circle) (1878-?) British

£7200	$12024	€10512	Summer pasture (49x75cm-19x30in) 14-Oct-3 Bearnes, Exeter #320/R est:600-900

LINTOTT, Edward Bernard (1875-1951) British

£378	$650	€552	Nude (25x33cm-10x13in) s. i.verso canvasboard. 7-Dec-3 Hindman, Chicago #812/R
£706	$1200	€1031	Floral still life (63x76cm-25x30in) s. 21-Nov-3 Skinner, Boston #383/R est:2000-3000
£900	$1647	€1314	Still life of summer flowers in a glass jug (76x64cm-30x25in) s. indis d. 8-Jul-4 Duke & Son, Dorchester #182/R

LINTZ, Frederik (1824-1909) Dutch

£318	$550	€464	Dutch interior (43x53cm-17x21in) s. 13-Dec-3 Charlton Hall, Columbia #280/R
£1176	$1965	€1717	Bird of mischief. Quick drink (17x12cm-7x5in) s. panel pair. 17-Nov-3 Waddingtons, Toronto #33/R (C.D 2600)

LINUS, Axel (1885-1980) American

£385	$662	€562	Smoke trees (50x60cm-20x24in) s. panel. 3-Dec-3 AB Stockholms Auktionsverk #2384/R (S.KR 5000)
£2060	$3750	€3008	Landscape (91x122cm-36x48in) s. 15-Jun-4 John Moran, Pasadena #50 est:3000-4000

LINZER, Fritz (20th C) German

£369	$687	€550	Lion in shadows (62x79cm-24x31in) s. 6-Mar-4 Arnold, Frankfurt #779

LION, Alexander (1823-1852) Belgian

£6986	$11877	€10200	Dejeuner des moissonneurs (61x80cm-24x31in) s.d.1849 panel. 10-Nov-3 Horta, Bruxelles #128/R
£10490	$17832	€15000	Fete dans la cour d'une maison de ville (97x77cm-38x30in) s.d.1845 panel. 18-Nov-3 Vanderkindere, Brussels #18/R est:9000-12000

LION, Fernand (19th C) ?

Sculpture			
£2222	$4000	€3244	Portrait of a woman (60cm-24in) i. marble. 21-Jan-4 Sotheby's, New York #197/R est:3000-5000

LION, Flora (1876-1958) British

£420	$743	€613	Portrait of a lady, seated in an embroidered pink dress (118x91cm-46x36in) s.d.1938. 29-Apr-4 Christie's, Kensington #59

LION, Pierre Joseph (1729-1809) Flemish

£3611	$6500	€5272	Portrait of Miss Lucy and Miss Frances Carpenter (107x92cm-42x36in) s. prov.exhib.lit. 23-Jan-4 Christie's, Rockefeller NY #119/R est:6000-8000

LIONE, Andrea di (1596-1675) Italian

£11000	$20130	€16060	Three Maries lamenting at the foot of the Cross (74x100cm-29x39in) prov. 8-Jul-4 Sotheby's, London #306/R est:10000-15000
£93960	$168188	€140000	Venus and ADonis (76x102cm-30x40in) s. prov.exhib.lit. 26-May-4 Porro, Milan #42/R est:220000-250000

LIONE, Andrea di (circle) (1596-1675) Italian

£28000	$51240	€42000	Poetry wins over Time (97x133cm-38x52in) 1-Jun-4 Sotheby's, Milan #150/R est:15000-20000

LIONEL, Percy (?) British

£270	$451	€394	Yacht towing rowing boat (33x48cm-13x19in) s.d.94. 17-Oct-3 Keys, Aylsham #621/R

LIOR (1971-) ?

£1668	$3002	€2435	Untitled (126x155cm-50x61in) s. 26-Apr-4 Bukowskis, Stockholm #575/R est:12000-15000 (S.KR 23000)

LIOTARD, Jean-Étienne (attrib) (1702-1789) Swiss

£19444	$35000	€28388	Portrait of a lady (67x53cm-26x21in) 21-Jan-4 Sotheby's, New York #103/R est:35000-45000

LIOZU, Charles (19/20th C) French

£284	$474	€400	Portrait of lady (65x54cm-26x21in) s. 20-Oct-3 Sant Agostino, Torino #59/R

LIPCHITZ, Jacques (1891-1973) French

Sculpture			
£3209	$6000	€4685	Gertrude Stein (20cm-8in) s. num.2/7 pat bronze prov.lit. 25-Feb-4 Christie's, Rockefeller NY #50/R est:8000-10000
£5000	$8350	€7300	L'enlevement d'Europe (24cm-9in) i.with sig. bronze num.6/7 st.f.Luigi Tommasi prov.lit. 22-Oct-3 Sotheby's, Olympia #145/R est:5000-7000
£8649	$16000	€12628	Study for Hagar - Maquette number 2 (16x23cm-6x9in) init. num.8/10 base plaster iron filings conceived 1948 lit. 12-Feb-4 Sotheby's, New York #6/R est:5000-7000
£11765	$22000	€17177	Course (37cm-15in) sts.ig. pat bronze lit. 25-Feb-4 Christie's, Rockefeller NY #71/R est:1400-18000
£14130	$26000	€20630	Rape of Europa (51x28x20cm-20x11x8in) i. num.1/7 brown pat bronze st.f.Tammari Pietrasanta exec 1969-70. 27-Jun-4 Freeman, Philadelphia #68/R est:15000-25000
£21000	$38640	€30660	Theseus and the minotaur (63cm-25in) s. bronze prov.lit. 24-Mar-4 Sotheby's, Olympia #178/R est:15000-20000
£36313	$65000	€53017	Rape of Europa I (41cm-16in) i.sig. num.3/7 brown pat bronze conceived 1938 lit. 6-May-4 Sotheby's, New York #388/R est:40000-60000
£85294	$145000	€124529	Seated man - meditation (36cm-14in) s.base onyx exec 1925 prov.lit. 5-Nov-3 Christie's, Rockefeller NY #266/R est:90000-145000
£223464	$400000	€326257	Baigneuse (65cm-26in) s. num.1/7 pat bronze prov.exhib. 6-May-4 Sotheby's, New York #151/R est:400000-600000
Works on paper			
£1816	$3250	€2651	Struggle (30x23cm-12x9in) s.d.1940 brush India ink wash prov. 6-May-4 Doyle, New York #109/R est:1500-2500
£2797	$4755	€4000	Figures (55x43cm-22x17in) s. gouache over pencil. 29-Nov-3 Villa Grisebach, Berlin #293/R est:4000-6000
£51397	$92000	€75040	Still life of a newspaper and musical instruments (21x29cm-8x11in) s. gouache pencil exec 1917 prov.exhib. 5-May-4 Christie's, Rockefeller NY #112/R est:60000-80000
£82353	$140000	€120235	Femme assise (46x37cm-18x15in) s. gouache over pencil panel executed 1918 prov.exhib. 5-Nov-3 Christie's, Rockefeller NY #264/R est:70000-90000

LIPENSKY, Franz (1934-) German
Sculpture
£1467 $2669 €2200 Family of ducks (26cm-10in) i. num.1/15 bronze. 1-Jul-4 Van Ham, Cologne #1039/R est:1900

LIPHART, Ernest Friedrich von (1847-1934) Russian
£11189 $19021 €16000 Reclining female nude on divan (88x140cm-35x55in) s.cyrillic d.1898. 20-Nov-3 Van Ham, Cologne #1721/R est:15000

LIPKAT, Maria (1893-1971) Austrian
£490 $842 €700 Allegory of music (97x72cm-38x28in) s.d.20 board. 4-Dec-3 Schopman, Hamburg #691/R

LIPKE, Alexis Christian (1819-1885) Danish
£280 $442 €409 Portrait of a young woman with embroidery anglaise collar and black dress (25x22cm-10x9in) s.d.1838. 27-Apr-3 Wilkinson, Doncaster #316/R

LIPOT, Herman (1884-1972) Hungarian
£2254 $3741 €3200 In the harem (62x65cm-24x26in) s. 16-Jun-3 Dorotheum, Vienna #140/R est:2600-3000

LIPP, Kilian (1953-) German
£503 $921 €750 Path on a snow covered mountain (60x70cm-24x28in) s.d.88 i.verso lit. 8-Jul-4 Allgauer, Kempten #2156/R

LIPPENS, Piet (1890-1981) Belgian
£278 $464 €400 Roulotte (40x55cm-16x22in) s. 21-Oct-3 Campo, Vlaamse Kaai #924
£333 $600 €500 Landscape with church (48x59cm-19x23in) s. 26-Apr-4 Bernaerts, Antwerp #279/R

LIPPI, Filippino (1457-1504) Italian
Works on paper
£1399 $2336 €2000 Madonna appearing to St John the Evangelist (21x16cm-8x6in) pen. 28-Jun-3 Bolland & Marotz, Bremen #582/R est:2200

LIPPI, Lorenzo (1606-1665) Italian
£100000 $173000 €146000 Judith (121x97cm-48x38in) 11-Dec-3 Sotheby's, London #20/R est:35000-45000
Works on paper
£260 $450 €380 Monk holding a candle (22x15cm-9x6in) i. red chk prov. 12-Dec-3 Christie's, Kensington #332
£1703 $3100 €2486 Saint gesturing to the right, with study of the left arm (40x24cm-16x9in) red chk. 4-Feb-4 Christie's, Rockefeller NY #123/R est:1500-2000

LIPPINCOTT, William H (1849-1920) American
£1657 $3000 €2419 Woods and stream (63x76cm-25x30in) s.indis.i. s.verso prov. 31-Mar-4 Sotheby's, New York #96/R est:3000-7000
£2096 $3500 €3060 Little helper (56x37cm-22x15in) s.i. 7-Oct-3 Sotheby's, New York #84/R est:4000-6000
£25568 $45000 €37329 Marginal Way (58x74cm-23x29in) s.d.1915 i.verso prov.exhib.lit. 19-May-4 Sotheby's, New York #27/R est:50000-70000

LIPPMANN, Karl Friedrich (1883-1957) German
£382 $603 €550 Yellow, violet and rose coloured mallow in ceramic jug (100x69cm-39x27in) s.d.1928. 6-Sep-3 Arnold, Frankfurt #608/R
£500 $900 €750 Summer view of Runkel an der Lahn from Schadek (50x65cm-20x26in) s.d. panel. 24-Apr-4 Reiss & Sohn, Konigstein #5364/R

LIPPS, Richard (1857-1926) German
£336 $617 €500 House on village street (51x62cm-20x24in) s. board. 27-Mar-4 Dannenberg, Berlin #587/R
£915 $1639 €1300 Young girl praying to Madonna in a night-time town scene (71x43cm-28x17in) s. lit. 8-Jan-4 Allgauer, Kempten #2452/R

LIPS, Harry (1918-1979) Dutch
£753 $1281 €1100 City mine (49x59cm-19x23in) s.d.56 board. 5-Nov-3 Vendue Huis, Gravenhage #510/R
Works on paper
£909 $1564 €1300 Vrouwe Church in Maastricht (47x62cm-19x24in) s.d.70 gouache. 3-Dec-3 Auction Maastricht #1014/R

LIPS, Harry (attrib) (1918-1979) Dutch
Works on paper
£909 $1564 €1300 Vrouwe church in Maastricht (47x62cm-19x24in) s.d.70 gouache. 4-Dec-3 Vendue Huis, Gravenhage #1014

LIPS, Johann Heinrich (1758-1817) Swiss
Works on paper
£995 $1593 €1453 Two seated men. Woman at water pump (19x15cm-7x6in) pencil Indian ink board three. 19-Sep-3 Koller, Zurich #3129/R est:1200-1800 (S.FR 2200)
£4600 $8418 €6716 Portrait of Johann Casper Lavater, seated and reading a book (30x23cm-12x9in) W/C over engraved outlines prov. 6-Jul-4 Christie's, London #186/R est:1000-1500

LIPSCOMBE, Guy (fl.1908-1937) British
£520 $972 €759 Sunlit house. House overlooking a bay (40x51cm-16x20in) s. one d.1943 pair. 24-Feb-4 Bonhams, Knowle #50

LIPSHITZ, Lippy (1903-1980) South African
Sculpture
£1345 $2434 €1964 Endless nude (287cm-113in) s.d.1959 teak. 30-Mar-4 Stephan Welz, Johannesburg #544 est:7000-10000 (SA.R 16000)

LIPTAI (1893-?) German
£1678 $2853 €2400 Woodcutter in summer wood (101x142cm-40x56in) s. 20-Nov-3 Van Ham, Cologne #1722 est:1900

LIRA, Armando (1903-1959) Chilean
£515 $875 €752 Vase with gladiola (70x50cm-28x20in) s. 23-Nov-3 Subastas Odalys, Caracas #146/R
£637 $1000 €930 Fruit and wine (50x60cm-20x24in) s. 23-Nov-2 Subastas Odalys, Caracas #15
£637 $1000 €930 Still life (63x52cm-25x20in) s. 23-Nov-2 Subastas Odalys, Caracas #47
£658 $1020 €961 Landscape (50x59cm-20x23in) s. painted 1937. 3-Nov-2 Subastas Odalys, Caracas #41/R
£958 $1600 €1399 Landscape in a village (36x45cm-14x18in) painted 1939. 13-Jul-3 Subastas Odalys, Caracas #101
£1012 $1690 €1478 Landscape (60x70cm-24x28in) s. painted 1957. 19-Oct-3 Subastas Odalys, Caracas #107/R
£1123 $1875 €1640 Landscape in a village (51x61cm-20x24in) s. painted 1957. 13-Jul-3 Subastas Odalys, Caracas #20
£1266 $2000 €1848 Landscape (59x72cm-23x28in) s. 1-Dec-2 Subastas Odalys, Caracas #13/R
Works on paper
£441 $750 €644 Carlos III Bridge (60x46cm-24x18in) mixed media exec.1939. 23-Nov-3 Subastas Odalys, Caracas #21

LISA, Mario (1908-1992) Italian
£336 $594 €500 Canal in Venice (50x38cm-20x15in) s. board oval. 1-May-4 Meeting Art, Vercelli #290
£467 $859 €700 Casalborgone (8x16cm-3x6in) s. s.i.d.1968 verso board. 14-Jun-4 Sant Agostino, Torino #211/R
£533 $981 €800 Rural houses (30x24cm-12x9in) s.d.1952 s.i.verso board. 14-Jun-4 Sant Agostino, Torino #226/R
£748 $1339 €1100 Around Livorno (23x45cm-9x18in) s.d.1966 exhib. 22-Mar-4 Sant Agostino, Torino #165/R
£851 $1421 €1200 Paris, Place Blanch (17x23cm-7x9in) s.i.d.1952 board. 20-Oct-3 Sant Agostino, Torino #165/R
£1361 $2435 €2000 Still life (46x55cm-18x22in) s. exhib. 22-Mar-4 Sant Agostino, Torino #546/R est:2500
£1931 $3206 €2800 Still life (38x49cm-15x19in) s. cardboard. 1-Oct-3 Della Rocca, Turin #24/R

LISAERT, Pieter (16th C) Flemish
£6111 $11000 €8922 Adoration of the shepherds (28x22cm-11x9in) copper. 23-Jan-4 Christie's, Rockefeller NY #163/R est:10000-15000

LISAERT, Pieter IV (1595-c.1629) Flemish
£2818 $4931 €4000 L'annonciation (54x40cm-21x16in) panel. 18-Dec-3 Tajan, Paris #71/R est:5000-7000

LISAERT, Pieter IV (attrib) (1595-c.1629) Flemish
£706 $1235 €1000 La nativite (26x21cm-10x8in) copper. 18-Dec-3 Tajan, Paris #73

LISCHKE, Emmy (1860-1919) German
£352 $563 €500 Mary with Christ child in evening sun (52x80cm-20x31in) s. 18-Sep-3 Rieber, Stuttgart #989/R
£443 $691 €700 Forest clearing (39x26cm-15x10in) i. verso canvas on panel. 18-Oct-2 Von Zezschwitz, Munich #38/R

LISENKOV, Valentin Aleksandrovich (1938-) Russian
£550 $1001 €803 Field workers (47x68cm-19x27in) s.d.61 card on board. 21-Jun-4 Bonhams, New Bond Street #35/R

LISIEWSKA, Anna Dorothea (1721-1782) German
£9028 $14715 €13000 Portrait of King Friedrich Wilhelm II of Prussia (110x87cm-43x34in) prov. 25-Sep-3 Dr Fritz Nagel, Stuttgart #1250/R est:3000

LISIEWSKA, Anna Rosina (1716-1783) German
£2083 $3750 €3041 Portrait of Jean Marie Louise Kernezabre (81x65cm-32x26in) i.verso canvas on masonite. 21-Jan-4 Doyle, New York #84/R est:2000-3000

LISIO, Arnaldo de (1869-1949) Italian
£556 $1000 €812 Portrait of a lady, in traditional costume (86x61cm-34x24in) s. 25-Jan-4 Hindman, Chicago #1047/R
£600 $1104 €900 Portrait of Chieffo (53x44cm-21x17in) s.d.29. 10-Jun-4 Christie's, Rome #63
£791 $1400 €1155 Figures dining on a balcony on a Mediterranean night (53x74cm-21x29in) s. 2-May-4 Bonhams & Butterfields, San Francisco #1030/R est:2500-3500
Works on paper
£520 $962 €759 Portrait of a gypsy girl (69x49cm-27x19in) s.i. W/C. 13-Jul-4 Rosebery Fine Art, London #544
£1119 $1869 €1600 Serenade (50x70cm-20x28in) s.i. W/C card. 26-Jun-3 Sant Agostino, Torino #36/R est:1400

LISKA, Hans (20th C) German
Works on paper
£299 $536 €440 Paula Wessely and Wily Birgel (50x40cm-20x16in) s.d.39 W/C lit. 20-Mar-4 Bergmann, Erlangen #1173

LISMER, Arthur (1885-1969) Canadian
£3252 $5821 €4748 Rocky Shore (30x40cm-12x16in) s. prov. 31-May-4 Sotheby's, Toronto #166/R est:5000-7000 (C.D 8000)
£3378 $5743 €4932 C O D (30x41cm-12x16in) s.d.46 panel prov. 18-Nov-3 Sotheby's, Toronto #86/R est:5000-7000 (C.D 7500)
£3604 $6126 €5262 Interior still life with totem fragment (30x30cm-12x12in) s.verso panel prov.exhib. 18-Nov-3 Sotheby's, Toronto #183/R est:4000-6000 (C.D 8000)
£4054 $6892 €5919 Dock still life (30x41cm-12x16in) s. panel prov. 18-Nov-3 Sotheby's, Toronto #85/R est:5000-7000 (C.D 9000)
£4241 $7295 €6192 Long Beach, Vancouver (30x40cm-12x16in) s. i.verso board prov. 2-Dec-3 Joyner Waddington, Toronto #127/R est:10000-15000 (C.D 9500)
£4878 $8732 €7122 BC Forest (45x35cm-18x14in) init. s.i.d.1965 verso canvasboard prov. 6-May-4 Heffel, Vancouver #86/R est:8000-12000 (C.D 12000)
£4955 $8423 €7234 Dark spruce and logs (16x12cm-6x5in) s.d.55 i.d.verso panel prov.lit. 18-Nov-3 Sotheby's, Toronto #43/R est:10000-12000 (C.D 11000)
£5285 $9459 €7716 Forest interior (40x30cm-16x12in) s. i.d.c.1960 verso board lit. 27-May-4 Heffel, Vancouver #165/R est:8000-12000 (C.D 13000)
£5357 $9214 €7821 Killicks and Anchors (30x40cm-12x16in) s.d.45 panel prov. 2-Dec-3 Joyner Waddington, Toronto #99/R est:12000-15000 (C.D 12000)
£6098 $10915 €8903 Trees on a rocky coastline, Vancouver Island, BC (45x35cm-18x14in) s.d.1964 canvasboard prov. 27-May-4 Heffel, Vancouver #167/R est:12000-16000 (C.D 15000)
£7600 $13908 €11096 B C Forest (51x41cm-20x16in) s. panel prov. 1-Jun-4 Joyner Waddington, Toronto #154/R est:10000-15000 (C.D 19000)
£7724 $13825 €11277 Bridge at the forks of the Credit (25x30cm-10x12in) d.1928 panel prov. 31-May-4 Sotheby's, Toronto #80/R est:15000-20000 (C.D 19000)
£8929 $15357 €13036 Rock and Pine,Georgian Bay (30x40cm-12x16in) s.d.1950 panel. 2-Dec-3 Joyner Waddington, Toronto #69/R est:15000-20000 (C.D 20000)
£10163 $18191 €14838 Rough weather, Georgian Bay (41x51cm-16x20in) s. s.i.d.1959 verso prov.exhib.lit. 31-May-4 Sotheby's, Toronto #85/R est:15000-20000 (C.D 25000)
£13211 $23648 €19288 View of the lake through the trees (30x39cm-12x15in) s.i. canvas on board prov. 31-May-4 Sotheby's, Toronto #56/R est:20000-25000 (C.D 32500)
Works on paper
£440 $805 €642 Rocky landscape (29x39cm-11x15in) s. ink brush. 1-Jun-4 Joyner Waddington, Toronto #405 (C.D 1100)
£631 $1072 €921 Starfish and dock litter, Cape Breton (33x40cm-13x16in) init. i.verso conte executed c.1938 prov. 27-Nov-3 Heffel, Vancouver #160/R (C.D 1400)
£773 $1260 €1129 Rocky shore, Cape Breton (29x39cm-11x15in) s. graphite prov. 23-Sep-3 Ritchie, Toronto #151/R est:1500-2000 (C.D 1700)
£95041 $172025 €138760 Old mill, Baie St. Paul (66x81cm-26x32in) s.i. 18-Apr-4 Levis, Calgary #64/R est:50000-60000 (C.D 230000)

LISMONDE, Jules (1908-2001) Belgian
Works on paper
£350 $594 €500 Le moulin rose a Linkebeek (50x65cm-20x26in) s.d.50 chl. 18-Nov-3 Vanderkindere, Brussels #188
£490 $817 €700 View of the room with throne in Brussels (64x84cm-25x33in) s. chl dr. 11-Oct-3 De Vuyst, Lokeren #228
£733 $1342 €1100 Rome I (47x62cm-19x24in) s.d.54 chl exhib. 7-Jun-4 Palais de Beaux Arts, Brussels #183/R
£872 $1544 €1300 Composition (73x92cm-29x36in) s.d.1969 dr. 27-Apr-4 Campo & Campo, Antwerp #151

LISS, Jan (attrib) (c.1595-1629) Dutch
£18421 $33895 €28000 David holding Goliath's head (69x56cm-27x22in) exhib. 24-Jun-4 Christie's, Paris #77/R est:6000-8000

LISS, Jan (circle) (c.1595-1629) Dutch
£17808 $30274 €26000 Man stealing a lady's purse (64x50cm-25x20in) 5-Nov-3 Christie's, Amsterdam #36/R est:4000-6000

LISSAC, Pierre (1878-) French
Works on paper
£2128 $3553 €3000 Fete devant les remparts (48x63cm-19x25in) s. gouache crayon. 16-Jun-3 Gros & Delettrez, Paris #396/R est:2800-3000

LISSE, Dirck van der (?-1669) Dutch
£2000 $3740 €2920 Diana and Actaeon (21x32cm-8x13in) mono. copper prov. 27-Feb-4 Christie's, Kensington #81/R est:1500-2500
£6787 $10860 €9909 Sleeping nymph in southern landscape (50x37cm-20x15in) mono. panel prov. 19-Sep-3 Koller, Zurich #3028/R est:15000-20000 (S.FR 15000)

LISSE, Dirck van der (attrib) (?-1669) Dutch
£559 $962 €800 Diane et ses nymphes au bain (48x41cm-19x16in) panel. 8-Dec-3 Piasa, Paris #3
£1133 $2029 €1700 Satyr and nymph with living creatures by a grotto (26cm-10in circular) panel. 17-May-4 Glerum, Amsterdam #48/R est:2000-3000

LISSITZKY, El (1890-1941) Russian
Photographs
£14493 $23768 €20000 Untitled (9x13cm-4x5in) i. verso photogram vintage silver gelatin prov.lit. 30-May-3 Villa Grisebach, Berlin #1266/R est:20000-30000
Prints
£115000 $209300 €167900 Die plastische gestaltung der elktro-mechanischen schau (55x46cm-22x18in) s. col lithograph portfolio of ten. 30-Jun-4 Christie's, London #247/R est:100000-150000
Works on paper
£70000 $127400 €102200 Path of Energy and Dynamic Flows (21x29cm-8x11in) i. gouache W/C pencil tracing paper exec c.1920 prov. 5-Feb-4 Christie's, London #347/R est:45000-65000

LIST, Franz (1898-1986) ?
£398 $637 €581 Daning at Sonderho Inn (90x145cm-35x57in) s. 22-Sep-3 Rasmussen, Vejle #304 (D.KR 4200)

LIST, Herbert (1903-1974) German
Photographs
£1916 $3200 €2797 Blick aus dem Fenster II, der Tanz der Roecke - Dance of the skirts (22x29cm-9x11in) gelatin silver print exec.1953 prov.lit. 17-Oct-3 Phillips, New York #122/R est:2500-3500
£1944 $3500 €2838 Jean Cocteau (28x22cm-11x9in) i.d.1948 gelatin silver print. 23-Apr-4 Phillips, New York #195/R est:4000-6000
£2083 $3542 €3000 View from window I, Trastevere (29x17cm-11x7in) gelatin silver lit. 31-Oct-3 Lempertz, Koln #220/R est:3000
£2333 $4293 €3500 Hyde Park, London (24x19cm-9x7in) i. verso bromide silver gelatin prov.lit.exhib. 10-Jun-4 Villa Grisebach, Berlin #1190/R est:3000-4000
£2639 $4486 €3800 Le couple (29x36cm-11x14in) s.d. verso gelatin silver lit. prov. 31-Oct-3 Lempertz, Koln #217/R est:4000
£2727 $4636 €3900 Wooden stakes in still water of the Bodensee (29x19cm-11x7in) s.i. verso silver gelatin prov. 27-Nov-3 Villa Grisebach, Berlin #1295/R est:2800-3200

LISTER, Edward d'Arcy (1911-) British
£2000 $3400 €2920 Boatyard scene with various yachts laid up for repair (74x61cm-29x24in) s.d.66. 30-Oct-3 Grant, Worcester #607/R est:2000-3000

LISTER, William Lister (1859-1943) Australian
£611 $1111 €892 River landscape with seated figure (48x63cm-19x25in) s. hessian on board. 16-Jun-4 Deutscher-Menzies, Melbourne #549/R est:2000-4000 (A.D 1600)
£1349 $2252 €2024 Fields in the valley (87x109cm-34x43in) s. 27-Oct-3 Goodman, Sydney #216/R est:2500-3500 (A.D 3250)
Works on paper
£249 $415 €364 Queensland coast (25x90cm-10x35in) s. W/C. 17-Nov-3 Waddingtons, Toronto #24/R (C.D 550)
£345 $538 €500 Pulpit Rock, Blue Mountains (32x49cm-13x19in) s. W/C. 1-Aug-2 Joel, Victoria #221 est:1200-1400 (A.D 1000)
£732 $1149 €1061 Approaching storm (27x91cm-11x36in) s. W/C. 26-Aug-3 Lawson Menzies, Sydney #70 est:2000-3000 (A.D 1800)
£813 $1455 €1187 Coming storm (27x90cm-11x35in) s. W/C gouache. 10-May-4 Joel, Victoria #389/R est:1500-2000 (A.D 2000)
£1277 $2170 €1864 The Blue Mountains (50x33cm-20x13in) s. W/C. 25-Nov-3 Christie's, Melbourne #264 est:1500-2500 (A.D 3000)

LISZEWSKI, Christian Friedrich Reinhold (1725-1794) German
£8451 $14620 €12000 Portrait of Kasimire, Countess zur Lippe-Detmold (83x67cm-33x26in) prov. 10-Dec-3 Christie's, Amsterdam #885/R est:12000-16000
£15493 $26803 €22000 Portrait of Henriette Catharine Agnes, Baroness von Loen auf Kappeln (126x113cm-50x44in) s.d.1764 prov.lit. 10-Dec-3 Christie's, Amsterdam #884/R est:15000-20000

LISZT, Maria (20th C) American
£233 $400 €340 Birches (51x41cm-20x16in) s. painted c.1950. 7-Dec-3 Treadway Gallery, Cincinnati #538/R

LITHOW, Leo (20th C) British?
£2300 $4232 €3358 Sunshine at Arbe, mother and children outside cliff top house (36x46cm-14x18in) s. panel. 26-Mar-4 ELR Auctions, Sheffield #337/R est:200-300
£3000 $5520 €4380 Italian street scene (53x34cm-21x13in) s. panel. 26-Mar-4 ELR Auctions, Sheffield #340/R est:150-250

LITOVCHENKO, Boris (1938-) Russian
£359 $600 €524 San Francisco Harbour scene. s. 15-Nov-3 Harvey Clar, Oakland #1270

LITTECZKY, Endre (1880-1953) Hungarian
£454 $804 €663 Venice (51x66cm-20x26in) s. 28-Apr-4 Kieselbach, Budapest #113/R (H.F 170000)

LITTLE, George Léon (fl.1884-1926) British
£516 $950 €753 Landscape (25x36cm-10x14in) s. board. 27-Jun-4 Hindman, Chicago #1018 est:500-700
£581 $1000 €848 Landscape near Fay Gate, Sussex (20x28cm-8x11in) s. board. 7-Dec-3 Hindman, Chicago #761/R
Works on paper
£450 $833 €657 Pastoral with sheep grazing (25x36cm-10x14in) s. W/C. 13-Feb-4 Keys, Aylsham #444/R

LITTLE, James (fl.1880-1910) British
Works on paper
£267 $461 €390 Dutch canal view (30x20cm-12x8in) s. W/C. 9-Dec-3 Pinneys, Montreal #72 (C.D 600)
£300 $501 €438 On the harbour quay (52x35cm-20x14in) s. W/C. 16-Oct-3 Lyon & Turnbull, Edinburgh #153
£340 $626 €496 Quai du Pollil Dieppe, fisher folk with the days catch (30x39cm-12x15in) s. W/C. 26-Mar-4 ELR Auctions, Sheffield #322
£420 $672 €613 French townscape (48x33cm-19x13in) s. W/C. 15-May-3 Bonhams, Edinburgh #349
£450 $788 €657 Edinburgh Castle from Johnstone Terrace (30x20cm-12x8in) s. prov. 18-Dec-3 John Nicholson, Haslemere #1072

£700 $1281 €1022 Dordrecht (23x33cm-9x13in) s. W/C. 8-Apr-4 Bonhams, Edinburgh #134
£1000 $1860 €1460 St. Giles Kirk, Edinburgh (25x32cm-10x13in) s. pencil W/C htd white. 4-Mar-4 Christie's, Kensington #248/R est:1000-1500

LITTLE, John C (1928-) Canadian
£680 $1244 €993 Norman D Clement, Toronto, at Bickerdike Pier, (21x26cm-8x10in) s. painted 1960. 1-Jun-4 Joyner Waddington, Toronto #50/R est:1800-2200 (C.D 1700)
£1440 $2635 €2102 Poetic melancholy of Rue la Gauchetiere MTL - Sunday apres midi (25x35cm-10x14in) s.d.68 verso prov. 1-Jun-4 Joyner Waddington, Toronto #324/R est:2000-3000 (C.D 3600)
£1518 $2611 €2216 Rue Arcade, Montreal (21x26cm-8x10in) s. prov. 2-Dec-3 Joyner Waddington, Toronto #6/R est:2000-2500 (C.D 3400)
£1563 $2688 €2282 Summer morning, Matin estival, Rue de Bullion a Varennes, Montreal (30x40cm-12x16in) s. painted 1981 prov. 2-Dec-3 Joyner Waddington, Toronto #172/R est:3500-4500 (C.D 3500)
£2009 $3455 €2933 Rue Coursol at Vinet, St Henri (20x25cm-8x10in) s. canvasboard painted 1971 prov. 2-Dec-3 Joyner Waddington, Toronto #178/R est:2000-2500 (C.D 4500)
£2140 $3638 €3124 Flaque d'eau, Rue Logan et Plessis (30x40cm-12x16in) s. s.i.d.1987 verso prov. 27-Nov-3 Heffel, Vancouver #44/R est:1500-2500 (C.D 4750)
£2400 $4392 €3504 Epicerie G Faucher, corner of Notre Dame and Marche Champlain, Quebec (25x20cm-10x8in) s. canvasboard painted 1960. 1-Jun-4 Joyner Waddington, Toronto #108/R est:3000-5000 (C.D 6000)
£2800 $5124 €4088 La Gauchetiere St, Chinatown, Montreal (30x40cm-12x16in) s. canvasboard prov. 1-Jun-4 Joyner Waddington, Toronto #2/R est:3000-4000 (C.D 7000)
£3049 $5457 €4452 Rue St Eustache, Quebec (30x40cm-12x16in) s. s.i.d.1968 verso prov. 27-May-4 Heffel, Vancouver #133/R est:3500-4500 (C.D 7500)
£3153 $5360 €4603 Rue Henri Julien, le matin apres la neige, Montreal (61x76cm-24x30in) s. s.i.d.1981 verso prov. 27-Nov-3 Heffel, Vancouver #43/R est:4000-6000 (C.D 7000)
£3491 $5935 €5097 Dimanche matin, anse a Beaufils Gape, Quebec (71x91cm-28x36in) s. s.i.d.1969 stretcher verso prov. 18-Nov-3 Sotheby's, Toronto #95/R est:7000-9000 (C.D 7750)
£5600 $10248 €8176 Rue de Bullion vers Av. Mont-Royal, D'Autrefois, Montreal (60x90cm-24x35in) s. prov. 1-Jun-4 Joyner Waddington, Toronto #64/R est:12000-15000 (C.D 14000)
£7200 $13176 €10512 Rue St Dominic with old General Hospital at La Gauchetiere St (60x75cm-24x30in) s. 1-Jun-4 Joyner Waddington, Toronto #22/R est:5000-7000 (C.D 18000)

LITTLE, John Wesley (1867-1923) American
Works on paper
£353 $600 €515 Afternoon concert. s.d.1886 W/C. 22-Nov-3 New Orleans Auction, New Orleans #1173/R

LITTLE, Philip (1857-1942) American
£2683 $4750 €3917 Spring landscape with wildflowers (76x61cm-30x24in) s.d.1932. 2-May-4 Grogan, Boston #85/R

LITTLECHILD, George (20th C) North American
Works on paper
£432 $721 €631 Horses talking no.2 (75x75cm-30x30in) s.i.d. mixed media. 17-Nov-3 Hodgins, Calgary #150/R est:750-1000 (C.D 955)

LITTLEFIELD, William Horace (1902-1969) American
£307 $500 €448 Statue of a young boy (23x25cm-9x10in) s.verso board painted 1949. 19-Jul-3 Outer Cape Auctions, Provincetown #179/R
£389 $700 €568 Collision (41x58cm-16x23in) s.d.March 21 1951 s.i.verso masonite. 23-Jan-4 Freeman, Philadelphia #254/R
Works on paper
£258 $475 €377 Boxers (46x33cm-18x13in) s.d.1929 ink. 25-Jun-4 Freeman, Philadelphia #56/R

LITTLEJOHN, William (1929-) British
Works on paper
£480 $802 €701 Chalice and fish shrine (54x86cm-21x34in) s.d.90 W/C. 16-Oct-3 Bonhams, Edinburgh #16
£500 $835 €730 Blue paper fish and mirror (56x94cm-22x37in) s.d.1988 W/C oval. 16-Oct-3 Lyon & Turnbull, Edinburgh #53
£600 $1002 €876 Mirror and origami crane - yellow (62x95cm-24x37in) s.d.1988 W/C mixed media. 16-Oct-3 Bonhams, Edinburgh #26/R

LITTLEJOHNS, John (1874-?) British
Works on paper
£319 $578 €466 Harbour on the French Riviera (35x48cm-14x19in) s.d.1948 W/C. 30-Mar-4 Stephan Welz, Johannesburg #152 est:2000-3000 (SA.R 3800)

LITTROW, Leo von (1860-1914) Austrian
£933 $1671 €1400 Fishing boats (24x36cm-9x14in) s. 12-May-4 Stadion, Trieste #678/R
£2657 $4517 €3800 In the Lagoon, Venice (33x64cm-13x25in) s. 24-Nov-3 Dorotheum, Vienna #7/R est:2800-3200
£4027 $7128 €6000 Woman sewing (42x30cm-17x12in) s. panel. 28-Apr-4 Wiener Kunst Auktionen, Vienna #64/R est:5000-10000
£4027 $7208 €6000 Flowers near the forest path (65x53cm-26x21in) i.verso board. 27-May-4 Dorotheum, Vienna #236/R est:5000-6000
£4861 $8264 €7000 Garden of Villa Hojos near Fiume (46x70cm-18x28in) i. stretcher. 28-Oct-3 Wiener Kunst Auktionen, Vienna #56/R est:7000-25000

LITVINOVSKY, Pinchas (1894-1985) Israeli
£437 $800 €638 Figures in a landscape (40x28cm-16x11in) s. oil paper. 1-Feb-4 Ben-Ami, Tel Aviv #4652/R
£440 $800 €660 Figures in the room (27x38cm-11x15in) s. cardboard painted c.1930. 1-Jul-4 Ben-Ami, Tel Aviv #4942/R
£519 $950 €758 The dance (59x44cm-23x17in) s. oil paper painted c.1940. 1-Feb-4 Ben-Ami, Tel Aviv #4653/R
£667 $1200 €974 Young man (53x38cm-21x15in) 24-Apr-4 Du Mouchelle, Detroit #3160/R est:500-800
£833 $1500 €1216 Two men (46x30cm-18x12in) oil paper on wood panel. 24-Apr-4 Du Mouchelle, Detroit #3161/R est:700-1200
£847 $1500 €1237 Young girl by the house (61x45cm-24x18in) s. oil silk paper on canvas. 1-May-4 Ben-Ami, Tel Aviv #4813/R est:2200-3000
£934 $1700 €1401 Figures and animals (60x45cm-24x18in) s. oil paper on canvas painted c.1930. 1-Jul-4 Ben-Ami, Tel Aviv #4992/R est:1800-2400
£1186 $2100 €1732 Figures and animals (78x57cm-31x22in) s. cardboard painted c.1930. 1-May-4 Ben-Ami, Tel Aviv #4812/R est:2600-3200
£1582 $2800 €2310 Interior with figures (55x75cm-22x30in) s. oil paper on canvas painted c.1931 prov. 1-May-4 Ben-Ami, Tel Aviv #4776/R est:3000-4000
£2596 $4750 €3790 Family (68x92cm-27x36in) s. s.verso. 1-Jun-4 Ben-Ami, Tel Aviv #4922/R est:6000-8000
£4011 $7100 €5856 Nargilla smoker and three women (130x195cm-51x77in) s.verso painted 1950. 1-May-4 Ben-Ami, Tel Aviv #4814/R est:8000-12000
Works on paper
£412 $750 €618 Young boy (48x35cm-19x14in) s. W/C. 1-Jul-4 Ben-Ami, Tel Aviv #4939/R

LIU BAOGUO (1963-) Chinese
Works on paper
£608 $1089 €900 Jeune fille au poisson (40x60cm-16x24in) pigment canvas. 5-May-4 Coutau Begarie, Paris #128/R

LIU CHI-WEI (1912-2002) Chinese
Works on paper
£898 $1500 €1311 Sight zebra (51x74cm-20x29in) W/C gouache. 14-Nov-3 Du Mouchelle, Detroit #2023/R est:1500-2000
£2489 $4481 €3634 Cat, three wisemen (31x38cm-12x15in) s.d.96 mixed media. 25-Apr-4 Christie's, Hong Kong #767/R est:35000-45000 (HK.D 35000)
£3201 $5761 €4673 Artist self portrait (37x49cm-15x19in) s.d.97 mixed media. 25-Apr-4 Christie's, Hong Kong #764/R est:45000-50000 (HK.D 45000)
£4979 $8962 €7269 Po you niau, whisper in the cloud (38x24cm-15x9in) s.d.90 mixed media. 25-Apr-4 Christie's, Hong Kong #765/R est:45000-55000 (HK.D 70000)

LIU DAN (1953-) Chinese
Works on paper
£5405 $9027 €7891 Rock (46x83cm-18x33in) s.i.d.2003 ink. 27-Oct-3 Sotheby's, Hong Kong #379/R est:70000-90000 (HK.D 70000)

LIU DANZHAI (1931-) Chinese
Works on paper
£4118 $7000 €6012 Playing the qin under pines (244x178cm-96x70in) s.d.1980 ink col hanging scroll. 4-Nov-3 Bonhams & Butterfields, San Francisco #3449/R est:2000-3000
£15444 $25792 €22548 Ten poets (33x272cm-13x107in) s.i. ink col handscroll. 26-Oct-3 Christie's, Hong Kong #298/R est:200000-300000 (HK.D 200000)

LIU GUOSONG (1932-) Chinese
£3557 $6367 €5300 Untitled (76x153cm-30x60in) st.sig.d.1967 paint ink. 27-May-4 Beaussant & Lefèvre, Paris #270/R est:4000-6000
Works on paper
£2353 $4000 €3435 Abstract blue (216x142cm-85x56in) s.d.64 ink col rice paper. 4-Nov-3 Bonhams & Butterfields, San Francisco #3460/R est:4000-6000
£2794 $4750 €4079 Abstract landscape (152x234cm-60x92in) s.d.1967 mixed media rice paper. 4-Nov-3 Bonhams & Butterfields, San Francisco #3459/R est:4000-6000

LIU HAI (18/19th C) Chinese
Works on paper
£1892 $3330 €2800 Lui Hai on toad (190x124cm-75x49in) Indian ink col hanging scroll. 21-May-4 Dr Fritz Nagel, Stuttgart #1297/R est:1800

LIU JIA DI (20th C) Chinese?
£689 $1150 €1006 Autumn Forest (64x79cm-25x31in) s.d. 11-Oct-3 Nadeau, Windsor #142/R

LIU KUILING (1885-1968) Chinese
Works on paper
£5690 $10242 €8307 Horse (87x38cm-34x15in) s.i.d.1939 ink col hanging scroll. 25-Apr-4 Christie's, Hong Kong #145/R est:45000-55000 (HK.D 80000)

LIU SHENGYANG (1968-) Chinese
£187 $350 €273 Floral still life (79x60cm-31x24in) s. 29-Feb-4 Bonhams & Butterfields, San Francisco #4476

LIU XUN (1958-) Chinese
Works on paper
£8494 $14185 €12401 Misty gorge (237x59cm-93x23in) s.i.d.2003 col hanging scroll. 27-Oct-3 Sotheby's, Hong Kong #377/R est:60000-80000 (HK.D 110000)
£9246 $16643 €13499 River bank (70x152cm-28x60in) s.i.d.2003 ink. 26-Apr-4 Sotheby's, Hong Kong #538/R est:50000-70000 (HK.D 130000)

LIU YONGLANG (19th C) Chinese
Works on paper
£1233 $2096 €1800 Landscape with men and horses (154x66cm-61x26in) i. seal Indian ink col silk hanging scroll. 7-Nov-3 Dr Fritz Nagel, Stuttgart #857/R est:1300

LIVEMONT, Franz (19th C) Belgian
£294 $505 €420 Pecheur sur l'eau (53x80cm-21x31in) s. panel. 2-Dec-3 Campo & Campo, Antwerp #216
£317 $555 €450 Village de campagne anime (35x55cm-14x22in) s. 16-Dec-3 Galerie Moderne, Brussels #770
£950 $1511 €1378 Portrait of two scottie dogs (52x75cm-20x30in) s.d.1922. 9-Sep-3 Bonhams, Knightsbridge #202/R

LIVEMONT, Privat (1861-1936) Belgian
£355 $592 €500 Portrait du pere de l'artiste (38x26cm-15x10in) s.i.d.12 septembre 1889 panel. 15-Oct-3 Hotel des Ventes Mosan, Brussels #106
£567 $948 €800 Still life with fish (48x74cm-19x29in) s.d.1913. 20-Oct-3 Bernaerts, Antwerp #478/R
£1351 $2554 €2000 Le reveil (44x116cm-17x46in) s. 17-Feb-4 Vanderkindere, Brussels #80 est:1800-2500
Works on paper
£265 $482 €400 Portrait d'Anna Boch (27x20cm-11x8in) sanguine. 15-Jun-4 Galerie Moderne, Brussels #198/R
£461 $770 €650 La conversation (29x29cm-11x11in) s.d.1917 mixed media. 15-Oct-3 Hotel des Ventes Mosan, Brussels #134
£1678 $2853 €2400 Jeune fille dans un entourage de fleurs (43x28cm-17x11in) s. pastel. 1-Dec-3 Palais de Beaux Arts, Brussels #104/R est:1500-2000

LIVENS, Henry (19th C) British
£400 $716 €584 Still life of bird's nest and eggs, yellow roses and other flora (36x46cm-14x18in) s.d.1878. 6-May-4 Amersham Auction Rooms, UK #285/R
£462 $850 €675 Still life with flowers and robin's nest on a mossy bank (36x43cm-14x17in) s. 9-Jun-4 Doyle, New York #3054
£2700 $5049 €4050 Fruit on a mossy bank. Flowers on a mossy bank (50x60cm-20x24in) s.d.1880 pair. 26-Jul-4 Bonhams, Bath #82/R est:1000-1500

LIVENS, Horace Mann (1862-1936) British
£449 $836 €656 Cows in river in autumn woods (31x40cm-12x16in) indis.sig. 2-Mar-4 Rasmussen, Copenhagen #1341/R (D.KR 5000)
£539 $900 €787 Outdoor still life with flowers (51x61cm-20x24in) s.d.1898. 20-Jun-3 Freeman, Philadelphia #261/R
£1400 $2506 €2044 Still life of primroses, on a mossy bank. Still life of fruit and flowers on a mossy bank (34x44cm-13x17in) s.d.1879-1880 pair. 11-May-4 Bonhams, Knightsbridge #214/R est:800-1200
£1912 $3250 €2792 Spring flowers (51x61cm-20x24in) s.d.1880. 19-Nov-3 Bonhams & Butterfields, San Francisco #147/R

LIVERMORE, Annbel (20th C) American
£950 $1700 €1387 Good habits (64x64cm-25x25in) oil on wood. 13-May-4 Dallas Auction Gallery, Dallas #321/R est:2000-4000

LIVERSEEGE, Henry (1803-1832) British
£850 $1607 €1241 Scholar (61x51cm-24x20in) s.d.1831. 19-Feb-4 Christie's, Kensington #78/R
£950 $1520 €1387 Portrait of a King Charles Spaniel (18x15cm-7x6in) mock circle. 18-Sep-3 Scarborough Perry Fine Arts, Hove #666
£2072 $3750 €3025 Head of a King Charles spaniel (18x17cm-7x7in) board painted c.1828. 30-Mar-4 Bonhams & Butterfields, San Francisco #33/R est:1800-2500
£4000 $7360 €5840 Elegant figure seated at a table reading a book (30x25cm-12x10in) panel prov. 11-Jun-4 Christie's, London #35/R est:1000-1500

LIVERSEEGE, Henry (attrib) (1803-1832) British
£750 $1380 €1095 Performing dogs outside a family home (30x34cm-12x13in) 29-Mar-4 Bonhams, Bath #99/R

LIVESAY, Richard (1753-1823) British
£1500 $2580 €2190 Le juste and L'America in Portsmouth Harbour (69x91cm-27x36in) paper on board. 2-Dec-3 Sotheby's, London #11/R est:1500-2500
£1676 $3000 €2447 Portrait of a Royal Navy Post Captain (28x23cm-11x9in) wood panel oval painted c.1780. 18-Mar-4 Richard Opfer, Timonium #89/R est:4000-5000
£3073 $5500 €4487 British Grenadier Officer (28x23cm-11x9in) panel painted c.1780. 18-Mar-4 Richard Opfer, Timonium #40/R est:6000-7000

LIVESAY, Richard (attrib) (1753-1823) British
£1600 $2672 €2336 Portrait of an officer of the 1st Royal Dragoons (74x61cm-29x24in) 14-Oct-3 Sotheby's, London #463 est:1000-1500

LIVESEY, Algernon M (1874-1951) British
£280 $448 €409 Villa, St Raphael (50x81cm-20x32in) 16-Sep-3 Bonhams, Knightsbridge #117/R

LIVESEY, John (1926-1990) British
£400 $732 €584 Summer flowers, fruit and a jar on a table by a window (70x43cm-28x17in) s. board. 8-Apr-4 Christie's, Kensington #213/R

LIVINGSTON, Edward (1837-1898) American
Works on paper
£1111 $1800 €1611 Huts on the bayou (22x41cm-9x16in) s. W/C prov. 8-Aug-3 Barridorf, Portland #222/R est:2000-3000

LIVINGSTON, Ruth (20th C) American
£2593 $4200 €3760 Desert (41x107cm-16x42in) i.verso. 8-Aug-3 Barridorf, Portland #227/R est:2000-3000

LIX, Frederic Theodore (1830-1897) French
£8242 $15000 €12033 Cueilleuse de Violettes (95x140cm-37x55in) s. 29-Jun-4 Sotheby's, New York #63/R est:15000-20000

LIZARS, Ch (?) ?
£510 $913 €750 Femmes sur la cote Bretonne a maree bassee (54x65cm-21x26in) s. peinture exhib. 20-Mar-4 Binoche, Orleans #45

LIZCANO Y ESTEBAN, Angel (1846-1929) Spanish
£986 $1706 €1400 Couple Espagnol dans un patio (20x25cm-8x10in) s. panel. 10-Dec-3 Rossini, Paris #93/R
£1645 $2977 €2500 Bull scene (62x37cm-24x15in) s.d.1904. 14-Apr-4 Ansorena, Madrid #168/R est:2500
£1678 $3003 €2500 What a story ! (20x25cm-8x10in) s. board. 25-May-4 Durán, Madrid #107/R est:2500
£2289 $3960 €3250 Figures (44x32cm-17x13in) s.i.d.1874 board. 10-Dec-3 Castellana, Madrid #216/R

LIZEN, Marcel (1887-?) ?
£395 $726 €600 Entree du village (75x75cm-30x30in) s. 22-Jun-4 Palais de Beaux Arts, Brussels #277
£436 $807 €650 Marche aux fleurs en Provence (54x65cm-21x26in) s. 15-Mar-4 Horta, Bruxelles #273

LJUBA (1934-) Yugoslavian
£552 $921 €800 Cavernes de lincoscience (34x25cm-13x10in) s.i.d.1978 verso canvas on cardboard. 11-Jul-3 Rabourdin & Choppin de Janvry, Paris #30/R
£604 $1111 €900 L'air de la tempete (46x55cm-18x22in) s.i.d.1991 verso. 24-Mar-4 Joron-Derem, Paris #92
£671 $1235 €1000 Impression d'ete (45x89cm-18x35in) s.i.d.1989 verso. 24-Mar-4 Joron-Derem, Paris #91
£2200 $3960 €3300 A Georges Fall l'hommage a Herman Melville (33x41cm-13x16in) s.i.d.1979. 25-Apr-4 Versailles Encheres #178 est:800-1000
£4082 $7306 €6000 Les dieux eux memes (73x60cm-29x24in) i.d.1974 s.verso prov. 21-Mar-4 Calmels Cohen, Paris #137/R est:3000-4000
Works on paper
£263 $484 €400 Personnages (20x29cm-8x11in) s.d.1976 felt pen drawings framed together four. 28-Jun-4 Joron-Derem, Paris #154
£263 $484 €400 Sodomija (63x48cm-25x19in) d.1974 ink wash. 28-Jun-4 Joron-Derem, Paris #155
£405 $726 €600 Personnages fantastiques (20x25cm-8x10in) s.d.1966 Chinese ink. 4-May-4 Calmels Cohen, Paris #201

LJUNGBERG, Sven (1913-) Swedish
£476 $843 €695 Field landscape from Banyuls-sur-Mer, France (43x66cm-17x26in) s. 27-Apr-4 AB Stockholms Auktionsverk #657/R (S.KR 6500)
£769 $1323 €1123 Skyscraper and figures carrying brief-cases, Stockholm (80x31cm-31x12in) s. 7-Dec-3 Uppsala Auktionskammare, Uppsala #275/R (S.KR 10000)
£2266 $3852 €3308 Ljungby centre (55x100cm-22x39in) s. 5-Nov-3 AB Stockholms Auktionsverk #816/R est:30000-40000 (S.KR 30000)
£2266 $3852 €3308 View from Ljungby market (45x67cm-18x26in) s.d.93. 4-Nov-3 Bukowskis, Stockholm #295/R est:30000-35000 (S.KR 30000)
£3776 $6420 €5513 Flowers against the studio wall (117x103cm-46x41in) s.d.95. 5-Nov-3 AB Stockholms Auktionsverk #657/R est:30000-35000 (S.KR 50000)
£4683 $7961 €6837 Flowerbed with cosmos (100x116cm-39x46in) s.d.88. 5-Nov-3 AB Stockholms Auktionsverk #658/R est:30000-35000 (S.KR 62000)

LJUNGGREN, Reinhold (1920-) Swedish
£2217 $3969 €3237 Dancing by the roadside (32x40cm-13x16in) s.d.44 panel. 28-May-4 Uppsala Auktionskammare, Uppsala #281/R est:30000-40000 (S.KR 30000)

LJUNGQUIST, Birger (1898-1965) Swedish
£517 $926 €755 Eva (55x32cm-22x13in) s.d.1948 panel. 28-May-4 Uppsala Auktionskammare, Uppsala #355 (S.KR 7000)
£769 $1323 €1123 Fishing village with two young girls (61x75cm-24x30in) s. 7-Dec-3 Uppsala Auktionskammare, Uppsala #286/R (S.KR 10000)
Works on paper
£408 $751 €612 The ball (24x38cm-9x15in) s.d.1960 W/C. 14-Jun-4 Lilla Bukowskis, Stockholm #333 (S.KR 5600)

LLANECES, Jose (1863-1919) Spanish
£3618 $6549 €5500 Card players (53x50cm-21x20in) s. board. 14-Apr-4 Ansorena, Madrid #103/R
£5369 $10040 €8000 Satyre (99x138cm-39x54in) s. 24-Feb-4 Durán, Madrid #237/R est:6500
£9420 $15449 €13000 Un libro satirico (99x138cm-39x54in) s. 27-May-3 Durán, Madrid #257/R est:13000
Works on paper
£3080 $5051 €4250 Jugando a los dados (43x48cm-17x19in) s. W/C. 27-May-3 Durán, Madrid #157/R est:3250

LLASERA Y DIAZ, Jose (1882-1943) Spanish
£704 $1232 €1000 Isabel (99x95cm-39x37in) s. i.verso. 16-Dec-3 Durán, Madrid #64/R

LLEDO, Guillermo (20th C) Spanish
Works on paper
£1486 $2750 €2170 Garbage Cans (42x61cm-17x24in) s.d.74 W/C exhib.lit. 12-Feb-4 Sotheby's, New York #168/R est:400-600

LLEO, Lluis (20th C) American?
£2000 $3660 €3000 Trecento cinque (183x213cm-72x84in) s.i.d.1997 verso. 7-Jun-4 Palais de Beaux Arts, Brussels #375/R est:3000-4000
£5333 $9760 €8000 Quattro cento uno (183x213cm-72x84in) s.i.d.1997 verso. 7-Jun-4 Palais de Beaux Arts, Brussels #374/R est:3000-4000

LLEWELLYN, Sir William (1858-1941) British
£3000 $5670 €4380 Southwold Beach (14x23cm-6x9in) s.i. panel. 17-Feb-4 Bonhams, New Bond Street #73/R est:1000-1500

LLIMONA Y BRUGUERA, Juan (1860-1926) Spanish
£319 $571 €475 Mountainous landscape (17x25cm-7x10in) s. board. 25-May-4 Durán, Madrid #158/R

LLIMONA, Rafael (1896-1957) Spanish
£3873 $6701 €5500 Spinning (73x60cm-29x24in) 15-Dec-3 Ansorena, Madrid #47/R est:5500

LLIMOS, Robert (1943-) Spanish
£1056 $1690 €1500 Rite (183x91cm-72x36in) s.d.1984 s.i.d.verso. 16-Sep-3 Segre, Madrid #177/R
£1831 $2930 €2600 Ort XI (102x73cm-40x29in) s.d.1979 casein cardboard on board prov.exhib.lit. 16-Sep-3 Segre, Madrid #247/R est:1900
£1831 $3204 €2600 Hort X (101x72cm-40x28in) s.d.1979 casein cardboard on board prov.exhib.lit. 16-Dec-3 Segre, Madrid #172/R est:2000

LLOPIS, Francesca (1956-) Spanish
£414 $745 €600 Composition (147x116cm-58x46in) s.d.81. 26-Jan-4 Durán, Madrid #47/R

LLORENS CIFRE, Ricardo (1926-) Spanish
£552 $993 €800 Allegory of Jesus (54x46cm-21x18in) s.d.78. 26-Jan-4 Durán, Madrid #604/R

LLOVERA BUFILL, Josep (1846-1896) Spanish
£3147 $5255 €4500 Seated young woman in a garden (59x44cm-23x17in) s. 30-Jun-3 Ansorena, Madrid #331/R
£3546 $5922 €5000 Young people meeting monks (38x54cm-15x21in) s.d.1880 board. 20-Oct-3 Durán, Madrid #125/R est:2250

LLOVERAS, Federico (1912-1983) Spanish
£362 $666 €550 Paris (50x61cm-20x24in) s. 22-Jun-4 Durán, Madrid #60/R
£1479 $2558 €2100 The Seine (50x130cm-20x51in) s. 15-Dec-3 Ansorena, Madrid #298/R est:2100
Works on paper
£629 $1051 €900 Madrid (46x62cm-18x24in) s.d.1944 W/C. 24-Jun-3 Segre, Madrid #292/R
£629 $1051 €900 Puerta Cerrada, Madrid (30x46cm-12x18in) s. W/C. 24-Jun-3 Segre, Madrid #294/R
£629 $1051 €900 Puente de Segovia (30x46cm-12x18in) s.d.1943 W/C. 24-Jun-3 Segre, Madrid #295/R
£769 $1285 €1100 Atocha (48x64cm-19x25in) W/C. 24-Jun-3 Segre, Madrid #296/R

LLOVET, Ramon (1917-1987) Spanish
£979 $1635 €1400 Village (65x92cm-26x36in) s. s.verso. 30-Jun-3 Ansorena, Madrid #248/R
£1316 $2382 €2000 Toreador, bull and sun (65x92cm-26x36in) s. 14-Apr-4 Ansorena, Madrid #262/R est:2000

LLOYD, Arthur John (20th C) New Zealander
£521 $828 €761 Shipping, Auckland Harbour (49x70cm-19x28in) s.d.1922. 1-May-3 Dunbar Sloane, Wellington #131 est:600-1000 (NZ.D 1500)

LLOYD, Donald H (?) British
£700 $1295 €1022 Winter landscape with a stream and trees (76x61cm-30x24in) s. 11-Mar-4 Duke & Son, Dorchester #183/R

LLOYD, Edward (19th C) British
£1800 $3312 €2628 Disturbed (51x61cm-20x24in) s.i.d.1873. 10-Jun-4 Christie's, Kensington #88/R est:1000-1500

LLOYD, Ethel A (fl.1893-1916) British
£360 $569 €526 Path through the garden (60x73cm-24x29in) bears sig. 24-Jul-3 Lawrence, Crewkerne #964
£360 $601 €526 Garden path (62x74cm-24x29in) s. 11-Nov-3 Bonhams, Knightsbridge #92h/R

LLOYD, James (1905-1974) British
Works on paper
£460 $837 €672 Feeding Time (33x43cm-13x17in) s. W/C. 3-Feb-4 Gorringes, Bexhill #973/R
£470 $855 €686 Cows grazing (36x51cm-14x20in) s. W/C. 3-Feb-4 Gorringes, Bexhill #974
£500 $910 €730 Cow and Calf (48x33cm-19x13in) s. W/C. 3-Feb-4 Gorringes, Bexhill #975
£540 $983 €788 Lamb (33x48cm-13x19in) s.d.1959 W/C. 3-Feb-4 Gorringes, Bexhill #976
£1000 $1820 €1500 Girl on a wagon wheel (35x25cm-14x10in) s. gouache pen ink. 2-Jul-4 Bloomsbury, London #183/R est:300-500
£1622 $3000 €2368 James Lloyd and family. Boy walking in Cotswolds village (36x51cm-14x20in) s.d.59 gouache board sold with work by P Le Vasseur three prov. 15-Jul-4 Sotheby's, New York #127/R est:1000-1500

LLOYD, Llewelyn (1879-1950) Italian
Works on paper
£13333 $24533 €20000 Sunset in Procchio Bay (45x64cm-18x25in) s.d.908 pastel card lit. 10-Jun-4 Christie's, Rome #184/R est:22000-25000

LLOYD, Mary Constance (fl.1903-1920) British
£2800 $4760 €4088 Santa Maria della Salute, Venice (33x41cm-13x16in) s.i.d.1903. 21-Nov-3 Christie's, London #77/R est:800-1200

LLOYD, Norman (1897-1985) Australian
£420 $773 €613 Corn stooks (43x54cm-17x21in) s. 23-Jun-4 Cheffins, Cambridge #526/R
£432 $800 €631 Market scene in the village square (33x41cm-13x16in) s. board. 17-Jan-4 New Orleans Auction, New Orleans #508
£450 $774 €657 Summer river landscape with figures in rowing boat (33x41cm-13x16in) s. 2-Dec-3 Canterbury Auctions, UK #134/R
£541 $1000 €790 View from across the River Seine (33x41cm-13x16in) s. 17-Jan-4 New Orleans Auction, New Orleans #507/R est:1200-1800
£600 $1110 €876 Still life (71x76cm-28x30in) s. 11-Feb-4 Sotheby's, Olympia #184/R
£650 $1021 €943 Figures gathered before an Islamic town (63x76cm-25x30in) s. 28-Aug-3 Christie's, Kensington #252
£1245 $2079 €1868 Spanish landscape (76x97cm-30x38in) s. board. 27-Oct-3 Goodman, Sydney #209/R est:2000-3000 (A.D 3000)
£1736 $3072 €2535 Sydney Harbour (19x91cm-7x36in) s. panel. 3-May-4 Christie's, Melbourne #94/R est:4000-6000 (A.D 4200)

LLOYD, P H Stuart (1875-1929) British
Works on paper
£1450 $2639 €2117 Bosham, figures and boats on a river at sunset (29x90cm-11x35in) W/C exhib. 15-Jun-4 Bonhams, Oxford #56/R est:1000-1200

LLOYD, R Malcolm (1855-1945) British
£285 $510 €416 Old Shoreham Harbour, Sussex (24x32cm-9x13in) s.d.1886 paper. 26-May-4 Christie's, Kensington #689/R
Works on paper
£210 $375 €307 Malden, Essex, England (14x18cm-6x7in) s. W/C gouache paperboard prov. 14-May-4 Skinner, Boston #128/R
£350 $550 €508 Broadstairs, early morning (25x36cm-10x14in) s. W/C. 15-Dec-2 Desmond Judd, Cranbrook #836
£377 $600 €550 Unloading (20x40cm-8x16in) s.d.1899 W/C gouache. 12-Sep-3 Skinner, Boston #238/R
£380 $699 €555 Barges before the Houses of Parliament (13x18cm-5x7in) s.indis.d.99 pencil W/C bodycol. 25-Mar-4 Christie's, Kensington #249/R
£400 $688 €584 Shipping in a slight swell (16x24cm-6x9in) s.d.1889 W/C bodycol. 2-Dec-3 Sworder & Son, Bishops Stortford #537/R
£450 $774 €657 Stormy seas (32x52cm-13x20in) s. indis d. W/C. 2-Dec-3 Sotheby's, London #83/R
£450 $747 €657 Fishing boats preparing to sail with passing paddle steamer (30x57cm-12x22in) s.d.1890 W/C. 2-Oct-3 Lane, Penzance #118
£550 $985 €803 Fishing fleet returns (43x76cm-17x30in) s.d.1889 W/C. 4-May-4 Gorringes, Bexhill #1342/R

LLOYD, Robert (1969-) British
Works on paper
£400 $716 €584 Blue Star Line's Brisbane Star in San Francisco Bay (43x76cm-17x30in) s.d.1996 pencil W/C bodycol. 26-May-4 Christie's, Kensington #533/R
£850 $1522 €1241 Blue Star Line vessel Argentina Star (37x83cm-15x33in) s.d.95 pencil W/C bodycol. 26-May-4 Christie's, Kensington #535/R
£850 $1522 €1241 Blue Star Line vessel Viking Star at Shanghai (55x85cm-22x33in) s.d.1997 pencil W/C bodycol. 26-May-4 Christie's, Kensington #536/R

LLOYD, T Ivester (1873-1942) British
£380 $692 €555 Portrait of a bay hunter in a stable interior (39x49cm-15x19in) s. 15-Jun-4 Bonhams, Oxford #71
£400 $728 €584 Portrait of a bay horse in a stable interior (40x50cm-16x20in) s. 15-Jun-4 Bonhams, Oxford #83/R
£480 $888 €701 Portrait of a horse in a stable (40x50cm-16x20in) s. 9-Mar-4 Bonhams, Knightsbridge #324/R
£900 $1647 €1314 Otter hunting (25x33cm-10x13in) s. board. 8-Apr-4 Christie's, Kensington #134/R
£2300 $3657 €3358 Exercise. Slip. Course. Kill, four horse scenes (24x32cm-9x13in) s. panel four. 9-Sep-3 Rowley Fine Art, Newmarket #428/R est:1500-2500
Works on paper
£360 $659 €526 Graceful jump (21x32cm-8x13in) s. W/C htd white. 28-Jul-4 Bonhams, Knightsbridge #84/R
£700 $1204 €1022 Ploughing teams (22x33cm-9x13in) s. W/C pair. 2-Dec-3 Sworder & Son, Bishops Stortford #477/R
£1000 $1670 €1460 Hunt in full cry (49x65cm-19x26in) s. W/C. 21-Oct-3 Sworder & Son, Bishops Stortford #311/R est:1000-1500
£1300 $2392 €1898 On the scent (48x66cm-19x26in) s. W/C bodycol. 10-Jun-4 Christie's, Kensington #129/R est:1500-2000

LLOYD, Thomas James (1849-1910) British
£8077 $13892 €11792 Primrose gatherers (107x183cm-42x72in) s. exhib. 2-Dec-3 Bukowskis, Stockholm #289/R est:50000-70000 (S.KR 105000)
Works on paper
£700 $1274 €1022 A shepherd and his flock returning home at sunset (39x90cm-15x35in) s.d.1909 pencil W/C. 1-Jul-4 Christie's, Kensington #220/R
£800 $1296 €1160 Moonrise (20x46cm-8x18in) s.d.1896 W/C. 7-Aug-3 Amersham Auction Rooms, UK #285/R
£850 $1547 €1241 Fen folk (39x71cm-15x28in) s.d.1908 pencil W/C scratching out. 1-Jul-4 Christie's, Kensington #198/R
£854 $1400 €1238 Yew Tree House, Sussex (41x71cm-16x28in) s.d.1908 W/C. 4-Jun-3 Alderfer's, Hatfield #250/R est:500-700
£1400 $2226 €2030 Evening stroll (18x36cm-7x14in) s.d.1904 W/C. 23-Mar-3 Desmond Judd, Cranbrook #1045

£1450 $2320 €2117 Coastal scene with boats, mother and child (18x33cm-7x13in) s.d.1898 W/C. 16-Sep-3 Louis Taylor, Stoke on Trent #1050
£2200 $3938 €3212 Shepherd's return (50x34cm-20x13in) s.d.1890 W/C. 26-May-4 Sotheby's, Olympia #200/R est:1000-1500
£3000 $5520 €4380 Otter hunting, Bolton Abbey (39x100cm-15x39in) s. indid d. W/C htd white. 10-Jun-4 Christie's, Kensington #128/R est:3000-4000
£4000 $7360 €5840 In the fields (33x70cm-13x28in) s.d.1896 W/C. 24-Mar-4 Hamptons Fine Art, Godalming #242/R
£4200 $7728 €6132 Above Pulborough, Sussex (28x69cm-11x27in) s.d.1898 W/C bodycol. 8-Jun-4 Bonhams, New Bond Street #130/R est:2000-3000

LLOYD, Trevor (1864-1937) New Zealander
£735 $1375 €1073 Marsh landscape with Pukeko (19x24cm-7x9in) s.verso canvasboard. 24-Feb-4 Peter Webb, Auckland #5/R (NZ.D 2000)

LLOYD, Trevor (attrib) (1864-1937) New Zealander
£202 $378 €295 Coastal landscape with Pohutukawa (14x30cm-6x12in) canvasboard. 24-Feb-4 Peter Webb, Auckland #6/R (NZ.D 550)

LLOYD, W Stuart (fl.1875-1929) British
£252 $450 €368 Portrait of a steer (43x58cm-17x23in) s. board. 8-Jan-4 James Julia, Fairfield #1183/R
£1923 $3308 €2808 St. Monaco, Scotland (40x100cm-16x39in) s.d.905. 3-Dec-3 AB Stockholms Auktionsverk #2607/R est:12000-15000 (S.KR 25000)
Works on paper
£280 $512 €409 Figures by a lake with a church beyond (48x74cm-19x29in) s. W/C. 7-Apr-4 Woolley & Wallis, Salisbury #48/R
£350 $641 €525 Bell Quay, Chichester Harbour (28x64cm-11x25in) s.i. W/C. 30-Jul-4 Bigwood, Stratford on Avon #356/R
£370 $588 €537 Silver birch by tranquil rural river (41x36cm-16x14in) s. W/C. 23-Mar-3 Desmond Judd, Cranbrook #1023
£370 $585 €537 Mother and child by millpond. W/C. 27-Jul-3 Desmond Judd, Cranbrook #1136
£460 $828 €672 Golden evening, Battcock's Island, Hemingford backwaters (24x44cm-9x17in) s. W/C. 21-Apr-4 Cheffins, Cambridge #461/R
£500 $920 €730 Village harbour (50x75cm-20x30in) s. W/C bodycol. 8-Jun-4 Bonhams, Knightsbridge #51/R
£550 $1012 €803 Springtime at the mill (75x49cm-30x19in) s. W/C bodycol. 22-Jun-4 Bonhams, Knightsbridge #180/R
£600 $1104 €876 River with a church in the distance (48x38cm-19x15in) s. pencil W/C bodycol. 25-Mar-4 Christie's, Kensington #172
£650 $1086 €949 Rye (49x74cm-19x29in) s. W/C bodycol. 14-Oct-3 Bonhams, Knightsbridge #24/R
£660 $1221 €964 River scene with ferry boat and figures, a village church beyond (49x75cm-19x30in) s. W/C. 14-Jul-4 Bonhams, Chester #478
£720 $1303 €1051 Coastal scene with boats and figures before sand dunes (74x36cm-29x14in) s.d.1911 W/C. 1-Apr-4 Biddle & Webb, Birmingham #904
£775 $1318 €1132 Riverscape with boats, figures and church beyond (23x43cm-9x17in) s. W/C sold with another by the same hand. 27-Nov-3 Morphets, Harrogate #464
£778 $1400 €1136 Caernarvon Castle, North Wales (48x71cm-19x28in) s. W/C. 23-Jan-4 Freeman, Philadelphia #48/R
£870 $1400 €1270 Landscape with fisherman in boat in foreground and castle and cottage (102x76cm-40x30in) s. W/C. 24-Feb-3 O'Gallerie, Oregon #794/R
£900 $1503 €1314 View of Lincoln from the river (29x90cm-11x35in) s.d.1910 W/C. 26-Jun-3 Greenslade Hunt, Taunton #495/R
£950 $1748 €1387 Haven, Christchurch (30x65cm-12x26in) s.d.1906 pencil W/C. 25-Mar-4 Christie's, Kensington #174/R
£972 $1653 €1400 Border of Windsor Forest, men with gun dogs. Near Yarmouth, men with dogs. s.i.d.1878 W/C pair. 28-Oct-3 Mealy's, Castlecomer #217/R
£1250 $2363 €1825 Estuary and harbour scene at low tide with fisherfolk, boats and town (48x74cm-19x29in) W/C. 19-Feb-4 Rendalls, Ashburton #1605
£1400 $2478 €2044 Sunset scene with canal barge and church beyond (41x74cm-16x29in) s. W/C. 28-Apr-4 Halls, Shrewsbury #481/R est:1000-1500
£1507 $2562 €2200 Christchurch near Bornemouth (30x90cm-12x35in) s. W/C. 10-Nov-3 Horta, Bruxelles #221 est:1000-1500
£1600 $2672 €2336 Rowing on a meandering river (49x100cm-19x39in) s. W/C bodycol. 14-Oct-3 Bonhams, Knightsbridge #53/R est:1000-1500
£1750 $3273 €2555 River landscape with figures and boats (50x75cm-20x30in) s. W/C bodycol. 20-Jul-4 Sworder & Son, Bishops Stortford #707/R est:1800-2200
£1800 $3312 €2628 Fishing boats in the harbour at Polperro (47x74cm-19x29in) s. pencil W/C bodycol. 25-Mar-4 Christie's, Kensington #175/R est:800-1200
£2000 $3660 €2920 Golden evening on the Arun, Sussex (42x102cm-17x40in) s.d.1903 W/C htd white. 27-Jan-4 Bonhams, Knightsbridge #330/R est:1200-1800
£2000 $3640 €2920 Sorting the catch at dusk, Babbacombe Bay, South Devon (29x89cm-11x35in) s. pencil W/C bodycol. 1-Jul-4 Christie's, Kensington #214/R est:800-1200
£2100 $3507 €3066 At the ferry (41x99cm-16x39in) s.d.1903 W/C. 12-Nov-3 Halls, Shrewsbury #248/R est:1500-2500
£5900 $10207 €8614 On the Yealm (36x74cm-14x29in) s. W/C. 11-Dec-3 Rendalls, Ashburton #1729

LOAN, Dorothy van (1904-1999) American
£462 $850 €675 Anachronism (79x94cm-31x37in) s.verso. 25-Jun-4 Freeman, Philadelphia #146/R
£539 $900 €787 Sewing circle (51x46cm-20x18in) s. exhib. 20-Jun-3 Freeman, Philadelphia #98/R
£543 $1000 €793 In the dressing tent (107x94cm-42x37in) s. 25-Jun-4 Freeman, Philadelphia #145/R
£1337 $2300 €1952 Nude bathers (51x61cm-20x24in) s.verso attrib to Cezanne. 7-Dec-3 Freeman, Philadelphia #176 est:1800-2500
£1512 $2600 €2208 Wissahickon Picnic (51x61cm-20x24in) 7-Dec-3 Freeman, Philadelphia #175 est:1800-2500

LOATES, Glen (1945-) Canadian
Works on paper
£201 $342 €293 Ruby-throated hummingbird and columbine (20x24cm-8x9in) s.i.d.1985 pencil prov. 6-Nov-3 Heffel, Vancouver #74/R (C.D 450)

LOBATCHEV, Youri (1941-) Russian
£333 $600 €500 Vladimir (41x50cm-16x20in) mono. 26-Apr-4 Millon & Associes, Paris #91/R

LOBEDAN, Clara (1840-1918) German
£1400 $2520 €2100 Chrysanthemums (78x125cm-31x49in) s.d.1900. 26-Apr-4 Rieber, Stuttgart #1074/R est:1980
£6928 $11500 €10115 Astrolobe with chrysanthemums (137x88cm-54x35in) s.d.1890. 30-Sep-3 Christie's, Rockefeller NY #438/R est:6000-8000

LOBEL-RICHE, Almery (1880-1950) French
£2041 $3653 €3000 Portrait de Mademoiselle Evelyne Janney (210x100cm-83x39in) s. 19-Mar-4 Millon & Associes, Paris #62 est:3000-4000
Works on paper
£408 $678 €580 Mosquee de Fes (26x21cm-10x8in) s.i.d.1918 W/C. 16-Jun-3 E & Eve, Paris #205
£922 $1540 €1300 Reunion dans la mosquee (26x21cm-10x8in) s.i.d.1918 W/C. 19-Oct-3 Rabourdin & Choppin de Janvry, Paris #92/R

LOBERG, Gunnar (1893-1950) Swedish
£806 $1426 €1177 Portrait of Ernst Zierer (73x60cm-29x24in) exhib. 27-Apr-4 AB Stockholms Auktionsverk #854/R (S.KR 11000)

LOBISSER, Switbert (1878-1943) Austrian
Works on paper
£458 $760 €650 Landscape with stream (26x25cm-10x10in) s.d.17 W/C. 12-Jun-3 Dorotheum, Graz #169
£775 $1286 €1100 Landscape with stream (25x25cm-10x10in) s.d.17 W/C. 12-Jun-3 Dorotheum, Graz #168/R
£2703 $4757 €4000 Karnburg (38x32cm-15x13in) mono.i.d.1942 W/C. 19-May-4 Dorotheum, Klagenfurt #49/R est:3000

LOBLEY, James (1829-1888) British
Works on paper
£380 $692 €555 Remember the poor (28x18cm-11x7in) s. W/C bodycol. 15-Jun-4 Rosebery Fine Art, London #631/R
£380 $692 €555 Little girl in a church interior (30x24cm-12x9in) s.d.1886 W/C bodycol. 15-Jun-4 Rosebery Fine Art, London #632

LOBLEY, John Hodgson (1878-?) British
£260 $481 €380 Winter landscape (88x102cm-35x40in) s. 15-Jan-4 Christie's, Kensington #783/R

LOBO, Balthazar (1910-1993) Spanish
Sculpture
£3846 $6538 €5500 Maternite (12cm-5in) s. yellow pat.bronze Cast Susse fondeur stone socle. 29-Nov-3 Villa Grisebach, Berlin #345/R est:3000-4000
£4564 $8489 €6800 Stella (29x13x8cm-11x5x3in) s. num.2/4 gilded pat bronze f.Susse prov.lit. 3-Mar-4 Tajan, Paris #133/R est:4000-6000
£5200 $8996 €7592 Femme assise par terre (21cm-8in) s.num.3/4 brown pat bronze conceived 1943 st.f.Susse. 11-Dec-3 Christie's, Kensington #208/R est:5000-7000
£5294 $9000 €7729 Feme se coiffant (15x15cm-6x6in) s. bronze prov. 22-Nov-3 Jackson's, Cedar Falls #386/R est:1500-2500
£6500 $11245 €9490 La reve (24cm-9in) s.num.6/8 green pat bronze conceived 1989 st.f.Susse. 11-Dec-3 Christie's, Kensington #212/R est:5000-7000
£7667 $13800 €11500 Courseulles (29x20x10cm-11x8x4in) s. num.1/8 pat bronze lit. 24-Apr-4 Cornette de St.Cyr, Paris #618/R est:10000-12000
£12000 $21840 €17520 Pensive a genoux (45cm-18in) s. num.1/8 st.f.Susse dark brown green pat bronze prov. 3-Feb-4 Christie's, London #275/R est:15000-20000
£15000 $25950 €21900 Marielle et Maria Alexandra (47cm-19in) s.num.4/8 green pat bronze st.f. lit. 11-Dec-3 Christie's, Kensington #214/R est:15000-20000
£16667 $30667 €25000 A la source (15cm-6in) s.st.f.Susse num.8 green black pat bronze exec. 1982 prov. 12-Jun-4 Villa Grisebach, Berlin #382/R est:25000-35000
£18000 $32760 €26280 Mere et enfant (61cm-24in) s. num.3/4 st.f.Bonvicini black pat bronze conceived c.1947. 3-Feb-4 Christie's, London #291/R est:15000-20000
£18000 $33120 €26280 Allongee (48x71cm-19x28in) s. num.3/8 green brown pat bronze exec. 1996 Cast Susse prov. 23-Jun-4 Christie's, London #239/R est:18000-24000
£19000 $34960 €27740 Repos sur socle (47cm-19in) i. num.3/8 bronze f.Susse Freres edn of 8 lit. 22-Jun-4 Sotheby's, London #297/R est:15000-20000
£19553 $35000 €28547 Jeune fille a genoux (37cm-15in) s.st.f.Susse Paris num.1/8 green pat bronze prov.lit. 5-May-4 Christie's, Rockefeller NY #309/R est:18000-22000
£20000 $36400 €29200 Femme, mains au dos (77cm-30in) s. num.4/8 brown green pat bronze conceived 1970 lit. 3-Feb-4 Christie's, London #282/R est:25000-35000
£29412 $50000 €42942 Repos sur socle (46cm-18in) s. num.1/8 brown green pat bronze Cast S Fondeur prov.lit. 5-Nov-3 Christie's, Rockefeller NY #302/R est:25000-35000
Works on paper
£524 $902 €750 Nu (24x18cm-9x7in) s. dr. 3-Dec-3 Tajan, Paris #74
£650 $1125 €949 Mujer recostada VI (14x21cm-6x8in) s. pencil pen col ink brush prov. 11-Dec-3 Christie's, Kensington #207/R
£774 $1200 €1130 Figures (48x62cm-19x24in) s. ink. 29-Sep-2 Subastas Odalys, Caracas #84/R

LOBRICHON, Timoleon Marie (1831-1914) French
£7042 $12606 €10000 Portrait de fillette avec ses jouets (105x81cm-41x32in) s. prov.exhib. 11-Jan-4 Rouillac, Vendome #375
£17647 $30000 €25765 Champ de Bataille (81x111cm-32x44in) s. 28-Oct-3 Sotheby's, New York #144/R est:30000-40000

LOCATELLI, A (17/19th C) Italian
£1644 $2795 €2400 Paysage anime (49x64cm-19x25in) 9-Nov-3 Versailles Encheres #28a est:3000-3500

LOCATELLI, Andrea (1693-1741) Italian
£8725 $16054 €13000 Roman landscape with travellers (58x81cm-23x32in) lit. 27-Mar-4 Farsetti, Prato #318/R est:16000
£17986 $29496 €25000 Market scene with blacksmith (73x99cm-29x39in) prov.lit. 4-Jun-3 Sotheby's, Milan #134/R est:25000-35000

£38621 $64497 €56000 Architectural capriccio with fountain (73x98cm-29x39in) prov.lit. 15-Nov-3 Lempertz, Koln #1087/R est:60000-80000
£43662 $76408 €62000 Five figures in Mediterranean landscape (73x97cm-29x38in) prov.lit. 17-Dec-3 Christie's, Rome #491/R est:30000-40000
£206897 $345517 €300000 Venus and Volcano. Venus and Adonis (63x99cm-25x39in) one mono. pair lit. 12-Nov-3 Sotheby's, Milan #165/R est:120000-160000

LOCATELLI, Andrea (attrib) (1693-1741) Italian
£10000 $18300 €15000 Mercurius and Argo (63x75cm-25x30in) 1-Jun-4 Sotheby's, Milan #99/R est:15000-20000
Works on paper
£1014 $1784 €1500 Man and his dog under a tree. Studies of dogs and chapel frescoes (20x15cm-8x6in) pen brown ink black lead wash double-sided exhib. 19-May-4 Sotheby's, Amsterdam #172/R est:800-1200

LOCATELLI, Andrea (circle) (1693-1741) Italian
£10000 $17000 €14600 Architectural capriccio with figures amongst ruins (60x50cm-24x20in) 30-Oct-3 Sotheby's, Olympia #181/R est:5000-7000

LOCATELLI, Raffaelo (1915-) Italian
£870 $1426 €1200 Young painter (100x70cm-39x28in) 27-May-3 Il Ponte, Milan #898/R

LOCATELLI, Romualdo (1905-1943) Italian
£2667 $4907 €4000 Bergere et mouton (100x79cm-39x31in) s. 9-Jun-4 Oger, Dumont, Paris #66/R est:1000
£5334 $9761 €8000 Mere et fille (81x60cm-32x24in) s. isorel. 3-Jun-4 Tajan, Paris #283/R est:6000-8000
£6452 $10323 €9420 Boy on a donkey (100x70cm-39x28in) s. 18-May-3 Sotheby's, Singapore #23/R est:30000-40000 (S.D 18000)
£9028 $15076 €13181 My wife (97x52cm-38x20in) s.d.1937. 12-Oct-3 Sotheby's, Singapore #29/R est:25000-30000 (S.D 26000)
£29412 $53235 €42942 Boy fluter (93x74cm-37x29in) s.d.1939. 4-Apr-4 Sotheby's, Singapore #38/R est:90000-120000 (S.D 90000)

LOCATELLO, Gianfranco (19th C) Italian
£380 $680 €555 Per sepelirla (74cm-29in circular) 18-Mar-4 Neales, Nottingham #783
£500 $895 €730 Italian girl (74x85cm-29x33in) i. oval. 11-May-4 Bonhams, Knightsbridge #62/R

LOCCA, Albert (1895-1966) Swiss
£259 $463 €378 Portrait of young woman (60x50cm-24x20in) s.d.38. 12-May-4 Dobiaschofsky, Bern #3721 (S.FR 600)
£352 $599 €514 Nature morte (48x51cm-19x20in) s. i. stretcher. 5-Nov-3 Dobiaschofsky, Bern #754/R (S.FR 800)
£524 $964 €765 Still life (50x50cm-20x20in) s. 8-Jun-4 Germann, Zurich #828 (S.FR 1200)

LOCHEN, Karl (1865-1893) Norwegian
£2846 $5207 €4155 Self-portrait (24x16cm-9x6in) 7-Jun-4 Blomqvist, Oslo #374/R est:35000-45000 (N.KR 35000)

LOCHER, C (1851-1915) Danish
£378 $677 €552 Seascape with sailing boats (40x63cm-16x25in) bears sig.d.74. 12-Jan-4 Rasmussen, Vejle #46/R (D.KR 4000)

LOCHER, Carl (1851-1915) Danish
£303 $485 €442 Seascape with sailing vessels off coast (16x18cm-6x7in) panel. 22-Sep-3 Rasmussen, Vejle #310/R (D.KR 3200)
£467 $738 €677 Summer's day at sea with view towards the coast (26x36cm-10x14in) init. 2-Sep-3 Rasmussen, Copenhagen #1918 (D.KR 5000)
£474 $758 €692 Fishermen on beach (27x36cm-11x14in) s. 22-Sep-3 Rasmussen, Vejle #147/R (D.KR 5000)
£500 $925 €730 Fisherman watching the sea (28x36cm-11x14in) s. 10-Feb-4 Bonhams, Knightsbridge #77/R
£681 $1218 €994 Seascape with men-o-war (29x53cm-11x21in) s. 12-Jan-4 Rasmussen, Vejle #45/R (D.KR 7200)
£756 $1375 €1134 Coastal landscape with beached boats (40x62cm-16x24in) s.d.74. 19-Jun-4 Rasmussen, Havnen #2246/R (D.KR 8500)
£812 $1501 €1186 Ship's portrait of Gallileae of Helsingor (42x69cm-17x27in) 15-Mar-4 Rasmussen, Vejle #132/R (D.KR 9000)
£1348 $2507 €1968 Cattle grazing in meadow by the sea (130x208cm-51x82in) s. 2-Mar-4 Rasmussen, Copenhagen #1237/R est:30000-50000 (D.KR 15000)
£1374 $2500 €2006 Ship on (43x61cm-17x24in) s.indis.d. 7-Feb-4 Sloans & Kenyon, Bethesda #1275/R est:2000-3000
£1514 $2800 €2210 Sakgen Strand (61x97cm-24x38in) s.d.1885. 17-Jul-4 New Orleans Auction, New Orleans #735/R est:3000-5000
£1682 $2658 €2439 Skagen's Sonderstrand (28x38cm-11x15in) s. 2-Sep-3 Rasmussen, Copenhagen #1581/R est:12000 (D.KR 18000)
£1758 $2831 €2567 Full sails ahead (77x107cm-30x42in) s.d.72. 25-Aug-3 Lilla Bukowskis, Stockholm #163 est:12000-15000 (S.KR 23000)
£1801 $2882 €2629 Coastal landscape (29x50cm-11x20in) s.indis.i.d.95. 22-Sep-3 Rasmussen, Vejle #273/R est:15000 (D.KR 19000)
£1890 $3270 €2759 Fishing boat at sea off the coast (90x146cm-35x57in) s. 9-Dec-3 Rasmussen, Copenhagen #1448/R est:20000-25000 (D.KR 20000)
£2246 $4178 €3279 Big breakers hitting the pier on a windy day (168x262cm-66x103in) s.d.1904. 2-Mar-4 Rasmussen, Copenhagen #1383/R est:25000 (D.KR 25000)
£2268 $3924 €3311 Sailing boats off Skagen Sonderstrand (30x51cm-12x20in) s.d.1898. 9-Dec-3 Rasmussen, Copenhagen #1492/R est:12000-15000 (D.KR 24000)
£2336 $4345 €3411 Loading a sailing ship with barrels on the beach at Scheveningen (82x98cm-32x39in) s.i.d.1885. 2-Mar-4 Rasmussen, Copenhagen #1454/R est:30000-40000 (D.KR 26000)
£2417 $4423 €3529 The life boat going out (58x88cm-23x35in) s.d.98 exhib.prov. 9-Jun-4 Rasmussen, Copenhagen #1787/R est:30000 (D.KR 27000)
£2516 $4679 €3673 Life-boat going out (82x142cm-32x56in) s. prov. 2-Mar-4 Rasmussen, Copenhagen #1266/R est:25000-50000 (D.KR 28000)
£2705 $5005 €3949 Fishermen coming ashore, Skagen (37x46cm-15x18in) s.i.d.7-12-1900 panel. 15-Mar-4 Rasmussen, Vejle #79/R est:12000-15000 (D.KR 30000)
£3156 $5839 €4608 Fishermen at Skagen Strand (46x64cm-18x25in) init.i.d.1900. 15-Mar-4 Rasmussen, Vejle #77/R est:35000-40000 (D.KR 35000)
£3223 $5898 €4706 Seascape with boats in the calm (59x85cm-23x33in) s.d.95. 9-Jun-4 Rasmussen, Copenhagen #1821/R est:30000 (D.KR 36000)
£3970 $6868 €5796 Lifeboat going out (60x93cm-24x37in) s. 9-Dec-3 Rasmussen, Copenhagen #1489/R est:30000 (D.KR 42000)

LOCHER, Jens (1825-1869) Danish
£567 $981 €828 The sailing ship Marie off Kronborg (43x66cm-17x26in) s.d.1866. 9-Dec-3 Rasmussen, Copenhagen #1457/R (D.KR 6000)
£2937 $4905 €4200 Three masted Ceres off coast (52x77cm-20x30in) s.d.1866 lit. 11-Oct-3 Hans Stahl, Hamburg #149/R est:3000

LOCHHEAD, John (1866-1921) British
£320 $560 €467 Village street, summer (26x62cm-10x24in) s. 18-Dec-3 Bonhams, Edinburgh #312
£800 $1480 €1168 Summer's day by the river (41x62cm-16x24in) s. 9-Mar-4 Bonhams, Knightsbridge #278/R

LOCHHEAD, Kenneth (1926-) Canadian
£1118 $2001 €1632 Foothills (61x61cm-24x24in) s.d.1980 s.i.d.verso board. 6-May-4 Heffel, Vancouver #88/R est:1200-1600 (C.D 2750)
£1802 $3063 €2631 The snow fence (76x40cm-30x16in) s. painted c.1956 prov. 27-Nov-3 Heffel, Vancouver #203/R est:4000-5000 (C.D 4000)
Works on paper
£366 $655 €534 St Lawrence (66x101cm-26x40in) s.i.d.1982 pastel prov. 6-May-4 Heffel, Vancouver #89/R (C.D 900)
£766 $1302 €1118 Simple shapes (94x64cm-37x25in) s.d.1963 W/C prov. 23-Nov-3 Levis, Calgary #311/R (C.D 1700)

LOCK, Anton (1893-1971) British
£420 $760 €613 Woodland pastures (43x33cm-17x13in) i.verso. 16-Apr-4 Keys, Aylsham #820

LOCK, Edith (19/20th C) British
£280 $515 €409 Teddy - A bay hunter in a stable yard (40x50cm-16x20in) s.d.1924. 14-Jun-4 Bonhams, Bath #48

LOCK, William (younger-attrib) (1767-1847) British
Works on paper
£6500 $11050 €9490 Studies of fairies and a pair of hands (38x55cm-15x22in) i. pen brown ink wash htd white pencil red chk prov.exhib. 20-Nov-3 Christie's, London #35/R est:2500-3500

LOCKER, Thomas (?) ?
£376 $700 €549 Homage to church (30x46cm-12x18in) s. painted c.1990 exhib. 7-Mar-4 Treadway Gallery, Cincinnati #703/R est:500-700

LOCKER, W A (19/20th C) ?
£1173 $1900 €1713 Still life with trout, creel, rod and reel (21x27cm-8x11in) s. 31-Jul-3 Eldred, East Dennis #1212/R est:300-500

LOCKHART, Sharon (1964-) American
Photographs
£17365 $29000 €25353 Julie. Thomas (152x122cm-60x48in) two c-prints executed 1993 prov. 14-Nov-3 Phillips, New York #239/R est:20000-30000
£35928 $60000 €52455 Four groups (114x96cm-45x38in) cibachrome prints four prov. 12-Nov-3 Christie's, Rockefeller NY #542/R est:70000-90000

LOCKHART, William Ewart (1846-1900) British
Works on paper
£444 $729 €644 Courtyard (35x55cm-14x22in) s. W/C. 5-Jun-3 Heffel, Vancouver #14 (C.D 1000)
£2200 $3982 €3212 Historical interior with two figures, one holding a sword (69x61cm-27x24in) s.d.1880 W/C. 16-Apr-4 Keys, Aylsham #526/R est:1500-2000

LOCKWOOD, John Ward (1894-1963) American
£1676 $3000 €2447 Road among the pines and birches (61x46cm-24x18in) prov. 26-May-4 Doyle, New York #129/R est:6000-8000
Works on paper
£2429 $4250 €3546 Mountains (39x56cm-15x22in) s. gouache pencil. 19-Dec-3 Sotheby's, New York #1138/R est:1500-2000

LOCKWOOD, Wilton (1862-1914) American
£610 $1000 €885 Portrait of a woman (76x64cm-30x25in) 2-Jun-3 Grogan, Boston #608a/R

LODDER, Captain Charles A (fl.1880-1885) British
£310 $493 €453 Corpach, from Fort William, a moonlit scene (12x21cm-5x8in) mono.d.1899 panel. 9-Sep-3 Bamfords, Derby #1147/R
£650 $1086 €949 Corpack from Fort William (10x18cm-4x7in) mono.d.99. 17-Oct-3 Keys, Aylsham #816
Works on paper
£400 $716 €584 HMS Duke of Wellington in Portsmouth harbour (37x53cm-15x21in) s.d.1866 W/C htd white. 25-May-4 Bonhams, Knightsbridge #24/R
£620 $1035 €905 Coastal scene (59x98cm-23x39in) s.d.1881 W/C. 19-Jun-3 Bonhams, Edinburgh #363

£1600 $2832 €2336 Royal Navy brig on anti slavery patrol heaving to off the African coast (35x52cm-14x20in) s.d.1866 W/C. 27-Apr-4 Bonhams, New Bond Street #87/R est:800-1200

LODER OF BATH, Edwin (1827-1885) British
£320 $589 €467 Success (24x29cm-9x11in) s.d.1867. 29-Mar-4 Thomson Roddick & Medcalf, Edinburgh #212
£414 $750 €604 Norwich terrier (17x22cm-7x9in) board. 30-Mar-4 Bonhams & Butterfields, San Francisco #26/R
£460 $823 €672 Chestnut hunter in a loosebox (46x61cm-18x24in) s.d.1887. 17-Mar-4 Bonhams, Chester #394
£500 $925 €730 Racehorse in a stable (30x51cm-12x20in) s.d.1845. 9-Mar-4 Gorringes, Lewes #1977
£550 $985 €803 Dignity and impudence (30x23cm-12x9in) s. board after Sir Edwin Landseer. 18-Mar-4 Christie's, Kensington #485
£1519 $2750 €2218 The lesson. Star pupil (22x30cm-9x12in) board pair. 30-Mar-4 Bonhams & Butterfields, San Francisco #32/R est:2800-3500
£2624 $4750 €3831 Greyhound and beagle in a stable (25x30cm-10x12in) s.d.1845. 30-Mar-4 Bonhams & Butterfields, San Francisco #28/R est:3500-5000

LODER OF BATH, James (1784-1860) British
£2700 $4266 €3915 Huntsman on a bay hunter in a landscape (56x75cm-22x30in) bears sig.d.1842. 24-Jul-3 Lawrence, Crewkerne #921/R est:800-1200
£3000 $5520 €4380 Gundog and a spaniel in a landscape (39x51cm-15x20in) s.i.d.1829. 10-Jun-4 Christie's, Kensington #391/R est:3000-4000
£3200 $5216 €4672 Portrait of Colonel Bouverie on Mr Hobson's Challenger (58x76cm-23x30in) s.i.d.1837. 24-Sep-3 Dreweatt Neate, Newbury #104/R est:3500-4500
£5000 $8300 €7300 Three prized park cattle (53x74cm-21x29in) s.d.1843. 2-Oct-3 Neales, Nottingham #752/R est:4000-5000

LODGE, George Edward (1860-1954) British
£400 $732 €584 Seagulls (17x33cm-7x13in) s. board. 28-Jan-4 Dreweatt Neate, Newbury #81
£2400 $3768 €3480 Snowy owl (31x23cm-12x9in) s. canvas on board. 27-Aug-3 Sotheby's, London #1007/R est:2000-3000
Works on paper
£270 $451 €394 Winter forage, snow covered woodland scene with cock and hen pheasants (25x46cm-10x18in) s. W/C htd white. 16-Oct-3 Neales, Nottingham #871
£350 $585 €511 Pechora pipit, grey headed wagtail, black headed wagtail (29x23cm-11x9in) s. W/C bodycol. 14-Oct-3 Bonhams, Knightsbridge #30/R
£420 $701 €613 Western black eared wheatear (28x22cm-11x9in) s. W/C bodycol. 14-Oct-3 Bonhams, Knightsbridge #29/R
£820 $1394 €1197 Grey legged partridge (22x28cm-9x11in) s. W/C. 19-Nov-3 Sotheby's, Olympia #86/R
£1000 $1800 €1460 Falcon (28x21cm-11x8in) s. W/C. 21-Jan-4 Sotheby's, Olympia #259/R est:500-700
£2600 $4758 €3796 Pink Grosbeak, Crossbill, Red backed Shrike, Wall creeper and Water pipet (27x21cm-11x8in) s. W/C bodycol set of five. 28-Jul-4 Bonhams, Knightsbridge #43/R est:2500-3000
£2800 $5124 €4088 Partridge in stubble (29x45cm-11x18in) s. bodycol. 28-Jul-4 Bonhams, Knightsbridge #44/R est:2000-3000
£3400 $5780 €4964 Gyr Falcon on a rocky outcrop (39x50cm-15x20in) s. pencil W/C bodycol prov. 30-Oct-3 Christie's, London #43/R est:3000-5000

LODOLA, Marco (1955-) Italian
£369 $683 €550 Mask (40x30cm-16x12in) s.verso perspex. 11-Mar-4 Galleria Pace, Milan #37/R
£399 $654 €550 Horse (60x80cm-24x31in) s. acrylic collage. 29-May-3 Galleria Pace, Milan #52/R
£399 $654 €550 Mask (42x31cm-17x12in) s.d.1996 verso on perspex. 29-May-3 Galleria Pace, Milan #116/R
£400 $736 €600 Figure (75x30cm-30x12in) on perspex painted 2000. 10-Jun-4 Galleria Pace, Milan #14/R
£403 $745 €600 Mask (31x41cm-12x16in) s.verso perspex. 11-Mar-4 Galleria Pace, Milan #10/R
£414 $691 €600 Mask (40x30cm-16x12in) s.d. perspex. 13-Nov-3 Galleria Pace, Milan #67/R
£433 $797 €650 Saturday night at the disco (80x60cm-31x24in) s. enamel collage. 12-Jun-4 Meeting Art, Vercelli #319/R
£435 $713 €600 Mask (42x31cm-17x12in) s.d.1996 perspex. 29-May-3 Galleria Pace, Milan #109/R
£448 $749 €650 Mask (40x30cm-16x12in) s.d.1996 verso perspex. 13-Nov-3 Galleria Pace, Milan #26/R
£471 $772 €650 Dancers (80x60cm-31x24in) s. acrylic collage. 29-May-3 Galleria Pace, Milan #14/R
£567 $1043 €850 From the key hole (80x60cm-31x24in) s. enamel collage. 12-Jun-4 Meeting Art, Vercelli #824/R
£667 $1227 €1000 Violin player (150x100cm-59x39in) s. enamel collage. 11-Jun-4 Farsetti, Prato #118/R
£667 $1227 €1000 Applause (150x100cm-59x39in) s. enamel collage. 12-Jun-4 Meeting Art, Vercelli #473/R
£667 $1227 €1000 Dance (150x100cm-59x39in) s. enamel collage. 12-Jun-4 Meeting Art, Vercelli #835/R
£669 $1111 €950 Ballerine (72x134cm-28x53in) s. s.d.2002 verso oil collage. 14-Jun-3 Meeting Art, Vercelli #631/R
£690 $1152 €1000 Two dancers (100x55cm-39x22in) s.i.d.1999 verso perspex. 13-Nov-3 Galleria Pace, Milan #44/R
£733 $1349 €1100 Musicals (150x100cm-59x39in) s. enamel collage. 12-Jun-4 Meeting Art, Vercelli #122/R
£764 $1207 €1100 Dance (100x150cm-39x59in) enamel collage painted 2002. 6-Sep-3 Meeting Art, Vercelli #693
£833 $1533 €1250 Figures (122x83cm-48x33in) s. enamel collage. 10-Jun-4 Galleria Pace, Milan #120/R est:2200
£845 $1403 €1200 Deposizione (100x150cm-39x59in) s. s.d.2002 verso oil collage canvas. 14-Jun-3 Meeting Art, Vercelli #480/R
£845 $1403 €1200 Passi di Danza (150x100cm-59x39in) s. s.d.2002 verso oil collage. 14-Jun-3 Meeting Art, Vercelli #711/R
£867 $1569 €1300 Dancers (116x100cm-46x39in) s. enamel collage. 2-Apr-4 Farsetti, Prato #270/R
£872 $1562 €1300 Figure (150x100cm-59x39in) s. enamel collage painted 2002. 28-May-4 Farsetti, Prato #37/R
£872 $1614 €1300 Marilyn (150x100cm-59x39in) s. enamel collage. 13-Mar-4 Meeting Art, Vercelli #114
£906 $1676 €1350 Dancer (90x53cm-35x21in) s. painted 2001. 11-Mar-4 Galleria Pace, Milan #72/R
£933 $1689 €1400 Royal wedding (120x198cm-47x78in) s.i.d.2002 verso enamel perspex. 2-Apr-4 Farsetti, Prato #324/R
£966 $1612 €1400 Punk (130x90cm-51x35in) s.i.d.1997 verso perspex. 13-Nov-3 Galleria Pace, Milan #106/R est:2300
£972 $1536 €1400 Dance steps (150x100cm-59x39in) enamel collage. 6-Sep-3 Meeting Art, Vercelli #306
£1174 $2173 €1750 Dancers (100x57cm-39x22in) s.i.verso perspex. 13-Mar-4 Meeting Art, Vercelli #82 est:750
£1497 $2679 €2200 Frames (75x138cm-30x54in) s.d.1996 verso plexiglas. 22-Mar-4 Sant Agostino, Torino #453/R est:2500
Sculpture
£1408 $2338 €2000 Corrida (95x130x12cm-37x51x5in) s.i.d.2002 verso neon perspex. 14-Jun-3 Meeting Art, Vercelli #236/R est:2000
£1408 $2338 €2000 Il Cavallo (130x79x12cm-51x31x5in) s.i.d.2002 neon perspex. 14-Jun-3 Meeting Art, Vercelli #461/R est:2000
£1689 $2973 €2500 Vespa (79x80x12cm-31x31x5in) s.i.d.2000 verso perspex neon light. 22-May-4 Galleria Pananti, Florence #391/R est:2800-3000
£1745 $3228 €2600 Buddha (149x85x12cm-59x33x5in) s.i.d.2000 verso perspex neon light. 13-Mar-4 Meeting Art, Vercelli #523 est:2000
£2238 $3804 €3200 Car (76x122x12cm-30x48x5in) s.i.d.2000 verso perspex neon light. 28-Nov-3 Farsetti, Prato #91/R est:3000-3500
£2391 $3922 €3300 Roman holiday (99x97x12cm-39x38x5in) s.i.d.2002 verso perspex neon light. 30-May-3 Farsetti, Prato #418/R
£2483 $4445 €3700 Larilene (100x105x12cm-39x41x5in) s.i.verso perspex neon light. 30-May-4 Meeting Art, Vercelli #13 est:2000
Works on paper
£423 $701 €600 La Balera (74x38cm-29x15in) s.i.d.2003 verso perspex. 14-Jun-3 Meeting Art, Vercelli #159/R
£604 $1117 €900 Dancers (90x118cm-35x46in) s. paper on canvas exec.2000. 13-Mar-4 Meeting Art, Vercelli #19

LOEB, John (20th C) American
Works on paper
£595 $1100 €869 Portrait of Jacqueline Kennedy (46x60cm-18x24in) s. gouache. 13-Jul-4 Christie's, Rockefeller NY #107/R

LOEB, Michel (1930-) French
£839 $1427 €1200 Partie de chasse en Provence (24x33cm-9x13in) d.2003 acrylic. 27-Nov-3 Calmels Cohen, Paris #88/R

LOEB, Pierre (1934-) French
£993 $1658 €1400 Musiciens Afghans II (100x81cm-39x32in) s. prov. 19-Oct-3 Charbonneaux, Paris #146/R
£1538 $2615 €2200 Sonneur de Shofar (61x46cm-24x18in) s. 27-Nov-3 Calmels Cohen, Paris #75/R est:2000-2500

LOEBER, Lou (1894-1983) Dutch
£2536 $4159 €3500 Geranium (40x28cm-16x11in) mono.d.28 s.i.d.1928 cardboard. 27-May-3 Sotheby's, Amsterdam #358/R est:3500-4500
£2600 $4784 €3796 Zonnelbloemen (28x28cm-11x11in) init.d.28 s.i.d.1928 verso board. 24-Jun-4 Sotheby's, Olympia #510/R est:1500-2000
£3467 $6379 €5200 Schuitenvoerder I (40x58cm-16x23in) s.i.d.1928 verso board prov.exhib. 8-Jun-4 Sotheby's, Amsterdam #215/R est:4500-5500
£3667 $6747 €5500 Sneeuw-Maan-Lamp (33x32cm-13x13in) s.d.25 board prov.exhib. 8-Jun-4 Sotheby's, Amsterdam #220/R est:2200-2800
£3867 $7115 €5800 Landscape (51x51cm-20x20in) s.d.35 s.i.d.1935 verso cardboard prov. 8-Jun-4 Sotheby's, Amsterdam #219/R est:3500-4500
£4000 $7360 €6000 Landschap met Vuurtoren (50x74cm-20x29in) s.d.29 s.i.d.1929 verso board prov.exhib. 8-Jun-4 Sotheby's, Amsterdam #214/R est:6000-8000
£4000 $7360 €5840 Fabriekje (35x54cm-14x21in) init.d.23 s.i.d.1923 verso. 24-Jun-4 Sotheby's, Olympia #512/R est:2000-3000
£4333 $7973 €6500 Stad aan het water (62x60cm-24x24in) s.d.27 s.i.d. verso prov.lit. 8-Jun-4 Sotheby's, Amsterdam #222/R est:3500-4500
£5000 $9200 €7300 Schilder in atelier (48x36cm-19x14in) init.d.26 s.i.d.1926 verso board. 24-Jun-4 Sotheby's, Olympia #513/R est:2500-3500
£8000 $14720 €12000 Village (46x86cm-18x34in) init.d.22 lit. 9-Jun-4 Christie's, Amsterdam #64/R est:4000-6000
£9790 $16839 €14000 Man bij de kachel I (93x75cm-37x30in) mono.d.46 s.i.d.1946 verso panel prov. 2-Dec-3 Sotheby's, Amsterdam #109/R est:10000-15000

LOEDING, Harmen (1637-1673) Dutch
£6000 $10920 €9000 Fruit and shells on ledge (48x39cm-19x15in) panel. 29-Jun-4 Sotheby's, Paris #33/R est:10000-12000
£36000 $61200 €52560 Lobsters and cherries in a porcelain bowl, partly peeled lemon on a p ewter platter (58x45cm-23x18in) panel prov.exhib. 29-Oct-3 Christie's, London #29/R est:15000-25000

LOEMANS, Alexander François (c.1816-1898) Canadian/French
£586 $995 €856 Rocky Mountain stream (46x29cm-18x11in) s. board. 21-Nov-3 Walker's, Ottawa #88/R (C.D 1300)
£631 $1072 €921 South American landscapes (7x13cm-3x5in) one s. panel pair. 21-Nov-3 Walker's, Ottawa #87/R (C.D 1400)
£893 $1536 €1304 Rescue attempt (54x90cm-21x35in) s. 2-Dec-3 Joyner Waddington, Toronto #389 est:2000-3000 (C.D 2000)
£3911 $7000 €5710 Harvesters in a river landscape (56x91cm-22x36in) s. 6-May-4 Shannon's, Milford #183/R est:4000-6000
Works on paper
£318 $519 €464 Tropical landscape (42x67cm-17x26in) s. pastel. 23-Sep-3 Ritchie, Toronto #66/R (C.D 700)

LOENEN, Cor van (1942-) Dutch
£278 $439 €400 Paterswoldse meer, Groningen (80x110cm-31x43in) s. board prov. 2-Sep-3 Christie's, Amsterdam #440

LOEW, Michael (1907-1985) American
£926 $1500 €1343 Fog red (127x114cm-50x45in) s. s.i.d.1962 verso prov. 8-Aug-3 Barridorf, Portland #238/R est:2000-3000

LOEWER, Claude (1917-) Swiss
£690 $1234 €1007 La guitarre (81x65cm-32x26in) s.d.51. 12-May-4 Dobiaschofsky, Bern #752 est:1600 (S.FR 1600)

LOEWY, Raymond (1893-1986) French
Works on paper
£278 $464 €400 Etude de bras de maintien telescopique (34x42cm-13x17in) st.sig.d.May 3 1971 crayon col marker. 21-Oct-3 Artcurial Briest, Paris #109/R
£278 $464 €400 Homme au repos sur son siege (36x33cm-14x13in) mono.d.68 ink col marker. 21-Oct-3 Artcurial Briest, Paris #110/R
£312 $521 €450 Etude de couchette reversible contenant la combinaison spatiale (31x41cm-12x16in) mono.d.68 crayon col marker. 21-Oct-3 Artcurial Briest, Paris #108/R
£347 $580 €500 Etude d'un cabine individuelle (34x40cm-13x16in) mono.d.68 ink col marker. 21-Oct-3 Artcurial Briest, Paris #105/R
£431 $719 €620 Studbaker (22x29cm-9x11in) st.sig.d.December 48 graphite pastel. 25-Oct-3 Cornette de St.Cyr, Paris #526
£451 $754 €650 Etude de siege-capsule modulable (33x36cm-13x14in) st.sig.d.Jul 1 1971 ink col marker. 21-Oct-3 Artcurial Briest, Paris #106/R
£451 $754 €650 Etude d'un ceinturon gonflable permettant le guidage (32x41cm-13x16in) ink col marker. 21-Oct-3 Artcurial Briest, Paris #112/R
£486 $812 €700 Etude d'une ceinture (34x42cm-13x17in) st.sig.d.Aug 28 1972 ink col marker. 21-Oct-3 Artcurial Briest, Paris #111/R
£498 $832 €715 Personnage Nasa (20x16cm-8x6in) ink. 21-Oct-3 Artcurial Briest, Paris #113/R
£604 $1081 €900 Helicopter study, greyhound system (60x44cm-24x17in) st.sig.d.1943 crayon. 27-May-4 Sotheby's, Paris #244/R
£764 $1276 €1100 Arizona highway (50x60cm-20x24in) s.i.d.70 verso mixed media gouache collage. 21-Oct-3 Artcurial Briest, Paris #114/R
£940 $1682 €1400 Flying wing helicopter (39x55cm-15x22in) st.sig.d.1943 crayon. 27-May-4 Sotheby's, Paris #243/R est:400-600
£1111 $1855 €1600 Un appareil pour faciliter les periodes de sommeil de courtes durees (32x40cm-13x16in) s.d.1968 col crayon. 21-Oct-3 Artcurial Briest, Paris #107/R est:600-800

LOFDAHL, Eva (1953-) Swedish
£1020 $1733 €1489 Untitled (50x70cm-20x28in) s.d.85 prov. 4-Nov-3 Bukowskis, Stockholm #555d/R est:10000-12000 (S.KR 13500)

LOFFLER, August (1822-1866) German
Works on paper
£1310 $2384 €1913 Ebene von Plataa (28x38cm-11x15in) mono.d.1857 W/C over brush bistre ink over pencil. 17-Jun-4 Kornfeld, Bern #31/R est:3000 (S.FR 3000)

LOFFLER, Bertold (1874-1960) Austrian
Works on paper
£374 $681 €550 Schwallenbach, Wachau (27x27cm-11x11in) s.i. col pen. 9-Feb-4 Dorotheum, Vienna #131
£476 $867 €700 Schwallenbach a D (37x29cm-15x11in) s.i.d.1928 chl col pen. 9-Feb-4 Dorotheum, Vienna #132

LOFFLER, Emma (1843-1929) Danish
£455 $773 €650 Nature morte aux fleurs et aux livres (47x38cm-19x15in) s. 18-Nov-3 Vanderkindere, Brussels #3

LOFFLER, Franz Karl (1875-1955) German
£671 $1235 €1000 Wasserburg (20x30cm-8x12in) s. board. 27-Mar-4 Geble, Radolfzell #738/R

LOFFLER, Richard (1956-) American
Sculpture
£1955 $3500 €2854 Silent twitch (30cm-12in) bronze edn of 15. 15-May-4 Altermann Galleries, Santa Fe #162/R

LOFFREDO, Silvio (1920-) Italian
£225 $410 €340 Battistero (33x24cm-13x9in) s. card. 21-Jun-4 Pandolfini, Florence #496/R
£247 $427 €350 Woman (70x50cm-28x20in) s. card on canvas. 9-Dec-3 Pandolfini, Florence #144
£282 $487 €400 Female nude (50x70cm-20x28in) s. card on canvas. 9-Dec-3 Pandolfini, Florence #145
£331 $603 €500 Battistero (40x28cm-16x11in) s. board. 17-Jun-4 Galleria Pananti, Florence #459/R
£331 $603 €500 Battistero (50x40cm-20x16in) s. canvas on cardboard. 21-Jun-4 Pandolfini, Florence #359
£430 $783 €650 Kittens (19x50cm-7x20in) s. s.verso board. 17-Jun-4 Galleria Pananti, Florence #494/R
£430 $783 €650 Peasant man (60x45cm-24x18in) s. s.i.d.87 verso. 21-Jun-4 Pandolfini, Florence #488
£563 $975 €800 Battistero (40x30cm-16x12in) s.d.62. 9-Dec-3 Pandolfini, Florence #116/R
£576 $944 €800 Nude (70x50cm-28x20in) s.d.78 tempera card on canvas. 10-Jun-3 Pandolfini, Florence #377/R

LOFGREN, Clara (1843-1923) Swedish
£363 $653 €545 Girl by small holding (26x34cm-10x13in) s.d.94 cardboard. 25-Apr-4 Goteborg Auktionsverk, Sweden #y/R (S.KR 5000)

LOFQUIST, Ann (1964-) American
£4198 $6800 €6087 Deerfield pasture in October (89x254cm-35x100in) s.verso dyptich prov. 8-Aug-3 Barridorf, Portland #232/R est:3000-5000

LOFTUS, Peter (20th C) American
£1173 $2100 €1713 Spring rain. s.i. 13-May-4 Dallas Auction Gallery, Dallas #120/R est:1000-2000

LOGAN, Maurice (1886-1977) American
£978 $1800 €1428 Rocks on the Monterey Coast (35x45cm-14x18in) s. canvasboard prov. 8-Jun-4 Bonhams & Butterfields, San Francisco #4239/R est:3000-5000
Works on paper
£449 $750 €656 Coastal cliffs of Monterey (49x69cm-19x27in) s. W/C. 16-Nov-3 Bonhams & Butterfields, Los Angeles #7019/R
£726 $1300 €1060 Autumn landscape (28x36cm-11x14in) s. W/C. 16-Mar-4 Matthew's, Oregon #91/R
£1016 $1900 €1483 Boats tied up to a pier (49x63cm-19x25in) s. pencil W/C exhib. 29-Feb-4 Bonhams & Butterfields, San Francisco #4544 est:2000-3000
£1188 $1900 €1734 Zion National Park. s. W/C. 20-Sep-3 Harvey Clar, Oakland #1316
£2198 $4000 €3209 Boat beached (53x74cm-21x29in) s. i.verso W/C prov. 15-Jun-4 John Moran, Pasadena #88 est:3000-4000

LOGAN, Robert Henry (1874-1942) American
£958 $1600 €1399 Trees in summer (33x41cm-13x16in) s. prov. 23-Oct-3 Shannon's, Milford #223/R est:1500-2500

LOGAN, Thayne J (1900-1990) American
Works on paper
£238 $425 €347 Fisher Towers, Colorado River, near Moab Utah (30x41cm-12x16in) s.i.d.10-11-36 verso W/C. 16-Mar-4 Matthew's, Oregon #9/R
£256 $460 €374 Lake Louise Banee Nat Park Canada (38x56cm-15x22in) s.d.10-12-45 i.verso W/C. 16-Mar-4 Matthew's, Oregon #10/R

LOGELAIN, Henri (1889-1968) Belgian
£445 $757 €650 Vue de la Seine a Paris (27x34cm-11x13in) s. panel. 4-Nov-3 Servarts Themis, Bruxelles #592
£461 $834 €700 Visage de fillette (34x87cm-13x34in) s. panel. 19-Apr-4 Horta, Bruxelles #387
£805 $1426 €1200 La rade d'Anvers (39x45cm-15x18in) s. panel. 27-Apr-4 Campo, Vlaamse Kaai #495

LOGELAIN, Henri (attrib) (1889-1968) Belgian
£267 $477 €400 Vase de fleurs (50x40cm-20x16in) panel. 11-May-4 Vanderkindere, Brussels #127

LOGGAN, David (1635-1692) British
Miniatures
£2200 $3960 €3212 Daniel Pryce, Dean of St Asaph, in black robes (12cm-5in) init.d.168 i.verso plumbago W/C vellum oval exhib. 22-Apr-4 Bonhams, New Bond Street #20/R est:1200-1800

LOGSDAIL, Marian (19/20th C) British
£2800 $5012 €4088 Through the vestry door (91x39cm-36x15in) s.d.89. 22-Mar-4 Bonhams & Brooks, Norfolk #278/R est:150-250

LOGSDAIL, William (1859-1944) British
£400 $680 €584 Wadham College Chapel, Oxford (40x30cm-16x12in) s. canvasboard. 1-Dec-3 Bonhams, Bath #25/R
£700 $1190 €1022 Portrait of Fred Hall (61x51cm-24x20in) i.stretcher. 1-Dec-3 Bonhams, Bath #1/R
£5500 $9350 €8030 Portrait of a young girl in a pink dress (20x13cm-8x5in) s.d.1900 verso board. 25-Nov-3 Christie's, London #119/R est:3000-5000

LOGSDAIL, William (attrib) (1859-1944) British
£2600 $4654 €3796 Entrance to the Grand Canal (28x45cm-11x18in) 11-May-4 Bonhams, Knightsbridge #99/R est:2000-3000

LOHAN, Mary (20th C) Irish?
£1818 $3091 €2600 Coastal landscape (41x51cm-16x20in) s. diptych. 25-Nov-3 De Veres Art Auctions, Dublin #195/R est:2500-3500

LOHMANN, Adolf (1928-) German
£1207 $2160 €1762 Ducks on pond (30x40cm-12x16in) s. panel. 12-May-4 Dobiaschofsky, Bern #753/R est:2600 (S.FR 2800)

LOHMANN, Theo (1880-1963) Dutch
£336 $621 €500 Farm with hay stack, Blaricum (33x43cm-13x17in) s. 15-Mar-4 Sotheby's, Amsterdam #285

LOHR, August (1843-1919) German
£800 $1256 €1160 Bridge in Mexican landscape (67x45cm-26x18in) s.d.August 1912. 28-Aug-3 Christie's, Kensington #223/R
£3425 $5342 €5000 Landscape (90x137cm-35x54in) s.d.1917. 10-Apr-3 Weidler, Nurnberg #6600
£6500 $10855 €9490 Woman on a track near Mexico City (25x37cm-10x15in) s. board. 14-Oct-3 Sotheby's, London #224/R est:3000-5000
£47486 $85000 €69330 Popocatepetl (95x140cm-37x55in) s.i.d.1917. 26-May-4 Sotheby's, New York #81/R est:60000-80000
Works on paper
£1983 $3549 €2895 River in Mexico (25x40cm-10x16in) s.i.d.1894 W/C. 12-May-4 Dobiaschofsky, Bern #754/R est:6000 (S.FR 4600)

£3622 $6483 €5288 Temple in Mexico (36x52cm-14x20in) s.i.d.1910 W/C. 26-May-4 AB Stockholms Auktionsverk #2488/R est:25000-30000 (S.KR 49000)
£5200 $8684 €7592 Village in Mexico (27x41cm-11x16in) s. W/C over pencil. 14-Oct-3 Sotheby's, London #225/R est:2000-3000
£5882 $10000 €8588 Mexican village (36x52cm-14x20in) s.d.1909 W/C prov. 19-Nov-3 Sotheby's, New York #74/R est:10000-15000
£7059 $12000 €10306 Paisaje de xochimilco (44x55cm-17x22in) s.d.1909 W/C. 19-Nov-3 Sotheby's, New York #73/R est:10000-15000

LOHR, Hugo (19th C) ?
£1243 $2200 €1815 Summer landscape with figures haymaking (36x51cm-14x20in) s.d.1907. 2-May-4 Bonhams & Butterfields, San Francisco #1052/R est:600-800

LOHR, O (19/20th C) German
Works on paper
£2353 $4000 €3435 Three glimpses into the life of General Von Steuben (13x28cm-5x11in) s. gouache mixed media on kid skin. 18-Nov-3 Doyle, New York #24 est:1000-1500

LOHSE, Carl (20th C) German
£764 $1245 €1100 Two dancing children in park (34x34cm-13x13in) mono. 25-Sep-3 Dr Fritz Nagel, Stuttgart #1312/R
£5369 $9611 €8000 Portrait of seated man in blue suit (90x60cm-35x24in) s.d.33. 25-May-4 Karl & Faber, Munich #392/R est:9000
£6389 $10669 €9200 Hay harvest (60x79cm-24x31in) s. 25-Oct-3 Dr Lehr, Berlin #318/R est:8500
Works on paper
£4000 $7160 €6000 Lausitz landscape (79x60cm-31x24in) s. W/C chl prov. 14-May-4 Ketterer, Munich #53/R est:1800-2400

LOHSE, Richard Paul (1902-1988) Swiss
£4909 $8346 €7167 Vertikalstufung gelb-grun-blau (120x12cm-47x5in) s.d.1977 verso. 5-Nov-3 AB Stockholms Auktionsverk #1171/R est:80000-120000 (S.KR 65000)
£9063 $15408 €13232 Untitled (120x20cm-47x8in) s.d.1950 verso prov. 5-Nov-3 AB Stockholms Auktionsverk #1167/R est:80000-120000 (S.KR 120000)
£16107 $28832 €24000 Four colours on four rectangles (59x60cm-23x24in) s.i.d.52 prov. 25-May-4 Sotheby's, Milan #170/R est:8000-10000
£39301 $72314 €57379 Composition (120x120cm-47x47in) s. verso s.i.d. stretcher exhib. 8-Jun-4 Germann, Zurich #64/R est:35000-40000 (S.FR 90000)

LOHSE-WACHTLER, Elfriede (1899-1940) German
£33094 $54273 €46000 Blue tunic - self portrait IV (44x56cm-17x22in) mono.d. s.i. verso w/C. 4-Jun-3 Ketterer, Hamburg #617/R est:1500-2000

LOIR, Luigi (1845-1916) French
£300 $552 €438 Tuilleries, Paris (16x21cm-6x8in) s. 23-Jun-4 Cheffins, Cambridge #511/R
£872 $1605 €1300 Evening walk by lake (17x29cm-7x11in) s. canvas on panel. 26-Mar-4 Bolland & Marotz, Bremen #554/R
£1781 $3027 €2600 Paris street (32x45cm-13x18in) s.d.05. 5-Nov-3 Vendue Huis, Gravenhage #367/R est:2500-3000
£3020 $5406 €4500 Parisian suburb with figures (46x55cm-18x22in) s. 27-May-4 Dorotheum, Graz #46/R est:2000
£3600 $5976 €5256 En plein air (23x33cm-9x13in) s.i. board. 1-Oct-3 Sotheby's, Olympia #289/R est:2500-3500
£6250 $11000 €9125 Parisian nighttime scene of the Seine (61x74cm-24x29in) s. 21-May-4 Pook & Pook, Downington #279/R est:12000-15000
£14706 $25000 €21471 Parisian street scene (52x52cm-20x20in) s. 29-Oct-3 Christie's, Rockefeller NY #185/R est:20000-30000
£24706 $42000 €36071 On the quai in Le Havre (38x56cm-15x22in) s. exhib. 29-Oct-3 Christie's, Rockefeller NY #183/R est:40000-60000
Works on paper
£268 $494 €400 Symphonie des Hannetons (29x20cm-11x8in) s. s. lead pencil scratching out board. 24-Mar-4 Joron-Derem, Paris #76
£799 $1334 €1150 Pietons a Paris (11x21cm-4x8in) s. wash htd gouache. 25-Oct-3 Binoche, Orleans #35
£1379 $2552 €2000 Rue animee a MOntmartre (45x21cm-18x8in) s. pen dr htd white. 16-Feb-4 Giraudeau, Tours #26
£5960 $10848 €9000 Le bassin du Treport (30x44cm-12x17in) s. W/C crayon. 18-Jun-4 Piasa, Paris #45/R est:9000-10000
£8235 $14000 €12023 Evening promenade, Le Havre (21x33cm-8x13in) s. W/C gouache pencil htd gum arabic. 29-Oct-3 Christie's, Rockefeller NY #184/R est:10000-15000

LOIR, Marianne (c.1715-1769) French
£4967 $9089 €7500 Portrait de Francoise de Mailly-Nesle, Princesse de Montbarey (92x74cm-36x29in) oval. 7-Apr-4 Libert, Castor, Paris #34/R est:8000-10000

LOIR, Marianne (attrib) (c.1715-1769) French
£1776 $3268 €2700 Portrait de jeune femme a la robe bleue et au petit chien (81x64cm-32x25in) 25-Jun-4 Rossini, Paris #51/R est:3000-5000

LOIR, Nicolas (attrib) (1624-1679) French
Works on paper
£1020 $1827 €1500 L'Aurore avec Apollon pret a monter su son char, figures mythologiques (62cm-24in circular) pen brown ink wash htd gouache prov. 19-Mar-4 Piasa, Paris #25/R est:2000-2500

LOIRAND, Maurice (1922-) French
£280 $481 €400 Colonne Maurice sous la neige (54x81cm-21x32in) s. 3-Dec-3 Tajan, Paris #273

LOIS, Jacob (c.1620-1676) Dutch
Works on paper
£18310 $32042 €26000 Portrait d'un homme portant un fraise et appuye sur un epee (19x16cm-7x6in) s.d.1659 col chk blue wash prov. 17-Dec-3 Christie's, Paris #29/R est:15000-20000

LOISEAU, Gustave (1865-1935) French
£1549 $2680 €2200 Statuettes en faience (37x27cm-15x11in) studio st. panel. 14-Dec-3 Eric Pillon, Calais #71/R
£2667 $4853 €4000 Nature morte a la coupe de fruits (32x40cm-13x16in) s. panel. 4-Jul-4 Eric Pillon, Calais #145/R
£3262 $5448 €4600 Nature morte aux poissons, gardons (38x47cm-15x19in) s. panel. 19-Jun-3 Millon & Associes, Paris #215/R est:3000-4000
£4698 $8691 €7000 Trois gardons (38x47cm-15x19in) s. panel lit. 14-Mar-4 Eric Pillon, Calais #124/R
£5594 $9510 €8000 Soupiere, citron et faience de Quimper. Paysage (46x56cm-18x22in) s. double-sided painted c.1916. 27-Nov-3 Millon & Associes, Paris #193/R est:9000-12000
£8741 $15035 €12500 Cote rocheuse (54x65cm-21x26in) s. 5-Dec-3 Maigret, Paris #16/R est:15000-18000
£11173 $20000 €16313 Falaises d'Yport (55x66cm-22x26in) s. painted c.1924. 6-May-4 Sotheby's, New York #423/R est:20000-30000
£13667 $24463 €20500 La meule pres des chaumes (46x55cm-18x22in) s. 16-May-4 Thierry & Lannon, Brest #156/R est:18000-20000
£13761 $22982 €19953 Le marronnier de la Sous Prefecture, Pontoise (65x50cm-26x20in) s. prov. 23-Jun-3 Philippe Schuler, Zurich #3567/R est:30000-50000 (S.FR 30000)
£13966 $25000 €20390 Deux grillons, Saint-Cyr-Du-Vaudreuil (65x54cm-26x21in) s. painted c.1931 prov. 6-May-4 Sotheby's, New York #417/R est:25000-35000
£15676 $29000 €22887 Maison des soeurs, Pontoise (54x65cm-21x26in) s.d.1924 prov. 11-Feb-4 Sotheby's, New York #13/R est:25000-30000
£16000 $29120 €23360 Barrage de St. Maryin Pontoise (46x61cm-18x24in) s.d.1907 prov. 4-Feb-4 Sotheby's, London #306/R est:18000-25000
£18000 $32760 €26280 Au bord de la mer (60x76cm-24x30in) s. prov.exhib. 4-Feb-4 Sotheby's, London #301/R est:20000-30000
£18000 $33120 €26280 L'Hotel Julia a Pont-Aven (46x61cm-18x24in) s. painted 1928 prov. 23-Jun-4 Christie's, London #139/R est:20000-30000
£18438 $29500 €26919 Passage a niveau (46x61cm-18x24in) s. prov. 20-Sep-3 New Orleans Auction, New Orleans #541/R est:50000
£20000 $36400 €29200 Le pont de la Poissonnerie, Dieppe (54x65cm-21x26in) s. 3-Feb-4 Christie's, London #146/R est:20000-30000
£20588 $35000 €30058 Maisons a Pont-Aven - Finistere - l'auberge (54x46cm-21x18in) s. i.stretcher prov. 5-Nov-3 Christie's, Rockefeller NY #242/R est:35000-45000
£23529 $40000 €34352 Paysage de Bretagne, Pont-Aven (73x60cm-29x24in) s.d.1903 i.stretcher prov. 5-Nov-3 Christie's, Rockefeller NY #221/R est:40000-60000
£24000 $43680 €35040 L'Arc de Triomphe, la Place de l'Etoile (54x64cm-21x25in) s. painted 1929 prov.exhib.lit. 3-Feb-4 Christie's, London #160/R est:22000-26000
£25000 $45500 €36500 Rue a Pont-Aven (46x38cm-18x15in) s. prov. 3-Feb-4 Christie's, London #265/R est:25000-35000
£25140 $45000 €36704 Marronnier de la sous prefecture, Pontoise (65x50cm-26x20in) s. painted 1922 prov. 6-May-4 Sotheby's, New York #265/R est:40000-60000
£25352 $44366 €36000 Animation sur la place de Pont-Aven (65x50cm-26x20in) s. 21-Dec-3 Thierry & Lannon, Brest #175/R est:30000-32000
£29412 $50000 €42942 Marine, baie de Douarnenez (65x81cm-26x32in) s. painted c.1913 prov. 5-Nov-3 Christie's, Rockefeller NY #216/R est:50000-70000
£32000 $58240 €46720 Le port de Dieppe (60x72cm-24x28in) s. painted 1929. 4-Feb-4 Sotheby's, London #223/R est:35000-45000
£35000 $64400 €51100 Rue de village au Vaudreuil (46x55cm-18x22in) s.d.1903 prov. 22-Jun-4 Sotheby's, London #243/R est:25000-35000
£35000 $64400 €51100 Moret-sur-Loing (60x81cm-24x32in) s. painted c.1932-1935. 23-Jun-4 Christie's, London #137/R est:30000-40000
£44693 $80000 €65252 Maison de Campagne (50x62cm-20x24in) s. painted 1897 prov. 6-May-4 Sotheby's, New York #243/R est:8000-120000
£44693 $80000 €65252 Port de Dieppe (60x73cm-24x29in) s.d.1926 prov. 6-May-4 Sotheby's, New York #264/R est:60000-80000
£60000 $109200 €87600 Printemps (54x65cm-21x26in) s.d.1906 prov. 3-Feb-4 Christie's, London #136/R est:60000-80000
£67039 $120000 €97877 Verger en fleur, printemps (65x81cm-26x32in) s.d.1902 prov. 6-May-4 Sotheby's, New York #268/R est:70000-90000
£70000 $127400 €102200 Le Loing a Moret (60x73cm-24x29in) s. prov. 3-Feb-4 Christie's, London #191/R est:40000-60000
£85000 $156400 €124100 La rue de Clignancourt (73x61cm-29x24in) s.d.1924 prov. 23-Jun-4 Christie's, London #138/R est:80000-120000
£134078 $240000 €195754 Mer a Pornic (61x74cm-24x29in) s. painted c.1900 prov. 6-May-4 Sotheby's, New York #259/R est:70000-90000
Works on paper
£1800 $3258 €2628 Notre Dame (27x44cm-11x17in) studio st. pencil W/C. 1-Apr-4 Christie's, Kensington #33/R est:2000-3000

LOISEAU-ROUSSEAU, Paul Louis Émile (attrib) (1861-1927) French
Sculpture
£1067 $1909 €1600 Femme vegetale (44cm-17in) s. pat bronze. 14-May-4 Camard, Paris #157 est:400-600

LOISEL, Wilhelm (1914-) Austrian?
£743 $1308 €1100 Little stream in winter (69x94cm-27x37in) s.d.52 board. 19-May-4 Dorotheum, Klagenfurt #17
Works on paper
£278 $442 €400 Flowers (50x38cm-20x15in) s. W/C. 10-Sep-3 Dorotheum, Vienna #145
£315 $535 €450 Worthersee with view of Karawanken (33x45cm-13x18in) s.d.55 W/C board. 19-Nov-3 Dorotheum, Klagenfurt #55

LOJACONO, Francesco (1841-1915) Italian
£9058 $14855 €12500 Seascape with cliffs (46x88cm-18x35in) s. 27-May-3 Finarte Semenzato, Milan #65/R est:15000
£13768 $22580 €19000 Sicilian landscape (63x96cm-25x38in) canvas on board. 27-May-3 Finarte Semenzato, Milan #73/R est:14000-16000
£18667 $34347 €28000 Landscape (50x120cm-20x47in) s. 8-Jun-4 Sotheby's, Milan #85/R est:18000-25000
£19500 $33540 €28470 Country girl and the lamp (49x97cm-19x38in) s. 4-Dec-3 Christie's, Kensington #37/R est:10000-15000
£22222 $40000 €32444 Going to market (54x102cm-21x40in) s. 23-Apr-4 Sotheby's, New York #72/R est:30000-50000
£22917 $37354 €33000 Fishermen returning to village harbour (58x103cm-23x41in) s. i. verso. 25-Sep-3 Dr Fritz Nagel, Stuttgart #1374/R est:30000
£28623 $46942 €39500 After the storm (46x96cm-18x38in) s. 27-May-3 Finarte Semenzato, Milan #81/R est:18000

£30072 $49319 €41500 Palermo bay (48x96cm-19x38in) s. 27-May-3 Finarte Semenzato, Milan #66/R est:22000-24000

LOKHORST, Dirk Pieter van (1848-?) Dutch
£262 $461 €383 Cows in summer landscape (42x56cm-17x22in) s. prov. 22-May-4 Galerie Gloggner, Luzern #104 (S.FR 600)
£1800 $3096 €2628 Cattle at the waters' edge (100x150cm-39x59in) s.d.1872. 4-Dec-3 Christie's, Kensington #212/R est:2000-4000
£2072 $3750 €3025 Bull and cow in a pasture (76x127cm-30x50in) 3-Apr-4 Neal Auction Company, New Orleans #291/R est:4000-6000

LOKHORST, Dirk van (1818-1893) Dutch
£625 $1019 €900 Three cows in meadow (24x30cm-9x12in) s. panel. 24-Sep-3 Neumeister, Munich #485/R
£789 $1453 €1200 Sheep (29x35cm-11x14in) s. panel. 28-Jun-4 Sotheby's, Amsterdam #13/R

LOKHORST, Jan van (1837-1874) Dutch
£2721 $4952 €4000 By the bridge (62x104cm-24x41in) s.d.1875. 3-Feb-4 Christie's, Amsterdam #265/R est:4000-6000

LOKKE, Karl (1870-1943) Norwegian
£244 $449 €366 Trabelisaeter, Ringebu (49x51cm-19x20in) s. 14-Jun-4 Blomqvist, Lysaker #1231 (N.KR 3000)
£260 $479 €390 Outfarm in the mountains (37x45cm-15x18in) s. 14-Jun-4 Blomqvist, Lysaker #1230 (N.KR 3200)
£260 $479 €390 Spring, Gulbransdalen (52x66cm-20x26in) s. 14-Jun-4 Blomqvist, Lysaker #1233 (N.KR 3200)
£301 $553 €452 Farm, Ringebu (47x59cm-19x23in) s. 14-Jun-4 Blomqvist, Lysaker #1232 (N.KR 3700)
£417 $668 €605 Winter's day (46x70cm-18x28in) s. 22-Sep-3 Blomqvist, Lysaker #1198 (N.KR 4900)
£489 $856 €714 Landscape from Gudbrandsdalen (50x69cm-20x27in) s. i.stretcher. 16-Dec-3 Grev Wedels Plass, Oslo #197/R (N.KR 5700)

LOKKE, Marie (1876-1948) Norwegian
£407 $748 €594 Fjord landscape (40x60cm-16x24in) s. 10-Jun-4 Grev Wedels Plass, Oslo #206/R (N.KR 5000)
£1027 $1745 €1499 Coastal landscape with woman (25x30cm-10x12in) s. panel. 19-Nov-3 Grev Wedels Plass, Oslo #74/R est:15000-20000 (N.KR 12000)
£1308 $2250 €1910 Haystacks (46x61cm-18x24in) s. sold with a pastel of sailboats at sunset by the same artist. 7-Dec-3 Grogan, Boston #107/R
£1681 $3010 €2454 Landscape with geese (72x80cm-28x31in) s. 22-Mar-4 Blomqvist, Oslo #393/R est:18000-20000 (N.KR 21000)

LOLMO, Giovanni Paolo (1550-1593) Italian
£7692 $13231 €11000 Madonna and Child (74x97cm-29x38in) 2-Dec-3 Sotheby's, Milan #18/R est:4000-6000

LOMAKIN, Oleg (1924-) Russian
£430 $800 €628 Sunset (61x46cm-24x18in) s.i. 7-Mar-4 William Jenack, New York #287
£567 $948 €800 Model (61x43cm-24x17in) s. 20-Oct-3 Durán, Madrid #715/R

LOMAX, John Arthur (1857-1923) British
£800 $1384 €1168 Bowl of bishop (23x33cm-9x13in) s. board. 9-Dec-3 Louis Taylor, Stoke on Trent #1191
£1350 $2336 €1971 When I was a boy (23x28cm-9x11in) s. board. 9-Dec-3 Louis Taylor, Stoke on Trent #1190
£2700 $4671 €3942 How happy I would be with either (34x52cm-13x20in) s. exhib. 9-Dec-3 Anderson & Garland, Newcastle #427/R est:2000-3000
£2700 $5022 €3942 Wish clouded cave and broider dreams and very artful ways' (41x30cm-16x12in) s. panel. 4-Mar-4 Christie's, Kensington #636/R est:3000-5000
£3600 $6552 €5256 Curiosities (34x44cm-13x17in) s. exhib. 29-Jun-4 Anderson & Garland, Newcastle #497/R est:3000-5000
£10500 $17850 €15330 Bachelor. Spinster (30x25cm-12x10in) s. panel pair. 28-Oct-3 Henry Adams, Chichester #440/R est:4000-6000
Works on paper
£400 $680 €584 Reliving the chase (17x24cm-7x9in) s. W/C. 29-Oct-3 Bonhams, Chester #507
£580 $1021 €847 A country girl paused on a track beside a scarecrow (53x36cm-21x14in) s. W/C. 19-May-4 Dreweatt Neate, Newbury #38/R

LOMAZZO, Giovanni Paolo (1538-1600) Italian
Works on paper
£3611 $6500 €5272 Study of a draped figure, his hands raised (25x16cm-10x6in) black chk htd white. 21-Jan-4 Sotheby's, New York #25/R est:3500-4500

LOMBARD SCHOOL (16th C) Italian
£5036 $8259 €7000 Saint Sebastian (93x50cm-37x20in) board. 4-Jun-3 Sotheby's, Milan #27/R est:4000-6000
£5694 $9681 €8200 L'Arcangelo Michele (136x101cm-54x40in) tempera. 28-Oct-3 Della Rocca, Turin #210/R est:4000-4500
£6000 $10980 €9000 Portrait of gentleman (85x63cm-33x25in) 1-Jun-4 Sotheby's, Milan #108/R est:5000-7000
£7000 $12600 €10220 Holy Family with the infant Saint John the Baptist and saint Elisabeth (55x42cm-22x17in) panel. 21-Apr-4 Christie's, London #86/R est:7000-10000
£13333 $24133 €20000 Madonna and Child (68x49cm-27x19in) board. 31-Mar-4 Finarte Semenzato, Milan #609/R est:18000-20000

LOMBARD SCHOOL (17th C) Italian
£5944 $9927 €8500 Madonna and Child (54x38cm-21x15in) board oval. 7-Oct-3 Pandolfini, Florence #447/R est:5500-6000
£7000 $12110 €10220 Mary Magdalane washing Christ's feet (10x82cm-4x32in) 12-Dec-3 Christie's, Kensington #222/R est:7000-10000
£8276 $13738 €12000 Allegory of the seasons (95x134cm-37x53in) prov. 1-Oct-3 Dorotheum, Vienna #66/R est:6000-10000
£10000 $18200 €15000 Saint Sebastian (92x72cm-36x28in) 29-Jun-4 Pandolfini, Florence #64/R est:15000-18000
£11702 $19543 €16500 Holy scene (150x168cm-59x66in) 17-Jun-3 Finarte Semenzato, Milan #401/R est:20000
£23944 $41901 €34000 Vase with flowers (65x51cm-26x20in) oval set of 4. 17-Dec-3 Il Ponte, Milan #286/R est:40000-50000
£34899 $62470 €52000 Basket with apricots and asparagus. Basket with pears and courgettes (74x104cm-29x41in) pair. 26-May-4 Porro, Milan #35/R est:60000-80000

LOMBARD SCHOOL (18th C) Italian
£4965 $8291 €7000 Still life (93x137cm-37x54in) 17-Jun-3 Finarte Semenzato, Milan #622/R est:8000-12000
£5616 $8762 €8200 Salome (110x75cm-43x30in) 8-Apr-3 Il Ponte, Milan #187
£8800 $15840 €12848 Temptation of Saint Anthony (121x88cm-48x35in) painted c.1700. 23-Apr-4 Christie's, Kensington #213/R est:6000-8000
£17361 $28993 €25000 Portrait of woman (102x86cm-40x34in) 23-Oct-3 Finarte Semenzato, Milan #340/R est:9000
£31690 $51021 €45000 Scena di genere (112x182cm-44x72in) 8-May-3 Farsetti, Prato #683/R est:35000-45000

LOMBARD SCHOOL (19th C) Italian
£6623 $12053 €10000 Rural fair (55x86cm-22x34in) 17-Jun-4 Finarte Semenzato, Milan #263/R est:9000-10000
Sculpture
£7534 $12808 €11000 River nymph (60x50x28cm-24x20x11in) marble. 8-Nov-3 Finarte, Venice #206/R est:9000-11000

LOMBARD, Henri Edouard and VERLET, Charles Raoul (19/20th C) French
Sculpture
£418919 $749865 €620000 Four seasons (286cm-113in) white marble set of 4 prov.lit. 9-May-4 Sotheby's, Amsterdam #554/R est:900000-1400000

LOMBARD, Jean (1895-1983) French
£986 $1637 €1400 Rue sous l'aqueduc (54x65cm-21x26in) s.d.1944. 11-Jun-3 Delorme & Bocage, Paris #57/R

LOMBARD, Lambert (attrib) (1506-1566) Flemish
Works on paper
£2568 $4519 €3800 Death of Lucretia (21x31cm-8x12in) pen brown ink blue wash black chk prov.lit. 19-May-4 Sotheby's, Amsterdam #9/R est:2500-3500

LOMBARDI, Carmen (1902-2002) American
£213 $350 €311 Parkway, facing William Penn (51x61cm-20x24in) s. 4-Jun-3 Alderfer's, Hatfield #324
£231 $425 €337 Landscape with outdoor concert (51x61cm-20x24in) s. 9-Jun-4 Alderfer's, Hatfield #482/R
£244 $400 €356 Market street, Philadelphia (61x76cm-24x30in) s. 4-Jun-3 Alderfer's, Hatfield #323/R
£274 $475 €400 Philadelphia street scene (51x61cm-20x24in) s. 10-Dec-3 Alderfer's, Hatfield #458/R
£326 $600 €476 Urban landscape with street market (61x51cm-24x20in) s. 9-Jun-4 Alderfer's, Hatfield #484/R
£403 $750 €588 Philadelphia street scene (51x61cm-20x24in) s.d.1963. 3-Mar-4 Alderfer's, Hatfield #406/R
£407 $750 €594 Urban landscape with Logan Circle fountain in Philadelphia (61x91cm-24x36in) s. 9-Jun-4 Alderfer's, Hatfield #483
£409 $650 €597 Independence Hall, 5th and Chestnut Streets, Philadelphia (51x61cm-20x24in) s. 10-Sep-3 Alderfer's, Hatfield #423/R
£462 $850 €675 Urban landscape with figures on sidewalk (61x51cm-24x20in) s. 9-Jun-4 Alderfer's, Hatfield #485

LOMBARDI, Giovanni Battista (1823-c.1880) Italian
£34483 $57241 €50000 Elegant party in palace (103x142cm-41x56in) 1-Oct-3 Dorotheum, Vienna #56/R est:40000-60000

LOMBARDO, Salvo (1948-) Italian
£567 $1043 €850 Father and daughter (40x50cm-16x20in) init. painted 2003. 12-Jun-4 Meeting Art, Vercelli #928
£633 $1165 €950 Doberman (40x50cm-16x20in) s. i.verso painted 2003. 12-Jun-4 Meeting Art, Vercelli #202

LOMBARDO, Sergio (1939-) Italian
£6711 $12013 €10000 Politician (170x155cm-67x61in) s.d.1964 on stretcher acrylic prov.exhib. 25-May-4 Sotheby's, Milan #207/R est:13000-18000
£9058 $14855 €12500 Portrait oF mambor (170x100cm-67x39in) s.d.1964 on stretcher acrylic prov.exhib. 27-May-3 Sotheby's, Milan #209f/R est:10000-15000
£20979 $35664 €30000 Plinio and I (144x176cm-57x69in) acrylic painted c.1962 exhib. 25-Nov-3 Sotheby's, Milan #155/R est:10000-15000

LOMI, Giovanni (1889-1969) Italian
£263 $484 €400 Farmhouses in Tuscany (39x29cm-15x11in) s. board prov. 28-Jun-4 Sotheby's, Amsterdam #108/R
£423 $731 €600 Cock and hens (13x18cm-5x7in) s. board. 11-Dec-3 Christie's, Rome #90
£667 $1227 €1000 Sunset on the sea (7x12cm-3x5in) s. board. 14-Jun-4 Sant Agostino, Torino #228/R
£704 $1218 €1000 Hen in the courtyard (30x40cm-12x16in) s. board. 10-Dec-3 Sotheby's, Milan #86/R
£1208 $2162 €1800 Around Lecco (19x24cm-7x9in) s. board. 25-May-4 Finarte Semenzato, Milan #46/R est:1000-1300
£1275 $2257 €1900 Portoferraio Gulf (15x21cm-6x8in) s. i.verso board. 1-May-4 Meeting Art, Vercelli #333 est:1500

£1348 $2250 €1900 Street in Bergamo (10x17cm-4x7in) s. board. 14-Oct-3 Finarte Semenzato, Milan #23
£1377 $2258 €1900 Beach with boats (35x25cm-14x10in) s. s.verso masonite. 29-May-3 Galleria Pace, Milan #91/R est:2800
£1479 $2558 €2100 Village in the mountains (19x29cm-7x11in) s. board. 9-Dec-3 Pandolfini, Florence #361/R est:1600-1700
£1867 $3341 €2800 Horses in the square (29x37cm-11x15in) s. board. 12-May-4 Stadion, Trieste #669/R est:1000-1500
£1901 $3289 €2700 Morning on the beach (23x30cm-9x12in) s. masonite. 9-Dec-3 Pandolfini, Florence #274/R est:2200-2400
£2000 $3340 €2900 Washerwomen (24x35cm-9x14in) s. board. 14-Nov-3 Farsetti, Prato #568/R est:2400-2800
£2086 $3422 €2900 Water carriers (15x20cm-6x8in) s. board. 10-Jun-3 Pandolfini, Florence #243/R est:2100-2300
£2958 $5117 €4200 Boats in Tozzo (29x48cm-11x19in) s.i.verso board. 9-Dec-3 Pandolfini, Florence #268/R est:2800-3200
£3944 $6823 €5600 Nap (35x71cm-14x28in) s. i.verso board. 9-Dec-3 Pandolfini, Florence #267/R est:2800-3200
Works on paper
£282 $487 €400 Nuns (10x9cm-4x4in) s. chl. 9-Dec-3 Pandolfini, Florence #309/R

LOMMAERT, Léon (1904-) Belgian
£268 $481 €400 Barques a l'estran (80x100cm-31x39in) s. 25-May-4 Campo & Campo, Antwerp #152

LONBLAD, Emilia (1865-1946) Swedish
£1700 $3043 €2482 Small girl reading (54x65cm-21x26in) s.d.1895. 26-May-4 AB Stockholms Auktionsverk #2105/R est:15000-20000 (S.KR 23000)

LONCIN, Louis (1875-1946) Belgian
£464 $844 €700 Sous-bois automnal (100x150cm-39x59in) s. 16-Jun-4 Hotel des Ventes Mosan, Brussels #215
£777 $1469 €1150 L'epluchage de betteraves (72x100cm-28x39in) s. 17-Feb-4 Vanderkindere, Brussels #11/R
£861 $1567 €1300 Cour de ferme avec chevaux (90x120cm-35x47in) s.d.1901. 16-Jun-4 Hotel des Ventes Mosan, Brussels #213
£3916 $6657 €5600 En embuscade (101x150cm-40x59in) s. 18-Nov-3 Vanderkindere, Brussels #70/R est:2000-3000

LONDERSEEL, Jan van (1582-?) Dutch
Prints
£1788 $3200 €2610 Christ and his Disciples at Emmaus (30x48cm-12x19in) engraving after Vinckboons. 6-May-4 Swann Galleries, New York #44/R est:2500-3500

LONDON, Terence (attrib) (?) British
£1100 $2013 €1606 Still life with flowers in a glass vase (61x51cm-24x20in) 28-Jan-4 Dreweatt Neate, Newbury #114/R est:600-800

LONDOT, Charles (1887-1968) Belgian
£293 $531 €440 Port de peche a Ostende (61x67cm-24x26in) s. panel. 30-Mar-4 Palais de Beaux Arts, Brussels #643

LONE WOLF (1882-?) American
£1235 $2000 €1791 Western genre scene (38x48cm-15x19in) s.d.1928. 26-Jul-3 Thomaston Place, Thomaston #114/R
£1647 $2800 €2405 Rider in moonlight (25x20cm-10x8in) canvasboard. 1-Nov-3 Altermann Galleries, Santa Fe #50

LONECHILD, Ken (1960-) Canadian
£289 $524 €422 They bite after sunset (46x61cm-18x24in) s. s.i.d.1996 verso acrylic. 18-Apr-4 Levis, Calgary #490/R (C.D 700)

LONG, A (?) ?
£2365 $4234 €3453 Landscapes with waterways (74x101cm-29x40in) s.d.863 pair. 28-May-4 Uppsala Auktionskammare, Uppsala #106/R est:15000-18000 (S.KR 32000)

LONG, Edwin (1829-1891) British
£4000 $6320 €5800 Entrance to the cathedral at Burgos, Spain (58x49cm-23x19in) mono.i.d.1858. 4-Sep-3 Christie's, Kensington #252/R est:4000-6000
£6800 $11288 €9928 Mrs Patrick Campbell in Balkan dress (66x48cm-26x19in) mono.d.1880. 1-Oct-3 Sotheby's, Olympia #177/R est:4000-6000
£8000 $14720 €11680 Esther (59x43cm-23x17in) mono.d.18EL79. 23-Mar-4 Bonhams, New Bond Street #79/R est:10000-15000
£10544 $18874 €15500 Hadassah, that is Esther (55x42cm-22x17in) mono.d.1879. 17-Mar-4 Maigret, Paris #2/R est:6000-8000
£45198 $80000 €65989 Eastern favourite (107x61cm-42x24in) mono.d.1880 prov. 2-May-4 Bonhams & Butterfields, San Francisco #1056/R est:25000-35000
£222222 $371111 €320000 Le marche aux esclaves dans l'Antiquite (151x243cm-59x96in) s.d.1874 prov. 22-Oct-3 Ribeyre & Baron, Paris #20/R

LONG, Edwin (attrib) (1829-1891) British
£3100 $5766 €4526 Portrait of young lady (130x100cm-51x39in) bears sig. 2-Mar-4 Bearnes, Exeter #465/R est:600-900
£8000 $13360 €11680 Letter (102x152cm-40x60in) 13-Nov-3 Christie's, Kensington #322/R est:8000-12000

LONG, Leonard (1911-) Australian
£696 $1093 €1016 Wattamalla Hills, Kangaroo Valley, 1972 (34x45cm-13x18in) s. canvas board. 24-Nov-2 Goodman, Sydney #14/R est:1500-2500 (A.D 1950)
£2439 $4366 €3561 In the Ormiston Gorge, Northern Territory (90x121cm-35x48in) s.d.1980 canvas on board. 10-May-4 Joel, Victoria #287 est:6000-8000 (A.D 6000)

LONG, Lieutenant (19th C) ?
£2797 $4811 €4000 Halte apres la chasse (40x65cm-16x26in) s. 8-Dec-3 Tajan, Paris #302/R est:3000-3500
£2800 $5124 €4200 Halte derriere la Mosquee (40x65cm-16x26in) s.d.1885. 3-Jun-4 Tajan, Paris #295/R est:3000-3500

LONG, Marion (1882-1970) Canadian
£428 $727 €625 An arrangement (66x56cm-26x22in) s. s.i.verso. 21-Nov-3 Walker's, Ottawa #49/R (C.D 950)
£1124 $2092 €1641 Street scene (26x22cm-10x9in) s. i.verso beaver board. 2-Mar-4 Ritchie, Toronto #111/R est:1000-1500 (C.D 2800)

LONG, Richard (1945-) British
Photographs
£3073 $5500 €4487 Sincholagua summit shadow stones a 12 day walk in Ecuador (81x112cm-32x44in) photo text prov.exhib.lit. 14-May-4 Phillips, New York #242/R est:7000-10000
Sculpture
£29940 $50000 €43712 Valle pellice stone chair (160x160cm-63x63in) stone pietra di Luserna prov. 13-Nov-3 Sotheby's, New York #587/R est:30000-40000
£35928 $60000 €52455 Little tejunga canyon line (15x105x122cm-6x41x48in) granite stones prov.exhib. 13-Nov-3 Sotheby's, New York #140/R est:60000-80000
Works on paper
£4167 $7500 €6084 Mud finger spiral (17x24cm-7x9in) mud paper exec.c.1986 prov.exhib. 24-Apr-4 David Rago, Lambertville #166/R est:2000-3000
£9497 $17000 €13866 Untitled (190x160cm-75x63in) china clay prov. 14-May-4 Phillips, New York #248/R est:15000-20000

LONG, Robert Dickson (1884-?) American
£367 $650 €536 Landscape (64x91cm-25x36in) s.d.1942. 1-May-4 Harvey Clar, Oakland #1437

LONG, Stanley (1892-1972) American
Works on paper
£588 $1000 €858 Rendezvous of the clan and mesa riders (48x69cm-19x27in) W/C. 1-Nov-3 Altermann Galleries, Santa Fe #138

LONG, Sydney (1871-1955) Australian
£2295 $3718 €3351 The Boathouse, Lake Narrabeen (26x37cm-10x15in) s. panel prov. 30-Jul-3 Goodman, Sydney #110/R est:6000-8000 (A.D 5600)
£2697 $4504 €4046 Tranquil waters (51x76cm-20x30in) s. 27-Oct-3 Goodman, Sydney #130/R est:8000-12000 (A.D 6500)
£8594 $16070 €12891 Drover (28x20cm-11x8in) s. board painted c.1896 prov. 20-Jul-4 Goodman, Sydney #27/R est:12000-18000 (A.D 22000)
£31837 $58580 €46482 Vaucluse, view towards Watson's Bay (25x38cm-10x15in) s. prov. 29-Mar-4 Goodman, Sydney #110/R est:20000-30000 (A.D 78000)
£66802 $107551 €97531 West Wind (74x151cm-29x59in) s.d.1916 prov.lit. 25-Aug-3 Sotheby's, Paddington #176/R est:190000-220000 (A.D 165000)
Works on paper
£407 $728 €594 Bledlow, Buckinghamshire (26x36cm-10x14in) s.i.d.1912 W/C. 10-May-4 Joel, Victoria #307 (A.D 1000)
£569 $893 €825 Marketplace, Bruges (47x30cm-19x12in) s.d.1914 W/C. 26-Aug-3 Lawson Menzies, Sydney #33 est:1500-2500 (A.D 1400)
£1829 $2872 €2652 The Lake's edge (32x36cm-13x14in) s.d.1910 W/C. 26-Aug-3 Christie's, Sydney #320/R est:3000-5000 (A.D 4500)
£2863 $5210 €4180 Lake (27x37cm-11x15in) s.d.1917 W/C. 16-Jun-4 Deutscher-Menzies, Melbourne #153/R est:6000-8000 (A.D 7500)

LONG, Ted (1933-) American
£1180 $1900 €1711 Evening set (61x91cm-24x36in) 22-Aug-3 Altermann Galleries, Santa Fe #75

LONG, Woodie (20th C) American
£240 $400 €350 New York Cosmos (51x61cm-20x24in) prov. 15-Nov-3 Slotin Folk Art, Buford #324/R
£333 $600 €486 Jumping on grandma's bed (43x51cm-17x20in) tempera on paper. 24-Apr-4 Slotin Folk Art, Buford #419/R
£333 $600 €486 Plowing with a mule (30x53cm-12x21in) oil on tin. 24-Apr-4 Slotin Folk Art, Buford #420/R
£359 $600 €524 Country bard (20x25cm-8x10in) 15-Nov-3 Slotin Folk Art, Buford #322/R
£361 $650 €527 Homemage dresses 1999 (41x38cm-16x15in) acrylic on paper. 24-Apr-4 Slotin Folk Art, Buford #423/R
£419 $700 €612 Woman going to church (46x61cm-18x24in) acrylic paper prov. 15-Nov-3 Slotin Folk Art, Buford #323/R
£444 $800 €648 Girl band 1999 (28x79cm-11x31in) board. 24-Apr-4 Slotin Folk Art, Buford #421/R
£539 $900 €787 Five teenagers and four kids (61x46cm-24x18in) acrylic paper prov. 15-Nov-3 Slotin Folk Art, Buford #321/R
£599 $1000 €875 Family fishing (71x48cm-28x19in) acrylic tin prov. 15-Nov-3 Slotin Folk Art, Buford #320/R
£611 $1100 €892 Plowing at sunset (46x61cm-18x24in) acrylic on paper. 24-Apr-4 Slotin Folk Art, Buford #422/R est:500-800

LONGA, Hugo (1934-1990) South American
Works on paper
£568 $1000 €829 Yellow collage (80x60cm-31x24in) s.d.67 collage. 5-Jan-4 Galeria y Remates, Montevideo #114/R
£568 $1000 €829 Red collage (80x60cm-31x24in) s.d.66 collage. 5-Jan-4 Galeria y Remates, Montevideo #115/R
£688 $1300 €1004 Composition (120x100cm-47x39in) s.d.67 collage on canvas. 22-Feb-4 Galeria y Remates, Montevideo #133/R
£882 $1500 €1288 Colourful (120x72cm-47x28in) s.d.72 mixed media on canvas. 25-Nov-3 Galeria y Remates, Montevideo #96

LONGA, Louis Anselme (attrib) (1809-1869) French
£1067 $1963 €1600 Scene animee a l'entree d'une ville, Algerie (32x46cm-13x18in) cardboard. 14-Jun-4 Gros & Delettrez, Paris #83/R est:800-1200

LONGA, Rene Charles Eugène (1878-?) French
£580 $986 €847 Portrait of a lady, holding a tulip (90x60cm-35x24in) s.d.1943 board. 8-Nov-3 Shapes, Edinburgh #410/R

LONGABOUGH, Charles Oglesby (1885-1944) American
£362 $605 €529 Pine against cloudy sky (41x46cm-16x18in) s. canvas on board. 17-Nov-3 Waddingtons, Toronto #2/R (C.D 800)
Works on paper
£375 $600 €548 Pirate's Alley in spring (15x18cm-6x7in) s.i. W/C. 20-Sep-3 Jeffery Burchard, Florida #44/R

LONGARETTI, Trento (1916-) Italian
£528 $877 €750 Vecchio con bambino (20x10cm-8x4in) s. panel painted 2002. 14-Jun-3 Meeting Art, Vercelli #147
£764 $1207 €1100 Mimosa (22x12cm-9x5in) board. 6-Sep-3 Meeting Art, Vercelli #421
£915 $1520 €1300 Madre (30x20cm-12x8in) s. s.i.verso. 14-Jun-3 Meeting Art, Vercelli #195/R
£933 $1717 €1400 Mother in blue (32x14cm-13x6in) s. s.verso board painted 2002. 12-Jun-4 Meeting Art, Vercelli #590/R
£1034 $1655 €1500 Mother (30x20cm-12x8in) s. s.i.verso. 13-Mar-3 Galleria Pace, Milan #72/R est:1600-2400
£1049 $1752 €1500 Mother (30x20cm-12x8in) s. s.i.verso. 26-Jun-3 Sant Agostino, Torino #269/R est:1800
£1067 $1963 €1600 Travellers and Russian churches (20x30cm-8x12in) s. 12-Jun-4 Meeting Art, Vercelli #374/R est:1000
£1078 $1929 €1574 Dedicato a un quartetto di Mozart (44x37cm-17x15in) s. i.d.95 verso. 12-May-4 Dobiaschofsky, Bern #761/R est:1400 (S.FR 2500)
£1111 $1756 €1600 Family with boy wearing red hat (20x30cm-8x12in) painted 1997. 6-Sep-3 Meeting Art, Vercelli #681 est:1000
£1127 $1870 €1600 Viandanti Felici (22x27cm-9x11in) s. s.i.verso painted 1988. 14-Jun-3 Meeting Art, Vercelli #629 est:1000
£1141 $2111 €1700 Running away (20x30cm-8x12in) s. s.i.d.2000 verso. 13-Mar-4 Meeting Art, Vercelli #456 est:1000
£1293 $2315 €1888 Il rabbi de KLuzzick (65x45cm-26x18in) s.i. 12-May-4 Dobiaschofsky, Bern #759/R est:2600 (S.FR 3000)
£1342 $2483 €2000 Jolly musicians (20x30cm-8x12in) s. painted 1993. 13-Mar-4 Meeting Art, Vercelli #175 est:1000
£1533 $2821 €2300 Venice with big moon (20x30cm-8x12in) s. painted 2003. 12-Jun-4 Meeting Art, Vercelli #715/R est:1000
£1678 $3104 €2500 Figures walking (30x40cm-12x16in) s. s.i.verso. 13-Mar-4 Meeting Art, Vercelli #459 est:1500
£1793 $2994 €2600 Musician and fairy (40x30cm-16x12in) s. s.i.d.1997 verso. 17-Nov-3 Sant Agostino, Torino #89/R est:2500-3000
£1793 $2994 €2600 Head of boy (40x30cm-16x12in) s. s.i.d.1977 verso. 17-Nov-3 Sant Agostino, Torino #92/R est:3000
£2198 $3935 €3209 Torero in rosso con cappello a cono (70x50cm-28x20in) s.i.d.92. 12-May-4 Dobiaschofsky, Bern #760/R est:2600 (S.FR 5100)
£2400 $4416 €3600 Old man and boy (50x40cm-20x16in) s. s.i.verso. 12-Jun-4 Meeting Art, Vercelli #978/R est:3000
£2802 $5015 €4091 Mendicante con organetto blu (110x80cm-43x31in) s. i.d.1988 verso. 12-May-4 Dobiaschofsky, Bern #755/R est:5000 (S.FR 6500)
£2953 $5286 €4400 Old man with boy and parrot (48x34cm-19x13in) s. s.i.verso board. 30-May-4 Meeting Art, Vercelli #72 est:4000
£3060 $5478 €4468 Flora con beretto viola (73x59cm-29x23in) s. i. verso. 12-May-4 Dobiaschofsky, Bern #757/R est:3500 (S.FR 7100)
£3233 $5787 €4720 Viandanti e collina azzurra (65x100cm-26x39in) s. i.d.84 verso. 12-May-4 Dobiaschofsky, Bern #756/R est:4500 (S.FR 7500)
£3356 $6208 €5000 Old traveller and grandson (60x50cm-24x20in) s. s.i.verso. 13-Mar-4 Meeting Art, Vercelli #277a est:5000
£3448 $6172 €5034 Attori di teatri dei poveri (100x73cm-39x29in) s. i. verso. 12-May-4 Dobiaschofsky, Bern #758/R est:4500 (S.FR 8000)
£8451 $14028 €12000 Violinista in Azzurro (120x100cm-47x39in) s.d.1999 s.i.d.verso. 14-Jun-3 Meeting Art, Vercelli #491/R est:10000
Works on paper
£352 $585 €500 La Famiglia (50x38cm-20x15in) s. gouache cardboard. 14-Jun-3 Meeting Art, Vercelli #430
£367 $675 €550 Untitled (31x41cm-12x16in) s. mixed media paper on canvas. 12-Jun-4 Meeting Art, Vercelli #157/R
£483 $806 €700 Figures (38x25cm-15x10in) s. pencil paper on canvas. 13-Nov-3 Galleria Pace, Milan #8/R

LONGCROFT, Thomas (fl.1786-1811) British
Works on paper
£6000 $9780 €8760 Sal trees in the north Rohilcund (38x56cm-15x22in) i.d.1792 indis.init.verso pencil grey wash prov.exhib. 24-Sep-3 Christie's, London #32/R est:3000-5000

LONGENECKIR, Paul (20th C) American
£2647 $4500 €3865 Untitled (183x184cm-72x72in) panel in 4 parts prov. 25-Nov-3 Christie's, Rockefeller NY #223/R est:2000-3000

LONGFELLOW, Ernest Wadsworth (1845-1921) American
£2374 $4250 €3466 Gathering branches, Nahant (46x76cm-18x30in) s.d.74. 26-May-4 Doyle, New York #35/R est:2000-3000
£2395 $4000 €3497 Manchester by the sea (41x61cm-16x24in) s. prov. 23-Oct-3 Shannon's, Milford #4/R est:2500-3500

LONGHI, Alessandro (1733-1813) Italian
Works on paper
£371 $619 €530 Female allegory of hope (15x12cm-6x5in) pen wash. 28-Jun-3 Bolland & Marotz, Bremen #583/R

LONGHI, Pietro (attrib) (1702-1785) Italian
£1351 $2324 €1972 Peasant with dead game (61x43cm-24x17in) pair. 8-Dec-3 Philippe Schuler, Zurich #3420/R est:3000-5000 (S.FR 3000)

LONGHI, Pietro (school) (1702-1785) Italian
£6111 $10206 €8800 Interior with figures (58x45cm-23x18in) 22-Oct-3 Finarte Semenzato, Milan #10/R est:6000-8000

LONGI, Alberto (20th C) Italian
£905 $1511 €1321 Young woman disrobing (80x90cm-31x35in) s.d.71. 17-Nov-3 Waddingtons, Toronto #264/R est:1000-1500 (C.D 2000)

LONGLEY, Sarah (20th C) Irish?
Works on paper
£650 $1066 €949 Female nude study (45x78cm-18x31in) s.d.2001 chl. 4-Jun-3 John Ross, Belfast #85

LONGMIRE, William Taylor (1841-1914) British
£300 $555 €438 Rowing on calm waters (40x55cm-16x22in) s.d.1870. 15-Jan-4 Christie's, Kensington #883
£420 $714 €613 Blea Tarn, Langdale (29x43cm-11x17in) s.d.1881. 19-Nov-3 James Thompson, Kirby Lonsdale #63

LONGO, Jacobino (attrib) (?-c.1542) Italian
£5634 $9859 €8000 Madonna of the Milk (27x22cm-11x9in) indis.sig. board. 17-Dec-3 Christie's, Rome #386/R est:6000-9000

LONGO, Robert (1953-) American
Prints
£1657 $3000 €2419 Sandy (178x102cm-70x40in) s.i. lithograph. 19-Apr-4 Bonhams & Butterfields, San Francisco #281/R est:4000-5000
£1695 $3000 €2475 James (177x101cm-70x40in) s.d.1999 num.30/50 lithograph. 30-Apr-4 Sotheby's, New York #395a est:2500-3000
£1933 $3500 €2822 Raphael (117x76cm-46x30in) s.d.1998 num.26/120 black grey lithograph. 19-Apr-4 Bonhams & Butterfields, San Francisco #280/R est:2000-3000
£2500 $4550 €3650 Eric, from men in the cities (182x91cm-72x36in) s.d.1985 num.6/48 black grey lithograph. 30-Jun-4 Christie's, London #248/R est:2500-3500
£2500 $4550 €3650 Gretchen, from men in the cities (182x91cm-72x36in) s.d.1985 num.6/48 black grey lithograph. 30-Jun-4 Christie's, London #249/R est:2500-3500
£3038 $5500 €4435 Joseph (178x102cm-70x40in) s.num.6/50 lithograph. 19-Apr-4 Bonhams & Butterfields, San Francisco #282/R est:4000-5000
£3235 $5500 €4723 Eric (172x99cm-68x39in) s. lithograph. 31-Oct-3 Sotheby's, New York #666/R
£5650 $10000 €8249 Eric. Cindy (172x99cm-68x39in) s.i.d.1984 lithograph two. 30-Apr-4 Sotheby's, New York #396 est:8000-10000
Works on paper
£11173 $20000 €16313 Untitled - Alien (100x152cm-39x60in) chk pencil prov. 13-May-4 Sotheby's, New York #480/R est:15000-20000
£24540 $40000 €35828 Untitled, Gretchen (244x152cm-96x60in) s.i.verso chl graphite prov.exhib.lit. 23-Sep-3 Christie's, Rockefeller NY #146/R est:25000-35000

LONGOBARDI, Nino (1953-) Italian
£317 $539 €463 Untitled (35x30cm-14x12in) s.d.1987 verso. 4-Nov-3 Bukowskis, Stockholm #555c/R (S.KR 4200)
£369 $653 €550 Head (77x56cm-30x22in) s.d. tempera board. 30-Apr-4 Dr Fritz Nagel, Stuttgart #327/R
£1503 $2600 €2194 Untitled (81x168cm-32x66in) acrylic chl pastel oil wash paper prov. 10-Dec-3 Phillips, New York #478/R est:1500-2500
Works on paper
£293 $519 €428 Senza titulo (35x30cm-14x12in) s.d.1987 verso mixed media. 27-Apr-4 AB Stockholms Auktionsverk #925/R (S.KR 4000)
£563 $975 €800 Sans titre (76x57cm-30x22in) s. mixed media paper on canvas prov. 14-Dec-3 Versailles Encheres #227/R

LONGONI, Baldassare (1876-1956) Italian
£805 $1442 €1200 Landscape with mountains covered in snow (15x22cm-6x9in) s. board. 25-May-4 Finarte Semenzato, Milan #136/R
£805 $1442 €1200 Lake landscape with trees (15x22cm-6x9in) s. board. 25-May-4 Finarte Semenzato, Milan #135/R
£2600 $4810 €3796 Sunlit paysage (36x51cm-14x20in) s. board. 15-Jan-4 Christie's, Kensington #980/R est:1000-1500

LONGONI, Emilio (1859-1933) Italian
£5986 $10356 €8500 Bushes (25x39cm-10x15in) s. cardboard on canvas prov.lit. 10-Dec-3 Sotheby's, Milan #70/R est:6000-8000
£7746 $13401 €11000 Val Cavallina, valtellina (21x39cm-8x15in) s. cardboard on canvas prov.lit. 10-Dec-3 Sotheby's, Milan #69/R est:4000-6000
£9155 $15838 €13000 Alpine lake (29x39cm-11x15in) s. canvas on cardboard. 11-Dec-3 Christie's, Rome #170/R est:15000-20000
£29577 $51761 €42000 Bernina Peak (35x45cm-14x18in) s.d.1908 canvas on cardboard lit. 17-Dec-3 Finarte Semenzato, Milan #41/R est:10000-12000
£45139 $75382 €65000 Life spring (190x55cm-75x22in) painted 1899 prov.exhib.lit. 21-Oct-3 Sotheby's, Milan #393/R est:10000-15000

LONGPRE, Paul de (1855-1911) American/French
£3593 $6000 €5246 Bouquet with roses and lilacs (53x72cm-21x28in) s. W/C gouache. 9-Oct-3 Christie's, Rockefeller NY #23/R est:6000-8000
Works on paper
£1300 $2249 €1898 English iris (21x28cm-8x11in) s. black lead W/C bodycol. 12-Dec-3 Christie's, Kensington #498 est:1000-1500
£5163 $9500 €7538 Iris and lilac on a stone shelf (50x69cm-20x27in) s.d. gouache. 8-Jun-4 Bonhams & Butterfields, San Francisco #4196/R est:5000-7000

LONGPRE, Raoul de (1859-1920) French
£1236 $2100 €1805 Still life with lilacs and roses (37x28cm-15x11in) s. gouache paper on board. 21-Nov-3 Skinner, Boston #277/R est:1500-2000
£2216 $4100 €3235 Pink roses and white lilacs (51x71cm-20x28in) s. tempera gouache. 12-Mar-4 Jackson's, Cedar Falls #779/R est:4000-5000
Works on paper
£2100 $3360 €3066 Yellow roses and white lilac on a ledge (51x71cm-20x28in) s. gouache paper on board. 16-Sep-3 Rosebery Fine Art, London #576/R est:800-1200
£2300 $4209 €3358 Roses and white lilacs on a ledge (51x71cm-20x28in) s. W/C gouache. 7-Apr-4 Woolley & Wallis, Salisbury #61/R est:2500-3500
£2300 $4209 €3358 Irises and white lilacs on a ledge (51x71cm-20x28in) s. W/C gouache. 7-Apr-4 Woolley & Wallis, Salisbury #62/R est:2500-3500
£2446 $4500 €3571 Lilacs and yellow roses on a stone ledge (51x70cm-20x28in) s. W/C. 27-Jun-4 Freeman, Philadelphia #93a/R est:3000-5000
£2600 $4810 €3796 Roses and lilacs (53x73cm-21x29in) s. gouache. 9-Mar-4 Bonhams, New Bond Street #3/R est:1500-2000
£2649 $4900 €3868 Still life of bouquet of pale pink roses in full bloom with white lilacs (51x71cm-20x28in) s. conte W/C. 16-Jan-4 Aspire, Cleveland #127/R est:4000-6000
£2700 $4941 €3942 Roses and white lilacs on a ledge (51x71cm-20x28in) s. W/C gouache. 7-Apr-4 Woolley & Wallis, Salisbury #63/R est:2500-3500
£3704 $7000 €5408 Still life of lilacs and roses (63x51cm-25x20in) s. gouache pair. 21-Feb-4 Weschler, Washington #273 est:3000-5000
£4070 $7000 €5942 Still life of yellow roses and pink lilacs (48x71cm-19x28in) s. gouache W/C. 6-Dec-3 Pook & Pook, Downington #195/R est:3000-5000
£4420 $8000 €6453 Lilacs and roses (68x53cm-27x21in) s. 31-Mar-4 Sotheby's, New York #60/R est:3000-5000
£4420 $8000 €6453 Lilacs (67x50cm-26x20in) s. gouache prov. 31-Mar-4 Sotheby's, New York #63/R est:3000-5000

LONGSDON, David (fl.1867-1901) British
£260 $468 €380 Country landscape with stream (25x35cm-10x14in) s. 20-Jan-4 Bonhams, Knightsbridge #82

LONGSTAFF, Sir John (1861-1941) Australian
£729 $1173 €1064 English landscape (39x49cm-15x19in) s.d.1916. 13-Oct-3 Joel, Victoria #275 est:1500-2500 (A.D 1800)
£2979 $5064 €4349 Portrait of young woman (49x37cm-19x15in) s.d.1901. 25-Nov-3 Christie's, Melbourne #283/R est:3000-5000 (A.D 7000)

LONGSTAFF, William (1879-1953) Australian
£350 $616 €511 Still life with flowers (76x63cm-30x25in) s. 19-May-4 Sotheby's, Olympia #134/R
Works on paper
£500 $835 €730 Houses of Parliament. Admiralty Arch at night (17x17cm-7x7in) s. pencil W/C pair prov. 16-Oct-3 Christie's, Kensington #160/R

LONGSTAFFE, Edgar (1849-1912) British
£500 $835 €730 On the dart (41x61cm-16x24in) s.i. 7-Oct-3 Bonhams, Knightsbridge #188
£2600 $4862 €3796 Near Loch Lomond, river landscape (76x102cm-30x40in) i.verso stretcher. 22-Jul-4 Tennants, Leyburn #851/R est:1800-2200
£2800 $4676 €4088 Country landscape with figure outside a cottage (31x51cm-12x20in) s. sold with a companion. 7-Oct-3 Bonhams, Knightsbridge #278/R est:2000-3000

LONGSTREET, Stephen (20th C) American
£216 $400 €315 Table (74x89cm-29x35in) s. board. 18-Jul-4 Bonhams & Butterfields, Los Angeles #7018/R
Works on paper
£216 $400 €315 Jazz musician (69x58cm-27x23in) s. W/C. 18-Jul-4 Bonhams & Butterfields, Los Angeles #7019/R

LONGUET, Alexandre Marie (?-1850) French
£1594 $2614 €2200 Le repos des nymphes pres de la riviere (24x33cm-9x13in) s. panel. 11-May-3 Osenat, Fontainebleau #180 est:2500-2800

LONGUET, Alexandre Marie (attrib) (?-1850) French
£393 $723 €574 Wooded landscape with Venus and Cupid (20x26cm-8x10in) s. panel. 14-Jun-4 Philippe Schuler, Zurich #5865 (S.FR 900)

LONGUEVILLE, James (1942-) British
£280 $496 €409 Old wharf market Drayton (26x41cm-10x16in) s. board. 28-Apr-4 Peter Wilson, Nantwich #103/R
£360 $666 €526 Beeston Castle (38x59cm-15x23in) s. board. 14-Jul-4 Bonhams, Chester #346
£600 $1062 €876 Chester races (19x28cm-7x11in) s.i.d.1982 verso board. 28-Apr-4 Peter Wilson, Nantwich #16
Works on paper
£1486 $2809 €2200 Pembroke Place, Dublin. Fitzwilliam Street from Merrion Square (29x39cm-11x15in) s. pastel pair prov. 17-Feb-4 Whyte's, Dublin #96/R est:2000-3000

LONN, George (20th C) Canadian
£311 $516 €454 Untitled, Inuit child with toy sled (51x41cm-20x16in) s. canvasboard. 5-Oct-3 Levis, Calgary #269/R (C.D 700)

LONNBERG, William (1887-1949) Finnish
£745 $1371 €1110 Landscape (55x38cm-22x15in) S. 25-Mar-4 Hagelstam, Helsinki #990
£2267 $4057 €3400 Still life of bottle and apples (70x94cm-28x37in) s. 15-May-4 Hagelstam, Helsinki #156/R est:2500

LONNE, Le Facteur (1910-1989) French
Works on paper
£467 $859 €700 Untitled (13x19cm-5x7in) s.d.1965 ball pen. 9-Jun-4 Artcurial Briest, Paris #313
£634 $1097 €900 Untitled (31x22cm-12x9in) s. ink gouache pr. 9-Dec-3 Artcurial Briest, Paris #472/R
£733 $1349 €1100 Untitled (17x25cm-7x10in) s.d.81 gouache. 9-Jun-4 Artcurial Briest, Paris #312
£845 $1462 €1200 Untitled (21x30cm-8x12in) s. s.d.1970 verso Chinese ink prov. 9-Dec-3 Artcurial Briest, Paris #471/R
£967 $1779 €1450 La foret (46x61cm-18x24in) s. india ink gouache exec. c.1969 prov. 11-Jun-4 Pierre Berge, Paris #49

LONNGREN, Carl Ewald (1839-1902) Swedish
£1700 $3043 €2482 Landscape from Visby (49x33cm-19x13in) s.i.d.15 Aug 1891. 25-May-4 Bukowskis, Stockholm #3/R est:15000-18000 (S.KR 23000)
£3287 $5587 €4700 On the path to home (58x87cm-23x34in) s.d.1888. 29-Nov-3 Bukowskis, Helsinki #370/R est:1800-2000

LONNROTH, Arvid Fredrik (1823-1880) Swedish
£493 $888 €740 Stable interior with two horses (38x51cm-15x20in) s. 25-Apr-4 Goteborg Auktionsverk, Sweden #161/R (S.KR 6800)
£923 $1588 €1348 Family of horses (37x46cm-15x18in) s. 3-Dec-3 AB Stockholms Auktionsverk #2461/R (S.KR 12000)

LONZA, Antonio (1846-1918) Italian
£1000 $1660 €1460 Vegetable market, Italy (27x37cm-11x15in) s. board. 1-Oct-3 Sotheby's, Olympia #225/R est:1000-1500
£1400 $2548 €2044 Artist's studio (45x53cm-18x21in) s. 16-Jun-4 Christie's, Kensington #83/R est:1500-2000
£1702 $2843 €2400 La lecture (22x15cm-9x6in) s. panel. 19-Jun-3 Millon & Associes, Paris #108/R est:2000-3000

LOO, Amedee van (1719-1795) French
Works on paper
£230 $424 €350 Scene d'offrande (25x37cm-10x15in) i. graphite. 22-Jun-4 Calmels Cohen, Paris #10

LOO, Amedee van (attrib) (1719-1795) French
£17105 $31474 €26000 Four seasons (79x64cm-31x25in) set of 4 oval. 25-Jun-4 Piasa, Paris #52/R est:20000-30000
Works on paper
£467 $850 €682 Study of a man on a horse (41x25cm-16x10in) chl htd white. 4-Feb-4 Christie's, Rockefeller NY #132/R

LOO, Carle van (1705-1765) French
Works on paper
£2000 $3460 €2920 Portrait of Marguerite Carbois (25x24cm-10x9in) s.i. red chk inscribed circle. 12-Dec-3 Christie's, Kensington #444/R est:1000-2000

LOO, Carle van (attrib) (1705-1765) French
£2013 $3705 €3000 The first kiss (55x45cm-22x18in) 25-Mar-4 Dr Fritz Nagel, Stuttgart #632/R est:5500
Works on paper
£420 $777 €613 Study of a reclining youth (34x47cm-13x19in) red chk. 9-Mar-4 Bonhams, Knightsbridge #79/R
£612 $1096 €900 La tragedie (32x36cm-13x14in) graphite htd white prov. 17-Mar-4 Maigret, Paris #38/R

LOO, Carle van (circle) (1705-1765) French
£13158 $24211 €20000 Suzanne et les vieillards (130x118cm-51x46in) 24-Jun-4 Tajan, Paris #39/R est:12000-15000

LOO, Carle van (studio) (1705-1765) French
£19737 $36316 €30000 Sultane jouant instrument a cordes (74x60cm-29x24in) 23-Jun-4 Sotheby's, Paris #18/R est:10000-15000

LOO, Huub van der (1962-) Dutch
£1333 $2453 €2000 Untitled (300x200cm-118x79in) s.d.2000 verso oil tempera beeswax. 9-Jun-4 Christie's, Amsterdam #385/R est:2000-3000

LOO, Jan van der (1585-?) Dutch
£667 $1200 €1000 Still life with flowers (80x64cm-31x25in) s.d.62. 26-Apr-4 Bernaerts, Antwerp #443

LOO, Jean Baptiste van (1684-1745) French
£3864 $7032 €5835 Moise et le buisson ardent (71x92cm-28x36in) s.d.1714. 21-Jun-4 Tajan, Paris #95/R est:6000-8000
£9155 $16021 €13000 Portrait de gentilhomme en habit bleu (125x99cm-49x39in) 18-Dec-3 Tajan, Paris #41/R est:12000-14000

LOO, Jean Baptiste van (attrib) (1684-1745) French
£2958 $5176 €4200 Allegorie a la poesie pastorale (106x136cm-42x54in) 16-Dec-3 Artcurial Briest, Paris #223/R est:2000-2500
£3600 $6480 €5256 Portrait of Augusta, Princess of Wales (70x57cm-28x22in) oval. 21-Jan-4 Sotheby's, Olympia #19/R est:2000-3000
£3800 $6460 €5548 Portrait of a gentleman wearing a red coat (74x62cm-29x24in) 27-Nov-3 Sotheby's, London #136/R est:3000-4000

LOO, Jean Baptiste van (studio) (1684-1745) French
£17931 $29766 €26000 Equestrian portrait of Louis XIV of France in armour (260x307cm-102x121in) prov. 1-Oct-3 Dorotheum, Vienna #265/R est:25000-30000

LOO, Jean Baptiste van (style) (1684-1745) French
£7500 $12525 €10950 Portrait of a gentleman, wearing an armoured tunic (74x61cm-29x24in) oval. 13-Nov-3 Christie's, Kensington #32/R est:800-1200

LOO, Jules Cesar Denis van (1743-1821) French
£5634 $9859 €8000 Stormy landscape (25x33cm-10x13in) 17-Dec-3 Christie's, Rome #469/R est:7000-9000

LOO, Louis-Michel van (1707-1771) French
£4027 $7410 €6000 Portrait de jeune femme (68x53cm-27x21in) s.d.1767 oval. 24-Mar-4 Tajan, Paris #124/R est:6000-8000
£7931 $13245 €11500 Portrait d'une jeune fille (72x59cm-28x23in) s.d.17 prov. 17-Nov-3 Delorme & Bocage, Paris #67/R est:6000-8000
£48000 $87840 €70080 Allegorical portrait of lady as Diana (165x157cm-65x62in) prov.lit. 8-Jul-4 Sotheby's, London #329/R est:20000-30000
£58659 $105000 €85642 The Devin family (110x150cm-43x59in) s.d.1767 prov.exhib. 27-May-4 Sotheby's, New York #42/R est:70000-90000

LOO, Louis-Michel van (attrib) (1707-1771) French
£986 $1637 €1400 Portrait d'un erudit (49x39cm-19x15in) 13-Jun-3 Renaud, Paris #12
£9396 $17289 €14000 Portrait of Louis Jean Marie de Bourbon (129x97cm-51x38in) 24-Mar-4 Dorotheum, Vienna #296/R est:18000-25000

LOO, Louis-Michel van (studio) (1707-1771) French
£5389 $9000 €7868 Portrait of an admiral (129x98cm-51x39in) 7-Oct-3 Sotheby's, New York #31/R est:6000-8000
£6500 $11895 €9490 Portrait of the Duc de Berry (61x49cm-24x19in) prov. 9-Jul-4 Christie's, Kensington #101/R est:4000-6000
£10000 $17000 €14600 Portrait of a young gentleman, probably the Comte d'Artois, later King Charles X of France (65x55cm-26x22in) prov. 29-Oct-3 Christie's, London #58/R est:6000-8000

LOO, Marten van der (1880-1920) Belgian
£867 $1560 €1300 Mechlin city view with figures (80x100cm-31x39in) s. 26-Apr-4 Bernaerts, Antwerp #313/R

LOO, Pieter van (1731-1784) Dutch
Works on paper
£2500 $4500 €3650 Mareschal de France, a hyacinth (47x29cm-19x11in) s.i. black chk bodycol. 22-Jan-4 Christie's, Rockefeller NY #262/R est:2500-3500

LOOBY, Keith (1940-) Australian
£2439 $3829 €3537 Kindergaten class 45, Bondi Beach (166x166cm-65x65in) i. exhib.lit. 27-Aug-3 Christie's, Sydney #560/R est:4000-6000 (A.D 6000)

LOOKING ELK, Albert (?-1941) American
£1420 $2500 €2073 Pueblo (23x30cm-9x12in) s. board painted c.1920. 23-May-4 Treadway Gallery, Cincinnati #557/R est:2000-3000

LOOMIS, Andrew (1892-1959) American
£3892 $6500 €5682 Test take (89x86cm-35x34in) s. painted c.1940. 15-Nov-3 Illustration House, New York #122/R est:6000-9000

LOOMIS, Charles Russell (19th C) American
£963 $1800 €1406 Woodland fairies dancing in the moonlight (23x18cm-9x7in) s.d.83 board. 29-Feb-4 Grogan, Boston #72/R
Works on paper
£281 $450 €410 Harbour scene. s. W/C. 20-Sep-3 Nadeau, Windsor #322

LOOMIS, Manchus C (20th C) American
£301 $550 €439 Morning (36x25cm-14x10in) s. paper on board. 10-Apr-4 Auctions by the Bay, Alameda #1556/R
£1279 $2200 €1867 Cattle in a landscape (89x102cm-35x40in) s. painted c.1920. 7-Dec-3 Treadway Gallery, Cincinnati #555/R est:2000-3000

LOON, Theodoor van (c.1585-c.1667) Flemish
£68966 $114483 €100000 Manoah's wife giving birth to Simson (198x157cm-78x62in) lit. 1-Oct-3 Dorotheum, Vienna #271/R est:50000-80000

LOOP, Edith Harrison (1873-1952) American
£435 $800 €653 Portrait of a woman (102x76cm-40x30in) 23-Mar-4 American Auctioneer #453632/R

LOOP, Leota Williams (1893-1961) American
£323 $600 €472 Violets (23x20cm-9x8in) s. canvas on board painted c.1930. 7-Mar-4 Treadway Gallery, Cincinnati #619/R
£860 $1600 €1256 Autumn flowers (51x61cm-20x24in) s.i.stretcher painted c.1930. 7-Mar-4 Treadway Gallery, Cincinnati #512/R est:2400-4500

LOOS, Friedrich (1797-1890) Austrian
£1667 $2717 €2400 Konigssee with St Bartholoma (29x40cm-11x16in) s.d.1835 paper on board. 24-Sep-3 Neumeister, Munich #486/R est:1500
Works on paper
£537 $988 €800 Landscape with travellers on bridge, near Vienna (19x24cm-7x9in) s.i.d.1870 pen htd white over pen. 26-Mar-4 Dorotheum, Vienna #66/R
£1441 $2623 €2104 Fonte de Papa, alla strada de porto d'Anzo (19x22cm-7x9in) i. W/C prov.exhib. 17-Jun-4 Kornfeld, Bern #34/R est:2000 (S.FR 3300)

LOOS, Henry (19/20th C) Belgian
£3200 $5440 €4672 Three-masted barque (52x77cm-20x30in) s.i.d.1872. 19-Nov-3 Christie's, Kensington #499/R

LOOS, John F (19th C) Belgian
£1361 $2163 €2000 Trois-mats (60x91cm-24x36in) s.i.d.1893. 21-Mar-3 Bailly Pommery, Paris #112 est:2000

LOOS, John F (attrib) (19th C) Belgian
£2014 $3304 €2800 English clipper, Elbe at sea (66x89cm-26x35in) prov. 4-Jun-3 Ketterer, Hamburg #10/R est:2000-3200

LOOSE, Basile de (1809-1885) Dutch
£490 $842 €700 Portrait d'un noble (88x73cm-35x29in) s. 2-Dec-3 Campo & Campo, Antwerp #101
£629 $1082 €900 Traveller (25x21cm-10x8in) s.d.1850 panel. 7-Dec-3 Sotheby's, Amsterdam #573/R
£9574 $15989 €13500 Music class (58x50cm-23x20in) s.d.1845 panel. 14-Oct-3 Vanderkindere, Brussels #30/R
£13000 $22360 €18980 Feeding the children (55x44cm-22x17in) s.d.1844 panel. 3-Dec-3 Christie's, London #3/R est:10000-15000

LOOTEN, Jan (1618-1681) Dutch
£4000 $7200 €5840 Mountainous wooded landscape with wooden bridge over a river (126x189cm-50x74in) s. 23-Apr-4 Christie's, Kensington #42/R est:4000-6000

LOOTZ, Eva (1940-) ?
£942 $1545 €1300 Composition (130x101cm-51x40in) s.d.76 verso panel. 27-May-3 Durán, Madrid #69/R

LOOY, Jacobus van (1855-1930) Dutch
Works on paper
£2000 $3600 €3000 Clouds over a farm field, Soest (29x38cm-11x15in) col chk pastel exhib. 21-Apr-4 Christie's, Amsterdam #138/R est:4000-6000

LOP-MONTEL, Alfred (20th C) German
£2013 $3705 €3000 Baigneuses (81x100cm-32x39in) s.d.1944. 28-Mar-4 Anaf, Lyon #190/R est:2000-2500

LOPES, Sousa (1879-1944) Portuguese
£1544 $2763 €2300 Beach with boats (13x31cm-5x12in) board. 31-May-4 Cabral Moncada Leiloes, Lisbon #89/R est:2000-3000

LOPEZ ARMENTIA, Gustavo (20th C) Argentinian
Works on paper
£824 $1500 €1203 Fishermen (37x56cm-15x22in) W/C. 5-Jul-4 Arroyo, Buenos Aires #92/R est:1500

LOPEZ CANCIO, Mariana (1909-1996) Spanish
£280 $445 €409 Still life of hydrangeas in a glass vase (74x58cm-29x23in) s. 9-Sep-3 Gorringes, Lewes #1837

LOPEZ CANITO, Jose (1942-) Spanish
£403 $721 €600 The ritual to wear the toreador costume (46x65cm-18x26in) s.d.83. 25-May-4 Durán, Madrid #665/R

LOPEZ CLARO, Cesar (?) Argentinian
£939 $1700 €1371 Figure (90x70cm-35x28in) 30-Mar-4 Arroyo, Buenos Aires #15

LOPEZ GARCIA, Antonio (1936-) Spanish
£110000 $202400 €160600 Tomelloso (68x95cm-27x37in) s.i.d.1958 board. 24-Jun-4 Sotheby's, London #203/R est:15000-20000

LOPEZ GARCIA, Ezequiel (1940-) Spanish
£369 $683 €550 Clowns (35x50cm-14x20in) s. oil mixed media card exhib.lit. 13-Mar-4 Meeting Art, Vercelli #494

LOPEZ GARCIA, Juan Luis (1894-1978) Spanish
£5137 $8733 €7500 Manuela's house (65x81cm-26x32in) s. s.i.verso. 4-Nov-3 Ansorena, Madrid #909/R est:6000
£7183 $12427 €10200 Still life with apples (66x81cm-26x32in) s. s.i.verso. 15-Dec-3 Ansorena, Madrid #27/R est:12000

LOPEZ LEAO DE LAGUNA, Baruch (1864-1943) Dutch
£658 $1211 €1000 Teatime (65x55cm-26x22in) s. 22-Jun-4 Christie's, Amsterdam #244/R est:1200-1600
£972 $1604 €1400 Taking tea (66x56cm-26x22in) s. 3-Jul-3 Van Ham, Cologne #1322

LOPEZ MENDEZ, Luis Alfredo (1901-) Venezuelan
£449 $835 €656 Araguaney (35x26cm-14x10in) s. 14-Mar-4 Subastas Odalys, Caracas #87/R
£457 $750 €667 Seascape (50x40cm-20x16in) s. painted 1986. 1-Jun-3 Subastas Odalys, Caracas #107
£503 $935 €734 Las Mercedes (31x41cm-12x16in) s. masonite painted 1951. 14-Mar-4 Subastas Odalys, Caracas #29/R

£506 $845 €739 Apamate (30x23cm-12x9in) s. painted 1973. 13-Jul-3 Subastas Odalys, Caracas #88
£534 $875 €780 Seascape (35x25cm-14x10in) s. 1-Jun-3 Subastas Odalys, Caracas #6
£565 $1040 €848 Vase of flowers (33x24cm-13x9in) s. painted 1953. 27-Jun-4 Subastas Odalys, Caracas #79/R
£570 $900 €832 Roses (31x22cm-12x9in) s. painted 1962. 1-Dec-2 Subastas Odalys, Caracas #22/R
£594 $920 €867 Still life (39x46cm-15x18in) s. cardboard on canvas. 29-Sep-2 Subastas Odalys, Caracas #39/R
£686 $1125 €1002 Spring (46x62cm-18x24in) s. 1-Jun-3 Subastas Odalys, Caracas #17
£839 $1560 €1225 Girl (91x66cm-36x26in) s. painted 1936. 14-Mar-4 Subastas Odalys, Caracas #13/R
£934 $1560 €1364 Chrysanthemums (55x42cm-22x17in) s. painted 1977. 13-Jul-3 Subastas Odalys, Caracas #76/R
£1012 $1690 €1478 Roses (45x35cm-18x14in) s. painted 1973. 13-Jul-3 Subastas Odalys, Caracas #72/R
£1035 $1925 €1511 Nude (38x30cm-15x12in) s. painted 1971. 14-Mar-4 Subastas Odalys, Caracas #84/R
£1046 $1925 €1527 Seascape (40x50cm-16x20in) s. painted 1984. 28-Mar-4 Subastas Odalys, Caracas #81/R
£1094 $1750 €1597 Still life (54x37cm-21x15in) s. panel painted 1966. 21-Sep-3 Subastas Odalys, Caracas #7/R
£1123 $1875 €1640 Roses (50x40cm-20x16in) s. painted 1971. 13-Jul-3 Subastas Odalys, Caracas #25/R
£1176 $2000 €1717 Roses (60x50cm-24x20in) s. painted 1988. 23-Nov-3 Subastas Odalys, Caracas #22
£1274 $2345 €1860 Untitled (80x60cm-31x24in) s. painted 1965. 28-Mar-4 Subastas Odalys, Caracas #11
£1347 $2250 €1967 Untitled (80x60cm-31x24in) s. painted 1965. 19-Oct-3 Subastas Odalys, Caracas #143/R
£1383 $2310 €2019 Dusk in La Guaira (33x24cm-13x9in) s. painted 1973. 13-Jul-3 Subastas Odalys, Caracas #105/R
£1422 $2375 €2076 Araguaney (61x51cm-24x20in) s. 19-Oct-3 Subastas Odalys, Caracas #73/R
£1471 $2500 €2148 Flowers (50x60cm-20x24in) s. painted 1963. 23-Nov-3 Subastas Odalys, Caracas #102/R
£1529 $2600 €2232 Seascape (42x36cm-17x14in) s. painted 1971. 23-Nov-3 Subastas Odalys, Caracas #7/R
£1582 $2500 €2310 Flowers (100x50cm-39x20in) s. painted 1944. 1-Dec-2 Subastas Odalys, Caracas #77
£1698 $3125 €2479 Flowers (63x38cm-25x15in) s. painted 1948. 28-Mar-4 Subastas Odalys, Caracas #9/R
£1719 $2750 €2510 Flowers (50x40cm-20x16in) s. painted 1981. 21-Sep-3 Subastas Odalys, Caracas #44/R
£1765 $3000 €2577 Macuto (60x52cm-24x20in) s. painted 1940. 23-Nov-3 Subastas Odalys, Caracas #149/R
£2000 $3100 €2920 Flowers (80x100cm-31x39in) s. painted 1965. 29-Sep-2 Subastas Odalys, Caracas #94/R
£2548 $4740 €3720 Roses (60x51cm-24x20in) s. painted 1971. 14-Mar-4 Subastas Odalys, Caracas #62/R
£2574 $4685 €3861 River Caribe (55x66cm-22x26in) s. panel painted 1955. 21-Jun-4 Subastas Odalys, Caracas #30/R
£2863 $5210 €4295 Flowers and pomegranates (89x59cm-35x23in) s. painted 1967. 21-Jun-4 Subastas Odalys, Caracas #19/R
£2976 $5060 €4345 Flowers (65x30cm-26x12in) s. panel. 23-Nov-3 Subastas Odalys, Caracas #122/R est:5000
£3771 $6410 €5506 Roses (61x50cm-24x20in) s. panel painted 1963. 23-Nov-3 Subastas Odalys, Caracas #136/R est:5000
£3897 $6625 €5690 Roses (70x40cm-28x16in) s. panel painted 1968. 23-Nov-3 Subastas Odalys, Caracas #80/R

LOPEZ MEZQUITA, Jose Maria (1883-1954) Spanish
£625 $1019 €900 Alhambra interior (21x15cm-8x6in) s. board painted 1900. 23-Sep-3 Durán, Madrid #148/R
£7534 $12808 €11000 Woman with fan (84x54cm-33x21in) s. 4-Nov-3 Ansorena, Madrid #140/R est:11000

LOPEZ MURIAS, Isidoro (20th C) Spanish
£355 $592 €500 Landscape near Zaragoza (16x22cm-6x9in) s. board. 20-Oct-3 Durán, Madrid #1193/R

LOPEZ NAGUIL, Gregorio (1894-1953) Argentinian
£586 $973 €850 Landscape in Majorca (16x22cm-6x9in) s. cardboard. 1-Oct-3 Ansorena, Madrid #725/R

LOPEZ RAMON, Ramon (1905-1989) Spanish
£517 $859 €750 Urban scene (51x61cm-20x24in) s. 1-Oct-3 Ansorena, Madrid #747/R
Works on paper
£284 $460 €400 Monasterio de Poblet (31x40cm-12x16in) s. W/C. 20-May-3 Ansorena, Madrid #968/R

LOPEZ TAJES, Agustin (1938-) Spanish
£336 $628 €500 Train to Medina (48x70cm-19x28in) s.d.2001 s.i.d.verso board. 24-Feb-4 Durán, Madrid #600/R
£423 $739 €600 Oviedo Cathedral (41x27cm-16x11in) s.d.2003 cardboard. 16-Dec-3 Durán, Madrid #48/R
£426 $711 €600 Burgos cathedral (41x27cm-16x11in) s. board. 20-Oct-3 Durán, Madrid #672/R
£426 $711 €600 Toledo cathedral (41x23cm-16x9in) s. s.i.d.2003 verso board. 20-Oct-3 Durán, Madrid #671/R
£805 $1442 €1200 Still life with colours (60x73cm-24x29in) s.d.2004 s.i.d.verso. 25-May-4 Durán, Madrid #693/R

LOPEZ TOMAS, Jose (1860-?) Spanish
£709 $1184 €1000 Playing in the garden (51x85cm-20x33in) s.i.d.93. 20-Oct-3 Durán, Madrid #177/R

LOPEZ Y MARTINEZ, Enrique (1853-1875) Spanish
£306 $557 €450 Soldier (29x20cm-11x8in) s. board. 3-Feb-4 Segre, Madrid #36/R

LOPEZ Y PORTANA, Vicente (1772-1850) Spanish
Works on paper
£674 $1125 €950 Two male nudes (32x21cm-13x8in) s.d.1794 dr. 20-Oct-3 Durán, Madrid #132/R
£780 $1303 €1100 Male nude (65x46cm-26x18in) s.d.1790 dr. 20-Oct-3 Durán, Madrid #15/R

LOPEZ, Abraham Lucis (20th C) Spanish?
£400 $716 €584 Multiple portrait of Yehudi (109x99cm-43x39in) s. oil collage board. 11-May-4 Sotheby's, Olympia #559

LOPEZ, Andres Joseph (fl.1768-1812) Mexican
£20719 $32736 €30250 True portrait of Lady Maria Francisca Prieto (92x72cm-36x28in) s.i. 24-Jul-3 Louis Morton, Mexico #12/R est:120000 (M.P 340000)

LOPEZ, Francisco (16/17th C) Spanish
Works on paper
£1892 $3500 €2762 Self Portrait (98x66cm-39x26in) s.d.1973 pencil prov.exhib. 12-Feb-4 Sotheby's, New York #167/R est:2000-3000

LOPEZ, Gasparo (1650-1732) Italian
£8000 $14560 €12000 Vases with flowers (40x31cm-16x12in) pair prov. 4-Jul-4 Finarte, Venice #34/R est:9000-11000
£32000 $58560 €46720 Still lives of garlands of flowers (64x50cm-25x20in) one i. pair. 8-Jul-4 Sotheby's, London #168/R est:15000-20000

LOPEZ, Juan Luis (20th C) Spanish
£2095 $3959 €3100 Florero (75x65cm-30x26in) s. d.1947 verso. 17-Feb-4 Vanderkindere, Brussels #142 est:300-400

LOPEZ, L (19/20th C) ?
£2113 $3782 €3000 Slaughter scene (82x124cm-32x49in) s. 8-Jan-4 Allgauer, Kempten #2453/R est:1200
£2254 $4034 €3200 Slaughter scene (82x124cm-32x49in) s. 8-Jan-4 Allgauer, Kempten #2454/R est:1200

LOPEZ-CABRERA, Ricardo (1866-1950) Spanish
£282 $524 €420 Landscape (18x24cm-7x9in) s. board. 2-Mar-4 Ansorena, Madrid #183/R
£1250 $2125 €1800 Portrait of girl (47x32cm-19x13in) s.i.d.1903 oval. 28-Oct-3 Segre, Madrid #101a/R est:1500
£1342 $2376 €2000 Arab (56x47cm-22x19in) s. 27-Apr-4 Durán, Madrid #57/R est:1200

LOPEZ-CURVAL, Catherine (1954-) French
£347 $549 €500 Baiser dans la rue (20x20cm-8x8in) s.d.1998 s.i.d.verso panel. 27-Apr-3 Versailles Encheres #150
£2113 $3655 €3000 Kaleidoscope (130x97cm-51x38in) s.i.d.1954 verso prov. 15-Dec-3 Charbonneaux, Paris #220/R est:2500-3000

LOPEZ-SOLDADO MATO, Francisco (1940-) Spanish
£336 $624 €500 Forms in space (116x86cm-46x34in) s.i. on stretcher. 2-Mar-4 Ansorena, Madrid #889/R

LOPP, Harry Leonard (1888-1966) American
£344 $650 €502 Mountain landscape in winter (51x76cm-20x30in) s. 23-Feb-4 O'Gallerie, Oregon #130/R

LOPPE, Gabriel (1825-1913) French
£11207 $20060 €16362 Sur la mer de glace a Chamonix (40x30cm-16x12in) s. 12-May-4 Dobiaschofsky, Bern #762/R est:1600 (S.FR 26000)
Photographs
£2111 $3800 €3082 Lightning striking the Eiffel Tower, Paris (18x13cm-7x5in) printing-out-paper. 22-Apr-4 Phillips, New York #54/R est:4000-6000

LORAINE, Nevison Arthur (fl.1889-1908) British
£3000 $5100 €4380 Trimmed and spurred fighting cock (70x55cm-28x22in) s. 27-Nov-3 Christie's, Kensington #207/R est:600-800

LORAN, Erle (1905-1999) American
£1056 $1700 €1531 Ancient rocks (61x91cm-24x36in) s.d.1949 masonite. 23-Aug-3 Harvey Clar, Oakland #1376
£1078 $1800 €1574 Realm of nature (130x48cm-51x19in) s.d.1952. 25-Oct-3 David Rago, Lambertville #162 est:800-1200
£1156 $2000 €1688 House in Provence (61x73cm-24x29in) s. 10-Dec-3 Bonhams & Butterfields, San Francisco #6292/R est:2500-3500
£1317 $2200 €1923 Black genesis, abstract (69x58cm-27x23in) s. masonite. 25-Oct-3 David Rago, Lambertville #161 est:800-1200
£3022 $5500 €4412 Urban landscape (48x64cm-19x25in) s.d.40 tempera oil exhib. 15-Jun-4 John Moran, Pasadena #63 est:4500-6500
Works on paper
£647 $1100 €945 Mending the nets (48x74cm-19x29in) s.d.47 gouache. 18-Nov-3 John Moran, Pasadena #150a

LORANGE, A (1833-1875) Danish
£302 $541 €441 Coastal landscape (20x29cm-8x11in) s. 12-Jan-4 Rasmussen, Vejle #117/R (D.KR 3200)

£537 $983 €784 Italian woman wearing shawl over dark hair (47x37cm-19x15in) s.d.1864. 9-Jun-4 Rasmussen, Copenhagen #1551 (D.KR 6000)

LORANGER, Georges (1931-1993) Canadian
£215 $335 €312 Prospero's magic (76x102cm-30x40in) s.i.d.1992 prov. 26-Mar-3 Walker's, Ottawa #426/R (C.D 500)

LORBER, Stephen (20th C) American
£440 $700 €642 Still life with thin cube (163x137cm-64x54in) s. 14-Sep-3 Susanin's, Chicago #6015/R

LORCA DI CORCIA, Philip (1953-) American
Photographs
£3200 $5440 €4672 Brent Booth, 21 Des Moines, Lowa dollar 30 (38x58cm-15x23in) s.d.1990-92 num.7/20 chromogenic print. 18-Nov-3 Christie's, Kensington #230/R est:4000-6000

LORCHER, Alfred (1875-1962) ?
Sculpture
£2937 $5052 €4200 Four women carrying jugs (15x12x9cm-6x5x4in) bronze. 2-Dec-3 Hauswedell & Nolte, Hamburg #381/R est:3500

LORCK, Karl Julius (1829-1882) Norwegian
£2439 $4463 €3561 From at farmer's cottage with couple (48x39cm-19x15in) s.d.80. 7-Jun-4 Blomqvist, Oslo #329/R est:40000-60000 (N.KR 30000)

LORD, Don W (1929-) American
£361 $650 €527 Windy day (91x122cm-36x48in) s.d.1953 board exhib. 23-Jan-4 Freeman, Philadelphia #289/R

LORDON, Pierre Jerome (1780-1838) French
£2069 $3828 €3000 Enfance de Semiramis (24x32cm-9x13in) lit. 16-Feb-4 Giraudeau, Tours #47

LORENTSON, Waldemar (1899-1982) Swedish
£668 $1155 €975 Twilight (20x41cm-8x16in) s. s.i.verso panel. 15-Dec-3 Lilla Bukowskis, Stockholm #551 (S.KR 8500)
£689 $1240 €1006 From Altea la Veija (20x45cm-8x18in) s. d.1972 verso panel. 26-Apr-4 Bukowskis, Stockholm #81/R (S.KR 9500)
£879 $1416 €1283 Dawn (19x24cm-7x9in) s. s.d.1968 verso panel. 25-Aug-3 Lilla Bukowskis, Stockholm #333 (S.KR 11500)
£1000 $1720 €1460 Loaded atmosphere (29x49cm-11x19in) s. d.1964 verso panel. 7-Dec-3 Uppsala Auktionskammare, Uppsala #267/R (S.KR 13000)
£1077 $1852 €1572 Gates against space (34x26cm-13x10in) s. panel. 7-Dec-3 Uppsala Auktionskammare, Uppsala #270/R (S.KR 14000)
£1109 $1984 €1619 Cliffs by the sea (16x41cm-6x16in) s. d.1953 verso panel. 28-May-4 Uppsala Auktionskammare, Uppsala #307/R est:18000-20000 (S.KR 15000)
£1114 $1815 €1626 Spanish scene II (16x9cm-6x4in) s. panel. 29-Sep-3 Lilla Bukowskis, Stockholm #506 (S.KR 14500)
£2115 $3595 €3088 In Provence (30x50cm-12x20in) s.d.1969 verso panel. 4-Nov-3 Bukowskis, Stockholm #151/R est:20000-25000 (S.KR 28000)
£2231 $3837 €3257 Pastoral (43x27cm-17x11in) s. panel. 7-Dec-3 Uppsala Auktionskammare, Uppsala #266/R est:20000-25000 (S.KR 29000)
£2417 $4109 €3529 Surrealistic shore landscape (61x122cm-24x48in) s. panel. 5-Nov-3 AB Stockholms Auktionsverk #674/R est:40000-50000 (S.KR 32000)
£3323 $5650 €4852 Harbour (27x41cm-11x16in) s. 4-Nov-3 Bukowskis, Stockholm #45/R est:20000-25000 (S.KR 44000)
£3776 $6420 €5513 View from Halmstad with Palace mill (32x25cm-13x10in) s. d.1921 verso prov. 5-Nov-3 AB Stockholms Auktionsverk #659/R est:30000-40000 (S.KR 50000)
£13973 $23754 €20401 The sea gives - fishermen with fish (90x101cm-35x40in) s. 4-Nov-3 Bukowskis, Stockholm #47/R est:140000-160000 (S.KR 185000)

LORENTZEN, C A (1746-1828) Danish
£1522 $2785 €2222 Portrait of Frederick VI wearing red uniform (45x34cm-18x13in) s.stretcher oval. 9-Jun-4 Rasmussen, Copenhagen #1897/R est:10000-15000 (D.KR 17000)
£1701 $2943 €2483 Portrait of Adolphine Fabritius de Tengnagel wearing red jacket (75x57cm-30x22in) oval. 9-Dec-3 Rasmussen, Copenhagen #1374/R est:20000-25000 (D.KR 18000)

LORENTZEN, Christian August (1746-1828) Danish
£2875 $5348 €4198 Portrait of Ulrich Chr von Schmidten (70x56cm-28x22in) s. oval painted c.1812 lit. 2-Mar-4 Rasmussen, Copenhagen #1491/R est:20000-25000 (D.KR 32000)
£19696 $36043 €28756 A Greenlander fisherman and fisher woman after nature (37x57cm-15x22in) 9-Jun-4 Rasmussen, Copenhagen #1439a (D.KR 220000)
£23000 $41860 €33580 The Silke Saugen sawmill by the Honefossen Falls, Norway (44x58cm-17x23in) s. sold with aquatint. 15-Jun-4 Sotheby's, London #301/R est:20000-30000

LORENTZEN, Christian August (attrib) (1746-1828) Danish
£739 $1323 €1079 Dyveke's death - Interior scene with figures (72x90cm-28x35in) canvas on panel. 28-May-4 Uppsala Auktionskammare, Uppsala #30/R (S.KR 10000)

LORENTZON, Ida (1951-) Swedish
£5133 $8725 €7494 On one's own legs (160x131cm-63x52in) exhib.lit. 19-Nov-3 Grev Wedels Plass, Oslo #96/R est:60000-80000 (N.KR 60000)

LORENZ, Carl (1871-1945) Austrian
£1400 $2240 €2030 Lovers by the side of a lake, a classical temple beyond (65x98cm-26x39in) s. 18-Sep-3 Christie's, Kensington #160/R est:1000-2000

LORENZ, Ernest (1872-?) German
£769 $1323 €1123 Interior (79x120cm-31x47in) s. 7-Dec-3 Uppsala Auktionskammare, Uppsala #164/R (S.KR 10000)

LORENZ, Richard (1858-1915) German
£304 $535 €450 Three sailing boats on high seas in evening (68x48cm-27x19in) s. lit. 21-May-4 Mehlis, Plauen #15143/R
£1105 $2000 €1613 Portrait of a saddle horse (30x36cm-12x14in) s. board. 2-Apr-4 Eldred, East Dennis #1019/R est:3000-4000
£4412 $7500 €6442 On the trail, winter (28x38cm-11x15in) s. canvas on board prov. 1-Nov-3 Santa Fe Art, Santa Fe #104/R est:3000-5000
Works on paper
£8140 $14000 €11884 Profile of Indian Chief with headdress (56x51cm-22x20in) s. prov. 2-Dec-3 Christie's, Rockefeller NY #80/R est:2500-3500

LORENZ, Willi (1901-1981) German
£470 $869 €700 Wild boar in winter wooded landscape (79x59cm-31x23in) s. 10-Mar-4 James Adam, Dublin #21/R
£567 $1026 €850 Stag mountain landscape (80x60cm-31x24in) s. 1-Apr-4 Van Ham, Cologne #1523
£625 $987 €900 Pheasants in field (50x60cm-20x24in) s. 6-Sep-3 Schopman, Hamburg #809/R
£769 $1308 €1100 Wild boar (60x80cm-24x31in) s. 20-Nov-3 Van Ham, Cologne #1727
£793 $1442 €1158 Pheasant (34x48cm-13x19in) s. tempera W/C board. 20-Jun-4 Agra, Warsaw #27/R (P.Z 5500)
£833 $1375 €1200 Wild boar (70x60cm-28x24in) s. 3-Jul-3 Van Ham, Cologne #1337
£1119 $1902 €1600 Lion pair in the Savannah (40x60cm-16x24in) s. 20-Nov-3 Van Ham, Cologne #1725/R est:2000
£1189 $2021 €1700 Herd of elephants in the Savannah (59x79cm-23x31in) s. 20-Nov-3 Van Ham, Cologne #1726/R est:2000

LORENZ-MUROWANA, Ernst Hugo (1872-?) German
£830 $1535 €1212 Ships in a calm (70x100cm-28x39in) 14-Mar-4 Agra, Warsaw #29/R (P.Z 6000)
£1107 $2047 €1616 Fishing in moonlight (36x48cm-14x19in) 14-Mar-4 Agra, Warsaw #30/R (P.Z 8000)
£1338 $2315 €1900 Berlin, River Spree by moonlight (80x102cm-31x40in) s. 10-Dec-3 Dorotheum, Vienna #188/R est:3200-3600

LORENZL, J (1892-1950) Austrian
Sculpture
£1300 $2171 €1898 Figure (23cm-9in) s. pat bronze onyx. 15-Oct-3 Christie's, Kensington #666/R
£1900 $3173 €2774 Figure (38cm-15in) s. pat bronze. 13-Nov-3 Christie's, Kensington #302/R

LORENZL, Josef (1892-1950) Austrian
Sculpture
£1100 $1870 €1606 Nude dancer (25cm-10in) s. gilt bronze onyx pedestal st.f.BK. 25-Nov-3 Sotheby's, Olympia #131/R est:1000-1200
£1171 $1990 €1710 Nude female figure (36cm-14in) s. pat.bronze on onyx socle. 4-Nov-3 Bukowskis, Stockholm #1343/R est:6000-8000 (S.KR 15500)
£1200 $2196 €1752 Figure of a nude (37cm-15in) s. bronze onyx base. 3-Jun-4 Sotheby's, Olympia #249/R
£1208 $2162 €1800 Girl (26cm-10in) i. pat.bronze. 26-May-4 Dorotheum, Vienna #345/R est:1800-2200
£1282 $2179 €1872 Figure of a dancer (31cm-12in) incised sig. gold pat. green marble base. 10-Nov-3 Stephan Welz, Johannesburg #775/R est:8000-12000 (SA.R 15000)
£1400 $2618 €2044 Dancer (25cm-10in) bronze ivory green onyx pedestal exec.c.1930. 24-Feb-4 Sotheby's, Olympia #267/R est:1000-1500
£1408 $2254 €2000 Dancer (28cm-11in) s.i. bronze. 18-Sep-3 Rieber, Stuttgart #2202 est:2400
£1806 $2871 €2600 Nude girl with fan (35cm-14in) i. verso metallic pat.bronze onyx socle. 15-Sep-3 Dorotheum, Vienna #189/R est:2000-2500
£2500 $4425 €3650 Dancing girl with floral painted skirt (34cm-13in) s. silvered bronze green marble base exec.c.1925. 27-Apr-4 Bonhams, Chester #92/R est:400-600
£3000 $4770 €4380 Two nude dancers (47cm-19in) st.sig. bronze. 9-Sep-3 Sotheby's, Olympia #376/R est:2500-3500
£3400 $6018 €4964 Dancing girl (39cm-15in) s. silvered bronze green marble base. 27-Apr-4 Bonhams, Chester #91/R est:800-1000
£4200 $6636 €6132 Art Deco figure holding a clock (54cm-21in) s. bronze onyx base. 2-Sep-3 Woolley & Wallis, Salisbury #456/R est:1500-2000

LORENZL, Josef (attrib) (1892-1950) Austrian
Sculpture
£1400 $2380 €2044 Lady leaning forwards pouting (24cm-9in) ivory on green onyx pedestal. 25-Nov-3 Sotheby's, Olympia #130/R est:1000-1200

LORENZO MONACO (c.1370-c.1425) Italian
£905172 $1665517 €1321551 Annunciation (136x98cm-54x39in) tempera gold panel prov.exhib.lit. 26-Mar-4 Koller, Zurich #3008/R est:1200000-1800000 (S.FR 2100000)

LORIA, Vincenzo (1850-?) Italian
£1014 $1784 €1500 Fishermen coming back (36x62cm-14x24in) s.i. 19-May-4 Il Ponte, Milan #501 est:200-300
Works on paper
£280 $476 €409 Neapolitan fishermen in a boat with a rocky coastline (18x36cm-7x14in) s.i. W/C. 30-Oct-3 Duke & Son, Dorchester #83/R
£347 $590 €500 Benevento (25x36cm-10x14in) s. s.i.d.1913 verso W/C. 1-Nov-3 Meeting Art, Vercelli #56/R
£496 $829 €700 Seascape in Sorrento (24x40cm-9x16in) s. W/C. 14-Oct-3 Finarte Semenzato, Milan #81/R
£1250 $2037 €1800 View of Naples (39x76cm-15x30in) s. W/C. 23-Sep-3 Durán, Madrid #80/R

LORIMER, John Henry (1856-1936) British
£16000 $25280 €23360 Jeanie Gray (118x94cm-46x37in) mono.d.1880 exhib. 6-Sep-3 Shapes, Edinburgh #301/R est:10000-15000

LORIOT, Bernard (1925-) French
£276 $458 €400 Planches a Deauville (22x27cm-9x11in) s. s.i.verso. 1-Oct-3 Millon & Associes, Paris #189
£310 $515 €450 Bateaux a Honfleur (22x27cm-9x11in) s. 1-Oct-3 Millon & Associes, Paris #187
£352 $584 €510 Plage a Trouville (33x41cm-13x16in) s. s.i.verso. 1-Oct-3 Millon & Associes, Paris #188
£369 $687 €550 Bord de l'eau a Vasouy sur Honfleur (38x46cm-15x18in) s. 7-Mar-4 Lesieur & Le Bars, Le Havre #146
£448 $744 €650 Port de Honfleur (38x55cm-15x22in) s. 1-Oct-3 Millon & Associes, Paris #190
£537 $999 €800 La falaise de Sainte Adresse en ete (65x81cm-26x32in) s. 7-Mar-4 Lesieur & Le Bars, Le Havre #144
£552 $916 €800 Plage de Deauville (27x35cm-11x14in) s. i.d.1967 verso. 1-Oct-3 Millon & Associes, Paris #181/R
Works on paper
£959 $1505 €1400 Trouville, retour des bateaux (32x46cm-13x18in) s. W/C. 20-Apr-3 Deauville, France #24
£1644 $2581 €2400 View of Venice (51x67cm-20x26in) s. pastel. 20-Apr-3 Deauville, France #23 est:2000-2500

LORIS, Vincenzo (1848-1939) Italian
Works on paper
£386 $641 €560 Sunset over bay (23x39cm-9x15in) s. W/C. 13-Jun-3 Zofingen, Switzerland #2484/R (S.FR 850)

LORJOU, Bernard (1908-1986) French
£359 $600 €524 Pot de fleurs (30x28cm-12x11in) s. masonite. 11-Oct-3 Auctions by the Bay, Alameda #1648/R
£872 $1623 €1300 Trois portraits (54x73cm-21x29in) s. paper on canvas. 3-Mar-4 Tajan, Paris #162/R est:1300-1500
£1241 $2061 €1800 Paysage (100x81cm-39x32in) s. 30-Sep-3 Blanchet, Paris #293 est:800-1000
£1622 $3000 €2368 Still life with sunflowers (33x46cm-13x18in) s. panel prov. 13-Jul-4 Christie's, Rockefeller NY #175/R est:4000-6000
£1678 $3121 €2500 Bateaux (54x65cm-21x26in) s. prov. 3-Mar-4 Ferri, Paris #69 est:2500-2700
£1867 $3435 €2800 Vase aux fleurs blanches (81x65cm-32x26in) s. 14-Jun-4 Tajan, Paris #152/R est:2800-3000
£2237 $4116 €3400 Barques (73x116cm-29x46in) s.d.55. 22-Jun-4 Ribeyre & Baron, Paris #67/R est:2500-3500
£2473 $4500 €3611 Still life of flowers in a yellow pitcher (100x73cm-39x29in) s. 29-Jun-4 Sotheby's, New York #379/R est:4000-6000
£2658 $4571 €3800 Fruits dans un plat, fond bleu (55x65cm-22x26in) s. 3-Dec-3 Tajan, Paris #425 est:3500-4500
£2797 $4811 €4000 Tete d'Arlequin (102x73cm-40x29in) s. 3-Dec-3 Tajan, Paris #424 est:3000-5000
£2917 $4871 €4200 Bouquets de fleurs (92x73cm-36x29in) s. 23-Oct-3 Credit Municipal, Paris #107/R est:3000-3500
£2941 $5500 €4294 Nature morte avec pasteques (89x106cm-35x42in) s. prov. 25-Feb-4 Christie's, Rockefeller NY #105/R est:4000-6000
£3374 $5500 €4926 Vase avec fleurs rouge et blanc (93x76cm-37x30in) s. 25-Sep-3 Christie's, Rockefeller NY #605/R est:6000-8000
£3618 $6658 €5500 Picador (160x130cm-63x51in) s. 24-Jun-4 Credit Municipal, Paris #45/R est:5000-6000
£3631 $6500 €5301 Tete d'arlequin (92x60cm-36x24in) s. 6-May-4 Doyle, New York #135/R est:3000-5000
£3688 $6159 €5200 Vase rouge aux fleurs (92x65cm-36x26in) s. exhib. 19-Jun-3 Millon & Associes, Paris #250/R est:3000-4000
£3741 $6135 €5200 La cathedrale de Chartres (100x67cm-39x26in) s. zinc. 6-Jun-3 David Kahn, Paris #40 est:7000-7500
£3988 $6500 €5822 Vase de fleurs blanches et jaunes (103x67cm-41x26in) s. prov. 25-Sep-3 Christie's, Rockefeller NY #558/R est:3000-5000
£3988 $6500 €5822 Arlequin en rouge (99x63cm-39x25in) s. 25-Sep-3 Christie's, Rockefeller NY #631/R est:3000-5000
£3988 $6500 €5822 Arlequin en bleu (96x61cm-38x24in) s. 25-Sep-3 Christie's, Rockefeller NY #632/R est:4000-6000
£4027 $7490 €6000 Taureau et torero (106x91cm-42x36in) s. acrylic felt tip paper on canvas painted c.1969 prov. 3-Mar-4 Ferri, Paris #68/R est:6000-6200
£4225 $7310 €6000 Cruche et poisson (81x65cm-32x26in) s. prov. 10-Dec-3 Ferri, Paris #70/R est:6000-6500
£4278 $8000 €6246 Vase de fleurs (68x48cm-27x19in) s. paper on canvas prov. 25-Feb-4 Christie's, Rockefeller NY #83/R est:5000-7000
£4437 $7675 €6300 Table de cuisine (91x73cm-36x29in) s. painted c.1944-45 prov. 10-Dec-3 Ferri, Paris #69/R est:6000-6500
£4545 $8500 €6636 Vase avec fleurs rouges (92x72cm-36x28in) s. prov. 25-Feb-4 Christie's, Rockefeller NY #57/R est:5000-7000
£4832 $8650 €7200 Arlequin (102x73cm-40x29in) s. 30-May-4 Eric Pillon, Calais #200/R
£5775 $9990 €8200 Vase de fleurs (92x73cm-36x29in) s. 14-Dec-3 Eric Pillon, Calais #263/R
£18121 $33162 €27000 L'arlequin au bouquet de fleurs (146x89cm-57x35in) s. d.30.11.74 verso prov. 7-Jul-4 Artcurial Briest, Paris #162/R est:4000-6000
Works on paper
£524 $902 €750 Le dejeuner (50x70cm-20x28in) s.d.29 VIII 74 gouache ink. 3-Dec-3 Tajan, Paris #100
£979 $1664 €1400 Le coq (59x44cm-23x17in) s.d.1958 ink wax pastel. 23-Nov-3 Cornette de St.Cyr, Paris #614/R

LORME, Anthonie de (1610-1673) Dutch
£19444 $35000 €28388 Interior of the Laurenskerk (85x69cm-33x27in) s.d.1668 prov. 22-Jan-4 Sotheby's, New York #39/R est:40000-60000

LORRAIN, Robert le (attrib) (1666-1743) French
Sculpture
£84507 $146197 €120000 Andromede (62cm-24in) bronze exec.c.1700 prov.lit. 15-Dec-3 Sotheby's, Paris #26/R est:35000-45000

LORY, Gabriel Ludwig (1763-1840) Swiss
Works on paper
£6787 $11742 €9909 Vallee de Lauterbrunnen (46x69cm-18x27in) s. pencil W/C. 9-Dec-3 Sotheby's, Zurich #5/R est:8000-12000 (S.FR 15000)

LORY, Matthias Gabriel (1784-1846) Swiss
Works on paper
£390 $697 €569 Shepherds in grotto (16x22cm-6x9in) s. W/C. 22-Mar-4 Philippe Schuler, Zurich #6349 (S.FR 900)

LOS CARPINTEROS (20th C) Cuban
Works on paper
£4118 $7000 €6012 Sin titulo. Bloque no.23 (161x132cm-63x52in) s. one d.1999 one i.d.1998 W/C two prov. 18-Nov-3 Christie's, Rockefeller NY #9/R est:8000-12000

LOS, Waldemar (1849-1888) Polish
£2802 $5015 €4091 Autumn day in Poland (40x30cm-16x12in) s. 12-May-4 Dobiaschofsky, Bern #763/R est:8000 (S.FR 6500)

LOSCA, Joseph (19th C) ?
Works on paper
£374 $591 €542 View towards Wartha Monastery (30x44cm-12x17in) i.verso gouache. 2-Sep-3 Rasmussen, Copenhagen #1983/R (D.KR 4000)

LOSCHKIN, A (19/20th C) Russian
Works on paper
£756 $1308 €1104 Snow covered woodland path (30x20cm-12x8in) s.d.19 gouache W/C prov. 9-Dec-3 Rasmussen, Copenhagen #1526/R (D.KR 8000)
£851 $1472 €1242 Woman by red and green painted monastery (22x30cm-9x12in) mono. pencil W/C. 9-Dec-3 Rasmussen, Copenhagen #1523/R (D.KR 9000)
£945 $1635 €1380 Sunshine coming through tree trunks (34x52cm-13x20in) s.d.1911 gouache W/C prov. 9-Dec-3 Rasmussen, Copenhagen #1527/R (D.KR 10000)

LOSIK, Thomas (1849-1896) Polish
£2000 $3700 €2920 By the Fire (56x46cm-22x18in) s. 10-Mar-4 Sotheby's, Olympia #274/R est:2000-3000

LOSSEN, Dr Otto (1875-?) German
Photographs
£6154 $10462 €8800 Kitchen, Stuttgart (17x23cm-7x9in) i.verso silver gelatin exec.with others lit.exhib. 27-Nov-3 Villa Grisebach, Berlin #1301/R est:2000-2500
£6294 $10699 €9000 Living room, Stuttgart (17x23cm-7x9in) i.verso silver gelatin exec.with others. 27-Nov-3 Villa Grisebach, Berlin #1302/R est:2000-2500

LOSSOW, Heinrich (1843-1897) German
£1333 $2413 €2000 Erotic scene (30x23cm-12x9in) panel. 2-Apr-4 Dr Fritz Nagel, Leipzig #3971/R est:250
£4800 $8736 €7008 Precarious game (30x23cm-12x9in) s. panel. 16-Jun-4 Christie's, Kensington #266/R est:4000-6000

LOSTUTTER, Robert (1939-) American
£459 $850 €670 After crossing the line (56x53cm-22x21in) s. acrylic. 17-Jan-4 Susanin's, Chicago #121/R
£1471 $2500 €2148 Map to the morning dance (135x91cm-53x36in) s.i.d.1972. 9-Nov-3 Wright, Chicago #478 est:2500-3500

LOT, Hendrik (1821-1878) Dutch
£8163 $14612 €12000 Deer in forest clearing (137x124cm-54x49in) s. 17-Mar-4 Neumeister, Munich #523/R est:5000

LOTE, B J (20th C) German
Sculpture
£2400 $3984 €3504 Amazon on horseback (48x38cm-19x15in) s. num.II rich green brown pat bronze. 30-Sep-3 Sotheby's, London #390/R est:1500-2500

LOTH, Johann Karl (1632-1698) German
£3067 $5000 €4478 Portrait of Silenus. 27-Sep-3 Thomaston Place, Thomaston #155

LOTH, Johann Karl (after) (1632-1698) German
£10738 $19758 €16000 Mythological scene (78x80cm-31x31in) 25-Mar-4 Dr Fritz Nagel, Stuttgart #646/R est:2500

LOTH, Johann Karl (attrib) (1632-1698) German
£6897 $11448 €10000 Apollo and Marsyas (106x131cm-42x52in) prov. 1-Oct-3 Dorotheum, Vienna #18/R est:6000-8000
£7586 $12593 €11000 St Sebastian (107x79cm-42x31in) prov. 1-Oct-3 Dorotheum, Vienna #299/R est:5000-7000
£17544 $29298 €25614 Flora (118x97cm-46x38in) prov. 15-Nov-3 Galerie Gloggner, Luzern #77/R est:5800-6500 (S.FR 40000)
£18881 $32476 €27000 Allegory of Astronomy. Allegory of Geometry (113x97cm-44x38in) pair. 2-Dec-3 Sotheby's, Milan #104/R est:30000-40000

LOTH, Wilhelm (1920-1993) German

Sculpture			
£2000	$3580	€3000	Relief 11/59 (58x45x6cm-23x18x2in) bronze prov.lit. 15-May-4 Van Ham, Cologne #760/R est:2500
£2448	$4210	€3500	Relief (55x44x6cm-22x17x2in) mono. bronze prov. 4-Dec-3 Van Ham, Cologne #300/R est:2500
£2448	$4210	€3500	Relief (54x41x6cm-21x16x2in) mono. num.5/60 bronze exec.1960 prov. 4-Dec-3 Van Ham, Cologne #299/R est:2500

LOTI, Pierre (1850-1923) French?

Works on paper			
£1333	$2453	€2000	Paysage de Grece (26x39cm-10x15in) i.d.12 fevr 70 crayon exhib. 9-Jun-4 Piasa, Paris #145/R est:2000-2500
£1400	$2576	€2100	Paysage. Composition aux squelettes. Calendrier (17x15cm-7x6in) two pen one crayon three exhib. 9-Jun-4 Piasa, Paris #143 est:1800-2000
£1667	$3067	€2500	Paysage d'Asie mineure, avec une mosquee de compagne (39x27cm-15x11in) i.d.20 fevr 70 exhib. 9-Jun-4 Piasa, Paris #147/R est:2500-3000
£1867	$3435	€2800	Paysage de foret (25x23cm-10x9in) s. crayon. 9-Jun-4 Piasa, Paris #148 est:1500-2000
£2000	$3680	€3000	Femmes de la grande Kybylie (13x19cm-5x7in) s. crayon exec.1869 exhib. 9-Jun-4 Piasa, Paris #144/R est:2000-2500

LOTIRON, Robert (1886-1966) French

£927	$1687	€1400	Peniches a quai (31x46cm-12x18in) s. 18-Jun-4 Piasa, Paris #155
£1343	$2497	€2000	Bord de Seine a Paris (60x73cm-24x29in) s. s.i.verso. 2-Mar-4 Artcurial Briest, Paris #217 est:2000-3000
Works on paper			
£1127	$1949	€1600	Pressoir (20x26cm-8x10in) s. gouache. 10-Dec-3 Piasa, Paris #149 est:400-500

LOTT, Frederick Tully (fl.1852-1879) British

Works on paper			
£900	$1629	€1314	Hauling in the nets at Plemont Bay, Jersey (29x44cm-11x17in) s. W/C. 1-Apr-4 Martel Maides, Guernsey #214/R

LOTTER, Heinrich (1875-1941) German

£933	$1699	€1400	Landscape, Insel Reichenau (39x49cm-15x19in) i.verso canvas on board. 3-Jul-4 Geble, Radolfzell #409/R
£1597	$2635	€2300	Bodensee landscape in the summer (55x79cm-22x31in) s.i. 3-Jul-3 Dr Fritz Nagel, Stuttgart #502/R est:1600
Works on paper			
£280	$481	€400	St Ulrich in Augsburg (31x20cm-12x8in) s. mixed media on pencil. 5-Dec-3 Michael Zeller, Lindau #694

LOTTIER, Louis (1815-1892) French

£552	$922	€800	Barques Espagnoles a Biscaye (40x75cm-16x30in) s. 17-Nov-3 Tajan, Paris #66
£833	$1492	€1250	Vue de bord de mer (31x50cm-12x20in) s. 16-May-4 other European Auctioneer #30
£1986	$3377	€2900	Vue du Bosphore (38x60cm-15x24in) s. 5-Nov-3 Rabourdin & Choppin de Janvry, Paris #55/R est:3000-3500
£2100	$3759	€3150	Vue du Bosphore (35x47cm-14x19in) s.d. panel. 16-May-4 other European Auctioneer #29

LOTTO, Lorenzo (style) (1480-1556) Italian

£7237	$13316	€11000	Portrait d'homme tenant des livres (78x70cm-31x28in) prov.exhib.lit. 24-Jun-4 Christie's, Paris #71/R est:4000-6000

LOTZ, Karl (1833-1904) Hungarian

£1900	$3155	€2774	Blue eyed woman (61x47cm-24x19in) s. 4-Oct-3 Kieselbach, Budapest #24/R (H.F 700000)
£3425	$6200	€5001	Greyhound (29x38cm-11x15in) s. oil on wood. 16-Apr-4 Mu Terem Galeria, Budapest #98/R (H.F 1300000)
£4887	$8112	€7135	Nude (65x145cm-26x57in) s. 4-Oct-3 Kieselbach, Budapest #25/R (H.F 1800000)
£4887	$8112	€7135	Portrait of a girl (69x55cm-27x22in) s. 4-Oct-3 Kieselbach, Budapest #72/R (H.F 1800000)
£4959	$8579	€7240	Stud resting (32x43cm-13x17in) s. 12-Dec-3 Kieselbach, Budapest #133/R (H.F 1900000)
£8431	$15261	€12309	Stick carver (32x43cm-13x17in) s. 16-Apr-4 Mu Terem Galeria, Budapest #97/R (H.F 3200000)
Works on paper			
£731	$1264	€1067	Aquarius (54x86cm-21x34in) s. chl golden paint cardboard. 12-Dec-3 Kieselbach, Budapest #132/R (H.F 280000)

LOTZ, Marie (1871-1970) Swiss

£437	$795	€638	Still life with flowers in a vase (34x28cm-13x11in) s. 16-Jun-4 Fischer, Luzern #2258/R (S.FR 1000)

LOU, Liza (1969-) American

Sculpture			
£21229	$38000	€30994	Untitled (15x25x19cm-6x10x7in) s.d.1996 cigar box cigars wood col beads prov. 12-May-4 Christie's, Rockefeller NY #316/R est:15000-20000

LOUBCHANSKY, Marcelle (1917-1988) French

£280	$476	€400	Composition (16x22cm-6x9in) s.d.1962. 28-Nov-3 Blanchet, Paris #214
£317	$548	€450	Via Saigon (32x24cm-13x9in) s. i.d.1954 verso panel. 14-Dec-3 Versailles Encheres #9
£400	$720	€600	Composition (57x42cm-22x17in) s. oil essence paper. 25-Apr-4 Versailles Encheres #35
£467	$840	€700	Composition (37x55cm-15x22in) s. paper painted 1962. 25-Apr-4 Versailles Encheres #5
£493	$853	€700	Composition (80x59cm-31x23in) s. acrylic paper on canvas. 14-Dec-3 Versailles Encheres #36/R
£600	$1074	€900	Composition (81x130cm-32x51in) s.d.1960. 15-May-4 De Vuyst, Lokeren #194
Works on paper			
£280	$467	€400	Composition (55x79cm-22x31in) s. mixed media paper on canvas. 29-Jun-3 Versailles Encheres #31/R
£423	$680	€600	Composition (57x78cm-22x31in) s. mixed media paper on canvas. 11-May-3 Versailles Encheres #222

LOUBERE, J (19th C) French

£1020	$1622	€1500	Jeunes enfantsa la fontaine (128x55cm-50x22in) s.i. 21-Mar-3 Bailly Pommery, Paris #109/R est:1200

LOUBERE, Roger Lambert (20th C) French?

£300	$537	€450	Village (48x65cm-19x26in) s. panel. 16-May-4 Renault-Aubry, Pontivy #460

LOUCHE, Constant (19/20th C) French

£377	$640	€550	Lavandiere a Ouid El Saida (37x46cm-15x18in) s. panel. 8-Nov-3 Gerard, Besancon #86
£1135	$1895	€1600	Marabout (34x82cm-13x32in) s. 19-Oct-3 Rabourdin & Choppin de Janvry, Paris #138/R est:1500-2000
£1389	$2194	€2000	Les porteuses d'eau (34x100cm-13x39in) s. 25-Apr-3 Etude de Provence, Marseille #199
£2000	$3320	€2920	Middle Eastern landscape. Setting up camp (43x123cm-17x48in) both s. pair. 1-Oct-3 Sotheby's, Olympia #264/R est:2000-4000
Works on paper			
£2676	$4630	€3800	Vue deColomb Bechar (51x157cm-20x62in) s.i. 15-Dec-3 Gros & Delettrez, Paris #91/R est:3000-4500

LOUCHET, Paul-François (1854-1936) French

£2467	$4514	€3700	Neige a Fontainebleau (46x55cm-18x22in) s. 6-Jun-4 Osenat, Fontainebleau #146/R est:3500-4000

LOUDEN, Albert (1943-) British

£400	$716	€584	Untitled (66x61cm-26x24in) s. 14-May-4 Christie's, Kensington #565/R

LOUDER, Thomas (attrib) (?) ?

£650	$1034	€949	Interior of a cottage, man smoking a pipe, sitting besides open fire (41x43cm-16x17in) 1-May-3 John Nicholson, Haslemere #736

LOUDERBACK, Walt (1887-1941) American

£1860	$3200	€2716	Columbus and the King of Spain (56x117cm-22x46in) i.verso. 6-Dec-3 Pook & Pook, Downington #175/R est:4000-5000

LOUDON, Terence (fl.1921-1940) British

£520	$884	€759	Christmas roses (40x30cm-16x12in) s. board. 1-Dec-3 Bonhams, Bath #129/R

LOUGHEED, Robert Elmer (1910-1982) Canadian

£2353	$4000	€3435	Colorado adobe (30x41cm-12x16in) masonite. 1-Nov-3 Altermann Galleries, Santa Fe #149
£3911	$7000	€5710	My South pasture along the Santa Fe Trail (30x61cm-12x24in) board. 15-May-4 Altermann Galleries, Santa Fe #120/R
£5294	$9000	€7729	In the San Pedros (30x38cm-12x15in) board. 1-Nov-3 Altermann Galleries, Santa Fe #4
£8235	$14000	€12023	Dark skies over Arroyo Tesuque (25x51cm-10x20in) masonite. 1-Nov-3 Altermann Galleries, Santa Fe #150
£8824	$15000	€12883	Willow wind break (30x61cm-12x24in) board. 1-Nov-3 Altermann Galleries, Santa Fe #148
£9412	$16000	€13742	Follow the Pecas Trail (28x61cm-11x24in) masonite. 1-Nov-3 Altermann Galleries, Santa Fe #147
£14706	$25000	€21471	Sunday afternoon (51x76cm-20x30in) masonite. 1-Nov-3 Altermann Galleries, Santa Fe #146
Works on paper			
£3727	$6000	€5441	Winter shadows (11x23cm-4x9in) W/C. 22-Aug-3 Altermann Galleries, Santa Fe #106

LOUGUININE-WOLKONSKY, Maria (1875-1960) Russian

£530	$970	€800	Paysage au lac de Montagne (30x42cm-12x17in) s. 7-Apr-4 Piasa, Paris #103b
£2897	$4837	€4200	Ville Mediterranee (54x65cm-21x26in) s. 17-Nov-3 Claude Boisgirard, Paris #58 est:1000-1200

LOUIS, Morris (1912-1962) American

£311377	$520000	€454610	Alphard (218x137cm-86x54in) acrylic painted 1961 prov.exhib.lit. 12-Nov-3 Sotheby's, New York #58/R est:200000-300000
£418994	$750000	€611731	Saf (250x358cm-98x141in) magna painted 1959 prov.exhib.lit. 11-May-4 Christie's, Rockefeller NY #15/R est:400000-600000

LOUIS, Rene J (20th C) Haitian

£273	$500	€399	Peasants outside cottages (51x61cm-20x24in) s. board. 3-Jun-4 Christie's, Rockefeller NY #1125/R

LOUIS-PAUL, Auguste-Albert (1854-1922) French

£490	$832	€700	Le menage dans l'atelier du peintre (46x31cm-18x12in) s. panel. 24-Nov-3 Boscher, Cherbourg #727/R

LOUKASIEVITCH, Thaddaus (?-1842) Polish

£1525 $2531 €2227 Portrait of a girl (53x40cm-21x16in) s.d.1841. 15-Jun-3 Agra, Warsaw #24/R est:9000 (P.Z 9500)

LOUKOTA, Josef (1879-1967) Czechoslovakian

£438 $727 €639 In train (26x29cm-10x11in) s. board. 4-Oct-3 Dorotheum, Prague #114/R est:20000-30000 (C.KR 20000)

£746 $1269 €1089 Girl with a basket of flowers (80x63cm-31x25in) s. 29-Nov-3 Dorotheum, Prague #41/R (C.KR 34000)

£1121 $1772 €1625 Female nude in the studio (99x55cm-39x22in) s.d.1901. 2-Sep-3 Rasmussen, Copenhagen #1702/R est:8000-10000 (D.KR 12000)

LOUND, Thomas (1802-1861) British

£340 $615 €496 Coastal view with beached fishing boats and figures (10x20cm-4x8in) 16-Apr-4 Keys, Aylsham #585/R

LOUND, Thomas (attrib) (1802-1861) British

£280 $465 €409 Figures by a ruined abbey (41x35cm-16x14in) 1-Oct-3 Woolley & Wallis, Salisbury #266/R

LOUP, Arnold (1882-1972) Swiss

£679 $1174 €991 Tours d'Ai (58x75cm-23x30in) s. canvas on cardboard. 12-Dec-3 Galerie du Rhone, Sion #549/R (S.FR 1500)

LOUPOT, Charles (19/20th C) ?

Prints

£2054 $3800 €2999 Securit (120x80cm-47x31in) s. col lithograph exec.c.1931. 9-Mar-4 Christie's, Rockefeller NY #242/R est:2000-3000

LOUREIRO, Arthur Jose de Souza (1853-1932) Portuguese

£567 $913 €828 Haystacks, box hill (16x10cm-6x4in) mono. board. 13-Oct-3 Joel, Victoria #446 est:1200-1500 (A.D 1400)

LOURENCO, Armand (c.1925-) French

£395 $726 €600 Paris - La Madeleine sous la neige (38x46cm-15x18in) 27-Jun-4 Teitgen, Nancy #77

£455 $773 €650 Paris, Place Blanche la nuit (22x27cm-9x11in) 30-Nov-3 Teitgen, Nancy #106

LOUTCHANSKY, Jacob (c.1882-1978) French

Sculpture

£963 $1800 €1406 Man riding a horse (46cm-18in) s.num.7/7 green pat bronze exec.c.1950. 1-Mar-4 Ben-Ami, Tel Aviv #4708/R est:2400-3000

LOUTHERBOURG, Jacques Philippe de II (1740-1812) French

Works on paper

£400 $748 €600 Aaron stopping the plague (41x36cm-16x14in) s. pen ink W/C arched top. 22-Jul-4 Dominic Winter, Swindon #249/R

£719 $1151 €1000 Pastorale (21x30cm-8x12in) brown grey wash traces of blk crayon. 16-May-3 Tajan, Paris #74

£1538 $2646 €2200 Vue d'un petit port avec promeneurs et pecheurs (22x38cm-9x15in) s. pen ink ink wash. 8-Dec-3 Rossini, Paris #31 est:750-900

LOUTHERBOURG, Jacques Philippe de II (attrib) (1740-1812) French

£1200 $2160 €1752 River landscape with shepherdess resting her flock (40x33cm-16x13in) indis.sig. prov. 23-Apr-4 Christie's, Kensington #145/R est:1500-2000

£4000 $7480 €5840 Jason and the dragon (68x50cm-27x20in) panel. 27-Feb-4 Christie's, Kensington #47/R est:1500-2500

LOUTHERBOURG, Philipp Jakob I (1698-1768) Swiss

Works on paper

£873 $1590 €1275 Landscape with harvesters and animals (19x30cm-7x12in) brush bister on chk. 17-Jun-4 Kornfeld, Bern #73 est:2000 (S.FR 2000)

LOUTTRE, Marc Antoine (1926-) French

Works on paper

£764 $1245 €1100 Il etait une fois dans l'eau (80x80cm-31x31in) s. W/C prov. 29-Sep-3 Sotheby's, Amsterdam #310

LOUVRIER, Maurice (1878-1954) French

£861 $1567 €1300 Poupees dans un jardin (24x33cm-9x13in) panel. 20-Jun-4 Imberdis, Pont Audemer #24

£1391 $2531 €2100 Impression matinal environs de Grandcourt (27x41cm-11x16in) panel painted 1943. 20-Jun-4 Imberdis, Pont Audemer #26

£1788 $3254 €2700 Rue de la Place Saint-Hilaire sous la neige (20x15cm-8x6in) s. 20-Jun-4 Imberdis, Pont Audemer #27

£1854 $3375 €2800 Notre-Dame de Paris sous la neige (33x41cm-13x16in) s. panel. 20-Jun-4 Imberdis, Pont Audemer #20

£1854 $3375 €2800 Cathedrale de Rouen (46x38cm-18x15in) s. 20-Jun-4 Imberdis, Pont Audemer #21

£1987 $3616 €3000 Effet de brume (31x36cm-12x14in) s. panel. 20-Jun-4 Imberdis, Pont Audemer #23

£2800 $5068 €4200 Le Pont Boieldieu, matin de brume (33x41cm-13x16in) s. d.1921 verso panel. 4-Apr-4 Salle des ventes Pillet, Lyon la Foret #44/R est:4000-5000

LOUYOT, Edmond (1861-1909) German

£237 $425 €346 Landscape with mountains and rock outcroppings (61x79cm-24x31in) s. 29-May-4 Brunk, Ashville #331/R

£302 $541 €441 Interior scene with young man (16x11cm-6x4in) s.d.93. 12-Jan-4 Rasmussen, Vejle #270 (D.KR 3200)

LOUYS, Pierre (1870-1925) French

Works on paper

£433 $797 €650 Le bal de l'ecole. Croquis d'apres nature (21x34cm-8x13in) pen two sheets exhib. 9-Jun-4 Piasa, Paris #150

LOVAAS, Hans (1848-1890) Norwegian

£476 $875 €695 Fjord landscape with fishermen (29x51cm-11x20in) s. 29-Mar-4 Blomqvist, Lysaker #1197/R (N.KR 6000)

£1951 $3571 €2848 Evening on the fjord (86x70cm-34x28in) s. 7-Jun-4 Blomqvist, Oslo #303/R est:30000-35000 (N.KR 24000)

LOVAGHY, Denes (20th C) Hungarian

£3819 $6226 €5500 Skier (172x122cm-68x48in) s. 23-Sep-3 Galerie Moderne, Brussels #862/R est:800-1000

LOVATTI (?) Italian

Works on paper

£919 $1700 €1342 Minstrel with girl (53x36cm-21x14in) s. W/C. 13-Mar-4 Susanin's, Chicago #6163/R est:1000-1500

LOVATTI, Matteo (1861-?) Italian

£4000 $7360 €5840 At the races (25x48cm-10x19in) s.i. panel. 23-Mar-4 Bonhams, New Bond Street #91/R est:4000-6000

LOVE, Horace Beevor (1800-1836) British

Works on paper

£550 $919 €803 Portrait of young gentleman (25x18cm-10x7in) s. W/C. 17-Oct-3 Keys, Aylsham #651

LOVE, Ralph (1907-) American

£1176 $2000 €1717 Golden valley (61x76cm-24x30in) s. 1-Nov-3 Santa Fe Art, Santa Fe #138/R est:3000-4000

£1471 $2500 €2148 Last moment (30x41cm-12x16in) canvas on board prov. 1-Nov-3 Santa Fe Art, Santa Fe #81/R est:3000-5000

LOVEJOY, Rupert (1885-1975) American

£759 $1200 €1108 Autumn, Maine (36x41cm-14x16in) s. masonite. 7-Sep-3 Treadway Gallery, Cincinnati #609/R

£886 $1400 €1294 Hessian Hill (46x56cm-18x22in) 7-Sep-3 Treadway Gallery, Cincinnati #645/R

LOVELESS, Kenneth (1919-1954) Canadian

£227 $411 €331 Poet (20x25cm-8x10in) s.d.1948 board prov. 18-Apr-4 Levis, Calgary #67/R (C.D 550)

£244 $405 €356 Untitled, forest interior, autumn (20x25cm-8x10in) wood board prov. 5-Oct-3 Levis, Calgary #66/R (C.D 550)

£466 $774 €680 Untitled, birch trees in winter (41x51cm-16x20in) s. prov. 5-Oct-3 Levis, Calgary #65/R (C.D 1050)

£537 $972 €784 Flowering plants (51x56cm-20x22in) prov. 18-Apr-4 Levis, Calgary #66/R est:1200-1500 (C.D 1300)

LOVELL, Katharine Adams (1877-1965) American

£378 $700 €552 Back of studio on beach (30x41cm-12x16in) s. canvasboard. 13-Mar-4 DeFina, Austinburg #591/R

£483 $850 €705 View from Telegraph Hill (41x51cm-16x20in) 3-Jan-4 Outer Cape Auctions, Provincetown #88/R

LOVELL, Tom (1909-1997) American

£2095 $3750 €3059 Mother and two daughters with garlands if daisies (36x53cm-14x21in) s. board. 15-May-4 Illustration House, New York #68/R est:4000-6000

£3892 $6500 €5682 Woman take aback by painting in artist's garret (51x48cm-20x19in) s. board. 15-Nov-3 Illustration House, New York #136/R est:5000-8000

£6704 $12000 €9788 Cowboy and his gal at night (71x51cm-28x20in) s.d.1935. 15-May-4 Illustration House, New York #31/R est:9000-12000

Works on paper

£348 $650 €508 Boat moored in icy waters, seagulls congregating (13x20cm-5x8in) s. gouache exec.c.1950. 26-Feb-4 Illustration House, New York #114

LOVELL-SMITH, Colin (1894-1961) New Zealander

£350 $636 €511 Vezelay Bourgogue (34x42cm-13x17in) s.d.1950 canvasboard. 29-Jun-4 Peter Webb, Auckland #191/R est:1500-2000 (NZ.D 1000)

£558 $959 €815 Goose Bay (34x44cm-13x17in) s. 7-Dec-3 International Art Centre, Auckland #294/R (NZ.D 1500)

LOVELL-SMITH, Rata (1900-1969) New Zealander

£311 $576 €454 Punakaiki Rocks (72x90cm-28x35in) s. board. 9-Mar-4 Watson's, Christchurch #204 (NZ.D 850)

£346 $619 €505 Two thumb range, South Canterbury (34x43cm-13x17in) s. board painted c.1930. 12-May-4 Dunbar Sloane, Wellington #246 est:800-1500 (NZ.D 1000)

£403 $746 €588 Magnolia grandiflora on a table cloth (44x49cm-17x19in) s. board. 9-Mar-4 Watson's, Christchurch #72 est:300-1000 (NZ.D 1100)

£421 $779 €615 Ben Ohu, Benmore Ranges from Pukaki (35x43cm-14x17in) s. board. 9-Mar-4 Watson's, Christchurch #3 (NZ.D 1150)

£450 $805 €657 Rocky shoreline, Pukaki (35x44cm-14x17in) s.d.60 board. 11-May-4 Watson's, Christchurch #7/R (NZ.D 1300)

£496 $918 €724 Limestone country, mid Canterbury, Porters Pass (36x46cm-14x18in) s. board. 13-Jul-4 Watson's, Christchurch #47/R est:300-1000 (NZ.D 1400)

£558 $959 €815 Bush Tramway Viaduct near Mahinapua, West Coast of South Island, NZ (34x44cm-13x17in) s.d.1952. 7-Dec-3 International Art Centre, Auckland #365/R (NZ.D 1500)
£616 $979 €899 Maymery landscape (44x34cm-17x13in) s. board. 9-Sep-3 Watson's, Christchurch #23 (NZ.D 1700)
£996 $1614 €1444 Rue Gaillard Vezelay (48x36cm-19x14in) s.d.1950 board. 31-Jul-3 International Art Centre, Auckland #85/R est:2500-3500 (NZ.D 2750)
£1504 $2556 €2196 Duchess Avenue, Dunedin (44x34cm-17x13in) s. board. 27-Nov-3 International Art Centre, Auckland #120/R est:3000-5000 (NZ.D 4000)
£2927 $4595 €4273 Headwaters of the Waimakariri (71x91cm-28x36in) s.d.1942. 1-Sep-3 Shapiro, Sydney #318/R est:5000-7000 (A.D 7200)
£7519 $12782 €10978 Headwaters of the Waimakariri (71x91cm-28x36in) s. 27-Nov-3 International Art Centre, Auckland #19/R est:20000-30000 (NZ.D 20000)

LOVEN, Frank W (1869-1941) American
£444 $800 €648 Vernal Falls, Yosemite (50x40cm-20x16in) init. i. stretcher prov. 25-Apr-4 Bonhams & Butterfields, San Francisco #5514/R

LOVERIDGE, Clinton (19th C) American
£599 $1000 €875 Cows in the water (20x15cm-8x6in) s. 16-Nov-3 CRN Auctions, Cambridge #24/R
£1075 $2000 €1570 Landscape with cattle by a stream (15x30cm-6x12in) init. board. 3-Mar-4 Christie's, Rockefeller NY #19/R est:1500-2500
£1956 $3500 €2856 Cattle and sheep in a river landscape (30x51cm-12x20in) s. 6-May-4 Shannon's, Milford #229/R est:4000-6000

LOVERIDGE, Clinton (attrib) (19th C) American
£1018 $1700 €1486 Cows in a pasture (38x64cm-15x25in) 18-Jun-3 Doyle, New York #54/R est:800-1200

LOVESEY, Roderick (1944-) British
£250 $455 €365 Derelict aeroplane (5x64cm-2x25in) s. indis d. 5-Feb-4 Mellors & Kirk, Nottingham #575

LOVET-LORSKI, Boris (1894-1973) Russian/American
Sculpture
£11377 $19000 €16610 Polynesian lady (53cm-21in) s. golden brown pat bronze marble base sold with a book prov.lit. 9-Oct-3 Christie's, Rockefeller NY #113/R est:15000-25000
£26471 $45000 €38648 Cretan woman (57cm-22in) i. veined marble on black marble mount. 30-Oct-3 Phillips, New York #88/R est:15000-25000

LOVINFOSSE, Pierre Michel de (1745-1821) French
£16667 $30000 €24334 Elegant party in countryside with a lady playing the harp and gentleman playing guitar (89x114cm-35x45in) s.i.d.1771. 22-Jan-4 Sotheby's, New York #257/R est:20000-30000

LOVMAND, Christine Marie (1803-1872) Danish
£930 $1600 €1358 Wild flowers (16x13cm-6x5in) init. panel. 2-Dec-3 Christie's, Rockefeller NY #56/R est:2000-4000
£2500 $4250 €3650 Still life with grapes on a vine and a peach on a stone ledge (38x32cm-15x13in) init. 30-Oct-3 Sotheby's, Olympia #179/R est:2500-3500
£7162 $13107 €10457 Strawberries in basket with other fruit on table (28x40cm-11x16in) s. 9-Jun-4 Rasmussen, Copenhagen #1438/R est:30000-40000 (D.KR 80000)

LOW, Charles (fl.1870-1902) British
£560 $1002 €818 Sporting man and his dog in a wooded landscape (38x59cm-15x23in) s. 16-Mar-4 Bonhams, Leeds #634/R
Works on paper
£350 $616 €511 Landscape with female figure walking (33x49cm-13x19in) s. W/C. 19-May-4 Dreweatt Neate, Newbury #11

LOW, Fritzi (1891-1975) Austrian
Works on paper
£517 $880 €740 Interior (22x30cm-9x12in) mono.d.1934. 29-Nov-3 Bassenge, Berlin #6880

LOW, Sanford Ballard Dale (1905-1964) American
£231 $400 €337 Mexican landscape (76x102cm-30x40in) s. i.verso. 15-Dec-3 Winter Associates, Plainville #93/R

LOW, Will Hicock (1853-1932) American
£8556 $16000 €12492 Beauty that is a rose (51x71cm-20x28in) s.d.1888. 25-Feb-4 Doyle, New York #49/R est:2000-3000

LOWCOCK, Charles Frederick (fl.1878-1922) British
£550 $913 €803 Grave Digger (76x51cm-30x20in) s.d.1880. 1-Oct-3 Sotheby's, Olympia #80/R
£5200 $8632 €7592 Duet (46x35cm-18x14in) s.d.83 panel. 1-Oct-3 Sotheby's, Olympia #114/R est:3000-5000

LOWDON, Stewart (1932-) British
£280 $442 €409 Breaking waves (60x121cm-24x48in) s. 7-Sep-3 Lots Road Auctions, London #344

LOWE, Arthur (20th C) British
Works on paper
£253 $400 €369 Black man with bag (38x20cm-15x8in) s. W/C. 6-Apr-3 William Jenack, New York #382

LOWE, Geoffrey (1952-) Australian
Works on paper
£1316 $2118 €1921 History from the series ten famous feeling for man (152x106cm-60x42in) s.i.d.1984 synthetic polymer on linen. 13-Oct-3 Joel, Victoria #386 est:800-1200 (A.D 3250)

LOWE, Robert Allensmore (1873-?) British
Works on paper
£560 $1014 €818 Steam cargo boat, Rhenenea, unloading timber into a barge (73x128cm-29x50in) s. W/C. 30-Mar-4 David Duggleby, Scarborough #145/R

LOWELL, Lemuel L (?-1914) American
£457 $850 €667 Winter scene (36x33cm-14x13in) s. 7-Mar-4 William Jenack, New York #206/R

LOWELL, Milton H (1848-1927) American
£529 $900 €772 Country cottage (20x33cm-8x13in) s. 5-Nov-3 Doyle, New York #55/R
£604 $1100 €882 Houses by a wooded river (61x91cm-24x36in) s.d.09 prov. 15-Jun-4 John Moran, Pasadena #176
£1195 $1900 €1745 Pastoral setting with pond and road running past tree-shaded farm buildings (61x91cm-24x36in) s. 10-Sep-3 Alderfer's, Hatfield #283 est:2000-3000
£3352 $6000 €4894 Path by the river (61x91cm-24x36in) s. prov. 6-May-4 Shannon's, Milford #252/R est:4000-6000

LOWELL, Orson Byron (1871-1956) American
£1070 $2000 €1562 Fawn and doe nibbling at branches (58x43cm-23x17in) s. painted c.1930. 26-Feb-4 Illustration House, New York #115 est:1800-2400
£1557 $2600 €2273 Patriotic turkey with World War I vintage helmet (79x66cm-31x26in) s. 15-Nov-3 Illustration House, New York #2/R est:3000-5000
Works on paper
£503 $900 €734 Widow and her suitors (51x76cm-20x30in) s. pen ink. 15-May-4 Illustration House, New York #99/R

LOWENSBERG, Verena (1912-1986) Swiss
£3620 $6154 €5285 Composition (139x139cm-55x55in) 25-Nov-3 Germann, Zurich #30/R est:10000-15000 (S.FR 8000)
£8597 $14357 €12552 Composition Nr 52a (50x85cm-20x33in) s.i. prov. 24-Jun-3 Germann, Zurich #8/R est:14000-18000 (S.FR 19000)
£11765 $19647 €17177 Composition Nr 108 (61x60cm-24x24in) s.i.d.1956 prov. 24-Jun-3 Germann, Zurich #9/R est:18000-22000 (S.FR 26000)
£11765 $19647 €17177 Composition Nr 135 (64x64cm-25x25in) s.i.d.1953 verso prov. 24-Jun-3 Germann, Zurich #18/R est:18000-22000 (S.FR 26000)
£13100 $24105 €19126 Untitled (120x120cm-47x47in) s.d.1982 s.d. stretcher. 8-Jun-4 Germann, Zurich #49/R est:25000-35000 (S.FR 30000)
£14932 $25385 €21801 Untitled (33x80cm-13x31in) s.d.1973 prov. 22-Nov-3 Burkhard, Luzern #179/R est:34000-40000 (S.FR 33000)
£17195 $28715 €25105 Composition Nr 71 (61x67cm-24x26in) s.i.d. verso prov. 24-Jun-3 Germann, Zurich #15/R est:20000-25000 (S.FR 38000)

LOWER RHINE SCHOOL (15th C) German
Sculpture
£5743 $10280 €8500 St Hieronymus (72cm-28in) lime wood. 8-May-4 Dawo, Saarbrucken #187/R est:8500

LOWES, Jason (20th C) British
Works on paper
£550 $880 €803 Portrait of a lady (30x21cm-12x8in) s.d.99 W/C. 16-Sep-3 Bonhams, Knightsbridge #113/R

LOWITH, Wilhelm (1861-1932) Austrian
£2100 $3486 €3066 Good read (19x26cm-7x10in) s. panel. 1-Oct-3 Sotheby's, Olympia #226/R est:1200-1800
£2177 $3962 €3200 Gentleman reading (14x12cm-6x5in) s. panel. 3-Feb-4 Christie's, Amsterdam #101/R est:2000-3000
£2533 $4560 €3800 Engrossed in a book (15x10cm-6x4in) s. panel. 21-Apr-4 Christie's, Amsterdam #26/R est:2000-3000

LOWNDES, Alan (1921-1978) British
£700 $1295 €1022 Under the moonlight (26x23cm-10x9in) s.d.1958 oil paper on board. 11-Mar-4 Christie's, Kensington #265/R
£4500 $8235 €6570 Serene sunset (91x122cm-36x48in) s.d.1965 s.i.d.verso. 2-Jun-4 Sotheby's, London #92/R est:5000-7000
£5000 $8800 €7300 Dieppe (36x54cm-14x21in) s. 19-May-4 Sotheby's, Olympia #232/R est:5000-7000
£7500 $13875 €10950 Chip shop (76x50cm-30x20in) s.d.1970 i.d.Feb 1970 verso. 11-Feb-4 Sotheby's, Olympia #273/R est:1000-1500
£7500 $13200 €10950 Cyclist in the snow (51x76cm-20x30in) s.d.1969. 19-May-4 Sotheby's, Olympia #203/R est:4000-6000
Works on paper
£500 $915 €730 David Andersons Felt Works Trafford Park (25x33cm-10x13in) s.d.1960 crayon. 6-Apr-4 Capes Dunn, Manchester #816/R

LOWRY, L S (1887-1976) British
Works on paper
£2800 $5124 €4088 Street scene - possibly Stockport (23x30cm-9x12in) s.d.1934 pencil sketch. 6-Apr-4 Capes Dunn, Manchester #817/R

LOWRY, Laurence Stephen (1887-1976) British

£15000	$25800	€21900	Girl (18x11cm-7x4in) indis sig. panel prov. 2-Dec-3 Bonhams, New Bond Street #78/R est:18000-25000
£18000	$30600	€26280	Farm buildings on a country lane (23x30cm-9x12in) s.d.13 board. 21-Nov-3 Christie's, London #116/R est:20000-30000
£20000	$36600	€29200	Glencoe (23x30cm-9x12in) s.d.1959 panel prov.exhib. 4-Jun-4 Christie's, London #67/R est:12000-18000
£20000	$36600	€29200	Pooh Bear (30x23cm-12x9in) s.d.1945 sold with stuffed toy Pooh bear prov. 4-Jun-4 Christie's, London #86/R est:12000-18000
£26000	$44200	€37960	Standing woman (18x11cm-7x4in) s.d.1954 panel prov. 21-Nov-3 Christie's, London #111/R est:15000-20000
£26000	$44720	€37960	Family group (22x16cm-9x6in) s.d.1951 panel prov. 2-Dec-3 Bonhams, New Bond Street #79/R est:25000-35000
£50000	$91500	€73000	Seascape (20x30cm-8x12in) s.d.1938 prov. 4-Jun-4 Christie's, London #68/R est:20000-30000
£92000	$168360	€134320	On a promenade: Hartlepool (40x51cm-16x20in) s.d.1970 s.i.d.verso. 2-Jun-4 Sotheby's, London #89/R est:40000-60000
£100000	$170000	€146000	Board meeting. Road through a wood (36x30cm-14x12in) s.d.1942 panel double-sided prov.exhib. 21-Nov-3 Christie's, London #110/R est:50000-80000
£110000	$201300	€160600	Yachts (35x49cm-14x19in) s.d.1947 panel prov.exhib. 4-Jun-4 Christie's, London #76/R est:50000-70000
£120000	$219600	€175200	Dwellings (39x53cm-15x21in) s.d.1932 board prov.exhib. 4-Jun-4 Christie's, London #85/R est:120000-180000
£125000	$228750	€182500	Sudden illness (25x46cm-10x18in) s.d.1920 s.i.d.verso panel prov.exhib.lit. 4-Jun-4 Christie's, London #75/R est:70000-100000
£130000	$237900	€189800	Beach at Penarth (61x76cm-24x30in) s.d.1960 prov. 2-Jun-4 Sotheby's, London #87/R est:60000-80000
£135000	$229500	€197100	Lady crossing a bridge (54x39cm-21x15in) s.d.1961 board prov. 21-Nov-3 Christie's, London #106/R est:120000-160000
£155000	$277450	€226300	Three children (46x27cm-18x11in) s.d.1962 board prov. 16-Mar-4 Bonhams, New Bond Street #68/R est:80000-100000
£220000	$402600	€321200	Organ grinder (25x36cm-10x14in) s.d.1934 prov.exhib. 4-Jun-4 Christie's, London #81/R est:120000-180000
£400000	$732000	€584000	Punch and Judy (41x56cm-16x22in) s.d.1943 prov.exhib.lit. 4-Jun-4 Christie's, London #79/R est:250000-350000
£440000	$805200	€642400	Senhouse Street, Maryport (51x91cm-20x36in) s.d.1955 prov.exhib. 4-Jun-4 Christie's, London #70/R est:350000-500000
Works on paper			
£3800	$6536	€5548	Figures and building (25x18cm-10x7in) init.d.1924 pencil prov. 2-Dec-3 Peter Francis, Wales #75/R est:3000-5000
£4000	$6680	€5840	Man with a pram and two dogs (16x11cm-6x4in) init. red crayon prov. 16-Oct-3 Christie's, Kensington #547/R est:800-1200
£4000	$6800	€5840	Farm at Lytham (12x18cm-5x7in) s.i.d.1921 pencil chk prov. 26-Nov-3 Sotheby's, Olympia #1/R est:2000-3000
£4000	$7320	€5840	Head of a man (21x21cm-8x8in) s. s.d.1920 verso pencil three. 4-Jun-4 Christie's, London #74/R est:4000-6000
£4200	$7518	€6132	Standing male figure (49x29cm-19x11in) init. pencil. 16-Mar-4 Bonhams, New Bond Street #21/R est:4000-6000
£4600	$8234	€6716	Man and dog (8x5cm-3x2in) init. blue biro prov. 17-Mar-4 Bonhams, Chester #265/R est:1000-1500
£4800	$8160	€7008	Boats on the beach at Lytham (12x18cm-5x7in) init. pencil prov. 21-Nov-3 Christie's, London #115/R est:5000-7000
£5200	$9464	€7592	Figures in a landscape (7x12cm-3x5in) s.d.61 pencil ink. 15-Jun-4 Bonhams, New Bond Street #79/R est:2000-3000
£5300	$9593	€7738	Salford Street (25x34cm-10x13in) s.d.1936 pencil. 30-Mar-4 David Duggleby, Scarborough #155/R est:2000-3000
£5500	$9845	€8030	Lytham 1923 (9x13cm-4x5in) s. bears i. pencil drawing exec 1923. 17-Mar-4 Bonhams, Chester #264/R est:3500-4500
£6500	$11050	€9490	Two landscape drawing, Lytham (13x17cm-5x7in) init.d.1918 pencil pastel two prov.exhib. 21-Nov-3 Christie's, London #113/R est:6000-8000
£6500	$11830	€9490	Figures on a beach (17x25cm-7x10in) s.d.1960 pen ink. 15-Jun-4 Bonhams, New Bond Street #78/R est:5000-7000
£6800	$12580	€9928	Head of a girl (29x22cm-11x9in) s. cardboard pencil drawing. 14-Jul-4 Bonhams, Chester #378/R est:2000-3000
£7000	$12810	€10220	Figures in the street (13x9cm-5x4in) s.d.23 Nov 1970 pencil ball point pen autograph book prov. 4-Jun-4 Christie's, London #84/R est:2000-3000
£8200	$14924	€11972	Conversation at a lodging house (34x24cm-13x9in) s.d.1920 pencil. 15-Jun-4 Bonhams, Leeds #56/R est:7000-10000
£9000	$16470	€13140	Kanga (28x20cm-11x8in) s.d.1961 pencil sold with knitted toy Kanga and Roo prov.exhib. 4-Jun-4 Christie's, London #87/R est:5000-8000
£9500	$16150	€13870	In Whitehaven (18x23cm-7x9in) init.i. pencil. 21-Nov-3 Christie's, London #109/R est:2000-3000
£9500	$17385	€13870	Street scene (12x18cm-5x7in) s.d.1919 pencil prov.exhib. 4-Jun-4 Christie's, London #72/R est:3000-5000
£10000	$16300	€14500	Application for a job (20x21cm-8x8in) s.d.1968 pencil dr. 23-Sep-3 Bonhams, Leeds #96/R est:7000-9000
£11500	$21275	€16790	The only one on the coast, Skerries (30x42cm-12x17in) init.i.d.1970 s.d. verso black felt-tip pen. 14-Jul-4 Bonhams, Chester #379/R est:1800-2500
£12000	$20400	€17520	Study for man drinking water (33x25cm-13x10in) s.d.1962 pencil exhib. 18-Nov-3 Bonhams, Leeds #117/R est:12000-15000
£13000	$22100	€18980	Factory gate (19x20cm-7x8in) s.d.1928 black ink prov.exhib. 21-Nov-3 Christie's, London #112/R est:7000-10000
£13000	$23790	€18980	Surgery (25x37cm-10x15in) s.d.1961 pencil prov. 4-Jun-4 Christie's, London #71/R est:7000-10000
£15000	$25500	€21900	Going to the elections (25x35cm-10x14in) s.d.1925 pencil exhib. 21-Nov-3 Christie's, London #114/R est:12000-18000
£16000	$27200	€23360	Ferry, South Shields (24x34cm-9x13in) s.d.1967 s.i.d.verso pencil. 21-Nov-3 Christie's, London #107/R est:12000-18000
£17000	$31110	€24820	Bridge, Ringley (24x34cm-9x13in) s.d.1926 pencil prov. 4-Jun-4 Christie's, London #77/R est:8000-12000
£17500	$32025	€25550	Men's club (25x36cm-10x14in) s.d.1918 pencil prov. 4-Jun-4 Christie's, London #73/R est:7000-10000
£19000	$34770	€27740	Canal, Worsley (24x34cm-9x13in) init. pencil prov. 4-Jun-4 Christie's, London #78/R est:7000-10000
£20000	$36600	€29200	Figures in a street (33x25cm-13x10in) s.d.1956 pencil prov. 4-Jun-4 Christie's, London #82/R est:8000-12000
£20000	$36600	€29200	Brewery train, high street, Burton (23x35cm-9x14in) s.d.1960 pencil prov. 4-Jun-4 Christie's, London #83/R est:10000-15000
£26000	$44200	€37960	Lady in a straw hat without a dog (34x24cm-13x9in) init.d.1964 pencil prov.exhib. 21-Nov-3 Christie's, London #101/R est:15000-20000
£26000	$48100	€37960	Head of a bearded man (35x26cm-14x10in) s.d.1956 pencil drawing. 14-Jul-4 Bonhams, Chester #377/R est:5000-7000
£28000	$48160	€40880	Piccadilly, Manchester (27x38cm-11x15in) s.d.1930 s.i.d.verso pencil prov.lit. 2-Dec-3 Bonhams, New Bond Street #76/R est:15000-20000
£35000	$59500	€51100	Co-op, Market Square, Cleator Moor (23x36cm-9x14in) s.d.1950 pencil prov.exhib.lit. 21-Nov-3 Christie's, London #108/R est:25000-35000
£38000	$69540	€55480	Leaving work (24x34cm-9x13in) s.d.1959 W/C gouache prov. 2-Jun-4 Sotheby's, London #96/R est:15000-20000
£40000	$68800	€58400	St. Michael and All Angel, Angel meadow, Manchester (38x27cm-15x11in) s.d.1931 pencil. 2-Dec-3 Bonhams, New Bond Street #80/R est:30000-40000
£46000	$84180	€67160	Industrial scene (29x36cm-11x14in) s.d.1951 pencil prov.exhib. 4-Jun-4 Christie's, London #80/R est:20000-30000
£65000	$118950	€94900	Coal queue (28x38cm-11x15in) s.i.d.1937 pencil. 4-Jun-4 Christie's, London #69/R est:30000-50000

LOWRY, Will J (19th C) American

£1676	$3000	€2447	Cottage nestled among flowering trees (61x107cm-24x42in) s. 20-Mar-4 Selkirks, St. Louis #149/R est:3000-5000

LOXTON, John S (1903-1971) Australian

£330	$610	€482	Yachting redcliffs (63x75cm-25x30in) s. board. 9-Mar-4 Watson's, Christchurch #9 est:800-2000 (NZ.D 900)
£402	$671	€583	Still life (61x51cm-24x20in) s. 30-Jun-3 Australian Art Auctions, Sydney #126 (A.D 1000)
£403	$746	€588	Country road, west coast (63x76cm-25x30in) s. board. 9-Mar-4 Watson's, Christchurch #32 est:1000-1800 (NZ.D 1100)
£407	$728	€594	Still life with azaleas (59x49cm-23x19in) s. 10-May-4 Joel, Victoria #356/R (A.D 1000)
£407	$728	€594	Still life with azaleas (59x49cm-23x19in) s. 10-May-4 Joel, Victoria #215 est:1000-1200 (A.D 1000)
£488	$873	€712	Still life with camellias (59x49cm-23x19in) s. 10-May-4 Joel, Victoria #294 (A.D 1200)
£569	$1019	€831	Fisherman's cottage, Cley-on-Sea, East coast, England (49x59cm-19x23in) s. canvas on board. 10-May-4 Joel, Victoria #235/R est:1000-1200 (A.D 1400)
£621	$968	€900	Sunset, Mordialloc creek (61x74cm-24x29in) s. canvasboard. 1-Aug-2 Joel, Victoria #220 est:1400-1800 (A.D 1800)
£1232	$1983	€1799	Hayricks near Kaiapoi (70x90cm-28x35in) s. board. 20-Aug-3 Peter Webb, Auckland #2050 est:1000-2000 (NZ.D 3400)
£1518	$2444	€2216	Mount Buffalo (75x62cm-30x24in) s. 13-Oct-3 Joel, Victoria #230/R est:2000-2500 (A.D 3750)
Works on paper			
£376	$639	€549	Sunny corner, Yugoslavia (36x43cm-14x17in) s. W/C executed c.1965. 26-Nov-3 Dunbar Sloane, Wellington #403 est:300-500 (NZ.D 1000)
£447	$801	€653	Alpine Country (33x49cm-13x19in) s. W/C. 10-May-4 Joel, Victoria #302 (A.D 1100)
£813	$1455	€1187	Ross Bridge, Tasmania (51x71cm-20x28in) s. W/C. 10-May-4 Joel, Victoria #325 est:1000-1500 (A.D 2000)

LOY, Abie (c.1935-) Australian

Works on paper			
£1545	$2441	€2256	Untitled (91x150cm-36x59in) i.verso synthetic polymer paint linen prov. 28-Jul-3 Sotheby's, Paddington #362/R est:2000-3000 (A.D 3800)

LOZANO SANCHIS, Francisco (1912-2000) Spanish

£1007	$1872	€1500	Peasant man (77x70cm-30x28in) s.d.1963 s.d.verso. 2-Mar-4 Ansorena, Madrid #49/R est:15000
£2931	$5422	€4250	Basket of fruit (29x38cm-11x15in) s.d.72 verso. 14-Jan-4 Castellana, Madrid #218/R est:3000
£3221	$5992	€4800	View of village (32x41cm-13x16in) s.indis.d. board. 2-Mar-4 Ansorena, Madrid #91/R est:4800
£4828	$8062	€7000	Mediterranean landscape (46x55cm-18x22in) s.d.73. 17-Nov-3 Durán, Madrid #223/R est:7000
£7333	$13347	€11000	Mediterraneo (38x46cm-15x18in) s.d.1979 s.i.d. verso. 29-Jun-4 Segre, Madrid #106/R est:5000
£13103	$23586	€19000	Female nude (105x170cm-41x67in) s. 26-Jan-4 Ansorena, Madrid #216/R est:18000
£14493	$23768	€20000	Arenal, Valencia (60x73cm-24x29in) s.d.75 s.i.d.verso. 27-May-3 Durán, Madrid #234/R est:16000
£19718	$34113	€28000	Rice fields (53x73cm-21x29in) s.d.63 board. 15-Dec-3 Ansorena, Madrid #41/R est:20000
Works on paper			
£532	$888	€750	Benidorm (32x22cm-13x9in) s. pen drawing. 23-Jun-3 Durán, Madrid #17/R

LOZANO, Lee (20th C) American

£13889	$25000	€20278	Untitled, wrench. Untitled (12x18cm-5x7in) three s. oil crayon graphite four. 24-Apr-4 David Rago, Lambertville #313/R est:600-900
Works on paper			
£1500	$2700	€2190	Untitled (22x17cm-9x7in) graphite crayon two. 24-Apr-4 David Rago, Lambertville #143/R est:400-600
£2778	$5000	€4056	Untitled. Evolution of men. one i.d.1962 ink one pair pen ink in 1 frame one chl three. 24-Apr-4 David Rago, Lambertville #372/R est:400-800
£3889	$7000	€5678	Untitled. graphite 4 in 1 frame graphite col pencil 6 in 1 frame two works. 24-Apr-4 David Rago, Lambertville #229/R est:400-600
£5278	$9500	€7706	Untitled. Be this occasionally. s.i. four s.d.1964 verso one s.d.1963-64 verso graphite seven. 24-Apr-4 David Rago, Lambertville #39/R est:500-1000
£11111	$20000	€16222	Untitled Subway series, bullshit 62 (19x24cm-7x9in) one s.i.d.62 graphite crayon one chl oil crayon two. 24-Apr-4 David Rago, Lambertville #540/R est:600-1200
£18056	$32500	€26362	Untitled Pot ball (11x9cm-4x4in) one s.i.d.1968 graphite one pair of oils in one mount two. 24-Apr-4 David Rago, Lambertville #450/R est:1000-2000

LOZOWICK, Louis (1892-1973) American

£8523	$15000	€12444	Japanese lanterns (61x46cm-24x18in) s.verso painted c.1931. 19-May-4 Sotheby's, New York #131/R est:15000-25000
Prints			
£1796	$3000	€2622	Mural study, lower Manhattan (33x18cm-13x7in) s.i.d.1936 lithograph. 11-Nov-3 Doyle, New York #316/R est:1500-2000
£1828	$3400	€2669	Roofs and sky (25x33cm-10x13in) s.i. col screenprint executed c.1939. 2-Mar-4 Swann Galleries, New York #372/R est:1500-2500
£2260	$4000	€3300	Subway construction (17x33cm-7x13in) s.d.1931 num.11/50 lithograph. 30-Apr-4 Sotheby's, New York #23/R est:5000-7000
£2375	$3800	€3468	First avenue market (30x23cm-12x9in) s.d.1934 num.16/50 lithograph. 18-Sep-3 Swann Galleries, New York #379/R est:1500-2500
£3059	$5200	€4466	Hanover Square (38x23cm-15x9in) s.d.1929 num. I/X lithograph. 6-Nov-3 Swann Galleries, New York #611/R est:5000-8000

Works on paper

£1099	$2000	€1605	Untitled (27x20cm-11x8in) s. mixed media prov. 29-Jun-4 Sotheby's, New York #321/R est:2000-3000
£8791	$16000	€12835	Panama (51x35cm-20x14in) s. s.i.verso ink executed c.1923-24 prov.exhib. 29-Jun-4 Sotheby's, New York #303/R est:8000-12000

LOZZA, Raul (20th C) Argentinian

£7650	$14000	€11169	Composition 83 (40x41cm-16x16in) oil pencil board. 1-Jun-4 Arroyo, Buenos Aires #50

LU SHENG ZHONG (1952-) Chinese

Works on paper

£4633	$7737	€6764	Shenbei folk custom (312x110cm-123x43in) mixed media. 26-Oct-3 Christie's, Hong Kong #109/R est:60000-120000 (HK.D 60000)

LU SHOUKUN (1919-1975) Chinese

Works on paper

£1494	$2688	€2181	Island view (23x43cm-9x17in) s.d.1961 ink col. 26-Apr-4 Sotheby's, Hong Kong #530/R est:20000-30000 (HK.D 21000)
£3041	$5351	€4500	Composition (94x31cm-37x12in) i. seal Indian ink seal col. 21-May-4 Dr Fritz Nagel, Stuttgart #1105/R est:2500
£3201	$5761	€4673	Landscape in moonlight (84x33cm-33x13in) s.i.d.1956 ink col scroll. 25-Apr-4 Christie's, Hong Kong #63/R est:50000-70000 (HK.D 45000)
£6046	$10882	€8827	Reservoir in Hong Kong (119x58cm-47x23in) s.i.d.1963 ink col scroll. 25-Apr-4 Christie's, Hong Kong #7/R est:25000-30000 (HK.D 85000)
£7722	$12896	€11274	Rapid river (46x46cm-18x18in) s.d.1963 ink col hanging scroll prov. 27-Oct-3 Sotheby's, Hong Kong #383/R est:25000-35000 (HK.D 100000)
£10669	$19203	€15577	Zen (139x69cm-55x27in) s.i.d.1971 ink col scroll. 25-Apr-4 Christie's, Hong Kong #131/R est:40000-50000 (HK.D 150000)

LU YANSHAO (1909-1993) Chinese

Works on paper

£3800	$6992	€5548	Cloudy ravines (67x44cm-26x17in) s.d.1980 ink hanging scroll. 8-Jun-4 Bonhams, New Bond Street #54 est:1500-2500
£5019	$8382	€7328	Mount Yandang (82x51cm-32x20in) s.i.d.1979 ink col hanging scroll. 26-Oct-3 Christie's, Hong Kong #293/R est:35000-45000 (HK.D 65000)
£5405	$9027	€7891	Majestic view of Lake Dongting (67x45cm-26x18in) s.i.d.1979 ink col hanging scroll. 27-Oct-3 Sotheby's, Hong Kong #269/R est:50000-70000 (HK.D 70000)
£6401	$11522	€9345	Landscape (42x21cm-17x8in) s.i. ink. 26-Apr-4 Sotheby's, Hong Kong #641/R est:40000-60000 (HK.D 90000)
£6950	$11606	€10147	Clouds over Mount Huang (89x47cm-35x19in) s.i.d.January 1979 ink col hanging scroll. 26-Oct-3 Christie's, Hong Kong #295/R est:60000-80000 (HK.D 90000)
£6950	$11606	€10147	Sailing through the gorges (19x53cm-7x21in) s.i.d.1946 ink col hanging scroll fan. 27-Oct-3 Sotheby's, Hong Kong #280/R est:45000-60000 (HK.D 90000)
£7112	$12802	€10384	Landscape (19x40cm-7x16in) s.i. ink col hand scroll pair. 25-Apr-4 Christie's, Hong Kong #109/R est:100000-150000 (HK.D 100000)
£7336	$12251	€10711	Landscape (89x50cm-35x20in) s.i.d.August 1978 ink col hanging scroll. 26-Oct-3 Christie's, Hong Kong #296/R est:50000-70000 (HK.D 95000)
£7722	$12896	€11274	Scene of Fuchun (49x93cm-19x37in) s.i.d.October 1979 ink col. 27-Oct-3 Sotheby's, Hong Kong #266/R est:50000-70000 (HK.D 100000)
£8535	$15363	€12461	Sage under a tree (67x37cm-26x15in) s.i.d.1963 ink col hanging scroll lit. 26-Apr-4 Sotheby's, Hong Kong #660/R est:120000-180000 (HK.D 120000)
£9957	$17923	€14537	Excursion in autumn (67x32cm-26x13in) s.i. ink col hanging scroll. 26-Apr-4 Sotheby's, Hong Kong #665/R est:60000-80000 (HK.D 140000)
£11380	$20484	€16615	Hermitage (97x46cm-38x18in) s.i.d.1980 ink col hanging scroll exhib.lit. 26-Apr-4 Sotheby's, Hong Kong #631/R est:80000-100000 (HK.D 160000)
£11380	$20484	€16615	Plum blossom and rock (95x88cm-37x35in) s.i.d.1986 ink col. 26-Apr-4 Sotheby's, Hong Kong #678/R est:80000-120000 (HK.D 160000)
£12355	$20633	€18038	Seascape from Pu Tu Island (95x58cm-37x23in) s.i.d.1982 ink col hanging scroll. 26-Oct-3 Christie's, Hong Kong #294/R est:50000-70000 (HK.D 160000)
£12802	$23044	€18691	Industrial city (22x31cm-9x12in) seal of artist ink col scroll set of twelve. 25-Apr-4 Christie's, Hong Kong #110/R est:200000-250000 (HK.D 180000)
£13127	$21923	€19165	Landscape after ancient masters (68x38cm-27x15in) s.i.d.1975 ink col hanging scroll. 27-Oct-3 Sotheby's, Hong Kong #326/R est:150000-250000 (HK.D 170000)
£18492	$33286	€26998	Scholar's studio (89x55cm-35x22in) s.i.d.1978 ink col. 26-Apr-4 Sotheby's, Hong Kong #634/R est:70000-90000 (HK.D 260000)
£20077	$33529	€29312	Figures (22x31cm-9x12in) artist seal eleven i. ink col leaves 12 album. 26-Oct-3 Christie's, Hong Kong #297/R est:200000-250000 (HK.D 260000)
£23166	$38687	€33822	Woods and ravines (34x386cm-13x152in) s.i.d.1989 ink col handscroll exhib. 27-Oct-3 Sotheby's, Hong Kong #333/R est:300000-400000 (HK.D 300000)
£32006	$57610	€46729	Dwelling among misty mountains (22x231cm-9x91in) s.i.d.1984 ink col handscroll. 26-Apr-4 Sotheby's, Hong Kong #595/R est:180000-220000 (HK.D 450000)
£47876	$79954	€69899	Qutang gorge (99x34cm-39x13in) s.i. ink col hanging scroll prov. 27-Oct-3 Sotheby's, Hong Kong #268/R est:200000-300000 (HK.D 620000)
£48364	$87055	€70611	Mount Huang (145x48cm-57x19in) s.i.d.1942 ink col hanging scroll lit. 26-Apr-4 Sotheby's, Hong Kong #579/R est:220000-300000 (HK.D 680000)
£53343	$96017	€77881	Sunset gorge (90x60cm-35x24in) s.i.d.1985 ink col hanging scroll exhib.lit. 26-Apr-4 Sotheby's, Hong Kong #627/R est:300000-500000 (HK.D 750000)
£53343	$96017	€77881	River gorge (97x34cm-38x13in) s.i. ink col hanging scroll lit. 26-Apr-4 Sotheby's, Hong Kong #630/R est:250000-350000 (HK.D 750000)
£60232	$100587	€87939	Landscapes (13x17cm-5x7in) i.d.1963 ink col sixteen leaves album. 27-Oct-3 Sotheby's, Hong Kong #329/R est:280000-350000 (HK.D 780000)
£92664	$154749	€135289	Landscapes (27x35cm-11x14in) s.i. ink col thirteen leaves album lit. 26-Oct-3 Christie's, Hong Kong #292/R est:1200000-1500000 (HK.D 1200000)

LUARD, Elizabeth (20th C) British

Works on paper

£1000	$1630	€1450	Eagle owl. Tawny owl. Shorteared owl (45x35cm-18x14in) s.i.d.1977 ink W/C three. 21-Jul-3 Sotheby's, London #551 est:600-800

LUARD, Lowes Dalbiac (1872-1944) British

Works on paper

£537	$993	€800	Chevaux de halage l'hiver (55x100cm-22x39in) s.d.1899 pastel. 14-Mar-4 St-Germain-en-Laye Encheres #5/R

LUBBERS, Adriaan (1892-1954) Dutch

£1678	$3104	€2500	Portrait of a gentleman (102x74cm-40x29in) s.d.37. 15-Mar-4 Sotheby's, Amsterdam #152/R est:2500-3000
£4333	$7973	€6500	Portrait of Piet Mondrian (81x55cm-32x22in) s.d.1931 s.i.d. verso prov. 8-Jun-4 Sotheby's, Amsterdam #195/R est:3000-4000

LUBBERS, Holger (1850-1931) Danish

£301	$512	€439	Seascape with vessels and rowing boat (35x57cm-14x22in) s. 29-Nov-3 Rasmussen, Havnen #2009/R (D.KR 3200)
£332	$531	€485	Coastal landscape with beached boats and seagulls (14x22cm-6x9in) mono. i.verso. 22-Sep-3 Rasmussen, Vejle #472 (D.KR 3500)
£352	$658	€514	Seascape with two frigates (21x27cm-8x11in) s.d.1927. 25-Feb-4 Kunsthallen, Copenhagen #538 (D.KR 3900)
£358	$655	€523	Seascape with sailing boat in Oresund (36x26cm-14x10in) i. 7-Jun-4 Museumsbygningen, Copenhagen #63 (D.KR 4000)
£366	$667	€534	Coastal landscape with sailing vessels (25x39cm-10x15in) s.d.1908. 7-Feb-4 Rasmussen, Havnen #2174/R (D.KR 4000)
£374	$591	€542	Beached boats on shore (31x48cm-12x19in) 3-Sep-3 Museumsbygningen, Copenhagen #187 (D.KR 4000)
£384	$626	€561	Fisherwomen at Gammel Strand (31x37cm-12x15in) s.d.1905. 28-Sep-3 Hindemae, Ullerslev #141/R (D.KR 4100)
£393	$620	€570	Coastal landscape with sailing boats (13x20cm-5x8in) mono. 3-Sep-3 Museumsbygningen, Copenhagen #178 (D.KR 4200)
£407	$729	€594	Cattle at Saltholm (37x61cm-15x24in) s.d.1901. 10-May-4 Rasmussen, Vejle #147/R (D.KR 4500)
£451	$844	€658	Beach near Agger (26x35cm-10x14in) s.d.1911. 25-Feb-4 Kunsthallen, Copenhagen #541/R (D.KR 5000)
£474	$758	€687	Seascape (18x25cm-7x10in) s.d.1923. 17-Sep-3 Kunsthallen, Copenhagen #445 (D.KR 5000)
£717	$1290	€1047	The entrance to Copenhagen Harbour (27x39cm-11x15in) s.d.1919. 24-Apr-4 Rasmussen, Havnen #2351/R (D.KR 8000)
£722	$1350	€1054	From Copenhagen's outer harbour with Flak Fort (26x40cm-10x16in) mono. 25-Feb-4 Kunsthallen, Copenhagen #571/R (D.KR 8000)
£771	$1311	€1126	Coastal landscape with sailing vessels, figures on beach (54x47cm-21x19in) s. 29-Nov-3 Rasmussen, Havnen #2004/R (D.KR 8200)
£932	$1463	€1361	Fishermen fixing nets by beached boat (29x42cm-11x17in) s. 30-Aug-3 Rasmussen, Havnen #2070/R (D.KR 10000)
£1083	$2025	€1581	View of the sea (60x79cm-24x31in) s.d.1912. 25-Feb-4 Museumsbygningen, Copenhagen #118/R est:12000-15000 (D.KR 12000)
£1134	$1962	€1656	From Limfjorden, with fisherman carrying the day's catch ashore (66x70cm-26x28in) s.d.1909. 9-Dec-3 Rasmussen, Copenhagen #1470/R est:10000 (D.KR 12000)
£1305	$2048	€1905	Canal view from Copenhagen (66x92cm-26x36in) init. 30-Aug-3 Rasmussen, Havnen #2199 est:10000-12000 (D.KR 14000)
£1715	$3207	€2504	From Copenhagen Harbour (82x113cm-32x44in) s.d.1903. 25-Feb-4 Museumsbygningen, Copenhagen #168/R est:12000-15000 (D.KR 19000)
£5551	$10158	€8104	Prawn fishermen in North Sjaelland (75x105cm-30x41in) s.d.1905 prov. 9-Jun-4 Rasmussen, Copenhagen #1836/R est:75000 (D.KR 62000)

LUBIN, Arieh (1897-1980) Israeli

£984	$1800	€1437	Still life with a vase of flowers (34x25cm-13x10in) s. canvas on board. 1-Jun-4 Ben-Ami, Tel Aviv #4842/R est:2200-3000

LUBITCH, Ossip (1896-1986) French

£173	$310	€253	Still life (38x46cm-15x18in) s. 22-Mar-4 Philippe Schuler, Zurich #6166 (S.FR 400)
£302	$540	€441	Still life with flowers in glass jug (41x24cm-16x9in) s. 12-May-4 Dobiaschofsky, Bern #3729/R (S.FR 700)
£940	$1748	€1400	Chevaux de cirque (73x50cm-29x20in) s. s.i.verso. 2-Mar-4 Artcurial Briest, Paris #175 est:1500-1800
£993	$1808	€1500	Orchestre (33x24cm-13x9in) s. oil W/C cardboard. 16-Jun-4 Claude Boisgirard, Paris #99 est:1500-1800

Works on paper

£414	$691	€600	La Gare sous la neige (53x63cm-21x25in) s. W/C gouache. 17-Nov-3 Claude Boisgirard, Paris #60
£552	$921	€800	Village sous la neige (53x63cm-21x25in) s. gouache. 17-Nov-3 Claude Boisgirard, Paris #59

LUBLIN, Lea (1929-) Argentinian

£3187	$5800	€4653	Painting (50x70cm-20x28in) s.d.63. 29-Jun-4 Arroyo, Buenos Aires #60/R est:5500

LUBOVITCH, Norman (20th C) ?

£264	$475	€385	Seated nude (127x89cm-50x35in) s. 23-Jan-4 Freeman, Philadelphia #208/R

LUBSCHITZ, John Leopold (1858-1941) Danish

£487	$794	€711	Boat bridge with children fishing in sunshine (111x95cm-44x37in) s.d.87. 27-Sep-3 Rasmussen, Havnen #2147 (D.KR 5200)

LUCA, A de (?) ?

Sculpture

£2374	$4250	€3466	Three boys crabbing (213cm-84in) verdigris brown pat bronze. 20-Mar-4 Freeman, Philadelphia #864/R est:3500-5000
£5435	$10000	€7935	Centaurs (157x135cm-62x53in) s. brown pat bronze pair. 23-Mar-4 Arthur James, Florida #93/R est:12000-16000

LUCA, Arturo de (?) ?

£559	$1000	€816	Still life (80x103cm-31x41in) 11-May-4 Arroyo, Buenos Aires #29

LUCA, F de (20th C) ?

Sculpture

£3911	$7000	€5710	Female nude (163cm-64in) s. verdigris pat. 20-Mar-4 Freeman, Philadelphia #602/R est:5000-8000
£7162	$12605	€10600	Dancers. s.verso silver marble base. 19-May-4 Il Ponte, Milan #599/R est:5000-6000

LUCANDER, Anitra (1918-2000) Finnish

£1533	$2745	€2300	Still life (34x41cm-13x16in) s. 15-May-4 Hagelstam, Helsinki #2000/R est:2000
£1761	$3046	€2500	Branch with blossom (40x29cm-16x11in) s. 13-Dec-3 Hagelstam, Helsinki #175/R est:1800
£2254	$3899	€3200	Marshy landscape (38x46cm-15x18in) s. 13-Dec-3 Hagelstam, Helsinki #177/R est:3000
£2341	$3980	€3418	Town view (46x55cm-18x22in) s. panel. 5-Nov-3 AB Stockholms Auktionsverk #1156/R est:15000-20000 (S.KR 31000)
£2365	$4233	€3500	Still life of flowers in vase (35x25cm-14x10in) s. 8-May-4 Bukowskis, Helsinki #279/R est:1600-1800
£2838	$5080	€4200	Clump of trees (65x65cm-26x26in) s.d.67. 8-May-4 Bukowskis, Helsinki #261/R est:5000-6000
£3169	$5482	€4500	Composition (41x56cm-16x22in) s.d.1960. 13-Dec-3 Hagelstam, Helsinki #174/R est:3000
£3239	$5604	€4600	In the rain (37x48cm-15x19in) s. board. 13-Dec-3 Hagelstam, Helsinki #176/R est:4000
£3380	$5848	€4800	Two women (81x61cm-32x24in) s. 13-Dec-3 Hagelstam, Helsinki #178/R est:4000
£3636	$6182	€5200	Temple in the rain (54x65cm-21x26in) s.d.68. 29-Nov-3 Bukowskis, Helsinki #301/R est:3000-4000

LUCANDER, Robert (20th C) Finnish

£1511	$2568	€2206	Unsere Bestseller (100x70cm-39x28in) s.d.97 verso varnish panel. 5-Nov-3 AB Stockholms Auktionsverk #974/R est:6000-8000 (S.KR 20000)

LUCANO, Pietro (1878-1972) Italian

£294	$505	€420	Peace morning (28x43cm-11x17in) s. cardboard exhib. 3-Dec-3 Stadion, Trieste #1136
£364	$663	€550	Roses (32x26cm-13x10in) s. cardboard. 18-Jun-4 Stadion, Trieste #463/R
£367	$656	€550	Path (34x31cm-13x12in) s. board. 12-May-4 Stadion, Trieste #637a
£397	$723	€600	Girls in the garden (38x50cm-15x20in) s. canvas on board. 18-Jun-4 Stadion, Trieste #460/R
£397	$723	€600	View of Chiusaforte (40x50cm-16x20in) s. board. 18-Jun-4 Stadion, Trieste #459/R
£397	$723	€600	Houses in Carso (40x50cm-16x20in) s. board. 18-Jun-4 Stadion, Trieste #458/R
£400	$716	€600	Still life (50x39cm-20x15in) s. cardboard. 12-May-4 Stadion, Trieste #675
£400	$716	€600	Symbolical landscape (30x40cm-12x16in) s. cardboard. 12-May-4 Stadion, Trieste #786/R
£430	$783	€650	Field idyll (30x40cm-12x16in) s. board. 18-Jun-4 Stadion, Trieste #462/R
£464	$844	€700	Carso (40x50cm-16x20in) s. board. 18-Jun-4 Stadion, Trieste #457/R
£497	$904	€750	Bell tower in Basovizza (32x42cm-13x17in) s. board. 18-Jun-4 Stadion, Trieste #461/R
£530	$964	€800	Rural houses (50x68cm-20x27in) s. board. 18-Jun-4 Stadion, Trieste #451
£530	$964	€800	Rainbow over the village (48x60cm-19x24in) s. 18-Jun-4 Stadion, Trieste #453/R
£541	$1022	€800	Book on the sofa (80x56cm-31x22in) s. board. 20-Feb-4 Stadion, Trieste #221/R
£559	$962	€800	Haystacks in the wood (30x39cm-12x15in) s. cardboard on canvas. 3-Dec-3 Stadion, Trieste #999/R
£563	$1025	€850	Green trees (50x60cm-20x24in) s. board. 18-Jun-4 Stadion, Trieste #454/R
£563	$1025	€850	Chinese objects (60x50cm-24x20in) s. board. 18-Jun-4 Stadion, Trieste #455/R
£662	$1205	€1000	Angels (82x64cm-32x25in) s. board. 18-Jun-4 Stadion, Trieste #450/R
£662	$1205	€1000	Boats and masks (40x50cm-16x20in) s. board. 18-Jun-4 Stadion, Trieste #456/R
£667	$1193	€1000	Harmony (45x60cm-18x24in) s. board. 12-May-4 Stadion, Trieste #674
£685	$1068	€1000	Morning (55x55cm-22x22in) s. i.verso. 8-Apr-3 Il Ponte, Milan #628
£795	$1446	€1200	Courtyard in Basovizza (52x64cm-20x25in) s. board. 18-Jun-4 Stadion, Trieste #452
£800	$1432	€1200	Seated on the bank (25x35cm-10x14in) s. cardboard. 12-May-4 Stadion, Trieste #685/R

LUCAS Y PADILLA, Eugenio (attrib) (1824-1870) Spanish

£3620	$5792	€5285	Procession in cathedral (22x17cm-9x7in) panel. 16-Sep-3 Philippe Schuler, Zurich #3340/R est:2000-2500 (S.FR 8000)

LUCAS Y VILLAAMIL, Eugenio (1858-1918) Spanish

£625	$1063	€900	Man with hat (15x10cm-6x4in) s. board. 28-Oct-3 Segre, Madrid #29/R
£625	$1063	€900	Toreador (15x10cm-6x4in) s. board. 28-Oct-3 Segre, Madrid #28/R
£3667	$6673	€5500	Anciano pretendiente (29x25cm-11x10in) s. 29-Jun-4 Segre, Madrid #88/R est:5300
£3691	$6866	€5500	Gallant scene (30x23cm-12x9in) s. board. 2-Mar-4 Ansorena, Madrid #82/R est:5500
£4225	$6761	€6000	Gallant scene (35x29cm-14x11in) s. prov. 16-Sep-3 Segre, Madrid #17/R est:6000
£5369	$9611	€8000	What beautiful flowers ! (36x54cm-14x21in) s. 25-May-4 Durán, Madrid #190/R est:4500
£10870	$17826	€15000	Salida de la boda (65x42cm-26x17in) s. 27-May-3 Durán, Madrid #300/R est:12000
£19928	$32681	€27500	El contrato nupcial (73x46cm-29x18in) s. 27-May-3 Durán, Madrid #254/R est:12000
£20833	$33958	€30000	Celebration in village (38x56cm-15x22in) s. board. 23-Sep-3 Durán, Madrid #193/R est:19000

LUCAS, Albert Durer (1828-1918) British

£750	$1373	€1095	Wild heath, butterflies amongst heather (127cm-50in) s.d.1877 i.verso. 7-Apr-4 Bonhams, Bury St Edmunds #435
£800	$1360	€1168	English autumn leaves (42x52cm-17x20in) s. 30-Oct-3 Locke & England, Leamington Spa #207/R
£3600	$6696	€5256	Heather and a butterfly. Primulas and violas (20x15cm-8x6in) s.d.1890 pair. 4-Mar-4 Christie's, Kensington #663/R est:2000-3000
Works on paper			
£600	$1002	€876	Heather in flower (24x19cm-9x7in) s.d.1868 W/C gum arabic bodycol. 12-Nov-3 Sotheby's, Olympia #60/R

LUCAS, August Georg Friedrich (1803-1863) German

£6490	$11812	€9800	Evening country landscape near Olevana (63x83cm-25x33in) mono.d.1839. 16-Jun-4 Hugo Ruef, Munich #1025/R est:9800
Works on paper			
£1216	$2141	€1800	Roman villa (25x34cm-10x13in) d.1832 pencil double-sided prov. 22-May-4 Lempertz, Koln #1433/R est:2000
£6332	$11524	€9245	At the washing grotto of Subiaco (32x47cm-13x19in) mono.i.d.1850 prov. 17-Jun-4 Kornfeld, Bern #35/R est:7500 (S.FR 14500)

LUCAS, Charlie (1951-) American

Sculpture			
£1198	$2000	€1749	Violinist (208x112x76cm-82x44x30in) welded metal. 15-Nov-3 Slotin Folk Art, Buford #155/R est:3000-5000
£1497	$2500	€2186	Ezekial's vision, a wheel within a wheel (234x69cm-92x27in) welded metal. 15-Nov-3 Slotin Folk Art, Buford #154/R est:3000-5000
Works on paper			
£444	$800	€648	Woman's face (53x69cm-21x27in) crayon graphite ink. 24-Apr-4 Slotin Folk Art, Buford #564/R

LUCAS, David (1802-1881) British

Prints			
£6000	$10920	€8760	English landscape (33x45cm-13x18in) mezzotints after John Constable folio prov. 1-Jul-4 Sotheby's, London #97/R est:3000-4000

LUCAS, Edward George Handel (1861-1936) British

£1848	$3307	€2698	Study for Fast falls the eventide (56x47cm-22x19in) s.d.1906 exhib. 26-May-4 AB Stockholms Auktionsverk #2421/R est:25000-30000 (S.KR 25000)
£2252	$3874	€3288	Of the past (15x20cm-6x8in) s.d.1883 panel. 8-Dec-3 Philippe Schuler, Zurich #3421/R est:3000-4000 (S.FR 5000)

LUCAS, François (?) French

Sculpture			
£3028	$5239	€4300	Femme (56x29cm-22x11in) s.d.1782 marble sold with base. 11-Dec-3 Binoche, Paris #43 est:6000-8000
Works on paper			
£775	$1340	€1100	Cinq scenes de la vie d'Alexandre et une scene de triomphe antique (17x30cm-7x12in) one s. bears indis.d. pen blk ink grey wash five. 10-Dec-3 Piasa, Paris #37/R

LUCAS, George (19th C) British

£3000	$5550	€4380	Harvesting on the Downs (77x109cm-30x43in) 13-Jan-4 Bonhams, Knightsbridge #260/R est:3000-5000

LUCAS, Henry Frederick Lucas (c.1848-1943) British

£430	$675	€624	Victorian hunt and pack in English landscape (30x46cm-12x18in) s. 15-Dec-2 Desmond Judd, Cranbrook #876/R
£550	$1012	€803	Brampton, a chestnut hunter (28x37cm-11x15in) mono.i. prov. 10-Jun-4 Christie's, Kensington #82
£600	$948	€876	Trixy - Study of a horse in a stable (26x36cm-10x14in) s.d.98 i.verso. 2-Sep-3 Gildings, Market Harborough #436/R
£650	$1196	€949	Brownie, a bay hunter (36x46cm-14x18in) s.i. prov. 10-Jun-4 Christie's, Kensington #80
£900	$1638	€1314	All Gold, horse in a stable (36x46cm-14x18in) s.d.1908 prov. 4-Feb-4 John Nicholson, Haslemere #125/R
£900	$1647	€1314	Rally, a beagle (20x28cm-8x11in) s.i.d.1921 i.verso. 7-Apr-4 Woolley & Wallis, Salisbury #287/R
£1000	$1700	€1460	Tom Thumb, chestnut hunter (28x38cm-11x15in) s.i. 27-Nov-3 Christie's, Kensington #136/R est:1500-2000
£1000	$1600	€1460	Goodwin (49x65cm-19x26in) s.d.1887 s.i.d.verso. 18-Sep-3 Bonhams, Edinburgh #376/R est:1000-1500
£1000	$1820	€1460	Chatterbox, horse in a stable (36x46cm-14x18in) s.d.1909 prov. 4-Feb-4 John Nicholson, Haslemere #124/R est:800-1000
£1000	$1840	€1460	Rally, champion hound bitch (23x30cm-9x12in) s.d.1921 i.verso. 10-Jun-4 Christie's, Kensington #419/R est:1000-1500
£1374	$2500	€2006	Racehorse Minting by Lord Lyon out of mint sauce (51x66cm-20x26in) s.d.1888 s.i.d.verso prov. 29-Jun-4 Sotheby's, New York #169/R est:4000-6000
£1436	$2600	€2097	Second whip (38x55cm-15x22in) s. s.i.d.1879 verso. 30-Mar-4 Christie's, Rockefeller NY #42/R est:1500-2000
£1500	$2550	€2190	Goodwin, bay hunter in a stable (51x66cm-20x26in) s.d.1887 i.verso. 27-Nov-3 Christie's, Kensington #133/R est:1500-2000
£1800	$3060	€2628	Holderness Truemon, a beagle (28x37cm-11x15in) s.i. 27-Nov-3 Christie's, Kensington #379/R est:1800-2200
£2348	$4250	€3428	Damsel and Gaylass. Henbane and Caroline. Fencer (28x37cm-11x15in) s.d.96 i.d.Sept 1896 verso three. 30-Mar-4 Bonhams & Butterfields, San Francisco #68/R est:4500-6000
£5800	$10440	€8468	Five ponies from the Bostock Hall polo stud (28x37cm-11x15in) s.d.1924 1929 i.verso six sold with photo. 21-Apr-4 Christie's, Kensington #380/R est:3000-5000
£10497	$19000	€15326	Portrait of dogs, Whip-cord and Democrat (50x66cm-20x26in) s.d.1900 i.verso pair. 30-Mar-4 Bonhams & Butterfields, San Francisco #67/R est:4500-6000
£20718	$37500	€30248	Group of Percy bitches (71x102cm-28x40in) s.d.1900 i.d.1900 verso. 30-Mar-4 Bonhams & Butterfields, San Francisco #69/R est:12000-18000
£20718	$37500	€30248	Group of Percy hounds (71x102cm-28x40in) s.d.98 i.d.Sept and Oct 1898 verso. 30-Mar-4 Bonhams & Butterfields, San Francisco #70/R est:12000-18000
Works on paper			
£400	$632	€584	Noggs - study of a horse in a field (23x30cm-9x12in) s.d.1910 i.verso. 2-Sep-3 Gildings, Market Harborough #416/R

LUCAS, Jean (1823-?) French
£3000 $5400 €4380 L'Arc de Triomphe, Paris (50x61cm-20x24in) s. 21-Jan-4 Sotheby's, Olympia #454/R est:1500-2000

LUCAS, John Seymour (1849-1923) British
£750 $1343 €1095 On the Thames at Twickenham (33x40cm-13x16in) s.d.1894. 26-May-4 Christie's, Kensington #722/R
£3200 $5056 €4640 An important letter (51x41cm-20x16in) s.d.1877. 4-Sep-3 Christie's, Kensington #250/R est:2500-3500
Works on paper
£650 $1196 €949 Prayer before battle (49x39cm-19x15in) s.d.1878 pencil W/C bodycol. 25-Mar-4 Christie's, Kensington #239/R

LUCAS, Lucas W (20th C) British
£3243 $6000 €4735 Ch Crackley Sensational, wirehaired fox terrier (30x36cm-12x14in) s.i.d.1925 canvasboard. 10-Feb-4 Doyle, New York #270/R est:1800-2400

LUCAS, Marie Seymour (1855-1921) British
£1250 $2288 €1825 Mother and child cleaning a basin and spoon in a kitchen (38x28cm-15x11in) s. prov. 7-Apr-4 Gardiner & Houlgate, Bath #345/R est:300-450
£1900 $3553 €2850 Four sisters (30x50cm-12x20in) s. 26-Jul-4 Bonhams, Bath #90/R est:800-1000

LUCAS, Ralph W (attrib) (fl.1821-1851) British
£600 $1074 €876 Country landscape with cattle, sheep and figures by gate (46x60cm-18x24in) 11-May-4 Bonhams, Knightsbridge #215/R

LUCAS, Sarah (1962-) British
Photographs
£7784 $13000 €11365 Pierre de Toucher (78x53cm-31x21in) c-print edition 8 of 10 prov. 13-Nov-3 Sotheby's, New York #450/R est:12000-18000
£25140 $45000 €36704 Self portrait with skull (161x130cm-63x51in) c-print executed1997 prov.exhib.lit. 13-May-4 Phillips, New York #3/R est:50000-70000
Sculpture
£1800 $3312 €2628 Beer can penis (17x15x7cm-7x6x3in) init.d.00 num.6/20 cast aluminium prov. 24-Jun-4 Sotheby's, Olympia #405/R est:2000-3000
£83832 $140000 €122395 Bunny gets snookered no.10 (118x62x51cm-46x24x20in) tan tights red stocking chair kapok wire executed 1997 prov.exhib. 13-Nov-3 Phillips, New York #9/R est:120000-150000
Works on paper
£60000 $110400 €87600 Seven up (218x312cm-86x123in) i. photocopy collage executed 1991 prov.exhib.lit. 23-Jun-4 Sotheby's, London #41/R est:14000-18000

LUCAS, Sydney Seymour (fl.1904-1940) British
£250 $455 €365 Gentleman seated in his study (36x30cm-14x12in) s.d.1912. 15-Jun-4 David Lay, Penzance #83

LUCAS, W Lucas (20th C) British
£2210 $4000 €3227 Wire fox terrier, Beau Brocade of Courtwood (30x36cm-12x14in) s.i.d.1931 canvasboard. 30-Mar-4 Bonhams & Butterfields, San Francisco #88/R est:1800-2800

LUCAS, Wilhelm (1884-1918) German
£432 $800 €631 Lubeck from the river (74x53cm-29x21in) s. 24-Jan-4 Jeffery Burchard, Florida #32/R
£1667 $2750 €2400 Old buildings by stream in autumn landscape (50x70cm-20x28in) s.d.05. 3-Jul-3 Van Ham, Cologne #1339 est:2500

LUCAS, William (1840-1895) British
Works on paper
£222 $400 €324 Young girl with basket of eggs (30x25cm-12x10in) s.d.1862 W/C oval. 23-Jan-4 Freeman, Philadelphia #29/R

LUCAS-ROBIQUET, Marie Aimee (1858-1959) French
£1326 $2400 €1936 Portrait of Catherine Woodruff (65x54cm-26x21in) s. 30-Mar-4 Christie's, Rockefeller NY #70/R est:3000-5000
£16667 $30000 €24334 Jeune femme se tirant les cartes (172x218cm-68x86in) s.d.90 prov. 23-Apr-4 Sotheby's, New York #114/R est:40000-60000
£126761 $219296 €180000 Tahadat et Khadidja (102x77cm-40x30in) s. painted c.1914 exhib. 15-Dec-3 Gros & Delettrez, Paris #162/R est:200000-300000

LUCASSEN, Reinier (1939-) Dutch
£2667 $4907 €4000 Systeem (70x80cm-28x31in) s.i.d.989 prov. 9-Jun-4 Christie's, Amsterdam #179/R est:4000-6000
£9441 $16049 €13500 Interior scene (200x170cm-79x67in) s.d.72-73 verso acrylic prov. 25-Nov-3 Christie's, Amsterdam #325/R est:15000-20000
£10667 $19627 €16000 Een Holpartij met Moeder (180x120cm-71x47in) s.d.71 verso acrylic prov.exhib. 8-Jun-4 Sotheby's, Amsterdam #126/R est:18000-25000
Works on paper
£278 $439 €400 E MC2 (29x36cm-11x14in) init.d.98 pencil W/C ballpoint prov. 2-Sep-3 Christie's, Amsterdam #482
£278 $439 €400 Eclectique (29x35cm-11x14in) s.i.d.985 pencil brush ink prov. 2-Sep-3 Christie's, Amsterdam #484
£1608 $2766 €2300 Mellow and proud (28x21cm-11x8in) i. s.d.99 verso col crayon pencil ballpoint pen three. 2-Dec-3 Sotheby's, Amsterdam #360/R est:2300-3400

LUCCHESI, Andrea Carlo (1860-1924) British
Sculpture
£16000 $29440 €23360 Myrtle's altar (37cm-15in) s. brown green pat. black marble plinth prov.lit. 11-Jun-4 Christie's, London #76/R est:6000-8000

LUCCHESI, Bruno (1926-) American
Sculpture
£800 $1400 €1168 Drying-off (22x15cm-9x6in) i.verso golden brown pat bronze wooden base. 19-Dec-3 Sotheby's, New York #1023/R est:1000-1500
£811 $1500 €1217 Weighing game birds (56cm-22in) s. brown pat. bronze prov. 17-Jul-4 Skinner, Boston #110/R est:1000-1500
£1081 $2000 €1578 Women on the steps (76x36cm-30x14in) sig. brown pat bronze relief stone base exec 1961 prov. 12-Feb-4 Sotheby's, New York #185/R est:3000-5000
£1816 $3250 €2651 Washing her face (51cm-20in) s. bronze prov. 14-May-4 Skinner, Boston #376/R est:1000-1500
£2000 $3500 €2920 The pedicure (33x25cm-13x10in) i. golden brown pat bronze wooden base. 19-Dec-3 Sotheby's, New York #1024/R est:2000-3000

LUCCHESI, Rafaelo (19th C) ?
£1829 $3000 €2652 Portrait of Louise Elizabeth Vigee LeBrun (99x81cm-39x32in) s.d.1896 verso prov. 31-May-3 Brunk, Ashville #178/R est:800-1200

LUCCHINI, Cesare (1941-) Swiss
£1310 $2410 €1913 Untitled (107x92cm-42x36in) s.d.1989 oil collage board on panel prov. 8-Jun-4 Germann, Zurich #10/R est:3500-4000 (S.FR 3000)

LUCE, Maximilien (1858-1941) French
£563 $975 €800 Baignade sur les berges (10x25cm-4x10in) cardboard painted c.1925. 10-Dec-3 Millon & Associes, Paris #71
£694 $1160 €1000 Le chemin (24x33cm-9x13in) s. oil paper on canvas. 25-Oct-3 Cornette de St.Cyr, Paris #528
£704 $1218 €1000 Sur sa toile d'origine (27x35cm-11x14in) s.i. 10-Dec-3 Millon & Associes, Paris #72/R
£1000 $1800 €1500 La briquettere de Bressy-sur-Cure (26x35cm-10x14in) st.sig. panel painted 1908 prov.lit. 26-Apr-4 Tajan, Paris #108 est:1000-1200
£1000 $1800 €1500 Park landscape with numerous figures (40x52cm-16x20in) s. lit. 22-Apr-4 Allgauer, Kempten #3636/R est:2500
£1049 $1783 €1500 Soldat au repos (42x54cm-17x21in) s. cardboard. 23-Nov-3 Cornette de St.Cyr, Paris #615/R est:1500-2000
£1096 $1721 €1600 Paris, les quais (19x24cm-7x9in) s. panel. 20-Apr-3 Deauville, France #126/R est:1200-1500
£1127 $1972 €1600 Bord de mer (21x29cm-8x11in) cardboard. 16-Dec-3 Claude Aguttes, Neuilly #3/R est:2000-3000
£1189 $2021 €1700 Soldat a la canne (54x42cm-21x17in) s.d.1917 cardboard. 23-Nov-3 Cornette de St.Cyr, Paris #616/R est:1500-2000
£1250 $2088 €1800 Cote rocheuse (33x50cm-13x20in) s. oil paper on canvas. 25-Oct-3 Cornette de St.Cyr, Paris #527/R est:1500-2000
£1259 $2165 €1800 Remorqueur a Rolleboise (10x25cm-4x10in) bears st.sig. cardboard. 3-Dec-3 Tajan, Paris #358 est:2000-3000
£1467 $2669 €2200 Attelage (19x15cm-7x6in) s. panel. 4-Jul-4 Eric Pillon, Calais #83/R
£1549 $2711 €2200 Le regate (14x23cm-6x9in) s. cardboard prov. 16-Dec-3 Claude Aguttes, Neuilly #2/R est:2000-2500
£1656 $3030 €2500 Rolleboise, L'eglise (18x27cm-7x11in) s. panel. 7-Apr-4 Piasa, Paris #83/R est:2500-2800
£1667 $3067 €2500 Exode (34x98cm-13x39in) 14-Jun-4 Tajan, Paris #66 est:3000-4000
£1776 $3268 €2700 Oree du bois (24x33cm-9x13in) s. 22-Jun-4 Chassaing Rivet, Toulouse #311
£1879 $3477 €2800 Peniche sur la Seine (14x28cm-6x11in) st.sig. cardboard. 14-Mar-4 Eric Pillon, Calais #115/R
£1915 $3198 €2700 Autoportrait (53x40cm-21x16in) s. oil paper on canvas. 19-Oct-3 Anaf, Lyon #202/R est:12000-13000
£1958 $3329 €2800 La gaignade (26x35cm-10x14in) s. cardboard painted c.1925. 27-Nov-3 Millon & Associes, Paris #226/R est:1500-1800
£2000 $3680 €2920 Les bords de la Loire a Saint-Ayr (36x27cm-14x11in) st.sig. oil paper on canvas. 24-Mar-4 Sotheby's, Olympia #78/R est:2000-3000
£2055 $3226 €3000 Rentree des champs (20x57cm-8x22in) s. panel. 20-Apr-3 Deauville, France #125/R est:3000-3500
£2134 $3840 €3200 Trois ouvriers dressant un echafaudage (46x27cm-18x11in) st.sig. prov.lit. 26-Apr-4 Tajan, Paris #110 est:1000-1200
£2134 $3840 €3200 Trois ouvriers dressant un echafaudage (46x27cm-18x11in) st.sig. prov.lit. 26-Apr-4 Tajan, Paris #111 est:1000-1200
£2148 $3995 €3200 Rolleboise, baignade (15x40cm-6x16in) s. panel lit. 2-Mar-4 Artcurial Briest, Paris #135/R est:4000-6000
£2267 $4171 €3400 Embarcation en mer (46x55cm-18x22in) bears st.sig. oil paper on canvas. 14-Jun-4 Tajan, Paris #65 est:4000-6000
£2416 $4470 €3600 Rolleboise (20x31cm-8x12in) s. panel lit. 14-Mar-4 Eric Pillon, Calais #112/R
£2500 $4175 €3650 Bourgogne landscape (23x43cm-9x17in) s. painted c.1905. 22-Oct-3 Sotheby's, Olympia #114/R est:3000-4000
£2587 $4450 €3700 Deux paysans dans un champ a Mirecourt (3x62cm-1x24in) s. cardboard on canvas. 3-Dec-3 Tajan, Paris #353/R est:4000-6000
£2733 $4893 €4100 Maisons a l'ecluse de Mericourt (30x41cm-12x16in) s. 16-May-4 Lombrail & Teucquam, Paris #153/R
£2733 $5029 €4100 Les quais de la Seine (100x74cm-39x29in) 14-Jun-4 Tajan, Paris #67 est:3000-4000
£2800 $5040 €4200 La carriere de Pierre (35x44cm-14x17in) st.sig. cardboard prov. 26-Apr-4 Tajan, Paris #107/R est:2000-3000
£3000 $5370 €4500 Bouquet d'arbres a Bussy sur Cure (26x34cm-10x13in) s. panel. 16-May-4 Lombrail & Teucquam, Paris #154/R
£3020 $5618 €4500 Baignades dans la marne (37x47cm-15x19in) bears st.sig. board on canvas. 3-Mar-4 Tajan, Paris #55/R est:3000-5000
£3147 $5413 €4500 Le bac (32x51cm-13x20in) s. cardboard on canvas. 3-Dec-3 Tajan, Paris #355/R est:5000-6000
£3222 $5992 €4800 Rolleboise (33x51cm-13x20in) s.d.28 paper on canvas. 3-Mar-4 Tajan, Paris #56/R est:4000-4500
£3289 $6053 €5000 Jetee au Treport (46x55cm-18x22in) s.d.30 paper on masonite. 25-Jun-4 Millon & Associes, Paris #94 est:4000-6000
£3333 $5567 €4800 Rolleboise, la route au bord de la Seine (23x67cm-9x26in) s. lit. 21-Oct-3 Artcurial Briest, Paris #169/R est:5000-6000
£3497 $5944 €5000 Bords de Seine (34x42cm-13x17in) s. panel. 18-Nov-3 Pierre Berge, Paris #57/R est:5000-6000
£3667 $6600 €5500 Les quais de Paris, le docker a la ceinture (63x47cm-25x19in) st.sig. paper on panel prov.lit. 26-Apr-4 Tajan, Paris #106/R est:4000-5000
£4000 $7280 €6000 Rolleboise (38x55cm-15x22in) s. painted c.1925 lit. 5-Jul-4 Le Mouel, Paris #24/R est:6000-8000

£4133	$7605	€6200	Rolleboise, la maison de l'artiste (36x46cm-14x18in) s. panel. 14-Jun-4 Tajan, Paris #69/R est:5000-6000
£4200	$7644	€6300	Jardin de Rolleboise (50x65cm-20x26in) s.d.1930 s.i.d.verso paper on canvas. 5-Jul-4 Neret-Minet, Paris #42/R est:7000-9000
£4533	$8251	€6800	Paysans dans les champs pres de Mirecourt (32x51cm-13x20in) s. cardboard on canvas. 4-Jul-4 Eric Pillon, Calais #102/R
£4667	$8400	€7000	Soldats et secouristes a la Gare de l'Est (52x68cm-20x27in) s.d.1916 cardboard prov.lit. 26-Apr-4 Tajan, Paris #109/R est:2000-3000
£4685	$7965	€6700	Enfants jouant pres du lavoir (27x35cm-11x14in) s. oil paper on canvas prov. 18-Nov-3 Pierre Berge, Paris #59/R est:4000-5000
£4800	$8640	€7200	Le treport, la plage et la falaise (54x73cm-21x29in) s. prov.lit. 26-Apr-4 Tajan, Paris #105/R est:8000-10000
£4865	$9000	€7103	Rolleboise, la Seine (40x54cm-16x21in) st.sig. paper on canvas prov.lit. 11-Feb-4 Sotheby's, New York #26/R est:10000-12000
£5000	$8350	€7300	Le repos sous le pont (53x58cm-21x23in) s. oil paper on canvas painted c.1935 prov. 21-Oct-3 Sotheby's, London #124/R est:6000-8000
£5000	$9100	€7500	Petite maison dans le parc (55x46cm-22x18in) s. 4-Jul-4 Eric Pillon, Calais #82/R
£5369	$9503	€8000	Cote sauvage, coucher de soleil, effet de vent (40x48cm-16x19in) st.sig. board prov. 27-Apr-4 Artcurial Briest, Paris #138/R est:8000-10000
£5556	$9278	€8000	Bord de Loire (65x54cm-26x21in) s. prov.lit. 21-Oct-3 Fraysse & Associes, Paris #18
£6000	$10860	€8760	Les bords de la Marne (27x35cm-11x14in) s. s.i.verso board. 1-Apr-4 Christie's, Kensington #18/R est:4000-6000
£7000	$12670	€10220	Rolleboise, le passeur (32x51cm-13x20in) s. oil paper on canvas painted c.1930. 1-Apr-4 Christie's, Kensington #13/R est:6000-8000
£7027	$13000	€10259	Port de Dieppe (33x46cm-13x18in) s. board painted c.1922. 11-Feb-4 Sotheby's, New York #17/R est:15000-20000
£7059	$12000	€10306	Auvers-sur-Oise, Paysage (50x65cm-20x26in) s. painted c.1915 prov.lit. 6-Nov-3 Sotheby's, New York #147/R est:12000-15000
£7642	$13908	€11157	Paysage a Moulineux (32x40cm-13x16in) s. canvas on board prov. 17-Jun-4 Kornfeld, Bern #533/R est:5000 (S.FR 17500)
£8735	$14500	€12753	Jeune femme a son chevalet (55x46cm-22x18in) s. 2-Oct-3 Christie's, Tel Aviv #45/R est:15000-20000
£9000	$14310	€13050	Le remouleur (54x66cm-21x26in) s. painted c.1907 prov.exhib.lit. 11-Sep-3 Christie's, Kensington #37/R est:7000-9000
£9091	$15636	€13000	Honfleur (80x73cm-31x29in) s.d.31 lit. 2-Dec-3 Calmels Cohen, Paris #49/R est:15000-20000
£9202	$15000	€13435	Vase de fleurs (44x37cm-17x15in) s.d.1912 board prov. 25-Sep-3 Christie's, Rockefeller NY #519/R est:15000-20000
£9500	$15105	€13775	Hollande, paysage au moulin (25x37cm-10x15in) board executed c.1908. 11-Sep-3 Christie's, Kensington #17/R est:12000-18000
£10000	$17300	€14600	Rolleboise, le dejeuner en plein air (40x54cm-16x21in) s. 11-Dec-3 Christie's, Kensington #28/R est:10000-15000
£10067	$18725	€15000	Moissons (54x74cm-21x29in) s. 3-Mar-4 Tajan, Paris #54/R est:6000-8000
£10490	$17517	€15000	Cote rocheuse (25x40cm-10x16in) s. panel lit. 29-Jun-3 Eric Pillon, Calais #101/R
£11000	$20240	€16060	Les baigneuses (73x54cm-29x21in) s. prov.lit. 24-Mar-4 Sotheby's, Olympia #41/R est:6000-8000
£11268	$19493	€16000	Paysage anime aux meules de foin (40x50cm-16x20in) s.d.1902 panel. 9-Dec-3 Vanderkindere, Brussels #55/R est:7500-10000
£12000	$22080	€17520	Moulinex, l'entree du village (25x38cm-10x15in) s.d.1903 canvas on board painted 1903. 23-Jun-4 Christie's, London #128/R est:12000-16000
£14706	$25000	€21471	Ouvriers sur un chantier a Paris (81x65cm-32x26in) s. painted c.1920. 6-Nov-3 Sotheby's, New York #326/R est:30000-40000
£16760	$30000	€24470	Guernes, la Seine (65x81cm-26x32in) s. prov.lit. 6-May-4 Sotheby's, New York #430/R est:30000-40000
£20000	$36800	€29200	Le saule au bord de la Cure (37x45cm-15x18in) s. board painted 1906 prov. 23-Jun-4 Christie's, London #129/R est:12000-18000
£20950	$37500	€30587	Saint-Ay, paysage (65x54cm-26x21in) s. prov.lit. 6-May-4 Sotheby's, New York #429/R est:15000-20000
£25503	$45651	€38000	Moulin en Hollande (54x65cm-21x26in) s.d.1908-09 prov. 26-May-4 Christie's, Paris #24/R est:20000-30000
£29412	$50000	€42942	Peupliers, Automne (81x60cm-32x24in) s.d.1907 prov.exhib.lit. 5-Nov-3 Christie's, Rockefeller NY #217/R est:50000-70000
£32353	$55000	€47235	Verger a Eragny (26x40cm-10x16in) s. s.i.verso board painted 1895 prov. 6-Nov-3 Sotheby's, New York #151/R est:40000-60000
£38000	$69920	€55480	Good Samaritan (76x101cm-30x40in) s. s.d.1896 stretcher prov.exhib.lit. 22-Jun-4 Sotheby's, London #228/R est:12000-16000
£38733	$62748	€55000	La fabrique de briquettes sur les bords de la Sambre (60x73cm-24x29in) s.d.1896 prov.exhib.lit. 5-Aug-3 Tajan, Paris #7/R est:60000-80000
£39106	$70000	€57095	Cathedrale de Gisors - vue du Foss aux Tanneurs (50x41cm-20x16in) s.d.97 prov. 6-May-4 Sotheby's, New York #248/R est:40000-60000
£46089	$82500	€67290	Guinguette au bord de l'eau (38x54cm-15x21in) s.d.97 paper on canvas prov. 6-May-4 Sotheby's, New York #249/R est:50000-70000
£118000	$214760	€172280	Paris, la Seine et le quai de la Megisserie vue du quai de l'Horloge (26x39cm-10x15in) s.d.92 cardboard. 3-Feb-4 Christie's, London #137/R est:70000-90000
£175000	$318500	€255500	Le port de Rotterdam, Le Soir (65x81cm-26x32in) s.d.1908 prov. 4-Feb-4 Sotheby's, London #227/R est:100000-150000

Works on paper

£268	$491	€400	Champs a Rolleboise (11x20cm-4x8in) i. ink traces crayon lit. 7-Jul-4 Artcurial Briest, Paris #90
£280	$467	€400	Etudes de figures (32x23cm-13x9in) s. chl. 25-Jun-3 Blanchet, Paris #5
£280	$502	€409	Landscape (4x3cm-2x1in) s. chl Indian ink wash. 12-May-4 Dobiaschofsky, Bern #1788 (S.FR 650)
£331	$606	€500	Rolleboise, les coteaux (27x37cm-11x15in) s. chl stump lit. 7-Apr-4 Doutrebente, Paris #51
£340	$609	€500	Enfants plongeant d'un ponton (18x25cm-7x10in) s. pen brown ink. 17-Mar-4 Tajan, Paris #155
£342	$538	€500	Paysage aux grands arbres (16x21cm-6x8in) s. W/C crayon. 20-Apr-3 Deauville, France #4
£347	$580	€500	Scene de la commune (38x29cm-15x11in) s. ink wash htd gouache. 21-Oct-3 Artcurial Briest, Paris #170
£350	$584	€500	Le chanteur des rues (23x10cm-9x4in) s. conte crayon. 25-Jun-3 Rabourdin & Choppin de Janvry, Paris #140
£350	$602	€511	Wooded landscape, St Tropez (20x25cm-8x10in) s.i. pencil. 3-Dec-3 Christie's, Kensington #213/R
£403	$737	€600	Femme au seau et enfant (28x20cm-11x8in) s. ink lead pencil. 7-Jul-4 Artcurial Briest, Paris #91
£450	$819	€657	Etude pour en echafaudage (22x28cm-9x11in) studio st. pen ink. 21-Jun-4 Bonhams, New Bond Street #7/R
£493	$853	€700	La Seine a Billancourt (14x21cm-6x8in) s.i. ink dr over crayon lit. 9-Dec-3 Artcurial Briest, Paris #83
£604	$1124	€900	Les Saltimbanques (27x20cm-11x8in) s. ink wash pencil. 2-Mar-4 Artcurial Briest, Paris #18
£800	$1336	€1168	Gardien de prison (29x22cm-11x9in) s. black crayon. 22-Oct-3 Bonhams, New Bond Street #23/R
£903	$1507	€1300	Les jeunes lutteurs (32x25cm-13x10in) s. gouache W/C. 21-Oct-3 Artcurial Briest, Paris #171 est:500-600
£1074	$1987	€1600	Libertaires (32x22cm-13x9in) s. Chinese ink htd gouache col crayon. 14-Mar-4 Eric Pillon, Calais #139/R
£1135	$1895	€1600	Paysage a Gisors (27x34cm-11x13in) s.i. col crayon. 20-Jun-3 Drouot Estimations, Paris #116 est:350-450
£1409	$2437	€2000	Coteaux de Rosny (30x47cm-12x19in) s.d.1924 W/C pastel chl prov.lit. 9-Dec-3 Artcurial Briest, Paris #82/R est:2000-2500
£2113	$3655	€3000	Paysage pres de Gisors (26x34cm-10x13in) s.i. pastel chl. 14-Dec-3 Eric Pillon, Calais #77/R
£2148	$3844	€3200	Rue des Abbesses (28x38cm-11x15in) s.i. chl graphite exec.1896. 26-May-4 Christie's, Paris #7/R est:1500-2000
£6376	$11413	€9500	Jeune femme mettant ses bas (46x36cm-18x14in) s.d.89 pastel htd chk. 26-May-4 Christie's, Paris #19/R est:9000-12000

LUCE, Molly (1896-1986) American

£3294	$5500	€4809	Church at Little Compton, Rhode Island (76x61cm-30x24in) s. masonite prov. 23-Oct-3 Shannon's, Milford #221/R est:6000-8000

LUCEBERT (1924-1994) Dutch

£1221	$2038	€1783	Face (32x46cm-13x18in) s.d.55 paper prov. 7-Oct-3 Rasmussen, Copenhagen #19/R est:10000 (D.KR 13000)
£2098	$3608	€3000	Untitled (24x18cm-9x7in) s. ac, painted 1988. 2-Dec-3 Sotheby's, Amsterdam #311/R est:3500-4500
£2400	$4392	€3600	Two figures near a tree (60x90cm-24x35in) s.d.74 paper. 7-Jun-4 Glerum, Amsterdam #411/R est:4000-6000
£2533	$4661	€3800	Untitled (78x63cm-31x25in) s.d.75.XI.10 oil gouache col crayons. 8-Jun-4 Sotheby's, Amsterdam #273/R est:3000-5000
£2899	$4754	€4000	Untitled (74x98cm-29x39in) s.d.86 acrylic gouache W/C col crayon. 27-May-3 Sotheby's, Amsterdam #400/R est:4000-6000
£2937	$4993	€4200	Big cloud (100x80cm-39x31in) s.d.73 i.stretcher. 25-Nov-3 Christie's, Amsterdam #273/R est:5000-7000
£3623	$5942	€5000	Birth of a tyrant (80x100cm-31x39in) s.d.81 i. on stretcher. 27-May-3 Sotheby's, Amsterdam #417/R est:6000-8000
£3667	$6747	€5500	Snoek in de bai of het gevecht met de Muze (115x143cm-45x56in) s.d.88 i. stretcher prov. 9-Jun-4 Christie's, Amsterdam #180/R est:3000-5000
£4667	$8587	€7000	Blind sculptor (30x40cm-12x16in) s.d.69 i. stretcher oil W/C wax crayon collage paper on canvas ex. 9-Jun-4 Christie's, Amsterdam #159/R est:3000-5000
£8392	$14434	€12000	De opstandigen (140x100cm-55x39in) s.d.62 i.d.62 stretcher prov. 2-Dec-3 Sotheby's, Amsterdam #139/R est:18000-25000
£23188	$38029	€32000	Strange family (145x115cm-57x45in) s.d.64 i.d.64 verso prov.lit. 27-May-3 Sotheby's, Amsterdam #403/R est:32000-42000
£23333	$42933	€35000	Strange lady (60x40cm-24x16in) s.d.60 prov. 8-Jun-4 Sotheby's, Amsterdam #89/R est:30000-40000

Works on paper

£267	$477	€400	Composition with figures (29x21cm-11x8in) s.i.d.94 pastel feltip pen pencil. 15-May-4 De Vuyst, Lokeren #197
£333	$597	€500	Composition with heads (29x21cm-11x8in) s.i.d.94. 15-May-4 De Vuyst, Lokeren #198
£433	$776	€650	The painter paints (32x23cm-13x9in) s.i.d.91 pastel W/C felttip pen. 15-May-4 De Vuyst, Lokeren #196/R
£436	$807	€650	Le jardinier (34x22cm-13x9in) s.d.48 ink prov. 15-Mar-4 Sotheby's, Amsterdam #238/R
£500	$915	€750	HHAA (26x20cm-10x8in) s.i.d.65 Indian ink. 7-Jun-4 Glerum, Amsterdam #400/R
£543	$923	€793	Untitled (29x21cm-11x8in) s.d.1989 china ink W/C. 22-Nov-3 Burkhard, Luzern #115/R (S.FR 1200)
£563	$941	€822	Figure composition (34x45cm-13x18in) s.d.89-1-2 Indian ink W/C prov. 7-Oct-3 Rasmussen, Copenhagen #181 (D.KR 6000)
£600	$1098	€900	Figure and sun (26x20cm-10x8in) s.d.69 Indian ink. 7-Jun-4 Glerum, Amsterdam #401/R
£657	$1098	€959	Mask composition (50x65cm-20x26in) s.d.75 -VIII.13 Indian ink W/C prov. 7-Oct-3 Rasmussen, Copenhagen #182 (D.KR 7000)
£733	$1342	€1100	Figure with lance (26x20cm-10x8in) s.d.60 Indian ink. 7-Jun-4 Glerum, Amsterdam #386/R
£987	$1816	€1500	Figures (31x41cm-12x16in) s.d.77.VIII.28 W/C blk chk. 28-Jun-4 Sotheby's, Amsterdam #263/R est:1000-1500
£1007	$1862	€1500	Untitled (25x20cm-10x8in) Indian ink set of three. 15-Mar-4 Sotheby's, Amsterdam #223/R est:900-1200
£1133	$2074	€1700	Ladies and gentlemen (27x21cm-11x8in) s.d.73 Indian ink prov.lit. two in one frame. 7-Jun-4 Glerum, Amsterdam #391/R est:800-1200
£1267	$2267	€1900	Composition (28x38cm-11x15in) s.i.d.90 pastel W/C. 15-May-4 De Vuyst, Lokeren #195/R est:700-1000
£1304	$2139	€1800	Untitled (47x61cm-19x24in) s.d.82 gouache col crayon. 27-May-3 Sotheby's, Amsterdam #539/R est:2500-3500
£1321	$2140	€1929	Untitled (47x33cm-19x13in) s.d.90.11.14 mixed media. 24-May-3 Burkhard, Luzern #140/R est:3000-3500 (S.FR 2800)
£1333	$2453	€2000	Two heads (50x65cm-20x26in) s.d.75 gouache col chk. 12-Jun-4 Villa Grisebach, Berlin #788/R est:2000-2500
£1379	$2483	€2000	Composition (47x34cm-19x13in) s.d.1990 ink chl crayon. 25-Jan-4 Chayette & Cheval, Paris #306/R est:2200-2500
£1467	$2699	€2200	Untitled (50x64cm-20x25in) s.d.25/X/75 pastel gouache W/C. 9-Jun-4 Christie's, Amsterdam #178/R est:2200-3000
£1818	$3091	€2600	Figure (26x18cm-10x7in) s.d.48 gouache. 25-Nov-3 Christie's, Amsterdam #42/R est:3000-5000
£1958	$3329	€2800	Armen vogel zonnen en porten (21x27cm-8x11in) s.i.d.II 52 pen brush blk ink. 25-Nov-3 Christie's, Amsterdam #64/R est:1200-1600
£1974	$3632	€3000	Fantasy figures (28x26cm-11x10in) s.d.51 ink pastel W/C black chk wax crayon prov. 22-Jun-4 Christie's, Amsterdam #325/R est:3000-5000
£2000	$3680	€3000	Composition (74x99cm-29x39in) s.d.86 gouache W/C wax crayon prov. 9-Jun-4 Christie's, Amsterdam #160/R est:4000-6000
£2536	$4159	€3500	Untitled (67x97cm-26x38in) s.d.91 gouache col crayon. 27-May-3 Sotheby's, Amsterdam #533/R est:3500-4500
£3200	$5888	€4800	Ein Merkwurdiger hase (64x50cm-25x20in) s.d.V 10 1961 gouache pastel prov. 8-Jun-4 Sotheby's, Amsterdam #263/R est:2000-3000
£4203	$6893	€5800	Untitled (54x75cm-21x30in) s.indis.i.d.62 gouache col crayons prov. 27-May-3 Sotheby's, Amsterdam #390/R est:4000-6000
£4545	$7818	€6500	Untitled (76x51cm-30x20in) s.i.d.14.VII.65 gouache W/C col crayon. 2-Dec-3 Sotheby's, Amsterdam #301/R est:4500-6500

LUCENA, Tomas Munoz (?) Spanish

Works on paper

£330	$538	€475	Campensina (41x25cm-16x10in) s. pen drawing. 16-Jul-3 Durán, Madrid #595

LUCERNI, Ugo (1900-) Italian
£297 $550 €434 Tenda al Mare Pietra Santa (46x51cm-18x20in) s. board. 13-Mar-4 Susanin's, Chicago #6128/R

LUCHFORD, Glen and SAVILLE, Jenny (20th C) ?
Photographs
£15569 $26000 €22731 Closed contact no.13 (60x120cm-24x47in) s.i. num.6. c-print mounted on plexiglas prov.exhib. 13-Nov-3 Phillips, New York #45/R est:25000-35000

LUCHINGER, Roland (1949-) Swiss
£588 $1000 €858 Composition (58x83cm-23x33in) s.d.85 bears i. oil collage board. 18-Nov-3 Hans Widmer, St Gallen #1145 (S.FR 1300)

LUCIANI, Ascanio (attrib) (1621-1706) Italian
£11348 $18950 €16000 Capriccio architettonico con astanti in primo piano (31x67cm-12x26in) 18-Jun-3 Christie's, Rome #454/R est:14000-18000

LUCIANI, Ascanio (style) (1621-1706) Italian
£6600 $11418 €9636 Architectural capriccio with figures amongst ruins with the Anthonine column (119x155cm-47x61in) 9-Dec-3 Sotheby's, Olympia #431/R est:6000-8000

LUCIONI, Luigi (1900-1988) American
£4278 $8000 €6246 Shelburne pastoral (18x25cm-7x10in) s. board prov. 24-Jul-4 Coeur d'Alene, Hayden #270/R est:3000-6000
£4969 $8000 €7255 Landscape with trees (51x41cm-20x16in) s. board. 20-Aug-3 James Julia, Fairfield #1396/R est:8000-12000
£10270 $19000 €14994 Retrospections (86x71cm-34x28in) s.d.1952 prov. 11-Mar-4 Christie's, Rockefeller NY #70/R est:7000-10000
£13408 $24000 €19576 Nostalgic echoes (87x71cm-34x28in) s.d.1954 prov. 14-May-4 Skinner, Boston #362/R est:25000-35000
£19318 $34000 €28204 Bread and fruit (36x46cm-14x18in) s.d.1940 prov.exhib.lit. 18-May-4 Christie's, Rockefeller NY #112/R est:15000-25000
Works on paper
£323 $550 €472 Tree study (30x20cm-12x8in) s. graphite. 21-Nov-3 Skinner, Boston #466/R
£976 $1600 €1415 Still life with vases and cloth (51x36cm-20x14in) s.d. W/C. 7-Jun-3 Treadway Gallery, Cincinnati #1501 est:1500-2500
£5028 $9000 €7341 Vermont barns. s. W/C. 31-May-4 William A Smith, Plainfield #353/R

LUCIUS, Sebastian (19/20th C) Italian
£2652 $4800 €3872 Twilight idyll (100x150cm-39x59in) s. indis d.XXVI. 30-Mar-4 Christie's, Rockefeller NY #73/R est:3000-5000

LUCKER, Eugene (1876-1943) Dutch
£526 $968 €800 View of a pond (47x65cm-19x26in) s. 28-Jun-4 Sotheby's, Amsterdam #162/R
£764 $1245 €1100 Farm in a landscape, Limburg (62x77cm-24x30in) s. panel. 29-Sep-3 Sotheby's, Amsterdam #275/R

LUCKHARDT, Karl (1886-1970) German
£667 $1220 €1000 In front of the blacksmiths (30x41cm-12x16in) s. i.verso fibreboard. 5-Jun-4 Arnold, Frankfurt #656/R
£1275 $2372 €1900 Village street with horses and ox cart (60x80cm-24x31in) s. 6-Mar-4 Arnold, Frankfurt #781/R est:1200

LUCKNER, Heinrich Alexander Graf von (1891-1970) German
£500 $835 €730 View of Provence (70x90cm-28x35in) s. 21-Oct-3 Bonhams, Knightsbridge #171/R

LUCKNOW SCHOOL (19th C) Indian
Works on paper
£5000 $8150 €7300 Noblewoman smoking a hookah with attendants (28x41cm-11x16in) i. pencil pen blk ink W/C htd bodycol gold. 24-Sep-3 Christie's, London #117/R est:4000-6000

LUCOP, Thomas (19th C) British?
£900 $1701 €1314 Two-decker making sail with a cutter crossing her bow (30x49cm-12x19in) s. board. 17-Feb-4 Bonhams, New Bond Street #15/R
£900 $1701 €1314 Ships at anchor in the dying light (30x49cm-12x19in) s. board. 17-Feb-4 Bonhams, New Bond Street #16/R
£1350 $2147 €1958 Ship's portrait Zsar steam and sail vessel (56x87cm-22x34in) 9-Sep-3 David Duggleby, Scarborough #289/R est:1500-2000
£2000 $3580 €2920 Light airs at dusk (30x47cm-12x19in) s. board. 26-May-4 Christie's, Kensington #695/R est:1200-1800

LUCY, Charles (1814-1873) British
£1800 $3006 €2628 Count and Countess Rapp (85x69cm-33x27in) s.d.1845. 12-Nov-3 Sotheby's, Olympia #18/R est:1000-1500
£2000 $3700 €2920 Lady and Gentleman under a tree, said to the Count and Coutess Rapp (85x69cm-33x27in) s.d.1845. 10-Mar-4 Sotheby's, Olympia #184/R est:1000-1500

LUDBY, Max (1858-1943) British
Works on paper
£600 $1092 €876 The hay wagon returning home at dusk (20x25cm-8x10in) s. pencil W/C. 1-Jul-4 Christie's, Kensington #210/R
£1048 $1929 €1530 Evening, High Street, Guildford (50x73cm-20x29in) s. W/C. 9-Jun-4 Walker's, Ottawa #367/R est:900-1200 (C.D 2600)

LUDDERS, Hinrich P (1826-1897) German?
Works on paper
£979 $1684 €1400 Sailing boat Victoria seen from Finkenwarder (57x72cm-22x28in) s.i.d.1862 gouache. 6-Dec-3 Quittenbaum, Hamburg #25/R

LUDECKE-CLEVE, August (1868-1957) German
£625 $1044 €900 Cows in meadow (30x40cm-12x16in) s. 24-Oct-3 Ketterer, Hamburg #86/R
£1467 $2669 €2200 Cows in meadow (81x106cm-32x42in) s. 30-Jun-4 Neumeister, Munich #605/R est:2200

LUDLOW, Mary Sophia (fl.1908-1909) British
£800 $1480 €1200 Farm landscape (45x54cm-18x21in) s. 14-Jul-4 Sotheby's, Olympia #280/R
£950 $1758 €1425 Landscape over fields (45x54cm-18x21in) s. 14-Jul-4 Sotheby's, Olympia #281/R

LUDOVICI, Albert (1820-1894) British
£950 $1748 €1425 Minnie F Clark Kennedy, aged two years and three months (46x35cm-18x14in) s.i.d.1863 verso oval. 10-Jun-4 Morphets, Harrogate #510/R
Works on paper
£300 $549 €438 The unwanted suitor (28x22cm-11x9in) s. W/C. 28-Jan-4 Hampton & Littlewood, Exeter #378/R
£460 $842 €672 Bath time (24x18cm-9x7in) s. W/C. 28-Jan-4 Hampton & Littlewood, Exeter #377/R
£1600 $2864 €2336 Perfect enjoyment. Spinning tops (9x15cm-4x6in) W/C pair. 26-May-4 Sotheby's, Olympia #94/R est:800-1200

LUDOVICI, Albert (attrib) (1820-1894) British
£620 $1128 €905 Portrait of a young lady (52x41cm-20x16in) bears mono.d.1880 i. verso. 15-Jun-4 Dreweatt Neate, Newbury #588/R

LUDOVICI, Albert (jnr) (1852-1932) British
£320 $534 €467 Sunday by the sea (41x51cm-16x20in) s. 8-Oct-3 Christie's, Kensington #914
Works on paper
£282 $519 €412 Harbour view with boatmen (18x25cm-7x10in) s. W/C. 14-Jun-4 Waddingtons, Toronto #49/R (C.D 700)
£1800 $3330 €2628 Busy afternoon on the river (42x72cm-17x28in) W/C bodycol. 9-Mar-4 Bonhams, New Bond Street #102/R est:1500-2000

LUDOVICI, Julius (19th C) Italian
Works on paper
£346 $550 €505 Relic of the past (20x16cm-8x6in) s. W/C. 13-Sep-3 Weschler, Washington #757/R

LUDUENA, Jorge (1927-) Argentinian
£586 $973 €850 Still life (51x45cm-20x18in) s.d.70 board. 1-Oct-3 Ansorena, Madrid #603/R

LUDWIG, Karl Julius Emil (1839-1901) German
£267 $480 €400 Peasant couple harvesting in the high mountains (65x46cm-26x18in) s.d.2/9 1900. 21-Apr-4 Neumeister, Munich #2677/R
£1338 $2315 €1900 In Thuringer forest (100x78cm-39x31in) s. 10-Dec-3 Hugo Ruef, Munich #2451/R est:1500

LUDWIG, William (20th C) American
Sculpture
£1405 $2600 €2108 Face (147cm-58in) s.d.74 cast bronze base. 17-Jul-4 Susanin's, Chicago #5013/R est:100-200

LUEDERS, Jimmy (1927-1994) American
£249 $450 €364 Landscape (41x51cm-16x20in) s. 2-Apr-4 Freeman, Philadelphia #198
£359 $650 €524 Schuylkill view (36x56cm-14x22in) s. 2-Apr-4 Freeman, Philadelphia #199
£500 $800 €730 Abstract (196x160cm-77x63in) s.i.verso. 19-Sep-3 Freeman, Philadelphia #65/R

LUENGO, Cesar (20th C) ?
£1056 $1827 €1500 Wood in winter (25x40cm-10x16in) s. board. 15-Dec-3 Ansorena, Madrid #938/R est:1300
Works on paper
£340 $619 €500 Entry (45x40cm-18x16in) s. pencil dr prov. 3-Feb-4 Segre, Madrid #239/R
£764 $1299 €1100 Window (53x39cm-21x15in) s.i.d.1984 pencil col crayon exhib. 28-Oct-3 Segre, Madrid #145/R
£1189 $1985 €1700 Saliendo del Invierno (37x45cm-15x18in) s.i. col pencil prov.exhib. 24-Jun-3 Segre, Madrid #169/R est:900

LUGARDON, Albert (1827-1909) French
£789 $1318 €1152 Anes sous un pont (24x34cm-9x13in) s.d.1878 cardboard. 16-Nov-3 Koller, Geneva #1262 (S.FR 1800)
£948 $1697 €1384 Cows grazing on alpine pasture (48x35cm-19x14in) s. board. 14-May-4 Dobiaschofsky, Bern #2/R est:2400 (S.FR 2200)
£4825 $8057 €7045 Paysage de montagne avec vaches et lac (69x60cm-27x24in) s. 16-Nov-3 Koller, Geneva #1261/R est:5000-9000 (S.FR 11000)
£6608 $11233 €9648 Cows on alpine meadow in the summer in the Bernese Oberland (99x144cm-39x57in) s.d.1893. 7-Nov-3 Dobiaschofsky, Bern #47/R est:22000 (S.FR 15000)
£7240 $12525 €10570 Vue de la Jungfrau (60x86cm-24x34in) s. 9-Dec-3 Sotheby's, Zurich #7/R est:10000-15000 (S.FR 16000)

LUGARDON, Jean-Leonard (1801-1884) Swiss
Works on paper
£352 $599 €514 Prison visit (30x22cm-12x9in) s. 5-Nov-3 Dobiaschofsky, Bern #760/R (S.FR 800)

LUGER, Alfons (1869-1945) Austrian
£267 $491 €400 Woman wearing red dress- Johanna Berchthold (76x56cm-30x22in) s. 9-Jun-4 Dorotheum, Salzburg #556/R

LUGERTH, Ferdinand (fl.1885-1915) Dutch?
Sculpture
£2153 $3509 €3100 Lady sitting holding a mirror (25cm-10in) s. bronze ivory onyx base. 29-Sep-3 Glerum, Amsterdam #329/R est:1500-2000

LUGINBUHL, Bernhard (1929-) Swiss
Sculpture
£1606 $2681 €2329 Small head volume (55cm-22in) iron. 19-Jun-3 Kornfeld, Bern #637/R est:3000 (S.FR 3500)
Works on paper
£1101 $1839 €1596 Bull (30x29cm-12x11in) s.d.60 Indian ink. 19-Jun-3 Kornfeld, Bern #639/R est:4000 (S.FR 2400)
£1193 $1992 €1730 Composition (30x29cm-12x11in) s.d.60 Indian ink. 19-Jun-3 Kornfeld, Bern #640/R est:4000 (S.FR 2600)
£1193 $1992 €1730 Drawing for 'Emmentaler' (27x38cm-11x15in) s.d.1967 Indian ink. 19-Jun-3 Kornfeld, Bern #642 est:3000 (S.FR 2600)

LUGRIS GONZALEZ, Urbano (1908-1973) Spanish
£4138 $6869 €6000 Lonely boat (58x40cm-23x16in) s. board. 1-Oct-3 Ansorena, Madrid #572/R est:10000

LUHN, Joachim (c.1640-1717) German
£2230 $3991 €3300 Hanseatic judge (60x45cm-24x18in) s.i.d.1670. 8-May-4 Hans Stahl, Toestorf #108/R est:3200

LUIGI, Ludovico de (1933-) Italian
£335 $600 €489 Venice relocated in the Rocky Mountains (71x51cm-28x20in) s. s.d.1969 verso. 7-May-4 Sloans & Kenyon, Bethesda #1735/R
£938 $1500 €1369 Venetian canal scene (61x99cm-24x39in) s. 20-Sep-3 Bunte, Elgin #1265 est:1500-2500
Works on paper
£261 $475 €381 Pianeta delle Piogge, Venice export (28x20cm-11x8in) s. s.i.d.1969 verso. 7-Feb-4 Sloans & Kenyon, Bethesda #863/R

LUIGI, Mario de (1908-1978) Italian
£725 $1188 €1000 Cor Stima e auguri (29x23cm-11x9in) s.i.d.1964 verso board. 27-May-3 Sotheby's, Amsterdam #435/R
£2000 $3340 €2900 Red grattage (55x46cm-22x18in) s. 14-Nov-3 Farsetti, Prato #273 est:550-750

LUIGINI, Ferdinand-Jean (1870-1943) French
£335 $600 €489 Figures by a fountain (18x24cm-7x9in) s. panel. 14-May-4 Skinner, Boston #302a/R
£403 $749 €600 Paysage presume de la Vallee du Rhone (46x65cm-18x26in) s.d.98. 3-Mar-4 Ferri, Paris #383/R
£461 $834 €700 Still life with asters in a vase (20x27cm-8x11in) s. panel. 19-Apr-4 Glerum, Amsterdam #293

LUINI, Aurelio (1530-1593) Italian
Works on paper
£70000 $128100 €102200 Hermit contemplating a crucifix, with studies of putti and a head in profile (23x18cm-9x7in) black chk pen ink htd white corners made up prov. 6-Jul-4 Christie's, London #37/R est:15000-20000

LUINI, Bernardino (1475-1532) Italian
£310000 $567300 €452600 Female martyr (90x59cm-35x23in) panel prov.exhib.lit. 7-Jul-4 Sotheby's, London #42/R est:80000-120000

LUINI, Bernardino (after) (1475-1532) Italian
£6800 $12240 €9928 Madonna and Child (86x64cm-34x25in) panel. 23-Apr-4 Christie's, Kensington #202/R est:7000-10000

LUINI, Bernardino (attrib) (1475-1532) Italian
£30769 $52923 €44923 Saint Katarina of Alexandria (57x44cm-22x17in) panel. 2-Dec-3 Bukowskis, Stockholm #322/R est:200000-250000 (S.KR 400000)

LUINI, Bernardino (style) (1475-1532) Italian
£5500 $9900 €8030 Madonna and Child (35x26cm-14x10in) panel prov. 20-Apr-4 Sotheby's, Olympia #213/R est:2000-3000

LUIS, Jacinto (1945-) Portuguese
£638 $1141 €950 Factory (35x27cm-14x11in) s.d.1987. 31-May-4 Cabral Moncada Leiloes, Lisbon #88c/R

LUISADA, Avigdor Renzo (1905-1987) Israeli
£791 $1400 €1155 Still life with a bottle and a vase of flowers (60x50cm-24x20in) s. painted 1930. 1-May-4 Ben-Ami, Tel Aviv #4832/R est:1600-2200

LUKA, Madeleine (1900-1989) French
£314 $562 €458 Landscape in Normandie (64x53cm-25x21in) s. i.verso prov. 31-May-4 Stephan Welz, Johannesburg #74 (SA.R 3800)
£317 $548 €450 Jeune fille (17x13cm-7x5in) s. board. 9-Dec-3 Chambelland & Giafferi, Paris #91/R
£699 $1203 €1000 Les roses blanches (73x60cm-29x24in) s. 3-Dec-3 Beaussant & Lefèvre, Paris #48/R
£1000 $1790 €1500 Jeune femme au chapeau (79x63cm-31x25in) s. 11-May-4 Christie's, Paris #210/R est:800-1200

LUKASCHEWSKI, Rolf (1947-) German
£1477 $2717 €2200 Ankunft III (160x200cm-63x79in) s.d.1982 i.d.verso. 24-Mar-4 Joron-Derem, Paris #185 est:1800-2000

LUKASIEWICZ, Jozef Ignacy (1789-1850) Lithuanian
£956 $1750 €1396 Tadeusz Kosciuszko in uniform on a rearing horse (33x30cm-13x12in) 10-Apr-4 Cobbs, Peterborough #124c/R

LUKE, Alexandra (1901-1967) Canadian
Works on paper
£803 $1494 €1172 Composition (25x33cm-10x13in) s. W/C. 2-Mar-4 Ritchie, Toronto #157/R est:1000-1500 (C.D 2000)

LUKE, John (1906-1975) British
Works on paper
£750 $1290 €1095 Botanical study (43x28cm-17x11in) s. pencil. 3-Dec-3 John Ross, Belfast #166
£750 $1290 €1095 Botanical study (43x28cm-17x11in) s. pencil. 3-Dec-3 John Ross, Belfast #167

LUKE, John (attrib) (1906-1975) British
Works on paper
£700 $1106 €1022 Study of a young woman head (35x25cm-14x10in) pencil. 7-Sep-3 Lots Road Auctions, London #346

LUKER, William (1828-1905) British
£350 $553 €511 Stream near Burnham. 27-Jul-3 Desmond Judd, Cranbrook #1110
£350 $553 €511 Donkeys in landscape. 27-Jul-3 Desmond Judd, Cranbrook #1111
£1525 $2532 €2227 Highland cattle resting in a mountainous landscape (61x109cm-24x43in) s.i.d.1878. 30-Sep-3 Andrew Smith, Winchester #148/R est:2500-3500
£3823 $6500 €5582 Stud pointer Major (46x69cm-18x27in) s.d.1866 prov. 19-Nov-3 Bonhams & Butterfields, San Francisco #134/R

LUKIN, Sven (1934-) American
£289 $500 €422 Untitled L no 4 (117x94cm-46x37in) s.verso prov. 15-Dec-3 Hindman, Chicago #93/R

LUKOMSKI, George (1884-1954) Russian
£1408 $2437 €2000 Interior (69x53cm-27x21in) s. Cyrillic d.1919. 10-Dec-3 Dorotheum, Vienna #79/R est:2000-2300
£1690 $2806 €2400 Interior (69x53cm-27x21in) s.cyrillic d.1919. 16-Jun-3 Dorotheum, Vienna #143/R est:2000-2300
Works on paper
£374 $670 €550 Le jardin des Tuileries (24x31cm-9x12in) s.i.d.1920 crayon W/C. 17-Mar-4 Maigret, Paris #126/R

LUKS, George (1867-1933) American
£249 $450 €364 Still life with pink and red roses (43x36cm-17x14in) s. 3-Apr-4 Nadeau, Windsor #109
£1647 $2800 €2405 Reclining nude (15x23cm-6x9in) panel prov. 30-Oct-3 Phillips, New York #68/R est:3000-5000
£8840 $16000 €12906 Old salt (51x41cm-20x16in) prov.exhib. 31-Mar-4 Sotheby's, New York #9/R est:15000-20000
Works on paper
£335 $600 €489 Family in a living room (20x25cm-8x10in) s. graphite. 20-Mar-4 Rachel Davis, Shaker Heights #226/R
£894 $1600 €1305 Distant view of Niagara Falls (18x23cm-7x9in) s. W/C prov. 8-Jan-4 James Julia, Fairfield #930/R est:2000-3000
£1196 $2200 €1746 Figure procession. Market scene (25x36cm-10x14in) one s. chl one ink. 10-Jun-4 Swann Galleries, New York #156/R est:1000-1500
£1622 $3000 €2368 Buffalo chasing fox in man's clothing (36x24cm-14x9in) s.d.1900 gouache pencil en grisaille board. 11-Mar-4 Christie's, Rockefeller NY #43/R est:4000-6000

LULPUNDA, Anguburra Patsy (20th C) Australian
Works on paper
£1176 $2106 €1717 My dogs (53x66cm-21x26in) natural earth pigments canvas exec 2000. 25-May-4 Lawson Menzies, Sydney #168/R est:3000-5000 (A.D 3000)
£1255 $2246 €1832 Birds in the rain (69x74cm-27x29in) natural earth pigments canvas exec 2000. 25-May-4 Lawson Menzies, Sydney #169/R est:3000-6000 (A.D 3200)

LULVES, Jean (1833-1889) German
£461 $751 €673 Youth making music (46x37cm-18x15in) s. panel. 29-Sep-3 Lilla Bukowskis, Stockholm #536 (S.KR 6000)
£2431 $4010 €3500 Court scene (94x76cm-37x30in) s. 3-Jul-3 Van Ham, Cologne #1341/R est:2500

LUM, Bertha Boynton (1879-1954) American
Prints
£2500 $4250 €3650 Mother west wind (38x25cm-15x10in) s. col woodcut prov. 18-Nov-3 John Moran, Pasadena #210 est:1200-1800
Works on paper
£1359 $2500 €1984 Dancers (69x48cm-27x19in) s. gouache. 8-Jun-4 Auctions by the Bay, Alameda #1098/R

LUM, Ken (1956-) American
Sculpture
£5978 $11000 €8728 Jim and Susan (167x153x5cm-66x60x2in) Plexiglas lacquered aluminum plastic enamel edition of 2 prov. 10-Jun-4 Phillips, New York #554/R est:4000-6000

LUMBROSO, Alain (1955-) ?
£3497 $5944 €5000 Memoire (160x130cm-63x51in) s. oil acrylic collage mixed media. 27-Nov-3 Calmels Cohen, Paris #102/R est:4500-5500

LUMINAIS, Evariste-Vital (1822-1896) French
£302 $541 €441 The Good Samaritan (38x46cm-15x18in) init. 12-Jan-4 Rasmussen, Vejle #182/R (D.KR 3200)
£1400 $2576 €2100 Gaulois et romaines au bord d'une riviere (32x41cm-13x16in) s. panel. 11-Jun-4 Maigret, Paris #84/R est:4000-6000
£7823 $14003 €11500 La halte (73x59cm-29x23in) s. 19-Mar-4 Oger, Dumont, Paris #15/R est:5000-6000

LUMIS, Harriet Randall (1870-1953) American
£816 $1460 €1191 Old beech (56x46cm-22x18in) s. prov.exhib. 8-Jan-4 James Julia, Fairfield #985/R est:800-1200
£10465 $18000 €15279 On the moor, Gloucester (45x55cm-18x22in) s. i.on stretcher prov. 3-Dec-3 Doyle, New York #208/R est:6000-8000

LUMLEY, Arthur (1837-1912) American
£216 $400 €315 Bustling canal in Venice (20x25cm-8x10in) s. board. 15-Jul-4 Doyle, New York #56/R

LUMPKINS, William (1909-) American
Works on paper
£1285 $2300 €1876 Abards. s.i. W/C. 13-May-4 Dallas Auction Gallery, Dallas #380/R est:800-1200

LUNA Y NOVICIO, Juan (1857-1900) Philippino
£651 $1106 €950 Portrait of lady. Portrait of gentleman (58x44cm-23x17in) s.d.1881 pair. 4-Nov-3 Ansorena, Madrid #303/R
£651 $1106 €950 Portrait of lady. Portrait of gentleman (58x44cm-23x17in) s.d.1881 pair. 4-Nov-3 Ansorena, Madrid #304/R
Works on paper
£280 $467 €400 Academia masculina (23x31cm-9x12in) s. chl. 24-Jun-3 Segre, Madrid #45/R

LUNA, Antonio Rodriguez (1910-) Spanish
£306 $550 €447 Three figures (28x28cm-11x11in) 24-Apr-4 Du Mouchelle, Detroit #3163/R
£500 $900 €730 Two men (51x33cm-20x13in) 24-Apr-4 Du Mouchelle, Detroit #3166/R
£722 $1300 €1054 Art critic (51x58cm-20x23in) 24-Apr-4 Du Mouchelle, Detroit #3164/R est:800-1200
£1389 $2500 €2028 Still life with cheese (76x152cm-30x60in) 24-Apr-4 Du Mouchelle, Detroit #3162/R est:800-1200
Works on paper
£220 $350 €321 Figures (52x37cm-20x15in) s. mixed media. 12-Sep-3 Skinner, Boston #541/R

LUNAR, Emerio Dario (1940-1990) Venezuelan
£305 $500 €445 Untitled (90x78cm-35x31in) s. painted 1979. 1-Jun-3 Subastas Odalys, Caracas #35
£584 $935 €853 Untitled (80x56cm-31x22in) s. painted 1978. 21-Sep-3 Subastas Odalys, Caracas #26/R
£935 $1450 €1365 Untitled (68x80cm-27x31in) s. painted 1979. 3-Nov-2 Subastas Odalys, Caracas #77/R

LUND, Aage (1892-1972) Danish
£341 $613 €498 Summer landscape with yellow houses at Laesoe (68x80cm-27x31in) s.i.d.1955. 24-Apr-4 Rasmussen, Havnen #2004 (D.KR 3800)

LUND, Anker Niels (1840-1922) Danish
£2268 $4060 €3311 King Erik Ejegod telling his people the reason for travelling to The Holy Land (99x122cm-39x48in) s.d.1879. 12-Jan-4 Rasmussen, Vejle #202/R est:30000-40000 (D.KR 24000)

LUND, Bernt (1812-1885) Norwegian
£3245 $5419 €4738 Forest and river (64x81cm-25x32in) s.d.1850. 13-Oct-3 Blomqvist, Oslo #253/R est:35000-45000 (N.KR 38000)
£21386 $36356 €31224 Christiania seen from Trondheimsveien near Sinsen (95x137cm-37x54in) s.d.1847 canvas on panel. 19-Nov-3 Grev Wedels Plass, Oslo #43/R est:200000-300000 (N.KR 250000)

LUND, Carl Emil (1855-1928) Danish
£280 $467 €400 Danish shepherdess (80x120cm-31x47in) s. 28-Jun-3 Bolland & Marotz, Bremen #698/R
£356 $647 €534 Young shepherd and sheep in heath landscape (41x62cm-16x24in) s. 19-Jun-4 Rasmussen, Havnen #2180 (D.KR 4000)

LUND, F C (1826-1901) Danish
£374 $591 €542 Musketeer with bottle and glass (25x20cm-10x8in) s.d.1880 panel. 2-Sep-3 Rasmussen, Copenhagen #1848/R (D.KR 4000)
£561 $886 €813 Monk with his pack ass (35x40cm-14x16in) s.i.indis.d.1874. 2-Sep-3 Rasmussen, Copenhagen #1781/R (D.KR 6000)
£1438 $2674 €2099 The brave soldier (51x23cm-20x9in) s.d.84. 2-Mar-4 Rasmussen, Copenhagen #1327/R est:10000-12000 (D.KR 16000)
£4537 $7849 €6624 The print collector (88x65cm-35x26in) s.d.1873 exhib.prov. 9-Dec-3 Rasmussen, Copenhagen #1202/R est:40000-50000 (D.KR 48000)

LUND, Harold Marrat (1904-) American
Works on paper
£324 $600 €473 Provincetown boats (43x58cm-17x23in) s. W/C. 15-Feb-4 Outer Cape Auctions, Provincetown #55/R

LUND, Henrik (1879-1935) Norwegian
£420 $713 €600 Fjord landscape (70x97cm-28x38in) s. 28-Nov-3 Schloss Ahlden, Ahlden #716/R
£10000 $18200 €14600 Knut Hamsun in his study (33x41cm-13x16in) s.d.25 prov. 15-Jun-4 Sotheby's, London #360/R est:6000-8000
£12777 $21976 €18654 Gunbjor working (70x75cm-28x30in) s. exhib.prov. 8-Dec-3 Blomqvist, Oslo #485/R est:70000-90000 (N.KR 150000)
£20392 $36501 €29772 Woman seated on bed (103x86cm-41x34in) s.d.1908 lit. 25-May-4 Grev Wedels Plass, Oslo #81/R est:250000 (N.KR 250000)

LUND, Johan Ludvig (1777-1867) Danish
£3378 $5946 €5000 Madonna with Child and young saint before landscape (33x26cm-13x10in) s.d.1832 panel. 22-May-4 Lempertz, Koln #1556/R est:6000

LUND, Johan Ludvig (attrib) (1777-1867) Danish
£1701 $2943 €2483 Landscape from Frederiksdal (47x39cm-19x15in) s.d.1822 exhib. 9-Dec-3 Rasmussen, Copenhagen #1400/R est:15000 (D.KR 18000)

LUND, Soren (1852-1933) Danish
£269 $484 €393 Landscape with horses in meadow (35x57cm-14x22in) s.d.1924. 24-Apr-4 Rasmussen, Havnen #2005 (D.KR 3000)
£417 $676 €609 Cow grazing in clover meadow (35x55cm-14x22in) s.d.1910. 9-Aug-3 Hindemae, Ullerslev #105/R (D.KR 4400)

LUND, Unni (1914-) Norwegian
£516 $831 €753 Composition 5 (90x60cm-35x24in) s. 25-Aug-3 Blomqvist, Lysaker #1169 (N.KR 6000)

LUNDAHL, Amelie (1850-1914) Finnish
£27027 $48378 €40000 At the spinning wheel (60x45cm-24x18in) s. 8-May-4 Bukowskis, Helsinki #40/R est:20000-25000
Works on paper
£403 $741 €600 Wooded landscape (32x24cm-13x9in) s. W/C. 25-Mar-4 Hagelstam, Helsinki #944
£5775 $9990 €8200 Portrait of lady, possibly Anna Aspelin (80x62cm-31x24in) s. pastel exhib.lit. 13-Dec-3 Hagelstam, Helsinki #117/R est:10000

LUNDAHL, Nadine (1958-) Finnish
£667 $1227 €1000 Fruit in glass dish (29x39cm-11x15in) s.d.1985. 9-Jun-4 Bukowskis, Helsinki #464/R
£1354 $2261 €1950 Still life (40x30cm-16x12in) s. 23-Oct-3 Hagelstam, Helsinki #1021 est:1200

LUNDBERG, August Frederick (1878-1928) American
£307 $550 €448 Old man with a pipe (76x61cm-30x24in) s. 7-May-4 Sloans & Kenyon, Bethesda #1702/R
£529 $900 €772 Impressionistic wooded landscape (64x76cm-25x30in) s. 7-Nov-3 Selkirks, St. Louis #493/R

LUNDBERG, Gerhard (1903-) Swedish
£376 $627 €549 Parisian view (33x40cm-13x16in) s.d.38. 7-Oct-3 Rasmussen, Copenhagen #320/R (D.KR 4000)
£479 $861 €719 Window composition (120x104cm-47x41in) init. 25-Apr-4 Goteborg Auktionsverk, Sweden #379/R (S.KR 6600)

LUNDBERG, Gustaf (1695-1786) Swedish
Works on paper
£1478 $2646 €2158 Princess Sofia Albertina (39x30cm-15x12in) pastel prov. 25-May-4 Bukowskis, Stockholm #533/R est:25000-30000 (S.KR 20000)
£1769 $3043 €2583 Portrait of a noble lady (65x49cm-26x19in) pastel. 3-Dec-3 AB Stockholms Auktionsverk #2348/R est:30000-40000 (S.KR 23000)
£2769 $4763 €4043 Portrait of Countess Fredrika de la Gardie (47x38cm-19x15in) pastel. 3-Dec-3 AB Stockholms Auktionsverk #2457/R est:20000-25000 (S.KR 36000)
£7692 $13231 €11230 Archbishop Samuel Troilius and his wife Brita Elisabet (65x50cm-26x20in) pastel pair prov.lit. 2-Dec-3 Bukowskis, Stockholm #437/R est:100000-150000 (S.KR 100000)

LUNDBERG, Lars-Gosta (1938-) Swedish
£508 $914 €742 Suspicious objects (85x64cm-33x25in) s.d.1992 s.d.verso panel. 26-Apr-4 Bukowskis, Stockholm #492/R (S.KR 7000)

£513 $908 €749 Storm (100x73cm-39x29in) s.d.1987. 27-Apr-4 AB Stockholms Auktionsverk #982/R (S.KR 7000)
£580 $1044 €847 Bodies in landscape (130x130cm-51x51in) s.d.1970 verso exhib. 26-Apr-4 Bukowskis, Stockholm #493b/R (S.KR 8000)
£659 $1167 €962 Untitled (72x61cm-28x24in) s.d.1969. 27-Apr-4 AB Stockholms Auktionsverk #954/R (S.KR 9000)
£1133 $1926 €1654 Stella Beach II (24x21cm-9x8in) s.d.71 lit. 4-Nov-3 Bukowskis, Stockholm #530/R est:4000-5000 (S.KR 15000)
Works on paper
£415 $706 €606 The flag (56x38cm-22x15in) s.d.1987 mixed media. 4-Nov-3 Bukowskis, Stockholm #612/R (S.KR 5500)
£415 $706 €606 Untitled (56x38cm-22x15in) s.d.1987 mixed media. 4-Nov-3 Bukowskis, Stockholm #613/R (S.KR 5500)
£718 $1220 €1048 The fall (130x97cm-51x38in) s.d.1989 s.d.verso mixed media. 4-Nov-3 Bukowskis, Stockholm #614/R (S.KR 9500)

LUNDBERG, Mikael (1952-) Swedish
£1233 $2219 €1800 Untitled (124x90cm-49x35in) oil silver gold leaf glass painted c.1987-88 exhib. 26-Apr-4 Bukowskis, Stockholm #467/R est:10000-15000 (S.KR 17000)

LUNDBERG, Robert (1861-1903) Swedish
£2587 $4630 €3777 The main guards (80x99cm-31x39in) s.i.d.1888. 26-May-4 AB Stockholms Auktionsverk #2337/R est:20000-25000 (S.KR 35000)

LUNDBOHM, Sixten (1895-1982) Swedish
£1360 $2311 €1986 Town scene - Cadaques (27x34cm-11x13in) s.d.1950 panel. 5-Nov-3 AB Stockholms Auktionsverk #862/R est:10000-12000 (S.KR 18000)
£1586 $2696 €2316 Landscape with white houses (77x96cm-30x38in) s. 4-Nov-3 Bukowskis, Stockholm #208/R est:15000-20000 (S.KR 21000)

LUNDBYE, J T (1818-1848) Danish
Works on paper
£328 $564 €479 Seated bird (10x7cm-4x3in) pencil pen i. verso page of sketchbook exhib. 3-Dec-3 Museumsbygningen, Copenhagen #118 (D.KR 3500)
£514 $812 €745 A cow on the run, man in background (11x16cm-4x6in) init.i. pen prov. 3-Sep-3 Museumsbygningen, Copenhagen #185/R (D.KR 5500)

LUNDBYE, Johan Thomas (1818-1848) Danish
£629 $1070 €900 Danish coastal scene with harbour (24x32cm-9x13in) mono. lit. 28-Nov-3 Schloss Ahlden, Ahlden #1504/R
£1388 $2539 €2026 Red cow in meadow (12x12cm-5x5in) mono. panel. 9-Jun-4 Rasmussen, Copenhagen #1969/R est:12000-15000 (D.KR 15500)
£4608 $7834 €6728 Klingo II - horse grazing (28x37cm-11x15in) mono.i.d.47 exhib.lit. 10-Nov-3 Rasmussen, Vejle #131/R est:75000-100000 (D.KR 50000)
£15123 $26163 €22080 Gigantic stones at night (29x47cm-11x19in) mono.d.1844 exhib.prov. 9-Dec-3 Rasmussen, Copenhagen #1232/R est:100000-125000 (D.KR 160000)
Works on paper
£269 $491 €393 Oxen and cart on heath road (13x20cm-5x8in) mono.i.d.45 wash pencil. 9-Jun-4 Rasmussen, Copenhagen #2061 (D.KR 3000)
£756 $1308 €1104 Young girl (19x13cm-7x5in) mono.d.27 Juny 1841 pen pencil. 9-Dec-3 Rasmussen, Copenhagen #1716/R (D.KR 8000)
£1028 $1624 €1491 Thatched farm (19x24cm-7x9in) mono.i.d.6 juni 1847 pen W/C prov. 2-Sep-3 Rasmussen, Copenhagen #2015/R (D.KR 11000)
£1880 $3440 €2745 From a stable (31x42cm-12x17in) i. pen wash exhib.prov. 7-Jun-4 Museumsbygningen, Copenhagen #8/R est:15000 (D.KR 21000)

LUNDE, Anders (1809-1886) Danish
£3581 $6553 €5228 Country place high above Rome with visitors (38x57cm-15x22in) s. 9-Jun-4 Rasmussen, Copenhagen #1485/R est:30000-50000 (D.KR 40000)

LUNDEBERG, Helen (1908-) American
£1437 $2400 €2098 Winter pear (16x25cm-6x10in) s. cardboard painted 1949. 11-Nov-3 Christie's, Rockefeller NY #145/R est:3000-5000

LUNDEBY, Alf (1870-1961) Norwegian
£1463 $2443 €2136 From Huskeliseter (86x100cm-34x39in) s. 20-Oct-3 Blomqvist, Lysaker #1199/R est:20000-25000 (N.KR 17000)

LUNDEEN, George W (1948-) American
Sculpture
£1180 $1900 €1723 New friends (64cm-25in) s. num.2/100 bronze. 20-Aug-3 James Julia, Fairfield #1392/R est:1500-2500
£1304 $2100 €1904 Chelsea (107cm-42in) s. num.24/25 bronze. 20-Aug-3 James Julia, Fairfield #1391/R est:3000-5000
£1553 $2500 €2267 Field of blue (124cm-49in) s. num.5/50 bronze. 20-Aug-3 James Julia, Fairfield #1390/R est:4000-8000
£8380 $15000 €12235 Field of blue (119cm-47in) bronze polychrome. 15-May-4 Altermann Galleries, Santa Fe #147/R

LUNDEGARD, Justus (1860-1924) Swedish
£887 $1588 €1295 Sailing boats in fog (23x31cm-9x12in) s. 26-May-4 AB Stockholms Auktionsverk #2309/R (S.KR 12000)
£1078 $1800 €1574 Swedish sound. s.d.98. 7-Oct-3 Sotheby's, New York #229 est:1500-2000
£3104 $5557 €4532 Harbour in Skaane (63x92cm-25x36in) s.d.1887. 25-May-4 Bukowskis, Stockholm #221/R est:30000-40000 (S.KR 42000)
£6731 $12250 €9827 Snowy landscape (72x90cm-28x35in) s.i. 29-Jun-4 Sotheby's, New York #134/R est:12000-15000

LUNDGREN, Charles (19/20th C) American
£1913 $3500 €2793 Eagle (56x76cm-22x30in) s. board. 29-Jul-4 Christie's, Rockefeller NY #287/R est:6000-8000

LUNDGREN, Egron Sillif (1815-1875) Swedish
£875 $1609 €1313 Pretty Italian woman (55x45cm-22x18in) s. oval. 14-Jun-4 Lilla Bukowskis, Stockholm #722 (S.KR 12000)
Works on paper
£277 $510 €416 Southern girl in landscape (27x18cm-11x7in) init. W/C. 14-Jun-4 Lilla Bukowskis, Stockholm #323 (S.KR 3800)
£280 $501 €409 The Domenican Friar (43x30cm-17x12in) W/C gouache htd white exhib. 4-May-4 Gorringes, Bexhill #1306
£300 $489 €435 Harvest time (45x32cm-18x13in) W/C. 23-Sep-3 Bonhams, Knightsbridge #38/R
£1014 $1824 €1480 Oriental scene with caravan (22x37cm-9x15in) i.verso mixed media prov. 26-Jan-4 Lilla Bukowskis, Stockholm #375 (S.KR 13500)
£2000 $3540 €2920 Lady going to church, Calcutta. Native groom (23x36cm-9x14in) W/C htd white two sold with a book. 27-Apr-4 Bonhams, New Bond Street #43/R est:2000-3000

LUNDGREN, Egron Sillif (attrib) (1815-1875) Swedish
Works on paper
£380 $600 €551 Portrait of a young girl with flowers in her hair (27x21cm-11x8in) W/C. 3-Sep-3 Bonhams, Bury St Edmunds #376

LUNDGREN, Eric (20th C) ?
£870 $1600 €1270 Huntsman with his hounds (46x61cm-18x24in) board. 26-Jun-4 Sloans & Kenyon, Bethesda #268/R est:700-900

LUNDH, Theodor (1812-1896) Swedish
£1077 $1852 €1572 Still life of hanging birds (49x39cm-19x15in) s. 3-Dec-3 AB Stockholms Auktionsverk #2510/R est:12000-15000 (S.KR 14000)
£1284 $2298 €1900 Still life of game (48x59cm-19x23in) s. 8-May-4 Bukowskis, Helsinki #375/R est:900-1000

LUNDMARK, Leon (1875-?) American
£652 $1200 €952 Sunset over crashing surf (40x61cm-16x24in) s. 8-Jun-4 Auctions by the Bay, Alameda #1107/R

LUNDQUIST, Evert (1904-1994) Swedish
£1088 $1958 €1588 Park landscape (38x46cm-15x18in) init. s.d.1950 verso. 26-Apr-4 Bukowskis, Stockholm #190/R est:15000-18000 (S.KR 15000)
£1088 $1958 €1588 Still life of straw sheaf (54x66cm-21x26in) s. verso. 26-Apr-4 Bukowskis, Stockholm #190a/R est:20000-25000 (S.KR 15000)
£1109 $1785 €1619 Female head (46x27cm-18x11in) s.d.1948 verso. 25-Aug-3 Lilla Bukowskis, Stockholm #640 (S.KR 14500)
£1203 $2213 €1805 Abstract composition (46x55cm-18x22in) 14-Jun-4 Lilla Bukowskis, Stockholm #500 est:12000-15000 (S.KR 16500)
£1284 $2183 €1875 The stone (21x21cm-8x8in) s. panel. 5-Nov-3 AB Stockholms Auktionsverk #723/R est:10000-12000 (S.KR 17000)
£1392 $2464 €2032 The stone (30x38cm-12x15in) init. s.verso. 27-Apr-4 AB Stockholms Auktionsverk #832/R est:18000-20000 (S.KR 19000)
£1586 $2696 €2316 The spade (25x23cm-10x9in) s. verso panel. 5-Nov-3 AB Stockholms Auktionsverk #817/R est:10000-12000 (S.KR 21000)
£1668 $3002 €2435 Woman (27x20cm-11x8in) init. canvas on panel. 26-Apr-4 Bukowskis, Stockholm #191b/R est:20000-25000 (S.KR 23000)
£1822 $3353 €2733 Glistening sun on the ocean (46x39cm-18x15in) init. s. verso. 14-Jun-4 Lilla Bukowskis, Stockholm #836 est:20000-25000 (S.KR 25000)
£2039 $3467 €2977 Still life of apples (25x31cm-10x12in) s. 5-Nov-3 AB Stockholms Auktionsverk #881/R est:10000-12000 (S.KR 27000)
£4381 $7447 €6396 Reclining woman (92x72cm-36x28in) init. s.d.1961 verso. 5-Nov-3 AB Stockholms Auktionsverk #824/R est:60000-80000 (S.KR 58000)
£6344 $10785 €9262 The small easel (82x65cm-32x26in) init. s.verso. 4-Nov-3 Bukowskis, Stockholm #205/R est:80000-100000 (S.KR 84000)
£7931 $13482 €11579 The man on the hill (65x54cm-26x21in) init. d.1974 verso exhib.prov. 5-Nov-3 AB Stockholms Auktionsverk #813/R est:75000-100000 (S.KR 105000)
£9065 $16316 €13235 The spring (92x73cm-36x29in) init. s. verso. 26-Apr-4 Bukowskis, Stockholm #188/R est:125000-150000 (S.KR 125000)
£10877 $19579 €15880 The road (85x40cm-33x16in) s. verso exhib. 26-Apr-4 Bukowskis, Stockholm #191/R est:150000-175000 (S.KR 150000)
£14350 $24396 €20951 The axe. Portrait of man (83x65cm-33x26in) init.d.56 double-sided lit. 4-Nov-3 Bukowskis, Stockholm #202/R est:40000-45000 (S.KR 190000)
£16484 $29176 €24067 The glass (74x91cm-29x36in) s.i.verso oval painted 1962 exhib.lit. 27-Apr-4 AB Stockholms Auktionsverk #833/R est:125000-150000 (S.KR 225000)

LUNDQUIST, Sven (1918-) Swedish
Sculpture
£2462 $4234 €3595 The green mare (64cm-25in) s. green pat.bronze. 7-Dec-3 Uppsala Auktionskammare, Uppsala #363/R est:25000-30000 (S.KR 32000)

LUNDQVIST, Rita (1953-) Swedish?
£2341 $3980 €3418 The Holy Communion (34x26cm-13x10in) s.d.2001 verso panel exhib.lit. 5-Nov-3 AB Stockholms Auktionsverk #994/R est:20000-25000 (S.KR 31000)

LUNDSTROM, Knut (1892-1945) Swedish
£875 $1609 €1313 By the river (46x55cm-18x22in) s. panel. 14-Jun-4 Lilla Bukowskis, Stockholm #656 (S.KR 12000)

LUNDSTROM, Vilhelm (1893-1950) Danish
£1327 $2123 €1924 Final scene from Tosca (42x61cm-17x24in) exhib.lit. 17-Sep-3 Kunsthallen, Copenhagen #60/R est:15000 (D.KR 14000)
£10329 $17249 €15080 Still life (81x65cm-32x26in) init.d.42 verso prov. 7-Oct-3 Rasmussen, Copenhagen #132/R est:100000-125000 (D.KR 110000)
£31588 $58123 €46118 Seated model by still life (130x97cm-51x38in) init.d.42 verso prov.exhib.lit. 29-Mar-4 Rasmussen, Copenhagen #11/R est:300000-400000 (D.KR 350000)
Works on paper
£307 $565 €448 House behind trees (28x37cm-11x15in) mono. crayon pencil exhib. 29-Mar-4 Rasmussen, Copenhagen #446 (D.KR 3400)
£343 $641 €501 Seated model (40x25cm-16x10in) i. verso pencil. 25-Feb-4 Museumsbygningen, Copenhagen #35/R (D.KR 3800)

£373 $585 €545 Model study of woman (37x25cm-15x10in) mono. chl sketch. 30-Aug-3 Rasmussen, Havnen #4340/R (D.KR 4000)
£379 $697 €553 Houses with trees in foreground (26x30cm-10x12in) mono. W/C pencil prov. 29-Mar-4 Rasmussen, Copenhagen #555/R (D.KR 4200)

LUNGREN, Fernand Harvey (1859-1932) American
£924 $1700 €1349 Grove of trees in the sun (34x45cm-13x18in) s. 8-Jun-4 Bonhams & Butterfields, San Francisco #4132/R est:3000-5000
Works on paper
£1278 $2250 €1866 Man asleep on a horse (27x42cm-11x17in) s.d.94 W/C exhib. 23-May-4 Bonhams & Butterfields, San Francisco #6604/R

LUNN, Augustus (1905-1986) British
£2800 $4816 €4088 Figures in a niche (108x146cm-43x57in) s. indis.i. board exhib. 3-Dec-3 Sotheby's, London #53/R est:3000-5000

LUNOIS, Alexandre (1863-1916) French
Works on paper
£2069 $3455 €3000 Les banderilles (82x61cm-32x24in) pastel exhib. 17-Nov-3 Tajan, Paris #5 est:1500-2000

LUNY, T (1759-1837) British
£1000 $1590 €1450 Hauling in the boats, Ryde Isle of Wight (82x120cm-32x47in) 9-Sep-3 David Duggleby, Scarborough #354 est:1000-1500

LUNY, Thomas (1759-1837) British
£1074 $1902 €1568 Frigate in the Channel (30x41cm-12x16in) s.d.1833 panel. 3-May-4 Lawson Menzies, Sydney #385 est:2000-3000 (A.D 2600)
£1850 $3312 €2701 Gossiping on the foreshore on the Devonshire coast (19x28cm-7x11in) s.d.1832 board. 26-May-4 Christie's, Kensington #578/R est:1000-1500
£3600 $6444 €5256 Frigate under tow at the entrance to Dartmouth harbour (23x30cm-9x12in) s.d.1821 panel. 26-May-4 Christie's, Kensington #579/R est:2000-3000
£3800 $6460 €5548 Extensive Estuary Scene at evening with numberous fisherfolk and boats (60x84cm-24x33in) s. 29-Oct-3 Hampton & Littlewood, Exeter #612/R est:3000-5000
£3911 $7000 €5710 HMS Zephyr engaging the French frigate, La Senegal on the river Gambia (86x147cm-34x58in) s. indis.d.178 prov. 16-Mar-4 Bonhams & Butterfields, San Francisco #6121/R est:8000-12000
£4000 $6880 €5840 Shipping off a mountains coast in stormy seas (50x68cm-20x27in) s.d.1830 panel. 2-Dec-3 Sotheby's, London #5/R est:4000-6000
£4000 $7160 €5840 Frigate running out to sea with a cutter astern of her and a fishing boat (61x86cm-24x34in) s.d.1830. 26-May-4 Christie's, Kensington #592/R est:5000-7000
£5700 $9063 €8322 Beach scene near Teignmouth (30x40cm-12x16in) s.d.1825 panel. 10-Sep-3 Edgar Horn, Eastbourne #377/R est:3000-4000
£8108 $15000 €11838 Royal Naval warships lying at anchor in a stiff breeze (38x51cm-15x20in) s.d.1824 prov. 10-Feb-4 Christie's, Rockefeller NY #168/R est:15000-20000
£8197 $15000 €11968 Running home before the gale. Running up the estuary (30x41cm-12x16in) panel two. 29-Jul-4 Christie's, Rockefeller NY #231/R est:15000-25000
£15000 $27600 €21900 Royal Navy frigate and other shipping off Harwich (84x149cm-33x59in) s.d.1783. 11-Jun-4 Christie's, London #50/R est:15000-20000
£22000 $37400 €32120 Shipping on the River Dart at Dittisham with women selling fish in the foreground (61x86cm-24x34in) s.d.1815 prov. 25-Nov-3 Christie's, London #84/R est:15000-20000
£30000 $55200 €43800 Siege of Algiers (91x151cm-36x59in) 26-Mar-4 Sotheby's, London #36/R est:30000-40000

LUNY, Thomas (attrib) (1759-1837) British
£500 $895 €730 Sunset beach scene with boats, figures and a dog (18x25cm-7x10in) s.d.1832 panel. 17-Mar-4 John Nicholson, Haslemere #748/R
£550 $1007 €803 Rescue at sea (30x38cm-12x15in) 6-Jul-4 Bearnes, Exeter #512/R
£12195 $19146 €17683 Shipping under sail (80x145cm-31x57in) indis.sig.indis.d. 26-Aug-3 Christie's, Sydney #159/R est:30000-40000 (A.D 30000)

LUO QING (1948-) Chinese
£915 $1656 €1336 Overstretched shirt (145x58cm-57x23in) s.verso. 3-Apr-4 Glerum, Singapore #59/R est:3000-4000 (S.D 2800)

LUO ZHONGLI (1948-) Chinese
£3201 $5761 €4673 Still life (49x60cm-19x24in) s.d.1985.4. 25-Apr-4 Christie's, Hong Kong #737/R est:40000-80000 (HK.D 45000)

LUONG XUAN NHI (1913-) Vietnamese
£5208 $8698 €7604 Under the tree (73x54cm-29x21in) s. 12-Oct-3 Sotheby's, Singapore #92/R est:15000-20000 (S.D 15000)
Works on paper
£22569 $37691 €32951 Vietnamese Women (38x31cm-15x12in) s. ink gouache silk. 12-Oct-3 Sotheby's, Singapore #101/R est:55000-65000 (S.D 65000)

LUOSTARINEN, Leena (1949-) Finnish
£3333 $5967 €5000 Heavenly dragons (75x350cm-30x138in) s. exhib.lit. 15-May-4 Hagelstam, Helsinki #221/R est:5000

LUPERTZ, Markus (1941-) Czechoslovakian
£1141 $2019 €1700 Parsifal (70x100cm-28x39in) mono. tempera on col lithograph board. 30-Apr-4 Dr Fritz Nagel, Stuttgart #882/R est:1500
£1189 $2021 €1700 Untitled (21x15cm-8x6in) mono. acrylic Indian ink pen brush board. 27-Nov-3 Lempertz, Koln #256/R est:1500
£3401 $6088 €5000 Hill with Cross (36x48cm-14x19in) s.i.d.1988 prov. 16-Mar-4 Finarte Semenzato, Milan #393/R est:3000
£9333 $17080 €14000 Scene from Othello I (81x100cm-32x39in) mono. s.i. verso prov.lit. 4-Jun-4 Lempertz, Koln #286/R est:18000-20000
£10563 $18275 €15000 Vogue (101x81cm-40x32in) s. verso i. stretcher. 13-Dec-3 Lempertz, Koln #165/R est:12000
£11189 $19021 €16000 Cacti discussion (162x130cm-64x51in) mono. s.i. stretcher. 27-Nov-3 Lempertz, Koln #254/R est:20000-30000
£13575 $22670 €19820 Untitled (200x170cm-79x67in) mono. prov. 24-Jun-3 Germann, Zurich #62/R est:50000-70000 (S.FR 30000)
£13986 $23776 €20000 Grating picture (162x130cm-64x51in) mono. oil chk prov. 29-Nov-3 Villa Grisebach, Berlin #394/R est:20000-25000
£14667 $26840 €22000 Scene from Othello II (81x100cm-32x39in) mono. s.i. verso prov.lit. 4-Jun-4 Lempertz, Koln #287/R est:18000-20000
£24476 $41608 €35000 Stage fight (130x163cm-51x64in) mono. s.i. stretcher prov.lit. 27-Nov-3 Lempertz, Koln #253/R est:20000-30000
Prints
£2215 $3920 €3300 Parsifal (83x50cm-33x20in) i. verso gouache board. 30-Apr-4 Dr Fritz Nagel, Stuttgart #883/R est:3900
£2533 $4636 €3800 Untitled - female nude (69x49cm-27x19in) mono. etching col chk. 4-Jun-4 Lempertz, Koln #289/R est:3700
£6643 $11294 €9500 Men without women - Parsifal (140x106cm-55x42in) mono. col monotype. 29-Nov-3 Villa Grisebach, Berlin #395/R est:10000-12000
Sculpture
£2207 $3686 €3200 Dithyrambe (16x18x14cm-6x7x6in) mono. num.302/998 two-part bronze Cast ARA Kunst. 13-Nov-3 Neumeister, Munich #580/R est:1800-2000
Works on paper
£600 $1074 €900 Untitled (43x31cm-17x12in) s. pencil col pen. 15-May-4 Van Ham, Cologne #768
£647 $1062 €900 Untitled (27x19cm-11x7in) mono. gouache oil chk. 4-Jun-3 Ketterer, Hamburg #619/R
£725 $1188 €1000 Untitled (29x21cm-11x8in) s. gouache acrylic paper on card. 27-May-3 Sotheby's, Amsterdam #542/R
£769 $1323 €1100 Composition with guitar (29x30cm-11x12in) mono. chk gouache cardboard. 4-Dec-3 Van Ham, Cologne #307/R
£1200 $2208 €1800 Untitled (50x70cm-20x28in) mono. gouache prov. 9-Jun-4 Artcurial Briest, Paris #527 est:1200-1500
£1267 $2267 €1900 Theatre (50x35cm-20x14in) s. gouache chk. 15-May-4 Van Ham, Cologne #767/R est:1650
£1467 $2699 €2200 Giant soft brush (22x30cm-9x12in) s. pencil W/C. 12-Jun-4 Villa Grisebach, Berlin #789/R est:1200-1500
£1533 $2760 €2300 Harlequin (100x70cm-39x28in) mono. gouache on lithograph. 24-Apr-4 Dr Lehr, Berlin #262/R est:2500
£1538 $2646 €2200 Untitled (61x42cm-24x17in) s. W/C crayon black chk pencil oil executed 1979 prov. 2-Dec-3 Sotheby's, Amsterdam #337/R est:1500-2000
£1538 $2646 €2200 Landscape (42x60cm-17x24in) s. W/C chk crayon executed 1978 prov. 2-Dec-3 Sotheby's, Amsterdam #345/R est:1500-2000
£1736 $2899 €2500 Untitled (22x31cm-9x12in) s. pencil Indian ink chk collage. 24-Oct-3 Ketterer, Hamburg #447/R est:2500-2700
£1958 $3329 €2800 Untitled (36x26cm-14x10in) mono. gouache graphite biro collage paper on board. 27-Nov-3 Lempertz, Koln #258/R est:2800-3000
£2098 $3608 €3000 Auto (30x40cm-12x16in) s. mono.i.verso gouache W/C black chk prov. 5-Dec-3 Ketterer, Munich #167/R est:3000-3500
£2238 $3804 €3200 Untitled (34x24cm-13x9in) mono. gouache chk Indian ink graphite. 27-Nov-3 Lempertz, Koln #257/R est:2800-3000
£2800 $5124 €4200 Untitled (62x45cm-24x18in) mono. gouache pencil col pen. 4-Jun-4 Lempertz, Koln #285/R est:3500
£4000 $7360 €5840 Untitled (41x54cm-16x21in) s. W/C gouache col crayon prov. 24-Jun-4 Sotheby's, Olympia #582/R est:4000-6000
£4196 $7133 €6000 Alice in Wonderland (61x43cm-24x17in) mono. mixed media. 29-Nov-3 Arnold, Frankfurt #358/R est:9000
£5594 $9510 €8000 Olevano (49x67cm-19x26in) s.i. mixed media pastel gouache. 26-Nov-3 Dorotheum, Vienna #86/R est:5500-7500

LUPIANEZ Y CARRASCO, Jose (1864-1933) Spanish
£769 $1285 €1100 Landscape with trees and village (80x37cm-31x15in) s. 30-Jun-3 Ansorena, Madrid #236/R
£1974 $3572 €3000 Landscape with stream (21x33cm-8x13in) s.d.1906 board. 14-Apr-4 Ansorena, Madrid #51/R est:3000
£2349 $4205 €3500 Landscape (23x35cm-9x14in) s. board. 25-May-4 Durán, Madrid #152/R est:2000
£2517 $4505 €3750 Landscape (30x50cm-12x20in) s. 25-May-4 Durán, Madrid #153/R est:2500
£2759 $4579 €4000 Landscape with mountains covered in snow (35x45cm-14x18in) s. 30-Sep-3 Ansorena, Madrid #75/R est:4000
£3020 $5617 €4500 River landscape (30x51cm-12x20in) s. 2-Mar-4 Ansorena, Madrid #89/R est:4500

LUPICINI, Francesco (1588-?) Italian
£7343 $12483 €10500 Mary Magdalene at her toilet (121x95cm-48x37in) 1-Dec-3 Babuino, Rome #126/R est:10000-15000

LUPLAU, Marie (1848-1925) Danish
£376 $677 €549 Evening near Fredensborg (37x69cm-15x27in) s.i.d.1898. 24-Apr-4 Rasmussen, Havnen #2344 (D.KR 4200)

LUPO, Alessandro (1876-1953) Italian
£1400 $2576 €2100 Grey day, Pieve Ligure (27x34cm-11x13in) s. i.d.1941 verso exhib. 14-Jun-4 Sant Agostino, Torino #283/R est:2000-2500
£1469 $2526 €2100 Cottage in the mountains (50x75cm-20x30in) s. 3-Dec-3 Stadion, Trieste #1101/R
£1701 $3044 €2500 Shepherdess (26x39cm-10x15in) s. cardboard. 22-Mar-4 Sant Agostino, Torino #254/R
£1733 $3189 €2600 Lights and shadows (29x29cm-11x11in) s.d.1943 cardboard. 14-Jun-4 Sant Agostino, Torino #219/R est:1500-2000
£3691 $6534 €5500 Fruit market (25x30cm-10x12in) s. board. 1-May-4 Meeting Art, Vercelli #365 est:5000
£7047 $12473 €10500 Corpus Domini in Aosta Valley (48x56cm-19x22in) s.i.d.1918 cardboard lit. 1-May-4 Meeting Art, Vercelli #117 est:9000
£7383 $13067 €11000 Carnival (51x59cm-20x23in) s. canvas on board lit. 1-May-4 Meeting Art, Vercelli #468 est:10000
£15541 $27351 €23000 Sunset in Venice with gondola (110x88cm-43x35in) s. 19-May-4 Il Ponte, Milan #656 est:25000-30000
Works on paper
£567 $1043 €850 Seascape (15x25cm-6x10in) s.d.1907 W/C. 14-Jun-4 Sant Agostino, Torino #192/R
£1586 $2633 €2300 Exit from the church (20x18cm-8x7in) s. W/C card. 1-Oct-3 Della Rocca, Turin #85/R

LUPPEN, Gerard Josef Adrian van (1834-1891) Belgian
£306 $548 €450 Vue d'une fagne a Esneux (18x23cm-7x9in) panel. 22-Mar-4 Amberes, Antwerp #262
£479 $815 €700 Paysage montagneux (35x50cm-14x20in) s. 4-Nov-3 Servarts Themis, Bruxelles #638
£537 $961 €800 Personnages dans un paysage (67x88cm-26x35in) s.d.1874. 25-May-4 Campo & Campo, Antwerp #317
£1972 $3411 €2800 Gardeurs de betail dans un paysage (89x63cm-35x25in) s.d.1881. 9-Dec-3 Campo, Vlaamse Kaai #464/R est:3000-4000

LUPPEN, J van (19th C) Belgian?
£1000 $1840 €1500 Chasseur dans un paysage montagneux (50x41cm-20x16in) panel painted 1877. 14-Jun-4 Amberes, Antwerp #138

LURCAT, Jean (1892-1966) French
£993 $1818 €1500 Porteurs de drapeaux en bord de mer (29x36cm-11x14in) s. 7-Apr-4 Piasa, Paris #217 est:800-1000
£1028 $1717 €1450 Paysage maritime (27x35cm-11x14in) s. i.verso. 19-Jun-3 Millon & Associes, Paris #266/R
£2096 $3500 €3060 Still life with vegetables (42x45cm-17x18in) s.d.27 prov. 7-Oct-3 Sotheby's, New York #265 est:1000-1500
£2937 $4993 €4200 Deux nus (52x27cm-20x11in) s. panel prov. 23-Nov-3 Cornette de St.Cyr, Paris #230/R est:800-1000
£3357 $5706 €4800 Paysage surrealiste (52x23cm-20x9in) s. panel prov. 23-Nov-3 Cornette de St.Cyr, Paris #229/R est:600-800
£3380 $5848 €4800 Nature morte aux fruits (42x45cm-17x18in) s.d.1927. 14-Dec-3 Eric Pillon, Calais #259/R
£3514 $6500 €5130 Nu fond vert (35x24cm-14x9in) s. panel exhib.lit. 12-Feb-4 Sotheby's, New York #17/R est:2000-3000
£4000 $7280 €6000 Deux nus (53x27cm-21x11in) s. panel lit. 4-Jul-4 Eric Pillon, Calais #292/R
£6000 $11040 €9000 Breton landscape (90x116cm-35x46in) s.d.27 prov.lit. 8-Jun-4 Sotheby's, Amsterdam #14/R est:10000-15000
£6417 $12000 €9369 Femme assise (36x26cm-14x10in) s. panel prov. 25-Feb-4 Christie's, Rockefeller NY #74/R est:1000-1500
£10403 $19349 €15500 L'orage (195x129cm-77x51in) s.d.1931 prov.exhib.lit. 3-Mar-4 Tajan, Paris #70/R est:12000-15000
£11000 $20130 €16500 L'ocean (55x82cm-22x32in) s.d.1922 si. verso prov. 5-Jun-4 Lempertz, Koln #835/R est:10000-15000
£11888 $20448 €17000 La baigneuse (33x24cm-13x9in) s. panel painted 1931. 2-Dec-3 Sotheby's, Amsterdam #88/R est:10000-15000
Works on paper
£282 $454 €400 Guerres (29x23cm-11x9in) s.i. W/C gouache. 11-May-3 Versailles Encheres #133
£556 $900 €812 Three standing female figures (66x76cm-26x30in) s. mixed media. 3-Aug-3 North East Auctions, Portsmouth #1980/R
£642 $1072 €931 Chouette (52x46cm-20x18in) s. gouache. 23-Jun-3 Philippe Schuler, Zurich #3051/R (S.FR 1400)
£667 $1227 €1000 L'oiseau pris dans les filets (34x52cm-13x20in) s.d.1949 gouache with poem. 9-Jun-4 Beaussant & Lefèvre, Paris #93/R
£750 $1380 €1095 Le coq (31x18cm-12x7in) s. W/C gouache pencil. 24-Mar-4 Sotheby's, Olympia #170/R
£1333 $2453 €2000 Untitled (36x52cm-14x20in) s.d.1953 gouache. 8-Jun-4 Sotheby's, Amsterdam #247/R est:2000-3000
£1678 $3104 €2500 Chateau au ciel etoile (57x43cm-22x17in) s. gouache exec.1949 lit. 14-Mar-4 St-Germain-en-Laye Encheres #133/R est:2000-2500
£2349 $4158 €3500 Mediterranee (23x57cm-9x22in) s.d.1938 gouache prov.exhib.lit. 27-Apr-4 Artcurial Briest, Paris #52/R est:4000-5000
£2533 $4661 €3800 Barques au ciel bleu (29x40cm-11x16in) s.d.44 gouache prov.exhib.lit. 8-Jun-4 Sotheby's, Amsterdam #248/R est:2000-3000
£6952 $13000 €10150 Femme debout (46x29cm-18x11in) s.d.26 gouache pencil cardboard. 25-Feb-4 Christie's, Rockefeller NY #80/R est:1800-2500
£8500 $15640 €12410 La collerette (49x38cm-19x15in) s.d.1921 W/C lit. 24-Mar-4 Sotheby's, Olympia #187/R est:4000-6000

LUSCHER, Ingeborg (1936-) German
Works on paper
£1310 $2410 €1913 Untitled (148x186cm-58x73in) s.d.1986 verso ash soot pigment acrylic chl prov. 8-Jun-4 Germann, Zurich #133/R est:3000-4000 (S.FR 3000)

LUSCHER, Jean Jacques (1884-1955) Swiss
£261 $477 €381 Landscape in the Jura region (62x80cm-24x31in) s.i.d.1911 verso. 4-Jun-4 Zofingen, Switzerland #2876 (S.FR 600)

LUSCOMB, William Henry (1805-1866) American
£1087 $1750 €1587 Shipping off entrance to Salem Harbour (46x56cm-18x22in) board. 20-Aug-3 James Julia, Fairfield #1445/R est:2000-3000

LUSCOMBE, H A (1820-?) British
£1450 $2639 €2117 Frigate passing before Drake Island, Plymouth Sound. board. 6-Feb-4 Honiton Galleries, Honiton #332 est:300-500

LUSCOMBE, Henry A (1820-?) British
Works on paper
£700 $1190 €1022 H.M.S. Victory (27x43cm-11x17in) s. pencil W/C htd white. 19-Nov-3 Christie's, Kensington #342/R

LUSENKO, Yuri (20th C) Russian
£600 $1092 €876 Cafe (70x80cm-28x31in) s. 20-Jun-4 Lots Road Auctions, London #340/R

LUSH, Isaac (19th C) British?
Works on paper
£2038 $3750 €2975 HMS Euryalus blockading Cronstad (43x64cm-17x25in) s.i.d.1858 pen ink W/C. 10-Jun-4 Sotheby's, New York #639/R est:600-800

LUSK, Doris (1916-1990) New Zealander
£4275 $7353 €6242 Mt Taranki (60x91cm-24x36in) s.d.1956 board prov. 3-Dec-3 Dunbar Sloane, Auckland #33/R est:20000-30000 (NZ.D 11500)
Works on paper
£433 $706 €632 Lyttelton Harbour (13x40cm-5x16in) init.i. W/C. 23-Sep-3 Peter Webb, Auckland #142/R (NZ.D 1200)
£484 $867 €707 Portrait of woman (41x29cm-16x11in) s.d.89 W/C. 12-May-4 Dunbar Sloane, Wellington #244 est:800-1600 (NZ.D 1400)
£761 $1233 €1103 Cabbage tree, Port Hills (38x54cm-15x21in) s.i.d.1970 W/C ink. 31-Jul-3 International Art Centre, Auckland #129/R est:2200-2800 (NZ.D 2100)
£1562 $2484 €2281 Arrowtown landscape (53x75cm-21x30in) s.d.1967 crayon W/C. 1-May-3 Dunbar Sloane, Wellington #61/R est:3000-4000 (NZ.D 4500)
£1608 $2927 €2348 Goat Bay (36x53cm-14x21in) s.i.d.1971 W/C. 29-Jun-4 Peter Webb, Auckland #133/R est:4500-6500 (NZ.D 4600)
£2083 $3312 €3041 Spanish village scene (32x50cm-13x20in) s.d.1988 W/C. 1-May-3 Dunbar Sloane, Wellington #47/R est:6000-8000 (NZ.D 6000)
£3014 $5576 €4400 Porters Pass (54x79cm-21x31in) s.d.1969 W/C. 13-Jul-4 Watson's, Christchurch #60/R (NZ.D 8500)
£7246 $11739 €10507 Portrait of Tony Fomison (54x40cm-21x16in) s.d.1969 W/C. 31-Jul-3 International Art Centre, Auckland #45/R est:16000-24000 (NZ.D 20000)

LUSSANET, Paul de (1940-) Dutch
Works on paper
£490 $832 €700 Reclining female nude (130x105cm-51x41in) s.d.86 gouache prov. 24-Nov-3 Glerum, Amsterdam #241/R

LUSSENBURGH, Johannes (1889-1975) Dutch
£604 $1123 €900 Washing day (30x40cm-12x16in) s. 4-Mar-4 Auction Maastricht #1073
£625 $987 €900 Thatched cottage by a country lane (50x80cm-20x31in) s. 2-Sep-3 Christie's, Amsterdam #280

LUSSIE, Jacques (1924-) Belgian
£1007 $1652 €1400 Portrait. panel. 6-Jun-3 Chochon-Barre & Allardi, Paris #72a

LUSSIGNY, E (19th C) French
Works on paper
£3217 $5469 €4600 L'escrimeur (39x46cm-15x18in) s.d.1808 chl crayon. 18-Nov-3 Vanderkindere, Brussels #112 est:375-625

LUSSO, Paola (1962-) Italian
£336 $621 €500 Sun (73x83cm-29x33in) s. fresco board. 13-Mar-4 Meeting Art, Vercelli #27
£369 $683 €550 Newborn star (100x70cm-39x28in) s. fresco board. 13-Mar-4 Meeting Art, Vercelli #370
Works on paper
£333 $613 €500 Pure earth (76x78cm-30x31in) s. fresco board exec.2003. 12-Jun-4 Meeting Art, Vercelli #438/R
£352 $585 €500 KU (110x80cm-43x31in) s. s.i.d.2002 verso fresco gold leaf panel. 14-Jun-3 Meeting Art, Vercelli #70/R

LUST, Abraham de (17th C) Dutch
£11000 $19030 €16060 Garland of roses and other flowers suspended from bronze handles (69x109cm-27x43in) 12-Dec-3 Christie's, Kensington #46/R est:8000-12000

LUSTICHUYS, Simon (attrib) (16th C) ?
£778 $1300 €1136 Portrait of a man (41x36cm-16x14in) mono.i. panel. 22-Oct-3 Doyle, New York #28

LUSTIG, Otto (?) ?
£379 $709 €553 Seascape with paddle-steamer (63x95cm-25x37in) s. 25-Feb-4 Kunsthallen, Copenhagen #539 (D.KR 4200)

LUSURIER, Catherine (attrib) (1753-1781) French
£1958 $3270 €2800 Portrait d'homme (97x78cm-38x31in) oval. 26-Jun-3 Artcurial Briest, Paris #487 est:3000-3500

LUTES, Jim (20th C) American
£2907 $5000 €4244 Artist in his studio (155x102cm-61x40in) canvas on board painted c.1982. 7-Dec-3 Treadway Gallery, Cincinnati #634/R est:4500-6500

LUTHER, Adolf (1912-1990) German
Sculpture
£1133 $2029 €1700 Untitled - landscape (28x51x9cm-11x20x4in) s.d. verso mirror glass. 15-May-4 Dr Sturies, Dusseldorf #122/R
£1958 $3329 €2800 Untitled (45x45x8cm-18x18x3in) s.d.69 verso mirrors plexiglass. 27-Nov-3 Lempertz, Koln #263/R est:2500-3000
£2098 $3566 €3000 Untitled (34x34x5cm-13x13x2in) s.d.78 verso mirrors panel glass prov. 27-Nov-3 Lempertz, Koln #262/R est:1500
£2262 $3778 €3303 Sight is beautiful (52x63x8cm-20x25x3in) s.i.d.1987 verso plastic mirros wood. 24-Jun-3 Germann, Zurich #64/R est:5000-6000 (S.FR 5000)
£2378 $4042 €3400 Untitled (45x45x8cm-18x18x3in) s.d.69 verso mirrors wood plexiglass. 27-Nov-3 Lempertz, Koln #259/R est:2500-3000
£2517 $4280 €3600 Untitled (45x45x8cm-18x18x3in) s.d.70 verso mirrors plexiglass wood. 27-Nov-3 Lempertz, Koln #260/R est:2500-3000
£2533 $4636 €3800 Mirrors (66x66x8cm-26x26x3in) s.d.75 mirrors. 4-Jun-4 Lempertz, Koln #290/R est:4000
£2657 $4517 €3800 Untitled (45x45x8cm-18x18x3in) s.d.70 verso mirrors plexiglass. 27-Nov-3 Lempertz, Koln #261/R est:2500-3000

LUTHI, Bernhard (20th C) Swiss
Works on paper
£845 $1462 €1200 Untitled (73x85cm-29x33in) s.i.d.72 W/C. 13-Dec-3 Lempertz, Koln #332/R

LUTHI, Ernest (1906-1983) Canadian
£498 $831 €727 Summer near the south west corner of Katepwa Lake (25x30cm-10x12in) s.i. board. 17-Nov-3 Hodgins, Calgary #24/R est:600-800 (C.D 1100)

LUTHI, Urs (1947-) Swiss
£1584 $2692 €2313 Untitled (155x110cm-61x43in) s. acrylic. 25-Nov-3 Germann, Zurich #9/R est:3300-5000 (S.FR 3500)
£1991 $3325 €2907 Evergreen (65x50cm-26x20in) s.i.d.1988/1989 verso. 24-Jun-3 Germann, Zurich #114/R est:4500-5000 (S.FR 4400)
£2941 $4912 €4294 Self portrait (200x160cm-79x63in) s.i. verso exhib. 24-Jun-3 Germann, Zurich #132/R est:10000-20000 (S.FR 6500)
£4196 $7133 €6000 The sign of love (160x200cm-63x79in) s.i.d.82 verso. 26-Nov-3 Dorotheum, Vienna #92/R est:6000-8000
Works on paper
£317 $538 €463 Self portrait (37x25cm-15x10in) s.d.1985 pencil. 25-Nov-3 Germann, Zurich #835 (S.FR 700)

LUTHY, Johannes (1803-1873) Swiss
£786 $1431 €1148 Portraits of a husband and wife (62x48cm-24x19in) s.d.1826 pair. 16-Jun-4 Fischer, Luzern #1304/R (S.FR 1800)
£1135 $2089 €1657 Anna Justine Gehret with dog (56x43cm-22x17in) s.d. i. verso. 14-Jun-4 Philippe Schuler, Zurich #4219/R est:1800-2400 (S.FR 2600)

LUTHY, Oskar Wilhelm (1882-1945) Swiss
£351 $586 €512 Self portrait (40x30cm-16x12in) s.d.1914 verso prov. 15-Nov-3 Galerie Gloggner, Luzern #79/R (S.FR 800)
£995 $1593 €1453 Still life with roses (81x66cm-32x26in) s.d.1931 panel. 16-Sep-3 Philippe Schuler, Zurich #3243/R est:3000-3500 (S.FR 2200)
£1136 $1886 €1647 Holy Family (145x171cm-57x67in) s.d.1930 panel. 13-Jun-3 Zofingen, Switzerland #2925/R est:2000 (S.FR 2500)
£1310 $2410 €1913 Still life with roses (66x55cm-26x22in) s.d. masonite. 14-Jun-4 Philippe Schuler, Zurich #4220/R est:3000-3500 (S.FR 3000)
£2619 $4190 €3798 Spring landscape in the Anniviers valley (145x205cm-57x81in) s.d.1909. 15-May-3 Stuker, Bern #1368/R est:4000-5000 (S.FR 5500)
£5238 $8381 €7595 Winter landscape in the Anniviers valley (145x205cm-57x81in) s.d.1909. 15-May-3 Stuker, Bern #1367/R est:4000-5000 (S.FR 11000)
£7018 $11719 €10246 Flock of sheep in autumn sun (126x200cm-50x79in) s.d.08 s.i. verso prov. 15-Nov-3 Galerie Gloggner, Luzern #78/R est:5000-6000 (S.FR 16000)
£13913 $25461 €20313 Requiem dans les Alpes (144x204cm-57x80in) s.d.09 prov. 5-Jun-4 Galerie du Rhone, Sion #550/R est:40000-50000 (S.FR 32000)

LUTI, Benedetto (1666-1724) Italian
£7222 $13000 €10544 Saint Sebastian tended by saint Irene (137x102cm-54x40in) 23-Jan-4 Christie's, Rockefeller NY #200/R est:8000-12000
£18000 $32940 €26280 Christ in the house of Simon the Pharisee (36x47cm-14x19in) feigned oval. 7-Jul-4 Christie's, London #101/R est:20000-30000

LUTI, Benedetto (attrib) (1666-1724) Italian
£1400 $2520 €2044 Saint Peter (49x36cm-19x14in) canvas on panel. 23-Apr-4 Christie's, Kensington #219/R est:3000-5000
£5500 $10065 €8030 Portrait of young boy (38x30cm-15x12in) 9-Jul-4 Christie's, Kensington #174/R est:6000-8000
Works on paper
£508 $950 €742 Seated male nude (48x38cm-19x15in) red chk. 25-Feb-4 Dallas Auction Gallery, Dallas #27/R

LUTKEN, Eirik (1962-) Norwegian
£604 $1003 €876 Self-portrait (60x43cm-24x17in) painted c.1997. 16-Jun-3 Blomqvist, Lysaker #1128/R (N.KR 7000)

LUTTER, Vera (20th C) ?
Photographs
£4749 $8500 €6934 Fulton Ferry landing (35x53cm-14x21in) s.i.d.1996 verso unique camera obscura gelatin silver print prov. 13-May-4 Sotheby's, New York #385/R est:4000-6000
£25150 $42000 €36719 Rockefeller Centre, West III (221x284cm-87x112in) s.d.March 17, 1998 verso obscura gelatin silver print linen prov. 17-Oct-3 Phillips, New York #22/R est:30000-40000
£33520 $60000 €48939 Frankfurt Airport IV (205x425cm-81x167in) gelatin silver print prov.exhib. 12-May-4 Christie's, Rockefeller NY #443/R est:60000-80000

LUTTEROTH, Ascan (1842-1923) German
£900 $1503 €1314 Stroll by lake (70x56cm-28x22in) s. 12-Nov-3 Sotheby's, Olympia #151/R
£1250 $2037 €1800 Spring landscape with canal (65x55cm-26x22in) s. 24-Sep-3 Neumeister, Munich #487a/R est:2500
£1259 $2102 €1800 Tree blossom (55x80cm-22x31in) s. 28-Jun-3 Bolland & Marotz, Bremen #700/R est:2000
£1667 $2633 €2400 Spring (75x118cm-30x46in) s. i. stretcher. 6-Sep-3 Schopman, Hamburg #760/R est:2000
£1788 $3254 €2700 View of Capri in the evening sunshine (130x100cm-51x39in) s. 18-Jun-4 Bolland & Marotz, Bremen #680/R est:2700
£2361 $3896 €3400 Monte Pellegrino from Palermo (54x81cm-21x32in) s. 3-Jul-3 Van Ham, Cologne #1342/R est:2900
£3020 $5346 €4500 The four seasons (206x246cm-81x97in) mono.i. four parts. 28-Apr-4 Schopman, Hamburg #633/R est:6000
Works on paper
£280 $467 €400 Boys working on Ferioli coast, Italy (36x51cm-14x20in) s.d.20/885. 28-Jun-3 Bolland & Marotz, Bremen #701/R
£490 $832 €700 Campagna landscape with Roman ruins (16x26cm-6x10in) s.d.1877 W/C. 27-Nov-3 Bassenge, Berlin #5613/R
£600 $960 €870 Caves at Posillipo (34x24cm-13x9in) s.i.d.29.5.73 W/C. 18-Sep-3 Christie's, Kensington #90/R
£3521 $6092 €5000 Rome, Appia Antica. Rome, convent (22x34cm-9x13in) s.d.1876 W/C card pair. 11-Dec-3 Christie's, Rome #24/R est:1300-1800

LUTTEROTH, Emma (1854-1894) German
£1678 $2853 €2400 Fishermen with boats in the Lagoon (71x129cm-28x51in) s. 20-Nov-3 Van Ham, Cologne #1732/R est:4500

LUTTICHUYS, Isaak (1616-1673) Dutch
£8333 $15000 €12166 Portrait of a woman with a fan (102x78cm-40x31in) prov. 22-Jan-4 Sotheby's, New York #214/R est:20000-30000

LUTTICHUYS, Isaak (attrib) (1616-1673) Dutch
£3297 $6000 €4814 Portrait of a lady, three-quarter length, in a black dress (94x81cm-37x32in) 4-Feb-4 Christie's, Rockefeller NY #72/R est:3000-5000

LUTTMANN, August (1830-1882) German
£526 $968 €800 Travellers walking through the Ruhr valley (50x70cm-20x28in) s.d.1852 s.i. on stretcher. 22-Jun-4 Christie's, Amsterdam #78/R

LUTTRINGSHAUSEN, Johann Heinrich (1783-1857) German
Works on paper
£544 $974 €800 Vue de Harfleur en Normandie, avec un marche sur les berges de la Seine (21x29cm-8x11in) graphite pen black ink. 18-Mar-4 Christie's, Paris #301/R

LUTY, Max (1859-?) German
£1487 $2320 €2350 Snow village on Dachauer Moor (75x96cm-30x38in) s. s. stretcher. 18-Oct-2 Von Zezschwitz, Munich #29/R est:2500

LUTYENS, Charles Augustus Henry (1829-1915) British
£775 $1340 €1100 Putti (45x80cm-18x31in) s. 9-Dec-3 Pandolfini, Florence #192/R
£900 $1611 €1314 Cherubs Saints Francis. John the Baptist. Christopher (20x16cm-8x6in) s. set of three. 16-Mar-4 Bonhams, Oxford #64
£1000 $1700 €1460 Putti disporting in clouds. Putti amidst clouds (32x25cm-13x10in) s. pair. 26-Nov-3 Hamptons Fine Art, Godalming #197 est:500-700
£1100 $1837 €1606 Putti disporting in the clouds (30x91cm-12x36in) s. 12-Nov-3 Sotheby's, Olympia #105/R est:600-800

LUTYENS, Frederick M (1860-1924) British
£800 $1488 €1168 Dapple grey horse in stable (41x51cm-16x20in) s. indis d. 4-Mar-4 Mitchells, Cockermouth #793/R

LUTZ, Anton (20th C) ?
£1467 $2625 €2200 Landscape with cross (31x41cm-12x16in) s.d.53 panel. 13-May-4 Dorotheum, Linz #470/R est:3000-3800
£2133 $3819 €3200 Still life of flowers (63x54cm-25x21in) s.d.63 board. 13-May-4 Dorotheum, Linz #463/R est:6400-8000
£2517 $4280 €3600 Attersee landscape (37x46cm-15x18in) s. board. 27-Nov-3 Dorotheum, Linz #455/R est:6000-8000
£3846 $6538 €5500 On the Danube (78x98cm-31x39in) s.d.42. 27-Nov-3 Dorotheum, Linz #453/R est:8000-10000

LUTZ, Dan (1906-1978) American
£279 $500 €407 Sandpipers (61x76cm-24x30in) s. 21-Mar-4 Bonhams & Butterfields, Los Angeles #7334/R
£326 $600 €476 Still life with cornupia (76x61cm-30x24in) s. 13-Jun-4 Bonhams & Butterfields, Los Angeles #7034/R
£682 $1200 €996 Maguey (102x127cm-40x50in) s. 23-May-4 Bonhams & Butterfields, Los Angeles #7040/R
£765 $1300 €1117 Sittin, figure in rocking chair (30x23cm-12x9in) s. 18-Nov-3 John Moran, Pasadena #199

LUTZ, Louis (1940-) French
Sculpture
£933 $1717 €1400 Couple enlace (39x31x30cm-15x12x12in) s.d.1968 num.3/8 brown pat bronze socle. 14-Jun-4 Tajan, Paris #172 est:1200-1500

LUTZ, Lucien (20th C) French
£1164 $1979 €1700 Port de Saint-Tropez (65x92cm-26x36in) s. 9-Nov-3 Eric Pillon, Calais #224/R

LUTZ-WALDNER, Erwin (1912-1975) Austrian
£800 $1472 €1200 Southern village in hilly landscape (100x118cm-39x46in) s. 9-Jun-4 Dorotheum, Salzburg #646/R

LUU CONG NHAN (1931-) Oriental
£2614 $4732 €3816 Village scene (50x65cm-20x26in) s. 4-Apr-4 Sotheby's, Singapore #178/R est:6000-8000 (S.D 8000)

LUVONI, Luigi (1859-1904) Italian
£336 $594 €500 Alagna Valle Sesia (39x31cm-15x12in) s.i.d.1883 cardboard on canvas. 1-May-4 Meeting Art, Vercelli #140
£369 $653 €550 Lavena Valle Torrazza (39x29cm-15x11in) s. i.d.1884 verso cardboard on canvas. 1-May-4 Meeting Art, Vercelli #296

LUX, Theodore (1910-) German
£8380 $15000 €12235 Seine near Honfleur (51x97cm-20x38in) s. exhib. 14-May-4 Skinner, Boston #312/R est:1200-1800

LUXBURY, Mary Ellen (1839-?) American
£1765 $3300 €2577 Child holding doll seated in a Windsor rocker (71x61cm-28x24in) s.verso. 28-Feb-4 William A Smith, Plainfield #56/R

LUXMOORE, Frances (?) British?
Works on paper
£780 $1435 €1139 Portrait of a lady in a green dress and feathered hat (33x24cm-13x9in) W/C. 23-Jun-4 Cheffins, Cambridge #461/R

LUXORO, Alfredo (1859-1918) Italian
£1689 $2973 €2500 Portrait of girl in interior (174x110cm-69x43in) 19-May-4 Il Ponte, Milan #604 est:2500-2800

LUXTON, Doris E (?) British?
Works on paper
£500 $880 €730 The golf links, westward ho (21x49cm-8x19in) s. W/C sold with oil by Francis E Hiley. 19-May-4 Dreweatt Neate, Newbury #42

LUYKEN, Jan (1649-1712) Dutch
Works on paper
£3767 $6404 €5500 Crowning of William and Mary in Westminster (11x15cm-4x6in) i.verso pen brown ink wash prov.exhib. 4-Nov-3 Sotheby's, Amsterdam #131/R est:1500-3000

LUYKEN, Jan (attrib) (1649-1712) Dutch
Works on paper
£1370 $2329 €2000 King Udislaus of Poland being hit by fireworks set off in his honour (15x20cm-6x8in) i.verso pen brown ink grey wash over black chk. 4-Nov-3 Sotheby's, Amsterdam #130/R est:2000-3000

LUYKX, Christiaan (1623-c.1653) Flemish
£3497 $5944 €5000 Roses (40x58cm-16x23in) panel. 20-Nov-3 Van Ham, Cologne #1376/R est:7000
£4800 $8304 €7008 Garland of roses and other flowers around a stone cartouche (91x74cm-36x29in) 12-Dec-3 Christie's, Kensington #92/R est:5000-8000

LUYPAERT, Jean (1893-1954) Belgian
£355 $592 €500 Vue deSainte-Maxime (24x33cm-9x13in) s. canvas on cardboard. 14-Oct-3 Vanderkindere, Brussels #127

LUYT, Arie Marthinus (1879-1951) Dutch
Works on paper
£408 $743 €600 Soldiers at the Grebbeberg during the First World War (45x38cm-18x15in) s. W/C bodycol. 3-Feb-4 Christie's, Amsterdam #362
£940 $1738 €1400 View of Trafalgar Square (48x32cm-19x13in) s. pencil W/C. 15-Mar-4 Sotheby's, Amsterdam #113/R est:1000-1500

LUZ, Arturo Iz (1926-) Philippino
£4731 $7570 €6907 Moon magic (86x56cm-34x22in) s.i.d.1962 verso. 18-May-3 Sotheby's, Singapore #92/R est:11000 15000 (S.D 13200)
£7190 $13013 €10497 Two men on a wire (122x183cm-48x72in) s. s.verso acrylic collage panel. 4-Apr-4 Sotheby's, Singapore #112/R est:22000-32000 (S.D 22000)
Works on paper
£6882 $11011 €10048 Acrobats (78x121cm-31x48in) s. mixed media. 18-May-3 Sotheby's, Singapore #73/R est:9000-12000 (S.D 19200)

LUZRO, Giovanni (attrib) (fl.1850-1877) Italian
Works on paper
£1118 $1900 €1632 British brig providential of Dartmouth, Joshua Collings , Commander, entering port of Venice (38x58cm-15x23in) W/C. 31-Oct-3 North East Auctions, Portsmouth #1710

LUZURIAGA, Juan Ramon (1938-) Spanish
£699 $1168 €1000 Bilbao market (54x65cm-21x26in) s. s.i.d.1976 verso. 30-Jun-3 Ansorena, Madrid #239/R
£704 $1127 €1000 Low tide in Deusto (64x53cm-25x21in) s. s.i.d.1977 verso. 16-Sep-3 Segre, Madrid #156/R
£733 $1327 €1100 Bilbao market (54x65cm-21x26in) s.d.1976 s.i.d.verso exhib. 30-Mar-4 Segre, Madrid #247/R
£789 $1429 €1200 Lezama Station, Bilbao (81x65cm-32x26in) s. s.i.d.1976 verso. 14-Apr-4 Ansorena, Madrid #31/R
£872 $1632 €1300 Balcony (65x54cm-26x21in) s. s.i.d.1976 verso. 24-Feb-4 Durán, Madrid #172/R
£897 $1488 €1300 Old embarcadero (60x73cm-24x29in) s. s.i.d.1978 verso. 1-Oct-3 Ansorena, Madrid #557/R
£1056 $1827 €1500 Reflexions (81x65cm-32x26in) s. s.i.d.1975 verso. 15-Dec-3 Ansorena, Madrid #285/R est:1150
£1064 $1723 €1500 Paseando por la ribera (73x92cm-29x36in) s. s.i.d.1978 verso. 20-May-3 Ansorena, Madrid #298/R est:1300
£1096 $1863 €1600 Cargo boats (81x100cm-32x39in) s. 4-Nov-3 Ansorena, Madrid #348/R est:1500
£1181 $2007 €1700 Dam and bridge, Bilbao (73x92cm-29x36in) s. s.i.d.1977 verso. 28-Oct-3 Segre, Madrid #327/R est:1300
£1552 $2591 €2250 Rainy day (65x54cm-26x21in) s. s.d.1975 verso. 17-Nov-3 Durán, Madrid #115/R est:1000
£1597 $2540 €2300 Bilbao gris (81x100cm-32x39in) s. s.i.d.1976 verso. 29-Apr-3 Durán, Madrid #129/R est:1500

LUZZI, Cleto (19/20th C) Italian
£7200 $13104 €10512 Recital (56x85cm-22x33in) s.i. prov. 16-Jun-4 Bonhams, New Bond Street #79/R est:7000-10000

LUZZO, Anthony (1855-1907) Italian?
£1818 $3091 €2600 The Annie Lloydf (38x64cm-15x25in) s.d.1885 tempera paperpair. 18-Nov-3 Cambi, Genoa #383/R est:2500-3000
Works on paper
£580 $1073 €847 Larunda at sea (26x47cm-10x19in) s.d.1898 W/C gouache. 17-Jul-4 Bonhams, Knightsbridge #193a/R

LUZZO, Giovanni (19/20th C) Italian
Works on paper
£839 $1427 €1200 The Polynesia (45x66cm-18x26in) s.d.1921 gouache. 18-Nov-3 Cambi, Genoa #353/R

LUZZO, Vincenzo (attrib) (fl.1855-1875) Italian
Works on paper
£1200 $2268 €1752 Barque - Ariadne of Sunderland leaving Venice (32x52cm-13x20in) W/C arched top. 17-Feb-4 Bonhams, New Bond Street #6/R est:700-1000

LVOV, Piotr Ivanovich (1882-1944) Russian
Works on paper
£364 $663 €550 Village landscape (12x17cm-5x7in) s. Cyrillic i.d.1930 W/C. 19-Jun-4 Bergmann, Erlangen #877

LVOV, Piotr Ivanovich (attrib) (1882-1944) Russian
£350 $553 €511 Sunny path through snowy woods (45x54cm-18x21in) s. 24-Jul-3 Lawrence, Crewkerne #937/R

LYALL, Laura Adeline (1860-1930) Canadian
£2800 $5124 €4088 Young girl in a garden (57x44cm-22x17in) s. 1-Jun-4 Joyner Waddington, Toronto #186/R est:8000-10000 (C.D 7000)
£3252 $5821 €4748 Portrait of Margo, Jack and Eleanor Goldie Breckenridge (74x69cm-29x27in) s.d.1911 prov. 31-May-4 Sotheby's, Toronto #75/R est:6000-8000 (C.D 8000)
£6306 $10721 €9207 Woman in wide-brimmed hat (45x53cm-18x21in) s. canvas on masonite prov. 18-Nov-3 Sotheby's, Toronto #2/R est:6000-8000 (C.D 14000)
£8130 $14553 €11870 Portrait of Dorothy (39x49cm-15x19in) board prov. 31-May-4 Sotheby's, Toronto #112/R est:6000-8000 (C.D 20000)
£9350 $16736 €13651 Portrait of Margo Breckenridge (56x46cm-22x18in) s.d.11 prov. 31-May-4 Sotheby's, Toronto #76/R est:9000-12000 (C.D 23000)
£11200 $20496 €16352 Mother and child (65x55cm-26x22in) s.d.April 88. 1-Jun-4 Joyner Waddington, Toronto #83/R est:10000-15000 (C.D 28000)
Works on paper
£225 $383 €329 Seascape (31x33cm-12x13in) s. W/C prov. 27-Nov-3 Heffel, Vancouver #102 (C.D 500)
£2846 $5093 €4155 Portrait of a young lady (38x30cm-15x12in) s.d.1902 s.i.verso. 31-May-4 Sotheby's, Toronto #184/R est:2500-3500 (C.D 7000)

LYBAERT, Theophile Marie Françoise (1848-1927) Belgian
£5000 $9150 €7500 Garde en priere (61x35cm-24x14in) s.d.89 panel. 3-Jun-4 Tajan, Paris #288/R est:7500-8000

LYDEN, Edvin (1879-1956) Finnish
£423 $731 €600 Gypsy camp (44x53cm-17x21in) s. painted c.1917 lit. 13-Dec-3 Hagelstam, Helsinki #154/R
£563 $975 €800 Landscape with Nadendals Church (43x53cm-17x21in) s.d.1914 lit. 13-Dec-3 Hagelstam, Helsinki #153/R

LYDIS, Mariette (1890-1970) Austrian
£336 $625 €500 Portrait de fillette (41x33cm-16x13in) s.d.1946 prov. 3-Mar-4 Tajan, Paris #124
£1678 $3121 €2500 Portrait d'une elegante (65x53cm-26x21in) s.i.d.1937. 2-Mar-4 Artcurial Briest, Paris #212/R est:2000-2500
Works on paper
£235 $437 €350 Femmes, Afrique du Nord (21x24cm-8x9in) studio st. W/C graphite. 2-Mar-4 Artcurial Briest, Paris #47
£336 $625 €500 Keltoum assise, Marrakech (34x25cm-13x10in) s.i.d.1925 W/C graphite. 2-Mar-4 Artcurial Briest, Paris #45

LYDZBA, Jacek (20th C) Polish
£229 $381 €334 Two children (120x100cm-47x39in) painted 1999. 2-Oct-3 Agra, Warsaw #56/R (P.Z 1500)

LYKASCHEWSKI, Rolf (?) ?
£659 $1100 €962 Untitled (140x100cm-55x39in) s. acrylic. 20-Oct-3 Sotheby's, New York #118/R

LYMAN, Harry (19th C) ?
£1271 $2250 €1856 Racehorse, Morello, in a stable (56x43cm-22x17in) s.d.1893. 27-Apr-4 Doyle, New York #24a/R est:1000-1500

LYMAN, John Goodwin (1886-1967) Canadian
£2027 $3446 €2959 Lake Massawippi V (46x38cm-18x15in) s. i.verso panel prov.exhib. 18-Nov-3 Sotheby's, Toronto #176/R est:5000-7000 (C.D 4500)
£2200 $4026 €3212 Coral and shells (40x55cm-16x22in) s. prov. 1-Jun-4 Joyner Waddington, Toronto #213/R est:3500-4000 (C.D 5500)
£5856 $9955 €8550 Hydrangeas and birch trees (46x37cm-18x15in) s. i.verso masonite prov.exhib. 18-Nov-3 Sotheby's, Toronto #174/R est:6000-9000 (C.D 13000)
£9350 $16736 €13651 Group on Provincetown beach (30x40cm-12x16in) s. canvasboard prov. 6-May-4 Heffel, Vancouver #90/R est:12000-15000 (C.D 23000)
Works on paper
£545 $889 €796 Seated nude (43x23cm-17x9in) s. chl. 23-Sep-3 Ritchie, Toronto #154/R est:1000-1500 (C.D 1200)
£602 $1120 €879 Reclining nude (23x44cm-9x17in) chl graphite. 2-Mar-4 Ritchie, Toronto #162/R (C.D 1500)
£676 $1149 €987 Family promenade (26x32cm-10x13in) s. W/C sepia executed 1936 prov. 27-Nov-3 Heffel, Vancouver #152/R (C.D 1500)
£1829 $3274 €2670 The family (26x32cm-10x13in) s. gouache exec. 1936 prov. 6-May-4 Heffel, Vancouver #91/R est:5000-7000 (C.D 4500)

LYMAN, Joseph (jnr) (1843-1913) American
£649 $1200 €948 Lakeside landscape (43x56cm-17x22in) s. 15-Jul-4 Sotheby's, New York #48/R

LYMBEROPOULOU-ARGYROU, Eugenia (1902-1975) Greek
£750 $1343 €1095 Still life of roses (50x55cm-20x22in) s. prov. 11-May-4 Bonhams, New Bond Street #53/R

LYMBURNER, Francis (1916-1972) Australian
£305 $556 €445 Elizabeth (38x32cm-15x13in) s.i.d.1946 oil on paper. 16-Jun-4 Deutscher-Menzies, Melbourne #578/R (A.D 800)
£363 $660 €530 Mother and daughter (43x28cm-17x11in) s. canvas on board. 16-Jun-4 Deutscher-Menzies, Melbourne #564/R (A.D 950)
£496 $903 €724 At rehearsal (38x30cm-15x12in) s. i.verso canvas on board. 16-Jun-4 Deutscher-Menzies, Melbourne #415/R est:1500-2000 (A.D 1300)
£766 $1302 €1118 Red Dress (34x24cm-13x9in) i.verso board. 26-Nov-3 Deutscher-Menzies, Melbourne #249/R (A.D 1800)
£1301 $2042 €1899 Circus audience (39x48cm-15x19in) s. canvasboard. 1-Sep-3 Shapiro, Sydney #323/R est:3000-5000 (A.D 3200)
£1653 $3058 €2413 Figure on the beach (30x61cm-12x24in) board painted c.1950 prov. 10-Mar-4 Deutscher-Menzies, Melbourne #60/R est:4000-6000 (A.D 4000)
Works on paper
£248 $421 €362 Resting kangaroo (20x29cm-8x11in) s. pen ink wash. 29-Oct-3 Lawson Menzies, Sydney #180/R (A.D 600)
£267 $486 €390 Boys from Syracuse (36x46cm-14x18in) s.i. ink wash. 16-Jun-4 Deutscher-Menzies, Melbourne #574/R (A.D 700)
£286 $521 €418 Shakespeare from the wings (35x21cm-14x8in) s.i.d.1964 W/C ink wash. 16-Jun-4 Deutscher-Menzies, Melbourne #575/R (A.D 750)
£360 $612 €526 Strip Club, London. s.i.d.60 ink wash prov.exhib. 24-Nov-3 Sotheby's, Melbourne #201 (A.D 850)
£638 $1085 €931 Dressing room study (30x32cm-12x13in) s.i. W/C ink. 25-Nov-3 Christie's, Melbourne #300 (A.D 1500)
£1277 $2170 €1864 At the dressing table (26x32cm-10x13in) s.d.1960 W/C ink. 25-Nov-3 Christie's, Melbourne #244/R est:1800-2500 (A.D 3000)

LYNAS-GRAY (1869-1940) British
Works on paper
£420 $752 €613 Cottages at Newlyn (29x44cm-11x17in) s. W/C. 17-Mar-4 James Thompson, Kirby Lonsdale #129

LYNAS-GRAY, John Abernethy (1869-1940) British
Works on paper
£320 $506 €467 Young girl with dog before a thatched cottage on the Anglesey coast (29x44cm-11x17in) s.d.1919 W/C. 5-Sep-3 Honiton Galleries, Honiton #32/R
£620 $1110 €905 Village street, Sussex (28x44cm-11x17in) s.d.1922 W/C. 26-May-4 Sotheby's, Olympia #95/R

LYNCH, Albert (1851-?) Peruvian
£3889 $7000 €5678 Young woman in white (99x65cm-39x26in) s. 21-Jan-4 Sotheby's, New York #211/R est:10000-15000
£16667 $30000 €24334 Morning walk (115x82cm-45x32in) s. prov. 22-Apr-4 Christie's, Rockefeller NY #73/R est:18000-25000

LYNCH, Henrietta (fl.1882-1919) Irish
Works on paper
£520 $941 €759 Ireland (38x28cm-15x11in) W/C. 2-Apr-4 Bracketts, Tunbridge Wells #430/R

LYNCH, Justo (1870-1953) Argentinian
£4372 $8000 €6383 Evening light (20x24cm-8x9in) canvas on cardboard. 1-Jun-4 Arroyo, Buenos Aires #51

LYNCH, Padraig (1940-) Irish
£1611 $2883 €2400 At Loughshinney (50x75cm-20x30in) s. 26-May-4 James Adam, Dublin #102/R est:1250-1750

LYNDE, Raymond (19/20th C) British
£460 $842 €672 Bearded gentleman in a conservatory interior (29x40cm-11x16in) s. 6-Jul-4 Bearnes, Exeter #473/R

LYNDSAY, Roy (20th C) Irish?
£352 $616 €500 Study of an old cart (28x32cm-11x13in) s. board. 16-Dec-3 James Adam, Dublin #92/R
£366 $641 €520 Waterfall (52x30cm-20x12in) s. 16-Dec-3 James Adam, Dublin #97/R
£805 $1442 €1200 Thursday morning, Spain (38x49cm-15x19in) s. i. verso. 31-May-4 Hamilton Osborne King, Dublin #27/R
£2517 $4280 €3600 Laytown and Betystown races (41x99cm-16x39in) s. i.verso. 25-Nov-3 De Veres Art Auctions, Dublin #161/R est:4000-6000
£4225 $7310 €6000 Galway races (40x100cm-16x39in) s. i.verso. 10-Dec-3 Bonhams & James Adam, Dublin #120/R est:3000-5000
£6250 $10188 €9000 Meeting at the Last Stakes in the Phoenix Park (40x100cm-16x39in) s.i.verso. 24-Sep-3 James Adam, Dublin #43/R est:3000-5000

LYNE, Michael (1912-1989) British
£600 $1098 €876 Pursuit (51x74cm-20x29in) s. 7-Apr-4 Woolley & Wallis, Salisbury #269/R
£900 $1656 €1314 Show jumpers (61x76cm-24x30in) s. 10-Jun-4 Christie's, Kensington #202/R
£1100 $2024 €1606 Pursuit (51x76cm-20x30in) s. 10-Jun-4 Christie's, Kensington #201/R est:1200-1800
£1497 $2500 €2186 Grand National, Bechers 1968 (61x91cm-24x36in) s. prov. 7-Oct-3 Sotheby's, New York #167 est:4000-6000
£3000 $5280 €4380 Going home (61x91cm-24x36in) s. prov. 21-May-4 Christie's, London #4/R est:3000-5000
£3352 $6000 €4894 Vaguely Noble beating Sir Ivor (61x91cm-24x36in) s. prov. 27-May-4 Sotheby's, New York #301/R est:6000-8000
£8000 $14080 €11680 Hitting off (71x107cm-28x42in) s. prov. 21-May-4 Christie's, London #1/R est:5000-8000
Works on paper
£350 $648 €511 Fox crossing a woodland path (13x25cm-5x10in) s. W/C. 13-Feb-4 Keys, Aylsham #488
£350 $648 €511 Fox hounds crossing a field (18x28cm-7x11in) s. W/C. 13-Feb-4 Keys, Aylsham #490/R
£920 $1684 €1343 Dogs study (33x51cm-13x20in) s.d.1946 W/C bodycol. 28-Jul-4 Mallams, Oxford #162/R
£1000 $1840 €1460 Too windy (23x33cm-9x13in) s.d.1981 gouache prov. 10-Jun-4 Christie's, Kensington #190/R est:700-900

LYNEN, Amedee (1852-1938) Belgian
£347 $552 €500 Paysage avec berger (45x72cm-18x28in) s.d.1919 cardboard. 9-Sep-3 Palais de Beaux Arts, Brussels #250
Works on paper
£270 $511 €400 Un consommateur terrace (24x19cm-9x7in) s.d.1932 chl htd W/C. 17-Feb-4 Vanderkindere, Brussels #408
£694 $1104 €1000 La joyeuse entree (17x26cm-7x10in) s. pen W/C dr. 15-Sep-3 Horta, Bruxelles #355
£759 $1403 €1100 Fantaisie (23x18cm-9x7in) s.d.89 Indian ink drawing htd wash. 19-Jan-4 Horta, Bruxelles #299
£2133 $3925 €3200 Joyeuse entree (39x55cm-15x22in) s.d.1911 mixed media. 14-Jun-4 Horta, Bruxelles #102/R est:3500-5000

LYNEN, Andre (1888-1984) Belgian
£268 $497 €400 Coastal scene (40x50cm-16x20in) s.d.1927 board. 15-Mar-4 Sotheby's, Amsterdam #148/R

LYNES, George Platt (1907-1955) American
Photographs
£1693 $3200 €2472 Jared French (11x9cm-4x4in) i. verso silver print. 17-Feb-4 Swann Galleries, New York #63/R est:1800-2200
£2328 $4400 €3399 Francisco Moncion (23x18cm-9x7in) silver print. 17-Feb-4 Swann Galleries, New York #86/R est:4000-5000

LYNGBO, Christen (1871-1968) Danish
£280 $517 €409 Landscape (41x71cm-16x28in) s. 15-Mar-4 Rasmussen, Vejle #431 (D.KR 3100)
£287 $516 €419 Evening sunshine over village (34x45cm-13x18in) init.d.1916. 24-Apr-4 Rasmussen, Havnen #2065 (D.KR 3200)
£289 $534 €422 Dune landscape (47x71cm-19x28in) s.d.64. 15-Mar-4 Rasmussen, Vejle #432 (D.KR 3200)
£305 $548 €445 Heath landscape (65x99cm-26x39in) s.d.1952. 24-Apr-4 Rasmussen, Havnen #2064/R (D.KR 3400)
£361 $667 €527 Dune landscape (48x71cm-19x28in) s. 15-Mar-4 Rasmussen, Vejle #433 (D.KR 4000)
£376 $677 €549 Interior scene with woman by spinning wheel (69x61cm-27x24in) s.d.1951. 24-Apr-4 Rasmussen, Havnen #2061 (D.KR 4200)
£379 $701 €553 Dune landscape with dune roses (61x100cm-24x39in) s.d.63. 15-Mar-4 Rasmussen, Vejle #417 (D.KR 4200)
£389 $622 €568 Thatched house in sunshine (66x69cm-26x27in) s.d.1961. 22-Sep-3 Rasmussen, Vejle #533 (D.KR 4100)
£541 $1001 €790 View of the ocean (52x71cm-20x28in) s. 15-Mar-4 Rasmussen, Vejle #434 (D.KR 6000)
£559 $1034 €816 Sheep grazing, Sondervig (63x52cm-25x20in) s. 15-Mar-4 Rasmussen, Vejle #467/R (D.KR 6200)

LYNN, Elwyn Augustus (1917-1997) Australian
£264 $415 €383 Untitled - still life (52x70cm-20x28in) s.d.55. 26-Aug-3 Lawson Menzies, Sydney #135 est:500-700 (A.D 650)
£2439 $3829 €3537 Tidal (122x152cm-48x60in) s.i.d.1965 verso oil mixed media. 27-Aug-3 Christie's, Sydney #686/R est:5000-7000 (A.D 6000)
Works on paper
£234 $438 €351 Finn's breakfast table (24x31cm-9x12in) s. i.verso collage. 20-Jul-4 Goodman, Sydney #71/R (A.D 600)
£288 $521 €420 Downhill (59x79cm-23x31in) s.d.1977 mixed media string banknote photo synthetic polymer. 30-Mar-4 Lawson Menzies, Sydney #106/R (A.D 700)
£514 $920 €750 Mocca (25x43cm-10x17in) collage. 15-May-4 Christie's, Sydney #473/R (A.D 1300)
£909 $1682 €1327 Untitled (45x61cm-18x24in) s.d.1970 i.verso mixed media on board. 10-Mar-4 Deutscher-Menzies, Melbourne #482/R est:2000-3000 (A.D 2200)
£1061 $1953 €1549 Last snow (60x70cm-24x28in) s.i.d.verso mixed media prov. 29-Mar-4 Goodman, Sydney #65/R est:1500-2500 (A.D 2600)

LYNN, John (fl.1826-1838) British
£1800 $3402 €2628 Distress signal answered (25x36cm-10x14in) prov. 17-Feb-4 Bonhams, New Bond Street #20/R est:2000-3000
£3500 $6020 €5110 British naval brig chasing a Dutch lugger (30x45cm-12x18in) s.d.1833. 2-Dec-3 Sotheby's, London #19/R est:2000-3000

LYNN, Robert (1940-) British
£979 $1664 €1400 Meadow, County Wicklow (76x57cm-30x22in) s.d.1984 i.verso. 18-Nov-3 Whyte's, Dublin #93/R

LYNTON, Henry S (19/20th C) British
Works on paper
£621 $1030 €900 Nile by Cairo (27x70cm-11x28in) s.d.909 W/C. 30-Sep-3 Dorotheum, Vienna #272/R

LYON, Danny (1942-) American
Photographs
£2395 $4000 €3497 McHenry, Illinois (20x30cm-8x12in) s.i.d.1966/1968 verso gelatin silver print. 21-Oct-3 Bonhams & Butterfields, San Francisco #1559/R

LYON, Harold (1930-) Canadian
£452 $756 €660 Leaning barn. After rain, Swampland. board three. 17-Nov-3 Hodgins, Calgary #398/R est:500-700 (C.D 1000)
£560 $1025 €818 Desert sun (45x60cm-18x24in) s.i. 1-Jun-4 Hodgins, Calgary #370/R (C.D 1400)

LYON, Henry J (fl.1897-1933) British
Works on paper
£280 $512 €409 Walberswick, Suffolk, with boats pulled up onto riverbank (27x37cm-11x15in) s. W/C. 6-Jul-4 Peter Wilson, Nantwich #83/R

LYON, John Howard (?-1921) British
£500 $910 €730 Mountainous landscape with highland cattle on a path near a pool of water (40x50cm-16x20in) s. 16-Jun-4 Rupert Toovey, Partridge Green #25/R
£950 $1739 €1387 Loch scene (46x63cm-18x25in) s. board. 7-Apr-4 Bonhams, Bury St Edmunds #459/R

LYON, Thomas Bonar (1873-1955) British
£560 $980 €818 Ayrshire lane, summer (29x36cm-11x14in) s. board. 18-Dec-3 Bonhams, Edinburgh #332
£605 $1113 €883 Millers House in the Grange Estates by Culroy. River landscape (30x38cm-12x15in) s. s.i.d.1938 verso panel two. 14-Jun-4 Waddingtons, Toronto #183/R est:1500-2000 (C.D 1500)
£950 $1663 €1387 Dunure harbour, Ayrshire (30x40cm-12x16in) s. board. 18-Dec-3 Bonhams, Edinburgh #331

LYONS, Arthur J (fl.1911-1921) British
£550 $990 €803 Study of a female ballet dancer seated on a stool (89x71cm-35x28in) s.d.15 prov. 21-Apr-4 Tennants, Leyburn #1219

LYONS, Catherine (?) ?
Works on paper
£500 $905 €750 Bergeres au bord du lac (54x40cm-21x16in) s.d.1851 W/C. 30-Mar-4 Campo & Campo, Antwerp #165/R

LYONS, Fergus (?) Irish
£4000 $7160 €5840 Ballinasloe horse fair (93x122cm-37x48in) s.d.92 s.i.d.1992 verso exhib. 14-May-4 Christie's, Kensington #416/R est:1000-1500

LYR, Claude (1916-) Belgian
Works on paper
£350 $584 €500 Ville fantastique (30x40cm-12x16in) s.d.1965 mixed media. 13-Oct-3 Horta, Bruxelles #458

LYRE, Adolphe la (1850-1935) French
£1418 $2369 €2000 La rencontre sur le chime de Halage (38x56cm-15x22in) s.d.1875. 12-Oct-3 St-Germain-en-Laye Encheres #34/R est:2000-2500
£5556 $10000 €8112 Songs of the seas (150x198cm-59x78in) s.i.d.MDCCCXII prov. 21-Jan-4 Sotheby's, New York #182/R est:12000-18000

LYSSAK, Nikolai (1951-) Russian
£590 $986 €850 Silk sock (105x100cm-41x39in) s. 21-Oct-3 Campo & Campo, Antwerp #202

LYSSIENKO, Youri (1957-) Russian
£476 $867 €700 Le billard. s. 8-Feb-4 Lesieur & Le Bars, Le Havre #141

LYTENS, Gysbrecht (attrib) (17th C) Flemish
£12000 $21600 €17520 Forest landscape with travellers near a stream (54x83cm-21x33in) panel. 22-Apr-4 Sotheby's, London #7/R est:15000-20000

LYTKEN, Anna Maria (1917-) Danish
£609 $1016 €889 The artist's self portrait (100x91cm-39x36in) init. exhib. 25-Oct-3 Rasmussen, Havnen #4035/R (D.KR 6500)
£611 $1040 €892 Interior scene with the artist (71x82cm-28x32in) init. 29-Nov-3 Rasmussen, Havnen #4124 (D.KR 6500)

LYTRAS, Nicolas (1883-1927) Greek
£19000 $34010 €27740 Slope in Parnassos (32x37cm-13x15in) s. 11-May-4 Bonhams, New Bond Street #76/R est:10000-15000
£30000 $53700 €43800 The artist in his studio (27x41cm-11x16in) s. prov. 10-May-4 Sotheby's, Olympia #6/R est:15000-20000
£40000 $70000 €58400 Mountain village (47x66cm-19x26in) s. prov. 16-Dec-3 Bonhams, New Bond Street #75/R est:16000-20000

LYTRAS, Nikiforos (1832-1904) Greek
£10000 $17000 €14600 Study for the 'Dirge of Psara' (20x24cm-8x9in) s. canvas on board prov.exhib. 18-Nov-3 Sotheby's, London #20/R est:10000-15000
£14000 $25060 €20440 Portrait of an Arab (29cm-11in circular) leather back of tambourine prov. 11-May-4 Bonhams, New Bond Street #19/R est:12000-18000
£22000 $37400 €32120 Weaver (19x27cm-7x11in) s. canvas on board prov.exhib. 18-Nov-3 Sotheby's, London #21/R est:10000-15000

LYTRAS, Pericles (1888-1940) Greek
£22000 $37400 €32120 Church in pine forest (80x56cm-31x22in) s. 18-Nov-3 Sotheby's, London #6/R est:12000-18000

LYTTON, Neville Stephen (1879-1951) British
Works on paper
£650 $1170 €949 Sisina (25x43cm-10x17in) s.d.1934 W/C wash htd gilt. 21-Apr-4 Lyon & Turnbull, Edinburgh #244/R

LYTZEN, N A (1826-1890) Danish
£328 $564 €479 Oak-tree in Dyrehaven with deer in background (55x48cm-22x19in) s. 3-Dec-3 Museumsbygningen, Copenhagen #150 (D.KR 3500)

LYYTIKAINEN, Olli (1949-1987) Finnish
Works on paper
£3108 $5564 €4600 Negreiffel (35x49cm-14x19in) s.d.1984 W/C. 8-May-4 Bukowskis, Helsinki #260/R est:2500-3500

M M (?) ?
£450 $819 €657 Abstract - nine people in an interior (76x122cm-30x48in) mono. board. 4-Feb-4 John Nicholson, Haslemere #75/R

MA DAI (1885-1936) Chinese
Works on paper
£6401 $11522 €9345 Troopers (104x49cm-41x19in) s.i.d.1927 ink col hanging scroll. 26-Apr-4 Sotheby's, Hong Kong #569/R est:15000-25000 (HK.D 90000)

MA JIN (1900-1971) Chinese
Works on paper
£1991 $3585 €2907 Two horses (39x24cm-15x9in) s.i.d.1948 ink col scroll. 25-Apr-4 Christie's, Hong Kong #144/R est:20000-30000 (HK.D 28000)
£6757 $12162 €9865 Two running horses (36x73cm-14x29in) s.i.d.1941 ink col scroll silk. 25-Apr-4 Christie's, Hong Kong #81/R est:80000-100000 (HK.D 95000)
£21337 $38407 €31152 Phoenix (123x239cm-48x94in) s.i.d.1959 ink col scroll. 25-Apr-4 Christie's, Hong Kong #82/R est:100000-150000 (HK.D 300000)

MA LIN (17/18th C) Chinese
Works on paper
£1014 $1784 €1500 Fisherman by river (62x75cm-24x30in) s. seal hanging scroll. 21-May-4 Dr Fritz Nagel, Stuttgart #1678/R est:3000

MA SHOUZHEN (1548-1604) Chinese
Works on paper
£6757 $12162 €9865 Landscapes and flowers (29x26cm-11x10in) s.i. ink col leaves eight album. 25-Apr-4 Christie's, Hong Kong #340/R est:60000-80000 (HK.D 95000)

MA YUANYU (1625-1705) Chinese
Works on paper
£4267 $7681 €6230 Peach blossoms in ink (106x47cm-42x19in) s.i.d.1695 ink hanging scroll. 25-Apr-4 Christie's, Hong Kong #428/R est:40000-50000 (HK.D 60000)

MAANEN, Henriette van (1938-) Dutch
£342 $582 €500 Four seasons (124x124cm-49x49in) s.verso. 5-Nov-3 Vendue Huis, Gravenhage #470/R

MAAR, Dora (1909-1997) French
£397 $727 €600 Paysage (24x35cm-9x14in) s.verso. 7-Apr-4 Doutrebente, Paris #67
£1918 $3260 €2800 The Durance (53x80cm-21x31in) s. s.verso. 4-Nov-3 Ansorena, Madrid #61/R est:2800
£2333 $4246 €3500 New York (161x92cm-63x36in) studio st. prov. 30-Jun-4 Calmels Cohen, Paris #66/R est:4000-5000
£2381 $4262 €3500 Paysage (38x46cm-15x18in) s. painted 1957 exhib. 21-Mar-4 Calmels Cohen, Paris #26/R est:5000-6000
Photographs
£2537 $4160 €3500 Picasso a Golfe-Juan tenant un crane de vache (17x9cm-7x4in) Kodak silver print. 2-Jun-3 Tajan, Paris #167 est:1000-1500

Works on paper
£329 $595 €500 Portrait (29x23cm-11x9in) s. felt-tip pen dr. 14-Apr-4 Ansorena, Madrid #818/R

MAAREL, Marinus van der (1857-1921) Dutch
£350 $601 €500 Milkmaid (34x22cm-13x9in) s. 8-Dec-3 Glerum, Amsterdam #33/R

MAARNI, Elvi (1907-) Finnish
£1408 $2437 €2000 Mother and child (28x23cm-11x9in) s. 13-Dec-3 Hagelstam, Helsinki #171/R est:2000
£2533 $4535 €3800 Mother and child (21x16cm-8x6in) s. canvas on board. 15-May-4 Hagelstam, Helsinki #188/R est:3500
£3200 $5728 €4800 Portrait of girl (42x35cm-17x14in) s. 15-May-4 Hagelstam, Helsinki #183/R est:5000
£4056 $6895 €5800 Playing the violin (47x30cm-19x12in) s. canvas on board. 29-Nov-3 Bukowskis, Helsinki #100/R est:2200-2500
£4366 $7554 €6200 In the park (40x46cm-16x18in) s. canvas on board. 13-Dec-3 Hagelstam, Helsinki #170/R est:1500
Works on paper
£324 $518 €460 Vase (21x14cm-8x6in) wax crayon. 18-Sep-3 Hagelstam, Helsinki #822
£347 $580 €500 House (31x23cm-12x9in) chl. 23-Oct-3 Hagelstam, Helsinki #802
£458 $732 €650 Fruit (29x20cm-11x8in) s. mixed media. 18-Sep-3 Hagelstam, Helsinki #802
£493 $789 €700 Pears (30x21cm-12x8in) s. wax crayon. 18-Sep-3 Hagelstam, Helsinki #808
£528 $845 €750 Woman thinking (29x20cm-11x8in) s. mixed media. 18-Sep-3 Hagelstam, Helsinki #801
£563 $901 €800 Violin player (30x21cm-12x8in) s. wax crayon. 18-Sep-3 Hagelstam, Helsinki #800/R
£563 $901 €800 Three women (30x21cm-12x8in) s. chl. 18-Sep-3 Hagelstam, Helsinki #803
£634 $1014 €900 Violin player (21x14cm-8x6in) s. wax crayon. 18-Sep-3 Hagelstam, Helsinki #804/R
£729 $1218 €1050 Sick boy (42x29cm-17x11in) s. mixed media. 23-Oct-3 Hagelstam, Helsinki #800
£733 $1349 €1100 Road to the park (25x17cm-10x7in) s. chl. 9-Jun-4 Bukowskis, Helsinki #470/R
£800 $1472 €1200 Girl with flowers (38x28cm-15x11in) s. chl. 9-Jun-4 Bukowskis, Helsinki #471/R
£915 $1465 €1300 Horses (32x23cm-13x9in) s. crayon. 18-Sep-3 Hagelstam, Helsinki #1002
£1111 $1856 €1600 Horsemen (35x29cm-14x11in) s. wax crayon. 23-Oct-3 Hagelstam, Helsinki #987/R est:900
£1127 $1803 €1600 Flute players (24x18cm-9x7in) s. crayon. 18-Sep-3 Hagelstam, Helsinki #1003 est:600
£1268 $2028 €1800 Girl (23x20cm-9x8in) s. mixed media. 18-Sep-3 Hagelstam, Helsinki #805 est:800
£1667 $3067 €2500 Playing the guitar (30x23cm-12x9in) s. pastel. 9-Jun-4 Bukowskis, Helsinki #469/R est:2000
£2028 $3448 €2900 Yellow flowers in vase (23x19cm-9x7in) s. pastel. 29-Nov-3 Bukowskis, Helsinki #131/R est:1200-1500
£2109 $3838 €3100 Embracing (30x23cm-12x9in) s. mixed media. 8-Feb-4 Bukowskis, Helsinki #399/R est:1500
£2517 $4280 €3600 A beauty wearing a hat (18x16cm-7x6in) s. mixed media. 29-Nov-3 Bukowskis, Helsinki #132/R est:1000-1200
£2685 $4940 €4000 Horses grazing (26x22cm-10x9in) s. crayon. 25-Mar-4 Hagelstam, Helsinki #935/R est:1300
£2727 $4636 €3900 Green landscape (25x22cm-10x9in) s. pastel. 29-Nov-3 Bukowskis, Helsinki #78/R est:1200-1500
£3200 $5728 €4800 White horse (27x22cm-11x9in) s. mixed media. 15-May-4 Hagelstam, Helsinki #187/R est:2500
£4133 $7399 €6200 The violin player (28x40cm-11x16in) s. mixed media. 15-May-4 Hagelstam, Helsinki #184/R est:2500
£5070 $8772 €7200 Violin player (50x43cm-20x17in) s. mixed media canvas. 13-Dec-3 Hagelstam, Helsinki #169/R est:3000
£5374 $9781 €7900 Violin players (29x21cm-11x8in) s. mixed media. 8-Feb-4 Bukowskis, Helsinki #400/R est:1500
£5467 $9785 €8200 In the park (40x32cm-16x13in) s. mixed media canvas on board. 15-May-4 Hagelstam, Helsinki #185/R est:2500

MAAS, Dirck (1659-1717) Dutch
£5369 $9879 €8000 Horsemen resting in mountainous landscape (56x73cm-22x29in) s. 24-Mar-4 Dorotheum, Vienna #361/R est:10000-15000
Works on paper
£2448 $4161 €3500 Riders with dogs (19x30cm-7x12in) s. W/C pencil Indian ink. 21-Nov-3 Reiss & Sohn, Konigstein #97/R est:3800

MAAS, Ernst (1904-1971) Swiss
Works on paper
£480 $884 €701 Raven time (60x46cm-24x18in) s.d.1960 mixed media collage. 8-Jun-4 Germann, Zurich #831/R (S.FR 1100)
£524 $964 €765 Composition (47x62cm-19x24in) s.d.1956 mixed media. 8-Jun-4 Germann, Zurich #830 (S.FR 1200)

MAAS, Harry (1906-1982) Dutch
£592 $1089 €900 Portrait of a young woman (40x30cm-16x12in) s.d.67 d. verso board. 28-Jun-4 Sotheby's, Amsterdam #217/R
£658 $1211 €1000 Reclining female nude (55x40cm-22x16in) s.d.1966 d. verso. 28-Jun-4 Sotheby's, Amsterdam #214/R
£694 $1097 €1000 In front of the mirror (76x56cm-30x22in) s.d.1950. 2-Sep-3 Christie's, Amsterdam #371/R est:1000-1500
£778 $1400 €1136 The rakes progress, Ninette de Valais, Sadler's Wells Ballet (61x76cm-24x30in) s.d.1961 s.i.verso. 23-Jan-4 Freeman, Philadelphia #150/R
£940 $1738 €1400 Female nude (55x40cm-22x16in) s.d.1974. 15-Mar-4 Sotheby's, Amsterdam #220/R est:1000-1500
£1049 $1783 €1500 Bathers on a beach near Loevestijn (50x70cm-20x28in) s.d.1974 i.verso. 24-Nov-3 Glerum, Amsterdam #53/R est:1000-1500
£1275 $2359 €1900 Uitkleden (39x29cm-15x11in) s.d.1967 board. 15-Mar-4 Sotheby's, Amsterdam #273 est:1000-1500
£1644 $2795 €2400 Girl and sailors on Dort quai (89x69cm-35x27in) s.i.d.1968. 5-Nov-3 Vendue Huis, Gravenhage #215/R est:2200-2600
£1645 $3026 €2500 Going for a swim (70x90cm-28x35in) s.d.1963. 22-Jun-4 Christie's, Amsterdam #577/R est:3000-5000
£1667 $2717 €2400 Boats in the harbour of Spakenburg (70x90cm-28x35in) s. 29-Sep-3 Sotheby's, Amsterdam #245/R
£1842 $3389 €2800 Hop on (100x80cm-39x31in) s.d.1961. 22-Jun-4 Christie's, Amsterdam #584/R est:3000-5000
£4276 $7868 €6500 Relaxing on the sofa (80x100cm-31x39in) s.d.1960. 22-Jun-4 Christie's, Amsterdam #576/R est:3000-5000
Works on paper
£329 $605 €500 Lovers (28x35cm-11x14in) s.d.1954 W/C. 22-Jun-4 Christie's, Amsterdam #580/R
£347 $565 €500 Female nude (65x50cm-26x20in) s.d.1946 pastel. 29-Sep-3 Sotheby's, Amsterdam #321/R
£658 $1211 €1000 Two girls in the woods (48x32cm-19x13in) s.d.1959 W/C two. 22-Jun-4 Christie's, Amsterdam #578/R
£658 $1211 €1000 A girl undressing in the artist's studio (49x33cm-19x13in) W/C two. 22-Jun-4 Christie's, Amsterdam #579/R

MAAS, Hendrik (1793-1873) Dutch
£497 $900 €726 Panoramic winter landscape with townspeople on a frozen river (25x41cm-10x16in) s. prov. 18-Apr-4 Jeffery Burchard, Florida #58/R

MAAS, Lorenz Johann (1845-1882) German
£2098 $3566 €3000 Idyllic courtyard with view into kitchen (23x17cm-9x7in) 22-Nov-3 Arnold, Frankfurt #585/R est:2000

MAAS, Marise (1969-) Australian
£992 $1835 €1448 High tide at Oyster Bay (100x100cm-39x39in) s.d.00 s.d.verso prov. 15-Mar-4 Sotheby's, Melbourne #219/R est:500-800 (A.D 2400)

MAAS, Paul (1890-1962) Belgian
£333 $600 €500 Het gele boeket (65x50cm-26x20in) s. lit. 26-Apr-4 Bernaerts, Antwerp #1038/R
£594 $1010 €850 Les amoureux a Etikhove (26x34cm-10x13in) s. painted c.1935 panel. 1-Dec-3 Palais de Beaux Arts, Brussels #83
£1241 $2297 €1800 La plage d'Honfleur animee (50x60cm-20x24in) s. panel. 13-Jan-4 Vanderkindere, Brussels #53 est:2000-3000
£1528 $2551 €2200 Still life (81x116cm-32x46in) s. exhib. 21-Oct-3 Campo & Campo, Antwerp #203/R est:2300-2600

MAASS, David (20th C) American
£7487 $14000 €10931 Mallards (51x71cm-20x28in) s. board. 24-Jul-4 Coeur d'Alene, Hayden #9/R est:6000-8000

MAATSCH, Thilo (1900-1983) German
£1118 $2058 €1700 Untitled (74x60cm-29x24in) s.d.16.10.27 verso. 28-Jun-4 Sotheby's, Amsterdam #240/R est:1500-2000
£4615 $7661 €6738 Composition, ship (39x57cm-15x22in) s.verso. 4-Oct-3 Kieselbach, Budapest #158/R (H.F 1700000)
£5072 $8319 €7000 Untitled (56x47cm-22x19in) s.verso board prov. 27-May-3 Sotheby's, Amsterdam #361/R est:7000-9000
£5797 $9507 €8000 Untitled (60x86cm-24x34in) s.verso board prov. 27-May-3 Sotheby's, Amsterdam #366/R est:8000-12000
£12528 $21674 €18291 Blue composition (72x103cm-28x41in) s.d.39 verso. 12-Dec-3 Kieselbach, Budapest #209/R (H.F 4800000)
Works on paper
£305 $500 €445 Das rote dreieck number 309 (17x12cm-7x5in) mono. s.d.1933 verso gouache ink prov. 28-May-3 Sotheby's, Amsterdam #166/R

MABE (1924-) Brazilian
£5037 $9217 €7556 Untitled (79x79cm-31x31in) s.d.1962. 6-Jul-4 Bolsa de Arte, Rio de Janeiro #160/R (B.R 27500)
£6777 $11995 €10166 Untitled (125x125cm-49x49in) s.d.1969. 27-Apr-4 Bolsa de Arte, Rio de Janeiro #113/R (B.R 37000)
£7509 $13291 €11264 Untitled (50x60cm-20x24in) s.i.d.1959 masonite. 27-Apr-4 Bolsa de Arte, Rio de Janeiro #127/R (B.R 41000)
£10989 $19451 €16484 Untitled (102x102cm-40x40in) s.d.1972. 27-Apr-4 Bolsa de Arte, Rio de Janeiro #125/R (B.R 60000)

McADAM, Walter (1866-1935) British
£2517 $4280 €3600 Spring in Mallorca (34x44cm-13x17in) i. verso canvas on panel. 24-Nov-3 Dorotheum, Vienna #211/R est:3600-4000

McAFEE, Ila Mae (1897-1995) American
£2941 $5000 €4294 Ghost Ranch, Kitchen Rock (51x61cm-20x24in) s. prov.lit. 1-Nov-3 Santa Fe Art, Santa Fe #219/R est:15000-20000
£4237 $7500 €6186 Silence is golden (87x70cm-34x28in) s. s.i. stretcher prov. 28-Apr-4 Christie's, Los Angeles #1/R est:6000-8000

MACAIONE, Tommy (1907-1992) American
£260 $475 €390 Impressionistic landscape (46x91cm-18x36in) s.d.1981 acrylic. 7-Jun-4 O'Gallerie, Oregon #75

MACALA, Ben (1938-1997) South African
Works on paper
£276 $461 €403 Two figures with a horse (145x75cm-57x30in) s.d.70 mixed media. 20-Oct-3 Stephan Welz, Johannesburg #653 est:2000-3000 (SA.R 3200)

McALEER, Clement (1949-) Irish
£1500 $2685 €2190 Irish bogland (69x75cm-27x30in) s. s.i.d.1989 verso acrylic pastel. 14-May-4 Christie's, Kensington #465/R est:2000-3000

£1892	$3576	€2800	Landscape (86x89cm-34x35in) s. acrylic on paper. 17-Feb-4 Whyte's, Dublin #38/R est:3000-4000

McALLISTER, Ian (20th C) Irish

£2517	$4280	€3600	Still life with stoneware and hydrangea (43x55cm-17x22in) mono.d.1995 board. 18-Nov-3 Whyte's, Dublin #165/R est:3000-4000

McALLISTER, Therese (20th C) Irish

£933	$1689	€1400	Table top still life (36x46cm-14x18in) s. canvasboard. 30-Mar-4 De Veres Art Auctions, Dublin #172
£1067	$1931	€1600	Red onions on a tablecloth (38x56cm-15x22in) s. canvasboard. 30-Mar-4 De Veres Art Auctions, Dublin #118/R est:1500-2000

MACALLUM, Hamilton (1841-1896) British

£362	$666	€550	Peasant farmers ploughing a beachside field (51x76cm-20x30in) s. 22-Jun-4 Mealy's, Castlecomer #322
£628	$1136	€917	Boat by the pier (41x71cm-16x28in) s. prov. 1-Apr-4 Heffel, Vancouver #73/R (C.D 1500)
£2300	$3818	€3358	A Scilly anchorage, sailing boats off the Isles of Scilly (39x70cm-15x28in) s.d.1886 s.i.verso. 2-Oct-3 Lane, Penzance #320/R est:2500-3000
£13500	$22950	€19710	Walberswick ferry (82x155cm-32x61in) s.d.1875. 25-Nov-3 Christie's, London #170/R est:10000-15000
Works on paper			
£300	$543	€438	Fishermen unloading the boat (20x38cm-8x15in) s.d.94 W/C. 16-Apr-4 Keys, Aylsham #517/R
£800	$1456	€1168	Agoni fishing on the Arno (21x38cm-8x15in) s.d.1873-4 W/C bodycol. 3-Feb-4 Sworder & Son, Bishops Stortford #289/R
£1500	$2700	€2190	Heave ho (38x89cm-15x35in) s.d.1877 W/C. 21-Jan-4 Sotheby's, Olympia #240/R est:2000-3000

McALPINE, William (19th C) British

£300	$537	€438	Big ships in an anchorage (20x41cm-8x16in) 26-May-4 Christie's, Kensington #691/R
£450	$765	€657	Loss of H.M.S. Bombay (51x76cm-20x30in) 19-Nov-3 Christie's, Kensington #509/R
£1900	$3230	€2774	Trading brigs (30x61cm-12x24in) 19-Nov-3 Christie's, Kensington #506/R

MACARA, Andrew (1944-) British

£400	$648	€580	On Paignton Beach (41x51cm-16x20in) s.i.d.1998. 30-Jul-3 Hamptons Fine Art, Godalming #224
£400	$736	€584	Poole (30x36cm-12x14in) s.i.d.97 stretcher. 23-Mar-4 Rosebery Fine Art, London #773
£440	$713	€638	Swimming pool (30x56cm-12x22in) s.d.2001. 30-Jul-3 Hamptons Fine Art, Godalming #182/R
£440	$704	€642	Green Mosque, Luxor (35x45cm-14x18in) s.d.1992 i.d.verso. 16-Sep-3 Bonhams, Knowle #98
£440	$704	€642	Ribandar, Goa (89x73cm-35x29in) s.d.1994 i.d.verso. 16-Sep-3 Bonhams, Knowle #99
£480	$883	€701	Watching the waves (51x61cm-20x24in) s.d.1999. 24-Mar-4 Hamptons Fine Art, Godalming #299/R
£550	$985	€803	Playa de Pals, Costa Brava (41x51cm-16x20in) s.d.2002 i.verso. 14-May-4 Christie's, Kensington #619/R
£550	$985	€803	Children playing on the swings (41x51cm-16x20in) s.d.1999. 14-May-4 Christie's, Kensington #622/R
£550	$968	€803	Markeaton Park, Derby (63x76cm-25x30in) s.d.2001 i.verso. 19-May-4 Sotheby's, Olympia #207/R
£550	$968	€803	On the beach (63x76cm-25x30in) s.d.2002. 19-May-4 Sotheby's, Olympia #245/R
£550	$1001	€803	Playing on the rocks (41x51cm-16x20in) s.d.2002. 1-Jul-4 Christie's, Kensington #279/R
£580	$1067	€847	Winter afternoon, Allestree Park, Derby. Tobogganing, Allestree Park (25x51cm-10x20in) pair. 24-Mar-4 Hamptons Fine Art, Godalming #298/R
£600	$972	€870	Feeding the swans (47x57cm-19x22in) s.d.1995. 30-Jul-3 Hamptons Fine Art, Godalming #248
£600	$1020	€876	Pool (30x40cm-12x16in) s.d.2001 i.on stretcher. 26-Nov-3 Sotheby's, Olympia #134/R
£600	$1020	€876	Swans at a lake-side (51x41cm-20x16in) s.d.2001. 26-Nov-3 Hamptons Fine Art, Godalming #232/R
£620	$1141	€905	St Palais sur Mer, SW France (30x35cm-12x14in) s.i.verso. 23-Mar-4 Rosebery Fine Art, London #772/R
£650	$1034	€949	Marrakech market (40x50cm-16x20in) s.d.1993. 10-Sep-3 Sotheby's, Olympia #257/R
£650	$1105	€949	Street in Ribanda, Goa (41x51cm-16x20in) s.d.1994 i.verso. 26-Nov-3 Hamptons Fine Art, Godalming #202/R
£650	$1151	€949	Boys on the beach, Cape Town (30x55cm-12x22in) s. 27-Apr-4 Bonhams, Knightsbridge #91/R
£700	$1190	€1022	Santorini in May (31x36cm-12x14in) s.d.2002 i.verso. 26-Nov-3 Sotheby's, Olympia #133/R
£700	$1232	€1022	St Palais, Royan (40x75cm-16x30in) s. i.verso. 19-May-4 Sotheby's, Olympia #212/R
£700	$1274	€1022	Children's teaching pool (41x51cm-16x20in) s.d.1986 exhib. 1-Jul-4 Christie's, Kensington #281/R
£700	$1274	€1022	Autumn, Markeaton Park, Derby (41x51cm-16x20in) s.d.2002. 1-Jul-4 Christie's, Kensington #282/R
£750	$1320	€1095	Bathing (51x61cm-20x24in) s.d.2001. 19-May-4 Dreweatt Neate, Newbury #71/R
£800	$1360	€1168	Isle of Wight (39x49cm-15x19in) s.d.1999 i.verso. 26-Nov-3 Sotheby's, Olympia #115/R
£800	$1472	€1168	Clacton beach. South Africa, January (30x41cm-12x16in) s. pair. 24-Mar-4 Hamptons Fine Art, Godalming #291/R
£820	$1492	€1197	Chickens, Paphos, Cyprus (39x49cm-15x19in) s.d.1996 i.verso. 1-Jul-4 Mellors & Kirk, Nottingham #800/R
£850	$1352	€1241	Ballet dancers (45x55cm-18x22in) s. 10-Sep-3 Sotheby's, Olympia #246/R
£850	$1572	€1241	Roller skating (40x50cm-16x20in) s. 11-Feb-4 Sotheby's, Olympia #208/R
£850	$1505	€1241	Allestree Park, Derby, in the snow (30x55cm-12x22in) s. 27-Apr-4 Bonhams, Knightsbridge #95/R
£850	$1496	€1241	Purple lilo, Playa de Pals, Spain (71x91cm-28x36in) s.d.1997. 19-May-4 Sotheby's, Olympia #247/R
£900	$1665	€1314	Derby Academy of Dance (63x76cm-25x30in) s.d.1993 i.verso. 11-Feb-4 Sotheby's, Olympia #213/R est:600-800
£900	$1638	€1314	Children playing on a beach (34x45cm-13x18in) s.d.1999. 5-Feb-4 Mellors & Kirk, Nottingham #529
£900	$1584	€1314	On the beach (45x35cm-18x14in) s. 19-May-4 Sotheby's, Olympia #229/R
£950	$1511	€1387	Boating (63x76cm-25x30in) s.d.2000. 10-Sep-3 Sotheby's, Olympia #256/R
£1100	$1947	€1606	Summer's day on the beach (45x93cm-18x37in) s. 27-Apr-4 Bonhams, Knightsbridge #200/R est:800-1000
£1100	$1936	€1606	Isle of Wight (40x50cm-16x20in) s. 19-May-4 Sotheby's, Olympia #244/R est:800-1200
£1300	$2405	€1898	French garden (63x76cm-25x30in) s.d.2001. 11-Feb-4 Sotheby's, Olympia #219/R est:1200-1800
£1400	$2590	€2044	Tree shadow, Allestree Park, Derby (63x76cm-25x30in) s.d.2003. 11-Feb-4 Sotheby's, Olympia #211/R est:600-800
£2000	$3700	€2920	Sailing boats, Sa Rieva, Costa Brava (71x91cm-28x36in) s.d.1999 i.stretcher. 11-Feb-4 Sotheby's, Olympia #209/R est:2000-3000
£3200	$5632	€4672	Diabolo, Santorini (91x101cm-36x40in) s.d.2002. 19-May-4 Sotheby's, Olympia #220/R est:2000-3000

McARA, Don (20th C) ?

Works on paper			
£326	$518	€476	Over the wall, Volterra, Italy (51x34cm-20x13in) s.d.94 W/C. 9-Sep-3 Watson's, Christchurch #69 (NZ.D 900)

MACARRON, Ricardo (1926-) Spanish

£775	$1356	€1100	Yellow flowers (41x33cm-16x13in) s. board. 16-Dec-3 Durán, Madrid #114/R
£937	$1594	€1350	Blue arlequin (65x46cm-26x18in) s.d.1966. 28-Oct-3 Segre, Madrid #284/R
£1379	$2303	€2013	Las flores II (115x88cm-45x35in) s. 20-Oct-3 Stephan Welz, Johannesburg #215/R est:7000-10000 (SA.R 16000)
£1471	$2750	€2148	Harlequin (102x97cm-40x38in) s. 25-Feb-4 Dallas Auction Gallery, Dallas #415/R
£1944	$3306	€2800	Landscape (59x92cm-23x36in) s.d.1966. 28-Oct-3 Segre, Madrid #358/R est:2400
£2013	$3745	€3000	Flowers II (115x88cm-45x35in) s.d.71. 2-Mar-4 Ansorena, Madrid #831/R est:3000

McARTHUR (?) British?

Works on paper			
£420	$794	€613	Still life of cyclamen (55x42cm-22x17in) s. W/C. 19-Feb-4 Lyon & Turnbull, Edinburgh #7

MACARTHUR, Blanche (fl.1870-1903) British

£506	$800	€734	Gypsy girl (18x36cm-7x14in) s.d.1880. 27-Jul-3 Simpson's, Houston #190

MACARTHUR, Charles M (fl.1860-1892) British

£380	$692	€555	River scene with figure in the foreground (41x53cm-16x21in) s.d.1889. 16-Jun-4 Andrew Hartley, Ilkley #1099
£500	$910	€730	Canal scene near Matlock (46x71cm-18x28in) s.d.1887. 16-Jun-4 Andrew Hartley, Ilkley #1100
Works on paper			
£600	$1122	€876	Children and other figures with a dog in the grounds of a country mansion (42x68cm-17x27in) s. pencil W/C htd white. 22-Jul-4 Tennants, Leyburn #664

MACARTNEY, Carlile Henry Hayes (1842-1924) British

£420	$756	€613	Figures on path crossing Tidmarsh Meads (30x51cm-12x20in) s. 25-Jan-4 Desmond Judd, Cranbrook #1043

MACARTNEY, Jack (1893-1976) American

£1324	$2250	€1933	California autumn (24x36cm-9x14in) s. i.d.1968 verso. 18-Nov-3 John Moran, Pasadena #122 est:2000-4000

McAULEY, Charles (1910-1999) British

£750	$1290	€1095	View along the coast (41x67cm-16x26in) s. 3-Dec-3 Christie's, Kensington #518/R
£900	$1548	€1314	Rathlin from Cushendall, County Antrim (35x45cm-14x18in) s. 3-Dec-3 John Ross, Belfast #3
£1000	$1640	€1460	Country Antrim coast (45x50cm-18x20in) s. board. 4-Jun-3 John Ross, Belfast #231
£1000	$1660	€1460	Cattle grazing near Cushendun, Co. Antrim (40x63cm-16x25in) s. 1-Oct-3 John Ross, Belfast #187 est:1200-1400
£1000	$1830	€1460	Road in the glens (35x45cm-14x18in) s. board. 2-Jun-4 John Ross, Belfast #110a est:1000-1200
£1100	$1804	€1606	Rowing boats (33x45cm-13x18in) s. board. 4-Jun-3 John Ross, Belfast #4
£1200	$2196	€1752	Waiting by the rowing boat (30x40cm-12x16in) s. board. 2-Jun-4 John Ross, Belfast #254 est:800-1000
£1329	$2259	€1900	Glens of Antrim landscape (50x72cm-20x28in) s. board. 18-Nov-3 Whyte's, Dublin #103/R est:2000-3000
£1350	$2471	€1971	In the Glens of Antrim (40x61cm-16x24in) s. board. 2-Jun-4 John Ross, Belfast #12 est:1200-1500
£1400	$2408	€2044	Looking towards Waterfoot from Glenariff, County Antrim (40x61cm-16x24in) s. board. 3-Dec-3 John Ross, Belfast #30 est:1500-1800
£1400	$2604	€2044	River, Kilmacrennan, Co. Donegal (40x61cm-16x24in) s. 3-Mar-4 John Ross, Belfast #12 est:1500-1800
£1400	$2562	€2044	My lady's view Killarney (50x76cm-20x30in) s. board. 2-Jun-4 John Ross, Belfast #169a est:1400-1600
£1450	$2494	€2117	Lough reflections, Donegal (40x50cm-16x20in) s. board. 3-Dec-3 John Ross, Belfast #219 est:1500-1600
£1500	$2460	€2190	Stroll in the Glens (30x40cm-12x16in) s. 4-Jun-3 John Ross, Belfast #63
£1500	$2580	€2190	Sunshine and shadow, Donegal (35x45cm-14x18in) s. 3-Dec-3 John Ross, Belfast #116 est:1600-1800
£1500	$2790	€2190	Vanishing lake in winter (40x50cm-16x20in) s. board. 3-Mar-4 John Ross, Belfast #86 est:1500-1600
£1550	$2542	€2263	Antrim coast (35x45cm-14x18in) s.board. 4-Jun-3 John Ross, Belfast #98

£1600 $2656 €2336 Red Bay, Co. Antrim (30x45cm-12x18in) s. 1-Oct-3 John Ross, Belfast #12 est:1800-2000
£1600 $2752 €2336 Turf stacks, Donegal (40x50cm-16x20in) s. board. 3-Dec-3 John Ross, Belfast #199 est:1500-1750
£1700 $3162 €2482 Muckish Mountain Donegal (40x56cm-16x22in) s. 3-Mar-4 John Ross, Belfast #128 est:1800-2000
£1700 $3162 €2482 Cattle grazing by the river Dun (33x44cm-13x17in) s. 3-Mar-4 John Ross, Belfast #167 est:1400-1500
£1800 $2952 €2628 River in the Glens (35x53cm-14x21in) s. 4-Jun-3 John Ross, Belfast #12
£1900 $3154 €2774 Cattle near Glendun (35x45cm-14x18in) s. 1-Oct-3 John Ross, Belfast #135 est:1600-1800
£2000 $3320 €2920 Corn stacks (53x68cm-21x27in) s. 1-Oct-3 John Ross, Belfast #48 est:2000-2500
£2000 $3720 €2920 Bridge at Cushendun (38x50cm-15x20in) s. board. 3-Mar-4 John Ross, Belfast #210 est:1000-1200
£2162 $4086 €3200 Lurig from the rocks at Cushendall, County Antrim (47x67cm-19x26in) s.i.d.September 1958 board. 17-Feb-4 Whyte's, Dublin #126/R est:3500-4500
£2300 $3818 €3358 Stroll in the Glens (45x61cm-18x24in) s. 1-Oct-3 John Ross, Belfast #32 est:2250-2500
£2333 $4223 €3500 Cattle on the Dun (45x59cm-18x23in) s.i.d.85 verso. 30-Mar-4 De Veres Art Auctions, Dublin #22/R est:3000-4000
£3087 $5464 €4600 Driving the cows home (41x51cm-16x20in) s. 27-Apr-4 Whyte's, Dublin #200/R est:3500-4500
£3200 $5312 €4672 Heading home with the turf (45x61cm-18x24in) s. board. 1-Oct-3 John Ross, Belfast #158 est:2250-2500
£3300 $6138 €4818 Digging for bait (35x45cm-14x18in) s.d.77 verso. 3-Mar-4 John Ross, Belfast #53 est:3500-4000
£3800 $7068 €5548 Footing the turf, Co. Antrim (35x53cm-14x21in) s. 3-Mar-4 John Ross, Belfast #155 est:4000-5000
Works on paper
£600 $1116 €876 Waterfall, Glenariff, Co. Antrim (28x35cm-11x14in) s. W/C. 3-Mar-4 John Ross, Belfast #35

McAULEY, John (1865-?) American
£242 $450 €353 Jesus on the Red Sea (58x84cm-23x33in) s. 7-Mar-4 William Jenack, New York #298

McAULEY, Michael (20th C) Irish?
Works on paper
£278 $436 €400 Fountain head (31x32cm-12x13in) s. mixed media. 26-Aug-3 James Adam, Dublin #194/R

McAULIFFE, James J (1848-1921) American
£5914 $11000 €8634 Out for a carriage ride with two trotters (51x69cm-20x27in) s. stock. 6-Mar-4 North East Auctions, Portsmouth #1122/R

MACAVOY (1905-1991) French
£1076 $1798 €1550 Vue de la baie (60x79cm-24x31in) s.d.1943. 25-Oct-3 Cornette de St.Cyr, Paris #529 est:1200-1500

MACAVOY, Edouard (1905-1991) French
£524 $876 €750 Petite fille contemplant la mer (11x25cm-4x10in) s. paper painted 1948. 25-Jun-3 Blanchet, Paris #91
Works on paper
£233 $420 €350 Venise (32x48cm-13x19in) s.d.80 gouache. 26-Apr-4 Tajan, Paris #78

MACBETH, James (1847-1891) British
£2131 $3750 €3111 Fairground by night (88x62cm-35x24in) s.d.1878. 18-May-4 Bonhams & Butterfields, San Francisco #170/R est:3000-5000
Works on paper
£2600 $4420 €3796 Elegant lady seated by a fire in a chinese influenced interior (20x28cm-8x11in) init.d.73 pencil W/C bodycol htd white. 20-Nov-3 Christie's, London #143/R est:2000-3000

MACBETH, Norman (1821-1888) British
£520 $868 €759 Half length of Hugh Watson seated (90x75cm-35x30in) s. 19-Jun-3 Bonhams, Edinburgh #343

MACBETH, Robert Walker (1848-1910) British
Works on paper
£360 $601 €526 Roadside tragedy (45x69cm-18x27in) init. en grisaille W/C. 19-Jun-3 Bonhams, Edinburgh #318
£600 $1104 €876 Gypsy mother travelling with her chidlren (30x25cm-12x10in) init. pencil W/C. 25-Mar-4 Christie's, Kensington #217
£1000 $1660 €1460 Yealscombe (19x29cm-7x11in) s.i.d.aug 1896 W/C. 1-Oct-3 Sotheby's, Olympia #112/R est:1000-1500

McBEY, James (1883-1959) British
£850 $1445 €1241 Reading (24x20cm-9x8in) 30-Oct-3 Christie's, London #215/R
£1900 $3154 €2774 On the Thames (34x68cm-13x27in) s.d.1928 prov. 1-Oct-3 Woolley & Wallis, Salisbury #220/R est:1000-1500
£6600 $10428 €9636 Venice, mooring posts, salute (44x62cm-17x24in) s. 6-Sep-3 Shapes, Edinburgh #345/R est:3000-4000
£6700 $10586 €9782 Easdale (49x66cm-19x26in) s. 6-Sep-3 Shapes, Edinburgh #351 est:2000-3000
£7000 $12110 €10220 September sunset, Venice (25x40cm-10x16in) s.i.d.20 September 1925 board prov. 11-Dec-3 Lyon & Turnbull, Edinburgh #113/R est:2000-3000
£7900 $12482 €11534 Venice gondolier (40x60cm-16x24in) s.d.1924. 6-Sep-3 Shapes, Edinburgh #344/R est:3000-4000
Works on paper
£340 $585 €496 Tangier (16x17cm-6x7in) s.d.28 January 1913 pen ink. 6-Dec-3 Shapes, Edinburgh #403
£600 $948 €876 Hastings, fishermen and boats (26x39cm-10x15in) s.d.21 May 1923 W/C. 6-Sep-3 Shapes, Edinburgh #353/R
£620 $1054 €905 Lerma, a North African street scene (25x18cm-10x7in) s.i.d.1932 pen ink W/C. 27-Nov-3 Greenslade Hunt, Taunton #982/R
£650 $1125 €949 Barges at Rochester (26x44cm-10x17in) s. i.d. April 1928 W/C. 10-Dec-3 Bonhams, Bury St Edmunds #519
£700 $1253 €1022 Wivenhoe (20x31cm-8x12in) s.i.d. pen ink W/C. 28-May-4 Lyon & Turnbull, Edinburgh #59
£720 $1138 €1051 Veure figures before a windmill (27x41cm-11x16in) s.d.20 June 1923 mixed media W/C. 6-Sep-3 Shapes, Edinburgh #354/R
£750 $1343 €1095 Acle (21x34cm-8x13in) s.i.d.1920 pen ink W/C. 28-May-4 Lyon & Turnbull, Edinburgh #12/R
£820 $1468 €1197 Boston (29x45cm-11x18in) s.i.d.1929 pen ink W/C prov. 28-May-4 Lyon & Turnbull, Edinburgh #10
£850 $1343 €1241 Venice (24x42cm-9x17in) s.d.September 1924 W/C. 6-Sep-3 Shapes, Edinburgh #342
£850 $1547 €1241 Scottish fishing village (23x36cm-9x14in) s. W/C. 4-Feb-4 John Nicholson, Haslemere #34/R
£920 $1454 €1343 East Sussex fisherman preparing the boat (26x39cm-10x15in) s.d.8 April 1924 mixed media. 6-Sep-3 Shapes, Edinburgh #355
£950 $1501 €1387 Rochester from Strood (24x41cm-9x16in) d.April 1928 mixed media pen ink W/C. 6-Sep-3 Shapes, Edinburgh #331/R
£960 $1517 €1402 Glass blowers, Murano (33x21cm-13x8in) s.d.22 September 1925 W/C. 6-Sep-3 Shapes, Edinburgh #343/R
£1300 $2301 €1898 View of Greenhithe (22x40cm-9x16in) s.i.d.1928 W/C black ink. 27-Apr-4 Bonhams, Knightsbridge #14/R est:1000-1500
£1300 $2327 €1898 Johnshaven (29x44cm-11x17in) s.i.d.1947 pen ink W/C. 28-May-4 Lyon & Turnbull, Edinburgh #77/R est:700-900
£1400 $2212 €2044 Glass blower (19x25cm-7x10in) s.i. W/C. 6-Sep-3 Shapes, Edinburgh #337 est:600-800
£1500 $2415 €2175 Dawn, San Giorgio, Venice (18x38cm-7x15in) s.i.d.14.Sep 1925 ink W/C. 21-Aug-3 Bonhams, Edinburgh #1097/R est:1000-1500
£1500 $2370 €2190 Veure with figures on a jetty waiting for the fishing boat (27x42cm-11x17in) s.d.22 June 1923 mixed media. 6-Sep-3 Shapes, Edinburgh #356/R est:600-800
£1700 $2686 €2482 Venice (26x40cm-10x16in) s.d.September 1924 W/C. 6-Sep-3 Shapes, Edinburgh #334 est:800-1200
£2125 $3400 €3103 Venice (28x50cm-11x20in) s.i.d.1925 W/C. 18-Sep-3 Swann Galleries, New York #390/R est:2000-3000
£2200 $4026 €3212 Boddam (26x44cm-10x17in) s.i.d.15 Sep 1930 ink W/C prov. 8-Apr-4 Bonhams, Edinburgh #142/R est:1500-2500
£3900 $6630 €5694 Street scene in Tetnon. Morning in Marrakesh (38x25cm-15x10in) s.i.d.1938 W/C pair prov. 5-Nov-3 John Nicholson, Haslemere #569/R est:500-1000
£4400 $7568 €6424 Under the cliffs, Kingsgate (25x33cm-10x13in) s.i.d.1919 ink W/C. 4-Dec-3 Bonhams, Edinburgh #17/R est:1000-1500

MacBRIDE, Alexander (1859-1955) British
Works on paper
£250 $458 €365 Evening on the Grand Canal, Venice (17x23cm-7x9in) s. W/C. 8-Apr-4 Bonhams, Edinburgh #111
£550 $1023 €803 Still life with paint brushes in a Japanese vase (44x27cm-17x11in) s.i. pencil W/C. 4-Mar-4 Christie's, Kensington #183/R

McBRIDE, Clifford (1901-1951) American
Works on paper
£348 $650 €508 Radio broadcast is interrupted by ad, to Napoleon and Uncle Elby's dismay (56x41cm-22x16in) s. pen ink. 26-Feb-4 Illustration House, New York #124

MacBRIDE, William (1856-1913) British
£360 $648 €526 Drying and mending the nets (48x69cm-19x27in) 21-Apr-4 Brightwells, Leominster #812/R

MACBRYDE, Robert (1913-1966) British
£6000 $10860 €8760 Still life with a melon (51x61cm-20x24in) 19-Apr-4 Sotheby's, London #153/R est:3000-5000
£18000 $32940 €26280 Green still life (41x51cm-16x20in) s. prov.exhib. 4-Jun-4 Christie's, London #122/R est:10000-15000

MACCABE, Gladys (1918-) Irish
£350 $574 €511 Male portrait (38x30cm-15x12in) s. board. 4-Jun-3 John Ross, Belfast #213
£350 $574 €511 Saint John (35x33cm-14x13in) s. board. 4-Jun-3 John Ross, Belfast #252
£620 $1029 €905 Clown (40x20cm-16x8in) s. board. 1-Oct-3 John Ross, Belfast #200
£900 $1476 €1314 Still life (40x30cm-16x12in) s.board. 4-Jun-3 John Ross, Belfast #7
£900 $1494 €1314 Cottages, Donegal (45x56cm-18x22in) s. board. 1-Oct-3 John Ross, Belfast #49
£950 $1739 €1387 Rides on the sands, Co. Antrim (30x43cm-12x17in) s. board. 2-Jun-4 John Ross, Belfast #35
£1056 $1849 €1500 Jockeys and trainers (39x50cm-15x20in) s. board. 16-Dec-3 James Adam, Dublin #74/R est:600-800
£1085 $1898 €1540 Study of a clown (40x20cm-16x8in) s. board. 16-Dec-3 James Adam, Dublin #88/R est:1200-1500
£1200 $2064 €1752 Still life (45x35cm-18x14in) s. board. 3-Dec-3 John Ross, Belfast #6 est:1400-1500
£1342 $2403 €2000 From upstairs side window, No 8 Robin Hill (35x45cm-14x18in) s. board. 31-May-4 Hamilton Osborne King, Dublin #125/R est:2000-3000
£1400 $2408 €2044 The May Queen (25x35cm-10x14in) s. board. 3-Dec-3 John Ross, Belfast #95 est:1600-1800
£1500 $2490 €2190 Stroll in the park (30x50cm-12x20in) s. board. 1-Oct-3 John Ross, Belfast #98 est:1600-1800
£1549 $2479 €2200 Road to Carlingford Lough (27x33cm-11x13in) s. board. 16-Sep-3 Whyte's, Dublin #211/R est:2000-3000
£1611 $2851 €2400 People in the park (22x28cm-9x11in) s. board. 27-Apr-4 Whyte's, Dublin #191/R est:1500-2000
£1611 $2851 €2400 Still life with fruit and flowers (46x36cm-18x14in) s. board. 27-Apr-4 Whyte's, Dublin #255/R est:2000-3000
£1800 $2988 €2628 On the beach (38x50cm-15x20in) s. board. 1-Oct-3 John Ross, Belfast #1 est:1200-1500

£1800	$2988	€2628	Market (40x48cm-16x19in) s. board. 1-Oct-3 John Ross, Belfast #127 est:1600-2000
£2013	$3604	€3000	Market Day (45x34cm-18x13in) s. board. 31-May-4 Hamilton Osborne King, Dublin #178/R est:3000-5000
£2027	$3831	€3000	Booterstown carnival (34x42cm-13x17in) s. i.verso board. 17-Feb-4 Whyte's, Dublin #224/R est:3000-4000
£2200	$3938	€3212	Clown with cat (48x33cm-19x13in) s. i.verso board. 14-May-4 Christie's, Kensington #394/R est:1200-1500
£2300	$3818	€3358	Market day (38x50cm-15x20in) s. board. 1-Oct-3 John Ross, Belfast #203 est:2000-2500
£2368	$4358	€3600	Fruit cart, Connemara market (41x57cm-16x22in) s. board. 22-Jun-4 De Veres Art Auctions, Dublin #154/R est:4000-5000
£2400	$3984	€3504	Horse fair, Galway (40x50cm-16x20in) s. board. 1-Oct-3 John Ross, Belfast #60 est:2500-2800
£2676	$4282	€3800	Still life (51x84cm-20x33in) s. i.verso board. 16-Sep-3 Whyte's, Dublin #33/R est:4000-5000
£2685	$4752	€4000	Donkey ride (51x61cm-20x24in) s. board. 27-Apr-4 Whyte's, Dublin #250/R est:4000-6000
£2817	$4507	€4000	Race meeting (23x36cm-9x14in) s. board. 16-Sep-3 Whyte's, Dublin #125/R est:2000-3000
£3467	$6275	€5200	An open air market (50x60cm-20x24in) s. board. 30-Mar-4 De Veres Art Auctions, Dublin #49/R est:3000-5000
£4545	$7727	€6500	Graduation Day, Queen's University, Belfast (57x57cm-22x22in) s. board exhib. 18-Nov-3 Whyte's, Dublin #33/R est:5000-7000

Works on paper

£600	$996	€876	Pony rides (40x56cm-16x22in) s. W/C. 1-Oct-3 John Ross, Belfast #206
£800	$1464	€1168	Day excursion (25x76cm-10x30in) s. W/C. 2-Jun-4 John Ross, Belfast #194
£850	$1462	€1241	London park (27x38cm-11x15in) s. pen ink W/C wash. 3-Dec-3 John Ross, Belfast #114c

MACCABE, Max (1917-2000) British

£265	$482	€400	Deep sea (38x50cm-15x20in) s. board. 15-Jun-4 James Adam, Dublin #143/R
£282	$493	€400	Bowl of fruit (16x25cm-6x10in) s. board. 16-Dec-3 James Adam, Dublin #42/R
£352	$616	€500	Deep sea (38x50cm-15x20in) s. board. 16-Dec-3 James Adam, Dublin #63/R
£366	$641	€520	Bottle and fruit (45x38cm-18x15in) s.d.1962. 16-Dec-3 James Adam, Dublin #8/R
£401	$702	€570	Fish (28x44cm-11x17in) s. board. 16-Dec-3 James Adam, Dublin #20/R
£458	$801	€650	Fish (34x48cm-13x19in) s. board. 16-Dec-3 James Adam, Dublin #32/R

Works on paper

£282	$493	€400	Picnic at dusk (28x38cm-11x15in) s. W/C. 16-Dec-3 James Adam, Dublin #64/R
£324	$567	€460	Fishes (25x35cm-10x14in) s.i.verso W/C. 16-Dec-3 James Adam, Dublin #59/R
£352	$616	€500	Glowing tree (25x7cm-10x3in) s.i.verso W/C. 16-Dec-3 James Adam, Dublin #50/R
£423	$739	€600	Swirling fishes (40x52cm-16x20in) s.i.verso pastel. 16-Dec-3 James Adam, Dublin #18/R
£563	$986	€800	Bricks and backyards (27x38cm-11x15in) s.i.verso W/C. 16-Dec-3 James Adam, Dublin #61/R

McCAFFREY, Polly (1944-) American

£1176	$2000	€1717	Peonies (63x53cm-25x21in) s. board. 30-Oct-3 Phillips, New York #60/R est:2000-3000

McCAHON, Colin (1930-1977) New Zealander

£3279	$5180	€4787	Michael Nicholson's studio, Auckland (20x27cm-8x11in) s.d.April 57 pen prov. 2-Sep-3 Deutscher-Menzies, Melbourne #20/R est:8000-12000 (A.D 8000)
£10656	$16836	€15558	Waterfall (30x23cm 12x9in) init.d.64 oil synthetic polymer board prov. 2-Sep-3 Deutscher-Menzies, Melbourne #18/R est:25000-35000 (A.D 26000)
£12295	$19426	€17951	North Otago (22x27cm-9x11in) s.i.d.1967 oil synthetic polymer paint prov. 2-Sep-3 Deutscher-Menzies, Melbourne #19/R est:15000-20000 (A.D 30000)
£21429	$38786	€31286	Landscape (60x60cm-24x24in) s.d.July August 1965 s.i.d.verso acrylic sawdust hardboard prov. 30-Mar-4 Peter Webb, Auckland #34/R est:70000-120000 (NZ.D 60000)
£22541	$35614	€32910	Hill crest (36x25cm-14x10in) s. board prov. 2-Sep-3 Deutscher-Menzies, Melbourne #17/R est:30000-40000 (A.D 55000)
£65217	$105652	€94565	Black and white French Bay (76x61cm-30x24in) s.d.11.1.59 enamel sand hardboard exhib. 31-Jul-3 International Art Centre, Auckland #39/R est:170000-225000 (NZ.D 180000)
£90909	$160909	€132727	Can you hear me St Francis (30x90cm-12x35in) s.i.d.June 69 acrylic hardboard three panels lit. 3-May-4 Christie's, Melbourne #33/R est:220000-250000 (A.D 220000)

Works on paper

£1885	$2978	€2752	North from Mt Atkinson (21x28cm-8x11in) s.d.57 pen prov. 2-Sep-3 Deutscher-Menzies, Melbourne #21/R est:5000-8000 (A.D 4600)
£7435	$12788	€10855	Michael Nicholson's Studio, Auckland (21x27cm-8x11in) s.d.1957 pen ink drawing. 3-Dec-3 Dunbar Sloane, Auckland #66/R est:18000-22000 (NZ.D 20000)
£7942	$12946	€11595	North Otago Landscape (68x43cm-27x17in) s.d.1967 ink. 23-Sep-3 Peter Webb, Auckland #70/R est:25000-35000 (NZ.D 22000)
£14336	$26091	€20931	Light falling through a darl landscape (45x60cm-18x24in) s.i.d.October 1971 conte crayon. 29-Jun-4 Peter Webb, Auckland #45/R est:35000-45000 (NZ.D 41000)
£15217	$24500	€22217	No one should say (153x54cm-60x21in) s.d.Sept 8 1969 conte. 20-Aug-3 Dunbar Sloane, Auckland #52/R est:45000-55000 (NZ.D 42000)
£16667	$26833	€24334	Whoever loves life (152x55cm-60x22in) s.d.August 18 1969 conte prov. 20-Aug-3 Dunbar Sloane, Auckland #27/R est:50000-70000 (NZ.D 46000)
£21429	$39429	€31286	Waterfall (60x45cm-24x18in) s.d.1964 verso mixed media hardboard. 25-Mar-4 International Art Centre, Auckland #50/R est:60000-100000 (NZ.D 60000)
£28926	$51198	€42232	North Otago no 17 (57x83cm-22x33in) s.i.d.1967 polyvinyl acetate hardboard prov.exhib. 3-May-4 Christie's, Melbourne #41/R est:70000-100000 (A.D 70000)
£40650	$63821	€58943	View from the top of the cliff Muriwai, no 3 (108x71cm-43x28in) s.i.d.1970 water-based crayon wash prov.lit. 26-Aug-3 Christie's, Sydney #102/R est:100000-150000 (A.D 100000)
£50000	$90500	€73000	Necessary protection (110x73cm-43x29in) s.d.1971 ink acrylic prov. 30-Mar-4 Peter Webb, Auckland #33/R est:130000-180000 (NZ.D 140000)
£58209	$100701	€84985	Fall of light illuminating darkness (58x77cm-23x30in) s.i.d.July 1971 s.d.July 1971 verso crayon acrylic W/C. 9-Dec-3 Peter Webb, Auckland #48/R est:100000-150000 (NZ.D 156000)

McCAIG, Norman J (1929-2001) Irish

£550	$1007	€803	Rough seas, Co. Antrim Coast (30x40cm-12x16in) s. 2-Jun-4 John Ross, Belfast #26
£620	$1085	€880	Galway hookers (20x26cm-8x10in) s. board. 16-Dec-3 James Adam, Dublin #152/R
£700	$1204	€1022	Harbour at Portstewart (33x91cm-13x36in) s. board. 3-Dec-3 John Ross, Belfast #137
£805	$1442	€1200	Country cottage (28x39cm-11x15in) s. canvasboard. 31-May-4 Hamilton Osborne King, Dublin #140/R
£867	$1560	€1300	Sailing boats in estuary (34x29cm-13x11in) s. board. 20-Apr-4 James Adam, Dublin #82/R
£872	$1562	€1300	Roundstone, Galway (30x24cm-12x9in) s. board. 31-May-4 Hamilton Osborne King, Dublin #33/R
£986	$1725	€1400	Grand canal, Robertstown (24x29cm-9x11in) s. 16-Dec-3 James Adam, Dublin #149/R
£1007	$1782	€1500	Near Kill, County Kildare (25x36cm-10x14in) s. i.verso. 27-Apr-4 Whyte's, Dublin #231/R est:1500-2000
£1074	$1922	€1600	River Errif, Leenane, Connemara (25x30cm-10x12in) s. board. 31-May-4 Hamilton Osborne King, Dublin #7/R est:1000-1500
£1074	$1922	€1600	Flying kites (35x45cm-14x18in) s. board. 31-May-4 Hamilton Osborne King, Dublin #114/R est:800-1200
£1118	$2058	€1700	Snowfall, Enisscree (23x30cm-9x12in) canvasboard. 22-Jun-4 De Veres Art Auctions, Dublin #207/R est:600-900
£1200	$1992	€1752	Donaghadee Harbour, Co. Down (35x91cm-14x36in) s. board. 1-Oct-3 John Ross, Belfast #140 est:800-1000
£1329	$2259	€1900	Boats on the Slaney River, Co.Wexford (30x41cm-12x16in) s.i. 25-Nov-3 De Veres Art Auctions, Dublin #1/R est:1600-2200
£1342	$2376	€2000	Rosses, Donegal (30x41cm-12x16in) s. i.verso. 27-Apr-4 Whyte's, Dublin #204/R est:1800-2200
£1400	$2296	€2044	Walk in the fields (35x45cm-14x18in) s. 4-Jun-3 John Ross, Belfast #1
£1400	$2604	€2044	Fishing boats, Ballywalter (40x50cm-16x20in) s. board. 3-Mar-4 John Ross, Belfast #1 est:1400-1800
£1408	$2437	€2000	Coastal scene with sailing boats (41x61cm-16x24in) s. 10-Dec-3 Bonhams & James Adam, Dublin #111/R est:2500-4000
£1477	$2613	€2200	Coastal bay with cottages and mountains (46x91cm-18x36in) s. 27-Apr-4 Whyte's, Dublin #197/R est:2000-4000
£1479	$2588	€2100	Winter, Avoca, Co Wicklow (28x34cm-11x13in) s. board. 16-Dec-3 James Adam, Dublin #240/R est:1200-1800
£1533	$2760	€2300	At the seaside (35x44cm-14x17in) s. canvasboard. 20-Apr-4 James Adam, Dublin #87/R est:1000-1500
£1678	$2970	€2500	Farmland, Celbridge, County Kildare (41x51cm-16x20in) s. i.verso acrylic canvasboard. 27-Apr-4 Whyte's, Dublin #235/R est:2500-3500
£1700	$2924	€2482	Lough Na Fooey, Connemara (40x50cm-16x20in) s. board. 3-Dec-3 John Ross, Belfast #1 est:1600-1800
£1736	$2830	€2500	Summer, St Stephen's Green (41x51cm-16x20in) s. canvas on board. 23-Sep-3 De Veres Art Auctions, Dublin #217/R est:2000-3000
£1757	$3320	€2600	On the Grand Canal, Dublin (46x36cm-18x14in) s. i.verso canvasboard. 17-Feb-4 Whyte's, Dublin #177/R est:2500-3000
£1867	$3379	€2800	Group of children at the beach (35x46cm-14x18in) s. 30-Mar-4 De Veres Art Auctions, Dublin #48/R est:3000-4000
£1900	$3268	€2774	On the river Bann (40x50cm-16x20in) s. board. 3-Dec-3 John Ross, Belfast #106 est:2000-2500
£1950	$3569	€2847	Fishing boats, low tide, Strangford (40x50cm-16x20in) s. board. 2-Jun-4 John Ross, Belfast #1 est:1600-1800
£1974	$3632	€3000	Sunday on the farm, Normandy (30x40cm-12x16in) s.i.verso canvasboard. 22-Jun-4 De Veres Art Auctions, Dublin #6/R est:3000-4000
£1974	$3632	€3000	Children on a beach at summertime (35x43cm-14x17in) s. canvasboard. 22-Jun-4 De Veres Art Auctions, Dublin #47/R est:2500-3500
£2000	$3280	€2920	Achill Isle (40x50cm-16x20in) s. board. 4-Jun-3 John Ross, Belfast #116a est:1600
£2098	$3566	€3000	Fishing on the river Moy (30x41cm-12x16in) s. board. 18-Nov-3 Whyte's, Dublin #172/R est:3000-3500
£2133	$3861	€3200	The Band Stand, St Stephens Green, Dublin (35x44cm-14x17in) s. board. 31-Mar-4 James Adam, Dublin #156/R est:2000-3000
£2148	$3844	€3200	Cottage on a country road (50x75cm-20x30in) s. 31-May-4 Hamilton Osborne King, Dublin #230/R est:3000-5000
£2297	$4342	€3400	Rowing boat on an open lake (61x91cm-24x36in) s. canvasboard. 17-Feb-4 Whyte's, Dublin #175/R est:3000-4000
£2300	$3979	€3358	Cottages by the water (41x51cm-16x20in) s. sold with companion pair. 10-Dec-3 Bonhams, Bury St Edmunds #581/R est:1800-2500
£2361	$3849	€3400	Horn Head, Donegal (25x35cm-10x14in) s. canvas board. 24-Sep-3 James Adam, Dublin #104/R est:2000-3000
£2378	$4042	€3400	Cottages, the Maam Valley (36x46cm-14x18in) s. board. 18-Nov-3 Whyte's, Dublin #176/R est:2500-3000
£2400	$4344	€3600	Morning catch (29x24cm-11x9in) s. canvasboard. 30-Mar-4 De Veres Art Auctions, Dublin #134/R est:2000-3000
£2606	$4560	€3700	Hookers in harbour (46x65cm-18x26in) s. board. 16-Dec-3 James Adam, Dublin #147/R est:2000-3000
£2635	$4980	€3900	Fishing boats, quayside (41x51cm-16x20in) s. board. 17-Feb-4 Whyte's, Dublin #179/R est:2000-3000
£2657	$4517	€3800	Fishing boats Arklow (51x41cm-20x16in) s. board. 18-Nov-3 Whyte's, Dublin #200/R est:3000-4000
£2703	$5108	€4000	Children at the duck pond, St. Stephen's Green (36x46cm-14x18in) s. canvasboard. 17-Feb-4 Whyte's, Dublin #234/R est:2500-3500
£3200	$5792	€4800	On the Grand Canal near Newcastle, Co Dublin (29x39cm-11x15in) s. board. 31-Mar-4 James Adam, Dublin #154/R est:2000-3000
£3378	$6385	€5000	Safely home (41x51cm-16x20in) s. canvasboard. 17-Feb-4 Whyte's, Dublin #176/R est:3000-4000
£3467	$6275	€5200	In the park (41x51cm-16x20in) s. board. 31-Mar-4 James Adam, Dublin #46/R est:4000-5000
£3521	$6092	€5000	Cashel harbour, Connemara (51x76cm-20x30in) s. 10-Dec-3 Bonhams & James Adam, Dublin #121/R est:4000-6000
£3611	$5886	€5200	Evening, Howth Harbour (61x92cm-24x36in) s. 24-Sep-3 James Adam, Dublin #44/R est:4000-6000

McCAIN, Buck (20th C) American

£2050	$3300	€2973	Indian by river (56x66cm-22x26in) board. 22-Aug-3 Altermann Galleries, Santa Fe #38

Sculpture
£932 $1500 €1351 Invocation (43cm-17in) bronze. 22-Aug-3 Altermann Galleries, Santa Fe #34

McCALL, Charles (1907-1989) British
£420 $773 €613 Girl in a bathroom (26x22cm-10x9in) s. board. 10-Jun-4 Lyon & Turnbull, Edinburgh #144
£550 $919 €803 Off Montpelier Square, London (41x30cm-16x12in) s.d.65. 16-Oct-3 Christie's, Kensington #432/R
£600 $1098 €876 Victorian Gown (30x21cm-12x8in) s.d.1982 board. 6-Jul-4 Bearnes, Exeter #486
£620 $1054 €905 Bedtime (25x20cm-10x8in) s.d.67 board. 1-Dec-3 Bonhams, Bath #48/R
£750 $1253 €1095 Melanie (29x20cm-11x8in) board. 16-Oct-3 Christie's, Kensington #303/R
£1000 $1850 €1460 The letter (26x32cm-10x13in) s.d.78 board. 11-Feb-4 Sotheby's, Olympia #182/R est:1000-1500
£1300 $2041 €1885 Girl at a mirror (22x18cm-9x7in) s.d.1979 board prov. 27-Aug-3 Sotheby's, London #1149/R est:1500-2000
£1300 $2327 €1898 Sleep (40x30cm-16x12in) s.d.83 board. 28-May-4 Lyon & Turnbull, Edinburgh #4/R est:1000-1500
£1550 $2744 €2263 Bedroom with a figure seated in the light of a window (37x0cm-15x0in) i.verso board exhib. 28-Apr-4 Peter Wilson, Nantwich #36 est:400-600
£1600 $2816 €2336 Warwick Place (46x36cm-18x14in) s.d.61 prov.exhib. 19-May-4 Sotheby's, Olympia #193/R est:1500-2000
£3000 $5430 €4380 Chateau at Chartres. Portrait of a lady (52x42cm-20x17in) s.d.1942 board double-sided. 19-Apr-4 Sotheby's, London #126/R est:3000-4000
£3800 $7030 €5548 Girl in front of mantelpiece (22x17cm-9x7in) s.d.1978 board. 11-Feb-4 Sotheby's, Olympia #224/R est:1000-1500

McCALLIEN, William J (fl.1899-1913) British
£300 $546 €438 Sailing vessels in a harbour (45x61cm-18x24in) s. 15-Jun-4 Rosebery Fine Art, London #538

McCALLUM, Andrew (1821-1902) British
£700 $1295 €1022 The Beeches (56x132cm-22x52in) s.i.d.1894. 13-Jan-4 Bonhams, Knightsbridge #65/R
£5500 $9350 €8030 Twilight, Burnham Beeches (90x90cm-35x35in) s.d.1880. 25-Nov-3 Christie's, London #123/R est:7000-10000
Works on paper
£650 $1190 €949 Fortress of Bard, Val d'Aosta, Italy (34x49cm-13x19in) s.i.d.1861 W/C. 27-Jan-4 Bonhams, Knightsbridge #66/R

McCANCE, William (1894-1970) British
Works on paper
£3500 $5950 €5110 Industrial landscape (36x50cm-14x20in) blk chk prov.exhib. 30-Oct-3 Christie's, London #150/R est:2000-3000

McCANN, Gerald Patrick (1916-) American
£1294 $2200 €1889 Hunter (58x84cm-23x33in) board. 1-Nov-3 Altermann Galleries, Santa Fe #139

McCANNELL, Ursula (1923-) British
£840 $1554 €1226 Leary's a landscape with farm and cattle (50x51cm-20x20in) s. board. 13-Feb-4 Sworder & Son, Bishops Stortford #139/R

McCARA, Don (20th C) New Zealander
Works on paper
£1812 $2935 €2627 Late summer afternoon, near Cass (52x70cm-20x28in) s.d.2002 W/C. 31-Jul-3 International Art Centre, Auckland #63/R est:2500-3500 (NZ.D 5000)

MACCARI, Mino (1898-1989) Italian
£267 $491 €400 Two halves (29x29cm-11x11in) s. paper. 14-Jun-4 Sant Agostino, Torino #368/R
£397 $723 €600 Face of woman (24x16cm-9x6in) s. 21-Jun-4 Pandolfini, Florence #360
£629 $1051 €900 Surprise (35x45cm-14x18in) s. paper. 26-Jun-3 Sant Agostino, Torino #178/R
£655 $1094 €950 Figures (27x17cm-11x7in) s. board. 14-Nov-3 Farsetti, Prato #23
£667 $1200 €1000 Portrait in blue (24x20cm-9x8in) s. cardboard on canvas prov. 22-Apr-4 Finarte Semenzato, Rome #156/R
£1042 $1646 €1500 Tantrum (20x30cm-8x12in) board. 6-Sep-3 Meeting Art, Vercelli #463 est:1500
£1197 $1987 €1700 Three girls (31x21cm-12x8in) s. 13-Jun-3 Farsetti, Prato #429/R
£1268 $2104 €1800 At the bar (35x50cm-14x20in) s. paper on canvas. 13-Jun-3 Farsetti, Prato #92/R
£1333 $2453 €2000 Figures (30x40cm-12x16in) s. cardboard on canvas. 12-Jun-4 Meeting Art, Vercelli #250/R
£1351 $2378 €2000 Suburbs (20x30cm-8x12in) s. 22-May-4 Galleria Pananti, Florence #448/R est:1200-1500
£1379 $2303 €2000 You do not need a veil (22x23cm-9x9in) s. tempera paper. 17-Nov-3 Sant Agostino, Torino #175/R est:1600
£1408 $2437 €2000 Roman scene (34x25cm-13x10in) s. card exhib. 9-Dec-3 Pandolfini, Florence #142 est:2000-2500
£1467 $2655 €2200 Figures under the umbrellas (40x29cm-16x11in) s. canvas on cardboard. 2-Apr-4 Farsetti, Prato #514/R est:1600-1900
£1589 $2893 €2400 Female nude (34x24cm-13x9in) s. canvas on board. 21-Jun-4 Pandolfini, Florence #382/R est:2300-2500
£1611 $2980 €2400 Figures (40x25cm-16x10in) s. cardboard on canvas prov. 11-Mar-4 Galleria Pace, Milan #114/R est:2800-3600
£1667 $3067 €2500 Untitled (30x40cm-12x16in) s. board. 12-Jun-4 Meeting Art, Vercelli #620/R est:2500
£1701 $3044 €2500 Approach (45x25cm-18x10in) d. painted 1964 prov. 16-Mar-4 Finarte Semenzato, Milan #327/R est:2600
£1793 $2994 €2600 Salute (35x50cm-14x20in) s. canvas on cardboard. 14-Nov-3 Farsetti, Prato #484/R est:2600-3000
£1854 $3375 €2800 Faces (40x53cm-16x21in) s. canvas on board. 21-Jun-4 Pandolfini, Florence #461/R est:2800-3200
£1958 $3329 €2800 Dancers (40x34cm-16x13in) s.s.verso cardboard on canvas prov. 24-Nov-3 Christie's, Milan #65/R est:1800-2200
£1959 $3449 €2900 Three figures (30x41cm-12x16in) s. 22-May-4 Galleria Pananti, Florence #449/R est:1600-1800
£1987 $3616 €3000 Figures (45x34cm-18x13in) s. cardboard. 21-Jun-4 Pandolfini, Florence #387/R est:3000-3500
£2432 $4281 €3600 Three figures (37x38cm-15x15in) s. cardboard on canvas. 24-May-4 Christie's, Milan #46/R est:2000-3000
£2465 $4313 €3500 Planes and ships (40x60cm-16x24in) s. board prov. 17-Dec-3 Il Ponte, Milan #1104/R est:4000-5000
£2649 $4821 €4000 Man and woman (39x49cm-15x19in) s. 21-Jun-4 Pandolfini, Florence #381/R est:2800-3200
£2649 $4821 €4000 Soldiers and girls (39x53cm-15x21in) s. board. 21-Jun-4 Pandolfini, Florence #462/R est:3200-3400
£2800 $5152 €4200 Sisters (35x50cm-14x20in) s. 11-Jun-4 Farsetti, Prato #581/R est:4000-5000
£2867 $5160 €4300 Meetings (60x40cm-24x16in) s. 22-Apr-4 Finarte Semenzato, Rome #309/R est:4500-5000
£2914 $5303 €4400 Figures in landscape (35x50cm-14x20in) s. 21-Jun-4 Pandolfini, Florence #490/R est:2400-2600
£3000 $5430 €4500 Ball (49x35cm-19x14in) s.d.1961 canvas on cardboard. 2-Apr-4 Farsetti, Prato #605/R est:4000-5000
£3034 $5068 €4400 Last hours of Don Giovanni (40x50cm-16x20in) s.d.1949. 17-Nov-3 Sant Agostino, Torino #264/R est:4000-5000
£3133 $5671 €4700 Masked ball (40x50cm-16x20in) s. 2-Apr-4 Farsetti, Prato #617/R est:4500-5500
£3311 $6026 €5000 Three faces (39x48cm-15x19in) s. board prov. 21-Jun-4 Pandolfini, Florence #356/R est:2800-3000
£3448 $5759 €5000 Carousel (50x60cm-20x24in) s. 13-Nov-3 Finarte Semenzato, Rome #396/R est:4500-5500
£3576 $6509 €5400 Soldier with women (51x67cm-20x26in) s. 21-Jun-4 Pandolfini, Florence #357/R est:2800-3200
£3716 $6541 €5500 Four figures (36x45cm-14x18in) s. painted c.1975. 24-May-4 Christie's, Milan #58/R est:2500-3500
£3793 $6334 €5500 Figures (49x60cm-19x24in) s. i.verso board. 14-Nov-3 Farsetti, Prato #498/R est:4700-5200
£3846 $6423 €5500 Pirouette (40x60cm-16x24in) s. board. 26-Jun-3 Sant Agostino, Torino #250/R est:5500-6500
£4533 $8341 €6800 Masked ball (45x55cm-18x22in) s.d.1960 cardboard on canvas. 12-Jun-4 Meeting Art, Vercelli #972/R est:4000
£6376 $11859 €9500 Figures (60x90cm-24x35in) s. 4-Mar-4 Babuino, Rome #77 est:5000-6000
Works on paper
£298 $542 €450 Tonino (30x20cm-12x8in) s. ink. 17-Jun-4 Galleria Pananti, Florence #142/R
£303 $507 €440 Temptations (20x31cm-8x12in) s. W/C pencil. 14-Nov-3 Farsetti, Prato #47
£303 $507 €440 Praying (28x22cm-11x9in) s. ink lit. 17-Nov-3 Sant Agostino, Torino #171/R
£310 $518 €450 Study for boy (35x25cm-14x10in) s.i. pencil W/C pastel. 14-Nov-3 Farsetti, Prato #237
£333 $613 €500 Face of woman (49x35cm-19x14in) s. chl. 8-Jun-4 Finarte Semenzato, Milan #169/R
£333 $613 €500 Untitled (35x25cm-14x10in) s. pastel oil. 12-Jun-4 Meeting Art, Vercelli #321
£340 $609 €500 Politic prisoner (16x13cm-6x5in) pencil. 22-Mar-4 Sant Agostino, Torino #421/R
£385 $642 €550 Woman (27x25cm-11x10in) s. mixed media. 26-Jun-3 Sant Agostino, Torino #171/R
£397 $723 €600 Untitled (14x15cm-6x6in) s. mixed media. 17-Jun-4 Galleria Pananti, Florence #141/R
£397 $723 €600 Painter (30x43cm-12x17in) s. W/C dr. 17-Jun-4 Galleria Pananti, Florence #439/R
£420 $701 €600 Lieutenant (25x23cm-10x9in) s. mixed media. 26-Jun-3 Sant Agostino, Torino #172/R
£436 $807 €650 My boredom comes inevitably (22x11cm-9x4in) s. pen. 13-Mar-4 Meeting Art, Vercelli #247
£448 $749 €650 Red hair and blue eyes (34x13cm-13x5in) s. chl W/C. 17-Nov-3 Sant Agostino, Torino #41/R
£468 $767 €650 Dance (33x24cm-13x9in) s. W/C pencil. 10-Jun-3 Pandolfini, Florence #332
£476 $852 €700 Surprise box (18x17cm-7x7in) mixed media. 22-Mar-4 Sant Agostino, Torino #415/R
£533 $981 €800 Cameraman (30x24cm-12x9in) wax crayon. 14-Jun-4 Sant Agostino, Torino #367/R
£634 $1096 €900 Quando meno te l'aspetti - When you don't expect it (50x37cm-20x15in) s.i. mixed media card. 9-Dec-3 Pandolfini, Florence #143/R
£655 $1048 €950 Face (23x15cm-9x6in) s. chl W/C. 13-Mar-3 Galleria Pace, Milan #16/R
£690 $1152 €1000 Odalisk (28x47cm-11x19in) s. W/C tempera. 13-Nov-3 Finarte Semenzato, Rome #148
£725 $1188 €1000 Composition (35x51cm-14x20in) s. mixed media paper on canvas. 29-May-3 Galleria Pace, Milan #25/R
£764 $1207 €1100 Mythological figure (40x50cm-16x20in) mixed media exec.1969. 6-Sep-3 Meeting Art, Vercelli #735 est:1000
£1020 $1827 €1500 Couple (51x40cm-20x16in) s. mixed media. 16-Mar-4 Finarte Semenzato, Milan #160/R est:850
£1467 $2640 €2200 Wishes (48x49cm-19x19in) s. pastel exec.1969. 22-Apr-4 Finarte Semenzato, Rome #100/R est:1800-2400
£1736 $2743 €2500 Study for Falstaff (49x70cm-19x28in) mixed media. 6-Sep-3 Meeting Art, Vercelli #633 est:2500

McCARTHY, Brian (20th C) Irish
£694 $1090 €1000 Still life with fruit bowl and yukka plant (50x40cm-20x16in) s. 26-Aug-3 James Adam, Dublin #45/R est:800-1200

McCARTHY, Doris Jean (1910-) Canadian
£720 $1318 €1051 Reflecting (30x40cm-12x16in) s. canvasboard. 1-Jun-4 Joyner Waddington, Toronto #318/R est:1500-2000 (C.D 1800)
£887 $1632 €1295 Bon Echo. Sailboats, New Brunswick (29x34cm-11x13in) s. board double-sided. 9-Jun-4 Walker's, Ottawa #81/R est:2500-3500 (C.D 2200)
£1423 $2547 €2078 Rocky Mountain (29x34cm-11x13in) s. panel prov. 6-May-4 Heffel, Vancouver #96/R est:1500-2500 (C.D 3500)

£1429	$2457	€2086	Pond inlet, NWT (30x40cm-12x16in) s. panel. 2-Dec-3 Joyner Waddington, Toronto #282/R est:1500-2000 (C.D 3200)
£1700	$3111	€2482	Pines at the Keyhole (30x40cm-12x16in) s. panel prov. 1-Jun-4 Joyner Waddington, Toronto #189/R est:2000-3000 (C.D 4250)
£2400	$4392	€3504	Trees, Revelstoke (29x34cm-11x13in) s. panel painted c.1937-38 unfinished sketch verso. 1-Jun-4 Joyner Waddington, Toronto #123/R est:3000-4000 (C.D 6000)
£2439	$4366	€3561	Haliburton Village (29x34cm-11x13in) s. i.d.1937 verso panel prov. 6-May-4 Heffel, Vancouver #95/R est:1500-2500 (C.D 6000)
£2602	$4345	€3799	Foothills (60x75cm-24x30in) s.i. 17-Nov-3 Hodgins, Calgary #317/R est:3000-5000 (C.D 5750)
£2893	$5236	€4224	Rock puddle below the pine, Baie Fine (29x34cm-11x13in) s. board prov. 18-Apr-4 Levis, Calgary #76/R est:3000-4000 (C.D 7000)
£3348	$5759	€4888	Lily pads (21x26cm-8x10in) s. board oil sketch verso double-sided. 2-Dec-3 Joyner Waddington, Toronto #198/R est:2000-3000 (C.D 7500)
£9009	$15315	€13153	Longpoint, Newfoundland (91x121cm-36x48in) s. i.verso. 27-Nov-3 Heffel, Vancouver #113/R est:4000-6000 (C.D 20000)
Works on paper			
£1727	$3092	€2521	Rocky shore, Newfoundland (38x55cm-15x22in) s. W/C prov. 27-May-4 Heffel, Vancouver #60/R est:2500-3000 (C.D 4250)
£2232	$3839	€3259	Glacier starting to the sea (54x72cm-21x28in) s. W/C. 2-Dec-3 Joyner Waddington, Toronto #152/R est:2000-3000 (C.D 5000)
£3200	$5856	€4672	Complete Barachois, a panoramic view of the fishing village, Gaspe (60x90cm-24x35in) s. W/C exhib. 1-Jun-4 Joyner Waddington, Toronto #25/R est:5000-7000 (C.D 8000)

McCARTHY, Frank (1924-2002) American

£1618	$2750	€2362	Law of the West (48x28cm-19x11in) s. board. 1-Nov-3 Santa Fe Art, Santa Fe #244/R est:3500-5500
£2733	$4400	€3963	Gunslinger (51x36cm-20x14in) 22-Aug-3 Altermann Galleries, Santa Fe #18
£2941	$5000	€4294	Pursued (20x25cm-8x10in) board. 1-Nov-3 Altermann Galleries, Santa Fe #122
£3230	$5200	€4684	River crossing (41x61cm-16x24in) 22-Aug-3 Altermann Galleries, Santa Fe #17
£3727	$6000	€5404	Sentinel of the superstitions (30x20cm-12x8in) board. 22-Aug-3 Altermann Galleries, Santa Fe #1
£3955	$7000	€5774	Into the shadows (34x30cm-13x12in) s.i.d.1982 verso canvasboard prov. 28-Apr-4 Christie's, Los Angeles #69/R est:7000-9000
£4412	$7500	€6442	Stolen ponies (30x46cm-12x18in) 1-Nov-3 Altermann Galleries, Santa Fe #119
£4706	$8000	€6871	Crack in the rock (41x30cm-16x12in) board. 1-Nov-3 Altermann Galleries, Santa Fe #120
£11377	$19000	€16610	At the timberline (61x76cm-24x30in) s.d.1978 s.i.verso tempera gessoed masonite. 9-Oct-3 Christie's, Rockefeller NY #77/R est:10000-15000
£23529	$40000	€34352	Heading back (51x102cm-20x40in) 1-Nov-3 Altermann Galleries, Santa Fe #118
£24022	$43000	€35072	Buffalo Hunt (61x102cm-24x40in) 15-May-4 Altermann Galleries, Santa Fe #36/R
£26738	$50000	€39037	Cold trail (46x81cm-18x32in) s. board prov. 24-Jul-4 Coeur d'Alene, Hayden #152/R est:15000-25000
£34759	$65000	€50748	Apache scouts (51x102cm-20x40in) s. 24-Jul-4 Coeur d'Alene, Hayden #153/R est:25000-45000
£54900	$93330	€80154	On the Old North Trail (61x203cm-24x80in) s.d.1989 triptych prov.lit. 1-Nov-3 Santa Fe Art, Santa Fe #174/R est:100000-130000

McCARTHY, Justin (1892-1977) American

£359	$600	€524	Three birds (15x61cm-6x24in) board prov. 15-Nov-3 Slotin Folk Art, Buford #226/R
£479	$800	€699	Six flowers (48x64cm-19x25in) acrylic board prov. 15-Nov-3 Slotin Folk Art, Buford #224/R
£556	$1000	€812	Three birds (23x71cm-9x28in) acrylic. 24-Apr-4 Slotin Folk Art, Buford #387/R est:1000-2000
£659	$1100	€962	Woman doing backstroke (76x51cm-30x20in) board prov. 15-Nov-3 Slotin Folk Art, Buford #228/R
£1056	$1900	€1542	Elizabeth Taylor and Pie, her horse. Taylor with Lassie (23x28cm-9x11in) painted manila envelopes two pieces. 24-Apr-4 Slotin Folk Art, Buford #389/R est:1000-1500
£1111	$2000	€1622	Poodle puppies (38x58cm-15x23in) board prov. 24-Apr-4 Slotin Folk Art, Buford #386/R est:1000-2000
£1138	$1900	€1661	Landscape with river (61x61cm-24x24in) acrylic board prov. 15-Nov-3 Slotin Folk Art, Buford #227/R est:1000-1500
£1916	$3200	€2797	Tiger in the grass (64x94cm-25x37in) acrylic board prov. 15-Nov-3 Slotin Folk Art, Buford #225/R est:1000-2000
Works on paper			
£278	$500	€406	Movie stars - Ingrid Bergman and Virginia Mays (23x28cm-9x11in) ink. 24-Apr-4 Slotin Folk Art, Buford #388/R
£389	$700	€568	Sweater styles 1961 (56x71cm-22x28in) crayon pencil posterboard. 24-Apr-4 Slotin Folk Art, Buford #385/R
£539	$900	€787	Kiwi bird of New Zealand (36x41cm-14x16in) graphite prov. 15-Nov-3 Slotin Folk Art, Buford #231/R

McCARTHY, Paul (1945-) American

£410	$750	€599	Untitled (112x84cm-44x33in) 10-Jul-4 Hindman, Chicago #332/R
£872	$1500	€1273	Chicago (122x76cm-48x30in) s.d.1983. 7-Dec-3 Susanin's, Chicago #6069/R est:1500-3000
Photographs			
£5533	$10126	€8300	Heidi (76x102cm-30x40in) s.d.1993 verso varnished cibachrome lit. 4-Jun-4 Lempertz, Koln #303/R est:6000
£8152	$15000	€11902	Rat blue, propo objects (183x122cm-72x48in) s.d.1995 num.3 verso c-print prov. 10-Jun-4 Phillips, New York #428/R est:8000-12000
£10615	$19000	€15498	Propo object, ken-pink head (183x122cm-72x48in) s.i.d.1995 num. of three verso cibachrome prov.exhib.lit. 14-May-4 Phillips, New York #148/R est:10000-15000
£12291	$22000	€17945	Propo object, ken-no head (183x122cm-72x48in) s.i.d.1995 num. of three cibachrome prov.exhib.lit. 14-May-4 Phillips, New York #150/R est:10000-15000
£23952	$40000	€34970	White line painted on the floor with my face (155x99cm-61x39in) s.num.1/3 verso gelatin silver print 2 exec.1972 prov.exhib.lit. 13-Nov-3 Sotheby's, New York #445/R est:40000-60000
£41916	$70000	€61197	Propo, miracle whip, girl with penis, baby lotion (183x122cm-72x48in) cibachrome prints on aluminum set of three executed 1991. 13-Nov-3 Phillips, New York #50/R est:30000-40000
Prints			
£12291	$22000	€17945	Propo (183x126cm-72x50in) s. col coupler print on aluminum edition of 3 prov.exhib. 12-May-4 Christie's, Rockefeller NY #332/R est:18000-22000
Sculpture			
£20112	$36000	€29364	Untitled, A (97x30x45cm-38x12x18in) s.d.1996 polyurethane wood prov. 14-May-4 Phillips, New York #121/R est:40000-60000
£30726	$55000	€44860	Dwarf head, light blue (96x65x65cm-38x26x26in) platinum-based silicone wood series of 7 prov.exhib. 12-May-4 Christie's, Rockefeller NY #331/R est:35000-45000
Works on paper			
£2793	$5000	€4078	Untitled (48x59cm-19x23in) init.d.90 verso ink prov. 12-May-4 Christie's, Rockefeller NY #334/R est:10000-15000
£17877	$32000	€26100	Yaa-hoo (61x48cm-24x19in) s.verso graphite photo collage six parts prov. 14-May-4 Phillips, New York #152/R est:8000-12000

McCARTHY, Stephen (1954-) Australian

Works on paper			
£351	$650	€512	Towards the golden dawn II (122x91cm-48x36in) s.d.1991 i.verso synthetic polymer. 15-Mar-4 Sotheby's, Melbourne #221 est:800-1200 (A.D 850)

McCAW, Dan (1942-) American

£1176	$2000	€1717	Watchful eye (36x46cm-14x18in) s. masonite panel prov.lit. 1-Nov-3 Santa Fe Art, Santa Fe #87/R est:2500-3500
£1912	$3250	€2792	Their land (51x61cm-20x24in) s. masonite panel prov.lit. 1-Nov-3 Santa Fe Art, Santa Fe #86/R est:2500-3500

McCAW, Terence (1913-1979) South African

£330	$591	€482	Self portrait (45x85cm-18x33in) s.d.55 canvasboard. 31-May-4 Stephan Welz, Johannesburg #315 (SA.R 4000)
£385	$654	€562	Landscape with huts (49x60cm-19x24in) s.d.53. 4-Nov-3 Stephan Welz, Johannesburg #683 est:5000-8000 (SA.R 4500)
£400	$668	€584	Harbour scene (39x50cm-15x20in) s.d.61 board. 18-Oct-3 Windibank, Dorking #368/R
£504	$913	€736	St. Joseph lilies in a glass vase (29x23cm-11x9in) s. board. 30-Mar-4 Stephan Welz, Johannesburg #531 est:4000-6000 (SA.R 6000)
£517	$864	€755	View of a canal, Venice (59x48cm-23x19in) s.d.57 canvas on board. 20-Oct-3 Stephan Welz, Johannesburg #288/R est:6000-8000 (SA.R 6000)
£673	$1239	€983	Rural huts (50x60cm-20x24in) 8-Jun-4 Dales, Durban #6 (SA.R 8000)
£733	$1224	€1070	East Rand headgear - old quarry pit (49x59cm-19x23in) s.d.42. 20-Oct-3 Stephan Welz, Johannesburg #298/R est:7000-10000 (SA.R 8500)
£826	$1478	€1206	Cape farmstead (29x39cm-11x15in) s.d.49 canvas on board. 31-May-4 Stephan Welz, Johannesburg #499 (SA.R 10000)
£826	$1478	€1206	Spanish street (39x49cm-15x19in) s. i. verso. 31-May-4 Stephan Welz, Johannesburg #557/R (SA.R 10000)
£991	$1774	€1447	Cape street scene (39x49cm-15x19in) s.d.46 canvasboard. 31-May-4 Stephan Welz, Johannesburg #502 (SA.R 12000)
£1001	$1722	€1461	Street scene, Mamre (40x50cm-16x20in) s. canvasboard. 3-Dec-3 Stephan Welz, Johannesburg #30/R est:9000-12000 (SA.R 11000)
£1239	$2217	€1809	Sea, Hermanus (56x76cm-22x30in) s.d.75 i. verso board. 31-May-4 Stephan Welz, Johannesburg #542/R est:8000-12000 (SA.R 15000)
£1513	$2738	€2209	Small fishing village on a river (39x50cm-15x20in) s.d.50 canvasboard. 30-Mar-4 Stephan Welz, Johannesburg #439/R est:8000-12000 (SA.R 18000)
£1513	$2738	€2209	Still life of flowes in a jug (75x55cm-30x22in) s.d.1939 canvas on board. 30-Mar-4 Stephan Welz, Johannesburg #535/R est:7000-10000 (SA.R 18000)
£1552	$2591	€2266	Fishermens cottages (37x55cm-15x22in) s. board. 20-Oct-3 Stephan Welz, Johannesburg #286/R est:8000-12000 (SA.R 18000)
£1638	$2735	€2391	Cottages, Waenhuiskrans (40x50cm-16x20in) s.d.75 board. 20-Oct-3 Stephan Welz, Johannesburg #287/R est:9000-12000 (SA.R 19000)
£1638	$2735	€2391	Street scene, Johannesburg, mine dump in the distance (50x40cm-20x16in) s.d.42. 20-Oct-3 Stephan Welz, Johannesburg #299/R est:6000-9000 (SA.R 19000)
£1817	$3252	€2653	Malay quarter (39x49cm-15x19in) s.d.50 canvas on board. 31-May-4 Stephan Welz, Johannesburg #506/R est:9000-12000 (SA.R 22000)
£2069	$3455	€3021	Village man mine, Johannesburg (54x69cm-21x27in) s.d.41. 20-Oct-3 Stephan Welz, Johannesburg #297/R est:12000-16000 (SA.R 24000)
£2586	$4319	€3776	In the harbour at Gans Bay (50x60cm-20x24in) s.d.48 i.verso. 20-Oct-3 Stephan Welz, Johannesburg #354/R est:12000-18000 (SA.R 30000)
£3303	$5912	€4822	Hout bay harbour (39x49cm-15x19in) s.d.61 canvas on board. 31-May-4 Stephan Welz, Johannesburg #548/R est:10000-15000 (SA.R 40000)
£4542	$8130	€6631	Onrust river (60x96cm-24x38in) s.d.50 i. mount canvas on board. 31-May-4 Stephan Welz, Johannesburg #486/R est:20000-30000 (SA.R 55000)
Works on paper			
£325	$552	€475	View of Jerusalem (46x61cm-18x24in) s.d.71 W/C. 4-Nov-3 Stephan Welz, Johannesburg #370 est:2000-3000 (SA.R 3800)
£362	$605	€529	Still life with flowers in a bowl (50x60cm-20x24in) s.d.70 W/C. 20-Oct-3 Stephan Welz, Johannesburg #575 est:2500-3500 (SA.R 4200)
£682	$1174	€996	Facade, Petra (90x69cm-35x27in) s.d.71 W/C. 3-Dec-3 Stephan Welz, Johannesburg #31 est:3000-4000 (SA.R 7500)

McCAY, Winsor (1869-1934) American

Works on paper			
£2246	$3750	€3279	Frog followed by ape, followed by man, followed by giant eye (20x56cm-8x22in) s. pen ink exec.c.1915. 15-Nov-3 Illustration House, New York #25/R est:2000-3000

McCHESNEY, Robert Pearson (1913-) American

£2222	$4000	€3244	Untitled (48x62cm-19x24in) s.d.1961/1944/1945 enamel sand canvas gouache paper three. 25-Apr-4 Bonhams & Butterfields, San Francisco #5649/R

MACCHI, Aurelio (1916-) South American
Sculpture
£1648 $3000 €2406 Resting (28cm-11in) init.d.93 pat bronze marble base. 29-Jun-4 Arroyo, Buenos Aires #35/R est:2800

MACCHI, Lorenzo (1804-?) Italian
Works on paper
£308 $524 €450 Veduta alle vicinanze de Milano (18x30cm-7x12in) i. gouache htd white. 5-Nov-3 Dobiaschofsky, Bern #1148 (S.FR 700)

MACCIO, Gerard di (?) ?
Works on paper
£1812 $3316 €2700 Fille assise (142x110cm-56x43in) s. mixed media paper on panel. 7-Jul-4 Artcurial Briest, Paris #247 est:3000-4000

MACCIO, Romulo (1931-) Argentinian
£3352 $6000 €4894 Figure (60x43cm-24x17in) s. tempera paper. 4-May-4 Arroyo, Buenos Aires #16/R est:6000
£7059 $12000 €10306 Rufina (200x200cm-79x79in) s.d.68 acrylic prov.exhib. 19-Nov-3 Sotheby's, New York #160/R est:15000-20000
Works on paper
£2793 $5000 €4078 Figure (54x38cm-21x15in) mixed media. 11-May-4 Arroyo, Buenos Aires #59

MACCIOTTA, Giovanni (1927-1993) Italian
£517 $864 €750 Southwest wind (31x34cm-12x13in) s.i.d.1969 acrylic masonite. 17-Nov-3 Sant Agostino, Torino #111/R
£517 $864 €750 Human element in landscape (21x36cm-8x14in) s.i.d.1969 board. 17-Nov-3 Sant Agostino, Torino #112/R
£533 $981 €800 Dialogue (52x25cm-20x10in) s.i.d.1969 board. 14-Jun-4 Sant Agostino, Torino #178/R
£748 $1339 €1100 Fragment (80x55cm-31x22in) s. i.verso acrylic. 22-Mar-4 Sant Agostino, Torino #350/R
£800 $1472 €1200 Snow (40x58cm-16x23in) s.d.1961 board. 14-Jun-4 Sant Agostino, Torino #230/R
Works on paper
£828 $1382 €1200 Straw (35x50cm-14x20in) s.i.d.1971 mixed media cardboard. 17-Nov-3 Sant Agostino, Torino #95/R

McCLEAN, Sheila (1932-) Irish
£480 $893 €701 Landscape III (45x61cm-18x24in) s. board. 3-Mar-4 John Ross, Belfast #83

McCLELLAND, Robert John (1906-1977) American
£503 $800 €734 Road home (61x51cm-24x20in) s. i.d.1941 verso. 12-Sep-3 Skinner, Boston #393/R
£578 $1000 €844 Waiting for Washington (56x79cm-22x31in) s. masonite. 10-Dec-3 Alderfer's, Hatfield #415/R est:800-1000

McCLOY, Samuel (1831-1904) British
Works on paper
£7042 $11268 €10000 Flowers for the teacher (38x24cm-15x9in) mono. W/C prov. 16-Sep-3 Whyte's, Dublin #97/R est:5000-7000

McCLUNG, Florence (1896-1992) American
£2703 $5000 €4055 Texas landscape with bluebonnets and trees. s.stretcher. 14-Jul-4 Dallas Auction Gallery, Dallas #369/R est:1500-2500
£5988 $10000 €8742 Lake Worth (51x61cm-20x24in) painted c.1940. 18-Oct-3 David Dike, Dallas #234/R est:8000-12000
Works on paper
£1078 $1800 €1574 Wash day in Trinity valley (30x48cm-12x19in) pencil. 18-Oct-3 David Dike, Dallas #59/R est:2500-3500

McCLURE, Daphne (1930-) British
£850 $1471 €1241 Boats at Porthleven (69x36cm-27x14in) s. card. 11-Dec-3 Lane, Penzance #45/R
Works on paper
£520 $863 €759 The Ship Inn (30x41cm-12x16in) s. mixed media. 2-Oct-3 Lane, Penzance #186
£550 $919 €803 Mexic Towans (56x46cm-22x18in) s. gouache acrylic. 14-Oct-3 David Lay, Penzance #549
£600 $996 €876 Hayle River (61x48cm-24x19in) s. gouache acrylic prov. 2-Oct-3 Lane, Penzance #348
£900 $1494 €1314 Levant Mine (54x80cm-21x31in) s. i.verso mixed media board. 2-Oct-3 Lane, Penzance #190/R

McCLURE, David (1926-1998) British
£1200 $1884 €1740 Myna bird and white jug (29x39cm-11x15in) s. i.verso panel. 27-Aug-3 Sotheby's, London #1159/R est:1500-2000
£1200 $2004 €1752 Room interior with red chair, settee, Japanese prints (50x60cm-20x24in) s. board. 11-Oct-3 Shapes, Edinburgh #363 est:800-1200
£1800 $2898 €2610 Nude with Norwegian church (66x44cm-26x17in) board painted c.1963 exhib. 21-Aug-3 Bonhams, Edinburgh #1111/R est:2000-3000
£2200 $3872 €3212 Kite and dried leaf (27x39cm-11x15in) s. s.i.d.78 verso board. 19-May-4 Sotheby's, Olympia #256/R est:2000-3000
£2500 $4525 €3650 Wick Harbour (46x64cm-18x25in) board. 19-Apr-4 Sotheby's, London #146/R est:3000-5000
£3000 $4830 €4350 Objects on a blue ground (71x91cm-28x36in) s. s.i.verso. 21-Aug-3 Bonhams, Edinburgh #1110/R est:3000-5000
£5000 $9050 €7300 Pink marble with bird (63x76cm-25x30in) s. i.verso. 19-Apr-4 Sotheby's, London #151/R est:5000-7000
£5000 $8800 €7300 Black cockerel (76x101cm-30x40in) s.d.1968 s.i.verso. 18-May-4 Woolley & Wallis, Salisbury #239/R est:2000-3000
£5500 $9350 €8030 Japanese Kite (102x127cm-40x50in) s. s.i.d.1980 verso. 30-Oct-3 Christie's, London #228/R est:6000-8000
£8000 $12560 €11600 Grey marble with melon (63x76cm-25x30in) s. i.verso prov. 27-Aug-3 Sotheby's, London #1165/R est:3000-5000
£8500 $14450 €12410 Red studio (76x102cm-30x40in) s. s.i.d.1967 verso. 26-Nov-3 Sotheby's, Olympia #148/R est:8000-12000
Works on paper
£600 $966 €870 White bird and flowers (19x31cm-7x12in) s.d.67 s.i.verso pastel W/C monotype. 21-Aug-3 Bonhams, Edinburgh #1041/R

McCLURE, Emma (1962-) British
£350 $655 €511 Pink lillies (29x30cm-11x12in) s.i.d.2000 verso. 26-Feb-4 Lane, Penzance #78
£460 $860 €672 Boat and fishing gear V (38x41cm-15x16in) i.d.2002-03 verso board. 26-Feb-4 Lane, Penzance #77

MACCO, Georg (1863-1933) German
£300 $471 €435 Street scenes before a fortified gateway, Rhodes (25x37cm-10x15in) s.d.23.3.1933 i.verso oil gouache on card. 28-Aug-3 Christie's, Kensington #248
£417 $679 €600 Constantinople (39x52cm-15x20in) s. 24-Sep-3 Neumeister, Munich #489/R
£559 $962 €800 Sphinx in Gizeh (47x33cm-19x13in) s.d.30/3/03 i.verso. 3-Dec-3 Neumeister, Munich #661/R
£667 $1213 €1000 Rocky coast near Monterosso (33x47cm-13x19in) s. i. verso. 30-Jun-4 Neumeister, Munich #608/R
£884 $1583 €1300 Concordia Temple in Agrigent (34x47cm-13x19in) s.d.20.2.03 i. verso. 17-Mar-4 Neumeister, Munich #525/R
£933 $1689 €1400 Jerusalem (27x47cm-11x19in) s. 1-Apr-4 Van Ham, Cologne #1527
£1399 $2406 €2000 Ecole Allemande - Vue de Jerusalem (33x47cm-13x19in) s.i. board. 8-Dec-3 Tajan, Paris #294/R est:2000-3000
£1418 $2369 €2000 Le marche aux abords de la mosquee (24x40cm-9x16in) s.d.1914. 16-Jun-3 Gros & Delettrez, Paris #508/R est:1900-2300
£1528 $2490 €2200 Oriental street scene (37x50cm-15x20in) s.d.1905. 25-Sep-3 Dr Fritz Nagel, Stuttgart #1371/R est:3500
£1667 $2717 €2400 Interior of Orthodox church (80x111cm-31x44in) s.d.1931. 24-Sep-3 Neumeister, Munich #488/R est:2300
£1958 $3368 €2800 Market scene in Jerusalem (79x110cm-31x43in) s.d.1931. 3-Dec-3 Neumeister, Munich #660/R est:2300
£2000 $3620 €3000 Constantinople (71x102cm-28x40in) s.d.1903. 1-Apr-4 Van Ham, Cologne #1526/R est:2400
£2177 $4006 €3178 Palmenhain, Kairo (38x52cm-15x20in) s.d.1905. 14-Jun-4 Waddingtons, Toronto #304/R est:5500-7000 (C.D 5400)
£2334 $4270 €3500 Scene de rue au Caire (53x39cm-21x15in) s. 3-Jun-4 Tajan, Paris #287/R est:3000-3500
£3546 $5922 €5000 La Mosqueee Omar a Jerusalem (54x78cm-21x31in) s. i.verso. 16-Jun-3 Gros & Delettrez, Paris #255/R est:5000-6000
£6114 $11127 €8926 View towards Istanbul (56x88cm-22x35in) s.d.1910. 16-Jun-4 Fischer, Luzern #1244/R est:3000-4000 (S.FR 14000)
£8000 $14640 €12000 Marche a Jerusalem (79x110cm-31x43in) s.d.1931 i.verso. 3-Jun-4 Tajan, Paris #290/R est:6000-8000
Works on paper
£1400 $2478 €2044 Garden of Gethsemane, Jerusalem (38x51cm-15x20in) s.i.d.1926 W/C bodycol. 27-Apr-4 Bonhams, New Bond Street #54/R est:1500-2000
£3667 $6673 €5500 Mecca (71x100cm-28x39in) s.d.1917 gouache. 30-Jun-4 Neumeister, Munich #421/R est:700

McCOLLUM, Allan (1944-) American
£2054 $3800 €2999 Four surrogates (40x21cm-16x8in) each s. verso enamel on hydrocal four. 13-Jul-4 Christie's, Rockefeller NY #87/R est:3000-5000
£2973 $5500 €4341 Ten surrogates (23x28cm-9x11in) each s.d.1982/90 verso enamel on hydrocal ten. 13-Jul-4 Christie's, Rockefeller NY #86/R est:7000-9000
Sculpture
£3784 $7000 €5525 Plaster Surrogates (20x18cm-8x7in) s.i.d.1983 verso cast plaster enamel paint 6 parts prov. 12-Feb-4 Sotheby's, New York #206/R est:2500-3500
£6993 $11888 €10000 Nine perfect vehicles (107x78x77cm-42x31x30in) s.i.d.1985/90 vases. 27-Nov-3 Lempertz, Koln #274/R est:10000
£13772 $23000 €20107 Thirty plaster surrogates no 9 (376x161x5cm-148x63x2in) enamel stone prov. 13-Nov-3 Sotheby's, New York #511/R est:15000-20000
£18000 $32760 €26280 20 surrogates (104x231cm-41x91in) s.num.1-20 verso enamel solid cast hydrocal prov. 6-Feb-4 Sotheby's, London #260/R est:6000-8000
£18000 $32760 €26280 Perfect vehicle (196x93x93cm-77x37x37in) acrylic cast fibreglass reinforced concrete prov.exhib. 6-Feb-4 Sotheby's, London #261/R est:15000-20000

McCOLVIN, John (?) British?
£260 $416 €380 Fishergirl seated on a wall (23x19cm-9x7in) s. panel. 16-Sep-3 Holloways, Banbury #303/R
£380 $616 €551 Country girl (61x41cm-24x16in) s. 30-Jul-3 Hamptons Fine Art, Godalming #185
£7000 $11620 €10220 Young Maidens (61x30cm-24x12in) s. pair. 1-Oct-3 Sotheby's, Olympia #78/R est:600-800

McCOMAS, Francis (1874-1938) American
Works on paper
£1099 $2000 €1605 Monterey home in landscape (30x46cm-12x18in) s.d.99 W/C. 15-Jun-4 John Moran, Pasadena #88a est:2500-3500
£2647 $4500 €3865 Oaks (20x25cm-8x10in) s.d.1902 W/C prov. 18-Nov-3 John Moran, Pasadena #3 est:2000-3000

McCONAHA, Lawrence (1894-?) American
£568 $1000 €829 Pitcher and potatoes, with city view outside window (51x61cm-20x24in) s. painted c.1940 prov. 23-May-4 Treadway Gallery, Cincinnati #651/R
£806 $1500 €1177 Farm scene (46x61cm-18x24in) s. board painted c.1940. 7-Mar-4 Treadway Gallery, Cincinnati #655/R est:1500-2000
£872 $1500 €1273 Still life of apples (51x61cm-20x24in) s. painted c.1920. 7-Dec-3 Treadway Gallery, Cincinnati #588/R est:1000-2000

McCONNELL, Charles Lawrence (20th C) American
£297 $475 €434 On the scent (61x56cm-24x22in) s. 19-Sep-3 Freeman, Philadelphia #177/R

McCONNELL, George (1852-1929) American
£254 $475 €371 Autumn landscape (40x61cm-16x24in) s. 26-Feb-4 Skinner, Bolton #510/R
£376 $700 €549 New Hampshire birches (48x38cm-19x15in) s.d.1919 prov. 6-Mar-4 North East Auctions, Portsmouth #560/R
£765 $1400 €1117 Seascape (25x51cm-10x20in) s.d.1891 board. 6-Jun-4 Skinner, Boston #209 est:800-1200

MACCONVILLE, Charles (fl.1938-1940) British
Works on paper
£300 $510 €438 On the high seas (35x52cm-14x20in) s. W/C. 1-Dec-3 David Duggleby, Scarborough #245/R

McCORD, George (1848-1909) American
£419 $675 €612 Moonlight Amsterdam Holland (41x30cm-16x12in) s. 20-Aug-3 James Julia, Fairfield #1803/R
£1163 $2000 €1698 Village winter landscape (36x53cm-14x21in) s. 6-Dec-3 South Bay, Long Island #231a/R
£1497 $2500 €2186 Ships in a harbour (43x36cm-17x14in) s. prov. 23-Oct-3 Shannon's, Milford #240/R est:3000-5000
£1648 $3000 €2406 Ships in harbour (51x91cm-20x36in) indis.s. prov. 15-Jun-4 John Moran, Pasadena #158 est:2000-4000
£1648 $3000 €2406 Rushing stream (51x76cm-20x30in) s. 29-Jun-4 Sotheby's, New York #190/R est:4000-6000
£1816 $3250 €2651 Shipping on the Hudson at West Point (51x66cm-20x26in) s. i.stretcher. 26-May-4 Doyle, New York #42/R est:4000-6000
£1934 $3500 €2824 Seascape at moonrise with becalmed schooners (64x76cm-25x30in) s. 3-Apr-4 Nadeau, Windsor #87/R est:3000-5000
£2096 $3500 €3060 Sunset over the harbour (102x76cm-40x30in) s. 9-Oct-3 Christie's, Rockefeller NY #34/R est:4000-6000
£2994 $5000 €4371 Moonlight, journey's end (64x86cm-25x34in) s. canvas on masonite prov. 23-Oct-3 Shannon's, Milford #262/R est:5000-7000

McCORD, Jake (20th C) American
£278 $500 €406 Girl in red bikini (122x61cm-48x24in) housepaint on board prov. 24-Apr-4 Slotin Folk Art, Buford #629/R
£333 $600 €486 Woman in the garden (122x81cm-48x32in) housepaint wood board. 24-Apr-4 Slotin Folk Art, Buford #627/R

MACCORMACK, Bill (20th C) New Zealander?
£567 $1050 €851 Old miners cottage Arrowtown (29x39cm-11x15in) s. board. 13-Jul-4 Watson's, Christchurch #82/R est:1600-2000 (NZ.D 1600)

MACCORMACK, Richard (1962-) American
Works on paper
£368 $600 €537 Blue Sunday morning (66x76cm-26x30in) s. W/C. 19-Jul-3 Outer Cape Auctions, Provincetown #47/R

McCORMACK, Selma (19/20th C) British?
£280 $459 €409 Two figures in red landscape (50x61cm-20x24in) s. acrylic paper. 4-Jun-3 John Ross, Belfast #131
£400 $656 €584 Blue Weir (58x43cm-23x17in) s. acrylic paper. 4-Jun-3 John Ross, Belfast #211
£600 $1116 €876 Diptych abstract (30x22cm-12x9in) s.d.03 board. 3-Mar-4 John Ross, Belfast #133
Sculpture
£1600 $2624 €2336 Lovers (22cm-9in) s. bronze. 4-Jun-3 John Ross, Belfast #228 est:2000
Works on paper
£300 $516 €438 Harbour house (35x30cm-14x12in) s.d.03 mixed media. 3-Dec-3 John Ross, Belfast #242
£320 $550 €467 The visitor (35x30cm-14x12in) s.d.03 mixed media. 3-Dec-3 John Ross, Belfast #122

McCORMACK, Thomas Arthur (1883-1973) New Zealander
Works on paper
£415 $743 €606 Autumn tints, river scene (28x39cm-11x15in) s. W/C executed c.1948. 12-May-4 Dunbar Sloane, Wellington #202 est:1000-2000 (NZ.D 1200)
£752 $1278 €1098 Hawkes Bay Road (30x47cm-12x19in) s. W/C pastel. 26-Nov-3 Dunbar Sloane, Wellington #96/R est:2500-3000 (NZ.D 2000)

McCORMICK, Arthur David (1860-1943) British
£1900 $3230 €2774 Pirate's tribune (46x61cm-18x24in) indis.sig. 19-Nov-3 Tennants, Leyburn #1031/R est:1800-2500
£2000 $3680 €2920 Ploughing team (25x35cm-10x14in) s. board. 23-Mar-4 Bonhams, New Bond Street #130/R est:2000-3000
£2200 $3674 €3212 Reviewing the plans (50x66cm-20x26in) s.d.18. 12-Nov-3 Sotheby's, Olympia #115/R est:1500-2500
£3200 $5344 €4672 Lord Nelson makes his point (49x59cm-19x23in) s. 16-Oct-3 Lawrence, Crewkerne #750/R
£4200 $7686 €6132 Huntsman's tale (49x74cm-19x29in) s. 28-Jul-4 Bonhams, Knightsbridge #88/R est:2500-3500
Works on paper
£650 $1183 €949 Mountaineers crossing a crevasse (27x49cm-11x19in) s. grisaille W/C. 1-Jul-4 Mellors & Kirk, Nottingham #727
£700 $1169 €1022 At the Pembrokes (61x49cm-24x19in) s. pencil W/C prov. 8-Oct-3 Christie's, Kensington #1123/R

McCORMICK, Katherine Hood (1880-1960) American
£1308 $2250 €1910 Girl in a garden (30x45cm-12x18in) s. i.verso canvasboard prov. 3-Dec-3 Doyle, New York #221/R est:3000-5000
£1468 $2700 €2143 Rushes in a river (25x35cm-10x14in) s.d.20 board. 27-Jun-4 Freeman, Philadelphia #205/R est:1500-2500
Works on paper
£432 $800 €631 Chestnut houses (28x33cm-11x13in) s.d.1947 pastel. 13-Feb-4 David Rago, Lambertville #60/R

McCORMICK, M Evelyn (1869-1948) American
£3533 $6500 €5158 Gondola in Venice (64x48cm-25x19in) s. prov. 8-Jun-4 Bonhams & Butterfields, San Francisco #4253/R est:7000-10000

McCORMICK, Robert (1800-1890) British
Works on paper
£8500 $13174 €12410 Voyages of discovery in the Arctic and Antarctic Seas. pencil sketches set of 34. 25-Sep-2 Christie's, London #38/R est:10000-15000

McCOUCH, Gordon Mallet (1885-1956) American
£776 $1389 €1133 Man in a bar (58x49cm-23x19in) mono. board. 12-May-4 Dobiaschofsky, Bern #783/R est:1600 (S.FR 1800)

McCOURT, John (?) Irish?
£362 $666 €550 Thinking back to half past six (92x92cm-36x36in) s.i.verso board. 22-Jun-4 De Veres Art Auctions, Dublin #266

McCOY, Ann Wyeth (20th C) American
Works on paper
£552 $950 €806 Church Graveyard (51x36cm-20x14in) s. W/C pencil bodycol. 7-Dec-3 Freeman, Philadelphia #147

McCOY, John W (1909-) American
Works on paper
£320 $550 €467 Drowned rock (76x56cm-30x22in) s. W/C exhib. 7-Dec-3 Freeman, Philadelphia #211
£4360 $7500 €6366 Cosmos (53x74cm-21x29in) s. W/C. 7-Dec-3 Freeman, Philadelphia #216 est:400-600

McCOY, Wilton Guy (1902-1986) American
£392 $725 €572 Desert landscape with smoky mountains and sandy plains (43x58cm-17x23in) s. board. 16-Jan-4 Aspire, Cleveland #50/R
£487 $775 €711 Desert landscape with mountains and sandy plains (43x58cm-17x23in) s. board. 12-Sep-3 Aspire, Cleveland #115
£804 $1382 €1174 Saguara cacti (46x61cm-18x24in) s.d.57 s.i.verso canvasboard. 2-Dec-3 Ritchie, Toronto #92/R (C.D 1800)

McCRACKEN, Francis (1879-1959) British
£2888 $4708 €4216 One Tree Hill (40x45cm-16x18in) s. prov. 23-Sep-3 Peter Webb, Auckland #126/R est:8000-10000 (NZ.D 8000)
Works on paper
£616 $1047 €899 Fishing boats in harbour (24x27cm-9x11in) s. W/C prov. 4-Nov-3 Peter Webb, Auckland #66 est:1000-2000 (NZ.D 1700)

McCRACKEN, James (20th C) American
£1105 $1900 €1613 Tropical garden (71x61cm-28x24in) s. board painted c.1940. 7-Dec-3 Treadway Gallery, Cincinnati #702/R est:2000-3000
£1582 $2500 €2310 Herons (61x51cm-24x20in) s. board. 7-Sep-3 Treadway Gallery, Cincinnati #654/R est:2500-3500

McCRACKEN, John (1934-) American
Sculpture
£4908 $8000 €7166 Untitled (295x63x9cm-116x25x4in) init.d.85 fiberglass over wood prov. 23-Sep-3 Christie's, Rockefeller NY #185/R est:5000-7000
£16766 $28000 €24478 Untitled (46x4x242cm-18x2x95in) with sig.d.72 fibreglass wood prov. 12-Nov-3 Christie's, Rockefeller NY #600/R est:10000-15000
£40223 $72000 €58726 Untitled (54x237x6cm-21x93x2in) s.d.1973 verso fiberglass wood. 12-May-4 Christie's, Rockefeller NY #421/R est:12000-18000
Works on paper
£5000 $9050 €7300 VIII black plank (282x11cm-111x4in) init.i.d.98 polyester resin fibreglass on plywood. 1-Apr-4 Christie's, Kensington #274/R est:6000-8000

McCRADY, John (1911-1968) American
£16867 $28000 €24626 Metamorphosis (56x71cm-22x28in) s. multi-stage on masonite prov. 4-Oct-3 Neal Auction Company, New Orleans #580/R est:30000-50000
Works on paper
£1453 $2500 €2121 Frightened horses (36x48cm-14x19in) pencil prov. 6-Dec-3 Neal Auction Company, New Orleans #563 est:3000-5000
£1657 $3000 €2419 Wrestlers (36x48cm-14x19in) pencil. 3-Apr-4 Neal Auction Company, New Orleans #540/R est:3000-5000

McCRANE, Ruth Mae (20th C) American
£599 $1000 €875 Gardener (61x46cm-24x18in) acrylic paper. 18-Oct-3 David Dike, Dallas #297/R

McCREA, Harold Wellington (1887-1969) Canadian
£1120 $2050 €1635 Winter logging (48x74cm-19x29in) s. board. 1-Jun-4 Hodgins, Calgary #405/R est:3250-3750 (C.D 2800)

McCREA, S Harkness (1867-?) American

£278 $500 €406 Autumn (51x61cm-20x24in) s.d.1901. 23-Jan-4 Freeman, Philadelphia #103/R
£1198 $2000 €1749 Dock scene (51x61cm-20x24in) painted 1901. 17-Oct-3 Du Mouchelle, Detroit #2017/R est:2000-2500

McCROSSAN, Mary (?-1934) British

£480 $864 €701 Figures by a fisherman's cottage on the coast (29x40cm-11x16in) s. canvas on board. 22-Apr-4 Lawrence, Crewkerne #947
£580 $1073 €847 Wash day (30x41cm-12x16in) s.d.1894 board sold with another by same hand. 10-Feb-4 David Lay, Penzance #476

McCUBBIN, Frederick (1855-1917) Australian

£2642 $4730 €3857 Portrait of Mrs Mary Moriarty (45x34cm-18x13in) canvas on board prov. 4-May-4 Sotheby's, Melbourne #92/R est:10000-15000 (A.D 6500)
£6198 $10971 €9049 Landscape (24x34cm-9x13in) s.d.1907 canvasboard prov. 3-May-4 Christie's, Melbourne #57/R est:15000-20000 (A.D 15000)
£6707 $12006 €9792 Old man with caged birds (55x44cm-22x17in) canvas on board painted c.1879 prov. 4-May-4 Sotheby's, Melbourne #93/R est:20000-30000 (A.D 16500)
£9924 $18061 €14489 Ti tree at Mentone (25x35cm-10x14in) s.d.1901 panel prov.exhib. 16-Jun-4 Deutscher-Menzies, Melbourne #49/R est:25000-35000 (A.D 26000)
£10569 $18919 €15431 Woodcutter and son (48x33cm-19x13in) s. prov. 4-May-4 Sotheby's, Melbourne #86/R est:25000-35000 (A.D 26000)
£14754 $23311 €21541 Flinders Street, early morning (24x35cm-9x14in) s. panel prov. 2-Sep-3 Deutscher-Menzies, Melbourne #69/R est:35000-45000 (A.D 36000)
£14876 $27521 €21719 View towards the city, from Kensington Road, South Yarra (24x34cm-9x13in) s. canvas on board prov. 10-Mar-4 Deutscher-Menzies, Melbourne #99/R est:30000-40000 (A.D 36000)
£50813 $90955 €74187 Cottage at Mount Macedon (51x60cm-20x24in) s. 4-May-4 Sotheby's, Melbourne #29/R est:100000-150000 (A.D 125000)
£57851 $107025 €84462 Melbourne in 1888 (124x90cm-49x35in) s.d.1879 prov.exhib. 10-Mar-4 Deutscher-Menzies, Melbourne #48/R est:160000-200000 (A.D 140000)
£64050 $118492 €93513 Glade (118x92cm-46x36in) s.d.1913 prov. 10-Mar-4 Deutscher-Menzies, Melbourne #69/R est:100000-150000 (A.D 155000)
£433884 $802686 €633471 Childhood fancies (69x138cm-27x54in) s.d.1905 prov.exhib. 10-Mar-4 Deutscher-Menzies, Melbourne #36/R est:1200000-1500000 (A.D 1050000)

McCUBBIN, Louis (1890-1952) Australian

£691 $1237 €1009 Spring morning (60x49cm-24x19in) s.d.23. 10-May-4 Joel, Victoria #295 est:1800-2500 (A.D 1700)

McCULLOCH, Horatio (1805-1867) British

£720 $1174 €1051 On the cart (32x45cm-13x18in) panel. 17-Jul-3 Bonhams, Edinburgh #358
£750 $1388 €1095 Blasted Oak, Cadzow (36x45cm-14x18in) s. board. 14-Jul-4 Christie's, Kensington #1073
£3300 $6039 €4818 Mooring (51x61cm-20x24in) s. 8-Apr-4 Bonhams, Edinburgh #104/R est:2000-3000
£4000 $6800 €5840 Highland cottage, Aberfoyle (40x61cm-16x24in) s.d.Sep'22 1855. 30-Oct-3 Christie's, London #68/R est:3000-5000
£4200 $6762 €6090 On a drove road (34x44cm-13x17in) s. 21-Aug-3 Bonhams, Edinburgh #1014/R est:3000-5000

McCULLOCH, Horatio (attrib) (1805-1867) British

£920 $1693 €1343 View of Edinburgh from the North (46x83cm-18x33in) panel. 24-Mar-4 Hamptons Fine Art, Godalming #282/R
£1350 $2417 €1971 Hunters and their dogs before an extensive view of Edinburgh (51x84cm-20x33in) 27-May-4 Christie's, Kensington #208/R est:1500-2000

MACCULLOCH, James (?-1915) British

Works on paper
£300 $540 €438 Loch Katrine (27x46cm-11x18in) s.d.1890 W/C. 22-Apr-4 Bonhams, Edinburgh #301

McCULLOCH, Jane (20th C) American

Works on paper
£898 $1500 €1311 Storm on the plains (56x71cm-22x28in) pastel. 18-Oct-3 David Dike, Dallas #141/R est:1500-3000

McCURRACH, Bryan (20th C) New Zealander

Sculpture
£1087 $1750 €1587 Carved Panel (184x58cm-72x23in) wood paua. 20-Aug-3 Peter Webb, Auckland #2092/R est:1500-2000 (NZ.D 3000)
£1178 $1896 €1720 Standing figure on box (120x43x43cm-47x17x17in) wood. 20-Aug-3 Peter Webb, Auckland #2089/R est:2000-3000 (NZ.D 3250)
£1178 $1896 €1720 Carved Panel (184x58cm-72x23in) wood paua. 20-Aug-3 Peter Webb, Auckland #2090/R est:1500-2000 (NZ.D 3250)
£1721 $2771 €2513 Standing figure (186cm-73in) wood. 20-Aug-3 Peter Webb, Auckland #2088/R est:2500-3500 (NZ.D 4750)
£1993 $3208 €2910 Standing figure holding a kotiate (200cm-79in) wood paua. 20-Aug-3 Peter Webb, Auckland #2086/R est:3000-4000 (NZ.D 5500)
£1993 $3208 €2910 Standing figure holding a kotiate (224cm-88in) d.1969 wood. 20-Aug-3 Peter Webb, Auckland #2087/R est:3000-4000 (NZ.D 5500)
£2174 $3500 €3174 Te Rauparaha and Te Pehi Kupe (96x65x65cm-38x26x26in) wood greenstone mere. 20-Aug-3 Peter Webb, Auckland #2091/R est:2500-3500 (NZ.D 6000)

McCURRY, Steve (20th C) American

Photographs
£2222 $4000 €3244 Afghan girl (51x76cm-20x30in) s.verso dye transfer print. 24-Apr-4 Phillips, New York #110/R est:5000-7000

McDERMITT, William Thomas (1884-1961) American

£1000 $1700 €1460 Stage in atmospheric landscape (25x30cm-10x12in) s.d.49 prov. 18-Nov-3 John Moran, Pasadena #114a est:1500-2500

McDERMOTT and McGOUGH (20th C) American

£400 $716 €600 Christ (96x30cm-38x12in) s. 12-May-4 Chochon-Barre & Allardi, Paris #59/R
£433 $776 €650 Handsome strong and durable (77x56cm-30x22in) panel exhib. 12-May-4 Chochon-Barre & Allardi, Paris #57
£958 $1600 €1399 American pansey (61x46cm-24x18in) s. oil linen prov. 7-Oct-3 Sotheby's, New York #413 est:3000-5000
Photographs
£2395 $4000 €3497 Ones worth (44x29cm-17x11in) d.2/9/93 num.2 palladium print one of three prov. 17-Oct-3 Phillips, New York #289/R est:2500-3500

McDEVITT, Patrick (19th C) American

£894 $1600 €1305 Portrait of a naval commodore (53x41cm-21x16in) i.verso. 20-Mar-4 Pook & Pook, Downington #305/R est:2500-3500

MACDIARMID, Douglas (1922-) New Zealander

£277 $496 €404 Extensive valley scene, France (63x90cm-25x35in) s.d.84. 12-May-4 Dunbar Sloane, Wellington #118/R (NZ.D 800)
£1119 $1937 €1634 Landscape near Perpignan, France (23x33cm-9x13in) s.d.1956 board. 9-Dec-3 Peter Webb, Auckland #1/R est:2500-3500 (NZ.D 3000)
Works on paper
£1455 $2284 €2110 Portrait of Helen Hitchings (46x61cm-18x24in) s. W/C. 27-Aug-3 Dunbar Sloane, Wellington #67/R est:2500-4000 (NZ.D 4000)

McDONAGH, Bernard (20th C) Irish

£539 $993 €820 Collage green (41x38cm-16x15in) s.i.verso canvasboard prov. 22-Jun-4 De Veres Art Auctions, Dublin #161/R

MACDONALD, Albert Angus (1909-1986) Canadian

£1250 $2150 €1825 Sailing on the lake (87x105cm-34x41in) s.d.34. 2-Dec-3 Joyner Waddington, Toronto #368/R est:1500-2500 (C.D 2800)

MACDONALD, Alexander (1839-1921) British

£300 $546 €438 Small blue box head (30x30cm-12x12in) s. verso. 1-Jul-4 Christie's, Kensington #378

MacDONALD, Arthur (fl.1897-1940) British

Works on paper
£700 $1274 €1022 Magdalen College from the meadows with men cutting hay (33x49cm-13x19in) W/C. 15-Jun-4 Bonhams, Oxford #64/R

MACDONALD, Elizabeth (20th C) American

£281 $450 €410 Manayunk (51x76cm-20x30in) s.d.61. 19-Sep-3 Freeman, Philadelphia #178/R

MACDONALD, Grant (1944-) American

£621 $1000 €907 Landscape with house (30x41cm-12x16in) acrylic board. 22-Aug-3 Altermann Galleries, Santa Fe #170
£2353 $4000 €3435 Hill country reflection (61x46cm-24x18in) 1-Nov-3 Altermann Galleries, Santa Fe #173
£3073 $5500 €4487 Autumn kaleidoscope (46x61cm-18x24in) board. 15-May-4 Altermann Galleries, Santa Fe #160/R
£4969 $8000 €7255 Evening in the land of enchantment (40x30cm-16x12in) 22-Aug-3 Altermann Galleries, Santa Fe #141

MACDONALD, Grant Kenneth (1909-) Canadian

£491 $845 €717 Renaissance Woman (36x26cm-14x10in) s.d.47 board. 2-Dec-3 Joyner Waddington, Toronto #335/R (C.D 1100)

MACDONALD, James Edward Hervey (1873-1932) Canadian

£250 $457 €365 Paysage (20x15cm-8x6in) panel. 27-Jan-4 Iegor de Saint Hippolyte, Montreal #22 (C.D 600)
£3125 $5375 €4563 Early spring run-off at dusk (22x17cm-9x7in) init. board. 2-Dec-3 Joyner Waddington, Toronto #277/R est:8000-10000 (C.D 7000)
£3659 $6549 €5342 Untitled (17x22cm-7x9in) indis.init. board prov. 27-May-4 Heffel, Vancouver #98/R est:6000-8000 (C.D 9000)
£4054 $6892 €5919 Winter hillside, Thornhill (17x22cm-7x9in) i.verso panel prov. 27-Nov-3 Heffel, Vancouver #97/R est:8000-10000 (C.D 9000)
£5200 $9516 €7592 Field Elm, Thornhill (21x26cm-8x10in) init.d.29 board. 1-Jun-4 Joyner Waddington, Toronto #69/R est:12000-15000 (C.D 13000)
£5285 $9459 €7716 Elm (22x26cm-9x10in) init.d.23 i.verso board prov. 31-May-4 Sotheby's, Toronto #3/R est:7000-9000 (C.D 13000)
£5804 $9982 €8474 Breaking wave, Nova Scotia (21x26cm-8x10in) init.d.1922 board prov.lit. 2-Dec-3 Joyner Waddington, Toronto #139/R est:8000-10000 (C.D 13000)
£5856 $9955 €8550 At York Mills (21x27cm-8x11in) s.i. painted c.1917-1918. 18-Nov-3 Sotheby's, Toronto #9/R est:15000-20000 (C.D 13000)
£7263 $13000 €10604 Lake Simova (22x27cm-9x11in) init.i.d.19 board. 14-May-4 Skinner, Boston #267/R est:5500-7500
£14286 $24571 €20858 Mount Goodsir in cloud (21x26cm-8x10in) s.i.verso board prov.lit. 2-Dec-3 Joyner Waddington, Toronto #79/R est:15000-20000 (C.D 32000)
£17857 $30714 €26071 Evening, Hungabee and Biddle Mounts, L. O'Hara (21x26cm-8x10in) s.d.24 board prov.lit. 2-Dec-3 Joyner Waddington, Toronto #26/R est:20000-25000 (C.D 40000)
£26000 $47580 €37960 Fresh wind, Lake Simcoe (21x26cm-8x10in) s. verso board. 1-Jun-4 Joyner Waddington, Toronto #113/R est:15000-18000 (C.D 65000)
£29279 $49775 €42747 Lake O'Hara (22x27cm-9x11in) init.d.29 s.i.d.29 verso board prov. 18-Nov-3 Sotheby's, Toronto #58/R est:20000-30000 (C.D 65000)
£33482 $57589 €48884 Algoma (21x26cm-8x10in) i.verso board prov.lit. 2-Dec-3 Joyner Waddington, Toronto #74/R est:75000-100000 (C.D 75000)

Works on paper
£357 $614 €521 Cathedral Mountain from Lake O'Hara (6x8cm-2x3in) s.i. pencil. 2-Dec-3 Joyner Waddington, Toronto #460 (C.D 800)
£400 $732 €584 White pine (20x11cm-8x4in) s.i.d.1902 ink. 1-Jun-4 Hodgins, Calgary #203/R (C.D 1000)

MACDONALD, James Edward Hervey (attrib) (1873-1932) Canadian
£1506 $2802 €2199 Corn flowers (25x30cm-10x12in) s. prov. 2-Mar-4 Ritchie, Toronto #122/R est:2000-3000 (C.D 3750)

MACDONALD, James W G (1897-1960) Canadian
£1760 $3221 €2570 Spring on the riviera (30x40cm-12x16in) s. board painted c.1954-55 prov.lit. 1-Jun-4 Joyner Waddington, Toronto #385/R est:2500-3000 (C.D 4400)
£2236 $4002 €3265 Garibaldi Lake (30x38cm-12x15in) i.verso panel painted c.1932-1936 double-sided prov. 6-May-4 Heffel, Vancouver #93a/R est:6000-8000 (C.D 5500)
£2236 $4002 €3265 Sphinx Glacier, Garibaldi Park (30x38cm-12x15in) s.d.1935 i.verso panel prov.exhib. 6-May-4 Heffel, Vancouver #93b/R est:6000-8000 (C.D 5500)
£7317 $13098 €10683 Glenmore, Alkali Lake, near Kelowna, BC (30x38cm-12x15in) s.d.1944 s.i.verso panel double-sided prov.lit. 27-May-4 Heffel, Vancouver #8/R est:4000-6000 (C.D 18000)

McDONALD, John B (20th C) British
£300 $480 €438 In Glenlyon (50x75cm-20x30in) s. 15-May-3 Bonhams, Edinburgh #348

MACDONALD, John Blake (1829-1901) British
£320 $589 €467 Figures by a woodland stream (70x45cm-28x18in) s. board. 10-Jun-4 Lyon & Turnbull, Edinburgh #1
£385 $700 €562 Mountain landscape with horseman on road across bridge (30x40cm-12x16in) s. 7-Feb-4 Rasmussen, Havnen #2302 (D.KR 4200)
£680 $1258 €993 Woman and child in an interior (46x65cm-18x26in) s.d.1867. 9-Mar-4 Bonhams, Knightsbridge #169/R
£913 $1671 €1333 Seaweed gatherers (17x33cm-7x13in) s. cardboard. 4-Jun-4 Zofingen, Switzerland #2357 (S.FR 2100)

MACDONALD, Manly Edward (1889-1971) Canadian
£446 $768 €651 Hayfield with lake and farmhouse (20x25cm-8x10in) s. board. 2-Dec-3 Joyner Waddington, Toronto #465 (C.D 1000)
£484 $890 €707 Winter near Thornhill (21x26cm-8x10in) s.i.d.1931 panel. 9-Jun-4 Walker's, Ottawa #1/R (C.D 1200)
£545 $889 €796 Plowing (23x27cm-9x11in) s. panel. 23-Sep-3 Ritchie, Toronto #53/R est:700-900 (C.D 1200)
£600 $1098 €876 Stream in winter (30x40cm-12x16in) s. board prov. 1-Jun-4 Hodgins, Calgary #95/R (C.D 1500)
£691 $1237 €1009 Early morning, Bay of Quinte (30x40cm-12x16in) s. i.verso panel prov. 6-May-4 Heffel, Vancouver #92/R (C.D 1700)
£691 $1237 €1009 Lake shore (27x35cm-11x14in) s. board prov. 6-May-4 Heffel, Vancouver #93/R (C.D 1700)
£763 $1419 €1114 Autumn evening on the river Rouge (30x41cm-12x16in) s. i.verso canvasboard. 2-Mar-4 Ritchie, Toronto #119/R est:1500-2000 (C.D 1900)
£804 $1382 €1174 Shoreline - Autumn (30x40cm-12x16in) s. canvasboard. 2-Dec-3 Joyner Waddington, Toronto #485 est:800-1200 (C.D 1800)
£818 $1334 €1194 Spring blossoms (21x27cm-8x11in) s. canvas on board. 23-Sep-3 Ritchie, Toronto #52/R est:800-1000 (C.D 1800)
£880 $1610 €1285 Country Road, Autumn (45x60cm-18x24in) s. 1-Jun-4 Joyner Waddington, Toronto #285/R est:2500-3000 (C.D 2200)
£900 $1530 €1314 Stream in spring sun (27x35cm-11x14in) s. canvas on board. 4-Nov-3 Bonhams, New Bond Street #146/R
£946 $1608 €1381 Autumn ploughing (21x27cm-8x11in) s. panel. 21-Nov-3 Walker's, Ottawa #41/R est:2000-2500 (C.D 2100)
£960 $1757 €1402 Stream in winter (27x34cm-11x13in) s. canvas on board. 1-Jun-4 Joyner Waddington, Toronto #348/R est:1800-2200 (C.D 2400)
£982 $1689 €1434 Pioneer Home, Napanee River (30x40cm-12x16in) s. board. 2-Dec-3 Joyner Waddington, Toronto #448 est:1000 1500 (C.D 2200)
£1111 $1822 €1622 Spring (25x36cm-10x14in) s. 28-May-3 Maynards, Vancouver #116/R est:2500-3000 (C.D 2500)
£1116 $1920 €1629 Ducks on a pond (21x29cm-8x11in) s.d.15 board. 2-Dec-3 Joyner Waddington, Toronto #526 est:800-1200 (C.D 2500)
£1126 $1914 €1644 Red house on the Moyra River (28x36cm-11x14in) s. board. 21-Nov-3 Walker's, Ottawa #4/R est:2500-3500 (C.D 2500)
£1126 $1914 €1644 Winter stream (41x51cm-16x20in) s. board. 21-Nov-3 Walker's, Ottawa #5/R (C.D 2500)
£1339 $2304 €1955 Stream in winter (26x34cm-10x13in) s. panel. 2-Dec-3 Joyner Waddington, Toronto #436 est:1200-1500 (C.D 3000)
£1360 $2489 €1986 Winter landscape with horses and sleigh (26x35cm-10x14in) s. canvasboard. 1-Jun-4 Joyner Waddington, Toronto #311/R est:1800-2200 (C.D 3400)
£1556 $2551 €2272 Bay of Quinte, Ontario (41x51cm-16x20in) s. canvasboard. 28-May-3 Maynards, Vancouver #78/R est:3800-4500 (C.D 3500)
£1760 $3221 €2570 Logging road in winter (30x40cm-12x16in) s. board painted c.1935 prov. 1-Jun-4 Joyner Waddington, Toronto #126/R est:3000-4000 (C.D 4400)
£1802 $3063 €2631 Cape Breton, Nova Scotia. The mill at Millhaven (41x51cm-16x20in) s. canvasboard two prov. 18-Nov-3 Sotheby's, Toronto #39/R est:5000-6000 (C.D 4000)
£2009 $3455 €2933 Winding river, Autumn (36x43cm-14x17in) s. 2-Dec-3 Joyner Waddington, Toronto #243/R est:3000-4000 (C.D 4500)
£2027 $3446 €2959 Country Inn. The Barn, Hay Bay (30x41cm-12x16in) canvasboard two prov. 18-Nov-3 Sotheby's, Toronto #10/R est:4000-6000 (C.D 4500)
£2200 $4026 €3212 Village in winter (45x60cm-18x24in) s. prov. 1-Jun-4 Joyner Waddington, Toronto #23/R est:5000-7000 (C.D 5500)
£2232 $3839 €3259 Tilling his fields (50x60cm-20x24in) s. 2-Dec-3 Joyner Waddington, Toronto #274/R est:3000-4000 (C.D 5000)
£2240 $4099 €3270 Winter stream (50x66cm-20x26in) s. 1-Jun-4 Joyner Waddington, Toronto #143/R est:4000-5000 (C.D 5600)
£2455 $4223 €3584 Ploughing the field (60x75cm-24x30in) s. 2-Dec-3 Joyner Waddington, Toronto #137/R est:5000-7000 (C.D 5500)
£2477 $4212 €3616 Belleville Harbour (40x50cm-16x20in) s. s.i.d.April 1947 verso canvasboard prov. 27-Nov-3 Heffel, Vancouver #192/R est:3500-4000 (C.D 5500)
£2590 $4403 €3781 Horse with coloured blanket in winter woods (43x53cm-17x21in) s. prov. 18-Nov-3 Sotheby's, Toronto #102/R est:3500-4000 (C.D 5750)
£2600 $4758 €3796 Cottage on the bay of Quinte (60x75cm-24x30in) s. prov. 1-Jun-4 Joyner Waddington, Toronto #5/R est:5000-7000 (C.D 6500)
£3125 $5375 €4563 Horse-drawn sleigh (50x65cm-20x26in) s. 2-Dec-3 Joyner Waddington, Toronto #25/R est:5000-7000 (C.D 7000)
£3252 $5821 €4748 Skiers (61x76cm-24x30in) with sig. masonite prov. 31-May-4 Sotheby's, Toronto #109/R est:6000-8000 (C.D 8000)
£3795 $6527 €5541 Haying with a three-horse hitch (60x75cm-24x30in) s. 2-Dec-3 Joyner Waddington, Toronto #2/R est:5000-7000 (C.D 8500)

MACDONALD, Murray (fl.1889-1910) British
£420 $781 €613 Crofter (28x23cm-11x9in) s.d.1896 i.verso. 4-Mar-4 Amersham Auction Rooms, UK #284
£541 $919 €790 The flight of Dorothy Vernon, Haddon Hall (61x91cm-24x36in) s.d.1902 s.i.d.1902 verso. 21-Nov-3 Walker's, Ottawa #266/R (C.D 1200)
Works on paper
£340 $564 €496 Loch Tummel from the Queen's view (30x45cm-12x18in) s.d.1905 gouache. 1-Oct-3 Woolley & Wallis, Salisbury #78/R

MACDONALD, Thomas Reid (1908-1978) Canadian
£207 $374 €302 Lighthouse, New Brunswick (16x22cm-6x9in) init. s.i.d.1947 verso panel. 18-Apr-4 Levis, Calgary #493/R (C.D 500)
£244 $423 €356 Sandy (61x46cm-24x18in) s. i.verso. 9-Dec-3 Pinneys, Montreal #171 (C.D 550)
£267 $461 €390 Early autumn, Laurentians (53x74cm-21x29in) s.d.1942. 9-Dec-3 Maynards, Vancouver #223 (C.D 600)

MACDONALD, W Alister (1861-c.1948) British
Works on paper
£248 $450 €362 Tahiti, an ocean view at sunset with distant volcanoes (13x23cm-5x9in) s.i. W/C. 2-Apr-4 Eldred, East Dennis #1005/R
£380 $646 €555 Gateway in Vatican Wall, Rome (27x17cm-11x7in) s.i.d.1908 W/C. 25-Nov-3 Bonhams, Knightsbridge #55/R
£600 $1092 €876 San Giorgio Maggiore from the Dogana, Venice (23x18cm-9x7in) s. pencil W/C. 1-Jul-4 Christie's, Kensington #359/R
£660 $1122 €964 Carriage on Westminster bridge (15x11cm-6x4in) s. W/C. 18-Nov-3 Bonhams, Leeds #56
£1371 $2523 €2002 Tahitian landscape (25x30cm-10x12in) W/C set of five. 14-Jun-4 Waddingtons, Toronto #66/R est:2000-2500 (C.D 3400)

McDONALD, Walter (20th C) American
£291 $475 €425 Forest scene with lake (61x91cm-24x36in) s. 27-Sep-3 Charlton Hall, Columbia #585/R

MACDONALD, William Purcell (1863-?) American
£820 $1500 €1197 Spring brook (41x51cm-16x20in) s. painted c.1920. 5-Jun-4 Treadway Gallery, Cincinnati #639/R est:2500-3500

MACDONALD-WRIGHT, Stanton (1890-1973) American
£4237 $7500 €6186 I listen to the thunder (48x61cm-19x24in) init.i.verso masonite. 28-Apr-4 Christie's, Los Angeles #81/R est:8000-12000
£4348 $8000 €6348 Departing spring (61x48cm-24x19in) i.verso panel prov. 8-Jun-4 Bonhams & Butterfields, San Francisco #4365/R est:8000-12000
Works on paper
£2446 $4500 €3571 Imaginary sill life (36x48cm-14x19in) init.i.d.1950 pencil W/C gouache prov. 8-Jun-4 Bonhams & Butterfields, San Francisco #4366/R est:5000-7000

MACDONALL, Angus Peter (1876-1927) American
£335 $600 €489 Lessons in the class room (51x51cm-20x20in) s. 21-Mar-4 Jeffery Burchard, Florida #46/R

McDONNELL, Hector (1947-) British
£1622 $3065 €2400 Woodbines (25x18cm-10x7in) canvasboard prov. 17-Feb-4 Whyte's, Dublin #191/R est:2500-3500
£1958 $3329 €2800 Porter and shopfront, Little Italy, New York (36x30cm-14x12in) s.i.d.91 verso board. 25-Nov-3 De Veres Art Auctions, Dublin #216/R est:3000-4000
£2676 $4282 €3800 Man leaving a pub (36x46cm-14x18in) s.d.1980 i.verso canvas on board prov.exhib. 16-Sep-3 Whyte's, Dublin #31/R est:2500-3500
£2733 $4947 €4100 Dancing couple outside Walsh's Pub (26x16cm-10x6in) board exhib. 30-Mar-4 De Veres Art Auctions, Dublin #3/R est:2500-3500
£5734 $9748 €8200 Quays near Christchurch (152x137cm-60x54in) s. prov. 25-Nov-3 De Veres Art Auctions, Dublin #129/R est:9000-12000

McDOUGAL, John (fl.1877-1941) British
Works on paper
£250 $418 €365 Coastal landscape with fishing harbour (12x29cm-5x11in) s.d.1900 W/C. 20-Oct-3 Bonhams, Bath #132
£260 $484 €380 Talland Sands, Cornwall (24x34cm-9x13in) s.d.1865 W/C. 2-Mar-4 Bearnes, Exeter #332/R
£340 $568 €496 Ever restless sea - seascape with sailing vessels (64x39cm-25x15in) s.d.1918 W/C htd white. 7-Oct-3 Fellows & Sons, Birmingham #489/R
£550 $995 €803 Children before a thatched coastal cottage (23x33cm-9x13in) s. W/C. 16-Apr-4 Keys, Aylsham #482/R
£700 $1288 €1022 Point Lynas, Anglesey (61x109cm-24x43in) s.d.1904 pencil W/C prov. 25-Mar-4 Christie's, Kensington #269
£760 $1414 €1110 Coastal scene with low cliffs and cornfields, fishing fleet beyond (50x75cm-20x30in) s.d.1893 W/C. 4-Mar-4 Bonhams, Cornwall #236/R
£1050 $1712 €1533 Thatched roadside cottage with figures and ducks (28x48cm-11x19in) s.d.1889 W/C. 27-Sep-3 Rogers Jones, Clwyd #34/R
£1700 $3043 €2482 Cornfield by beach with fishing boats beyond (48x74cm-19x29in) s.d.1893 W/C. 13-May-4 Rendalls, Ashburton #1855
£2800 $5012 €4088 Last of the glow near Port St Mary, Isle of Man (42x75cm-17x30in) s.d.1894 W/C. 25-May-4 Bonhams, Knightsbridge #160/R est:1000-1500

MacDOUGALL, Allan (fl.1840-1889) British
£800 $1480 €1168 Dumbarton Rock. Ormidale, Kyle of Bute, Scotland (36x53cm-14x21in) s. pair. 15-Jan-4 Christie's, Kensington #903/R

MACDOUGALL, Norman M (1852-1939) British
£440 $823 €642 Portrait of Laura, standing by a path (43x23cm-17x9in) s. 25-Feb-4 Mallams, Oxford #153/R

McDOWELL, Robert J (?) New Zealander?
£588 $1053 €858 Lindis River (60x121cm-24x48in) s.d.81 board. 12-May-4 Dunbar Sloane, Wellington #496/R (NZ.D 1700)

McDOWELL, William John Patton (1888-1950) British
Works on paper
£520 $915 €759 The morning after Trafalgar, Victory in tow. Victory joins the fleet (33x44cm-13x17in) s.i.d.49 pen black ink W/C. 18-May-4 Rosebery Fine Art, London #704
£700 $1253 €1022 Booth Line's Hildebrand arriving at Liverpool under tug escort (37x52cm-15x20in) mono. pencil W/C htd white. 26-May-4 Christie's, Kensington #542/R
£1700 $3111 €2482 Shipping on the Thames (31x48cm-12x19in) s. W/C. 7-Apr-4 Woolley & Wallis, Salisbury #37/R est:800-1200

McDUFF, Frederick H (1931-) American
£865 $1600 €1298 Balloon lady (58x46cm-23x18in) s. prov. 14-Jul-4 American Auctioneer #490345/R est:2500-3500

MACDUFF, William (1824-1881) British
£970 $1736 €1416 The Ingle-Neuk (28x23cm-11x9in) 28-May-4 Lyon & Turnbull, Edinburgh #91

MACE, Jill del (1947-) Australian
£1721 $2770 €2513 Harlequins (150x122cm-59x48in) s. 13-Oct-3 Joel, Victoria #417/R est:3000-5000 (A.D 4250)

MACE, John Edmund (1889-?) British
£450 $810 €675 Fishing boats with figures and buildings on opposite shore (44x59cm-17x23in) s. 24-Apr-4 Windibank, Dorking #275

MACE, Nicholas (20th C) British
£1000 $1700 €1460 Partridge shoot by the estuary. Winter morning. Evening on the estuary (19x30cm-7x12in) two s. board set of three. 27-Nov-3 Christie's, Kensington #210/R est:1000-1500

MACEGAN, Darius J (1856-1939) Irish
£1056 $1690 €1500 La Tour Eiffel (27x21cm-11x8in) s.d.1925 board prov.exhib. 16-Sep-3 Whyte's, Dublin #159/R est:1500-2000
£1549 $2479 €2200 Irish village, women scutching flax, Ballsbridge (30x38cm-12x15in) s.d.1921 i.verso prov. 16-Sep-3 Whyte's, Dublin #158/R est:1500-2000

McELCHERAN, William (1927-1999) Canadian
Sculpture
£732 $1310 €1069 Study for the gates of Limbo (27x17x7cm-11x7x3in) init.d.1987 bronze prov. 27-May-4 Heffel, Vancouver #16 est:1500-2000 (C.D 1800)
£759 $1290 €1108 Two businessmen (11x5x4cm-4x2x2in) brown pat bronze six of 12. 6-Nov-3 Heffel, Vancouver #81/R est:1500-2000 (C.D 1700)
£813 $1455 €1187 Three businessmen (14x20x20cm-6x8x8in) s.d.1985 num.6/12 brown pat. incl. bronze marble base. 6-May-4 Heffel, Vancouver #98/R est:2000-3000 (C.D 2000)
£1016 $1819 €1483 Four businessmen (11x5x3cm-4x2x1in) s.d.1985 num.11/12 brown pat. bronze prov. 27-May-4 Heffel, Vancouver #125/R est:2500-3500 (C.D 2500)
£1451 $2467 €2118 Three businessmen (11x5x4cm-4x2x2in) s.d.1985 brown pat bronze five of 12. 6-Nov-3 Heffel, Vancouver #80/R est:2000-3000 (C.D 3250)
£1577 $2680 €2302 Two businessmen (11x5x3cm-4x2x1in) s.d.1985 num.5/12 brown pat bronze prov. 27-Nov-3 Heffel, Vancouver #162 est:1500-2000 (C.D 3500)
£1600 $2928 €2336 Man with muse (24cm-9in) verde antico base marble plinth bronze. 1-Jun-4 Joyner Waddington, Toronto #249/R est:3000-4000 (C.D 4000)
£2477 $4212 €3616 Five businessmen (11x5x3cm-4x2x1in) s.d.1985 num.8/12 brown pat bronze prov. 27-Nov-3 Heffel, Vancouver #62/R est:3000-4000 (C.D 5500)
£4000 $7320 €5840 Peripatetics (40cm-16in) init. d.69 num.0/4 bronze. 1-Jun-4 Joyner Waddington, Toronto #221/R est:5000-7000 (C.D 10000)
£5183 $9277 €7567 Mediator (73x29x30cm-29x11x12in) s.d.1996 num.7/9 brown pat. bronze prov. 27-May-4 Heffel, Vancouver #73/R est:12000-16000 (C.D 12750)
£6757 $11486 €9865 The deal (73x38x30cm-29x15x12in) s.d.1996 num.9/9 brown pat bronze prov.lit. 27-Nov-3 Heffel, Vancouver #61/R est:12000-16000 (C.D 15000)
£7600 $13908 €11096 Preoccupied (70cm-28in) init.d.94 num.A.P. 1/3. 1-Jun-4 Joyner Waddington, Toronto #76/R est:12000-15000 (C.D 19000)

McENTAGGART, Brett (1939-) Irish?
Works on paper
£694 $1132 €1000 Side street near the Duomo Assisi (44x28cm-17x11in) s.d.73 W/C. 24-Sep-3 James Adam, Dublin #76/R est:1000-1500
£724 $1332 €1100 Blessington (33x44cm-13x17in) s. W/C. 22-Jun-4 De Veres Art Auctions, Dublin #237/R

McENTEE, Jervis (1828-1891) American
£4000 $7000 €5840 Where the trout run (30x46cm-12x18in) s.i.d.1871 verso. 19-Dec-3 Sotheby's, New York #1064/R est:10000-15000
£5587 $10000 €8157 Approaching storm, early evening (61x51cm-24x20in) init. 26-May-4 Doyle, New York #23/R est:15000-25000
£6522 $12000 €9522 Ulster County scene, November (34x55cm-13x22in) mono. board prov. 8-Jun-4 Bonhams & Butterfields, San Francisco #4019/R est:10000-15000
£18895 $32500 €27587 Landscape (51x76cm-20x30in) mono. prov. 3-Dec-3 Sotheby's, New York #127/R est:18000-24000
£22727 $40000 €33181 October in the Catskills (41x71cm-16x28in) s.d.1866 i.d.verso prov.exhib. 18-May-4 Christie's, Rockefeller NY #3/R est:50000-70000
Works on paper
£475 $750 €694 Pastoral scene (43x71cm-17x28in) init. W/C. 27-Jul-3 Simpson's, Houston #167

MACENTYRE, Eduardo (1929-) Argentinian
£1676 $3000 €2447 Untitled (100x46cm-39x18in) acrylic paper. 11-May-4 Arroyo, Buenos Aires #58
£2682 $4800 €3916 Red relief II (50x50cm-20x20in) s.d.1989-97 acrylic. 4-May-4 Arroyo, Buenos Aires #48/R est:3500

McEVOY, Ambrose (1878-1927) British
£400 $728 €584 View from Abbotsleigh, Freshford, Somerset (76x63cm-30x25in) 1-Jul-4 Christie's, Kensington #109/R
£1500 $2685 €2190 Portrait of a woman (77x63cm-30x25in) s. exhib. 14-May-4 Christie's, Kensington #488/R est:1500-2000
Works on paper
£280 $445 €409 Portrait of a lady (35x25cm-14x10in) W/C pencil. 10-Sep-3 Sotheby's, Olympia #137/R

McEVOY, Henry Nesbitt (1828-1914) Canadian
£924 $1718 €1349 Landscape with crane (36x69cm-14x27in) s.d.1889. 2-Mar-4 Ritchie, Toronto #35/R est:2000-3000 (C.D 2300)
£1285 $2300 €1876 Landscape with distant mountains and crane (36x51cm-14x20in) s.d.1889. 7-May-4 Sloans & Kenyon, Bethesda #1716/R est:2500-3000

McEVOY, William (fl.1858-1880) Irish
£420 $668 €613 Traveller on a packhorse bridge by a Scottish loch (75x126cm-30x50in) s. 10-Sep-3 Cheffins, Cambridge #528/R
£887 $1588 €1295 River landscape (46x83cm-18x33in) s. 28-May-4 Uppsala Auktionskammare, Uppsala #110/R (S.KR 12000)
£1000 $1770 €1460 Irish lake and river landscape (20x43cm-8x17in) s. pair. 30-Apr-4 Dee Atkinson & Harrison, Driffield #762/R est:700-1000
£1933 $3499 €2900 View of Dublin Bay from Killiney (29x59cm-11x23in) init. 31-Mar-4 James Adam, Dublin #4/R est:2500-4000

McEWAN, Mary B (fl.1890-1891) British
£500 $800 €730 Peasant girl with basket on a terrace. 16-Sep-3 Lawrences, Bletchingley #1942

McEWAN, Tom (1846-1914) British
£280 $476 €409 Somebody coming (41x31cm-16x12in) s. i.verso. 19-Nov-3 Tennants, Leyburn #1236
£280 $448 €409 Father's chair (35x44cm-14x17in) s.d.98. 15-May-3 Bonhams, Edinburgh #318
£350 $630 €511 Mending (36x26cm-14x10in) s. 22-Apr-4 Bonhams, Edinburgh #362
£650 $1164 €949 Bairn's tout (40x29cm-16x11in) s. 26-May-4 Outhwaite & Litherland, Liverpool #307
£900 $1656 €1314 Royal Brig o Turk, cottage interior (11x13cm-4x5in) s.d.73. 11-Jun-4 Keys, Aylsham #621/R
£968 $1781 €1413 Quiet time (45x61cm-18x24in) s.d.84. 9-Jun-4 Walker's, Ottawa #340/R est:1200-1600 (C.D 2400)
£1200 $2148 €1752 Liberal defeat (46x36cm-18x14in) s.d.84 s.i.verso. 27-May-4 Christie's, Kensington #306/R est:1500-2000
£1550 $2852 €2263 Nurslings (46x36cm-18x14in) s. 8-Jun-4 Lawrences, Bletchingley #1407/R est:1500-2000
£2500 $3925 €3625 From the far west (50x60cm-20x24in) s.d.85 canvas on board. 27-Aug-3 Sotheby's, London #929/R est:2500-3000
£2500 $4400 €3650 Interesting news, cottage interior with elderly couple (46x36cm-18x14in) s. i.verso. 30-Dec-3 British Auctioneer #802 est:2500-3000
£4400 $7964 €6424 Interesting news (46x35cm-18x14in) s. s.i.verso. 19-Apr-4 Sotheby's, London #10/R est:3000-4000
Works on paper
£290 $464 €423 Cottage interior (22x30cm-9x12in) s.d.91. 15-May-3 Bonhams, Edinburgh #368

McEWAN, Tom (attrib) (1846-1914) British
£230 $403 €336 Cottage interior. 18-Dec-3 Bonhams, Edinburgh #334

McEWEN, Jean (1923-1999) Canadian
£670 $1152 €978 Untitled (25x25cm-10x10in) s.d.88 prov. 2-Dec-3 Joyner Waddington, Toronto #81/R (C.D 1500)
£811 $1378 €1184 Trou de memoire II (31x36cm-12x14in) s. prov. 27-Nov-3 Heffel, Vancouver #204/R est:2000-2500 (C.D 1800)
£811 $1378 €1184 Trou de memoire I (31x36cm-12x14in) s.d.1992 verso prov. 27-Nov-3 Heffel, Vancouver #205 est:2000-2500 (C.D 1800)
£1674 $2796 €2427 Paysage Inacheve No.31 (35x45cm-14x18in) s.d.89 s.i.d.verso. 17-Jun-3 Pinneys, Montreal #24 est:4000-5000 (C.D 3750)
£1680 $3074 €2453 Abstract (30x27cm-12x11in) s. painted 1972. 1-Jun-4 Joyner Waddington, Toronto #173/R est:1000-1500 (C.D 4200)
£4911 $8446 €7170 Nuit a Myconos (90x80cm-35x31in) s.d.65 verso prov.exhib. 2-Dec-3 Joyner Waddington, Toronto #148/R est:8000-10000 (C.D 11000)
£6667 $11533 €9734 Untitled (99x127cm-39x50in) s.d.1960 verso prov. 9-Dec-3 Maynards, Vancouver #243 est:16000-18000 (C.D 15000)
£11789 $21102 €17212 Si je suis, si je fus, si je dors, ou je veille (183x303cm-72x119in) s.d.89-90 s.i.d.verso prov. 31-May-4 Sotheby's, Toronto #41/R est:30000-40000 (C.D 29000)
£13333 $23067 €19466 L'aque d'un pays Jaune (157x157cm-62x62in) s.i.d.1972 verso prov. 9-Dec-3 Maynards, Vancouver #245 (C.D 30000)
£20444 $35369 €29848 La drapeau inconnu - troisieu theme no.1 (183x168cm-72x66in) prov. 9-Dec-3 Maynards, Vancouver #237 (C.D 46000)

McEWEN, Rory (1932-1982) British
Works on paper
£260 $416 €380 Upper club, Eton (34x30cm-13x12in) s.i.verso W/C on vellum. 19-May-3 Bruton Knowles, Cheltenham #160

McEWEN, Walter (1860-1943) American
£5689 $9500 €8306 Hudson River Landscape, day. Hudson River Landscape, night (46x56cm-18x22in) prov. pair. 23-Oct-3 Shannon's, Milford #142/R est:12000-18000
Works on paper
£1105 $2000 €1613 Quiet moment (51x38cm-20x15in) s. with artist device gouache pencil paper on board. 31-Mar-4 Sotheby's, New York #53/R est:2000-3000

McFADYEN, Keneta (20th C) New Zealander
£580 $933 €847 Timber mill, Taupo (64x78cm-25x31in) s. board. 20-Aug-3 Peter Webb, Auckland #2053 (NZ.D 1600)

McFADYEN, Ron (1943-) Canadian
£579 $1047 €845 King of Spanish Banks (91x122cm-36x48in) s. i.d.2003 verso. 18-Apr-4 Levis, Calgary #77/R est:2000-2500 (C.D 1400)
£1875 $3225 €2738 Long way home (90x90cm-35x35in) s. acrylic. 2-Dec-3 Joyner Waddington, Toronto #260/R est:1000-1200 (C.D 4200)
Works on paper
£300 $549 €438 Night birds (24x22cm-9x9in) s.i. W/C. 1-Jun-4 Hodgins, Calgary #124/R (C.D 750)

MACFARLANE, Quentin (1935-) New Zealander
£344 $547 €502 Untitled (52x41cm-20x16in) s. acrylic. 9-Sep-3 Watson's, Christchurch #80 (NZ.D 950)
£550 $1017 €803 Untitled (37x30cm-15x12in) s. acrylic. 9-Mar-4 Watson's, Christchurch #7 est:1500-2500 (NZ.D 1500)
£550 $1017 €803 Landscape as still life (30x38cm-12x15in) s. acrylic. 9-Mar-4 Watson's, Christchurch #37 est:1500-2500 (NZ.D 1500)
£725 $1152 €1059 Mahurangi series 2002 (37x50cm-15x20in) s. acrylic. 9-Sep-3 Watson's, Christchurch #60 (NZ.D 2000)

McFARLANE, Shona (20th C) New Zealander
£313 $497 €457 Reclining nude 1960 (49x59cm-19x23in) s. canvas on board. 1-May-3 Dunbar Sloane, Wellington #111 (NZ.D 900)
Works on paper
£347 $552 €507 Gargil Monument Dunedin (54x45cm-21x18in) s. W/C. 1-May-3 Dunbar Sloane, Wellington #487 est:400-600 (NZ.D 1000)
£714 $1314 €1042 Still life (39x50cm-15x20in) s. W/C. 25-Mar-4 International Art Centre, Auckland #138/R (NZ.D 2000)

MACFARLANE, Stewart (1953-) Australian
£413 $702 €603 Simone with a green bottle (46x36cm-18x14in) s.d.2002. 29-Oct-3 Lawson Menzies, Sydney #149/R est:1500-2000 (A.D 1000)
£537 $914 €784 Red towl - Claire (57x43cm-22x17in) s.d.2002 board. 29-Oct-3 Lawson Menzies, Sydney #148/R est:2000-2500 (A.D 1300)
£1707 $2680 €2475 Room 305 (122x152cm-48x60in) s.d.1995 s.i.stretcher prov. 27-Aug-3 Christie's, Sydney #725/R est:3000-5000 (A.D 4200)
£2426 $4196 €3542 Melbourne night (136x150cm-54x59in) s.d.84. 10-Dec-3 Shapiro, Sydney #5/R est:3000-5000 (A.D 5700)
£3192 $5426 €4660 Conservatory (183x244cm-72x96in) s.d.1988 s.i.d.verso prov. 26-Nov-3 Deutscher-Menzies, Melbourne #260/R est:6000-8000 (A.D 7500)

McFAYDEN, Ron (20th C) Canadian?
£724 $1209 €1057 Safe passage (90x120cm-35x47in) s.i.d.2003. 17-Nov-3 Hodgins, Calgary #39/R est:1500-2000 (C.D 1600)

McFEE, Henry Lee (1886-1953) American
£9091 $16000 €13273 Still life (51x41cm-20x16in) s.d.12 prov.exhib. 18-May-4 Christie's, Rockefeller NY #118/R est:20000-30000
£10778 $18000 €15736 Petunias and phlox (77x61cm-30x24in) s. prov.exhib.lit. 7-Oct-3 Sotheby's, New York #215 est:6000-9000
Works on paper
£428 $775 €625 Rural scene (30x36cm-12x14in) pencil. 16-Apr-4 American Auctioneer #268/R
£2647 $4500 €3865 Out of the window, Woodstock (58x45cm-23x18in) s. graphite prov. 30-Oct-3 Phillips, New York #90/R est:2500-4500

McGARY, Dave (1958-) American
Sculpture
£932 $1500 €1351 Head with feather (56x33cm-22x13in) num.2/7 bronze. 22-Aug-3 Altermann Galleries, Santa Fe #51
£2545 $4250 €3716 Muralist at Pottery Mound (81x117x46cm-32x46x18in) num.20/30 bronze. 11-Oct-3 Nadeau, Windsor #36/R est:8000-12000
£2844 $4750 €4152 War deeds (104x53x36cm-41x21x14in) bronze one of 25. 11-Oct-3 Nadeau, Windsor #34/R est:6500-10000

McGAVIN, Margaret (?) British
£480 $907 €701 Still life with flag (72x92cm-28x36in) s. 19-Feb-4 Lyon & Turnbull, Edinburgh #69
£520 $983 €759 Still life of roses (71x91cm-28x36in) s. 19-Feb-4 Lyon & Turnbull, Edinburgh #137

McGEE, Barry (1966-) American
£10056 $18000 €14682 Untitled (91x61cm-36x24in) acrylic spray paint laminated map prov. 14-May-4 Phillips, New York #126/R est:15000-20000
£14371 $24000 €20982 Untitled (86x105cm-34x41in) oil ink paper on canvas painted 1995 prov. 12-Nov-3 Christie's, Rockefeller NY #509/R est:20000-30000
£14371 $24000 €20982 Untitled (91x61cm-36x24in) oil on laminated map painted 1997 prov. 12-Nov-3 Christie's, Rockefeller NY #512/R est:8000-12000
£16168 $27000 €23605 Untitled. acrylic enamel oil on wood nine parts painted 1997 prov. 14-Nov-3 Phillips, New York #112/R est:30000-40000
Sculpture
£39106 $70000 €57095 Untitled. enamel on 60 glass bottles executed 2001 prov.lit. 13-May-4 Phillips, New York #54/R est:30000-50000
£56886 $95000 €83054 Bottles. enamel on 103 glass bottles exec 2000 prov.exhib. 12-Nov-3 Christie's, Rockefeller NY #511/R est:25000-35000
Works on paper
£1087 $2000 €1587 Untitled (28x22cm-11x9in) pen ink two works prov. 10-Jun-4 Phillips, New York #485/R est:2500-3500

MacGEORGE, William Stewart (1861-1931) British
£1000 $1790 €1460 River town scene (27x35cm-11x14in) s. board. 26-May-4 Sotheby's, Olympia #233/R est:1000-1500
£1700 $3162 €2482 In Tarff Glen (30x41cm-12x16in) s. canvasboard. 4-Mar-4 Christie's, Kensington #140/R est:1000-1500
£2500 $3925 €3625 Fruits of autumn (38x28cm-15x11in) s. panel prov. 27-Aug-3 Sotheby's, London #1113/R est:2000-3000
£3892 $6500 €5682 Landscape with three girls picking flowers by the riverside (51x61cm-20x24in) s. 19-Oct-3 Jeffery Burchard, Florida #26
£5200 $8840 €7592 Children in a glen (51x61cm-20x24in) s. prov.exhib. 30-Oct-3 Christie's, London #121/R est:500-600
£6900 $11730 €10074 Portrait of Ducarol Steuart, as a young girl (46x41cm-18x16in) s. 19-Nov-3 Tennants, Leyburn #1290/R est:6000-9000
£28000 $43960 €40600 My lady's train (112x86cm-44x34in) s. prov.exhib.lit. 27-Aug-3 Sotheby's, London #1084/R est:30000-40000
£38000 $64600 €55480 Nutting (91x127cm-36x50in) s. 30-Oct-3 Christie's, London #120/R est:40000-60000

McGHIE, John (1867-1952) British
£800 $1488 €1168 At the quayside (25x36cm-10x14in) s. panel. 4-Mar-4 Christie's, Kensington #127a
£980 $1725 €1431 Little harbour. Fishermen on a harbour wall (35x27cm-14x11in) s.d.98 one s. board pair. 19-May-4 Christie's, Kensington #587/R
£2100 $3843 €3066 Mull and Ben More from Iona (70x90cm-28x35in) s. prov. 8-Apr-4 Bonhams, Edinburgh #182/R est:1500-2500
£4839 $8903 €7065 Waiting for the fleet (71x91cm-28x36in) s. prov. 14-Jun-4 Waddingtons, Toronto #197/R est:14000-16000 (C.D 12000)
£20000 $34000 €29200 By the sea (87x112cm-34x44in) s. prov. 30-Oct-3 Christie's, London #105/R est:5000-8000

McGILL, Donald (1875-1962) British
Works on paper
£250 $430 €365 At the seaside (13x26cm-5x10in) s. pencil W/C. 3-Dec-3 Christie's, Kensington #290/R
£250 $430 €365 I'se got it - so who cares who's who (23x15cm-9x6in) s. i.verso pencil W/C. 3-Dec-3 Christie's, Kensington #292/R
£250 $430 €365 Say old man, does your wife pick your suits (23x16cm-9x6in) s. i.verso pencil W/C. 3-Dec-3 Christie's, Kensington #299/R
£250 $430 €365 This is such a fine place - I'm booking up for two months (23x16cm-9x6in) s. i.verso pencil W/C. 3-Dec-3 Christie's, Kensington #300/R
£250 $430 €365 If I stay here much longer by goom I will bust (23x17cm-9x7in) s. i.verso pencil W/C. 3-Dec-3 Christie's, Kensington #301/R
£250 $430 €365 You should be very careful, you know, you might get interested in your work (13x23cm-5x9in) s. pencil W/C. 3-Dec-3 Christie's, Kensington #303
£270 $500 €405 The girl who took the wrong turning (23x17cm-9x7in) s. W/C gouache. 14-Jul-4 Rupert Toovey, Partridge Green #1/R
£300 $516 €438 For a jolly fine time, if your wanting ar-rest, you've really no option (25x16cm-10x6in) s.i. pencil W/C. 3-Dec-3 Christie's, Kensington #291/R
£300 $516 €438 Take this away and bring me oysters (23x16cm-9x6in) s. i.verso pencil W/C. 3-Dec-3 Christie's, Kensington #294/R
£300 $540 €438 Here's jolly good luck to Tommy and Jack (20x15cm-8x6in) W/C. 24-Jan-4 British Auctioneer #279
£310 $558 €453 Lascivious gent admiring a painting of a naked girl (23x18cm-9x7in) W/C sold with printed postcard version. 24-Jan-4 British Auctioneer #278
£320 $573 €467 No - I don't want a Doctor (19x14cm-7x6in) s. bears i. W/C. 17-Mar-4 Bonhams, Chester #316
£350 $602 €511 I know he's wagging his tail, but it's this end that bites (14x17cm-6x7in) s. i.verso pencil W/C. 3-Dec-3 Christie's, Kensington #286/R
£430 $774 €628 You'll enjoy the sun, but you'll miss the sons (15x25cm-6x10in) W/C sold with printed postcard version. 24-Jan-4 British Auctioneer #280
£450 $774 €657 He would have lovely kittens too, but he ain't that kind of cat (21x16cm-8x6in) s. i.verso pencil W/C. 3-Dec-3 Christie's, Kensington #293/R
£450 $774 €657 Thomas, we are sent on earth to help others (23x16cm-9x6in) s. i.verso pencil W/C. 3-Dec-3 Christie's, Kensington #298/R
£550 $919 €803 Should think he is a fat baby, it took four storks to bring him. He isn't a he, he's er one (20x15cm-8x6in) s. W/C pair. 22-Oct-3 Cheffins, Cambridge #493/R
£650 $1118 €949 That woman used to mean the world to me (15x27cm-6x11in) s. i.verso pencil W/C. 3-Dec-3 Christie's, Kensington #285/R
£650 $1118 €949 We just keep popping in and popping out (15x27cm-6x11in) s. pencil W/C. 3-Dec-3 Christie's, Kensington #289/R
£650 $1118 €949 I was coming all the way by charabanc, but I got off before I reached here (13x25cm-5x10in) s. i.verso pencil W/C. 3-Dec-3 Christie's, Kensington #287/R
£700 $1204 €1022 I feel a perfect ass when I'm alone (23x16cm-9x6in) s. i.verso pencil W/C. 3-Dec-3 Christie's, Kensington #302/R
£850 $1462 €1241 A jolly happy Christmas (23x15cm-9x6in) s. pencil W/C. 3-Dec-3 Christie's, Kensington #296/R

McGILL, Marjorie R (fl.1936-1939) British
£400 $740 €584 The king and the beggar maid (43x45cm-17x18in) i.verso board prov. 11-Feb-4 Cheffins, Cambridge #466/R

MACGILVARY, Norwood Hodge (1874-1950) American
£472 $750 €689 Morning fog (35x36cm-14x14in) s.verso board. 12-Sep-3 Skinner, Boston #402/R
£1720 $3250 €2511 Woman seated on porch with panoramic landscape beyond (20x25cm-8x10in) s. canvasboard. 17-Feb-4 John Moran, Pasadena #31/R est:2000-3000
£2353 $4000 €3435 Artist and his family, Vermont (154x169cm-61x67in) bears sig prov. 21-Nov-3 Skinner, Boston #437/R est:7000-9000

MACGINNIS, Robert E (1926-) American
£3073 $5500 €4487 Nearly nude lounging woman, looking up from a fashion magazine (23x33cm-9x13in) s. tempera gouache litho pencil. 15-May-4 Illustration House, New York #126/R est:4000-6000

£5090 $8500 €7431 Relaxed nude seated in elegant interior (30x41cm-12x16in) s. tempera painted c.1958. 15-Nov-3 Illustration House, New York #22/R est:9000-12000

McGLYNN, Thomas A (1878-1966) American

£5026 $9500 €7338 Landscape - Morning pebble beach (64x76cm-25x30in) i. verso. 17-Feb-4 John Moran, Pasadena #40/R est:4000-6000

McGOLDRICK, Tom (?) British

£300 $558 €438 Collecting turf (40x50cm-16x20in) s. 3-Mar-4 John Ross, Belfast #188

McGONIGAL, Maurice (1900-1979) British

£660 $1075 €950 Incroyable (60x50cm-24x20in) board prov.exhib. 23-Sep-3 De Veres Art Auctions, Dublin #172
£2000 $3620 €3000 Calm (31x38cm-12x15in) s. i.verso board prov. 30-Mar-4 De Veres Art Auctions, Dublin #17/R est:2000-3000
£2400 $3816 €3504 Figgin's cottage on Gabalennaun (29x38cm-11x15in) s. board. 10-Sep-3 Sotheby's, Olympia #209/R est:2000-3000
£2763 $5084 €4200 Storm clouds, Lough Inah, Connemara (35x46cm-14x18in) s. canvasboard. 22-Jun-4 De Veres Art Auctions, Dublin #10/R est:4000-6000
£3916 $6657 €5600 On Gubalennaun, Achill - Figgis's cottage (31x39cm-12x15in) s.i.verso board. 25-Nov-3 De Veres Art Auctions, Dublin #53/R est:6000-9000
£3916 $6657 €5600 Busy street scene. Landscape (36x46cm-14x18in) s. board double-sided. 25-Nov-3 De Veres Art Auctions, Dublin #81/R est:6000-9000
£4895 $8322 €7000 West of Ireland landscape with mother and child on the road (33x46cm-13x18in) canvasboard. 25-Nov-3 De Veres Art Auctions, Dublin #9/R est:6000-8000
£6376 $11413 €9500 Sea inlet, early moring, Ballygaw, Co. Kerry (30x61cm-12x24in) s. board prov. 26-May-4 James Adam, Dublin #94/R est:8000-12000
£6711 $12013 €10000 Village, Feothanoch, Dingle Peninsula (51x61cm-20x24in) s. prov. 26-May-4 James Adam, Dublin #92/R est:10000-15000
£7639 $12451 €11000 Connemara village with flowers (44x60cm-17x24in) s. 24-Sep-3 James Adam, Dublin #81/R est:8000-10000
£10067 $17819 €15000 Desmond Stephenson Arha coming home in Connemara (37x27cm-15x11in) s. s.i.verso canvas on wood prov.exhib. 27-Apr-4 Whyte's, Dublin #37/R est:15000-18000
£18881 $32098 €27000 Races, Ballyconneely, Connemara (96x129cm-38x51in) s.d.1974 verso. 25-Nov-3 De Veres Art Auctions, Dublin #120/R est:20000-30000

Works on paper

£345 $636 €525 Pigs on Arran (24x35cm-9x14in) i.verso W/C. 22-Jun-4 Mealy's, Castlecomer #743
£400 $716 €584 Strolling by the banks of the river (17x24cm-7x9in) s. W/C bodycol. 14-May-4 Christie's, Kensington #324
£704 $1218 €1000 Study for poster for the Irish National Ballet (15x7cm-6x3in) s. W/C exec.c.1950/55. 10-Dec-3 Bonhams & James Adam, Dublin #147/R
£1216 $2299 €1800 Spring grazing (13x33cm-5x13in) s.d.1978 W/C pencil prov.exhib. 17-Feb-4 Whyte's, Dublin #141/R est:1200-1500

McGORAN, Kieran (1932-1990) British

£550 $902 €803 Landscape (38x56cm-15x22in) board. 4-Jun-3 John Ross, Belfast #214

Works on paper

£300 $558 €438 Old shawlie (43x33cm-17x13in) s. mixed media. 3-Mar-4 John Ross, Belfast #107
£400 $744 €584 Grannie (40x30cm-16x12in) s.d.68 pastel. 3-Mar-4 John Ross, Belfast #62
£500 $915 €730 Conversation (56x48cm-22x19in) s. mixed media. 2-Jun-4 John Ross, Belfast #187
£600 $1116 €876 Chat over a cup of tea (45x38cm-18x15in) s. pastel. 3-Mar-4 John Ross, Belfast #43
£750 $1395 €1095 Playing marbles (28x38cm-11x15in) s. pastel. 3-Mar-4 John Ross, Belfast #113
£1300 $2379 €1898 Downpatrick races (28x40cm-11x16in) s. pastel. 2-Jun-4 John Ross, Belfast #38 est:800-1200
£1400 $2562 €2044 After the first jump (28x40cm-11x16in) s. pastel. 2-Jun-4 John Ross, Belfast #156 est:800-1000
£1600 $2752 €2336 Downpatrick Races (30x38cm-12x15in) s. pastel. 3-Dec-3 John Ross, Belfast #42 est:1200-1400
£1600 $2752 €2336 The Paddock, Downpatrick Races (35x30cm-14x12in) s. pastel. 3-Dec-3 John Ross, Belfast #194 est:1200-1400
£1700 $3111 €2482 Before the start, Downpatrick Races (50x43cm-20x17in) s. pastel. 2-Jun-4 John Ross, Belfast #225 est:1000-1200
£2000 $3720 €2920 Last jump, Downpatrick races (30x38cm-12x15in) s. pastel. 3-Mar-4 John Ross, Belfast #127b est:1800-2000

McGREGOR, Robert (1848-1922) British

£880 $1514 €1285 Old Edinburgh Close (19x8cm-7x3in) s. board. 4-Dec-3 Bonhams, Edinburgh #33/R
£1250 $2263 €1825 The haystack (15x23cm-6x9in) Sketch at Littleworth, Sussex. 3-Apr-4 British Auctioneer #264
£1359 $2500 €2039 Racing yachts (55x76cm-22x30in) s. 8-Jun-4 Bonhams & Butterfields, San Francisco #4055/R est:3000-5000
£1600 $2752 €2336 Study for - The Knife Grinder (20x14cm-8x6in) s. 4-Dec-3 Bonhams, Edinburgh #32/R est:700-1000
£1700 $3111 €2550 Jackdaw (34x24cm-13x9in) s. board. 27-Jul-4 Henry Adams, Chichester #475/R est:2000-3000
£2900 $5249 €4234 Reading the letter (30x22cm-12x9in) panel. 3-Apr-4 British Auctioneer #265
£4500 $7650 €6570 Fishwife and her children (61x46cm-24x18in) s. 30-Oct-3 Christie's, London #113/R est:5000-8000
£4800 $7728 €6960 Little shrimper (23x18cm-9x7in) s. board. 21-Aug-3 Bonhams, Edinburgh #1189/R est:600-800
£4800 $8160 €7008 Homewards at the close of day (67x49cm-26x19in) s. prov. 30-Oct-3 Christie's, London #112/R est:4000-6000

Works on paper

£667 $1207 €1000 Les ramaseuses de pommes de terre (22x32cm-9x13in) s. W/C. 30-Mar-4 Campo & Campo, Antwerp #173/R

McGREGOR, William York (1855-1923) British

£376 $650 €549 English landscape (61x91cm-24x36in) s.i. 10-Dec-3 Alderfer's, Hatfield #300/R
£1600 $2512 €2320 Pastoral (25x35cm-10x14in) s.d.1891 panel prov. 27-Aug-3 Sotheby's, London #1041/R est:1500-2000

McGREW, Ralph Brownell (1916-1994) American

£1676 $3000 €2514 Little hills, shall praise thee (76x102cm-30x40in) s. masonite. 16-May-4 Abell, Los Angeles #425/R
£14525 $26000 €21207 Tsosie Ahzonie (61x51cm-24x20in) board. 15-May-4 Altermann Galleries, Santa Fe #22/R

McGREW, Ralph Brownell (attrib) (1916-1994) American

£284 $475 €415 Desert landscape. Portrait of woman (51x61cm-20x24in) panel double-sided. 14-Jul-3 O'Gallerie, Oregon #130/R

McGUINNESS, Michael (?) Irish?

£1100 $1804 €1606 Sp. (91x66cm-36x26in) s. 4-Jun-3 John Ross, Belfast #241
£2500 $4650 €3650 Harbour and promenade, Portstewart (66x71cm-26x28in) s.d.89 verso. 3-Mar-4 John Ross, Belfast #185 est:700-800

McGUINNESS, Norah (1903-1980) British

£3357 $5706 €4800 At Lhote's, Paris (51x36cm-20x14in) init. i.verso paper painted 1930 exhib. 18-Nov-3 Whyte's, Dublin #22/R est:5000-7000
£3846 $6538 €5500 Cottages in a mountainous landscape (39x51cm-15x20in) 25-Nov-3 De Veres Art Auctions, Dublin #93/R est:6000-8000
£8000 $14320 €11680 Black wings (41x56cm-16x22in) init. 14-May-4 Christie's, Kensington #449/R est:6000-8000
£10667 $19307 €16000 Blue pool (55x70cm-22x28in) 30-Mar-4 De Veres Art Auctions, Dublin #68/R est:14000-18000
£18792 $33262 €28000 Flight over Mulroy Bay (51x76cm-20x30in) s. prov. 27-Apr-4 Whyte's, Dublin #18/R est:12000-15000

Works on paper

£362 $666 €550 Costume design for stage set (46x31cm-18x12in) s. col chk. 22-Jun-4 De Veres Art Auctions, Dublin #219
£1208 $2138 €1800 Garden landscape with pond (20x30cm-8x12in) init. col crayon ink. 27-Apr-4 Whyte's, Dublin #152/R est:1200-1500
£1389 $2264 €2000 Clady River, Co Donegal (24x34cm-9x13in) s.verso W/C. 24-Sep-3 James Adam, Dublin #33/R est:2000-3000
£2067 $3741 €3100 Jagged rocks, Ballycotton (34x49cm-13x19in) s. gouache. 31-Mar-4 James Adam, Dublin #50/R est:2500-3500
£2254 $3606 €3200 Duomo, Assisi (25x36cm-10x14in) i. W/C gouache. 16-Sep-3 Whyte's, Dublin #118/R est:2500-3000
£2400 $4344 €3600 Pastoral landscape with distant mountains (33x48cm-13x19in) s.d.1942 gouache. 31-Mar-4 James Adam, Dublin #96/R est:1500-2000
£2517 $4280 €3600 Mill stream, Kilkenny (24x34cm-9x13in) s.i.verso gouache. 25-Nov-3 De Veres Art Auctions, Dublin #20/R est:2000-3000
£2600 $4654 €3796 Dunloe, Donegal (30x40cm-12x16in) s.i. pencil chl W/C brush black ink. 14-May-4 Christie's, Kensington #450/R est:3000-5000
£2700 $4833 €3942 Interior at Lisheen, Sligo (44x30cm-17x12in) init. pencil W/C. 14-May-4 Christie's, Kensington #399/R est:1000-1500
£3300 $5907 €4818 Lisheen, Sligo (44x30cm-17x12in) indis.init. pencil W/C. 14-May-4 Christie's, Kensington #401/R est:1000-1500
£3662 $5859 €5200 Fahan, Donegal (25x38cm-10x15in) init. W/C gouache artist's board prov.exhib. 16-Sep-3 Whyte's, Dublin #117/R est:5000-7000
£5594 $9510 €8000 New York, skyline (36x56cm-14x22in) s.d.89 gouache. 25-Nov-3 De Veres Art Auctions, Dublin #46/R est:7000-10000

McGUINNESS, Tom (20th C) British

£450 $752 €657 At the rally (70x91cm-28x36in) board. 8-Oct-3 Christie's, Kensington #940/R
£480 $797 €701 Miner (58x58cm-23x23in) s.d.58 hardboard. 2-Oct-3 Neales, Nottingham #756
£600 $1002 €876 Road to work (61x122cm-24x48in) s.d.64 board. 8-Oct-3 Christie's, Kensington #943/R
£1350 $2457 €1971 Durham Miners Gala (40x70cm-16x28in) s.d.77 board. 29-Jun-4 Anderson & Garland, Newcastle #396/R est:200-350

Works on paper

£580 $1056 €847 Meeting station - miners underground (23x34cm-9x13in) s.d.86. 29-Jun-4 Anderson & Garland, Newcastle #121

McGUINNESS, William Bingham (1849-1928) British

Works on paper

£282 $519 €412 Village pond, Donegal (35x18cm-14x7in) s. i.verso W/C. 9-Jun-4 Walker's, Ottawa #366/R (C.D 700)
£320 $579 €480 Errigal, from near Falcarragh (18x26cm-7x10in) s. W/C prov. 31-Mar-4 James Adam, Dublin #28/R
£336 $601 €500 Cattle in lake and mountain landscape (26x35cm-10x14in) s. W/C. 26-May-4 James Adam, Dublin #42/R
£470 $841 €700 Continental village scene (25x35cm-10x14in) s.d.1884 W/C. 31-May-4 Hamilton Osborne King, Dublin #105/R
£638 $1141 €950 Shepherd and his flock in village (37x26cm-15x10in) s. W/C. 26-May-4 James Adam, Dublin #177/R
£669 $1157 €950 Coastal lighthouse, Figures by a mountain cottage (25x36cm-10x14in) s. W/C pair. 10-Dec-3 Bonhams & James Adam, Dublin #41/R
£724 $1332 €1100 River landscape (60x97cm-24x38in) s. W/C htd white. 22-Jun-4 De Veres Art Auctions, Dublin #150/R
£750 $1275 €1095 Wagon passing through a village (34x58cm-13x23in) s.d.1885 pencil W/C htd white. 4-Nov-3 Holloways, Banbury #496/R
£764 $1245 €1100 Sailing boats off shore (25x37cm-10x15in) s. W/C. 24-Sep-3 James Adam, Dublin #16/R est:400-600
£775 $1239 €1100 Continental street with crowds and carriages (33x23cm-13x9in) s. W/C. 16-Sep-3 Whyte's, Dublin #113/R
£940 $1663 €1400 Glen Burn, Scotland (23x34cm-9x13in) s. i.verso W/C pencil. 27-Apr-4 Whyte's, Dublin #220/R
£1000 $1670 €1460 Figures outside buildings, probably on the Continent (30x20cm-12x8in) s. W/C sold with another by the same hand. 26-Jun-3 Greenslade Hunt, Taunton #475/R est:300-500
£1000 $1810 €1500 Old world estuary, Ireland (24x34cm-9x13in) s. W/C prov. 31-Mar-4 James Adam, Dublin #29/R est:1000-1500

£1007 $1802 €1500 Louch Marre, Benn Slioch (51x76cm-20x30in) s.d.1887 W/C. 26-May-4 James Adam, Dublin #43/R est:1500-2500
£1127 $1803 €1600 Lisiuex, Normandy (32x39cm-13x15in) s.i.d.1878 W/C exhib. 16-Sep-3 Whyte's, Dublin #170/R est:1800-2200
£1250 $2037 €1800 In Connemara (27x44cm-11x17in) s. W/C on board. 28-Sep-3 Hamilton Osborne King, Dublin #155 est:1500-2000
£1333 $2413 €2000 Old church at Louvain, Belgiam (24x34cm-9x13in) s.i.d.1979 verso W/C. 31-Mar-4 James Adam, Dublin #11/R est:1500-2000
£1333 $2413 €2000 Canal scene, Venice (35x16cm-14x6in) s. W/C prov. 31-Mar-4 James Adam, Dublin #12/R est:1500-2000
£1479 $2558 €2100 Street scene, San Remo (34x24cm-13x9in) s. W/C. 10-Dec-3 Bonhams & James Adam, Dublin #34/R est:1500-2000
£1690 $2924 €2400 Street scene, Bruges (39x21cm-15x8in) s. W/C. 10-Dec-3 Bonhams & James Adam, Dublin #35/R est:1000-1500
£1831 $3168 €2600 Coastal village with figures and donkey (25x35cm-10x14in) s. W/C. 10-Dec-3 Bonhams & James Adam, Dublin #39/R est:1400-1800
£2400 $4344 €3600 Village scene with figures, horses and cart (34x58cm-13x23in) s.d.1885 W/C. 31-Mar-4 James Adam, Dublin #23/R est:2500-3500
£2500 $4475 €3650 Venice (52x90cm-20x35in) s. W/C. 26-May-4 Sotheby's, Olympia #177/R est:1000-1500

McGUIRE, Michael (1953-) American
£216 $400 €315 Untitled (76x76cm-30x30in) s.d.1998. 17-Jul-4 Outer Cape Auctions, Provincetown #64/R
£235 $400 €343 Red farm (61x46cm-24x18in) s. painted c.2003. 9-Nov-3 Outer Cape Auctions, Provincetown #55/R
£514 $950 €750 Town wharf (76x102cm-30x40in) s. 15-Feb-4 Outer Cape Auctions, Provincetown #90/R

McGUIRE, Senator Edward Augustine (1901-1992) Irish
£839 $1427 €1200 Moonlit river (51x66cm-20x26in) s. prov. 18-Nov-3 Whyte's, Dublin #79/R

MACH, David (1956-) British
Sculpture
£5000 $9050 €7300 African matches (43x20x20cm-17x8x8in) burnt matches executed c.1986 prov. 1-Apr-4 Christie's, Kensington #304/R est:3000-5000

MACHADO, Juares (1941-) South American
£2824 $4800 €4123 Taba (46x61cm-18x24in) s.d.1988. 25-Nov-3 Galeria y Remates, Montevideo #210
£3294 $5600 €4809 Imagination (100x72cm-39x28in) s.d.1988. 25-Nov-3 Galeria y Remates, Montevideo #209
£4824 $8200 €7043 Two women seated (97x131cm-38x52in) s.d.1988. 25-Nov-3 Galeria y Remates, Montevideo #208/R

MACHAL, Svatopluk (1895-1947) Czechoslovakian?
£535 $996 €781 Ferrying on Sunday at Kunetice (45x68cm-18x27in) s. board. 6-Mar-4 Dorotheum, Prague #133/R est:26000-38000 (C.KR 26000)

MACHARD, J L (1839-1900) French
Works on paper
£1188 $1900 €1734 Before the ball (112x86cm-44x34in) s.d.1891 pastel. 21-Sep-3 Grogan, Boston #18

MACHEN, William H (1832-1911) American
£1188 $1900 €1734 Still life of fish (20x30cm-8x12in) 19-Sep-3 Du Mouchelle, Detroit #2290/R est:300-500

MACHETANZ, Fred (1908-2002) American
£12032 $22500 €17567 Forest trail (66x81cm-26x32in) board. 24-Jul-4 Coeur d'Alene, Hayden #135a est:20000-30000

MACHO, Victorio (1887-1966) Spanish
Works on paper
£270 $476 €400 Woman holding jug (29x20cm-11x8in) mono. pencil dr. 18-May-4 Segre, Madrid #36/R

MACHUCA, Pedro (?-1550) Spanish
£282759 $472207 €410000 Dieu le Pere entoure d'anges (84x134cm-33x53in) panel. 14-Nov-3 Drouot Estimations, Paris #34/R est:120000-150000

MACIEJEWSKI, Zbyslaw (1946-1999) Polish
£1310 $2188 €1900 Portrait of a female (80x90cm-31x35in) s.d.94. 16-Nov-3 Agra, Warsaw #23/R est:1000

MACIEL, Leonel (1939-) Mexican
£448 $761 €654 Nautilus (60x50cm-24x20in) s.d.1974. 30-Oct-3 Louis Morton, Mexico #133 (M.P 8500)

McILFATRICK, Hugh (?) Irish
£260 $426 €380 Donegal cottage (28x38cm-11x15in) s. board. 4-Jun-3 John Ross, Belfast #249
£300 $549 €438 Muckish Mountain, Donegal (30x40cm-12x16in) s. board. 2-Jun-4 John Ross, Belfast #43
£320 $586 €467 Bathers on the Antrim Coast (30x40cm-12x16in) s. board. 2-Jun-4 John Ross, Belfast #186
£350 $574 €511 Cottages on the Donegal coast (50x76cm-20x30in) s. board. 4-Jun-3 John Ross, Belfast #198
£350 $651 €511 Fishing on the River Dunn, Co. Antrim (50x76cm-20x30in) s. board. 3-Mar-4 John Ross, Belfast #242
£380 $654 €555 Connemara Cottage (30x40cm-12x16in) s. board. 3-Dec-3 John Ross, Belfast #41
£400 $744 €584 Connemara boglands (53x68cm-21x27in) s. board. 3-Mar-4 John Ross, Belfast #192
£450 $747 €657 Connemara (61x91cm-24x36in) s. board. 1-Oct-3 John Ross, Belfast #243
£450 $824 €657 Cottage on the Donegal Coast (50x76cm-20x30in) s. 2-Jun-4 John Ross, Belfast #82
£460 $856 €672 Muckish, Co. Donegal (61x91cm-24x36in) s. 3-Mar-4 John Ross, Belfast #127
£500 $860 €730 Away up the glen (76x101cm-30x40in) s. 3-Dec-3 John Ross, Belfast #90
£500 $860 €730 Bathing near Garron Point (76x101cm-30x40in) s. board. 3-Dec-3 John Ross, Belfast #190
£500 $915 €730 Bathers near Fairhead, Co. Atrim (71x91cm-28x36in) s. board. 2-Jun-4 John Ross, Belfast #229
£550 $913 €803 Cottage by the shore, Donegal (76x101cm-30x40in) s. 1-Oct-3 John Ross, Belfast #104

McILHENNY, Charles Morgan (1858-c.1908) American
£559 $1000 €816 Sunset over bog. s. 10-Jan-4 Pook & Pook, Downington #130/R

McINNES, Robert (1801-1886) British
£320 $534 €467 Portrait of a lady (28x25cm-11x10in) s. 11-Nov-3 Bonhams, Knightsbridge #125/R

McINNES, Violet (1892-1971) Australian
£298 $507 €435 Flowers in a pewter jug (21x17cm-8x7in) s. canvas on board. 26-Nov-3 Deutscher-Menzies, Melbourne #271/R (A.D 700)
£407 $728 €594 Still life with freesias (44x39cm-17x15in) s.d.1945 board. 10-May-4 Joel, Victoria #408 (A.D 1000)

McINNES, W B (1889-1939) Australian
£553 $1007 €807 Soft sunlight (31x40cm-12x16in) s. s.i.d.1916 verso canvas on board. 16-Jun-4 Deutscher-Menzies, Melbourne #541/R est:1000-1200 (A.D 1450)
£1653 $3058 €2413 Portrait of H.S. Gilkes, the connoisseur (112x92cm-44x36in) s.d.38 prov. 10-Mar-4 Deutscher-Menzies, Melbourne #64/R est:5000-8000 (A.D 4000)

McINNES, William Beckwith (1889-1939) Australian
£1057 $1659 €1533 Windmill (24x34cm-9x13in) s. board. 26-Aug-3 Christie's, Sydney #322 est:2500-3500 (A.D 2600)

McINNIS, Robert (1942-) Canadian
£226 $378 €330 Ava Tired - Ava Nagy (90x40cm-35x16in) s.i.d.1982. 17-Nov-3 Hodgins, Calgary #186/R (C.D 500)
£240 $439 €350 Westmount, QC (60x75cm-24x30in) s. 1-Jun-4 Hodgins, Calgary #190/R (C.D 600)
£267 $443 €390 Late day, sky effect (23x30cm-9x12in) s.d.1991 s.i.verso oil paperboard prov. 5-Oct-3 Levis, Calgary #76/R (C.D 600)
£317 $529 €463 Toronto, wicker chair (75x60cm-30x24in) s.i.d.1980. 17-Nov-3 Hodgins, Calgary #331/R (C.D 700)
£333 $577 €486 Girl in the window (102x86cm-40x34in) s.d.1980 acrylic. 9-Dec-3 Maynards, Vancouver #246 (C.D 750)
£400 $732 €584 Storm front (60x75cm-24x30in) s.i.d.1979. 1-Jun-4 Hodgins, Calgary #146/R (C.D 1000)
£826 $1496 €1206 8511 DRS 17a buit 1954 (61x76cm-24x30in) s. s.i.d.1978 verso. 18-Apr-4 Levis, Calgary #78/R est:1000-1200 (C.D 2000)
£1000 $1730 €1460 Figure in a winter landscape (112x127cm-44x50in) s. acrylic. 9-Dec-3 Maynards, Vancouver #239 est:1200-1500 (C.D 2250)

McINTIRE, Samuel (attrib) (1757-1811) American
Sculpture
£15054 $28000 €21979 Salem carved and gilded eagle (23cm-9in) salem carved gilded lit. 6-Mar-4 North East Auctions, Portsmouth #417/R est:25000-35000

McINTOSH, Dwight (20th C) American?
Works on paper
£479 $800 €699 Face and hands (38x56cm-15x22in) ink. 15-Nov-3 Slotin Folk Art, Buford #270/R
£838 $1400 €1223 Tom Mix and his horse, Bruce (48x64cm-19x25in) crayon mixed media exhib. 15-Nov-3 Slotin Folk Art, Buford #269/R
£1198 $2000 €1749 Animals (48x64cm-19x25in) W/C ink exhib. 15-Nov-3 Slotin Folk Art, Buford #268/R est:1000-1500

MACINTOSH, John Macintosh (1847-1913) British
£260 $442 €380 Beach scene with figures at the shore (16x21cm-6x8in) mono. board. 4-Nov-3 Dreweatt Neate, Newbury #97/R

McINTOSH, Pleasant Ray (1897-?) American
£838 $1500 €1223 At Tarpon Springs (36x53cm-14x21in) s. 13-May-4 Dallas Auction Gallery, Dallas #4/R est:800-1200
£838 $1500 €1223 Boat at Tarpon (64x76cm-25x30in) s.i. 13-May-4 Dallas Auction Gallery, Dallas #151/R est:800

McINTOSH, Pleasant Ray (attrib) (1897-?) American
£254 $475 €371 Spectators (99x142cm-39x56in) painted c.1962. 25-Feb-4 Dallas Auction Gallery, Dallas #462/R
£267 $500 €390 Mexican villagers (102x142cm-40x56in) s. painted c.1962. 25-Feb-4 Dallas Auction Gallery, Dallas #386/R
£348 $650 €508 Abstract figural landscape (99x142cm-39x56in) s. painted c.1962. 25-Feb-4 Dallas Auction Gallery, Dallas #175/R
£455 $850 €664 Marine landscape (76x104cm-30x41in) s. painted c.1950. 25-Feb-4 Dallas Auction Gallery, Dallas #92/R

McINTYRE, Donald (1923-) British

£360	$637	€526	Soldiers saluting an officer (48x74cm-19x29in) s. 29-Apr-4 Gorringes, Lewes #2502
£460	$837	€672	Port Vendres no.2, south west France (40x28cm-16x11in) init. acrylic on paper. 21-Jun-4 Bonhams, Bath #365
£500	$850	€730	Two figures, stormy sea (61x40cm-24x16in) s. board. 10-Nov-3 Thomson Roddick & Medcalf, Edinburgh #269/R
£553	$940	€807	House by the sea No.7 (35x25cm-14x10in) init. prov. 25-Nov-3 Christie's, Melbourne #219/R (A.D 1300)
£580	$922	€847	Three bathers (25x35cm-10x14in) init. s.i.verso board. 10-Sep-3 Sotheby's, Olympia #234/R
£620	$1054	€905	Harbour (23x34cm-9x13in) init. i.verso board. 29-Oct-3 Hampton & Littlewood, Exeter #543/R
£700	$1274	€1022	Beach scene no.1 (24x29cm-9x11in) 21-Jun-4 Bonhams, Bath #364
£750	$1350	€1095	Pale evening, winter (26x36cm-10x14in) s. board. 20-Jan-4 Bonhams, Knightsbridge #57/R
£800	$1456	€1168	Resting, Sandend (20x28cm-8x11in) init. acrylic board. 15-Jun-4 Bonhams, Knightsbridge #218
£820	$1394	€1197	Bessie's Cove no.1 (20x28cm-8x11in) init. board. 29-Oct-3 Bonhams, Chester #380
£850	$1505	€1241	Trees, evening sun (22x35cm-9x14in) init. oil on card double-sided. 27-Apr-4 Bonhams, Knightsbridge #35/R
£880	$1628	€1285	Beach Portsoy No 1 (37x44cm-15x17in) init. board. 14-Jul-4 Bonhams, Chester #371
£900	$1530	€1314	Sullen sea, Iona (20x29cm-8x11in) s. board. 29-Oct-3 Bonhams, Chester #381
£920	$1674	€1343	Rocky Shore No 3 (35x43cm-14x17in) init. acrylic board. 15-Jun-4 Bonhams, Knightsbridge #213
£950	$1511	€1387	Sunlight on the sea (28x38cm-11x15in) init. board. 10-Sep-3 Sotheby's, Olympia #245/R
£950	$1710	€1387	House in the snow (30x40cm-12x16in) s. board. 20-Jan-4 Bonhams, Knightsbridge #123/R
£980	$1813	€1431	Green sea, Dolan (27x37cm-11x15in) init. board. 14-Jul-4 Bonhams, Chester #372/R
£1200	$2160	€1752	Two figures stormy sea (61x41cm-24x16in) s.i.verso board. 24-Apr-4 Rogers Jones, Clwyd #182
£1300	$2210	€1898	Village by the sea, no.7 (20x28cm-8x11in) init. board. 29-Oct-3 Bonhams, Chester #379 est:500-700
£1300	$2171	€1898	Small boats in a harbour (18x20cm-7x8in) init. board. 14-Oct-3 David Lay, Penzance #624/R est:1200-1500
£1300	$2210	€1898	Two girls and sea (39x56cm-15x22in) s. s.i.verso board. 26-Nov-3 Sotheby's, Olympia #90/R est:1000-1500
£1300	$2366	€1898	Figures on the beach (30x25cm-12x10in) init. s.i. verso board. 1-Jul-4 Christie's, Kensington #319/R est:600-800
£1300	$2405	€1898	Beach Iona No 23 (29x39cm-11x15in) init. board. 14-Jul-4 Bonhams, Chester #375 est:700-1000
£1350	$2241	€1971	Mevagissey. init. i.verso board. 2-Oct-3 Lane, Penzance #99 est:500-700
£1500	$2730	€2190	Calm Sea Iona (51x61cm-20x24in) s. acrylic board. 15-Jun-4 Bonhams, Knightsbridge #217 est:1500-2000
£1500	$2775	€2190	Landscape with horses and caravan (39x49cm-15x19in) s. board. 14-Jul-4 Bonhams, Chester #374/R est:800-1200
£1550	$2868	€2263	Rocky shore No 1 (36x43cm-14x17in) init. board. 14-Jul-4 Bonhams, Chester #373/R est:800-1200
£1600	$2992	€2400	Road to Llangefni (38x63cm-15x25in) s.i.verso oil paper. 21-Jul-4 Anthemion, Cardiff #602/R est:400-600
£1700	$2992	€2482	Carrying a curragh (15x25cm-6x10in) init. board. 19-May-4 Sotheby's, Olympia #208/R est:600-800
£1700	$3043	€2482	Interior no 1 (59x49cm-23x19in) s. board. 14-May-4 Christie's, Kensington #602/R est:1000-1500
£1750	$2975	€2555	Rocky coast (40x80cm-16x31in) s. board prov. 29-Oct-3 Bonhams, Chester #382/R est:1000-1500
£1800	$3006	€2628	Snow, river Ogwen Valley, north Wales (61x122cm-24x48in) s. board. 16-Oct-3 Christie's, Kensington #465/R est:1500-2000
£1800	$3186	€2628	Pleasure boat, grey day (51x61cm-20x24in) s. board. 27-Apr-4 Bonhams, Knightsbridge #139/R est:1800-2200
£1800	$3276	€2628	Farm in Autumn (51x61cm-20x24in) s. acrylic board. 15-Jun-4 Bonhams, Knightsbridge #219 est:1200-1800
£1800	$3168	€2628	House and cottages (51x61cm-20x24in) s. board. 19-May-4 Sotheby's, Olympia #228/R est:2000-3000
£1800	$3222	€2628	Cottages near Dolan (51x61cm-20x24in) s. board. 14-May-4 Christie's, Kensington #601/R est:1500-2000
£1900	$3515	€2774	Cottage Rhosgadfan (51x61cm-20x24in) s. board. 11-Feb-4 Sotheby's, Olympia #215/R est:1500-2000
£1900	$3458	€2774	Farm, Angle Bay West (50x125cm-20x49in) s. i.verso board. 21-Jun-4 Bonhams, Bath #363/R est:1000-1500
£1950	$3608	€2847	Estuary (28x39cm-11x15in) init. board. 14-Jul-4 Bonhams, Chester #376/R est:700-900
£2000	$3180	€2920	Harbour window (101x76cm-40x30in) s. 18-Mar-3 Anderson & Garland, Newcastle #424/R est:800-1200
£2000	$3700	€2920	Boat shed (30x36cm-12x14in) s. board. 10-Feb-4 David Lay, Penzance #407/R est:600-800
£2000	$3700	€2920	Table in the garden (53x63cm-21x25in) s. board. 11-Feb-4 Sotheby's, Olympia #232/R est:800-1200
£2200	$3586	€3212	Stormy coastalscape (51x61cm-20x24in) s. board. 27-Sep-3 Rogers Jones, Clwyd #96/R
£2200	$4070	€3212	Landscape (46x7cm-18x3in) s. board. 11-Feb-4 Sotheby's, Olympia #225/R est:1200-1800
£2200	$3894	€3212	Bust jetty (30x38cm-12x15in) s. board. 27-Apr-4 Bonhams, Knightsbridge #140/R est:1200-1800
£2200	$3960	€3212	Welsh farmstead (48x61cm-19x24in) s. acrylic board. 24-Apr-4 Rogers Jones, Clwyd #185/R
£2200	$4004	€3212	Boats on the sea (51x61cm-20x24in) s. board. 1-Jul-4 Christie's, Kensington #317/R est:1000-1500
£2300	$4255	€3358	Mevagissey (32x42cm-13x17in) init. board. 11-Feb-4 Sotheby's, Olympia #220/R est:2000-3000
£2400	$4080	€3504	White boats Bunowen (32x42cm-13x17in) s. board. 18-Nov-3 Sotheby's, Olympia #190/R est:2000-3000
£2600	$4680	€3796	Church colours (58x104cm-23x41in) s. board. 20-Jan-4 Bonhams, Knightsbridge #111/R est:1500-2000
£2800	$4676	€4088	Rocks and mountains (51x153cm-20x60in) s. 21-Oct-3 Bonhams, Knightsbridge #64/R est:3000-5000
£2800	$5180	€4088	Norfolk (51x76cm-20x30in) s. exhib. 11-Mar-4 Christie's, Kensington #266/R est:1500-2000
£3000	$5370	€4380	Anglesey stream (61x122cm-24x48in) s. s.i.verso canvas on board. 14-May-4 Christie's, Kensington #599/R est:3000-5000
£3400	$5406	€4964	Clachan (52x77cm-20x30in) s. board. 10-Sep-3 Sotheby's, Olympia #243/R est:2500-3000
£3800	$6460	€5548	Cemaes Harbour (51x76cm-20x30in) s. s.i.verso canvasboard prov. 18-Nov-3 Sotheby's, Olympia #199/R est:3000-5000

MACINTYRE, James (1926-) British

£500	$910	€730	Seated woman (45x37cm-18x15in) s. board. 15-Jun-4 Bonhams, Knightsbridge #47/R
£650	$1183	€949	Girl from Connemara (40x50cm-16x20in) s. board. 15-Jun-4 Bonhams, Knightsbridge #44/R
£1100	$1826	€1606	River bush, Bushmill, Co. Antrim (56x66cm-22x26in) s. board. 1-Oct-3 John Ross, Belfast #224 est:1200-1500
Works on paper			
£550	$946	€803	Winter, Knockagh, Greenisland (50x60cm-20x24in) s.d.1976 W/C. 3-Dec-3 John Ross, Belfast #62
£620	$1029	€905	Cattle grazing by the farm (45x35cm-18x14in) s.d.89 W/C. 1-Oct-3 John Ross, Belfast #15
£650	$1118	€949	The happy sow (35x56cm-14x22in) s.d.98 W/C. 3-Dec-3 John Ross, Belfast #83
£900	$1476	€1314	The remains of Headman's Farm, Greenisland (40x56cm-16x22in) s.d.99 W/C. 4-Jun-3 John Ross, Belfast #72
£900	$1494	€1314	Thatcher (30x40cm-12x16in) s.d.89 W/C. 1-Oct-3 John Ross, Belfast #112
£900	$1647	€1314	Carrying kelp (33x40cm-13x16in) s.d.88 W/C. 2-Jun-4 John Ross, Belfast #69
£950	$1577	€1387	Old pub (40x50cm-16x20in) s.d.78 W/C. 1-Oct-3 John Ross, Belfast #251
£1351	$2297	€1972	Misty day, Glens of Antrim (39x53cm-15x21in) s.d.1999 s.i.d.verso W/C. 27-Nov-3 Heffel, Vancouver #2/R est:2000-2500 (C.D 3000)
£1399	$2378	€2000	The fisherman's dogs, Roundstone, Connemara (44x56cm-17x22in) s.i.d.1998 verso W/C exhib. 18-Nov-3 Whyte's, Dublin #163/R est:1800-2200
£1464	$2651	€2137	Conversation in Roundstone (44x35cm-17x14in) s. i.verso W/C prov. 1-Apr-4 Heffel, Vancouver #71/R est:4000-5000 (C.D 3500)

McINTYRE, John H (fl.1896-1904) British

£2941	$5000	€4294	Extensive mountainous landscape with a river leading into a lake and a figure with two dogs (76x127cm-30x50in) s. 19-Nov-3 Bonhams & Butterfields, San Francisco #130/R

McINTYRE, Joseph Wrightson (fl.1866-1888) British

£820	$1525	€1197	Highland landscape (30x47cm-12x19in) s. card pair. 2-Mar-4 Bearnes, Exeter #405/R
£1040	$1800	€1518	Fishermen and ducks by a fishing shack (61x91cm-24x36in) s. s.i.verso. 13-Dec-3 Sloans & Kenyon, Bethesda #788/R est:3000-4000

McINTYRE, Mary (fl.1982) New Zealander

Works on paper			
£399	$642	€583	Scenes of Auckland, One tree hill and Tony Fomison (57x76cm-22x30in) s.i. pastel prov. 12-Aug-3 Peter Webb, Auckland #102/R (NZ.D 1100)

McINTYRE, Peter (1910-1995) New Zealander

£906	$1458	€1323	The Kingston Arm, Lake Wakatipu (47x55cm-19x22in) s. i.verso. 12-Aug-3 Peter Webb, Auckland #88 (NZ.D 2500)
£1203	$2250	€1805	New Zealander (61x76cm-24x30in) s. prov. 25-Jul-4 Bonhams & Butterfields, San Francisco #6146/R est:1500-2500
£1786	$3286	€2608	Relics of the outback (58x74cm-23x29in) s. board. 25-Mar-4 International Art Centre, Auckland #88/R est:8000-12000 (NZ.D 5000)
£1812	$2935	€2627	Willow pool (40x50cm-16x20in) s. board. 31-Jul-3 International Art Centre, Auckland #123/R est:4500-6500 (NZ.D 5000)
£1880	$3195	€2745	Trout fishing, Lake Taupo (48x54cm-19x21in) s. 26-Nov-3 Dunbar Sloane, Wellington #47/R est:5000-8000 (NZ.D 5000)
£2257	$3589	€3295	Portrait of a young Asian girl (74x58cm-29x23in) s. canvas on board. 1-May-3 Dunbar Sloane, Wellington #59/R est:4000-8000 (NZ.D 6500)
£2632	$4474	€3843	Kakahi (45x73cm-18x29in) s. board. 27-Nov-3 International Art Centre, Auckland #117/R est:7000-11000 (NZ.D 7000)
£2972	$5409	€4339	View of National park across Lake Taupo (40x50cm-16x20in) s. board. 29-Jun-4 Peter Webb, Auckland #132/R est:10000-15000 (NZ.D 8500)
£3000	$4740	€4380	Sheep shearers at work (69x58cm-27x23in) board. 23-Jul-3 Grant, Worcester #479/R est:1500-2000
£3383	$5752	€4939	Ghost town, Madrid, New Mexico (64x80cm-25x31in) s. 27-Nov-3 International Art Centre, Auckland #56/R est:8000-12000 (NZ.D 9000)
£3607	$5698	€5266	Abandoned stockyards, Anthony's Lagoon, Northern Territory (61x86cm-24x34in) s. board prov.exhib. 2-Sep-3 Deutscher-Menzies, Melbourne #164/R est:8000-10000 (A.D 8800)
£3759	$6391	€5488	Lambton quay, Wellington (54x85cm-21x33in) s. 26-Nov-3 Dunbar Sloane, Wellington #46/R est:5000-8000 (NZ.D 10000)
£4511	$7669	€6586	The bush, coast road to Russell (64x72cm-25x28in) s. canvasboard prov.exhib. 27-Nov-3 International Art Centre, Auckland #69/R est:15000-20000 (NZ.D 12000)
£4875	$8970	€7118	Rangitikei river (54x75cm-21x30in) board. 25-Mar-4 International Art Centre, Auckland #103/R est:15000-20000 (NZ.D 13650)
£5714	$10514	€8342	Sun and shadow, Rangitikei river (50x60cm-20x24in) s. board. 25-Mar-4 International Art Centre, Auckland #64/R est:15000-20000 (NZ.D 16000)
£8514	$13708	€12430	Waitarere Valley (50x60cm-20x24in) s. board. 20-Aug-3 Peter Webb, Auckland #2033/R est:15000-20000 (NZ.D 23500)
£8664	$14123	€12649	Shearers (69x60cm-27x24in) s. board lit. 23-Sep-3 Peter Webb, Auckland #36/R est:20000-30000 (NZ.D 24000)
£8696	$14000	€12696	Country scene (62x75cm-24x30in) s. board. 20-Aug-3 Peter Webb, Auckland #2039/R est:15000-20000 (NZ.D 24000)
£10140	$18455	€14804	Sheep mustering in Kawarau Gorge (70x90cm-28x35in) s. 29-Jun-4 Peter Webb, Auckland #77/R est:28000-35000 (NZ.D 29000)
Works on paper			
£350	$637	€511	Buckingham Palace (52x73cm-20x29in) s. W/C. 15-Jun-4 Bonhams, Knightsbridge #65
£362	$616	€529	St. Andrews on the terrace, Wellington (53x43cm-21x17in) s. ink wash. 4-Nov-3 Peter Webb, Auckland #216/R est:1000-2000 (NZ.D 1000)
£390	$671	€569	Whakapapa river (36x43cm-14x17in) s. ink. 7-Dec-3 International Art Centre, Auckland #224 (NZ.D 1050)
£595	$1023	€869	Flotilla in the Pacific Islands (29x36cm-11x14in) s. W/C. 7-Dec-3 International Art Centre, Auckland #295/R (NZ.D 1600)
£709	$1312	€1035	Four children (53x72cm-21x28in) W/C. 13-Jul-4 Watson's, Christchurch #55/R est:3000-5000 (NZ.D 2000)

£929 $1599 €1356 Floating market, Bangkok (52x71cm-20x28in) s. W/C. 7-Dec-3 International Art Centre, Auckland #219/R (NZ.D 2500)
£996 $1604 €1454 Waterfront scene (42x55cm-17x22in) s. ink W/C. 20-Aug-3 Peter Webb, Auckland #2036/R (NZ.D 2750)
£1064 $1968 €1553 Venice (53x71cm-21x28in) W/C. 13-Jul-4 Watson's, Christchurch #11/R (NZ.D 3000)
£1178 $1896 €1720 University Tower (45x55cm-18x22in) s. ink W/C. 20-Aug-3 Peter Webb, Auckland #2034/R est:3000-5000 (NZ.D 3250)
£1389 $2208 €2028 China sea (51x68cm-20x27in) s. W/C. 1-May-3 Dunbar Sloane, Wellington #54/R est:6000-10000 (NZ.D 4000)
£1399 $2545 €2043 Lake scene (49x58cm-19x23in) s. W/C. 29-Jun-4 Peter Webb, Auckland #170/R est:4000-6000 (NZ.D 4000)
£1812 $2917 €2646 Queen Street (44x55cm-17x22in) s. ink W/C. 20-Aug-3 Peter Webb, Auckland #2035/R est:3000-5000 (NZ.D 5000)
£2393 $4403 €3494 New Guineau girls, market day (49x73cm-19x29in) W/C. 25-Mar-4 International Art Centre, Auckland #121/R est:8000-12000 (NZ.D 6700)
£3895 $6193 €5687 Boys going fishing (54x73cm-21x29in) s. W/C. 9-Sep-3 Watson's, Christchurch #8 (NZ.D 10750)

McINTYRE, Raymond (fl.1880-1931) British
£18182 $33091 €26546 River tug boat (26x20cm-10x8in) s. board prov. 29-Jun-4 Peter Webb, Auckland #65/R est:28000-35000 (NZ.D 52000)

McINTYRE, Robert Finlay (fl.1892-1897) British
£1100 $1969 €1606 Figures in highland landscape. Approaching storm (28x47cm-11x19in) s. board pair. 27-May-4 Christie's, Kensington #218/R est:1000-1500

McINTYRE, Simon (?) ?
£536 $970 €783 Untitled (100x65cm-39x26in) s. oil paper. 4-Apr-4 International Art Centre, Auckland #347/R (NZ.D 1500)
£564 $959 €823 Untitled (100x65cm-39x26in) s. oil paper. 27-Nov-3 International Art Centre, Auckland #67/R (NZ.D 1500)

MACIVER, Loreen (1909-1998) American
£1198 $2000 €1749 Fall of snow (104x74cm-41x29in) s. painted 1948 prov. 11-Nov-3 Christie's, Rockefeller NY #146/R est:3000-5000
£1437 $2400 €2098 Study of flowers (25x36cm-10x14in) masonite prov. 11-Nov-3 Christie's, Rockefeller NY #147/R est:2000-3000
£10465 $18000 €15279 Circus (132x138cm-52x54in) s. prov.exhib. 3-Dec-3 Doyle, New York #85/R est:4000-6000
£11047 $19000 €16129 Cyclamen (71x81cm-28x32in) s. prov.exhib. 3-Dec-3 Doyle, New York #51/R est:3000-5000
Works on paper
£240 $400 €350 Flowers (33x25cm-13x10in) s.i.d.90 crayon. 11-Nov-3 Christie's, Rockefeller NY #148/R

MACK, Heinz (1931-) German
£1067 $1909 €1600 Untitled - light graphic (43x41cm-17x16in) s.d. scratching silver wax pen. 15-May-4 Dr Sturies, Dusseldorf #124/R
£11189 $19245 €16000 Schleier zu sais (130x120cm-51x47in) s.i.d.62 prov.exhib. 2-Dec-3 Sotheby's, Amsterdam #166/R est:18000-22000
£12195 $20000 €17805 Untitled (85x100cm-33x39in) s.d.57 on stretcher acrylic prov.exhib. 28-May-3 Sotheby's, Amsterdam #28/R est:20000-30000
Sculpture
£1000 $1840 €1500 Small triad (64cm-25in) s. highly polished lacquered bronze one of 35. 12-Jun-4 Villa Grisebach, Berlin #790/R est:2000-3000
£1333 $2453 €2000 Gemini-atlas (31cm-12in) s. highly polished lacquered bronze one of 35. 12-Jun-4 Villa Grisebach, Berlin #791/R est:2000-3000
£1600 $2864 €2400 Untitled - light relief (48x48x4cm-19x19x2in) s.i.d. verso aluminium masonite. 15-May-4 Dr Sturies, Dusseldorf #123/R
£2667 $4773 €4000 Light pyramid (48x68x4cm-19x27x2in) s.i.d.64 verso aluminium relief panel. 15-May-4 Van Ham, Cologne #771/R est:8000
£5594 $9622 €8000 Paravent fur das licht (200x263x2cm-79x104x1in) aluminium perspex prov.lit. 2-Dec-3 Sotheby's, Amsterdam #171/R est:8000-12000
£9500 $15865 €13870 Oeuvre 662 (198x198cm-78x78in) s.i.d.65 verso aluminium relief laid on wood panel prov. 21-Oct-3 Sotheby's, London #340/R est:5000-7000
Works on paper
£322 $547 €460 Lighthouse (62x49cm-24x19in) s.d.1969 spray technique. 29-Nov-3 Arnold, Frankfurt #359
£1000 $1790 €1500 White structure (64x49cm-25x19in) s.d. bodycol prov. 13-May-4 Neumeister, Munich #691/R est:1500-1800
£1408 $2437 €2000 Structures (62x48cm-24x19in) s.d.63 gouache black. 13-Dec-3 Lempertz, Koln #166/R est:2000
£1829 $3000 €2670 Untitled (25x24cm-10x9in) s.d.62 pencil prov. 28-May-3 Sotheby's, Amsterdam #41/R est:3000-4000
£2113 $3655 €3000 Colour chromatic (106x77cm-42x30in) s.d.91 col wax chk pastel chk prov. 13-Dec-3 Lempertz, Koln #334/R est:2500-3000
£4268 $7000 €6231 Lichtrelief 499 A (29x35cm-11x14in) s.d.58 verso aluminium board prov.exhib.lit. 28-May-3 Sotheby's, Amsterdam #57/R est:7000-10000
£9146 $15000 €13353 Lichtrelief (50x65cm-20x26in) s.d.60 verso aluminium wood prov.exhib. 28-May-3 Sotheby's, Amsterdam #67/R est:15000-20000

McKAIN, Bruce (1900-) American
£511 $900 €746 Untitled townscape with boat (38x56cm-15x22in) s. paper. 3-Jan-4 Outer Cape Auctions, Provincetown #83a/R
£1081 $2000 €1578 Untitled sailboat (61x51cm-24x20in) s. 15-Feb-4 Outer Cape Auctions, Provincetown #77/R
£1892 $3500 €2762 Mary Heaton Vorse's home (51x61cm-20x24in) s. board. 17-Jul-4 Outer Cape Auctions, Provincetown #60/R
£2159 $3800 €3152 Shoreline, Provincetown (51x61cm-20x24in) s. 3-Jan-4 Outer Cape Auctions, Provincetown #65/R
Works on paper
£601 $950 €877 Little red house, Provincetown, Mass (48x36cm-19x14in) s. W/C exec.c.1960. 6-Apr-3 William Jenack, New York #74

McKAY, Brian (1926-) Australian
£1382 $2170 €2018 Coast (42x55cm-17x22in) s.d.63 board. 26-Aug-3 Lawson Menzies, Sydney #324 est:300-500 (A.D 3400)

MACKAY, Collin (19th C) British
£400 $720 €584 East coast fishing harbour (60x90cm-24x35in) s.d.1891. 22-Apr-4 Bonhams, Edinburgh #327

McKAY, F H (1880-?) American
£1138 $1900 €1661 To the bay, Maine (61x76cm-24x30in) s. s.i.stretcher. 18-Jun-3 Doyle, New York #58/R est:800-1200

MACKAY, Florence (fl.1890-1920) British
Works on paper
£480 $768 €701 Feeding time; mother and daughter in garden with birds (18x23cm-7x9in) s.i. W/C. 18-Sep-3 Scarborough Perry Fine Arts, Hove #626

McKAY, Frances H (1880-?) American
£261 $450 €381 Connecticut village (41x51cm-16x20in) s.i.verso. 6-Dec-3 Neal Auction Company, New Orleans #346/R
£782 $1400 €1142 Dutch farmyard (61x91cm-24x36in) s. 8-Jan-4 James Julia, Fairfield #829/R est:900-1200

MACKAY, Thomas (19/20th C) British
Works on paper
£800 $1432 €1168 Cottage garden (15x21cm-6x8in) s. W/C htd white. 25-May-4 Bonhams, Knightsbridge #193/R
£1000 $1790 €1460 Country village lane with brook (19x31cm-7x12in) s. W/C. 17-Mar-4 Bonhams, Chester #226 est:600-800
£1400 $2548 €2044 Feeding the ducks. Gathering the hay (15x22cm-6x9in) s. W/C bodycol pair. 1-Jul-4 Christie's, Kensington #204/R est:1200-1800

McKAY, Thomas Hope (fl.1900-1930) British
£260 $442 €380 Autumnal colours (40x30cm-16x12in) s. 10-Nov-3 Thomson Roddick & Medcalf, Edinburgh #273
£1000 $1840 €1460 Gathering wild flowers (50x75cm-20x30in) s. board. 10-Jun-4 Lyon & Turnbull, Edinburgh #123 est:1000-1500

McKAY, William Darling (1844-1924) British
£500 $835 €730 Gathering wood (26x36cm-10x14in) s. 23-Oct-3 Bonhams, Edinburgh #372
£550 $886 €798 Holy Island sands (25x36cm-10x14in) init. canvasboard. 21-Aug-3 Bonhams, Edinburgh #1160
£700 $1274 €1022 Errand girl (25x19cm-10x7in) init. panel. 5-Feb-4 Mellors & Kirk, Nottingham #558/R
£1100 $2046 €1606 Cattle watering (25x31cm-10x12in) init. canvas on board prov. 4-Mar-4 Christie's, Kensington #71/R est:1000-1500
£1300 $2093 €1885 Haugh, Haddington, afternoon shadow (30x40cm-12x16in) init. 21-Aug-3 Bonhams, Edinburgh #1197/R est:1200-1800
£2000 $3340 €2920 Huntsmen entering a village. Ploughing (23x30cm-9x12in) init. panel pair. 16-Oct-3 Bonhams, Edinburgh #164/R est:2000-3000

MACKE, August (1887-1914) German
£80000 $145600 €116800 Still life of bunch of flowers in front of a window (65x47cm-26x19in) s.d.1913 prov.lit. 3-Feb-4 Sotheby's, London #16/R est:100000-150000
£1500000 $2730000 €2190000 Woman bathing. Pierrot with dancing couple (101x72cm-40x28in) double-sided painted 1913 prov.exhib.lit. 21-Jun-4 Sotheby's, London #41/R est:1500000-2500000
Works on paper
£979 $1684 €1400 Mother with child (15x10cm-6x4in) Indian ink. 2-Dec-3 Hauswedell & Nolte, Hamburg #383/R
£2533 $4661 €3800 Female dancer II (20x16cm-8x6in) i.d.1913 i.verso pencil. 12-Jun-4 Villa Grisebach, Berlin #608/R est:2000-2500
£2667 $4907 €4000 Walter playing (28x21cm-11x8in) pencil. 12-Jun-4 Villa Grisebach, Berlin #170/R est:4000-6000
£3497 $6014 €5000 Dancers with veils (12x19cm-5x7in) W/C brush two exec.1907/08 prov.exhib. 5-Dec-3 Ketterer, Munich #41/R est:5000-7000
£9000 $16110 €13500 Under the arches in Thun 1 (21x14cm-8x6in) chl whisked prov.exhib. 14-May-4 Ketterer, Munich #154/R est:15000-20000
£12587 $21399 €18000 Landscape with Lake Thun (17x11cm-7x4in) chl. 26-Nov-3 Lempertz, Koln #817/R est:7000
£13333 $24400 €20000 Studio I (20x16cm-8x6in) i.d.1913 pencil. 5-Jun-4 Lempertz, Koln #383/R est:18000-20000
£17361 $28993 €25000 Under the arches in Thun I (21x14cm-8x6in) chl wash prov.exhib. 24-Oct-3 Ketterer, Hamburg #450/R est:25000-30000
£18667 $34347 €28000 Flowers in a vase and fruit (31x27cm-12x11in) W/C gouache exec. 1912 prov.exhib.lit. 12-Jun-4 Villa Grisebach, Berlin #175/R est:30000-40000
£20000 $36800 €30000 Different people from Tegernsee (34x23cm-13x9in) i.d.1910 W/C gouache prov.exhib. 12-Jun-4 Villa Grisebach, Berlin #171/R est:20000-30000
£22667 $41480 €34000 Riverside cafe (21x16cm-8x6in) i.d.1913 pencil. 5-Jun-4 Lempertz, Koln #837/R est:18000-20000
£23490 $42047 €35000 Lamp (21x19cm-8x7in) W/C prov.lit. 27-May-4 Hassfurther, Vienna #60/R est:40000-60000
£52000 $95160 €78000 Tulips in blue and white vase (29x23cm-11x9in) s. verso pastel prov. 5-Jun-4 Lempertz, Koln #836/R est:50000-70000
£60000 $109200 €87600 Vor der Regatta (35x44cm-14x17in) i.d.1912 verso W/C chl brush blk ink prov.exhib.lit. 5-Feb-4 Christie's, London #367/R est:60000-90000
£90000 $163800 €131400 Nachmittag im garten - Afternoon in the garden (54x35cm-21x14in) i.d.1913 W/C brush ink prov.exhib.lit. 3-Feb-4 Sotheby's, London #13/R est:90000-120000

MACKE, Helmuth (1891-1936) German
Works on paper
£1310 $2410 €1913 Landscape with cows (25x32cm-10x13in) s.d.1918 Indian ink W/C gouache. 8-Jun-4 Germann, Zurich #130/R est:3000-4000 (S.FR 3000)
£1333 $2387 €2000 Carousel by the Rhine (16x21cm-6x8in) s.d. W/C gouache pencil prov. 14-May-4 Ketterer, Munich #55/R est:1500-2000
£2133 $3819 €3200 Landscape with timbered house (25x32cm-10x13in) s.d. W/C chk prov. 14-May-4 Ketterer, Munich #56/R est:1500-2000

McKECHNIE, Jessie (20th C) British

Works on paper

£1300	$2041	€1885	Oh- C'est affreuse. i. W/C exhib. 27-Aug-3 Sotheby's, London #1065/R est:1000-1500

McKEE, John (1941-) Canadian

£1451	$2467	€2118	Country road, country sky, one solitary house (107x122cm-42x48in) s. s.i.d.1987 verso acrylic prov. 6-Nov-3 Heffel, Vancouver #82/R est:2000-4000 (C.D 3250)

McKEEVER, Ian (1946-) British

£1310	$2410	€1913	Column II (250x108cm-98x43in) s.d.1988 verso oil acrylic photo canvas prov. 8-Jun-4 Germann, Zurich #98/R est:3000-5000 (S.FR 3000)

McKELL, James (1885-1956) American

£883	$1500	€1289	Stagecoach shootout (61x81cm-24x32in) s. board. 21-Nov-3 Skinner, Boston #328/R est:1500-2500

McKELVEY, Frank (1895-1974) Irish

£2700	$5022	€3942	Homeward bound, Donegal (30x45cm-12x18in) s. board. 3-Mar-4 John Ross, Belfast #8 est:2000-2500
£2937	$4993	€4200	Evening Island Magee (25x35cm-10x14in) s. canvasboard. 25-Nov-3 De Veres Art Auctions, Dublin #148/R est:4000-6000
£3221	$5702	€4800	Donegal landscape (30x43cm-12x17in) s. panel. 27-Apr-4 Whyte's, Dublin #202/R est:4000-6000
£4196	$7133	€6000	Moyola river at Castle Dawson (35x43cm-14x17in) s. board. 25-Nov-3 De Veres Art Auctions, Dublin #55/R est:6000-8000
£4500	$8370	€6570	Upper reaches of the river Lagan (30x43cm-12x17in) s. board. 3-Mar-4 John Ross, Belfast #119 est:5000-6000
£4667	$8447	€7000	Errigal from Falcarragh (31x42cm-12x17in) s. i.verso canvasboard exhib. 30-Mar-4 De Veres Art Auctions, Dublin #75/R est:7000-10000
£5000	$8200	€7300	Still life of roses (61x50cm-24x20in) s. 4-Jun-3 John Ross, Belfast #157
£5333	$9653	€8000	Boating on the river (31x41cm-12x16in) s. canvas on board. 30-Mar-4 De Veres Art Auctions, Dublin #59/R est:8000-12000
£5500	$10230	€8030	Sheep grazing, Lagan Meadows (38x50cm-15x20in) s. 3-Mar-4 John Ross, Belfast #162 est:6000-7000
£5500	$9845	€8030	Cattle grazing (30x43cm-12x17in) s. panel. 14-May-4 Christie's, London #176/R est:6000-8000
£5594	$9510	€8000	Beach at Falcarragh, Co. Donegal (38x49cm-15x19in) s.i. 25-Nov-3 De Veres Art Auctions, Dublin #127/R est:8000-12000
£5667	$10257	€8500	Near Castlebar, Co Mayo (31x42cm-12x17in) s. canvasboard exhib. 30-Mar-4 De Veres Art Auctions, Dublin #51/R est:7000-10000
£5705	$10211	€8500	Atlantic drive, Co. Donegal (51x68cm-20x27in) s. 26-May-4 James Adam, Dublin #156/R est:8000-12000
£6376	$11285	€9500	Picnic on Lagan, Belfast (23x30cm-9x12in) s. i.d.1935 verso panel prov. 27-Apr-4 Whyte's, Dublin #43/R est:7000-9000
£6434	$10937	€9200	View of Ben Bulben (51x69cm-20x27in) s. prov. 25-Nov-3 De Veres Art Auctions, Dublin #78/R est:10000-15000
£6713	$11413	€9600	Donegal coastal landscape (31x42cm-12x17in) s. prov. 25-Nov-3 De Veres Art Auctions, Dublin #47/R est:6000-9000
£7000	$11480	€10220	Landscape at Bunbeg (40x50cm-16x20in) s. 4-Jun-3 John Ross, Belfast #162a
£9000	$16110	€13140	The road to the sea, coast of Donegal (51x66cm-20x26in) s. i. on stretcher prov. 14-May-4 Christie's, London #208/R est:7000-10000
£9000	$16110	€13140	Church Island on the Bann River. Gunn Island, Ballyhornan, Co Down (15x20cm-6x8in) s. canvasboard two. 13-May-4 Sotheby's, London #36/R est:6000-8000
£10500	$19530	€15330	Lagan River at Maze, Co. Down (45x61cm-18x24in) s. 3-Mar-4 John Ross, Belfast #31 est:10000-12000
£10500	$19215	€15330	Unloading the catch Donegal (50x68cm-20x27in) s. 2-Jun-4 John Ross, Belfast #119 est:11000-12000
£11500	$20585	€16790	Landscape after rain (51x68cm-20x27in) s. prov. 13-May-4 Sotheby's, London #49/R est:12000-18000
£12081	$21624	€18000	Wooded lakeside with cattle grazing (53x66cm-21x26in) s. prov. 26-May-4 James Adam, Dublin #91/R est:20000-30000
£13380	$21408	€19000	Landscape with figure and cattle on a river path (41x51cm-16x20in) s. 16-Sep-3 Whyte's, Dublin #93/R est:20000-25000
£14000	$25060	€20440	Ballycastle (38x51cm-15x20in) s. board. 14-May-4 Christie's, London #171/R est:15000-25000
£17000	$30430	€24820	Gathering wild flowers (30x40cm-12x16in) s. canvasboard. 13-May-4 Sotheby's, London #88/R est:10000-15000
£18000	$30960	€26280	Feeding ducks, St Stephen's Green, Dublin (38x50cm-15x20in) s. 3-Dec-3 John Ross, Belfast #158 est:18000-20000
£21127	$33803	€30000	Back road (51x69cm-20x27in) s. exhib. 16-Sep-3 Whyte's, Dublin #91/R est:30000-40000
£22819	$40389	€34000	Fishermen on Strangford Lough, County Down (51x66cm-20x26in) s. prov. 27-Apr-4 Whyte's, Dublin #61/R est:30000-40000
£25503	$45141	€38000	Mixed flock (38x51cm-15x20in) s. prov. 27-Apr-4 Whyte's, Dublin #57/R est:40000-50000
£29371	$49930	€42000	After rain, Bunbeg, Co Donegal (51x68cm-20x27in) s. 25-Nov-3 De Veres Art Auctions, Dublin #72/R est:35000-45000
£48320	$85530	€72000	Swans on the Lagan (51x69cm-20x27in) s. prov.exhib. 27-Apr-4 Whyte's, Dublin #55/R est:70000-90000

Works on paper

£560	$890	€812	Irish river scene (24x34cm-9x13in) s. W/C. 9-Sep-3 David Duggleby, Scarborough #61
£600	$960	€876	River landscape with wooded hills beyond (20x25cm-8x10in) s. W/C. 18-Sep-3 Goldings, Lincolnshire #850/R
£811	$1265	€1200	Donegal landscape (13x20cm-5x8in) s. 29-Mar-3 Woodwards, Cork #10
£1342	$2403	€2000	Lake and mountain landscape with cottages (26x35cm-10x14in) s. W/C. 26-May-4 James Adam, Dublin #98/R est:2000-3000
£1400	$2296	€2044	Cattle grazing (25x35cm-10x14in) s.d.12 W/C. 4-Jun-3 John Ross, Belfast #151 est:1800
£1458	$2377	€2100	Bridge over a river in landscape with distant cottage (26x37cm-10x15in) s. W/C. 24-Sep-3 James Adam, Dublin #35/R est:1000-1500
£1700	$2924	€2482	Bathers on the beach, Donegal (35x56cm-14x22in) s. W/C. 3-Dec-3 John Ross, Belfast #153 est:3000-4000
£1800	$3294	€2628	River in the glens (28x38cm-11x15in) s. W/C. 2-Jun-4 John Ross, Belfast #143 est:1500-1750
£2254	$3606	€3200	Portrait of a lady with green drop earrings (34x25cm-13x10in) s.d.1931 W/C prov. 16-Sep-3 Whyte's, Dublin #95/R est:2000-3000
£2800	$5208	€4088	Collecting turf, Donegal (35x50cm-14x20in) s. W/C. 3-Mar-4 John Ross, Belfast #158 est:3000-4000
£2800	$5040	€4088	Unloading the catch (37x53cm-15x21in) s. pencil W/C. 21-Apr-4 Christie's, Kensington #179/R est:700-1000
£2958	$4732	€4200	Working in the yard (25x37cm-10x15in) s. W/C over chl prov. 16-Sep-3 Whyte's, Dublin #89/R est:2500-3500
£3000	$5490	€4380	Digging for bait, Donegal (35x50cm-14x20in) s. W/C. 2-Jun-4 John Ross, Belfast #152 est:3000-4000
£4200	$7812	€6132	Feeding the hens (35x25cm-14x10in) s. W/C. 3-Mar-4 John Ross, Belfast #55 est:4000-5000
£21000	$37590	€30660	Fair day at Camlough, Co Armagh (36x51cm-14x20in) s. pencil W/C. 14-May-4 Christie's, London #177/R est:5000-7000

MACKENDREE, William (1950-) American

£417	$696	€600	Sans titre (150x150cm-59x59in) s.i.d.1985 acrylic. 25-Oct-3 Cornette de St.Cyr, Paris #753
£533	$960	€800	Odoo chicken (150x50cm-59x20in) s.d.1987 verso prov. 24-Apr-4 Cornette de St.Cyr, Paris #626

MACKENDRICK, Lilian (1906-1987) American

£968	$1800	€1413	Still life with blue canister (51x76cm-20x30in) s. 3-Mar-4 Christie's, Rockefeller NY #51/R est:3000-5000
£1029	$1800	€1502	Fields of Agosteim (35x59cm-14x23in) s. 19-Dec-3 Sotheby's, New York #1060/R est:3000-4000

McKENNA, Alex (?) ?

£300	$492	€438	Heading home (40x61cm-16x24in) s. board. 4-Jun-3 John Ross, Belfast #77
£333	$603	€500	Fair day (29x41cm-11x16in) s. canvasboard. 30-Mar-4 De Veres Art Auctions, Dublin #233/R

McKENNA, Noel Vincent Joseph (1956-) Australian

£1319	$2243	€1926	Bus terminus (35x41cm-14x16in) s.i.d.87 verso exhib.prov. 25-Nov-3 Christie's, Melbourne #111/R est:2800-3500 (A.D 3100)

Works on paper

£1405	$2599	€2051	Yearling sale (56x40cm-22x16in) s.d.89 s.i.d.89 verso oil on plywood. 15-Mar-4 Sotheby's, Melbourne #79 est:2000-3000 (A.D 3400)

McKENNA, Stephen (1939-) Irish?

£5000	$8950	€7300	Isabella (183x122cm-72x48in) init. s.i.d.1987 verso prov. 13-May-4 Sotheby's, London #77/R est:5000-7000

MACKENNAL, B (20th C) British?

Sculpture

£2700	$4590	€3942	Long haired woman, seated upon a sphere four pairs of wings above. bronze. 5-Nov-3 Rupert Toovey, Partridge Green #1109/R

MACKENNAL, Sir Edgar Bertram (1863-1931) Australian

Sculpture

£2744	$4912	€4006	Circe (57cm-22in) s. st.base num.83/100 bonded bronze powder polymer resin. 4-May-4 Sotheby's, Melbourne #236/R est:4000-6000 (A.D 6750)
£3953	$7075	€5771	George V in uniform (55cm-22in) s.d.1911 bronze marble gilt base. 15-May-4 Christie's, Sydney #336/R est:5000-8000 (A.D 10000)
£22764	$40748	€33235	Truth (62cm-24in) s.d.June 12 1894 i.base bronze st.f.Gruet Paris exhib. 4-May-4 Sotheby's, Melbourne #136/R est:50000-70000 (A.D 56000)

MACKENSEN, Fritz (1866-?) German

Works on paper

£470	$864	€700	Portrait of seated mother (33x25cm-13x10in) s. pen wash chk. 26-Mar-4 Bolland & Marotz, Bremen #346/R

MACKENZIE, Alexander (1923-2002) British

£500	$915	€730	Slate variations South Hill (43x61cm-17x24in) s.d.1969 oil pencil. 3-Jun-4 Lane, Penzance #36
£600	$1092	€876	Reds and blacks (13x18cm-5x7in) s.i.d.1962 verso. 15-Jun-4 David Lay, Penzance #251/R
£1200	$2004	€1752	Farm buildings (15x20cm-6x8in) s.i.d.1987 oil collage. 14-Oct-3 David Lay, Penzance #263/R est:700-900

Works on paper

£400	$732	€584	Untitled abstract (51x62cm-20x24in) s.d.66/67 sprayed stencil painting. 3-Jun-4 Lane, Penzance #35/R
£450	$752	€657	Spoure stone (50x60cm-20x24in) s.i.d.1968 pencil W/C. 8-Oct-3 Rupert Toovey, Partridge Green #6
£820	$1517	€1197	Rock face (15x15cm-6x6in) s.i.d.2001 verso mixed media. 10-Feb-4 David Lay, Penzance #365
£3000	$5610	€4380	Stonehenge (44x59cm-17x23in) mixed media board exec.c.1972 prov. 26-Feb-4 Lane, Penzance #80/R est:3000-4000

McKENZIE, Carl (1905-) American

Sculpture

£898	$1500	€1311	Statue of Liberty (56cm-22in) paint wood prov. 15-Nov-3 Slotin Folk Art, Buford #318/R est:500-800
£1737	$2900	€2536	Noah's ark (56x51x10cm-22x20x4in) paint wood prov. 15-Nov-3 Slotin Folk Art, Buford #315/R est:1000-2000
£2246	$3750	€3279	Adam and Eve in the garden with birds in the tree (74x43x20cm-29x17x8in) paint wood prov. 15-Nov-3 Slotin Folk Art, Buford #316/R est:1000-2000

MACKENZIE, Frederick (1787-1854) British

Works on paper

£3953	$7075	€5771	Westminster Abbey, Edward the Confessor's Chapel (54x74cm-21x29in) W/C prov. 15-May-4 Christie's, Sydney #233/R est:5000-7000 (A.D 10000)

MACKENZIE, Frederick (attrib) (1787-1854) British

Works on paper

£750 $1275 €1095 Christ Church from the south west (20x35cm-8x14in) W/C. 4-Nov-3 Dreweatt Neate, Newbury #46 est:400-600

MACKENZIE, Jim (1953-) Canadian

Works on paper

£314 $518 €458 Georgeson Island (53x81cm-21x32in) s. pastel. 3-Jul-3 Heffel, Vancouver #21/R (C.D 700)

£625 $1063 €913 Glenda at Oyster Bay (42x63cm-17x25in) s.d.1985 i.verso W/C. 6-Nov-3 Heffel, Vancouver #83/R est:1500-2000 (C.D 1400)

MACKENZIE, Kenneth (1884-1899) British

£800 $1416 €1168 Farmer with flock of sheep in a meadow (38x76cm-15x30in) s.d.85. 28-Apr-4 Halls, Shrewsbury #540/R

MACKENZIE, Marie Henrie (1878-1961) Dutch

£362 $666 €550 Kostverloren canal, Amsterdam (12x19cm-5x7in) s. s.i.verso cardboard. 22-Jun-4 Christie's, Amsterdam #265/R

£890 $1514 €1300 Prince canal, Amsterdam near Noordermarkt (18x24cm-7x9in) s. board. 5-Nov-3 Vendue Huis, Gravenhage #127/R

£952 $1733 €1400 Building site (46x54cm-18x21in) s. board. 3-Feb-4 Christie's, Amsterdam #215/R est:1500-2000

£952 $1733 €1400 Old Amsterdam (25x32cm-10x13in) s. cardboard. 3-Feb-4 Christie's, Amsterdam #335/R est:1200-1600

£1106 $1881 €1615 Amsterdam (63x73cm-25x29in) s. board. 25-Nov-3 Christie's, Melbourne #154/R (A.D 2600)

£7237 $13316 €11000 Winter in Oude Damrak, Amsterdam (65x101cm-26x40in) s. s.i.verso plywood exhib. 22-Jun-4 Christie's, Amsterdam #200/R est:3000-5000

Works on paper

£503 $926 €750 Round Luthers tower (16x12cm-6x5in) s. W/C prov. 29-Mar-4 Glerum, Amsterdam #144

£888 $1608 €1350 Boats in the ice in the winter (25x35cm-10x14in) s. pastel. 19-Apr-4 Glerum, Amsterdam #168/R

McKENZIE, Queenie (c.1930-1998) Australian

Works on paper

£2539 $4748 €3809 Girrgilabany, Place of Galahs (60x80cm-24x31in) bears name.verso earth pigments canvas prov. 26-Jul-4 Sotheby's, Melbourne #216/R est:6000-8000 (A.D 6500)

£3252 $5138 €4715 Turrwurrngan, fertility hill (61x76cm-24x30in) earth pigments binders canvas exec.c.1995 prov.lit. 28-Jul-3 Sotheby's, Paddington #289/R est:8000-12000 (A.D 8000)

£5859 $10957 €8789 Karyang, waterlillies (90x120cm-35x47in) s.i.verso earth pigments bush gum prov. 26-Jul-4 Sotheby's, Melbourne #123/R est:15000-20000 (A.D 15000)

£10938 $20453 €16407 Yhunhud (92x163cm-36x64in) earth pigments prov. 26-Jul-4 Sotheby's, Melbourne #124/R est:18000-25000 (A.D 28000)

£16260 $25691 €23577 White mountain and Duncan highway (70x110cm-28x43in) i.verso earth pigments binders canvas prov.exhib. 28-Jul-3 Sotheby's, Paddington #104/R est:15000-25000 (A.D 40000)

McKENZIE, Rhona (20th C) New Zealander

£3160 $5435 €4614 Fendalton (22x27cm-9x11in) s. board. 7-Dec-3 International Art Centre, Auckland #358/R est:500-1000 (NZ.D 8500)

McKENZIE, Robert Tait (1867-1938) American

Sculpture

£4878 $8732 €7122 Sprinter (28cm-11in) s.i. bronze prov.exhib. 31-May-4 Sotheby's, Toronto #118/R est:6000-8000 (C.D 12000)

£5856 $9955 €8550 Blighty (40cm-16in) s.i.d.1916 bronze prov.lit. 18-Nov-3 Sotheby's, Toronto #123/R est:10000-12000 (C.D 13000)

£6936 $12000 €10127 Athlete (43cm-17in) with sig. bronze. 11-Dec-3 Sotheby's, New York #164/R est:3000-5000

MACKENZIE, Roderick D (1865-1941) American

£500 $835 €730 Simla (24x60cm-9x24in) s.i.d.1897. 16-Oct-3 Lyon & Turnbull, Edinburgh #126

MACKENZIE, William G (?-1925) British

£1000 $1720 €1460 Pond at Belvoir Park (38x48cm-15x19in) s.d.1905. 3-Dec-3 John Ross, Belfast #67 est:1000-1200

MACKENZIE, William Murray (fl.1850-1908) British

£11500 $19550 €16790 Winnowing Corn - Ana Capri (101x144cm-40x57in) s.d.1883 exhib. 30-Oct-3 Christie's, London #119/R est:1200-18000

MACKEPRANG, A (1833-1911) Danish

£474 $758 €687 Oxen and cart by Italian farm (40x23cm-16x9in) mono. 17-Sep-3 Kunsthallen, Copenhagen #436/R (D.KR 5000)

MACKEPRANG, Adolf (1833-1911) Danish

£430 $774 €628 Landscape with deer (71x45cm-28x18in) mono. 24-Apr-4 Rasmussen, Havnen #2153/R (D.KR 4800)

£520 $899 €759 Hare on woodland path (40x29cm-16x11in) mono. 9-Dec-3 Rasmussen, Copenhagen #1421/R (D.KR 5500)

£599 $1018 €875 Pair of doves by nest (59x51cm-23x20in) mono.d.1872. 10-Nov-3 Rasmussen, Vejle #128/R (D.KR 6500)

£724 $1296 €1057 Landscape with hare (40x29cm-16x11in) mono. 10-May-4 Rasmussen, Vejle #281/R (D.KR 8000)

£842 $1533 €1229 Wooded landscape with deer in glade (80x60cm-31x24in) s. 7-Feb-4 Rasmussen, Havnen #2041/R (D.KR 9200)

£1040 $1799 €1518 Roe-deer running in forest (53x42cm-21x17in) s.d.1874. 9-Dec-3 Rasmussen, Copenhagen #1422/R (D.KR 11000)

£1198 $2037 €1749 Summer landscape with calf and goat playing, Southern Sweden (59x40cm-23x16in) mono. exhib. 10-Nov-3 Rasmussen, Vejle #127/R est:12000-15000 (D.KR 13000)

£1382 $2350 €2018 Wooded landscape with two deer and kid (79x61cm-31x24in) mono.d.1910. 10-Nov-3 Rasmussen, Vejle #125/R est:15000 (D.KR 15000)

£1418 $2538 €2070 Woodland with two gundogs running (56x61cm-22x24in) s. 12-Jan-4 Rasmussen, Vejle #177/R est:15000-20000 (D.KR 15000)

£1422 $2275 €2076 Cattle in meadow, possibly Bjornemosegaard near Faaborg (89x152cm-35x60in) mono.d.1900. 22-Sep-3 Rasmussen, Vejle #253/R est:15000-20000 (D.KR 15000)

£1443 $2669 €2107 Deer in woodland glade (65x52cm-26x20in) s. 15-Mar-4 Rasmussen, Vejle #487/R est:10000-12000 (D.KR 16000)

£1629 $2916 €2378 Woodland with stag running (80x60cm-31x24in) s. 10-May-4 Rasmussen, Vejle #280/R est:18000 (D.KR 18000)

£1890 $3270 €2759 Roe-deer hunted by dog (53x93cm-21x37in) mono. 9-Dec-3 Rasmussen, Copenhagen #1424/R est:20000 (D.KR 20000)

£2238 $4096 €3267 Wooded landscape with boy on white horse (80x61cm-31x24in) mono. prov. 9-Jun-4 Rasmussen, Copenhagen #1695/R est:15000 (D.KR 25000)

£3760 $6881 €5490 Landscape with deer, young calf watching butterfly (74x68cm-29x27in) s. prov. 9-Jun-4 Rasmussen, Copenhagen #1697/R est:20000-25000 (D.KR 42000)

£6267 $11468 €9150 Fox hunting a mallard (90x115cm-35x45in) mono. prov. 9-Jun-4 Rasmussen, Copenhagen #1715/R est:30000 (D.KR 70000)

MACKESY, Charlie (1956-) British

Works on paper

£550 $985 €803 Dog studies. s.d. chl pair. 11-Jan-4 Lots Road Auctions, London #370

MACKETANZ, Ferdinand (1902-1970) Polish

Works on paper

£1133 $2063 €1700 Still life with flowers (72x52cm-28x20in) s. W/C. 3-Jul-4 Geble, Radolfzell #447/R est:500

McKEWAN, David Hall (c.1816-1875) British

Works on paper

£260 $447 €380 River landscape with cattle drover (25x36cm-10x14in) s. W/C. 2-Dec-3 Gorringes, Lewes #2537

£600 $1020 €876 Balie Lake, North Wales (24x34cm-9x13in) s. W/C. 25-Nov-3 Bonhams, Knightsbridge #165/R

£1400 $2590 €2044 Checking the salmon trap (41x53cm-16x21in) W/C. 9-Mar-4 Bonhams, New Bond Street #48/R est:1000-1500

MACKEY, Haydn Reynolds (1883-?) British

£480 $850 €701 Portrait of Harry Chapman (40x30cm-16x12in) s.d.1914. 27-Apr-4 Bonhams, Knowle #83

MACKEY, Kim (20th C) American

£750 $1200 €1095 Saddle pals (23x30cm-9x12in) board. 19-Sep-3 Altermann Galleries, Santa Fe #10

£750 $1200 €1095 Sky lined (23x30cm-9x12in) board. 19-Sep-3 Altermann Galleries, Santa Fe #11

£750 $1200 €1095 Summer evening (23x30cm-9x12in) board. 19-Sep-3 Altermann Galleries, Santa Fe #12

£813 $1300 €1187 Fishing (20x30cm-8x12in) board. 19-Sep-3 Altermann Galleries, Santa Fe #3

£938 $1500 €1369 Night on Pinon Ridge (36x28cm-14x11in) board. 19-Sep-3 Altermann Galleries, Santa Fe #8

£1188 $1900 €1734 Patio light (36x46cm-14x18in) 19-Sep-3 Altermann Galleries, Santa Fe #9

£1188 $1900 €1734 Hardscrabble (36x46cm-14x18in) board. 19-Sep-3 Altermann Galleries, Santa Fe #4

£1500 $2400 €2190 Hobbles (41x51cm-16x20in) 19-Sep-3 Altermann Galleries, Santa Fe #5

£1500 $2400 €2190 New Mexico travelers (41x51cm-16x20in) 19-Sep-3 Altermann Galleries, Santa Fe #7

£1688 $2700 €2464 Winter hunters (61x46cm-24x18in) 19-Sep-3 Altermann Galleries, Santa Fe #13

£3063 $4900 €4472 Loco weed (61x91cm-24x36in) 19-Sep-3 Altermann Galleries, Santa Fe #6

£3395 $5500 €4923 Catchin a tadpole (76x102cm-30x40in) 23-May-3 Altermann Galleries, Santa Fe #63

£4190 $7500 €6117 Along the old trails (76x102cm-30x40in) 15-May-4 Altermann Galleries, Santa Fe #19/R

McKIBBEN, Robert (20th C) American

Works on paper

£273 $500 €410 Barbado, rain slick road (76x104cm-30x41in) pastel. 10-Jul-4 Hindman, Chicago #338/R

£437 $800 €656 Landscape with train (56x76cm-22x30in) pastel. 10-Jul-4 Hindman, Chicago #339/R

MACKIE, Charles H (1862-1920) British

£1100 $1749 €1595 At Milngavie (28x39cm-11x15in) s.i. panel. 9-Sep-3 David Duggleby, Scarborough #341/R est:500-700

£1500 $2505 €2190 Crossing the brook (40x61cm-16x24in) s.d.1886. 7-Oct-3 Bonhams, Knightsbridge #280/R est:1500-2000

£2100 $3906 €3066 Riber Tiber and the Castel Sant Angelo, Rome (80x102cm-31x40in) s. 6-Mar-4 Shapes, Edinburgh #427/R est:2000-3000

MACKIE, John (1953-) British

£300 $510 €438 St Tropez sails (41x51cm-16x20in) s.d.95 prov.exhib. 19-Nov-3 Tennants, Leyburn #1264

£580 $1056 €847 Red roofs, Canel village (69x84cm-27x33in) s.d.88. 15-Jun-4 Bonhams, Leeds #40/R

£1400	$2506	€2044	Port Grimaud, near St. Tropez (69x90cm-27x35in) s.d.89. 16-Mar-4 Bonhams, Leeds #577/R est:1500-2000

MACKIE, Kathleen Isabella (attrib) (1899-1996) Irish?

£270	$489	€394	Donegal coast (19x29cm-7x11in) i.verso. 30-Mar-4 David Duggleby, Scarborough #205/R

MACKIE, Peter R M (1867-1959) British

£1300	$2119	€1898	Scottish coastal landscape (36x51cm-14x20in) s.d.1915 board. 24-Sep-3 Dreweatt Neate, Newbury #179/R est:600-800

MACKIEWICZ, Konstanty (1894-1985) Polish

£1724	$2690	€2517	Resting in the shade (72x58cm-28x23in) s. painted c.1930. 30-Mar-3 Agra, Warsaw #30/R est:10000 (P.Z 11000)

McKIM, Charles C (1872-1939) American

£1933	$3460	€2822	West Portland hills (30x41cm-12x16in) s. canvasboard. 16-Mar-4 Matthew's, Oregon #104/R est:2500-3500
£4469	$8000	€6525	Patton Creek (51x66cm-20x26in) s. i.verso. 16-Mar-4 Matthew's, Oregon #102/R est:10000-12000
£5307	$9500	€7748	Mountain at sunset (41x56cm-16x22in) s. 16-Mar-4 Matthew's, Oregon #100/R est:7000-9000

McKINLEY, Hazel (20th C) American?

£1630	$3000	€2380	Costume party (64x76cm-25x30in) s. 27-Mar-4 New Orleans Auction, New Orleans #814/R est:4000-7000
Works on paper			
£471	$800	€688	Abstract dream of Wagnerian Iperas. s.i.d.1954 W/C. 22-Nov-3 New Orleans Auction, New Orleans #1241

MACKINNON, Archibald (19th C) British

£15000	$25500	€21900	Tarporley hunt steeplechases (76x180cm-30x71in) mono.d.1896. 19-Nov-3 Sotheby's, Olympia #48/R est:15000-25000

MACKINNON, Charles (20th C) British

£1600	$2608	€2320	Portrait of Lieutenant Colonel Sir William Rowley, 6th BT of Hill House (74x62cm-29x24in) with another portrait after George Sanders two. 21-Jul-3 Sotheby's, London #474 est:400-600

MACKINNON, Finlay (fl.1891-1930) British

Works on paper			
£260	$484	€380	Cuillins, Skye (57x89cm-22x35in) s. pencil W/C. 4-Mar-4 Christie's, Kensington #131
£500	$835	€730	View of Cuillin Mountain and river (36x51cm-14x20in) s. W/C. 12-Nov-3 Halls, Shrewsbury #270/R

MACKINNON, Sine (1901-1997) British

£667	$1193	€1000	Early morning in Cucuron. s. 15-May-4 other European Auctioneer #41
£667	$1193	€1000	Cassis harbour. s.d.32 masonite. 15-May-4 other European Auctioneer #43
£2550	$4514	€3800	Children with a donkey outside farm buildings in a valley (65x81cm-26x32in) s. 27-Apr-4 Whyte's, Dublin #69/R est:3000-4000
Works on paper			
£1000	$1790	€1500	Honfleur. s. W/C. 15-May-4 other European Auctioneer #37

McKINSTRY, Cherith (1928-) British

£450	$824	€657	Landscape 2 (39x49cm-15x19in) s. exhib. 7-Jul-4 Cheffins, Cambridge #112

MACKINSTRY, Hieronymus (1926-) German

Works on paper			
£276	$475	€403	San Rafael del Rio (48x61cm-19x24in) s.i.d.87 pastel. 6-Dec-3 Skinner, Boston #585

MACKINTOSH, Colin J (19/20th C) British

£407	$680	€594	Figure on the riverbank (50x76cm-20x30in) s.d.98 prov. 17-Nov-3 Waddingtons, Toronto #95/R (C.D 900)

MACKLEM, Sutherland (19/20th C) Canadian

£880	$1610	€1285	View of the Horseshoe Falls, Niagara Falls (41x55cm-16x22in) s.d.1906. 1-Jun-4 Joyner Waddington, Toronto #391/R est:800-1200 (C.D 2200)

MACKLEY, Evan (1940-) Australian

£293	$533	€428	May my day. board. 5-Feb-4 Joel, Victoria #118 (A.D 700)

MACKLIN, Thomas Eyre (1867-1943) British

£300	$531	€438	Heart of England (18x25cm-7x10in) s.d.92 board. 28-Apr-4 Halls, Shrewsbury #546
£650	$1203	€949	Angling on a rocky riverbank (51x76cm-20x30in) s. indis d. 15-Jan-4 Christie's, Kensington #873/R
£1700	$3162	€2482	Figures in a gondola, Santa Maria della Salute beyond (13x32cm-5x13in) board prov. 4-Mar-4 Christie's, Kensington #565/R est:700-1000

McKNIGHT, Robert Johnson (1905-1989) American

Sculpture			
£9783	$18000	€14283	Bust of Katharine Hepburn (36cm-14in) with sig.i.d.41 white marble. 10-Jun-4 Sotheby's, New York #116/R est:4000-6000
£12228	$22500	€17853	Two nudes of Katharine Hepburn (10cm-4in) brown pat. bronze two. 10-Jun-4 Sotheby's, New York #233/R est:2000-4000
£17663	$32500	€25788	Bust of Katharine Hepburn (36cm-14in) i. brown pat. bronze executed 1935. 10-Jun-4 Sotheby's, New York #127/R est:5000-7000

MACKRILL, Martyn (1961-) British

£22000	$39380	€32120	Valkyrie III leading Britannia off Hunter's Quay during the Clyde Regatta 1895 (102x152cm-40x60in) s. lit. 26-May-4 Christie's, Kensington #517/R est:10000-15000
Works on paper			
£2200	$3740	€3212	Favell (53x73cm-21x29in) s. W/C htd white. 19-Nov-3 Christie's, Kensington #379/R

McLANE, Murtle Jean (1878-1964) American

£2172	$3410	€3171	Woman in formal dress (102x71cm-40x28in) s. painted c.1900. 1-Sep-3 William A Smith, Plainfield #17/R
£9581	$16000	€13988	On the beach, Devonshire (101x101cm-40x40in) s.verso prov.exhib.lit. 7-Oct-3 Sotheby's, New York #221 est:5000-10000
£10056	$18000	€14682	Portrait of a girl with hat (102x74cm-40x29in) s.d.1914 prov. 26-May-4 Doyle, New York #112/R est:8000-12000
£11377	$19000	€16610	Country dog show (127x101cm-50x40in) s.d.1934 s.d.1933 verso prov.exhib.lit. 7-Oct-3 Sotheby's, New York #222 est:5000-10000

MACLARDIE, Peter (20th C) American

£434	$750	€634	Coastal view (30x41cm-12x16in) s.d.1910. 13-Dec-3 Sloans & Kenyon, Bethesda #547/R
£503	$900	€734	Coastal view (30x41cm-12x16in) s.d.1910. 7-May-4 Sloans & Kenyon, Bethesda #1202/R

MACLAREN, Helen (20th C) British

£300	$558	€438	Still life (60x50cm-24x20in) s. 7-Mar-4 Lots Road Auctions, London #367

McLAREN, Peter (20th C) British

£2850	$5301	€4161	Man with cycle (121x121cm-48x48in) board painted c.1989 prov. 4-Mar-4 Christie's, Kensington #264/R est:3000-5000
Works on paper			
£1000	$1860	€1460	Figure in a car - yellow sky (66x89cm-26x35in) s.d.88 brush ink W/C bodycol. 4-Mar-4 Christie's, Kensington #267/R est:1000-1500
£1300	$2418	€1898	Cyclist with upstretched arms (77x58cm-30x23in) s.d.88 brush ink W/C bodycol. 4-Mar-4 Christie's, Kensington #266/R est:1000-1500
£1550	$2883	€2263	Leith cyclist (60x80cm-24x31in) s.d.88 pencil brush ink W/C bodycol prov. 4-Mar-4 Christie's, Kensington #265/R est:1000-1500

McLARNON, Samuel (?) British?

£250	$410	€365	Horn Head, Donegal (40x58cm-16x23in) s. board. 4-Jun-3 John Ross, Belfast #66
£280	$465	€409	Near Ballyliffen, Donegal (30x40cm-12x16in) s. 1-Oct-3 John Ross, Belfast #7
£300	$516	€438	Fishing boats, County Antrim coast (40x50cm-16x20in) s. 3-Dec-3 John Ross, Belfast #28
£300	$516	€438	Winter trees, Castlegreen, Cushendun (40x76cm-16x30in) s. 3-Dec-3 John Ross, Belfast #39
£300	$558	€438	Mamorte gap, Donegal (40x76cm-16x30in) s. 3-Mar-4 John Ross, Belfast #41
£320	$525	€467	Wet day, Glendum (40x76cm-16x30in) s. 4-Jun-3 John Ross, Belfast #248
£350	$581	€511	Cushendun (40x76cm-16x30in) s. 1-Oct-3 John Ross, Belfast #119a
£350	$651	€511	Black Arch, Larne (40x76cm-16x30in) s. 3-Mar-4 John Ross, Belfast #92
£400	$656	€584	Inishowen, Donegal (40x76cm-16x30in) s. 4-Jun-3 John Ross, Belfast #78
£420	$689	€613	River reflections (40x76cm-16x30in) s. 4-Jun-3 John Ross, Belfast #183

MACLAUGHLIN, Donald Shaw (1876-1938) American

£568	$1000	€829	Venice (20x25cm-8x10in) s.d.1910 board. 23-May-4 Treadway Gallery, Cincinnati #592/R

McLAUGHLIN, John (1898-1976) American

£3955	$7000	€5774	Untitled (52x42cm-20x17in) s. masonite. 2-May-4 Bonhams & Butterfields, Los Angeles #3034/R est:3000-5000
£10588	$18000	€15458	V-1958 (122x81cm-48x32in) s. i.d.1958 verso prov. 9-Nov-3 Wright, Chicago #377 est:20000-25000

MACLAURIN, Robert (1961-) British

£280	$515	€409	Cliff and green tent (41x41cm-16x16in) s.verso board. 10-Jun-4 Lyon & Turnbull, Edinburgh #27
£380	$718	€555	Memory of a bus journey (15x20cm-6x8in) d.1994 oil on ceramic tile. 19-Feb-4 Lyon & Turnbull, Edinburgh #62
£400	$756	€584	When we were in Armenia (30x30cm-12x12in) s.i.d.1988 verso. 19-Feb-4 Lyon & Turnbull, Edinburgh #47
£450	$779	€657	Yayla-tea-picking (40x50cm-16x20in) d.1991 panel. 11-Dec-3 Lyon & Turnbull, Edinburgh #23/R
Works on paper			
£360	$680	€526	Rest at the bottle trees (19x29cm-7x11in) s.1995 W/C. 19-Feb-4 Lyon & Turnbull, Edinburgh #46

MACLE, Andre (?) French?
Works on paper
£2000 $3660 €3000 Mimosa dans un vase (99x71cm-39x28in) s. W/C. 6-Jun-4 Anaf, Lyon #422/R est:3000-4000

McLEA, Duncan Fraser (1841-1916) British
£300 $561 €438 River in a highland scene (46x36cm-18x14in) s.d.1879. 27-Feb-4 Thomson, Roddick & Medcalf, Carlisle #278
£460 $791 €672 Shipping off the coast (33x51cm-13x20in) s. 2-Dec-3 Gorringes, Lewes #2271
£620 $1141 €905 Highland loch scenes at morning and evening (47x36cm-19x14in) s. pair. 23-Mar-4 Anderson & Garland, Newcastle #334

McLEA, John Watson (19th C) British
£500 $945 €730 View of Edinburgh from the Firth of Forth (40x83cm-16x33in) indis sig.verso panel. 19-Feb-4 Lyon & Turnbull, Edinburgh #115/R
£800 $1472 €1168 Figures by the lochside (31x41cm-12x16in) s. board. 10-Jun-4 Lyon & Turnbull, Edinburgh #9

McLEAN, Bruce (1942-) British
£2054 $3800 €2999 Ladder (168x137cm-66x54in) acrylic prov. 13-Jul-4 Christie's, Rockefeller NY #67/R est:3000-5000

McLEAN, Howard (1879-?) American
£1844 $3300 €2692 Ladies on street at night (30x41cm-12x16in) s. board. 20-Mar-4 Sloans & Kenyon, Bethesda #1195/R est:800-1200

McLEAN, Jack Lee (1924-) Canadian
£446 $759 €651 Chilcotin canyon (46x61cm-18x24in) s. board prov. 6-Nov-3 Heffel, Vancouver #84/R (C.D 1000)
£600 $1098 €876 Shoshone (60x50cm-24x20in) s.i.d.1980 board. 1-Jun-4 Hodgins, Calgary #359/R (C.D 1500)
£760 $1391 €1110 Rider and pack horse above the Fraser River (60x90cm-24x35in) s. board. 1-Jun-4 Hodgins, Calgary #174/R (C.D 1900)

McLEAN, John (1939-) British
£1500 $2745 €2190 Peasiehill (345x223cm-136x88in) acrylic painted 1971. 2-Jun-4 Sotheby's, London #132/R est:5000-7000

McLEAN, Pantijiti Mary (c.1938-) Australian
£305 $482 €442 All the people are looking for food (57x76cm-22x30in) i.verso acrylic. 22-Jul-3 Lawson Menzies, Sydney #70/R (A.D 750)
Works on paper
£313 $584 €468 Plenty of crows eating food (75x56cm-30x22in) synthetic polymer paper on board exec. 1996 prov. 21-Jul-4 Shapiro, Sydney #130a/R (A.D 800)

McLEAN, Thomas Wesley (1881-1951) Canadian
£363 $668 €530 The end of a lake (43x30cm-17x12in) s. s.i.verso board exhib. 9-Jun-4 Walker's, Ottawa #90/R (C.D 900)

McLEAN, Wilson (1937-) American
£249 $415 €364 Mineral exploration (66x51cm-26x20in) s. i.verso prov. 17-Nov-3 Waddingtons, Toronto #4/R (C.D 550)
£294 $491 €429 Oil and gas exploration (77x62cm-30x24in) i.verso prov. 17-Nov-3 Waddingtons, Toronto #5/R (C.D 650)

MACLEAY, Kenneth (1802-1878) British
Miniatures
£1000 $1840 €1460 Lady Isabella and Donald Campbell, as children (7cm-3in) pair. 24-Jun-4 Bonhams, New Bond Street #142/R est:1000-1500

MACLEAY, McNeil (19th C) British
£5000 $8500 €7300 View on the Tay from Perth. View on the Tay at North Inch (33x45cm-13x18in) one s.d.1842 pair prov.exhib. 30-Oct-3 Christie's, London #18/R est:6000-8000
Works on paper
£1900 $3496 €2774 Morning effect near Glen Coe (28x46cm-11x18in) s.d.1869 i.verso. 24-Mar-4 Hamptons Fine Art, Godalming #260/R
£2800 $4396 €4060 Fishing near the abbey. Fishing by the falls (30x47cm-12x19in) one s.d.1887 one s. W/C. 27-Aug-3 Sotheby's, London #928/R est:1500-2000

MACLEAY, McNeil (attrib) (19th C) British
£720 $1224 €1051 Scottish landscape with boats on a loch and figures (33x48cm-13x19in) panel. 27-Nov-3 Clevedon Sale Rooms #125

McLEAY, Neil (fl.1829-1848) British
Works on paper
£2000 $3240 €2920 Lakeland landscape (20x30cm-8x12in) s. gouache. 30-Jul-3 Hamptons Fine Art, Godalming #76/R est:2000-3000

McLEAY, Neil (attrib) (fl.1829-1848) British
£1271 $2161 €1856 William Wallace Memorial (66x91cm-26x36in) 24-Nov-3 Sotheby's, Melbourne #287/R est:1500-2500 (A.D 3000)

McLELLAN, Charles A (1887-1941) American
£3892 $6500 €5682 Young boy helps out by drying dishes, but isn't thrilled about it (48x38cm-19x15in) s.d.1913. 15-Nov-3 Illustration House, New York #102/R est:2500-4000

McLELLAN, Ralph (1884-1952) American
Works on paper
£189 $350 €276 The home of a wharf rat (20x28cm-8x11in) s. W/C. 16-Jan-4 Aspire, Cleveland #141/R

MACLENNAN, Stewart (20th C) New Zealander
Works on paper
£694 $1104 €1013 Wellington Wharf (33x40cm-13x16in) s. W/C. 1-May-3 Dunbar Sloane, Wellington #94/R est:2000-3000 (NZ.D 2000)

MACLEOD, Euan (1956-) New Zealander
£826 $1529 €1206 Two figures and reflections (63x77cm-25x30in) d.15.8.89 oil on paper prov. 15-Mar-4 Sotheby's, Melbourne #164 est:500-800 (A.D 2000)
£1148 $1813 €1676 Jack (56x61cm-22x24in) s.i.d.4-6/01 verso prov. 2-Sep-3 Deutscher-Menzies, Melbourne #188/R est:2500-3500 (A.D 2800)
£1322 $2446 €1930 Figure walking, Neilsen Park (64x80cm-25x31in) d.30.6.90 s.i.d.verso oil paper on canvas prov. 15-Mar-4 Sotheby's, Melbourne #230 est:500-800 (A.D 3200)
£1829 $2872 €2652 Figure in mist (56x78cm-22x31in) s.i.d.95-96 verso prov. 27-Aug-3 Christie's, Sydney #524/R est:6000-8000 (A.D 4500)
£2066 $3822 €3016 Canal study 2 torso (56x77cm-22x30in) d.10.91 s,i.d.verso oil paper on canvas prov. 15-Mar-4 Sotheby's, Melbourne #231/R est:500-800 (A.D 5000)
£3074 $4857 €4488 Medium hole (83x122cm-33x48in) s.i.d.0-10/92 verso prov. 2-Sep-3 Deutscher-Menzies, Melbourne #132/R est:3500-5500 (A.D 7500)
£3074 $4857 €4488 Frame (120x84cm-47x33in) s.i.d.4-6/01 verso prov.exhib. 2-Sep-3 Deutscher-Menzies, Melbourne #133/R est:4000-6000 (A.D 7500)
£3719 $6880 €5430 Boat on green (138x183cm-54x72in) s.d.6.8.89 i.verso prov. 15-Mar-4 Sotheby's, Melbourne #92/R est:2500-3500 (A.D 9000)
£8197 $12951 €11968 Bridge and reflections (137x182cm-54x72in) s.i.d.10/1/89 verso prov. 2-Sep-3 Deutscher-Menzies, Melbourne #4/R est:8000-12000 (A.D 20000)
Works on paper
£309 $485 €451 Maternal drawings (18x24cm-7x9in) pastels. 27-Aug-3 Dunbar Sloane, Wellington #508 (NZ.D 850)

MACLEOD, Pegi Nichol (1904-1949) Canadian
£424 $729 €619 Portrait of Kay Echlin (30x27cm-12x11in) panel painted c.2931. 2-Dec-3 Joyner Waddington, Toronto #361/R (C.D 950)
£3140 $5684 €4584 Untitled - basket weaver (46x43cm-18x17in) board. 18-Apr-4 Levis, Calgary #71/R est:8000-10000 (C.D 7600)
£3604 $6126 €5262 Indian boy (30x24cm-12x9in) board prov.exhib. 18-Nov-3 Sotheby's, Toronto #5/R est:4000-6000 (C.D 8000)
Works on paper
£909 $1482 €1327 Forest (35x42cm-14x17in) s. W/C prov. 23-Sep-3 Ritchie, Toronto #114/R est:2000-3000 (C.D 2000)

McLEOD, Robert (1948-) New Zealander
£2545 $3996 €3690 Into two (182x158cm-72x62in) s.i.d.30 July 1978 verso acrylic. 27-Aug-3 Dunbar Sloane, Wellington #41/R est:8000-12000 (NZ.D 7000)
Works on paper
£294 $526 €429 Glaik I, 1987 (100x134cm-39x53in) mixed media. 12-May-4 Dunbar Sloane, Wellington #213 (NZ.D 850)
£346 $619 €505 Copris II (153x153cm-60x60in) s.i.d.14/10/85 verso mixed media. 12-May-4 Dunbar Sloane, Wellington #212 est:1500-3000 (NZ.D 1000)

McLEOD, Simon (20th C) Irish
£282 $505 €420 Dublin Bay, evening (60x65cm-24x26in) s. i.verso. 31-May-4 Hamilton Osborne King, Dublin #5/R

MACLES, Jean Denis (1912-) French
Works on paper
£800 $1472 €1200 Les quatre chevaliers du monde de la lune (29x43cm-11x17in) s.i. W/C gouache. 11-Jun-4 Pierre Berge, Paris #114/R

MACLET (1881-1962) French
£1259 $2165 €1800 La place du Tertre (46x55cm-18x22in) s. 2-Dec-3 Claude Aguttes, Neuilly #52 est:3000-4000

MACLET, Elisee (1881-1962) French
£676 $1209 €1000 Le grand arbre face a la mer (33x41cm-13x16in) s. panel. 5-May-4 Coutau Begarie, Paris #48d
£699 $1202 €1000 Village (24x19cm-9x7in) s. 3-Dec-3 Tajan, Paris #391
£738 $1374 €1100 Residence a Ceylan (33x41cm-13x16in) s. painted 1919. 3-Mar-4 Tajan, Paris #86/R
£845 $1462 €1200 Petit port mediterraneen (35x28cm-14x11in) s. panel. 12-Dec-3 Piasa, Paris #148
£944 $1605 €1350 L'Eglise Saint Etienne du Mont (73x54cm-29x21in) s.d.19. 27-Nov-3 Millon & Associes, Paris #238/R
£1049 $1783 €1500 Rue de Paris (41x28cm-16x11in) s. 28-Nov-3 Drouot Estimations, Paris #149/R est:1200-1500
£1127 $1949 €1600 Entree du port (27x35cm-11x14in) s. panel. 9-Dec-3 Artcurial Briest, Paris #266 est:1500-2000
£1141 $2123 €1700 Fort Sainte-Marguerite a la Pointe Fourmi (32x40cm-13x16in) s. prov. 3-Mar-4 Tajan, Paris #88/R est:800-1000
£1154 $1962 €1650 Paris, Montmartre, le Sacre Coeur (63x48cm-25x19in) s. isorel panel. 27-Nov-3 Millon & Associes, Paris #200/R est:4000-5000
£1154 $2100 €1685 Floral still life (69x53cm-27x21in) s. panel. 19-Jun-4 Charlton Hall, Columbia #104/R est:2000-2500
£1207 $2003 €1750 Canaux (50x69cm-20x27in) s. 1-Oct-3 Millon & Associes, Paris #115/R
£1208 $2247 €1800 Menton, le jardin public (32x40cm-13x16in) s. prov. 3-Mar-4 Tajan, Paris #87/R est:800-1000
£1216 $2177 €1800 Effet de neige a Montmartre (27x34cm-11x13in) s. lit. 4-May-4 Calmels Cohen, Paris #152/R est:1500-2000
£1259 $2102 €1800 Campement gitan (32x22cm-13x9in) s. panel. 29-Jun-3 Eric Pillon, Calais #201/R

£1267	$2331	€1900	Suisse, une ville (52x73cm-20x29in) s. 14-Jun-4 Tajan, Paris #54/R est:2500-3000
£1316	$2421	€2000	Moulin de la Galette (3x845cm-1x333in) s. panel. 28-Jun-4 Joron-Derem, Paris #247/R est:2000-2500
£1343	$2497	€2000	Saint Jean Cap-Ferrat (32x40cm-13x16in) s. prov. 3-Mar-4 Tajan, Paris #89/R est:600-800
£1391	$2545	€2100	Une place a Paris (37x46cm-15x18in) s. board. 7-Apr-4 Piasa, Paris #93/R est:2200-2500
£1399	$2378	€2000	Fleurs dans un vase jaune (27x21cm-11x8in) s. 21-Nov-3 Lombrail & Teucquam, Paris #130/R est:1800-2000
£1399	$2378	€2000	Place de l'eglise (72x96cm-28x38in) cardboard. 27-Nov-3 Millon & Associes, Paris #201/R est:3000-4000
£1500	$2400	€2190	Windmill on hillside with house (48x64cm-19x25in) s. 20-Sep-3 Sloans & Kenyon, Bethesda #1170/R est:2000-4000
£1510	$2703	€2250	Hotel de Rohan, Paris (61x45cm-24x18in) s. cardboard. 25-May-4 Chambelland & Giafferi, Paris #43/R est:3000-4000
£1667	$2983	€2500	Place de village (41x33cm-16x13in) s. 16-May-4 Lombrail & Teucquam, Paris #161/R
£1678	$3121	€2500	Bouquet de fleurs au vase bleu (34x27cm-13x11in) s. prov. 3-Mar-4 Tajan, Paris #97/R est:400-600
£1700	$3094	€2550	Paris, Montmartre (27x35cm-11x14in) s. 4-Jul-4 Eric Pillon, Calais #186/R
£1761	$3046	€2500	Port mediterraneen (27x35cm-11x14in) s. panel. 12-Dec-3 Piasa, Paris #147/R est:1500-2000
£1854	$3393	€2800	Rue de Banlieue (49x60cm-19x24in) s. isorel. 7-Apr-4 Piasa, Paris #97/R est:2500-3000
£1879	$3364	€2800	Petit port mediterraneen (35x28cm-14x11in) s. panel. 30-May-4 Eric Pillon, Calais #83/R
£1892	$3576	€2800	La maison de Mimi Pinson (41x33cm-16x13in) s. 21-Feb-4 Cornette de St.Cyr, Paris #214/R est:3000-4000
£1931	$3206	€2800	Ruelle a Montmartre (62x46cm-24x18in) s. panel. 1-Oct-3 Millon & Associes, Paris #116/R
£1958	$3368	€2800	Vue d'Antibes (54x73cm-21x29in) s. 3-Dec-3 Tajan, Paris #392 est:3000-4000
£1987	$3636	€3000	Rue a Montmartre (37x45cm-15x18in) s. board. 7-Apr-4 Piasa, Paris #92/R est:2200-2400
£2013	$3604	€3000	Jardin fleuri a Menton (33x41cm-13x16in) s. 30-May-4 Eric Pillon, Calais #85/R
£2013	$3745	€3000	Ferte Allais (32x46cm-13x18in) s. prov. 3-Mar-4 Tajan, Paris #90/R est:600-800
£2013	$3745	€3000	Montmartre, La maison de Berlioz (35x27cm-14x11in) s. prov. 3-Mar-4 Tajan, Paris #95/R est:500-600
£2027	$3628	€3000	Le marche (47x57cm-19x22in) s. 5-May-4 Coutau Begarie, Paris #48c est:3000-4000
£2039	$3467	€2977	Le printemps (45x54cm-18x21in) s. 5-Nov-3 AB Stockholms Auktionsverk #1102/R est:20000-30000 (S.KR 27000)
£2148	$3995	€3200	Montmartre, Le Moulin de la Galette (35x27cm-14x11in) s. prov. 3-Mar-4 Tajan, Paris #93/R est:600-800
£2168	$3620	€3100	Sainte-Maxime (25x32cm-10x13in) s. panel. 29-Jun-3 Eric Pillon, Calais #205/R
£2248	$4024	€3350	Theatre de l'Atelier (37x46cm-15x18in) s. panel. 30-May-4 Eric Pillon, Calais #79/R
£2282	$4244	€3400	Pavillon de chasse d'Henri IV, vieux Montmartre (35x27cm-14x11in) s. 7-Mar-4 Lesieur & Le Bars, Le Havre #86
£2300	$3841	€3358	Ile St Louis (27x35cm-11x14in) s.i. prov. 22-Oct-3 Sotheby's, Olympia #116/R est:2000-3000
£2315	$4145	€3450	Vase de fleurs (55x46cm-22x18in) s. 30-May-4 Eric Pillon, Calais #77/R
£2340	$3909	€3300	Le Pre-Saint-Gervais (50x65cm-20x26in) s. 19-Jun-3 Millon & Associes, Paris #244/R est:3000-4000
£2349	$4205	€3500	Montmartre (35x27cm-14x11in) s. painted c.1940. 30-May-4 Eric Pillon, Calais #75/R
£2374	$4250	€3466	Le moulin de la Gallette. s.i. 13-May-4 Dallas Auction Gallery, Dallas #126/R est:2000-4000
£2383	$4265	€3550	Theatre de l'Atelier (27x35cm-11x14in) s. 30-May-4 Eric Pillon, Calais #78/R
£2400	$4416	€3504	Vue de St Paul de Vence (50x65cm-20x26in) s. 24-Mar-4 Sotheby's, Olympia #92/R est:2500-3500
£2416	$4325	€3600	Vase de fleurs (35x27cm-14x11in) s. 30-May-4 Eric Pillon, Calais #76/R
£2448	$4210	€3500	Place du theatre sous la neige (46x55cm-18x22in) s. 3-Dec-3 Tajan, Paris #390 est:3500-4500
£2482	$4220	€3624	Untitled (46x32cm-18x13in) s. masonite. 23-Nov-3 Subastas Odalys, Caracas #76 est:4000
£2551	$4744	€3800	Moulin Rouge (46x55cm-18x22in) s. 3-Mar-4 Tajan, Paris #84 est:4000-6000
£2551	$4744	€3800	Montmartre, la Rue Norvins sous le neige (35x27cm-14x11in) s. prov. 3-Mar-4 Tajan, Paris #92/R est:600-800
£2584	$4625	€3850	Petite rue bordee d'arbres (48x60cm-19x24in) s. panel. 30-May-4 Eric Pillon, Calais #81/R
£2587	$4321	€3700	Lapin Agile (27x35cm-11x14in) s. 29-Jun-3 Eric Pillon, Calais #197/R
£2587	$4321	€3700	Maison de Mimi Pinson (27x35cm-11x14in) s. 29-Jun-3 Eric Pillon, Calais #196/R
£2654	$4750	€3875	Winter snow scene (43x53cm-17x21in) s.i. 13-May-4 Dallas Auction Gallery, Dallas #159/R est:3000-6000
£2727	$4636	€3900	Arlesienne (46x38cm-18x15in) s.i.d.1925 lit. 21-Nov-3 Lombrail & Teucquam, Paris #129/R est:3000-3400
£2759	$4579	€4000	Rue a Montmartre (18x26cm-7x10in) s. panel. 1-Oct-3 Millon & Associes, Paris #113/R
£2793	$5000	€4078	Le canal (48x58cm-19x23in) s.i. board. 13-May-4 Dallas Auction Gallery, Dallas #250/R est:3500-6500
£2819	$5243	€4200	Pecheurs a Montigny-sur-Loire (32x45cm-13x18in) s. prov. 3-Mar-4 Tajan, Paris #94/R est:600-800
£2886	$5166	€4300	Petite eglise a Villefranche-sur-Mer (55x38cm-22x15in) s. panel. 30-May-4 Eric Pillon, Calais #84/R
£2958	$5117	€4200	Pre Saint-Gervais (50x65cm-20x26in) s. cardboard prov. 9-Dec-3 Artcurial Briest, Paris #267/R est:3000-4000
£2958	$5117	€4200	Petit coin de Paris (46x55cm-18x22in) s. panel. 14-Dec-3 Eric Pillon, Calais #168/R
£3020	$5618	€4500	Moulins a Montmartre (27x35cm-11x14in) s. prov. 3-Mar-4 Tajan, Paris #96/R est:600-800
£3020	$5617	€4500	Le clown (62x46cm-24x18in) s. cardboard painted c.1910 lit. 3-Mar-4 Fraysse & Associes, Paris #17/R est:2500-3500
£3147	$5255	€4500	Ruelle a Montmartre (45x55cm-18x22in) s. panel. 29-Jun-3 Eric Pillon, Calais #195/R
£3352	$6000	€4894	Le pont Michele (46x56cm-18x22in) s.i. 13-May-4 Dallas Auction Gallery, Dallas #190/R est:3000-6000
£3352	$6000	€4894	Les bords de la Bievre. s.i. 13-May-4 Dallas Auction Gallery, Dallas #279/R est:3000-6000
£3352	$6000	€4894	Notre Dame. s.i. 13-May-4 Dallas Auction Gallery, Dallas #322/R est:4000-8000
£3356	$6242	€5000	Place du Tertre sous la neige (27x35cm-11x14in) s. prov.e. 3-Mar-4 Tajan, Paris #91/R est:600-800
£3357	$5606	€4800	Paris, Hotel de la Tourelle (33x41cm-13x16in) s. 29-Jun-3 Eric Pillon, Calais #191/R
£3380	$5848	€4800	Moulin a Montmartre (54x65cm-21x26in) s. 9-Dec-3 Artcurial Briest, Paris #265/R est:3000-4000
£3380	$5915	€4800	Montmartre sous la neige (27x35cm-11x14in) s. 19-Dec-3 Delvaux, Paris #40/R est:2000-3000
£3404	$5685	€4800	Au velocipede, rue du Polygone (46x55cm-18x22in) s. s.i.verso. 12-Oct-3 St-Germain-en-Laye Encheres #105/R est:4500-5000
£3423	$6298	€5100	Lapin agile (45x55cm-18x22in) s. 29-Mar-4 Lombrail & Teucquam, Paris #122/R
£3467	$6309	€5200	Paris, Moulin Rouge (46x38cm-18x15in) s. 4-Jul-4 Eric Pillon, Calais #187/R
£4011	$7500	€5856	Port de Dieppe (48x70cm-19x28in) s.i.d.1923 board. 25-Feb-4 Christie's, Rockefeller NY #19/R est:5000-7000
£4027	$7490	€6000	Place duTertre, le cafe Labille (49x64cm-19x25in) s. cardboard. 7-Mar-4 Lesieur & Le Bars, Le Havre #85/R
£4027	$7208	€6000	Paris le Theatre de l'Atelier sous la neige (46x55cm-18x22in) s. 30-May-4 Eric Pillon, Calais #80/R
£4094	$7328	€6100	Montmartre (55x46cm-22x18in) s. 30-May-4 Eric Pillon, Calais #71/R
£4192	$7000	€6120	Landscape with bridge and houses (45x54cm-18x21in) s. 7-Oct-3 Sotheby's, New York #276 est:7000-10000
£4278	$8000	€6246	Moulin de la Galette (65x50cm-26x20in) s. board. 25-Feb-4 Christie's, Rockefeller NY #32/R est:7000-9000
£4601	$7500	€6717	Le port de Cassis (46x55cm-18x22in) s. 25-Sep-3 Christie's, Rockefeller NY #554/R est:7000-9000
£4755	$7941	€6800	Montmartte, maison de Mimi Pinson (35x41cm-14x16in) s. 29-Jun-3 Eric Pillon, Calais #194/R
£4813	$9000	€7027	Maison du Docteur Guillatin (43x55cm-17x22in) s. masonite. 25-Feb-4 Christie's, Rockefeller NY #43/R est:7000-9000
£5034	$9010	€7500	Montmartre, le Lapin Agile (46x55cm-18x22in) s. 30-May-4 Eric Pillon, Calais #70/R
£5175	$8642	€7400	Montmartre, maison de Mimi Pinson (46x55cm-18x22in) s. 29-Jun-3 Eric Pillon, Calais #190/R
£5233	$9368	€7850	Les glaneurs, paysage jaune (54x65cm-21x26in) s.i. 16-May-4 Thierry & Lannon, Brest #158/R est:8000-9000
£6376	$11860	€9500	Impasse Preme - La tour du Philosophe et Utrillo (50x65cm-20x26in) s. board. 3-Mar-4 Tajan, Paris #83/R est:10000-12000
£10490	$17832	€15000	Montmartre (60x73cm-24x29in) s. exhib.lit. 21-Nov-3 Lombrail & Teucquam, Paris #128/R est:14000-16000
Works on paper			
£280	$481	€400	Paysage de course (21x27cm-8x11in) s. W/C. 3-Dec-3 Tajan, Paris #122
£282	$487	€400	Antibes (17x24cm-7x9in) s.i. W/C. 12-Dec-3 Piasa, Paris #146
£284	$474	€400	Sortie du port (28x36cm-11x14in) s. W/C ink. 14-Oct-3 Millon & Associes, Paris #84/R
£369	$653	€550	Voiliers sur le lac (21x27cm-8x11in) s. ink W/C. 29-Apr-4 Claude Aguttes, Neuilly #54
£458	$792	€650	Dieppe (18x25cm-7x10in) s.i. W/C. 12-Dec-3 Piasa, Paris #145
£482	$805	€680	Les hauts de Montmartre (14x9cm-6x4in) s. W/C. 12-Oct-3 St-Germain-en-Laye Encheres #202
£537	$993	€800	Vieilles maisons a menton. s. W/C. 15-Mar-4 Blanchet, Paris #87/R
£552	$1021	€800	Les matelots (21x27cm-8x11in) s. W/C. 13-Feb-4 Charbonneaux, Paris #58
£559	$934	€800	Paris, Tour Saint-Jacques (24x17cm-9x7in) s. W/C. 29-Jun-3 Eric Pillon, Calais #203/R
£560	$963	€800	Le port de Honfleur et le voilier en mer (20x30cm-8x12in) s. one i. W/C pair. 3-Dec-3 Tajan, Paris #220
£600	$1104	€900	Voiliers (23x29cm-9x11in) s. W/C prov. 14-Jun-4 Tajan, Paris #58/R
£604	$1081	€900	Barques a l'entree du port d'Antibes (17x24cm-7x9in) s.i. W/C. 30-May-4 Eric Pillon, Calais #89/R
£629	$1051	€900	Sortie du port (20x29cm-8x11in) s. W/C. 29-Jun-3 Eric Pillon, Calais #206/R
£629	$1083	€900	Vue de Cassis (21x30cm-8x12in) s. W/C. 3-Dec-3 Tajan, Paris #219/R
£634	$1096	€900	Vue de Cannes (18x23cm-7x9in) s. W/C. 15-Dec-3 Bailly Pommery, Paris #122/R
£683	$1121	€950	Rue a Montmartre (14x9cm-6x4in) s. W/C. 6-Jun-3 Chochon-Barre & Allardi, Paris #73
£733	$1313	€1100	L'Oise (18x23cm-7x9in) s.i. W/C. 16-May-4 Lombrail & Teucquam, Paris #173/R
£734	$1226	€1050	Baignade (20x28cm-8x11in) s. W/C. 29-Jun-3 Eric Pillon, Calais #207/R
£769	$1285	€1100	Maison rose a Montmartre (26x33cm-10x13in) s. gouache. 29-Jun-3 Eric Pillon, Calais #204/R
£900	$1611	€1350	La Seine et le viaduc de Bir Hakem (18x23cm-7x9in) s. W/C. 16-May-4 Lombrail & Teucquam, Paris #172/R
£1056	$1849	€1500	Rue a Montmartre (27x22cm-11x9in) s. W/C. 17-Dec-3 Rabourdin & Choppin de Janvry, Paris #61 est:1000-1200
£1958	$3270	€2800	Mere Catherine (41x56cm-16x22in) s. W/C gouache. 29-Jun-3 Eric Pillon, Calais #200/R
£2028	$3387	€2900	Moulin a Montmartre (19x25cm-7x10in) s. gouache. 29-Jun-3 Eric Pillon, Calais #198/R
£3497	$5839	€5000	Terrasse animee sur Place du Tertre (44x58cm-17x23in) s. W/C gouache. 29-Jun-3 Eric Pillon, Calais #199/R

MACLIAMMOIR, Michael (1899-1978) Irish

Works on paper			
£1748	$2972	€2500	An old woman beholds a fairy parade at night (32x24cm-13x9in) s. W/C pen ink. 18-Nov-3 Whyte's, Dublin #131/R est:2500-3500

MACLISE, D (1806-1870) British/Irish

£1200	$2184	€1752	Young mother with boy and babe in arme, with a view over field of battle (76x61cm-30x24in) s.d.1879. 4-Feb-4 Goldings, Lincolnshire #481/R

MACLISE, Daniel (1806-1870) British/Irish
£729 $1189 €1050 Portrait of Justin McCarthy (30x24cm-12x9in) i.verso. 24-Sep-3 James Adam, Dublin #13/R est:700-1000
£6704 $12000 €9788 Ship voyage. s.i. 13-May-4 Dallas Auction Gallery, Dallas #301b/R est:10000-15000
Works on paper
£450 $752 €657 Lovers (23x13cm-9x5in) mono. W/C prov. 17-Oct-3 Keys, Aylsham #482
£1056 $1690 €1500 Loves labour lost (20x30cm-8x12in) s.d.1848 W/C. 16-Sep-3 Whyte's, Dublin #168/R est:1500-2000

MACLOT, Armand (1877-1960) Belgian
£1133 $2040 €1700 Antwerp roadstead (50x70cm-20x28in) s.d.1904. 26-Apr-4 Bernaerts, Antwerp #973/R est:250-375

McLOUGHLIN, Rosemary (20th C) Irish?
£921 $1695 €1400 Lock Walkway, Grand Canal (51x41cm-20x16in) s. board. 22-Jun-4 De Veres Art Auctions, Dublin #196/R
£1189 $2021 €1700 The Liffey at Butt Bridge (51x76cm-20x30in) s. panel. 18-Nov-3 Whyte's, Dublin #167/R est:1200-1500

McLOY, Samuel (1831-1904) British
Works on paper
£3200 $5760 €4672 Girl with foxgloves (24x19cm-9x7in) mono. W/C. 21-Jan-4 Sotheby's, Olympia #192/R est:1500-2000

McLUCKIE, Bill (1932-) Canadian
Works on paper
£300 $549 €438 The roads of English Bay (49x74cm-19x29in) s. i.verso W/C prov. 3-Jun-4 Heffel, Vancouver #37/R (C.D 750)

McMAHON, Brian (20th C) Irish?
£592 $1089 €900 Bishop's Island, Kilkee (61x76cm-24x30in) s.d.03 i.verso. 22-Jun-4 De Veres Art Auctions, Dublin #105/R

McMANUS, James Goodwin (1882-1958) American
£419 $750 €612 Path to the pier, a north shore view (30x41cm-12x16in) estate st.verso board. 14-May-4 Skinner, Boston #230/R

McMASTER, James (1856-1913) British
Works on paper
£300 $501 €438 Sketch at Largo (17x25cm-7x10in) s.i. W/C. 16-Oct-3 Lyon & Turnbull, Edinburgh #150
£360 $673 €526 Waltham Abbey (34x24cm-13x9in) s.i. W/C. 22-Jul-4 Bonhams, Edinburgh #326
£524 $965 €765 St. David's (24x34cm-9x13in) s.i. W/C. 14-Jun-4 Waddingtons, Toronto #178/R est:700-900 (C.D 1300)
£550 $919 €803 Entering harbour (17x25cm-7x10in) s. W/C. 16-Oct-3 Lyon & Turnbull, Edinburgh #155
£595 $1100 €869 Village street (36x18cm-14x7in) s.i. i.verso W/C bodycol board. 17-Jul-4 Brunk, Ashville #808/R
£816 $1486 €1200 Village au bord de l'eau (69x101cm-27x40in) W/C. 9-Feb-4 Amberes, Antwerp #275
£850 $1547 €1241 Unloading on the quayside (19x29cm-7x11in) s.indis.i. pencil W/C gum arabic. 1-Jul-4 Christie's, Kensington #460/R
£1900 $3534 €2774 Ary Harbour (34x25cm-13x10in) s.i. W/C bodycol. 4-Mar-4 Christie's, Kensington #105/R est:500-700

McMEIN, Neysa (1890-1949) American
Works on paper
£3892 $6500 €5682 Seated woman with red hair and white gloves (81x66cm-32x26in) s.i. pastel. 15-Nov-3 Illustration House, New York #147/R est:5000-7000

MACMIADHACHAIN, Padraig (1929-) Irish
£500 $800 €730 Below the Down (61x74cm-24x29in) s.d.Oct.1990 verso. 16-Sep-3 Gorringes, Bexhill #1519
£680 $1217 €993 Ladder to the sky (20x25cm-8x10in) s. 14-May-4 Christie's, Kensington #447/R
£850 $1445 €1241 Sand wind (46x122cm-18x48in) i.verso board. 30-Oct-3 Duke & Son, Dorchester #256

McMILLAN, Hamilton (19th C) British
Works on paper
£550 $1007 €803 On the shore at Kilcreggan (36x66cm-14x26in) mono.d.1876. 31-Jan-4 Shapes, Edinburgh #370

McMILLAN, Sam (20th C) American
£319 $575 €466 No one lives on the moon there isn't a Wal-Mart (51x61cm-20x24in) board. 24-Apr-4 Slotin Folk Art, Buford #785/R

MACMONNIES, Frederick William (1863-1937) American
Sculpture
£1148 $2100 €1722 Pan atop a ball with fish at base (38cm-15in) i. bronze Cast Rouard. 7-Jun-4 Everard, Savannah #476375/R est:1000-1500
£7647 $13000 €11165 Bacchante and infant faun (85cm-33in) s.i.d.1894 bronze prov. 21-Nov-3 Skinner, Boston #394/R est:15000-20000
£8380 $15000 €12235 Bacchante and infant fawn (89cm-35in) s.d.1894 brown pat bronze st.f.F.Cruet Jeune prov. 6-May-4 Shannon's, Milford #171/R est:15000-20000
£17045 $30000 €24886 Diana (76cm-30in) i.d.1890 dark green pat bronze marble pedestal prov.lit. 19-May-4 Sotheby's, New York #1261/R est:15000-25000
£17964 $30000 €26227 Pan of Rohallion (76cm-30in) s.st.f.Jaboeuf and Rouard weathered pat bronze lit. 9-Oct-3 Christie's, Rockefeller NY #39/R est:15000-25000

MACMONNIES, Frederick William (attrib) (1863-1937) American
Sculpture
£2654 $4750 €3875 Lovers embracing (29cm-11in) bronze black plinth prov. 14-May-4 Skinner, Boston #374/R est:3000-5000

McMURTRY, Arthur W (20th C) American
Works on paper
£365 $675 €533 Sailing scene (64x48cm-25x19in) s. W/C. 15-Feb-4 Outer Cape Auctions, Provincetown #48a/R

MACNAB, Iain (1890-1967) British
£450 $774 €657 Still life (41x51cm-16x20in) s. 3-Dec-3 Christie's, Kensington #718
Works on paper
£450 $837 €657 Caribbean port (37x55cm-15x22in) s. pencil W/C bodycol. 4-Mar-4 Christie's, Kensington #149

MACNAB, Peter (?-1900) British
£600 $1134 €876 Couple in partially harvested field of corn (43x58cm-17x23in) s. 19-Feb-4 Rendalls, Ashburton #1606

McNAB, Theo (1940-) Irish?
Works on paper
£265 $482 €400 The room (22x34cm-9x13in) s. pencil W/C prov. 15-Jun-4 James Adam, Dublin #73/R

MACNAIR, J Herbert (1868-1955) British
Works on paper
£3500 $5565 €5110 Sacred dove and lowly bird, met in love by holy word (19x6cm-7x2in) s.d.1897 pencil prov. 9-Sep-3 Sotheby's, Olympia #131/R est:600-800

McNAIRN, Caroline (1955-) British
£600 $1038 €876 Farm (84x76cm-33x30in) s.d.85. 11-Dec-3 Lyon & Turnbull, Edinburgh #22/R
Works on paper
£750 $1253 €1095 Early street (53x73cm-21x29in) pastel. 16-Oct-3 Lyon & Turnbull, Edinburgh #55

McNALLY, Matthew James (1874-1943) Australian
Works on paper
£813 $1276 €1179 Under the gum trees (59x73cm-23x29in) s.d.1933 W/C. 26-Aug-3 Lawson Menzies, Sydney #26 est:2800-3800 (A.D 2000)
£830 $1386 €1245 Sunlit hillside (30x36cm-12x14in) s.d.1927 W/C. 27-Oct-3 Goodman, Sydney #133/R (A.D 2000)
£1277 $2170 €1864 Sylvan glade (55x79cm-22x31in) s.d.1933 W/C. 25-Nov-3 Christie's, Melbourne #306/R est:3000-5000 (A.D 3000)

MACNEE, Robert Russell (1880-1952) British
£1056 $1700 €1542 Misty morning in the pasture (42x52cm-17x20in) s. 14-Jan-4 Christie's, Rockefeller NY #69/R est:2000-3000
£1600 $2576 €2320 Poultry by a cart (30x45cm-12x18in) s.d.18. 21-Aug-3 Bonhams, Edinburgh #1199/R est:1000-1500
£2200 $3454 €3190 Two hens (25x30cm-10x12in) s.d.16 board prov. 27-Aug-3 Sotheby's, London #1089a/R est:1500-2000
£5800 $9860 €8468 Country lane in summer (51x62cm-20x24in) s.d.13 prov. 30-Oct-3 Christie's, London #116/R est:4000-6000

MACNEE, Sir Daniel (1806-1882) British
£800 $1416 €1168 Ride on the pony (51x71cm-20x28in) 28-Apr-4 Halls, Shrewsbury #533/R
£900 $1674 €1314 Portrait of two ladies, with a spaniel, under a tree (36x25cm-14x10in) init. board. 4-Mar-4 Christie's, Kensington #17/R
£2679 $4607 €3911 Peggy and Jenny, from The Gentle Shepherd (98x72cm-39x28in) s. prov.exhib. 2-Dec-3 Ritchie, Toronto #53/R est:6000-8000 (C.D 6000)

McNEIL, George (1908-1995) American
£973 $1800 €1421 Baiser (71x56cm-28x22in) s.d.79 oil acrylic paper on panel prov. 10-Mar-4 Doyle, New York #78/R est:500-700

McNELLIS, Laura Craig (1957-) American
£944 $1700 €1378 Christmas tree (56x66cm-22x26in) oil on paper painted c.1982. 24-Apr-4 Slotin Folk Art, Buford #483/R est:1000-2000
Works on paper
£1437 $2400 €2098 Red house with two trees (53x74cm-21x29in) mixed media newsprint prov. 15-Nov-3 Slotin Folk Art, Buford #267/R est:500-800

MACNELLY, Jeffrey Kenneth (1947-2000) American
Works on paper
£374 $700 €546 Jimmy Carter and Ted Kennedy have a traffic mishap (23x33cm-9x13in) s. pen ink craftint. 26-Feb-4 Illustration House, New York #119

MACNIADHACHAIN, Padraig (?) Irish?
£440 $801 €642 Mediterranean landscape with white buildings (58x119cm-23x47in) s. board. 7-Feb-4 Windibank, Dorking #340/R

McNICOL, Ian (fl.1928-1938) British
£650 $1203 €949 On the Derg (56x76cm-22x30in) s. 11-Feb-4 Sotheby's, Olympia #143/R

MACOUN, Gustav (1892-1934) Czechoslovakian
£615 $1045 €898 Landscape of Cesky (46x64cm-18x25in) s. cardboard. 29-Nov-3 Dorotheum, Prague #63/R est:15000-23000 (C.KR 28000)
£759 $1336 €1139 Spring (96x128cm-38x50in) s. 22-May-4 Dorotheum, Prague #106/R est:36000-60000 (C.KR 36000)
£1576 $2900 €2301 Church viewed through the trees (89x122cm-35x48in) s.d.1911. 26-Jun-4 Sloans & Kenyon, Bethesda #1059/R est:1000-1500

McPHAIL, Roger (1953-) British
£1900 $3496 €2774 Taking the fly (51x61cm-20x24in) s. 10-Jun-4 Christie's, Kensington #233/R est:700-900
Works on paper
£1100 $1870 €1606 Great bustards (51x72cm-20x28in) s.d.77 W/C. 19-Nov-3 Sotheby's, Olympia #83/R est:1000-1500
£2600 $4420 €3796 Spectators (35x52cm-14x20in) s. W/C prov. 19-Nov-3 Sotheby's, Olympia #85/R est:1500-2000

McPHAIL, Wayne (20th C) New Zealander?
Works on paper
£326 $518 €476 Evening at Tairi river mouth, South of Dunedin (48x63cm-19x25in) s. pastel. 9-Sep-3 Watson's, Christchurch #84 (NZ.D 900)

McPHEE, Charles C (1910-) New Zealander
£833 $1417 €1216 Tahitian woman (89x67cm-35x26in) s. oil on velvet. 4-Nov-3 Peter Webb, Auckland #196 est:800-1000 (NZ.D 2300)

MACPHERSON, Alexander (1904-1970) British
Works on paper
£360 $601 €526 War weapons week, Glasgow, Nov 1940 (37x51cm-15x20in) s.i. pencil W/C. 16-Oct-3 Lyon & Turnbull, Edinburgh #146

MACPHERSON, J (fl.1865-1884) British
Works on paper
£500 $945 €730 Farm building with shepherdess (24x41cm-9x16in) W/C. 17-Feb-4 Patersons, Paisley #266
£900 $1503 €1314 Cattle watering (47x83cm-19x33in) s.d.1890 W/C. 21-Oct-3 Bruton Knowles, Cheltenham #395/R

MACPHERSON, John (fl.1865-1884) British
£2800 $5124 €4088 Waiting for the tide (88x135cm-35x53in) s.d.1864. 8-Apr-4 Bonhams, Edinburgh #100/R est:2000-3000
Works on paper
£250 $438 €365 Children and a woman before a house with wisteria (25x36cm-10x14in) s. 18-Dec-3 John Nicholson, Haslemere #1074
£260 $416 €380 Sheep on a country lane (24x42cm-9x17in) s. W/C. 21-Sep-3 Lots Road Auctions, London #369
£270 $497 €394 Bringing home the hay through the ford (48x72cm-19x28in) s. W/C. 14-Jun-4 Bonhams, Bath #108
£320 $509 €467 Shepherd and sheep on a roadway with farm building and landscape in distance (23x42cm-9x17in) s. W/C. 13-Sep-3 Windibank, Dorking #168

MACPHERSON, M Campbell (fl.1885-1904) British
£2185 $3955 €3190 Portrait of a lady (97x73cm-38x29in) s. oval. 30-Mar-4 Stephan Welz, Johannesburg #400/R est:25000-35000 (SA.R 26000)

MacPHERSON, Neil (1954-) British
£370 $592 €540 Blue dog looking for blue Danube (47cm-19in circular) 19-May-3 Bruton Knowles, Cheltenham #223

MACPHERSON, Robert (1937-) Australian
£4938 $8938 €7209 Group 2 1976-77 (176x10cm-69x4in) i.verso acrylic triptych. 30-Mar-4 Lawson Menzies, Sydney #151/R est:8000-10000 (A.D 12000)

MACPHERSON, Robert (1811-1872) British
Photographs
£1889 $3400 €2758 Temple of Vesta, Rome (28x39cm-11x15in) albumen print lit. 22-Apr-4 Phillips, New York #151/R est:5000-7000

McQUALTER, John (1949-) Australian
£766 $1302 €1118 Beach at Rye (12x75cm-5x30in) s. s.i. verso canvas on board. 25-Nov-3 Christie's, Melbourne #282 (A.D 1800)

MACQUEEN, Kenneth (1897-1960) Australian
Works on paper
£389 $712 €584 Gums. W/C. 3-Jun-4 Joel, Victoria #200/R (A.D 1000)
£744 $1264 €1116 Farm scene (36x41cm-14x16in) s.d.1926 W/C. 28-Oct-3 Goodman, Sydney #321/R (A.D 1800)
£1055 $1973 €1583 Cows resting in the shade (36x46cm-14x18in) s. W/C. 20-Jul-4 Goodman, Sydney #20/R est:2500-4000 (A.D 2700)
£1207 $1883 €1750 Arboretum (36x44cm-14x17in) s. W/C. 1-Aug-2 Joel, Victoria #308 est:4000-6000 (A.D 3500)

MACQUOID, Percy (1852-1925) British
Works on paper
£1300 $2171 €1898 Lady standing in an interior, holding a peacock, with two dogs (36x48cm-14x19in) s.d.1881 pencil W/C. 16-Oct-3 Christie's, Kensington #100/R est:1200-1800
£3000 $5100 €4380 Promenade, Hampton Court (51x71cm-20x28in) s.i. W/C htd bodycol. 27-Nov-3 Sotheby's, London #381/R est:3000-5000

MACQUOID, Thomas (1820-1912) British
Works on paper
£550 $919 €803 Spanish patio (41x52cm-16x20in) s.i.d.86 W/C. 16-Oct-3 Lyon & Turnbull, Edinburgh #127

MACRAE, Elmer (1875-1953) American
£4491 $7500 €6557 Summer reflections (61x51cm-24x20in) s. prov. 23-Oct-3 Shannon's, Milford #205/R est:4000-6000
£5191 $9500 €7579 Knoll with haystack (76x66cm-30x26in) s.d.1911 exhib. 10-Apr-4 Cobbs, Peterborough #44/R
Works on paper
£235 $400 €343 On the beach (14x16cm-6x6in) s.d.1912 mixed media canvasboard prov. 21-Nov-3 Skinner, Boston #568/R
£471 $800 €688 Floral still with tulips (37x44cm-15x17in) s.d.1915 mixed media pair prov. 21-Nov-3 Skinner, Boston #380/R
£765 $1300 €1117 Still life with zinnias (61x52cm-24x20in) s.d.95 mixed media canvasboard. 21-Nov-3 Skinner, Boston #376/R est:500-700

McRAE, Jennifer (1959-) British
£500 $945 €730 Young girl with a mole (22x17cm-9x7in) s.d.96 board. 19-Feb-4 Lyon & Turnbull, Edinburgh #50

McRAE, Tommy (c.1836-1901) Australian
Works on paper
£7317 $11561 €10610 Corroboree (24x35cm-9x14in) i. ink exec.c.1890 prov. 28-Jul-3 Sotheby's, Paddington #79/R est:20000-30000 (A.D 18000)
£8537 $13488 €12379 Corroboree (24x35cm-9x14in) i. ink exec.c.1890 prov. 28-Jul-3 Sotheby's, Paddington #78/R est:20000-30000 (A.D 21000)
£15625 $29219 €23438 Spearing the kangaroo (23x33cm-9x13in) bears i. ink prov. 26-Jul-4 Sotheby's, Melbourne #9/R est:20000-30000 (A.D 40000)
£23438 $43828 €35157 Aboriginal fight scenes (24x34cm-9x13in) bears i. ink exec.c.1890 four prov. 26-Jul-4 Sotheby's, Melbourne #11/R est:70000-100000 (A.D 60000)

MACREAU, Michel (1935-) French
£1958 $3270 €2800 Femme poulpe (97x86cm-38x34in) s. prov.exhib. 29-Jun-3 Versailles Encheres #180/R
£2797 $4671 €4000 Untitled (116x89cm-46x35in) prov.exhib.lit. 29-Jun-3 Versailles Encheres #153/R
£2937 $4905 €4200 Dents (161x132cm-63x52in) mono.d.1989 acrylic masonite prov.exhib. 29-Jun-3 Versailles Encheres #152/R
£3077 $5138 €4400 Untitled (130x97cm-51x38in) s.d.1963. 29-Jun-3 Versailles Encheres #161/R
£3357 $5606 €4800 Plancher du chateau (145x94cm-57x37in) s.d.1960 prov.exhib. 29-Jun-3 Versailles Encheres #160/R
£3636 $6073 €5200 Untitled (122x94cm-48x37in) masonite prov.exhib.lit. 29-Jun-3 Versailles Encheres #155/R
£4336 $7241 €6200 Voile de la mariee (130x97cm-51x38in) s.d.1962 s.i.d.verso prov.exhib. 29-Jun-3 Versailles Encheres #151/R
£5594 $9343 €8000 Untitled (162x130cm-64x51in) s.d.1962 prov.exhib. 29-Jun-3 Versailles Encheres #156/R
£6993 $11678 €10000 Histoire et surface (165x110cm-65x43in) s.i.d.1961 prov.exhib. 29-Jun-3 Versailles Encheres #162/R
£9091 $15182 €13000 Toile monumentale (200x160cm-79x63in) s.d.1961 prov.exhib.lit. 29-Jun-3 Versailles Encheres #163/R
£9441 $15766 €13500 Untitled (140x220cm-55x87in) s.d.1963 prov.exhib. 29-Jun-3 Versailles Encheres #164/R
Works on paper
£530 $964 €800 Autoportrait a la plage (32x25cm-13x10in) s.i.d.1953 india ink red ink. 15-Jun-4 Blanchet, Paris #259
£2797 $4671 €4000 Ciel et terre (175x140cm-69x55in) s.d.1987 mixed media masonite prov.exhib. 29-Jun-3 Versailles Encheres #158/R
£5315 $8876 €7600 Untitled (260x140cm-102x55in) mono. chl canvas on panel. 29-Jun-3 Versailles Encheres #157/R

MACRUAIDHRI, Patsy Dan (20th C) Irish?
£528 $914 €750 Tory at sunset (41x60cm-16x24in) s. i.d.5th March 1983 verso board. 10-Dec-3 Bonhams & James Adam, Dublin #188/R
£1133 $2051 €1700 Beanna Thorai, a coastal scene off Tory Island (45x60cm-18x24in) s.i. board. 31-Mar-4 James Adam, Dublin #134/R est:800-1200

MACRUM, George (1888-?) American
£599 $1000 €875 Grand canal, Venice (30x41cm-12x16in) board painted 1888. 17-Oct-3 Du Mouchelle, Detroit #2179/R
£1494 $2750 €2181 The tramp, Venice (30x40cm-12x16in) s. i.verso canvasboard. 8-Jun-4 Bonhams & Butterfields, San Francisco #4057/R est:3000-5000
£4790 $8000 €6993 View of the Palisades from New York (64x76cm-25x30in) s. prov. 23-Oct-3 Shannon's, Milford #181/R est:2500-3500

MACSOUD, Nicolas S (1884-1972) American
£1374 $2500 €2006 View of Fifth Avenue with the Empire State Building in the background (81x63cm-32x25in) painted c.1930 prov. 29-Jun-4 Sotheby's, New York #277/R est:3000-5000

McSWEENEY, Sean (1935-) Irish

£839 $1427 €1200 Spring pool (25x35cm-10x14in) s.d.95 tempera. 25-Nov-3 De Veres Art Auctions, Dublin #212/R est:900-1200
£1400 $2506 €2044 Sligo boglands (25x35cm-10x14in) s.d.89 s.i.d.87 verso board. 14-May-4 Christie's, Kensington #460/R est:1500-2000
£1611 $2851 €2400 Trees on the hill (14x19cm-6x7in) s.i.verso board exhib. 27-Apr-4 Whyte's, Dublin #17/R est:1500-2000
£1800 $3222 €2628 Kelly's bog (35x25cm-14x10in) s.d.86 s.i.d.86 verso board. 14-May-4 Christie's, Kensington #459/R est:1500-2000
£1800 $3222 €2628 Blue lake (40x45cm-16x18in) s.d.87 s.i.d.87 verso board. 14-May-4 Christie's, Kensington #462/R est:2000-2500
£1972 $3155 €2800 Blue pool (30x41cm-12x16in) s.d.2001 s.i.verso board prov. 16-Sep-3 Whyte's, Dublin #53/R est:3000-4000
£2133 $3861 €3200 White pool (26x36cm-10x14in) s.d.98 i.verso board. 30-Mar-4 De Veres Art Auctions, Dublin #102/R est:3000-4000
£2308 $3923 €3300 Bogland foliage (26x36cm-10x14in) s.d.88 s.i.d.verso board. 25-Nov-3 De Veres Art Auctions, Dublin #16/R est:2500-3500
£2400 $4296 €3504 September strand (35x45cm-14x18in) s.d.90 s.i.d.90 verso board. 14-May-4 Christie's, Kensington #464/R est:1500-2000
£2432 $4597 €3600 Where ladybirds play (36x46cm-14x18in) s. 17-Feb-4 Whyte's, Dublin #39/R est:3000-4000
£2517 $4280 €3600 Wetland (26x34cm-10x13in) s.d.2000. 25-Nov-3 De Veres Art Auctions, Dublin #40/R est:3000-4000
£2657 $4517 €3800 Wetland (46x61cm-18x24in) s.d.1998 s.i.verso board. 18-Nov-3 Whyte's, Dublin #154/R est:4000-5000
£2667 $4827 €4000 Shoreline pools (46x61cm-18x24in) s. i.d.2002 verso. 30-Mar-4 De Veres Art Auctions, Dublin #79/R est:4500-6000
£2667 $4827 €4000 Grey bogland (26x31cm-10x12in) s.d.02 s.i.verso board prov. 30-Mar-4 De Veres Art Auctions, Dublin #101/R est:3000-4000
£2817 $4507 €4000 Bogland fields. Rough ground, Wicklow (25x18cm-10x7in) s.d.1981 s.i.verso canvasboard pair. 16-Sep-3 Whyte's, Dublin #52/R est:3000-4000
£2838 $5364 €4200 White bogland pool (25x36cm-10x14in) s.d.1998 s.i.verso board prov. 17-Feb-4 Whyte's, Dublin #73/R est:2500-3500
£3200 $5728 €4672 Bogland pools and sea (35x45cm-14x18in) s.d.87 s.i.d.87 verso board. 14-May-4 Christie's, Kensington #458/R est:2000-3000
£3733 $6757 €5600 Cloch ceim (46x77cm-18x30in) s.d.86 i.verso board triptych exhib. 30-Mar-4 De Veres Art Auctions, Dublin #97/R est:4000-6000
£5500 $9845 €8030 Roskeeragh (81x110cm-32x43in) s.i.d.88 verso board. 14-May-4 Christie's, Kensington #463/R est:3000-5000
£8667 $15687 €13000 Yellow ochre bog (127x174cm-50x69in) s.i.stretcher prov. 30-Mar-4 De Veres Art Auctions, Dublin #82/R est:10000-13000
Works on paper
£413 $748 €620 The lane, Lugglass (14x20cm-6x8in) s. s.i.verso mixed media prov. 30-Mar-4 De Veres Art Auctions, Dublin #158/R
£868 $1415 €1250 Landscape (20x29cm-8x11in) s. W/C prov. 24-Sep-3 James Adam, Dublin #58/R est:1000-1500

McSWINEY, Eugène (1866-?) British

£880 $1646 €1285 Street scene (43x79cm-17x31in) s. 23-Jul-4 Tring Auctions, Tring #290/R

MacTAGGART, Sir William (1903-1981) British

£2200 $3806 €3212 Lauderdale (18x25cm-7x10in) s. board. 11-Dec-3 Lyon & Turnbull, Edinburgh #13/R est:1500-2000
£2400 $4128 €3504 Cornfield (17x25cm-7x10in) s. board. 4-Dec-3 Bonhams, Edinburgh #71/R est:1500-2000
£2400 $4152 €3504 Angry sea (18x25cm-7x10in) s. board exhib. 11-Dec-3 Lyon & Turnbull, Edinburgh #14/R est:1500-2000
£2500 $4025 €3625 Woodland (25x31cm-10x12in) s. board. 21-Aug-3 Bonhams, Edinburgh #1050/R est:2000-3000
£2500 $4175 €3650 Gifford, East Lothian (35x44cm-14x17in) s. board. 16-Oct-3 Bonhams, Edinburgh #44/R est:2000-3000
£2600 $4472 €3796 Towards Denmark (16x24cm-6x9in) board prov. 4-Dec-3 Bonhams, Edinburgh #21/R est:1500-2000
£2800 $4508 €4060 Luce Bay (17x25cm-7x10in) s. s.i.verso board. 21-Aug-3 Bonhams, Edinburgh #1049/R est:2500-3500
£3100 $5332 €4526 After rain (30x40cm-12x16in) s. canvasboard prov. 4-Dec-3 Bonhams, Edinburgh #24/R est:3000-5000
£3400 $5848 €4964 On the Solway (30x40cm-12x16in) s. board prov. 4-Dec-3 Bonhams, Edinburgh #68/R est:2500-3500
£4000 $6280 €5800 Sunset over the sea (41x51cm-16x20in) s.d.67 board. 27-Aug-3 Sotheby's, London #1160/R est:4000-6000
£4000 $7440 €5840 Sunset (41x51cm-16x20in) s.d.57. 4-Mar-4 Christie's, Kensington #228/R est:2500-3500
£5000 $9050 €7300 Abstract, sombre harmony (76x60cm-30x24in) s. board exhib. 19-Apr-4 Sotheby's, London #135/R est:5000-7000
£5000 $9050 €7300 Summers day, Loch Tay (20x24cm-8x9in) s. panel prov. 19-Apr-4 Sotheby's, London #137/R est:5000-7000
£9500 $14915 €13775 View - still life with roses (51x61cm-20x24in) s. board prov. 27-Aug-3 Sotheby's, London #1161/R est:7000-9000
£13000 $23530 €18980 Pianist's bouquet (62x52cm-24x20in) s. board prov. 19-Apr-4 Sotheby's, London #139/R est:10000-15000
Works on paper
£1200 $2064 €1752 Red roofs (46x61cm-18x24in) W/C gouache prov. 4-Dec-3 Bonhams, Edinburgh #50/R est:1200-1800
£1250 $2150 €1825 Norwegian harbour (22x25cm-9x10in) pencil W/C buff paper. 4-Dec-3 Bonhams, Edinburgh #70/R est:600-800
£2600 $4472 €3796 Winter Road, East Lothian (44x37cm-17x15in) s.d.1923 col chks prov. 4-Dec-3 Bonhams, Edinburgh #51/R est:800-1200
£3200 $5792 €4672 Norwegian village (22x25cm-9x10in) W/C pencil. 19-Apr-4 Sotheby's, London #138/R est:2000-2500

McTAGGART, William (1835-1910) British

£6000 $11160 €8760 Children by a wood (27x34cm-11x13in) s. panel. 4-Mar-4 Christie's, Kensington #113/R est:7000-9000
£9000 $14490 €13050 Fields near Broomieknowe (61x79cm-24x31in) prov. 21-Aug-3 Bonhams, Edinburgh #1139/R est:8000-12000
£9000 $14130 €13050 Puir weans (38x33cm-15x13in) s.d.1863 prov.exhib. 27-Aug-3 Sotheby's, London #1187/R est:10000-15000
£9500 $16150 €13870 Bird's nest (40x50cm-16x20in) s.d.1869 prov.exhib. 30-Oct-3 Christie's, London #110/R est:10000-15000
£14000 $21980 €20300 In rough seas (26x35cm-10x14in) s.i. panel prov. 27-Aug-3 Sotheby's, London #1192/R est:8000-12000
£28000 $47600 €40880 Harvest Moon at twilight (88x110cm-35x43in) s.d.1897 prov.exhib.lit. 30-Oct-3 Christie's, London #140/R est:30000-50000
£80000 $125600 €116000 As happy as the day is long (60x85cm-24x33in) s. prov.exhib.lit. 27-Aug-3 Sotheby's, London #1189/R est:80000-120000
Works on paper
£6800 $11560 €9928 Shipwreck (35x52cm-14x20in) s.d.1878 W/C bodycol. 30-Oct-3 Christie's, London #142/R est:3500-5500

McVEIGH, Blanche (1895-1970) American

Prints
£1916 $3200 €2797 Lawdy, lawdy (20x25cm-8x10in) aquatint. 18-Oct-3 David Dike, Dallas #46/R est:1000-2000

McVITTIE, Robert (1935-2002) Canadian

£227 $370 €331 Fishing boat on calm sea (30x41cm-12x16in) s. canvasboard prov. 23-Sep-3 Ritchie, Toronto #142/R (C.D 500)
£261 $486 €381 Evening light, the frigate (41x61cm-16x24in) s. i.verso canvasboard prov. 2-Mar-4 Ritchie, Toronto #133/R (C.D 650)
£360 $659 €526 Capture of the Dos Amigos (61x91cm-24x36in) s. i.verso prov. 3-Jun-4 Heffel, Vancouver #38/R (C.D 900)
£440 $805 €642 Up coast (45x61cm-18x24in) s. i.verso. 3-Jun-4 Heffel, Vancouver #39/R (C.D 1100)
£448 $740 €650 Moshula (61x76cm-24x30in) s. i.verso. 3-Jul-3 Heffel, Vancouver #23/R (C.D 1000)
£548 $877 €800 Barquentine Alexa (61x76cm-24x30in) s. 16-Sep-3 Maynards, Vancouver #357 est:800-1200 (C.D 1200)

McWHANNELL, Richard (1952-) New Zealander

£357 $657 €521 Toy motorbike (11x9cm-4x4in) s.d.1979 canvasboard. 25-Mar-4 International Art Centre, Auckland #87/R (NZ.D 1000)
£882 $1579 €1288 Knotted curtain (35x30cm-14x12in) i.d.1982. 11-May-4 Peter Webb, Auckland #55/R est:2000-3000 (NZ.D 2550)
£1429 $2586 €2086 Lover slopes (60x76cm-24x30in) i. s.d.1992 verso. 30-Mar-4 Peter Webb, Auckland #146/R est:4000-6000 (NZ.D 4000)
£1449 $2348 €2101 Memento Mori (83x60cm-33x24in) s.d.1987 verso. 31-Jul-3 International Art Centre, Auckland #24/R est:4000-6000 (NZ.D 4000)
£1986 $3236 €2900 Heading south (38x58cm-15x23in) s.i.d.2000-2001 verso board. 23-Sep-3 Peter Webb, Auckland #109/R est:3500-4500 (NZ.D 5500)

MacWHIRTER, John (1839-1911) British

£950 $1615 €1387 Autumn woodlands (47x34cm-19x13in) mono. 8-Nov-3 Shapes, Edinburgh #422/R
£1800 $3348 €2628 At the edge of the forest (49x75cm-19x30in) s. 4-Mar-4 Christie's, Kensington #101/R est:2000-3000
£2000 $3140 €2900 Shepherd's bridge, Arran (51x76cm-20x30in) s. prov. 27-Aug-3 Sotheby's, London #1085/R est:2000-3000
£2700 $4968 €3942 In the Highlands (127x84cm-50x33in) s. 24-Mar-4 Hamptons Fine Art, Godalming #280
£5200 $8840 €7592 Mountain road, Invernesshire (75x48cm-30x19in) init. s.i.stretcher. 30-Oct-3 Christie's, London #115/R est:2000-3000
£6000 $9420 €8700 Alpine meadow (66x97cm-26x38in) s. prov. 27-Aug-3 Sotheby's, London #1098/R est:4000-6000
Works on paper
£250 $418 €365 Alpine flowers (25x18cm-10x7in) mono. W/C. 12-Nov-3 Halls, Shrewsbury #278
£300 $543 €438 Rainy day, Berisal on the Simpleton Route (18x12cm-7x5in) init. W/C. 1-Apr-4 Martel Maides, Guernsey #261
£320 $509 €464 Highland landscape with an estuary, castle and fishing boats (32x24cm-13x9in) s. W/C. 9-Sep-3 Sworder & Son, Bishops Stortford #438/R
£380 $631 €555 View in the Italian lakes (20x13cm-8x5in) init. W/C. 2-Oct-3 Neales, Nottingham #676
£400 $680 €584 Faggot gatherers on a path (49x34cm-19x13in) mono. W/C. 8-Nov-3 Shapes, Edinburgh #502
£430 $679 €624 Landscape with silver birch trees beside a pond with kingfisher (54x37cm-21x15in) s. W/C gouache. 24-Jul-3 Dominic Winter, Swindon #48/R
£1000 $1790 €1460 Alpine meadow of wildflowers (24x34cm-9x13in) s. W/C gouache. 26-May-4 Sotheby's, Olympia #214/R est:1000-1500
£12500 $21250 €18250 British rural scenes. W/C pencil pen ink album prov. 27-Nov-3 Sotheby's, London #353/R est:5000-7000

McWILLIAM, Frederick Edward (1909-1992) British

Sculpture
£2703 $5108 €4000 Winged figure (27cm-11in) cast bronze. 17-Feb-4 Whyte's, Dublin #20/R est:3000-4000
£6000 $10860 €9000 Lazarus and his sisters (42x30cm-17x12in) composite wire exec.c.1953. 31-Mar-4 James Adam, Dublin #140/R est:4000-6000
£12676 $21930 €18000 Seated woman in a hat (72cm-28in) init. metal wire metal armature prov.exhib. 10-Dec-3 Bonhams & James Adam, Dublin #89/R est:15000-20000
£14000 $23800 €20440 Girl with cloth cap (43cm-17in) init.num.4/5 brown pat. bronze conceived 1978 exhib.lit. 21-Nov-3 Christie's, London #173/R est:10000-15000

McWILLIAMS, Joe (1938-) Irish

Works on paper
£340 $622 €496 Farm near Strangford (20x25cm-8x10in) s.d.1982 W/C. 2-Jun-4 John Ross, Belfast #234

MACY, Wendell Ferdinand (1845-1913) American

£1257 $2100 €1823 Seascape with rower in dory approaching shoreline (13x15cm-5x6in) s.d.1903 panel. 30-Jun-3 Winter Associates, Plainville #128/R
£2471 $4250 €3608 Macy lane, Nantucket, Massachusetts (25x36cm-10x14in) s.d.89. 7-Dec-3 Grogan, Boston #55/R

MADDEN, Anne (1932-) British

£704 $1218 €1000 No 1 lemon yellow hill (33x41cm-13x16in) s.i.d.December 1963 verso. 10-Dec-3 Bonhams & James Adam, Dublin #154/R

Works on paper
£839 $1427 €1200 Leda and the swan (29x36cm-11x14in) s.d.1992 graphite after Gericault exhib. 18-Nov-3 Whyte's, Dublin #155/R

MADDEN, Jan (20th C) American
£333 $600 €486 Fishing boats in a harbour (51x61cm-20x24in) s. 23-Jan-4 Freeman, Philadelphia #227/R

MADDEN, John McIntosh (1856-1922) New Zealander
£353 $639 €515 Lake in the mountains (34x54cm-13x21in) s.d.1900 board. 30-Mar-4 Stephan Welz, Johannesburg #417 est:4000-6000 (SA.R 4200)
£600 $1020 €876 Mitre Peak, Milford Sound, New Zealand (30x46cm-12x18in) s. board. 4-Nov-3 Bonhams, New Bond Street #1/R

MADDERSON, Arthur K (20th C) Irish?
Works on paper
£296 $518 €420 Man playing the fiddle (36x26cm-14x10in) s. W/C. 16-Dec-3 James Adam, Dublin #85/R
£1275 $2346 €1900 Towards evening, Conemara (109x79cm-43x31in) s.i. mixed media. 23-Mar-4 Mealy's, Castlecomer #1128/R est:1200-1800
£1611 $2964 €2400 September sunset, near Youghal (109x79cm-43x31in) mixed media on board. 23-Mar-4 Mealy's, Castlecomer #1127/R est:2500-3500
£1812 $3334 €2700 Winter sunset, St. Laurent le Minier, France (79x109cm-31x43in) s.i.verso mixed media on board. 23-Mar-4 Mealy's, Castlecomer #1129/R est:2500-3500

MADDOX, Alan (1948-2000) New Zealander
£621 $1098 €907 In the studio, Apr/May (27x33cm-11x13in) acrylic. 28-Apr-4 Dunbar Sloane, Auckland #86 (NZ.D 1750)
£632 $1087 €923 Hamlet (117x13cm-46x5in) i. prov. 3-Dec-3 Dunbar Sloane, Auckland #62/R (NZ.D 1700)
£709 $1255 €1035 In the studio, Apr/May (27x33cm-11x13in) acrylic. 28-Apr-4 Dunbar Sloane, Auckland #83/R (NZ.D 2000)
£922 $1632 €1346 Untitled (33x27cm-13x11in) s. oil paper. 28-Apr-4 Dunbar Sloane, Auckland #6/R (NZ.D 2600)
£982 $1807 €1434 Untitled, crosses (76x57cm-30x22in) s.d.1994 oil paper. 25-Mar-4 International Art Centre, Auckland #27/R (NZ.D 2750)
£982 $1807 €1434 Untitled (33x46cm-13x18in) s.d.1994 canvasboard. 25-Mar-4 International Art Centre, Auckland #28/R (NZ.D 2750)
£1000 $1810 €1460 Al-Lita's for Lala (101x103cm-40x41in) init.i.d.15.15.76 acrylic on paper. 30-Mar-4 Peter Webb, Auckland #164/R est:3000-5000 (NZ.D 2800)
£1224 $2227 €1787 Untitled grid (166x141cm-65x56in) s.d.3.74 acrylic prov. 29-Jun-4 Peter Webb, Auckland #154/R est:5000-7000 (NZ.D 3500)
£1487 $2558 €2171 Red tower (80x28cm-31x11in) s.i.d.1976. 3-Dec-3 Dunbar Sloane, Auckland #63 est:2000-3000 (NZ.D 4000)
£1692 $2876 €2470 Untitled (45x45cm-18x18in) s.d.1997 verso. 27-Nov-3 International Art Centre, Auckland #13/R est:3500-4500 (NZ.D 4500)
£1880 $3195 €2745 Lattice 141 (82x89cm-32x35in) s.i.d.15/7/76 acrylic on paper. 26-Nov-3 Dunbar Sloane, Wellington #19/R est:7000-12000 (NZ.D 5000)
£2604 $4141 €3802 2 forms (79x79cm-31x31in) s. i.d.6-75 verso prov. 1-May-3 Dunbar Sloane, Wellington #40/R est:5000-7000 (NZ.D 7500)
£2935 $4725 €4285 Proclivity picture (91x91cm-36x36in) s.d.verso. 20-Aug-3 Dunbar Sloane, Auckland #36/R est:10000-15000 (NZ.D 8100)
£3172 $5487 €4631 Grid (74x119cm-29x47in) 9-Dec-3 Peter Webb, Auckland #134/R est:5000-7000 (NZ.D 8500)
£4286 $7757 €6258 From blue to white (91x91cm-36x36in) s.i.d.2000 prov. 30-Mar-4 Peter Webb, Auckland #56/R est:12000-18000 (NZ.D 12000)
£4851 $8392 €7082 Composition with blue (98x80cm-39x31in) init.i.d.17.7.76. 9-Dec-3 Peter Webb, Auckland #131/R est:10000-15000 (NZ.D 13000)
£5455 $8564 €7910 In memory of Tony Fomison (91x91cm-36x36in) s.i.verso. 27-Aug-3 Dunbar Sloane, Wellington #27/R est:18000-25000 (NZ.D 15000)
Works on paper
£297 $512 €434 Untitled (110x72cm-43x28in) crayon prov. 3-Dec-3 Dunbar Sloane, Auckland #21 (NZ.D 800)
£346 $619 €505 Untitled Union Jack lattice (29x25cm-11x10in) s.d.4/84 W/C acrylic. 12-May-4 Dunbar Sloane, Wellington #210 est:1250-2000 (NZ.D 1000)
£346 $619 €505 Untitled abstract (41x58cm-16x23in) init.d.6.2.83 W/C. 11-May-4 Peter Webb, Auckland #62/R est:1000-2000 (NZ.D 1000)
£440 $813 €642 Alpha, omega and anchor. s.i.d.89 W/C. 9-Mar-4 Watson's, Christchurch #70 est:2000-3000 (NZ.D 1200)
£519 $929 €758 Grid (76x80cm-30x31in) W/C. 11-May-4 Peter Webb, Auckland #163/R est:1500-3000 (NZ.D 1500)
£564 $959 €823 Omega (38x37cm-15x15in) s.d.1989 W/C. 27-Nov-3 International Art Centre, Auckland #25/R (NZ.D 1500)
£746 $1291 €1089 Abstract grid composition (21x24cm-8x9in) mixed media card. 9-Dec-3 Peter Webb, Auckland #173/R (NZ.D 2000)
£839 $1527 €1225 Alpha omega and anchor - eternal hope (60x42cm-24x17in) init.i.d.26.9.89 W/C. 29-Jun-4 Peter Webb, Auckland #188/R est:3000-4000 (NZ.D 2400)
£865 $1548 €1263 Untitled lattice (40x57cm-16x22in) init.d.3/2/83 W/C pastel. 12-May-4 Dunbar Sloane, Wellington #137/R est:2000-4000 (NZ.D 2500)
£1224 $2227 €1787 Behind the bridge (111x72cm-44x28in) init.i.d.9.10.77 pastel. 29-Jun-4 Peter Webb, Auckland #155/R est:5000-8000 (NZ.D 3500)
£1493 $2582 €2180 Fear of the world, alpha, omega and order (63x41cm-25x16in) init.i.d.29.9.89 W/C. 9-Dec-3 Peter Webb, Auckland #170/R est:4000-6000 (NZ.D 4000)
£1504 $2556 €2196 Old memories (55x75cm-22x30in) s.d.17/1/94 mixed media. 27-Nov-3 International Art Centre, Auckland #24/R est:3500-4500 (NZ.D 4000)

MADDOX, Conroy (1912-) British
£850 $1505 €1241 Manual of childhood (60x86cm-24x34in) s.d.83. 27-Apr-4 Bonhams, Knightsbridge #287/R
£900 $1665 €1314 The catch (29x24cm-11x9in) s.d.65 s.i.d.1965 verso oil collage board. 11-Feb-4 Sotheby's, Olympia #253/R est:1000-1500
£1400 $2590 €2044 Free associations (27x21cm-11x8in) s.d.48 canvas on board. 11-Mar-4 Christie's, Kensington #305/R est:400-600
£2600 $4134 €3796 Custodian of the street (96x76cm-38x30in) s.d.73 s.i.d.verso. 10-Sep-3 Sotheby's, Olympia #295/R est:2500-3500
£5200 $9620 €7592 Cabinet of curiosities (61x48cm-24x19in) s. 11-Feb-4 Sotheby's, Olympia #268/R est:3000-5000

MADDOX, Ronald (1930-) British
Works on paper
£300 $555 €438 Vineyard pattern Hertfordshire (21x29cm-8x11in) s. pen ink W/C. 13-Feb-4 Sworder & Son, Bishops Stortford #11/R

MADDOX, Willes (1813-1853) British
£16000 $29600 €23360 Scenes from the New Testament (36x84cm-14x33in) four over door panels lunette shaped prov. 11-Mar-4 Duke & Son, Dorchester #204/R

MADE, Ida Bagus (1915-) Indonesian
£7843 $14196 €11451 Bali life (55x67cm-22x26in) s.i. tempera cloth. 3-Apr-4 Glerum, Singapore #49/R est:15000-20000 (S.D 24000)
Works on paper
£476 $852 €700 Family preparing dinner (33x23cm-13x9in) gouache. 16-Mar-4 Christie's, Amsterdam #116/R
£476 $852 €700 Water buffaloes crossing the river (32x23cm-13x9in) gouache. 16-Mar-4 Christie's, Amsterdam #120/R
£476 $852 €700 Picking mangoes (33x23cm-13x9in) gouache. 16-Mar-4 Christie's, Amsterdam #125/R

MADELAIN, G (1867-1944) French
£1034 $1893 €1500 Notre-Dame, vue des quais (29x45cm-11x18in) s. peinture panel. 1-Feb-4 Robin & Fattori, Granville #27

MADELAIN, Gustave (1867-1944) French
£567 $948 €800 Les travailleurs pres de l'hotel de Sens a Paris (26x44cm-10x17in) s. panel. 19-Jun-3 Millon & Associes, Paris #153/R
£629 $1070 €900 Le rendez-vous des clochards (61x50cm-24x20in) s.i. 27-Nov-3 Millon & Associes, Paris #191
£1118 $2024 €1700 View of the Seine with figures and a bridge (32x43cm-13x17in) s. panel. 19-Apr-4 Glerum, Amsterdam #292 est:700-800
£1176 $2000 €1717 Vieux Montmartre (45x37cm-18x15in) s.i.d.1927. 28-Nov-3 Zofingen, Switzerland #2624 est:3000 (S.FR 2600)
£1418 $2369 €2000 Peniche sous le Pont Marie, borde de Seine, Paris (38x61cm-15x24in) s. 20-Jun-3 Drouot Estimations, Paris #66 est:1500-2000
£2273 $4000 €3319 Faubourge de la Madeleine (53x46cm-21x18in) s. prov. 23-May-4 Hindman, Chicago #59/R
£2759 $4579 €4000 Foire a la ferraille (73x92cm-29x36in) s. 1-Oct-3 Millon & Associes, Paris #70/R
£2759 $4579 €4000 Notre-Dame sous la neige (66x81cm-26x32in) s. 1-Oct-3 Millon & Associes, Paris #68/R
£2958 $5117 €4200 Paris, bords de Seine animes (39x62cm-15x24in) s. 14-Dec-3 Eric Pillon, Calais #58/R

MADELIN, Jean (20th C) French
Works on paper
£629 $1070 €900 Art de la liseuse (41x32cm-16x13in) s. col crayon chl. 27-Nov-3 Calmels Cohen, Paris #44/R

MADELINE, Paul (1863-1920) French
£570 $1061 €850 Les falaises (33x41cm-13x16in) s. 3-Mar-4 Ferri, Paris #32
£1133 $2097 €1700 Paysage au moulin (33x46cm-13x18in) s. 14-Jul-4 Livinec, Gaudcheau & Jezequel, Rennes #167
£2113 $3655 €3000 Paysage (46x55cm-18x22in) s. 9-Dec-3 Artcurial Briest, Paris #132/R est:3000-4000
£2448 $4161 €3500 Bord de riviere en Bretagne (54x65cm-21x26in) s. 28-Nov-3 Doutrebente, Paris #40/R est:4000-5000
£2482 $4145 €3500 Paysage (38x46cm-15x18in) s.i.d.05. 19-Jun-3 Millon & Associes, Paris #185/R est:3000-4000
£2667 $4907 €4000 Paysage (46x55cm-18x22in) s. prov. 14-Jun-4 Tajan, Paris #70/R est:4000-5000
£3311 $6026 €5000 Femme creusoise (54x65cm-21x26in) s. 18-Jun-4 Piasa, Paris #105/R est:5000-6000
£3620 $6154 €5285 Washing in Pyrennean village (54x65cm-21x26in) s. prov. 19-Nov-3 Fischer, Luzern #1116/R est:8000-12000 (S.FR 8000)
£3841 $7029 €5800 Vue de la Creuse (55x65cm-22x26in) s.prov. 9-Apr-4 Bailly Pommery, Paris #77/R est:4000-6000
£3841 $7029 €5800 Village au bord de l'eau (37x46cm-15x18in) s. prov. 9-Apr-4 Bailly Pommery, Paris #79/R est:3000-4000
£4133 $7523 €6200 Bord de riviere ombrage (38x46cm-15x18in) s. 4-Jul-4 Eric Pillon, Calais #88/R
£4636 $8483 €7000 Paris - Le pont du Carroussel (46x54cm-18x21in) s.d.18. 7-Apr-4 Piasa, Paris #119/R est:5000-6000
£4967 $9040 €7500 Sechage des filets, Douarnenez (60x73cm-24x29in) 18-Jun-4 Piasa, Paris #24/R est:5000-7000
£5233 $9000 €7640 Warm afternoon in autumn, Crozant (60x73cm-24x29in) prov. 3-Dec-3 Doyle, New York #136/R est:6000-8000
£6993 $11888 €10000 Bord de riviere, automne (60x77cm-24x30in) s.d.16. 28-Nov-3 Doutrebente, Paris #41/R est:5000-6000
£16556 $30298 €25000 View of Brittany (81x100cm-32x39in) s. 9-Apr-4 Bailly Pommery, Paris #78/R est:6000-8000

MADER, Bruno (19/20th C) ?
£982 $1699 €1434 Game of chess (66x54cm-26x21in) s.i.d.1903/05 verso after K Vermehren. 15-Dec-3 Lilla Bukowskis, Stockholm #917 (S.KR 12500)

MADER, Heribert (1937-) Austrian
Works on paper
£267 $491 €400 Italian houses (31x44cm-12x17in) s.d.91 W/C. 9-Jun-4 Dorotheum, Salzburg #714/R

MADERSON, Arthur (1942-) British
£440 $792 €642 Summer landscape scene on the Somerset Levels (28x30cm-11x12in) s. oil pastel canvas on board. 22-Apr-4 Lawrence, Crewkerne #959
£460 $828 €672 Early morning, low tide, Kilve (24x29cm-9x11in) init. s.d.18.5.86 board. 22-Apr-4 Lawrence, Crewkerne #963
£570 $1021 €850 Overhearing a word in confidence (24x19cm-9x7in) s. i.verso panel. 31-May-4 Hamilton Osborne King, Dublin #13/R

£647 $1170 €970 Street scene. Beach scene (39x29cm-15x11in) s.verso board double-sided. 30-Mar-4 De Veres Art Auctions, Dublin #128/R
£750 $1403 €1125 Winter sunshine, Charlton Mackerell (47x70cm-19x28in) s. s.d.18.5.86 verso board. 26-Jul-4 Bonhams, Bath #37/R
£780 $1404 €1139 Evening study, near Glastonbury (49x57cm-19x22in) s. board. 22-Apr-4 Lawrence, Crewkerne #961
£800 $1440 €1168 Hazy sun, Weston (34x34cm-13x13in) s. board. 22-Apr-4 Lawrence, Crewkerne #964/R
£820 $1476 €1197 Distant rain, view on the Somerset Levels (62x89cm-24x35in) s. canvas on board. 22-Apr-4 Lawrence, Crewkerne #962
£1250 $2250 €1825 End of a hot day, Weymouth (47x51cm-19x20in) s. canvas on board. 22-Apr-4 Lawrence, Crewkerne #965/R est:500-700
£1600 $2880 €2336 Studio by moonlight (59x46cm-23x18in) s. s.d.18.5.86 verso board. 22-Apr-4 Lawrence, Crewkerne #960 est:300-400
£2013 $3604 €3000 From the Upper Pool (74x74cm-29x29in) s. i. verso board. 31-May-4 Hamilton Osborne King, Dublin #112/R est:3000-4000
£2535 $4437 €3600 Figures against evening light, Lerici, Tuscany coast (61x56cm-24x22in) s. s.i.verso board. 16-Dec-3 James Adam, Dublin #135/R est:1500-2500
£2568 $4853 €3800 Point of sunset , study San Terenzo, Lerici, Tuscany Coast (62x57cm-24x22in) s. s.i.verso board. 17-Feb-4 Whyte's, Dublin #183/R est:3000-4000
£3467 $6275 €5200 Beach study, Lerici, Italy (107x78cm-42x31in) s.i.verso board. 31-Mar-4 James Adam, Dublin #137/R est:3000-5000
£4430 $7840 €6600 A particular time of day, Tallow horse fair, County Waterford (81x112cm-32x44in) s. s.i.verso acrylic gouache oil pastel board. 27-Apr-4 Whyte's, Dublin #193/R est:4000-5000
£6993 $11888 €10000 September evening, river Dordogne (163x122cm-64x48in) s. s.i.verso panel. 18-Nov-3 Whyte's, Dublin #209/R est:5000-7000
Works on paper
£570 $1021 €850 Orchard, September evening (25x30cm-10x12in) s. i. mixed media. 31-May-4 Hamilton Osborne King, Dublin #231
£620 $1116 €905 Early morning, Dordogne (59x48cm-23x19in) s. pastel. 22-Apr-4 Lawrence, Crewkerne #958
£1667 $3000 €2500 Bourgeoisie at sunset, Lerici, Ligurian coast, Italy (78x73cm-31x29in) s. i.verso mixed media. 20-Apr-4 James Adam, Dublin #13/R est:1500-2500
£2013 $3604 €3000 Dusk le Vigan (81x112cm-32x44in) s.i.verso mixed media. 26-May-4 James Adam, Dublin #137/R est:3000-5000
£2953 $5286 €4400 In a glancing light (81x112cm-32x44in) s.i.verso mixed media. 26-May-4 James Adam, Dublin #138/R est:3000-5000
£4014 $6423 €5700 Point of sunset, study, Tallow Horse Fair (49x409cm-19x161in) s. s.i.d.April 2003 verso mixed media board. 16-Sep-3 Whyte's, Dublin #206/R est:4000-5000

MADEYSKA, Arika (1928-) Polish
£424 $767 €636 Landscape (45x54cm-18x21in) s. oil collage painted 1956-60. 4-Apr-4 Agra, Warsaw #50/R (P.Z 3000)

MADGE, Donald James (1920-) South African
£347 $621 €507 Street scene with Cape cottages (29x59cm-11x23in) s. canvas on board. 31-May-4 Stephan Welz, Johannesburg #153 (SA.R 4200)
£454 $813 €663 Street scene with figures (60x90cm-24x35in) s. canvas on board. 31-May-4 Stephan Welz, Johannesburg #278 (SA.R 5500)

MADGWICK, Clive (1934-) British
£250 $468 €375 Morning catch (33x53cm-13x21in) s. 21-Jul-4 John Nicholson, Haslemere #106
£300 $561 €438 Hill farm, mid Wales, spring (20x30cm-8x12in) s. 24-Feb-4 Canterbury Auctions, UK #150
£480 $878 €720 Moving to a new draw (50x75cm-20x30in) s.i.verso. 12-Jul-4 Mullucks Wells, Bishop's Stortford #425/R
£520 $962 €759 Fisherman's hut on a pebble beach (30x40cm-12x16in) s. 16-Feb-4 Bonhams, Bath #147
£920 $1592 €1343 Sunday Morning, Chelsworth (29x47cm-11x19in) s. 11-Dec-3 Olivers, Sudbury #119/R

MADIAI, Mario (1944-) Italian
£364 $663 €550 Venice (70x60cm-28x24in) s.i.d.1976. 17-Jun-4 Galleria Pananti, Florence #13/R
£633 $1165 €950 Islamic town (60x80cm-24x31in) s. s.verso. 11-Jun-4 Farsetti, Prato #442

MADIGAN, Martha (1950-) American
Photographs
£2156 $3600 €3148 Geneta Mana (146x100cm-57x39in) s.i.d.2000 gelatin silver photogram. 17-Oct-3 Phillips, New York #204/R est:7000-10000

MADIOL, Adrien Jean (1845-1892) Dutch
£1408 $2465 €2000 In de Branding (47x35cm-19x14in) s.d.1888 panel. 16-Dec-3 Galerie Moderne, Brussels #742/R est:3000-4000

MADLENER, Josef (1881-1967) German
£6000 $10800 €9000 Children and sheep by wayside shrine (60x82cm-24x32in) s. lit. 22-Apr-4 Allgauer, Kempten #3639/R est:5000
£6338 $11345 €9000 Young girl in front of wayside shrine in an extensive landscape (60x81cm-24x32in) s. lit. 8-Jan-4 Allgauer, Kempten #2456/R est:5000
Works on paper
£322 $590 €480 Field worker in extensive wooded hilly landscape (17x24cm-7x9in) s. W/C gouache lit. 8-Jul-4 Allgauer, Kempten #2009/R

MADONI, Enrico (1862-1928) Italian
£3684 $6779 €5600 Landscape with buffaloes at pasture and shepherd (45x64cm-18x25in) init.d.1886. 22-Jun-4 Babuino, Rome #433/R est:2000-2500

MADOU, Jean Baptiste (1796-1877) Belgian
£500 $895 €750 Interieur anime (40x29cm-16x11in) mono. canvas on panel. 11-May-4 Vanderkindere, Brussels #589
£578 $1000 €844 Interior scene (20x18cm-8x7in) init. panel. 13-Dec-3 Charlton Hall, Columbia #448/R est:1000-1500
£2000 $3600 €3000 At the bookshop (32x19cm-13x7in) s.d.1873 panel. 21-Apr-4 Christie's, Amsterdam #188/R est:3000-4000
£17763 $32151 €27000 Hunting day (48x60cm-19x24in) s.d.1863 board. 14-Apr-4 Ansorena, Madrid #60a/R est:25000
Works on paper
£413 $756 €620 Les politiques (28x22cm-11x9in) mono.d.1870 crayon wash prov.exhib. 7-Jun-4 Palais de Beaux Arts, Brussels #274/R
£427 $781 €640 Le cordonnier (34x28cm-13x11in) mono.d.1872 crayon wash. 7-Jun-4 Palais de Beaux Arts, Brussels #273/R
£458 $792 €650 Smoker (19x15cm-7x6in) mono. black chl gouache prov. 13-Dec-3 De Vuyst, Lokeren #213
£629 $1070 €900 Interieur d'auberge anime (15x17cm-6x7in) s.d.49 ink chl W/C. 18-Nov-3 Vanderkindere, Brussels #2
£845 $1462 €1200 Grenadier (18x15cm-7x6in) s.d.1833 W/C. 13-Dec-3 De Vuyst, Lokeren #212
£867 $1560 €1300 Tavern scene (29x43cm-11x17in) mono. chl gouache washed ink. 26-Apr-4 Bernaerts, Antwerp #42/R
£1918 $3260 €2800 Famille de l'artiste (42x68cm-17x27in) dr set of 13. 10-Nov-3 Horta, Bruxelles #70
£2465 $4264 €3500 La vendeuse de bijoux (24x29cm-9x11in) s. W/C. 9-Dec-3 Campo, Vlaamse Kaai #351/R est:3500-4000
£4167 $6625 €6000 Liseur (32x48cm-13x19in) s. W/C. 9-Sep-3 Vanderkindere, Brussels #50/R

MADOU, Jean Baptiste (attrib) (1796-1877) Belgian
£2098 $3566 €3000 La prison du temple (36x50cm-14x20in) panel. 18-Nov-3 Vanderkindere, Brussels #8 est:2000-3000

MADRASSI, Luca (1848-1919) Italian
Sculpture
£1711 $3147 €2600 Couple de jeunes gens (74cm-29in) s. pat bronze. 25-Jun-4 Rossini, Paris #157/R est:2000-3000
£2465 $4264 €3500 Bust of girl (50cm-20in) s. terracotta. 10-Dec-3 Sotheby's, Milan #151/R est:500-700
£2500 $4550 €3650 Shepherd's star (96cm-38in) s. copper brown pat bronze lit. 15-Jun-4 Sotheby's, Olympia #133/R est:1500-2000
£6200 $11346 €9052 Figure of a maiden (81cm-32in) bronze. 3-Jun-4 Sotheby's, Olympia #117/R est:4000-5000

MADRASSI, Ludovic Lucien (1881-1956) French
Sculpture
£1701 $3113 €2483 Mother and child (85cm-33in) s. pat.bronze on red marble base. 2-Jun-4 Rasmussen, Copenhagen #1306/R est:15000-20000 (D.KR 19000)
Works on paper
£749 $1340 €1100 Portrait de jeune fille, un noeud dans les cheveux (25x19cm-10x7in) s. pastel exhib. 17-Mar-4 Tajan, Paris #176/R

MADRAZO DE OCHOA, Federico de (1875-1934) Spanish
£7500 $13800 €10950 Un momento de pensiero (86x58cm-34x23in) s. 25-Mar-4 Christie's, Kensington #158/R est:3000-4000

MADRAZO Y GARRETA, Raimundo de (1841-1920) Spanish
£4000 $7360 €5840 Elegant lady (26x17cm-10x7in) s. panel. 23-Mar-4 Bonhams, New Bond Street #94/R est:4000-6000
£27586 $49655 €40000 Portrait of lady (81x65cm-32x26in) s.d.90. 26-Jan-4 Durán, Madrid #208/R est:24000
£68966 $124138 €100000 Aline (61x43cm-24x17in) s. board. 26-Jan-4 Durán, Madrid #220/R est:95000
£88235 $150000 €128823 Hot Chocolate (86x66cm-34x26in) s. prov.exhib. 28-Oct-3 Sotheby's, New York #9/R est:100000-150000
£90909 $151818 €130000 Aline in the changing room (64x50cm-25x20in) s. 30-Jun-3 Ansorena, Madrid #349/R est:130000
Works on paper
£5594 $9343 €8000 Portrait of Aline Masson (56x38cm-22x15in) chl dr. 30-Jun-3 Ansorena, Madrid #349a/R est:8000

MADRAZO Y GARRETA, Ricardo de (1852-1917) Spanish
£8163 $14612 €12000 Lady (114x80cm-45x31in) s. 22-Mar-4 Durán, Madrid #211/R est:1300

MADRAZO Y KUNTZ, Luis (1825-1879) Spanish
£1552 $2591 €2250 Court figure (66x45cm-26x18in) s. 17-Nov-3 Durán, Madrid #137/R est:1200

MADRAZO Y KUNTZ, don Federigo de (1815-1894) Spanish
£2241 $3743 €3250 Portrait of woman (66x54cm-26x21in) s.d.1873. 17-Nov-3 Durán, Madrid #196/R est:3000

MADRAZO, Federico and Luis de (19th C) Spanish
£4770 $8776 €7250 Last Supper (55x122cm-22x48in) s.d.1842. 22-Jun-4 Durán, Madrid #182/R est:6500

MADRIGAL ARCIA, Mario (20th C) Latin American
£310 $514 €450 Presencia ante el crepusculo (120x130cm-47x51in) d.1997. 12-Jun-3 Louis Morton, Mexico #84/R est:1500-1800 (M.P 5400)

MADRIGALI, Olynthe (20th C) ?
£2553 $4264 €3600 Vers la pointe pescade, environs d'Alger (45x65cm-18x26in) s. panel exhib.lit. 16-Jun-3 Gros & Delettrez, Paris #250/R est:3500-4000

MADRITSCH, Karl (1908-1986) Swiss
£517 $926 €755 Reclining female nude (34x54cm-13x21in) s.d.60 canvas on board. 12-May-4 Dobiaschofsky, Bern #768/R (S.FR 1200)

MADRIZ, Leopoldo la (20th C) Venezuelan?
£323 $500 €472 Seascape (50x65cm-20x26in) s. panel. 29-Sep-2 Subastas Odalys, Caracas #71/R

MADSEN, H C (19/20th C) Danish
£269 $484 €393 Chr IV and Kristen Munk walking by Rosenborg Palace (52x43cm-20x17in) s.d.1903. 24-Apr-4 Rasmussen, Havnen #2224 (D.KR 3000)

MADSEN, Sophie (1829-1856) Danish
£2249 $3869 €3284 The Devil's dandelion (21x15cm-8x6in) s. study panel painted c.1852 prov. 3-Dec-3 Museumsbygningen, Copenhagen #192/R est:12000-15000 (D.KR 24000)

MADSEN, Viggo (1885-1954) Danish
£282 $480 €412 Green landscape (72x100cm-28x39in) mono. 29-Nov-3 Rasmussen, Havnen #2091 (D.KR 3000)
£303 $485 €442 Sitting room interior (53x67cm-21x26in) mono.d.1904 exhib. 22-Sep-3 Rasmussen, Vejle #46/R (D.KR 3200)
£452 $810 €660 Landscape from Skagen (72x100cm-28x39in) mono. exhib. 10-May-4 Rasmussen, Vejle #681/R (D.KR 5000)

MADURA, Jean (19/20th C) Italian
£262 $477 €383 Oriental birdcatcher (79x48cm-31x19in) s. 16-Jun-4 Fischer, Luzern #2262/R (S.FR 600)

MADYOL, Jacques (1871-1950) Belgian
£322 $537 €460 Eze en Provence (32x23cm-13x9in) s. panel. 13-Oct-3 Horta, Bruxelles #475
£496 $829 €700 La bohemienne (100x80cm-39x31in) s. 17-Jun-3 Vanderkindere, Brussels #24
£496 $829 €700 Joie maternelle (72x57cm-28x22in) s. 17-Jun-3 Vanderkindere, Brussels #108
£503 $931 €750 La vallee du Var, Alpes Maritimes (60x80cm-24x31in) s. 15-Mar-4 Horta, Bruxelles #23
£1000 $1810 €1500 La surprise (36x27cm-14x11in) s.d.1886 panel. 30-Mar-4 Campo & Campo, Antwerp #167/R est:2000-4000
£1259 $2140 €1800 Port de Cassis, Provence (54x65cm-21x26in) s.d.1914. 1-Dec-3 Palais de Beaux Arts, Brussels #277 est:1800-2400

MAECKER, Franz Wilhelm (1855-1913) German
£811 $1451 €1200 Sailing boats on Fjord near Ekensund (60x110cm-24x43in) s. lit. 8-May-4 Hans Stahl, Toestorf #73

MAEDA, Josaku (1926-) Japanese
£1529 $2600 €2232 No.7 jardin des delices (114x89cm-45x35in) s. oil ink on burlap prov.exhib. 9-Nov-3 Wright, Chicago #418 est:3000-4000
£3691 $6903 €5500 Paysage humain (116x81cm-46x32in) s. s.i.d.1961 verso prov. 29-Feb-4 Versailles Encheres #268 est:250-300
£8000 $14720 €11680 Jardin des delices no. 7 (116x89cm-46x35in) s. s.i.d.1959 verso oil ink paper on burlap prov.exhib. 24-Jun-4 Sotheby's, London #171/R est:8000-10000
Works on paper
£3741 $6697 €5500 Mystagogie d'espace (80x61cm-31x24in) s.i.d.1964 verso mixed media canvas prov. 21-Mar-4 Calmels Cohen, Paris #138/R est:4000-5000

MAEDA, Maiko (?) ?
£282 $487 €400 Reclining female nude (97x116cm-38x46in) s.d.73. 15-Dec-3 Ansorena, Madrid #1003/R
£282 $487 €400 Mother and daughter (100x73cm-39x29in) s.d.73. 15-Dec-3 Ansorena, Madrid #1018/R
£403 $749 €600 Nude, raised hands (130x90cm-51x35in) s. 2-Mar-4 Ansorena, Madrid #878/R
£625 $1031 €900 Kleelong woman (92x73cm-36x29in) s.d.73. 2-Jul-3 Ansorena, Madrid #901/R

MAEHLE, Ole (1904-1990) Norwegian
£244 $449 €366 White spring morning by the sea (60x85cm-24x33in) s. 14-Jun-4 Blomqvist, Lysaker #1276 (N.KR 3000)
£285 $525 €416 Autumn in the woods (60x72cm-24x28in) s. panel. 29-Mar-4 Blomqvist, Lysaker #1209/R (N.KR 3600)
£894 $1431 €1296 Winter night in Lofoten (90x98cm-35x39in) s. 22-Sep-3 Blomqvist, Lysaker #1216/R (N.KR 10500)

MAEHLY, Otto (1869-1953) Swiss
Works on paper
£283 $517 €413 Autumn landscape in the Jura region (37x56cm-15x22in) mono.i.d.05 s.i.verso mixed media. 4-Jun-4 Zofingen, Switzerland #2877 (S.FR 650)

MAENPAA, Arvid (1899-1976) Finnish
£952 $1733 €1400 Every day life (15x18cm-6x7in) s.d.1933. 8-Feb-4 Bukowskis, Helsinki #406/R

MAENTEL, Jacob (1763-1863) American
Works on paper
£2469 $4000 €3605 Woman holding rose. Man in blue jacket and trousers (25x18cm-10x7in) W/C pair lit. 1-Aug-3 North East Auctions, Portsmouth #607/R
£2568 $4750 €3749 Woman in blue dress (25x16cm-10x6in) W/C ink executed c.1825. 15-Jan-4 Sotheby's, New York #297/R est:6000-8000
£5398 $9500 €7881 Portrait of a dark haired young woman seated in a chair with a child on her lap (20x15cm-8x6in) W/C pen ink sold with another. 18-May-4 Sotheby's, New York #102/R est:12000-18000
£7027 $13000 €10259 Portrait of Elizabeth Culp Bixler and Joseph Bixler (27x32cm-11x13in) i. W/C pen ink pair. 15-Jan-4 Sotheby's, New York #298/R est:6000-10000
£7386 $13000 €10784 Two young girls holding hands (20x15cm-8x6in) W/C. 21-May-4 Pook & Pook, Downington #251/R est:8000-10000
£12791 $22000 €18675 Portraits of Henry and Christiannah Hubbert Welsh (33x20cm-13x8in) W/C pair prov. 6-Dec-3 Pook & Pook, Downington #200/R est:10000-15000

MAENTEL, Jacob (attrib) (1763-1863) American
Works on paper
£3194 $5750 €4663 Portrait of a woman (18x28cm-7x11in) W/C. 20-Apr-4 Bunch, West Chester #391/R est:5000-7000

MAERTELAERE, Edmond de (1876-1938) Belgian
£5245 $8916 €7500 Bouquets de fleurs sur une table (100x150cm-39x59in) s. 1-Dec-3 Palais de Beaux Arts, Brussels #42/R est:4500-5000
Works on paper
£1000 $1660 €1460 Lady with a fan (95x67cm-37x26in) s. pastel. 1-Oct-3 Sotheby's, Olympia #188/R est:1000-1500

MAERTENS, Medard (1875-1946) Belgian
£382 $638 €550 Nature morte au moulin a cafe (60x75cm-24x30in) s. panel. 21-Oct-3 Galerie Moderne, Brussels #356/R
£436 $807 €650 Le lecteur satisfait (66x55cm-26x22in) s. 15-Mar-4 Horta, Bruxelles #316
£461 $847 €700 Paysage meridional (39x61cm-15x24in) s. 22-Jun-4 Palais de Beaux Arts, Brussels #279
£533 $965 €800 Vue de village (38x46cm-15x18in) s. panel. 30-Mar-4 Palais de Beaux Arts, Brussels #648
£1818 $3091 €2600 Jeune artiste devant son chevalet (29x19cm-11x7in) s. cardboard. 1-Dec-3 Palais de Beaux Arts, Brussels #276/R est:800-1200
£3311 $6026 €5000 Paysage (70x60cm-28x24in) s. 15-Jun-4 Galerie Moderne, Brussels #396/R est:1000-1500

MAERZ, Richard (1810-1871) Austrian
£1342 $2470 €2000 Tyrolean dance evening in tavern (35x41cm-14x16in) s.d.1851. 24-Mar-4 Hugo Ruef, Munich #1038/R est:2500

MAES, E R (1849-1931) Belgian
£10000 $17900 €15000 Hen fight (60x94cm-24x37in) s. 15-May-4 De Vuyst, Lokeren #424/R est:15000-17000

MAES, Eugène Remy (1849-1931) Belgian
£688 $1100 €1004 Chickens and roosters (13x18cm-5x7in) s. panel. 21-Sep-3 William Jenack, New York #308
£816 $1486 €1200 Haybarges and two master on a calm (21x31cm-8x12in) s.d.1873 panel. 3-Feb-4 Christie's, Amsterdam #56/R est:1500-2000
£950 $1587 €1387 Cockerels and mallards on a sheltered bank (19x27cm-7x11in) s. panel. 8-Oct-3 Christie's, Kensington #729/R
£1453 $2600 €2121 Sheep and poultry (25x36cm-10x14in) s. 31-May-4 William A Smith, Plainfield #352/R
£1536 $2750 €2243 Hens and chicks in the farmyard (27x36cm-11x14in) s. i.verso panel. 6-May-4 Doyle, New York #53/R est:4000-6000
£1613 $3000 €2355 Barnyard chickens (25x40cm-10x16in) s. panel. 5-Mar-4 Skinner, Boston #243/R est:2000-4000
£1912 $3250 €2792 Stable interior with a ewe, lamb and a chicken (27x37cm-11x15in) s. s.i.verso. 19-Nov-3 Bonhams & Butterfields, San Francisco #69/R
£4667 $8447 €7000 Le poulailler (44x72cm-17x28in) s.d.1882. 30-Mar-4 Campo & Campo, Antwerp #168/R est:8000-10000
£6667 $12200 €10000 Chien surveillant le poulailler (61x95cm-24x37in) s. 7-Jun-4 Palais de Beaux Arts, Brussels #78/R est:8000-12000
£8824 $15000 €12883 Sheep, roosters and chickens in a barn (60x80cm-24x31in) s. 29-Oct-3 Christie's, Rockefeller NY #5/R est:15000-20000

MAES, Giacomo (attrib) (19th C) Italian
£5369 $9879 €8000 Extensive Campagna landscape with ruins of Acquedotto Romano (108x71cm-43x28in) s.i. 25-Mar-4 Dr Fritz Nagel, Stuttgart #739/R est:3000

MAES, Godfried (1649-1700) Flemish
Works on paper
£1300 $2379 €1898 Allegory (21x27cm-8x11in) i. pen ink wash. 7-Jul-4 Bonhams, Knightsbridge #82/R est:1500-2000

MAES, Jacques (1905-1968) Belgian
£331 $603 €500 Les avoines (50x60cm-20x24in) s. 15-Jun-4 Galerie Moderne, Brussels #332/R
£364 $663 €550 Nature morte aux legumes (80x65cm-31x26in) s.d.1937. 15-Jun-4 Galerie Moderne, Brussels #188/R
£382 $638 €550 Fauteuil rouge (46x38cm-18x15in) s. panel. 21-Oct-3 Campo & Campo, Antwerp #208
£467 $845 €700 Deux personnages attables (38x46cm-15x18in) s. panel. 30-Mar-4 Palais de Beaux Arts, Brussels #651
£541 $968 €800 Vue du Palais Royal (65x80cm-26x31in) s.d.1938 s.verso sold with another oil. 10-May-4 Horta, Bruxelles #470
£567 $948 €800 Le Palais Royal a Bruxelles (65x80cm-26x31in) s. 17-Jun-3 Galerie Moderne, Brussels #335
£625 $994 €900 Composition a la figurine et au bouquet fleuri (80x65cm-31x26in) s.d.1928. 15-Sep-3 Horta, Bruxelles #432
£769 $1285 €1100 L'enfant a la poupee (80x65cm-31x26in) s. 13-Oct-3 Horta, Bruxelles #335
£946 $1665 €1400 Girl with doll (80x65cm-31x26in) s. 24-May-4 Bernaerts, Antwerp #642

MAES, Jan (1876-1974) Belgian
£533 $965 €800 Bergere sous le soleil du printemps (91x68cm-36x27in) s. 30-Mar-4 Campo & Campo, Antwerp #169

MAES, Jan Baptist Lodewyck (1794-1856) Flemish
£7059 $12000 €10306 Young maiden filling an oil lamp (96x72cm-38x28in) s.d.1835. 29-Oct-3 Christie's, Rockefeller NY #139/R est:10000-15000

MAES, Nicolaes (1632-1693) Dutch
£5500 $9130 €8030 Portrait of Anna de Veer, three quarter length wearing black and white dress (95x77cm-37x30in) 30-Sep-3 Sotheby's, London #330/R est:6000-8000
£8333 $15000 €12166 Portrait of a nobleman wearing a European order (44x31cm-17x12in) s.d.1675 painted oval prov.exhib.lit. 23-Jan-4 Christie's, Rockefeller NY #179/R est:15000-20000
£14000 $23800 €20440 Portrait of Rochus van der Does, Raadsheer and Schepen of Utrecht (107x91cm-42x36in) s.d.1675 prov.lit. 29-Oct-3 Christie's, London #38/R est:10000-15000

MAES, Nicolaes (circle) (1632-1693) Dutch
£433 $775 €632 Peasant woman with pots of vegetables (47x37cm-19x15in) 22-Mar-4 Philippe Schuler, Zurich #4416/R (S.FR 1000)

MAES, Nicolaes (style) (1632-1693) Dutch
£388 $694 €566 Man's portrait (53x52cm-21x20in) 13-May-4 Stuker, Bern #241 (S.FR 900)

MAES, Victor (20th C) Belgian?
£467 $835 €700 In the kitchen garden (80x100cm-31x39in) s. 15-May-4 De Vuyst, Lokeren #203

MAESTRI, Michelangelo (?-1812) Italian
£2500 $4600 €3800 Day, hour V (38x27cm-15x11in) s. tempera paper. 22-Jun-4 Finarte Semenzato, Rome #253/R est:3000-3500
Prints
£2448 $4088 €3500 Les quatre heures, d'apres Raphael (38x27cm-15x11in) s. engraving htd gouache. 26-Jun-3 Artcurial Briest, Paris #514 est:3000-4500
Works on paper
£3800 $6992 €5548 Medea in a chariot (36x52cm-14x20in) W/C gouache sold with another by the same hand. 24-Mar-4 Hamptons Fine Art, Godalming #235/R
£7382 $13731 €11000 Venus, Junon, Mercure et Diane (36x43cm-14x17in) s. gouache set of four after Raphael. 8-Mar-4 Artcurial Briest, Paris #11/R est:15000

MAESTRI, Michelangelo (attrib) (?-1812) Italian
Works on paper
£596 $1085 €900 Marte - man in two horse chariot (45x58cm-18x23in) s.i. gouache. 19-Jun-4 Dannenberg, Berlin #594/R

MAETZEL-JOHANNSEN, Dorothea (1886-1930) German
Works on paper
£467 $835 €700 Nude couple in landscape (24x31cm-9x12in) chk. 15-May-4 Bassenge, Berlin #7009/R

MAEXMONTAN, Frans (1847-1901) Finnish
£4545 $7727 €6500 Seascape with vessels by coast (60x97cm-24x38in) s. 29-Nov-3 Bukowskis, Helsinki #56/R est:7000-9000

MAEYER, Jacky de (20th C) Belgian?
£417 $696 €600 Zeefaun 1 (125x100cm-49x39in) s. d.1967 verso panel. 21-Oct-3 Campo, Vlaamse Kaai #410
£556 $928 €800 Zeekoningin (170x125cm-67x49in) s. d.1965 verso panel. 21-Oct-3 Campo, Vlaamse Kaai #411

MAEYER, Marcel (1920-) Belgian
£1944 $3247 €2800 Trottoir (122x85cm-48x33in) s.d.1975. 21-Oct-3 Campo, Vlaamse Kaai #490 est:2500-3500

MAEZTU, Gustavo de (1887-1947) Spanish
Works on paper
£461 $847 €700 Nude (100x64cm-39x25in) s. dr. 22-Jun-4 Durán, Madrid #58/R
£987 $1816 €1500 Resting (65x100cm-26x39in) s. dr. 22-Jun-4 Durán, Madrid #77/R
£1678 $3003 €2500 Female nude (99x62cm-39x24in) s. chl dr. 25-May-4 Durán, Madrid #161/R est:800

MAFAI, Antonietta Raphael (1900-1975) Italian
Works on paper
£769 $1308 €1100 Woman with glove (28x22cm-11x9in) s. Chinese ink double-sided. 20-Nov-3 Finarte Semenzato, Milan #132/R est:1000-1400
£1399 $2378 €2000 Face (28x22cm-11x9in) Chinese ink prov. 20-Nov-3 Finarte Semenzato, Milan #140/R est:2000-2200

MAFAI, Mario (1902-1965) Italian
£6944 $10972 €10000 Dry flowers (50x60cm-20x24in) painted 1958. 6-Sep-3 Meeting Art, Vercelli #746 est:10000
£10345 $17276 €15000 Rooftops in Rome (37x64cm-15x25in) s. 17-Nov-3 Sant Agostino, Torino #254/R est:14000-18000

MAFFEI, Alessandro (c.1780-1859) Italian
Works on paper
£5352 $9259 €7600 Street in Siena (24x30cm-9x12in) s. pen ink W/C. 9-Dec-3 Pandolfini, Florence #190/R est:1600-1800

MAFFEI, Francesco (circle) (1620-1660) Italian
£9061 $16672 €13500 Le Christ (69x57cm-27x22in) 24-Mar-4 Tajan, Paris #33/R est:3000-4000

MAFFEI, Francesco (style) (1620-1660) Italian
£7800 $13494 €11388 Madonna and Child (52x37cm-20x15in) oil on alabaster. 9-Dec-3 Sotheby's, Olympia #399/R est:5000-7000

MAFLI, Walter (1915-) Swiss
£229 $383 €332 Femme au debarcadere, St Tropez (42x32cm-17x13in) s. i.verso cardboard. 21-Jun-3 Galerie du Rhone, Sion #393 (S.FR 500)
£302 $540 €441 Young woman with red hat (48x38cm-19x15in) s.d.57 canvas on board. 12-May-4 Dobiaschofsky, Bern #3732 (S.FR 700)
£362 $615 €529 Portrait of young woman wearing white blouse (65x54cm-26x21in) s. 19-Nov-3 Fischer, Luzern #2199/R (S.FR 800)
£448 $749 €654 Corsy (54x65cm-21x26in) s.d.61 s.i. stretcher. 24-Oct-3 Hans Widmer, St Gallen #68/R (S.FR 1000)
£455 $755 €660 Le port d'Ouchy (54x65cm-21x26in) s.i. verso. 13-Jun-3 Zofingen, Switzerland #2927 (S.FR 1000)
Works on paper
£529 $899 €772 Winter landscape (50x61cm-20x24in) s. i. verso mixed media canvas. 5-Nov-3 Dobiaschofsky, Bern #762/R (S.FR 1200)

MAGAARD, Valdemar (1864-1937) Danish
£374 $591 €542 Mother and daughter washing (43x38cm-17x15in) s.d.1917. 2-Sep-3 Rasmussen, Copenhagen #1997 (D.KR 4000)

MAGAFAN, Ethel (1916-) American
£516 $950 €753 Grey mountain (15x33cm-6x13in) s.i.verso board. 10-Jun-4 Swann Galleries, New York #157/R

MAGALHAES, Roberto (1940-) Brazilian
£4304 $7876 €6456 The hunter, Saturn (46x65cm-18x26in) s.i.d.1997. 6-Jul-4 Bolsa de Arte, Rio de Janeiro #175/R (B.R 23500)
£21978 $38901 €32967 Imaginary city (100x200cm-39x79in) s.d.1986. 27-Apr-4 Bolsa de Arte, Rio de Janeiro #87/R (B.R 120000)

MAGANI, Mick (c.1920-1984) Australian
Works on paper
£781 $1461 €1172 Wongar dog story (75x35cm-30x14in) earth pigments eucalyptus bark exec.c.1962 prov. 26-Jul-4 Sotheby's, Melbourne #405/R (A.D 2000)
£2148 $4018 €3222 Untitled, fish ceremony (102x55cm-40x22in) earth pigments eucalyptus bark exec.c.1965 prov. 26-Jul-4 Sotheby's, Melbourne #407/R est:7000-10000 (A.D 5500)

MAGANZA, Alessandro (1556-1630) Italian
Works on paper
£952 $1705 €1400 Un pape entoure de cardinaux recevant un moine (21x28cm-8x11in) black chk pen brown ink. 18-Mar-4 Christie's, Paris #14/R

MAGANZA, Alessandro (attrib) (1556-1630) Italian
Works on paper
£7483 $13395 €11000 L'adoration du veau d'or (26x21cm-10x8in) pen brown ink wash black crayon. 19-Mar-4 Piasa, Paris #1/R est:4000-5000
£8333 $15000 €12166 Study of the three fates. Partial study for a Solomonic column (20x20cm-8x8in) i. pen ink wash over black chk prov. 21-Jan-4 Sotheby's, New York #28/R est:8000-12000

MAGARAM, Alexandre (1894-?) Russian
£526 $968 €800 Marine (73x92cm-29x36in) s. 25-Jun-4 Daguerre, Paris #161

MAGAZZINI, Salvatore (1955-) Italian
£265 $482 €400 Jemaa el Fna (50x60cm-20x24in) s. s.i.verso board. 17-Jun-4 Galleria Pananti, Florence #31/R
£265 $482 €400 Marrakech (50x40cm-20x16in) s. board. 17-Jun-4 Galleria Pananti, Florence #257/R
£352 $585 €500 Concerie (50x70cm-20x28in) s. s.i.verso panel. 14-Jun-3 Meeting Art, Vercelli #181/R
£352 $585 €500 Tende (50x70cm-20x28in) s. 14-Jun-3 Meeting Art, Vercelli #543
£352 $585 €500 Marrakech (50x70cm-20x28in) s. s.i.verso panel. 14-Jun-3 Meeting Art, Vercelli #396/R
£367 $675 €550 Marrakech (50x70cm-20x28in) s. board. 12-Jun-4 Meeting Art, Vercelli #561/R
£367 $675 €550 Tunis (50x70cm-20x28in) s. s.i.verso board. 12-Jun-4 Meeting Art, Vercelli #925/R
£400 $736 €600 Marrakech (50x70cm-20x28in) s. s.i.verso board. 12-Jun-4 Meeting Art, Vercelli #675/R
£433 $797 €650 Ferrandina (50x70cm-20x28in) s. s.i.verso board. 12-Jun-4 Meeting Art, Vercelli #307/R
£433 $797 €650 Tiznit (50x70cm-20x28in) s. s.i.verso board. 12-Jun-4 Meeting Art, Vercelli #896/R
£470 $869 €700 Tunis (50x70cm-20x28in) s. s.i.verso board. 13-Mar-4 Meeting Art, Vercelli #155

£503	$931	€750	Houses (60x80cm-24x31in) s.s.i.verso board. 13-Mar-4 Meeting Art, Vercelli #448
£528	$877	€750	Cortile a Zagora (80x60cm-31x24in) s. s.i.verso panel. 14-Jun-3 Meeting Art, Vercelli #218/R
£528	$877	€750	Figure (80x60cm-31x24in) s. s.i.verso panel. 14-Jun-3 Meeting Art, Vercelli #666/R
£537	$993	€800	Marrakech (50x70cm-20x28in) s. s.i.verso board. 13-Mar-4 Meeting Art, Vercelli #446
£599	$994	€850	Venezia (60x80cm-24x31in) s. s.i.verso panel. 14-Jun-3 Meeting Art, Vercelli #451/R
£604	$1117	€900	Beach (60x80cm-24x31in) s. s.i.verso board. 13-Mar-4 Meeting Art, Vercelli #173
£667	$1227	€1000	Sharm El Sheik (70x100cm-28x39in) s. card on canvas. 12-Jun-4 Meeting Art, Vercelli #227/R
£700	$1288	€1050	Landscape (70x100cm-28x39in) s. board. 12-Jun-4 Meeting Art, Vercelli #602/R
£739	$1227	€1050	Chioggia (60x80cm-24x31in) s. s.i.verso panel. 14-Jun-3 Meeting Art, Vercelli #678/R

MAGEE, Alan (1947-) American

£25926	$42000	€37593	Casting of runes 1985 (122x183cm-48x72in) acrylic prov.lit. 8-Aug-3 Barridorf, Portland #228/R est:15000-20000
Works on paper			
£746	$1350	€1089	Backview of head (41x56cm-16x22in) W/C. 16-Apr-4 American Auctioneer #259/R

MAGEE, James C (1846-1924) American

£222	$400	€324	Shepherd and his flock at dusk (64x76cm-25x30in) s. 23-Jan-4 Freeman, Philadelphia #173/R
£857	$1500	€1251	End of day (76x97cm-30x38in) s. i. on stretcher. 19-Dec-3 Sotheby's, New York #1083/R est:2000-3000

MAGER, Gus (1878-1956) American

£258	$475	€377	Sand Brook Farm (48x61cm-19x24in) s. 11-Jun-4 David Rago, Lambertville #243/R

MAGERER, H (20th C) ?

£1192	$2170	€1800	Flower seller on the Mole (65x92cm-26x36in) s. 21-Jun-4 Dorotheum, Vienna #26/R est:2000-2200

MAGGI, Cesare (1881-1961) Italian

£280	$467	€400	Bather (44x15cm-17x6in) s. board. 26-Jun-3 Sant Agostino, Torino #96/R
£284	$474	€400	Cottages in the mountains (27x34cm-11x13in) s. board. 20-Oct-3 Sant Agostino, Torino #123/R
£612	$1096	€900	Mountains (15x22cm-6x9in) s. board. 22-Mar-4 Sant Agostino, Torino #49/R
£851	$1421	€1200	Mountainous landscape (50x31cm-20x12in) s. board. 20-Oct-3 Sant Agostino, Torino #88/R
£884	$1583	€1300	Reclining female nude (34x52cm-13x20in) board. 22-Mar-4 Sant Agostino, Torino #50/R
£1409	$2495	€2100	Mountainous landscape (50x31cm-20x12in) s. board double-sided. 1-May-4 Meeting Art, Vercelli #179 est:1500
£1448	$2404	€2100	Mountainous landscape (13x18cm-5x7in) s. board. 1-Oct-3 Della Rocca, Turin #89/R
£2517	$4204	€3600	Bardonecchia (40x50cm-16x20in) s. masonite exhib. 26-Jun-3 Sant Agostino, Torino #291/R est:3000-3500
£2685	$4752	€4000	Bardonecchia (40x50cm-16x20in) s. masonite lit. 1-May-4 Meeting Art, Vercelli #223 est:4000
£3356	$5940	€5000	Summer in the mountains (41x33cm-16x13in) s.d.1921 board. 1-May-4 Meeting Art, Vercelli #452 est:5000
£6400	$11776	€9600	Flowers (73x44cm-29x17in) s. board. 14-Jun-4 Sant Agostino, Torino #329/R est:8000-10000
£9929	$16582	€14000	Houses in Courmayeur (69x60cm-27x24in) s. board painted 1930. 20-Oct-3 Sant Agostino, Torino #310/R est:14000-18000
£13000	$23920	€19500	Mount Cervino (74x100cm-29x39in) s. 8-Jun-4 Della Rocca, Turin #299/R est:15000-20000
£14094	$24946	€21000	Alleghe Church (100x70cm-39x28in) s. i.verso lit. 1-May-4 Meeting Art, Vercelli #258/R est:20000
£18792	$33638	€28000	Usseglio, Ponte dei Ladri (72x102cm-28x40in) s. i.verso. 25-May-4 Finarte Semenzato, Milan #188/R est:35000-40000
£18807	$31408	€27270	Winter landscape with figures (50x70cm-20x28in) s.d.908. 23-Jun-3 Philippe Schuler, Zurich #3568/R est:8000-12000 (S.FR 41000)
£21739	$35652	€30000	Sunset on Mount Blanc (101x100cm-40x39in) s.d.911. 27-May-3 Finarte Semenzato, Milan #57/R est:32000-35000
£25362	$41594	€35000	Mount Cervino (100x140cm-39x55in) s. 27-May-3 Finarte Semenzato, Milan #82/R est:34000
Works on paper			
£280	$467	€400	Skier (22x28cm-9x11in) s.i.d.1951 pencil. 26-Jun-3 Sant Agostino, Torino #34/R

MAGGI, Cesare (attrib) (1881-1961) Italian

£2817	$4873	€4000	Mountainous landscape covered in snow (49x69cm-19x27in) panel. 11-Dec-3 Christie's, Rome #27/R est:4300-4800

MAGGI, Gianpietro (1934-) Italian

£342	$582	€500	Loneliness (40x60cm-16x24in) s.d.1934. 7-Nov-3 Galleria Rosenberg, Milan #21/R

MAGGIONE, Piero (1931-1995) Italian

£669	$1111	€950	Giocatori di Bocce (30x40cm-12x16in) s. panel. 14-Jun-3 Meeting Art, Vercelli #90/R
£759	$1214	€1100	Landscape with sailing boats (40x50cm-16x20in) s. masonite. 13-Mar-3 Galleria Pace, Milan #11/R
£1253	$2306	€1880	Landscape (50x70cm-20x28in) s. 12-Jun-4 Meeting Art, Vercelli #843/R est:1000

MAGGIORANI, Luigi (19th C) Italian

£3049	$5457	€4452	Jeux d'Adresse (37x49cm-15x19in) s.d.1874 prov. 4-May-4 Ritchie, Toronto #90/R est:5000-7000 (C.D 7500)
Works on paper			
£270	$451	€394	Offer accepted (52x36cm-20x14in) s. W/C. 20-Oct-3 Bonhams, Bath #117
£393	$723	€574	Tambourine girl (54x37cm-21x15in) s. W/C. 25-Mar-4 International Art Centre, Auckland #163/R (NZ.D 1100)

MAGGIOTTO, Domenico (1713-1794) Italian

£2676	$4683	€3800	Girl with caged bird (46x29cm-18x11in) 17-Dec-3 Christie's, Rome #372/R est:4000-6000

MAGGIOTTO, Domenico (attrib) (1713-1794) Italian

£13333	$24000	€19466	Portrait of a young woman holding an apple (56x46cm-22x18in) 21-Jan-4 Sotheby's, New York #114/R est:6000-8000
Works on paper			
£3401	$6088	€5000	Un homme barbu assis devant une femme (41x31cm-16x12in) black white chk prov. 18-Mar-4 Christie's, Paris #43/R est:5000-7000

MAGGS, John Charles (1819-1896) British

£850	$1462	€1241	The Manchester to London mail coach on the road (40x76cm-16x30in) s. 4-Dec-3 Mellors & Kirk, Nottingham #945
£950	$1757	€1387	Exeter to Plymouth coach (30x61cm-12x24in) s.d.1873. 10-Mar-4 Sotheby's, Olympia #187/R est:600-800
£1000	$1700	€1460	Meeting on the highway (36x61cm-14x24in) 19-Nov-3 Sotheby's, Olympia #31/R est:1000-2000
£1187	$1900	€1733	George Inn, Guildford. s.d.1888. 16-Sep-3 Maynards, Vancouver #376 est:4000-6000 (C.D 2600)
£1200	$2040	€1752	London to Manchester mail coach outside the Sun Inn (35x68cm-14x27in) s. 27-Nov-3 Christie's, Kensington #105/R est:1500-2500
£1400	$2324	€2044	Outside the Bell Inn, Christmas Eve (34x67cm-13x26in) s. prov. 1-Oct-3 Woolley & Wallis, Salisbury #261/R est:800-1200
£1400	$2576	€2044	Mail coach outside the Old Fox Inn, hunt beyond (38x66cm-15x26in) s. 10-Jun-4 Christie's, Kensington #117/R est:1500-2000
£2000	$3680	€2920	Bristol, Bath and London coach in snow before an inn. Bath to Reading and London coach (30x66cm-12x26in) s. pair. 10-Jun-4 Christie's, Kensington #115/R est:2000-3000
£2500	$4425	€3650	London to Bath Mail coach outside a hostelry in winter (49x74cm-19x29in) s.d.1872. 28-Apr-4 Hampton & Littlewood, Exeter #570/R est:3500-4500
£3500	$5950	€5110	Leeds to London stagecoach (36x60cm-14x24in) s. 27-Nov-3 Sotheby's, London #373/R est:3500-5000
£3700	$6919	€5550	Exeter and London coach stopping at the Crown on a winter evening (34x65cm-13x26in) s.i.d.1882 sold with a companion. 26-Jul-4 Bonhams, Bath #78/R est:1500-2000

MAGIASSIS, Stavros (1921-1976) Greek

£1200	$2148	€1752	Boats by the harbour of Leros (59x74cm-23x29in) s. 11-May-4 Bonhams, New Bond Street #40/R est:1200-1800
£1800	$3150	€2628	View of Leros (50x70cm-20x28in) s. hardboard. 16-Dec-3 Bonhams, New Bond Street #54/R est:1200-1500

MAGIASSIS, Vassilis (1880-1926) Greek

£1300	$2275	€1898	Village house (19x24cm-7x9in) s. card. 16-Dec-3 Bonhams, New Bond Street #55/R est:1000-1500
£2000	$3580	€2920	Fishing in calm waters. Landscape (36x45cm-14x18in) one init. cardboard. 11-May-4 Bonhams, New Bond Street #28/R est:2000-3000

MAGIDEY, Vladimir (1881-?) Russian?

£317	$538	€463	Serenade (50x60cm-20x24in) s. 28-Nov-3 Zofingen, Switzerland #2625 (S.FR 700)

MAGINI, Carlo (1720-1806) Italian

£27778	$50000	€40556	Cakes, bread and fruit with decorated boxes on a partly draped table (81x102cm-32x40in) i. 23-Jan-4 Christie's, Rockefeller NY #84/R est:60000-80000

MAGINNIS, Charles Donagh (19/20th C) American

Works on paper			
£215	$400	€314	House at Annisquam (11x13cm-4x5in) mono.i. W/C paper on board. 5-Mar-4 Skinner, Boston #552/R

MAGISTRETTI, Emilio (1851-1936) Italian

£1575	$2458	€2300	Divine justice (100x50cm-39x20in) s.d.1880. 8-Apr-3 Il Ponte, Milan #608 est:2000-2500

MAGNASCO, Alessandro (1667-1749) Italian

£10417	$17708	€15000	Saint Jerome in rocky landscape (110x90cm-43x35in) prov. 28-Oct-3 Il Ponte, Milan #383/R
£13889	$23611	€20000	Saint John in landscape (110x90cm-43x35in) prov. 28-Oct-3 Il Ponte, Milan #384/R
£19444	$35000	€28388	Wooded river landscape with hermits (94x130cm-37x51in) painted with studio prov. 23-Jan-4 Christie's, Rockefeller NY #166/R est:30000-50000
£39735	$72318	€60000	Travellers resting by river (117x175cm-46x69in) 16-Jun-4 Christie's, Rome #518/R est:80000-120000
£39735	$72318	€60000	Travellers resting by river (117x175cm-46x69in) i. 16-Jun-4 Christie's, Rome #519/R est:80000-120000
£49296	$78873	€70000	Landscape with washerwomen (130x198cm-51x78in) 21-Sep-3 Finarte, Venice #26/R
£66667	$122000	€100000	Preaching to the monks (57x42cm-22x17in) prov.exhib.lit. 1-Jun-4 Sotheby's, Milan #151/R est:100000-150000

MAGNASCO, Alessandro (circle) (1667-1749) Italian

£10072	$16518	€14000	Jesus entering Jerusalem (116x196cm-46x77in) 4-Jun-3 Sotheby's, Milan #75/R est:15000-20000

MAGNASCO, Alessandro (style) (1667-1749) Italian
£7042 $12183 €10000 Landscape with two monks in prayer (58x73cm-23x29in) 11-Dec-3 Dr Fritz Nagel, Stuttgart #498/R est:15000

MAGNASCO, Alessandro and PERUZZINI, Anton Francesco (17/18th C) Italian
£14085 $24366 €20000 Landscapes with figures (75x99cm-30x39in) pair. 11-Dec-3 Dr Fritz Nagel, Stuttgart #429/R est:30000
£55556 $90556 €80000 Landscapes (72cm-28in circular) four prov. 25-Sep-3 Dr Fritz Nagel, Stuttgart #1218/R

MAGNASCO, Alessandro and PERUZZINI, Anton Francesco (studio) (17/18th C) Italian
£5263 $9684 €8000 Landscape with countryfolk resting (75x29cm-30x11in) pair. 24-Jun-4 Dr Fritz Nagel, Stuttgart #646/R est:15000

MAGNASCO, Alessandro and SPERA, Clemente (17/18th C) Italian
£58621 $97897 €85000 Burying a trunk. Unburying a trunk (46x61cm-18x24in) pair. 12-Nov-3 Sotheby's, Milan #118/R est:80000-120000

MAGNASCO, Stefano (1635-1681) Italian
£6383 $10660 €9000 Ascension of the Virgin (173x122cm-68x48in) 18-Jun-3 Christie's, Rome #438/R est:7000-9000
£26000 $44980 €37960 Penitent Magdalen (124x147cm-49x58in) mono. 10-Dec-3 Christie's, London #93/R est:20000-30000
Works on paper
£600 $1038 €876 Christ healing the lame man (25x22cm-10x9in) red chk prov. 12-Dec-3 Christie's, Kensington #361/R

MAGNAVACCA, Ubaldo (1885-1957) Italian
£227 $400 €331 Tree in storm landscape (61x46cm-24x18in) s. board. 23-May-4 Hindman, Chicago #986/R
£822 $1397 €1200 Village in the mountains. s. 7-Nov-3 Tuttarte, Modena #606

MAGNE, Desire Alfred (1855-1936) French
£573 $974 €837 Still life with bread, fruit and sugar shaker (46x61cm-18x24in) s. 5-Nov-3 Dobiaschofsky, Bern #764/R (S.FR 1300)
£987 $1816 €1500 Bouquet de fleurs (63x90cm-25x35in) s. 28-Jun-4 Rossini, Paris #100/R est:2000-2500

MAGNELLI, Alberto (1888-1971) Italian
£4362 $7809 €6500 Compositions (50x45cm-20x18in) s.d.65 tempera ink pencil cardboard two prov.lit. 25-May-4 Sotheby's, Milan #98/R
£20134 $36040 €30000 Colloques 8 (46x55cm-18x22in) s.d.65 s.i.d.verso exhib.lit. 29-May-4 Farsetti, Prato #489/R est:30000-40000
£24161 $43248 €36000 Composition (50x60cm-20x24in) s.d.1937. 29-May-4 Farsetti, Prato #487/R est:30000-40000
£26846 $48054 €40000 Variations 4 (100x81cm-39x32in) s.d.58 s.i.d.verso prov.lit. 25-May-4 Sotheby's, Milan #288/R est:30000-40000
£31469 $53497 €45000 Harmonique (73x60cm-29x24in) s.d.46 s.i.d.verso prov.exhib.lit. 25-Nov-3 Sotheby's, Milan #212/R est:35000-45000
£47101 $77246 €65000 Visages (97x130cm-38x51in) s.d.34 prov.lit. 27-May-3 Sotheby's, Milan #266/R est:80000-120000
£72464 $118841 €100000 Rythme saccade (97x130cm-38x51in) s.d.38 s.i.d.verso prov.exhib.lit. 27-May-3 Sotheby's, Milan #278/R est:90000-120000
£120000 $200400 €175200 La sposa (100x73cm-39x29in) s.i.d.1914 verso prov.exhib.lit. 21-Oct-3 Christie's, London #2/R est:150000-200000
£190476 $340952 €280000 Donna alla blusa gialla - woman in a yellow blouse (100x76cm-39x30in) s.i.d.1916-1917 verso exhib.lit. 21-Mar-4 Calmels Cohen, Paris #179/R est:200000-250000
Works on paper
£800 $1472 €1200 Female nude (41x27cm-16x11in) s. chl. 8-Jun-4 Finarte Semenzato, Milan #170/R
£900 $1638 €1314 Untitled (21x27cm-8x11in) s.d.36 pencil. 4-Feb-4 Sotheby's, Olympia #179/R
£1000 $1800 €1500 Composition (18x13cm-7x5in) s.d.1962 pen dr. 25-Apr-4 Versailles Encheres #190 est:500-600
£1067 $1920 €1600 Seated figure (33x24cm-13x9in) s. pencil exec.1914. 22-Apr-4 Finarte Semenzato, Rome #80/R est:1400-1700
£2318 $4242 €3500 Composition (28x22cm-11x9in) s.i.d.1964 pastel. 7-Apr-4 Doutrebente, Paris #68/R est:5000
£2747 $4752 €3900 Composition (27x21cm-11x8in) Chinese ink col ink crayon prov. 9-Dec-3 Artcurial Briest, Paris #500/R est:3000-4000
£3147 $5350 €4500 Composition (31x24cm-12x9in) s.d.53 collage cardboard prov. 25-Nov-3 Sotheby's, Milan #96/R est:4000-6000
£3357 $5706 €4800 Composition (27x21cm-11x8in) s.d.42 gouache card prov. 25-Nov-3 Sotheby's, Milan #95/R est:4000-6000
£3761 $6282 €5453 Composition (17x22cm-7x9in) s. collage Indianin. 19-Jun-3 Kornfeld, Bern #666/R est:10000 (S.FR 8200)
£5141 $8894 €7300 Composition (36x24cm-14x9in) s. gouache W/C felt pen crayon exec.c.1956-1957 prov.lit. 14-Dec-3 Versailles Encheres #89/R est:8000-9000
£5594 $9510 €8000 Composition (43x74cm-17x29in) s.d.42 collage pencil W/C pastel chl iron cardboard prov.exhib.li. 25-Nov-3 Sotheby's, Milan #16/R est:8000-10000
£8609 $15669 €13000 Untitled (30x23cm-12x9in) s.d.40 i.verso gouache prov. 18-Jun-4 Piasa, Paris #198/R est:6000-8000
£10135 $17838 €15000 Collage au fond noir (66x56cm-26x22in) s.d.1948 collage board on board prov.exhib.lit. 18-May-4 Tajan, Paris #29/R est:12000-15000
£10204 $18266 €15000 Nineteen fifty nine (63x48cm-25x19in) s.d.59 felt tip pen crayon. 21-Mar-4 Calmels Cohen, Paris #156/R est:12000-15000
£11565 $20701 €17000 Nineteen thirty three (31x22cm-12x9in) s.d.33 gouache. 21-Mar-4 Calmels Cohen, Paris #155/R est:8000-10000

MAGNI, Giuseppe (1869-1956) Italian
£563 $1025 €850 Bridge (59x80cm-23x31in) s. 21-Jun-4 Pandolfini, Florence #133/R
£1319 $2243 €1900 Inn interior (23x32cm-9x13in) s. cardboard. 1-Nov-3 Meeting Art, Vercelli #89/R est:1000

MAGNUS, Camille (1850-?) French
£1468 $2700 €2143 Figure in a sunlit woodland setting (45x67cm-18x26in) s. 27-Jun-4 Freeman, Philadelphia #3173/R est:3000-5000
£1739 $2852 €2400 Village a l'oree de la foret (23x32cm-9x13in) s. panel. 11-May-3 Osenat, Fontainebleau #111/R est:2200-2400
£2014 $3182 €2900 Peasant woman in Fontainebleau wood (51x61cm-20x24in) s.d.73 canvas on panel lit. 19-Sep-3 Schloss Ahlden, Ahlden #1538/R est:2800
£2411 $3930 €3520 Paysanne dans la foret (90x130cm-35x51in) s. 17-Jul-3 Naón & Cia, Buenos Aires #7/R
£2448 $4210 €3500 Boisiere en foret (46x60cm-18x24in) s. 7-Dec-3 Osenat, Fontainebleau #134 est:3800-4000

MAGNUS, Emma (1856-1936) British
£1700 $3043 €2482 Visiting the fortune teller (86x74cm-34x29in) s. 26-May-4 AB Stockholms Auktionsverk #2440/R est:15000-20000 (S.KR 23000)

MAGNUS, Reidar (1896-1968) Danish
£338 $615 €507 Study of female nude (107x98cm-42x39in) init.d.45. 19-Jun-4 Rasmussen, Havnen #4197 (D.KR 3800)

MAGNUSSEN, Christian Carl (1821-1896) German
Works on paper
£556 $928 €800 Shepherd resting (32x23cm-13x9in) W/C Indian ink. 24-Oct-3 Ketterer, Hamburg #193/R

MAGNUSSON, Gustaf (1890-1957) Swedish
£429 $776 €626 Street scene viewed from an upstairs window (59x49cm-23x19in) s.d.1941 board. 30-Mar-4 Peter Webb, Auckland #123/R est:1500-2500 (NZ.D 1200)

MAGNUSSON, Ragnvald (1904-1984) Swedish
£319 $574 €479 Landscape with road (49x64cm-19x25in) s. 25-Apr-4 Goteborg Auktionsverk, Sweden #328/R (S.KR 4400)
£566 $1018 €849 Verandah II (52x59cm-20x23in) s. exhib. 25-Apr-4 Goteborg Auktionsverk, Sweden #364/R (S.KR 7800)

MAGRATH, William (1838-1918) British
Works on paper
£2254 $3606 €3200 Jealousy (36x66cm-14x26in) s. W/C. 16-Sep-3 Whyte's, Dublin #167/R est:2000-3000

MAGRINI, R (?) Italian?
£2500 $4000 €3625 Mischievous pupils (54x85cm-21x33in) s. 18-Sep-3 Christie's, Kensington #70a/R est:2000-3000

MAGRITTE, René (1898-1967) Belgian
£7947 $14464 €12000 Vue de Bruges (46x33cm-18x13in) s. prov.lit. 16-Jun-4 Hotel des Ventes Mosan, Brussels #267/R est:5000-7000
£176666 $325066 €265000 Recolte des nuages (65x50cm-26x20in) s. prov.lit. 9-Jun-4 Tajan, Paris #24/R est:80000-100000
£220000 $400400 €321200 Nu allonge (44x59cm-17x23in) s.d.1923 prov.exhib.lit. 3-Feb-4 Christie's, London #234/R est:100000-150000
£315642 $565000 €460837 A la rencontre du plaisir (50x60cm-20x24in) s. s.i.d.1950 verso prov.exhib.lit. 5-May-4 Christie's, Rockefeller NY #303a/R est:500000-700000
£320000 $585600 €467200 Les amants - IV (54x73cm-21x29in) s. i.verso painted 1928 prov.exhib.lit. 2-Feb-4 Christie's, London #87/R est:280000-340000
£390000 $709800 €569400 Jeunes amours (33x41cm-13x16in) s. s.i.verso painted 1963 prov.exhib.lit. 21-Jun-4 Sotheby's, London #57/R est:300000-400000
£500000 $910000 €730000 Beau langage (41x33cm-16x13in) s. i.verso painted 1952 prov.exhib.lit. 21-Jun-4 Sotheby's, London #59/R est:200000-300000
£520000 $951600 €759200 Le trait d'union (60x73cm-24x29in) s. painted 1942 prov.exhib.lit. 2-Feb-4 Christie's, London #68/R est:400000-600000
£550000 $1012000 €803000 Belle captive (30x40cm-12x16in) s. painted c.1950 prov.exhib.lit. 22-Jun-4 Christie's, London #35/R est:400000-600000
£600000 $1104000 €876000 Reconnaissance infinie (97x73cm-38x29in) s. s.i.d.1933 on stretcher prov.exhib.lit. 22-Jun-4 Christie's, London #36/R est:600000-800000
£614525 $1100000 €897207 Eternite (65x81cm-26x32in) s. s.i.d.1935 verso prov.exhib.lit. 4-May-4 Christie's, Rockefeller NY #32/R est:800000-1200000
£780000 $1435200 €1138800 Recherche de l'absolu (73x60cm-29x24in) s. painted 1940 prov.exhib.lit. 22-Jun-4 Christie's, London #34/R est:320000-380000
Prints
£1676 $3000 €2447 Le viol (73x53cm-29x21in) s.num.173/300 color lithograph. 6-May-4 Swann Galleries, New York #498/R est:1000-1500
£1761 $3081 €2500 Pommes masquees (28x23cm-11x9in) s. col eau forte prov. 16-Dec-3 Finarte Semenzato, Milan #39/R est:700-900
£2333 $4177 €3500 La Comtesse de Monte Christo (38x29cm-15x11in) s. etching. 13-May-4 Neumeister, Munich #420/R est:1500-1800
£2381 $3810 €3452 Marche des snobs pour piano par Fernand Rousseau (33x26cm-13x10in) s.d.24 col lithograph. 15-May-3 Stuker, Bern #1371/R est:5000-6000 (S.FR 5000)
£2933 $5251 €4400 Les deux mysteres - ceci n'est pas une pipe (18x13cm-7x5in) s. etching. 13-May-4 Neumeister, Munich #421/R est:1800-2000
£3200 $5824 €4672 Les bijoux indiscrets (32x41cm-13x16in) s.num.70/75 col lithograph. 1-Jul-4 Sotheby's, London #196/R est:3000-5000
£3235 $5500 €4723 Paysage de Baucis (38x28cm-15x11in) s.i. etching exec.1966. 4-Nov-3 Christie's, Rockefeller NY #105/R est:6000-8000
£3490 $6526 €5200 Paysage de Baucis (38x28cm-15x11in) s. eau forte. 1-Mar-4 Artcurial Briest, Paris #119/R est:3000-4000
£3586 $5989 €5200 Paysage de Baucis (37x27cm-15x11in) s. num.42/100 engraving. 17-Nov-3 Sant Agostino, Torino #184/R est:1500-2000
£3800 $6954 €5548 Paysage de Baucis (23x17cm-9x7in) s.i. etching. 3-Jun-4 Christie's, Kensington #89/R est:3000-4000
Sculpture
£135000 $245700 €197100 Femme bouteille (29cm-11in) s. oil on glass bottle painted c.1941 prov.exhib.lit. 3-Feb-4 Sotheby's, London #61/R est:80000-120000

Works on paper

£1188	$1900	€1734	Animal and plant studies (22x19cm-9x7in) bears another sig.i. pencil. 18-Sep-3 Swann Galleries, New York #393/R est:1500-2500
£1200	$2004	€1752	Sans, landscape (36x28cm-14x11in) W/C prov. 14-Oct-3 Canterbury Auctions, UK #132/R est:900-1200
£2617	$4816	€3900	Colinet faisant dans son vase (32x16cm-13x6in) s.i. ball pen prov. 24-Mar-4 Joron-Derem, Paris #98/R est:5000-6000
£2797	$4811	€4000	Trois postillons (22x19cm-9x7in) s. pen ink prov. 5-Dec-3 Ketterer, Munich #125/R est:5000-6000
£11409	$20195	€17000	Nouveau porte-nez economique (27x21cm-11x8in) s.i. dr. 29-Apr-4 Christie's, Paris #151/R est:20000-30000
£16084	$26860	€23000	Musique (10x27cm-4x11in) s. Indian ink lit. 25-Jun-3 Digard, Paris #89/R est:15000-20000
£35000	$63700	€51100	Smoking pipes (25x15cm-10x6in) s. ink executed 1938 prov.lit. 3-Feb-4 Sotheby's, London #80/R est:35000-45000
£55866	$100000	€81564	Seducteur (13x18cm-5x7in) s. gouache exec 1952 prov.lit. 6-May-4 Sotheby's, New York #361/R est:100000-150000
£70000	$128100	€102200	Untitled (61x45cm-24x18in) s. W/C col crayons brush ink collage exec.1926 prov.exhib.lit. 2-Feb-4 Christie's, London #51/R est:50000-70000
£85000	$155550	€124100	L'autre parole (27x33cm-11x13in) s. s.i.d.1955 gouache prov.exhib.lit. 2-Feb-4 Christie's, London #73/R est:40000-70000
£85000	$155550	€124100	Untitled (269x21cm-106x8in) s. gouache executed 1935-36 prov.exhib.lit. 2-Feb-4 Christie's, London #86/R est:60000-80000
£94118	$160000	€137412	Le principe d'Archimede (16x18cm-6x7in) s. gouache paper on board prov.exhib.lit. 5-Nov-3 Christie's, Rockefeller NY #129/R est:100000-150000
£110000	$200200	€160600	La paix du soir (42x30cm-17x12in) s. i.d.1945 verso g. col crayons prov.exhib. 3-Feb-4 Sotheby's, London #66/R est:120000-160000
£125000	$227500	€182500	La clairvoyance (42x29cm-17x11in) s.i. s.i.d.1937 verso col crayons pastel g. prov.exhib.lit. 3-Feb-4 Sotheby's, London #67/R est:120000-150000
£130000	$239200	€189800	Sense propre (19x25cm-7x10in) s. gouache collage pencil chl exec 1961 prov.exhib.lit. 24-Jun-4 Christie's, London #428/R est:100000-150000
£130000	$239200	€189800	Automate (35x27cm-14x11in) s. gouache paper on board exec.1962 prov.lit. 22-Jun-4 Sotheby's, London #485/R est:150000-200000
£140000	$256200	€210000	Le seducteur (26x34cm-10x13in) s. gouache exec. 1960 prov.exhib.lit. 7-Jun-4 Palais de Beaux Arts, Brussels #123/R est:150000-200000
£180000	$329400	€262800	Le banquet (36x46cm-14x18in) s. g. executed 1956 prov.exhib.lit. 2-Feb-4 Christie's, London #55/R est:140000-180000
£265000	$482300	€386900	Le pretre marie (27x35cm-11x14in) s. i.verso g. prov.exhib.lit. 3-Feb-4 Sotheby's, London #65/R est:180000-250000
£880000	$1610400	€1284800	Le retour (29x42cm-11x17in) s. gouache executed 1950 prov. 2-Feb-4 Christie's, London #69/R est:400000-600000

MAGROTTI, Ercole (1890-1958) Italian

£385	$654	€562	D'intorni d'ischia (56x113cm-22x44in) s. i.verso. 4-Nov-3 Stephan Welz, Johannesburg #587 est:3000-4000 (SA.R 4500)
£433	$776	€650	Mountainous landscape (50x70cm-20x28in) s. 12-May-4 Stadion, Trieste #665
£442	$800	€645	Old mill (48x69cm-19x27in) s. 2-Apr-4 Freeman, Philadelphia #147
£520	$957	€759	Fisherman mending nets on the shore in the Bay of Naples (68x100cm-27x39in) s. 23-Jun-4 Bonhams, Bury St Edmunds #367
£537	$961	€784	Venetian canal scene (68x96cm-27x38in) s. canvas on board. 31-May-4 Stephan Welz, Johannesburg #465/R (SA.R 6500)
£560	$936	€818	Bringing in the catch (48x68cm-19x27in) s. canvas on board. 20-Oct-3 Stephan Welz, Johannesburg #202/R est:5000-7000 (SA.R 6500)
£563	$975	€800	Winter lake landscape (40x50cm-16x20in) s. 9-Dec-3 Finarte Semenzato, Milan #109/R
£570	$1021	€850	Old houses on the lake (40x50cm-16x20in) s. 25-May-4 Finarte Semenzato, Milan #84/R
£604	$1081	€900	Winter landscape (50x70cm-20x28in) s. 25-May-4 Finarte Semenzato, Milan #83/R
£671	$1188	€1000	Alpine landscape with stream (70x100cm-28x39in) s. 1-May-4 Meeting Art, Vercelli #163
£704	$1218	€1000	Lake landscape with angler (49x70cm-19x28in) s. 9-Dec-3 Finarte Semenzato, Milan #110/R
£733	$1224	€1070	Lakeside landscape (45x63cm-18x25in) s. canvas on board. 20-Oct-3 Stephan Welz, Johannesburg #465 est:3000-5000 (SA.R 8500)
£993	$1658	€1400	Varese lake (40x50cm-16x20in) s. 14-Oct-3 Finarte Semenzato, Milan #15/R

MAGROU, Jean Marie Joseph (1869-1945) French

Sculpture

£1645	$3026	€2500	Mooglie (28cm-11in) s. gilded bronze blk veined marble base st.f.Barbedienne. 25-Jun-4 Tajan, Paris #31/R est:2500-3000

MAGSAYSAY-HO, Anita Corpus (1914-) Philippino

£2355	$3650	€3438	Girls with a fan (38x32cm-15x13in) s.d.2002 denim jacket. 6-Oct-2 Sotheby's, Singapore #79/R est:5000-10000 (S.D 6500)
£13194	$22035	€19263	Woman with baskets (61x34cm-24x13in) s.d.68 canvas on board. 12-Oct-3 Sotheby's, Singapore #77/R est:30000-40000 (S.D 38000)
£23551	$36504	€34384	Peanut vendors (46x53cm-18x21in) s.d.1979. 6-Oct-2 Sotheby's, Singapore #92/R est:60000-80000 (S.D 65000)
£23656	$37849	€34538	Three women with bird cages (41x51cm-16x20in) s.d.1985. 18-May-3 Sotheby's, Singapore #84/R est:55000-80000 (S.D 66000)
£30108	$48172	€43958	Harvest (50x40cm-20x16in) s.d.1957 board. 18-May-3 Sotheby's, Singapore #72/R est:45000-65000 (S.D 84000)
£56899	$102418	€83073	Six senses (122x91cm-48x36in) s.d.1995 acrylic diptych prov.lit. 25-Apr-4 Christie's, Hong Kong #554/R est:900000-1400000 (HK.D 800000)
£159420	$247101	€232753	Fruit vendors (40x50cm-16x20in) s. wood exhib.lit. 6-Oct-2 Sotheby's, Singapore #88/R est:100000-150000 (S.D 440000)

MAGUES, Isidore Jean Baptiste (19th C) French

Works on paper

£280	$448	€409	Portrait of Lord William Russell, head and shoulders (20x15cm-8x6in) s.i.d.1839 pastel drawing lit. 16-Sep-3 Gorringes, Bexhill #1553/R

MAGUIRE, Brian (20th C) Irish

£1184	$2179	€1800	The bath (140x104cm-55x41in) s.d.1983. 22-Jun-4 De Veres Art Auctions, Dublin #192 est:2000-4000

MAGUIRE, Cecil (1930-) British

£1284	$2426	€1900	Parkland landscape, thought to be Brownlow House, Lurgan, County Armagh (46x33cm-18x13in) s. board. 17-Feb-4 Whyte's, Dublin #171/R est:2000-3000
£1342	$2376	€2000	Fountain in a village square, France (51x41cm-20x16in) s. board. 27-Apr-4 Whyte's, Dublin #196/R est:2000-3000
£1549	$2680	€2200	Volunteer at Roundstone (20x25cm-8x10in) s.d.87 i.verso board. 10-Dec-3 Bonhams & James Adam, Dublin #117/R est:2000-3000
£1800	$2988	€2628	Venice (38x30cm-15x12in) s.d.03 board. 1-Oct-3 John Ross, Belfast #153 est:2000-2500
£2416	$4277	€3600	Men of Aran, Kilronan (25x30cm-10x12in) s. panel. 27-Apr-4 Whyte's, Dublin #39/R est:3000-4000
£2431	$3962	€3500	Early morning, Larne Lough (41x121cm-16x48in) s.d.63. 23-Sep-3 De Veres Art Auctions, Dublin #132 est:3000-5000
£2838	$5364	€4200	Ballynahinch, Connemara (25x30cm-10x12in) s.d.1974 board exhib. 17-Feb-4 Whyte's, Dublin #125/R est:3000-4000
£3077	$5231	€4400	Gathering cockles (29x25cm-11x10in) s.d.1983 i.verso board. 18-Nov-3 Whyte's, Dublin #3/R est:3000-4000
£3800	$6308	€5548	Potato patch, Mannin (45x61cm-18x24in) s.d.86 board. 1-Oct-3 John Ross, Belfast #202 est:2500-2800
£4027	$7128	€6000	Evening light, Gorteen Beach, Roundstone (61x91cm-24x36in) s. i.verso board prov. 27-Apr-4 Whyte's, Dublin #66/R est:6000-8000
£4097	$6678	€5900	Giant Banyan Tree, Yang Sho, Guilin, China (61x85cm-24x33in) s.d.1990 s.i.verso board. 24-Sep-3 James Adam, Dublin #113/R est:6000-8000
£4133	$7481	€6200	Horse fair at Clifden (60x92cm-24x36in) s.d.85 board. 30-Mar-4 De Veres Art Auctions, Dublin #91/R est:6000-8000
£4189	$7918	€6200	Santa Maria Della Salute, Venezia (41x61cm-16x24in) s.d.1979 i.verso board. 17-Feb-4 Whyte's, Dublin #184/R est:6000-8000
£4400	$8140	€6424	Dividing the catch (61x48cm-24x19in) s. board. 9-Mar-4 Gorringes, Lewes #2223 est:800-1200
£4500	$8055	€6570	Thatcher, Errisberg (41x61cm-16x24in) s. s.i.verso board. 14-May-4 Christie's, Kensington #378/R est:5000-8000
£4527	$8556	€6700	Cottages, Ballyconneely (41x61cm-16x24in) s. i.verso. 17-Feb-4 Whyte's, Dublin #95/R est:5000-7000
£4667	$8447	€7000	Twelfth, Lurgan (59x74cm-23x29in) s.i.d.72 verso board. 31-Mar-4 James Adam, Dublin #109/R est:7000-10000
£5034	$8909	€7500	Turf boat, Kilronan (61x46cm-24x18in) s. i.verso board. 27-Apr-4 Whyte's, Dublin #104/R est:6000-8000
£5245	$8916	€7500	Cutting rye, Inishmaan (46x36cm-18x14in) s.d.1985 i.verso board lit. 18-Nov-3 Whyte's, Dublin #38/R est:5000-7000
£5282	$8451	€7500	Dawn, Killary harbour (61x91cm-24x36in) s.d.1971 i.verso board. 16-Sep-3 Whyte's, Dublin #142/R est:6000-8000
£6690	$10704	€9500	Twelve Pins from Roundstone, Connemara (38x91cm-15x36in) s.d.1965 i.verso. 16-Sep-3 Whyte's, Dublin #124/R est:8000-10000
£6711	$11879	€10000	Swans at Letterdyfe, Roundstone, Connemara (61x76cm-24x30in) s. i.verso board. 27-Apr-4 Whyte's, Dublin #238/R est:8000-10000
£7042	$11268	€10000	Low tide, Roundstone, Connemara (51x69cm-20x27in) s. s.i.verso canvasboard. 16-Sep-3 Whyte's, Dublin #129/R est:8000-10000
£9500	$17005	€13870	Waiting for the boat, Kilronan, Inishmore (46x61cm-18x24in) s.d.94 s.i.d.verso canvasboard. 14-May-4 Christie's, Kensington #414/R est:4000-6000
£10135	$19155	€15000	Cross Street, Galway (51x61cm-20x24in) s.d.1979 board. 17-Feb-4 Whyte's, Dublin #65/R est:8000-10000
£11409	$20195	€17000	Sunday morning mass, Roundstone (46x61cm-18x24in) s.d.1982 i.verso board. 27-Apr-4 Whyte's, Dublin #101/R est:7000-9000
£14667	$26547	€22000	The dark parade, Falls Road (91x60cm-36x24in) s.i.d.72 verso canvasboard. 31-Mar-4 James Adam, Dublin #101/R est:7000-10000

Works on paper

£1200	$2172	€1800	Group of shawlies in conversation (46x36cm-18x14in) s.d.76 chl wash. 30-Mar-4 De Veres Art Auctions, Dublin #2/R est:2000-3000

MAGUIRE, Edith (20th C) American

Works on paper

£412	$750	€602	Fishing pier (23x28cm-9x11in) s. W/C. 7-Feb-4 Auctions by the Bay, Alameda #1560/R

MAGUIRE, Edward (1932-1986) Irish

£1042	$1698	€1500	Two figures in a landscape (62x75cm-24x30in) 24-Sep-3 James Adam, Dublin #121/R est:1500-2500

MAGUIRE, Helena (1860-1909) British

Works on paper

£1141	$2042	€1700	Gate to the sea (24x19cm-9x7in) s.d.1880 W/C. 26-May-4 James Adam, Dublin #188/R est:2000-3000

MAGUIRE, Tim (1958-) Australian/British

£1872	$3183	€2733	Slits (50x50cm-20x20in) s.i.d.1994 verso. 26-Nov-3 Deutscher-Menzies, Melbourne #209/R est:4000-6000 (A.D 4400)
£2127	$3617	€3105	Slits (50x50cm-20x20in) s.i.d.1994 verso. 26-Nov-3 Deutscher-Menzies, Melbourne #210/R est:4000-6000 (A.D 5000)
£16674	$30680	€24344	Untitled, white rose (120x120cm-47x47in) i.d.02 verso oil polyester. 29-Mar-4 Goodman, Sydney #82/R est:60000-70000 (A.D 40850)
£19672	$31082	€28721	Flower piece (152x111cm-60x44in) s.d.95 paper on canvas prov. 2-Sep-3 Deutscher-Menzies, Melbourne #7/R est:20000-30000 (A.D 48000)
£32787	$51803	€47869	Untitled - apples (150x200cm-59x79in) s.i.d.98 verso prov. 2-Sep-3 Deutscher-Menzies, Melbourne #28/R est:80000-120000 (A.D 80000)
£46748	$83679	€68252	Untitled (160x148cm-63x58in) s.d.00 i.verso. 4-May-4 Sotheby's, Melbourne #4/R est:75000-95000 (A.D 115000)
£53719	$99380	€78430	Untitled 2002 0201 2002 (160x148cm-63x58in) prov. 10-Mar-4 Deutscher-Menzies, Melbourne #25/R est:90000-120000 (A.D 130000)
£68085	$115745	€99404	Untitled 2000U52 (180x440cm-71x173in) s.i.d.2000 verso prov.exhib. 26-Nov-3 Deutscher-Menzies, Melbourne #25/R est:150000-180000 (A.D 160000)
£77236	$121260	€111992	Untitled 20010805 (212x252cm-83x99in) diptych prov.exhib.lit. 26-Aug-3 Christie's, Sydney #26/R est:200000-280000 (A.D 190000)
£119149	$202553	€173958	Untitled 1997 (200x400cm-79x157in) diptych prov. 25-Nov-3 Christie's, Melbourne #57/R est:180000-220000 (A.D 280000)

Prints

£4065	$6382	€5894	Untitled, 9522M (112x153cm-44x60in) monotype two sheets prov. 26-Aug-3 Christie's, Sydney #58/R est:10000-15000 (A.D 10000)

Works on paper

£383	$651	€559	Study for Faith and reason (17x26cm-7x10in) i.verso W/C ink pastel exec c.1989 prov. 26-Nov-3 Deutscher-Menzies, Melbourne #208/R (A.D 900)

MAGURK, John (20th C) New Zealander
Works on paper
£291 $457 €425 New woolshed (34x49cm-13x19in) s. W/C. 27-Aug-3 Dunbar Sloane, Wellington #154 (NZ.D 800)

MAGYAR-MANNHEIMER, Gustav (1859-1937) Hungarian
£1159 $2098 €1692 Bathing children (41x55cm-16x22in) s. oil on wood. 16-Apr-4 Mu Terem Galeria, Budapest #170/R (H.F 440000)
£1567 $2664 €2288 Approaching storm, mountains in background (42x51cm-17x20in) s. panel. 10-Nov-3 Rasmussen, Vejle #352/R est:3000 (D.KR 17000)

MAHAFFEY, Josephine (1903-1982) American
£599 $1000 €875 Indian (76x61cm-30x24in) 18-Oct-3 David Dike, Dallas #149/R
Works on paper
£449 $750 €656 Eisenhower birthplace (76x56cm-30x22in) W/C. 18-Oct-3 David Dike, Dallas #147/R
£539 $900 €787 Northside (46x61cm-18x24in) W/C. 18-Oct-3 David Dike, Dallas #101/R
£719 $1200 €1050 The cross (76x66cm-30x26in) mixed media. 18-Oct-3 David Dike, Dallas #136/R

MAHAFFEY, Noel (1944-) American
£1913 $3500 €2793 Realist city street. s.i.d.1974 verso. 5-Jun-4 Dan Ripley, Indianapolis #257
£2000 $3640 €2920 Hooker Chemical Corp, Grand Island N Y (76x92cm-30x36in) s.i.d.1971 prov.lit. 4-Feb-4 Sotheby's, Olympia #215/R est:2000-3000

MAHAUX, Eugène (1874-1946) Belgian
£303 $561 €440 Composition a la poupee et aux fleurs (42x65cm-17x26in) s. 19-Jan-4 Horta, Bruxelles #444
£342 $582 €500 Jeune femme dans les dunes (39x58cm-15x23in) s. 10-Nov-3 Horta, Bruxelles #258/R
£586 $1084 €850 Trois-mats au coucher du soleil (111x139cm-44x55in) s. 19-Jan-4 Horta, Bruxelles #443

MAHDAVI, Rafael (1946-) American
£240 $400 €348 Anonimo 2 (155x178cm-61x70in) acrylic col photographic paper on canvas. 29-Jun-3 Butterfields, Los Angeles #7059/R

MAHDY, Wadie (1921-) Canadian
£220 $402 €321 City street, Winter (50x60cm-20x24in) s. canvasboard prov. 1-Jun-4 Joyner Waddington, Toronto #395/R (C.D 550)
£290 $499 €423 Jeune femme en blue (30x22cm-12x9in) s. canvasboard prov. 2-Dec-3 Joyner Waddington, Toronto #330/R (C.D 650)

MAHLANGU, Speelman (1958-) South African
£314 $562 €458 Ritual bull (50x80cm-20x31in) s. canvasboard. 31-May-4 Stephan Welz, Johannesburg #231 (SA.R 3800)
Works on paper
£1121 $1872 €1637 End of Eden (98x68cm-39x27in) s. mixed media. 20-Oct-3 Stephan Welz, Johannesburg #423/R est:5000-8000 (SA.R 13000)

MAHLAU, Alfred (20th C) ?
Works on paper
£268 $475 €400 Red cliffs - Sylt (16x23cm-6x9in) mono.d.IX 56 W/C. 28-Apr-4 Schopman, Hamburg #636/R

MAHLER, Richard (1896-?) Austrian
£594 $1010 €850 Farmhouse (61x82cm-24x32in) s. panel. 27-Nov-3 Dorotheum, Linz #526/R

MAHLER, Rudolf (20th C) German
£517 $926 €755 Abstract expressive composition with figure (140x115cm-55x45in) s.d.64 i. verso. 12-May-4 Dobiaschofsky, Bern #770/R (S.FR 1200)

MAHLKNECHT, Edmund (1820-1903) Austrian
£1370 $2329 €2000 Mountain lake (38x47cm-15x19in) s.d.1852. 5-Nov-3 Hugo Ruef, Munich #1062 est:1200
£1944 $3208 €2800 Bull and goat standing in lake (40x50cm-16x20in) s. 2-Jul-3 Neumeister, Munich #702/R est:1500
£2797 $4755 €4000 Cows on alpine pasture (53x37cm-21x15in) mono. 24-Nov-3 Dorotheum, Vienna #72/R est:4500-5500
£3020 $5406 €4500 On the homeward journey (38x58cm-15x23in) s.indis.d. 27-May-4 Dorotheum, Vienna #41/R est:5500-6000
£6711 $12013 €10000 Animal herd with shepherd family (63x79cm-25x31in) s.d.854. 27-May-4 Dorotheum, Vienna #210/R est:8000-10000

MAHLKNECHT, Edmund (attrib) (1820-1903) Austrian
£1974 $3632 €3000 Cow with calf (33x30cm-13x12in) 22-Jun-4 Wiener Kunst Auktionen, Vienna #49/R est:3000

MAHMOUD, Ben (1935-) American
£297 $550 €434 Under the blanket (124x122cm-49x48in) s.d.1980 acrylic. 17-Jan-4 Susanin's, Chicago #203/R

MAHONEY, James (1816-1879) Irish
£500 $850 €730 Clouds over Madaget, Nantucket (63x76cm-25x30in) s. s.i.d.80/81 verso. 21-Nov-3 Skinner, Boston #456/R est:500-700
Works on paper
£2900 $5336 €4234 Smoke on the sly (12x14cm-5x6in) s. W/C gouache. 8-Jun-4 Holloways, Banbury #234/R est:800-1200

MAHOOD, Kenneth (20th C) ?
Works on paper
£733 $1327 €1100 Abstract (19x24cm-7x9in) s. mixed media. 31-Mar-4 James Adam, Dublin #53/R

MAHOOD, Marguerite Callaway (1901-1989) Australian
Works on paper
£492 $777 €718 Medusa (54x37cm-21x15in) s.d.1923 i. verso W/C ink wash card. 2-Sep-3 Deutscher-Menzies, Melbourne #348/R (A.D 1200)

MAHORCIG, Josef (1843-1923) Austrian
£268 $481 €400 Coastal landscape (22x32cm-9x13in) s. board. 27-May-4 Dorotheum, Graz #48/R

MAHRENHOLZ, Harald (1904-1994) British/Danish
£1678 $2803 €2400 Interior with white flowers and sofa (63x75cm-25x30in) mono. 10-Oct-3 Winterberg, Heidelberg #1630/R est:2950

MAHRINGER, Anton (1902-1974) German
£2676 $4282 €3800 Young woman (69x48cm-27x19in) s. board. 18-Sep-3 Rieber, Stuttgart #785/R est:2800
£7692 $13077 €11000 San Angelo d'Ischia (51x65cm-20x26in) mono.d.52 i.d.verso lit. 28-Nov-3 Schloss Ahlden, Ahlden #1608/R est:6800
£13423 $23758 €20000 Wood and mountain - Dobratsch (60x70cm-24x28in) mono.d.1966 panel. 28-Apr-4 Wiener Kunst Auktionen, Vienna #114/R est:7000-14000
£16783 $28531 €24000 Evening landscape in the Gail valley (57x72cm-22x28in) mono.d.50 i. verso panel prov. 26-Nov-3 Dorotheum, Vienna #189/R est:13000-18000
£23776 $40420 €34000 My house (66x71cm-26x28in) mono.d.51 i. verso prov. 26-Nov-3 Dorotheum, Vienna #92/R est:12000-17000
Works on paper
£3020 $5406 €4500 Woodland's edge (45x57cm-18x22in) s.d.57 chk W/C. 25-May-4 Dorotheum, Vienna #218/R est:3800-5000
£3147 $5350 €4500 Wood and Dobratsch (46x40cm-18x16in) mono.d.70 chl W/C prov. 26-Nov-3 Dorotheum, Vienna #235/R est:2200-3000

MAHU, Cornelis (1613-1689) Flemish
£3500 $6405 €5110 Peasants eating, drinking and conversing in front of a cottage (28x34cm-11x13in) panel. 6-Jul-4 Sotheby's, Olympia #537/R est:4000-6000
£11724 $19462 €17000 Still life with goblet, pewter jug and herring (48x64cm-19x25in) s. panel lit.prov. 1-Oct-3 Dorotheum, Vienna #115/R est:18000-25000
£16783 $28531 €24000 Fantasy harbour with lighthouse (41x57cm-16x22in) s. panel prov.lit. 20-Nov-3 Van Ham, Cologne #1377/R est:18000
£24658 $41918 €36000 Still life with silverware, pewterware, various fruits and nuts on a table (91x122cm-36x48in) mono. panel prov.exhib.lit. 4-Nov-3 Sotheby's, Amsterdam #31/R est:30000-40000
£34483 $57586 €50000 Still life (58x87cm-23x34in) s. panel prov.lit. 15-Nov-3 Lempertz, Koln #1093/R est:50000-70000

MAHU, Cornelis (attrib) (1613-1689) Flemish
£6000 $10800 €8760 Kitchen interior with peasants (41x67cm-16x26in) bears another sig. panel. 23-Apr-4 Christie's, Kensington #97/R est:3000-5000

MAHU, Cornelis (circle) (1613-1689) Flemish
£23288 $39589 €34000 Upturned tazza, roemer, facon de Venise glass, oyster and lemon on a draped ledge (91x178cm-36x70in) prov.lit. 5-Nov-3 Christie's, Amsterdam #41/R est:12000-18000

MAHU, Victor (?-1700) Flemish
£13575 $23077 €19820 Quack doctor's surgery (58x84cm-23x33in) s. 19-Nov-3 Fischer, Luzern #1037/R est:35000-40000 (S.FR 30000)

MAHY-BOSSU, Maria (1880-?) Belgian
£1310 $2188 €1900 La lavandiere (130x105cm-51x41in) s. 17-Nov-3 Tajan, Paris #112 est:2000-3000

MAI THU (1906-1980) Vietnamese
£7667 $14107 €11500 L'offrande (25x24cm-10x9in) s.d. peinture silk. 14-Jun-4 Tajan, Paris #99/R est:12000-15000
£8667 $15860 €13000 A la riviere (55x46cm-22x18in) s. silk. 6-Jun-4 Anaf, Lyon #423/R est:12000-15000
£16667 $30667 €25000 Mere jouant avec ses enfants (56x33cm-22x13in) s.d.1942 peinture silk. 14-Jun-4 Tajan, Paris #102/R est:25000-30000
£28672 $49315 €41000 Mere et ses deux enfants (45x39cm-18x15in) s. prov. 3-Dec-3 Tajan, Paris #372/R est:15000-20000
Works on paper
£4667 $8447 €7000 L'enfant sur le dos (29x16cm-11x6in) s. mono. gouache ink. 1-Apr-4 Credit Municipal, Paris #31/R est:5000-6000
£4902 $8873 €7157 L'idylle (24x33cm-9x13in) s.d.45 ink gouache. 4-Apr-4 Sotheby's, Singapore #52/R est:15000-20000 (S.D 15000)
£4902 $8873 €7157 Mother and child (28x24cm-11x9in) s.d.73 ink gouache on silk. 4-Apr-4 Sotheby's, Singapore #53/R est:10000-15000 (S.D 15000)
£5229 $9464 €7634 Girl with cherry blossoms (13x18cm-5x7in) s.d.56 ink gouache silk on paper. 4-Apr-4 Sotheby's, Singapore #62/R est:12000-15000 (S.D 16000)
£8497 $15379 €12406 Tea party (60x58cm-24x23in) s.d.71 ink gouache silk on paper. 4-Apr-4 Sotheby's, Singapore #72/R est:28000-35000 (S.D 26000)
£9722 $16236 €14194 Young Tonkinese (45x34cm-18x13in) s.d.1933 ink gouache silk. 12-Oct-3 Sotheby's, Singapore #100/R est:28000-35000 (S.D 28000)

£15385 $26154 €22000 Femmes se coiffant (23x14cm-9x6in) s. gouache pair. 28-Nov-3 Drouot Estimations, Paris #191/R est:2500-3000
£16344 $26151 €23862 Sleep (66x56cm-26x22in) s.d.1938 gouache ink silk. 18-May-3 Sotheby's, Singapore #102/R est:20000-25000 (S.D 45600)
£19608 $35490 €28628 La lettre - the letter (42x48cm-17x19in) s.i.d.1942 verso ink gouache silk on paper. 4-Apr-4 Sotheby's, Singapore #64/R est:60000-80000 (S.D 60000)

MAIDMENT, Henry (19/20th C) British
£260 $458 €380 River landscape with two children fishing by the water's edge (38x28cm-15x11in) s. 18-May-4 Fellows & Sons, Birmingham #59/R
£500 $850 €730 Farm near Elstree (50x76cm-20x30in) mono. s.i.on stretcher. 29-Oct-3 Bonhams, Chester #505
£500 $920 €730 Shepherd and flock in a landscape (53x43cm-21x17in) mono. 8-Jun-4 Gorringes, Lewes #2248
£850 $1420 €1241 Tranquil stretch of the river (30x61cm-12x24in) mono.d.1905. 13-Nov-3 Christie's, Kensington #156/R
£850 $1496 €1241 Duck pond (53x43cm-21x17in) mono.d.1905. 19-May-4 Christie's, Kensington #542/R
£900 $1503 €1314 Children beside a rustic gate overlooking a valley (51x41cm-20x16in) d.98 mono. 18-Jun-3 John Nicholson, Haslemere #718/R
£1450 $2625 €2117 On the River Stour. River landscape with sheep and drover (14x24cm-6x9in) mono.d.1903 panel pair. 30-Mar-4 Sworder & Son, Bishops Stortford #559/R est:600-800

MAIDMENT, Kathleen (fl.1908-1926) Irish
Works on paper
£465 $758 €670 Old lady darning by the window (62x47cm-24x19in) s. W/C. 23-Sep-3 De Veres Art Auctions, Dublin #336

MAIDMENT, Thomas (1871-1952) British
Works on paper
£260 $473 €380 Pudding Bay Lane, St Ives, Cornwall (36x26cm-14x10in) s. W/C. 15-Jun-4 Bonhams, Oxford #48/R
£500 $835 €730 Smeaton's Pier, St. Ives (23x36cm-9x14in) s. W/C bodycol. 14-Oct-3 David Lay, Penzance #497

MAIGNAN (19th C) French
Sculpture
£1226 $1950 €1790 Plowing bulls (56x28x33cm-22x11x13in) s. green brown pat bronze marble base. 12-Sep-3 Aspire, Cleveland #224 est:1500-2500

MAIGNAN, Albert Pierre René (1845-1908) French
£3000 $5490 €4380 Portrait of a young woman, in a landscape (63x39cm-25x15in) s. panel. 6-Apr-4 Bonhams, Knightsbridge #191/R est:2000-3000

MAIK, Henri (20th C) ?
£306 $550 €447 Meeting (97x130cm-38x51in) s.d.64 s.i.verso prov. 20-Jan-4 Arthur James, Florida #172
£531 $850 €775 Untitled (23x33cm-9x13in) s. 20-Sep-3 Nadeau, Windsor #56/R

MAILICK, Erik (20th C) German
£267 $491 €400 In the woods, near Moritzburg (71x81cm-28x32in) s. s.i.verso. 11-Jun-4 Wendl, Rudolstadt #4152/R

MAILLARD, Charles (?) Canadian
£246 $410 €357 Tree lined boulevard (51x35cm-20x14in) s. board. 17-Jun-3 Pinneys, Montreal #173 (C.D 550)

MAILLARD, Émile (1846-?) French
£704 $1169 €1000 Soleil couchant (31x41cm-12x16in) s.i. panel. 10-Jun-3 Renaud, Paris #22/R
£1088 $1948 €1600 Voiliers en mer (32x40cm-13x16in) s. panel. 19-Mar-4 Millon & Associes, Paris #47/R est:500-600
£1871 $3068 €2600 Coucher de soleil sur la mer (60x81cm-24x32in) s.d.1915. 3-Jun-3 Livinec, Gaudcheau & Jezequel, Rennes #54

MAILLART, Diogene Ulysse Napoleon (1840-1926) French
£280 $481 €400 Portrait of a young girl (36x31cm-14x12in) s. 2-Dec-3 Christie's, Paris #226/R

MAILLART, Jean Denis (1913-) French
£1818 $3127 €2600 Dancer (72x60cm-28x24in) s. 2-Dec-3 Christie's, Paris #227/R est:300-400
Works on paper
£559 $962 €800 Dancer (32x25cm-13x10in) s.i. chl crayon. 2-Dec-3 Christie's, Paris #228/R

MAILLAUD, Fernand (1863-1948) French
£620 $992 €905 La cherette pres de la riviere (30x41cm-12x16in) s. panel. 16-Sep-3 Rosebery Fine Art, London #522
£667 $1213 €1000 Sous-bois (28x35cm-11x14in) s. 29-Jun-4 Chenu & Scrive, Lyon #127/R
£800 $1272 €1160 Les baigneuses (58x72cm-23x28in) s. board. 11-Sep-3 Christie's, Kensington #21/R
£800 $1416 €1168 Crossing the brook (31x41cm-12x16in) s. board. 29-Apr-4 Christie's, Kensington #179/R
£1391 $2531 €2100 Retour des champs (33x41cm-13x16in) s. i.verso cardboard. 15-Jun-4 Blanchet, Paris #111 est:1000-1200
£2252 $4098 €3400 Semailles (60x73cm-24x29in) s. panel. 19-Jun-4 St-Germain-en-Laye Encheres #110/R est:3000
£2267 $4080 €3400 Bruyeres en Creuse (46x55cm-18x22in) s. exhib. 20-Apr-4 Chenu & Scrive, Lyon #119/R est:1200-1500
£2400 $4320 €3600 Scene de moisson (71x100cm-28x39in) s. panel. 20-Apr-4 Chenu & Scrive, Lyon #118/R est:1500-2000
£2657 $4517 €3800 Scene de marche (46x55cm-18x22in) s. 28-Nov-3 Drouot Estimations, Paris #147/R est:3000-4000
£3267 $5880 €4900 Le repas des moissonneurs (61x72cm-24x28in) s. panel. 20-Apr-4 Chenu & Scrive, Lyon #117/R est:3000-3500
£3533 $6325 €5300 Bergere et troupeau aupres de l'etang de Rouffant (54x65cm-21x26in) s. 16-May-4 Lombrail & Teucquam, Paris #152/R
£4138 $6869 €6000 Stroll in the woods (137x99cm-54x39in) s.d.1903. 1-Oct-3 Della Rocca, Turin #237/R
Works on paper
£667 $1213 €1000 Attelage (20x88cm-8x35in) s. gouache. 29-Jun-4 Chenu & Scrive, Lyon #126/R

MAILLET, Jacques Leonard (1823-1895) French
Sculpture
£15294 $26000 €22329 Water bearers (122cm-48in) one s. pat bronze pair. 28-Oct-3 Christie's, Rockefeller NY #33/R est:15000-25000

MAILLET, Leo (1902-) ?
£270 $465 €394 Violinist (35x24cm-14x9in) s. board. 8-Dec-3 Philippe Schuler, Zurich #5867 (S.FR 600)
£383 $659 €559 Guitarist (24x33cm-9x13in) s. board. 8-Dec-3 Philippe Schuler, Zurich #5866 (S.FR 850)
£452 $756 €660 Le violoncelliste (47x46cm-19x18in) s.d.1946 canvas on board. 24-Jun-3 Germann, Zurich #1005 (S.FR 1000)
£1435 $2396 €2095 Nora (102x58cm-40x23in) mono.d.60 lit. 24-Oct-3 Hans Widmer, St Gallen #18/R est:1500-2800 (S.FR 3200)
£2152 $3595 €3142 Sculptor (60x69cm-24x27in) s.d.45 canvas on board lit. 24-Oct-3 Hans Widmer, St Gallen #19/R est:1600-3500 (S.FR 4800)

MAILLOL, Aristide (1861-1944) French
Prints
£2067 $3803 €3100 Femme nue etendue (11x34cm-4x13in) engraving. 10-Jun-4 Piasa, Paris #161/R
£6471 $11000 €9448 La vague (17x20cm-7x8in) init. woodcut. 6-Nov-3 Swann Galleries, New York #614/R est:15000-20000
£10000 $18400 €15000 Vague (17x20cm-7x8in) mono.i. engraving. 10-Jun-4 Piasa, Paris #162
Sculpture
£1384 $2200 €2021 Reclining female nude (22x21cm-9x8in) mono. plaster relief. 12-Sep-3 Skinner, Boston #346/R
£23651 $42336 €34530 Jeune fille habilee, siise (18cm-7in) mono.num.2/6 pat.bronze Cast Alixis Rudier exec.1900 prov. 26-May-4 AB Stockholms Auktionsverk #2479/R est:200000-250000 (S.KR 320000)
£32000 $58240 €48000 Baigneuse accroupie (21x8x10cm-8x3x4in) mono. pat bronze Cast Godard exec.1900. 2-Jul-4 Binoche, Paris #30/R est:45000-50000
£33333 $60667 €50000 Jeune fille assise (22x9x13cm-9x4x5in) mono. pat bronze Cast Godard. 2-Jul-4 Binoche, Paris #28/R est:60000-80000
£33520 $60000 €48939 Baigneuse aux bras leves (28cm-11in) mono. num.4/6 i.f.Alexis Rudier brown green pat bronze prov.lit. 5-May-4 Christie's, Rockefeller NY #228/R est:60000-80000
£34667 $63788 €52000 Venus (36cm-14in) mono. pat bronze. 9-Jun-4 Tajan, Paris #13/R est:55000-60000
£34667 $63788 €52000 Mediterranee (21cm-8in) mono. terracotta. 9-Jun-4 Tajan, Paris #14/R est:55000-60000
£36000 $65520 €54000 Coude leve (29x12x5cm-11x5x2in) bronze Cast Godard exec.1921. 2-Jul-4 Binoche, Paris #33/R est:30000-50000
£40000 $72800 €60000 Se voilant les yeux (21x18x6cm-8x7x2in) s. bronze Cast Godard. 2-Jul-4 Binoche, Paris #29/R est:35000-55000
£44693 $80000 €65252 Tete Heroique (58cm-23in) mono. num.4/6 st.f.Valsuani brown green pat bronze prov.lit. 6-May-4 Sotheby's, New York #292/R est:80000-120000
£47486 $85000 €69330 La nuit (18cm-7in) mono.d.3 brown pat bronze conceived 1909 prov.lit. 5-May-4 Christie's, Rockefeller NY #263/R est:100000-150000
£54667 $99493 €82000 Baigneuse se coiffant (27x12x10cm-11x5x4in) mono. bronze Cast Godard. 2-Jul-4 Binoche, Paris #27/R est:45000-55000
£55000 $100100 €80300 Se tenant un pied (15cm-6in) mono. num.4/6 st.f.Rudier brown green pat bronze. 3-Feb-4 Christie's, London #128/R est:40000-60000
£58824 $100000 €85883 Femme a l'epine (17cm-7in) mono.num.5/6 green brown pat bronze Cast A.Rudier prov.lit. 6-Nov-3 Sotheby's, New York #139/R est:50000-70000
£60000 $110400 €87600 Dina assise (22cm-9in) mono. num.1/6 bronze st.f.Alexis Rudier conceived 1937 prov.lit. 22-Jun-4 Sotheby's, London #111/R est:60000-80000
£66067 $121563 €99100 Demi-nature (78cm-31in) mono. pat bronze. 9-Jun-4 Tajan, Paris #12/R est:110000-120000
£72626 $130000 €106034 Young woman kneeling (20cm-8in) mono. i.num.2/4 green blk pat bronze f.A Rudier prov.lit. 5-May-4 Christie's, Rockefeller NY #238/R est:60000-80000
£89385 $160000 €130502 Leda (29cm-11in) st.mono.st.f.Rudier black green pat bronze exec.1921 prov.lit. 6-May-4 Sotheby's, New York #121/R est:200000-300000
Works on paper
£1042 $1740 €1500 Seated woman (25x17cm-10x7in) mono. ochre paper on board. 24-Oct-3 Ketterer, Hamburg #452/R est:1500-1800
£1500 $2385 €2175 Dos debout (31x20cm-12x8in) mon. chl. 11-Sep-3 Christie's, Kensington #39/R est:1800-2500
£1974 $3632 €3000 Jeune fille au repos (31x19cm-12x7in) blk crayon stump prov. 23-Jun-4 Maigret, Paris #12/R est:1500-2000
£2125 $3400 €3103 Croquis pour l'actin enchainee (28x23cm-11x9in) init. pencil. 18-Sep-3 Swann Galleries, New York #395/R est:2500-3500
£2139 $4000 €3123 Femme debout (34x23cm-13x9in) mono. chk paper on board. 25-Feb-4 Christie's, Rockefeller NY #49/R est:4000-6000
£2819 $5243 €4200 Etude pour l'action enchainee (30x20cm-12x8in) init. crayon drawing exec 1905. 3-Mar-4 Tajan, Paris #63 est:3500-4000
£2937 $5052 €4200 Nu feminin au bras leve. Femme debout a la draperie (36x20cm-14x8in) mono. crayon white chk double-sided exec.c.1921. 2-Dec-3 Calmels Cohen, Paris #22/R est:5000-6000
£3200 $5824 €4672 Nu accroupi (12x22cm-5x9in) mono. pencil. 4-Feb-4 Sotheby's, London #455/R est:2000-3000
£4085 $7148 €5800 Nu de dos (29x19cm-11x7in) mono. sanguine lit. 21-Dec-3 Thierry & Lannon, Brest #115 est:6000-8000

£4110 $6986 €6000 Dina couchee (23x36cm-9x14in) mono. sanguine. 6-Nov-3 Tajan, Paris #225/R
£4167 $6958 €6000 Etude de baigneuse a la draperie. Etude de corps (33x24cm-13x9in) red chk htd white chk chl double-sided. 21-Oct-3 Christie's, Paris #84/R est:6000-8000
£4333 $7973 €6500 Baigneuse debout (30x21cm-12x8in) chl. 8-Jun-4 Artcurial Briest, Paris #109/R est:7000-9000
£4367 $7948 €6376 Standing male nude (38x27cm-15x11in) st.mono. ochre. 17-Jun-4 Kornfeld, Bern #538/R est:7500 (S.FR 10000)
£4514 $7538 €6500 Nu femme allonge de dos (22x27cm-9x11in) mono red chk. 21-Oct-3 Christie's, Paris #83/R est:3000-4000
£5369 $9987 €8000 Nu assis (25x21cm-10x8in) mono. sanguine. 3-Mar-4 Ferri, Paris #341/R est:6000-8000
£6000 $11040 €9000 Etude de nu (32x23cm-13x9in) mono. sanguine. 9-Jun-4 Tajan, Paris #15/R est:9000-12000
£7000 $12880 €10220 Trois baigneuses. Untitled (24x28cm-9x11in) mono. gouache pencil double-sided prov. 22-Jun-4 Sotheby's, London #431/R est:8000-12000
£7500 $13650 €10950 Femme nue (31x23cm-12x9in) mono. pencil W/C. 4-Feb-4 Sotheby's, London #454/R est:5000-7000
£7947 $14464 €12000 Dina debout de face (39x25cm-15x10in) mono. chl htd chk prov. 18-Jun-4 Piasa, Paris #31/R est:12000-15000
£8500 $15470 €12410 Dina couchee (23x32cm-9x13in) mono. sanguine white chk exec.1940 prov. 4-Feb-4 Sotheby's, London #440/R est:6000-8000
£50000 $92000 €75000 Iva (118x74cm-46x29in) mono. crayon pastel chk exec. 1930. 10-Jun-4 Camard, Paris #104/R est:60000-65000
£58000 $105560 €84680 La douleur, etude pour le monument aux morts de Ceret (62x44cm-24x17in) mono. chl pencil exec.1921 prov.exhib. 4-Feb-4 Sotheby's, London #437/R est:60000-80000

MAILLOT, Theodore Pierre Nicolas (1826-1888) French
£6897 $12759 €10000 Chez le barbier perruquier (53x65cm-21x26in) s.d.1861. 16-Feb-4 Horta, Bruxelles #106/R est:10000-12000
Works on paper
£704 $1218 €1000 Allegorie de la Danse. Allegorie de la Musique (37x94cm-15x37in) s. blk crayon pen blk pen htd white gouache beige paper two. 10-Dec-3 Piasa, Paris #80

MAIMON, Isaac (20th C) ?
£329 $550 €480 Ballet (132x201cm-52x79in) s. acrylic. 19-Oct-3 Susanin's, Chicago #6001/R

MAIN, Monique (20th C) French
£828 $1374 €1200 Coucher de soleil (50x50cm-20x20in) s. 1-Oct-3 Millon & Associes, Paris #270
£828 $1374 €1200 Paysage ensoleille (61x46cm-24x18in) s. 1-Oct-3 Millon & Associes, Paris #271/R

MAINARDI, Andrea (c.1550-1620) Italian
£42282 $74839 €63000 Table with fruit, vegetable and figures (115x126cm-45x50in) 2-May-4 Finarte, Venice #39/R est:60000-70000

MAINCENT, Gustave (1850-1887) French
£845 $1462 €1200 Nude woman on a couch (51x74cm-20x29in) s. 12-Dec-3 Berlinghof, Heidelberg #1089/R est:440
£2797 $4811 €4000 Bord de riviere (54x65cm-21x26in) s. 7-Dec-3 Osenat, Fontainebleau #186 est:4000-4500
£3315 $6000 €4840 Peaceful afternoon by the river (51x61cm-20x24in) s. 3-Apr-4 Neal Auction Company, New Orleans #676/R est:5000-8000
£4028 $6726 €5800 Au cafe sur les hauteurs de Montmartre (36x48cm-14x19in) s. 22-Oct-3 Ribeyre & Baron, Paris #21/R est:6000-7500
£5556 $10000 €8112 Saint Gervais vu du quai a Paris (66x54cm-26x21in) s. 23-Apr-4 Sotheby's, New York #137/R est:10000-150000

MAINDS, Allan Douglass (1881-1945) British
£820 $1484 €1197 View of a lake within a parkland setting and sawn trees to the fore (76x127cm-30x50in) s.d.1920. 17-Apr-4 Dickins, Middle Claydon #41

MAINELLA, Raffaele (1858-1907) Italian
£4790 $8000 €6993 Desert Caravan (58x99cm-23x39in) s. W/C. 23-Oct-3 Shannon's, Milford #119/R est:8000-12000
Works on paper
£403 $713 €600 Gondoliere in Venice (32x18cm-13x7in) s. W/C card. 1-May-4 Meeting Art, Vercelli #144
£979 $1684 €1400 Two small anglers in Venice (16x32cm-6x13in) s. W/C. 5-Dec-3 Bolland & Marotz, Bremen #602/R
£1549 $2680 €2200 Night in the lagoon (40x70cm-16x28in) W/C. 14-Dec-3 Finarte, Venice #22/R est:2000-2500
£1600 $2560 €2320 In the Venetian lagoon (30x44cm-12x17in) s. pencil W/C. 18-Sep-3 Christie's, Kensington #82/R est:1800-2200
£1690 $2806 €2400 Prayer (250x450cm-98x177in) s. W/C cardboard. 11-Jun-3 Christie's, Rome #141 est:2300-2800
£1972 $3411 €2800 Lagoon (16x31cm-6x12in) s. W/C. 14-Dec-3 Finarte, Venice #21/R est:1600-2000

MAINSSIEUX, Lucien (1885-1958) French
£340 $609 €500 Pour le centenaire de Blida (54x64cm-21x25in) s.i.d.1955. 19-Mar-4 Ribeyre & Baron, Paris #84
£664 $1109 €950 Remorqueurs (26x44cm-10x17in) s. 7-Oct-3 Livinec, Gaudcheau & Jezequel, Rennes #57
£1060 $1939 €1600 Promenade (48x56cm-19x22in) s.d.38. 7-Apr-4 Doutrebente, Paris #55 est:600-800
£1934 $3480 €2900 Nu au voile noir (128x87cm-50x34in) s.d.1925. 26-Apr-4 Tajan, Paris #154/R est:3000-4000
Works on paper
£604 $1123 €900 Vue de Voiron (24x30cm-9x12in) s.d.1927 W/C. 3-Mar-4 Ferri, Paris #389

MAIO, Paolo de (attrib) (?-1784) Italian
£2676 $4683 €3800 Saint Paul preaching (75x50cm-30x20in) 17-Dec-3 Christie's, Rome #353/R est:1500-2000

MAIONE, Robert (19th C) British
£387 $700 €565 Chrysamthemums (41x33cm-16x13in) 16-Apr-4 American Auctioneer #260/R
£405 $700 €591 The cliff, Capri (93x114cm-37x45in) s. prov. 13-Dec-3 Weschler, Washington #570
£983 $1700 €1435 View from the Palatine (93x114cm-37x45in) s. prov. 13-Dec-3 Weschler, Washington #571 est:1200-1800

MAIRE, Andre (1898-1985) French
£1655 $2764 €2400 Femmes vietnamiennes et enfant (46x55cm-18x22in) 14-Nov-3 Claude Boisgirard, Paris #26/R est:1000-1500
£1705 $3000 €2489 King of Emir of Northern Dahomey (132x109cm-52x43in) s. 21-May-4 North East Auctions, Portsmouth #986/R
£2796 $4473 €4082 Women in the Vietnamese countryside (48x63cm-19x25in) s.d.1960 i.d.verso panel. 18-May-3 Sotheby's, Singapore #112/R est:6000-8000 (S.D 7800)
£3793 $6941 €5500 Femmes mois et enfant a la sieste (60x72cm-24x28in) s. isorel panel. 28-Jan-4 Piasa, Paris #21/R est:2000-2500
Works on paper
£411 $699 €600 Escurial (29x37cm-11x15in) s. sepia ink wash. 5-Nov-3 Tajan, Paris #10/R
£544 $974 €800 Marche malgache (32x49cm-13x19in) s.d.1959 pastel. 21-Mar-4 St-Germain-en-Laye Encheres #108/R
£658 $1211 €1000 Vue du Mekong (46x63cm-18x25in) s.d.1956 chl sanguine. 28-Jun-4 Joron-Derem, Paris #263
£658 $1210 €1000 Mosquee (28x36cm-11x14in) s. W/C. 25-Jun-4 Tajan, Paris #14/R
£667 $1220 €1000 Venise (28x36cm-11x14in) s. sepia prov. 6-Jun-4 Rouillac, Vendome #48
£667 $1220 €1000 Venise (58x73cm-23x29in) s.d.1928 sepia prov. 6-Jun-4 Rouillac, Vendome #49
£671 $1235 €1000 Deesse allongee (36x55cm-14x22in) s.d.1951 chl estompe htd sanguine. 28-Mar-4 Anaf, Lyon #191/R
£680 $1218 €1000 Zebus malgaches (25x32cm-10x13in) s.d.1959 pastel. 21-Mar-4 St-Germain-en-Laye Encheres #107/R
£800 $1456 €1200 Conversation (63x48cm-25x19in) s.d.1956 chl gouache. 4-Jul-4 Eric Pillon, Calais #171/R
£1034 $1728 €1500 Scene vietnamienne (50x65cm-20x26in) s.d.1957 gouache. 14-Nov-3 Claude Boisgirard, Paris #16 est:1400-1600
£1190 $2131 €1750 Belle malgache (50x65cm-20x26in) s.d.1959 pastel. 21-Mar-4 St-Germain-en-Laye Encheres #116/R est:2200-2500
£1241 $2073 €1800 La sieste (50x65cm-20x26in) s.d.1956 gouache. 14-Nov-3 Claude Boisgirard, Paris #18/R est:1600-1800
£1338 $2315 €1900 Elephants (52x49cm-20x19in) s.d.1953 chl gouache. 14-Dec-3 Eric Pillon, Calais #138/R
£1379 $2524 €2000 Marche malgache (50x65cm-20x26in) s.d.1959 black conte crayon sanguine. 28-Jan-4 Piasa, Paris #16 est:1200-1500
£1486 $2661 €2200 Pagode (65x50cm-26x20in) s.d.1952 conte sanguine. 5-May-4 Claude Boisgirard, Paris #17
£1489 $2487 €2100 Maternite Africaine (49x64cm-19x25in) s.d.1959 crayon pastel. 16-Jun-3 Gros & Delettrez, Paris #244/R est:2300-2800
£1517 $2777 €2200 Alcazar de Tolede (48x54cm-19x21in) s.d.1930 ink panel. 28-Jan-4 Piasa, Paris #22 est:1000-1200
£1548 $2477 €2260 Scene de plage. Bateaux sur le Mekong (50x65cm-20x26in) s. one d.1955 one d.1956 chl chk pair. 18-May-3 Sotheby's, Singapore #100/R est:4000-6000 (S.D 4320)
£1586 $2649 €2300 Femmes Moi a la cascade (65x50cm-26x20in) s.d.1949 gouache. 14-Nov-3 Claude Boisgirard, Paris #19/R est:2000-2500
£1824 $3266 €2700 Elephants aux chutes de Gouga (65x50cm-26x20in) s.d.1956 conte sanguine. 5-May-4 Claude Boisgirard, Paris #19/R est:1800-2000
£1831 $3168 €2600 Cavaliers africains (50x65cm-20x26in) s. gouache. 15-Dec-3 Gros & Delettrez, Paris #385/R est:2300-2800
£1972 $3411 €2800 Cornac et son elephant (64x49cm-25x19in) s.d.1952 crayon sanguine. 15-Dec-3 Gros & Delettrez, Paris #386/R est:2800-3500
£2000 $3660 €2900 Palais Venitien et gondole sur un canal (75x60cm-30x24in) s.d.1930 sepia. 28-Jan-4 Piasa, Paris #15 est:1500-2000
£2027 $3628 €3000 Lecture (50x65cm-20x26in) s.d.1958 gouache. 5-May-4 Claude Boisgirard, Paris #20/R est:2500-3000
£2061 $3689 €3050 Etudiantes vietnamiennes (50x65cm-20x26in) s.d.1953 conte sanguine. 5-May-4 Claude Boisgirard, Paris #18/R est:1800-2000
£2065 $3303 €3015 Buddhas (65x50cm-26x20in) s.d.1957 chl chk lit. 18-May-3 Sotheby's, Singapore #101/R est:2500-3500 (S.D 5760)
£2414 $4031 €3500 Famille Moi au cheval (65x50cm-26x20in) s.d.1949 gouache. 14-Nov-3 Claude Boisgirard, Paris #20/R est:2000-2500
£2432 $4354 €3600 Famille Moi (50x65cm-20x26in) s.d.1958 gouache. 5-May-4 Claude Boisgirard, Paris #21/R est:2500-3000

MAIRE, Arthur (1877-1939) French
£1552 $2778 €2266 Jura landscape with cows grazing (75x130cm-30x51in) s.d.1918. 14-May-4 Dobiaschofsky, Bern #100/R est:2000 (S.FR 3600)

MAIRINGER, Peter (1950-) Austrian
£355 $592 €500 Composition (80x100cm-31x39in) s.d.97. 16-Oct-3 Dorotheum, Salzburg #781/R
£533 $981 €800 Vanity (100x80cm-39x31in) s.d.97 acrylic. 9-Jun-4 Dorotheum, Salzburg #745/R

MAIROVICH, Zvi (1911-1973) Israeli
£605 $1113 €883 Israeli coastal village (45x37cm-18x15in) s. 9-Jun-4 Walker's, Ottawa #332/R (C.D 1500)
£769 $1400 €1154 Portrait of a young girl (62x38cm-24x15in) s. 1-Jul-4 Ben-Ami, Tel Aviv #4930/R est:1800-2200
£874 $1600 €1276 Still life with flowers (46x33cm-18x13in) s. oil paper on canvas painted c.1950. 1-Feb-4 Ben-Ami, Tel Aviv #4643/R est:2000-3000
£1000 $1700 €1460 Landscape of Haifa (33x41cm-13x16in) s. painted late 1940's. 1-Dec-3 Ben-Ami, Tel Aviv #4318/R est:2000-3000
£1176 $2000 €1717 Still life with pomegranates (50x61cm-20x24in) s. paper on canvas painted late 1940's prov. 1-Dec-3 Ben-Ami, Tel Aviv #4313/R est:2600-3400
£1412 $2400 €2062 Landscape of Haifa (50x61cm-20x24in) s. exec. 1950's prov. 1-Dec-3 Ben-Ami, Tel Aviv #4312/R est:3000-4000

£1420	$2500	€2073	Interior with vases of flowers (61x50cm-24x20in) s. painted c.1940. 1-Jan-4 Ben-Ami, Tel Aviv #4401/R est:3000-4000
£1511	$2750	€2206	Haifa (66x81cm-26x32in) s. prov. 29-Jun-4 Sotheby's, New York #407/R est:2000-3000
£1528	$2750	€2231	Haifa harbor (64x84cm-25x33in) 24-Apr-4 Du Mouchelle, Detroit #3168/R est:1000-2000
£1807	$3000	€2638	Girl in Blue (70x50cm-28x20in) s. 2-Oct-3 Christie's, Tel Aviv #98/R est:3000-5000
£2159	$3800	€3152	Haifa by night (61x50cm-24x20in) s. painted c.1950-51 prov. 1-Jan-4 Ben-Ami, Tel Aviv #4383/R est:4500-6000
Works on paper			
£604	$1100	€906	Landscape of Haifa (40x54cm-16x21in) s. gouache exec.c.1940. 1-Jul-4 Ben-Ami, Tel Aviv #4936/R
£3005	$5500	€4387	Self portrait (99x99cm-39x39in) s. mixed media on cardboard exhib. 1-Jun-4 Ben-Ami, Tel Aviv #4841/R est:8000-10000
£3279	$6000	€4787	Bird in the bush (100x50cm-39x20in) s. panda on cardboard. 1-Jun-4 Ben-Ami, Tel Aviv #4861/R est:7000-9000

MAISONNEUVE, Louis (?-1926) French

£709	$1184	€1000	Marchand d'oranges dans une vue d'Orient (55x111cm-22x44in) s. 19-Oct-3 Peron, Melun #319

MAISSEN, Fernand (1873-?) French

Works on paper			
£278	$453	€400	Pose de canards sur etang (28x40cm-11x16in) W/C. 29-Sep-3 Coutau Begarie, Paris #263/R

MAISTRE, Roy de (1894-1968) Australian

£2033	$3191	€2948	Grey still life. Still life with vases (28x38cm-11x15in) s. board double-sided prov. 26-Aug-3 Christie's, Sydney #297/R est:5000-8000 (A.D 5000)
£6383	$10851	€9319	Still life of fruit. Grey still life (29x38cm-11x15in) s. verso board double-sided prov. 25-Nov-3 Christie's, Melbourne #77/R est:15000-20000 (A.D 15000)
£6612	$12231	€9654	Tulips in a vase (61x51cm-24x20in) s. prov. 10-Mar-4 Deutscher-Menzies, Melbourne #77/R est:15000-20000 (A.D 16000)
£6809	$11574	€9941	St Jean de Luz (49x60cm-19x24in) s. panel prov. 25-Nov-3 Christie's, Melbourne #74/R est:15000-25000 (A.D 16000)
£7692	$12385	€11230	House amongst the trees (20x26cm-8x10in) s. card painted c.1920 prov. 25-Aug-3 Sotheby's, Paddington #132/R est:15000-20000 (A.D 19000)
£7724	$12126	€11200	Woman in red, portrait of Betty Morrison (43x33cm-17x13in) s. board painted c.1927 prov.lit. 26-Aug-3 Christie's, Sydney #138/R est:18000-25000 (A.D 19000)
£7851	$13897	€11462	Quayside, St Jean de Luz (32x40cm-13x16in) s. canvasboard. 3-May-4 Christie's, Melbourne #91/R est:12000-15000 (A.D 19000)
£9924	$18061	€14489	Still life, artist's studio (50x35cm-20x14in) s. board prov. 16-Jun-4 Deutscher-Menzies, Melbourne #101/R est:25000-35000 (A.D 26000)
£10526	$16947	€15368	Suburban House (19x17cm-7x7in) s. indis.d.192 card prov. 25-Aug-3 Sotheby's, Paddington #131/R est:15000-20000 (A.D 26000)
£11570	$20479	€16892	Harbour entrance, St Jean de Luz (56x61cm-22x24in) s.d.1926. 3-May-4 Christie's, Melbourne #95/R est:22000-28000 (A.D 28000)
Works on paper			
£850	$1573	€1241	Study for Jacob and the angel (11x17cm-4x7in) s. W/C gouache over pencil. 14-Jan-4 Lawrence, Crewkerne #1356/R

MAITLAND, Paul (1869-1909) British

£3200	$5824	€4672	Bright winter morning (19x22cm-7x9in) indis.init. panel prov. 15-Jun-4 Bonhams, New Bond Street #14/R est:3000-5000
£6500	$11895	€9490	Cheyne walk west, afternoon (30x41cm-12x16in) s. s.i.stretcher. 4-Jun-4 Christie's, London #5/R est:7000-10000

MAITLAND, Percy (?) ?

£420	$773	€613	Fishing scene with boats, harbour and fisherfolk (45x75cm-18x30in) s. 14-Jun-4 Bonhams, Bath #27

MAJAV, Karoly (fl.1890s) ?

£260	$434	€380	The one that got away (70x45cm-28x18in) s.d.1892. 8-Oct-3 Christie's, Kensington #732/R

MAJCHER, Stephen B (20th C) Canadian

Sculpture			
£1667	$2883	€2434	Moonwalker (122x79x124cm-48x31x49in) d.1979 bronze. 9-Dec-3 Maynards, Vancouver #240 est:2000-3000 (C.D 3750)

MAJERUS, Michel (1967-2002) American?

£1317	$2200	€1923	264 (59x59cm-23x23in) s.i.d.98 acrylic on cotton prov. 14-Nov-3 Phillips, New York #327/R est:2000-3000
£1916	$3200	€2797	437 (59x59cm-23x23in) s.i.d.99v. acrylic on cotton prov. 14-Nov-3 Phillips, New York #326/R est:2000-3000
£17877	$32000	€26100	Skul (210x210cm-83x83in) s.i.verso acrylic prov. 14-May-4 Phillips, New York #109/R est:25000-35000
£27545	$46000	€40216	Enough (250x400cm-98x157in) s.i.d.1999 acrylic prov. 14-Nov-3 Phillips, New York #212/R est:15000-20000

MAJEWICZ, George (1897-1965) German?

£342	$582	€500	Leopard on branch (40x30cm-16x12in) s. i. verso oil gold leaf panel lit. 6-Nov-3 Allgauer, Kempten #3491/R
£822	$1397	€1200	Leopard watching water hole (80x120cm-31x47in) s.i.d.1962. 6-Nov-3 Allgauer, Kempten #3492/R est:1200
£1931	$3225	€2800	Jaguar on riverbank stalking crane (70x60cm-28x24in) s. lit. 10-Jul-3 Allgauer, Kempten #2592/R est:500

MAJEWSKI, Andrzej (1836-?) Polish

£604	$1117	€900	Patineurs au coucher du soleil en Hollande (70x105cm-28x41in) s. 15-Mar-4 Horta, Bruxelles #47

MAJOR, Charlotte (fl.1872-1888) British

£30000	$55200	€43800	Wander in the Elysian fields (125x58cm-49x23in) s. exhib.lit. 11-Jun-4 Christie's, London #102/R est:20000-30000

MAJOR, Ernest (1864-1950) American

£2957	$5500	€4317	The water's edge (60x76cm-24x30in) s.d.1891 board. 5-Mar-4 Skinner, Boston #450/R est:3000-5000

MAJOR, Henry A (fl.1859-1873) British

£500	$860	€730	Still life of plums (20x25cm-8x10in) s.d.1883. 2-Dec-3 Gorringes, Lewes #2287

MAJOR, Theodore (1908-1999) British

£4400	$7876	€6424	Five bottles and fruit (45x54cm-18x21in) board prov. 17-Mar-4 Bonhams, Chester #267 est:4000-6000
£5000	$7850	€7300	Cyclamens in a pot (64x66cm-25x26in) s.verso board. 16-Apr-3 Bamfords, Derby #631/R est:3000-4000
£5000	$8500	€7300	Dark and light (31x37cm-12x15in) s. i.verso canvasboard. 29-Oct-3 Bonhams, Chester #373/R est:2500-3500
£5100	$8007	€7446	The Storm (77x94cm-30x37in) s.verso board. 16-Apr-3 Bamfords, Derby #632/R est:3000-4000
£12000	$20640	€17520	Lancashire town (76x94cm-30x37in) board. 3-Dec-3 Christie's, Kensington #469 est:600-800
Works on paper			
£300	$537	€438	Working woman (51x43cm-20x17in) pastel. 17-Mar-4 Bonhams, Chester #269
£300	$555	€438	Ploughman and horses (15x19cm-6x7in) init.d.1923 W/C. 14-Jul-4 Bonhams, Chester #366
£320	$592	€467	Working woman (51x43cm-20x17in) pastel. 14-Jul-4 Bonhams, Chester #363
£420	$777	€613	Street scene with telegraph pole (27x36cm-11x14in) chl. 14-Jul-4 Bonhams, Chester #362
£480	$888	€701	Windmill (32x30cm-13x12in) s. W/C. 14-Jul-4 Bonhams, Chester #365
£640	$1146	€934	Sprititualist (56x45cm-22x18in) s.i.d.1948 pastel. 17-Mar-4 Bonhams, Chester #268
£1600	$2928	€2336	River landscape with telegraph poles (25x36cm-10x14in) pastel drawing. 6-Apr-4 Capes Dunn, Manchester #838/R

MAJOREL, Fernand (1898-1965) French

£2448	$4210	€3500	Tahitiennes (160x220cm-63x87in) s. 5-Dec-3 Gros & Delettrez, Paris #94/R est:1500-2300
Works on paper			
£567	$1031	€850	Ballerine se reposant (30x23cm-12x9in) s. pastel. 29-Jun-4 Chenu & Scrive, Lyon #128/R

MAJORELLE, Jacques (1886-1962) French

£1879	$3477	€2800	Soir a Marg, Egypte (16x22cm-6x9in) s. i.d.1912 verso. 15-Mar-4 Gros & Delettrez, Paris #201/R est:3200-3500
£8451	$14620	€12000	Ruelle a Tanger (44x36cm-17x14in) i.d.18 cardboard. 15-Dec-3 Gros & Delettrez, Paris #168/R est:12000-15000
£9239	$16537	€13489	Souk des Teinturiers, Marrakesh (37x49cm-15x19in) indis sig. i.d.44 verso paper exhib. 26-May-4 AB Stockholms Auktionsverk #2451/R est:50000-60000 (S.KR 125000)
£63333	$114633	€95000	Harmonie en noir (60x78cm-24x31in) s.i. tempera gouache htd gold prov. 31-Mar-4 Sotheby's, Paris #153/R est:15000-20000
Works on paper			
£563	$975	€800	Souk et Khemis (38x28cm-15x11in) studio st. crayon. 15-Dec-3 Gros & Delettrez, Paris #53/R
£851	$1421	€1200	Ruelle animee, les remparts, Marrakech (29x25cm-11x10in) studio st. pen graphite. 16-Jun-3 Gros & Delettrez, Paris #169
£2817	$4873	€4000	Jeune marocaine pensive (34x25cm-13x10in) s.d.26 Chinese ink. 15-Dec-3 Gros & Delettrez, Paris #37/R est:1500-2500
£4667	$8587	€7000	Assemblee de femmes Africaines (42x54cm-17x21in) studio st. gouache graphite. 14-Jun-4 Gros & Delettrez, Paris #317/R est:6000-10000
£11972	$20711	€17000	Marrakech (61x47cm-24x19in) mixed media chl graphite col crayon lit. 15-Dec-3 Gros & Delettrez, Paris #39/R est:8000-10000
£12057	$20135	€17000	Beaute noire au bijoux (60x50cm-24x20in) s. pastel. 16-Jun-3 Gros & Delettrez, Paris #205/R est:12000-18000
£12416	$22970	€18500	Marrakech (63x54cm-25x21in) mixed media chl graphite col. 15-Mar-4 Gros & Delettrez, Paris #202/R est:8000-10000
£20408	$36531	€30000	Tam-tam (58x72cm-23x28in) d.45. 21-Mar-4 Teitgen, Nancy #67
£21000	$38640	€31500	Le charmant charmeur (105x73cm-41x29in) gouache tempera mixed media prov.lit. 9-Jun-4 Oger, Dumont, Paris #68/R est:25000-30000
£24832	$45940	€37000	Souk aux tissus a Marrakech (65x53cm-26x21in) s.i.d.1955 pastel distemper metal powder. 15-Mar-4 Gros & Delettrez, Paris #99/R est:25000-30000
£25352	$43859	€36000	Souk au cuir (64x52cm-25x20in) s.i. mixed media htd gold silver powder exec.c.1955. 15-Dec-3 Gros & Delettrez, Paris #47/R est:18000-25000
£27027	$47568	€40000	Vue des terrasses de Toundout (54x63cm-21x25in) s.d.49 gouache stump masonite. 18-May-4 Christie's, Paris #49/R est:25000-35000
£28369	$47376	€40000	Ruelle de la Medina, Marrakech (71x59cm-28x23in) s.i. mixed media. 16-Jun-3 Gros & Delettrez, Paris #82/R est:30000-40000
£29787	$49745	€42000	Le regime de dattes (66x49cm-26x19in) s.i. mixed media htd gold powder. 16-Jun-3 Gros & Delettrez, Paris #35/R est:25000-35000
£34966	$60141	€50000	Grande Kasbah vue d'une terrasse (78x89cm-31x35in) s.i.d.49 gouache isorel. 8-Dec-3 Tajan, Paris #296/R est:30000-35000
£48000	$86880	€72000	Femme dans une orangeraie (87x96cm-34x38in) s.i. col chk htd gold powder prov. 31-Mar-4 Sotheby's, Paris #156/R est:35000-50000
£59574	$99489	€84000	La Difa, fete Marocaine (64x80cm-25x31in) i. mixed media canvas. 16-Jun-3 Gros & Delettrez, Paris #327/R est:50000-65000

MAJORELLE, Jacques (attrib) (1886-1962) French

£333	$603	€500	Modele nu. cardboard. 3-Apr-4 Gerard, Besancon #61

MAJORES, Rosso H (1911-1996) German

£1333	$2400	€2000	Baltic beach (33x42cm-13x17in) s.d. 24-Apr-4 Dr Lehr, Berlin #264/R est:2500

MAJOUX, Louis Francois (19/20th C) French
£820 $1500 €1197 Nature morte of rabbits and quail (81x53cm-32x21in) s. indis d. 5-Jun-4 Neal Auction Company, New Orleans #550/R est:1500-2500

MAJZNER, Victor (1945-) Australian
£823 $1490 €1202 Untitled (124x168cm-49x66in) 30-Mar-4 Lawson Menzies, Sydney #126/R est:2000-3000 (A.D 2000)
£1240 $2194 €1810 Saint suit (183x152cm-72x60in) s.d.2000 s.i.d.2000 verso. 3-May-4 Christie's, Melbourne #222/R est:4000-7000 (A.D 3000)
Works on paper
£1382 $2474 €2018 Clear skin (183x153cm-72x60in) s.d.1994 i.verso synthetic polymer canvas. 4-May-4 Sotheby's, Melbourne #176/R est:3000-5000 (A.D 3400)
£1610 $2737 €2351 Vent Suit Spirit (198x183cm-78x72in) s.d.2001 s.i.d.verso synthetic polymer paint canvas. 24-Nov-3 Sotheby's, Melbourne #161/R est:3000-5000 (A.D 3800)

MAK (20th C) Iranian
Works on paper
£5500 $9735 €8030 Dervish (23x10cm-9x4in) s. pen wash htd gold. 27-Apr-4 Christie's, London #118/R est:2500-3500

MAK, Paul (20th C) Russian
Works on paper
£5000 $9200 €7500 La promenade du levrier (26x19cm-10x7in) s. gouache. 11-Jun-4 Claude Aguttes, Neuilly #43/R est:7000-8000
£10135 $18142 €15000 Princesse nue a cheval devant un chateau (30x25cm-12x10in) s.d.1938 mixed media. 10-May-4 Horta, Bruxelles #225/R est:2500-3500

MAKAROVA, Irina (1950-) Russian
Works on paper
£347 $566 €500 Nu renverse (42x58cm-17x23in) s.d.1987 gouache. 18-Jul-3 Charbonneaux, Paris #209

MAKART, Hans (1840-1884) Austrian
£987 $1816 €1500 The entrance into Anwerp by Karl V (14x22cm-6x9in) i.verso paper lit. 22-Jun-4 Wiener Kunst Auktionen, Vienna #2/R est:1500
£2238 $3804 €3200 Reclining Venus with two Cupids (24x45cm-9x18in) mono. lit. 28-Nov-3 Wiener Kunst Auktionen, Vienna #432/R est:3000-10000
£2500 $4600 €3800 Secret love (11x20cm-4x8in) board lit. 22-Jun-4 Wiener Kunst Auktionen, Vienna #3/R est:3000
£10490 $17832 €15000 Flowers (202x117cm-80x46in) 20-Nov-3 Dorotheum, Salzburg #191/R est:20000-28000
£10738 $19221 €16000 Flower painting (181x104cm-71x41in) 27-May-4 Dorotheum, Vienna #149/R est:16000-18000
£58000 $105560 €84680 Sleeping Snow White (220x126cm-87x50in) prov.exhib.lit. 15-Jun-4 Sotheby's, London #31/R est:50000-70000
£65000 $118300 €94900 Snow White receives the poisoned comb (220x126cm-87x50in) prov.exhib.lit. 15-Jun-4 Sotheby's, London #30/R est:50000-70000
Works on paper
£664 $1129 €950 Sad procession (22x33cm-9x13in) Indian ink pencil paper on board. 20-Nov-3 Dorotheum, Salzburg #234/R
£664 $1129 €950 Last confession (22x33cm-9x13in) pencil. 20-Nov-3 Dorotheum, Salzburg #235/R
£769 $1308 €1100 Inquisition (33x22cm-13x9in) d.1861 pencil. 20-Nov-3 Dorotheum, Salzburg #236/R

MAKELA, Juho (1885-1943) Finnish
£1409 $2621 €2100 Park scene (43x36cm-17x14in) s.d.1908 prov. 7-Mar-4 Bukowskis, Helsinki #394/R est:350
Works on paper
£268 $499 €400 Pine trees on the mountains (29x23cm-11x9in) s.d.1926 W/C prov. 7-Mar-4 Bukowskis, Helsinki #395/R

MAKELA, Jukka (1949-) Finnish
£507 $907 €750 Untitled (36x67cm-14x26in) s.d.91. 8-May-4 Bukowskis, Helsinki #291/R
£541 $968 €800 Landscape (45x45cm-18x18in) s.d.2000 verso acrylic. 8-May-4 Bukowskis, Helsinki #292/R
£623 $1102 €910 Untitled (22x38cm-9x15in) s.d.89 oil varnish paper. 27-Apr-4 AB Stockholms Auktionsverk #930/R (S.KR 8500)

MAKELA, Marika (1947-) Finnish
£473 $847 €700 Painting (59x80cm-23x31in) s/d/88 board. 8-May-4 Bukowskis, Helsinki #290/R
£1133 $2029 €1700 Composition "-U-" (150x130cm-59x51in) s.d.1975. 15-May-4 Hagelstam, Helsinki #220/R est:2500

MAKILA, Jarmo (1952-) Finnish
£1081 $1935 €1600 The journey to the mountains (101x166cm-40x65in) s.d.85 acrylic exhib. 8-May-4 Bukowskis, Helsinki #310/R est:1200-1500

MAKILA, Otto (1904-1955) Finnish
Works on paper
£733 $1313 €1100 Machine compositions (22x17cm-9x7in) s. pencil pair. 15-May-4 Hagelstam, Helsinki #211/R

MAKIN, James K (fl.1873-1906) British
£1450 $2349 €2117 Duet (46x38cm-18x15in) s.d.1866 verso. 26-Jan-3 Desmond Judd, Cranbrook #846

MAKIN, Jeffrey (1943-) Australian
£732 $1149 €1061 Wild Dog creek III (91x91cm-36x36in) s.d.85 s.i.d.1985 stretcher prov. 27-Aug-3 Christie's, Sydney #580/R est:2500-3500 (A.D 1800)
£1033 $1828 €1508 Fleurieu Peninsula (121x167cm-48x66in) s. s.i.stretcher. 3-May-4 Christie's, Melbourne #386/R est:4000-6000 (A.D 2500)
£1141 $1906 €1712 Untitled (121x101cm-48x40in) s. 27-Oct-3 Goodman, Sydney #235/R (A.D 2750)
£1271 $2161 €1856 Three sisters, Flinders Ranges (121x151cm-48x59in) s.d.99. 24-Nov-3 Sotheby's, Melbourne #234/R est:3000-5000 (A.D 3000)
£1322 $2340 €1930 Almond blossom (84x122cm-33x48in) s. 3-May-4 Christie's, Melbourne #353/R est:2000-3000 (A.D 3200)
£1429 $2629 €2086 Lower Aspley Falls (185x124cm-73x49in) s. s.i.d.2001 verso. 29-Mar-4 Goodman, Sydney #219/R est:3000-5000 (A.D 3500)
£1702 $2894 €2485 Flinders Ranges (83x182cm-33x72in) s.d.87 i.d.1987 verso. 25-Nov-3 Christie's, Melbourne #125/R est:3000-5000 (A.D 4000)
£2979 $5064 €4349 Glen Helen Gorge (122x153cm-48x60in) s. i.stretcher. 25-Nov-3 Christie's, Melbourne #267/R est:122-153 (A.D 7000)
£3099 $5485 €4525 Boab trees (122x152cm-48x60in) s. 3-May-4 Christie's, Melbourne #310/R est:4000-6000 (A.D 7500)

MAKK, Americo (20th C) American/Hungarian
£1534 $2500 €2240 The thinker (61x91cm-24x36in) s. 28-Sep-3 Simpson's, Houston #378/R

MAKLOTH, Johann (attrib) (19/20th C) Austrian
£1111 $1811 €1600 Priest with peasant family (19x25cm-7x10in) s. panel. 24-Sep-3 Neumeister, Munich #490 est:1600

MAKO, Sergej Alexandrovic (1885-1953) Russian
£1391 $2531 €2100 Fille au livre (92x73cm-36x29in) s. 16-Jun-4 Claude Boisgirard, Paris #103/R est:1500-1800

MAKOKIAN, Vartan (1869-1937) Armenian
£539 $1003 €787 Gebirgslandschaft im winter (17x23cm-7x9in) s. 2-Mar-4 Rasmussen, Copenhagen #1650/R (D.KR 6000)

MAKOVSKY, Konstantin (1839-1915) Russian
£1762 $2996 €2573 Young Russian woman (25cm-10in circular) s. paenl. 5-Nov-3 Dobiaschofsky, Bern #767/R est:5500 (S.FR 4000)
£2438 $3900 €3559 Portrait of a wealthy woman (91x71cm-36x28in) s. 21-Sep-3 William Jenack, New York #299 est:3000-5000
£8000 $14320 €11680 Lady in mourning (91x71cm-36x28in) s. 26-May-4 Sotheby's, London #23/R est:8000-12000
£8000 $14320 €11680 Portrait of an officer (88x67cm-35x26in) s.d.1883. 26-May-4 Sotheby's, London #24/R est:8000-12000
£16667 $27500 €24000 Angler's luck (85x66cm-33x26in) s.cyrillic i.d.1856. 2-Jul-3 Neumeister, Munich #705/R est:6000
£16667 $30000 €24334 Young woman kneeling (65x45cm-26x18in) s. prov. 23-Apr-4 Sotheby's, New York #11/R est:20000-30000
£17598 $31500 €25693 Katys, portrait of the artist daughter (23x20cm-9x8in) init. panel. 19-Mar-4 Aspire, Cleveland #5/R est:10000-15000
£29577 $51169 €42000 Portrait of lady (36x26cm-14x10in) s. panel. 13-Dec-3 Hagelstam, Helsinki #30/R est:20000
£30769 $48000 € Portrait of Tzaigane Raisova (46x37cm-18x15in) s. i.verso board prov. 11-Apr-3 Christie's, Rockefeller NY #16/R est:60000-70000
£51351 $91919 €76000 Girl with cat (35x27cm-14x11in) s. 8-May-4 Bukowskis, Helsinki #448/R est:35000-40000
£62084 $111131 €90643 Young beauty resting on a cushion (28x33cm-11x13in) s. panel. 28-May-4 Uppsala Auktionskammare, Uppsala #118/R est:200000-250000 (S.KR 840000)
£83333 $137500 €120000 Young girl carrying water (109x84cm-43x33in) s.cyrillic d.1874. 2-Jul-3 Neumeister, Munich #704/R est:7000
£88889 $160000 €129778 Ophelia (117x47cm-46x19in) s.i. prov. 23-Apr-4 Sotheby's, New York #10/R est:60000-80000
£160000 $286400 €233600 Beauty preparing to bathe (62x31cm-24x12in) s. panel. 26-May-4 Sotheby's, London #46/R est:80000-100000
Works on paper
£6000 $10740 €8760 Two Cossacks (23x28cm-9x11in) s. ink wash. 26-May-4 Sotheby's, Olympia #368/R est:2500-3500
£18919 $33865 €28000 Brother and sister (21x29cm-8x11in) s. gouache. 8-May-4 Bukowskis, Helsinki #470/R est:6000-8000
£27778 $50000 €40556 Warm embrace (29x22cm-11x9in) s. gouache on board. 23-Apr-4 Sotheby's, New York #12/R est:20000-30000

MAKOVSKY, Konstantin (attrib) (1839-1915) Russian
£3000 $5460 €4380 Portrait of the artist daughter (35x25cm-14x10in) board. 17-Jun-4 Clevedon Sale Rooms #1040/R est:1000-1500
£5397 $9500 €7880 Russian beauty (22x16cm-9x6in) bears sig board. 18-May-4 Bonhams & Butterfields, San Francisco #85/R est:4000-6000

MAKOVSKY, Vladimir (1846-1920) Russian
£10743 $19660 €15685 Two small girls watching bird on stone (74x90cm-29x35in) s. 9-Jun-4 Rasmussen, Copenhagen #1618/R est:100000 (D.KR 120000)
£30000 $53700 €43800 Old Baroness taking a walk (41x27cm-16x11in) s.d.1877 board. 26-May-4 Sotheby's, London #42/R est:30000-40000
£35000 $59500 €51100 Christ below the Mount (41x26cm-16x10in) s.d.1890 board. 19-Nov-3 Sotheby's, London #33/R est:6000-8000
£42868 $76733 €62587 Brothers (46x39cm-18x15in) s. panel prov. 26-May-4 AB Stockholms Auktionsverk #2423/R est:150000-200000 (S.KR 580000)
£130000 $232700 €189800 Mushroom pickers in Finland (125x179cm-49x70in) s.d.1898. 26-May-4 Sotheby's, London #45/R est:60000-80000

MAKOWSKI (19/20th C) ?
£24476 $41608 €35000 Cows and figures in forest clearing (125x178cm-49x70in) s.d.1898. 20-Nov-3 Weidler, Nurnberg #6507/R est:2500

MAKOWSKI, Alexander W (1869-1924) Russian
£7343 $12262 €10500 Village view with livestock (23x37cm-9x15in) s.d.1922 board. 11-Oct-3 De Vuyst, Lokeren #237/R est:2400-3000

£10211 $17665 €14500 Young girl (33x24cm-13x9in) s. panel. 13-Dec-3 Lempertz, Koln #233/R est:1000
£15278 $27500 €22306 Portrait of a young girl (33x24cm-13x9in) s. panel. 23-Apr-4 Sotheby's, New York #16/R est:20000-25000
£18000 $30600 €27000 Village pond (26x42cm-10x17in) s.d.97 panel. 25-Nov-3 Christie's, London #118/R est:12000-16000
£30000 $53700 €43800 Provincial Russian village (24x37cm-9x15in) s.d.1922 board. 26-May-4 Sotheby's, London #43/R est:15000-20000
£55000 $93500 €80300 Russian provincial village (70x90cm-28x35in) s.d.1917. 19-Nov-3 Sotheby's, London #34/R est:30000-40000
£60000 $102000 €90000 Village scene (76x62cm-30x24in) s.indis.d.i. 25-Nov-3 Christie's, London #136/R est:7000-9000

MAKOWSKI, Tade (1882-1932) Polish
£23513 $43499 €34329 Young boy (28x40cm-11x16in) 14-Mar-4 Agra, Warsaw #73/R (P.Z 170000)
Works on paper
£3974 $7232 €6000 Toutes mes felicitations (20x26cm-8x10in) mono. india ink W/C exec.1931 prov.lit. 16-Jun-4 Claude Boisgirard, Paris #104/R est:6000-8000

MAKOWSKI, Theodore (1890-1971) ?
£537 $993 €800 Maries (41x33cm-16x13in) s.d.1930. 14-Mar-4 Eric Pillon, Calais #262/R

MAKOWSKI, Zbigniew (1930-) Polish
£690 $1152 €1000 Arsenal (56x76cm-22x30in) s.d.1972 tempera card. 13-Nov-3 Finarte Semenzato, Rome #164
£690 $1152 €1000 Non saturetur oculus viso (56x76cm-22x30in) s.d.1972 tempera card. 13-Nov-3 Finarte Semenzato, Rome #177
£724 $1231 €1057 Avec quatre soleils (41x41cm-16x16in) s.d.1968 prov. 25-Nov-3 Germann, Zurich #840 est:800-1200 (S.FR 1600)
Works on paper
£423 $800 €618 Things about sunset (56x81cm-22x32in) s. Indian ink gouache. 22-Feb-4 Bonhams & Butterfields, Los Angeles #7049

MAKS, Cornelis Johannes (1876-1967) Dutch
£1316 $2421 €2000 Prinseneiland in Sneeuw (32x54cm-13x21in) s. i. stretcher. 28-Jun-4 Sotheby's, Amsterdam #244/R est:2000-3000
£4525 $7692 €6607 Before the rendezvous (74x60cm-29x24in) s. 28-Nov-3 Zofingen, Switzerland #2626/R est:5000 (S.FR 10000)
£6294 $10699 €9000 Horserider (50x60cm-20x24in) s. board prov. 25-Nov-3 Christie's, Amsterdam #194/R est:6000-8000
£8696 $14261 €12000 Paul Fratellini (68x52cm-27x20in) s. exhib. 27-May-3 Sotheby's, Amsterdam #317/R est:7000-9000
£9420 $15449 €13000 Albert Fratellini (68x51cm-27x20in) s. exhib. 27-May-3 Sotheby's, Amsterdam #316/R est:7000-9000
£9420 $15449 €13000 Francois Fratellini (68x51cm-27x20in) s. exhib. 27-May-3 Sotheby's, Amsterdam #318/R est:7000-9000
£11333 $20853 €17000 Circusdirecteur Jean Houcke (52x69cm-20x27in) s. 8-Jun-4 Sotheby's, Amsterdam #8/R est:15000-20000
£12000 $22080 €18000 View of Ronde Lutherse Kerk, from Haarlemmerstraat, Amsterdam (64x75cm-25x30in) s. board. 8-Jun-4 Sotheby's, Amsterdam #1/R est:8000-12000
£16667 $30667 €25000 Circus Paard (64x77cm-25x30in) s. board. 8-Jun-4 Sotheby's, Amsterdam #9/R est:15000-20000
£17105 $31474 €26000 Before the rendez-vous (74x60cm-29x24in) s. 22-Jun-4 Christie's, Amsterdam #559/R est:6000-8000
£28986 $47536 €40000 Lord Ernst Schuman in the Hooge School (99x94cm-39x37in) s. 27-May-3 Sotheby's, Amsterdam #320/R est:30000-50000
Works on paper
£3333 $6133 €5000 Flamingo dancers (46x63cm-18x25in) s. gouache. 8-Jun-4 Sotheby's, Amsterdam #294/R est:5000-7000
£3667 $6747 €5500 Stads gezicht bij Avond (23x28cm-9x11in) s. s.i. verso W/C. 8-Jun-4 Sotheby's, Amsterdam #193/R est:4000-6000
£6294 $10825 €9000 Two ladies (14x21cm-6x8in) s. gouache. 2-Dec-3 Sotheby's, Amsterdam #1/R est:4000-6000

MAKSIMENKO, Taras Nikitiyevich (1890-1969) Russian
£1074 $1976 €1600 Still life with asters (73x99cm-29x39in) s. canvasboard. 24-Mar-4 Hugo Ruef, Munich #1243 est:400

MALA-REIWALD, Hilde (1895-1993) German
£413 $689 €599 Portrait of girl (51x61cm-20x24in) s.d.1957 masonite. 23-Jun-3 Philippe Schuler, Zurich #8617 (S.FR 900)

MALACARNE, Claudio (1956-) Italian
£333 $613 €500 Venice (60x70cm-24x28in) s. s.i.verso. 12-Jun-4 Meeting Art, Vercelli #709
£352 $585 €500 Positano (70x80cm-28x31in) s. s.i.verso. 14-Jun-3 Meeting Art, Vercelli #647
£400 $736 €600 Embarcadero (70x80cm-28x31in) s. 12-Jun-4 Meeting Art, Vercelli #950
£467 $859 €700 Young anglers (120x80cm-47x31in) s. s.i.verso. 12-Jun-4 Meeting Art, Vercelli #949/R

MALACHOWSKI-NAUEN, Marie von (1880-1943) German
Works on paper
£633 $1159 €950 River landscape with trees (42x36cm-17x14in) mono. chl prov. 5-Jun-4 Lempertz, Koln #840/R

MALACREA, Francesco (1812-1886) Italian
£530 $964 €800 Dead game (55x44cm-22x17in) 18-Jun-4 Stadion, Trieste #518
£1014 $1916 €1500 Still life with fish and onion (61x77cm-24x30in) 20-Feb-4 Stadion, Trieste #119/R est:1600-2000
£1467 $2625 €2200 Still life with figs and melon (53x70cm-21x28in) 12-May-4 Stadion, Trieste #833/R est:1800-2200
£2133 $3819 €3200 Still life of fruit (52x71cm-20x28in) 12-May-4 Stadion, Trieste #832/R est:1800-2200

MALAGODI, Giuseppe (1890-1968) Italian
£872 $1500 €1273 In Campagna (53x64cm-21x25in) s.d.1958 board. 7-Dec-3 Treadway Gallery, Cincinnati #569/R est:1000-2000
£933 $1717 €1400 Life in Anticoli Corrado (48x50cm-19x20in) init.i.verso board. 14-Jun-4 Sant Agostino, Torino #332/R

MALANCA, Jose (1897-1967) Argentinian
£400 $692 €584 Farmhouses and mountains (42x53cm-17x21in) s. 9-Dec-3 Rosebery Fine Art, London #644/R
£9290 $17000 €13563 Autumn (70x76cm-28x30in) 1-Jun-4 Arroyo, Buenos Aires #87

MALANGI, David (1927-1999) Australian
Sculpture
£11382 $17984 €16504 Gunmirringu and his wife (56cm-22in) earth pigments wood exec.c.1961 pair prov. 28-Jul-3 Sotheby's, Paddington #235/R est:16000-24000 (A.D 28000)
Works on paper
£353 $632 €515 Djikaria - Catfish (35x67cm-14x26in) natural ochre's bark exec 1989 prov. 25-May-4 Lawson Menzies, Sydney #265/R (A.D 900)
£391 $730 €587 Dhamala site (123x60cm-48x24in) bears name.verso earth pigments eucalyptus bark exec.c.1990 prov. 26-Jul-4 Sotheby's, Melbourne #406/R (A.D 1000)
£508 $950 €762 Gunmirringu mortuary rites (51x27cm-20x11in) earth pigments eucalyptus bark prov. 26-Jul-4 Sotheby's, Melbourne #539/R (A.D 1300)
£813 $1285 €1179 Gunmirringu story (75x46cm-30x18in) earth pigments eucalyptus bark exec.c.1968 prov. 28-Jul-3 Sotheby's, Paddington #473/R est:2000-4000 (A.D 2000)
£1016 $1899 €1524 Gunmirringu mortuary rites. bears name.i.d.1968 verso earth pigments eucalyptus bark prov. 26-Jul-4 Sotheby's, Melbourne #537/R (A.D 2600)
£2941 $5265 €4294 Gunmirringu - The Great Hunter (86x63cm-34x25in) natural earth pigments eucalyptus bark exec c.1985 prov. 25-May-4 Lawson Menzies, Sydney #264/R est:3000-5000 (A.D 7500)

MALATESTA, Adeodato (1806-1891) Italian
£2734 $4483 €3800 Portrait of woman (29x23cm-11x9in) 5-Jun-3 Adma, Formigine #911 est:3900-4100

MALAVAL, Robert (1937-1980) French
Sculpture
£2448 $4210 €3500 Faux portrait d'Helene (77x35x23cm-30x14x9in) s.i.d.1963 verso resin wood box. 4-Dec-3 Piasa, Paris #8/R est:4000-6000

MALBET, Aurelie Leontine (fl.1868-1906) French
£1100 $1969 €1606 Still life of fruit. Still life of game (27x41cm-11x16in) s. pair. 26-May-4 Sotheby's, Olympia #299/R est:1000-1500

MALBON, William (1805-1877) British
£2800 $4760 €4088 Birdseye (69x90cm-27x35in) s.d.Oct 17 186. 27-Nov-3 Christie's, Kensington #76/R est:3000-4000

MALCHAIR, John Baptiste (1731-1817) British
Works on paper
£1400 $2576 €2044 Tom Tivey's hole in the woods near East Cranmore, Somerset. House at East Cranmore (27x50cm-11x20in) i.d.Sept 25 1794 W/C set of three. 26-Mar-4 Sotheby's, London #106/R est:1500-2000

MALCHE, Brigitta (1938-) Swiss
£270 $500 €394 Plinthos (84x84cm-33x33in) s. verso acrylic board. 18-Jan-4 Bonhams & Butterfields, Los Angeles #7042/R

MALCHUS, Carl Freiherr von (1835-1889) German
£1250 $2338 €1875 Dutch canal landscape with mindmill and cattle (78x108cm-31x43in) s.d.1882 exhib. 26-Jul-4 Bonhams, Bath #62/R est:1500-2500

MALCLES, Jean Denis (1912-) French
Works on paper
£397 $723 €600 L'envol sur Paris. s. gouache exec. 1997. 15-Jun-4 Blanchet, Paris #236

MALCZEWSKI, Jacek (1854-1929) Polish
£5000 $9100 €7300 Study of three young boys (18x30cm-7x12in) s.d.1890 panel prov. 15-Jun-4 Sotheby's, London #79/R est:5000-7000
£10156 $16961 €14828 Portrait of Ignacego Bobrowskiego (81x66cm-32x26in) s. painted c.1910-14. 19-Oct-3 Agra, Warsaw #4/R est:36000 (P.Z 65000)
£27663 $51176 €40388 Thanatos (81x65cm-32x26in) d.1917. 14-Mar-4 Agra, Warsaw #23/R (P.Z 200000)

MALCZEWSKI, Rafal (1892-1965) Polish
£324 $600 €473 Burning of the rossa (51x69cm-20x27in) s.d.1942. 15-Jul-4 Doyle, New York #57/R

MALDEGHEM, Romain Eugène van (1813-1867) Belgian
£3846 $6538 €5500 Le songe de Marie Amelie (113x76cm-44x30in) s. 27-Nov-3 Millon & Associes, Paris #104/R est:6000-8000

MALEAS, Constantine (1879-1928) Greek

£15000	$26250	€21900	Pine trees in Halki (29x39cm-11x15in) s. hardboard prov.exhib.lit. 16-Dec-3 Bonhams, New Bond Street #104/R est:15000-25000
£36000	$61200	€52560	Santorini at dusk (47x56cm-19x22in) s. panel on board prov.lit. 18-Nov-3 Sotheby's, London #7/R est:25000-35000
£40000	$71600	€58400	Landscape in the Peloponise (32x35cm-13x14in) s.i. i.verso board prov.lit. 10-May-4 Sotheby's, Olympia #13/R est:20000-30000
£42000	$75180	€61320	View of the Acropolis (50x69cm-20x27in) s. cardboard prov. 11-May-4 Bonhams, New Bond Street #75/R est:30000-40000

Works on paper

£3000	$5370	€4380	Springs of the Nile (36x37cm-14x15in) s. chl. 11-May-4 Bonhams, New Bond Street #29/R est:3000-5000
£4000	$7160	€5840	The Gate (29x39cm-11x15in) s. pastel prov. 10-May-4 Sotheby's, Olympia #3/R est:4000-6000
£5000	$8950	€7300	House in Lesvos. House in Messolonghi (30x39cm-12x15in) s. one d. 1921 one crayon chl one pencil two. 11-May-4 Bonhams, New Bond Street #23/R est:5000-7000

MALECKI, Vladislav (1836-1900) Polish

£2500	$4475	€3650	Forward patrol (26x40cm-10x16in) s.d.1876. 28-May-4 Lyon & Turnbull, Edinburgh #46/R est:1000-1500

MALENCON, Paul (1817-1880) French

£537	$1004	€800	Les chevaux (65x81cm-26x32in) s.d.1851. 29-Feb-4 Osenat, Fontainebleau #216

MALER, Hans (style) (16th C) Austrian

£5495	$10000	€8023	Portrait of a girl holding a goldfinch (42x34cm-17x13in) panel on panel. 4-Feb-4 Christie's, Rockefeller NY #50/R est:10000-15000

MALERBA, Frank (1950-) Australian?

£1423	$2233	€2063	Slim (152x122cm-60x48in) s. acrylic. 26-Aug-3 Christie's, Sydney #259/R est:3500-5500 (A.D 3500)
£1844	$2988	€2692	Girls in red bikinis (137x163cm-54x64in) s. painted c.1990. 30-Jul-3 Goodman, Sydney #68/R est:4500-5500 (A.D 4500)

Works on paper

£1707	$3056	€2492	Behind (122x122cm-48x48in) s. synthetic polymer paint canvas. 4-May-4 Sotheby's, Melbourne #314/R est:4000-8000 (A.D 4200)

MALERBA, Gian Emilio (1880-1926) Italian

£1946	$3113	€2841	Portrait of young woman (40x43cm-16x17in) s. d.Marzo 1916 verso. 16-Sep-3 Philippe Schuler, Zurich #3367/R est:3000-4000 (S.FR 4300)

MALESCI, Giovanni (1884-1969) Italian

Works on paper

£616	$1010	€850	Farm in Maremma (34x49cm-13x19in) s. mixed media board prov. 27-May-3 Il Ponte, Milan #918

MALESPINA, Louis Ferdinand (1874-1940) French

£1042	$1635	€1500	Course a Chantilly. s. cardboard. 29-Aug-3 Deauville, France #167/R est:1500-1800

MALET, Albert (1905-1986) French

£414	$691	€600	Foret en automne (41x33cm-16x13in) s. masonite. 11-Nov-3 Lesieur & Le Bars, Le Havre #81
£537	$999	€800	Oleron, la plage (50x65cm-20x26in) s. 7-Mar-4 Lesieur & Le Bars, Le Havre #103
£570	$1061	€850	L'eglise du village (55x46cm-22x18in) s. isorel. 7-Mar-4 Lesieur & Le Bars, Le Havre #98
£586	$979	€850	Etang en foret (54x82cm-21x32in) s. 11-Nov-3 Lesieur & Le Bars, Le Havre #83
£671	$1248	€1000	Foret de Vaupalliere (46x38cm-18x15in) s. isorel. 7-Mar-4 Lesieur & Le Bars, Le Havre #103
£759	$1267	€1100	Orage (65x81cm-26x32in) s. 11-Nov-3 Lesieur & Le Bars, Le Havre #80
£851	$1421	€1200	Bord de Seine (23x31cm-9x12in) 19-Oct-3 Imberdis, Pont Audemer #45
£872	$1623	€1300	Paysage d'hiver (38x46cm-15x18in) s.d.1933. 7-Mar-4 Lesieur & Le Bars, Le Havre #99
£872	$1623	€1300	Jardin fleuri (38x46cm-15x18in) s.verso. 7-Mar-4 Lesieur & Le Bars, Le Havre #100
£1000	$1820	€1500	Voiliers pres du rivage (46x55cm-18x22in) s. 4-Jul-4 Eric Pillon, Calais #101/R
£1007	$1872	€1500	En foret l'etang (54x82cm-21x32in) s. 7-Mar-4 Lesieur & Le Bars, Le Havre #104
£1033	$1901	€1550	Champs de lavande en bord de mer (14x23cm-6x9in) s. panel. 8-Jun-4 Livinec, Gaudcheau & Jezequel, Rennes #136/R
£1074	$1997	€1600	Bord de Seine a Duclair (37x40cm-15x16in) s. isorel. 7-Mar-4 Lesieur & Le Bars, Le Havre #104
£1074	$1922	€1600	Vue de Rouen (45x63cm-18x25in) s. 25-May-4 Chambelland & Giafferi, Paris #77/R est:1500-2000
£1099	$1836	€1550	Etang de Gouville Claville Motteville (46x55cm-18x22in) s. 19-Oct-3 Imberdis, Pont Audemer #46
£1119	$1902	€1600	Rouen vu de Canteleu (38x55cm-15x22in) s. s.i.verso. 28-Nov-3 Blanchet, Paris #61/R est:1800-2000
£1141	$2122	€1700	Bord de Seine (73x93cm-29x37in) s. 7-Mar-4 Lesieur & Le Bars, Le Havre #102
£1275	$2372	€1900	Pont sur Saone a Auzouville (46x55cm-18x22in) s. isorel. 7-Mar-4 Lesieur & Le Bars, Le Havre #96
£1275	$2372	€1900	La Seine a Villequier (38x5cm-15x2in) s. isorel. 7-Mar-4 Lesieur & Le Bars, Le Havre #97
£1333	$2387	€2000	La Seine a Rouen (54x81cm-21x32in) s. 12-May-4 Brissoneau, France #92/R est:2000-3000
£1600	$2912	€2400	Inondation a Henouville (51x65cm-20x26in) s. 4-Jul-4 Eric Pillon, Calais #100/R
£1611	$2996	€2400	Rouen, vue de Canteleu (60x81cm-24x32in) s. 7-Mar-4 Lesieur & Le Bars, Le Havre #91/R
£1611	$2996	€2400	Honfleur, la lieutenance et le bassin (54x66cm-21x26in) s. isorel. 7-Mar-4 Lesieur & Le Bars, Le Havre #93
£1678	$3121	€2500	Les meules de foins (54x82cm-21x32in) s. 7-Mar-4 Lesieur & Le Bars, Le Havre #90
£1678	$3003	€2500	Rouen, la cote Ste Catherine (54x82cm-21x32in) s. 25-May-4 Chambelland & Giafferi, Paris #78/R est:1500-2000
£1812	$3370	€2700	Bord de mer (65x81cm-26x32in) s. 7-Mar-4 Lesieur & Le Bars, Le Havre #89/R
£1879	$3495	€2800	Le port de Rouen (50x65cm-20x26in) s. d.69 verso. 7-Mar-4 Lesieur & Le Bars, Le Havre #92
£2282	$4244	€3400	La Bouille a Duclair (60x92cm-24x36in) s. 7-Mar-4 Lesieur & Le Bars, Le Havre #88
£2464	$4041	€3400	Panorama de Rouen vu de Canteleu (54x73cm-21x29in) s. 11-May-3 Osenat, Fontainebleau #230/R est:4000-4500

Works on paper

£265	$482	€400	Paysage (25x34cm-10x13in) s. gouache. 20-Jun-4 Imberdis, Pont Audemer #38

MALEVICH, Kasimir (1878-1935) Russian

£650000	$1183000	€949000	Suprematist figure (71x44cm-28x17in) s. i.verso painted c.1931-1932 prov. 21-Jun-4 Bonhams, New Bond Street #28/R est:700000-900000

Photographs

£6818	$12000	€9954	Views of his constructivist exhibition at the Grosse Berliner Kunsthaus (15x23cm-6x9in) photograph set of three. 20-May-4 Swann Galleries, New York #333/R est:15000-25000

Works on paper

£26000	$47840	€37960	Sensations melangees (13x20cm-5x8in) pencil buff paper exec c.1916 prov.exhib.lit. 24-Jun-4 Christie's, London #372/R est:8000-12000
£140000	$254800	€204400	Self portrait (25x25cm-10x10in) varnished gouache W/C pencil round exec 1909-1910 prov.exhib.lit. 5-Feb-4 Christie's, London #348/R est:140000-180000

MALFAIT, Hubert (1898-1971) Belgian

£2448	$4087	€3500	Winter landscape (50x67cm-20x26in) mono. 11-Oct-3 De Vuyst, Lokeren #238/R est:5000-6000
£2667	$4880	€4000	Baignade (67x50cm-26x20in) s. prov. 7-Jun-4 Palais de Beaux Arts, Brussels #81/R est:3500-5000
£4196	$7133	€6000	Vue portuaire avec personnages sur l'estacade (75x90cm-30x35in) s. 1-Dec-3 Palais de Beaux Arts, Brussels #285/R est:6000-8000
£5175	$8797	€7400	Horse riders on the beach (50x67cm-20x26in) s. 25-Nov-3 Christie's, Amsterdam #240/R est:1000-1500
£5245	$8916	€7500	Trois enfants dans une rue enneigee (50x38cm-20x15in) s. 1-Dec-3 Palais de Beaux Arts, Brussels #279/R est:4500-6000
£5594	$9510	€8000	Fillette et vaches dans les champs (38x50cm-15x20in) s. 1-Dec-3 Palais de Beaux Arts, Brussels #283/R est:7500-10000
£8054	$14255	€12000	Harvesting (75x90cm-30x35in) s.d.1962 panel lit. 27-Apr-4 Campo & Campo, Antwerp #157/R est:12000-16000
£12324	$21320	€17500	Potato harvest (60x90cm-24x35in) s. panel exhib.lit. 13-Dec-3 De Vuyst, Lokeren #493/R est:20000-25000
£13986	$23776	€20000	Chasseur au faisan et au lapin devant le chateau d'Ooidonk (128x91cm-50x36in) s. prov. 1-Dec-3 Palais de Beaux Arts, Brussels #284/R est:20000-30000

Works on paper

£500	$895	€750	Hay harvest (30x38cm-12x15in) s. chk sepia lit. 15-May-4 De Vuyst, Lokeren #207
£733	$1313	€1100	Two horses in the field (36x46cm-14x18in) s. sepia. 15-May-4 De Vuyst, Lokeren #206/R

MALFATTI, Nino (1940-) Austrian

£400	$736	€600	Wire clothes hangers (105x86cm-41x34in) s.i.d.1974 verso. 12-Jun-4 Villa Grisebach, Berlin #792/R

MALFRAY, Charles Alexandre (1887-1940) French

£1000	$1730	€1460	Near Tonlon, Southern (46x66cm-18x26in) s. 9-Dec-3 Maynards, Vancouver #131 est:1000-1500 (C.D 2250)

Sculpture

£1677	$3118	€2500	Baigneuse (61cm-24in) s.num.7/8 antique pat bronze st.f.Godart. 2-Mar-4 Artcurial Briest, Paris #209/R est:2500-3000

Works on paper

£276	$461	€400	Femme se coiffant (30x23cm-12x9in) s. sanguine. 11-Nov-3 Lesieur & Le Bars, Le Havre #84

MALFROY (19/20th C) French

£588	$1000	€858	Port de Sausset - Provence (33x46cm-13x18in) s. i. stretcher. 18-Nov-3 Hans Widmer, St Gallen #1146 (S.FR 1300)
£3521	$6092	€5000	Les Martigues (45x65cm-18x26in) s. 12-Dec-3 Piasa, Paris #76c/R est:5000-7000

MALFROY, Charles (1862-1918) French

£933	$1717	€1400	Les Martigues (27x46cm-11x18in) s. prov. 11-Jun-4 Pierre Berge, Paris #203
£1184	$2179	€1800	Bateaux a quai (26x21cm-10x8in) s.d.1889 wood. 28-Jun-4 Joron-Derem, Paris #129/R est:2000-2500
£1397	$2500	€2040	Port in France (46x66cm-18x26in) s. prov. 6-May-4 Shannon's, Milford #194/R est:2500-3500
£1622	$2903	€2400	Mediterranean coast (38x55cm-15x22in) s. canvas on panel lit. 8-May-4 Dawo, Saarbrucken #62/R est:2200
£2603	$4425	€3800	South European fishing ground (45x63cm-18x25in) s. 5-Nov-3 Vendue Huis, Gravenhage #181/R est:1000-1500
£2643	$4493	€3859	Sunny beach (24x41cm-9x16in) s.d.1908. 5-Nov-3 Dobiaschofsky, Bern #768/R est:3800 (S.FR 6000)
£5000	$8950	€7300	Shipping in the harbour at Nantes (46x65cm-18x26in) s.i. 26-May-4 Christie's, Kensington #661/R est:2000-3000

MALFROY, H (1895-1944) French

£2238	$3849	€3200	Les martigues (60x92cm-24x36in) s. 3-Dec-3 Beaussant & Lefèvre, Paris #56/R est:1500-2000

MALFROY, Henry (1895-1944) French

£621	$1148	€900	Paris (26x40cm-10x16in) s. d.1928 verso. 14-Feb-4 Hans Stahl, Hamburg #113
£833	$1350	€1208	La Madeleine (22x27cm-9x11in) s. 29-Jul-3 Galeria y Remates, Montevideo #34/R
£900	$1548	€1314	Bonne brise (60x92cm-24x36in) s.i. 2-Dec-3 Sotheby's, London #106/R
£915	$1520	€1300	Place du Chatelet (22x27cm-9x11in) s. 15-Jun-3 Peron, Melun #166
£947	$1752	€1383	Coastal landscape, Martiques (45x64cm-18x25in) s.i.d.1919. 15-Mar-4 Rasmussen, Vejle #191/R (D.KR 10500)
£1210	$2226	€1767	La place de la Bastille (28x41cm-11x16in) s. 14-Jun-4 Waddingtons, Toronto #288/R est:3000-4000 (C.D 3000)
£1250	$1962	€1800	Paris - cars and pedestrians near Madeleine (26x40cm-10x16in) s. d.1928 verso. 30-Aug-3 Hans Stahl, Toestorf #38/R est:1200
£1748	$2920	€2500	Port mediterraneen (53x63cm-21x25in) 12-Oct-3 Teitgen, Nancy #83
£1862	$3408	€2700	Steamer de la CGT par grand vent (90x54cm-35x21in) s.i. 31-Jan-4 Neret-Minet, Paris #160/R est:2500-3000
£2013	$3725	€3000	Paris, marche aux fleurs (27x35cm-11x14in) s. 14-Mar-4 Eric Pillon, Calais #127/R
£2055	$3493	€3000	Paris, Notre-Dame (30x40cm-12x16in) s. 9-Nov-3 Eric Pillon, Calais #117/R
£2466	$3871	€3600	Les Martigues (33x46cm-13x18in) s. 20-Apr-3 Deauville, France #127/R est:3600-4300
£2958	$5117	€4200	Harbour towns in the south of France (35x55cm-14x22in) s. 13-Dec-3 Lempertz, Koln #234/R est:3000
£3226	$5935	€4710	Fishing port near Martigues (60x91cm-24x36in) s. 14-Jun-4 Waddingtons, Toronto #292/R est:6000-8000 (C.D 8000)
£3267	$5945	€4900	Port de Cassis (38x55cm-15x22in) s. 4-Jul-4 Eric Pillon, Calais #20/R

MALFROY, Henry (attrib) (1895-1944) French

£1329	$2285	€1900	Paysage de bord de mer (32x63cm-13x25in) 5-Dec-3 Gros & Delettrez, Paris #53 est:600-800

MALHERBE, William (1884-1951) French

£353	$636	€530	Croissy-sur-Seine (32x41cm-13x16in) s. panel. 24-Apr-4 Cornette de St.Cyr, Paris #384
£353	$636	€530	Au bord de l'eau (37x46cm-15x18in) s.d.1923 panel. 24-Apr-4 Cornette de St.Cyr, Paris #383
£400	$720	€600	Bouquet (61x50cm-24x20in) s.d.1913. 24-Apr-4 Cornette de St.Cyr, Paris #387
£433	$780	€650	Nu debout (61x46cm-24x18in) s. 24-Apr-4 Cornette de St.Cyr, Paris #385
£700	$1260	€1050	Bouquet (50x60cm-20x24in) 24-Apr-4 Cornette de St.Cyr, Paris #386
£1267	$2267	€1900	Deux baigneuses (55x45cm-22x18in) panel prov. 15-May-4 De Vuyst, Lokeren #208/R est:1800-2000
£1267	$2267	€1900	Nude (64x53cm-25x21in) prov. 15-May-4 De Vuyst, Lokeren #209/R est:2000-2400
£1390	$2600	€2029	Nature morte avec vase de fleurs (51x40cm-20x16in) s.d.45 prov. 25-Feb-4 Christie's, Rockefeller NY #102/R est:1000-1500
£1479	$2558	€2100	Jeune femme assise (57x50cm-22x20in) s.d.1913. 13-Dec-3 De Vuyst, Lokeren #218/R est:2000-2400
£1479	$2558	€2100	Baigneuse (72x50cm-28x20in) s. 13-Dec-3 De Vuyst, Lokeren #219/R est:2000-2400
£2081	$3849	€3100	Portrait d'elegante (53x43cm-21x17in) s. 14-Mar-4 St-Germain-en-Laye Encheres #90/R est:2500

MALHOA, Jose Vital Branco (1855-1933) Portuguese

Works on paper

£7383	$13215	€11000	Chatting in the street (41x33cm-16x13in) s. dr. 31-May-4 Cabral Moncada Leiloes, Lisbon #399/R est:6000-9000

MALI, Christian (1832-1906) German

£855	$1574	€1300	Ox cart laden with hay (24x44cm-9x17in) bears sig.i. canvas on board. 24-Jun-4 Dr Fritz Nagel, Stuttgart #730/R
£987	$1816	€1500	Herdsman and cattle watering (51x71cm-20x28in) s.i.d.1895. 22-Jun-4 Wiener Kunst Auktionen, Vienna #51/R est:1500
£1867	$3416	€2800	Cows watering (50x65cm-20x26in) s.d.1889. 5-Jun-4 Arnold, Frankfurt #659/R est:2400
£1875	$3056	€2700	Lakeside idyll (33x55cm-13x22in) s.i. 25-Sep-3 Dr Fritz Nagel, Stuttgart #1376/R est:2900
£2083	$3396	€3000	Young herder with cattle by stream (25x42cm-10x17in) s.d.1883 panel. 24-Sep-3 Neumeister, Munich #493/R est:3200
£2676	$4630	€3800	Girl herding sheep in mountains (31x23cm-12x9in) s. panel. 13-Dec-3 Lempertz, Koln #31/R est:3000
£3125	$5156	€4500	Cattle outside mountain farmstead (32x73cm-13x29in) s.i. bears d.18. 2-Jul-3 Neumeister, Munich #707/R est:4000
£4895	$8322	€7000	Pastoral mountain scene (55x41cm-22x16in) s.i. lit. 28-Nov-3 Schloss Ahlden, Ahlden #1474/R est:7000
£5282	$9137	€7500	Herder with cattle and sheep outside village (77x16cm-30x6in) s.i. d.1880 stretcher. 11-Dec-3 Dr Fritz Nagel, Stuttgart #534/R est:9000
£6241	$10111	€8800	On the mountain pasture (55x86cm-22x34in) s. i. verso lit. 23-May-3 Karlheinz Kaupp, Staufen #1984/R est:8800
£9155	$15838	€13000	Herder with cattle at ford (58x54cm-23x21in) s.d.1859. 11-Dec-3 Dr Fritz Nagel, Stuttgart #535/R est:14000
£11333	$20400	€17000	Frauenchimsee shore with loaded punts and figures (39x84cm-15x33in) s.d.1864. 26-Apr-4 Rieber, Stuttgart #1260/R est:13500

MALIAVINE, Philippe (1869-1940) Russian

£2027	$3628	€3000	Mr Messerschmidt (28x22cm-11x9in) s.d.1940. 8-May-4 Bukowskis, Helsinki #439/R est:1500-2000
£2700	$4590	€3942	Portrait of a seated gentleman with book (100x80cm-39x31in) s.d.1940. 19-Nov-3 Sotheby's, London #145/R est:3000-4000
£3147	$5350	€4500	Portrait de femme assise (26x21cm-10x8in) s. crayon W/C. 27-Nov-3 Millon & Associes, Paris #19/R est:1200-1500
£5822	$9897	€8500	Jeune fille assise dans le jardin (37x49cm-15x19in) s. panel. 9-Nov-3 Eric Pillon, Calais #100/R
£6092	$10478	€8894	Winter landscape with troika driving, windmills in background (73x92cm-29x36in) s. 3-Dec-3 Museumsbygningen, Copenhagen #102/R est:20000-25000 (D.KR 65000)
£10000	$17000	€14600	Old peasant (73x60cm-29x24in) s. 19-Nov-3 Sotheby's, London #144/R est:4000-6000
£16556	$30132	€25000	Jeune paysanne (55x38cm-22x15in) s. 15-Jun-4 Rossini, Paris #53/R est:8000-12000
£20000	$34000	€29200	Peasant women in the field (56x72cm-22x28in) s. 19-Nov-3 Sotheby's, London #148/R est:20000-30000
£42000	$75180	€61320	Troika (73x92cm-29x36in) s. 26-May-4 Sotheby's, London #171/R est:15000-20000
£47222	$85000	€68944	Laughing Baba (81x65cm-32x26in) s. 23-Apr-4 Sotheby's, New York #15/R est:50000-70000

Works on paper

£276	$505	€400	Dancer (36x27cm-14x11in) s. pencil col pen prov. 27-Jan-4 Dorotheum, Vienna #58/R
£447	$800	€653	Baba (43x32cm-17x13in) pencil exec. 1900-1910. 29-May-4 Shishkin Gallery, Moscow #2/R
£495	$900	€723	Portrait of a peasant (66x51cm-26x20in) graphite col pencil. 19-Jun-4 Jackson's, Cedar Falls #267/R
£556	$1000	€812	Country girl (34x26cm-13x10in) pastel. 24-Apr-4 Shishkin Gallery, Moscow #2/R est:2000-3000
£1300	$2210	€1898	Fighting centaurs (38x52cm-15x20in) s. pencil col pencil crayon. 19-Nov-3 Sotheby's, London #146/R est:1500-2000
£1796	$3000	€2622	Portrait of a woman (65x51cm-26x20in) s. col pencil. 21-Oct-3 Christie's, Rockefeller NY #102 est:3000-5000
£3474	$6218	€5072	The hunter (66x50cm-26x20in) gouache chl. 26-May-4 AB Stockholms Auktionsverk #2484/R est:20000-30000 (S.KR 47000)
£4444	$8000	€6488	Peasant woman in the village (64x49cm-25x19in) s. mixed media. 23-Apr-4 Sotheby's, New York #13/R est:10000-15000
£5000	$8950	€7300	Centaur (36x51cm-14x20in) s. pencil crayon. 26-May-4 Sotheby's, Olympia #448/R est:1800-2500
£8333	$13000	€	Portrait of Leon Davidovich Trotsky (44x32cm-17x13in) s.cyrillic d.1922 pencil col crayon. 11-Apr-3 Christie's, Rockefeller NY #39/R est:8000-10000

MALICOAT, Philip Cecil (1908-1981) American

£914	$1700	€1334	Provincetown Cottages (26x30cm-10x12in) s. canvasboard. 3-Mar-4 Christie's, Rockefeller NY #54/R est:1200-1800
£9189	$17000	€13416	Storm over the sea (152x127cm-60x50in) s.d.1970 exhib. 17-Jul-4 Outer Cape Auctions, Provincetown #75/R

Works on paper

£1193	$2100	€1742	Dune scape (30x46cm-12x18in) s.i. W/C. 3-Jan-4 Outer Cape Auctions, Provincetown #73/R

MALINCONICO, Andrea (1624-1698) Italian

£17333	$31373	€26000	Judith's triumph (150x203cm-59x80in) prov. 30-Mar-4 Segre, Madrid #56/R est:15000

MALINCONICO, Nicola (1654-1721) Italian

£20000	$35800	€30000	Vase of flowers and fruit in a garden (94x120cm-37x47in) exhib.lit. 17-May-4 Finarte Semenzato, Rome #125/R est:40000-45000

MALINCONICO, Nicola (attrib) (1654-1721) Italian

£2113	$3507	€3000	La resurrection (70x50cm-28x20in) 13-Jun-3 Ferri, Paris #52/R est:3000-4000

MALINOWSKY, Lise (1957-) Danish

£711	$1137	€1031	Soren Lerby (100x80cm-39x31in) s.d.86. 17-Sep-3 Kunsthallen, Copenhagen #98 (D.KR 7500)
£1083	$1993	€1581	A different dog (89x116cm-35x46in) s.d.96 verso prov. 29-Mar-4 Rasmussen, Copenhagen #336/R est:10000-12000 (D.KR 12000)
£1176	$2106	€1717	Man 19" - figure composition (80x60cm-31x24in) s.d.92 verso. 10-May-4 Rasmussen, Vejle #705/R est:15000 (D.KR 13000)
£1878	$3136	€2742	J.B. - a fantasy (200x195cm-79x77in) s.d.82 exhib. 7-Oct-3 Rasmussen, Copenhagen #98/R est:40000 (D.KR 20000)
£2629	$4391	€3838	Paraphrase over Rembrandt - Portrait of old man in armchair (210x140cm-83x55in) s.d.1985 verso lit.exhib. 7-Oct-3 Rasmussen, Copenhagen #100/R est:25000-30000 (D.KR 28000)

Works on paper

£378	$677	€552	Figure composition (38x32cm-15x13in) s.d.90 W/C crayon. 12-Jan-4 Rasmussen, Vejle #602/R (D.KR 4000)

MALINVERNI, Angelo (1877-1947) Italian

£336	$594	€500	Cottages in the mountains (27x35cm-11x14in) s. cardboard. 1-May-4 Meeting Art, Vercelli #181
£336	$594	€500	Cottage (38x48cm-15x19in) s. canvas on board. 1-May-4 Meeting Art, Vercelli #173
£367	$675	€550	Landscape (35x45cm-14x18in) s. cardboard. 14-Jun-4 Sant Agostino, Torino #141/R
£433	$797	€650	Terrace in bloom (34x44cm-13x17in) s. cardboard. 8-Jun-4 Della Rocca, Turin #350/R
£533	$981	€800	Anemones (55x71cm-22x28in) s. cardboard. 14-Jun-4 Sant Agostino, Torino #109/R
£694	$1181	€1000	August morning (55x65cm-22x26in) s. 1-Nov-3 Meeting Art, Vercelli #205/R
£780	$1303	€1100	Alpine village (44x34cm-17x13in) s. cardboard. 20-Oct-3 Sant Agostino, Torino #144/R

MALINVERNO, Atilio (1890-1936) Argentinian

£2793	$5000	€4078	Ranch at dusk (21x15cm-8x6in) s. canvas on cardboard. 4-May-4 Arroyo, Buenos Aires #66/R est:1700
£4396	$8000	€6418	Ranch (45x55cm-18x22in) s. 29-Jun-4 Arroyo, Buenos Aires #58/R est:4000

MALIOUTIN, Serge (1859-1937) Russian

Works on paper

£900	$1530	€1350	Portrait of man in shapka, with pipe and stick (57x43cm-22x17in) s.d.1921 pencil chl. 25-Nov-3 Christie's, London #222/R

MALIQUET, Claire (1878-1964) French
£1056 $1827 €1500 Jeune femme dans les fleurs (130x89cm-51x35in) s.d.1929. 10-Dec-3 Millon & Associes, Paris #31/R est:1500-2000
£1241 $2073 €1800 Le modele au miroir (115x147cm-45x58in) s. exhib. 17-Nov-3 Tajan, Paris #133 est:2000-3000

MALISSARD, Georges (1877-1942) French
Sculpture
£1258 $2290 €1900 Trotting horse (40cm-16in) s.i.d.1909 green brown pat. bronze. 16-Jun-4 Hugo Ruef, Munich #1759/R est:900

MALKIN, Albert (?) ?
Works on paper
£331 $603 €500 River landscape with castle (32x46cm-13x18in) s. W/C. 21-Jun-4 Pandolfini, Florence #15

MALKINE, Georges (1898-1970) French
£6123 $10959 €9000 Emotion (46x38cm-18x15in) s.d.27. 21-Mar-4 Calmels Cohen, Paris #18/R est:8000-10000
£11333 $20513 €17000 Soleil de l'Inoui (46x55cm-18x22in) s. i.d.1926 verso. 1-Apr-4 Credit Municipal, Paris #54 est:5000-6000

MALKOWSKY, Heiner (1920-1988) German
Works on paper
£347 $566 €500 Composition (101x72cm-40x28in) s. gouache Indian ink chk. 26-Sep-3 Bolland & Marotz, Bremen #783/R
£486 $792 €700 Composition (73x101cm-29x40in) s.d.73 gouache. 26-Sep-3 Bolland & Marotz, Bremen #784/R
£833 $1392 €1200 Girl's head (45x47cm-18x19in) s.d. chl sketch verso. 24-Oct-3 Ketterer, Hamburg #453/R

MALLE, Charles (1935-) French
£464 $844 €700 Saint-Denis, place de la Gare (38x46cm-15x18in) s. 15-Jun-4 Blanchet, Paris #237
£704 $1218 €1000 Quai des Hollandais a Dunkerque (46x48cm-18x19in) s. 13-Dec-3 Martinot & Savignat, Pontoise #240
£888 $1608 €1350 Maison Catherine (46x61cm-18x24in) s. 19-Apr-4 Boscher, Cherbourg #759/R
£1007 $1621 €1500 Le chargement en quai de Seine (50x65cm-20x26in) s. 23-Feb-3 St-Germain-en-Laye Encheres #214 est:1500
£1007 $1782 €1500 Auteuil, appontement du point du jour (46x55cm-18x22in) s. 28-Apr-4 Charbonneaux, Paris #199/R est:1200-1500
£1074 $1997 €1600 Le Havre, les quais (33x46cm-13x18in) s. 7-Mar-4 Lesieur & Le Bars, Le Havre #105
£1379 $2303 €2000 Neuilly-sur-Seine, Bd Bineau (38x61cm-15x24in) s. 17-Nov-3 Charbonneaux, Paris #215 est:2000

MALLEBRANCHE, Louis-Claude (attrib) (1790-1838) French
£800 $1448 €1200 Cavaliers entrant dans un chateau par temps de neige (24x32cm-9x13in) 30-Mar-4 Rossini, Paris #67

MALLET, Jean Baptiste (1759-1835) French
£4444 $8000 €6488 Young woman standing in an archway (44x35cm-17x14in) panel. 22-Jan-4 Sotheby's, New York #250/R est:10000-15000
£12222 $22000 €17844 La veille du mariage, nude woman standing by a bedridden man. Le lendemain du mariage (25x20cm-10x8in) pair prov. 23-Jan-4 Christie's, Rockefeller NY #74/R est:15000-20000
Works on paper
£1333 $2413 €2000 Portrait of young woman holding letter (82x61cm-32x24in) s. pastel board. 1-Apr-4 Van Ham, Cologne #1219/R est:3000
£2152 $3917 €3250 Petite precaution (22x16cm-9x6in) indis.sig. gouache W/C prov.lit. 15-Jun-4 Claude Aguttes, Neuilly #1/R est:4500-5000
£17778 $32000 €25956 Young man piercing the ear of a young girl seated on the knees of a woman (24x33cm-9x13in) bodycol prov. 22-Jan-4 Christie's, Rockefeller NY #109/R est:30000-50000

MALLET, Jean Baptiste (attrib) (1759-1835) French
Works on paper
£900 $1557 €1314 Woman seated on a bench tying posies, a garden beyond (23x17cm-9x7in) W/C bodycol. 12-Dec-3 Christie's, Kensington #476/R

MALLIONI, E (20th C) ?
£1342 $2483 €2000 Woman with bread (100x81cm-39x32in) s. 9-Mar-4 Dorotheum, Vienna #87/R est:1200-1500

MALLO, Cristino (1905-1987) Spanish
Sculpture
£3200 $5792 €4800 Balcony (15cm-6in) s. num.1/1 bronze prov.lit. 30-Mar-4 Segre, Madrid #126/R est:4000
£4422 $7915 €6500 Make up scene (36x27cm-14x11in) s. bronze relief exhib.lit. 22-Mar-4 Durán, Madrid #145/R est:6000
£7660 $12409 €10800 Desnudo de pie (32cm-13in) s. s.i.base bronze. 20-May-3 Ansorena, Madrid #809/R est:9800
Works on paper
£280 $510 €420 Torero (35x29cm-14x11in) s. chl drawing double-sided exec c.1930-37. 29-Jun-4 Segre, Madrid #286/R
£317 $571 €460 Composition (16x19cm-6x7in) s. W/C. 26-Jan-4 Ansorena, Madrid #870/R
£435 $713 €600 Personajaes (32x24cm-13x9in) s. drawing. 27-May-3 Durán, Madrid #751/R
£458 $732 €650 Figure (15x11cm-6x4in) s.d.1974 ink wash prov. 16-Sep-3 Segre, Madrid #306/R
£604 $1069 €900 Vase of flowers (18x11cm-7x4in) s. gouache. 27-Apr-4 Durán, Madrid #634/R

MALLOCH, Stirling (19/20th C) British
£500 $900 €730 Little shepherds (30x45cm-12x18in) s.d.1900. 22-Apr-4 Bonhams, Edinburgh #321

MALLORY, Ronald (1935-) American
Sculpture
£1173 $2100 €1713 Diffused mercury (28x23cm-11x9in) prov. 16-May-4 Wright, Chicago #435/R est:1000-1500

MALM, Ulla (1930-) Finnish
£979 $1664 €1400 Blue shades (62x86cm-24x34in) s.d.70. 29-Nov-3 Bukowskis, Helsinki #245/R
£1162 $1859 €1650 Reflections (59x79cm-23x31in) s. 18-Sep-3 Hagelstam, Helsinki #911 est:2000
£1333 $2387 €2000 Seascape (55x61cm-22x24in) s.d.2003 board. 15-May-4 Hagelstam, Helsinki #204/R est:1500

MALMSJO, F (?) Norwegian?
Works on paper
£270 $496 €394 Solhaug - Norway (17x34cm-7x13in) s. gouache. 29-Mar-4 Blomqvist, Lysaker #1198 (N.KR 3400)

MALMSTROM, August (1829-1901) Swedish
£458 $820 €669 The pink dress - study of girl (46x38cm-18x15in) 26-May-4 AB Stockholms Auktionsverk #2210/R (S.KR 6200)
£702 $1257 €1025 The dying Norna Gest (96x75cm-38x30in) lit. 25-May-4 Bukowskis, Stockholm #209/R (S.KR 9500)

MALMSTROM, August (attrib) (1829-1901) Swedish
£459 $739 €670 Woman and girl (51x34cm-20x13in) canvas on board. 25-Aug-3 Lilla Bukowskis, Stockholm #112 (S.KR 6000)

MALNOVITZER, Zvi (1945-) Israeli
£7186 $12000 €10492 Old man and the sea (73x99cm-29x39in) s. 7-Oct-3 Sotheby's, New York #345 est:12000-15000

MALOMBRA, Pietro (1556-1618) Italian
Works on paper
£795 $1446 €1200 La vierge a l'Enfant avec Saint Joseph (15x11cm-6x4in) pen ink wash black crayon htd white gouache prov. 16-Jun-4 Piasa, Paris #27
£2300 $4209 €3358 Scene of streetfighting (15x10cm-6x4in) pen brown ink wash traces blk chk double-sided prov. 8-Jul-4 Sotheby's, London #34/R est:2000-2500

MALONE, Henry (1950-) Australian
£305 $479 €445 Autumn tumut (75x100cm-30x39in) s. canvas on board. 27-Aug-3 Christie's, Sydney #632 (A.D 750)

MALONEY, Martin (1961-C) British
£3200 $5792 €4672 Untitled portrait youth (56x81cm-22x32in) s.i.d.1996 stretcher prov.exhib.lit. 1-Apr-4 Christie's, Kensington #302/R est:2000-3000
£12000 $22080 €17520 Rehearsal (168x275cm-66x108in) s.i.d.1999 verso prov. 24-Jun-4 Sotheby's, London #121/R est:12000-15000
£16000 $26720 €23360 Adoration of the Magi (152x183cm-60x72in) s.i.d.May 2000 verso prov. 21-Oct-3 Sotheby's, London #303/R est:6000-8000

MALRIC (?) ?
Sculpture
£2013 $3604 €3000 Bacchus enfant (63cm-25in) biscuit de Sevres. 25-May-4 Palais de Beaux Arts, Brussels #97/R est:1750-2500

MALSKAT, Lothar (1913-1988) German
£420 $722 €600 Untitled (55x69cm-22x27in) s. acrylic paper. 4-Dec-3 Van Ham, Cologne #310
£559 $951 €800 Still life with poppies (59x49cm-23x19in) mono. panel lit. 28-Nov-3 Schloss Ahlden, Ahlden #1614/R
£839 $1427 €1200 Sailing boat (76x51cm-30x20in) s. cardboard lit. 28-Nov-3 Schloss Ahlden, Ahlden #1613/R
Works on paper
£350 $594 €500 Tulips (31x24cm-12x9in) s. W/C lit. 28-Nov-3 Schloss Ahlden, Ahlden #1621/R
£629 $1070 €900 Peony (56x47cm-22x19in) s. W/C lit. 28-Nov-3 Schloss Ahlden, Ahlden #1620/R
£662 $1205 €1000 Garden with flowers (73x55cm-29x22in) s. W/C. 19-Jun-4 Hans Stahl, Hamburg #76/R

MALTENI, Giovanni (1898-?) Italian
£857 $1371 €1243 Oliveto di Marzo (70x60cm-28x24in) s. i. verso. 15-May-3 Stuker, Bern #1372 est:1200-1400 (S.FR 1800)

MALTERRE, Andre (1889-?) French
£789 $1429 €1200 Still life with bottles and copper (90x146cm-35x57in) s.d.1916. 14-Apr-4 Ansorena, Madrid #83/R

MALTHOUSE, Eric (1914-1997) British

£800	$1272	€1168	Garden (44x24cm-17x9in) s. 10-Sep-3 Sotheby's, Olympia #206/R
Works on paper			
£310	$555	€453	Abstract design with birds (15x15cm-6x6in) s. W/C. 7-May-4 Mallams, Oxford #152

MALTON, James (1761-1803) British

Prints			
£11258	$20490	€17000	Views of the city of Dublin. hand col aquatint folio. 17-Jun-4 Hamilton Osborne King, Dublin #281/R est:10000-15000
Works on paper			
£16000	$27680	€23360	View of the Provost's house and Trinity College, Dublin (53x77cm-21x30in) i.d.1796 pen ink pencil W/C. 11-Dec-3 Lyon & Turnbull, Edinburgh #27/R est:4000-6000

MALY, Elga (1921-) German

£979	$1684	€1400	Figuration 4 (80x100cm-31x39in) s. 4-Dec-3 Dorotheum, Graz #18/R
Works on paper			
£315	$541	€450	Romantic landscape (49x64cm-19x25in) s. mixed media board. 4-Dec-3 Dorotheum, Graz #152/R

MALY, Michel (1936-) French

£733	$1335	€1100	Paysage anime (50x71cm-20x28in) s. 29-Jun-4 Chenu & Scrive, Lyon #129/R

MALYSHEV, Nikolai Tarasievich (1851-?) Russian

Works on paper			
£1200	$2040	€1752	Scenes of peasant life (50x36cm-20x14in) s. ink gouache W/C study verso. 19-Nov-3 Sotheby's, London #68/R est:1500-2000

MALYSHEVA, O V (1920-) Russian

£4167	$7500	€6084	Girl in a tree (79x64cm-31x25in) 24-Apr-4 Shishkin Gallery, Moscow #25/R est:6000-8000

MALZACHER, Bertha (1866-?) German

£528	$845	€750	Boy with beer jugs and radishes (102x68cm-40x27in) s.i.d.1897. 18-Sep-3 Rieber, Stuttgart #923/R

MAMAK, Andrzej (1964-) ?

£1748	$3007	€2500	Child with toys (76x64cm-30x25in) s. d.1993 on stretcher. 2-Dec-3 Sotheby's, Amsterdam #332/R est:2500-3500

MAMBOR, Renato (1936-) Italian

£2391	$3922	€3300	Untitled (79x100cm-31x39in) s.d.65 verso acrylic. 30-May-3 Farsetti, Prato #10/R

MAMBOUR, Auguste (1896-1968) Belgian

£4000	$7160	€6000	Tete de negresse (48x40cm-19x16in) s. cardboard. 11-May-4 Vanderkindere, Brussels #110 est:6000-8000
£6338	$10965	€9000	Buste d'Africaine. s. panel lit. 10-Dec-3 Hotel des Ventes Mosan, Brussels #194/R est:10000-12000
£6690	$11574	€9500	Buste d'Africaine (60x50cm-24x20in) s. panel painted c.1929. 10-Dec-3 Hotel des Ventes Mosan, Brussels #189/R est:10000-12000
£9929	$16582	€14000	Negresse en buste (74x60cm-29x24in) s. painted c.1925. 15-Oct-3 Hotel des Ventes Mosan, Brussels #191/R est:8000-10000
Works on paper			
£667	$1193	€1000	Child running (44x34cm-17x13in) s. black chk. 15-May-4 De Vuyst, Lokeren #211
£1722	$3134	€2600	Jeune fille debout (101x78cm-40x31in) s.d.1950 chl. 16-Jun-4 Hotel des Ventes Mosan, Brussels #268 est:2400-2800

MAMINYAMANJA, Nagaguma (20th C) Australian

£650	$1021	€949	Untitled (46x76cm-18x30in) natural pigments bark. 27-Aug-3 Christie's, Sydney #778 est:500-800 (A.D 1600)

MAMMEN, Jeanne (1890-1976) German

Works on paper			
£867	$1595	€1300	Female nude, half-length (63x50cm-25x20in) mono. pencil. 12-Jun-4 Villa Grisebach, Berlin #609/R est:1400-1600
£1295	$2124	€1800	Portrait with woman wearing necklace (42x23cm-17x9in) mono. pencil. 4-Jun-3 Ketterer, Hamburg #627/R est:1500-2000
£1333	$2453	€2000	The smoker (50x38cm-20x15in) mono. pencil. 12-Jun-4 Villa Grisebach, Berlin #610/R est:1600-1800
£1806	$3015	€2600	Ice coffee (43x37cm-17x15in) s.mono. brush Indian ink pen. 25-Oct-3 Dr Lehr, Berlin #322/R est:2400

MAMMERI, Azouaou (1890-1954) Algerian

Works on paper			
£340	$569	€480	Dans les souks (48x62cm-19x24in) s. Indian ink dr. 16-Jun-3 Gros & Delettrez, Paris #214

MAMPASO, Manuel (1924-) Spanish

£680	$1238	€1000	Seascape (54x72cm-21x28in) s. painted 2000. 3-Feb-4 Segre, Madrid #344/R

MAN, Cornelis de (1621-1706) Dutch

£31507	$53562	€46000	Interior of the Oude Kerk in Delft, with figures and men digging (72x59cm-28x23in) s. panel prov.lit. 4-Nov-3 Sotheby's, Amsterdam #79/R est:15000-20000

MAN-RAY (1890-1976) American

£4200	$7728	€6132	Composition (8x10cm-3x4in) init. panel mounted on masonite painted c.1954 prov. 24-Mar-4 Sotheby's, Olympia #156/R est:3000-4000
£6338	$10204	€9000	Fan (31x38cm-12x15in) s.d.1954 s.i.verso panel. 22-Aug-3 Deauville, France #131/R est:12000-15000
£7586	$13655	€11000	L'Eventail (31x38cm-12x15in) s.d.1954 s.i.verso panel. 25-Jan-4 Chayette & Cheval, Paris #207/R est:10000-12000
£8973	$14087	€13100	Q.E.D. (40x30cm-16x12in) s. panel painted 1947 prov.exhib.lit. 20-Apr-3 Deauville, France #147/R est:12000-15000
£10500	$19320	€15330	Novembre (37x45cm-15x18in) s. acrylic masonite painted 1958 prov. 22-Jun-4 Sotheby's, London #300/R est:8000-12000
£16000	$29120	€23360	Mythologie moderne (50x50cm-20x20in) s.d.1955 board prov. 3-Feb-4 Christie's, London #238/R est:15000-20000
£32000	$58880	€46720	L'Arc de Triomphe (50x61cm-20x24in) s.d.1923 i.stretcher prov.lit. 22-Jun-4 Sotheby's, London #189/R est:35000-45000
£190000	$347700	€277400	Wall (50x64cm-20x25in) s.d.1938 prov.exhib.lit. 2-Feb-4 Christie's, London #85b/R est:170000-250000
£420000	$764400	€613200	Les gens en colere d'un apres-midi (162x114cm-64x45in) s.d.1928 prov.exhib. 3-Feb-4 Sotheby's, London #78/R est:300000-400000
Photographs			
£1944	$3500	€2838	Mathematical object (30x23cm-12x9in) i.verso gelatin silver print prov.exhib.lit. 23-Apr-4 Phillips, New York #16/R est:8000-12000
£2158	$3453	€3000	Portrait of poet (60x41cm-24x16in) mono.verso silver gelatin print exec.1954. 19-May-3 Sotheby's, Milan #85/R est:3000-4000
£2200	$4026	€3212	Gertrude Stein (21x16cm-8x6in) i.d.1924 verso silver print. 8-Jul-4 Sotheby's, London #406/R est:1800-2200
£2400	$4224	€3504	Breton and Eluard (30x21cm-12x8in) s. gelatin silver print lit. 19-May-4 Christie's, London #140/R est:2500-3500
£2401	$4250	€3505	Mathematical object (29x23cm-11x9in) s.num. i.verso photo exec.c.1936 prov. 28-Apr-4 Sotheby's, New York #186/R est:7000-10000
£2700	$4941	€3942	Paul Hamann making a life mask of Man Ray (12x22cm-5x9in) i.verso silver print. 8-Jul-4 Sotheby's, London #402/R est:3000-5000
£2778	$4722	€4000	Verve boude (23x18cm-9x7in) s. i.d. verso gelatin silver. 30-Oct-3 Van Ham, Cologne #134/R est:4000
£2825	$5000	€4125	Juliet in exotic costume (25x20cm-10x8in) i.verso gelatin silver print executed c.1946. 27-Apr-4 Christie's, Rockefeller NY #58/R est:6000-8000
£3067	$5489	€4600	Portrait de Simone Kahn (28x27cm-11x11in) s. photograph exec.1923. 15-May-4 Renaud, Paris #166/R
£3107	$5500	€4536	Danses horizons, 1934 (19x29cm-7x11in) gelatin silver print lit. 27-Apr-4 Christie's, Rockefeller NY #52/R est:6000-8000
£3593	$6000	€5246	Self-portrait in car (23x17cm-9x7in) st.sig.verso exec. c.1943 prov.lit. 17-Oct-3 Phillips, New York #130/R est:8000-12000
£3623	$5942	€5000	Georges Braque (23x17cm-9x7in) i. verso vintage silver gelatin. 30-May-3 Villa Grisebach, Berlin #1277/R est:7000-9000
£3672	$6500	€5361	Henri Matisse (21x15cm-8x6in) i.d. gelatin silver print executed c.1926. 27-Apr-4 Christie's, Rockefeller NY #55/R est:8000-10000
£3672	$6500	€5361	Rue Sade, au chat botte, Antibes, 1936 (14x9cm-6x4in) gelatin silver print lit. 27-Apr-4 Christie's, Rockefeller NY #117/R est:8000-10000
£4192	$7000	€6120	Francis Picabia (47x37cm-19x15in) s.i.d.1923 verso photo lit. 17-Oct-3 Sotheby's, New York #216/R est:8000-12000
£4333	$7757	€6500	Mannequin de Salvador Dali' (23x16cm-9x6in) photograph exec.1938. 15-May-4 Renaud, Paris #172/R
£4790	$8000	€6993	Self portrait, California (25x20cm-10x8in) i.d.1944 verso gelatin silver print. 20-Oct-3 Christie's, Rockefeller NY #73/R est:9000-12000
£4800	$8448	€7008	Man's hat (18x21cm-7x8in) gelatin silver print lit. 19-May-4 Christie's, London #143/R est:6000-8000
£4802	$8500	€7011	Jules Pascin, 1923 (21x17cm-8x7in) init.i.d.1923 verso gelatin silver print. 27-Apr-4 Christie's, Rockefeller NY #56/R est:8000-10000
£4802	$8500	€7011	Untitled - sunflower (11x9cm-4x4in) gelatin silver print. 27-Apr-4 Christie's, Rockefeller NY #283/R est:7000-9000
£5085	$9000	€7424	Nude, 1930 (14x9cm-6x4in) gelatin silver print. 27-Apr-4 Christie's, Rockefeller NY #50/R est:10000-15000
£5085	$9000	€7424	James Joyce, 1922 (12x9cm-5x4in) gelatin silver print lit. 27-Apr-4 Christie's, Rockefeller NY #54/R est:8000-10000
£5389	$9000	€7868	Jean Cocteau with gloves (27x21cm-11x8in) s.i.d.1924 gelatin silver print prov.exhib. 20-Oct-3 Christie's, Rockefeller NY #74/R est:10000-15000
£5667	$10483	€8500	Andre Derain a bord de sa Bugatti modele 43 (15x20cm-6x8in) gelatin silver print exec.1927 prov.exhib.lit. 18-Jul-4 Sotheby's, Paris #294/R est:8000-12000
£5689	$9500	€8306	Study of danger/dancer and other works (12x7cm-5x3in) i.verso photo exec.c.1920. 17-Oct-3 Sotheby's, New York #215/R est:5000-7000
£6250	$10625	€9000	Hans Richter (22x17cm-9x7in) gelatin silver lit. 31-Oct-3 Lempertz, Koln #227/R est:10000-12000
£6667	$12133	€10000	Echiquier (50x50cm-20x20in) mono. gelatin silver print prov. 30-Jun-4 Calmels Cohen, Paris #65/R est:12000-15000
£8000	$14080	€11680	Bouquet (29x23cm-11x9in) gelatin silver print lit. 19-May-4 Christie's, London #142/R est:8000-12000
£10734	$19000	€15672	Untitled - study of legs (15x12cm-6x5in) init.verso gelatin silver print. 27-Apr-4 Christie's, Rockefeller NY #51/R est:7000-9000
£10778	$18000	€15736	Nusch Eluard (38x22cm-15x9in) s.d.1935 photo warm toned photo lit. 17-Oct-3 Sotheby's, New York #218/R est:15000-25000
£13174	$22000	€19234	Jean Cocteau sculpting his own head in wire (23x17cm-9x7in) i.d.1928 gelatin silver print exec.c.1926 prov.lit. 20-Oct-3 Christie's, Rockefeller NY #75/R est:30000-50000
£15569	$26000	€22731	La priere (32x23cm-13x9in) s.i. gelatin silver print exec.1930 printed later lit. 17-Oct-3 Sotheby's, New York #219/R est:18000-22000
£15819	$28000	€23096	Madame Xupery (23x18cm-9x7in) i.verso gelatin silver print prov. 27-Apr-4 Christie's, Rockefeller NY #48/R est:20000-30000
£16949	$30000	€24746	Icelandic mask collage, 1920s (51x33cm-20x13in) gelatin silver print prov. 27-Apr-4 Christie's, Rockefeller NY #286/R est:18000-22000
£24859	$44000	€36294	Harry Melvill (22x16cm-9x6in) s.i. photo exec.c.1925 prov. 28-Apr-4 Sotheby's, New York #188/R est:30000-50000
£33898	$60000	€49491	Sur impression, Paris, 1930 (27x21cm-11x8in) s.d.1930 gelatin silver print. 27-Apr-4 Christie's, Rockefeller NY #49/R est:30000-50000
£35928	$60000	€52455	Still life composition with chess set and plaster cast (16x22cm-6x9in) gelatin silver print prov.exhib.lit. 20-Oct-3 Christie's, Rockefeller NY #78/R est:40000-60000
£37778	$68000	€55156	Untitled (29x22cm-11x9in) gelatin silver print prov. 23-Apr-4 Phillips, New York #55/R est:60000-80000
£50847	$90000	€74237	Anatomies, grand dos noir (29x23cm-11x9in) i.num.verso solarized photo exec.c.1930 prov.exhib.lit. 27-Apr-4 Sotheby's, New York #27/R est:50000-70000

£141243	$250000	€206215	Untitled, rayograph with shapes of a vase and flowrs (39x29cm-15x11in) s.d.1926 i.verso rayograph prov.exhib.lit. 27-Apr-4 Sotheby's, New York #28/R est:150000-250000

Prints

£1875	$3000	€2738	Rope dancer accompanies herself with her shadows (50x70cm-20x28in) s.num.III/X col lithograph. 18-Sep-3 Swann Galleries, New York #534/R est:2000-3000
£3497	$5840	€5000	Nu bleute (68x41cm-27x16in) s. num.4/25 serigraph. 10-Oct-3 Tajan, Paris #255/R
£9040	$16000	€13198	Revolving doors (57x39cm-22x15in) col pochoirs set of 10 album. 28-Apr-4 Christie's, Rockefeller NY #66/R est:20000-25000

Sculpture

£942	$1545	€1300	Cadeau (17cm-7in) s.i. num.2004/5000 iron lit. 27-May-3 Sotheby's, Milan #98 est:1500
£1049	$1804	€1500	Herma (28cm-11in) i.num278/550 polished pewter on wood base lit. 2-Dec-3 Sotheby's, Amsterdam #290/R est:2000-3000
£1119	$1902	€1600	Priape (53cm-21in) init.num.104/500 marble exec.1972 lit. 25-Nov-3 Sotheby's, Milan #116/R est:1500-2000
£1141	$2099	€1700	Priape (50x30x30cm-20x12x12in) mono. num.240/500 marble four parts lit. 24-Mar-4 Joron-Derem, Paris #108/R est:2000-2500
£1200	$1908	€1740	Cadeau (16x10cm-6x4in) num.4593/5000 brown pat. bronze executed 1974. 11-Sep-3 Christie's, Kensington #103/R est:800-1200
£1411	$2399	€2060	Cadeau - 1921/1974 (9x9x17cm-4x4x7in) s. iron - shape of iron. 26-Nov-3 Kunsthallen, Copenhagen #128/R est:5000 (D.KR 15000)
£1500	$2385	€2175	Cadeau (16x10cm-6x4in) num.4570/5000 brown pat. bronze executed 1974. 11-Sep-3 Christie's, Kensington #102/R est:800-1200
£2083	$3292	€3000	Priape (50x30x30cm-20x12x12in) s. num.191/500 Paros marble lit. 27-Apr-3 Versailles Encheres #126
£2098	$3503	€3000	Priape (50x30x30cm-20x12x12in) s.i. marble exec.1975 lit. 29-Jun-3 Versailles Encheres #192/R
£2113	$3655	€3000	Hermaphrodite (26cm-10in) s. bronze prov. 13-Dec-3 Lempertz, Koln #335/R est:3000
£2819	$5187	€4200	Femme et poison. Femme sur le pont (41x57x4cm-16x22x2in) mono.i. brown pat.brass relief two. 26-Mar-4 Ketterer, Hamburg #541/R est:2000-3000
£5405	$10000	€7891	Objet indestructible (22cm-9in) s.i.d.1923-1975 metronome plaque photograph lit. 11-Feb-4 Sotheby's, New York #42/R est:10000-15000
£6000	$10380	€8760	Objet indestructible (20x18cm-8x7in) metronome photo box conceived 1923 to 1965 edition 63 of 100. 11-Dec-3 Christie's, Kensington #98/R est:7000-9000
£15000	$27600	€21900	Chess set. init. num.6/25 32 aluminium pieces board velvet case exec.1972-73. 23-Jun-4 Christie's, London #247/R est:15000-25000
£16949	$30000	€24746	Chess set (10x57cm-4x22in) s.i.d.1962 num.17/50 bronze 32 pieces enamel metal board lit. 2-May-4 Bonhams & Butterfields, Los Angeles #3030/R est:15000-20000
£17059	$29000	€24906	Chess set (46x46cm-18x18in) i.d.1947 aluminium prov.lit. 6-Nov-3 Sotheby's, New York #253/R est:30000-35000
£17877	$32000	€26100	Pechage (35x23x10cm-14x9x4in) init.i. num.8/9 wood artificial peaches plexiglass prov.exhib.lit. 5-May-4 Christie's, Rockefeller NY #304/R est:40000-60000
£20958	$35000	€30599	Grande herma (61cm-24in) s.num.5/8 brown pat bronze taupe pillow st.f.Blanchet. 7-Oct-3 Sotheby's, New York #333 est:6000-8000
£27933	$50000	€40782	En dernier ressort - tournez (29x24x14cm-11x9x6in) s.i.d.1956 wood metal construction prov.exhib.lit. 5-May-4 Christie's, Rockefeller NY #302/R est:40000-60000
£42178	$75498	€62000	L'oeuf plat (110cm-43in) stone exec 1957-1960 prov.lit. 21-Mar-4 Calmels Cohen, Paris #67/R est:60000-80000
£62000	$112840	€90520	Indestructable object (23cm-9in) s.d.1959 photographic eye prov.lit. 3-Feb-4 Sotheby's, London #64/R est:15000-20000

Works on paper

£2200	$3740	€3212	Compass (36x51cm-14x20in) init.verso multiple in mixed media. 18-Nov-3 Bonhams, Knightsbridge #177/R est:2500-3500
£2667	$4907	€4000	It's a small world (34x27cm-13x11in) s. Chinese ink exec.1952 prov. 8-Jun-4 Finarte Semenzato, Milan #461/R est:4400-4800
£3209	$6000	€4685	Souvenir de Remiremont (30x42cm-12x17in) s.i.d.1966 collage pen ink wax crayon paper on panel prov. 25-Feb-4 Christie's, Rockefeller NY #123/R est:4000-6000
£6000	$11040	€9000	Temps meles (31x23cm-12x9in) s.i.d.1948 india ink prov. 8-Jun-4 Artcurial Briest, Paris #183/R est:10000-12000
£9412	$16000	€13742	Boardwalk (58x64cm-23x25in) s.d.1917-1973 cord wood fabric pen India ink panel prov.exhib.lit. 5-Nov-3 Christie's, Rockefeller NY #306/R est:25000-35000
£101695	$180000	€148475	Boite a conserves (26x31cm-10x12in) matchboxes gelatin silver prints exec.c.1960 fifteen prov.exhib. 27-Apr-4 Sotheby's, New York #29/R est:30000-50000

MAN-RAY and BASSET, Rene (20th C) American

Photographs

£6587	$11000	€9617	Coin du Studio rue Campagne Premiere. Juliet and Man Ray in studio (23x17cm-9x7in) one i. gelatin silver print exec.1926 and c.1960 2 prov.exhib.lit. 20-Oct-3 Christie's, Rockefeller NY #77/R est:10000-15000

MANAGO, Vincent (1880-1936) French

£378	$642	€540	Southern coastal town (40x54cm-16x21in) s. 20-Nov-3 Weidler, Nurnberg #4501/R
£800	$1448	€1200	Port de Martigues (46x55cm-18x22in) s. panel. 1-Apr-4 Credit Municipal, Paris #48
£1000	$1840	€1500	Porte de Tunis (41x33cm-16x13in) s. cardboard. 14-Jun-4 Gros & Delettrez, Paris #106 est:1500-1800
£1277	$2132	€1800	Au bord de l'oued (46x60cm-18x24in) s. panel. 16-Jun-3 Gros & Delettrez, Paris #97 est:1200-1800
£1467	$2699	€2200	Rue Orientale animee (80x60cm-31x24in) s. 14-Jun-4 Gros & Delettrez, Paris #534/R est:2300-3800
£1918	$3260	€2800	Grand Canal a Venise (50x73cm-20x29in) s. 10-Nov-3 Horta, Bruxelles #83
£5674	$9475	€8000	Lavandieres tunisiennes (65x92cm-26x36in) s. 19-Oct-3 Rabourdin & Choppin de Janvry, Paris #77/R est:8000-9000

MANAIGO, Silvestro (1670-1734) Italian

£17241	$28793	€25000	Moses walking onto the pharaoh's crown (76x95cm-30x37in) prov.lit. 15-Nov-3 Porro, Milan #226/R est:25000

MANAKOV, Boris (1829-?) Russian

£595	$1083	€875	Les lilas. s. 8-Feb-4 Lesieur & Le Bars, Le Havre #65

MANANOS, Asterio (1861-1935) Spanish

£986	$1725	€1400	Portrait of Hussar (190x110cm-75x43in) s.d.1908. 16-Dec-3 Durán, Madrid #92/R

MANANSALA, Vicente (1910-1981) Philippino

£16667	$27833	€24334	Mother and child (47x56cm-19x22in) s.d.81. 12-Oct-3 Sotheby's, Singapore #66/R est:35000-55000 (S.D 48000)
£17361	$28993	€25347	Still life (65x75cm-26x30in) s.d.80 canvas on board. 12-Oct-3 Sotheby's, Singapore #55/R est:50000-70000 (S.D 50000)
£25806	$41290	€37677	Woman with a cat (65x54cm-26x21in) s.d.65 prov. 18-May-3 Sotheby's, Singapore #63/R est:50000-70000 (S.D 72000)
£34420	$53351	€50253	Pounding rice (92x123cm-36x48in) s.d.1980. 6-Oct-2 Sotheby's, Singapore #78/R est:85000-95000 (S.D 95000)
£39855	$61775	€58188	Harvest (86x58cm-34x23in) s.d.57 board. 6-Oct-2 Sotheby's, Singapore #70/R est:50000-70000 (S.D 110000)
£51613	$82581	€75355	Jeepneys (43x51cm-17x20in) s.d.54 board. 18-May-3 Sotheby's, Singapore #81/R est:30000-40000 (S.D 144000)
£52083	$86979	€76041	Family at a meal (94x102cm-37x40in) s.d.75. 12-Oct-3 Sotheby's, Singapore #52/R est:65000-85000 (S.D 150000)
£52083	$86979	€76041	Three musicians (141x88cm-56x35in) s.d.73. 12-Oct-3 Sotheby's, Singapore #86/R est:125000-185000 (S.D 150000)
£67568	$121622	€98649	Juan luna,- blood compact (86x168cm-34x66in) s.i.d.62 canvas on board prov. 25-Apr-4 Christie's, Hong Kong #560/R est:950000-1100000 (HK.D 950000)

Works on paper

£1961	$3549	€2863	Paranague. Cadena de amor (55x75cm-22x30in) s.d.57 W/C paper on panel two. 4-Apr-4 Sotheby's, Singapore #94/R est:4000-6000 (S.D 6000)
£2083	$3479	€3041	Fish vendor (40x30cm-16x12in) s.d.55 W/C. 12-Oct-3 Sotheby's, Singapore #51/R est:4000-6000 (S.D 6000)
£2431	$4059	€3549	Candle vendor (31x26cm-12x10in) s.d.74 W/C. 12-Oct-3 Sotheby's, Singapore #50/R est:5000-7000 (S.D 7000)
£2717	$4212	€3967	Nipa huts (50x70cm-20x28in) s.d.59 W/C. 6-Oct-2 Sotheby's, Singapore #75/R est:7000-9000 (S.D 7500)
£2941	$5324	€4294	Fish and lace (56x55cm-22x22in) s.d.66 W/C. 4-Apr-4 Sotheby's, Singapore #114/R est:10000-15000 (S.D 9000)
£3011	$4817	€4396	Tinapang bangus (36x55cm-14x22in) s.d.69 W/C. 18-May-3 Sotheby's, Singapore #86/R est:6000-8000 (S.D 8400)
£3268	$5915	€4771	Abaca trees (61x46cm-24x18in) s.d.80 W/C. 4-Apr-4 Sotheby's, Singapore #93/R est:10000-15000 (S.D 10000)
£3986	$6178	€5820	In the park (52x73cm-20x29in) s.d.57 W/C. 6-Oct-2 Sotheby's, Singapore #90/R est:10000-15000 (S.D 11000)
£4267	$7681	€6230	Two reclining nudes (77x151cm-30x59in) s.d.72 chl lit. 25-Apr-4 Christie's, Hong Kong #553/R est:48000-65000 (HK.D 60000)

MANARA, Gianfranco (20th C) Italian

£694	$1146	€1000	Landscape (60x70cm-24x28in) s. s.d.1957 verso. 1-Jul-3 Il Ponte, Milan #795

MANARESI, Ugo (1851-1917) Italian

£5034	$9413	€7500	Tuscan coast (10x23cm-4x9in) s. board prov.lit. 25-Feb-4 Porro, Milan #12/R est:7000-8000
£7746	$12859	€11000	Livorno harbour (32x47cm-13x19in) s.d.1879. 13-Jun-3 Farsetti, Prato #529/R
£25352	$43859	€36000	Livorno, canal (64x100cm-25x39in) s.d.1883. 11-Dec-3 Christie's, Rome #191/R est:12000-15000

MANASSE (20th C) ?

Photographs

£2133	$3925	€3200	My little sugar (22x17cm-9x7in) s. silver gelatin lit.exhib. 10-Jun-4 Villa Grisebach, Berlin #1197/R est:1000-1500

MANAURE, Mateo (1926-) Venezuelan

£310	$480	€453	My country (31x23cm-12x9in) s. 29-Sep-2 Subastas Odalys, Caracas #29
£313	$500	€457	My country (30x40cm-12x16in) s. 16-Mar-3 Subastas Odalys, Caracas #78
£335	$560	€489	My country (30x40cm-12x16in) s. painted 1971. 13-Jul-3 Subastas Odalys, Caracas #36
£357	$650	€536	My land (30x23cm-12x9in) s. painted 1975. 21-Jun-4 Subastas Odalys, Caracas #8/R
£424	$780	€619	My country (30x40cm-12x16in) s. painted 1982. 28-Mar-4 Subastas Odalys, Caracas #53/R
£492	$885	€718	My country (30x40cm-12x16in) s. painted 1975. 25-Apr-4 Subastas Odalys, Caracas #11/R
£538	$990	€785	My country (23x32cm-9x13in) s.verso masonite painted 1969. 28-Mar-4 Subastas Odalys, Caracas #96/R
£581	$970	€848	My country (41x51cm-16x20in) s. painted 1975. 13-Jul-3 Subastas Odalys, Caracas #42
£616	$1145	€899	Untitled (41x31cm-16x12in) s. painted 1975. 14-Mar-4 Subastas Odalys, Caracas #97
£674	$1125	€984	Orinoquia (30x40cm-12x16in) s. painted 1993. 13-Jul-3 Subastas Odalys, Caracas #59
£727	$1250	€1061	My country (30x40cm-12x16in) s. painted 1985. 7-Dec-3 Subastas Odalys, Caracas #106/R
£857	$1560	€1286	My country (50x60cm-20x24in) s. painted 1967. 21-Jun-4 Subastas Odalys, Caracas #87/R
£1161	$1800	€1695	Cube (100x100cm-39x39in) s. panel painted 1991. 29-Sep-2 Subastas Odalys, Caracas #77/R
£7444	$12655	€10868	Colour rythm (40x40cm-16x16in) s.verso acrylic panel painted 1956. 23-Nov-3 Subastas Odalys, Caracas #164/R est:12000

Sculpture

£956	$1720	€1396	Untitled (21x13x2cm-8x5x1in) bronze. 25-Apr-4 Subastas Odalys, Caracas #90/R

Works on paper

£294	$500	€429	Untitled (48x43cm-19x17in) s. mixed media exec.1970. 23-Nov-3 Subastas Odalys, Caracas #33

£297	$460	€434	Untitled (31x26cm-12x10in) s. mixed media. 3-Nov-2 Subastas Odalys, Caracas #83
£343	$625	€515	Untitled (37x28cm-15x11in) s. mixed media exec.1977. 21-Jun-4 Subastas Odalys, Caracas #23

MANAUT VIGLIETTI, Jose (1899-1971) Spanish

£724	$1310	€1100	Idyllic landscape (60x73cm-24x29in) s.d.1961. 14-Apr-4 Ansorena, Madrid #299/R

MANCADAN, Jacobus Sibrandi (1602-1680) Dutch

£24324	$42811	€36000	Hilly landscape with shepherds and their herd near a stream (103x151cm-41x59in) mono. prov.lit. 18-May-4 Sotheby's, Amsterdam #84/R est:10000-15000

MANCIET, Charles (1874-1963) French

£733	$1327	€1100	Elegante a la capeline (33x24cm-13x9in) s.i. 4-Apr-4 St-Germain-en-Laye Encheres #8/R
£4800	$7680	€7008	Nue allongee (54x73cm-21x29in) s. 18-Sep-3 Christie's, Kensington #185/R est:3000-5000

MANCINELLI, Giuseppe (1813-1875) Italian

£4967	$9040	€7500	Joseph interpreting the pharaoh's dreams (132x105cm-52x41in) s. 16-Jun-4 Christie's, Rome #396/R est:6500-8000

MANCINI ARDIZZONE, Francesco (1863-?) Italian

£915	$1520	€1300	Barche e pescatori a riva. Marina con barche di pescatori (35x50cm-14x20in) panel two. 11-Jun-3 Christie's, Rome #68

MANCINI, Antonio (1852-1930) Italian

£1500	$2640	€2190	Roses in a vase (53x44cm-21x17in) s. board. 19-May-4 Christie's, Kensington #716/R est:1500-2000
£1549	$2572	€2200	Composition with figure (14x43cm-6x17in) s. oil monochrome three ceramic tiles. 11-Jun-3 Christie's, Rome #170/R est:800-1200
£6954	$12656	€10500	Toast (80x70cm-31x28in) s. 17-Jun-4 Finarte Semenzato, Milan #259/R est:10000-12000
£9060	$16218	€13500	Luigiello (28x18cm-11x7in) i.verso board. 25-May-4 Finarte Semenzato, Milan #228/R est:10000-12000
£9412	$16000	€13742	Italian town view (97x60cm-38x24in) s. oil mixed media. 28-Oct-3 Sotheby's, New York #109/R est:18000-25000
£9859	$17056	€14000	Portrait of a boy (53x39cm-21x15in) s. board. 11-Dec-3 Dr Fritz Nagel, Stuttgart #450/R est:20000
£15493	$25718	€22000	I fiori bianchi (33x26cm-13x10in) s. 11-Jun-3 Christie's, Rome #201/R est:15000-25000
£24161	$44456	€36000	Male nude with yellow turban (100x75cm-39x30in) s. prov.lit. 24-Mar-4 Finarte Semenzato, Rome #10/R est:38000-40000
£26174	$46852	€39000	Portrait of man with sculpture (101x61cm-40x24in) s. 25-May-4 Finarte Semenzato, Milan #184/R est:18000-20000
Works on paper			
£613	$1104	€920	Female nude (36x27cm-14x11in) s. pencil. 21-Apr-4 Finarte Semenzato, Milan #591/R
£845	$1462	€1200	Mancini taken ill (18x12cm-7x5in) i. pencil chl. 11-Dec-3 Christie's, Rome #62
£3521	$5845	€5000	Giovane in preghiera (650x550cm-256x217in) s. chl htd white cardboard. 11-Jun-3 Christie's, Rome #162/R est:5500-7000
£4967	$9040	€7500	Neapolitan boy (97x63cm-38x25in) i. chl pastel cardboard. 17-Jun-4 Finarte Semenzato, Milan #257/R est:2000-3000
£5333	$9813	€8000	View of the Marinella (14x24cm-6x9in) s.i.d.1877 W/C prov.exhib.lit. 10-Jun-4 Christie's, Rome #77/R est:2800-3200
£9722	$16236	€14000	Girl with hat (79x58cm-31x23in) pastel paper on canvas. 21-Oct-3 Sotheby's, Milan #392/R est:2000-4000

MANCINI, Antonio (attrib) (1852-1930) Italian

£1333	$2453	€2000	Landscape with cable pole (22x13cm-9x5in) board. 10-Jun-4 Christie's, Rome #48 est:1500-2000

MANCINI, Bartolommeo (attrib) (fl.1630) Italian

£2027	$3649	€2959	Madonna and Child (58x51cm-23x20in) 26-Jan-4 Lilla Bukowskis, Stockholm #95 est:20000-25000 (S.KR 27000)
£4832	$8891	€7200	Saint Margherita of Antiochia (72x56cm-28x22in) 29-Mar-4 Pandolfini, Florence #784/R est:7000-9000

MANCINI, Francesco (1679-1758) Italian

£10345	$17172	€15000	Portrait of young lady as Flora (56x45cm-22x18in) 1-Oct-3 Dorotheum, Vienna #1/R est:15000-20000

MANCINI, Francesco (1829-1905) Italian

Works on paper			
£1469	$2526	€2100	Conversation a la sortie du village (54x37cm-21x15in) s. mixed media. 8-Dec-3 Horta, Bruxelles #92 est:1200-1800

MANCINI, Francesco Longo (1880-1954) Italian

Works on paper			
£1067	$1909	€1600	Nude (42x24cm-17x9in) s. pastel card. 13-May-4 Babuino, Rome #393/R est:400-600

MANCOBA, Sonja Ferlov (1911-1984) Danish

Sculpture			
£3128	$5005	€4536	Figure (109cm-43in) init. plaster prov. 17-Sep-3 Kunsthallen, Copenhagen #47/R est:25000 (D.KR 33000)
£3412	$5460	€4947	Figure (24cm-9in) init.num.2/6 bronze. 17-Sep-3 Kunsthallen, Copenhagen #7/R est:35000 (D.KR 36000)
£8451	$14113	€12338	Rider (123cm-48in) init.num.1/6 dark pat.bronze lit. 7-Oct-3 Rasmussen, Copenhagen #17/R est:100000-125000 (D.KR 90000)
Works on paper			
£1127	$1882	€1645	Figure composition (98x49cm-39x19in) init.d.64 collage prov. 7-Oct-3 Rasmussen, Copenhagen #36/R est:12000 (D.KR 12000)

MANDARRG, Wally (1915-1987) Australian

Works on paper			
£305	$482	€442	Murul, the devil man spirit (74x32cm-29x13in) earth pigments eucalyptus bark exec.c.1968 prov.exhib.lit. 28-Jul-3 Sotheby's, Paddington #249 (A.D 750)
£332	$621	€498	Untitled, totemic fish (46x100cm-18x39in) earth pigments eucalyptus bark exec.c.1975 prov. 26-Jul-4 Sotheby's, Melbourne #395/R (A.D 850)
£1289	$2411	€1934	Untitled (105x38cm-41x15in) i. pigment bark exec. c.1980. 21-Jul-4 Shapiro, Sydney #13/R est:3500-5000 (A.D 3300)
£1707	$2698	€2475	Standing man with spears (134x34cm-53x13in) earth pigments eucalyptus bark exec.c.1985 prov. 28-Jul-3 Sotheby's, Paddington #350/R est:4000-6000 (A.D 4200)

MANDELBAUM, Arie (1939-) Belgian

Works on paper			
£417	$696	€600	Femme debout (147x65cm-58x26in) s.d.1967 chl pastel. 21-Oct-3 Campo, Vlaamse Kaai #473

MANDELBERG, Johan Edvard (1730-1786) Danish

£981	$1550	€1422	Battle scene (19x23cm-7x9in) i.verso. 2-Sep-3 Rasmussen, Copenhagen #1842/R (D.KR 10500)
Works on paper			
£614	$1063	€896	Injured soldier (20x28cm-8x11in) pen chl. 9-Dec-3 Rasmussen, Copenhagen #1331/R (D.KR 6500)

MANDELLI, Pompilio (1912-) Italian

£471	$772	€650	Figures (35x24cm-14x9in) s.d.59 acrylic board. 30-May-3 Farsetti, Prato #57
£500	$920	€750	Hill (40x50cm-16x20in) s.d.1989 s.i.d.verso. 12-Jun-4 Meeting Art, Vercelli #37/R
£1400	$2576	€2100	Autumn (60x50cm-24x20in) s.d.1990. 12-Jun-4 Meeting Art, Vercelli #360/R est:1000

MANDELMAN, Beatrice (20th C) American

£1235	$2100	€1803	No.12 (58x79cm-23x31in) acrylic. 9-Nov-3 Wright, Chicago #390 est:2000-3000

MANDELSLOH, Gustav von (1806-?) German

£298	$498	€432	Winter woodland with huts and ravens (41x31cm-16x12in) s.d.91 board. 23-Jun-3 Philippe Schuler, Zurich #8618 (S.FR 650)

MANDER, Karel van (attrib) (16/17th C) Dutch

£3081	$5391	€4375	L'histoire de Joseph (104x102cm-41x40in) 18-Dec-3 Tajan, Paris #91/R est:5000-6000

MANDER, Karel van I (attrib) (1548-1606) Dutch

£6081	$10703	€9000	Adoration of the Magi (40x107cm-16x42in) panel. 18-May-4 Sotheby's, Amsterdam #77/R est:10000-15000

MANDER, Karel van III (1610-1672) Dutch

£190000	$347700	€277400	Allegory of taste, young man drinking from a silver tankard (57x46cm-22x18in) panel prov.exhib.lit. 7-Jul-4 Christie's, London #51/R est:70000-100000

MANDER, W H (1850-1922) British

£1892	$3500	€2762	Oil mill town - Dolgelly (61x91cm-24x36in) s.i. 14-Jan-4 Dallas Auction Gallery, Dallas #122/R est:3000-5000
£6486	$12000	€9470	Landscapes (33x53cm-13x21in) s. pair. 14-Jan-4 Dallas Auction Gallery, Dallas #416/R est:2500-4500

MANDER, William Henry (1850-1922) British

£850	$1607	€1241	Tranquil river in wooded landscape with mountains (48x72cm-19x28in) s.d.94 canvas on board. 17-Feb-4 Rosebery Fine Art, London #601
£1441	$2580	€2104	In the Valley of the Lleds, North Wales (57x97cm-22x38in) s.d.87. 25-May-4 Bukowskis, Stockholm #362/R est:20000-25000 (S.KR 19500)
£1500	$2805	€2190	Falls on the Lledr, North Wales (26x36cm-10x14in) s. 22-Jul-4 Tennants, Leyburn #838/R est:1800-2200
£1850	$3145	€2701	On the River Llugwy, North Wales (40x60cm-16x24in) s. s.i.verso. 18-Nov-3 Bonhams, Leeds #217/R est:700-900
£2100	$3780	€3066	Children fishing beside a river (31x46cm-12x18in) s. prov. 21-Apr-4 Tennants, Leyburn #1132/R est:1800-2500
£3243	$6000	€4735	Lledr valley near Dolwyddelan North Wales (76x112cm-30x44in) i. 14-Jan-4 Dallas Auction Gallery, Dallas #84 est:4000-6000
£3600	$6732	€5256	On the Conway, Bettws-y-Coed, North Wales (26x36cm-10x14in) s. 22-Jul-4 Tennants, Leyburn #839/R est:1800-2200
£3800	$6080	€5548	On the Llugwy; river scene with figures and cottage (41x61cm-16x24in) s. s.d.1896 verso. 17-Sep-3 Brightwells, Leominster #862 est:4000-5000
£4000	$7360	€5840	Mountainous river landscapes (46x36cm-18x14in) s. pair. 8-Jun-4 Lawrences, Bletchingley #1496/R est:3000-5000
£4600	$8372	€6716	On the river Llugwy, nr Capel Curig. In the Llugwy Valley (24x34cm-9x13in) s. s.i.verso pair. 15-Jun-4 Bonhams, Leeds #157/R est:2000-3000
£4800	$7632	€7008	Gwernon Villa lake, Dolgelley (58x89cm-23x35in) s.i. s.i.d.95 verso. 12-Sep-3 Gardiner & Houlgate, Bath #232/R est:3000-4000
£5800	$10846	€8468	Old footbridge at Goring. Banks of the Thames, nr Abingdon (61x41cm-24x16in) s. one d.11 one d.10 i.verso pair. 24-Feb-4 Bonhams, Knowle #85/R est:3000-5000
£11000	$19800	€16060	On the Llugwy below Capel Curig. In the Lledr Valley above Betws-y-Coed (51x76cm-20x30in) s.d.08 s.i.d.verso pair. 21-Apr-4 Tennants, Leyburn #1133/R est:4000-6000

Works on paper
£420 $764 €613 Rocky river landscape (35x51cm-14x20in) s. W/C. 29-Jun-4 Bonhams, Knowle #49

MANDLER, Ernst (1886-?) German
£790 $1343 €1153 Fishermen (93x87cm-37x34in) s.d.1929. 29-Nov-3 Dorotheum, Prague #48 est:30000-45000 (C.KR 36000)

MANDLICK, Auguste (1860-?) Austrian
Works on paper
£533 $960 €800 Woman's portrait (54x46cm-21x18in) i. pastel chk paper on canvas. 24-Apr-4 Quittenbaum, Munich #598/R

MANDON, Edouard (20th C) French
£333 $600 €500 Marine (49x99cm-19x39in) s. 20-Apr-4 Chenu & Scrive, Lyon #121/R
£633 $1140 €950 Marine (58x122cm-23x48in) s.d.1936. 20-Apr-4 Chenu & Scrive, Lyon #122/R

MANDRUP, Peter (1949-) Danish
£542 $1013 €791 Composition (146x114cm-57x45in) s.d.1986 verso. 25-Feb-4 Kunsthallen, Copenhagen #86 (D.KR 6000)

MANDYN, Jan (style) (1500-1560) Dutch
£7718 $13815 €11500 La tentation de Saint Antoine (29x43cm-11x17in) panel. 25-May-4 Palais de Beaux Arts, Brussels #78/R est:12000-18000

MANE KATZ (1894-1962) French
£462 $800 €675 Face of a bearded man (36x25cm-14x10in) bears sig. oil paper. 12-Dec-3 Du Mouchelle, Detroit #2156/R
£611 $1100 €892 Mediterranean sea (51x66cm-20x26in) 24-Apr-4 Du Mouchelle, Detroit #3174/R est:2000-4000
£806 $1500 €1177 Trumpeter (15x25cm-6x10in) 6-Mar-4 Page, Batavia #142
£1301 $2212 €1900 Nu en buste (25x19cm-10x7in) s. canvas on panel. 9-Nov-3 Eric Pillon, Calais #180/R
£1439 $2360 €2000 La maison rouge (49x65cm-19x26in) s.d.32 peinture a l'essence cardboard. 6-Jun-3 Chochon-Barre & Allardi, Paris #77/R est:1800-2000
£1538 $2569 €2200 Vase de fleurs (18x14cm-7x6in) s.verso. 29-Jun-3 Eric Pillon, Calais #259/R
£1700 $2703 €2465 Trois maisons (51x65cm-20x26in) s. prov. 11-Sep-3 Christie's, Kensington #81/R est:2000-3000
£2398 $3860 €3501 Still life vase with flowers (53x41cm-21x16in) s. board. 20-Aug-3 James Julia, Fairfield #628a/R est:2000-3000
£2454 $4000 €3583 Hasidic scholars (25x15cm-10x6in) s. prov. 25-Sep-3 Christie's, Rockefeller NY #639/R est:4000-6000
£4167 $7500 €6084 Bullfight (53x74cm-21x29in) 24-Apr-4 Du Mouchelle, Detroit #3178/R est:10000-15000
£4500 $7515 €6570 Village with cows (65x92cm-26x36in) s. lit. 22-Oct-3 Sotheby's, Olympia #181/R est:5000-7000
£4545 $7591 €6500 DEux garcons (31x31cm-12x12in) s. 29-Jun-3 Eric Pillon, Calais #262/R
£5594 $9510 €8000 Tete de rabin (60x50cm-24x20in) s.d.32. 1-Dec-3 Palais de Beaux Arts, Brussels #372/R est:3000-5000
£5723 $9500 €8356 Chevaux et cavaliers (55x55cm-22x22in) s. two. 2-Oct-3 Christie's, Tel Aviv #74/R est:10000-15000
£6000 $10020 €8760 Drinker (93x73cm-37x29in) s.d.27 prov.lit. 21-Oct-3 Sotheby's, London #147/R est:8000-12000
£6000 $11040 €9000 Paysage d'Ukraine (60x73cm-24x29in) s. 8-Jun-4 Artcurial Briest, Paris #158/R est:7000-9000
£6024 $10000 €8795 Les maries (24x35cm-9x14in) s. prov.exhib.lit. 2-Oct-3 Christie's, Tel Aviv #5/R est:9000-12000
£6145 $11000 €8972 Yeshiva boy (41x31cm-16x12in) s. prov. 18-Mar-4 Sotheby's, New York #288/R est:10000-15000
£6145 $11000 €8972 Concert (41x33cm-16x13in) s. canvasboard prov. 14-May-4 Skinner, Boston #354/R est:10000-20000
£6200 $11222 €9052 La charrette de fleurs (81x99cm-32x39in) s. canvasboard. 1-Apr-4 Christie's, Kensington #125/R est:6000-8000
£6643 $11094 €9500 Deux musiciens (28x22cm-11x9in) init. s.verso. 29-Jun-3 Eric Pillon, Calais #263/R
£7986 $13337 €11500 Grand bouquet de fleurs roses (81x100cm-32x39in) s. 21-Oct-3 Artcurial Briest, Paris #268/R est:8000-10000
£8000 $14560 €11680 Rabbi with young disciple (46x34cm-18x13in) s. canvas on board. 21-Jun-4 Bonhams, New Bond Street #49/R est:6000-8000
£12432 $23000 €18151 Femme avec pichet (73x60cm-29x24in) s. painted 1930 - 1939 prov.lit. 12-Feb-4 Sotheby's, New York #53/R est:15000-20000
£13907 $25311 €21000 Bouquet et statuette (100x81cm-39x32in) s.d.1933. 15-Jun-4 Rossini, Paris #80/R est:20000-22000
£14124 $25000 €20621 Biblical figures (159x120cm-63x47in) s. prov.lit. 1-May-4 Ben-Ami, Tel Aviv #4821/R est:30000-40000
£14667 $26253 €22000 Ruth a la chevre (130x89cm-51x35in) s. 17-May-4 Chayette & Cheval, Paris #138/R est:22000-25000
£15000 $27600 €21900 Bowl of flowers (61x46cm-24x18in) s. painted 1937 prov.lit. 23-Jun-4 Christie's, London #225/R est:12000-16000
£22346 $40000 €32625 Shepherd (81x63cm-32x25in) s. prov.lit. 18-Mar-4 Sotheby's, New York #102/R est:40000-60000
£30769 $51385 €44000 Mariage (60x73cm-24x29in) s. 29-Jun-3 Eric Pillon, Calais #258/R
£39106 $70000 €57095 Quartet (81x96cm-32x38in) s. prov.lit. 5-May-4 Christie's, Rockefeller NY #345/R est:50000-70000
£48000 $88320 €70080 Dancer, Simchat Torah (195x131cm-77x52in) s. prov.exhib. 22-Jun-4 Sotheby's, London #313/R est:35000-45000
Sculpture
£1719 $2871 €2510 Le musicien (36cm-14in) s. one of six dark brown pat bronze incl. marble base prov. 17-Nov-3 Waddingtons, Toronto #215/R est:1500-2000 (C.D 3800)
Works on paper
£297 $550 €434 Shepherd with sheep (61x51cm-24x20in) s. ink wash. 10-Feb-4 Sotheby's, New York #271
£300 $540 €438 Tetes de chevaux, study of two horses (24x18cm-9x7in) s. pen ink prov. 21-Apr-4 Tennants, Leyburn #990
£348 $550 €508 Cottage (23x30cm-9x12in) s.i. W/C. 7-Sep-3 Treadway Gallery, Cincinnati #729/R
£361 $650 €527 Emigrants (36x28cm-14x11in) ink. 24-Apr-4 Du Mouchelle, Detroit #3171/R
£472 $850 €689 Sitting girl (20x28cm-8x11in) wash. 24-Apr-4 Du Mouchelle, Detroit #3170/R
£531 $850 €775 Man with a bottle (48x39cm-19x15in) s. brush ink wash. 18-Sep-3 Swann Galleries, New York #334/R
£611 $1100 €892 Four Hassidim (71x53cm-28x21in) ink. 24-Apr-4 Du Mouchelle, Detroit #3177/R est:1000-2000
£722 $1300 €1054 Motherhood (66x51cm-26x20in) ink. 24-Apr-4 Du Mouchelle, Detroit #3169/R est:1000-2000
£722 $1300 €1054 Tree and house (71x56cm-28x22in) W/C gouache. 24-Apr-4 Du Mouchelle, Detroit #3185/R est:2000-4000
£874 $1600 €1276 Three Hassidim (38x46cm-15x18in) s. gouache. 1-Feb-4 Ben-Ami, Tel Aviv #4644/R est:1800-2400
£1250 $2250 €1825 Maabara (51x66cm-20x26in) gouache. 24-Apr-4 Du Mouchelle, Detroit #3175/R est:1500-2500
£1322 $2247 €1930 Le phare de Saint Malo (46x61cm-18x24in) s.d.38 bodycol paper on canvas. 5-Nov-3 Dobiaschofsky, Bern #771/R est:4000 (S.FR 3000)
£1399 $2336 €2000 Promenade des amoureux (49x64cm-19x25in) init. gouache W/C. 29-Jun-3 Eric Pillon, Calais #261/R
£1400 $2506 €2100 Le musicien (30x22cm-12x9in) W/C. 16-May-4 Osenat, Fontainebleau #39/R est:200-300
£1577 $2823 €2350 Scene d'interieur (63x48cm-25x19in) s. gouache W/C lit. 30-May-4 Eric Pillon, Calais #195/R
£1611 $2883 €2400 Marchande de fleurs (68x54cm-27x21in) s. gouache. 30-May-4 Eric Pillon, Calais #194/R
£1647 $2750 €2405 Les barques (50x66cm-20x26in) s. gouache prov. 7-Oct-3 Sotheby's, New York #305 est:3000-5000
£1676 $3000 €2447 Rabbi and student (29x23cm-11x9in) s. W/C ink prov. 18-Mar-4 Sotheby's, New York #287/R est:3000-5000
£2119 $3750 €3094 Study of a Rabbi (65x48cm-26x19in) s.d.35 gouache prov. 2-May-4 Bonhams & Butterfields, Los Angeles #3007/R est:2500-3500
£2747 $5000 €4011 Family in Israel (59x50cm-23x20in) s. gouache executed c.1950 prov. 29-Jun-4 Sotheby's, New York #342/R est:6000-8000
£3087 $5681 €4600 Les toits de Jerusalem (50x64cm-20x25in) s.d.1928 gouache. 29-Mar-4 Rieunier, Paris #54/R est:3000-4000
£3497 $5839 €5000 Garcon priant (48x30cm-19x12in) s. gouache W/C. 29-Jun-3 Eric Pillon, Calais #264/R

MANE KATZ (attrib) (1894-1962) French
£2174 $4000 €3261 Still life with vase of flowers (58x53cm-23x21in) s. 26-Jun-4 Selkirks, St. Louis #432/R est:4000-6000

MANEGLIA, Edmondo (1925-2003) Italian
£367 $675 €550 Turin in the Thirties (30x50cm-12x20in) s. s.i.verso cardboard on canvas. 12-Jun-4 Meeting Art, Vercelli #953

MANERA, Enrico (1947-) Italian
£333 $613 €500 Frankenstein (80x80cm-31x31in) s.i.d.1997 verso acrylic. 12-Jun-4 Meeting Art, Vercelli #161/R
£333 $613 €500 Columbia Pictures (64x44cm-25x17in) s.i.d.1999 verso oil acrylic. 12-Jun-4 Meeting Art, Vercelli #695/R
£336 $621 €500 Danger toy (40x50cm-16x20in) s.i.verso acrylic on PVC painted 2001. 13-Mar-4 Meeting Art, Vercelli #305
£352 $585 €500 Ex Balla (50x50cm-20x20in) s.i.d.1989 verso acrylic PVC. 14-Jun-3 Meeting Art, Vercelli #429
£387 $643 €550 Caravaggio Verde (40x30cm-16x12in) s.i.d.2001 verso acrylic PVC. 14-Jun-3 Meeting Art, Vercelli #501
£403 $745 €600 Porsche (60x60cm-24x24in) s. i.d.200 verso acrylic. 13-Mar-4 Meeting Art, Vercelli #189
£403 $745 €600 Metro Goldwin Mayer (60x50cm-24x20in) s.i.d.1992 acrylic. 13-Mar-4 Meeting Art, Vercelli #293
£458 $760 €650 Danger Toy (40x50cm-16x20in) s.i.verso acrylic PVC painted 2001. 14-Jun-3 Meeting Art, Vercelli #614
£503 $931 €750 Little mouse (70x50cm-28x20in) s. i.d.1995 verso acrylic. 13-Mar-4 Meeting Art, Vercelli #358
£528 $877 €750 Marilyn (50x40cm-20x16in) s.i.d.2001 acrylic on PVC. 14-Jun-3 Meeting Art, Vercelli #175/R
£528 $877 €750 Zeta come Zorro (70x60cm-28x24in) s.i.d.2001 verso acrylic on pvc. 14-Jun-3 Meeting Art, Vercelli #221/R
£563 $1025 €850 Spiderman (80x100cm-31x39in) s.i.d.2003 verso. 17-Jun-4 Galleria Pananti, Florence #454/R
£704 $1169 €1000 Don't worry (170x170cm-67x67in) s.d.2000 acrylic PVC. 14-Jun-3 Meeting Art, Vercelli #627/R
£733 $1349 €1100 Arabian nights (100x100cm-39x39in) s.d.1999 verso acrylic. 12-Jun-4 Meeting Art, Vercelli #241/R
£805 $1442 €1200 Mars attacks (130x90cm-51x35in) s.i.d.2001 verso acrylic photograph on PVC lit. 30-May-4 Meeting Art, Vercelli #1
£942 $1545 €1300 Homage to Masaccio (129x129cm-51x51in) s.d.94 verso acrylic. 30-May-3 Farsetti, Prato #16
£1000 $1840 €1500 Riders (120x100cm-47x39in) s.i.verso acrylic painted 1996. 12-Jun-4 Meeting Art, Vercelli #955/R est:1500
£1275 $2359 €1900 Andy (101x101cm-40x40in) s.i.d.2001 verso acrylic lit. 13-Mar-4 Meeting Art, Vercelli #396 est:1000
£7667 $14107 €11500 Transfer (120x150cm-47x59in) s.i.d.1978 verso acrylic on plastic. 12-Jun-4 Meeting Art, Vercelli #640/R est:5000
Sculpture
£1854 $3375 €2800 Transfers (95x120x13cm-37x47x5in) s.i.d.1981 mixed media on canvas neon plexiglas. 17-Jun-4 Galleria Pananti, Florence #238/R est:3000-3200
Works on paper
£302 $559 €450 Coke (20x20cm-8x8in) s.i.d.2003 verso mixed media collage cardboard. 13-Mar-4 Meeting Art, Vercelli #207
£333 $613 €500 God with us (20x20cm-8x8in) s.i.d.2003 verso mixed media collage cardboard. 12-Jun-4 Meeting Art, Vercelli #419
£500 $920 €750 Alpine landscape (70x100cm-28x39in) s. mixed media collage on canvas exec.1992. 12-Jun-4 Meeting Art, Vercelli #310/R

MANERO DE MIGUEL, Luis (1876-1937) Spanish
£586 $973 €850 Landscape in Burgos (18x27cm-7x11in) s. canvas on cardboard. 1-Oct-3 Ansorena, Madrid #711/R

MANES, Pablo (c.1891-1963) South American
Sculpture
£17033 $31000 €24868 Saint Teresita (22cm-9in) s. pat bronze exhib.lit. 29-Jun-4 Arroyo, Buenos Aires #39/R est:30000

MANESSIER, Alfred (1911-1993) French
£1690 $2924 €2400 Untitled (10x47cm-4x19in) s.d.58 oil gouache paper. 12-Dec-3 Piasa, Paris #213 est:2000-3000
£1800 $3006 €2628 Untitled (22x22cm-9x9in) s.d.66 board prov. 22-Oct-3 Bonhams, New Bond Street #77/R est:2000-3000
£2416 $4470 €3600 La vigne (22x35cm-9x14in) s.d.65. 15-Mar-4 Blanchet, Paris #179/R est:3000-4000
£2448 $4087 €3500 Composition (20x20cm-8x8in) s.d.1967 panel prov. 29-Jun-3 Versailles Encheres #52/R
£3000 $5460 €4380 Woman and child (18x24cm-7x9in) s.d.1946 i. verso prov. 4-Feb-4 Sotheby's, Olympia #176/R est:3000-5000
£3147 $5255 €4500 Bouquet ensoleille (22x22cm-9x9in) s.d.1967 panel prov. 29-Jun-3 Versailles Encheres #53/R
£3497 $5839 €5000 Bruyere I (27x25cm-11x10in) s.d. paper on canvas prov. 29-Jun-3 Versailles Encheres #64/R
£4667 $8400 €7000 Flanc de colline (47x69cm-19x27in) s.d.1960 i.verso prov. 25-Apr-4 Versailles Encheres #101 est:8000-10000
£5282 $9137 €7500 A flanc de colline (47x70cm-19x28in) s.d.60 i. stretcher. 13-Dec-3 Lempertz, Koln #167/R est:8000-10000
£6434 $10744 €9200 Objets de la passion (24x41cm-9x16in) s.d.1947 prov. 29-Jun-3 Versailles Encheres #65/R
£6892 $12130 €10200 Mattoon (24x19cm-9x7in) s. painted c.1946 prov. 18-May-4 Tajan, Paris #26/R est:6000-7000
£7000 $12880 €10220 Les fruits qui tombent (46x38cm-18x15in) s.d.49 oil paper on canvas exhib. 25-Jun-4 Christie's, London #110/R est:8000-12000
£7279 $13029 €10700 Composition (81x65cm-32x26in) s.d.1944. 19-Mar-4 Ribeyre & Baron, Paris #99/R est:7000-10000
£10461 $19247 €15900 Composition (33x55cm-13x22in) s.d.1957 lit. 27-Jun-4 Versailles Encheres #79/R est:15000-20000
£13986 $23357 €20000 Sceau (162x97cm-64x38in) s.d.63 prov. 25-Jun-3 Blanchet, Paris #135/R
£16084 $26860 €23000 Durance (130x97cm-51x38in) s.d.59 prov. 25-Jun-3 Blanchet, Paris #136/R
£16434 $27444 €23500 Sentier de la Ermita (100x100cm-39x39in) s.d.1969 s.i.d.verso prov. 29-Jun-3 Versailles Encheres #84/R
Works on paper
£300 $540 €450 Composition (20x25cm-8x10in) s.d.53 pastel. 22-Apr-4 Christie's, Paris #157
£450 $752 €657 Untitled (21x27cm-8x11in) s.d.68 W/C crayon prov. 22-Oct-3 Bonhams, New Bond Street #76/R
£1316 $2421 €2000 Composition (18x16cm-7x6in) s. W/C. 27-Jun-4 Versailles Encheres #19/R est:2000-3000
£1329 $2219 €1900 Etude pour Cymbaluh (30x23cm-12x9in) s.i. W/C. 11-Oct-3 Cornette de St.Cyr, Paris #61/R est:2000-3000
£1612 $2853 €2354 Pastel Number 11 (12x16cm-5x6in) s.d.77 mixed media prov. 27-Apr-4 AB Stockholms Auktionsverk #1218/R est:25000-30000 (S.KR 22000)
£1908 $3511 €2900 Composition (20x25cm-8x10in) s.d.1953 chl pastel prov. 27-Jun-4 Versailles Encheres #27/R est:3000-3500
£2448 $4087 €3500 Composition (54x54cm-21x21in) s. W/C ink prov. 29-Jun-3 Versailles Encheres #55/R
£2797 $4811 €4000 Sans titre (29x10cm-11x4in) s. gouache collage pair. 3-Dec-3 Beaussant & Lefèvre, Paris #11/R est:1500-2000

MANET, Edouard (1832-1883) French
£720000 $1317600 €1051200 Deux poires (28x32cm-11x13in) init. painted 1864 prov.exhib.lit. 2-Feb-4 Christie's, London #3/R est:300000-400000
£13128493 $23500000 €19167600 Courses au Bois de Boulogne (73x94cm-29x37in) s.d.1872 prov.exhib.lit. 5-May-4 Sotheby's, New York #13/R est:20000000-30000000
Prints
£1816 $3250 €2651 Gitanos (28x20cm-11x8in) etching. 14-May-4 Du Mouchelle, Detroit #2120/R est:2000-3000
£1875 $3000 €2738 Les gitanos (32x24cm-13x9in) sepia etching. 18-Sep-3 Swann Galleries, New York #400/R est:2500-3500
£2000 $3400 €2920 Le chanteur Espagnol (30x25cm-12x10in) etching. 6-Nov-3 Swann Galleries, New York #372/R est:3000-5000
£2000 $3640 €3000 Berthe morisot (32x25cm-13x10in) lithograph edition of 50. 2-Jul-4 Bloomsbury, London #29/R est:2000-2500
£2346 $4200 €3425 Le Buveur d'absinthe (29x16cm-11x6in) etching aquatint. 6-May-4 Swann Galleries, New York #298/R est:2000-3000
£2375 $3800 €3468 Olympia (9x18cm-4x7in) etching aquatint. 18-Sep-3 Swann Galleries, New York #403/R est:2500-3500
£2400 $4392 €3504 Les chats (18x22cm-7x9in) tone etching. 3-Jun-4 Christie's, Kensington #92/R est:800-1200
£2676 $4630 €3800 Lola de Valence (26x18cm-10x7in) i. etching aquatint. 11-Dec-3 Piasa, Paris #92/R
£2750 $4400 €4015 Le chanteur Espagnol (30x25cm-12x10in) col etching. 18-Sep-3 Swann Galleries, New York #401a/R est:3000-5000
£3800 $6992 €5700 La toilette (28x22cm-11x9in) mono. etching. 10-Jun-4 Hauswedell & Nolte, Hamburg #448/R est:7500
£11000 $18920 €16060 Untitled (56x41cm-22x16in) etchings 29 of 30 album 1 heliogravure after Fantin-Latour. 4-Dec-3 Sotheby's, London #157/R est:12000-15000
£19774 $35000 €28870 Execution of Maximilian (33x43cm-13x17in) lithograph. 30-Apr-4 Sotheby's, New York #122/R est:40000-60000
Works on paper
£7333 $13346 €11000 Untitled (7x10cm-3x4in) W/C four parts on board prov. 30-Jun-4 Calmels Cohen, Paris #10/R est:10000-12000
£13699 $23288 €20000 Etude de femme agenouillee (47x30cm-19x12in) studio st. wash htd gouache over crayon. 6-Nov-3 Tajan, Paris #192/R

MANETAS, Miltos (1964-) Greek
£2667 $4773 €4000 Grey (130x181cm-51x71in) d.96. 12-May-4 Chochon-Barre & Allardi, Paris #33 est:1000-1500

MANETTI, Rutilio (1571-1639) Italian
£17778 $32000 €25956 Finding of Moses (72x107cm-28x42in) 23-Jan-4 Christie's, Rockefeller NY #188/R est:20000-30000
£26000 $44980 €37960 Rest on the flight into Egypt (31x24cm-12x9in) copper. 11-Dec-3 Sotheby's, London #185/R est:8000-12000
£122148 $216201 €182000 Presentation at the temple (108x151cm-43x59in) 27-Apr-4 Porro, Milan #322/R est:200000

MANEV, Nicolas (c.1940-) Bulgarian
Works on paper
£238 $426 €350 Untitled (75x55cm-30x22in) s.d.80 pastel prov. 21-Mar-4 Calmels Cohen, Paris #139/R

MANFREDI, Alberto (1930-2001) Italian
£1081 $1903 €1600 Self-portrait (20x20cm-8x8in) s.d.1979 board. 22-May-4 Galleria Pananti, Florence #381/R est:2000-3000
£2324 $3858 €3300 Widow (50x40cm-20x16in) s. exhib. 11-Jun-3 Finarte Semenzato, Milan #714/R
£2848 $5183 €4300 Chimneys (62x52cm-24x20in) s.d.1997 board. 17-Jun-4 Galleria Pananti, Florence #446/R est:4700-5000
£3724 $6219 €5400 Composition (36x50cm-14x20in) s.d.71 paper on canvas. 14-Nov-3 Farsetti, Prato #94/R est:4200-4700
Works on paper
£497 $904 €750 Nude (34x24cm-13x9in) s. W/C. 17-Jun-4 Galleria Pananti, Florence #445/R
£738 $1366 €1100 Figure (45x32cm-18x13in) s.d.1972 pastel. 11-Mar-4 Galleria Pace, Milan #122/R

MANFREDI, Bartolomeo (circle) (1580-1620) Italian
£8000 $14480 €12000 Cain and Abel (124x154cm-49x61in) lit. 30-Mar-4 Babuino, Rome #58/R est:8000

MANFREDI, Giuseppe (1934-1987) Italian
£725 $1188 €1000 Composition (70x55cm-28x22in) s.d.78 wood panel. 31-May-3 Farsetti, Prato #746/R
£1259 $2140 €1800 Bar (72x35cm-28x14in) s. cardboard. 26-Nov-3 Pandolfini, Florence #1/R est:1400-1600
£1267 $2293 €1900 Vase with roses. Rider (70x50cm-28x20in) s.d.1975 double-sided. 2-Apr-4 Farsetti, Prato #515/R est:1800-2200
£1457 $2652 €2200 Flowers (77x56cm-30x22in) s. cardboard. 17-Jun-4 Galleria Pananti, Florence #532/R est:2000-2200
£1748 $2972 €2500 Vase with roses (70x60cm-28x24in) board. 26-Nov-3 Pandolfini, Florence #2/R est:2200-2400

MANG, Hans (1892-?) German
£733 $1349 €1100 Passer-bys (69x57cm-27x22in) s.d.1916 panel. 11-Jun-4 Wendl, Rudolstadt #4153/R

MANGASARYAN, Sarkis (1918-1991) Armenian
Works on paper
£280 $510 €409 In the Hermitage Museum (41x30cm-16x12in) s. W/C. 20-Jun-4 Lots Road Auctions, London #382/R

MANGER, Chris (20th C) British?
£400 $748 €600 Nelsons harbour (43x56cm-17x22in) s.d.1978. 21-Jul-4 John Nicholson, Haslemere #118

MANGIN, Charles (1892-1977) Belgian
£270 $476 €400 Hydrangeas in vase (85x120cm-33x47in) s. 24-May-4 Bernaerts, Antwerp #477/R
£367 $664 €550 Nature morte au mimosa (80x129cm-31x51in) s. 30-Mar-4 Campo & Campo, Antwerp #172
£500 $910 €750 Bouquet de roses jaunes (70x80cm-28x31in) s. 4-Jul-4 MonsAntic, Maisieres #385

MANGITAK, Kellypalik (1940-) North American
Works on paper
£1081 $1838 €1578 Arctic gull (43x29cm-17x11in) skin stencil. 3-Nov-3 Waddingtons, Toronto #298/R est:1500-2000 (C.D 2400)

MANGLARD, Adrien (1695-1760) French
Works on paper
£503 $805 €700 Navire en rade (17x24cm-7x9in) i. pen brown ink grey wash. 16-May-3 Tajan, Paris #57
£1224 $2192 €1800 Des figures dans un port, des bateaux a l'arrier plan. Un sermon (26x41cm-10x16in) s. red chk conte double-sided. 18-Mar-4 Christie's, Paris #252/R est:2000-3000
£1972 $3411 €2800 Attroupement autour d'une scene de lutte dans un village (35x45cm-14x18in) i. sanguine. 10-Dec-3 Piasa, Paris #50/R est:3000

MANGLARD, Adrien (attrib) (1695-1760) French
£19655 $32824 €28500 Seascapes (151x217cm-59x85in) pair. 14-Nov-3 Marc Kohn, Paris #25/R est:30000-40000

MANGO, Leonardo de (1843-1930) Italian
£10563 $18275 €15000 Figures in Constantinoples (49x34cm-19x13in) s.d.1912 canvas on cardboard. 10-Dec-3 Castellana, Madrid #189/R est:15000
Works on paper
£352 $609 €500 Market (9x13cm-4x5in) s.d.1916 sepia wash. 10-Dec-3 Castellana, Madrid #72/R
£805 $1490 €1200 Reunion de sages a Beyrouth (29x24cm-11x9in) s.d.1883 mixed media. 15-Mar-4 Horta, Bruxelles #421

£1127	$1949	€1600	Blind beggar (27x20cm-11x8in) s.d.1918 W/C. 10-Dec-3 Castellana, Madrid #73/R est:2000
£1408	$2437	€2000	Bosphorus (16x35cm-6x14in) s.d.1911 W/C. 10-Dec-3 Castellana, Madrid #74/R est:2000

MANGOLD, Anton (attrib) (1863-1907) German

£397	$723	€600	Female nude seated on a park bench under the trees (120x108cm-47x43in) 16-Jun-4 Hugo Ruef, Munich #1032

MANGOLD, Josef (1884-1942) German

£667	$1207	€1000	Summer landscape in the Harz (66x55cm-26x22in) s. 1-Apr-4 Van Ham, Cologne #1530
£1538	$2646	€2200	Winter landscape (56x66cm-22x26in) s. 4-Dec-3 Van Ham, Cologne #312/R est:1400
£1748	$3007	€2500	Still life (88x74cm-35x29in) s.d.19 board. 4-Dec-3 Van Ham, Cologne #311/R est:3000

MANGOLD, Robert (1937-) American

£4790	$8000	€6993	Plane/figure II (58x76cm-23x30in) s.d.1993 acrylic pencil col pencil paper prov.exhib. 13-Nov-3 Sotheby's, New York #580/R est:6000-8000
£29940	$50000	€43712	Untitled - red (240x140cm-94x55in) acrylic graphite cut paper painted 1977 prov. 14-Nov-3 Phillips, New York #156/R est:40000-60000
£31000	$56420	€45260	Triangle with three rectangles (51x106cm-20x42in) s.i.d.1977 s.stretcher acrylic pencil masonite prov. 6-Feb-4 Sotheby's, London #138/R est:20000-30000
Works on paper			
£7027	$13000	€10259	Four Arcs within a square (45x45cm-18x18in) s.i.d.1975 verso chl. ochre coloured paper. 12-Feb-4 Sotheby's, New York #152/R est:5000-7000
£11976	$20000	€17485	Triangle with three squares of diminishing size (70x100cm-28x39in) s.i.d.1996 pencil col pencil prov.exhib. 13-Nov-3 Sotheby's, New York #579/R est:7000-9000
£18994	$34000	€27731	Red/grey/black zone painting (76x170cm-30x67in) s.d.1996 conte crayon graphite prov. 14-May-4 Phillips, New York #238/R est:30000-50000

MANGOLD, Sylvia (1938-) American

£659	$1200	€962	Untitled (34x46cm-13x18in) s.d.July 31 1984 verso oil on paper prov.exhib. 29-Jun-4 Sotheby's, New York #560/R est:2000-3000
Works on paper			
£2500	$4500	€3650	Four rulers four corners with a 38 vanishing RT (12x22cm-5x9in) s.i.d.1976 ink acrylic two sheets. 24-Apr-4 David Rago, Lambertville #471/R est:1000-2000
£2703	$5000	€3946	Tree Studies - a Suite of 4 (46x57cm-18x22in) s.i.d.1985 mixed media paper four prov. 12-Feb-4 Sotheby's, New York #289/R est:1500-2000
£4167	$7500	€6084	22 1/2 inches of floorboard (18x24cm-7x9in) s.i.d.1974 W/C. 24-Apr-4 David Rago, Lambertville #78/R est:2000-4000

MANGOS, Vyron (1924-) Greek

£900	$1575	€1314	View of Myconos (35x49cm-14x19in) s. hardboard. 16-Dec-3 Bonhams, New Bond Street #56/R
£1500	$2685	€2190	The red boat (50x70cm-20x28in) s. s.d.1972 verso. 11-May-4 Bonhams, New Bond Street #42/R est:1500-2000

MANGRAVITE, Peppino (1896-1978) American

£4624	$8000	€6751	Dancing in the moonlight (110x83cm-43x33in) s. i.verso painted 1937 prov.exhib. 10-Dec-3 Bonhams & Butterfields, San Francisco #6067/R est:7000-10000

MANGU PUTRA, Gusti Agung (1963-) Balinese

£2124	$3845	€3101	Ikan Putih di atas Latar Hijau dan Merah (100x120cm-39x47in) s.d.2002 i.d.2002 verso acrylic. 3-Apr-4 Glerum, Singapore #42/R est:6000-8000 (S.D 6500)

MANGU, Roberto (1948-) Italian

£2148	$3952	€3200	Las piedritas no 1 (33x22cm-13x9in) s.i.d.1997 1998 verso. 24-Mar-4 Binoche, Paris #95/R est:2500-3000

MANGUIN, Henri (1874-1949) French

£748	$1362	€1100	Branches in brown vase (50x39cm-20x15in) s. board on canvas. 6-Feb-4 Paul Kieffer, Pforzhiem #8060
£2113	$3655	€3000	Asperges (27x41cm-11x16in) studio st. prov.lit. 9-Dec-3 Artcurial Briest, Paris #175/R est:2000-3000
£3169	$5483	€4500	Madame Henri Manguin (40x32cm-16x13in) prov.lit. 9-Dec-3 Artcurial Briest, Paris #173/R est:500-700
£3873	$6701	€5500	Odette au foulard (55x46cm-22x18in) studio st. prov.lit. 9-Dec-3 Artcurial Briest, Paris #161/R est:6000-8000
£4667	$8493	€7000	Odette assise (56x47cm-22x19in) s. lit. 4-Jul-4 Eric Pillon, Calais #105/R
£4930	$8528	€7000	Auto-portrait (55x46cm-22x18in) studio st. prov.lit. 9-Dec-3 Artcurial Briest, Paris #158/R est:8000-12000
£5282	$9138	€7500	Torse nu (35x27cm-14x11in) studio st. prov.lit. 9-Dec-3 Artcurial Briest, Paris #157/R est:7000-10000
£5986	$10356	€8500	Personnage lisant (33x41cm-13x16in) studio st. prov.lit. 9-Dec-3 Artcurial Briest, Paris #152/R est:10000-15000
£5986	$10356	€8500	Femme nue (19x27cm-7x11in) studio st. canvas on cardboard prov. 9-Dec-3 Artcurial Briest, Paris #156/R est:2000-3000
£8190	$14659	€11957	Nature morte a la rhubarbe (38x46cm-15x18in) s. 12-May-4 Dobiaschofsky, Bern #773/R est:12000 (S.FR 19000)
£8451	$14620	€12000	Toulon, entree de rade, hiver (27x41cm-11x16in) st.sig. lit. 10-Dec-3 Rossini, Paris #95/R
£9189	$17000	€13416	Petit vase de roses (42x33cm-17x13in) s. painted 1940 prov.lit. 11-Feb-4 Sotheby's, New York #19/R est:10000-15000
£9412	$16000	€13742	Nature morte, coings, grenades et raisins (38x47cm-15x19in) s. painted 1924 prov.lit. 6-Nov-3 Sotheby's, New York #172/R est:20000-25000
£9507	$16448	€13500	Auto-portrait (46x38cm-18x15in) studio st. prov.lit. 9-Dec-3 Artcurial Briest, Paris #155/R est:8000-12000
£9910	$17045	€14469	Nature morte: le the (53x64cm-21x25in) s. prov. 2-Dec-3 Koller, Zurich #3082/R est:25000-35000 (S.FR 22000)
£11258	$20490	€17000	Jeune femme, assise, bras derriere la tete (46x38cm-18x15in) s. painted c.1924 exhib. 18-Jun-4 Piasa, Paris #21/R est:18000-20000
£14000	$24220	€20440	Tulipes perroquet (54x46cm-21x18in) s. prov.lit. 11-Dec-3 Christie's, Kensington #47/R est:9000-12000
£14000	$25760	€20440	Saint-Paul de Vence (46x55cm-18x22in) s. painted autumn 1938 prov.lit. 23-Jun-4 Christie's, London #158/R est:14000-18000
£17333	$31547	€26000	Mourillon, Toulon (42x58cm-17x23in) s. canvas on cardboard painted 1926 prov.exhib.lit. 29-Jun-4 Sotheby's, Paris #11/R est:18000-25000
£18000	$30060	€26280	Le Reinerie, vallee chevreuse (73x60cm-29x24in) s. 22-Oct-3 Bonhams, New Bond Street #12/R est:20000-30000
£20000	$36400	€29200	Grenades raisins (44x56cm-17x22in) s. painted 1929 lit. 4-Feb-4 Sotheby's, London #232/R est:20000-30000
£20979	$36084	€30000	Pavots (92x73cm-36x29in) s. lit. 5-Dec-3 Chochon-Barre & Allardi, Paris #132/R est:30000-35000
£23777	$39707	€34000	Nu debout s'essuyant (86x49cm-34x19in) s. prov.lit. 30-Jun-3 Artcurial Briest, Paris #736/R est:35000-40000
£31690	$54824	€45000	Saint-Tropez, femme au hamac (54x65cm-21x26in) s. 12-Dec-3 Renaud, Paris #161/R est:16000
£40223	$72000	€58726	Lever (97x130cm-38x51in) s. painted 1910 prov.exhib.lit. 5-May-4 Christie's, Rockefeller NY #286/R est:50000-70000
£55882	$95000	€81588	Jeanne en jaune dans le jardin de Neuilly (100x81cm-39x32in) s. painted 1910 prov.exhib.lit. 5-Nov-3 Christie's, Rockefeller NY #250/R est:60000-80000
£94972	$170000	€138659	Jeanne a la fontaine, Villa Demiere (116x89cm-46x35in) s. painted 1904 prov.exhib.lit. 5-May-4 Christie's, Rockefeller NY #259/R est:200000-300000
Works on paper			
£282	$487	€400	Saint-Tropez (12x18cm-5x7in) s. Chinese ink dr prov. 9-Dec-3 Artcurial Briest, Paris #137
£317	$548	€450	Ile d'Or (11x18cm-4x7in) studio st. Chinese ink dr prov. 9-Dec-3 Artcurial Briest, Paris #176
£423	$731	€600	Etude pour baigneuses (21x27cm-8x11in) studio st. graphite dr pr. 9-Dec-3 Artcurial Briest, Paris #138
£423	$731	€600	Odette Manguin de dos (18x16cm-7x6in) studio st. Chinese ink dr prov. 9-Dec-3 Artcurial Briest, Paris #144
£423	$731	€600	Deux amies (22x28cm-9x11in) studio st. graphite dr prov. 9-Dec-3 Artcurial Briest, Paris #162
£438	$700	€639	Femme nue assise (28x22cm-11x9in) s. brush ink. 18-Sep-3 Swann Galleries, New York #398/R
£458	$792	€650	Etude pour composition (22x28cm-9x11in) studio st. chl dr prov. 9-Dec-3 Artcurial Briest, Paris #140
£471	$816	€670	Terrasse sur l'atelier (23x18cm-9x7in) studio st. Chinese ink dr prov. 9-Dec-3 Artcurial Briest, Paris #146
£493	$853	€700	Nu allonge (16x27cm-6x11in) studio st. Chinese ink dr. 9-Dec-3 Artcurial Briest, Paris #169
£528	$913	€750	Nu allonge (25x32cm-10x13in) studio st. Chinese ink dr prov. 9-Dec-3 Artcurial Briest, Paris #143
£564	$975	€800	Lucile Manguin (22x28cm-9x11in) studio st. chl dr prov. 9-Dec-3 Artcurial Briest, Paris #147
£564	$975	€800	Nu sur tapis (27x21cm-11x8in) studio st. Chinese ink wash dr prov. 9-Dec-3 Artcurial Briest, Paris #164
£634	$1097	€900	Vue de l'Oustalet (18x22cm-7x9in) studio st. Chinese ink dr prov. 9-Dec-3 Artcurial Briest, Paris #174
£634	$1097	€900	Nu debout (21x12cm-8x5in) studio st. wash dr prov. 9-Dec-3 Artcurial Briest, Paris #172
£704	$1218	€1000	Bouquet de fleurs (23x18cm-9x7in) studio st. Chinese ink dr prov. 9-Dec-3 Artcurial Briest, Paris #163/R
£704	$1218	€1000	Foux (12x18cm-5x7in) studio st. Chinese ink dr prov. 9-Dec-3 Artcurial Briest, Paris #170
£845	$1462	€1200	Jeanne au divan (22x29cm-9x11in) s. graphite dr prov. 9-Dec-3 Artcurial Briest, Paris #148
£845	$1462	€1200	Nu de dos (15x10cm-6x4in) studio st. Chinese ink dr prov. 9-Dec-3 Artcurial Briest, Paris #167 est:400-600
£915	$1584	€1300	Paysage provencal (21x27cm-8x11in) studio st. ink wash prov. 9-Dec-3 Artcurial Briest, Paris #150/R est:1000-1500
£1111	$1855	€1600	Sanary, bateaux en Cales seches (28x44cm-11x17in) st.sig.i. ink exhib. 21-Oct-3 Artcurial Briest, Paris #38/R est:1200-1500
£1127	$1949	€1600	Canal (24x31cm-9x12in) studio st. Chinese ink wash dr prov. 9-Dec-3 Artcurial Briest, Paris #149/R est:1500-2000
£1127	$1949	€1600	Nu de dos (27x21cm-11x8in) s. chl. 12-Dec-3 Renaud, Paris #160 est:300
£1268	$2193	€1800	Grenouillette (20x26cm-8x10in) studio st. sanguine dr prov. 9-Dec-3 Artcurial Briest, Paris #154 est:1800-2200
£1338	$2315	€1900	Jeanne a la tunique (28x21cm-11x8in) studio st. ink wash dr prov. 9-Dec-3 Artcurial Briest, Paris #139/R est:2000
£1831	$3168	€2600	Jeanne au coussin (19x16cm-7x6in) Chinese ink wash dr prov. 9-Dec-3 Artcurial Briest, Paris #171 est:1500-2000
£2183	$3777	€3100	Nu de dos (28x22cm-11x9in) s. graphite dr prov. 9-Dec-3 Artcurial Briest, Paris #168 est:1200-1800
£3169	$5483	€4500	Jeune femme se coiffant (20x16cm-8x6in) s.i. W/C graphite prov. 9-Dec-3 Artcurial Briest, Paris #141/R est:5000-7000
£3169	$5483	€4500	Odette Manguin lisant (27x23cm-11x9in) s. W/C prov. 9-Dec-3 Artcurial Briest, Paris #151/R est:4000-6000
£3380	$5848	€4800	Jeanne assise (27x21cm-11x8in) studi st. ink wash dr prov. 9-Dec-3 Artcurial Briest, Paris #145/R est:1500-2000
£3500	$5845	€5110	Bouquet de coquelicots et de fleurs (32x25cm-13x10in) st.sig. W/C over pencil executed c.1939 prov. 21-Oct-3 Sotheby's, London #85/R est:4000-6000
£5986	$10356	€8500	Chateau-Martin (29x37cm-11x15in) s.i. W/C over graphite prov.exhib. 9-Dec-3 Artcurial Briest, Paris #136/R est:6000-8000

MANHART, Eduard (1880-?) Austrian

Works on paper			
£304	$535	€450	Winter landscape (21x14cm-8x6in) s.d.9.III.08 W/C. 19-May-4 Dorotheum, Klagenfurt #50
£524	$892	€750	First World War scene in snowy woodland (24x35cm-9x14in) s.d.1916 W/C htd white. 19-Nov-3 Dorotheum, Klagenfurt #57

MANIATTY, Stephen G (1910-) American

£214	$400	€312	Approaching fog, Monhegan Island, Maine (33x58cm-13x23in) s. board. 28-Feb-4 Thomaston Place, Thomaston #231/R
£588	$1000	€858	Along the Deerfield River (63x76cm-25x30in) s. i.verso. 21-Nov-3 Skinner, Boston #492/R est:2000-4000
£988	$1600	€1442	Old Deerfield, Massachusetts landscape (51x76cm-20x30in) s. 31-Jul-3 Eldred, East Dennis #882/R est:1500-2500
£1105	$2000	€1613	Birth place Mary p Wells Smith (41x61cm-16x24in) board. 2-Apr-4 Douglas, South Deerfield #38
£1713	$3100	€2501	Sugar house in winter (41x25cm-16x10in) board. 2-Apr-4 Douglas, South Deerfield #8
£2044	$3700	€2984	Spring Freshet (61x41cm-24x16in) 2-Apr-4 Douglas, South Deerfield #7
£3315	$6000	€4840	Our roots are here (76x64cm-30x25in) 2-Apr-4 Douglas, South Deerfield #6

MANIGLIER, Yvette (1922-) French
£1342 $2376 €2000 Californie jazz (116x73cm-46x29in) s. acrylic. 29-Apr-4 Claude Aguttes, Neuilly #125 est:2000-2200

MANIQUET, Marius (1822-1896) French
£1133 $2074 €1700 Cabane au bord de la mare aux canards (46x65cm-18x26in) s. 6-Jun-4 Osenat, Fontainebleau #278 est:1000-1200

MANISCO, Lucio (1928-) ?
Works on paper
£909 $1545 €1300 Composition (29x42cm-11x17in) s.d.49 mixed media. 24-Nov-3 Christie's, Milan #257/R est:1000-1500

MANJEWITSCH, Abraham (1883-1942) Russian
£8889 $16000 €12978 Camden (50x56cm-20x22in) s.i.d.1923. 23-Apr-4 Sotheby's, New York #59/R est:8000-12000

MANKELL, Otto August (?) Swedish
£393 $679 €574 Field landscape with view of town (60x80cm-24x31in) s. 15-Dec-3 Lilla Bukowskis, Stockholm #335 (S.KR 5000)

MANKES, Jan (1889-1920) Dutch
£173333 $318933 €260000 Self portrait (28x23cm-11x9in) s. painted 1913 prov.exhib.lit. 9-Jun-4 Christie's, Amsterdam #235/R est:200000-300000
£246667 $453867 €370000 Bomenrij (69x52cm-27x20in) s.d.1915 prov.exhib.lit. 9-Jun-4 Christie's, Amsterdam #220/R est:100000-150000
Works on paper
£282 $519 €420 Study of a crow (25x25cm-10x10in) studio st. black chk. 29-Mar-4 Glerum, Amsterdam #111

MANN, Alexander (1853-1908) British
£900 $1611 €1314 Loch Lomond (21x32cm-8x13in) panel pair prov. 27-May-4 Christie's, Kensington #222/R
£2800 $5124 €4088 Portrait of a girl at dusk (33x24cm-13x9in) panel prov. 7-Apr-4 Woolley & Wallis, Salisbury #222/R est:800-1200

MANN, Cathleen (1896-1959) British
£867 $1569 €1300 Portrait de Jeanne de Rothschild (62x51cm-24x20in) s.d.1945. 31-Mar-4 Sotheby's, Paris #77/R est:1500-2000
£900 $1638 €1314 Flowerpiece (76x64cm-30x25in) s.d.1943 portrait verso double-sided. 1-Jul-4 Christie's, Kensington #139139/R
£3000 $4710 €4350 On the Grand canal, Venice (46x61cm-18x24in) s.d.1949. 27-Aug-3 Sotheby's, London #1144/R est:3000-5000
Works on paper
£1900 $3021 €2774 Filmstars use Shell (54x96cm-21x38in) pastel W/C gouache collage exhib.lit. 10-Sep-3 Sotheby's, Olympia #78/R est:600-800

MANN, David (1948-) American
£1350 $2200 €1971 Drum beat (30cm-12in circular) 18-Jul-3 Altermann Galleries, Santa Fe #4
£1687 $2750 €2463 Winter's hunt (41x30cm-16x12in) 18-Jul-3 Altermann Galleries, Santa Fe #18
£2454 $4000 €3583 Cheyenne winter (51x41cm-20x16in) 18-Jul-3 Altermann Galleries, Santa Fe #3
£2454 $4000 €3583 Winchester magic (41x51cm-16x20in) 18-Jul-3 Altermann Galleries, Santa Fe #17
£3006 $4900 €4389 Buffalo Springs (61x46cm-24x18in) 18-Jul-3 Altermann Galleries, Santa Fe #1/R
£3006 $4900 €4389 Signal at sunrise (61x46cm-24x18in) 18-Jul-3 Altermann Galleries, Santa Fe #15
£3374 $5500 €4926 Medicine ridge (61x51cm-24x20in) 18-Jul-3 Altermann Galleries, Santa Fe #8
£3374 $5500 €4926 Red Lodge smoke (61x51cm-24x20in) 18-Jul-3 Altermann Galleries, Santa Fe #12
£4118 $7000 €6012 Old scout (61x46cm-24x18in) 1-Nov-3 Altermann Galleries, Santa Fe #86
£4706 $8000 €6871 Distant gleam (61x76cm-24x30in) 1-Nov-3 Altermann Galleries, Santa Fe #85
£5215 $8500 €7614 Look out point (61x76cm-24x30in) 18-Jul-3 Altermann Galleries, Santa Fe #7
£5215 $8500 €7614 Ride a yellow horse (76x61cm-30x24in) 18-Jul-3 Altermann Galleries, Santa Fe #13
£5828 $9500 €8509 Lakota man (91x61cm-36x24in) 18-Jul-3 Altermann Galleries, Santa Fe #6
£5828 $9500 €8509 Pawnee man (91x61cm-36x24in) 18-Jul-3 Altermann Galleries, Santa Fe #11
£5828 $9500 €8509 Off the trail (61x91cm-24x36in) 18-Jul-3 Altermann Galleries, Santa Fe #10
£7362 $12000 €10749 Horse raid (102x76cm-40x30in) 18-Jul-3 Altermann Galleries, Santa Fe #5
£7362 $12000 €10749 Night watch (102x76cm-40x30in) 18-Jul-3 Altermann Galleries, Santa Fe #9
£7362 $12000 €10749 Canyon voices (102x76cm-40x30in) 18-Jul-3 Altermann Galleries, Santa Fe #2
£7362 $12000 €10749 White bird (102x76cm-40x30in) 18-Jul-3 Altermann Galleries, Santa Fe #16
£11656 $19000 €17018 Shadows in the sun (102x152cm-40x60in) 18-Jul-3 Altermann Galleries, Santa Fe #14
£12849 $23000 €18760 Medicine Lodge (122x152cm-48x60in) 15-May-4 Altermann Galleries, Santa Fe #58/R
£13408 $24000 €19576 Kiowa Pass (102x76cm-40x30in) 15-May-4 Altermann Galleries, Santa Fe #57/R

MANN, Edward (19th C) ?
£450 $828 €657 Old couple before a fireside in a cottage interior (30x40cm-12x16in) s.d.1874. 8-Jun-4 Bonhams, Knightsbridge #159/R

MANN, Gother Victor Fyers (1863-1948) Australian
£810 $1304 €1183 Autumn landscape (26x14cm-10x6in) s. board. 13-Oct-3 Joel, Victoria #304/R est:2000-2500 (A.D 2000)

MANN, Harrington (1864-1937) British
£450 $774 €657 Farm (16x23cm-6x9in) s. panel. 4-Dec-3 Bonhams, Edinburgh #2
£4200 $7602 €6132 Girl with red hair (33x28cm-13x11in) s. 19-Apr-4 Sotheby's, London #128/R est:3000-4000
£8108 $15000 €11838 Portrait of Alicia du Pont with her basset hound (132x112cm-52x44in) s.d.1915. 24-Jan-4 Jeffery Burchard, Florida #70/R est:15000-25000

MANN, Robert (19th C) British
£320 $582 €467 Camp fire (60x86cm-24x34in) s. 15-Jun-4 Bonhams, Knightsbridge #208
£750 $1403 €1095 Welsh cottage. Welsh river scene (24x40cm-9x16in) s. i.d.1892 verso board pair. 22-Jul-4 Tennants, Leyburn #837

MANN, Sally (1951-) American
Photographs
£1739 $3200 €2539 Untitled (61x51cm-24x20in) s.d.1990 num.verso cibachrome prov. 10-Jun-4 Phillips, New York #630/R est:3000-4000
£2395 $4000 €3497 Jessie bites (20x25cm-8x10in) s.i.d.1985 num.13/25 i.verso photo. 17-Oct-3 Sotheby's, New York #305/R est:5000-7000
£2395 $4000 €3497 Big girls (57x48cm-22x19in) s.i.d.1992 num.7/25 i.verso photo prov. 17-Oct-3 Sotheby's, New York #307/R est:3000-5000
£2500 $4400 €3650 Bath (51x61cm-20x24in) with sig.i.d.1989 silver print. 20-May-4 Swann Galleries, New York #524/R est:4000-6000
£2542 $4500 €3711 Perfect tomato, 1990 (19x24cm-7x9in) s.i.d.1990 gelatin silver print lit. 27-Apr-4 Christie's, Rockefeller NY #188/R est:5000-7000
£2994 $5000 €4371 Black eye (47x59cm-19x23in) s.i.d.1991 num.7/25 i.verso photo. 17-Oct-3 Sotheby's, New York #306/R est:5000-7000
£3114 $5200 €4546 Virginia at six (24x19cm-9x7in) gelatin silver print executed 1991 prov. 14-Nov-3 Phillips, New York #267/R est:5000-7000
£3800 $6460 €5548 Three Graces (20x24cm-8x9in) s.i.d,1994 num.12/25 gelatin silver print. 18-Nov-3 Christie's, Kensington #252/R est:2000-3000
£3955 $7000 €5774 Jessie at 5 (20x25cm-8x10in) s.i.d.1987 num.17/25 i.verso photo prov. 28-Apr-4 Sotheby's, New York #167/R est:8000-12000
£4000 $7040 €5840 Three Graces (48x57cm-19x22in) s. num.12/25 gelatin silver print. 19-May-4 Christie's, London #197/R est:4000-6000
£4192 $7000 €6120 Jessie bites (48x58cm-19x23in) s.i.d.1985 num.12/25 verso gelatin silver print prov.lit. 17-Oct-3 Phillips, New York #246/R est:8000-12000
£4444 $8000 €6488 Shiva at Whistle Creek (20x25cm-8x10in) s.i.d.1994 gelatin silver print prov.lit. 23-Apr-4 Phillips, New York #118/R est:9000-12000
£4722 $8500 €6894 Untitled (76x96cm-30x38in) s.d.1996 gelatin silver print lit. 23-Apr-4 Phillips, New York #235/R est:9000-12000
£5085 $9000 €7424 The last time Emmett modeled nude (20x25cm-8x10in) s.i.d.1987 num.16/25 i.verso photo prov. 28-Apr-4 Sotheby's, New York #166/R est:8000-12000
£5988 $10000 €8742 Jessie in the wind (48x57cm-19x22in) s.i.d.num.17/25 verso gelatin silver print lit. 20-Oct-3 Christie's, Rockefeller NY #226/R est:12000-18000
£6587 $11000 €9617 Holding the weasel (49x59cm-19x23in) s.i.d.1989 num.11/25 i.verso photo. 17-Oct-3 Sotheby's, New York #303/R est:10000-15000
£6587 $11000 €9617 Modest child no 1 (59x49cm-23x19in) i.d.1988 num.20/25 i.verso photo. 17-Oct-3 Sotheby's, New York #304/R est:7000-10000
£6780 $12000 €9899 Venus after school, 1992 (48x58cm-19x23in) s.i.d.1992 num.15/25 gelatin silver print. 27-Apr-4 Christie's, Rockefeller NY #187/R est:12000-18000
£7778 $14000 €11356 Jessi at 12 (20x25cm-8x10in) s. num.16/25 verso gelatin silver print. 23-Apr-4 Phillips, New York #131/R est:8000-12000
£15819 $28000 €23096 Deep South no 32 (102x127cm-40x50in) s.i.d.1998 num.10/10 verso toned photo printed 1999 prov.lit. 27-Apr-4 Sotheby's, New York #38/R est:15000-25000

MANNA, Francisco (1879-1943) ?
£2381 $4357 €3572 An evening in the botanical gardens (98x148cm-39x58in) s.i.d.1922. 6-Jul-4 Bolsa de Arte, Rio de Janeiro #118/R (B.R 13000)

MANNERS, William (fl.1885-c.1910) British
£460 $851 €672 Gathering the harvest (18x28cm-7x11in) s.i. verso board. 12-Feb-4 Andrew Hartley, Ilkley #891
£500 $910 €730 Lakeland scene with shepherd and flock (15x23cm-6x9in) s. 16-Jun-4 Andrew Hartley, Ilkley #1094/R
£600 $960 €870 Stick gatherers, carter and dog on a woodland path (30x44cm-12x17in) s. 17-Sep-3 James Thompson, Kirby Lonsdale #171/R
£600 $1032 €876 Early winter (18x30cm-7x12in) s.d.1907 board. 3-Dec-3 Andrew Hartley, Ilkley #1226
£620 $1128 €905 Landscape with shepherd and flock (18x25cm-7x10in) s. pair. 16-Jun-4 Andrew Hartley, Ilkley #1096
£650 $1177 €949 Landscape with figures on a path beside farm buildings (20x31cm-8x12in) s.d.1892 board. 30-Mar-4 Sworder & Son, Bishops Stortford #561/R
£700 $1295 €1022 Returning home (20x30cm-8x12in) s.d.1905. 13-Jan-4 Bonhams, Knightsbridge #33/R
£760 $1201 €1110 Country landscape with grazing horses and cottage (28x20cm-11x8in) s.d. board. 23-Jul-3 Grant, Worcester #499/R
£800 $1360 €1168 Evening landscape with figure and geese on a country lane (20x30cm-8x12in) s. board. 19-Nov-3 Tennants, Leyburn #1095
£800 $1456 €1168 Yorkshire town on a winters night (18x30cm-7x12in) s. 16-Jun-4 Andrew Hartley, Ilkley #1088
£1100 $2024 €1606 Extensive river landscape at sunset, with a figure in the foreground (20x31cm-8x12in) s.d.1889 board. 8-Jun-4 Bonhams, Knightsbridge #172/R est:600-800
£3100 $4960 €4526 Landscapes (75x50cm-30x20in) d.1894 pair. 17-Sep-3 Bonhams, Brooks & Langlois, Jersey #89/R est:3000-4000
Works on paper
£320 $573 €467 Shepherd with flock (17x25cm-7x10in) s. W/C. 17-Mar-4 James Thompson, Kirby Lonsdale #100/R
£380 $600 €551 Herding sheep on an autumn lane (29x43cm-11x17in) s. W/C bodycol. 24-Jul-3 Lawrence, Crewkerne #853
£500 $900 €730 River landscape (34x24cm-13x9in) s. W/C. 21-Jan-4 James Thompson, Kirby Lonsdale #188/R
£520 $941 €759 Homewards, near Kendall (30x44cm-12x17in) s. W/C. 30-Mar-4 David Duggleby, Scarborough #147/R
£540 $918 €788 Men and shire horses in the field. Figures with a cart and horses beside a river (16x24cm-6x9in) s. W/C pair. 18-Nov-3 Bonhams, Leeds #40

£630	$1141	€920	Two figures on a road. Four figures on a road. s.d.1910 W/C pair. 30-Mar-4 Stephan Welz, Johannesburg #394 est:4000-6000 (SA.R 7500)
£640	$1158	€934	Winter woodland, Leven (25x35cm-10x14in) s. W/C. 30-Mar-4 David Duggleby, Scarborough #87/R
£850	$1530	€1241	At close of day (17x25cm-7x10in) s. pencil W/C htd white. 22-Apr-4 Mellors & Kirk, Nottingham #1049
£900	$1449	€1305	Autumnal landscape with figures (33x23cm-13x9in) s. W/C pair. 13-Aug-3 Andrew Hartley, Ilkley #794
£900	$1494	€1314	Winter street scene at night (25x33cm-10x13in) s. W/C. 2-Oct-3 Mitchells, Cockermouth #836/R
£1400	$2520	€2044	Scene near Grange. Autumn (16x24cm-6x9in) s.i. W/C htd white pair. 21-Apr-4 Tennants, Leyburn #1050 est:600-800
£1400	$2520	€2044	Off to market. Across the common (16x24cm-6x9in) s.i. W/C htd white pair. 21-Apr-4 Tennants, Leyburn #1051/R est:600-800

MANNERS, William (attrib) (fl.1885-c.1910) British

£323	$550	€472	Figures along a road in an expansive landscape (51x76cm-20x30in) s. 22-Nov-3 Jackson's, Cedar Falls #19/R

MANNEVILLE, Andre (fl.1893-1922) French

Sculpture

£1067	$1931	€1600	Danseuse au tambourin (27cm-11in) s. ivory bronze. 30-Mar-4 Campo & Campo, Antwerp #64/R est:1000-1500

MANNHEIM, Jean (1863-1945) American/German

£385	$700	€562	Desert landscape with distant hills (30x41cm-12x16in) init. masonite. 7-Feb-4 Auctions by the Bay, Alameda #1591/R
£432	$800	€631	Portrait of a woman's head (51x36cm-20x14in) s. 24-Jan-4 Jeffery Burchard, Florida #84a/R
£541	$1000	€790	Portrait of Net Mender (61x48cm-24x19in) s. 24-Jan-4 Jeffery Burchard, Florida #84/R
£1156	$2000	€1688	Eternity (39x30cm-15x12in) s. i.verso canvas on board prov. 10-Dec-3 Bonhams & Butterfields, San Francisco #6225/R est:3000-5000
£1323	$2500	€1932	Figures in landscape (38x46cm-15x18in) s. board prov. 17-Feb-4 John Moran, Pasadena #116/R est:3000-5000
£1471	$2500	€2148	The rainbow (53x64cm-21x25in) s. masonite. 18-Nov-3 John Moran, Pasadena #142 est:3000-5000
£1587	$3000	€2317	The abandoned road (30x41cm-12x16in) s. canvasboard prov. 17-Feb-4 John Moran, Pasadena #38/R est:3000-4000
£1648	$3000	€2406	The New Bridge, Pasadena (30x38cm-12x15in) s. board. 15-Jun-4 John Moran, Pasadena #25 est:3000-5000
£1667	$3000	€2434	California coastal view at sunset (30x38cm-12x15in) s. masonite prov. 24-Apr-4 Weschler, Washington #612/R est:3000-5000
£1734	$3000	€2532	Yellow field with fence (30x38cm-12x15in) s. masonite prov. 10-Dec-3 Bonhams & Butterfields, San Francisco #6224/R est:3000-5000
£1852	$3500	€2704	Houses in eucalyptus landscape (30x41cm-12x16in) i. verso canvasboard. 17-Feb-4 John Moran, Pasadena #20a/R est:3000-4000
£1852	$3500	€2704	Harbour scene - Newport (30x38cm-12x15in) s. board. 17-Feb-4 John Moran, Pasadena #39/R est:2500-3500
£1852	$3500	€2704	Houses in coastal landscape (38x46cm-15x18in) s. board prov. 17-Feb-4 John Moran, Pasadena #115/R est:3000-5000
£2333	$4200	€3406	California desert landscape (30x38cm-12x15in) s. canvas on board prov. 24-Apr-4 Weschler, Washington #614/R est:3000-5000
£3297	$6000	€4814	At the dam (51x61cm-20x24in) s. prov. 15-Jun-4 John Moran, Pasadena #36 est:4000-6000
£5291	$10000	€7725	Woman/interior kitchen/green leaf vegetables (81x69cm-32x27in) s. prov. 17-Feb-4 John Moran, Pasadena #179/R est:10000-15000
£6878	$13000	€10042	Dairy farm in the Arroyo Seco (71x91cm-28x36in) s. prov. 17-Feb-4 John Moran, Pasadena #74/R est:10000-15000
£8995	$17000	€13133	Pathway to church (71x91cm-28x36in) s. prov. 17-Feb-4 John Moran, Pasadena #104a/R est:20000-30000

MANNINEN, Jaakko (1926-1985) Finnish

£403	$673	€580	From the deep (195x130cm-77x51in) s.d.61. 26-Oct-3 Bukowskis, Helsinki #410/R

MANNING, James (?) ?

£1399	$2378	€2000	Coastal landscape, boatyard (41x46cm-16x18in) s. board. 25-Nov-3 De Veres Art Auctions, Dublin #156/R est:2000-3000
£1399	$2378	€2000	Row of houses in a mountain landscape (41x51cm-16x20in) s. board. 25-Nov-3 De Veres Art Auctions, Dublin #157/R est:2000-3000

MANNIX, Max (1939-) Australian

£262	$482	€383	Have you fed the dogs (21x26cm-8x10in) s. board. 28-Jun-4 Australian Art Auctions, Sydney #94 (A.D 700)
£286	$526	€418	On tour. board. 26-Mar-4 Lawson Menzies, Sydney #2116 (A.D 700)
£298	$506	€447	24 Hour trading (24x28cm-9x11in) board. 28-Oct-3 Goodman, Sydney #261/R (A.D 720)
£321	$582	€469	Day of adventure (39x49cm-15x19in) s. board. 4-Apr-4 International Art Centre, Auckland #241/R (NZ.D 900)
£361	$604	€523	Chip 'n run (26x31cm-10x12in) s. board. 30-Jun-3 Australian Art Auctions, Sydney #89 (A.D 900)
£522	$872	€757	No one by that name here (30x37cm-12x15in) s. board. 30-Jun-3 Australian Art Auctions, Sydney #129 (A.D 1300)
£749	$1378	€1094	Up and down the creek (38x31cm-15x12in) s. board. 28-Jun-4 Australian Art Auctions, Sydney #131 (A.D 2000)

MANNUCCI, Cipriano (1882-1970) Italian

£313	$509	€450	Bowler. board. 24-Sep-3 Cambi, Genoa #1138
£503	$941	€750	Trees (30x40cm-12x16in) 26-Feb-4 Cambi, Genoa #542/R
£1039	$1860	€1517	Carneval - young woman with mask (35x45cm-14x18in) s.d.1939. 22-Mar-4 Philippe Schuler, Zurich #4452 est:1500-2000 (S.FR 2400)
£1200	$2148	€1800	Jeune Venitienne (56x40cm-22x16in) s.i.d.1925 panel. 15-May-4 De Vuyst, Lokeren #212/R est:1300-1600
£1275	$2385	€1900	Vase of flowers (50x60cm-20x24in) 26-Feb-4 Cambi, Genoa #533/R est:400-500
£3521	$6092	€5000	Lady in white (190x130cm-75x51in) s. 11-Dec-3 Christie's, Rome #148/R est:5000-8000

Works on paper

£299	$500	€437	Cellist (47x64cm-19x25in) s. W/C. 16-Nov-3 Bonhams & Butterfields, Los Angeles #7028/R
£1600	$2960	€2336	Minuette (57x78cm-22x31in) s. W/C. 14-Jul-4 Sotheby's, Olympia #203/R est:1000-1500

MANO, Ugo (?) ?

£216	$400	€315	Sorrento, Naples (30x46cm-12x18in) s. 13-Mar-4 DeFina, Austinburg #788/R

MANOLIDIS, Theodoros (1940-) Greek

£5500	$9845	€8030	Still life (55x45cm-22x18in) s. 10-May-4 Sotheby's, Olympia #65/R est:3000-5000

MANOLO (1872-1945) Spanish

Sculpture

£2133	$3819	€3200	Portrait of woman (24cm-9in) bronze wooden socle. 15-May-4 Van Ham, Cologne #672/R est:1000

MANOTTI, Luigi (20th C) Italian

£500	$925	€730	At the Customs House, Venice (41x51cm-16x20in) s. panel. 15-Jan-4 Christie's, Kensington #959/R

MANRIQUE, Cesar (1920-1992) Spanish

£800	$1456	€1200	Personage (30x24cm-12x9in) s. oil acrylic gouache ink paper. 29-Jun-4 Segre, Madrid #215/R
£1067	$1952	€1600	Untitled (45x47cm-18x19in) s.d.75 oil on cloth collage board. 4-Jun-4 Lempertz, Koln #292/R est:1600
£1067	$1952	€1600	Untitled (57x39cm-22x15in) s.d.89 oil on material collage board. 4-Jun-4 Lempertz, Koln #294/R est:1600
£5467	$10004	€8200	Rotura (81x100cm-32x39in) s.d.89 s.i.d.89 verso acrylic sand prov.exhib. 4-Jun-4 Lempertz, Koln #293/R est:7000-7500
£10870	$17826	€15000	Enterrado en fango (92x73cm-36x29in) s.d.78 s.i.d.verso. 27-May-3 Durán, Madrid #297/R est:15000

Works on paper

£6333	$11526	€9500	Pintura No 67 (73x92cm-29x36in) s.d.60 mixed media canvas. 30-Jun-4 Calmels Cohen, Paris #70/R est:6500-8000

MANSCHGO, Johann (attrib) (1800-1867) Austrian

£1579	$2905	€2400	Portrait of nobleman and woman (78x62cm-31x24in) i. stretcher pair. 24-Jun-4 Dr Fritz Nagel, Stuttgart #732/R est:2500

MANSER, Albert (1937-) Swiss

£383	$659	€559	Looking after pigs in the Alps (16x12cm-6x5in) s. board. 8-Dec-3 Philippe Schuler, Zurich #4050 (S.FR 850)
£860	$1462	€1256	Cats (22x17cm-9x7in) s.d.74 pavatex prov. 18-Nov-3 Hans Widmer, St Gallen #1253 est:1500-2800 (S.FR 1900)
£973	$1654	€1421	Kittens playing (21x17cm-8x7in) s.d.73. 18-Nov-3 Hans Widmer, St Gallen #1251 est:1300-2600 (S.FR 2150)
£1086	$1846	€1586	Winter (16x31cm-6x12in) s.d.73 pavatex. 18-Nov-3 Hans Widmer, St Gallen #1250 est:1500-2800 (S.FR 2400)
£1164	$2083	€1699	Cattle in the snow (20x30cm-8x12in) s. panel. 14-May-4 Dobiaschofsky, Bern #238/R est:2800 (S.FR 2700)
£1166	$1947	€1702	Alpine descent (15x22cm-6x9in) s. pavatex prov. 24-Oct-3 Hans Widmer, St Gallen #47/R est:1800-3500 (S.FR 2600)
£1176	$2000	€1717	Winter evening (17x32cm-7x13in) s.d.73 pavatex prov. 18-Nov-3 Hans Widmer, St Gallen #1252/R est:1500-2800 (S.FR 2600)
£1293	$2315	€1888	Cattle going up the mountains with wedding party (16x27cm-6x11in) s.d.83 board. 14-May-4 Dobiaschofsky, Bern #236/R est:2800 (S.FR 3000)
£1345	$2247	€1964	Winter landscape near Appenzell (44x58cm-17x23in) s.d.72 pavatex. 24-Oct-3 Hans Widmer, St Gallen #48/R est:3000-5500 (S.FR 3000)
£1379	$2469	€2013	Autumn baptism (24x129cm-9x51in) s.d.1981 board. 14-May-4 Dobiaschofsky, Bern #237/R est:2600 (S.FR 3200)
£1441	$2623	€2104	New Year's Eve parade (17x32cm-7x13in) s. panel prov. 16-Jun-4 Fischer, Luzern #2264/R est:1800-2500 (S.FR 3300)
£1570	$2621	€2292	Winter landscape near Appenzell (25x55cm-10x22in) s.d.70 pavatex. 24-Oct-3 Hans Widmer, St Gallen #139/R est:3500-6000 (S.FR 3500)
£1570	$2621	€2292	Winter evening (21x31cm-8x12in) s.d.74 pavatex. 24-Oct-3 Hans Widmer, St Gallen #136/R est:2000-3500 (S.FR 3500)
£1948	$3487	€2844	Winter - baptism (26x56cm-10x22in) s. masonite prov. 22-Mar-4 Philippe Schuler, Zurich #4346 est:2300-2600 (S.FR 4500)
£2242	$3744	€3273	Cattle coming down from the alpine meadows in autumn (25x41cm-10x16in) s.d.73 pavatex prov. 24-Oct-3 Hans Widmer, St Gallen #2/R est:2500-4500 (S.FR 5000)

MANSER, Percy L (1886-1973) American

£447	$800	€653	Pioneer's cabin (46x56cm-18x22in) s. board. 16-Mar-4 Matthew's, Oregon #108/R
£950	$1700	€1387	Winter on the Columbia (56x71cm-22x28in) s. canvasboard. 16-Mar-4 Matthew's, Oregon #110/R est:2000-3000
£1069	$1700	€1561	Mountainscape in winter (76x91cm-30x36in) s. 5-May-3 O'Gallerie, Oregon #781/R est:1500-2000

MANSFELD, Heinrich August (1816-1901) Austrian

£1824	$3211	€2700	Remembrance - interior with two figures (37x29cm-15x11in) s.d.1845 panel prov. 22-May-4 Lempertz, Koln #1558/R est:3000

MANSFELD, Josef (1819-1894) Austrian

£1389	$2361	€2000	Hunting still life (31x26cm-12x10in) s.d.1883 panel. 28-Oct-3 Dorotheum, Vienna #253/R est:2200-2500
£1974	$3632	€3000	Music hour (40x32cm-16x13in) s.d.1854 canvas on canvas. 22-Jun-4 Wiener Kunst Auktionen, Vienna #19/R est:3000

MANSFELD, Moritz (fl.1850-1890) Austrian
£400 $720 €600 Still life on table (32x25cm-13x10in) s.d.1889 panel. 26-Apr-4 Rieber, Stuttgart #1143/R
£690 $1152 €1000 Still life with silver jug, fruit and books (25x32cm-10x13in) s.d.1882 panel. 9-Jul-3 Hugo Ruef, Munich #141/R

MANSFIELD, Louise (1876-?) American
£1000 $1640 €1460 Collecting shells (50x76cm-20x30in) s. board. 4-Jun-3 John Ross, Belfast #121
Works on paper
£252 $400 €368 Will of the wisps (69x43cm-27x17in) s. pastel. 4-May-3 William Jenack, New York #258

MANSHIP, John Paul (1927-2000) American
£265 $425 €387 Coastal view (38x66cm-15x26in) s.d.50. 21-Sep-3 Grogan, Boston #88/R

MANSHIP, Paul Howard (1885-1966) American
Sculpture
£966 $1700 €1410 Sagittarius (15x15cm-6x6in) s. bronze medallion exec.c.1930. 23-May-4 Treadway Gallery, Cincinnati #747/R est:1000-1500
£46512 $80000 €67908 Briseis (55cm-22in) i.d.1916 pat bronze prov.exhib. 4-Dec-3 Christie's, Rockefeller NY #85/R est:40000-60000
£104651 $180000 €152790 Flight of night (65cm-26in) i.d.1916 pat bronze. 4-Dec-3 Christie's, Rockefeller NY #86/R est:100000-150000

MANSKIRCH, Franz Joseph (1770-1830) German
£1914 $3100 €2775 Romantic landscape with figures (65x53cm-26x21in) s. panel. 4-Aug-3 Rasmussen, Vejle #200/R est:20000-30000 (D.KR 20000)

MANSO, Leo (1914-1993) American
£276 $450 €403 Darius (51x51cm-20x20in) s. acrylic. 19-Jul-3 Outer Cape Auctions, Provincetown #33/R
£795 $1400 €1161 Untitled (130x130cm-51x51in) acrylic painted c.1970. 23-May-4 Treadway Gallery, Cincinnati #752/R

MANSON, James (1791-1862) British
Works on paper
£700 $1141 €1022 Village scene in Dhampur. View of the Himalayas (28x38cm-11x15in) s.d.1826 i.verso pencil W/C gum arabic blk ink prov.exhib. two. 24-Sep-3 Christie's, London #46/R

MANSON, James Bolivar (1879-1945) British
£380 $711 €570 Windmill, Storrington (25x36cm-10x14in) s.d.1911 wood panel. 22-Jul-4 Gorringes, Lewes #1893
£380 $711 €570 Jean Manson, the artist's daughter (36x25cm-14x10in) wood panel. 22-Jul-4 Gorringes, Lewes #1894/R

MANSON, James Bolivar (attrib) (1879-1945) British
£400 $736 €584 Portrait of a young boy in a green shirt (35x25cm-14x10in) board. 23-Jun-4 Bonhams, Bury St Edmunds #407

MANSON, John (?) Irish
£250 $410 €365 Collecting shells (25x35cm-10x14in) s. board. 4-Jun-3 John Ross, Belfast #184

MANSOUROFF, Paul (1896-1983) French
£3691 $6533 €5500 Construction (100x24cm-39x9in) s.i.d.1965-64 panel prov. 28-Apr-4 Artcurial Briest, Paris #341/R est:6000-8000
£15385 $26462 €22000 Composition geometrique (93x31cm-37x12in) s. panel. 4-Dec-3 Piasa, Paris #98/R est:2000-3000
Works on paper
£470 $874 €700 Cinq spheres (25x8cm-10x3in) s. graphite col crayon. 2-Mar-4 Artcurial Briest, Paris #69
£1049 $1804 €1500 Composition (37x14cm-15x6in) s.d.51 graphite. 4-Dec-3 Piasa, Paris #99/R est:400-500
£1189 $2021 €1700 Composition (24x13cm-9x5in) s. chl pastel. 23-Nov-3 Cornette de St.Cyr, Paris #231/R est:120-150
£1399 $2378 €2000 Composition (25x13cm-10x5in) s. chl pastel. 23-Nov-3 Cornette de St.Cyr, Paris #232/R est:120-150
£3020 $5618 €4500 Composition (64x50cm-25x20in) s.d.59-60 pastel col crayon. 2-Mar-4 Artcurial Briest, Paris #68/R est:2000-3000

MANSSON, Per (1896-1949) Swedish
£369 $601 €539 Landscape (50x42cm-20x17in) s. 29-Sep-3 Lilla Bukowskis, Stockholm #110 (S.KR 4800)
£1208 $2054 €1764 Southern mountain town with girl and pigeons (62x49cm-24x19in) 5-Nov-3 AB Stockholms Auktionsverk #754/R est:12000-15000 (S.KR 16000)
£1885 $3394 €2752 Spanish landscape, Majorca (74x56cm-29x22in) s.i.d.1922. 26-Apr-4 Bukowskis, Stockholm #108/R est:20000-25000 (S.KR 26000)

MANSUETI, Giovanni (?-1527) Italian
£27000 $45900 €39420 Madonna and Child (59x48cm-23x19in) panel. 29-Oct-3 Christie's, London #91/R est:12000-18000

MANSUROFF, Pavel (1896-1984) Russian
Works on paper
£750 $1343 €1095 Abstract composition (31x23cm-12x9in) s.i.d.59 pen pastel. 26-May-4 Sotheby's, Olympia #503/R

MANTEGAZZA, Giacomo (1853-1920) Italian
£349 $600 €510 Standing lady (28x15cm-11x6in) s. panel. 7-Dec-3 Grogan, Boston #27/R
£12319 $20203 €17000 Presenting the heir (89x122cm-35x48in) s.d.1888. 27-May-3 Finarte Semenzato, Milan #59/R est:17000-20000
£12941 $22000 €18894 Presenting the new prince (86x124cm-34x49in) s.i. canvas on board. 19-Nov-3 Bonhams & Butterfields, San Francisco #49/R
£18310 $31676 €26000 Diogenes (149x87cm-59x34in) s.i. 10-Dec-3 Sotheby's, Milan #114/R est:30000-40000

MANTELET, Albert Goguet (1858-?) French
£276 $461 €400 La loi Fuller (73x51cm-29x20in) panel. 12-Nov-3 Chassaing Rivet, Toulouse #210

MANTLEY, Thekla (19th C) ?
£376 $688 €549 Still life of flowers on marble ledge (12x17cm-5x7in) i. verso panel. 7-Jun-4 Museumsbygningen, Copenhagen #50 (D.KR 4200)

MANTON, G Grenville (?-1932) British
£1400 $2562 €2044 Portrait of a seated lady wearing a gold satin dress (110x83cm-43x33in) s.d.1890. 6-Jul-4 Bonhams, Knightsbridge #254/R est:1500-2500

MANTON, Maria (1915-) French?
£578 $1052 €850 Kalamaki (45x54cm-18x21in) s.d.68 canvas on board prov. 3-Feb-4 Christie's, Amsterdam #633/R

MANTOVANI, Guido (1916-) Italian
£750 $1418 €1095 Autumno (49x70cm-19x28in) s. 19-Feb-4 Christie's, Kensington #170/R

MANTOVANI, Luigi (1880-1957) Italian
£600 $1074 €900 Duomo Square, Milan (20x30cm-8x12in) s. board. 12-May-4 Stadion, Trieste #666/R
£700 $1288 €1050 Little market (23x32cm-9x13in) s. board. 14-Jun-4 Sant Agostino, Torino #422/R
£1200 $2208 €1800 Milan Duomo (26x36cm-10x14in) s. board. 14-Jun-4 Sant Agostino, Torino #423/R est:1000-1400
£1408 $2437 €2000 Bellagio, Italy (35x44cm-14x17in) s.d.938 canvas on cardboard. 9-Dec-3 Finarte Semenzato, Milan #12/R est:2000-2200
£1946 $3484 €2900 The Duomo in Milan (44x53cm-17x21in) s. cardboard. 25-May-4 Finarte Semenzato, Milan #3/R est:3300-3500

MANTOVANI, Rudy (1973-) Indonesian?
£1961 $3549 €2863 Terbatas biru (145x145cm-57x57in) s.d.2003 acrylic. 4-Apr-4 Sotheby's, Singapore #182/R est:3000-4000 (S.D 6000)
Works on paper
£1042 $1740 €1521 Menghembus Angin (145x360cm-57x142in) s.d.2002 mixed media canvas. 12-Oct-3 Sotheby's, Singapore #196/R est:3000-4000 (S.D 3000)

MANTOVANI-GUTTI, Rosina (19th C) Italian
Works on paper
£331 $603 €500 Portrait of three small children (32x46cm-13x18in) s. mixed media. 19-Jun-4 Bergmann, Erlangen #829

MANTOVANO, Francesco (fl.1636-1663) Italian
£22000 $38060 €32120 Still life of tulips, roses and other flowers in a blue and white ceramic vase (63x49cm-25x19in) 11-Dec-3 Sotheby's, London #229/R est:12000-18000

MANTUA SCHOOL (15th C) Italian
Sculpture
£6200000 $10726001 €9052000 Mars, Venus, Cupid and Vulcan (42x42cm-17x17in) i. dark brown pat bronze roundel. 11-Dec-3 Christie's, London #20/R est:1000000-1500000

MANTUA SCHOOL (16th C) Italian
£16000 $29280 €23360 Bacchanalian scene (31x55cm-12x22in) panel. 8-Jul-4 Sotheby's, London #302/R est:15000-20000

MANTYNEN, Jussi (1886-1978) Finnish
Sculpture
£1042 $1740 €1500 Bear (9cm-4in) s.d.1967 bronze. 23-Oct-3 Hagelstam, Helsinki #750/R est:650
£1067 $1909 €1600 Oxen (25cm-10in) s.d.1921 bronze. 15-May-4 Hagelstam, Helsinki #6/R est:1500
£1268 $2193 €1800 Calves in spring (25cm-10in) s. bronze prov.lit. 13-Dec-3 Hagelstam, Helsinki #5/R est:1500
£1733 $3103 €2600 Cow and calf (24cm-9in) s.d.1922 bronze. 15-May-4 Hagelstam, Helsinki #7/R est:2000
£1846 $3175 €2695 Bear cub (19cm-7in) s.d.1936 dark pat.bronze. 3-Dec-3 AB Stockholms Auktionsverk #2638/R est:30000-35000 (S.KR 24000)
£1848 $3307 €2698 Lemminkainen and hiisis elk (38cm-15in) s.d.1917 dark pat.bronze. 25-May-4 Bukowskis, Stockholm #307/R est:15000-20000 (S.KR 25000)
£2000 $3580 €3000 Eagle (33cm-13in) s.d.1952 bronze. 15-May-4 Hagelstam, Helsinki #8/R est:3000
£2113 $3655 €3000 Lynx scenting danger (19x21cm-7x8in) s.d.1940 bronze lit. 13-Dec-3 Hagelstam, Helsinki #4/R est:2000
£2231 $3837 €3257 Lynx (19cm-7in) s.d.1940 bronze. 7-Dec-3 Uppsala Auktionskammare, Uppsala #358/R est:20000-25000 (S.KR 29000)
£2324 $4020 €3300 Conventional lynx (32cm-13in) s.d.1940 bronze Cast Pettersson prov.lit. 13-Dec-3 Hagelstam, Helsinki #3/R est:4000

£2365 $4233 €3500 Small bear (19cm-7in) s.d.1936 bronze lit. 8-May-4 Bukowskis, Helsinki #24/R est:3500-4000
£2462 $4234 €3595 Lynx with young (28cm-11in) s.d.1944 pat.bronze. 3-Dec-3 AB Stockholms Auktionsverk #2637/R est:30000-35000 (S.KR 32000)
£2535 $4056 €3600 Lioness (35cm-14in) s.d.1957 bronze Cast Pettersson. 18-Sep-3 Hagelstam, Helsinki #734/R est:2500
£2809 $5027 €4101 Cranes (42cm-17in) s. pat.bronze Cast A Pettersson. 25-May-4 Bukowskis, Stockholm #306/R est:15000-20000 (S.KR 38000)
£2817 $4873 €4000 Bear cubs playing (31cm-12in) s.indis.d. carved stone prov. 13-Dec-3 Hagelstam, Helsinki #7/R est:3000
£3217 $5469 €4600 Young lynx (22cm-9in) s.d.1940 bronze. 29-Nov-3 Bukowskis, Helsinki #1/R est:4200-4700
£3333 $5967 €5000 Woodland atmosphere - young elk (24cm-9in) s.d.1927 bronze lit. 15-May-4 Hagelstam, Helsinki #9/R est:5000
£3378 $6047 €5000 Elk cow (36cm-14in) s.d.1930 bronze lit. 8-May-4 Bukowskis, Helsinki #9/R est:5000-5500
£3427 $5825 €4900 The old man - a bear (23cm-9in) s.d.1941 bronze lit. 29-Nov-3 Bukowskis, Helsinki #11/R est:4000-4500
£3944 $6823 €5600 Excelsior (53cm-21in) s.d.1940 bronze. 13-Dec-3 Hagelstam, Helsinki #6/R est:4500
£4196 $7133 €6000 The Dever lynx (21cm-8in) s.d.1945 bronze lit. 29-Nov-3 Bukowskis, Helsinki #20/R est:4000-5000
£4527 $8103 €6700 Swans about to fly (28cm-11in) s.d.1955 bronze. 8-May-4 Bukowskis, Helsinki #21/R est:4500-5000
£5986 $10356 €8500 Bear by ant-hill (42x38cm-17x15in) s.d.1927 mahogany prov.lit. 13-Dec-3 Hagelstam, Helsinki #2/R est:7000
£7692 $13231 €11230 Excelsior (128cm-50in) s.d.1943 green pat.bronze Cast Sthlms lit. 2-Dec-3 Bukowskis, Stockholm #240/R est:100000-125000 (S.KR 100000)
£8869 $15876 €12949 Irritated lynx - the shah's lynx (46cm-18in) s.d.1938 green pat.bronze Cast A Pettersson exhib.lit. 25-May-4 Bukowskis, Stockholm #305/R est:50000-60000 (S.KR 120000)

MANTZ, Werner (1901-1983) German
Photographs
£3986 $6536 €5500 Untitled (22x14cm-9x6in) s.d. vintage silver gelatin on board. 30-May-3 Villa Grisebach, Berlin #1278/R est:6000-8000
£3986 $6536 €5500 Sinn Department Store, Gelsenkirch, Architect: Bruno Paul (16x23cm-6x9in) vintage silver gelatin. 30-May-3 Villa Grisebach, Berlin #1279/R est:6000-8000

MANUEL, David (1940-) American
Sculpture
£1486 $2750 €2170 John Wayne. s.i. bronze. 14-Jan-4 Dallas Auction Gallery, Dallas #160/R est:5000-10000

MANUEL, Victor (1897-1969) Cuban
£2647 $4500 €3865 Retrato de mujer - Portrait of a woman (25x20cm-10x8in) s. board painted c.1945 prov. 18-Nov-3 Christie's, Rockefeller NY #148/R est:4000-6000
£3529 $6000 €5152 Mujer - Woman (50x40cm-20x16in) s. cardboard painted c.1945 prov. 18-Nov-3 Christie's, Rockefeller NY #147/R est:8000-10000
£70588 $120000 €103058 Mujeres en el balcon - Women on the balcony (128x96cm-50x38in) s. panel painted c.1945 prov. 18-Nov-3 Christie's, Rockefeller NY #44/R est:100000-150000

MANUWA (1917-1979) Australian
Works on paper
£508 $803 €737 Legendary stingray (76x41cm-30x16in) i.verso earth pigments eucalyptus bark prov.exhib.lit. 28-Jul-3 Sotheby's, Paddington #255 est:800-1200 (A.D 1250)

MANVILLE, Elsie (1922-) American
£276 $500 €403 Brown eggs, breadsticks and pasta (112x122cm-44x48in) 16-Apr-4 American Auctioneer #262/R

MANZ, Curt (1900-1989) Swiss
£339 $577 €495 Cerises, melon, pot bleu (26x45cm-10x18in) s. 28-Nov-3 Zofingen, Switzerland #3058/R (S.FR 750)
£430 $731 €628 Irises (65x46cm-26x18in) s. 28-Nov-3 Zofingen, Switzerland #3059 (S.FR 950)

MANZ, Ewald (20th C) German?
£559 $962 €800 Bathing in the pond (55x55cm-22x22in) s.d.1907. 5-Dec-3 Bolland & Marotz, Bremen #843/R

MANZ-MONDIN, Yvonne (1888-1967) French
£173 $310 €253 Still life with apple blossom (33x24cm-13x9in) s. 22-Mar-4 Philippe Schuler, Zurich #6036 (S.FR 400)

MANZANA-PISSARRO, Georges (1871-1961) French
£3800 $6992 €5548 Au parc (25x20cm-10x8in) s.d.1938 board. 24-Mar-4 Sotheby's, Olympia #49/R est:2000-3000
£3916 $6540 €5600 Vue de ma fenetre (46x54cm-18x21in) s.d.1953 masonite. 29-Jun-3 St-Germain-en-Laye Encheres #8/R
£4500 $8280 €6570 La maison (54x65cm-21x26in) s. 24-Mar-4 Sotheby's, Olympia #64/R est:4000-6000
£5634 $9352 €8000 Jardin a Rauze (54x65cm-21x26in) s.d.1905. 15-Jun-3 Peron, Melun #167
Works on paper
£420 $713 €600 La voyante (17x21cm-7x8in) s.i. pencil col crayon. 27-Nov-3 Millon & Associes, Paris #75
£671 $1248 €1000 Paysage pres de la riviere (22x19cm-9x7in) s.d.1910 W/C. 2-Mar-4 Artcurial Briest, Paris #16
£699 $1189 €1000 Poisson chinois (12x20cm-5x8in) s.d.1930 W/C htd gold silver. 27-Nov-3 Millon & Associes, Paris #71/R
£2098 $3566 €3000 Leda et le cygne (49x32cm-19x13in) s. wash chl gouache htd gold. 24-Nov-3 Tajan, Paris #9/R est:3000-4000
£2465 $4264 €3500 Baigneuse au bord de l'eau (44x34cm-17x13in) s. W/C htd gold. 12-Dec-3 Piasa, Paris #174 est:2000-3000

MANZANET, Riccardo (19th C) Spanish
£1206 $2013 €1700 Landscape (70x116cm-28x46in) s. 20-Oct-3 Durán, Madrid #58/R est:1700
£2685 $4993 €4000 Seascape (70x116cm-28x46in) s. 2-Mar-4 Ansorena, Madrid #98/R est:4000

MANZANI, Luca (20th C) Spanish
£789 $1429 €1200 Sailing boats (44x31cm-17x12in) s. board. 14-Apr-4 Ansorena, Madrid #259/R

MANZINI, Ferdinando (1817-1886) Italian?
Works on paper
£935 $1534 €1300 Modena Accademy (26x39cm-10x15in) W/C. 5-Jun-3 Adma, Formigine #880

MANZON, Serge (c.1935-1998) French
Sculpture
£1712 $2911 €2500 Femme (130x100cm-51x39in) pipes metal. 5-Nov-3 Pierre Berge, Paris #29/R est:1500-2000
£1849 $3144 €2700 Profil de femme (73x35x21cm-29x14x8in) painted metal. 5-Nov-3 Pierre Berge, Paris #28/R est:1000-1500
£2192 $3726 €3200 Naja (124x36x60cm-49x14x24in) painted metal. 5-Nov-3 Pierre Berge, Paris #27/R
£2397 $4075 €3500 Composition (173x40x40cm-68x16x16in) painted metal. 5-Nov-3 Pierre Berge, Paris #45/R est:2000-3000
£2603 $4425 €3800 Visage (79x100cm-31x39in) painted metal. 5-Nov-3 Pierre Berge, Paris #44/R est:1000-1500
£2740 $4658 €4000 Vitesse (126cm-50in) painted metal. 5-Nov-3 Pierre Berge, Paris #37/R est:1000-1500
£2877 $4890 €4200 Danseuse (53x56cm-21x22in) painted metal wood. 5-Nov-3 Pierre Berge, Paris #36/R est:1000-1500
£2877 $4890 €4200 Arcs (66x50x25cm-26x20x10in) painted metal. 5-Nov-3 Pierre Berge, Paris #43/R est:1500
£3288 $5589 €4800 Femme agenouillee (119x32x60cm-47x13x24in) painted metal. 5-Nov-3 Pierre Berge, Paris #22/R est:2000-3000
£3288 $5589 €4800 Personnage (174x110cm-69x43in) painted metal. 5-Nov-3 Pierre Berge, Paris #31/R est:3000-4000
£3425 $5822 €5000 Deux profils de femmes (77x48x18cm-30x19x7in) painted metal. 5-Nov-3 Pierre Berge, Paris #32/R est:2000
£3904 $6637 €5700 Outil de precision (80x80x30cm-31x31x12in) painted metal. 5-Nov-3 Pierre Berge, Paris #23/R est:2000-3000
£4795 $8151 €7000 Composition (215x130x55cm-85x51x22in) painted metal. 5-Nov-3 Pierre Berge, Paris #38/R est:3000-4000
£24658 $41918 €36000 Screen (189x265cm-74x104in) painted metal. 5-Nov-3 Pierre Berge, Paris #30/R est:4000-5000
£26027 $44247 €38000 Bar (81x81x81cm-32x32x32in) chromed steel. 5-Nov-3 Pierre Berge, Paris #46/R est:3000-4000

MANZONE, Giuseppe (1887-1983) Italian
£4653 $7910 €6700 Countryside lord (80x60cm-31x24in) s. 1-Nov-3 Meeting Art, Vercelli #431/R est:2500

MANZONI, Piero (1933-1963) Italian
£42667 $76373 €64000 Paradoxus Smith (100x130cm-39x51in) s.d.57 panel. 15-May-4 Van Ham, Cologne #773/R est:80000
Sculpture
£6993 $11888 €10000 Egg (7x8x6cm-3x3x2in) s.i.d.60 ink egg wooden box prov.lit. 25-Nov-3 Sotheby's, Milan #244/R est:8000-10000
£10615 $19000 €15498 Linea, m 5,65 (22x565cm-9x222in) s.i.d.5,65 verso ink rolled paper cardboard cylinder prov.lit. 14-May-4 Phillips, New York #262/R est:20000-30000
£27439 $45000 €40061 Achrome (21x14cm-8x6in) s.d.59 verso twelve foam rubber parts prov.exhib.lit. 28-May-3 Sotheby's, Amsterdam #23/R est:60000-80000
£75000 $125250 €109500 Achrome (45x39cm-18x15in) fibre synthetic board in artist's box exec.1961 prov.exhib.lit. 20-Oct-3 Sotheby's, London #22/R est:45000
Works on paper
£12291 $22000 €17945 Line (60x50cm-24x20in) s. ink prov. 14-May-4 Phillips, New York #257/R est:15000-20000
£15385 $26462 €22000 Impronte (50x60cm-20x24in) s. artist's fingerprints executed 1961 prov.exhib.lit. 2-Dec-3 Sotheby's, Amsterdam #168/R est:14000-16000
£16000 $29440 €24000 Artist's breath (18x18cm-7x7in) mixed media board exec.1960 prov.lit. 14-Jun-4 Porro, Milan #56/R est:16000-18000
£20979 $35664 €30000 Achrome (11x10cm-4x4in) s.d.61 cotton wool cardboard lit. 28-Nov-3 Farsetti, Prato #376/R est:30000-35000
£150838 $270000 €220223 Achrome (60x51cm-24x20in) s.d.58 stretcher kaolin on canvas prov.lit. 13-May-4 Phillips, New York #38/R est:250000-350000
£200000 $364000 €292000 Achrome (55x46cm-22x18in) kaolin canvas exec 1960 prov.exhib.lit. 5-Feb-4 Sotheby's, London #9/R est:200000-300000
£251497 $420000 €367186 Achrome (50x61cm-20x24in) kaolin exec 1960 prov.exhib.lit. 11-Nov-3 Christie's, Rockefeller NY #37/R est:300000-400000
£400000 $736000 €584000 Achrome (74x94cm-29x37in) kaolin on canvas executed 1958 prov.exhib.lit. 23-Jun-4 Sotheby's, London #20/R est:400000-500000
£480000 $801600 €700800 Achrome (100x80cm-39x31in) kaolin on canvas exec.1959 prov.exhib.lit. 20-Oct-3 Sotheby's, London #13/R est:450000
£480000 $801600 €700800 Achrome (62x82cm-24x32in) kaolin canvas exec.c.1959 prov.exhib.lit. 21-Oct-3 Christie's, London #28/R est:250000-350000
£780000 $1302600 €1138800 Achrome (60x80cm-24x31in) kaolin on canvas exec.1959 prov.exhib.lit. 20-Oct-3 Sotheby's, London #14/R est:450000

MANZU, Giacomo (1908-1991) Italian
Sculpture
£6000 $10020 €8760 La pace (42x60cm-17x24in) st. bronze relief executed 1968 prov. 21-Oct-3 Sotheby's, London #97/R est:8000-12000
£6587 $11000 €9617 Mother and child (43cm-17in) bronze. 17-Oct-3 Du Mouchelle, Detroit #2138/R est:12000-15000
£7000 $12880 €10220 Testa Di Donna (18cm-7in) s. bronze prov. 24-Mar-4 Sotheby's, Olympia #141/R est:7000-9000

£9000	$16380	€13140	Pattinatrice (50cm-20in) s. st.f.Maf dark brown pat bronze. 3-Feb-4 Christie's, London #230/R est:12000-18000
£11377	$19000	€16610	Head of a young man (37cm-15in) s.st.f.MAFM Milano brown pat bronze sold with base. 7-Oct-3 Sotheby's, New York #331 est:10000-15000
£12353	$21000	€18035	La famiglia nel lavoro e nel risparmio (33x93cm-13x37in) st.sig. brown pat bronze relief st.f.Manz NFMM prov. 5-Nov-3 Christie's, Rockefeller NY #293/R est:25000-35000
£16216	$28541	€24000	Giulia and Mileto on the carriage (30x79x34cm-12x31x13in) st.sig. bronze exec.1967. 24-May-4 Christie's, Milan #207/R est:22000-28000
£17000	$30940	€24820	Fanciulla - girl (81cm-32in) bronze st.f.NFMM prov. 4-Feb-4 Sotheby's, London #341/R est:15000-20000
£23448	$39159	€34000	Chair (48x28x32cm-19x11x13in) s.verso bronze lit. 17-Nov-3 Sant Agostino, Torino #257/R est:35000-45000
£28000	$51520	€40880	Strip-tease (69cm-27in) st.sig. bronze st.f.NFMM exec 1965 prov.exhib. 22-Jun-4 Sotheby's, London #282/R est:18000-25000
£29412	$50000	€42942	Busto di Inge (120cm-47in) st.sig. brown pat bronze st.f.MANZ NFMM prov. 5-Nov-3 Christie's, Rockefeller NY #294/R est:40000-60000
£40000	$73600	€58400	Ballerina, passo de danza (91cm-36in) st.sig. brown pat. bronze conceived 1969 unique st.f. Manzu. 23-Jun-4 Christie's, London #241/R est:35000-45000
£44118	$75000	€64412	Cardinale seduto (44cm-17in) st.sig. brown pat bronze cast 1960 st.f.Manzu. 5-Nov-3 Christie's, Rockefeller NY #354/R est:60000-80000
£77500	$129425	€113150	Cardinale (91cm-36in) s.num.1/3 brown pat bronze exec.c.1968 st.f.Manzu. 21-Oct-3 Christie's, London #15/R est:80000-120000
£100000	$167000	€146000	Cardinal (72cm-28in) st.f.NFMM bronze exec.1968 prov. 20-Oct-3 Sotheby's, London #8/R est:120000
£101449	$166377	€140000	Ragazza sdraiata (138x135x54cm-54x53x21in) bronze lit. 31-May-3 Farsetti, Prato #714/R est:140000-170000
£134078	$240000	€195754	Cardinale Seduto (111cm-44in) st.s. brown pat bronze cast 1982 prov. 5-May-4 Christie's, Rockefeller NY #324/R est:200000-300000

Works on paper

£1655	$2764	€2400	Study for war (24x32cm-9x13in) s. ink exec.1960 lit. 17-Nov-3 Sant Agostino, Torino #192/R est:2500-3500
£1748	$2972	€2500	Botanical studies (29x16cm-11x6in) s.d.1944 Chinese ink set of 3. 25-Nov-3 Sotheby's, Milan #78/R est:3000-4000
£1884	$3090	€2600	Nude (58x43cm-23x17in) s. chl prov. 27-May-3 Sotheby's, Milan #85/R est:1000-1500
£2069	$3455	€3000	Conversation (34x24cm-13x9in) s.d.31 pencil. 13-Nov-3 Finarte Semenzato, Rome #199/R est:3000-3500
£4362	$7809	€6500	Cardinal (92x63cm-36x25in) s. chl water. 29-May-4 Farsetti, Prato #423/R est:6000-7000

MANZUR, David (1929-) Colombian

£950	$1700	€1387	Flowers (80x39cm-31x15in) s.d.61. 14-May-4 Skinner, Boston #409/R est:800-1200

MAO LIZI (1950-) Chinese

£3556	$6401	€5192	Door with graffiti (73x65cm-29x26in) s. board. 25-Apr-4 Christie's, Hong Kong #745/R est:25000-35000 (HK.D 50000)

MAPPLETHORPE, Robert (1946-1989) American

Photographs

£1946	$3250	€2841	Agapanthus (35x35cm-14x14in) s.d.1980 num.3/15 photo prov. 17-Oct-3 Sotheby's, New York #288/R est:4000-6000
£1977	$3500	€2886	Flower, tulip, 1983 (55x45cm-22x18in) s.num.27/40 photogravure. 27-Apr-4 Christie's, Rockefeller NY #193/R est:5000-7000
£2133	$3925	€3200	Femme denudee (50x40cm-20x16in) s. num.2/10 s.d.198 verso photograph. 11-Jun-4 Pierre Berge, Paris #13/R est:1500-2000
£2210	$4000	€3227	Self portrait (20x20cm-8x8in) s.num.23/25 gelatin silver print prov.lit. 19-Apr-4 Bonhams & Butterfields, San Francisco #450/R est:3000-4000
£2210	$4000	€3227	Clifton (38x38cm-15x15in) s.d.1981 num.4/10 gelatin silver print prov. 19-Apr-4 Bonhams & Butterfields, San Francisco #451/R est:4000-6000
£2275	$3800	€3322	Freesias in a bowl, from the Flowers portfolio (55x45cm-22x18in) s.num. 2/10 photogravure. 20-Oct-3 Christie's, Rockefeller NY #244/R est:4000-6000
£2395	$4000	€3497	Dollar bill (49x58cm-19x23in) s.d.1987 num.1/2 photo. 17-Oct-3 Sotheby's, New York #289/R est:5000-7000
£2695	$4500	€3935	Doris Saatchi (50x40cm-20x16in) s.i.d.1983 verso num.1 gelatin silver print one of 10 prov.lit. 17-Oct-3 Phillips, New York #243/R est:5000-7000
£2778	$5000	€4056	Flower (38x38cm-15x15in) s.d.1983 num.num.2/10 gelatin silver print prov. 23-Apr-4 Phillips, New York #210/R est:5000-7000
£2838	$5080	€4200	Untitled (35x35cm-14x14in) s.i.d. silver gelatin. 8-May-4 Lempertz, Koln #195/R est:4000
£3107	$5500	€4536	Flower, chrysanthemums, 1983 (55x45cm-22x18in) s.num.27/40 photogravure. 27-Apr-4 Christie's, Rockefeller NY #192/R est:5000-7000
£3107	$5500	€4536	Flower, tiger orchids, 1983 (55x45cm-22x18in) s.num.27/40 photogravure. 27-Apr-4 Christie's, Rockefeller NY #195/R est:5000-7000
£3175	$6000	€4636	Dying lilies (55x45cm-22x18in) s.num.7/40 photogravure. 17-Feb-4 Christie's, Rockefeller NY #261/R est:4000-6000
£3390	$6000	€4949	Desmond (38x39cm-15x15in) s.d.1983 num.2/10 photo. 28-Apr-4 Sotheby's, New York #249/R est:5000-7000
£3693	$6500	€5392	Werner Dannheisser. Elaine Dannheisser (48x48cm-19x19in) with sig.d.1987 silver print two. 20-May-4 Swann Galleries, New York #522/R est:6000-9000
£3892	$6500	€5682	Iris (49x49cm-19x19in) bears another sig.i.d.1989 num.8/10 verso gelatin silver print. 20-Oct-3 Christie's, Rockefeller NY #242/R est:6000-8000
£3955	$7000	€5774	Flower - Oriental composition (48x38cm-19x15in) s.i.d.1983 num.2/10 gelatin silver print. 27-Apr-4 Christie's, Rockefeller NY #191/R est:5000-7000
£4192	$7000	€6120	Blue rose (50x51cm-20x20in) s.i.d.1988 num.2/5 toned photogravure lit. 21-Oct-3 Bonhams & Butterfields, San Francisco #1561/R
£4237	$7500	€6186	Calla lily (49x49cm-19x19in) i.d.1986 num.8/10 photo. 28-Apr-4 Sotheby's, New York #247/R est:10000-15000
£4491	$7500	€6557	Blue Calla Lily (50x51cm-20x20in) s.i.d.1988 num.2/5 toned photogravure lit. 21-Oct-3 Bonhams & Butterfields, San Francisco #1560/R
£4722	$8500	€6894	Fish (49x59cm-19x23in) s.i.d.1985 s.d.verso platinum print lit. 23-Apr-4 Phillips, New York #88/R est:20000-30000
£4762	$9000	€6953	Leaf (49x49cm-19x19in) s.i.d. s.d. verso silver print. 17-Feb-4 Swann Galleries, New York #109/R est:4000-6000
£4802	$8500	€7011	Derrick Cross (19x49cm-7x19in) i.d.1982 num.6/10 photo. 28-Apr-4 Sotheby's, New York #248/R est:5000-7000
£5090	$8500	€7431	Lily and tulip (39x39cm-15x15in) i.d.1984-85 num.3/10 photo two. 17-Oct-3 Sotheby's, New York #284/R est:7000-10000
£5090	$8500	€7431	Lily (49x49cm-19x19in) bears another sig.i.d.1989 num.7/10 verso gelatin silver print. 20-Oct-3 Christie's, Rockefeller NY #241/R est:6000-8000
£5650	$10000	€8249	Roses (49x49cm-19x19in) s.d.1986 num.2/10 i.d.verso photo. 28-Apr-4 Sotheby's, New York #244/R est:8000-12000
£5650	$10000	€8249	Flower, wheat (48x48cm-19x19in) s.d.1986 num.2/10 gelatin silver print. 27-Apr-4 Christie's, Rockefeller NY #190/R est:5000-7000
£5650	$10000	€8249	Flower, freesias, 1983 (55x45cm-22x18in) s.num.27/40 photogravure. 27-Apr-4 Christie's, Rockefeller NY #194/R est:5000-7000
£5689	$9500	€8306	Rose (49x49cm-19x19in) bears another sig.d.1989 num.10/10 verso gelatin silver print. 20-Oct-3 Christie's, Rockefeller NY #243/R est:6000-8000
£5820	$11000	€8497	Tulips (39x38cm-15x15in) s.d.1982 s.i.d.verso num.1/10 gelatin silver print. 17-Feb-4 Christie's, Rockefeller NY #260/R est:8000-10000
£6215	$11000	€9074	Parrot tulip (49x49cm-19x19in) s.d.1987 num.1/10 i.d.verso photo. 28-Apr-4 Sotheby's, New York #245/R est:8000-12000
£6587	$11000	€9617	Stems (39x39cm-15x15in) i.d.1985 num.7/10 photo. 17-Oct-3 Sotheby's, New York #290/R est:4000-6000
£8383	$14000	€12239	Calla lily (39x38cm-15x15in) i.d.1985 num.3/10 photo. 17-Oct-3 Sotheby's, New York #283/R est:7000-10000
£9040	$16000	€13198	Roses (58x56cm-23x22in) i.num.2/5 dye transfer print printed 1989. 28-Apr-4 Sotheby's, New York #243/R est:20000-30000
£9040	$16000	€13198	Irises (86x81cm-34x32in) s.d.1987 photogravure on silk lit. 27-Apr-4 Christie's, Rockefeller NY #189/R est:12000-16000
£11458	$19479	€16500	Tulip in black vase (25x25cm-10x10in) s.i.d. gelatin silver prov.lit. 31-Oct-3 Lempertz, Koln #230/R est:7000-9000
£12575	$21000	€18360	Self portrait with cigarette (35x35cm-14x14in) s.d.1980 num.7/15 photo. 17-Oct-3 Sotheby's, New York #285/R est:15000-25000
£13559	$24000	€19796	Orchid (83x82cm-33x32in) s.d.1987 num.13/27 photogravure prov.exhib. 28-Apr-4 Sotheby's, New York #242/R est:10000-15000
£13772	$23000	€20107	Fish (49x59cm-19x23in) s.d.85 num.3/3 platinum print prov.exhib.lit. 17-Oct-3 Phillips, New York #15/R est:15000-20000
£13772	$23000	€20107	Flag (61x50cm-24x20in) i.d.1987 num.2/2 verso gelatin silver print one of ten prov. 17-Oct-3 Phillips, New York #16/R est:20000-30000
£14689	$26000	€21446	Calla lily (39x39cm-15x15in) s.d.1984 num.7/10 photo. 28-Apr-4 Sotheby's, New York #246/R est:15000-25000
£15000	$27450	€21900	Coral sea (50x40cm-20x16in) bears another sig.i.d.1983 verso silver print card edition 9/10. 8-Jul-4 Sotheby's, London #439/R est:10000-15000
£20000	$36600	€29200	Tulip (61x51cm-24x20in) bears another sig. dye transfer print prov. 8-Jul-4 Sotheby's, London #441/R est:8000-12000
£21557	$36000	€31473	Calla lily (56x42cm-22x17in) s.d.1988 num.5/7 s.i.d.verso dye-transfer print. 17-Oct-3 Sotheby's, New York #281/R est:15000-25000
£22754	$38000	€33221	Calla lilly (61x50cm-24x20in) s.i.verso num.6 gelatin silver print exec.1988 one of ten prov. 17-Oct-3 Phillips, New York #14/R est:10000-15000
£39548	$70000	€57740	Torso, Lisa Marie (59x49cm-23x19in) s.d.1987 num.7/10 verso photo. 28-Apr-4 Sotheby's, New York #250/R est:15000-25000
£48000	$87840	€70080	Self portrait with skull cane (58x49cm-23x19in) silver print edition 5/10 prov. 8-Jul-4 Sotheby's, London #438/R est:12000-18000

MARA, Pol (1920-1998) Belgian

£833	$1392	€1200	Armoire abandonnee (110x130cm-43x51in) s.d.1988 verso. 21-Oct-3 Campo, Vlaamse Kaai #476/R
£1133	$2074	€1700	Composition (160x130cm-63x51in) s.d.60 verso. 7-Jun-4 Palais de Beaux Arts, Brussels #339/R est:1500-2000
£1250	$2088	€1800	Nu assis (100x80cm-39x31in) s.d.1969 verso. 21-Oct-3 Campo, Vlaamse Kaai #475/R est:1200-1500
£1958	$3270	€2800	Le mur et les amaryllis (100x80cm-39x31in) s.verso prov. 11-Oct-3 De Vuyst, Lokeren #241/R est:2500-3500
£2133	$3904	€3200	Xuchmal (195x130cm-77x51in) s.d.69 verso. 7-Jun-4 Palais de Beaux Arts, Brussels #340/R est:2000-3000
£3077	$5138	€4400	May tree (162x195cm-64x77in) s.d.1976 prov.lit. 11-Oct-3 De Vuyst, Lokeren #562/R est:4500-5500
£3099	$5361	€4400	Les fleurs du paradis (114x114cm-45x45in) s.d.1977 verso. 13-Dec-3 De Vuyst, Lokeren #584/R est:4000-5000

Works on paper

£278	$464	€400	Visage (65x50cm-26x20in) s.d.1964 W/C. 21-Oct-3 Campo, Vlaamse Kaai #477
£347	$580	€500	A l'ile de mar egee (110x72cm-43x28in) s. W/C. 21-Oct-3 Campo, Vlaamse Kaai #478
£369	$653	€550	Composition (65x50cm-26x20in) s.d.1960 W/C. 27-Apr-4 Campo, Vlaamse Kaai #499
£379	$702	€550	Femme de profil au ballon (70x107cm-28x42in) s.d.72 mixed media collage. 16-Feb-4 Horta, Bruxelles #280
£400	$720	€600	Blauwe symphonie (92x98cm-36x39in) s.d.63 mixed media. 26-Apr-4 Bernaerts, Antwerp #546/R
£436	$807	€650	Jeune femme nue au collier (107x69cm-42x27in) s.d.75 mixed media sold with a book. 15-Mar-4 Horta, Bruxelles #349
£470	$832	€700	Composition (105x67cm-41x26in) s.d.61 W/C. 27-Apr-4 Campo, Vlaamse Kaai #500
£500	$900	€750	I love you (76x113cm-30x44in) s.d.64 W/C. 26-Apr-4 Bernaerts, Antwerp #542/R
£634	$1096	€900	To open with a white hand (110x72cm-43x28in) s.d.1976 W/C. 9-Dec-3 Campo, Vlaamse Kaai #352/R
£764	$1276	€1100	Figures (64x49cm-25x19in) s.d.1956 gouache. 21-Oct-3 Campo, Vlaamse Kaai #480
£1034	$1717	€1500	Room in the sky (114x146cm-45x57in) mixed media on canvas. 6-Oct-3 Amberes, Antwerp #237

MARAGALL, Julio (1936-) Latin American

Sculpture

£1613	$2500	€2355	Figure (34x65x40cm-13x26x16in) s. num.1/1 bronze exec.1981. 3-Nov-2 Subastas Odalys, Caracas #88/R est:2200

MARAGLIANO, Antonio Maria (1664-1741) Italian

Sculpture

£1342	$2510	€2000	Madonna and Child with two Saints (56cm-22in) white stone. 29-Feb-4 Finarte, Venice #53/R est:1500-2000

MARAGLIANO, Federico (1873-1952) Italian

£1074	$1901	€1600	Genoa, Lighthouse (18x13cm-7x5in) s. i.d.1927 verso cardboard on canvas. 1-May-4 Meeting Art, Vercelli #329 est:1000
£1477	$2613	€2200	Levante Riviera, Portofino (18x13cm-7x5in) s. cardboard on canvas. 1-May-4 Meeting Art, Vercelli #331 est:1000

MARAIS, Jean (20th C) French
Works on paper
£317 $548 €450 Etude de cerf (27x20cm-11x8in) s. ink W/C. 13-Dec-3 Martinot & Savignat, Pontoise #17/R
£3147 $5413 €4500 Portrait de Jean Cocteau (32x24cm-13x9in) s.d.fevrier 1928 dr. 6-Dec-3 Renaud, Paris #75/R

MARAIS, Wessel (20th C) South African
£294 $532 €429 Country market (49x75cm-19x30in) s. canvas on board. 30-Mar-4 Stephan Welz, Johannesburg #217 est:2500-4000 (SA.R 3500)

MARAIS-MILTON, Victor (1872-1948) French
£2410 $4000 €3519 Introduction (55x38cm-22x15in) s. 30-Sep-3 Christie's, Rockefeller NY #429/R est:5000-7000
£4930 $7887 €7000 The confession (54x65cm-21x26in) s. lit. 19-Sep-3 Karlheinz Kaupp, Staufen #2036/R est:800
£5000 $8500 €7300 Petits compagnons (46x38cm-18x15in) s. 18-Nov-3 Sotheby's, London #331/R
£5638 $9190 €8231 Cardinal and dogs (46x38cm-18x15in) s. board. 17-Jul-3 Naón & Cia, Buenos Aires #20/R
£6897 $12759 €10000 Prelats jouant aux cartes (46x55cm-18x22in) s. panel. 19-Jan-4 Horta, Bruxelles #88/R est:7500-9500
£7000 $12740 €10220 Le sermon (61x50cm-24x20in) s. prov. 15-Jun-4 Sotheby's, London #199/R est:7000-10000
Works on paper
£966 $1612 €1400 La degustation (40x32cm-16x13in) s. W/C. 17-Nov-3 Bernaerts, Antwerp #5

MARAK, Julius Eduard (1832-1899) Bohemian
£7593 $13364 €11390 Rocky landscape (70x40cm-28x16in) s. exhib. 22-May-4 Dorotheum, Prague #25/R est:360000-500000 (C.KR 360000)

MARAKOVA, Pepa (1872-1907) Austrian
£412 $766 €602 From the Way to Bread and its End cycle (24x34cm-9x13in) four. 6-Mar-4 Dorotheum, Prague #95/R est:20000-30000 (C.KR 20000)

MARANDAT, Louis (1850-1899) French
£1119 $1902 €1600 Les lavandieres (44x70cm-17x28in) s.d.1884. 24-Nov-3 Boscher, Cherbourg #828 est:1200-1500

MARANIELLO, Giuseppe (1945-) Italian
Sculpture
£1724 $2879 €2500 Ulysses (20x105x8cm-8x41x3in) s.d.1989 bronze exhib. 13-Nov-3 Finarte Semenzato, Rome #477/R est:4000-5000
£2200 $4048 €3300 Graffiti (50x67x13cm-20x26x5in) metal fabric. 12-Jun-4 Meeting Art, Vercelli #98/R est:3000
Works on paper
£5634 $9859 €8000 Anfesibena (166x236cm-65x93in) s.i.d.1983 mixed media polymer on canvas. 16-Dec-3 Finarte Semenzato, Milan #209/R est:7800-8200

MARANTZ, Irving (1912-1973) American
£348 $550 €508 Tightrope walker (51x41cm-20x16in) s.d.1937 canvasboard. 7-Sep-3 Treadway Gallery, Cincinnati #680/R

MARASCO, Antonio (1886-1975) Italian
£759 $1267 €1100 Still life (34x18cm-13x7in) s.d.16 tempera collage card. 13-Nov-3 Finarte Semenzato, Rome #163/R
£897 $1497 €1300 War message (15x20cm-6x8in) s. s.i.verso cardboard. 13-Nov-3 Finarte Semenzato, Rome #289 est:1400-1600
£1467 $2640 €2200 Autumn. Frozen village (13x18cm-5x7in) s. cardboard two. 22-Apr-4 Finarte Semenzato, Rome #188 est:2000-2400
£47101 $77246 €65000 Atmosphere in Year VIII (152x200cm-60x79in) s.d. painted 1929 exhib.lit. 27-May-3 Sotheby's, Milan #214/R est:48000-55000
Works on paper
£915 $1520 €1300 Composition (20x30cm-8x12in) s. mixed media canvasboard. 14-Jun-3 Meeting Art, Vercelli #88/R
£1733 $3120 €2600 Portraits (12x8cm-5x3in) pencil Chinese ink tempera set of 14. 22-Apr-4 Finarte Semenzato, Rome #83/R est:1300-1600

MARASTONI, Giacomo (1804-1860) Italian
£1203 $2128 €1756 Young woman in blue dress (76x60cm-30x24in) s.i.d.1838. 28-Apr-4 Kieselbach, Budapest #186/R (H.F 450000)

MARATTA, Carlo (1625-1713) Italian
£604 $1111 €900 Marie-Madeleine (55x45cm-22x18in) 23-Mar-4 Galerie Moderne, Brussels #363
Works on paper
£1639 $3000 €2393 Head of Saint Francis of Assisi (22x17cm-9x7in) red chk. 29-Jan-4 Swann Galleries, New York #69/R est:4000-6000
£2111 $3800 €3082 Christ holding an orb, His right arm raised in benediction (38x25cm-15x10in) i. black chk. 22-Jan-4 Christie's, Rockefeller NY #46/R est:2000-4000
£14085 $24648 €20000 Le martyre de Saint Jean-Baptiste (26x17cm-10x7in) black chk pen brown ink wash prov. 17-Dec-3 Christie's, Paris #9/R est:20000-30000
£27778 $50000 €40556 Infant Romulus and two studies of a man's left arm (26x34cm-10x13in) i.mount col chk prov.exhib.lit. 22-Jan-4 Christie's, Rockefeller NY #45/R est:30000-40000
£70000 $128100 €102200 Madonna and Child appearing to Saint Ambrosius, Francis of Sales and Nicholas of Bari (40x22cm-16x9in) black chk pen ink wash arched. 6-Jul-4 Christie's, London #55/R est:30000-50000

MARATTA, Carlo (attrib) (1625-1713) Italian
Works on paper
£462 $794 €675 Meeting of St Elisabeth and the Virgin (29x22cm-11x9in) red chk. 7-Dec-3 Uppsala Auktionskammare, Uppsala #20/R (S.KR 6000)
£626 $1120 €920 Etude de chevalier (37x23cm-15x9in) sanguine htd white. 22-Mar-4 Digard, Paris #31
£1311 $2400 €1914 Seated woman seen from behind and study of an extended arm (41x26cm-16x10in) col chk. 29-Jan-4 Swann Galleries, New York #71/R est:1200-1800
£1639 $3000 €2393 Study of two cherubs (15x19cm-6x7in) col chk. 29-Jan-4 Swann Galleries, New York #70/R est:1500-2500
£2778 $5000 €4056 Study for a Madonna and Child in the clouds (18x17cm-7x7in) red black chk prov. 21-Jan-4 Sotheby's, New York #125/R est:3500-4000
£3333 $6000 €4866 Seated man writing on a tablet, turning back to a woman (20x17cm-8x7in) i. col chk prov. 22-Jan-4 Christie's, Rockefeller NY #31/R est:5000-7000
£18056 $32500 €26362 Portrait of a man, said to be Alessandro Algardi (39x30cm-15x12in) i. red chk. 21-Jan-4 Sotheby's, New York #78/R est:15000-20000

MARATTA, Carlo (studio) (1625-1713) Italian
£8392 $14434 €12000 Flight to Egypt (166x162cm-65x64in) 2-Dec-3 Sotheby's, Milan #81/R est:10000-15000

MARATTA, Carlo (style) (1625-1713) Italian
£4167 $7500 €6084 Saints Stephen and Sebastian with the Madonna and Child (61x42cm-24x17in) 22-Jan-4 Sotheby's, New York #278/R est:8000-12000
£7292 $12396 €10500 Bacchus and Arianna (87x119cm-34x47in) 29-Oct-3 Il Ponte, Milan #811/R est:10000-12000

MARATTA, Hardesty (1864-1924) American
£511 $900 €746 Illinois farm (13x18cm-5x7in) s. board painted c.1910. 23-May-4 Treadway Gallery, Cincinnati #501/R

MARAVER MORENO, Jose Luis (20th C) Spanish
Works on paper
£1127 $1972 €1600 Cariatidis and friends (130x162cm-51x64in) s. s.i.verso mixed media collage exhib. 16-Dec-3 Durán, Madrid #88/R

MARAWARR (1967-) Australian
Works on paper
£386 $610 €564 Caterpillars. earth pigments eucalyptus bark exec.c.1980 prov. 28-Jul-3 Sotheby's, Paddington #33 (A.D 950)

MARAZ, Roman (20th C) American
£1173 $2100 €1713 Woman reading in a Mathsson lounge chair (74x56cm-29x22in) s.d.1942 masonite. 16-May-4 Wright, Chicago #167/R est:2000-3000

MARBLE, John Nelson (1855-1918) American
Works on paper
£1455 $2750 €2124 Early view of Santa Barbara Mission (13x23cm-5x9in) s. marble W/C. 17-Feb-4 John Moran, Pasadena #91a/R est:1000-1500

MARBURG, Amanda (1976-) Australian
£840 $1528 €1226 Fly lightly my heart (90x60cm-35x24in) s.d.2003 verso exhib. 16-Jun-4 Deutscher-Menzies, Melbourne #186/R est:1500-2500 (A.D 2200)

MARC, Franz (1880-1916) German
£12416 $22225 €18500 Small mountain pasture study (15x24cm-6x9in) paper exhib.lit. 25-May-4 Karl & Faber, Munich #399/R est:23000-25000
Prints
£1765 $3000 €2577 Schopfungsgeschichte II (24x20cm-9x8in) estate st. bears another sig.verso col woodcut. 6-Nov-3 Swann Galleries, New York #616/R est:3500-5000
£2333 $4293 €3500 History of creation II (24x20cm-9x8in) col woodcut. 10-Jun-4 Hauswedell & Nolte, Hamburg #456/R est:4000
£2797 $4755 €4000 Horse and hedgehog (16x22cm-6x9in) woodcut. 29-Nov-3 Villa Grisebach, Berlin #160/R est:4000-5000
£3240 $5800 €4730 Spielende wiesel (28x19cm-11x7in) s. lithograph. 6-May-4 Swann Galleries, New York #502/R est:6000-9000
£5944 $10105 €8500 Reconciliation (20x26cm-8x10in) s.i. woodcut prov. 28-Nov-3 Villa Grisebach, Berlin #30/R est:4000-6000
£9441 $16049 €13500 Leaping horses (13x9cm-5x4in) s.i. woodcut prov. 28-Nov-3 Villa Grisebach, Berlin #29/R est:4000-6000
£16667 $30667 €25000 Horses at rest (17x23cm-7x9in) col woodcut prov. 11-Jun-4 Villa Grisebach, Berlin #22/R est:20000-30000
Works on paper
£10000 $18400 €15000 Cows resting in the shade of the trees (20x16cm-8x6in) i.verso pencil prov. 12-Jun-4 Villa Grisebach, Berlin #180/R est:18000-24000

MARC, Robert (1943-1993) French
£282 $487 €400 Composition (20x30cm-8x12in) s. cardboard. 10-Dec-3 Millon & Associes, Paris #115
£1040 $1945 €1550 Composition cubiste (81x60cm-32x24in) s. prov. 29-Feb-4 Versailles Encheres #275 est:600-800
£1294 $2200 €1889 Untitled (33x41cm-13x16in) s. s.verso. 9-Nov-3 Wright, Chicago #337 est:2500-3500
£3082 $5240 €4500 Composition (80x65cm-31x26in) s. 9-Nov-3 Eric Pillon, Calais #279/R
£5141 $8894 €7300 Portrait (92x73cm-36x29in) s. 15-Dec-3 Marc Kohn, Paris #115/R est:6000-10000

MARCA-RELLI, Conrad (1913-2000) American
£1408 $2465 €2000 Figure (51x67cm-20x26in) s. paint collage tissue paper. 18-Dec-3 Cornette de St.Cyr, Paris #75/R est:2500-4000
£1831 $3204 €2600 Figure (67x51cm-26x20in) s. paint collage tissue paper. 18-Dec-3 Cornette de St.Cyr, Paris #73/R est:2500-4000

£3873 $6778 €5500 L-7-73 (123x175cm-48x69in) s. s.i.d.1973 verso oil collage lit. 16-Dec-3 Segre, Madrid #202/R est:4500
£5034 $9262 €7500 Composition (65x50cm-26x20in) s.d.1955 oil collage painted canvas. 29-Mar-4 Cornette de St.Cyr, Paris #32/R est:8000-10000
£5235 $9632 €7800 Composition (52x60cm-20x24in) s. oil collage painted canvas. 29-Mar-4 Cornette de St.Cyr, Paris #33/R est:8000-10000
£6000 $10920 €9000 Composition (60x69cm-24x27in) s. s.d.1965 paint collage. 29-Jun-4 Cornette de St.Cyr, Paris #48/R est:9000-10000
£6000 $10920 €9000 Composition (57x60cm-22x24in) s.d.1965 paint collage. 29-Jun-4 Cornette de St.Cyr, Paris #47/R est:9000-10000
£15363 $27500 €22430 Untitled - R2 - 57 (43x60cm-17x24in) s. s.i.d.2-57 stretcher oil canvas collage prov. 13-May-4 Sotheby's, New York #110/R est:15000-20000
£21472 $35000 €31349 M-6-57 (86x147cm-34x58in) s. s.i.d.6-57 stretcher oil canvas collage on canvas prov.exhib. 23-Sep-3 Christie's, Rockefeller NY #39/R est:12000-18000
£41916 $70000 €61197 X-L-31-62 (152x152cm-60x60in) s. s.i.d.X-L-31-62 verso oil canvas collage on canvas prov.exhib. 13-Nov-3 Sotheby's, New York #177/R est:25000-35000
Works on paper
£359 $600 €524 Birds (13x15cm-5x6in) s. gouache prov. 15-Nov-3 Sloans & Kenyon, Bethesda #89/R

MARCACCIO, Fabian (1963-) Argentinian
£276 $450 €403 Geography (76x71cm-30x28in) s. 28-Sep-3 Bonhams & Butterfields, Los Angeles #7060
Works on paper
£330 $584 €482 Untitled (69x49cm-27x19in) s.d.93 Indian ink pen prov. 27-Apr-4 AB Stockholms Auktionsverk #933/R (S.KR 4500)

MARCARA, P (20th C) American?
Sculpture
£2210 $4000 €3227 Statue of Liberty (180cm-71in) s.d. carved floor sculpture. 3-Apr-4 David Rago, Lambertville #310/R est:1500-2500

MARCED FURIO, Jose (1896-?) Spanish
£1042 $1656 €1500 Flowers (91x71cm-36x28in) s. 29-Apr-3 Durán, Madrid #94/R est:1100

MARCEL, Didier (1961-) French
Works on paper
£608 $1149 €900 Sans titre (50x74cm-20x29in) s. dr. 21-Feb-4 Cornette de St.Cyr, Paris #348/R

MARCEL-BERONNEAU, Pierre Amedee (1869-1937) French
£350 $630 €511 Study for Orphee (65x81cm-26x32in) indis.i.stretcher. 21-Jan-4 Sotheby's, Olympia #482/R
£600 $1080 €876 Study for Salome with the head of John the Baptist (40x31cm-16x12in) bears st.verso panel. 21-Jan-4 Sotheby's, Olympia #476/R
£700 $1260 €1022 Susanna and the Elders (42x33cm-17x13in) i.verso panel. 21-Jan-4 Sotheby's, Olympia #477/R
£700 $1260 €1022 Flood plain at sunset (65x94cm-26x37in) bears studio st.verso. 21-Jan-4 Sotheby's, Olympia #480/R
£750 $1350 €1095 Study for femme au serpent (54x45cm-21x18in) board oval. 21-Jan-4 Sotheby's, Olympia #479/R
£769 $1308 €1100 Le rosier grimpant (65x50cm-26x20in) s. oil cardboard. 28-Nov-3 Doutrebente, Paris #42
£1500 $2700 €2190 Terrace in Corsica (64x81cm-25x32in) bears studio st.verso board. 21-Jan-4 Sotheby's, Olympia #485/R est:700-900
£1800 $3240 €2628 Diane (100x80cm-39x31in) i.d.1929 verso. 21-Jan-4 Sotheby's, Olympia #483/R est:2000-3000
£2000 $3600 €2920 Cherry trees in a landscape (73x92cm-29x36in) s. 21-Jan-4 Sotheby's, Olympia #487/R est:800-1200
Works on paper
£900 $1665 €1314 Portrait of a lady, with a scarf (22x19cm-9x7in) bears studio st. col chk prov. 14-Jul-4 Sotheby's, Olympia #284/R

MARCEL-CLEMENT, Amedee Julien (1873-?) French
£2057 $3435 €2900 Barques de peche (38x46cm-15x18in) s. s.i.verso panel. 12-Oct-3 St-Germain-en-Laye Encheres #63/R est:3000-4000
£2800 $5124 €4200 Cancale, retour des cotres (27x35cm-11x14in) s. masonite. 4-Jun-4 Pierre Berge, Paris #56/R est:1000-1500
£3200 $5312 €4672 Aux sables d'Orlonne (33x46cm-13x18in) s. board. 1-Oct-3 Sotheby's, Olympia #283/R est:1000-1500
£3310 $5726 €4700 Bateaux de peche (38x46cm-15x18in) s. panel. 14-Dec-3 Eric Pillon, Calais #155/R
£4000 $7200 €5840 Sailing boats (46x113cm-18x44in) s. board. 21-Jan-4 Sotheby's, Olympia #523/R est:4000-6000
£6289 $10000 €9182 Le vent fraichit (81x116cm-32x46in) s. s.i.verso. 13-Sep-3 Weschler, Washington #681/R est:3000-5000

MARCEL-LAURENT, Emmanuel (1892-1948) French
£1268 $2218 €1800 Jour anime sur la place de Locronan (54x65cm-21x26in) s. 21-Dec-3 Thierry & Lannon, Brest #182/R est:2000-3000
£1788 $3344 €2700 Jour de Pardon a Ste Anne la Palud (24x85cm-9x33in) s. isorel. 24-Jul-4 Thierry & Lannon, Brest #196/R est:2000-2500
Works on paper
£3099 $5423 €4400 Projet No 1, 2 et 3 de la decoration pour la grand foyer de Brest (46x62cm-18x24in) s. gouache sold with lots 368 and 369. 16-Dec-3 Adjug'art, Brest #367/R

MARCEL-LAURENT, Ernest (20th C) French
£921 $1667 €1400 Canot a la godille. 17-Apr-4 Deburaux, Boulogne #81

MARCEL-LENOIR, Jules (1872-1931) French
Works on paper
£288 $460 €400 Etude de visage (22x30cm-9x12in) s. crayon. 18-May-3 Salle des ventes Pillet, Lyon la Foret #85/R
£302 $553 €450 Bapteme du Christ (34x29cm-13x11in) s. ink stumping chl htd white chk. 7-Jul-4 Artcurial Briest, Paris #51
£389 $728 €580 Visage (38x31cm-15x12in) s. chl. 29-Feb-4 Versailles Encheres #162

MARCEL-LENOIR, Jules (attrib) (1872-1931) French
£2914 $4662 €4050 Danse champetre (90x200cm-35x79in) 18-May-3 Salle des ventes Pillet, Lyon la Foret #84/R est:2500-3000

MARCELIN, Renoud (20th C) ?
£506 $844 €739 Wooded landscape with figures and animals (146x203cm-57x80in) s,. 25-Oct-3 Rasmussen, Havnen #4240 (D.KR 5400)
£995 $1782 €1453 Rain forest with exotic birds (147x186cm-58x73in) s. 10-May-4 Rasmussen, Vejle #790/R (D.KR 11000)

MARCELLO (?) Italian?
Sculpture
£12000 $20760 €17520 Pythia (45cm-18in) s.st.f.Thiebaut Freres brown pat bronze lit. 12-Dec-3 Sotheby's, London #255/R est:6000-8000

MARCETTE, Alexandre (1853-1929) Belgian
£490 $842 €700 Lever de lune sur le moulin (65x81cm-26x32in) s. 8-Dec-3 Horta, Bruxelles #501
£1088 $1981 €1600 Voiliers dans un paysage fluvial (70x152cm-28x60in) 9-Feb-4 Amberes, Antwerp #276/R
Works on paper
£333 $603 €500 Voiliers au coucher du soleil (53x45cm-21x18in) s. W/C. 30-Mar-4 Palais de Beaux Arts, Brussels #652
£490 $877 €720 Vue sur canal (43x54cm-17x21in) s. mixed media. 17-Mar-4 Hotel des Ventes Mosan, Brussels #148
£592 $1072 €900 Barque de peche echouee pres des Ducs d'Albe (63x78cm-25x31in) s. gouache. 19-Apr-4 Horta, Bruxelles #437

MARCH, Elsie (19/20th C) British?
Sculpture
£8000 $14720 €11680 World and the soul (38cm-15in) s.d.1919 brown pat. bronze. 11-Jun-4 Christie's, London #82/R est:3000-5000

MARCH, Giovanni (1894-1974) Tunisian
£759 $1267 €1100 Campolecciano, Italy (18x26cm-7x10in) s. board. 14-Nov-3 Farsetti, Prato #451/R
£915 $1520 €1300 Landscape (35x45cm-14x18in) s.i.verso. 13-Jun-3 Farsetti, Prato #567/R
£2185 $3977 €3300 Under the parasol (50x70cm-20x28in) s. s.d.1966 verso. 17-Jun-4 Galleria Pananti, Florence #465/R est:3300-3500

MARCH, Horacio (1899-1978) Argentinian
£503 $900 €734 Harbour (14x19cm-6x7in) tempera paper. 11-May-4 Arroyo, Buenos Aires #62
£503 $900 €734 Around Lima (13x16cm-5x6in) tempera paper. 11-May-4 Arroyo, Buenos Aires #60
£1006 $1800 €1469 Huancayo (14x20cm-6x8in) tempera cardboard. 11-May-4 Arroyo, Buenos Aires #61
Works on paper
£330 $600 €482 Landscape (14x18cm-6x7in) s. W/C. 5-Jul-4 Arroyo, Buenos Aires #76/R
£357 $650 €521 Boats (13x18cm-5x7in) s. W/C. 5-Jul-4 Arroyo, Buenos Aires #75/R
£989 $1800 €1444 Buenos Aires (15x22cm-6x9in) s. W/C pair. 29-Jun-4 Arroyo, Buenos Aires #9/R est:700

MARCH, J (20th C) ?
£933 $1699 €1400 Picnic at the Forum (54x105cm-21x41in) 3-Jul-4 Finarte, Venice #193/R est:1400-1800

MARCH, Miguel (1633-1670) Spanish
£33333 $60000 €48666 Peasants mocking an old man (152x175cm-60x69in) prov. 23-Jan-4 Christie's, Rockefeller NY #9/R est:15000-20000
£58333 $105000 €85166 Personification of the Liberal Arts (152x176cm-60x69in) i. prov. 23-Jan-4 Christie's, Rockefeller NY #8/R est:15000-20000

MARCH, Vernon (20th C) British?
£360 $612 €526 Port scene (59x73cm-23x29in) s.d.1919. 2-Nov-3 Lots Road Auctions, London #332

MARCH, Vicente (1859-1914) Spanish
£33000 $56100 €48180 Washerwomen (46x66cm-18x26in) s.i. prov. 18-Nov-3 Sotheby's, London #202/R

MARCHAL, Henri (1878-?) French
£387 $643 €550 Paysage lorrain (78x102cm-31x40in) panel. 15-Jun-3 Teitgen, Nancy #84

MARCHAND, Andre (1907-1998) French
£268 $494 €400 Homard (45x64cm-18x25in) s. 24-Mar-4 Joron-Derem, Paris #64
£420 $722 €600 Derniers instants du soir (22x27cm-9x11in) s. s.i.verso. 8-Dec-3 Christie's, Paris #81/R
£559 $962 €800 Aix en Provence (57x75cm-22x30in) canvas laid down. 2-Dec-3 Claude Aguttes, Neuilly #58

£639	$1003	€920	Course a Longchamp (38x61cm-15x24in) s.i. panel. 29-Aug-3 Deauville, France #161
£738	$1321	€1100	Provence, les derniers instants du soir (22x27cm-9x11in) s. 30-May-4 Eric Pillon, Calais #186/R
£839	$1427	€1200	Vase de fleurs (46x54cm-18x21in) s. panel. 28-Nov-3 Blanchet, Paris #129/R
£1007	$1802	€1500	Soir dans les avoines folles (46x55cm-18x22in) s. s.i.verso. 27-May-4 Christie's, Paris #133/R est:1500-2000
£1333	$2400	€2000	Jeune femme au fond rouge (40x31cm-16x12in) s. 24-Apr-4 Cornette de St.Cyr, Paris #388 est:2000
£1538	$2646	€2200	Rayon vert sur 'Ocean (46x55cm-18x22in) s. s.i.d.1967 verso. 8-Dec-3 Christie's, Paris #82/R est:900-1200
£1958	$3368	€2800	Respiration marine (81x65cm-32x26in) s. s.i.verso. 8-Dec-3 Christie's, Paris #79/R est:1500-2200
£1972	$3411	€2800	Nature morte aux figues (46x55cm-18x22in) s. 14-Dec-3 Eric Pillon, Calais #233/R
Works on paper			
£350	$601	€500	Baigneuse (48x63cm-19x25in) s.d. chl. 3-Dec-3 Beaussant & Lefèvre, Paris #60
£403	$749	€600	Flamants en vol au soleil couchant (78x58cm-31x23in) s. W/C exhib. 3-Mar-4 Tajan, Paris #156

MARCHAND, Andre (1877-1951) French

£1645	$3026	€2500	Bouquet de tulipes (71x90cm-28x35in) s. 28-Jun-4 Rossini, Paris #60/R est:1500-1800

MARCHAND, Jean Hippolyte (1883-1940) French

£450	$747	€657	Still life with artichoke (27x40cm-11x16in) s. oil traces pencil board prov. 1-Oct-3 Sotheby's, Olympia #279/R
£1600	$2672	€2336	Bateaux au port (55x65cm-22x26in) s. prov.exhib. 22-Oct-3 Sotheby's, Olympia #46/R est:1800-2500
£2200	$3894	€3212	Landscape with viaduct (62x50cm-24x20in) s.d.1912. 27-Apr-4 Bonhams, Knightsbridge #73/R est:1500-2500
£3667	$6747	€5500	Maison dans les arbres a Garches (66x54cm-26x21in) s. i.d.1919 verso. 8-Jun-4 Artcurial Briest, Paris #140/R est:2000-3000

MARCHAND, John N (1875-1921) American

£2747	$5000	€4011	Indians on a bison hunt (71x102cm-28x40in) s. 15-Jun-4 John Moran, Pasadena #125a est:1800-2200
£2747	$5000	€4011	Sheep hunting, the long shot (23x30cm-9x12in) s.d.1915 board prov. 15-Jun-4 John Moran, Pasadena #125b est:800-1200

MARCHAND, Marie Odile (?) French?

Works on paper			
£420	$689	€580	Chamois (48x69cm-19x27in) W/C board. 28-May-3 Coutau Begarie, Paris #136/R

MARCHANT, Alfred (?) ?

£420	$781	€613	Coastal scene with beached sailing boats and shrimpers on shore (48x73cm-19x29in) s. board. 5-Mar-4 Moore Allen & Innocent, Cirencester #334

MARCHANT, Bob (1938-) Australian

£1406	$2630	€2109	Untitled (92x121cm-36x48in) s. i.verso. 21-Jul-4 Shapiro, Sydney #143 est:4000-6000 (A.D 3600)
£1797	$3360	€2696	Preparing for the Wollombi show at Holly Brook Farm (77x91cm-30x36in) s.i.d.1986. 21-Jul-4 Shapiro, Sydney #144/R est:5000-7000 (A.D 4600)
£4219	$7889	€6329	As usual a large crowd turned up to watch the annual social cricket match (152x123cm-60x48in) s. 21-Jul-4 Shapiro, Sydney #141/R est:12000-18000 (A.D 10800)
£6445	$12053	€9668	Sitting ducks (195x120cm-77x47in) s. i.verso exec. 1989. 21-Jul-4 Shapiro, Sydney #142/R est:12000-18000 (A.D 16500)

MARCHANT, Jean (1808-1864) Belgian

£2883	$4700	€4209	Children playing at the farmyard (43x53cm-17x21in) s.d.1835. 17-Jul-3 Naón & Cia, Buenos Aires #22/R

MARCHBANK, John (19th C) British

£300	$501	€438	Figures seated before a cottage (23x30cm-9x12in) s. 8-Oct-3 Andrew Hartley, Ilkley #1152/R

MARCHENKO, Sergei (20th C) Russian

£400	$716	€584	Still life with poppies (55x46cm-22x18in) s. 5-May-4 John Nicholson, Haslemere #40/R

MARCHENNIKOV, Serguei (1977-) Russian

£296	$545	€450	Still life with blue cup (46x55cm-18x22in) s. 22-Jun-4 Durán, Madrid #706/R
£381	$693	€560	Lecture. s. 8-Feb-4 Lesieur & Le Bars, Le Havre #51/R

MARCHESCHI, Jean-Paul (20th C) French

Works on paper			
£382	$638	€550	11000 nuits, fragments (120x114cm-47x45in) peinture soot wax felt lead prov. 25-Oct-3 Cornette de St.Cyr, Paris #430
£382	$638	€550	Dante, chant V (65x50cm-26x20in) s.d.1985 asphalt oil wax graphite prov. 25-Oct-3 Cornette de St.Cyr, Paris #433
£486	$812	€700	11000 nuits, fragments (120x114cm-47x45in) peinture soot wax felt lead prov. 25-Oct-3 Cornette de St.Cyr, Paris #431
£660	$1102	€950	11000 nuits, fragments (120x114cm-47x45in) peinture soot wax felt lead prov. 25-Oct-3 Cornette de St.Cyr, Paris #429/R

MARCHESI, Salvatore (1852-1926) Italian

£1733	$3155	€2600	Church interior with monks (42x61cm-17x24in) s. cardboard on canvas. 12-Jul-4 Il Ponte, Milan #528 est:1600-1800

MARCHESINI, Alessandro (1664-1738) Italian

£53691	$100403	€80000	Do not give the bad example. Let the children come to me (100x133cm-39x52in) s.d.MDCCVIII pair prov.exhib.lit. 25-Feb-4 Porro, Milan #54/R est:80000
£127586	$213069	€185000	Let the children come to me. Do not create a scandal amongst the children (100x133cm-39x52in) s.d.MDCCVIII pair prov.exhib.lit. 15-Nov-3 Porro, Milan #253/R est:80000

MARCHESINI, Alessandro (attrib) (1664-1738) Italian

£24161	$44456	€36000	Heathendom paying homage to Christianity (67x88cm-26x35in) prov. 24-Mar-4 Dorotheum, Vienna #82/R est:35000-45000

MARCHESINI, Nella (1901-1953) Italian

£503	$891	€750	Bathers (21x35cm-8x14in) cardboard. 1-May-4 Meeting Art, Vercelli #268

MARCHETTI DA FAENZA, Marco (attrib) (?-1588) Italian

Works on paper			
£1200	$2076	€1752	Studies of part of an overdoor and three figures (23x16cm-9x6in) black red chk pen brown ink wash prov. 12-Dec-3 Christie's, Kensington #307/R est:800-1200

MARCHETTI, G (18th C) Italian

£2400	$4368	€3504	Confirmation day (127x81cm-50x32in) s.d.1911. 16-Jun-4 Christie's, Kensington #89/R est:1500-2000

MARCHETTI, Lou (1920-1992) American

£2953	$5286	€4400	The men from the boys (79x56cm-31x22in) cardboard. painted 1957. 27-May-4 Sotheby's, Paris #148/R est:2000-3000

MARCHETTI, Ludovico (1853-1909) Italian

£1676	$3000	€2447	Allegorical scenes with putti (44x15cm-17x6in) s.d.1883 panel two. 14-May-4 Skinner, Boston #57/R est:1200-1800
£2937	$4905	€4200	Jeune femme au bouquet de fleurs (80x65cm-31x26in) s.d.92. 26-Jun-3 Artcurial Briest, Paris #526 est:4000-5000
£3800	$6840	€5548	Cavalieri (23x40cm-9x16in) s.d.1879 panel. 21-Jan-4 Sotheby's, Olympia #447/R est:2000-4000
£4300	$7310	€6278	Fair connoisseur (60x42cm-24x17in) indis.sig.d.1881. 19-Nov-3 Bonhams, New Bond Street #83/R est:4000-6000
Works on paper			
£3546	$5922	€5000	Royal dinner (41x32cm-16x13in) s. W/C. 20-Oct-3 Sant Agostino, Torino #248/R est:6000

MARCHI, Mario Vellani (1895-1979) Italian

£2254	$3741	€3200	Burano, Merlettaia a riposo (52x40cm-20x16in) s.d.1944 board. 14-Jun-3 Meeting Art, Vercelli #699/R est:2000
£2878	$4719	€4000	Madonna (55x71cm-22x28in) 5-Jun-3 Adma, Formigine #947 est:4300-4500
Works on paper			
£267	$488	€400	Rialto Bridge (17x23cm-7x9in) W/C Chinese ink exec.1952. 4-Jun-4 Tuttarte, Modena #240
£333	$610	€500	Venice (17x25cm-7x10in) W/C Chinese ink exec.1951. 4-Jun-4 Tuttarte, Modena #270

MARCHIGIAN SCHOOL (16th C) Italian

Works on paper			
£10000	$18300	€14600	Last supper (27x38cm-11x15in) i. black chk pen ink wash prov. 6-Jul-4 Christie's, London #31/R est:6000-10000

MARCHINGTON, Philip (19/20th C) ?

£360	$601	€526	Merchantman entering Portsmouth Harbour (51x76cm-20x30in) s. 11-Nov-3 Bonhams, Knightsbridge #51/R

MARCHINI, Paolo Alberto (1929-1977) Italian

£306	$548	€450	Snow on the Appennini (40x60cm-16x24in) s. s.i.d.1973 verso. 22-Mar-4 Sant Agostino, Torino #51/R

MARCHIOLIVY, G (?) ?

£353	$575	€515	Nude men in crashing wave reaching towards rowboat, woman inside (33x48cm-13x19in) s. artist board. 26-Sep-3 York Town, York #1068

MARCHIONI, Elisabetta (18th C) Italian

£4667	$8353	€7000	Still life of flowers (65x38cm-26x15in) 12-May-4 Finarte Semenzato, Milan #98/R est:5000-7000

MARCHIONI, Elisabetta (attrib) (18th C) Italian

£20000	$34600	€29200	Still lifes of tulips, roses, carnations and other flowers in bronze urns (72x97cm-28x38in) pair. 11-Dec-3 Sotheby's, London #228/R est:15000-20000

MARCHIS, Alessio de (attrib) (1684-1752) Italian

£3901	$6514	€5500	Landscape before the storm (29x47cm-11x19in) 14-Oct-3 Finarte Semenzato, Rome #259/R est:6000
£6338	$11092	€9000	River landscape (59x73cm-23x29in) 17-Dec-3 Christie's, Rome #407/R est:10000-15000

MARCHOT DE TOMBECKEM, Louis Meriade (19th C) Belgian

£319	$533	€450	Nature morte aux prunes (51x75cm-20x30in) s. 14-Oct-3 Vanderkindere, Brussels #29

MARCHOU, Georges (1898-1984) French

£284 $474 €400 Deux nus dans un paysage (65x50cm-26x20in) 23-Jun-3 Lombrail & Teucquam, Paris #206
£319 $533 €450 Nu a l'ombrelle (38x46cm-15x18in) panel. 23-Jun-3 Lombrail & Teucquam, Paris #204
£355 $592 €500 Nu au drape rouge (50x65cm-20x26in) 23-Jun-3 Lombrail & Teucquam, Paris #193
£355 $592 €500 Nu dans la clairiere (81x65cm-32x26in) 23-Jun-3 Lombrail & Teucquam, Paris #198
£426 $711 €600 Nu blonde au canape bleu (81x130cm-32x51in) 23-Jun-3 Lombrail & Teucquam, Paris #191
£461 $770 €650 Eve. 23-Jun-3 Lombrail & Teucquam, Paris #199
£532 $888 €750 Le nu en Provence (65x81cm-26x32in) panel. 23-Jun-3 Lombrail & Teucquam, Paris #189
£638 $1066 €900 La cueillette des pommes (81x60cm-32x24in) panel. 23-Jun-3 Lombrail & Teucquam, Paris #197
£671 $1242 €1000 La baigneuse a la draperie jaune (100x81cm-39x32in) s. 14-Mar-4 Feletin, Province #216
£709 $1184 €1000 Femme nue exotique (73x100cm-29x39in) panel. 23-Jun-3 Lombrail & Teucquam, Paris #194

MARCIL, René (1917-1993) Canadian

£387 $630 €565 Abstract composition (41x58cm-16x23in) s.d.73 oil on paper. 23-Sep-3 Ritchie, Toronto #178/R (C.D 850)
£1786 $3036 €2608 Bouquet (46x36cm-18x14in) s.d.1947. 6-Nov-3 Heffel, Vancouver #77/R est:5000-6000 (C.D 4000)
£3000 $5490 €4380 Bellboy du Ritz (109x74cm-43x29in) s.d.88 acrylic paper on canvas prov. 1-Jun-4 Joyner Waddington, Toronto #165/R est:12000-15000 (C.D 7500)
£17857 $30714 €26071 Mere et l'enfant a la plage (242x120cm-95x47in) s.d.86 panel prov. 2-Dec-3 Joyner Waddington, Toronto #114/R est:25000-35000 (C.D 40000)
Works on paper
£268 $461 €391 Portrait of Evelyn (11x12cm-4x5in) s.d.51 pencil. 2-Dec-3 Joyner Waddington, Toronto #290/R (C.D 600)
£2333 $4200 €3500 Robot and its sexual life (110x74cm-43x29in) s.d.1988 gouache. 24-Apr-4 Cornette de St.Cyr, Paris #635/R est:2000-3000
£2500 $4300 €3650 Tete de femme (38x57cm-15x22in) s.d.78 pastel prov. 2-Dec-3 Joyner Waddington, Toronto #168/R est:3000-5000 (C.D 5600)
£2500 $4725 €3700 Reglement de comptes (120x80cm-47x31in) s.d.1987 gouache. 21-Feb-4 Cornette de St.Cyr, Paris #349/R est:800-1200

MARCIUS-SIMONS, Pinky (1867-1909) American

£1250 $2088 €1800 Vue d'une ville (36x21cm-14x8in) s. panel. 21-Oct-3 Artcurial Briest, Paris #269/R est:2000-3000

MARCKE DE LUMMEN, Émile van (1827-1890) French

£441 $749 €644 River landscape (28x39cm-11x15in) s. board. 5-Nov-3 Dobiaschofsky, Bern #785/R (S.FR 1000)
£633 $1077 €924 Herder and cow in meadow (33x46cm-13x18in) s. 28-Nov-3 Zofingen, Switzerland #2473/R (S.FR 1400)
£1389 $2500 €2028 Cattle at pasture (30x41cm-12x16in) s. 21-Jan-4 Sotheby's, New York #238/R est:3000-5000
£1538 $2646 €2200 Cattle in a meadow (56x83cm-22x33in) s. 7-Dec-3 Sotheby's, Amsterdam #675
£1879 $3495 €2800 Les barques echouees (22x32cm-9x13in) s. panel. 3-Mar-4 Ferri, Paris #358 est:2500-3000
£5000 $9200 €7300 Cattle at the river (86x67cm-34x26in) s. 25-Mar-4 Christie's, Kensington #175/R est:3000-5000
£5245 $9021 €7500 Vaches dans la prairie (57x84cm-22x33in) s. prov.exhib. 7-Dec-3 Osenat, Fontainebleau #40 est:8000

MARCKE DE LUMMEN, Jean van (1875-1918) French

£2098 $3608 €3000 Horserace at Haymarket (49x64cm-19x25in) s. board. 2-Dec-3 Christie's, Paris #360/R est:4000-6000
£6704 $12000 €9788 Course at Newmarket (61x84cm-24x33in) s. prov. 6-May-4 Shannon's, Milford #144/R est:8000-12000

MARCKE, Émile van (1797-1839) Belgian

£1695 $3000 €2475 Study of a bull in a field (48x71cm-19x28in) s. 2-May-4 Bonhams & Butterfields, San Francisco #1034/R est:3000-5000

MARCKE, Marie Jaqueline Francoise van (1800-1882) Belgian

£1000 $1810 €1500 Bouquet of flowers including roses, poppies and aster (21x16cm-8x6in) s. 1-Apr-4 Van Ham, Cologne #1531/R est:1100

MARCKS, Gerhard (1889-1981) German

Prints
£1800 $3312 €2700 Two cats (23x38cm-9x15in) s.d.1921 woodcut one of 120. 11-Jun-4 Villa Grisebach, Berlin #1578/R est:1000-1500
Sculpture
£1133 $2029 €1700 Portrait of Herbert (35x18x22cm-14x7x9in) mono. verso bronze granite socle. 15-May-4 Van Ham, Cologne #783/R est:1500
£1533 $2806 €2300 Small Aliena (70cm-28in) i. verso terracotta prov. 5-Jun-4 Lempertz, Koln #850/R est:1500
£1608 $2734 €2300 Small seated Sappho (49cm-19in) terracotta. 26-Nov-3 Lempertz, Koln #830/R est:2500
£2326 $4000 €3396 Tischgebet (33cm-13in) mono. num.5/6 gold pat bronze st.f.Guss Barth Berlin prov. 7-Dec-3 Freeman, Philadelphia #49 est:2000-3000
£3000 $5520 €4500 Meeting - old woman and pregnant woman (18x10x5cm-7x4x2in) bronze. 10-Jun-4 Hauswedell & Nolte, Hamburg #459/R est:4500
£4000 $7360 €6000 Raffaelo (49x19x9cm-19x7x4in) red brown pat.bronze. 10-Jun-4 Hauswedell & Nolte, Hamburg #458/R est:8000
£4667 $8540 €7000 Sword tester (28cm-11in) s. pat.bronze Cast.Rich. Barth BLN Mariendorf. 5-Jun-4 Lempertz, Koln #845/R est:6000
£4667 $8540 €7000 Lovers standing together (45cm-18in) s. pat.bronze Cast.Barth Rinteln. 5-Jun-4 Lempertz, Koln #849/R est:4000-5000
£5333 $9547 €8000 Donkey and rider (42x11x36cm-17x4x14in) light gold brown pat.bronze prov.exhib.lit. 14-May-4 Ketterer, Munich #203/R est:8000-12000
£6667 $12267 €10000 Standing figure (73cm-29in) gold brown pat.bronze exhib. 10-Jun-4 Hauswedell & Nolte, Hamburg #461/R est:9000
£6993 $12028 €10000 Standing horse (42x44x12cm-17x17x5in) bronze. 2-Dec-3 Hauswedell & Nolte, Hamburg #394/R est:8000
£8042 $13671 €11500 Hella (94cm-37in) i. verso bronze Cast.Barth Berlin exhib. 26-Nov-3 Lempertz, Koln #829/R est:10000-12000
£9333 $16707 €14000 Zoe (95cm-37in) s. brown pat.bronze. 15-May-4 Van Ham, Cologne #784/R est:15000
£10490 $18042 €15000 Figure of a woman (82cm-32in) num.3/10 bronze exec.1978 st.f. Barth Rinteln. 4-Dec-3 Van Ham, Cologne #317/R est:18000
£12000 $21960 €18000 Chloe (72cm-28in) s.i. bronze Cast.Barth Rinteln exhib. 5-Jun-4 Lempertz, Koln #847/R est:18000-20000
£13333 $24533 €20000 Standing figure (97cm-38in) gold brown pat.bronze. 10-Jun-4 Hauswedell & Nolte, Hamburg #460/R est:24000
£15569 $26000 €22731 Mutter mit kind (131cm-52in) st.f.Guss R Barth green pat bronze lit. 7-Oct-3 Sotheby's, New York #289 est:7000-10000
£133333 $244000 €200000 Selene (88cm-35in) prov.exhib.lit. muschelkalk. 5-Jun-4 Lempertz, Koln #844/R est:100000-150000
Works on paper
£320 $589 €480 Portrait of Schikoradi (17x10cm-7x4in) s.i. pencil. 10-Jun-4 Hauswedell & Nolte, Hamburg #464/R
£420 $722 €600 Standing female nude (37x12cm-15x5in) s. pencil. 2-Dec-3 Hauswedell & Nolte, Hamburg #397/R
£570 $1050 €850 Portrait of Alex Vomel (17x11cm-7x4in) s. pencil wash. 26-Mar-4 Ketterer, Hamburg #1021/R

MARCLAY, Christian (20th C) American

Sculpture
£4865 $9000 €7103 Cube (30x30x30cm-12x12x12in) s.d.1989 phonographic records prov. 12-Feb-4 Sotheby's, New York #232/R est:700-900

MARCOLA, Giovanni Battista (1711-1780) Italian

Works on paper
£422 $755 €620 Le jugement de Suzanne (31x38cm-12x15in) i. black chk pen brown ink green wash prov. 18-Mar-4 Christie's, Paris #39/R

MARCOLA, Marco (1740-1793) Italian

Works on paper
£709 $1184 €1000 Rinaldo e Armida (28x20cm-11x8in) s.i.d.1760 blk pencil pen brown ink brown W/C prov. 18-Jun-3 Christie's, Rome #405/R
£1608 $2734 €2300 Two mounted officers (26x40cm-10x16in) brush. 27-Nov-3 Bassenge, Berlin #5476 est:2000

MARCOLA, Marco (attrib) (1740-1793) Italian

£2289 $3800 €3342 Arlecchino, Colombina and other Commedia dell'Arte characters (52x42cm-20x17in) 30-Sep-3 Christie's, Rockefeller NY #362/R est:5000-7000
£22000 $40260 €32120 Carnival scene (73x98cm-29x39in) prov. 8-Jul-4 Sotheby's, London #330/R est:8000-12000
£26000 $47580 €37960 Carnival scene (73x98cm-29x39in) prov. 8-Jul-4 Sotheby's, London #331/R est:8000-12000
£57000 $104310 €83220 Carnival scene (73x98cm-29x39in) prov. 8-Jul-4 Sotheby's, London #332/R est:8000-12000

MARCON, Charles (1920-) French

£1476 $2746 €2200 Personnages a la table (77x56cm-30x22in) s.d.60 s.i.d.1960 verso. 2-Mar-4 Artcurial Briest, Paris #275 est:500-700
£3179 $5785 €4800 Mozart au clavecin (70x70cm-28x28in) mono. s.i.d.1995 verso panel. 18-Jun-4 Charbonneaux, Paris #156/R est:5000-6000
Works on paper
£300 $552 €450 Three people (30x30cm-12x12in) s.d.1979 mixed media board. 9-Jun-4 Le Roux & Morel, Paris #75
£331 $603 €500 Untitled (30x30cm-12x12in) mono. s.d.2003 verso pastel india ink paper on panel. 18-Jun-4 Charbonneaux, Paris #154
£333 $613 €500 Nature morte (30x30cm-12x12in) s.d.82 felt pen. 9-Jun-4 Le Roux & Morel, Paris #74
£397 $723 €600 Rouge ardent (30x30cm-12x12in) mono. s.d.2002 verso paint india ink. 18-Jun-4 Charbonneaux, Paris #155

MARCONI, Rocco (?-1529) Italian

£7285 $13259 €11000 Le Christ et la femme adultere (117x170cm-46x67in) 21-Jun-4 Tajan, Paris #5/R est:10000-12000
£21477 $38443 €32000 Madonna and Child, Saint Joseph and Saint John the Baptist (51x68cm-20x27in) board prov.lit. 26-May-4 Porro, Milan #14/R est:40000-50000

MARCOTTE, Marie Antoinette (1869-1929) French

£276 $510 €400 Le bouquet de roses en cadeau (70x60cm-28x24in) s. 16-Feb-4 Horta, Bruxelles #425

MARCOUSSIS, Louis (1883-1941) French

£15278 $25514 €22000 Composition au visage et au coquillage (35x44cm-14x17in) s.d.1939 canvas on panel lit. 21-Oct-3 Artcurial Briest, Paris #222/R est:15000-18000
£33784 $58108 €49325 Still life before window (45x37cm-18x15in) s.d.26 prov. 2-Dec-3 Koller, Zurich #3070/R est:40000-55000 (S.FR 75000)
£34000 $61201 €51000 Femme au balcon (33x19cm-13x7in) s.d.30 prov. 26-Apr-4 Tajan, Paris #133/R est:12000-15000
£223529 $380000 €326352 Le bar du port (81x65cm-32x26in) s.i.d.1913 canvas on panel prov.exhib.lit. 5-Nov-3 Christie's, Rockefeller NY #265/R est:200000-300000
£264706 $450000 €386471 Bouteille de Whisky et le paquet de scaferlati (55x46cm-22x18in) s.d.1913 oil papier colle prov.exhib.lit. 6-Nov-3 Sotheby's, New York #208/R est:120000-180000
Prints
£30000 $54600 €43800 Portrait de Guillaume Apollinaire (50x28cm-20x11in) init. etching aquatint drypoint. 30-Jun-4 Christie's, London #252/R est:25000-35000
Works on paper
£2148 $3930 €3200 Autoportrait (14x13cm-6x5in) s. Indian ink drawing. 7-Jul-4 Artcurial Briest, Paris #71 est:1200-1500

£3222 $5992 €4800 Pichet et six de trefle (24x35cm-9x14in) s.i. W/C. 3-Mar-4 Tajan, Paris #72/R est:5000-6000
£4100 $6847 €5986 Nature morte au violon et archet (33x47cm-13x19in) s. W/C gouache brush ink pencil prov. 22-Oct-3 Sotheby's, Olympia #128/R est:3000-5000
£4514 $7132 €6500 Nature morte au pichet (19x23cm-7x9in) s. gouache exec.c.1927. 25-Apr-3 Etude de Provence, Marseille #236 est:4000-5000
£53691 $95034 €80000 Alcools. i. dr album. 29-Apr-4 Christie's, Paris #155/R est:100000-150000

MARCUCCI, Lucia (1933-) Italian
£400 $724 €600 Exercise (51x49cm-20x19in) s.i.d.97 verso acrylic collage. 2-Apr-4 Farsetti, Prato #62/R
Works on paper
£839 $1427 €1200 I think that a crown. (130x87cm-51x34in) s.d.72 emulsion acrylic on canvas exhib. 28-Nov-3 Farsetti, Prato #15/R

MARCUCCI, Mario (1910-1992) Italian
£288 $472 €400 Vase of flowers (50x33cm-20x13in) s. cardboard. 10-Jun-3 Pandolfini, Florence #412
£318 $579 €480 Strolling at night (23x16cm-9x6in) s. paper. 17-Jun-4 Galleria Pananti, Florence #478/R
£324 $531 €450 Landscape (39x33cm-15x13in) card. 10-Jun-3 Pandolfini, Florence #300
£533 $981 €800 Square in Viareggio, Tuscany (45x31cm-18x12in) s. cardboard. 11-Jun-4 Farsetti, Prato #445/R
£728 $1326 €1100 Seascape with beach (20x24cm-8x9in) s. cardboard. 17-Jun-4 Galleria Pananti, Florence #477/R
£728 $1326 €1100 Seascape with cliffs (23x32cm-9x13in) s.d.1964 cardboard. 17-Jun-4 Galleria Pananti, Florence #588/R
£743 $1308 €1100 Bottle, glass and egg (22x30cm-9x12in) s. cardboard. 22-May-4 Galleria Pananti, Florence #432/R
£927 $1687 €1400 Boy with red hat (42x29cm-17x11in) s. board. 17-Jun-4 Galleria Pananti, Florence #618/R
£927 $1687 €1400 Basket with peaches (21x35cm-8x14in) cardboard. 17-Jun-4 Galleria Pananti, Florence #587/R
£1014 $1784 €1500 Bather (64x25cm-25x10in) board. 22-May-4 Galleria Pananti, Florence #437/R est:1800-2000
£1014 $1784 €1500 Portrait of Mario Tobino (24x19cm-9x7in) s. board. 22-May-4 Galleria Pananti, Florence #438/R est:1300-1500
£1200 $2208 €1800 Still life (58x48cm-23x19in) s.d.1958. 11-Jun-4 Farsetti, Prato #563/R est:1500-2000
£1748 $2972 €2500 Flowers (53x60cm-21x24in) board. 19-Nov-3 Cambi, Genoa #419/R est:1800-2200
£1757 $3092 €2600 Still life with shell (49x67cm-19x26in) s. cardboard. 22-May-4 Galleria Pananti, Florence #458/R est:2500-3000
£2635 $4638 €3900 Seashore (73x77cm-29x30in) s.d.1968 cardboard. 22-May-4 Galleria Pananti, Florence #457/R est:3000-5000
£2838 $4995 €4200 Self-portrait (50x35cm-20x14in) s.d.1946 board lit. 22-May-4 Galleria Pananti, Florence #439/R est:1500-1800

MARCUS, Gert (1914-) German
Sculpture
£2190 $3724 €3197 Sfera Centripeta - Centrifuga (22x22cm-9x9in) s.d.1970 circular cut marble sold with black wood base. 5-Nov-3 AB Stockholms Auktionsverk #795/R est:15000-20000 (S.KR 29000)

MARCUS, Peter (1889-1934) American
£671 $1100 €973 Landscape (30x41cm-12x16in) s. painted c.1910. 7-Jun-3 Treadway Gallery, Cincinnati #1401

MARCZUKIEWICZ, Adam (1958-) Polish
£828 $1382 €1200 Still life with bowl of fruit (80x60cm-31x24in) s.d.2003 s.i.verso. 16-Nov-3 Agra, Warsaw #64/R

MARCZYNSKI, Adam (1908-) Polish
£1007 $1862 €1500 Houses near the waterfront (62x71cm-24x28in) s.verso. 15-Mar-4 Sotheby's, Amsterdam #180/R est:1100-2000
Works on paper
£2119 $3835 €3094 Untitled (60x49cm-24x19in) s.d.1953 collage paper board. 4-Apr-4 Agra, Warsaw #21/R (P.Z 15000)

MARDEN, Brice (1938-) American
£1317365 $2200000 €1923353 10 dialog 2 (213x152cm-84x60in) s.i.d,1987-88 oil on linen prov.exhib.lit. 12-Nov-3 Sotheby's, New York #22/R est:2000000-3000000
Prints
£1765 $3000 €2577 Five threes (53x75cm-21x30in) s. etching aquatint. 31-Oct-3 Sotheby's, New York #671/R
£2147 $3500 €3135 Untitled (99x128cm-39x50in) s.d.1983 num.PP1/2 screenprint handmade Kurotani Kozo. 24-Sep-3 Christie's, Rockefeller NY #301/R est:1500-2500
£2941 $5000 €4294 Untitled (37x60cm-15x24in) s.d.1971 etching. 31-Oct-3 Sotheby's, New York #668/R
£10000 $17000 €14600 Views (67x52cm-26x20in) etching aquatint album. 31-Oct-3 Sotheby's, New York #672/R
£11299 $20000 €16497 Untitled (81x91cm-32x36in) s.i.d.1979 etching. 30-Apr-4 Sotheby's, New York #397/R est:6000-8000
£19774 $35000 €28870 Etchings to Rexroth (50x40cm-20x16in) s.d.1986 num.44/45 portfolio. 30-Apr-4 Sotheby's, New York #397a/R est:40000-60000
Works on paper
£11976 $20000 €17485 Untitled, suicide drawing (29x20cm-11x8in) s.d.72 ink prov. 13-Nov-3 Sotheby's, New York #132/R est:7000-9000
£19461 $32500 €28413 Untitled, suicide drawing (29x20cm-11x8in) s.d.72 ink prov. 13-Nov-3 Sotheby's, New York #129/R est:10000-12000
£145251 $260000 €212066 Hydra, Summer 1990 IV (35x21cm-14x8in) init.i.d.90 ink gouache prov.exhib. 11-May-4 Christie's, Rockefeller NY #55/R est:200000-250000
£245810 $440000 €358883 Untitled (66x101cm-26x40in) s.d.67 graphite beeswax prov. 11-May-4 Christie's, Rockefeller NY #56/R est:25000-350000
£642458 $1150000 €937989 Teddy's drawing (102x66cm-40x26in) s.d.64 graphite beeswax prov.exhib.lit. 11-May-4 Christie's, Rockefeller NY #54/R est:300000-400000

MARDIGAN, Charlie (1926-1986) Australian
Works on paper
£1176 $2106 €1717 Billabong and dreaming tracks (63x26cm-25x10in) natural earth pigments on eucalyptus bark exec c.1959 prov. 25-May-4 Lawson Menzies, Sydney #142/R est:4000-6000 (A.D 3000)

MARE, Andre (1885-1932) French
£811 $1451 €1200 Cheval en foret (56x46cm-22x18in) painted c.1924. 5-May-4 Coutau Begarie, Paris #52/R
£2267 $4171 €3400 Charlotte au jardin (65x81cm-26x32in) s. painted c.1905. 10-Jun-4 Camard, Paris #114/R est:3000-4000

MARE, Andre and SUE, Louis (20th C) French
Works on paper
£436 $798 €650 Study for ship decoration (52x37cm-20x15in) st.sig.i. Chinese ink chl dr. 6-Jul-4 Maigret, Paris #5/R

MARECHAL, Alice (19/20th C) Belgian
Works on paper
£533 $971 €800 Portrait of a young woman in a pink dress (75x55cm-30x22in) s.d.1925 pastel oval. 1-Jul-4 Van Ham, Cologne #1489

MARECHAL, Émile (19th C) French
£1000 $1810 €1500 Arcadian harbour with figures (35x654cm-14x257in) s. panel lit. 3-Apr-4 Hans Stahl, Hamburg #56/R est:1700

MARECHAL, François (1861-?) Belgian
£282 $487 €400 Village d'Italie (40x50cm-16x20in) s. 10-Dec-3 Hotel des Ventes Mosan, Brussels #244
Works on paper
£775 $1340 €1100 Jeune femme silencieuse (18x25cm-7x10in) s.d.19.01.1897 mixed media graphite col crayon. 10-Dec-3 Hotel des Ventes Mosan, Brussels #219/R

MARECHAL, Jacques (1953-) Belgian?
Works on paper
£420 $713 €600 L'arbre mecanique (35x19cm-14x7in) graphite ink. 23-Nov-3 Cornette de St.Cyr, Paris #217

MARECHAL, Jean Baptiste (attrib) (18th C) French
Works on paper
£1639 $3000 €2393 Figures in a garden below an amphitheatre. Figures gathered at a pool (30x43cm-12x17in) black chk pen ink W/C pair prov. 3-Jun-4 Christie's, Rockefeller NY #1143/R est:1000-1500
£4762 $8524 €7000 Vue de parc avec terrasse (21x34cm-8x13in) pen ink htd W/C. 19-Mar-4 Beaussant & Lefèvre, Paris #29/R est:3000-4000

MARECHAL, Louis (1884-1971) French
£440 $800 €642 Spring landscape (46x69cm-18x27in) s.verso. 7-Feb-4 Sloans & Kenyon, Bethesda #1262/R

MAREELS, Maurice (1893-1975) Belgian
£367 $675 €550 Hiver a Uccle (70x55cm-28x22in) s. 14-Jun-4 Horta, Bruxelles #397

MAREK, Charles S (20th C) American
£378 $650 €552 Moonlight marine, Hawaii (46x56cm-18x22in) s.d.1958 board. 7-Dec-3 Treadway Gallery, Cincinnati #533/R

MAREK, Dusan Tomas (1926-1993) Australian
£305 $482 €442 Untitled (18x24cm-7x9in) s.i. acrylic on card. 22-Jul-3 Lawson Menzies, Sydney #156/R (A.D 750)
£840 $1528 €1226 Rays (20x54cm-8x21in) i.verso board prov. 16-Jun-4 Deutscher-Menzies, Melbourne #523/R est:800-1200 (A.D 2200)

MAREK, Emil van (19th C) German?
£284 $474 €400 Washerwomen in front of farmstead (39x34cm-15x13in) s. canvas on panel. 17-Oct-3 Berlinghof, Heidelberg #1068/R

MAREK, Jeremy (20th C) British?
£480 $878 €701 Children playing (28x38cm-11x15in) s.d.1969 board. 6-Apr-4 Capes Dunn, Manchester #854/R

MAREMBERT, Jean (c.1900-1968) French
£521 $869 €750 Fantome du Moulin - Mesnil (73x92cm-29x36in) s. 21-Oct-3 Artcurial Briest, Paris #226
Works on paper
£243 $406 €350 Personnages au cabaret (38x50cm-15x20in) s. gouache. 21-Oct-3 Artcurial Briest, Paris #225

MARESCA, Mario (20th C) Italian
£317 $538 €463 Strada di Genova (40x80cm-16x31in) s. 28-Nov-3 Zofingen, Switzerland #2627 (S.FR 700)
£629 $1051 €900 Capri, Marina Grande (65x92cm-26x36in) s. 24-Jun-3 Finarte Semenzato, Rome #119/R

MARET, Jacques (1901-) French
£799 $1318 €1150 Composition surrealiste (54x65cm-21x26in) s.d. s.verso. 1-Jul-3 Lemoine & Ferrando, Paris #74/R

MAREVNA, Marie (1892-1984) Russian
£1049 $1783 €1500 Palmiers a Alexandrie (57x38cm-22x15in) s.i. 18-Nov-3 Vanderkindere, Brussels #88 est:1500-2000
£10000 $17900 €14600 Spring landscape with vase of flowers (110x60cm-43x24in) s. oil pencil on board. 26-May-4 Sotheby's, London #296/R est:10000-15000
£60000 $107400 €87600 Descent from the Cross (153x183cm-60x72in) s.d.1955 verso exhib. 26-May-4 Sotheby's, London #293/R est:30000-40000
Works on paper
£604 $1105 €900 Portrait of a woman (31x23cm-12x9in) s.d.40 W/C. 7-Jul-4 Artcurial Briest, Paris #130
£650 $1196 €949 Study of two boys with a ball (30x23cm-12x9in) s.d.46 W/C. 8-Jun-4 Gorringes, Lewes #2058
£1312 $2073 €1850 Pont d'Avignon (45x58cm-18x23in) s. W/C. 24-Jul-3 Claude Boisgirard, Paris #51/R
£1600 $2864 €2336 Mother and child (37x25cm-15x10in) s. ink. 26-May-4 Sotheby's, Olympia #476/R est:1000-1500
£2721 $4871 €4000 Deux amies (44x63cm-17x25in) s. lead pencil col crayons. 19-Mar-4 Millon & Associes, Paris #98/R est:5000-6000
£4225 $7310 €6000 Le petit marin (62x47cm-24x19in) s.d.1939 graphite col crayon. 9-Dec-3 Chambelland & Giafferi, Paris #93/R est:8000-10000

MAREY, Étienne Jules (1830-1904) ?
Photographs
£9444 $17000 €13788 Man jumping over hurdle (6x9cm-2x4in) i. gelatin silver print lit. 22-Apr-4 Phillips, New York #66/R est:20000-30000

MARFAING, Andre (1925-1987) French
£2013 $3564 €3000 Composition (61x50cm-24x20in) s.d.74 prov. 28-Apr-4 Artcurial Briest, Paris #276/R est:3000-5000
£2168 $3620 €3100 Composition (61x50cm-24x20in) s.d.1974. 29-Jun-3 Versailles Encheres #25/R
£2500 $4600 €3800 Composition (126x79cm-50x31in) s.d.1977 acrylic paper on canvas. 27-Jun-4 Versailles Encheres #59/R est:4000-5000
£4200 $7644 €6300 Untitled (92x73cm-36x29in) s. d.1971 verso acrylic. 29-Jun-4 Cornette de St.Cyr, Paris #45/R est:4000-5000
£4578 $7920 €6500 Composition (114x146cm-45x57in) s.d.64 s.i.d.verso prov. 9-Dec-3 Artcurial Briest, Paris #419/R est:4000-5000

MARFFY, Odon (1878-1959) Hungarian
£2610 $4515 €3811 Landscape with orange - coloured sky (34x49cm-13x19in) s. cardboard. 12-Dec-3 Kieselbach, Budapest #16/R (H.F 1000000)
£3162 $5723 €4617 Italian landscape (38x60cm-15x24in) s. 16-Apr-4 Mu Terem Galeria, Budapest #24/R (H.F 1200000)
£3226 $5935 €4710 Seated woman with hand mirror (63x46cm-25x18in) s. board exhib. 14-Jun-4 Waddingtons, Toronto #314/R est:8000-10000 (C.D 8000)
£3915 $6773 €5716 Girl combing (49x60cm-19x24in) s. 12-Dec-3 Kieselbach, Budapest #158/R (H.F 1500000)
£4543 $8041 €6633 Gladioli (60x50cm-24x20in) s. 28-Apr-4 Kieselbach, Budapest #19/R (H.F 1700000)
£4887 $8112 €7135 Fruit bowl (46x55cm-18x22in) s. 4-Oct-3 Kieselbach, Budapest #64/R (H.F 1800000)
£5742 $9934 €8383 Hillside with the Lake Balaton in the background (34x49cm-13x19in) s. cardboard. 12-Dec-3 Kieselbach, Budapest #99/R (H.F 2200000)
£7904 $14307 €11540 Csinszka with lion's tooth (56x45cm-22x18in) s. 16-Apr-4 Mu Terem Galeria, Budapest #36/R (H.F 3000000)
£10316 $17125 €15061 Sunflowers in a glass vase (76x60cm-30x24in) s. 4-Oct-3 Kieselbach, Budapest #43/R (H.F 3800000)
£12292 $21757 €17946 Lady in a straw hat (81x64cm-32x25in) s. cardboard. 28-Apr-4 Kieselbach, Budapest #196/R (H.F 4600000)
£17126 $30998 €25004 Picking fruits (61x50cm-24x20in) 16-Apr-4 Mu Terem Galeria, Budapest #122/R (H.F 6500000)
£34739 $61488 €50719 Rumour (115x120cm-45x47in) s. painted c.1920. 28-Apr-4 Kieselbach, Budapest #141/R (H.F 13000000)
£45428 $80407 €66325 Still life (44x55cm-17x22in) s. 28-Apr-4 Kieselbach, Budapest #200/R (H.F 17000000)
£83520 $144490 €121939 Boy and girl on a green bench (95x115cm-37x45in) s. painted c.1907. 12-Dec-3 Kieselbach, Budapest #32/R (H.F 32000000)
Works on paper
£422 $763 €616 Self portrait (31x29cm-12x11in) s. W/C. 16-Apr-4 Mu Terem Galeria, Budapest #165/R (H.F 160000)
£1140 $1893 €1664 Csinszka (34x45cm-13x18in) s. mixed media. 4-Oct-3 Kieselbach, Budapest #20/R (H.F 420000)
£7482 $13244 €10924 Dynamic self portrait (90x73cm-35x29in) s. pastel. 28-Apr-4 Kieselbach, Budapest #73/R (H.F 2800000)

MARGALEF PALACIN, Jose (1900-1985) Spanish
£362 $655 €550 Still life of fruit (65x81cm-26x32in) s. 14-Apr-4 Ansorena, Madrid #86/R

MARGAT, Andre (1903-1999) French
£1126 $2060 €1700 Chouettes (64x53cm-25x21in) s. cardboard. 7-Apr-4 Maigret, Paris #5/R est:1500-2000
Works on paper
£838 $1500 €1223 Three bats (51x79cm-20x31in) s. W/C. 13-May-4 Dallas Auction Gallery, Dallas #176/R est:400-600
£2600 $4862 €3796 Two wild boars (49x65cm-19x26in) s.d.30 chl pastel silver leaf. 24-Feb-4 Sotheby's, Olympia #197/R est:2000-2500
£13380 $23415 €19000 Pantheres (60x160cm-24x63in) s.d.1963 lacquer gold leaf panel. 17-Dec-3 Rabourdin & Choppin de Janvry, Paris #151/R est:7500-9000

MARGESON, Gilbert Tucker (1852-?) American
£215 $400 €314 High seas (23x30cm-9x12in) s. i.verso board. 5-Mar-4 Skinner, Boston #567/R
£1584 $2550 €2313 Rockport Harbour (41x51cm-16x20in) s. 20-Aug-3 James Julia, Fairfield #1659/R est:800-1200

MARGETSON, Helen Howard (1860-?) British
Works on paper
£2000 $3580 €2920 Beryl sewing (65x43cm-26x17in) s. W/C. 26-May-4 Sotheby's, Olympia #188/R est:2000-3000

MARGETSON, William Henry (1861-1940) British
£9000 $15480 €13140 A woman in white (73x61cm-29x24in) s.d.1904. 4-Dec-3 Mellors & Kirk, Nottingham #878/R est:3000-4000
Works on paper
£450 $810 €657 The amulet (44x33cm-17x13in) s. W/C exhib. 21-Jan-4 Sotheby's, Olympia #256/R
£800 $1472 €1168 First Noel (28x18cm-11x7in) s. W/C. 23-Mar-4 Bonhams, Knightsbridge #11/R

MARGOLIES, Samuel L (1898-1974) American
Prints
£2044 $3250 €2984 Men of steel (37x30cm-15x12in) s. drypoint. 12-Sep-3 Skinner, Boston #116/R est:600
£2096 $3500 €3060 Builders of Babylon (36x28cm-14x11in) inti.i. etching aquatint edition of 250. 21-Oct-3 Bonhams & Butterfields, San Francisco #1070/R
£2542 $4500 €3711 Men of steel (38x30cm-15x12in) s.i. etching executed c.1940. 30-Apr-4 Sotheby's, New York #24/R est:3000-5000
£3128 $5600 €4567 Man's canyons (30x22cm-12x9in) s.i. aquatint etching. 6-May-4 Swann Galleries, New York #504/R est:6000-9000

MARGOTTI, Anacleto (1899-1984) Italian
£1267 $2280 €1900 Mechanic ploughing (50x60cm-20x24in) s. board. 22-Apr-4 Finarte Semenzato, Rome #172 est:500-600

MARGOTTI, Francesco (1868-1946) Italian
£336 $628 €500 View of Paris (14x18cm-6x7in) board. 26-Feb-4 Cambi, Genoa #558/R
£369 $690 €550 Beach (12x20cm-5x8in) card. 26-Feb-4 Cambi, Genoa #553/R

MARGOTTON, René (20th C) French
£350 $601 €500 Paysage provencal (54x65cm-21x26in) s. 7-Dec-3 Lesieur & Le Bars, Le Havre #235

MARGRY, Antoine (19th C) French
£2844 $4750 €4152 Floral still lifes (60x49cm-24x19in) s. pair. 7-Oct-3 Sotheby's, New York #78/R est:4000-6000

MARGUERAY, Michel (1938-) French
£979 $1684 €1400 La plage du Havre (55x65cm-22x26in) s. 7-Dec-3 Lesieur & Le Bars, Le Havre #244

MARGULIES, Joseph (1896-1984) American
£435 $800 €635 Rowboats, Gloucester harbour (23x30cm-9x12in) s. canvasboard exhib. 25-Jun-4 Freeman, Philadelphia #153/R
Works on paper
£242 $450 €353 Harbour view (51x71cm-20x28in) W/C. 5-Mar-4 Skinner, Boston #540/R

MARIA, Francesco de (1845-1908) Italian
£11111 $20000 €16222 Tambourine player (105x81cm-41x32in) s. prov. 22-Apr-4 Christie's, Rockefeller NY #203/R est:20000-30000

MARIA, Nicola de (1954-) Italian
£1964 $3338 €2867 Untitled (15x23cm-6x9in) s. verso. 4-Nov-3 Bukowskis, Stockholm #616/R est:15000-20000 (S.KR 26000)
£4895 $8322 €7000 Untitled (34x25cm-13x10in) tempera col pencil collage. 25-Nov-3 Sotheby's, Milan #145/R est:4000-5000
£6000 $10860 €8760 Testa della poesia (27x18cm-11x7in) i. i.d.1983 verso acrylic two joined canvases prov. 1-Apr-4 Christie's, Kensington #231/R est:5000-7000
£8000 $13360 €11680 Pace (51x40cm-20x16in) i.stretcher prov. 22-Oct-3 Christie's, London #45/R est:8000-12000
£8054 $14416 €12000 Pre-historical uncounsciousness (21x15cm-8x6in) s.i.d.1989 verso paper double-sided prov. 25-May-4 Sotheby's, Milan #319/R est:8000-10000
£17000 $30940 €24820 Testa de Donna (40x50cm-16x20in) s.d.1987 i.overlap oil pencil prov. 6-Feb-4 Sotheby's, London #247/R est:12000-15000
£21000 $38220 €30660 Poesia dipinta in estate (150x109cm-59x43in) i. d.1999 2000 verso acrylic prov.exhib. 5-Feb-4 Christie's, London #142/R est:14000-18000
Sculpture
£8500 $14195 €12410 Testa del pittore (30x24x3cm-12x9x1in) s.d.1985 overlap two canvases mounted together prov. 22-Oct-3 Christie's, London #46/R est:8000-12000
Works on paper
£671 $1242 €1000 Untitled (23x23cm-9x9in) s. pastel. 15-Mar-4 Sotheby's, Amsterdam #267 est:250-350
£1000 $1840 €1460 Regno dei fiori (27x44cm-11x17in) s. col crayon prov. 24-Jun-4 Sotheby's, Olympia #585/R est:1000-1500

£2193 $4035 €3202 Acqua di pioggia (16x20cm-6x8in) s.i.d.1978 W/C gouache. 23-Jun-4 Koller, Zurich #3121/R est:2000-3000 (S.FR 5000)
£13000 $23530 €18980 Universo senza bombe, Regno dei fiori (97x128cm-38x50in) s.i. s.i.d.MCXXXVI W/C pencil collage on printed world map. 1-Apr-4 Christie's, Kensington #240/R est:6000-8000

MARIAN, Aldo (20th C) Italian
£385 $642 €550 Canal in Venice (50x70cm-20x28in) s. 26-Jun-3 Sant Agostino, Torino #56/R

MARIANI, C (19th C) Italian
£2897 $5214 €4200 Landscape with houses (65x92cm-26x36in) s. 26-Jan-4 Ansorena, Madrid #188/R est:4200

MARIANI, Carlo Maria (1931-) Italian
Works on paper
£3793 $6334 €5500 Face (54x49cm-21x19in) s.d.92 verso graphite W/C. 13-Nov-3 Finarte Semenzato, Rome #182/R est:2500-3000

MARIANI, Francisco (20th C) Argentinian
£440 $800 €642 Station, Cacheuta (13x20cm-5x8in) s.d.1947. 5-Jul-4 Arroyo, Buenos Aires #17/R
£663 $1200 €968 Lifts (24x34cm-9x13in) board. 30-Mar-4 Arroyo, Buenos Aires #2

MARIANI, Pompeo (1857-1927) Italian
£1736 $2951 €2500 Beached boats (17x45cm-7x18in) s.i.d.1889 board. 28-Oct-3 Il Ponte, Milan #147
£4965 $8291 €7000 Pastoral scene (50x70cm-20x28in) s.i.d.1919 cardboard lit. 20-Oct-3 Sant Agostino, Torino #304/R est:9000
£5594 $9343 €8000 Stream with ducks (58x72cm-23x28in) s. cardboard. 26-Jun-3 Sant Agostino, Torino #305/R est:10000-14000
Works on paper
£399 $654 €550 Untitled (12x18cm-5x7in) s. pencil. 29-May-3 Galleria Pace, Milan #85/R
£694 $1181 €1000 Seascape (18x25cm-7x10in) W/C. 1-Nov-3 Meeting Art, Vercelli #67/R
£933 $1680 €1400 Landscape with herd and goats (23x30cm-9x12in) init. W/C. 21-Apr-4 Finarte Semenzato, Milan #597/R est:1200-1500
£1014 $1664 €1400 Summer lights (8x13cm-3x5in) s.i.d.904 mixed media. 27-May-3 Il Ponte, Milan #948/R
£1216 $2141 €1800 Ships at high sea (8x13cm-3x5in) s.i. W/C card. 19-May-4 Il Ponte, Milan #572 est:1500-2000
£1611 $2883 €2400 Lake landscape (24x34cm-9x13in) s. W/C canvas on paper. 25-May-4 Finarte Semenzato, Milan #161/R est:2000-2300
£3356 $6007 €5000 Woman on the cliff (27x20cm-11x8in) s. W/C. 25-May-4 Finarte Semenzato, Milan #162/R est:3500-3800

MARIANI, Umberto (1936-) Italian
£439 $773 €650 Untitled (53x43cm-21x17in) s.d.1999 acrylic lead board on masonite. 19-May-4 Il Ponte, Milan #1135
Works on paper
£333 $613 €500 Untitled (30x24cm-12x9in) s.d.1994 lead board. 12-Jun-4 Meeting Art, Vercelli #785
£400 $736 €600 Untitled (45x33cm-18x13in) s.d.1995 lead board. 12-Jun-4 Meeting Art, Vercelli #769/R
£513 $945 €770 Untitled (36x40cm-14x16in) s.i.d.2003 verso lead. 12-Jun-4 Meeting Art, Vercelli #803
£633 $1165 €950 OK (60x60cm-24x24in) s.i.d.1990 verso mixed media plastic board. 12-Jun-4 Meeting Art, Vercelli #791

MARIANO DA PERUGIA (c.1470-c.1527) Italian
£46667 $85400 €70000 Madonna and Child with angels (29x24cm-11x9in) board. 1-Jun-4 Sotheby's, Milan #145/R est:15000-20000

MARICH, Geza (1913-1975) Canadian
£203 $344 €296 Autumn River (61x91cm-24x36in) s. prov. 23-Nov-3 Levis, Calgary #504/R (C.D 450)

MARIE ALEXANDRINE (1849-1922) German
£433 $797 €650 Young beggar (88x60cm-35x24in) s.d.1874. 11-Jun-4 Wendl, Rudolstadt #4154/R

MARIE, Adrien Emmanuel (1848-1891) French
Works on paper
£361 $596 €520 Fantasia (55x39cm-22x15in) W/C. 3-Jul-3 Claude Aguttes, Neuilly #124a

MARIEN, Marcel (1920-1993) Belgian
Sculpture
£1200 $2196 €1800 Les memoires de Jack l'Eventreur (17x31cm-7x12in) s.d.1971 wood knife. 7-Jun-4 Palais de Beaux Arts, Brussels #187/R est:600-800
£1342 $2376 €2000 Le cantique des cantiques (29x22x16cm-11x9x6in) s.d.1969 collage. 27-Apr-4 Campo, Vlaamse Kaai #505 est:1000-1200
Works on paper
£320 $573 €480 La double vie des chretiens (17x24cm-7x9in) s.i.d.87 collage. 15-May-4 De Vuyst, Lokeren #216
£563 $975 €800 Le cantique des cantiques (36x19cm-14x7in) s.i.d.1978 pastel. 13-Dec-3 De Vuyst, Lokeren #223
£1000 $1830 €1500 Le plaisir au soleil (20x27cm-8x11in) s.d.74 collage. 7-Jun-4 Palais de Beaux Arts, Brussels #186 est:500-700

MARIESCHI, Jacopo (1711-1791) Italian
£8144 $13520 €11890 Three Magi (42x46cm-17x18in) s. 4-Oct-3 Kieselbach, Budapest #168/R (H.F 3000000)

MARIESCHI, Michele (1696-1743) Italian
£11111 $18889 €16000 Capriccio with ruins and obelisk (58x73cm-23x29in) prov. 28-Oct-3 Il Ponte, Milan #386/R
£11458 $19479 €16500 Capriccio with ruins and fountain (58x73cm-23x29in) prov. 28-Oct-3 Il Ponte, Milan #387/R
£105556 $190000 €154112 Capriccio of a Mediterranean coastal town with fishermen by a bridge (83x110cm-33x43in) prov. 23-Jan-4 Christie's, Rockefeller NY #87/R est:200000-300000
£120000 $216000 €175200 San Giorgio Maggiore, Venice, with the Doge's Palace and the Riva degli schiavoni in the distance (62x99cm-24x39in) painted with studio prov. 21-Apr-4 Christie's, London #102/R est:30000-50000
£240000 $436800 €360000 Prison and Palazzo Ducale seen from San Marco, Venice (55x83cm-22x33in) prov. 29-Jun-4 Sotheby's, Paris #38/R est:300000-450000
Prints
£1800 $3240 €2700 View of Rialto Bridge (31x46cm-12x18in) engraving lit. 21-Apr-4 Finarte Semenzato, Milan #446/R est:2500-3500
£2014 $3223 €2800 View of Saint Basso Square, Venice (46x62cm-18x24in) engraving. 14-May-3 Finarte Semenzato, Milan #371/R est:2000-3000
£20000 $34400 €29200 Magnificentiores selectioresque urbis venetiarum prospectus. etchings folio. 4-Dec-3 Sotheby's, London #38/R est:20000-25000

MARIESCHI, Michele (style) (1696-1743) Italian
£19000 $32300 €27740 Venice, view of the Grand Canal with the Fondaco Deiturchi (62x98cm-24x39in) 30-Oct-3 Sotheby's, Olympia #188/R est:8000-12000
£26951 $45008 €38000 Views of Venice (44x60cm-17x24in) set of four. 17-Oct-3 Tajan, Paris #40/R est:20000-30000

MARIKA, Mawalan (1908-1967) Australian
Works on paper
£267 $425 €387 Yirrkala-Sacred story (61x33cm-24x13in) d.1963 pigment bark board three panels. 12-Sep-3 Aspire, Cleveland #77
£330 $525 €479 Turtle and fish dance (66x20cm-26x8in) pigment bark board. 12-Sep-3 Aspire, Cleveland #76
£332 $621 €498 Turtle and fish dance (45x21cm-18x8in) earth pigments eucalyptus bark prov. 26-Jul-4 Sotheby's, Melbourne #528 (A.D 850)
£781 $1461 €1172 Untitled (43x35cm-17x14in) s. earth pigments eucalyptus bark exec.c.1962 prov. 26-Jul-4 Sotheby's, Melbourne #524/R (A.D 2000)
£938 $1753 €1407 Yirrkala, sacred story (61x32cm-24x13in) bears name.i.d.1963 verso earth pigments eucalyptus bark prov. 26-Jul-4 Sotheby's, Melbourne #527/R (A.D 2400)
£976 $1541 €1415 Untitled (29x16cm-11x6in) earth pigments eucalyptus bark exec.c.1960 multi artists 3 prov. 28-Jul-3 Sotheby's, Paddington #330 est:1000-1500 (A.D 2400)
£1626 $2569 €2358 Djanda (74x47cm-29x19in) earth pigments eucalyptus bark exec.c.1960 prov. 28-Jul-3 Sotheby's, Paddington #233/R est:4000-6000 (A.D 4000)
£1626 $2569 €2358 Untitled (88x44cm-35x17in) earth pigments eucalyptus bark exec.c.1963 prov. 28-Jul-3 Sotheby's, Paddington #234/R est:4000-6000 (A.D 4000)
£1829 $2890 €2652 Picture of plenty. Daymirri the whale. Untitled (41x22cm-16x9in) earth pigments eucalyptus exec.c.1960 multi artists 3 prov. 28-Jul-3 Sotheby's, Paddington #328 est:1500-2500 (A.D 4500)
£2500 $4675 €3750 Bremer Island turtle hunter (56x69cm-22x27in) i.verso earth pigments eucalyptus bark exec.c.1960 prov. 26-Jul-4 Sotheby's, Melbourne #153/R est:8000-12000 (A.D 6400)
£2846 $4496 €4127 Djambuwal. Seagull. Sacred dreaming. Djambuwal the thunderman (36x18cm-14x7in) earth pigments eucalyptus bark exec.c.1960 four prov. 28-Jul-3 Sotheby's, Paddington #326/R est:4000-6000 (A.D 7000)
£3008 $4753 €4362 Yalangbara. Crow and turkey. Bush turkey (48x26cm-19x10in) earth pigments eucalyptus bark exec.c.1960 three prov. 28-Jul-3 Sotheby's, Paddington #325/R est:3000-5000 (A.D 7400)
£3049 $4817 €4421 Djanda. Jarwolawal. Sacred bush turkey (49x17cm-19x7in) earth pigments eucalyptus bark exec.c.1960 three prov. 28-Jul-3 Sotheby's, Paddington #324/R est:5000-7000 (A.D 7500)
£20325 $32114 €29471 Yalangbara (185x63cm-73x25in) earth pigments eucalyptus bark exec.c.1960 multi artists. 28-Jul-3 Sotheby's, Paddington #83/R est:40000-60000 (A.D 50000)

MARIKA, Milirrpum (1908-?) Australian
Works on paper
£1951 $3083 €2829 Legend of Djang'Kawu (182x69cm-72x27in) earth pigments eucalyptus bark exec.c.1972 prov.exhib.lit. 28-Jul-3 Sotheby's, Paddington #253/R est:3000-5000 (A.D 4800)

MARIKA, Wandjuk (1927-1987) Australian
Works on paper
£313 $584 €470 Djanda, goannas, and snake (47x19cm-19x7in) ep eucalyptus bark exec.c.1962. 26-Jul-4 Sotheby's, Melbourne #526 (A.D 800)
£586 $1096 €879 Untitled (121x39cm-48x15in) earth pigments eucalyptus bark prov. 26-Jul-4 Sotheby's, Melbourne #525/R (A.D 1500)
£3659 $5780 €5306 Wawilak sisters. Boibaigaine. Sacred burial (46x27cm-18x11in) earth pigments eucalyptus bark exec.c.1960 three prov. 28-Jul-3 Sotheby's, Paddington #322/R est:4000-6000 (A.D 9000)

MARIKA, Wandjuk (attrib) (1927-1987) Australian
Works on paper
£1484 $2776 €2226 Untitled (37x98cm-15x39in) d.1962 verso earth pigments eucalyptus bark prov. 26-Jul-4 Sotheby's, Melbourne #154/R est:7000-10000 (A.D 3800)

MARIL, Herman (1908-1986) American

£455 $800 €664 Rocky Cliffs (33x25cm-13x10in) s. acrylic paper. 3-Jan-4 Outer Cape Auctions, Provincetown #63/R
£483 $850 €705 Pines and deep dunes (25x33cm-10x13in) s. acrylic. 3-Jan-4 Outer Cape Auctions, Provincetown #89/R
Works on paper
£813 $1300 €1187 Net and shore (30x46cm-12x18in) s. W/C. 20-Sep-3 Sloans & Kenyon, Bethesda #673/R est:300-400

MARILHAT, Prosper (1811-1847) French

Works on paper
£282 $487 €400 Un chateau sur une colline (31x36cm-12x14in) i. blk crayon stumping. 10-Dec-3 Piasa, Paris #89

MARILHAT, Prosper (attrib) (1811-1847) French

Works on paper
£267 $483 €400 Estaminet Oriental, Basse Egypte (29x46cm-11x18in) i. graphite black crayon. 30-Mar-4 Rossini, Paris #1027

MARIN BAGUES, Francisco (1879-1961) Spanish

£2819 $5243 €4200 Girl with dog (75x65cm-30x26in) s. 2-Mar-4 Ansorena, Madrid #159/R est:550

MARIN LOPEZ, Diego (1865-?) Spanish

£268 $475 €400 Portrait of Arabian man (37x27cm-15x11in) s. 27-Apr-4 Durán, Madrid #1129
£268 $475 €400 Portrait of Arabian man (35x27cm-14x11in) s. 27-Apr-4 Durán, Madrid #1128

MARIN MARIE (1901-1987) French

£517 $947 €750 Trois mats barque par temps de brume (46x58cm-18x23in) 31-Jan-4 Neret-Minet, Paris #157/R
Works on paper
£2857 $5114 €4200 Bateaux de guerre (48x63cm-19x25in) s. W/C gouache. 20-Mar-4 Binoche, Orleans #28 est:1500-2000
£3724 $6815 €5400 Portrait de bateau (29x39cm-11x15in) s. W/C gouache. 31-Jan-4 Robin & Fattori, Granville #128a
£9195 $16918 €13700 Voilier en mer (53x73cm-21x29in) s. gouache. 29-Mar-4 Lombrail & Teucquam, Paris #44/R
£11034 $20193 €16000 Trois mats barque, calem blanc (52x63cm-20x25in) s. W/C gouache. 31-Jan-4 Robin & Fattori, Granville #128

MARIN RAMOS, Eustaquio (1873-1959) Spanish

£4106 $7473 €6200 Fete espagnole (118x168cm-46x66in) s. cardboard. 20-Jun-4 Salle des ventes Pillet, Lyon la Foret #30/R est:5000-7000

MARIN, Enrique (1876-1940) Spanish

Works on paper
£297 $550 €446 Village street with burro and man (36x25cm-14x10in) s. W/C graphite paper on board. 17-Jul-4 Skinner, Boston #370
£530 $964 €800 Rue a Grenade (38x28cm-15x11in) s.i. W/C. 15-Jun-4 Blanchet, Paris #127/R
£600 $1086 €900 Village street (18x10cm-7x4in) s. W/C. 30-Mar-4 Segre, Madrid #1/R

MARIN, Javier (1962-) Mexican

Sculpture
£4121 $7500 €6017 Fin (79x84cm-31x33in) i.d.15.V.95 brown pat. bronze steel base. 29-Jun-4 Sotheby's, New York #676/R est:12000-18000
£12849 $23000 €18760 Little man standing (88x28x32cm-35x11x13in) st.sig. num.4/4 pat bronze. 26-May-4 Sotheby's, New York #168/R est:12000-18000

MARIN, John (1870-1953) American

£1796 $3000 €2622 Restaurant (13x15cm-5x6in) s. pencil prov. 23-Oct-3 Shannon's, Milford #249/R est:4000-6000
£45455 $80000 €66364 City skyline (20x25cm-8x10in) s.d.35 canvasboard prov.exhib.lit. 19-May-4 Sotheby's, New York #124/R est:80000-120000
£85227 $150000 €124431 Two sloops on a squally sea (36x46cm-14x18in) s.d.39 i.d.verso canvasboard prov. 19-May-4 Sotheby's, New York #125/R est:125000-175000
Prints
£2011 $3600 €2936 Downtown, the El (17x22cm-7x9in) s. etching. 6-May-4 Swann Galleries, New York #506/R est:2500-3500
£5882 $10000 €8588 Broad street (21x17cm-8x7in) s.i. etching. 6-Nov-3 Swann Galleries, New York #617/R est:4000-6000
Works on paper
£346 $550 €505 Landscape with house (20x33cm-8x13in) s. W/C. 9-Mar-3 William Jenack, New York #416
£1429 $2500 €2086 Circus elephants (20x25cm-8x10in) s.d.48 col pencil graphite. 19-Dec-3 Sotheby's, New York #1017/R est:2500-3500
£1713 $3100 €2501 Five boat movement (18x23cm-7x9in) sketch. 19-Apr-4 Caddigan, Hanover #3/R
£2174 $4000 €3174 Paris from the Seine (13x18cm-5x7in) s.i. pencil exec. c.1906. 10-Jun-4 Swann Galleries, New York #163/R est:2000-3000
£2762 $5000 €4033 White Lake, Sullivan County, New York (25x33cm-10x13in) s.d.88 i.d.1888 verso W/C prov.exhib.lit. 31-Mar-4 Sotheby's, New York #16/R est:7000-10000
£4469 $8000 €6525 Cow and two year old bull (41x48cm-16x19in) s.d.18 W/C pencil exhib. 26-May-4 Doyle, New York #154/R est:8000-10000
£5946 $11000 €8681 City Hall, World and Tribune, New York City (18x23cm-7x9in) s. pencil col crayon exec.c.1924 prov.exhib. 11-Mar-4 Christie's, Rockefeller NY #91/R est:8000-12000
£6145 $11000 €8972 Maine Island (30x38cm-12x15in) s.d.27 W/C. 8-Jan-4 James Julia, Fairfield #710/R est:5000-10000
£6250 $10000 €9125 Spring (23x33cm-9x13in) s.d.49 W/C pencil prov. 20-Sep-3 Sloans & Kenyon, Bethesda #1197/R est:12000-18000
£7821 $14000 €11419 New York street movement and figure (25x20cm-10x8in) s. crayon prov.exhib. 16-May-4 Wright, Chicago #140/R est:15000-20000
£11364 $20000 €16591 New York (56x69cm-22x27in) s.d.25 prov.exhib.lit. 19-May-4 Sotheby's, New York #134/R est:25000-35000
£12500 $22000 €18250 Movement, sea and sky, Cape Split, Maine (44x57cm-17x22in) s.d.42 W/C pencil prov.exhib.lit. 18-May-4 Christie's, Rockefeller NY #136/R est:30000-50000
£12941 $22000 €18894 Castorland, New York (41x36cm-16x14in) s.d.13 W/C prov. 30-Oct-3 Phillips, New York #86/R est:25000-45000
£19886 $35000 €29034 Herring Weirs, Deer Isle, Maine (39x51cm-15x20in) s.d.28 W/C pencil prov.exhib. 18-May-4 Christie's, Rockefeller NY #140/R est:40000-60000
£21802 $37500 €31831 Pertaining to Cape Split, Maines (46x70cm-18x28in) s.d.39 W/C prov.exhib. 3-Dec-3 Sotheby's, New York #62/R est:20000-30000
£22727 $40000 €33181 New York Stock Exchange (34x25cm-13x10in) s. crayon exec c.1924 prov.exhib.lit. 18-May-4 Christie's, Rockefeller NY #138/R est:25000-35000
£23256 $40000 €33954 New Mexico landscape (38x52cm-15x20in) s.d.29 W/C prov.exhib.lit. 3-Dec-3 Sotheby's, New York #50/R est:40000-60000
£116279 $200000 €169767 Near spring valley, New York (55x68cm-22x27in) s.d.31 W/C prov.exhib.lit. 3-Dec-3 Sotheby's, New York #49/R est:80000-120000

MARIN, Joseph Charles (style) (1759-1834) French

Sculpture
£4420 $8000 €6453 Nymph and two Bacchic putti (11x18cm-4x7in) s.verso terracotta. 16-Apr-4 Sotheby's, New York #24/R est:8000-12000

MARINALI, Orazio (attrib) (1643-1720) Italian

Sculpture
£3403 $5785 €4900 Moses. white marble. 29-Oct-3 Il Ponte, Milan #657/R
£4800 $8304 €7008 Head of an old woman (25cm-10in) white marble col marble socle lit. 12-Dec-3 Sotheby's, London #221/R est:4000-6000

MARINARI, Onorio (after) (1627-1715) Italian

£6000 $10200 €8760 Saint Agnes (72x56cm-28x22in) 31-Oct-3 Christie's, Kensington #118/R est:6000-8000

MARINARI, Onorio (attrib) (1627-1715) Italian

£1389 $2500 €2028 Portrait of a scholar (116x87cm-46x34in) prov.lit. 21-Jan-4 Sotheby's, New York #95/R est:4000-6000
£10140 $16934 €14500 Saint Agatha (67x50cm-26x20in) 7-Oct-3 Pandolfini, Florence #540/R est:12000-14000

MARINETTI, Antonio (c.1710-1796) Italian

Works on paper
£2632 $4842 €4000 Allegorical figures (25x18cm-10x7in) sanguine over pencil. 22-Jun-4 Sotheby's, Milan #74/R est:2000-3000

MARINI, Antonio (1788-1861) Italian

£3750 $6900 €5700 Stormy sea (77x120cm-30x47in) 22-Jun-4 Finarte Semenzato, Rome #303/R est:6000-8000
£6623 $12119 €10000 Storm (96x133cm-38x52in) 9-Apr-4 Bailly Pommery, Paris #26/R est:7500-8000

MARINI, Antonio (attrib) (19th C) Italian

£8278 $15149 €12500 Marines (96x72cm-38x28in) two oval. 7-Apr-4 Libert, Castor, Paris #13/R est:8000-12000

MARINI, Antonio Maria (attrib) (1668-1725) Italian

£5282 $9243 €7500 Washerwomen (74x59cm-29x23in) oval. 17-Dec-3 Christie's, Rome #468/R

MARINI, Marino (1901-1980) Italian

£1056 $1827 €1500 Rider (65x49cm-26x19in) s.i. col lithograph lit. 13-Dec-3 Lempertz, Koln #168/R est:1500
£7746 $13556 €11000 Horse and rider (32x23cm-13x9in) s. tempera W/C paper prov. 16-Dec-3 Porro, Milan #9/R est:15000-20000
£12227 $22498 €17851 Acrobata (43x32cm-17x13in) s. oil grattage collage prov. 8-Jun-4 Germann, Zurich #30/R est:30000-40000 (S.FR 28000)
£14118 $24000 €20612 Cavalli e cavalieri (40x37cm-16x15in) s. tempera gouache pen India ink prov. 5-Nov-3 Christie's, Rockefeller NY #144/R est:30000-40000
£14118 $24000 €20612 Cavalli e cavalieri (40x37cm-16x15in) s. tempera pen India ink col crayons prov. 5-Nov-3 Christie's, Rockefeller NY #145/R est:30000-40000
£156425 $280000 €228381 Composition (99x79cm-39x31in) s.d.1952 prov.exhib.lit. 5-May-4 Christie's, Rockefeller NY #325/R est:150000-200000
£300000 $501000 €438000 Jugglers (150x120cm-59x47in) s.verso painted 1956 prov.exhib.lit. 20-Oct-3 Sotheby's, London #7/R est:300000
Prints
£1958 $3368 €2800 Marino from Shakespeare II (48x38cm-19x15in) s.i. col aquatint drypoint one of 20 artist's proofs. 5-Dec-3 Ketterer, Munich #127/R est:2800-3000
£2011 $3600 €2936 Marino from Shakespeare II (48x38cm-19x15in) s. num.41/75 color aquatint. 6-May-4 Swann Galleries, New York #507/R est:3000-5000
£2118 $3600 €3092 From colour to form I (40x52cm-16x20in) s.i. col lithograph. 6-Nov-3 Swann Galleries, New York #619/R est:2000-3000
£2125 $3400 €3103 Orizzonte (72x52cm-28x20in) init.num.44/75 col lithograph. 18-Sep-3 Swann Galleries, New York #414/R est:3000-5000
£2378 $4090 €3400 Marino from Shakespeare II (48x37cm-19x15in) s.i. col aquatint drypoint one of 20 artist's proofs. 5-Dec-3 Ketterer, Munich #128/R est:2800-3000
£2825 $5000 €4125 Quadriga (48x57cm-19x22in) s.num.14/60 col lithograph. 30-Apr-4 Sotheby's, New York #124/R est:3000-4000
£12162 $21405 €18000 Graphics (44x36cm-17x14in) s.i. eau forte drypoint album lit. 24-May-4 Christie's, Milan #255/R est:20000-30000

Sculpture

£6757 $11892 €10000 Head of girl (21x15x15cm-8x6x6in) init.num.1/2 bronze exec.c.1940. 24-May-4 Christie's, Milan #209/R est:10000-15000
£34118 $58000 €49812 Composition - Piccolo cavaliere (18cm-7in) st.init. green blk pat bronze conceived 1956 prov.lit. 5-Nov-3 Christie's, Rockefeller NY #352/R est:30000-40000
£43357 $73706 €62000 Composition (20x40x19cm-8x16x7in) init. bronze conceived 1956 prov.exhib.lit. 25-Nov-3 Christie's, Amsterdam #136136/R est:25000-35000
£62937 $106993 €90000 Arlequin (161x63x14cm-63x25x6in) init. pat bronze prov.exhib.lit. 24-Nov-3 Christie's, Milan #288/R est:60000-90000
£88000 $146960 €128480 Cavallo filiforme (32x17x12cm-13x7x5in) init. grey brown pat bronze edition of six prov.lit. 21-Oct-3 Christie's, London #3/R est:40000-70000
£100000 $167000 €146000 Toro (83x95x37cm-33x37x15in) init. grey pat bronze edition of 5 prov.exhib.lit. 21-Oct-3 Christie's, London #9/R est:50000-80000
£160000 $291200 €233600 Young girl (130cm-51in) st.init. i. d.1944 bronze prov.exhib.lit. 3-Feb-4 Sotheby's, London #41/R est:80000-120000
£250000 $417500 €365000 Piccolo miracolo (49x67x32cm-19x26x13in) init. grey pat bronze edition of seven prov.exhib.lit. 21-Oct-3 Christie's, London #10/R est:300000-500000
£1100000 $2024000 €1606000 Rider (116cm-46in) st.init. pat bronze exec.c.1954 prov.exhib.lit. 22-Jun-4 Christie's, London #25/R est:1200000-1600000
£1600000 $2672000 €2336000 Rider (132cm-52in) st.init. pat bronze prov.lit. 20-Oct-3 Sotheby's, London #19/R est:1200000-1800000

Works on paper

£1448 $2418 €2114 Paesaggio con bicicletta (14x20cm-6x8in) ink paper on canvas prov. 24-Jun-3 Germann, Zurich #1007 est:3200-3500 (S.FR 3200)
£1613 $3000 €2355 Abstract figure (23x33cm-9x13in) s. W/C gouache. 7-Mar-4 William Jenack, New York #74 est:2500-3500
£2727 $4691 €3900 Start olympiade (27x25cm-11x10in) s.d.1938 ink prov. 2-Dec-3 Sotheby's, Amsterdam #97/R est:4000-6000
£3000 $5520 €4380 Horse and rider (30x40cm-12x16in) s.d.1947 brush ink. 22-Jun-4 Sotheby's, London #509/R est:4000-6000
£3374 $5500 €4926 Ballerino (43x33cm-17x13in) indis.sig. gouache brush Indian ink. 25-Sep-3 Christie's, Rockefeller NY #593/R est:7000-9000
£4000 $7280 €5840 Nudo di Donna (29x21cm-11x8in) s.d.44 col crayon pencil exhib.lit. 4-Feb-4 Sotheby's, London #459/R est:4000-6000
£4000 $7360 €5840 Nudo (34x26cm-13x10in) s.d.1949 pen ink. 24-Jun-4 Christie's, London #445/R est:6000-8000
£4225 $7014 €6000 Horse and rider (38x29cm-15x11in) s.d.1941 pencil. 13-Jun-3 Farsetti, Prato #343/R
£4392 $7730 €6500 Horse (27x19cm-11x7in) s. ink. 22-May-4 Galleria Pananti, Florence #441/R est:5000-6000
£4667 $8353 €7000 Cavallo e Cavalcatrice (31x20cm-12x8in) s.d. i. verso Indian ink W/C prov. 14-May-4 Ketterer, Munich #234/R est:7000-9000
£5000 $9100 €7300 Nudo (38x29cm-15x11in) s. pencil htd white exec.1941 exhib.lit. 4-Feb-4 Sotheby's, London #458/R est:4000-6000
£5068 $8919 €7500 Horse (28x22cm-11x9in) s. Chinese ink prov. 24-May-4 Christie's, Milan #133/R est:6000-8000
£6294 $10699 €9000 Composition (35x60cm-14x24in) s. ink paper on canvas. 24-Nov-3 Christie's, Milan #121/R est:10000-15000
£6422 $10725 €9312 Cavallo (33x58cm-13x23in) s. gouache bodycol. 19-Jun-3 Kornfeld, Bern #690/R est:7500 (S.FR 14000)
£14500 $26390 €21170 Riratto (40x32cm-16x13in) s.d.1944 gouache W/C exhib.lit. 4-Feb-4 Sotheby's, London #460/R est:8000-12000
£14706 $25000 €21471 Cavallo e cavaliere che cadono (62x43cm-24x17in) s.d.1955 gouache brush India ink paper on canvas prov. 5-Nov-3 Christie's, Rockefeller NY #147/R est:35000-45000
£15000 $27600 €21900 Cavallo e cavaliere (70x49cm-28x19in) s.d.1954 verso gouache India ink wall-paper prov. 24-Jun-4 Christie's, London #402/R est:15000-20000
£17647 $30000 €25765 Cavallo e cavalieri (40x37cm-16x15in) s. gouache brush pen India ink prov. 5-Nov-3 Christie's, Rockefeller NY #143/R est:30000-40000
£18500 $34040 €27010 Il Circo (48x33cm-19x13in) s.d.1946 gouache brush pen India ink prov.lit. 24-Jun-4 Christie's, London #413/R est:15000-20000
£18824 $32000 €27483 Cavallo e cavaliere (63x43cm-25x17in) s.d.1950 gouache caesin pen India ink blk wash prov. 5-Nov-3 Christie's, Rockefeller NY #148/R est:35000-45000
£20588 $35000 €30058 Cavallo e cavaliere (40x37cm-16x15in) s. gouache pen brush India ink prov. 5-Nov-3 Christie's, Rockefeller NY #146/R est:30000-40000
£21903 $37236 €31978 Giocoliere e Cavallo (60x43cm-24x17in) s.d.1951 gouache. 4-Nov-3 Bukowskis, Stockholm #277/R est:200000-250000 (S.KR 290000)
£22000 $40480 €32120 Iberia (76x55cm-30x22in) s.d.1960 gouache paper on canvas prov.exhib.lit. 22-Jun-4 Sotheby's, London #510/R est:25000-35000
£24000 $40080 €35040 Miracolo. Composition (66x50cm-26x20in) s.d.1955 gouache W/C brush pen lithograph double-sided prov.lit. 21-Oct-3 Christie's, London #4/R est:18000-25000
£24000 $44160 €35040 Magia (62x42cm-24x17in) s.d.1953 gouache pen ink prov.lit. 24-Jun-4 Christie's, London #412/R est:30000-40000
£25000 $45500 €36500 Cavallo e cavaliere (51x34cm-20x13in) s. gouache India ink exec 1951 prov.exhib. 5-Feb-4 Christie's, London #430/R est:25000-35000
£26000 $47840 €37960 Horse (86x62cm-34x24in) s.d.1955 gouache paper on canvas prov. 22-Jun-4 Sotheby's, London #506/R est:20000-30000
£30000 $50100 €43800 Cavallo e cavaliere (69x50cm-27x20in) s.d.1951 gouache pastel brush Indian ink prov.lit. 21-Oct-3 Christie's, London #7/R est:20000-30000
£67039 $120000 €97877 Cavallo e Cavaliere (82x61cm-32x24in) s.d.1954 gouache pen India ink prov. 6-May-4 Sotheby's, New York #389/R est:40000-60000

MARINO DI TEANA (1920-) Italian

Sculpture

£7467 $13589 €11200 Tour de jardin (210cm-83in) metal exec.1975. 2-Jul-4 Binoche, Paris #20 est:3000-4000

MARINO, Bepi (20th C) Italian

£550 $919 €803 Rio de la Sensa, Venice (48x58cm-19x23in) s. 22-Oct-3 Cheffins, Cambridge #548/R

MARINO, Francesco di (1892-1954) Italian

£533 $981 €800 Boats and sailing boats (36x47cm-14x19in) s. board. 10-Jun-4 Christie's, Rome #71/R
£563 $975 €800 Market in Porta Capuana (24x35cm-9x14in) s. board. 10-Dec-3 Finarte Semenzato, Rome #250/R
£855 $1574 €1300 Coastal landscape (37x46cm-15x18in) s. board. 23-Jun-4 Finarte Semenzato, Rome #68/R

MARINO, Giuseppe (1903-1980) Italian

£274 $427 €400 Still life (50x70cm-20x28in) s. 8-Apr-3 Il Ponte, Milan #984
£459 $850 €670 Fondamenta misericordia, Venezia (69x102cm-27x40in) s. prov. 15-Jul-4 Sotheby's, New York #88
£486 $826 €700 Venice (70x100cm-28x39in) s. 1-Nov-3 Meeting Art, Vercelli #149
£837 $1515 €1222 Rio a Burano, Venice (48x67cm-19x26in) s. i.verso prov. 1-Apr-4 Heffel, Vancouver #74/R est:2500-3500 (C.D 2000)

MARINO, di (?) Italian

£1549 $2680 €2200 Fishermen in Naples (44x52cm-17x20in) s. panel. 11-Dec-3 Christie's, Rome #33/R est:1200-1500

MARINONI, Alessandra (20th C) Italian

£764 $1299 €1100 Onions (40x30cm-16x12in) s.d.1997. 28-Oct-3 Il Ponte, Milan #236/R

MARINOT, Maurice (1882-1960) French

£537 $983 €800 Paysage a la route (22x27cm-9x11in) studio st. i.d.1910 verso board. 7-Jul-4 Artcurial Briest, Paris #88
£704 $1288 €1050 Paysage a Vermoise (22x27cm-9x11in) studio st. i.d.1949 verso board. 7-Jul-4 Artcurial Briest, Paris #87

MARIONI, Joseph (1943-) American

£5233 $9000 €7640 Painting no.10-79 (113x98cm-44x39in) mono.overlap acrylic on linen prov. 3-Dec-3 Doyle, New York #90/R est:2000-4000
£22378 $38042 €32000 Painting no.9 - red (200x200cm-79x79in) s.i.d.1985 verso acrylic exhib. 27-Nov-3 Lempertz, Koln #273/R est:25000-30000
£29333 $53680 €44000 Painting No 8 (200x200cm-79x79in) s.i.d.1985 verso acrylic prov.lit. 4-Jun-4 Lempertz, Koln #302/R est:40000-45000

MARIOTON, Eugène (1854-1925) French

Sculpture

£847 $1541 €1237 Clytie (61cm-24in) s. brown pat. bronze marble base. 15-Jun-4 Waddingtons, Toronto #705/R est:2000-2500 (C.D 2100)
£1000 $1800 €1460 Art Nouveau Maiden (81cm-32in) s. base ormolu incl base. 24-Apr-4 Weschler, Washington #517/R est:1500-2500
£1050 $1638 €1523 Travail (53cm-21in) s.verso bronze exec.c.1890. 22-Sep-2 Desmond Judd, Cranbrook #584
£1154 $1985 €1685 Young with bow (44cm-17in) s. gold pat.bronze Cast Colin. 2-Dec-3 Bukowskis, Stockholm #250/R est:15000-18000 (S.KR 15000)
£1371 $2495 €2002 Vainqueur (69cm-27in) brown pat. bronze. 15-Jun-4 Waddingtons, Toronto #706/R est:1000-1500 (C.D 3400)
£1633 $2971 €2400 Soldier (97cm-38in) s.i. pat bronze. 4-Feb-4 Segre, Madrid #639/R est:1000
£1676 $3000 €2447 La pense (86cm-34in) s. golden brown pat bronze. 20-Mar-4 Freeman, Philadelphia #855/R est:3000-4000
£1897 $3396 €2770 Vainqueur (32cm-13in) s.i. bronze cast 1909. 15-May-4 Christie's, Sydney #281/R est:1500-2500 (A.D 4800)

MARIOTTI, Teobaldo (1907-1981) Italian

£839 $1443 €1200 Cosmic aeropainting (44x58cm-17x23in) s. oil tempera cardboard. 3-Dec-3 Stadion, Trieste #1044/R

MARIS, Ferdinand Johannes Jacobus (1873-1935) Dutch

£272 $495 €400 Poland rooster and hen in a landscape (31x37cm-12x15in) s. 3-Feb-4 Christie's, Amsterdam #221

MARIS, Jacob (1837-1899) Dutch

£300 $501 €438 Dutch landscape (36x53cm-14x21in) s. 14-Oct-3 David Lay, Penzance #110/R
£900 $1665 €1314 River scene (18x27cm-7x11in) s. panel. 13-Jan-4 Bonhams, Knightsbridge #76/R
£950 $1492 €1378 Barges on a river at a Dutch settlement (47x71cm-19x28in) s. 28-Aug-3 Christie's, Kensington #204a/R
£1087 $2000 €1587 Windmills on a stormy day (20x35cm-8x14in) s. canvas laid down prov. 27-Jun-4 Freeman, Philadelphia #10/R est:2000-3000
£1151 $2083 €1680 On the Mass (56x73cm-22x29in) s. prov. 1-Apr-4 Heffel, Vancouver #75/R est:3000-5000 (C.D 2750)
£1259 $2102 €1800 River landscape with windmill (41x56cm-16x22in) s. 28-Jun-3 Bolland & Marotz, Bremen #704/R est:1600
£1500 $2655 €2190 Weary traveller (36x20cm-14x8in) s.d.1868. 28-Apr-4 Halls, Shrewsbury #545/R est:1500-2000
£3600 $6552 €5256 Zwolle Holland (25x35cm-10x14in) s. panel. 1-Jul-4 Mellors & Kirk, Nottingham #847/R est:3000-5000
£4167 $6958 €6000 Loading the hay barge (36x24cm-14x9in) s. 21-Oct-3 Sotheby's, Amsterdam #114/R est:8000-12000
£4514 $7538 €6500 Italienne (15x12cm-6x5in) panel prov. 21-Oct-3 Sotheby's, Amsterdam #149/R est:3000-5000
£4861 $8118 €7000 Portrait of a child (36x28cm-14x11in) init. prov.lit. 21-Oct-3 Sotheby's, Amsterdam #223/R est:8000-12000
£5333 $9600 €8000 Motherly love (61x46cm-24x18in) s. 20-Apr-4 Sotheby's, Amsterdam #136/R est:8000-12000
£9028 $15076 €13000 On the tow path (47x30cm-19x12in) s. painted c.1877 prov.exhib. 21-Oct-3 Sotheby's, Amsterdam #91/R est:15000-20000
£13889 $23611 €20000 Shipping on the Merwede by Dordrecht (58x89cm-23x35in) s. prov. 28-Oct-3 Christie's, Amsterdam #136/R est:15000-20000
£18000 $30600 €26280 Beached fishing vessels (23x31cm-9x12in) s.d.72 panel. 19-Nov-3 Bonhams, New Bond Street #9/R est:7000-10000

Works on paper

£753 $1281 €1100 Retour au village (17x29cm-7x11in) s. gouache. 10-Nov-3 Horta, Bruxelles #442
£2533 $4560 €3800 Farmer ploughing a field (33x45cm-13x18in) s. W/C bodycol. 21-Apr-4 Christie's, Amsterdam #99/R est:3000-5000
£7639 $12757 €11000 View of Dordrecht (34x47cm-13x19in) s. W/C prov. 21-Oct-3 Sotheby's, Amsterdam #215/R est:10000-15000
£19444 $32472 €28000 Deux barques de pecheur (39x22cm-15x9in) s. W/C prov.exhib. 21-Oct-3 Sotheby's, Amsterdam #218/R est:10000-15000

MARIS, Matthijs (1839-1917) Dutch
£4500 $8100 €6750 Return of the Prodigal son (45x62cm-18x24in) mono.d.59 panel prov.exhib.lit. 20-Apr-4 Sotheby's, Amsterdam #153/R est:7000-10000
Works on paper
£1250 $1975 €1800 Bride at the altar (58x37cm-23x15in) init. pencil prov.lit. 2-Sep-3 Christie's, Amsterdam #218 est:1000-1500
£5333 $9600 €8000 Aurelia, the Golden (19x15cm-7x6in) mono. W/C prov. 21-Apr-4 Christie's, Amsterdam #121/R est:8000-12000

MARIS, Simon (1873-1935) Dutch
£331 $553 €480 Portrait of the Honourable Voorst van Beest (34x27cm-13x11in) s. maroufle. 11-Nov-3 Vendu Notarishuis, Rotterdam #20
£503 $931 €750 Portrait of an elegant lady (18x13cm-7x5in) s.d.24.5.26 panel. 15-Mar-4 Sotheby's, Amsterdam #67/R
£526 $968 €800 Portrait of an elegant lady (50x40cm-20x16in) s. 28-Jun-4 Sotheby's, Amsterdam #96/R
£724 $1310 €1100 Girl in a white dress seated by a river (30x22cm-12x9in) panel. 19-Apr-4 Glerum, Amsterdam #252/R
£1586 $2538 €2300 Woman playing with necklace (97x61cm-38x24in) s.d.1918. 12-Mar-3 Auction Maastricht #1127

MARIS, Willem (1844-1910) Dutch
£3947 $7145 €6000 Cows watering (80x102cm-31x40in) s. 19-Apr-4 Glerum, Amsterdam #111/R est:6000-8000
£4000 $7200 €6000 Watering cows in summer (61x50cm-24x20in) s. 21-Apr-4 Christie's, Amsterdam #111/R est:4000-6000
£9028 $15347 €13000 Cows on a riverbank (53x81cm-21x32in) s. 28-Oct-3 Christie's, Amsterdam #127/R est:10000-15000
Works on paper
£263 $484 €400 A grazing cow (29x48cm-11x19in) s. pencil black brown ink wash. 22-Jun-4 Christie's, Amsterdam #148/R
£382 $623 €550 Couple on a horse (21x33cm-8x13in) s. pencil prov. 29-Sep-3 Sotheby's, Amsterdam #84

MARIS, Willem Matthijs (1872-1929) Dutch
Works on paper
£680 $1238 €1000 Sweet siblings, double portrait of a boy and a girl (64x53cm-25x21in) s.d.1920 pencil W/C htd white painted oval. 3-Feb-4 Christie's, Amsterdam #204/R est:1000-1500

MARISALDI, Elena Falco (1902-1986) Italian
£521 $885 €750 Watering (50x40cm-20x16in) s. cardboard on canvas. 1-Nov-3 Meeting Art, Vercelli #38
£552 $916 €800 Still life of fruit and dead game (69x50cm-27x20in) s. cardboard. 1-Oct-3 Della Rocca, Turin #304/R
£600 $1104 €900 In the hen house (35x50cm-14x20in) s. cardboard. 14-Jun-4 Sant Agostino, Torino #193/R

MARISOL (1930-) American/Venezulean
Sculpture
£26816 $48000 €39151 Magritte III in Heaven - White (180x96x94cm-71x38x37in) oil chl graphite wood umbrella exec 1998 prov.exhib. 12-May-4 Christie's, Rockefeller NY #207/R est:35000-45000
£65868 $110000 €96167 Baby boy (223x79x61cm-88x31x24in) oil pencil wood fabric collage prov.exhib.lit. 13-Nov-3 Sotheby's, New York #153/R est:40000-50000

MARITONOV, Nicolai (1880-1944) ?
£789 $1453 €1200 Jeune fille blonde (31x26cm-12x10in) s. paper. 25-Jun-4 Millon & Associes, Paris #163

MARIZZA, A (20th C) Italian
£949 $1500 €1386 Clam gathers on the lido (76x117cm-30x46in) s. 27-Jul-3 Simpson's, Houston #356

MARJORAM, Gerard (1936-) Irish
£278 $464 €400 Bogland near Cashel, Connemara (25x46cm-10x18in) s. 22-Oct-3 Woodwards, Cork #23
£291 $530 €440 In the Gap of Dunloe, County Kerry (24x34cm-9x13in) s. board. 15-Jun-4 James Adam, Dublin #121/R
£307 $552 €460 Boys on the beach, Connemara (24x35cm-9x14in) s. board. 20-Apr-4 James Adam, Dublin #80/R
£345 $604 €490 Sunlight on Roundstone Bog (24x34cm-9x13in) s. board. 16-Dec-3 James Adam, Dublin #249/R
£347 $545 €500 Summer's day near Clifden (24x35cm-9x14in) s. board. 26-Aug-3 James Adam, Dublin #50/R
£382 $600 €550 Cattle grazing near Roundstone bog (24x35cm-9x14in) s. board. 26-Aug-3 James Adam, Dublin #49/R
£411 $747 €620 Sunlight on Round Stone Bog, Connemara (24x35cm-9x14in) s. board. 15-Jun-4 James Adam, Dublin #124/R
£451 $754 €650 Quiet day on Roundstone bog (25x46cm-10x18in) s. 22-Oct-3 Woodwards, Cork #13
£456 $817 €680 Children on the beach, Connemara (26x36cm-10x14in) s. board. 31-May-4 Hamilton Osborne King, Dublin #220/R
£456 $817 €680 Saving the hay near Leenane (25x35cm-10x14in) s. board. 31-May-4 Hamilton Osborne King, Dublin #221/R
£500 $790 €725 Roundstone Bog (60x91cm-24x36in) 7-Sep-3 Lots Road Auctions, London #360a
£500 $915 €730 Summer's day near Clifden, Connemara (25x35cm-10x14in) s. board. 2-Jun-4 John Ross, Belfast #216
£694 $1090 €1000 Summer light near Ballynahinch, Connemara (33x59cm-13x23in) s. 26-Aug-3 James Adam, Dublin #48/R est:1000-1500

MARK, Brenda (?) British?
Works on paper
£680 $1136 €993 Pink house, St. Tropez (54x37cm-21x15in) s. W/C. 16-Oct-3 Bonhams, Edinburgh #35

MARK, F Myron (20th C) American
£791 $1400 €1155 Frigate on the high seas (51x66cm-20x26in) s. 2-May-4 Bonhams & Butterfields, San Francisco #1072/R est:1000-1500

MARK, Lajos (1867-1942) Hungarian
£276 $461 €400 Still life of flowers (127x168cm-50x66in) s. canvas on panel lit. 12-Jul-3 Bergmann, Erlangen #665/R
£407 $728 €594 Portrait of a lady (57x42cm-22x17in) s.i.d.1910 exhib. 4-May-4 Ritchie, Toronto #105/R est:1000-1500 (C.D 1000)
£428 $800 €625 Still life with potted plants (79x58cm-31x23in) s. 25-Feb-4 Doyle, New York #40/R
£481 $900 €702 Female nude seated on a draped armchair (79x58cm-31x23in) s. 25-Feb-4 Doyle, New York #39/R
£489 $900 €714 Woman applying lipstick (79x58cm-31x23in) s. s.indis.i.verso. 9-Jun-4 Doyle, New York #3056
£2540 $4750 €3708 Draped nude seated before a mirror (104x99cm-41x39in) s. 25-Feb-4 Doyle, New York #41/R est:1000-1500
£5080 $9500 €7417 Preparing for tea (99x127cm-39x50in) s. exhib. 25-Feb-4 Doyle, New York #42/R est:1500-2500

MARK, Sharon (1955-) Canadian
£226 $378 €330 Fantastic fall (40x50cm-16x20in) s. acrylic. 17-Nov-3 Hodgins, Calgary #335/R (C.D 500)
£270 $494 €394 New puppies (25x30cm-10x12in) s.i.d.1998 acrylic. 1-Jun-4 Hodgins, Calgary #286/R (C.D 675)
£271 $453 €396 Old white farmhouse (20x40cm-8x16in) s.i.d.2003 acrylic. 17-Nov-3 Hodgins, Calgary #14/R (C.D 600)
£289 $479 €422 Bright winter day (36x46cm-14x18in) s. i.d.1998 verso acrylic. 5-Oct-3 Levis, Calgary #271/R (C.D 650)
£480 $878 €701 Autumn splendour (50x60cm-20x24in) s.i.d.1997 acrylic. 1-Jun-4 Hodgins, Calgary #140/R (C.D 1200)

MARKES, Albert Ernest (1865-1901) British
Works on paper
£280 $456 €409 Yacht sailing out from harbour (34x27cm-13x11in) s. W/C. 24-Sep-3 Dreweatt Neate, Newbury #13
£300 $498 €438 Two-decker at anchor (21x17cm-8x7in) s. W/C. 1-Oct-3 Bonhams, Knightsbridge #79a
£450 $806 €657 On the mooring (12x17cm-5x7in) s. W/C. 25-May-4 Bonhams, Knightsbridge #6/R
£780 $1271 €1139 Liner at sunset (34x27cm-13x11in) s. W/C. 24-Sep-3 Dreweatt Neate, Newbury #14
£1000 $1660 €1460 Newry fishing vessel at low tide (76x60cm-30x24in) s. W/C. 1-Oct-3 Bonhams, Knightsbridge #104/R est:1000-1500

MARKES, Richmond (19th C) British
Works on paper
£450 $747 €657 Yachting at full sail (22x49cm-9x19in) s. W/C. 1-Oct-3 Bonhams, Knightsbridge #53/R
£1034 $1717 €1500 Three master in storm (24x52cm-9x20in) mono. W/C. 30-Sep-3 Dorotheum, Vienna #274/R est:1400-1600

MARKHAM, Kyra (1891-1967) American
Prints
£2375 $3800 €3468 Flag raising in Leroy Street (33x25cm-13x10in) s.i.d.42 lithograph. 18-Sep-3 Swann Galleries, New York #415/R est:3500-5000
Works on paper
£699 $1300 €1021 Abstract composition (51x41cm-20x16in) s.d.1960 gouache. 7-Mar-4 Treadway Gallery, Cincinnati #752/R est:1000-1500

MARKIDIS, Christos (1954-) Greek
£1000 $1790 €1460 Lady in black (64x54cm-25x21in) s.d.86 paper on canvas. 10-May-4 Sotheby's, Olympia #87/R est:1000-1500

MARKIEWICS, Comte Kasimir Dunin (1874-1932) Polish
£1049 $1783 €1500 River landscape (33x45cm-13x18in) s. 25-Nov-3 Hamilton Osborne King, Dublin #140a est:1000-1500
£18182 $30909 €26000 Self portrait, standing smoking a pipe (83x65cm-33x26in) 25-Nov-3 Hamilton Osborne King, Dublin #240/R est:3000-5000

MARKINO, Yoshio (1874-1956) British/Japanese
Works on paper
£1500 $2760 €2190 Windsor Castle (30x23cm-12x9in) s. pencil W/C. 25-Mar-4 Christie's, Kensington #210/R est:1000-1500

MARKKULA, Mauno (1905-1959) Finnish
£1200 $2148 €1800 Towards the light (46x37cm-18x15in) s. board. 15-May-4 Hagelstam, Helsinki #207/R est:1000
£1757 $3145 €2600 Evening light (22x27cm-9x11in) s. 8-May-4 Bukowskis, Helsinki #280/R est:1300-1600
£2027 $3628 €3000 On the train (48x80cm-19x31in) s. 8-May-4 Bukowskis, Helsinki #271/R est:2000-2500

MARKLE, Robert Nelson (1936-) Canadian
Works on paper
£1607 $2764 €2346 Seated woman (97x72cm-38x28in) s.d.60 gouache. 2-Dec-3 Joyner Waddington, Toronto #145/R est:1500-2000 (C.D 3600)

MARKO, Andreas (1824-1895) Austrian
£510 $913 €750 Vaches au pre (17x23cm-7x9in) s. panel. 16-Mar-4 Vanderkindere, Brussels #373
£4176 $7225 €6097 Shepherdess on Italian beach (34x41cm-13x16in) s.d.1880. 12-Dec-3 Kieselbach, Budapest #38/R (H.F 1600000)
£4196 $7133 €6000 Gathering storm (47x63cm-19x25in) s.d.1852. 24-Nov-3 Dorotheum, Vienna #54/R est:7000-9000
£5944 $10105 €8500 Italian landscape with herders resting (50x76cm-20x30in) s. 24-Nov-3 Dorotheum, Vienna #130/R est:7000-9000
£5986 $10356 €8500 View of Florence (53x82cm-21x32in) s.d.1893. 9-Dec-3 Pandolfini, Florence #56/R est:5000-6000
£6040 $10812 €9000 Herdsman with cattle watering (70x118cm-28x46in) s.indis.d. 27-May-4 Dorotheum, Vienna #75/R est:9000-12000
£6667 $12000 €9734 Crossing the stream (76x100cm-30x39in) s.d.1868. 21-Jan-4 Sotheby's, New York #247/R est:6000-9000
£7500 $13650 €10950 Surveying the vista (81x114cm-32x45in) s.d.1886 prov. 15-Jun-4 Sotheby's, London #13/R est:4000-6000
£8687 $14421 €12683 Meeting by the well in an Italian landscape (50x70cm-20x28in) s.d.1868. 4-Oct-3 Kieselbach, Budapest #131/R (H.F 3200000)

MARKO, Henry (1855-1921) Italian
£503 $891 €750 Landscape (70x35cm-28x14in) s. 1-May-4 Meeting Art, Vercelli #392
£537 $950 €800 Seascape (62x38cm-24x15in) s. canvas on board. 1-May-4 Meeting Art, Vercelli #499
£599 $1036 €850 Landscape with figures (23x40cm-9x16in) s. board. 9-Dec-3 Finarte Semenzato, Milan #140
£694 $1132 €1000 Southern sea coast (35x58cm-14x23in) s. 24-Sep-3 Neumeister, Munich #494/R
£933 $1671 €1400 Wood at sunset (99x48cm-39x19in) s. 17-May-4 Finarte Semenzato, Rome #1/R
£1736 $2951 €2500 Alpine lake (61x119cm-24x47in) s. 1-Nov-3 Meeting Art, Vercelli #189/R est:2500
£1761 $3046 €2500 View of Florence (39x78cm-15x31in) s. 9-Dec-3 Pandolfini, Florence #52/R est:2000-2500
£2013 $3564 €3000 Alpine lake (61x119cm-24x47in) s. 1-May-4 Meeting Art, Vercelli #230 est:3000

MARKO, Karl (elder) (1791-1860) Hungarian
£6944 $11458 €10000 Landscape with Diana's nymphs resting and hunting (50x63cm-20x25in) s. 2-Jul-3 Neumeister, Munich #708/R est:4000
£7601 $12618 €11097 View of campagna (12x17cm-5x7in) s. 4-Oct-3 Kieselbach, Budapest #186/R (H.F 2800000)
£46152 $76612 €67382 Biblical scene (44x57cm-17x22in) s. 4-Oct-3 Kieselbach, Budapest #144/R (H.F 17000000)

MARKO, Karl (younger) (1822-1891) Hungarian
£2113 $3401 €3000 Paesaggio con torre antica (22x31cm-9x12in) 8-May-3 Farsetti, Prato #766 est:3800-4200
£2113 $3401 €3000 Paesaggio (22x31cm-9x12in) 8-May-3 Farsetti, Prato #793 est:3800-4200
£4333 $7973 €6500 Rural life (57x74cm-22x29in) s.d.1849. 10-Jun-4 Christie's, Rome #111/R est:4000-5600
£4479 $8107 €6539 Corsican landscape (41x33cm-16x13in) s. 16-Apr-4 Mu Terem Galeria, Budapest #107/R (H.F 1700000)
£8144 $13520 €11890 Italian landscape with ruins of a castle (28x38cm-11x15in) s.d.1858 panel. 4-Oct-3 Kieselbach, Budapest #30/R (H.F 3000000)
£11888 $20210 €17000 Extensive river landscape in the evening (85x104cm-33x41in) s.d.863. 20-Nov-3 Van Ham, Cologne #1735/R est:16000
£12025 $21284 €17557 Northern Italian landscape (72x98cm-28x39in) s.d.1877. 28-Apr-4 Kieselbach, Budapest #160/R (H.F 4500000)

MARKO, Karl (younger-attrib) (1822-1891) Hungarian
£500 $935 €750 Goat herder on a country track (8x36cm-3x14in) s.d.1847. 22-Jul-4 Sotheby's, Olympia #405/R
£563 $975 €800 Florence seen from Girone (10x15cm-4x6in) i.verso board. 9-Dec-3 Pandolfini, Florence #58

MARKO, Serge (1925-) ?
Works on paper
£385 $608 €600 Chalutiers au sec en baie de Saint Brieuc (50x32cm-20x13in) s. W/C. 12-Nov-2 Adjug'art, Brest #76/R

MARKOS, Lajos (1917-1993) American/Rumanian
£927 $1687 €1400 Intimacy (101x80cm-40x31in) s.d.1942. 18-Jun-4 Stadion, Trieste #515/R
£993 $1808 €1500 Chatting in the kitchen (104x83cm-41x33in) s.d.1942. 18-Jun-4 Stadion, Trieste #514/R est:1200-1600
£1946 $3250 €2841 Duck hunters (41x51cm-16x20in) s. 16-Nov-3 Simpson's, Houston #239/R

MARKOWSKI, Eugeniusz (1912-) Polish
£327 $563 €477 Composition with shell (49x37cm-19x15in) s. 4-Dec-3 Agra, Warsaw #45/R (P.Z 2200)

MARKS, Claude (fl.1899-1915) British
Works on paper
£452 $756 €660 Grand Canal, Venice (27x39cm-11x15in) s. W/C gouache. 17-Nov-3 Waddingtons, Toronto #45/R (C.D 1000)
£724 $1209 €1057 Exeter Cathedral after snowstorm. Sussex dyke near Arundel. Clovelly, Cornwall (24x34cm-9x13in) s. two i.verso W/C gouache three. 17-Nov-3 Waddingtons, Toronto #65/R (C.D 1600)
£900 $1656 €1314 Exeter Cathedral (26x36cm-10x14in) s. W/C. 23-Mar-4 Bonhams, Knightsbridge #154/R
£1448 $2418 €2114 St Paul's from Waterloo Bridge. Cleopatra's Needle. Nelson's Column (22x35cm-9x14in) s. i.verso W/C gouache three. 17-Nov-3 Waddingtons, Toronto #66/R (C.D 3200)

MARKS, George (fl.1876-1922) British
Works on paper
£900 $1494 €1314 Spring on the moors (18x23cm-7x9in) s. W/C. 2-Oct-3 Neales, Nottingham #637/R

MARKS, George B (1923-1983) American
Sculpture
£1471 $2500 €2148 Wild and running free (38cm-15in) bronze. 1-Nov-3 Altermann Galleries, Santa Fe #2

MARKS, Henry Stacy (1829-1898) British
£1500 $2685 €2190 Feeding time (60x45cm-24x18in) s.d.1891. 27-May-4 Christie's, Kensington #283/R est:1500-2000
£1650 $2690 €2409 Two young boys seated beneath a window (46x29cm-18x11in) init. 24-Sep-3 Dreweatt Neate, Newbury #119/R est:1000-1500

MARKS, Henry Stacy (attrib) (1829-1898) British
Works on paper
£280 $504 €409 Study of a donkey's head (18x12cm-7x5in) mono. W/C. 23-Jan-4 British Auctioneer #623/R

MARKUS, Ans (1947-) Dutch
£3147 $5350 €4500 Sigrid (100x200cm-39x79in) s. lit. 24-Nov-3 Glerum, Amsterdam #273/R est:5000-7000
£3497 $5944 €5000 Ennia house (80x100cm-31x39in) s. painted c.1985-1987 prov. 25-Nov-3 Christie's, Amsterdam #289/R est:6000-8000

MARKUS, Antoon (1870-1955) Dutch
£426 $711 €600 River landscape near Arnhem (43x57cm-17x22in) s.d.1915. 20-Oct-3 Glerum, Amsterdam #129

MARLAT, V (19th C) ?
£1267 $2267 €1900 Fleurs, dans un vase et sur un entablement (90x116cm-35x46in) s. 11-May-4 Vanderkindere, Brussels #245 est:1000-1500

MARLE, Felix del (1889-1952) French
£1748 $2972 €2500 Composition (66x40cm-26x16in) oil paper on canvas prov. 23-Nov-3 Cornette de St.Cyr, Paris #89/R est:150-200
£20000 $36800 €30000 Composition 1 (83x57cm-33x22in) s.i.d.1946 verso board prov.exhib. 8-Jun-4 Sotheby's, Amsterdam #17/R est:30000-40000

MARLE, del (20th C) ?
Works on paper
£2545 $4250 €3716 Cubist portrait (63x48cm-25x19in) chl. 16-Nov-3 Bonhams & Butterfields, Los Angeles #7084/R est:500-700

MARLET, Ricard (1896-1976) Spanish
£1127 $1803 €1600 Pastoral scene (50x61cm-20x24in) s.d.1934. 16-Sep-3 Segre, Madrid #99/R est:1200

MARLIAVE, François (1874-1953) French
Works on paper
£280 $476 €400 Vue de petit Trianon de Versailles (24x30cm-9x12in) s.i.d.Mai 1900 W/C. 24-Nov-3 E & Eve, Paris #161
£533 $965 €800 Man Lang Son (23x15cm-9x6in) s.d.7 juin 1920 gouache W/C lead pencil. 1-Apr-4 Credit Municipal, Paris #39

MARLIN, Brigid (20th C) Irish?
Works on paper
£383 $685 €570 Portrait of Hilda van Stockum (47x41cm-19x16in) s.i. W/C. 26-May-4 James Adam, Dublin #161/R

MARLOW, William (1740-1813) British
£3200 $5312 €4672 Landscape with classical ruins and cattle in the foreground (42x55cm-17x22in) 30-Sep-3 Sotheby's, London #331/R est:3000-5000
Works on paper
£550 $935 €803 Ferry crossing a river (25x35cm-10x14in) s. W/C over pencil prov. 4-Nov-3 Bonhams, New Bond Street #30/R
£5800 $10556 €8468 Coach and horses entering York (24x37cm-9x15in) W/C over pencil. 1-Jul-4 Sotheby's, London #198/R est:2500-3500

MARLOW, William (attrib) (1740-1813) British
£9200 $14996 €13432 Distant view of Florence (60x77cm-24x30in) prov. 24-Sep-3 Dreweatt Neate, Newbury #136/R est:10000-15000

MARLOW, William (circle) (1740-1813) British
£12000 $18960 €17400 Messrs Peach and Larkin's barge building yard on the Lambeth banks of the Thames (47x63cm-19x25in) s. 4-Sep-3 Christie's, Kensington #89/R est:4000-6000

MARLOW, William (style) (1740-1813) British
£6500 $10270 €9425 Westminster Abbey, hall and bridge from the Lambeth bank of the Thames (60x109cm-24x43in) 4-Sep-3 Christie's, Kensington #85/R est:4000-6000

MARMA, Rodolfo (1923-1997) Italian
£278 $506 €420 Door in San Frediano (30x20cm-12x8in) s.d.1977 cardboard on canvas. 17-Jun-4 Galleria Pananti, Florence #570/R
£288 $472 €400 Volta dei Girolami (30x20cm-12x8in) s.d.1982 canvas on cardboard. 10-Jun-3 Pandolfini, Florence #411
£298 $542 €450 Little nuns (35x20cm-14x8in) s.d.1972 cardboard on canvas. 17-Jun-4 Galleria Pananti, Florence #504/R
£298 $542 €450 Little nuns (30x20cm-12x8in) s. s.i.verso card on canvas. 21-Jun-4 Pandolfini, Florence #345/R
£298 $542 €450 Fish market (40x50cm-16x20in) s. s.i.verso. 21-Jun-4 Pandolfini, Florence #378
£301 $475 €439 Birotondo al mare (38x48cm-15x19in) s.d.1967 board. 6-Apr-3 William Jenack, New York #224
£324 $531 €450 Nuns and pupils (20x30cm-8x12in) s.d.1982 canvas on cardboard. 10-Jun-3 Pandolfini, Florence #402/R
£423 $731 €600 Via dei Servi, Florence (30x20cm-12x8in) s.d.1976. 9-Dec-3 Pandolfini, Florence #72/R
£533 $981 €800 Wall of San Giorgio (30x80cm-12x31in) s.d.1967. 11-Jun-4 Farsetti, Prato #410
Works on paper
£251 $458 €380 Santo Spirito Square (49x34cm-19x13in) s.d.56 W/C. 21-Jun-4 Pandolfini, Florence #328
£397 $723 €600 Piazza Castellani (25x35cm-10x14in) s. W/C. 17-Jun-4 Galleria Pananti, Florence #552/R
£414 $691 €600 Nun and students (47x34cm-19x13in) s.d.1980 W/C. 14-Nov-3 Farsetti, Prato #48

MARMOL, Ignacio (1934-1994) Spanish
Works on paper
£1532 $2650 €2237 Plaza (166x228cm-65x90in) s.i.d.1968 verso aluminium paint mixed media. 10-Dec-3 Shapiro, Sydney #27a est:4000-6000 (A.D 3600)

MARNEFFE, Ernest (1866-1921) Belgian
£2199 $3672 €3100 L'espagnole (45x35cm-18x14in) s. cardboard. 17-Jun-3 Vanderkindere, Brussels #441 est:750-1000
£2517 $4580 €3800 Le camee (45x35cm-18x14in) s. cardboard. 16-Jun-4 Hotel des Ventes Mosan, Brussels #158/R est:4200-5600
£3521 $6092 €5000 L'amulette (35x44cm-14x17in) s. oil paper prov. 10-Dec-3 Hotel des Ventes Mosan, Brussels #221/R est:5000-7000

MARNY, Paul (1829-1914) British
Works on paper
£250 $473 €365 Continental market place (43x29cm-17x11in) s. W/C. 23-Feb-4 David Duggleby, Scarborough #649/R
£280 $468 €409 Cottage on a river (15x29cm-6x11in) s. W/C. 14-Oct-3 Bonhams, Knightsbridge #81/R
£320 $573 €467 River scene (20x34cm-8x13in) s. W/C. 17-May-4 David Duggleby, Scarborough #643/R
£340 $636 €496 Continental port and town (39x50cm-15x20in) s. W/C. 26-Feb-4 Lane, Penzance #314
£360 $612 €526 St Lo, Normandy (25x19cm-10x7in) s. W/C htd white. 25-Nov-3 Bonhams, Knightsbridge #182/R
£360 $680 €526 Stream's confluence with the sea, possibly Hayburn Wyke Scarborough (36x58cm-14x23in) s. W/C. 23-Feb-4 David Duggleby, Scarborough #622/R
£360 $648 €526 Continental street scene with figures, horse drawn vehicles (38x28cm-15x11in) s. W/C. 21-Apr-4 Brightwells, Leominster #824/R
£380 $631 €555 Bayeaux, Normandy, townscape with barge in foreground (40x27cm-16x11in) s. W/C. 6-Oct-3 David Duggleby, Scarborough #279
£380 $623 €555 Continental Medieval coastal town (20x38cm-8x15in) s. W/C htd white. 29-May-3 Neales, Nottingham #743/R
£380 $646 €555 Calvados (43x33cm-17x13in) s.i. W/C. 1-Dec-3 David Duggleby, Scarborough #267
£400 $664 €584 Beauvais, France, townscape with market place and statue (40x27cm-16x11in) s. W/C. 6-Oct-3 David Duggleby, Scarborough #281
£400 $680 €584 Post de l'arsenal (20x31cm-8x12in) s.i. W/C. 25-Nov-3 Bonhams, Knightsbridge #196/R
£520 $946 €759 French River estuary scene with cathedral building, bridge and figures (28x43cm-11x17in) W/C. 4-Feb-4 Brightwells, Leominster #972
£520 $983 €759 Continental river townscapes (16x44cm-6x17in) s. W/C pair. 23-Feb-4 David Duggleby, Scarborough #647/R
£550 $946 €803 Warwick Castle with mill (17x27cm-7x11in) s. W/C htd white. 4-Dec-3 Locke & England, Leamington Spa #151/R
£580 $986 €847 Church interior with choir and congregation (44x31cm-17x12in) s.d.1888 W/C. 1-Dec-3 David Duggleby, Scarborough #265/R
£800 $1336 €1168 Carentau, Normandy (30x43cm-12x17in) s.i. W/C. 12-Nov-3 Halls, Shrewsbury #265/R
£1350 $2336 €1971 Low tide, Bourgneuf, Brittany (61x109cm-24x43in) s.i. W/C htd white. 11-Dec-3 Neales, Nottingham #542/R est:1200-1600
£1400 $2506 €2044 Lavaur France, bridge over the river (38x68cm-15x27in) s. W/C. 17-May-4 David Duggleby, Scarborough #627/R est:1000-1500

MAROHN, Ferdinand (19th C) French
£353 $600 €515 Fox hunter (25x36cm-10x14in) s. i.verso panel. 22-Nov-3 Jackson's, Cedar Falls #3/R
Works on paper
£650 $1196 €949 Shooting lunch (27x31cm-11x12in) s. pen ink W/C. 23-Mar-4 Rosebery Fine Art, London #778

MAROLD, Ludwig (1865-1898) Czechoslovakian
Works on paper
£340 $609 €500 Jeune femme peintre dans son atelier (36x45cm-14x18in) s.d.93 black crayon grey wash W/C htd white gouache. 17-Mar-4 Tajan, Paris #153

MARON, Anton von (1733-1808) Austrian
£28082 $47740 €41000 Portrait of the Prince of Scilla (94x74cm-37x29in) i. 9-Nov-3 Finarte, Venice #128/R est:45000-55000

MARON, Anton von (attrib) (1733-1808) Austrian
£1970 $3604 €2876 Self-portrait wearing green coat (75x62cm-30x24in) 7-Jun-4 Museumsbygningen, Copenhagen #113/R est:15000-25000 (D.KR 22000)

MARONIEZ (1865-1933) French
£1818 $3127 €2600 Voiliers au soleil couchant (22x27cm-9x11in) s. panel. 2-Dec-3 Claude Aguttes, Neuilly #51 est:800-1200

MARONIEZ, Georges Philibert Charles (1865-1933) French
£315 $535 €450 Voiliers au couchant (12x17cm-5x7in) s. 27-Nov-3 Millon & Associes, Paris #157
£315 $535 €450 Moulin au bord de l'eau (23x31cm-9x12in) s. cardboard. 23-Nov-3 Cornette de St.Cyr, Paris #617/R
£403 $713 €600 Thonier (27x40cm-11x16in) s. cardboard. 30-Apr-4 Tajan, Paris #212
£424 $708 €615 Bringing in the catch, Brittany (22x26cm-9x10in) s. board prov. 17-Jun-3 Pinneys, Montreal #38a (C.D 950)
£461 $847 €700 Bateaux au clair de lune (9x13cm-4x5in) s. cardboard. 24-Jun-4 Credit Municipal, Paris #38
£470 $874 €700 Rochers a Saint Malo (11x15cm-4x6in) mono. cardboard. 7-Mar-4 Lesieur & Le Bars, Le Havre #107
£662 $1238 €1000 Bord de mer, soleil couchant (19x24cm-7x9in) s. panel. 24-Jul-4 Thierry & Lannon, Brest #244
£986 $1637 €1400 Soleil couchant a maree basse (12x21cm-5x8in) s. cardboard. 15-Jun-3 Peron, Melun #124
£1429 $2386 €2072 Retour des pecheurs (46x55cm-18x22in) s. 17-Jun-3 Pinneys, Montreal #64 est:3500-4500 (C.D 3200)
£1608 $2686 €2300 St Tropez (53x65cm-21x26in) s. 29-Jun-3 Feletin, Province #100
£1722 $3134 €2600 Marsh landscape with bundles of reeds (30x55cm-12x22in) s.d.86 panel. 21-Jun-4 Dorotheum, Vienna #135/R est:2600-3200
£2600 $4758 €3900 Bateau de peche (38x55cm-15x22in) s. 6-Jun-4 Osenat, Fontainebleau #193/R est:3000-3500
£3172 $5806 €4600 Personnages et maisons bord de mer (61x81cm-24x32in) s. peinture. 1-Feb-4 Robin & Fattori, Granville #13

MAROTTA, Gino (1935-) Italian
Works on paper
£1333 $2453 €2000 Venus of Manila (110x86cm-43x34in) s.d.1972 mixed media prov. 14-Jun-4 Porro, Milan #42/R est:1800-2800

MARPLE, William (1827-1910) American
£1984 $3750 €2897 Sailboats at slack tide (61x71cm-24x28in) init. i. verso panel prov. 17-Feb-4 John Moran, Pasadena #43/R est:3000-4000
£4444 $7200 €6444 Western Idyll (34x60cm-13x24in) s. canvas on board. 8-Aug-3 Barridorf, Portland #258/R est:6000-9000

MARQUARD, Otto (1881-1969) German
£274 $466 €400 View from Rohrenberg over vineyards to Allensbach (35x50cm-14x20in) mono. 8-Nov-3 Geble, Radolfzell #792/R

MARQUARDT, Hedwig (1884-1969) German
£6667 $12200 €10000 Wellwisher (91x56cm-36x22in) mono.d.09 mono.d. verso. 5-Jun-4 Lempertz, Koln #857/R est:8000-10000

MARQUERIE, Louis (attrib) (1825-?) French
£270 $511 €400 Rue de ville animee (35x46cm-14x18in) s.d.avril 1896. 17-Feb-4 Vanderkindere, Brussels #521

MARQUES GARCIA, Jose Maria (1862-1936) Spanish
£345 $621 €500 Landscape with herd (27x45cm-11x18in) s.i.d.1885. 26-Jan-4 Ansorena, Madrid #140/R
£655 $1179 €950 Fishing day (29x46cm-11x18in) s.d.1879. 26-Jan-4 Ansorena, Madrid #160/R
£1042 $1656 €1500 Cabeza de arabe (21x16cm-8x6in) s.d.1892 panel. 29-Apr-3 Durán, Madrid #100/R est:1400
£1096 $1863 €1600 Portrait of boy (38x30cm-15x12in) s. board. 4-Nov-3 Ansorena, Madrid #431/R est:1600
Works on paper
£345 $621 €500 Dutch canal (30x48cm-12x19in) s. W/C. 26-Jan-4 Durán, Madrid #43/R
£379 $683 €550 Dutch landscape (30x48cm-12x19in) s. W/C. 26-Jan-4 Durán, Madrid #42/R

MARQUES PUIG, Jose Maria (1890-1950) Spanish
£1208 $2247 €1800 Rainy day (73x100cm-29x39in) s.d.MCMXLII. 2-Mar-4 Ansorena, Madrid #114/R est:1800

MARQUES, Guilherme d'Oliveira (1887-?) ?
£302 $559 €450 Le village indigene (27x41cm-11x16in) s. canvas on panel. 15-Mar-4 Gros & Delettrez, Paris #174
£533 $981 €800 Scene de village Africain (35x27cm-14x11in) s. panel. 14-Jun-4 Gros & Delettrez, Paris #299
£1208 $2235 €1800 Le village Africain (50x60cm-20x24in) s. isorel panel. 15-Mar-4 Gros & Delettrez, Paris #175/R est:1200-1800

MARQUESTE, Laurent Honore (1848-1920) French
Sculpture
£3262 $5448 €4600 La renommee (121cm-48in) s. brown pat bronze marble socle Cast F. Barbedienne. 17-Jun-3 Vanderkindere, Brussels #450/R est:3000-4000
£8054 $14255 €12000 Persee et Meduse (46cm-18in) s.st.f.Barbedienne pat bronze. 29-Apr-4 Sotheby's, Paris #208/R est:7000-9000
£12500 $22750 €18250 Perseus and Medusa (47cm-19in) s. brown pat bronze prov. 17-Jun-4 Christie's, London #61/R est:6000-8000

MARQUET, Albert (1875-1947) French

£15646	$28007	€23000	Quais de la Seine au soleil, Paris (32x46cm-13x18in) s. painted c.1905-1907 prov. 21-Mar-4 Calmels Cohen, Paris #176/R est:30000-40000
£18000	$32760	€26280	Le chevalet (21x12cm-8x5in) s. canvas on panel painted 1944 prov.lit. 3-Feb-4 Christie's, London #198/R est:12000-18000
£21479	$37158	€30500	Barque a Porquerolles (33x40cm-13x16in) s. i.verso panel. 15-Dec-3 Marc Kohn, Paris #107/R est:40000-50000
£23334	$42934	€35000	Baie de Tunis (33x41cm-13x16in) s. canvas on cardboard prov.lit. 9-Jun-4 Tajan, Paris #54/R est:40000-50000
£24000	$43680	€35040	La Seine a Herblay, automne (32x40cm-13x16in) s. canvasboard prov. 3-Feb-4 Christie's, London #255/R est:25000-35000
£26000	$47840	€37960	La place (33x41cm-13x16in) s. panel prov.exhib.lit. 23-Jun-4 Christie's, London #181/R est:14000-18000
£34965	$59441	€50000	Davos sous la neige (32x40cm-13x16in) s. panel painted c.1936. 18-Nov-3 Pierre Berge, Paris #63/R est:50000-60000
£35000	$63700	€51100	Le Pont Neuf dans la brume (54x73cm-21x29in) s. painted c.1945-1946 prov. 3-Feb-4 Christie's, London #167/R est:40000-50000
£35294	$60000	€51529	Vue de Sidi-Bou-Said (50x61cm-20x24in) s. painted 1923 prov.exhib.lit. 6-Nov-3 Sotheby's, New York #173/R est:50000-70000
£35526	$65368	€54000	Brumes a la Frette (50x61cm-20x24in) s. prov.exhib. 23-Jun-4 Maigret, Paris #20/R est:20000-30000
£40000	$72800	€58400	Champ en fleurs (32x41cm-13x16in) s. panel painted 1923 prov.lit. 3-Feb-4 Christie's, London #224/R est:35000-45000
£48000	$87360	€70080	L'allee du jardin (33x41cm-13x16in) s. panel painted c.1944 prov.lit. 4-Feb-4 Sotheby's, London #204/R est:40000-60000
£52000	$95680	€75920	Le Bou-Regreg vue de la Casbah (32x41cm-13x16in) s. panel painted 1935 prov.exhib.lit. 22-Jun-4 Sotheby's, London #62400/R est:35000-45000
£53073	$95000	€77487	Cargos a quai (61x80cm-24x31in) s. painted 1925 prov.exhib.lit. 6-May-4 Sotheby's, New York #271/R est:70000-90000
£62000	$114080	€90520	Port de Marseille (50x61cm-20x24in) s. painted 1916 prov.exhib. 22-Jun-4 Sotheby's, London #265/R est:50000-70000
£68000	$123760	€99280	Bateaux de guerre dans le port (65x81cm-26x32in) s. painted 1930-1932 prov.exhib.lit. 3-Feb-4 Christie's, London #253/R est:50000-70000
£72000	$132480	€105120	Venise (38x55cm-15x22in) s. painted 1936 prov.exhib. 23-Jun-4 Christie's, London #189/R est:40000-60000
£88028	$141725	€125000	Porquerolles (65x85cm-26x33in) s. 22-Aug-3 Deauville, France #56/R est:100000-120000
£88235	$150000	€128823	Pont-Neuf sous la neige (63x75cm-25x30in) s. painted c.1910. 6-Nov-3 Sotheby's, New York #186/R est:120000-150000
£100559	$180000	€146816	Le Pin, St Tropez (50x61cm-20x24in) s. i.verso painted c.1906 prov.exhib.lit. 6-May-4 Sotheby's, New York #272/R est:100000-150000

Works on paper

£284	$508	€420	Nu (19x28cm-7x11in) s. pen dr. 10-May-4 Giraudeau, Tours #57
£333	$613	€500	Nu sur un genou (10x17cm-4x7in) bears st.sig. ink prov. 14-Jun-4 Tajan, Paris #35/R
£440	$805	€642	Coastal landscape with a pier (18x28cm-7x11in) mono. wash. 8-Jul-4 Duke & Son, Dorchester #105
£600	$1086	€900	Nu de dox (18x13cm-7x5in) bears init. lead pencil note-book sheet. 1-Apr-4 Credit Municipal, Paris #27
£634	$1096	€900	Modele agenouille (17x10cm-7x4in) crayon. 12-Dec-3 Piasa, Paris #123
£704	$1218	€1000	Le fiacre (21x33cm-8x13in) init. crayon. 12-Dec-3 Piasa, Paris #120
£764	$1276	€1100	Jeune Marocain (19x13cm-7x5in) mono. ink drawing. 21-Oct-3 Artcurial Briest, Paris #34 est:400-600
£789	$1453	€1200	Esquisse de trois figures. Esquisse de deux hommes au chapeau. Esquisse de bateau (9x14cm-4x6in) pen ink set of 3. 25-Jun-4 Millon & Associes, Paris #102/R
£795	$1446	€1200	Femme et enfant (16x9cm-6x4in) st.sig. ink. 15-Jun-4 Rossini, Paris #35/R
£906	$1685	€1350	La voile (20x17cm-8x7in) mono. ink exhib. 2-Mar-4 Artcurial Briest, Paris #33 est:400-600
£986	$1706	€1400	Modele de profil (21x11cm-8x4in) init. crayon. 12-Dec-3 Piasa, Paris #122
£1043	$1910	€1523	Le fiacre (11x9cm-4x4in) s. ink. 4-Jun-4 Zofingen, Switzerland #2484 (S.FR 2400)
£1060	$1928	€1600	Quai (16x9cm-6x4in) st.sig. ink. 15-Jun-4 Rossini, Paris #36/R est:700-1000
£1074	$1922	€1600	Pin, Saint-Tropez (10x15cm 4x6in) init. graphitc prov.exhib. 26-May-4 Christie's, Paris #9/R est:700-900
£1119	$1902	€1600	Vieux mendiant Arabe (21x28cm-8x11in) s. pen prov. 18-Nov-3 Pierre Berge, Paris #87 est:1100-1500
£1259	$2165	€1800	Couple d'elegants. Homme marchant (15x12cm-6x5in) s. ink wash double-sided. 2-Dec-3 Calmels Cohen, Paris #9/R est:1200-1500
£1325	$2411	€2000	Couple, le baiser (22x33cm-9x13in) st.sig. pen. 18-Jun-4 Piasa, Paris #89 est:1500-1800
£1523	$2772	€2300	Modele de profil (33x21cm-13x8in) init. black crayon. 18-Jun-4 Piasa, Paris #90 est:1200-1500
£1761	$3046	€2500	Les deux amies (21x29cm-8x11in) init. ink. 12-Dec-3 Piasa, Paris #119 est:2500-3500
£2252	$4121	€3400	Bateau (17x25cm-7x10in) init. blk ink wash. 7-Apr-4 Piasa, Paris #68/R est:2000-2500
£3427	$5722	€4900	Saint-Jean-de-Luz (11x16cm-4x6in) s.i. W/C prov. 29-Jun-3 Eric Pillon, Calais #120/R
£3800	$6992	€5548	Sulina (11x13cm-4x5in) s.i. W/C pencil. 24-Mar-4 Sotheby's, Olympia #12/R est:4000-6000
£4000	$7360	€5840	St. Jean de Luz (11x17cm-4x7in) s.i.d.1927 W/C pencil. 24-Mar-4 Sotheby's, Olympia #2/R est:3000-4000
£4079	$7505	€6200	Le port d'Alger (28x31cm-11x12in) s.i.d.1941 W/C. 28-Jun-4 Rossini, Paris #35/R est:2000-3000
£4196	$7217	€6000	La plameraie a Alger (12x17cm-5x7in) s. W/C. 3-Dec-3 Tajan, Paris #28/R est:5000-7500
£4225	$7310	€6000	Palmeraie (25x17cm-10x7in) s. W/C over crayon. 15-Dec-3 Bailly Pommery, Paris #116/R est:3000-3500
£5000	$9200	€7300	Bateaux sur la riviere (10x13cm-4x5in) s. W/C pencil. 24-Mar-4 Sotheby's, Olympia #11/R est:3000-4000
£8310	$14376	€11800	Vienne, le Ring (17x25cm-7x10in) s. W/C. 12-Dec-3 Piasa, Paris #26/R est:6000-8000
£8392	$14014	€12000	Ruelle dans la casbah (25x17cm-10x7in) s.d.1929 W/C gouache. 29-Jun-3 Eric Pillon, Calais #109/R
£8500	$13515	€12325	Sables d'Olonne (17x25cm-7x10in) s.i. pencil W/C prov. 11-Sep-3 Christie's, Kensington #43/R est:4000-6000

MARQUEZ (19th C) Spanish?

£1064	$1777	€1500	Village Africain (60x130cm-24x51in) s. 17-Jun-3 Galerie Moderne, Brussels #204 est:800-1000

MARQUEZ, Jose (1937-) Spanish

£390	$632	€550	Paloma (84x70cm-33x28in) 20-May-3 Ansorena, Madrid #379/R
£474	$857	€720	Camaleon (54x65cm-21x26in) s. 14-Apr-4 Ansorena, Madrid #296/R
£503	$941	€750	Horse (81x100cm-32x39in) s. 24-Feb-4 Durán, Madrid #130/R
£2270	$3677	€3200	Untitled (61x45cm-24x18in) s. 20-May-3 Ansorena, Madrid #308/R est:3200

MARQUEZ, Rafael (?) Spanish?

£426	$711	€600	Landscape (47x38cm-19x15in) s. 23-Jun-3 Durán, Madrid #773/R

MARQUEZANNE, Juanita (?) Spanish

Works on paper

£479	$815	€700	La jeune espagnole (48x59cm-19x23in) s. pastel on canvas. 5-Nov-3 Rabourdin & Choppin de Janvry, Paris #61/R

MARQUIS, Alexander (19th C) British

£500	$835	€730	Half length portrait of William Leith Downie holding a fishing rod (33x26cm-13x10in) s.d.1842 i.verso sold with companion portrait two. 16-Oct-3 Lyon & Turnbull, Edinburgh #148
£500	$925	€730	Young man with a fishing rod, thought to be William Leight Downie (32x25cm-13x10in) s.d.1840 verso painted oval sold with a companion. 9-Mar-4 Bonhams, Knightsbridge #340/R

MARQUIS, J Richard (?-1885) British

£1259	$2140	€1800	Coastal view, near Dublin (41x61cm-16x24in) s. prov. 25-Nov-3 De Veres Art Auctions, Dublin #203/R est:2000-3000
£4800	$8016	€7008	Port in Dublin (28x51cm-11x20in) s.d.1875. 11-Nov-3 Bonhams, Knightsbridge #68/R est:800-1200

Works on paper

£1000	$1810	€1500	Extensive landscape (50x84cm-20x33in) s.d.1854 W/C. 31-Mar-4 James Adam, Dublin #13/R est:1500-2500

MARR, Carl Ritter von (1858-1936) German/American

£1056	$1849	€1500	Country path (47x37cm-19x15in) s. board. 19-Dec-3 Dorotheum, Vienna #73/R est:1500-2000
£1736	$2830	€2500	Peasant woman at open farmstead gate (23x29cm-9x11in) mono.d.85 panel. 25-Sep-3 Dr Fritz Nagel, Stuttgart #1375/R est:3800
£3691	$6792	€5500	Between heaven and earth (159x110cm-63x43in) s.i. 27-Mar-4 L & B, Essen #152/R est:5000
£5455	$9109	€7800	Funeral in Friesland (106x185cm-42x73in) s.i.d.82. 27-Jun-3 Michael Zeller, Lindau #613/R est:6500

Works on paper

£592	$1089	€900	Princess grieving over her lover (55x35cm-22x14in) gouache mixed media. 25-Jun-4 Michael Zeller, Lindau #742/R

MARR, J W Hamilton (1846-?) British

£410	$656	€599	Moorland solitude (51x76cm-20x30in) s. i.verso. 16-Sep-3 Bonhams, Knowle #80

MARR, Joseph Heinrich Ludwig (1807-1871) German

£341	$600	€512	Ferrymen on horseback pulling riverboats (28x38cm-11x15in) s. panel. 21-May-4 North East Auctions, Portsmouth #1514/R
£3077	$5138	€4400	Country scene with peasants and cattle outside tavern on Tegernsee (52x73cm-20x29in) s.d.1853. 26-Jun-3 Weidler, Nurnberg #301/R est:4000

MARR, Leslie (1922-) British

£2000	$3640	€2920	Moel Hebog, Wales (72x122cm-28x48in) s.d.48. 15-Jun-4 Bonhams, Knightsbridge #109/R est:1400-1600

MARRALWANGA, Peter (20th C) Australian

Works on paper

£781	$1461	€1172	Jati, the frogs (98x38cm-39x15in) bears name.verso earth pigments eucalyptus bark prov. 26-Jul-4 Sotheby's, Melbourne #402 (A.D 2000)
£1172	$2191	€1758	Narbalek rock wallaby (93x42cm-37x17in) name.i.verso earth pigment eucalyptus bark exec.c.1987 prov. 26-Jul-4 Sotheby's, Melbourne #399/R est:3000-5000 (A.D 3000)
£1220	$1927	€1769	Ngalyod the rainbow serpent (89x47cm-35x19in) i.verso earth pigments eucalyptus bark exec.c.1980 prov.exhib. 28-Jul-3 Sotheby's, Paddington #349/R est:6000-8000 (A.D 3000)

MARREL, Jacob (1614-1681) Dutch

£3448	$6345	€5034	Study of the tulip - Schipio (32x21cm-13x8in) i. W/C. 26-Mar-4 Koller, Zurich #3033/R est:8000-12000 (S.FR 8000)
£3448	$6345	€5034	Study of the tulip - Amrael van der Eyck (32x21cm-13x8in) i. i. verso W/C pen. 26-Mar-4 Koller, Zurich #3034/R est:8000-12000 (S.FR 8000)
£3448	$6345	€5034	Study of the tulip - Gouda (32x21cm-13x8in) i. i. verso W/C pen. 26-Mar-4 Koller, Zurich #3035/R est:8000-12000 (S.FR 8000)

Works on paper

£3233	$5948	€4720	Study of a tulip - Buyseloo (32x21cm-13x8in) i. i. verso W/C pen. 26-Mar-4 Koller, Zurich #3032/R est:8000-12000 (S.FR 7500)

MARRGULULU, Andrew (20th C) Australian
Works on paper
£320 $550 €467 Fish and animals (71x33cm-28x13in) i. red ochre white pigments. 2-Dec-3 Sotheby's, Olympia #368/R

MARRINON, Linda (1959-) Australian
£620 $1147 €905 Figure with yellow spots (111x91cm-44x36in) s.d.1989 i.verso prov. 15-Mar-4 Sotheby's, Melbourne #67 est:700-900 (A.D 1500)

MARRON, Joan (1934-) American
£278 $500 €406 Rocky Mountain snow (76x61cm-30x24in) init. s.i. stretcher. 25-Apr-4 Bonhams & Butterfields, San Francisco #5569/R

MARROS, Basil (1897-1954) Greek
£6000 $10500 €8760 Figures in a forest (53x41cm-21x16in) s. hardboard exhib. 16-Dec-3 Bonhams, New Bond Street #100/R est:6000-8000

MARSANS, Luis (1930-) Spanish
Works on paper
£2027 $3750 €2959 Estudio (24x27cm-9x11in) s.d.1983 paper on panel prov.lit. 12-Feb-4 Sotheby's, New York #170/R est:800-1200

MARSCHALL, Nicola (1829-1917) American
£929 $1700 €1356 Napoleon Lockett (61x51cm-24x20in) s.d.1883. 5-Jun-4 Neal Auction Company, New Orleans #450/R est:1500-2500
£1205 $2000 €1759 Mrs Maxwell (69x56cm-27x22in) 4-Oct-3 Neal Auction Company, New Orleans #513/R est:2000-4000

MARSCHELAS, Felix (?) ?
£1111 $1744 €1600 Young girl resting (40x20cm-16x8in) s. 26-Aug-3 Thomas Adams, Dublin #1

MARSDEN, Edith Frances (1880-?) American
£368 $600 €537 Two boats (30x41cm-12x16in) s. board. 19-Jul-3 Outer Cape Auctions, Provincetown #96/R

MARSH, Barbara (20th C) British
£300 $501 €438 Still life of pink tulips in a vase (59x50cm-23x20in) s. 22-Oct-3 Cheffins, Cambridge #554

MARSH, Dale (1940-) Australian
£840 $1528 €1226 Two ladies of Sydney (40x50cm-16x20in) s.i.d.1978 canvas on board. 16-Jun-4 Deutscher-Menzies, Melbourne #612/R est:1200-1800 (A.D 2200)
£2276 $3574 €3300 Spirit of summer (43x117cm-17x46in) s.i.d.1977-78-79-80 board prov.lit. 27-Aug-3 Christie's, Sydney #543/R est:1800-2500 (A.D 5600)

MARSH, Diane (20th C) American
£273 $500 €410 Alaska (89x64cm-35x25in) oil on paper. 10-Jul-4 Hindman, Chicago #322/R

MARSH, Georgia (20th C) American
Works on paper
£270 $450 €394 Spectacle pond (27x142cm-11x56in) chl. 19-Oct-3 Bonhams & Butterfields, Los Angeles #7100/R

MARSH, Reginald (1898-1954) American
£432 $700 €626 U.S Marine (20x22cm-8x9in) s.d.1934 masonite. 8-Aug-3 Barridorf, Portland #45/R
£1902 $3500 €2777 Ladies walking (28x40cm-11x16in) s.d.1948 board prov. 8-Jun-4 Bonhams & Butterfields, San Francisco #4106/R est:4000-6000
£3867 $7000 €5646 Girl in yellow dress (25x14cm-10x6in) s.d.50 masonite. 31-Mar-4 Sotheby's, New York #13/R est:3000-5000
£4118 $7000 €6012 Carousel (38x28cm-15x11in) s.d.1947 board. 9-Nov-3 Wright, Chicago #212 est:9000-12000
£8840 $16000 €12906 Two women walking. Two women (41x30cm-16x12in) board double-sided. 31-Mar-4 Sotheby's, New York #11/R est:10000-15000
£13514 $25000 €19730 Afternoon stroll (51x41cm-20x16in) s.d.1942-53 gessoed masonite. 11-Mar-4 Christie's, Rockefeller NY #76/R est:10000-15000
£116279 $200000 €169767 Girl in green on the bowery and acrobats at Coney Island (91x122cm-36x48in) s.d.47 panel double-sided prov.exhib.lit. 3-Dec-3 Sotheby's, New York #79/R est:200000-300000
Prints
£4570 $8500 €6672 Tattoo shave haircut (25x24cm-10x9in) etching drypoint. 2-Mar-4 Swann Galleries, New York #404/R est:6000-9000
Works on paper
£313 $550 €457 Addressing the ball (13x10cm-5x4in) s. W/C double-sided prov. 3-Jan-4 Collins, Maine #46/R
£323 $600 €472 Export line (19x24cm-7x9in) s.i. pen ink. 5-Mar-4 Skinner, Boston #419/R
£324 $600 €473 Thames at London (25x36cm-10x14in) s.d.1926 W/C. 15-Jul-4 Doyle, New York #58/R
£719 $1200 €1050 Older woman reading Bible to a girl. Man hailed on street (20x20cm-8x8in) pen ink pair. 15-Nov-3 Illustration House, New York #40/R
£745 $1200 €1088 Maine beach scene (46x53cm-18x21in) W/C. 20-Aug-3 James Julia, Fairfield #1618/R
£761 $1400 €1111 Nude studies (25x36cm-10x14in) s.d.1939 pen ink. 10-Jun-4 Swann Galleries, New York #164/R
£769 $1400 €1123 Nude studies (20x18cm-8x7in) s. graphite. 19-Jun-4 Rachel Davis, Shaker Heights #247 est:1200-1800
£815 $1500 €1190 Nude studies (23x30cm-9x12in) s.i. pen ink. 10-Jun-4 Swann Galleries, New York #165/R est:2000-3000
£978 $1800 €1428 Figure studies (18x28cm-7x11in) brush ink wash. 10-Jun-4 Swann Galleries, New York #166/R est:1000-1500
£1105 $1900 €1613 New York City Harbor (32x42cm-13x17in) W/C chl. 3-Dec-3 Doyle, New York #264/R est:2000-3000
£1317 $2200 €1923 Woman reading the paper (36x25cm-14x10in) s.d.40 pen ink crayon W/C. 18-Jun-3 Doyle, New York #55/R est:1500-2000
£1429 $2500 €2086 Nude sketch number 2. Nude sketch number 8 (27x43cm-11x17in) conte crayon two prov. 19-Dec-3 Sotheby's, New York #1046/R est:2000-3000
£2035 $3500 €2971 View of New York from the Brooklyn Bridge (22x32cm-9x13in) W/C pencil htd white. 3-Dec-3 Doyle, New York #263/R est:5000-7000
£3774 $6000 €5510 Locomotive (34x49cm-13x19in) s.i. W/C. 12-Sep-3 Skinner, Boston #476/R
£4000 $7000 €5840 Girl walking (51x36cm-20x14in) s.d.1952 W/C ink inkwash. 19-Dec-3 Sotheby's, New York #1007/R est:6000-9000
£4144 $7500 €6050 Havana (35x48cm-14x19in) s.i.d.1930 W/C prov. 31-Mar-4 Sotheby's, New York #12/R est:2000-4000
£6077 $11000 €8872 Coney Island beach (57x77cm-22x30in) i.d.1951 pen ink wash en grisaille prov. 31-Mar-4 Sotheby's, New York #10/R est:7000-10000
£6358 $11000 €9283 Day on the docks (34x49cm-13x19in) s.d.1938 pencil W/C. 10-Dec-3 Bonhams & Butterfields, San Francisco #6065/R est:5000-7000
£7558 $13000 €11035 Street walker (55x38cm-22x15in) s. ink wash en grisaille double-sided prov. 3-Dec-3 Sotheby's, New York #89/R est:12000-18000
£9783 $18000 €14283 Bowery beauty (56x76cm-22x30in) s.d.1946 blk ink wash traces W/C pencil prov. 27-Jun-4 Freeman, Philadelphia #128/R est:20000-30000
£9884 $17000 €14431 Girl on a carousel yellow skirt (47x51cm-19x20in) s.d.1950 gouache on board prov. 3-Dec-3 Sotheby's, New York #82/R est:12000-18000
£10180 $17000 €14863 Fat men's shop (77x56cm-30x22in) s.d.1944 W/C prov. 9-Oct-3 Christie's, Rockefeller NY #98/R est:20000-30000
£13174 $22000 €19234 Tug boats in New York (36x51cm-14x20in) s.d.1936 W/C prov. 9-Oct-3 Christie's, Rockefeller NY #114/R est:10000-15000
£18605 $32000 €27163 Coney Island Beach (67x100cm-26x39in) s.i.d.1945 prov.exhib.lit. 4-Dec-3 Christie's, Rockefeller NY #100/R
£22093 $38000 €32256 Waistline (57x79cm-22x31in) s. ink wash W/C prov.lit. 4-Dec-3 Christie's, Rockefeller NY #99/R est:30000-50000
£25000 $44000 €36500 Burlesque Dancers (56x80cm-22x31in) s.d.1950 verso W/C ink prov. 18-May-4 Christie's, Rockefeller NY #110/R est:30000-50000

MARSHALL, Ben (1767-1835) British
£111732 $200000 €163129 Burleigh with Sam Chifney up (87x101cm-34x40in) s.i.d.1812 prov.lit. 27-May-4 Sotheby's, New York #263/R est:180000-200000

MARSHALL, Charles (1806-1896) British
£380 $695 €555 The village of Simplon, High Alps (27x44cm-11x17in) s.d.63 paper on board. 28-Jan-4 Hampton & Littlewood, Exeter #400/R

MARSHALL, Charles Edward (fl.1872-1903) British
£8803 $15229 €12500 Beaute orientale a la ceinture rouge (102x77cm-40x30in) s.d.1911. 15-Dec-3 Gros & Delettrez, Paris #459/R est:10000-12000

MARSHALL, Clark Summers (1861-1944) American
£314 $500 €458 Maryland landscape with stand of trees at sunset (51x38cm-20x15in) s. 13-Sep-3 Weschler, Washington #738/R
£598 $950 €873 Maryland landscape with pond (56x46cm-22x18in) s. prov. 13-Sep-3 Weschler, Washington #736/R
£692 $1100 €1010 Rural Maryland landscape with winding road (51x36cm-20x14in) s. prov. 13-Sep-3 Weschler, Washington #735/R
£755 $1200 €1102 Summer landscape (36x57cm-14x22in) s. 13-Sep-3 Weschler, Washington #739/R
£755 $1200 €1102 Rural Maryland landscape at sunset (61x46cm-24x18in) s. 13-Sep-3 Weschler, Washington #740/R

MARSHALL, David (20th C) ?
Sculpture
£1556 $2691 €2272 Duality (178x76x94cm-70x30x37in) d.1979 bronze. 9-Dec-3 Maynards, Vancouver #247 est:2000-3000 (C.D 3500)

MARSHALL, Duard (1914-) American
£1559 $2900 €2276 Busy harbour, Spain (94x124cm-37x49in) s. painted c.1940. 7-Mar-4 Treadway Gallery, Cincinnati #650/R est:2000-4000

MARSHALL, Herbert Menzies (1841-1913) British
Works on paper
£350 $641 €511 View down the Thames, thought to be Waterloo Bridge (9x13cm-4x5in) init. W/C. 27-Jan-4 Bonhams, Knightsbridge #202/R
£360 $659 €526 Pool of London, dusk (19x27cm-7x11in) s. W/C htd white. 27-Jan-4 Bonhams, Knightsbridge #199/R
£500 $865 €730 View of Dorrecht from the river at sunset (17x25cm-7x10in) s.d.1898 W/C. 9-Dec-3 Bonhams, Oxford #62
£1000 $1730 €1460 Boats in the harbour, Ipswich (29x55cm-11x22in) s.d.1883 W/C. 10-Dec-3 Bonhams, Bury St Edmunds #512/R est:1000-1500
£1100 $1892 €1606 Westminster (20x13cm-8x5in) s. pencil W/C. 3-Dec-3 Christie's, Kensington #88/R est:700-900
£1650 $2855 €2409 Westminster at sunset (26x36cm-10x14in) s. W/C. 9-Dec-3 Bonhams, Oxford #28/R est:400-600
£1800 $3006 €2628 Fleet Street looking towards St Paul's (26x18cm-10x7in) s.d.1900 i.verso pencil W/C. 16-Oct-3 Christie's, Kensington #151/R est:800-1200
£2000 $3660 €2920 Looking towards Trafalgar Square (19x29cm-7x11in) s. W/C pencil. 7-Apr-4 Woolley & Wallis, Salisbury #163/R est:1000-1500
£4000 $6800 €5840 Westminster Bridge (49x67cm-19x26in) s.d.1907 W/C exhib. 4-Nov-3 Bonhams, New Bond Street #152/R est:4000-6000

MARSHALL, John Fitz (1859-1932) British
£1200 $2064 €1752 Fox terriers in a scullery (20x23cm-8x9in) s. board. 2-Dec-3 Gorringes, Lewes #2495/R est:1000-1500

MARSHALL, John Miller (fl.1881-1927) British
Works on paper
£500 $835 €730 Camping out at St Bennett's Abbey on the Bur. Last road for the night (18x48cm-7x19in) s. pencil W/C pair. 8-Oct-3 Christie's, Kensington #1072/R

MARSHALL, R A K (1849-c.1923) British
Works on paper
£648 $1043 €946 Near Abergavenny, Monmothshire (51x37cm-20x15in) s. W/C. 13-Oct-3 Joel, Victoria #279/R est:1500-2000 (A.D 1600)

MARSHALL, Richard (1944-) British
£600 $1134 €876 Making sand pies (19x25cm-7x10in) s. board. 23-Feb-4 David Duggleby, Scarborough #602/R
£700 $1190 €1022 Children playing on the beach at Flamborough (25x30cm-10x12in) s. board. 1-Dec-3 David Duggleby, Scarborough #317/R
£940 $1598 €1372 Donkeys on the beach at Scarborough, the harbour and castle beyond (25x32cm-10x13in) s. board. 1-Dec-3 David Duggleby, Scarborough #316/R

MARSHALL, Roberto Angelo Kittermaster (1849-c.1923) British
£227 $400 €331 Loch Long off the Clyde (20x51cm-8x20in) s. painted c.1880 board. 23-May-4 Treadway Gallery, Cincinnati #583/R
£280 $481 €400 Mountainous landscape (51x77cm-20x30in) s. 7-Dec-3 Sotheby's, Amsterdam #587/R
Works on paper
£300 $546 €450 Sheep grazing in the evening light (51x39cm-20x15in) s. pencil W/C. 1-Jul-4 Christie's, Kensington #195/R
£330 $525 €479 Traveller and dog on path (23x38cm-9x15in) s. W/C. 23-Mar-3 Desmond Judd, Cranbrook #1090
£440 $801 €642 View of Snowdon from Llyn Lwellyn, North Wales (46x69cm-18x27in) s. W/C. 5-Feb-4 Biddle & Webb, Birmingham #953
£850 $1462 €1241 Figures on a path in an extensive landscape (34x53cm-13x21in) s. pencil W/C. 3-Dec-3 Christie's, Kensington #119/R
£1200 $2208 €1752 Near Ashburnham, Sussex (24x34cm-9x13in) s. W/C. 8-Jun-4 Bonhams, New Bond Street #120/R est:1000-1500
£1750 $3098 €2555 Sheep grazing in a wooded river landscape (33x51cm-13x20in) s. W/C htd white. 27-Apr-4 Bonhams, Knowle #53/R est:800-1200
£1800 $3276 €2628 Extensive wooded landscape with sheep (33x58cm-13x23in) s. 3-Feb-4 Gorringes, Bexhill #997 est:800-1200
£2200 $4004 €3212 River Idle west Retford Nottinghamshire (41x65cm-16x26in) s. pencil W/C htd white. 5-Feb-4 Mellors & Kirk, Nottingham #489/R est:1200-1600

MARSHALL, William Edgar (1837-1906) American
£549 $1000 €802 Envisioning Lincoln in his old age (46x61cm-18x24in) s. 19-Jun-4 Harvey Clar, Oakland #2400

MARSHENKOV, Sergei (20th C) Russian
£600 $1092 €876 Grace (61x40cm-24x16in) s. 20-Jun-4 Lots Road Auctions, London #355/R
£750 $1365 €1095 Beauty by the pond (65x50cm-26x20in) s. 20-Jun-4 Lots Road Auctions, London #343/R
£1000 $1820 €1460 Reclining nude (45x65cm-18x26in) s. 20-Jun-4 Lots Road Auctions, London #345/R est:800-1200
£4000 $7280 €5840 Nude in red (55x90cm-22x35in) s. 20-Jun-4 Lots Road Auctions, London #339/R est:800-1200

MARSHENNIKOV, Sergei (1971-) Russian
£1000 $1860 €1460 Reclining nude (53x89cm-21x35in) 7-Mar-4 Lots Road Auctions, London #370 est:500-700

MARSILI, G (20th C) Italian
£1034 $1728 €1500 Ponte Vecchio, Lungarno Torrigiani, Florence (50x70cm-20x28in) s. 14-Nov-3 Farsetti, Prato #458 est:1300-1600

MARSTBOOM, Antoon (1905-1960) Belgian
£805 $1426 €1200 Composition (70x43cm-28x17in) s.d.1956 panel. 27-Apr-4 Campo, Vlaamse Kaai #506

MARSTON, Byrne (1931-) American
£243 $450 €355 Pamet Harbour (30x41cm-12x16in) s. board. 15-Feb-4 Outer Cape Auctions, Provincetown #49/R

MARSTON, Freda (1895-1949) British
£600 $1098 €876 Still life with a vase of roses and a bowl on a table (40x50cm-16x20in) s. 28-Jan-4 Dreweatt Neate, Newbury #52/R

MARSTRAND, Wilhelm (1810-1873) Danish
£361 $667 €527 Portrait of gentleman wearing brown coat (30x24cm-12x9in) i. verso. 15-Mar-4 Rasmussen, Vejle #407/R (D.KR 4000)
£440 $758 €642 Erasmus Montanus (28x12cm-11x5in) study. 3-Dec-3 Museumsbygningen, Copenhagen #194 (D.KR 4700)
£526 $853 €763 Wooded landscape with rider and children (31x66cm-12x26in) prov. 4-Aug-3 Rasmussen, Vejle #421/R (D.KR 5500)
£756 $1308 €1104 Tobias F Pronk's wife Wilhelmine (10x8cm-4x3in) 9-Dec-3 Rasmussen, Copenhagen #1744/R (D.KR 8000)
£945 $1635 €1380 Judgement of Paris (48x42cm-19x17in) prov. 9-Dec-3 Rasmussen, Copenhagen #1342/R (D.KR 10000)
£1229 $2126 €1794 Italian woman (42x40cm-17x16in) 9-Dec-3 Rasmussen, Copenhagen #1341/R est:20000 (D.KR 13000)
£1512 $2616 €2208 Judgement of Paris (35x34cm-14x13in) prov. 9-Dec-3 Rasmussen, Copenhagen #1344/R est:10000-15000 (D.KR 16000)
£1522 $2785 €2222 Young woman with curly hair (30x24cm-12x9in) 9-Jun-4 Rasmussen, Copenhagen #1589/R est:8000-12000 (D.KR 17000)
£1701 $3113 €2483 Inn keeper pouring wine to an Italian girl (31x24cm-12x9in) prov. 9-Jun-4 Rasmussen, Copenhagen #1401/R est:10000-15000 (D.KR 19000)
£1797 $3342 €2624 Italian woman with tambourine (42x31cm-17x12in) i.d.47. 2-Mar-4 Rasmussen, Copenhagen #1278/R est:25000 (D.KR 20000)
£1797 $3342 €2624 Portrait of professor Shiern (66x55cm-26x22in) mono.d.1861 oval. 2-Mar-4 Rasmussen, Copenhagen #1559/R est:20000-25000 (D.KR 20000)
£1890 $3270 €2759 Portrait of lady professor Shiern (66x54cm-26x21in) oval. 9-Dec-3 Rasmussen, Copenhagen #1656/R est:25000 (D.KR 20000)
£2149 $3932 €3138 Italian woman standing (37x27cm-15x11in) study prov. 9-Jun-4 Rasmussen, Copenhagen #1914/R est:20000-25000 (D.KR 24000)
£2617 $4135 €3795 Study of an Italian woman dancing (38x27cm-15x11in) 2-Sep-3 Rasmussen, Copenhagen #1780/R est:15000 (D.KR 28000)
£2647 $4578 €3865 The sisters inviting the monk to dance (15x21cm-6x8in) prov. 9-Dec-3 Rasmussen, Copenhagen #1233/R est:15000-25000 (D.KR 28000)
£8505 $15564 €12417 Holberg got out of the way for two jesters (44x34cm-17x13in) exhib.prov. 9-Jun-4 Rasmussen, Copenhagen #1402/R est:100000-125000 (D.KR 95000)
£10397 $17987 €15180 Neapolitan man serenading young girls (48x58cm-19x23in) mono.d.1866. 9-Dec-3 Rasmussen, Copenhagen #1256/R est:100000-125000 (D.KR 110000)
Works on paper
£271 $506 €396 A reluctant minuet (15x11cm-6x4in) s.i.d.1866 pen pencil. 25-Feb-4 Museumsbygningen, Copenhagen #130 (D.KR 3000)
£281 $484 €410 Greeting the legation (19x22cm-7x9in) i. pen pencil prov. 3-Dec-3 Museumsbygningen, Copenhagen #170 (D.KR 3000)
£319 $548 €466 Figure studies. pencil pen eight in one frame. 2-Dec-3 Kunsthallen, Copenhagen #561 (D.KR 3400)
£654 $1034 €948 Moving day scene (23x25cm-9x10in) pen pencil wash study exec.c.1831. 2-Sep-3 Rasmussen, Copenhagen #2019/R (D.KR 7000)
£1253 $2294 €1829 Young Italian woman seated on window ledge (55x38cm-22x15in) s.i.d.1847 pastel. 7-Jun-4 Museumsbygningen, Copenhagen #9/R est:15000-18000 (D.KR 14000)

MART, Juliao (19th C) Portuguese
£300 $500 €438 Gentleman in uniform (71x55cm-28x22in) s.i.d.1883. 25-Oct-3 Rasmussen, Havnen #2032/R (D.KR 3200)

MARTEGANI, Amedeo (1961-) Italian
Works on paper
£352 $616 €500 Jordaens (20x14cm-8x6in) s.i.d.1990 verso mixed media. 16-Dec-3 Finarte Semenzato, Milan #229/R

MARTEL, J (1896-1966) French
Sculpture
£5070 $8417 €7200 La pie (32x23cm-13x9in) s. pat bronze Cast Susse. 13-Jun-3 Renaud, Paris #55/R est:3000

MARTEL, Jan (1896-1966) French
Sculpture
£9929 $16085 €14000 L'hermine (17x43x7cm-7x17x3in) s. grey marble exec.c.1920 lit. 24-May-3 Martinot & Savignat, Pontoise #102/R est:13000-15000

MARTEL, Jan and Joel (1896-1966) French
Sculpture
£2023 $3500 €2954 Le danseur Malkovsky (50cm-20in) i. glazed earthenware wood. 11-Dec-3 Sotheby's, New York #203/R est:4000-6000
£4545 $7727 €6500 La belette, attaquant (14x11x20cm-6x4x8in) s. polished mahogany rec. base lit. 24-Nov-3 Tajan, Paris #20/R est:5000-6000
£4730 $8324 €7000 Sainte-Suzanne (123x26x21cm-48x10x8in) s. plaster lit. 18-May-4 Christie's, Paris #32/R est:2000-3000
£12162 $21405 €18000 Martyre de Saint-Sebastien (257x161cm-101x63in) plaster relief. 18-May-4 Christie's, Paris #31/R est:10000-15000
£12766 $21319 €18000 Accordeoniste (64cm-25in) s. terracotta exhib.lit. 17-Jun-3 Camard, Paris #140/R est:12000-15000
£15603 $26057 €22000 Joueuse de luth (61cm-24in) s. terracotta lit. 17-Jun-3 Camard, Paris #141/R est:8000-10000

MARTELLI, Achille (1829-1903) Italian
£338 $595 €500 Seascape (51x70cm-20x28in) s. 19-May-4 Il Ponte, Milan #504

MARTELLY, John S de (1903-1979) American
£1647 $2750 €2405 Untitled (43x53cm-17x21in) masonite. 17-Oct-3 Du Mouchelle, Detroit #2011/R est:2500-3500

MARTEN, Elliot H (fl.1886-1910) British
Works on paper
£300 $492 €438 Rural landscape with sheep grazing (52x25cm-20x10in) s. W/C. 3-Jun-3 Fellows & Sons, Birmingham #120/R
£300 $477 €438 Arun and Amberley Mount from South woods (43x30cm-17x12in) s. W/C. 9-Sep-3 Gorringes, Lewes #1920
£380 $703 €555 River scene (45x60cm-18x24in) W/C. 16-Jul-4 Charterhouse, Sherborne #533/R
£400 $668 €584 Derwentwater, Keswick (34x51cm-13x20in) s. pencil W/C. 16-Oct-3 Christie's, Kensington #180/R

MARTENS, Conrad (1801-1878) Australian
Works on paper
£800 $1464 €1168 Gomera (12x19cm-5x7in) i.d.1833 W/C. 7-Apr-4 Christie's, London #99/R
£1220 $1915 €1769 Double bay (16x25cm-6x10in) i.d.15.4.70 W/C gouache. 26-Aug-3 Christie's, Sydney #397 est:3000-5000 (A.D 3000)
£1300 $2171 €1898 Artist's house at St. Leonard's Sydney (20x29cm-8x11in) s. pencil htd white. 14-Oct-3 Sotheby's, London #178/R est:800-1200
£1781 $2868 €2600 Cottage at St Leonards near Sydney - Martens Home (20x32cm-8x13in) s.i.d.1847 pencil white gouache. 25-Aug-3 Sotheby's, Paddington #457/R est:4000-6000 (A.D 4400)

£7025 $12996 €10257 Cox's River (31x46cm-12x18in) W/C executed c.1835 prov.exhib. 10-Mar-4 Deutscher-Menzies, Melbourne #165/R est:14000-18000 (A.D 17000)
£8907 $14340 €13004 Colyton Church, Devon (51x71cm-20x28in) s.d.1854 W/C prov. 25-Aug-3 Sotheby's, Paddington #10/R est:20000-30000 (A.D 22000)
£20325 $31911 €29471 View of Wiseman's Road, New South Wales (64x43cm-25x17in) s. W/C bodycol prov.lit. 26-Aug-3 Christie's, Sydney #71/R est:50000-70000 (A.D 50000)

MARTENS, Gysbert George (1894-1979) Dutch
£1974 $3632 €3000 Still life with fruits, flowers and a bottle (50x50cm-20x20in) s.d.33. 22-Jun-4 Christie's, Amsterdam #521/R est:2500-3500

MARTENS, Hans Ditlev Christian (1795-1864) German
£14178 $24527 €20700 View over Rome from Via Sacra (80x58cm-31x23in) prov. 9-Dec-3 Rasmussen, Copenhagen #1241/R est:60000-80000 (D.KR 150000)

MARTENS, Henry (?-1860) British
£2200 $3938 €3212 7th Queens own Hussars (46x61cm-18x24in) init. prov. 26-May-4 Sotheby's, Olympia #84/R est:1200-1800
Works on paper
£750 $1328 €1095 North African horseman (21x28cm-8x11in) init. W/C bodycol. 27-Apr-4 Bonhams, New Bond Street #70/R
£2400 $4248 €3504 Sowar, in full dress, Nizam's 3rd Cavalry (21x28cm-8x11in) init. W/C htd white set of three. 27-Apr-4 Bonhams, New Bond Street #40/R est:2000-3000

MARTENS, Medard (20th C) ?
£769 $1308 €1100 Nu feminin (75x25cm-30x10in) s.d.1912. 18-Nov-3 Galerie Moderne, Brussels #818/R

MARTENS, Theodor (1822-1884) German
£360 $659 €526 River landscape at dusk (27x35cm-11x14in) s. panel. 6-Jul-4 Bonhams, Knightsbridge #42/R

MARTENS, Willem Johannes (1838-1895) Dutch
£1275 $2359 €1900 Confession (66x48cm-26x19in) s. 15-Mar-4 Sotheby's, Amsterdam #54/R est:4000-6000
£1310 $2424 €1900 Le depart des pecheurs (14x21cm-6x8in) s. panel. 16-Feb-4 Horta, Bruxelles #201 est:1200-1800
£1517 $2807 €2200 Le chaperon discret (23x31cm-9x12in) s. panel. 16-Feb-4 Horta, Bruxelles #200/R est:2500-3500

MARTENS, Willy (1856-1927) Dutch
£559 $1029 €850 In half light: girl in an interior (36x32cm-14x13in) s. s.i.verso canvas on cardboard. 22-Jun-4 Christie's, Amsterdam #169/R
£1189 $2200 €1736 Pastoral scene with mother, child and goat (51x61cm-20x24in) s. 17-Jul-4 New Orleans Auction, New Orleans #185/R est:3000-5000
£2273 $4000 €3319 Mother and daughter in a landscape (41x48cm-16x19in) s. 21-May-4 Pook & Pook, Downington #64/R est:3000-4000
£4321 $7000 €6265 Two children and a goat. s. prov. 8-Aug-3 Barridorf, Portland #91/R est:6000-9000
£4605 $8474 €7000 A sunny day in the dunes (75x56cm-30x22in) s. 22-Jun-4 Christie's, Amsterdam #151/R est:4000-6000
£6250 $10625 €9000 Sur la veranda - a seductive glance (66x55cm-26x22in) s.d.82 prov. 28-Oct-3 Christie's, Amsterdam #56/R est:10000-15000

MARTI VALLS, Oriol (20th C) Spanish
£284 $460 €400 Landscape (37x46cm-15x18in) s.d.47 canvas on panel. 20-May-3 Ansorena, Madrid #9/R
£496 $804 €700 Coastal view (37x48cm-15x19in) s. canvas on masonite. 20-May-3 Ansorena, Madrid #7/R

MARTI Y AGUILO, Ricardo (1868-1936) Spanish
£1611 $2996 €2400 Still life with fish (116x70cm-46x28in) s.d.1878. 2-Mar-4 Ansorena, Madrid #6/R

MARTI Y ALSINA, Ramon (1826-1894) Spanish
£14667 $26693 €22000 Pendiente de Montjuich hacia al sur (56x110cm-22x43in) s.d.1877. 29-Jun-4 Segre, Madrid #93/R est:11000
£19718 $34113 €28000 Flowers and fan in the garden (111x69cm-44x27in) s. 15-Dec-3 Ansorena, Madrid #28/R est:26000
Works on paper
£532 $862 €750 Desnudo (30x44cm-12x17in) s.i. pencil sketch grey paper. 20-May-3 Segre, Madrid #102/R
£603 $977 €850 Desnudo femenino (29x18cm-11x7in) s.i. pencil wax crayon htd white brown paper. 20-May-3 Segre, Madrid #100/R

MARTI, Agostino (1485-c.1537) Italian
£15789 $29053 €24000 Adoration of the Shepherds (184x185cm-72x73in) prov.exhib. 24-Jun-4 Christie's, Paris #57/R est:12000-18000

MARTI, Joan (1936-) Spanish
£387 $670 €550 Singer (55x38cm-22x15in) s. 15-Dec-3 Ansorena, Madrid #361/R
£423 $731 €600 Woman at balcony (38x46cm-15x18in) s. 15-Dec-3 Ansorena, Madrid #65/R
£599 $1036 €850 Female nude (80x50cm-31x20in) s.d. 15-Dec-3 Ansorena, Madrid #362/R

MARTIAL, Lucien (1892-1987) French/Canadian
£1192 $2229 €1800 Le port de St Jean de Luz (54x73cm-21x29in) s. paper. 25-Jul-4 Feletin, Province #84

MARTIKAINEN, Olavi (1920-1979) Finnish
£286 $520 €420 By the bonfire (68x99cm-27x39in) s.d.74. 8-Feb-4 Bukowskis, Helsinki #402/R

MARTIN GIMENEZ, Juan (1855-1901) Spanish
£18116 $29710 €25000 El pretendiente (82x144cm-32x57in) s. 27-May-3 Durán, Madrid #256/R est:20000
Works on paper
£2174 $3565 €3000 Escena de serrallo (53x39cm-21x15in) s. W/C. 27-May-3 Durán, Madrid #108/R est:3000

MARTIN REBOLLO, Tomas (attrib) (1858-1919) Spanish
£426 $689 €600 Militar montando a caballo (21x13cm-8x5in) panel. 20-May-3 Segre, Madrid #34/R est:750

MARTIN, A (?) ?
£1074 $1987 €1600 Composition au vase de Sevres (130x90cm-51x35in) s. 15-Mar-4 Horta, Bruxelles #247 est:1200-1500

MARTIN, Agnes (1912-) American/Canadian
£39106 $70000 €57095 Buds (127x127cm-50x50in) s.verso oil graphite painted c.1960 prov. 12-May-4 Christie's, Rockefeller NY #409/R est:100000-150000
£47904 $80000 €69940 Desert Rain (63x63cm-25x25in) s. painted 1957 prov.exhib. 12-Nov-3 Christie's, Rockefeller NY #597/R est:80000-120000
£227545 $380000 €332216 Untitled (30x30cm-12x12in) oil ink wash on canvas painted c.1961 prov.exhib. 12-Nov-3 Sotheby's, New York #4/R est:250000-350000
£346369 $620000 €505699 Love (152x152cm-60x60in) s.d.99 verso acrylic graphite prov.exhib. 11-May-4 Christie's, Rockefeller NY #42/R est:500000-700000
£401198 $670000 €585749 Untitled no 6 (183x183cm-72x72in) s.d.1992 verso acrylic graphite prov. 11-Nov-3 Christie's, Rockefeller NY #33/R est:700000-900000
£718563 $1200000 €1049102 Desert (183x183cm-72x72in) s.d.1985 verso oil pencil prov. 12-Nov-3 Sotheby's, New York #44/R est:800000-1200000
£1377246 $2300000 €2010779 Leaves (183x183cm-72x72in) s.i.d.1966 acrylic pencil on canvas prov.exhib. 12-Nov-3 Sotheby's, New York #7/R est:1800000-2200000
Works on paper
£44693 $80000 €65252 Untitled (24x30cm-9x12in) s.d.60 verso pen ink prov. 13-May-4 Phillips, New York #44/R est:80000-120000
£53892 $90000 €78682 Drift of summer (3x30cm-1x12in) s.i.d.64 ink prov.exhib. 13-Nov-3 Sotheby's, New York #117/R est:50000-70000
£53892 $90000 €78682 Untitled, yellow no 6 (30x30cm-12x12in) i. s.d.1966 verso ink wash prov.exhib. 13-Nov-3 Sotheby's, New York #133/R est:50000-70000
£143713 $240000 €209821 Wood (20x20cm-8x8in) s.i.d.64 s.d.1966 verso ink grey wash prov.exhib. 12-Nov-3 Sotheby's, New York #9/R est:80000-120000
£155689 $260000 €227306 Untitled (22x21cm-9x8in) s.d.1962 ink blue wash prov.exhib. 12-Nov-3 Sotheby's, New York #2/R est:100000-150000

MARTIN, Alex Louis (1887-1954) Belgian
£676 $1209 €1000 Fillette a la robe bleue (90x80cm-35x31in) s. 10-May-4 Horta, Bruxelles #195
£1119 $1869 €1600 Fillette au chale (81x71cm-32x28in) s. 13-Oct-3 Horta, Bruxelles #371 est:1000-1500
Works on paper
£448 $829 €650 Le repos du travailleur (99x180cm-39x71in) s. chl. 16-Feb-4 Horta, Bruxelles #422

MARTIN, Alfred (1888-1950) Belgian
£327 $584 €480 Nu de dos assis (35x27cm-14x11in) s. panel. 17-Mar-4 Hotel des Ventes Mosan, Brussels #144
£596 $1085 €900 Vallee mosane (69x99cm-27x39in) s. i.verso cardboard. 16-Jun-4 Hotel des Ventes Mosan, Brussels #207

MARTIN, Andreas (18th C) Dutch
£11034 $18317 €16000 Skating pleasures (47x70cm-19x28in) s. 1-Oct-3 Dorotheum, Vienna #205/R est:16000-20000

MARTIN, Andreas (attrib) (18th C) Dutch
£2695 $4501 €3800 Pecheur pres d'une riviere (24x33cm-9x13in) panel. 17-Oct-3 Tajan, Paris #51 est:3000-4000
£10000 $17300 €14600 Village scene with waggoners on a road and boors watering their cattle (49x62cm-19x24in) panel. 11-Dec-3 Sotheby's, London #104/R est:12000-16000

MARTIN, Anson A (fl.1840-1861) British
£1700 $3060 €2482 Portrait of John Hosken on a bay hunter (55x44cm-22x17in) painted 1865. 21-Apr-4 Christie's, Kensington #323/R est:1000-1500

MARTIN, Anthony (1941-) American
£419 $700 €612 White house (18x30cm-7x12in) masonite. 18-Oct-3 David Dike, Dallas #83/R

MARTIN, Charles (19/20th C) ?
£10241 $17000 €14952 DeSoto crossing the Mississippi at Baton Rouge (74x122cm-29x48in) s. 4-Oct-3 Neal Auction Company, New Orleans #466/R est:7000-10000

MARTIN, David (fl.1887-1935) British
Works on paper
£300 $501 €438 Clyde at Port Glasgow (33x51cm-13x20in) s.i. W/C. 16-Oct-3 Bonhams, Edinburgh #161

MARTIN, Eddie Owens (1908-1986) American
Works on paper
£599 $1000 €875 Woman's face or possibly a portrait of the artist as a young man (56x76cm-22x30in) W/C. 15-Nov-3 Slotin Folk Art, Buford #243/R

MARTIN, Elias (1739-1818) Swedish
£5692 $9791 €8310 Baron Knut von Troil and his wife Margareta Johanna (17x14cm-7x6in) oval panel pair exhib. 2-Dec-3 Bukowskis, Stockholm #312/R est:25000-30000 (S.KR 74000)
£6154 $10585 €8985 Portrait of Ulrika von Hopken in pastoral landscape (72x60cm-28x24in) oval exhib. 3-Dec-3 AB Stockholms Auktionsverk #2346/R est:75000-100000 (S.KR 80000)
£9978 $17860 €14568 A wedding at Roslagen (69x110cm-27x43in) prov.exhib.lit. 26-May-4 AB Stockholms Auktionsverk #2257/R est:100000-125000 (S.KR 135000)
Works on paper
£350 $648 €511 Portrait of Roxelana, wife of Sulyman the Magnificent (13x10cm-5x4in) pencil W/C. 10-Mar-4 Sotheby's, Olympia #23/R

MARTIN, Elias (attrib) (1739-1818) Swedish
£1589 $2893 €2400 Patineurs sur un lac gele pres d'une forteresse (32x37cm-13x15in) panel. 21-Jun-4 Tajan, Paris #79/R est:3000-4000

MARTIN, Ethel Selina (1873-?) British
£300 $567 €438 Peonies (58x48cm-23x19in) mono. 21-Feb-4 Nigel Ward, Hereford #1482/R

MARTIN, Étienne Philippe (1858-1945) French
Sculpture
£23427 $39825 €33500 La nuit Nina (136cm-54in) s.num.2/9 black pat bronze st.f.Bonvicini prov.exhib.lit. 27-Nov-3 Millon & Associes, Paris #100/R est:28000-35000

MARTIN, Eugène-Louis (1880-1954) Swiss
£273 $453 €396 Matin en etet (60x70cm-24x28in) s.i.d.1924 verso. 13-Jun-3 Zofingen, Switzerland #2932 (S.FR 600)

MARTIN, Fletcher (1904-1979) American
£882 $1500 €1288 Jody (94x61cm-37x24in) s. prov. 7-Nov-3 Selkirks, St. Louis #496 est:1500-2000
£898 $1500 €1311 Pineapple (23x30cm-9x12in) s. s.i.verso canvas on board prov. 23-Oct-3 Shannon's, Milford #230/R est:1200-1500
£972 $1565 €1419 The flowered hat (66x41cm-26x16in) s. s.i. stretcher. 20-Aug-3 James Julia, Fairfield #1732/R est:3000-5000
£1445 $2500 €2110 Flowered hat (66x40cm-26x16in) s. 10-Dec-3 Bonhams & Butterfields, San Francisco #6058/R est:3000-5000

MARTIN, Fletcher (attrib) (1904-1979) American
£403 $650 €588 The artist (30x41cm-12x16in) bears sig. verso board. 20-Aug-3 James Julia, Fairfield #1734/R

MARTIN, Florence Beresford (1908-) Australian
£420 $756 €613 Paddington Cottages (42x52cm-17x20in) s. board prov. 20-Jan-4 Bonhams, Knightsbridge #298/R

MARTIN, Floyd Thornton (20th C) American
£404 $650 €590 Pheasants amidst the birches (107x234cm-42x92in) s.d.1940. 21-Aug-3 Doyle, New York #42/R

MARTIN, Franc P (1883-1966) British
£380 $635 €555 Roses (39x49cm-15x19in) s. canvas on board. 13-Nov-3 Bonhams, Edinburgh #381
£2473 $4500 €3611 Three nymphs (128x102cm-50x40in) s. 29-Jun-4 Sotheby's, New York #160/R est:6000-8000

MARTIN, François (19th C) French
£687 $1202 €1003 Sailing vessels in harbour (42x65cm-17x26in) s.d.1885. 16-Dec-3 Grev Wedels Plass, Oslo #359 (N.KR 8000)

MARTIN, Hardy (20th C) American
£294 $550 €429 Texas landscape of bluebonnets (41x51cm-16x20in) s. 25-Feb-4 Dallas Auction Gallery, Dallas #210/R

MARTIN, Henri (1860-1943) French
£4225 $7310 €6000 Apparition (55x35cm-22x14in) s. 10-Dec-3 Rossini, Paris #96/R
£4444 $8000 €6488 Le port de Cherbourg (109x79cm-43x31in) s.d.1874. 23-Apr-4 Sotheby's, New York #214/R est:8000-12000
£9000 $16560 €13140 Etude pour travaux sur la place de la Concorde (65x54cm-26x21in) painted c.1925 prov. 24-Mar-4 Sotheby's, Olympia #74/R est:10000-15000
£10067 $18725 €15000 Femme en tablier bleu et chapeau de paille, ramassant une gerbe (36x46cm-14x18in) painted c.1919. 2-Mar-4 Artcurial Briest, Paris #124/R est:8000-10000
£11656 $19000 €17018 Auto portrait (117x99cm-46x39in) s. board. 19-Jul-3 Outer Cape Auctions, Provincetown #75/R
£15000 $27300 €21900 Femme au chapeau de paille (46x32cm-18x13in) s. panel. 3-Feb-4 Christie's, London #166/R est:14000-18000
£16000 $29440 €23360 Femme en tablier bleu et chapeau de paille, ramassant une gerbe (38x46cm-15x18in) painted c.1919. 22-Jun-4 Sotheby's, London #123/R est:12000-15000
£18000 $32220 €27000 Le bateau-lavoir sur les quais de la Garonne (45x36cm-18x14in) s. panel. 16-May-4 Thierry & Lannon, Brest #159/R est:30000-35000
£18182 $31273 €26000 Lys dans un vase (73x50cm-29x20in) s. prov. 3-Dec-3 Fraysse & Associes, Paris #111/R est:20000-25000
£19000 $34960 €27740 Recifs (65x54cm-26x21in) s. painted c.1920. 23-Jun-4 Christie's, London #140/R est:15000-20000
£20112 $36000 €29364 Paysage (53x89cm-21x35in) s. prov.exhib. 5-May-4 Christie's, Rockefeller NY #252/R est:30000-40000
£24476 $40874 €35000 Paris, Place de la Concorde (54x37cm-21x15in) s. panel. 29-Jun-3 Eric Pillon, Calais #90/R
£33520 $60000 €48939 Bastide-du-vert (90x82cm-35x32in) s. prov. 5-May-4 Christie's, Rockefeller NY #276/R est:60000-80000
£35294 $60000 €51529 Foret (74x56cm-29x22in) s.d.95. 6-Nov-3 Sotheby's, New York #159/R est:35000-45000
£38667 $70373 €58000 Bateaux de peche (40x55cm-16x22in) s. canvas on panel prov. 29-Jun-4 Sotheby's, Paris #6/R est:30000-40000
£39106 $70000 €57095 Terrasse en ete (63x54cm-25x21in) s. prov. 6-May-4 Sotheby's, New York #260/R est:40000-60000
£40000 $73600 €58400 Jeune fille cousant (65x54cm-26x21in) s. 23-Jun-4 Christie's, London #183/R est:50000-70000
£44014 $70863 €62500 Paysage sur le pont dans la vallee du Vert (73x90cm-29x35in) s. 22-Aug-3 Deauville, France #66/R est:50000-60000
£44118 $75000 €64412 Porte de potager dans la tonnelle sud de Marquayrol (82x94cm-32x37in) s. painted c.1920 prov. 5-Nov-3 Christie's, Rockefeller NY #222/R est:80000-100000
£44693 $80000 €65252 Femme de l'artiste (45x54cm-18x21in) s. prov. 6-May-4 Sotheby's, New York #254/R est:40000-60000
£48000 $87360 €70080 La riviere du Vert au printemps (81x60cm-32x24in) s. 3-Feb-4 Christie's, London #189/R est:40000-60000
£48000 $87360 €70080 Automne sur Labastide du Vert (67x88cm-26x35in) s. painted 1920 prov. 3-Feb-4 Christie's, London #164/R est:50000-70000
£50279 $90000 €73407 Dans les fleurs (48x48cm-19x19in) s. exhib. 6-May-4 Sotheby's, New York #244/R est:50000-70000
£55866 $100000 €81564 Bassin de Marquayrol (66x103cm-26x41in) s. prov. 5-May-4 Christie's, Rockefeller NY #264/R est:120000-160000
£58000 $105560 €84680 Remparts a collioure (81x65cm-32x26in) s. painted c.1915. 4-Feb-4 Sotheby's, London #224/R est:35000-45000
£61765 $105000 €90177 L'Eglise de la Bastide du Vert (116x90cm-46x35in) s. prov. 6-Nov-3 Sotheby's, New York #165/R est:100000-150000
£64706 $110000 €94471 Saule se refletant dans la vert (90x64cm-35x25in) bears sig. painted c.1915 prov. 6-Nov-3 Sotheby's, New York #158/R est:80000-120000
£65000 $119600 €94900 Vue d'un palais a Venise (55x46cm-22x18in) s. panel painted 1910 prov. 23-Jun-4 Christie's, London #165/R est:50000-70000
£70588 $120000 €103058 Le port de Collioure (90x110cm-35x43in) s. prov. 19-Nov-3 Bonhams & Butterfields, San Francisco #124/R est:150000-200000
£90000 $165600 €131400 Baie de Collioure, avec le port (94x81cm-37x32in) s. prov.exhib. 22-Jun-4 Sotheby's, London #132/R est:70000-100000
£94118 $160000 €137412 Paysage pres de Toulouse (74x92cm-29x36in) s. painted c.1910 prov. 6-Nov-3 Sotheby's, New York #150/R est:100000-150000
£100559 $180000 €146816 Village dans le Lot - Rue Ensoleillee (91x76cm-36x30in) s. prov. 6-May-4 Sotheby's, New York #251/R est:120000-180000
£111732 $200000 €163129 Madame Henri Martin assise sur la margelle d'un des bassins de Marquayrol (72x93cm-28x37in) s. painted c.1900. 6-May-4 Sotheby's, New York #262/R est:150000-200000
£113333 $206267 €170000 Gondoles sur le Grand Canal, Venise (60x73cm-24x29in) prov. 29-Jun-4 Sotheby's, Paris #8/R est:150000-200000
£125000 $230000 €182500 Barque bleue dans le port de Collioure (82x99cm-32x39in) s. painted c.1930 prov. 22-Jun-4 Sotheby's, London #134/R est:120000-180000
£145000 $263900 €211700 La maison sur l'eau (84x73cm-33x29in) s. prov. 4-Feb-4 Sotheby's, London #211/R est:60000-80000
£152318 $277219 €230000 Gondoles a Venise (70x98cm-28x39in) indis.sig. painted c.1909. 18-Jun-4 Piasa, Paris #16/R est:50000-60000
Works on paper
£315 $535 €450 Etude de nu (18x12cm-7x5in) s. crayon pen. 27-Nov-3 Millon & Associes, Paris #11

MARTIN, Henriette (19th C) French?
Works on paper
£861 $1567 €1300 Bouquet de roses (34x26cm-13x10in) s. W/C. 20-Jun-4 Versailles Encheres #63/R

MARTIN, Henry (1835-1908) British
£380 $616 €555 St. Michael's Mount (20x34cm-8x13in) s.i. 30-Jul-3 Hamptons Fine Art, Godalming #285
£400 $636 €584 Fishing boats at Newlyn harbour (28x43cm-11x17in) s. 12-Sep-3 Gardiner & Houlgate, Bath #163/R
£750 $1403 €1095 Newlyn harbour (28x43cm-11x17in) s. 26-Feb-4 Lane, Penzance #35/R
£920 $1592 €1343 St Michael's Mount from the foreshore (20x34cm-8x13in) s.i. 11-Dec-3 Lane, Penzance #230/R

MARTIN, Henry Byam (1837-1902) Canadian
Works on paper
£317 $529 €463 Fontaine bleau beeches (30x48cm-12x19in) s.d.1882 W/C. 17-Nov-3 Hodgins, Calgary #58/R (C.D 700)

MARTIN, Homer D (1836-1897) American
£2683 $4400 €3890 Boat at water's edge with birch trees (48x28cm-19x11in) s.d.1866 prov. 31-May-3 Brunk, Ashville #477/R est:2000-4000
£4192 $7000 €6120 Silence of the brooks (18x28cm-7x11in) s. i.verso panel prov. 23-Oct-3 Shannon's, Milford #260/R est:1000-1500
£5028 $9000 €7341 Autumn, Adirondacks (28x25cm-11x10in) s. 8-Jan-4 James Julia, Fairfield #665a/R est:3000-4000
£7186 $12000 €10492 Mountain landscape in Autumn (41x36cm-16x14in) s. prov. 23-Oct-3 Shannon's, Milford #148/R est:12000-18000
£10778 $18000 €15736 View of the lake (36x61cm-14x24in) s. prov. 23-Oct-3 Shannon's, Milford #26/R est:10000-15000

MARTIN, J (?) ?
Works on paper
£2198 $4000 €3209 View of the forum, Rome (49x72cm-19x28in) s. W/C. 29-Jun-4 Sotheby's, New York #68/R est:3000-5000

MARTIN, Jack (20th C) Canadian
£640 $1171 €934 Country snow (28x32cm-11x13in) s. panel unfinished sketch verso prov. 1-Jun-4 Joyner Waddington, Toronto #351/R (C.D 1600)

MARTIN, Jacques (1844-1919) French

£667	$1200	€1000	Bouquet de roses (50x39cm-20x15in) s. panel. 20-Apr-4 Chenu & Scrive, Lyon #125/R
£1074	$1987	€1600	Vase de fleurs et nature morte aux fruits (59x43cm-23x17in) s. panel. 14-Mar-4 Eric Pillon, Calais #68/R
£2837	$4738	€4000	Bouquet de pivoines (73x92cm-29x36in) s. 19-Oct-3 Anaf, Lyon #203 est:3800-4000
Works on paper			
£288	$460	€400	Alix, les barbares (30x21cm-12x8in) s. crayon bic dr. 18-May-3 Coutau Begarie, Paris #100
£302	$483	€420	Olympia (13x23cm-5x9in) Indian ink W/C dr. 18-May-3 Coutau Begarie, Paris #6
£302	$483	€420	Alix, la tour de Babel, guerrier perse (25x19cm-10x7in) pencil dr. 18-May-3 Coutau Begarie, Paris #74
£432	$691	€600	Guy Lefranc, la grande menace (51x37cm-20x15in) s. dr. 18-May-3 Coutau Begarie, Paris #138
£468	$748	€650	L'alchimiste, Francesco Prelati (36x22cm-14x9in) graphite dr. 18-May-3 Coutau Begarie, Paris #191
£576	$921	€800	Guy Lefranc, page de garde (47x68cm-19x27in) s. crayon dr. 18-May-3 Coutau Begarie, Paris #135
£647	$1036	€900	Personnages (18x24cm-7x9in) s. col dr. 18-May-3 Coutau Begarie, Paris #187
£1079	$1727	€1500	Alix, O Alexandrie, projet de couverture (51x36cm-20x14in) s. pencil dr. 18-May-3 Coutau Begarie, Paris #89 est:1500-1600
£1871	$2993	€2600	Alix, le spectre de carthage (29x36cm-11x14in) mono.d.77 Indian ink. 18-May-3 Coutau Begarie, Paris #67 est:2500-2800
£1978	$3165	€2750	Alix et Enak, temple Romain (49x64cm-19x25in) s. Indian ink dr. 18-May-3 Coutau Begarie, Paris #29 est:1500-1600
£2086	$3338	€2900	Alix - L'Ile Maudite (51x36cm-20x14in) s. crayon dr. 18-May-3 Coutau Begarie, Paris #47 est:1500-1700
£2158	$3453	€3000	Les voyages d'Alix (51x73cm-20x29in) s.i. Indian ink. 18-May-3 Coutau Begarie, Paris #131 est:2500-2800
£2230	$3568	€3100	Jacobs avec Black et Mortimer (51x36cm-20x14in) s.d.90 Indian ink dr. 18-May-3 Coutau Begarie, Paris #21 est:2800-3000
£2302	$3683	€3200	Couverture odyssee d'Alix 1 (49x35cm-19x14in) mono.i. Indian ink dr. 18-May-3 Coutau Begarie, Paris #108 est:3000-3200
£2446	$3914	€3400	Odyssee l, Carthage (51x36cm-20x14in) mono.i. Indian ink dr. 18-May-3 Coutau Begarie, Paris #111 est:3000-3200
£3237	$5180	€4500	Alix l'Intrepide, combat de gladiateur (53x41cm-21x16in) s.i. Indian ink two parts exec.c.1948/49. 18-May-3 Coutau Begarie, Paris #36 est:4500-4800
£3237	$5180	€4500	Ile Maudite, Alix en Enak (47x36cm-19x14in) s.i. Indian ink two parts. 18-May-3 Coutau Begarie, Paris #45 est:4500-4800
£3597	$5755	€5000	Alix, la griffe noire (47x36cm-19x14in) s.i. Indian ink two parts. 18-May-3 Coutau Begarie, Paris #53 est:5000-5200
£3597	$5755	€5000	Alix, le gouffre du diable (48x36cm-19x14in) s.i. Indian ink. 18-May-3 Coutau Begarie, Paris #69 est:5000-5200
£3597	$5755	€5000	L'ouragan de feu (48x36cm-19x14in) s.i. Indian ink. 18-May-3 Coutau Begarie, Paris #143 est:5000-5200
£3885	$6216	€5400	Grande menace (47x37cm-19x15in) s.i. Indian ink two parts. 18-May-3 Coutau Begarie, Paris #137 est:5500-5800
£3957	$6331	€5500	Reflexion sur l'enigme (48x36cm-19x14in) Indian ink. 18-May-3 Coutau Begarie, Paris #145 est:5500-5800
£4460	$7137	€6200	Alix, le dernier spartiate (48x37cm-19x15in) s.i. Indian ink. 18-May-3 Coutau Begarie, Paris #56 est:5500-5800
£6835	$10935	€9500	Les Legions perdues Alix (48x36cm-19x14in) s.i. Indian ink two parts. 18-May-3 Coutau Begarie, Paris #54 est:5500-5800

MARTIN, Jacques and MORALES, Rafael (19th C) French

Works on paper			
£1151	$1842	€1600	Alix et Enak marchands a Pompei (21x29cm-8x11in) s. W/C dr sold with another by Jacques Martin. 18-May-3 Coutau Begarie, Paris #199
£2158	$3453	€3000	Alix, l'Egypte 2, Medinet haboue (51x73cm-20x29in) s. Indian ink dr. 18-May-3 Coutau Begarie, Paris #124 est:3000-3200
£3597	$5755	€5000	Alix, l'Egypte 1, Temple de Louxor (51x73cm-20x29in) s. Indian ink dr sold with a screenprint by the same artists. 18-May-3 Coutau Begarie, Paris #123 est:4800-5000

MARTIN, Jacques and SIMON, Christophe (19th C) French

Works on paper			
£2158	$3453	€3000	L'Odyssee d'Alix II, Abou, Simbel (51x36cm-20x14in) s.i. Indian ink dr. 18-May-3 Coutau Begarie, Paris #114 est:2400-2600

MARTIN, Jason (1970-) British

£3500	$6440	€5110	Untitled (23x23cm-9x9in) s.i.d.Nov 93 overlap oil linen perspex box prov. 24-Jun-4 Sotheby's, Olympia #418/R est:1500-2000
£8000	$14560	€11680	Spirit (120x120cm-47x47in) s.i.d.1997 verso acrylic gel medium polished copper prov. 21-Jun-4 Bonhams, New Bond Street #120/R est:8000-10000
£8700	$16008	€12702	Untitled, aerolum num 8 (40x60cm-16x24in) s.i.d.1997 i.verso oil melamine aluminium aerolum m-board prov. 24-Jun-4 Sotheby's, Olympia #420/R est:3000-4000
£10500	$19110	€15330	Ozone (120x120cm-47x47in) s.i.d.1997 verso acrylic gel medium polished stainless steel prov. 21-Jun-4 Bonhams, New Bond Street #121/R est:8000-10000
£12432	$23000	€18151	Slap Jack (121x122cm-48x48in) s.i.d.1998 verso oil aluminium prov. 12-Feb-4 Sotheby's, New York #339/R est:10000-15000

MARTIN, Johan Fredrik (1755-1816) Swedish

Prints			
£3548	$6350	€5180	View of Stockholm taken from Mosebacke (46x72cm-18x28in) s. hand col line etching. 25-May-4 Bukowskis, Stockholm #534/R est:50000-60000 (S.KR 48000)

MARTIN, John (1789-1854) British

£223	$384	€326	Pink boat at blue rocks (36x54cm-14x21in) board. 2-Dec-3 Joyner Waddington, Toronto #382/R (C.D 500)
£9000	$16560	€13140	View of Dolbadern Castle, North Wales (22x27cm-9x11in) panel. 26-Mar-4 Sotheby's, London #57/R est:8000-12000
Works on paper			
£900	$1647	€1314	Tower of Babel (25x33cm-10x13in) W/C pencil prov. 8-Jul-4 Duke & Son, Dorchester #64/R
£2000	$3700	€2920	Classical landscape with figures and a fountain (17x23cm-7x9in) s.d.1817 W/C. 10-Mar-4 Sotheby's, Olympia #18/R est:1500-2000
£7883	$13559	€11509	Victory arch with figures (134x98cm-53x39in) s.i. W/C. 8-Dec-3 Philippe Schuler, Zurich #4216/R est:5000-7000 (S.FR 17500)

MARTIN, Kenneth (1905-) British

£11000	$20130	€16060	Oval painting (46x71cm-18x28in) card on board prov.exhib. 2-Jun-4 Sotheby's, London #110/R est:6000-8000

MARTIN, Léon (19th C) French

£352	$630	€500	Jeune fille espagnole (54x37cm-21x15in) s.d.1873. 11-Jan-4 Rouillac, Vendome #379
£2587	$4399	€3700	Still life with flowers and fruit (122x90cm-48x35in) s. lit. 28-Nov-3 Schloss Ahlden, Ahlden #1560/R est:1600

MARTIN, Mandy (1952-) Australian

£2439	$3829	€3537	No go area from Yarra ridge (130x300cm-51x118in) i. s.i.d.93 verso. 27-Aug-3 Christie's, Sydney #622/R est:6000-12000 (A.D 6000)

MARTIN, Maurice (1894-1978) French

£467	$845	€700	Pont Neuf (45x55cm-18x22in) s. panel. 1-Apr-4 Credit Municipal, Paris #74
£604	$1130	€900	Champ de coquelicots (54x65cm-21x26in) s. 29-Feb-4 Versailles Encheres #165

MARTIN, Milo (attrib) (1893-1970) Swiss

Sculpture			
£4405	$7489	€6431	Crouching figure (137cm-54in) mono.d.34 dark green pat.bronze. 5-Nov-3 Dobiaschofsky, Bern #2457/R est:12000 (S.FR 10000)

MARTIN, Pierre (?) ?

£1206	$2013	€1700	Young girls with fans (69x60cm-27x24in) s. board. 23-Jun-3 Durán, Madrid #198/R est:1500

MARTIN, Pompey Japanangka (c.1932-1989) Australian

Works on paper			
£586	$1096	€879	Janynki jukurrpa (71x55cm-28x22in) name.i.d.1987 verso synthetic polymer paint canvasboard prov. 26-Jul-4 Sotheby's, Melbourne #415/R (A.D 1500)

MARTIN, Raymond (20th C) French

Works on paper			
£599	$1036	€850	Nu debout (36x24cm-14x9in) crayon. 10-Dec-3 Ferri, Paris #74

MARTIN, Ronald Albert (1943-) Canadian

Works on paper			
£241	$448	€352	No 43 (76x56cm-30x22in) s.i.d.March 1970 W/C. 2-Mar-4 Ritchie, Toronto #178/R (C.D 600)
£301	$561	€439	No 15 (76x56cm-30x22in) s.i.d.Feb 1970 W/C pencil. 2-Mar-4 Ritchie, Toronto #179 (C.D 750)

MARTIN, Sylvester (fl.1856-1906) British

£250	$473	€365	The sportsman's return (25x30cm-10x12in) s.d.1906. 17-Feb-4 Fellows & Sons, Birmingham #10/R
£850	$1352	€1241	Four hunting scenes (16x31cm-6x12in) s.d.1885 board. 9-Sep-3 Rowley Fine Art, Newmarket #429/R
£950	$1482	€1387	Portrait of a pair of greyhounds, a coursing scene beyond. s.d.1879 i.verso. 28-Mar-3 Greenslade Hunt, Taunton #501
£1200	$2040	€1752	In full cry, Gilberts Green, Tamworth. Gone away. Kill (51x76cm-20x30in) s.d.1901 set of three. 27-Nov-3 Christie's, Kensington #32/R est:1200-1800
£1500	$2580	€2190	Hampton coppier. Thornleys bog (24x47cm-9x19in) s.d.1888 board pair. 3-Dec-3 Bonhams, Knightsbridge #170/R est:1000-1500
£1700	$2890	€2482	Kenelworth, Warks. Chace woods (41x66cm-16x26in) s.d.1878 s.i.verso pair. 25-Nov-3 Bonhams, Knowle #260/R est:1800-2500
£2200	$3740	€3212	Meet. Setting off. On the sent. Drawing cover (18x33cm-7x13in) s.d.1885 board set of four in one frame. 27-Nov-3 Christie's, Kensington #15/R est:2500-3500
£3198	$5500	€4669	Meet of the Cheshire Hunt (76x102cm-30x40in) s. 7-Dec-3 Freeman, Philadelphia #41 est:7000-9000

MARTIN, Therese (1933-) French

Works on paper			
£349	$636	€510	Composition (44x53cm-17x21in) s.d.68 mixed media cardboard. 16-Jun-4 Fischer, Luzern #2266/R (S.FR 800)

MARTIN, Thomas Mower (1838-1934) Canadian

£260	$476	€380	Twelve mile point on the Kaministiquia River (18x26cm-7x10in) s.i.d.1898. 1-Jun-4 Hodgins, Calgary #25/R (C.D 650)
£413	$748	€603	2nd concession, Eglinton and York (36x51cm-14x20in) s. 18-Apr-4 Levis, Calgary #72/R est:1200-1800 (C.D 1000)
£600	$1098	€876	Young woman fishing (50x40cm-20x16in) s. 1-Jun-4 Joyner Waddington, Toronto #352/R (C.D 1500)
£670	$1118	€972	Fishing from the river bank (56x88cm-22x35in) s. 17-Jun-3 Pinneys, Montreal #123 est:1800-2400 (C.D 1500)
£880	$1610	€1285	Country road, autumn (55x88cm-22x35in) s. 1-Jun-4 Hodgins, Calgary #339/R est:2500-3000 (C.D 2200)
£3125	$5375	€4563	Rocky stream at forest's edge (140x110cm-55x43in) s. canvas on board. 2-Dec-3 Joyner Waddington, Toronto #292/R est:4000-6000 (C.D 7000)

Works on paper

£200 $366 €292 Indian women at the water's edge (17x32cm-7x13in) s. W/C. 1-Jun-4 Joyner Waddington, Toronto #493 (C.D 500)
£220 $403 €321 Coastal mountains (16x33cm-6x13in) s. W/C. 1-Jun-4 Hodgins, Calgary #380/R (C.D 550)
£331 $598 €483 Untitled - forest stream (22x50cm-9x20in) s.d.1891 W/C. 18-Apr-4 Levis, Calgary #73/R (C.D 800)
£340 $622 €496 Riverscape (20x49cm-8x19in) s. W/C. 1-Jun-4 Joyner Waddington, Toronto #534 (C.D 850)
£342 $548 €499 Don River (25x36cm-10x14in) s. W/C. 16-Sep-3 Maynards, Vancouver #391 (C.D 750)
£362 $605 €529 Quiet corner (33x48cm-13x19in) s.i.d.1888 W/C. 17-Nov-3 Hodgins, Calgary #305/R (C.D 800)
£432 $721 €631 Lake Louise (33x24cm-13x9in) s. W/C. 17-Nov-3 Hodgins, Calgary #79/R est:1000-1500 (C.D 955)
£450 $766 €657 View of Illecilliwaet Glacier, BC (30x50cm-12x20in) s.i. W/C prov. 27-Nov-3 Heffel, Vancouver #19/R (C.D 1000)
£495 $842 €723 Rushing river in the Rocky Mountain Glacier field (33x47cm-13x19in) s.i. W/C prov. 27-Nov-3 Heffel, Vancouver #20/R (C.D 1100)
£633 $1058 €924 Mount Sir Donald, in the Selkirks (51x71cm-20x28in) s. W/C. 17-Nov-3 Hodgins, Calgary #114/R est:2000-2500 (C.D 1400)

MARTIN, Vicente (1911-1998) Uruguayan

£250 $400 €365 Rooster (33x43cm-13x17in) s.d.1975. 20-Sep-3 Sloans & Kenyon, Bethesda #1040/R
£261 $480 €381 Youth (71x53cm-28x21in) s.d.59 cardboard. 22-Jun-4 Galeria y Remates, Montevideo #149/R
£293 $480 €428 Moon gypsy (72x72cm-28x28in) s.d.78 enamel oil card. 3-Jun-3 Galeria y Remates, Montevideo #49
£299 $550 €437 Purple moon (73x73cm-29x29in) s. acrylic. 22-Jun-4 Galeria y Remates, Montevideo #146/R
£353 $650 €515 Moon and cahpel (50x65cm-20x26in) s.d.72. 22-Jun-4 Galeria y Remates, Montevideo #148/R
£353 $600 €515 Boat and tree (72x92cm-28x36in) s.d. 25-Nov-3 Galeria y Remates, Montevideo #8
£370 $700 €540 Pears and watermelon (74x93cm-29x37in) s. acrylic. 22-Feb-4 Galeria y Remates, Montevideo #22
£389 $650 €568 Blue moon (100x101cm-39x40in) s.d.73. 7-Oct-3 Galeria y Remates, Montevideo #84/R
£412 $700 €602 Birds and moon (61x71cm-24x28in) s. acrylic. 25-Nov-3 Galeria y Remates, Montevideo #103/R
£471 $800 €688 Fortress (85x85cm-33x33in) s.d.77. 25-Nov-3 Galeria y Remates, Montevideo #7/R
£471 $800 €688 Boat and moon (91x71cm-36x28in) s.d.79 acrylic. 25-Nov-3 Galeria y Remates, Montevideo #104
£483 $850 €705 H242 (91x71cm-36x28in) s.d.93 acrylic. 5-Jan-4 Galeria y Remates, Montevideo #4
£500 $850 €730 Castle (73x60cm-29x24in) s.d.75 acrylic. 25-Nov-3 Galeria y Remates, Montevideo #105
£511 $900 €746 Nude (91x71cm-36x28in) s.d.57 verso. 5-Jan-4 Galeria y Remates, Montevideo #112/R
£568 $1000 €829 Nude (91x71cm-36x28in) s.d.57. 5-Jan-4 Galeria y Remates, Montevideo #111/R
£802 $1300 €1163 Moon (60x73cm-24x29in) s. s.d.50 verso. 29-Jul-3 Galeria y Remates, Montevideo #84/R

MARTIN, William Alison (c.1878-1936) British

£270 $440 €394 Farmhouse scene and trees (36x48cm-14x19in) s. i.verso board. 27-Sep-3 Rogers Jones, Clwyd #86

MARTIN-CARO SOTO, Julio (1933-1968) Spanish

Works on paper

£286 $520 €420 Bakers II (64x49cm-25x19in) s. W/C ink exec.1957 prov. 3-Feb-4 Segre, Madrid #306/R
£320 $582 €470 The Karamazov brothers (64x49cm-25x19in) s. gouache ink wash prov. 3-Feb-4 Segre, Madrid #304/R
£352 $616 €500 Untitled (25x32cm-10x13in) s. gouache wash double-sided prov. 16-Dec-3 Segre, Madrid #245/R
£423 $739 €600 Untitled (25x35cm-10x14in) s. gouache prov. 16-Dec-3 Segre, Madrid #246/R
£442 $805 €650 Madrid scenes (64x50cm-25x20in) s. ink wash exec.1957 prov. 3-Feb-4 Segre, Madrid #307/R
£845 $1479 €1200 Untitled (50x66cm-20x26in) s. gouache double-sided prov. 16-Dec-3 Segre, Madrid #247/R

MARTIN-FERRIERES, Jac (1893-1972) French

£470 $869 €700 Bord de riviere (33x46cm-13x18in) s.i. 15-Mar-4 Blanchet, Paris #68/R
£667 $1200 €1000 Tulipes dans un pot. Vue de port (38x46cm-15x18in) s. panel double-sided. 26-Apr-4 Tajan, Paris #123
£704 $1218 €1000 Plage d'Irlande (25x40cm-10x16in) s. panel. 10-Dec-3 Rossini, Paris #97/R
£922 $1540 €1300 Neige a l'Artandiere (27x39cm-11x15in) s. panel. 15-Oct-3 Rabourdin & Choppin de Janvry, Paris #6/R
£940 $1738 €1400 Bord de mer (34x46cm-13x18in) s. panel. 14-Mar-4 Feletin, Province #79
£1129 $2077 €1648 Paysage (65x80cm-26x31in) s. 14-Jun-4 Waddingtons, Toronto #287/R est:3000-4000 (C.D 2800)
£1197 $2071 €1700 Clair de lune (38x42cm-15x17in) s.d.22 panel. 10-Dec-3 Claude Boisgirard, Paris #25 est:1500-2000
£1275 $2283 €1900 Paysage vallonne (41x51cm-16x20in) s.d.1925. 25-May-4 Chambelland & Giafferi, Paris #107/R est:1500-1800
£1867 $3360 €2800 Propriete de Saint-Circq La Poupi (96x74cm-38x29in) d.1945. 24-Apr-4 Hotel des Ventes de Vienne, Vienne #190
£2113 $3655 €3000 Neige (65x65cm-26x26in) s.d.23. 10-Dec-3 Claude Boisgirard, Paris #26/R est:3000-4000
£2817 $4873 €4000 Barque de peche (50x80cm-20x31in) s.d.27. 10-Dec-3 Claude Boisgirard, Paris #23/R est:4000-5000
£2848 $5211 €4300 Allee bordee d'arbres (64x49cm-25x19in) s.d.20. 7-Apr-4 Piasa, Paris #111/R est:4000-6000
£3333 $6000 €5000 Landscape (61x94cm-24x37in) d.1927. 24-Apr-4 Hotel des Ventes de Vienne, Vienne #192
£4400 $7920 €6600 Scene de marche (86x81cm-34x32in) d.1927. 24-Apr-4 Hotel des Ventes de Vienne, Vienne #189
£4536 $8302 €6850 Ruisseau a travers les arbres (65x80cm-26x31in) s.d.22. 7-Apr-4 Piasa, Paris #110/R est:6000-8000
£12667 $22800 €19000 Landscape (100x138cm-39x54in) d.1927. 24-Apr-4 Hotel des Ventes de Vienne, Vienne #191

MARTIN-GOURDAULT, Marie (1880-1938) French

£671 $1235 €1000 Flowers (81x65cm-32x26in) s.d.1911 lit. 25-Mar-4 Karlheinz Kaupp, Staufen #2599/R

MARTIN-KAVEL, François (1861-1918) French

£474 $849 €692 Young woman at spinning wheel (100x72cm-39x28in) s. 12-May-4 Dobiaschofsky, Bern #3740 (S.FR 1100)
£1208 $2138 €1800 Jeune femme au rouet (100x80cm-39x31in) s. 29-Apr-4 David Kahn, Paris #214/R est:3000-3500

MARTINA, Piero (1912-) Italian

£544 $974 €800 My school teacher (45x33cm-18x13in) s. board painted 1942 prov.exhib.lit. 16-Mar-4 Finarte Semenzato, Milan #175/R
£748 $1339 €1100 Back from fishing (49x84cm-19x33in) s.d.1956 i.verso board exhib. 22-Mar-4 Sant Agostino, Torino #358/R

Works on paper

£310 $518 €450 Untitled (47x68cm-19x27in) s. collage cardboard. 17-Nov-3 Sant Agostino, Torino #150/R
£400 $736 €600 Study of seated nude (32x40cm-13x16in) s. chl. 8-Jun-4 Finarte Semenzato, Milan #174/R

MARTINAGE, Louis Alexandre (1878-?) French

£933 $1699 €1400 Marche aux poissons sous les ponchettes (73x54cm-29x21in) s. 29-Jun-4 Gioffredo, Nice #1/R

MARTINE, Martine (1932-) French

£2098 $3566 €3000 Gouter d'enfants (89x116cm-35x46in) s. i.verso. 1-Dec-3 Camard, Paris #114/R est:3000-4000

MARTINEAU, Edith (1842-1909) British

Works on paper

£1000 $1720 €1460 Loch an Eilan Aviemore (31x48cm-12x19in) s, pencil W/C htd white. 4-Dec-3 Mellors & Kirk, Nottingham #863/R est:600-800
£1364 $2400 €1991 Landscape with child seated on woman's lap in the garden (41x30cm-16x12in) s. W/C. 21-May-4 Pook & Pook, Downington #63/R est:3000-5000

MARTINEAU, Gertrude (1840-1924) British

Works on paper

£850 $1462 €1241 Loch Morlich (24x39cm-9x15in) pencil W/C htd white. 4-Dec-3 Mellors & Kirk, Nottingham #864/R

MARTINEAU, Louise (1952-) Canadian

£579 $1053 €845 Belle Journee pour etendre (91x122cm-36x48in) s. i.verso prov.exhib. 5-Feb-4 Heffel, Vancouver #051/R (C.D 1400)
£579 $1053 €845 Fleurs d'ete (76x91cm-30x36in) s. prov.exhib. 5-Feb-4 Heffel, Vancouver #052/R (C.D 1400)

MARTINELLI, Ezio (1913-1980) American

£380 $600 €555 Reclining nude (51x71cm-20x28in) s. 27-Jul-3 William Jenack, New York #280

MARTINELLI, Giovanni (1610-1659) Italian

£8000 $14640 €11680 Young man holding crown (73x58cm-29x23in) 8-Jul-4 Sotheby's, London #310/R est:8000-12000
£16000 $29280 €23360 Head of female saint (32x32cm-13x13in) panel octagonal lit. 8-Jul-4 Sotheby's, London #191/R est:3000-5000

MARTINELLI, Giovanni (attrib) (1610-1659) Italian

£6356 $10805 €9280 Two women (85x101cm-33x40in) 24-Nov-3 Sotheby's, Melbourne #332/R est:15000-20000 (A.D 15000)

MARTINELLI, Ulrich (1911-1989) Swiss

£987 $1648 €1441 Peasant boy with two goats and cow before mountain landscape (10x16cm-4x6in) s. board. 24-Oct-3 Hans Widmer, St Gallen #113/R est:1500-3000 (S.FR 2200)

MARTINET, Christophe (?) ?

Works on paper

£315 $535 €450 Empire (50x50cm-20x20in) s.verso mixed media canvas. 29-Nov-3 Neret-Minet, Paris #200/R
£336 $571 €480 Orient (60x60cm-24x24in) s.verso mixed media canvas. 29-Nov-3 Neret-Minet, Paris #125/R

MARTINETTI, Angelo (19th C) Italian

£17000 $30940 €24820 Commanding performance (64x48cm-25x19in) s.i. 17-Jun-4 Christie's, London #86/R est:12000-18000

MARTINETTI, Maria (1864-?) Italian

Works on paper

£1189 $2200 €1736 Untitled (56x74cm-22x29in) W/C. 12-Mar-4 Du Mouchelle, Detroit #2121/R est:2500-3000
£1800 $3276 €2628 Palace guard (52x34cm-20x13in) s.i.d.1883 w, bodycol. 16-Jun-4 Christie's, Kensington #280/R est:2000-3000

MARTINEZ ALCOVER, Manuel (1927-) Spanish
£532 $888 €750 Fishermen (22x27cm-9x11in) s. board. 20-Oct-3 Durán, Madrid #601/R
£532 $888 €750 Harbour scene (22x27cm-9x11in) s. board. 20-Oct-3 Durán, Madrid #602/R
£621 $1117 €900 Fishermen (34x41cm-13x16in) s. board. 26-Jan-4 Durán, Madrid #89/R

MARTINEZ DE HOYOS, Ricardo (1918-) American/Mexican
£1765 $3000 €2577 Untitled - choir boys and parrot (91x70cm-36x28in) s.d.4.42. 9-Nov-3 Bonhams & Butterfields, Los Angeles #4136/R est:6000-8000

MARTINEZ DE LA VEGA, Joaquin (1846-1905) Spanish
£1400 $2534 €2100 Portrait of Mallarme (16x22cm-6x9in) s. board. 30-Mar-4 Segre, Madrid #86/R est:2100

MARTINEZ DIAZ, Rafael (1915-1991) Spanish
£1316 $2421 €2000 Woman with jug (73x60cm-29x24in) s. 22-Jun-4 Durán, Madrid #42/R est:1000
£1316 $2421 €2000 Woman with vase (80x65cm-31x26in) s. 22-Jun-4 Durán, Madrid #41/R est:1000
£2069 $3724 €3000 Square with fountain (100x81cm-39x32in) s. 26-Jan-4 Ansorena, Madrid #182/R est:3000
£4605 $8474 €7000 Landscape (70x106cm-28x42in) s. 22-Jun-4 Durán, Madrid #44/R est:1500

MARTINEZ HOWARD, Julio (1932-1999) Spanish
£820 $1500 €1197 Rembrandt (43x33cm-17x13in) cardboard. 1-Jun-4 Arroyo, Buenos Aires #14
£1547 $2800 €2259 Nude (60x60cm-24x24in) acrylic cardboard. 30-Mar-4 Arroyo, Buenos Aires #21
Works on paper
£385 $700 €562 Figure (41x29cm-16x11in) s. ink. 5-Jul-4 Arroyo, Buenos Aires #43/R
£440 $800 €642 Nude with cat (25x20cm-10x8in) s. mixed media. 5-Jul-4 Arroyo, Buenos Aires #20/R
£820 $1500 €1197 Figures (46x65cm-18x26in) mixed media. 1-Jun-4 Arroyo, Buenos Aires #6
£829 $1500 €1210 Figures (32x43cm-13x17in) mixed media. 30-Mar-4 Arroyo, Buenos Aires #7
£1341 $2400 €1958 Figure (108x68cm-43x27in) chl. 11-May-4 Arroyo, Buenos Aires #63

MARTINEZ MARTIN, Santiago (1890-1979) Spanish
£1027 $1747 €1500 Lady in the garden (50x60cm-20x24in) s. 4-Nov-3 Ansorena, Madrid #369/R est:1050

MARTINEZ NOVILLO, Cirilo (1921-) Spanish
£1552 $2793 €2250 Grey landscape (22x30cm-9x12in) s. board. 26-Jan-4 Durán, Madrid #111/R
£4264 $7250 €6225 Village (74x93cm-29x37in) s. prov. 9-Nov-3 Bonhams & Butterfields, Los Angeles #4018/R
£5028 $9000 €7341 Granada, Iglesia Blanca (65x81cm-26x32in) s. 6-May-4 Doyle, New York #71/R est:5000-7000
£5556 $8833 €8000 Landscape (33x41cm-13x16in) s. s.d.98 verso exhib.lit. 29-Apr-3 Durán, Madrid #146/R est:8000
£6207 $10366 €9000 Landscape (60x73cm-24x29in) s. 17-Nov-3 Durán, Madrid #224/R est:9000
£6294 $10510 €9000 Landscape with houses and figures (55x44cm-22x17in) s. panel. 24-Jun-3 Segre, Madrid #112/R est:9000
£7292 $12396 €10500 Segovia (81x64cm-32x25in) s. painted c.1950. 28-Oct-3 Segre, Madrid #180/R est:10500
Works on paper
£1567 $2836 €2350 Landscape in Castilla (30x39cm-12x15in) s. gouache prov. 30-Mar-4 Segre, Madrid #256/R est:2350
£1748 $2920 €2500 Landscape (32x44cm-13x17in) s. mixed media. 30-Jun-3 Ansorena, Madrid #27/R

MARTINEZ ORTIZ, Nicolas (1907-1990) Spanish
Works on paper
£290 $475 €400 Market (19x25cm-7x10in) s.i. drawing. 27-May-3 Durán, Madrid #58/R
£295 $469 €425 El Monasterio de El Escorial (14x12cm-6x5in) s. col drawing W/C. 29-Apr-3 Durán, Madrid #46/R
£387 $670 €550 Castillian village (24x30cm-9x12in) s. pencil dr. 15-Dec-3 Ansorena, Madrid #195/R
£426 $711 €600 Iglesia (24x32cm-9x13in) s. W/C. 23-Jun-3 Durán, Madrid #13/R
£669 $1171 €950 Ploughing (19x24cm-7x9in) s. W/C. 16-Dec-3 Durán, Madrid #609/R

MARTINEZ PUEYRREDON, Alberto (20th C) Argentinian
£769 $1400 €1123 Composition with pomegranates (30x54cm-12x21in) s. cardboard. 5-Jul-4 Arroyo, Buenos Aires #78/R

MARTINEZ SIERRA, Pedro (1948-) Spanish
Works on paper
£280 $481 €400 Female nude (35x50cm-14x20in) s.d. chl. 3-Dec-3 Hauswedell & Nolte, Hamburg #996/R

MARTINEZ TARRASSO, Casimiro (1900-1980) Spanish
£2270 $3677 €3200 Pirineo catalan (60x55cm-24x22in) s. 20-May-3 Ansorena, Madrid #335/R est:1800
£17103 $30786 €24800 Polychrome (81x100cm-32x39in) s. 26-Jan-4 Ansorena, Madrid #213/R est:22800

MARTINEZ VAZQUEZ, Eduardo (1886-1971) Spanish
Works on paper
£3080 $5051 €4250 Rural landscape (54x65cm-21x26in) s. 27-May-3 Durán, Madrid #158/R est:3500

MARTINEZ VILLAFINEZ, Lino (1892-1960) Spanish
£1119 $1869 €1600 View of Santiago de Compostela (17x48cm-7x19in) s. 30-Jun-3 Ansorena, Madrid #220/R

MARTINEZ, Alfredo Ramos (1872-1946) Mexican
£1117 $2000 €1631 Portrait of and old sailor (58x41cm-23x16in) s. oil on newsprint. 21-Mar-4 Bonhams & Butterfields, Los Angeles #7322/R est:1000-1500
£13408 $24000 €19576 Tehuana (33x53cm-13x21in) s. tempera gouache prov. 26-May-4 Sotheby's, New York #96/R est:25000-30000
£83799 $150000 €122347 Mexican family (71x99cm-28x39in) s. tempera pencil chl prov.exhib. 26-May-4 Sotheby's, New York #1/R est:175000-225000
Works on paper
£1445 $2500 €2110 Figure seated by a table (61x46cm-24x18in) s. conte crayon prov. 10-Dec-3 Bonhams & Butterfields, San Francisco #6287/R est:3000-5000
£5914 $11000 €8634 Three men in conversation (38x54cm-15x21in) s. pen ink pencil. 2-Mar-4 Swann Galleries, New York #533/R est:2000-3000
£6849 $11644 €10000 Blue volcano (50x75cm-20x30in) s.i.d.1916 pastel lit. 30-Oct-3 Louis Morton, Mexico #88/R est:140000-160000 (M.P 130000)
£11173 $20000 €16313 Three figures (38x53cm-15x21in) s. ink. 26-May-4 Sotheby's, New York #84/R est:20000-30000
£27933 $50000 €40782 Mother and son (99x91cm-39x36in) s. chl prov.exhib. 26-May-4 Sotheby's, New York #85/R est:20000-25000

MARTINEZ, C (?) ?
£1600 $2928 €2400 Arrivee au relais (35x55cm-14x22in) s. 6-Jun-4 Rouillac, Vendome #5

MARTINEZ, Cesar (?) ?
£660 $1089 €950 Landscape with bell tower (74x93cm-29x37in) s.d.78. 2-Jul-3 Ansorena, Madrid #837/R
£2793 $5000 €4078 Brushpile of the imagination in South Texas. i. oil canvas metal. 13-May-4 Dallas Auction Gallery, Dallas #291/R est:10000-15000

MARTINEZ, F E (?) ?
£2400 $4344 €3504 Red setter and spaniel. Soaniels on the hill (49x65cm-19x26in) s. pair. 31-Mar-4 Bonhams, Knightsbridge #39/R est:1500-2000

MARTINEZ, Jose Esteban (20th C) Mexican
£215 $400 €314 Surrealist scene (99x80cm-39x31in) s.d.86 prov. 5-Mar-4 Skinner, Boston #597/R

MARTINEZ, Julian (1879-1943) American
Works on paper
£272 $500 €397 Pueblo dancers (28x43cm-11x17in) s. gouache on board. 14-Jun-4 Bonhams & Butterfields, San Francisco #1110/R
£870 $1600 €1270 Untitled (47x39cm-19x15in) W/C two. 24-Jun-4 Sotheby's, New York #246/R est:800-1200

MARTINEZ, Pedro Antonio (1886-?) Spanish
£816 $1461 €1200 Young woman with headscarf (33x26cm-13x10in) s.d.1940. 22-Mar-4 Durán, Madrid #185/R

MARTINEZ, Prospero (1885-1966) Venezuelan
£297 $475 €434 Village in Carrizal (50x70cm-20x28in) s. panel painted 1975. 21-Sep-3 Subastas Odalys, Caracas #31

MARTINEZ, Raoul (1876-1973) Dutch/Cuban
£548 $932 €800 Chrysanthemum (53x44cm-21x17in) s.d.45. 5-Nov-3 Vendue Huis, Gravenhage #389/R est:800-1000

MARTINEZ, Raymundo (1938-) Mexican
£316 $537 €461 Landscape (44x59cm-17x23in) s.d.1973 paper. 30-Oct-3 Louis Morton, Mexico #151 (M.P 6000)
£2107 $3583 €3076 Popocatepetl (61x30cm-24x12in) s.d.1967. 30-Oct-3 Louis Morton, Mexico #107/R est:45000-50000 (M.P 40000)

MARTINEZ, Ricardo (1918-) Mexican
£948 $1612 €1384 Couple (31x24cm-12x9in) s.d.1967 paper. 30-Oct-3 Louis Morton, Mexico #39/R est:30000 (M.P 18000)
£1511 $2750 €2206 Profile portrait (25x20cm-10x8in) s.d.59. 29-Jun-4 Sotheby's, New York #420/R est:3000-5000
£1686 $2866 €2462 Drink (30x20cm-12x8in) s. 30-Oct-3 Louis Morton, Mexico #128/R est:20000-25000 (M.P 32000)
£1765 $3000 €2577 Untitled - portrait (61x41cm-24x16in) s.d.86 prov. 9-Nov-3 Bonhams & Butterfields, Los Angeles #4130/R est:5000-7000
£8000 $14720 €12000 Woman with apple (127x81cm-50x32in) s.d.58 prov.exhib. 10-Jun-4 Christie's, Paris #70/R est:20000-28000
£12670 $21158 €18498 Mujer con pano blanco (114x84cm-45x33in) s.d.1961 prov. 17-Nov-3 Waddingtons, Toronto #281/R est:20000-30000 (C.D 28000)
£20588 $35000 €30058 Desnudo (129x199cm-51x78in) s.d.80 prov.lit. 19-Nov-3 Sotheby's, New York #118/R est:35000-45000
£25000 $42500 €36500 Madre de tres hijos (175x112cm-69x44in) s.d.60 prov.exhib.lit. 19-Nov-3 Sotheby's, New York #125/R est:30000-40000

MARTINEZ, Xavier (1869-1943) American

£2312 $4000 €3376 Canyon in Arizona (25x30cm-10x12in) mono. i.verso board prov. 10-Dec-3 Bonhams & Butterfields, San Francisco #6179/R est:4000-6000

MARTINI, Alberto (1876-1954) Italian

£333 $613 €500 Sonata (40x50cm-16x20in) s.i.d.2003. 12-Jun-4 Meeting Art, Vercelli #434/R

£4558 $8159 €6700 Concert (22x14cm-9x6in) s. i.verso. 22-Mar-4 Sant Agostino, Torino #528/R est:8000

£6250 $10625 €9000 Smiling tree (73x60cm-29x24in) s. cardboard prov. 28-Oct-3 Il Ponte, Milan #249/R

Works on paper

£769 $1308 €1123 Profilo di fanciulla (23x15cm-9x6in) s. Indian ink. 28-Nov-3 Zofingen, Switzerland #2630/R est:2000 (S.FR 1700)

£1014 $1784 €1500 Portrait of Lady Casati (22x18cm-9x7in) s.i.d.1925 pencil. 19-May-4 Il Ponte, Milan #1067 est:2000-2200

£1014 $1784 €1500 Soldiers crossing river (6x17cm-2x7in) s.d.1896 Chinese ink. 19-May-4 Il Ponte, Milan #1063 est:2000-2200

£1351 $2378 €2000 Tondo with monkey. Tondo with crab and foot (16x14cm-6x6in) mono.i.d. pen dr pair prov.exhib. 19-May-4 Il Ponte, Milan #1065 est:3000-3500

MARTINI, Arturo (1889-1947) Italian

Sculpture

£1812 $2971 €2500 Bathers (26x17x12cm-10x7x5in) lithoceramic lit. 27-May-3 Sotheby's, Milan #88 est:3000-4000

£9732 $17419 €14500 Bust of young woman (62x49x31cm-24x19x12in) s.verso bronze exec.1921 exhib.lit. 29-May-4 Farsetti, Prato #457/R est:8000-10000

£9790 $16643 €14000 Jesus meeting Mary. Jesus meeting Veronica (41x32cm-16x13in) painted terracotta pair. 29-Nov-3 Farsetti, Prato #439/R est:10000-15000

£10870 $17826 €15000 Girl resting (37x27x18cm-15x11x7in) init. terracotta prov. 27-May-3 Sotheby's, Milan #248/R est:15000-20000

£22069 $36855 €32000 Charity (60x69x14cm-24x27x6in) num.2/3 bronze relief lit. 17-Nov-3 Sant Agostino, Torino #241/R est:32000-40000

MARTINI, Bruno (1911-1979) Italian

£566 $962 €826 The women bathing in landscape with two horses (78x147cm-31x58in) 28-Nov-3 Zofingen, Switzerland #3060 (S.FR 1250)

MARTINI, Felix Lewis (1893-1965) American

£519 $950 €758 California ranch (41x46cm-16x18in) s. painted c.1930. 5-Jun-4 Treadway Gallery, Cincinnati #617/R

MARTINI, Gaetano de (1845-1917) Italian

£4167 $7500 €6084 Tambourin girl (128x70cm-50x28in) s.d.1883. 21-Jan-4 Sotheby's, New York #171/R est:10000-15000

MARTINI, Joseph de (1896-1984) American

£556 $1000 €812 Interior (30x21cm-12x8in) s. i.verso masonite prov. 25-Apr-4 Bonhams & Butterfields, San Francisco #5534/R

£811 $1500 €1184 Surf on the Rocks. Nocturn (28x37cm-11x15in) each s. first oil on paperboard other mixed media two prov. 13-Jul-4 Christie's, Rockefeller NY #113/R est:1500-2000

£1189 $2200 €1736 Figure in hammock. Downing sun (46x100cm-18x39in) each s. s.i. verso two prov. 13-Jul-4 Christie's, Rockefeller NY #114/R est:1500-2000

£1189 $2200 €1736 Lighthouse. Wave (26x36cm-10x14in) each s. board two prov.exhib. 13-Jul-4 Christie's, Rockefeller NY #115/R est:1000-1500

£1189 $2200 €1736 Window on the harbour (90x63cm-35x25in) s. prov. 13-Jul-4 Christie's, Rockefeller NY #116/R est:800-1200

£1543 $2500 €2237 Wreck (25x30cm-10x12in) s. board. 8-Aug-3 Barridorf, Portland #335/R est:900 1200

£2160 $3500 €3132 Morning mist (41x51cm-16x20in) s. s.i.verso. 8-Aug-3 Barridorf, Portland #319/R est:3000-5000

MARTINI, Sandro (1941-) Italian

£667 $1227 €1000 Board 8 (44x35cm-17x14in) s.i.d.1966 verso tempera. 12-Jun-4 Meeting Art, Vercelli #52

£878 $1546 €1300 Composition (120x120cm-47x47in) s.d.1970 verso tempera collage prov. 24-May-4 Christie's, Milan #38

£2797 $4755 €4000 Page 87 (140x140cm-55x55in) s.i.d.1970 verso tempera collage prov. 20-Nov-3 Finarte Semenzato, Milan #22/R est:3500-4000

MARTINI, Vivaldo (1908-1989) Italian

£437 $795 €638 Female nude (30x45cm-12x18in) s.d.44. 16-Jun-4 Fischer, Luzern #2267/R (S.FR 1000)

£1121 $2006 €1637 Composition (70x88cm-28x35in) s. pavatex. 13-May-4 Stuker, Bern #247/R est:3000-4000 (S.FR 2600)

MARTINO, Antonio Pietro (1902-1989) American

£252 $400 €368 Urban landscape with narrow alley opening to white buildings (51x76cm-20x30in) s. W/C. 10-Sep-3 Alderfer's, Hatfield #432

£535 $850 €781 Bananas (23x30cm-9x12in) s. 10-Sep-3 Alderfer's, Hatfield #433/R

£1195 $1900 €1745 Bass Rocks (51x61cm-20x24in) s.i.d.1933. 10-Sep-3 Alderfer's, Hatfield #428/R est:3000-4000

£1209 $2250 €1765 Perce, seascape with prominently featured cliffs (69x114cm-27x45in) s. 3-Mar-4 Alderfer's, Hatfield #408/R est:2000-3000

£1572 $2500 €2295 Petunias (61x51cm-24x20in) s. 10-Sep-3 Alderfer's, Hatfield #430/R est:2000-2500

£1630 $3000 €2380 Stonebridge, Maine (33x43cm-13x17in) s. s.i. verso board. 27-Jun-4 Freeman, Philadelphia #166/R est:2000-3000

£1730 $2750 €2526 Mixed Bouquet (51x61cm-20x24in) s. painted 1983. 10-Sep-3 Alderfer's, Hatfield #429/R est:2000-2500

£1734 $3000 €2532 Still life of orange flowers in a green vase (51x41cm-20x16in) s.d.31. 10-Dec-3 Alderfer's, Hatfield #434/R est:2000-3000

£1829 $3000 €2652 Figures by the coast (61x76cm-24x30in) s. 4-Jun-3 Alderfer's, Hatfield #377/R est:2000-3000

£1981 $3250 €2872 Sailboats on lake (76x114cm-30x45in) s. 4-Jun-3 Alderfer's, Hatfield #373/R est:4000-5000

£2174 $4000 €3174 Winter's day (38x50cm-15x20in) s. board. 27-Jun-4 Freeman, Philadelphia #167/R est:1500-2500

£2516 $4000 €3673 Leo Carillo (91x102cm-36x40in) s. 10-Sep-3 Alderfer's, Hatfield #427/R est:3000-5000

£2673 $4250 €3903 Blocks, Manayunk (76x102cm-30x40in) s. 10-Sep-3 Alderfer's, Hatfield #426/R est:5000-7000

£3779 $6500 €5517 Street in winter (25x30cm-10x12in) s. panel. 7-Dec-3 Freeman, Philadelphia #204 est:2500-4000

£4076 $7500 €5951 Gobbler's shop (66x102cm-26x40in) s. 9-Jun-4 Alderfer's, Hatfield #486 est:4000-6000

£4301 $8000 €6279 Manayunk scene (58x99cm-23x39in) s. 3-Mar-4 Alderfer's, Hatfield #407/R est:3000-5000

£4865 $9000 €7103 East Manayunk (76x13cm-30x5in) s. 13-Feb-4 David Rago, Lambertville #10/R est:7000-9000

£4878 $8000 €7073 Wet day, with fishing boats at dock (51x61cm-20x24in) s.d.1929. 4-Jun-3 Alderfer's, Hatfield #359/R est:5000-7000

£5978 $11000 €8728 Two bridges (64x76cm-25x30in) s.d.1928 s.i.d. stretcher verso. 27-Jun-4 Freeman, Philadelphia #210/R est:10000-15000

£7558 $13000 €11035 The Blocks, Manayunk (76x114cm-30x45in) i. 6-Dec-3 Pook & Pook, Downington #99/R est:8000-10000

£9434 $15000 €13774 Darby Creek (64x76cm-25x30in) s.d.30. 10-Sep-3 Alderfer's, Hatfield #425/R est:12000-15000

£10227 $18000 €14931 Landscape of Bucks County millpond with buildings in the background (76x76cm-30x30in) s. 21-May-4 Pook & Pook, Downington #309/R est:18000-25000

£20381 $37500 €29756 Canal, New Hope (63x76cm-25x30in) s. 27-Jun-4 Freeman, Philadelphia #208/R est:12000-18000

£59783 $110000 €87283 Winter landscape (76x81cm-30x32in) s.d.1926. 27-Jun-4 Freeman, Philadelphia #168/R est:15000-25000

Works on paper

£692 $1100 €1010 Along the Delaware (38x69cm-15x27in) s. W/C. 10-Sep-3 Alderfer's, Hatfield #431/R

MARTINO, Edoardo (1838-1912) Italian

£1529 $2600 €2232 Fregatta (53x63cm-21x25in) s.d.1870 oval. 25-Nov-3 Galeria y Remates, Montevideo #169/R

£4000 $6400 €5840 Argentinian cruiser with frigate in background (46x74cm-18x29in) s. 16-Sep-3 Bonhams, New Bond Street #71/R est:4000-5000

£5495 $10000 €8023 Steam boat on fire (92x62cm-36x24in) s. painted 1889. 29-Jun-4 Arroyo, Buenos Aires #50/R est:10000

£10000 $16000 €14600 Royal Yacht Ophir disembarking the Duke and Duchess of York in Sydney Harbour (36x76cm-14x30in) s. prov. 16-Sep-3 Bonhams, New Bond Street #69/R est:10000-15000

Works on paper

£1600 $2672 €2336 Brazilian views (20x27cm-8x11in) s.i.d.21 Apr 68 W/C over pencil folio. 14-Oct-3 Sotheby's, London #248/R est:1500-2000

£2200 $3740 €3212 Britannia (31x23cm-12x9in) s.i.d.94 pencil W/C htd white. 19-Nov-3 Christie's, Kensington #406/R

£3000 $4800 €4380 Royal Yacht Ophir disembarking the Duke and Duchess of York in Sydney Harbour (20x50cm-8x20in) bears i.verso W/C htd white. 16-Sep-3 Bonhams, New Bond Street #70/R est:2500-3500

MARTINO, Giovanni (1908-1998) American

£1223 $2250 €1786 Rector Street (41x51cm-16x20in) s. 9-Jun-4 Alderfer's, Hatfield #489/R est:3000-5000

£1445 $2500 €2110 Gloucester docks (51x61cm-20x24in) s. d.1929 verso. 10-Dec-3 Alderfer's, Hatfield #433/R est:2500-2750

£2038 $3750 €2975 Urban landscape (30x46cm-12x18in) s. board. 9-Jun-4 Alderfer's, Hatfield #490/R est:2000-4000

£4403 $7000 €6428 Canton Street (64x102cm-25x40in) s. 10-Sep-3 Alderfer's, Hatfield #395/R est:4000-6000

MARTINO, Nicola Maria (1946-) Italian

£1103 $1843 €1600 Italian factories in the South (70x100cm-28x39in) s.i.d.1983 verso. 13-Nov-3 Finarte Semenzato, Rome #458 est:1800-2400

MARTINO, Romeo de (1880-1897) Italian

Works on paper

£1500 $2445 €2175 HRH Prince of Wales. Chinese ambassador Li Hung Chang reviews the fleet (16x42cm-6x17in) s.i.d.96 W/C two. 21-Jul-3 Sotheby's, London #592/R est:800-1200

MARTINY, Theodor (1880-1949) Austrian

£500 $900 €750 Inner courtyard with clocktower (63x45cm-25x18in) s.d.16. 22-Apr-4 Dorotheum, Graz #19/R

MARTINZ, Fritz (1924-2002) ?

£733 $1349 €1100 Man looking at woman (45x45cm-18x18in) s.d.1964 panel. 9-Jun-4 Dorotheum, Salzburg #653/R

£2500 $4600 €3800 Report (76x180cm-30x71in) s.d.1976 i.d.verso chipboard lit. 22-Jun-4 Wiener Kunst Auktionen, Vienna #323/R est:3000

MARTON, Franz (1884-?) Czechoslovakian

£329 $595 €500 The secret little spot (32x23cm-13x9in) s. panel. 19-Apr-4 Glerum, Amsterdam #302

MARTORELL, Vicente (?) Spanish

£423 $739 €600 Still life (60x80cm-24x31in) s. 16-Dec-3 Durán, Madrid #29/R

£845 $1479 €1200 Still life with flowers (75x92cm-30x36in) s. 16-Dec-3 Durán, Madrid #31/R

MARTOS, Manuel (1950-) Spanish

£302 $562 €450 Sofa, fruit and flowers (65x81cm-26x32in) s. 2-Mar-4 Ansorena, Madrid #887/R

£302	$541	€450	Two pink trees (54x65cm-21x26in) s. 25-May-4 Durán, Madrid #66/R
£319	$583	€475	Landscape with poplars (50x61cm-20x24in) s.d.74. 12-Jul-4 Durán, Madrid #82/R
£336	$601	€500	Landscape in Quesada (65x81cm-26x32in) s.d.77. 25-May-4 Durán, Madrid #85/R
£473	$832	€700	Path in the countryside (73x92cm-29x36in) s.d.1976. 18-May-4 Segre, Madrid #108/R

MARTOS, Nikita Ivanovich (1787-1813) Russian

Works on paper

£3593	$6000	€5246	View of St Petersburg Stock Exchange (20x41cm-8x16in) i. W/C prov. 21-Oct-3 Christie's, Rockefeller NY #83 est:4000-6000

MARTOUGEN, Stanislas (1873-?) ?

£586	$1084	€850	Nu a la fontaine (65x48cm-26x19in) s.d.1939 panel. 16-Feb-4 Giraudeau, Tours #85

MARTSEN, Jan (younger) (1609-c.1647) Flemish

£1500	$2550	€2190	Landscape with waggoners being ambushed by bandits (34x48cm-13x19in) mono. prov. 30-Oct-3 Sotheby's, Olympia #127/R est:3000-5000
£6164	$10479	€9000	Cavalry battle (47x64cm-19x25in) mono. panel. 4-Nov-3 Sotheby's, Amsterdam #76/R est:6000-8000
£7308	$12569	€10670	Battle scene (52x82cm-20x32in) indis.sig.d.164. 2-Dec-3 Bukowskis, Stockholm #375/R est:50000-80000 (S.KR 95000)

MARTSEN, Jan (younger-attrib) (1609-c.1647) Flemish

£1523	$2773	€2300	Scene de choc de cavalerie (41x53cm-16x21in) panel. 21-Jun-4 Tajan, Paris #50 est:2500-3000

MARTTINEN, Veikko (1917-2003) Finnish

£1486	$2661	€2200	The guitar player (75x45cm-30x18in) s.d.64. 8-May-4 Bukowskis, Helsinki #265/R est:2500-3500
£1538	$2615	€2200	Girl with seagulls (46x55cm-18x22in) s.d.68 board. 29-Nov-3 Bukowskis, Helsinki #299/R est:2500-2800
£1944	$3247	€2800	The gaze (61x33cm-24x13in) s.d.61. 26-Oct-3 Bukowskis, Helsinki #413/R est:2000
£2937	$4993	€4200	From the Mediterranean (75x70cm-30x28in) s.d.69 board. 29-Nov-3 Bukowskis, Helsinki #308/R est:3000-4000

MARUSIC, Zivko (1944-) Balkan

£1049	$1804	€1500	In the wood (100x60cm-39x24in) s.d.90 s.d.verso paper on canvas. 3-Dec-3 Stadion, Trieste #1067/R est:1000-1500

MARUSSIG, Piero (1879-1937) Italian

£2098	$3608	€3000	Landscape in Veneto (28x34cm-11x13in) s. cardboard. 3-Dec-3 Stadion, Trieste #1167/R est:2200-3200
£3873	$6430	€5500	Still life (39x50cm-15x20in) s. s.i.verso. 11-Jun-3 Finarte Semenzato, Milan #521/R
£4196	$7133	€6000	Visit (59x50cm-23x20in) s. board exhib.lit. 25-Nov-3 Sotheby's, Milan #136/R est:8000-10000
£6897	$11517	€10000	Landscape with pink house (50x59cm-20x23in) s. board. 13-Nov-3 Finarte Semenzato, Rome #411/R est:10000-12000
£9420	$15449	€13000	Still life (39x34cm-15x13in) s. cardboard prov. 27-May-3 Sotheby's, Milan #233/R est:8000-10000
£13605	$24354	€20000	Seated woman (84x68cm-33x27in) s. painted 1916-18 exhib. 16-Mar-4 Finarte Semenzato, Milan #450/R est:22000

Works on paper

£600	$1104	€900	Reclining woman (20x25cm-8x10in) s. pencil prov. 10-Jun-4 Galleria Pace, Milan #54/R

MARUSSO, Vittorio (?) Italian

Works on paper

£300	$546	€438	A Venetian beauty (29x20cm-11x8in) s.i. pencil W/C. 1-Jul-4 Christie's, Kensington #416/R

MARVAL, Jacqueline (1866-1932) French

£1498	$2546	€2187	Still life (54x65cm-21x26in) s.d.1906. 5-Nov-3 Dobiaschofsky, Bern #790/R est:5500 (S.FR 3400)
£3333	$6100	€5000	Le bain, etude pour Daphne et Chloe (38x61cm-15x24in) s. prov.lit. 6-Jun-4 Anaf, Lyon #437/R est:5000-6000
£5517	$10207	€8000	Head of lady (27x22cm-11x9in) 14-Jan-4 Castellana, Madrid #235/R est:6000

MARVILLE, Charles (1816-c.1880) French

Photographs

£1705	$3000	€2489	Place du chatelet (34x25cm-13x10in) with sig. salted paper print. 20-May-4 Swann Galleries, New York #216/R est:3500-4500
£2667	$4800	€3894	La porte rouge, portail septentrional de l'eglise metropolitaine a Paris (21x15cm-8x6in) i.num.46 salt print lit. 22-Apr-4 Phillips, New York #74/R est:6000-8000

MARX, Ernst Bernhard (1864-?) German

£1341	$2468	€2012	Woman at her toilet (186x115cm-73x45in) s. 14-Jun-4 Blomqvist, Lysaker #1250 est:20000-25000 (N.KR 16500)

MARX, Franz (1889-1960) German

£400	$720	€600	Goat (44x54cm-17x21in) s.d.17. 21-Apr-4 Dorotheum, Vienna #26/R
£784	$1223	€1145	Flamingos (50x60cm-20x24in) s. cardboard. 30-Mar-3 Agra, Warsaw #48/R (P.Z 5000)
£795	$1446	€1200	Flamingos in a park (51x60cm-20x24in) s. 18-Jun-4 Bolland & Marotz, Bremen #822/R
£1042	$1719	€1500	Flamingos (51x60cm-20x24in) s. 2-Jul-3 Neumeister, Munich #709/R est:1200
£1400	$2422	€2044	Bullfight (45x55cm-18x22in) s. 11-Dec-3 Christie's, Kensington #61/R est:1500-2000

MARX, Gustav (1855-1928) German

£1189	$2045	€1700	Lady in white dress (34x26cm-13x10in) s.i.d.91 board. 3-Dec-3 Neumeister, Munich #664/R est:1300

MARXEN, Herbert (1900-1954) German

£347	$545	€500	House in the dunes by moonlight (47x63cm-19x25in) s.d.25 lit. 30-Aug-3 Hans Stahl, Toestorf #84/R

MARXER, Alfred (1876-1945) Swiss

£195	$349	€285	Self portrait in studio (70x60cm-28x24in) s.d. prov. 22-Mar-4 Philippe Schuler, Zurich #6032 (S.FR 450)
£303	$542	€442	Bathseba (110x95cm-43x37in) s.d. prov. 22-Mar-4 Philippe Schuler, Zurich #6031 (S.FR 700)
£567	$1020	€850	Interior with female nude and petroleum lamp (50x43cm-20x17in) s.d. 24-Apr-4 Dr Lehr, Berlin #278/R

MARXMUELLER, Anton (1898-?) German

£342	$582	€500	Still life with fishes and fruit (89x74cm-35x29in) s.d.1929. 5-Nov-3 Hugo Ruef, Munich #1061

MARY, Josephine (fl.1866-1870) French

£1000	$1820	€1500	Still life with mackerels and artichokes (49x60cm-19x24in) s. 30-Jun-4 Pierre Berge, Paris #82/R est:1000-1500

MARYAN (1927-1977) American

£1127	$1882	€1645	Figure composition (80x64cm-31x25in) s.d.59. 7-Oct-3 Rasmussen, Copenhagen #74/R est:15000 (D.KR 12000)

MARYAN, Burstein Pinchas (1927-1977) American

£2941	$5000	€4294	Personnage (76x61cm-30x24in) s.d.1961 prov.exhib. 9-Nov-3 Wright, Chicago #352 est:2000-3000

Works on paper

£347	$580	€500	Visage de profil (56x45cm-22x18in) s.d.1971 chl. 25-Oct-3 Cornette de St.Cyr, Paris #750
£451	$754	€650	Personnage criant (45x56cm-18x22in) s.d.1971 chl. 25-Oct-3 Cornette de St.Cyr, Paris #749/R
£451	$754	€650	Visage souriant (45x56cm-18x22in) s.d.1971 chl. 25-Oct-3 Cornette de St.Cyr, Paris #751
£940	$1757	€1400	Personnage (64x49cm-25x19in) s.d.1970 pastel on pastel. 29-Feb-4 Versailles Encheres #277/R

MARZELLE, Jean (1916-) French

£298	$542	€450	Baigneurs (24x33cm-9x13in) s. 15-Jun-4 Blanchet, Paris #238
£382	$650	€558	Olive trees (25x36cm-10x14in) s. prov. 22-Nov-3 Jackson's, Cedar Falls #402/R
£451	$754	€650	Les oliviers (54x65cm-21x26in) s. 21-Oct-3 Artcurial Briest, Paris #342
£800	$1456	€1200	Village surplombant la riviere (27x35cm-11x14in) s. 4-Jul-4 Eric Pillon, Calais #248/R
£1678	$3070	€2500	Paysage a la riviere (66x92cm-26x36in) s. 7-Jul-4 Artcurial Briest, Paris #159 est:1300-1800

MARZI, Bruno (1908-1981) Italian

£1399	$2336	€2000	Saint Dorothy (39x40cm-15x16in) tempera gold lit. 7-Oct-3 Pandolfini, Florence #465/R est:1200-1500

MARZI, Ezio (1875-?) Italian

£872	$1500	€1273	Children in an interior (61x76cm-24x30in) s.i.d.1945 board. 7-Dec-3 Treadway Gallery, Cincinnati #507/R est:2500-3500
£4000	$7360	€6000	In the study (45x30cm-18x12in) s.i. 8-Jun-4 Sotheby's, Milan #137/R est:4000-6000

MARZOCCHI DE BELLUCI, Numa (19/20th C) French

£26389	$47500	€38528	Lesson in the Koran (116x89cm-46x35in) s. 23-Apr-4 Sotheby's, New York #95/R est:50000-70000
£32110	$53624	€46560	Studying the Koran in a mosque (116x89cm-46x35in) s.d.78. 23-Jun-3 Philippe Schuler, Zurich #3535 est:8000-12000 (S.FR 70000)

MARZOHL, Johann Baptiste (1792-1862) Swiss

Works on paper

£1092	$1987	€1594	Country landscape (34x50cm-13x20in) s. W/C. 16-Jun-4 Fischer, Luzern #2795/R est:2500-3500 (S.FR 2500)

MAS Y FONDEVILA, Arcadio (1852-1934) Spanish

Works on paper

£828	$1490	€1200	Coastal view (15x20cm-6x8in) s. W/C. 26-Jan-4 Ansorena, Madrid #294/R
£993	$1658	€1400	Japanese garden (33x46cm-13x18in) s. mixed media. 20-Oct-3 Durán, Madrid #147/R
£2254	$3944	€3200	Choir boy (52x30cm-20x12in) W/C. 16-Dec-3 Segre, Madrid #64/R est:3000

MAS, Ernesto (19/20th C) ?

£483	$801	€700	Landscape (80x100cm-31x39in) s.d.1912. 1-Oct-3 Ansorena, Madrid #721/R

MAS, Felix (20th C) Spanish
£231 $415 €337 Dream (60x50cm-24x20in) s. 25-Apr-4 Subastas Odalys, Caracas #72
£284 $475 €415 Green light (25x41cm-10x16in) s. painted 1976. 13-Jul-3 Subastas Odalys, Caracas #15
£387 $670 €550 Bull scene (40x30cm-16x12in) s.d.1977 s.i.d.1977 verso. 15-Dec-3 Ansorena, Madrid #369/R

MASANOBU, Okumura (1686-1764) Japanese
Prints
£2200 $4048 €3212 Mitate of Fugen Bosatsu (30x15cm-12x6in) s. print exec. late 1720's lit. 8-Jun-4 Sotheby's, London #18/R est:1200-1500
£2600 $4784 €3796 Saigyo Hoshi contemplating Fuji (31x15cm-12x6in) s. print exec. late 1730's lit. 8-Jun-4 Sotheby's, London #21/R est:900-1200
£2657 $4517 €3800 Scene de drame (30x16cm-12x6in) col print lit. 25-Nov-3 Sotheby's, Paris #112/R est:4500-5500
£6500 $11960 €9490 Sanagawa Ichimatsu II as a puppeteer (72x26cm-28x10in) s. print exec. late 1740's one of three lit. 8-Jun-4 Sotheby's, London #14/R est:4500-5000
£16000 $29440 €23360 Daikoku and Ebisu performing a New Year's Manzai dance (56x31cm-22x12in) s. print exec. late 1710's unique prov. 8-Jun-4 Sotheby's, London #15/R est:5000-8000

MASARYK, Herbert G (attrib) (1880-1915) Austrian
£309 $575 €451 Landscape study (23x25cm-9x10in) mono.d.1911 canvas on board. 6-Mar-4 Dorotheum, Prague #43/R est:15000-23000 (C.KR 15000)

MASATSUNE, Ju (19th C) Japanese
Sculpture
£3288 $5589 €4800 Eagle on rock (35cm-14in) i. silvered bronze. 8-Nov-3 Dr Fritz Nagel, Stuttgart #1879/R est:3500

MASAYOSHI, Kitao (1764-1824) Japanese
Prints
£5500 $10120 €8030 Perspective view of the evening cool at the Ryogokubashi in Edo (31x44cm-12x17in) s. print. 8-Jun-4 Sotheby's, London #144/R est:3200-4000

MASAZUMI, Ryusai (19th C) Japanese
Prints
£5200 $9568 €7592 Chinese warrior on horseback shooting an arrow towards a tiger (21x36cm-8x14in) s. print diptych. 8-Jun-4 Sotheby's, London #440/R est:1000-1500

MASCARINI, Giuseppe (1877-?) Italian
£273 $453 €396 La bellezza (40x31cm-16x12in) s.d.1915 panel. 13-Jun-3 Zofingen, Switzerland #2491/R (S.FR 600)

MASCART, Gustave (1834-1914) French
£851 $1421 €1200 Les pecheurs assis et la fregate Francaise (33x46cm-13x18in) s. 19-Jun-3 Millon & Associes, Paris #212
£872 $1500 €1273 Le depart en Barque (48x64cm-19x25in) s. 6-Dec-3 Neal Auction Company, New Orleans #56/R est:2000-3000
£1098 $2020 €1647 French harbour view. s. 14-Jun-4 Blomqvist, Lysaker #1251 est:8000-12000 (N.KR 13500)
£1268 $2193 €1800 Le cirque (33x44cm-13x17in) s. 10-Dec-3 Millon & Associes, Paris #50/R est:1500-2000
£1812 $3352 €2700 Bruges, le beguinage (46x61cm-18x24in) s. 14-Mar-4 St-Germain-en-Laye Encheres #65/R est:1800-2000
£1921 $3497 €2805 At the pier (49x65cm-19x26in) s.i.d.1890. 16-Jun-4 Fischer, Luzern #2268/R est:1200-1500 (S.FR 4400)
£2081 $3870 €3100 Promenade en bord de mer (43x53cm-17x21in) s. 7-Mar-4 Lesieur & Le Bars, Le Havre #108
£2267 $4125 €3400 Treport (46x65cm-18x26in) s.i.d.1892. 4-Jul-4 Eric Pillon, Calais #58/R
£2434 $4479 €3700 Plage du nord (33x46cm-13x18in) s. 28-Jun-4 Joron-Derem, Paris #109/R est:1000-1200

MASCHERINI, Marcello (1906-1983) Italian
Sculpture
£2867 $4931 €4100 Gladiator (47cm-19in) s. bronze lit. 3-Dec-3 Stadion, Trieste #1088/R est:2500-3500
£4533 $8115 €6800 Angel (160x100cm-63x39in) pat. plaster. 12-May-4 Stadion, Trieste #801/R est:2500-3500

MASCI, Edolo (1938-) Italian
£255 $474 €380 Hilly landscape (46x54cm-18x21in) s.d.1963 verso canvas on cardboard. 4-Mar-4 Babuino, Rome #484
£268 $499 €400 Road and house with figure (30x40cm-12x16in) painted c.1965. 4-Mar-4 Babuino, Rome #383
£288 $536 €430 Bell game (40x25cm-16x10in) s.i.d.1964 verso. 4-Mar-4 Babuino, Rome #125

MASCO, Pam (1953-) British/American
£390 $729 €569 Flower shop interior (76x91cm-30x36in) s. prov. 24-Feb-4 Bonhams, Knowle #124

MASCRET, Jean Etienne (19th C) French?
Sculpture
£2235 $3800 €3263 Charles X (32cm-13in) d.1829b Sevres biscuit after Bosio. 25-Nov-3 Christie's, Rockefeller NY #397/R est:2000-3000

MASELLI, Titina (1924-) Italian
£1467 $2640 €2200 Football (100x70cm-39x28in) s. acrylic paper on canvas. 22-Apr-4 Finarte Semenzato, Rome #139/R est:2200-2500
£2333 $4200 €3500 Winter morning (62x69cm-24x27in) s.verso board painted 1954 exhib. 22-Apr-4 Finarte Semenzato, Rome #210/R est:3800-4500
£3586 $5989 €5200 Baseball, trees and skyscraper (195x130cm-77x51in) s.d.1975 verso acrylic. 13-Nov-3 Finarte Semenzato, Rome #350/R est:6000-7000
£5161 $8773 €7380 Boxers (113x146cm-44x57in) s.i.d.1969 verso. 18-Nov-3 Babuino, Rome #60/R est:2500-3000

MASEREEL, Frans (1889-1972) Belgian
£600 $1074 €900 Torse nu de docker devant le port (48x63cm-19x25in) mono.d.1950 paper lit. 15-May-4 De Vuyst, Lokeren #217
£833 $1317 €1200 White cat (32x48cm-13x19in) init.d.1955 cardboard. 2-Sep-3 Christie's, Amsterdam #420 est:1000-1500
£972 $1624 €1400 La barmaid en rose (50x65cm-20x26in) mono. oil paper. 21-Oct-3 Campo, Vlaamse Kaai #485
£1056 $1827 €1500 Blonde en maillot rouge sur la plage (48x63cm-19x25in) mono.d.1959 paper on board lit. 13-Dec-3 De Vuyst, Lokeren #227/R est:1400-1600
£1208 $2235 €1800 Le banc (50x65cm-20x26in) mono.d.1965 paper lit. 13-Mar-4 De Vuyst, Lokeren #238 est:1400-1600
£1259 $2140 €1800 Nageuse I (48x62cm-19x24in) mono.d.1952 paper on board. 29-Nov-3 Villa Grisebach, Berlin #620/R est:2400-2600
£1399 $2336 €2000 Tamise (50x70cm-20x28in) mono.i.d.1948 s.i.d.1948 verso board prov.lit. 11-Oct-3 De Vuyst, Lokeren #245/R est:1300-1500
£1399 $2378 €2000 Clothes seller (65x50cm-26x20in) mono.d.1968 paper on masonite. 29-Nov-3 Bassenge, Berlin #6894 est:3000
£1733 $3189 €2600 Baigneuse entre les Nochers II (46x54cm-18x21in) mono.d.1950 s.i.d.1950 verso panel lit. 9-Jun-4 Dorotheum, Salzburg #669/R est:4500-6000
£1748 $2972 €2500 Pecheur et enfant en Equihen (24x32cm-9x13in) mono.d.1939 paper on panel. 21-Nov-3 Reiss & Sohn, Konigstein #470/R est:3000
£1761 $3046 €2500 Clochards sur un banc (46x62cm-18x24in) mono.d.1959 paper on panel. 13-Dec-3 De Vuyst, Lokeren #226/R est:1400-1600
£1875 $3131 €2700 Autoportrait au modele (56x38cm-22x15in) mono.d.1967 s.verso. 21-Oct-3 Campo, Vlaamse Kaai #483/R est:3000-3500
£1958 $3368 €2800 Torse nue a la toilette (33x24cm-13x9in) mono.d.1944 paper. 2-Dec-3 Hauswedell & Nolte, Hamburg #411/R est:2800
£2667 $4907 €4000 Pecheur au panier (66x54cm-26x21in) mono.d.1929 s.d. verso. 10-Jun-4 Hauswedell & Nolte, Hamburg #467/R est:2000
£2797 $4811 €4000 Boulogne, maisons sur le quai et bateaux dans le port (59x80cm-23x31in) mono.d.1930 i. verso. 2-Dec-3 Hauswedell & Nolte, Hamburg #405/R est:5000
£2933 $5397 €4400 Arbres dans les dunes (73x100cm-29x39in) mono.d.1930 s.d. verso. 10-Jun-4 Hauswedell & Nolte, Hamburg #468/R est:5000
£4196 $7133 €6000 Brune a la fenetre (65x50cm-26x20in) mono.d.1953 paper on panel. 29-Nov-3 Villa Grisebach, Berlin #220/R est:3500-4500
£6100 $11102 €8906 Panorama de Boulogne - view of the city and port (91x71cm-36x28in) s.d.1927. 29-Jun-4 Anderson & Garland, Newcastle #463/R est:5000-8000
Prints
£3147 $5350 €4500 Femme a la cigarette - jeune femme a la cigarette (43x34cm-17x13in) mono.d.1923 i. verso prov.lit. 29-Nov-3 Villa Grisebach, Berlin #151/R est:5000-7000
Works on paper
£342 $582 €500 Le marin (43x31cm-17x12in) mono.d.1946 W/C china ink. 4-Nov-3 Servarts Themis, Bruxelles #599
£400 $716 €600 Paysage imaginaire (48x63cm-19x25in) mono.d.1956 pencil Indian ink lit. 15-May-4 De Vuyst, Lokeren #219
£556 $928 €800 Warmonger (32x25cm-13x10in) mono.d. Indian ink brush. 25-Oct-3 Dr Lehr, Berlin #334/R
£638 $1129 €950 Civilisation (49x63cm-19x25in) s.d.1937 ink dr. 27-Apr-4 Campo & Campo, Antwerp #160
£664 $1129 €950 Reclining nude (21x30cm-8x12in) mono.d.1937 W/C Indian ink. 29-Nov-3 Villa Grisebach, Berlin #622/R est:600-800
£769 $1308 €1100 Chat noir (47x63cm-19x25in) mono.d.1954 Indian ink brush. 29-Nov-3 Villa Grisebach, Berlin #625/R est:800-900
£800 $1440 €1200 Deux cygnes IV (31x40cm-12x16in) mono.d. W/C Indian ink brush. 24-Apr-4 Dr Lehr, Berlin #280/R
£909 $1545 €1300 City at night (30x31cm-12x12in) init. W/C gouache. 25-Nov-3 Christie's, Amsterdam #226/R
£1049 $1752 €1500 Sailor (41x30cm-16x12in) mono.d.1929 ink lit. 11-Oct-3 De Vuyst, Lokeren #246 est:750-1000
£1049 $1783 €1500 Trois plongeurs (48x63cm-19x25in) mono.d.1953 paper on board. 29-Nov-3 Villa Grisebach, Berlin #621/R est:2000-2500
£1538 $2615 €2200 On the Flight (32x49cm-13x19in) mono.d.1940 W/C. 29-Nov-3 Villa Grisebach, Berlin #623/R est:2000-2500
£1733 $3137 €2600 La secretaire (62x46cm-24x18in) mono.d.1924 W/C. 30-Mar-4 Palais de Beaux Arts, Brussels #654/R est:3000-4000
£1818 $3091 €2600 Giant in city (120x76cm-47x30in) mono.d.50 Indian ink brush htd white. 29-Nov-3 Villa Grisebach, Berlin #219/R est:3000-4000
£2937 $5052 €4200 Au theatre (107x74cm-42x29in) mono.d.1923 Indian ink pen brush exhib. 2-Dec-3 Hauswedell & Nolte, Hamburg #408/R est:2000
£3100 $4929 €4526 Fille sur un banc (49x59cm-19x23in) init.d. W/C. 9-Sep-3 Rowley Fine Art, Newmarket #432/R est:500-800
£5594 $9510 €8000 Soir a Paris (105x73cm-41x29in) mono.d.1923 chl prov.exhib. 29-Nov-3 Villa Grisebach, Berlin #207/R est:5000-7000
£5734 $9863 €8200 A la terrasse (63x49cm-25x19in) mono.d.1924 Indian ink brush W/C. 2-Dec-3 Hauswedell & Nolte, Hamburg #409/R est:3500
£5734 $9863 €8200 Paris, la nuit (74x54cm-29x21in) mono.d.1927 Indian ink brush W/C. 2-Dec-3 Hauswedell & Nolte, Hamburg #410/R est:6000

MASEY, Philip Edward (19th C) British
Works on paper
£340 $626 €496 Chigi Palace at Larigia, Italy (10x14cm-4x6in) W/C pencil. 23-Mar-4 Bonhams, Knightsbridge #48/R

MASHKOV, Ilya (1881-1944) Russian
£1364 $2264 €1978 Fishing boats on beach (23x28cm-9x11in) s. 13-Jun-3 Zofingen, Switzerland #2492 est:800 (S.FR 3000)

MASHKOV, Ilya (attrib) (1881-1944) Russian
Works on paper
£363 $650 €530 Cathedral (41x53cm-16x21in) gouache. 11-Jan-4 William Jenack, New York #215

MASI, Diego (1965-) Uruguayan
£309 $500 €448 Suspended (61x76cm-24x30in) s. s.i.d.2003 verso acrylic. 29-Jul-3 Galeria y Remates, Montevideo #62
£423 $800 €618 Tower (92x73cm-36x29in) s.i.verso acrylic. 22-Feb-4 Galeria y Remates, Montevideo #137/R
£483 $850 €705 Plastic shape (76x61cm-30x24in) s.i.d.2003 acrylic. 5-Jan-4 Galeria y Remates, Montevideo #30/R

MASI, Paolo (20th C) Italian
Works on paper
£244 $400 €356 Untitled (40x40cm-16x16in) s.d.76 verso pencil paper on cardboard prov. 28-May-3 Sotheby's, Amsterdam #107/R
£244 $400 €356 Untitled (40x40cm-16x16in) s.d.75 verso pencil on cardboard prov. 28-May-3 Sotheby's, Amsterdam #108/R

MASI, Roberto (1940-) Italian
£533 $981 €800 Fishermen (50x40cm-20x16in) s. s.verso. 12-Jun-4 Meeting Art, Vercelli #525/R

MASIA, Roberto (1958-) Italian
£268 $497 €400 Sailing boats in Portacarbone (40x60cm-16x24in) s. s.i.verso. 13-Mar-4 Meeting Art, Vercelli #248
£369 $683 €550 Mending the nets (60x50cm-24x20in) s. s.i.verso. 13-Mar-4 Meeting Art, Vercelli #555
£423 $701 €600 Vele a Portacarbone (40x60cm-16x24in) s. s.i.verso. 14-Jun-3 Meeting Art, Vercelli #710

MASIDE, Carlos (1897-1958) Spanish
Works on paper
£563 $975 €800 Peasant woman (19x24cm-7x9in) s. dr. 15-Dec-3 Ansorena, Madrid #222/R
£600 $1092 €900 Pescadoras (22x16cm-9x6in) s. ink drawing. 29-Jun-4 Segre, Madrid #112/R
£676 $1189 €1000 Sailors (21x27cm-8x11in) s. inik dr. 18-May-4 Segre, Madrid #317/R
£694 $1181 €1000 Strolling (21x22cm-8x9in) s. ink. 28-Oct-3 Segre, Madrid #212/R
£890 $1514 €1300 Peasant women (22x28cm-9x11in) s. dr. 4-Nov-3 Ansorena, Madrid #214/R

MASINELLI, Leo (1902-1983) Italian?
£540 $885 €750 Still life (30x42cm-12x17in) cardboard. 5-Jun-3 Adma, Formigine #752

MASKELL, Christopher M (1846-1933) British
£500 $925 €730 Flatford, Orwell (23x28cm-9x11in) s. pair. 13-Feb-4 Keys, Aylsham #650/R

MASLOWSKI, Stanislaw (1853-1926) Polish
£938 $1566 €1369 Landscape (15x33cm-6x13in) s. plywood painted c.1900. 19-Oct-3 Agra, Warsaw #58/R est:4000 (P.Z 6000)
£1016 $1696 €1483 Glade (15x33cm-6x13in) s. plywood painted c.1900. 19-Oct-3 Agra, Warsaw #52/R est:3000 (P.Z 6500)
£3906 $6523 €5703 On the way to the village (18x34cm-7x13in) s.d.78. 19-Oct-3 Agra, Warsaw #17/R est:22000 (P.Z 25000)

MASO, Felipe (1851-1929) Spanish
£1678 $2970 €2500 On the beach (46x37cm-18x15in) s. board. 27-Apr-4 Durán, Madrid #136/R est:2500
£2395 $4000 €3497 Afternoon in the park (55x74cm-22x29in) s. panel. 7-Oct-3 Sotheby's, New York #92 est:4000-6000

MASOLINO DA PANICALE (c.1383-c.1447) Italian
£11333 $20400 €17000 Madonna with Infant Jesus (142x63cm-56x25in) i. verso panel. 22-Apr-4 Weidler, Nurnberg #333/R

MASON, Albert E (1895-1950) British/South African
£248 $443 €362 2000 feet below, Rand Leases gold mine, Johannesburg (47x43cm-19x17in) s.d.1946 i.verso. 31-May-4 Stephan Welz, Johannesburg #286 (SA.R 3000)

MASON, Barry (1927-) British
£380 $695 €555 Twilight on the Thames (28x39cm-11x15in) s. s.i.d.75 verso. 6-Jul-4 Bonhams, Knightsbridge #54/R

MASON, Bateson (1910-1977) British
£300 $537 €438 Facade over water (91x122cm-36x48in) s. s.i.verso board. 14-May-4 Christie's, Kensington #623/R

MASON, Emily Florence (1870-?) British
£390 $651 €550 Personification of summer (61x51cm-24x20in) s. 17-Oct-3 Berlinghof, Heidelberg #1069/R

MASON, Ernold A (fl.1883) British
Works on paper
£260 $416 €380 Mother and child in a cot (46x33cm-18x13in) s. W/C. 16-Sep-3 Bonhams, Knowle #70

MASON, Frank H (1876-1965) British
£250 $460 €365 Yacht and a coaster passing one another in an estuary (29x39cm-11x15in) s. board. 23-Mar-4 Anderson & Garland, Newcastle #410
£270 $467 €394 Three masted sailing ship in stormy seas (24x34cm-9x13in) s. board. 9-Dec-3 Bonhams, Oxford #85
£320 $534 €467 Stormy weather (20x46cm-8x18in) s. board. 10-Oct-3 Richardson & Smith, Whitby #128
£600 $1002 €876 Durham Castle leaving harbour (51x76cm-20x30in) s.i.d.1904 i.verso. 18-Jun-3 John Nicholson, Haslemere #719/R
£720 $1145 €1051 Steam coaster on a blustery day (30x39cm-12x15in) s. board. 18-Mar-3 Anderson & Garland, Newcastle #529
£800 $1432 €1168 Four-master in the Channel off Dover with a pilot cutter standing by (51x76cm-20x30in) s. 26-May-4 Christie's, Kensington #732/R
£1600 $2720 €2336 Galleons with full sails in flat calm estuary (102x63cm-40x25in) 1-Dec-3 David Duggleby, Scarborough #340/R est:1000-2000
£1600 $3024 €2336 Hunt is up (51x71cm-20x28in) s.d.1940. 17-Feb-4 Bonhams, New Bond Street #67/R est:800-1200
£1810 $3023 €2643 Shipping by the Tower of London (49x74cm-19x29in) s. 17-Nov-3 Waddingtons, Toronto #123/R est:4000-6000 (C.D 4000)
£2000 $3180 €2920 Steamship Singularity docking in a French port (59x79cm-23x31in) s. 18-Mar-3 Anderson & Garland, Newcastle #528/R est:2000-3000
Works on paper
£260 $442 €380 Yacht in choppy seas with steamer in the background (20x27cm-8x11in) s. pen ink prov. 1-Dec-3 David Duggleby, Scarborough #254/R
£300 $498 €438 The Lido (24x34cm-9x13in) s.i. W/C. 1-Oct-3 Bonhams, Knightsbridge #105/R
£300 $543 €438 Off Beachy Head (13x23cm-5x9in) init. i.verso W/C gouache. 16-Apr-4 Keys, Aylsham #524
£400 $656 €584 Cove scene with various figures on the sandy beach (17x26cm-7x10in) s.d.49 W/C. 30-May-3 Bigwood, Stratford on Avon #290
£400 $716 €584 Coastal scene with fishing smacks at low tide (23x43cm-9x17in) s. W/C. 13-May-4 Grant, Worcester #336/R
£520 $827 €759 River scene (15x21cm-6x8in) s. W/C. 9-Sep-3 David Duggleby, Scarborough #219
£540 $918 €788 Hay cart and figures in a field (22x29cm-9x11in) s. W/C. 18-Nov-3 Bonhams, Leeds #60
£550 $935 €803 Shipping off the pier (34x52cm-13x20in) s. W/C bodycol. 18-Nov-3 Bonhams, Leeds #59
£550 $995 €803 S.S. Lord Warwick beached in Scarborough South Bay (25x36cm-10x14in) s.d.1900 i.verso pen ink. 15-Apr-4 Richardson & Smith, Whitby #111/R
£580 $922 €847 Moonrise on the Trent (15x22cm-6x9in) s. W/C. 9-Sep-3 David Duggleby, Scarborough #220
£580 $969 €847 Evening on a Dutch Canal (20x33cm-8x13in) s. i.verso W/C. 10-Oct-3 Richardson & Smith, Whitby #122
£600 $954 €876 Portuguese inlet (24x34cm-9x13in) mono. W/C. 9-Sep-3 David Duggleby, Scarborough #100/R
£600 $1134 €876 Figures on the shore (18x25cm-7x10in) s. W/C. 23-Feb-4 David Duggleby, Scarborough #645/R
£650 $1105 €949 Off Cape Pilas (20x42cm-8x17in) s.i. W/C bodycol. 19-Nov-3 Christie's, Kensington #388/R
£680 $1156 €993 Steam and fishing boats leaving harbour (25x35cm-10x14in) s. W/C. 1-Dec-3 David Duggleby, Scarborough #237/R
£680 $1217 €993 View of Vigo (23x35cm-9x14in) s. W/C htd white. 25-May-4 Bonhams, Knightsbridge #154/R
£700 $1113 €1022 Off the Tyne (15x25cm-6x10in) s. W/C. 1-May-3 John Nicholson, Haslemere #641/R
£760 $1201 €1110 Off the South Foreland (15x22cm-6x9in) s. W/C bodycol. 24-Jul-3 Dominic Winter, Swindon #50/R
£780 $1435 €1139 Inward bound (24x36cm-9x14in) s. W/C. 23-Jun-4 Cheffins, Cambridge #466/R
£800 $1432 €1168 Booth Line vessel departing from Le Havre (23x34cm-9x13in) s.i. pencil W/C htd white. 26-May-4 Christie's, Kensington #544/R
£920 $1647 €1380 Fishing boats, Chioggia (30x43cm-12x17in) s. W/C. 28-May-4 Tring Auctions, Tring #381/R
£980 $1813 €1431 Shipping in the Bacino Venice (23x36cm-9x14in) s. 12-Feb-4 Andrew Hartley, Ilkley #794/R
£1000 $1810 €1460 Tall ship by the quayside (33x25cm-13x10in) mono. W/C htd white. 30-Mar-4 David Duggleby, Scarborough #200/R est:800-1200
£1100 $1870 €1606 Man-o'-war and other shipping in a Venetian lagoon (44x59cm-17x23in) s. pencil W/C gouache. 19-Nov-3 Tennants, Leyburn #898/R est:1200-1500
£1100 $1969 €1606 Shipping in the Channel off Dover (39x59cm-15x23in) s.d.1903 W/C bodycol scratching out. 26-May-4 Christie's, Kensington #437/R est:1000-1500
£1100 $2057 €1650 Fishing fleet (30x33cm-12x13in) s. W/C. 23-Jul-4 Tring Auctions, Tring #272/R est:900-1200
£1200 $1992 €1752 North Bay Scarborough with Castle beyond (18x28cm-7x11in) s. W/C. 6-Oct-3 David Duggleby, Scarborough #248/R est:1200-1500
£1200 $2184 €1752 Busy shipping scenes (17x43cm-7x17in) s.i. one d.97 W/C pair. 15-Jun-4 Rosebery Fine Art, London #617 est:1000-1500
£1250 $1988 €1825 Racing yachts (35x57cm-14x22in) s. W/C. 9-Sep-3 David Duggleby, Scarborough #64/R est:700-1000
£1600 $2720 €2336 Scarborough beach (18x44cm-7x17in) s. W/C. 18-Nov-3 Bonhams, Leeds #58 est:1500-2000
£1600 $2768 €2336 Figures in St Mark's Square (50x75cm-20x30in) s. W/C. 11-Dec-3 Lyon & Turnbull, Edinburgh #1/R est:700-1000
£1800 $2880 €2628 Fishing boats off Calais (25x76cm-10x30in) s. W/C htd white scratching out. 16-Sep-3 Bonhams, New Bond Street #21/R est:1500-2000
£2083 $3542 €3000 Fishing vessels near a harbour (52x37cm-20x15in) s. W/C. 28-Oct-3 Mealy's, Castlecomer #216/R
£2200 $3498 €3212 Wreck in the Channel (37x74cm-15x29in) s. W/C. 9-Sep-3 David Duggleby, Scarborough #24/R est:2000-3000
£2900 $4930 €4234 Katwijk (40x100cm-16x39in) s. W/C. 1-Dec-3 Bonhams, Bath #66/R est:1000-1500
£3500 $6440 €5110 Scarborough (53x75cm-21x30in) s. W/C. 24-Mar-4 Hamptons Fine Art, Godalming #255/R
£3800 $7030 €5548 Shipping off the coast (38x76cm-15x30in) s. W/C. 9-Mar-4 Capes Dunn, Manchester #654/R

MASON, Frank Herbert (1921-) American
Works on paper
£219 $400 €320 Life drawing (32x30cm-13x12in) s.d.1976 conte crayon. 10-Jul-4 Auctions by the Bay, Alameda #486/R

MASON, George Finch (1850-1915) British
Works on paper
£280 $515 €409 Eclipse stakes, Sandown Park, 1888 (28x36cm-11x14in) s.i.d.1888 pen ink W/C htd white. 10-Jun-4 Christie's, Kensington #158/R

£320 $589 €467 Eclipse stakes, Sandown Park, 1886 (25x45cm-10x18in) s. W/C htd white. 10-Jun-4 Christie's, Kensington #159/R
£350 $644 €511 Derby, 1899, Flying Fox wins (25x35cm-10x14in) s.i.d.1899 pen ink W/C htd white. 10-Jun-4 Christie's, Kensington #152/R
£1600 $2720 €2336 The railway stakes (24x34cm-9x13in) s.i. pencil W/C gouache four. 19-Nov-3 Tennants, Leyburn #910 est:1200-1500
£1600 $2912 €2336 The Grand National, 1900. The Grand National, 1897 (25x32cm-10x13in) s.i. pencil W/C bodycol pair. 1-Jul-4 Christie's, Kensington #241/R est:1000-1500

MASON, George Hemming (1818-1872) British
£650 $1027 €943 Study for the gander (11x15cm-4x6in) board. 4-Sep-3 Christie's, Kensington #312/R
£1000 $1670 €1460 Derbyshire farm (25x71cm-10x28in) s. oil paper on board exhib. 13-Nov-3 Christie's, Kensington #161/R est:1200-1800

MASON, Mary Townsend (1886-?) American
Works on paper
£229 $425 €334 Interior scene (41x51cm-16x20in) casein gouache on board. 3-Mar-4 Alderfer's, Hatfield #410
£284 $475 €415 Plantation, Captiva Island, Florida (51x33cm-20x13in) s.d.1952 gouache. 20-Jun-3 Freeman, Philadelphia #11/R
£349 $650 €510 Interior scene (28x43cm-11x17in) s. casein gouache on board. 3-Mar-4 Alderfer's, Hatfield #409/R

MASON, Robert (1946-) British
£720 $1310 €1051 Family portrait II (102x62cm-40x24in) acrylic chl prov.exhib. 4-Feb-4 Sotheby's, Olympia #246/R

MASON, Roy M (1886-1972) American
£2174 $3500 €3174 Carrying the stone (76x64cm-30x25in) s. 20-Aug-3 James Julia, Fairfield #1557/R est:6000-8000
Works on paper
£323 $600 €472 Old Doc Dunbar. pencil. 6-Mar-4 Page, Batavia #104

MASON, Sanford (1798-1862) American
£9259 $15000 €13518 Capt Stephen T Northam. Mary Langley Northam (84x69cm-33x27in) s.d.1832 verso pair prov. 1-Aug-3 North East Auctions, Portsmouth #772/R est:8000-12000

MASON, William (1906-) British
£300 $480 €438 Flower lesson (64x54cm-25x21in) init. 16-Sep-3 Bonhams, Knightsbridge #165
£1259 $2140 €1800 Fishing boats and figures on a strand (61x76cm-24x30in) s. 18-Nov-3 Whyte's, Dublin #26/R est:1800-2200

MASON, William Henry (fl.1858-1885) British
£260 $450 €380 Extensive view over an Italian City (28x41cm-11x16in) init.d.1880. 11-Dec-3 Neales, Nottingham #586/R
£280 $507 €409 Port Loe, Cornwall (22x33cm-9x13in) init.d.1881. 30-Mar-4 Sworder & Son, Bishops Stortford #587/R
£400 $664 €584 Portloe, Cornwall (38x61cm-15x24in) init.d.1881. 2-Oct-3 Neales, Nottingham #717
£400 $664 €584 Old oaks in Sherwood Forest (76x64cm-30x25in) init.d.1881. 2-Oct-3 Neales, Nottingham #722
£500 $865 €730 Edge of the wood, with foxgloves (41x51cm-16x20in) 11-Dec-3 Neales, Nottingham #582/R
£900 $1494 €1314 Distant view of Tenby, South Wales (41x61cm-16x24in) init.d.1885. 2-Oct-3 Neales, Nottingham #719/R
Works on paper
£280 $484 €409 Middle Hill, Gloucestershire (33x48cm-13x19in) init.d.1882 W/C. 11-Dec-3 Neales, Nottingham #575
£400 $692 €584 Italian Landscape, town with castle (41x56cm-16x22in) init. W/C. 11-Dec-3 Neales, Nottingham #577/R
£400 $692 €584 Near Leukerbad, Switzerland (43x58cm-17x23in) init.d.1876 W/C htd white. 11-Dec-3 Neales, Nottingham #580/R
£480 $830 €701 Fishing smack leaving Littlehampton harbour. W/C. 14-Dec-3 Desmond Judd, Cranbrook #1147

MASON, William Sanford (1824-1864) American
£615 $1100 €898 Country girl (43x36cm-17x14in) s.d.1855 i.stretcher prov. 26-May-4 Doyle, New York #26/R

MASRIADI, Nyoman (1973-) Indonesian?
£3656 $5849 €5338 Cuci tangan (125x125cm-49x49in) s.i.d.19 Nov 2002 acrylic. 18-May-3 Sotheby's, Singapore #185/R est:4000-6000 (S.D 10200)

MASRIERA VILA, Frederico (1892-1943) Spanish
£600 $1092 €900 Casa rural (19x24cm-7x9in) s.d.1922 canvas on panel. 29-Jun-4 Segre, Madrid #76a/R

MASRIERA Y MANOVENS, Francisco (1842-1902) Spanish
£1000 $1820 €1460 Track running through a sunlit glade (55x79cm-22x31in) s. 16-Jun-4 Christie's, Kensington #147/R est:1000-1500
£1972 $3451 €2800 Portrait of Arab man (61x49cm-24x19in) s.d.1878. 16-Dec-3 Segre, Madrid #71/R est:1800
£6667 $12067 €10000 Ball (57x43cm-22x17in) s.d.1899. 30-Mar-4 Segre, Madrid #90/R est:10000
£8844 $15830 €13000 Bust of Arab man (61x49cm-24x19in) s. 22-Mar-4 Durán, Madrid #222/R est:6000
£11748 $19620 €16800 Odalisk (51x41cm-20x16in) s. 30-Jun-3 Ansorena, Madrid #345a/R

MASRIERA Y MANOVENS, Jose (1841-1912) Spanish
£1275 $2283 €1900 Village in the mountains (40x55cm-16x22in) s. 25-May-4 Durán, Madrid #181/R est:900

MASRIERA Y ROSES, Luis (1872-1958) Spanish
£1915 $3102 €2700 The studio (27x35cm-11x14in) s. 20-May-3 Ansorena, Madrid #188/R est:2700

MASSANI, Pompeo (1850-1920) Italian
£1000 $1850 €1460 Tuning the guitar (34x26cm-13x10in) s.d.1877. 14-Jul-4 Sotheby's, Olympia #196/R est:1000-1500
£1304 $2400 €1956 Couple in an interior scene enjoying the news (33x25cm-13x10in) s. 23-Mar-4 American Auctioneer #453738/R
£1408 $2437 €2000 Photo album (30x39cm-12x15in) s.i. 10-Dec-3 Sotheby's, Milan #107/R est:2000-4000
£1690 $2806 €2400 Elegant couple (30x22cm-12x9in) 16-Jun-3 Dorotheum, Vienna #76/R est:2800-3200
£2953 $5434 €4400 Man with moustache (46x38cm-18x15in) s. lit. 25-Mar-4 Karlheinz Kaupp, Staufen #2600/R est:600
£5517 $9159 €8000 De zangles (48x78cm-19x31in) 6-Oct-3 Amberes, Antwerp #238/R

MASSE, Jean Eugène Julien (1856-1950) French
£436 $772 €650 River landscape (44x37cm-17x15in) s. 30-Apr-4 Dr Fritz Nagel, Stuttgart #338/R
£1632 $2693 €2350 La maison derrier la roseraie (54x73cm-21x29in) s.d.31. 1-Jul-3 Lemoine & Ferrando, Paris #75/R est:400-500
Works on paper
£2039 $3753 €3100 Paysage, riviere le soir (60x73cm-24x29in) s. pastel. 23-Jun-4 Maigret, Paris #64/R est:1000-1500

MASSERONI, Giulio (1900-1980) Italian
£268 $475 €400 View of village (33x25cm-13x10in) s.d.1927 board. 1-May-4 Meeting Art, Vercelli #15

MASSEY, Willie (20th C) American
£240 $400 €350 Black bird (28x36cm-11x14in) tempera cardboard prov. 15-Nov-3 Slotin Folk Art, Buford #374/R
£240 $400 €350 White bird and tree (13x33cm-5x13in) acrylic wood prov. 15-Nov-3 Slotin Folk Art, Buford #376/R

MASSIMI, Cardinal Camillo (attrib) (1620-1677) Italian
Works on paper
£642 $1130 €950 Interior scene with a woman writing a letter (25x19cm-10x7in) s. pen brown ink col wash black chk. 19-May-4 Sotheby's, Amsterdam #26/R

MASSIRONI, Manfredo (1937-) Italian
£1067 $1963 €1600 Untitled (19x23cm-7x9in) s.d.1959 verso cardboard. 12-Jun-4 Meeting Art, Vercelli #853/R est:1000

MASSMANN, Carl (1859-1929) Austrian
£2098 $3566 €3000 Getting ready for market (40x60cm-16x24in) s. 24-Nov-3 Dorotheum, Vienna #93/R est:3000-3500

MASSON, Alex (19/20th C) French
£1056 $1849 €1500 Retour de peche a Douarnenez (45x54cm-18x21in) s. 21-Dec-3 Thierry & Lannon, Brest #339 est:1500-1800

MASSON, Andre (1896-1987) French
£2708 $4523 €3900 Paysage de Mediterranee (32x39cm-13x15in) studio st. 25-Oct-3 Cornette de St.Cyr, Paris #530 est:3000-4000
£4595 $8500 €6709 Devoration 2 (22x68cm-9x27in) s.i.d.1956 verso prov. 11-Feb-4 Sotheby's, New York #47/R est:8000-12000
£6952 $13000 €10150 Poisson et euphorbes (55x33cm-22x13in) s.i. prov.exhib. 25-Feb-4 Christie's, Rockefeller NY #85/R est:8000-12000
£17007 $30443 €25000 Cheval Irlandais (100x81cm-39x32in) s. i.d.1969 verso prov.exhib.lit. 21-Mar-4 Calmels Cohen, Paris #53/R est:25000-30000
£18000 $33120 €26280 Flore (81x65cm-32x26in) s. i.verso painted 1976 prov. 23-Jun-4 Christie's, London #266/R est:18000-24000
£21000 $38640 €30660 Il descend de la montagne (145x89cm-57x35in) s. i.d.1960 verso prov.exhib.lit. 22-Jun-4 Sotheby's, London #301/R est:20000-30000
£21333 $38400 €32000 Roi David (73x60cm-29x24in) s. painted 1971 prov.exhib. 25-Apr-4 Versailles Encheres #130 est:30000-35000
£22000 $40480 €32120 L'orphee (65x81cm-26x32in) s. painted 1946. 23-Jun-4 Christie's, London #260/R est:22000-28000
£23649 $41622 €35000 Procession (100x81cm-39x32in) s. painted 1976 prov. 18-May-4 Tajan, Paris #12/R est:40000-50000
£30000 $55200 €43800 Enlevement (46x61cm-18x24in) s. painted 1933 prov. 22-Jun-4 Sotheby's, London #295/R est:20000-30000
£30000 $55200 €43800 Juillet (54x65cm-21x26in) s. painted 1948 prov.exhib. 23-Jun-4 Christie's, London #263/R est:25000-35000
£32886 $58866 €49000 Georges Limbour et Roland Tual (55x38cm-22x15in) s. oil crayon painted 1922 prov.exhib. 26-May-4 Christie's, Paris #43/R est:50000-70000
£36667 $67100 €55000 Composition aux deux hommes dans le foret (89x116cm-35x46in) oil pastel crayon painted c.1931-32 prov.lit. 7-Jun-4 Artcurial Briest, Paris #31/R est:60000-80000
£37163 $65407 €55000 Cenotaphe dans les nuages (130x97cm-51x38in) s. i.d.1969 verso prov.exhib. 18-May-4 Tajan, Paris #11/R est:45000-50000
£38000 $69160 €55480 Vagabond (100x81cm-39x32in) s. indis.i. stretcher painted 1966 prov. 3-Feb-4 Christie's, London #235/R est:25000-35000
£38000 $69160 €55480 Entre la plante et l'oiseau (145x114cm-57x45in) s. painted 1961 prov. 3-Feb-4 Christie's, London #236/R est:25000-35000
£38000 $69920 €55480 Petit don quichotte (22x27cm-9x11in) s. painted 1935 prov. 22-Jun-4 Sotheby's, London #196/R est:12000-15000
£43103 $77155 €62930 Petite bacchanale (28x42cm-11x17in) s. prov. 12-May-4 Dobiaschofsky, Bern #781/R est:36000 (S.FR 100000)
£60000 $109200 €87600 Le repas de la mante religieuse (20x40cm-8x16in) s.verso painted 1937 prov.exhib. 3-Feb-4 Sotheby's, London #75/R est:60000-80000

£70588	$120000	€103058	Nu eclaire par le feu (126x105cm-50x41in) s. painted c.1946 prov.exhib. 6-Nov-3 Sotheby's, New York #285/R est:150000-200000
£76870	$137598	€113000	Poursuite (81x116cm-32x46in) s. painted 1933 prov.exhib.lit. 21-Mar-4 Calmels Cohen, Paris #59/R est:120000-140000
£118310	$207042	€168000	Reve tauromachique (45x54cm-18x21in) s. prov.exhib. 16-Dec-3 Claude Aguttes, Neuilly #33/R est:80000-100000
£122905	$220000	€179441	Poissonniere (97x131cm-38x52in) s.d.30 prov.exhib.lit. 4-May-4 Christie's, Rockefeller NY #30/R est:200000-300000
£164706	$280000	€240471	L'arbre en fleurs (96x76cm-38x30in) s.i.d.1947 prov.exhib. 5-Nov-3 Sotheby's, New York #47/R est:350000-450000
£170000	$311100	€248200	Figure ou personnage animal (41x16cm-16x6in) oil sand painted 1926-1927 prov.exhib.lit. 2-Feb-4 Christie's, London #56/R est:150000-200000
£189944	$340000	€277318	Etoile (47x38cm-19x15in) painted 1925 prov.exhib.lit. 6-May-4 Sotheby's, New York #118/R est:90000-120000
Prints			
£110000	$201300	€160600	Pygmalion (38x46cm-15x18in) s. painted 1938 prov.exhib. 2-Feb-4 Christie's, London #63/R est:120000-180000
Sculpture			
£29412	$50000	€42942	Extase (95cm-37in) num.1/8 green pat bronze st.f.Brustolin prov.exhib.lit. 6-Nov-3 Sotheby's, New York #283/R est:50000-70000
Works on paper			
£533	$960	€800	Fleur. Study (15x15cm-6x6in) init. Chinese ink two. 22-Apr-4 Finarte Semenzato, Rome #84/R
£600	$1002	€876	Tossa, 1934 (32x40cm-13x16in) s.i. pencil W/C. 21-Oct-3 Bonhams, Knightsbridge #164a/R
£646	$1157	€950	Composition (28x19cm-11x7in) s. ink. 19-Mar-4 Millon & Associes, Paris #113
£789	$1453	€1152	L'Arbre au Rocher (23x31cm-9x12in) s. pen over pencil. 23-Jun-4 Koller, Zurich #3109 (S.FR 1800)
£880	$1523	€1250	Personnage au clair de lune (31x24cm-12x9in) studio st. wax crayon. 14-Dec-3 Versailles Encheres #140/R
£1049	$1783	€1500	La tour Eiffel sur un chariot (20x15cm-8x6in) s.d.XLVI Indian ink prov. 23-Nov-3 Cornette de St.Cyr, Paris #233/R est:150-200
£1067	$1920	€1600	Nu (31x24cm-12x9in) s. pastel pencil. 22-Apr-4 Finarte Semenzato, Rome #135/R est:1400-1600
£1133	$2040	€1700	Chambre (15x20cm-6x8in) studio st. pastel. 25-Apr-4 Versailles Encheres #123 est:1500-1800
£1334	$2400	€2000	Les delires de l'amour, fete galante chez les ecorches (33x50cm-13x20in) i. ink. 26-Apr-4 Tajan, Paris #80/R est:1500-1800
£1399	$2378	€2000	Figure Study I. Figure Study II (21x15cm-8x6in) s.d. bears i. Indian ink prov. 29-Nov-3 Villa Grisebach, Berlin #843/R est:2000-2400
£1409	$2437	€2000	Europhagie (32x24cm-13x9in) s.i. col crayon. 9-Dec-3 Artcurial Briest, Paris #303/R est:2000-3000
£1479	$2558	€2100	Fille tourmentee par une ombre (32x24cm-13x9in) mono.i.d.1961 ink. 14-Dec-3 Versailles Encheres #141/R est:1800-2000
£1517	$2534	€2200	Study for 'Charrette bleue' (48x31cm-19x12in) pastel paper on canvas. 13-Nov-3 Finarte Semenzato, Rome #215/R est:1800-2400
£1549	$2680	€2200	Composition (33x25cm-13x10in) s. gouache. 9-Dec-3 Artcurial Briest, Paris #308/R est:3000-4000
£1724	$3103	€2500	Meditation par le songe (32x24cm-13x9in) i. gouache coloured paper exec c.1960. 25-Jan-4 Chayette & Cheval, Paris #277/R est:2800-3500
£1901	$3289	€2700	Untitled (46x36cm-18x14in) s. ink exec. c.1929 prov. 14-Dec-3 Rabourdin & Choppin de Janvry, Paris #54/R est:2700-3000
£2448	$4087	€3500	Baigneuse couchee devant la mer (20x26cm-8x10in) mono.d.1957 ink wash. 29-Jun-3 Versailles Encheres #129/R
£2708	$4279	€3900	Couple (43x50cm-17x20in) s. col ink dr prov. 27-Apr-3 Versailles Encheres #69
£2958	$5117	€4200	Nu (62x48cm-24x19in) s. ink wash. 9-Dec-3 Artcurial Briest, Paris #302/R est:5000-7000
£3000	$5190	€4380	La naissance de la femme (27x27cm-11x11in) init.i. pen black ink. 11-Dec-3 Christie's, Kensington #91/R est:2000-3000
£3000	$5190	€4380	Sans titre (29x22cm-11x9in) s.d.41 pen black ink. 11-Dec-3 Christie's, Kensington #99/R est:3000-4000
£3289	$6053	€5000	Mascarade erotique (16x14cm-6x6in) pastel. 27-Jun-4 Versailles Encheres #110/R est:3500-4000
£3289	$6051	€4900	Tragediens et massacre (37x47cm-15x19in) s.studio st.i. ink. 24-Mar-4 Joron-Derem, Paris #96/R est:5000-6000
£3357	$5606	€4800	Reitre (58x39cm-23x15in) mono.d.1964 pastel ink prov. 29-Jun-3 Versailles Encheres #128/R
£3440	$5745	€4988	Minotaur (46x36cm-18x14in) s. Indian ink. 19-Jun-3 Kornfeld, Bern #702/R est:8000 (S.FR 7500)
£3741	$6697	€5500	Autoportrait - Etude pour le dialogue avec l'aigle (22x31cm-9x12in) pastel chl. 21-Mar-4 Calmels Cohen, Paris #39/R est:6000-8000
£4167	$6583	€6000	Entre l'oiseau et la plante (26x19cm-10x7in) i. pastel ball-point pen. 27-Apr-3 Versailles Encheres #67
£4832	$8553	€7200	Histoire de l'oeil (31x24cm-12x9in) graphite pen collage. 29-Apr-4 Christie's, Paris #35/R est:4000-6000
£6000	$10020	€8760	Conversation II (60x49cm-24x19in) s. pastel chl on canvas executed 1958 prov. 21-Oct-3 Sotheby's, London #84/R est:7000-9000
£6000	$10800	€9000	Illustration (38x56cm-15x22in) s. pastel exec.1961. 25-Apr-4 Versailles Encheres #125 est:10000-12000
£10000	$17000	€14600	La Marguerite (65x50cm-26x20in) s.d.1969 i.d.verso col felt-tip pens pastel prov. 5-Nov-3 Christie's, Rockefeller NY #153/R est:10000-15000
£11000	$20020	€16060	Metamorphose (48x63cm-19x25in) s. pen ink prov. 4-Feb-4 Sotheby's, London #493/R est:12000-15000
£11500	$20930	€16790	Coq et centaure (56x76cm-22x30in) s. pen ink wash prov. 4-Feb-4 Sotheby's, London #494/R est:12000-18000
£16471	$28000	€24048	Femme violoncelle, instrument anthropomorphique (37x53cm-15x21in) s.d.42 i.verso India ink prov. 6-Nov-3 Sotheby's, New York #256/R est:20000-30000
£16784	$28532	€24000	Portrait d'Isabelle d'Este (63x47cm-25x19in) pastel chl col chk dr exec.1942 prov. 19-Nov-3 Tajan, Paris #15/R est:28000-35000
£50000	$91000	€73000	Le coq (60x73cm-24x29in) s. chl pastel executed 1930 prov.exhib.lit. 3-Feb-4 Sotheby's, London #79/R est:60000-80000

MASSON, Clovis (1838-1913) French

Sculpture			
£872	$1544	€1300	Combat de felins (34x45x20cm-13x18x8in) s. pat bronze. 30-Apr-4 Tajan, Paris #21/R
£896	$1497	€1300	Chien epagneul (17x14x35cm-7x6x14in) s. green brown pat bronze. 17-Nov-3 Tajan, Paris #38/R est:600-800
£2360	$3800	€3446	Standing bull (30cm-12in) i. bronze. 14-Jan-4 Christie's, Rockefeller NY #302/R est:2500-3500

MASSON, Edouard (1881-1950) Belgian

£284	$474	€400	Verger au printemps (65x92cm-26x36in) s. 15-Oct-3 Hotel des Ventes Mosan, Brussels #182
£887	$1480	€1250	Femme lisant (55x45cm-22x18in) s. 14-Oct-3 Vanderkindere, Brussels #136
Works on paper			
£461	$770	€650	Nature morte (56x46cm-22x18in) s.d.35 pastel. 15-Oct-3 Hotel des Ventes Mosan, Brussels #166
£532	$888	€750	Nature morte aux roses (54x37cm-21x15in) s.d.1950 pastel panel. 15-Oct-3 Hotel des Ventes Mosan, Brussels #238

MASSON, Ernest (19th C) French

£2989	$5500	€4364	Cavalry charge (51x94cm-20x37in) s. 27-Jun-4 Freeman, Philadelphia #46/R est:5000-8000

MASSON, Georges Armand (1892-1977) French

£2857	$4543	€4200	Maison de l'Infante a Saint-Jean-de-Luz (19x24cm-7x9in) s. s.i.verso panel. 23-Mar-3 St-Germain-en-Laye Encheres #57/R est:500-600

MASSON, Henri L (1907-1996) Canadian

£640	$1171	€934	Boy's head (30x25cm-12x10in) s. board prov. 1-Jun-4 Joyner Waddington, Toronto #429 (C.D 1600)
£714	$1229	€1042	Venetian church (37x45cm-15x18in) s. 2-Dec-3 Joyner Waddington, Toronto #252/R (C.D 1600)
£785	$1429	€1146	Woods - Gatineau Park (30x41cm-12x16in) s. s.i.verso prov. 5-Feb-4 Heffel, Vancouver #53/R (C.D 1900)
£811	$1378	€1184	Venetian gondolier (41x30cm-16x12in) s. lit. 21-Nov-3 Walker's, Ottawa #111/R est:2000-3000 (C.D 1800)
£893	$1536	€1304	Little Canal, Venice (40x30cm-16x12in) s.d.57. 2-Dec-3 Joyner Waddington, Toronto #316/R est:2000-2500 (C.D 2000)
£1016	$1819	€1483	Rainy day (22x26cm-9x10in) s. board double-sided prov.lit. 27-May-4 Heffel, Vancouver #135/R est:1500-2500 (C.D 2500)
£1116	$1920	€1629	Spring (45x55cm-18x22in) s. 2-Dec-3 Joyner Waddington, Toronto #171/R est:3500-4000 (C.D 2500)
£1126	$1914	€1644	Autumn in the Gatineau (30x40cm-12x16in) s. board prov. 27-Nov-3 Heffel, Vancouver #92/R est:2500-3500 (C.D 2500)
£1280	$2342	€1869	River in winter (29x39cm-11x15in) s. 1-Jun-4 Joyner Waddington, Toronto #101/R est:2500-3000 (C.D 3200)
£1321	$2365	€1929	Porte Neuf (35x45cm-14x18in) s. s.i.d.1977 verso prov. 27-May-4 Heffel, Vancouver #63/R est:2500-3500 (C.D 3250)
£1339	$2304	€1955	Beamish Hill (45x60cm-18x24in) s. prov. 2-Dec-3 Joyner Waddington, Toronto #136/R est:3500-4500 (C.D 3000)
£1351	$2297	€1972	Bic, Gaspe (30x40cm-12x16in) s. s.i.verso. 27-Nov-3 Heffel, Vancouver #33/R est:2000-3000 (C.D 3000)
£1351	$2297	€1972	Perkins Mill, PQ (48x56cm-19x22in) s. i.verso. 21-Nov-3 Walker's, Ottawa #65/R est:3000-4000 (C.D 3000)
£1612	$2917	€2354	Untitled - Newfoundland village scene (46x61cm-18x24in) s. hard board prov. 18-Apr-4 Levis, Calgary #74/R est:3000-3500 (C.D 3900)
£1696	$2918	€2476	Grande Vallee, Gaspe (37x45cm-15x18in) s. 2-Dec-3 Joyner Waddington, Toronto #19/R est:3000-3500 (C.D 3800)
£1786	$3071	€2608	Cloridorme, Gaspe (37x45cm-15x18in) s. 2-Dec-3 Joyner Waddington, Toronto #208/R est:3000-3500 (C.D 4000)
£1802	$3063	€2631	Premiere neige, St Irene, Quebec (55x71cm-22x28in) s. s.i.verso prov. 27-Nov-3 Heffel, Vancouver #198/R est:4000-5000 (C.D 4000)
£1829	$3274	€2670	March, Perkins (46x61cm-18x24in) s. s.i.d.79 verso prov. 31-May-4 Sotheby's, Toronto #18/R est:3500-4000 (C.D 4500)
£1895	$3487	€2767	The new studio (50x40cm-20x16in) s. i.verso board painted c.1967 prov. 9-Jun-4 Walker's, Ottawa #149/R est:6000-7000 (C.D 4700)
£2000	$3660	€2920	Autumnal landscape (30x40cm-12x16in) s. board prov. 1-Jun-4 Joyner Waddington, Toronto #41/R est:2000-3000 (C.D 5000)
£2232	$3839	€3259	Fishing boats, Perce, Que. (40x50cm-16x20in) s. 2-Dec-3 Joyner Waddington, Toronto #220/R est:3000-3500 (C.D 5000)
£2236	$4002	€3265	Nova Scotia still life (55x46cm-22x18in) s.d.53 prov.exhib. 31-May-4 Sotheby's, Toronto #65/R est:4000-4500 (C.D 5500)
£2439	$4366	€3561	Autumn in Perkins, Quebec (46x56cm-18x22in) s.d.48 prov. 31-May-4 Sotheby's, Toronto #167/R est:5000-6000 (C.D 6000)
£4464	$7679	€6517	Patineurs, Parc Flora (45x52cm-18x20in) s. painted 1944 prov. 2-Dec-3 Joyner Waddington, Toronto #33/R est:15000-18000 (C.D 10000)
Works on paper			
£181	$336	€264	Paysage Gatineau (58x46cm-23x18in) s.d.63 chl prov. 2-Mar-4 Ritchie, Toronto #95/R (C.D 450)
£330	$600	€482	Gaspe coast (13x16cm-5x6in) s. W/C. 7-Feb-4 Sloans & Kenyon, Bethesda #892/R
£357	$614	€521	Le petit cure (31x17cm-12x7in) s. pastel exec 1940 prov. 2-Dec-3 Joyner Waddington, Toronto #475 (C.D 800)
£403	$742	€588	The artist with observers (36x43cm-14x17in) s.d.1942 verso W/C prov. 9-Jun-4 Walker's, Ottawa #152/R (C.D 1000)
£440	$805	€642	Figures (61x47cm-24x19in) s.d.69 gouache prov. 1-Jun-4 Joyner Waddington, Toronto #271/R (C.D 1100)
£440	$805	€642	Procession (27x34cm-11x13in) s. pastel. 1-Jun-4 Joyner Waddington, Toronto #339/R (C.D 1100)
£536	$921	€783	Duo (26x21cm-10x8in) s. W/C pastel. 2-Dec-3 Joyner Waddington, Toronto #283/R (C.D 1200)
£756	$1307	€1104	Laurentian village in winter (46x61cm-18x24in) s. mixed media. 9-Dec-3 Pinneys, Montreal #156 (C.D 1700)
£1423	$2547	€2078	Street scene, rainy day (50x66cm-20x26in) s. chk pastel prov. 27-May-4 Heffel, Vancouver #116/R est:2000-3000 (C.D 3500)

MASSON, Jules-Edmond (1871-1932) French

Sculpture			
£1793	$3317	€2600	Cerf et biche (71cm-28in) s.st.f.Societe Bronzes col pat bronze. 16-Feb-4 Horta, Bruxelles #126 est:1800-2000
£1921	$3497	€2805	Napoleon I on horseback (46cm-18in) i. brown pat. bronze Cast Susse. 16-Jun-4 Fischer, Luzern #1569/R est:4000-6000 (S.FR 4400)
£3000	$5010	€4380	Group of stages (59x50cm-23x20in) mono. gold green pat. bronze st.f.Linjl. 14-Oct-3 Sotheby's, Olympia #58/R est:2000-2500
£4967	$8096	€7500	Le grand Cerf (80cm-31in) s. brown pat bronze. 1-Feb-3 Dubee & Berron, Vernou en Sologne #91
£5172	$9466	€7500	Napoleon 1er a cheval (55cm-22in) light pat bronze marble socle. 31-Jan-4 Osenat, Fontainebleau #592

MASSON, Marcel (1911-1988) French
£364 $604 €528 Village (22x27cm-9x11in) s. 13-Jun-3 Zofingen, Switzerland #2493/R (S.FR 800)
£385 $654 €562 Montmartre - Rue de l'abreuvoir (46x56cm-18x22in) s. 19-Nov-3 Fischer, Luzern #2207/R (S.FR 850)

MASSONI, Egisto (fl.1880-1885) Italian
£1871 $3349 €2750 Venice (61x46cm-24x18in) s.d.1891. 22-Mar-4 Durán, Madrid #131/R

MASSOT, Firmin (1766-1849) Swiss
Miniatures
£1750 $3133 €2555 Portrait of George Haldinand seated on a wicker chair (13cm-5in) en grisaille W/C. 22-Mar-4 Bonhams & Brooks, Norfolk #91/R est:150-250

MASSOULE, Andre Paul Arthur (1851-1901) French
Sculpture
£4200 $7014 €6132 Young Viking (75cm-30in) s. dark brown pat. 14-Oct-3 Sotheby's, Olympia #55/R est:1500-2000

MASTENBROEK, Clary (1947-) Dutch
£280 $512 €420 Her spooky dream (50x70cm-20x28in) init.d.68. 7-Jun-4 Glerum, Amsterdam #346/R

MASTENBROEK, Hans van (1900-1934) Dutch
£658 $1211 €1000 Still life with bottles, bread and brushes (58x90cm-23x35in) init.d.33. 28-Jun-4 Sotheby's, Amsterdam #104/R est:1000-1500

MASTENBROEK, Johann Hendrik van (1875-1945) Dutch
£2778 $4389 €4000 Along the water in winter (26x51cm-10x20in) s.d.1909 panel. 2-Sep-3 Christie's, Amsterdam #301/R est:3500-4500
£3151 $5356 €4600 Rotterdam houses by canal (14x17cm-6x7in) s. panel. 5-Nov-3 Vendue Huis, Gravenhage #124/R est:2000-3000
£3472 $5799 €5000 Winter day in Delfshaven (13x17cm-5x7in) s.d.1920 panel. 21-Oct-3 Sotheby's, Amsterdam #100 est:3000-5000
£3819 $6493 €5500 View of the Semafoor, Scheveningen (70x100cm-28x39in) s.d.1937. 28-Oct-3 Christie's, Amsterdam #152/R est:7000-9000
£4706 $8000 €6871 Canal scene with boats (39x55cm-15x22in) s.d.1893. 19-Nov-3 Bonhams & Butterfields, San Francisco #63/R
£5319 $8883 €7500 Rotterdam harbour activity (41x47cm-16x19in) s. 20-Oct-3 Glerum, Amsterdam #108/R est:6000-8000
£9211 $16671 €14000 View of Maasluis Harbour (28x35cm-11x14in) s.d.1917. 19-Apr-4 Glerum, Amsterdam #158/R est:9000-11000
£9220 $15397 €13000 Horse and wagon at the toll gate in winter (40x60cm-16x24in) s.d.1905. 20-Oct-3 Glerum, Amsterdam #71/R est:8000-12000
£12667 $22800 €19000 Maas river, Rotterdam (47x71cm-19x28in) s.d.1926. 21-Apr-4 Christie's, Amsterdam #152/R est:12000-16000
£16000 $28800 €24000 Kolen lossen (70x130cm-28x51in) s.d.1924 s.i.d.verso. 20-Apr-4 Sotheby's, Amsterdam #108/R est:10000-15000
£22727 $40000 €33181 View of a town with barges on a canal and figures by a wag on in the foreground (86x131cm-34x52in) s.d.99 i.verso. 18-May-4 Bonhams & Butterfields, San Francisco #74/R est:15000-20000
Works on paper
£333 $603 €500 Barquettes dans le canal (20x29cm-8x11in) s. mixed media. 30-Mar-4 Campo & Campo, Antwerp #318
£403 $745 €600 Duck hunt (23x44cm-9x17in) s. W/C. 15-Mar-4 Sotheby's, Amsterdam #50/R
£411 $699 €600 City port (15x22cm-6x9in) s. chl. 5-Nov-3 Vendue Huis, Gravenhage #123/R
£766 $1302 €1118 Antwerp harbour (29x49cm-11x19in) s.d.1898 W/C prov. 21-Nov-3 Walker's, Ottawa #204/R est:2000-3000 (C.D 1700)
£855 $1574 €1300 View of the Willemskade in winter, Rotterdam (13x21cm-5x8in) s.i.d.1933 pencil W/C bodycol. 22-Jun-4 Christie's, Amsterdam #109/R est:1000-1500
£1200 $2184 €1752 Punting on a Dutch canal (20x16cm-8x6in) s.d.1930 pencil W/C. 1-Jul-4 Christie's, Kensington #427/R est:300-400
£1597 $2667 €2300 Moored boats in Rotterdam (21x27cm-8x11in) s.d.1892 W/C prov. 21-Oct-3 Sotheby's, Amsterdam #136/R est:2000-3000
£1769 $3219 €2600 Avond in Volendam (34x50cm-13x20in) s. indis d. W/C htd white prov. 3-Feb-4 Christie's, Amsterdam #348/R est:2000-3000
£2446 $4500 €3571 Busy Dutch harbour (33x31cm-13x12in) s. indis.d. W/C htd white. 27-Jun-4 Freeman, Philadelphia #14/R est:3000-5000
£4000 $7200 €6000 Canal scene in winter (42x34cm-17x13in) s.d.99 W/C htd white. 20-Apr-4 Sotheby's, Amsterdam #152/R est:3000-5000
£5333 $9600 €8000 Awaiting the closing of the bridge (23x50cm-9x20in) s.d.1903 pen black ink W/C bodycol. 21-Apr-4 Christie's, Amsterdam #144/R est:4000-6000

MASTER M Z (c.1477-c.1555) German
Prints
£6000 $10320 €8760 Embrace (15x11cm-6x4in) engraving. 2-Dec-3 Christie's, London #45/R est:5000-7000

MASTER OF 1518 (16th C) Flemish
£16552 $27641 €24000 Adoration of the Magi (100x74cm-39x29in) panel prov. 15-Nov-3 Lempertz, Koln #1098/R est:25000

MASTER OF ASTORGA (16th C) Italian?
£10345 $18621 €15000 Saint John and Saint Peter (81x63cm-32x25in) board. 26-Jan-4 Ansorena, Madrid #27/R est:10200

MASTER OF CANILLO (16th C) Spanish
£7895 $14526 €12000 Saint Sylvestre combattant le dragon (130x94cm-51x37in) panel. 24-Jun-4 Christie's, Paris #12/R est:10000-12000

MASTER OF CARMIGNANO (15th C) Italian
£50336 $94128 €75000 Madonna and Child with Saints (124x62cm-49x24in) tempera gold board. 29-Feb-4 Finarte, Venice #47/R est:65000-80000

MASTER OF FLORA (attrib) (16th C) French
£57047 $104966 €85000 Ceres entouree d'amour figurant les quatre elements (108x148cm-43x58in) panel prov. 28-Mar-4 Anaf, Lyon #129/R est:8000-100000

MASTER OF FOSSA (14th C) Italian
£154362 $276309 €230000 Madonna and Child enthroned with Saint Francis and Ludwig of Toulouse (92x71cm-36x28in) boardprov.lit. 27-May-4 Semenzato, Florence #196/R est:180000-250000

MASTER OF FRANKFURT (studio) (c.1490-1515) Dutch
£45000 $77850 €65700 Deposition of Christ (110x73cm-43x29in) oak panel arched top prov.exhib.lit. 11-Dec-3 Sotheby's, London #1/R est:20000-30000

MASTER OF HOOGSTRAETEN (16th C) Flemish
£11972 $20711 €17000 Portrait of a man (34x28cm-13x11in) panel. 13-Dec-3 Lempertz, Koln #2/R est:4000

MASTER OF MONTEFALCO (14th C) Italian
£93333 $169867 €140000 Madonna and Child with Martyrs and Apostles (34x36cm-13x14in) tempera gold board diptych prov.lit. 4-Jul-4 Finarte, Venice #48/R est:190000-220000

MASTER OF SAINT CHIARA (fl.1290-1330) Italian
£125000 $230000 €182500 Procession cross (32x27cm-13x11in) tempera gold panel prov.lit. 26-Mar-4 Koller, Zurich #3010/R est:100000-150000 (S.FR 290000)

MASTER OF SAN MINIATO (fl.1478-1500) Italian
£32000 $58560 €46720 Madonna and Child with angels (86x63cm-34x25in) tempera gold panel exhib.lit. 8-Jul-4 Sotheby's, London #197/R est:25000-40000

MASTER OF SAN TORPE (14th C) Italian
£27465 $45592 €39000 Madonna and Child with two angels (32x23cm-13x9in) tempera gold board lit. 11-Jun-3 Semenzato, Florence #165/R est:40000-44000

MASTER OF TEPLICE (14th C) Italian
£25000 $43250 €36500 Saint Anthony. Saint Nicholas. Saint Catherine (26x16cm-10x6in) i. altarpiece pointed tops three. 10-Dec-3 Christie's, London #105/R est:25000-35000

MASTER OF THE ANNUNCIATION OF SPINOLA (14th C) Italian
£344828 $634483 €503449 The nativity (20x16cm-8x6in) tempera gold panel prov.exhib.lit. 26-Mar-4 Koller, Zurich #3009/R est:500000-900000 (S.FR 800000)

MASTER OF THE ANTWERP ADORATION, Flemish
£7095 $12486 €10500 Last supper (97x57cm-38x22in) panel. 18-May-4 Sotheby's, Amsterdam #33/R est:10000-15000

MASTER OF THE CARNATIONS (15th C) Italian
£58273 $95568 €81000 Le martyr de Saint Jean Baptiste (45x37cm-18x15in) s. panel prov. 6-Jun-3 Drouot Estimations, Paris #37/R est:20000-25000

MASTER OF THE CARPETS (17th C) Italian
£28378 $49946 €42000 Still life of carpets, mirror, a blanket with fruit on a draped red gilt curtain (88x107cm-35x42in) prov.exhib.lit. 18-May-4 Sotheby's, Amsterdam #101/R est:30000-50000

MASTER OF THE CORRER ALTAR (14th C) Italian
£29078 $48560 €41000 Madonna dell'umilta coronata da due angeli (57x44cm-22x17in) tempera panel prov.lit. 17-Jun-3 Finarte Semenzato, Milan #639/R est:40000-60000

MASTER OF THE CORTEGES (attrib) (fl.1645-1660) French
£2961 $5447 €4500 La chasse au cerf (81x116cm-32x46in) 23-Jun-4 Millon & Associes, Paris #25/R est:4000-6000

MASTER OF THE CORTONA TONDO (15/16th C) Italian
£60000 $103800 €87600 Madonna and Child with two female Saints (55x38cm-22x15in) i. panel prov.lit. 10-Dec-3 Christie's, London #111/R est:60000-80000

MASTER OF THE EGMONT ALBUMS (?) ?
Works on paper
£2800 $5124 €4088 Flagellation (15x10cm-6x4in) pen ink wash framing lines corner made up. 6-Jul-4 Christie's, London #169/R est:2500-3500

MASTER OF THE FEAST OF BELSHAZZAR (17TH c) Flemish
£13699 $23288 €20000 Feast of Belshazzar (74x104cm-29x41in) panel. 4-Nov-3 Sotheby's, Amsterdam #120/R est:8000-12000

MASTER OF THE FEMALE HALF LENGTHS (16th C) Flemish
£14847 $27022 €21677 The Virgin Mary reading (36x27cm-14x11in) panel prov.lit. 16-Jun-4 Fischer, Luzern #1013/R est:16000-18000 (S.FR 34000)
£35000 $63000 €51100 Penitent Saint Jerome in an extensive river landscape (55x42cm-22x17in) panel. 21-Apr-4 Christie's, London #6/R est:15000-25000

£38000 $68400 €55480 Woman as the Magdalen, writing a letter at a table in an interior (54x41cm-21x16in) panel. 21-Apr-4 Christie's, London #7/R est:15000-25000
£60000 $103800 €87600 Magdalene, half-length, holding a jar of unguent (62x47cm-24x19in) oak panel prov. 11-Dec-3 Sotheby's, London #6/R est:40000-50000
£70000 $121100 €102200 Virgin and Child (23x17cm-9x7in) panel arched top. 10-Dec-3 Christie's, London #4/R est:30000-40000

MASTER OF THE FEMALE HALF LENGTHS (attrib) (16th C) Flemish
£12500 $20875 €18250 Magdalene (42x30cm-17x12in) panel. 16-Oct-3 Lawrence, Crewkerne #714/R

MASTER OF THE FEMALE HALF LENGTHS (studio) (16th C) Flemish
£20000 $36600 €29200 Woman as the Magdalen writing at a table in an interior (42x31cm-17x12in) panel prov. 7-Jul-4 Bonhams, New Bond Street #12/R est:15000-20000

MASTER OF THE FERTILITY OF THE EGG (17th C) Italian
£9333 $17080 €14000 Cat playing drum (91x140cm-36x55in) 1-Jun-4 Sotheby's, Milan #158/R est:10000-12000

MASTER OF THE GROTESQUE VASES (17th C) Italian
£8333 $15000 €12166 Tulips, peonies and other flowers in a sculpted vase (77x54cm-30x21in) 23-Jan-4 Christie's, Rockefeller NY #129/R est:5000-7000
£10556 $19000 €15412 Tulips, poppies and other flowers in a sculpted vase (77x54cm-30x21in) 23-Jan-4 Christie's, Rockefeller NY #128/R est:5000-7000

MASTER OF THE HOLY BLOOD (studio) (16th C) Flemish
£22000 $40260 €32120 Lamentation of the Christ (104x130cm-41x51in) panel arched top prov.lit. 8-Jul-4 Sotheby's, London #106/R est:25000-35000

MASTER OF THE HOLY KINSHIP (circle) (fl.1450-1515) German
£27586 $46069 €40000 Martyrdom of the Maccabian brothers (102x72cm-40x28in) mono. panel prov. 15-Nov-3 Lempertz, Koln #1078/R est:40000-50000

MASTER OF THE JOHNSON NATIVITY (15th C) Italian
£11667 $21000 €17034 Madonna and Child (85x51cm-33x20in) panel prov. 21-Jan-4 Sotheby's, New York #59/R est:8000-12000

MASTER OF THE LANGMATT FOUNDATION VIEW (fl.1740-1770) Italian
£10000 $17900 €15000 View of Santa Maria del Rosario, Venice (33x51cm-13x20in) 12-May-4 Finarte Semenzato, Milan #68/R est:15000-20000
£19231 $35000 €28077 Grand Canal, Venice, looking east towards the Dogana (29x46cm-11x18in) 17-Jun-4 Christie's, Rockefeller NY #56/R est:10000-15000
£50000 $86500 €73000 Arch of Constantine and the Coliseum, Rome (71x110cm-28x43in) with sig.d.MDCCXXXVI. 10-Dec-3 Christie's, London #49/R est:50000-70000
£70000 $121100 €102200 View of the river Brenta at Stra with the Villa Cappello and the Villa Pisani (72x120cm-28x47in) 11-Dec-3 Sotheby's, London #43/R est:40000-60000
£70000 $128800 €105000 Vue du grand canal avec les eglises des Scalzi. Vue du grand canal avec San Simeone Piccola (38x57cm-15x22in) pair. 11-Jun-4 Maigret, Paris #53/R est:40000-60000
£75000 $137250 €109500 Venice, Saint Mark's Square (83x113cm-33x44in) 8-Jul-4 Sotheby's, London #183/R est:30000-50000
£83333 $150000 €121666 View of the Grand canal looking north. View of the Grand Canal from the Palazzo Vendramin Calergi (71x110cm-28x43in) i.verso pair prov.lit. 22-Jan-4 Sotheby's, New York #182/R est:60000-80000
£105000 $189000 €153300 Bacino di San Marco, Venice. Riva deglia Schiavoni. Entrance of the Arsenal Giudecca, Venice (39x62cm-15x24in) set of four prov. 21-Apr-4 Christie's, London #103/R est:80000-120000

MASTER OF THE LANGMATT FOUNDATION VIEW (attrib) (fl.1740-1770) Italian
£22000 $40260 €32120 Grand Canal with Palazzo Balbi (54x87cm-21x34in) prov. 9-Jul-4 Christie's, Kensington #205/R est:8000-12000

MASTER OF THE LANGMATT FOUNDATION VIEW (style) (fl.1740-1770) Italian
£8451 $14789 €12000 Grand Canal (35x57cm-14x22in) 17-Dec-3 Piasa, Paris #62/R est:3000-4000

MASTER OF THE MADONNA OF MARBLE (attrib) (fl.1470-1500) Italian
Sculpture
£5986 $9637 €8500 Testa di cherubino con festone e nastri (21x74x8cm-8x29x3in) Part of architectural frieze bas-relief stone. 8-May-3 Farsetti, Prato #149/R est:1000-12000

MASTER OF THE MANSI MAGDALEN (16th C) Flemish
£60000 $109800 €87600 Entombment (86x48cm-34x19in) panel prov. 7-Jul-4 Christie's, London #15/R est:60000-80000

MASTER OF THE MANSI MAGDALEN (studio) (16th C) Flemish
£8054 $14819 €12000 Mary Magdalene (46x43cm-18x17in) panel prov. 24-Mar-4 Dorotheum, Vienna #108/R est:14000-17000

MASTER OF THE MARTYRDOM OF ST SEBASTIAN (attrib) (17th C) Austrian
Sculpture
£220000 $380600 €321200 Captive Hercules (21cm-8in) ivory perspex stand exec.c.1655 lit. 12-Dec-3 Sotheby's, London #166/R est:40000-60000

MASTER OF THE PARROT (attrib) (16th C) Flemish
£10000 $17000 €14600 Holy Family (43x31cm-17x12in) panel. 29-Oct-3 Christie's, London #6/R est:10000-15000

MASTER OF THE PIETA DI SAN CONTANZO (15th C) Italian
£90000 $164700 €131400 Christ the Redeemer. Christ carrying the cross. Crucifixion (113x42cm-44x17in) gold ground panel triptych lit. 7-Jul-4 Christie's, London #14/R est:20000-30000

MASTER OF THE PRODIGAL SON (attrib) (16th C) Flemish
£3873 $6779 €5500 Le mariage de la Vierge (78x103cm-31x41in) panel. 18-Dec-3 Tajan, Paris #94/R est:4000-6000
£7042 $12324 €10000 Recolte de la manne (57x79cm-22x31in) panel. 17-Dec-3 Piasa, Paris #12/R est:10000-15000
£13333 $24400 €20000 Deploration (75x106cm-30x42in) panel prov. 6-Jun-4 Rouillac, Vendome #19
£26667 $47733 €40000 Lot and his daughters (79x109cm-31x43in) panel. 17-May-4 Christie's, Amsterdam #64/R est:10000-15000

MASTER OF THE RIFLESSI (18th C) Italian
£18000 $32940 €26280 Meeting between procurator and wife (73x55cm-29x22in) 8-Jul-4 Sotheby's, London #170/R est:20000-30000

MASTER OF THE SCANDICCI LAMENTATIONS (?) Italian?
£125000 $228750 €182500 Madonna and Child seated beneath green draped curtain (86x67cm-34x26in) panel prov.lit. 7-Jul-4 Sotheby's, London #43/R est:60000-80000

MASTER OF THE SMALL LANDSCAPES (attrib) (16th C) ?
Works on paper
£238889 $430000 €348778 Landscape with an avenue of trees through a village (14x21cm-6x8in) pen ink. 21-Jan-4 Sotheby's, New York #57/R est:6000-8000

MASTER OF THE UNRULY CHILDREN (16th C) Italian
Sculpture
£10563 $17535 €15000 Charity (54x38x22cm-21x15x9in) painted terracotta prov. 11-Jun-3 Semenzato, Florence #86/R est:21000

MASTER OF TROGNANO (15th C) Italian
Sculpture
£7718 $13661 €11500 Baptism of Christ (105x63x12cm-41x25x5in) carved wood relief lit. 2-May-4 Finarte, Venice #71/R est:10000-12000

MASTER P V L (16th C) ?
Prints
£2600 $4472 €3796 Man playing a game of dice (9cm-4in circular) engraving executed c.1520. 2-Dec-3 Christie's, London #46/R est:3000-5000

MASTERS, Edward (19th C) British
£780 $1435 €1139 Busy farmyard scene (23x33cm-9x13in) s. 8-Jun-4 Gorringes, Lewes #2173
£2016 $3710 €2943 Busy farmyard. Travelers outside an inn (25x46cm-10x18in) pair prov. 14-Jun-4 Waddingtons, Toronto #141/R est:6000-8000 (C.D 5000)

MASTERS, Edwin (19th C) British
£1100 $2046 €1606 Figures in a village. In the farmyard (30x46cm-12x18in) pair. 4-Mar-4 Christie's, Kensington #482/R est:1500-2000
£3000 $4740 €4350 At the end of the day (51x76cm-20x30in) mono. 4-Sep-3 Christie's, Kensington #165/R est:2000-3000

MASTRO, Luis (20th C) Argentinian
£659 $1200 €962 Harbour (50x60cm-20x24in) s. 5-Jul-4 Arroyo, Buenos Aires #41/R

MASTROIANNI, Umberto (1910-1998) Italian
£278 $439 €400 Space car (25x35cm-10x14in) card. 6-Sep-3 Meeting Art, Vercelli #290
£282 $468 €400 Macchina Spaziale (21x33cm-8x13in) s. retouching cardboard. 14-Jun-3 Meeting Art, Vercelli #575
£347 $549 €500 Spatial car (25x35cm-10x14in) card. 6-Sep-3 Meeting Art, Vercelli #539
£667 $1227 €1000 Composition (100x70cm-39x28in) s. cardboard. 14-Jun-4 Sant Agostino, Torino #381/R
£699 $1189 €1000 Untitled (17x30cm-7x12in) s. cardboard. 24-Nov-3 Christie's, Milan #72
£952 $1705 €1400 Composition (69x52cm-27x20in) s. cardboard. 22-Mar-4 Sant Agostino, Torino #559/R
Sculpture
£1034 $1728 €1500 Ghosts (30x20cm-12x8in) col lead exec.1985. 17-Nov-3 Sant Agostino, Torino #58/R est:2000
£1103 $1843 €1600 Composition (30x24x20cm-12x9x8in) s. silver exec.1961. 17-Nov-3 Sant Agostino, Torino #59/R est:1400
£1667 $3067 €2500 Bull (67x103x25cm-26x41x10in) s. stone lit. 12-Jun-4 Meeting Art, Vercelli #99/R est:2500
£1724 $2862 €2500 Horse. bronze. 1-Oct-3 Della Rocca, Turin #268/R
£1862 $3110 €2700 Rider (31x26x14cm-12x10x6in) s. bronze. 17-Nov-3 Sant Agostino, Torino #304/R est:2000-2500
£2098 $3566 €3000 Face of woman (45cm-18in) pat bronze. 29-Nov-3 Farsetti, Prato #440/R est:3000-4000
£2394 $3975 €3400 Mask (25cm-10in) s. bronze. 11-Jun-3 Finarte Semenzato, Milan #669/R est:4000
£2778 $4389 €4000 Iopa (76x60x22cm-30x24x9in) marble. 6-Sep-3 Meeting Art, Vercelli #558 est:4000
£2819 $5215 €4200 Mythological cock (71x20cm-28x8in) s. Carrara marble exec.1993 lit. 13-Mar-4 Meeting Art, Vercelli #354 est:3000
£3034 $5068 €4400 Left-overs (51x51cm-20x20in) s.d.1973 col lead exhib.lit. 17-Nov-3 Sant Agostino, Torino #289/R est:3000-4000

£5517 $9214 €8000 Portrait of gentleman (70x80x45cm-28x31x18in) s. bronze. 17-Nov-3 Sant Agostino, Torino #70/R est:2500
£5594 $9343 €8000 Courses de bateaux a moteurs (32x73x25cm-13x29x10in) s. brown pat bronze stone socle. 25-Jun-3 Maigret, Paris #193/R est:1200-1500
£6000 $11040 €9000 Cactus (58x36x20cm-23x14x8in) s. bronze exec.1973 exhib.lit. 14-Jun-4 Sant Agostino, Torino #386/R est:8000-10000
£6122 $10959 €9000 Symbol (80x59x10cm-31x23x4in) s. bronze exec.1969. 22-Mar-4 Sant Agostino, Torino #477/R est:9000-12000
Works on paper
£490 $832 €700 Abstract (29x50cm-11x20in) gouache cardboard. 26-Nov-3 Pandolfini, Florence #56
£966 $1603 €1400 Found image (50x35cm-20x14in) s. mixed media graphite card. 1-Oct-3 Della Rocca, Turin #60/R
£1200 $2160 €1800 Untitled (70x100cm-28x39in) s. mixed media exec.1974. 22-Apr-4 Finarte Semenzato, Rome #98/R est:1800
£1399 $2336 €2000 Lemuri (55x80cm-22x31in) s. mixed media cardboard exec.1977. 26-Jun-3 Sant Agostino, Torino #219/R est:2500
£1769 $3166 €2600 Gerdur (90x63cm-35x25in) s. mixed media cardboard. 22-Mar-4 Sant Agostino, Torino #557/R est:3200

MASTURZIO, Marzio (attrib) (fl.1670) Italian
£15000 $27450 €21900 Cavalry battle between Turks and Christians (90x122cm-35x48in) 7-Jul-4 Bonhams, New Bond Street #49/R est:8000-12000

MASUCCI, Agostino (1691-1758) Italian
Works on paper
£984 $1800 €1437 Bust study of Saint Francis, looking up (14x12cm-6x5in) black chk htd white. 29-Jan-4 Swann Galleries, New York #111/R est:800-1200
£5500 $10065 €8030 Marriage of Prince James Stuart, the Old Pretender, and Princess Maria Clementina Sobieska (34x42cm-13x17in) black chk pen ink htd white. 6-Jul-4 Christie's, London #61/R est:3000-5000

MASUCCI, Agostino (attrib) (1691-1758) Italian
Works on paper
£2778 $5000 €4056 Calling of St. Peter (11x45cm-4x18in) i. pen ink wash black chk. 21-Jan-4 Sotheby's, New York #128/R est:2500-3500

MASUDA, Makoto (20th C) Japanese?
£568 $1000 €829 Paris (74x99cm-29x39in) s. painted c.1960. 23-May-4 Treadway Gallery, Cincinnati #691/R
£791 $1298 €1100 Rue de Montmartre (48x55cm-19x22in) s. 6-Jun-3 Chochon-Barre & Allardi, Paris #74/R

MASUI, Paul Auguste (1888-1981) Luxembourger
£265 $482 €400 Bord de mer en Bretagne (60x70cm-24x28in) s. 15-Jun-4 Vanderkindere, Brussels #41
£270 $484 €400 Au bord de la Sure (35x40cm-14x16in) s. panel. 10-May-4 Horta, Bruxelles #495
£400 $716 €600 Port de peche (60x70cm-24x28in) s. panel. 11-May-4 Vanderkindere, Brussels #230
£473 $847 €700 Barques et reflets a Ostende (32x41cm-13x16in) s. oil paper laid down. 10-May-4 Horta, Bruxelles #494
£514 $873 €750 Peniches (45x50cm-18x20in) s. 10-Nov-3 Horta, Bruxelles #426
£552 $1021 €800 Barque de peche an Zelande (40x50cm-16x20in) s. panel. 16-Feb-4 Horta, Bruxelles #315
£1027 $1747 €1500 Passeur (88x78cm-35x31in) s. 10-Nov-3 Horta, Bruxelles #425
£1206 $2013 €1700 Port (100x110cm-39x43in) s. 17-Jun-3 Vanderkindere, Brussels #1 est:625-875

MASUNOBU, Tanaka (fl.1736-1760s) Japanese
Prints
£3600 $6624 €5256 Perspective view of Genji Junidan No Soshi (32x45cm-13x18in) s. print exec. late 1740's prov.lit. 8-Jun-4 Sotheby's, London #31/R est:900-1200

MASVDA, Makoto (20th C) ?
£874 $1486 €1250 Le port (38x46cm-15x18in) s. 24-Nov-3 Boscher, Cherbourg #788/R

MASWIENS, Joseph (1828-1880) Belgian
£1250 $2300 €1900 Interior of Brou Church (60x70cm-24x28in) s. 24-Jun-4 Christie's, Paris #139/R est:1500-2000
£3521 $6092 €5000 Les stalles de l'eglise Ste Gertrude a Louvain (49x39cm-19x15in) s.d.66 i.verso panel. 13-Dec-3 De Vuyst, Lokeren #527/R est:6500-7500

MATA PACHECO, Juan de (19th C) South American
£527 $896 €769 Patio (46x46cm-18x18in) s.d.1920. 30-Oct-3 Louis Morton, Mexico #14a (M.P 10000)

MATA, Carlos (20th C) ?
Sculpture
£3497 $5944 €5000 Caballo (41cm-16in) s.num.1/1 green pat bronze Cast Fien Fumesant. 20-Nov-3 Claude Aguttes, Neuilly #150/R est:5000-5300

MATA, Emelio Garcia (1910-1985) French
£615 $1100 €898 Sirenitas - mermaid (36x25cm-14x10in) s. i.d.61 verso pair. 21-Mar-4 Jeffery Burchard, Florida #33/R

MATAL, Bohumir (1922-1988) Czechoslovakian
£1756 $2985 €2564 Woman in front of a mirror (28x20cm-11x8in) s.d.52 cardboard. 29-Nov-3 Dorotheum, Prague #102/R est:80000-120000 (C.KR 80000)
Works on paper
£316 $557 €474 Composition (34x21cm-13x8in) s.d.68 pastel. 22-May-4 Dorotheum, Prague #257/R est:15000-28000 (C.KR 15000)

MATANGALE, Maudi (c.1932-) Australian
Works on paper
£702 $1300 €1025 Bush tucker dream, Woomchi, in the Tanami Desert, W.A (90x60cm-35x24in) synthetic polymer prov. 15-Mar-4 Sotheby's, Melbourne #29 est:2000-4000 (A.D 1700)
£1172 $2191 €1758 Tjalyuwangu (90x60cm-35x24in) bears name.verso synthetic polymer paint canvas prov.exhib.lit. 26-Jul-4 Sotheby's, Melbourne #435/R est:3000-4000 (A.D 3000)

MATANIA, Fortunino (1881-1963) Italian
£504 $826 €700 Naples Bay (24x22cm-9x9in) s. s.i.verso cardboard. 10-Jun-3 Pandolfini, Florence #82
£1000 $1840 €1460 Lady in a long dress seated at a keyboard (43x28cm-17x11in) s. 24-Jun-4 Ewbank, Send #571/R est:2000-3000
£1050 $1932 €1533 Alpine landscape with rocky mountains, and figure (41x30cm-16x12in) s.d.1885. 24-Jun-4 Ewbank, Send #573/R est:800-1200
£3200 $5888 €4672 Dinner party with guests in 18th century dress (38x61cm-15x24in) s. 24-Jun-4 Ewbank, Send #572/R est:1500-2500
£3800 $6992 €5548 Lady seated on her chair, with an artist painting her portrait (28x38cm-11x15in) s. 24-Jun-4 Ewbank, Send #570/R est:3000-5000
£7000 $12740 €10220 Ballroom (34x49cm-13x19in) s. 5-Feb-4 Mellors & Kirk, Nottingham #556/R est:5000-6000
Works on paper
£270 $451 €394 Death of Cola di Rienzi (23x23cm-9x9in) s.i. pencil wash bodycol. 12-Nov-3 Sotheby's, Olympia #189/R
£588 $1000 €858 Picnickers (26x40cm-10x16in) s. gouache. 21-Nov-3 Skinner, Boston #436/R est:800-1200
£4800 $8832 €7008 On the terrace at the Hotel Excelsior, Venice (34x51cm-13x20in) s. pencil W/C. 25-Mar-4 Christie's, Kensington #79/R est:5000-7000

MATANIA, Franco (20th C) ?
Works on paper
£360 $576 €522 Reclining nude (31x48cm-12x19in) s. conte crayon sold with 7 others by the same hand. 16-Sep-3 Bonhams, Knightsbridge #93

MATARE, Ewald (1887-1965) German
Prints
£1867 $3435 €2800 Cows on a windy day (18x27cm-7x11in) s.i. woodcut exec. 1928 one of 25 prov. 12-Jun-4 Villa Grisebach, Berlin #297/R est:2500-3500
£2533 $4661 €3800 Grazing (16x27cm-6x11in) s.i. col woodcut. 10-Jun-4 Hauswedell & Nolte, Hamburg #482/R est:5000
£2933 $5251 €4400 Horses in meadow (12x32cm-5x13in) s.i. col woodcut. 15-May-4 Dr Sturies, Dusseldorf #128/R
£2933 $5368 €4400 Three cows (41x36cm-16x14in) s.i. col woodcut. 5-Jun-4 Lempertz, Koln #866/R est:500-6000
£4133 $7399 €6200 Night meadow (19x45cm-7x18in) s.i. col woodcut. 15-May-4 Dr Sturies, Dusseldorf #127/R
£5667 $10143 €8500 Signs of a meadow (38x45cm-15x18in) s.i. col woodcut. 15-May-4 Dr Sturies, Dusseldorf #129/R
Sculpture
£6667 $12200 €10000 Cockerel (40x46cm-16x18in) s. bronze relief prov.exhib.lit. 5-Jun-4 Lempertz, Koln #864/R est:10000-15000
£6800 $12512 €9928 Steinbock (5x3x7cm-2x1x3in) mono. dark brown pat bronze exec c.1935 edn of 19 lit. 24-Jun-4 Sotheby's, London #223/R est:7000-9000
£6800 $12512 €9928 Kihzeichen (3x8x13cm-1x3x5in) mono. dark brown pat bronze exec c.1945 edn of 5 lit. 24-Jun-4 Sotheby's, London #224/R est:7000-9000
£9790 $16643 €14000 Abstract cow (14x6x1cm-6x2x0in) bronze prov. 26-Nov-3 Lempertz, Koln #842/R est:10000-12000
£11333 $20287 €17000 Mathematical cow I (4x11x7cm-2x4x3in) mono. gold brown pat.bronze prov.exhib.lit. 14-May-4 Ketterer, Munich #191/R est:15000-20000
£12000 $22080 €18000 Mathematical cow I (4x11x7cm-2x4x3in) mono. bronze. 10-Jun-4 Hauswedell & Nolte, Hamburg #479/R est:12000
£32000 $58560 €48000 Female torso (19cm-7in) mono. pat.bronze. 5-Jun-4 Lempertz, Koln #863/R est:25000
£34965 $60140 €50000 Finnish cow (20x18x33cm-8x7x13in) mono. dark brown pat bronze one of c.15 prov.exhib.lit. 5-Dec-3 Ketterer, Munich #101/R est:28000-35000
£44000 $79640 €64240 Grosse liegende Kih (57cm-22in) mono.num.IIII/V brown pat bronze lit. 1-Apr-4 Christie's, Kensington #47/R est:15000-20000
£53691 $95034 €80000 Cow lying down (12x29cm-5x11in) s. verso brown pat.bronze prov. 30-Apr-4 Dr Fritz Nagel, Stuttgart #899/R est:20000
Works on paper
£1667 $3067 €2500 On the edge of the forest (23x31cm-9x12in) s. pencil exec. c.1930-31 prov. 12-Jun-4 Villa Grisebach, Berlin #296/R est:2500-3500
£2517 $4280 €3600 Hiddensee (29x39cm-11x15in) s. W/C. 26-Nov-3 Lempertz, Koln #844/R est:4000
£3467 $6205 €5200 Forest path (25x35cm-10x14in) s. W/C on pencil. 15-May-4 Dr Sturies, Dusseldorf #126/R
£4545 $7727 €6500 Landscape with house (29x39cm-11x15in) s. W/C over pencil. 29-Nov-3 Villa Grisebach, Berlin #223/R est:3500-4500

MATARRANZ, Mariano (1952-) Spanish
£306 $557 €450 Walden Series (200x78cm-79x31in) s.i.d.1986 verso oil metal net mixed media prov.exhib. 3-Feb-4 Segre, Madrid #211/R

MATASSONI, Terry (1959-) Australian
£244 $383 €356 In the small hours (121x167cm-48x66in) s.i.verso linen prov.exhib.lit. 27-Aug-3 Christie's, Sydney #664 (A.D 600)
£936 $1591 €1367 Getting out (152x182cm-60x72in) s.i.verso painted 1988 prov. 26-Nov-3 Deutscher-Menzies, Melbourne #263/R (A.D 2200)

MATCHITT, Paratene (1933-) New Zealander
Sculpture
£1429 $2429 €2086 White Union Jack (61x90cm-24x35in) s.d.1984 verso canvas strips timber frame. 26-Nov-3 Dunbar Sloane, Wellington #5/R est:3000-5000 (NZ.D 3800)
£3304 $5979 €4824 Untitled (135x72cm-53x28in) s.d.7/90 steel wall sculpture. 30-Mar-4 Peter Webb, Auckland #166/R est:4000-6000 (NZ.D 9250)

MATEJKO, Jan (1838-1893) Polish
£32532 $57256 €47497 Portrait of lady (57x47cm-22x19in) painted 1861. 23-May-4 Agra, Warsaw #3/R (P.Z 230000)

MATEJKO, Theo (?-1946) Austrian
Works on paper
£503 $921 €750 PAK Garrison in Second World War (34x70cm-13x28in) s.d.41 pastel lit. 8-Jul-4 Allgauer, Kempten #2011/R

MATELDI, Filiberto (1885-1942) Italian
Works on paper
£247 $427 €350 I ask for your love and you give me lies (33x38cm-13x15in) s.i.verso Chinese ink. 9-Dec-3 Pandolfini, Florence #332/R

MATEOS, Francisco (1894-1976) Spanish
£5106 $8272 €7200 Still life (59x78cm-23x31in) s.d.52. 20-May-3 Ansorena, Madrid #315/R est:7200
£5319 $8883 €7500 El castillo (81x100cm-32x39in) s. s.i.d.74 verso. 23-Jun-3 Durán, Madrid #216/R est:7500
£6122 $11143 €9000 Brujo (99x81cm-39x32in) s.d.1972 s.i.d.verso. 3-Feb-4 Segre, Madrid #349/R est:9000
£9091 $15182 €13000 La Jaula esmaltada (100x81cm-39x32in) s. s.i.d.1972. 24-Jun-3 Segre, Madrid #165/R est:8400
£12500 $21250 €18000 Meteorites (100x81cm-39x32in) s. s.i.d.1969 verso. 28-Oct-3 Segre, Madrid #151/R est:9500

MATET, Charles (1791-1870) French
£11538 $19846 €16500 Portrait de Casimir Perier en costume de Pair de France (100x78cm-39x31in) s.d.1840. 8-Dec-3 Claude Aguttes, Neuilly #39/R est:15000-20000

MATHAM, Jacob (1571-1631) Dutch
Prints
£2378 $4042 €3400 Portrait of Jan van de Velde (20x15cm-8x6in) copperplate. 27-Nov-3 Bassenge, Berlin #5267/R est:1500
£2667 $4773 €4000 Rich at the table and poor Lazarus at the door (40x53cm-16x21in) copperplate after Sebastian Vrancks. 13-May-4 Bassenge, Berlin #5211/R est:2400
£9333 $16707 €14000 Minerva, Venus and Juno (34x25cm-13x10in) copperplate 3. 13-May-4 Bassenge, Berlin #5212/R est:6000
Works on paper
£360 $659 €526 Portrait of Poliander (25x19cm-10x7in) s. black chk prov. 7-Jul-4 Bonhams, Knightsbridge #44/R
£2817 $4873 €4000 Un jeune homme et une vieille femme vus en buste (16x16cm-6x6in) s. pen brown ink prov. 12-Dec-3 Renaud, Paris #111/R est:4000-5000
£3333 $6000 €4866 Diana the huntress (14x11cm-6x4in) i.verso black chk pen brown ink wash. 22-Jan-4 Christie's, Rockefeller NY #111/R est:7000-10000
£8889 $16000 €12978 Venus and Cupid (16x18cm-6x7in) black chk oval prov. 22-Jan-4 Christie's, Rockefeller NY #110/R est:7000-10000

MATHELIN, Lucien (1905-1981) French
£805 $1425 €1200 Chouette (65x54cm-26x21in) s. acrylic. 28-Apr-4 Artcurial Briest, Paris #505
£1007 $1782 €1500 Puce d'apres Georges de la tour (83x65cm-33x26in) s. acrylic. 28-Apr-4 Artcurial Briest, Paris #508 est:1500-1800
£1410 $2495 €2100 Visage de profil d'apres Piero di Cosimo et Goya (60x73cm-24x29in) s. acrylic. 28-Apr-4 Artcurial Briest, Paris #507/R est:1200-1500
£1476 $2613 €2200 Composition surrealiste (72x72cm-28x28in) s.d.1979 acrylic isorel. 28-Apr-4 Artcurial Briest, Paris #506/R est:1500-1800
£1678 $2970 €2500 Diderot (72x72cm-28x28in) s. s.d. verso panel. 28-Apr-4 Artcurial Briest, Paris #504 est:1200-1500

MATHER, John (1848-1916) British
£344 $625 €502 Marysville (33x25cm-13x10in) s.d.84 board. 16-Jun-4 Deutscher-Menzies, Melbourne #542/R (A.D 900)
£511 $868 €746 Mouth of Stony Creek, Lorne (18x23cm-7x9in) s.d.1.06 i.verso board. 26-Nov-3 Deutscher-Menzies, Melbourne #226/R (A.D 1200)
£992 $1806 €1448 Coastal scene (45x76cm-18x30in) s.d.99. 16-Jun-4 Deutscher-Menzies, Melbourne #598/R est:1500-2500 (A.D 2600)
£1296 $2086 €1892 Sunlight and shadow, gums by the creek (52x42cm-20x17in) s.d.88. 13-Oct-3 Joel, Victoria #348/R est:2000-3000 (A.D 3200)
£1702 $2894 €2485 Australian Paper Mill overlooking the Yarra River from Kew (50x62cm-20x24in) s.d.7.10 prov. 26-Nov-3 Deutscher-Menzies, Melbourne #167/R est:6000-9000 (A.D 4000)
Works on paper
£265 $443 €384 Landscape with road (33x51cm-13x20in) s.d.1897 W/C. 13-Jul-3 James Lawson, Sydney #452 est:800-1200 (A.D 650)
£1538 $2477 €2245 Fitzory Garden (27x42cm-11x17in) s.d.May 92 W/C. 13-Oct-3 Joel, Victoria #331/R est:2000-2500 (A.D 3800)

MATHER, Margrethe (1886-1952) American
Photographs
£2542 $4500 €3711 Jetta Goudal and Harold Grieve (17x21cm-7x8in) i.d.1930 i.verso platinum print. 28-Apr-4 Sotheby's, New York #174/R est:5000-7000

MATHER, Sydney (1944-) Australian
£405 $652 €591 White trees (48x74cm-19x29in) s.i. board painted c.1990. 13-Oct-3 Joel, Victoria #356 est:1000-1200 (A.D 1000)
£648 $1043 €946 Spring, Kingower District (76x50cm-30x20in) s. board. 13-Oct-3 Joel, Victoria #426 est:1200-1500 (A.D 1600)

MATHET, Louis Dominique (1853-1920) French
Sculpture
£2183 $3777 €3100 Eve (68x30cm-27x12in) s. Carrare marble exec.c.1890-1900. 13-Dec-3 Martinot & Savignat, Pontoise #63/R est:3200-4000

MATHEWS, Arthur F (1860-1945) American
£52198 $95000 €76209 Woman and children picking poppies in landscape (30x23cm-12x9in) s. panel prov. 15-Jun-4 John Moran, Pasadena #33 est:15000-20000
Works on paper
£611 $1100 €892 Canoe by the river's edge (24x34cm-9x13in) s. W/C. 25-Apr-4 Bonhams & Butterfields, San Francisco #5505/R

MATHEWS, Binny (1960-) British
£260 $460 €380 Still life with Benin head (62x76cm-24x30in) s.d.1991. 27-Apr-4 Bonhams, Knightsbridge #299/R
£300 $510 €438 Still life with pot plants (86x91cm-34x36in) s.d.91. 4-Nov-3 Dreweatt Neate, Newbury #131

MATHEWS, John Chester (fl.1884-1912) British
£2000 $3400 €2920 Liver chestnut charger of the Hussars (63x76cm-25x30in) s.d.1889. 27-Nov-3 Christie's, Kensington #74/R est:2000-3000

MATHEWS, John Chester (attrib) (fl.1884-1912) British
£1872 $3500 €2808 Horse and two hounds (63x77cm-25x30in) bears sig.indis.d.18. 25-Jul-4 Bonhams & Butterfields, San Francisco #6019/R est:600-800

MATHEWS, P (19th C) British
£8200 $13940 €11972 Trial of Bill Burns, under Martin's act (66x81cm-26x32in) prov. 27-Nov-3 Sotheby's, London #205/R est:5000-7000

MATHEWSON, Frank Convers (1862-1941) American
Works on paper
£299 $475 €437 Floral still life (25x20cm-10x8in) s.d.1924 W/C. 10-Sep-3 Alderfer's, Hatfield #466

MATHEY, Jacques (attrib) (1883-1973) French
£1233 $2096 €1800 View of Marrakech (49x81cm-19x32in) s. cardboard lit. 4-Nov-3 Ansorena, Madrid #73/R est:1800
£1334 $2440 €2000 Animation devant les remparts (52x73cm-20x29in) s. 3-Jun-4 Tajan, Paris #291/R est:2000-2500

MATHEY, Maurice (1878-?) Swiss
£1667 $2783 €2434 L'ombre s'etend (43x125cm-17x49in) s.d.1908. 16-Nov-3 Koller, Geneva #1284/R est:900-1200 (S.FR 3800)

MATHEY, Paul (1844-1929) French
£1500 $2385 €2190 Bouquet d'ete (73x92cm-29x36in) s. 9-Sep-3 Bonhams, Knightsbridge #66/R est:1200-1800

MATHEY, Paul (1891-1972) Swiss
£294 $500 €429 Le fichu valaisain (74x60cm-29x24in) s.i. verso. 28-Nov-3 Zofingen, Switzerland #3062 (S.FR 650)

MATHIESEN, Egon (1907-1976) Danish
£379 $607 €550 Night (100x78cm-39x31in) init.d.73-74 verso. 17-Sep-3 Kunsthallen, Copenhagen #74c (D.KR 4000)
£487 $838 €711 Cyclists in landscape - cubist composition (67x82cm-26x32in) s.i.d.april-maj 1939 verso. 3-Dec-3 Museumsbygningen, Copenhagen #48 (D.KR 5200)
£722 $1350 €1054 Composition (86x62cm-34x24in) init.d.54 verso. 25-Feb-4 Kunsthallen, Copenhagen #153/R (D.KR 8000)
£1083 $1993 €1581 Figure in landscape (94x76cm-37x30in) init.d.54 verso. 29-Mar-4 Rasmussen, Copenhagen #431/R est:12000 (D.KR 12000)

MATHIEU, Cornelius (17th C) Dutch
£6000 $10380 €8760 Extensive river landscape with a fisherman sitting before a bridge (42x54cm-17x21in) s. 11-Dec-3 Sotheby's, London #158/R est:6000-8000

MATHIEU, Gabriel (1843-1921) French
£331 $550 €483 River landscape (54x73cm-21x29in) s. 30-Sep-3 Christie's, Rockefeller NY #433/R

MATHIEU, Georges (1921-) French
£606 $1085 €885 Abstract composition (14x24cm-6x9in) s.d.59. 22-Mar-4 Philippe Schuler, Zurich #4453/R (S.FR 1400)
£2533 $4661 €3800 Untitled (48x38cm-19x15in) s.d.58 indis.i. oil gouache canvas on board prov. 8-Jun-4 Sotheby's, Amsterdam #76/R est:5000-7000
£3125 $5219 €4500 Sans titre (88x72cm-35x28in) s. paper on canvas. 21-Oct-3 Artcurial Briest, Paris #403/R est:5000-7000
£4196 $7133 €6000 Plainte captive (55x75cm-22x30in) s. i.verso oil paper prov. 25-Nov-3 Tajan, Paris #22/R est:5000-6000
£4546 $7728 €6500 Composition (51x56cm-20x22in) s.i.d.1957 oil paper prov. 25-Nov-3 Tajan, Paris #19/R est:5000-6000
£6338 $10521 €9000 Composition (56x76cm-22x30in) s. acrylic paper. 14-Jun-3 Meeting Art, Vercelli #79/R est:8000

£6376 $11795 €9500 Untitled (72x88cm-28x35in) s. paper on canvas. 13-Mar-4 Meeting Art, Vercelli #93 est:5000
£9091 $15182 €13000 Composition jaune, blanche et noire (49x64cm-19x25in) s.i. oil paper on canvas. 11-Oct-3 Cornette de St.Cyr, Paris #54/R est:12000-15000
£9868 $18158 €15000 Passion indicible (81x100cm-32x39in) s. i.verso. 23-Jun-4 Maigret, Paris #39/R est:6000-8000
£10135 $19155 €15000 L'espace eclate (89x116cm-35x46in) s. 21-Feb-4 Cornette de St.Cyr, Paris #352/R est:12000-15000
£10211 $16440 €14500 Lieux jaloux (92x73cm-36x29in) s. painted c.1980. 22-Aug-3 Deauville, France #129/R est:15000-18000
£12000 $22200 €18000 Illusion (69x69cm-27x27in) s.i.d.1949 prov.exhib.lit. 18-Jul-4 Sotheby's, Paris #242/R est:18000-25000
£12676 $21042 €18000 Ardeurs illuminees (73x92cm-29x36in) s. 14-Jun-3 Meeting Art, Vercelli #597/R est:15000
£12752 $22826 €19000 Avadel (50x81cm-20x32in) s.d.1969. 30-May-4 Meeting Art, Vercelli #55 est:15000
£13000 $21710 €18980 Ce soir Salle 7 (285x99cm-112x39in) s.d.58 s.i.d.stretcher prov.exhib. 21-Oct-3 Sotheby's, London #390/R est:10000-15000
£13542 $21396 €19500 Composition (97x162cm-38x64in) prov. 27-Apr-3 Versailles Encheres #46
£14000 $25760 €20440 Composition sur fond blanc (89x146cm-35x57in) s.verso painted 1960 prov. 25-Jun-4 Christie's, London #112/R est:14000-18000
£15493 $26803 €22000 Ivresses extremes (89x116cm-35x46in) s. 9-Dec-3 Artcurial Briest, Paris #420/R est:25000-30000
£15972 $26674 €23000 Misteorix (89x146cm-35x57in) s.d.70 exhib. 21-Oct-3 Artcurial Briest, Paris #388/R est:20000-25000
£18000 $33300 €27000 Untitled (130x80cm-51x31in) s.d.56 verso prov. 18-Jul-4 Sotheby's, Paris #243/R est:25000-35000
£20000 $36400 €29200 Le Comte de Guibes (81x129cm-32x51in) s.d.59 i.stretcher prov. 6-Feb-4 Sotheby's, London #173/R est:20000-30000
£21831 $37768 €31000 Composition (130x89cm-51x35in) s.d.58 prov. 9-Dec-3 Artcurial Briest, Paris #414/R est:30000-40000
£42667 $78933 €64000 Eginhardt (152x252cm-60x99in) s.d.51 prov.exhib. 18-Jul-4 Sotheby's, Paris #241/R est:50000-60000
£55945 $95107 €80000 Hommage a Philippe III le Hardi (200x400cm-79x157in) s.d.22 janv.52 prov.exhib.lit. 25-Nov-3 Tajan, Paris #16/R est:80000-100000
£57047 $102114 €85000 Massacre de Vassy (97x162cm-38x64in) s.d.54 exhib. 26-May-4 Christie's, Paris #71/R est:40000-60000
£63087 $112926 €94000 Bataille de Lepante (200x500cm-79x197in) s.i.d.59 exhib.lit. 26-May-4 Christie's, Paris #75/R est:80000-100000

Works on paper
£280 $476 €400 Composition (18x21cm-7x8in) s.i. col ink. 28-Nov-3 Drouot Estimations, Paris #186
£350 $595 €511 Composition (23x28cm-9x11in) s.i.d.64 ink prov. 2-Nov-3 Lots Road Auctions, London #335
£833 $1392 €1200 Composition (10x23cm-4x9in) s.i.d.64 ink collage blk paper. 21-Oct-3 Artcurial Briest, Paris #668
£1342 $2403 €2000 Composition (46x61cm-18x24in) s.i.d.1960 chl pastel. 26-May-4 Christie's, Paris #97/R
£1352 $2379 €2000 Composition (27x19cm-11x7in) Indian ink exec 1950 prov.lit. 18-May-4 Tajan, Paris #52/R est:1600-1800
£1711 $3149 €2550 Composition abstraite (73x55cm-29x22in) s.d.1965 ink collage. 24-Mar-4 Joron-Derem, Paris #142/R est:2500-3000
£1905 $3410 €2800 Composition. s.d.59 ink W/C. 19-Mar-4 Millon & Associes, Paris #181/R est:3000-4000
£2014 $3363 €2900 Corydon (65x49cm-26x19in) s.d.1971 mixed media collage cardboard prov. 25-Oct-3 Cornette de St.Cyr, Paris #752/R est:3000-4000
£2448 $4161 €3500 Untitled (57x77cm-22x30in) s.d.65 collage ink. 25-Nov-3 Sotheby's, Milan #1/R est:3000-4000
£2536 $4159 €3500 Untitled (56x77cm-22x30in) s.d.61 ink prov. 27-May-3 Sotheby's, Milan #99 est:4000
£2554 $4750 €3729 Abstract composition (56x76cm-22x30in) s.d.59 ink was prov. 5-Mar-4 Skinner, Boston #612/R est:3500-5000
£2703 $4757 €4000 Chateau de fleury (54x76cm-21x30in) s.d.1965 i. verso ink ink wash collage Arches paper prov.exhib. 18-May-4 Tajan, Paris #57/R est:3800-4000
£2703 $4757 €4000 Untitled (50x65cm-20x26in) s.d.1954 gouache black paper prov. 18-May-4 Tajan, Paris #54/R est:4000-5000
£3108 $5874 €4600 Composition (50x65cm-20x26in) s.d.1953 ink oil paper on canvas. 21-Feb-4 Cornette de St.Cyr, Paris #353/R est:4500-5000
£3333 $5967 €5000 Composition (37x47cm 15x19in) s.d. gouache bronze board prov. 14-May-4 Ketterer, Munich #275/R est:3500-4000
£3379 $5946 €5000 Composition (30x40cm-12x16in) s.i.d.1962 Indian ink gouache prov.exhib. 18-May-4 Tajan, Paris #53/R est:5000-6000
£4000 $7360 €6000 Rouille (50x65cm-20x26in) s.d.1972 mixed media collage card. 12-Jun-4 Meeting Art, Vercelli #828/R est:4000
£4392 $7730 €6500 Untitled (49x64cm-19x25in) s.d.1954 gouache prov. 18-May-4 Tajan, Paris #51/R est:5000-6000
£4595 $8087 €6800 Enveitg (56x77cm-22x30in) s.d.1969 gouache ink prov.exhib. 18-May-4 Tajan, Paris #58/R est:6500-7000

MATHIEU, Paul (1872-1932) Belgian
£385 $700 €562 Souvenir du Pavillon (46x51cm-18x20in) s.i.d.1905 panel. 7-Feb-4 Auctions by the Bay, Alameda #1521/R
£528 $914 €750 Boulaie (80x70cm-31x28in) s. 9-Dec-3 Campo, Vlaamse Kaai #355
£616 $1048 €900 Paysage flamand (36x46cm-14x18in) s. panel. 4-Nov-3 Servarts Themis, Bruxelles #512
£667 $1227 €1000 Bord de riviere (35x46cm-14x18in) s. panel. 14-Jun-4 Horta, Bruxelles #52
£724 $1332 €1100 Maison au bord de l'etang (40x55cm-16x22in) s.d.1895 panel. 22-Jun-4 Chassaing Rivet, Toulouse #317
£839 $1443 €1200 Reflets de la maison dans le lac (24x35cm-9x14in) panel. 8-Dec-3 Horta, Bruxelles #163
£2238 $3849 €3200 Peniche en bord de Meuse (40x55cm-16x22in) s. cardboard. 8-Dec-3 Horta, Bruxelles #162 est:3000-5000
£6294 $10699 €9000 Maisons ensoleillees au bord du lac (72x100cm-28x39in) s. 1-Dec-3 Palais de Beaux Arts, Brussels #97/R est:8000-12000
£6597 $10490 €9500 Peniche accostee au bord de la Meuse (72x100cm-28x39in) s. 15-Sep-3 Horta, Bruxelles #108/R est:8000-10000
£6643 $11294 €9500 L'elevateur (72x100cm-28x39in) s. prov. 1-Dec-3 Palais de Beaux Arts, Brussels #95/R est:12000-15000
£6757 $12770 €10000 Coin de Seine Pont de Chatou (60x80cm-24x31in) s.d.21. 17-Feb-4 Vanderkindere, Brussels #3 est:3750-5000

Works on paper
£268 $494 €400 Vue de la Seine a Paris (40x53cm-16x21in) s. chl. 28-Mar-4 MonsAntic, Maisieres #1314

MATHIS, Leonie (1883-1952) Argentinian
Works on paper
£3785 $6170 €5526 Independence Square (28x38cm-11x15in) s. gouache. 17-Jul-3 Naón & Cia, Buenos Aires #2/R
£4588 $7800 €6698 Old town, Montevideo (28x37cm-11x15in) s. W/C cardboard exhib.lit. 25-Nov-3 Galeria y Remates, Montevideo #171/R

MATHISEN, Jens (1926-) Norwegian?
£294 $487 €426 Woman at table (100x81cm-39x32in) s. 16-Jun-3 Blomqvist, Lysaker #1132 (N.KR 3400)

MATHON, Émile (19th C) French
£652 $1070 €900 Bords de l'Oise pres d'Anvers. s.d.1872 panel. 11-May-3 Osenat, Fontainebleau #228

MATHORNE, Carl (1878-1942) Danish
£385 $700 €562 Interior scene with harlequin (52x42cm-20x17in) mono. 7-Feb-4 Rasmussen, Havnen #2142/R (D.KR 4200)

MATHYS, Adolf (1889-1993) Swiss
£317 $538 €463 Landscape near Koniz (53x68cm-21x27in) mono. board. 22-Nov-3 Burkhard, Luzern #64/R (S.FR 700)

MATHYS, Albert François (1885-1956) Belgian
£1600 $2880 €2400 Still life with flowers, pears and jugs on a table (70x60cm-28x24in) s.d.1917 verso. 26-Apr-4 Bernaerts, Antwerp #403/R est:2500-2750

MATHYS, Hendrik (20th C) Belgian
£1348 $2250 €1900 Retour du berger et troupeau (100x150cm-39x59in) s. 14-Oct-3 Vanderkindere, Brussels #129 est:1000-1500
£2308 $3854 €3300 Shepherd with flock (96x118cm-38x46in) s. 11-Oct-3 De Vuyst, Lokeren #249/R est:2800-3000

MATICSKA, Jeno (1885-1906) Hungarian
£1283 $2270 €1873 Girl in a field (39x45cm-15x18in) s. 28-Apr-4 Kieselbach, Budapest #179/R (H.F 480000)

MATIFAS, Louis Remy (1847-1896) French
£451 $745 €650 Ducks by stream (51x81cm-20x32in) s. 3-Jul-3 Van Ham, Cologne #1349 est:1350

MATIGNON, Albert (1869-?) French
£1500 $2730 €2190 Flower girl (81x55cm-32x22in) 16-Jun-4 Christie's, Kensington #259/R est:1500-2000

MATILLA Y MARINA, Segundo (1862-1937) Spanish
£1549 $2479 €2200 Children at the seaside (15x11cm-6x4in) d.1921 cardboard. 16-Sep-3 Segre, Madrid #310/R est:2200
£2517 $4204 €3600 Still life of fruit and grapes (27x19cm-11x7in) s.d.33 cardboard. 30-Jun-3 Ansorena, Madrid #370/R
£4710 $7725 €6500 River landscape (34x43cm-13x17in) s.d.35. 27-May-3 Durán, Madrid #231/R est:6500

MATINO, Vittorio (1943-) Italian
£872 $1562 €1300 Eidos (185x115cm-73x45in) s. i.d.80 verso acrylic prov. 25-May-4 Sotheby's, Milan #160/R
£2448 $4161 €3500 Untitled (75x161cm-30x63in) s. acrylic set of 3. 24-Nov-3 Christie's, Milan #59 est:1000-1500
£3357 $5706 €4800 White (190x45cm-75x18in) s.d.76 verso acrylic set of 3. 24-Nov-3 Christie's, Milan #57 est:2000-2500

MATISSE, Camille (20th C) French
£233 $415 €340 Flower jar (38x30cm-15x12in) s. 8-Jan-4 James Julia, Fairfield #977/R
£350 $641 €511 Roses, daisies and other summer flowers in a vase (25x20cm-10x8in) s. canvasboard oval. 8-Apr-4 Christie's, Kensington #235
£1250 $2213 €1825 Still life of vase of summer flowers (60x44cm-24x17in) s. 27-Apr-4 Henry Adams, Chichester #681 est:1200-1500

MATISSE, Henri (1869-1954) French
£6630 $12000 €9680 Oriental sur lit de repos, sol de carreaux rouges (27x48cm-11x19in) s.num.25/50 lithograph. 19-Apr-4 Bonhams & Butterfields, San Francisco #172/R est:10000-15000
£83916 $144336 €120000 Maison de Renoir a Cannes (39x46cm-15x18in) s. prov.exhib.lit. 8-Dec-3 Artcurial Briest, Paris #31/R est:130000-180000
£131004 $238428 €191266 Paysage des environs de Toulouse (38x46cm-15x18in) s. painted 1898-1899 prov.exhib.lit. 18-Jun-4 Kornfeld, Bern #108/R est:350000 (S.FR 300000)
£152941 $260000 €223294 Bateau a Etretat (38x46cm-15x18in) s. painted c.1920 prov.exhib.lit. 6-Nov-3 Sotheby's, New York #192/R est:250000-350000
£180000 $331200 €262800 Bosquet au bord de la Garonne (46x38cm-18x15in) s. painted 1900 prov.exhib.lit. 22-Jun-4 Sotheby's, London #153/R est:150000-200000
£200873 $365590 €293275 La plage d'Etretat avec baigneurs (38x45cm-15x18in) s. painted 1923 prov. 18-Jun-4 Kornfeld, Bern #109/R est:500000 (S.FR 460000)
£500000 $915000 €730000 Falaises d'Aval, pecheurs (38x46cm-15x18in) s. canvas on board painted 1920 prov.exhib.lit. 2-Feb-4 Christie's, London #43/R est:300000-500000
£921788 $1650000 €1345810 Nature morte au pourpre II (28x36cm-11x14in) s. painted c.1904-05 prov.exhib.lit. 5-May-4 Sotheby's, New York #25/R est:1500000-2000000
£2200000 $4004000 €3212000 Torse nu, bras leves (46x33cm-18x13in) s. painted 1923 prov.exhib.lit. 21-Jun-4 Sotheby's, London #19/R est:500000-700000
£5900000 $10856001 €8614000 Odalisque au fauteuil noir (38x46cm-15x18in) s.d.42 prov.exhib.lit. 22-Jun-4 Christie's, London #26/R

Prints

£1882	$3200	€2748	Teeny (30x23cm-12x9in) s.num.56/100 linoleum cut. 6-Nov-3 Swann Galleries, New York #623/R est:3000-5000
£2125	$3400	€3103	Tete de femme (31x24cm-12x9in) frontispiece lithograph edition of 2850. 18-Sep-3 Swann Galleries, New York #423 est:1500-2500
£2183	$3777	€3100	Odalisque couchee (20x30cm-8x12in) etching vellum edition of 150. 11-Dec-3 Piasa, Paris #100
£2246	$3750	€3279	Autoportrait de trois quarts (28x20cm-11x8in) s.num.6/25 lithograph. 11-Nov-3 Doyle, New York #321/R est:5000-7000
£2256	$4219	€3294	Masque de jeune garcon (33x25cm-13x10in) s.d.45 one of six trial prints. 25-Feb-4 Kunsthallen, Copenhagen #316/R est:30000 (D.KR 25000)
£2260	$4000	€3300	Jeune fille souriant et fleurs (41x31cm-16x12in) etching edition of 12 printed in 1980. 28-Apr-4 Christie's, Rockefeller NY #76/R est:3000-4000
£2344	$4149	€3422	Jeune fille en robe fleurie au col d'organdi (22x15cm-9x6in) s.num.33/50 lithograph prov.lit. 27-Apr-4 AB Stockholms Auktionsverk #1322/R est:30000-40000 (S.KR 32000)
£2353	$4000	€3435	Isaia (40x31cm-16x12in) init. linocut exec.1938. 4-Nov-3 Christie's, Rockefeller NY #123/R est:4000-6000
£2378	$4042	€3400	Nu agenouille (29x16cm-11x6in) s. etching. 26-Nov-3 Dorotheum, Vienna #170/R est:3400-3600
£2564	$4538	€3743	Pierres Levees - frontispiece (20x15cm-8x6in) s.num.246/300 lithograph chine applique. 27-Apr-4 AB Stockholms Auktionsverk #1323/R est:20000-25000 (S.KR 35000)
£2667	$4907	€4000	Repos du modele (22x30cm-9x12in) s.i. lithograph exec.1922. 10-Jun-4 Piasa, Paris #170
£2676	$4630	€3800	Jeune femme au repos (13x18cm-5x7in) s. etching edition of 28. 11-Dec-3 Piasa, Paris #105
£2676	$4630	€3800	Nu couche au visage incomplet, etude de jambes (29x52cm-11x20in) s. lithograph edition of 60. 11-Dec-3 Piasa, Paris #112
£2762	$5000	€4033	Le repos du modele (22x31cm-9x12in) s.num.19/50 lithograph. 19-Apr-4 Bonhams & Butterfields, San Francisco #169/R est:4000-6000
£2797	$4811	€4000	Le repos du modele (22x30cm-9x12in) s. lithograph. 2-Dec-3 Hauswedell & Nolte, Hamburg #426/R est:5000
£2903	$5400	€4238	Marie jose en robe jaune (54x42cm-21x17in) aquatint. 2-Mar-4 Swann Galleries, New York #410/R est:5000-8000
£2958	$5117	€4200	Nu assis, chevelure foncee (38x24cm-15x9in) s.num. lithograph edition of 64. 11-Dec-3 Piasa, Paris #110/R
£3021	$5136	€4411	Grand masque (35x25cm-14x10in) s.num.36/50 lithograph prov.lit. 4-Nov-3 Bukowskis, Stockholm #401/R est:30000-35000 (S.KR 40000)
£3028	$5239	€4300	Nu au rocking-chair (48x27cm-19x11in) s.num. lithograph edition of 55. 11-Dec-3 Piasa, Paris #109
£3151	$5356	€4600	Catherinette. lithograph. 6-Nov-3 Piasa, Paris #139
£3200	$5504	€4672	Martiniquaise (14x11cm-6x4in) s.num.24/25 etching. 2-Dec-3 Christie's, London #191/R est:2000-3000
£3287	$5653	€4700	La pompadour (52x37cm-20x15in) s.i.num.6/200 lithograph vellum. 3-Dec-3 Beaussant & Lefèvre, Paris #7/R est:1500-2000
£3293	$5400	€4775	Le repos du modele (23x30cm-9x12in) s. lithograph exec.c.1922 prov. 31-May-3 Brunk, Ashville #519/R est:2000-4000
£3310	$5726	€4700	Odalisque sur fond a carreaux (15x12cm-6x5in) s.i. drypoint velum edition of 29. 11-Dec-3 Piasa, Paris #101/R
£3380	$5848	€4800	Nu assis sur le sol, un coude pose sur la jambe (9x12cm-4x5in) s.i. etching vellum edition of 32. 11-Dec-3 Piasa, Paris #102
£3390	$6000	€4949	Jazz formes (42x65cm-17x26in) col pochoir print. 30-Apr-4 Sotheby's, New York #133 est:6000-8000
£3400	$6222	€4964	Trois Tetes (43x35cm-17x14in) aquatint. 3-Jun-4 Christie's, Kensington #103/R est:1000-2000
£3430	$6310	€5008	Jeune Chinoise - female head (46x33cm-18x13in) s.num.22/29 lithograph prov.lit. 29-Mar-4 Rasmussen, Copenhagen #150/R est:25000 (D.KR 38000)
£3467	$6379	€5200	Visage de profil (30x24cm-12x9in) lithograph exec.1924. 10-Jun-4 Piasa, Paris #173
£3500	$6370	€5110	Nu au rocking chair (50x33cm-20x13in) s.num.46/50 lithograph. 1-Jul-4 Sotheby's, London #201/R est:4000-6000
£3521	$6162	€5000	Jeune fille aux bouches brunes (24x20cm-9x8in) s. num.13/100 lithograph. 16-Dec-3 Segre, Madrid #240/R est:4500
£3529	$6000	€5152	Le repos du modele (22x31cm-9x12in) s. lithograph. 6-Nov-3 Swann Galleries, New York #619a/R est:8000-12000
£3529	$6000	€5152	Vierge et Enfant sans indication des visages II (34x19cm-13x7in) s.i. lithograph. 6-Nov-3 Swann Galleries, New York #630/R est:8000-12000
£3593	$6000	€5246	Nu, epoque du chapeau jaune (25x12cm-10x5in) s.num.13/25 etching. 21-Oct-3 Bonhams & Butterfields, San Francisco #1206/R
£3662	$6335	€5200	Nu couche, jambe repliee, etude de jambes (25x47cm-10x19in) s.num. lithograph edition of 60. 11-Dec-3 Piasa, Paris #111/R
£3662	$6335	€5200	Grand visage (50x34cm-20x13in) s.num. lithograph edition of 67. 11-Dec-3 Piasa, Paris #113/R
£3667	$6747	€5500	Nu assis (39x24cm-15x9in) s.i. lithograph exec.1922. 10-Jun-4 Piasa, Paris #172
£3670	$6128	€5322	Etude pour la nappe liturgique de la Chapelle de Vence II. s.d.Nov 50 aquatint. 19-Jun-3 Kornfeld, Bern #710/R est:7500 (S.FR 8000)
£3776	$6495	€5400	Nu assis, bras gauche sur la tete (41x44cm-16x17in) s.i. lithograph. 2-Dec-3 Hauswedell & Nolte, Hamburg #427/R est:7000
£3800	$6460	€5548	Nausicaa (29x23cm-11x9in) s.num.72/150 etching. 30-Oct-3 Christie's, Kensington #304/R est:2000-2500
£3800	$6536	€5548	Madeleine (20x18cm-8x7in) s.num.150/200 lithograph. 2-Dec-3 Christie's, London #194/R est:2000-3000
£3824	$6500	€5583	Nu pour Cleveland (37x29cm-15x11in) s.num.33/250 etching. 6-Nov-3 Swann Galleries, New York #622/R est:7000-10000
£3824	$6500	€5583	Nu (38x28cm-15x11in) s. num.7/25 et exec.1929 prov. 4-Nov-3 Christie's, Rockefeller NY #117/R est:8000-12000
£3867	$7000	€5646	Vierge et enfant sur fond de fleurs et d'etoiles (32x25cm-13x10in) s.num.199/200 lithograph. 19-Apr-4 Bonhams & Butterfields, San Francisco #173/R est:4000-6000
£3899	$6511	€5654	Orientale sur lit de repost. s.i. lithograph. 19-Jun-3 Kornfeld, Bern #709 est:8000 (S.FR 8500)
£3911	$7000	€5710	Femme. le pouch sur les levres, fond raye (28x20cm-11x8in) s.num.14/25 linoleum cut prov. 7-May-4 Sloans & Kenyon, Bethesda #1732/R est:3000-5000
£3916	$6736	€5600	Marie Jose en robe jaune (54x41cm-21x16in) aquatint etching. 2-Dec-3 Hauswedell & Nolte, Hamburg #424/R est:5000
£3955	$7000	€5774	Nu de trois-quarts, latete penchee (45x28cm-18x11in) num.10/25 lithograph. 28-Apr-4 Christie's, Rockefeller NY #68/R est:5000-7000
£4000	$7360	€6000	Nu assis (39x25cm-15x10in) s.i. lithograph exec.1922. 10-Jun-4 Piasa, Paris #171
£4000	$7360	€6000	Correspondance (20x12cm-8x5in) s.i. eau forte exec.1929. 10-Jun-4 Piasa, Paris #165
£4000	$7360	€6000	Jeune femme accoudee, voile sur la tete (15x12cm-6x5in) s. drypoint exec. 1929 one of 25 prov. 12-Jun-4 Villa Grisebach, Berlin #368/R est:6000-8000
£4118	$7000	€6012	Buste de femme (35x22cm-14x9in) s.i. lithograph edition of 25. 6-Nov-3 Swann Galleries, New York #625/R est:6000-9000
£4118	$7000	€6012	Autoportrait de trois-quarts (23x19cm-9x7in) s.num.5/25 lithograph. 6-Nov-3 Swann Galleries, New York #627/R est:7000-10000
£4190	$7500	€6117	Nu couchee au visage incomplet - etude de jambes (45x56cm-18x22in) s.num.36/50 lithograph. 6-May-4 Swann Galleries, New York #511/R est:10000-15000
£4200	$7728	€6300	La main (15x20cm-6x8in) s. eau forte lit. 10-Jun-4 Camard, Paris #72/R est:5000-5500
£4333	$7973	€6500	La sieste (40x43cm-16x17in) s.i. lithograph. 10-Jun-4 Hauswedell & Nolte, Hamburg #484/R est:8000
£4345	$7256	€6300	Lettre (15x24cm-6x9in) s. num.22/25 eau forte prov.lit. 13-Nov-3 Finarte Semenzato, Rome #103/R est:6500-7000
£4375	$7000	€6388	Nu allonge, jambes repliees (10x14cm-4x6in) s.i. etching. 18-Sep-3 Swann Galleries, New York #422a/R est:7000-10000
£4412	$7500	€6442	Fillette, bloue fleurie (14x10cm-6x4in) s. etching exec.1920. 31-Oct-3 Sotheby's, New York #310/R
£4491	$7500	€6557	Tete de jeune fille (20x15cm-8x6in) s.num.47/50 lithograph. 11-Nov-3 Doyle, New York #320/R est:5000-7000
£4500	$7740	€6570	Cinq visages feminins (5x25cm-2x10in) s.num.2/20 aquatint. 2-Dec-3 Christie's, London #188/R est:3000-5000
£4500	$8190	€6570	Nu au bracelet (32x25cm-13x10in) s.i.num.12 drypoint. 1-Jul-4 Sotheby's, London #199/R est:2500-3500
£4513	$8303	€6589	Etudes pour la Vierge, tete voilee (50x38cm-20x15in) s.num.158/200 lithograph prov.lit. 29-Mar-4 Rasmussen, Copenhagen #151/R est:25000 (D.KR 50000)
£4706	$8000	€6871	Nu sur chaise de repos sur fond moucharabieh (49x40cm-19x16in) s.num.23/50 lithograph. 6-Nov-3 Swann Galleries, New York #620/R est:7000-10000
£4706	$8000	€6871	Nu renverse (66x50cm-26x20in) s. num.3/50 lithograph exec.1929 prov. 4-Nov-3 Christie's, Rockefeller NY #118/R est:10000-15000
£4749	$8500	€6934	Buste de femme (35x22cm-14x9in) s.i. lithograph. 6-May-4 Swann Galleries, New York #513/R est:6000-9000
£4802	$8500	€7011	Orientale, tatouage en croix sur la poitrine (15x11cm-6x4in) s.num.23/25 etching. 28-Apr-4 Christie's, Rockefeller NY #73/R est:8000-10000
£5000	$8500	€7300	Marguerite II (32x26cm-13x10in) s.num.5/25 lithograph. 6-Nov-3 Swann Galleries, New York #626/R est:7000-10000
£5000	$8500	€7300	Marie-Jose en robe jaune (54x42cm-21x17in) s.i. aquatint. 6-Nov-3 Swann Galleries, New York #628/R est:8000-12000
£5000	$8500	€7300	Vierge et Enfant (32x22cm-13x9in) s.num.9/100 lithograph. 6-Nov-3 Swann Galleries, New York #629/R est:8000-12000
£5000	$8500	€7300	Repos du modele (32x50cm-13x20in) s. lithograph exec.1922. 4-Nov-3 Christie's, Rockefeller NY #108/R est:4000-6000
£5000	$9200	€7500	Etude pour la Viergem tete voilee (28x23cm-11x9in) s. num.58/200 lithograph. 9-Jun-4 Beaussant & Lefèvre, Paris #85/R est:2500
£5000	$9200	€7500	Torse reposant sur les bras (9x12cm-4x5in) s.i. drypoint exec. 1929 one of 25 prov. 12-Jun-4 Villa Grisebach, Berlin #367/R est:6000-8000
£5000	$9100	€7300	L'enterrement de pierrot (42x65cm-17x26in) col pochoir edition of 250. 21-Jun-4 Bonhams, New Bond Street #69/R est:5000-7000
£5175	$8901	€7400	Nu au collier et aux cheveux longs (15x19cm-6x7in) s.i. etching. 2-Dec-3 Hauswedell & Nolte, Hamburg #423/R est:7500
£5333	$9813	€8000	Reflexion (12x8cm-5x3in) s.i. drypoint exec.1929. 10-Jun-4 Piasa, Paris #167
£5493	$9503	€7800	Nu assis, bras croises supportant la tete (26x10cm-10x4in) s.i. etching vellum edition of 27. 11-Dec-3 Piasa, Paris #107
£5500	$9130	€8030	Une religieuse a l'expression ironique (29x22cm-11x9in) s.num.2/25 etching. 6-Oct-3 Sotheby's, London #97/R est:2000-3000
£5667	$10427	€8500	Petit bois clair (34x27cm-13x11in) engraving exec.1906. 10-Jun-4 Piasa, Paris #169/R
£5801	$10500	€8469	Figure voilee aux deux bracelets (43x37cm-17x15in) s.i.num.1/5 lithograph. 19-Apr-4 Bonhams & Butterfields, San Francisco #171/R est:9000-12000
£5882	$10000	€8588	Nu couche (28x38cm-11x15in) s.i. etching exec.1929 prov. 4-Nov-3 Christie's, Rockefeller NY #115/R est:7500-8500
£5882	$10000	€8588	Danseuse debout (50x33cm-20x13in) s. num.95/130 lithograph exec.1927. 4-Nov-3 Christie's, Rockefeller NY #112/R est:9000-12000
£6000	$11040	€9000	Nu a genoux (18x13cm-7x5in) i. eau forte exec.1930. 10-Jun-4 Piasa, Paris #168/R
£6145	$11000	€8972	La robe d'organdi (42x28cm-17x11in) s.num.44/50 lithograph on chine. 6-May-4 Swann Galleries, New York #510/R est:10000-15000
£6200	$11284	€9052	Etude pour la Vierge (47x36cm-19x14in) s.num.59/200 lithograph. 1-Jul-4 Sotheby's, London #200/R est:3000-4000
£6215	$11000	€9074	Jazz, l'avaleau des sabres (42x65cm-17x26in) col pochoir print. 30-Apr-4 Sotheby's, New York #129/R est:6000-8000
£6471	$11000	€9448	Nu pour Cleveland (36x28cm-14x11in) s. etching. 31-Oct-3 Sotheby's, New York #311/R
£6471	$11000	€9448	Figure drapee (28x38cm-11x15in) s. num.15/25 etching exec.1929 prov. 4-Nov-3 Christie's, Rockefeller NY #116/R est:8000-12000
£6479	$11208	€9200	Torse vu de trois quarts (25x10cm-10x4in) s.i. etching drypoint vellum edition of 29. 11-Dec-3 Piasa, Paris #106/R
£6500	$11180	€9490	Liseuse au bouquet de roses (16x24cm-6x9in) s.num.45/50 lithograph. 2-Dec-3 Christie's, London #196/R est:6000-8000
£6500	$11180	€9490	Odalisque au magnolia (28x39cm-11x15in) s.num.30/50 lithograph. 2-Dec-3 Christie's, London #197/R est:6000-8000
£6667	$12267	€10000	Grand nu couche (24x18cm-9x7in) s.i. drypoint exec.1929. 10-Jun-4 Piasa, Paris #166/R
£6667	$12200	€10000	Tete voilee (28x23cm-11x9in) s. lithograph. 5-Jun-4 Lempertz, Koln #868/R est:5000-6000
£6780	$12000	€9899	Jeune femme au balcon observant des perruches (24x17cm-9x7in) s.num.17/25 etching. 28-Apr-4 Christie's, Rockefeller NY #74/R est:8000-12000
£6780	$12000	€9899	Jazz, le cauchemar de l'elephant blanc (42x65cm-17x26in) col pochoir print. 30-Apr-4 Sotheby's, New York #132/R est:6000-8000
£6897	$12345	€10070	Petit interieur bleu (51x42cm-20x17in) s.i. col aquatint. 12-May-4 Dobiaschofsky, Bern #1828/R est:9000 (S.FR 16000)
£7059	$12000	€10306	Danseuse allongee (32x50cm-13x20in) s. num.10/15 lithograph exec.1927. 4-Nov-3 Christie's, Rockefeller NY #113/R est:8000-10000
£7200	$13032	€10800	Nu de profil sur une chaise longue (48x36cm-19x14in) mono. woodcut. 2-Apr-4 Winterberg, Heidelberg #1315/R est:13500
£7263	$13000	€10604	L'homme endormi (25x17cm-10x7in) s.num.29/150 aquatint. 6-May-4 Swann Galleries, New York #512/R est:7000-10000
£7345	$13000	€10724	Jeune femme de profil, blouse en dentelle (15x11cm-6x4in) s.i.num.4/5 etching. 28-Apr-4 Christie's, Rockefeller NY #75/R est:6000-8000
£7386	$13000	€10784	Dancer number 3 from series Dix Danseuses (46x25cm-18x10in) s. num.3/15 lithograph Japan paper. 23-May-4 Hindman, Chicago #954/R est:6000-8000
£7401	$13617	€10805	Bedouine au large visage (50x38cm-20x15in) s.num.22/29 aquatint. 29-Mar-4 Rasmussen, Copenhagen #152/R est:35000 (D.KR 82000)
£7667	$14107	€11500	Nu au fauteuil bistre (31x23cm-12x9in) s.i. num. lithograph exec.1925. 10-Jun-4 Piasa, Paris #174/R
£7910	$14000	€11549	Jazz, la nageuse dans l'aquarium (42x65cm-17x26in) col pochoir print. 30-Apr-4 Sotheby's, New York #130/R est:6000-8000
£8059	$14264	€11766	Nu assis dans un fauteuil au decor fleuri (48x32cm-19x13in) s.num.25/250 lithograph lit. 27-Apr-4 AB Stockholms Auktionsverk #1324/R est:80000-100000 (S.KR 110000)

£8235	$14000	€12023	Visage de profil (45x42cm-18x17in) s.i. num.9/10 lithograph exec.1924 prov. 4-Nov-3 Christie's, Rockefeller NY #109/R est:10000-12000
£8287	$15000	€12099	Grande liseuse (66x51cm-26x20in) s.i.num.6/12 lithograph. 19-Apr-4 Bonhams & Butterfields, San Francisco #170/R est:10000-15000
£8451	$14620	€12000	Figure au visage coupe assise dans un interieur (15x23cm-6x9in) s.i. etching vellum edition of 30. 11-Dec-3 Piasa, Paris #103/R
£8824	$15000	€12883	Arabesque (63x46cm-25x18in) s. num.4/50 lithograph exec.1924 prov. 4-Nov-3 Christie's, Rockefeller NY #110/R est:12000-15000
£8824	$15000	€12883	Grand visage (65x50cm-26x20in) init.i. lithograph exec.1929 prov. 4-Nov-3 Christie's, Rockefeller NY #122/R est:8000-12000
£9000	$15300	€13140	Tete de jeune garcon, masque (31x21cm-12x8in) s.num.18/25 aquatint. 30-Oct-3 Christie's, Kensington #303/R est:6000-8000
£9040	$16000	€13198	La robe jaune au Ruban noir (54x38cm-21x15in) init. lithograph. 30-Apr-4 Sotheby's, New York #126/R est:10000-15000
£9412	$16000	€13742	Nu (46x56cm-18x22in) s. num.3/10 lithograph exec.1926 prov. 4-Nov-3 Christie's, Rockefeller NY #111/R est:12000-15000
£9412	$16000	€13742	Nu couche (51x66cm-20x26in) s. num.4/50 lithograph exec.1929 prov. 4-Nov-3 Christie's, Rockefeller NY #119/R est:12000-15000
£9500	$17290	€13870	Patitvha, masque (36x27cm-14x11in) s.i. aquatint exhib. 30-Jun-4 Christie's, London #258/R est:5000-7000
£10000	$17200	€14600	Nu couche sur sol fleuri (46x56cm-18x22in) s.num.35/50 lithograph. 4-Dec-3 Sotheby's, London #158/R est:8000-10000
£13000	$23660	€18980	Nu sur chaise de repos sur fond moucharabieh (50x40cm-20x16in) s.i.num.5/10 lithograph. 1-Jul-4 Sotheby's, London #202/R est:8000-10000
£14000	$25480	€20440	Odalisque, brasero et couple de fruits (28x37cm-11x15in) s.num.61/100 lithograph prov. 30-Jun-4 Christie's, London #257/R est:10000-15000
£14667	$26987	€22000	Repos sur la banquette (44x54cm-17x21in) s.i. lithograph exec. 1929 one of 68. 11-Jun-4 Villa Grisebach, Berlin #1588/R est:25000-35000
£14689	$26000	€21446	Nu assis a la chemise de tulle (37x28cm-15x11in) s.num.24/50 lithograph. 28-Apr-4 Christie's, Rockefeller NY #72/R est:25000-35000
£15294	$26000	€22329	Odalisque (38x57cm-15x22in) s. num.20/100 lithograph exec.1929. 4-Nov-3 Christie's, Rockefeller NY #120/R est:15000-20000
£15721	$28611	€22953	Jeune fille a la chaise-longue dans un sous-bois (41x51cm-16x20in) s. num.50 lithograph exec. 1922. 18-Jun-4 Kornfeld, Bern #111/R est:35000 (S.FR 36000)
£15819	$28000	€23096	La capeline de paille d'Italie (45x40cm-18x16in) s.num.26/50 lithograph. 28-Apr-4 Christie's, Rockefeller NY #69/R est:20000-30000
£15819	$28000	€23096	Hindoue a la jupe de julle (28x37cm-11x15in) s.num.34/50 lithograph. 30-Apr-4 Sotheby's, New York #128/R est:25000-35000
£19774	$35000	€28870	Odalisque a la culotte de satin rouge (19x27cm-7x11in) s.num.31/50 lithograph. 30-Apr-4 Sotheby's, New York #127/R est:35000-45000
£20588	$35000	€30058	Persane (62x44cm-24x17in) s.i. lithograph exec.1929. 4-Nov-3 Christie's, Rockefeller NY #121/R est:35000-45000
£22059	$37500	€32206	Persane (44x29cm-17x11in) s. lithograph. 31-Oct-3 Sotheby's, New York #312/R
£158192	$280000	€230960	Grande odalisque a la culotte bayadere (54x44cm-21x17in) s.num.30/50 lithograph. 28-Apr-4 Christie's, Rockefeller NY #71/R est:300000-500000

Sculpture

£54782	$95868	€77790	Tete de Marguerite (16cm-6in) s. num.1/0 pat bronze prov.lit. 18-Dec-3 Tajan, Paris #19/R est:120000-150000
£88235	$150000	€128823	Nu debout - Katia (44cm-17in) st.f.C.Valsuani num.4/10 brown pat bronze prov.lit. 6-Nov-3 Sotheby's, New York #198/R est:180000-250000

Works on paper

£6000	$10920	€8760	Femme assise (26x21cm-10x8in) s. pen ink exhib. 4-Feb-4 Sotheby's, London #452/R est:7000-9000
£7821	$14000	€11419	Faun (24x32cm-9x13in) st.init. pencil exec c.1935 prov. 5-May-4 Christie's, Rockefeller NY #118/R est:15000-20000
£8725	$16228	€13000	Les acrobates (27x21cm-11x8in) st.mono. ink prov. 2-Mar-4 Artcurial Briest, Paris #34/R est:13000-18000
£8824	$15000	€12883	Casbah - Le marabout (17x18cm-7x7in) s. pen India ink prov.exhib.lit. 5-Nov-3 Christie's, Rockefeller NY #125/R est:15000-20000
£10067	$18523	€15000	Denise (32x24cm-13x9in) studio st. chl exec 1951 prov. 24-Mar-4 Joron-Derem, Paris #84 est:18000-20000
£12000	$21840	€17520	Femme debout (26x20cm-10x8in) s. pen ink exhib. 4-Feb-4 Sotheby's, London #453/R est:12000-15000
£13500	$24570	€19710	Branchage (21x26cm-8x10in) init. pen ink prov. 4-Feb-4 Sotheby's, London #442/R est:10000-15000
£14866	$26759	€21704	Figure (50x30cm-20x12in) s.i.d.1950 verso col chk. 26-Apr-4 Bukowskis, Stockholm #246b/R est:100000-125000 (S.KR 205000)
£15000	$27300	€21900	Seated nude (32x25cm-13x10in) s.d.1920 pencil prov. 5-Feb-4 Christie's, London #423/R est:15000-20000
£15000	$27600	€21900	Nu (21x26cm-8x10in) s. brush ink exec.c.1905-06 prov. 22-Jun-4 Sotheby's, London #444/R est:10000-15000
£17857	$32500	€26071	Tete de femme (49x34cm-19x13in) s.d.50 pencil prov.exhib. 29-Jun-4 Sotheby's, New York #349/R est:18000-25000
£20000	$36400	€29200	Woman (26x20cm-10x8in) s.d.42 pencil prov. 5-Feb-4 Christie's, London #409/R est:20000-30000
£20000	$36400	€29200	Head of a woman (28x22cm-11x9in) s.i.d.48 pencil prov. 5-Feb-4 Christie's, London #418/R est:20000-30000
£20135	$37451	€30000	Jeune femme nue allongee (58x48cm-23x19in) s. ink wash two joined sheets. 2-Mar-4 Artcurial Briest, Paris #35/R est:40000-60000
£23529	$40000	€34352	Nu (25x33cm-10x13in) s. pencil prov. 6-Nov-3 Sotheby's, New York #270a/R est:30000-40000
£26021	$45537	€36950	Modele nu assis (38x27cm-15x11in) s. graphite W/C dr prov.exhib. 18-Dec-3 Tajan, Paris #40/R est:40000-50000
£26667	$49067	€40000	La danseuse (31x23cm-12x9in) s. graphite. 8-Jun-4 Artcurial Briest, Paris #111/R est:40000-45000
£27000	$45090	€39420	Polypheme (32x25cm-13x10in) i. chl executed 1934 prov. 21-Oct-3 Sotheby's, London #92/R est:30000-40000
£28671	$48741	€41000	Jeune fille aux amaryllis (20x26cm-8x10in) s.d.41 pen ink exhib. 28-Nov-3 Blanchet, Paris #190/R est:30000-40000
£29167	$48708	€42000	Femme nue allongee (24x33cm-9x13in) ink prov. 21-Oct-3 Christie's, Paris #120/R est:20000-30000
£30000	$54600	€43800	Jeune fille se coiffant (28x20cm-11x8in) st.init. pencil exec 1939 prov. 5-Feb-4 Christie's, London #411/R est:25000-35000
£32477	$55211	€47416	Femme nue, etendue, les bras relevese (23x30cm-9x12in) s. Indian ink exhib.prov. 4-Nov-3 Bukowskis, Stockholm #270/R est:375000-400000 (S.KR 430000)
£34437	$63020	€52000	Odalisque couchee (33x50cm-13x20in) s.d.28 pen. 7-Apr-4 Fraysse & Associes, Paris #6/R est:40000-50000
£36913	$66074	€55000	Annelise dessinant des fleurs (52x40cm-20x16in) s.d.45 graphite prov.lit. 27-May-4 Christie's, Paris #121/R est:50000-70000
£41333	$76467	€62000	Nu assis. Etude de feuilles (26x20cm-10x8in) init. graphite double-sided prov. 18-Jul-4 Sotheby's, Paris #290/R est:30000-40000
£42254	$73099	€60000	Visage (37x28cm-15x11in) init. black crayon exhib. 12-Dec-3 Piasa, Paris #29/R est:60000-80000
£43296	$77500	€63212	Artiste et le Modele (27x38cm-11x15in) s.d.37 pen India ink prov. 6-May-4 Sotheby's, New York #269/R est:90000-120000
£44693	$80000	€65252	Odalisque nue allongee (26x37cm-10x15in) st.sig. pencil exec 1928 prov. 6-May-4 Sotheby's, New York #367/R est:60000-80000
£48000	$87360	€70080	Femme de face (49x31cm-19x12in) s.d.47 brush ink prov. 5-Feb-4 Christie's, London #407/R est:50000-70000
£53073	$95000	€77487	Jeune femme accoudee (52x40cm-20x16in) s.d.Juin 11.44 pen ink prov.exhib. 6-May-4 Sotheby's, New York #385/R est:60000-80000
£54000	$98280	€78840	Femme allongee (22x28cm-9x11in) st.init. pencil prov. 4-Feb-4 Sotheby's, London #439/R est:40000-60000
£55000	$100100	€80300	Portrait of a woman (52x40cm-20x16in) s.d.49 chl prov. 5-Feb-4 Christie's, London #404/R est:50000-70000
£57353	$97500	€83735	Tete de jeune femme (42x37cm-17x15in) s.d.1949 pen ink prov. 6-Nov-3 Sotheby's, New York #294/R est:80000-120000
£58000	$106720	€84680	Jeune femme accoudee a la blouse roumaine (42x33cm-17x13in) d.15/12 pencil exec 1939 prov. 24-Jun-4 Christie's, London #408/R est:60000-80000
£72626	$130000	€106034	Madame Skira (43x33cm-17x13in) s.i.d.48 pen India ink prov.exhib. 5-May-4 Christie's, Rockefeller NY #149/R est:90000-120000
£78000	$143520	€113880	Portrait de femme (38x28cm-15x11in) st.init. pen ink exec.1937 prov. 22-Jun-4 Sotheby's, London #454/R est:60000-80000
£97765	$175000	€142737	Nu debout (52x39cm-20x15in) s.d.49 chl prov. 6-May-4 Sotheby's, New York #374/R est:150000-200000
£111765	$190000	€163177	Themes et variations - Buste de femme (41x53cm-16x21in) s.i.d.42 pen India ink prov. 6-Nov-3 Sotheby's, New York #307/R est:140000-180000
£130000	$237900	€189800	Lydia en blouse roumaine (37x51cm-15x20in) s.d.36 pen ink paper on board prov.lit. 2-Feb-4 Christie's, London #34/R est:150000-200000
£164706	$280000	€240471	Grande tete de femme - Marie Josee (56x38cm-22x15in) s.d.47 brush ink prov. 6-Nov-3 Sotheby's, New York #270/R est:200000-300000
£209497	$375000	€305866	La France (52x40cm-20x16in) s.d.9 Nov 39 chl prov.exhib.lit. 6-May-4 Sotheby's, New York #345/R est:400000-600000
£280000	$515200	€408800	Carmen (53x40cm-21x16in) s.d.46 chl prov. 22-Jun-4 Christie's, London #28/R est:280000-350000
£335196	$600000	€489386	Arabesques noires et violettes sur un fond orange (40x27cm-16x11in) s. gouache papier colle exec 1947 prov.exhib.lit. 6-May-4 Sotheby's, New York #339/R est:400000-600000
£1284916	$2300000	€1875977	Les quatre rosaces aux motifs bleus (37x53cm-15x21in) s. gouache paper on canvas exec.1949-50 prov.exhib.lit. 6-May-4 Sotheby's, New York #110/R est:2500000-3500000

MATISSE, Henri (after) (1869-1954) French

Prints

£4412	$7500	€6442	L'Espagnole (40x28cm-16x11in) s.num.101/200 col etching aquatint roulette. 6-Nov-3 Swann Galleries, New York #634/R est:5000-8000
£7042	$12183	€10000	L'Espagnole (40x28cm-16x11in) s.num.44/200 col etching aquatint roulette. 11-Dec-3 Piasa, Paris #114/R
£7059	$12000	€10306	Odalisque sur la terrace (48x60cm-19x24in) s.num.117/200 col aquatint. 6-Nov-3 Swann Galleries, New York #633/R est:10000-15000
£7692	$13077	€11000	Odalisque au coffret rouge (42x55cm-17x22in) s. col aquatint. 29-Nov-3 Villa Grisebach, Berlin #305/R est:4000-6000
£10000	$17000	€14600	Odalisque au coffret rouge (41x55cm-16x22in) s. num.189/200 col aquatint. 31-Oct-3 Sotheby's, New York #313/R est:10000-14000
£10056	$18000	€14682	L'Espagnole (40x27cm-16x11in) s.num.12/200 color etching. 6-May-4 Swann Galleries, New York #515/R est:8000-12000

MATISSE, Henri and METTHEY, Andre (20th C) French

£8108	$15000	€11838	Tete de femme (35cm-14in circular) mono. painted glazed ceramic prov. 11-Feb-4 Sotheby's, New York #36/R est:20000-30000

MATOSSY, Pierre (1891-1969) French

£1200	$2148	€1800	Villa Medici (130x132cm-51x52in) s.i. 13-May-4 Babuino, Rome #550/R est:800-1200

MATSCH, Franz von (1861-1942) Austrian

£420	$701	€613	Amazon woman (50x34cm-20x13in) s. prov. 8-Oct-3 Christie's, Kensington #694

Works on paper

£2890	$5000	€4219	Winged woman (18x38cm-7x15in) s. pencil chl collage cut photographs prov. 11-Dec-3 Sotheby's, New York #135/R est:4000-6000

MATSCHINSKY-DENNINGHOFF, Brigitte and Martin (20th C) German

Sculpture

£3733	$6869	€5600	Composition (29x35x10cm-11x14x4in) mono.i.d. brass zinc. 11-Jun-4 Hauswedell & Nolte, Hamburg #1426/R est:3000
£10000	$18000	€15000	Untitled (38x36x28cm-15x14x11in) mono.d. brass tin. 24-Apr-4 Dr Lehr, Berlin #282/R est:18000
£18881	$32476	€27000	Wrestler (100x80x65cm-39x31x26in) brass tin lit. 5-Dec-3 Ketterer, Munich #348/R est:18000-24000

MATSSON, Lind Lars (19th C) Swedish

£786	$1359	€1148	His Royal Highness the Crown-Prince on horseback (94x110cm-37x43in) i.d.1835. 15-Dec-3 Lilla Bukowskis, Stockholm #1270 (S.KR 10000)

MATSSON, Lind Lars (attrib) (19th C) Swedish

£377	$652	€550	When Jesus was twelve years old (80x128cm-31x50in) i. 15-Dec-3 Lilla Bukowskis, Stockholm #1272 (S.KR 4800)
£566	$978	€826	Valley picture (94x109cm-37x43in) i. 15-Dec-3 Lilla Bukowskis, Stockholm #1271 (S.KR 7200)

MATSUDA, Fumiko (20th C) ?

£283	$517	€413	Children and cats (35x47cm-14x19in) s. tempera. 4-Jun-4 Zofingen, Switzerland #2486 (S.FR 650)

MATT, Hans von (1899-1985) Swiss

Works on paper

£362	$615	€529	View of country house and lake (33x23cm-13x9in) W/C. 19-Nov-3 Fischer, Luzern #2645/R (S.FR 800)
£452	$769	€660	Lake view (33x26cm-13x10in) s. W/C tempera. 19-Nov-3 Fischer, Luzern #2644/R (S.FR 1000)

MATTA (1911-2002) Chilean

£2143	$3750	€3129	Three figures (33x44cm-13x17in) s.indis.i. oil pencil col pencil paper. 19-Dec-3 Sotheby's, New York #1178/R est:3000-4000
£6704	$12000	€9788	Green muscles (52x50cm-20x20in) s. s.i.d.1989 verso prov. 26-May-4 Sotheby's, New York #131/R est:12000-18000
£10952	$18618	€15990	Composition (62x62cm-24x24in) s. prov. 5-Nov-3 AB Stockholms Auktionsverk #1143/R est:100000-120000 (S.KR 145000)
£12500	$20000	€18250	Quietly happy (67x48cm-26x19in) s. 18-Sep-3 Swann Galleries, New York #428/R est:10000-15000
£12500	$20875	€18250	Vivant l'homme (73x62cm-29x24in) s. i.d.1976 verso prov. 22-Oct-3 Christie's, London #33/R est:10000-15000
£12849	$23000	€18760	Composition (95x74cm-37x29in) s. painted 1970 prov. 26-May-4 Sotheby's, New York #184/R est:18000-22000
£14813	$27256	€22220	Untitled (65x55cm-26x22in) s. painted 1971. 8-Jun-4 Artcurial Briest, Paris #217/R est:25000-30000
£16783	$28531	€24000	Aube permanente (101x97cm-40x38in) s. s.i.d.72 verso prov. 25-Nov-3 Sotheby's, Milan #164/R est:15000-20000
£17000	$30940	€24820	Untitled (46x59cm-18x23in) s.d.1968 prov. 6-Feb-4 Sotheby's, London #190/R est:8000-12000
£18824	$32000	€27483	Composicion - Composition (83x103cm-33x41in) painted c.1958-1964 prov.exhib. 18-Nov-3 Christie's, Rockefeller NY #153/R est:40000-50000
£19118	$32500	€27912	Flame (72x64cm-28x25in) s.d.1973 verso prov. 19-Nov-3 Sotheby's, New York #139/R est:35000-40000
£19737	$36316	€30000	Composition (104x85cm-41x33in) s. painted c.1960 prov. 27-Jun-4 Versailles Encheres #69/R est:30000-40000
£21477	$38443	€32000	Vous sentez-vous? (64x73cm-25x29in) s. verso prov. 25-May-4 Dorotheum, Vienna #60/R est:34000-40000
£22000	$40040	€32120	Etre ete (83x103cm-33x41in) s.i. prov.exhib. 6-Feb-4 Sotheby's, London #170/R est:15000-20000
£22000	$40480	€32120	Untitled (70x67cm-28x26in) painted c.1977 prov. 25-Jun-4 Christie's, London #123/R est:15000-20000
£22346	$40000	€32625	Nudes in space (90x110cm-35x43in) painted c.1970 prov.exhib. 26-May-4 Sotheby's, New York #135/R est:40000-60000
£23750	$38000	€34675	Trois voix dans une (110x104cm-43x41in) s.i. 18-Sep-3 Swann Galleries, New York #427/R est:35000-45000
£24000	$43680	€36000	Convolviente (90x102cm-35x40in) s. i.verso prov. 29-Jun-4 Cornette de St.Cyr, Paris #37/R est:30000-40000
£26667	$49067	€40000	Green hard, you green (64x76cm-25x30in) painted 1955 prov. 10-Jun-4 Christie's, Paris #76/R est:48000-65000
£26667	$49067	€40000	Etre-La (60x73cm-24x29in) s. painted c.1950 prov. 8-Jun-4 Artcurial Briest, Paris #215/R est:35000-40000
£30000	$54600	€45000	Untitled (145x140cm-57x55in) s. painted 1961 prov. 29-Jun-4 Cornette de St.Cyr, Paris #40/R est:45000-50000
£30667	$56733	€46000	Proces Rosenberg (59x39cm-20x15in) s. exhib. 18-Jul-4 Sotheby's, Paris #246/R est:50000-70000
£32000	$58240	€46720	Untitled (61x74cm-24x29in) prov.exhib. 6-Feb-4 Sotheby's, London #168/R est:25000-30000
£36313	$65000	€53017	Leda demain (143x206cm-56x81in) s. painted 1983 prov. 26-May-4 Sotheby's, New York #53/R est:70000-90000
£39597	$73255	€59000	Carrefour de violence (135x150cm-53x59in) s.i. s.i.d.1968 verso. 13-Mar-4 Meeting Art, Vercelli #130 est:50000
£40268	$72081	€60000	Jeo-graphy (166x203cm-65x80in) s.i.d.68. 25-May-4 Sotheby's, Milan #305/R est:40000-60000
£40817	$73062	€60000	Untitled (81x100cm-32x39in) s. 21-Mar-4 Calmels Cohen, Paris #58/R est:40000-50000
£41899	$75000	€61173	Elasticite du risible (105x93cm-41x37in) s. painted 1968 prov. 26-May-4 Sotheby's, New York #176/R est:50000-70000
£50000	$92500	€75000	Oscillation du present (150x201cm-59x79in) painted 1957 prov. 18-Jul-4 Sotheby's, Paris #247/R est:80000-120000
£52941	$90000	€77294	N'abolira (200x300cm-79x118in) s.d.1990 verso prov. 19-Nov-3 Sotheby's, New York #40/R est:80000-100000
£52941	$90000	€77294	Foot-coreography (181x239cm-71x94in) s.i.d.1990 verso prov.exhib. 19-Nov-3 Sotheby's, New York #128/R est:90000-120000
£60000	$109200	€87600	Les orienteur (114x145cm-45x57in) s.i. painted c.1957 prov. 6-Feb-4 Sotheby's, London #188/R est:60000-80000
£61594	$101014	€85000	Untitled (116x148cm-46x58in) painted 1958. 27-May-3 Sotheby's, Milan #273/R est:50000-70000
£66434	$112937	€95000	Composition (151x202cm-59x80in) s. painted 1970 exhib.lit. 29-Nov-3 Farsetti, Prato #482/R est:90000-120000
£68000	$123760	€99280	Untitled (99x79cm-39x31in) s.d.54 prov. 6-Feb-4 Sotheby's, London #169/R est:40000-60000
£76471	$130000	€111648	Que se despierte el lenador (144x198cm-57x78in) s. i.verso painted 1951 prov. 18-Nov-3 Christie's, Rockefeller NY #46/R est:140000-180000
£91176	$155000	€133117	Je t'ange (326x259cm-128x102in) s. i.d.87/12 verso prov. 18-Nov-3 Christie's, Rockefeller NY #56/R est:150000-200000
£93333	$171733	€140000	Composition (147x203cm-58x80in) s. prov. 8-Jun-4 Artcurial Briest, Paris #214/R est:100000-150000
£94118	$160000	€137412	Untitled, from the Morphology series (30x41cm-12x16in) s.d.1939 prov. 18-Nov-3 Christie's, Rockefeller NY #31/R est:200000-300000
£94118	$160000	€137412	Sin titulo - Untitled (200x381cm-79x150in) s. painted c.1965 prov. 18-Nov-3 Christie's, Rockefeller NY #59/R est:200000-250000
£109387	$195802	€159705	A que saint (120x294cm-47x116in) s.d.59 verso triptych prov. 28-May-4 Uppsala Auktionskammare, Uppsala #316/R est:1000000-1500000 (S.KR 1480000)
£411765	$700000	€601177	Morphologie psychologique de l'attente (71x91cm-28x36in) s. painted 1938 prov.exhib. 19-Nov-3 Sotheby's, New York #10/R est:1000000-1500000
Sculpture			
£5000	$7950	€7250	Le roi. La reine (40cm-16in) s.num.117/150 gold painted metal pair. 11-Sep-3 Christie's, Kensington #208/R est:1500-2000
£5705	$10611	€8500	Personnage (64x32x18cm-25x13x7in) s.num.6/6 antique green pat bronze st.f.Susse. 3-Mar-4 Artcurial Briest, Paris #494 est:8000-10000
£14118	$24000	€20612	Design of intention (39x72x22cm-15x28x9in) s. num.VII/X black pat. bronze prov.exhib. 19-Nov-3 Sotheby's, New York #137/R est:12000-18000
Works on paper			
£700	$1190	€1022	Untitled (20x16cm-8x6in) s. wax crayon. 18-Nov-3 Bonhams, Knightsbridge #155/R
£1657	$3000	€2419	Erotic conversation II (9x11cm-4x4in) pastel pencil. 30-Mar-4 Arroyo, Buenos Aires #56
£1800	$3240	€2700	Musicians (40x60cm-16x24in) pastel frottage graphite prov. 24-Apr-4 Cornette de St.Cyr, Paris #640/R est:4000
£1867	$3360	€2800	Musicians (40x60cm-16x24in) pastel frottage graphite prov. 24-Apr-4 Cornette de St.Cyr, Paris #639/R est:4000
£1867	$3360	€2800	Musicians (40x60cm-16x24in) pastel frottage graphite prov. 24-Apr-4 Cornette de St.Cyr, Paris #641/R est:4000
£1933	$3480	€2900	Musicians (40x60cm-16x24in) pastel frottage graphite prov. 24-Apr-4 Cornette de St.Cyr, Paris #638/R est:4000
£2027	$3831	€3000	Les joueurs et l'enfer (26x33cm-10x13in) i. pastel graphite. 21-Feb-4 Cornette de St.Cyr, Paris #351/R est:2000-3000
£2113	$3507	€3000	Bou (32x24cm-13x9in) s.i.d.1974 pencil pastel. 14-Jun-3 Meeting Art, Vercelli #97/R est:3000
£2210	$4000	€3227	Erotic conversation (9x11cm-4x4in) pastel pencil. 30-Mar-4 Arroyo, Buenos Aires #54
£2237	$4116	€3400	Untitled (50x65cm-20x26in) s. pastel wax crayon. 27-Jun-4 Versailles Encheres #39/R est:5000-6000
£2637	$4668	€3850	La soie de la maitreise (49x64cm-19x25in) s. pastel prov. 27-Apr-4 AB Stockholms Auktionsverk #1156/R est:20000-25000 (S.KR 36000)
£2721	$4871	€4000	Scene erotique (40x60cm-16x24in) s.i. pastel. 22-Mar-4 Digard, Paris #119 est:5000-7000
£3020	$5618	€4500	Composition (46x75cm-18x30in) s.indis.i. pastel wax crayon. 3-Mar-4 Artcurial Briest, Paris #496/R est:4000-5000
£3021	$5136	€4411	Le soi de la maihise (49x64cm-19x25in) s. mixed media prov. 5-Nov-3 AB Stockholms Auktionsverk #1141/R est:20000-25000 (S.KR 40000)
£3289	$6053	€5000	Sur et sou-venir d'un vol (32x50cm-13x20in) s.i. wax crayon. 27-Jun-4 Versailles Encheres #38/R est:5000-6000
£3497	$5944	€5000	Behind the back (76x56cm-30x22in) i.d.1990 verso gouache coffee pastel chl prov.exhib. 26-Nov-3 Pandolfini, Florence #143/R est:5500-6500
£3600	$6552	€5400	Untitled (48x62cm-19x24in) s. pastel prov. 29-Jun-4 Cornette de St.Cyr, Paris #38/R est:5000-7000
£3800	$6916	€5548	Composition (48x70cm-19x28in) s. pencil col crayon exec c.1960 prov. 4-Feb-4 Sotheby's, Olympia #85/R est:4000-6000
£3846	$7000	€5615	St. Tropez (35x50cm-14x20in) s.i.d.1958 pastel pencil prov. 29-Jun-4 Sotheby's, New York #418/R est:10000-15000
£3873	$6701	€5500	Bisou (50x56cm-20x22in) pastel exec.c.1980 prov. 14-Dec-3 Versailles Encheres #103/R est:6000-8000
£3893	$6968	€5800	Untitled (52x66cm-20x26in) s.d.62 crayon. 26-May-4 Christie's, Paris #68/R est:3000-4000
£4800	$8688	€7008	Sintitulo (109x74cm-43x29in) s. wax crayon. 1-Apr-4 Christie's, Kensington #247/R est:5000-7000
£4832	$8650	€7200	Untitled (30x38cm-12x15in) s.d.1960 crayon. 26-May-4 Christie's, Paris #70/R est:2000-3000
£5406	$9676	€8000	Dance de demenageurs (48x63cm-19x25in) s.i.d.59 graphite col crayon. 4-May-4 Calmels Cohen, Paris #204/R est:8000-10000
£6000	$10920	€8760	Untitled (43x75cm-17x30in) s. col crayon pencil prov.exhib. 6-Feb-4 Sotheby's, London #186/R est:5000-7000
£6897	$11517	€10000	One sun (100x101cm-39x40in) s. pastel exec.1981 prov. 13-Nov-3 Finarte Semenzato, Rome #220/R est:8000-10000
£7182	$13000	€10486	Study for mural (43x63cm-17x25in) pastel crayon. 30-Mar-4 Arroyo, Buenos Aires #55
£11111	$17556	€16000	Black light (106x150cm-42x59in) pastel oil card on canvas. 6-Sep-3 Meeting Art, Vercelli #367 est:15000
£19553	$35000	€28547	Untitled (23x31cm-9x12in) pencil wax crayon exec.1937 prov. 26-May-4 Sotheby's, New York #9/R est:50000-70000
£20134	$35638	€30000	Figure IV Burundun (92x67cm-36x26in) s. pastel exec.1970 exhib.lit. 27-Apr-4 Durán, Madrid #193/R est:30000
£20409	$36532	€30000	Couple (181x90cm-71x35in) s.verso ink pastel board exec c.1945. 21-Mar-4 Calmels Cohen, Paris #40/R est:15000-20000
£20588	$35000	€30058	L'assasin Philantrope (151x100cm-59x39in) chl pastel paper on canvas exec. 1951 prov.exhib. 18-Nov-3 Christie's, Rockefeller NY #163/R est:40000-50000
£21769	$38966	€32000	Untitled (39x51cm-15x20in) i. collage col crayons black paper exec c.1940 prov. 21-Mar-4 Calmels Cohen, Paris #56/R
£70000	$128100	€102200	Untitled (25x32cm-10x13in) col crayon executed 1937 prov.exhib. 2-Feb-4 Christie's, London #62/R est:80000-120000
£75000	$136500	€109500	Le glaive et la parole (86x60cm-34x24in) s. pastel chk graphite on card executed 1944 prov.exhib. 3-Feb-4 Sotheby's, London #83/R est:50000-70000
£86667	$159467	€130000	Untitled (28x44cm-11x17in) s.d.1939 verso ink crayon gouache paint prov. 10-Jun-4 Christie's, Paris #13/R est:80000-100000
£125000	$227500	€182500	Femme jouant a la belle devant un volcan (28x38cm-11x15in) s.d.40 col crayons pencil prov.exhib.lit. 3-Feb-4 Sotheby's, London #81/R est:90000-120000

MATTAS, Ake (1920-1962) Finnish

£811	$1451	€1200	Coastal town (20x26cm-8x10in) s.d.58 canvas on board. 8-May-4 Bukowskis, Helsinki #150/R
£2703	$4838	€4000	It is complete (70x50cm-28x20in) s.d.1962 exhib. 8-May-4 Bukowskis, Helsinki #62/R est:4000-5000
Works on paper			
£694	$1160	€1000	Model (125x100cm-49x39in) s.d.1962 mixed media exhib. 23-Oct-3 Hagelstam, Helsinki #842
£1014	$1814	€1500	Ellen (62x49cm-24x19in) s. pastel exhib. 8-May-4 Bukowskis, Helsinki #138/R est:1200-1500

MATTEINI, Theodoro (1754-1831) Italian

£1489	$2413	€2100	Portrait of officer (63x59cm-25x23in) 21-May-3 Babuino, Rome #48/R est:2000-3000

MATTEIS, Paolo de (1662-1728) Italian

£381	$681	€556	Young female Saint in adoration (69x56cm-27x22in) s.verso. 11-May-4 Peter Webb, Auckland #263/R est:1000-2000 (NZ.D 1100)
£1000	$1830	€1460	Young woman, holding a carnival mask (64x53cm-25x21in) prov. 6-Apr-4 Bonhams, Knightsbridge #253/R est:1000-1500
£27972	$48112	€40000	Immaculate Conception (110x77cm-43x30in) 2-Dec-3 Sotheby's, Milan #79/R est:20000-30000

MATTEIS, Paolo de (attrib) (1662-1728) Italian

£6667	$12000	€9734	God the Father in glory (42x47cm-17x19in) 23-Jan-4 Christie's, Rockefeller NY #167/R est:10000-15000
£17931	$29766	€26000	Venus asleep with putti (83x68cm-33x27in) lit.prov. 1-Oct-3 Dorotheum, Vienna #55/R est:6000-10000

MATTELE, Gustave (fl.1880) Belgian

£403	$737	€600	Ecrevisses de la Meuse (16x34cm-6x13in) s.d.1881 panel. 8-Jul-4 Campo, Vlaamse Kaai #178

MATTEO, David J de (1941-) American

£647	$1100	€945	A time of peace (9x15cm-4x6in) s. acrylic painted c.1975. 18-Nov-3 John Moran, Pasadena #115

MATTEO, Gabriele di (1957-) Italian

£952	$1705	€1400	Sissi (21x15cm-8x6in) acrylic in 2 pars. 16-Mar-4 Finarte Semenzato, Milan #119/R est:1400-1600

£1224 $2192 €1800 Self-portrait (21x15cm-8x6in) acrylic in 4 parts. 16-Mar-4 Finarte Semenzato, Milan #120/R est:1600-1800
£4155 $7271 €5900 Devant la vitrine du chocolatier (190x145cm-75x57in) init.i.d.1992-93 verso. 16-Dec-3 Finarte Semenzato, Milan #228/R est:5600-6000

MATTER, Herbert (20th C) ?
Photographs
£1944 $3500 €2838 Trylon and perisphere construction, New York World fair (25x20cm-10x8in) gelatin silver print prov. 22-Apr-4 Phillips, New York #225/R est:4000-6000

MATTERN, Walter (20th C) American
£229 $375 €332 Landscape with bridge and pier (30x36cm-12x14in) s.verso board prov. 4-Jun-3 Alderfer's, Hatfield #392
£518 $850 €756 Autumn landscape with country road (28x33cm-11x13in) board prov. 4-Jun-3 Alderfer's, Hatfield #367/R
£549 $900 €796 Landscape with farm (51x56cm-20x22in) board prov. 4-Jun-3 Alderfer's, Hatfield #368/R
£732 $1200 €1061 Landscape with barn (30x36cm-12x14in) board prov. 4-Jun-3 Alderfer's, Hatfield #393
£1478 $2750 €2158 Landscape with figures on horseback riding on road with barn alongside (51x64cm-20x25in) s. board. 3-Mar-4 Alderfer's, Hatfield #411/R est:2000-3000
£5488 $9000 €7958 Autumn landscape with country road (64x76cm-25x30in) board prov. 4-Jun-3 Alderfer's, Hatfield #356/R est:5000-7000

MATTESON, Bartow V (1894-?) American
£321 $600 €469 Woman bringing pot of tea to seated well dressed gentleman (48x61cm-19x24in) mono. board painted c.1920. 26-Feb-4 Illustration House, New York #122

MATTESON, Tompkins Harrison (attrib) (1813-1884) American
£865 $1600 €1263 Rogues slighted Falstaff into the Thames with little remorse (61x51cm-24x20in) bears sig.d.1873. 15-Jul-4 Doyle, New York #59/R est:1500-2000

MATTHAEY, Heinrich (1808-1880) German
£1911 $2943 €3000 Stream landscape with deer hunt (110x145cm-43x57in) i. verso. 4-Sep-2 Schopman, Hamburg #29/R est:4000

MATTHAI, Johann Friedrich (1777-1845) German
£5282 $9137 €7500 Portrait of a lady, with a red shawl, standing by a balcony (105x85cm-41x33in) indis.sig. prov. 10-Dec-3 Christie's, Amsterdam #13/R est:1500-2500

MATTHES, Christophe George (1738-1805) German
Works on paper
£3404 $5685 €4800 Cain batit la ville d'Henoch. s.i.d.1804 pen ink Chinese ink wash. 15-Oct-3 Sotheby's, Paris #178/R est:400-600

MATTHEWS, Cally (attrib) (19th C) American
£2216 $4100 €3235 Washington crossing the Delaware (58x99cm-23x39in) s. i.verso copy of Emanuel Gottlieb Leutze. 19-Jan-4 Winter Associates, Plainville #246/R est:125-250

MATTHEWS, Edward (19/20th C) British
Works on paper
£450 $828 €657 Glen Coe (37x51cm-15x20in) s.i.d.1875 W/C. 25-Mar-4 Bonhams, Edinburgh #325/R

MATTHEWS, James (19th C) British
Works on paper
£600 $1080 €876 Icklesham, Sussex (25x33cm-10x13in) s.i. W/C. 20-Apr-4 Canterbury Auctions, UK #170

MATTHEWS, Marmaduke (1837-1913) Canadian
£520 $952 €759 Fishing on a rocky point (30x55cm-12x22in) init. 1-Jun-4 Hodgins, Calgary #387/R (C.D 1300)
£3182 $5759 €4646 Fraser Canyon below North Bend (77x51cm-30x20in) s.d.1892. 18-Apr-4 Levis, Calgary #75/R est:10000-12000 (C.D 7700)
Works on paper
£200 $366 €292 Gleams at sea (35x46cm-14x18in) s. W/C. 1-Jun-4 Joyner Waddington, Toronto #388/R (C.D 500)
£201 $373 €293 Mountain landscape (37x49cm-15x19in) s.d.81 W/C. 2-Mar-4 Ritchie, Toronto #62/R (C.D 500)
£241 $448 €352 Fishing (38x51cm-15x20in) s. W/C. 2-Mar-4 Ritchie, Toronto #63/R (C.D 600)
£249 $416 €364 Rider beside a mountain river (14x35cm-6x14in) s. W/C. 17-Nov-3 Hodgins, Calgary #78/R (C.D 550)
£272 $500 €397 Bear in mountain landscape (48x5cm-19x2in) s. W/C htd white. 23-Mar-4 Arthur James, Florida #15/R
£289 $524 €422 Untitled - stormy seas on the east coast (31x60cm-12x24in) s. W/C. 18-Apr-4 Levis, Calgary #75a/R (C.D 700)
£380 $700 €555 View from Rogers Pass, Selkirk Range (74x48cm-29x19in) s. W/C htd white prov. 23-Mar-4 Arthur James, Florida #16/R
£528 $946 €771 View of the Selkirk Mountains (38x55cm-15x22in) s. W/C prov. 6-May-4 Heffel, Vancouver #94/R (C.D 1300)
£622 $1033 €908 Riding in the Rockies (75x49cm-30x19in) init. W/C. 5-Oct-3 Levis, Calgary #73a/R (C.D 1400)
£714 $1229 €1042 Cattle grazing at the forest's edge (31x49cm-12x19in) s. W/C. 2-Dec-3 Joyner Waddington, Toronto #311/R (C.D 1600)

MATTHEWS, Michael (20th C) British
£440 $774 €642 Dutch winter village scene with figures skating on the frozen canal (75x49cm-30x19in) s. 18-May-4 Fellows & Sons, Birmingham #41/R
£460 $810 €672 Clippers on a choppy sea (35x23cm-14x9in) s. 18-May-4 Fellows & Sons, Birmingham #40/R

MATTHEWS, William (20th C) British
Works on paper
£4190 $7500 €6117 In the chutes (48x43cm-19x17in) W/C. 15-May-4 Altermann Galleries, Santa Fe #4/R
£4706 $8000 €6871 No slack (48x46cm-19x18in) W/C. 1-Nov-3 Altermann Galleries, Santa Fe #25

MATTHIASDOTTIR, Louisa (1918-2000) Icelandic
£3693 $6500 €5392 Still life with squash and tomato (56x61cm-22x24in) s. prov. 23-May-4 Hindman, Chicago #1013/R est:3000-5000

MATTHIESEN, Oscar Adam Otto (1861-1957) German
£3318 $5308 €4844 Dragoons on horseback going into the sea, Skaane (95x189cm-37x74in) s.d.1906 exhib. 22-Sep-3 Rasmussen, Vejle #1/R est:50000-75000 (D.KR 35000)

MATTHIESSEN, Hjalmar (1880-1955) Danish
£332 $531 €485 Prospect view of a Danish landscape (70x97cm-28x38in) s.d.april 1905. 22-Sep-3 Rasmussen, Vejle #325/R (D.KR 3500)
£341 $546 €498 Parisian view with bridge across the Seine (53x40cm-21x16in) s.i.d.1913. 22-Sep-3 Rasmussen, Vejle #405/R (D.KR 3600)

MATTHIEU, Rosina Christiana (1748-1795) German
Works on paper
£315 $526 €450 Portrait of young man with lace collar (12x9cm-5x4in) s. gouache oval. 28-Jun-3 Dannenberg, Berlin #730/R

MATTHISON, William (fl.1883-1923) British
Works on paper
£300 $561 €438 Country house at dusk with lake in foreground, trees and rhododendrons (59x49cm-23x19in) pencil W/C. 22-Jul-4 Tennants, Leyburn #660
£320 $605 €467 River landscape with windmills to the shore (52x23cm-20x9in) s. W/C. 17-Feb-4 Fellows & Sons, Birmingham #117/R
£320 $598 €467 Country house with lake, gentleman seated in a punt fishing (53x35cm-21x14in) s.i. pencil W/C. 22-Jul-4 Tennants, Leyburn #661
£400 $732 €584 Market day, Banbury (16x35cm-6x14in) s. W/C bodycol. 27-Jan-4 Bonhams, Knightsbridge #69/R
£450 $815 €657 Evening on the estuary (25x51cm-10x20in) s. W/C. 16-Apr-4 Keys, Aylsham #472
£460 $833 €672 Sandsend from Lythe Bank (18x28cm-7x11in) s. W/C. 30-Mar-4 David Duggleby, Scarborough #187/R
£800 $1264 €1160 Nanny and baby standing in the rose garden of a Cotswold stone house (27x44cm-11x17in) s. W/C. 2-Sep-3 Bonhams, Oxford #51/R
£1100 $2013 €1606 Town centre, Banbury (24x54cm-9x21in) s. W/C. 27-Jan-4 Bonhams, Knightsbridge #70/R est:800-1200

MATTHYS, von (19th C) ?
£6000 $10200 €8760 Vessels before the Dogana, Venice. Vessels on the Grand Canal, Venice (77x127cm-30x50in) s.d.90 pair. 6-Nov-3 Christie's, Kensington #856/R est:4000-6000

MATTIACCI, Eliseo (1940-) Italian
Sculpture
£13768 $22580 €19000 House and houses (190x80x40cm-75x31x16in) s.d.1978 iron copper exhib. 27-May-3 Sotheby's, Milan #290 est:15000-20000
Works on paper
£2319 $3803 €3200 Plinth (68x47cm-27x19in) s.i.d.79 graphite pen felt-tip pen card. 27-May-3 Sotheby's, Milan #100/R est:2000-3000
£3800 $6916 €5548 Study (70x49cm-28x19in) col crayons sold with four crayon studies by same hand five. 4-Feb-4 Sotheby's, Olympia #232/R est:600-800

MATTINEN, Seppo (1930-) Finnish
£517 $880 €755 Figure composition (36x39cm-14x15in) s.d.72 masonite. 26-Nov-3 Kunsthallen, Copenhagen #8 (D.KR 5500)
£587 $1097 €857 Figure composition in landscape (100x100cm-39x39in) s.d.67. 25-Feb-4 Kunsthallen, Copenhagen #177 (D.KR 6500)

MATTIOLI, Carlo (1911-1994) Italian
£1477 $2643 €2200 Woman (35x25cm-14x10in) s. paper. 30-May-4 Meeting Art, Vercelli #43 est:2000
£2536 $4159 €3500 Nude. Portrait of Carra' (50x35cm-20x14in) s tempera card double-sided. 27-May-3 Sotheby's, Milan #101/R est:4000-5000
£3793 $6334 €5500 Red landscape (50x30cm-20x12in) s. oil pencil. 13-Nov-3 Finarte Semenzato, Rome #359/R est:2000-2500
£4000 $7360 €6000 Mercurius (89x54cm-35x21in) cardboard on canvas painted 1954. 10-Jun-4 Galleria Pace, Milan #138/R est:8000
£4336 $7371 €6200 Sea (44x20cm-17x8in) s.i.d.1987 verso prov.exhib.lit. 26-Nov-3 Pandolfini, Florence #189/R est:6000-7000
£6897 $11517 €10000 Landscapes (49x30cm-19x12in) s. oil pencil card pair. 13-Nov-3 Finarte Semenzato, Rome #360/R est:4000-5000
£13793 $23034 €20000 Pine grove (63x84cm-25x33in) s. painted 1984. 13-Nov-3 Finarte Semenzato, Rome #454/R est:18000-22000
£16552 $27641 €24000 Summer (90x81cm-35x32in) s. s.i.d.1975 verso. 13-Nov-3 Finarte Semenzato, Rome #453/R est:20000-22000
£24161 $43248 €36000 Landscape (136x105cm-54x41in) painted 1992. 29-May-4 Farsetti, Prato #478/R est:35000-45000

MATTIONI, Eszter (1902-) Hungarian
£1470 $2601 €2146 Sunny landscape (80x60cm-31x24in) s. 28-Apr-4 Kieselbach, Budapest #1/R (H.F 550000)

MATTIS-TEUTSCH, Janos (1884-1960) Bohemian
£14491 $26229 €21157 Composition (29x36cm-11x14in) s. oil on paper. 16-Apr-4 Mu Terem Galeria, Budapest #81/R (H.F 5500000)

£48867 $81119 €71346 Spring (36x46cm-14x18in) init. s.d.1909 verso cardboard. 4-Oct-3 Kieselbach, Budapest #204/R (H.F 18000000)
Works on paper
£805 $1490 €1200 Composition rose et verte (67x54cm-26x21in) s. gouache W/C cardboard. 15-Mar-4 Claude Boisgirard, Paris #78/R
£5879 $10406 €8583 Hilly landscape with trees (24x33cm-9x13in) s. W/C. 28-Apr-4 Kieselbach, Budapest #198/R (H.F 2200000)

MATTISON, Donald M (1905-1975) American
Works on paper
£247 $400 €361 Study of a man (30x20cm-12x8in) s.d.1937 pencil. 2-Aug-3 Neal Auction Company, New Orleans #559

MATTO, Francisco (1911-1995) Uruguayan
£1647 $2800 €2405 Harbour (42x42cm-17x17in) s. cardboard. 25-Nov-3 Galeria y Remates, Montevideo #67/R
£2941 $5000 €4294 Landscape with tram (39x45cm-15x18in) s. cardboard. 25-Nov-3 Galeria y Remates, Montevideo #66/R
£4261 $7500 €6221 Black and white composition (63x100cm-25x39in) s.d.88 cardboard prov. 5-Jan-4 Galeria y Remates, Montevideo #37/R est:7000-9000
£6704 $12000 €9788 Sun (60x60cm-24x24in) s.d.63 cardboard prov.exhib. 26-May-4 Sotheby's, New York #104/R est:12000-18000
£16760 $30000 €24470 Composition, New York (105x79cm-41x31in) board prov.exhib. 26-May-4 Sotheby's, New York #14/R est:20000-25000

MATTON, Arsene (1873-1933) Belgian
Sculpture
£2867 $5275 €4300 Maternite congolaise (40cm-16in) s. brown pat bronze marble socle. 14-Jun-4 Gros & Delettrez, Paris #285/R est:4000-6000

MATTON, Charles (1933-) French
Sculpture
£13333 $24667 €20000 A Marcel Proust (57x79x49cm-22x31x19in) s.d.2000 num.3/3 wood resin mixed media prov. 18-Jul-4 Sotheby's, Paris #288/R est:20000-25000
£21333 $39467 €32000 Grande Lulu (202x130x106cm-80x51x42in) s.st.f.Bocquel num.1/8 pat bronze exec.2000 prov. 18-Jul-4 Sotheby's, Paris #168/R est:20000-25000

MATTONI DE LA FUENTE, Virgilio (1842-1923) Spanish
£690 $1152 €1000 Lake creatures (98x39cm-39x15in) s.d.1903 i.verso. 17-Nov-3 Durán, Madrid #165/R

MATTSON, Dennis (20th C) American
Works on paper
£383 $700 €575 Rhododendron (64x51cm-25x20in) pastel. 10-Jul-4 Hindman, Chicago #327/R

MATTSON, Henry Elis (1887-1971) American
£778 $1300 €1136 Big rock pool (63x81cm-25x32in) s. s.i.stretcher painted c.1942 prov.exhib.lit. 7-Oct-3 Sotheby's, New York #234

MATULKA, Jan (1890-1972) American
£1796 $3000 €2622 Village scene (61x81cm-24x32in) s. 7-Oct-3 Sotheby's, New York #207 est:5000-7000
Works on paper
£707 $1300 €1032 Fishermen (20x28cm-8x11in) s. W/C. 10-Jun-4 Swann Galleries, New York #170/R
£882 $1500 €1288 Three peasant (53x58cm-21x23in) s.d.1921 graphite. 9-Nov-3 Wright, Chicago #226 est:1500-2000
£1033 $1900 €1508 Road near Turi Pole (41x30cm-16x12in) s. brush india ink pencil exec. c.1921. 10-Jun-4 Swann Galleries, New York #168/R est:1500-2500
£1630 $3000 €2380 Toilette (28x23cm-11x9in) s. pencil exec. c.1925 dr verso. 10-Jun-4 Swann Galleries, New York #169/R est:4000-6000
£5294 $9000 €7729 Gathering (46x61cm-18x24in) pastel prov. 1-Nov-3 Santa Fe Art, Santa Fe #159/R est:15000-20000

MATUSHEVSKI, Yuri (1930-1999) Russian
£350 $634 €511 Bathers (48x58cm-19x23in) s.d.64 oil paper. 4-Apr-4 Lots Road Auctions, London #357/R
£850 $1547 €1241 Orange sunset (28x39cm-11x15in) s. board painted 1964. 20-Jun-4 Lots Road Auctions, London #385/R
£1000 $1820 €1460 Forest Pond (40x50cm-16x20in) s. board painted 1969. 20-Jun-4 Lots Road Auctions, London #350a/R est:800-1200
£2000 $3640 €2920 Crispy winter (60x80cm-24x31in) s. board painted 1961. 20-Jun-4 Lots Road Auctions, London #357a/R est:2000-3000
£2000 $3640 €2920 Christmas morning (50x70cm-20x28in) s. board painted 1965. 20-Jun-4 Lots Road Auctions, London #365a/R est:2000-3000
£2000 $3640 €2920 Grandeur (60x80cm-24x31in) s. board painted 1962. 20-Jun-4 Lots Road Auctions, London #377a/R est:1600-2000
£2100 $3822 €3066 Violet Winter (50x70cm-20x28in) s. board painted 1960. 20-Jun-4 Lots Road Auctions, London #341a/R est:2000-3000

MATWIJKIW, Edward (1937-) Scandinavian
£812 $1519 €1186 Joy of life and pain (145x120cm-57x47in) s. 25-Feb-4 Kunsthallen, Copenhagen #127/R (D.KR 9000)

MAUBERT, James (1666-1746) British
£3800 $6460 €5548 Portrait of a young girl, wearing a green dress, seated in landscape with her dog at her side (125x100cm-49x39in) s.d.1729. 29-Oct-3 Bonhams, New Bond Street #60/R est:4000-6000

MAUBOULES, Jean (1943-) Swiss
Sculpture
£1131 $1889 €1651 Sans titre (120x195x25cm-47x77x10in) iron glass prov. 24-Jun-3 Germann, Zurich #27/R est:2800-3500 (S.FR 2500)
Works on paper
£308 $523 €450 Collage de verre (15x21cm-6x8in) s.d. collage glass ink. 22-Nov-3 Burkhard, Luzern #47/R (S.FR 680)
£724 $1231 €1057 Collage de verre (65x65cm-26x26in) collage glass board. 22-Nov-3 Burkhard, Luzern #45/R (S.FR 1600)
£769 $1308 €1123 Cube (100x90cm-39x35in) s. i.verso collage glass board exec. 1972. 22-Nov-3 Burkhard, Luzern #42/R (S.FR 1700)
£1086 $1846 €1586 Falling triangle (120x90cm-47x35in) s.d.1978 collage glass board. 22-Nov-3 Burkhard, Luzern #46/R (S.FR 2400)

MAUDSLEY, Helen (1927-) Australian
£620 $1147 €905 Glory and the triumph (77x77cm-30x30in) s.d.1995 i.verso prov.exhib. 15-Mar-4 Sotheby's, Melbourne #129/R est:1200-1800 (A.D 1500)

MAUFRA, Maxime (1861-1918) French
£2267 $4193 €3400 Moulin sur la riviere (27x35cm-11x14in) s. 14-Jul-4 Livinec, Gaudcheau & Jezequel, Rennes #129
£2676 $4630 €3800 Paysage (30x35cm-12x14in) s.d.1890. 15-Dec-3 Bailly Pommery, Paris #112/R est:1500-2500
£4000 $7360 €5840 Rivage en Bretagne (35x57cm-14x22in) s. painted 1906 prov.exhib. 24-Mar-4 Sotheby's, Olympia #83/R est:5000-7000
£4698 $8409 €7000 Oued d'Oued-Djellal, Sahara (60x73cm-24x29in) s.d.1913 prov. 26-May-4 Christie's, Paris #23/R est:4000-6000
£5099 $9281 €7700 Le feu d'artifice du 14 juillet devant le bateau-lavoir (46x38cm-18x15in) s. painted 1893. 15-Jun-4 Blanchet, Paris #141/R est:8000-10000
£6040 $10812 €9000 Dunes a Beg-Meil (60x81cm-24x32in) s.d.1904. 25-May-4 Chambelland & Giafferi, Paris #52/R est:6000-8000
£7000 $11690 €10220 Soleil couchant (54x73cm-21x29in) s. painted 1905. 21-Oct-3 Sotheby's, London #133/R est:5000-7000
£7042 $12324 €10000 Village de Lavardin (81x65cm-32x26in) s.d.1907. 21-Dec-3 Thierry & Lannon, Brest #181/R est:12000-15000
£7655 $14162 €11100 Soleil couchant, Yport (54x65cm-21x26in) s.d.1900 prov. 13-Feb-4 Rossini, Paris #28/R est:13000-15000
£8589 $14000 €12540 Automne, foret de Fontainebleau (60x73cm-24x29in) s.d.1909 i.stretcher prov. 25-Sep-3 Christie's, Rockefeller NY #523/R est:18000-24000
£10000 $17900 €15000 Les rochers rouges (61x74cm-24x29in) i. 16-May-4 Thierry & Lannon, Brest #161/R est:15000-20000
£10000 $18400 €15000 Paysage (50x70cm-20x28in) s.d.1904 prov.lit. 14-Jun-4 Tajan, Paris #47/R est:15000-20000
£11656 $19000 €17018 La vallee de Glencoe-Ecose (73x92cm-29x36in) s.d.1895 prov. 25-Sep-3 Christie's, Rockefeller NY #539/R est:15000-20000
£12583 $22901 €19000 Port de Kerhostin (60x81cm-24x32in) s. lit. 15-Jun-4 Rossini, Paris #37/R est:18000-22000
£13475 $22504 €19000 Les voiles rouges pres de Saint Guenole (61x74cm-24x29in) s.d.1898. 15-Oct-3 Rabourdin & Choppin de Janvry, Paris #26/R est:15000-17000
£17450 $31235 €26000 Automne a Saint-Jean du Doigt (60x73cm-24x29in) s.d.1895 s.i.verso. 26-May-4 Christie's, Paris #14/R est:15000-20000
£21831 $38204 €31000 Soir dore Paimpol. s. painted c.1893. 21-Dec-3 Thierry & Lannon, Brest #179/R est:24000-28000
£22535 $39437 €32000 Village de Locronan (81x100cm-32x39in) s.d.1898. 21-Dec-3 Thierry & Lannon, Brest #178/R est:30000-40000
£23944 $41901 €34000 Arbres fantastiques, le Pouldu (61x72cm-24x28in) s.d.1893. 21-Dec-3 Thierry & Lannon, Brest #180/R est:22000-25000
Prints
£2819 $4989 €4200 Vague (57x38cm-22x15in) s. eau forte aquatint. 29-Apr-4 Piasa, Paris #275/R est:2500-3000
Works on paper
£704 $1218 €1000 Moulin (22x30cm-9x12in) s. W/C chl. 14-Dec-3 Eric Pillon, Calais #54/R
£733 $1313 €1100 Cote rocheuse (13x18cm-5x7in) i.d.92 W/C chl. 16-May-4 Thierry & Lannon, Brest #66
£1192 $2170 €1800 Carteret (22x31cm-9x12in) s.i.d.94 W/C. 18-Jun-4 Piasa, Paris #87/R est:2500-3000
£1200 $2208 €1800 Les menhirs de Saint-Pierre, Quiberon, Morbihan (25x47cm-10x19in) s.d.1911 W/C gouache. 9-Jun-4 Beaussant & Lefèvre, Paris #191/R est:500-600
£1268 $2193 €1800 Montagnes noires (20x30cm-8x12in) s. W/C over chl. 9-Dec-3 Artcurial Briest, Paris #85 est:1000-1200
£1549 $2711 €2200 Ruisseau dans le vallon (25x32cm-10x13in) s. W/C drawing. 21-Dec-3 Thierry & Lannon, Brest #117/R est:2200-2400
£1620 $2802 €2300 Route dans un paysage de Bretagne (23x31cm-9x12in) s. chl W/C. 12-Dec-3 Renaud, Paris #87/R est:1200-1500
£1901 $3327 €2700 Goelette a quai a Port Haliguen (24x32cm-9x13in) studio st. chl. 21-Dec-3 Thierry & Lannon, Brest #448 est:2000-2500
£1933 $3461 €2900 Chapelle en bord de mer (32x39cm-13x15in) s. chl gouache exec. 96. 16-May-4 Thierry & Lannon, Brest #91 est:3000-3500
£1972 $3451 €2800 Bourg et l'eglise de Locronan (27x21cm-11x8in) s. chl pastel. 21-Dec-3 Thierry & Lannon, Brest #116 est:2800-3000
£2667 $4773 €4000 Le port du Havre vu des hauteurs de Ste Adresse (29x46cm-11x18in) s.d.1905 W/C gouache. 16-May-4 Thierry & Lannon, Brest #67/R est:4000-5000
£2733 $4893 €4100 Hameau et champs verts pres du Pouldu (22x30cm-9x12in) W/C chl exec. c.1890. 16-May-4 Thierry & Lannon, Brest #65/R est:3000-4000
£3356 $5940 €5000 L'anse du port, Morbihan (26x46cm-10x18in) s.d.1909 W/C gouache traces crayon. 27-Apr-4 Artcurial Briest, Paris #6/R est:4000-5000

MAUGHAN, Karl (1964-) New Zealander
£652 $1109 €952 Garden path (111x105cm-44x41in) oil on paper. 4-Nov-3 Peter Webb, Auckland #208/R est:2000-3000 (NZ.D 1800)
£893 $1616 €1304 Floral study (35x38cm-14x15in) exhib. 30-Mar-4 Peter Webb, Auckland #7/R est:2500-3500 (NZ.D 2500)
£1128 $1917 €1647 Love, lies bleeding, suite 4 (41x38cm-16x15in) s.d.February 1996. 27-Nov-3 International Art Centre, Auckland #157/R est:3000-4000 (NZ.D 3000)
£1241 $2197 €1812 Chrysthanemums and fence (92x71cm-36x28in) s.d.1987 verso. 28-Apr-4 Dunbar Sloane, Auckland #10/R est:3000-5000 (NZ.D 3500)
£1413 $2247 €2063 Love lies bleeding suite no.4 (41x38cm-16x15in) 9-Sep-3 Watson's, Christchurch #51 (NZ.D 3900)
£3846 $7000 €5615 Garden study (150x120cm-59x47in) s.d.1991 verso. 29-Jun-4 Peter Webb, Auckland #38/R est:12000-16000 (NZ.D 11000)
£5263 $8947 €7684 Stone wall and sunflowers (160x190cm-63x75in) s.d.1994 verso exhib. 27-Nov-3 International Art Centre, Auckland #87/R est:15000-20000 (NZ.D 14000)

MAULBERTSCH, Franz Anton (circle) (1724-1796) Austrian
£5556 $9056 €8000 Martyrdom of St Andreas (93x54cm-37x21in) 24-Sep-3 Neumeister, Munich #352/R est:8000

MAULDIN, Bill (20th C) American
Works on paper
£629 $1100 €918 Jeez, Willie, now they've drafted radios (38x30cm-15x12in) s. red col acetate overlay ink paper on ills board exec 1975. 17-Dec-3 Christie's, Rockefeller NY #249/R

MAULNOIR, Esther de (19th C) French
£2483 $4146 €3500 Une rose tremiere (40x32cm-16x13in) mono.d.1841. 17-Oct-3 Tajan, Paris #144/R est:3000-4000

MAULWURF, Hans (19th C) German
£382 $607 €550 Frank village with herd of sheep (67x79cm-26x31in) s.d.1923. 11-Sep-3 Weidler, Nurnberg #7004/R
£503 $841 €720 Manngasse in Norlingen (61x52cm-24x20in) s.d.1923. 26-Jun-3 Weidler, Nurnberg #7013/R
£517 $864 €750 Boy with two lambs fishing (38x47cm-15x19in) s. bears d. board on panel lit. 10-Jul-3 Allgauer, Kempten #2597/R

MAUPASSANT, Guy de (1850-1893) French
Works on paper
£3400 $6256 €5100 Lettre illustree de dessins de son ami de canotage sur la Seine (21x19cm-8x7in) d.8 fevrier 1875 pen two sheets exhib. 9-Jun-4 Piasa, Paris #152/R est:5000-7000

MAURA Y MONTANER, Antonio (1853-1925) Spanish
Works on paper
£839 $1401 €1200 Landscapes with buildings (35x25cm-14x10in) s.d.1920 W/C pair. 30-Jun-3 Ansorena, Madrid #6/R

MAURA Y MONTANER, Francisco (1857-1931) Spanish
£3077 $5138 €4400 Venetian canal (95x73cm-37x29in) s. 30-Jun-3 Ansorena, Madrid #199/R est:3600

MAURE, Jacob (18th C) ?
£2151 $3850 €3140 Shepherd children with a dog teasing a goat (51x66cm-20x26in) s.d.1775. 11-May-4 Roland's, New York #473288/R

MAURER, Alfred H (1868-1932) American
£2857 $5000 €4171 Landscape (53x45cm-21x18in) s. panel prov. 19-Dec-3 Sotheby's, New York #1032/R est:7000-10000
£8725 $16228 €13000 Paysage de printemps (21x27cm-8x11in) s. panel painted c.1906-1907 prov. 2-Mar-4 Artcurial Briest, Paris #130/R est:8000-10000
£35135 $65000 €51297 Sisters (55x46cm-22x18in) s. board painted c.1925 prov.exhib. 11-Mar-4 Christie's, Rockefeller NY #102/R est:20000-30000
£38636 $68000 €56409 Still life no 7 (46x55cm-18x22in) s. paperboard painted c.1930 prov. 18-May-4 Christie's, Rockefeller NY #120/R est:15000-25000
£39106 $70000 €57095 House and trees. Tropical forest interior (53x43cm-21x17in) board double-sided. 26-May-4 Doyle, New York #155/R est:40000-60000
Works on paper
£408 $750 €596 Female nude (41x25cm-16x10in) s. pencil. 10-Jun-4 Swann Galleries, New York #171/R
£11364 $20000 €16591 Floral still life (53x46cm-21x18in) s.i. gouache chl prov. 19-May-4 Sotheby's, New York #129/R est:20000-30000
£18466 $32500 €26960 Portrait of a woman (53x46cm-21x18in) s. gouache prov. 19-May-4 Sotheby's, New York #154/R est:15000-25000

MAURER, Friedrich (19th C) German
£1389 $2292 €2000 Farmstead in the mountains (60x73cm-24x29in) s. 2-Jul-3 Neumeister, Munich #711/R est:1800

MAURER, Hans (20th C) German
£317 $567 €450 Still life with peonies, grapes and peaches (64x62cm-25x24in) s.i. 8-Jan-4 Allgauer, Kempten #2460/R

MAURER, Ingo (20th C) German
Sculpture
£1100 $2002 €1650 Bulb (60cm-24in) GRP plastic exec.c.1980. 30-Jun-4 Christie's, Kensington #149/R est:500-800

MAUREY BARISSON, Olivia (20th C) French?
Works on paper
£315 $535 €450 Jeudi 8h17 (56x50cm-22x20in) s. mixed media panel. 29-Nov-3 Neret-Minet, Paris #129/R

MAURIE, Gaston (?-1912) French
Works on paper
£514 $807 €750 Place du village (29x12cm-11x5in) s. gouache. 20-Apr-3 Deauville, France #42

MAURIER, Georges du (1834-1896) French
Works on paper
£412 $700 €602 Morning swim (14x22cm-6x9in) s. ink pencil prov. 25-Nov-3 Christie's, Rockefeller NY #487/R
£700 $1204 €1022 The Du Maurier family (16x23cm-6x9in) s. pen ink. 3-Dec-3 Cheffins, Cambridge #572

MAURIGE, Jean Francois (20th C) French
£278 $464 €400 Sans titre (135x185cm-53x73in) acrylic prov. 25-Oct-3 Cornette de St.Cyr, Paris #436

MAURITZ-LARSEN, Bjarne (1897-1967) Norwegian
£345 $573 €500 Goats at the mountain farm (57x82cm-22x32in) s. 16-Jun-3 Blomqvist, Lysaker #1133 (N.KR 4000)

MAURO, Mario (1920-1984) Canadian
£380 $695 €555 Ferme a St Ferreal (45x60cm-18x24in) s.i.d.1978. 1-Jun-4 Hodgins, Calgary #13/R (C.D 950)

MAURUS, Hans (1901-1942) German
£280 $481 €400 Matterhorn and riffelsee (62x81cm-24x32in) s. bears i. 4-Dec-3 Neumeister, Munich #2801/R
£347 $573 €500 Alpine farmstead (60x80cm-24x31in) s. 3-Jul-3 Van Ham, Cologne #1350
£377 $640 €550 Matterhorn and Winklmann (60x80cm-24x31in) s.i. i. verso lit. 6-Nov-3 Allgauer, Kempten #3499/R
£400 $720 €600 Near Kitzbuhl (65x80cm-26x31in) s.i. i. verso. 21-Apr-4 Neumeister, Munich #2683/R
£414 $691 €600 Landscape with farmstead and Zugspitze (60x80cm-24x31in) s.i. lit. 10-Jul-3 Allgauer, Kempten #2598/R
£451 $736 €650 Farmstead in mountains (60x80cm-24x31in) s.d.1923. 24-Sep-3 Neumeister, Munich #495
£486 $812 €700 Heiligenblut on Grossglockner (66x80cm-26x31in) s.i. 22-Oct-3 Neumeister, Munich #734/R
£503 $921 €750 View of Tegernsee with castle (51x41cm-20x16in) s.i. i.verso lit. 8-Jul-4 Allgauer, Kempten #2161/R
£533 $955 €800 Lake Starnberger (64x80cm-25x31in) s. i.verso. 14-May-4 Behringer, Furth #1589/R
£570 $1050 €850 High mountain pasture (68x80cm-27x31in) s. bears i. 27-Mar-4 L & B, Essen #153/R
£667 $1227 €1000 Matterhorn and Findelen (60x80cm-24x31in) s. i. verso. 9-Jun-4 Dorotheum, Salzburg #636/R
£1250 $2037 €1800 St Leonard in Pitztal (66x81cm-26x32in) s.i. i.verso. 23-Sep-3 Wiener Kunst Auktionen, Vienna #30/R est:1800-3000

MAURY, François (1861-1933) French
£289 $500 €422 Two figures by a forest pool (18x24cm-7x9in) s. 13-Dec-3 Auctions by the Bay, Alameda #1841/R
£814 $1385 €1188 Bearded man (32x22cm-13x9in) s. panel. 19-Nov-3 Fischer, Luzern #2208/R (S.FR 1800)
£2098 $3608 €3000 Femmes aux bains (50x61cm-20x24in) s. 3-Dec-3 Tajan, Paris #310 est:3000-3500
£2238 $3804 €3200 Jeunes femmes dans les bois (65x80cm-26x31in) s. pair. 1-Dec-3 Palais de Beaux Arts, Brussels #364 est:2600-3200
£2292 $3735 €3300 Le concert champetre (100x140cm-39x55in) s.d.22 or 92. 26-Sep-3 Rabourdin & Choppin de Janvry, Paris #53/R est:4000-5000

MAUTLOA, Kagiso Patrick (1952-) South African
Works on paper
£661 $1182 €965 Traveller (98x70cm-39x28in) s.d.99 mixed media. 31-May-4 Stephan Welz, Johannesburg #583/R (SA.R 8000)
£690 $1152 €1007 Trader (98x69cm-39x27in) s.d.99 mixed media. 20-Oct-3 Stephan Welz, Johannesburg #348/R est:10000-15000 (SA.R 8000)

MAUVE, Anton (1838-1888) Dutch
£662 $1079 €1000 Troupeau (23x43cm-9x17in) s. 1-Feb-3 Dubee & Berron, Vernou en Sologne #20
£667 $1207 €1000 Breakfast (43x53cm-17x21in) s. 3-Apr-4 Badum, Bamberg #35/R
£812 $1501 €1186 Shepherd and sheep on marshes (54x73cm-21x29in) s.d.1875. 15-Mar-4 Rasmussen, Vejle #460/R (D.KR 9000)
£1184 $2143 €1800 Figure in the meadow under a cloudy sky (26x36cm-10x14in) init. paper on panel. 19-Apr-4 Glerum, Amsterdam #109/R est:2000-3000
£1259 $2102 €1800 Peasant girl with cow and sheep (31x49cm-12x19in) s. panel. 28-Jun-3 Bolland & Marotz, Bremen #705/R est:2700
£3014 $5123 €4400 Country path with horse and wagon by a mill (25x19cm-10x7in) s. panel. 5-Nov-3 Vendue Huis, Gravenhage #56/R est:3000-3500
£6667 $12000 €10000 Peasant woman by a barn (39x44cm-15x17in) s. canvas on panel prov.exhib.lit. 20-Apr-4 Sotheby's, Amsterdam #218/R est:10000-15000
£8667 $15600 €13000 Resting cows (17x27cm-7x11in) s. panel prov. 20-Apr-4 Sotheby's, Amsterdam #222/R est:15000-20000
£25333 $45600 €38000 Sand cart (33x28cm-13x11in) s. lit. 20-Apr-4 Sotheby's, Amsterdam #203/R est:20000-30000
Works on paper
£447 $800 €653 Sheep in farmyard (15x20cm-6x8in) W/C. 14-May-4 Du Mouchelle, Detroit #2013/R
£1060 $1727 €1600 Retour du troupeau (40x55cm-16x22in) s. pastel. 1-Feb-3 Dubee & Berron, Vernou en Sologne #19
£6500 $11895 €9490 Shepherd and sheep in a winter landscape at sunset (38x51cm-15x20in) s. W/C bodycol prov. 8-Jul-4 Duke & Son, Dorchester #135/R
£6944 $11597 €10000 Horse drawn cart on a country road (35x47cm-14x19in) s. W/C prov. 21-Oct-3 Sotheby's, Amsterdam #129/R est:10000-15000

MAUVE, Anton (attrib) (1838-1888) Dutch
Works on paper
£559 $934 €800 Farmer (21x26cm-8x10in) s. W/C. 10-Oct-3 Vendue Huis, Gravenhage #866

MAUZEY, Merritt (1898-1973) American
£898 $1500 €1311 Misty morning (30x41cm-12x16in) board. 18-Oct-3 David Dike, Dallas #312/R est:2500-4000

MAVRO, Mania (1889-1969) Russian

£331 $603 €500 Quais de Seine pres la tour Eiffel (65x82cm-26x32in) s. 20-Jun-4 Salle des ventes Pillet, Lyon la Foret #32/R
£1325 $2411 €2000 Nu sur un fond bleu (81x65cm-32x26in) 16-Jun-4 Claude Boisgirard, Paris #107/R est:2000-2500
£1611 $2996 €2400 Paysage (27x34cm-11x13in) s. cardboard laid down. 2-Mar-4 Artcurial Briest, Paris #191 est:300-400
£1724 $2879 €2500 Roses dans un cruche blanche (50x40cm-20x16in) s. panel. 17-Nov-3 Claude Boisgirard, Paris #63/R est:2000-2500

MAVROGORDATO, Alexander James (fl.1892-1933) British

Works on paper
£407 $650 €594 Interior scene (53x36cm-21x14in) s.d.1918 W/C gouache. 20-Sep-3 Bunte, Elgin #1489
£1600 $2752 €2336 Athenian cobbler. Modern Athens (24x34cm-9x13in) pencil W/C pair. 3-Dec-3 Christie's, Kensington #32/R est:1500-2000

MAVROIDIS, Giorgios (1913-) Greek

£2800 $5012 €4088 Still life with fruit (32x26cm-13x10in) s. 10-May-4 Sotheby's, Olympia #36/R est:2800-3200
£6300 $11277 €9198 Landscape (73x54cm-29x21in) s. 10-May-4 Sotheby's, Olympia #123/R est:4000-5000

MAWANDJUL, John (1952-) Australian

Works on paper
£440 $757 €642 Wayarra and mornorr (108x27cm-43x11in) red black white pigment. 2-Dec-3 Sotheby's, Olympia #364/R

MAWSON, Elizabeth Cameron (1849-1939) British

Works on paper
£300 $501 €438 Portrait of a girl in a green dress (36x25cm-14x10in) s. W/C. 8-Oct-3 Andrew Hartley, Ilkley #1038

MAWUNDJUL, John (1957-) Australian

Works on paper
£488 $771 €712 Bone of Namorrordo, shooting star spirit (155x23cm-61x9in) earth pigments eucalyptus bark prov. 28-Jul-3 Sotheby's, Paddington #544 (A.D 1200)
£4878 $7707 €7122 Ngalyod the rainbow serpent at Milmilngkan (162x82cm-64x32in) earth pigments eucalyptus bark prov. 28-Jul-3 Sotheby's, Paddington #355/R est:8000-12000 (A.D 12000)

MAX (20th C) ?

£470 $841 €700 Untitled - man (32x25cm-13x10in) s. chk prov. 25-May-4 Dorotheum, Vienna #284/R

MAX, Columbus Josef (1877-1970) German

£385 $654 €550 Demon (51x43cm-20x17in) s. i.verso board. 28-Nov-3 Wendl, Rudolstadt #4086/R
£1987 $3616 €3000 Young girl with a bunch of cowslips (68x70cm-27x28in) s. 16-Jun-4 Hugo Ruef, Munich #1035/R est:400

MAX, Corneille (1875-1924) German

£556 $917 €800 Portrait of boy with whip (69x53cm-27x21in) s.d.1922. 2-Jul-3 Neumeister, Munich #712/R

MAX, Gabriel von (1840-1915) Czechoslovakian

£805 $1482 €1200 Woman's portrait (33x26cm-13x10in) s.i. 26-Mar-4 Altus, Berlin #613/R
£903 $1490 €1300 Glance into the future (34x26cm-13x10in) s.i. 2-Jul-3 Neumeister, Munich #713
£1042 $1646 €1500 Girl with boy and flowers in southern ruins (67x56cm-26x22in) s.d.1880. 6-Sep-3 Arnold, Frankfurt #611/R est:2500
£1042 $1771 €1500 Girl with flowers in hair (49x40cm-19x16in) s. 28-Oct-3 Dorotheum, Vienna #252/R est:2000-2500
£1081 $1935 €1600 Portrait of a woman as Thalia (51x42cm-20x17in) s.d.1857 lit. 8-May-4 Schloss Ahlden, Ahlden #742/R est:1800
£1268 $2193 €1800 Blond maiden (45x37cm-18x15in) s. 10-Dec-3 Christie's, Amsterdam #665/R est:2000-3000
£1867 $3379 €2800 Happy hour (25x28cm-10x11in) s.i. 2-Apr-4 Winterberg, Heidelberg #486/R est:980
£2238 $3737 €3200 Maria Magdalena (68x57cm-27x22in) s. 28-Jun-3 Bolland & Marotz, Bremen #706/R est:3000
£2254 $3741 €3200 Person praying (58x43cm-23x17in) s. 16-Jun-3 Dorotheum, Vienna #202/R est:2000-2300
£2339 $4303 €3415 Epignonen (85x65cm-33x26in) s.i.verso. 14-Jun-4 Waddingtons, Toronto #204/R est:6000-7000 (C.D 5800)
£2587 $4450 €3700 Portrait of a girl with laurel leaves in her hair (46x36cm-18x14in) s. 3-Dec-3 Neumeister, Munich #666a/R est:1500
£3217 $5469 €4600 Ave Maria (67x55cm-26x22in) s.i. 28-Nov-3 Schloss Ahlden, Ahlden #1438/R est:3800
£3258 $5408 €4757 Young girl with roses (47x37cm-19x15in) s. 4-Oct-3 Kieselbach, Budapest #38/R (H.F 1200000)
£4133 $7440 €6200 Monkey drinking (60x45cm-24x18in) s. 26-Apr-4 Rieber, Stuttgart #1209/R est:5800
£5667 $10313 €8500 Maria Magdalena at the foot of the cross (86x65cm-34x26in) s.d.99. 30-Jun-4 Neumeister, Munich #612/R est:3000

MAX, Gabriel von (attrib) (1840-1915) Czechoslovakian

£1818 $3091 €2600 Little monkey with melon (34x26cm-13x10in) i. 20-Nov-3 Van Ham, Cologne #1736/R est:2600

MAX, Peter (1937-) American/German

£1347 $2250 €1967 Striped umbrella (84x74cm-33x29in) s. 23-Oct-3 Shannon's, Milford #231/R est:1500-2500
£7059 $12000 €10306 Miss Liberty (152x152cm-60x60in) s.d.89 i.verso acrylic. 20-Nov-3 Auctions by the Bay, Alameda #1134/R
Works on paper
£258 $475 €377 Seated dega, collage 2 (216x267cm-85x105in) s. mixed media acrylic. 27-Jun-4 Bonhams & Butterfields, San Francisco #3884/R
£307 $550 €448 Seated dega (23x28cm-9x11in) s. mixed media. 15-May-4 Susanin's, Chicago #5064/R
£435 $700 €631 Figures (23x29cm-9x11in) s. mixed media. 24-Aug-3 Bonhams & Butterfields, Los Angeles #7063
£838 $1400 €1223 New York flower (61x48cm-24x19in) s. mixed media. 16-Nov-3 Bonhams & Butterfields, Los Angeles #7081/R est:1000-1500
£958 $1600 €1399 Better world (60x44cm-24x17in) s. mixed media. 16-Nov-3 Bonhams & Butterfields, Los Angeles #7080/R est:1000-1500

MAXENCE, Edgard (1871-1954) French

£379 $683 €550 Vase de fleurs (32x24cm-13x9in) s. isorel. 26-Jan-4 Gros & Delettrez, Paris #21
£1000 $1600 €1450 Roses dans une vase (33x41cm-13x16in) s. panel. 18-Sep-3 Christie's, Kensington #27/R est:1000-1500
£2000 $3640 €2920 Waiting at the avenue entrance (81x55cm-32x22in) s. board. 16-Jun-4 Christie's, Kensington #49/R est:3000-5000
£2500 $4550 €3650 White roses in a vase, lace handkerchief and a book on a table (46x37cm-18x15in) s. 16-Jun-4 Christie's, Kensington #48/R est:3000-5000
£3000 $5460 €4380 Red and white roses in a bowl before a Chines lacquer screen (45cm-18in circular) s. board. 16-Jun-4 Christie's, Kensington #46/R est:3000-5000
£10200 $18258 €14892 Portrait of d'enfant (47x38cm-19x15in) s.d.1900 panel exhib. 26-May-4 Sotheby's, Olympia #326/R est:4000-6000
£11000 $20020 €16060 Chrysanthemums in a Chinese Imari jardiniere with a decanter and glasses on a table (54x65cm-21x26in) s. board. 16-Jun-4 Christie's, Kensington #47/R est:4000-6000
£78000 $134160 €113880 Legend of Brittany (150x221cm-59x87in) s.d.1906 prov.exhib.lit. 3-Dec-3 Christie's, London #59/R est:100000-150000
Works on paper
£1469 $2497 €2100 Jeune femme en priere (33x23cm-13x9in) s. W/C. 30-Nov-3 Anaf, Lyon #148/R est:1200-1500

MAXIM, Ora Inge (1895-1982) American

Prints
£2654 $4750 €3875 Mallards in flight (18x24cm-7x9in) s. col woodcut sold with woodblock. 4-May-4 Doyle, New York #220/R est:2000-3000

MAXWELL, Donald (1877-1936) British

Works on paper
£450 $765 €657 Moonlit harbour (18x30cm-7x12in) s. W/C htd gouache. 25-Nov-3 Bonhams, Knightsbridge #51/R

MAXWELL, James Scott (1845-1922) British?

Works on paper
£279 $500 €407 American Schooner Intrepid (13x20cm-5x8in) s.i.d.1881 W/C gouache. 16-Mar-4 Bonhams & Butterfields, San Francisco #6192/R

MAXWELL, John (1905-1962) British

Works on paper
£407 $650 €594 Hilltown No. 7 (91x61cm-36x24in) s. s.i.verso mixed media oil col paper. 20-Sep-3 Bunte, Elgin #1208
£10200 $18666 €14892 Fruit on stool (53x34cm-21x13in) s.d.55 W/C prov.exhib.lit. 8-Apr-4 Bonhams, Edinburgh #149/R est:7000-10000

MAXWELL, Paul (1926-) American

£246 $450 €359 No.521 (58x89cm-23x35in) acrylic print hand cast. 10-Jul-4 Hindman, Chicago #328/R

MAXWELL, Stuart (1925-) Australian

Works on paper
£455 $841 €664 Container ship (134x185cm-53x73in) s.d.89 i.verso synthetic polymer. 15-Mar-4 Sotheby's, Melbourne #73 est:1000-2000 (A.D 1100)

MAY, Ferdinand (?) British?

£4802 $8500 €7011 Coastal scene with sailing boat in the distance (33x89cm-13x35in) s.d.94. 2-May-4 Bonhams & Butterfields, San Francisco #1075/R est:300-500

MAY, Frank (fl.1882-1895) British

£467 $849 €700 Sailing boats close to a rocky coastline (20x30cm-8x12in) s. panel. 1-Jul-4 Van Ham, Cologne #1494/R

MAY, Joannah (20th C) British

£3200 $5952 €4672 Zee and little Zee (150x120cm-59x47in) 8-Mar-4 Christie's, London #19

MAY, Olivier le (1734-1797) French

Works on paper
£900 $1647 €1314 View of Latomia del Paradiso, Syracuse (24x37cm-9x15in) s. pen ink brown grey wash over chk prov. 7-Jul-4 Bonhams, Knightsbridge #15/R
£2133 $3925 €3200 Paysages italiens (44x59cm-17x23in) s. sanguine pair. 9-Jun-4 Oger, Dumont, Paris #30/R est:3000-3500

MAY, Phil (1864-1903) British
Works on paper
£400 $668 €584 Frankness. Hobby horse (24x18cm-9x7in) s.d.1902 pen ink two. 14-Oct-3 Bonhams, New Bond Street #239

MAY, Walter William (1831-1896) British
£1958 $3329 €2800 Yacht Kara in the Arctic regions (40x58cm-16x23in) s.d.82. 25-Nov-3 Hamilton Osborne King, Dublin #77/R est:1500-2500
Works on paper
£280 $484 €409 Female peasant on path to harvest field (18x28cm-7x11in) s. W/C. 14-Dec-3 Desmond Judd, Cranbrook #1091
£750 $1275 €1095 Low tide (25x38cm-10x15in) s.d.80 pencil W/C. 19-Nov-3 Christie's, Kensington #332/R
£950 $1701 €1387 Breached coasters at low tide (21x32cm-8x13in) s.d.66 W/C htd white gum Arabic. 26-May-4 Christie's, Kensington #418/R

MAYA CORTES, Antonio (1950-) Spanish
£993 $1658 €1400 Flowers (50x61cm-20x24in) s.d.86. 23-Jun-3 Durán, Madrid #1/R
£1773 $2961 €2500 Mesa de trabajo (91x130cm-36x51in) s.d.82. 23-Jun-3 Durán, Madrid #3/R est:100

MAYA, Francisco (1915-) ?
£671 $1201 €1000 Farmhouse in Fonte Santa, Loures (28x36cm-11x14in) s.d.1941 panel. 31-May-4 Cabral Moncada Leiloes, Lisbon #225/R

MAYBANK, Thomas (19/20th C) British
£7000 $12040 €10220 The glow worm (59x44cm-23x17in) s.d.1904 s.i.verso. 4-Dec-3 Mellors & Kirk, Nottingham #940/R est:4000-5000

MAYBURGER, Josef (1813-1908) Austrian
£839 $1427 €1200 View of Salzburg (29x42cm-11x17in) s.i.verso board. 27-Nov-3 Dorotheum, Linz #421/R
£1528 $2490 €2200 Extensive landscape with lakeside town (44x64cm-17x25in) s. 25-Sep-3 Dr Fritz Nagel, Stuttgart #1378/R est:3600
£3147 $5350 €4500 Wallersee (81x115cm-32x45in) s.d.1859. 24-Nov-3 Dorotheum, Vienna #168/R est:5000-6000

MAYER, Alois (1855-?) German
Sculpture
£2109 $3775 €3100 Young hunter (87cm-34in) s. dark pat.bronze lit. 20-Mar-4 Bergmann, Erlangen #1209 est:3100

MAYER, Auguste Étienne (1805-1890) French
£3028 $5239 €4300 Bay of Naples. At Bosporus (15x21cm-6x8in) s. board pair. 12-Dec-3 Berlinghof, Heidelberg #1092/R est:330
£3099 $5361 €4400 View of Constantinoples (8x14cm-3x6in) on marble pair. 9-Dec-3 Pandolfini, Florence #229/R est:4200-4500

MAYER, Constance (attrib) (1775-1821) French
£1854 $3375 €2800 Portrait de jeune fille pensive (40x32cm-16x13in) 21-Jun-4 Tajan, Paris #114/R est:3000-4000

MAYER, Erich (1876-1960) South African
£276 $461 €403 Landscape on the farm stirum, Potgietersrus (17x22cm-7x9in) s.d.1943 board. 20-Oct-3 Stephan Welz, Johannesburg #537 est:1800-2400 (SA.R 3200)
£310 $518 €453 Figures outside a hartbeeshuis (16x28cm-6x11in) s.d.1940 board. 20-Oct-3 Stephan Welz, Johannesburg #510 est:4000-6000 (SA.R 3600)

MAYER, Frank Blackwell (1827-1899) American
£4747 $7500 €6931 Woman with map (33x28cm-13x11in) s. 6-Sep-3 Brunk, Ashville #187

MAYER, Friedrich (1825-1875) German
£769 $1323 €1100 Day trippers in Bavarian highland (71x56cm-28x22in) s. 4-Dec-3 Schopman, Hamburg #633/R
£2245 $4018 €3300 Peasant returning home beneath stormy skies (72x107cm-28x42in) s. bears d. 17-Mar-4 Neumeister, Munich #527/R est:1800

MAYER, L (?) ?
£2534 $4636 €3800 Constantinople, les Deux Douches (21x41cm-8x16in) s. panel. 3-Jun-4 Tajan, Paris #296/R est:3000-4000

MAYER, Louis (1791-1843) German
£2500 $4075 €3600 Extensive landscape with Burg Rechberg (68x94cm-27x37in) 25-Sep-3 Dr Fritz Nagel, Stuttgart #1377/R est:2500

MAYER, Louis (attrib) (1791-1843) German
£395 $726 €600 Landscape with travellers on lakeshore (29x25cm-11x10in) panel. 24-Jun-4 Dr Fritz Nagel, Stuttgart #734/R

MAYER, Luigi (18th C) Italian
£17778 $32000 €25956 View of Villa Scabrosa, Catania (54x93cm-21x37in) s.i. prov. 23-Jan-4 Christie's, Rockefeller NY #204/R est:8000-12000
Works on paper
£667 $1200 €1000 Catacombs in Syracuse (46x50cm-18x20in) i. verso W/C bodycol. 24-Apr-4 Reiss & Sohn, Konigstein #5525
£2300 $4071 €3358 Entrance of the village of Ciali Kavak, Bulgaria (38x52cm-15x20in) s.i. W/C bodycol. 29-Apr-4 Christie's, Kensington #190/R est:2000-3000
£2533 $4560 €3800 Camere taliate nel sasso con porte di communicazione (46x61cm-18x24in) s. W/C bodycol. 24-Apr-4 Reiss & Sohn, Konigstein #5524/R est:1200
£3000 $5310 €4380 Ancient port and ruins of the theatre at Cape Crio in the Bay of Caramania (46x61cm-18x24in) s.i. W/C bodycol. 29-Apr-4 Christie's, Kensington #187/R est:4000-6000
£4000 $7080 €5840 View of Rhodes from the sea (46x62cm-18x24in) s.i. W/C bodycol prov. 29-Apr-4 Christie's, Kensington #188/R est:6000-8000

MAYER, Peter Bela (1888-1954) American
£435 $800 €635 View through the trees (43x36cm-17x14in) s. s.d.1920 verso canvasboard. 25-Jun-4 Freeman, Philadelphia #298/R
£2143 $3750 €3129 Lake fishing (41x51cm-16x20in) s. canvas on board prov. 19-Dec-3 Sotheby's, New York #1051/R est:2500-3500

MAYER-BECK, Friedrich (1907-) Austrian
£382 $623 €550 Saint Barbara (51x26cm-20x10in) mono.d.69 glass painting. 25-Sep-3 Dorotheum, Graz #95/R

MAYER-FELICE, Felix (1876-?) German
£1761 $3151 €2500 Edith and Ilse, portrait of artist's children (138x85cm-54x33in) s.d.1912 i.verso lit. 8-Jan-4 Allgauer, Kempten #2461/R est:2500

MAYES, William Edward (1861-1952) British
Works on paper
£400 $668 €584 Wherry and yachts (20x33cm-8x13in) s. W/C. 17-Oct-3 Keys, Aylsham #636/R
£410 $742 €599 Sailing yachts on the Norfolk Broads (20x30cm-8x12in) s. W/C. 16-Apr-4 Keys, Aylsham #621/R
£450 $833 €657 Wherry and a sailing yacht on the Broads nearing Irstead Church (20x33cm-8x13in) s.d.1918 W/C. 13-Feb-4 Keys, Aylsham #592/R
£520 $941 €759 White hulled sailing yacht passing a wherry on the Norfolk Broads (20x28cm-8x11in) s. W/C. 16-Apr-4 Keys, Aylsham #620

MAYET, Léon (1858-?) French
£4800 $8016 €7008 Morning (122x91cm-48x36in) s.d.1914 exhib. 12-Nov-3 Sotheby's, Olympia #238/R est:3000-5000

MAYEUR, Adrien le (1844-1923) Belgian
£517 $931 €750 Bateau a Maree basse (16x24cm-6x9in) s. panel. 20-Jan-4 Galerie Moderne, Brussels #138/R
£517 $931 €750 Marine (16x22cm-6x9in) s. panel. 20-Jan-4 Galerie Moderne, Brussels #202/R
£2778 $4639 €4000 Bateaux sur riviere (106x151cm-42x59in) s. 21-Oct-3 Campo & Campo, Antwerp #171/R est:4000-5000

MAYEUR, Jean le (1880-1958) Belgian
£2533 $4535 €3800 Le port de Nieuport (29x41cm-11x16in) s. canvas on panel. 11-May-4 Vanderkindere, Brussels #44 est:1500-2000
£2759 $5103 €4000 Deux jeunes femmes conversant (46x60cm-18x24in) s. chl paper on silver sheet. 19-Jan-4 Horta, Bruxelles #212/R est:4000-5000
£3595 $6507 €5249 Harbour scene (22x27cm-9x11in) s. panel. 4-Apr-4 Sotheby's, Singapore #21/R est:7500-9500 (S.D 11000)
£4362 $7721 €6500 Le marche a Bruges (36x45cm-14x18in) s. panel. 27-Apr-4 Campo, Vlaamse Kaai #485/R est:5000-7000
£4861 $8118 €7097 Boat (29x41cm-11x16in) s. 12-Oct-3 Sotheby's, Singapore #43/R est:6000-8000 (S.D 14000)
£5435 $8424 €7935 Boat (46x54cm-18x21in) s. board. 6-Oct-2 Sotheby's, Singapore #16/R est:13000-18000 (S.D 15000)
£8497 $15379 €12406 Boats (46x65cm-18x26in) s. panel. 4-Apr-4 Sotheby's, Singapore #20/R est:15000-20000 (S.D 26000)
£8784 $15723 €13000 Caravane sur fond de ville, Orientaliste (22x27cm-9x11in) s. cardboard. 10-May-4 Horta, Bruxelles #153/R est:4000-6000
£9420 $14601 €13753 Ladies on the beach (22x27cm-9x11in) s. board. 6-Oct-2 Sotheby's, Singapore #46/R est:20000-30000 (S.D 26000)
£10145 $15725 €14812 Boats by the canal Flander (36x55cm-14x22in) s. board. 6-Oct-2 Sotheby's, Singapore #51/R est:20000-30000 (S.D 28000)
£11183 $17892 €16327 Church (35x55cm-14x22in) s. panel. 18-May-3 Sotheby's, Singapore #35/R est:15000-20000 (S.D 31200)
£12081 $21383 €18000 Algerienne a la cigarette (46x55cm-18x22in) s. cardboard. 27-Apr-4 Campo, Vlaamse Kaai #486/R est:15000-20000
£14225 $25605 €20769 Sailing boats (29x40cm-11x16in) s. 25-Apr-4 Christie's, Hong Kong #511/R est:95000-130000 (HK.D 200000)
£14493 $22464 €21160 Girls by the canal (70x120cm-28x47in) s. 6-Oct-2 Sotheby's, Singapore #15/R est:30000-40000 (S.D 40000)
£20077 $33529 €29312 Harbour of Venice (46x55cm-18x22in) s. 26-Oct-3 Christie's, Hong Kong #6/R est:110000-150000 (HK.D 260000)
£23551 $36504 €34384 Balinese maidens (101x118cm-40x46in) 6-Oct-2 Sotheby's, Singapore #56/R est:50000-70000 (S.D 65000)
£26144 $47320 €38170 Ville de Flanders (106x151cm-42x59in) s. 4-Apr-4 Sotheby's, Singapore #17/R est:50000-70000 (S.D 80000)
£32680 $59150 €47713 Women by the beach (45x55cm-18x22in) s. 3-Apr-4 Glerum, Singapore #69/R est:120000-150000 (S.D 100000)
£36559 $58495 €53376 Women by the beach (52x61cm-20x24in) s. 18-May-3 Sotheby's, Singapore #29/R est:50000-70000 (S.D 102000)
£61594 $95471 €89927 Sur la terrasse (91x111cm-36x44in) s. lit. 6-Oct-2 Sotheby's, Singapore #28/R est:100000-150000 (S.D 170000)
£78236 $140825 €114225 Nudes under foliage (100x120cm-39x47in) s. i.verso. 25-Apr-4 Christie's, Hong Kong #516/R est:750000-850000 (HK.D 1100000)
£84967 $153791 €124052 Two Balinese beauties flanking an offering in the garden (43x53cm-17x21in) s. prov. 3-Apr-4 Glerum, Singapore #41/R est:150000-200000 (S.D 260000)
£90278 $150764 €131806 Four women in the garden, working on a loom (45x54cm-18x21in) s. lit. 12-Oct-3 Sotheby's, Singapore #28/R est:9000-120000 (S.D 260000)
£126812 $196558 €185146 A l'ombre des cocotiers Tahiti (90x120cm-35x47in) s. i.d.1931 verso prov.lit. 6-Oct-2 Sotheby's, Singapore #45/R est:300000-350000 (S.D 350000)
£200772 $335290 €293127 Atelier de Tissage (90x120cm-35x47in) i.verso prov. 26-Oct-3 Christie's, Hong Kong #23/R est:1800000-2800000 (HK.D 2600000)
£285156 $533242 €427734 Garden at Sanur, Bali (100x120cm-39x47in) s. prov. 20-Jul-4 Goodman, Sydney #37/R (A.D 730000)
£298720 $537696 €436131 Balinese ladies in the garden (100x120cm-39x47in) s. prov. 25-Apr-4 Christie's, Hong Kong #515/R est:2400000-2800000 (HK.D 4200000)

Works on paper

£1522	$2359	€2222	Indian woman (28x38cm-11x15in) pastel. 6-Oct-2 Sotheby's, Singapore #35/R est:3000-5000 (S.D 4200)
£3986	$6178	€5820	Horse carriage (45x59cm-18x23in) s. mixed media. 6-Oct-2 Sotheby's, Singapore #54/R est:9000-12000 (S.D 11000)
£4054	$7257	€6000	L'oasis de Nefta en Tunisie (43x58cm-17x23in) s. mixed media. 10-May-4 Horta, Bruxelles #152/R est:5000-6000
£4730	$8466	€7000	Cafe Arabe a Kairouan, Tunisie (43x58cm-17x23in) s. mixed media. 10-May-4 Horta, Bruxelles #151 est:5000-6000
£5072	$7862	€7405	Canal scene. Winter landscape (45x60cm-18x24in) mixed media two. 6-Oct-2 Sotheby's, Singapore #37/R est:8000-10000 (S.D 14000)
£5161	$8258	€7535	View at Chameaux (45x60cm-18x24in) s.d.1919 mixed media. 18-May-3 Sotheby's, Singapore #33/R est:12000-15000 (S.D 14400)
£6452	$10323	€9420	Market square (45x60cm-18x24in) s.d.1919 mixed media. 18-May-3 Sotheby's, Singapore #32/R est:12000-15000 (S.D 18000)
£7190	$13013	€10497	Benares. Jaipur (14x21cm-6x8in) s.d.1921 mixed media two. 4-Apr-4 Sotheby's, Singapore #18/R est:12000-18000 (S.D 22000)
£7312	$11699	€10676	Ni pollok (35x28cm-14x11in) s. pastel. 18-May-3 Sotheby's, Singapore #5/R est:8000-12000 (S.D 20400)
£7609	$11793	€11109	Three women by the window (30x35cm-12x14in) s. pastel. 6-Oct-2 Sotheby's, Singapore #10/R est:8000-12000 (S.D 21000)
£7742	$12387	€11303	Indian women (43x59cm-17x23in) mixed media. 18-May-3 Sotheby's, Singapore #9/R est:7000-9000 (S.D 21600)
£9524	$17048	€14000	Ni pollok in the artist's house in Sanur, Bali (37x35cm-15x14in) black chk W/C executed c.1937-38. 16-Mar-4 Christie's, Amsterdam #84/R est:8000-12000
£10145	$15725	€14812	Street scene in Africa (46x60cm-18x24in) s.d.1919 mixed media. 6-Oct-2 Sotheby's, Singapore #33/R est:10000-15000 (S.D 28000)
£13072	$23660	€19085	Ni Pollok and maidens (27x35cm-11x14in) gouache prov. 4-Apr-4 Sotheby's, Singapore #30/R est:25000-30000 (S.D 40000)
£18056	$30153	€26362	Portrait of Ni Pollok (68x51cm-27x20in) s. mixed media lit. 12-Oct-3 Sotheby's, Singapore #10/R est:30000-40000 (S.D 52000)
£19305	$32239	€28185	Balinese girls in the garden (54x70cm-21x28in) s. chl pastel htd white. 26-Oct-3 Christie's, Hong Kong #4/R est:90000-120000 (HK.D 250000)
£23529	$42588	€34352	Woman at a loom (55x70cm-22x28in) s. mixed media. 4-Apr-4 Sotheby's, Singapore #8/R est:18000-28000 (S.D 72000)
£64011	$115220	€93456	Balinese girl preparing offerings in the garden (48x64cm-19x25in) s. chl pastel. 25-Apr-4 Christie's, Hong Kong #507/R est:280000-350000 (HK.D 900000)

MAYFIELD, Robert Bledsoe (1869-1934) American

£273	$500	€399	Where Dwelt the Aristocracy, New Orleans (25x13cm-10x5in) s. i.verso chl chk. 5-Jun-4 Neal Auction Company, New Orleans #389
£1958	$3250	€2859	Dr Isaac Monroe Cline at Home (46x56cm-18x22in) s.d.1910 prov. 4-Oct-3 Neal Auction Company, New Orleans #539/R est:5000-7000

MAYMURA, Narritjin (1922-1982) Australian

Works on paper

£1172	$2191	€1758	Untitled (73x43cm-29x17in) earth pigments eucalyptus bark exec.c.1955 prov. 26-Jul-4 Sotheby's, Melbourne #532/R est:3000-4000 (A.D 3000)
£1172	$2191	€1758	Possum tree (132x46cm-52x18in) earth pigments eucalyptus bark prov. 26-Jul-4 Sotheby's, Melbourne #533/R est:4000-6000 (A.D 3000)
£2148	$4018	€3222	Evolution of the Manggalili Clan (171x72cm-67x28in) earth pigments eucalyptus bark exec.c.1970. 26-Jul-4 Sotheby's, Melbourne #235/R est:7000-10000 (A.D 5500)
£8235	$14741	€12023	Possum Tree (78x33cm-31x13in) ochres on bark exec 1964 prov. 25-May-4 Lawson Menzies, Sydney #28/R est:10000-12000 (A.D 21000)

MAYMURU, Bokara (1932-1982) Australian

Works on paper

£1953	$3652	€2930	Guwak the night bird, Marrnyu the possum, the sacred tree at Djarrakpi (141x70cm-56x28in) bears name.verso earth pigments eucalyptus bark exec.c.1975 prov. 26-Jul-4 Sotheby's, Melbourne #234/R est:7000-10000 (A.D 5000)

MAYMURU, Nanyin (1918-1969) Australian

Works on paper

£244	$385	€354	Guardian spirit of the paperbark tree (83x35cm-33x14in) earth pigments eucalyptus bark exec.c.1968 prov.exhib.lit. 28-Jul-3 Sotheby's, Paddington #256 (A.D 600)

MAYNARD, William (1921-) American

£257	$475	€375	Provincetown from High Head (61x97cm-24x38in) s. 15-Feb-4 Outer Cape Auctions, Provincetown #57/R
£270	$475	€394	Sal's Dory (30x61cm-12x24in) s. acrylic. 3-Jan-4 Outer Cape Auctions, Provincetown #55/R
£387	$700	€565	Dawn (56x76cm-22x30in) s. acrylic. 3-Apr-4 Outer Cape Auctions, Provincetown #58/R
£399	$650	€583	Captain Jack's Wharf (56x94cm-22x37in) s. acrylic. 19-Jul-3 Outer Cape Auctions, Provincetown #40/R
£478	$750	€698	The poet (56x71cm-22x28in) s. acrylic. 20-Apr-3 Outer Cape Auctions, Provincetown #63/R
£568	$1050	€829	First light (30x61cm-12x24in) s. acrylic. 17-Jul-4 Outer Cape Auctions, Provincetown #111a/R

Works on paper

£757	$1400	€1105	Fisherman (38x53cm-15x21in) s. W/C. 15-Feb-4 Outer Cape Auctions, Provincetown #45/R

MAYNE, Arthur Jocelyn (attrib) (1837-1893) British?

£1800	$3222	€2628	Sugar Loaf Mountain, Glengariffe (61x91cm-24x36in) indis.sig.d.1874. 14-May-4 Christie's, Kensington #307/R est:2000-3000

MAYNE, Jean (1850-1905) Belgian

£855	$1574	€1300	Ferme a Veere (54x76cm-21x30in) s.d.1898. 22-Jun-4 Palais de Beaux Arts, Brussels #285
£1067	$1941	€1600	Mother and her daughter reading (55x45cm-22x18in) s. 1-Jul-4 Van Ham, Cologne #1495 est:1400

MAYO, Antoine Malliarakis (1905-1990) French/Egyptian

Works on paper

£349	$618	€520	Le baiser (30x17cm-12x7in) s. gouache. 28-Apr-4 Charbonneaux, Paris #202

MAYO, Ethel Baker (?) American

£230	$375	€336	Christopher Wren Church (51x41cm-20x16in) s. board. 19-Jul-3 Outer Cape Auctions, Provincetown #41/R

MAYO, Nickerson (20th C) American

£279	$475	€407	Untitled, landscape (46x61cm-18x24in) s. painted c.1966. 9-Nov-3 Outer Cape Auctions, Provincetown #58/R

MAYODON, Jean (1893-1967) French

Works on paper

£317	$548	€450	Bouquet de roses jaunes (47x30cm-19x12in) s. W/C. 10-Dec-3 Ferri, Paris #75

MAYOL TRESERRA, Luis (1918-) Spanish

£352	$609	€500	Still life of fruit (36x49cm-14x19in) s.d.943. 15-Dec-3 Ansorena, Madrid #9/R

MAYOLEZ, A (19/20th C) French?

£1342	$2403	€2000	Attributs de pecheurs et poissons en guise d'ornement mural (145x60cm-57x24in) s.d.1899 pair. 25-May-4 Palais de Beaux Arts, Brussels #372/R est:2000-3000

MAYOR, Fred (1868-1916) British

£950	$1710	€1387	Picardy landscape (16x24cm-6x9in) s. board. 21-Jan-4 Sotheby's, Olympia #350/R est:500-700

MAYOR, Igor (1946-1991) Russian

£313	$522	€450	Couple (37x27cm-15x11in) s. W/C bodycol Indian ink. 24-Oct-3 Ketterer, Hamburg #957/R

Works on paper

£347	$580	€500	Woman at table (41x30cm-16x12in) s. W/C bodycol Indian ink. 24-Oct-3 Ketterer, Hamburg #956/R
£347	$580	€500	Guitar player (41x29cm-16x11in) s. W/C bodycol Indian ink. 24-Oct-3 Ketterer, Hamburg #958/R
£347	$580	€500	Evening (41x29cm-16x11in) s. W/C bodycol Indian ink. 24-Oct-3 Ketterer, Hamburg #959/R
£403	$741	€600	Woman at bar (40x28cm-16x11in) s. W/C bodycol Indian ink. 26-Mar-4 Ketterer, Hamburg #1032/R

MAYOR, William Frederick (1868-1916) British

Works on paper

£1800	$3240	€2628	Village scene with figures. Figures beside eastern buildings (15x21cm-6x8in) s.i. W/C two. 21-Apr-4 Tennants, Leyburn #964/R est:600-800

MAYR, Johann Ulrich (1630-1704) German

£6667	$11933	€10000	The muse Thalia, Poet Laureate (66x51cm-26x20in) prov. 17-May-4 Glerum, Amsterdam #41/R est:10000-20000

MAYR, Michael (1794-?) German

£940	$1729	€1400	Mill by mountain stream (30x23cm-12x9in) s.d. 24-Mar-4 Hugo Ruef, Munich #1043/R

MAYRHOFER, Johann Nepomuk (1764-1832) Austrian

£10738	$19758	€16000	Still life of fruit with roses (61x50cm-24x20in) s. 27-Mar-4 Dannenberg, Berlin #595/R est:1000

MAYRSHOFER, Max (1875-1950) German

£369	$661	€550	Self portrait (38x27cm-15x11in) s. 25-May-4 Karl & Faber, Munich #408/R
£690	$1152	€1000	The painter Schrader-Velgen (40x33cm-16x13in) s.i.d.1915 board. 13-Nov-3 Neumeister, Munich #394/R

MAZE, Paul (1887-1979) French

£500	$920	€730	Navy day (19x32cm-7x13in) canvasboard. 24-Mar-4 Hamptons Fine Art, Godalming #296/R
£500	$895	€730	Coastal trader (71x93cm-28x37in) s. prov. 26-May-4 Christie's, Kensington #730/R
£550	$935	€803	Portrait of Jessie in deckchair (43x35cm-17x14in) board prov. 26-Nov-3 Sotheby's, Olympia #52/R
£700	$1295	€1022	Horse and cart in a field (23x29cm-9x11in) s. indis d. s.i.verso panel. 11-Mar-4 Christie's, Kensington #67/R
£850	$1522	€1241	Compton Downs (46x55cm-18x22in) s. i.d.1950 stretcher. 14-May-4 Christie's, Kensington #542/R
£900	$1593	€1314	Country lane (44x73cm-17x29in) board. 27-Apr-4 Bonhams, Knightsbridge #36/R
£900	$1593	€1314	Le Harve with distant view of the Seine (33x40cm-13x16in) s. 27-Apr-4 Henry Adams, Chichester #770/R
£900	$1638	€1314	Bosham Harbour (30x38cm-12x15in) board. 1-Jul-4 Christie's, Kensington #120/R
£950	$1720	€1387	Horses in paddock (25x30cm-10x12in) s. 16-Apr-4 Keys, Aylsham #841
£1200	$2184	€1752	Fishing boats on the beach (35x51cm-14x20in) s. 1-Jul-4 Christie's, Kensington #121/R est:700-1000
£1500	$2715	€2190	Ostend Harbour (38x43cm-15x17in) s. 16-Apr-4 Keys, Aylsham #705/R est:1500-2000

£1500	$2685	€2190	Boats in an estuary (33x41cm-13x16in) s. board. 14-May-4 Christie's, Kensington #541/R est:800-1200
£1600	$2672	€2336	London embankment (38x46cm-15x18in) 21-Oct-3 Gorringes, Lewes #2183/R
£1900	$3515	€2774	Thames from the Embankment (39x47cm-15x19in) s.i.d.Nov 12 1960 panel. 11-Mar-4 Christie's, Kensington #64/R est:2000-3000
£2200	$3740	€3212	Boating in Summer (38x55cm-15x22in) s. 26-Nov-3 Sotheby's, Olympia #62/R est:800-1200
£2400	$4224	€3504	Relaxing in the garden (74x92cm-29x36in) s. board. 18-May-4 Bonhams, Knightsbridge #60/R est:1000-1500
£3600	$6192	€5256	Jessie in the garden (50x61cm-20x24in) s. 3-Dec-3 Christie's, Kensington #449/R est:2500-3500
Works on paper			
£300	$528	€438	Vase of pink and blue bloom (28x35cm-11x14in) s. pastel. 18-May-4 Bonhams, Knightsbridge #190/R
£300	$528	€438	Snow scene (28x44cm-11x17in) s. pastel. 18-May-4 Bonhams, Knightsbridge #194/R
£350	$585	€511	Tea laid (38x55cm-15x22in) s. pastel. 16-Oct-3 Christie's, Kensington #263/R
£350	$595	€511	Study of seated woman (26x28cm-10x11in) s. col chk. 26-Nov-3 Sotheby's, Olympia #64/R
£360	$612	€526	Blenheim Park in winter (25x36cm-10x14in) s. pastel. 26-Nov-3 Sotheby's, Olympia #61/R
£420	$739	€613	Vase of roses in a blue and white vase (36x52cm-14x20in) s. pastel. 18-May-4 Bonhams, Knightsbridge #191/R
£450	$792	€657	Vase of irises (23x26cm-9x10in) s. pastel. 18-May-4 Bonhams, Knightsbridge #205/R
£450	$806	€657	Boats on a riverbank (26x36cm-10x14in) s. pastel. 14-May-4 Christie's, Kensington #540
£480	$768	€696	Flowers in a blue vase (75x55cm-30x22in) s. pastel. 16-Sep-3 Bonhams, Knightsbridge #58/R
£500	$860	€730	Trooping the colour (11x17cm-4x7in) s. gouache. 3-Dec-3 Christie's, Kensington #450
£500	$860	€730	Sunset, Antibes (28x37cm-11x15in) s.d.39 pastel. 3-Dec-3 Christie's, Kensington #515/R
£500	$925	€730	Yacht (24x35cm-9x14in) s. pastel. 17-Jul-4 Bonhams, Knightsbridge #181/R
£500	$915	€730	Bridge over the River Seine, Paris (33x53cm-13x21in) W/C. 28-Jul-4 Mallams, Oxford #271/R
£510	$882	€745	In the paddock, Ascot (27x37cm-11x15in) s.i.d.1955 W/C. 9-Dec-3 Bristol Auction Rooms #404/R
£550	$946	€803	The Common in Sussex (24x37cm-9x15in) s. pastel. 3-Dec-3 Christie's, Kensington #509/R
£600	$1002	€876	Black boat on beach (18x24cm-7x9in) s. pastel exhib. 16-Oct-3 Christie's, Kensington #267/R
£600	$1002	€876	Seine, Paris (27x34cm-11x13in) s.i.d.November 22 pencil W/C. 16-Oct-3 Christie's, Kensington #271/R
£600	$1074	€876	Sailing boats at anchor, naval boat in the background (25x36cm-10x14in) s. pastel. 17-Mar-4 John Nicholson, Haslemere #653/R
£600	$1074	€876	Fishing boats pulled onto the sands (23x33cm-9x13in) s.i. pastel. 17-Mar-4 John Nicholson, Haslemere #654
£600	$1074	€876	Fishing boats on the shore beneath cliffs (25x33cm-10x13in) s. pastel. 17-Mar-4 John Nicholson, Haslemere #660
£600	$1074	€876	Fishing and other boats on the beach, others in the sea (25x33cm-10x13in) s. pastel. 17-Mar-4 John Nicholson, Haslemere #661
£650	$1164	€949	Still life with grapes. Flowers in a basket (25x34cm-10x13in) s.d.39 pastel pair. 14-May-4 Christie's, Kensington #544
£700	$1204	€1022	Study of a hill top town. Study of trees (19x25cm-7x10in) s. pastel pair. 3-Dec-3 Christie's, Kensington #508/R
£740	$1347	€1080	Roses in a jug (26x19cm-10x7in) s. pastel. 3-Jul-4 Shapes, Edinburgh #474/R
£750	$1253	€1095	Jessie in the garden (59x79cm-23x31in) s. pen black ink W/C. 16-Oct-3 Christie's, Kensington #261/R
£750	$1290	€1095	Frigates (35x44cm-14x17in) studio st. pastel. 3-Dec-3 Christie's, Kensington #513/R
£750	$1365	€1095	Mimosa and anemones. Roses (38x55cm-15x22in) s. pastel two. 1-Jul-4 Christie's, Kensington #119
£800	$1384	€1168	Horsedrawn carriage (36x53cm-14x21in) s. W/C. 10-Dec-3 Bonhams, Bury St Edmunds #460
£800	$1448	€1168	Mounted life guards in London street scene (25x41cm-10x16in) s. W/C. 16-Apr-4 Keys, Aylsham #504/R
£800	$1416	€1168	Jessie dressing, rear view (27x38cm-11x15in) s. pastel. 27-Apr-4 Henry Adams, Chichester #606
£800	$1408	€1168	Still life of daffodils and table lamp. Still life of flowers and figurine (24x30cm-9x12in) s. pastel two. 19-May-4 Sotheby's, Olympia #97/R
£800	$1456	€1168	Jessie at her dressing table. Nude in front of a fireplace (25x35cm-10x14in) s. pastel two. 1-Jul-4 Christie's, Kensington #128/R
£850	$1496	€1241	Boating lake near the sea (25x36cm-10x14in) s. pastel. 18-May-4 Bonhams, Knightsbridge #195/R
£900	$1422	€1305	Jessie nude (43x55cm-17x22in) s. red chk. 7-Sep-3 Lots Road Auctions, London #338
£900	$1548	€1314	House in a landscape. Winter landscape (55x76cm-22x30in) s.d.55 pastel pair. 3-Dec-3 Christie's, Kensington #511/R
£900	$1665	€1314	Dieppe (41x54cm-16x21in) s.d.88 pastel bodycol. 11-Mar-4 Christie's, Kensington #65/R
£900	$1593	€1314	Central Park, New York (26x37cm-10x15in) s. pastel. 27-Apr-4 Henry Adams, Chichester #604
£900	$1593	€1314	Jessie at her dressing table (25x37cm-10x15in) s. pastel. 27-Apr-4 Henry Adams, Chichester #605
£1000	$1670	€1460	Still life with cyclamen. Primula. Anemones in bloom (28x37cm-11x15in) s. pastel three. 16-Oct-3 Christie's, Kensington #266/R est:600-800
£1000	$1720	€1460	Woods at Uppark, Sussex. Sussex, autumn (55x75cm-22x30in) s. one d.1948 pastel pair. 3-Dec-3 Christie's, Kensington #510/R est:800-1200
£1000	$1720	€1460	Frescia with Chinese pot. Flowers against a screen (38x55cm-15x22in) s. pastel pair. 3-Dec-3 Christie's, Kensington #528/R est:800-1200
£1000	$1720	€1460	Tea and roses. Frescias in a vase (37x56cm-15x22in) s. pastel pair. 3-Dec-3 Christie's, Kensington #531/R est:600-800
£1100	$1837	€1606	Winter walk. Snow capped hills, Sussex (37x56cm-15x22in) s. pastel. 16-Oct-3 Christie's, Kensington #272/R est:700-1000
£1100	$1892	€1606	Oxford eight (12x36cm-5x14in) s.i.d.1930 pastel. 3-Dec-3 Christie's, Kensington #514/R est:1000-1500
£1100	$2002	€1606	Regent's Park in autumn. Cornfield (38x56cm-15x22in) s. pastel two. 1-Jul-4 Christie's, Kensington #122/R est:800-1200
£1200	$2064	€1752	Red roses and tea tin. Flowers and lamp. Primula in pot. Flowers in vase (28x31cm-11x12in) s. pastel four. 3-Dec-3 Christie's, Kensington #530/R est:600-800
£1200	$2112	€1752	Harbour in Brittany (22x22cm-9x9in) s. W/C. 19-May-4 Sotheby's, Olympia #95/R est:1000-1500
£1300	$2366	€1898	Cafe on the promenade (35x76cm-14x30in) s.d.58 pastel. 1-Jul-4 Christie's, Kensington #124/R est:1200-1800
£1400	$2338	€2044	Girls by the loch, Black Loch at Achnachlock, Argyll (53x7cm-21x3in) s. s.i.verso pastel. 16-Oct-3 Christie's, Kensington #259/R est:1500-2000
£1400	$2506	€2044	Bosham (34x52cm-13x20in) s. pastel prov. 14-May-4 Christie's, Kensington #539/R est:1000-1500
£1500	$2580	€2190	Brooklyn Bridge (27x37cm-11x15in) s. pastel. 3-Dec-3 Christie's, Kensington #498/R est:1500-2000
£1600	$2816	€2336	Trooping the colour (42x55cm-17x22in) s. W/C. 19-May-4 Sotheby's, Olympia #96/R est:800-1200
£1700	$2839	€2482	Yachts at St Tropez. Ducks at low tide (57x77cm-22x30in) s. W/C pair. 16-Oct-3 Christie's, Kensington #269/R est:700-1000
£1900	$3401	€2774	Off to the start from the Stands (41x53cm-16x21in) s. pencil W/C. 14-May-4 Christie's, Kensington #546/R est:1000-1500
£2000	$3400	€2920	Jessie combing her hair (72x53cm-28x21in) s.d.55 pastel. 20-Nov-3 Christie's, London #189/R est:2000-3000
£2000	$3580	€2920	Tulips and telephone. Roses in a vase. Books and flowers (56x77cm-22x30in) s.d.57 pastel three. 14-May-4 Christie's, Kensington #509/R est:1500-2000
£2200	$3784	€3212	Goodwood, the last furlong (38x56cm-15x22in) s.d.1950 pastel. 3-Dec-3 Christie's, Kensington #512/R est:1000-1500
£2300	$3818	€3358	Cowes Isle of Wight (35x53cm-14x21in) s. pastel. 1-Oct-3 Woolley & Wallis, Salisbury #144/R est:800-1200
£2400	$4296	€3504	Waiting, Goodwood (38x56cm-15x22in) s. pastel. 14-May-4 Christie's, Kensington #545/R est:1000-1500
£2500	$4475	€3650	The Stands, Goodwood (38x56cm-15x22in) s. pastel. 14-May-4 Christie's, Kensington #543/R est:1000-1500
£2500	$4550	€3650	Summer landscape (74x91cm-29x36in) s. 1-Jul-4 Christie's, Kensington #126/R est:2000-3000
£3000	$4770	€4380	New York skyline (36x54cm-14x21in) s.i.d.52 pastel. 10-Sep-3 Sotheby's, Olympia #142/R est:2500-3000
£3000	$5160	€4380	Flowers in a pot. Irises in a vase. Lilies in a jug. Still life with telephone (56x76cm-22x30in) s.d.56 pastel four. 3-Dec-3 Christie's, Kensington #529/R est:1000-1500
£3000	$5460	€4380	Skyscrapers of Manhattan (45x74cm-18x29in) s. W/C. 1-Jul-4 Christie's, Kensington #118/R est:2000-3000
£3200	$5440	€4672	Jessie in an interior (53x74cm-21x29in) s.d.55 pastel. 20-Nov-3 Christie's, London #185/R est:2000-3000
£5000	$8000	€7300	Yacht race during Cowes Regatta with Royal Yacht Victoria and Albert III (53x74cm-21x29in) bears studio st. pastel. 16-Sep-3 Bonhams, New Bond Street #46/R est:5000-8000

MAZIARSKA, Jadwiga (1913-) Polish

£1700	$3042	€2482	Untitled (90x100cm-35x39in) painted 1985. 6-May-4 Agra, Warsaw #21/R (P.Z 12000)
Works on paper			
£1793	$2994	€2600	Collage (75x55cm-30x22in) s.verso collage oil canvas. 16-Nov-3 Agra, Warsaw #52/R est:1000

MAZO, Juan Bautista Martinez del (attrib) (1612-1667) Spanish

£1007	$1852	€1500	Portrait d'un gentilhomme de trois quarts (60x51cm-24x20in) 24-Mar-4 Tajan, Paris #21 est:2000-3000

MAZO, Maurice (1901-) Algerian

£719	$1180	€1000	Nature morte a l'Afrique. 6-Jun-3 Chochon-Barre & Allardi, Paris #77a
£719	$1180	€1000	Scene symboliste. panel. 6-Jun-3 Chochon-Barre & Allardi, Paris #77c

MAZOT, Louis (1919-) French

£486	$900	€710	Street scene (58x71cm-23x28in) s. i.verso. 19-Jul-4 Winter Associates, Plainville #188/R

MAZUMDAR, Hemen (1894-1943) Indian

£10870	$20000	€15870	Lady in her dressing room (91x60cm-36x24in) 24-Mar-4 Sotheby's, New York #155/R est:25000-35000

MAZZA, Achille (19th C) Italian

£387	$670	€550	Last light (94x55cm-37x22in) s. 10-Dec-3 Finarte Semenzato, Rome #227

MAZZA, Giuseppe Maria (style) (1653-1741) Italian

Sculpture			
£10417	$17188	€15000	Ceres (49cm-19in) terracotta. 2-Jul-3 Neumeister, Munich #18/R est:1200

MAZZA, Salvatore (1819-1886) Italian

£603	$1007	€850	View of village (17x13cm-7x5in) cardboard. 14-Oct-3 Finarte Semenzato, Milan #44
£3546	$5922	€5000	Interiors with peasants (92x74cm-36x29in) s. pair. 17-Jun-3 Finarte Semenzato, Milan #375/R est:5000-8000

MAZZACURATI, Marino (1907-1969) Italian

£1067	$1920	€1600	Riding horses (77x96cm-30x38in) s. tempera paper. 22-Apr-4 Finarte Semenzato, Rome #97/R
Sculpture			
£1000	$1840	€1500	Seated obese (26x17x19cm-10x7x7in) pat bronze exec.1941-42. 8-Jun-4 Finarte Semenzato, Milan #179/R est:1500-1800
£1293	$2314	€1900	Victory (87cm-34in) s. bronze exec.1958. 16-Mar-4 Finarte Semenzato, Milan #446/R est:2400
£1831	$3039	€2600	Saint Jerome (41cm-16in) s. bronze exhib. 11-Jun-3 Finarte Semenzato, Milan #681/R
Works on paper			
£467	$840	€700	Seated girl (100x65cm-39x26in) s. graphite. 22-Apr-4 Finarte Semenzato, Rome #85

MAZZANOVICH, Lawrence (1872-1946) American
£3911 $7000 €5710 Saugatuck, Westport, Connecticut (30x41cm-12x16in) s. prov. 6-May-4 Shannon's, Milford #185/R est:3000-5000

MAZZANTI, Lodovico (attrib) (1679-1775) Italian
£11489 $19187 €16200 Suicide of Cleopatra (99x136cm-39x54in) 18-Jun-3 Christie's, Rome #433/R est:6000-8000

MAZZETTI, Emo (1870-1955) Italian
£1528 $2521 €2200 Evening river landscape (41x60cm-16x24in) s.d.1903 panel. 3-Jul-3 Neumeister, Munich #2878/R
£24306 $40104 €35000 Antiquary (54x73cm-21x29in) s.d.1901. 2-Jul-3 Neumeister, Munich #714/R est:3500

MAZZEY, Luis (?) South American
£741 $1200 €1074 Street car in summer - Old Montevideo (45x63cm-18x25in) fibre-board prov. 29-Jul-3 Galeria y Remates, Montevideo #103/R

MAZZOLA, Francesco (1503-1540) Italian
Works on paper
£22000 $40040 €33000 Figure drapee tenant un violon de sa main gauche (10x5cm-4x2in) i.verso pen ink prov. 5-Jul-4 Neret-Minet, Paris #14/R est:10000-12000
£24667 $44893 €37000 Figure drapee tenant un violon de sa main gauche (10x5cm-4x2in) i.verso pen ink prov. 5-Jul-4 Neret-Minet, Paris #15/R est:10000-12000

MAZZOLA, Francesco (circle) (1503-1540) Italian
Works on paper
£6111 $11000 €8922 Man leaning against a laden horse (11x9cm-4x4in) pen brown ink wash prov. 22-Jan-4 Christie's, Rockefeller NY #1/R est:3000-5000

MAZZOLA, Francesco (style) (1503-1540) Italian
£5667 $10370 €8500 Adoration of the Infant (76x58cm-30x23in) 1-Jun-4 Sotheby's, Milan #131/R est:4000-6000

MAZZOLA, Girolamo Bedoli (1500-1569) Italian
Works on paper
£5000 $9150 €7300 Standing King in a niche (19x9cm-7x4in) pen brown ink red wash htd white prov.lit. 8-Jul-4 Sotheby's, London #41/R est:4000-6000
£27778 $50000 €40556 Saint Alexander filling a censer held by an angel (21x14cm-8x6in) black chk pen brown ink wash prov. 22-Jan-4 Christie's, Rockefeller NY #17/R est:30000-50000

MAZZOLANI, Enrico (1876-1967) Italian
£347 $590 €500 Summer by the mountains (27x18cm-11x7in) s. board. 1-Nov-3 Meeting Art, Vercelli #250
£369 $653 €550 Lake landscape (46x30cm-18x12in) s. board. 1-May-4 Meeting Art, Vercelli #32
£738 $1307 €1100 Landscape with figure and lake (46x30cm-18x12in) s. board. 1-May-4 Meeting Art, Vercelli #348
Sculpture
£1389 $2361 €2000 Anacreontica (60cm-24in) s.d.1901 bronze exhib. 28-Oct-3 Il Ponte, Milan #277/R est:2500-3000

MAZZOLARI, Ugo (1873-1946) Italian
£1812 $3207 €2700 Reading (56x46cm-22x18in) s.d.1911 oval lit. 1-May-4 Meeting Art, Vercelli #149 est:1500
£2162 $3805 €3200 View of lake (60x80cm-24x31in) s. 19-May-4 Il Ponte, Milan #535 est:600-700

MAZZOLINI, G (1806-1876) Italian
£3000 $5100 €4380 Samian Sybil (117x95cm-46x37in) s. after Guercino. 30-Oct-3 Sotheby's, Olympia #106/R est:2000-3000

MAZZOLINI, Giuseppe (1806-1876) Italian
£1629 $2720 €2378 Mother and child at a window (63x49cm-25x19in) s. 17-Nov-3 Waddingtons, Toronto #267/R est:1500-2000 (C.D 3600)
£2200 $3498 €3190 Mother and child (61x49cm-24x19in) s. 9-Sep-3 Bonhams, Knightsbridge #96/R est:1000-1500
£2254 $3899 €3200 Good watchful sleep (62x49cm-24x19in) s.d.1869. 10-Dec-3 Dorotheum, Vienna #170/R est:3000-3400
£2800 $5040 €4088 Peaceful slumber (64x51cm-25x20in) s.i.d.1858. 21-Jan-4 Sotheby's, Olympia #406/R est:1500-2000

MAZZOLINI, Giuseppe (attrib) (1806-1876) Italian
£1626 $2976 €2374 Mother by sleeping child (60x50cm-24x20in) indis.sig.d.1862. 7-Jun-4 Blomqvist, Oslo #337/R est:30000-35000 (N.KR 20000)

MAZZOLINO, Ludovico (attrib) (1480-1528) Italian
£10856 $19974 €16500 Madonna and Child with Saints (35x30cm-14x12in) i. panel. 24-Jun-4 Tajan, Paris #33/R est:12000-15000

MAZZON, Galliano (1896-1978) Italian
£400 $736 €600 Colourful (92x72cm-36x28in) s.d.1974. 8-Jun-4 Finarte Semenzato, Milan #181/R
£680 $1218 €1000 Magic (65x48cm-26x19in) s.d.1965 s.i.d.verso masonite prov. 16-Mar-4 Finarte Semenzato, Milan #163/R
£1905 $3410 €2800 Apocalypse (100x70cm-39x28in) s. painted 1966 exhib.lit. 22-Mar-4 Sant Agostino, Torino #472/R est:2600

MAZZONI, Giulio (c.1525-c.1618) Italian
Works on paper
£437 $800 €638 Virgin and child adored by saints (24x19cm-9x7in) i. pen brown ink wash. 29-Jan-4 Swann Galleries, New York #28/R

MAZZUCHELLI, Pietro Francesco (1571-1626) Italian
£283893 $530879 €423000 Magdalen taken to Heaven by angels (184x135cm-72x53in) lit. 25-Feb-4 Porro, Milan #74/R est:170000

MAZZUCHELLI, Pietro Francesco (studio) (1571-1626) Italian
£13673 $24475 €19963 The Penitent Magdalene attended by angels (80x69cm-31x27in) lit. 25-May-4 Bukowskis, Stockholm #433/R est:180000-200000 (S.KR 185000)

MAZZULLO, Giuseppe (1913-1988) Italian
Sculpture
£1724 $2879 €2500 Female nude. Nude. Woman undressing. two pat bronze one plaster three. 13-Nov-3 Finarte Semenzato, Rome #276/R est:2200-2500

MEACCI, Ricciardo (1856-?) Italian
Works on paper
£1285 $2300 €1876 La Corte Gioiosa (18x50cm-7x20in) s. W/C gouache paperboard prov. 14-May-4 Skinner, Boston #339/R est:3500-5500

MEAD, Ben Carlton (1902-1986) American
£273 $500 €399 Wyatt Earp (51x41cm-20x16in) s.d.1957 prov. 5-Jun-4 Neal Auction Company, New Orleans #430/R

MEAD, David (19/20th C) British
£550 $1029 €803 Cuxton Wood, Kent (61x51cm-24x20in) s. i.verso board. 22-Jul-4 Tennants, Leyburn #924

MEAD, Larkin Goldsmith (1835-1910) American
Sculpture
£17442 $30000 €25465 Venice (65cm-26in) s.i. marble. 4-Dec-3 Christie's, Rockefeller NY #52/R est:25000-35000

MEAD, Ray John (1921-1998) Canadian
£221 $411 €323 Untitled (25x30cm-10x12in) s.d.90 verso acrylic. 2-Mar-4 Ritchie, Toronto #193/R (C.D 550)

MEADE, Arthur (1863-1948) British
£720 $1195 €1051 Ploughing above the estuary, Lelant, Cornwall (39x30cm-15x12in) s. panel. 2-Oct-3 Lane, Penzance #178
£2000 $3740 €2920 Waves breaking on the foreshore St Ives (38x48cm-15x19in) s.d.1891. 26-Feb-4 Lane, Penzance #125/R est:1500-2000
£2300 $3680 €3358 Lonely road (198x132cm-78x52in) s.i. 16-Sep-3 Bonhams, Knowle #90/R est:800-1200
£2400 $3816 €3504 Attentive audience (64x77cm-25x30in) s. 9-Sep-3 Bamfords, Derby #1176/R est:600-1000
£2400 $4296 €3504 Lonely road (132x198cm-52x78in) s.i. i.verso. 27-May-4 Christie's, Kensington #231/R est:800-1200
£5000 $9350 €7300 Notre Dame, barges on the Seine (80x114cm-31x45in) s.d.1886. 26-Feb-4 Lane, Penzance #45/R est:5000-6000

MEADMORE, Clement (1929-) American/Australian
Sculpture
£950 $1700 €1387 Hereabout (23x15cm-9x6in) s.d.1971 painted cast resin one of 150. 16-May-4 Wright, Chicago #277/R est:1500-2000
£2395 $4000 €3497 Study for U-Turn (9x18x13cm-4x7x5in) painted cardboard executed 1968 prov. 11-Nov-3 Christie's, Rockefeller NY #150/R est:800-1200
£20747 $34647 €31121 Dervish (66x135x78cm-26x53x31in) num.2/4 steel st.f. Meadmore prov. 27-Oct-3 Goodman, Sydney #31/R est:25000-35000 (A.D 50000)

MEADOWS, Alfred (19th C) British
£2005 $3750 €3008 Derbyshire landscape (76x127cm-30x50in) s. 25-Jul-4 Bonhams & Butterfields, San Francisco #6027/R est:2000-3000

MEADOWS, Arthur Joseph (1843-1907) British
£420 $777 €613 Coast near Weymouth (23x33cm-9x13in) s.d.1879 i.verso. 11-Mar-4 Duke & Son, Dorchester #141/R
£700 $1309 €1050 Fishing smacks and other shipping off coast. Yachts and other vessels off coast (23x39cm-9x15in) s. pair. 22-Jul-4 Hobbs Parker, Ashford #595/R
£739 $1323 €1079 Coastal landscape with sailing vessels near harbour jetty (22x45cm-9x18in) s.d.1873. 26-May-4 AB Stockholms Auktionsverk #293/R (S.KR 10000)
£1500 $2550 €2190 Pozzuoli, Bay of Naples (31x51cm-12x20in) s.d.1901 s.i.d.verso. 19-Nov-3 Bonhams, New Bond Street #57/R est:2000-4000
£1600 $2944 €2336 Huy on the Meuse, morning (35x61cm-14x24in) s. 23-Mar-4 Bonhams, New Bond Street #71/R est:1500-2000
£1617 $3008 €2361 Sailing vessels off the breakwater (26x36cm-10x14in) s. 2-Mar-4 Rasmussen, Copenhagen #1455/R est:20000 (D.KR 18000)
£1700 $2890 €2482 Barges (25x46cm-10x18in) s.d.1871. 19-Nov-3 Christie's, Kensington #546/R
£1800 $3312 €2628 Estuary scene (34x60cm-13x24in) s. 8-Jun-4 Bonhams, Knightsbridge #350c/R est:1200-1800
£2400 $4536 €3504 Unloading the catch (46x76cm-18x30in) s.d.1888. 17-Feb-4 Bonhams, New Bond Street #40/R est:2500-3500
£2500 $4425 €3650 San Giorgio Maggiore, Venice (30x25cm-12x10in) s.d.96 panel. 27-Apr-4 Bonhams, Knowle #90 est:500-800
£2500 $4675 €3750 Saumur on the Loire (25x36cm-10x14in) s.d.1884. 22-Jul-4 Gorringes, Lewes #1891/R est:1500-2000
£3700 $6401 €5402 Isle of Capri with market boats landing in the foreground (19x29cm-7x11in) s. panel. 9-Dec-3 Anderson & Garland, Newcastle #439a/R est:3000-5000

£4000 $6800 €5840 Mentone (30x51cm-12x20in) s.d.1901 s.i.d.verso prov. 19-Nov-3 Bonhams, New Bond Street #79/R est:4000-6000
£5500 $8800 €8030 Breezy weather off Portland (36x61cm-14x24in) s.d.1884 s.i.d.1884 verso. 16-Sep-3 Bonhams, New Bond Street #78/R est:5000-7000
£7200 $13320 €10512 Shipping in stormy seas (36x61cm-14x24in) s.d.1882. 10-Mar-4 Sotheby's, Olympia #196/R est:3000-5000
£9500 $16150 €13870 Antwerp on the Scheldt (76x127cm-30x50in) s.d.1878 prov. 19-Nov-3 Christie's, Kensington #527/R
£11000 $19690 €16060 Grand Canal, Venice (69x89cm-27x35in) s.d.1897. 5-May-4 John Nicholson, Haslemere #529/R est:5000-7500
£14000 $25760 €20440 Venice from beyond S Giorgio. Venice with the Doge's Palace (31x51cm-12x20in) s.d.1905 s.i.d.verso pair. 23-Mar-4 Bonhams, New Bond Street #72/R est:15000-20000

MEADOWS, Bernard (1915-) British
Sculpture
£2162 $4000 €3157 Head for wounded bird (28x36cm-11x14in) dark green pat bronze exec c.1960-65. 12-Feb-4 Sotheby's, New York #138/R est:3000-5000
£2200 $4070 €3212 Fallen bird (11x29cm-4x11in) mono. black pat bronze. 11-Feb-4 Sotheby's, Olympia #281/R est:1000-1500
£2297 $4250 €3354 Running Bird (33cm-13in) mono.base dark brown pat bronze Cast 1957 edn of 6. 12-Feb-4 Sotheby's, New York #137/R est:3000-5000
£3600 $6552 €5256 Running bird (33cm-13in) init. num.0/6 black pat bronze incl. base one of six lit. 15-Jun-4 Bonhams, New Bond Street #94/R est:3000-5000
Works on paper
£550 $875 €803 Sculpture design (13x17cm-5x7in) mono. pencil pastel W/C. 10-Sep-3 Sotheby's, Olympia #302/R

MEADOWS, Edwin L (fl.1854-1872) British
£1500 $2685 €2190 Gossip at the Dog (50x76cm-20x30in) s.i.d.1878 i.verso. 11-May-4 Bonhams, Knightsbridge #179/R est:800-1200

MEADOWS, Gordon Arthur (1868-?) British
£320 $598 €467 Fishing on the lagoons, Venice (14x22cm-6x9in) s. i.verso board. 22-Jul-4 Tennants, Leyburn #815

MEADOWS, Harvey H (20th C) American
Works on paper
£688 $1100 €1004 Drawings with military men. one chl two pencil three. 21-Sep-3 Grogan, Boston #72/R

MEADOWS, James (snr) (1798-1864) British
£2229 $3700 €3254 Ships off the coast of Brittany (30x56cm-12x22in) 4-Oct-3 South Bay, Long Island #180
£7500 $12750 €10950 Fishermen (76x127cm-30x50in) s.d.1858. 19-Nov-3 Christie's, Kensington #526/R

MEADOWS, James Edwin (1828-1888) British
£1050 $1785 €1533 Old church on the cliff, Bonchurch, Isle of Wight (42x72cm-17x28in) 26-Nov-3 Hamptons Fine Art, Godalming #155/R est:800-1200
£1556 $2800 €2272 Views of the Devon countryside (25x30cm-10x12in) one s. pair. 24-Apr-4 Weschler, Washington #542/R est:1500-2500
£2500 $4250 €3650 Cottages (76x122cm-30x48in) s.d.1862. 21-Nov-3 Skinner, Boston #218/R est:4000-6000
£2700 $4914 €3942 On the Usk near Brecon (49x75cm-19x30in) s.d.1879. 15-Jun-4 Bonhams, Oxford #110/R est:3000-5000
£2747 $5000 €4011 Gypsy encampment in the New Forest (71x92cm-28x36in) s. prov. 29-Jun-4 Sotheby's, New York #149/R est:8000-12000
£3200 $5504 €4672 Entering the harbour (60x105cm-24x41in) s.d.1869 canvas on board. 2-Dec-3 Sotheby's, London #47/R est:2000-3000
£3500 $5530 €5075 Children before a cottage, Surrey (61x107cm-24x42in) init. 4-Sep-3 Christie's, Kensington #285 est:1000-1500
£4500 $8100 €6570 Plodding home, figures with a horse and cart on a country lane (66x105cm-26x41in) 21-Apr-4 Tennants, Leyburn #1161/R est:4500-5500
£4610 $7699 €6500 Fishing village with boats in stormy seas (43x79cm-17x31in) s.d.1867. 17-Oct-3 Behringer, Furth #1650/R est:6000
£5000 $9450 €7300 Shipping off a pier (46x81cm-18x32in) s.d.1867. 17-Feb-4 Bonhams, New Bond Street #18/R est:2000-3000

MEADOWS, James Edwin (attrib) (1828-1888) British
£617 $1048 €901 Landscape with farmstead (30x51cm-12x20in) i. 5-Nov-3 Dobiaschofsky, Bern #793/R (S.FR 1400)
£1154 $1985 €1685 River landscape with cattle (61x91cm-24x36in) s.d.1859. 3-Dec-3 AB Stockholms Auktionsverk #2548/R est:20000-25000 (S.KR 15000)

MEADOWS, W G (19th C) British
£850 $1445 €1241 Period battle scene with four run-away heavy artillery horse and cannon (62x92cm-24x36in) s.d.1890. 31-Oct-3 Moore Allen & Innocent, Cirencester #856/R
£870 $1600 €1270 Children gleaning wheat (76x127cm-30x50in) s. 27-Mar-4 New Orleans Auction, New Orleans #593 est:800-1200
£1000 $1670 €1460 Stable friends (51x77cm-20x30in) s.d.1897 pair. 12-Nov-3 Sotheby's, Olympia #86/R est:1000-1500

MEADOWS, William (fl.1870-1895) British
£600 $1074 €876 On the Grand Canal, Venice (20x41cm-8x16in) s. 18-Mar-4 Christie's, Kensington #629/R

MEADOWS, William (circle) (19th C) British
£1500 $2775 €2190 View from the Riva Degli Schiavoni towards the Grand Canal (23x40cm-9x16in) bears indis.sig. 10-Mar-4 Sotheby's, Olympia #199/R est:600-900

MEAGHER, Eileen (20th C) British?
£480 $787 €701 Fishing near Ballynahinch (25x30cm-10x12in) s.d.1999 verso. 4-Jun-3 John Ross, Belfast #134
£1250 $2325 €1825 Evening Errislannon, Connemara (40x50cm-16x20in) s.d.1998 verso board. 3-Mar-4 John Ross, Belfast #196 est:1200-1400
£1250 $2288 €1825 Ponies in the Inagh Valley, Connemare (40x30cm-16x12in) s.d.2001 verso. 2-Jun-4 John Ross, Belfast #215 est:1000-1200
£1400 $2296 €2044 Lough Inagh (50x61cm-20x24in) s.d.1997 verso. 4-Jun-3 John Ross, Belfast #76

MEAKIN, Lewis Henry (1853-1917) American
£430 $800 €628 In the mountains (20x46cm-8x18in) s. i.verso board. 5-Mar-4 Skinner, Boston #428/R
£820 $1500 €1197 Clouded peak (48x61cm-19x24in) painted c.1913. 5-Jun-4 Treadway Gallery, Cincinnati #561/R est:2000-3000

MEARNS, John (19th C) British
£2200 $4004 €3212 Setters putting up a pheasant (69x89cm-27x35in) s.d.1875. 15-Jun-4 Dreweatt Neate, Newbury #684/R est:1000-1500

MEARS, George (1865-1910) British
£400 $664 €584 Three master under reduced sail off a coast line (46x76cm-18x30in) s.d.1889. 1-Oct-3 Bonhams, Knightsbridge #156/R
£1304 $2100 €1904 Paddle packet, Victoria (51x91cm-20x36in) s. prov. 20-Aug-3 James Julia, Fairfield #910/R est:2000-3000

MEATYARD, Ralph Eugene (1925-1972) American
Photographs
£1796 $3000 €2622 Untitled (17x17cm-7x7in) d.61 verso gelatin silver print. 17-Oct-3 Phillips, New York #76/R est:3000-5000
£2874 $4800 €4196 Untitled (18x19cm-7x7in) gelatin silver print exec.1961 lit. 17-Oct-3 Phillips, New York #78/R est:3000-5000

MECATI, Dario (1909-1976) Italian
£978 $1800 €1428 Market (72x90cm-28x35in) 22-Jun-4 Galeria y Remates, Montevideo #39/R est:900-1100

MECHAU, Frank (1904-1946) American
Works on paper
£258 $475 €377 Study for the left panel of the battle of the Alamo (41x36cm-16x14in) pencil vellum exec. c.1939 exhib. 10-Jun-4 Swann Galleries, New York #172/R
£707 $1300 €1032 Study for the mural fighting a prairie fire (25x58cm-10x23in) pencil prov.exhib. 25-Jun-4 Freeman, Philadelphia #96/R est:600-1000
£881 $1400 €1286 Study for Tommy Kenny comes home (70x114cm-28x45in) pencil tracing paper prov.exhib. 13-Sep-3 Weschler, Washington #784/R est:2000-3000
£1105 $1900 €1613 Horses, South Park, Colorado (61x74cm-24x29in) pencil tracing paper exec.c.1937 exhib. 7-Dec-3 Treadway Gallery, Cincinnati #686/R est:2000-3000

MECHAU, Jakob Wilhelm (attrib) (1745-1808) German
Works on paper
£2345 $3892 €3400 Oak by water (49x68cm-19x27in) brush over chk. 30-Sep-3 Dorotheum, Vienna #97/R est:1500-1700

MECKEL, Adolf von (1856-1893) German
£1867 $3360 €2800 Waterfall (120x90cm-47x35in) s.d.1881 lit. 22-Apr-4 Allgauer, Kempten #3645/R est:2800

MECKENEM, Israhel van (15/16th C) German
Prints
£1818 $3200 €2654 Foolish virgin (10x13cm-4x5in) copper plate engraving. 28-May-4 Aspire, Cleveland #89/R est:5000-7000
£5588 $9500 €8158 Flagellation. Crucifixion. Christ at Emmaus (21x14cm-8x6in) engraving three. 31-Oct-3 Sotheby's, New York #151/R

MECKLENBURG, Ludwig (1820-1882) German
£694 $1160 €1000 Italian city (17x13cm-7x5in) s. panel. 25-Oct-3 Bergmann, Erlangen #914/R

MECKSEPER, Friedrich (1936-) German?
Works on paper
£1176 $2000 €1717 Labyrinth (47x52cm-19x20in) s. pencil executed c.1966. 21-Nov-3 Swann Galleries, New York #126/R est:1000-1500

MEDCALF, William (20th C) American
£1879 $3364 €2800 Under pressure (91x75cm-36x30in) s. 27-May-4 Sotheby's, Paris #116/R est:2000-2500
£3691 $6607 €5500 The maid (101x76cm-40x30in) s. panel. 27-May-4 Sotheby's, Paris #118/R est:2000-2500
Works on paper
£2550 $4565 €3800 By the pool (98x75cm-39x30in) W/C cardboard painted c.1950. 27-May-4 Sotheby's, Paris #117/R est:2500-3000

MEDEARIS, Roger (1920-) American
£1618 $2800 €2362 South of St Louis (22x32cm-9x13in) s. i.verso tempera panel prov. 13-Dec-3 Weschler, Washington #616 est:500-700
£2428 $4200 €3545 Red stable (33x61cm-13x24in) s. i.verso tempera masonite prov. 13-Dec-3 Weschler, Washington #617 est:1000-1500
£22099 $40000 €32265 We shall come rejoicing (64x142cm-25x56in) acrylic. 16-Apr-4 American Auctioneer #287/R est:45000-65000

MEDGYES, Ladislas (?) ?

£662 $1205 €1000 View of port (27x35cm-11x14in) s. paint panel. 15-Jun-4 Rossini, Paris #158
£728 $1326 €1100 Route au bord de mer (27x35cm-11x14in) s. paint panel. 15-Jun-4 Rossini, Paris #157

MEDICI DEL VASCELLO, Osvaldo (1902-1978) Italian

£1049 $1783 €1500 Pont Royal and Tuileries (33x46cm-13x18in) s. s.i.d.1931 verso. 24-Nov-3 Christie's, Milan #195/R est:1000-1500

MEDINA SERRANO, Antonio (1944-) Spanish

£651 $1106 €950 View of village with figures (34x62cm-13x24in) s. board. 4-Nov-3 Ansorena, Madrid #342/R
£828 $1374 €1200 Market in the square (46x70cm-18x28in) s. 1-Oct-3 Ansorena, Madrid #734/R
£959 $1630 €1400 Interior scene (54x67cm-21x26in) s. board. 4-Nov-3 Ansorena, Madrid #366/R

MEDINA VERA, Inocenzio (1876-1917) Spanish

Works on paper
£455 $759 €650 Two on a donkey (27x32cm-11x13in) s. W/C ink. 30-Jun-3 Ansorena, Madrid #13/R
£704 $1232 €1000 Argentinian scene (27x32cm-11x13in) s. wash ink dr. 16-Dec-3 Durán, Madrid #664/R

MEDINA, Angel (1924-) Spanish

Works on paper
£289 $518 €425 Scarecrow (50x65cm-20x26in) s. mixed media card. 22-Mar-4 Durán, Madrid #1287/R
£289 $518 €425 Harbour (65x50cm-26x20in) s. mixed media card. 22-Mar-4 Durán, Madrid #1285/R
£306 $548 €450 Carriage (50x65cm-20x26in) s. mixed media card. 22-Mar-4 Durán, Madrid #1286/R
£323 $578 €475 French campment (65x50cm-26x20in) s. mixed media card. 22-Mar-4 Durán, Madrid #1290/R
£323 $578 €475 Astrologists (65x50cm-26x20in) s. mixed media card. 22-Mar-4 Durán, Madrid #1289/R

MEDINA, Efren (20th C) Latin American

£184 $305 €267 Landscape with nudes (119x199cm-47x78in) d.1997. 12-Jun-3 Louis Morton, Mexico #128 est:2000-2500 (M.P 3200)

MEDINA, Enrique (1935-) ?

£263 $440 €384 Red abstraction (73x60cm-29x24in) s.d.74. 7-Oct-3 Galeria y Remates, Montevideo #75/R
£441 $750 €644 Decorative (64x64cm-25x25in) s. 25-Nov-3 Galeria y Remates, Montevideo #120
£462 $850 €675 Door (80x80cm-31x31in) s. acrylic. 22-Jun-4 Galeria y Remates, Montevideo #162/R
£618 $1050 €902 Door (80x80cm-31x31in) s. 25-Nov-3 Galeria y Remates, Montevideo #119/R
£735 $1250 €1073 Vase of flowers (80x80cm-31x31in) s. 25-Nov-3 Galeria y Remates, Montevideo #118/R

MEDINA, M (?) ?

Works on paper
£400 $688 €584 Alhambra Palace, Granada (65x48cm-26x19in) s. pencil W/C. 3-Dec-3 Christie's, Kensington #27/R

MEDINI, Giulio (20th C) ?

£709 $1184 €1000 Souk de Talea, Fes (62x46cm-24x18in) s.d.41. 16-Jun-3 Gros & Delettrez, Paris #468

MEDIZ, Karl (1868-1944) Austrian

£2128 $3553 €3000 On the Adria (64x97cm-25x38in) prov. 14-Oct-3 Dorotheum, Vienna #15/R est:3600-5000

MEDIZ-PELIKAN, Emilie (1861-1908) Austrian

£1528 $2490 €2200 Rocky arc near Duino (89x122cm-35x48in) s. lit. 23-Sep-3 Wiener Kunst Auktionen, Vienna #109/R est:2000-3000

MEDLEEYS, Leopoleys (?) ?

£320 $595 €467 Child awake in cot (35x44cm-14x17in) bears sig. 2-Mar-4 Bearnes, Exeter #457/R

MEDLEY, Robert (1905-) British

£260 $468 €380 Mohican (35x25cm-14x10in) s.i.d.1984 canvasboard. 20-Apr-4 Rosebery Fine Art, London #576
£360 $637 €526 Geometric abstract forms (66x66cm-26x26in) s.d.70 verso. 27-Apr-4 Bonhams, Knowle #150/R

MEDLYCOTT, Sir Hubert (1841-1920) British

Works on paper
£600 $1002 €876 View of Westminster from the South Bank. View of St Paul's (28x44cm-11x17in) s.d.1906 pencil W/C pair. 16-Oct-3 Christie's, Kensington #152/R
£733 $1224 €1070 Pool of London (45x74cm-18x29in) s.d.1895 W/C. 20-Oct-3 Stephan Welz, Johannesburg #188/R est:6000-8000 (SA.R 8500)
£1000 $1670 €1460 View of Battersea bridge and old Chelsea church from the Southbank (24x46cm-9x18in) s.i.d.March 1881 verso W/C. 7-Oct-3 Bonhams, Knightsbridge #30/R est:800-1200
£2400 $4416 €3504 Pool of London (58x85cm-23x33in) s. W/C. 8-Jun-4 Bonhams, New Bond Street #91/R est:1200-1800

MEDNYANSZKY, Laszlo von (1852-1919) Hungarian

£1201 $2077 €1753 Blue twilight (24x34cm-9x13in) cardboard. 12-Dec-3 Kieselbach, Budapest #130/R (H.F 460000)
£1357 $2253 €1981 Blooming trees (21x26cm-8x10in) s. canvas on board. 4-Oct-3 Kieselbach, Budapest #4/R (H.F 500000)
£1449 $2623 €2116 In the studio (34x21cm-13x8in) s. canvas on card. 16-Apr-4 Mu Terem Galeria, Budapest #102/R (H.F 550000)
£1600 $2832 €2336 Mountain view (34x23cm-13x9in) s. panel. 29-Apr-4 Christie's, Kensington #143/R est:1000-1500
£1871 $3311 €2732 Autumn twilight (23x29cm-9x11in) s. 28-Apr-4 Kieselbach, Budapest #120/R (H.F 700000)
£1958 $3386 €2859 Boy in a hat (63x42cm-25x17in) 12-Dec-3 Kieselbach, Budapest #69/R (H.F 750000)
£1976 $3577 €2885 Riverscape (28x35cm-11x14in) s. canvas on card. 16-Apr-4 Mu Terem Galeria, Budapest #47/R (H.F 750000)
£2200 $3960 €3212 Forest view (50x63cm-20x25in) s. 21-Jan-4 Sotheby's, Olympia #474/R est:2000-3000
£3162 $5723 €4617 On the veranda (33x28cm-13x11in) s. canvas on card. 16-Apr-4 Mu Terem Galeria, Budapest #90/R (H.F 1200000)
£4008 $7095 €5852 White walled cottage amongst trees (27x37cm-11x15in) s. cardboard. 28-Apr-4 Kieselbach, Budapest #63/R (H.F 1500000)
£4276 $7568 €6243 Landscape in the Tatra mountains (23x31cm-9x12in) s. panel. 28-Apr-4 Kieselbach, Budapest #108/R (H.F 1600000)
£4479 $8107 €6539 Flowery hillside (24x31cm-9x12in) s. canvas on card. 16-Apr-4 Mu Terem Galeria, Budapest #46/R (H.F 1700000)
£4543 $8041 €6633 Spring (25x32cm-10x13in) s. canvas on cardboard. 28-Apr-4 Kieselbach, Budapest #8/R (H.F 1700000)
£4810 $8514 €7023 Babbling brook in dawn light (34x36cm-13x14in) s. 28-Apr-4 Kieselbach, Budapest #180/R (H.F 1800000)
£6516 $10816 €9513 Landscape by twilight (75x100cm-30x39in) s. 4-Oct-3 Kieselbach, Budapest #57/R (H.F 2400000)
£7377 $13353 €10770 Tramp (59x73cm-23x29in) s. 16-Apr-4 Mu Terem Galeria, Budapest #103/R (H.F 2800000)
£9086 $16081 €13266 Mood after rain (38x50cm-15x20in) s. 28-Apr-4 Kieselbach, Budapest #72/R (H.F 3400000)
£14355 $24834 €20958 Blossoming trees (55x69cm-22x27in) s. 12-Dec-3 Kieselbach, Budapest #161/R (H.F 5500000)
£14491 $26229 €21157 Twilight forest (100x85cm-39x33in) s. 16-Apr-4 Mu Terem Galeria, Budapest #52/R (H.F 5500000)
£16033 $28379 €23408 Rest by the riverside (81x101cm-32x40in) s. 28-Apr-4 Kieselbach, Budapest #61/R (H.F 6000000)
£19575 $33865 €28580 Landscape with blue clouds (60x101cm-24x40in) s. 12-Dec-3 Kieselbach, Budapest #197/R (H.F 7500000)
£20880 $36123 €30485 Autumn Mood (120x111cm-47x44in) s.i. 12-Dec-3 Kieselbach, Budapest #50/R (H.F 8000000)
£21718 $36053 €31708 Blooming trees, spring (71x101cm-28x40in) s. 4-Oct-3 Kieselbach, Budapest #152/R (H.F 8000000)
£24050 $42569 €35113 The edge of the city (126x187cm-50x74in) s. 28-Apr-4 Kieselbach, Budapest #163/R (H.F 9000000)
Works on paper
£896 $1621 €1308 Fort Hermann (33x46cm-13x18in) s. gouache. 16-Apr-4 Mu Terem Galeria, Budapest #91/R (H.F 340000)
£940 $1626 €1372 Landscape (31x40cm-12x16in) s. mixed media. 12-Dec-3 Kieselbach, Budapest #221/R (H.F 360000)
£1305 $2258 €1905 Spring (46x32cm-18x13in) s. mixed media. 12-Dec-3 Kieselbach, Budapest #187/R (H.F 500000)

MEDWEDJEW, Andrei (1950-) Russian

£671 $1235 €1000 Parade portrait (174x134cm-69x53in) mono.d.1991 i. verso. 26-Mar-4 Bolland & Marotz, Bremen #677

MEE, Anne (c.1770-1851) British

Miniatures
£1600 $2768 €2336 Miss Molyneux (8cm-3in) silver-gilt frame oval. 9-Dec-3 Christie's, London #116/R est:800-1200

MEEGAN, Walter (1859-1944) British

£340 $629 €496 Moonlit harbour scene (43x33cm-17x13in) s. 12-Feb-4 Andrew Hartley, Ilkley #887
£360 $612 €526 Boats in Scarborough harbour (22x32cm-9x13in) s. 1-Dec-3 David Duggleby, Scarborough #306
£460 $782 €672 North Bay Scarborough with the pier by moonlight (21x29cm-8x11in) s. board. 1-Dec-3 David Duggleby, Scarborough #343
£550 $1018 €803 Cattle watering by a woodland river (51x76cm-20x30in) s. 15-Jan-4 Christie's, Kensington #900/R
£600 $1002 €876 Lights in Scarborough Harbour (28x38cm-11x15in) s.d.1892 i.verso. 10-Oct-3 Richardson & Smith, Whitby #123/R
£640 $1024 €934 Figure and cart on a moonlit road (30x46cm-12x18in) s. 16-Sep-3 Bonhams, Knowle #89
£740 $1325 €1080 Moonlit street scene (30x45cm-12x18in) s. 17-May-4 David Duggleby, Scarborough #646/R
£820 $1394 €1197 Sailing boats in Scarborough harbour (24x35cm-9x14in) s. 1-Dec-3 David Duggleby, Scarborough #300/R
£851 $1379 €1200 Pareja de marinas con Londres al fondo (30x22cm-12x9in) s. pair. 20-May-3 Segre, Madrid #82/R
£1100 $1870 €1606 Whitby by moonlight (50x76cm-20x30in) s. canvas on board. 18-Nov-3 Bonhams, Leeds #164 est:500-700
£1500 $2685 €2190 Scarborough Spa and South Bay by moonlight (29x44cm-11x17in) s. 17-May-4 David Duggleby, Scarborough #602/R est:1000-1500
£3150 $5009 €4568 Whitby inner harbour. Whitby outer harbour (27x37cm-11x15in) s. board pair. 9-Sep-3 David Duggleby, Scarborough #266/R est:2000-3000

MEEGAN, Walter (attrib) (1859-1944) British

£450 $747 €657 Moonlight on the Thames (16x22cm-6x9in) panel. 1-Oct-3 Sotheby's, Olympia #28/R
£880 $1575 €1285 Thames at night (45x77cm-18x30in) bears sig verso. 26-May-4 Sotheby's, Olympia #78/R est:800-1200

MEEGEREN, Han van (1889-1947) Dutch

£267	$488	€400	Goats on a sandy path (24x29cm-9x11in) i.d.1945 verso. 7-Jun-4 Glerum, Amsterdam #77/R
£280	$468	€409	Good Samaritan (81x61cm-32x24in) s. 11-Nov-3 Bonhams, Knightsbridge #15
£647	$1080	€945	Church interior (49x39cm-19x15in) s. 20-Oct-3 Stephan Welz, Johannesburg #200/R est:8000-12000 (SA.R 7500)
£1265	$2264	€1847	Mother and Child (17x12cm-7x5in) s. wood panel prov.exhib. 15-May-4 Christie's, Sydney #489/R est:1000-1500 (A.D 3200)
Works on paper			
£559	$951	€800	Dahlia's (79x89cm-31x35in) studio st. pastel. 24-Nov-3 Glerum, Amsterdam #125/R
£1528	$2414	€2200	Fireworks at the fun fair (46x62cm-18x24in) s. pastel. 2-Sep-3 Christie's, Amsterdam #360 est:1500-2000
£3537	$6332	€5200	The man and the woman (127x423cm-50x167in) pastel diptych. 17-Mar-4 De Zwann, Amsterdam #4637a/R est:5000-7000
£4138	$6910	€6000	Sailors with woman (61x24cm-24x9in) s.d.1927 gouache. 11-Nov-3 Vendu Notarishuis, Rotterdam #135/R est:1000-1500

MEEKER, Joseph R (1827-1889) American

£3614	$6000	€5276	Birches on Lake Pepin (30x25cm-12x10in) s.d.73 mono.i.d.verso. 4-Oct-3 Neal Auction Company, New Orleans #544/R est:6000-8000
£4706	$8000	€6871	Louisiana Bayou landscape (18x13cm-7x5in) s. 22-Nov-3 New Orleans Auction, New Orleans #1064/R est:6000-9000
£6145	$11000	€8972	Bend in the river (36x76cm-14x30in) s.d.1884 prov. 26-May-4 Doyle, New York #121/R est:8000-12000
£6780	$12000	€9899	The morning walk (43x35cm-17x14in) s.d.1881 mono.i.d.verso prov.exhib. 28-Apr-4 Christie's, Los Angeles #40/R est:15000-25000
£10615	$19000	€15923	Trees in the everglades (33x58cm-13x23in) s. 16-May-4 Abell, Los Angeles #239/R
£13253	$22000	€19349	Live Oaks, Louisiana (36x61cm-14x24in) s.d.82 mono.i.d.verso. 4-Oct-3 Neal Auction Company, New Orleans #516/R est:25000-35000
£24324	$45000	€35513	Sunlight on the bayou (36x30cm-14x12in) s.d.1877 prov. 11-Mar-4 Christie's, Rockefeller NY #16/R est:15000-25000

MEEKS, Eugene (1843-?) American

£1163	$2000	€1698	Herd of cows (41x61cm-16x24in) s. 6-Dec-3 Neal Auction Company, New Orleans #345/R est:1500-2500

MEELES, Derk Willem (1872-1958) Dutch

£296	$536	€450	Mixed bouquet in a copper vase (70x45cm-28x18in) s. 19-Apr-4 Glerum, Amsterdam #149/R
£329	$595	€500	Still life with chrysanthemums in a vase (75x67cm-30x26in) s. 19-Apr-4 Glerum, Amsterdam #165

MEENAN, Anton (20th C) Irish?

£380	$654	€555	Tor Mor (61x61cm-24x24in) s. 3-Dec-3 John Ross, Belfast #214

MEENE, Hellen van (1972-) Dutch

Photographs			
£2611	$4700	€3812	Untitled no.117 (39x39cm-15x15in) s. num.5/10 chromogenic colour print. 23-Apr-4 Phillips, New York #236/R est:2000-3000

MEER, Barend van der (attrib) (1659-?) Dutch

£3474	$6218	€5072	The fruit seller (126x105cm-50x41in) 26-May-4 AB Stockholms Auktionsverk #2511/R est:40000-50000 (S.KR 47000)

MEER, Barend van der (style) (1659-?) Dutch

£5244	$8758	€7500	Still life with a roemer (61x71cm-24x28in) 30-Jun-3 Sotheby's, Amsterdam #5/R

MEER, Charles van (19th C) Belgian?

£4336	$7371	€6200	Deux hommes lisant la lettre a l'auberge (56x45cm-22x18in) s.d.1841 panel. 18-Nov-3 Vanderkindere, Brussels #59/R est:5000-7500

MEER, Eduard Alphonse Victor Auguste van der (1846-1889) Dutch

£625	$987	€900	Eagle in flight (24x30cm-9x12in) s. board. 6-Sep-3 Schopman, Hamburg #678/R
£1027	$1747	€1500	Farmhouse by the ditch. Washday (31x45cm-12x18in) s. panel pair. 5-Nov-3 Vendue Huis, Gravenhage #43/R est:1500-2000

MEER, Kurt (20th C) American

£546	$1000	€819	River landscape (76x122cm-30x48in) s.d.1998 verso board. 31-Jul-4 Sloans & Kenyon, Bethesda #279

MEERBERGEN, Rudolf (1908-1987) Belgian

£604	$1069	€900	Abstraction geometrique (71x53cm-28x21in) s.d.1958 paper. 27-Apr-4 Campo & Campo, Antwerp #162
£872	$1614	€1300	Tormented (179x89cm-70x35in) s.d.51 prov.lit. 13-Mar-4 De Vuyst, Lokeren #241/R
Works on paper			
£280	$467	€400	Les guerriers (56x73cm-22x29in) mono.d.51 ink pastel. 11-Oct-3 De Vuyst, Lokeren #250

MEERE, Charles M (1890-1961) Australian

£826	$1405	€1206	Indoor plant (43x35cm-17x14in) s.d.1958 board. 29-Oct-3 Lawson Menzies, Sydney #163/R est:2200-2800 (A.D 2000)
£1831	$3204	€2600	Viaduc a Dinan (61x50cm-24x20in) s. 21-Dec-3 Thierry & Lannon, Brest #343 est:2500-3000

MEERE, Jozef de (18th C) Dutch

£360	$619	€526	Portrait of a servant girl selling oranges (20x18cm-8x7in) s.d.1765. 3-Dec-3 Neal & Fletcher, Woodbridge #331

MEERHOUD, Jan (?-1677) Dutch

£1733	$3155	€2600	River landscape (31x39cm-12x15in) s. panel. 30-Jun-4 Neumeister, Munich #468/R est:1500

MEERHOUD, Jan (attrib) (?-1677) Dutch

£1042	$1698	€1500	Evening landscape with windmill (43x58cm-17x23in) 25-Sep-3 Neumeister, Munich #353/R est:3000
£1735	$2758	€2550	Dutch estuary at moonlight (55x79cm-22x31in) 23-Mar-3 St-Germain-en-Laye Encheres #20/R est:3000
£2245	$4018	€3300	Evening landscape with riverside village (43x58cm-17x23in) 17-Mar-4 Neumeister, Munich #361/R est:1500

MEERKOTTER, Dirk Adriaan (1922-) South African

£259	$432	€378	Still life of paint, pots and brushes (40x49cm-16x19in) s.d.54 board. 20-Oct-3 Stephan Welz, Johannesburg #644 est:2000-3000 (SA.R 3000)

MEERTENS, Abraham van (1757-1823) German

Works on paper			
£1351	$2378	€2000	Silver pheasant (43x28cm-17x11in) W/C black chk prov.exhib. 19-May-4 Sotheby's, Amsterdam #225/R est:2500-3500
£1892	$3330	€2800	Hind (44x28cm-17x11in) W/C prov.exhib.lit. 19-May-4 Sotheby's, Amsterdam #232/R est:2500-3500
£2162	$3805	€3200	Six South American birds (37x27cm-15x11in) W/C graphite prov. 19-May-4 Sotheby's, Amsterdam #229/R est:3500-4500
£2568	$4519	€3800	Whimbrel (27x43cm-11x17in) W/C prov.exhib. 19-May-4 Sotheby's, Amsterdam #230/R est:4500-6000

MEERTS, Frans (1836-1896) Belgian

Works on paper			
£369	$683	€550	Boulanger dans le quotidien (41x32cm-16x13in) s.d.93 W/C. 15-Mar-4 Horta, Bruxelles #365
£470	$869	€700	Conversation au coin de la table (34x40cm-13x16in) s.d.93 W/C. 15-Mar-4 Horta, Bruxelles #364

MEESER, Leo (19th C) German

£3169	$5261	€4500	Paysage Mexicain aux deux volcans (57x86cm-22x34in) s. 15-Jun-3 Muizon & Le Coent, Paris #10b

MEESER, Lillian B (1864-1942) American

£815	$1500	€1190	Floral still life (51x41cm-20x16in) s. 27-Jun-4 Freeman, Philadelphia #109/R est:1500-2500

MEESON, Dora (1869-1955) Australian

£366	$655	€534	In the garden of the villa of the Kaiser, Fraserti, Rome (33x24cm-13x9in) s.d.1918 board. 10-May-4 Joel, Victoria #421 (A.D 900)
£900	$1656	€1314	St Mark's Square, Venice with figures and boats (33x28cm-13x11in) panel. 8-Jun-4 Lawrences, Bletchingley #1321

MEESTER DE BETZENBROECK, Raymond de (1904-1995) Belgian

Sculpture			
£1216	$2177	€1800	Mouflon sur un rocher (61cm-24in) bears sig. green pat bronze. 10-May-4 Horta, Bruxelles #38 est:1200-1500
£1531	$2740	€2250	Tigre assis rugissant (28x24cm-11x9in) s. terracotta socle. 17-Mar-4 Hotel des Ventes Mosan, Brussels #159/R est:1400-1600
£1818	$3091	€2600	Cheval de trait (51x64x18cm-20x25x7in) green pat bronze. 1-Dec-3 Palais de Beaux Arts, Brussels #239/R est:2500-3500
£1944	$3247	€2800	Elephant (44cm-17in) s. bronze. 21-Oct-3 Campo & Campo, Antwerp #84/R est:3000-5000
£2069	$3828	€3000	Ours marchant (28x46cm-11x18in) s. num.6/12 gilt pat bronze Cast Rocher. 19-Jan-4 Horta, Bruxelles #84/R est:3500-5500
£2535	$4386	€3600	Ostrich (40x30cm-16x12in) s.d.1929 num.III/VII st.f.Batardy lit. 13-Dec-3 De Vuyst, Lokeren #472/R est:3000-4000
£2857	$5114	€4200	Couple de perruches (47x39cm-19x15in) s. brown pat bronze socle. 17-Mar-4 Hotel des Ventes Mosan, Brussels #154/R est:2800-3200
£3421	$6192	€5200	Lion assis (31cm-12in) s. pat bronze. 19-Apr-4 Horta, Bruxelles #57 est:3500-4500
£6993	$12028	€10000	Lionne en marche (30cm-12in) s. dark pat bronze. 8-Dec-3 Horta, Bruxelles #174/R est:10000-12000

MEESTERS, Dirk (1899-1950) British

£995	$1662	€1453	Wood gatherer (44x60cm-17x24in) s. prov. 17-Nov-3 Waddingtons, Toronto #160/R est:2000-3000 (C.D 2200)

MEETEREN BROUWER, Menno van (1882-1974) Dutch

£272	$487	€400	Plough team (30x24cm-12x9in) s. board. 16-Mar-4 Christie's, Amsterdam #38

MEGERT, Christian (1937-) Swiss

£915	$1500	€1336	Untitled (32x21cm-13x8in) s.d.60 verso oil cement mirror on canvas prov. 28-May-3 Sotheby's, Amsterdam #34/R est:1500-2000
Sculpture			
£2439	$4000	€3561	No 111160 (69x69cm-27x27in) s.d.65 three moveable mirrors on wood prov.exhib. 28-May-3 Sotheby's, Amsterdam #63/R est:4000-5000

MEHEUT, François (?) French

Sculpture

£3133	$5609	€4700	Le pecheur breton (34x43cm-13x17in) brown red pat bronze cire perdue Cast Susse. 16-May-4 Thierry & Lannon, Brest #18/R est:3000-4000
£3618	$6549	€5500	Porteurs de filets. bronze. 17-Apr-4 Bretagne Encheres, St Malo #123 est:6000-8000

MEHEUT, Mathurin (1882-1958) French

£1620	$2835	€2300	Mer houleuse pres des roches (37x50cm-15x20in) mono. board. 21-Dec-3 Thierry & Lannon, Brest #340/R est:800-900
£1656	$3096	€2500	La chapelle St Bruno a Penmerc Morbihan (38x57cm-15x22in) s.i. tempera. 24-Jul-4 Thierry & Lannon, Brest #109/R est:2500-3000
£2797	$4811	€4000	Paons (76x116cm-30x46in) mono. one masonite one panel two. 7-Dec-3 Livinec, Gaudcheau & Jezequel, Rennes #69/R
£4930	$8627	€7000	Etude de la foret, l'hiver (63x50cm-25x20in) mono. board. 21-Dec-3 Thierry & Lannon, Brest #341 est:7000-8000
£8099	$14173	€11500	Etude de la foret, l'automne (65x50cm-26x20in) mono. board. 21-Dec-3 Thierry & Lannon, Brest #183/R est:7000-8000

Sculpture

£3618	$6549	€5500	Porteurs de filet (31x52x20cm-12x20x8in) s. num.2/8 bronze Cast Mohon. 17-Apr-4 Livinec, Gaudcheau & Jezequel, Rennes #123/R

Works on paper

£367	$656	€550	Cormoran et poisson (30x23cm-12x9in) wash htd gouache. 16-May-4 Thierry & Lannon, Brest #403
£380	$680	€570	Lisieux (18x15cm-7x6in) i. wash. 16-May-4 Thierry & Lannon, Brest #268
£387	$692	€580	Boulangerie dans les ruines, Lisieux (22x33cm-9x13in) i. W/C chl. 16-May-4 Thierry & Lannon, Brest #270
£433	$776	€650	Langouste et tourteau (21x25cm-8x10in) i. chl sanguine. 16-May-4 Thierry & Lannon, Brest #35
£458	$801	€650	Etude de tetes de tigres (27x38cm-11x15in) studio st. chl pastel. 16-Dec-3 Adjug'art, Brest #359
£461	$847	€700	Jeune fille et charettes (25x32cm-10x13in) s. conte col crayon W/C. 28-Jun-4 Rossini, Paris #128
£461	$847	€700	La roulotte (21x27cm-8x11in) s. graphite col crayon W/C. 28-Jun-4 Rossini, Paris #129
£461	$847	€700	Etude de personnage (24x32cm-9x13in) s. conte col crayon. 28-Jun-4 Rossini, Paris #132
£470	$874	€700	Untitled (18x21cm-7x8in) st.mono. 7-Mar-4 Livinec, Gaudcheau & Jezequel, Rennes #37a
£503	$936	€750	Barque de pecheur (27x33cm-11x13in) st.sig. dr. 7-Mar-4 Livinec, Gaudcheau & Jezequel, Rennes #36a
£533	$955	€800	Les deux faucons (38x28cm-15x11in) mono. crayon chl. 16-May-4 Thierry & Lannon, Brest #37
£559	$1029	€850	Pecheur. Personnage pres d'une statue de sainte Anne (22x26cm-9x10in) one i. one s. conte two. 28-Jun-4 Rossini, Paris #115
£592	$1089	€900	Au marche. Paysans pres d'une charette (23x19cm-9x7in) s. ink conte col crayon two. 28-Jun-4 Rossini, Paris #161
£613	$1098	€920	Sortie de messe dans le nord (44x31cm-17x12in) mono. gouache. 16-May-4 Thierry & Lannon, Brest #70
£625	$1150	€950	Fontaine du village. Procession pres d'une eglise (22x25cm-9x10in) s. crayon conte two. 28-Jun-4 Rossini, Paris #106
£625	$1150	€950	Bretonne et cure. Bretonne de dos (22x26cm-9x10in) s. conte two. 28-Jun-4 Rossini, Paris #126
£629	$1176	€950	La rue Kereon a Quimper (32x24cm-13x9in) mono. chl. 24-Jul-4 Thierry & Lannon, Brest #42
£658	$1211	€1000	Personnes et eglise en Bretagne. (24x32cm-9x13in) s.i. graphite two. 28-Jun-4 Rossini, Paris #109
£658	$1211	€1000	Personnage de dos. Cure de dos (25x33cm-10x13in) s. chl conte two. 28-Jun-4 Rossini, Paris #144
£724	$1332	€1100	Les religieux. Messe en Bretagne (23x30cm-9x12in) s. graphite col crayon conte two. 28-Jun-4 Rossini, Paris #102
£724	$1332	€1100	Ceremonie. Bretons a la messe (32x37cm-13x15in) s. col crayon conte two. 28-Jun-4 Rossini, Paris #107
£724	$1332	€1100	Enfants de choeur de dos. Personnages en procession (30x25cm-12x10in) s. chl gouache col crayon conte two. 28-Jun-4 Rossini, Paris #108
£724	$1332	€1100	Personnages. Autour de la fontaine (18x26cm-7x10in) s. conte stump graphite two. 28-Jun-4 Rossini, Paris #134
£724	$1332	€1100	Les trois coiffes. Bretonne en costume traditionnel (25x32cm-10x13in) s. conte. 28-Jun-4 Rossini, Paris #136
£724	$1332	€1100	Les repos des paysans. Les Bretonnes (19x26cm-7x10in) s. one i.verso conte. 28-Jun-4 Rossini, Paris #143
£724	$1332	€1100	Paysans aux champs. Panorama de la Benediction sur mer (24x32cm-9x13in) s. conte col crayon two. 28-Jun-4 Rossini, Paris #164
£789	$1453	€1200	Calvaire pres d'une petite chapelle. Bretonnes assises pres d'un calvaire (31x42cm-12x17in) s. one i. col crayon conte. 28-Jun-4 Rossini, Paris #110
£789	$1453	€1200	Etude de meule de foin et petit village (28x21cm-11x8in) mono. graphite. 28-Jun-4 Rossini, Paris #137/R
£789	$1453	€1200	La buvette au marche, et etude de couple. Reunion de paysans (23x30cm-9x12in) s. graphite W/C graphite stump two. 28-Jun-4 Rossini, Paris #141
£789	$1453	€1200	Personnages. Les bannieres et coiffes (15x21cm-6x8in) s. conte stump col crayon two. 28-Jun-4 Rossini, Paris #142
£789	$1453	€1200	Groupes de Bretonnes. Voitures et tambours (15x20cm-6x8in) s. conte col crayon two. 28-Jun-4 Rossini, Paris #152
£789	$1453	€1200	Les pecheurs. Personnages admirant le panorama (22x26cm-9x10in) s. conte col crayon stump graphite two. 28-Jun-4 Rossini, Paris #154
£789	$1453	€1200	Etudes de Bretonnes. Etendards et utensils (25x32cm-10x13in) s. conte col crayon two. 28-Jun-4 Rossini, Paris #158
£845	$1479	€1200	Etude d'algues (42x30cm-17x12in) mono. gouache. 21-Dec-3 Thierry & Lannon, Brest #257
£855	$1574	€1300	Procession (25x32cm-10x13in) s. one i. conte col crayon two. 28-Jun-4 Rossini, Paris #111
£855	$1574	€1300	Pendant la messe Sainte Anne (25x32cm-10x13in) i. conte ink wash two. 28-Jun-4 Rossini, Paris #112
£855	$1574	€1300	Les preparatifs pour la noce a Ouessant. Boufflage du mouton a Ouessant (26x30cm-10x12in) one s.i. one mono.i. conte col crayon graphite two. 28-Jun-4 Rossini, Paris #138
£855	$1574	€1300	La charette pres de la petite chapelle (25x32cm-10x13in) mono. conte. 28-Jun-4 Rossini, Paris #139
£855	$1574	€1300	L'eglise et le puit. Paysans attablees (22x43cm-9x17in) s. conte W/C ink two. 28-Jun-4 Rossini, Paris #162
£867	$1551	€1300	L'abbatage du cochon (22x29cm-9x11in) i. chl col crayon double-sided. 16-May-4 Thierry & Lannon, Brest #36/R
£888	$1634	€1350	Preparatifs pour la fete. Preparatifs pres de la roulotte (21x27cm-8x11in) s. graphite col crayon conte two. 28-Jun-4 Rossini, Paris #165
£921	$1695	€1400	Les voeux. Breton a la bequille (24x32cm-9x13in) s. one i. conte graphite two. 28-Jun-4 Rossini, Paris #125
£921	$1695	€1400	Groupe de Bretons en habits traditionnels. Les laveuses bretonnes (24x32cm-9x13in) s. conte col crayon W/C two. 28-Jun-4 Rossini, Paris #166
£921	$1695	€1400	Voeux de Douarnenez. L'auberge sous la bache (24x32cm-9x13in) one s. one mono.i. conte two. 28-Jun-4 Rossini, Paris #167
£933	$1717	€1400	Caboteur (17x22cm-7x9in) dr W/C. 8-Jun-4 Livinec, Gaudcheau & Jezequel, Rennes #87/R
£987	$1816	€1500	Bretons en habit traditionnel (25x32cm-10x13in) mono. conte. 28-Jun-4 Rossini, Paris #127 est:150-200
£987	$1816	€1500	Au marche (25x33cm-10x13in) mono. conte col crayon W/C. 28-Jun-4 Rossini, Paris #130 est:150-200
£987	$1816	€1500	Etude de Bretonnes et Breton au beret mauve (25x32cm-10x13in) s.i. conte W/C. 28-Jun-4 Rossini, Paris #135 est:150-200
£987	$1816	€1500	Le croyant et son chien. Le mendiant a la bequille (25x33cm-10x13in) s. conte two. 28-Jun-4 Rossini, Paris #147 est:150-200
£987	$1816	€1500	Les pecheurs. Le pelerin (24x32cm-9x13in) s. conte two. 28-Jun-4 Rossini, Paris #153 est:150-200
£987	$1816	€1500	Etude de coiffes (33x21cm-13x8in) s. graphite gouache. 28-Jun-4 Rossini, Paris #170 est:150-200
£1053	$1937	€1600	Jeune bretonne. Bretonnes a la fontaine (25x33cm-10x13in) s. conte two. 28-Jun-4 Rossini, Paris #146 est:150-200
£1053	$1937	€1600	Bretonnes attablees. Preparatifs pres de l'eglise (25x33cm-10x13in) s. conte stump two. 28-Jun-4 Rossini, Paris #157 est:150-200
£1053	$1937	€1600	Les baches. Les baches, les cuisinieres et les deux Bretons (25x31cm-10x12in) s. conte two. 28-Jun-4 Rossini, Paris #159 est:150-200
£1053	$1937	€1600	La marque des moutons. La fete sous la bache (34x26cm-13x10in) one s. one mono. graphite W/C conte two. 28-Jun-4 Rossini, Paris #168 est:150-200
£1056	$1849	€1500	Singes (51x39cm-20x15in) mono. chl. 21-Dec-3 Thierry & Lannon, Brest #449 est:800-1000
£1107	$2060	€1650	En bateau (27x19cm-11x7in) s.i. crayon. 7-Mar-4 Livinec, Gaudcheau & Jezequel, Rennes #36
£1118	$2024	€1700	Etudes de paons. gouache. 17-Apr-4 Bretagne Encheres, St Malo #111 est:1500-2000
£1118	$2024	€1700	Etude de paons (44x30cm-17x12in) mono. gouache. 17-Apr-4 Livinec, Gaudcheau & Jezequel, Rennes #111
£1118	$2058	€1700	A l'auberge (25x33cm-10x13in) mono. conte. 28-Jun-4 Rossini, Paris #145 est:150-200
£1184	$2179	€1800	La traite des vaches. Paysage a la chapelle. Paysans a la priere (25x32cm-10x13in) s. conte col crayon two one double-sided. 28-Jun-4 Rossini, Paris #160 est:150-200
£1217	$2203	€1850	Chapelle Saint Bruno, Penmere (49x64cm-19x25in) mono.i. gouache. 17-Apr-4 Deburaux, Boulogne #145
£1250	$2300	€1900	Villageois pres de la fontaine. Etudes de personnages d'Ouessant (26x33cm-10x13in) s. conte two. 28-Jun-4 Rossini, Paris #148 est:150-200
£1316	$2421	€2000	Etude de personnages. Bretons de dos (20x14cm-8x6in) s. conte gouache two. 28-Jun-4 Rossini, Paris #156 est:150-200
£1382	$2501	€2100	Cassis, l'entree du mas (53x64cm-21x25in) mono.i. gouache. 17-Apr-4 Deburaux, Boulogne #144
£1409	$2621	€2100	La Poterie, Cotes du Nord (28x22cm-11x9in) s.i. gouache Indian ink. 7-Mar-4 Livinec, Gaudcheau & Jezequel, Rennes #37
£1579	$2905	€2400	Couple de Bretons (26x21cm-10x8in) mono.i. conte. gouache. 28-Jun-4 Rossini, Paris #155 est:150-200
£1645	$3026	€2500	Etude de Bretons (25x33cm-10x13in) mono. conte gouache. 28-Jun-4 Rossini, Paris #171 est:150-200
£1656	$3030	€2500	Poterie (31x50cm-12x20in) mono.i. gouache. 7-Apr-4 Piasa, Paris #95 est:400-700
£1761	$3081	€2500	Etude de coqs (42x50cm-17x20in) mono. W/C htd gouache. 21-Dec-3 Thierry & Lannon, Brest #65 est:2800-3200
£1809	$3275	€2750	Moulin a maree de Pomper pres Baden Morbihan (49x64cm-19x25in) mono.i. gouache. 17-Apr-4 Deburaux, Boulogne #142
£1842	$3389	€2800	Etudes de Bretonnes. Bretonnes assises (25x32cm-10x13in) s. conte col crayon two. 28-Jun-4 Rossini, Paris #150/R est:150-200
£1866	$3266	€2650	Composition aux moules (44x30cm-17x12in) studio st. gouache. 21-Dec-3 Thierry & Lannon, Brest #96/R est:2200-2500
£1987	$3636	€3000	Voiliers a Douelan (20x26cm-8x10in) mono.i. W/C. 7-Apr-4 Piasa, Paris #94 est:400-500
£2500	$4600	€3800	La ferme a Sainte Anne, le jour de Pardon (24x32cm-9x13in) mono. conte W/C. 28-Jun-4 Rossini, Paris #133 est:150-200
£2697	$4963	€4100	La part des pauvres (30x23cm-12x9in) mono.i. ink W/C. 28-Jun-4 Rossini, Paris #149/R est:150-200
£3158	$5811	€4800	La baie du Stiff Ouessant (60x25cm-24x10in) mono. graphite col crayon. 28-Jun-4 Rossini, Paris #169 est:150-200
£3882	$7142	€5900	La tonte a la pointe de Pern (26x35cm-10x14in) mono.i. ink W/C. 28-Jun-4 Rossini, Paris #140/R est:150-200
£4577	$8011	€6500	Femme de Roscoff a l'Ile de Batz pres du troupeau (26x20cm-10x8in) mono. gouache. 21-Dec-3 Thierry & Lannon, Brest #97/R est:4800-5000
£4895	$8420	€7000	Scene de basse-cour (53x81cm-21x32in) mono. caseine masonite. 7-Dec-3 Livinec, Gaudcheau & Jezequel, Rennes #68/R
£8000	$14320	€12000	Marche a Quimper (61x49cm-24x19in) s. W/C gouache. 16-May-4 Thierry & Lannon, Brest #68/R est:6000-8000
£10333	$18497	€15500	Le pardon de Folgoet (74x104cm-29x41in) mono. gouache. 16-May-4 Thierry & Lannon, Brest #92/R est:15000-20000
£13158	$23816	€20000	Releve des casiers en baie de Morlaix (135x175cm-53x69in) mono. casein. 17-Apr-4 Deburaux, Boulogne #146

MEHL, Eilert (1865-1941) Norwegian

£304	$527	€444	Stand (33x57cm-13x22in) s. 13-Dec-3 Blomqvist, Lysaker #1234 (N.KR 3500)
£366	$673	€534	Setter and two grouse (44x63cm-17x25in) s.d.1918. 10-Jun-4 Grev Wedels Plass, Oslo #207/R (N.KR 4500)
£417	$722	€609	Dog (25x30cm-10x12in) s. 13-Dec-3 Blomqvist, Lysaker #1235 (N.KR 4800)
£439	$808	€659	Dogs hunting for birds (36x65cm-14x26in) s. 14-Jun-4 Blomqvist, Lysaker #1257/R (N.KR 5400)
£488	$898	€712	English setter in landscape (30x70cm-12x28in) s.d.1918 panel. 10-Jun-4 Grev Wedels Plass, Oslo #208/R (N.KR 6000)

MEHL, Jan (1912-) ?

£328	$545	€479	Puppet master workshop II (97x130cm-38x51in) s. exhib. 4-Oct-3 Dorotheum, Prague #146/R est:15000-28000 (C.KR 15000)

MEHOFFER, Jozef (1869-1946) Polish

£10502	$16382	€15333	On the way to school (51x37cm-20x15in) 30-Mar-3 Agra, Warsaw #7/R est:50000 (P.Z 67000)

Works on paper

£908	$1570	€1326	Crucifixion (14x14cm-6x6in) s. W/C gouache pencil painted 1900-1914. 14-Dec-3 Agra, Warsaw #68/R est:3000 (P.Z 6000)

MEHRETU, Julie (1970-) American
Works on paper

£38037	$62000	€55534	Ringside (183x213cm-72x84in) s.d.1999 verso ink polymer canvas over panel prov.exhib. 23-Sep-3 Christie's, Rockefeller NY #77/R est:20000-30000

MEHTA, Tyeb (1925-) Indian

£17391	$32000	€25391	Untitled (125x94cm-49x37in) 25-Mar-4 Christie's, Rockefeller NY #212/R est:30000-40000
£46196	$85000	€67446	Drummer (115x90cm-45x35in) s.d.87 verso acrylic. 25-Mar-4 Christie's, Rockefeller NY #223/R est:70000-80000

MEHUS, Livio (circle) (1630-1691) Flemish

£50000	$90000	€73000	Saint George and the dragon (86x73cm-34x29in) 23-Jan-4 Christie's, Rockefeller NY #193/R est:8000-12000

MEI, Bernardino (attrib) (1615-1676) Italian
Works on paper

£1761	$3046	€2500	Lutteurs sur une place publique (21x17cm-8x7in) ink lavis. 10-Dec-3 Maigret, Paris #8 est:2500-2800

MEICHSNER, Johann Nepomuk Michael van (1737-?) German

£324	$531	€450	Scene allegorique (48x39cm-19x15in) s.verso panel. 6-Jun-3 Drouot Estimations, Paris #39

MEID, Hans (1883-1957) German
Works on paper

£567	$1043	€850	Horse-drawn carriage, night-time (35x48cm-14x19in) W/C ink chl exec. c.1926 exhib. 11-Jun-4 Villa Grisebach, Berlin #1552/R

MEIDNER, Ludwig (1884-1966) German

£2797	$4755	€4000	Portrait of a young man (65x50cm-26x20in) s.d. panel double-sided. 29-Nov-3 Villa Grisebach, Berlin #233/R est:4000-6000
£3333	$6133	€5000	Self portrait (80x60cm-31x24in) mono.d.1959 board. 10-Jun-4 Hauswedell & Nolte, Hamburg #486/R est:6000
£14333	$25657	€21500	Self portrait (67x53cm-26x21in) s.mono.d. board prov.exhib. 14-May-4 Ketterer, Munich #209/R est:9000-12000

Prints

£2667	$4773	€4000	Street in Flanders (27x21cm-11x8in) etching. 15-May-4 Bassenge, Berlin #7029/R est:1200

Works on paper

£1250	$2088	€1800	Mother of the artist (38x44cm-15x17in) mono.d. Indian ink over pencil study verso. 24-Oct-3 Ketterer, Hamburg #470/R est:2000-2200
£1608	$2766	€2300	Portrait of Georg Koch (44x28cm-17x11in) s.i.d.1916 Indian ink. 2-Dec-3 Hauswedell & Nolte, Hamburg #430/R est:3000
£5208	$8229	€7500	Grand Cafe, Schoneberg (70x56cm-28x22in) mono.d.53 chl W/C lit. 19-Sep-3 Schloss Ahlden, Ahlden #1667/R est:7800
£7500	$13650	€10950	Apokalyptische landschaft - apocalyptic landscape (33x46cm-13x18in) s.d.1912 black crayon prov. 4-Feb-4 Sotheby's, London #472/R est:8000-12000

MEIER, Theo (1908-1982) Swiss

£308	$524	€450	Still life with flowers (27x17cm-11x7in) mono. 5 Nov 3 Dobiaschofsky, Bern #799/R (S.FR 700)
£318	$528	€461	City with river and bridge (45x53cm-18x21in) s.d.1932. 13-Jun-3 Zofingen, Switzerland #2938 (S.FR 700)
£969	$1648	€1415	Reclining female nude (52x65cm-20x26in) s.d.31. 5-Nov-3 Dobiaschofsky, Bern #797/R (S.FR 2200)
£2398	$3837	€3501	Portrait of young woman from Thailand (51x41cm-20x16in) s.d.1961. 16-Sep-3 Philippe Schuler, Zurich #3244/R est:2500-3000 (S.FR 5300)
£2604	$4349	€3802	Balinese Maiden (54x44cm-21x17in) s.d.36. 12-Oct-3 Sotheby's, Singapore #6/R est:6000-8000 (S.D 7500)
£2643	$4493	€3859	Balinese woman combing hair (68x58cm-27x23in) s.d.1955. 5-Nov-3 Dobiaschofsky, Bern #796/R est:6000 (S.FR 6000)
£3080	$4774	€4497	Balinese au chapeau bleu (32x32cm-13x13in) s.d.68. 6-Oct-2 Sotheby's, Singapore #2/R est:5000-7000 (S.D 8500)
£3261	$5054	€4761	Balinese de profil. Djena la Matisse (43x35cm-17x14in) one s.d.1967 one s.d.36 i.verso two. 6-Oct-2 Sotheby's, Singapore #8/R est:10000-12000 (S.D 9000)
£3299	$5509	€4817	Divinity under a tree (100x76cm-39x30in) s.d.61. 12-Oct-3 Sotheby's, Singapore #39/R est:9000-15000 (S.D 9500)
£3394	$5871	€4955	Jeune asiatique a la robe jaune (90x75cm-35x30in) s. 12-Dec-3 Galerie du Rhone, Sion #552/R est:1500-2000 (S.FR 7500)
£3595	$6507	€5249	Landscape (40x48cm-16x19in) s. 4-Apr-4 Sotheby's, Singapore #26/R est:4000-6000 (S.D 11000)
£3846	$6154	€5615	Portrait of young woman with blossom in hair (69x60cm-27x24in) s.d.1962. 16-Sep-3 Philippe Schuler, Zurich #32345/R est:2500-3000 (S.FR 8500)
£3986	$6178	€5820	Nude (106x52cm-42x20in) s.d.76. 6-Oct-2 Sotheby's, Singapore #11/R est:9000-12000 (S.D 11000)
£5442	$9741	€8000	Portrait of Madeh Pergi, wife of the artist (24x20cm-9x8in) board prov. 16-Mar-4 Christie's, Amsterdam #102/R est:2000-3000
£5591	$8946	€8163	Temple entrance (60x70cm-24x28in) 18-May-3 Sotheby's, Singapore #40/R est:8000-12000 (S.D 15600)
£6667	$10667	€9734	Gunung agung (40x48cm-16x19in) s. board. 18-May-3 Sotheby's, Singapore #46/R est:10000-12000 (S.D 18600)
£7246	$11232	€10579	Vase of Mimosa (70x60cm-28x24in) s.d.32. 6-Oct-2 Sotheby's, Singapore #40/R est:8000-12000 (S.D 20000)
£8389	$15017	€12500	Tahitiennes (60x70cm-24x28in) s. painted 1933. 30-May-4 Eric Pillon, Calais #222/R
£9892	$15828	€14442	Young girls (47x39cm-19x15in) s.d.48. 18-May-3 Sotheby's, Singapore #16/R est:18000-25000 (S.D 27600)
£10811	$18054	€15784	Portrait of a lady (51x40cm-20x16in) s.d.48 burlap on board. 26-Oct-3 Christie's, Hong Kong #7/R est:65000-95000 (HK.D 140000)
£14583	$24354	€21291	Girls under the tree (57x37cm-22x15in) s.d.1947. 12-Oct-3 Sotheby's, Singapore #7/R est:15000-20000 (S.D 42000)
£20077	$33529	€29312	Made Pergi with offering (65x54cm-26x21in) s.d.36. 26-Oct-3 Christie's, Hong Kong #19/R est:160000-200000 (HK.D 260000)
£23656	$37849	€34538	Repos sous les cocotiers (101x141cm-40x56in) s. 18-May-3 Sotheby's, Singapore #18/R est:40000-60000 (S.D 66000)
£25362	$39312	€37029	Pegie en tjoeplik (70x60cm-28x24in) lit. 6-Oct-2 Sotheby's, Singapore #13/R est:15000-20000 (S.D 70000)
£27083	$45229	€39541	Nude with gladiola (78x103cm-31x41in) s.d.71 board. 12-Oct-3 Sotheby's, Singapore #27/R est:60000-80000 (S.D 78000)
£29247	$46796	€42701	Balinese maidens (95x75cm-37x30in) s.d.70 i.verso. 18-May-3 Sotheby's, Singapore #28/R est:40000-60000 (S.D 81600)
£32609	$50543	€47609	Offerings to the goddess (200x120cm-79x47in) s.d.1961. 6-Oct-2 Sotheby's, Singapore #24/R est:50000-70000 (S.D 90000)
£35562	$64011	€51921	Balinese nude (90x75cm-35x30in) s. lit. 25-Apr-4 Christie's, Hong Kong #522/R est:500000-700000 (HK.D 500000)
£61594	$95471	€89927	Going to the temple (92x76cm-36x30in) s.d.60. 6-Oct-2 Sotheby's, Singapore #55/R est:35000-45000 (S.D 170000)

Works on paper

£261	$477	€381	Vahine tani (31x24cm-12x9in) s.d.33 sanguine chl crayon. 5-Jun-4 Galerie du Rhone, Sion #365 (S.FR 600)
£317	$507	€463	Portrait of Balinese girl (64x49cm-25x19in) ochre chk wash. 16-Sep-3 Philippe Schuler, Zurich #3159 (S.FR 700)
£609	$1114	€889	Portrait of an exotic beauty (43x32cm-17x13in) s.indis.d. red chk. 4-Jun-4 Zofingen, Switzerland #2879/R (S.FR 1400)
£819	$1466	€1196	Portrait of an Asian woman (38x28cm-15x11in) s.d.1964 ochre. 12-May-4 Dobiaschofsky, Bern #788/R est:1900 (S.FR 1900)
£948	$1697	€1384	Portrait of Asian woman (55x37cm-22x15in) s.d.1961 ochre wash. 12-May-4 Dobiaschofsky, Bern #786/R est:2400 (S.FR 2200)
£1057	$1797	€1543	Portrait of Balinese woman (42x32cm-17x13in) s.d.51 ochre. 5-Nov-3 Dobiaschofsky, Bern #798/R est:1500 (S.FR 2400)

MEIER-DENNINGHOFF, Brigitte (1923-) German
Sculpture

£1067	$1909	€1600	Stone head II (25cm-10in) i. stone lit. 13-May-4 Neumeister, Munich #696/R est:1200-1500

MEIER-MICHEL (1880-?) Austrian
Sculpture

£2036	$3462	€2973	Coming of age (41cm-16in) i. dark pat.bronze Cast.Broma lit. 19-Nov-3 Fischer, Luzern #1445/R est:4500-5500 (S.FR 4500)

MEIFFRE, Louis (19th C) European

£1000	$1840	€1460	Suitor (36x43cm-14x17in) s. panel. 8-Jun-4 Bonhams, Knightsbridge #197/R est:1000-1500

MEIFREN Y ROIG, Eliseo (1859-1940) Spanish

£15517	$27931	€22500	Seascape (23x30cm-9x12in) s. board. 26-Jan-4 Durán, Madrid #164/R est:7500
£17450	$32456	€26000	Venice (68x82cm-27x32in) s.i. 2-Mar-4 Ansorena, Madrid #54/R est:26000
£18116	$29710	€25000	Fisherwoman on the beach (48x72cm-19x28in) s. exhib. 27-May-3 Durán, Madrid #238/R est:22500
£38194	$62257	€55000	Night view in Cadaques (70x99cm-28x39in) s. 23-Sep-3 Durán, Madrid #187/R est:55000
£40141	$69444	€57000	Coastal landscape (72x97cm-28x38in) s. 15-Dec-3 Ansorena, Madrid #33/R est:57000
£71053	$128605	€108000	Naples (74x130cm-29x51in) s.d.90. 14-Apr-4 Ansorena, Madrid #60e/R est:108000
£120000	$204000	€175200	Seascape, Southern France (130x220cm-51x87in) s. prov. 18-Nov-3 Sotheby's, London #244/R
£5033557	$9362417	€7500000	My garden (81x86cm-32x34in) s. 2-Mar-4 Ansorena, Madrid #53/R est:75000

Works on paper

£775	$1340	€1100	Cafe Novedades (13x10cm-5x4in) pencil dr lit. 15-Dec-3 Ansorena, Madrid #182/R
£775	$1340	€1100	Patio (11x15cm-4x6in) s. pencil dr. 15-Dec-3 Ansorena, Madrid #193/R
£1776	$3215	€2700	Waterfall (52x70cm-20x28in) s. pastel. 14-Apr-4 Ansorena, Madrid #48/R est:2500
£6690	$11708	€9500	View of Sitges (49x69cm-19x27in) s. chl. 16-Dec-3 Segre, Madrid #275/R est:3300

MEIFREN Y ROIG, Eliseo (attrib) (1859-1940) Spanish

£1620	$2802	€2300	Landscape with pond (36x25cm-14x10in) s. 15-Dec-3 Ansorena, Madrid #301/R est:2300

MEIJER, Cristoffel (1776-1813) Dutch
Works on paper

£582	$990	€850	Two market vendors wheeling a barrow full of cabbages (14x19cm-6x7in) s.d.1804 pen brown ink W/C over black chk. 4-Nov-3 Sotheby's, Amsterdam #136/R

MEIJER, Fritz (1900-1970) Swiss

£333	$603	€500	Tessin (49x61cm-19x24in) s. 1-Apr-4 Van Ham, Cologne #1533

MEIJER, Gerhardus (1816-1875) Dutch

£733	$1349	€1100	Landscapes (13x18cm-5x7in) one s. board pair. 11-Jun-4 Wendl, Rudolstadt #4162/R
£1007	$1862	€1500	Peasant woman on a path in a wooded landscape (31x47cm-12x19in) s. panel. 15-Mar-4 Sotheby's, Amsterdam #80/R est:1000-1500

MEIJI DYNASTY (19th C) Japanese
Sculpture

£5600	$9688	€8176	Doves on the edge of a nest. s. amber horn ivory. 11-Dec-3 Sotheby's, Olympia #135/R est:3000-4000

£8000 $14080 €11680 Hawk (23x57cm-9x22in) bronze wood stand. 18-May-4 Woolley & Wallis, Salisbury #1230/R est:1000-1500
£9932 $16884 €14500 Jurojin (26cm-10in) s. metal gold. 8-Nov-3 Dr Fritz Nagel, Stuttgart #1900/R est:12000
£12291 $22000 €17945 Shishi, guardian lion (187cm-74in) green pat. bronze. 10-May-4 Bonhams & Butterfields, San Francisco #4009/R est:15000-25000
£15278 $25972 €22000 Kanshoshi with flute (243cm-96in) bronze. 28-Oct-3 Il Ponte, Milan #316/R

MEILERTS, Ludmilla (1908-1997) Australian
£345 $538 €500 Still life (48x58cm-19x23in) s.d.80 board. 1-Aug-2 Joel, Victoria #158 est:1200-1500 (A.D 1000)
£517 $807 €750 Flowers (75x59cm-30x23in) s.d.70 board. 1-Aug-2 Joel, Victoria #334 est:1500-2000 (A.D 1500)

MEILINGER, Lothar Rudolf (1887-1935) German
£299 $536 €440 Roses in vase (64x53cm-25x21in) s.d.1931 i. verso panel. 18-Mar-4 Neumeister, Munich #2725

MEINDL, Albert (1891-1967) Austrian
£466 $750 €680 River scene in Austria (66x53cm-26x21in) s.d.1923. 17-Aug-3 Bonhams & Butterfields, San Francisco #5797

MEINEMA, Ger (1939-) Dutch
£489 $817 €700 Silence (90x90cm-35x35in) s.d.77. 30-Jun-3 Sotheby's, Amsterdam #536

MEINERS, C H (1819-1894) Dutch
£1250 $2088 €1800 Retour des pecheurs (80x140cm-31x55in) s. panel. 21-Oct-3 Galerie Moderne, Brussels #235 est:1500-2000

MEINERS, Claas Hendrik (1819-1894) Dutch
£2657 $4438 €3800 Landscape (35x52cm-14x20in) s.d.1878 panel prov. 30-Jun-3 Sotheby's, Amsterdam #181/R

MEINERS, Piet (1857-1903) Dutch
£336 $571 €480 Polder landscape with farm in the sun (25x33cm-10x13in) init.d.97 canvas on panel. 24-Nov-3 Glerum, Amsterdam #70/R

MEINHARD, Friedrich (1910-1997) German
£1399 $2336 €2000 Field of flowers before woodland (172x125cm-68x49in) s.d.76 tempera board. 9-Oct-3 Michael Zeller, Lindau #866/R est:2000
Works on paper
£350 $584 €500 Reclining Odaliske (28x37cm-11x15in) s.d.72 mixed media. 9-Oct-3 Michael Zeller, Lindau #863

MEINTJES, Johannes (1923-1980) South African
£372 $665 €543 Night bather (49x25cm-19x10in) s.d.1947. 31-May-4 Stephan Welz, Johannesburg #606 (SA.R 4500)
£413 $739 €603 Tree in a landscape (64x44cm-25x17in) s.d.1960 board. 31-May-4 Stephan Welz, Johannesburg #525 (SA.R 5000)
£756 $1369 €1104 Horses in the wind (37x26cm-15x10in) s.d.1948 board two. 30-Mar-4 Stephan Welz, Johannesburg #518/R est:5000-8000 (SA.R 9000)
£940 $1598 €1372 Two embracing figures (48x47cm-19x19in) s.d.49 board. 4-Nov-3 Stephan Welz, Johannesburg #647/R est:7000-10000 (SA.R 11000)
£1293 $2159 €1888 Seun met visbak (81x55cm-32x22in) s.d.1965 s.i.d.verso board. 20-Oct-3 Stephan Welz, Johannesburg #418/R est:5000-8000 (SA.R 15000)

MEIRELES, Cildo (1948-) Brazilian
Sculpture
£23529 $40000 €34352 Arte fisica (50x38x13cm-20x15x5in) s. ink industrial cord map wooden box exec. 1969 prov.lit. 18-Nov-3 Christie's, Rockefeller NY #16/R est:30000-40000

MEIREN, Jan Baptist van der (1664-1708) Flemish
£3691 $6607 €5500 Vue de village avec personnages devant l'entree d'une eglise (24x33cm-9x13in) panel. 25-May-4 Palais de Beaux Arts, Brussels #548/R est:4500-6000
£4730 $8324 €7000 Cavalry battle between Turkish and other troops. Cavalry battle between Turkish and Austrian (48x63cm-19x25in) pair. 18-May-4 Sotheby's, Amsterdam #16/R est:7000-9000
£6291 $11450 €9500 Southern port with anchoring frigates, numerous boats and figures (41x59cm-16x23in) 16-Jun-4 Dorotheum, Vienna #49/R est:6000-8000
£10811 $19027 €16000 Mediterranean harbour scene with figures (63x76cm-25x30in) prov. 18-May-4 Sotheby's, Amsterdam #124/R est:12000-18000

MEIREN, Jan Baptist van der (attrib) (1664-1708) Flemish
£4564 $8397 €6800 Navires de commerce pres de ports Mediterraneens (30x68cm-12x27in) pair. 26-Mar-4 Piasa, Paris #23/R est:3000-5000

MEIRHANS, Joseph (1890-1981) American
£295 $550 €431 Abstract (51x61cm-20x24in) s. board. 3-Mar-4 Alderfer's, Hatfield #351
£323 $600 €472 Abstract (51x36cm-20x14in) s. board. 3-Mar-4 Alderfer's, Hatfield #352
£353 $650 €515 Abstract in yellows and greens with blues (36x38cm-14x15in) s. masonite. 9-Jun-4 Alderfer's, Hatfield #418/R
£457 $750 €663 Abstract composition (76x58cm-30x23in) s. masonite. 4-Jun-3 Alderfer's, Hatfield #314
£751 $1300 €1096 Abstract on silver ground (114x46cm-45x18in) s. masonite. 10-Dec-3 Alderfer's, Hatfield #345/R est:1500-1800
£751 $1300 €1096 Abstract on silver ground (114x46cm-45x18in) s. masonite. 10-Dec-3 Alderfer's, Hatfield #346/R est:1500-1800
£978 $1800 €1428 Abstract expression in yellow, oranges and greens (71x76cm-28x30in) s. masonite. 9-Jun-4 Alderfer's, Hatfield #416 est:2000-3000
£978 $1800 €1428 Abstract cubist in yellow, greens and blues (91x56cm-36x22in) s. 9-Jun-4 Alderfer's, Hatfield #417/R est:2000-3000
£1156 $2000 €1688 Abstract composition (51x81cm-20x32in) s. masonite. 10-Dec-3 Alderfer's, Hatfield #348 est:1000-1500
£1195 $1900 €1745 Abstract (81x61cm-32x24in) s. masonite. 10-Sep-3 Alderfer's, Hatfield #367/R est:1500-2500
£1344 $2500 €1962 Abstract (122x81cm-48x32in) oil on plywood. 3-Mar-4 Alderfer's, Hatfield #350 est:3000-5000
£1613 $3000 €2355 Abstract (71x86cm-28x34in) 3-Mar-4 Alderfer's, Hatfield #349 est:3000-5000
Works on paper
£326 $600 €476 Lyrical abstract (25x30cm-10x12in) s. mixed media on masonite. 11-Jun-4 David Rago, Lambertville #221/R
£380 $700 €555 Lyrical abstract (15x61cm-6x24in) s. mixed media on board. 11-Jun-4 David Rago, Lambertville #223/R
£462 $800 €675 Abstract landscape (25x33cm-10x13in) s.d.1946 pastel. 10-Dec-3 Alderfer's, Hatfield #349

MEIRING, Dalene (?) New Zealander?
£301 $511 €439 Tuscan hills (100x100cm-39x39in) s. 26-Nov-3 Dunbar Sloane, Wellington #276 (NZ.D 800)

MEIRVENNE, Alfons van (1932-) Belgian
£300 $543 €450 Paire de perroquets (100x80cm-39x31in) s.d.1963. 30-Mar-4 Campo & Campo, Antwerp #319
£705 $1290 €1050 Grenouilles vertes (80x100cm-31x39in) s. 8-Jul-4 Campo, Vlaamse Kaai #273
Works on paper
£633 $1146 €950 L'aigle (151x100cm-59x39in) s.d.1958 chl. 30-Mar-4 Campo & Campo, Antwerp #320

MEISEL, Ernst (1838-1895) German
£2303 $4168 €3500 Proposal of the musician (64x75cm-25x30in) s. 19-Apr-4 Glerum, Amsterdam #304/R est:3500-4000
£3521 $6092 €5000 New gift (75x64cm-30x25in) s. 10-Dec-3 Christie's, Amsterdam #616/R est:5000-7000
£14085 $24366 €20000 King Louis XVI of France bidding farewell to his family in the Temple prison (110x180cm-43x71in) s.i. prov.exhib.lit. 10-Dec-3 Christie's, Amsterdam #698/R est:15000-20000

MEISEL, Hugo (1887-1966) German
Sculpture
£2069 $3455 €3000 Indian dancer (29cm-11in) marble socle. 14-Nov-3 Von Zezschwitz, Munich #814/R est:2300

MEISEL, Steven (20th C) American
Photographs
£3200 $5856 €4672 Christy Turlington (43x35cm-17x14in) i.verso silver print. 8-Jul-4 Sotheby's, London #494/R est:2000-2500

MEISELAS, Susan (1948-) American
Photographs
£1556 $2800 €2272 Girk show, 1974 (16x24cm-6x9in) gelatin silver print. 24-Apr-4 Phillips, New York #105/R est:3000-5000
£1667 $3000 €2434 Shortie on the bally (16x24cm-6x9in) gelatin silver print. 24-Apr-4 Phillips, New York #104/R est:3000-5000

MEISSER, Leonhard (1902-1977) Swiss
£727 $1207 €1054 Spring bouquet (61x50cm-24x20in) s.d.39 double-sided. 13-Jun-3 Zofingen, Switzerland #2940 est:2500 (S.FR 1600)
£948 $1697 €1384 Hoarfrost II (45x38cm-18x15in) s.d.64. 14-May-4 Dobiaschofsky, Bern #196/R est:3000 (S.FR 2200)
£969 $1648 €1415 Sailing boats on beach in the Lagoon, Venice (65x81cm-26x32in) s. 7-Nov-3 Dobiaschofsky, Bern #144/R (S.FR 2200)
£1121 $2006 €1637 Quiet bay (65x81cm-26x32in) s.d.48. 13-May-4 Stuker, Bern #249/R est:3000-4000 (S.FR 2600)
£1357 $2308 €1981 Mountain stream in wood (101x80cm-40x31in) mono.d.36 prov. 19-Nov-3 Fischer, Luzern #1307/R est:3500-4500 (S.FR 3000)

MEISSL, August Ritter von (1867-?) Hungarian
£1976 $3577 €2885 Dance on the meadow (60x87cm-24x34in) s. 16-Apr-4 Mu Terem Galeria, Budapest #172/R (H.F 750000)

MEISSNER, Adolf Ernst (1837-1902) German
£470 $879 €700 Evening river landscape (25x37cm-10x15in) s. board. 27-Feb-4 Altus, Berlin #445
£477 $868 €720 Sheep grazing in a sunny meadow (16x50cm-6x20in) 18-Jun-4 Bolland & Marotz, Bremen #687/R
£1769 $3166 €2600 Herder with animals on shore of mountain lake (50x63cm-20x25in) s. 17-Mar-4 Neumeister, Munich #528/R est:2500

MEISSNER, Gustav (1830-?) German
£420 $794 €613 Moonlit lake scene (39x31cm-15x12in) canvas on canvas. 23-Feb-4 David Duggleby, Scarborough #667/R

MEISSNER, Johann Heinrich (attrib) (1700-1770) German
Sculpture
£2500 $4575 €3650 Pan (25cm-10in) wood lit. 9-Jul-4 Sotheby's, London #48/R est:3000-4000

MEISSONIER, Jean Charles (1848-1917) French

£987	$1816	€1500	Port de Martigues (46x65cm-18x26in) s. 24-Jun-4 Credit Municipal, Paris #31/R est:400-600

MEISSONIER, Jean Louis Ernest (1815-1891) French

£1500	$2505	€2190	Study of a bridled horse (17x14cm-7x6in) mono. panel. 8-Oct-3 Christie's, Kensington #724/R est:700-1000
£2899	$4754	€4000	Le gentilhomme en habit rouge (11x8cm-4x3in) s. 11-May-3 Osenat, Fontainebleau #183/R est:5000-6000
£4110	$6986	€6000	Portrait (25x19cm-10x7in) mono. 6-Nov-3 Sotheby's, Paris #43/R est:3000-5000
£7333	$13200	€11000	Playing jeu de boules (14x20cm-6x8in) s.d.1847 panel. 20-Apr-4 Sotheby's, Amsterdam #74/R est:9000-12000
£8392	$14434	€12000	Draught players (31x24cm-12x9in) panel. 2-Dec-3 Christie's, Paris #720/R est:6000-8000
£11111	$20000	€16222	Bonaparte, Armee d'Italie, traversee des Alpes (41x65cm-16x26in) mono. panel prov. 23-Apr-4 Sotheby's, New York #184/R est:25000-35000
£24476	$42098	€35000	Chessplayers (20x14cm-8x6in) s. panel prov.exhib.lit. 2-Dec-3 Christie's, Paris #721/R est:12000-15000
£153846	$264615	€220000	Painting amateurs (28x21cm-11x8in) s. panel prov.exhib.lit. 2-Dec-3 Christie's, Paris #719/R est:20000-30000

MEISTER, Otto (1887-1969) Swiss

£273	$453	€396	Caslano street (61x46cm-24x18in) s.d.1928. 13-Jun-3 Zofingen, Switzerland #2941 (S.FR 600)
£302	$540	€441	Landscape with house (60x81cm-24x32in) s.d.25. 12-May-4 Dobiaschofsky, Bern #791/R (S.FR 700)
£480	$874	€701	Springtime (73x100cm-29x39in) s.d.51. 16-Jun-4 Fischer, Luzern #2273/R (S.FR 1100)
£485	$824	€708	Caslano landscape (65x88cm-26x35in) s.d.52 i. stretcher. 5-Nov-3 Dobiaschofsky, Bern #802/R (S.FR 1100)
£655	$1192	€956	Summer landscape (65x81cm-26x32in) s.d.48. 16-Jun-4 Fischer, Luzern #2272/R (S.FR 1500)

MEIXMORON, Charles de (1839-1912) French

£362	$666	€550	Le parc du chateau (15x22cm-6x9in) s. panel. 25-Jun-4 Daguerre, Paris #150

MEJA, Nyoman (1950-) Balinese

£6536	$11830	€9543	Baris dancer (150x117cm-59x46in) s.i. tempera. 3-Apr-4 Glerum, Singapore #31/R est:14000-18000 (S.D 20000)

MEJIAZ, Mauro (1930-) Venezuelan

£574	$935	€838	Untitled (97x129cm-38x51in) s. 20-Jul-3 Subastas Odalys, Caracas #136
£949	$1500	€1386	Untitled (89x106cm-35x42in) s. panel painted 1986. 1-Dec-2 Subastas Odalys, Caracas #88 est:1500
£1852	$3185	€2704	Suspended child (65x50cm-26x20in) s.verso masonite painted 1964. 7-Dec-3 Subastas Odalys, Caracas #10/R

MELANDRI, Pietro (1885-1976) Italian

Sculpture

£5208	$8854	€7500	Allegories (36x38cm-14x15in) s. ceramic relief on panel set of 4. 28-Oct-3 Il Ponte, Milan #282/R est:10000-12000

MELAVI, S (20th C) ?

Sculpture

£1292	$2313	€1900	Lanceur de javelot (33x90x20cm-13x35x8in) s. pat bronze onyx socle. 17-Mar-4 Tajan, Paris #16/R est:1500-2000

MELBYE, Anton (1818 1875) Danish

£700	$1295	€1022	Shipping off Copenhagen (15x21cm-6x8in) s. indis.d. panel. 10-Mar-4 Sotheby's, Olympia #241/R
£716	$1311	€1045	Seascape with sailing vessel in rough seas (21x30cm-8x12in) s.d.47. 7-Jun-4 Museumsbygningen, Copenhagen #31 (D.KR 8000)
£909	$1564	€1300	Sailing boats on a restless sea (11x16cm-4x6in) i.verso panel. 6-Dec-3 Hans Stahl, Toestorf #135/R
£1041	$1863	€1520	Sailing vessel at sunset off coast (42x55cm-17x22in) s.d.1856. 10-May-4 Rasmussen, Vejle #336/R (D.KR 11500)
£1327	$2123	€1937	Seascape with sailing vessels (40x51cm-16x20in) s.d.1845. 22-Sep-3 Rasmussen, Vejle #303/R est:4000-6000 (D.KR 14000)
£2865	$5243	€4183	Fishermen and their boats on shore, white lighthouse in background (48x66cm-19x26in) s. prov. 9-Jun-4 Rasmussen, Copenhagen #1829/R est:40000-50000 (D.KR 32000)
£3472	$5486	€5000	Oriental harbour by moonlight (95x74cm-37x29in) s.d.1864. 2-Sep-3 Christie's, Amsterdam #175/R est:2000-3000
£8000	$14560	€11680	Boats on the coast of Constantinople (42x76cm-17x30in) s.d.1860. 15-Jun-4 Sotheby's, London #142/R est:7000-10000

Works on paper

£280	$515	€420	Evening at the lakeside (22x27cm-9x11in) s.d.1863 mixed media. 12-Jun-4 Karlheinz Kaupp, Staufen #1131/R
£426	$689	€600	Boats on Terafina beach (20x28cm-8x11in) s.i.d.1853 W/C chl. 23-May-3 Karlheinz Kaupp, Staufen #1758

MELBYE, W (1824-1882) Danish

Works on paper

£1350	$2498	€2025	Ships at sea, believed to be the coast of Melbourne (20x33cm-8x13in) s. 14-Jul-4 John Bellman, Billingshurst #1750/R

MELBYE, Wilhelm (1824-1882) Danish

£816	$1460	€1191	Sailing vessel with union flag in rough seas (35x45cm-14x18in) s.d.1850 i.verso. 25-May-4 Grev Wedels Plass, Oslo #8/R (N.KR 10000)
£905	$1620	€1321	Seascape with vessels (19x28cm-7x11in) init.d.77. 10-May-4 Rasmussen, Vejle #356/R (D.KR 10000)
£1511	$2750	€2267	Fishing boat with figures off coastal cliffs (75x102cm-30x40in) s. 19-Jun-4 Rasmussen, Havnen #2084/R est:15000 (D.KR 17000)
£1527	$2841	€2229	Norwegian fjord landscape with boats (31x53cm-12x21in) s.i. verso. 2-Mar-4 Rasmussen, Copenhagen #1395/R est:8000-12000 (D.KR 17000)
£2062	$3546	€3011	Seascape with sailing vessels and boats in Storebaelt, evening (29x43cm-11x17in) s.d.1874. 3-Dec-3 Museumsbygningen, Copenhagen #120/R est:20000-25000 (D.KR 22000)
£2076	$3882	€3031	Seascape with sailing boat in rough seas (40x58cm-16x23in) s.d.48. 25-Feb-4 Museumsbygningen, Copenhagen #123/R est:8000-12000 (D.KR 23000)
£2079	$3722	€3035	Seascape with sailing vessels off rocky coast (35x53cm-14x21in) s.d.49. 12-Jan-4 Rasmussen, Vejle #21/R est:12000 (D.KR 22000)
£2538	$4366	€3705	Sailing vessels by Straights of Bosphorus (40x77cm-16x30in) s.d.1860. 2-Dec-3 Bukowskis, Stockholm #257/R est:20000-25000 (S.KR 33000)
£3407	$5860	€4974	Seascape with barque and full-rigged ship, Kattegat (43x70cm-17x28in) s.d.1879. 8-Dec-3 Blomqvist, Oslo #437/R est:30000-40000 (N.KR 40000)
£3615	$6218	€5278	Shipwreck by the coast (66x108cm-26x43in) s.d.59. 2-Dec-3 Bukowskis, Stockholm #256/R est:40000-50000 (S.KR 47000)
£3738	$5907	€5420	Seascape with paddle-steamer (56x97cm-22x38in) s.d.1868. 2-Sep-3 Rasmussen, Copenhagen #1578/R est:50000 (D.KR 40000)
£3804	$7000	€5554	Paddle steamer in storm (56x97cm-22x38in) s.d.1868. 28-Mar-4 Carlsen Gallery, Greenville #370/R
£4730	$8466	€7000	Shipwrecked (104x155cm-41x61in) s.d.1855. 8-May-4 Bukowskis, Helsinki #396/R est:3000-5000
£12287	$21257	€17939	View towards Sundet from Langelinie, afternoon (86x142cm-34x56in) s.d.1871 exhib. 9-Dec-3 Rasmussen, Copenhagen #1221/R est:50000-75000 (D.KR 130000)

MELCARTH, Edward (1914-) American

£726	$1300	€1060	Facade, aka goodbye Marc, the funeral. s.i. 13-May-4 Dallas Auction Gallery, Dallas #220/R est:600-1000

MELCHER-TILMES, Jan Hermanus (1847-1920) Dutch

£526	$953	€800	Bloem Canal in Amsterdam by night (55x43cm-22x17in) s. 19-Apr-4 Glerum, Amsterdam #153/R
£671	$1242	€1000	Landscape with a peasant woman on a country road (39x30cm-15x12in) s. panel. 15-Mar-4 Sotheby's, Amsterdam #83/R est:1000-1500
£1748	$2972	€2500	Paysage anime (64x92cm-25x36in) s. 18-Nov-3 Vanderkindere, Brussels #12 est:1500-2500
£2200	$4048	€3212	Canal in Amsterdam (36x46cm-14x18in) s. 25-Mar-4 Christie's, Kensington #168/R est:1500-2000

MELCHERS, Gari (1860-1932) American

£1934	$3500	€2824	Portrait of a woman (66x53cm-26x21in) 16-Apr-4 Du Mouchelle, Detroit #2078/R est:2000-4000
£14205	$25000	€20739	Early morning, North River (46x56cm-18x22in) s. i.backing painted c.1907 prov.exhib. 19-May-4 Sotheby's, New York #19/R est:15000-25000
£42614	$75000	€62216	Crimson Rambler (81x84cm-32x33in) s. painted c.1914-15 prov. 19-May-4 Sotheby's, New York #29/R est:40000-60000

MELCHERT, Samuel (1916-) Swiss

£262	$477	€383	Boots at the quayside in Gandria (51x68cm-20x27in) mono. masonite. 16-Jun-4 Fischer, Luzern #2274/R (S.FR 600)

MELCHIOR, Wilhelm (1817-1860) German

£1081	$1903	€1600	Outside the tavern (24x33cm-9x13in) s.d.46 prov. 22-May-4 Lempertz, Koln #1561/R est:1500

MELCHIORRE, Enzo (1931-) Italian

£333	$613	€500	Reflections in Mikonos (46x60cm-18x24in) s. cardboard painted 1993. 12-Jun-4 Meeting Art, Vercelli #893/R

MELDRUM, Duncan Max (1875-1955) Australian

£389	$712	€584	Portrait of Mrs Nellie Govett. board. 3-Jun-4 Joel, Victoria #279/R (A.D 1000)
£830	$1386	€1245	Newport, N S Wales (33x40cm-13x16in) s. board. 27-Oct-3 Goodman, Sydney #221/R (A.D 2000)
£840	$1528	€1226	Roses (45x38cm-18x15in) s. board exhib. 16-Jun-4 Deutscher-Menzies, Melbourne #328/R est:2500-3500 (A.D 2200)
£1277	$2170	€1864	Floral still life (41x33cm-16x13in) s. board. 25-Nov-3 Christie's, Melbourne #279/R est:3000-5000 (A.D 3000)
£1626	$2911	€2374	Pont de Grenelle, Paris (31x39cm-12x15in) s. s.i.d.1929 verso board. 10-May-4 Joel, Victoria #268/R est:3000-5000 (A.D 4000)

MELDRUM, James Michael (1931-) Australian

£533	$842	€778	Angry crucifix - Spain (71x96cm-28x38in) init.d.59 enamel prov.exhib. 2-Sep-3 Deutscher-Menzies, Melbourne #321/R est:1200-1800 (A.D 1300)

MELE, Juan (1923-) Argentinian

Works on paper

£345	$621	€500	Composition madi (38x48cm-15x19in) s.d.1990 gouache. 25-Jan-4 Chayette & Cheval, Paris #304

MELENDEZ, Luis (1716-1780) Italian

£1000000	$1730000	€1460000	Pears on a plate, a melon and a decorated Manises jar with plums on a wooden ledge (36x49cm-14x19in) init. prov. 10-Dec-3 Christie's, London #62/R est:450000-650000
£2000000	$3600000	€2920000	Arbutus berries on a plate, apples, a wood barrel and bread rolls on a wooden table (35x48cm-14x19in) init. prov.exhib.lit. 23-Jan-4 Christie's, Rockefeller NY #83/R est:1500000-2000000

MELENDEZ, Luis (attrib) (1716-1780) Italian

£6419	$11490	€9500	Still life with fruit, flowers and ceramics (63x81cm-25x32in) 8-May-4 Hans Stahl, Toestorf #109/R est:4500

MELERO, Mercedes (1959-) Spanish
£845 $1352 €1200 Crimean lion (160x206cm-63x81in) s.i. acrylic paper on canvas prov.exhib. 16-Sep-3 Segre, Madrid #179/R

MELGAARD, Bjarne (1967-) Norwegian
£2033 $3720 €2968 Composition (146x115cm-57x45in) s.d.1997 verso. 7-Jun-4 Blomqvist, Oslo #451/R est:30000-40000 (N.KR 25000)
£2520 $4612 €3679 Composition (156x140cm-61x55in) painted c.1996-97. 7-Jun-4 Blomqvist, Oslo #471/R est:25000-30000 (N.KR 31000)
Works on paper
£322 $588 €470 A Jack Smith penguin floating (110x70cm-43x28in) s. mixed media collage. 2-Feb-4 Blomqvist, Lysaker #1180 (N.KR 4000)
£403 $713 €588 Sketch for painting (50x65cm-20x26in) s.d.99 mixed media prov. 27-Apr-4 AB Stockholms Auktionsverk #1080/R (S.KR 5500)
£952 $1686 €1390 Very ape - The only thing that really interest me is love - John Cassawettes (126x110cm-50x43in) s.d.2001 verso mixed media canvas prov. 27-Apr-4 AB Stockholms Auktionsverk #1079/R (S.KR 13000)
£1208 $2054 €1764 Mickey Rourke (81x110cm-32x43in) s.d.2001 verso mixed media. 5-Nov-3 AB Stockholms Auktionsverk #1034/R est:10000-12000 (S.KR 16000)
£1758 $3112 €2567 I'm nowhere when I get there (99x99cm-39x39in) s.d.1988/1999 mixed media canvas exhib.prov. 27-Apr-4 AB Stockholms Auktionsverk #1052/R est:25000-30000 (S.KR 24000)

MELGERS, Hendrik Johan (1899-1973) Dutch
£959 $1630 €1400 Ditch at Leek near Groning (49x39cm-19x15in) s.v. 5-Nov-3 Vendue Huis, Gravenhage #347/R

MELGERS, Henk (20th C) Dutch
£3618 $6658 €5500 View of the Amstel with Carre in winter (60x80cm-24x31in) s. verso. 28-Jun-4 Sotheby's, Amsterdam #76/R est:1200-1500

MELILLI, Cering (19/20th C) French?
Sculpture
£782 $1400 €1142 Female figure (49cm-19in) s. bronze. 14-May-4 Skinner, Boston #314/R est:1000-1500

MELIN, Joseph Urbain (1814-1886) French
£738 $1343 €1107 Landscape with woman and three greyhounds (28x37cm-11x15in) s. 19-Jun-4 Rasmussen, Havnen #2120/R (D.KR 8300)
£3200 $5920 €4672 Diana the huntress (74x92cm-29x36in) s.d.1875. 14-Jul-4 Sotheby's, Olympia #146/R est:1000-2000

MELINGUE, Étienne Marin (1808-1875) French
Sculpture
£2685 $4752 €4000 Kaiser Karl V (45cm-18in) i. brown pat.bronze. 29-Apr-4 Dorotheum, Vienna #2/R est:2500-3500

MELINGUE, Gaston (1840-1914) French
£3297 $6000 €4814 Jean Bart in the Galerie des Glaces at Versailles (181x134cm-71x53in) s.d.1896 exhib. 29-Jun-4 Sotheby's, New York #73/R est:7000-9000

MELIS MARINI, Felice (1871-1953) Italian
£1645 $3026 €2500 Girl at balcony (32x23cm-13x9in) mono. board. 23-Jun-4 Finarte Semenzato, Rome #101/R est:900-1000
£2105 $3874 €3200 Landscape with peasants (30x40cm-12x16in) s. board. 23-Jun-4 Finarte Semenzato, Rome #105/R est:1800-2000

MELIS, Fritz (1913-1982) German
Sculpture
£1549 $2479 €2200 Two cranes (49cm-19in) bronze. 18-Sep-3 Rieber, Stuttgart #2253 est:4800

MELIS, Henricus Johannes (1845-1923) Dutch
£651 $1106 €950 Children with small goat (54x38cm-21x15in) s. 5-Nov-3 Vendue Huis, Gravenhage #165/R
Works on paper
£1700 $2941 €2482 Maternal cares (46x36cm-18x14in) s. W/C. 11-Dec-3 Lyon & Turnbull, Edinburgh #33/R est:1000-1500

MELISSENT, Maurice (?) French
£483 $899 €720 Port d'Urk en Hollande (50x73cm-20x29in) s.i.d.1967 verso. 7-Mar-4 Livinec, Gaudcheau & Jezequel, Rennes #34
Works on paper
£302 $562 €450 Le Havre, le port (34x52cm-13x20in) s. W/C. 7-Mar-4 Livinec, Gaudcheau & Jezequel, Rennes #28
£389 $724 €580 Trois mats (47x34cm-19x13in) s.i.d.aout 1941 W/C. 7-Mar-4 Livinec, Gaudcheau & Jezequel, Rennes #27

MELKEBEKE, Jacques van (1904-1983) Belgian
£284 $474 €400 Dernier dimanche deseptembre a l'Hotel Welington d'Ostende (40x60cm-16x24in) s. d.1975 verso. 14-Oct-3 Vanderkindere, Brussels #114

MELKOV, A (20th C) Russian
Works on paper
£2500 $4475 €3650 Interior (42x60cm-17x24in) s. gouache. 26-May-4 Sotheby's, Olympia #424/R est:2500-3000

MELKUS, H (20th C) ?
£1399 $2406 €2000 Bearded peasant reading book (30x24cm-12x9in) s. panel. 3-Dec-3 Neumeister, Munich #670/R est:2000

MELLE (1908-1976) Dutch
£4348 $7130 €6000 Heilige Antonius (46x37cm-18x15in) s.d.40 panel prov. 27-May-3 Sotheby's, Amsterdam #342/R est:7000-9000
£6667 $12267 €10000 Pike-perche (50x60cm-20x24in) s. painted c.1970. 8-Jun-4 Sotheby's, Amsterdam #28/R est:12000-15000
£10000 $18400 €15000 Het jaar van de Vrouw (43x40cm-17x16in) s. panel painted c.1973. 8-Jun-4 Sotheby's, Amsterdam #31/R est:8000-12000

MELLE, Léon Auguste (1816-1889) French
£550 $1018 €803 Ruins before the Roman Campagna (37x28cm-15x11in) indis sig. panel. 15-Jan-4 Christie's, Kensington #948/R
£1064 $1777 €1500 Cascade a Narcia, Toscane (30x50cm-12x20in) panel. 15-Oct-3 Claude Aguttes, Neuilly #12/R est:1000-2000

MELLER, Reijo (1944-) Finnish
£367 $675 €550 Many coloured dressing gown (19x15cm-7x6in) s.d.86. 9-Jun-4 Bukowskis, Helsinki #478/R
£867 $1595 €1300 Spanish fan (40x30cm-16x12in) s.d.87. 9-Jun-4 Bukowskis, Helsinki #477/R

MELLERUP, Tage (1910-1988) Danish
£516 $862 €753 Friday (64x62cm-25x24in) s.d.1947 verso. 7-Oct-3 Rasmussen, Copenhagen #225/R (D.KR 5500)
£6318 $11625 €9224 Figure composition with fantasy animals (94x135cm-37x53in) s. painted c.1945. 29-Mar-4 Rasmussen, Copenhagen #31/R est:20000-25000 (D.KR 70000)

MELLERY, Xavier (1845-1921) Belgian
£3191 $5330 €4500 Accord (58x77cm-23x30in) s. cardboard prov. 20-Oct-3 Bernaerts, Antwerp #216 est:4000-5000
£4895 $8322 €7000 Allegorie de l'Agriculture. Allegorie de l'Industrie (60x32cm-24x13in) s. panel pair. 28-Nov-3 Drouot Estimations, Paris #155 est:1200-1500
Works on paper
£486 $812 €700 Au marche (18x24cm-7x9in) mono. dr. 21-Oct-3 Campo, Vlaamse Kaai #491
£3846 $6615 €5500 La dame (13x27cm-5x11in) mono. ink black chk. 2-Dec-3 Sotheby's, Amsterdam #72/R est:2000-3000

MELLI, Roberto (1885-1958) Italian
£10000 $16700 €14500 Self-portrait (70x60cm-28x24in) s.d.936 exhib.lit. 13-Nov-3 Finarte Semenzato, Rome #381/R est:16000-18000
Sculpture
£2098 $3503 €3000 Mask (18x15x8cm-7x6x3in) bronze exec.1913 lit. 26-Jun-3 Sant Agostino, Torino #276/R est:3000-3500

MELLIN, Charles (c.1597-1647) French
£36242 $64872 €54000 Virtue triumphing over Disagreement (136x100cm-54x39in) 26-May-4 Porro, Milan #20/R est:50000-60000

MELLING, Antoine Ignace (attrib) (1763-1831) French
Works on paper
£3500 $5705 €5110 Nouvelle Caserne Imperiale a Ramis-Tchiflik, Constantinople (48x91cm-19x36in) i.verso W/C. 24-Sep-3 Christie's, London #193/R est:4000-6000

MELLING, Joseph (attrib) (1724-1796) French
£1810 $2896 €2643 Holy Family with St John the Baptist (58x43cm-23x17in) panel. 16-Sep-3 Philippe Schuler, Zurich #3341/R est:3000-4000 (S.FR 4000)
£4362 $8027 €6500 Holy Family with St John (58x43cm-23x17in) panel. 24-Mar-4 Dorotheum, Vienna #405/R est:5000-6000

MELLISH, Thomas (attrib) (18th C) British
£2400 $4296 €3504 Two-decker announcing her departure from her anchorage on the Medway (58x91cm-23x36in) 26-May-4 Christie's, Kensington #563/R est:2000-3000

MELLON, Campbell (1876-1955) British
£1050 $1806 €1533 Beccles Church from the river (28x20cm-11x8in) s. prov. 5-Dec-3 Keys, Aylsham #587/R est:1000-1500
£1750 $3168 €2555 Late November. Stormy unsettled morning, mid September (20x28cm-8x11in) pair. 16-Apr-4 Keys, Aylsham #809 est:1200-1500
£1800 $3096 €2628 The Wye, near Symonds Yat (56x69cm-22x27in) s. prov. 3-Dec-3 Christie's, Kensington #484/R est:2000-3000
£2200 $3872 €3212 Country landscape with cattle grazing (46x60cm-18x24in) s. 18-May-4 Bonhams, Knightsbridge #13/R est:1200-1500

MELLON, Campbell (attrib) (1876-1955) British
£420 $739 €613 View of the Thames (15x18cm-6x7in) board. 18-May-4 Bonhams, Knightsbridge #98/R
£820 $1443 €1197 View of Gorleston from Hopton Beach (24x35cm-9x14in) 18-May-4 Bonhams, Knightsbridge #118/R

MELLOR, Everett W (1878-1965) British
£1900 $3040 €2774 Ullswater (23x33cm-9x13in) s.i.mount board. 15-May-3 Mitchells, Cockermouth #1002 est:1000-1500
£2200 $3520 €3212 Peep of Derwentwater (23x33cm-9x13in) s.i.mount panel. 15-May-3 Mitchells, Cockermouth #1001/R est:1000-1500
£3200 $5984 €4672 Drover and his dog with sheep beside a gate in a meadow (31x46cm-12x18in) s. 22-Jul-4 Tennants, Leyburn #828/R est:1800-2200

Works on paper

£900	$1683	€1314	On the Lledr, North Wales (29x45cm-11x18in) s.i. pencil W/C htd white. 22-Jul-4 Tennants, Leyburn #776/R

MELLOR, Joseph (fl.1850-1885) British

£350	$585	€511	Lady ambling along a riverside track (46x35cm-18x14in) s. 8-Oct-3 Christie's, Kensington #880/R
£500	$835	€730	Girls picking berries (36x53cm-14x21in) s. 13-Nov-3 Christie's, Kensington #293/R
£700	$1190	€1022	Children beside a ford with cattle watering and thatched cottages beyond (41x61cm-16x24in) s. 30-Oct-3 Duke & Son, Dorchester #134/R
£950	$1634	€1387	Figure on woodland path (43x33cm-17x13in) s. 3-Dec-3 Andrew Hartley, Ilkley #1236
£1000	$1800	€1460	Herding cattle on a riverside path. Children by a river in wooded landscape (39x65cm-15x26in) s. pair. 22-Apr-4 Lawrence, Crewkerne #905 est:1000-1500
£1200	$2220	€1752	Three children berry picking by woodland stream (33x51cm-13x20in) s. 12-Feb-4 Andrew Hartley, Ilkley #888/R est:1200-2000
£1950	$3140	€2828	Goitstock, waterfall near Bingley (43x33cm-17x13in) s. 13-Aug-3 Andrew Hartley, Ilkley #854/R est:700-900
£2000	$3640	€2920	Figures at the Strid, Bolton Abbey (58x89cm-23x35in) s. 16-Jun-4 Andrew Hartley, Ilkley #1136/R est:2000-3000

MELLOR, William (1851-1931) British

£320	$509	€464	Rocky gorge (33x25cm-13x10in) s. 9-Sep-3 David Duggleby, Scarborough #275
£500	$850	€730	River landscape (59x43cm-23x17in) s. 18-Nov-3 Bonhams, Leeds #232/R
£1150	$1840	€1668	Nidderdale (20x30cm-8x12in) s. i.verso. 17-Sep-3 James Thompson, Kirby Lonsdale #175
£1150	$2139	€1679	Waterfall (38x64cm-15x25in) 4-Mar-4 Mitchells, Cockermouth #850/R est:1200-1800
£1200	$2220	€1752	Summer river landscape with waterfall (46x36cm-18x14in) 11-Mar-4 Ewbank, Send #462/R est:1200-1800
£1257	$2250	€1835	Double waterfall (30x23cm-12x9in) s. board. 8-Jan-4 James Julia, Fairfield #1008/R est:1500-2500
£1300	$2106	€1885	River in the dales (61x51cm-24x20in) s. 30-Jul-3 Hamptons Fine Art, Godalming #257 est:1500-1800
£1500	$2760	€2190	On the Greta. Barnard Castle (43x34cm-17x13in) s. pair. 23-Jun-4 Cheffins, Cambridge #524 est:800-1200
£1550	$2635	€2263	Waterfall scene (91x70cm-36x28in) s. indis sig.i.verso. 18-Nov-3 Bonhams, Leeds #231/R est:1000-1500
£1700	$3162	€2482	In Bolton Woods (76x63cm-30x25in) s. i.stretcher. 4-Mar-4 Christie's, Kensington #466/R est:1500-2000
£1700	$3145	€2482	Mother and children by the rivers edge (61x91cm-24x36in) s. 12-Mar-4 Dickins, Middle Claydon #14 est:1500-2500
£1800	$3276	€2628	The Strid, Bolton Woods, Yorkshire (60x53cm-24x21in) s. i.verso. 15-Jun-4 Bonhams, Leeds #148/R est:2000-3000
£1850	$3275	€2701	Near Barnard Castle (58x43cm-23x17in) s.i.d.1886 verso. 30-Apr-4 Dee Atkinson & Harrison, Driffield #751 est:1500-2000
£2000	$3720	€2920	Fairy glen, North Wales (76x63cm-30x25in) s. i.verso. 4-Mar-4 Christie's, Kensington #465/R est:2000-3000
£2300	$3634	€3335	Morning on the Derwent. Evening, Ullswater (61x46cm-24x18in) s. pair. 3-Sep-3 Bonhams, Bury St Edmunds #457/R est:3000-5000
£2374	$4250	€3466	River landscape with figures (61x91cm-24x36in) s. 6-May-4 Doyle, New York #24/R est:8000-10000
£2374	$4250	€3466	Falls in North Wales (61x91cm-24x36in) s. i.verso. 6-May-4 Doyle, New York #25/R est:8000-12000
£2400	$4440	€3504	Fairy glen, North Wales (91x60cm-36x24in) s. i.verso. 14-Jul-4 Sotheby's, Olympia #90/R est:2500-3500
£2454	$4000	€3583	Welsh scene (61x46cm-24x18in) s.i.verso. 28-Sep-3 Bonhams & Butterfields, Los Angeles #7028 est:2000-3000
£2500	$4175	€3650	Loch Katrine, Scotland (30x21cm-12x8in) s. prov. 13-Nov-3 Christie's, Kensington #202/R est:3000-5000
£2500	$4300	€3650	On the Conway (30x45cm-12x18in) s. 4-Dec-3 Mellors & Kirk, Nottingham #895/R est:3000-4000
£2500	$4550	€3650	Bolton Woods, Yorkshire (76x61cm-30x24in) s.i.verso. 16-Jun-4 Andrew Hartley, Ilkley #1134/R est:3000-4000
£2600	$4238	€3796	Shipley Glen, Yorkshire (60x90cm-24x35in) s. i.verso. 23-Sep-3 Anderson & Garland, Newcastle #327/R est:200-300
£2600	$4810	€3796	Ingleton Falls and stream (30x20cm-12x8in) s. pair. 9-Mar-4 Gorringes, Lewes #2257 est:1500-2000
£2667	$4853	€4000	View on the Wharfe Bollon, Yorkshire (31x46cm-12x18in) s. i.verso. 1-Jul-4 Van Ham, Cologne #1500 est:800
£2700	$4590	€3942	On the Wharfe, Bolton Woods, Yorkshire (20x30cm-8x12in) s. i.verso. 18-Nov-3 Bonhams, Leeds #234/R est:700-900
£2800	$4452	€4060	Skelwith Force, nr Ambleside, Westmoreland (91x71cm-36x28in) s. i.verso. 11-Sep-3 Morphets, Harrogate #255/R est:3000-3500
£2800	$4816	€4088	On the Greta (30x45cm-12x18in) s. 4-Dec-3 Mellors & Kirk, Nottingham #896/R est:3000-4000
£2800	$5040	€4088	River landscape with a figure on a stone bridge (61x91cm-24x36in) s. 21-Apr-4 Tennants, Leyburn #1155/R est:2500-3000
£3000	$5010	€4380	Near Capel Curig, north Wales (20x30cm-8x12in) s. bears i.stretcher sold with a companion. 26-Jun-3 Greenslade Hunt, Taunton #541/R est:1500-2500
£3000	$5400	€4380	Cumberland hills. On the hills Westmorland (20x30cm-8x12in) s. i.verso pair. 21-Jan-4 Sotheby's, Olympia #334/R est:3000-5000
£3200	$5120	€4672	On the wharf, Bolton Woods, Yorkshire (30x46cm-12x18in) s. i.verso. 16-Sep-3 Capes Dunn, Manchester #760/R
£3300	$6006	€4818	On the Wharfe, Wharfedale, Yorkshire (49x75cm-19x30in) s. i. verso. 29-Jun-4 Anderson & Garland, Newcastle #468/R est:1500-2500
£3500	$6300	€5110	View on the Greta, near Barnard Castle, Durham (76x127cm-30x50in) s. prov. 21-Apr-4 Tennants, Leyburn #1154/R est:3000-4000
£3800	$6460	€5548	Ullswater from the hills, Westmorland (46x31cm-18x12in) s. i.verso. 19-Nov-3 Tennants, Leyburn #1073/R est:2500-3500
£3800	$7068	€5548	On the river Llugwy. On the river Lledr, Wales (30x51cm-12x20in) s. i.verso pair. 4-Mar-4 Christie's, Kensington #467/R est:2000-3000
£4000	$6800	€5840	Loughrigg from Rydal Lake, Westmoreland (51x76cm-20x30in) s. i.verso. 27-Nov-3 Sotheby's, London #358/R est:5000-7000
£4000	$6880	€5840	On the wharf near Ilkley (28x43cm-11x17in) s.i.verso. 3-Dec-3 Andrew Hartley, Ilkley #1235 est:4000-5000
£4200	$7770	€6132	View near Goathland, near Whitby, Yorkshire (76x127cm-30x50in) s. 11-Mar-4 Morphets, Harrogate #303/R est:4000-5000
£4200	$7518	€6132	On the Wharfe, Bolton Woods, Yorkshire (31x51cm-12x20in) s.i.verso. 16-Mar-4 Bonhams, Leeds #669/R est:1200-1500
£4533	$8250	€6618	On the Scardale (91x71cm-36x28in) s. i.verso. 7-Feb-4 Neal Auction Company, New Orleans #461/R est:5000-7000
£5200	$8216	€7540	Highland river landscape with cows and sheep (30x46cm-12x18in) s. pair. 3-Sep-3 Bonhams, Bury St Edmunds #458/R est:3000-5000
£5500	$9900	€8030	Lakeland landscape with cattle beside a river (91x71cm-36x28in) s. 21-Apr-4 Tennants, Leyburn #1156/R est:3500-4000
£5600	$10192	€8176	On the Nidd, near Knaresborough, Yorkshire (40x59cm-16x23in) s. i.verso. 15-Jun-4 Bonhams, Leeds #146/R est:4000-6000
£5800	$10266	€8468	Rokeby. Near Barnard Castle, landscapes (45x34cm-18x13in) s. pair. 28-Apr-4 Peter Wilson, Nantwich #51 est:5000-6000
£5800	$10556	€8468	Lakeland landscape with figures. River landscape with cattle and sheep (59x105cm-23x41in) s. pair. 15-Jun-4 Bonhams, Leeds #145/R est:6000-8000
£5900	$10738	€8614	On the Lledr, North Wales (49x75cm-19x30in) s. i. verso. 29-Jun-4 Anderson & Garland, Newcastle #467/R est:1500-2500
£6400	$11456	€9344	River landscape with cattle watering, possibly on the Wharfe. Lakeland landscape (28x49cm-11x19in) s. pair. 16-Mar-4 Bonhams, Leeds #668/R est:6000-8000
£7200	$12024	€10512	Cattle and drover on a woodland path. River landscape (28x48cm-11x19in) s. pair. 8-Oct-3 Andrew Hartley, Ilkley #1153/R est:5000-7000
£7600	$13680	€11096	Loughrigg, Rydal Water. On the Wharfe, Bolton Woods (26x36cm-10x14in) s. board pair prov. 21-Apr-4 Tennants, Leyburn #1157/R est:2500-3000
£7800	$13260	€11388	On the wharfe, Bolton Woods, Yorkshire (61x91cm-24x36in) s. i.verso. 19-Nov-3 Tennants, Leyburn #1074/R est:4000-6000
£10500	$19425	€15330	On the Wharfe, near Beamsley. On the Glaslyn, North Wales (29x44cm-11x17in) s. board pair prov. 10-Mar-4 Sotheby's, Olympia #209/R est:4000-6000
£13000	$23270	€18980	Ullswater. Derwent water (48x73cm-19x29in) s. pair. 16-Mar-4 Bonhams, Leeds #666/R est:8000-12000

MELLOR, William (attrib) (1851-1931) British

£950	$1577	€1387	Waterfall, Bolton woods, Yorkshire (91x71cm-36x28in) bears sig. i.stretcher. 1-Oct-3 Sotheby's, Olympia #123/R

MELLY, Ferdinand (1863-1903) German

Works on paper

£604	$1111	€900	Woman smoking (69x57cm-27x22in) s.d.94 pastel. 26-Mar-4 Dorotheum, Vienna #344/R

MELNICK, Camillo (19th C) Austrian

£4167	$6583	€6000	Conversation by window (43x34cm-17x13in) s.i.d.1891 panel lit. 19-Sep-3 Schloss Ahlden, Ahlden #1479/R est:6500

MELNIKOV, Fedor Ivanovich (fl.1920s) Russian

£2800	$4760	€4088	Two puppies (40x43cm-16x17in) s. card. 19-Nov-3 Sotheby's, London #76/R est:3000-5000

MELO, Attilio (1917-) Italian

£467	$849	€700	Porto Cervo. View of village. s. pair. 12-Jul-4 Il Ponte, Milan #1046

MELONI, Gino (1905-1989) Italian

£451	$767	€650	Composition (80x60cm-31x24in) s. i.verso. 28-Oct-3 Il Ponte, Milan #228
£6643	$11294	€9500	Interior with figure (88x57cm-35x22in) s. double-sided. 20-Nov-3 Finarte Semenzato, Milan #201/R est:6000-8000

Works on paper

£433	$784	€650	Composition (50x50cm-20x20in) s.d.1973 hydropaint. 2-Apr-4 Farsetti, Prato #216
£483	$772	€700	Cock (47x32cm-19x13in) s. W/C paper on board prov. 13-Mar-3 Galleria Pace, Milan #129/R
£517	$828	€750	Vase of flowers (59x42cm-23x17in) s.i.d.1952 W/C. 13-Mar-3 Galleria Pace, Milan #38/R
£544	$974	€800	Landscape (35x49cm-14x19in) s. mixed media on canvas prov. 16-Mar-4 Finarte Semenzato, Milan #164

MELOTTI, Fausto (1901-1986) Italian

£1088	$1948	€1600	Untitled (29x23cm-11x9in) s.verso tempera pencil paper prov. 16-Mar-4 Finarte Semenzato, Milan #165/R est:1200

Sculpture

£1033	$1901	€1550	Pendulum (50x15x8cm-20x6x3in) s. num.21/500 steel. 12-Jun-4 Meeting Art, Vercelli #454/R est:750
£1958	$3329	€2800	Sculpture A (40x15x8cm-16x6x3in) s. num.100/500 steel exhib.lit. 20-Nov-3 Finarte Semenzato, Milan #32/R est:2800-3000
£2657	$4517	€3800	Cup (32x15cm-13x6in) s. glazed ceramic exec.c.1960. 25-Nov-3 Sotheby's, Milan #125/R est:3000-4000
£4545	$7727	€6500	Rising moon (26x17x11cm-10x7x4in) s. brass lit. 24-Nov-3 Christie's, Milan #159/R est:6000-8000
£6040	$10812	€9000	Vase (47x14x10cm-19x6x4in) ceramic exec.1956 prov.lit. 25-May-4 Sotheby's, Milan #300/R est:10000-15000
£7343	$12483	€10500	Counterpoint (62x180x12cm-24x71x5in) s. num.71/99 brass exhib.lit. 20-Nov-3 Finarte Semenzato, Milan #190/R est:8000-9000
£7383	$13215	€11000	Theme and variations II (30x7x4cm-12x3x2in) s. num.9/9. 25-May-4 Sotheby's, Milan #263/R est:15000-20000
£7718	$13815	€11500	Theme and varaitions II (30x7x4cm-12x3x2in) s. num.9/9 gold. 25-May-4 Sotheby's, Milan #264/R est:15000-20000
£9296	$16268	€13200	Girl in blue dress (45cm-18in) s. ceramic. 17-Dec-3 Il Ponte, Milan #1107/R est:8000-9000
£10811	$19027	€16000	Suddenly (53x26x12cm-21x10x5in) brass exhib.lit. 24-May-4 Christie's, Milan #260/R est:18000-24000
£14094	$25228	€21000	Cart (27x16x13cm-11x6x5in) s. ceramic exec.c.1955. 25-May-4 Sotheby's, Milan #299/R est:15000-20000
£45000	$75150	€65700	La balancoire aux violettes (115x38x39cm-45x15x15in) brass paint polystyrene prov.exhib.lit. 21-Oct-3 Christie's, London #36/R est:40000-60000
£55000	$91850	€80300	Virgin I (45x29x6cm-18x11x2in) s.verso painted terracotta glazed ceramic prov.exhib.lit. 20-Oct-3 Sotheby's, London #12/R est:60000
£55000	$91850	€80300	White fire (48x34x11cm-19x13x4in) s.verso painted terracotta paper brass glazed ceramic pumice prov. 20-Oct-3 Sotheby's, London #18/R est:60000

Works on paper

£1232	$2020	€1700	Untitled (31x23cm-12x9in) s. pencil W/C tempera exec.1979. 27-May-3 Sotheby's, Milan #103/R est:1500-2000
£1399	$2378	€2000	Composition (35x24cm-14x9in) s.verso pencil prov. 20-Nov-3 Finarte Semenzato, Milan #136/R est:2000-2200
£1538	$2615	€2200	Composition (32x23cm-13x9in) s. verso pencil prov. 20-Nov-3 Finarte Semenzato, Milan #137/R est:2000-2200

£1769 $3166 €2600 Untitled (31x23cm-12x9in) s. paint on plaster. 16-Mar-4 Finarte Semenzato, Milan #293 est:2200
£1931 $3090 €2800 Composition (29x23cm-11x9in) pencil exec 1980-81. 13-Mar-3 Galleria Pace, Milan #65/R est:3500-5000
£2937 $4993 €4200 Untitled (35x50cm-14x20in) s. mixed media lit. 26-Nov-3 Pandolfini, Florence #137/R est:3600-4000
£5245 $8916 €7500 Untitled (26x24cm-10x9in) s. mixed media chk board exec.1975 prov.lit. 25-Nov-3 Sotheby's, Milan #166/R est:3000-4000

MELROSE, Andrew (1836-1901) American
£886 $1400 €1294 Figure by a rushing stream (48x41cm-19x16in) s. 7-Sep-3 Treadway Gallery, Cincinnati #557/R est:2000-3000
£1250 $2000 €1825 Sunlit river landscape with a figure reclining on the shoreline (25x20cm-10x8in) s.d.1878. 20-Sep-3 Pook & Pook, Downington #534/R est:1500-2500
£2018 $3250 €2946 Shipwreck off Dover (56x86cm-22x34in) mono. 20-Aug-3 James Julia, Fairfield #774/R est:4000-6000
£3779 $6500 €5517 Sunrise harbour scene with sailors loading a ship (56x91cm-22x36in) s. i.verso. 6-Dec-3 Pook & Pook, Downington #280/R est:4000-6000

MELROSE, D (19th C) British?
£1166 $1900 €1702 Derwentwater, Cumberland (51x76cm-20x30in) s. i.verso. 24-Sep-3 Doyle, New York #59 est:1500-2500

MELS, Jacques (1899-1974) Dutch
£280 $481 €400 Owl (61x50cm-24x20in) s.d.56. 8-Dec-3 Glerum, Amsterdam #212/R

MELSEN, Marten (1870-1947) Belgian
£1141 $2019 €1700 Nettoyage (28x24cm-11x9in) s.d.1917. 27-Apr-4 Campo & Campo, Antwerp #163/R est:1600-1800
£1342 $2376 €2000 Le garde de chasse Willems (50x40cm-20x16in) s.d.1907 panel. 27-Apr-4 Campo & Campo, Antwerp #164/R est:2000-2250

MELTON, Diane (20th C) American
Works on paper
£519 $950 €779 Still life with Casa Blanca (104x48cm-41x19in) W/C. 10-Jul-4 Hindman, Chicago #343/R est:500-700

MELTSNER, Paul R (1905-1966) American
£1313 $2100 €1917 Saloon dancers (61x76cm-24x30in) s. 21-Sep-3 William Jenack, New York #72 est:1000-1500

MELTZER, Arthur (1893-1989) American
£925 $1600 €1351 Pont Neuf, landscape with view of Notre Dame (25x36cm-10x14in) s. board. 10-Dec-3 Alderfer's, Hatfield #424/R est:800-1200
£1075 $2000 €1570 Forst patterns, frosty window (56x81cm-22x32in) s. 3-Mar-4 Alderfer's, Hatfield #413/R est:3000-5000
£1220 $2000 €1769 Still life with magnolia blossoms and silver bowl (41x51cm-16x20in) s. d.1936 verso. 4-Jun-3 Alderfer's, Hatfield #353/R est:3000-5000
£1879 $3250 €2743 Voices in the garden (41x51cm-16x20in) s. 10-Dec-3 Alderfer's, Hatfield #423/R est:2000-4000
£3468 $6000 €5063 Winter landscape with trees on snowy hills (30x56cm-12x22in) s. 10-Dec-3 Alderfer's, Hatfield #422/R est:3000-5000
£5031 $8000 €7345 Landscape with rocky terrain and tree in foreground (33x36cm-13x14in) s.d.30. 10-Sep-3 Alderfer's, Hatfield #400/R est:4000-6000
£8939 $16000 €15007 The marsh, autumnal landscape (51x61cm-20x24in) s.d.22 prov. 20-Mar-4 Pook & Pook, Downington #200/R est:20000-30000
£23121 $40000 €33757 Winter landscape with farm buildings with rolling hills (64x76cm-25x30in) s. 10-Dec-3 Alderfer's, Hatfield #421/R est:15000-20000

MELVILLE, Arthur (1858-1904) British
Works on paper
£900 $1629 €1314 African figures outside a walled city (18x17cm-7x7in) s.d.1892 W/C. 3-Apr-4 British Auctioneer #263
£2600 $4602 €3796 St. Mark's Square, Venice (15x24cm-6x9in) W/C prov. 28-Apr-4 George Kidner, Lymington #202/R est:300-400
£7000 $12810 €10220 Two moorish guards (74x53cm-29x21in) s.d.91 W/C htd white exhib. 8-Apr-4 Bonhams, Edinburgh #191/R est:8000-12000

MELVILLE, Harden Sidney (attrib) (fl.1837-1881) British
£760 $1345 €1110 Winter landscape with figures and horse drawn carts (251x124cm-99x49in) 27-Apr-4 Lawrences, Bletchingley #1701

MELVILLE, John (1902-1986) British
£340 $568 €496 Fantasy landscape with colourful trees and foliage (137x135cm-54x53in) s. 17-Oct-3 Biddle & Webb, Birmingham #304
£340 $612 €496 Skyscrapers (76x101cm-30x40in) s.d.1974 i.verso. 20-Apr-4 Rosebery Fine Art, London #408
£350 $574 €511 Abstract depicting nude figures (112x140cm-44x55in) s.d.1962. 6-Jun-3 Biddle & Webb, Birmingham #442
£450 $833 €657 Portrait of Theo Melville (102x98cm-40x39in) s. i.verso. 11-Mar-4 Christie's, Kensington #243
£500 $925 €730 Portrait of a seated lady (98x67cm-39x26in) s. board. 11-Mar-4 Christie's, Kensington #198
£500 $885 €730 Portrait of the artist's wife (41x33cm-16x13in) 27-Apr-4 Bonhams, Knightsbridge #28/R
£920 $1702 €1343 Forest glade (145x180cm-57x71in) s.d.1968. 11-Mar-4 Christie's, Kensington #241/R
£1000 $1590 €1460 Border stone (79x102cm-31x40in) s.d.1968. 10-Sep-3 Sotheby's, Olympia #248/R est:1000-1500

MELZER, Moritz (1877-1966) German
£5208 $8698 €7500 Excursion (89x116cm-35x46in) s. paper on canvas. 25-Oct-3 Dr Lehr, Berlin #341/R est:3000

MENA, Daniel (1945-) Spanish?
£340 $609 €500 Cubist still life (38x46cm-15x18in) s. board. 22-Mar-4 Durán, Madrid #54/R
£355 $592 €500 Still life (38x46cm-15x18in) s. board. 20-Oct-3 Durán, Madrid #21/R
£972 $1546 €1400 Still life - Cubist (65x54cm-26x21in) s. 29-Apr-3 Durán, Madrid #99/R
£1215 $1908 €1750 Ecuyere 14 (54x65cm-21x26in) s. 29-Aug-3 Deauville, France #193/R
Works on paper
£496 $804 €700 Mujeres al cava (39x31cm-15x12in) s. gouache. 20-May-3 Ansorena, Madrid #354/R

MENA, Jorge (20th C) ?
Sculpture
£4005 $7290 €6008 Rose (136x42x57cm-54x17x22in) pat bronze. 21-Jun-4 Subastas Odalys, Caracas #95/R est:10000

MENARD, Emile René (1862-1930) French
£426 $711 €600 Varangeville (26x37cm-10x15in) cardboard. 19-Jun-3 Millon & Associes, Paris #170
£855 $1574 €1300 Tour Hassan (50x72cm-20x28in) s. 22-Jun-4 Palais de Beaux Arts, Brussels #286
£1000 $1810 €1500 Paysage de Provence, le soir (50x73cm-20x29in) s. 30-Mar-4 Rossini, Paris #337/R est:1500-2000
£1208 $2235 €1800 Rivage mediterraneen (50x73cm-20x29in) s. 14-Mar-4 Eric Pillon, Calais #152/R
£2168 $3685 €3100 Etude (92x65cm-36x26in) 27-Nov-3 Millon & Associes, Paris #156/R est:3000-5000
Works on paper
£634 $1096 €900 Cotes rocheuses (46x54cm-18x21in) s. pastel. 15-Dec-3 Bailly Pommery, Paris #114
£1727 $2970 €2521 Bagneuse au bord de l'eau (75x100cm-30x39in) pastel. 3-Dec-3 Naón & Cia, Buenos Aires #21/R est:3000-4000
£2817 $4873 €4000 L'enlevement d'Europe (81x150cm-32x59in) s. pastel. 10-Dec-3 Millon & Associes, Paris #34/R est:4000-5000
£26667 $49067 €40000 Harmonie du soir (95x138cm-37x54in) pastel cardboard on canvas. 11-Jun-4 Claude Aguttes, Neuilly #62/R est:25000-30000

MENARD, René-Joseph (1827-1887) French
£385 $654 €550 Le port (65x81cm-26x32in) s. 23-Nov-3 Cornette de St.Cyr, Paris #619/R

MENARDEAU, Maurice (1897-1977) French
£1208 $2247 €1800 Landscape in the French countryside (66x81cm-26x32in) s. 2-Mar-4 Ansorena, Madrid #116/R est:1800

MENASCO, Milton (?) ?
£3488 $6000 €5092 In the paddock (51x76cm-20x30in) s. 5-Dec-3 Christie's, Rockefeller NY #133/R est:4000-6000

MENCHETTI, R (?) ?
£2013 $3765 €3000 Approaching storm (46x36cm-18x14in) i. verso one of pair. 24-Feb-4 Dorotheum, Vienna #44/R est:3500-4000

MENCIA, Antoine Garcia (attrib) (19th C) Italian
£860 $1600 €1256 Genre scenes with ladies (21x13cm-8x5in) one indis.s. panel two. 5-Mar-4 Skinner, Boston #220/R est:1000-1500

MENDELSON, Anthony (20th C) British
£250 $450 €365 Portrait of a clown (34x29cm-13x11in) s.d.1956 board. 20-Jan-4 Rosebery Fine Art, London #602/R

MENDELSON, Marc (1915-) Belgian
£3472 $5799 €5000 Antibes (28x34cm-11x13in) mono.d.1947. 21-Oct-3 Campo, Vlaamse Kaai #492/R est:3500-4000
Works on paper
£336 $594 €500 Untitled (27x35cm-11x14in) mono.d.1953 dr. 27-Apr-4 Campo & Campo, Antwerp #167

MENDENHALL, Emma (1873-?) American
£305 $500 €442 Hillside tree (25x20cm-10x8in) estate st. board painted c.1920. 7-Jun-3 Treadway Gallery, Cincinnati #1382

MENDENHALL, Jack (1937-) American
£13497 $22000 €19706 Interior (109x150cm-43x59in) s.d.91 prov. 23-Sep-3 Christie's, Rockefeller NY #143/R est:15000-20000

MENDES DA COSTA, Joseph (1863-1939) Dutch
Sculpture
£6643 $11294 €9500 Baboon (13cm-5in) mono.verso sandstone excl wooden base exec 1900 lit. 25-Nov-3 Christie's, Amsterdam #127/R est:12000-16000
£8000 $14640 €12000 St Anna (55cm-22in) mono.i.d.1924 brown pat. bronze incl. wooden base. 7-Jun-4 Sotheby's, Amsterdam #121/R est:12000-15000

MENDEZ MAGARINOS, Melchor (1885-1945) South American
£259 $420 €376 Landscape scene (60x71cm-24x28in) s. fibre-board. 29-Jul-3 Galeria y Remates, Montevideo #69/R
£1941 $3300 €2834 Landscape with figures (65x75cm-26x30in) s. 25-Nov-3 Galeria y Remates, Montevideo #33/R

£1989 $3500 €2904 Washerwomen in Malvin (90x70cm-35x28in) prov. 5-Jan-4 Galeria y Remates, Montevideo #77/R est:4000-5000

MENDEZ OSUNA, Elbano (20th C) Venezuelan

£573 $900 €837 Flowers (60x50cm-24x20in) s. painted 1970. 23-Nov-2 Subastas Odalys, Caracas #30/R

MENDEZ RUIZ, Jose (1936-) Spanish

£470 $879 €700 Ruins and landscape (81x100cm-32x39in) s. s.d.77 exhib. 24-Feb-4 Durán, Madrid #59/R

MENDHAM, Robert (fl.1821-1858) British

£600 $1074 €876 Peter the faithful servant of Henry Carr, 15 years old (47x35cm-19x14in) s.i.d.1846 verso. 22-Mar-4 Bonhams & Brooks, Norfolk #231/R

MENDIETA, Ana (1948-1985) Cuban

Photographs

£2162 $4000 €3157 Untitled (40x51cm-16x20in) colour photograph edn 5/10 exec 1983 prov. 12-Feb-4 Sotheby's, New York #264/R est:6000-8000
£11173 $20000 €16313 Esculturas Rupestres (25x18cm-10x7in) portfolio photo-etchings 10 exec 1981 prov.lit. 13-May-4 Sotheby's, New York #378/R est:20000-30000
£23333 $42933 €35000 Silhouettes, Mexico (50x41cm-20x16in) cibachrome set of 12 exec.c.1975. 10-Jun-4 Christie's, Paris #83/R est:18000-24000

MENDILAHARZU, Gratien (19th C) Argentinian

£4670 $8500 €6818 Self-portrait (25x19cm-10x7in) s.d.1894. 29-Jun-4 Arroyo, Buenos Aires #77/R est:7500

MENDJISKY, Maurice (1889-1951) Polish

£414 $745 €600 Peniches sur le canal (54x65cm-21x26in) s. painted c.1935. 25-Jan-4 Chayette & Cheval, Paris #170
£570 $1055 €850 Paysage d'automne (50x65cm-20x26in) s.d.1915. 15-Mar-4 Claude Boisgirard, Paris #80
£570 $1055 €850 Paysage Montagneux (50x65cm-20x26in) s.d.1915. 15-Mar-4 Claude Boisgirard, Paris #81
£795 $1446 €1200 Fleurs dans un vase (89x58cm-35x23in) s. 16-Jun-4 Claude Boisgirard, Paris #110/R
£1788 $3254 €2700 La Colombe d'Or (91x73cm-36x29in) s. 16-Jun-4 Claude Boisgirard, Paris #111/R est:3000-3500

MENDJISKY, Serge (1929-) French

£400 $724 €600 Paysage (64x91cm-25x36in) s. 30-Mar-4 Gioffredo, Nice #335
£1000 $1670 €1460 Champ Elysees (50x65cm-20x26in) s. 8-Oct-3 Christie's, Kensington #934/R est:1000-1500
£1200 $2160 €1800 Nu assoupi (61x50cm-24x20in) s. 26-Apr-4 Tajan, Paris #195 est:1000-1200

MENDJUZKY, Serge (20th C) ?

£278 $506 €420 Mediterranean villa (71x45cm-28x18in) board. 15-Jun-4 James Adam, Dublin #175/R

MENDLIK, Oscar Johan Alfred (1871-1963) Hungarian/Dutch

£316 $581 €480 A rocky mountain stream (54x41cm-21x16in) s.d.1906 canvas on board. 22-Jun-4 Christie's, Amsterdam #285/R

MENDOLA, Rosolino (1949-) Italian

£387 $643 €550 Alfabeto (100x100cm-39x39in) s. s.i.d.2001 verso. 14-Jun-3 Meeting Art, Vercelli #213/R
£600 $1104 €900 Patterns (90x116cm-35x46in) s. 12-Jun-4 Meeting Art, Vercelli #946/R

Works on paper

£436 $807 €650 Prints (100x100cm-39x39in) s. mixed media on canvas. 13-Mar-4 Meeting Art, Vercelli #333

MENE, P J (1810-1879) French

Sculpture

£1000 $1790 €1500 Chien epagneul a l'arret (14x31cm-6x12in) s. green brown pat bronze. 12-May-4 Coutau Begarie, Paris #236/R est:1500-1800
£1400 $2380 €2044 Stallion tethered to a tree trunk (18x36cm-7x14in) s.d.1877 bronze. 29-Oct-3 Mallams, Oxford #633/R est:1200-1500
£1500 $2700 €2190 Study of North American elks. i. bronze. 25-Jan-4 Desmond Judd, Cranbrook #764
£1974 $3632 €3000 L'accolade (33x53x21cm-13x21x8in) brown pat. bronze. 24-Jun-4 Claude Boisgirard, Paris #96 est:3000-4000
£2235 $4000 €3263 Arab falconer (69cm-27in) brown pat bronze. 20-Mar-4 Freeman, Philadelphia #842/R est:4000-6000
£2727 $4636 €3900 Le jockey (42x42cm-17x17in) s. brown pat bronze. 20-Nov-3 Millon & Associes, Paris #534/R
£3000 $5460 €4500 Chasse au cerf (28cm-11in) pat bronze. 20-Jun-4 Wilkinson, Doncaster #142 est:4000-6000
£4545 $7727 €6500 Combat de cerf. bronze green marble socle Cast Susse. 20-Nov-3 Millon & Associes, Paris #537/R
£10738 $20081 €16000 Deux chiens attaquant un renard (27x49cm-11x19in) s.d.1849 brown pat bronze. 1-Mar-4 Coutau Begarie, Paris #237/R est:1000-12000

MENE, Pierre Jules (1810-1879) French

Sculpture

£783 $1300 €1143 Retriever (18cm-7in) s. brown pat. bronze. 4-Oct-3 Skinner, Boston #757 est:1500-2000
£798 $1300 €1165 Chase au cerf - stag attacked by three hounds (30cm-12in) s. brown pat bronze ovoid base lit. 19-Jul-3 Skinner, Boston #224 est:700-900
£848 $1535 €1238 Hound (10x28x9cm-4x11x4in) s. bronze. 31-Mar-4 Louis Morton, Mexico #56/R est:5000-8000 (M.P 17000)
£900 $1530 €1314 Pointer (12x31cm-5x12in) s. pat bronze. 28-Oct-3 Sotheby's, London #131/R
£919 $1700 €1342 Setter on point (23x33cm-9x13in) s. brown pat.bronze. 10-Feb-4 Doyle, New York #195/R est:1000-1500
£1000 $1700 €1460 Standing retriever (20x28cm-8x11in) s. pat bronze. 28-Oct-3 Sotheby's, London #129/R
£1000 $1820 €1460 Goat and kid (23cm-9in) s. brown pat bronze. 15-Jun-4 Sotheby's, Olympia #122/R est:800-1200
£1047 $1800 €1529 Chien epagneul. bronze. 3-Dec-3 Naón & Cia, Buenos Aires #591/R est:800-1200
£1064 $1777 €1500 L'epagneul (22x31cm-9x12in) s. black pat bronze. 20-Jun-3 Drouot Estimations, Paris #205 est:1500-2000
£1064 $1777 €1500 Cheval (19cm-7in) s. brown pat bronze. 14-Oct-3 Vanderkindere, Brussels #146/R
£1100 $1980 €1606 Two antelopes (35cm-14in) s. brown pat, bronze. 21-Apr-4 Cheffins, Cambridge #591/R est:800-1200
£1156 $1839 €1700 Setter a l'arret (32cm-13in) s. brown pat bronze. 23-Mar-3 St-Germain-en-Laye Encheres #95
£1163 $2000 €1698 Groupe de renards. bronze. 3-Dec-3 Naón & Cia, Buenos Aires #589/R est:2000-3000
£1167 $2112 €1750 Cheval libre (37x16x30cm-15x6x12in) s.d.1868 brown pat bronze. 1-Apr-4 Credit Municipal, Paris #93 est:2000-3000
£1222 $2200 €1784 Barbary stallion, Djinn (25x18cm-10x7in) bronze. 24-Jan-4 Skinner, Boston #644 est:1500-2500
£1439 $2360 €2000 Cerf a la branche (37x38cm-15x15in) st.f.Susse brown pat bronze. 6-Jun-3 Maigret, Paris #212/R est:1200-1800
£1565 $2488 €2300 Cerf (38x39cm-15x15in) s. pat bronze. 23-Mar-3 Salle des ventes Pillet, Lyon la Foret #164
£1600 $2880 €2336 Chien limiere - bloodhound tethered to tree (32cm-13in) s. brown pat. bronze. 21-Apr-4 Cheffins, Cambridge #592/R
£1655 $2764 €2400 L'etalon (16x37cm-6x15in) s. brown pat bronze. 17-Nov-3 Tajan, Paris #33/R est:2000-3000
£1656 $3030 €2500 Deux levrettes jouant avec une boule (22cm-9in) s. brown green pat. bronze. 6-Apr-4 Sotheby's, Amsterdam #233/R est:2000-3000
£1837 $2920 €2700 Taureau (24x40cm-9x16in) s. plaster. 23-Mar-3 Salle des ventes Pillet, Lyon la Foret #163
£1842 $3389 €2800 Jockey (42cm-17in) s. pat bronze. 24-Jun-4 Credit Municipal, Paris #68 est:2000-3000
£1854 $3375 €2800 Chatte nourissant ses petits (10x21cm-4x8in) s. brown pat. bronze cire perdue Cast Susse. 15-Jun-4 Vanderkindere, Brussels #202/R est:3000-5000
£1921 $3495 €2900 Le cheval Ibrahim (31x36cm-12x14in) s.i. brown pat. bronze lit. 16-Jun-4 Renaud, Paris #151/R est:2500-3000
£2000 $3400 €2920 Chasse au lapin (20x38cm-8x15in) s.i.d.1865 brown pat bronze. 19-Nov-3 Sotheby's, Olympia #152/R est:2000-3000
£2013 $3564 €3000 Deux chiens de chasse (41x21cm-16x8in) s. pat bronze Cast Barbedienne. 30-Apr-4 Tajan, Paris #27/R est:3500-4000
£2198 $4000 €3209 Deux chiens de chasse a l'arret devant un faisan (23x41cm-9x16in) s. brown pat bronze. 19-Jun-4 Jackson's, Cedar Falls #118/R est:2500-3500
£2200 $3674 €3190 Cow with suckling calf (23x33cm-9x13in) s. bronze. 22-Jun-3 Desmond Judd, Cranbrook #609
£2200 $3740 €3212 Groupe levrettes (15x21cm-6x8in) s. pat bronze. 28-Oct-3 Sotheby's, London #148/R
£2200 $4158 €3212 Pointer with dead game (28cm-11in) s. brown pat bronze. 17-Feb-4 Sotheby's, Olympia #25/R est:2500-3500
£2215 $3566 €3300 Chien braque portant un lievre (31cm-12in) s. brown pat bronze. 23-Feb-3 St-Germain-en-Laye Encheres #61/R est:3000
£2235 $3800 €3263 Chasse a la perdrix (22cm-9in) s. pat bronze. 28-Oct-3 Christie's, Rockefeller NY #243/R
£2353 $4000 €3435 Jumente normande (42cm-17in) s.st.f.Barbedienne pat bronze prov.lit. 28-Oct-3 Christie's, Rockefeller NY #203/R
£2365 $4233 €3500 Moroccan falconer on horseback (77x60cm-30x24in) s. dark brown pat.bronze lit. 8-May-4 Dawo, Saarbrucken #199/R est:3500
£2400 $3744 €3480 Fauconnier Arabe a pied (66cm-26in) s. brown pat bronze. 20-Oct-2 Desmond Judd, Cranbrook #527
£2500 $4250 €3600 Vase, sujet de chasse (39x21x14cm-15x8x6in) brown pat bronze. 28-Oct-3 Rabourdin & Choppin de Janvry, Paris #54/R est:3600-4000
£2500 $4600 €3800 Horse and dog (49cm-19in) s. gold brown pat bronze incl. base. 22-Jun-4 Sotheby's, Amsterdam #97/R est:1500-2000
£2550 $4693 €3800 Racehorse and dog (47cm-19in) s. dark pat.bronze. 25-Mar-4 Dr Fritz Nagel, Stuttgart #942/R est:800
£2600 $4784 €3900 Couple de chevreuils (27cm-11in) s. pat bronze. 9-Jun-4 Beaussant & Lefèvre, Paris #126/R est:1500-1800
£2817 $4873 €4000 Group of dogs, hunt of a partridge (22cm-9in) s.d.1847 pat bronze lit. 10-Dec-3 Hugo Ruef, Munich #2786/R est:700
£2900 $4582 €4205 Chasseur Africain a cheval (61cm-24in) s. bronze exec.c.1860-1870. 17-Nov-2 Desmond Judd, Cranbrook #603
£2923 $5028 €4268 Stags fighting (60cm-24in) s. dark pat.bronze. 2-Dec-3 Bukowskis, Stockholm #246/R est:30000-35000 (S.KR 38000)
£3400 $5372 €4964 Animal group with dogs attacking a wild boar (25x22x48cm-10x9x19in) s. gold brown pat bronze oval naturalistic base. 27-Apr-3 Wilkinson, Doncaster #3/R
£3500 $5495 €5075 Valet de limier - Huntsman with a bloodhound (48x36cm-19x14in) s.d.1879 brown pat. bronze. 27-Aug-3 Sotheby's, London #970/R est:4000-6000
£3700 $5883 €5402 Jument a l'ecurie Juodunt avec un chien (25x46cm-10x18in) s. bronze. 11-Sep-3 John Nicholson, Haslemere #297/R est:3750-4000
£3895 $6700 €5687 Levrette jouant. bronze. 3-Dec-3 Naón & Cia, Buenos Aires #590/R est:3000-4000
£4000 $6280 €5800 Cheval a la barriere-djinn - Stallion by a fence (29x38cm-11x15in) s.i.d.1846 brown pat. bronze. 27-Aug-3 Sotheby's, London #968/R est:4000-6000
£4333 $7843 €6500 Jument Normande (43x49cm-17x19in) s.base pat bronze. 2-Apr-4 Coutau Begarie, Paris #215 est:6500-7000
£4333 $7887 €6500 Chasseur avec chien (8x41cm-3x16in) s. pat bronze marble socle. 29-Jun-4 Sotheby's, Paris #84/R est:4500-6000
£4452 $7568 €6500 Accolade (31x55cm-12x22in) s.st.f.Susse pat bronze. 5-Nov-3 Beaussant & Lefèvre, Paris #172/R
£4500 $7650 €6570 Fauconnier arabe (78x59cm-31x23in) s. pat bronze lit. 28-Oct-3 Sotheby's, London #152/R
£4545 $7591 €6500 Accolade (54cm-21in) s. pat bronze. 7-Oct-3 Sotheby's, Amsterdam #255/R est:4000-6000
£4564 $7850 €6663 Chien braque. bronze. 3-Dec-3 Naón & Cia, Buenos Aires #588/R est:3500-5000
£4600 $7820 €6716 Djinn (29x38cm-11x15in) s.d.1846 pat bronze. 28-Oct-3 Sotheby's, London #160/R
£4667 $8587 €7000 L'accolade (34x52cm-13x20in) s. brown pat. bronze. 14-Jun-4 Horta, Bruxelles #161/R est:6500-8000
£4700 $7661 €6862 Two Arab horses (33x52cm-13x20in) bronze. 28-Sep-3 Wilkinson, Doncaster #4/R
£4800 $8640 €7008 Jument a l'ecurie jouant avec un chien (48cm-19in) s. dark brown pat. bronze. 21-Apr-4 Cheffins, Cambridge #590/R est:1200-1500

£4861 $8118 €7000 La chasse au renard en ecosse (54x73x35cm-21x29x14in) s. verso brown pat.bronze lit. 24-Oct-3 Ketterer, Hamburg #87/R est:8000-10000
£5000 $9000 €7300 Boar brought down by four hounds (28x49cm-11x19in) s.d.1846 brown pat bronze ebonised wood base. 21-Apr-4 Sotheby's, London #91/R est:3000-4000
£5034 $9312 €7500 Cheval breton (36x37x14cm-14x15x6in) s. pat bronze. 14-Mar-4 St-Germain-en-Laye Encheres #88/R est:7000-8000
£5081 $8740 €7418 Djinn, cheval a la barriere. bronze. 3-Dec-3 Naón & Cia, Buenos Aires #595/R est:5000-7000
£5100 $8058 €7395 Pauconnier Arabe a cheval (91x76cm-36x30in) s. bronze. 27-Jul-3 Desmond Judd, Cranbrook #564
£5729 $8995 €8250 Djinn (29x44cm-11x17in) s.i.d.1846 pat bronze. 29-Aug-3 Deauville, France #206/R est:7000-7500
£6338 $10965 €9000 Valet de chasse a cheval (61x62cm-24x24in) s.d.1874 bronze. 10-Dec-3 Beaussant & Lefèvre, Paris #99/R est:10000-15000
£6667 $12200 €10000 Fauconnier arabe a cheval (79cm-31in) i. num.396 brown pat. bronze lit. 3-Jun-4 Tajan, Paris #294/R est:10000-12000
£6879 $11489 €9700 Fauconnier Arabe a cheval (75x59cm-30x23in) s. gilt pat bronze. 19-Oct-3 Peron, Melun #363
£7059 $12000 €10306 Kemlem-Handani (30cm-12in) s. pat bronze prov.lit. 28-Oct-3 Christie's, Rockefeller NY #202/R
£7616 $13861 €11500 La jument normande et son poulain (45x61cm-18x24in) s.d.1868 brown pat. bronze lit. 16-Jun-4 Renaud, Paris #150/R est:8000-10000
£8000 $14000 €11680 Vanquer Du Derby (41x41cm-16x16in) bronze group. 18-Dec-3 John Nicholson, Haslemere #534 est:7500-8000
£8000 $14320 €12000 Valet de chasse Louis XV a cheval avec deux chiens (41x47x24cm-16x19x9in) s. dark pat bronze oak socle. 12-May-4 Coutau Begarie, Paris #260/R est:12000-13000
£8500 $15300 €12410 Mare and stallion (34x54cm-13x21in) s. dark brown pat bronze. 21-Apr-4 Sotheby's, London #78/R est:5000-7000
£9000 $16380 €13500 Valet de chiens (66x75cm-26x30in) s. pat bronze. 4-Jul-4 Eric Pillon, Calais #18/R
£9589 $16301 €14000 Groupe de chevaux arabes (33x54x21cm-13x21x8in) s.i.d.1876 brown pat bronze. 9-Nov-3 Eric Pillon, Calais #64/R
£10490 $18042 €15000 Equestrian bronze group (66cm-26in) s.d.1869 pat bronze. 2-Dec-3 Christie's, Paris #52/R est:15000-20000
£12000 $18840 €17400 Ecossais montrant un renard a son chien - Scottish huntsman showing a fox to the hounds (54cm-21in) s. brown pat. bronze pair. 27-Aug-3 Sotheby's, London #952/R est:8000-12000
£18000 $28260 €26100 Valet de chiens a chaval menant sa harde - Mounted huntsman leading his hounds (67x77cm-26x30in) s.d.1869 brown pat. bronze. 27-Aug-3 Sotheby's, London #980/R est:18000-25000

MENEELY, Leslie Stewart (20th C) American
Sculpture
£1471 $2500 €2148 Bust of Hippocrates (48cm-19in) bronze black marble base. 31-Oct-3 North East Auctions, Portsmouth #1884

MENEGALDO, Giovanni (1927-) Italian
Works on paper
£282 $468 €400 Untitled (50x50cm-20x20in) s.i.verso col plaster panel. 14-Jun-3 Meeting Art, Vercelli #21
£317 $526 €450 Untitled (50x60cm-20x24in) s.d.1995 col plaster panel. 14-Jun-3 Meeting Art, Vercelli #293

MENEGHELLI, Enrico (1853-1891) Italian
£484 $900 €707 Cows at pasture (40x60cm-16x24in) s. 5-Mar-4 Skinner, Boston #241/R
£2235 $4000 €3263 Golden sunset over Boston (23x30cm-9x12in) s. canvasboard painted c.1880 exhib. 26-May-4 Doyle, New York #69/R est:2000-3000

MENENDEZ PIDAL, Luis (1864-1932) Spanish
£1596 $2665 €2250 La panderata rota (38x24cm-15x9in) s. canvas on panel. 23-Jun-3 Durán, Madrid #203/R est:1200
Works on paper
£567 $948 €800 Landscape of Grado, Austria (14x21cm-6x8in) s.d.80 W/C. 23-Jun-3 Durán, Madrid #54/R

MENENDEZ ROJAS, Jose Manuel (1956-) Spanish
£599 $1048 €850 Untitled (46x38cm-18x15in) s.d.1993 prov. 16-Dec-3 Segre, Madrid #187/R

MENENDEZ, Cesar (1954-) American?
£2747 $5000 €4011 La adolescente de Balthus (120x119cm-47x47in) s.d.98 s.i.d.verso exhib. 29-Jun-4 Sotheby's, New York #680/R est:6000-8000

MENESCARDI, Giustino (attrib) (18th C) Italian
£3893 $7162 €5800 Joseph's dream (44x31cm-17x12in) i.verso. 29-Mar-4 Pandolfini, Florence #645/R est:6000

MENESES DEL BARCO, Jesus (1924-) Spanish
Works on paper
£476 $794 €680 Landscape with marsh (69x48cm-27x19in) s. W/C. 30-Jun-3 Ansorena, Madrid #14/R

MENESES, Jesus (?) Spanish
Works on paper
£517 $864 €750 Landscape (68x98cm-27x39in) s. W/C. 17-Nov-3 Durán, Madrid #634/R

MENEVILLE (19/20th C) French
Sculpture
£1148 $1860 €1665 Art deco figure of a woman (47cm-19in) pat metal ivory marble alabaster exec.c.1925 lit. 4-Aug-3 Rasmussen, Vejle #1094/R est:12000 (D.KR 12000)

MENG, Josef (20th C) Austrian
£367 $675 €550 Wilde Kaiser (50x60cm-20x24in) s. masonite. 9-Jun-4 Dorotheum, Salzburg #593/R

MENGARD, Leontine (19th C) French
£795 $1454 €1200 Les lavandieres (53x42cm-21x17in) s.d.1851. 9-Apr-4 Claude Aguttes, Neuilly #24/R

MENGE, Charles (1920-) Swiss
£661 $1123 €965 Still life with raspberries (22x28cm-9x11in) s.d.1970 board. 7-Nov-3 Dobiaschofsky, Bern #87/R (S.FR 1500)
£661 $1123 €965 Still life with pots, candle, cheese and keys (20x25cm-8x10in) s.d.1969 panel. 7-Nov-3 Dobiaschofsky, Bern #89/R (S.FR 1500)
£849 $1417 €1231 Plaine du Rhone dans la brume (42x52cm-17x20in) s.d. cardboard. 21-Jun-3 Galerie du Rhone, Sion #396 (S.FR 1850)
£1034 $1852 €1510 Workers in the vineyards of Branson (17x24cm-7x9in) s.i.d.1985 board. 14-May-4 Dobiaschofsky, Bern #165/R est:2800 (S.FR 2400)
£1086 $1879 €1586 Collines de Finges (15x31cm-6x12in) s.d.1989 panel. 12-Dec-3 Galerie du Rhone, Sion #556 est:2000-2500 (S.FR 2400)
£1718 $2921 €2508 Old town of Sion (40x50cm-16x20in) s.d.1968 panel. 7-Nov-3 Dobiaschofsky, Bern #107/R est:4500 (S.FR 3900)
£2026 $3445 €2958 Houses by lake (50x65cm-20x26in) s.d.1981 panel. 7-Nov-3 Dobiaschofsky, Bern #88/R est:6000 (S.FR 4600)
£2579 $4462 €3765 Nature morte au faisan et aux noix (62x86cm-24x34in) s.d.1965 prov. 12-Dec-3 Galerie du Rhone, Sion #658/R est:5000-7000 (S.FR 5700)
Works on paper
£486 $812 €700 Paysage anime (41x33cm-16x13in) s.i.d.1971 gouache. 23-Oct-3 Credit Municipal, Paris #105
£517 $926 €755 Personnages (28x20cm-11x8in) s.d.1963 mixed media. 12-May-4 Dobiaschofsky, Bern #793/R (S.FR 1200)
£1267 $2192 €1850 Ecole enfantine (16x21cm-6x8in) s.i.d.1986 gouache. 12-Dec-3 Galerie du Rhone, Sion #553/R est:2000-3000 (S.FR 2800)

MENGELS, Hubertus Johannus (1921-1995) Dutch
£769 $1323 €1100 Maassluis II (55x70cm-22x28in) s. 8-Dec-3 Glerum, Amsterdam #150/R

MENGHI, Jose Luis (1869-?) Argentinian
£385 $700 €562 Vase of flowers (24x19cm-9x7in) s. cardboard. 5-Jul-4 Arroyo, Buenos Aires #74/R
£495 $900 €723 Poppies (35x27cm-14x11in) s. 5-Jul-4 Arroyo, Buenos Aires #16/R
£495 $900 €723 Vase of flowers (39x34cm-15x13in) s. cardboard. 5-Jul-4 Arroyo, Buenos Aires #60/R
£531 $950 €775 White roses (33x25cm-13x10in) cardboard. 11-May-4 Arroyo, Buenos Aires #64

MENGIN, Lecreulx Vincent (20th C) ?
£336 $594 €500 Aurelia (130x292cm-51x115in) mono. triptych. 27-Apr-4 Campo & Campo, Antwerp #168

MENGIN, Paul Eugène (1853-1937) French
Sculpture
£12500 $20000 €18250 At the wishing well (76cm-30in) s. bronze. 20-Sep-3 Sloans & Kenyon, Bethesda #1200a/R est:8500-9500

MENGS, Anton Raphael (1728-1779) German
£40000 $73200 €58400 Holy Family with Saint John (200x136cm-79x54in) prov.lit. 7-Jul-4 Sotheby's, London #50/R est:40000-60000
£42000 $76860 €61320 Portrait sketch of the head of young man (40x35cm-16x14in) i.verso exhib.lit. 8-Jul-4 Sotheby's, London #229/R est:8000-12000
£170213 $275745 €240000 The adoration of the shepherds (253x163cm-100x64in) prov.lit. 20-May-3 Ansorena, Madrid #97/R est:240000

MENGS, Anton Raphael (attrib) (1728-1779) German
Works on paper
£724 $1332 €1100 Allegorical figure (28x23cm-11x9in) sanguine. 22-Jun-4 Sotheby's, Milan #92/R

MENGS, Anton Raphael (style) (1728-1779) German
£8500 $15300 €12410 Madonna and Child (37x27cm-15x11in) 23-Apr-4 Christie's, Kensington #154/R est:1500-2000

MENGUY, Frederic (1927-) French
£352 $609 €500 Nu rouge (60x73cm-24x29in) s. 13-Dec-3 Touati, Paris #146/R
£733 $1327 €1100 Marchande de fruits (49x49cm-19x19in) s. 1-Apr-4 Credit Municipal, Paris #60
£733 $1327 €1100 Regate (49x49cm-19x19in) s. 1-Apr-4 Credit Municipal, Paris #61

MENINSKY, Bernard (1891-1950) British
£320 $598 €480 Portrait of Laura Jane-Bowers (61x51cm-24x20in) s. 22-Jul-4 Gorringes, Lewes #1897
£1200 $2196 €1752 Reclining figure in a landscape (64x36cm-25x14in) 8-Jul-4 Duke & Son, Dorchester #274/R est:1000-2000
£1600 $2864 €2336 Portrait of a woman (51x41cm-20x16in) 14-May-4 Christie's, Kensington #506/R est:800-1200
£1850 $3367 €2701 Portrait of a girl in a red dress (61x51cm-24x20in) 15-Jun-4 Bonhams, Knightsbridge #81/R est:1200-1800

£11000 $18920 €16060 Reclining woman (45x56cm-18x22in) exhib. 3-Dec-3 Sotheby's, London #49/R est:10000-15000
Works on paper
£280 $510 €409 Portrait of a young lady (54x40cm-21x16in) s. pencil W/C. 1-Jul-4 Christie's, Kensington #47
£320 $550 €467 Study of a male nude (55x18cm-22x7in) s. brown chk. 3-Dec-3 Christie's, Kensington #402
£400 $740 €584 Standing female nude (37x15cm-15x6in) s. pencil. 11-Mar-4 Christie's, Kensington #20
£520 $868 €759 Portrait of a young boy seated (38x30cm-15x12in) s.d.1917 pencil chl. 11-Oct-3 Shapes, Edinburgh #365
£700 $1239 €1022 Seated female figure (26x15cm-10x6in) pencil ink over pencil. 27-Apr-4 Bonhams, Knightsbridge #87/R
£750 $1343 €1095 Summer landscape (23x30cm-9x12in) s. gouache. 16-Mar-4 Bonhams, New Bond Street #42/R
£800 $1456 €1168 Guardian Angel (30x21cm-12x8in) pen brush blk ink W/C. 1-Jul-4 Christie's, Kensington #34/R
£850 $1522 €1241 Landscape in Hampshire (38x51cm-15x20in) s.d.26 W/C. 16-Mar-4 Bonhams, New Bond Street #43/R
£1701 $3095 €2500 Maternity (49x32cm-19x13in) s. gouache W/C prov. 3-Feb-4 Christie's, Amsterdam #456 est:800-1200
£2000 $3400 €2920 Study (26x17cm-10x7in) pen ink W/C. 26-Nov-3 Sotheby's, Olympia #15/R est:2000-3000
£3800 $6916 €5548 Maternity (49x33cm-19x13in) s. gouache prov. 15-Jun-4 Bonhams, New Bond Street #58/R est:2500-3500

MENINSKY, Phillip (1919-) British?
£360 $572 €526 Table top and plants (18x23cm-7x9in) s. board. 9-Sep-3 Gorringes, Lewes #1860/R

MENKES, Zygmunt (1896-1986) Polish
£2473 $4500 €3611 Still life of flowers in a vase (61x46cm-24x18in) s. prov. 29-Jun-4 Sotheby's, New York #376/R est:4000-6000
£2596 $4750 €3790 Femme et fleurs (56x46cm-22x18in) s. painted c.1950. 5-Jun-4 Treadway Gallery, Cincinnati #734/R est:4000-6000
£2994 $5000 €4371 Boy playing a harmonica (51x41cm-20x16in) s. 7-Oct-3 Sotheby's, New York #304 est:2500-3500
£4037 $6500 €5894 Mysterious woman (61x46cm-24x18in) s. 22-Feb-3 Bunte, Elgin #1203 est:3000-5000
£6052 $11014 €8836 Female portrait (67x52cm-26x20in) s. painted 1960. 20-Jun-4 Agra, Warsaw #29/R (P.Z 42000)
£6150 $11500 €8979 Encounter (53x46cm-21x18in) i.verso. 29-Feb-4 Grogan, Boston #92/R
£6250 $10438 €9125 Fruit picking (61x82cm-24x32in) s. painted c.1930. 19-Oct-3 Agra, Warsaw #11/R est:35000 (P.Z 40000)
£9366 $17046 €13674 Female nude (41x33cm-16x13in) s. painted 1950. 20-Jun-4 Agra, Warsaw #28/R (P.Z 65000)
£9901 $17426 €14455 Lady (99x74cm-39x29in) painted 1930. 23-May-4 Agra, Warsaw #8/R (P.Z 70000)
Works on paper
£438 $731 €639 Standing woman (28x22cm-11x9in) Indian ink parchment exec.c.1960. 19-Oct-3 Agra, Warsaw #69/R (P.Z 2800)
£1724 $2879 €2500 Fille au bouquet (53x38cm-21x15in) s. Indian ink W/C. 17-Nov-3 Claude Boisgirard, Paris #66 est:3000-3500

MENKOV, Mikhail Ivanovich (1885-1926) Russian
Works on paper
£362 $568 €529 F A R (33x23cm-13x9in) mono. gouache collage. 26-Aug-3 Iegor de Saint Hippolyte, Montreal #109 (C.D 800)
£362 $568 €529 G E (28x21cm-11x8in) mono. gouache collage. 26-Aug-3 Iegor de Saint Hippolyte, Montreal #110 (C.D 800)
£407 $639 €594 Graf (23x20cm-9x8in) mono.d.1913 gouache collage. 26-Aug-3 Iegor de Saint Hippolyte, Montreal #111 (C.D 900)

MENN, Barthelemy (1815-1893) Swiss
Works on paper
£588 $983 €858 Paysage du lac leman (11x15cm-4x6in) dr. 16-Nov-3 Koller, Geneva #427 (S.FR 1340)

MENNERET, Charles Louis (1876-?) French
£366 $641 €520 Paysage maritime (50x73cm-20x29in) s. panel. 21-Dec-3 Thierry & Lannon, Brest #342

MENNEVILLE, E (20th C) French
Sculpture
£1044 $1900 €1566 Figure of a maiden and a songbird (66x13x20cm-26x5x8in) s. ivorine marble base executed c.1925. 19-Jun-4 Harvey Clar, Oakland #2090

MENNYEY, Francesco (1889-1950) Italian
£567 $948 €800 Alpine village (30x39cm-12x15in) s. cardboard. 20-Oct-3 Sant Agostino, Torino #266/R
£604 $1069 €900 Seascape (25x33cm-10x13in) s.d.1926 board. 1-May-4 Meeting Art, Vercelli #215
£2308 $3854 €3300 Park (47x68cm-19x27in) s. cardboard. 26-Jun-3 Sant Agostino, Torino #289/R est:3000-4000

MENON, Anjolie Ela (1940-) Indian
£9957 $17923 €14537 Brahmin boy (50x45cm-20x18in) s. masonite. 25-Apr-4 Christie's, Hong Kong #613/R est:60000-70000 (HK.D 140000)

MENPES, Mortimer L (1860-1938) British
£1800 $3096 €2628 On the balcony (39x25cm-15x10in) s. board. 2-Dec-3 Bonhams, New Bond Street #39/R est:2000-3000

MENS, Isidorus Maria Cornelis van (1890-1985) Belgian
£514 $873 €750 Berbere (20x15cm-8x6in) s. panel. 10-Nov-3 Horta, Bruxelles #316
£642 $1149 €950 Porte a Segovie (47x38cm-19x15in) s.d.1951. 10-May-4 Horta, Bruxelles #69
£1064 $1777 €1500 Portrait de jeune Arabe (19x15cm-7x6in) s. panel. 16-Jun-3 Gros & Delettrez, Paris #451 est:1500-1800
£1250 $1962 €1800 Paysage Algerien (50x70cm-20x28in) s. 26-Aug-3 Galerie Moderne, Brussels #282/R est:2000-3000
£1389 $2264 €2000 A miner (90x100cm-35x39in) s.d.1931. 29-Sep-3 Sotheby's, Amsterdam #399
£1408 $2437 €2000 Fillette marocaine (30x25cm-12x10in) s. panel. 15-Dec-3 Gros & Delettrez, Paris #219/R est:2200-3200
£1655 $3062 €2400 Saint-Tropez (80x90cm-31x35in) s. painted 1937. 19-Jan-4 Horta, Bruxelles #70 est:2000-2500
£1972 $3411 €2800 Deux jeunes marocains (50x60cm-20x24in) s.i.d.1932. 15-Dec-3 Gros & Delettrez, Paris #388/R est:2800-3500
£2400 $4296 €3600 Assemblee d'hommes en Afrique du nord (100x80cm-39x31in) s. 16-May-4 MonsAntic, Maisieres #479 est:1200-1800
£3125 $4969 €4500 Le marchand de beignets, Orientaliste (60x50cm-24x20in) s. 15-Sep-3 Horta, Bruxelles #30 est:1500-2000
£5000 $7950 €7200 Le souk des femmes, Orientaliste (75x68cm-30x27in) s.d.1941. 15-Sep-3 Horta, Bruxelles #29 est:1500-2000
£5068 $9071 €7500 La fete du Caid a Ghardaia (42x65cm-17x26in) s. 10-May-4 Horta, Bruxelles #68/R est:6000-8000
£5986 $10356 €8500 North African scene (100x120cm-39x47in) s.d.1929. 13-Dec-3 De Vuyst, Lokeren #358/R est:1800-2200
£7386 $13000 €10784 Market, Moulay-Idris, Morocco (100x121cm-39x48in) s.i.d.1936. 18-May-4 Bonhams & Butterfields, San Francisco #79/R est:10000-15000
£8392 $14434 €12000 Jour de marche a Ghardiaia (59x90cm-23x35in) s.i.d.1949. 8-Dec-3 Tajan, Paris #327/R est:12000-15000
£18000 $32941 €27000 Fete de nuit a Ghardaia (88x286cm-35x113in) s.i.d.1933 triptych. 3-Jun-4 Tajan, Paris #343/R est:30000-40000
Works on paper
£278 $453 €400 Entree du temple a Bali. s. W/C exec.1929. 23-Sep-3 Galerie Moderne, Brussels #829
£490 $842 €700 Sur la route de Djerba (26x36cm-10x14in) s. W/C. 8-Dec-3 Horta, Bruxelles #329
£699 $1202 €1000 Marcha a Ghardaia (22x31cm-9x12in) s.i. crayon. 8-Dec-3 Tajan, Paris #335/R
£1007 $1862 €1500 Puits dans l'oasis (32x25cm-13x10in) s.i.d.1926 W/C. 15-Mar-4 Gros & Delettrez, Paris #89/R est:1500-2000

MENSA, Carlos (1936-1982) Spanish
£3793 $6828 €5500 Figure (100x78cm-39x31in) s. s.i.verso. 26-Jan-4 Durán, Madrid #140/R est:3000

MENSA, Manuel (1875-?) Spanish
£1348 $2250 €1900 Gypsy meeting (48x70cm-19x28in) s. 20-Oct-3 Durán, Madrid #145/R est:1900

MENSE, Carlo (1886-1965) German
£2000 $3660 €3000 Portrait of Boris Pasternak (80x60cm-31x24in) s. prov.exhib.lit. 5-Jun-4 Lempertz, Koln #873/R est:2500
£2238 $3804 €3200 Siebengebirg landscape (53x66cm-21x26in) s. panel. 26-Nov-3 Lempertz, Koln #855/R est:3500
£17333 $31720 €26000 Landscape with village - Hennef (69x58cm-27x23in) mono. canvas on board prov.lit. 5-Jun-4 Lempertz, Koln #872/R est:25000
Works on paper
£280 $512 €420 Industrial landscape (21x25cm-8x10in) s. chl. 5-Jun-4 Lempertz, Koln #874/R
£2000 $3580 €3000 Southern landscape (30x39cm-12x15in) s.d. gouache pencil prov. 14-May-4 Ketterer, Munich #60/R est:1500-2000

MENSION, Cornelis Jan (1882-1950) Dutch
£292 $461 €420 Crane on a riverbank (63x53cm-25x21in) s.d.1916. 2-Sep-3 Christie's, Amsterdam #255

MENTA, Edouard (1858-1915) Swiss/French
£730 $1291 €1066 Clown and monkeys (46x32cm-18x13in) s. i. stretcher. 12-Jun-4 Falk & Falk, Zurich #1036/R est:3000 (S.FR 1700)

MENTELER, Franz Josef (1777-1833) Swiss
£317 $538 €463 Man's portrait (64x51cm-25x20in) s.i. 19-Nov-3 Fischer, Luzern #2210/R (S.FR 700)
£1223 $2225 €1786 Portrait of Melchior Fidel. Portrait of Maria Josepha Achermann-Traxler (44x38cm-17x15in) s.i.d.1810 verso pair. 16-Jun-4 Fischer, Luzern #1274/R est:2500-3500 (S.FR 2800)

MENTOR, Blasco (1918-) Spanish
£1400 $2506 €2100 Paysage aux toits rouges (54x65cm-21x26in) s. 16-May-4 Lombrail & Teucquam, Paris #167/R
£1761 $3046 €2500 Couple (65x47cm-26x19in) s. 15-Dec-3 Ansorena, Madrid #1025/R est:2500
Works on paper
£267 $477 €400 Jeune femme a la mantille (30x22cm-12x9in) W/C. 16-May-4 Osenat, Fontainebleau #37/R
£350 $584 €500 Bull scene (47x64cm-19x25in) s. W/C felt-tip pen. 30-Jun-3 Ansorena, Madrid #8/R

MENU, Alfred (1873-1952) Belgian
Works on paper
£317 $587 €460 Barque de peche au soleil (37x54cm-15x21in) s. 19-Jan-4 Horta, Bruxelles #321

MENU, Julien (20th C) ?

£334	$600	€500	L'halterophile a l'hippopotame (50x60cm-20x24in) s. 26-Apr-4 Tajan, Paris #284

MENYAYEV, Sergei (1953-) Russian

£320	$589	€467	Harbour scene (59x75cm-23x30in) s. 28-Mar-4 Lots Road Auctions, London #369
£460	$837	€672	Roses on the window sill (60x60cm-24x24in) s. painted 1990. 20-Jun-4 Lots Road Auctions, London #344/R
£480	$874	€701	Village street (75x60cm-30x24in) s. 20-Jun-4 Lots Road Auctions, London #347
£550	$1001	€803	Sunday Morning (59x69cm-23x27in) s. 20-Jun-4 Lots Road Auctions, London #346/R
£600	$1092	€876	Sea view (60x75cm-24x30in) s. 20-Jun-4 Lots Road Auctions, London #348/R
£620	$1128	€905	Girl by the window (74x59cm-29x23in) s. 20-Jun-4 Lots Road Auctions, London #369/R

MENZEL, Adolph (1815-1905) German

£144796	$231674	€211402	Frederick the Great the Barbarina with Chevalier de Chasot (34x26cm-13x10in) s.d.1852 prov.exhib.lit. 19-Sep-3 Koller, Zurich #3078/R est:320000-420000 (S.FR 320000)
£734266	$1248252	€1050000	Schafgraben in Berlin (60x47cm-24x19in) mono.bears d.1846 prov.exhib.lit. 28-Nov-3 Villa Grisebach, Berlin #6/R est:500000-700000
Works on paper			
£533	$981	€800	Leather knots (16x10cm-6x4in) mono. pencil. 11-Jun-4 Hauswedell & Nolte, Hamburg #1045/R
£972	$1624	€1400	Study for Sister Emilie in wedding dress (15x7cm-6x3in) st.mono. pencil. 24-Oct-3 Ketterer, Hamburg #88/R
£2222	$4000	€3244	Study of legs and lower torso (21x12cm-8x5in) init. black pencil. 21-Jan-4 Sotheby's, New York #146/R est:4000-6000
£2917	$4608	€4200	Woman by table with material (21x14cm-8x6in) mono.d.1843 pencil. 6-Sep-3 Arnold, Frankfurt #613/R est:2800
£2933	$5397	€4400	Back view of a seated child (15x8cm-6x3in) pencil. 12-Jun-4 Villa Grisebach, Berlin #105/R est:5000-7000
£5705	$10211	€8500	Thankyou letter with coin and cat's head (14x12cm-6x5in) s.i.d.77 W/C pen silver coin. 25-May-4 Karl & Faber, Munich #114/R est:10000-12000
£11972	$20711	€17000	Two women's heads (17x11cm-7x4in) s. pencil chk. 13-Dec-3 Lempertz, Koln #34/R est:12000
£15000	$27450	€21900	Two carthorses in harness, seen from behind (11x18cm-4x7in) s.i. soft black lead exhib.lit. 6-Jul-4 Christie's, London #201/R est:8000-12000
£23776	$40420	€34000	Female heads - head and hat studies (21x15cm-8x6in) mono.d.7.97 pencil wash prov. 28-Nov-3 Villa Grisebach, Berlin #7/R est:30000-40000
£25000	$45000	€36500	Portraits of a girl and an old woman (13x20cm-5x8in) s.d.86 pencil stumped lit. 22-Jan-4 Christie's, Rockefeller NY #19/R est:20000-30000
£30000	$54900	€43800	Portrait of a girl in profile, wearing a straw hat (39x26cm-15x10in) s.d.92 soft black lead prov.lit. 6-Jul-4 Christie's, London #202/R est:15000-25000
£32000	$58560	€46720	Otto von Wittelsbach fountain the Munich residence (20x12cm-8x5in) init. blk chk prov.exhib.lit. 8-Jul-4 Sotheby's, London #151/R est:25000-35000
£41958	$71329	€60000	Consultation at advocate's office (38x29cm-15x11in) exhib.lit.prov. 28-Nov-3 Villa Grisebach, Berlin #2/R est:60000-80000
£54545	$92727	€78000	Sleeping child (13x21cm-5x8in) pencil prov. 28-Nov-3 Villa Grisebach, Berlin #5/R est:40000-60000
£59441	$101049	€85000	Blind man's bluff (29x23cm-11x9in) s.d.1867 gouache prov.exhib.lit. 28-Nov-3 Villa Grisebach, Berlin #4/R est:80000-120000

MENZEL, E (19th C) Austrian?

£1119	$1902	€1600	St Wolfgang on Wolfgangsee (45x53cm-18x21in) s.d.81. 20-Nov-3 Dorotheum, Salzburg #148/R est:1200-1800

MENZEL, Julius (19/20th C) German

£308	$514	€440	Old mill in the Alps on sunny day (24x15cm-9x6in) s. panel. 9-Oct-3 Michael Zeller, Lindau #687

MENZI, Ernst (1895-?) German?

£217	$369	€317	Peat moorland in Rhine valley (25x33cm-10x13in) s. board. 18-Nov-3 Hans Widmer, St Gallen #1149 (S.FR 480)

MENZIES, John (?-1939) British

£8500	$14705	€12410	On the riverbank (50x66cm-20x26in) s. 11-Dec-3 Lyon & Turnbull, Edinburgh #74/R est:3000-5000

MENZIO, Francesco (1899-1979) Italian

£1517	$2534	€2200	Lina, model from Turin (32x23cm-13x9in) board. 17-Nov-3 Sant Agostino, Torino #88/R est:2600
£2029	$3328	€2800	Open window (41x33cm-16x13in) s.prov. 27-May-3 Sotheby's, Milan #104/R est:2500-3000
£2083	$3292	€3000	Open window (41x33cm-16x13in) 6-Sep-3 Meeting Art, Vercelli #450 est:3000
£3521	$6162	€5000	Composition with chair (70x50cm-28x20in) s. 17-Dec-3 Il Ponte, Milan #1088/R
£3846	$6423	€5500	Landscape seen from the window (100x60cm-39x24in) s. 26-Jun-3 Sant Agostino, Torino #265/R est:4000-5000
£4196	$7133	€6000	Flowers and still life (67x53cm-26x21in) s. prov. 25-Nov-3 Sotheby's, Milan #103/R est:3500-4000
£4483	$7486	€6500	Still life (60x100cm-24x39in) s. board. 17-Nov-3 Sant Agostino, Torino #221/R est:6000-8000
£4800	$8016	€7008	The letter (68x56cm-27x22in) s. 22-Oct-3 Sotheby's, Olympia #194/R est:800-1200
£9091	$15182	€13000	Study interior (93x36cm-37x14in) s. board painted 1945 exhib.lit. 26-Jun-3 Sant Agostino, Torino #243/R est:9000-12000
£9655	$16124	€14000	Landscape in Turin (70x90cm-28x35in) s. painted 1952. 17-Nov-3 Sant Agostino, Torino #205/R est:14000-18000
£21379	$35703	€31000	Girl with blue book (85x57cm-33x22in) s. prov.exhib.lit. 17-Nov-3 Sant Agostino, Torino #206/R est:16000-20000
Works on paper			
£690	$1152	€1000	Boy sleeping, in profile (32x22cm-13x9in) s. pencil. 13-Nov-3 Finarte Semenzato, Rome #210
£1154	$1927	€1650	Carla (100x70cm-39x28in) s. mixed media card. 26-Jun-3 Sant Agostino, Torino #242/R est:1500-2000
£3862	$6450	€5600	Carla (97x68cm-38x27in) s. mixed media paper on canvas exec.1969. 17-Nov-3 Sant Agostino, Torino #220/R est:4000-5000

MENZLER, Wilhelm (1846-1926) German

£5650	$10000	€8249	Portrait of a lady, holding a rose (102x61cm-40x24in) s. 2-May-4 Bonhams & Butterfields, San Francisco #1048/R est:10000-15000

MERANDON (19/20th C) French?

£1049	$1783	€1500	Yacht devant une cote montagneuse (44x70cm-17x28in) s.d.1901. 23-Nov-3 Claude Boisgirard, Paris #181/R est:1300-1500

MERANO, Giovanni Battista (1632-c.1698) Italian

Works on paper			
£7000	$12810	€10220	Daedalus attaching wings to Icarus (16x20cm-6x8in) i. pen ink wash squared in red chk. 6-Jul-4 Christie's, London #66/R est:3000-5000

MERCADE, Jaime (1889-1967) Spanish

£604	$1069	€900	From the window (28x23cm-11x9in) s. cardboard. 27-Apr-4 Durán, Madrid #130/R
£5211	$8338	€7400	Still life with mushrooms and jugs (55x65cm-22x26in) s.d.1944. 16-Sep-3 Segre, Madrid #96/R
£7333	$13347	€11000	Paisaje del Bosc de Valls (40x65cm-16x26in) s.d.1938. 29-Jun-4 Segre, Madrid #96/R est:9000
£18116	$29710	€25000	La cuina (132x178cm-52x70in) s.d.52 s.i.d.verso exhib.lit. 27-May-3 Durán, Madrid #235/R est:25000

MERCER, Frederick (fl.1881-1937) British

Works on paper			
£280	$459	€409	Coastal landscape with farm buildings and figures (53x26cm-21x10in) s. W/C. 3-Jun-3 Fellows & Sons, Birmingham #119/R
£300	$552	€438	Figures before old cottages in summer (7x13cm-3x5in) s.d.79 W/C. 11-Jun-4 Keys, Aylsham #328
£780	$1420	€1139	St. Ives from Tregenna (26x50cm-10x20in) s.d.76 i.verso W/C. 21-Jun-4 Bonhams, Bath #458

MERCER, Stanley (1889-1932) British

£662	$1205	€1000	Portrait of a young girl wearing a green dress (90x70cm-35x28in) s. 17-Jun-4 Hamilton Osborne King, Dublin #371/R est:1000-1500
£1300	$2236	€1898	Portrait of Mrs Richmond Temple (91x71cm-36x28in) prov. 7-Dec-3 Lots Road Auctions, London #360 est:1200-1800

MERCIE, M J A (1845-1916) French

Sculpture			
£1690	$2806	€2400	David Vainqueur (60cm-24in) s. greenish pat. bronze. 11-Jun-3 Sotheby's, Amsterdam #374/R est:2200-2800

MERCIE, Marius Jean Antonin (1845-1916) French

£1977	$3677	€2886	The model (81x53cm-32x21in) s. 2-Mar-4 Rasmussen, Copenhagen #1470/R est:20000 (D.KR 22000)
Sculpture			
£987	$1816	€1500	Quand Meme (63cm-25in) s. st.f.Barbedienne bronze. 22-Jun-4 Glerum, Amsterdam #102/R est:1600-1800
£1382	$2542	€2100	David (94cm-37in) s. pat bronze. 28-Jun-4 Joron-Derem, Paris #258/R est:2500-3000
£1528	$2551	€2200	David Vainqueur (61x15x18cm-24x6x7in) s.st.f.F. Barbedienne gold brown pat bronze. 23-Oct-3 Credit Municipal, Paris #124 est:1300-1800
£2282	$4244	€3400	La danse du sabre (72x21x41cm-28x8x16in) brown pat bronze exec.c.1890. 7-Mar-4 Lesieur & Le Bars, Le Havre #209
£2569	$4599	€3751	David with the Head of Goliath (28cm-11in) s. bronze red marble socle prov. 15-May-4 Christie's, Sydney #396/R est:2000-3000 (A.D 6500)
£2649	$4848	€4000	David Vainqueur (73cm-29in) bronze. 6-Apr-4 Sotheby's, Amsterdam #292/R est:2500-3000
£2897	$5214	€4200	David vainqueur (91cm-36in) s.st.f.Barbedienne brown pat bronze. 20-Jan-4 Galerie Moderne, Brussels #1508/R est:4000-5000
£2941	$5000	€4294	David with Goliath's head (72cm-28in) s.d.1892 pat bronze Cast Barbedienne. 28-Oct-3 Christie's, Rockefeller NY #104/R
£3716	$6541	€5500	David, the winner (91cm-36in) s.st.f.Barbedienne pat bronze lit. 19-May-4 Segre, Madrid #885/R est:4200
£4000	$7280	€5840	David apres le combat (10cm-4in) s. i.f.Barbedienne dark brown pat bronze prov.lit. 17-Jun-4 Christie's, London #59/R est:4000-6000
£4722	$8500	€6894	David Vainqueur (89cm-35in) s.i. bronze st.f.F. Barbedienne. 23-Apr-4 Christie's, Rockefeller NY #152/R est:5000-8000
£5000	$8650	€7300	David apres le combat (88cm-35in) s.num.226 brown pat bronze st.f.F.Barbedienne. 12-Dec-3 Sotheby's, London #256/R est:3500-4500
£5000	$7900	€7300	Gloria Victis (89cm-35in) s. gold pat bronze stop-fluted scotia plinth Cast.f.Barbedienne. 27-Apr-3 Wilkinson, Doncaster #23/R
£5000	$9100	€7300	Gloria Victis (84cm-33in) s.st.f.F. Barbedienne brown pat bronze red marble base lit. 15-Jun-4 Sotheby's, Olympia #71/R est:3000-5000
£8500	$15300	€12410	Gloria Victis (93cm-37in) s.i.num.141 brown pat bronze htd gilding st.f.F. Barbedienne. 21-Apr-4 Sotheby's, London #105/R est:7000-10000
£13125	$21000	€19163	Gloria Victis (109cm-43in) s. parcel gilt bronze Cast F. Barbedienne. 21-Sep-3 William Jenack, New York #163 est:6000-10000
£15294	$26000	€22329	Gloria Victis (203cm-80in) s.i. i.verso brown parcel-gilt pat bronze incl. base lit. 29-Oct-3 Christie's, Rockefeller NY #124/R est:25000-35000
£15556	$28000	€22712	Gloria Victis (88cm-35in) s.i. gold brown pat bronze marble pedestal lit. 22-Apr-4 Christie's, Rockefeller NY #124/R est:30000-40000

MERCIER (?) French

£242	$450	€353	Sheep in a manger (33x48cm-13x19in) s. painted c.1880. 7-Mar-4 Treadway Gallery, Cincinnati #517/R

MERCIER, Jean Baptiste (18th C) French
Works on paper
£280 $467 €400 Couple sous un portique au clair de lune (22x35cm-9x14in) s.d. W/C pen ink over crayon. 30-Jun-3 Bailly Pommery, Paris #10

MERCIER, Louise (19th C) French
£3444 $6302 €5200 Repos de l'odalisque (46x55cm-18x22in) s.d.1880. 7-Apr-4 Piasa, Paris #56 est:1000-1200

MERCIER, Philippe (1689-1760) French
£6000 $11040 €8760 Double portrait of a girl and a boy , girl seated on a rocking horse, boy holding a flag (62x74cm-24x29in) lit. 11-Jun-4 Christie's, London #17/R est:7000-10000
£24000 $43920 €35040 Young girl carrying a basket of flowers, said to be daughter of Governor of Greenwich hospital (89x71cm-35x28in) i.verso. 8-Jul-4 Duke & Son, Dorchester #282/R
£28000 $47600 €40880 Young artists (71x61cm-28x24in) mono. prov.exhib.lit. 27-Nov-3 Sotheby's, London #191/R est:30000-40000
£75000 $138000 €109500 Young woman in fawn dress (127x101cm-50x40in) init.i. prov.lit. 9-Jun-4 Christie's, London #8/R est:50000-70000

MERCIER, Philippe (attrib) (1689-1760) French
£1974 $3632 €3000 Fortune teller (33x28cm-13x11in) panel. 24-Jun-4 Dr Fritz Nagel, Stuttgart #618/R est:5000
£2500 $4175 €3650 Portrait of lady wearing a yellow dress (73x62cm-29x24in) 14-Oct-3 Sotheby's, London #434 est:2000-3000
£5587 $10000 €8157 Portrait of young man (92x71cm-36x28in) prov. 27-May-4 Sotheby's, New York #239/R est:15000-20000
Works on paper
£246 $450 €359 Man dressed as a pilgrim to St James of Compostella with an elegant woman (32x25cm-13x10in) black chk vellum. 29-Jan-4 Swann Galleries, New York #292/R

MERCIER, V (?) French
Miniatures
£1517 $2534 €2200 Lady Elizabeth Leveson-Gower (9cm-4in) exec.c.1830. 12-Nov-3 Sotheby's, Milan #63/R est:1000-1500

MERCK, Jacob Franz van der (1610-1664) Dutch
£5500 $9350 €8030 Portrait of a gentleman in black coat. Portrait of a lady in a black dress, holing a fan (76x64cm-30x25in) s.d.1660 pair. 31-Oct-3 Christie's, Kensington #24/R est:4000-6000
£8276 $14897 €12000 Portrait of lady. Portrait of gentleman (76x63cm-30x25in) pair prov. 26-Jan-4 Ansorena, Madrid #67/R est:12000
£10072 $16518 €14000 Portrait de famille devant une balustrade (166x220cm-65x87in) s.d.1658. 6-Jun-3 Drouot Estimations, Paris #30/R est:15000-20000

MERCKAERT, Jules (1872-1924) Belgian
£280 $467 €400 L'entree de la vallee (61x49cm-24x19in) s. s.i.d.1904. 11-Oct-3 De Vuyst, Lokeren #253
£526 $953 €800 Vallee de la Marne (50x60cm-20x24in) s.d.1921. 19-Apr-4 Horta, Bruxelles #434
£676 $1189 €1000 Canal in Flanders (50x75cm-20x30in) s.d.1909. 24-May-4 Bernaerts, Antwerp #562/R
£3497 $5839 €5000 Brume sur la riviere (98x139cm-39x55in) s.d.1917. 13-Oct-3 Horta, Bruxelles #220/R est:3500-4500
Works on paper
£338 $639 €500 Pont sur la Seine a Paris (33x42cm-13x17in) s.d.24 pastel. 17-Feb-4 Vanderkindere, Brussels #13/R

MERCKER, Erich (1891-1973) German
£280 $476 €400 Steamer in fjord (40x51cm-16x20in) s.i. board. 21-Nov-3 Reiss & Sohn, Konigstein #22/R
£352 $609 €500 Beach near Rugen (29x36cm-11x14in) s. cardboard. 10-Dec-3 Hugo Ruef, Munich #2459
£352 $609 €500 View of chapel, Wurzburg (39x48cm-15x19in) s. fibreboard. 10-Dec-3 Hugo Ruef, Munich #2460/R
£400 $720 €600 Chiemsee landscape (55x70cm-22x28in) s. 26-Apr-4 Rieber, Stuttgart #1263/R
£423 $731 €600 Sailing boats (40x50cm-16x20in) s. fibreboard. 10-Dec-3 Hugo Ruef, Munich #2457/R
£479 $815 €700 Grain harvest (33x46cm-13x18in) s. panel. 5-Nov-3 Hugo Ruef, Munich #1064
£483 $806 €700 Stormy seas off rocky coast (178x254cm-70x100in) s. lit. 12-Jul-3 Bergmann, Erlangen #669/R
£524 $892 €750 Fjord landscape with huts in background (40x51cm-16x20in) s.i. board. 21-Nov-3 Reiss & Sohn, Konigstein #23
£570 $1044 €850 Sailing ships on choppy sea (66x85cm-26x33in) s.i. lit. 8-Jul-4 Allgauer, Kempten #2168/R
£590 $974 €850 Old Nurnberg in winter (60x80cm-24x31in) s.i. i. verso. 3-Jul-3 Neumeister, Munich #2879/R
£616 $1048 €900 Fishing huts on Chiemsee (40x50cm-16x20in) s.i. panel. 6-Nov-3 Allgauer, Kempten #3501/R
£660 $1201 €990 Celebration in Wurzburg (49x59cm-19x23in) s. 1-Jul-4 Weidler, Nurnberg #7044/R
£738 $1321 €1100 Waves breaking by Genua (60x80cm-24x31in) s.i. 25-May-4 Karl & Faber, Munich #415/R
£753 $1281 €1100 Ships in Hamburg harbour (40x50cm-16x20in) s.i. panel. 6-Nov-3 Allgauer, Kempten #3502/R est:900
£753 $1281 €1100 Neumeyer factory, Nurnberg (39x49cm-15x19in) s.i. verso board. 6-Nov-3 Allgauer, Kempten #3504/R
£800 $1448 €1200 Old town of Cologne (61x81cm-24x32in) s. 1-Apr-4 Van Ham, Cologne #1537/R
£811 $1265 €1200 Beach (97x116cm-38x46in) s.i. 31-Mar-3 Bloss, Merzhausen #1582/R
£811 $1265 €1200 Rocky coast in evening. s.i. 31-Mar-3 Bloss, Merzhausen #1583/R
£833 $1325 €1200 Fraueninsel, Chiemsee (52x65cm-20x26in) s.i. panel. 13-Sep-3 Quittenbaum, Hamburg #59/R
£867 $1560 €1300 Hamburg harbour (80x120cm-31x47in) s. 26-Apr-4 Rieber, Stuttgart #1291/R est:1800
£909 $1518 €1300 Sylt, before the storm (63x83cm-25x33in) s. i. verso board. 11-Oct-3 Hans Stahl, Hamburg #24/R
£972 $1536 €1400 Goods yard (70x80cm-28x31in) s.i. i. verso lit. 19-Sep-3 Schloss Ahlden, Ahlden #1612/R
£1014 $1693 €1450 Moselle near Traben-Trarbach (60x80cm-24x31in) s.i. 10-Oct-3 Winterberg, Heidelberg #1674/R
£1094 $1827 €1597 View of Norymbergi (80x61cm-31x24in) s. painted c.1920. 19-Oct-3 Agra, Warsaw #48/R est:7000 (P.Z 7000)
£1133 $2029 €1700 Clouds over the Chiemsee (40x49cm-16x19in) s.i. i. verso board. 13-May-4 Neumeister, Munich #430/R est:1700-1800
£1133 $2029 €1700 Chiemsee in the morning (38x49cm-15x19in) s.i. i. verso board. 13-May-4 Neumeister, Munich #431/R est:1700-1800
£1208 $2223 €1800 Southern coastline (50x100cm-20x39in) s. lit. 25-Mar-4 Karlheinz Kaupp, Staufen #2612/R
£1233 $2096 €1800 Fortress on Bodensee (90x110cm-35x43in) s.i. panel. 6-Nov-3 Allgauer, Kempten #3503/R est:1200
£1233 $2096 €1800 Ships in Hamburg harbour (66x86cm-26x34in) s.i. bears i. verso. 6-Nov-3 Allgauer, Kempten #3506/R est:1800
£1575 $2678 €2300 Factory furnaces (66x71cm-26x28in) s.i. verso. 6-Nov-3 Allgauer, Kempten #3505/R est:2800
£1600 $2592 €2320 Venetian fishing boats in a calm (61x81cm-24x32in) s.i. 30-Jul-3 Hamptons Fine Art, Godalming #192 est:300-500
£1818 $3091 €2600 Factories on the Rhine (80x120cm-31x47in) s. 20-Nov-3 Van Ham, Cologne #1737/R est:1800
£2133 $3840 €3200 Monaco coast (92x131cm-36x52in) s. 21-Apr-4 Dorotheum, Vienna #111/R est:3200-3600
£3265 $5845 €4800 Village in southern France with stone bridge (61x80cm-24x31in) s.i. i. stretcher. 17-Mar-4 Neumeister, Munich #529/R est:1500

MERDY, Jean le (1928-) French
£1267 $2267 €1900 Composition aux lampes a petrole (81x40cm-32x16in) s.d.79. 16-May-4 Thierry & Lannon, Brest #217/R est:1000-1500
£2167 $3878 €3250 Raguennes, cote rocheuses, la tempete. s.d.74 panel. 16-May-4 Thierry & Lannon, Brest #218/R est:1500-2000

MEREDITH, Alfred (?) British
£700 $1281 €1022 Sheep and sheep dog in an extensive upland landscape (76x127cm-30x50in) indis sig.d. 8-Jul-4 Duke & Son, Dorchester #237/R

MERELLO, Amedeo (1890-1979) Italian
£403 $713 €600 Mushrooms and scales (59x50cm-23x20in) s.d.1966 board. 1-May-4 Meeting Art, Vercelli #159
£417 $708 €600 Giovi (24x33cm-9x13in) s.d.1941 board. 1-Nov-3 Meeting Art, Vercelli #413
£922 $1540 €1300 View in Liguria (32x21cm-13x8in) s.d.1913 board. 14-Oct-3 Finarte Semenzato, Milan #138/R

MERELLO, Rubaldo (1872-1922) Italian
£19310 $32248 €28000 Landscape in Liguria (26x19cm-10x7in) cardboard. 17-Nov-3 Sant Agostino, Torino #229/R est:22000-26000

MERET, Émile Louis (19/20th C) French
£562 $917 €821 River landscape with loading barge (38x61cm-15x24in) s.d.1902. 28-Sep-3 Hindemae, Ullerslev #158/R (D.KR 6000)

MERGAERT, Desire (1865-1890) Belgian
£1329 $2259 €1900 Portrait de Yves de Monti de Reze (65x53cm-26x21in) oval. 26-Nov-3 Daguerre, Paris #61 est:500-600

MERIAN, Matthaus (elder) (1593-1650) Swiss
Works on paper
£1701 $3044 €2500 Esau et Jacob dans un interieur (10x14cm-4x6in) pen brown ink grey wash prov. 19-Mar-4 Piasa, Paris #35/R est:3000
£2740 $4658 €4000 Extensive mountain landscape seen through trees, with peasants and their flocks (23x32cm-9x13in) chk pen ink wash htd white framing lines prov. 5-Nov-3 Christie's, Amsterdam #121/R est:4000-6000

MERIDA, Carlos (1891-1984) Guatemalan
£1648 $3000 €2406 Figure (65x55cm-26x22in) s.i.d.1913. 29-Jun-4 Arroyo, Buenos Aires #55/R est:3000
£3167 $5290 €4624 Biomorphic abstract forms (57x46cm-22x18in) s.d.1937 gouache pencil prov. 24-Jun-3 Germann, Zurich #57/R est:10000-15000 (S.FR 7000)
£3620 $6154 €5285 La ofrenda (47x33cm-19x13in) s.d.1975 s.i.d. verso paper on pavatex prov. 25-Nov-3 Germann, Zurich #12/R est:10000-15000 (S.FR 8000)
£9412 $16000 €13742 Kalel. Sin titulo (55x45cm-22x18in) s.d.1960 one acrylic polytec masonite one acrylic paper two. 18-Nov-3 Christie's, Rockefeller NY #125/R est:25000-30000
£13529 $23000 €19752 Motivo guatemalteco (97x71cm-38x28in) s.d.1919 s.i.verso prov.lit. 19-Nov-3 Sotheby's, New York #96/R est:18000-22000
£27933 $50000 €40782 Moon (80x59cm-31x23in) s.d.1972 s.i.d.verso acrylic petroplastic parchment on wood prov. 26-May-4 Sotheby's, New York #111/R est:35000-45000
Works on paper
£420 $764 €613 Abstracted figure of a jester (23x13cm-9x5in) gouache tree bark. 15-Jun-4 Rosebery Fine Art, London #459
£844 $1342 €1232 Peasants standing (26x21cm-10x8in) s. pastel. 29-Apr-3 Louis Morton, Mexico #109/R est:26000-30000 (M.P 14000)
£1786 $3250 €2608 Circo no.2 (23x13cm-9x5in) s. gouache prov. 29-Jun-4 Sotheby's, New York #419/R est:4000-5000
£4525 $7692 €6607 El chac coh (57x39cm-22x15in) s. i. verso gouache prov. 25-Nov-3 Germann, Zurich #24/R est:5000-7000 (S.FR 10000)
£6153 $10460 €8983 Untitled (25x18cm-10x7in) s. mixed media cardboard exec.1955. 23-Nov-3 Subastas Odalys, Caracas #4/R est:12000
£10056 $18000 €14682 Ubiquity (53x38cm-21x15in) s.d.1976 mixed media paper on masonite prov. 26-May-4 Sotheby's, New York #120/R est:25000-30000

MERIEL-BUSSY, Andre (1902-1985) French
£364 $681 €550 Pelerinage (27x22cm-11x9in) s. 24-Jul-4 Thierry & Lannon, Brest #276
£500 $895 €750 Port breton (38x46cm-15x18in) s.d.39. 16-May-4 Thierry & Lannon, Brest #162
£662 $1238 €1000 Le bain d'enfant (61x50cm-24x20in) s.d.1935. 24-Jul-4 Thierry & Lannon, Brest #200/R

MERIMEE, Prosper (1803-1870) French
Works on paper
£267 $491 €400 Dame en robe de Moyen-age (29x19cm-11x7in) i. pen exec. 1839. 9-Jun-4 Piasa, Paris #155
£267 $491 €400 Portrait de Mr. Wary, paysan breton en sabots et costume traditionnel (22x17cm-9x7in) s.i. pen exec. 1840. 9-Jun-4 Piasa, Paris #156
£267 $491 €400 Neuf tetes de femmes, en cheveux ou coiffees d'un chapeau (22x18cm-9x7in) pen exhib. 9-Jun-4 Piasa, Paris #168
£467 $859 €700 Composition de fantaisie avec insectes monstreux et homme a la broche (31x20cm-12x8in) s, pen sepia exhib. 9-Jun-4 Piasa, Paris #164
£567 $1043 €850 Prosper Merimee, en Senat (21x18cm-8x7in) i.d.17 septembre 1869 pen exhib. 9-Jun-4 Piasa, Paris #167/R
£1067 $1963 €1600 Beau paysage du Midi (19x29cm-7x11in) s. W/C htd gouache exhib. 9-Jun-4 Piasa, Paris #170/R est:1500-2000

MERINO, Daniel (1941-) Spanish
£448 $807 €650 Painter and model (61x50cm-24x20in) s. s.i.d.80 verso. 26-Jan-4 Durán, Madrid #87/R
£563 $975 €800 Two worlds meeting (85x85cm-33x33in) s.i.verso board. 15-Dec-3 Ansorena, Madrid #1007/R
£704 $1232 €1000 Chess (38x47cm-15x19in) s. s.i.d.84 verso board. 16-Dec-3 Durán, Madrid #71/R

MERINOV, A I (1942-) Russian
£462 $850 €675 The citadel in Volokolamsk (31x39cm-12x15in) painted 1990. 27-Mar-4 Shishkin Gallery, Moscow #30/R

MERITE, Edouard Paul (1867-1941) French
£300 $549 €450 Oiseau branche (27x18cm-11x7in) s.i. panel. 3-Jun-4 E & Eve, Paris #74
£699 $1203 €1000 Pic epeiche (35x21cm-14x8in) panel. 3-Dec-3 Coutau Begarie, Paris #85/R
£853 $1467 €1220 Le vol de perdreaux (24x34cm-9x13in) cardboard. 3-Dec-3 Coutau Begarie, Paris #190/R
£1329 $2285 €1900 Mesange tentant d'effaroucher un loir (22x35cm-9x14in) panel. 3-Dec-3 Coutau Begarie, Paris #87/R est:500-700
Works on paper
£304 $499 €420 Lapins de garenne (20x13cm-8x5in) s. crayon. 28-May-3 Coutau Begarie, Paris #314/R
£317 $548 €450 Etudes de chat sauvage (26x20cm-10x8in) graphite gouache. 12-Dec-3 Libert, Castor, Paris #23
£362 $594 €500 Loup (18x13cm-7x5in) s.i. W/C. 28-May-3 Coutau Begarie, Paris #313/R
£367 $656 €550 Tete de chat sauvage (23x15cm-9x6in) i.d.1939 W/C. 12-May-4 Coutau Begarie, Paris #101/R
£1233 $2096 €1800 Lievre (16x25cm-6x10in) s. W/C gouache over crayon. 6-Nov-3 Tajan, Paris #234

MERK, Eduard (1816-1888) German
£612 $1096 €900 Card game (49x61cm-19x24in) s. lit. 20-Mar-4 Bergmann, Erlangen #1078

MERKEL, Georg (1881-1976) Austrian
£6944 $11806 €10000 Tobias with angel (35x46cm-14x18in) s. 28-Oct-3 Wiener Kunst Auktionen, Vienna #77/R est:10000-18000
£40268 $71275 €60000 Summer idyll (100x127cm-39x50in) s. lit. 28-Apr-4 Wiener Kunst Auktionen, Vienna #76/R est:50000-100000

MERKIN, Richard (1938-) American
£444 $800 €648 Sons of the desert revisited (28x40cm-11x16in) s. tempera paper prov. 24-Apr-4 David Rago, Lambertville #533/R
Works on paper
£1667 $3000 €2434 Virgins in cellophane (48x72cm-19x28in) s. mixed media. 24-Apr-4 David Rago, Lambertville #219/R est:600-800

MERKLEN, Jean (20th C) French
£267 $477 €400 Moret sur Loing (38x56cm-15x22in) cardboard. 16-May-4 Osenat, Fontainebleau #92

MERLE, Hughes (1823-1881) French
£4624 $8000 €6751 Abraham banishing Hagar and Ishmael (92x54cm-36x21in) s.d.1872 prov. 11-Dec-3 Sotheby's, New York #94/R est:10000-15000
£20588 $35000 €30058 Embroidery lesson (97x80cm-38x31in) s. 29-Oct-3 Christie's, Rockefeller NY #135/R est:40000-60000
£28235 $48000 €41223 Mother and Child (101x81cm-40x32in) s.d.1869 prov. 28-Oct-3 Sotheby's, New York #40/R est:50000-70000
£34483 $57241 €50000 Legende des Willis (104x146cm-41x57in) s.d.1847 exhib. 2-Oct-3 Sotheby's, Paris #20/R est:45000
£38000 $68020 €57000 Vendanges (111x196cm-44x77in) s.d.1850. 16-May-4 Joron-Derem, Paris #124/R est:45000-60000

MERLE, Hughes (attrib) (1823-1881) French
£3816 $7021 €5800 Frere et soeur (101x74cm-40x29in) 23-Jun-4 Maigret, Paris #87/R est:6000-6500

MERLETTE, Charles (1861-1899) French
£470 $864 €700 Officier conversant avec un Abbe dans un salon (24x28cm-9x11in) s.d.84 panel. 28-Mar-4 Anaf, Lyon #194/R

MERLI, Alessandro (fl.1590-1608) Italian
Works on paper
£1100 $1903 €1606 Madonna and Child with an angel and a donor (21x15cm-8x6in) i. black lead W/C bodycol gold vellum. 12-Dec-3 Christie's, Kensington #351/R est:1000-1200

MERLIN, Daniel (1861-1933) French
£2098 $3566 €3000 Jeunes chatons au coffret a bijoux (27x35cm-11x14in) s. 1-Dec-3 Palais de Beaux Arts, Brussels #373/R est:2000-3000
£2486 $4500 €3630 Kittens (23x33cm-9x13in) s. 16-Apr-4 James Julia, Fairfield #655/R est:5000-7500
£5400 $8586 €7884 Jeunes chats (46x53cm-18x21in) s. 1-May-3 John Nicholson, Haslemere #735/R est:4000-5000

MERLO, Camillo (1856-1931) Italian
£336 $594 €500 Flowers (35x25cm-14x10in) init.d.1888 cardboard. 1-May-4 Meeting Art, Vercelli #176
£671 $1188 €1000 Hills in Turin (25x35cm-10x14in) s.d.1909 board. 1-May-4 Meeting Art, Vercelli #167
£671 $1188 €1000 Landscape (23x30cm-9x12in) s.d.1925 cardboard. 1-May-4 Meeting Art, Vercelli #336
£674 $1125 €950 Rural landscape (24x32cm-9x13in) s.d.1919 cardboard. 20-Oct-3 Sant Agostino, Torino #132/R
£748 $1339 €1100 The Devil's Bridge in Lanzo (26x37cm-10x15in) s.d.1901. 22-Mar-4 Sant Agostino, Torino #163/R
£805 $1426 €1200 Still life (28x43cm-11x17in) s.d.1912 board. 1-May-4 Meeting Art, Vercelli #341
£940 $1663 €1400 Valentino Alley (49x34cm-19x13in) s.d.1903 cardboard. 1-May-4 Meeting Art, Vercelli #263
£1033 $1901 €1550 Farmhouse (22x30cm-9x12in) s.d.1913 card. 8-Jun-4 Della Rocca, Turin #338/R est:1000-1600

MERLO, Metello (1886-1964) Italian
£333 $613 €500 Snow (23x28cm-9x11in) s. board. 14-Jun-4 Sant Agostino, Torino #139/R
£347 $590 €500 Along the Seine (22x27cm-9x11in) s.d.1960 board. 1-Nov-3 Meeting Art, Vercelli #425
£355 $592 €500 Winter landscape (22x43cm-9x17in) cardboard. 20-Oct-3 Sant Agostino, Torino #97/R
£426 $711 €600 Afternoon on the Po' (24x30cm-9x12in) s.d.1956 cardboard. 20-Oct-3 Sant Agostino, Torino #170/R
£451 $767 €650 Camaldolesi Park (28x37cm-11x15in) s. s.i.verso cardboard. 1-Nov-3 Meeting Art, Vercelli #350
£451 $767 €650 Pian Bausonn, sunset (23x27cm-9x11in) s. cardboard. 1-Nov-3 Meeting Art, Vercelli #389
£483 $801 €700 Blue door (60x49cm-24x19in) s.d.1956 tempera paper. 1-Oct-3 Della Rocca, Turin #308/R
£496 $829 €700 Sunset on the snow (23x28cm-9x11in) s. cardboard. 20-Oct-3 Sant Agostino, Torino #101/R
£503 $891 €750 Dam in Piovezzano (40x48cm-16x19in) s.d.1951 tempera card. 1-May-4 Meeting Art, Vercelli #27
£503 $891 €750 Church by the sea (50x33cm-20x13in) s. cardboard. 1-May-4 Meeting Art, Vercelli #390
£503 $891 €750 Sunset (40x50cm-16x20in) s.d.1963 cardboard. 1-May-4 Meeting Art, Vercelli #411
£517 $859 €750 Ripe rye (27x36cm-11x14in) s.d.42 cardboard. 1-Oct-3 Della Rocca, Turin #111/R
£521 $885 €750 Still life with mushrooms (35x38cm-14x15in) s.d.1945 board. 1-Nov-3 Meeting Art, Vercelli #221/R
£521 $885 €750 Autumn in Oggebbio (51x80cm-20x31in) s.d.1963 s.d.verso cardboard. 1-Nov-3 Meeting Art, Vercelli #417
£533 $981 €800 In the countryside (27x37cm-11x15in) s. cardboard prov. 14-Jun-4 Sant Agostino, Torino #198/R
£537 $961 €800 Ripe rye (29x38cm-11x15in) s.d.42 i.verso cardboard. 25-May-4 Finarte Semenzato, Milan #153/R
£667 $1227 €1000 Hilly landscape (34x44cm-13x17in) s.d.1918 card. 14-Jun-4 Sant Agostino, Torino #212/R
£667 $1227 €1000 Path in the wood (34x44cm-13x17in) s.d.1915 cardboard. 14-Jun-4 Sant Agostino, Torino #209/R
£671 $1188 €1000 Red expressions (49x40cm-19x16in) s.d.1962 cardboard. 1-May-4 Meeting Art, Vercelli #39
£671 $1188 €1000 Study in blue (40x50cm-16x20in) s.d.1957. 1-May-4 Meeting Art, Vercelli #81
£733 $1349 €1100 The Tanaro at Fossano (22x27cm-9x11in) s.i.d.1918 cardboard prov. 14-Jun-4 Sant Agostino, Torino #140/R
£733 $1349 €1100 Snow (30x37cm-12x15in) s.d.1931 cardboard. 14-Jun-4 Sant Agostino, Torino #213/R
£775 $1340 €1100 Ripe wheat (29x38cm-11x15in) s.d.1942 cardboard prov. 9-Dec-3 Finarte Semenzato, Milan #63/R
£993 $1658 €1400 Still life with onions and parsnips (60x70cm-24x28in) s.d.1936. 20-Oct-3 Sant Agostino, Torino #153/R
£1007 $1782 €1500 Blooming trees (60x69cm-24x27in) s. s.i.d.1964 verso cardboard. 1-May-4 Meeting Art, Vercelli #226 est:1500
£1042 $1771 €1500 Spring on Lake Maggiore (50x60cm-20x24in) s.d.1950 card. 1-Nov-3 Meeting Art, Vercelli #312/R est:1500
£1319 $2243 €1900 Oggebbio, Lake Maggiore (50x60cm-20x24in) s. cardboard. 1-Nov-3 Meeting Art, Vercelli #87/R est:1500
£1678 $2803 €2400 Serralunga Castle (76x76cm-30x30in) s.d. board. 26-Jun-3 Sant Agostino, Torino #284a/R est:1500-2000
£3688 $6159 €5200 Tuscolo (56x70cm-22x28in) s.d.1920 cardboard lit. 14-Oct-3 Finarte Semenzato, Milan #185/R
Works on paper
£1067 $1963 €1600 Punta Crena di Varigotti (49x59cm-19x23in) s.d.1956 mixed media card. 14-Jun-4 Sant Agostino, Torino #208/R est:1000-1400

MERO, Istvan (1873-?) Hungarian
£363 $650 €530 Young girl in a pasture landscape (48x58cm-19x23in) s. 15-May-4 Jeffery Burchard, Florida #395
£800 $1464 €1168 Budapest figures of ladies working in cabbage field and reading by meadow (34x27cm-13x11in) s. panel pair. 5-Jun-4 Windibank, Dorking #378/R

MERODACK-JEANNEAU, Alexis (1873-1919) French
£40000 $73200 €60000 A Verlaine - Portrait de Verlaine (55x46cm-22x18in) s.i. prov.exhib.lit. 5-Jun-4 Lempertz, Koln #875/R est:40000-45000

MERODE, Carl von (1853-1909) Austrian
£521 $885 €750 At the blacksmiths (21x15cm-8x6in) s. bears d.1900 panel. 28-Oct-3 Dorotheum, Vienna #218/R
£1690 $2806 €2400 Woman with vegetables (31x21cm-12x8in) s.d.94. 16-Jun-3 Dorotheum, Vienna #219/R est:2000-2600

MERODIO, Carlos (1944-) Spanish
£282 $487 €400 Untitled (81x100cm-32x39in) s.d.1972. 15-Dec-3 Ansorena, Madrid #928
£296 $512 €420 Geometry and still life (81x100cm-32x39in) s.d.73. 15-Dec-3 Ansorena, Madrid #1002/R
£428 $774 €650 Untitled (100x81cm-39x32in) s.d.1972. 14-Apr-4 Ansorena, Madrid #295/R
£479 $815 €700 Yellow composition (100x81cm-39x32in) s.d.1972. 4-Nov-3 Ansorena, Madrid #885/R
£548 $932 €800 Abstract (81x100cm-32x39in) s.d.1972. 4-Nov-3 Ansorena, Madrid #949/R
£556 $917 €800 Untitled (81x100cm-32x39in) s.d.1972. 2-Jul-3 Ansorena, Madrid #841/R

MERRIAM, James Arthur (1880-1951) American
£281 $450 €410 Neowashingtonian Palms. s. 20-Sep-3 Harvey Clar, Oakland #1328
£295 $475 €428 Desert palms (102x76cm-40x30in) s. 23-Aug-3 Harvey Clar, Oakland #1381
£503 $900 €734 Californian desert landscape (64x76cm-25x30in) s. 10-Jan-4 Auctions by the Bay, Alameda #532/R

MERRICK, James Kirk (1905-1985) American
Works on paper
£317 $575 €463 Heritage museum (76x53cm-30x21in) s. W/C executed c.1960. 3-Apr-4 Outer Cape Auctions, Provincetown #78/R

MERRIFIELD, Tom (1932-) Australian
Sculpture
£1800 $3222 €2628 Female torso (81cm-32in) bronze marble plinth. 16-Mar-4 Woolley & Wallis, Salisbury #101/R est:700-1000
£2000 $3340 €2920 Collette (70cm-28in) s.num.4/8 bronze. 21-Oct-3 Bonhams, Knightsbridge #96/R est:2500-3500
Works on paper
£300 $540 €438 Dancer (112x82cm-44x32in) s. pastel. 20-Jan-4 Bonhams, Knightsbridge #211
£500 $800 €725 Two ballerinas (76x65cm-30x26in) s. chl wax crayon. 16-Sep-3 Bonhams, Knightsbridge #91

MERRILL, Edward (1800-1884) American
£276 $500 €403 Gorge in Mexico (46x61cm-18x24in) s. board. 16-Apr-4 James Julia, Fairfield #1070/R

MERRILL, Katherine (1876-1962) American
£559 $900 €816 Market day in the Pyrenees (56x43cm-22x17in) s. canvasboard. 17-Aug-3 Jeffery Burchard, Florida #36a

MERRILL, Ruth E (19/20th C) American
£370 $650 €540 Clipper ship (69x102cm-27x40in) s. 21-May-4 Pook & Pook, Downington #97/R

MERRIOTT, Jack (1901-1968) British
£580 $1085 €847 Old hulk at Topsham, boats on the ship (49x23cm-19x9in) s. 26-Feb-4 Lane, Penzance #245
Works on paper
£250 $415 €365 Lobster pots, Polperro (67x50cm-26x20in) s. wash. 2-Oct-3 Lane, Penzance #284
£380 $684 €555 Rough water at Slaughden, Aldeburgh (26x36cm-10x14in) s. W/C. 20-Apr-4 Bonhams, Ipswich #207

MERRITT, Anna Lea (1844-1930) British
£300 $498 €438 Lady arranging a vase of flowers (75x55cm-30x22in) mono. 1-Oct-3 Woolley & Wallis, Salisbury #234/R
Works on paper
£260 $450 €380 A Christmas gift (46x30cm-18x12in) s.d. W/C. 11-Dec-3 Ewbank, Send #437

MERRITT, Marshall (20th C) American
£231 $400 €337 Moon over Point Lobos (38x76cm-15x30in) s. i.verso. 13-Dec-3 Charlton Hall, Columbia #574/R

MERRITT, Warren Chase (1897-1968) American
£3261 $6000 €4761 California hills with hollyoaks and a lily pond (167x221cm-66x87in) s.d.25 board four panel screen prov. 8-Jun-4 Bonhams & Butterfields, San Francisco #4290/R est:5000-7000

MERSCH, Cecile (1905-) Belgian
£308 $529 €440 Vue du parc de Bruxelles en automne (50x60cm-20x24in) s. 8-Dec-3 Horta, Bruxelles #328
£874 $1486 €1250 Femme nue assise (107x89cm-42x35in) s.d.1930. 18-Nov-3 Vanderkindere, Brussels #149

MERSFELDER, Jules (1865-1937) American
£341 $550 €498 Shepherd with sheep resting under sheltering tree (51x76cm-20x30in) s. 17-Aug-3 Bonhams & Butterfields, San Francisco #5802
£769 $1400 €1123 Mount Tamalpais. s. 7-Feb-4 Harvey Clar, Oakland #1578

MERSON, Luc-Olivier (1846-1920) French
Works on paper
£700 $1281 €1022 Final Benediction of the archbishop Turpin (28x19cm-11x7in) s. pen ink wash gouache lit. 7-Jul-4 Bonhams, Knightsbridge #78/R
£979 $1684 €1400 Nu (58x39cm-23x15in) s. col crayon. 3-Dec-3 Beaussant & Lefèvre, Paris #64
£986 $1706 €1400 Allegorie de la musique (18x9cm-7x4in) pen blk ink tracing paper. 10-Dec-3 Piasa, Paris #147
£1958 $3368 €2800 Nu (58x39cm-23x15in) s. col crayon. 3-Dec-3 Beaussant & Lefèvre, Paris #63 est:200-250

MERTEL, Christian (fl.1789-1800) American/German
Works on paper
£2500 $4000 €3650 The Princess of Braunswick (30x41cm-12x16in) W/C ink. 20-Sep-3 Pook & Pook, Downington #444/R est:4000-6000

MERTENS, Thomas (17th C) Dutch
£3800 $6840 €5548 Fruit in a porcelain bown, and shrimps in a pewter plate on a forest floor (54x69cm-21x27in) 23-Apr-4 Christie's, Kensington #86/R est:1200-1800

MERTON, Erling (1898-1967) Norwegian
£254 $467 €371 Olive trees, Toledo (38x46cm-15x18in) s. panel. 29-Mar-4 Blomqvist, Lysaker #1200/R (N.KR 3200)
£257 $471 €375 Grey day (44x55cm-17x22in) s. 2-Feb-4 Blomqvist, Lysaker #1181 (N.KR 3200)
£278 $481 €406 Southern town (65x81cm-26x32in) s. 13-Dec-3 Blomqvist, Lysaker #1236 (N.KR 3200)
£429 $751 €626 Rowing boat in the skerries (44x55cm-17x22in) s.d.44. 16-Dec-3 Grev Wedels Plass, Oslo #200/R (N.KR 5000)

MERTZ, Albert (1920-1990) Danish
£451 $830 €658 Glowing sky. s.d.1959 verso masonite exhib. 29-Mar-4 Rasmussen, Copenhagen #429/R (D.KR 5000)
£632 $1162 €923 Before the thunder storm (40x48cm-16x19in) s. verso panel. 29-Mar-4 Rasmussen, Copenhagen #325/R (D.KR 7000)
Works on paper
£271 $506 €396 Mill (50x50cm-20x20in) init.d.1-2-65 W/C. 25-Feb-4 Kunsthallen, Copenhagen #48 (D.KR 3000)
£1033 $1725 €1508 Red and blue composition (30x44cm-12x17in) init.d.16-4 61 gouache. 7-Oct-3 Rasmussen, Copenhagen #288/R (D.KR 11000)

MERTZ, Johann Cornelius (1819-1891) Dutch
£789 $1453 €1200 Burgemeester boom ontvangt slecht nieuws (33x26cm-13x10in) s. panel. 28-Jun-4 Sotheby's, Amsterdam #49/R

MERWART, Fritz (1882-1967) German
£280 $481 €400 Hamburg harbour (45x54cm-18x21in) s. panel. 4-Dec-3 Schopman, Hamburg #781/R

MERWART, Paul (1855-1902) Polish
£5986 $9937 €8500 Brody-Paris (42x60cm-17x24in) s.i.d.1882-1883. 13-Jun-3 Renaud, Paris #38/R est:4000-4500

MERWE, Eben van der (1932-) South African
£248 $443 €362 Still life with fruit and vessels (38x32cm-15x13in) s.d.82 board. 31-May-4 Stephan Welz, Johannesburg #181 (SA.R 3000)

MERY, Alfred Émile (1824-1896) French
Works on paper
£690 $1090 €1000 Heron cendre (47x66cm-19x26in) s. gouache. 6-Apr-3 Salle des ventes Pillet, Lyon la Foret #592

MERYON, Charles (1821-1868) French
Prints
£2059 $3500 €3006 Morgue (21x19cm-8x7in) etching drypoint. 31-Oct-3 Sotheby's, New York #315
£2500 $4250 €3650 San Francisco (18x94cm-7x37in) etching exec.1873. 1-Dec-3 Bonhams, New Bond Street #255a/R est:2500-3500

MERZ, Albert (1942-) Swiss
£317 $529 €463 Arche Noel (54x39cm-21x15in) s.d.1985 acrylic chl. 24-Jun-3 Germann, Zurich #1009 (S.FR 700)
£519 $841 €758 Untitled (57x39cm-22x15in) s.d.1985 acrylic chl. 24-May-3 Burkhard, Luzern #42/R (S.FR 1100)

MERZ, Jen (19th C) ?
£266 $425 €388 Portrait of a gentleman in profile (38x36cm-15x14in) s.d.1850. 20-Sep-3 Bunte, Elgin #1403

MERZ, Karl (1890-1970) German
£800 $1456 €1200 Summer landscape (61x80cm-24x31in) s.d.1936 panel. 3-Jul-4 Geble, Radolfzell #413/R

MERZ, Mario (1925-2003) Italian
£38000 $63460 €55480 Rinoceronte (201x500cm-79x197in) oil Indian ink spray paint neon linen prov.exhib. 21-Oct-3 Christie's, London #65/R est:38000-50000
Sculpture
£13000 $21710 €18980 Was machen? (18x68x14cm-7x27x6in) aluminium wax neon prov. 20-Oct-3 Sotheby's, London #40/R
£48000 $88320 €70080 Untitled (289x289cm-114x114in) metal tubes mixed media cloth neon tube executed 1979 prov.exhib. 25-Jun-4 Christie's, London #160/R est:20000-30000
Works on paper
£699 $1203 €1000 Iglo (23x20cm-9x8in) s. ballpoint pen paper on card executed 1993. 2-Dec-3 Sotheby's, Amsterdam #340/R est:1000-1500
£3289 $6053 €4802 Fibonacci number sequence (121x42cm-48x17in) s.d.1975 black ink. 23-Jun-4 Koller, Zurich #3117/R est:3500-5000 (S.FR 7500)
£3631 $6500 €5301 Untitled (122x42cm-48x17in) s.i.d.12-2-75 felt tipped pen two parts prov. 14-May-4 Phillips, New York #297/R est:6000-8000
£4196 $7133 €6000 Untitled (70x70cm-28x28in) s.d.1974 pencil ink spray paint card. 24-Nov-3 Christie's, Milan #142/R est:6000-8000
£4333 $7757 €6500 Luce e se te appoggianti allo spazio (50x73cm-20x29in) s.i.d. pencil W/C spray prov. 14-May-4 Ketterer, Munich #302/R est:2000-3000
£9170 $16690 €13388 Spiral of filomene connected with. (75x100cm-30x39in) s.i.d.68 chl snail. 17-Jun-4 Kornfeld, Bern #568/R est:25000 (S.FR 21000)
£10204 $18265 €15000 Untitled (74x103cm-29x41in) mixed media sand snail shell card exec.1982 prov. 16-Mar-4 Finarte Semenzato, Milan #411/R est:20000

MESA BASAN, Jose Antonio (1938-) Spanish
£414 $691 €600 View of Madrid (89x172cm-35x68in) s. 17-Nov-3 Durán, Madrid #39/R

MESCHERSKY, Arsenii Ivanovich (1834-1902) Russian
£12000 $21480 €17520 Ships on the Narva (24x35cm-9x14in) s.d.1882 board. 26-May-4 Sotheby's, London #53/R est:5000-7000
£13000 $23270 €18980 Shipping in the Crimea (22x33cm-9x13in) s.d.1884. 26-May-4 Sotheby's, London #52/R est:6000-8000

MESCHIS, Renzo (1945-) Italian
£302 $559 €450 Prickly pears (80x70cm-31x28in) s. s.d.2000 verso. 13-Mar-4 Meeting Art, Vercelli #253
£470 $869 €700 Terrace overlooking the sea (70x80cm-28x31in) s. s.d.2002 verso. 13-Mar-4 Meeting Art, Vercelli #551

MESCIULAM, Plinio (1926-) Italian
£1224 $2192 €1800 Shape (47x68cm-19x27in) s.i.d.1951 verso tempera paper exhib.lit. 22-Mar-4 Sant Agostino, Torino #457/R est:1800-2200

MESDAG VAN HOUTEN, Sientje (1834-1909) Dutch
£638 $1066 €900 Landscape with travellers (29x43cm-11x17in) s. panel. 20-Oct-3 Glerum, Amsterdam #93
£909 $1564 €1300 Dune landscape (30x42cm-12x17in) mono. lit. 8-Dec-3 Glerum, Amsterdam #4/R
£2270 $3790 €3200 Still life with vases and tulips (70x95cm-28x37in) init. exhib. 20-Oct-3 Glerum, Amsterdam #91/R est:3500-4500
Works on paper
£1053 $1937 €1600 Cottage garden (38x25cm-15x10in) s. W/C gouache. 28-Jun-4 Sotheby's, Amsterdam #28/R est:800-1200

MESDAG, Hendrik-Willem (1831-1915) Dutch
£1988 $3200 €2902 Moonlight seascape (15x23cm-6x9in) s. panel. 20-Aug-3 James Julia, Fairfield #833/R est:3000-4000
£2657 $4571 €3800 Dutch village (20x25cm-8x10in) s. panel. 8-Dec-3 Glerum, Amsterdam #7/R est:4000-6000
£2937 $5052 €4200 Country path with cart (23x34cm-9x13in) s. lit. 8-Dec-3 Glerum, Amsterdam #5/R est:3000-5000
£3017 $5401 €4405 Fisherwomen and boats on beach (44x34cm-17x13in) s. 12-May-4 Dobiaschofsky, Bern #796/R est:9000 (S.FR 7000)
£4667 $8400 €7000 Fishing boats at dusk (21x18cm-8x7in) panel. 20-Apr-4 Sotheby's, Amsterdam #109/R est:4000-6000
£7483 $13619 €11000 Harvesting potatoes, Drenthe (48x78cm-19x31in) s. 3-Feb-4 Christie's, Amsterdam #133/R est:7000-9000
£8392 $14434 €12000 Sea by moonlight (53x31cm-21x12in) mono. panel prov.lit. 8-Dec-3 Glerum, Amsterdam #22/R est:12000-15000
£10490 $18042 €15000 Woman in cornfield (47x79cm-19x31in) s.d.1873 prov.exhib.lit. 8-Dec-3 Glerum, Amsterdam #15/R est:15000-18000
£16667 $28333 €24000 Bomschuitten by the coast (40x30cm-16x12in) s. canvas on panel lit. 28-Oct-3 Christie's, Amsterdam #122/R est:20000-30000
£31250 $53125 €45000 Bomschuiten at the break of dawn (31x25cm-12x10in) s. panel prov.exhib.lit. 28-Oct-3 Christie's, Amsterdam #130/R est:50000-70000
£31250 $52187 €45000 Bomschuiten at sea (51x40cm-20x16in) s. lit. 21-Oct-3 Sotheby's, Amsterdam #237/R est:50000-70000
£33333 $60000 €50000 Fishing boats near the coast (90x120cm-35x47in) s. 20-Apr-4 Sotheby's, Amsterdam #216/R est:60000-80000
£41333 $74400 €62000 Bomschuiten at sea, Scheveningen (51x39cm-20x15in) s. prov. 21-Apr-4 Christie's, Amsterdam #96/R est:40000-60000
£43333 $78000 €65000 Bomschuit Prinses Sophie on the beach, Scheveningen (80x100cm-31x39in) s.d.1870 prov.lit. 20-Apr-4 Sotheby's, Amsterdam #231/R est:30000-50000
£83333 $139167 €120000 Return of the fishing fleet, Scheveningen (78x112cm-31x44in) s.d.90 prov. 21-Oct-3 Sotheby's, Amsterdam #214/R est:80000-120000
£86667 $156000 €130000 Le depart du bateau de sauvetage (97x157cm-38x62in) s.d.1876 canvas on panel exhib.lit. 20-Apr-4 Sotheby's, Amsterdam #221/R est:60000-80000
£138889 $231944 €200000 Departure of the fishing fleet, Scheveningen (139x179cm-55x70in) s.d.1890 prov.lit. 21-Oct-3 Sotheby's, Amsterdam #242/R est:200000-300000
Works on paper
£559 $962 €800 Shell fishermen (21x28cm-8x11in) pencil lit. 8-Dec-3 Glerum, Amsterdam #9/R
£8333 $14167 €12000 Sailing vessels at sea by Scheveningen (38x29cm-15x11in) s. W/C. 28-Oct-3 Christie's, Amsterdam #139/R est:6000-8000
£15385 $26462 €22000 In front of the anchor (51x30cm-20x12in) s. W/C prov.exhib.lit. 8-Dec-3 Glerum, Amsterdam #27/R est:22000-28000
£24306 $41319 €35000 De Scheveningen 86, Sheveninger Bomschuiten (65x79cm-26x31in) s. W/C htd white prov.exhib.lit. 28-Oct-3 Christie's, Amsterdam #138/R est:35000-50000
£25333 $45600 €38000 Arrival of the fleet (63x40cm-25x16in) s. W/C htd white prov. 21-Apr-4 Christie's, Amsterdam #115/R est:35000-50000

MESDAG, Hendrik-Willem (attrib) (1831-1915) Dutch
Works on paper
£300 $537 €438 Scheveningen fishing fleet setting off to the fishing grounds (39x70cm-15x28in) s. pencil W/C bodycol scratching out. 26-May-4 Christie's, Kensington #440/R

MESDAG, Taco (1829-1902) Dutch
£570 $1055 €850 Shepherd with his flock (26x38cm-10x15in) s. panel. 15-Mar-4 Sotheby's, Amsterdam #98/R est:800-1200

MESEGUER, Jose (1900-1957) Spanish
£483 $869 €700 Couple (16x13cm-6x5in) s. board. 26-Jan-4 Durán, Madrid #1244
£655 $1179 €950 Toast (14x11cm-6x4in) s. paper. 26-Jan-4 Durán, Madrid #1243/R

MESENS, E L T (1903-1971) British
£1678 $2853 €2400 Sphinx de cirque (30x22cm-12x9in) s.i.d.1962 s.i.d.verso tempera pastel pencil collage cardboard. 25-Nov-3 Sotheby's, Milan #141/R est:1000-1500
Photographs
£8000 $14560 €11680 Arriere-pensee (23x16cm-9x6in) s.d.1926-27 black white photograph prov.lit. 3-Feb-4 Sotheby's, London #72/R est:9000-12000
Works on paper
£909 $1545 €1300 Desespoir II (27x21cm-11x8in) s.d.5/1968 mixed media. 1-Dec-3 Palais de Beaux Arts, Brussels #170/R
£1119 $1902 €1600 Desespoir (25x19cm-10x7in) s.d.4/1968 mixed media. 1-Dec-3 Palais de Beaux Arts, Brussels #172 est:1250-1750
£1259 $2140 €1800 Amas - amour - amovible (30x24cm-12x9in) s. collage prov. 1-Dec-3 Palais de Beaux Arts, Brussels #169/R est:1750-2500

MESENS, Edouard Léon Theodore (1903-1971) British
Works on paper
£313 $509 €450 E.LandscapeT. s. collage. 23-Sep-3 Galerie Moderne, Brussels #672/R
£313 $509 €450 Coeur de tournesol. s. collage. 23-Sep-3 Galerie Moderne, Brussels #680/R
£313 $509 €450 E.LT.M. s. collage. 23-Sep-3 Galerie Moderne, Brussels #826/R
£347 $566 €500 Coeur-fleurs. s. collage. 23-Sep-3 Galerie Moderne, Brussels #815/R

MESGRINY, Claude François Auguste de (1836-1884) French
£2254 $3899 €3200 Les pecheurs en bord de riviere (36x56cm-14x22in) s. 12-Dec-3 Piasa, Paris #56/R est:3500-4500

MESIBOV, Hugh (1916-) American
Works on paper
£326 $600 €476 Lost island (20x28cm-8x11in) s.i.d.1940 pencil. 10-Jun-4 Swann Galleries, New York #173/R
£326 $600 €476 Peoza (28x20cm-11x8in) s. s.i.d.1943 verso brush ink pencil. 10-Jun-4 Swann Galleries, New York #174/R

MESLY, David (1918-) ?
Sculpture
£2013 $3685 €3000 Seduisante (56cm-22in) s. num.6/8 blk pat bronze s.f.Serralheiro. 7-Jul-4 Artcurial Briest, Paris #169/R est:3000-4000
£2148 $3801 €3200 Simplicite (22x19cm-9x7in) s.num.4/8 dark pat bronze Cast Serralheird. 29-Apr-4 Claude Aguttes, Neuilly #88/R est:3000-3200
£2416 $4494 €3600 Isidore, l'hippopotame (13x29cm-5x11in) s.num.4/8 black pat bronze. 7-Mar-4 Lesieur & Le Bars, Le Havre #210/R
£3310 $5528 €4800 Simbad (29x29cm-11x11in) num.4/8 pat bronze. 11-Nov-3 Lesieur & Le Bars, Le Havre #124
£4362 $7721 €6500 Elephant et son elephanteau (24cm-9in) s.num.4/8 black pat bronze Cast Serralheiro. 28-Apr-4 Charbonneaux, Paris #203/R est:4500-5000

MESNAGER, Jerome (1961-) French
£486 $812 €700 Les arbres (73x92cm-29x36in) s.d.1996. 25-Oct-3 Cornette de St.Cyr, Paris #754/R
£636 $1082 €910 Palissade (64x58cm-25x23in) s. acrylic wood. 20-Nov-3 Claude Aguttes, Neuilly #180/R
£764 $1207 €1100 Ho hisse (78x38cm-31x15in) s. paint wooden fence. 27-Apr-3 Versailles Encheres #138
£833 $1317 €1200 A Bacchus et a Bercy (193x97cm-76x38in) s.d.1989 s.i.verso acrylic metal wood sand. 27-Apr-3 Versailles Encheres #146
£1007 $1782 €1500 L'atlans (104x72cm-41x28in) s. fence acrylic wood. 29-Apr-4 Claude Aguttes, Neuilly #247/R est:1500-1600
£1888 $3210 €2700 L'elan (130x90cm-51x35in) s. acrylic sand metal plaque. 20-Nov-3 Claude Aguttes, Neuilly #125/R est:1600-1800
Works on paper
£367 $660 €550 Homme blanc et nanometre (30x20cm-12x8in) s. mixed media panel on metal. 24-Apr-4 Cornette de St.Cyr, Paris #646
£405 $726 €600 Chasse d'amour (64x49cm-25x19in) s.d90 gouache collage. 5-May-4 Coutau Begarie, Paris #69/R
£699 $1189 €1000 Interdit sauf aux voitures de police (65x72cm-26x28in) s.d.88 mixed media canvas wood road sign. 29-Nov-3 Neret-Minet, Paris #112/R

MESS, George J (1898-1962) American

£1559	$2900	€2276	Summer lake scene (56x61cm-22x24in) painted c.1928. 7-Mar-4 Treadway Gallery, Cincinnati #656/R est:1800-2200

MESS, Sara (?) American

£310	$500	€453	Bouquet of flowers (39x38cm-15x15in) s. board. 24-Aug-3 Bonhams & Butterfields, Los Angeles #7066

MESSAC, Ivan (1948-) French

£2000	$3660	€3000	Le second eveil (130x97cm-51x38in) s.d.78-79 i.verso acrylic. 6-Jun-4 Anaf, Lyon #442/R est:2500-3000
£2200	$3960	€3300	Bad moon (33x24cm-13x9in) s.d.1972 acrylic. 24-Apr-4 Cornette de St.Cyr, Paris #651/R est:1000
£2778	$4583	€4000	Le musee de la rue (162x130cm-64x51in) s.i.d.1977 verso acrylic. 2-Jul-3 Cornette de St.Cyr, Paris #130/R est:2000-3000
£2817	$4873	€4000	Le noble art-orange no 2 (80x100cm-31x39in) s.i.d.1973 verso acrylic. 14-Dec-3 Versailles Encheres #169/R est:1200-1500
£3380	$5848	€4800	Peine capillaire (100x100cm-39x39in) s.i.d.1970 verso acrylic. 14-Dec-3 Versailles Encheres #167/R est:1200-1500

MESSAGIER, Jean (1920-1999) French

£369	$687	€550	Portrait d'Avril (36x46cm-14x18in) s.d.1962 verso panel. 3-Mar-4 Tajan, Paris #215
£420	$701	€600	Decisions climatiques (76x104cm-30x41in) s.i. acrylic paper prov. 29-Jun-3 Versailles Encheres #34/R
£592	$1089	€900	Neige en plus (55x85cm-22x33in) s.i. acrylic pastel paper prov. 27-Jun-4 Versailles Encheres #52/R
£940	$1719	€1400	Champs d'intervention de l'hiver 1975 en Bourgogne-Franche-Comte (116x192cm-46x76in) s.i. painted 1975 prov. 7-Jul-4 Artcurial Briest, Paris #311b est:3000-5000
£1625	$2989	€2373	De l'ombre au soleil (72x128cm-28x50in) s. s.d.Juillet 1962 verso prov. 29-Mar-4 Rasmussen, Copenhagen #403/R est:20000-25000 (D.KR 18000)
£1715	$3155	€2504	Antennes d'ete (59x110cm-23x43in) s. 29-Mar-4 Rasmussen, Copenhagen #341/R est:15000 (D.KR 19000)
£1812	$3371	€2700	Chemins de Juillet (64x110cm-25x43in) s. s.i.verso prov. 3-Mar-4 Tajan, Paris #214 est:1500-1800
£2349	$4205	€3500	Composition verte (104x170cm-41x67in) s. s.d.61 verso. 26-May-4 Christie's, Paris #78/R est:5000-7000
£2676	$4630	€3800	Courants a Perche (90x166cm-35x65in) s. s.i.d.1963 verso prov. 9-Dec-3 Artcurial Briest, Paris #509/R est:5000-7000
£2953	$5434	€4400	Bonjour monsieur (204x215cm-80x85in) s.i. s.i.d.1989 verso acrylic sequins. 24-Mar-4 Joron-Derem, Paris #175/R est:4000-5000
£3000	$5400	€4500	Moucheron rafraichissant (124x195cm-49x77in) s.i. acrylic prov. 25-Apr-4 Versailles Encheres #60 est:4000-5000
£3333	$6133	€5000	Haute prairie (105x160cm-41x63in) s. s.i.d.1957 verso prov.exhib. 14-Jun-4 Tajan, Paris #162/R est:3000-4000
£3497	$5944	€5000	Herons d'hiver (85x191cm-33x75in) s. s.i.d.1961 verso. 28-Nov-3 Drouot Estimations, Paris #220/R est:3000-3500
£3803	$6579	€5400	L'helicoptere (57x100cm-22x39in) s.d.1953 s.i.d.verso prov. 14-Dec-3 Versailles Encheres #65/R est:4000-5000
£4027	$7128	€6000	Moucherons et la chanterelle (205x198cm-81x78in) s.i. acrylic painted c.1986 prov.exhib. 28-Apr-4 Artcurial Briest, Paris #298/R est:6000-8000
£4054	$7135	€6000	On Marche sur l'herbe (203x196cm-80x77in) s.i. s.i.d.1989 verso acrylic prov.exhib. 18-May-4 Tajan, Paris #144/R est:5000-6000
£5705	$10211	€8500	Composition orange (132x191cm-52x75in) s. painted 1960. 26-May-4 Christie's, Paris #80/R est:5000-7000
Works on paper			
£267	$491	€400	Sans titre (49x63cm-19x25in) s.d.1947 verso gouache wax crayon. 14-Jun-4 Tajan, Paris #161
£267	$491	€400	Festin de campagnols en ionosphere (44x63cm-17x25in) s.i. mixed media. 14-Jun-4 Tajan, Paris #163
£420	$701	€600	Les tomates laissent un parfum sur les mains apres la taille (52x75cm-20x30in) s.i. mixed media paper on canvas. 29-Jun-3 Versailles Encheres #14
£451	$754	€650	Cinquieme machine a arreter le printemps (76x104cm-30x41in) s.i. W/C pencil prov. 25-Oct-3 Cornette de St.Cyr, Paris #757/R
£559	$1029	€850	Composition (74x104cm-29x41in) s. pastel prov. 27-Jun-4 Versailles Encheres #51/R
£839	$1427	€1200	Palais pour une innondation rose (69x106cm-27x42in) s.i. crayon. 30-Nov-3 Anaf, Lyon #163
£909	$1545	€1300	Toutes les frontieres des eaux et de la terre (76x104cm-30x41in) s.i. mixed media. 30-Nov-3 Anaf, Lyon #166 est:1500-2000
£909	$1545	€1300	Rose, orange, bleu (51x73cm-20x29in) s. mixed media prov. 30-Nov-3 Anaf, Lyon #168
£940	$1719	€1400	Composition (73x103cm-29x41in) s. W/C. 7-Jul-4 Artcurial Briest, Paris #311 est:1200-1500
£979	$1664	€1400	Palais des stupeurs (76x106cm-30x42in) s.i. crayon. 30-Nov-3 Anaf, Lyon #161/R
£987	$1816	€1500	Coeur d'ete (75x106cm-30x42in) s.i. W/C. 25-Jun-4 Millon & Associes, Paris #262/R est:1500-2000
£987	$1816	€1500	Composition (74x108cm-29x43in) s. W/C exhib. 22-Jun-4 Palais de Beaux Arts, Brussels #287/R est:700-1000

MESSEGUER, Benito (20th C) Mexican?

£198	$365	€289	Two figures (70x60cm-28x24in) s.d.1969. 25-Mar-4 Louis Morton, Mexico #22/R (M.P 4000)
£298	$548	€435	Study for mural I.M.A. and L (90x130cm-35x51in) s.d.1963 acrylic. 25-Mar-4 Louis Morton, Mexico #93/R (M.P 6000)

MESSEL, Oliver (1904-1978) British

£900	$1503	€1314	Head of Carl Chandler (48x38cm-19x15in) s. canvasboard. 21-Oct-3 Bonhams, Knightsbridge #148/R
Works on paper			
£1600	$2816	€2336	Designs for Fortnum and Mason's menu cards (35x27cm-14x11in) i. W/C black chk two. 19-May-4 Sotheby's, Olympia #82/R est:800-1200

MESSENSEE, Jurgen (1937-) Austrian

£1316	$2421	€2000	Untitled (40x46cm-16x18in) s.d.1985 oil pencil paper. 22-Jun-4 Wiener Kunst Auktionen, Vienna #412/R est:2500
£2657	$4517	€3800	Reclining small person (30x24cm-12x9in) s.d.1985/86. 28-Nov-3 Wiener Kunst Auktionen, Vienna #617/R est:2500-3500
£8333	$14167	€12000	Untitled (150x146cm-59x57in) s. s. verso acrylic. 28-Oct-3 Wiener Kunst Auktionen, Vienna #247/R est:12000-18000
£10490	$17832	€15000	Reclining nude (160x190cm-63x75in) s.d.86 Sept i.d. verso acrylic prov. 26-Nov-3 Dorotheum, Vienna #320/R est:10000-13000
Works on paper			
£347	$566	€500	Untitled (24x23cm-9x9in) s. W/C. 23-Sep-3 Wiener Kunst Auktionen, Vienna #155/R
£987	$1816	€1500	Untitled (31x46cm-12x18in) s.d.1984 mixed media. 22-Jun-4 Wiener Kunst Auktionen, Vienna #413/R est:1500
£1049	$1783	€1500	Untitled (50x65cm-20x26in) s. chk collage glass paper. 26-Nov-3 Dorotheum, Vienna #266/R est:1300-1800
£1172	$2146	€1700	Untitled (47x32cm-19x13in) s.d.82 mixed media. 27-Jan-4 Dorotheum, Vienna #241/R est:1700-2000
£1184	$2179	€1800	Untitled (83x58cm-33x23in) mixed media. 22-Jun-4 Wiener Kunst Auktionen, Vienna #415/R est:1800
£2550	$4718	€3800	Bust (59x56cm-23x22in) s.d.83 mixed media. 9-Mar-4 Dorotheum, Vienna #190/R est:2400-3000

MESSER, Ken (?) British

Works on paper			
£250	$455	€365	Magdalen College, Oxford from the Bridge (30x40cm-12x16in) s. W/C. 3-Feb-4 Bonhams, Oxford #221

MESSER, Sam (1955-) American

£389	$700	€568	Totem (74x21cm-29x8in) s.i.d.1983 prov. 24-Apr-4 David Rago, Lambertville #370/R
£2066	$3450	€3016	Composition with man and circular shape (177x123cm-70x48in) s.d.86 verso. 7-Oct-3 Rasmussen, Copenhagen #116/R est:25000 (D.KR 22000)
£3610	$6643	€5271	Composition with man and circle (177x123cm-70x48in) s.d.86 verso. 29-Mar-4 Rasmussen, Copenhagen #169/R est:25000 (D.KR 40000)

MESSERSCHMITT, Pius Ferdinand (1858-1915) German

£276	$461	€400	Portrait of a man in chainmail (18x15cm-7x6in) mono. board lit. 10-Jul-3 Allgauer, Kempten #2603/R

MESSIAEN, Jules (1869-1957) Belgian?

Works on paper			
£331	$612	€480	Force, adresse et justesse (63x48cm-25x19in) mono.d.1916 pastel. 19-Jan-4 Horta, Bruxelles #486

MESSINA, Francesco (1900-1995) Italian

Sculpture			
£1275	$2372	€1900	Flora (41x30cm-16x12in) s. num.1/75 pat bronze. 4-Mar-4 Babuino, Rome #469 est:1000-1500
£2000	$3680	€3000	Dancer (56x14x13cm-22x6x5in) s. num.187/230 pat bronze exec.1970. 12-Jun-4 Meeting Art, Vercelli #234/R est:3000
£2333	$4200	€3500	Dancer (50cm-20in) s. num.149/150 pat bronze. 22-Apr-4 Finarte Semenzato, Rome #42/R est:1500
£4698	$8409	€7000	Narcissus (22x15x16cm-9x6x6in) s. bronze exec.1944 exhib. 25-May-4 Sotheby's, Milan #18/R est:10000
£4730	$8324	€7000	Dancer fragment (51cm-20in) s. bronze. 24-May-4 Christie's, Milan #208/R est:7000-10000
£6643	$11294	€9500	Portrait of Luisa (45x40x30cm-18x16x12in) s. bronze exec.1946 exhib. 25-Nov-3 Sotheby's, Milan #37/R est:6000-8000
£12000	$22080	€18000	Horse (51x99x16cm-20x39x6in) s. bronze exec.1969 exhib. 8-Jun-4 Finarte Semenzato, Milan #350/R est:20000-25000
£13542	$23021	€19500	Dying horse (44x56cm-17x22in) s. bronze prov. 28-Oct-3 Il Ponte, Milan #271/R
Works on paper			
£1259	$2140	€1800	Nudes (24x32cm-9x13in) s. pencil double-sided. 20-Nov-3 Finarte Semenzato, Milan #70/R est:2000-2500

MESSMANN, Carl Ludvig Ferd (1826-1893) Danish

£375	$611	€548	Landscape with manor house (38x60cm-15x24in) s. 27-Sep-3 Rasmussen, Havnen #2044/R (D.KR 4000)

MESTON, Emily (c.1864-1914) Australian

£447	$800	€653	Roses (34x59cm-13x23in) s. 4-May-4 Sotheby's, Melbourne #145 (A.D 1100)

MESTRALLET, Paul Louis (1886-?) French

£433	$797	€650	La marche a Belle-Ile (21x27cm-8x11in) s. 11-Jun-4 Pierre Berge, Paris #248
£626	$1001	€914	From the Seine in Paris (81x116cm-32x46in) s.d.1916. 22-Sep-3 Rasmussen, Vejle #321/R (D.KR 6600)
£822	$1513	€1250	Bigoudenes (21x28cm-8x11in) s.d.1911 wood. 28-Jun-4 Joron-Derem, Paris #95

MESTROVIE, Mathilde von (1843-?) Austrian

£1049	$1804	€1500	Still life of flowers (114x35cm-45x14in) s.d.1895 three. 4-Dec-3 Dorotheum, Graz #22/R est:1500

MESZOLY, Geza (1844-1887) Hungarian

£2635	$4769	€3847	Late afternoon (25x46cm-10x18in) 16-Apr-4 Mu Terem Galeria, Budapest #48/R (H.F 1000000)
£5158	$8563	€7531	Girls by waterside with geese (19x35cm-7x14in) panel. 4-Oct-3 Kieselbach, Budapest #121/R (H.F 1900000)
£7377	$13353	€10770	Houses on the streambank (30x47cm-12x19in) s. 16-Apr-4 Mu Terem Galeria, Budapest #108/R (H.F 2800000)
£8551	$15135	€12484	Hen with her chick (26x21cm-10x8in) s. panel. 28-Apr-4 Kieselbach, Budapest #112/R (H.F 3200000)
£14355	$24834	€20958	Bath House (38x67cm-15x26in) s. board. 12-Dec-3 Kieselbach, Budapest #227/R (H.F 5500000)

METCALF, Conger (1914-1998) American
£395 $700 €577 Seated boy (46x30cm-18x12in) i.verso. 2-May-4 Grogan, Boston #108/R
Works on paper
£226 $400 €330 Dancing boys (23x30cm-9x12in) s. pencil sepia wash. 2-May-4 Grogan, Boston #107/R
£323 $550 €472 Interior sketch (30x27cm-12x11in) s. mixed media W/C. 21-Nov-3 Skinner, Boston #423/R
£353 $600 €515 Street urchin (49x40cm-19x16in) s. s.verso red crayon W/C. 21-Nov-3 Skinner, Boston #420/R
£531 $850 €775 Blue faces (38x38cm-15x15in) s. mixed media. 21-Sep-3 Grogan, Boston #76/R
£1037 $1700 €1504 Three figures (122x99cm-48x39in) mixed media. 2-Jun-3 Grogan, Boston #676

METCALF, Willard Leroy (1858-1925) American
£24419 $42000 €35652 First sketch for 'White mantle' (13x15cm-5x6in) s.d.07 i.verso prov. 4-Dec-3 Christie's, Rockefeller NY #74/R est:20000-30000
£116279 $200000 €169767 Road to Cape Porpoise (53x65cm-21x26in) s.d.20 prov.lit. 3-Dec-3 Sotheby's, New York #17/R est:200000-300000
£125000 $220000 €182500 Summer night no 2 (67x74cm-26x29in) s.d.1914 prov.lit. 18-May-4 Christie's, Rockefeller NY #101/R est:120000-180000
Works on paper
£682 $1200 €996 Under the archway (20x28cm-8x11in) chl dr prov. 3-Jan-4 Collins, Maine #50/R
£939 $1700 €1371 Landscape (15x33cm-6x13in) W/C. 16-Apr-4 Du Mouchelle, Detroit #2126/R est:1000-1500
£2639 $4250 €3853 The summer house (48x58cm-19x23in) s. pastel. 20-Aug-3 James Julia, Fairfield #1383/R est:3000-5000

METCALFE, Augusta Isabella (1881-1971) American
£275 $500 €413 Battle of soldiers and Indians (46x91cm-18x36in) s. prov. 19-Jun-4 Harvey Clar, Oakland #2200/R

METCALFE, Gerald Fenwick (fl.1894-1929) British
Works on paper
£280 $510 €409 Study for the war memorial at Albury, Surrey (49x34cm-19x13in) s.i.d.1913/1914 pencil W/C htd bodycol. 1-Jul-4 Christie's, Kensington #408/R

METCALFE, Muriel (1910-) British
£420 $760 €613 Scotch fisher girls at Scarborough (49x39cm-19x15in) s. i.verso. 30-Mar-4 David Duggleby, Scarborough #193/R

METHER-BORGSTROM, Ernst (1917-1996) Finnish
£946 $1693 €1400 View from Saint Paul (27x22cm-11x9in) s.d.51. 8-May-4 Bukowskis, Helsinki #286/R
£1133 $2029 €1700 Abstract composition I (19x28cm-7x11in) s.d.1952 canvas on board exhib. 15-May-4 Hagelstam, Helsinki #214/R est:1000
Works on paper
£385 $654 €550 Caviteter - composition (44x64cm-17x25in) s.d.91 gouache. 29-Nov-3 Bukowskis, Helsinki #295/R
£490 $832 €700 Gouache I (44x64cm-17x25in) s.d.91 gouache. 29-Nov-3 Bukowskis, Helsinki #268/R

METHFESSEL, Adolf (1836-1909) Argentinian
£7500 $11624 €10950 Iguacu Falls (88x156cm-35x61in) s. 26-Sep-2 Christie's, London #115/R est:4000-6000
Works on paper
£433 $789 €650 South American fishermen (23x32cm-9x13in) s. W/C. 30-Jun-4 Neumeister, Munich #423/R
£617 $1048 €901 Cainguas Indian with tiger trap (24x34cm-9x13in) s. W/C bodycol. 5-Nov-3 Dobiaschofsky, Bern #803/R (S.FR 1400)
£3911 $7000 €5710 Indiens du Paraguay a la chasse (23x33cm-9x13in) s. W/C gouache. 26-May-4 Sotheby's, New York #77/R est:10000-15000

METHUEN, Lord (1886-1974) British
£290 $537 €423 Burleigh House (33x51cm-13x20in) s. 13-Feb-4 Keys, Aylsham #777
£420 $714 €613 Amaryllis pot plant (80x65cm-31x26in) s.d.1931. 1-Dec-3 Bonhams, Bath #36/R
£450 $752 €657 Bath in winter (18x25cm-7x10in) s. canvasboard prov. 16-Oct-3 Christie's, Kensington #466/R
£480 $826 €701 Meconopsis regia and meconopsis betonicifolia, from the Himalayas (63x47cm-25x19in) s. board exhib. 3-Dec-3 Christie's, Kensington #533/R
£480 $874 €701 Aqueduct at Limpley Stoke (21x44cm-8x17in) s. board exhib. 1-Jul-4 Christie's, Kensington #108/R
£500 $830 €730 St Mary's, Redcliff, Bristol (48x34cm-19x13in) s.d.1957 board. 30-Sep-3 Bristol Auction Rooms #589/R
£1000 $1670 €1460 Melbury Stable building from the hexagonal Edward VI Tower (61x51cm-24x20in) s. board exhib. 16-Oct-3 Christie's, Kensington #399/R est:1200-1800
£1000 $1820 €1460 Claverton Manor (76x127cm-30x50in) s. exhib. 1-Jul-4 Christie's, Kensington #106/R est:800-1200
£1600 $2720 €2336 Brympton d'Evercy, Somerset (64x77cm-25x30in) s. prov.exhib.lit. 26-Nov-3 Sotheby's, Olympia #50/R est:1000-1500
£2500 $4400 €3650 Princes Buildings, Bath (56x76cm-22x30in) s. i. on stretcher prov. 19-May-4 Dreweatt Neate, Newbury #84/R est:500-700
Works on paper
£250 $395 €363 Florence from the Piazzale Michelangelo (44x57cm-17x22in) s. pen col chk. 7-Sep-3 Lots Road Auctions, London #354
£260 $458 €380 Lac d'Aiguebelette, Savoie (13x22cm-5x9in) s.d.56 pen chk prov. 19-May-4 Dreweatt Neate, Newbury #83/R
£360 $583 €522 Blenheim Palace (33x53cm-13x21in) s. pen ink htd pastel. 30-Jul-3 Hamptons Fine Art, Godalming #107

METHVEN, Cathcart William (1849-1925) South African
£991 $1774 €1447 Seascape (75x126cm-30x50in) s.d.1908. 31-May-4 Stephan Welz, Johannesburg #543/R (SA.R 12000)

METRAL, Francois (19/20th C) Swiss
£259 $463 €378 Schloss Chillon with Villeneuve and the Dents du Midi (25x44cm-10x17in) s. board. 12-May-4 Dobiaschofsky, Bern #3757 (S.FR 600)

METSU, Gabriel (1629-1667) Dutch
£12222 $22000 €17844 Woman drawing wine from barrel (37x33cm-15x13in) prov. 22-Jan-4 Sotheby's, New York #2/R est:10000-15000
£87248 $163154 €130000 Little dog on a chair (94x94cm-37x37in) prov. 29-Feb-4 Finarte, Venice #26/R est:95000-120000

METSYS, Cornelis (attrib) (1508-1580) Flemish
£3289 $6053 €5000 Bon Samaritain (22x34cm-9x13in) panel. 25-Jun-4 Piasa, Paris #4/R est:5000-7000
£6853 $11650 €9800 Le portement de croix (28x41cm-11x16in) panel. 1-Dec-3 Rieunier, Paris #12/R est:7000-9000

METSYS, Jan (c.1509-1575) Flemish
£42000 $75600 €61320 Bathsheba observed by King David (109x76cm-43x30in) panel prov.lit. 22-Apr-4 Sotheby's, London #14/R est:15000-20000

METSYS, Jan (attrib) (c.1509-1575) Flemish
£10738 $19758 €16000 Madonna and Child worshipped by two angels (95x71cm-37x28in) panel prov. 24-Mar-4 Dorotheum, Vienna #100/R est:10000-15000

METSYS, Jan (circle) (c.1509-1575) Flemish
£5901 $9500 €8615 Madonna and Child (102x30cm-40x12in) oil tempera panel. 20-Aug-3 James Julia, Fairfield #652/R est:10000-20000

METSYS, Jan (style) (c.1509-1575) Flemish
£12000 $20400 €17520 Mother and her children (62x57cm-24x22in) 30-Oct-3 Sotheby's, Olympia #43/R est:6000-8000
£12000 $21600 €17520 Virgin and Child (67x49cm-26x19in) panel prov. 21-Apr-4 Christie's, London #54/R est:12000-16000

METSYS, Quentin (circle) (1466-1530) Flemish
£10526 $19368 €16000 Portrait d'homme en buste derriere balustrade (55x48cm-22x19in) panel exhib. 24-Jun-4 Christie's, Paris #6/R est:20000-30000
£11268 $19718 €16000 Love promise (56x84cm-22x33in) board lit. 16-Dec-3 Segre, Madrid #43/R est:9000
£15000 $27450 €21900 Lamentation (122x77cm-48x30in) en grisaille panel triptych. 7-Jul-4 Christie's, London #16/R est:15000-20000

METSYS, Quentin (style) (1466-1530) Flemish
£8000 $13840 €11680 Virgin at prayer (35x25cm-14x10in) panel prov.lit. 12-Dec-3 Christie's, Kensington #11/R est:4000-6000
£23077 $42000 €33692 Money lenders (113x79cm-44x31in) panel. 17-Jun-4 Christie's, Rockefeller NY #9/R est:15000-20000

METTENHOVEN, Marcel (20th C) French
£915 $1483 €1300 Retour de la maison du bord de mer (50x65cm-20x26in) s.d.1920. 11-Aug-3 Boscher, Cherbourg #861/R

METTENLEITER, Johann Michael (1765-1853) German
Works on paper
£1467 $2625 €2200 Don Giovanni before the tomb of Komtur (34x27cm-13x11in) s.d.1787 pen brush. 13-May-4 Bassenge, Berlin #5435/R est:600

METTLING, Louis (1847-1904) French
£460 $768 €672 Tete de femme (21x81cm-8x32in) s. panel. 11-Nov-3 Bonhams, Knightsbridge #88/R

METTLING, Louis (attrib) (1847-1904) French
£333 $603 €500 Le plafond de la Galerie d'Apollon (100x81cm-39x32in) after Eugene Delacroix exhib. 30-Mar-4 Rossini, Paris #822

METTLING, Raoul Edmond (1876-?) French
£267 $483 €400 Les pelerins d'Emaus (46x38cm-18x15in) s. after Rembrandt. 30-Mar-4 Rossini, Paris #823

METTON, Edouard (1856-1927) Swiss
£545 $905 €790 Herder with cows on alpine pasture (72x93cm-28x37in) s. 13-Jun-3 Zofingen, Switzerland #2943/R (S.FR 1200)
£724 $1231 €1057 Cows on alpine meadow in evening (24x30cm-9x12in) s. 19-Nov-3 Fischer, Luzern #2214/R (S.FR 1600)

METZ, Conrad Martin (1749-1827) British
Works on paper
£1111 $2000 €1622 Two putti shearing a sheep (16x24cm-6x9in) s.d.1791 red chk. 21-Jan-4 Sotheby's, New York #116/R est:2500-3500

METZ, Friedrich (1820-1901) German
£1497 $2679 €2200 Extensive romantic river landscape (31x40cm-12x16in) s.d.52 lit. 20-Mar-4 Bergmann, Erlangen #1102 est:1500-2200

METZ, Gerry (1943-) American
£269 $425 €393 After the hunt (51x76cm-20x30in) s. board. 27-Jul-3 Bonhams & Butterfields, Los Angeles #7025/R
£1519 $2750 €2218 Color of war (76x102cm-30x40in) s.i.verso board. 3-Apr-4 Neal Auction Company, New Orleans #673/R est:3000-4000

METZ, Gertrud (1746-1793) German
£4595 $8224 €6800 Still life of fruit (33x42cm-13x17in) s. copper plate. 8-May-4 Bukowskis, Helsinki #393/R est:2000-2500

METZ, Johann Martin (1717-1790) German
£10959 $18630 €16000 Still life with tulips, roses and tea-cup (76x62cm-30x24in) s.d.1779. 5-Nov-3 Vendue Huis, Gravenhage #26/R est:6000-8000
£10959 $18630 €16000 Still life with tulip and roses (76x62cm-30x24in) s.d.1779. 5-Nov-3 Vendue Huis, Gravenhage #27/R est:6000-8000

METZ, Johann Martin (attrib) (1717-1790) German
£5369 $9879 €8000 Bouquet of flowers and other blossoms in basket (71x94cm-28x37in) 24-Mar-4 Dorotheum, Vienna #362/R est:8000-10000

METZENER, Alfred (1833-1905) Swiss
£1049 $1783 €1500 Mountain panorama (122x175cm-48x69in) s.d.1878. 20-Nov-3 Van Ham, Cologne #1739 est:700

METZGER, Eduard (1807-?) German
£3400 $6086 €4964 Figures in an extensive Greek landscape (41x64cm-16x25in) s. 11-May-4 Bonhams, New Bond Street #8/R est:3000-5000

METZGER, Henry (1876-1934) Canadian
£300 $549 €438 Old couple (49x66cm-19x26in) s. 1-Jun-4 Hodgins, Calgary #109/R (C.D 750)
£702 $1271 €1025 Untitled - plains Indian chief (51x41cm-20x16in) s. 18-Apr-4 Levis, Calgary #79/R est:2000-2500 (C.D 1700)
£1915 $3255 €2796 Chief Achim, Cree Indian (35x45cm-14x18in) s. i.verso prov. 27-Nov-3 Heffel, Vancouver #136/R est:2000-3000 (C.D 4250)

METZINGER, Jean (1883-1956) French
£4278 $8000 €6246 Flamants (33x41cm-13x16in) painted c.1906 prov. 25-Feb-4 Christie's, Rockefeller NY #106/R est:15000-20000
£16000 $29440 €23360 Suzanne (21x16cm-8x6in) s. board painted c.1935 exhib. 22-Jun-4 Sotheby's, London #298/R est:10000-12000
£17059 $29000 €24906 Paysage du Midi (46x55cm-18x22in) s. painted c.1940. 6-Nov-3 Sotheby's, New York #180/R est:20000-30000
£17483 $30070 €25000 Tete de femme (34x23cm-13x9in) s. panel prov.exhib.lit. 8-Dec-3 Artcurial Briest, Paris #20/R est:30000-35000
£22346 $40000 €32625 Nu allonge sur le divan (54x873cm-21x344in) s. painted c.1940 prov. 6-May-4 Sotheby's, New York #394/R est:50000-70000
£28000 $51520 €40880 Three red flamingoes (32x40cm-13x16in) painted c.1905 prov. 22-Jun-4 Sotheby's, London #154/R est:12000-15000
£28170 $49297 €40000 Nature morte aux coquillages (93x65cm-37x26in) s.prov. 18-Dec-3 Tajan, Paris #32/R est:40000-45000
£40000 $73600 €58400 L'Argonaute (53x73cm-21x29in) s. painted c.1927 prov.exhib. 23-Jun-4 Christie's, London #245/R est:25000-35000
£44693 $80000 €65252 Petit Port - pecheurs et bateaux au quai (54x72cm-21x28in) init. painted c.1906 prov. 6-May-4 Sotheby's, New York #258/R est:30000-40000
£46667 $85867 €70000 La jeune femme pensive aux roses rouges (81x60cm-32x24in) s.d.1923 exhib. 11-Jun-4 Villa Grisebach, Berlin #1586/R est:18000-24000
£58000 $96860 €84680 Femme assise devant la fenetre (81x65cm-32x26in) s. painted 1935-1944. 21-Oct-3 Sotheby's, London #57/R est:50000-70000
£60000 $110400 €90000 Young woman holding a fruit bowl (92x66cm-36x26in) s. painted 1924 exhib. 11-Jun-4 Villa Grisebach, Berlin #1516/R est:25000-30000
£134078 $240000 €195754 Nature morte a la carafe (81x60cm-32x24in) s. s.i.d.1914 verso prov.exhib.lit. 5-May-4 Christie's, Rockefeller NY #289/R est:250000-350000
£158824 $270000 €231883 Femme a sa toilette (92x60cm-36x24in) s. painted 1918 prov. 6-Nov-3 Sotheby's, New York #212a/R est:180000-250000
£205000 $373100 €299300 Baigneuses deux nus dans un paysage exotique (116x89cm-46x35in) s. painted c.1905 prov. 4-Feb-4 Sotheby's, London #251/R est:80000-180000
£411765 $700000 €601177 Nature morte aux poires (116x81cm-46x32in) painted c.1920-21 prov.exhib.lit. 5-Nov-3 Sotheby's, New York #42/R est:700000-900000
Works on paper
£268 $494 €400 La danse (17x12cm-7x5in) s. black crayon. 24-Mar-4 Binoche, Paris #69/R
£315 $535 €450 Femme dans un interieur (24x18cm-9x7in) s. sanguine exec.c.1913 prov. 23-Nov-3 Cornette de St.Cyr, Paris #235
£1259 $2140 €1800 Untitled (26x19cm-10x7in) s. ink prov. 25-Nov-3 Sotheby's, Milan #93/R est:1500-2000
£2100 $3507 €3066 Composition surrealiste au main et verre (18x12cm-7x5in) st.sig. pencil preparatory sketch verso. 22-Oct-3 Bonhams, New Bond Street #48/R est:2000-3000
£2700 $4509 €3942 Femme cubiste (32x24cm-13x9in) s. pencil prov. 22-Oct-3 Bonhams, New Bond Street #65/R est:1500-2000
£2797 $4755 €4000 Nu (25x20cm-10x8in) s. Indian ink prov. 23-Nov-3 Cornette de St.Cyr, Paris #234/R est:300-400
£5594 $9510 €8000 Femme dans un interieur (30x23cm-12x9in) s. graphite exec.c.1910 prov.exhib. 23-Nov-3 Cornette de St.Cyr, Paris #236/R est:600-800

METZKES, Harald (1929-) German
£872 $1605 €1300 Winter landscape at dusk (120x110cm-47x43in) s.d.89. 27-Mar-4 Dannenberg, Berlin #597/R
£933 $1680 €1400 Seated nude (40x30cm-16x12in) s.d. 24-Apr-4 Dr Lehr, Berlin #288/R

METZLER, Kurt Laurenz (1941-) Swiss
£359 $650 €524 Reformation (46x53cm-18x21in) s. masonite. 3-Apr-4 David Rago, Lambertville #110/R
Sculpture
£1171 $2014 €1710 Business man (31cm-12in) mono.d.96 brown green pat.bronze. 2-Dec-3 Koller, Zurich #3352/R est:2000-3000 (S.FR 2600)
£1376 $2298 €1995 Untitled (49cm-19in) mono.i.d. gold col bronze. 23-Jun-3 Philippe Schuler, Zurich #3302/R est:4000-6000 (S.FR 3000)
£1376 $2298 €1995 Untitled (52cm-20in) mono.i.d. gold col bronze. 23-Jun-3 Philippe Schuler, Zurich #3303/R est:4000-6000 (S.FR 3000)
£1485 $2732 €2168 Untitled (40x19x10cm-16x7x4in) mono.d.1974 iron. 8-Jun-4 Germann, Zurich #90/R est:4000-6000 (S.FR 3400)
£2081 $3538 €3038 Golfer (95x52x55cm-37x20x22in) pat.iron. 25-Nov-3 Germann, Zurich #148/R est:4000-6000 (S.FR 4600)
£3167 $5385 €4624 Street man (64x34x22cm-25x13x9in) mono.d.2001 bronze. 25-Nov-3 Germann, Zurich #41/R est:8000-10000 (S.FR 7000)
£3167 $5385 €4624 Woman with bag (63x30x15cm-25x12x6in) mono.d.2001 bronze. 25-Nov-3 Germann, Zurich #139/R est:8000-10000 (S.FR 7000)
Works on paper
£271 $462 €396 Untitled (102x68cm-40x27in) mono.d.1986 W/C gouache collage. 25-Nov-3 Germann, Zurich #844 (S.FR 600)

METZOLDT, Max (1859-?) German
£1074 $1997 €1600 Portrait of kitchen maid (60x50cm-24x20in) s.d.1892 panel. 6-Mar-4 Arnold, Frankfurt #791/R est:600

MEUCCI, Angiola (1880-1966) Italian
£336 $594 €500 Vase of flowers (45x35cm-18x14in) s. 1-May-4 Meeting Art, Vercelli #427
£442 $791 €650 Vase of flowers (69x88cm-27x35in) s. oval. 22-Mar-4 Sant Agostino, Torino #1/R

MEUCCI, Michelangelo (19th C) Italian
£300 $501 €438 Study of hanging dead game (46x36cm-18x14in) s.i. 17-Oct-3 Keys, Aylsham #735
£331 $603 €500 Punting (27x41cm-11x16in) s.d.1908 board. 21-Jun-4 Pandolfini, Florence #109/R
£335 $550 €489 Trompe l'oeil of birds (20x18cm-8x7in) s. board. 8-Feb-3 Auctions by the Bay, Alameda #385/R
£682 $1200 €996 Trompe l'oeil of still life with fish (66x53cm-26x21in) s.d.1871. 22-May-4 Harvey Clar, Oakland #2433
£694 $1160 €1000 Trophees d'oiseaux multicolores (29cm-11in) s.i.d.1874 peinture oval pair. 25-Oct-3 Binoche, Orleans #45
£700 $1190 €1022 Hanging songbirds (22x18cm-9x7in) s.i.d.1875 board pair. 6-Nov-3 Christie's, Kensington #928/R
£845 $1462 €1200 Still life with dead game (100x50cm-39x20in) s.d.1906. 9-Dec-3 Pandolfini, Florence #204/R
£1056 $1701 €1500 Still life with game (100x40cm-39x16in) s.d.1904. 8-May-3 Farsetti, Prato #236 est:1700-2000
£1056 $1701 €1500 Still life with game (100x40cm-39x16in) s.d.1904. 8-May-3 Farsetti, Prato #240 est:1700-2000
£1200 $2172 €1752 Hanging game (48x38cm-19x15in) s.i. board oval. 31-Mar-4 Bonhams, Knightsbridge #34/R est:600-800
£1250 $2288 €1875 Still life of fruit and vegetables (83x58cm-33x23in) 27-Jul-4 Henry Adams, Chichester #446/R est:500-800
£3611 $6500 €5272 Still lives with boar and deer (151x79cm-59x31in) s.d.1889 pair. 21-Jan-4 Sotheby's, New York #178/R est:10000-15000

MEUCCI, Nina (fl.1818-1826) American
Miniatures
£1386 $2300 €2024 Portrait of Jno B McClanahan (8x5cm-3x2in) s.i.d.1819 rec. 4-Oct-3 Neal Auction Company, New Orleans #512/R est:1500-2500

MEUGENS, Sibyl (fl.1917-1937) British
£380 $623 €555 Reflections, silver bowl and teapot on an embroidered cloth (25x30cm-10x12in) s. board. 29-May-3 Neales, Nottingham #817/R

MEULEN, Adam Frans van der (1632-1690) Flemish
£12587 $21021 €18000 Cavalry battle (51x66cm-20x26in) s.d.1654 copper. 9-Oct-3 Michael Zeller, Lindau #500/R est:18000
£18889 $34000 €27578 Louis XIV in a state coach accompanied by his gentleman (91x131cm-36x52in) s. prov. 22-Jan-4 Sotheby's, New York #195/R est:12000-16000
£80986 $141725 €115000 Entree triomphale de Louis XIV (92x120cm-36x47in) s. 17-Dec-3 Piasa, Paris #22/R est:120000-150000
Works on paper
£775 $1340 €1100 Cavaliers s'elancant, un jeune homme leur indiquant une direction (29x45cm-11x18in) pen brown ink htd. 10-Dec-3 Piasa, Paris #31/R
£32394 $56690 €46000 Une vue de la porte Saint-Pierre a Lille (12x23cm-5x9in) i. graphite W/C prov. 17-Dec-3 Christie's, Paris #38/R est:25000-35000

MEULEN, Adam Frans van der (attrib) (1632-1690) Flemish
£6667 $12133 €10000 Defeat of the Spanish Army on the Bruges canal (28x44cm-11x17in) paper on panel. 30-Jun-4 Neumeister, Munich #469/R est:15000
£9615 $16538 €14038 Etude de cheveaux (19x26cm-7x10in) paper. 3-Dec-3 AB Stockholms Auktionsverk #2665/R est:60000-80000 (S.KR 125000)
Works on paper
£541 $951 €800 Study of an elegantly dressed man (25x16cm-10x6in) black chk prov.exhib. 19-May-4 Sotheby's, Amsterdam #99/R
£4762 $8524 €7000 Scene de retour de chasse (46x127cm-18x50in) sanguine. 19-Mar-4 Piasa, Paris #42/R est:4000-5000
£5442 $9741 €8000 Scene de retour de chasse (46x127cm-18x50in) sanguine. 19-Mar-4 Piasa, Paris #41/R est:3000-4000

MEULEN, Adam Frans van der (style) (1632-1690) Flemish
£10000 $18100 €15000 Cavaliers devant la ville Courtrai (54x132cm-21x52in) 30-Mar-4 Millon & Associes, Paris #8/R est:12000-15000
£11644 $19795 €17000 Arrival of Louis XIV at the siege of Maastricht (86x122cm-34x48in) 4-Nov-3 Sotheby's, Amsterdam #78/R est:10000-15000

MEULEN, Edmond van der (1841-1905) Belgian
£1379 $2552 €2000 Deux cheins atteles a une carrette contenant des fleurs (110x85cm-43x33in) s. 19-Jan-4 Horta, Bruxelles #227/R est:2500-3500

MEULEN, Steven van der (16th C) Flemish
£28000 $50960 €40880 Portrait of the blessed Thomas Percy, 7th Earl of Northumberland (123x89cm-48x35in) i. panel. 1-Jul-4 Sotheby's, London #104/R est:20000-30000

MEULENAERE, Edmond de (1884-1963) Belgian
£267 $480 €400 Dockers (47x40cm-19x16in) s. cardboard. 20-Apr-4 Galerie Moderne, Brussels #346
£280 $507 €420 Bateaux au port (45x54cm-18x21in) s. cardboard. 30-Mar-4 Campo & Campo, Antwerp #66
£400 $736 €600 Vue des environs de Linkebeek. s. 14-Jun-4 Horta, Bruxelles #365

MEULENER, Pieter (1602-1654) Dutch
£3846 $6615 €5615 Battle scene (60x82cm-24x32in) s.d.1648. 2-Dec-3 Bukowskis, Stockholm #374/R est:25000-30000 (S.KR 50000)
£18792 $34953 €28000 Cavalry battle (44x65cm-17x26in) s.d.1650 board. 2-Mar-4 Ansorena, Madrid #297/R est:19000
£20690 $34345 €30000 Battle (44x65cm-17x26in) s. board. 30-Sep-3 Ansorena, Madrid #50/R est:28000

MEUNIER, Constantin (1831-1905) Belgian
£699 $1168 €1000 Chez le forgeron (40x32cm-16x13in) s. panel. 13-Oct-3 Horta, Bruxelles #370
£699 $1203 €1000 Portrait du Baron de Beeckman (46x32cm-18x13in) s. panel. 8-Dec-3 Horta, Bruxelles #26
£1972 $3411 €2800 La digue a Ostende (25x38cm-10x15in) s.i. panel prov. 13-Dec-3 De Vuyst, Lokeren #443/R est:2500-3500
£3147 $5255 €4500 Mine worker at the entrance to the mine (48x31cm-19x12in) s.d.1887. 11-Oct-3 De Vuyst, Lokeren #426/R est:4500-6500
Sculpture
£1042 $1740 €1500 Travailleuse de mine (47cm-19in) s. bronze. 21-Oct-3 Campo & Campo, Antwerp #213 est:1500-1600
£1275 $2359 €1900 Forest labourer (47x23cm-19x9in) s. dark brown pat bronze. 13-Mar-4 De Vuyst, Lokeren #242 est:1000-1250
£1678 $2853 €2400 Mineur assis (37x20x24cm-15x8x9in) s. pat bronze. 1-Dec-3 Palais de Beaux Arts, Brussels #289/R est:1000-1500
£1987 $3616 €3000 Homme a la pelle (47cm-19in) s. pat bronze. 19-Jun-4 St-Germain-en-Laye Encheres #35/R est:3000
£2000 $3400 €2920 Vieux cheval de mine (38x35cm-15x14in) s.st.f.Verbeyst pat bronze. 28-Oct-3 Sotheby's, London #157/R
£2400 $4296 €3600 Quarryman (59x23cm-23x9in) s. green brown pat.bronze Cast.B.Verbeyst Fondeur Bruxelles. 13-May-4 Bassenge, Berlin #5615/R est:2500
£2483 $4569 €3700 La Glebe (45x45x15cm-18x18x6in) s.i. dark brown pat.bronze lit. 26-Mar-4 Ketterer, Hamburg #557/R est:4000-5000
Works on paper
£537 $950 €800 Sortie de l'eglise (36x56cm-14x22in) s. mixed media. 27-Apr-4 Campo & Campo, Antwerp #171/R
£1469 $2452 €2100 Hiercheuse partant pour le travail (28x19cm-11x7in) s. W/C. 11-Oct-3 De Vuyst, Lokeren #255/R est:2000-2400
£2746 $4751 €3900 Old mining horse (45x60cm-18x24in) s.d.93 gouache W/C exhib.lit. 13-Dec-3 De Vuyst, Lokeren #547/R est:3500-4500

MEUNIER, Constantin (attrib) (1831-1905) Belgian
£645 $1078 €942 Factory chimneys (59x68cm-23x27in) s. panel. 20-Oct-3 Blomqvist, Lysaker #1203/R (N.KR 7500)
£4196 $7133 €6000 Mineurs au charbonnage (59x85cm-23x33in) 18-Nov-3 Vanderkindere, Brussels #22 est:3750-5000

MEUNIER, Georgette (1859-1951) Belgian
Works on paper
£1645 $2977 €2500 Composition florale sur un entablement (73x97cm-29x38in) s. pastel. 19-Apr-4 Horta, Bruxelles #84 est:3000-4000

MEUNIER, Jean Baptiste (1786-1858) French
Works on paper
£414 $691 €600 Pic-vert (31x24cm-12x9in) W/C gouache varnish brush col wash black crayon. 13-Nov-3 Binoche, Paris #95/R

MEUNIER, Jean-Baptiste and TRAVIES, Edouard (19th C) French
Works on paper
£1517 $2534 €2200 Various animals. s. two d.1835 one d.1837 W/C gouache crayon 3 sheets 1 mount. 13-Nov-3 Binoche, Paris #41/R est:1500
£2345 $3916 €3400 Various animals. s.d.1834/1836/1837 W/C gouache crayon 3 sheets 1 mount. 13-Nov-3 Binoche, Paris #34/R est:3000
£2483 $4146 €3600 Various animals. s.d.1833/1835/1836 W/C gouache black crayon 3 sheets 1 mount. 13-Nov-3 Binoche, Paris #42/R est:3000

MEUNIER, Monika (20th C) French?
£699 $1189 €1000 Le pin parasol (46x55cm-18x22in) s. 20-Nov-3 Gioffredo, Nice #170
£1538 $2615 €2200 Le soleil bleu (92x73cm-36x29in) 20-Nov-3 Gioffredo, Nice #19/R

MEUNIER, Pierre Louis (attrib) (c.1780-?) French
Works on paper
£4762 $8524 €7000 Vue de jardin d'agrement (14x25cm-6x10in) W/C prov.exhib. 19-Mar-4 Beaussant & Lefèvre, Paris #30/R est:3000-4000

MEURER, Charles A (1865-1955) American
£438 $700 €639 Cows to pasture with farmer (15x23cm-6x9in) init. board. 20-Sep-3 Sloans & Kenyon, Bethesda #640/R
£10270 $19000 €14994 Still life with money, pipe and letters (28x36cm-11x14in) s.d.1914. 11-Mar-4 Christie's, Rockefeller NY #11/R est:8000-12000

MEURER, Ernst (1884-1956) German
£400 $716 €600 Black diamonds (80x100cm-31x39in) s. i. stretcher lit. 14-May-4 Schloss Ahlden, Ahlden #2901/R

MEURET, François (1800-1887) French
Miniatures
£2200 $3938 €3212 Young gentleman and lady (10cm-4in) s.d.1850 rec. gilt frame pair. 25-May-4 Christie's, London #192/R est:2000-3000

MEURICE, Jean Michel (1938-) French?
£571 $1010 €850 Tondo (60x60cm-24x24in) s.i.d.75 verso acrylic round. 28-Apr-4 Artcurial Briest, Paris #389
£1409 $2437 €2000 Portrait jumeau de femme (80x200cm-31x79in) s.i.d.77 verso acrylic prov.exhib. 9-Dec-3 Artcurial Briest, Paris #575/R est:800-1200

MEURIS (?) French?
Works on paper
£7895 $14526 €12000 Naples seen from Posillipo. Naples seen from Carmine (40x60cm-16x24in) s. gouache pair. 22-Jun-4 Sotheby's, Milan #192/R est:11000-13000

MEURIS, Emmanuel (1894-1969) Italian
£338 $585 €480 Le petit chateau au bord de l'Ambleve (54x65cm-21x26in) s.d,60. 10-Dec-3 Hotel des Ventes Mosan, Brussels #203
£397 $723 €600 La clairiere (55x65cm-22x26in) s.d.1922. 16-Jun-4 Hotel des Ventes Mosan, Brussels #229
Works on paper
£447 $800 €653 Figures on road traversing tunnel (33x25cm-13x10in) gouache. 20-Mar-4 Sloans & Kenyon, Bethesda #1143/R

MEURON, Albert de (1823-1897) Swiss
£647 $1190 €945 Shore of Lake Geneva (16x28cm-6x11in) mono.d.75. 26-Mar-4 Koller, Zurich #3098/R est:1800-2200 (S.FR 1500)
£2941 $5000 €4294 Baigneuses a l'ombre (70x100cm-28x39in) s.d.1848. 25-Nov-3 Germann, Zurich #54/R est:8000-12000 (S.FR 6500)
£3664 $6558 €5349 Vaches a l'alpage (51x68cm-20x27in) mono.d.1870 prov. 13-May-4 Pierre Berge, Paris #15/R est:12000-15000 (S.FR 8500)
£6987 $12507 €10201 Baigneuses a l'ombre (72x105cm-28x41in) s.i.d.1848. 26-May-4 Sotheby's, Zurich #18/R est:10000-15000 (S.FR 16000)

MEURON, Louis de (1868-1939) Swiss
£271 $462 €396 L'arbre a Sanary (46x38cm-18x15in) s.i.d.1923 board double-sided. 28-Nov-3 Zofingen, Switzerland #3079 (S.FR 600)
£679 $1086 €991 Interior with still life (46x46cm-18x18in) mono. 16-Sep-3 Philippe Schuler, Zurich #3246/R est:1200-1500 (S.FR 1500)

MEURS, Harmen (1891-1964) Dutch
£952 $1705 €1400 Boats in the harbour (46x56cm-18x22in) d.1927. 17-Mar-4 De Zwann, Amsterdam #4641a/R est:1000-2000
£1000 $1800 €1500 Flowers in vase (54x47cm-21x19in) s.d.1923 lit. 22-Apr-4 Allgauer, Kempten #3647/R est:1500

MEUSHAUSEN, Helen (19th C) German
£490 $817 €700 Forbidden dreams (66x54cm-26x21in) s.i.d.1893. 26-Jun-3 Sant Agostino, Torino #99/R

MEVIUS, Hermann (1820-1864) German
£1110 $2043 €1621 Boats in rough seas near harbour town (56x80cm-22x31in) s. 29-Mar-4 Blomqvist, Lysaker #1202/R est:10000-15000 (N.KR 14000)
£4545 $8136 €6636 Ships in stormy sea off coast (80x123cm-31x48in) s.d.1860. 22-Mar-4 Philippe Schuler, Zurich #4418/R est:8000-12000 (S.FR 10500)

MEW, Thomas Hillier (?) British
£500 $920 €730 Jockey on a grey in full gallop (32x48cm-13x19in) s.i. board. 10-Jun-4 Christie's, Kensington #67/R

MEWAR SCHOOL (18th C) Indian
£21739 $40000 €31739 Portrait of Maharana Jai Singh of Mewar (203x127cm-80x50in) distemper htd gold cloth. 24-Mar-4 Sotheby's, New York #129/R est:40000-60000

MEWHINNEY, Ella (1891-1975) American
£898 $1500 €1311 Bluebonnets (20x25cm-8x10in) canvasboard. 18-Oct-3 David Dike, Dallas #180/R est:1500-3000

MEXIA, Juan Frances (1873-1954) Spanish
£816 $1461 €1200 Portrait of young woman (93x75cm-37x30in) s.d.1918. 22-Mar-4 Durán, Madrid #59/R

MEXICAN SCHOOL
£13408 $24000 €19576 Bull scene. Attacking the carriage (35x47cm-14x19in) pair. 26-May-4 Sotheby's, New York #71/R est:10000-15000

MEXICAN SCHOOL, 18th C
£3937 $6417 €5748 Heavenly choir (343x152cm-135x60in) 24-Sep-3 Louis Morton, Mexico #224/R est:55000-70000 (M.P 70000)
£4988 $9027 €7282 Coronation of the VIrgin (135x195cm-53x77in) 31-Mar-4 Louis Morton, Mexico #96/R est:120000-130000 (M.P 100000)

£9484 $16122 €13847 Virgin of Guadalupe (156x111cm-61x44in) 29-Oct-3 Louis Morton, Mexico #58/R est:50000-70000 (M.P 180000)
£9890 $18000 €14439 Wedding of Joseph and Mary (295x178cm-116x70in) painted c.1750. 19-Jun-4 Jackson's, Cedar Falls #73/R est:6000-9000
£12645 $21496 €18462 Jesus (98x63cm-39x25in) 29-Oct-3 Louis Morton, Mexico #25/R est:180000-200000 (M.P 240000)
£13408 $24000 €19576 Virgin of Guadalupe (14cm-6in circular) oil gilt copper. 26-May-4 Sotheby's, New York #68/R est:18000-22000
£15132 $27842 €23000 Virgin of Mexico appearing (46x35cm-18x14in) s. copper. 24-Jun-4 Christie's, Paris #49/R est:3000-5000
£23743 $42500 €34665 Virgin of Guadalupe (102x79cm-40x31in) 26-May-4 Sotheby's, New York #66/R est:10000-15000
Sculpture
£3952 $6718 €5770 Immaculate (78cm-31in) painted wood. 29-Oct-3 Louis Morton, Mexico #77/R est:28000-30000 (M.P 75000)

MEXICAN SCHOOL, 19th C
£3688 $6270 €5384 Lady in pink (68x51cm-27x20in) 29-Oct-3 Louis Morton, Mexico #29/R est:25000-30000 (M.P 70000)
£14525 $26000 €21207 Puebla cathedral (54x101cm-21x40in) canvas on masonite prov. 26-May-4 Sotheby's, New York #74/R est:12000-18000
£15363 $27500 €22430 Mazatlan harbour (67x117cm-26x46in) 26-May-4 Sotheby's, New York #79/R est:20000-25000

MEY, Jos de (1928-) Belgian
£699 $1189 €1000 Souvenir de voyage des temps perdus (65x80cm-26x31in) s.d.1984 verso. 1-Dec-3 Palais de Beaux Arts, Brussels #238/R
£733 $1327 €1100 Avec les compliments tardifs de Monsieur Le Notre (100x85cm-39x33in) s.d.1983 panel. 30-Mar-4 Palais de Beaux Arts, Brussels #503
£769 $1308 €1100 Riante rekonstruktie van een Romaanse retro-ruine (100x86cm-39x34in) s.d.1982. 1-Dec-3 Palais de Beaux Arts, Brussels #240/R

MEYBODEN, Hans (1901-1965) German
£267 $477 €400 Village square (23x31cm-9x12in) s. oil chk. 15-May-4 Van Ham, Cologne #801
£490 $842 €700 Bunch of flowers in a white jug (53x42cm-21x17in) mono.d.17 panel. 5-Dec-3 Bolland & Marotz, Bremen #385/R
£780 $1303 €1100 Garden flowers (40x50cm-16x20in) mono.d.1956. 16-Oct-3 Dorotheum, Salzburg #669/R
£1467 $2640 €2200 In the garden (40x50cm-16x20in) mono.d.1956. 26-Apr-4 Rieber, Stuttgart #1290/R est:2200

MEYENDORFF, Isabelle B (?) ?
£500 $895 €730 Self portrait as a young man (63x52cm-25x20in) s. panel after Rembrandt. 18-Mar-4 Christie's, Kensington #416

MEYER VON BREMEN, Johann Georg (1813-1886) German
£1200 $2004 €1752 Story teller (10x12cm-4x5in) s.i. board. 12-Nov-3 Sotheby's, Olympia #194/R est:800-1200
£2059 $3500 €3006 Landmadchen auf dem heimweg (27x21cm-11x8in) s.d.1867 panel. 21-Nov-3 Skinner, Boston #244/R est:7000-9000
£4167 $6792 €6000 Peasant girl decorating wayside shrine (28x18cm-11x7in) s.d.1870 panel. 24-Sep-3 Neumeister, Munich #498/R est:7000
£8333 $13583 €12000 Boy reading (20x16cm-8x6in) s.d.1852. 24-Sep-3 Neumeister, Munich #497/R est:8000
£8982 $15000 €13114 In the boudoir (56x42cm-22x17in) s.d.1872. 7-Oct-3 Sotheby's, New York #75/R est:15000-20000
£16860 $29000 €24616 Little flower girl (58x41cm-23x16in) s.i.d.1882. 7-Dec-3 Freeman, Philadelphia #23 est:30000-50000
£18056 $32500 €26362 New baby (46x34cm-18x13in) s.i. panel. 23-Apr-4 Sotheby's, New York #168/R est:15000-20000
£18750 $30000 €27375 Untitled (58x48cm-23x19in) painted 1865. 19-Sep-3 Du Mouchelle, Detroit #2013/R est:20000-25000
£29839 $54903 €43565 Making a floral garland (63x49cm-25x19in) s.d.1880. 14-Jun-4 Waddingtons, Toronto #308/R est:40000-60000 (C.D 74000)

MEYER VON KAMPTZ, Edith (1884-1969) German
£867 $1560 €1300 Dancer (85x72cm-33x28in) s. 24-Apr-4 Dr Lehr, Berlin #290/R
Works on paper
£278 $464 €400 Man under sun (38x23cm-15x9in) pastel W/C over pencil. 24-Oct-3 Ketterer, Hamburg #970/R

MEYER, Adolph Campbell (1888-1918) British
£360 $655 €526 Retiring from work (39x29cm-15x11in) s. i.verso. 15-Jun-4 Bonhams, Leeds #118
Works on paper
£450 $842 €675 Acropolis, Athens (43x69cm-17x27in) s.i. W/C htd bodycol. 22-Jul-4 Dominic Winter, Swindon #70/R

MEYER, C (19/20th C) German
£2308 $3969 €3300 Oldenburger Lotsenschoner in front of fireboat Weser (62x92cm-24x36in) mono. painted on back of glass. 5-Dec-3 Bolland & Marotz, Bremen #604/R est:4700

MEYER, Carl Vilhelm (1870-1938) Danish
£504 $917 €736 Small girl with curly hair (51x47cm-20x19in) s.d.1912. 7-Feb-4 Rasmussen, Havnen #2067/R (D.KR 5500)

MEYER, Carl Walter (1965-) South African
£1207 $2016 €1762 Cottage with cyprus trees (49x59cm-19x23in) init.d.95. 20-Oct-3 Stephan Welz, Johannesburg #417/R est:5000-7000 (SA.R 14000)

MEYER, Christophe (1958-) ?
Works on paper
£267 $480 €400 Homme tronc en marche (210x120cm-83x47in) mixed media exhib. 24-Apr-4 Cornette de St.Cyr, Paris #653

MEYER, Claus (1856-1919) German
£503 $926 €750 Portrait of Werner v Bake (85x78cm-33x31in) s.d.1914 lit. 26-Mar-4 Karrenbauer, Konstanz #1748/R
£800 $1456 €1200 Playing dice (95x82cm-37x32in) s. 1-Jul-4 Van Ham, Cologne #1502/R
£1267 $2293 €1900 Reading at window (17x24cm-7x9in) s.d.1882 panel. 1-Apr-4 Van Ham, Cologne #1540/R est:1600
£1633 $2922 €2400 Figures in tavern (108x130cm-43x51in) s. 17-Mar-4 Neumeister, Munich #531/R est:1400

MEYER, Conrad (1618-1689) Swiss
£1267 $2027 €1850 Portrait of Zurich councillor (88x69cm-35x27in) s.i.d.1664. 16-Sep-3 Philippe Schuler, Zurich #3247/R est:2500-3000 (S.FR 2800)
£1554 $2735 €2300 Portrait of an elderly bearded gentleman, aged 46 (10x8cm-4x3in) s.i.d.1653 copper. 18-May-4 Sotheby's, Amsterdam #57/R est:1000-1500

MEYER, Edgar (1853-1925) Austrian
Works on paper
£638 $1173 €950 Rome (24x35cm-9x14in) s. W/C. 26-Mar-4 Ketterer, Hamburg #201/R

MEYER, Émile (19th C) French
£439 $786 €650 Composition aux raisins et grenades (64x54cm-25x21in) s. 10-May-4 Horta, Bruxelles #508

MEYER, Ernst (1796-1861) Danish
£336 $527 €491 By the well near a monastery in Italy (26x34cm-10x13in) study panel. 30-Aug-3 Rasmussen, Havnen #2074 (D.KR 3600)
£6944 $11319 €10000 Public letter writer (62x76cm-24x30in) s.i. 25-Sep-3 Dr Fritz Nagel, Stuttgart #1380/R est:20000
Works on paper
£415 $705 €606 Coastal landscape with Italian woman praying (22x17cm-9x7in) i.verso W/C. 10-Nov-3 Rasmussen, Vejle #6/R (D.KR 4500)

MEYER, Eugene (attrib) (1853-1907) Belgian
£1172 $2169 €1700 Trois victoires ailees aux fleurs (112x130cm-44x51in) s.d.1883 canvas on panel prov. 13-Jan-4 Vanderkindere, Brussels #85 est:800-1200

MEYER, Felicia (1913-) American
£430 $800 €628 Floral still life (60x50cm-24x20in) s. 5-Mar-4 Skinner, Boston #368/R

MEYER, Hans Rudolf (1913-) Swiss
£323 $585 €472 House with water wheel (78x110cm-31x43in) s.d.1969 board. 31-Mar-4 Zurichsee Auktionen, Erlenbach #70/R (S.FR 750)
£433 $775 €632 Winter landscape (91x81cm-36x32in) s.d. board. 22-Mar-4 Philippe Schuler, Zurich #6035 (S.FR 1000)

MEYER, Heiner (1953-) German
£1275 $2283 €1900 Reconstruction (60x50cm-24x20in) s. s.d.98/99 verso. 25-May-4 Dorotheum, Vienna #406/R est:2000-2200

MEYER, Hendrik de II (1737-1793) Dutch
£9091 $15636 €13000 Seascape (25x30cm-10x12in) panel prov. 8-Dec-3 Claude Aguttes, Neuilly #35/R est:12000-15000
Works on paper
£4138 $6910 €6000 Ferry by the church (18x23cm-7x9in) W/C. 11-Nov-3 Vendu Notarishuis, Rotterdam #144/R est:1000-1500
£30556 $55000 €44612 Thatched mill with shepherd and flock. Thatched house under snow (37x48cm-15x19in) s.d.1787 black chk pen brown ink bodycol pair. 22-Jan-4 Christie's, Rockefeller NY #131/R est:20000-30000

MEYER, Hendrik de II (attrib) (1737-1793) Dutch
£909 $1627 €1327 Coast with ships, animals and figures (58x82cm-23x32in) s. panel. 22-Mar-4 Philippe Schuler, Zurich #6169 (S.FR 2100)
£3600 $6588 €5256 Horse drawn cart, a rider and travellers on a track before a farmstead (40x52cm-16x20in) panel. 6-Jul-4 Bonhams, Knightsbridge #104/R est:3500-4500

MEYER, Herbert (1882-1960) American
£296 $550 €432 Still life with currants and plums (57x41cm-22x16in) s. 5-Mar-4 Skinner, Boston #381/R
£625 $1100 €938 Still life of summer flowers in a glass vase (61x51cm-24x20in) s. 21-May-4 North East Auctions, Portsmouth #658/R
Works on paper
£323 $600 €472 Hillside landscape (34x32cm-13x13in) s. pastel. 5-Mar-4 Skinner, Boston #451/R

MEYER, Jacob (1895-1971) Danish
£275 $500 €402 Interior scene with girl seen from behind (30x28cm-12x11in) s.d.1918. 7-Feb-4 Rasmussen, Havnen #2141 (D.KR 3000)

MEYER, Jan (1927-1995) Dutch
£350 $594 €500 Mediterranean fishing port (101x66cm-40x26in) s.d.1950. 24-Nov-3 Glerum, Amsterdam #96/R
£680 $1238 €1000 Harbour (75x100cm-30x39in) s.d.1953. 3-Feb-4 Christie's, Amsterdam #544 est:1000-1500

£699 $1189 €1000 Landscape in yellow (100x80cm-39x31in) s.d.8/60 s.i.d.verso. 25-Nov-3 Christie's, Amsterdam #47/R

MEYER, Jeremiah (1735-1789) German
Miniatures
£2973 $5500 €4341 Edward Gibbon (3x3cm-1x1in) oval. 12-Mar-4 Du Mouchelle, Detroit #2034/R est:1000-2000
£4500 $8100 €6570 Gentleman wearing a brown velvet coat (6cm-2in) gold frame oval exhib.lit. 22-Apr-4 Bonhams, New Bond Street #64/R est:1200-1800
£9500 $17100 €13870 King George III, in Staff Officer's uniform (3cm-1in circular) s.i.d.1767 enamel gilt metal frame exhib. 22-Apr-4 Bonhams, New Bond Street #41/R est:3000-5000

MEYER, Jeremiah (attrib) (1735-1789) German
Miniatures
£1500 $2445 €2190 Officer wearing his powdered hair en queue (4x3cm-2x1in) oval. 25-Sep-3 Mellors & Kirk, Nottingham #677/R est:1500-2000

MEYER, Johan (1885-1970) Dutch
£395 $714 €600 Autumn on the heather (41x61cm-16x24in) s. 19-Apr-4 Glerum, Amsterdam #219/R
£395 $726 €600 Birch trees in a summer landscape (26x37cm-10x15in) s. 28-Jun-4 Sotheby's, Amsterdam #141/R
£592 $1089 €900 Hay harvest (37x27cm-15x11in) s. 28-Jun-4 Sotheby's, Amsterdam #102/R
£867 $1586 €1300 Autumn morning at the Gooier canal of Laren (60x100cm-24x39in) s. 7-Jun-4 Glerum, Amsterdam #68/R

MEYER, Johan (attrib) (1885-1970) Dutch
£243 $396 €350 View of a winter landscape (27x52cm-11x20in) 29-Sep-3 Sotheby's, Amsterdam #276/R

MEYER, Johan Hendrik Louis (1809-1866) Dutch
£1810 $3077 €2643 Harbour at river mouth (35x58cm-14x23in) s. panel. 19-Nov-3 Fischer, Luzern #1095/R est:4000-4200 (S.FR 4000)
Prints
£294 $499 €420 Dansko (45x60cm-18x24in) col copperplate. 20-Nov-3 Van Ham, Cologne #1379

MEYER, Maurice de (1911-) Belgian
£467 $835 €700 Enfants jouant sur la plage (40x60cm-16x24in) s. 11-May-4 Vanderkindere, Brussels #158
£604 $1117 €900 View of beach (45x59cm-18x23in) s. 13-Mar-4 De Vuyst, Lokeren #109

MEYER, Rolf (1913-) Swiss
£524 $922 €765 Child's portrait - Sandra (110x54cm-43x21in) s.i.d.1958 verso prov. 22-May-4 Galerie Gloggner, Luzern #73/R (S.FR 1200)
£1310 $2306 €1913 Still life with flowers and pots (90x110cm-35x43in) s. prov. 22-May-4 Galerie Gloggner, Luzern #72/R est:3800-4500 (S.FR 3000)

MEYER, Rudolph Theodor (1605-1638) Swiss
Works on paper
£232 $425 €339 Old man seated before a chest of gold surrounded by soldiers (13x16cm-5x6in) pen black ink brown wash. 29-Jan-4 Swann Galleries, New York #289/R

MEYER, Sal (1877-1965) Dutch
£789 $1453 €1200 Schotse collie (40x31cm-16x12in) s. board. 28-Jun-4 Sotheby's, Amsterdam #209/R
£921 $1695 €1400 Houses in a landscape (57x71cm-22x28in) s. 28-Jun-4 Sotheby's, Amsterdam #212/R
£1250 $2300 €1900 Man with a top hat (38x25cm-15x10in) s. 28-Jun-4 Sotheby's, Amsterdam #210/R est:1500-2500
£1739 $2852 €2400 Still life with flowers (40x30cm-16x12in) s. 27-May-3 Sotheby's, Amsterdam #504/R est:2500-3500
£3667 $6747 €5500 Naakt met strik - nude with red bow (12x10cm-5x4in) s. painted c.1914 prov.lit. 9-Jun-4 Christie's, Amsterdam #3/R est:3000-5000

MEYER, Siri (1898-?) Swedish
Works on paper
£1015 $1827 €1482 Der Verbruckte Schwerpunkt (20x14cm-8x6in) s.d.22 W/C Indian ink exhib. 26-Apr-4 Bukowskis, Stockholm #151/R (S.KR 14000)

MEYER, Ton (1892-?) Dutch
£280 $476 €400 Mountain village in Spain (61x80cm-24x31in) s. 24-Nov-3 Glerum, Amsterdam #613/R
£315 $535 €450 Bridge over a river in a French town (50x70cm-20x28in) 24-Nov-3 Glerum, Amsterdam #610/R
£385 $654 €550 Menton (65x54cm-26x21in) s. linen. 24-Nov-3 Glerum, Amsterdam #616/R
£385 $654 €550 Fortress of Antibes (22x43cm-9x17in) 24-Nov-3 Glerum, Amsterdam #621/R
£490 $832 €700 Castle in Belgium, near Maastricht (80x100cm-31x39in) s. 24-Nov-3 Glerum, Amsterdam #612/R
£559 $951 €800 Moored barge in an Amsterdam canal (36x46cm-14x18in) s. panel. 24-Nov-3 Glerum, Amsterdam #625/R
£699 $1189 €1000 Small port in southern France (27x52cm-11x20in) canvas on panel. 24-Nov-3 Glerum, Amsterdam #622/R
£769 $1308 €1100 View of the Sarphatipark, Amsterdam, from the studio (80x70cm-31x28in) 24-Nov-3 Glerum, Amsterdam #611/R
£839 $1427 €1200 View of Canne, near Maastricht (70x80cm-28x31in) s. 24-Nov-3 Glerum, Amsterdam #609/R

MEYER-AMDEN, Otto (1885-1933) Swiss
Works on paper
£3478 $6365 €5078 Fabric pattern, study of Child at the Door (27x21cm-11x8in) i. i.verso pencil col crayon prov.exhib. 7-Jun-4 Christie's, Zurich #76/R est:10000-15000 (S.FR 8000)
£10917 $19541 €15939 Self portrait in room full of furniture in Wollishofen (27x20cm-11x8in) pencil ink W/C prov.exhib. 26-May-4 Sotheby's, Zurich #38/R est:25000-30000 (S.FR 25000)
£13575 $23484 €19820 Market scene (20x27cm-8x11in) ink W/C prov.exhib. 9-Dec-3 Sotheby's, Zurich #66/R est:30000-40000 (S.FR 30000)
£15837 $27398 €23122 Boy standing (24x15cm-9x6in) pencil paper on paper prov.lit. 9-Dec-3 Sotheby's, Zurich #56/R est:35000-45000 (S.FR 35000)

MEYER-BASEL, Carl Theodor (1860-1932) Swiss
£436 $811 €650 Bleaching the washing on rivershore in summer (24x32cm-9x13in) s. panel. 6-Mar-4 Arnold, Frankfurt #792/R
£905 $1538 €1321 Untersee (39x73cm-15x29in) s. i. verso exhib. 28-Nov-3 Zofingen, Switzerland #3081/R est:2500 (S.FR 2000)

MEYER-BERNBURG, Alfred (1872-?) German
£377 $588 €550 Stolen glance (85x71cm-33x28in) s.d.1904 board. 10-Apr-3 Weidler, Nurnberg #328/R

MEYER-EBERHARDT, Curt (1895-1977) German
£541 $930 €790 Snowy mountainous landscape with chamois (79x100cm-31x39in) s. 8-Dec-3 Philippe Schuler, Zurich #5870 (S.FR 1200)

MEYER-KASSEL, Hans (1872-1952) German
£4533 $8251 €6800 At the beach (52x70cm-20x28in) s. 1-Jul-4 Van Ham, Cologne #1493/R est:7200

MEYER-RUBRITIUS, Friedrich (1890-1950) Austrian
£524 $902 €750 Mountain landscape in late summer (36x53cm-14x21in) s. 4-Dec-3 Dorotheum, Graz #25/R

MEYER-WALDECK, Kunz (1859-1953) German
£927 $1687 €1400 Fishermen bringing in their nets (62x91cm-24x36in) s. 18-Jun-4 Bolland & Marotz, Bremen #690/R
£1528 $2597 €2200 Boys with boat (60x80cm-24x31in) s.i. 28-Oct-3 Dorotheum, Vienna #199/R est:2200-2600
£2568 $4519 €3800 Fishermen (60x90cm-24x35in) s. 22-May-4 Lempertz, Koln #1563/R est:2000

MEYERHEIM, F E (19th C) German
£994 $1800 €1451 Portrait of two girls and a dog (18x15cm-7x6in) s. 14-Apr-4 Dallas Auction Gallery, Dallas #36/R est:900-1500

MEYERHEIM, Franz Eduard (1838-1880) German
£28966 $48372 €42000 Sleeping Beauty (188x142cm-74x56in) s.d.1870 prov.exhib.lit. 15-Nov-3 Lempertz, Koln #1654/R est:20000-25000

MEYERHEIM, Friedrich Edouard (1808-1879) German
£2420 $3727 €3800 Winter pleasures (41x58cm-16x23in) s. 4-Sep-2 Schopman, Hamburg #31/R est:3500

MEYERHEIM, Hermann (1840-1880) German
£1445 $2268 €2110 Figures and houses by frozen river (59x85cm-23x33in) s. 30-Aug-3 Rasmussen, Havnen #2172/R est:10000-15000 (D.KR 15500)

MEYERHEIM, Paul Friedrich (1842-1915) German
£250 $418 €365 Studies of goats (27x24cm-11x9in) s. canvasboard. 7-Oct-3 Bonhams, Knightsbridge #213/R
£719 $1180 €1000 Hieronymous and the lion (85x67cm-33x26in) s.d. 4-Jun-3 Ketterer, Hamburg #75/R
£1736 $2743 €2500 Girl with goats (60x94cm-24x37in) s. lit. 19-Sep-3 Schloss Ahlden, Ahlden #1493/R est:2800
Works on paper
£315 $568 €460 Fairy story scene with animals and insects in poppy field (21x25cm-8x10in) s.d.1861 W/C. 26-Jan-4 Lilla Bukowskis, Stockholm #730 (S.KR 4200)
£347 $566 €500 Woodland (35x25cm-14x10in) s. W/C gouache. 26-Sep-3 Bolland & Marotz, Bremen #576/R
£2800 $5124 €4088 Large house with a blooming garden, a rider with a horse in the foreground (54x72cm-21x28in) s.d.9.8.1887 pencil W/C bodycol htd white. 6-Jul-4 Christie's, London #203/R est:3000-5000

MEYERHEIM, Paul Friedrich (attrib) (1842-1915) German
£867 $1577 €1300 Stable interior with a dead squirrel (60x49cm-24x19in) i. 1-Jul-4 Van Ham, Cologne #1503/R

MEYERHEIM, Wilhelm Alexander (1815-1882) German
£2552 $4261 €3700 Peasant woman winding wool with children and poultry (18x24cm-7x9in) s.d.1846 oval lit. 10-Jul-3 Allgauer, Kempten #2605/R est:3500

MEYERHOFF, Pedro Moreno (1951-) Spanish
£3514 $6500 €5130 Botiquin (80x69cm-31x27in) init.d.1988-89 wood panel prov. 12-Feb-4 Sotheby's, New York #332/R est:2000-3000
£4324 $8000 €6313 Afueras IV (150x120cm-59x47in) init.d.1988-89 wood panel. 12-Feb-4 Sotheby's, New York #333/R est:3000-5000
£14054 $26000 €20519 Gran Vista - Las Afueras X (140x170cm-55x67in) init.d.1991-92 s.i.d.verso wood panel prov. 12-Feb-4 Sotheby's, New York #337/R est:3000-5000

MEYERING, Albert (1645-1714) Dutch
£3200 $5760 €4672 Classical landscape with a mother and a child on a donkey (55x48cm-22x19in) s. 20-Apr-4 Sotheby's, Olympia #279/R est:2500-4000
£4500 $7470 €6570 Italianate river landscape with cowherd and shepherdess (64x72cm-25x28in) s. prov. 30-Sep-3 Sotheby's, London #329/R est:5000-7000

MEYERING, Albert (attrib) (1645-1714) Dutch
£1478 $2646 €2158 Landscape with waterway (23x33cm-9x13in) panel. 26-May-4 AB Stockholms Auktionsverk #2528/R est:25000-30000 (S.KR 20000)

MEYERN, Ellen von (19/20th C) New Zealander
£2888 $4708 €4216 Maori women and children cooking at a geothermal Hangi Pit (36x55cm-14x22in) s.d.1903 board. 23-Sep-3 Peter Webb, Auckland #24/R est:8000-12000 (NZ.D 8000)

MEYEROWITZ, Joel (1938-) American
Photographs
£1916 $3200 €2797 The Arch, St Louis (38x48cm-15x19in) s.verso num.8/75 chromogenic col print exec. c.1978-79 prov.lit. 17-Oct-3 Phillips, New York #263/R est:3000-5000
£2328 $4400 €3399 Porch series, Provincetown (49x38cm-19x15in) s.i.d. verso chromogenic print. 17-Feb-4 Swann Galleries, New York #104/R est:4000-6000

MEYEROWITZ, William (1887-1981) American
£435 $800 €635 Sambatian Horses (46x20cm-18x8in) s. board sold with etching. 10-Jun-4 Swann Galleries, New York #176/R
£642 $1200 €937 Three dancers (51x66cm-20x26in) s. 29-Feb-4 Grogan, Boston #96/R
£650 $1040 €949 Ceremonial horsemen (49x30cm-19x12in) s. canvas on board. 16-Sep-3 Rosebery Fine Art, London #593/R
£1173 $1900 €1701 Dancer (53x24cm-21x9in) s. board prov. 8-Aug-3 Barridorf, Portland #320/R est:900-1200
£2027 $3750 €2959 Still life with apples before a window with a view (76x91cm-30x36in) s. 10-Mar-4 Doyle, New York #38/R est:2000-3000
£3580 $5800 €5191 Artist, Gloucester harbor (51x62cm-20x24in) s. 8-Aug-3 Barridorf, Portland #188/R est:4000-6000
Works on paper
£252 $400 €368 At work (71x50cm-28x20in) s. mixed media oil board. 12-Sep-3 Skinner, Boston #378/R
£761 $1400 €1111 Houses with trees (36x56cm-14x22in) s. W/C. 10-Jun-4 Swann Galleries, New York #175/R

MEYERS, Isidore (1836-1917) Belgian
£280 $507 €420 Hiver en campine (12x22cm-5x9in) s. panel. 30-Mar-4 Campo & Campo, Antwerp #178
£608 $1149 €900 Sous-bois anime (33x54cm-13x21in) s. 17-Feb-4 Vanderkindere, Brussels #406
£867 $1569 €1300 Le moulin de Mariekerke (24x36cm-9x14in) s.verso. 30-Mar-4 Campo & Campo, Antwerp #176/R
£915 $1602 €1300 Village de campagne (42x62cm-17x24in) s. 16-Dec-3 Galerie Moderne, Brussels #755/R
£1316 $2421 €2000 A peasant woman passing a windmill on a sunny day (47x59cm-19x23in) s. 22-Jun-4 Christie's, Amsterdam #133/R est:2000-3000

MEYERSON, Vera (1903-?) Swedish
£24795 $42896 €36201 Composition (114x48cm-45x19in) s.d.25. 12-Dec-3 Kieselbach, Budapest #203/R (H.F 9500000)

MEYNART, Maurice (1894-1976) Belgian
£300 $537 €450 Paysage ensoleille (46x60cm 18x24in) s. 11-May-4 Vanderkindere, Brussels #585

MEYNER, Walter (19/20th C) American
£299 $500 €437 Figure along the coast (41x51cm-16x20in) s.d.06. 20-Jun-3 Freeman, Philadelphia #231/R

MEYNIER, Charles (1768-1832) French
£1479 $2588 €2100 Priam tue par Pyrrhus (32x41cm-13x16in) s. 19-Dec-3 Delvaux, Paris #116 est:1000-2000
Works on paper
£3020 $5617 €4500 Alexandre cedant Campaspe a Appelle (34x43cm-13x17in) s.d.1822 pen wash prov. 7-Mar-4 Livinec, Gaudcheau & Jezequel, Rennes #43

MEYRICK, Myra (fl.1886-1891) British
Works on paper
£500 $900 €730 Wooded landscape with pond and horse-drawn cart (51x33cm-20x13in) indis.sig.i. 20-Apr-4 Canterbury Auctions, UK #160

MEYS, Louis (1902-1995) Dutch
£433 $793 €650 Clearing up on a spring day (17x25cm-7x10in) s. canvas on panel. 7-Jun-4 Glerum, Amsterdam #79/R
£521 $823 €750 In the park (40x60cm-16x24in) s. 2-Sep-3 Christie's, Amsterdam #375
£1164 $1979 €1700 Portrait of a girl (48x58cm-19x23in) s. board. 5-Nov-3 Vendue Huis, Gravenhage #443/R est:900-1400
£1507 $2562 €2200 Boulevard (58x78cm-23x31in) s.d.56 board. 5-Nov-3 Vendue Huis, Gravenhage #442/R est:1200-1500

MEZA, Guillermo (1917-) Mexican
£1161 $1938 €1695 Nina con perro (43x33cm-17x13in) board prov. 17-Jun-3 Maynards, Vancouver #320 est:3000-5000 (C.D 2600)
Works on paper
£359 $600 €524 Nude. s.d.1980 pastel. 15-Nov-3 Harvey Clar, Oakland #1322

MEZEROVA, Juliana Winterova (1893-?) Czechoslovakian
£217 $400 €317 Lilacs (66x51cm-26x20in) prov. 23-Jun-4 Doyle, New York #5052/R

MEZIAT, Renato (1952-) Latin American
£6471 $11000 €9448 Still life with apples (75x110cm-30x43in) s. s.i.d.Mar 2003 verso. 19-Nov-3 Sotheby's, New York #180/R est:10000-15000

MEZZOLI, Olmedo (attrib) (20th C) Italian
£254 $475 €381 Origami hats (81x48cm-32x19in) s.d.62 masonite prov. 25-Jul-4 Bonhams & Butterfields, San Francisco #6125/R

MGUDLANDLU, Gladys (1925-1979) South African
£1817 $3252 €2653 Houses near a roadway (39x64cm-15x25in) canvas on board. 31-May-4 Stephan Welz, Johannesburg #553/R est:12000-15000 (SA.R 22000)
£1849 $3346 €2700 Anthrinums (25x15cm-10x6in) s.d.1960 board lit. 30-Mar-4 Stephan Welz, Johannesburg #538/R est:7000-10000 (SA.R 22000)
Works on paper
£3248 $5521 €4742 Two huts and a kraal (48x64cm-19x25in) s.d.1958 W/C gouache. 4-Nov-3 Stephan Welz, Johannesburg #684/R est:9000-12000 (SA.R 38000)
£4103 $6974 €5990 Five birds in a field (50x58cm-20x23in) s.d.1962 gouache. 4-Nov-3 Stephan Welz, Johannesburg #662/R est:9000-12000 (SA.R 48000)

MI WANZHONG (1570-1628) Chinese
Works on paper
£8494 $14185 €12401 Lin Fu with plum blossoms and crane (72x37cm-28x15in) ink. 26-Oct-3 Christie's, Hong Kong #445/R (HK.D 110000)

MICAELLES, Ruggero (1898-1976) Italian
£800 $1448 €1200 Garfagnana (47x55cm-19x22in) s.d.50 board. 2-Apr-4 Farsetti, Prato #410/R

MICALESCO, Sergio (1937-) Italian
£629 $1083 €900 Little bar (120x140cm-47x55in) s.d.1969 oil tempera. 3-Dec-3 Stadion, Trieste #1172/R
£699 $1203 €1000 Sacchetta (60x80cm-24x31in) s. 3-Dec-3 Stadion, Trieste #1069/R

MICCINI, Eugenio (20th C) Italian
Works on paper
£1200 $2172 €1800 Naif and funny (50x70cm-20x28in) s.d.1979 collage metal board exhib.lit. 2-Apr-4 Farsetti, Prato #58 est:1800-2200
£1259 $2140 €1800 Ex libris (70cm-28in circular) s.d.1992 verso collage cardboard exhib. 28-Nov-3 Farsetti, Prato #14/R est:1800-2200
£2174 $3565 €3000 Come on Europe ! (69x49cm-27x19in) s.d.1970 collage board. 30-May-3 Farsetti, Prato #435/R

MICEU, Giuseppe (1873-1908) Italian
£2133 $3819 €3200 Fishermen on the lake (95x59cm-37x23in) s. 12-May-4 Stadion, Trieste #640/R est:3500-4500

MICH, Jean T (1871-1919) Luxembourger
Sculpture
£1126 $2060 €1700 Chin-Fan Han Yang-Chin (42cm-17in) s.i. terracotta Cast f.Susse Freres. 7-Apr-4 Piasa, Paris #158 est:300-500

MICH, Jerry (20th C) Polish?
£285 $447 €413 Time, private move II (41x53cm-16x21in) s.d.93. 26-Aug-3 Lawson Menzies, Sydney #334/R (A.D 700)

MICHA, Maurice Jean (1890-1969) Belgian
£304 $575 €450 La pergola fleurie (55x40cm-22x16in) s. 17-Feb-4 Vanderkindere, Brussels #189
£514 $873 €750 Jeune femme a sa toilette (60x50cm-24x20in) s. 10-Nov-3 Horta, Bruxelles #418
£795 $1446 €1200 Nu a la fenetre (75x50cm-30x20in) s. 15-Jun-4 Galerie Moderne, Brussels #222/R
£933 $1671 €1400 Fontaine sur une place Italienne animee (70x60cm-28x24in) s. 11-May-4 Vanderkindere, Brussels #583

MICHAEL, Anne (20th C) British?
£250 $430 €365 Jazz man (40x30cm-16x12in) s. board. 3-Dec-3 John Ross, Belfast #196
£300 $516 €438 Study of a child (25x20cm-10x8in) s. board. 3-Dec-3 John Ross, Belfast #45

MICHAEL, Creighton (1949-) American
Sculpture
£838 $1500 €1223 Tor (188x15cm-74x6in) s.i.d.1989 verso prov. 16-May-4 Wright, Chicago #455/R est:900-1200

MICHAEL, Gregory (20th C) American
£424 $750 €619 Portrait of a lady, in a black evening gown (102x84cm-40x33in) s. 2-May-4 Bonhams & Butterfields, San Francisco #1071/R

MICHAEL, Lemon Hart (19th C) British?
Works on paper
£300 $561 €450 South coast cliffs, Guernsey (38x56cm-15x22in) s.d.1886 W/C. 22-Jul-4 Martel Maides, Guernsey #192

MICHAEL, Loui (1933-) Danish
£292 $496 €426 Imaginary scenery (135x112cm-53x44in) s.d.71-72 verso. 26-Nov-3 Kunsthallen, Copenhagen #185 (D.KR 3100)
£343 $641 €501 Composition (82x100cm-32x39in) s.d.1968 verso. 25-Feb-4 Kunsthallen, Copenhagen #95 (D.KR 3800)
£378 $677 €552 King and Birthe outside (122x100cm-48x39in) mono. s.d.1983-84 verso. 12-Jan-4 Rasmussen, Vejle #628/R (D.KR 4000)
£466 $839 €680 Looking at each other (100x122cm-39x48in) mono. panel. 24-Apr-4 Rasmussen, Havnen #4072/R (D.KR 5200)

MICHAEL, Max (1823-1891) German
£786 $1431 €1148 Mother playing with her child (49x36cm-19x14in) s.i.d.1856 prov. 16-Jun-4 Fischer, Luzern #1214/R (S.FR 1800)
£1700 $3145 €2482 In the forest (87x61cm-34x24in) s. 10-Feb-4 Bonhams, Knightsbridge #161/R est:1000-1500

MICHAELIS, Gerrit Jan (1775-1857) Dutch
£1067 $1931 €1600 Water behind farmstead (41x49cm-16x19in) s. 1-Apr-4 Van Ham, Cologne #1543/R est:2200
Works on paper
£2192 $3726 €3200 Wooded landscape near Haarlem, with windmill and figures (25x38cm-10x15in) s.i.verso black chk grey wash. 4-Nov-3 Sotheby's, Amsterdam #154/R est:2000-3000

MICHAELIS, Oskar (1872-?) German
£350 $594 €500 Nude on sofa (40x55cm-16x22in) s.i.d.1924 board. 22-Nov-3 Arnold, Frankfurt #591/R

MICHAHELLES, Ernesto (1893-1959) Italian
Sculpture
£1467 $2625 €2200 Futuristic portrait (25cm-10in) s. polished metal. 12-May-4 Stadion, Trieste #739/R est:500-700

MICHAILOW, Nikola (1876-1960) Bulgarian
£467 $859 €700 Portrait of a gentleman (100x90cm-39x35in) s.d.1936. 11-Jun-4 Wendl, Rudolstadt #4163/R

MICHALIK, Marian (1947-) Polish
£461 $839 €673 Still life with cloudy landscape (81x91cm-32x36in) s.d.1993. 20-Jun-4 Agra, Warsaw #30/R (P.Z 3200)

MICHALLON, Achille Etna (1796-1822) French
£8667 $15687 €13000 Le hetre (36x29cm-14x11in) i.verso exhib.lit. 30-Mar-4 Rossini, Paris #108/R est:1800-3000
£10560 $18269 €15418 Wooded landscape with figures (32x41cm-13x16in) s.d.1815 prov. 9-Dec-3 Sotheby's, Olympia #450/R est:4000-6000
£52000 $94120 €78000 Paysage d'Auvergne (35x48cm-14x19in) mono. oil paper on canvas lit. 30-Mar-4 Rossini, Paris #107/R est:5000-8000
£88816 $163421 €135000 Paysans romains au pied de la cascade de Tivoli (49x62cm-19x24in) s. lit. 23-Jun-4 Sotheby's, Paris #62/R est:30000-40000
Works on paper
£1156 $2070 €1700 Une route longant des murs, une foret a l'arriere plan (30x30cm-12x12in) black white chk prov. 18-Mar-4 Christie's, Paris #282/R est:1500-2000

MICHALOVSKI, Piotr (1801-1855) Polish
£69823 $115907 €101942 French troops on horseback (55x67cm-22x26in) painted c.1835. 15-Jun-3 Agra, Warsaw #2/R est:400000 (P.Z 435000)

MICHALOWSKI, Herman V (1849-1912) Russian
£475 $850 €694 Farm scene with turkeys (41x56cm-16x22in) s. 8-May-4 Susanin's, Chicago #6055/R
£559 $1000 €816 Farm scene with chicken and chicks (41x56cm-16x22in) s.d.1901. 8-May-4 Susanin's, Chicago #6054/R est:800-1200

MICHALS, Duane (1932-) American
Photographs
£1796 $3000 €2622 Rene Magritte (16x25cm-6x10in) s.num.VII/VII silver print. 21-Oct-3 Swann Galleries, New York #290/R est:2000-3000
£2222 $4200 €3244 Letter from my father (12x18cm-5x7in) s.i.d.1975 num.16/25 gelatin silver print. 17-Feb-4 Christie's, Rockefeller NY #154/R est:4000-6000
£4058 $6655 €5600 Rene Magritte (12x18cm-5x7in) s.i.d. verso lit. 30-May-3 Villa Grisebach, Berlin #1290/R est:2000-3000
£4192 $7000 €6120 Portrait of Andy Warhol (8x12cm-3x5in) s.i.d.1973 num.10/25 gelatin silver print 3 one frame prov.lit. 17-Oct-3 Phillips, New York #116/R est:8000-12000

MICHAU, Theobald (1676-1765) Flemish
£5986 $9937 €8500 Scene de dechargement de bateaux pres d'un rivage (40x57cm-16x22in) s.d.17. 10-Jun-3 Renaud, Paris #10/R est:15000-20000
£15646 $24878 €23000 Idylle champetre (29x35cm-11x14in) oak panel. 23-Mar-3 Mercier & Cie, Lille #142/R est:25000-28000
£18000 $31140 €26280 Village scene with boors playing skittles outside a tavern (34x49cm-13x19in) mono. prov. 11-Dec-3 Sotheby's, London #105/R est:20000-30000
£28000 $48440 €40880 River landscape with fishermen unloading and selling their catch (46x67cm-18x26in) s. panel. 11-Dec-3 Sotheby's, London #52/R est:30000-40000
£75000 $137250 €109500 Village landscape with peasants merrymaking outside an inn. River landscape with peasants unloading (28x39cm-11x15in) with sig. copper pair prov. 7-Jul-4 Christie's, London #36/R est:70000-100000

MICHAU, Theobald (attrib) (1676-1765) Flemish
£1150 $2070 €1679 Travellers fording a river (13x17cm-5x7in) fragment panel. 23-Apr-4 Christie's, Kensington #121/R est:800-1200

MICHAU, Theobald (circle) (1676-1765) Flemish
£11000 $20130 €16060 River landscape with a wagon and travellers. River landscape with traveller (65x77cm-26x30in) pair. 7-Jul-4 Bonhams, New Bond Street #69/R est:6000-8000

MICHAU, William (1931-1990) French
£352 $609 €500 Village mediterraneen (46x38cm-18x15in) s.d.82. 15-Dec-3 Marc Kohn, Paris #11/R
£1620 $2802 €2300 Self-portrait with palette (81x65cm-32x26in) s. 15-Dec-3 Marc Kohn, Paris #1/R est:1800-2500

MICHAUD, Jean Luc (1910-2004) French
£298 $542 €450 Marche a Besancon (116x81cm-46x32in) s. 19-Jun-4 Gerard, Besancon #89

MICHAUD, Yves (20th C) Haitian
£740 $1325 €1110 L'orchestre (40x30cm-16x12in) s. 17-May-4 Rogeon, Paris #134

MICHAUX, Henri (1899-1984) Belgian
£1476 $2613 €2200 Untitled (25x35cm-10x14in) mono. canvas on board. 28-Apr-4 Artcurial Briest, Paris #310 est:2500-3500
£1832 $3242 €2675 Sans titre (33x41cm-13x16in) mono.d.1983 panel prov. 27-Apr-4 AB Stockholms Auktionsverk #1230/R est:30000-35000 (S.KR 25000)
£2013 $3745 €3000 Sans titre (19x27cm-7x11in) mono. painted c.1980. 3-Mar-4 Artcurial Briest, Paris #503/R est:3500-4000
£2349 $4158 €3500 Untitled (41x27cm-16x11in) board. 28-Apr-4 Artcurial Briest, Paris #320 est:5000-6000
£3000 $5520 €4380 Untitled (46x33cm-18x13in) prov.exhib. 24-Jun-4 Sotheby's, Olympia #562/R est:3000-4000
£3020 $5618 €4500 Sans titre (14x22cm-6x9in) mono. cardboard painted c.1980. 3-Mar-4 Artcurial Briest, Paris #504 est:4000-5000
£3356 $6242 €5000 Sans titre (33x46cm-13x18in) cardboard painted c.1980. 3-Mar-4 Artcurial Briest, Paris #505 est:5000-6000
£3667 $6747 €5500 Untitled (38x57cm-15x22in) mono. acrylic W/C Arches paper prov.exhib. 9-Jun-4 Artcurial Briest, Paris #468/R est:6000-8000
£3846 $6615 €5500 Untitled (35x27cm-14x11in) init. canvas on card. 2-Dec-3 Sotheby's, Amsterdam #333/R est:5500-7500
£4027 $7128 €6000 Untitled (33x40cm-13x16in) mono. 28-Apr-4 Artcurial Briest, Paris #312 est:7000-8000
£4698 $8738 €7000 Sans titre (39x46cm-15x18in) canvas on canvas painted c.1980. 3-Mar-4 Artcurial Briest, Paris #498/R est:7000-8000
£5705 $10611 €8500 Sans titre (40x55cm-16x22in) painted c.1980. 3-Mar-4 Artcurial Briest, Paris #500/R est:7000-8000
£5743 $10108 €8500 Untitled (32x25cm-13x10in) mono. W/C gouache prov. 18-May-4 Tajan, Paris #10/R est:9000-10000
£8026 $14768 €12200 Composition (41x60cm-16x24in) Chinese ink prov. 27-Jun-4 Versailles Encheres #76/R est:1000-12000
Works on paper
£1200 $2184 €1800 Untitled (32x50cm-13x20in) s. ink acrylic exec.1975. 29-Jun-4 Cornette de St.Cyr, Paris #25/R est:3000
£1543 $2732 €2300 Untitled (58x44cm-23x17in) gouache. 28-Apr-4 Artcurial Briest, Paris #311 est:2500-3500
£1678 $3121 €2500 Sans titre (38x26cm-15x10in) gouache wax crayon exec.c.1975. 3-Mar-4 Artcurial Briest, Paris #501/R est:2500-3500
£1813 $3082 €2647 Pour trouver l'Orient (26x33cm-10x13in) mono. gouache prov. 5-Nov-3 AB Stockholms Auktionsverk #1158/R est:30000-40000 (S.KR 24000)
£2000 $3680 €2920 Untitled (20x14cm-8x6in) init. ballpoint pen prov. 24-Jun-4 Sotheby's, Olympia #561/R est:2000-3000
£2000 $3640 €3000 Untitled (50x33cm-20x13in) s. W/C. 29-Jun-4 Cornette de St.Cyr, Paris #28/R est:3000-4000
£2081 $3849 €3100 Mouvements XXXVII (30x23cm-12x9in) mono. Chinese ink exec.1949. 14-Mar-4 St-Germain-en-Laye Encheres #153/R est:2000
£2148 $3973 €3200 Mouvements III (30x23cm-12x9in) mono. Chinese ink. 14-Mar-4 St-Germain-en-Laye Encheres #156/R est:2000
£2198 $3890 €3209 Untitled (55x74cm-22x29in) init. Indian ink prov. 27-Apr-4 AB Stockholms Auktionsverk #1177/R est:50000-60000 (S.KR 30000)
£2448 $4161 €3500 Sans titre (39x29cm-15x11in) mono. W/C prov. 25-Nov-3 Tajan, Paris #38/R est:4000-5000
£2527 $4650 €3689 Figure composition (50x65cm-20x26in) mono. W/C Indian ink exhib.prov. 29-Mar-4 Rasmussen, Copenhagen #170/R est:30000 (D.KR 28000)
£2644 $4494 €3860 Composition (50x65cm-20x26in) mono. gouache prov. 5-Nov-3 AB Stockholms Auktionsverk #1084/R est:40000-50000 (S.KR 35000)
£2684 $4751 €4000 Untitled (37x30cm-15x12in) mono. gouache exec c.1967. 28-Apr-4 Artcurial Briest, Paris #308/R est:3000-4000
£3169 $5483 €4500 Mouvements (32x24cm-13x9in) mono. Chinese ink. 9-Dec-3 Artcurial Briest, Paris #494a/R est:2800-3200
£3267 $5945 €4900 Untitled (31x24cm-12x9in) ink prov. 29-Jun-4 Cornette de St.Cyr, Paris #27/R est:5000-7000
£3333 $6133 €5000 Composition abstraite (49x62cm-19x24in) s. W/C exec. c.1958 prov. 9-Jun-4 Piasa, Paris #172/R est:5000-7000
£3497 $5944 €5000 Untitled (55x74cm-22x29in) mono. blk ink. 25-Nov-3 Christie's, Amsterdam #243/R est:5000-7000
£3497 $5944 €5000 Untitled (50x65cm-20x26in) mono. blk ink. 25-Nov-3 Christie's, Amsterdam #244/R est:5000-7000
£3497 $6014 €5000 Composition (39x25cm-15x10in) s. Indian ink. 6-Dec-3 Renaud, Paris #198
£3667 $6600 €5500 Untitled (58x75cm-23x30in) s. ink prov. 24-Apr-4 Cornette de St.Cyr, Paris #654/R est:8000
£3691 $6792 €5500 Visage rouge a lunettes et long nez (50x32cm-20x13in) mono. gouache prov. 24-Mar-4 Binoche, Paris #108/R est:5000-6000
£3919 $6897 €5800 Untitled (44x62cm-17x24in) mono. ink Japan paper prov. 18-May-4 Tajan, Paris #62/R est:5000-6000
£3947 $7263 €5920 Composition (55x74cm-22x29in) mono. India ink Arches paper exec c.1962 prov. 9-Jun-4 Artcurial Briest, Paris #467/R est:6000-8000

£4333 $7887 €6500 Untitled (57x78cm-22x31in) s. i.verso Chinese ink. 29-Jun-4 Cornette de St.Cyr, Paris #23/R est:6000
£4667 $8353 €7000 Untitled (38x56cm-15x22in) mono. i.d. verso Indian ink W/C. 13-May-4 Neumeister, Munich #697/R est:7000-8000
£4895 $8322 €7000 Sans titre (50x65cm-20x26in) mono. Indian ink exec.c.1960-65. 25-Nov-3 Tajan, Paris #14/R est:5000-6000
£5128 $9077 €7487 Sans titre (82x68cm-32x27in) mono.d.1958 prov. 27-Apr-4 AB Stockholms Auktionsverk #1228/R est:60000-70000 (S.KR 70000)
£5333 $9600 €8000 Untitled (32x41cm-13x16in) mono. mixed media cardboard. 25-Apr-4 Versailles Encheres #103 est:8000-10000
£6993 $11678 €10000 Untitled (60x40cm-24x16in) mono. Chinese ink prov. 29-Jun-3 Versailles Encheres #91/R
£7333 $13200 €11000 Composition (40x61cm-16x24in) mono. Chinese ink prov. 25-Apr-4 Versailles Encheres #89 est:10000-12000
£8500 $14195 €12410 Untitled (68x104cm-27x41in) init. ink. 21-Oct-3 Sotheby's, London #399/R est:8000-12000
£8667 $15947 €13000 Composition (104x72cm-41x28in) s. ink. 11-Jun-4 Pierre Berge, Paris #89/R est:10000-12000
£9333 $16707 €14000 La fuite (67x105cm-26x41in) mono. Indian ink board prov.exhib. 14-May-4 Ketterer, Munich #289/R est:10000-12000
£13986 $24056 €20000 Untitled (36x27cm-14x11in) s. W/C exec.c.1946. 6-Dec-3 Renaud, Paris #197/R
£16783 $28867 €24000 Untitled, composition sur fond noir (18x27cm-7x11in) mono. pastel prov.exhib.lit. 5-Dec-3 Chochon-Barre & Allardi, Paris #131/R est:15000-18000
£18531 $31874 €26500 Untitled (65x148cm-26x58in) mono. Indian ink prov. 2-Dec-3 Calmels Cohen, Paris #69/R est:10000-12000
£24000 $42960 €36000 Paix dans les brisements. dr album. 15-May-4 Renaud, Paris #207/R

MICHAUX, John (1876-1956) Belgian
£313 $522 €450 Matin (31x41cm-12x16in) s. s.verso cardboard. 21-Oct-3 Campo & Campo, Antwerp #215
£355 $592 €500 Yachts at the river (54x63cm-21x25in) s. 20-Oct-3 Bernaerts, Antwerp #194/R
£662 $1205 €1000 Automne (54x59cm-21x23in) s. panel. 16-Jun-4 Hotel des Ventes Mosan, Brussels #236
£667 $1200 €1000 Moonlight (54x73cm-21x29in) s.d.verso. 26-Apr-4 Bernaerts, Antwerp #285/R
£1757 $3145 €2600 Au bord de la plage (29x40cm-11x16in) s. canvas on panel. 10-May-4 Horta, Bruxelles #468 est:800-1000
Works on paper
£408 $743 €600 On the boulevard (17x33cm-7x13in) s. W/C. 3-Feb-4 Christie's, Amsterdam #598

MICHEAL, David (20th C) American
£284 $500 €415 Abstract composition in yellow, white, brown and blue (198x137cm-78x54in) oil linen. 22-May-4 Selkirks, St. Louis #595/R

MICHEL, Charles (19th C) French/Belgian
£322 $596 €480 Lisiere de foret (25x33cm-10x13in) s. panel. 15-Mar-4 Horta, Bruxelles #417
£350 $584 €500 L'arriere pays de Nice (22x32cm-9x13in) s. cardboard. 13-Oct-3 Horta, Bruxelles #411

MICHEL, Ernest (1833-1902) French
£9868 $18158 €15000 Allegorie de la musique (320cm-126in circular) s.d.1868. 25-Jun-4 Rossini, Paris #76/R est:4500-6000

MICHEL, Geo (1885-?) French
£20645 $33032 €30142 Thai woman (195x113cm-77x44in) s. painted c.1935 exhib. 18-May-3 Sotheby's, Singapore #113/R est:25000-35000 (S.D 57600)

MICHEL, Georges (1763-1843) French
£1667 $3017 €2500 La halte de militaires au pied d'une forteresse (22x30cm-9x12in) panel. 30-Mar-4 Rossini, Paris #94/R est:2000-3000
£1676 $3000 €2447 Approaching storm (54x71cm-21x28in) 6-May-4 Doyle, New York #31/R est:3000-5000
£2818 $4931 €4000 Vue d'une plaine dans la region Parisienne (26x59cm-10x23in) exhib.lit. 18-Dec-3 Tajan, Paris #158/R est:4000-5000
£3333 $6033 €5000 Chemin tournant aux deux moulins (81x102cm-32x40in) lit. 30-Mar-4 Rossini, Paris #95/R est:4000-6000
£6667 $12000 €9734 Moulin dans un paysage (75x105cm-30x41in) oil paper. 22-Apr-4 Christie's, Rockefeller NY #111/R est:10000-15000
£6667 $12067 €10000 L'orage approche (47x68cm-19x27in) panel lit. 30-Mar-4 Rossini, Paris #93/R est:4000-6000
£7667 $13877 €11500 Les moulins sur la colline (25x38cm-10x15in) i.verso panel lit. 30-Mar-4 Rossini, Paris #96/R est:3000-5000
Works on paper
£400 $724 €600 Scene d'auberge. Sous-bois (27x43cm-11x17in) chl white chk double-sided. 30-Mar-4 Rossini, Paris #97/R
£1333 $2413 €2000 La clairiere (38x48cm-15x19in) init.verso chl exhib. 30-Mar-4 Rossini, Paris #98 est:800-1200

MICHEL, Georges (attrib) (1763-1843) French
£1678 $3087 €2500 Vue des environs de Paris (51x73cm-20x29in) paper on canvas. 24-Mar-4 Tajan, Paris #171 est:1000

MICHEL, Gustave Frederic (1851-1924) French
Sculpture
£2937 $4905 €4200 La Pensee (48cm-19in) s. bronze st.f.Susse lit. 25-Jun-3 Segre, Madrid #571/R est:1680
£3315 $6000 €4840 Sea nymph emerging from a wave (30x58x41cm-12x23x16in) cast sig. gold pat. bronze. 3-Apr-4 Neal Auction Company, New Orleans #284/R est:3000-5000
£52941 $90000 €77294 Dans le reve (211cm-83in) s. marble pair exhib. lit. 28-Oct-3 Christie's, Rockefeller NY #172/R

MICHEL, Louise (1830-1905) French
Works on paper
£1400 $2576 €2100 Curieux personnage, aux cheveux longs, de profil, marchant dans la foret (23x14cm-9x6in) s.i. chl. 9-Jun-4 Piasa, Paris #173/R est:1000-1500

MICHEL, Pierre (1924-) Swiss
£391 $716 €571 Vers les champs (60x100cm-24x39in) s. pavatex exhib. 5-Jun-4 Galerie du Rhone, Sion #370/R (S.FR 900)

MICHEL, Robert (1897-1983) German
Works on paper
£24000 $44160 €35040 Herr-As-Sesor-im-Bad (50x45cm-20x18in) s.i.d.1919-1920 pen India ink pencil W/C collage prov.exhib.lit. 24-Jun-4 Christie's, London #374/R est:10000-15000

MICHEL-HENRY (1928-) French
£724 $1332 €1100 La Seine a Paris (38x46cm-15x18in) s. 27-Jun-4 Feletin, Province #88

MICHEL-LEVY, Henri (1845-1914) French
£1733 $3155 €2600 Quais pres du Pont Neuf (60x73cm-24x29in) s. 29-Jun-4 Chenu & Scrive, Lyon #125/R est:2000-3000
£7292 $12177 €10500 Au cafe (24x26cm-9x10in) s. panel. 22-Oct-3 Ribeyre & Baron, Paris #22/R est:2500-3800

MICHELACCI, Luigi (attrib) (1879-1959) Italian
£317 $549 €450 Sunset on the Arno (27x37cm-11x15in) card. 9-Dec-3 Pandolfini, Florence #44

MICHELANGELO (after) (1475-1564) Italian
Sculpture
£4698 $8315 €7000 Lorenzo de Medici (92cm-36in) s.st.f.Barbedienne pat bronze. 29-Apr-4 Sotheby's, Paris #173/R est:8000-12000

MICHELENA, Arturo (1863-1898) Venezuelan
£8609 $15755 €13000 Jeux d'enfants (72x41cm-28x16in) s.i.d.1889 panel. 9-Apr-4 Claude Aguttes, Neuilly #22/R est:3000-5000
Works on paper
£703 $1125 €1026 Untitled (20x13cm-8x5in) ink. 21-Sep-3 Subastas Odalys, Caracas #63
£975 $1560 €1424 Untitled (19x28cm-7x11in) graphite. 21-Sep-3 Subastas Odalys, Caracas #47/R
£1198 $2000 €1749 Study (49x31cm-19x12in) Chinese ink. 13-Jul-3 Subastas Odalys, Caracas #34

MICHELET, Georges (1873-?) French
£709 $1184 €1000 Bord de mer en Orient (38x45cm-15x18in) s. canvas on cardboard. 19-Oct-3 Rabourdin & Choppin de Janvry, Paris #90

MICHELET, Georges (attrib) (1873-?) French
£1333 $2453 €2000 Les fumeurs a Damas (46x37cm-18x15in) s.i.d.1988 oil paper on canvas. 14-Jun-4 Gros & Delettrez, Paris #50/R est:2500-3500

MICHELET, Johan Fredrik (1905-1975) Norwegian
£402 $736 €587 Fruit and jug (93x115cm-37x45in) s. painted c.1953-54 exhib. 2-Feb-4 Blomqvist, Lysaker #1183/R (N.KR 5000)
£5873 $10512 €8575 Yellow nude's rhythms (115x70cm-45x28in) s.d.53 i.stretcher exhib.lit. 25-May-4 Grev Wedels Plass, Oslo #92/R est:50000-70000 (N.KR 72000)

MICHELETTI, Mario (1892-1975) Italian
£333 $613 €500 Numana (50x60cm-20x24in) s. i.verso. 14-Jun-4 Sant Agostino, Torino #201/R
£600 $1104 €900 London suburbs (24x34cm-9x13in) s. board. 8-Jun-4 Della Rocca, Turin #323/R
Works on paper
£280 $467 €400 SS.Quattro Cloister (20x29cm-8x11in) s. W/C. 26-Jun-3 Sant Agostino, Torino #132/R

MICHELEZ, Léon Auguste (1830-1895) French
£573 $883 €900 Cows grazing near trees (31x49cm-12x19in) s.d.1870. 4-Sep-2 Schopman, Hamburg #32/R

MICHELI, G Armando (20th C) American
£387 $700 €565 Roses and vase (64x56cm-25x22in) s. trompe l'oeil. 18-Apr-4 Jeffery Burchard, Florida #155/R
£884 $1600 €1291 San Gennero-Lucca (76x152cm-30x60in) s. by artist and by T L Macrini i.d.1933. 18-Apr-4 Jeffery Burchard, Florida #157/R
Works on paper
£442 $800 €645 Interior scene of the St Stanislaus Kostka Polish Church in Chicago (64x53cm-25x21in) W/C exec.c.1930. 18-Apr-4 Jeffery Burchard, Florida #156/R

MICHELIN, Jean (1623-1696) French
£4605 $8474 €7000 Couple de paysans attables (53x63cm-21x25in) indis.sig. 24-Jun-4 Christie's, Paris #31/R est:7000-10000

MICHELIN, Jean (attrib) (1623-1696) French
£144860 $228879 €210047 The Holy Family in stable surrounded by peasants, young girl has given basket of eggs (85x126cm-33x50in) mono. panel prov. 2-Sep-3 Rasmussen, Copenhagen #1592/R est:150000-200000 (D.KR 1550000)

MICHELIS, Alexander (1823-1868) German
£1329 $2259 €1900 Cattle in extensive pre Alpine landscape (60x87cm-24x34in) s.d.1854. 20-Nov-3 Van Ham, Cologne #1741/R est:1400

MICHELIS, Franz (19th C) German
£636 $1082 €910 Italian woman with a child and young shepherd boy (60x50cm-24x20in) s.d.1855. 28-Nov-3 Wendl, Rudolstadt #4091/R

MICHELL, Edward (20th C) Canadian
Works on paper
£180 $329 €263 Canadian entity (30x40cm-12x16in) s.i.d.1999 mixed media board. 1-Jun-4 Hodgins, Calgary #464/R (C.D 450)

MICHELOZZI, Corrado (1883-1965) Italian
£288 $472 €400 Vase of flowers (17x12cm-7x5in) init. board. 10-Jun-3 Pandolfini, Florence #274/R
£933 $1689 €1400 Vase of flowers (32x19cm-13x7in) s. board. 2-Apr-4 Farsetti, Prato #401/R

MICHELS, Theo (1908-1981) Dutch
£293 $525 €440 Orange background (110x90cm-43x35in) s. i.d.71 verso. 11-May-4 Vendu Notarishuis, Rotterdam #551/R

MICHELSON, Eric Gustavus (1884-1964) American
£1070 $2000 €1562 Allegory of peace (76x53cm-30x21in) s. board painted c.1924 exhib. 25-Feb-4 Doyle, New York #963/R est:3000-4000

MICHETTI, Francesco Paolo (1851-1929) Italian
£517 $926 €755 Sunny landscape (23x28cm-9x11in) s.d.XI 17 panel. 12-May-4 Dobiaschofsky, Bern #798/R (S.FR 1200)
£1409 $2523 €2100 Cross bearer (46x34cm-18x13in) tempera canvas on cardboard. 25-May-4 Finarte Semenzato, Milan #112/R est:2300-2500
£1600 $2512 €2320 Little shepherdess (48x52cm-19x20in) s. en grisaille. 28-Aug-3 Christie's, Kensington #360 est:600-800
£1972 $3411 €2800 Shepherds (12x9cm-5x4in) s. cardboard. 11-Dec-3 Christie's, Rome #141/R est:1800-2500
£2778 $5000 €4056 Washerwoman. Study of a tree (14x21cm-6x8in) s. oil on paper double-sided prov. 23-Apr-4 Sotheby's, New York #75/R est:5000-7000
£2826 $4635 €3900 Shepherdess with goat (58x38cm-23x15in) s.d. canvas on board. 29-May-3 Galleria Pace, Milan #86/R est:6000
£3087 $5526 €4600 Self-portrait (54x41cm-21x16in) s.d.1872 tempera card. 25-May-4 Finarte Semenzato, Milan #113/R est:5000-6000
£6376 $11413 €9500 Face of woman (52x33cm-20x13in) s. tempera pastel paper. 25-May-4 Finarte Semenzato, Milan #185/R est:10000-12000
£11268 $19493 €16000 Girls from Abruzzo (25x1cm-10x0in) s. 10-Dec-3 Sotheby's, Milan #51/R est:1000-15000
£12081 $21624 €18000 Study for 'The Vow' (49x81cm-19x32in) 25-May-4 Finarte Semenzato, Milan #183/R est:20000-22000
Works on paper
£633 $1165 €950 Shepherdess (15x5cm-6x2in) pastel pen W/C. 10-Jun-4 Christie's, Rome #44
£1611 $3012 €2400 Peasant scene (35x45cm-14x18in) pastel. 26-Feb-4 Cambi, Genoa #579/R est:2000-2500
£2483 $4445 €3700 Peasant woman from Abruzzo (31x47cm-12x19in) s. mixed media paper on canvas prov. 25-May-4 Finarte Semenzato, Milan #71/R est:4000-5000

MICHIE, Alastair (1921-) British
Works on paper
£250 $463 €365 Quarry at Creech (27x32cm-11x13in) s.d.1990 i.verso pencil grey wash. 13-Feb-4 Sworder & Son, Bishops Stortford #18/R

MICHIE, David (1928-) British
£244 $437 €356 Landscape in Languedoc (107x132cm-42x52in) s.d.1971 prov. 10-May-4 Joel, Victoria #259 (A.D 600)
£400 $728 €584 Still life of Sweet William in a jug (38x51cm-15x20in) s. 15-Jun-4 Bonhams, Knightsbridge #151/R
£500 $885 €730 Bouquet with Helenium (45x59cm-18x23in) s. board. 27-Apr-4 Bonhams, Knowle #127
£680 $1136 €993 Boon Valley (55x101cm-22x40in) s.d.66 prov. 16-Oct-3 Bonhams, Edinburgh #24
£1000 $1860 €1460 Rosebed, corner of the park (35x51cm-14x20in) s. prov. 4-Mar-4 Christie's, Kensington #245/R est:1000-1500
£1700 $3162 €2482 White pigeons (35x50cm-14x20in) s. 4-Mar-4 Christie's, Kensington #243/R est:1000-1500

MICHIE, James Coutts (1861-1919) British
£2600 $4836 €3796 Nocturne in blue and gold, Valparaiso (76x51cm-30x20in) after James Abbot McNeill Whistler. 4-Mar-4 Christie's, Kensington #158/R est:4000-6000
£4200 $6762 €6090 Gathering firewood (90x131cm-35x52in) s. 21-Aug-3 Bonhams, Edinburgh #1168 est:2500-4000

MICHIELI, Andrea dei (1542-1617) Italian
£166667 $303333 €250000 Dogaress Morosina Morosini Grimani (117x325cm-46x128in) lit. 4-Jul-4 Finarte, Venice #73/R est:140000-180000

MICHIELI, Andrea dei (attrib) (1542-1617) Italian
£2685 $4940 €4000 Christ raising the Youth of Naim (55x49cm-22x19in) prov. 24-Mar-4 Dorotheum, Vienna #330/R est:4000-5000

MICHIELS, Johann Franz (1823-1887) German
Photographs
£5676 $10159 €8400 Cologne Cathedral under construction (43x53cm-17x21in) salt paper lit. 8-May-4 Lempertz, Koln #28/R est:2000

MICHONZE, Gregoire (1902-1982) French
£326 $600 €476 Farm by the sea, Brittany (20x33cm-8x13in) s. prov. 25-Jun-4 Freeman, Philadelphia #314/R
£353 $650 €515 Paysage breton (33x46cm-13x18in) s.d.60 i.verso stretcher prov. 25-Jun-4 Freeman, Philadelphia #267/R
£410 $750 €599 Figures on the beach (13x45cm-5x18in) s.d.1957 masonite. 1-Feb-4 Ben-Ami, Tel Aviv #4654/R
£671 $1248 €1000 Famille en bord de mer (28x23cm-11x9in) s.d.64 panel. 2-Mar-4 Artcurial Briest, Paris #179
£772 $1443 €1150 Sans titre (8x20cm-3x8in) s. panel. 29-Feb-4 Versailles Encheres #167/R
£805 $1498 €1200 La charrette de foin (65x25cm-26x10in) s.d.61 oil paper on canvas. 2-Mar-4 Artcurial Briest, Paris #178
£1400 $2534 €2044 Tetes (25x65cm-10x26in) s.d.60 oil paper on canvas. 1-Apr-4 Christie's, Kensington #136/R est:800-1200
£2000 $3640 €3000 Conversation devant le village (13x26cm-5x10in) s.d.1944 wood. 5-Jul-4 Le Mouel, Paris #40/R est:2300-3000
Works on paper
£1800 $3258 €2628 Au finistere (38x46cm-15x18in) s.d.66 s.i.d.66 verso gouache. 1-Apr-4 Christie's, Kensington #134/R est:1500-2000

MICKELBORG, Finn (1932-) Danish
£493 $789 €715 Metaphysic - Nov.72 (80x98cm-31x39in) mono. 17-Sep-3 Kunsthallen, Copenhagen #122 (D.KR 5200)
£569 $910 €825 Composition (110x128cm-43x50in) s.verso. 17-Sep-3 Kunsthallen, Copenhagen #102 (D.KR 6000)

MIDDELEER, Joseph (1865-1939) Belgian
£2517 $4204 €3600 Pastorale (196x430cm-77x169in) s.d.1891. 13-Oct-3 Horta, Bruxelles #201/R est:3500-5500

MIDDELHOEK, Martinus Leonardus (1898-1986) Dutch
£343 $631 €501 Dutch canal (70x80cm-28x31in) s. 14-Jun-4 Waddingtons, Toronto #221/R (C.D 850)

MIDDELHOEK, Pieter (1930-) Dutch
£294 $491 €420 Still life with bouquet (50x70cm-20x28in) s. i. on stretcher. 30-Jun-3 Sotheby's, Amsterdam #451/R

MIDDENDORF, Helmut (1953-) German
£1208 $2054 €1764 Revolt (70x100cm-28x39in) s.d.1990 verso acrylic. 5-Nov-3 AB Stockholms Auktionsverk #1072/R est:15000-18000 (S.KR 16000)
£1223 $2250 €1786 Sun (98x68cm-39x27in) s.i.d.1988 acrylic paper. 8-Jun-4 Germann, Zurich #99/R est:3000-4000 (S.FR 2800)
£6748 $11000 €9852 Caligari (185x236cm-73x93in) s.i.d.1984/87 verso prov. 23-Sep-3 Christie's, Rockefeller NY #153/R est:7000-9000
£7263 $13000 €10604 City of the red lights I (220x349cm-87x137in) s.i.d.81 verso oil resin diptych prov.lit. 14-May-4 Phillips, New York #275/R est:12000-18000
£10000 $18400 €15000 Painter (230x180cm-91x71in) s.i.d.1984 acrylic. 12-Jun-4 Villa Grisebach, Berlin #428/R est:5000-7000
Works on paper
£417 $679 €600 Untitled (100x71cm-39x28in) s.d.1990 gouache. 27-Sep-3 Dr Fritz Nagel, Stuttgart #9290/R
£486 $812 €700 Study for print (100x70cm-39x28in) s.i. W/C gouache over lithograph. 24-Oct-3 Ketterer, Hamburg #972/R
£867 $1586 €1300 Untitled (40x30cm-16x12in) s.i.d.82 pastel chk Indian ink W/C pencil. 4-Jun-4 Lempertz, Koln #308/R
£1250 $2088 €1800 Couple (700x70cm-276x28in) s.d.1985 mixed media. 21-Oct-3 Campo, Vlaamse Kaai #497 est:2000-2400
£1415 $2292 €2066 City head (62x87cm-24x34in) mono.i.d.1979 gouache prov. 24-May-3 Burkhard, Luzern #67/R est:1600-2000 (S.FR 3000)
£1810 $3077 €2643 Star (61x87cm-24x34in) s.i.d.80 gouache oil chk prov. 25-Nov-3 Germann, Zurich #91/R est:3500-4500 (S.FR 4000)

MIDDLEDITCH, Edward (1923-1987) British
£2000 $3180 €2920 Trafalgar Square (69x61cm-27x24in) board prov. 10-Sep-3 Sotheby's, Olympia #202/R est:2000-3000
£4500 $8235 €6570 Flower composition (127x101cm-50x40in) painted c.1958-9. 2-Jun-4 Sotheby's, London #83/R est:5000-7000

MIDDLETON, C (?) British
£860 $1436 €1256 Industrial landscape (56x119cm-22x47in) s.i.verso board. 8-Oct-3 Andrew Hartley, Ilkley #1129

MIDDLETON, Colin (1910-1983) British
£2100 $3486 €3066 Caddicks Road, Bangor (15x15cm-6x6in) mono. board. 1-Oct-3 John Ross, Belfast #22 est:2500-3000
£2958 $5117 €4200 Landscape (18x16cm-7x6in) mono. board. 10-Dec-3 Bonhams & James Adam, Dublin #83/R est:3000-4000
£3500 $6510 €5110 Iris, Achill (20x20cm-8x8in) mono.d.1969 verso board. 3-Mar-4 John Ross, Belfast #77 est:1500-1800
£3550 $6568 €5183 Industrial landscape (61x122cm-24x48in) i.verso board. 11-Mar-4 Morphets, Harrogate #308/R est:3000-4000
£4196 $7133 €6000 The reader (41x25cm-16x10in) mono. panel. 18-Nov-3 Whyte's, Dublin #66/R est:8000-10000
£4500 $7740 €6570 Belmullet Green (30x30cm-12x12in) mono. d.December 1968 verso. 3-Dec-3 John Ross, Belfast #150 est:5000-6000
£4800 $8688 €7200 Boa Island, Loch Erne (30x30cm-12x12in) s. board prov. 31-Mar-4 James Adam, Dublin #128/R est:3000-4000
£6800 $12308 €10200 Meditation (60x49cm-24x19in) mono. i.verso. 30-Mar-4 De Veres Art Auctions, Dublin #86/R est:8000-10000
£7042 $12183 €10000 Houses and trees in a surreal landscape (44x54cm-17x21in) s.d.1940. 10-Dec-3 Bonhams & James Adam, Dublin #130/R est:10000-15000
£7500 $13425 €10950 View from Ballymote house (28x38cm-11x15in) s. s.i.d.1951 verso prov. 14-May-4 Christie's, Kensington #379/R est:4000-6000

£8451 $13521 €12000 Miss Kitt (64x76cm-25x30in) mono. mixed media board. 16-Sep-3 Whyte's, Dublin #40/R est:15000-20000
£9060 $16037 €13500 Seated woman in blue (61x61cm-24x24in) mono. board. 27-Apr-4 Whyte's, Dublin #13/R est:12000-15000
£9732 $17419 €14500 Louth Coast I (60x60cm-24x24in) mono. mono.i.d.70 verso board exhib. 26-May-4 James Adam, Dublin #74/R est:6000-10000
£10738 $19221 €16000 Point of Phenick (50x75cm-20x30in) mono. s.i.d.June 1951 verso. 26-May-4 James Adam, Dublin #60/R est:10000-15000
£11409 $20423 €17000 Sycamores, Ballgrawley (46x61cm-18x24in) s. s.i.d.1953 prov. 26-May-4 James Adam, Dublin #72/R est:10000-15000
£11824 $22348 €17500 Seven creatures (122x122cm-48x48in) s.i.d.1970 s.verso masonite board prov.lit. 17-Feb-4 Whyte's, Dublin #92/R est:10000-15000
£13028 $22539 €18500 Farm buildings, Ballyrashane (30x41cm-12x16in) mono. s.i.d.1956 verso. 10-Dec-3 Bonhams & James Adam, Dublin #160/R est:12000-15000
£15436 $27631 €23000 Linnet (60x60cm-24x24in) s. s.i.verso prov.exhib. 26-May-4 James Adam, Dublin #77/R est:10000-15000
£16000 $26240 €23360 Sea road (20x30cm-8x12in) s.d.1951 verso. 4-Jun-3 John Ross, Belfast #110a
£16000 $28640 €23360 The dark lady (61x51cm-24x20in) s.d.1941 paper on board prov.exhib. 13-May-4 Sotheby's, London #97/R est:10000-15000
£16901 $27042 €24000 Glen Lough (61x61cm-24x24in) s. s.i.d.1976 verso board prov.exhib. 16-Sep-3 Whyte's, Dublin #60/R est:25000-35000
£21396 $36374 €31238 Oies blanches (30x40cm-12x16in) s. i.verso prov.exhib.lit. 27-Nov-3 Heffel, Vancouver #4/R est:55000-65000 (C.D 47500)
£22000 $39380 €32120 August landscape, Ballygrainey (51x76cm-20x30in) s. s.i.d.1953 verso. 14-May-4 Christie's, London #174/R est:15000-20000
£30872 $55262 €46000 Outward bound (45x60cm-18x24in) s. s.i.d.March 1958 prov.exhib. 26-May-4 James Adam, Dublin #121/R est:30000-40000
Works on paper
£336 $601 €500 Female nude study (25x20cm-10x8in) s.d.2 November 1947 pen ink prov. 26-May-4 James Adam, Dublin #183/R
£500 $895 €730 Figure with raised arms (7x5cm-3x2in) mono.d.Dec.22.42 pencil. 14-May-4 Christie's, Kensington #426/R
£550 $985 €803 Landscape with buildings (8x9cm-3x4in) mono.d.Dec.18.42 pencil. 14-May-4 Christie's, Kensington #425/R
£650 $1209 €949 Bird (28x20cm-11x8in) s. pen ink. 3-Mar-4 John Ross, Belfast #136
£750 $1395 €1095 Western Sky I (7x7cm-3x3in) mono. W/C. 3-Mar-4 John Ross, Belfast #21
£850 $1522 €1241 Madonna and Child (10x9cm-4x4in) mono.d.Dec.22.42 pencil. 14-May-4 Christie's, Kensington #423/R
£872 $1544 €1300 Abstract form (24x17cm-9x7in) s.d.1967 ink wash. 27-Apr-4 Whyte's, Dublin #12/R
£900 $1611 €1314 Madonna (10x8cm-4x3in) mono.d.Dec.22.42 pencil. 14-May-4 Christie's, Kensington #424/R
£950 $1767 €1387 Sunburst (15x15cm-6x6in) mono.d.1983 W/C. 3-Mar-4 John Ross, Belfast #170
£1100 $1804 €1606 Female study (22x12cm-9x5in) mono. pencil. 4-Jun-3 John Ross, Belfast #80
£1622 $3065 €2400 Tambourine dancer (10x13cm-4x5in) mono. black crayon sold with two others prov. 17-Feb-4 Whyte's, Dublin #27/R est:1800-2400
£1818 $3091 €2600 Nude study (38x27cm-15x11in) s.d.1959 W/C crayon. 18-Nov-3 Whyte's, Dublin #153/R est:1500-2000
£2000 $3660 €2920 Four heads (25x20cm-10x8in) s. mixed media. 2-Jun-4 John Ross, Belfast #14 est:2000-2500
£4000 $7440 €5840 Cage (15x15cm-6x6in) mono. mixed media. 3-Mar-4 John Ross, Belfast #156 est:1400-1600
£4189 $7918 €6200 Mayo (15x15cm-6x6in) studio st.verso gouache on card prov. 17-Feb-4 Whyte's, Dublin #88/R est:3000-4000

MIDDLETON, James Godsell (fl.1826-1872) British
£340 $612 €496 Mrs Ramsden (27x22cm-11x9in) s.d.1843 verso board. 23-Apr-4 Charterhouse, Sherborne #670/R
£58000 $103820 €84680 Portrait of Charles William Stewart, 3rd Marquis of Londonderry (289x194cm-114x76in) s.i.d.1855 prov. 13-May-4 Sotheby's, London #52/R est:15000-20000

MIDDLETON, Janet (1922-) Canadian
Works on paper
£271 $453 €396 Peyto Lake (36x50cm-14x20in) s.i.d.1965 W/C. 17-Nov-3 Hodgins, Calgary #411/R (C.D 600)

MIDDLETON, John (1828-1856) British
£2517 $4280 €3600 Figures on bicycle. Two women (91x61cm-36x24in) s.d.1966 board pair. 18-Nov-3 Whyte's, Dublin #64/R est:4000-5000
Works on paper
£2800 $5124 €4088 Timber yard (32x46cm-13x18in) s.d.1847 pencil W/C prov.exhib. 3-Jun-4 Christie's, London #117/R est:3000-5000
£3200 $5824 €4672 Pont Neath, Vaughan (34x50cm-13x20in) i. W/C over pencil htd bodycol prov. 1-Jul-4 Sotheby's, London #218/R est:3000-5000
£4500 $7650 €6570 High rocks, Tonbridge (30x41cm-12x16in) pencil W/C htd white. 20-Nov-3 Christie's, London #63/R est:5000-8000

MIDDLETON, Max (1922-) Australian
£496 $903 €724 Still life, coffee pot, turnips, parsnips and cauliflower (51x61cm-20x24in) s. 16-Jun-4 Deutscher-Menzies, Melbourne #561/R est:1000-1500 (A.D 1300)
£526 $847 €768 Still life with rhododendrons (49x60cm-19x24in) s.d.46. 13-Oct-3 Joel, Victoria #267 est:1000-1500 (A.D 1300)
£526 $847 €768 On the road to Tallangatta (33x39cm-13x15in) s.d.45 canvas on board. 13-Oct-3 Joel, Victoria #387 est:900-1200 (A.D 1300)
£584 $1068 €876 Ploughing. board. 3-Jun-4 Joel, Victoria #242 (A.D 1500)
£674 $1240 €984 Beach reflections (30x46cm-12x18in) s. board. 28-Jun-4 Australian Art Auctions, Sydney #114 (A.D 1800)
£1162 $1940 €1743 Nude at the water's edge (35x50cm-14x20in) s. board. 27-Oct-3 Goodman, Sydney #166/R (A.D 2800)

MIDDLETON, Sam (1927-) American
£1377 $2258 €1900 Amsterdam (95x63cm-37x25in) s. oil paper collage board prov. 27-May-3 Sotheby's, Amsterdam #561/R est:2000-3000
Works on paper
£280 $512 €420 Fallen feathers (44x61cm-17x24in) s.d.62 collage prov. 7-Jun-4 Glerum, Amsterdam #234/R

MIDELFART, Willi (1904-1975) Norwegian
£489 $876 €714 Landscape from Holmsbu (46x55cm-18x22in) s.d.49 s.i.d.1949 verso panel. 25-May-4 Grev Wedels Plass, Oslo #86/R (N.KR 6000)
£500 $836 €730 Orange, South of France (33x41cm-13x16in) s. panel. 17-Nov-3 Blomqvist, Lysaker #1196 (N.KR 6000)
£783 $1354 €1143 Romantic couple in Venice (73x92cm-29x36in) s. panel. 13-Dec-3 Blomqvist, Lysaker #1239/R (N.KR 9000)

MIDGLEY, Waldo Park (1888-1986) American
£235 $425 €343 Flower still life, seascape (56x61cm-22x24in) 2-Apr-4 Douglas, South Deerfield #11
Works on paper
£252 $450 €368 Tugboats on the East River (46x58cm-18x23in) s.d.69 W/C prov.exhib. 14-May-4 Skinner, Boston #278/R
£280 $500 €409 Tiger at rest (25x34cm-10x13in) s.d.69 W/C prov.exhib. 14-May-4 Skinner, Boston #216/R

MIDIKURIA, Les (1943-) Australian
Works on paper
£863 $1544 €1260 Rainbow Serpent (56x147cm-22x58in) natural earth pigments bark exec 1992 prov. 25-May-4 Lawson Menzies, Sydney #293/R (A.D 2200)

MIDJAW, Midjaw (c.1897-1985) Australian
Works on paper
£1055 $1972 €1583 Mimih figure (89x23cm-35x9in) bears name.verso earth pigments eucalyptus bark exec.c.1970 prov. 26-Jul-4 Sotheby's, Melbourne #391/R (A.D 2700)
£1250 $2338 €1875 Freshwater turtles (88x35cm-35x14in) i.verso earth pigments eucalyptus bark exec.c.1970 prov. 26-Jul-4 Sotheby's, Melbourne #389/R est:4000-6000 (A.D 3200)
£2344 $4383 €3516 Male and female Mimihs (66x38cm-26x15in) earth pigments eucalyptus bark exec.c.1959 prov. 26-Jul-4 Sotheby's, Melbourne #33/R est:6000-8000 (A.D 6000)

MIDWOOD, William Henry (fl.1867-1871) British
£5000 $9200 €7300 Planning the future (69x91cm-27x36in) bears sig.d.1875. 26-Mar-4 Sotheby's, London #64/R est:5000-7000
£8000 $14720 €11680 Sailor's tune (35x47cm-14x19in) s.d.1870 panel. 11-Jun-4 Christie's, London #181/R est:4000-6000

MIDY, Arthur (1887-1944) French
£377 $600 €550 Narrow European village street with hill in background (53x46cm-21x18in) s. plywood. 10-Sep-3 Alderfer's, Hatfield #297

MIECKLITZ, Franz (1852-?) German
Works on paper
£286 $511 €420 Japanese Palace in Dresden (24x42cm-9x17in) s. d.1852 gouache. 20-Mar-4 Bergmann, Erlangen #1175
£563 $901 €800 Japanese Palace, Dresden (24x42cm-9x17in) s.d.August 1852 gouache. 19-Sep-3 Sigalas, Stuttgart #401/R

MIEDUCH, Dan (1947-) American
£1061 $1900 €1549 Two cowboys on horseback in a snowy landscape (30x41cm-12x16in) s.d.1988 board. 20-Mar-4 Selkirks, St. Louis #166 est:4000-6000
£4813 $9000 €7027 Moonlight express (61x91cm-24x36in) s. board. 24-Jul-4 Coeur d'Alene, Hayden #179/R est:12000-18000
£9412 $16000 €13742 Weapons and warpaint (91x122cm-36x48in) board. 1-Nov-3 Altermann Galleries, Santa Fe #30

MIEG, Peter (1906-1990) Swiss
Works on paper
£413 $756 €603 The charm of flowers (83x59cm-33x23in) s.d.1970 W/C. 4-Jun-4 Zofingen, Switzerland #2884 (S.FR 950)

MIEGHEM, Eugène van (1875-1930) Belgian
£2953 $5463 €4400 Three children (29x25cm-11x10in) s. oil paper. 13-Mar-4 De Vuyst, Lokeren #543/R est:1800-2000
£4698 $8691 €7000 Marieke on Saint-Anna beach (30x48cm-12x19in) s. board. 13-Mar-4 De Vuyst, Lokeren #455/R est:6000-8000
£5705 $10554 €8500 Harbour view (47x71cm-19x28in) s. 13-Mar-4 De Vuyst, Lokeren #451/R est:5000-6000
£10067 $18624 €15000 Two brothers (32x46cm-13x18in) s. s.i.verso. 13-Mar-4 De Vuyst, Lokeren #450/R est:10000-12000
£10738 $19866 €16000 Portrait of a woman (24x33cm-9x13in) s. oil on paper. 15-Mar-4 Sotheby's, Amsterdam #216/R est:800-1200
£26389 $44069 €38000 Old men (56x70cm-22x28in) s.d.1926 cardboard lit. 21-Oct-3 Campo & Campo, Antwerp #331/R est:30000-40000
£27778 $46389 €40000 Devant la rade d'Anvers (39x52cm-15x20in) s. lit. 21-Oct-3 Campo & Campo, Antwerp #330/R est:32500-35000
Prints
£3333 $6033 €5000 La cale seche (28x33cm-11x13in) s. monotype. 30-Mar-4 Campo, Vlaamse Kaai #205/R est:5000-6000
£5369 $9503 €8000 Dockers devant la cale seche (42x32cm-17x13in) s. monotype. 27-Apr-4 Campo, Vlaamse Kaai #630/R est:7000-8000
£6250 $10438 €9000 Docker (42x32cm-17x13in) s. monotype. 21-Oct-3 Campo, Vlaamse Kaai #598/R est:5000-6000
Works on paper
£298 $542 €450 Elegantes (27x19cm-11x7in) mono. W/C. 15-Jun-4 Galerie Moderne, Brussels #207
£300 $543 €450 Homme au chapeau boule (18x13cm-7x5in) mono. blue chk. 30-Mar-4 Campo, Vlaamse Kaai #207
£355 $592 €500 Beach view with tourists (14x28cm-6x11in) mono. pencil. 20-Oct-3 Bernaerts, Antwerp #187

£400	$724	€600	Couturiere (33x25cm-13x10in) s. chl. 30-Mar-4 Campo, Vlaamse Kaai #203
£436	$772	€650	Scene de port (6x12cm-2x5in) mono. black chk. 27-Apr-4 Campo & Campo, Antwerp #248/R
£533	$960	€800	Soldiers (19x35cm-7x14in) mono. chl col chk cardboard. 26-Apr-4 Bernaerts, Antwerp #323/R
£533	$960	€800	Nude in an interior (36x25cm-14x10in) s. pencil red chk. 26-Apr-4 Bernaerts, Antwerp #427/R
£563	$975	€800	Travailleuse portuaire devant le port (27x21cm-11x8in) mono. ink. 9-Dec-3 Campo, Vlaamse Kaai #468
£570	$1010	€850	Couple en promenade (10x12cm-4x5in) mono. black chk. 27-Apr-4 Campo & Campo, Antwerp #249/R
£600	$1086	€900	Deux femmes (31x24cm-12x9in) s. chl. 30-Mar-4 Campo, Vlaamse Kaai #204
£604	$1105	€900	Couple (21x28cm-8x11in) mono. chl. 8-Jul-4 Campo, Vlaamse Kaai #275
£671	$1188	€1000	Deux dames causant (12x18cm-5x7in) sanguine. 27-Apr-4 Campo & Campo, Antwerp #246/R
£671	$1188	€1000	Dame en promenade (12x18cm-5x7in) sanguine. 27-Apr-4 Campo & Campo, Antwerp #247/R
£704	$1218	€1000	Femme devant la ville (22x17cm-9x7in) mono. chl. 9-Dec-3 Campo, Vlaamse Kaai #469
£805	$1474	€1200	Deux jeunes femmes (25x35cm-10x14in) mono. sanguine. 8-Jul-4 Campo, Vlaamse Kaai #274/R
£972	$1624	€1400	A l'attaque (27x35cm-11x14in) mono. dr exhib. 21-Oct-3 Campo, Vlaamse Kaai #599/R
£1007	$1782	€1500	Immigrants (15x9cm-6x4in) mono. chl. 27-Apr-4 Campo, Vlaamse Kaai #631
£1064	$1777	€1500	Standing nude (34x24cm-13x9in) s. 20-Oct-3 Bernaerts, Antwerp #189 est:1500-1750
£1111	$1856	€1600	Porteur de journaux (20x16cm-8x6in) mono. chl. 21-Oct-3 Campo & Campo, Antwerp #332/R est:1200-1250
£1342	$2376	€2000	Couple sur un banc dans le parc (26x17cm-10x7in) mono. wash. 27-Apr-4 Campo & Campo, Antwerp #251/R est:2000-2500
£1467	$2655	€2200	Docker (16x14cm-6x6in) mono.d.1898 pastel. 30-Mar-4 Campo, Vlaamse Kaai #206/R est:1800-2400
£1690	$2924	€2400	La servante (21x13cm-8x5in) mono. chl. 9-Dec-3 Campo, Vlaamse Kaai #470/R est:1400-1800
£2041	$3653	€3000	Vue d'un village. Etude (31x17cm-12x7in) pastel sanguine double-sided. 22-Mar-4 Amberes, Antwerp #263
£2148	$3930	€3200	Chat endormi. Soldats marchant (34x26cm-13x10in) s. mixed media double-sided. 8-Jul-4 Campo, Vlaamse Kaai #276 est:2000-2300
£2685	$4966	€4000	Woman with two donkeys on the beach (36x46cm-14x18in) s. pastel black chalk. 13-Mar-4 De Vuyst, Lokeren #542/R est:2000-2800
£2917	$4871	€4200	Joueur d'orgue (33x25cm-13x10in) s. col chk chl. 21-Oct-3 Campo & Campo, Antwerp #334/R est:2500-3500
£10067	$17819	€15000	Emigrants juifs en attente (18x42cm-7x17in) s. pastel. 27-Apr-4 Campo, Vlaamse Kaai #628/R est:11000-14500
£10563	$18275	€15000	Les gamins des bassins (28x26cm-11x10in) s. mixed media. 9-Dec-3 Campo, Vlaamse Kaai #466/R est:9000-11000
£11268	$19493	€16000	Enfants des bassins (42x31cm-17x12in) s. mixed media. 9-Dec-3 Campo, Vlaamse Kaai #465/R est:9000-11000

MIEHE, Walter (1883-?) German

£417	$679	€600	Street musician receiving donation (35x29cm-14x11in) s.d.23 board. 26-Sep-3 Bolland & Marotz, Bremen #670

MIEL, Jan (1599-1663) Flemish

£20690	$34552	€30000	Roman carnival (58x73cm-23x29in) 12-Nov-3 Sotheby's, Milan #111/R est:30000-40000

MIEL, Jan (attrib) (1599-1663) Flemish

£19580	$32699	€28000	Paysage anime (79x97cm-31x38in) 25-Jun-3 Digard, Paris #34/R est:7000-9000

MIEL, Jan (circle) (1599-1663) Flemish

£7000	$12600	€10220	Riders and elegant women drinking outside an inn (80x82cm-31x32in) prov. 20-Apr-4 Sotheby's, Olympia #286/R est:6000-8000

MIEL, Jan and SALUCCI, Alessandro (17th C) Flemish/Italian

£106667	$190933	€160000	View of harbour with travellers (144x220cm-57x87in) 12-May-4 Finarte Semenzato, Milan #56/R est:150000-200000

MIELDS, Rune (1935-) German

£802	$1299	€1171	Untiteld (140x80cm-55x31in) s.d.10/69 verso acrylic. 24-May-3 Burkhard, Luzern #160/R (S.FR 1700)
£2254	$3899	€3200	Nr 20 (150x100cm-59x39in) s.i.d.20/1969 verso cotton. 13-Dec-3 Lempertz, Koln #340/R est:2500

MIELE, Franco (1904-1983) Swiss

£333	$613	€500	Malaga (80x60cm-31x24in) s. s.i.verso. 12-Jun-4 Meeting Art, Vercelli #322/R
£543	$923	€793	Rythme de poteaux (49x68cm-19x27in) s.d.53 prov. 19-Nov-3 Fischer, Luzern #2218/R (S.FR 1200)
£748	$1339	€1100	Rural road (50x70cm-20x28in) s. 22-Mar-4 Sant Agostino, Torino #461/R
£839	$1401	€1200	Landscape (50x60cm-20x24in) s. 26-Jun-3 Sant Agostino, Torino #273/R

MIELICH, Alfons Leopold (1863-1929) Austrian

£769	$1308	€1100	Pipe smoking Oriental (39x28cm-15x11in) s. 27-Nov-3 Dorotheum, Linz #444/R est:2000-2600
£940	$1738	€1400	Marchand de profil (32x27cm-13x11in) s. panel. 15-Mar-4 Horta, Bruxelles #233
£8000	$13760	€11680	An Oriental street (52x32cm-20x13in) s. panel. 4-Dec-3 Christie's, Kensington #226/R est:8000-12000

MIELZINER, Leo (1869-1935) American

£895	$1638	€1307	Young girl seated on woodland path in sunshine (46x37cm-18x15in) s.d.95. 9-Jun-4 Rasmussen, Copenhagen #1704/R (D.KR 10000)

MIERES, Alejandro (1927-) Spanish

Works on paper

£503	$921	€750	Composition (46x55cm-18x22in) s.d.69 mixed media. 12-Jul-4 Durán, Madrid #24/R
£633	$1146	€950	Abstract composition (83x67cm-33x26in) s. ink wash. 30-Mar-4 Segre, Madrid #156/R

MIEREVELT, Michiel Jans van (1567-1641) Dutch

£5000	$9000	€7300	Portrait of a lady wearing black dress with ruff and lace cap, holding gloves (78x61cm-31x24in) s.d.1634 panel prov. 21-Apr-4 Bonhams, New Bond Street #41/R est:3000-5000

MIEREVELT, Michiel Jans van (attrib) (1567-1641) Dutch

£6500	$11895	€9490	Portrait of a gentleman said to be Hugo Grotius (70x56cm-28x22in) panel. 6-Jul-4 Sotheby's, Olympia #451/R est:5000-7000
£7292	$12396	€10500	Portrait of lady with fan (120x94cm-47x37in) 29-Oct-3 Il Ponte, Milan #796
£8000	$14640	€11680	Portrait of gentleman with hand on book (111x81cm-44x32in) i.d.1608 panel prov.exhib.lit. 8-Jul-4 Sotheby's, London #263/R est:8000-12000

MIEREVELT, Michiel Jans van (circle) (1567-1641) Dutch

£6500	$11700	€9490	Portrait of Henry de Vere, 18th Earl of Oxford (71x57cm-28x22in) panel. 21-Apr-4 Bonhams, New Bond Street #22/R est:2000-3000

MIEREVELT, Michiel Jans van (studio) (1567-1641) Dutch

£5500	$10065	€8030	Portrait of Edward Cecil, Viscount Wimbledon (75x62cm-30x24in) i. 8-Jul-4 Sotheby's, London #208/R est:3000-4000
£6200	$11284	€9052	Portrait of Frederick V Elector Palatine and King of Bohemia (66x55cm-26x22in) panel. 1-Jul-4 Sotheby's, London #105 est:5000-7000

MIEREVELT, Michiel Jans van (style) (1567-1641) Dutch

£6000	$10980	€8760	Portrait of lady holding fan (68x46cm-27x18in) d.1628 panel prov. 9-Jul-4 Christie's, Kensington #59/R est:2000-3000

MIERIS, Frans van (elder-attrib) (1635-1681) Dutch

£1379	$2303	€2000	Portrait of woman with parrot (14x13cm-6x5in) panel prov. 15-Nov-3 Lempertz, Koln #1100/R est:2500

MIERIS, Jan van (1660-1690) Dutch

£2703	$4757	€4000	Nude woman sleeping in a forest, with silver gilt jug beside her (40x32cm-16x13in) 18-May-4 Sotheby's, Amsterdam #71/R est:3000-5000

MIERIS, Willem van (1662-1747) Dutch

£9868	$18158	€15000	Courtisanne comptant de l'argent (29x23cm-11x9in) panel prov. 24-Jun-4 Christie's, Paris #30/R est:15000-20000
£100000	$183000	€146000	Interior with mother attending her children (44x38cm-17x15in) s.d.1728 panel prov.lit. 7-Jul-4 Sotheby's, London #18/R est:80000-120000
£101351	$178378	€150000	Man holding a pipe (13x11cm-5x4in) s.d.1710 panel oval. 18-May-4 Sotheby's, Amsterdam #11/R est:20000-30000
£222973	$392432	€330000	Man seated holding a beremeier and a pipe in his hand, river landscape beyond (21x17cm-8x7in) s.d.1688 panel prov.exhib.lit. 18-May-4 Sotheby's, Amsterdam #9/R est:50000-70000

Works on paper

£1300	$2249	€1898	Massacre of the Innocents (18x27cm-7x11in) s.d.1696 black chk vellum. 9-Dec-3 Bonhams, Knightsbridge #7/R est:1500-2000

MIERLO, Eugène Victor Joseph van (1880-1972) Belgian

£355	$592	€500	Village dans le sud de la France (65x82cm-26x32in) s.d. 17-Jun-3 Vanderkindere, Brussels #12
£455	$759	€650	Coucher de soleil sur la fermette (80x100cm-31x39in) s. 13-Oct-3 Horta, Bruxelles #478

MIESENBERGER, Maria (1965-) Swedish

Photographs

£2719	$4622	€3970	Untitled - the child - From Sverige/Schweden (105x160cm-41x63in) s.d.93 verso num.1/5 silver gelatin prov.lit. 4-Nov-3 Bukowskis, Stockholm #630/R est:30000-35000 (S.KR 36000)
£3191	$5743	€4659	Untitled (123x81cm-48x32in) s.num.3/10 verso silver gelatin prov.lit. 26-Apr-4 Bukowskis, Stockholm #533/R est:30000-35000 (S.KR 44000)
£4683	$7961	€6837	Untitled - Gentlemen in the garden (99x157cm-39x62in) s.d.93-98 C-print one of three lit. 5-Nov-3 AB Stockholms Auktionsverk #971/R est:60000-80000 (S.KR 62000)

MIESTCHANINOFF, Oscar (1886-?) Russian

Sculpture

£4196	$7133	€6000	Tete de jeune femme, ler Eve (34cm-13in) st.f.J. Salvi pat bronze marble socle prov. 1-Dec-3 Palais de Beaux Arts, Brussels #374/R est:1500-2500

MIETTINEN, Olli (1899-1969) Finnish

£403	$741	€600	View of fields (54x45cm-21x18in) s.d.1936. 25-Mar-4 Hagelstam, Helsinki #909
£549	$879	€780	The old bridge (44x53cm-17x21in) s.d.34. 21-Sep-3 Bukowskis, Helsinki #398/R
£738	$1358	€1100	House (38x46cm-15x18in) s.d.1934. 25-Mar-4 Hagelstam, Helsinki #910

MIGADIS, Yannis (1926-) Greek
£1800 $3222 €2628 Admiring the sea (37x53cm-15x21in) s. tempera cardboard. 11-May-4 Bonhams, New Bond Street #92/R est:1700-2300

MIGHELL, Anthony (20th C) Australian?
Works on paper
£247 $447 €361 Conversation with a fish (74x55cm-29x22in) s. i.d.1989 verso gouache. 30-Mar-4 Lawson Menzies, Sydney #22/R (A.D 600)

MIGLIARA, Giovanni (1785-1837) Italian
£7200 $12960 €10512 Temple of Karnack, Luxor. Romanesque portal (21x17cm-8x7in) board pair. 20-Apr-4 Sotheby's, Olympia #399/R est:4000-6000
£9589 $16301 €14000 Saint Mark's School, Venice (40x58cm-16x23in) 9-Nov-3 Finarte, Venice #5/R est:12000-15000
£17266 $28317 €24000 Grand Canal (20x26cm-8x10in) pair. 4-Jun-3 Sotheby's, Milan #144/R est:20000-30000
£50000 $85000 €72000 View of Loggia dei Lanzi, Florence (43x34cm-17x13in) board. 28-Oct-3 Il Ponte, Milan #288/R
£111111 $200000 €162222 Washerwomen and gentlemen among classical ruins, church beyond (47x89cm-19x35in) prov. 22-Jan-4 Sotheby's, New York #98/R est:100000-150000
Miniatures
£5000 $8950 €7300 Arcadian landscape, woman in classical robes (9x9cm-4x4in) gilt metal frame. 25-May-4 Christie's, London #186/R est:2000-3000
Works on paper
£2400 $4320 €3600 Begging (26x20cm-10x8in) s. pencil. 21-Apr-4 Finarte Semenzato, Milan #566/R est:1400-1600
£7586 $12669 €11000 Grand Canal (5x9cm-2x4in) gouache. 12-Nov-3 Sotheby's, Milan #131/R est:2000-4000
£9155 $16387 €13000 The crypt in Milan Cathedral, interior scene with many figures (47x39cm-19x15in) s.i. W/C gouache. 8-Jan-4 Allgauer, Kempten #2122/R est:2500
£11972 $21430 €17000 Main nave of Milan Cathedral, interior scene with many figures (47x38cm-19x15in) s.i. W/C gouache. 8-Jan-4 Allgauer, Kempten #2121/R est:2500
£30345 $50676 €44000 Grand Canal (14x19cm-6x7in) gouache paper on copper. 12-Nov-3 Sotheby's, Milan #134/R est:8000-12000
£41379 $69103 €60000 Views of Venice (17x22cm-7x9in) gouache pair. 12-Nov-3 Sotheby's, Milan #133/R est:20000-30000

MIGLIARA, Giovanni (school) (1785-1837) Italian
£9655 $16124 €14000 Florence, Palazzo della Signoria (15x20cm-6x8in) copper. 12-Nov-3 Sotheby's, Milan #145/R est:6000-8000

MIGLIARO, Vincenzo (1858-1938) Italian
£420 $713 €600 Western motif (50x40cm-20x16in) s. canvas on board. 24-Nov-3 Glerum, Amsterdam #207/R
£800 $1472 €1200 Vase of flowers (22x14cm-9x6in) s. board. 10-Jun-4 Christie's, Rome #47
£1549 $2680 €2200 Naples Bay and the Vesuvius (18x30cm-7x12in) s. board. 10-Dec-3 Finarte Semenzato, Rome #217/R est:2300-2500
£2465 $4092 €3500 Il trovatello (22x17cm-9x7in) s. wood prov. 11-Jun-3 Christie's, Rome #74/R est:1500-2000
£5000 $8600 €7300 Young beauty (49x69cm-19x27in) s. 4-Dec-3 Christie's, Kensington #161/R est:4000-6000
£5944 $9927 €8500 Woman in narrow street (26x20cm-10x8in) s. board. 24-Jun-3 Finarte Semenzato, Rome #191/R
£12587 $21021 €18000 The doctor's visit (35x31cm-14x12in) s. board. 24-Jun-3 Finarte Semenzato, Rome #192/R
£19930 $33283 €28500 Windy day in town (54x41cm-21x16in) s. 24-Jun-3 Finarte Semenzato, Rome #194/R est:37000

MIGLIORINI, Dino (1909-) Italian
£298 $542 €450 Chimney (70x50cm-28x20in) s. board. 17-Jun-4 Galleria Pananti, Florence #466/R
£364 $663 €550 Farms (48x69cm-19x27in) s. board. 21-Jun-4 Pandolfini, Florence #363

MIGNARD, Nicolas (1606-1668) French
£7308 $12569 €10670 Sainte Cecile (138x97cm-54x38in) 3-Dec-3 AB Stockholms Auktionsverk #2693/R est:60000-80000 (S.KR 95000)

MIGNARD, Pierre (17/18th C) French
£3333 $6000 €4866 Portrait of a lady (41x30cm-16x12in) i.verso panel. 26-Jan-4 Schrager Galleries, Milwaukee #1318
Works on paper
£1892 $3330 €2800 Portrait of Louis Prince de Conde in armout (14x11cm-6x4in) s.i.d.1649 silverpoint vellum prov.exhib.lit. 19-May-4 Sotheby's, Amsterdam #136/R est:4500-5500

MIGNARD, Pierre (circle) (17/18th C) French
£17582 $32000 €25670 Portrait of a Lady said to be Mue Mertain, as Minerva (136x112cm-54x44in) prov. 4-Feb-4 Christie's, Rockefeller NY #79/R est:20000-30000

MIGNARD, Pierre (style) (17/18th C) French
£3352 $6000 €4894 Portrait of girl, said to be Jeanne de Fleurieu (45x36cm-18x14in) prov. 27-May-4 Sotheby's, New York #45/R est:4000-6000
£6376 $11732 €9500 Une scene d'offrande a ceres ou allegorie de l'ete (93x125cm-37x49in) 24-Mar-4 Tajan, Paris #119/R est:10000-12000

MIGNARD, Pierre I (attrib) (1612-1695) French
£1400 $2562 €2044 Portrait of a gentleman, in a gold coat (67x47cm-26x19in) oval. 6-Apr-4 Bonhams, Knightsbridge #83/R est:800-1200
£3311 $6026 €5000 Portrait de Catherine Mignard (73x58cm-29x23in) 15-Jun-4 Claude Aguttes, Neuilly #58b/R est:5000-7000

MIGNECO, Giuseppe (1908-1997) Italian
£1879 $3477 €2800 Seated woman (66x52cm-26x20in) s.d.1963 tempera paper on canvas. 11-Mar-4 Galleria Pace, Milan #102/R est:3300-4300
£2365 $4162 €3500 Fisherman (44x32cm-17x13in) s. tempera paper on canvas. 24-May-4 Christie's, Milan #22/R est:3500-5000
£2585 $4627 €3800 Fig harvest (30x20cm-12x8in) s. 16-Mar-4 Finarte Semenzato, Milan #288/R est:2200
£2609 $4278 €3600 Figure (47x32cm-19x13in) s.d.1962 tempera paper. 29-May-3 Galleria Pace, Milan #108/R est:5600
£2953 $5463 €4400 Woman combing her hair (49x38cm-19x15in) s. tempera paper on canvas painted 1971. 11-Mar-4 Galleria Pace, Milan #97/R est:4400-5600
£4218 $7550 €6200 Woman and cock (50x40cm-20x16in) s. 16-Mar-4 Finarte Semenzato, Milan #329/R est:4400
£5034 $9312 €7500 Gun firer (46x57cm-18x22in) s.d.1973 verso tempera paper on canvas. 11-Mar-4 Galleria Pace, Milan #64/R est:8800-11000
£5072 $8319 €7000 Woman and cat (50x35cm-20x14in) s. tempera paper on canvas. 29-May-3 Galleria Pace, Milan #106/R est:10000
£5944 $10105 €8500 Grapes picker (61x50cm-24x20in) s. s.verso prov. 25-Nov-3 Sotheby's, Milan #29/R est:7000-9000
£5944 $10105 €8500 Husker (40x30cm-16x12in) s. 29-Nov-3 Farsetti, Prato #442/R est:8000-10000
£5986 $9937 €8500 Peasant man (30x25cm-12x10in) s. 13-Jun-3 Farsetti, Prato #337/R
£6711 $12416 €10000 Waiting for a miracle (60x50cm-24x20in) s. 11-Mar-4 Galleria Pace, Milan #136/R est:11000-14000
£11224 $20429 €16500 Grapes picker (61x50cm-24x20in) s. prov. 6-Feb-4 Galleria Rosenberg, Milan #92/R est:15000
Works on paper
£537 $993 €800 Woman (28x23cm-11x9in) s. gouache paper on canvas. 13-Mar-4 Meeting Art, Vercelli #191
£563 $986 €800 Self-portrait (24x17cm-9x7in) s.i.d.1955 verso mixed media. 17-Dec-3 Il Ponte, Milan #1091/R
£629 $1145 €950 Figure (39x29cm-15x11in) s.d.1972 Chinese ink. 17-Jun-4 Galleria Pananti, Florence #403/R
£633 $1146 €950 Woman (29x21cm-11x8in) s.d.70 Chinese ink paper on canvas. 2-Apr-4 Farsetti, Prato #205/R
£699 $1168 €1000 Figure (28x22cm-11x9in) s. W/C paper on canvas. 26-Jun-3 Sant Agostino, Torino #189/R
£861 $1567 €1300 Harvest (27x21cm-11x8in) s. mixed media paper on canvas. 21-Jun-4 Pandolfini, Florence #333/R
£884 $1583 €1300 Head of woman (28x23cm-11x9in) s. W/C paper on canvas. 16-Mar-4 Finarte Semenzato, Milan #185
£1033 $1901 €1550 Figures (29x23cm-11x9in) s.d.1970 Chinese ink W/C paper on canvas. 10-Jun-4 Galleria Pace, Milan #77/R est:2600
£1067 $1963 €1600 Figure (29x23cm-11x9in) s.d.1970 Chinese ink W/C paper on canvas. 10-Jun-4 Galleria Pace, Milan #30/R est:2600
£1103 $1843 €1600 Woman at source (21x29cm-8x11in) s. Chinese ink paper on canvas. 13-Nov-3 Galleria Pace, Milan #48/R
£1159 $1901 €1600 Peasant with basket of figs (29x21cm-11x8in) s. Chinese ink paper on canvas. 29-May-3 Galleria Pace, Milan #64/R est:2400
£1159 $1901 €1600 Peasant woman (21x29cm-8x11in) s. Chinese ink paper on canvas. 29-May-3 Galleria Pace, Milan #60/R est:2400
£1172 $1876 €1700 Peasant woman (29x21cm-11x8in) Indian ink paper on canvas. 13-Mar-3 Galleria Pace, Milan #80/R est:2000-2400
£1172 $1876 €1700 Drinker (29x21cm-11x8in) s. Indian ink paper on canvas. 13-Mar-3 Galleria Pace, Milan #82/R est:2000-2400
£1200 $2172 €1800 Angler with fish (29x21cm-11x8in) s. Chinese ink paper on canvas lit. 2-Apr-4 Farsetti, Prato #3/R est:1100-1400
£1224 $2229 €1800 Peasant man (21x29cm-8x11in) s. wash paper on canvas. 6-Feb-4 Galleria Rosenberg, Milan #103/R est:1800
£1224 $2192 €1800 Prickly pears picker (25x39cm-10x15in) s. col Chinese ink exec.1989. 16-Mar-4 Finarte Semenzato, Milan #289/R est:1200
£1733 $3137 €2600 Fisherman (29x21cm-11x8in) s. Chinese ink paper on canvas. 2-Apr-4 Farsetti, Prato #32/R est:2600-2900

MIGNERY, Herb (1937-) American
Sculpture
£1788 $3200 €2610 Daddy of en all - A Cheyenne Tradition (51cm-20in) bronze edn of 20. 15-May-4 Altermann Galleries, Santa Fe #126/R

MIGNON, Abraham (1640-1679) German
£8681 $13715 €12500 Still life of fruit (67x80cm-26x31in) lit. 19-Sep-3 Schloss Ahlden, Ahlden #1422/R est:9500
£1450000 $2508500 €2117000 Still life of roses, poppies and other flowers, blackberries and redcurrants and insects (47x36cm-19x14in) s. panel prov.exhib.lit. 10-Dec-3 Bonhams, New Bond Street #53/R est:500000-700000

MIGNON, Abraham (after) (1640-1679) German
£3691 $6903 €5500 Still life with grapes, peaches, melons, snail (47x41cm-19x16in) i. stretcher. 28-Feb-4 Bolland & Marotz, Bremen #287/R est:4900

MIGNON, Léon (1847-1898) Belgian
Sculpture
£1034 $1914 €1500 Combat de taureaux romains (51x65x27cm-20x26x11in) s. green pat bronze. 19-Jan-4 Horta, Bruxelles #83 est:800-1200
£1060 $1727 €1600 Standing peasant with ox (51cm-20in) s. bronze. 31-Jan-3 Altus, Berlin #1955/R est:2400
£1241 $2234 €1800 Israeli boy (48cm-19in) s.st.f.Compagnie des Bronzes pat bronze prov. 21-Jan-4 Tajan, Paris #112 est:1000-2000
£4930 $8528 €7000 Le dompteur de taureaux (48x58cm-19x23in) black pat bronze exec.c.1879 lit. 10-Dec-3 Hotel des Ventes Mosan, Brussels #258/R est:6000-8000

MIGNON, Lucien (1865-1944) French
£379 $630 €550 Portrait de jeune fille (48x39cm-19x15in) s. panel. 1-Oct-3 Millon & Associes, Paris #67/R
£738 $1374 €1100 L'Allee (32x50cm-13x20in) 3-Mar-4 Tajan, Paris #28
£1275 $2372 €1900 Theiere (24x33cm-9x13in) s. 3-Mar-4 Tajan, Paris #27 est:1000-1200
£2467 $4489 €3700 Jeune danseuse (55x37cm-22x15in) s. 4-Jul-4 Eric Pillon, Calais #76/R

£2500 $4175 €3650 Beach scene (27x41cm-11x16in) s. 22-Oct-3 Sotheby's, Olympia #34/R est:3000-4000
£3034 $5614 €4400 Danseuse assise (73x60cm-29x24in) s. 16-Feb-4 Giraudeau, Tours #91

MIGONNEY, Jules (1876-1929) French
Works on paper
£3333 $6133 €5000 Messaouda au turban bleu (21x27cm-8x11in) s.i.d.1911 graphite htd chk exhib. 14-Jun-4 Gros & Delettrez, Paris #545/R est:3000-3500

MIGUEL, Juan Diego de (1955-) Spanish
Sculpture
£1224 $2192 €1800 Continuous flow (213x88cm-84x35in) i. s.i.d.1989 verso painted wood slate. 22-Mar-4 Durán, Madrid #118/R est:1800

MIHALIK, Daniel (1869-1910) Hungarian
£339 $587 €495 Riverside by Szolnok (28x33cm-11x13in) s. cardboard. 12-Dec-3 Kieselbach, Budapest #5/R (H.F 130000)

MIHALOVITS, Miklos (1888-1960) Hungarian
£410 $750 €615 Nude female in front of a mirror (61x91cm-24x36in) 9-Jul-4 Du Mouchelle, Detroit #2195/R
£1497 $2500 €2186 Slave girl (76x61cm-30x24in) 17-Oct-3 Du Mouchelle, Detroit #2218/R est:150-300

MIHURA, Miguel (1905-1977) Spanish
Works on paper
£1645 $3026 €2500 Murdered (29x18cm-11x7in) s. gouache. 22-Jun-4 Durán, Madrid #645/R est:180

MIJARES, Jose M (1921-) Cuban
£1081 $2000 €1578 Clown (49x41cm-19x16in) s. board. 13-Jul-4 Christie's, Rockefeller NY #192/R est:3000-5000
£1189 $2200 €1736 Portrait of a woman (50x39cm-20x15in) s. panel. 13-Jul-4 Christie's, Rockefeller NY #191/R est:3000-5000
£1580 $2687 €2260 Untitled (73x55cm-29x22in) s.d.1955 tempera card prov. 18-Nov-3 Babuino, Rome #538/R est:1500-2000

MIKESCH, Fritz (1939-) Austrian
£280 $504 €420 Hope (65x55cm-26x22in) s.i.d.1973 verso. 26-Apr-4 Rieber, Stuttgart #1252/R

MIKHAILOV, Oleg (1934-) Russian
£329 $605 €500 Winter day (78x65cm-31x26in) s. 22-Jun-4 Durán, Madrid #707/R

MIKI, Andy (1918-1983) North American
Sculpture
£946 $1608 €1381 Animal (14cm-6in) s. mottled grey soapstone. 3-Nov-3 Waddingtons, Toronto #789/R est:600-900 (C.D 2100)
£991 $1685 €1447 Arctic hare (19cm-7in) s. antler. 3-Nov-3 Waddingtons, Toronto #804/R est:700-1000 (C.D 2200)
£1116 $2008 €1629 Arctic hare (10cm-4in) s. grey soapstone. 26-Apr-4 Waddingtons, Toronto #611/R est:600-900 (C.D 2700)
£2252 $3829 €3288 Arctic hare (16cm-6in) mottled grey soapstone exec.c.1972. 3-Nov-3 Waddingtons, Toronto #374/R est:500-700 (C.D 5000)
£2973 $5054 €4341 Reclining dog (15cm-6in) mottled dark soapstone. 3-Nov-3 Waddingtons, Toronto #371/R est:1000-1500 (C.D 6600)
£8108 $13784 €11838 Arctic hare (25cm-10in) dark soapstone. 3-Nov-3 Waddingtons, Toronto #380/R est:2000-3000 (C.D 18000)

MIKI, Tomio (1937-) American
Sculpture
£20270 $37500 €29594 Ear II (56x33x10cm-22x13x4in) impressed name verso aluminium exec 1972 lit. 12-Feb-4 Sotheby's, New York #173/R est:300-500

MIKKELSEN, Lauritz (1879-1966) Danish
£466 $839 €680 Ploughing the field (53x74cm-21x29in) mono.d.1914. 24-Apr-4 Rasmussen, Havnen #2091 (D.KR 5200)

MIKL, Josef (1929-) Austrian
£805 $1490 €1200 Untitled (33x29cm-13x11in) s.d.1964 board. 9-Mar-4 Dorotheum, Vienna #155/R
£7383 $13067 €11000 Composition (50x70cm-20x28in) s.d. 28-Apr-4 Wiener Kunst Auktionen, Vienna #253/R est:6000-10000
£9396 $16819 €14000 Untitled (100x80cm-39x31in) mono.d.72 mono.d. stretcher. 25-May-4 Dorotheum, Vienna #347/R est:14000-18000
£12500 $21250 €18000 From the studio (160x95cm-63x37in) s. 28-Oct-3 Wiener Kunst Auktionen, Vienna #235/R est:18000-32000
Works on paper
£667 $1200 €1000 Flower (23x32cm-9x13in) mono.d.73. 21-Apr-4 Dorotheum, Vienna #244/R

MIKLOS, Gustave (1888-1967) French
Sculpture
£4333 $7973 €6500 Tete cubiste (13cm-5in) s. num.2/4 brown pat. bronze incl. marble base. 8-Jun-4 Artcurial Briest, Paris #175/R est:5000-7000
£14865 $26162 €22000 Untitled (65x39cm-26x15in) copper wood prov. 18-May-4 Christie's, Paris #8/R est:25000-35000
Works on paper
£350 $594 €500 Composition (11x10cm-4x4in) gouache prov. 23-Nov-3 Cornette de St.Cyr, Paris #237

MIKOLA, Andreas Armas (1884-1970) Finnish
£935 $1655 €1365 Under the free sky of God (75x95cm-30x37in) s. 28-Apr-4 Kieselbach, Budapest #151/R (H.F 350000)
£1015 $1797 €1482 House under blue sky (65x96cm-26x38in) s. 28-Apr-4 Kieselbach, Budapest #89/R (H.F 380000)
£1737 $3074 €2536 Spring in Nagybanya (100x113cm-39x44in) s. 28-Apr-4 Kieselbach, Budapest #111/R (H.F 650000)

MIKOLA, Armas (1901-1983) Finnish
£302 $556 €450 Villa (29x39cm-11x15in) s.d.1933. 25-Mar-4 Hagelstam, Helsinki #833
£400 $736 €600 House in the country (49x59cm-19x23in) s.d.31. 9-Jun-4 Bukowskis, Helsinki #482/R
£739 $1183 €1050 Naadendal Church (40x50cm-16x20in) s.d.1950. 18-Sep-3 Hagelstam, Helsinki #788/R
£1275 $2346 €1900 Fisherman (70x85cm-28x33in) s.d.1957. 25-Mar-4 Hagelstam, Helsinki #1005/R est:2000

MIKOLA, Nandor (1911-) Finnish
Works on paper
£347 $580 €500 Winter landscape (46x70cm-18x28in) s. W/C. 26-Oct-3 Bukowskis, Helsinki #419/R
£569 $951 €820 Cherry tree (70x48cm-28x19in) s. W/C. 26-Oct-3 Bukowskis, Helsinki #418/R
£573 $1055 €860 Autumn landscape (70x48cm-28x19in) s.d.1984 W/C. 9-Jun-4 Bukowskis, Helsinki #485/R
£587 $1079 €880 Apple blossom in vase (69x46cm-27x18in) s.d.1984 W/C. 9-Jun-4 Bukowskis, Helsinki #483/R

MIKULSKI, Kazimierz (1918-) Polish
£4207 $7026 €6100 Saying goodbye (55x46cm-22x18in) s.d.96. 16-Nov-3 Agra, Warsaw #10/R est:4000

MILANESE SCHOOL (16th C) Italian
£28000 $48440 €40880 The Lamentation (124x146cm-49x57in) panel. 11-Dec-3 Sotheby's, London #173/R est:15000-20000

MILANI, Aureliano (1675-1749) Italian
Works on paper
£7000 $12600 €10220 Rape of Helena (29x50cm-11x20in) s. pen black ink grey wash. 20-Apr-4 Sotheby's, Olympia #18/R est:2000-3000

MILANI, Umberto (1912-1969) Italian
£2254 $3741 €3200 Composition (100x100cm-39x39in) s. s.d.1963 verso. 11-Jun-3 Finarte Semenzato, Milan #575/R
Sculpture
£1023 $1800 €1494 Figure of an Indian chief in war bonnet (30cm-12in) bronze. 21-May-4 Pook & Pook, Downington #293/R est:2000-2500
£1189 $2021 €1700 Nude (46cm-18in) s. plaster. 20-Nov-3 Finarte Semenzato, Milan #99/R est:1500-1800
£2349 $4205 €3500 Woman (40x16x19cm-16x6x7in) s.d.943 wax plaster exhib. 25-May-4 Sotheby's, Milan #20/R est:4000

MILATZ, Frans Andreas (attrib) (1763-1808) Dutch
Works on paper
£822 $1397 €1200 Farmstead among trees, figures on a road (20x33cm-8x13in) black chk pen ink wash prov. 5-Nov-3 Christie's, Amsterdam #115/R est:600-800

MILAYBUMA, David (20th C) Australian
Works on paper
£938 $1753 €1407 Namu-miyak, mali-malin and norna, rainbow serpent (87x51cm-34x20in) bears name.i.verso earth pigments eucalyptus bark prov. 26-Jul-4 Sotheby's, Melbourne #401/R est:3000-5000 (A.D 2400)

MILBOURNE, Henry (1781-1826) British
£3709 $6750 €5600 Transport de betail sur la riviere (63x76cm-25x30in) s. 19-Jun-4 St-Germain-en-Laye Encheres #78/R est:5000

MILBU, Geoffrey (fl.1979-1981) Australian
Works on paper
£430 $804 €645 Fish and eel (60x100cm-24x39in) pigment eucalyptus bark. 21-Jul-4 Shapiro, Sydney #11/R (A.D 1100)
£430 $804 €645 Barramundi and waterlily (50x110cm-20x43in) i.verso pigment eucalyptus bark exec. 1985. 21-Jul-4 Shapiro, Sydney #12/R (A.D 1100)

MILBY, Frank (?) American
£429 $700 €626 Trees (61x51cm-24x20in) s. 19-Jul-3 Outer Cape Auctions, Provincetown #76/R
Works on paper
£351 $650 €512 Highland light lighthouse (28x38cm-11x15in) s. W/C. 17-Jul-4 Outer Cape Auctions, Provincetown #15/R

MILEN, Eduard (1891-?) Czechoslovakian
£333 $597 €500 Great evening (38x35cm-15x14in) s. board. 12-May-4 Stadion, Trieste #633

MILENKOVIC, John (20th C) Australian
£232 $364 €339 Wetland (49x75cm-19x30in) s. board. 24-Nov-2 Goodman, Sydney #79 (A.D 650)

MILES OF NORTHLEACH, John (19th C) British
£480 $830 €701 Carters and their horses frightened by a thunderstorm (53x64cm-21x25in) s.d.1838. 12-Dec-3 Moore Allen & Innocent, Cirencester #361

MILES, Annie Stewart (fl.1888-1907) British
£450 $806 €657 At prayer (91x61cm-36x24in) s. 27-May-4 Christie's, Kensington #278/R

MILES, Arthur (fl.1851-1872) British
Works on paper
£260 $465 €380 Rolling landscape with sheep in the foreground (31x45cm-12x18in) s.d.1973 W/C. 17-Mar-4 Anthemion, Cardiff #377

MILES, Donald E (1921-) American
£190 $350 €277 Blue Tohoe (41x61cm-16x24in) s. canvas on board. 13-Jun-4 Bonhams & Butterfields, Los Angeles #7046/R
£1000 $1700 €1460 Show of colour (46x69cm-18x27in) s. i.verso canvas on masonite prov. 18-Nov-3 John Moran, Pasadena #140 est:2000-3000

MILES, Edward (1752-1828) British
Miniatures
£3400 $6256 €4964 Gentleman, wearing viridian green coat with black collar (6cm-2in) gold fausse montre frame pale blue white enamel border. 24-Jun-4 Bonhams, New Bond Street #98/R est:2000-3000

MILES, Frank (1852-1891) British
Works on paper
£400 $652 €584 Portrait, head and shoulders of a pretty young girl (28x23cm-11x9in) s.d.1877 W/C oval. 23-Sep-3 John Nicholson, Haslemere #107

MILES, J P (19th C) ?
£460 $727 €672 Portrait of John Keynes in a black suit (74x62cm-29x24in) i.d.1853 verso. 24-Jul-3 Dominic Winter, Swindon #105/R

MILES, Manuel M (20th C) American
£404 $700 €590 Patio of the Mission San Juan Capistrano (76x96cm-30x38in) s. 10-Dec-3 Bonhams & Butterfields, San Francisco #6312/R

MILES, Mary (19/20th C) British
Works on paper
£420 $752 €613 Two sisters (56x61cm-22x24in) s.d.1900 pastel. 17-Mar-4 Bonhams, Chester #408

MILES, R (?) ?
£4500 $8055 €6570 Caught red handed (107x152cm-42x60in) s. 26-May-4 Sotheby's, Olympia #85/R est:5000-7000

MILES, T R (fl.1869-1906) British
£1750 $3220 €2555 Stormy seascape with paddle steamer in difficulty assisted by two vessels (58x89cm-23x35in) s. 24-Jun-4 Scarborough Perry Fine Arts, Hove #780

MILES, Thomas Rose (fl.1869-1906) British
£452 $756 €660 Entrance to Portsmouth Harbour (45x61cm-18x24in) s. s.i. verso. 17-Nov-3 Waddingtons, Toronto #140/R (C.D 1000)
£550 $985 €803 Coming storm, ebb-tide on the Goodwin Sands (76x127cm-30x50in) s. i.verso. 18-Mar-4 Christie's, Kensington #529/R
£1028 $1624 €1491 Evening, sailing vessels at sea (41x66cm-16x26in) s.i. 2-Sep-3 Rasmussen, Copenhagen #1639/R (D.KR 11000)
£1180 $1900 €1723 Drifting ashore (74x124cm-29x49in) s. i. verso. 20-Aug-3 James Julia, Fairfield #945/R est:1750-2250
£1300 $2236 €1898 Marine study of fishermen rowing out to waiting fishing boats (58x104cm-23x41in) s. 4-Dec-3 Biddle & Webb, Birmingham #930
£1800 $3060 €2628 Coming ashore (61x102cm-24x40in) indis.sig. 19-Nov-3 Christie's, Kensington #547/R
£1810 $3077 €2643 Seascape (76x127cm-30x50in) s. i.verso. 1-Dec-3 Koller, Zurich #6464 est:4000-6000 (S.FR 4000)
£1850 $3386 €2701 Going to sea (61x91cm-24x36in) 7-Apr-4 Bonhams, Bury St Edmunds #476 est:1500-2500
£2200 $3740 €3212 Day break on the Goodwins, not a soul was lost (76x128cm-30x50in) s. i.verso. 19-Nov-3 Tennants, Leyburn #1054/R est:2000-2500
£2819 $5046 €4200 Fishers returning, morning at Stone Head, Connemara (53x91cm-21x36in) s.i. 26-May-4 James Adam, Dublin #22/R est:4500-5500
£3200 $5152 €4640 Salmon fishing Loch Connemare (25x41cm-10x16in) s. i.verso. 13-Aug-3 Andrew Hartley, Ilkley #824/R est:800-1200
£3600 $6444 €5256 Wind and sea rising - Knock-na carra, Galway Bay (51x76cm-20x30in) s. s.i.verso. 26-May-4 Christie's, Kensington #682/R est:2000-3000
£4000 $6440 €5800 Trout fishing on the Ballanahinch Connemare (25x41cm-10x16in) s.i.verso. 13-Aug-3 Andrew Hartley, Ilkley #825/R est:800-1200
£4400 $7876 €6424 Polack fishers - Cliffs of Mohur, Country Clare (51x76cm-20x30in) s. s.i.verso. 26-May-4 Christie's, Kensington #681/R est:3000-4000
£4500 $8325 €6570 Breezy morning, Scarborough (75x126cm-30x50in) s. s.i.verso. 14-Jul-4 Sotheby's, Olympia #72/R est:2000-3000
£5000 $8500 €7200 Daybreak on the Goodwins (76x127cm-30x50in) s. 28-Oct-3 Mealy's, Castlecomer #218/R
£6376 $11413 €9500 Outward bound from Whitby (67x127cm-26x50in) s.d.1899 s.i.verso. 26-May-4 James Adam, Dublin #14/R est:10000-15000
£6711 $12013 €10000 Homeward bound to Plymouth (67x127cm-26x50in) s.d.1899 s.i.verso. 26-May-4 James Adam, Dublin #13/R est:10000-15000
£10563 $18275 €15000 Fishing on Loch Corrib and on the Ballinahinch, Connemara (27x41cm-11x16in) s. i.verso pair. 10-Dec-3 Bonhams & James Adam, Dublin #13/R est:15000-20000

MILESI, Alessandro (1856-1945) Italian
£671 $1201 €1000 Kitchen interior (10x15cm-4x6in) s. board painted 1887. 25-May-4 Finarte Semenzato, Milan #132/R
£2384 $4339 €3600 Portrait of Giulio Fradeletto (54x39cm-21x15in) s.d.1922 cardboard. 17-Jun-4 Finarte Semenzato, Milan #308/R est:3500-4000
£4710 $7725 €6500 Motherly love (53x40cm-21x16in) s. i.verso card. 27-May-3 Il Ponte, Milan #974/R est:10000
£4967 $9040 €7500 Girl amongst cherry trees (55x40cm-22x16in) s.i. 17-Jun-4 Finarte Semenzato, Milan #297/R est:5000-6000
£6383 $10660 €9000 Carmela (50x40cm-20x16in) s. cardboard painted c.1900. 20-Oct-3 Sant Agostino, Torino #302/R est:10000
£6667 $12000 €9734 Venetian lagoon (28x38cm-11x15in) s. board. 23-Apr-4 Sotheby's, New York #79/R est:6000-8000
£9000 $16560 €13500 The fisherman's daughter (45x30cm-18x12in) s. cardboard. 10-Jun-4 Christie's, Rome #98/R est:6000-9000
£9060 $16218 €13500 Little orphan (44x29cm-17x11in) s.d.1922 cardboard prov. 25-May-4 Finarte Semenzato, Milan #199/R est:10000-12000
Works on paper
£268 $502 €400 Girl (15x10cm-6x4in) pencil card exhib.lit. 28-Feb-4 Finarte, Venice #173/R

MILEY, R A (19th C) British
£700 $1204 €1022 Equestrian portrait (51x66cm-20x26in) s. 7-Dec-3 Lots Road Auctions, London #362

MILGATE, Rodney A (1934-) Australian
£851 $1472 €1242 Rhythm of live (122x122cm-48x48in) s.d.69 i.verso board. 10-Dec-3 Shapiro, Sydney #91/R (A.D 2000)

MILHAZES, Beatriz (1960-) Brazilian
£36471 $62000 €53248 Mundo civilizado - Civilised world (150x250cm-59x98in) s.d.1998 verso prov. 18-Nov-3 Christie's, Rockefeller NY #6/R est:25000-30000

MILIADIS, Stelios (1881-1965) Greek
£3000 $5370 €4380 Sailing along the coast (26x36cm-10x14in) s. board. 10-May-4 Sotheby's, Olympia #110/R est:3000-5000
£5000 $8750 €7300 Dandy (57x47cm-22x19in) s.d.05. 16-Dec-3 Bonhams, New Bond Street #66/R est:5000-7000
Works on paper
£900 $1530 €1314 Greek town scene (24x33cm-9x13in) W/C over pencil. 18-Nov-3 Sotheby's, London #72/R
£1100 $1969 €1606 Village street (27x23cm-11x9in) s. W/C. 10-May-4 Sotheby's, Olympia #153/R est:750-1000
£2000 $3580 €2920 Village harbour (24x34cm-9x13in) s. W/C. 10-May-4 Sotheby's, Olympia #150/R est:750-1000

MILIAN, Raul (1914-1986) Cuban
Works on paper
£6471 $11000 €9448 Untitled (38x28cm-15x11in) three s.d.66 one s.d.65 one s.d.61 one s.d.64 W/C six prov. 18-Nov-3 Christie's, Rockefeller NY #177/R est:4000-6000

MILIANI, Marco (1933-) Venezuelan
£231 $415 €337 Untitled (80x66cm-31x26in) s. painted 1978. 25-Apr-4 Subastas Odalys, Caracas #78

MILIOTI, Nikolai Dimitrievich (1874-1962) Russian
£20000 $34000 €29200 Daydreams (49x37cm-19x15in) s.d.1923 board. 19-Nov-3 Sotheby's, London #137/R est:20000-30000
£35000 $59500 €52500 Night fancy-dress party (50x61cm-20x24in) s.i. board prov.exhib. 25-Nov-3 Christie's, London #225/R est:10000-15000

MILLAIS, Raoul (1901-) British
£376 $700 €549 Man on a horse being pursued thru the desert (33x43cm-13x17in) s.d.1921 board. 6-Mar-4 Dan Ripley, Indianapolis #255
£620 $1011 €905 Horses paused in a forest clearing (25x31cm-10x12in) s. panel. 24-Sep-3 Dreweatt Neate, Newbury #138/R
£1700 $2890 €2482 On the beach (19x24cm-7x9in) s. board. 26-Nov-3 Sotheby's, Olympia #131/R est:400-600
£1850 $3016 €2701 Study of a bay (51x60cm-20x24in) s. board. 24-Sep-3 Dreweatt Neate, Newbury #88/R est:400-600
£3200 $5440 €4672 Mares and foals in a paddock (25x30cm-10x12in) s. 27-Nov-3 Christie's, Kensington #154/R est:1500-2000
£4800 $8784 €7008 Figures and carriages in a park (24x29cm-9x11in) s.i. pair. 27-Jan-4 Holloways, Banbury #362 est:800-1200
£5200 $9568 €7592 Racing at Newmarket (51x61cm-20x24in) s. 10-Jun-4 Christie's, Kensington #205/R est:4000-6000
£5500 $10120 €8030 Sanctuary (51x61cm-20x24in) 10-Jun-4 Christie's, Kensington #225/R est:2500-3500
£6000 $11040 €8760 Sunday in the park (25x30cm-10x12in) s. pair. 10-Jun-4 Christie's, Kensington #206/R est:6000-8000
Works on paper
£260 $434 €380 Leaping horse (37x26cm-15x10in) s. brown chk. 21-Oct-3 Bruton Knowles, Cheltenham #409
£340 $622 €496 Study of a grazing horse (26x22cm-10x9in) init.d. pen wash. 28-Jul-4 Bonhams, Knightsbridge #124/R
£380 $688 €555 Foal (17x18cm-7x7in) s. pastel. 31-Mar-4 Bonhams, Knightsbridge #67

£500 $920 €730 White horses (26x38cm-10x15in) s. pencil white chk prov. 10-Jun-4 Christie's, Kensington #200/R
£700 $1099 €1015 Lady in her carriage. Three matadors (28x19cm-11x7in) s. pencil W/C two. 28-Aug-3 Christie's, Kensington #499/R
£800 $1456 €1168 Bullfighting scenes (26x18cm-10x7in) s. sepia wash two prov. 30-Jun-4 Mervyn Carey, Tenterden #148
£820 $1394 €1197 Jockeys at the start (18x27cm-7x11in) s. pencil pastel prov. 19-Nov-3 Sotheby's, Olympia #126/R

MILLAIS, Sir John Everett (1829-1896) British
£2486 $4600 €3630 On Hampstead Heath (23x33cm-9x13in) mono. board painted c.1848 prov.exhib. 13-Mar-4 Susanin's, Chicago #6103/R est:4000-6000
£280000 $476000 €408800 Getting better (103x91cm-41x36in) mono.d.1876 prov.exhib.lit. 26-Nov-3 Christie's, London #28/R est:400000-600000
£1000000 $1820000 €1460000 Cherry ripe (134x89cm-53x35in) mono.d.1879 prov.exhib.lit. 1-Jul-4 Sotheby's, London #21/R est:800000-1200000

MILLAIS, William Henry (1828-1899) British
Works on paper
£700 $1169 €1022 Rabbits in a wood. Rabbit and stoat in a woodland setting (28x39cm-11x15in) one s.d.1859 pencil W/C bodycol pair. 16-Oct-3 Christie's, Kensington #214/R

MILLAN FERRIZ, Emilio (19th C) Spanish
£390 $651 €550 Landscape (75x58cm-30x23in) s.i. 23-Jun-3 Durán, Madrid #98/R
£660 $1075 €950 Farm (53x43cm-21x17in) s. 23-Sep-3 Durán, Madrid #653/R

MILLAN, Manuel (1948-) Spanish
£1020 $1827 €1500 Still life (69x100cm-27x39in) s. 22-Mar-4 Durán, Madrid #192/R est:1500

MILLAN, Victor (1909-1991) Venezuelan
£275 $495 €402 Virgin of the Valley (66x33cm-26x13in) s. painted 1988. 25-Apr-4 Subastas Odalys, Caracas #91/R
£312 $530 €456 Untitled (70x94cm-28x37in) s. painted 1977. 23-Nov-3 Subastas Odalys, Caracas #103
£764 $1200 €1115 Untitled (50x69cm-20x27in) s. 23-Nov-2 Subastas Odalys, Caracas #20/R

MILLAR, Addison T (1860-1913) American
£254 $425 €371 Still life (5x10cm-2x4in) s. board. 16-Nov-3 William Jenack, New York #300
£604 $1100 €882 Houses by the canal (15x23cm-6x9in) s. board. 7-Feb-4 Sloans & Kenyon, Bethesda #1287/R
£7778 $14000 €11356 Arab cafe (25x20cm-10x8in) s. i.verso panel. 22-Apr-4 Christie's, Rockefeller NY #215/R est:15000-20000

MILLAR, Beatriz (1967-) Swiss
£533 $981 €800 Tv soul century (44x65cm-17x26in) s. acrylic plastic board painted 1990. 8-Jun-4 Finarte Semenzato, Milan #187/R
£533 $981 €800 Tv soul century (47x34cm-19x13in) acrylic board painted 1990. 8-Jun-4 Finarte Semenzato, Milan #188/R

MILLAR, Jack (1921-) British
£320 $512 €464 Gardener (75x63cm-30x25in) s. board. 16-Sep-3 Bonhams, Knightsbridge #64/R

MILLAR, James H C (fl.1884-1903) British
£380 $703 €555 St Michael's Mount at high tide (50x101cm-20x40in) s. 16-Feb-4 Bonhams, Bath #47
£650 $1105 €949 Coastal scene with seabirds beside rocky cliffs (122x183cm-48x72in) s. prov. 19-Nov-3 Tennants, Leyburn #1034

MILLAR, Joseph (?) ?
£2700 $4914 €3942 Maths lesson, kitchen interior with grandmother teaching a young girl (68x55cm-27x22in) s. 15-Jun-4 Bonhams, Oxford #97/R est:800-1200

MILLAR, Ronald Grenville (1927-) Australian
£1220 $1915 €1769 The visit (101x126cm-40x50in) s. s.i.d.1996 stretcher. 27-Aug-3 Christie's, Sydney #592/R est:3000-5000 (A.D 3000)

MILLARD, Frederick (1857-1937) British
£3000 $4740 €4350 News from afar (71x51cm-28x20in) s. 4-Sep-3 Christie's, Kensington #259/R est:3000-4000
£5400 $8964 €7884 The letter (70x49cm-28x19in) s. 2-Oct-3 Lane, Penzance #350/R est:6000-8000

MILLARD, Pieter (20th C) British?
£340 $609 €496 Young ladies picking flowers (102x81cm-40x32in) s. board. 13-May-4 Grant, Worcester #368
£900 $1611 €1314 Gone horse riding (89x119cm-35x47in) s. board. 13-May-4 Grant, Worcester #367/R

MILLARES, Manolo (1926-1972) Spanish
£25362 $41594 €35000 Black, red and white (48x69cm-19x27in) s. paper painted 1961. 27-May-3 Durán, Madrid #294/R est:15000
£61350 $100000 €89571 Humboldt en el Orinoco (64x80cm-25x31in) s. s.i.d.1969 verso prov. oil string burlap. 23-Sep-3 Christie's, Rockefeller NY #5/R est:35000-45000
£75000 $125250 €109500 Cuadro 17 (81x100cm-32x39in) s. s.i.d.1959 stretcher oil string burlap prov.exhib.lit. 22-Oct-3 Christie's, London #9/R est:50000-70000
£110000 $200200 €160600 Cuadre 83 (130x162cm-51x64in) s. burlap painted 1959 prov.lit. 5-Feb-4 Sotheby's, London #39/R est:100000-150000
£110000 $200200 €160600 Homuncule (100x81cm-39x32in) s. oil mixed media burlap prov.lit. 6-Feb-4 Sotheby's, London #194/R est:60000-80000
£200000 $364000 €292000 El personaje (81x300cm-32x118in) s. s.i.d.1966 on stretcher acrylic metal sheet three burlap. 4-Feb-4 Christie's, London #27/R est:90000-120000
Works on paper
£3000 $5430 €4500 Study for wall (9x15cm-4x6in) s.i.d.1956-57 gouache ink wash. 30-Mar-4 Segre, Madrid #322/R est:4500
£3793 $6334 €5500 Composition (33x46cm-13x18in) s.d.1953 mixed media. 17-Nov-3 Durán, Madrid #101/R
£4514 $7358 €6500 Wood worker (65x48cm-26x19in) s.d.55 ink dr. 23-Sep-3 Durán, Madrid #229/R est:3000
£7547 $12000 €11019 Composition in red and black (69x48cm-27x19in) s.i.d.1968 verso ink gouache. 13-Sep-3 Weschler, Washington #705/R est:10000-15000
£12500 $20375 €18000 Composition (53x66cm-21x26in) s.d.65 mixed media. 23-Sep-3 Durán, Madrid #230/R est:18000

MILLASSON, Anne (20th C) French?
Works on paper
£2183 $3820 €3100 Port de Bretagne (50x65cm-20x26in) s. pastel. 21-Dec-3 Thierry & Lannon, Brest #401/R est:2200-2500

MILLDE, Helena Mathilda (?) ?
£424 $734 €619 Man by festive table (39x29cm-15x11in) s. 15-Dec-3 Lilla Bukowskis, Stockholm #690 (S.KR 5400)

MILLENET, Hippolyte (1802-1844) Swiss
£3493 $6358 €5100 Coastal landscape with herdsman and cattle returning home (71x98cm-28x39in) s. 16-Jun-4 Fischer, Luzern #1270/R est:8000-10000 (S.FR 8000)

MILLER (?) ?
Works on paper
£1901 $3156 €2700 Paysage lacustre anime (44x63cm-17x25in) s.d.1818 W/C. 16-Jun-3 E & Eve, Paris #45

MILLER VON HAUENFELS, Erich (1889-1972) Austrian
£2797 $4755 €4000 Harbour at night (59x71cm-23x28in) s. 28-Nov-3 Wiener Kunst Auktionen, Vienna #514/R est:4000-7000

MILLER, Alfred Jacob (1810-1874) American
£894 $1600 €1305 Keep the mill-a-going (20x25cm-8x10in) oil paper. 7-May-4 Sloans & Kenyon, Bethesda #1728/R est:2500-3000
£894 $1600 €1305 Paul, the art student, encounters the elegant model (15x15cm-6x6in) mono. i.verso oil paper. 7-May-4 Sloans & Kenyon, Bethesda #1729/R est:2000-2500
£1117 $2000 €1631 September gale (18x25cm-7x10in) mono. i.verso. 7-May-4 Sloans & Kenyon, Bethesda #1727/R est:1500-2000
£6145 $11000 €8972 Charles Street Avenue, Baltimore (10x13cm-4x5in) oil paper. 7-May-4 Sloans & Kenyon, Bethesda #1730/R est:1800-2200
£272727 $480000 €398181 Death of a Cougar (85x71cm-33x28in) painted c.1840-41 prov.lit. 18-May-4 Christie's, Rockefeller NY #49/R est:600000-800000
Works on paper
£23256 $40000 €33954 Starving trappers (20x33cm-8x13in) init.i. wash ink pencil prov.exhib.lit. 4-Dec-3 Christie's, Rockefeller NY #64/R est:30000-50000

MILLER, Anna (20th C) British
£2600 $4654 €3796 Bed of roses (167x75cm-66x30in) s.verso. 28-May-4 Lyon & Turnbull, Edinburgh #73 est:800-1200

MILLER, Arv (20th C) American
Works on paper
£571 $1000 €834 One should always be in love that is reason one should never marry (28x25cm-11x10in) s. st.init. ink wash illus board exec 1955 two. 17-Dec-3 Christie's, Rockefeller NY #23/R
£1371 $2400 €2002 I suspect foul play. Wha d'ya mean you'll call the detective. Diamonds Miss Moore (42x31cm-17x12in) s. W/C board sold with W/C by J.Dedman and one by A.Stine. 17-Dec-3 Christie's, Rockefeller NY #30/R est:2000-3000

MILLER, Barse (1904-1973) American
£56886 $95000 €83054 Factory town (66x91cm-26x36in) s. s.i.verso prov.exhib.lit. 7-Oct-3 Sotheby's, New York #212 est:7000-10000
Works on paper
£1734 $3000 €2532 Harbour Nocturne (42x52cm-17x20in) s. W/C. 10-Dec-3 Bonhams & Butterfields, San Francisco #6298/R est:3000-5000
£7182 $13000 €10486 Sailor come home, on the waterfront (38x58cm-15x23in) s. s.i.d.1936 verso W/C. 31-Mar-4 Sotheby's, New York #112/R est:1000-1500

MILLER, Beatrice M (?) British
Works on paper
£650 $1079 €949 Still life of sweet peas in an iridescent glass vase on a stone balustrade (30x46cm-12x18in) s. W/C. 2-Oct-3 Neales, Nottingham #611/R

MILLER, Captain Ralph Willett (1762-1799) American
Works on paper
£5000 $9450 €7300 Theseus engaging the Guerrier at the Battle of the Nile, 1798 (36x53cm-14x21in) bears i.verso W/C exec 1798. 17-Feb-4 Bonhams, New Bond Street #83/R est:5000-8000
£5500 $10395 €8030 Battle off Cape St Vincent, February 14th 1797 (33x48cm-13x19in) bears i.verso pen ink pair exec 1797. 17-Feb-4 Bonhams, New Bond Street #82/R est:6000-8000

MILLER, Charles Henry (1842-1922) American
£237 $425 €346 Wooded landscape with an elder woman and child walking in the rain (33x43cm-13x17in) s. 11-May-4 Roland's, New York #473264/R
£459 $850 €670 Hudson Valley landscape (41x51cm-16x20in) s. canvas on panel. 18-Jul-4 William Jenack, New York #239/R
£537 $950 €784 Fall river landscape (43x74cm-17x29in) s. 2-May-4 William Jenack, New York #195
£710 $1300 €1037 Old mill (46x61cm-18x24in) s. board exhib. 5-Jun-4 Treadway Gallery, Cincinnati #661/R est:1000-1500

MILLER, Charles Henry (attrib) (1842-1922) American
£435 $800 €635 Cow in a landscape (41x51cm-16x20in) init.d.July 4 1873 canvas on board. 25-Mar-4 Doyle, New York #44/R

MILLER, Charles Keith (19th C) British
£510 $806 €745 Lifeboat making for distressed sailing ship on the Goodwin Sands (38x51cm-15x20in) s.verso. 7-Sep-3 Desmond Judd, Cranbrook #708

MILLER, David (?) ?
£480 $878 €701 Carp and water lilies (59x120cm-23x47in) s.d.97 board exhib. 7-Apr-4 Woolley & Wallis, Salisbury #327/R

MILLER, Felix Martin (fl.1842-1880) British
Sculpture
£2500 $4550 €3650 Bust of the Naiad Oenone (163cm-64in) s.i. white marble scagliola column sold with a bust of Caesar. 15-Jun-4 Sotheby's, Olympia #66/R est:2000-3000

MILLER, Ferdinand von II (1842-1929) German
Sculpture
£1549 $2680 €2200 Game hunter (36cm-14in) s.d.1874 pat bronze. 10-Dec-3 Hugo Ruef, Munich #2787/R est:1800

MILLER, Francis (attrib) (1885-1930) American
£1230 $2300 €1796 Still life with coconuts and nuts (41x56cm-16x22in) s. 29-Feb-4 Grogan, Boston #53/R

MILLER, Frederick (19th C) British
£290 $542 €423 Beached boat with figures (23x33cm-9x13in) s. 24-Feb-4 Rogers Jones, Clwyd #152

MILLER, Gary Fabian (1957-) British
Photographs
£2500 $4550 €3650 Sections of England, snowscapes (53x53cm-21x21in) s.verso cibachrome print edition 3 of 5 prov. 21-Jun-4 Bonhams, New Bond Street #106/R est:2000-3000
£2500 $4550 €3650 Sections of England, snowscapes (53x53cm-21x21in) s.verso cibachrome print edition 3 of 5 prov. 21-Jun-4 Bonhams, New Bond Street #107/R est:2000-3000

MILLER, Godfrey Clive (1893-1964) Australian
£992 $1755 €1448 Harbour sketch (15x20cm-6x8in) canvasboard prov. 3-May-4 Christie's, Melbourne #355/R est:2000-3000 (A.D 2400)
£3099 $5733 €4525 Still life (23x26cm-9x10in) canvas on board prov. 10-Mar-4 Deutscher-Menzies, Melbourne #322/R est:4500-6500 (A.D 7500)
£13115 $21246 €19148 Ginger jar and fruit (44x59cm-17x23in) prov. 30-Jul-3 Goodman, Sydney #79/R est:30000-40000 (A.D 32000)
Sculpture
£7287 $11733 €10639 Female figure (32cm-13in) bronze exhib.lit. 25-Aug-3 Sotheby's, Paddington #309/R est:8000-12000 (A.D 18000)
Works on paper
£275 $443 €402 Nude drawing (27x37cm-11x15in) init. bears i.verso pencil exhib. 25-Aug-3 Sotheby's, Paddington #357 (A.D 680)
£279 $450 €407 Female nude (36x25cm-14x10in) init. i.verso pencil exhib. 25-Aug-3 Sotheby's, Paddington #293 (A.D 690)

MILLER, Harold (?) British
Works on paper
£400 $716 €584 Manx Farm (38x43cm-15x17in) s.d.54. 7-May-4 Chrystals Auctions, Isle of Man #311

MILLER, Harry Garrison (20th C) American
£1471 $2500 €2148 Old tree in the spring (76x91cm-30x36in) s.d.47 s.i.d.July 1 1947 verso prov. 1-Nov-3 Santa Fe Art, Santa Fe #146/R est:15000-20000

MILLER, Henry (1891-1980) American
Works on paper
£2067 $3803 €3100 Composition (20x14cm-8x6in) s.d.novembre 1957 india ink. 9-Jun-4 Piasa, Paris #174/R est:2500-3000

MILLER, Jack (1920-) American
£1229 $2200 €1794 Walker (175x43cm-69x17in) oil gouache. 13-May-4 Dallas Auction Gallery, Dallas #257/R est:600-800

MILLER, James (18/20th C) British
£1500 $2700 €2190 Thames at Richmond (49x71cm-19x28in) 21-Jan-4 Sotheby's, Olympia #86/R est:1200-1800
Works on paper
£5800 $9860 €8468 View of Westminster Bridge from Millbank (37x61cm-15x24in) pen ink W/C htd bodycol. 27-Nov-3 Sotheby's, London #266/R est:4000-6000

MILLER, James Robertson (fl.1880-1912) British
Works on paper
£360 $601 €526 View of Amiens (36x25cm-14x10in) s. W/C. 14-Oct-3 Bonhams, Knightsbridge #221/R

MILLER, Jan (20th C) American
£519 $950 €779 Oranges quartered (102x137cm-40x54in) acrylic. 10-Jul-4 Hindman, Chicago #347/R est:300-500

MILLER, John (1931-2002) British
£1550 $2821 €2263 Misty cathedral (70x100cm-28x39in) s.i.verso. 21-Jun-4 Bonhams, Bath #412/R est:1500-2500
£5000 $8300 €7300 The Beacon Sancreed (71x81cm-28x32in) s.d.1992 i.verso prov. 2-Oct-3 Lane, Penzance #40/R est:6000-7000
Sculpture
£2800 $5012 €4200 These fooling things. resin bas-relief. 12-May-4 Chochon-Barre & Allardi, Paris #116 est:150-200
Works on paper
£333 $597 €500 Village (11x16cm-4x6in) crayon. 12-May-4 Chochon-Barre & Allardi, Paris #115
£367 $656 €550 Salle de bains (14x13cm-6x5in) crayon. 12-May-4 Chochon-Barre & Allardi, Paris #114
£400 $740 €584 Wave (13x10cm-5x4in) s. s.i.verso gouache. 10-Feb-4 David Lay, Penzance #125
£500 $835 €730 Church in Penwith (30x53cm-12x21in) s.i. W/C. 14-Oct-3 David Lay, Penzance #5
£540 $896 €788 First day cover, alternative landscape (15x22cm-6x9in) s.i. W/C prov. 2-Oct-3 Lane, Penzance #228
£660 $1181 €964 Penzance from Tredavot (25x35cm-10x14in) s. W/C. 16-Mar-4 Bonhams, Oxford #12/R

MILLER, Joseph (19th C) German
£1761 $3046 €2500 Little apples thieves (77x63cm-30x25in) s.d.1865. 10-Dec-3 Christie's, Amsterdam #684/R est:3000-5000
£2742 $5045 €4003 Toy horse (70x80cm-28x31in) s.d.1867 canvas on masonite. 14-Jun-4 Waddingtons, Toronto #306/R est:10000-15000 (C.D 6800)

MILLER, Keith (20th C) American
Works on paper
£776 $1250 €1133 Sappho and Livonia (43x74cm-17x29in) prov. W/C. 20-Aug-3 James Julia, Fairfield #934/R

MILLER, Kenneth Hayes (1876-1952) American
£433 $776 €650 Woman's head (37x30cm-15x12in) panel. 15-May-4 Van Ham, Cologne #804
£1538 $2646 €2200 Three female heads (40x48cm-16x19in) board. 4-Dec-3 Van Ham, Cologne #326/R est:1000
£11602 $21000 €16939 Woman sleeping (87x114cm-34x45in) s.d.26 prov.exhib. 31-Mar-4 Sotheby's, New York #131/R est:12000-18000

MILLER, Kenneth Hayes (attrib) (1876-1952) American
£1200 $2148 €1800 Two women (60x40cm-24x16in) panel. 15-May-4 Van Ham, Cologne #803/R est:1800

MILLER, Lee (20th C) American
Photographs
£16766 $28000 €24478 Self-portrait (23x17cm-9x7in) s.verso gelatin silver print exec.1931. 17-Oct-3 Phillips, New York #87/R est:15000-20000

MILLER, Lewis (1959-) Australian
£1106 $1881 €1615 Large reclining nude (101x181cm-40x71in) s.d.99 s.i.d.verso. 26-Nov-3 Deutscher-Menzies, Melbourne #52/R est:3000-5000 (A.D 2600)

MILLER, Lilian May (1895-1943) American
£320 $550 €467 Forest monarch (20x48cm-8x19in) s. 7-Dec-3 Treadway Gallery, Cincinnati #149/R

MILLER, Melvin (1937-) American
£249 $450 €364 No 9 Front Street (91x147cm-36x58in) whiting gesso masonite. 16-Apr-4 American Auctioneer #291/R

MILLER, Milton (19th C) American
Photographs
£3222 $5800 €4704 Cantones Mandarin and his wife (19x24cm-7x9in) albumen print executed c.1861 lit. 22-Apr-4 Phillips, New York #189/R est:8000-12000

MILLER, Nick (20th C) British
£1733 $3137 €2600 Cloud above II (41x46cm-16x18in) s. i.d.2001 verso prov. 30-Mar-4 De Veres Art Auctions, Dublin #115/R est:2000-3000

MILLER, Oscar (1867-?) American
£1447 $2300 €2113 Young woman mending (41x61cm-16x24in) s. 12-Sep-3 Skinner, Boston #257/R est:1200

MILLER, Paton (1953-) American
£649 $1200 €948 White Dog (212x245cm-83x96in) s.i.d.88 verso oil chl unprimed canvas painted 1987-88 prov. 12-Feb-4 Sotheby's, New York #351/R

MILLER, Peter (19/20th C) British
£989 $1800 €1444 Pony express station, Echo country, Utah. Stage coach (97x122cm-38x48in) s. pair painted c.1990. 29-Jun-4 Sotheby's, New York #254/R est:3000-5000

MILLER, Ralph Davison (1858-1946) American
£335 $600 €489 Landscape with a stag (60x77cm-24x30in) s. 21-Mar-4 Bonhams & Butterfields, Los Angeles #7368/R
£706 $1200 €1031 No 6 Cypress Point (41x51cm-16x20in) indis.sig. panel. 18-Nov-3 John Moran, Pasadena #24a
£732 $1200 €1061 Landscape with eucalyptus trees and distant mountains (61x76cm-24x30in) s. laid down wax on masonite prov. 31-May-3 Brunk, Ashville #582/R
£809 $1504 €1181 Mexican seated on stone steps smoking (60x47cm-24x19in) s.d.1902. 2-Mar-4 Rasmussen, Copenhagen #1355/R (D.KR 9000)
£1000 $1700 €1460 Oaks in river landscape (46x66cm-18x26in) s.d.1910 canvas on canvas prov. 18-Nov-3 John Moran, Pasadena #146 est:1500-2500
£2152 $3400 €3142 Native American driving oxen with bright sun (76x102cm-30x40in) s. 6-Sep-3 Brunk, Ashville #877

MILLER, Richard E (1875-1943) American
£13812 $25000 €20166 Le deshabille bleu (65x54cm-26x21in) prov. 31-Mar-4 Sotheby's, New York #52/R est:15000-25000
£48295 $85000 €70511 Portrait of Alice Carey (76x61cm-30x24in) s. painted c.1905 prov.exhib.lit. 19-May-4 Sotheby's, New York #38/R est:30000-50000
£84302 $145000 €123081 Reading in the garden (27x22cm-11x9in) i.verso panel painted c.1911-13. 3-Dec-3 Sotheby's, New York #1/R est:50000-70000
£204545 $360000 €298636 Resting by the riverbank (53x64cm-21x25in) s. painted c.1910-11 prov. 19-May-4 Sotheby's, New York #26/R est:250000-450000

MILLER, Roy (1938-) British
£250 $398 €365 Slums, Manchester (43x30cm-17x12in) s. painted 1959 prov. 1-May-3 John Nicholson, Haslemere #691

MILLER, Thad (20th C) American
£288 $525 €420 Psych painting 6 1969 Beatles (183x119cm-72x47in) s.d.1969 plywood. 7-Feb-4 Dan Ripley, Indianapolis #35

MILLER, Werner (1892-1959) Swiss
£345 $617 €504 House under trees (78x70cm-31x28in) mono.d.21 i. stretcher. 12-May-4 Dobiaschofsky, Bern #802/R (S.FR 800)

MILLER, William (fl.1878-1933) British
£333 $600 €486 Forest scene with cascading stream (76x51cm-30x20in) s. 24-Apr-4 Weschler, Washington #540/R

MILLER, William Rickarby (1818-1893) American
£1006 $1800 €1469 Moonlight on the Passaic river, Paterson, NJ (20x15cm-8x6in) s. board. 8-Jan-4 James Julia, Fairfield #958/R est:1200-1800
£1183 $2200 €1727 Figures at a country inn (46x36cm-18x14in) s.d.1874. 3-Mar-4 Christie's, Rockefeller NY #3/R est:2500-3000
£1358 $2200 €1969 Walk in the woods (18x26cm-7x10in) s.d.1818 board. 8-Aug-3 Barridorf, Portland #347/R est:2500-3500
£1963 $3200 €2866 Poe's cottage, Fordham (18x25cm-7x10in) s.d.1885. 27-Sep-3 Charlton Hall, Columbia #502/R est:1500-2500
£2159 $3800 €3152 Adirondack landscape (30x51cm-12x20in) s.d.1876 prov. 3-Jan-4 Collins, Maine #32/R est:3500-4500
£5988 $10000 €8742 Long Island Homestead, Bowery Bay, Long Island (36x51cm-14x20in) s. 23-Oct-3 Shannon's, Milford #31/R est:10000-15000
£10753 $20000 €15699 Mississippi sunset (36x48cm-14x19in) s.i.stretcher painted c.1852. 7-Mar-4 Treadway Gallery, Cincinnati #489/R est:15000-20000

MILLES, Carl (1875-1955) Swedish/American
Sculpture
£809 $1400 €1181 Ung kvinde - woman head (25cm-10in) s. green pat. bronze on stone pedestal. 10-Dec-3 Alderfer's, Hatfield #232/R est:2500-3000
£1626 $2911 €2374 The water carrier (10cm-4in) s. brown pat.bronze Cast H Bergman. 25-May-4 Bukowskis, Stockholm #293/R est:15000-20000 (S.KR 22000)
£1996 $3572 €2914 Dutch fisherman (10cm-4in) s. brown pat.bronze Cast H Bergman. 25-May-4 Bukowskis, Stockholm #294/R est:15000-20000 (S.KR 27000)
£2333 $4293 €3500 Le baiser vole (25cm-10in) s. terracotta. 11-Jun-4 Claude Aguttes, Neuilly #112/R est:2000-3000
£3000 $5160 €4380 Carl Vilhelm Heele (49cm-19in) s. green pat.bronze Cast Bergman. 2-Dec-3 Bukowskis, Stockholm #235a/R est:35000-40000 (S.KR 39000)
£3800 $6840 €5548 Struggle for existence (19x22cm-7x9in) s. brown pat bronze. 21-Apr-4 Sotheby's, London #153/R est:4000-6000
£6282 $11245 €9172 Europa - from Europa and the bull (57cm-22in) init. green pat.bronze Cast Rasmussen. 26-May-4 AB Stockholms Auktionsverk #2159/R est:100000-125000 (S.KR 85000)
£14231 $24477 €20777 Children playing on guard dogs (165cm-65in) s. green pat.bronze incl. marble pedestals cire perdue pair. 2-Dec-3 Bukowskis, Stockholm #235/R est:80000-100000 (S.KR 185000)

MILLESON, Royal Hill (1849-1926) American
£604 $1100 €882 Fall landscape with distant village (51x61cm-20x24in) s. 19-Jun-4 Jackson's, Cedar Falls #7/R
Works on paper
£323 $600 €472 Summer landscape with a small stream (36x51cm-14x20in) s. W/C executed c.1900. 7-Mar-4 Treadway Gallery, Cincinnati #511/R

MILLET, Clarence (1897-1959) American
£1768 $3200 €2581 French quarter homes (18x15cm-7x6in) s. board. 3-Apr-4 Neal Auction Company, New Orleans #513/R est:1500-2500
£1989 $3600 €2904 French quitter courtyard (20x18cm-8x7in) s. 3-Apr-4 Neal Auction Company, New Orleans #514/R est:1500-2500
£2703 $5000 €3946 Chartres Street, New Orleans (25x20cm-10x8in) s.i. panel. 17-Jan-4 New Orleans Auction, New Orleans #743/R est:4500-7000
£2907 $5000 €4244 Little Theatre courtyard (46x38cm-18x15in) s. s.i.verso canvasboard. 6-Dec-3 Neal Auction Company, New Orleans #573/R est:4000-6000
£3198 $5500 €4669 Exchange Alley, New Orleans (46x38cm-18x15in) s. s.i.verso canvasboard. 6-Dec-3 Neal Auction Company, New Orleans #562/R est:5000-7000
£3198 $5500 €4669 Autumn (36x43cm-14x17in) s. s.i.verso canvasboard. 6-Dec-3 Neal Auction Company, New Orleans #587/R est:5000-7000
£4360 $7500 €6366 Jackson Square rainy day (36x46cm-14x18in) s. s.i.verso canvasboard. 6-Dec-3 Neal Auction Company, New Orleans #586/R est:7000-10000
£4784 $7750 €6985 Apple blossoms (38x46cm-15x18in) s. canvasboard. 2-Aug-3 Neal Auction Company, New Orleans #407/R est:5000-7000
£7831 $13000 €11433 Plantation Home-Moonlight (56x66cm-22x26in) s. s.i.verso. 4-Oct-3 Neal Auction Company, New Orleans #583/R est:15000-25000
£8721 $15000 €12733 River shacks (56x66cm-22x26in) s. s.i.verso. 6-Dec-3 Neal Auction Company, New Orleans #561a/R est:8000-12000
£10843 $18000 €15831 Road from Woodville (56x66cm-22x26in) s. s.i.verso. 4-Oct-3 Neal Auction Company, New Orleans #541/R est:10000-15000
£18675 $31000 €27266 Shadow (76x91cm-30x36in) 4-Oct-3 Neal Auction Company, New Orleans #537/R est:15000-25000

MILLET, Clarence (attrib) (1897-1959) American
£328 $600 €479 Delachaise Plantation in Louisiana (30x41cm-12x16in) board. 5-Jun-4 Neal Auction Company, New Orleans #370

MILLET, Francis Davis (1846-1912) American
£2095 $3750 €3059 Cardinal's garden (32x21cm-13x8in) init. board. 14-May-4 Skinner, Boston #139/R est:1000-1500

MILLET, Francisque (attrib) (17/18th C) French
£805 $1482 €1200 Vue panoramique d'un paysage de riviere (14x10cm-6x4in) i.verso cardboard. 26-Mar-4 Piasa, Paris #48

MILLET, Francisque (17/18th C) French
£927 $1688 €1400 Voyageurs sur une route dans un paysage boise (27cm-11in circular) panel. 21-Jun-4 Tajan, Paris #111 est:1000-1500

MILLET, Francisque I (attrib) (1642-1679) French
£2600 $4420 €3796 Figures taking fright in a storm as lightning strikes a coastal town (63x92cm-25x36in) prov. 29-Oct-3 Bonhams, New Bond Street #130/R est:3000-5000
£3158 $5811 €4800 Figures in landscape (102x131cm-40x52in) 22-Jun-4 Ribeyre & Baron, Paris #34/R est:4000-6000

MILLET, François (1851-1917) French
£1042 $1646 €1500 Grain harvest (40x60cm-16x24in) s. lit. 19-Sep-3 Schloss Ahlden, Ahlden #1509/R est:950
Works on paper
£3669 $6017 €5100 La fermiere aux dindons (64x46cm-25x18in) s. pastel. 6-Jun-3 Chochon-Barre & Allardi, Paris #78/R est:4300-4500

MILLET, Frederic (1786-1859) French
Miniatures
£2500 $4325 €3650 Young lady (13cm-5in) s.d.1833 oval. 9-Dec-3 Christie's, London #224/R est:2500-3500

MILLET, Jean Baptiste (1831-1906) French
Works on paper
£816 $1461 €1200 Paysage aux lavandieres (33x26cm-13x10in) W/C pen ink. 21-Mar-4 Muizon & Le Coent, Paris #40/R

MILLET, Jean Charles (19/20th C) French
£872 $1544 €1300 Fermieres et son enfant devant ses oies (55x45cm-22x18in) s. 30-Apr-4 Tajan, Paris #133/R est:2000

MILLET, Jean François (1814-1875) French
£2218 $3594 €3150 Etude de paysans (8x6cm-3x2in) blk crayon. 11-Aug-3 Boscher, Cherbourg #747/R est:2000-3000
Prints
£1587 $3000 €2317 Les becheurs (23x33cm-9x13in) etching. 21-Feb-4 Brunk, Ashville #297/R est:1000-2000
£1882 $3200 €2748 Paysan retrant du fumier (16x13cm-6x5in) etching. 6-Nov-3 Swann Galleries, New York #382/R est:2500-3500
£2118 $3600 €3092 Les becheurs (24x34cm-9x13in) brown etching. 6-Nov-3 Swann Galleries, New York #384/R est:4000-6000
£2235 $3800 €3263 La grande bergere (32x24cm-13x9in) sepia etching. 6-Nov-3 Swann Galleries, New York #387/R est:3500-5000
£2533 $4636 €3800 Cardeuse (18x126cm-7x50in) s. prov.lit. 6-Jun-4 Osenat, Fontainebleau #158/R est:3000-3500
£3529 $6000 €5152 Depart pour le travail (39x31cm-15x12in) sepia etching. 6-Nov-3 Swann Galleries, New York #389/R est:5000-8000
£5000 $8500 €7300 Les glaneuses (19x25cm-7x10in) black etching. 6-Nov-3 Swann Galleries, New York #383/R est:6000-9000
Works on paper
£691 $1250 €1009 Female figure (18x8cm-7x3in) black chk. 16-Apr-4 Du Mouchelle, Detroit #2130/R est:1500-2500
£755 $1208 €1050 Etude d'ane et de paysans (9x13cm-4x5in) blk crayon brown wash. 16-May-3 Tajan, Paris #162
£1049 $1783 €1500 Etude pour la Vierge a l'enfant Jesus (14x6cm-6x2in) st.init. pierre noire. 24-Nov-3 Boscher, Cherbourg #761/R est:1500-1800

£1477	$2702	€2200	Etude pour le tableau - Paysanne coulant sa lessive ou la lessiveuse (22x16cm-9x6in) studio st. lead pencil. 7-Jul-4 Artcurial Briest, Paris #44 est:800-1000
£1748	$2972	€2500	Les planteurs de pommes de terre (29x22cm-11x9in) st.init. black crayon exec.c.1860/1862. 24-Nov-3 Boscher, Cherbourg #762/R est:3000-3500
£2313	$4140	€3400	Jeune femme de profil la tete appuyee sur une main (11x11cm-4x4in) black crayon blue paper prov. 17-Mar-4 Tajan, Paris #146/R est:2000
£2797	$4671	€4000	Semeur (19x14cm-7x6in) st.init. chl dr. 29-Jun-3 Eric Pillon, Calais #115/R
£2857	$4543	€4200	Two views of hamlet in the Hague (6x12cm-2x5in) s. studio st. pen blk ink. 23-Mar-3 Mercier & Cie, Lille #258/R est:5000-7000
£2999	$5158	€4379	Study for Le repos des Moissonneurs (15x26cm-6x10in) pen exec.c.1851 prov.lit. 3-Dec-3 Museumsbygningen, Copenhagen #174/R est:45000-50000 (D.KR 32000)
£3000	$5490	€4380	Shepherdess carrying a bay, with sheep. Marguerite Sensier (20x12cm-8x5in) black double-sided. 6-Jul-4 Christie's, London #195/R est:2000-3000
£3093	$5320	€4516	Chaumieres a Gruchy (10x12cm-4x5in) i. pen ink chk prov. 3-Dec-3 Museumsbygningen, Copenhagen #175/R est:30000-40000 (D.KR 33000)
£5000	$9000	€7300	Seated male nude academy (21x31cm-8x12in) init. graphite black chk. 20-Apr-4 Sotheby's, Olympia #194/R est:3000-4000
£6993	$11888	€10210	Soir (15x22cm-6x9in) crayon prov. 6-Nov-3 Tajan, Paris #199/R
£10000	$18000	€14600	Study of a woman breaking flax (22x15cm-9x6in) pencil chl htd white prov.exhib. 23-Apr-4 Sotheby's, New York #21/R est:20000-30000
£12941	$22000	€18894	Portrait of a man, said to be Leopold Desbrosses (54x42cm-21x17in) blk crayon blue-grey paper prov.exhib.lit. 28-Oct-3 Sotheby's, New York #97/R est:25000-35000
£19000	$34770	€27740	Ferme sur les hauteurs de Vichy, possibly Les Malavaux (13x21cm-5x8in) black chk pen ink W/C htd prov.exhib. 6-Jul-4 Christie's, London #193/R est:10000-15000
£65000	$118300	€94900	Les bucherons prenant leur repas (27x45cm-11x18in) s. black crayon prov.exhib.lit. 15-Jun-4 Sotheby's, London #161/R est:70000-100000

MILLET, Jean François (attrib) (1814-1875) French

£6376	$11732	€9500	Ideal landscape with figures (129x168cm-51x66in) 24-Mar-4 Dorotheum, Vienna #220/R est:8000-12000

MILLET, Jean François (studio) (1814-1875) French

£11000	$19030	€16060	Classical landscape with women gathering flowers, a town beyond (94x118cm-37x46in) 11-Dec-3 Sotheby's, London #203/R est:8000-12000

MILLIERE, Maurice (1871-1946) French

£671	$1188	€1000	Joyeuses Paques (38x30cm-15x12in) s. W/C gouache. 30-Apr-4 Tajan, Paris #187
£724	$1332	€1100	Bain de soleil (22x35cm-9x14in) s. 25-Jun-4 Millon & Associes, Paris #142/R
Works on paper			
£329	$605	€500	Portrait de jeune femme (26x19cm-10x7in) s. crayon col crayon. 25-Jun-4 Millon & Associes, Paris #143

MILLIKEN, James W (fl.1887-1930) British

Works on paper			
£300	$546	€438	A Dutch flower market (24x34cm-9x13in) s. pencil W/C. 1-Jul-4 Christie's, Kensington #442/R
£380	$604	€551	Village street scene with thatched cottages (17x25cm-7x10in) s. W/C. 9-Sep-3 David Duggleby, Scarborough #203
£450	$824	€657	Riva, Venice (18x25cm-7x10in) s. W/C. 27-Jan-4 Bonhams, Knightsbridge #155/R
£625	$1044	€906	Old church. Cheshire village (18x25cm-7x10in) s. W/C pair. 17-Jun-3 Pinneys, Montreal #87 est:600-800 (C.D 1400)
£800	$1464	€1168	Market scenes (17x24cm-7x9in) s. W/C pair. 27-Jan-4 Bonhams, Knightsbridge #362/R
£1900	$3363	€2774	Monckston Lane, Hampshire. Afternoon Warrington (27x45cm-11x18in) s. W/C pair. 28-Apr-4 Peter Wilson, Nantwich #132 est:1500-1800

MILLIKEN, Rob (20th C) British?

£320	$563	€467	Chance meeting (20x29cm-8x11in) init. tempera. 18-May-4 Woolley & Wallis, Salisbury #126/R

MILLIKEN, Robert W (1920-) British

Works on paper			
£260	$484	€380	Ducks over Lough Neagh, Co, Antrim (20x25cm-8x10in) s. W/C. 3-Mar-4 John Ross, Belfast #28
£320	$531	€467	Hawk among the ducks (54x74cm-21x29in) s. W/C. 1-Oct-3 Woolley & Wallis, Salisbury #118/R
£550	$935	€803	Black game (27x37cm-11x15in) s. pencil W/C htd white. 27-Nov-3 Christie's, Kensington #221/R
£550	$935	€803	Widgeon in flight (27x37cm-11x15in) s. W/C. 27-Nov-3 Christie's, Kensington #225/R
£550	$935	€803	French partridge in flight (27x37cm-11x15in) s. pencil W/C. 27-Nov-3 Christie's, Kensington #226/R
£550	$995	€803	Cock pheasant foraging. Woodcock in flight (37x50cm-15x20in) s. W/C pair. 31-Mar-4 Bonhams, Knightsbridge #21/R
£650	$1105	€949	Snipe and woodcock in flight (18x28cm-7x11in) s. W/C. 27-Nov-3 Christie's, Kensington #227/R

MILLINGER, Josef Stoitzner (1911-1982) Austrian

£352	$616	€500	Landscape with trees (66x50cm-26x20in) s.d.59 tempera paper. 19-Dec-3 Dorotheum, Vienna #181

MILLINGTON, James Heath (1799-1872) British

Miniatures			
£1000	$1700	€1460	Gentleman (7cm-3in) oval. 18-Nov-3 Bonhams, New Bond Street #166/R est:1000-1500

MILLINGTON, John (1891-1948) British

Works on paper			
£520	$884	€759	Sailing off Whitby (25x34cm-10x13in) s. W/C. 18-Nov-3 Bonhams, Leeds #63
£1800	$2934	€2628	The House of Parliament. Tower Bridge (30x43cm-12x17in) s. W/C pair. 23-Sep-3 John Nicholson, Haslemere #47 est:100-200

MILLNER, Karl (1825-1894) German

£1733	$3155	€2600	In Ramsau (55x46cm-22x18in) s.d.1888 i. stretcher. 30-Jun-4 Neumeister, Munich #617/R est:2000
£1879	$3326	€2800	Devil's Bridge on the St Gotthard (80x94cm-31x37in) s.d.1857. 28-Apr-4 Schopman, Hamburg #495/R est:1800
£2013	$3564	€3000	Classical alpine landscape (75x100cm-30x39in) s. bears d.185. 28-Apr-4 Schopman, Hamburg #496/R est:2200
£3077	$5231	€4400	High mountain outing (108x130cm-43x51in) s.d.1866. 20-Nov-3 Weidler, Nurnberg #335/R est:4900
£5282	$9454	€7500	Mountain landscape with cows in a pond and farmhouse in foreground (111x143cm-44x56in) mono. lit. 8-Jan-4 Allgauer, Kempten #2465/R est:9500

MILLNER, Karl (attrib) (1825-1894) German

£345	$576	€500	Tower in wooded landscape with view of high mountains (32x47cm-13x19in) i. paper on panel lit. 10-Jul-3 Allgauer, Kempten #2606/R
£448	$749	€650	Romantic mountain lnadscape with lake (86x124cm-34x49in) lit. 12-Jul-3 Bergmann, Erlangen #689/R

MILLNER, William Edward (1849-1885) British

£950	$1615	€1387	Summer souvenirs (32x24cm-13x9in) board. 19-Nov-3 Bonhams, New Bond Street #59/R

MILLOT, Adolphe (1857-1921) French

Works on paper			
£333	$603	€500	Mouse in nest in cornfield (21x14cm-8x6in) s. board. 2-Apr-4 Winterberg, Heidelberg #490

MILLS, Arthur W (19/20th C) British

Works on paper			
£260	$411	€377	Feeding time (25x36cm-10x14in) s. W/C. 27-Apr-3 Desmond Judd, Cranbrook #1035

MILLS, M (19th C) British?

£5298	$9642	€8000	Paris, le Champ de Mars, Prix Royal (41x81cm-16x32in) init. painted 1826. 16-Jun-4 Beaussant & Lefèvre, Paris #1/R est:10000-12000

MILLS, Reginald (20th C) British

£350	$595	€511	Mounted policeman in Trafalgar Square (38x54cm-15x21in) s. 27-Nov-3 Christie's, Kensington #127/R

MILLWARD, Clem (1929-) Australian

£1545	$2425	€2240	Landscape (121x121cm-48x48in) s.d.80 i.verso. 27-Aug-3 Christie's, Sydney #643 est:2000-4000 (A.D 3800)
£1829	$2872	€2652	Untitled, spinifex and mulga (120x150cm-47x59in) s.d prov.exhib.lit. 27-Aug-3 Christie's, Sydney #558 est:2000-4000 (A.D 4500)

MILNE, David Brown (1882-1953) Canadian

£9459	$16081	€13810	Petunias and bottle (51x21cm-20x8in) prov.exhib.lit. 18-Nov-3 Sotheby's, Toronto #71/R est:12000-15000 (C.D 21000)
£13514	$22973	€19730	Grey sunset (30x36cm-12x14in) s.d.1935 i.verso prov. 18-Nov-3 Sotheby's, Toronto #94/R est:30000-40000 (C.D 30000)
£16892	$28716	€24662	Cabin (30x35cm-12x14in) s.d.1935 canvas on panel backed with canvas. 18-Nov-3 Sotheby's, Toronto #93/R est:30000-40000 (C.D 37500)
£38288	$65090	€55900	House and shed (41x46cm-16x18in) s. i.verso prov.exhib. 18-Nov-3 Sotheby's, Toronto #148/R est:40000-60000 (C.D 85000)
£58559	$99550	€85496	Pool, Temagami, Lake Temagami, Ontario (50x61cm-20x24in) s. painted 1929 prov.exhib.lit. 27-Nov-3 Heffel, Vancouver #127/R est:90000-110000 (C.D 130000)
£81081	$137838	€118378	Woman and bright trees, West Saugerties, NY (55x50cm-22x20in) i.d.1914 verso prov.lit. 27-Nov-3 Heffel, Vancouver #116/R est:150000-175000 (C.D 180000)
Prints			
£8559	$14550	€12496	Blind road (13x18cm-5x7in) s.num./25 col drypoint prov.lit. 18-Nov-3 Sotheby's, Toronto #32/R est:10000-15000 (C.D 19000)
£11179	$20010	€16321	St. Michael's cathedral (19x21cm-7x8in) s.i. i.verso etching prov.lit. 31-May-4 Sotheby's, Toronto #62/R est:10000-15000 (C.D 27500)
£12195	$21829	€17805	Outlet of the pond (17x23cm-7x9in) s.num.50 col drypoint prov.lit. 31-May-4 Sotheby's, Toronto #11/R est:10000-12000 (C.D 30000)
Works on paper			
£3252	$5821	€4748	Sun Dogs II (30x40cm-12x16in) i.verso W/C exec. 1950 prov.exhib.lit. 27-May-4 Heffel, Vancouver #115/R est:8000-10000 (C.D 8000)
£6911	$12370	€10090	Trees and buildings with flag pole (40x51cm-16x20in) i.d.1915 pencil ink prov.exhib.lit. 31-May-4 Sotheby's, Toronto #12/R est:20000-30000 (C.D 17000)
£14444	$23689	€21088	Stump fence IV (36x53cm-14x21in) d.1946 W/C prov.exhib. 28-May-3 Maynards, Vancouver #70/R est:40000-50000 (C.D 32500)
£20325	$36382	€29675	Tower at night - scaffolding III (37x55cm-15x22in) i.verso W/C prov.exhib. 31-May-4 Sotheby's, Toronto #120/R est:30000-40000 (C.D 50000)
£22523	$38288	€32884	Pig and cat (37x56cm-15x22in) W/C prov.exhib.lit. 18-Nov-3 Sotheby's, Toronto #70/R est:50000-60000 (C.D 50000)
£27027	$45946	€39459	Snow bank and apple trees (39x57cm-15x22in) s.d.22 i.verso W/C prov.exhib.lit. 18-Nov-3 Sotheby's, Toronto #34/R est:50000-70000 (C.D 60000)

MILNE, Joe (fl.1905-1908) British

£400	$644	€584	Buckhaven (28x41cm-11x16in) s. 15-Aug-3 Keys, Aylsham #718/R
£800	$1464	€1168	Sheep in pasture (22x32cm-9x13in) s. canvas on panel. 8-Apr-4 Bonhams, Edinburgh #138
£1200	$2244	€1752	Children by the Tay (30x45cm-12x18in) s. 22-Jul-4 Bonhams, Edinburgh #320 est:800-1200

£2200	$3938	€3212	Fishing boats in harbour (51x76cm-20x30in) s. 28-May-4 Lyon & Turnbull, Edinburgh #7/R est:2000-3000

MILNE, John E (1931-1978) British

Sculpture

£850	$1572	€1241	Delphi (31x28cm-12x11in) init.d.69 num.6/9 verso fiber glass lit. 11-Feb-4 Sotheby's, Olympia #279/R est:600-800
£900	$1665	€1314	Cylindrical form (26cm-10in) init.d.1974 num.1/6 polished bronze lit. 11-Feb-4 Sotheby's, Olympia #275/R est:1000-1500
£1100	$2035	€1606	Horus (46cm-18in) init.d.1969 num.8/9 polished bronze lit. 11-Feb-4 Sotheby's, Olympia #277/R est:1200-1800
£1300	$2405	€1898	Bronze form (23cm-9in) init. num.5/9 bronze. 10-Feb-4 David Lay, Penzance #546/R est:600-700
£1400	$2380	€2044	Horus (42cm-17in) init.d.1969 num.2/9 polished pat. bronze, prov.lit. 21-Nov-3 Christie's, London #180/R est:1500-2500
£2600	$4420	€3796	Poseidon III (59cm-23in) init.d.1971 num.7/9 polished pat, bronze stone base prov.lit. 21-Nov-3 Christie's, London #179/R est:2500-3500
£4000	$6360	€5840	Rising sun (65cm-26in) bronze black marble base. 10-Sep-3 Sotheby's, Olympia #344/R est:3000-5000
£4800	$8736	€7008	Vertical form (84cm-33in) guarea incl. base exec. 1954 lit. 15-Jun-4 Bonhams, New Bond Street #91/R est:5000-7000

Works on paper

£420	$777	€613	Untitled (36x26cm-14x10in) chl pastel. 13-Jul-4 Bonhams, Knightsbridge #108/R
£500	$860	€730	Vortex (55x37cm-22x15in) chl prov. 3-Dec-3 Christie's, Kensington #757/R

MILNE, John Maclaughlan (1885-1957) British

£500	$860	€730	Still life with vase of flowers (51x38cm-20x15in) s. 4-Dec-3 Biddle & Webb, Birmingham #959
£680	$1136	€993	Driving the flock (14x19cm-6x7in) s. board. 12-Nov-3 Sotheby's, Olympia #128/R
£720	$1318	€1051	Dutch polder (43x55cm-17x22in) s. 8-Apr-4 Bonhams, Edinburgh #95
£950	$1767	€1387	Returning home (14x18cm-6x7in) s. board. 4-Mar-4 Christie's, Kensington #146/R
£4000	$6480	€5800	Sannox Bay, Arran (37x46cm-15x18in) s. board. 30-Jul-3 Hamptons Fine Art, Godalming #276/R est:1200-2400
£6500	$11050	€9490	Red Cart, Provence (46x61cm-18x24in) s. 30-Oct-3 Christie's, London #191/R est:4000-6000
£7000	$12670	€10220	Arran cottages (38x46cm-15x18in) s. board prov. 19-Apr-4 Sotheby's, London #78/R est:7000-10000
£9500	$17195	€13870	Mountain burn (38x46cm-15x18in) s. prov. 19-Apr-4 Sotheby's, London #79/R est:6000-8000
£9800	$16856	€14308	La Place, St Tropez (51x61cm-20x24in) s. bears i.stretcher prov. 4-Dec-3 Bonhams, Edinburgh #89/R est:10000-15000
£10500	$17010	€15225	Bridge over river in a town (28x36cm-11x14in) s. 30-Jul-3 Hamptons Fine Art, Godalming #275/R est:2500-4000
£10500	$18060	€15330	West coast silver sands (51x61cm-20x24in) s. prov. 4-Dec-3 Bonhams, Edinburgh #95/R est:7000-10000
£11000	$19030	€16060	Huts on the beach, Arran (51x61cm-20x24in) s. 11-Dec-3 Lyon & Turnbull, Edinburgh #114/R est:6000-8000
£12000	$20400	€17520	Haymaking (51x65cm-20x26in) s.d.31. 30-Oct-3 Christie's, London #189/R est:10000-15000
£18500	$29785	€26825	French hill town (60x75cm-24x30in) s.d.24 prov. 21-Aug-3 Bonhams, Edinburgh #1143/R est:8000-12000

Works on paper

£450	$752	€657	Tarbert, Loch Fyne (18x27cm-7x11in) s. W/C. 16-Oct-3 Bonhams, Edinburgh #148
£620	$1141	€905	St Tropez (28x33cm-11x13in) s.i.d.24 pen ink. 10-Jun-4 Lyon & Turnbull, Edinburgh #97
£900	$1548	€1314	French farm on the coast (36x24cm-14x9in) s. W/C buff paper sold with similar W/C two. 4-Dec-3 Bonhams, Edinburgh #104

MILNE, Joseph (1861-1911) British

£318	$550	€464	Ships sailing around an island (28x41cm-11x16in) s. board. 13-Dec-3 Sloans & Kenyon, Bethesda #546/R
£460	$782	€672	Landscape with cattle grazing (40x60cm-16x24in) s. 29-Oct-3 Bonhams, Chester #450
£600	$954	€870	Sheep and a cart on a country road (31x41cm-12x16in) s. 9-Sep-3 Bonhams, Knightsbridge #271/R
£600	$1020	€876	Scottish coastal scene with seabirds in a rocky pool (28x44cm-11x17in) s. board. 19-Nov-3 Tennants, Leyburn #1042
£1800	$3222	€2628	River in Angus (40x61cm-16x24in) s.d.04. 26-May-4 Sotheby's, Olympia #222/R est:2000-3000
£2100	$3297	€3045	Cattle watering (45x20cm-18x8in) s. prov. 27-Aug-3 Sotheby's, London #972/R est:1500-2000
£2200	$3454	€3190	Road home (47x62cm-19x24in) s. board. 27-Aug-3 Sotheby's, London #1124/R est:1500-2000

MILNE, William (19/20th C) British

£920	$1693	€1343	Homewards (25x36cm-10x14in) s.d.98. 25-Mar-4 Bonhams, Edinburgh #355

MILNE, William Watt (fl.1900-1915) British

£400	$736	€584	Waves breaking on a rocky coast (31x46cm-12x18in) s.d.95. 10-Jun-4 Lyon & Turnbull, Edinburgh #31
£550	$974	€803	Coastal landscape at low tide (30x46cm-12x18in) s. 29-Apr-4 Gorringes, Lewes #2488
£800	$1440	€1168	East coast fishing village (16x24cm-6x9in) s.d.1908 panel. 22-Apr-4 Bonhams, Edinburgh #331
£1860	$3291	€2716	Fieldworkers at Cambuskenneth (12x21cm-5x8in) s. i.verso panel pair. 3-May-4 Lawson Menzies, Sydney #396 est:2000-3000 (A.D 4500)
£2300	$3956	€3358	Fishing village (40x51cm-16x20in) s. 6-Dec-3 Shapes, Edinburgh #409/R est:250-350
£2600	$4914	€3796	Dusk, Gyles Pittenweem (63x76cm-25x30in) s. 19-Feb-4 Lyon & Turnbull, Edinburgh #101 est:1500-2000
£2900	$5017	€4234	Busy harbour scene, Pittenweem (30x38cm-12x15in) s. 11-Dec-3 Lyon & Turnbull, Edinburgh #54/R est:2000-3000
£4600	$7912	€6716	Landing the catch (50x61cm-20x24in) s. 6-Dec-3 Shapes, Edinburgh #408/R est:300-500

MILNER, Boxer (1935-) Australian

Works on paper

£1020	$1825	€1489	Wirrimangaru (60x90cm-24x35in) synthetic polymer paint linen exec 2001 prov. 25-May-4 Lawson Menzies, Sydney #130/R est:3000-4000 (A.D 2600)
£2941	$5265	€4294	Purkitji (150x75cm-59x30in) synthetic polymer paint linen exec 2002. 25-May-4 Lawson Menzies, Sydney #117/R est:8000-10000 (A.D 7500)

MILNER, Donald Ewart (1898-1993) British

£620	$1054	€905	Port of Bristol (70x91cm-28x36in) s. board. 4-Nov-3 Bristol Auction Rooms #591/R

MILNER, Frederick (1863-1939) British

£480	$888	€701	Street in Portalagre, Portugal (25x20cm-10x8in) s. board. 9-Mar-4 Gorringes, Lewes #2244
£520	$962	€759	Moon rising behind a mill (25x36cm-10x14in) s. board. 10-Feb-4 David Lay, Penzance #300

MILNER, William (19th C) British

£3125	$5000	€4563	Untitled (43x33cm-17x13in) painted c.1850. 19-Sep-3 Du Mouchelle, Detroit #2109/R est:3000-5000

MILNES-SMITH, John (1912-) British

£450	$774	€657	Horizontal painting, brown (51x61cm-20x24in) init. board. 3-Dec-3 Christie's, Kensington #787

MILO, Jean (1906-1993) Belgian

£738	$1366	€1100	Bathers and seaweed (65x23cm-26x9in) s.d.1962 s.i.d.1962 verso. 13-Mar-4 De Vuyst, Lokeren #244

MILONE, Antonio (?-1920) Italian

£250	$418	€365	Farmer and his donkey before Vesuvius (18x23cm-7x9in) s. 14-Oct-3 David Lay, Penzance #252/R
£671	$1201	€1000	In the stable (16x23cm-6x9in) s. board prov. 25-May-4 Finarte Semenzato, Milan #117/R

MILPURRURRU, George (1934-1998) Australian

Works on paper

£784	$1404	€1145	Long Grass at Maningrida (46x27cm-18x11in) natural earth pigment fixative on bark exec 1967 prov. 25-May-4 Lawson Menzies, Sydney #259/R est:2000-3000 (A.D 2000)
£1563	$2922	€2345	Mudukuntja hollow log ceremony (133x58cm-52x23in) bears name.i.verso earth pigments eucalyptus bark prov. 26-Jul-4 Sotheby's, Melbourne #233/R est:5000-7000 (A.D 4000)
£1626	$2569	€2358	Garr the spider (195x74cm-77x29in) earth pigments eucalyptus bark exec.c.1986 prov. 28-Jul-3 Sotheby's, Paddington #477/R est:4000-6000 (A.D 4000)
£1707	$2698	€2475	Gumang, magpie geese (101x75cm-40x30in) earth pigments canvas prov. 28-Jul-3 Sotheby's, Paddington #471/R est:1500-2500 (A.D 4200)
£1870	$2954	€2712	Gandayala, red kangaroo, hunting ceremony (121x91cm-48x36in) earth pigments exec.c.1990 prov. 28-Jul-3 Sotheby's, Paddington #469/R est:5000-8000 (A.D 4600)
£2344	$4383	€3516	Pythons and waterlilies (181x75cm-71x30in) earth pigments eucalyptus bark exec.c.1988 prov. 26-Jul-4 Sotheby's, Melbourne #538/R est:3000-4000 (A.D 6000)

MILROY, Lisa (1959-) Canadian

£6500	$11765	€9490	Greek vases (175x255cm-69x100in) init.d.85 prov.lit. 1-Apr-4 Christie's, Kensington #317/R est:6000-8000
£9000	$16290	€13140	Sailor's caps (190x239cm-75x94in) init.d.85 lit. 1-Apr-4 Christie's, Kensington #318/R est:7000-9000
£19500	$35490	€28470	Shoes (203x259cm-80x102in) init.d.86 overlap prov.exhib. 21-Jun-4 Bonhams, New Bond Street #176/R est:8000-12000

MILSTEIN, Zvi (1934-) Israeli

£315	$558	€470	Personnages (49x44cm-19x17in) s. 29-Apr-4 Claude Aguttes, Neuilly #99
£1034	$1862	€1500	La passionnee (100x73cm-39x29in) s. acrylic painted 1986 lit. 25-Jan-4 Chayette & Cheval, Paris #189 est:2000-2500

Works on paper

£420	$713	€600	Composition (62x48cm-24x19in) s. W/C pastel. 27-Nov-3 Calmels Cohen, Paris #73/R

MILTON, Carole (20th C) Australian

£637	$1172	€930	Roses and antiques silver (65x54cm-26x21in) s. 27-Jun-4 Joel, Victoria #189 (A.D 1700)
£1124	$2067	€1641	Hydrangeas (87x110cm-34x43in) s. 27-Jun-4 Joel, Victoria #188/R (A.D 3000)
£1260	$2256	€1840	David Austin Roses (76x61cm-30x24in) s. painted 2003. 10-May-4 Joel, Victoria #303/R est:2000-3000 (A.D 3100)

MILTON, Peter Winslow (1930-) American

Prints

£2706	$4600	€3951	Daylilies (50x81cm-20x32in) s.d.1975 num.X/XVIII photosensitive etching engraving. 21-Nov-3 Swann Galleries, New York #128/R est:4000-6000

MILTON-JENSEN, C (1855-1928) Danish

£289	$534	€422	Calm evening, Flynderso (83x125cm-33x49in) s.d.1910. 15-Mar-4 Rasmussen, Vejle #477 (D.KR 3200)
£300	$500	€438	Spring day in the wood (72x102cm-28x40in) s.d.1923. 25-Oct-3 Rasmussen, Havnen #2155/R (D.KR 3200)

£469 $867 €685 Farmyard with cat and chickens (54x68cm-21x27in) s. 15-Mar-4 Rasmussen, Vejle #445/R (D.KR 5200)
£478 $775 €693 Hilly landscape with lake and boat (52x92cm-20x36in) s.d.1912. 4-Aug-3 Rasmussen, Vejle #311/R (D.KR 5000)
£492 $901 €718 Woman seated by farm house (57x80cm-22x31in) s.d.1881. 9-Jun-4 Rasmussen, Copenhagen #1740/R (D.KR 5500)

MIMRAN, Patrick (1956-) American?
Prints
£6644 $11294 €9500 Last orange puff (200x50cm-79x20in) s.num.2/6 verso ink jet plexiglas. 25-Nov-3 Tajan, Paris #81/R est:7000-9000
£6993 $11888 €10000 Last green puff (200x50cm-79x20in) s.num.2/6 verso ink jet plexiglas. 25-Nov-3 Tajan, Paris #82/R est:7000-9000

MIN, Jaap (1914-1987) Dutch
£3623 $5942 €5000 Dunes of Schoorl (86x100cm-34x39in) s. 27-May-3 Sotheby's, Amsterdam #485/R est:5000-7000
Works on paper
£302 $559 €450 Portrait of a girl (39x29cm-15x11in) s. gouache. 15-Mar-4 Sotheby's, Amsterdam #203/R

MINAMI, Keiko (20th C) Japanese
£649 $1200 €948 Castle (23x18cm-9x7in) s. acrylic. 13-Mar-4 Susanin's, Chicago #6023/R
£919 $1700 €1342 Bird resting on sunflower (30x20cm-12x8in) s. a.c. 13-Mar-4 Susanin's, Chicago #6022/R est:250-400

MINARDI, Tommaso (1787-1871) Italian
Works on paper
£450 $779 €657 Head of a young girl, her hair tied with a ribbon (36x29cm-14x11in) s. col chk inscribed oval prov. 12-Dec-3 Christie's, Kensington #406/R

MINARIK, Jan B (1862-1937) Czechoslovakian
£985 $1635 €1438 Winter market at Old Town Square (48x49cm-19x19in) s.i. 4-Oct-3 Dorotheum, Prague #72/R est:30000-45000 (C.KR 45000)

MINARTZ, Tony (1873-1944) French
£1000 $1850 €1460 Figures in the park (40x28cm-16x11in) s. board. 14-Jul-4 Sotheby's, Olympia #268/R est:800-1200

MINAUX, Andre (1923-1988) French
£1200 $2208 €1800 Portrait de femme en pied (202x89cm-80x35in) s. cut panel. 9-Jun-4 Le Roux & Morel, Paris #44 est:1000-1200
£1301 $2212 €1900 Portrait de jeune fille (65x50cm-26x20in) s. 9-Nov-3 Eric Pillon, Calais #177/R
£1371 $2523 €2002 Woman in kimono holding a pitcher (131x70cm-52x28in) s. 14-Jun-4 Waddingtons, Toronto #291/R est:5000-7000 (C.D 3400)
Works on paper
£400 $736 €600 Portrait de femme (118x78cm-46x31in) chl pastel. 9-Jun-4 Le Roux & Morel, Paris #45
£420 $701 €600 Double vision (32x25cm-13x10in) s.i.d.1970 W/C. 25-Jun-3 Blanchet, Paris #100/R

MINCHIE, James Coutts (19th C) ?
£664 $1129 €950 Boy carrying a little girl through a wooded landscape (44x73cm-17x29in) s.d.1879. 26-Nov-3 James Adam, Dublin #26/R

MINCHIN, Eric (20th C) Australian
£265 $443 €384 Stormy sky (50x75cm-20x30in) s.d.1985 board. 13-Jul-3 James Lawson, Sydney #488 est:800-1200 (A.D 650)

MINCIEL, Eugeniusz (20th C) Polish
£398 $660 €581 Composition (245x121cm-96x48in) oil acrylic sand painted 1991-1992. 2-Oct-3 Agra, Warsaw #18/R (P.Z 2600)

MIND, Gottfried (1768-1814) Swiss
Works on paper
£271 $462 €396 Two cats (9x15cm-4x6in) i. W/C pen. 18-Nov-3 Hans Widmer, St Gallen #1153 (S.FR 600)
£594 $993 €850 Cat (7x9cm-3x4in) W/C graphite col pen. 10-Oct-3 Winterberg, Heidelberg #702
£633 $1077 €924 Cat with kittens (13x22cm-5x9in) i. W/C pen. 18-Nov-3 Hans Widmer, St Gallen #1152/R (S.FR 1400)
£874 $1460 €1250 Cat and kittens at milk dish (13x20cm-5x8in) W/C bodycol htd graphite col pen. 10-Oct-3 Winterberg, Heidelberg #701/R

MIND, Gottfried (attrib) (1768-1814) Swiss
Works on paper
£323 $579 €472 White cat (14x10cm-6x4in) gouache. 12-May-4 Dobiaschofsky, Bern #1149/R (S.FR 750)

MINDEN, Ottilie von (19th C) German
£650 $1079 €949 Autumnal landscape (85x117cm-33x46in) s. 1-Oct-3 Sotheby's, Olympia #277/R

MINDERHOUT, Andries (1920-) Dutch
£280 $476 €400 Child with fish (17x11cm-7x4in) board. 24-Nov-3 Glerum, Amsterdam #208/R

MINDERHOUT, Hendrik van (1632-1696) Dutch
£9155 $15838 €13000 Marchands Turcs dans un port Mediterraneen (58x81cm-23x32in) s. 14-Dec-3 St-Germain-en-Laye Encheres #13/R est:10000-12000
£13158 $24211 €20000 Harbour scene (154x276cm-61x109in) s.d.1685. 24-Jun-4 Christie's, Paris #23/R est:20000-30000
£33784 $59459 €50000 Roads of a city with a large flute, small cargo ship (93x121cm-37x48in) s. prov. 18-May-4 Sotheby's, Amsterdam #25/R est:50000-70000

MINE, T (20th C) Japanese
Sculpture
£2045 $3600 €2986 Seated figure (56x46x13cm-22x18x5in) s. bronze. 23-May-4 Hindman, Chicago #1101/R est:500-700

MINEL, Antonia (19th C) French
Works on paper
£411 $699 €600 Abside de Saint-Germain-des-Pres (51x36cm-20x14in) s.i.d.1825 W/C gouache. 6-Nov-3 Tajan, Paris #123

MINET, Louis Émile (1855-1920) French
£12583 $23026 €19000 Nature morte aux fleurs (145x200cm-57x79in) s. 9-Apr-4 Claude Aguttes, Neuilly #43/R est:20000-25000

MINET, Pierre (1909-1975) French
Works on paper
£267 $491 €400 Composition surrealiste (15x15cm-6x6in) s.i.d.1936 pen. 9-Jun-4 Piasa, Paris #176/R

MINEWSKI, Alexander (1917-1979) American
£250 $400 €365 Reclining nude on red (23x43cm-9x17in) s.i. canvas on masonite. 21-Sep-3 William Jenack, New York #84

MING DYNASTY, Chinese
Sculpture
£33784 $59459 €50000 Brushpot (14cm-6in) carved wood. 21-May-4 Dr Fritz Nagel, Stuttgart #1168/R est:6000

MINGELMANGANU, Alec (?-1981) Australian
Sculpture
£1953 $3652 €2930 Spearthrower (138x8cm-54x3in) earth pigments bush gum string sinew softwood exec.c.1980 prov. 26-Jul-4 Sotheby's, Melbourne #14/R est:5000-7000 (A.D 5000)
Works on paper
£1707 $2698 €2475 Wanjina (28x9cm-11x4in) i. earth pigments wood exec.c.1978 prov. 28-Jul-3 Sotheby's, Paddington #465/R est:2000-3000 (A.D 4200)
£60976 $96341 €88415 Wanjina (121x65cm-48x26in) earth pigments binders canvas exec.c.1980 prov. 28-Jul-3 Sotheby's, Paddington #161/R est:150000-200000 (A.D 150000)

MINGLE, Joseph F (1839-1903) American
£488 $800 €712 Shipwreck scene (38x61cm-15x24in) s.d.1894. 4-Jun-3 Alderfer's, Hatfield #416

MINGORANCE ACIEN, Manuel (1920-) Spanish
£313 $575 €475 Poet from Fuengirola (14x22cm-6x9in) s. s.i.d.1978 verso egg tempera. 22-Jun-4 Durán, Madrid #80/R
£313 $575 €475 Yellow umbrella (15x9cm-6x4in) s. s.i.d.1979 verso egg tempera. 22-Jun-4 Durán, Madrid #81/R
£417 $663 €600 El rio (46x38cm-18x15in) s. s.i.verso. 29-Apr-3 Durán, Madrid #758/R

MINGUET, Andre Joseph (1818-1860) Belgian
£2148 $3973 €3200 Interior of the Pauluskerk, Antwepen (72x58cm-28x23in) s. panel. 15-Mar-4 Sotheby's, Amsterdam #70/R est:2500-3500

MINGUILLON, Julia (1907-1965) Spanish
£6711 $12013 €10000 Women chatting (93x60cm-37x24in) s. board. 25-May-4 Durán, Madrid #94/R est:1800
£14789 $25585 €21000 Virgin of the Air (135x98cm-53x39in) s. painted 1939. 15-Dec-3 Ansorena, Madrid #35/R est:21000

MINGUZZI, Luciano (1911-) Italian
Sculpture
£1016 $1819 €1483 Bozettino per l'eco (20x38cm-8x15in) incised sig. bronze wood base. 4-May-4 Ritchie, Toronto #113/R est:4000-6000 (C.D 2500)
£1056 $1754 €1500 Goat (16x32x11cm-6x13x4in) st.sig. bronze. 11-Jun-3 Finarte Semenzato, Milan #682/R
£1594 $2614 €2200 Lights in the wood (16x50x9cm-6x20x4in) s. bronze exec.c.1961 prov. 27-May-3 Sotheby's, Milan #93/R est:2000
£1594 $2614 €2200 Cock (19x25x11cm-7x10x4in) s. bronze exec.1960 prov. 27-May-3 Sotheby's, Milan #92/R est:1000-1500
£1633 $2922 €2400 Untitled (58cm-23in) s. bronze. 16-Mar-4 Finarte Semenzato, Milan #187/R est:1200
£2029 $3328 €2800 Bust (47x23x11cm-19x9x4in) init. bronze exec.1954 prov.exhib. 27-May-3 Sotheby's, Milan #95/R est:2500-3000
£2899 $4754 €4000 Shadows in the wood 4 (51x33x13cm-20x13x5in) s. bronze exec.1956. 27-May-3 Sotheby's, Milan #91/R est:4500
£3623 $5942 €5000 Woman jumping (34x20x7cm-13x8x3in) init. bronze exec.1954 prov.exhib. 27-May-3 Sotheby's, Milan #94/R est:3000-4000

£3623	$5942	€5000	Man and cock (84x46x12cm-33x18x5in) s. bronze exec.1951-57. 27-May-3 Sotheby's, Milan #90/R est:5000-6000
£3636	$6182	€5200	Lovers (30cm-12in) s. bronze. 29-Nov-3 Farsetti, Prato #444/R est:5000-6000
£4348	$7130	€6000	Acrobats (70x20x11cm-28x8x4in) init. bronze exhib. 27-May-3 Sotheby's, Milan #96/R est:3500-4500
£4396	$8000	€6418	Warrior (86cm-34in) mono. black pat. bronze executed 1958 prov. 29-Jun-4 Sotheby's, New York #438/R est:6000-8000
£4865	$9000	€7103	Cathedral (69x35x15cm-27x14x6in) bronze blk marble base prov. 12-Feb-4 Sotheby's, New York #142/R est:3000-5000
£8242	$15000	€12033	Echo (49x123cm-19x48in) mono. iron black pat. bronze prov. 29-Jun-4 Sotheby's, New York #439/R est:6000-8000
Works on paper			
£600	$1104	€900	Untitled (22x17cm-9x7in) s. mixed media card on canvas sold with serigraph by M Kostabi. 10-Jun-4 Galleria Pace, Milan #36/R

MINIER, Suzanne (1884-?) French

£1133	$2029	€1700	Marche de Bretagne (55x65cm-22x26in) 16-May-4 Osenat, Fontainebleau #93/R est:1500-2000

MINKER, Gustav (1866-?) American

£258	$475	€377	Landscape with fields (66x81cm-26x32in) s. 9-Jun-4 Alderfer's, Hatfield #491

MINKO, Tachibana (18th C) Japanese

Prints			
£48913	$90000	€71413	Kitsune no yomeiri - Fox wedding (20x27cm-8x11in) six prints executed with his circle. 23-Mar-4 Christie's, Rockefeller NY #6/R est:40000-50000

MINNE, George (1866-1941) Belgian

Sculpture			
£909	$1564	€1300	Portrait of a woman (49cm-19in) i. bronze. 2-Dec-3 Sotheby's, Amsterdam #75/R est:1000-1700
£1933	$3480	€2900	Buste de femme (53x50x35cm-21x20x14in) s. num.1/8 bronze. 24-Apr-4 Cornette de St.Cyr, Paris #390/R est:4000
£2000	$3600	€3000	L'adolescent (42x31x14cm-17x12x6in) s.d. black pat.bronze. 24-Apr-4 Dr Lehr, Berlin #291/R est:4000
£3357	$5606	€4800	Tete d'homme (66x86cm-26x34in) plaster lit. 11-Oct-3 De Vuyst, Lokeren #425/R est:5000-6000
£4895	$8420	€7000	Buste d'homme (40cm-16in) i. brown pat. bronze wooden base prov.exhib. 2-Dec-3 Sotheby's, Amsterdam #73/R est:7000-10000
£7333	$13127	€11000	Female nude (57x37cm-22x15in) s.d.1931 brown pat bronze lit. 15-May-4 De Vuyst, Lokeren #448/R est:10000-12000
£8392	$14014	€12000	Jeune mere (38x26cm-15x10in) s. green pat bronze prov.lit. 11-Oct-3 De Vuyst, Lokeren #453/R est:11000-13000
£8667	$15947	€13000	Adolescent (42cm-17in) brown pat. bronze prov. 12-Jun-4 Villa Grisebach, Berlin #121/R est:9000-12000
£9790	$16839	€14000	Adolescent nu agenouille (60cm-24in) s.d.1931 brown pat bronze. 8-Dec-3 Horta, Bruxelles #128/R est:12000-15000
£10417	$16563	€15000	Torse de mere a l'enfant (64cm-25in) s. brown pat bronze. 15-Sep-3 Horta, Bruxelles #167/R est:12000-18000
£12000	$21600	€18000	Agenouille (144cm-57in) s. num.3/8 pat bronze lit. 24-Apr-4 Cornette de St.Cyr, Paris #391/R est:10000-15000
Works on paper			
£272	$487	€400	Pieta (18x11cm-7x4in) s. chl. 16-Mar-4 Vanderkindere, Brussels #81

MINNEBO, Hubert (1940-) Belgian

Sculpture			
£6000	$10740	€9000	Composition, during a cycle of thousand years (139x44cm-55x17in) bronze stone base one of one exhib. 15-May-4 De Vuyst, Lokeren #519/R est:10000-12000

MINNIE, Nancy and NAPANANGKA, Sarah (20th C) Australian

£1098	$1965	€1603	Women's site (67x51cm-26x20in) acrylic artist board painted 1986 prov. 25-May-4 Lawson Menzies, Sydney #134/R est:3000-5000 (A.D 2800)

MINNS, B E (1864-1937) Australian

Works on paper			
£1149	$1953	€1678	Helen (27x24cm-11x9in) s. s.i.verso W/C. 26-Nov-3 Deutscher-Menzies, Melbourne #270/R est:3000-3500 (A.D 2700)

MINNS, Benjamin Edwin (1864-1937) Australian

Works on paper			
£569	$894	€831	Une musicienne jeune (56x39cm-22x15in) s.d.1919 W/C. 1-Sep-3 Shapiro, Sydney #387 (A.D 1400)
£898	$1652	€1311	Abo woman New South Wales (32x25cm-13x10in) s.i. W/C. 29-Mar-4 Goodman, Sydney #11/R (A.D 2200)
£898	$1652	€1311	Australian Aboriginal (27x25cm-11x10in) s.i. W/C. 29-Mar-4 Goodman, Sydney #12/R (A.D 2200)

MINOLI, Paolo (1942-) Italian

£629	$1070	€900	Poema - antgeli notturni - Tempo B (60x60cm-24x24in) s.d.1988 i. verso acrylic. 29-Nov-3 Arnold, Frankfurt #376/R
£660	$1070	€964	Un'aria celestrina di rugiada (60x60cm-24x24in) s.i.d.1997 verso acrylic. 24-May-3 Burkhard, Luzern #85/R (S.FR 1400)
£1310	$2410	€1913	Via Grassi 5-Canu-Como (120x120cm-47x47in) acrylic on canvas on panel 3 part relief. 8-Jun-4 Germann, Zurich #62/R est:4000-5000 (S.FR 3000)

MINON, Edward (20th C) American?

Works on paper			
£602	$1000	€873	Nude torso (51x36cm-20x14in) chl. 13-Jun-3 Du Mouchelle, Detroit #2226/R

MINOR, Robert Crannell (1839-1904) American

£914	$1700	€1334	Barbizon landscape at dusk (30x41cm-12x16in) s. 3-Mar-4 Christie's, Rockefeller NY #20/R est:1500-2000
£1358	$2200	€1983	Landscape with farmhouse at sunset (66x38cm-26x15in) s. 31-Jul-3 Eldred, East Dennis #853/R est:1000-1300
£2727	$4800	€3981	September afternoon (66x91cm-26x36in) s. prov. 3-Jan-4 Collins, Maine #35/R est:5000-7000

MINOZZI, Bernardino (1699-1769) Italian

£66897	$111717	€97000	Landscape with church. Landscape with village and stream (110x148cm-43x58in) pair prov.exhib.lit. 15-Nov-3 Porro, Milan #255/R est:80000
Works on paper			
£748	$1339	€1100	Un paysage avec un rocher au dessus d'un etang, un monastiere au fond (30x44cm-12x17in) brush brown ink wash htd white prov.exhib. 18-Mar-4 Christie's, Paris #31/R

MINOZZI, Filiberto (1887-1936) Italian

£403	$713	€600	Landscape (16x34cm-6x13in) s. cardboard. 1-May-4 Meeting Art, Vercelli #219
£1042	$1771	€1500	Seascape in Cap Martin (15x25cm-6x10in) s. s.verso board. 1-Nov-3 Meeting Art, Vercelli #179/R est:1500
£1884	$3090	€2600	Venice, Saint Mark's Square (52x75cm-20x30in) s.i.d.1908. 27-May-3 Il Ponte, Milan #932
Works on paper			
£1141	$2042	€1700	French landscapes. s. mixed media set of 24 in 6 frames. 25-May-4 Finarte Semenzato, Milan #1/R est:1200-1500
£1333	$2453	€2000	Stormy evening (39x54cm-15x21in) s.d.903 pastel cardboard prov. 8-Jun-4 Sotheby's, Milan #149/R est:2000-4000

MINSHEW, Roy (20th C) American

Sculpture			
£1111	$2000	€1622	Flying angel dog (33x147cm-13x58in) caved painted wood cooper sheet wings eyehooks. 24-Apr-4 Slotin Folk Art, Buford #569/R est:400-600

MINSKY, Grigorii (1912-1958) Russian

£1049	$1783	€1500	Sunflower field (65x98cm-26x39in) i.verso. 28-Nov-3 Wiener Kunst Auktionen, Vienna #489/R est:1500-3000

MINTCHINE, Abraham (1898-1931) Russian

£2482	$4021	€3500	Vase de fleurs et coquillage (33x24cm-13x9in) s. 23-May-3 Sotheby's, Paris #48/R est:2000-3000
£11976	$20000	€17485	Market, Place d'Alleray, Paris (89x116cm-35x46in) s. painted c.1925 lit. 7-Oct-3 Sotheby's, New York #303 est:10000-15000
Works on paper			
£2400	$4008	€3504	Nu allonge (45x58cm-18x23in) s.d.29 W/C glaze prov. 22-Oct-3 Sotheby's, Olympia #196/R est:1000-2000

MINTCHINE, Isaac (1900-1941) Russian

£927	$1687	€1400	Nature morte aux tulipes (46x38cm-18x15in) panel. 16-Jun-4 Claude Boisgirard, Paris #115

MINTON, John (1917-1957) British

Works on paper			
£420	$752	€613	Study for Coriolanus (14x15cm-6x6in) pen brush black ink. 14-May-4 Christie's, Kensington #559
£520	$931	€759	Boy, Cornwall (23x18cm-9x7in) pen col ink exhib. 14-May-4 Christie's, Kensington #554/R
£650	$1164	€949	Young man asleep. Seated man in suit (18x13cm-7x5in) pencil pair. 14-May-4 Christie's, Kensington #555
£650	$1164	€949	Portrait of a seated man (38x35cm-15x14in) pen black ink. 14-May-4 Christie's, Kensington #557
£720	$1325	€1051	Stage set with Roman statues (30x45cm-12x18in) s. gouache. 14-Jun-4 Bonhams, Bath #148
£750	$1193	€1095	Services on tap (23x21cm-9x8in) init. ink gouache. 10-Sep-3 Sotheby's, Olympia #294/R
£1700	$2924	€2482	Desolate stage (30x47cm-12x19in) s.d.1939 pen ink wash prov. 2-Dec-3 Bonhams, New Bond Street #81/R est:1500-2000
£3000	$5100	€4380	Village in Corsica (28x38cm-11x15in) s.d.1949 ink W/C bodycol. 21-Nov-3 Christie's, London #150/R est:3000-5000
£4000	$7160	€5840	Sunflower (38x28cm-15x11in) s.d.1948 ink W/C wax resist prov. 16-Mar-4 Bonhams, New Bond Street #54/R est:1500-2000

MINUNBOC, Rodolfo (?) South American

Sculpture			
£2668	$4375	€3895	Dance (16x9x8cm-6x4x3in) s.verso bronze. 1-Jun-3 Subastas Odalys, Caracas #98

MIOLA, Camillo (1840-1919) Italian

£358	$655	€523	Interior scene with dignified figures (17x21cm-7x8in) s. study. 7-Jun-4 Museumsbygningen, Copenhagen #65 (D.KR 4000)

MIOLEE, Adrianus (1879-1961) Dutch

£320	$573	€480	Polder landscape with mill (31x36cm-12x14in) panel. 11-May-4 Vendu Notarishuis, Rotterdam #79

MIOT, Paul Emile (1827-1900) French
Photographs
£3222 $5800 €4704 View of the interior of a temporary fish warehouse, Newfoundland (20x24cm-8x9in) albumenized salt print lit. 22-Apr-4 Phillips, New York #56/R est:8000-12000

MIOTTE, Jean (1926-) French
£333 $597 €500 Composition (65x49cm-26x19in) s. acrylic prov. 15-May-4 Van Ham, Cologne #805
£2013 $3564 €3000 Composition (50x65cm-20x26in) trace sig. painted c.1960. 28-Apr-4 Artcurial Briest, Paris #297/R est:3000-4000
£4698 $8409 €7000 Songe exultante (120cm-47in circular) mono.i. stretcher. 25-May-4 Dorotheum, Vienna #122/R est:7500-8500
£38667 $70373 €58000 Attirance (162x130cm-64x51in) s.i.d.1997 verso acrylic. 29-Jun-4 Cornette de St.Cyr, Paris #144/R est:20000-25000
Works on paper
£336 $594 €500 Composition (65x50cm-26x20in) s.d.1984 W/C. 29-Apr-4 Claude Aguttes, Neuilly #235/R

MIR Y TRINXET, Joaquin (1873-1940) Spanish
£21233 $36096 €31000 Autumn landscape (66x66cm-26x26in) s. 4-Nov-3 Ansorena, Madrid #356/R est:21000
£22368 $40487 €34000 Cold and poverty (100x150cm-39x59in) exhib.lit. 14-Apr-4 Ansorena, Madrid #157/R est:34000

MIR Y TRINXET, Joaquin (attrib) (1873-1940) Spanish
£1096 $1863 €1600 Spanish view (16x25cm-6x10in) s.d.1903 board. 4-Nov-3 Ansorena, Madrid #66/R est:1600

MIRA, Alfred S (1900-1981) American
£5405 $10000 €7891 Washington Square rally (30x41cm-12x16in) s.d.42 i.verso canvasboard prov. 11-Mar-4 Christie's, Rockefeller NY #66/R est:5000-7000
£6486 $12000 €9470 Chinatown (41x30cm-16x12in) s.indis.d.4 i.verso canvasboard prov. 11-Mar-4 Christie's, Rockefeller NY #60/R est:5000-7000
£12973 $24000 €18941 MacDougal Alley (63x76cm-25x30in) s.d.42 prov. 11-Mar-4 Christie's, Rockefeller NY #41/R est:10000-15000
£29730 $55000 €43406 Washington Square (61x72cm-24x28in) s. prov. 11-Mar-4 Christie's, Rockefeller NY #57/R est:10000-15000

MIRA, Alfred S (attrib) (1900-1981) American
£1069 $1700 €1561 Boulevard des Capucines (31x22cm-12x9in) i. canvas on board. 12-Sep-3 Skinner, Boston #482/R

MIRA, Victor (1949-) Spanish
£1316 $2382 €2000 Bow culture (67x55cm-26x22in) s.i.d.1980 paper. 14-Apr-4 Ansorena, Madrid #261/R est:2000
£1736 $2951 €2500 Horses-74-horses (50x110cm-20x43in) s.i.d.1974 tempera paper on board. 28-Oct-3 Segre, Madrid #271/R est:900
£2740 $4658 €4000 Web (80x64cm-31x25in) sid.1974. 4-Nov-3 Ansorena, Madrid #906/R est:4000
£2759 $4579 €4000 March with tomato (67x110cm-26x43in) s.i.d.1978 lit. 1-Oct-3 Ansorena, Madrid #589/R est:2500
£2837 $4596 €4000 Spinnning (61x50cm-24x20in) s. s.i.d.1983 verso. 20-May-3 Ansorena, Madrid #279/R est:4000
£3333 $5500 €4800 Star from hell (91x59cm-36x23in) s.d.1983 s.i.d.verso. 2-Jul-3 Ansorena, Madrid #935/R
£3333 $6033 €5000 Great march with tomato (68x112cm-27x44in) s.i.d.1978 paper on canvas. 30-Mar-4 Segre, Madrid #273/R est:5000
£4965 $8043 €7000 Hilatura (130x60cm-51x24in) s. s.i.d.1984 verso. 20-May-3 Ansorena, Madrid #278/R est:7000
£5797 $9507 €8000 Montjuich (50x140cm-20x55in) s.d.1983 acrylic panel. 27-May-3 Durán, Madrid #197/R est:8000
£5921 $10895 €9000 Untitled (92x60cm-36x24in) s.d.1983. 22-Jun-4 Durán, Madrid #137/R est:9000
£5986 $9577 €8500 Untitled (92x60cm-36x24in) s. painted 1983. 16-Sep-3 Segre, Madrid #147/R est:7900
£6207 $10303 €9000 Guillotine (172x99cm-68x39in) s.i.d.1980 paper on board. 1-Oct-3 Ansorena, Madrid #575/R est:7000
£6250 $10313 €9000 Still life with upturned table (130x97cm-51x38in) s. s.i.d.verso. 2-Jul-3 Ansorena, Madrid #851/R
£7895 $14289 €12000 Walking to the grave (166x121cm-65x48in) s.i.d.1980. 14-Apr-4 Ansorena, Madrid #270/R est:12000
Sculpture
£2717 $4457 €3750 Bach Cantata (60x36cm-24x14in) s.i.d.1992 stone. 27-May-3 Durán, Madrid #201/R est:3500
Works on paper
£611 $1125 €892 Nerioda (105x49cm-41x19in) s.i. mixed media collage board prov. 8-Jun-4 Germann, Zurich #836 (S.FR 1400)
£1103 $1832 €1600 Night painting (91x43cm-36x17in) s.i.d.1981 mixed media prov. 1-Oct-3 Ansorena, Madrid #592/R est:1500

MIRABELLA, Mario (1870-1931) Italian
£2188 $3500 €3194 Naples, view off the shore (102x203cm-40x80in) s. 18-May-3 Auctions by the Bay, Alameda #1016/R

MIRABELLA, Saro (1914-) Italian
£467 $840 €700 Trees. Sunset in Acicastello (44x23cm-17x9in) s.d.59 s.i.d.verso pair. 22-Apr-4 Finarte Semenzato, Rome #168

MIRABENT Y CATELL, Jose (1831-1899) Spanish
£3611 $5886 €5200 Avant-premiere a l'Eden Theatre (100x59cm-39x23in) s. 26-Sep-3 Rabourdin & Choppin de Janvry, Paris #81/R est:6000-7000

MIRAGLIA, Ermogene (1907-1964) Italian
£789 $1453 €1200 Seated peasant (61x41cm-24x16in) s. 23-Jun-4 Finarte Semenzato, Rome #73/R
£789 $1453 €1200 Market scene (30x39cm-12x15in) s. 23-Jun-4 Finarte Semenzato, Rome #71/R
£1316 $2421 €2000 Two women (95x65cm-37x26in) s. 23-Jun-4 Finarte Semenzato, Rome #72/R est:1500-1700

MIRALDA, Antoni (1942-) Spanish
Sculpture
£4861 $8021 €7000 Soldats (74x93x10cm-29x37x4in) s.d.1971 verso plastic soldiers plastic. 2-Jul-3 Cornette de St.Cyr, Paris #224/R est:1500-2000

MIRALLES DARMANIN, Jose (1851-1900) Spanish
£2431 $3962 €3500 Modelling (38x46cm-15x18in) s. 23-Sep-3 Durán, Madrid #206/R
£2551 $4566 €3750 Posing (38x46cm-15x18in) s. 22-Mar-4 Durán, Madrid #215/R est:3000
£6897 $11517 €10000 Inn (52x80cm-20x31in) s. 17-Nov-3 Durán, Madrid #135/R est:9000
£19000 $32300 €27740 Music class (74x102cm-29x40in) s.d.1892. 18-Nov-3 Sotheby's, London #267/R

MIRALLES, Francisco (1848-1901) Spanish
£2536 $4159 €3500 Portrait of a young boy (61x50cm-24x20in) s.d.1874. 27-May-3 Durán, Madrid #269/R est:3500
£3041 $5443 €4500 Goose keeper (56x46cm-22x18in) 10-May-4 Giraudeau, Tours #160
£3873 $6197 €5500 Portrait of girl (32x24cm-13x9in) s.d.1878 board. 16-Sep-3 Segre, Madrid #79/R
£29514 $48108 €42500 Paris, strolling on Avenue Foch (31x40cm-12x16in) s. 23-Sep-3 Durán, Madrid #191/R est:42500

MIRANDA, Celso (1954-) Spanish
£299 $545 €440 Seascape (23x33cm-9x13in) s. board. 3-Feb-4 Segre, Madrid #339/R
£380 $688 €570 Seascape (38x58cm-15x23in) s. board. 30-Mar-4 Segre, Madrid #364/R
£563 $901 €800 Seascape (40x60cm-16x24in) s. board. 16-Sep-3 Segre, Madrid #271/R

MIRANDA, Juan de (17th C) Mexican
£4800 $8640 €7008 Archangel Michael (76x57cm-30x22in) s.d.1738. 20-Apr-4 Sotheby's, Olympia #318/R est:1000-2000

MIRANDA, Marc (1948-) French
£567 $948 €800 Le plat emaille (73x60cm-29x24in) s. 19-Oct-3 Anaf, Lyon #218

MIRANDA, P (19th C) Mexican
£1370 $2329 €2000 Christ Redemptor (86x45cm-34x18in) oil silk thread. 29-Oct-3 Louis Morton, Mexico #66/R est:20000-25000 (M.P 26000)

MIRANDOLI, Enrico (19th C) Italian
Sculpture
£14000 $25760 €21000 Figure of Faith in God, kneeling with her hands clasped in her lap (183cm-72in) i.d.1846 marble base pedestal after Lorenzo Bartolini prov.lit. 10-Jun-4 Christie's, London #172/R est:6000-9000

MIRANI, Everardus Pagano (1810-1881) Dutch
£30667 $55200 €46000 Skaters and a sportsman on the ice, a windmill beyond (45x62cm-18x24in) s.d.1846 panel prov. 21-Apr-4 Christie's, Amsterdam #239/R est:15000-20000

MIRBEAU, Octave (1848-1917) French
£1267 $2331 €1900 Paysage de la cote mediterraneen (31x39cm-12x15in) s. painted c.1888 exhib. 9-Jun-4 Piasa, Paris #178/R est:1500-2000

MIRBEL, Lizinka Aimee Zoe de (1796-1849) French
Miniatures
£1208 $2223 €1800 Portrait de Xavier Vincent Feuillant (11x8cm-4x3in) s. oval. 26-Mar-4 Daguerre, Paris #133 est:2000-3000

MIRKO (1910-1969) Italian
£1319 $2085 €1900 Figure (50x35cm-20x14in) tempera painted 1967. 6-Sep-3 Meeting Art, Vercelli #640 est:1500
£2416 $4325 €3600 Fantasy (40x62cm-16x24in) s.d.1954. 30-May-4 Meeting Art, Vercelli #68 est:3000
£2708 $4279 €3900 Illusion (40x62cm-16x24in) 6-Sep-3 Meeting Art, Vercelli #550 est:3000
Sculpture
£1647 $2750 €2405 Untitled (32cm-13in) s. patinated copper sold with wood base prov. 7-Oct-3 Sotheby's, New York #390 est:2500-3500
£4930 $8627 €7000 Totem (60x25x13cm-24x10x5in) s. bronze exec.1966 prov. 16-Dec-3 Porro, Milan #29/R est:5000-7000

MIRO LLEO, Gaspar (1859-1930) Spanish
£307 $549 €460 View of Paris with Notre-Dame (31x45cm-12x18in) s. 11-May-4 Vendu Notarishuis, Rotterdam #3/R
£320 $573 €480 Place de la Madeleine in Paris (31x45cm-12x18in) s. 11-May-4 Vendu Notarishuis, Rotterdam #4/R
£528 $914 €750 Landscape with bridge (25x34cm-10x13in) s. cardboard. 10-Dec-3 Castellana, Madrid #43/R

£1020	$1857	€1500	Venice (15x24cm-6x9in) s. cardboard. 3-Feb-4 Segre, Madrid #21/R est:1500
£1370	$2329	€2000	View of Venice (16x22cm-6x9in) s. panel. 9-Nov-3 Eric Pillon, Calais #13/R
£1370	$2329	€2000	View of Venice (16x22cm-6x9in) s. panel. 9-Nov-3 Eric Pillon, Calais #12/R
£2448	$4087	€3500	Paris, rue animee pres de l'Eglise des Cordeliers (15x24cm-6x9in) s. panel. 29-Jun-3 Eric Pillon, Calais #78/R
£3000	$5160	€4380	Place de la Republique, Paris (23x33cm-9x13in) s. panel. 4-Dec-3 Christie's, Kensington #31/R est:2500-3500

MIRO, Joachim (1875-1941) Spanish

£972	$1624	€1400	Bateaux dans un port (25x34cm-10x13in) s. panel. 21-Oct-3 Artcurial Briest, Paris #199/R est:1500-2000
£1361	$2476	€2000	Place Bellecour et Fourviere (16x24cm-6x9in) s. cardboard. 8-Feb-4 Anaf, Lyon #226a
£2200	$4070	€3212	Scene in the Atlas Mountains (27x40cm-11x16in) s. 14-Jul-4 Sotheby's, Olympia #277/R est:800-1200
£8156	$13621	€11500	La recolte des pasteques (47x72cm-19x28in) i.verso. 19-Jun-3 Millon & Associes, Paris #224/R est:8000-12000

MIRO, Joan (1893-1983) Spanish

£2647	$4500	€3865	Lezard aux plumes d'or (33x48cm-13x19in) s. col lithograph. 31-Oct-3 Sotheby's, New York #328
£48000	$87360	€70080	Composition (70x52cm-28x20in) s. gouache brush ink printed base on paper exec 1980 prov. 5-Feb-4 Christie's, London #440/R est:20000-30000
£70588	$120000	€103058	Deux personnages (48x63cm-19x25in) s. s.i.d.26/10/37 verso oil gouache W/C prov.exhib. 6-Nov-3 Sotheby's, New York #235/R est:120000-180000
£78212	$140000	€114190	Deux personnages (74x103cm-29x41in) s. oil chl board painted 1962 prov.exhib. 5-May-4 Christie's, Rockefeller NY #159/R est:100000-150000
£100000	$170000	€146000	Femme devant la lune (34x23cm-13x9in) s. i.d.15/XI/77 verso. 6-Nov-3 Sotheby's, New York #298/R est:120000-180000
£111732	$200000	€163129	Femme et oiseau devant le soleil (35x27cm-14x11in) painted 1944 prov.exhib.lit. 5-May-4 Christie's, Rockefeller NY #301/R est:250000-350000
£165000	$300300	€240900	Femme et enfant II (27x35cm-11x14in) s. s.i.d.12/IX/69 verso prov.lit. 3-Feb-4 Christie's, London #243/R est:150000-200000
£172000	$313040	€251120	Personnage (81x58cm-32x23in) s. i.d.76 verso oil gouache dechirage card prov. 4-Feb-4 Sotheby's, London #520/R est:150000-200000
£173184	$310000	€252849	Femmes dans la nuit (21x16cm-8x6in) s.d.1944 verso i.stretcher prov.exhib.lit. 5-May-4 Christie's, Rockefeller NY #310/R est:350000-450000
£183333	$337333	€275000	Femme 27/III (90x59cm-35x23in) s. tempera mixed media paper painted 1970 prov. 8-Jun-4 Finarte Semenzato, Milan #383/R est:280000-300000
£195531	$350000	€285475	Femme etoiles (21x16cm-8x6in) s.d.1944 verso prov.exhib.lit. 5-May-4 Christie's, Rockefeller NY #298/R est:350000-450000
£205882	$350000	€300588	Femme devant la lune (16x22cm-6x9in) s.d.1944 verso prov.exhib.lit. 6-Nov-3 Sotheby's, New York #233a/R est:350000-450000
£300000	$549000	€438000	Tete bleue et oiseau fleche (100x81cm-39x32in) s. s.i.d.31/XII/65 prov.exhib.lit. 2-Feb-4 Christie's, London #71/R est:250000-350000
£320000	$585600	€467200	La lueur de la lune le soleil couchant nous caresse (14x18cm-6x7in) s. s.d.1952 prov.lit. 2-Feb-4 Christie's, London #65/R est:120000-160000
£335196	$600000	€489386	Tete (74x104cm-29x41in) s. s.i.d.62 verso oil pastel gouache cardboard prov.exhib.lit. 6-May-4 Sotheby's, New York #152/R est:350000-450000
£400000	$680000	€584000	Oiseaux dans l'espace (131x81cm-52x32in) init. s.i.d.20/11/59 verso prov.exhib.lit. 4-Nov-3 Christie's, Rockefeller NY #44/R est:700000-900000
£400000	$732000	€584000	Peinture (73x198cm-29x78in) s. s.i.d.1953 verso prov.exhib.lit. 2-Feb-4 Christie's, London #85/R est:400000-500000
£420000	$768600	€613200	Femmes et oiseau dans la nuit (33x24cm-13x9in) s. painted October 1946 prov.lit. 2-Feb-4 Christie's, London #64/R est:400000-600000
£600000	$1098000	€876000	Peinture sur fond blanc (61x51cm-24x20in) s.d.1927 s.d.verso prov.lit. 2-Feb-4 Christie's, London #76/R est:600000-800000
£2681564	$4800000	€3915083	Rouge, bleu et bel espoir (47x62cm-19x24in) s. s.i.d.1947 verso prov.exhib.lit. 4-May-4 Christie's, Rockefeller NY #33/R est:4000000-6000000

Prints

£1695	$3000	€2475	Solar bird, Lunar bird, sparks (38x80cm-15x31in) s.num.22/75 col lithograph. 30-Apr-4 Sotheby's, New York #141/R est:4000-6000
£1703	$3100	€2486	Serie Mallorca (24x19cm-9x7in) s.num.16/75 col etching aquatint prov. 7-Feb-4 Sloans & Kenyon, Bethesda #1216/R est:3000-4000
£1796	$3000	€2622	Exhibition at the Pasadena Art Museum (64x48cm-25x19in) s.num.31/100 col lithograph. 21-Oct-3 Bonhams & Butterfields, San Francisco #1216/R
£1808	$3200	€2640	People and animals (76x57cm-30x22in) s.num.4/75 col lithograph. 28-Apr-4 Christie's, Rockefeller NY #77/R est:3500-4500
£1808	$3200	€2640	Terres de grand feu (39x58cm-15x23in) s.num.79/100 col lithograph. 28-Apr-4 Christie's, Rockefeller NY #83/R est:2500-3000
£1836	$3250	€2681	Homenatge a Joan Prats (65x85cm-26x33in) s.num.16/75 col lithograph. 30-Apr-4 Sotheby's, New York #151/R est:3000-5000
£1836	$3250	€2681	Barcelona (70x104cm-28x41in) s.num.44/50 etching aquatint. 30-Apr-4 Sotheby's, New York #153/R est:3000-4000
£1882	$3200	€2748	Femmes (65x48cm-26x19in) s.num.27/50 lithograph. 6-Nov-3 Swann Galleries, New York #636/R est:3500-5000
£1882	$3200	€2748	Les brisants (19x14cm-7x6in) s.num.VI/X col aquatint. 6-Nov-3 Swann Galleries, New York #640/R est:2500-3500
£1882	$3200	€2748	Archipel sauvage IV (59x92cm-23x36in) s.i. col etching aquatint. 6-Nov-3 Swann Galleries, New York #643/R est:1500-2500
£1882	$3200	€2748	Fusees (25x36cm-10x14in) s. etching col aquatint exec.1959. 4-Nov-3 Christie's, Rockefeller NY #130/R est:2500-3500
£1899	$3400	€2773	Montcada I (32x47cm-13x19in) s.num.5/75 color lithograph. 6-May-4 Swann Galleries, New York #532/R est:2500-3500
£1900	$3174	€2774	L'oiseau rouge II (33x51cm-13x20in) s.d.1950 num.58/75 col lithograph prov. 16-Oct-3 Waddingtons, Toronto #198/R est:3000-5000 (C.D 4200)
£1935	$3600	€2825	Serie mallorca (54x68cm-21x27in) s.i.d.4/IX/73 col aquatint. 2-Mar-4 Swann Galleries, New York #443/R est:3500-5000
£1977	$3500	€2886	Watchers (90x61cm-35x24in) s.num.22/75 col lithograph. 30-Apr-4 Sotheby's, New York #139/R est:3000-5000
£1977	$3500	€2886	Le puisatier (99x59cm-39x23in) s.num.25/75 col aquatint etching. 30-Apr-4 Sotheby's, New York #149/R est:4000-6000
£1982	$3409	€2894	Composition (69x52cm-27x20in) s. lithograph. 2-Dec-3 Koller, Zurich #3357/R est:2600-3400 (S.FR 4400)
£1987	$3616	€3000	Grand vent (29x78cm-11x31in) s. num.30/90 col etching exec. 1960. 15-Jun-4 James Adam, Dublin #91/R est:3000-4000
£2000	$3400	€2920	Foreign woman (66x51cm-26x20in) s.num.51/75 col lithograph. 6-Nov-3 Swann Galleries, New York #639/R est:3500-5000
£2000	$3680	€2920	Maravillas Con varicionres arcosticas (47x33cm-19x13in) s.i. lithograph. 29-Mar-4 Bonhams, New Bond Street #196/R est:800-1200
£2000	$3680	€3000	Affiche pour l'exposition 'Peintres, gouaches, dessins' (74x34cm-29x13in) s.i. col lithograph. 10-Jun-4 Hauswedell & Nolte, Hamburg #496/R est:3000
£2013	$3705	€3000	From: La bague d'Aurore (14x11cm-6x4in) s.i. col aquatint. 26-Mar-4 Ketterer, Hamburg #562/R est:2000-3000
£2013	$3765	€3000	Puisatier (105x68cm-41x27in) s. eau forte aquatint. 1-Mar-4 Artcurial Briest, Paris #133/R est:3000-4000
£2013	$3765	€3000	Passge de l'egyptienne (60x42cm-24x17in) s. col aquatint eau forte. 1-Mar-4 Artcurial Briest, Paris #135/R est:3000
£2067	$3782	€3100	From: Passage de l'Egyptienne (60x42cm-24x17in) 198s. col etching. 5-Jun-4 Lempertz, Koln #879/R est:1800
£2069	$3455	€3000	Lezard aux plumes d'or (35x50cm-14x20in) s. col lithograph exec.1971. 17-Nov-3 Sant Agostino, Torino #48/R est:4000
£2072	$3750	€3025	From Oda a Joan Miro (84x61cm-33x24in) s.num.VII/XXV col lithograph. 19-Apr-4 Bonhams & Butterfields, San Francisco #188/R est:3000-4000
£2081	$3476	€3038	L'equarrisseur a l'ouvrage (55x55cm-22x22in) s.num.70/75 col lithograph prov. 16-Oct-3 Waddingtons, Toronto #200/R est:5000-7000 (C.D 4600)
£2098	$3608	€3000	Untitled (14x11cm-6x4in) s. col etching. 4-Dec-3 Van Ham, Cologne #327/R est:4000
£2113	$3655	€3000	Grand vent (30x79cm-12x31in) s. num.60/90 col etching col aquatint lit. 13-Dec-3 De Vuyst, Lokeren #501/R est:4000-5000
£2133	$3819	€3200	La fille du jardinier (44x60cm-17x24in) s.i. col lithograph. 15-May-4 Bassenge, Berlin #7033/R est:2200
£2133	$3925	€3200	La lutte rituelle (60x89cm-24x35in) s. col lithograph exec. 1964 one of 75. 11-Jun-4 Villa Grisebach, Berlin #1602/R est:3000-4000
£2147	$3800	€3135	L'aieule des 10 000 ages (57x86cm-22x34in) s.num.21/50 col lithograph. 28-Apr-4 Christie's, Rockefeller NY #102/R est:4000-6000
£2168	$3685	€3100	Signes et meteores (43x48cm-17x19in) s. col lithograph. 26-Nov-3 Lempertz, Koln #856/R est:2000
£2174	$3565	€3000	Personaje romantico (81x63cm-32x25in) s.i.d.1975 etching engraving aquatint num.VIII/XXIV. 27-May-3 Durán, Madrid #79/R est:1200
£2200	$4004	€3212	Les voyants (64x49cm-25x19in) s.num.49/75 col lithograph. 30-Jun-4 Christie's, London #263/R est:2000-3000
£2200	$4004	€3212	Grave sur le givre III (57x48cm-22x19in) s.i. etching aquatint. 30-Jun-4 Christie's, London #273/R est:1500-2000
£2200	$4004	€3212	Le Marteau sans Maitre (65x43cm-26x17in) s.num.III/L etching aquatint. 30-Jun-4 Christie's, London #274/R est:1500-2000
£2210	$4000	€3227	Sponge fisherman (120x75cm-47x30in) s.num.26/50 col lithograph. 19-Apr-4 Bonhams & Butterfields, San Francisco #186/R est:3500-5500
£2210	$4000	€3227	L'enfance d'ubu (30x51cm-12x20in) s.num.43/120 col lithograph. 3-Apr-4 David Rago, Lambertville #241/R est:2500-3500
£2235	$3800	€3263	Maravillas con variacones acrosticas en el jardin de Miro (75x53cm-30x21in) s.num.31/75 col lithograph. 6-Nov-3 Swann Galleries, New York #648/R est:2000-3000
£2238	$3804	€3200	Le jour (38x27cm-15x11in) s. col lithograph. 29-Nov-3 Villa Grisebach, Berlin #316/R est:2500-3500
£2245	$3750	€3278	Le fantome de d'atelier (91x64cm-36x25in) s.num.32/65 etching col lithograph. 21-Oct-3 Bonhams & Butterfields, San Francisco #1217/R
£2258	$4200	€3297	Watchers (90x60cm-35x24in) s.num.12/75 col lithograph. 2-Mar-4 Swann Galleries, New York #434/R est:3000-5000
£2271	$4133	€3316	Composition. s.i. col etching. 17-Jun-4 Kornfeld, Bern #569 est:3000 (S.FR 5200)
£2308	$3854	€3300	Fundacio Joan Miro (46x56cm-18x22in) s. lithograph. 24-Jun-3 Segre, Madrid #220/R
£2331	$3800	€3403	Person in the garden (49x65cm-19x26in) s.d.1951 num.46/75 col lithograph wove paper. 24-Sep-3 Christie's, Rockefeller NY #111/R est:3000-4000
£2331	$3800	€3403	Espriu (87x70cm-34x28in) s. num.26/50 etching aquating col carborundum Guarro. 24-Sep-3 Christie's, Rockefeller NY #118/R est:3500-4500
£2349	$4369	€3500	L'Oiseau (72x94cm-28x37in) s.num.71/75 aquagravure. 4-Mar-4 Auction Maastricht #1088/R est:3000-4000
£2373	$4200	€3465	Suite la bague d'aurore (14x11cm-6x4in) s.num.32/60col aquatint. 28-Apr-4 Christie's, Rockefeller NY #81/R est:1800-2200
£2400	$4392	€3504	Monument a Christophe Colomb et a Marcel Duchamp (34x25cm-13x10in) s.num.93/125 col etching aquatint. 3-Jun-4 Christie's, Kensington #105/R est:1000-1500
£2400	$4368	€3504	Archipel sauvage II (59x92cm-23x36in) s.i. col etching aquatint. 1-Jul-4 Sotheby's, London #210/R est:2500-3000
£2432	$4500	€3551	Le lezard aux plumes d'or (33x48cm-13x19in) s.i. col lithograph deckled on two sides. 12-Feb-4 Christie's, Rockefeller NY #344/R est:2800-3200
£2448	$4161	€3500	From 'Oda a Joan Miro' (79x61cm-31x24in) s. col lithograph. 29-Nov-3 Villa Grisebach, Berlin #315/R est:2500-3500
£2455	$4223	€3584	Composition from Oda a Joan Miro (88x61cm-35x24in) s. num.25/75 col lithograph. 2-Dec-3 Ritchie, Toronto #161/R est:6000-8000 (C.D 5500)
£2465	$4264	€3500	Les essences de la Terre (50x35cm-20x14in) s. col lithograph htd black W/C one of eight. 10-Dec-3 Millon & Associes, Paris #26/R est:3500-4000
£2467	$4514	€3700	Frome: Le lezard aux plumes d'or (34x48cm-13x19in) s. col lithograph. 5-Jun-4 Lempertz, Koln #877/R est:3000
£2491	$4409	€3637	La Presidente (64x47cm-25x19in) s.num.44/75 etching aquatint craborundum lit. 27-Apr-4 AB Stockholms Auktionsverk #1337/R est:35000-40000 (S.KR 34000)
£2500	$4250	€3650	Poster for the opening of the Mourlot Atelier (73x55cm-29x22in) s. col lithograph. 31-Oct-3 Sotheby's, New York #323
£2500	$4250	€3650	Fissures (49x59cm-19x23in) s. col etching aquatint embossing. 31-Oct-3 Sotheby's, New York #325
£2500	$4300	€3650	Archipel sauvage (58x92cm-23x36in) s.i. col etching aquatint. 4-Dec-3 Sotheby's, London #168/R est:3000-3500
£2500	$4300	€3650	Archipel sauvage IV (58x92cm-23x36in) s.i. col etching aquatint. 4-Dec-3 Sotheby's, London #171/R est:3000-3500
£2500	$4300	€3650	Altamira (45x61cm-18x24in) s.num.17/75 col lithograph. 2-Dec-3 Christie's, London #214/R est:2000-3000
£2542	$4500	€3711	Archipel sauvage II (58x91cm-23x36in) s.i. col etching aquatint. 28-Apr-4 Christie's, Rockefeller NY #93/R est:4000-6000
£2570	$4600	€3752	Le lezard aux plumes d'or (34x48cm-13x19in) s. num.48/50 lithograph. 6-May-4 Swann Galleries, New York #522/R est:3000-5000
£2600	$4758	€3796	Montroig 2 (76x57cm-30x22in) s.i. col lithograph. 3-Jun-4 Christie's, Kensington #106/R est:1200-1600
£2620	$4821	€3825	La longue de l'evaporee (92x63cm-36x25in) s.num.20/75 col etching aquatint lit. 8-Jun-4 Germann, Zurich #541/R est:7000-9000 (S.FR 6000)
£2644	$4494	€3860	From - La Bague d'Aurore (11x14cm-4x6in) s.num.40/60 col etching aquatint lit. 4-Nov-3 Bukowskis, Stockholm #407/R est:25000-30000 (S.KR 35000)
£2644	$4494	€3860	Femme-oiseau (35x46cm-14x18in) s.num.43/90 softground etching aquatint lit. 4-Nov-3 Bukowskis, Stockholm #410/R est:35000-40000 (S.KR 35000)
£2647	$4500	€3865	Oda a Joan Miro (88x61cm-35x24in) s. col lithograph. 31-Oct-3 Sotheby's, New York #329/R
£2667	$4907	€4000	Seers (66x51cm-26x20in) s. num.1/5 lithograph exec 1970. 8-Jun-4 Sotheby's, Amsterdam #322/R est:3500-4500
£2667	$4907	€4000	Le chien bleu (62x48cm-24x19in) s. col aquatinta one of 300. 12-Jun-4 Villa Grisebach, Berlin #802/R est:1800-2400
£2700	$4644	€3942	Archipel sauvage VI (58x92cm-23x36in) s.i. col etching aquatint. 4-Dec-3 Sotheby's, London #173/R est:3000-3500
£2703	$5000	€3946	Poster for the Miro exhibition at Casino of Knokke-le-Zoute (57x77cm-22x30in) s.num.38/75 col lithograph vellum printed to two sides. 12-Feb-4 Christie's, Rockefeller NY #343/R est:3000-3500

£2712	$4800	€3960	Els castellers (67x47cm-26x19in) s.num.48/50 col etching. 28-Apr-4 Christie's, Rockefeller NY #95/R est:4000-6000
£2721	$4871	€4000	Composition (90x63cm-35x25in) s. num.36/50 col lithograph. 22-Mar-4 Sant Agostino, Torino #490/R est:4500
£2733	$5029	€4100	La destruction du miroir (34x25cm-13x10in) s. cal aquatint etching one of 60. 12-Jun-4 Villa Grisebach, Berlin #803/R est:2000-3000
£2793	$5000	€4078	Figure on a blue background (32x24cm-13x9in) s.num.43/75 col lithograph. 4-May-4 Doyle, New York #224/R est:2000-3000
£2794	$4750	€4079	El Pi de Formenter (88x74cm-35x29in) s. col etching aquatint. 31-Oct-3 Sotheby's, New York #335
£2797	$4811	€4000	Le carrosse d'oiseaux (59x63cm-23x25in) s. col etching aquatint. 2-Dec-3 Hauswedell & Nolte, Hamburg #439/R est:4500
£2797	$4755	€4000	From 'Oda a Joan Miro' (87x59cm-34x23in) s. col lithograph. 29-Nov-3 Villa Grisebach, Berlin #317/R est:2500-3500
£2800	$4648	€4088	Feuilles eparses (21x18cm-8x7in) s.num.iii/xii hand col etching. 6-Oct-3 Sotheby's, London #101/R est:3000-4000
£2800	$4816	€4088	Archipel sauvage V (58x92cm-23x36in) s.i. col etching aquatint. 4-Dec-3 Sotheby's, London #172/R est:3000-3500
£2800	$5096	€4088	La longue et l'evaporee (92x63cm-36x25in) s.i. col etching aquatint. 1-Jul-4 Sotheby's, London #222/R est:2500-3000
£2825	$5000	€4125	Homage to helion (58x46cm-23x18in) s.d.June 1976 col lithograph. 3-May-4 O'Gallerie, Oregon #793/R est:1000-1500
£2851	$5246	€4162	Exposition XXIle Salon de Mai (67x52cm-26x20in) s. lithograph. 23-Jun-4 Koller, Zurich #3266/R est:3000-4500 (S.FR 6500)
£2857	$5114	€4200	Barcelona (105x70cm-41x28in) s. eau forte one of 13 lit. 16-Mar-4 Finarte Semenzato, Milan #347/R est:2700
£2896	$4836	€4228	Personnages et animaux (119x91cm-47x36in) s.d.1950 num.44/75 col lithograph prov. 16-Oct-3 Waddingtons, Toronto #199/R est:4000-6000 (C.D 6400)
£2905	$5200	€4241	Le lezard aux plumes d'or (34x48cm-13x19in) s.num.48/50 lithograph. 6-May-4 Swann Galleries, New York #525/R est:3000-5000
£2933	$5397	€4400	King Ubu (41x62cm-16x24in) s. col lithograph exec. 1966 sheet 7 in series of 13. 12-Jun-4 Villa Grisebach, Berlin #381/R est:3000-4000
£2941	$5000	€4294	Colpir sense nafrar 2 (96x73cm-38x29in) s. col lithograph. 31-Oct-3 Sotheby's, New York #337
£2945	$4800	€4300	Balance on the Moon (85x60cm-33x24in) s. num.27/75 col lithograph executed 1969. 24-Sep-3 Christie's, Rockefeller NY #114/R est:2000-4000
£2983	$5250	€4355	Personatge I estels num 55 (89x61cm-35x24in) s.num.31/50 col aquatint woodcut collage. 22-May-4 Selkirks, St. Louis #867/R est:4000-6000
£3000	$5160	€4380	La translunaire (61x17cm-24x7in) s.i. col etching aquatint. 4-Dec-3 Sotheby's, London #164/R est:1800-2200
£3000	$5160	€4380	L'homme au balancier (68x50cm-27x20in) s.num.19/75 etching aquatint. 2-Dec-3 Christie's, London #206/R est:2500-3500
£3000	$5460	€4380	Grand vent (30x79cm-12x31in) s.num.70/90 col etching aquatint. 30-Jun-4 Christie's, London #268/R est:2000-3000
£3017	$5400	€4405	Montroig I (71x57cm-28x22in) s.i. color lithograph. 6-May-4 Swann Galleries, New York #533/R est:3000-5000
£3021	$5136	€4411	Le Presidente (64x47cm-25x19in) s.num.25/75 etching aquatint carborundum lit. 5-Nov-3 AB Stockholms Auktionsverk #1266/R est:30000-40000 (S.KR 40000)
£3046	$5482	€4447	From - La bague d'Aurore (11x14cm-4x6in) s.num.50/60 col etching aquatint. 26-Apr-4 Bukowskis, Stockholm #380/R est:25000-30000 (S.KR 42000)
£3107	$5500	€4536	The fitting II (120x80cm-47x31in) s.num.29/30 col lithograph. 28-Apr-4 Christie's, Rockefeller NY #92/R est:4000-6000
£3107	$5500	€4536	Horse ride blue, brown. Horse ride, blue (84x60cm-33x24in) s.num.50/75 col lithograph two. 30-Apr-4 Sotheby's, New York #147 est:3000-5000
£3107	$5500	€4536	Demi mondaine a sa fenetre (91x63cm-36x25in) s.num.30/50 col etching aquatint. 30-Apr-4 Sotheby's, New York #157/R est:3000-5000
£3144	$5722	€4590	Germination nocturne. s.i.d.1955 col lithograph. 17-Jun-4 Kornfeld, Bern #573 est:6000 (S.FR 7200)
£3167	$5290	€4624	Prise a l'hamecon (107x67cm-42x26in) s.num.40/75 col etching aquatint prov. 16-Oct-3 Waddingtons, Toronto #201/R est:8000-10000 (C.D 7000)
£3200	$5312	€4672	Feverish Eskimo (89x60cm-35x24in) s.num.61/75 col lithograph. 6-Oct-3 Sotheby's, London #103/R est:1500-2000
£3200	$5856	€4672	Barcelona (70x104cm-28x41in) s.num.48/50 col aquatint carborundum. 3-Jun-4 Christie's, Kensington #112/R est:1400-1600
£3200	$5888	€4800	A toute epreuve (31x44cm-12x17in) s.d.221/IV/58 col woodcut. 10-Jun-4 Hauswedell & Nolte, Hamburg #498/R est:5000
£3235	$5500	€4723	Montroig 4 (76x57cm-30x22in) s. col lithograph. 4-Nov-3 Christie's, Rockefeller NY #137/R est:5000-7000
£3297	$5835	€4814	Petit fille devant le Mere (58x92cm-23x36in) s.i. col. etching aquatint lit. 27-Apr-4 AB Stockholms Auktionsverk #1332/R est:50000-60000 (S.KR 45000)
£3333	$6067	€5000	Las Conchas (75x102cm-30x40in) s. lithograph Arches paper exec 1969 lit. 29-Jun-4 Segre, Madrid #261/R est:3600
£3374	$5500	€4926	Tete Fleche (66x50cm-26x20in) s. num.61/75 aquatint carborundum col on Arches. 24-Sep-3 Christie's, Rockefeller NY #113/R est:3000-5000
£3374	$5500	€4926	Sea Shells (77x113cm-30x44in) s. i.verso num.41/75 col lithograph Arches vellum. 24-Sep-3 Christie's, Rockefeller NY #116/R est:3000-5000
£3472	$5660	€5000	Les sourires aux ailes flamboyantes (48x64cm-19x25in) s.i.d.1954 col lithograph. 27-Sep-3 Dr Fritz Nagel, Stuttgart #9585/R est:3900
£3474	$5906	€5072	L'astre du marecage (104x72cm-41x28in) s.num.59/75 col aquatint lit. 4-Nov-3 Bukowskis, Stockholm #412/R est:50000-60000 (S.KR 46000)
£3500	$6370	€5110	Polypheme (94x65cm-37x26in) s.num.57/75 col etching aquating carborundum. 1-Jul-4 Sotheby's, London #215/R est:4000-5000
£3500	$6370	€5110	L'exile noir (106x68cm-42x27in) s.i. col etching aquatint. 1-Jul-4 Sotheby's, London #219/R est:3500-4500
£3538	$6086	€5165	Composition - L'astre du labyrinthe, Paris (104x71cm-41x28in) s.num.53/75 etching drypoint acrylic. 7-Dec-3 Uppsala Auktionskammare, Uppsala #326/R est:40000-50000 (S.KR 46000)
£3550	$6035	€5183	Les armes du sommeil (51x62cm-20x24in) s.num.35/75 col etching aquatint carborundum. 4-Nov-3 Bukowskis, Stockholm #417/R est:40000-50000 (S.KR 47000)
£3591	$6500	€5243	Demi-mondaine a sa fenetre (92x64cm-36x25in) s.num.28/50 col etching aquatint. 19-Apr-4 Bonhams & Butterfields, San Francisco #187/R est:5000-6000
£3631	$6500	€5301	Defile de mannequis en laponie (126x86cm-50x34in) s.num.44/75 lithograph. 6-May-4 Swann Galleries, New York #526/R est:3000-5000
£3670	$6128	€5322	Les formigues. s.i. col etching aquatint. 19-Jun-3 Kornfeld, Bern #719/R est:10000 (S.FR 8000)
£3712	$6830	€5420	Petite fille devant la mer (74x105cm-29x41in) s. col etching aquatint carborundum. 8-Jun-4 Germann, Zurich #543/R est:8000-10000 (S.FR 8500)
£3800	$6536	€5548	La demoiselle a bascule (57x47cm-22x19in) s.i. col etching aquatint. 4-Dec-3 Sotheby's, London #163/R est:2500-3000
£3800	$6536	€5548	La magie quotidienne (16x41cm-6x16in) s.num.30/70 etching aquatint. 2-Dec-3 Christie's, London #198/R est:4000-6000
£3824	$6500	€5583	Pese-mouche (66x50cm-26x20in) s. col etching aquatint. 31-Oct-3 Sotheby's, New York #333/R
£3853	$6435	€5587	Partie de campagne III. s.i. col etching aquatint. 19-Jun-3 Kornfeld, Bern #716 est:6000 (S.FR 8400)
£3955	$7000	€5774	Regne vegetal (47x34cm-19x13in) s.num.23/75 col aquatint carborundum. 30-Apr-4 Sotheby's, New York #145/R est:3000-5000
£3973	$6237	€5800	Captive (93x71cm-37x28in) s.i. eau forte lit. 20-Apr-3 Deauville, France #141/R est:3800-4500
£4000	$7280	€5840	Maravillas con variaciones acrosticas en el jardin de Miro (53x75cm-21x30in) s.num.13/75 col lithograph. 30-Jun-4 Christie's, London #266/R est:2000-3000
£4000	$7280	€5840	Sumo (76x57cm-30x22in) s.num.21/75 col etching carborundum. 1-Jul-4 Sotheby's, London #216/R est:3500-4000
£4000	$7280	€5840	From Alfred Jarry Ubu Roi (41x63cm-16x25in) s.i. col lithograph edition of 280. 1-Jul-4 Sotheby's, London #208/R est:2500-3500
£4000	$7280	€5840	Le jardin de mousse (59x68cm-23x27in) s.i. col etching carborundum prov. 1-Jul-4 Sotheby's, London #212/R est:3000-4000
£4054	$7257	€6000	Ubu roi (54x75cm-21x30in) s. num.4/75 col lithograph. 4-May-4 Calmels Cohen, Paris #86/R est:4500-5000
£4118	$7000	€6012	Invention du regard (50x66cm-20x26in) s. col etching aquatint carborundum. 31-Oct-3 Sotheby's, New York #327/R
£4118	$7000	€6012	L'ogre enjoue (74x107cm-29x42in) s.num.37 aquatint carborundum. 9-Nov-3 Wright, Chicago #491 est:9000-12000
£4200	$7644	€6132	Oda a Joan Miro (88x61cm-35x24in) s.num.16/75 col lithograph. 30-Jun-4 Christie's, London #264/R est:2000-3000
£4200	$7644	€6132	La magie quotidienne (16x41cm-6x16in) s.num.10/70 etching aquatint. 30-Jun-4 Christie's, London #267/R est:2000-3000
£4220	$7048	€6119	Partie de campagne IV. s.i. col etching aquatint. 19-Jun-3 Kornfeld, Bern #717 est:6000 (S.FR 9200)
£4279	$7360	€6247	Composition with Harlequin (34x44cm-13x17in) s.i. aquatint etching. 2-Dec-3 Koller, Zurich #3358/R est:3000-4500 (S.FR 9500)
£4358	$7800	€6363	Le rebelle (91x64cm-36x25in) s. col etching aquatint. 21-Mar-4 Hindman, Chicago #863/R est:7000-9000
£4392	$7862	€6500	Ubu roi (54x75cm-21x30in) s. num.4/75 col lithograph. 4-May-4 Calmels Cohen, Paris #85/R est:4500-5000
£4412	$7500	€6442	Literate man-green. Literate man-red (85x60cm-33x24in) s. col lithograph pair. 31-Oct-3 Sotheby's, New York #326
£4412	$7500	€6442	Nestor (95x63cm-37x25in) s. col lithograph. 31-Oct-3 Sotheby's, New York #332/R
£4437	$7365	€6300	Ubo roi (54x75cm-21x30in) s.num.4/75 col lithograph. 13-Jun-3 Calmels Cohen, Paris #48/R est:6000-6500
£4469	$8000	€6525	Le lezard aux plumes d'or (33x48cm-13x19in) s.num.VI/X lithograph. 6-May-4 Swann Galleries, New York #527/R est:4000-6000
£4500	$7740	€6570	L'oiseau destructeur (72x94cm-28x37in) s.num.26/75 col etching aquatint carborundum. 2-Dec-3 Christie's, London #207/R est:4000-6000
£4500	$8190	€6570	La manucure evaporee (74x115cm-29x45in) s.i. etching aquatint. 30-Jun-4 Christie's, London #272/R est:4500-5500
£4500	$8190	€6570	From Alfred Jarry Ubu Roi (54x75cm-21x30in) s.num.42/75 col lithograph. 1-Jul-4 Sotheby's, London #207/R est:2500-3000
£4520	$8000	€6599	Personnage L Estels IV (90x63cm-35x25in) s.num.19/50 col etching. 30-Apr-4 Sotheby's, New York #159/R est:3000-5000
£4683	$7961	€6837	L'Antitete (12x10cm-5x4in) s.d.1949 etchings pochoir in col pair lit. 5-Nov-3 AB Stockholms Auktionsverk #1262/R est:40000-60000 (S.KR 62000)
£4706	$8000	€6871	Partie de campagne IV (58x92cm-23x36in) s. col etching aquatint. 31-Oct-3 Sotheby's, New York #324/R
£4706	$8000	€6871	Dandy (41x43cm-16x17in) s.i. col aquatint drypoint carborundum. 9-Nov-3 Wright, Chicago #492 est:9000-12000
£5000	$8500	€7300	Serie II (50x60cm-20x24in) s.d.1952-3 col etching. 4-Nov-3 Christie's, Rockefeller NY #128/R est:9000-12000
£5000	$9100	€7300	L'oiseau destructeur (72x94cm-28x37in) s.num.26/75 col etching aquatint carborundum. 30-Jun-4 Christie's, London #271/R est:4500-6500
£5085	$9000	€7424	Petite barriere (26x10cm-10x4in) s.num.65/75 col drypoint aquatint. 28-Apr-4 Christie's, Rockefeller NY #87/R est:7000-10000
£5085	$9000	€7424	L'adorateur du soleil (99x60cm-39x24in) s.num.65/75 col etching aquatint carborundum. 28-Apr-4 Christie's, Rockefeller NY #89/R est:12000-15000
£5136	$8731	€7499	L'oiseau destructeur (72x94cm-28x37in) s.num.43/75 col etching aquatint carborundum. 4-Nov-3 Bukowskis, Stockholm #415/R est:60000-80000 (S.KR 68000)
£5367	$9500	€7836	Joueuer de bugle aux oiseaux (66x93cm-26x37in) s.num.38/50 col etching aquatint carborundum. 28-Apr-4 Christie's, Rockefeller NY #94/R est:6000-8000
£5517	$9159	€8000	Untitled (101x68cm-40x27in) carborundum. 1-Oct-3 Ansorena, Madrid #423/R est:8000
£5525	$10000	€8067	Le chasseur de pieuvres (106x67cm-42x26in) s.num.63/75 col etching aquatint carborundum. 19-Apr-4 Bonhams & Butterfields, San Francisco #183/R est:6000-8000
£5588	$9500	€8158	Trace sur la Paroi (72x104cm-28x41in) s. num.34/75 et aquatint. 4-Nov-3 Christie's, Rockefeller NY #131/R est:9000-12000
£5588	$9500	€8158	Els Gossos IX (115x73cm-45x29in) s. num.14/30 etching aquatint exec.1979. 4-Nov-3 Christie's, Rockefeller NY #139/R est:6000-8000
£5650	$10000	€8249	Parie de campagne II (58x92cm-23x36in) s.i. col etching aquatint. 30-Apr-4 Sotheby's, New York #142/R est:7000-9000
£5656	$10181	€8258	Le chasseur de pieuvres (91x59cm-36x23in) s.i. col etching aquatint carborundum lit. 26-Apr-4 Bukowskis, Stockholm #388/R est:50000-60000 (S.KR 78000)
£6077	$11000	€8872	Manoletina (69x104cm-27x41in) s.num.68/75 col aquatint carborundum. 19-Apr-4 Bonhams & Butterfields, San Francisco #184/R est:7000-9000
£6135	$10000	€8957	Expriu (106x89cm-42x35in) s. num.26/50 etching aquating carborundum. 24-Sep-3 Christie's, Rockefeller NY #117/R est:3500-4500
£6215	$11000	€9074	Quatre colors aparien el mon (87x63cm-34x25in) s.i. col etching aquatint. 28-Apr-4 Christie's, Rockefeller NY #99/R est:6000-8000
£6215	$11000	€9074	Sumo (48x37cm-19x15in) s.num.5/75 col aquatint carborundum. 28-Apr-4 Christie's, Rockefeller NY #88/R est:6000-8000
£6215	$11000	€9074	Le vieil irlandais (105x70cm-41x28in) s.num.XXI/XXIV col etching aquatint carborundum. 28-Apr-4 Christie's, Rockefeller NY #91/R est:8000-12000
£6215	$11000	€9074	La metamorphose (107x75cm-42x30in) s.num.11/50 coletching aquatint scraping. 28-Apr-4 Christie's, Rockefeller NY #103/R est:8000-12000
£6215	$11000	€9074	Le dandy (42x43cm-17x17in) s.i. col etching aquatint carborundum. 28-Apr-4 Christie's, Rockefeller NY #90/R est:8000-12000
£6215	$11000	€9074	Le vieil irlandais (105x70cm-41x28in) s.num.5/75 etching aquatint. 30-Apr-4 Sotheby's, New York #150/R est:6000-8000
£6471	$11000	€9448	La metamorphose (107x74cm-42x29in) s.num.21/50 col etching aquatint carborundum grattoir. 6-Nov-3 Swann Galleries, New York #650/R est:10000-15000
£6471	$11000	€9448	Soleil ebouillante (106x68cm-42x27in) s. num.12/75 et aquatint exec.1969. 4-Nov-3 Christie's, Rockefeller NY #134/R est:8000-10000
£6497	$11500	€9486	Trace sur la paroi II (58x92cm-23x36in) s.num.8/75 col etching aquatint. 30-Apr-4 Sotheby's, New York #143/R est:8000-10000
£6500	$11830	€9490	L'astre du marecage (104x72cm-41x28in) s.num.57/75 col aquatint. 30-Jun-4 Christie's, London #269/R est:4500-6500
£6597	$10885	€9500	Untitled (70x105cm-28x41in) s.i. eau forte engraving. 2-Jul-3 Ansorena, Madrid #878/R est:9000
£6780	$12000	€9899	Les forestiers, blue (50x32cm-20x13in) s.num.42/75 col aquatint. 28-Apr-4 Christie's, Rockefeller NY #82/R est:8000-10000
£6780	$12000	€9899	L'oiseau destructeur (72x94cm-28x37in) s.num.11/75 etching aquatint. 30-Apr-4 Sotheby's, New York #146/R est:8000-12000
£6889	$12400	€10058	Les femme des sables (105x63cm-41x25in) s.i. one of 75 col etching aquatint prov.lit. 26-Apr-4 Bukowskis, Stockholm #389/R est:80000-100000 (S.KR 95000)
£7059	$12000	€10306	Adorateur du soleil (106x68cm-42x27in) s. num.40/75 et aquatint exec.1969. 4-Nov-3 Christie's, Rockefeller NY #133/R est:7000-10000
£7345	$13000	€10724	La harpie (94x70cm-37x28in) s.num.73/75 etching aquatint. 30-Apr-4 Sotheby's, New York #148/R est:6000-8000

£7500	$13650	€10950	Le chasseur des pieuvres (105x67cm-41x26in) s.num.7/75 col aquatint etching carborundum. 1-Jul-4 Sotheby's, London #217/R est:6000-8000
£7910	$14000	€11549	L'enrage (90x60cm-35x24in) s.num.55/75 col etching aquatint carborundum. 28-Apr-4 Christie's, Rockefeller NY #86/R est:10000-15000
£7910	$14000	€11549	Serie II (37x45cm-15x18in) s.d.1952-53 num.5/13 col etching. 30-Apr-4 Sotheby's, New York #135/R est:10000-12000
£7910	$14000	€11549	L'etrangle (114x73cm-45x29in) s.num.17/50 etching aquatint. 30-Apr-4 Sotheby's, New York #155/R est:6000-8000
£8000	$13760	€11680	La sorciere (105x70cm-41x28in) s.i. etching aquatint carborundum. 4-Dec-3 Sotheby's, London #166/R est:6000-7000
£8000	$13760	€11680	Series III (48x85cm-19x33in) s.num.IX/XII etching aquatint. 2-Dec-3 Christie's, London #201/R est:8000-12000
£8000	$14560	€11680	Le sarrasin a l'etoile bleue (138x60cm-54x24in) s.num.4/50 col etching aquatint carborundum. 1-Jul-4 Sotheby's, London #220/R est:6000-8000
£8383	$14000	€12239	Untitled (30x25cm-12x10in) s.d.1934 col pochoir. 11-Nov-3 Christie's, Rockefeller NY #151/R est:12000-15000
£9040	$16000	€13198	Robert Desnos (40x29cm-16x11in) s.num. col lithograph set of 32 album. 28-Apr-4 Christie's, Rockefeller NY #98/R est:20000-25000
£10000	$17000	€14600	Le pitre rose (116x74cm-46x29in) s.num.31/50 col etching aquatint. 6-Nov-3 Swann Galleries, New York #649/R est:12000-18000
£10000	$17000	€14600	Tristan Tzara (41x31cm-16x12in) col lithograph album. 4-Nov-3 Christie's, Rockefeller NY #127/R est:12000-18000
£10000	$18200	€14600	Le scieur de long (76x57cm-30x22in) s.num.21/75 aquatint drypoint cardorundum. 30-Jun-4 Christie's, London #270/R est:4000-6000
£10000	$18200	€14600	La main (36x48cm-14x19in) s.d.1953 num.57/75 col etching aquatint. 1-Jul-4 Sotheby's, London #214/R est:7000-9000
£10169	$18000	€14847	La femme aux bijoux (47x34cm-19x13in) s.num.59/75 col aquatint carborundum. 30-Apr-4 Sotheby's, New York #144/R est:12000-16000
£10526	$19368	€16000	Charivari (120x160cm-47x63in) s. num.17/50 aquatint Arches paper exec 1976 lit. 28-Jun-4 Joron-Derem, Paris #42/R est:10000-12000
£10667	$19520	€16000	Constellations (47x38cm-19x15in) s.i. 2 etchings 2 col lithographs. 5-Jun-4 Lempertz, Koln #880/R est:10000
£10989	$20110	€16484	Untitled (24x31cm-9x12in) s.d.1948 lithograph. 6-Jul-4 Bolsa de Arte, Rio de Janeiro #66/R (B.R 60000)
£11176	$19000	€16317	Gaudi XXI (115x72cm-45x28in) s. col etching. 31-Oct-3 Sotheby's, New York #336/R
£11299	$20000	€16497	Raymond Queneau (66x51cm-26x20in) mono.num. col lithograph set of 26. 28-Apr-4 Christie's, Rockefeller NY #84/R est:25000-35000
£11765	$20000	€17177	Femme au miroir (39x56cm-15x22in) s. col lithograph. 31-Oct-3 Sotheby's, New York #321/R
£11765	$20000	€17177	Untitled (32x49cm-13x19in) s. col monotype exec.1974. 4-Nov-3 Christie's, Rockefeller NY #136/R est:25000-35000
£12000	$20640	€17520	La femme au miroir (38x56cm-15x22in) s.num.44/150 col lithograph. 2-Dec-3 Christie's, London #213/R est:12000-18000
£12000	$21840	€17520	Le bagnard et sa compagne (121x160cm-48x63in) s.num.29/50 col aquatint. 1-Jul-4 Sotheby's, London #205/R est:7000-9000
£12155	$22000	€17746	Joan Miro lithographe III (45x37cm-18x15in) s.num.XXV/LXXX col lithograph set of eight. 19-Apr-4 Bonhams & Butterfields, San Francisco #190/R est:15000-20000
£12291	$22000	€17945	Serie Mallorca (55x70cm-22x28in) s.num. engraving portfolio of 9. 6-May-4 Swann Galleries, New York #531/R est:25000-35000
£12941	$22000	€18894	Femme toupie (117x74cm-46x29in) s. col etching aquatint. 31-Oct-3 Sotheby's, New York #330/R
£13000	$22360	€18980	Oiseau migrateur (65x51cm-26x20in) s.num.IX/XV set of five lithograph. 2-Dec-3 Christie's, London #215/R est:10000-15000
£14124	$25000	€20621	Serie noire et rouge (26x17cm-10x7in) s.num.6/30 black red etching. 30-Apr-4 Sotheby's, New York #134/R est:20000-30000
£14706	$25000	€21471	Untitled (33x50cm-13x20in) s. monotype paper exec 1974 prov. 6-Nov-3 Sotheby's, New York #299/R est:30000-40000
£15819	$28000	€23096	Woman at the mirror (39x56cm-15x22in) s.i. col lithograph edition of 150. 28-Apr-4 Christie's, Rockefeller NY #79/R est:35000-45000
£15882	$27000	€23188	Main (36x48cm-14x19in) s.d.1953 etching. 31-Oct-3 Sotheby's, New York #320/R
£15882	$27000	€23188	Untitled (32x49cm-13x19in) s. col monotype exec.1974. 4-Nov-3 Christie's, Rockefeller NY #135/R est:20000-25000
£16949	$30000	€24746	Le somnambule (114x74cm-45x29in) s.i. col etching aquatint edition of 50. 28-Apr-4 Christie's, Rockefeller NY #96/R est:25000-35000
£17112	$32000	€24984	Poissons (48x56cm-19x22in) s. monoprint exec.1976. 25-Feb-4 Christie's, Rockefeller NY #126/R est:15000-20000
£17647	$30000	€25765	Somnambule (114x74cm-45x29in) s. col etching aquatint. 31-Oct-3 Sotheby's, New York #331/R
£20588	$35000	€30058	Michel Leiris (50x60cm-20x24in) s. aquatint set of 13. 4-Nov-3 Christie's, Rockefeller NY #132/R est:40000-60000
£21469	$38000	€31345	Untitled, from l'issue derobee (33x50cm-13x20in) s. col monotype one of 15. 28-Apr-4 Christie's, Rockefeller NY #97/R est:25000-35000
£21765	$37000	€31777	Untitled (32x25cm-13x10in) d.14/4/62 monotype colouring brush India ink gouache. 5-Nov-3 Christie's, Rockefeller NY #152/R est:25000-35000
£23529	$40000	€34352	Woman at mirror (39x56cm-15x22in) s.d.1956 col lithograph. 4-Nov-3 Christie's, Rockefeller NY #129/R est:25000-35000
£23529	$40000	€34352	Enfance d'Ubu (50x32cm-20x13in) s.i. col lithograph set of 20. 4-Nov-3 Christie's, Rockefeller NY #138/R est:40000-60000
£48000	$87360	€70080	Suites pour ubu Roi (54x75cm-21x30in) s.num.67/75 col lithograph set of 13. 30-Jun-4 Christie's, London #261/R est:28000-35000

Sculpture

£6704	$12000	€9788	Femme (16cm-6in) s.indis.st.f.Parellada num.2/2 brown pat bronze prov.lit. 5-May-4 Christie's, Rockefeller NY #312/R est:15000-20000
£20588	$35000	€30058	Tete (18cm-7in) s. glazed ceramic exec 1956 prov.lit. 6-Nov-3 Sotheby's, New York #263/R est:40000-60000
£35294	$60000	€51529	Les trois cheveux magnetiques de la belle blonde attirent les papillons (42cm-17in) brown green pat bronze cast 1969 prov.lit. 5-Nov-3 Christie's, Rockefeller NY #324/R est:60000-80000
£73333	$134200	€110000	Untitled (15x22cm-6x9in) s.d.1945 ceramic paint enamel double-sided unique prov.exhib.lit. 7-Jun-4 Artcurial Briest, Paris #25/R est:60000-80000

Works on paper

£1202	$2127	€1755	Pour Mademoiselle Hedy Sciess, hommage de Miro (24x36cm-9x14in) i.d.2/XI/64 col chk double-sided. 12-Jun-4 Falk & Falk, Zurich #918 est:3200 (S.FR 2800)
£2752	$5063	€4100	Male profile (15x16cm-6x6in) s.d.55 Indian ink. 27-Mar-4 Dannenberg, Berlin #598/R est:4000
£3056	$5042	€4400	Figure and star (19x19cm-7x7in) wax crayon dr. 2-Jul-3 Ansorena, Madrid #869/R
£6500	$11960	€9490	Figures (26x20cm-10x8in) s.i.d.948 pen ink prov. 22-Jun-4 Sotheby's, London #517/R est:6000-8000
£7000	$11690	€10220	Quatre dessins (25x18cm-10x7in) s.i. col wax crayon executed September 1964 prov. 21-Oct-3 Sotheby's, London #82/R est:7000-9000
£7500	$11925	€10875	Sans titre (25x20cm-10x8in) s.i. pencil col felt-tipped pen. 11-Sep-3 Christie's, Kensington #196/R est:8000-12000
£8000	$13360	€11680	Personnage oiseau (38x28cm-15x11in) s.i. pastel prov. 21-Oct-3 Sotheby's, London #83/R est:7000-9000
£9800	$18032	€14308	Personnage (46x37cm-18x15in) s.d.I/XII/76 black crayon prov. 24-Mar-4 Sotheby's, Olympia #172/R est:8000-12000
£10000	$18200	€14600	Composition (24x32cm-9x13in) Indian ink. 21-Jun-4 Bonhams, New Bond Street #115/R est:10000-15000
£11409	$20423	€17000	Personnage (28x27cm-11x11in) s.i. wax crayon graphite prov. 26-May-4 Christie's, Paris #53/R est:10000-15000
£13529	$23000	€19752	Hommage a Shuzo Takiguchi (36x50cm-14x20in) s. gouache brush India ink two. 5-Nov-3 Christie's, Rockefeller NY #150/R est:30000-40000
£13768	$22580	€19000	Untitled (57x45cm-22x18in) s. W/C over xilograph exec.1965 prov. 27-May-3 Sotheby's, Milan #263/R est:15000-20000
£17333	$32067	€26000	Composition (27x84cm-11x33in) s.i. Chinese ink on 4 leaves exec.c.1969. 18-Jul-4 Sotheby's, Paris #299/R est:18000-25000
£19445	$32473	€28000	Les voyants (66x51cm-26x20in) s.d.VI/69 gouache on lithograph on paper. 21-Oct-3 Artcurial Briest, Paris #135/R est:25000-30000
£19928	$32681	€27500	Cultura catalana (21x20cm-8x8in) s. Indian ink gouache brown paper lit. 27-May-3 Durán, Madrid #284/R est:8500
£20270	$35676	€30000	Untitled (45x57cm-18x22in) init. s.i.d.60 verso gouache pastel prov.exhib.lit. 24-May-4 Christie's, Milan #253/R est:30000-35000
£20979	$36084	€30000	Sans titre (42x23cm-17x9in) s.d.1946 verso W/C black chk prov. 5-Dec-3 Ketterer, Munich #124/R est:30000-40000
£21477	$38013	€32000	Untitled (38x28cm-15x11in) s.i. wax crayon. 29-Apr-4 Christie's, Paris #162/R est:8000-12000
£22819	$40846	€34000	Figures (40x56cm-16x22in) s.i.d.67 wax crayon prov. 26-May-4 Christie's, Paris #51/R est:15000-20000
£24000	$40080	€35040	Composition (84x44cm-33x17in) s. brush ink over pencil gouache executed c.1970 prov. 21-Oct-3 Sotheby's, London #69/R est:18000-25000
£25171	$45055	€37000	Untitled (21x17cm-8x7in) s.i.d.3/7/56 W/C book page prov. 21-Mar-4 Calmels Cohen, Paris #50/R est:25000-30000
£25792	$43846	€57000	Composition (46x62cm-18x24in) s. s.verso W/C htd gouache. 25-Nov-3 Pierre Berge, Paris #8/R est:30000-40000
£30000	$50100	€43800	Composition (11x33cm-4x13in) s.d.29/X/57 gouache brush ink pencil. 21-Oct-3 Sotheby's, London #59/R est:12000-15000
£32402	$58000	€47307	Untitled (63x46cm-25x18in) s.d.6.11.930 verso pencil prov. 5-May-4 Christie's, Rockefeller NY #132/R est:40000-60000
£45000	$82350	€65700	Composition (46x63cm-18x25in) s.d.30.9.30 chl prov. 2-Feb-4 Christie's, London #75/R est:45000-65000
£55000	$100100	€80300	Composition pour le lezard aux plumes d'or (35x50cm-14x20in) s.d.63 gouache W/C pen India ink brush ink ink wash prov. 5-Feb-4 Christie's, London #437/R est:45000-65000
£55866	$100000	€81564	Femme dans la nuit (65x52cm-26x20in) s.i.d.7/IX/67 d.I/IX/71 verso pastel W/C prov. 6-May-4 Sotheby's, New York #382/R est:100000-150000
£55882	$95000	€81588	Femme, oiseaux (75x57cm-30x22in) s. i.d.26/XI/75 verso gouache W/C blk crayon prov. 6-Nov-3 Sotheby's, New York #273/R est:100000-150000
£60000	$109200	€87600	Personnage dans la nuit, oiseau qui s'envolve, etoile matinale (49x31cm-19x12in) s. s.i.d.1968 verso gouache W/C pen ink prov. 5-Feb-4 Christie's, London #431/R est:60000-80000
£65000	$118950	€94900	Composition (24x31cm-9x12in) s.i.d.1944 gouache col chk pencil prov.exhib. 2-Feb-4 Christie's, London #57/R est:60000-80000
£70000	$128100	€102200	Composition (14x22cm-6x9in) s.d.27.7.24 pencil gesso panel. 2-Feb-4 Christie's, London #52/R est:70000-100000
£70588	$120000	€103058	Graphisme concret (72x98cm-28x39in) s. s.i.d.1952 verso W/C pen India ink chl prov. 5-Nov-3 Christie's, Rockefeller NY #128/R est:120000-160000
£80000	$145600	€116800	Woman catching a bird (64x52cm-25x20in) s.i.d.72 verso W/C chl col crayon prov. 5-Feb-4 Christie's, London #438/R est:60000-80000
£82353	$140000	€120235	Personnage devant le soleil (51x65cm-20x26in) s. s.i.d.28-10-1942 verso gouache brush India ink prov. 5-Nov-3 Christie's, Rockefeller NY #141/R est:120000-160000
£135000	$248400	€197100	Personnages, oiseau (51x65cm-20x26in) s. s.i.d.1942 verso gouache W/C India ink prov. 24-Jun-4 Christie's, London #427/R est:130000-180000
£167598	$300000	€244693	Untitled (77x56cm-30x22in) s. gouache W/C exec c.1969-70 prov. 6-May-4 Sotheby's, New York #379/R est:250000-350000
£170000	$312800	€248200	Dancers (70x99cm-28x39in) s. s.i.d.21/3/63 verso gouache W/C India ink prov.lit. 24-Jun-4 Christie's, London #448/R est:120000-160000
£288235	$490000	€420823	Composition (62x50cm-24x20in) s.verso gouache paper collage paper on board executed 1934 prov. 5-Nov-3 Sotheby's, New York #50/R est:500000-700000
£382353	$650000	€558235	Personnages, oiseaux, etoiles (110x79cm-43x31in) s.i.d.7.8.1942 pencil India ink gouache chl prov.exhib.lit. 5-Nov-3 Sotheby's, New York #52/R est:700000-900000
£400000	$728000	€584000	Courtisan Grotesque (41x58cm-16x23in) each s. one i. gouache W/C India ink pastel pencil fourteen prov. 5-Feb-4 Christie's, London #432/R est:280000-350000

MIROU, Antoine (1583-1669) Flemish

£14474	$26632	€22000	River landscape (12x18cm-5x7in) copper. 25-Jun-4 Piasa, Paris #5/R est:20000-25000
£26000	$44980	€37960	Coastal landscape with fishing boats disembarking, the calling of Saint Peter beyond (17x22cm-7x9in) copper exhib. 10-Dec-3 Christie's, London #21/R est:20000-30000

MIROU, Antoine (attrib) (1583-1669) Flemish

£10000	$17000	€14600	Duck shooting (33x53cm-13x21in) panel. 19-Nov-3 Tennants, Leyburn #1008/R est:15000-20000

MIROU, Antoine (circle) (1583-1669) Flemish

£9615	$16538	€14038	Landscape with a procession (28x37cm-11x15in) bears sig. panel. 3-Dec-3 AB Stockholms Auktionsverk #2659/R est:125000-150000 (S.KR 125000)

MIRVAL, C (20th C) French

Sculpture

£2113	$3655	€3000	Jeune fille aux cygnes (77x58cm-30x23in) s. silver-blue red pat bronze onyz alabaster base. 13-Dec-3 De Vuyst, Lokeren #237/R est:3000-4000

MIRWALD, Ferdinand (1872-1948) German

£483	$806	€700	Evening street (74x58cm-29x23in) s. 15-Nov-3 Von Zezschwitz, Munich #44/R
£570	$1050	€850	Village landscape in spring (44x54cm-17x21in) s. panel. 24-Mar-4 Hugo Ruef, Munich #1047

MISBACH, Constant (1808-?) French
£909 $1545 €1300 Portrait de jeune fille (65x54cm-26x21in) s.d.1839. 1-Dec-3 Coutau Begarie, Paris #172

MISCHKINE, Olga (1910-1985) Russian
£369 $690 €550 Bouquet (55x38cm-22x15in) s. 29-Feb-4 Versailles Encheres #168

MISKEY, Julian de (20th C) American
Works on paper
£3911 $7000 €5710 Tourists at quayside outside of bar American (46x33cm-18x13in) init. W/C pastel. 15-May-4 Illustration House, New York #137/R est:8000-12000
£5389 $9000 €7868 Couple dancing to old cylinder record player, servant surprised (51x33cm-20x13in) init. W/C chl. 15-Nov-3 Illustration House, New York #53/R est:8000-12000

MISONNE, Eudore (1891-1968) Belgian
£367 $656 €550 Paysage a Godinne (32x41cm-13x16in) s. 16-May-4 MonsAntic, Maisieres #449
£500 $895 €750 Petite fille posant avec sa poupee (58x49cm-23x19in) s. 16-May-4 MonsAntic, Maisieres #446
£667 $1193 €1000 La sandale orange (70x60cm-28x24in) s. 16-May-4 MonsAntic, Maisieres #445
£667 $1193 €1000 Jeune garcon boudant (60x50cm-24x20in) s. 16-May-4 MonsAntic, Maisieres #447

MISONNE, Leonard (1870-1943) Belgian
£2222 $4000 €3244 Wet weather (29x39cm-11x15in) i.d.1936 verso oil print prov. 22-Apr-4 Phillips, New York #194/R est:4000-6000
Photographs
£1796 $3000 €2622 Tress and pasture (29x39cm-11x15in) with sig.d.1939 mediabrome print. 21-Oct-3 Swann Galleries, New York #136/R est:3000-4000

MISRACH, Richard (1949-) American
Photographs
£1657 $3000 €2419 Clearing storm near Kingman (27x58cm-11x23in) s.i.d.1985/1986 num.11/25 chromogenic print. 19-Apr-4 Bonhams & Butterfields, San Francisco #458/R est:2500-3500
£2156 $3600 €3148 Salton Sea (72x85cm-28x33in) s.i.d.1985/1988 chromogenic col print one of ten prov. 17-Oct-3 Phillips, New York #262/R est:3000-5000
£2395 $4000 €3497 Salton sea, slide (47x59cm-19x23in) s.i.d.1983 num.2/25 chromogenic print. 17-Oct-3 Sotheby's, New York #298/R est:5000-7000
£2800 $4760 €4088 Golden Gate 3.3.98.625 P.M (71x89cm-28x35in) s.i.d.2001 num.3/7 chromogenic print. 18-Nov-3 Christie's, Kensington #244/R est:1500-2500
£3955 $7000 €5774 Desert fire no 1, burning palms (71x92cm-28x36in) cibachrome print prov. 28-Apr-4 Sotheby's, New York #168/R est:8000-12000
£5026 $9500 €7338 Moon over black rock, 8:22pm-10:24pm (121x154cm-48x61in) chromogenic print. 17-Feb-4 Swann Galleries, New York #113/R est:6000-9000
£10556 $19000 €15412 World's fastest mobile home 96 mph, Bonneville Salt Flats, Nevada (102x127cm-40x50in) s.i.d.1992 num2/3 chromogenic colour print prov.lit. 23-Apr-4 Phillips, New York #44/R est:9000-12000

MISTCHENKO, Viktor (?) Russian
£510 $929 €750 Sous les glycines. s. 8-Feb-4 Lesieur & Le Bars, Le Havre #107

MISTI-MIFLIEZ, Ferdinand (1865-1923) French
Works on paper
£317 $513 €450 Jeune femme se deshabillant (26x44cm-10x17in) drawing. 11-Aug-3 Boscher, Cherbourg #711
£816 $1461 €1200 Elegante au chapeau noir (46x38cm-18x15in) s. pastel exhib. 16-Mar-4 Vanderkindere, Brussels #80

MISTRY, Dhruva (1957-) Indian
Sculpture
£1216 $2250 €1775 White elephant (27x42cm-11x17in) green pat bronze edn 3/5 Cast 1987 prov. 12-Feb-4 Sotheby's, New York #210/R est:700-900
£5946 $11000 €8681 Object 11 (120x53x60cm-47x21x24in) dark brown pat bronze exec 1987-88 prov. 12-Feb-4 Sotheby's, New York #224/R est:1000-1500

MITARAS, Dimitris (1934-) Greek
£3500 $6265 €5110 Woman in profile (70x50cm-28x20in) s. board. 10-May-4 Sotheby's, Olympia #86/R est:2000-3000
£9500 $17005 €13870 Woman (100x70cm-39x28in) s. 10-May-4 Sotheby's, Olympia #88/R est:4000-6000

MITCHELL OF MARYPORT, William (c.1806-1900) British
£1400 $2562 €2044 Scene at Windermere (106x61cm-42x24in) s.d.1893 verso. 7-Jun-4 Cumbria Auction Rooms, Carlisle #236
£2955 $5200 €4433 Sailing ship, Lady Gordon, leaving Maryport. Cumberland (56x74cm-22x29in) mono.d.1891. 21-May-4 North East Auctions, Portsmouth #644/R
Works on paper
£360 $612 €526 Lowes water looking South (58x89cm-23x35in) i.d.1876 verso. 29-Oct-3 Bonhams, Chester #322

MITCHELL, Alfred R (1888-1972) American
£2031 $3250 €2965 Coastal beach scene (102x152cm-40x60in) s.d.1922 board. 18-May-3 Auctions by the Bay, Alameda #1107/R
£2174 $4000 €3174 The road to Old Farm (19x24cm-7x9in) s. board prov. 8-Jun-4 Bonhams & Butterfields, San Francisco #4242/R est:3000-5000
£2581 $4750 €3768 Manayunk (23x30cm-9x12in) s. s.i. verso board. 27-Jun-4 Freeman, Philadelphia #195/R est:5000-8000
£3175 $6000 €4636 Arizona farm (20x25cm-8x10in) s. i. verso board. 17-Feb-4 John Moran, Pasadena #42a/R est:4000-6000
£3179 $5500 €4641 High Sierra Lake - Half Dome (20x25cm-8x10in) s. i.verso board. 10-Dec-3 Bonhams & Butterfields, San Francisco #6309/R est:5000-7000
£3824 $6500 €5583 Center Bridge, PA (41x51cm-16x20in) s.i.d.Aug 25 1926 verso board after E W Redfield. 18-Nov-3 John Moran, Pasadena #50 est:9000-12000
£3824 $6500 €5583 Houses in winter river landscape (41x51cm-16x20in) s.i.d.March 1936 board after E W Redfield. 18-Nov-3 John Moran, Pasadena #50a est:9000-12000
£4076 $7500 €5951 Winter on the Delaware (41x51cm-16x20in) i.d.1926 verso board after Gardner Symons. 27-Jun-4 Freeman, Philadelphia #175/R est:7000-10000
£4237 $7500 €6186 Road to Palm Canyon, Palm Springs vicinity (40x50cm-16x20in) s. s.i.verso board prov. 28-Apr-4 Christie's, Los Angeles #48/R est:8000-12000
£4348 $8000 €6348 Center Bridge PA (41x51cm-16x20in) s.i.d.1926 verso board after E W Redfield. 27-Jun-4 Freeman, Philadelphia #174/R est:7000-10000
£4620 $8500 €6745 Barren Hill near Norristown PA (25x35cm-10x14in) s. painted 1927 board. 27-Jun-4 Freeman, Philadelphia #164/R est:6000-8000
£5163 $9500 €7538 Winter landscape Delaware river (41x51cm-16x20in) s. i.d.1926 verso board. 27-Jun-4 Freeman, Philadelphia #206/R est:7000-10000
£5233 $9000 €7640 Jolla (20x25cm-8x10in) s. s.i.verso board. 7-Dec-3 Freeman, Philadelphia #185 est:2000-3000
£5233 $9000 €7640 Grey thaw (41x51cm-16x20in) i.verso board. 7-Dec-3 Freeman, Philadelphia #217 est:7000-10000
£5780 $10000 €8439 At La Jolla (41x51cm-16x20in) s. i.verso board. 10-Dec-3 Bonhams & Butterfields, San Francisco #6211/R est:10000-15000
£7065 $13000 €10315 Dorothea painting the tiger lilies, Mineral King (20x25cm-8x10in) s. i.d.1941 verso board prov. 8-Jun-4 Bonhams & Butterfields, San Francisco #4286/R est:8000-12000
£8092 $14000 €11814 Cliffs (41x51cm-16x20in) s. i.verso board. 10-Dec-3 Bonhams & Butterfields, San Francisco #6210/R est:15000-20000
£11047 $19000 €16129 Road to New Hope (41x51cm-16x20in) s. s.i.verso board prov. 7-Dec-3 Freeman, Philadelphia #186 est:8000-12000

MITCHELL, Brian (20th C) British
£250 $418 €365 Three boats (30x28cm-12x11in) s. panel. 14-Oct-3 David Lay, Penzance #481
£360 $601 €526 Low tide (71x61cm-28x24in) s.d.1987 board. 14-Oct-3 David Lay, Penzance #475

MITCHELL, Colin (20th C) British
£300 $474 €438 Scottish landscape (62x76cm-24x30in) s. 25-Apr-3 Bigwood, Stratford on Avon #255/R

MITCHELL, Colin Gillespie (?-1938) British
£280 $512 €409 Burn in Scotland (19x24cm-7x9in) s. 8-Jul-4 Lawrence, Crewkerne #1655

MITCHELL, Denis (1912-1993) British
Sculpture
£3200 $5824 €4672 Untitled (21cm-8in) num.0/200 brown green pat bronze incl. base one of 200. 15-Jun-4 Bonhams, New Bond Street #93/R est:1500-2000
£5500 $9350 €8030 Botallack (79cm-31in) polished pat. bronze black stone base prov. 21-Nov-3 Christie's, London #181/R est:5000-8000
£6500 $11440 €9490 Trevean Dam (65cm-26in) i.d.1971 num.4 green pat bronze marble base. 18-May-4 Woolley & Wallis, Salisbury #367/R est:800-1200

MITCHELL, George Bertrand (1874-1966) American
£313 $522 €454 Fishing returning to Cape Cod (23x30cm-9x12in) s. board. 17-Jun-3 Pinneys, Montreal #80 (C.D 700)
Works on paper
£1816 $3250 €2651 Red wagon (41x51cm-16x20in) s. pastel prov. 6-May-4 Shannon's, Milford #198/R est:2500-3500

MITCHELL, Glen (1894-1972) American
£818 $1300 €1194 Abstracted landscape (48x66cm-19x26in) s.verso. 12-Sep-3 Skinner, Boston #537/R
Works on paper
£409 $650 €597 Women of the hills (39x28cm-15x11in) s. mixed media chl. 12-Sep-3 Skinner, Boston #539/R

MITCHELL, Gordon K (1952-) British
£800 $1488 €1168 Stretch Limo (24x70cm-9x28in) painted 1977. 6-Mar-4 Shapes, Edinburgh #442/R

MITCHELL, Hutton (?) Canadian
£356 $615 €520 Twilight, Quebec City (38x56cm-15x22in) s. 9-Dec-3 Pinneys, Montreal #10 (C.D 800)
Works on paper
£300 $510 €438 Wild mustard (54x75cm-21x30in) s. pencil W/C. 19-Nov-3 Tennants, Leyburn #968

MITCHELL, Janet (1912-1998) Canadian
£496 $898 €724 Untitled - carousel (41x51cm-16x20in) s.d.1956 board prov. 18-Apr-4 Levis, Calgary #87/R est:700-900 (C.D 1200)
£620 $1122 €905 Untitled - pilgrimage (51x41cm-20x16in) s. s.i.verso board prov. 18-Apr-4 Levis, Calgary #86/R est:800-1000 (C.D 1500)
£661 $1197 €965 Untitled - celebration (61x61cm-24x24in) s.d.1958 hard board prov. 18-Apr-4 Levis, Calgary #82/R est:1800-2200 (C.D 1600)
£680 $1244 €993 Camp under a full moon (46x54cm-18x21in) s.d.1950 board. 1-Jun-4 Hodgins, Calgary #278/R (C.D 1700)
£1033 $1870 €1508 Three Janes (51x40cm-20x16in) s.d.1956 s.i.verso hard board prov. 18-Apr-4 Levis, Calgary #85/R est:800-1000 (C.D 2500)
£1136 $2057 €1659 Untitled - boy with yellow sweater (122x48cm-48x19in) s.d.62 hard board prov. 18-Apr-4 Levis, Calgary #83/R est:1000-1200 (C.D 2750)

£1136 $2057 €1659 Untitled - girl with red and black jumper (122x48cm-48x19in) s. i.d.1950 verso hard board prov. 18-Apr-4 Levis, Calgary #84/R est:1000-1200 (C.D 2750)
£2376 $4301 €3469 Untitled - Royal family (58x121cm-23x48in) s. hard board prov. 18-Apr-4 Levis, Calgary #81/R est:2500-3500 (C.D 5750)
£3202 $5796 €4675 Some children (122x97cm-48x38in) s.d.1964 hard board prov. 18-Apr-4 Levis, Calgary #80/R est:3000-3500 (C.D 7750)
Works on paper
£260 $476 €380 Autumn trees (17x25cm-7x10in) s. W/C. 1-Jun-4 Hodgins, Calgary #149/R (C.D 650)
£372 $673 €543 Untitled - on the street (41x30cm-16x12in) s.d.1958 W/C prov. 18-Apr-4 Levis, Calgary #502/R (C.D 900)
£428 $728 €625 Conversation (55x36cm-22x14in) s.d.1954 i.verso W/C. 27-Nov-3 Heffel, Vancouver #200 (C.D 950)
£440 $805 €642 Cabins in the mountains (35x54cm-14x21in) s.d.1955 W/C. 1-Jun-4 Hodgins, Calgary #22/R (C.D 1100)
£440 $805 €642 Night skies in the mountains (35x53cm-14x21in) s.d.1954 W/C. 1-Jun-4 Hodgins, Calgary #167/R (C.D 1100)
£520 $952 €759 Conversation (54x36cm-21x14in) s.d.1954 W/C. 1-Jun-4 Hodgins, Calgary #68/R (C.D 1300)

MITCHELL, Joan (1926-1992) American
£71856 $120000 €104910 Untitled (35x99cm-14x39in) s. four attached canvases painted c.1975-76 prov. 12-Nov-3 Christie's, Rockefeller NY #355/R est:90000-120000
£107784 $180000 €157365 Untitled (91x73cm-36x29in) painted c.1967-68 prov. 13-Nov-3 Phillips, New York #32/R est:200000-300000
£234637 $420000 €342570 Untitled (200x149cm-79x59in) s. painted 1966-1969 prov. 11-May-4 Christie's, Rockefeller NY #23/R est:400000-600000
£299401 $500000 €437125 No room at the end (281x381cm-111x150in) in two parts painted 1977 prov.exhib. 12-Nov-3 Sotheby's, New York #57/R est:550000-750000
£347305 $580000 €507065 Ploughed field (112x213cm-44x84in) s. triptych painted 1971 prov.exhib.lit. 11-Nov-3 Christie's, Rockefeller NY #31/R est:600000-800000
£446927 $800000 €652513 Untitled (243x199cm-96x78in) s. exec c.1960 prov.exhib. 12-May-4 Sotheby's, New York #26/R est:600000-800000
£474860 $850000 €693296 Bracket (260x462cm-102x182in) s. triptych painted 1989 prov.exhib.lit. 11-May-4 Christie's, Rockefeller NY #28/R est:600000-800000
£479042 $800000 €699401 No 3 (176x166cm-69x65in) s. painted 1953-54 prov.exhib.lit. 11-Nov-3 Christie's, Rockefeller NY #25/R est:400000-600000
£726257 $1300000 €1060335 Degel (221x200cm-87x79in) s. painted 1961-1962 prov.exhib. 11-May-4 Christie's, Rockefeller NY #14/R est:500000-700000
Prints
£3955 $7000 €5774 Sides of a river II (108x83cm-43x33in) s. num.12/70 col lithograph. 30-Apr-4 Sotheby's, New York #398 est:3000-4000
Works on paper
£5435 $10000 €7935 Drowned (36x22cm-14x9in) s. pastel typewritten text. 27-Jun-4 Freeman, Philadelphia #132/R est:7000-10000
£10056 $18000 €14682 Untitled (32x22cm-13x9in) s. pastel W/C prov. 14-May-4 Phillips, New York #268/R est:18000-22000

MITCHELL, John (1838-1926) British
£978 $1800 €1428 Scottish landscape (76x119cm-30x47in) s.d.1905. 27-Jun-4 Hindman, Chicago #797/R est:1200-1800
Works on paper
£620 $1110 €905 Balmoral Castle (17x25cm-7x10in) s.d.1894 W/C. 25-May-4 Bonhams, Knightsbridge #173/R

MITCHELL, John Campbell (1862-1922) British
£260 $447 €380 Kirkcudbrightshire moor (23x28cm-9x11in) s.d.1918 panel. 5-Dec-3 Chrystals Auctions, Isle of Man #243
£300 $516 €438 Landscape, Galloway (51x66cm-20x26in) 5-Dec-3 Chrystals Auctions, Isle of Man #242
£1150 $1852 €1668 Carse of Stirling (37x44cm-15x17in) s. 21-Aug-3 Bonhams, Edinburgh #1149 est:1000-1500
£2400 $4296 €3504 South Road, Arran (55x65cm-22x26in) s. 27-May-4 Christie's, Kensington #221/R est:800-1200
£7000 $12530 €10220 On the Solway (91x152cm-36x60in) s.d.1913 prov. 28-May-4 Lyon & Turnbull, Edinburgh #15/R est:5000-7000

MITCHELL, Leonard (1925-1980) New Zealander
£368 $688 €537 Summer window (63x100cm-25x39in) s.d.1969 board. 24-Feb-4 Peter Webb, Auckland #103/R (NZ.D 1000)

MITCHELL, Leonard Victor (fl.1950s) Australian
Works on paper
£827 $1406 €1207 History of wool (47x70cm-19x28in) s.d.1958 W/C ink. 26-Nov-3 Dunbar Sloane, Wellington #145/R est:900-1500 (NZ.D 2200)

MITCHELL, Mike (20th C) Irish?
£320 $576 €480 Red on green (34x34cm-13x13in) s. acrylic collage. 20-Apr-4 James Adam, Dublin #68/R

MITCHELL, Philip (1814-1896) British
Works on paper
£420 $769 €613 Scene on the Millbrook Lake, looking towards Devonport (33x51cm-13x20in) s.d.1868 W/C. 7-Apr-4 Dreweatt Neate, Newbury #57/R

MITCHELL, Reginald M (1959-) American
£359 $600 €524 City scene (99x79cm-39x31in) acrylic paper. 15-Nov-3 Slotin Folk Art, Buford #661/R

MITCHELL, Thomas Wilberforce (1879-1958) Canadian
£1118 $2001 €1632 The crossroads (61x91cm-24x36in) mono.d.1906 prov. 6-May-4 Heffel, Vancouver #102/R est:2500-3500 (C.D 2750)

MITCHELL, Wallace Macmahon (1911-1977) American
£1117 $2000 €1631 Untitled (137x76cm-54x30in) acrylic plexiglas exhib. 16-May-4 Wright, Chicago #303/R est:2000-3000

MITCHELL, William Frederick (1845-1914) British
£362 $583 €529 Stablefield Bay (57x92cm-22x36in) s.i.d.1876 or 1896. 12-Aug-3 Peter Webb, Auckland #144/R (NZ.D 1000)
Works on paper
£410 $750 €599 An 1885 drednought (30x39cm-12x15in) s.d.1885 W/C. 29-Jul-4 Christie's, Rockefeller NY #286/R est:1200-1800
£3000 $4800 €4380 HMS Trafalgar (51x72cm-20x28in) mono. W/C htd white. 16-Sep-3 Bonhams, New Bond Street #7/R est:3000-5000

MITELLI, Giuseppe Maria (1634-1718) Italian
Works on paper
£811 $1427 €1200 Chronos, God of time appearing before old couple (20x30cm-8x12in) ochre prov. 22-May-4 Lempertz, Koln #1319/R

MITELMAN, Allan (1946-) Australian
Works on paper
£382 $695 €558 Untitled (54x72cm-21x28in) init.d.74 gouache synthetic polymer prov. 16-Jun-4 Deutscher-Menzies, Melbourne #646 est:400-600 (A.D 1000)

MITES, Julia (19th C) Irish
Works on paper
£292 $496 €420 Mrs Rev. Conygham (26x23cm-10x9in) s.i. W/C wash two. 28-Oct-3 Mealy's, Castlecomer #495

MITHINARI (1929-1976) Australian
Works on paper
£549 $983 €802 Myth of Garrimala Lagoon (95x20cm-37x8in) natural earth pigments bark exec 1970 prov. 25-May-4 Lawson Menzies, Sydney #260/R (A.D 1400)

MITI-ZANETTI, Giuseppe (1859-1929) Italian
£362 $594 €500 Landscape with lake (20x33cm-8x13in) s. board. 27-May-3 Finarte Semenzato, Milan #68/R
£420 $701 €600 Venetian canal (35x26cm-14x10in) s. cardboard on canvas. 24-Jun-3 Finarte Semenzato, Rome #91
£4317 $7079 €6000 Sighs Bridge, Venice (67x70cm-26x28in) cardboard. 5-Jun-3 Adma, Formigine #545 est:6500-7500

MITLISCH, Juliane (19th C) ?
£4667 $8353 €7000 Visite des dependances (59x72cm-23x28in) s.i.d. 16-May-4 Joron-Derem, Paris #174/R est:3000-4000

MITORAJ, Igor (1944-) German
Sculpture
£2550 $4514 €3800 Ascleopios (36x28x10cm-14x11x4in) s. num.570/1000 verso pat bronze lit. 28-Apr-4 Artcurial Briest, Paris #306 est:1200-1500
£3265 $5845 €4800 Bust (36x29x12cm-14x11x5in) s. bronze. 22-Mar-4 Sant Agostino, Torino #498/R est:3300
£3333 $6133 €5000 Bust (28x23x10cm-11x9x4in) s. num.5/25 br. 14-Jun-4 Sant Agostino, Torino #385/R est:4000-5000
£5517 $9214 €8000 Bust of the heart (46cm-18in) s. num.49/1000 bronze. 16-Nov-3 Agra, Warsaw #19/R est:3000
£11268 $18254 €16000 Torse d'homme (64cm-25in) s. brown pat bronze. 5-Aug-3 Tajan, Paris #46/R est:10000-12000
£13287 $22587 €19000 Hunters and trap (34cm-13in) s. num.1/8 pat bronze terracotta. 26-Nov-3 Pandolfini, Florence #174/R est:19000-21000
£25362 $41594 €35000 Torso italico (82cm-32in) s.i. num 4/6 pat bronze exhib. 31-May-3 Farsetti, Prato #710/R est:35000-45000

MITSUUCHI, Kei (20th C) Japanese
£350 $594 €500 Autoportrait de l'artiste (34x28cm-13x11in) 29-Nov-3 Neret-Minet, Paris #154

MITTERFELLNER, Andreas (1912-1972) German
£470 $874 €700 Mountain landscape with a river (80x100cm-31x39in) s.d.1941. 5-Mar-4 Wendl, Rudolstadt #3781/R
£869 $1608 €1260 Staffelsee with figures (19x44cm-7x17in) s. panel. 12-Feb-4 Weidler, Nurnberg #323/R est:1400
£890 $1389 €1300 Chiemsee with figures and animals (20x44cm-8x17in) s. panel. 10-Apr-3 Weidler, Nurnberg #315/R
£966 $1612 €1400 Tegernsee (20x40cm-8x16in) s. panel. 9-Jul-3 Hugo Ruef, Munich #147

MITTEY, Joseph (1853-1936) Swiss?
£690 $1234 €1007 Still life with chrysanthemums and stoneware jug (70x92cm-28x36in) s. 12-May-4 Dobiaschofsky, Bern #803/R (S.FR 1600)

MITTHOFF, Anton (1862-1930) Bulgarian
£2685 $4805 €4000 Market day in Bulgaria (48x36cm-19x14in) s.d.903. 27-May-4 Dorotheum, Vienna #215/R est:4000-4500

MIURA, Mitsuo (20th C) ?
£1497 $2724 €2200 CH-1 (100x70cm-39x28in) s.d.1983 s.i.d.verso board prov. 3-Feb-4 Segre, Madrid #218/R est:1500

MIVILLE, Jakob Christoph (1786-1836) Swiss
Works on paper
£1100 $1980 €1606 Alpine views, two showing St Gothard and the Rigi (22x31cm-9x12in) s.verso W/C black chk three. 20-Apr-4 Sotheby's, Olympia #173/R est:1000-1500

MIYAJIMA, Tatsuo (1957) Japanese
Sculpture
£2703 $5000 €3946 Opposite Harmony 57083-74228 (11x26x3cm-4x10x1in) electronic LCD aluminium units transformer elec wire two. 13-Jul-4 Christie's, Rockefeller NY #97/R est:5000-7000
£8982 $15000 €13114 Opposite level (27x117cm-11x46in) diods IC electric wire aluminum panel 6 units prov. 13-Nov-3 Sotheby's, New York #492/R est:15000-20000
£11173 $20000 €16313 Opposite level (27x86x3cm-11x34x1in) electronic LED wire aluminum panel 6 parts. 12-May-4 Christie's, Rockefeller NY #345/R est:12000-18000
£11173 $20000 €16313 Model 16 (31x31cm-12x12in) LED lights electric wire aluminum panel prov. 14-May-4 Phillips, New York #198/R est:10000-15000
£13986 $23776 €20000 Model - 36 - No 11 - green (46x46x26cm-18x18x10in) i. verso LED IC aluminium cable prov.exhib. 27-Nov-3 Lempertz, Koln #286/R est:8000-10000
£14000 $25760 €20440 Time go round no 6 (219x219x35cm-86x86x14in) light emitting diode IC elec wire motor three units prov. 24-Jun-4 Sotheby's, London #142/R est:12000-15000
£23952 $40000 €34970 Counter line no.10 (11x285x5cm-4x112x2in) i. electric wire IC light emitting diode mounted on wood. 14-Nov-3 Phillips, New York #131/R est:40000-60000

MIYAO (?) Japanese
Sculpture
£1164 $1979 €1700 Boy playing flute (6cm-2in) s. bronze gilt. 8-Nov-3 Dr Fritz Nagel, Stuttgart #1833/R est:1200
£2055 $3493 €3000 Drummer (10cm-4in) s. bronze gilt. 8-Nov-3 Dr Fritz Nagel, Stuttgart #1834/R est:2800
£2600 $4498 €3796 Manzai dancers, one holding a hand drum, the other a fan (14cm-6in) s. bronze wooden stand pair. 11-Dec-3 Sotheby's, Olympia #105/R est:600-800
£3800 $6574 €5548 Shishimai dancer holding a taiko. Warrior wielding a scythe (20cm-8in) s. bronze pair. 11-Dec-3 Sotheby's, Olympia #104/R est:800-1200
£11184 $20243 €17000 Man with bow and arrow (74cm-29in) s. bronze. 16-Apr-4 Dorotheum, Vienna #51/R est:7000-9000

MIYAO, Zo (19th C) Japanese
Sculpture
£1757 $3092 €2600 Hunter (16cm-6in) bronze. 22-May-4 Dr Fritz Nagel, Stuttgart #2246/R est:1800
£4795 $8151 €7000 Standing girl (18cm-7in) s. bronze gilt. 8-Nov-3 Dr Fritz Nagel, Stuttgart #1890/R est:4800

MIYASAKI, George (1935-) American
Works on paper
£417 $750 €609 Buffalo Hill (121x91cm-48x36in) s.i.d.1984 verso mixed media collage canvas. 25-Apr-4 Bonhams & Butterfields, San Francisco #5647/R

MIZEN, Frederic Kimball (1888-1964) American
£2795 $4500 €4081 The joy of living (97x51cm-38x20in) s. painted c.1942. 22-Feb-3 Bunte, Elgin #1251a est:2000-3000
£4070 $7000 €5942 Opium smoker (90x90cm-35x35in) s. 3-Dec-3 Doyle, New York #193/R est:3000-5000

MIZRACHI, Moshe Ben Yitzach (attrib) (1870-c.1930) Israeli
£1955 $3500 €2854 David slaying Goliath (31x37cm-12x15in) glass painting. 18-Mar-4 Sotheby's, New York #229/R est:4000-6000
£3352 $6000 €4894 Sacrifice of Isaac (48x58cm-19x23in) d.1912 verso glass painting. 18-Mar-4 Sotheby's, New York #228/R est:6000-8000

MLODOZENIEC, Jan (1929-2000) Polish
£551 $947 €804 Louvre, VI (73x60cm-29x24in) s. i.d.1998 verso tempera. 4-Dec-3 Agra, Warsaw #14/R (P.Z 3700)
£1034 $1728 €1500 Nocturnal (65x50cm-26x20in) s.d. March 1999 tempera lit. 16-Nov-3 Agra, Warsaw #1/R est:200
Works on paper
£255 $456 €372 Untitled (49x35cm-19x14in) wash. 6-May-4 Agra, Warsaw #40/R (P.Z 1800)
£336 $558 €491 Six o'clock (49x35cm-19x14in) gouache. 2-Oct-3 Agra, Warsaw #32/R (P.Z 2200)
£336 $558 €491 Billboard (36x50cm-14x20in) gouache cardboard. 2-Oct-3 Agra, Warsaw #39/R (P.Z 2200)
£354 $622 €517 Portrait (50x35cm-20x14in) s. gouache. 27-May-4 Agra, Warsaw #1562/R (P.Z 2500)
£448 $749 €650 Debiut (50x35cm-20x14in) s. gouache. 16-Nov-3 Agra, Warsaw #79/R
£496 $887 €724 Polish futurism (56x40cm-22x16in) wax. 6-May-4 Agra, Warsaw #19/R (P.Z 3500)
£677 $1233 €988 Two birds (56x41cm-22x16in) s. gouache board. 20-Jun-4 Agra, Warsaw #32/R (P.Z 4700)

MLODOZENIEC, Piotr (1956-) Polish
£865 $1573 €1263 Composition with figure (137x102cm-54x40in) s.d.89. 20-Jun-4 Agra, Warsaw #33/R (P.Z 6000)
Works on paper
£1653 $2991 €2413 Composition (181x82cm-71x32in) s.d.87 stencil gouache canvas. 4-Apr-4 Agra, Warsaw #18/R (P.Z 11700)

MNGUNI, Simoni (1885-1956) South African
Works on paper
£276 $461 €403 Zulu Induna (30x25cm-12x10in) s.i. W/C. 20-Oct-3 Stephan Welz, Johannesburg #619 est:3000-4000 (SA.R 3200)

MNISZEK, Count Andre de (1823-1905) Polish
£7778 $14000 €11356 Still life (100x75cm-39x30in) mono.d.1873. 23-Apr-4 Sotheby's, New York #198/R est:15000-20000

MO SHILONG (attrib) (1537-1587) Chinese
Works on paper
£40411 $68699 €59000 Lake and mountain landscape (29x261cm-11x103in) i. Indian ink col handscroll two parts. 7-Nov-3 Dr Fritz Nagel, Stuttgart #776/R est:1900

MOAL, Jean le (1909-) French
£1049 $1752 €1500 Paysage de Bretagne (24x35cm-9x14in) s. 30-Jun-3 Bailly Pommery, Paris #112
£2961 $5447 €4500 Composition (19x35cm-7x14in) s.d.1974 s.d.verso prov.exhib. 27-Jun-4 Versailles Encheres #74/R est:4500-5000
£3333 $6000 €5000 Composition (27x46cm-11x18in) s.d.19576 prov. 25-Apr-4 Versailles Encheres #58 est:5000-6000
£3356 $6174 €5000 Le port (73x100cm-29x39in) s.d.1953 i.d.verso. 24-Mar-4 Binoche, Paris #99 est:5000-7000
£3566 $5956 €5100 Composition (46x110cm-18x43in) s.d.1963 s.d.verso prov. 29-Jun-3 Versailles Encheres #58/R
£4474 $8232 €6800 Composition (60x60cm-24x24in) s.d.1963 s.d.verso prov. 27-Jun-4 Versailles Encheres #75/R est:7000-8000
£6081 $10885 €9000 Untitled (46x110cm-18x43in) s.d.1963 s.d.verso. 4-May-4 Calmels Cohen, Paris #185 est:9000-10000
Works on paper
£300 $540 €450 Composition (17x17cm-7x7in) s.d.1969 W/C gouache. 24-Apr-4 Cornette de St.Cyr, Paris #613

MOCHI, Francesco (attrib) (1580-1654) Italian
Sculpture
£20000 $34600 €29200 Figure of a running man (27x19cm-11x7in) gilt bronze lit. 12-Dec-3 Sotheby's, London #208/R est:15000-20000

MOCHIZUKI GYOKUSEN (1744-1795) Chinese
Works on paper
£490 $842 €700 Bamboo tree (125x51cm-49x20in) s. ink silk hanging scroll. 5-Dec-3 Lempertz, Koln #758/R

MOCHTAR, But (1930-1986) Javanese
£2174 $3370 €3174 Self portrait (84x45cm-33x18in) s.d.1972. 6-Oct-2 Sotheby's, Singapore #120/R est:6000-9000 (S.D 6000)
£2581 $4129 €3768 Two figures (90x100cm-35x39in) s.d.1967. 18-May-3 Sotheby's, Singapore #178/R est:5000-7000 (S.D 7200)
Sculpture
£9420 $14601 €13753 Acrobatic family (156cm-61in) s. wood exhib. 6-Oct-2 Sotheby's, Singapore #126/R est:25000-30000 (S.D 26000)
£62500 $104375 €91250 Women with offerings (183cm-72in) bronze incl wooden base prov. 12-Oct-3 Sotheby's, Singapore #146/R est:35000-45000 (S.D 180000)

MODEL, Evsa (1901-1976) American
£353 $650 €515 Cityscape (46x76cm-18x30in) s. 11-Jun-4 David Rago, Lambertville #126/R

MODEL, Lisette (1902-) American
Photographs
£2646 $5000 €3863 Promenades des Anglais, Nice (35x28cm-14x11in) gelatin silver print. 17-Feb-4 Christie's, Rockefeller NY #150/R est:3000-5000
£2994 $5000 €4371 Promenades des Anglais, Nice (34x27cm-13x11in) s.i.d. verso gelatin silver print exec.1934 lit. 17-Oct-3 Phillips, New York #62/R est:7000-10000
£3333 $6000 €4866 Newspaper man, Paris (49x39cm-19x15in) s.i.d.1936 verso gelatin silver print lit. 23-Apr-4 Phillips, New York #80/R est:7000-10000

MODERSOHN, Christian (1916-) German
£530 $964 €800 Still life with pot plant and apples (58x40cm-23x16in) s.d.1938. 19-Jun-4 Hans Stahl, Hamburg #82/R
Works on paper
£430 $783 €650 Evening scene with flooded Wumme (30x47cm-12x19in) s.d.44 W/C. 18-Jun-4 Bolland & Marotz, Bremen #363/R

MODERSOHN, Otto (1865-1943) German
£1600 $2944 €2400 Woman at work in the field (18x20cm-7x8in) cardboard. 9-Jun-4 Christie's, Amsterdam #210/R est:1000-1500
£2333 $4293 €3500 Fischerhude (32x42cm-13x17in) init.i.d.27 cardboard. 9-Jun-4 Christie's, Amsterdam #211/R est:3000-5000
£3243 $6000 €4735 Landschaft mit Ergebnis fur und Wirtschaftsgebande - landscape with farmer's wife (104x69cm-41x27in) s. 19-Jan-4 O'Gallerie, Oregon #867a/R est:700-900
£4333 $7973 €6500 Still life with a plate of apples and two pot plants (50x61cm-20x24in) s.d.36. 11-Jun-4 Villa Grisebach, Berlin #1521/R est:8000-12000
£4336 $7457 €6200 An der wumme (49x68cm-19x27in) s.d.39. 2-Dec-3 Sotheby's, Amsterdam #80/R est:6000-8000
£4667 $8587 €7000 Landscape with a house (40x57cm-16x22in) d.XI/05 cardboard. 12-Jun-4 Villa Grisebach, Berlin #137/R est:6000-8000
£5556 $9056 €8000 Summer's day (45x34cm-18x13in) mono. board. 26-Sep-3 Bolland & Marotz, Bremen #345/R est:8500
£5594 $9510 €8000 Flowers in red (40x59cm-16x23in) s.d.35 prov. 29-Nov-3 Villa Grisebach, Berlin #120/R est:8000-10000
£5677 $10332 €8288 Wedding procession in Worpswede (29x37cm-11x15in) s. panel prov. 17-Jun-4 Kornfeld, Bern #580/R est:15000 (S.FR 13000)

£5944	$10224	€8500	Westfalischer farm (44x52cm-17x20in) canvas on board. 5-Dec-3 Bolland & Marotz, Bremen #388/R est:12000
£6040	$10691	€9000	Canal on the moor (40x58cm-16x23in) mono.d.X.o3 board prov. 30-Apr-4 Dr Fritz Nagel, Stuttgart #896/R est:9000
£6333	$11653	€9500	Landschaft und Bauern und Kindern - landscape with farmers and children (41x57cm-16x22in) cardboard painted c.1902. 9-Jun-4 Christie's, Amsterdam #205/R est:10000-15000
£8000	$14720	€12000	Late autumn on the moors (47x64cm-19x25in) s.d.38. 12-Jun-4 Villa Grisebach, Berlin #135/R est:12000-16000
£8054	$14819	€12000	Harvest waggon in Worpswede (36x45cm-14x18in) mono. board. 26-Mar-4 Bolland & Marotz, Bremen #348/R est:13000
£9272	$16874	€14000	Horses on the banks of the Wumme (58x40cm-23x16in) d.1911 board. 18-Jun-4 Bolland & Marotz, Bremen #365/R est:13000
£9333	$17173	€14000	Country landscape with fishing huts (57x74cm-22x29in) s.d.28 prov. 12-Jun-4 Villa Grisebach, Berlin #138/R est:14000-18000
£9722	$15847	€14000	Summer evening sky over the Wumme (56x74cm-22x29in) s.d.39. 26-Sep-3 Bolland & Marotz, Bremen #344/R est:9000
£9790	$16643	€14000	Autumn landscape (56x74cm-22x29in) s.d.41. 29-Nov-3 Villa Grisebach, Berlin #115/R est:15000-20000
£10738	$19758	€16000	Moor landscape (64x77cm-25x30in) s.d. i. stretcher prov. 26-Mar-4 Ketterer, Hamburg #566/R est:17000-20000
£10738	$19758	€16000	Evening moorland (40x57cm-16x22in) mono.d.IX 04 i. verso board. 26-Mar-4 Bolland & Marotz, Bremen #349/R est:13000
£11189	$19245	€16000	The moor in autumn (73x92cm-29x36in) s. 5-Dec-3 Bolland & Marotz, Bremen #387/R est:25000
£11333	$20853	€17000	Louise Modersohn-Breling (57x40cm-22x16in) s.d.8/10 cardboard. 9-Jun-4 Christie's, Amsterdam #204/R est:12000-16000
£12238	$20804	€17500	Hamme pasture (50x70cm-20x28in) s.d.38 exhib. 26-Nov-3 Lempertz, Koln #862/R est:20000
£16000	$29120	€23360	Sommerliche wummelandschaft mit madchen und boot (50x35cm-20x14in) d.VII II board prov. 4-Feb-4 Sotheby's, London #305/R est:15000-20000
£16000	$29440	€24000	Family Modersohn-Breling (30x40cm-12x16in) s. cardboard painted c.1910. 9-Jun-4 Christie's, Amsterdam #202/R est:12000-16000
£17483	$29720	€25000	Girl with pram (46x36cm-18x14in) s. prov. 29-Nov-3 Villa Grisebach, Berlin #113/R est:25000-30000
Works on paper			
£728	$1326	€1100	Bathers in the River Wumme (15x13cm-6x5in) chl. 18-Jun-4 Bolland & Marotz, Bremen #366/R
£759	$1267	€1100	Worpswede (13x21cm-5x8in) chk paper on board. 13-Nov-3 Neumeister, Munich #401/R
£839	$1443	€1200	Wumme swamp and meadow under high cloud (15x21cm-6x8in) chl chk. 5-Dec-3 Bolland & Marotz, Bremen #389/R
£927	$1687	€1400	Landscape with the River Wumme (14x20cm-6x8in) chk sanguine. 18-Jun-4 Bolland & Marotz, Bremen #367/R
£993	$1808	€1500	Children under the trees on the banks of the Wumme (16x26cm-6x10in) chk chl sanguine. 18-Jun-4 Bolland & Marotz, Bremen #368/R est:860
£2533	$4610	€3698	Child with pram in Worpswede (19x32cm-7x13in) mono.d.11 W/C. 17-Jun-4 Kornfeld, Bern #581/R est:5000 (S.FR 5800)

MODERSOHN-BECKER, Paula (1876-1907) German

£27074	$49275	€39528	White lilies on a green background (32x55cm-13x22in) cardboard painted c.1897 prov. 18-Jun-4 Kornfeld, Bern #112/R est:75000 (S.FR 62000)
£48951	$83217	€70000	Avenue of birch trees in autumn (46x58cm-18x23in) mono. verso oil tempera board double-sided prov.exhib. 28-Nov-3 Villa Grisebach, Berlin #17/R est:70000-90000
£66667	$122667	€100000	Little girl with apron (48x34cm-19x13in) cardboard on board prov.exhib. 11-Jun-4 Villa Grisebach, Berlin #5/R est:50000-70000
£133333	$238667	€200000	Seated girl with sheep in meadow I (54x69cm-21x27in) board on panel prov.exhib. 14-May-4 Ketterer, Munich #128/R est:140000-180000
£166667	$306667	€250000	Still life with cabbage and green beans II (71x89cm-28x35in) cardboard on board prov.exhib. 11-Jun-4 Villa Grisebach, Berlin #13/R est:250000-350000
Prints			
£1528	$2782	€2231	Seated nude girl. s. drypoint. 17-Jun-4 Kornfeld, Bern #586 est:2000 (S.FR 3500)
£1572	$2861	€2295	Portrait of peasant woman. s. etching. 17-Jun-4 Kornfeld, Bern #587 est:2000 (S.FR 3600)
£1659	$3020	€2422	Two peasant girls. s. etching roulette. 17-Jun-4 Kornfeld, Bern #589 est:2000 (S.FR 3800)
£2000	$3680	€3000	Blind woman in the woods (15x14cm-6x6in) s. Otto Modersohn etching aquatint exec. 1900-02. 12-Jun-4 Villa Grisebach, Berlin #164/R est:3000-4000
£3200	$5792	€4800	Goose maid (25x20cm-10x8in) aquatint etching. 2-Apr-4 Winterberg, Heidelberg #1352/R est:2800
£3667	$6747	€5500	The lady with the goose (12x17cm-5x7in) s. Otto Modersohn exec. 1902 etching aquatint. 12-Jun-4 Villa Grisebach, Berlin #163/R est:4000-5000
Works on paper			
£667	$1227	€1000	Male nude (31x23cm-12x9in) init. pencil prov. 9-Jun-4 Christie's, Amsterdam #206/R
£800	$1472	€1200	Landscape with bridge over a ditch (22x14cm-9x6in) init. pencil cardboard prov.exhib. 9-Jun-4 Christie's, Amsterdam #203/R
£1399	$2378	€2000	Woman walking (31x24cm-12x9in) i. chl. 29-Nov-3 Villa Grisebach, Berlin #635a/R est:2500-3000
£2013	$3705	€3000	Girl with jug (36x12cm-14x5in) i. pencil. 26-Mar-4 Ketterer, Hamburg #567/R est:3500-3800
£2215	$3964	€3300	Notre Dame (29x22cm-11x9in) chl. 25-May-4 Karl & Faber, Munich #423/R est:2500
£3000	$5520	€4500	Three figures (27x18cm-11x7in) init. blk chk prov. 9-Jun-4 Christie's, Amsterdam #207/R est:4000-6000

MODESITT, John (1955-) American

£541	$1000	€790	Flax field in La Goulee. s.i. 14-Jul-4 Dallas Auction Gallery, Dallas #366/R
£950	$1700	€1387	Chatel censoir during rain. s.i. 13-May-4 Dallas Auction Gallery, Dallas #133/R est:1500-2500
£973	$1800	€1421	Summer hike. s.i. 14-Jul-4 Dallas Auction Gallery, Dallas #315/R est:2000-3000
£1087	$2000	€1587	View from the High Desert (61x61cm-24x24in) s. i. stretcher lit. 8-Jun-4 Bonhams & Butterfields, San Francisco #4386/R est:3000-5000
£1135	$2100	€1657	Cuyamaca September. s. 14-Jul-4 Dallas Auction Gallery, Dallas #345/R est:2000-4000
£1471	$2750	€2148	Blue fields (51x61cm-20x24in) s. board. 25-Feb-4 Dallas Auction Gallery, Dallas #409/R
£1676	$3000	€2447	Garden at La Goulee. s.i. 13-May-4 Dallas Auction Gallery, Dallas #238/R est:1500-2500
£1923	$3500	€2808	Flower fields, Mt Lilac in Pauma Valley (53x61cm-21x24in) i. stretcher sold with book. 15-Jun-4 John Moran, Pasadena #113a est:3500-5000
£2059	$3500	€3006	Antelope valley poppies (51x76cm-20x30in) s. i.verso. 18-Nov-3 John Moran, Pasadena #160 est:4000-6000
£2060	$3750	€3008	Flower fields, Tehachapi Pass (46x76cm-18x30in) i. stretcher sold with book. 15-Jun-4 John Moran, Pasadena #113 est:3500-5000
£2206	$3750	€3221	Wild flowers near Big Sur (41x51cm-16x20in) s. i.verso. 18-Nov-3 John Moran, Pasadena #161 est:2000-3000
£2249	$4250	€3284	Wildflowers near Petaluma (41x51cm-16x20in) s. i. stretcher. 17-Feb-4 John Moran, Pasadena #105a/R est:2500-3500
£2400	$4344	€3504	Vue de Rouen depuis la Seine (44x60cm-17x24in) s. 1-Apr-4 Christie's, Kensington #38/R est:1500-2000

MODESPACHER, Theobald (1897-1955) Swiss

£273	$453	€396	Garden flowers (40x31cm-16x12in) mono.d.1925 tempera board. 13-Jun-3 Zofingen, Switzerland #2947 (S.FR 600)

MODIGLIANI, Amedeo (1884-1920) Italian

£60000	$110400	€87600	La Duse (32x24cm-13x9in) s. canvas on board painted c.1906-1907 prov.exhib.lit. 23-Jun-4 Christie's, London #259/R est:50000-70000
£440000	$805200	€642400	Mendiant de Livourne (66x52cm-26x20in) s.d.1909 prov.exhib.lit. 2-Feb-4 Christie's, London #37/R est:400000-600000
£764706	$1300000	€1116471	Portrait de Leopold Zborowski (46x29cm-18x11in) s. painted 1917 prov.exhib.lit. 5-Nov-3 Sotheby's, New York #25/R est:1200000-1600000
£1400000	$2548000	€2044000	Christina (80x69cm-31x27in) s. painted c.1916 prov.exhib. 21-Jun-4 Bonhams, New Bond Street #53/R est:700000-1000000
£5500000	$10010001	€8030000	Garcon a la veste bleue (92x61cm-36x24in) s. painted 1918 prov.exhib.lit. 21-Jun-4 Sotheby's, London #6/R est:3500000-4500000
£14117648	$24000000	€20611766	Nu couche - sur le cote gauche (89x146cm-35x57in) s. painted 1917 prov.exhib.lit. 4-Nov-3 Christie's, Rockefeller NY #29/R est:20000000-25000000
Sculpture			
£6881	$11491	€9977	Tete de femme (26cm-10in) i. bronze. 19-Jun-3 Kornfeld, Bern #724/R est:15000 (S.FR 15000)
£17195	$29231	€38000	Head of woman (81cm-32in) s.st.f.Valsuani num.HC pat bronze lit. 25-Nov-3 Pierre Berge, Paris #18/R est:25000-35000
£27334	$49747	€41000	Head of a young girl (65cm-26in) s. num.1/1V bronze st.f.Valsuani cire perdue prov.lit. 30-Jun-4 Calmels Cohen, Paris #59/R est:30000-40000
Works on paper			
£917	$1669	€1339	Head of a girl, de face (35x26cm-14x10in) i. pencil. 17-Jun-4 Kornfeld, Bern #591 est:3000 (S.FR 2100)
£5245	$8759	€7500	Portrait de femme de la serie du petit carnet (21x13cm-8x5in) s. graphite prov. 25-Jun-3 Rabourdin & Choppin de Janvry, Paris #82/R est:6000-7000
£10211	$17665	€14500	Cariatide (57x43cm-22x17in) s. graphite lit. 14-Dec-3 Rabourdin & Choppin de Janvry, Paris #58/R est:18000-20000
£12941	$22000	€18894	D'apres Watteau - femme et arlequins (43x26cm-17x10in) s.i. pencil paper on board prov.exhib.lit. 5-Nov-3 Christie's, Rockefeller NY #111/R est:25000-35000
£20270	$37500	€29594	Homme au chapeau (30x22cm-12x9in) s. pencil prov. 11-Feb-4 Sotheby's, New York #40/R est:30000-40000
£20961	$38568	€30603	Hommage de profil assis a une table (41x25cm-16x10in) s. pencil prov. 8-Jun-4 Germann, Zurich #38/R est:44000-48000 (S.FR 48000)
£22000	$40040	€32120	Portrait de Chaim Soutine (42x26cm-17x10in) i. pencil prov. 5-Feb-4 Christie's, London #349/R est:20000-30000
£34965	$59441	€50000	Three figures (43x26cm-17x10in) s. pencil exhib. 29-Nov-3 Farsetti, Prato #420/R est:50000-65000
£40000	$73200	€60000	Cariatide (35x27cm-14x11in) s. chk prov. 5-Jun-4 Lempertz, Koln #884/R est:60000-70000
£41176	$70000	€60117	Tete de femme (43x26cm-17x10in) s. oil gouache over pencil paper on board prov.exhib. 5-Nov-3 Christie's, Rockefeller NY #116/R est:80000-120000
£72000	$131040	€105120	Portrait of a woman seated (62x31cm-24x12in) s.d.17 pencil prov.exhib. 5-Feb-4 Christie's, London #344/R est:40000-60000
£106145	$190000	€154972	Tete de profil a gauche avec chignon et boucles d'oreilles (42x26cm-17x10in) blk crayon prov.exhib.lit. 6-May-4 Sotheby's, New York #344/R est:140000-180000
£167598	$300000	€244693	Tete de face avec double collier et boucles d'oreilles (43x27cm-17x11in) blk crayon prov.exhib.lit. 6-May-4 Sotheby's, New York #338/R est:200000-250000

MODLINSKI, Dominik J (1970-) Canadian

£380	$695	€555	Strathcona Range, Vancouver Island, BC (30x40cm-12x16in) s.i.d.2002 board. 1-Jun-4 Hodgins, Calgary #458/R (C.D 950)
£420	$769	€613	Waiting for spring, Banff (30x40cm-12x16in) s.i. board. 1-Jun-4 Hodgins, Calgary #459/R (C.D 1050)

MODOTTI, Tina (1896-1962) Italian

Photographs			
£2542	$4500	€3711	Clement Orozco, scene Della Rivoluzione (19x24cm-7x9in) photo prov. 28-Apr-4 Sotheby's, New York #140/R est:4000-6000
£5556	$10000	€8112	Untitled (24x19cm-9x7in) gelatin silver print prov. 23-Apr-4 Phillips, New York #30/R est:12000-15000
£5556	$10000	€8112	Police puppets (14x24cm-6x9in) i.verso gelatin silver print prov.lit. 23-Apr-4 Phillips, New York #31/R est:12000-15000
£5988	$10000	€8742	Untitled - coconut tree climber (8x5cm-3x2in) s. init.verso silver print. 21-Oct-3 Swann Galleries, New York #117/R est:9000-12000
£10734	$19000	€15672	Selected marionette studies (24x19cm-9x7in) i.verso photo group of three prov. 28-Apr-4 Sotheby's, New York #171/R est:5000-8000
£11976	$20000	€17485	Portrait of William Spratling (24x18cm-9x7in) s.i. i.verso col photo exec.c.1929-39. 17-Oct-3 Sotheby's, New York #173/R est:10000-20000
£15569	$26000	€22731	Edward Weston with a camera (12x9cm-5x4in) init.d.1924 verso photo prov.exhib.lit. 17-Oct-3 Sotheby's, New York #174/R est:20000-30000
£56497	$100000	€82486	Bandolier, corn, and guitar (24x19cm-9x7in) s.i. photo board prov.exhib.lit. 28-Apr-4 Sotheby's, New York #139/R est:80000-120000
£79096	$140000	€115480	Telegraph wires (24x18cm-9x7in) i.verso platinum print exec.c.1925 prov.lit. 27-Apr-4 Sotheby's, New York #21/R est:100000-150000

MODZELEWSKI, Jaroslaw (1955-) Polish

£521	$896	€761	Study (60x60cm-24x24in) s. i.d.1997 verso tempera. 4-Dec-3 Agra, Warsaw #9/R (P.Z 3500)

MOE, Carl (1889-1942) Norwegian

£257	$471	€375	Winter on the fjord (26x48cm-10x19in) s/. 2-Feb-4 Blomqvist, Lysaker #1184 (N.KR 3200)

£270 $466 €394 Winter landscape with river (40x60cm-16x24in) s. 13-Dec-3 Blomqvist, Lysaker #1242 (N.KR 3100)
£426 $681 €618 Landscape with lake (78x100cm-31x39in) s. 22-Sep-3 Blomqvist, Lysaker #1209/R (N.KR 5000)

MOE, Louis (1859-1945) Norwegian
£316 $591 €461 Victory - scull with laurel wreath (35x27cm-14x11in) s.d.40 panel. 25-Feb-4 Museumsbygningen, Copenhagen #20/R (D.KR 3500)
Works on paper
£314 $565 €458 Elves and insects (32x121cm-13x48in) s. Indian ink freeze. 24-Apr-4 Rasmussen, Havnen #4009 (D.KR 3500)
£393 $620 €570 Father owl being taken home from party where he has eaten too much (27x30cm-11x12in) s.i.d.29 W/C pen pencil. 2-Sep-3 Rasmussen, Copenhagen #2006/R (D.KR 4200)
£473 $818 €691 Illustration for Nar kraaken fick arfva (49x34cm-19x13in) s. W/C Indian ink. 9-Dec-3 Rasmussen, Copenhagen #1748/R (D.KR 5000)

MOE, Odd (1944-) Norwegian
£389 $697 €568 Composition (78x112cm-31x44in) s.d.87 verso. 10-May-4 Rasmussen, Vejle #758/R (D.KR 4300)

MOE, Terje (1943-) Norwegian
£258 $431 €377 Landscape from Bygdo (80x100cm-31x39in) s. 20-Oct-3 Blomqvist, Lysaker #1207 (N.KR 3000)
£259 $430 €376 Still life of wineglass and other objects (60x80cm-24x31in) s. 16-Jun-3 Blomqvist, Lysaker #1139 (N.KR 3000)
£731 $1178 €1067 Sculpture fragment (80x102cm-31x40in) s. 25-Aug-3 Blomqvist, Lysaker #1185 (N.KR 8500)

MOELL, Sven (1894-1974) Swedish
£348 $627 €522 On the bridge (52x61cm-20x24in) s. panel prov.lit. 25-Apr-4 Goteborg Auktionsverk, Sweden #386/R (S.KR 4800)
£406 $731 €609 Walking in the park (63x53cm-25x21in) s. panel. 25-Apr-4 Goteborg Auktionsverk, Sweden #367/R (S.KR 5600)

MOELLER, Arnold (1886-1963) German
£400 $728 €600 Farmer's wife knitting with two goats (39x50cm-15x20in) s. board. 1-Jul-4 Neumeister, Munich #2760
£642 $1149 €950 Flock of sheep (56x81cm-22x32in) s.d. lit. 8-May-4 Schloss Ahlden, Ahlden #769/R
£667 $1193 €1000 Still life of flowers (43x36cm-17x14in) s. board lit. 14-May-4 Schloss Ahlden, Ahlden #2950/R
£881 $1498 €1286 Evening landscape with herder and cattle (33x43cm-13x17in) s.d.1946 board. 5-Nov-3 Dobiaschofsky, Bern #806/R (S.FR 2000)
£1250 $2037 €1800 Returning home (47x61cm-19x24in) s. i. verso. 24-Sep-3 Neumeister, Munich #499/R est:2200

MOELLER, Louis C (1855-1930) American
£5389 $9000 €7868 Gentlemen's meeting (25x36cm-10x14in) s. prov. 23-Oct-3 Shannon's, Milford #175/R est:6000-8000
£6145 $11000 €8972 Gossips (46x61cm-18x24in) s.indis.i. painted c.1900. 26-May-4 Doyle, New York #56/R est:10000-15000
£8152 $15000 €11902 Stop fooling (46x61cm-18x24in) s.i. i. stretcher verso. 27-Jun-4 Freeman, Philadelphia #74/R est:10000-15000

MOELLER-SCHLUNZ, Fritz (1900-1990) German
£414 $638 €650 August afternoon in Althagen/Baltic (34x48cm-13x19in) s.d.1934. 4-Sep-2 Schopman, Hamburg #161/R
£446 $687 €700 Niendorf - Baltic Sea harbour (42x54cm-17x21in) s. i. verso board. 4-Sep-2 Schopman, Hamburg #160/R

MOER, Jean Baptiste van (1819-1884) Belgian
£680 $1218 €1000 Vue de Lisbonne (35x65cm-14x26in) s. 17-Mar-4 Hotel des Ventes Mosan, Brussels #93
£940 $1738 €1400 Vue plongeante sur la Meuse (22x30cm-9x12in) s. panel. 15-Mar-4 Horta, Bruxelles #466
Works on paper
£331 $612 €480 Vue de pont de Malines (19x27cm-7x11in) s. W/C. 16-Feb-4 Horta, Bruxelles #318

MOERENHOUT, Edward (19th C) Belgian
£336 $624 €500 Seascape with yachts in moonlight (11x20cm-4x8in) s. panel. 8-Mar-4 Bernaerts, Antwerp #258/R
£336 $614 €500 Crepuscule sur la riviere (15x26cm-6x10in) s.d.1887 panel. 8-Jul-4 Campo, Vlaamse Kaai #185
£360 $662 €526 Fishing by moonlight (18x22cm-7x9in) s. panel. 29-Mar-4 Bonhams, Bath #86/R
£451 $718 €650 Winter landscape with dog in front of a door (34x46cm-13x18in) s.d.1878. 15-Sep-3 Bernaerts, Antwerp #223

MOERENHOUT, Joseph Jodocus (1801-1874) Belgian
£2041 $3714 €3000 Pause from the hunt (35x44cm-14x17in) s.d.1827 panel. 3-Feb-4 Christie's, Amsterdam #62/R est:3000-5000
£2218 $4081 €3238 Travellers rest (71x59cm-28x23in) s. panel prov. 9-Jun-4 Walker's, Ottawa #305/R est:6000-8000 (C.D 5500)
£2308 $3854 €3300 Fishermen with horses on beach (42x56cm-17x22in) s.d.1868. 28-Jun-3 Bolland & Marotz, Bremen #711/R est:2700
£2411 $4027 €3400 Shoeing the horses (53x74cm-21x29in) s.d.7 panel. 20-Oct-3 Bernaerts, Antwerp #131/R est:3000-4000
Works on paper
£280 $481 €400 Trois vaches et un cheval dans la prairie (38x58cm-15x23in) s. pastel. 2-Dec-3 Campo & Campo, Antwerp #233

MOERLIN, G (19/20th C) ?
Sculpture
£2200 $3938 €3212 Nude female figure (32cm-13in) s. gilt bronze ivory diamond setting. 13-May-4 Christie's, Kensington #403/R est:2500-3500

MOERMAN, J L (1850-1896) Belgian
£2313 $4140 €3400 Scene d'auberge (25x17cm-10x7in) panel. 22-Mar-4 Amberes, Antwerp #218

MOERMAN, Johannes Lodewyk (1850-1896) Belgian
£2517 $4330 €3600 Joueurs de cartes dans l'auberge (17x25cm-7x10in) s.d.1895 panel. 2-Dec-3 Campo & Campo, Antwerp #234/R est:2000-2500

MOES, Tilly (19/20th C) ?
£256 $450 €374 Still life of sunflowers in an earthenware vase (61x41cm-24x16in) s. 22-May-4 Harvey Clar, Oakland #2207

MOESCHLIN, Elsa (1879-1950) Swedish
£1409 $2339 €2043 Arosa - Bruggerhorn (61x70cm-24x28in) mono.i.d.1918 lit. 13-Jun-3 Zofingen, Switzerland #2948/R est:3500 (S.FR 3100)

MOESCHLIN, Walter J (1902-1961) Swiss
£317 $538 €463 Cathedral (100x65cm-39x26in) mono. 28-Nov-3 Zofingen, Switzerland #3087 (S.FR 700)

MOEST, Hermann (1868-1945) German
£272 $487 €400 Reclining female nude (24x34cm-9x13in) canvas on board. 18-Mar-4 Neumeister, Munich #2728
£613 $1000 €895 Portrait of Winifred Hancock Sgittovich (53x69cm-21x27in) s. 28-Sep-3 Simpson's, Houston #358/R

MOEYAERT, Nicolaes Cornelisz (1592-1655) Dutch
£6000 $10800 €8760 Granida and Daifilo (39x55cm-15x22in) init. panel prov.lit. 21-Apr-4 Christie's, London #47/R est:7000-10000
£6849 $11644 €10000 Portrait of a bearded gentleman in a black suit with a white lace collar (79x59cm-31x23in) panel prov.exhib.lit. 4-Nov-3 Sotheby's, Amsterdam #36/R est:10000-15000
£10690 $17852 €15500 Portrait of young girl as goat herder (107x86cm-42x34in) i. panel prov.lit. 15-Nov-3 Lempertz, Koln #1103/R est:12000-15000
£13699 $23288 €20000 Sacrifice of Manoah (100x132cm-39x52in) mono.indis.d. prov.exhib.lit. 4-Nov-3 Sotheby's, Amsterdam #111/R est:20000-30000
Works on paper
£874 $1600 €1276 Ruth and Boaz (30x41cm-12x16in) red chk. 29-Jan-4 Swann Galleries, New York #160/R est:1500-2500

MOEYAERT, Nicolaes Cornelisz (attrib) (1592-1655) Dutch
Works on paper
£685 $1164 €1000 Christ in the house of Mary and Martha (19x30cm-7x12in) bears i.Rembrant pen brown ink wash prov. 4-Nov-3 Sotheby's, Amsterdam #17/R

MOFFAT, James (1775-1815) British
Works on paper
£2200 $3586 €3212 View of an entrance to the temple at Kerdah, near Barrackpore (43x66cm-17x26in) pencil pen brown ink W/C prov. 24-Sep-3 Christie's, London #30/R est:2500-3500

MOFFATT, Tracey (1960-) Australian
Photographs
£3404 $5787 €4970 Something more 9 1989 (100x150cm-39x59in) monochrome photograph on plexiglass prov. 26-Nov-3 Deutscher-Menzies, Melbourne #115/R est:10000-15000 (A.D 8000)
£6809 $11574 €9941 Something more 8 1989 (118x151cm-46x59in) cibachrome photograph on plexiglass prov. 26-Nov-3 Deutscher-Menzies, Melbourne #114/R est:18000-24000 (A.D 16000)
£7200 $13104 €10512 Something more no 3 (99x129cm-39x51in) cibachrome print prov.lit. 6-Feb-4 Sotheby's, London #276/R est:7000-10000
£7660 $13021 €11184 Something more 5 1989 (116x148cm-46x58in) cibachrome photograph on plexiglass prov. 26-Nov-3 Deutscher-Menzies, Melbourne #113/R est:15000-20000 (A.D 18000)
£11976 $20000 €17485 Something more 8 (97x127cm-38x50in) c-print prov.lit. 13-Nov-3 Sotheby's, New York #433/R est:20000-30000
£15000 $26400 €21900 Somethings more no.1 (82x104cm-32x41in) s.verso cibachrome print. 18-May-4 Bonhams, New Bond Street #557/R est:14500-18500
£19461 $32500 €28413 Something more no 1 (98x100cm-39x39in) s.d.89 num.A/P verso c-print prov.lit. 13-Nov-3 Sotheby's, New York #434/R est:30000-40000
£20809 $36000 €30381 Something more number 1 (98x128cm-39x50in) cibachrome on aluminium one of 30 prov. 10-Dec-3 Phillips, New York #580/R est:40000-60000
£22346 $40000 €32625 Something more no. 1 (107x137cm-42x54in) Cibachrome print on aluminium exec 1989 edn 23/30 lit. 13-May-4 Sotheby's, New York #320/R est:30000-40000
£30738 $48565 €44877 Something more (101x130cm-40x51in) cibachrome prov.exhib. 2-Sep-3 Deutscher-Menzies, Melbourne #40/R est:80000-120000 (A.D 75000)
£31915 $54255 €46596 Something more 1 1989 (115x149cm-45x59in) cibachrome photograph on plexiglass prov. 26-Nov-3 Deutscher-Menzies, Melbourne #112/R est:40000-60000 (A.D 75000)
Prints
£2081 $3600 €3038 Invocation number 5 (147x222cm-58x87in) photosilkscreen ultaviolet ink one of 60 prov. 10-Dec-3 Phillips, New York #649/R est:2000-3000

MOFFETT, Ross E (1888-1971) American

£1409 $2550 €2057 Wellfleet (33x51cm-13x20in) s.d.1968 oil on paper. 3-Apr-4 Outer Cape Auctions, Provincetown #75/R
£4586 $7200 €6696 Winter in Provincetown (30x41cm-12x16in) s. board painted c.1927. 20-Apr-3 Outer Cape Auctions, Provincetown #75

MOFFITT, Trevor (1936-) New Zealander

£1465 $2711 €2139 No. 21 upstream series (49x60cm-19x24in) s.d.71 board. 9-Mar-4 Watson's, Christchurch #15 (NZ.D 4000)
£1573 $2864 €2297 Miner sleeping (35x26cm-14x10in) s.d.1968 board. 29-Jun-4 Peter Webb, Auckland #172/R est:2500-3500 (NZ.D 4500)
£1692 $2876 €2470 Rakaia series no.2 1978 (62x81cm-24x32in) s.i.d.verso hardboard. 26-Nov-3 Dunbar Sloane, Wellington #30/R est:8000-12000 (NZ.D 4500)
£2098 $3818 €3063 Composition with nude reading (60x73cm-24x29in) s.d.1979 board. 29-Jun-4 Peter Webb, Auckland #190/R est:6000-7000 (NZ.D 6000)
£2679 $4848 €3911 Human condition series II - mother in attendance (88x58cm-35x23in) s.d.1994 board. 30-Mar-4 Peter Webb, Auckland #62/R est:8000-12000 (NZ.D 7500)
£2799 $4841 €4087 Rakaia river, series no 13 (58x68cm-23x27in) s.d.1982 i.verso board. 9-Dec-3 Peter Webb, Auckland #168/R est:5000-7000 (NZ.D 7500)
£2893 $5236 €4224 Human condition series II - ballet no.2 (89x25cm-35x10in) s.d.1994 i.verso board. 30-Mar-4 Peter Webb, Auckland #61/R est:8500-12500 (NZ.D 8100)
£3383 $5752 €4939 Airport pig, pig paddock no.5, Canterbury paddock series (88x58cm-35x23in) s.d.1990 board prov. 26-Nov-3 Dunbar Sloane, Wellington #16/R est:10000-15000 (NZ.D 9000)
£3383 $5752 €4939 Dunedin judge sampling the evidence, Hokonui moonshine series. s.i.d.1999 hardboard. 26-Nov-3 Dunbar Sloane, Wellington #29/R est:7000-11000 (NZ.D 9000)
£3909 $6137 €5668 Family dinner (60x90cm-24x35in) s.d.1994 i.verso board prov. 27-Aug-3 Dunbar Sloane, Wellington #25/R est:10000-15000 (NZ.D 10750)
£4364 $6851 €6328 Constable Best, checking Constable Jordan and Tulloch, is shot again (88x88cm-35x35in) s.d.1987 board. 27-Aug-3 Dunbar Sloane, Wellington #24/R est:12000-18000 (NZ.D 12000)
£5208 $8281 €7604 Canterbury paddock series, airport pig (88x88cm-35x35in) s.d.1993 prov. 1-May-3 Dunbar Sloane, Wellington #25/R est:10000-15000 (NZ.D 15000)
£5556 $8833 €8112 Human condition series 1 (60x60cm-24x24in) s.d.1974 board prov. 1-May-3 Dunbar Sloane, Wellington #24/R est:10000-15000 (NZ.D 16000)

MOGANO, Phoshoko David (1932-2000) South African

Works on paper
£276 $461 €403 Child and donkeys (41x56cm-16x22in) s.d.1960 W/C. 20-Oct-3 Stephan Welz, Johannesburg #660 est:2000-3000 (SA.R 3200)
£388 $648 €566 Rain maker of the N. Province (101x71cm-40x28in) s.i.d.1994 W/C. 20-Oct-3 Stephan Welz, Johannesburg #377/R est:5000-8000 (SA.R 4500)
£388 $648 €566 Ancient ancestral method (100x71cm-39x28in) s.i.d.1995 W/C. 20-Oct-3 Stephan Welz, Johannesburg #378/R est:5000-8000 (SA.R 4500)
£578 $1035 €844 Phokwane tribal village (51x70cm-20x28in) s.d.1983 s.i.d.verso W/C over pencil. 31-May-4 Stephan Welz, Johannesburg #421 (SA.R 7000)

MOGELGAARD, Ludvig (1873-1928) Danish

£1164 $2130 €1699 Lady in the dunes, Tisvild (44x36cm-17x14in) s.i.d.1918. 9-Jun-4 Rasmussen, Copenhagen #1979/R est:7000-10000 (D.KR 13000)

MOGENSEN, Paul (1941-) American

£722 $1300 €1054 Scarlet to scarlet on Davy's Gray (24cm-9in circular) prov. 24-Apr-4 David Rago, Lambertville #259/R
Works on paper
£306 $550 €447 Untitled (15x22cm-6x9in) W/C. 24-Apr-4 David Rago, Lambertville #257/R

MOGET, Piet (1928-) Dutch

£1361 $2476 €2000 Composition (60x60cm-24x24in) s.d.1987 s.d.on stretcher prov. 3-Feb-4 Christie's, Amsterdam #636 est:700-900

MOGFORD, John (1821-1885) British

£444 $816 €648 Shad fishing, Cornwall (13x22cm-5x9in) s.d.1877 i.verso panel prov. 9-Jun-4 Walker's, Ottawa #353/R (C.D 1100)
£1000 $1670 €1460 Young fisherboy coming through the dunes (23x33cm-9x13in) s. 7-Oct-3 Bonhams, Knightsbridge #254/R est:1000-1500
Works on paper
£800 $1336 €1168 Coastal village (23x33cm-9x13in) s.d.1870 W/C. 14-Oct-3 David Lay, Penzance #190
£800 $1336 €1168 Dunwich (25x36cm-10x14in) s.i.d.1877 W/C. 12-Nov-3 Sotheby's, Olympia #53/R
£1700 $3128 €2482 Wanted a breeze - The Isle of Arran (44x78cm-17x31in) s.d.1874 W/C. 23-Mar-4 Anderson & Garland, Newcastle #300/R est:800-1400
£3000 $5430 €4380 Gleam of light, near Oban (33x49cm-13x19in) s.d.1862 W/C prov. 19-Apr-4 Sotheby's, London #20/R est:1500-2000
£3000 $5370 €4380 Wanted a breeze off the Isle of Arran (44x77cm-17x30in) pencil W/C htd white. 26-May-4 Christie's, Kensington #416/R est:3000-4000

MOGGIOLI, Umberto (1886-1919) Italian

£14765 $26430 €22000 Nude and fruit (97x98cm-38x39in) i.verso. 29-May-4 Farsetti, Prato #442/R est:20000-25000
£19580 $33287 €28000 Mazzarbo Canal (35x44cm-14x17in) s. exhib.lit. 20-Nov-3 Finarte Semenzato, Milan #159/R est:15000-18000

MOGISSE, Robert (1932-) French

£403 $753 €600 Marine (21x27cm-8x11in) s. 29-Feb-4 Osenat, Fontainebleau #235

MOHAMMEDI, Nasreen (1937-1990) Indian

Works on paper
£1902 $3500 €2777 Untitled (56x74cm-22x29in) pencil pen black ink. 24-Mar-4 Sotheby's, New York #190/R est:4000-6000

MOHL, John Koenakeefe (1903-1985) South African

£4542 $8130 €6631 Caught on the way to the house of worship (54x75cm-21x30in) s. i. verso. 31-May-4 Stephan Welz, Johannesburg #559/R est:10000-15000 (SA.R 55000)

MOHN, Victor Paul (1842-1911) German

Works on paper
£280 $476 €400 Two missionaries on horseback before mountain landscape (31x49cm-12x19in) s.d.24/6 78 W/C bodycol over Indian ink pencil. 29-Nov-3 Villa Grisebach, Berlin #636/R

MOHOLY, Lucia (1894-1989) Czechoslovakian

Photographs
£1808 $3200 €2640 Self portrait (11x8cm-4x3in) s. gelatin silver print. 27-Apr-4 Christie's, Rockefeller NY #59/R est:3000-5000
£1808 $3200 €2640 Escalier vue d'en haut, Paris (23x18cm-9x7in) i. gelatin silver print executed c.1930. 27-Apr-4 Christie's, Rockefeller NY #126/R est:4000-6000
£2133 $3925 €3200 Portrait of Lily Hildebrandt lying down (16x22cm-6x9in) i. verso silver gelatin prov.lit.exhib. 10-Jun-4 Villa Grisebach, Berlin #1225/R est:2800-3200

MOHOLY-NAGY, Laszlo (1895-1946) American/Hungarian

Photographs
£5689 $9500 €8306 Light space modulator (13x18cm-5x7in) s.i.verso gelatin silver print prov.lit. 20-Oct-3 Christie's, Rockefeller NY #82/R est:6000-8000
£7667 $13723 €11500 New museum exhibit - everyone can shoot their own picture (27x37cm-11x15in) photo after W/C board prov.exhib. 14-May-4 Ketterer, Munich #404/R est:9000-12000
£13333 $23867 €20000 How do I stay young and beautiful? (30x23cm-12x9in) photo after photo montage prov.exhib. 14-May-4 Ketterer, Munich #409/R est:12000-15000
£17333 $31027 €26000 Envy (30x23cm-12x9in) photo after photo montage bodycol Indian ink prov.exhib. 14-May-4 Ketterer, Munich #405/R est:15000-20000
Prints
£80000 $145600 €116800 Kestner-mappe konstruktionen, Hanover (43x60cm-17x24in) s. black red lithograph set of six. 30-Jun-4 Christie's, London #275/R est:80000-120000
Works on paper
£4192 $7000 €6120 Seated man (44x29cm-17x11in) s.d.19 chl. 7-Oct-3 Sotheby's, New York #267 est:5000-7000
£6000 $11040 €9000 Composition (36x45cm-14x18in) s.d.46 col chk pencil W/C. 12-Jun-4 Villa Grisebach, Berlin #278/R est:8000-12000
£10480 $19074 €15301 Four elements in circle (45x36cm-18x14in) s.d.46 W/C pen ink pencil. 18-Jun-4 Kornfeld, Bern #113/R est:15000 (S.FR 24000)

MOHR, Alexandre Carl Adrian (1892-1974) German

£699 $1203 €1000 Men with horses (82x92cm-32x36in) prov. 4-Dec-3 Van Ham, Cologne #334/R

MOHR, Johann Georg (1864-1943) German

£294 $499 €420 Lahn between Ems and Dausenau (40x65cm-16x26in) s. i. verso board. 22-Nov-3 Arnold, Frankfurt #593/R

MOHR, Johann Georg Paul (1808-1843) Danish

£800 $1464 €1200 View of Eppstein (54x64cm-21x25in) s. board. 5-Jun-4 Arnold, Frankfurt #666/R

MOHR, Johannes Carolus van der Meer (1821-1876) Dutch

£5333 $9600 €8000 Church interior with worshippers (150x119cm-59x47in) s. 21-Apr-4 Christie's, Amsterdam #34/R est:8000-12000

MOHR, Karl (19/20th C) German

£347 $566 €500 Harvest (60x70cm-24x28in) s. 26-Sep-3 Bolland & Marotz, Bremen #672/R
£385 $654 €550 Farmer ploughing his field (80x70cm-31x28in) s. 28-Nov-3 Wendl, Rudolstadt #4093/R
£1873 $3409 €2735 Horse riders and dogs in a landscape (80x70cm-31x28in) s. painted 1910. 20-Jun-4 Agra, Warsaw #31/R (P.Z 13000)

MOHR, Louise (19th C) ?

£3000 $5100 €4380 Mount Vesuvius with a village and ruins in the foreground (50x64cm-20x25in) 29-Oct-3 Bonhams, New Bond Street #124/R est:3000-4000

MOHREN, Jean (1876-?) German

£467 $845 €700 Cologne (60x80cm-24x31in) s. 1-Apr-4 Van Ham, Cologne #1544

MOHRMANN, John Henry (1857-1916) American

£1000 $1700 €1460 Close quarters in the Channel (61x100cm-24x39in) s.d.1896. 19-Nov-3 Christie's, Kensington #579/R est:1500-2000
£1070 $2000 €1605 British steamer, Kelvinbank, in the English Channel (52x90cm-20x35in) s.d.1904 canvas laid down prov. 25-Jul-4 Bonhams & Butterfields, San Francisco #6028/R est:2000-3000
£3311 $6026 €5000 Portrait of the ship Olga (64x100cm-25x39in) s. 19-Jun-4 Quittenbaum, Hamburg #31/R est:5500
£3784 $7000 €5525 British registered steamer, Anglo-Indian, bound for Argentina (61x92cm-24x36in) s. prov. 10-Feb-4 Christie's, Rockefeller NY #174/R est:7000-10000
£5133 $9291 €7700 Three masted sailing ship, Melpomene off steep coast (60x90cm-24x35in) s.d.1888. 3-Apr-4 Hans Stahl, Hamburg #171/R est:3000
£6667 $12067 €10000 Bateau a vapeur Zeeland et son pilote (60x100cm-24x39in) s.d.1905. 30-Mar-4 Campo & Campo, Antwerp #171/R est:3000-5000

MOHWALD, Otto (1933-) German
£759 $1403 €1100 Petersberg near Halle (34x40cm-13x16in) s.d.69. 14-Feb-4 Hans Stahl, Hamburg #65
£1034 $1914 €1500 Street with red house (36x51cm-14x20in) s.d.65 board. 14-Feb-4 Hans Stahl, Hamburg #64/R est:500

MOIGNIEZ, J (1835-1894) French
Sculpture
£1350 $2457 €2025 Stag (29cm-11in) bronze. 20-Jun-4 Wilkinson, Doncaster #143 est:1400-1800

MOIGNIEZ, Jules (1835-1894) French
Sculpture
£838 $1500 €1223 Bird of prey (79cm-31in) s. brown pat bronze marble base. 20-Mar-4 Freeman, Philadelphia #815 est:1000-1500
£1000 $1580 €1450 Hunting bird alighting on a branch (61cm-24in) s. brown pat bronze. 27-Jul-3 Desmond Judd, Cranbrook #616
£1007 $1883 €1500 Perdreau (27cm-11in) green brown pat bronze. 1-Mar-4 Coutau Begarie, Paris #232/R est:1500-1800
£1049 $1804 €1500 Couple de cailles a l'epi (18x23cm-7x9in) brown pat bronze. 3-Dec-3 Coutau Begarie, Paris #235/R est:1600-1800
£1181 $1877 €1700 Coq guettant (74x64cm-29x25in) s. pat bronze. 15-Sep-3 Horta, Bruxelles #63/R est:1500-2000
£1361 $2163 €2000 Lievre (30x23cm-12x9in) s. pat bronze. 23-Mar-3 Salle des ventes Pillet, Lyon la Foret #165
£1375 $2200 €2008 Mother bird feeding a butterfly to her young in a nest (56cm-22in) s. bronze. 20-Sep-3 Jeffery Burchard, Florida #102/R
£1379 $2303 €2000 Poule faisane (27x27x12cm-11x11x5in) s. medaille pat bronze. 14-Nov-3 Claude Boisgirard, Paris #68/R est:1200-1500
£1437 $2400 €2098 Hunting dogs and elk (28x38cm-11x15in) s. bronze. 16-Nov-3 William Jenack, New York #165 est:2000-3000
£1447 $2663 €2200 Le persan etalon (28cm-11in) s.i. brown pat. bronze incl. base. 22-Jun-4 Sotheby's, Amsterdam #220/R est:1200-1600
£1667 $2983 €2500 Perdrix (30cm-12in) s. brown pat bronze marble socle. 12-May-4 Coutau Begarie, Paris #244/R est:2500-3000
£1888 $3248 €2700 Becasse. brown pat bronze medaillon oval. 3-Dec-3 Coutau Begarie, Paris #236/R est:2300-2500
£2000 $3400 €2920 Setter spotting a hiding hare (19x33cm-7x13in) s. brown pat bronze. 19-Nov-3 Sotheby's, Olympia #151/R est:2000-3000
£2162 $4000 €3157 Eagle carrying baby eagle (66x48x25cm-26x19x10in) bronze. 13-Feb-4 Du Mouchelle, Detroit #2124/R est:6500-7000
£2410 $4000 €3519 Horse at gallop (30x41x13cm-12x16x5in) s. bronze. 4-Oct-3 South Bay, Long Island #112
£2600 $4654 €3796 Etalon Arabe. s. bronze bronze base exec.c.1860-1870 lit. 21-Mar-4 Desmond Judd, Cranbrook #645
£2800 $4424 €4060 Galloping stallion and greyhound taking a gate (56cm-22in) s. brown pat bronze. 27-Jul-3 Desmond Judd, Cranbrook #609
£3073 $5500 €4487 Eagle (69cm-27in) s. bronze. 8-May-4 Susanin's, Chicago #6041/R est:1000-2000
£3230 $5200 €4716 Owl (89x61cm-35x24in) bronze. 20-Aug-3 James Julia, Fairfield #1465/R est:2250-2750
£3289 $6053 €5000 Chien et sauterelle (47x63x25cm-19x25x10in) s. pat bronze. 22-Jun-4 Palais de Beaux Arts, Brussels #629/R est:6000-8000
£3404 $5685 €4800 Cheval au repos (59x50cm-23x20in) s. brown pat bronze. 15-Oct-3 Rabourdin & Choppin de Janvry, Paris #156/R est:6500-7000
£3800 $6840 €5548 Boar attacked by two hounds (30x41cm-12x16in) s. brown pat bronze. 21-Apr-4 Sotheby's, London #89/R est:3000-5000
£4397 $7343 €6200 L'accolade (37x50cm-15x20in) s. brown pat bronze. 12-Oct-3 St-Germain-en-Laye Encheres #47/R est:6000-7000

MOIGNIEZ, Jules (attrib) (1835-1894) French
Sculpture
£1067 $1931 €1600 Le Persan (20cm-8in) bronze. 1-Apr-4 Van Ham, Cologne #1137/R est:1600

MOILLIET, Louis (1880-1962) Swiss
Works on paper
£2477 $4137 €3592 Sousse Kasbah (24x31cm-9x12in) W/C pencil. 19-Jun-3 Kornfeld, Bern #727 est:4000 (S.FR 5400)
£3624 $6052 €5255 House in hilly landscape, Cadaques (27x36cm-11x14in) s.i.d.1926 W/C. 19-Jun-3 Kornfeld, Bern #728/R est:7500 (S.FR 7900)
£4220 $7048 €6119 Farmstead in Andraitx, Mallorca (23x28cm-9x11in) s.d.1926W/C. 19-Jun-3 Kornfeld, Bern #729/R est:7500 (S.FR 9200)
£4405 $7489 €6431 Houses in Tunis (34x38cm-13x15in) s.i.d.1928 W/C. 7-Nov-3 Dobiaschofsky, Bern #192/R est:14000 (S.FR 10000)
£4587 $7661 €6651 House of Dr Jaggi in St Germain neaar Tunis (20x26cm-8x10in) i. W/C. 19-Jun-3 Kornfeld, Bern #726/R est:10000 (S.FR 10000)

MOILLON, Louise (1609-1696) French
£60000 $103800 €87600 Market stall with a young woman giving a basket of grapes to an older woman (122x168cm-48x66in) prov. 11-Dec-3 Sotheby's, London #58/R est:60000-80000

MOINE, Antonin (19th C) French
Works on paper
£333 $603 €500 Musiciennes dans un parc (27x42cm-11x17in) s. pastel. 1-Apr-4 Credit Municipal, Paris #16

MOIR, John (1776-1857) British
£260 $434 €380 Lady seated her hand resting on a table (65x62cm-26x24in) s.d.1852. 21-Oct-3 Bruton Knowles, Cheltenham #450

MOIRA, Gerald (1867-1959) British
Works on paper
£1600 $2656 €2336 Crusader (50x36cm-20x14in) s. W/C gold paint prov. 1-Oct-3 Sotheby's, Olympia #170/R est:1000-1500

MOIRAGHI, Anacleto (1880-1943) Italian
£922 $1540 €1300 Landscape with old farm (60x80cm-24x31in) s. i.verso. 14-Oct-3 Finarte Semenzato, Milan #43/R
£1277 $2132 €1800 The Fishermen's island on Lake Maggiore (60x80cm-24x31in) s. i.verso. 14-Oct-3 Finarte Semenzato, Milan #22/R est:1800-2000
£1711 $3147 €2600 Bellagio, Italy (26x40cm-10x16in) s. cardboard. 23-Jun-4 Finarte Semenzato, Rome #90/R est:800-900

MOIRAGHI, C (20th C) Italian
£1600 $2864 €2400 Lake Como (105x160cm-41x63in) s. 12-May-4 Stadion, Trieste #774 est:1200-1600

MOIRIGNOT, Edmond (1913-) French
Sculpture
£1119 $1869 €1600 Zorba, le grec (41cm-16in) s.st.f.Valsuani gilt pat bronze lit. 30-Jun-3 Bailly Pommery, Paris #119/R

MOISE, Theodore Sydney (attrib) (19th C) American
£608 $1100 €888 New Orleans gentleman (64x76cm-25x30in) i.verso. 3-Apr-4 Neal Auction Company, New Orleans #851/R est:1200-1800

MOISES, Julio (1888-1968) Spanish
£1277 $2132 €1800 Woman with crown (28x31cm-11x12in) s.d.MCMXVI board. 20-Oct-3 Durán, Madrid #140/R

MOISSET, Maurice (1860-1946) French
£503 $936 €750 Berger rentrant son troupeau (24x35cm-9x14in) s. 3-Mar-4 Tajan, Paris #45

MOITTE, Pierre Etienne (1722-1780) French
Works on paper
£850 $1556 €1241 Classical maiden in an open chariot with attendants (14x46cm-6x18in) brown wash pen ink. 7-Apr-4 Woolley & Wallis, Salisbury #134/R

MOJA, Frederico (1802-1885) Italian
Works on paper
£433 $780 €650 Milan, Saint Lorenzo's columns (22x16cm-9x6in) pencil. 21-Apr-4 Finarte Semenzato, Milan #570
£1944 $3306 €2800 View of alpine lake (8x13cm-3x5in) W/C. 28-Oct-3 Il Ponte, Milan #287/R

MOJAIEV, Aleksei (1918-) Russian
£313 $570 €460 Gondolier. s. 8-Feb-4 Lesieur & Le Bars, Le Havre #133/R

MOKADY, Moshe (1902-1975) Israeli
£1257 $2300 €1835 Portrait of a boy (33x25cm-13x10in) s. oil paper masonite painted c.1930. 1-Feb-4 Ben-Ami, Tel Aviv #4575/R est:3000-4000
£1257 $2300 €1835 Portrait of a young man (34x26cm-13x10in) s. oil paper board painted c.1930. 1-Feb-4 Ben-Ami, Tel Aviv #4574/R est:3000-4000
£3169 $5800 €4627 Father and son (65x50cm-26x20in) s. painted c.1935 prov. 1-Feb-4 Ben-Ami, Tel Aviv #4378/R est:7000-9000

MOKETARINJA, Richard (1918-1983) Australian
Works on paper
£508 $950 €762 Utnurungita, green caterpillar, story (54x37cm-21x15in) bears name.verso synthetic polymer paint board prov. 26-Jul-4 Sotheby's, Melbourne #552/R (A.D 1300)

MOKIIL, J A (19th C) ?
£356 $647 €534 Landscape from a Norwegian fishing village with cabin and figures (65x90cm-26x35in) s.d.1883. 19-Jun-4 Rasmussen, Havnen #2182 (D.KR 4000)

MOKROV, Nicolai (1926-) Russian
£267 $480 €400 Vieille Ladoga (34x48cm-13x19in) s.d.90. 26-Apr-4 Millon & Associes, Paris #92/R
£300 $540 €450 Halte des chevaux (34x50cm-13x20in) s. 26-Apr-4 Millon & Associes, Paris #94/R
£733 $1320 €1100 Pereslavl Zaluky (61x105cm-24x41in) s.d.86. 26-Apr-4 Millon & Associes, Paris #95/R

MOKUBEI, Aoki (1767-1833) Japanese
Works on paper
£411 $699 €600 Landscape (109x30cm-43x12in) s. seals Indian ink col hanging scroll prov. 8-Nov-3 Dr Fritz Nagel, Stuttgart #1922/R
£411 $699 €600 Landscape (117x36cm-46x14in) s.d.1832 Indian ink col silk. 8-Nov-3 Dr Fritz Nagel, Stuttgart #1923/R
£685 $1164 €1000 Tea ceremony objects (30x28cm-12x11in) s.d.1814 Indian ink col hanging scroll. 8-Nov-3 Dr Fritz Nagel, Stuttgart #1924/R
£1027 $1747 €1500 Nehan zu - dead budha (77x31cm-30x12in) s. seal Indian ink silk hanging scroll. 8-Nov-3 Dr Fritz Nagel, Stuttgart #1925/R est:600

MOKUBEI, Aoki (attrib) (1767-1833) Japanese
Works on paper
£1200 $2004 €1752 Chinese landscape (135x34cm-53x13in) s.d.1823 ink col. 12-Nov-3 Christie's, London #49/R

MOL, Leo (1915-) Canadian
Sculpture

£1080	$1976	€1577	Resting woman (31cm-12in) s.d.1984 num.6/15 bronze. 1-Jun-4 Hodgins, Calgary #106/R est:2000-3000 (C.D 2700)
£1422	$2460	€2076	Nu feminin debout (47cm-19in) s.d.68 num.3/10 bronze. 15-Dec-3 Iegor de Saint Hippolyte, Montreal #35b (C.D 3200)

MOL, Pieter van (1599-1650) Flemish

£828	$1531	€1200	Paysage de neige (40x50cm-16x20in) s. 16-Feb-4 Horta, Bruxelles #30

MOL, Pieter van (attrib) (1599-1650) Flemish

£5333	$9653	€8000	Worship (41x54cm-16x21in) lit. 1-Apr-4 Frank Peege, Freiburg #1109/R est:10000

MOL, Wouterus (1786-1857) Dutch

£838	$1400	€1223	Cavalier in an interior (35x32cm-14x13in) s. panel. 7-Oct-3 Sotheby's, New York #42/R

MOLA, Pier Francesco (1612-1666) Italian

£3262	$5285	€4600	Saint Joseph's dream (47x36cm-19x14in) 21-May-3 Babuino, Rome #42/R
£10000	$18300	€14600	Pan playing his pipes (60x45cm-24x18in) 9-Jul-4 Christie's, Kensington #158/R est:6000-8000
£43972	$71234	€62000	Archimedes' death (135x122cm-53x48in) 21-May-3 Babuino, Rome #22/R

Works on paper

£2177	$3897	€3200	Le Songe de Joseph (27x20cm-11x8in) pen brown ink htd white prov. 18-Mar-4 Christie's, Paris #86/R est:3000-5000
£2721	$4871	€4000	Le Christ accompagne d'anges apparaissant a un saint agenouille (25x18cm-10x7in) red chk pen brown ink wash prov. 18-Mar-4 Christie's, Paris #84/R est:4000-6000
£4626	$8280	€6800	Le Bapteme du Christ, avec deux etudes subsidiaires du Christ (28x20cm-11x8in) pen brown ink wash prov. 18-Mar-4 Christie's, Paris #85/R est:4000-6000
£5278	$9500	€7706	Caricature of Cardinal Crescenzi. Caricature of the same (27x19cm-11x7in) i.verso black chk pen brown ink wash double-sided. 22-Jan-4 Christie's, Rockefeller NY #51/R est:2000-3000
£6111	$11000	€8922	Extensive coastal landscape seen from a wooded headland (17x26cm-7x10in) red chk oil paper. 22-Jan-4 Christie's, Rockefeller NY #61/R est:3000-5000
£7483	$13395	€11000	Moise sauve des eaux (22x30cm-9x12in) i. red chk pen brown ink wash prov. 18-Mar-4 Christie's, Paris #87/R est:3000-5000
£15556	$28000	€22712	Caricature of Pier Francesco Mola interrupting Giovanni Battista Passeri (24x19cm-9x7in) i. pen brown ink wash. 22-Jan-4 Christie's, Rockefeller NY #50/R est:3000-5000

MOLA, Pier Francesco (attrib) (1612-1666) Italian

£4079	$7505	€6200	Portrait de femme au turban (68x50cm-27x20in) 25-Jun-4 Piasa, Paris #63/R est:3000-4000
£9934	$18080	€15000	Good Samaritan (128x149cm-50x59in) 15-Jun-4 Artcurial Briest, Paris #212/R est:15000-20000
£11111	$20000	€16222	Bearded Saint or prophet in a landscape, probably Saint Jerome (107x147cm-42x58in) i. prov. 22-Jan-4 Sotheby's, New York #207/R est:20000-30000
£21127	$36972	€30000	Old man warming his hands (96x76cm-38x30in) 17-Dec-3 Christie's, Rome #482/R est:30000-40000

Works on paper

£950	$1739	€1387	Figures in an architectural setting. Bird in flight (36x24cm-14x9in) pen ink brown wash double-sided. 7-Jul-4 Bonhams, Knightsbridge #64/R

MOLA, Pier Francesco (circle) (1612-1666) Italian

£7692	$13231	€11230	Pyrame and Thysbee (74x93cm-29x37in) 3-Dec-3 AB Stockholms Auktionsverk #2706/R est:60000-80000 (S.KR 100000)

MOLANUS, Mattheus (attrib) (?-1645) Dutch

£6711	$12349	€10000	Landscape with village (59x102cm-23x40in) panel. 25-Mar-4 Dr Fritz Nagel, Stuttgart #616/R est:9000

MOLARSKY, Abraham (c.1883-?) Russian/American

£342	$550	€499	Harbour scene (38x46cm-15x18in) s. board painted c.1920. 22-Feb-3 Bunte, Elgin #1289
£1916	$3200	€2797	Japanese lanterns (66x56cm-26x22in) s.d.1917 canvas on board. 23-Oct-3 Shannon's, Milford #35/R est:3000-5000
£4469	$8000	€6525	View of the harbour (72x61cm-28x24in) s.d.20. 14-May-4 Skinner, Boston #275/R est:5000-7000

MOLDOVAN, Kurt (1918-1977) Austrian
Works on paper

£423	$739	€600	Classical scene with faun playing the flute (32x48cm-13x19in) s.i.d.61 pen ink wash. 19-Dec-3 Dorotheum, Vienna #227/R
£600	$1080	€900	Cats (22x15cm-9x6in) s.d.70 Indian ink brush pen. 21-Apr-4 Dorotheum, Vienna #176/R
£987	$1816	€1500	Maya watching the Spanish navy (32x47cm-13x19in) s.d.1967 ink. 22-Jun-4 Wiener Kunst Auktionen, Vienna #307/R est:1800
£1208	$2235	€1800	Alice with telescope neck (47x32cm-19x13in) s.d.68 Indian ink wash. 9-Mar-4 Dorotheum, Vienna #143/R est:1500-2000
£1399	$2378	€2000	Ice skaters (47x32cm-19x13in) s.i.d.1976 ink. 28-Nov-3 Wiener Kunst Auktionen, Vienna #616/R est:3000-4000
£1538	$2615	€2200	Song of the mad hatter (45x31cm-18x12in) s.i.d.68 pen brush Indian ink. 26-Nov-3 Dorotheum, Vienna #232/R est:1500-2000
£2013	$3564	€3000	Rome, Palatine (32x48cm-13x19in) s.i.d.1972 W/C. 28-Apr-4 Wiener Kunst Auktionen, Vienna #203/R est:3000-6000
£2377	$4350	€3470	Landscape of Barcelona (31x47cm-12x19in) s.i.d.1973. 1-Feb-4 Ben-Ami, Tel Aviv #4563/R est:5000-6000
£2535	$4437	€3600	Southern railway (31x46cm-12x18in) s.d.61 W/C. 19-Dec-3 Dorotheum, Vienna #226/R est:4000-5500
£3147	$5350	€4500	Periphery (31x46cm-12x18in) s.d.70 W/C. 26-Nov-3 Dorotheum, Vienna #237/R est:4500-5500
£4895	$8322	€7000	March periphery (32x48cm-13x19in) s.i.d.1975 W/C. 28-Nov-3 Wiener Kunst Auktionen, Vienna #610/R est:7000-10000
£4895	$8322	€7000	Venice (32x48cm-13x19in) s.d.1976 W/C. 28-Nov-3 Wiener Kunst Auktionen, Vienna #624/R est:9000-12000
£4899	$8770	€7300	Venice (32x40cm-13x16in) s.d.67 W/C. 27-May-4 Hassfurther, Vienna #61/R est:7000-10000
£5594	$9510	€8000	Train line (32x48cm-13x19in) s.d.1976 W/C. 28-Nov-3 Wiener Kunst Auktionen, Vienna #625/R est:8000-11000

MOLDOVAN, Sacha (1901-1982) American/Russian

£1130	$2000	€1650	Still life with red vase (46x33cm-18x13in) s. canvasboard painted c.1958 lit. 2-May-4 Bonhams & Butterfields, Los Angeles #3006/R est:4000-6000
£2260	$4000	€3300	Untitled, bull fight (51x61cm-20x24in) s. prov. 2-May-4 Bonhams & Butterfields, Los Angeles #3004/R
£2654	$4750	€3875	Village with church. i. 13-May-4 Dallas Auction Gallery, Dallas #242/R est:1500-2500
£2793	$5000	€4078	Red roof cottages. s.i. 13-May-4 Dallas Auction Gallery, Dallas #112/R est:1500-2500
£3352	$6000	€4894	Peasant feeding chickens. i. 13-May-4 Dallas Auction Gallery, Dallas #289/R est:1500-2500

MOLE, J H (1814-1886) British

£660	$1195	€964	Seascape with ruined building on cliffs and figures on rocks (33x20cm-13x8in) s. 17-Apr-4 Jim Railton, Durham #1729

MOLE, John Henry (1814-1886) British
Works on paper

£260	$465	€380	Bringing home the catch (38x59cm-15x23in) s.d.1858 W/C. 20-Mar-4 Lacy Scott, Bury St.Edmunds #436
£300	$543	€438	Boy with a flagon (25x20cm-10x8in) s.d.1858 W/C htd white. 2-Apr-4 Moore Allen & Innocent, Cirencester #768/R
£400	$728	€584	View from Richmond Hill (22x34cm-9x13in) mono. W/C. 15-Jun-4 Bonhams, Oxford #50
£450	$828	€657	Peat gatherers (23x38cm-9x15in) s.d.1874 pencil W/C. 25-Mar-4 Christie's, Kensington #147/R
£537	$983	€784	Rocky coast with boy and girl fishing in a rock-pool (35x50cm-14x20in) s.d.1852 W/C pencil. 9-Jun-4 Rasmussen, Copenhagen #2098/R (D.KR 6000)
£660	$1181	€964	Girl collecting water, ducks in the foreground (29x44cm-11x17in) s.d.1880 W/C. 25-May-4 Sworder & Son, Bishops Stortford #418/R
£750	$1350	€1095	Near the Mumbles, south Wales (19x32cm-7x13in) s.d.1874 W/C over pencil bodycol. 21-Jan-4 Sotheby's, Olympia #157/R
£750	$1388	€1095	Young girl crossing the stream (13x22cm-5x9in) s.d.1867 W/C. 9-Mar-4 Bonhams, New Bond Street #82/R
£800	$1336	€1168	Fisher girl (32x22cm-13x9in) s.d.1858 W/C. 12-Nov-3 Sotheby's, Olympia #111/R
£850	$1462	€1241	Young anglers (25x37cm-10x15in) s. pencil W/C. 3-Dec-3 Christie's, Kensington #124/R
£900	$1548	€1314	Returning home from market (24x37cm-9x15in) s.d.1877 W/C. 3-Dec-3 Christie's, Kensington #126/R
£950	$1739	€1387	Farmhouses in a landscape (30x51cm-12x20in) pencil W/C prov. 27-Jan-4 Holloways, Banbury #325/R
£1000	$1700	€1460	Gathering mussels (37x28cm-15x11in) s.d.1853 W/C. 4-Nov-3 Bonhams, New Bond Street #97/R est:1000-1500
£3200	$5760	€4672	Fisherman's life (66x104cm-26x41in) s.d.1851 W/C exhib. 21-Jan-4 Sotheby's, Olympia #197/R est:3000-4000
£3200	$5728	€4672	Children at a rock pool (26x59cm-10x23in) s.d.1869 W/C. 17-Mar-4 Bonhams, Chester #289/R est:2500-3500
£5200	$8840	€7592	Yorkshire Beck (46x86cm-18x34in) s. W/C. 4-Nov-3 Bonhams, New Bond Street #101/R est:4000-6000

MOLEIRO, Raul (1903-) Venezuelan

£299	$500	€437	Landscape in Marquez (51x61cm-20x24in) s. painted 1969. 13-Jul-3 Subastas Odalys, Caracas #102
£323	$500	€472	Morning in the mountains (51x61cm-20x24in) s. painted 1977. 3-Nov-2 Subastas Odalys, Caracas #36/R
£376	$595	€549	Avila (41x51cm-16x20in) s. 27-Apr-3 Subastas Odalys, Caracas #95

MOLENAAR, Johannes Petrus (1914-1989) Dutch
Works on paper

£293	$525	€440	Activity in a Rotterdam harbour (58x98cm-23x39in) s.d.41 mixed media. 11-May-4 Vendu Notarishuis, Rotterdam #101

MOLENAAR, Pieter (20th C) Canadian

£600	$1098	€876	Winter on the canal (60x75cm-24x30in) s.i.d.2003. 1-Jun-4 Hodgins, Calgary #392/R (C.D 1500)

MOLENAER, Bartholomeus (1612-1650) Dutch

£5743	$10108	€8500	Interior of an inn with peasants sitting around a table drinking and playing dice (37x49cm-15x19in) mono. panel prov. 18-May-4 Sotheby's, Amsterdam #112/R est:7000-9000

MOLENAER, Bartholomeus (circle) (1612-1650) Dutch

£6040	$10812	€9000	Paysans dans un interieur de taverne (61x55cm-24x22in) bears mono. panel. 25-May-4 Palais de Beaux Arts, Brussels #79/R est:10000-13000

MOLENAER, Jan Jacobz (1654-?) Dutch

£872	$1614	€1300	Fight in a tavern (48x35cm-19x14in) s. panel. 15-Mar-4 Sotheby's, Amsterdam #34a/R est:800-1200

MOLENAER, Jan Miense (1610-1668) Dutch
£1878 $3305 €2742 In the tavern (30x23cm-12x9in) s. panel prov. 22-May-4 Galerie Gloggner, Luzern #74/R est:6000-8000 (S.FR 4300)
£2800 $5012 €4200 Peasants singing and making merry in an inn (37x41cm-15x16in) panel. 17-May-4 Christie's, Amsterdam #51/R est:2000-3000
£3500 $6300 €5110 Peasants smoking and drinking by a table (25x19cm-10x7in) s. panel. 23-Apr-4 Christie's, Kensington #50/R est:3000-4000
£3600 $6480 €5256 Peasants carousing in a tavern interior (30x34cm-12x13in) s. panel. 21-Apr-4 Bonhams, New Bond Street #53/R est:2000-4000
£4500 $7650 €6570 Tavern interior with a peasant woman playing the violin and other peasants singing (47x36cm-19x14in) panel. 31-Oct-3 Christie's, Kensington #14/R est:6000-8000
£4730 $8324 €7000 Peasants drinking and playing cards in an inn (34x25cm-13x10in) s. panel. 18-May-4 Sotheby's, Amsterdam #5/R est:8000-12000
£5000 $9150 €7300 Interior of a tavern with revellers (51x67cm-20x26in) s. panel. 6-Jul-4 Sotheby's, Olympia #532/R est:5000-7000
£13429 $24575 €19606 Many figures in the village (87x112cm-34x44in) s. 9-Jun-4 Rasmussen, Copenhagen #1525/R est:150000-175000 (D.KR 150000)

MOLENAER, Jan Miense (attrib) (1610-1668) Dutch
£1700 $3060 €2482 Peasants merrymaking in a tavern (27x32cm-11x13in) indis.sig. panel. 23-Apr-4 Christie's, Kensington #67/R est:800-1200
£3000 $5100 €4380 River landscape with Boors smoking and drinking outside a cottage (40x50cm-16x20in) panel. 30-Oct-3 Sotheby's, Olympia #57/R est:2000-3000
£3497 $5944 €5000 Fete a l'auberge (68x101cm-27x40in) 18-Nov-3 Vanderkindere, Brussels #56/R est:7500-10000

MOLENAER, Klaes (1630-1676) Dutch
£2267 $4057 €3400 River landscape with rowing boat and anglers by a fortified town (30x43cm-12x17in) indis.sig. panel. 17-May-4 Christie's, Amsterdam #33/R est:4000-6000
£2632 $4842 €4000 Landscape with skaters (28x22cm-11x9in) panel. 25-Jun-4 Piasa, Paris #85/R est:4000-5000
£2809 $5027 €4101 Dutch canal scene (44x55cm-17x22in) s. panel. 26-May-4 AB Stockholms Auktionsverk #2552/R est:25000-30000 (S.KR 38000)
£3500 $6300 €5110 Wooded river landscape with windmill (39x48cm-15x19in) panel. 23-Apr-4 Christie's, Kensington #37/R est:4000-6000
£3688 $5827 €5200 Winter landscape with skaters (30x38cm-12x15in) panel. 24-Jul-3 Adjug'art, Brest #346/R
£5517 $9214 €8000 Many people on the ice by the city well (75x65cm-30x26in) mono. 11-Nov-3 Vendu Notarishuis, Rotterdam #80/R est:6000-8000
£5822 $9897 €8500 Wooded landscape with travellers, horses and figures swimming (41x55cm-16x22in) s. panel. 4-Nov-3 Sotheby's, Amsterdam #52/R est:5000-7000
£5822 $9897 €8500 Landscape with travellers resting near a farm, a church beyond (32x43cm-13x17in) s. panel. 4-Nov-3 Sotheby's, Amsterdam #87/R est:6000-8000
£6294 $10699 €9000 Winter scene (75x107cm-30x42in) s. 20-Nov-3 Van Ham, Cologne #1381/R est:10000
£7586 $12593 €11000 Farmhouse on river with boat and peasants (37x29cm-15x11in) s. panel. 1-Oct-3 Dorotheum, Vienna #184/R est:8000-12000

MOLENAER, Klaes (attrib) (1630-1676) Dutch
£1905 $3467 €2800 River landscape with rowing boats by a fortified town, conversing figures on the river bank (47x64cm-19x25in) panel. 3-Feb-4 Christie's, Amsterdam #16/R est:2000-3000
£8904 $15137 €13000 Winter landscape with man pushing a sledge, and view of Haarlem (34x46cm-13x18in) prov.exhib.lit. 4-Nov-3 Sotheby's, Amsterdam #70/R est:10000-15000

MOLENAER, Klaes (circle) (1630-1676) Dutch
£6507 $11062 €9500 Winter landscape with townsfolk on a frozen waterway by a tavern (72x102cm-28x40in) indis sig. 5-Nov-3 Christie's, Amsterdam #9/R est:5000-7000

MOLENAER, Klaes (style) (1630-1676) Dutch
£6061 $10848 €8849 Skaters on the ice (104x168cm-41x66in) 28-May-4 Uppsala Auktionskammare, Uppsala #21/R est:60000-80000 (S.KR 82000)

MOLENKAMP, Nico (?) ?
£2797 $4755 €4000 Man met vis (140x120cm-55x47in) s. s.i.stretcher prov. 25-Nov-3 Christie's, Amsterdam #298/R est:5000-7000
£2797 $4755 €4000 Giraffe (140x130cm-55x51in) s. s.i.stretcher prov. 25-Nov-3 Christie's, Amsterdam #299/R est:3500-4500
Works on paper
£629 $1070 €900 Baboon (75x70cm-30x28in) s. W/C prov. 25-Nov-3 Christie's, Amsterdam #103/R

MOLEVELD, Pieter (1919-) Dutch
£313 $500 €457 Still life of current twigs and pewter cans. s. 20-Sep-3 Harvey Clar, Oakland #1264

MOLEZUN SUAREZ, Manuel (1920-) Spanish
£755 $1261 €1080 Abstracto (48x68cm-19x27in) s.d.1980 oil collage paper prov. 24-Jun-3 Segre, Madrid #156/R

MOLIN, Lei (1927-1990) Dutch
Works on paper
£470 $869 €700 Untitled (122x76cm-48x30in) s.d.1988 W/C pastel. 15-Mar-4 Sotheby's, Amsterdam #299
£629 $1051 €900 Untitled (120x80cm-47x31in) s.d.1988 gouache. 30-Jun-3 Sotheby's, Amsterdam #484

MOLINA CAMPOS, Florencio (1891-1959) Argentinian
£33607 $61500 €49066 Coming out of a bad situation (35x51cm-14x20in) tempera cardboard. 1-Jun-4 Arroyo, Buenos Aires #79
Works on paper
£3824 $6500 €5583 Discussing (18x28cm-7x11in) W/C tempera exhib.lit. 25-Nov-3 Galeria y Remates, Montevideo #179/R
£4412 $7500 €6442 Hudson (29x20cm-11x8in) W/C tempera exhib.lit. 25-Nov-3 Galeria y Remates, Montevideo #178/R
£5882 $10000 €8588 Alma Mula (19x29cm-7x11in) W/C tempera exhib.lit. 25-Nov-3 Galeria y Remates, Montevideo #177/R

MOLINA MONTERO, Francisco (1962-) Spanish
£4027 $7490 €6000 Looking at the horse's teeth (171x136cm-67x54in) s. 2-Mar-4 Ansorena, Madrid #68/R est:9000

MOLINA SANCHEZ, Jose Antonio (1918-) Spanish
£1250 $2125 €1800 Maternity (59x40cm-23x16in) s.d.1950 s.d.verso paper on board. 28-Oct-3 Segre, Madrid #287/R est:1800
£2041 $3714 €3000 Girl (55x46cm-22x18in) s.d.1980. 3-Feb-4 Segre, Madrid #160/R est:2800
£4082 $7429 €6000 Cautious virgins (120x90cm-47x35in) s.d.1953 exhib. 3-Feb-4 Segre, Madrid #137/R est:5000
Works on paper
£345 $572 €500 Woman (33x26cm-13x10in) s.d.1990 W/C gouache. 1-Oct-3 Ansorena, Madrid #344/R

MOLINA, Jesus (1904-1969) Spanish
£1277 $2068 €1800 Mujer cosiendo (100x70cm-39x28in) 20-May-3 Segre, Madrid #262/R est:1800

MOLINARI, Aleksander Ludwik (1795-1868) Polish
£2069 $3455 €3000 Boy against landscape (92x79cm-36x31in) mono.d.1840 canvas on panel prov. 15-Nov-3 Lempertz, Koln #1656/R est:3000

MOLINARI, Antonio (attrib) (1665-c.1728) Italian
Works on paper
£533 $981 €800 Angel leading Peter out of captivity (25x14cm-10x6in) wash pen. 11-Jun-4 Hauswedell & Nolte, Hamburg #869/R

MOLINARI, Antonio (circle) (1665-c.1728) Italian
£70000 $121100 €102200 Venus and Bacchus with cupid and satyr (112x183cm-44x72in) 12-Dec-3 Christie's, Kensington #183/R est:7000-10000

MOLINARI, Guido (1933-) Canadian
£1351 $2297 €1972 Multiple diagonal noir (66x76cm-26x30in) s.d.1963-1973 verso acrylic prov.exhib. 27-Nov-3 Heffel, Vancouver #60/R est:6000-8000 (C.D 3000)
£4505 $7658 €6577 Untitled (91x30cm-36x12in) s.d.65 verso canvas on board prov. 18-Nov-3 Sotheby's, Toronto #165/R est:3000-5000 (C.D 10000)
£9910 $16847 €14469 Untitled (76x66cm-30x26in) s.d.January 1967 acrylic verso prov.lit. 27-Nov-3 Heffel, Vancouver #57/R est:20000-25000 (C.D 22000)
£14286 $24571 €20858 Rhythmique (180x150cm-71x59in) s.i.d.1/66 verso lit. 2-Dec-3 Joyner Waddington, Toronto #36/R est:35000-45000 (C.D 32000)
Works on paper
£382 $710 €558 Studies (34x27cm-13x11in) s.d.88 chl pair. 2-Mar-4 Ritchie, Toronto #204/R (C.D 950)
£382 $710 €558 Study for a painting (23x15cm-9x6in) s.d.69 pastel graphite. 2-Mar-4 Ritchie, Toronto #205/R (C.D 950)

MOLINARI, Guido (19th C) Italian
£260 $424 €380 Portrait of a young boy smoking a clay pipe (65x50cm-26x20in) 24-Sep-3 Dreweatt Neate, Newbury #198
£755 $1261 €1080 Village by the sea (29x39cm-11x15in) s. 30-Jun-3 Ansorena, Madrid #233/R

MOLINER, Manes F (1921-) Spanish
£284 $474 €400 Campesinos (31x23cm-12x9in) s. board. 23-Jun-3 Durán, Madrid #1291

MOLINIER, Pierre (1900-1976) French
£4667 $8400 €7000 Nu au bouquet de fleurs (96x129cm-38x51in) s. panel. 24-Apr-4 Cornette de St.Cyr, Paris #392 est:10000

MOLINO, Walter (1915-1997) Italian
£420 $701 €600 Bather (35x25cm-14x10in) s. 10-Oct-3 Stadion, Trieste #648/R
Works on paper
£493 $853 €700 Jimmy took me to England (28x37cm-11x15in) s.i. pencil W/C. 9-Dec-3 Pandolfini, Florence #334
£528 $914 €750 It seemed a long time (35x51cm-14x20in) s. W/C. 9-Dec-3 Pandolfini, Florence #335

MOLINS, Alfred de (19th C) French
£776 $1389 €1133 Riders on path (40x32cm-16x13in) s. 12-May-4 Dobiaschofsky, Bern #805/R est:2400 (S.FR 1800)
£9155 $16021 €13000 Promenade au bois (32x56cm-13x22in) s.d.73. 17-Dec-3 Delorme & Bocage, Paris #32/R est:15000-20000

MOLINS, Auguste de (19th C) French
£2616 $4500 €3819 Chasse a courre en plaine (34x54cm-13x21in) s.d.74. 5-Dec-3 Christie's, Rockefeller NY #79/R est:3000-5000

MOLITOR, J Lauren (18th C) German
Works on paper
£2431 $3962 €3500 St Katharina von Alexandria in conversation with philosophers (19x23cm-7x9in) s.i. W/C bodycol. 25-Sep-3 Neumeister, Munich #249/R est:1300

MOLITOR, Martin von (1759-1812) Austrian

Works on paper

£2707	$4928	€3952	Arcadian landscape with waterfall and herd (51x64cm-20x25in) s.d.1803 W/C htd white prov.exhib. 17-Jun-4 Kornfeld, Bern #39/R est:4000 (S.FR 6200)

MOLITOR, Martin von (attrib) (1759-1812) Austrian

£738	$1358	€1100	River landscape with herders and animals (22x32cm-9x13in) bears sig.d.1795 paper on board. 25-Mar-4 Dr Fritz Nagel, Stuttgart #686/R

MOLITOR, Mathieu (1873-1929) German

£359	$621	€510	Windmill by snowy harbour (25x30cm-10x12in) bears sig. i. verso. 11-Dec-3 Dr Fritz Nagel, Stuttgart #537/R
£367	$664	€550	Yellow punt on sea (30x37cm-12x15in) 2-Apr-4 Dr Fritz Nagel, Leipzig #3941/R
£467	$845	€700	Fields (38x54cm-15x21in) 2-Apr-4 Dr Fritz Nagel, Leipzig #3938/R
£500	$905	€750	Snowy mountain village (23x30cm-9x12in) 2-Apr-4 Dr Fritz Nagel, Leipzig #3936/R
£972	$1585	€1400	Landscape (32x44cm-13x17in) s. i. verso board. 25-Sep-3 Dr Fritz Nagel, Stuttgart #1385/R

MOLL, Anton Cassian (attrib) (1722-1757) Austrian

Works on paper

£604	$1069	€900	Kaiserin Maria Theresia (11cm-4in circular) wax slate. 29-Apr-4 Dorotheum, Vienna #12/R

MOLL, Carl (1861-1945) Austrian

£3289	$6053	€5000	Still life with lobster (40x58cm-16x23in) mono. 22-Jun-4 Wiener Kunst Auktionen, Vienna #25/R est:5000
£13423	$23758	€20000	Still life (57x54cm-22x21in) mono. panel. 28-Apr-4 Wiener Kunst Auktionen, Vienna #94/R est:18000-28000
£20139	$34236	€29000	Sunlit forest clearing (34x35cm-13x14in) mono. panel prov. 28-Oct-3 Wiener Kunst Auktionen, Vienna #60/R est:15000-50000
£29167	$49583	€42000	Beaulieu (35x35cm-14x14in) mono. i. verso panel prov. 28-Oct-3 Wiener Kunst Auktionen, Vienna #61/R est:18000-35000
£33557	$60067	€50000	View of Perchtoldsdorf (36x51cm-14x20in) s.d.1886 panel. 27-May-4 Dorotheum, Vienna #179/R est:35000-45000
£35000	$64400	€51100	Im Garten - In the garden (60x60cm-24x24in) init. prov. 23-Jun-4 Christie's, London #161/R est:15000-20000
£42000	$77280	€61320	Blick auf den Kanal in Venedig - View of the Canal in Venice (60x60cm-24x24in) init. prov. 23-Jun-4 Christie's, London #162/R est:15000-20000
£45455	$77273	€65000	Heustadlwasser in the Prater (60x60cm-24x24in) mono. prov.exhib. 26-Nov-3 Dorotheum, Vienna #42/R est:50000-70000
£83333	$141667	€120000	Heiligenstadt and the Nussberg (79x79cm-31x31in) s. lit. 28-Oct-3 Wiener Kunst Auktionen, Vienna #59/R est:80000-140000

MOLL, Carl (attrib) (1861-1945) Austrian

£3147	$5350	€4500	Breitenstein (18x23cm-7x9in) i.verso panel. 28-Nov-3 Wiener Kunst Auktionen, Vienna #461/R est:3000-10000

MOLL, Evert (1878-1955) Dutch

£313	$494	€450	Rhododendrons (41x60cm-16x24in) s. s.i.verso. 2-Sep-3 Christie's, Amsterdam #291
£437	$803	€638	Seascape (14x18cm-6x7in) s. board. 14-Jun-4 Philippe Schuler, Zurich #5868 (S.FR 1000)
£486	$812	€700	Rotterdam port (20x24cm-8x9in) s. panel. 21-Oct-3 Campo & Campo, Antwerp #219
£548	$932	€800	Sea port (18x24cm-7x9in) s. maroufle. 5-Nov-3 Vendue Huis, Gravenhage #187
£667	$1193	€1000	Three-master in a harbour (29x23cm-11x9in) s. 11-May-4 Vendu Notarishuis, Rotterdam #174/R
£680	$1238	€1000	Shipping at Rotterdam Harbour (19x25cm-7x10in) s. 3-Feb-4 Christie's, Amsterdam #376 est:1200-1600
£690	$1152	€1000	Break water (39x59cm-15x23in) s. 11-Nov-3 Vendu Notarishuis, Rotterdam #138/R
£759	$1267	€1100	Harbour view (59x98cm-23x39in) s. 11-Nov-3 Vendu Notarishuis, Rotterdam #117
£764	$1207	€1100	Three master and other ships at Rotterdam Harbour (25x19cm-10x7in) s. canvas on plywood. 2-Sep-3 Christie's, Amsterdam #333 est:600-800
£822	$1397	€1200	Rotterdam harbour (16x13cm-6x5in) s. panel. 5-Nov-3 Vendue Huis, Gravenhage #190/R
£822	$1397	€1200	Sea port (23x17cm-9x7in) s. maroufle. 5-Nov-3 Vendue Huis, Gravenhage #194
£921	$1695	€1400	A three-master in Rotterdam harbour (29x53cm-11x21in) s. panel. 22-Jun-4 Christie's, Amsterdam #291/R est:1200-1600
£972	$1536	€1400	Harbour of Enkhuizen (32x63cm-13x25in) s. 2-Sep-3 Christie's, Amsterdam #274/R est:1500-2000
£987	$1786	€1500	Scene de port (39x50cm-15x20in) s. 18-Apr-4 Rouillac, Vendome #160
£1020	$1857	€1500	Windmill by a river (37x62cm-15x24in) s. 3-Feb-4 Christie's, Amsterdam #246/R est:1000-1500
£1020	$1857	€1500	View of the harbour of Enkhuizen (32x63cm-13x25in) with sig. 3-Feb-4 Christie's, Amsterdam #352 est:700-900
£1020	$1857	€1500	Cargo ship in Rotterdam Harbour (34x67cm-13x26in) s. panel. 3-Feb-4 Christie's, Amsterdam #375/R est:1500-2000
£1042	$1646	€1500	Shipping in the harbour of Rotterdam (41x60cm-16x24in) s. 2-Sep-3 Christie's, Amsterdam #320 est:1500-2000
£1088	$1981	€1600	Pot plants in an interior (90x80cm-35x31in) s. 3-Feb-4 Christie's, Amsterdam #207/R est:1200-1600
£1088	$1981	€1600	Harbour impression (40x60cm-16x24in) s. 3-Feb-4 Christie's, Amsterdam #377 est:1200-1600
£1096	$1863	€1600	Town on the harbour (55x63cm-22x25in) s.d.1911. 5-Nov-3 Vendue Huis, Gravenhage #193/R est:1500-2000
£1107	$2049	€1650	Harbour scene (57x95cm-22x37in) s. 15-Mar-4 Sotheby's, Amsterdam #169/R est:1800-2500
£1111	$1756	€1600	Barges on a river (26x40cm-10x16in) s. panel. 2-Sep-3 Christie's, Amsterdam #317 est:1000-1500
£1180	$1924	€1700	Harbour scene (60x100cm-24x39in) s. 29-Sep-3 Sotheby's, Amsterdam #301
£1184	$2179	€1800	Shipping in Rotterdam harbour (40x60cm-16x24in) s. 22-Jun-4 Christie's, Amsterdam #193/R est:2000-3000
£1293	$2352	€1900	Three master at anchor, Rotterdam (26x20cm-10x8in) s. cardboard. 3-Feb-4 Christie's, Amsterdam #379 est:400-600
£1301	$2212	€1900	Rotterdam harbour (59x99cm-23x39in) s. 5-Nov-3 Vendue Huis, Gravenhage #189/R est:2000-3000
£1399	$2336	€2000	Harbour scene, Nice (33x54cm-13x21in) s. 30-Jun-3 Sotheby's, Amsterdam #368/R
£1447	$2620	€2200	Two steamers and other boats in Rotterdam Harbour (39x59cm-15x23in) s. 19-Apr-4 Glerum, Amsterdam #175/R est:2400-2800
£1497	$2679	€2200	Trois mats au port (24x31cm-9x12in) 22-Mar-4 Amberes, Antwerp #219
£1538	$2569	€2200	Moored boats near a harbour (60x73cm-24x29in) s. 30-Jun-3 Sotheby's, Amsterdam #147/R
£1678	$2803	€2400	Ships docked in the harbour (50x100cm-20x39in) s. 30-Jun-3 Sotheby's, Amsterdam #219/R
£1711	$3096	€2600	View of harbour, Amsterdam (60x100cm-24x39in) s. 19-Apr-4 Glerum, Amsterdam #178/R est:1500-1700
£1736	$2743	€2500	Daily activities at Rotterdam Harbour (45x67cm-18x26in) s. 2-Sep-3 Christie's, Amsterdam #345/R est:3000-5000
£1781	$3027	€2600	Dordrecht harbour (48x58cm-19x23in) s. 5-Nov-3 Vendue Huis, Gravenhage #188/R est:1500-2000
£1812	$3370	€2700	Fishermen on canal and sailboats on lake (70x100cm-28x39in) s. 4-Mar-4 Auction Maastricht #1012/R est:2500-5000
£1842	$3389	€2800	Rotterdam Harbour (26x37cm-10x15in) s. 22-Jun-4 Christie's, Amsterdam #269/R est:1000-1500
£2431	$3840	€3500	Industrious trade on the Willemskade, Rotterdam (50x80cm-20x31in) s. 2-Sep-3 Christie's, Amsterdam #343/R est:3000-5000
£2639	$4169	€3800	White three master (46x65cm-18x26in) s. 2-Sep-3 Christie's, Amsterdam #326/R est:2500-3500
£2657	$4571	€3800	Harbour scene with steam ships in the background (61x102cm-24x40in) s. 7-Dec-3 Sotheby's, Amsterdam #691/R
£2979	$4974	€4200	Schevening harbour (41x51cm-16x20in) s. 20-Oct-3 Glerum, Amsterdam #110/R est:2500-3000
£3191	$5330	€4500	Rotterdam harbour with moored three-mast ship (67x56cm-26x22in) s. 20-Oct-3 Glerum, Amsterdam #112/R est:4500-5000
£3191	$5330	€4500	Rotterdam harbour with three-mast and inland navigation ships (34x54cm-13x21in) s. 20-Oct-3 Glerum, Amsterdam #113/R est:4500-5000
£3194	$5047	€4600	Three master in a busy harbour (51x65cm-20x26in) s. 2-Sep-3 Christie's, Amsterdam #334/R est:2500-3500
£3288	$5589	€4800	View of Schevening from sea (80x100cm-31x39in) s. 5-Nov-3 Vendue Huis, Gravenhage #191a est:5000-7000

Works on paper

£276	$461	€400	Inside the harbour (13x18cm-5x7in) s. W/C. 11-Nov-3 Vendu Notarishuis, Rotterdam #53/R

MOLL, Marg (1884-1977) German

Works on paper

£933	$1708	€1400	Landscape with red houses and trees (51x36cm-20x14in) s. gouache. 5-Jun-4 Lempertz, Koln #885/R

MOLL, Oskar (1875-1947) German

£3000	$5520	€4500	Coastline (38x46cm-15x18in) s. cardboard. 8-Jun-4 Sotheby's, Amsterdam #178/R est:4000-6000
£6944	$11597	€10000	Autumn woodland with village (100x110cm-39x43in) s. exhib. 24-Oct-3 Ketterer, Hamburg #480/R est:10000-15000
£34667	$63440	€52000	Still life with Clivia (107x110cm-42x43in) s. i. stretcher. 5-Jun-4 Lempertz, Koln #886/R est:40000-45000

Works on paper

£310	$518	€450	View of sea with fig leaves (17x21cm-7x8in) s. pencil prov. 13-Nov-3 Neumeister, Munich #405/R
£1000	$1840	€1500	Park landscape in winter, zoo (56x49cm-22x19in) s.d.46 W/C bodycol. 12-Jun-4 Villa Grisebach, Berlin #621/R est:2500-3000
£3497	$5944	€5000	River landscape (23x29cm-9x11in) s. wax chk. 29-Nov-3 Villa Grisebach, Berlin #226/R est:5000-7000

MOLLENDORF, Lorenz (20th C) ?

£348	$550	€508	Fishing vessels and figures with baskets (61x91cm-24x36in) s. 6-Sep-3 Brunk, Ashville #11

MOLLENHAUER, Ernst (1892-1963) German

£1611	$3012	€2400	Boats on beach (47x61cm-19x24in) s. i. verso oil W/C pencil paper on board. 28-Feb-4 Quittenbaum, Hamburg #96/R est:2300

MOLLER, Aenderly (1863-?) German

£625	$987	€900	Early autumn on the Alster (54x42cm-21x17in) s. 6-Sep-3 Schopman, Hamburg #762/R

MOLLER, Bruno (fl.1923-1924) Danish

£313	$500	€457	The student (64x72cm-25x28in) i.verso after Rembrandt. 22-Sep-3 Rasmussen, Vejle #500 (D.KR 3300)
£664	$1062	€969	Garden with old baptismal font (65x66cm-26x26in) i.verso after Jorgen Roed. 22-Sep-3 Rasmussen, Vejle #435 (D.KR 7000)

MOLLER, Carl Henrik Koch (1845-1920) Danish

£293	$533	€428	Seascape with fishermen by the coast (47x71cm-19x28in) s.d.97. 7-Feb-4 Rasmussen, Havnen #2190/R (D.KR 3200)
£3529	$6000	€5152	In the fields (55x79cm-22x31in) indis.s.d.1893. 29-Oct-3 Christie's, Rockefeller NY #22/R est:8000-12000

MOLLER, Hans (1905-) American

£525	$950	€767	Yellow bird (76x61cm-30x24in) s.d.47. 18-Apr-4 Bonhams & Butterfields, Los Angeles #7054 est:500-700
£838	$1400	€1223	White horizon (76x114cm-30x45in) s.d.61 prov. 15-Nov-3 Sloans & Kenyon, Bethesda #103/R est:700-900

MOLLER, J P (1783-1854) Danish

£806	$1474	€1177	Mountain landscape with busy traffic by river (38x55cm-15x22in) 9-Jun-4 Rasmussen, Copenhagen #1848/R (D.KR 9000)

£1078 $2005 €1574 Houses and church by lake in the Swiss Alps (55x70cm-22x28in) s. 2-Mar-4 Rasmussen, Copenhagen #1364/R est:12000-15000 (D.KR 12000)

MOLLER, Niels Bjornsson (1827-1887) Norwegian
£1283 $2181 €1873 Village with church by fjord, west coast of Norway (38x49cm-15x19in) s. 19-Nov-3 Grev Wedels Plass, Oslo #56/R est:20000-30000 (N.KR 15000)
£1538 $2646 €2245 Lake landscape with palace (57x83cm-22x33in) s. 7-Dec-3 Uppsala Auktionskammare, Uppsala #97/R est:20000-25000 (S.KR 20000)

MOLLER, Olivia Holm (1875-1970) Danish
£287 $465 €416 Cattle and sheep in meadow (46x62cm-18x24in) init. 4-Aug-3 Rasmussen, Vejle #660/R (D.KR 3000)
£302 $541 €441 Mountain landscape with trees in foreground (48x69cm-19x27in) init. 12-Jan-4 Rasmussen, Vejle #614 (D.KR 3200)
£360 $576 €526 Autumn landscape (31x45cm-12x18in) init. 22-Sep-3 Rasmussen, Vejle #544 (D.KR 3800)
£423 $706 €618 Green hilly landscape (66x89cm-26x35in) init.d.35. 7-Oct-3 Rasmussen, Copenhagen #319 (D.KR 4500)
£474 $758 €687 Still life (60x70cm-24x28in) init. 17-Sep-3 Kunsthallen, Copenhagen #275 (D.KR 5000)
£945 $1692 €1380 Vejby Beach (90x104cm-35x41in) init. 12-Jan-4 Rasmussen, Vejle #536/R (D.KR 10000)

MOLLER, Peter (1948-) Australian
£744 $1264 €1086 Untitled (55x70cm-22x28in) s. 29-Oct-3 Lawson Menzies, Sydney #141/R est:800-1200 (A.D 1800)

MOLLER, Rudolf (1881-1964) German
£1200 $2148 €1800 Figure composition (74x100cm-29x39in) s. 15-May-4 Van Ham, Cologne #808/R est:2800
£2800 $5012 €4200 Still life with child (51x68cm-20x27in) s. prov. 14-May-4 Ketterer, Munich #61/R est:2000-3000
Works on paper
£320 $573 €480 Two women in beach basket (33x24cm-13x9in) s.d. W/C on pencil. 15-May-4 Bassenge, Berlin #7038
£367 $656 €550 Bathers (36x51cm-14x20in) s.d. W/C on pencil. 15-May-4 Bassenge, Berlin #7037/R

MOLLER, Thorvald Christian Benjamin (1842-1925) Danish
£537 $983 €784 Sailing vessels off Kronborg (47x79cm-19x31in) s.d.1875. 9-Jun-4 Rasmussen, Copenhagen #1845/R (D.KR 6000)

MOLLER, Ulrik (1962-) Danish
£751 $1254 €1096 Landscape (60x90cm-24x35in) s.d.juni 98 verso prov. 7-Oct-3 Rasmussen, Copenhagen #278/R (D.KR 8000)

MOLLER, Valdemar (1864-1905) Danish
£1512 $2616 €2208 Kitchen interior with woman at dusk (77x56cm-30x22in) s. i.stretcher. 9-Dec-3 Rasmussen, Copenhagen #1511/R est:20000 (D.KR 16000)

MOLLGAARD, Christian (1919-) Danish
£275 $500 €402 Seascape with sailing boats off Kronborg (46x64cm-18x25in) s. 7-Feb-4 Rasmussen, Havnen #2206/R (D.KR 3000)

MOLLINO, Carlo (1905-1973) Italian
Photographs
£4000 $7200 €5840 Nude (11x9cm-4x4in) i.verso polaroid print prov. 23-Apr-4 Phillips, New York #138/R est:7000-10000

MOLLIS, Anton (fl.1830-1850) Austrian
£861 $1567 €1300 Still life with fruit and flowers (30x35cm-12x14in) mono. 18-Jun-4 Bolland & Marotz, Bremen #693/R
£927 $1687 €1400 Bunch of flowers (29x36cm-11x14in) s. 21-Jun-4 Dorotheum, Vienna #190/R

MOLLWEIDE, Werner (1889-1978) German
£411 $699 €600 Bodensee landscape (60x80cm-24x31in) s. pavatex. 8-Nov-3 Geble, Radolfzell #795/R
£426 $689 €600 Iris meadows by the Untersee (40x49cm-16x19in) s. i. verso panel lit. 23-May-3 Karlheinz Kaupp, Staufen #1978/R

MOLNAR (?) ?
£1250 $2000 €1825 Young peasant girl (76x61cm-30x24in) board. 19-Sep-3 Du Mouchelle, Detroit #2249/R est:1500-2000

MOLNAR, C Pal (1894-1981) Hungarian
£802 $1419 €1171 Nude in front of a mirror (31x48cm-12x19in) s. cardboard. 28-Apr-4 Kieselbach, Budapest #97/R (H.F 300000)
£1032 $1713 €1507 Sitting nude (43x34cm-17x13in) s. panel. 4-Oct-3 Kieselbach, Budapest #21/R (H.F 380000)
£1305 $2258 €1905 Italian landscape (36x76cm-14x30in) s. fibreboard. 12-Dec-3 Kieselbach, Budapest #144/R (H.F 500000)
£1436 $2483 €2097 Italian Landscape (26x37cm-10x15in) s. panel. 12-Dec-3 Kieselbach, Budapest #78/R (H.F 550000)
£1765 $2929 €2577 Fairy tale landscape (50x67cm-20x26in) s. board. 4-Oct-3 Kieselbach, Budapest #111/R (H.F 650000)
£1871 $3311 €2732 Italy (50x70cm-20x28in) s. board. 28-Apr-4 Kieselbach, Budapest #105/R (H.F 700000)
£1958 $3386 €2859 Italian landscape (43x60cm-17x24in) s.d.925 fibreboard. 12-Dec-3 Kieselbach, Budapest #47/R (H.F 750000)
£2219 $3838 €3240 Holy Family (45x55cm-18x22in) s. tempera board. 12-Dec-3 Kieselbach, Budapest #46/R (H.F 850000)
£3741 $6622 €5462 Eve with an apple (94x63cm-37x25in) s. 28-Apr-4 Kieselbach, Budapest #98/R (H.F 1400000)
£4072 $6760 €5945 Landscape with a bather (60x70cm-24x28in) s. 4-Oct-3 Kieselbach, Budapest #69/R (H.F 1500000)
£4072 $6760 €5945 Holy Family (61x51cm-24x20in) s. 4-Oct-3 Kieselbach, Budapest #143/R (H.F 1500000)
£7830 $13546 €11432 Madonna in Tuscan landscape (118x103cm-46x41in) s.d.1933 board. 12-Dec-3 Kieselbach, Budapest #34/R (H.F 3000000)

MOLNAR, Janos Z (1880-1960) Czechoslovakian
£594 $993 €850 Red flowers (70x100cm-28x39in) cardboard. 10-Oct-3 Stadion, Trieste #227/R
£839 $1401 €1200 Nature morte au pichet (66x55cm-26x22in) s. 25-Jun-3 Rabourdin & Choppin de Janvry, Paris #22/R

MOLNAR, Josef (1821-1899) Hungarian
£1044 $1806 €1524 Landscape (35x25cm-14x10in) s. canvas on cardboard. 12-Dec-3 Kieselbach, Budapest #37/R (H.F 400000)
£3132 $5418 €4573 Monks on the lake (37x47cm-15x19in) s.d.1853 cardboard. 12-Dec-3 Kieselbach, Budapest #36/R (H.F 1200000)

MOLNAR, Roza (1900-1977) Hungarian
£1107 $2003 €1616 Self portrait with mask (89x75cm-35x30in) s. 16-Apr-4 Mu Terem Galeria, Budapest #147/R (H.F 420000)

MOLNE, Luis Vidal (1907-1970) Spanish
£563 $986 €800 Jeunes femmes Espagnoles (60x73cm-24x29in) s. s.i.verso. 17-Dec-3 Rabourdin & Choppin de Janvry, Paris #59

MOLS, Adrienne (?) Belgian
£1189 $2045 €1700 Nature morte aux peches et aux raisins (26x36cm-10x14in) s.i.d.1865/1900 panel. 8-Dec-3 Horta, Bruxelles #135 est:2000-3000

MOLS, N P (1859-1921) Danish
£269 $491 €393 A puppy (31x25cm-12x10in) init.d.15. 7-Jun-4 Museumsbygningen, Copenhagen #32 (D.KR 3000)
£342 $553 €499 Landscape with peasant woman and cow (60x76cm-24x30in) i.verso. 9-Aug-3 Hindemae, Ullerslev #106/R (D.KR 3600)
£492 $901 €718 Sheep in meadow (10x52cm-4x20in) s.i.d.06. 7-Jun-4 Museumsbygningen, Copenhagen #133 (D.KR 5500)
£567 $981 €828 Cattle seeking shadow under large tree in summer (68x89cm-27x35in) init.d.07. 9-Dec-3 Rasmussen, Copenhagen #1598/R (D.KR 6000)
£756 $1308 €1104 Cattle in meadow at sunset (69x90cm-27x35in) init.d.07. 9-Dec-3 Rasmussen, Copenhagen #1601/R (D.KR 8000)
£769 $1377 €1123 Milkmaid in field with two cows (54x68cm-21x27in) init.d.10. 10-May-4 Rasmussen, Vejle #329/R (D.KR 8500)
£809 $1504 €1181 Cows at coastal meadow, Raabjerg Mile (50x78cm-20x31in) init.i.d.Sept 97. 2-Mar-4 Rasmussen, Copenhagen #1584/R (D.KR 9000)
£1253 $2294 €1829 Cattle in meadow by the coast (100x130cm-39x51in) s.d.1911. 9-Jun-4 Rasmussen, Copenhagen #1958/R est:15000 (D.KR 14000)
£1435 $2325 €2081 Cattle at sunset, Ribe (196x142cm-77x56in) s.i.d.08-19. 4-Aug-3 Rasmussen, Vejle #134/R est:15000-20000 (D.KR 15000)

MOLS, Niels Pedersen (1859-1921) Danish
£988 $1838 €1442 Calves and geese by fence in field (81x132cm-32x52in) s.d.06-09. 2-Mar-4 Rasmussen, Copenhagen #1207/R (D.KR 11000)
£1600 $2912 €2400 Giving the calves milk (78x70cm-31x28in) s. exhib. 19-Jun-4 Rasmussen, Havnen #2215/R est:20000 (D.KR 18000)
£1797 $3342 €2624 Autumn with wild geese and tame geese (52x85cm-20x33in) init.i.d.97. 2-Mar-4 Rasmussen, Copenhagen #1239/R est:15000-20000 (D.KR 20000)
£2695 $5013 €3935 Calves by fence (126x178cm-50x70in) s.d.88 exhib.prov. 2-Mar-4 Rasmussen, Copenhagen #1206/R est:40000-60000 (D.KR 30000)
£2875 $5348 €4198 October day towards evening, Hojsand near Rorvig (130x194cm-51x76in) s.d.1900-01 exhib. 2-Mar-4 Rasmussen, Copenhagen #1238/R est:20000-30000 (D.KR 32000)

MOLS, Robert (1848-1903) Belgian
£25532 $42638 €36000 View on the Willemdok in Antwerp (247x147cm-97x58in) s. painted c.1880-1890. 20-Oct-3 Bernaerts, Antwerp #195 est:37500-50000

MOLSTED, Chr (1862-1930) Danish
£520 $931 €759 Coastal landscape with town (43x63cm-17x25in) s.d.99. 12-Jan-4 Rasmussen, Vejle #5/R (D.KR 5500)
£851 $1472 €1242 Morning in Dragoer, three-master at sea, sunrise (31x43cm-12x17in) s. 9-Dec-3 Rasmussen, Copenhagen #1465/R (D.KR 9000)
£1985 $3434 €2898 Sailing vessels in Copenhagen Harbour at sunset (41x49cm-16x19in) s.d.1907. 9-Dec-3 Rasmussen, Copenhagen #1466/R est:7000-10000 (D.KR 21000)
£5391 $10027 €7871 Taking the geese by ship from Saltholmen, Dragor Harbour (96x142cm-38x56in) s.d.1895-96 exhib. 2-Mar-4 Rasmussen, Copenhagen #1265/R est:75000 (D.KR 60000)
£5840 $10863 €8526 Rainy day in the harbour at Honsebroen, Frigate Fyn in foreground (124x177cm-49x70in) s.d.1906-07 exhib. 2-Mar-4 Rasmussen, Copenhagen #1212/R est:60000-80000 (D.KR 65000)
£6616 $11446 €9659 Hans Rostgaard sailing out in stormy seas to Dutch fleet with letter from Fredrik III 1658 (108x87cm-43x34in) s.d.24. 9-Dec-3 Rasmussen, Copenhagen #1471/R est:40000 (D.KR 70000)

MOLTENI, Giovanni (1898-1967) Italian
£336 $621 €500 Landscape (70x60cm-28x24in) s.d.1957. 13-Mar-4 Meeting Art, Vercelli #467

MOLTENI, Giuseppe (1800-1867) Italian
£21127 $36549 €30000 Portrait of grand-mother and grand-daughter (83x94cm-33x37in) exhib. 14-Dec-3 Finarte, Venice #49/R est:35000-40000

MOLTINO, Francis (1818-1874) British
£400 $668 €584 Gossiping fishwives on the shore (30x50cm-12x20in) board. 11-Nov-3 Bonhams, Knightsbridge #154/R
£750 $1350 €1095 Vessels moored on the Thames, moonlight (57x70cm-22x28in) arched top. 22-Apr-4 Lawrence, Crewkerne #921/R
£800 $1336 €1168 Venetian canal scene (61x107cm-24x42in) 11-Nov-3 Bonhams, Knightsbridge #71/R
£800 $1336 €1168 Venetian canal scene (20x40cm-8x16in) bears sig pair. 11-Nov-3 Bonhams, Knightsbridge #115/R
£2500 $4575 €3650 Busy waterfront, Venice (28x59cm-11x23in) s. 8-Jul-4 Lawrence, Crewkerne #1643/R est:1000-1500
£2700 $4860 €3942 View of Venice. View of Ancient Carthage (30x35cm-12x14in) six init. board painted oval nine. 21-Jan-4 Sotheby's, Olympia #345/R est:600-900

MOLTINO, Francis (attrib) (1818-1874) British
£1700 $2703 €2482 Venice, busy harbour, with shipping gondolas and figures (60x105cm-24x41in) 9-Sep-3 Bamfords, Derby #1180

MOLTKE, Harald (1871-1960) Danish
£483 $893 €700 Farmstead with chestnut trees (33x43cm-13x17in) mono.d.1909. 14-Feb-4 Hans Stahl, Hamburg #66
£769 $1377 €1123 View from Stromfjord with walrus (47x62cm-19x24in) init. panel. 10-May-4 Rasmussen, Vejle #238/R (D.KR 8500)
£1719 $3078 €2510 Skinning the bear (48x57cm-19x22in) s. i.stretcher. 10-May-4 Rasmussen, Vejle #237/R est:20000 (D.KR 19000)
£2174 $3891 €3174 Hunter's family outside stone house, Greenland (69x95cm-27x37in) s. 12-Jan-4 Rasmussen, Vejle #11/R est:3000-5000 (D.KR 23000)
£2268 $3924 €3311 Family idyll in the park at Gjorslev (148x124cm-58x49in) s. 9-Dec-3 Rasmussen, Copenhagen #1562/R est:30000-40000 (D.KR 24000)

MOLVIG, John (1923-1970) Australian
£1191 $2026 €1739 Landscape after Cezanne (25x32cm-10x13in) s.verso canvas on board prov.exhib. 26-Nov-3 Deutscher-Menzies, Melbourne #256/R est:2000-3000 (A.D 2800)
£1702 $2894 €2485 Boy climbing onto a chair (47x36cm-19x14in) s.d.51 board. 25-Nov-3 Christie's, Melbourne #276/R est:4000-6000 (A.D 4000)
£1721 $2789 €2513 Carnival (69x102cm-27x40in) paper prov. 30-Jul-3 Goodman, Sydney #61/R est:2000-3000 (A.D 4200)
£1867 $3118 €2801 Portrait of Ruth Komon (60x45cm-24x18in) s.d.63 board. 27-Oct-3 Goodman, Sydney #83/R est:4000-6000 (A.D 4500)
£2846 $4467 €4127 Spirit of a dead land (90x121cm-35x48in) s.d.56 i.verso board exhib.lit. 27-Aug-3 Christie's, Sydney #568/R est:6000-10000 (A.D 7000)
£3617 $6149 €5281 Crucifixion (137x61cm-54x24in) s.d.53 composition board prov.exhib. 26-Nov-3 Deutscher-Menzies, Melbourne #62/R est:10000-15000 (A.D 8500)
Works on paper
£533 $842 €778 Figure study (44x33cm-17x13in) s.d.57 chl prov. 2-Sep-3 Deutscher-Menzies, Melbourne #361/R est:800-1200 (A.D 1300)

MOLVILLE, Arthur (19th C) ?
Works on paper
£1200 $2172 €1800 Rome - Piazza Barberini with Fontana del Tritone (28x20cm-11x8in) mono. W/C. 3-Apr-4 Badum, Bamberg #101/R est:800

MOLYN, Maria Aletta Femmigje (1837-1932) Dutch
£329 $595 €500 Cut flowers in the green (28x40cm-11x16in) s. panel. 19-Apr-4 Glerum, Amsterdam #146/R

MOLYN, Pieter (1595-1661) Dutch
£4525 $7240 €6607 Travellers in dune landscape (26x33cm-10x13in) panel. 19-Sep-3 Koller, Zurich #3027/R est:15000-20000 (S.FR 10000)
Works on paper
£3529 $6000 €5152 Landscape with hunters and dogs and trees beyond (15x20cm-6x8in) s.d.1654 pencil. 19-Nov-3 Bonhams & Butterfields, San Francisco #6/R
£6667 $12000 €9734 Extensive landscape with peasants watching a bird trap (14x19cm-6x7in) s. black chk grey wash prov.lit. 22-Jan-4 Christie's, Rockefeller NY #121/R est:8000-12000

MOLYN, Pieter (attrib) (1595-1661) Dutch
Works on paper
£800 $1448 €1200 Landscape with farmstead (15x19cm-6x7in) Indian ink wash chk. 2-Apr-4 Winterberg, Heidelberg #205
£1293 $2314 €1900 Un paysage avec des chaumieres, une figure assise au premier plan (20x26cm-8x10in) i. black chk pen col ink col wash prov. 18-Mar-4 Christie's, Paris #30/R est:2000-3000

MOLYNEUX, Edward (20th C) French?
£300 $537 €438 Quais de la Seine (18x25cm-7x10in) s. 7-May-4 Mallams, Oxford #292
£360 $644 €540 Les toits de Florence (15x18cm-6x7in) init. panel. 7-May-4 Mallams, Oxford #294
£680 $1217 €1020 Vieux pecheur. s. 7-May-4 Mallams, Oxford #293

MOLYNEUX, Edward (fl.1899-1904) British
£380 $657 €555 Terrace overlooking the sea (25x36cm-10x14in) s.d.49. 9-Dec-3 Rosebery Fine Art, London #602
£2400 $4440 €3600 Lake scene in Kashmir (53x85cm-21x33in) s. canvasboard sold with two others prov. 14-Jul-4 Sotheby's, Olympia #108/R est:1000-1500
Works on paper
£6500 $12025 €9750 Views in Kashmir. 2 s. 17 i. 1 d.1892 1 d.1898 W/C 21 sold with 2 sketchbooks prov. 14-Jul-4 Sotheby's, Olympia #107/R est:1000-1500

MOLYNEUX, Edward Frank (1896-?) American
£360 $659 €540 Vase d'oeillets jaunes (25x33cm-10x13in) s. 28-Jul-4 Mallams, Oxford #327/R

MOLZAHN, Johannes (1892-1965) German
Works on paper
£20000 $36800 €29200 Schopfung (44x30cm-17x12in) s. s.i.d.1917 prov.exhib.lit. 24-Jun-4 Christie's, London #364/R est:20000-30000

MOMBELLI, Eugenio (1950-) Italian
Works on paper
£387 $643 €550 Meditazione sull'arte rupestre (80x100cm-31x39in) s.i.verso mixed media collage canvas. 14-Jun-3 Meeting Art, Vercelli #344

MOMBUR, Jean Ossaye (1850-1896) French
Sculpture
£1972 $3451 €2800 Le baiser au faucheur (69cm-27in) s.i.d.1892 brown pat bronze green marble base. 19-Dec-3 Delvaux, Paris #323/R est:1200-1800

MOMEN, Karl (1935-) Swedish
£1449 $2608 €2116 Composition (100x100cm-39x39in) s.d.87. 26-Jan-4 Lilla Bukowskis, Stockholm #223 est:10000-12000 (S.KR 19300)

MOMMERS, Hendrik (1623-1693) Dutch
£1538 $2615 €2245 Southern landscape with figures in discussion by temple ruins (45x39cm-18x15in) bears sig. panel. 19-Nov-3 Fischer, Luzern #1028/R est:4000-6000 (S.FR 3400)
£1728 $2990 €2523 Landscape with figures by ruins (63x75cm-25x30in) s. 15-Dec-3 Lilla Bukowskis, Stockholm #222/R est:25000-30000 (S.KR 22000)
£2210 $4000 €3227 Market place amongst Italian ruins (79x95cm-31x37in) s. 30-Mar-4 Christie's, Rockefeller NY #27/R est:3000-5000
£8333 $15000 €12166 Port scene with figures gathered by a statue (49x64cm-19x25in) s. prov. 22-Jan-4 Sotheby's, New York #144/R est:6000-8000
£17000 $30600 €24820 River landscape with drovers and their animals (66x91cm-26x36in) 22-Apr-4 Sotheby's, London #70/R est:12000-18000
£17000 $30600 €24820 Market scene in an italianate landscape (66x91cm-26x36in) 22-Apr-4 Sotheby's, London #71/R est:12000-18000
£24648 $42641 €35000 Amsterdam Dam (92x120cm-36x47in) s. 14-Dec-3 Finarte, Venice #85/R est:40000

MOMPER, Frans de (1603-1660) Flemish
£6897 $11448 €10000 Landscape with peasants (44x62cm-17x24in) board. 30-Sep-3 Ansorena, Madrid #63/R est:10000
£7273 $12509 €10400 Paysans dans un paysage montagneux (40x54cm-16x21in) s. panel. 8-Dec-3 Claude Aguttes, Neuilly #29/R est:12000-15000

MOMPER, Frans de (attrib) (1603-1660) Flemish
£5000 $8950 €7500 View of Antwerp with townsfolk in the foreground (51x67cm-20x26in) panel. 17-May-4 Christie's, Amsterdam #62/R est:3000-5000
£11333 $20513 €17000 Extensive river landscape with city and village (66x110cm-26x43in) 1-Apr-4 Van Ham, Cologne #1225/R est:5000

MOMPER, Jan de (16/17th C) Flemish
£7586 $12669 €11000 Landscape with riders (33x55cm-13x22in) 12-Nov-3 Sotheby's, Milan #110/R est:8000-12000

MOMPER, Jan de (attrib) (16/17th C) Flemish
£2041 $3245 €3000 Fouille des tombes (50x98cm-20x39in) canvas on cardboard. 21-Mar-3 Bailly Pommery, Paris #55 est:2000-3000
Works on paper
£1892 $3330 €2800 Two boats on the shore, one of them wrecked (22x47cm-9x19in) s. pen brown ink col wash black chk prov.exhib. 19-May-4 Sotheby's, Amsterdam #107/R est:3500-4500

MOMPER, Joos de (1564-1635) Flemish
£3252 $5821 €4748 Mountain landscape with figures (16x44cm-6x17in) panel. 25-May-4 Bukowskis, Stockholm #456/R est:55000-65000 (S.KR 44000)
£15000 $27450 €21900 Extensive mountainous landscape with an angel appearing to Hagar (31x55cm-12x22in) panel prov. 7-Jul-4 Christie's, London #10/R est:15000-20000
£15172 $25186 €22000 Hilly landscape with chapel and peasant travellers (56x74cm-22x29in) panel exhib. 1-Oct-3 Dorotheum, Vienna #104/R est:18000-24000
£23490 $43221 €35000 Extensive landscape with travellers (49x93cm-19x37in) prov. panel. 24-Mar-4 Dorotheum, Vienna #143/R est:35000-45000
£50000 $86500 €73000 Mountainous river landscape with the rest on the flight into Egypt (88x124cm-35x49in) panel prov. 10-Dec-3 Christie's, London #11/R est:50000-70000
£86667 $157733 €130000 Landscape with travellers (113x162cm-44x64in) 5-Jul-4 Marc Kohn, Paris #24/R est:150000-180000
£200000 $346000 €292000 Extensive landscape with travellers on a road outside a chateau, village beyond (45x75cm-18x30in) oak panel prov. 11-Dec-3 Sotheby's, London #50/R est:200000-300000
Works on paper
£4200 $7686 €6132 Mountainous river landscape with travellers approaching a bridge (26x39cm-10x15in) bears sig.d. 1607 pen brown ink W/C over blk chk prov. 8-Jul-4 Sotheby's, London #68/R est:3000-4000

MOMPER, Joos de (circle) (1564-1635) Flemish
£8500 $15555 €12410 Extensive mountainous landscape with two hermits reading in the foreground (67x90cm-26x35in) prov.lit. 6-Jul-4 Sotheby's, Olympia #445/R est:6000-8000
£12329 $20959 €18000 Winter landscape with travelers and peasants by a bridge (57x103cm-22x41in) 5-Nov-3 Christie's, Amsterdam #23/R est:18000-22000

MOMPER, Joos de (studio) (1564-1635) Flemish
£12329 $20959 €18000 Winter landscape with horseman, peasants, and horse-drawn cart (48x76cm-19x30in) panel prov. 4-Nov-3 Sotheby's, Amsterdam #5/R est:20000-30000
£12500 $23000 €19000 Landscape with figures by lake (150x183cm-59x72in) 24-Jun-4 Christie's, Paris #21/R est:15000-20000
£14765 $27168 €22000 Vue d'un village enneige des Flandres (48x76cm-19x30in) 24-Mar-4 Tajan, Paris #66/R est:20000-30000

MOMPER, Joos de (style) (1564-1635) Flemish
£568 $1045 €829 River landscape (59x74cm-23x29in) 14-Jun-4 Philippe Schuler, Zurich #5869 (S.FR 1300)

MOMPER, Philips de (younger) (c.1610-1675) Flemish
£30000 $54900 €43800 Wooded landscape with figures on path. Open wooded landscape with figures and watermill (49x93cm-19x37in) panel pair prov. 8-Jul-4 Sotheby's, London #238/R est:30000-40000

MOMPO, H (20th C) ?
Works on paper
£2893 $4600 €4224 Abstract, Mallorca (48x69cm-19x27in) s.d.1966 W/C prov. 9-Mar-3 William Jenack, New York #187 est:500-700

MONA, Domenico (c.1550-1602) Italian
£16312 $27241 €23000 Pieta' (51x37cm-20x15in) board. 17-Jun-3 Finarte Semenzato, Milan #465/R

MONACHESI, Alessandro (19th C) Italian
£570 $1050 €850 Town and river (37x46cm-15x18in) bears sig.d.1866. 27-Mar-4 Farsetti, Prato #278

MONACHESI, Sante (1910-1991) Italian
£979 $1664 €1400 Still life with jug and bottle (80x60cm-31x24in) s. prov. 26-Nov-3 Pandolfini, Florence #196/R est:1600-1800
£1208 $2247 €1800 We will not fall down (50x60cm-20x24in) s. s.i.d.1972 verso oil tempera dye. 4-Mar-4 Babuino, Rome #429 est:1200-1800
£1224 $2192 €1800 Flowers (50x40cm-20x16in) s. 16-Mar-4 Finarte Semenzato, Milan #192/R est:1600
£1333 $2453 €2000 Vase of flowers (70x50cm-28x20in) s. 12-Jun-4 Meeting Art, Vercelli #268/R est:2000
£1389 $2194 €2000 Blind walls in Paris (60x50cm-24x20in) 6-Sep-3 Meeting Art, Vercelli #311 est:2000
£1467 $2699 €2200 Paris (50x70cm-20x28in) s. 11-Jun-4 Farsetti, Prato #8/R est:2100-2400
£1467 $2655 €2200 Paris from the Boulevard (70x60cm-28x24in) s. s.i.verso. 2-Apr-4 Farsetti, Prato #208 est:1600-1900
£1544 $2871 €2300 Back to the countryside (50x60cm-20x24in) s. s.i.verso prov. 4-Mar-4 Babuino, Rome #98 est:1800-2200
£1600 $2944 €2400 Agra symbol at moonlight (60x80cm-24x31in) s. i.verso acrylic painted 1973 lit. 12-Jun-4 Meeting Art, Vercelli #601/R est:2000
£1736 $2743 €2500 Maternity (80x60cm-31x24in) oil sand. 6-Sep-3 Meeting Art, Vercelli #479 est:2500
£1761 $2923 €2500 Autostrada (50x70cm-20x28in) s. painted 1962. 14-Jun-3 Meeting Art, Vercelli #414/R est:2500
£1946 $3620 €2900 Vases of flowers with duck (70x50cm-28x20in) s. painted 1955. 4-Mar-4 Babuino, Rome #80
£2414 $4031 €3500 Bridges on the Seine (70x50cm-28x20in) s. 13-Nov-3 Finarte Semenzato, Rome #227/R est:2800-3500
£2550 $4744 €3800 Lobsters from Ustica (60x80cm-24x31in) s. s.i.verso painted 1961. 4-Mar-4 Babuino, Rome #510 est:3000-3500
£3793 $6334 €5500 Landscape (38x48cm-15x19in) s. board double-sided. 13-Nov-3 Finarte Semenzato, Rome #391/R est:4000-5000

MONACO, Pasquale (1948-) Italian
£333 $613 €500 Usual three (30x60cm-12x24in) s. 12-Jun-4 Meeting Art, Vercelli #574/R
£567 $1043 €850 South of the sky (40x70cm-16x28in) s. 12-Jun-4 Meeting Art, Vercelli #947/R

MONAFO, Janet (1940-) American
Works on paper
£437 $800 €638 Piled up (81x74cm-32x29in) pastel. 10-Jul-4 Hindman, Chicago #355/R

MONAHAN, Herb (19/20th C) American
£349 $600 €510 Monahan opera house (36x56cm-14x22in) s.d.1918. 7-Dec-3 Grogan, Boston #34

MONAHAN, Hugh (1914-1970) Irish
£663 $1200 €968 Geese on a lake at sunset (61x51cm-24x20in) s. 18-Apr-4 Bonhams & Butterfields, Los Angeles #7003 est:2000-3000
£680 $1272 €993 Mallards alighting on a mere (16x20cm-6x8in) s. board. 25-Feb-4 Mallams, Oxford #111/R
£724 $1209 €1057 Gathering of the Canada's north country (55x75cm-22x30in) s.i. 17-Nov-3 Hodgins, Calgary #128/R est:1400-1800 (C.D 1600)
£1200 $2196 €1752 Rocky coastal scene with geese (87x122cm-34x48in) s.d.1951. 7-Jul-4 George Kidner, Lymington #145/R est:500-700
£1242 $2000 €1813 Geese in flight (30x41cm-12x16in) s.d.1930. 20-Aug-3 James Julia, Fairfield #331/R est:2250-2750
£1425 $2550 €2081 After the storm-canvas backs restless (56x76cm-22x30in) s. i.verso. 8-Jan-4 James Julia, Fairfield #447/R est:1500-2500
£1816 $3250 €2651 Deserted Islands Green Landers Landing near the ruins (51x76cm-20x30in) s. i.verso. 8-Jan-4 James Julia, Fairfield #448/R est:3000-4000

MONALDI, Paolo (18th C) Italian
£8000 $13840 €11680 Barber at work by a well with other peasants drinking and playing music (73x60cm-29x24in) 10-Dec-3 Bonhams, New Bond Street #111/R est:5000-7000

MONALDI, Paolo (attrib) (18th C) Italian
£2057 $3435 €2900 Paysage pres d'une riviere avec paysans (65x49cm-26x19in) oval. 19-Oct-3 St-Germain-en-Laye Encheres #9/R est:4000-6000

MONAMY, Peter (1689-1749) British
£850 $1522 €1241 Evening gun (16x23cm-6x9in) 26-May-4 Christie's, Kensington #565/R
£2200 $3740 €3212 Admiralty yacht (84x101cm-33x40in) 19-Nov-3 Christie's, Kensington #440/R
£3356 $6174 €5000 Boats off coast (49x63cm-19x25in) s. lit. 25-Mar-4 Karlheinz Kaupp, Staufen #2286/R est:3500
£7000 $12810 €10220 The morning gun (52x71cm-20x28in) bears sig. 7-Apr-4 Woolley & Wallis, Salisbury #294/R est:6000-8000
£8000 $13600 €11680 Man-o-war in a swell, with another ship beyond (77x63cm-30x25in) s. 25-Nov-3 Christie's, London #82/R est:8000-12000
£10000 $18300 €14600 Shipping off the coast (72x116cm-28x46in) bears sig. 7-Apr-4 Woolley & Wallis, Salisbury #295/R est:10000-15000
£11000 $20130 €16060 An Admiralty yacht in a swell (121x105cm-48x41in) bears sig. 7-Apr-4 Woolley & Wallis, Salisbury #297/R est:12000-18000
£12000 $21960 €17520 Battle of Cap la Hogue (76x120cm-30x47in) 7-Apr-4 Woolley & Wallis, Salisbury #296/R est:8000-12000
£18000 $30960 €26280 Albemarle 80/90 guns flagship of Admiral pf the fleet Sir John Leake (103x127cm-41x50in) s. indis d. 2-Dec-3 Sotheby's, London #138/R est:20000-30000
£41667 $70833 €60000 English fleet (107x158cm-42x62in) 28-Oct-3 Il Ponte, Milan #335/R est:60000

MONAMY, Peter (attrib) (1689-1749) British
£780 $1342 €1139 Man-o-war dismasted in heavy seas (58x82cm-23x32in) 2-Dec-3 Sotheby's, London #6/R
£2800 $5012 €4088 Squadron of the Red in a swell (61x76cm-24x30in) 26-May-4 Christie's, Kensington #566/R est:2500-3500
£4000 $7160 €5840 English man-o-war opening fire on a Spanish armed ship (71x91cm-28x36in) 26-May-4 Christie's, Kensington #567/R est:4000-6000

MONARD, Louis de (1873-?) French
Sculpture
£983 $1700 €1435 Saddled horse (30x46cm-12x18in) num.28 bronze. 12-Dec-3 Du Mouchelle, Detroit #2009/R est:1000-1500

MONCADA CALVACHE, Jose (1895-?) Spanish
£1159 $1901 €1600 Landscape (20x25cm-8x10in) s. 27-May-3 Durán, Madrid #621/R est:350

MONCADA, Arecio (20th C) South American
£674 $1125 €984 View of the Andes (100x130cm-39x51in) s. painted 1996. 19-Oct-3 Subastas Odalys, Caracas #139

MONCAYO, Emilio (20th C) ?
£227 $400 €331 Village with a snowcapped mountain beyond (51x85cm-20x33in) s. 23-May-4 Bonhams & Butterfields, Los Angeles #7092/R

MONCHABLON, Jean Ferdinand (1855-1904) French
£2684 $4993 €4000 Paysage de campagne en ete (40x56cm-16x22in) s. 2-Mar-4 Artcurial Briest, Paris #105/R est:4000-5000

MONCHOT, L (1850-1920) French
£946 $1665 €1400 Serving girl in Oriental interior (30x38cm-12x15in) s.d.74. 21-May-4 Mehlis, Plauen #15147/R est:600

MONCUIT, Philippe de (?) French?
Works on paper
£302 $565 €450 Nature morte aux perdrix grise et rouge (41x31cm-16x12in) pastel. 1-Mar-4 Coutau Begarie, Paris #179

MONDINO, Aldo (1938-) Italian
£2014 $3182 €2900 Suite (120x90cm-47x35in) 6-Sep-3 Meeting Art, Vercelli #333 est:2500
£2416 $4325 €3600 Turkish scene (80x60cm-31x24in) s.d.1999 oil collage. 30-May-4 Meeting Art, Vercelli #47 est:2000
£2703 $4757 €4000 Schiffbruch new spirit (149x149cm-59x59in) i. s.i.d.81 verso exhib. 24-May-4 Christie's, Milan #230/R est:4500-6500
£2797 $4755 €4000 Oran-Oran (80x60cm-31x24in) oil assemblage wood lit. 26-Nov-3 Pandolfini, Florence #132/R est:3400-3600
£2953 $5286 €4400 Rugs (166x101cm-65x40in) s.d.96 panel lit. 28-May-4 Farsetti, Prato #244/R est:3600-4200
£4196 $7133 €6000 Rug (130x180cm-51x71in) s.d.95 verso painted board prov. 24-Nov-3 Christie's, Milan #150/R est:7000-10000
Works on paper
£352 $585 €500 Giullare (70x50cm-28x20in) s. pastel cardboard. 14-Jun-3 Meeting Art, Vercelli #580
£580 $951 €800 Sun (50x70cm-20x28in) s.d.67 gouache collage. 30-May-3 Farsetti, Prato #62

MONDO, Domenico (attrib) (1717-1806) Italian
Works on paper
£448 $749 €650 Mythological scene (18x24cm-7x9in) pen wash prov. 15-Nov-3 Lempertz, Koln #1362/R

MONDRIAAN, Frits (1853-1932) Dutch

£612	$1114	€900	Avond aan de vijver, woman strolling by a lake at dusk (40x59cm-16x23in) s. 3-Feb-4 Christie's, Amsterdam #264
£616	$1048	€900	Ditch in the woods (49x69cm-19x27in) s. 5-Nov-3 Vendue Huis, Gravenhage #143/R
£724	$1310	€1100	Cloud effect (27x18cm-11x7in) s. panel exhib. 19-Apr-4 Glerum, Amsterdam #195/R

MONDRIAN, Piet (1872-1944) Dutch

£117329	$215884	€171300	The French Mill in moonlight, seen from east towards west (63x76cm-25x30in) s. i.stretcher painted c.1902-03 prov.lit. 29-Mar-4 Rasmussen, Copenhagen #148/R est:1200000-1800000 (D.KR 1300000)
£1450000	$2668000	€2117000	Composition II, with red in a square (50x51cm-20x20in) init.d.26 prov.exhib.lit. 22-Jun-4 Christie's, London #30/R est:1000000-1500000
£1675978	$3000000	€2446928	Composition in blue. yellow. red and grey (39x35cm-15x14in) init.d.22 prov.exhib.lit. 4-May-4 Christie's, Rockefeller NY #27/R est:3000000-5000000
Works on paper			
£66667	$122667	€100000	Farmyard with laundry and logs (29x45cm-11x18in) s.d.95 W/C prov.exhib.lit. 8-Jun-4 Sotheby's, Amsterdam #6/R est:40000-60000
£91176	$155000	€133117	Chrysanthemum (34x24cm-13x9in) s, W/C exec c.1925 prov.exhib.lit. 6-Nov-3 Sotheby's, New York #204/R est:80000-120000
£106145	$190000	€154972	Chrysanthemum (35x25cm-14x10in) s. gouache W/C over pen ink buff paper exec c.1920 prov.lit. 5-May-4 Christie's, Rockefeller NY #129/R est:120000-160000

MONDRUS, Martin (20th C) American

£605	$1113	€883	Village backyards (64x76cm-25x30in) s.d.47. 14-Jun-4 Waddingtons, Toronto #4/R est:800-1200 (C.D 1500)
£8235	$14000	€12023	Overpass at Venice Blvd (76x91cm-30x36in) s. painted c.1943 prov.exhib. 18-Nov-3 John Moran, Pasadena #75 est:9000-12000

MONDZAIN, Simon François Stanislas (1890-1979) French

£759	$1259	€1100	Eglise de Sollis-Ville (63x53cm-25x21in) s. i.verso. 1-Oct-3 Millon & Associes, Paris #119/R
£881	$1498	€1286	La fontaine a Sallies Pont (61x50cm-24x20in) s. i. verso. 5-Nov-3 Dobiaschofsky, Bern #809/R (S.FR 2000)
£2667	$4907	€4000	Landscape (81x65cm-32x26in) s.indis.i.d.1914. 12-Jun-4 Villa Grisebach, Berlin #306/R est:3000-4000
£4610	$7699	€6500	Cathedrale Saint-Philippe (84x98cm-33x39in) lit. 19-Oct-3 Rabourdin & Choppin de Janvry, Paris #130/R est:6500-8000

MONET, Claude (1840-1926) French

£69014	$120775	€98000	Nympheas (36x63cm-14x25in) prov.lit. 16-Dec-3 Claude Aguttes, Neuilly #10/R est:40000-45000
£85000	$154700	€124100	Tete de chien griffon, Follette (36x29cm-14x11in) painted 1882 prov.lit. 3-Feb-4 Christie's, London #116/R est:40000-60000
£268156	$480000	€391508	Binnen-Amstel, Amsterdam (56x74cm-22x29in) s. painted 1874 prov.exhib.lit. 4-May-4 Christie's, Rockefeller NY #18/R est:600000-800000
£350000	$644000	€511000	Hameau de falaise pres Giverny (60x81cm-24x32in) s.d.83 painted 1885 prov.exhib.lit. 23-Jun-4 Christie's, London #117/R est:350000-450000
£380000	$699200	€554800	Route e GIverny (65x80cm-26x31in) s. prov. 22-Jun-4 Christie's, London #23/R est:300000-400000
£391061	$700000	€570949	Vase de tulipes (50x37cm-20x15in) s. painted 1885 prov.lit. 6-May-4 Sotheby's, New York #209/R est:200000-300000
£418994	$750000	€611731	Sur la falaise pres de Dieppe, soleil couchant (65x100cm-26x39in) s.d.97 prov.exhib.lit. 4-May-4 Christie's, Rockefeller NY #10/R est:700000-900000
£418994	$750000	€611731	Hameau de Falaise, paysage d'hiver (60x73cm-24x29in) s. painted 1885 prov.lit. 5-May-4 Christie's, Rockefeller NY #220/R est:500000-700000
£441176	$750000	€644117	La Seine a Lavacourt (56x73cm-22x29in) s.d.1878 prov.lit. 5-Nov-3 Sotheby's, New York #8/R est:900000-1200000
£1000000	$1700000	€1460000	Le train a jeufosse (61x81cm-24x32in) s. painted 1884 prov.lit. 5-Nov-3 Sotheby's, New York #15/R est:1200000-1800000
£1100000	$2002000	€1606000	Iris (120x100cm-47x39in) st.sig. st.sig.verso prov.exhib.lit. 21-Jun-4 Sotheby's, London #17/R est:1000000-1500000
£1173184	$2100000	€1712849	La Seine en crue a Vetheuil (65x81cm-26x32in) s.d.1881 prov.exhib.lit. 4-May-4 Christie's, Rockefeller NY #3/R est:1800000-2500000
£2011173	$3600000	€2936313	Paysage de printemps a Giverny (92x65cm-36x26in) s.d.94 prov.exhib.lit. 4-May-4 Christie's, Rockefeller NY #13/R est:4000000-6000000
£2176471	$3700000	€3177648	Nympheas (169x123cm-67x48in) st.sig. painted 1914-17 prov.lit. 4-Nov-3 Christie's, Rockefeller NY #23/R est:2500000-3500000
£2234637	$4000000	€3262570	Bateaux sur le Galet (73x92cm-29x36in) s.d.84 prov.exhib.lit. 5-May-4 Sotheby's, New York #9/R est:2500000-3500000
£2350000	$4324000	€3431000	Plage de Juan-les-Pins (73x92cm-29x36in) s.d.88 prov.exhib.lit. 22-Jun-4 Christie's, London #12/R est:1800000-2400000
£2450000	$4459000	€3577000	Vetheuil (90x93cm-35x37in) s.d.1901 prov.exhib.lit. 3-Feb-4 Sotheby's, London #34/R est:2000000-3000000
£3750000	$6825000	€5475000	Nympheas (150x200cm-59x79in) st.sig. prov.exhib.lit. 21-Jun-4 Sotheby's, London #10/R est:4000000-6000000
£5470588	$9300000	€7987058	Nympheas (91x89cm-36x35in) s.d.1908 prov.exhib.lit. 5-Nov-3 Sotheby's, New York #16/R est:10000000-15000000
£8379889	$15000000	€12234638	Bassin aux nympheas (100x200cm-39x79in) st.sig. prov.exhib.lit. 6-May-4 Sotheby's, New York #133/R est:9000000-12000000

MONET, Claude (attrib) (1840-1926) French

£1014	$1664	€1400	Houses in Venice (22x18cm-9x7in) cardboard prov.lit. 27-May-3 Il Ponte, Milan #896

MONET, Claude and THORNLEY, Georges W (19th C) French

Prints			
£3529	$6000	€5152	Tempete a Belle-Ile (20x24cm-8x9in) s. lithograph exec.c.1908. 6-Nov-3 Swann Galleries, New York #391/R est:7000-10000
£4749	$8500	€6934	Tempete a belle-ile (20x24cm-8x9in) s. lithograph in blue white. 6-May-4 Swann Galleries, New York #304/R est:6000-9000
£5376	$10000	€7849	Bateaux de peche, Etretat (18x25cm-7x10in) s. lithograph. 2-Mar-4 Swann Galleries, New York #454/R est:7000-10000

MONEY, Keith (1935-) British

£4200	$7392	€6132	Red Rum at the start of the Grand National 1974 (61x71cm-24x28in) s. i.d.1974 verso board. 21-May-4 Christie's, London #3/R est:2500-3500

MONFARDINI, Alfonso (1887-1965) Italian

£725	$1188	€1000	Piano de Resinelli (59x50cm-23x20in) s.d.1922 cardboard. 27-May-3 Finarte Semenzato, Milan #10/R

MONFORT, Frans van (1889-1980) Belgian

£368	$667	€560	Composition au vase fleuri (74x60cm-29x24in) s.d.1922 oval. 19-Apr-4 Horta, Bruxelles #383
Works on paper			
£629	$1070	€900	L'entretien avec Dieu. s. W/C. 18-Nov-3 Galerie Moderne, Brussels #602/R
£1399	$2378	€2000	Discussion. s.d.1919 pastel. 18-Nov-3 Galerie Moderne, Brussels #583/R est:300-400

MONFREID, Georges Daniel de (1856-1929) French

£3333	$6100	€5000	Nu de dos (62x48cm-24x19in) s.i.d.1906 prov. 6-Jun-4 Rouillac, Vendome #50
£7000	$12810	€10500	Vases de roses (76x56cm-30x22in) s.d.1914 paper on canvas prov.lit. 6-Jun-4 Rouillac, Vendome #51

MONGE, Jules (1855-?) French

£856	$1600	€1284	Entering the barracks (42x33cm-17x13in) s. 25-Jul-4 Bonhams & Butterfields, San Francisco #6068/R est:1500-2000
£1007	$1782	€1500	Dragon a pied. Artilleur du 12 regiment. s. panel pair. 28-Apr-4 Beaussant & Lefèvre, Paris #96/R est:1000-1500

MONGIN, Antoine Pierre (attrib) (1761-1827) French

Works on paper			
£405	$714	€600	Chinoiserie, with pagoda on a bridge (28x18cm-11x7in) brush grey ink wash black chk prov.exhib. 19-May-4 Sotheby's, Amsterdam #175/R

MONGINOT, Charlotte (1872-?) French

Sculpture			
£740	$1325	€1080	Monginot (38x10cm-15x4in) s. brown pat. bronze. 19-Mar-4 Aspire, Cleveland #185 est:800-1200

MONGRELL Y TORRENT, Jose (1870-1934) Spanish

£65000	$110500	€94900	By the sea (75x100cm-30x39in) s.d.1936 prov. 18-Nov-3 Sotheby's, London #217/R
£75000	$127500	€109500	Women with flowers (75x100cm-30x39in) s. prov. 18-Nov-3 Sotheby's, London #220/R
£83333	$135833	€120000	Cullera sailors (71x115cm-28x45in) s. lit. 23-Sep-3 Durán, Madrid #204/R est:70000

MONI, Henry (?) ?

£380	$600	€555	Kitchen scene with two women with dishes and cat and possibly two rats (71x56cm-28x22in) s. 6-Sep-3 Brunk, Ashville #993

MONIEN, Julius (1842-1897) German

£1223	$2225	€1786	By the riverside (73x110cm-29x43in) s.indis.d. 16-Jun-4 Fischer, Luzern #1230/R est:2000-2500 (S.FR 2800)
£10000	$18100	€15000	Woodland pond (83x125cm-33x49in) s.d.1883 i. verso lit. 1-Apr-4 Frank Peege, Freiburg #1155/R est:3500

MONIER, Émile (20th C) French

Sculpture			
£3147	$5413	€4500	Buste Koumbo (45x28x20cm-18x11x8in) s.i. black pat bronze sold with black marble socle st.f. exhib. 3-Dec-3 Beaussant & Lefèvre, Paris #87/R est:1500-2000

MONIER, Julien (19/20th C) French

Sculpture			
£2715	$4344	€3964	Egyptian dancer (38cm-15in) s. bronze ivory. 19-Sep-3 Koller, Zurich #1290/R est:6000-9000 (S.FR 6000)

MONIER, Pierre (1641-1703) French

Works on paper			
£1944	$3500	€2838	General on horseback in a landscape (25x18cm-10x7in) black chk pen brown ink wash. 22-Jan-4 Christie's, Rockefeller NY #84/R est:4000-6000

MONIES, David (1812-1894) Danish

£270	$501	€394	Portrait of Mr Herholt (20x15cm-8x6in) s. oval. 2-Mar-4 Rasmussen, Copenhagen #1560/R (D.KR 3000)
£308	$529	€450	Park landscape with figures resting (27x39cm-11x15in) panel. 3-Dec-3 AB Stockholms Auktionsverk #2605/R (S.KR 4000)
£449	$836	€656	Sunday outing to the woods (27x38cm-11x15in) prov. 2-Mar-4 Rasmussen, Copenhagen #1593/R (D.KR 5000)
£494	$775	€721	Young woman standing by table reading a letter (19x15cm-7x6in) with sig. verso. 30-Aug-3 Rasmussen, Havnen #2271 (D.KR 5300)
£949	$1537	€1386	Children resting in Dyrehaven (25x37cm-10x15in) s. 9-Aug-3 Hindemae, Ullerslev #91/R (D.KR 10000)
£1300	$2158	€1898	Sad Farewell (58x48cm-23x19in) s.d.1859. 1-Oct-3 Sotheby's, Olympia #257/R est:1000-2000

MONINOT, Bernard (20th C) French

£2153	$3595	€3100	Peinture (72x45cm-28x18in) s.d.1978 oil emballage de bois prov.exhib. 25-Oct-3 Cornette de St.Cyr, Paris #760/R est:2000-3000

Works on paper
£268 $494 €400 Le Bar (48x63cm-19x25in) black ink prov. 24-Mar-4 Binoche, Paris #67

MONNI, Mariano (20th C) Italian
£302 $504 €441 Porte St. Denis, Paris (68x98cm-27x39in) s. 20-Oct-3 Stephan Welz, Johannesburg #466 est:3500-5000 (SA.R 3500)

MONNICKENDAM, Martin (1874-1943) Dutch
£1389 $2264 €2000 Gypsy cart escorted by police (21x27cm-8x11in) s.d.1929 panel. 29-Sep-3 Sotheby's, Amsterdam #176/R
£2013 $3705 €3000 Woman selling fish (84x103cm-33x41in) s.d.1919. 26-Mar-4 Bolland & Marotz, Bremen #561/R est:1100
£2917 $4754 €4200 Ocean steamer in harbour and figures on quay (45x60cm-18x24in) s.d. 29-Sep-3 Sotheby's, Amsterdam #169/R
Works on paper
£660 $1042 €950 Westertoren seen from a canal, Amsterdam (102x78cm-40x31in) s.d.1939 chl pencil. 2-Sep-3 Christie's, Amsterdam #292

MONNIER (?) ?
£2113 $3507 €3000 Bateau de commerce Britannique et pecheurs pres de la cote (72x92cm-28x36in) s.d.1841. 13-Jun-3 Renaud, Paris #34/R est:3000-4000

MONNIER, Charles (1925-) Swiss
£679 $1154 €991 Maree basse (33x46cm-13x18in) s. i.d.1972 verso. 19-Nov-3 Fischer, Luzern #2219/R (S.FR 1500)
£679 $1174 €991 Vieilles bergeries (33x46cm-13x18in) s. i.verso prov.exhib. 12-Dec-3 Galerie du Rhone, Sion #619 (S.FR 1500)
£814 $1385 €1188 Mas au Destet (60x81cm-24x32in) s. d.1974 verso. 19-Nov-3 Fischer, Luzern #1306/R (S.FR 1800)

MONNIER, Henri (1805-1877) French
Works on paper
£222 $400 €324 Two women (22x20cm-9x8in) W/C ink over pencil. 21-Jan-4 Sotheby's, New York #261/R
£288 $460 €400 Paysan vu de face et de dos (15x17cm-6x7in) s.i.d.1837 W/C traces of blk crayon. 16-May-3 Tajan, Paris #163
£393 $724 €590 Valet en costume bleu et bas blancs lisant le journal (21x13cm-8x5in) s. W/C. 9-Jun-4 Piasa, Paris #182
£500 $920 €750 Portrait en pied de Joseph Prudhomme (23x15cm-9x6in) s.d.1873 pen wash exhib. 9-Jun-4 Piasa, Paris #183/R
£800 $1456 €1200 Conversation ennuyeuse (27x22cm-11x9in) s. pen ink wash crayon. 30-Jun-4 Delvaux, Paris #126
£1200 $2172 €1800 Une bourgeoise (26x18cm-10x7in) mono. W/C. 5-Apr-4 Deburaux, Boulogne #77 est:800-1000

MONNOYER, Jean Baptiste (1636-1699) French
£5556 $10000 €8112 Peonies, narcissi and other flowers in an urn on a ledge (92x70cm-36x28in) 23-Jan-4 Christie's, Rockefeller NY #157/R est:10000-15000
£11111 $20000 €16222 Still life of hydrangeas, convolvuli and other flowers in an urn on a draped stone ledge (71x92cm-28x36in) s. prov.lit. 22-Jan-4 Sotheby's, New York #140/R est:25000-35000
£15385 $25692 €22000 Bouquet d'oeillets, fleurs d'orangers et grenades, et jasmins (63x52cm-25x20in) prov. 27-Jun-3 Millon & Associes, Paris #15/R est:20000-30000
£21127 $36549 €30000 Vase de fleurs (40x30cm-16x12in) pair. 15-Dec-3 Ansorena, Madrid #119/R est:30000
£22000 $38060 €32120 Still life of flowers in a glass vase on a stone ledge (49x62cm-19x24in) prov. 11-Dec-3 Sotheby's, London #222/R est:15000-20000
£28000 $47600 €40880 Carnations, morning glory and other flowers in a glass vase on a stone ledge. Parrot tulips in vase (46x37cm-18x15in) pair 29-Oct-3 Christie's, London #53/R est:15000-20000
£38000 $69540 €55480 Parrot tulips, chrysanthemums and other flowers on stone ledge (79x65cm-31x26in) 7-Jul-4 Christie's, London #66/R est:20000-30000

MONNOYER, Jean Baptiste (circle) (1636-1699) French
£5000 $8650 €7300 Chrysanthemums, narcissi and other flowers in a glass vase (49x41cm-19x16in) 10-Dec-3 Bonhams, New Bond Street #70/R est:5000-7000
£5245 $9021 €7500 Still life of flowers (76x56cm-30x22in) 2-Dec-3 Sotheby's, Milan #36/R est:7000-10000
£5667 $10370 €8500 Still life with vase of flowers (87x72cm-34x28in) 1-Jun-4 Sotheby's, Milan #88/R est:7000-10000
£5800 $9860 €8468 Roses, delphiniums and other flowers in a sculpted urn on a stone ledge (64x77cm-25x30in) 29-Oct-3 Bonhams, New Bond Street #44/R est:4000-6000
£6643 $11427 €9500 Still life of flowers (76x56cm-30x22in) 2-Dec-3 Sotheby's, Milan #35/R est:7000-10000
£8500 $14450 €12410 Chrysanthemums, peonies and other flowers in a sculpted urn on a ledge (63x54cm-25x21in) 31-Oct-3 Christie's, Kensington #93/R est:6000-8000
£8500 $15300 €12410 Carnations, roses and peonies with other flowers in a glass set on a stone ledge (49x41cm-19x16in) 20-Apr-4 Sotheby's, Olympia #363/R est:2000-3000
£8500 $15300 €12410 Tulips, carnation and other flowers in a stone ledge (75x62cm-30x24in) 21-Apr-4 Bonhams, New Bond Street #51/R est:8000-12000
£9000 $15570 €13140 Chrysanthemums, narcissi and other flowers in a gilt bronze mounted glass vase (60x48cm-24x19in) 10-Dec-3 Bonhams, New Bond Street #69/R est:2000-3000

MONNOYER, Jean Baptiste (studio) (1636-1699) French
£3611 $6500 €5272 Flower bed with blue chrysanthemum and lilies (93x79cm-37x31in) prov.exhib. 23-Jan-4 Christie's, Rockefeller NY #107/R est:8000-12000

MONNOYER, Jean Baptiste (style) (1636-1699) French
£7500 $13500 €10950 Flowers in a sculpted urn on a ledge (73x60cm-29x24in) oval. 23-Apr-4 Christie's, Kensington #174/R est:7000-10000
£52000 $95160 €75920 Still lives of flowers (104x83cm-41x33in) bear sig. pair prov. 8-Jul-4 Sotheby's, London #167/R est:30000-50000

MONOGRAMMIST A A (?) ?
£1325 $2411 €2000 View of Schevening (28x38cm-11x15in) mono.i. 21-Jun-4 Dorotheum, Vienna #133/R est:1500-1700

MONOGRAMMIST A B (?) ?
£369 $679 €550 Mountain landscape (74x99cm-29x39in) d.1875. 29-Mar-4 Dr Fritz Nagel, Stuttgart #7101/R
£1189 $2021 €1700 In front of the stable (70x90cm-28x35in) mono. 28-Nov-3 Schloss Ahlden, Ahlden #1466/R est:1800
£4333 $7887 €6500 Forest hut in a winter landscape (32x41cm-13x16in) mono. 1-Jul-4 Van Ham, Cologne #1507/R est:1200
Sculpture
£3061 $5571 €4500 Seal with hand and snake (14cm-6in) ivory silver. 5-Feb-4 Dorotheum, Salzburg #316/R est:1200

MONOGRAMMIST A B H (?) ?
£541 $951 €800 Goatherd (68x89cm-27x35in) mono.d.28 double-sided. 21-May-4 Mehlis, Plauen #15070/R

MONOGRAMMIST A D R (?) ?
Works on paper
£699 $1202 €1000 Tyrus 06 (32x40cm-13x16in) mono.d.1906 crayon htd gouache. 8-Dec-3 Tajan, Paris #231/R

MONOGRAMMIST A E (?) ?
£295 $543 €440 Winter landscape with figures and sledge (34x30cm-13x12in) mono. panel. 26-Mar-4 Auktionhaus Georg Rehm, Augsburg #8117/R
£496 $913 €724 Still life of flowers and fruit (62x47cm-24x19in) mono. 29-Mar-4 Rasmussen, Copenhagen #522/R (D.KR 5500)

MONOGRAMMIST A F (?) ?
£400 $724 €600 Mother and child (55x48cm-22x19in) d.1866. 2-Apr-4 Dr Fritz Nagel, Leipzig #3964/R

MONOGRAMMIST A G (?) ?
£525 $856 €767 Young girl by lily pond (51x38cm-20x15in) mono. 23-Sep-3 John Nicholson, Haslemere #323
£6333 $11590 €9500 Coastal landscape with castle and figures (56x89cm-22x35in) mono. 1-Jun-4 Sotheby's, Milan #181/R est:6000-8000

MONOGRAMMIST A K (?) ?
Works on paper
£480 $884 €701 Portrait of young woman painter at easel (42x35cm-17x14in) mono. pastel silk on paper. 14-Jun-4 Philippe Schuler, Zurich #4445/R (S.FR 1100)

MONOGRAMMIST A O I (?) ?
£436 $803 €650 Elegant young woman (69x55cm-27x22in) mono.d.1857. 26-Mar-4 Auktionhaus Georg Rehm, Augsburg #8118/R

MONOGRAMMIST A R (?) ?
£1119 $1902 €1600 Mother's joy (36x28cm-14x11in) mono. 22-Nov-3 Arnold, Frankfurt #594/R est:1200
£1361 $2435 €2000 Boats by shipwreck in stormy waters (57x80cm-22x31in) mono. 17-Mar-4 Neumeister, Munich #533/R est:1000

MONOGRAMMIST A T (?) ?
Works on paper
£490 $832 €700 Angler by mountain river (15x21cm-6x8in) mono. pen brush. 28-Nov-3 Bassenge, Berlin #6164

MONOGRAMMIST A T L (?) ?
£2027 $3568 €3000 Hilly wooded landscape with a mansion on the left, and poplars in a meadow (43x48cm-17x19in) mono. 18-May-4 Sotheby's, Amsterdam #47a/R est:3000-4000

MONOGRAMMIST A W (?) ?
£600 $1080 €900 Salzkammergut (68x54cm-27x21in) mono.d.1934 panel. 21-Apr-4 Dorotheum, Vienna #91/R
Works on paper
£286 $487 €418 Lake Geneva (22x35cm-9x14in) mono.d.25/10/99 W/C over pencil. 5-Nov-3 Dobiaschofsky, Bern #811/R (S.FR 650)

MONOGRAMMIST B (?) ?
Works on paper
£335 $600 €489 Venice Scene (15x23cm-6x9in) W/C. 20-Mar-4 Sloans & Kenyon, Bethesda #1144/R

MONOGRAMMIST B C K (?) ?
£634 $1052 €900 By the water source (18x14cm-7x6in) mono. panel. 16-Jun-3 Dorotheum, Vienna #211/R

MONOGRAMMIST B G (?) ?
Works on paper
£724 $1231 €1057 Southern landscape with deer (19x27cm-7x11in) mono. W/C over pencil. 28-Nov-3 Falk & Falk, Zurich #285 est:1200 (S.FR 1600)
£769 $1308 €1123 Caravan in western landscape (19x27cm-7x11in) mono. W/C over pencil. 28-Nov-3 Falk & Falk, Zurich #284/R est:1200 (S.FR 1700)

MONOGRAMMIST B Z (?) ?
Works on paper
£604 $1123 €900 Portrait of a lady with exposed shoulders (65x54cm-26x21in) mono.d.1902 pastel oval. 5-Mar-4 Wendl, Rudolstadt #3786/R

MONOGRAMMIST C A (?) ?
£257 $475 €375 Sea coast with sailing ships and fishermen (20x38cm-8x15in) mono. 17-Jul-4 Fallon, Copake #152/R
£420 $713 €600 Female nude balanced on a ball (79cm-31in circular) mono.d.1870 panel. 28-Nov-3 Wendl, Rudolstadt #4097/R

MONOGRAMMIST C A T (?) ?
£315 $535 €450 Femme a la bougie (52x57cm-20x22in) 30-Nov-3 Teitgen, Nancy #113

MONOGRAMMIST C E (?) ?
£1053 $1937 €1600 Extensive landscape with a castle (44x60cm-17x24in) 28-Jun-4 Dr Fritz Nagel, Stuttgart #7051/R est:800

MONOGRAMMIST C F (?) ?
£1208 $2223 €1800 Woman behind man asleep in window (28x23cm-11x9in) mono.d.1838 panel. 25-Mar-4 Dr Fritz Nagel, Stuttgart #742/R est:2200

MONOGRAMMIST C H (?) ?
£311 $567 €454 Woodland lake with deer watering (55x92cm-22x36in) mono.d.1894. 7-Feb-4 Rasmussen, Havnen #2022/R (D.KR 3400)
Works on paper
£1477 $2613 €2200 Black Forest landscape (24x35cm-9x14in) mono. W/C. 30-Apr-4 Dr Fritz Nagel, Stuttgart #347/R est:400

MONOGRAMMIST C K (?) ?
£470 $864 €700 Boy with sheep and cattle (44x61cm-17x24in) mono. paper on canvas. 27-Mar-4 Dannenberg, Berlin #599

MONOGRAMMIST C L (?) ?
£473 $846 €691 The drunken monk (52x72cm-20x28in) mono. 12-Jan-4 Rasmussen, Vejle #351/R (D.KR 5000)

MONOGRAMMIST C M (?) ?
£556 $906 €800 Female tennis player (20x40cm-8x16in) mono. copper. 26-Sep-3 Bolland & Marotz, Bremen #578/R
£1342 $2470 €2000 Figures by Rhine (39x51cm-15x20in) mono. 27-Mar-4 L & B, Essen #156/R est:200
£1879 $3458 €2800 Evening on the Mosel (39x51cm-15x20in) mono. i. verso. 27-Mar-4 L & B, Essen #157/R est:200
£36111 $65000 €52722 Portrait of Jacob Futterer (97x76cm-38x30in) mono.d.1556. 22-Jan-4 Sotheby's, New York #31/R est:50000-70000
Works on paper
£199 $356 €291 Snowy mountain train (31x39cm-12x15in) mono. W/C. 22-Mar-4 Philippe Schuler, Zurich #5874 (S.FR 460)

MONOGRAMMIST C P (?) ?
£278 $439 €400 Danish three master and fire ship (36x55cm-14x22in) mono.d.26. 6-Sep-3 Schopman, Hamburg #855/R

MONOGRAMMIST C R (?) ?
£320 $531 €467 Sailor's cottage interior with mother and son (39x35cm-15x14in) mono. 6-Oct-3 David Duggleby, Scarborough #223

MONOGRAMMIST C T (?) ?
£403 $741 €600 Cows in meadow (24x38cm-9x15in) 29-Mar-4 Dr Fritz Nagel, Stuttgart #7029/R

MONOGRAMMIST C V K (?) ?
£556 $917 €800 Winter landscapes with figures on ice (11x15cm-4x6in) mono. panel two. 3-Jul-3 Van Ham, Cologne #1360/R

MONOGRAMMIST C V S (?) ?
£388 $694 €566 Montagnola (50x60cm-20x24in) mono.d.17 i. stretcher. 13-May-4 Stuker, Bern #739/R (S.FR 900)

MONOGRAMMIST C W (?) ?
£282 $480 €412 Still life of iris (39x29cm-15x11in) mono.d.87. 29-Nov-3 Rasmussen, Havnen #2225 (D.KR 3000)

MONOGRAMMIST C W M (?) ?
£1164 $2083 €1699 Two shepherds making music (71x62cm-28x24in) mono. 12-May-4 Dobiaschofsky, Bern #806/R est:4500 (S.FR 2700)

MONOGRAMMIST D B (?) ?
£574 $1011 €850 Girl with parrot (75x63cm-30x25in) mono. 24-May-4 Bernaerts, Antwerp #804

MONOGRAMMIST D G (?) ?
£382 $607 €550 Marine au coucher de soleil (50x60cm-20x24in) mono.d.1863 panel. 9-Sep-3 Vanderkindere, Brussels #116

MONOGRAMMIST D V (17th C) Flemish?
£4000 $6800 €5840 Game still life with a gentleman holding a dead hare (103x131cm-41x52in) init. 31-Oct-3 Christie's, Kensington #48/R est:5000-8000

MONOGRAMMIST D W L (?) ?
£280 $467 €400 Barge transportant le foin (38x62cm-15x24in) mono.d.1906. 13-Oct-3 Horta, Bruxelles #460

MONOGRAMMIST E A (?) ?
£769 $1308 €1100 The winning stallion (50x65cm-20x26in) mono. 28-Nov-3 Schloss Ahlden, Ahlden #1463/R

MONOGRAMMIST E D (?) ?
£307 $564 €460 Oriental scene with a shepherd and his flock by a stream (32x40cm-13x16in) mono. 12-Jun-4 Karlheinz Kaupp, Staufen #1134/R

MONOGRAMMIST E F (?) ?
£775 $1239 €1100 Campagna landscape with ruins (33x62cm-13x24in) mono. 18-Sep-3 Rieber, Stuttgart #1047/R
£1399 $2378 €2000 Night time coastal scene (124x100cm-49x39in) mono.d.15. 28-Nov-3 Schloss Ahlden, Ahlden #1593/R est:1600

MONOGRAMMIST E H (?) ?
£420 $713 €600 Still life of antiques (65x51cm-26x20in) mono. 19-Nov-3 Dorotheum, Klagenfurt #46/R
£2098 $3608 €3000 Rocky coast with figures (30x45cm-12x18in) mono.d.1889 panel. 4-Dec-3 Neumeister, Munich #2880 est:600

MONOGRAMMIST E K (?) ?
£306 $556 €447 Bargaining with the cloth merchant (53x74cm-21x29in) mono. 16-Jun-4 Fischer, Luzern #2281/R (S.FR 700)
£1034 $1852 €1510 Summer landscape with Walensee (65x87cm-26x34in) mono. 13-May-4 Stuker, Bern #257/R est:1000-1500 (S.FR 2400)

MONOGRAMMIST E M C (?) ?
Works on paper
£1747 $3250 €2551 Country estate with horse drawn carriage crossing a river (18x53cm-7x21in) W/C. 6-Mar-4 North East Auctions, Portsmouth #516/R

MONOGRAMMIST E P (?) ?
£2937 $4993 €4200 Scene de plage animee (14x22cm-6x9in) mono.d.1886 panel. 18-Nov-3 Vanderkindere, Brussels #55 est:1000-1500

MONOGRAMMIST E V L (?) ?
£420 $701 €600 Fjord landscape (73x95cm-29x37in) mono.d.1865. 28-Jun-3 Bolland & Marotz, Bremen #712

MONOGRAMMIST E W (?) ?
Works on paper
£439 $773 €650 Portrait of four children in garden (33x44cm-13x17in) mono.i. verso pastel. 21-May-4 Mehlis, Plauen #15071/R

MONOGRAMMIST F B (?) ?
£556 $878 €800 French troops greeting Napoleon on country road (21x26cm-8x10in) mono.d.1893. 6-Sep-3 Arnold, Frankfurt #621
£738 $1358 €1100 Dans l'atelier du peintre (65x55cm-26x22in) mono. 23-Mar-4 Galerie Moderne, Brussels #326/R
Works on paper
£960 $1747 €1402 Children playing on a haycart, set in a rural landscape (44x72cm-17x28in) W/C. 6-Feb-4 Honiton Galleries, Honiton #351

MONOGRAMMIST F G (?) ?
£100671 $180201 €150000 Still life with grapes, apples and chestnuts. Raspberries, crab and butterfly (24x34cm-9x13in) board pair oval lit. 26-May-4 Porro, Milan #37/R est:150000-180000

MONOGRAMMIST F K (?) ?
£423 $739 €600 Farmhouse (53x43cm-21x17in) mono.d.19. 19-Dec-3 Dorotheum, Vienna #21/R

MONOGRAMMIST F L (?) ?
£300 $483 €435 Rocky coastal view with fishermen in his boat in foreground (43x33cm-17x13in) 15-Aug-3 Keys, Aylsham #743

MONOGRAMMIST F M (?) ?
Works on paper
£563 $975 €800 Trompe l'oeil (54x68cm-21x27in) i. pen W/C ink. 14-Dec-3 Finarte, Venice #118
£569 $945 €831 Portrait of Augusta Princess Salmova (20x18cm-8x7in) mono.d.1843 pencil W/C. 4-Oct-3 Dorotheum, Prague #183/R est:6000-9000 (C.KR 26000)

MONOGRAMMIST F M G (?) ?
Works on paper
£300 $489 €438 Harbour scene with fishing boats and figures (35x57cm-14x22in) mono.d.1898 W/C. 25-Sep-3 Clevedon Sale Rooms #156

MONOGRAMMIST F N (?) ?
£1329 $2219 €1900 Southern landscape with riders, waggon and other figures (36x49cm-14x19in) mono.i.d.1826. 28-Jun-3 Dannenberg, Berlin #739/R est:1500

MONOGRAMMIST F R (?) ?
£1678 $2887 €2400 Elves dancing (90x82cm-35x32in) mono.i.d.1892. 3-Dec-3 Neumeister, Munich #676/R est:2200

MONOGRAMMIST G (?) ?
£559 $962 €800 Orchard (50x62cm-20x24in) mono.d.99. 4-Dec-3 Neumeister, Munich #2882

MONOGRAMMIST G A (?) ?
Works on paper
£302 $540 €441 Venus erupting (7x10cm-3x4in) mono. gouache two. 13-May-4 Stuker, Bern #9185 (S.FR 700)
£517 $926 €755 Naples with Vesuvius erupting at night (20x26cm-8x10in) mono. gouache. 13-May-4 Stuker, Bern #9184 (S.FR 1200)

MONOGRAMMIST G C (?) ?
£2148 $4016 €3200 Still life with apples and pears (29x43cm-11x17in) mono.i.d. 28-Feb-4 Quittenbaum, Hamburg #15/R est:1200

MONOGRAMMIST G D E (?) ?
£940 $1663 €1400 La visite au musee (19x21cm-7x8in) mono. cardboard. 27-Apr-4 Campo, Vlaamse Kaai #421

MONOGRAMMIST G M (?) ?
£1333 $2427 €2000 Four dogs in courtyard (26x31cm-10x12in) mono. 30-Jun-4 Neumeister, Munich #619 est:1500

MONOGRAMMIST G S (?) ?
£476 $818 €680 Town harbour (60x48cm-24x19in) mono. 4-Dec-3 Schopman, Hamburg #744/R

MONOGRAMMIST G W (?) ?
Works on paper
£500 $850 €730 Bay of Naples (41x58cm-16x23in) mono. indis i. W/C. 30-Oct-3 Duke & Son, Dorchester #58/R
£500 $850 €730 Monaco (41x56cm-16x22in) mono.i.d.1877 W/C bodycol. 30-Oct-3 Duke & Son, Dorchester #60/R

MONOGRAMMIST H B (?) ?
£1067 $1941 €1600 Dairymaid seated in front of her hut at sunset (18x24cm-7x9in) mono. panel. 1-Jul-4 Van Ham, Cologne #1510/R est:2200

MONOGRAMMIST H C N (?) ?
£1626 $2911 €2374 Sailing vessels off a harbour (26x38cm-10x15in) mono.d.1864. 28-May-4 Uppsala Auktionskammare, Uppsala #131/R est:10000-12000 (S.KR 22000)

MONOGRAMMIST H D (?) ?
£280 $502 €409 Nude by wood (65x54cm-26x21in) mono.d.85 i. stretcher study verso. 12-May-4 Dobiaschofsky, Bern #3773 (S.FR 650)

MONOGRAMMIST H J (?) ?
£268 $491 €400 La robe neuve. mono. 8-Jul-4 Campo, Vlaamse Kaai #133
£1042 $1698 €1500 Monastery by southern mountain lake (22x18cm-9x7in) mono. 24-Sep-3 Neumeister, Munich #503/R est:2000

MONOGRAMMIST H J P (?) ?
£550 $1018 €825 Studies of hunters in a stable (25x36cm-10x14in) mono. pair. 14-Jul-4 Brightwells, Leominster #681

MONOGRAMMIST H K (?) ?
£2168 $3685 €3100 Fantassin. Soldat au tambour (30x17cm-12x7in) mono. panel painted c.1870 pair. 18-Nov-3 Vanderkindere, Brussels #63 est:2000-3000

MONOGRAMMIST H L (?) ?
£5903 $9858 €8500 Basket with dahlias and roses (85x70cm-33x28in) mono.d. 24-Oct-3 Ketterer, Hamburg #89/R est:9000-10000

MONOGRAMMIST H M (?) ?
£282 $487 €400 Peaches (25x19cm-10x7in) 15-Dec-3 Dr Fritz Nagel, Stuttgart #7110/R
£282 $487 €400 Pears (25x19cm-10x7in) 15-Dec-3 Dr Fritz Nagel, Stuttgart #7111/R
£449 $751 €656 Glucksborg Palace (21x29cm-8x11in) mono.indis.d.89. 25-Oct-3 Rasmussen, Havnen #2188 (D.KR 4800)

MONOGRAMMIST H P (?) ?
£360 $659 €526 Cows in a meadow by a river (61x91cm-24x36in) mono. 7-Apr-4 Gardiner & Houlgate, Bath #240/R

MONOGRAMMIST H S (?) ?
£329 $605 €500 Landscape near Neufahrn (42x58cm-17x23in) 28-Jun-4 Dr Fritz Nagel, Stuttgart #7019/R
£940 $1719 €1400 Mother with child in front of ideal landscape (96x96cm-38x38in) mono.d.1876. 8-Jul-4 Allgauer, Kempten #2170/R
£5517 $9214 €8000 Venice (28x35cm-11x14in) mono.d.41 panel. 15-Nov-3 Lempertz, Koln #1657/R est:7500

MONOGRAMMIST H V J (?) ?
£436 $811 €650 Coastal scene with cliffs, lighthouse and sailing boats (75x105cm-30x41in) mono.d.1905. 5-Mar-4 Wendl, Rudolstadt #3789/R

MONOGRAMMIST H W B (?) ?
Works on paper
£369 $650 €539 Mythological studies (16x20cm-6x8in) black pen grey wash. 19-May-4 Doyle, New York #6010/R

MONOGRAMMIST H Z (?) ?
£298 $483 €420 Still life with snail shells (32x52cm-13x20in) mono.d.79 panel. 23-May-3 Altus, Berlin #481

MONOGRAMMIST I A (?) ?
£385 $642 €550 Rijnlandscape (63x75cm-25x30in) mono. 10-Oct-3 Auction Maastricht #927/R

MONOGRAMMIST I B M (?) ?
£274 $466 €400 Christ on the cross (48x33cm-19x13in) 5-Nov-3 Hugo Ruef, Munich #873

MONOGRAMMIST I B X (?) ?
Sculpture
£42053 $76957 €63500 Bacchus. Pan (23cm-9in) one mono. wood one by Flemish School XVII Century. 7-Apr-4 Libert, Castor, Paris #125/R est:10000-12000

MONOGRAMMIST I D (?) ?
£315 $541 €450 Sledging (32x42cm-13x17in) mono.d.1845. 5-Dec-3 Bolland & Marotz, Bremen #609

MONOGRAMMIST I H (?) ?
£3056 $4981 €4400 Russian horse drawn sleigh (55x74cm-22x29in) mono i. verso. 24-Sep-3 Neumeister, Munich #504/R est:1000
£19000 $34770 €27740 Roemer with a steiner, pewter dishes of oysters, bread roll table (66x107cm-26x42in) mono. panel. 7-Jul-4 Bonhams, New Bond Street #116/R est:15000-20000
Works on paper
£6259 $11203 €9200 Paysage aux deux chaumieres et aux coquelicots (27x40cm-11x16in) mono. W/C. 17-Mar-4 Maigret, Paris #125/R est:800-1000

MONOGRAMMIST I K (?) ?
£530 $964 €800 Winter landscape with wood gatherers (12x20cm-5x8in) panel. 16-Jun-4 Hugo Ruef, Munich #994

MONOGRAMMIST I v D (?) ?
£1867 $3341 €2800 Still life with fish, birds and fruit (19x21cm-7x8in) mono. panel. 13-May-4 Bassenge, Berlin #5436/R est:750
Works on paper
£420 $713 €600 Scaliger monuments in Verona (64x43cm-25x17in) mono.d.1875 W/C. 27-Nov-3 Bassenge, Berlin #5620
£559 $951 €800 Basle cathedral (61x48cm-24x19in) mono.d.1876 W/C. 27-Nov-3 Bassenge, Berlin #5619/R

MONOGRAMMIST J B (?) ?
£2378 $4090 €3400 Bergers dans un paysage (33x45cm-13x18in) s. panel. 2-Dec-3 Campo & Campo, Antwerp #239 est:700-900

MONOGRAMMIST J C W (17th C) Dutch
£7692 $13077 €11000 Le carenage des bateaux (41x51cm-16x20in) mono. panel. 1-Dec-3 Millon & Associes, Paris #16/R est:12000-18000

MONOGRAMMIST J G (?) ?
£340 $619 €500 Capri (33x48cm-13x19in) i.d.1909. 4-Feb-4 Neumeister, Munich #771

MONOGRAMMIST J H (?) ?
£350 $641 €511 Cattle watering before a village (50x75cm-20x30in) mono. 29-Jan-4 Bonhams, Edinburgh #366

MONOGRAMMIST J M D (?) ?
Works on paper
£500 $915 €730 Mother and child seated in a chair (37x29cm-15x11in) mono. W/C oval. 31-Jan-4 Shapes, Edinburgh #369

MONOGRAMMIST J R (?) ?
£2917 $4608 €4200 Stettin harbour (70x112cm-28x44in) mono.i.d.99. 19-Sep-3 Schloss Ahlden, Ahlden #1566/R est:4800

MONOGRAMMIST J T H (?) ?
£420 $713 €600 Romantic landscape with castle (41x32cm-16x13in) mono.d.1889. 28-Nov-3 Wendl, Rudolstadt #4103/R

Works on paper
£530 $970 €800 Schloss mIramare (19x28cm-7x11in) mono. W/C. 8-Apr-4 Dorotheum, Vienna #158/R

MONOGRAMMIST J T R (?) ?
£390 $706 €569 Gypsy encampment (14x18cm-6x7in) mono. board. 30-Mar-4 David Duggleby, Scarborough #39/R

MONOGRAMMIST J V D (?) ?
£1806 $2943 €2600 Market square in Amsterdam (32x39cm-13x15in) mono. panel. 23-Sep-3 Galerie Moderne, Brussels #890/R est:2000-3000

MONOGRAMMIST K (?) ?
£553 $924 €780 Woman's portrait (86x70cm-34x28in) mono. 17-Oct-3 Berlinghof, Heidelberg #1075/R

MONOGRAMMIST L B (?) ?
£671 $1255 €1000 Wine drinker (31x25cm-12x10in) mono. panel. 28-Feb-4 Bolland & Marotz, Bremen #288
Works on paper
£385 $654 €550 Tete de Mercure (39x33cm-15x13in) mono.d.1924. 27-Nov-3 Claude Aguttes, Neuilly #54

MONOGRAMMIST L D (?) ?
Works on paper
£1469 $2497 €2100 Parade (64x103cm-25x41in) mono. Chinese ink W/C. 27-Nov-3 Claude Aguttes, Neuilly #52 est:1500-2000

MONOGRAMMIST L D N (?) ?
£972 $1604 €1400 Martyrdom of St Sebastian (41x33cm-16x13in) mono.i.d.1631 panel. 3-Jul-3 Dr Fritz Nagel, Stuttgart #460/R

MONOGRAMMIST L G (?) ?
£245 $450 €358 Vase of mixed flowers (46x43cm-18x17in) mono. board. 25-Jun-4 Freeman, Philadelphia #161/R
Works on paper
£400 $716 €600 La halte des cuirassiers (11x32cm-4x13in) mono.d.14 juillet 1860 wash. 11-May-4 Vanderkindere, Brussels #193

MONOGRAMMIST L H (?) ?
£676 $1209 €1000 Meeting in the Park (35x27cm-14x11in) mono.d.1830. 8-May-4 Dawo, Saarbrucken #31/R
£1486 $2661 €2200 La fiance du Rois de Garbe (35x27cm-14x11in) mono.d.1830 i. stretcher. 8-May-4 Dawo, Saarbrucken #29/R est:280

MONOGRAMMIST L S (?) ?
£661 $1123 €965 Cow in landscape (24x36cm-9x14in) mono. panel. 5-Nov-3 Dobiaschofsky, Bern #813/R (S.FR 1500)

MONOGRAMMIST L U (?) ?
£387 $670 €550 Petit chasseur aux oiseaux (51x39cm-20x15in) mono.d.1853. 9-Dec-3 Vanderkindere, Brussels #99

MONOGRAMMIST L V (?) ?
£382 $638 €550 Nature morte a la bouteille et a la pomme (55x33cm-22x13in) mono. 21-Oct-3 Campo, Vlaamse Kaai #904

MONOGRAMMIST L V H (?) ?
£1733 $3172 €2600 Study of twin children (32x43cm-13x17in) mono.i. canvas on canvas. 5-Jun-4 Arnold, Frankfurt #668/R est:500

MONOGRAMMIST M (?) ?
£881 $1498 €1286 Five boys (34x30cm-13x12in) mono. 5-Nov-3 Dobiaschofsky, Bern #814/R (S.FR 2000)
£1667 $2633 €2400 Cavalry battle by ruins (26x34cm-10x13in) d.1676 panel. 6-Sep-3 Arnold, Frankfurt #622/R est:1000

MONOGRAMMIST M B (?) ?
£5636 $9862 €8000 Paysage de la campagne Flamande animes de personnages (22x34cm-9x13in) one mono. panel pair. 18-Dec-3 Tajan, Paris #33/R est:6000-8000

MONOGRAMMIST M E (?) ?
£1611 $3012 €2400 Schloss Seltenheim near Wolfnitz, Karnten (40x42cm-16x17in) 24-Feb-4 Dorotheum, Vienna #239/R est:2500-3000

MONOGRAMMIST M E G (?) ?
£270 $505 €394 View of a monastery on a small island in a Mediterranean lake (16x20cm-6x8in) mono.d.1926. 24-Feb-4 Canterbury Auctions, UK #159/R

MONOGRAMMIST M K (?) ?
£436 $803 €650 Berlin fishermen bringing in the nets with their catch (100x150cm-39x59in) mono. board. 27-Mar-4 L & B, Essen #155/R

MONOGRAMMIST M O (?) ?
£354 $556 €517 Still life of flowers (19x19cm-7x7in) mono.d.1887. 30-Aug-3 Rasmussen, Havnen #2289 (D.KR 3800)

MONOGRAMMIST M R (?) ?
Works on paper
£385 $654 €550 Village fete (9x14cm-4x6in) mono. gouache ivory after David Teniers. 20-Nov-3 Dorotheum, Salzburg #256/R

MONOGRAMMIST M S (?) ?
£1712 $2911 €2500 Hilly landscape with shepherd and animals (50x135cm-20x53in) 5-Nov-3 Hugo Ruef, Munich #1157 est:1200
£6944 $10972 €10000 King David's triumphal procession to Jerusalem (30x47cm-12x19in) mono. panel. 6-Sep-3 Schopman, Hamburg #684/R est:12000
£21769 $34612 €32000 Waterfall scene (77x131cm-30x52in) mono. oak panel. 23-Mar-3 Mercier & Cie, Lille #159/R est:35000-45000

MONOGRAMMIST M S L (?) ?
Works on paper
£3380 $5848 €4800 Portrait of a gentleman. Portrait of a woman (100x75cm-39x30in) mono.d.1932 pastel paper on canvas oval pair prov. 9-Dec-3 Vanderkindere, Brussels #320 est:3000-4000

MONOGRAMMIST M T B (?) ?
£267 $480 €400 Dachauer Moos (58x65cm-23x26in) mono. board. 22-Apr-4 Allgauer, Kempten #3658/R

MONOGRAMMIST M U (?) ?
Prints
£310 $574 €450 Still life with cacti (44x32cm-17x13in) mono.d.1938. 13-Feb-4 Auktionhaus Georg Rehm, Augsburg #8091/R

MONOGRAMMIST M V H (?) ?
£1399 $2336 €2000 Interior (42x29cm-17x11in) mono. panel. 10-Oct-3 Auction Maastricht #859/R est:2000-3000
£1399 $2336 €2000 Interior (42x29cm-17x11in) mono. 10-Oct-3 Vendue Huis, Gravenhage #859

MONOGRAMMIST M W (?) ?
£3800 $6954 €5548 Deposition (38x28cm-15x11in) mono. canvas on panel. 6-Jul-4 Sotheby's, Olympia #420/R est:3000-4000

MONOGRAMMIST N L F (?) ?
£278 $453 €400 Boy with cap (29x24cm-11x9in) mono.d.1680. 27-Sep-3 Dannenberg, Berlin #597/R

MONOGRAMMIST O G (?) ?
£367 $667 €550 Young girl from Alsace (37x32cm-15x13in) mono.d.1848. 1-Jul-4 Van Ham, Cologne #1511

MONOGRAMMIST O K (?) ?
£805 $1482 €1200 Southern landscape with figures (23x28cm-9x11in) mono.d panel two. 26-Mar-4 Altus, Berlin #569/R

MONOGRAMMIST O S (?) ?
£306 $510 €440 Five ducks by pond (45x70cm-18x28in) 22-Oct-3 Neumeister, Munich #793

MONOGRAMMIST O V B (?) ?
£367 $656 €550 Children playing (18x24cm-7x9in) mono.d.74. 14-May-4 Schloss Ahlden, Ahlden #2887/R

MONOGRAMMIST P (?) ?
£2000 $3200 €2900 Still life of flowers (18x22cm-7x9in) mono. panel. 15-May-3 Stuker, Bern #1391 est:500-700 (S.FR 4200)

MONOGRAMMIST P F (?) ?
£903 $1472 €1300 Emissaries (53x42cm-21x17in) mono. 23-Sep-3 Wiener Kunst Auktionen, Vienna #17/R

MONOGRAMMIST P H P (?) ?
£1477 $2732 €2200 Satyr and the peasant (37x49cm-15x19in) mono.indis.d panel oval exhib. 15-Mar-4 Sotheby's, Amsterdam #5/R est:1500-2000

MONOGRAMMIST P S C (?) ?
£11500 $19550 €16790 Portrait of Emperor Charles V. Portrait of Philip II of Spain (34x25cm-13x10in) mono.d.1609 panel pair prov. 30-Oct-3 Sotheby's, Olympia #93/R est:4000-6000

MONOGRAMMIST P V A (?) ?
£979 $1684 €1400 Portrait of a gentleman, seated, three-quarter length (128x103cm-50x41in) mono.d.1694 verso. 7-Dec-3 Sotheby's, Amsterdam #505/R

MONOGRAMMIST P W (?) ?
£436 $816 €650 Castle with figures (34x29cm-13x11in) mono.d.877 i. verso. 24-Feb-4 Dorotheum, Vienna #229/R

MONOGRAMMIST R A (?) ?
£308 $524 €450 Still life with peaches on white tablecloth (21x33cm-8x13in) mono. 5-Nov-3 Dobiaschofsky, Bern #3609 (S.FR 700)

MONOGRAMMIST R H (?) ?

£369 $679 €550 Scene in tavern (40x45cm-16x18in) 29-Mar-4 Dr Fritz Nagel, Stuttgart #7170/R

MONOGRAMMIST R J (?) ?

£1190 $2167 €1737 Still life of fruit and wine caraffe on table (52x84cm-20x33in) mono.d.94. 7-Feb-4 Rasmussen, Havnen #2084 (D.KR 13000)

MONOGRAMMIST R W (?) ?

£2026 $3445 €2958 Reclining female nude (58x69cm-23x27in) mono. 5-Nov-3 Dobiaschofsky, Bern #815/R est:1200 (S.FR 4600)

MONOGRAMMIST S (?) ?

£400 $716 €600 Paysage anime (25x40cm-10x16in) mono. 11-May-4 Vanderkindere, Brussels #68

£552 $993 €800 Tropicale (145x97cm-57x38in) mono. 20-Jan-4 Galerie Moderne, Brussels #315

MONOGRAMMIST S B (attrib) (?) ?

£829 $1500 €1210 Portrait of a Major General (76x64cm-30x25in) mono.d.1811. 18-Apr-4 Jeffery Burchard, Florida #91/R

MONOGRAMMIST S W (?) ?

£1172 $1958 €1700 Mountain landscape with hut (53x68cm-21x27in) 9-Jul-3 Hugo Ruef, Munich #236 est:900

MONOGRAMMIST T R (?) ?

£3231 $5881 €4717 Still life with fish, cheese, glass and knife (35x46cm-14x18in) mono. 16-Jun-4 Fischer, Luzern #1183/R est:3000-4000 (S.FR 7400)

MONOGRAMMIST T T (?) ?

£1175 $1997 €1680 Reclining female nude (61x185cm-24x73in) mono. 28-Nov-3 Schloss Ahlden, Ahlden #1549/R est:1600

MONOGRAMMIST T V E (19th C) ?

£629 $1070 €900 Sheep and dog in pre Alpine landscape (32x40cm-13x16in) mono. 20-Nov-3 Dorotheum, Salzburg #124/R

MONOGRAMMIST T W (?) ?

£694 $1132 €1000 Cattle and goat by water (26x33cm-10x13in) mono.d.1842 panel. 24-Sep-3 Neumeister, Munich #505/R

MONOGRAMMIST V (?) ?

£6600 $12078 €9636 Equine portrait of a grey with his master, open landscape beyond (47x66cm-19x26in) mono. panel. 10-Jul-4 Windibank, Dorking #300/R est:3000-5000

MONOGRAMMIST V B (?) ?

£567 $948 €800 Evening landscape with fisherman and city view. mono. panel. 20-Oct-3 Bernaerts, Antwerp #21/R

£1310 $2384 €1913 Flora (79x62cm-31x24in) mono. 16-Jun-4 Fischer, Luzern #1080/R est:3000-4000 (S.FR 3000)

£1944 $3208 €2800 Pipe smoker (18x16cm-7x6in) mono. panel. 3-Jul-3 Van Ham, Cologne #995/R est:1800

MONOGRAMMIST V D (?) ?

£839 $1427 €1200 Still life with sea animals and water pipe (48x70cm-19x28in) mono.d.17 panel. 20-Nov-3 Van Ham, Cologne #1382/R est:1500

MONOGRAMMIST V H E (?) ?

Works on paper

£28378 $49946 €42000 Panoramic hilly landscape with view of Antwerp (13x35cm-5x14in) mono. gouache vellum on panel two sheets prov.exhib. 19-May-4 Sotheby's, Amsterdam #14/R est:12000-18000

MONOGRAMMIST V R (?) ?

£6164 $10479 €9000 Swag of grapes, other fruit, and insects, before a bust of Bacchus (127x103cm-50x41in) mono. prov. 4-Nov-3 Sotheby's, Amsterdam #26/R est:12000-18000

MONOGRAMMIST W (?) ?

£1007 $1852 €1500 Village with church and cemetery (28x30cm-11x12in) d.1844 board. 24-Mar-4 Hugo Ruef, Munich #1140/R est:1500

MONOGRAMMIST W F (?) ?

£267 $477 €400 Portrait d'un gentilhomme (61x45cm-24x18in) mono.d.1818. 11-May-4 Vanderkindere, Brussels #164

£733 $1335 €1100 Landscape (57x44cm-22x17in) mono. board. 1-Jul-4 Van Ham, Cologne #1513

MONOGRAMMIST W V K (?) ?

Works on paper

£331 $603 €500 Soldier on horseback (32x45cm-13x18in) W/C. 16-Jun-4 Hugo Ruef, Munich #1128

MONORY, Jacques (1924-) French

£1867 $3360 €2800 Etude pour depart en Amerique (38x46cm-15x18in) s.d.1964 s.i.d.verso. 24-Apr-4 Cornette de St.Cyr, Paris #657 est:3500

£3600 $6012 €5256 Alptraum No. 3 (230x460cm-91x181in) s.i.d.1988 i.verso acrylic film reel string prov. 21-Oct-3 Sotheby's, London #425/R est:5000-7000

£4014 $7025 €5700 Velvet jungle no.11 (124x124cm-49x49in) s.i.d.1970 verso lit. 18-Dec-3 Cornette de St.Cyr, Paris #127/R est:6000-8000

£4698 $8645 €7000 Peinture a Venre No 33, etude pour Felix (100x73cm-39x29in) s.i.d.1988 verso oil objects film. 29-Mar-4 Cornette de St.Cyr, Paris #121/R est:8000-10000

£5634 $9859 €8000 Nuit 2 (100x100cm-39x39in) i. s.i.d.1999 verso. 18-Dec-3 Cornette de St.Cyr, Paris #155/R est:8000-10000

£6944 $11458 €10000 Reve no 1 (146x114cm-57x45in) s.d.1972 s.i.verso lit. 2-Jul-3 Cornette de St.Cyr, Paris #127/R est:10000-12000

£6944 $10972 €10000 Exercice de style (92x73cm-36x29in) s.d.1968 s.i.d.verso prov.lit. 27-Apr-3 Versailles Encheres #75

£8333 $13750 €12000 14 juillet prive, no 291 (190x284cm-75x112in) s.d.1967 oil collage panel prov.lit. 2-Jul-3 Cornette de St.Cyr, Paris #16/R est:12000-15000

£9441 $15766 €13500 Velvet jungle no VI (121x90cm-48x35in) s.d.1969 s.i.d.verso lit. 11-Oct-3 Cornette de St.Cyr, Paris #93/R est:10000-12000

£12667 $23307 €19000 Toxique No 20 Ho! La! (150x231cm-59x91in) s.i.d.1983 verso acrylic in plexiglas. 8-Jun-4 Artcurial Briest, Paris #265/R est:20000-25000

£13732 $24032 €19500 Alptraum no. 3 (230x450cm-91x177in) s.i.d.1987 verso lit. 18-Dec-3 Cornette de St.Cyr, Paris #157/R est:18000-22000

Sculpture

£1608 $2686 €2300 Pastiche/postiche (36x36cm-14x14in) s.i.d.1982 verso mirror ball col felt varnish wood exhib.lit. 11-Oct-3 Cornette de St.Cyr, Paris #95/R est:2500-3000

MONOSILIO, Salvatore (?-1776) Italian

£4276 $7868 €6500 Assumption of the Virgin (69x54cm-27x21in) 22-Jun-4 Babuino, Rome #44/R est:2000-3000

MONOT, Pierre Étienne (1657-1733) French

Sculpture

£420000 $726600 €613200 Depicting the Depostion, with St. John supporting the boby of Christ (72x58cm-28x23in) carved marble lit. 11-Dec-3 Christie's, London #76/R est:30000-50000

MONSANTO, Bernardo (20th C) ?

£324 $510 €473 Landscape (76x55cm-30x22in) 27-Apr-3 Subastas Odalys, Caracas #56

MONSEN, Mons Gabriel (1836-1896) Norwegian

£2310 $3926 €3373 The manor house Hillevaag (40x49cm-16x19in) init.d.1868 lit. 19-Nov-3 Grev Wedels Plass, Oslo #24/R est:20000-30000 (N.KR 27000)

MONSIAUX, Nicolas Andre (1754-1837) French

£61538 $105846 €88000 Allegory of lazyness (162x130cm-64x51in) s.d.1821 prov.exhib.lit. 2-Dec-3 Christie's, Paris #129/R est:30000-50000

MONSTED, Peder (1859-1941) Danish

£435 $778 €635 Portrait of a young soldier (38x25cm-15x10in) s.i.d.1929. 12-Jan-4 Rasmussen, Vejle #142/R (D.KR 4600)

£922 $1567 €1346 Southern landscape with woman looking out to sea (34x28cm-13x11in) mono.d.85. 10-Nov-3 Rasmussen, Vejle #5/R (D.KR 10000)

£935 $1477 €1356 Drifting clouds over snow covered mountain tops (21x31cm-8x12in) s.d.1899. 2-Sep-3 Rasmussen, Copenhagen #1527/R (D.KR 10000)

£937 $1528 €1368 Landscape with Aarhus Cathedral in background (40x58cm-16x23in) init.d.79. 27-Sep-3 Rasmussen, Havnen #2002 (D.KR 10000)

£1000 $1660 €1460 Along the Nile (21x33cm-8x13in) s.i.d.93. 1-Oct-3 Sotheby's, Olympia #265/R est:1000-1500

£1028 $1624 €1491 Foaming rapids (23x53cm-9x21in) s.d.1897. 2-Sep-3 Rasmussen, Copenhagen #1766/R (D.KR 11000)

£1053 $1705 €1527 Landscape from Aarhus Bay (32x37cm-13x15in) s.d.77. 4-Aug-3 Rasmussen, Vejle #284/R (D.KR 11000)

£1119 $2048 €1634 Monk peeling vegetables in monastery yard (31x21cm-12x8in) s.d.1926. 9-Jun-4 Rasmussen, Copenhagen #1915/R est:15000 (D.KR 12500)

£1134 $1962 €1656 Landscape from the coast by Goletta (17x25cm-7x10in) s.i.d.1886. 9-Dec-3 Rasmussen, Copenhagen #1346/R est:10000-12000 (D.KR 12000)

£1229 $2126 €1794 Landscape, Grunstein near Konigsee (53x38cm-21x15in) s.i.d.1914. 9-Dec-3 Rasmussen, Copenhagen #1678/R est:12000-18000 (D.KR 13000)

£1308 $2067 €1897 Winter's day in the wood (31x50cm-12x20in) s.d.1917. 2-Sep-3 Rasmussen, Copenhagen #1536/R est:15000-20000 (D.KR 14000)

£1333 $2213 €1946 Untitled, winter scene (41x60cm-16x24in) 2-Oct-3 Heffel, Vancouver #26 (C.D 3000)

£1382 $2350 €2018 Landscape with Etna, figures and donkey (18x42cm-7x17in) s.i.d.1885 exhib. 10-Nov-3 Rasmussen, Vejle #11/R est:15000 (D.KR 15000)

£1402 $2215 €2033 Girl seated on steps knitting socks (23x25cm-9x10in) sketch. 2-Sep-3 Rasmussen, Copenhagen #1955/R est:15000-20000 (D.KR 15000)

£1475 $2507 €2154 Wooded landscape with river (24x34cm-9x13in) init.d.87. 10-Nov-3 Rasmussen, Vejle #37/R est:10000-15000 (D.KR 16000)

£1556 $2831 €2334 Street scene from Cairo with figures and donkey (47x31cm-19x12in) s.i.d.1893 panel. 19-Jun-4 Rasmussen, Havnen #2201/R est:20000-25000 (D.KR 17500)

£1724 $2707 €2517 Farmyard with woman feeding chickens (24x32cm-9x13in) s.d.1921 panel. 30-Aug-3 Rasmussen, Havnen #2079/R est:20000 (D.KR 18500)

£1796 $3107 €2622 Breakfast in the woods (14x21cm-6x8in) study. 9-Dec-3 Rasmussen, Copenhagen #1411/R est:10000-15000 (D.KR 19000)

£1810 $3240 €2643 Evening landscape with view of Saeby (35x61cm-14x24in) s.d.95 exhib. 10-May-4 Rasmussen, Vejle #71/R est:25000 (D.KR 20000)

£1890 $3270 €2759 Alpine landscape with two children (57x31cm-22x12in) s.i.d.1899. 9-Dec-3 Rasmussen, Copenhagen #1500/R est:20000 (D.KR 20000)

£1970 $3604 €2876 Hellingdoms cliffs, Bornholm (48x74cm-19x29in) s.d.1882. 9-Jun-4 Rasmussen, Copenhagen #1632/R est:20000 (D.KR 22000)

£2032 $3638 €2967 Feeding chickens in woodland glade (36x48cm-14x19in) s.d.96. 12-Jan-4 Rasmussen, Vejle #55/R est:15000 (D.KR 21500)

£2144 $3365 €3130 Girl milking cow, white church in background (35x50cm-14x20in) s.d.1932. 30-Aug-3 Rasmussen, Havnen #2071/R est:20000-30000 (D.KR 23000)

£2156 $4011 €3148 Path through wood on a clear day in autumn (44x42cm-17x17in) init.d.1888. 2-Mar-4 Rasmussen, Copenhagen #1344/R est:15000 (D.KR 24000)

£2201 $3566 €3191 Summer landscape with woman walking by lake, Denmark (40x29cm-16x11in) s.d.1888. 4-Aug-3 Rasmussen, Vejle #288/R est:20000-30000 (D.KR 23000)

£2217 $3969 €3237 Sailing trip, Lac Leman (41x27cm-16x11in) s. canvas on cardboard. 25-May-4 Bukowskis, Stockholm #316/R est:40000-50000 (S.KR 30000)

£2268 $4060 €3311 Wooded landscape with figures, Bornholm (27x41cm-11x16in) init. 12-Jan-4 Rasmussen, Vejle #56/R est:25000-30000 (D.KR 24000)

£2275 $3640 €3322 Autumn landscape (30x41cm-12x16in) s.i.d.1925. 22-Sep-3 Rasmussen, Vejle #225/R est:20000-25000 (D.KR 24000)

£2308	$3969	€3370	Winter landscape with horse and sleigh (35x51cm-14x20in) s.i.d.1936. 3-Dec-3 AB Stockholms Auktionsverk #2602/R est:40000-50000 (S.KR 30000)
£2336	$3692	€3387	From Aalsgarde with view of the beach and large stones (30x46cm-12x18in) s.i.d.1919 cardboard. 3-Sep-3 Museumsbygningen, Copenhagen #210/R est:15000 (D.KR 25000)
£2467	$3996	€3602	Landscape with waterway (56x43cm-22x17in) s.d.1896. 9-Aug-3 Hindemae, Ullerslev #42/R est:35000-40000 (D.KR 26000)
£2500	$4500	€3650	Harvesting (41x46cm-16x18in) s.i.d.1922. 21-Jan-4 Sotheby's, Olympia #472/R est:2500-3500
£2686	$4915	€3922	Thatched farm with sheaves of corn and country road (29x50cm-11x20in) s.i.d.1908. 7-Jun-4 Museumsbygningen, Copenhagen #147/R est:30000-40000 (D.KR 30000)
£2686	$4915	€3922	Winter landscape with children on sledge, Dyrehaven (31x41cm-12x16in) s.i.d.1924 prov. 9-Jun-4 Rasmussen, Copenhagen #1514/R est:30000-40000 (D.KR 30000)
£2765	$4700	€4037	Summer's day by woodland lake with man in small boat (35x50cm-14x20in) s.i.d.1929. 10-Nov-3 Rasmussen, Vejle #35/R est:30000-40000 (D.KR 30000)
£2778	$5000	€4056	Lake landscape with trees (35x27cm-14x11in) s.d.1902 panel. 24-Apr-4 Rasmussen, Havnen #2342/R est:10000-15000 (D.KR 31000)
£2785	$5181	€4066	Chickens at farmhouse in spring (35x27cm-14x11in) s.d.1903. 2-Mar-4 Rasmussen, Copenhagen #1400/R est:25000 (D.KR 31000)
£2865	$5243	€4183	Hammershus palace ruins in sunshine (40x63cm-16x25in) s.d.1921. 9-Jun-4 Rasmussen, Copenhagen #1630/R est:40000 (D.KR 32000)
£2930	$5245	€4278	Woodland lake with water-lilies (28x43cm-11x17in) s.d.1908. 12-Jan-4 Rasmussen, Vejle #65/R est:30000-40000 (D.KR 31000)
£3033	$4853	€4428	Winter landscape with farm (31x48cm-12x19in) s.i.d.1921. 22-Sep-3 Rasmussen, Vejle #226/R est:30000-40000 (D.KR 32000)
£3133	$5734	€4574	Peasant woman among her chickens and geese (50x69cm-20x27in) s.i.d.1936 prov. 9-Jun-4 Rasmussen, Copenhagen #1723/R est:40000-60000 (D.KR 35000)
£3156	$5839	€4608	Evening landscape with waterway and two men fishing (35x58cm-14x23in) s.d.1897. 15-Mar-4 Rasmussen, Vejle #21/R est:25000-30000 (D.KR 35000)
£3214	$5560	€4692	Summer in Aalborg - mother walking with her children near Budolfi church (45x63cm-18x25in) s.d.1880. 9-Dec-3 Rasmussen, Copenhagen #1436/R est:35000-40000 (D.KR 34000)
£3235	$6016	€4723	Coastal landscape with boats and children playing on beach at Aalsgaarde (48x37cm-19x15in) s.d.1919 prov. 2-Mar-4 Rasmussen, Copenhagen #1402/R est:25000-30000 (D.KR 36000)
£3252	$5821	€4748	Farm yard with chickens (34x49cm-13x19in) s.d.1916. 26-May-4 AB Stockholms Auktionsverk #2429/R est:50000-60000 (S.KR 44000)
£3556	$6471	€5334	Winter landscape from Taastrup with sleigh ride (27x50cm-11x20in) s.i.d.1929. 19-Jun-4 Rasmussen, Havnen #2313/R est:15000-20000 (D.KR 40000)
£3581	$6553	€5228	Harvesters on country road (51x61cm-20x24in) s.i.d.1928. 9-Jun-4 Rasmussen, Copenhagen #1727/R est:60000 (D.KR 40000)
£3594	$6685	€5247	Norwegian winter landscape with cabin (33x51cm-13x20in) s.i.d.1919. 2-Mar-4 Rasmussen, Copenhagen #1223/R est:40000 (D.KR 40000)
£3738	$5907	€5420	Early summer in Tranbjerg with lilacs and children with dog (61x42cm-24x17in) s.i.d.1930. 2-Sep-3 Rasmussen, Copenhagen #1746/R est:50000 (D.KR 40000)
£3843	$6880	€5611	In the vegetable garden (61x27cm-24x11in) s.d.1908 canvas on cardboard. 25-May-4 Bukowskis, Stockholm #326/R est:25000-30000 (S.KR 52000)
£3916	$6500	€5717	Sunset (31x107cm-12x42in) s.d.1896. 30-Sep-3 Christie's, Rockefeller NY #462/R est:6000-8000
£3925	$6202	€5691	Landscape from Silkeborgsoerne (52x78cm-20x31in) s.d.1904. 2-Sep-3 Rasmussen, Copenhagen #1522/R est:50000 (D.KR 42000)
£4043	$7520	€5903	Winter landscape with two crows on woodland road (40x61cm-16x24in) s.i.d.1917. 2-Mar-4 Rasmussen, Copenhagen #1209/R est:25000-35000 (D.KR 45000)
£4070	$7000	€5942	Winter landscape, Lillehammer (34x50cm-13x20in) s.d.1922. 2-Dec-3 Christie's, Rockefeller NY #43/R est:7000-9000
£4112	$6497	€5962	Helligdoms cliffs, Bornholm (81x65cm-32x26in) s.d.1882. 2-Sep-3 Rasmussen, Copenhagen #1519/R est:30000-40000 (D.KR 44000)
£4159	$7195	€6072	Early spring day in the woods, Soroegnen (50x30cm-20x12in) s.d.1903. 9-Dec-3 Rasmussen, Copenhagen #1394/R est:30000 (D.KR 44000)
£4424	$7521	€6459	Country road with girl and goat by thatched farmhouse (97x70cm-38x28in) s.i.d.1920. 10-Nov-3 Rasmussen, Vejle #23/R est:50000 (D.KR 48000)
£4486	$7088	€6505	From Traneberg with three small girls out playing (47x31cm-19x12in) s.i.d.1932. 2-Sep-3 Rasmussen, Copenhagen #1530/R est:40000 (D.KR 48000)
£4492	$8356	€6558	River landscape with cattle grazing (90x150cm-35x59in) s.d.1906. 2-Mar-4 Rasmussen, Copenhagen #1382/R est:50000 (D.KR 50000)
£4861	$7924	€7000	Sunny Roquebrune coast (80x53cm-31x21in) s.d.1906. 26-Sep-3 Bolland & Marotz, Bremen #580/R est:7500
£4977	$8910	€7266	River through spring wood (36x26cm-14x10in) s.d.1894. 10-May-4 Rasmussen, Vejle #12/R est:80000 (D.KR 55000)
£5217	$9548	€7617	Village summer fete (38x45cm-15x18in) s.i.d.1913. 4-Jun-4 Zofingen, Switzerland #2491/R est:15000 (S.FR 12000)
£5372	$9830	€7843	Watering the garden flowers (40x62cm-16x24in) s.i.d.1928. 9-Jun-4 Rasmussen, Copenhagen #1449/R est:50000-75000 (D.KR 60000)
£5607	$8860	€8130	Taffelbay near Hellerup (54x36cm-21x14in) s.d.1908. 2-Sep-3 Rasmussen, Copenhagen #1542/R est:60000 (D.KR 60000)
£5987	$10716	€8741	In the shade of the palm trees, Algiers (75x121cm-30x48in) s. 25-May-4 Bukowskis, Stockholm #315/R est:100000-125000 (S.KR 81000)
£6049	$10465	€8832	Summer's day by Saeby river (50x47cm-20x19in) s.d.1882. 9-Dec-3 Rasmussen, Copenhagen #1410/R est:75000-100000 (D.KR 64000)
£6075	$9598	€8809	Three children seated on the grass under a rosebush in village street (45x61cm-18x24in) s.d.1929. 2-Sep-3 Rasmussen, Copenhagen #1531/R est:50000-60000 (D.KR 65000)
£6075	$9598	€8809	Sunshine in the village one winter's day (46x61cm-18x24in) s.i.d.1923. 2-Sep-3 Rasmussen, Copenhagen #1538/R est:30000-40000 (D.KR 65000)
£6111	$11000	€8922	Hosterkob (50x35cm-20x14in) s.i.d.1938. 22-Apr-4 Christie's, Rockefeller NY #13/R est:12000-18000
£6500	$11050	€9490	Tranquil river (61x91cm-24x36in) s.d.1910. 19-Nov-3 Bonhams, New Bond Street #34/R est:7000-10000
£7561	$13081	€11039	Sunshine on road through woods, summer (102x71cm-40x28in) s.d.1909. 9-Dec-3 Rasmussen, Copenhagen #1274/R est:100000-125000 (D.KR 80000)
£7610	$13926	€11111	Pale blue sky over spring landscape with wood anemones (50x39cm-20x15in) s.d.1895 panel. 9-Jun-4 Rasmussen, Copenhagen #1635/R est:50000 (D.KR 85000)
£7647	$13000	€11165	December (47x61cm-19x24in) s.d.1924. 29-Oct-3 Christie's, Rockefeller NY #21/R est:10000-15000
£7800	$14196	€11388	Portrait of Professor Jacobsen (48x34cm-19x13in) s.i.d.11/6/1918 prov. 15-Jun-4 Sotheby's, London #361/R est:4000-6000
£8054	$14416	€12000	Part of the coast (79x90cm-31x35in) s.i.d.1906. 27-May-4 Dorotheum, Vienna #78/R est:12000-16000
£8295	$14101	€12111	Waterlilies on woodland lake, Munkebjerg near Vejle (70x50cm-28x20in) s.i.d.1921. 10-Nov-3 Rasmussen, Vejle #24/R est:40000 (D.KR 90000)
£8411	$13290	€12196	Spring landscape with waterway (33x74cm-13x29in) s.d.1899. 2-Sep-3 Rasmussen, Copenhagen #1565/R est:100000 (D.KR 90000)
£8597	$15389	€12552	Summer landscape from Munkebjerg with two young figures in foreground (70x100cm-28x39in) s.i.d.1920. 10-May-4 Rasmussen, Vejle #57/R est:100000 (D.KR 95000)
£8910	$14256	€13009	Beech trees by river in spring, Saebygaard Woods (80x53cm-31x21in) s. 22-Sep-3 Rasmussen, Vejle #227/R est:20000-30000 (D.KR 94000)
£9346	$14766	€13552	Egyptian river landscape, possibly the Nile with women carrying fruit from ship (86x58cm-34x23in) s.d.1893. 2-Sep-3 Rasmussen, Copenhagen #1560/R est:100000-125000 (D.KR 100000)
£10000	$17000	€14600	Woodland path (52x79cm-20x31in) s.d.1903. 18-Nov-3 Sotheby's, London #352/R
£10295	$18841	€15031	Ducks by pond (98x71cm-39x28in) s.i.d.1918 prov. 9-Jun-4 Rasmussen, Copenhagen #1499/R est:125000-150000 (D.KR 115000)
£10500	$19110	€15330	View across Lake Geneva, Switzerland (47x85cm-19x33in) s.d.1887. 15-Jun-4 Sotheby's, London #350/R est:7000-10000
£10782	$20054	€15742	Landscape from Raadvad Lake (79x53cm-31x21in) s.d.1899. 2-Mar-4 Rasmussen, Copenhagen #1204/R est:80000-100000 (D.KR 120000)
£10782	$20054	€15742	Winter landscape with brook, Brondbyvester (62x86cm-24x34in) s.d.1923. 2-Mar-4 Rasmussen, Copenhagen #1256/R est:60000-80000 (D.KR 120000)
£11000	$20020	€16060	Winter landscape with a timber shed (68x98cm-27x39in) s.d.1918. 17-Jun-4 Christie's, London #48/R est:15000-20000
£11189	$19021	€16000	Sunny landscape with woodland and stream after the rain (25x42cm-10x17in) s.d.1898 prov. 24-Nov-3 Dorotheum, Vienna #91/R est:20000-24000
£12098	$21656	€17663	Rosebed by old house, Sorup (47x61cm-19x24in) s.d.1934 exhib. 12-Jan-4 Rasmussen, Vejle #64/R est:75000-100000 (D.KR 128000)
£13000	$22100	€18980	Winter landscape (50x36cm-20x14in) s.i.d.1914. 18-Nov-3 Sotheby's, London #353/R
£13514	$24189	€20000	Deer in wood (52x96cm-20x38in) s.d.1918 i. verso lit. 8-May-4 Schloss Ahlden, Ahlden #745/R est:7500
£13986	$23776	€20000	Swans in the reeds (90x149cm-35x59in) s.d.1904. 20-Nov-3 Van Ham, Cologne #1746/R est:23000
£14324	$26213	€20913	Rings in the water, river on a sunny summer's day (54x82cm-21x32in) s.i.d.1915 prov. 9-Jun-4 Rasmussen, Copenhagen #1500/R est:100000-125000 (D.KR 160000)
£14747	$25069	€21531	Summer's day by an Italian pergola with two young women (110x74cm-43x29in) s.d.1890. 10-Nov-3 Rasmussen, Vejle #3/R est:100000 (D.KR 160000)
£16500	$28380	€24090	Bedouin camp at Gerzeirch after sunset (50x73cm-20x29in) s.d.1893. 3-Dec-3 Christie's, London #88/R est:8000-12000
£16667	$30000	€24334	Lady reading by a lake (70x50cm-28x20in) s.i.d.1920. 22-Apr-4 Christie's, Rockefeller NY #16/R est:30000-40000
£16667	$30000	€24334	Autumn landscape (76x118cm-30x46in) s.d.1907. 22-Apr-4 Christie's, Rockefeller NY #19/R est:25000-35000
£16667	$30000	€24334	Chemin dans un bois (101x70cm-40x28in) s.d.1909. 23-Apr-4 Sotheby's, New York #154/R est:15000-20000
£17905	$32766	€26141	Street steps up towards Villa d'Este, Tivoli near Rome (122x95cm-48x37in) s.d.1884 prov. 9-Jun-4 Rasmussen, Copenhagen #1482/R est:150000-200000 (D.KR 200000)
£18904	$32703	€27600	Sibyl Temple near Tivoli (121x95cm-48x37in) s.i.d.1884 exhib. 9-Dec-3 Rasmussen, Copenhagen #1255/R est:200000 (D.KR 200000)
£19000	$34580	€27740	Returning home, Hellebaek (85x53cm-33x21in) s.d.1906 i.verso prov. 15-Jun-4 Sotheby's, London #369/R est:18000-25000
£19849	$34338	€28980	Brook running through autumn wood (100x70cm-39x28in) s.d.1908. 9-Dec-3 Rasmussen, Copenhagen #1259/R est:100000 (D.KR 210000)
£22000	$40040	€32120	Snowy river bank (41x58cm-16x23in) s.d.1915. 15-Jun-4 Sotheby's, London #340/R est:12000-18000
£22381	$40958	€32676	Winter landscape near Engadin, Switzerland (70x100cm-28x39in) s.i.d.1920 prov. 9-Jun-4 Rasmussen, Copenhagen #1513/R est:100000-150000 (D.KR 250000)
£23000	$41860	€33580	Children playing in the snow (70x100cm-28x39in) s.d.1908 prov. 15-Jun-4 Sotheby's, London #341/R est:25000-35000
£28000	$47600	€40880	Grazing by river (81x123cm-32x48in) s.d.1908. 18-Nov-3 Sotheby's, London #355/R
£35917	$62136	€52439	Small boy fishing (140x100cm-55x39in) s.d.1910. 9-Dec-3 Rasmussen, Copenhagen #1275/R est:150000-200000 (D.KR 380000)
£42000	$76440	€61320	River landscape in spring (83x119cm-33x47in) s.d.1903 prov. 15-Jun-4 Sotheby's, London #345/R est:25000-35000
£50000	$85000	€73000	Heather hills by the lakes near Silkeborg (123x200cm-48x79in) s.d.1908. 29-Oct-3 Christie's, Rockefeller NY #20/R est:70000-90000
£52000	$94640	€75920	Stream in the woods (81x120cm-32x47in) s.d.1911 prov. 15-Jun-4 Sotheby's, London #346/R est:30000-50000
£58000	$98600	€84680	Temple of Olympeus Zeus (80x137cm-31x54in) s.d.1894 prov. 18-Nov-3 Sotheby's, London #70/R est:30000-50000

Works on paper

£290	$522	€435	In the garden (40x62cm-16x24in) s.d.1897 W/C. 25-Apr-4 Goteborg Auktionsverk, Sweden #223/R (S.KR 4000)
£662	$1145	€967	Family harvesting (46x30cm-18x12in) s.d.1925 crayon W/C gouache. 9-Dec-3 Rasmussen, Copenhagen #1418/R (D.KR 7000)

MONTAGNAC, Pierre Paul (1883-?) French

Works on paper

£528	$877	€750	Les trois graces (53x92cm-21x36in) s. col crayon. 16-Jun-3 E & Eve, Paris #90/R

MONTAGNE, Émile Pierre de la (1873-1956) Belgian

£4636	$8483	€7000	Jeune femme regardant une sculpture (84x101cm-33x40in) s. 9-Apr-4 Claude Aguttes, Neuilly #59/R est:7000-8000

MONTAGNE, Louis (1879-1960) French

£700	$1288	€1050	La fontaine (38x55cm-15x22in) s. 9-Jun-4 Beaussant & Lefèvre, Paris #194
£709	$1184	€1000	Le pont du Gard au coucher de soleil (24x35cm-9x14in) s. 19-Jun-3 Millon & Associes, Paris #183
£1538	$2615	€2200	Vue d'une ville (38x55cm-15x22in) s. 30-Nov-3 Salle des ventes Pillet, Lyon la Foret #134 est:1500-1800
£1748	$2972	€2500	Paysage de la Meuse (38x55cm-15x22in) s. 30-Nov-3 Salle des ventes Pillet, Lyon la Foret #133 est:1800-2000
£2483	$4543	€3600	Parc de la propriete de l'artiste (84x68cm-33x27in) s. 31-Jan-4 Gerard, Besancon #52
£2587	$4399	€3700	Paysage du Gard (39x56cm-15x22in) s. 30-Nov-3 Salle des ventes Pillet, Lyon la Foret #130 est:2300-2500
£2657	$4517	€3800	Paysage du Gard (38x55cm-15x22in) s. 30-Nov-3 Salle des ventes Pillet, Lyon la Foret #132 est:1800-2000

£2797	$4755	€4000	Paysage pres d'Avignon (38x55cm-15x22in) s. 30-Nov-3 Salle des ventes Pillet, Lyon la Foret #131 est:2300-2500
£3000	$5190	€4380	Coin de Provence (65x81cm-26x32in) s. 11-Dec-3 Christie's, Kensington #62/R est:3000-5000
£4828	$8834	€7000	Villeneuve-les-Avignon, la tour de Guet (173x130cm-68x51in) s. 31-Jan-4 Gerard, Besancon #51
£7000	$11900	€10220	Fishing vessels (65x81cm-26x32in) s. 19-Nov-3 Christie's, Kensington #600/R
Works on paper			
£263	$484	€400	Bouquet de fleurs (49x61cm-19x24in) s. W/C. 28-Jun-4 Rossini, Paris #53
£345	$631	€500	Rouen, vue de la cathedrale (61x45cm-24x18in) s. W/C. 31-Jan-4 Gerard, Besancon #9
£379	$694	€550	Bassin du Chateau de Versailles (30x44cm-12x17in) s. W/C. 31-Jan-4 Gerard, Besancon #11
£379	$694	€550	La commode (43x32cm-17x13in) s. W/C. 31-Jan-4 Gerard, Besancon #12
£483	$883	€700	La commode Louis Philippe (45x33cm-18x13in) s. W/C. 31-Jan-4 Gerard, Besancon #13
£552	$1010	€800	Paris, le chevet de Notre-Dame (46x60cm-18x24in) s. W/C. 31-Jan-4 Gerard, Besancon #16
£621	$1136	€900	Le vaisselier (45x31cm-18x12in) s. W/C. 31-Jan-4 Gerard, Besancon #18
£655	$1199	€950	Les amandiers en fleurs (32x45cm-13x18in) s. W/C. 31-Jan-4 Gerard, Besancon #20/R
£724	$1325	€1050	La coiffeuse (60x45cm-24x18in) s. W/C. 31-Jan-4 Gerard, Besancon #8
£724	$1325	€1050	Le cheminee de la cuisine (60x46cm-24x18in) s. W/C. 31-Jan-4 Gerard, Besancon #10
£897	$1641	€1300	La cheminee du salon (60x45cm-24x18in) s. W/C. 31-Jan-4 Gerard, Besancon #19
£1379	$2524	€2000	Chateau de Versailles, la Cour de marbre (46x60cm-18x24in) s. W/C. 31-Jan-4 Gerard, Besancon #14
£1724	$3155	€2500	Salon Parisien (60x73cm-24x29in) s. W/C. 31-Jan-4 Gerard, Besancon #15
£2690	$4922	€3900	Venise, la Place Saint-Marc (45x60cm-18x24in) s. W/C. 31-Jan-4 Gerard, Besancon #17

MONTAGUE, Alfred (fl.1832-1883) British

£270	$459	€394	Antwerp from the river, morning (28x20cm-11x8in) s.d.1863 i.verso panel. 25-Nov-3 Bonhams, Knowle #232
£320	$589	€467	Rotterdam (34x30cm-13x12in) s. 10-Jun-4 Lyon & Turnbull, Edinburgh #35
£450	$828	€657	Children playing by a stream (34x45cm-13x18in) s. indis d. i.verso. 8-Jun-4 Bonhams, Knightsbridge #212/R
£524	$965	€765	Sunny morning (15x25cm-6x10in) s. s.i.verso prov. 9-Jun-4 Walker's, Ottawa #352/R (C.D 1300)
£600	$1110	€876	View of Rotterdam (30x41cm-12x16in) s. 9-Mar-4 Gorringes, Lewes #2100
£638	$1034	€900	Lively street and canal in Paris (30x25cm-12x10in) s. lit. 23-May-3 Karlheinz Kaupp, Staufen #1760
£647	$1080	€945	Continental port (12x20cm-5x8in) init. board. 20-Oct-3 Stephan Welz, Johannesburg #431 est:3000-4000 (SA.R 7500)
£1000	$1670	€1460	Continental landscape with figures and houses beside a river (28x43cm-11x17in) s.d.61. 10-Jul-3 Gorringes, Worthing #750/R est:1000-1500
£1100	$1980	€1606	Gypsy encampment (36cm-14in circular) i.verso panel. 21-Apr-4 Tennants, Leyburn #1120 est:1000-1500
£1150	$1955	€1679	Old Hastings (46x61cm-18x24in) s. 29-Oct-3 Bonhams, Chester #510a est:700-1000
£1200	$1920	€1752	Fishing boats in rough seas off the coast (33x58cm-13x23in) s. 16-Sep-3 Gorringes, Bexhill #1549/R est:1200-1800
£1400	$2226	€2030	Continental canal scene (36x51cm-14x20in) 9-Sep-3 Bonhams, Knightsbridge #284/R est:800-1200
£1528	$2490	€2200	Capriccio of a town by sunset (30cm-12in circular) s. 29-Sep-3 Sotheby's, Amsterdam #33/R
£1789	$2808	€2612	Untitled, harbour scene (50x76cm-20x30in) s. 1-Sep-3 Shapiro, Sydney #355/R est:3500-4500 (A.D 4400)
£2300	$3956	€3358	Hauling in the nets (41x61cm-16x24in) s. 2-Dec-3 Sotheby's, London #45/R est:800-1200
£2595	$4800	€3789	Hauling in the lobster pots (35x61cm-14x24in) s.d.1871. 10-Feb-4 Christie's, Rockefeller NY #219/R est:6000-8000
£3200	$5440	€4672	Blustery day (43x77cm-17x30in) s.d.1861. 19-Nov-3 Christie's, Kensington #568/R
£3400	$6290	€4964	Shipping off Amsterdam (76x101cm-30x40in) s. 10-Mar-4 Sotheby's, Olympia #200/R est:3000-5000
Works on paper			
£2291	$4101	€3345	Coastal landscape with sailing vessel (85x120cm-33x47in) s.d.1865 W/C. 26-May-4 AB Stockholms Auktionsverk #2466/R est:20000-25000 (S.KR 31000)

MONTAGUE, Alfred (attrib) (fl.1832-1883) British

£284	$500	€415	Street scene, Normandy (36x25cm-14x10in) panel painted c.1870. 23-May-4 Treadway Gallery, Cincinnati #510/R
£900	$1665	€1314	Street scene, Rue de Grande Horloge, Rouen (66x46cm-26x18in) 14-Jul-4 Bonhams, Chester #509/R

MONTAGUE, C P (20th C) American

£306	$550	€447	Twin oaks (61x91cm-24x36in) s. i.stretcher. 24-Apr-4 Weschler, Washington #616/R

MONTAGUE, Clifford (fl.1883-1900) British

£300	$498	€438	Outskirts of the park, gypsy encampment in a woodland landscape (43x43cm-17x17in) s.d.1884. 4-Oct-3 Finan Watkins & Co, Mere #136
£800	$1440	€1168	At Rouen, figures in boats on a canal (46x36cm-18x14in) s.i.d.1894 prov. 21-Apr-4 Tennants, Leyburn #1119
£1000	$1670	€1460	Canal scene at Abbeville. Street at Dal (46x36cm-18x14in) s. pair. 7-Oct-3 Bonhams, Knightsbridge #270/R est:800-1200

MONTAGUE, Lady Shalimar (20th C) American

Works on paper			
£299	$500	€437	Zigfield Follies (30x46cm-12x18in) ink W/C prov. 15-Nov-3 Slotin Folk Art, Buford #717/R

MONTAIGU, Louis (1905-1988) French

£604	$1081	€900	Petit village pres de Berck (46x61cm-18x24in) s. panel. 30-May-4 Eric Pillon, Calais #48/R
£638	$1141	€950	Dunes a Berck (54x81cm-21x32in) s. panel. 30-May-4 Eric Pillon, Calais #50/R
£906	$1622	€1350	Chalutier dans la baie de la Canche a maree basse (38x46cm-15x18in) s. panel. 30-May-4 Eric Pillon, Calais #47/R

MONTALD, Constant (1862-1944) Belgian

£872	$1614	€1300	Soleil se levant sur les meules (37x45cm-15x18in) s. canvas on panel. 15-Mar-4 Horta, Bruxelles #73
£1867	$3379	€2800	Vue de parc en hiver (50x70cm-20x28in) s.d.1916 oil paper. 30-Mar-4 Campo, Vlaamse Kaai #117/R est:3000-3500
£2000	$3620	€3000	La ferme au clair de lune (51x70cm-20x28in) s.d.1916 oil paper. 30-Mar-4 Campo, Vlaamse Kaai #116/R est:3000-3500
£2345	$4338	€3400	Pommiers en fleurs (48x42cm-19x17in) bears sig.d.23. 16-Feb-4 Horta, Bruxelles #94 est:1500-2500
£5333	$9653	€8000	Le village sous la neige (71x90cm-28x35in) s.d.1928. 30-Mar-4 Campo, Vlaamse Kaai #118/R est:6000-8000
£6294	$10699	€9000	Jeunes femmes dans un jardin (61x81cm-24x32in) s.d.25. 1-Dec-3 Palais de Beaux Arts, Brussels #96/R est:8000-12000

MONTALTI, Alfredo (1858-1928) Italian

£667	$1227	€1000	Bazar interior (16x27cm-6x11in) s.d.81 board. 8-Jun-4 Della Rocca, Turin #210/R

MONTALTO, Giovanni Stefano Danedi (attrib) (1612-1690) Italian?

£778	$1400	€1136	Adoration of the Christ Child (60x101cm-24x40in) panel. 21-Jan-4 Sotheby's, New York #80/R est:2000-3000

MONTAN, Anders (1846-1917) Swedish

£3414	$6350	€4984	Cottage interior with young girl and man (46x59cm-18x23in) s.i.d.82. 2-Mar-4 Rasmussen, Copenhagen #1280/R est:25000 (D.KR 38000)

MONTANA, Carlo (?) Italian?

£612	$1003	€850	View of lake (54x74cm-21x29in) s. 10-Jun-3 Pandolfini, Florence #89

MONTANARI, Dante (1896-?) Italian

£336	$594	€500	Lights on the lake (70x90cm-28x35in) s. 1-May-4 Meeting Art, Vercelli #435

MONTANARINI, Luigi (1906-1998) Italian

£367	$675	€550	Abstract (39x47cm-15x19in) s.d.1966 acrylic paper. 12-Jun-4 Meeting Art, Vercelli #435/R
£467	$840	€700	Variations (60x50cm-24x20in) s.d.74. 22-Apr-4 Finarte Semenzato, Rome #176/R
£580	$987	€830	Untitled (60x80cm-24x31in) s.d.1985 oil cardboard on canvas. 18-Nov-3 Babuino, Rome #497/R
£690	$1152	€1000	Variations (40x30cm-16x12in) s. s.i.d.1978 verso. 13-Nov-3 Finarte Semenzato, Rome #330
£690	$1152	€1000	Untitled (100x70cm-39x28in) s.d.83. 13-Nov-3 Finarte Semenzato, Rome #292
£828	$1382	€1200	Variations (80x60cm-31x24in) s. painted 1979. 13-Nov-3 Finarte Semenzato, Rome #264/R
£1172	$1958	€1700	May roses (80x60cm-31x24in) s.d.1932. 13-Nov-3 Finarte Semenzato, Rome #274/R est:1800-2200

MONTANARINI, Luigi (attrib) (1906-1998) Italian

£273	$494	€399	Landscape with bridge over a river, figures and boatsmen in foreground (80x199cm-31x78in) s. 30-Mar-4 Cannon & Cannon, Pietermaritzburg #229 (SA.R 3250)

MONTANE, Roger (1916-) French

£320	$573	€480	Vue de San Georgio, Venise (65x50cm-26x20in) s. 16-May-4 Osenat, Fontainebleau #94
Works on paper			
£267	$491	€400	Mer et soleil a Saint-Cyprien (31x43cm-12x17in) s. pastel. 9-Jun-4 Oger, Dumont, Paris #65

MONTANER, M (20th C) ?

£867	$1577	€1300	Coming storm (70x100cm-28x39in) 3-Jul-4 Finarte, Venice #194/R

MONTANES, Jose (?) ?

£243	$450	€355	Whistling boy (76x61cm-30x24in) s. 18-Jan-4 Bonhams & Butterfields, Los Angeles #7023/R

MONTANEZ, Juan Martinez (1568-1649) Spanish

Sculpture			
£31250	$50937	€45000	Portrait bust (54cm-21in) wood glass. 25-Sep-3 Dr Fritz Nagel, Stuttgart #1492/R est:4000

MONTANI, Andres (1918-2000) Uruguayan

Works on paper			
£309	$500	€448	Abstract (92x73cm-36x29in) s.d.70 mixed media canvas. 29-Jul-3 Galeria y Remates, Montevideo #60/R

MONTANI, Carlo Giuseppe (1868-1936) Italian

£400	$680	€584	Orchids in a Roman studio (13x33cm-5x13in) s.i.verso board. 29-Oct-3 Mallams, Oxford #689/R

£590 $1003 €850 Cuntryside (26x36cm-10x14in) s.i. board. 1-Nov-3 Meeting Art, Vercelli #299
£800 $1432 €1200 Orchids in the greenhouse (25x35cm-10x14in) s.d.1933. 13-May-4 Babuino, Rome #288/R
£915 $1584 €1300 Villa garden (25x35cm-10x14in) s.i.d.1934 panel. 11-Dec-3 Christie's, Rome #4
£1329 $2219 €1900 Summer garden (37x48cm-15x19in) s.d.1928 cardboard. 24-Jun-3 Finarte Semenzato, Rome #154/R

MONTASSIER, Henri (1880-1946) French
£559 $962 €800 Villa entrance (61x51cm-24x20in) s. 3-Dec-3 Stadion, Trieste #1114/R
£724 $1325 €1050 Ruelle d'Afrique de Nord (27x20cm-11x8in) s. panel. 31-Jan-4 Gerard, Besancon #53

MONTE, Giovanni da (c.1520-c.1590) Italian
Works on paper
£2000 $3660 €3000 Resurrection (14x15cm-6x6in) i. black chk pen ink htd white corner cut. 6-Jul-4 Christie's, London #25/R est:2000-3000

MONTECECCON, Mario (1893-1979) Italian
Sculpture
£1250 $2088 €1800 Bust of man (60cm-24in) i. bronze. 23-Oct-3 Finarte Semenzato, Milan #33/R est:1000-1300

MONTEFORTE, Eduardo (1849-1933) Italian
£895 $1638 €1307 A worker having a rest (15x17cm-6x7in) i. panel prov. 7-Jun-4 Museumsbygningen, Copenhagen #135/R (D.KR 10000)

MONTEIRO, Vicente do Rego (1899-?) Brazilian
£5861 $10725 €8792 Woman playing the cello (18x12cm-7x5in) s.1960. 6-Jul-4 Bolsa de Arte, Rio de Janeiro #149/R (B.R 32000)
Works on paper
£7326 $13407 €10989 Amazon legends, the moon (18x25cm-7x10in) s.d.1920 W/C. 6-Jul-4 Bolsa de Arte, Rio de Janeiro #60/R (B.R 40000)

MONTEL, Alexander Warren (1921-2002) American?
Works on paper
£865 $1600 €1263 Lanvin Perfume illustration featuring Arpege and My Sin (25x34cm-10x13in) pencil pen ink W/C gouache sold with three others four. 13-Jul-4 Christie's, Rockefeller NY #179/R est:2000-3000

MONTELATICI, Francesco (1600-1661) Italian
Works on paper
£1769 $3166 €2600 Une femme devant un puit, un enfant a droite (14x9cm-6x4in) col chk prov. 18-Mar-4 Christie's, Paris #215/R est:1500-2000

MONTELL, Justus (?) ?
£559 $951 €800 Coastal landscape in summer (30x45cm-12x18in) s. 29-Nov-3 Bukowskis, Helsinki #27/R

MONTEMEZZO, Antonio (1841-1898) German
£872 $1605 €1300 Flock of geese by river (30x48cm-12x19in) s. i. verso board. 24-Mar-4 Hugo Ruef, Munich #1052/R
£1533 $2760 €2300 Two girls feeding geese (23x32cm-9x13in) s. board. 26-Apr-4 Rieber, Stuttgart #1062/R est:1980
£4027 $7208 €6000 The goose shepherdess (29x19cm-11x7in) s.d.76 panel. 27-May-4 Dorotheum, Vienna #231/R est:3000-3400

MONTENARD, Frederic (1849-1926) French
£3147 $5413 €4500 Reve symboliste (182x93cm-72x37in) s. 7-Dec-3 Livinec, Gaudcheau & Jezequel, Rennes #84/R
£3546 $5922 €5000 La cueillette au bord de la Mediterranee (70x10cm-28x4in) s. 19-Jun-3 Millon & Associes, Paris #207/R est:3000-4000
£7616 $13937 €11500 La baie de Marseille (70x100cm-28x39in) s. 9-Apr-4 Claude Aguttes, Neuilly #79/R est:6500-7500
£15521 $27783 €22661 In Marseilles Harbour (110x201cm-43x79in) s.d.1889. 25-May-4 Bukowskis, Stockholm #378/R est:30000-40000 (S.KR 210000)

MONTENEGRO CAPELL, Jose (1855-1924) Spanish
£594 $993 €850 Alcazar de Sevilla (30x17cm-12x7in) s.d.1893. 24-Jun-3 Segre, Madrid #51/R
£1256 $2249 €1834 View from Seville (49x21cm-19x8in) s.i.d.1914 panel. 26-May-4 AB Stockholms Auktionsverk #2463/R est:15000-20000 (S.KR 17000)

MONTENEGRO, Roberto (1885-1968) Mexican
£1111 $2000 €1622 Native boy (36x25cm-14x10in) canvasboard. 24-Apr-4 Du Mouchelle, Detroit #3207/R est:600-1000
£2059 $3500 €3006 Dos cabezas (51x61cm-20x24in) s.d.63 s.d.verso prov. 9-Nov-3 Bonhams & Butterfields, Los Angeles #2129/R est:6000-8000
£2162 $4000 €3157 El caballo blanco (51x58cm-20x23in) 12-Mar-4 Du Mouchelle, Detroit #2100/R est:4000-6000
£4571 $8000 €6674 La dama sola (27x35cm-11x14in) s.d.1943 board. 19-Dec-3 Sotheby's, New York #1171/R est:3000-5000
Works on paper
£1655 $2748 €2400 Symbolist woman (29x25cm-11x10in) s.d.MCMIX ink dr. 1-Oct-3 Ansorena, Madrid #535/R est:2400

MONTERO BUSTAMANTE, Jose Pedro (1875-1927) South American
£1176 $2000 €1717 Boats and sailing boats (60x80cm-24x31in) s. 25-Nov-3 Galeria y Remates, Montevideo #168/R

MONTES DE OCA, Antonio (20th C) South American
£459 $835 €689 Open space with bays (104x127cm-41x50in) s. acrylic painted 2000. 21-Jun-4 Subastas Odalys, Caracas #17

MONTES ITURRIOZ, Gaspar (1901-1999) Spanish
£470 $841 €700 Portrait of lady (55x40cm-22x16in) s. board. 25-May-4 Durán, Madrid #654/R
£704 $1232 €1000 Bridge with houses (22x16cm-9x6in) s. board. 16-Dec-3 Segre, Madrid #103/R
£1342 $2403 €2000 Dancer (34x22cm-13x9in) s. cardboard. 25-May-4 Durán, Madrid #655/R est:1000

MONTES LENGUAS, Jose (1929-2001) Uruguayan?
£341 $560 €498 Saint Paul highway, Brazil (56x67cm-22x26in) s.d.80 cardboard. 3-Jun-3 Galeria y Remates, Montevideo #111
£427 $700 €623 Gothic cathedral (70x60cm-28x24in) s.d.61. 3-Jun-3 Galeria y Remates, Montevideo #110

MONTESANO, Gian Marco (1949-) Italian
£367 $675 €550 One of my first jobs (30x40cm-12x16in) s.i.verso. 12-Jun-4 Meeting Art, Vercelli #463/R
£570 $1055 €850 Mater Christi (60x50cm-24x20in) s.i.verso. 13-Mar-4 Meeting Art, Vercelli #466
£1399 $2378 €2000 A nice party for Marinello (115x75cm-45x30in) s.i.d.1994 prov. 25-Nov-3 Sotheby's, Milan #168 est:2000-3000
£1689 $2973 €2500 Star (60x80cm-24x31in) s.i.d.verso. 22-May-4 Galleria Pananti, Florence #386/R est:2500-3500
£2365 $4162 €3500 Au balle des femmes (180x150cm-71x59in) s.i.d.2000 verso. 22-May-4 Galleria Pananti, Florence #399/R est:4500-5000

MONTESINOS, Ricardo (1942-) Spanish
£272 $487 €400 Yard (15x23cm-6x9in) s. board. 22-Mar-4 Durán, Madrid #9/R

MONTESQUIOU, Robert de (1855-1921) French
Works on paper
£367 $675 €550 Deux cygnes blancs nageant sur des eaux vertes (9x15cm-4x6in) i.verso pastel. 9-Jun-4 Piasa, Paris #185
£733 $1327 €1100 Untitled (15x11cm-6x4in) init. W/C. 1-Apr-4 Piasa, Paris #251 est:800-1000
£2067 $3741 €3100 Untitled (14x17cm-6x7in) mono.d.1884 Chinese ink dr. 1-Apr-4 Piasa, Paris #250/R est:1200-1500

MONTEVERDE, Giulio (1837-1917) Italian
Sculpture
£1200 $2184 €1752 Figure of the young Christopher Columbus (59cm-23in) s.i. bronze. 29-Jun-4 Bonhams, Knightsbridge #260/R est:1500-2000

MONTEYNE, Roland (1932-1993) Belgian
Sculpture
£1141 $2019 €1700 Elle revait de cathedrales (41cm-16in) s.d.1971 bronze incl. marble base. 27-Apr-4 Campo, Vlaamse Kaai #17 est:1200-1500

MONTEZIN, Pierre Eugène (1874-1946) French
£2349 $4369 €3500 Lavandieres (13x18cm-5x7in) s. 8-Mar-4 Artcurial Briest, Paris #36/R est:2000-3000
£2667 $4907 €4000 River on summer's day (50x60cm-20x24in) s.d.1936 masonite. 9-Jun-4 Dorotheum, Salzburg #603/R est:8000-12000
£2979 $4974 €4200 Vaches dans un pre au bord de l'eau (36x82cm-14x32in) s. 19-Jun-3 Millon & Associes, Paris #208/R est:4000-5000
£3000 $5010 €4380 Ferme (60x73cm-24x29in) s. 22-Oct-3 Sotheby's, Olympia #51/R est:4000-5000
£3521 $6092 €5000 Pecheur en briere (46x55cm-18x22in) s. prov.lit. 9-Dec-3 Artcurial Briest, Paris #133/R est:5000-7000
£3593 $6000 €5246 Les baigneuses (49x49cm-19x19in) st.sig. panel painted c.1935. 7-Oct-3 Sotheby's, New York #261 est:8000-12000
£3691 $6533 €5500 Bouquet de roses (50x61cm-20x24in) s. 27-Apr-4 Artcurial Briest, Paris #130/R est:3000-4000
£3706 $6301 €5300 Bord de riviere (50x65cm-20x26in) s. 28-Nov-3 Doutrebente, Paris #44/R est:6000-8000
£4192 $7000 €6120 Paysage au bord de la riviere (29x46cm-11x18in) s. canvasboard prov. 7-Oct-3 Sotheby's, New York #264 est:6000-8000
£4476 $7698 €6400 Bouquet de roses (61x50cm-24x20in) s. painted c.1914. 3-Dec-3 Beaussant & Lefèvre, Paris #57/R est:4000
£4500 $7155 €6525 Personnes assises sous un arbre (60x81cm-24x32in) s. 11-Sep-3 Christie's, Kensington #44/R est:6000-8000
£4626 $8280 €6800 Paysan dans son champ (31x46cm-12x18in) s. 19-Mar-4 Millon & Associes, Paris #89/R est:4000-5000
£4800 $8832 €7200 Carriole sur un chemin dans un village (55x73cm-22x29in) s. 14-Jun-4 Tajan, Paris #49/R est:8000-10000
£5405 $10000 €7891 L'ombre, animaux au bord de l'Avre (73x76cm-29x30in) s. i.verso. 12-Feb-4 Sotheby's, New York #28/R est:12000-18000
£5705 $10211 €8500 Vaches au bord de la riviere (46x55cm-18x22in) s. 26-May-4 Christie's, Paris #11/R est:4000-6000
£6200 $11408 €9052 Paysage avec Eglise (65x54cm-26x21in) s. 24-Mar-4 Sotheby's, Olympia #46/R est:7000-9000
£6294 $10825 €9000 La sortie du village (56x76cm-22x30in) 3-Dec-3 Tajan, Paris #362 est:10000-12000
£6522 $12000 €9522 Vase de roses (55x46cm-22x18in) s.d.1914. 27-Jun-4 Freeman, Philadelphia #63/R est:8000-12000
£7263 $13000 €10604 Barques sur l'etang (50x65cm-20x26in) s. 6-May-4 Sotheby's, New York #420/R est:15000-18000
£8108 $15000 €11838 Neige a Saint-Mammes (61x74cm-24x29in) s. burlap lit. 11-Feb-4 Sotheby's, New York #18/R est:15000-20000

£8940	$16361	€13500	Bretagne, pecheuses de crevettes (51x72cm-20x28in) s. painted c. 1912-13. 7-Apr-4 Doutrebente, Paris #53/R est:3000-4000
£8951	$15217	€12800	Bords de riviere sous la neige (51x65cm-20x26in) s. i.verso. 27-Nov-3 Millon & Associes, Paris #204/R est:9000-10000
£9000	$15030	€13140	Bord de Seine a Veneux-les-Sablons (60x73cm-24x29in) s. prov. 21-Oct-3 Sotheby's, London #18/R est:10000-15000
£9500	$17480	€13870	La drague (60x73cm-24x29in) s. prov. 24-Mar-4 Sotheby's, Olympia #42/R est:8000-10000
£10490	$18042	€15000	Figures sous la pluie (46x55cm-18x22in) s. prov. 8-Dec-3 Artcurial Briest, Paris #13/R est:8000-12000
£10588	$18000	€15458	Bord de riviere (73x73cm-29x29in) s. 6-Nov-3 Sotheby's, New York #356/R est:20000-30000
£11972	$20711	€17000	Saules a Cherizy (52x52cm-20x20in) s. 11-Dec-3 Binoche, Paris #7/R est:12000-16000
£12667	$23307	€19000	Paysage aux arbres (60x81cm-24x32in) s. 8-Jun-4 Artcurial Briest, Paris #141/R est:20000-30000
£13000	$23920	€18980	Bord de Seine (60x73cm-24x29in) s. prov. 23-Jun-4 Christie's, London #134/R est:15000-20000
£14184	$23688	€20000	Paysage de neige (55x65cm-22x26in) s. 15-Oct-3 Rabourdin & Choppin de Janvry, Paris #7/R est:20000-22000
£14525	$26000	€21207	Vase of roses (62x50cm-24x20in) s. 6-May-4 Sotheby's, New York #239/R est:12000-18000
£14765	$26135	€22000	Bord de riviere (42x60cm-17x24in) studio st. lit. 27-Apr-4 Artcurial Briest, Paris #165/R est:20000-25000
£17333	$31027	€26000	Pecheurs sur la riviere (61x73cm-24x29in) 16-May-4 Osenat, Fontainebleau #89/R est:15000-20000
£17333	$31027	€26000	Sortie de messe a Dreux (55x66cm-22x26in) exhib. 16-May-4 Osenat, Fontainebleau #96/R est:20000-25000
£18717	$35000	€27327	Sentier au bord de l'Eure (50x61cm-20x24in) s. prov. 25-Feb-4 Christie's, Rockefeller NY #31/R est:14000-18000
£20950	$37500	€30587	Neige sur le pont de Monthilet (51x65cm-20x26in) s. 6-May-4 Sotheby's, New York #432/R est:20000-30000
£26000	$47840	€37960	Les parterres fleuris de la Promenade des Anglais (73x91cm-29x36in) s. i.d.35 verso paper on canvas. 23-Jun-4 Christie's, London #136/R est:25000-35000
£27933	$50000	€40782	Bord d'une riviere (65x81cm-26x32in) s. prov. 6-May-4 Sotheby's, New York #431/R est:25000-35000
£44693	$80000	€65252	Promenade (72x91cm-28x36in) s. prov. 6-May-4 Sotheby's, New York #428/R est:25000-35000

Works on paper

£276	$460	€400	Bord de riviere (25x35cm-10x14in) bears st.sig. ink wash. 17-Nov-3 Tajan, Paris #167/R
£280	$476	€400	La souvenir, programme (46x34cm-18x13in) s. gouache chl. 18-Nov-3 Pierre Berge, Paris #81
£385	$654	€550	Voile blanche (11x24cm-4x9in) s. gouache. 28-Nov-3 Doutrebente, Paris #22
£533	$981	€800	Cavaliers au bois (12x20cm-5x8in) st.sig. gouache. 8-Jun-4 Livinec, Gaudcheau & Jezequel, Rennes #67
£667	$1227	€1000	Troupeau de vaches pres du Ruisseau (19x29cm-7x11in) s. gouache. 14-Jun-4 Tajan, Paris #50/R
£704	$1218	€1000	Personnages dans un paysage (11x18cm-4x7in) s. gouache cardboard. 14-Dec-3 Rabourdin & Choppin de Janvry, Paris #30/R
£957	$1599	€1350	Sur les quais (17x38cm-7x15in) s. gouache. 19-Jun-3 Millon & Associes, Paris #206
£1189	$2045	€1700	Meule de foin (33x30cm-13x12in) s. gouache. 8-Dec-3 Christie's, Paris #66/R est:2000-3000
£1399	$2378	€2000	Vaches au bord de l riviere (29x38cm-11x15in) gouache. 30-Nov-3 Teitgen, Nancy #114
£2381	$4262	€3500	Meule de foin (32x29cm-13x11in) s. gouache prov. 19-Mar-4 Millon & Associes, Paris #90/R est:2500-3000
£6200	$10354	€9052	Bords de riviere (46x55cm-18x22in) s. gouache chl pastel paper on canvas. 21-Oct-3 Sotheby's, London #19/R est:4000-6000

MONTFORT, Franz van (1889-1980) Belgian

£315	$536	€460	Etudes de caracteres (66x51cm-26x20in) s. panel. 4-Nov-3 Servarts Themis, Bruxelles #640
£500	$905	€750	Etudes de caractere (66x51cm-26x20in) s. panel. 30-Mar-4 Palais de Beaux Arts, Brussels #724

Works on paper

£800	$1432	€1200	Cecile au Balai (31x21cm-12x8in) s.d.1919 chk. 15-May-4 De Vuyst, Lokeren #363

MONTGOMERY, Alfred (1857-1922) American

£1766	$3250	€2578	Still life with ears of corn. Still life with two ears of corn (31x61cm-12x24in) s. paper on board pair prov. 8-Jun-4 Bonhams & Butterfields, San Francisco #4012/R est:3000-5000

MONTGOMERY, Anne (1908-1991) Australian

£267	$486	€390	Desolate rocky landscape (40x57cm-16x22in) s.d.1952 s.i.verso board. 16-Jun-4 Deutscher-Menzies, Melbourne #525/R (A.D 700)
£267	$486	€390	Head study (35x25cm-14x10in) s. s.i.verso board. 16-Jun-4 Deutscher-Menzies, Melbourne #579/R (A.D 700)
£916	$1667	€1337	Beach and jetty (41x51cm-16x20in) s. board. 16-Jun-4 Deutscher-Menzies, Melbourne #333/R est:2000-3000 (A.D 2400)

MONTGOMERY, Loran A D (1904-1999) American

£442	$800	€645	Interior with rug (66x38cm-26x15in) s. prov.exhib. 2-Apr-4 Freeman, Philadelphia #187

MONTHERLANT, Henry de (1895-1972) French

Works on paper

£300	$552	€450	Nu feminin de dos, appuye au mur (32x18cm-13x7in) chl india ink sold with another. 9-Jun-4 Piasa, Paris #187
£400	$736	€600	Footballer s'appretant a taper dans le ballon (16x11cm-6x4in) col crayon. 9-Jun-4 Piasa, Paris #191/R

MONTHOLON, François de (1856-1940) French

£797	$1307	€1100	La rentree du troupeau (54x73cm-21x29in) s. 11-May-3 Osenat, Fontainebleau #204

MONTI, Cesare (1891-1952) Italian

£748	$1339	€1100	Flowers (43x34cm-17x13in) s. i.verso board. 22-Mar-4 Sant Agostino, Torino #203/R
£1342	$2510	€2000	Road and houses (48x60cm-19x24in) board. 26-Feb-4 Cambi, Genoa #446/R est:500-600
£1342	$2510	€2000	Landscape with houses (50x60cm-20x24in) board. 26-Feb-4 Cambi, Genoa #566/R est:1000-1200

MONTI, Francesco (attrib) (17/18th C) Italian

£3404	$5685	€4800	Madonna (77x63cm-30x25in) oval. 18-Jun-3 Christie's, Rome #309/R est:5000-8000
£3846	$6615	€5615	Pope Leon I driving out Attila and Hunerna with help of Saints Peter and Paul (75x122cm-30x48in) 3-Dec-3 AB Stockholms Auktionsverk #2701/R est:60000-80000 (S.KR 50000)
£4930	$8627	€7000	Cavalry battle (72x100cm-28x39in) 17-Dec-3 Christie's, Rome #375/R est:7000-10000

MONTI, Francesco (school) (1646-1712) Italian

£15333	$27447	€23000	Battle scenes (84x117cm-33x46in) pair. 17-May-4 Finarte Semenzato, Rome #115/R est:28000-30000

MONTI, Piero (1910-1994) Italian

£552	$916	€800	Cherry trees in Revigliasco (50x40cm-20x16in) s. board. 1-Oct-3 Della Rocca, Turin #79/R

Works on paper

£897	$1488	€1300	Savoia Square in Turin (43x69cm-17x27in) s. mixed media canvas on masonite. 1-Oct-3 Della Rocca, Turin #25/R

MONTI, Virginio (1852-1942) Italian

£822	$1397	€1200	Bishop and scholars (49x34cm-19x13in) s. panel lit. 6-Nov-3 Allgauer, Kempten #3516/R
£1664	$2829	€2380	Saint Joachim (40x30cm-16x12in) 1-Dec-3 Babuino, Rome #228/R est:600-800
£1664	$2829	€2380	Four Evangelists (34x34cm-13x13in) 1-Dec-3 Babuino, Rome #229/R est:1000-1500

MONTICELLI, Adolphe (1824-1886) French

£421	$680	€615	At prayer (20x15cm-8x6in) board. 20-Aug-3 James Julia, Fairfield #1137/R
£1399	$2378	€2000	Bacchante (33x34cm-13x13in) s. panel. 28-Nov-3 Blanchet, Paris #50/R est:2500-3000
£2340	$3909	€3300	Femmes dans un parc (41x32cm-16x13in) s. 20-Jun-3 Drouot Estimations, Paris #60 est:3000-4000
£2778	$4639	€4000	Sur les bords de la durance, ganagolie (18x29cm-7x11in) s.i.d.1878 board prov.exhib. 21-Oct-3 Sotheby's, Amsterdam #225/R est:4000-6000
£3000	$5430	€4500	Reunion dans un parc (32x61cm-13x24in) panel prov. 31-Mar-4 Sotheby's, Paris #108/R est:5000-7000
£3529	$6000	€5152	Les trois amies (41x33cm-16x13in) s. panel prov.exhib.lit. 29-Oct-3 Christie's, Rockefeller NY #143/R est:8000-12000
£4000	$6400	€5800	Jeune femme a l'eventail (28x20cm-11x8in) s. panel. 18-Sep-3 Christie's, Kensington #24/R est:4000-6000
£4000	$7360	€6000	La terrasse (40x26cm-16x10in) s. panel exhib. 11-Jun-4 Claude Aguttes, Neuilly #176/R est:6000-8000
£4225	$7310	€6000	Jeunes femmes au parc (35x48cm-14x19in) indis.s. panel. 12-Dec-3 Piasa, Paris #2/R est:6000-8000
£5200	$9464	€7800	Scene animee dans le parc (32x40cm-13x16in) lit. 4-Jul-4 Eric Pillon, Calais #61/R
£5517	$9214	€8000	Femmes a la fontaine (61x50cm-24x20in) s. prov.exhib.lit. 16-Nov-3 Muizon & Le Coent, Paris #39/R
£7333	$13200	€11000	At the well (26x40cm-10x16in) s. panel prov. 20-Apr-4 Sotheby's, Amsterdam #72/R est:7000-9000
£7667	$13877	€11500	Portrait de Ziem (46x37cm-18x15in) s. panel painted c.1866-1867 lit. 30-Mar-4 Rossini, Paris #319/R est:3500-5000
£9000	$14400	€13050	Fete dans un parc (41x72cm-16x28in) s. panel. 18-Sep-3 Christie's, Kensington #25/R est:10000-15000
£9859	$17254	€14000	Elegantes (46x64cm-18x25in) s. panel prov.lit. 18-Dec-3 Cornette de St.Cyr, Paris #2/R est:13000-15000
£10764	$17976	€15500	Voliere (42x30cm-17x12in) s. 25-Oct-3 Dianous, Marseille #402
£17000	$31280	€24820	Boats in a harbour (48x37cm-19x15in) indis.sig. panel prov. 25-Mar-4 Christie's, Kensington #22/R est:5000-7000
£17881	$32722	€27000	Fete dans un parc (53x97cm-21x38in) s. 7-Apr-4 Piasa, Paris #11/R est:17000-18000
£18000	$33120	€26280	Les premiers pas (47x37cm-19x15in) s. panel prov. 23-Mar-4 Bonhams, New Bond Street #98/R est:20000-30000

Works on paper

£1049	$1783	€1500	Le singe savant (44x27cm-17x11in) s. wash gouache. 30-Nov-3 Anaf, Lyon #186 est:1500-2000

MONTICELLI, Adolphe (attrib) (1824-1886) French

£2400	$4368	€3504	Fete champetre (52x102cm-20x40in) 16-Jun-4 Christie's, Kensington #45/R est:2000-3000

MONTICELLI, G (19th C) Italian

£2500	$4400	€3700	Antique shop (22x17cm-9x7in) s.d.1877 board. 19-May-4 Il Ponte, Milan #636 est:900-1000

MONTIEL, Elio (20th C) Mexican?

£316	$503	€461	Animals partying (89x122cm-35x48in) s. board. 29-Apr-3 Louis Morton, Mexico #118/R (M.P 5250)

MONTIEL, Jonio (1924-1986) South American

£272	$500	€397	Landscape with moon (82x58cm-32x23in) s. acrylic. 22-Jun-4 Galeria y Remates, Montevideo #122/R
£289	$500	€422	Santa Maria del Fiore, Florence (60x48cm-24x19in) s. prov. 15-Dec-3 Galeria y Remates, Montevideo #82/R

£426 $750 €622 Shapes (34x43cm-13x17in) s. tempera cardboard. 5-Jan-4 Galeria y Remates, Montevideo #12
£653 $1150 €953 Boca harbour (58x74cm-23x29in) s. cardboard. 5-Jan-4 Galeria y Remates, Montevideo #104/R

MONTIGNY, Jenny (1875-1937) Belgian
£4828 $8931 €7000 L'interieur ensoleille (35x45cm-14x18in) s. s.d.1906 verso. 19-Jan-4 Horta, Bruxelles #184/R est:8000-10000
£8392 $14266 €12000 Esquisse pour la Cour d'ecole (95x115cm-37x45in) prov. 1-Dec-3 Palais de Beaux Arts, Brussels #98/R est:10000-14000
£14094 $25228 €21000 Champs de fleurs, Deurle (55x61cm-22x24in) s. init.i.verso. 26-May-4 Christie's, Paris #22/R est:4000-6000
£15385 $26154 €22000 Vue de la Lys en ete (63x88cm-25x35in) s. prov. 1-Dec-3 Palais de Beaux Arts, Brussels #100/R est:18000-27000

MONTIGNY, Jules Léon (1847-1899) Belgian
£451 $718 €650 Charrette attelee avant l'orage (25x36cm-10x14in) s. panel. 15-Sep-3 Horta, Bruxelles #241
£2192 $3726 €3200 Fermiere sortant le veau (43x55cm-17x22in) s.d.65. 10-Nov-3 Horta, Bruxelles #48

MONTINI, Umberto (1897-1978) Italian
£263 $439 €384 Autumn lake landscape (30x40cm-12x16in) s. panel prov. 15-Nov-3 Galerie Gloggner, Luzern #87 (S.FR 600)
£435 $713 €600 Snowfall in Glasgow (25x35cm-10x14in) s. masonite. 27-May-3 Il Ponte, Milan #849
£543 $891 €750 River landscape covered in snow (24x40cm-9x16in) s. masonite. 27-May-3 Il Ponte, Milan #891
£652 $1070 €900 Snowfall in Comobbio (35x49cm-14x19in) s. board. 27-May-3 Il Ponte, Milan #860
£694 $1146 €1000 Winter landscape (60x80cm-24x31in) s. masonite. 1-Jul-3 Il Ponte, Milan #794

MONTOBIO, Guillaume (1883-1962) Belgian
£1875 $2981 €2700 Marrooniers en fleurs (100x90cm-39x35in) s. 9-Sep-3 Vanderkindere, Brussels #18/R

MONTORSOLI, Giovanni Angelo (style) (c.1507-1563) Italian
Sculpture
£46000 $78200 €67160 Bust of faun (70cm-28in) marble prov. 29-Oct-3 Sotheby's, London #35/R est:20000-30000

MONTOYA, Gustavo (1905-) Mexican
£1117 $2000 €1631 Ninas en la playa (48x58cm-19x23in) s.d.27 Aug 66 verso acrylic. 8-May-4 Susanin's, Chicago #6045/R est:3000-4000
£1143 $2000 €1669 Still life with plate of eggs and compote (60x80cm-24x31in) s. 19-Dec-3 Sotheby's, New York #1197/R est:3000-4000
£1695 $3000 €2475 Girl in a yellow dress (56x46cm-22x18in) s. 2-May-4 Bonhams & Butterfields, Los Angeles #3100/R est:3000-5000
£1897 $3224 €2770 Market (50x60cm-20x24in) s. 30-Oct-3 Louis Morton, Mexico #32/R est:40000 (M.P 36000)

MONTPETIT, Raphael (1980-) Canadian
£520 $952 €759 Jeudi apres-midi, Rue Mont Royal (20x30cm-8x12in) s. board prov. 1-Jun-4 Joyner Waddington, Toronto #295/R (C.D 1300)
£560 $1025 €818 Nuit Magique (20x30cm-8x12in) s. board prov. 1-Jun-4 Joyner Waddington, Toronto #345/R (C.D 1400)

MONTPEZAT, Henri d'Ainecy Comte de (1817-1859) French
£1409 $2495 €2100 Le manege (12x19cm-5x7in) s. prov. 28-Apr-4 Beaussant & Lefèvre, Paris #40 est:1500-2000
£3125 $5094 €4500 La chasse aux faucons (67x92cm-26x36in) s.d.1847. 26-Sep-3 Rabourdin & Choppin de Janvry, Paris #13/R est:4500-5000
£13287 $22587 €19000 Madame Chabot Latour et sa fille en amazones (104x131cm-41x52in) s.d.1850. 27-Nov-3 Millon & Associes, Paris #107/R est:20000-30000
Works on paper
£676 $1189 €1000 Peregrine (15x11cm-6x4in) s.i. pencil col wash exhib. 19-May-4 Sotheby's, Amsterdam #361/R

MONTULLO (19/20th C) Italian
£1800 $3312 €2628 Ballando vicino la Baia di Napoli (56x93cm-22x37in) s. 25-Mar-4 Christie's, Kensington #141/R est:2000-3000

MONVOISIN, Raymond Auguste Quinsac de (1794-1870) French
£31279 $53800 €45667 Self-portrait (55x43cm-22x17in) s. paint. 3-Dec-3 Naón & Cia, Buenos Aires #4/R est:30000-40000

MONZA, Louis (1897-1984) American
£222 $400 €324 Flower in the window (23x13cm-9x5in) painted c.1943. 24-Apr-4 Slotin Folk Art, Buford #518/R

MONZON RELOVA, Rene (1966-) Cuban
£302 $535 €450 Trees (25x40cm-10x16in) s. canvas on board. 27-Apr-4 Durán, Madrid #673/R
£1197 $2071 €1700 Humidity (40x60cm-16x24in) s. i.d.2003 verso canvas on board. 15-Dec-3 Ansorena, Madrid #935/R est:750

MOODIE, Donald (1892-1963) British
£400 $736 €584 Harvest landscape (50x75cm-20x30in) 10-Jun-4 Lyon & Turnbull, Edinburgh #117
£520 $868 €759 Mount Resipol - Archaracle (36x44cm-14x17in) s. board. 16-Oct-3 Lyon & Turnbull, Edinburgh #21
Works on paper
£250 $460 €365 Deserted rocky beach, west coast (30x43cm-12x17in) s. W/C. 10-Jun-4 Lyon & Turnbull, Edinburgh #46
£400 $736 €584 On the harbour quay (36x52cm-14x20in) pen ink W/C. 10-Jun-4 Lyon & Turnbull, Edinburgh #76

MOODY, Fannie (fl.1885-1897) British
£2800 $5152 €4088 Four Cairn Terriers (63x86cm-25x34in) s. 10-Jun-4 Christie's, Kensington #370/R est:3000-4000
Works on paper
£486 $900 €710 Cairn terrier (36x43cm-14x17in) s. col chk. 10-Feb-4 Doyle, New York #176/R
£500 $920 €730 Cairn Terrier (47x36cm-19x14in) s.d.1918 bodycol sold with photograph. 10-Jun-4 Christie's, Kensington #371/R
£649 $1200 €948 Two fox terriers (51x38cm-20x15in) s. col chk. 10-Feb-4 Doyle, New York #190/R

MOODY, Francis Wollaston Thomas (attrib) (1824-1886) British
£440 $800 €642 Portrait of a boy in lace collar (51x41cm-20x16in) canvas on board. 7-Feb-4 Sloans & Kenyon, Bethesda #1269/R

MOODY, Gertrude (19/20th C) British
£340 $588 €496 Faggot gatherer, Robin Wood Derbyshire (76x64cm-30x25in) i.d.1897 stretcher. 11-Dec-3 Neales, Nottingham #642/R

MOODY, Roy (20th C) American
Sculpture
£1086 $1900 €1586 How not to elect a President (58x82x10cm-23x32x4in) acrylic felt-tip pen shaped panel fluorescent lights exhib. 17-Dec-3 Christie's, Rockefeller NY #193/R est:1500-2000

MOODY, Rufus (20th C) Canadian
Sculpture
£5285 $9459 €7716 Totem pole (91x15x19cm-36x6x7in) s.i. relief carving. 27-May-4 Heffel, Vancouver #142/R est:4000-6000 (C.D 13000)
£5435 $10000 €7935 Haida argillite totem pole (66cm-26in) wood. 14-Jun-4 Bonhams & Butterfields, San Francisco #1136/R est:7000-10000
£10870 $20000 €15870 Haida argillite totem pole (94cm-37in) wood. 14-Jun-4 Bonhams & Butterfields, San Francisco #1134/R est:10000-15000
£12228 $22500 €17853 Haida argillite totem pole (91cm-36in) wood. 14-Jun-4 Bonhams & Butterfields, San Francisco #1135/R est:10000-15000

MOODY, Victor Hume (1896-?) British
£700 $1295 €1022 Portrait of Jean Cottard (91x71cm-36x28in) s.d.1942. 15-Jan-4 Christie's, Kensington #765

MOOK, Friedrich (1888-1944) German
£333 $610 €500 Lower alpine landscape with running river (61x80cm-24x31in) s.d.1923 i.verso. 5-Jun-4 Arnold, Frankfurt #674/R
£667 $1220 €1000 Apple trees in summer landscape (60x80cm-24x31in) mono.d.10. 5-Jun-4 Arnold, Frankfurt #670/R

MOOLHUIZEN, Jan Jurrien (1900-) Dutch
£532 $888 €750 Still life with violets and roses (29x23cm-11x9in) s. canvas on panel. 20-Oct-3 Glerum, Amsterdam #215/R

MOON, Jeremy (1934-1974) British
Works on paper
£260 $442 €380 Untitled (17x21cm-7x8in) s.d.15/11/1971 wax crayon pencil prov. 18-Nov-3 Bonhams, Knightsbridge #158

MOONEY, Carmel (20th C) Irish?
£366 $641 €520 Volcano (14x20cm-6x8in) s. board. 16-Dec-3 James Adam, Dublin #112/R
£394 $690 €560 Abstract landscape (40x49cm-16x19in) s. 16-Dec-3 James Adam, Dublin #142/R
£467 $840 €700 Snowy volcano (17x23cm-7x9in) s. 20-Apr-4 James Adam, Dublin #103/R
£503 $901 €750 Waterfall (48x39cm-19x15in) s. 31-May-4 Hamilton Osborne King, Dublin #62/R
£556 $906 €800 Virgin Mary (61x51cm-24x20in) s.d.87. 23-Sep-3 De Veres Art Auctions, Dublin #162

MOONEY, Eddie (20th C) Irish?
Works on paper
£604 $985 €870 Balcony scene with girl (74x66cm-29x26in) s.d.83 pastel. 23-Sep-3 De Veres Art Auctions, Dublin #321

MOONEY, Edward Hartley (c.1878-1938) British
£600 $1110 €876 Still life with lilacs in a glass vase (49x59cm-19x23in) s.d.1917. 14-Jul-4 Bonhams, Chester #355/R
£3000 $5100 €4380 Vale of Clwyd (62x75cm-24x30in) s.d.1920. 29-Oct-3 Bonhams, Chester #353/R est:3000-5000

MOONEY, Martin (20th C) Irish?
£262 $482 €383 Study light (27x35cm-11x14in) s.d.87 s.d.July 1987 verso prov. 14-Jun-4 Waddingtons, Toronto #174/R (C.D 650)
£726 $1335 €1060 Facade toledo study (46x38cm-18x15in) s.d.87 s.i.d.July August 87 verso prov. 14-Jun-4 Waddingtons, Toronto #173/R est:3000-5000 (C.D 1800)
£872 $1562 €1300 Killydonnell friary, Donegal (13x15cm-5x6in) init.d.1996 panel. 26-May-4 James Adam, Dublin #86/R est:800-1200

£1946 $3484 €2900 Huband Bridge, Dublin (33x45cm-13x18in) s.d.1993 i.verso prov. 26-May-4 James Adam, Dublin #83/R est:1500-2500
£1958 $3329 €2800 Connemara II (13x24cm-5x9in) init. board prov. 25-Nov-3 De Veres Art Auctions, Dublin #123/R est:2500-3500
£2000 $3440 €2920 Dun Arran, Donegal (20x40cm-8x16in) mono.d.1997 board. 3-Dec-3 John Ross, Belfast #125a
£2000 $3580 €2920 Grattan Bridge, Dublin (15x30cm-6x12in) init.d.04 s.i.d.2004 verso canvas on board. 14-May-4 Christie's, Kensington #333/R est:1200-1800
£2238 $3804 €3200 Rooftops Udaipur II (26x35cm-10x14in) init.d.1999 board. 25-Nov-3 De Veres Art Auctions, Dublin #122/R est:3000-4000
£2400 $4296 €3504 Arch, Dungarpur, Rajasthan, Indian (35x25cm-14x10in) s.d.20MM04 s.i.d.2004 verso canvas on board. 14-May-4 Christie's, Kensington #334/R est:1500-2000
£2600 $4654 €3796 Four Courts and Liffey, Dublin (15x30cm-6x12in) init.d.MM 04 s.i.d.2004 verso canvas on board. 14-May-4 Christie's, Kensington #336/R est:1200-1800

MOONY, Robert James Enraght (1879-1946) British
Works on paper
£1597 $2603 €2300 Nymphs in a woodland (51x60cm-20x24in) s. W/C bodycol. 24-Sep-3 James Adam, Dublin #34/R est:2000-3000

MOOR, Carel de (1656-1738) Dutch
Works on paper
£533 $955 €800 Portrait of young man with long hair (36x25cm-14x10in) s. 13-May-4 Bassenge, Berlin #5230/R

MOOR, Carel de (studio) (1656-1738) Dutch
£2131 $3750 €3111 Portrait of a standing figure, thought to be Louis XIV (66x55cm-26x22in) 18-May-4 Bonhams & Butterfields, San Francisco #18/R est:3000-5000

MOOR, Christian de (1899-1991) Dutch
£559 $962 €800 Head (80x100cm-31x39in) prov.exhib. 8-Dec-3 Glerum, Amsterdam #171/R
£616 $1048 €900 View of Italien village (95x95cm-37x37in) s.d.1976. 5-Nov-3 Vendue Huis, Gravenhage #423/R
£664 $1143 €950 Vicopisano (65x70cm-26x28in) s.d.1969 prov. 8-Dec-3 Glerum, Amsterdam #134/R
£822 $1397 €1200 Italien landscape (80x100cm-31x39in) 5-Nov-3 Vendue Huis, Gravenhage #424/R
£1027 $1747 €1500 Ceres (90x90cm-35x35in) d.1975. 5-Nov-3 Vendue Huis, Gravenhage #422/R est:500-700
Works on paper
£338 $595 €500 Two owls (48x63cm-19x25in) s. W/C sold with another by Rudolf Ernst Penning. 19-May-4 Sotheby's, Amsterdam #386/R
£350 $601 €500 Family (49x64cm-19x25in) s. gouache prov. 8-Dec-3 Glerum, Amsterdam #196/R

MOOR, Karel de (attrib) (1695-?) Dutch
£18000 $32220 €26280 Peter the Great (77x61cm-30x24in) 26-May-4 Sotheby's, London #475/R est:8000-12000

MOOR, Karl (1904-1991) Swiss
£286 $487 €418 Still life with crockery and fruit (24x34cm-9x13in) i. verso panel. 5-Nov-3 Dobiaschofsky, Bern #819/R (S.FR 650)

MOOR, Pieter Cornelis de (1866-1953) Dutch
Works on paper
£294 $505 €420 La belle (37x29cm-15x11in) s. mixed media prov. 8-Dec-3 Glerum, Amsterdam #28/R

MOORBY, E E (20th C) British
£1730 $3200 €2526 Champion Grateley Ben, black labrador (30x41cm-12x16in) s.i. 10-Feb-4 Doyle, New York #263/R est:2000-3000

MOORE OF IPSWICH, John (1820-1902) British
£500 $895 €730 Fishing schooners coming out of port. Peaceful stretch of river (29x23cm-11x9in) s. board pair. 26-May-4 Christie's, Kensington #726/R
£850 $1556 €1241 Rural lock scene (23x30cm-9x12in) s. panel. 7-Apr-4 Bonhams, Bury St Edmunds #427/R
£900 $1557 €1314 Thatched cottage with chickens (20x26cm-8x10in) s. board. 10-Dec-3 Bonhams, Bury St Edmunds #590
£950 $1634 €1387 Gypsy encampment with caravan and figures round a fire, sunset (38x18cm-15x7in) s. 3-Dec-3 Neal & Fletcher, Woodbridge #305
£1000 $1720 €1460 Marine scene with fishing boats and buoy to foreground (23x48cm-9x19in) s. 3-Dec-3 Neal & Fletcher, Woodbridge #301 est:1000-1500
£1000 $1790 €1460 Windswept figures on a jetty looking out to sea (18x25cm-7x10in) 26-May-4 Christie's, Kensington #702/R est:700-900
£1200 $2232 €1752 Barges on an east Anglian river at dusk (41x61cm-16x24in) 4-Mar-4 Christie's, Kensington #493/R est:1500-2000
£1800 $3402 €2628 Off to the fishing grounds (18x25cm-7x10in) both s. panel pair. 17-Feb-4 Bonhams, New Bond Street #21/R est:2000-3000
£2000 $3340 €2920 Suffolk landscape with figures in lane and cottages in distance (18x20cm-7x8in) s. 17-Oct-3 Keys, Aylsham #691 est:1800-2200
£2700 $4671 €3942 Fishing boats and other vessels in a choppy sea (34x44cm-13x17in) s. 10-Dec-3 Bonhams, Bury St Edmunds #568/R est:3000-4000

MOORE OF IPSWICH, John (attrib) (1820-1902) British
£600 $1074 €876 Moonlit harbour scene with various boats (20x30cm-8x12in) indis.sig. panel. 5-May-4 John Nicholson, Haslemere #568

MOORE, A Harvey (?-1905) British
Works on paper
£340 $541 €496 Bishopsthorpe House, York (21x29cm-8x11in) s. W/C. 10-Sep-3 Cheffins, Cambridge #450/R

MOORE, Barlow (fl.1863-1891) British
£1200 $1896 €1752 Storm, Bampig - Running for shelter passing the Elbe Light Vessel (75x126cm-30x50in) mono.d.1870. 2-Sep-3 Gildings, Market Harborough #433 est:1200-1600
Works on paper
£480 $797 €701 Sunrise off the Champman light on the Thames, with shrimpers and smacks (21x33cm-8x13in) init.d.1881 pencil wash gouache. 1-Oct-3 Bonhams, Knightsbridge #41/R
£800 $1432 €1168 AT the turning mark. Rounding the lightship. Racing schooner on a beam reach (20x14cm-8x6in) s. brown ink W/C three. 26-May-4 Christie's, Kensington #498/R
£1500 $2550 €2190 Freda (28x22cm-11x9in) s.d.1862 pencil W/C htd white oval pair. 19-Nov-3 Christie's, Kensington #407/R

MOORE, Benson Bond (1882-1974) American
£306 $550 €447 Autumn woods, Bluemont, Virginia (33x30cm-13x12in) s. board. 24-Apr-4 Weschler, Washington #591/R
£495 $900 €723 Potomac at Four Mile Run, April 15, 1917 (15x23cm-6x9in) s.i. canvasboard. 20-Jun-4 Charlton Hall, Columbia #575/R
£531 $950 €775 Potomac at Chain Bridge (10x15cm-4x6in) s. d.1914 verso board. 20-Mar-4 Sloans & Kenyon, Bethesda #1191/R
£782 $1400 €1142 On the shore of the Potomac (51x61cm-20x24in) i.verso after Max Weyl. 7-May-4 Sloans & Kenyon, Bethesda #1698/R
£894 $1600 €1305 At Skyline Drive, VA (28x36cm-11x14in) s. i.d.August 24 1952 verso. 7-May-4 Sloans & Kenyon, Bethesda #1700/R est:1200-1500
£1446 $2400 €2111 Winter landscape (61x48cm-24x19in) s. 4-Oct-3 Neal Auction Company, New Orleans #613/R est:1500-2500
Works on paper
£235 $425 €343 Mallards in flight (38x48cm-15x19in) s. W/C. 2-Apr-4 Freeman, Philadelphia #170

MOORE, Charles Herbert (1840-1930) American
£236 $425 €345 A fall scene (18x30cm-7x12in) canvas on board. 25-Apr-4 Locati, Maple Glen #470183/R

MOORE, Claude T S (1853-1901) British
£8000 $14720 €11680 Oxford and Cambridge boat race at Westminster (64x114cm-25x45in) s. 11-Jun-4 Christie's, London #155/R est:8000-12000

MOORE, Claude T S (attrib) (1853-1901) British
£773 $1400 €1129 Harbour scene (36x51cm-14x20in) s. board. 3-Apr-4 Neal Auction Company, New Orleans #983/R est:1500-2500

MOORE, David Q (1927-2002) Australian
Photographs
£2227 $3585 €3251 Sisters of Charity, Washington (35x23cm-14x9in) s.d.1956/1999 i.verso gelatin silver print. 25-Aug-3 Sotheby's, Paddington #242/R est:5000-10000 (A.D 5500)
£8000 $14080 €11680 360 degree panorama of Sydney Harbour from Martello Tower at Fort Denison (165x135cm-65x53in) type c photographs 14 panel on board. 18-May-4 Bonhams, New Bond Street #569/R est:10000-12000

MOORE, Edward (?) British
£326 $597 €476 Fishing boats drawn up on the beach (46x88cm-18x35in) s. 4-Jun-4 Zofingen, Switzerland #2492 (S.FR 750)

MOORE, Edwin Augustus (1858-1925) American
£598 $1100 €873 Steady, old boy! (58x66cm-23x26in) s.i.d.1892 verso. 9-Jun-4 Alderfer's, Hatfield #381/R est:1200-1500
£2654 $4750 €3875 Still life with apple, grapes and champagne flute (23x30cm-9x12in) s.d.1876. 26-May-4 Doyle, New York #11/R est:2500-3500

MOORE, Frank Montague (1877-1967) American/British
£437 $800 €638 Desert wildflowers (51x76cm-20x30in) s. 5-Jun-4 Dan Ripley, Indianapolis #266
£2312 $4000 €3376 Pacific spray (76x102cm-30x40in) s. masonite. 13-Dec-3 Charlton Hall, Columbia #533/R est:3000-5000

MOORE, George Belton (1805-1875) British
£347 $641 €520 Bay in Connemara (45x46cm-18x18in) s. board. 13-Jul-4 James Adam, Dublin #144
£467 $863 €700 Near Dunfannaghy, County Donegal (43x53cm-17x21in) s.i.verso board. 13-Jul-4 James Adam, Dublin #117

MOORE, Harry Humphrey (1844-1926) American
£250 $400 €365 Lady in a black gown with colourful scarf (20x13cm-8x5in) s. wood panel. 20-Sep-3 Bunte, Elgin #1422
£2600 $4784 €3900 Les musiciens (34x26cm-13x10in) s. panel. 14-Jun-4 Gros & Delettrez, Paris #520/R est:2800-3500
£8379 $15250 €12233 Portrait of young sheperhdess with her lamb (84x56cm-33x22in) s. 7-Feb-4 Neal Auction Company, New Orleans #109/R est:15000-20000
£9848 $18021 €14378 Young girl with small dog in her arms (76x58cm-30x23in) s. 9-Jun-4 Rasmussen, Copenhagen #1576/R est:120000 (D.KR 110000)

MOORE, Henry O M (1898-1986) British
Prints
£2011 $3600 €2936 Reclining woman on beach (55x76cm-22x30in) s.num.4/50 color lithograph. 6-May-4 Swann Galleries, New York #534/R est:2500-3500
£2200 $4070 €3212 Four reclining figures. s. edn 19/75 etching. 13-Jul-4 Bonhams, Knightsbridge #110/R est:2200-2500
£3000 $5100 €4380 Figures sculptures (12x20cm-5x8in) woodblock exec.1931 lit. 1-Dec-3 Bonhams, New Bond Street #259/R est:3000-5000

£3400	$6256	€4964	Family group (28x23cm-11x9in) s.d.1950 col lithograph. 29-Mar-4 Bonhams, New Bond Street #200/R est:2000-3000
£4412	$7500	€6442	Woman holding cat (35x53cm-14x21in) s.d.1949 num.16/75 col colograph. 4-Nov-3 Christie's, Rockefeller NY #141/R est:5000-7000

Sculpture

£1963	$3200	€2866	Two bulb forms (10cm-4in) s.num.1/9 brown pat bronze conceived 1983 lit. 25-Sep-3 Christie's, Rockefeller NY #577/R est:4000-6000
£2032	$3800	€2967	Relief 2 (11x10cm-4x4in) pat bronze exec.1957 prov.lit. 25-Feb-4 Christie's, Rockefeller NY #70/R est:2500-3500
£2331	$3800	€3403	Figurine (10cm-4in) s.num.3/9 gold brown pat bronze conceived 1983 lit. 25-Sep-3 Christie's, Rockefeller NY #578/R est:4000-6000
£3571	$6500	€5214	Maquette for relief no.1 (13cm-5in) i.num.5/9 brown pat. bronze cast 1971 lit. 29-Jun-4 Sotheby's, New York #355/R est:7000-9000
£3593	$6000	€5246	Roman matron (13cm-5in) s. num.7/7 bronze. 25-Oct-3 Rachel Davis, Shaker Heights #438/R est:7000-10000
£4294	$7000	€6269	Upright motive, maquette no 4 (31cm-12in) brown pat bronze edition num.381 conceived 1955 lit. 25-Sep-3 Christie's, Rockefeller NY #580/R est:9000-12000
£4500	$8235	€6570	Maquette for carving (12cm-5in) i.num.1/9 green pat. bronze lit. 4-Jun-4 Christie's, London #147/R est:5000-8000
£4878	$7659	€7122	Study for hands of queen (13cm-5in) bronze. 26-Aug-3 Christie's, Sydney #157/R est:12000-16000 (A.D 12000)
£5028	$9000	€7341	Reclining Figure - bunched (15cm-6in) s. num.8/9 back brown pat bronze conceived 1961 prov.lit. 5-May-4 Christie's, Rockefeller NY #356/R est:10000-15000
£5521	$9000	€8061	Wall relief, maquette no 1 (25x56cm-10x22in) gold green pat bronze relief copper panel conceived 1955 prov.lit. 25-Sep-3 Christie's, Rockefeller NY #612/R est:9000-12000
£7500	$13725	€10950	Standing figure, pointed head (21cm-8in) inscribed sig.num.4/9 brown pat. bronze lit. 4-Jun-4 Christie's, London #146/R est:8000-12000
£8475	$14407	€12374	Horse's Head (19cm-7in) bronze edn 1/7 cast 1980 prov.exhib. 24-Nov-3 Sotheby's, Melbourne #281/R est:10000-15000 (A.D 20000)
£9000	$16560	€13140	Head and shoulders (8cm-3in) s.num.4/6 bronze lit. 24-Mar-4 Sotheby's, Olympia #175/R est:10000-15000
£9050	$15385	€20000	Duck (16x16x9cm-6x6x4in) pat bronze. 25-Nov-3 Pierre Berge, Paris #23/R est:20000-30000
£9626	$18000	€14054	Seated woman (18cm-7in) s. num.7/9 pat bronze lit. 25-Feb-4 Christie's, Rockefeller NY #135/R est:15000-20000
£9677	$17806	€14128	Woman (19x17cm-7x7in) s.num.6/9 bronze cast 1961 prov. 14-Jun-4 Waddingtons, Toronto #163/R est:15000-18000 (C.D 24000)
£9816	$16000	€14331	Reclining warrior (19cm-7in) s.num.6/9 brown pat bronze lit. 25-Sep-3 Christie's, Rockefeller NY #614/R est:10000-15000
£11765	$20000	€17177	Two piece reclining figure arch (20cm-8in) i. num.2/9 brown green pat bronze Cast 1981 lit. 6-Nov-3 Sotheby's, New York #246/R est:20000-30000
£12000	$21480	€18000	Maquette for sheep piece (9x13x7cm-4x5x3in) s.i. brown green pat.bronze prov. 14-May-4 Ketterer, Munich #274/R est:18000-25000
£14706	$25000	€21471	Warrior's Head (25cm-10in) brown green pat bronze conceived 1953 prov.lit. 5-Nov-3 Christie's, Rockefeller NY #353/R est:25000-35000
£16000	$29600	€23360	Reclining figure (16cm-6in) s.num.6/9 brown pat. bronze prov. 11-Mar-4 Christie's, Kensington #176/R est:8000-12000
£16760	$30000	€24470	Standing figure no 2 (28cm-11in) green pat bronze conceived 1952 edn of 9 prov.lit. 6-May-4 Sotheby's, New York #392/R est:25000-35000
£17647	$30000	€25765	Two piece reclining figure - Maquette no 1 (24cm-9in) s. num.6/12 brown pat bronze conceived 1960 st.f.Noack prov.lit. 5-Nov-3 Christie's, Rockefeller NY #360/R est:25000-35000
£25000	$45500	€36500	Fragment of king (16cm-6in) s. brown pat bronze exec. 1952 prov. 3-Feb-4 Christie's, London #278/R est:25000-35000
£29412	$50000	€42942	Madonna and Child (19cm-7in) terracotta exec 1943 prov.exhib.lit. 5-Nov-3 Christie's, Rockefeller NY #285/R est:50000-70000
£32000	$57280	€46720	Reclining figure (13cm-5in) s. green brown pat bronze prov.lit. 16-Mar-4 Bonhams, New Bond Street #51/R est:18000-25000
£35000	$59500	€51100	Seated figure, thin head (13cm-5in) s.num.3/5 sterling silver conceived 1980. 21-Nov-3 Christie's, London #170/R est:20000-30000
£35000	$59500	€51100	Pointed reclining figure (24cm-9in) s.num8/9 gold pat. bronze conceived 1948 prov.lit. 21-Nov-3 Christie's, London #171/R est:30000-50000
£35000	$59500	€51100	Goats head (20cm-8in) green pat. bronze conceived 1952 prov.exhib.lit. 21-Nov-3 Christie's, London #172/R est:25000-35000
£36000	$65520	€52560	Mother and child (38cm-15in) green pat bronze conceived 1959 one of 12 lit. 15-Jun-4 Bonhams, New Bond Street #97/R est:20000-30000
£38235	$65000	€55823	Armless seated figure against round wall (28cm-11in) brown pat bronze incl base conceived 1957 lit. 5-Nov-3 Christie's, Rockefeller NY #168/R est:80000-120000
£47486	$85000	€69330	Reclining figure No 6 (21cm-8in) brown pat bronze conceived 1954 cast 1956 prov.lit. 6-May-4 Sotheby's, New York #364/R est:60000-80000
£58824	$100000	€130000	Bust (79x53x28cm-31x21x11in) white marble. 25-Nov-3 Pierre Berge, Paris #24/R est:50000-80000
£65000	$118300	€94900	Three bathers (14cm-6in) s. num.7/7 after Cezanne brown green pat bronze prov.lit. 3-Feb-4 Christie's, London #279/R est:40000-60000
£70588	$120000	€103058	Seated woman with crossed feet (20cm-8in) i. num.1/6 brown gold pat bronze conceived 1957 prov.lit. 6-Nov-3 Sotheby's, New York #271/R est:80000-120000
£72626	$130000	€106034	Mother and child fragment (17cm-7in) brown pat bronze conceived 1956 cast 1976 edn 1/9 prov.lit. 6-May-4 Sotheby's, New York #366/R est:80000-100000
£80000	$137600	€116800	Seated girl (45cm-18in) painted red-tinted plaster. 3-Dec-3 Sotheby's, London #po32/R est:80000-120000
£106145	$190000	€154972	Maquette for reclining figure - Angles (21cm-8in) i. num.3/9 brown pat bronze conceived 1975 prov.lit. 6-May-4 Sotheby's, New York #374a/R est:150000-200000
£111732	$200000	€163129	Seated woman with crossed feet (20cm-8in) i. brown gold pat bronze conceived 1957 cast 1965 prov.lit. 6-May-4 Sotheby's, New York #386/R est:125000-175000
£117318	$210000	€171284	Working model for mother and child - hood (76cm-30in) i. num.1/9 light brown pat bronze f.H Noack prov.exhib.lit. 6-May-4 Sotheby's, New York #368/R est:250000-350000
£120000	$220800	€175200	Rocking chair no 4 miniature (15cm-6in) bronze conceived 1950 edn of 9 prov.exhib.lit. 22-Jun-4 Sotheby's, London #203/R est:60000-80000
£135000	$248400	€197100	Draped mother and child on curved bench (19cm-7in) i. num.7/9 bronze cast 1980 prov.lit. 22-Jun-4 Sotheby's, London #207a/R est:50000-70000
£178771	$320000	€261006	Working model for divided oval: butterfly (91cm-36in) s.st.f.Noack num.2/6 pat bronze exec.1982 prov.lit. 6-May-4 Sotheby's, New York #134/R est:200000-300000
£290000	$527800	€423400	Working model, horse (68cm-27in) s. num.2/9 bronze prov.lit. 21-Jun-4 Sotheby's, London #52/R est:200000-300000
£335196	$600000	€489386	Rocking chair 3 (32cm-13in) st.f.Valsuani green pat bronze exec.1950 one of 6 prov.exhib.lit. 6-May-4 Sotheby's, New York #106/R est:350000-450000
£441176	$750000	€644117	Seated woman, thin neck (64cm-25in) s. green pat bronze prov.lit. 4-Nov-3 Christie's, Rockefeller NY #42/R est:500000-700000
£705882	$1200000	€1030588	Marquette for King and Queen (27cm-11in) bronze prov.lit. 4-Nov-3 Christie's, Rockefeller NY #41/R est:500000-700000
£3235294	$5500000	€4723529	Three piece reclining figure, draped (473cm-186in) s.num.4/7 brown pat. bronze conceived 1975 prov.exhib.lit. 4-Nov-3 Christie's, Rockefeller NY #35/R est:4000000-5000000

Works on paper

£800	$1336	€1168	Five faces (10x17cm-4x7in) s. ballpoint pen exec 1981 prov.lit. 22-Oct-3 Sotheby's, Olympia #168/R
£2400	$4128	€3504	Textile design (17x25cm-7x10in) s.d.43 pencil crayon W/C. 2-Dec-3 Bonhams, New Bond Street #173/R est:1500-2000
£3000	$5550	€4380	Reclining figure (20x23cm-8x9in) crayon chl wash executed 1956. 11-Mar-4 Christie's, Kensington #175/R est:3000-5000
£3743	$7000	€5465	Seated nude (34x23cm-13x9in) s.d.27 pen ink brush wash prov.lit. 25-Feb-4 Christie's, Rockefeller NY #68/R est:7000-9000
£4196	$7133	€6000	Ideas for sculpture (27x18cm-11x7in) s.d.36 pencil col pencil prov.exhib.lit. 25-Nov-3 Sotheby's, Milan #94 est:6000-8000
£4500	$8280	€6570	Girl seated in armchair (22x17cm-9x7in) s.i.d.55 pencil pen ink prov.lit. 22-Jun-4 Sotheby's, London #514/R est:5000-7000
£5282	$9137	€7500	Ideas for sculpture (29x24cm-11x9in) s.d.1959 chk Indian ink lit. 13-Dec-3 Lempertz, Koln #169/R est:7000
£5500	$9185	€8030	Reclining figure (23x24cm-9x9in) s.d.66 pen ink W/C lit. 16-Oct-3 Christie's, Kensington #561/R est:3000-5000
£6952	$13000	€10150	One reclining and two standing figures (29x25cm-11x10in) s.d.32 pen ink brush wash paper on board exhib.lit. 25-Feb-4 Christie's, Rockefeller NY #69/R est:12000-16000
£7483	$13395	€11000	Ideas for sculptures (19x25cm-7x10in) s.d.34 pencil lit. 16-Mar-4 Finarte Semenzato, Milan #322/R est:11500
£8000	$14720	€11680	Two seated Women I (24x28cm-9x11in) s. gouache chl cream paper exec 1982-1983 prov.lit. 24-Jun-4 Christie's, London #399/R est:8000-12000
£10667	$19093	€16000	Two sheep (15x32cm-6x13in) s. Indian ink prov. 14-May-4 Ketterer, Munich #268/R est:7000-9000
£10778	$18000	€15736	Reclining figure (14x21cm-6x8in) s.i.d.1940 W/C wax crayon pencil pen ink paper on board prov.lit. 11-Nov-3 Christie's, Rockefeller NY #152/R est:30000-40000
£11000	$20020	€16060	Reclining figure (36x50cm-14x20in) s. pencil black crayon exec.1954 prov.lit. 4-Feb-4 Sotheby's, London #509/R est:8000-12000
£11765	$20000	€17177	Miner working at the coal face (23x18cm-9x7in) s.d.42 W/C col wax crayons brush India ink prov.exhib.lit. 5-Nov-3 Christie's, Rockefeller NY #155/R est:18000-22000
£12821	$23462	€19232	Study for a sculpture (21x16cm-8x6in) s.d.1943 mixed media graphite pastel. 6-Jul-4 Bolsa de Arte, Rio de Janeiro #24/R (B.R 70000)
£16525	$28093	€24127	Untitled sketches of mother and child (20x16cm-8x6in) i. mixed media prov. 24-Nov-3 Sotheby's, Melbourne #282/R est:20000-30000 (A.D 39000)
£17000	$31110	€24820	Studies of sheep with lambs (20x25cm-8x10in) s.verso pen wash prov.lit. 2-Jun-4 Sotheby's, London #127/R est:12000-15000
£18000	$30600	€26280	Studies for sculpture, seated figure 1950-1 (29x23cm-11x9in) s.i.d.50 pencil wax crayon chl wash prov. 21-Nov-3 Christie's, London #168/R est:15000-25000
£28000	$51520	€40880	Six seated women, four holding children (28x21cm-11x8in) s. gouache W/C pen ink wax crayon pencil exec c.1943 prov. 24-Jun-4 Christie's, London #375/R est:16000-20000
£32000	$54400	€46720	Three standing figures 1949 (39x26cm-15x10in) s.d.50 pencil wax crayon W/C wash prov.lit. 21-Nov-3 Christie's, London #169/R est:30000-40000
£41000	$75030	€59860	Two women (53x39cm-21x15in) s.d.49 pencil chl col crayon prov.exhib. 4-Jun-4 Christie's, London #90/R est:20000-30000
£66000	$120120	€96360	Reclining figure (33x58cm-13x23in) s.i.d.43 col crayon pen ink wash htd white prov.lit. 4-Feb-4 Sotheby's, London #521/R est:12000-15000
£69000	$126270	€100740	Coalminers (30x56cm-12x22in) s.d.42 pencil wax crayon W/C wash pen ink exhib.lit. 4-Jun-4 Christie's, London #89/R est:40000-60000
£92000	$164680	€134320	Shelterers (33x28cm-13x11in) s. pencil wax crayon W/C pen ink gouache prov.lit. 16-Mar-4 Bonhams, New Bond Street #50/R est:30000-40000

MOORE, Henry R A (1831-1895) British

£300	$501	€438	Where land meets sea (20x30cm-8x12in) s.d.88 board. 13-Nov-3 Christie's, Kensington #100/R
£500	$790	€725	Clipper on the coast (43x73cm-17x29in) s.d.1891 prov. 7-Sep-3 Lots Road Auctions, London #350
£2246	$4178	€3279	Return of the fishing fleet (47x93cm-19x37in) s. 2-Mar-4 Rasmussen, Copenhagen #1424/R est:20000 (D.KR 25000)
£3385	$5822	€4942	Coastal landscape with figures and boats (41x67cm-16x26in) s.d.1877. 2-Dec-3 Bukowskis, Stockholm #287/R est:30000-35000 (S.KR 44000)
£4800	$7584	€6960	Waves breaking on a beach (29x65cm-11x26in) s.d.1873 panel. 4-Sep-3 Christie's, Kensington #196/R est:5000-8000
£5000	$8500	€7300	Lonely sea and the sky (42x66cm-17x26in) s.d.1883. 19-Nov-3 Christie's, Kensington #605/R
£5000	$8350	€7300	On the Dart (46x71cm-18x28in) s.i.d.1855 exhib. 12-Nov-3 Sotheby's, Olympia #73/R est:5000-7000
£5400	$8586	€7830	Breezy day in the Channel (60x100cm-24x39in) s. exhib. 9-Sep-3 David Duggleby, Scarborough #264 est:5000-7000

Prints

£2825	$5000	€4125	Woman holding cat (30x49cm-12x19in) s.i. colograph print. 30-Apr-4 Sotheby's, New York #162/R est:7000-9000
£3529	$6000	€5152	Woman holding cat (35x53cm-14x21in) s. colograph lit. 31-Oct-3 Sotheby's, New York #340/R
£4412	$7500	€6442	Figures in settings (58x41cm-23x16in) s. colograph. 31-Oct-3 Sotheby's, New York #338/R

Sculpture

£4192	$7000	€6120	Mother and child and reclining figure (18x42cm-7x17in) s.num.1/9 brown pat bronze prov.lit. 7-Oct-3 Sotheby's, New York #335 est:8000-12000
£89385	$160000	€130502	Stringed mother and child (47cm-19in) s. num.1/8 brown pat bronze string conceived 1938 prov.lit. 6-May-4 Sotheby's, New York #296/R est:150000-200000

Works on paper

£1800	$3294	€2628	Among the peat, Skye (25x34cm-10x13in) s.d.1885 pencil W/C prov.exhib. 3-Jun-4 Christie's, London #21/R est:1200-1800
£4000	$7320	€5840	Highland stream (37x56cm-15x22in) s.d.1867 pencil W/C gum arabic scratching out prov. 3-Jun-4 Christie's, London #20/R est:3000-5000
£9000	$16380	€13140	Reclining figure (13x22cm-5x9in) s.d.28 ink W/C over chl. 4-Feb-4 Sotheby's, London #456/R est:5000-7000
£10615	$19000	€15498	Illustration for a poem by Herbert Read (28x23cm-11x9in) col crayon W/C pen ink pencil exec 1946 prov.lit. 6-May-4 Sotheby's, New York #362/R est:20000-30000

MOORE, Jack Tex (1865-?) American

£659	$1100	€962	Castle Rock, Gallatin river, Montana (30x58cm-12x23in) 18-Oct-3 David Dike, Dallas #319/R

MOORE, James (19/20th C) British
£396 $708 €578 Adrienne as the Lady of Shallot (51x66cm-20x26in) s.indis.d.1922 double-sided prov. 22-Mar-4 Waddingtons, Toronto #645/R (C.D 950)

MOORE, John Collingham (1829-1880) British
£1042 $1646 €1500 Landscapes (34x45cm-13x18in) s. pair. 6-Sep-3 Schopman, Hamburg #685/R est:1500

MOORE, John Drummond McPherson (1888-1958) Australian
£1626 $2553 €2358 Free speech, the Domain, Sydney (26x38cm-10x15in) s.d.1925 board prov.exhib. 26-Aug-3 Christie's, Sydney #318/R est:4000-6000 (A.D 4000)

MOORE, John L (1897-1965) New Zealander
Works on paper
£564 $959 €823 Atkinson homestead, Wairarpa (24x34cm-9x13in) s.d. W/C. 26-Nov-3 Dunbar Sloane, Wellington #105 est:1500-2500 (NZ.D 1500)

MOORE, Leslie (1913-1984) British
Works on paper
£410 $746 €599 Red tea pot (84x59cm-33x23in) s.d.73 mixed media. 21-Jun-4 Bonhams, Bath #349

MOORE, Leslie L H (1907-1997) British
Works on paper
£380 $692 €555 Slaughdon Quay, Suffolk (36x56cm-14x22in) s. i.verso W/C. 16-Jun-4 Andrew Hartley, Ilkley #960

MOORE, Nelson Augustus (1823-1902) American
£1768 $3200 €2581 Landscape with lake, Original Kensington reservoir (28x46cm-11x18in) s.i. 3-Apr-4 Nadeau, Windsor #138 est:2000-3000
£1882 $3500 €2748 View of Lake George (30x53cm-12x21in) s.d.96. 6-Mar-4 North East Auctions, Portsmouth #544/R est:300-500

MOORE, Robert (?) ?
Works on paper
£289 $540 €422 Seascape with sailing vessels (25x35cm-10x14in) s. W/C. 25-Feb-4 Kunsthallen, Copenhagen #537 (D.KR 3200)

MOORE, Robert Eric (1956-) American
Works on paper
£559 $1000 €816 Vaughan Island off Turbot's Creek (36x53cm-14x21in) exhib. 8-Jan-4 James Julia, Fairfield #860/R

MOORE, Yvonne (20th C) Irish
£514 $838 €740 Table top still life (41x41cm-16x16in) init. 23-Sep-3 De Veres Art Auctions, Dublin #221/R
£528 $860 €760 Shuttered window with balcony (41x41cm-16x16in) init. 23-Sep-3 De Veres Art Auctions, Dublin #320/R
£839 $1427 €1200 Table top still life (40x40cm-16x16in) init. 25-Nov-3 De Veres Art Auctions, Dublin #117/R est:800-1200
£1000 $1810 €1500 Crowded dresser (30x61cm-12x24in) init. 30-Mar-4 De Veres Art Auctions, Dublin #143/R est:900-1200
£1447 $2663 €2200 Flowers on a sideboard (92x102cm-36x40in) s. i.verso board. 22-Jun-4 De Veres Art Auctions, Dublin #188/R est:3000-4000

MOORE-JONES, Horace Millichamp (1868-1922) New Zealander
£551 $1031 €804 Maori figure on steps of Whare (18x30cm-7x12in) s. canvasboard. 24-Feb-4 Peter Webb, Auckland #47/R (NZ.D 1500)
£1176 $2200 €1717 Portrait of a Maori woman (32x24cm-13x9in) s. canvasboard. 24-Feb-4 Peter Webb, Auckland #151/R est:1800-2500 (NZ.D 3200)
Works on paper
£2340 $3979 €3416 Simpson and his donkey (33x25cm-13x10in) s.d.1920 W/C. 25-Nov-3 Christie's, Melbourne #209/R est:1500-2000 (A.D 5500)

MOORE-JONES, Horace Millichamp (attrib) (1868-1922) New Zealander
£441 $825 €644 Tangi (14x23cm-6x9in) canvasboard. 24-Feb-4 Peter Webb, Auckland #2/R (NZ.D 1200)

MOORHOUSE, Mortram (20th C) British
Works on paper
£300 $498 €438 Hunting scene (15x13cm-6x5in) s.d.1912 W/C. 2-Oct-3 Mitchells, Cockermouth #845/R

MOORMANS, Franz (1832-1893) Dutch
£1067 $1920 €1600 Bourgeois interior with man playing cards at a table (46x37cm-18x15in) s. panel. 26-Apr-4 Bernaerts, Antwerp #26/R est:1600-1800
£1370 $2329 €2000 Deux elegantes a la lecture (27x21cm-11x8in) s. panel. 10-Nov-3 Horta, Bruxelles #103
£1655 $3062 €2400 L'erudit a la lecture (41x32cm-16x13in) s.d.1869 panel. 19-Jan-4 Horta, Bruxelles #114 est:1000-1500
£11724 $21690 €17000 Au bistrot (26x36cm-10x14in) s.i.d.1889 panel. 19-Jan-4 Horta, Bruxelles #113/R est:18000-20000

MOORTGAT, Gerard (1908-) Belgian
£331 $603 €500 Vue de Venise (50x60cm-20x24in) s. 15-Jun-4 Vanderkindere, Brussels #134

MOOS, Ludwig (1890-?) German
£445 $757 €650 Mountain landscape with church and stream in evening (51x70cm-20x28in) s. board lit. 6-Nov-3 Allgauer, Kempten #3517/R

MOOS, Max von (1903-1979) Swiss
£284 $517 €415 Ulfilas (40x35cm-16x14in) s. tempera cardboard. 16-Jun-4 Fischer, Luzern #2798/R (S.FR 650)
£383 $700 €559 Three figures (38x53cm-15x21in) s.d.1954 board. 5-Jun-4 Susanin's, Chicago #5061/R
£769 $1331 €1123 Composition (83x121cm-33x48in) s.d.1959 tempera masonite lit. 9-Dec-3 Sotheby's, Zurich #131/R est:1400-1800 (S.FR 1700)
£810 $1295 €1175 Portrait (17x12cm-7x5in) oil tempera. 15-May-3 Stuker, Bern #1399 (S.FR 1700)
£905 $1538 €1321 Personnage au serpent (68x98cm-27x39in) s.d.1961 oil chk. 19-Nov-3 Fischer, Luzern #2649/R est:1800-2000 (S.FR 2000)
£952 $1524 €1380 Ghost (14x19cm-6x7in) s. i.d.1942 verso tempera. 15-May-3 Stuker, Bern #1398 (S.FR 2000)
£995 $1692 €1453 Untitled (20x29cm-8x11in) mono.d.52 tempera ink. 22-Nov-3 Burkhard, Luzern #3 (S.FR 2200)
£1053 $1758 €1537 Exhumation (26x15cm-10x6in) s. s.i. verso tempera varnish board prov.lit. 15-Nov-3 Galerie Gloggner, Luzern #108/R est:1200-1500 (S.FR 2400)
£2661 $4443 €3858 Composition (41x58cm-16x23in) s. s.d.1944 verso board. 19-Jun-3 Kornfeld, Bern #732/R est:6000 (S.FR 5800)
£4525 $7828 €6607 Untitled (33x24cm-13x9in) s.d.1946 tempera board prov.lit. 9-Dec-3 Sotheby's, Zurich #127/R est:4000-6000 (S.FR 10000)
£4751 $8077 €6936 Untitled (46x64cm-18x25in) s.d.1968 verso tempera oil board. 22-Nov-3 Burkhard, Luzern #33/R est:8000-12000 (S.FR 10500)
£6190 $9905 €8976 Still life with guitar (59x84cm-23x33in) s. i.d.1945 board. 15-May-3 Stuker, Bern #1397/R est:4000-5000 (S.FR 13000)
Works on paper
£261 $477 €381 Jester (29x21cm-11x8in) s.d.1948 ink. 4-Jun-4 Zofingen, Switzerland #2887 (S.FR 600)
£905 $1538 €1321 Untitled (61x81cm-24x32in) s.d.1960 verso mixed media pavatex. 19-Nov-3 Fischer, Luzern #1294/R (S.FR 2000)
£1267 $2154 €1850 Untitled (64x49cm-25x19in) s. W/C over Indian ink. 25-Nov-3 Germann, Zurich #147/R est:3000-4000 (S.FR 2800)
£3066 $4967 €4476 Pipe with bottles (20x29cm-8x11in) s. i.d.1943 verso tempera col pen board. 24-May-3 Burkhard, Luzern #10/R est:4500-5000 (S.FR 6500)

MOOSBRUGGER, Friedrich (1804-1836) German
Works on paper
£480 $869 €720 Medieval bridge on Subiaco (19x26cm-7x10in) mono.i.d. pencil. 2-Apr-4 Winterberg, Heidelberg #492/R

MOOSBRUGGER, Josef (1810-1869) German
£1842 $3389 €2800 Spring landscape, early morning (143x100cm-56x39in) 25-Jun-4 Michael Zeller, Lindau #500/R est:2800

MOOSBRUGGER, Wendelin (attrib) (1760-1849) Austrian
£315 $526 €450 Bischoff Ludwigsburg (62x50cm-24x20in) i. verso. 27-Jun-3 Michael Zeller, Lindau #475
£315 $526 €450 Man's portrait (62x50cm-24x20in) 27-Jun-3 Michael Zeller, Lindau #476

MOOY, Jaap (20th C) ?
£664 $1129 €950 Aeroplane landing (65x95cm-26x37in) s.d.59 i.verso. 24-Nov-3 Glerum, Amsterdam #261/R

MOOY, Jan (1776-1847) Dutch
Works on paper
£570 $1055 €850 De kozak (33x49cm-13x19in) s.i.d.1817 ink W/C. 15-Mar-4 Sotheby's, Amsterdam #19/R est:800-1200

MOPP (1885-?) ?
£1422 $2375 €2062 Circle (16x13cm-6x5in) s. Indian ink htd bodycol. 19-Jun-3 Kornfeld, Bern #735 est:1000 (S.FR 3100)

MOPPETT, Ronald Benjamin (1945-) Canadian
Works on paper
£905 $1511 €1321 Untitled (130x94cm-51x37in) s.d.1992 mixed media prov. 17-Nov-3 Hodgins, Calgary #84/R est:3000-5000 (C.D 2000)

MOR, Antonis (attrib) (1519-1575) Dutch
£11067 $19810 €16158 Portrait of a young girl (33x23cm-13x9in) d.1575 verso wood panel prov. 15-May-4 Christie's, Sydney #138/R est:20000-25000 (A.D 28000)

MOR, Antonis (style) (1519-1575) Dutch
£5800 $10614 €8468 Portrait of Philip II of Spain (66x52cm-26x20in) panel. 6-Jul-4 Sotheby's, Olympia #449/R est:2000-30000

MORA, Alphonse (1891-1977) Belgian
£272 $487 €400 Nature morte aux coquillages de mer (53x75cm-21x30in) 22-Mar-4 Amberes, Antwerp #221
£272 $487 €400 Nature morte aux coquillages de mer (49x63cm-19x25in) canvas laid down. 22-Mar-4 Amberes, Antwerp #222

MORA, Francis Luis (1874-1940) American
£422 $700 €616 Chestnut roaster (41x25cm-16x10in) s. 4-Oct-3 Neal Auction Company, New Orleans #430/R
£1796 $3000 €2622 Portrait with green scarf. s. 18-Oct-3 Harvey Clar, Oakland #1475

£2081 $3600 €3038 Portrait of John Taylor arms as a s a boy (76x64cm-30x25in) s. prov. 11-Dec-3 Sotheby's, New York #217/R est:2000-3000
£2125 $3400 €3103 Bright autumn landscape (74x61cm-29x24in) i. s.verso. 20-Sep-3 Pook & Pook, Downington #560/R est:2000-3000
£3825 $7000 €5585 Dance of Salome (168x221cm-66x87in) s. prov. 5-Jun-4 Neal Auction Company, New Orleans #420/R est:10000-15000
£3827 $6200 €5549 Mardi gras (28x36cm-11x14in) s.d.1936 board. 8-Aug-3 Barridorf, Portland #223/R est:6000-9000
£5028 $9000 €7341 Young beauty with fan (56x46cm-22x18in) s. 6-May-4 Shannon's, Milford #71/R est:9000-12000
£10778 $18000 €15736 Woman with shawls (41x30cm-16x12in) s. 23-Oct-3 Shannon's, Milford #131/R est:8000-12000
Works on paper
£707 $1300 €1032 Return home (59x44cm-23x17in) s.d.1902 W/C gouache. 27-Jun-4 Freeman, Philadelphia #103/R est:1500-2500

MORA, Francis Luis (attrib) (1874-1940) American
£223 $400 €326 View over mountains and lake (61x91cm-24x36in) s. 7-May-4 Sloans & Kenyon, Bethesda #1211/R

MORA, Joseph (18th C) Mexican
£2529 $4299 €3692 Saint Augustin inspired by Saint Matthew (167x107cm-66x42in) s.d.1718. 29-Oct-3 Louis Morton, Mexico #61/R est:20000-25000 (M.P 48000)

MORA, Mirka Madeleine (1928-) Australian
£371 $694 €557 Face (76x55cm-30x22in) s.d.67 chl. 21-Jul-4 Goodman, Sydney #164 (A.D 950)
£1157 $2048 €1689 Looking at you (55x76cm-22x30in) s.d.95 i.d.1995 stretcher prov. 3-May-4 Christie's, Melbourne #242/R est:1500-2500 (A.D 2800)
£1221 $2223 €1783 Two angels (63x50cm-25x20in) s.d.70 oil on paper. 16-Jun-4 Deutscher-Menzies, Melbourne #422/R est:1800-2500 (A.D 3200)
£2273 $4022 €3319 Together (50x61cm-20x24in) s.d.96 s.i.d.1996 stretcher prov. 3-May-4 Christie's, Melbourne #251/R est:1500-2500 (A.D 5500)
Works on paper
£425 $723 €621 Figure and bird (25x23cm-10x9in) s.d.67 pencil pen ink wash. 26-Nov-3 Deutscher-Menzies, Melbourne #230/R (A.D 1000)

MORACH, Otto (1887-1973) Swiss
£31674 $54796 €46244 Circus in Solothurn (81x65cm-32x26in) exhib.lit. 9-Dec-3 Sotheby's, Zurich #50/R est:70000-80000 (S.FR 70000)
Works on paper
£1310 $2345 €1913 Viaduct and boat (47x29cm-19x11in) mono.d.1913 s.verso pencil chl prov. 26-May-4 Sotheby's, Zurich #68/R est:2000-4000 (S.FR 3000)
£3394 $5871 €4955 Couple on the street (44x31cm-17x12in) s.d.1918 chl lit. 9-Dec-3 Sotheby's, Zurich #59/R est:3000-4000 (S.FR 7500)

MORADO, Jose Chavez (1909-) Mexican
£824 $1500 €1203 Naturaleza tarasca (97x74cm-38x29in) 19-Jun-4 Du Mouchelle, Detroit #3055/R est:2500-3000
£1250 $2250 €1825 Aquadora (69x112cm-27x44in) 24-Apr-4 Du Mouchelle, Detroit #3208/R est:2500-3000

MORAGAS Y TORRAS, Tomas (1837-1906) Spanish
£1232 $2020 €1700 Plants and flowers (20x13cm-8x5in) s. panel lit. 27-May-3 Durán, Madrid #67/R est:900

MORAGO, Carlos (1957-) Spanish
£272 $487 €400 Woman with blue suit (22x15cm-9x6in) s. board. 22-Mar-4 Durán, Madrid #1241/R
£442 $805 €650 Notelets (31x21cm-12x8in) s.d.1988 board. 3-Feb-4 Segre, Madrid #241/R
Works on paper
£395 $714 €600 Trees (35x34cm-14x13in) s. pastel. 14-Apr-4 Ansorena, Madrid #303/R

MORALES JORDAN, Fernando (20th C) Venezuelan?
£299 $500 €437 Sumy, fishing boat (74x60cm-29x24in) s. painted 1972. 13-Jul-3 Subastas Odalys, Caracas #22

MORALES VANDEN EYNDEN, Francisco (1811-1884) Mexican
£3952 $6718 €5770 Immaculate Conception (25x19cm-10x7in) s.d.1867 zinc. 29-Oct-3 Louis Morton, Mexico #59/R est:44000-46000 (M.P 75000)

MORALES, Armando (1927-) Nicaraguan
£950 $1700 €1387 Figure with bowl (58x38cm-23x15in) s. 11-Jan-4 William Jenack, New York #57 est:1500-2000
£1492 $2476 €2163 Ciclistas y auto antiguo (40x32cm-16x13in) s. 12-Jun-3 Louis Morton, Mexico #117/R est:28000-32000 (M.P 26000)
£2295 $3810 €3328 Bull fight (65x80cm-26x31in) s.d.1997. 12-Jun-3 Louis Morton, Mexico #114/R est:20000-25000 (M.P 40000)
£2410 $4000 €3495 Desnudo de pie (90x80cm-35x31in) 12-Jun-3 Louis Morton, Mexico #119b/R est:30000-40000 (M.P 42000)
£2983 $4952 €4325 Madre y sus dos hijas (80x65cm-31x26in) s.d.1997. 12-Jun-3 Louis Morton, Mexico #118/R est:35000-40000 (M.P 52000)
£5587 $10000 €8157 Deux pommes et boite de sardines dans le flou (16x22cm-6x9in) s.d.86 prov. 26-May-4 Sotheby's, New York #180/R est:10000-15000
£14118 $24000 €20612 Two bathers (47x24cm-19x9in) s.d.1991 oil paper on canvas prov. 19-Nov-3 Sotheby's, New York #124/R est:12000-18000
£14535 $25000 €21221 Red apple (81x66cm-32x26in) s.d.72 prov. 3-Dec-3 Doyle, New York #18/R est:25000-35000
£19118 $32500 €27912 Boite de sardines et cone tronque II. Sin titulo (16x22cm-6x9in) s.d.83 set of four prov. 19-Nov-3 Sotheby's, New York #133/R est:10000-15000
£23529 $40000 €34352 Estudio de figura (81x51cm-32x20in) s.d.71. 19-Nov-3 Sotheby's, New York #123/R est:40000-60000
£52941 $90000 €77294 Dos banistas (81x102cm-32x40in) s.d.81 oil paper on canvas. 19-Nov-3 Sotheby's, New York #37/R est:90000-120000
£58824 $100000 €85883 Dos mujeres desvistiendose - Two women undressing (130x109cm-51x43in) s.d.96 i.stretcher oil beeswax prov.exhib. 18-Nov-3 Christie's, Rockefeller NY #55/R est:120000-160000
£80000 $147200 €120000 Two figures (203x167cm-80x66in) s.d.71 oil wax prov. 10-Jun-4 Christie's, Paris #66/R est:145000-180000
Works on paper
£1606 $2667 €2329 Apocaliptico sueno de caballos (58x83cm-23x33in) s. mixed media wood. 12-Jun-3 Louis Morton, Mexico #115/R est:20000-25000 (M.P 28000)
£17647 $30000 €25765 Dos desnudos - Two nudes (56x79cm-22x31in) s.d.81 pastel prov. 18-Nov-3 Christie's, Rockefeller NY #157/R est:35000-40000

MORALES, Armando (attrib) (1927-) Nicaraguan
£1563 $2500 €2282 Figure with bowl (61x41cm-24x16in) s. 21-Sep-3 William Jenack, New York #368 est:1500-2500

MORALES, Dario (1944-1988) Colombian
Works on paper
£857 $1500 €1251 Study for sick self-portrait (31x37cm-12x15in) s.d.1977 i.verso pencil chk wash prov. 19-Dec-3 Sotheby's, New York #1208/R est:3000-5000

MORALES, Juan Antonio (19/20th C) Spanish
£1000 $1810 €1500 Interior with woman and girl (42x34cm-17x13in) s. acrylic cardboard. 30-Mar-4 Segre, Madrid #330/R est:1200

MORALES, Luis de (c.1509-1586) Spanish
£10274 $17466 €15000 Ecce Homo (50x43cm-20x17in) board. 4-Nov-3 Ansorena, Madrid #36/R est:9000

MORALES, Rodolfo (1925-2001) Mexican
£1491 $2400 €2177 Man working on sculpture (30x61cm-12x24in) s.d.61 board. 24-Aug-3 William Jenack, New York #155 est:1000-1500
£2429 $4250 €3546 Untitled (56x21cm-22x8in) s. 19-Dec-3 Sotheby's, New York #1195/R est:7000-9000
£5587 $10000 €8157 Untitled (95x100cm-37x39in) s. prov. 26-May-4 Sotheby's, New York #164/R est:12000-18000
£6145 $11000 €8972 Untitled (90x70cm-35x28in) s.d.85 prov. 26-May-4 Sotheby's, New York #165/R est:10000-15000
£12353 $21000 €18035 Piedad en el desierto (89x121cm-35x48in) s. prov. 19-Nov-3 Sotheby's, New York #117/R est:18000-22000
Sculpture
£23529 $40000 €34352 Columna (178x42cm-70x17in) oil canvas on cardboard tube prov. 19-Nov-3 Sotheby's, New York #23/R est:40000-60000
£50279 $90000 €73407 Column of life (235cm-93in) s. canvas on cardboard tube prov. 26-May-4 Sotheby's, New York #46/R est:40000-60000
Works on paper
£542 $863 €791 Music Muse (32x50cm-13x20in) s. collage. 29-Apr-3 Louis Morton, Mexico #115/R (M.P 9000)
£603 $958 €880 Untitled (32x50cm-13x20in) s. collage. 29-Apr-3 Louis Morton, Mexico #97 (M.P 10000)
£914 $1600 €1334 Untitled collages (61x44cm-24x17in) s. collage of paper fabric string two prov. 19-Dec-3 Sotheby's, New York #1227/R est:2000-3000
£1099 $2000 €1605 Untitled - Soccer players (62x46cm-24x18in) s. collage fabric foil. 29-Jun-4 Sotheby's, New York #692/R est:3000-4000

MORALES, Vicente (?) ?
£331 $550 €480 Untitled (79x58cm-31x23in) 13-Jun-3 Du Mouchelle, Detroit #209/R

MORALIS, Yannis (1916-) Greek
£18000 $30600 €26280 Portrait (68x43cm-27x17in) s.d.55. 18-Nov-3 Sotheby's, London #49/R est:8000-12000
£18000 $31500 €26280 Seated nude (68x32cm-27x13in) s. panel. 16-Dec-3 Bonhams, New Bond Street #110/R est:18000-22000
£46000 $82340 €67160 Summer (130x98cm-51x39in) s.i.d.83 acrylic exhib.lit. 11-May-4 Bonhams, New Bond Street #98/R est:30000-50000

MORALT, Willy (1884-1947) German
£903 $1490 €1300 Pre alpine landscape (50x66cm-20x26in) s. 2-Jul-3 Neumeister, Munich #724
£1119 $1869 €1600 Monk in wood inspecting wine in glass (39x27cm-15x11in) s. panel lit. 27-Jun-3 Auktionhaus Georg Rehm, Augsburg #8130/R est:1800
£1189 $1985 €1700 Chiemsee fisherman in boat (19x30cm-7x12in) i. 11-Oct-3 Dr Fritz Nagel, Leipzig #3928/R est:1000
£1250 $2063 €1800 Scene in the mountains (28x19cm-11x7in) s.i. 3-Jul-3 Dr Fritz Nagel, Stuttgart #501/R
£1458 $2304 €2100 Tiroler stadtchen - departure of the mailcoach (10x21cm-4x8in) s.i. s.verso panel. 2-Sep-3 Christie's, Amsterdam #195/R est:1200-1600
£2041 $3653 €3000 Studying (21x30cm-8x12in) s.i. i. verso panel. 17-Mar-4 Neumeister, Munich #542/R est:3500
£2215 $4075 €3300 Girls bathing in woodland lake (56x38cm-22x15in) s.i. panel. 25-Mar-4 Dr Fritz Nagel, Stuttgart #746/R est:3700
£2431 $3962 €3500 Children at country shrine in mountains (38x27cm-15x11in) s.i. board on panel. 25-Sep-3 Dr Fritz Nagel, Stuttgart #1384/R est:3500
£2600 $4472 €3796 Bringing in the catch (35x51cm-14x20in) s.i. panel. 4-Dec-3 Christie's, Kensington #178/R est:3000-5000
£2649 $4821 €4000 Young girl praying at a forest shrine (33x55cm-13x22in) s. panel. 16-Jun-4 Hugo Ruef, Munich #1043/R est:3000
£2721 $4871 €4000 Morning pipe (21x30cm-8x12in) s.i. i. verso panel. 17-Mar-4 Neumeister, Munich #543/R est:3200
£3056 $5042 €4400 Fishermen hauling in nets on lakeshore (68x85cm-27x33in) s.i. 2-Jul-3 Neumeister, Munich #723/R est:3000
£3333 $5500 €4800 Arrival of the post coach (27x38cm-11x15in) s.i. panel. 2-Jul-3 Neumeister, Munich #722/R est:5000
£3524 $5991 €5145 Woodland dip (55x38cm-22x15in) s.i. panel. 5-Nov-3 Dobiaschofsky, Bern #823/R est:9000 (S.FR 8000)

£3618	$6658	€5500	Sunday outing (36x54cm-14x21in) s.i. paper on panel. 24-Jun-4 Dr Fritz Nagel, Stuttgart #736/R est:2000
£3846	$6615	€5500	Outing to a beer cellar (31x50cm-12x20in) s.i. panel. 3-Dec-3 Neumeister, Munich #677/R est:4000
£3946	$7063	€5800	Gift from God (37x27cm-15x11in) s. panel lit. 20-Mar-4 Bergmann, Erlangen #1082 est:5800
£4082	$7306	€6000	Travelling actors (38x55cm-15x22in) s.i. i. verso panel. 17-Mar-4 Neumeister, Munich #540/R est:6000
£4196	$7133	€6000	Flower bouquet (55x38cm-22x15in) s. panel. 20-Nov-3 Van Ham, Cologne #1748/R est:6500
£5282	$9137	€7500	The evening post (32x56cm-13x22in) s. i.verso panel. 10-Dec-3 Hugo Ruef, Munich #2463/R est:7500
£5369	$9879	€8000	Two young girls presenting flowers to old man (38x55cm-15x22in) i. verso panel lit. prov. 26-Mar-4 Auktionhaus Georg Rehm, Augsburg #8121/R est:4000
Works on paper			
£455	$782	€650	Village fair on the banks of the river (49x64cm-19x25in) s. gouache. 3-Dec-3 Neumeister, Munich #418/R
£748	$1339	€1100	Mountains with Zugspitze (43x58cm-17x23in) s.i. gouache. 17-Mar-4 Neumeister, Munich #305/R
£1565	$2801	€2300	Garmisch-Partenkirchen and Wetterstein (43x59cm-17x23in) s.i. gouache. 17-Mar-4 Neumeister, Munich #304/R est:2500
£2238	$3849	€3200	View of Lenggries (38x55cm-15x22in) s.i.d.13 gouache. 3-Dec-3 Neumeister, Munich #417/R est:900

MORAN, E Percy (1862-1935) American

£930	$1600	€1358	Portrait of a woman in Gainsborough dress (66x36cm-26x14in) s. 6-Dec-3 South Bay, Long Island #165/R
£978	$1800	€1428	The suitor's tea (56x71cm-22x28in) s. 25-Jun-4 Freeman, Philadelphia #287/R est:1500-2500
£1377	$2300	€2010	Fortune teller (71x95cm-28x37in) s. 7-Oct-3 Sotheby's, New York #171 est:2500-3500
£1657	$3000	€2419	Vespers (61x46cm-24x18in) s. 31-Mar-4 Sotheby's, New York #79a/R est:4000-6000
£8649	$16000	€12628	Wildflower field in bloom (37x51cm-15x20in) s. 11-Mar-4 Christie's, Rockefeller NY #1/R est:6000-8000

MORAN, E Percy (attrib) (1862-1935) American

£1176	$2000	€1717	Flower girl (76x51cm-30x20in) s. 21-Nov-3 Skinner, Boston #275/R est:1500-3500

MORAN, Earl (1893-1984) American

£2282	$4085	€3400	Waking (61x48cm-24x19in) s. painted c.1950. 27-May-4 Sotheby's, Paris #119/R est:2500-3000
Works on paper			
£3593	$6000	€5246	Shapely young woman plugging electric cord into socket (79x64cm-31x25in) s. pastel exec.c.1940. 15-Nov-3 Illustration House, New York #143/R est:7000-10000
£7383	$13215	€11000	The mouse (88x68cm-35x27in) s. pastel cardboard. 27-May-4 Sotheby's, Paris #120/R est:3000-5000

MORAN, Edward (1829-1901) American

£1648	$2950	€2406	Moonlit sail (30x46cm-12x18in) 8-Jan-4 James Julia, Fairfield #536/R est:2000-4000
£3631	$6500	€5301	On the Jersey shore (48x76cm-19x30in) s. s.i.d.1855 verso. 26-May-4 Doyle, New York #30/R est:8000-12000
£4942	$8500	€7215	Marsh with heron (76x64cm-30x25in) s. canvas on board. 7-Dec-3 Freeman, Philadelphia #114 est:6000-8000
£6704	$12000	€9788	Full sail at sunset (33x46cm-13x18in) s. prov. 6-May-4 Shannon's, Milford #153/R est:7000-9000
£13115	$24000	€19148	Shipping at sunset (51x76cm-20x30in) s. 29-Jul-4 Christie's, Rockefeller NY #249/R est:15000-25000
£13408	$24000	€19576	Breaking light (20x36cm-8x14in) init.d.73 prov. 6-May-4 Shannon's, Milford #139/R est:15000-25000
£14205	$25000	€20739	Coastal view (30x51cm-12x20in) s. paper on board painted c.1865 prov. 19-May-4 Sotheby's, New York #91/R est:25000-35000
£24286	$42500	€35458	Approaching storm at sea (31x51cm-12x20in) s. 19-Dec-3 Sotheby's, New York #1092/R est:8000-12000
£34091	$60000	€49773	Signalling for a pilot off Sandy Hook (76x127cm-30x50in) s.i. verso prov. 19-May-4 Sotheby's, New York #90/R est:40000-60000
£35519	$65000	€51858	When the flowing tide comes in (90x135cm-35x53in) s.d.1892. 3-Jun-4 Christie's, Rockefeller NY #707/R est:20000-30000
Works on paper			
£479	$800	€699	Country landscape at dawn (25x46cm-10x18in) s. W/C. 20-Jun-3 Freeman, Philadelphia #65/R

MORAN, Patricia (?) Australian

£506	$926	€759	White camellias. board. 3-Jun-4 Joel, Victoria #204 (A.D 1300)

MORAN, Peter (1841-1914) American

£9412	$16000	€13742	El burro (36x23cm-14x9in) s. i.verso board painted c.1902 prov. 1-Nov-3 Santa Fe Art, Santa Fe #121/R est:15000-20000
Works on paper			
£363	$650	€530	Country road, Buck's County (13x33cm-5x13in) s.i.d.1878 verso graphite ink wash exhib. 7-May-4 Sloans & Kenyon, Bethesda #1123/R
£1620	$2900	€2365	My sketching outfit (30x23cm-12x9in) s.i. graphite exhib. 7-May-4 Sloans & Kenyon, Bethesda #1122/R est:800-1000
£2712	$4800	€3960	Sheep in a pasture (25x50cm-10x20in) s. W/C gouache board. 28-Apr-4 Christie's, Los Angeles #57/R est:4000-6000

MORAN, Thomas (1837-1926) American

£13966	$25000	€20390	Near Frankford (51x76cm-20x30in) s.indis.d.185 painted c.1854 prov. 26-May-4 Doyle, New York #32/R est:20000-30000
£36932	$65000	€53921	Near East Hampton, Long Island (30x51cm-12x20in) mono.d.94 prov. 19-May-4 Sotheby's, New York #68/R est:60000-80000
£37791	$65000	€55175	East Hampton, Long Island (23x36cm-9x14in) mono.d.1903 prov. 3-Dec-3 Sotheby's, New York #104/R est:30000-50000
£52326	$90000	€76396	View of Venice (52x77cm-20x30in) init.d.1919 prov. 4-Dec-3 Christie's, Rockefeller NY #39/R est:70000-100000
£93750	$165000	€136875	Venice (51x76cm-20x30in) mono.d.1907 prov.exhib. 19-May-4 Sotheby's, New York #81/R est:80000-120000
£105114	$185000	€153466	Long Island landscape (51x77cm-20x30in) mono.d.1902 prov. 18-May-4 Christie's, Rockefeller NY #34/R est:120000-180000
£2352941	$4400000	€3435294	Mist in the Yellowstone (76x114cm-30x45in) s.d.1908 prov.exhib.lit. 24-Jul-4 Coeur d'Alene, Hayden #118/R est:2000000-3000000
Prints			
£1720	$3200	€2511	Morning on the St. John's, Florida (15x22cm-6x9in) s. etching. 2-Mar-4 Swann Galleries, New York #461/R est:2000-3000
Works on paper			
£13966	$25000	€20390	Venice (36x25cm-14x10in) mono.d.1894 W/C pencil paper on board. 26-May-4 Doyle, New York #40/R est:10000-15000

MORANDI, Giorgio (1890-1964) Italian

£70470	$126141	€105000	Flowers (20x24cm-8x9in) s. painted c.1950 prov.lit. 25-May-4 Sotheby's, Milan #251/R est:80000-120000
£94203	$154493	€130000	Flowers (20x19cm-8x7in) s. lit. 31-May-3 Farsetti, Prato #740/R est:130000-150000
£140000	$257600	€210000	Flowers (28x29cm-11x11in) s. painted 1951 prov.exhib.lit. 14-Jun-4 Porro, Milan #22/R est:16000-180000
£146853	$249650	€210000	Landscape (40x30cm-16x12in) s. prov.exhib.lit. 26-Nov-3 Pandolfini, Florence #35/R est:235000-260000
£154362	$276309	€230000	Landscape (33x38cm-13x15in) s.verso painted 1960 exhib.lit. 29-May-4 Farsetti, Prato #494/R est:220000-280000
£168919	$297297	€250000	Landscape (35x49cm-14x19in) s. painted 1942 prov.exhib.lit. 24-May-4 Christie's, Milan #324/R est:250000-350000
£185315	$315035	€265000	Nature morte (37x40cm-15x16in) s. exhib.lit. 1-Dec-3 Rieunier, Paris #27/R est:250000-300000
£189189	$332973	€280000	Still life with four objects (33x38cm-13x15in) s. painted 1946 prov.exhib.lit. 24-May-4 Christie's, Milan #325/R est:300000-400000
£214765	$384430	€320000	Still life (31x36cm-12x14in) s. painted 1962 prov.lit. 25-May-4 Sotheby's, Milan #244/R est:200000-250000
£234899	$420470	€350000	Still life (37x40cm-15x16in) s. painted 1958 lit. 29-May-4 Farsetti, Prato #530/R est:350000-400000
£251748	$427972	€360000	Landscape (40x44cm-16x17in) s.d.942 exhib.lit. 29-Nov-3 Farsetti, Prato #511/R est:350000-400000
£355705	$636711	€530000	Still life (44x46cm-17x18in) s.d.1941 prov.exhib.lit. 25-May-4 Sotheby's, Milan #254/R est:500000-600000
£390000	$651300	€569400	Still life (35x47cm-14x19in) s. prov.exhib.lit. 20-Oct-3 Sotheby's, London #9/R est:450000
Prints			
£3020	$5406	€4500	Still life with bread and lemon (3x7cm-1x3in) s.d.1921 eau forte copper prov.lit. 25-May-4 Sotheby's, Milan #116/R est:7000
£4054	$7135	€6000	Landscape (25x23cm-10x9in) s.i.d.1924 eau forte prov.lit. 24-May-4 Christie's, Milan #287/R est:6000-8000
£4412	$7500	€6442	Objects on table (17x19cm-7x7in) s. etching exec.1931. 31-Oct-3 Sotheby's, New York #342/R
£4545	$7727	€6500	Poplars (26x18cm-10x7in) s.d.1930 num.23/65 eau forte prov.lit. 25-Nov-3 Sotheby's, Milan #127/R est:7000-9000
£5072	$8319	€7000	Bridge on the Savena in Bologna (16x22cm-6x9in) s.d.1912 num.50/50 eau forte lit. 27-May-3 Sotheby's, Milan #222/R est:7000-9000
£5405	$9514	€8000	Objects on a table (19x17cm-7x7in) s.d.1931 num.16/30 eau forte lit. 24-May-4 Christie's, Milan #286/R est:8000-12000
£5677	$10332	€8288	Flowers in a basket on an oval background (29x19cm-11x7in) s.d.1929 num.40 etching. 18-Jun-4 Kornfeld, Bern #114/R est:15000 (S.FR 13000)
£6207	$10366	€9000	Landscape in Crizzana (30x24cm-12x9in) s.d.1932 num.49/60 eau forte on copper lit. 17-Nov-3 Sant Agostino, Torino #195/R est:8000-10000
£6215	$11000	€9074	Nature morta con pere e uva (18x21cm-7x8in) s.num.7/40 etching. 30-Apr-4 Sotheby's, New York #165/R est:7000-10000
£6376	$11413	€9500	Landscape in Grizzana (30x24cm-12x9in) s.d.1932 num.58/60 eau forte copper lit. 25-May-4 Sotheby's, Milan #114/R est:12000
£6471	$11000	€9448	Grande natura morta con undici oggetti in un tondo (27x27cm-11x11in) s. etching edition of 50. 6-Nov-3 Swann Galleries, New York #656/R est:15000-20000
£7042	$12324	€10000	Flowers in cone (30x20cm-12x8in) s. eau forte on copper lit. 16-Dec-3 Finarte Semenzato, Milan #46/R est:10000-12000
£7343	$12483	€10500	Landscape near Bologna (23x24cm-9x9in) s. eau forte exec.1926 lit. 29-Nov-3 Farsetti, Prato #410/R est:10000-12000
£7692	$13077	€11000	Three objects (12x16cm-5x6in) s.d.1961 num.64/100 eau forte copper lit. 25-Nov-3 Sotheby's, Milan #174/R est:10000-15000
£7692	$13077	€11000	Zinnias in striped vase (30x26cm-12x10in) i. eau forte prov.lit. 25-Nov-3 Sotheby's, Milan #172/R est:13000-18000
£8982	$15000	€13114	Natura morta (23x24cm-9x9in) s.d.1933 etching. 11-Nov-3 Christie's, Rockefeller NY #153/R est:25000-35000
£9091	$15636	€13000	Natura morta a tratti sottilissimi (25x23cm-10x9in) s.d.1933 etching. 2-Dec-3 Hauswedell & Nolte, Hamburg #446/R est:15000
£9605	$17000	€14023	Natura morta (26x31cm-10x12in) s.num.5/30 etching. 28-Apr-4 Christie's, Rockefeller NY #107/R est:20000-25000
£10870	$17826	€15000	Three houses in Grizzana (25x30cm-10x12in) s.d.929 num.26/40 eau forte lit. 27-May-3 Sotheby's, Milan #223/R est:13000-18000
£12587	$21399	€18000	Still life with bowl and two bottles (24x18cm-9x7in) s.d.1917 eau forte prov.lit. 25-Nov-3 Sotheby's, Milan #171/R est:20000-25000
£12937	$21993	€18500	Still life with vase and shells (10x12cm-4x5in) s.d.1921 eau forte prov.exhib.lit. 26-Nov-3 Pandolfini, Florence #15/R est:19000-20000
£14000	$25480	€20440	Grande natura morta con undici oggetti (27x30cm-11x12in) s.i.d.1942 num18/50 etching. 30-Jun-4 Christie's, London #276/R est:15000-20000
£15721	$28611	€22953	Still life (23x29cm-9x11in) s.d.1930 num.30 etching. 18-Jun-4 Kornfeld, Bern #115/R est:30000 (S.FR 36000)
£15721	$28611	€22953	Still life (25x23cm-10x9in) s. num.27 etching exec. 1933. 18-Jun-4 Kornfeld, Bern #116/R est:40000 (S.FR 36000)
£16779	$30034	€25000	Three houses in Grizzana (25x30cm-10x12in) s.d.929 num.27/40 eau forte prov.lit. 25-May-4 Sotheby's, Milan #228/R est:15000-20000
£20805	$37242	€31000	Still life (24x23cm-9x9in) s.d.1933 num.17/21 eau forte prov.lit. 25-May-4 Sotheby's, Milan #227/R est:20000-25000
£21834	$39738	€31878	Still life with five objects (13x19cm-5x7in) s. num.150 etching exec. 1956. 18-Jun-4 Kornfeld, Bern #117/R est:40000 (S.FR 50000)
£22378	$38042	€32000	Still life (26x30cm-10x12in) s.d.1933 eau forte copper lit. 29-Nov-3 Farsetti, Prato #412/R est:30000-40000
£23649	$41622	€35000	Big still life with lamp on the right (25x35cm-10x14in) s.d.928 num.71/75 eau forte lit. 24-May-4 Christie's, Milan #252/R est:35000-45000
£25424	$45000	€37119	Natura morta con il panneggio a sinistra (25x35cm-10x14in) s.d.1927 etching. 30-Apr-4 Sotheby's, New York #164/R est:50000-70000
£31159	$51101	€43000	Big still life with coffee pot (30x39cm-12x15in) s.d.1934 num.33/40 eau forte lit. 27-May-3 Sotheby's, Milan #221/R est:30000-40000
£32168	$54685	€46000	Great still life with bottle and objects (26x32cm-10x13in) s.d.1946 eau forte copper prov.lit. 25-Nov-3 Sotheby's, Milan #173/R est:25000-30000

Works on paper
£3329 $5659 €4760 Glass and pipe (13x11cm-5x4in) s. ink paper on canvas. 18-Nov-3 Babuino, Rome #132/R est:3000-4000
£5594 $9343 €8000 Still life (17x23cm-7x9in) s. pencil exec.1960 exhib.lit. 26-Jun-3 Sant Agostino, Torino #199/R est:8000-10000
£6711 $12013 €10000 Still life (16x18cm-6x7in) s. pencil dr exec.1962. 29-May-4 Farsetti, Prato #416/R est:10000-12000
£13793 $23034 €20000 Still life (20x28cm-8x11in) s.d.1956 pencil prov.exhib.lit. 13-Nov-3 Finarte Semenzato, Rome #225/R est:20000-25000
£14000 $23380 €20440 Paesaggio (21x16cm-8x6in) s. W/C over pencil executed 1958 prov.exhib.lit. 21-Oct-3 Sotheby's, London #99/R est:12000-15000
£15035 $25559 €21500 Still life (23x32cm-9x13in) s.d.53 pencil dr lit. 29-Nov-3 Farsetti, Prato #411/R est:14000-18000
£17000 $28390 €24820 Landscape (24x28cm-9x11in) s.d.1934 pencil prov.exhib.lit. 20-Oct-3 Sotheby's, London #20/R est:9000
£28671 $48741 €41000 Still life (21x16cm-8x6in) s. W/C exec.1963 lit. 29-Nov-3 Farsetti, Prato #413/R est:35000-45000
£34899 $62470 €52000 Still life (16x21cm-6x8in) s. i.d.1959 verso W/C exhib.lit. 25-May-4 Sotheby's, Milan #229/R est:20000-25000
£35000 $58450 €51100 Still life (25x34cm-10x13in) s. W/C pencil prov.exhib.lit. 20-Oct-3 Sotheby's, London #1/R est:15000-20000
£35000 $58450 €51100 Still life (24x33cm-9x13in) s.d.1945 pencil prov.exhib.lit. 20-Oct-3 Sotheby's, London #2/R est:15000

MORANDI, Giovanni Maria (1622-1717) Italian
£8511 $14213 €12000 Wedding of the Virgin (75x47cm-30x19in) lit. 23-Jun-3 Finarte Semenzato, Rome #193/R est:12000
Works on paper
£417 $750 €609 Holy Family with lamb (15x20cm-6x8in) red black chk. 21-Jan-4 Doyle, New York #43

MORANDI, Martha (1936-) Uruguayan
£276 $461 €400 Untitled (19x25cm-7x10in) s. board. 11-Nov-3 Castellana, Madrid #36/R
£276 $461 €400 Untitled (21x28cm-8x11in) s. cardboard. 11-Nov-3 Castellana, Madrid #10/R
£276 $461 €400 Untitled (21x30cm-8x12in) s. cardboard. 11-Nov-3 Castellana, Madrid #58/R
£276 $461 €400 Untitled (20x24cm-8x9in) s. board. 11-Nov-3 Castellana, Madrid #190/R
£276 $461 €400 Untitled (20x24cm-8x9in) s. board. 11-Nov-3 Castellana, Madrid #208/R
£276 $461 €400 Untitled (20x23cm-8x9in) s. board. 11-Nov-3 Castellana, Madrid #215/R

MORANDINI, Francesco (1544-1597) Italian
Sculpture
£1707 $2800 €2492 Struttura di un cubo (60x41x19cm-24x16x7in) s.verso white wood. 28-May-3 Sotheby's, Amsterdam #100/R est:2000-3000

MORANDINI, Marcello (1940-) Italian?
Sculpture
£3659 $6000 €5342 No 88A (125x18x10cm-49x7x4in) i. spray paint wood prov. 28-May-3 Sotheby's, Amsterdam #10/R est:6000-7000

MORANDO, Pietro (1892-1980) Italian
£1379 $2290 €2000 Woodcutter (60x50cm-24x20in) s. 1-Oct-3 Della Rocca, Turin #276/R
£1477 $2643 €2200 Ulysses (50x60cm-20x24in) s. s.i.verso painted 1967. 30-May-4 Meeting Art, Vercelli #82 est:2000
£1528 $2414 €2200 Ulysses (50x60cm-20x24in) painted 1967. 6-Sep-3 Meeting Art, Vercelli #495
£1678 $3104 €2500 Big brothers (60x50cm-24x20in) s. 13-Mar-4 Meeting Art, Vercelli #249 est:2500
£1678 $3104 €2500 Story teller (50x60cm-20x24in) s. s.i.verso lit. 13-Mar-4 Meeting Art, Vercelli #531 est:2500
£1736 $2743 €2500 Nuns at the sea (65x55cm-26x22in) 6-Sep-3 Meeting Art, Vercelli #699 est:2500
£1933 $3557 €2900 Fortress (60x90cm-24x35in) s. lit. 12-Jun-4 Meeting Art, Vercelli #975/R est:2500
£2067 $3803 €3100 Angel falling (85x65cm-33x26in) s. s.i.verso lit. 12-Jun-4 Meeting Art, Vercelli #597/R est:2500
£3356 $6208 €5000 The poors' inn (55x90cm-22x35in) s. lit. 13-Mar-4 Meeting Art, Vercelli #276 est:5000
£4828 $8062 €7000 Still life with aubergines and jug (41x48cm-16x19in) s. board. 17-Nov-3 Sant Agostino, Torino #222/R est:7000-9000
£4895 $8175 €7000 Anglers (72x101cm-28x40in) s. cardboard. 26-Jun-3 Sant Agostino, Torino #259/R est:7000-9000
£20000 $36800 €30000 Altar (160x120cm-63x47in) s.d.1953 lit. 12-Jun-4 Meeting Art, Vercelli #280/R est:15000
Works on paper
£340 $609 €500 Study (60x50cm-24x20in) s. chl. 16-Mar-4 Finarte Semenzato, Milan #193/R
£387 $711 €580 Traveller (53x40cm-21x16in) s. W/C card. 14-Jun-4 Sant Agostino, Torino #248/R
£461 $770 €650 Traveller (70x50cm-28x20in) s.i. chl tempera. 20-Oct-3 Sant Agostino, Torino #119/R
£533 $981 €800 Big brother (67x48cm-26x19in) s. mixed media cardboard. 12-Jun-4 Meeting Art, Vercelli #201/R
£2041 $3653 €3000 Shepherd (76x97cm-30x38in) s. chl paper on canvas. 22-Mar-4 Sant Agostino, Torino #429/R est:3500

MORANG, Alfred (1901-1958) American
£4412 $7500 €6442 Boil's Store (41x51cm-16x20in) s. masonite panel painted c.1950 prov.lit. 1-Nov-3 Santa Fe Art, Santa Fe #142/R est:20000-25000

MORAS, Walter (1856-1925) German
£629 $1145 €950 Summer river landscape (60x100cm-24x39in) s. 17-Jun-4 Frank Peege, Freiburg #1187/R
£851 $1421 €1242 Winter landscape (81x120cm-32x47in) s. 17-Nov-3 Blomqvist, Lysaker #1206 (N.KR 10200)
£1146 $2051 €1673 Ile de Rugen (24x36cm-9x14in) s. panel. 25-May-4 Bukowskis, Stockholm #367/R est:10000-12000 (S.KR 15500)
£1277 $2068 €1800 Fishing hut by sea (56x100cm-22x39in) s. lit. 23-May-3 Karlheinz Kaupp, Staufen #1772/R est:1800
£1391 $2531 €2100 Moon rising over the Dutch coast (56x90cm-22x35in) s. 18-Jun-4 Bolland & Marotz, Bremen #697/R est:1600
£2246 $4178 €3279 Summer evening at the Norwegian coast (60x126cm-24x50in) s. 2-Mar-4 Rasmussen, Copenhagen #1334/R est:25000 (D.KR 25000)
£2252 $4121 €3400 Autumn in wood on the Spree (80x120cm-31x47in) s. 8-Apr-4 Dorotheum, Vienna #107/R est:3800-4200
£3490 $6421 €5200 Mother and child in village street (123x200cm-48x79in) s. prov.lit. 25-Mar-4 Karlheinz Kaupp, Staufen #2623/R est:3800
£4027 $7208 €6000 Winter landscape with figures (70x103cm-28x41in) s. board. 27-May-4 Dorotheum, Vienna #234/R est:4500-5000
£4800 $8688 €7200 Summer's day in Spreewald (80x121cm-31x48in) s. prov. 1-Apr-4 Van Ham, Cologne #1550/R est:6700
£5634 $9746 €8000 Forest in winter (80x120cm-31x47in) s. 10-Dec-3 Dorotheum, Vienna #111/R est:2200-2800
£5903 $9622 €8500 Winter wood (81x120cm-32x47in) s. 24-Sep-3 Neumeister, Munich #506/R est:2500
£10490 $18042 €15000 Winter woodland scene (81x120cm-32x47in) s. 3-Dec-3 Neumeister, Munich #678/R est:2800

MORAT, Johann Martin (1805-1867) German
£2215 $4075 €3300 Staufen (7x12cm-3x5in) i. prov.lit. 25-Mar-4 Karlheinz Kaupp, Staufen #2626/R est:1500
Works on paper
£496 $804 €700 Wiesental (23x37cm-9x15in) i. i. verso gouache lit. 23-May-3 Karlheinz Kaupp, Staufen #1761
£800 $1448 €1200 Atzenbach in Wiesental (22x36cm-9x14in) s.i. gouache lit. 1-Apr-4 Frank Peege, Freiburg #1236a/R
£1146 $1891 €1650 Constance (19x28cm-7x11in) gouache over lithograph. 5-Jul-3 Geble, Radolfzell #506/R est:1500
£1342 $2470 €2000 Rogggenbach castles near Bonndorf (24x37cm-9x15in) s. gouache prov.lit. 25-Mar-4 Karlheinz Kaupp, Staufen #2624/R est:2000
£2465 $3944 €3500 Munsterthal and St Trudpert (22x36cm-9x14in) s.i. gouache lit. 19-Sep-3 Karlheinz Kaupp, Staufen #2117/R est:2000
£2465 $3944 €3500 Belchen and lower Munsterthal (22x36cm-9x14in) i. gouache lit. 19-Sep-3 Karlheinz Kaupp, Staufen #2155/R est:2000
£2482 $4021 €3500 Views of Kappel, Black Forest (23x36cm-9x14in) i. gouache lit. pair. 23-May-3 Karlheinz Kaupp, Staufen #1828/R est:3500
£2817 $4507 €4000 Staufen (22x36cm-9x14in) i. gouache lit. 19-Sep-3 Karlheinz Kaupp, Staufen #2032/R est:2000
£2958 $4732 €4200 Laisackerhofgut (22x36cm-9x14in) i. gouache lit. 19-Sep-3 Karlheinz Kaupp, Staufen #2039/R est:2000
£3380 $5408 €4800 St Trudpert in Munster valley (22x36cm-9x14in) i. gouache lit. 19-Sep-3 Karlheinz Kaupp, Staufen #2014/R est:2000

MORATILLA, Felipe (1827-?) Spanish
Sculpture
£17778 $32000 €25956 Young boy collecting shellfish and crabs (136cm-54in) s.st. bronze oval base exec.c.1890 Cast Nelli. 23-Apr-4 Christie's, Rockefeller NY #87/R est:25000-35000

MORATO ARAGONES, Jose (1923-) Spanish
£599 $1036 €850 Still life with fish (61x73cm-24x29in) s. 15-Dec-3 Ansorena, Madrid #15/R
£638 $1186 €950 Still life (60x73cm-24x29in) s. 2-Mar-4 Ansorena, Madrid #13/R

MORBELLI, Angelo (1853-1919) Italian
£48000 $88320 €72000 Pumpkins in the field (35x55cm-14x22in) s. prov.exhib. 10-Jun-4 Christie's, Rome #213/R est:50000-70000
£88889 $160000 €129778 Tempi lontani - Days gone by (69x50cm-27x20in) s.d.1908 exhib.lit. 23-Apr-4 Sotheby's, New York #77/R est:100000-150000

MORBELLI, Gigi (1900-1980) Italian
£333 $613 €500 Zinnias (24x17cm-9x7in) s.d.1974 tempera card. 14-Jun-4 Sant Agostino, Torino #158/R
£374 $670 €550 Dahlias (22x17cm-9x7in) s. egg tempera card painted 1973. 22-Mar-4 Sant Agostino, Torino #321/R
£470 $832 €700 Portrait of lady (59x47cm-23x19in) s.d.1941 masonite. 1-May-4 Meeting Art, Vercelli #396
Works on paper
£433 $797 €650 Still life (40x36cm-16x14in) s.d.1955 mixed media. 8-Jun-4 Della Rocca, Turin #326/R
£433 $797 €650 Still life (27x23cm-11x9in) s.d. mixed media. 8-Jun-4 Della Rocca, Turin #327/R

MORCHAIN, Paul-Bernard (1876-1938) French
£563 $975 €800 Paris, la Seine et peniches a quai (26x35cm-10x14in) indis.s. i. panel. 12-Dec-3 Piasa, Paris #139
£1722 $3220 €2600 Plage du Ris a Dourarnenez (46x55cm-18x22in) panel. 24-Jul-4 Thierry & Lannon, Brest #202/R est:2500-3000
£1854 $3468 €2800 Retour de peche a Douarnenez (46x55cm-18x22in) s. 24-Jul-4 Thierry & Lannon, Brest #201/R est:2000-3000
£8940 $16272 €13500 Promenade au bord du port (110x90cm-43x35in) s.d.1925. 18-Jun-4 Piasa, Paris #125/R est:4000-6000

MORDECAI, Joseph (1851-1940) British
£450 $747 €657 Portrait of a young girl (61x51cm-24x20in) s. 1-Oct-3 Woolley & Wallis, Salisbury #340/R

MORDINA, J (19th C) Spanish?
£2759 $4607 €4000 The Bergantin Brillante (62x81cm-24x32in) s.i.d.1852. 17-Nov-3 Durán, Madrid #203/R est:3000

MORDT, Gustav (1826-1856) Norwegian
£1601 $2866 €2337 A reindeer by mountain lake (37x54cm-15x21in) s.d.52. 22-Mar-4 Blomqvist, Oslo #358/R est:30000-40000 (N.KR 20000)

MORE, Antonio (?) ?
£4698 $8691 €7000 Autoportrait du peintre Antonio More (72x58cm-28x23in) 15-Mar-4 Horta, Bruxelles #201 est:5000-7000

MORE, Tom (20th C) ?
£289 $500 €422 Dutch interior (71x99cm-28x39in) s. 13-Dec-3 Charlton Hall, Columbia #83/R

MOREAU, A (?) French
£1678 $2803 €2400 Composition (97x70cm-38x28in) s.d.84 acrylic vinylique. 25-Jun-3 Rabourdin & Choppin de Janvry, Paris #54/R est:2400-2800

MOREAU, Adrien (1843-1906) French
£1835 $3064 €2661 Elegante au bord de la riviere (33x20cm-13x8in) s. 21-Jun-3 Galerie du Rhone, Sion #503/R est:4000-6000 (S.FR 4000)
£2517 $4330 €3600 Femme a la barque (61x46cm-24x18in) s. 2-Dec-3 Claude Aguttes, Neuilly #40 est:1000-1200
£4276 $7141 €6200 Champ de hautes herbes et coquelicots (47x39cm-19x15in) studio st. panel. 14-Nov-3 Drouot Estimations, Paris #40 est:1000-1600
£20588 $35000 €30058 The ferry (74x93cm-29x37in) s. 20-Nov-3 Auctions by the Bay, Alameda #1014/R

MOREAU, Aimee (20th C) French
£2533 $4611 €3800 Amazone (56x44cm-22x17in) s.d.1890 wood. 5-Jul-4 Le Mouel, Paris #12/R est:4000-5000

MOREAU, Auguste (1834-1917) French
Sculpture
£938 $1500 €1369 Young girl with putti (43cm-17in) s. bronze. 20-Sep-3 Jeffery Burchard, Florida #32b/R
£950 $1700 €1387 Water carrier (89cm-35in) s. brown pat bronze polychrome marble base. 20-Mar-4 Freeman, Philadelphia #766/R est:2000-3000
£1020 $1827 €1500 Danseuse Orientale (50cm-20in) s. brown pat bronze. 16-Mar-4 Vanderkindere, Brussels #517/R est:1250-1750
£1133 $2085 €1700 Le baiser (45cm-18in) s. pat bronze. 9-Jun-4 Beaussant & Lefèvre, Paris #226/R est:1000-1200
£1399 $2378 €2000 Flora (63cm-25in) i. brown pat.bronze. 20-Nov-3 Van Ham, Cologne #1250/R est:1600
£1447 $2663 €2200 Mussel fisher (49cm-19in) s. num.3897 brown green pat bronze incl. marble base. 22-Jun-4 Sotheby's, Amsterdam #104/R est:1000-1200
£1500 $2730 €2250 Figure of a young girl with flowers in one hand and bird perched nearby (46cm-18in) brown pat. bronze. 20-Jun-4 Wilkinson, Doncaster #209 est:2400-2800
£1667 $2650 €2400 L'espiegle, enfant au canard (40cm-16in) s. gilt pat bronze marble socle. 15-Sep-3 Horta, Bruxelles #62 est:1500-2500
£1800 $3006 €2610 Fairy and a putto holding garlands for flowers (52cm-20in) bronze. 25-Jun-3 Dreweatt Neate, Newbury #1280/R est:2000-2500
£1900 $3458 €2850 Winged figure of the infant Psyche (53cm-21in) s. green pat bronze. 20-Jun-4 Wilkinson, Doncaster #211 est:1600-2200
£2168 $3750 €3165 Reine des pres - figure of a nymph in a flowing dress (168cm-66in) s. bronze. 10-Dec-3 Alderfer's, Hatfield #231/R est:2500-3000
£2553 $4264 €3600 Femme et son enfant (64cm-25in) s. gilt bronze marble socle. 15-Oct-3 Hotel des Ventes Mosan, Brussels #151 est:1800-2000
£2649 $4848 €4000 Mignon, young girl with mandolin (79cm-31in) s. brown par. bronze. 6-Apr-4 Sotheby's, Amsterdam #325/R est:4000-5000
£2837 $4738 €4000 Aurore (66cm-26in) s.i. brown pat bronze. 12-Oct-3 St-Germain-en-Laye Encheres #51/R est:3000-3500
£2923 $4851 €4150 Groupe d'enfants (60x30cm-24x12in) s. white marble. 10-Jun-3 Renaud, Paris #125/R
£4000 $7200 €5840 Le char de l'Aurore (84cm-33in) gilt bronze incl. plinth base. 21-Apr-4 Tennants, Leyburn #1288/R est:1800-2500
£4698 $8409 €7000 Cupidon (54cm-21in) pat bronze. 25-May-4 Palais de Beaux Arts, Brussels #103/R est:2500-3500
£18000 $30600 €26280 Printemps (82cm-32in) s.d.1881 marble. 28-Oct-3 Sotheby's, London #194/R

MOREAU, Charles (1830-?) French
£4000 $6800 €5840 Birthday present (57x70cm-22x28in) s. 1-Dec-3 Bonhams, Bath #136/R est:4000-6000

MOREAU, François Hippolyte (19th C) French
Sculpture
£2535 $4386 €3600 Little sparrow (57cm-22in) s. alabaster. 9-Dec-3 Pandolfini, Florence #280/R est:3000-3200

MOREAU, Gustave (1826-1898) French
£130000 $221000 €189800 Source surprise par un satyre (46x38cm-18x15in) s. panel prov.exhib.lit. 18-Nov-3 Sotheby's, London #312/R
£344444 $620000 €502888 Narcissus (65x37cm-26x15in) s. painted c.1890 prov.lit. 22-Apr-4 Christie's, Rockefeller NY #122/R est:400000-600000
Works on paper
£60000 $109200 €87600 Sainte Elizabeth de Hongrie (27x19cm-11x7in) s. W/C exec.1879 prov.exhib.lit. 15-Jun-4 Sotheby's, London #164/R est:60000-80000

MOREAU, Henri (1869-1943) Belgian
£280 $501 €409 Red Indian by a fire, mountains beyond (35x75cm-14x30in) s. board. 11-May-4 Bonhams, Knightsbridge #103
£300 $546 €450 Still life with pewter plate of oranges and a blue vase (48x65cm-19x26in) s. 20-Jun-4 Wilkinson, Doncaster #314
£464 $844 €700 Nu feminin (31x45cm-12x18in) s.d.1893. 16-Jun-4 Hotel des Ventes Mosan, Brussels #251
£490 $832 €700 Les anemones (65x50cm-26x20in) s. 18-Nov-3 Vanderkindere, Brussels #117
£580 $928 €847 Still life with white flowers in basket. Floral still life (49x40cm-19x16in) s. one d.1917 two. 16-Sep-3 Rosebery Fine Art, London #541
£764 $1215 €1100 Composition aux oranges (30x40cm-12x16in) s. 15-Sep-3 Horta, Bruxelles #49
£1049 $1804 €1500 Elegante a la gerbe de roses de profil (80x60cm-31x24in) s. 8-Dec-3 Horta, Bruxelles #46 est:1500-1800

MOREAU, Henri (?) French
£260 $424 €377 Red Indian chief by a camp fire (36x74cm-14x29in) s. board. 17-Jul-3 Thomson, Roddick & Medcalf, Carlisle #24/R

MOREAU, Hippolite (19th C) French
Sculpture
£1183 $2117 €1727 Le reve (51cm-20in) s. brown pat.bronze. 25-May-4 Bukowskis, Stockholm #311/R est:20000-25000 (S.KR 16000)
£1267 $2280 €1900 Young girl picking grapes (63cm-25in) s. bronze Cast.Societe des Bronzes Paris. 26-Apr-4 Rieber, Stuttgart #2201/R est:480
£1748 $2972 €2500 Girls playing (48cm-19in) i. bronze. 20-Nov-3 Van Ham, Cologne #1251/R est:900
£2759 $4607 €4000 L'odalisque (61cm-24in) s.st.f.Societe des Bronzes brown pat bronze. 17-Nov-3 Tajan, Paris #79/R est:3000-3500

MOREAU, Hippolyte François (1832-1927) French
Sculpture
£1042 $1719 €1500 Charmeuse (52cm-20in) i. bronze. 3-Jul-3 Van Ham, Cologne #921/R est:1800
£1154 $2100 €1685 Traveller (61x23cm-24x9in) cast sig. pat bronze. 7-Feb-4 Neal Auction Company, New Orleans #400/R est:2000-3000
£1597 $2635 €2300 Mignon et Priscilla (67cm-26in) i. bronze lit. 3-Jul-3 Van Ham, Cologne #920/R est:1800
£1600 $2912 €2336 Woman feeding birds (62cm-24in) s. brown pat bronze base. 15-Jun-4 Sotheby's, Olympia #87/R est:1500-2000
£3077 $5138 €4400 Le printemps (66x30cm-26x12in) s. white marble lit. 11-Oct-3 De Vuyst, Lokeren #517/R est:4000-5000

MOREAU, Jacob (20th C) French?
£789 $1429 €1200 Angels' concert (120x60cm-47x24in) s. panel. 14-Apr-4 Ansorena, Madrid #177/R

MOREAU, Jacques Gaston (1903-1994) French
£1450 $2654 €2117 New pearl necklace (79x106cm-31x42in) s.d.28 board. 8-Jul-4 Lawrence, Crewkerne #1620/R est:1200-1800

MOREAU, Jean (19/20th C) French
£850 $1573 €1241 Portrait of a girl (36x28cm-14x11in) indis.s. panel. 14-Jul-4 Christie's, Kensington #894/R

MOREAU, Jean Jacques (1899-1927) French
£1974 $3632 €3000 Arranging pink roses (90x60cm-35x24in) s. 22-Jun-4 Christie's, Amsterdam #224/R est:3000-5000

MOREAU, Louis (?) French
Works on paper
£18543 $33748 €28000 Landscapes (32x25cm-13x10in) W/C gouache on velin on panel pair prov.lit. 15-Jun-4 Artcurial Briest, Paris #234/R est:30000-35000

MOREAU, Louis Gabriel (1740-1806) French
Works on paper
£407 $700 €594 View of French village (13x25cm-5x10in) s. pencil ink wash. 2-Dec-3 Christie's, Rockefeller NY #152/R
£1027 $1747 €1500 Village au bord de la Seine (23x36cm-9x14in) wash prov. 6-Nov-3 Tajan, Paris #75/R
£1250 $2250 €1825 View of a park with a woman at a fountain (21cm-8in circular) init.d.1780 brush wash over graphite. 21-Jan-4 Sotheby's, New York #117/R est:2500-3500
£2603 $4425 €3800 Chaumiere (16x21cm-6x8in) gouache. 6-Nov-3 Tajan, Paris #74/R
£6122 $10959 €9000 Diane et Acteon. Un couple dans un parc sous un statue de Cupidon (6cm-2in circular) gouache pair prov.exhib.lit. 18-Mar-4 Christie's, Paris #143/R est:10000-15000

MOREAU, Louis Gabriel (attrib) (1740-1806) French
Works on paper
£2152 $3917 €3250 Pecheurs pres de la riviere (25x37cm-10x15in) W/C gouache. 15-Jun-4 Claude Aguttes, Neuilly #1b est:400-600

MOREAU, Louis Gabriel (circle) (1740-1806) French
£3867 $7000 €5646 Elegant figures in a park (72x93cm-28x37in) 30-Mar-4 Christie's, Rockefeller NY #29/R est:4000-6000

MOREAU, Louis-Auguste (1855-1919) French
Sculpture
£1119 $1902 €1600 Little girl standing on chair (45cm-18in) s. bronze. 29-Nov-3 Bukowskis, Helsinki #354/R est:1000-1200

MOREAU, Louis-Auguste (after) (1855-1919) French
Sculpture
£3552 $6500 €5186 Young psyche (79cm-31in) gold brown pat. bronze incl. marble plinth. 7-Jun-4 Bonhams & Butterfields, San Francisco #2176/R est:2500-3500

MOREAU, Mathurin (1822-1912) French
Sculpture
£1183 $2117 €1727 Woman with attribution for science (85cm-33in) s. dark pat.bronze. 25-May-4 Bukowskis, Stockholm #312/R est:25000-30000 (S.KR 16000)
£1200 $2172 €1800 La reconnaissance (60cm-24in) s. bronze. 30-Mar-4 Gioffredo, Nice #52/R
£1293 $2314 €1900 La rosee (49cm-19in) s. brown pat bronze. 19-Mar-4 Oger, Dumont, Paris #71/R est:1500
£1469 $2497 €2100 Source (68cm-27in) s.st.f. pat bronze. 28-Nov-3 Drouot Estimations, Paris #15 est:1600-1800
£1538 $2646 €2200 Summer, young girl sitting on a rock (50cm-20in) s. brown pat bronze lit. 3-Dec-3 Neumeister, Munich #270/R est:2000
£1736 $2830 €2500 Inspiration (67cm-26in) s. pat bronze. 23-Sep-3 Durán, Madrid #919/R est:1200
£1745 $3123 €2600 Nymphe donnant a boire a l'amour (62cm-24in) biscuit. 25-May-4 Palais de Beaux Arts, Brussels #104/R est:2500-3000
£2036 $3462 €2973 Nymphe fluvial (80cm-31in) i. bronze. 28-Nov-3 Zofingen, Switzerland #2393/R est:5500 (S.FR 4500)
£2098 $3504 €3000 Venus aux fleurs (85cm-33in) green pat bronze. 26-Jun-3 Artcurial Briest, Paris #714 est:3000-4000
£2113 $3655 €3000 Jeune chasseur rapportant un chevreuil (76cm-30in) s. medaille green brown pat bronze. 12-Dec-3 Libert, Castor, Paris #131 est:3000-4000
£2215 $4097 €3300 Vendangeuse (66cm-26in) s. white marble sold with base. 14-Mar-4 St-Germain-en-Laye Encheres #9/R est:2000-2500
£2350 $3737 €3431 Classical young girl playing a tambourine (48cm-19in) s. bronze. 1-May-3 John Nicholson, Haslemere #290/R est:2750-3000
£3423 $5511 €5100 La pecheuse de moules (72cm-28in) s.num.3877 brown pat bronze red marble socle. 23-Feb-3 St-Germain-en-Laye Encheres #44/R est:5000-6000
£3536 $6223 €5163 Lady (64cm-25in) s. pat bronze. 23-May-4 Agra, Warsaw #15/R (P.Z 25000)
£3642 $6629 €5500 Jeune femme guettant (74cm-29in) pat bronze. 15-Jun-4 Claude Aguttes, Neuilly #312/R est:3500-4000
£4000 $6680 €5840 Goddess Venus, clasping a shell (76cm-30in) white marble. 14-Oct-3 Sotheby's, Olympia #35/R est:4000-6000
£4667 $8353 €7000 La source (74x32cm-29x13in) st.sig. brown pat bronze lit. 15-May-4 De Vuyst, Lokeren #418/R est:7500-8500
£5369 $9933 €8000 Retour de moisson (84x42cm-33x17in) s. brown pat bronze marble wood base lit. 13-Mar-4 De Vuyst, Lokeren #415/R est:5000-7000
£5600 $9352 €8176 Song of the sea (115cm-45in) s. bronze. 21-Oct-3 Bruton Knowles, Cheltenham #683/R
£5704 $9868 €8100 Pensee (98cm-39in) i. brown red pat bronze. 14-Dec-3 St-Germain-en-Laye Encheres #92/R est:8000-10000
£7092 $11844 €10000 Les harmonies (225cm-89in) i. pat bronze red marble griotte mahogany base exec.c.1896 prov. 17-Jun-3 Christie's, Paris #118/R est:7000-10000
£11000 $19800 €16500 Young girl seated on a rock, holding a birds' nest (101cm-40in) s. marble. 26-Apr-4 Bernaerts, Antwerp #153/R est:10000-12000

MOREAU, Max (1902-1992) Belgian
£541 $968 €800 La petite marchande de fleurs (81x61cm-32x24in) s.d.1956. 10-May-4 Horta, Bruxelles #44
£3087 $5711 €4600 Le repos des sages (81x60cm-32x24in) s.d.1950. 15-Mar-4 Horta, Bruxelles #31 est:1000-1200
£3288 $5589 €4800 Acrobat (100x80cm-39x31in) s.d.29. 10-Nov-3 Horta, Bruxelles #245
£4225 $7310 €6000 Tete de Bedouin, tete de Bedouine (45x35cm-18x14in) s.d.1930 pair. 10-Dec-3 Hotel des Ventes Mosan, Brussels #218/R est:2000-2500
£6334 $11591 €9500 Portrait d'homme. Portrait de Bedouine (50x40cm-20x16in) s. pair. 3-Jun-4 Tajan, Paris #286/R est:8000-10000

MOREAU, Nicolas (19th C) French
£333 $597 €500 Deux chiens courant (23x29cm-9x11in) panel. 12-May-4 Coutau Begarie, Paris #170/R
£1267 $2305 €1900 Femme au cigare (89x94cm-35x37in) s.d. 2-Jul-4 Binoche, Paris #13/R est:1500-2000

MOREAU-VAUTHIER, Edme Augustin Jean (attrib) (1831-1893) French
Sculpture
£10500 $19110 €15750 Allegorical figure of a woman (130cm-51in) s.d.1878 brown pat. bronze st.f. Barbedienne. 20-Jun-4 Wilkinson, Doncaster #20 est:10000-15000

MOREAU-VAUTHIER, Paul (1871-1936) French
Sculpture
£1538 $2615 €2200 Terrassier a la pioche (61cm-24in) s. pat bronze. 28-Nov-3 Doutrebente, Paris #53/R est:1500-2000

MOREELSE, Johann (17th C) Dutch
£2533 $4535 €3800 Democritus (72x62cm-28x24in) lit. 13-May-4 Babuino, Rome #96/R est:3000-4000

MOREELSE, Paulus (1571-1638) Dutch
£5556 $9167 €8000 Madonna with child (75x59cm-30x23in) s.d.1615. 2-Jul-3 Neumeister, Munich #561/R est:7000
£7534 $12808 €11000 Portrait of a lady, in a black dress, wearing pearl jewellery. mono.d.1630 prov.exhib.lit. 4-Nov-3 Sotheby's, Amsterdam #42/R est:10000-15000
£13793 $22897 €20000 Portrait of a gentleman in ruff (55x37cm-22x15in) panel octagonal. 1-Oct-3 Dorotheum, Vienna #152/R est:20000-30000
£95890 $163014 €140000 Vanitas, young lady at a draped table before a black framed mirror (88x73cm-35x29in) mono.d.1632 prov.lit. 5-Nov-3 Christie's, Amsterdam #54/R est:50000-70000

MOREL FATIO, Antoine Léon (1810-1871) French
£4000 $7400 €5840 Caide au Caire (61x41cm-24x16in) s. 10-Mar-4 Sotheby's, Olympia #259/R est:4000-6000
£6667 $12267 €10000 Cavalier ottoman dans les souks du Caire (60x40cm-24x16in) s. 14-Jun-4 Gros & Delettrez, Paris #501/R est:12000-15000
£100000 $182000 €146000 La Corne d'Or (45x123cm-18x48in) s. prov. 15-Jun-4 Sotheby's, London #144/R est:80000-120000
Works on paper
£276 $505 €400 Au sec (31x23cm-12x9in) mono. 31-Jan-4 Neret-Minet, Paris #142/R

MOREL, Casparus Johannes (1798-1861) Dutch
£1736 $2743 €2500 Dutch coast. Seascape with boats (15x18cm-6x7in) s.d.31.8.29 i. verso lit. pair. 19-Sep-3 Schloss Ahlden, Ahlden #1431/R est:2800
£2207 $3686 €3200 Ship in difficulty by the coast with figures (58x83cm-23x33in) s.d.1856 panel. 11-Nov-3 Vendu Notarishuis, Rotterdam #150/R est:2500-3000

MOREL, E (19th C) French
£772 $1421 €1158 Still life of flowers (92x62cm-36x24in) s. 14-Jun-4 Blomqvist, Lysaker #1269/R (N.KR 9500)

MOREL, Henriette (20th C) French
Works on paper
£320 $576 €480 Village sous la neige. s.i.d.28 octobre 38 W/C. 20-Apr-4 Chenu & Scrive, Lyon #129/R

MOREL, Jan Baptist (attrib) (1662-1732) Flemish
£6000 $10380 €8760 Mixed flowers in a vase (77x70cm-30x28in) 12-Dec-3 Christie's, Kensington #43/R est:6000-8000

MOREL, Jan Evert I (1769-1808) Flemish
£14286 $26000 €20858 Grapes, pomegranates, peaches, cherries and flowers on a stone ledge in a landscape (89x66cm-35x26in) s.d.1801 panel. 17-Jun-4 Christie's, Rockefeller NY #24/R est:15000-20000

MOREL, Jan Evert II (1835-1905) Dutch
£1034 $1852 €1510 Dutch river landscape (15x20cm-6x8in) s.d.4 panel. 12-May-4 Dobiaschofsky, Bern #812/R est:1800 (S.FR 2400)
£1034 $1852 €1510 Winter scene with frozen waterway (15x21cm-6x8in) s. panel. 12-May-4 Dobiaschofsky, Bern #813/R est:2000 (S.FR 2400)
£1333 $2400 €2000 Hunter and his dog resting in a woodland landscape (32x25cm-13x10in) s. panel. 20-Apr-4 Sotheby's, Amsterdam #38/R est:2000-3000
£1867 $3416 €2800 Fun on the ice in evening time (61x81cm-24x32in) s. 5-Jun-4 Arnold, Frankfurt #678/R est:2000
£2200 $3674 €3212 Travellers in summer landscape (15x20cm-6x8in) s. panel. 12-Nov-3 Sotheby's, Olympia #166/R est:1000-1500
£3667 $6600 €5500 Figures resting by a ford, a town in a valley beyond (50x70cm-20x28in) s. 21-Apr-4 Christie's, Amsterdam #16/R est:5000-7000
£4000 $7200 €6000 Extensive summer landscape with a town beyond (26x34cm-10x13in) s. panel. 20-Apr-4 Sotheby's, Amsterdam #2/R est:4000-6000
£6200 $10974 €9052 Landscape (71x97cm-28x38in) 1-May-4 British Auctioneer #1 est:4000-5000
Works on paper
£476 $867 €700 Gathering wood in the forest (22x31cm-9x12in) s. pencil W/C. 3-Feb-4 Christie's, Amsterdam #128

MOREL, Jan Evert II (attrib) (1835-1905) Dutch
£764 $1260 €1100 Faggot gatherers in winter wood (36x54cm-14x21in) i. 3-Jul-3 Van Ham, Cologne #1362/R

MOREL, Willem F A I Vaarzon (1868-1955) Dutch
£604 $1117 €900 Market scene (30x40cm-12x16in) s. canvas on board. 15-Mar-4 Sotheby's, Amsterdam #171/R est:900-1200
£4276 $7868 €6500 Winkelen: shopping in the sun (17x27cm-7x11in) s. panel. 22-Jun-4 Christie's, Amsterdam #305/R est:2000-3000
£26316 $47632 €40000 In a dress shop (54x42cm-21x17in) s. 19-Apr-4 Glerum, Amsterdam #251/R est:9000-11000
Works on paper
£349 $583 €500 Duindigt paddock (34x49cm-13x19in) s. W/C. 30-Jun-3 Sotheby's, Amsterdam #443/R

MORELL, Abelardo (1948-) ?
Photographs
£1778 $3200 €2596 Book with wavy pages (56x46cm-22x18in) s.i.d.2001 gelatin silver print prov. 23-Apr-4 Phillips, New York #231/R est:2000-3000
£2994 $5000 €4371 Dictionary (45x57cm-18x22in) s.i.d.1994 verso gelatin silver print prov.lit. 17-Oct-3 Phillips, New York #17/R est:7000-10000

MORELL, Pit (1939-) German
£662 $1205 €1000 Composition with figures (44x35cm-17x14in) s.d.1975 canvas on panel. 18-Jun-4 Bolland & Marotz, Bremen #935/R
Works on paper
£288 $472 €400 Woman from Schoneberg (80x50cm-31x20in) s.i.d. col chk pencil transparent foil. 4-Jun-3 Ketterer, Hamburg #696/R

MORELLET, François (1926-) French
£7042 $11690 €10000 Trois doubles trames (80x80cm-31x31in) sid.1971 verso acrylic board. 11-Jun-3 Finarte Semenzato, Milan #570a/R est:12000-16000

Sculpture
£3067 $5612 €4600 Sphere-Trames (36x36x36cm-14x14x14in) steel. 4-Jun-4 Lempertz, Koln #311/R est:2400
Works on paper
£1000 $1840 €1500 Carre bascule a 45 degrees (20x28cm-8x11in) s.i.d.1976 two collage squared paper prov. 9-Jun-4 Artcurial Briest, Paris #536/R est:2000-2500
£1268 $2193 €1800 Untitled (18x90cm-7x35in) s.i. ink tracing paper. 9-Dec-3 Artcurial Briest, Paris #265 est:1800-2000
£2308 $3854 €3300 3-3 horizontal and 3-3 vertical (30x45cm-12x18in) s.i.d.1976 verso ink. 11-Oct-3 Cornette de St.Cyr, Paris #139/R est:3500-4000

MORELLI, Domenico (1826-1901) Italian
£355 $574 €500 Charity (17x20cm-7x8in) 21-May-3 Babuino, Rome #212/R
£845 $1462 €1200 Soldiers (11x22cm-4x9in) cardboard on canvas. 10-Dec-3 Sotheby's, Milan #97/R
£1000 $1840 €1500 Historical scene (40x31cm-16x12in) i. 10-Jun-4 Christie's, Rome #103/R est:1300-1800
£1690 $2924 €2400 Crucifixion (40x31cm-16x12in) 10-Dec-3 Sotheby's, Milan #96/R est:2000-4000
£1940 $3472 €2832 Watering the animals (21x39cm-8x15in) s. board. 12-May-4 Dobiaschofsky, Bern #814/R est:8000 (S.FR 4500)
£1940 $3472 €2832 In the desert (20x40cm-8x16in) s. panel. 12-May-4 Dobiaschofsky, Bern #815/R est:8000 (S.FR 4500)
£2676 $4442 €3800 Donna al calvario (38x25cm-15x10in) s. 11-Jun-3 Christie's, Rome #166/R est:3300-3800
£4577 $7919 €6500 Player (80x45cm-31x18in) s. 10-Dec-3 Sotheby's, Milan #113/R est:4000-6000
£40000 $73600 €60000 Maometto praying before the battle (53x119cm-21x47in) s. painted 1855 prov.lit. 8-Jun-4 Sotheby's, Milan #124/R est:60000-80000
Works on paper
£921 $1695 €1400 Woman reading (45x32cm-18x13in) s. ink. 23-Jun-4 Finarte Semenzato, Rome #8/R est:1000-1100
£1141 $2099 €1700 Seated woman (34x32cm-13x13in) s.i.d.1901 Chinese ink W/C dr. 24-Mar-4 Il Ponte, Milan #532/R est:1200
£1690 $2924 €2400 Arab (44x31cm-17x12in) s.d.1883 Chinese ink. 10-Dec-3 Finarte Semenzato, Rome #185/R est:800-1000
£2465 $4264 €3500 Scene from the Othello (25x43cm-10x17in) s. W/C card. 11-Dec-3 Christie's, Rome #65/R est:1500

MORELLI, Domenico (attrib) (1826-1901) Italian
£699 $1168 €1000 Saint Anthony's temptation (32x45cm-13x18in) 7-Oct-3 Livinec, Gaudcheau & Jezequel, Rennes #121
Works on paper
£399 $666 €570 Study (24x15cm-9x6in) ink. 24-Jun-3 Finarte Semenzato, Rome #2

MORELLI, F (1768-1830) French
£3472 $5903 €5000 Parting with precious possessions (67x76cm-26x30in) s. prov. 28-Oct-3 Christie's, Amsterdam #65/R est:5000-7000

MORELLO, F (19/20th C) ?
£1600 $2944 €2400 Palermo, fishing boats (70x100cm-28x39in) s. 10-Jun-4 Christie's, Rome #74/R est:2000-3000
£2000 $3640 €3000 Piedigrotta (90x90cm-35x35in) s. i.verso. 12-Jul-4 Il Ponte, Milan #535 est:1400-1500

MORELLO, Federico (19/20th C) Italian
£1200 $2148 €1800 People on the beach (90x112cm-35x44in) s. 12-May-4 Stadion, Trieste #775 est:2000-3000

MORENI, Mattia (1920-1999) Italian
£4483 $7486 €6500 Woman holding flower (80x51cm-31x20in) s.d.1944 i.verso. 17-Nov-3 Sant Agostino, Torino #274/R est:6000-8000
£5517 $9214 €8000 Red nude (50x70cm-20x28in) s.i.d.1943 verso. 17-Nov-3 Sant Agostino, Torino #275/R est:5000-6000
£11379 $19003 €16500 Watermelon in the grass (47x90cm-19x35in) s.d.1965. 17-Nov-3 Sant Agostino, Torino #290/R est:9000-12000
£14118 $24000 €20612 Sterpi (110x150cm-43x59in) s.d.55 s.i.d.verso prov.exhib. 9-Nov-3 Bonhams & Butterfields, Los Angeles #4086/R est:15000-20000
£32609 $53478 €45000 Landscape (85x166cm-33x65in) s.d.1959 s.i.d.verso prov.exhib. 27-May-3 Sotheby's, Milan #275/R est:18000-22000
Works on paper
£310 $518 €450 Nude (28x35cm-11x14in) s.d.1943 ink wash paper on cardboard. 14-Nov-3 Farsetti, Prato #241/R
£680 $1218 €1000 Figure (46x31cm-18x12in) s. wax crayon. 22-Mar-4 Sant Agostino, Torino #417/R
£748 $1339 €1100 Abstract composition (44x28cm-17x11in) s.d.1947 wax crayon. 22-Mar-4 Sant Agostino, Torino #418/R
£1329 $2219 €1900 Disco and computer (55x49cm-22x19in) s.d.1995 mixed media. 26-Jun-3 Sant Agostino, Torino #209/R est:1800-2200
£1329 $2219 €1900 Worker directed by computer (56x43cm-22x17in) s.d.1995 mixed media. 26-Jun-3 Sant Agostino, Torino #208/R est:2200
£1342 $2483 €2000 Project of shoe (46x71cm-18x28in) s.d.1998 mixed media card. 13-Mar-4 Meeting Art, Vercelli #95 est:2000
£1342 $2403 €2000 Life revolution (71x47cm-28x19in) s.d.1997 mixed media. 30-May-4 Meeting Art, Vercelli #5 est:2000
£1586 $2649 €2300 Computer genetics (70x50cm-28x20in) s.i.d.1995 mixed media. 17-Nov-3 Sant Agostino, Torino #54/R est:2200
£2759 $4607 €4000 Abstract composition (47x65cm-19x26in) s.i.d.1952 Chinese ink W/C. 17-Nov-3 Sant Agostino, Torino #138/R est:5000

MORENO VILLA, Jose (1887-1960) Spanish
£7237 $13316 €11000 Flute player (55x46cm-22x18in) s. 22-Jun-4 Durán, Madrid #191/R est:5500

MORENO, Benito (1940-) Spanish
£276 $497 €400 Basket (46x56cm-18x22in) init.d.1980 canvas on cardboard exhib. 26-Jan-4 Durán, Madrid #6/R
£276 $497 €400 Dusk in Seville (54x41cm-21x16in) init.d.79 board. 26-Jan-4 Durán, Madrid #7/R
£414 $745 €600 Strawberries (72x60cm-28x24in) init.d.79 board exhib. 26-Jan-4 Durán, Madrid #8/R

MORENO, Felicidad (1959-) Spanish
£667 $1207 €1000 Untitled (116x89cm-46x35in) s.d.1995 verso oil acrylic vinyl. 30-Mar-4 Segre, Madrid #167/R

MORENO, Genaro (20th C) ?
£261 $470 €381 Untitled (60x50cm-24x20in) s. 25-Apr-4 Subastas Odalys, Caracas #101

MORENO, Michel (1945-) French
£288 $472 €400 Composition (73x60cm-29x24in) s. 6-Jun-3 David Kahn, Paris #52
£800 $1448 €1168 La gitane (81x65cm-32x26in) s. s.i.verso. 1-Apr-4 Christie's, Kensington #143/R
Works on paper
£530 $964 €800 Composition Syntho-chromiste (40x32cm-16x13in) s.i. gouache. 15-Jun-4 Blanchet, Paris #249

MORENO, Salvador (1916-1999) Mexican
Works on paper
£500 $910 €750 Geranio (47x35cm-19x14in) s.d.1988 gouache. 29-Jun-4 Segre, Madrid #273/R

MORERA Y GALICIA, Jaime (1854-1927) Spanish
£1103 $1843 €1600 Landscape (19x33cm-7x13in) s. board. 17-Nov-3 Durán, Madrid #75/R est:900
£2069 $3724 €3000 Landscape with trees (35x23cm-14x9in) s. canvas on cardboard. 26-Jan-4 Ansorena, Madrid #176/R est:1800
£2174 $3565 €3000 Landscape (21x29cm-8x11in) s. panel. 27-May-3 Durán, Madrid #38/R est:900
£2368 $4287 €3600 Flowers (58cm-23in circular) s. on ceramic dish. 14-Apr-4 Ansorena, Madrid #71/R est:3600
£2552 $4593 €3700 Rocky landscape (18x29cm-7x11in) board. 26-Jan-4 Ansorena, Madrid #175/R
£16000 $29120 €23360 Plaza de la Iglesia Santa Colonna de Queralt (35x61cm-14x24in) s. panel. 17-Jun-4 Christie's, London #93/R est:7000-10000

MOREROD, Edouard (1879-1919) Swiss
£679 $1154 €991 L'Espagnol (73x60cm-29x24in) s.d.1909. 1-Dec-3 Koller, Zurich #6567 (S.FR 1500)

MORET, Henry (1856-1913) French
£2797 $4811 €4000 Mediterranean coast (56x78cm-22x31in) s. 4-Dec-3 Schopman, Hamburg #634/R est:9800
£2933 $5368 €4400 Le port (31x63cm-12x25in) s. 5-Jun-4 Arnold, Frankfurt #679/R est:4000
£4040 $7554 €6100 Calme plat. panel. 24-Jul-4 Thierry & Lannon, Brest #444
£8609 $16099 €13000 La vague. panel. 24-Jul-4 Thierry & Lannon, Brest #43
£11888 $20447 €17000 Charrue (49x65cm-19x26in) s.d.98 prov.exhib.lit. 8-Dec-3 Artcurial Briest, Paris #9/R est:18000-25000
£13333 $23867 €20000 Femme assise au setter devant la mer (40x27cm-16x11in) s. panel painted c.1907. 16-May-4 Thierry & Lannon, Brest #164/R est:20000-25000
£16290 $27204 €23783 Brittany Harbour (31x44cm-12x17in) s.d.1889 i. stretcher prov. 17-Nov-3 Waddingtons, Toronto #235/R est:20000-30000 (C.D 36000)
£20000 $33400 €29200 Moulin de Saint-Ouarneau (92x73cm-36x29in) s.d.09 i.on stretcher prov. 21-Oct-3 Sotheby's, London #6/R est:15000-20000
£20834 $34793 €30000 Rammasseur de Goemons, Glenans (37x52cm-15x20in) s. i.d.1904 verso. 21-Oct-3 Artcurial Briest, Paris #161/R est:18000-22000
£20834 $34793 €30000 Kernabat (60x73cm-24x29in) s.d.1910 exhib. 21-Oct-3 Artcurial Briest, Paris #162/R est:18000-22000
£21667 $39867 €32500 Paysage au clocher, Bois Morand, Loiret (46x61cm-18x24in) s. 11-Jun-4 Pierre Berge, Paris #251/R est:10000-12000
£24706 $42000 €36071 Les falaises pres de la mer (47x55cm-19x22in) s.d.96 prov. 5-Nov-3 Christie's, Rockefeller NY #235/R est:35000-45000
£25000 $45500 €36500 Pern, Ile d'ouessant (60x92cm-24x36in) s.d.1902 i.stretcher prov. 4-Feb-4 Sotheby's, London #302/R est:30000-40000
£26667 $49067 €40000 Bretonnes au bord de la riviere (71x53cm-28x21in) s. painted 1908 prov. 11-Jun-4 Pierre Berge, Paris #260/R est:20000-25000
£26761 $46296 €38000 Moulin a Saint-Ouarneau (92x73cm-36x29in) s.d.1909 lit. 14-Dec-3 Eric Pillon, Calais #69/R
£26846 $49934 €40000 Les Brisants - cote de Bretagne (54x74cm-21x29in) s. painted 1906 prov.lit. 3-Mar-4 Tajan, Paris #25/R est:40000-60000
£28000 $46760 €40880 Environs de belon, Finistere (46x61cm-18x24in) s.d.1913 prov. 21-Oct-3 Sotheby's, London #26/R est:15000-20000
£28333 $51567 €42500 Temps brumeux, barques de peche (38x55cm-15x22in) s.d.1908. 29-Jun-4 Gioffredo, Nice #10/R
£29412 $50000 €42942 Doelan, Basse mer (65x81cm-26x32in) s.d.1903 prov. 6-Nov-3 Sotheby's, New York #144/R est:50000-70000
£32000 $58880 €46720 Printemps a Pont Aven (65x50cm-26x20in) s.d.1902 prov. 22-Jun-4 Sotheby's, London #114/R est:20000-30000
£33113 $61921 €50000 Les goemonier au travail sur la cote bretonne (54x72cm-21x28in) s.d.1911. 24-Jul-4 Thierry & Lannon, Brest #204/R est:35000-40000
£33520 $60000 €48939 Rochers en Bretagne (47x62cm-19x24in) s.d.1913 prov. 6-May-4 Sotheby's, New York #425/R est:30000-40000
£35374 $63320 €52000 Le Goemon a Nevez, Finistere (38x65cm-15x26in) s. i.d.1898 verso. 21-Mar-4 Muizon & Le Coent, Paris #46/R
£38000 $69920 €55480 Cote du Large (60x73cm-24x29in) s.d.1897 prov. 22-Jun-4 Sotheby's, London #225/R est:25000-35000
£39106 $70000 €57095 Moulin a Doualan - Finistere (60x73cm-24x29in) s.d.1910 prov. 6-May-4 Sotheby's, New York #263/R est:40000-60000
£40000 $68000 €58400 Quimper, la riviere (46x55cm-18x22in) s. painted 1907 prov. 5-Nov-3 Christie's, Rockefeller NY #220/R est:50000-70000

£44000 $80960 €64240 Semaphore, Cote de Bretagne (65x92cm-26x36in) s.d.1906 prov.exhib. 22-Jun-4 Sotheby's, London #214/R est:25000-35000
£45000 $81900 €65700 Le calme, cote de Bretagne (73x92cm-29x36in) s.d.1906 i. stretcher prov. 3-Feb-4 Christie's, London #117/R est:25000-35000
£45638 $81691 €68000 Gros temps, les Cotes du Finistere (73x92cm-29x36in) s.d.1910. 25-May-4 Chambelland & Giafferi, Paris #51/R est:20000-30000
£49000 $90160 €71540 Belle-Ile-en-mer, Falaises (60x73cm-24x29in) s.i.d.92 prov. 22-Jun-4 Sotheby's, London #101/R est:25000-35000
£67039 $120000 €97877 Rade de Lorient (52x69cm-20x27in) s.i.d.92 prov. 6-May-4 Sotheby's, New York #250/R est:70000-90000
Works on paper
£282 $493 €400 Ouessant le Turrent Bell (14x18cm-6x7in) studio st. dr. 16-Dec-3 Adjug'art, Brest #360
£319 $533 €450 La chapelle de Saint Leger, Riec sur Belon (21x28cm-8x11in) studio st. graphite. 19-Jun-3 Millon & Associes, Paris #34
£604 $1124 €900 Etude de chiens (21x27cm-8x11in) bears studio st. pastel. 3-Mar-4 Tajan, Paris #26/R est:300-500
£861 $1610 €1300 Cote rocheuse en Bretagne (23x32cm-9x13in) graphite. 24-Jul-4 Thierry & Lannon, Brest #43
£3169 $5546 €4500 Le port du Conquet (22x30cm-9x12in) studio st.i. W/C. 21-Dec-3 Thierry & Lannon, Brest #66/R est:5500-6000

MORETEAU, Jules Louis (1886-?) French
£408 $731 €600 Foret exotique (81x100cm-32x39in) s. lit. 21-Mar-4 St-Germain-en-Laye Encheres #112/R

MORETH, J (18th C) French
Works on paper
£2449 $4384 €3600 Paysage anime avec un etang et l'aqueduc de Marly (65x97cm-26x38in) s.d.1817 gouache paper on cardboard. 19-Mar-4 Piasa, Paris #91/R est:2000-2500

MORETH, Jean (18th C) French
Works on paper
£3000 $5490 €4380 Rustic landscape with hills in the distance, peasants and his donkey crossing a bridge. Landscape (47x63cm-19x25in) gouache W/C pair. 7-Jul-4 Bonhams, Knightsbridge #95/R est:3000-5000

MORETTI, Antonio (?) Italian
£563 $975 €800 Lake landscape (33x43cm-13x17in) s. board. 9-Dec-3 Finarte Semenzato, Milan #104/R

MORETTI, G (?) Italian
Works on paper
£1070 $2000 €1562 Game of chess (36x53cm-14x21in) s. W/C. 24-Feb-4 Arthur James, Florida #73

MORETTI, Giacomo (1939-) Italian
£738 $1307 €1100 Neapolitan girl (60x50cm-24x20in) s. 1-May-4 Meeting Art, Vercelli #119
£1042 $1771 €1500 Kitten (82x67cm-32x26in) s. s.i.verso lit. 1-Nov-3 Meeting Art, Vercelli #294 est:1500

MORETTI, Giovanni Battista (18th C) Italian
£9777 $17500 €14274 Capriccio of ruins by port with figures and boats, Castel Sant'Angelo and city walls beyond (129x165cm-51x65in) prov. 27-May-4 Sotheby's, New York #54/R est:8000-12000

MORETTI, Lucien Philippe (1922-) French
£299 $500 €437 La ballerine (36x28cm-14x11in) s. i.verso. 11-Oct-3 Auctions by the Bay, Alameda #1701/R
£500 $900 €730 Carnival (53x66cm-21x26in) s. 25-Jan-4 Bonhams & Butterfields, San Francisco #3605/R
£671 $1188 €1000 Jeune enfant a la guitare (55x46cm-22x18in) s. 27-Apr-4 Artcurial Briest, Paris #234
£1575 $2473 €2300 Lecon de piano (55x46cm-22x18in) s. 20-Apr-3 Deauville, France #137/R est:2400-2600
£4533 $8251 €6800 Joie du cirque (72x92cm-28x36in) s. s.i.d.1988 verso prov. 29-Jun-4 Sotheby's, Paris #18/R est:2000-3000

MORETTI, Luigi (1884-?) Italian
£537 $993 €800 Venise, Rio Pesaro (70x30cm-28x12in) s. 14-Mar-4 Eric Pillon, Calais #76/R
£537 $993 €800 Venise, Rio Albizzi (69x29cm-27x11in) s. panel. 14-Mar-4 Eric Pillon, Calais #77/R
£550 $919 €798 Venise, la bassin de St-Marc (60x73cm-24x29in) s. exhib. 21-Jun-3 Galerie du Rhone, Sion #499/R (S.FR 1200)
£995 $1692 €1453 Venice (54x64cm-21x25in) s. panel. 19-Nov-3 Fischer, Luzern #1097/R (S.FR 2200)

MORETTI, P (20th C) Italian
£1374 $2500 €2006 Canal in Venice (53x30cm-21x12in) s. 7-Feb-4 Neal Auction Company, New Orleans #93/R est:2800-3200

MORETTI, Professor R (?) Italian?
£4000 $6320 €5840 Music Room (53x38cm-21x15in) s. 2-Sep-3 Gildings, Market Harborough #435/R est:2000-3000
Works on paper
£462 $800 €675 Cardinal in drawing room (71x51cm-28x20in) s. W/C. 13-Dec-3 Sloans & Kenyon, Bethesda #529/R

MORETTI, Raymond (1931-) French
Works on paper
£276 $458 €400 Portrait au chapeau (64x50cm-25x20in) s. W/C. 1-Oct-3 Millon & Associes, Paris #38
£403 $737 €600 Ville (73x102cm-29x40in) s. gouache. 7-Jul-4 Artcurial Briest, Paris #157

MORGAN, Alfred (fl.1862-1904) British
£6000 $10020 €8760 Spray of wild flowers on a bank (23x61cm-9x24in) s.d.1886. 13-Nov-3 Christie's, Kensington #371/R est:3000-5000

MORGAN, Alfred George (fl.1896-1919) British
£320 $573 €467 Fishermen and boats by the Quay, Whitby (70x122cm-28x48in) s. 17-May-4 David Duggleby, Scarborough #662/R

MORGAN, Amelia (20th C) Irish
Works on paper
£345 $638 €500 St Multose Church, Kinsale (36x32cm-14x13in) s.d.1933 W/C. 11-Feb-4 Woodwards, Cork #5/R

MORGAN, Barbara (1902-1992) American
Photographs
£1818 $3200 €2654 Martha Graham - letter to the World (26x34cm-10x13in) with sig.i.d.1940 silver print. 20-May-4 Swann Galleries, New York #392/R est:2000-3000
£2133 $3925 €3200 Cornleaf (33x24cm-13x9in) s. verso silver gelatin. 10-Jun-4 Villa Grisebach, Berlin #1226/R est:3000-3500
£4072 $6800 €5945 Martha Graham: lamentation and song (32x27cm-13x11in) s. photograph lit. 16-Oct-3 Phillips, New York #119/R est:6000-8000

MORGAN, Cole (1950-) Dutch
£724 $1332 €1100 Composition LVIII (70x50cm-28x20in) s.i.d.83 acrylic W/C paper. 22-Jun-4 Christie's, Amsterdam #379/R
£1958 $3329 €2800 LXVIII (68x47cm-27x19in) s.i.d.85 oil gouache prov. 25-Nov-3 Christie's, Amsterdam #82/R est:2000-3000
£3667 $6747 €5500 Sample 5 (80x80cm-31x31in) s. i.d.1997 verso oil mixed media. 8-Jun-4 Sotheby's, Amsterdam #297/R est:5000-7000
£4196 $7217 €6000 Schiller's letter (80x80cm-31x31in) s. s.i.d.1996 verso oil mixed media. 2-Dec-3 Sotheby's, Amsterdam #348/R est:5000-7000
£5944 $10224 €8500 32-C (100x125cm-39x49in) s. i.d.1985 acrylic oil pencil. 2-Dec-3 Sotheby's, Amsterdam #346/R est:7000-9000
£5944 $10224 €8500 Sample 5 (80x80cm-31x31in) indis sig.d.97 s.i.d.verso oil mixed media. 2-Dec-3 Sotheby's, Amsterdam #349/R est:5000-7000
Works on paper
£1812 $2971 €2500 Golfer (67x48cm-26x19in) s.d.86 mixed media. 27-May-3 Sotheby's, Amsterdam #560/R est:3000-4000
£3497 $5944 €5000 Fish out of water (74x105cm-29x41in) s.d.99 s.i.d.verso mixed media. 25-Nov-3 Christie's, Amsterdam #321/R est:5000-7000
£3667 $6710 €5500 Open book, yellow jacket (80x80cm-31x31in) s.d.1991 mixed media. 7-Jun-4 Glerum, Amsterdam #266/R est:5000-7000
£4200 $7728 €6300 5 Y s (120x120cm-47x47in) s.d.90 s.i.d. verso mixed media canvas. 8-Jun-4 Sotheby's, Amsterdam #148/R est:7000-9000
£5667 $10370 €8500 White hat on (180x130cm-71x51in) s.d.88 mixed media. 7-Jun-4 Glerum, Amsterdam #265/R est:8000-12000

MORGAN, David (1964-) British
£460 $782 €672 Dartmoor landscape with sheep in foreground (24x39cm-9x15in) s. board. 27-Nov-3 Clevedon Sale Rooms #181

MORGAN, Douglas (20th C) American
£225 $425 €329 California landscape with young fruit trees (41x51cm-16x20in) s. 23-Feb-4 O'Gallerie, Oregon #92/R

MORGAN, Evelyn de (1855-1919) British
Works on paper
£5200 $9464 €7592 Study for moonbeams dipping into the ocean (24x15cm-9x6in) pastel brown paper. 1-Jul-4 Sotheby's, London #282/R est:2000-3000

MORGAN, Frederick (1847-1927) British
£900 $1665 €1314 Portrait of a young girl from behind (33x25cm-13x10in) s. indis d. oval. 11-Mar-4 Duke & Son, Dorchester #190/R
£1500 $2685 €2190 Portrait of a girl, in profile (36x26cm-14x10in) s.d.1866 oval. 27-May-4 Christie's, Kensington #103/R est:1500-2000
£14000 $25900 €20440 Emigrant's departure (122x229cm-48x90in) s.d.1875 prov.exhib.lit. 14-Jul-4 Sotheby's, Olympia #122/R est:15000-20000
£22000 $41140 €32120 Two children in a garden with a Yorkshire terrier beside a chair (66x40cm-26x16in) s.i. 22-Jul-4 Tennants, Leyburn #909/R est:25000-30000
£58333 $105000 €85166 Skipping (76x51cm-30x20in) s. painted c.1896 prov.exhib. 22-Apr-4 Christie's, Rockefeller NY #67/R est:120000-180000
£60000 $109200 €87600 Willing hand (74x83cm-29x33in) s. 16-Jun-4 Bonhams, New Bond Street #57/R est:60000-80000
£97561 $174634 €142439 Teeter-totter (60x91cm-24x36in) s. prov. 4-May-4 Ritchie, Toronto #30/R est:100000-150000 (C.D 240000)
£282353 $480000 €412235 His first birthday (104x146cm-41x57in) s. painted 1899 prov.exhib.lit. 29-Oct-3 Christie's, Rockefeller NY #69/R est:500000-700000

MORGAN, Frederick R (?) British
£280 $524 €409 Church of St Ursula, Valetta (33x43cm-13x17in) s. 26-Feb-4 Mallams, Cheltenham #218/R

MORGAN, John (1823-1886) British
£3100 $5642 €4526 Gossips (75x50cm-30x20in) s. 21-Jun-4 Bonhams, Bath #362/R est:2000-3000

£18000 $33120 €26280 Cockshy (61x122cm-24x48in) s. 11-Jun-4 Christie's, London #107/R est:20000-30000
£30000 $51000 €43800 Ride (92x72cm-36x28in) s. exhib. 19-Nov-3 Bonhams, New Bond Street #69/R est:30000-50000
£100000 $170000 €146000 Village school in Bedfordshire (56x91cm-22x36in) prov.exhib. 26-Nov-3 Christie's, London #33/R est:100000-150000

MORGAN, K (19th C) ?
£962 $1654 €1405 Gluckliche reise (30x42cm-12x17in) s. panel. 3-Dec-3 AB Stockholms Auktionsverk #2563/R (S.KR 12500)

MORGAN, Mary de Neale (1868-1948) American
£1183 $2200 €1727 Mountain landscape (30x41cm-12x16in) s. board painted c.1930. 7-Mar-4 Treadway Gallery, Cincinnati #545/R est:3000-5000
£1511 $2750 €2206 Carmel Valley (30x30cm-12x12in) s. i.verso canvasboard prov. 15-Jun-4 John Moran, Pasadena #22 est:3000-4000
£1648 $3000 €2406 Foothill landscape (30x41cm-12x16in) s. masonite. 15-Jun-4 John Moran, Pasadena #78 est:3000-4000
£1768 $2900 €2564 Mountain landscape (30x41cm-12x16in) s. board painted c.1930. 7-Jun-3 Treadway Gallery, Cincinnati #1365 est:3000-5000
£1912 $3250 €2792 Coastal (10x15cm-4x6in) s. canvas on board prov. 18-Nov-3 John Moran, Pasadena #8 est:3000-4000
£2717 $5000 €3967 Near Palm Canyon (63x76cm-25x30in) s. i. stretcher prov. 8-Jun-4 Bonhams & Butterfields, San Francisco #4353/R est:5000-7000
£4118 $7000 €6012 Landscape (30x46cm-12x18in) s. 18-Nov-3 John Moran, Pasadena #167 est:4000-6000
£4335 $7500 €6329 Grey Day, Sand dune (50x40cm-20x16in) i.verso paper board prov. 10-Dec-3 Bonhams & Butterfields, San Francisco #6190/R est:4000-6000
Works on paper
£1058 $2000 €1545 Sand dunes (13x18cm-5x7in) s. W/C prov. 17-Feb-4 John Moran, Pasadena #9/R est:1500-2000
£1852 $3500 €2704 Landscape (18x23cm-7x9in) s. gouache prov. 17-Feb-4 John Moran, Pasadena #3/R est:2000-3000
£2890 $5000 €4219 View of the Californian Coast (20x20cm-8x8in) s. mixed media prov. 10-Dec-3 Bonhams & Butterfields, San Francisco #6192/R est:3000-5000
£4046 $7000 €5907 Old Custom's House, Carmel (29x37cm-11x15in) s. pencil W/C gouache prov. 10-Dec-3 Bonhams & Butterfields, San Francisco #6189/R est:3000-5000

MORGAN, Michael (?) British
Works on paper
£280 $442 €409 Devon panorama (14x35cm-6x14in) s. W/C. 5-Sep-3 Honiton Galleries, Honiton #22/R

MORGAN, Michele (20th C) French
Works on paper
£769 $1308 €1100 Composition abstraite (37x60cm-15x24in) s.d.99 mixed media. 27-Nov-3 Calmels Cohen, Paris #134/R est:2000-2500

MORGAN, R F (1929-) American
£2273 $4250 €3319 Buffalo (76x102cm-30x40in) s. 24-Jul-4 Coeur d'Alene, Hayden #281/R est:4000-6000

MORGAN, Randall (1920-) American
£898 $1500 €1311 Ponte Vecchio, Florence (66x76cm-26x30in) s. painted c.1949 prov.exhib.lit. 7-Oct-3 Sotheby's, New York #238 est:500-700

MORGAN, Sally (1951-) Australian
Works on paper
£1296 $2086 €1892 Untitled (197x167cm-78x66in) init. synthetic polymer paint canvas prov. 25-Aug-3 Sotheby's, Paddington #285/R est:2000-3000 (A.D 3200)

MORGAN, Sister Gertrude (1900-1980) American
£833 $1500 €1216 Self portrait (8x8cm-3x3in) 24-Apr-4 Slotin Folk Art, Buford #290/R est:1000-2000
£1944 $3500 €2838 Father and the Son with their little birdie (13x18cm-5x7in) acrylic. 24-Apr-4 Slotin Folk Art, Buford #289/R est:4000-6000
£3234 $5400 €4722 Eight figures (53x43cm-21x17in) acrylic paper prov. 15-Nov-3 Slotin Folk Art, Buford #132/R est:5000-8000
£3593 $6000 €5246 Jesus with six disciples (43x53cm-17x21in) acrylic paper prov. 15-Nov-3 Slotin Folk Art, Buford #133/R est:5000-8000
£3611 $6500 €5272 God the Father.Wife of God. The Son (20x28cm-8x11in) set of three. 24-Apr-4 Slotin Folk Art, Buford #288/R est:5000-8000
£11377 $19000 €16610 The grave of Lazyrus (30x66cm-12x26in) acrylic ink paper prov.lit. 15-Nov-3 Slotin Folk Art, Buford #131/R est:10000-15000

MORGAN, Walter Jenks (1847-1924) British
£983 $1700 €1435 In the Boboli Gardens, Florence (30x20cm-12x8in) s. s.i.verso board. 13-Dec-3 Sloans & Kenyon, Bethesda #785/R est:1200-1800

MORGAN-SMITH, Arthur C (fl.1905-) British
Works on paper
£450 $752 €657 Country landscape with figure and horse towing a barge along a canal (43x56cm-17x22in) s. W/C. 9-Jul-3 Peter Wilson, Nantwich #74

MORGARI, Paolo Emilio (1883-1947) Italian
£417 $688 €600 Tuscan cowboy (55x40cm-22x16in) s. 1-Jul-3 Il Ponte, Milan #303

MORGARI, Rodolfo (1827-1909) Italian
£671 $1188 €1000 Portrait of woman (75x65cm-30x26in) s. 1-May-4 Meeting Art, Vercelli #62
£1007 $1782 €1500 Portrait of man (75x65cm-30x26in) s. lit. 1-May-4 Meeting Art, Vercelli #59 est:1000
£2482 $4145 €3500 Thoughtful (64x44cm-25x17in) s. prov. 20-Oct-3 Sant Agostino, Torino #284/R est:4500
£6552 $10876 €9500 Sleeping beauty (76x151cm-30x59in) s. 1-Oct-3 Della Rocca, Turin #11/R

MORGENROTH, Johann Martin (1800-1859) German
Miniatures
£1100 $1969 €1606 Young officer (13x11cm-5x4in) s. porcelain rectangular. 25-May-4 Christie's, London #44 est:600-800

MORGENSTERN, Christian (1805-1867) German
£5245 $8916 €7500 Diebesturm, Lindau (28x34cm-11x13in) paper on board. 21-Nov-3 Reiss & Sohn, Konigstein #24/R est:8000
£9028 $14715 €13000 Country path in Dachau (58x46cm-23x18in) s. 24-Sep-3 Neumeister, Munich #507/R est:10000
Works on paper
£289 $533 €440 Sun shining on rocks and water (14x23cm-6x9in) i.d.14 Mai 1865 W/C. 25-Jun-4 Michael Zeller, Lindau #750/R
£3930 $7153 €5738 The Elbe downstream from Hamburg in moonlight (40x58cm-16x23in) s. brush bodycol over chk prov.exhib. 17-Jun-4 Kornfeld, Bern #40/R est:5000 (S.FR 9000)

MORGENSTERN, Christian (attrib) (1805-1867) German
£1181 $1865 €1700 Sunny wood (33x41cm-13x16in) panel. 6-Sep-3 Schopman, Hamburg #763/R est:1000
£1197 $2071 €1700 Study of part of the forest (17x21cm-7x8in) cardboard. 10-Dec-3 Hugo Ruef, Munich #2464 est:1000

MORGENSTERN, Friedrich Ernst (1853-1919) German
£1364 $2264 €1978 Marine (61x92cm-24x36in) 13-Jun-3 Zofingen, Switzerland #2505/R est:2000 (S.FR 3000)
£2267 $4125 €3400 Street in Muhlbach a d Rienz (58x43cm-23x17in) s.i.d.1897 i. stretcher. 30-Jun-4 Neumeister, Munich #625/R est:2800
Works on paper
£270 $484 €400 Fishing boat entering harbour (12x16cm-5x6in) s.d.1902 board. 8-May-4 Hans Stahl, Toestorf #27/R
£345 $576 €500 Unloading the boats on Baltic beach (10x15cm-4x6in) s. pencil sketch verso. 9-Jul-3 Hugo Ruef, Munich #287/R
£839 $1427 €1200 Sachsenhausen, Frankfurt (48x141cm-19x56in) s.d.Mai 1917 wash chl htd bodycol. 21-Nov-3 Reiss & Sohn, Konigstein #266/R est:1000
£1049 $1783 €1500 Frankfurt with cathedral (58x145cm-23x57in) s.d.Mai 1917 wash chk htd bodycol paper on board. 21-Nov-3 Reiss & Sohn, Konigstein #267/R est:1000

MORGENSTERN, Johann Christoph (1697-1767) German
£2113 $3655 €3000 Portrait of Magdalene Sofie, Countess von Schonburg-Hartenstein (107x86cm-42x34in) s.d.1727 i.verso prov. 10-Dec-3 Christie's, Amsterdam #20/R est:2000-3000

MORGENSTERN, Karl (1811-1893) German
£1333 $2453 €2000 Italian coastal landscape (21x31cm-8x12in) st.sig. 12-Jun-4 Villa Grisebach, Berlin #101/R est:2500-3500
£2667 $4773 €4000 Amalfi Cove with fishing boats in the evening light (18x24cm-7x9in) s.d.1847 panel. 14-May-4 Behringer, Furth #1601/R est:4000
£4333 $7887 €6500 Gulf of Naples near Sorrento (22x26cm-9x10in) s.d.1857 board painted oval. 30-Jun-4 Neumeister, Munich #624/R est:5500
£15278 $24903 €22000 Villa Franca bay near Nice (41x62cm-16x24in) s.d.1854. 25-Sep-3 Dr Fritz Nagel, Stuttgart #1381/R est:15000
Works on paper
£287 $516 €430 Mantuan ships in Venice in front of Dogana del Mare (23x30cm-9x12in) i. pencil. 24-Apr-4 Reiss & Sohn, Konigstein #5533/R
£320 $573 €480 Sailing ships at sea (11x15cm-4x6in) i. brush W/C. 13-May-4 Bassenge, Berlin #5619/R

MORGENSTERNE MUNTHE, Gerhard (1875-1927) Dutch
£448 $747 €654 Vessel by coast (12x19cm-5x7in) s. panel. 20-Oct-3 Blomqvist, Lysaker #1209 (N.KR 5200)
£559 $962 €800 Moonlight (26x42cm-10x17in) s. 7-Dec-3 Sotheby's, Amsterdam #685
£1549 $2680 €2200 Sailing boats at sea in evening (24x31cm-9x12in) s. canvas on panel. 11-Dec-3 Dr Fritz Nagel, Stuttgart #538/R est:1300
£1818 $3091 €2600 Boat on winter beach (21x15cm-8x6in) s. panel. 20-Nov-3 Van Ham, Cologne #1764/R est:1800
£1837 $3288 €2700 Le retour des pecheurs (11x19cm-4x7in) s. panel. 16-Mar-4 Vanderkindere, Brussels #44 est:1200-1500
£2055 $3493 €3000 Surf (23x29cm-9x11in) init. marouflé. 5-Nov-3 Vendue Huis, Gravenhage #354/R est:700-1000
£2177 $3897 €3200 Les pecheurs de crevettes (30x40cm-12x16in) s.d.21. 16-Mar-4 Vanderkindere, Brussels #30 est:2000-3000
£2238 $3849 €3200 Sailing vessels near the coast (20x15cm-8x6in) s. panel. 7-Dec-3 Sotheby's, Amsterdam #582/R
£2381 $4333 €3500 A waiting the return of the fleet (15x11cm-6x4in) s. cardboard. 3-Feb-4 Christie's, Amsterdam #135/R est:1200-1600
£3472 $5799 €5000 Volendam Harbour in the snow (27x21cm-11x8in) s.d.22 board. 21-Oct-3 Sotheby's, Amsterdam #111/R est:4000-6000
£3472 $5799 €5000 Bomschuit at dusk (26x40cm-10x16in) s.d.05. 21-Oct-3 Sotheby's, Amsterdam #115/R est:3000-5000
£3472 $5799 €5000 Unloading the catch (31x51cm-12x20in) s. 21-Oct-3 Sotheby's, Amsterdam #145/R est:4000-6000
£3496 $5838 €5000 View of a village with boats in a harbour (60x90cm-24x35in) s.d.07. 30-Jun-3 Sotheby's, Amsterdam #66/R
£4167 $7083 €6000 Collecting the catch (26x40cm-10x16in) s.d.1914. 28-Oct-3 Christie's, Amsterdam #144/R est:6000-8000
£4218 $7550 €6200 Pecheurs en bord de mer (41x30cm-16x12in) s. 16-Mar-4 Vanderkindere, Brussels #50 est:1000-1500
£4934 $8931 €7500 Winter polder landscape in winter (50x93cm-20x37in) s. prov. 19-Apr-4 Glerum, Amsterdam #101/R est:7000-9000
£6250 $10625 €9000 Bomschuit in the surf by Katwijk (40x32cm-16x13in) s. paintersboard. 28-Oct-3 Christie's, Amsterdam #142/R est:4000-6000

Works on paper

£2721 $4952 €4000 Bomschuit anchored in the surf, Katwijk (35x25cm-14x10in) s.d.1912 W/C bodycol htd white. 3-Feb-4 Christie's, Amsterdam #391/R est:2000-3000

MORGENSTERNE MUNTHE, Gerhard (attrib) (1875-1927) Dutch

£1655 $2764 €2400 Canalside fishmarket (80x141cm-31x56in) bears sig.d. 15-Nov-3 Lempertz, Koln #1660/R est:2500

MORGENTHALER, Ernst (1887-1962) Swiss

£280 $467 €406 Self portrait at easel (100x80cm-39x31in) mono. 23-Jun-3 Philippe Schuler, Zurich #8449 (S.FR 610)
£901 $1550 €1315 In front of the house (50x72cm-20x28in) mono. 8-Dec-3 Philippe Schuler, Zurich #3350 (S.FR 2000)
£996 $1782 €1454 Extensive landscape with waggon and horses (54x73cm-21x29in) mono.d. 22-Mar-4 Philippe Schuler, Zurich #4349/R est:2000-2300 (S.FR 2300)
£1087 $1989 €1587 Farm (70x90cm-28x35in) mono.d.51. 7-Jun-4 Christie's, Zurich #108/R est:3000-5000 (S.FR 2500)
£1390 $2322 €2029 Spring landscape with Jura mountains (50x73cm-20x29in) mono.d.44. 24-Oct-3 Hans Widmer, St Gallen #84/R est:2500-4800 (S.FR 3100)
£1397 $2543 €2040 Autumn in Hongg (54x73cm-21x29in) mono. prov. 16-Jun-4 Fischer, Luzern #1331/R est:3000-4000 (S.FR 3200)
£2036 $3523 €2973 Corner of the garden (92x64cm-36x25in) mono.d.1950 s.i.verso board. 9-Dec-3 Sotheby's, Zurich #82/R est:2500-3500 (S.FR 4500)
£2252 $3874 €3288 Factory interior (150x190cm-59x75in) mono.d.50 prov. 2-Dec-3 Koller, Zurich #3039/R est:5500-7000 (S.FR 5000)
£2252 $3874 €3288 Foundry (150x150cm-59x59in) mono.d.46 panel prov.exhib. 2-Dec-3 Koller, Zurich #3040/R est:4000-5500 (S.FR 5000)
£2586 $4759 €3776 Still life (44x47cm-17x19in) mono.d.25 panel double-sided. 26-Mar-4 Koller, Zurich #520/R est:2500-3500 (S.FR 6000)
£4803 $8598 €7012 Apple trees (54x54cm-21x21in) mono.d.1920 board. 26-May-4 Sotheby's, Zurich #141/R est:2500-3000 (S.FR 11000)
£5652 $10343 €8252 Summer in lower alpine landscape (100x120cm-39x47in) mono.d.38. 7-Jun-4 Christie's, Zurich #113/R est:4000-6000 (S.FR 13000)

Works on paper

£273 $453 €396 Busy street in Tunisia (25x30cm-10x12in) mono. W/C prov. 13-Jun-3 Zofingen, Switzerland #2951 (S.FR 600)
£296 $541 €432 Sheep in country landscape (23x29cm-9x11in) mono.d.1928 W/C. 4-Jun-4 Zofingen, Switzerland #2888 (S.FR 680)
£437 $782 €638 Two people sitting at a table (23x32cm-9x13in) mono.d.1952 pastel. 26-May-4 Sotheby's, Zurich #79/R (S.FR 1000)

MORGHEN, Antonio (attrib) (1788-1853) Italian

£1200 $1992 €1752 Figures and builings in a winter landscape (54x73cm-21x29in) 1-Oct-3 Woolley & Wallis, Salisbury #318/R est:1200-1800

MORGNER, Michael (1942-) German?

Works on paper

£4545 $7727 €6500 Figure in space (250x200cm-98x79in) mono.d.90 s.i.d. verso Indian ink lavage ashphalt paper on canvas. 29-Nov-3 Villa Grisebach, Berlin #386/R est:5000-7000

MORGNER, Wilhelm (1891-1917) German

£34965 $60140 €50000 Woman with cart (51x66cm-20x26in) mono.d.1911 i.verso cardboard prov.lit. 5-Dec-3 Ketterer, Munich #39/R est:50000-70000
£97902 $166434 €140000 Astral composition (74x99cm-29x39in) mono.d.12 board prov. 28-Nov-3 Villa Grisebach, Berlin #31/R est:90000-120000

Works on paper

£1538 $2646 €2200 Couple from Serbia (24x32cm-9x13in) mono.d.1917 pen ink prov.exhib. 5-Dec-3 Ketterer, Munich #71/R est:2000-2500
£1833 $3282 €2750 Apocalyptic scene (23x31cm-9x12in) mono.d. Indian ink. 15-May-4 Bassenge, Berlin #7043/R est:3000
£2308 $3923 €3300 Man wearing hat - self portrait (60x47cm-24x19in) mono.d.11 chl. 26-Nov-3 Lempertz, Koln #867/R est:3500
£2797 $4755 €4000 Man with wheelbarrow and tools (57x42cm-22x17in) mono.d.11 chl prov. 29-Nov-3 Villa Grisebach, Berlin #165/R est:6000-8000
£6667 $11933 €10000 Battle - blue riders (20x26cm-8x10in) W/C Indian ink. 15-May-4 Bassenge, Berlin #7042/R est:6000

MORHARDT, Joseph Emil (1906-) American

Works on paper

£228 $425 €333 Craggy coastline (33x51cm-13x20in) s. W/C. 6-Mar-4 Harvey Clar, Oakland #1287

MORI, Mariko (1967-) American

Photographs

£29940 $50000 €43712 Beginning of the end (100x376cm-39x148in) Fuji super gloss print exec 1986 prov. 12-Nov-3 Christie's, Rockefeller NY #558/R est:25000-35000

Sculpture

£1944 $3208 €2800 Star doll (29cm-11in) plastic doll fabric one of 99. 2-Jul-3 Cornette de St.Cyr, Paris #178/R est:2500-3000

MORI, Neno (1898-1970) Italian

£2042 $3268 €2900 Still life with fruit (60x80cm-24x31in) s.d.1963. 19-Sep-3 Finarte, Venice #454/R

MORI, Shoichiro (20th C) ?

£387 $643 €550 Composition (102x60cm-40x24in) s.i.d.verso. 16-Jun-3 E & Eve, Paris #107

MORIARTY, Peter (?) New Zealander

£429 $776 €626 Paradise Valley (39x49cm-15x19in) s. oil paper. 4-Apr-4 International Art Centre, Auckland #312/R (NZ.D 1200)
£446 $808 €651 Lake Wanaka (34x50cm-13x20in) s. oil paper. 4-Apr-4 International Art Centre, Auckland #314/R (NZ.D 1250)

MORIDE, Madelaine (19/20th C) French?

£450 $797 €657 Yellow chair (80x55cm-31x22in) 29-Apr-4 Christie's, Kensington #197/R

MORIER, David (1705-1770) Swiss

£5800 $9860 €8468 Equestrian portrait of H.R.H. William Augustus, Duke of Cumberland (52x42cm-20x17in) 27-Nov-3 Sotheby's, London #146/R est:6000-8000
£9000 $15300 €13140 Equestrian portrait of King George II (52x42cm-20x17in) prov. 27-Nov-3 Sotheby's, London #145/R est:8000-12000

MORIER, David (attrib) (1705-1770) Swiss

£2077 $3572 €3032 Nobleman on horseback - La courbette (63x52cm-25x20in) 2-Dec-3 Bukowskis, Stockholm #416/R est:25000-30000 (S.KR 27000)
£5000 $8350 €7300 Portrait of Major Thomas Burton, standing in a landscape (48x35cm-19x14in) prov.lit. 14-Oct-3 Sotheby's, London #454/R est:3000-4000

MORIGGIA, Giovanni (1796-1878) Italian

£633 $1077 €924 Portrait of Elisabeth Vonder Muhll-Bischoff von Basel (55x45cm-22x18in) 19-Nov-3 Fischer, Luzern #2225/R (S.FR 1400)

MORILLO FERRADAS, Jose (1853-1920) Spanish

£780 $1303 €1100 In the taverna (13x18cm-5x7in) s.d.1890 panel. 23-Jun-3 Durán, Madrid #22/R

MORILLON, Étienne (20th C) French

£1533 $2791 €2300 Dejeuner sur l'herbe (65x81cm-26x32in) s. 29-Jun-4 Chenu & Scrive, Lyon #137/R est:1200-1500

MORIMURA, Yasumasa (1951-) Japanese

Photographs

£5000 $8350 €7300 Self portrait, actress after Brigitte Bardot 1 (120x95cm-47x37in) ilfachrome prov. 22-Oct-3 Christie's, London #147/R est:6000-8000
£8939 $16000 €13051 Six brides (147x128cm-58x50in) s.num.3/5 verso col photo on canvas exec 1991 prov.exhib. 13-May-4 Sotheby's, New York #407/R est:10000-15000

MORIN, A H (19th C) French?

Photographs

£2587 $4321 €3700 Portrait de groupe. s. daguerrotype exec.c.1848-50. 10-Oct-3 Beaussant & Lefèvre, Paris #21/R est:600-800

MORIN, Arturo (1953-) Mexican

£948 $1612 €1384 Nuns (120x120cm-47x47in) s.d.2003. 30-Oct-3 Louis Morton, Mexico #35/R est:35000 (M.P 18000)

MORIN, Georges (1874-1928) German

Sculpture

£2408 $3997 €3516 Dancer with hulahoop (49cm-19in) s. pat bronze exec.c.1900. 15-Jun-3 Agra, Warsaw #17/R est:12000 (P.Z 15000)
£7456 $13719 €10886 Young falconer (231cm-91in) s. natural pat bronze incl base. 23-Jun-4 Koller, Zurich #3154/R est:6000-10000 (S.FR 17000)

MORIN, Gustave François (1809-1886) French

Works on paper

£625 $1131 €950 Village normand (40x57cm-16x22in) s.d.61 dr. 19-Apr-4 Boscher, Cherbourg #710/R

MORIN, M (19/20th C) ?

£1915 $3198 €2700 Jeune femme vendant des oranges (43x54cm-17x21in) s. 16-Jun-3 Gros & Delettrez, Paris #277/R est:1700-2500

MORINA, Giulio (c.1555-1609) Italian

Works on paper

£10000 $18000 €14600 Adoration of the Shepherds (35x24cm-14x9in) red white chk. 22-Jan-4 Christie's, Rockefeller NY #27/R est:20000-30000

MORINIERE, Elie de la (20th C) French

£1701 $2671 €2450 Pacha (33x41cm-13x16in) s. panel. 29-Aug-3 Deauville, France #138/R est:2500-2800
£13194 $20715 €19000 Pacha (73x92cm-29x36in) s.d.1941. 29-Aug-3 Deauville, France #130/R est:8000-10000

MORIS, Louis Marie (1818-1883) French

Sculpture

£4895 $8175 €7000 Portrait equestre de Francois Ier (84x65cm-33x26in) s. brown pat bronze. 27-Jun-3 Millon & Associes, Paris #77/R est:8000-10000

MORISON, J (jnr) (19th C) British

£756 $1300 €1104 Scottish highland valley (53x89cm-21x35in) s.d.1873. 7-Dec-3 Susanin's, Chicago #6004/R est:600-800

MORISOT, Berthe (1841-1895) French

£36313 $65000 €53017 Jeune femme assise dans l'herbe (46x68cm-18x27in) st.sig. painted 1884 prov.lit. 5-May-4 Christie's, Rockefeller NY #218/R est:60000-80000

£44693 $80000 €65252 Petite fille assise dans l'herbe (48x55cm-19x22in) st.sig. lit. 6-May-4 Sotheby's, New York #231/R est:80000-120000
£100000 $184000 €146000 Chrysanthemes (46x55cm-18x22in) s. painted 1885 prov.exhib.lit. 23-Jun-4 Christie's, London #114/R est:100000-150000
Works on paper
£5300 $8850 €7630 Etude pour jeune fille dessinant (18x25cm-7x10in) col crayons lead pencil. 21-Oct-3 Artcurial Briest, Paris #31/R est:7000-9000
£13793 $22897 €20000 Les Invalides (21x26cm-8x10in) studio st. W/C crayon prov.exhib.lit. 30-Sep-3 Christie's, Paris #20/R est:12000-16000
£20000 $33200 €29000 Tete de jeune fille (52x43cm-20x17in) studio st. pastel prov.exhib.lit. 30-Sep-3 Christie's, Paris #21/R est:25000-30000
£24706 $42000 €36071 Fillette assise dans l'herbe (40x50cm-16x20in) st.sig. pastel on stretched paper drawn 1889 prov.exhib.lit. 5-Nov-3 Christie's, Rockefeller NY #101/R est:30000-40000
£173184 $310000 €252849 Jeune fille aux epaules nues (56x46cm-22x18in) st.sig. pastel paper on board exec 1885 prov.exhib.lit. 6-May-4 Sotheby's, New York #226/R est:300000-400000

MORISSON, Philippe (1924-) French
£1408 $2338 €2000 Untitled (60x60cm-24x24in) s.d.1963 verso acrylic. 11-Jun-3 Finarte Semenzato, Milan #572/R

MORITA (19th C) ?
Sculpture
£4000 $6920 €5840 Crayfish (55x21cm-22x8in) s. bronze. 11-Dec-3 Sotheby's, Olympia #97/R est:1600-2000

MORITA, Shiryu (1912-) Japanese
£19653 $34000 €28693 Dragon knows dragon (163x325cm-64x128in) black gold lacquer 4 panel folding screen exec.c.1966 prov.exhib. 15-Dec-3 Hindman, Chicago #38/R est:5000-7000

MORITZ, Friedrich Wilhelm (attrib) (1783-1855) Swiss
Works on paper
£754 $1281 €1100 View of a courtyard in Palazzo Vecchio, Florence (43x35cm-17x14in) s.d.1839 W/C crayon. 6-Nov-3 Tajan, Paris #191

MORITZ, Fritz (1922-) German
£326 $532 €470 Lively Dutch canal side with flower market (60x90cm-24x35in) s. 27-Sep-3 Dannenberg, Berlin #598/R

MORITZ, Karl (1896-1963) German
£493 $908 €750 View of the Untersee (49x58cm-19x23in) s.d.1938. 26-Jun-4 Karrenbauer, Konstanz #1748
£987 $1816 €1500 Landscape in the Hegau region (50x62cm-20x24in) mono.d.49 masonite. 26-Jun-4 Karrenbauer, Konstanz #1752 est:1500
£1181 $1948 €1700 Hegau landscape (32x50cm-13x20in) s. board. 5-Jul-3 Geble, Radolfzell #475/R est:1000
Works on paper
£268 $494 €400 Hegau landscape (22x32cm-9x13in) s.d.48 W/C. 27-Mar-4 Geble, Radolfzell #791/R
£362 $666 €550 Village in the Hegau region (54x24cm-21x9in) s. W/C lit. 26-Jun-4 Karrenbauer, Konstanz #1750
£1042 $1719 €1500 View of Gottmadingen (35x50cm-14x20in) s.d.1936 W/C. 5-Jul-3 Geble, Radolfzell #502 est:600

MORITZ, Louis (circle) (1773-1850) Dutch
£10274 $17466 €15000 Elegant company making music in an interior, in a sculpted niche (44x34cm-17x13in) indis sig. panel. 5-Nov-3 Christie's, Amsterdam #68/R est:7000-10000

MORITZ, William (1816-1860) Swiss
£573 $974 €837 Two washerwomen by water trough (16x21cm-6x8in) s. board. 5-Nov-3 Dobiaschofsky, Bern #824/R (S.FR 1300)

MORIYAMA, Daido (20th C) American
Photographs
£2910 $5500 €4249 Stray dog, Misawa Aomori, 1971 (30x41cm-12x16in) s.verso gelatin silver print. 17-Feb-4 Christie's, Rockefeller NY #282/R est:2000-3000

MORIZOT, Henriette (19th C) French
£486 $773 €700 Portrait de jeune elegante (61x50cm-24x20in) s. 9-Sep-3 Palais de Beaux Arts, Brussels #254
£559 $951 €800 Vue de la Seine a Paris (14x22cm-6x9in) s. panel. 1-Dec-3 Palais de Beaux Arts, Brussels #375/R

MORK, Michael (1959-) Danish
£267 $485 €401 Composition with spots (100x80cm-39x31in) init.d.02 verso acrylic. 19-Jun-4 Rasmussen, Havnen #4096/R (D.KR 3000)

MORKEL, Karl (20th C) Australian
£1152 $2086 €1682 Birdlife (96x91cm-38x36in) s.d.84-85 verso. 30-Mar-4 Lawson Menzies, Sydney #181/R est:1000-1500 (A.D 2800)

MORLAND, G (1763-1804) British
£250 $408 €365 Woman riding a donkey (15x20cm-6x8in) mono. panel. 23-Sep-3 John Nicholson, Haslemere #252

MORLAND, George (1763-1804) British
£580 $963 €847 Drover with sheep and cattle watering in a stream (51x60cm-20x24in) 1-Oct-3 Sotheby's, Olympia #7/R
£1529 $2600 €2232 Return (31x45cm-12x18in) board. 25-Nov-3 Galeria y Remates, Montevideo #188
£1564 $2690 €2283 Tramps on the road (50x61cm-20x24in) s. 3-Dec-3 Naón & Cia, Buenos Aires #29/R
£1800 $3060 €2628 Young girl on coastal path (63x76cm-25x30in) s.d.1794. 19-Nov-3 Christie's, Kensington #467/R
£2207 $4083 €3200 La halte du cavalier (56x48cm-22x19in) s. 13-Jan-4 Vanderkindere, Brussels #15/R est:3750-5000
£2419 $4452 €3532 Wayfarers (47x63cm-19x25in) s.d.1784 panel prov. 14-Jun-4 Waddingtons, Toronto #151/R est:5000-7000 (C.D 6000)
£2600 $4316 €3796 Two Gloucester old spot piglets in a barn with vegetables and a barrel (34x45cm-13x18in) s.d.1797. 1-Oct-3 Woolley & Wallis, Salisbury #326/R est:1000-1500
£3000 $5490 €4380 Extensive wooded landscape, with three travellers resting before a cottage (19x26cm-7x10in) s.d.1795 panel. 28-Jan-4 Henry Adams, Chichester #281/R est:1000-1500
£4500 $8055 €6570 Figures crossing a stream with a church beyond (30x39cm-12x15in) s. 27-May-4 Christie's, Kensington #118/R est:5000-7000
£4500 $8190 €6570 Two men hunting rabbits with their dog a village beyond (44x57cm-17x22in) 1-Jul-4 Sotheby's, London #162/R est:5000-7000
£4800 $7968 €7008 Cottagers wealth (36x47cm-14x19in) init.d.79 panel. 1-Oct-3 Woolley & Wallis, Salisbury #325/R est:1500-2000
£5307 $9500 €7748 Baggage wagon (25x30cm-10x12in) s. prov. 27-May-4 Sotheby's, New York #223/R est:6000-8000
£6000 $10920 €8760 Taking refreshments outside a village inn (68x88cm-27x35in) mono. prov. 1-Jul-4 Sotheby's, London #158/R est:6000-8000
£7000 $13090 €10220 Smugglers unloading contraband (50x75cm-20x30in) panel. 21-Jul-4 Lyon & Turnbull, Edinburgh #131/R est:4000-6000
£10000 $18700 €14600 Landing the catch (100x140cm-39x55in) s.d.1792 prov. 21-Jul-4 Lyon & Turnbull, Edinburgh #132/R est:10000-15000
£12291 $22000 €17945 Before the storm (71x96cm-28x38in) init. prov. 27-May-4 Sotheby's, New York #276/R est:15000-20000
Works on paper
£600 $1002 €876 Study of a man reading (20x14cm-8x6in) init.d.1792 pencil. 16-Oct-3 Christie's, Kensington #9/R
£600 $1032 €876 Filling the trough. Punishing the dog (22x18cm-9x7in) s.d.1792 pencil col chk pair. 3-Dec-3 Christie's, Kensington #17/R

MORLAND, George (attrib) (1763-1804) British
£380 $612 €551 Sportsmen refreshing (33x46cm-13x18in) panel. 21-Aug-3 Richardson & Smith, Whitby #565
£588 $941 €858 Buccolic idyl (46x62cm-18x24in) 16-Sep-3 Philippe Schuler, Zurich #3345 (S.FR 1300)
£600 $954 €876 Reading the news (76x63cm-30x25in) init. 18-Mar-3 Anderson & Garland, Newcastle #538
£600 $1020 €876 Pig with piglets (25x30cm-10x12in) i. panel. 30-Oct-3 Duke & Son, Dorchester #200
£750 $1350 €1095 Returning home (21x29cm-8x11in) bears init. panel. 21-Jan-4 Sotheby's, Olympia #84/R
£751 $1300 €1096 Couple in wooded setting (25x30cm-10x12in) 10-Dec-3 Alderfer's, Hatfield #278 est:700-900
£1000 $1850 €1460 Sheep in a barn interior (45x60cm-18x24in) 10-Feb-4 Bonhams, Knightsbridge #218/R est:800-1200
£1050 $1838 €1533 Interior stable scene with mother and child feeding pigs (43x51cm-17x20in) 19-Dec-3 Mallams, Oxford #214/R est:600-800
£1100 $1969 €1606 Pet dog (59x44cm-23x17in) 11-May-4 Bonhams, Knightsbridge #171/R est:800-1200
£1420 $2500 €2073 Farmyard scene with a figure, horses, pigs and a dog (72x92cm-28x36in) bears sig prov. 18-May-4 Bonhams & Butterfields, San Francisco #49/R est:4000-6000
£1800 $3222 €2628 Figures and cattle in a winter landscape, cottage beyond (25x35cm-10x14in) prov. 27-May-4 Christie's, Kensington #124a est:2000-3000
£2400 $4464 €3504 Approaching storm (63x81cm-25x32in) with sig.d.1796. 4-Mar-4 Christie's, Kensington #511/R est:1200-1800
£2600 $4862 €3796 Figures with donkey and sheep (40x60cm-16x24in) bears sig. d.1790 prov. 21-Jul-4 Lyon & Turnbull, Edinburgh #133/R est:2000-3000
£3000 $5100 €4380 Landscape with a figure climbing up to a hay loft, and a pig (25x30cm-10x12in) 25-Nov-3 Christie's, London #63/R est:1000-2000

MORLAND, George (circle) (1763-1804) British
£5000 $9200 €7300 Figures by a cottage in a wooded landscape (83x116cm-33x46in) 11-Jun-4 Christie's, London #54/R est:5000-8000
£10000 $18300 €14600 English pointer in a landscape (95x109cm-37x43in) 7-Jul-4 Bonhams, New Bond Street #75/R est:3000-4000

MORLAND, Henry Robert (c.1719-1797) British
£6800 $12240 €9928 Butter churner (74x61cm-29x24in) 21-Apr-4 Bonhams, New Bond Street #113/R est:6000-8000
£8939 $16000 €13051 Kitchen maid (86x70cm-34x28in) s. 27-May-4 Sotheby's, New York #238/R est:12000-16000
Works on paper
£500 $910 €750 The young mussel gatherers (47x39cm-19x15in) pastel. 1-Jul-4 Christie's, Kensington #278

MORLAND, John (fl.1850-1860s) British
Works on paper
£450 $734 €657 Pietermaritzburg, Natal, from the Camp Hill (26x36cm-10x14in) mono. i.d.1865 pen ink W/C. 24-Sep-3 Christie's, London #141/R

MORLAND, Valere Alphonse (1846-?) French
£390 $651 €550 Promenade a cheval (22x16cm-9x6in) s. 14-Oct-3 Vanderkindere, Brussels #32

MORLE, Stuart (1960-) British
£1745 $3089 €2600 Roses in a white vase (69x39cm-27x15in) s. canvas on board. 27-Apr-4 Whyte's, Dublin #240/R est:1800-2200
£2517 $4280 €3600 Winter dawn, Echlin Street (36x46cm-14x18in) s. canvas on board. 18-Nov-3 Whyte's, Dublin #166/R est:2000-3000

MORLEY, Harry (1881-1943) British
Works on paper
£310 $570 €453 North Norfolk river estuary scene (9x11cm-4x4in) s. W/C. 11-Jun-4 Keys, Aylsham #559
£450 $828 €657 Teatime (37x50cm-15x20in) s. W/C pencil. 23-Mar-4 Bonhams, Knightsbridge #59/R

MORLEY, Henry (1869-1937) British
£559 $1000 €816 Farm Scene (25x29cm-10x11in) painted c.1890. 9-Jan-4 Du Mouchelle, Detroit #2140/R
Works on paper
£320 $544 €467 Shepherd and his flock (24x35cm-9x14in) s.d.1925 pencil W/C. 18-Nov-3 Bonhams, Leeds #36

MORLEY, Lewis (20th C) British
Photographs
£2800 $4928 €4200 Christine Keeler (46x40cm-18x16in) s. num.39/50 gelatin silver print. 18-May-4 Bonhams, New Bond Street #449/R est:3000-5000

MORLEY, Malcolm (1931-) British
£18436 $33000 €26917 Pamela passing freighters (97x132cm-38x52in) s. oil plastic gun replica prov.exhib. 14-May-4 Phillips, New York #226/R est:40000-60000
£53333 $98667 €80000 Chateau Romain II (137x167cm-54x66in) s. painted 1976 prov.exhib. 18-Jul-4 Sotheby's, Paris #230/R est:80000-120000
£80838 $135000 €118023 Remembrance of Things past (71x101cm-28x40in) s.i. verso painted 1976 prov. 12-Nov-3 Christie's, Rockefeller NY #616/R est:80000-120000
£83799 $150000 €122347 Icarus (203x279cm-80x110in) s. oil linen toy airplane boat prov.exhib.lit. 12-May-4 Christie's, Rockefeller NY #467/R est:150000-200000
£179641 $300000 €262276 Farewell to Crete (203x417cm-80x164in) s. painted 1984 prov.exhib.lit. 12-Nov-3 Christie's, Rockefeller NY #614/R est:120000-160000
Works on paper
£604 $1105 €900 Au restaurant (14x22cm-6x9in) s. W/C. 7-Jul-4 Artcurial Briest, Paris #313
£865 $1600 €1263 Untitled (46x37cm-18x15in) s. W/C exec 1982 prov. 13-Jul-4 Christie's, Rockefeller NY #101/R est:2000-3000
£973 $1800 €1421 Untitled (75x55cm-30x22in) s.d.78 W/C. 13-Jul-4 Christie's, Rockefeller NY #23/R est:1000-1500
£1389 $2500 €2028 Mini masters (24x35cm-9x14in) init.i.d.1977 crayon double-sided joined sheet. 24-Apr-4 David Rago, Lambertville #127/R est:1000-1500
£1500 $2715 €2190 Untitled (48x60cm-19x24in) s. ink pencil executed 1987 prov. 1-Apr-4 Christie's, Kensington #295/R est:1500-2500
£1786 $3250 €2608 Landscape (30x40cm-12x16in) s.i. W/C prov. 29-Jun-4 Sotheby's, New York #589/R est:3000-4000
£2027 $3750 €2959 Gericault Figure III (45x30cm-18x12in) s.d.1977 pencil pastel chl crayon exec 1977-78 prov.exhib. 12-Feb-4 Sotheby's, New York #116/R est:2000-3000
£2270 $4200 €3314 Study for Alexander Greeting AB Seaman Ulysses MA Evans (18x23cm-7x9in) s. W/C two attached sheets paper prov.exhib. 13-Jul-4 Christie's, Rockefeller NY #100/R est:2000-3000
£3571 $6500 €5214 Blue fish (71x105cm-28x41in) s. W/C executed 1981 prov. 29-Jun-4 Sotheby's, New York #550/R est:3000-5000
£4121 $7500 €6017 Drums in friendship, Maine (54x75cm-21x30in) s.i. s.verso W/C. 29-Jun-4 Sotheby's, New York #606/R est:8000-12000
£4444 $8000 €6488 Hollywood film stars and homes foldout (22x30cm-9x12in) s.d.1973 graphite. 24-Apr-4 David Rago, Lambertville #511/R est:800-1200
£300000 $546000 €438000 Buckingham Palace with first prize (164x225cm-65x89in) s.d.1970 liquitex encaustic ribbon on canvas water pistol. 4-Feb-4 Christie's, London #39/R est:300000-400000

MORLEY, Robert (1857-1941) British
£720 $1238 €1051 English garden scene with path running through borders filled with mixed flowers (56x76cm-22x30in) s. 2-Dec-3 Canterbury Auctions, UK #140

MORLEY, T W (1859-1925) British
Works on paper
£400 $748 €584 Study of monks and clergymen outside a church (36x53cm-14x21in) s. d.1912 W/C. 24-Feb-4 Tayler & Fletcher, Cheltenham #2

MORLEY, Thomas W (1859-1925) British
Works on paper
£280 $468 €409 Market scene (50x35cm-20x14in) s.d.15 W/C. 14-Oct-3 Bonhams, Knightsbridge #10/R
£280 $512 €409 Moroccan street scene (35x53cm-14x21in) s.d.19 W/C. 27-Jan-4 Bonhams, Knightsbridge #251

MORLON, Alexandre (1878-?) French
Sculpture
£3916 $6736 €5600 Danseuse et bouquetin (50x66cm-20x26in) s.st.f.Valsuani dark pat bronze. 8-Dec-3 Horta, Bruxelles #61/R est:3500-5500

MORLON, Alice (1959-) French
Sculpture
£1528 $2551 €2200 Sculpture (150x80cm-59x31in) 25-Oct-3 Cornette de St.Cyr, Paris #437 est:800-1000

MORLON, Paul Émile Antony (1835-?) French
Works on paper
£525 $950 €767 Elegant gentleman carrying a basket. Gentleman seated looking over his shoulder (44x34cm-17x13in) s. chl pair. 30-Mar-4 Christie's, Rockefeller NY #142/R

MORLOTTI, Ennio (1910-1992) Italian
£5517 $8828 €8000 Fragment (12x67cm-5x26in) s. card on canvas. 13-Mar-3 Galleria Pace, Milan #77/R est:9000-12000
£8163 $14612 €12000 Flowers (37x33cm-15x13in) s. painted 1965 prov. 16-Mar-4 Finarte Semenzato, Milan #440/R est:13000
£9396 $16819 €14000 Flowers (34x31cm-13x12in) painted 1965. 29-May-4 Farsetti, Prato #467/R est:13000-15000
£9655 $16124 €14000 Still life (45x60cm-18x24in) s. painted 1942 prov.lit. 13-Nov-3 Finarte Semenzato, Rome #335/R est:7000-8000
£10067 $18020 €15000 Leaves (90x65cm-35x26in) s. painted 1968 lit. 29-May-4 Farsetti, Prato #466/R est:15000-20000
£12081 $21624 €18000 Olive trees (52x63cm-20x25in) s.d.61 prov.exhib. 25-May-4 Sotheby's, Milan #119/R est:22000
£15217 $24957 €21000 Vegetazione (50x60cm-20x24in) s. s.d.63 verso. 31-May-3 Farsetti, Prato #684/R est:13000-16000
£15436 $27631 €23000 Wood (80x90cm-31x35in) s. lit. 30-May-4 Meeting Art, Vercelli #76 est:15000
£15493 $27113 €22000 Leaves (100x81cm-39x32in) s. d.1968 verso exhib.lit. 16-Dec-3 Finarte Semenzato, Milan #324/R est:21000-22500
£40580 $66551 €56000 Cactus (112x120cm-44x47in) s. painted 1963 lit. 29-May-3 Galleria Pace, Milan #130/R est:75000
Works on paper
£333 $603 €500 Woman with turban (44x31cm-17x12in) pencil. 2-Apr-4 Farsetti, Prato #43
£364 $663 €550 Figures in the wind (24x24cm-9x9in) s. ink dr. 18-Jun-4 Stadion, Trieste #395
£400 $724 €600 Portrait (44x31cm-17x12in) s. pencil. 2-Apr-4 Farsetti, Prato #128
£470 $869 €700 Figures in landscape (25x35cm-10x14in) s. Chinese ink. 13-Mar-4 Meeting Art, Vercelli #30
£503 $931 €750 Figures (23x17cm-9x7in) s. Chinese ink. 13-Mar-4 Meeting Art, Vercelli #282
£667 $1227 €1000 Three nudes (25x35cm-10x14in) s.d.1967 Chinese ink exhib. 8-Jun-4 Finarte Semenzato, Milan #197/R
£680 $1218 €1000 Nude (35x23cm-14x9in) s. ink exec.1945. 22-Mar-4 Sant Agostino, Torino #420/R
£1049 $1783 €1500 Nude (35x49cm-14x19in) s. wax crayon prov. 20-Nov-3 Finarte Semenzato, Milan #126/R est:1500-1700
£1333 $2453 €2000 Study of nude (35x47cm-14x19in) s. pastel. 12-Jun-4 Meeting Art, Vercelli #355/R est:2000
£1342 $2403 €2000 Figures. Flowers (23x32cm-9x13in) s. one pastel one chl two. 25-May-4 Sotheby's, Milan #37/R est:2000
£1399 $2378 €2000 Rocks (24x34cm-9x13in) s. pastel exec.1982 prov. 24-Nov-3 Christie's, Milan #29 est:2000-3000
£1528 $2414 €2200 Seated man (34x34cm-13x13in) pastel card. 6-Sep-3 Meeting Art, Vercelli #305 est:2000
£1667 $3067 €2500 Cactus (30x44cm-12x17in) s.d.1969 pastel card on canvas exec.1969. 12-Jun-4 Meeting Art, Vercelli #482/R est:2500
£1678 $3104 €2500 Nude (34x37cm-13x15in) s. pastel oil. 13-Mar-4 Meeting Art, Vercelli #176 est:2500
£2013 $3725 €3000 Flowers (35x37cm-14x15in) s. pastel oil. 13-Mar-4 Meeting Art, Vercelli #389 est:3000
£2083 $3292 €3000 Seated nude (34x28cm-13x11in) wax crayon card. 6-Sep-3 Meeting Art, Vercelli #411 est:3000
£2174 $3565 €3000 Flower (35x40cm-14x16in) s. pastel card. 29-May-3 Galleria Pace, Milan #31 est:3500-4500

MORNER, Stellan (1896-1979) Swedish
£307 $501 €448 Sunshine through the trees (27x35cm-11x14in) s. 29-Sep-3 Lilla Bukowskis, Stockholm #311 (S.KR 4000)
£522 $851 €762 Misty landscape (38x46cm-15x18in) s.d.56. 29-Sep-3 Lilla Bukowskis, Stockholm #934 (S.KR 6800)
£765 $1408 €1148 On the mountain a new town is being made (33x41cm-13x16in) s.d.71. 14-Jun-4 Lilla Bukowskis, Stockholm #44 (S.KR 10500)
£845 $1377 €1234 Composition (38x61cm-15x24in) s.d.63. 29-Sep-3 Lilla Bukowskis, Stockholm #295 (S.KR 11000)
£952 $1686 €1390 Market scene (46x38cm-18x15in) s. panel. 27-Apr-4 AB Stockholms Auktionsverk #649/R (S.KR 13000)
£1026 $1815 €1498 In the palace of the vizier (38x46cm-15x18in) s.d.58. 27-Apr-4 AB Stockholms Auktionsverk #732/R (S.KR 14000)
£1035 $1852 €1511 Tediousness one winter's day at a Russian village - Eugen Onegin (22x33cm-9x13in) s.d.62. 28-May-4 Uppsala Auktionskammare, Uppsala #304/R est:12000-15000 (S.KR 14000)
£1099 $1945 €1605 May (27x35cm-11x14in) s. panel. 27-Apr-4 AB Stockholms Auktionsverk #647/R est:15000-20000 (S.KR 15000)
£1109 $1984 €1619 Surrealistic composition (37x54cm-15x21in) s. 28-May-4 Uppsala Auktionskammare, Uppsala #302/R est:15000-18000 (S.KR 15000)
£1130 $2079 €1695 The old tower (24x33cm-9x13in) s. 14-Jun-4 Lilla Bukowskis, Stockholm #45 est:10000-12000 (S.KR 15500)
£1133 $1926 €1654 By the sea (41x33cm-16x13in) s.d.50 panel. 5-Nov-3 AB Stockholms Auktionsverk #888/R est:18000-20000 (S.KR 15000)
£1245 $2204 €1818 Greek evening (19x24cm-7x9in) s/. 27-Apr-4 AB Stockholms Auktionsverk #644/R est:15000-18000 (S.KR 17000)
£1284 $2183 €1875 The beggar opera (19x24cm-7x9in) s. 5-Nov-3 AB Stockholms Auktionsverk #883/R est:8000-10000 (S.KR 17000)
£1360 $2311 €1986 Gone with the wind (27x35cm-11x14in) s. 5-Nov-3 AB Stockholms Auktionsverk #743/R est:20000-25000 (S.KR 18000)
£1511 $2568 €2206 The King of Crete (46x55cm-18x22in) s. 5-Nov-3 AB Stockholms Auktionsverk #647/R est:20000-25000 (S.KR 20000)
£1813 $3263 €2647 Landscape with farm in Soder (27x42cm-11x17in) s. 26-Apr-4 Bukowskis, Stockholm #14/R est:12000-15000 (S.KR 25000)
£1895 $3487 €2843 Dancing couple (55x46cm-22x18in) s. panel. 14-Jun-4 Lilla Bukowskis, Stockholm #281 est:15000-18000 (S.KR 26000)
£1952 $3514 €2850 Surrealistic composition with candle-holder (50x60cm-20x24in) s. 26-Jan-4 Lilla Bukowskis, Stockholm #119 est:15000-20000 (S.KR 26000)
£2321 $4177 €3389 Interior of a manor house (37x46cm-15x18in) s. panel. 26-Apr-4 Bukowskis, Stockholm #11/R est:15000-20000 (S.KR 32000)
£2344 $4149 €3422 Window towards sunset (27x35cm-11x14in) s. d.63 verso panel. 27-Apr-4 AB Stockholms Auktionsverk #667/R est:30000-35000 (S.KR 32000)
£2615 $4498 €3818 Soon everything will disappear in the haze - Surrealistic interior (49x60cm-19x24in) s. 7-Dec-3 Uppsala Auktionskammare, Uppsala #273/R est:12000-15000 (S.KR 34000)
£2719 $4622 €3970 The manor - landscape with sculptures (38x55cm-15x22in) s. 5-Nov-3 AB Stockholms Auktionsverk #635/R est:25000-30000 (S.KR 36000)

£3663	$6484	€5348	Announcement at night (60x73cm-24x29in) mono. panel. 27-Apr-4 AB Stockholms Auktionsverk #695/R est:50000-60000 (S.KR 50000)
£5076	$9137	€7411	Grandmother is moving (101x83cm-40x33in) s. exhib. 26-Apr-4 Bukowskis, Stockholm #15/R est:50000-70000 (S.KR 70000)
Works on paper			
£360	$649	€526	Landscape with many stars (22x26cm-9x10in) s. W/C. 26-Jan-4 Lilla Bukowskis, Stockholm #139 (S.KR 4800)
£1160	$2088	€1694	Composition in blue and green (44x54cm-17x21in) s. pastel chk. 26-Apr-4 Bukowskis, Stockholm #65/R est:12000-15000 (S.KR 16000)

MORO ESCALONA, Milagros (1936-) Spanish

£470	$879	€700	Hunt day (38x46cm-15x18in) s. s.i.verso acrylic board. 24-Feb-4 Durán, Madrid #52/R

MORO, Franz (1900-1940) Austrian

Works on paper			
£345	$572	€500	Chinone de la Polo, Dolomites (74x57cm-29x22in) s.i. verso W/C paper on board. 30-Sep-3 Dorotheum, Vienna #343/R

MORO, Gino (1901-1977) Italian

£467	$859	€700	Seascape at the Elba island (33x41cm-13x16in) s. cardboard. 12-Jun-4 Meeting Art, Vercelli #875
£878	$1546	€1300	Against the light (50x70cm-20x28in) s. 19-May-4 Il Ponte, Milan #1044 est:700-750
£946	$1665	€1400	Landscape (60x86cm-24x34in) s. 19-May-4 Il Ponte, Milan #1042 est:700-800
£1000	$1840	€1500	The Po' (50x75cm-20x30in) s. 12-Jun-4 Meeting Art, Vercelli #990/R est:1500
£1014	$1784	€1500	Composition (80x60cm-31x24in) s. 19-May-4 Il Ponte, Milan #1050 est:600-650

MORONEY, Ken (1949-) British

£400	$704	€584	Artist at her easel (31x41cm-12x16in) s. board. 18-May-4 Bonhams, Knightsbridge #149
£400	$704	€584	On the river (33x38cm-13x15in) s. board. 18-May-4 Bonhams, Knightsbridge #150
£450	$752	€657	Clown (91x62cm-36x24in) s. board. 16-Oct-3 Christie's, Kensington #368
£500	$835	€730	Still life with cherries in a bowl (26x61cm-10x24in) s. 16-Oct-3 Christie's, Kensington #360
£550	$968	€803	Girl on a beach (30x40cm-12x16in) s. board. 18-May-4 Bonhams, Knightsbridge #151
£662	$1205	€1000	Winter in New York (48x75cm-19x30in) s.d.1993 board. 15-Jun-4 James Adam, Dublin #17/R
£950	$1672	€1387	Still life with silver pitcher (51x61cm-20x24in) s. 18-May-4 Bonhams, Knightsbridge #125/R
£1126	$2049	€1700	On the promenade (40x49cm-16x19in) s. board. 15-Jun-4 James Adam, Dublin #101/R est:700-1000
£1150	$2024	€1679	Girl on a beach (50x62cm-20x24in) s. board. 18-May-4 Bonhams, Knightsbridge #137/R est:1500-2000

MOROT, Aime (1850-1913) French

£1931	$3225	€2800	La captivite des juifs a Babylone (43x34cm-17x13in) s.d.73 s.i.verso. 17-Nov-3 Tajan, Paris #86/R est:3000-4000
£2013	$3725	€3000	Chasseur dans l'oued (38x46cm-15x18in) s.d.89. 15-Mar-4 Gros & Delettrez, Paris #70/R est:3000-3500

MOROZOV, Aleksandr Ivanovich (1835-1904) Russian

£1007	$1862	€1500	Homme assis sur la plage (14x16cm-6x6in) s. 14-Mar-4 Eric Pillon, Calais #111/R
£5175	$8797	€7400	A little wanderer (27x21cm-11x8in) s.d.95 panel. 29-Nov-3 Bukowskis, Helsinki #411/R est:2000-2500

MORPER, Daniel (1944-) American

Works on paper			
£301	$550	€439	Forest of Civilization (84x74cm-33x29in) gouache. 10-Jul-4 Hindman, Chicago #357/R

MORRELL, Wayne (1923-) American

£258	$475	€377	Yellow umbrella girl, Cape Ann (30x25cm-12x10in) s. d.1985 verso board. 9-Jun-4 Alderfer's, Hatfield #420
£296	$550	€432	Essex marshes (20x25cm-8x10in) s. s.i.d.Sept 15 1984 verso masonite. 5-Mar-4 Skinner, Boston #537/R
£353	$650	€515	Walking the dog, winter (15x25cm-6x10in) s. board prov. 25-Jun-4 Freeman, Philadelphia #320/R
£376	$700	€549	Sunlit wooded path (20x25cm-8x10in) s. panel prov. 5-Mar-4 Skinner, Boston #471/R
£376	$700	€549	Winter vista (23x30cm-9x12in) s. masonite prov. 5-Mar-4 Skinner, Boston #488/R
£380	$700	€555	East Stroudsburg express (30x41cm-12x16in) s. board. 9-Jun-4 Alderfer's, Hatfield #419/R
£430	$800	€628	Marsh sunset (30x40cm-12x16in) i.d.21 April 1971 s.i.verso masonite prov. 5-Mar-4 Skinner, Boston #566/R
£484	$900	€707	Harbour mist and sunrise (50x40cm-20x16in) s. prov. 5-Mar-4 Skinner, Boston #549/R
£531	$950	€775	Beach side stroll (30x41cm-12x16in) s. 8-Jan-4 James Julia, Fairfield #758/R
£531	$950	€775	Mr Evans Window-King St, Rockport, Mass (28x36cm-11x14in) s.i.d.July 1985 board. 8-Jan-4 James Julia, Fairfield #759/R
£538	$1000	€785	Winter stream at dusk near Peterborough, New Hampshire (40x50cm-16x20in) s. s.i.d.1977 verso board prov. 5-Mar-4 Skinner, Boston #495/R
£559	$1000	€816	Rockport seaside gardens (20x25cm-8x10in) d.July 1994 board prov. 8-Jan-4 James Julia, Fairfield #760/R
£588	$1000	€858	Indian camp by the Rio Grande New Mexico (38x48cm-15x19in) board exhib. 21-Nov-3 Shelley, Hendersonville #713/R
£703	$1300	€1026	View of Rockport Headlands (25x36cm-10x14in) 13-Feb-4 Du Mouchelle, Detroit #2133/R
£833	$1500	€1216	Old Essex Harbour (30x41cm-12x16in) s.i.d.1975 board. 24-Apr-4 Weschler, Washington #597/R est:800-1200
£860	$1600	€1256	A November day (60x91cm-24x36in) s. i.verso. 5-Mar-4 Skinner, Boston #476/R est:1000-1500
£860	$1600	€1256	Turning towards the wind. Off Rockport waters. Homeward bound. (20x25cm-8x10in) s. two i. board three prov. 5-Mar-4 Skinner, Boston #551/R est:2000-3000
£1129	$2100	€1648	Marsh haze (30x40cm-12x16in) s. s.i.d.1975 verso masonite prov. 5-Mar-4 Skinner, Boston #564/R est:800-1200
£1313	$2100	€1917	Monet's pond, Giverny (99x99cm-39x39in) s. board. 21-Sep-3 Grogan, Boston #68/R

MORREN, Auguste (19th C) Belgian

£890	$1514	€1300	Repos du troupeau (35x30cm-14x12in) s.d.1885 panel. 10-Nov-3 Horta, Bruxelles #376

MORREN, Georges (1868-1941) Belgian

£300	$516	€438	Still life of daisies and poppies (56x50cm-22x20in) s.d.29 board. 3-Dec-3 Cheffins, Cambridge #662
£1702	$2843	€2400	Petit canal a Venise (54x45cm-21x18in) s.d.1922. 17-Jun-3 Vanderkindere, Brussels #114/R est:1500-2500
£2536	$4159	€3500	Village by a river (42x55cm-17x22in) s.d.1926. 27-May-3 Sotheby's, Amsterdam #493/R est:4000-6000
£17568	$31446	€26000	Petite baigneuse a contre-jour. Une dame dans une pergola (80x90cm-31x35in) s.d.1923 s.i.d.verso double-sided. 10-May-4 Horta, Bruxelles #148/R est:20000-30000
Sculpture			
£4483	$8293	€6500	Jeune femme nue (26cm-10in) s.d.99 dark pat bronze. 16-Feb-4 Horta, Bruxelles #59 est:2000-3000
Works on paper			
£1600	$2896	€2400	Jeune Zelandaise en priere (23x30cm-9x12in) s. pastel. 30-Mar-4 Campo, Vlaamse Kaai #120 est:300-350

MORRICE, James Wilson (1865-1924) Canadian

£4225	$7310	€6000	Bonsecourt market, Montreal (15x12cm-6x5in) s. panel. 10-Dec-3 Dorotheum, Vienna #186/R est:3200-3800
£5285	$9459	€7716	Little church in England (22x31cm-9x12in) s. canvas on masonite prov. 31-May-4 Sotheby's, Toronto #103/R est:9000-12000 (C.D 13000)
£15766	$26802	€23018	Pavillon de Flore, Palais de Tuileries, Paris (12x15cm-5x6in) panel on masonite prov. 18-Nov-3 Sotheby's, Toronto #187/R est:40000-50000 (C.D 35000)
£28455	$50935	€41544	Parame, la plage (12x15cm-5x6in) s. s.i.verso panel prov.lit. 31-May-4 Sotheby's, Toronto #1/R est:40000-50000 (C.D 70000)
£52846	$94593	€77155	Le palais des Doges, Venice (46x62cm-18x24in) s. painted c.1901. 31-May-4 Sotheby's, Toronto #135/R est:100000-125000 (C.D 130000)
£675676	$1148649	€986487	Effet de Neige (65x81cm-26x32in) s. prov.exhib.lit. 18-Nov-3 Sotheby's, Toronto #92/R est:250000-350000 (C.D 1500000)
Works on paper			
£1915	$3255	€2796	La Synagogue, Dijon (21x25cm-8x10in) i.d.99 graphite prov. 18-Nov-3 Sotheby's, Toronto #55/R est:5000-6000 (C.D 4250)
£12195	$21829	€17805	Farm and horse (34x55cm-13x22in) W/C gouache prov.exhib.lit. 31-May-4 Sotheby's, Toronto #16/R est:30000-50000 (C.D 30000)

MORRIEN, Johann Hendrik (1819-1878) Dutch

£1700	$3043	€2482	Washwoman by a river with a cottage beyond (44x57cm-17x22in) s. 27-May-4 Christie's, Kensington #134/R est:1200-1800

MORRIS, Alfred (19th C) British

£243	$450	€355	Portrait of a cairn terrier (23x23cm-9x9in) s.d.64. 10-Feb-4 Doyle, New York #177/R
£380	$688	€555	Highland sheep overlooked by watchful sheepdog (76x62cm-30x24in) s.d.1892. 2-Apr-4 Bracketts, Tunbridge Wells #457/R
£625	$1031	€900	Hunter with dogs in Scottish Highlands (60x90cm-24x35in) s.d.1869 canvas on panel. 3-Jul-3 Van Ham, Cologne #1363
£1600	$2864	€2336	Sheep in a highland landscape (91x71cm-36x28in) s.d.1856. 27-May-4 Christie's, Kensington #200/R est:600-800
£1900	$3477	€2774	Sheep in a landscape (61x91cm-24x36in) s.d.1871. 7-Apr-4 Gardiner & Houlgate, Bath #353/R est:2000-3000

MORRIS, Alfred (attrib) (19th C) British

£2238	$3804	€3200	Sheep and watchdogs (76x115cm-30x45in) 29-Nov-3 Bukowskis, Helsinki #373/R est:3700-4000

MORRIS, C R (20th C) British

Works on paper			
£1300	$2067	€1898	Judges prefer Shell (51x72cm-20x28in) s.d.35 gouache. 10-Sep-3 Sotheby's, Olympia #72/R est:300-500

MORRIS, Carey (1882-1968) British

£580	$1067	€847	Dynevor Castle, Llandeilo, Carmarthenshire (58x73cm-23x29in) s. 23-Jun-4 Cheffins, Cambridge #527/R

MORRIS, Carl (1911-1993) American

£335	$600	€489	Men working near trucks (41x51cm-16x20in) s.i. canvas on paper on masonite painted c.1930. 16-Mar-4 Matthew's, Oregon #111/R

MORRIS, Cedric (1889-1982) British

£2600	$4810	€3796	Villa on the coast (48x61cm-19x24in) 11-Mar-4 Christie's, Kensington #116/R est:2000-3000
£4500	$7470	€6570	Monkshood with tulips and bluebells (46x53cm-18x21in) s.d.28 board prov. 30-Sep-3 Sotheby's, London #208/R est:4000-6000
£13000	$23270	€18980	Newlyn Harbour (53x66cm-21x26in) s.d.24 board. 7-May-4 Mallams, Oxford #415/R est:2500-3500
£15000	$24900	€21900	Crisis (120x90cm-47x35in) prov.exhib. 30-Sep-3 Sotheby's, London #210/R est:10000-15000

MORRIS, Cedric (attrib) (1889-1982) British
£300 $555 €438 Still life study of mixed spring flowers in gold coloured vase (74x51cm-29x20in) 13-Feb-4 Keys, Aylsham #711

MORRIS, Charles (19th C) British
£1600 $2560 €2336 Six scenes including moonlit harbour (12x18cm-5x7in) s. six. 16-Sep-3 Bonhams, Knowle #91 est:400-600

MORRIS, Charles (attrib) (19th C) British
£528 $950 €771 Bucolic landscapes (25x20cm-10x8in) s. pair. 24-Jan-4 Skinner, Boston #270/R est:800-1200

MORRIS, Charles (snr) (19th C) British
£340 $612 €496 Landscape with gnarled tree and grazing sheep, a cottage behind (9x13cm-4x5in) init.d.1866 panel. 21-Apr-4 Rupert Toovey, Partridge Green #88/R

MORRIS, Charles (snr-attrib) (19th C) British
£500 $925 €730 River landscape with ducks by house. Riverside path (51x61cm-20x24in) pair. 14-Jul-4 Bonhams, Chester #432

MORRIS, Charles Greville (1861-1922) British
£300 $516 €438 Woodland pool (58x48cm-23x19in) s. 5-Dec-3 Keys, Aylsham #631

MORRIS, Desmond (1928-) British
Works on paper
£450 $819 €657 Rank and File (29x30cm-11x12in) mono.d.49 pen black ink W/C prov. 1-Jul-4 Christie's, Kensington #389/R

MORRIS, Ellerman (?) British
£1418 $2453 €2070 Timber load - man collecting timber with horse and cart in winter (76x130cm-30x51in) s. 9-Dec-3 Rasmussen, Copenhagen #1658/R est:10000-12000 (D.KR 15000)

MORRIS, Franklin E (1938-) American
£1397 $2500 €2040 Washington Arch, New York (51x61cm-20x24in) s. i.verso. 26-May-4 Doyle, New York #135/R est:2000-3000

MORRIS, Garman (fl.c.1900-1930) British
Works on paper
£267 $477 €400 Off the Essex coast (18x54cm-7x21in) s. W/C. 11-May-4 Vendu Notarishuis, Rotterdam #20/R
£280 $507 €409 Morning in Scarborough (27x69cm-11x27in) s.i. W/C. 30-Mar-4 David Duggleby, Scarborough #222/R
£500 $905 €730 Maldon, Essex. Rye, Sussex (30cm-12in circular) s.i. W/C pair. 30-Mar-4 David Duggleby, Scarborough #30/R

MORRIS, George L K (1905-1975) American
£824 $1500 €1203 Abstract composition (25x33cm-10x13in) s. oil ink W/C board. 7-Feb-4 Neal Auction Company, New Orleans #516/R est:3000-5000
£1850 $3200 €2701 Excavation (20x25cm-8x10in) s.i.d.1956 verso prov. 15-Dec-3 Hindman, Chicago #19/R est:3000-5000
£2695 $4500 €3935 Spatial perspectives (41x33cm-16x13in) s.i.d.1953 verso prov. 9-Oct-3 Christie's, Rockefeller NY #111/R est:6000-8000
Works on paper
£304 $575 €450 Composition abstraite. s. gouache ink. 21-Feb-4 Cornette de St.Cyr, Paris #317
£304 $575 €450 Composition abstraite (30x27cm-12x11in) s. chl. 21-Feb-4 Cornette de St.Cyr, Paris #318

MORRIS, Hilda (1911-1991) American
Sculpture
£2515 $4200 €3672 Little fish (10x14cm-4x6in) verdigris pat. bronze executed 1954. 11-Nov-3 Christie's, Rockefeller NY #154/R est:200-300

MORRIS, J (19th C) British
£1208 $2247 €1800 Bringing in the tithe (116x155cm-46x61in) s.indis.i. i.d.1838 verso. 5-Mar-4 Wendl, Rudolstadt #3800/R est:950

MORRIS, J C (19th C) British
£1376 $2216 €2009 Rabbit (59cm-23in circular) s. 25-Aug-3 Lilla Bukowskis, Stockholm #638 est:15000-20000 (S.KR 18000)
£2000 $3740 €2920 Terriers and a rabbit in a moorland landscape (69x91cm-27x36in) 26-Feb-4 Mallams, Cheltenham #238/R est:2000-3000
£2500 $4475 €3650 Guarding the flock (127x102cm-50x40in) s.d.1877. 27-May-4 Christie's, Kensington #202/R est:3000-5000

MORRIS, J W (19th C) British
£2300 $4071 €3358 Sheep and collie in highland landscape (61x107cm-24x42in) s. 1-May-4 Shapes, Edinburgh #407/R est:2000-3000

MORRIS, John (19th C) British
£280 $515 €409 Farmyard friends (24x34cm-9x13in) s.d.80. 14-Jun-4 Bonhams, Bath #44
£347 $624 €520 Inch beach, Co Kerry (43x58cm-17x23in) s. board. 20-Apr-4 James Adam, Dublin #212/R
£414 $750 €604 Sheep and chickens in barn (25x36cm-10x14in) 2-Apr-4 Douglas, South Deerfield #34
£440 $792 €642 Waiting for the guns (24x19cm-9x7in) s. 22-Apr-4 Lawrence, Crewkerne #920/R
£540 $902 €788 Highland cattle in repose (61x91cm-24x36in) s. 23-Oct-3 Bonhams, Edinburgh #330
£540 $902 €788 Highland cattle in a glen (61x92cm-24x36in) s. 23-Oct-3 Bonhams, Edinburgh #333
£667 $1207 €1000 Summer Dollymount beach (51x51cm-20x20in) s. board. 30-Mar-4 De Veres Art Auctions, Dublin #234/R
£671 $1201 €1000 Ballinskelligs Beach (43x49cm-17x19in) s. i. verso panel. 31-May-4 Hamilton Osborne King, Dublin #93/R
£1500 $2370 €2175 Highland cattle (91x71cm-36x28in) s. pair. 4-Sep-3 Christie's, Kensington #168/R est:2000-3000
£1800 $2988 €2628 Sheepdog (61x91cm-24x36in) s. 1-Oct-3 Sotheby's, Olympia #37/R est:1200-1800
£1977 $3500 €2886 Terriers at a fox hole (76x127cm-30x50in) s. 2-May-4 Bonhams & Butterfields, San Francisco #1058/R est:2500-3500
£2600 $4316 €3796 Shepherd and his flock (71x92cm-28x36in) s. 1-Oct-3 Sotheby's, Olympia #43/R est:800-1200
£2700 $4509 €3942 Gun dogs with the day's bag (90x70cm-35x28in) s. 16-Oct-3 Bonhams, Edinburgh #230 est:1500-2000
£3800 $6992 €5548 Setters with the day's bag (91x71cm-36x28in) s. 10-Jun-4 Christie's, Kensington #408/R est:2500-3500
£4200 $6972 €6132 Highland cattle. Highland cattle and sheep (61x91cm-24x36in) s. pair. 1-Oct-3 Sotheby's, Olympia #36/R est:3000-5000
£8000 $13040 €11680 Retriever and a pony resting by trees. Setters and a pony in a highland landscape (70x90cm-28x35in) s. pair. 25-Sep-3 Mellors & Kirk, Nottingham #755/R est:6000-8000

MORRIS, John W (19th C) British
£420 $769 €613 Sheep in a winter landscape (50x76cm-20x30in) s.d.1883. 6-Jul-4 Bonhams, Knightsbridge #119/R
£761 $1400 €1111 Sheep in a winter landscape (76x130cm-30x51in) s.d.1875. 23-Jun-4 Doyle, New York #5055/R est:800-1200

MORRIS, Kathleen (1893-1986) Canadian
£13514 $22973 €19730 Notre Dame Church (30x35cm-12x14in) s. i.verso panel painted c.1925. 27-Nov-3 Heffel, Vancouver #107/R est:20000-25000 (C.D 30000)
£14228 $25467 €20773 Market day, Ottawa (25x35cm-10x14in) s. i.verso panel painted c.1923 prov.exhib. 27-May-4 Heffel, Vancouver #82/R est:18000-22000 (C.D 35000)

MORRIS, Kyle (1918-1979) American
£1946 $3250 €2841 Number 10 (142x170cm-56x67in) s. exhib. 7-Oct-3 Sotheby's, New York #320 est:2000-4000

MORRIS, Lincoln Godfrey (1887-1967) Canadian
£711 $1166 €1038 Mount Royal in autumn (41x51cm-16x20in) s. canvasboard painted c.1950. 28-May-3 Maynards, Vancouver #2/R (C.D 1600)

MORRIS, Louise (1896-?) American
Works on paper
£541 $860 €790 Laguna fiesta (102x119cm-40x47in) s. pigment fabric on board. 12-Sep-3 Aspire, Cleveland #56

MORRIS, Margaret (1891-1980) British
£1300 $2392 €1898 Composite impression of Ram Gopal (74x53cm-29x21in) s.d.1960 exhib. 8-Jun-4 Gorringes, Lewes #1999 est:400-600

MORRIS, Michael (1942-) Canadian
£602 $1120 €879 Berliner landschaft mit tennisplatz und spree (202x234cm-80x92in) s.i.d.1987 verso acrylic diptych prov. 2-Mar-4 Ritchie, Toronto #209/R (C.D 1500)

MORRIS, Philip Richard (1838-1902) British
£780 $1240 €1139 Stray Calf (48x74cm-19x29in) s. 18-Mar-3 Anderson & Garland, Newcastle #503/R
£980 $1784 €1431 Rural lake scene with figures before a lake (48x74cm-19x29in) 3-Feb-4 Lawrences, Bletchingley #1914/R
£1250 $1975 €1800 Orange seller, London Cry (56x41cm-22x16in) s. 6-Sep-3 Schopman, Hamburg #686/R est:2200
£3885 $6371 €5400 Portrait of mother and daughter (140x90cm-55x35in) s. 10-Jun-3 Pandolfini, Florence #99/R est:5700-6000
£4000 $7440 €5840 Fond farewell (74x48cm-29x19in) s. 4-Mar-4 Christie's, Kensington #623/R est:5000-7000
£8000 $13280 €11680 Feeding the swans (78x60cm-31x24in) init.d.1887. 1-Oct-3 Sotheby's, Olympia #117/R est:3500-4500
£27778 $50000 €40556 Sunday best (69x51cm-27x20in) s. prov. 22-Apr-4 Christie's, Rockefeller NY #65/R est:60000-80000

MORRIS, Rebecca (20th C) American
£1098 $1900 €1603 Remix (69x69cm-27x27in) prov. 10-Dec-3 Phillips, New York #597/R est:3000-4000

MORRIS, Robert (1931-) American
Works on paper
£724 $1303 €1050 Etude (21x28cm-8x11in) felt pen. 25-Jan-4 Cornette de St.Cyr, Paris #447/R
£1000 $1840 €1460 Untitled (21x27cm-8x11in) ball point pen. 24-Jun-4 Sotheby's, Olympia #473/R est:1200-1500
£16467 $27500 €24042 Untitled, '76/felt (284x320cm-112x126in) black felt metal grommets prov.exhib. 13-Nov-3 Sotheby's, New York #563/R est:15000-20000

MORRIS, Sarah (1967-) American
Works on paper
£533 $955 €800 Pieds (21x15cm-8x6in) col crayon. 12-May-4 Chochon-Barre & Allardi, Paris #110

MORRIS, William Bright (1844-?) British
£3400 $5780 €4964 Capri cornfield (44x64cm-17x25in) s.d.1870 exhib. 19-Nov-3 Bonhams, New Bond Street #60/R est:2000-4000

MORRIS, William and WEBB, Phillip (19th C) British
Works on paper
£6800 $12444 €9928 Sketches for a shield (33x28cm-13x11in) pair in one frame. 7-Apr-4 Andrew Hartley, Ilkley #1045 est:500-700

MORRISET, Andre (?) ?
Works on paper
£378 $650 €552 Moonlit seascape (23x18cm-9x7in) s. W/C. 7-Dec-3 Treadway Gallery, Cincinnati #312/R

MORRISH, Bertram (19/20th C) British
Works on paper
£700 $1309 €1050 Devon scenes (28x76cm-11x30in) s. W/C pair. 21-Jul-4 John Nicholson, Haslemere #61

MORRISH, William S (1844-1917) British
Works on paper
£260 $473 €380 Cattle on Dartmoor (28x43cm-11x17in) s.d.1892 W/C htd white. 21-Jun-4 Bonhams, Bath #456/R
£320 $586 €467 A Dartmoor stream with sheep grazing nearby (29x45cm-11x18in) s.d.1895 W/C. 28-Jan-4 Hampton & Littlewood, Exeter #361/R
£360 $659 €526 Leather Tor, near Devonford Leat (26x45cm-10x18in) s.d.1897 W/C. 28-Jan-4 Hampton & Littlewood, Exeter #357/R
£520 $848 €754 Highland landscapes (17x51cm-7x20in) s. W/C pair. 23-Sep-3 Bonhams, Knightsbridge #76/R

MORRISON, Alexander (fl.1873-1888) British
£500 $885 €730 Duenna - study of two Spanish ladies (64x51cm-25x20in) s. i.verso. 28-Apr-4 Halls, Shrewsbury #542/R

MORRISON, David (20th C) New Zealander
£507 $862 €740 Study of harbour 30 (120x137cm-47x54in) i. s.d.1998 verso. 4-Nov-3 Peter Webb, Auckland #88 est:1000-2000 (NZ.D 1400)
£551 $1031 €804 Study of harbour 52 (120x120cm-47x47in) s.i.d.1999 verso. 24-Feb-4 Peter Webb, Auckland #133/R (NZ.D 1500)

MORRISON, George C (?) British?
Works on paper
£280 $512 €409 Co. Downs farmhouse (35x50cm-14x20in) s. W/C. 2-Jun-4 John Ross, Belfast #155

MORRISON, George William (20th C) Irish
Works on paper
£250 $430 €365 Fairhead, County Antrim (25x35cm-10x14in) s.d.37 W/C. 3-Dec-3 John Ross, Belfast #216
£250 $458 €365 Creeslough (25x35cm-10x14in) s. W/C. 2-Jun-4 John Ross, Belfast #8
£260 $476 €380 Lough Finn (15x30cm-6x12in) s. W/C. 2-Jun-4 John Ross, Belfast #209
£280 $456 €406 Dhulough (25x37cm-10x15in) s.i. W/C. 23-Sep-3 Bonhams, Knightsbridge #192/R
£280 $482 €409 Atlantic Drive, Donegal (17x35cm-7x14in) s. W/C. 3-Dec-3 John Ross, Belfast #17
£280 $482 €409 Errigal, County Donegal (25x35cm-10x14in) s.d.1935 W/C. 3-Dec-3 John Ross, Belfast #240
£280 $482 €409 Port Braddon (25x35cm-10x14in) s. W/C. 3-Dec-3 John Ross, Belfast #257
£280 $521 €409 Muckish, Donegal (17x25cm-7x10in) s.d.1930 W/C. 3-Mar-4 John Ross, Belfast #97
£300 $516 €438 White Rocks, Portrush (15x28cm-6x11in) s.d.1936 W/C. 3-Dec-3 John Ross, Belfast #68
£300 $558 €438 Scrabo (17x25cm-7x10in) s.d.1930 W/C. 3-Mar-4 John Ross, Belfast #88
£300 $558 €438 In the Mournes (15x30cm-6x12in) s. W/C. 3-Mar-4 John Ross, Belfast #247
£300 $549 €438 Red Bay, Co. Antrim (15x30cm-6x12in) s. W/C. 2-Jun-4 John Ross, Belfast #247
£310 $577 €453 White rocks, Portrush (15x30cm-6x12in) s. W/C. 3-Mar-4 John Ross, Belfast #248
£310 $577 €453 Near Trassay Bridge (17x25cm-7x10in) s. W/C. 3-Mar-4 John Ross, Belfast #9
£320 $525 €467 Connemara (25x35cm-10x14in) s. W/C. 4-Jun-3 John Ross, Belfast #17
£320 $586 €467 Dundrum, Co.Down (15x30cm-6x12in) s.d.27 W/C. 2-Jun-4 John Ross, Belfast #28
£330 $614 €482 Cushendun Bay, Antrim Coast (17x25cm-7x10in) s. W/C. 3-Mar-4 John Ross, Belfast #18
£340 $622 €496 Browns Bay (17x38cm-7x15in) s. W/C. 2-Jun-4 John Ross, Belfast #70
£340 $622 €496 Ballintoy (17x35cm-7x14in) s. W/C. 2-Jun-4 John Ross, Belfast #237
£350 $574 €511 Thatched cottage (25x35cm-10x14in) s. W/C. 4-Jun-3 John Ross, Belfast #8
£350 $641 €511 Cockle strand from downings (25x35cm-10x14in) s. W/C. 2-Jun-4 John Ross, Belfast #4
£380 $623 €555 Glenveigh (17x38cm-7x15in) s. W/C. 4-Jun-3 John Ross, Belfast #109a
£380 $654 €555 Spelga Pass, Mournes (25x35cm-10x14in) s. W/C. 3-Dec-3 John Ross, Belfast #36
£400 $656 €584 Sheephaven (17x38cm-7x15in) s. W/C. 4-Jun-3 John Ross, Belfast #112a
£400 $664 €584 Glenveagh, Co. Donegal (25x35cm-10x14in) W/C. 1-Oct-3 John Ross, Belfast #18
£400 $688 €584 Horn Head, County Donegal (25x35cm-10x14in) s. W/C. 3-Dec-3 John Ross, Belfast #104
£450 $747 €657 Narrow water castle (30x61cm-12x24in) s. W/C. 1-Oct-3 John Ross, Belfast #132
£450 $824 €657 Scrabo from Whiterock (25x35cm-10x14in) s. W/C. 2-Jun-4 John Ross, Belfast #17
£450 $824 €657 Errigal (15x30cm-6x12in) s. W/C. 2-Jun-4 John Ross, Belfast #200
£600 $1116 €876 Glenveagh, Co. Donegal (23x58cm-9x23in) s. W/C. 3-Mar-4 John Ross, Belfast #32

MORRISON, Hal Alexander Courtney (1848-1927) American
£3963 $6500 €5786 Still life with wood duck and mallard duck (81x46cm-32x18in) s. prov. 31-May-3 Brunk, Ashville #553/R est:400-800

MORRISON, James (1932-) British
£480 $802 €701 Tree study (44x80cm-17x31in) s.d.1983 board. 16-Oct-3 Lyon & Turnbull, Edinburgh #115
£500 $835 €730 Salmon nets drying (31x92cm-12x36in) s.d.1962. 16-Oct-3 Bonhams, Edinburgh #21
£550 $919 €803 Plough (36x56cm-14x22in) board. 14-Oct-3 Bearnes, Exeter #402/R
£600 $1098 €876 Angus landscape (31x152cm-12x60in) s.d.1961. 8-Apr-4 Bonhams, Edinburgh #23
£800 $1336 €1168 On the riverbank (75x105cm-30x41in) s.d.1976 board. 16-Oct-3 Lyon & Turnbull, Edinburgh #52
£820 $1320 €1189 Kinnaird (27x63cm-11x25in) s.d.1971 board. 21-Aug-3 Bonhams, Edinburgh #1047
£1600 $2720 €2336 Silver Birch (72x65cm-28x26in) s.d.1983 board. 30-Oct-3 Christie's, London #211/R est:2000-3000
£2000 $3580 €2920 L'Obiou from the Ravine des Achards (91x152cm-36x60in) s.d.80 panel prov. 28-May-4 Lyon & Turnbull, Edinburgh #34/R est:2000-3000
£3000 $4710 €4350 Summer clouds (91x151cm-36x59in) board prov. 27-Aug-3 Sotheby's, London #1174/R est:3000-4000
£3000 $4710 €4350 Winter sea, Montrose (79x110cm-31x43in) board. 27-Aug-3 Sotheby's, London #1175/R est:2500-3000
£3000 $5370 €4380 Peel street, Glasgow (46x69cm-18x27in) s.d.1957. 26-May-4 Sotheby's, Olympia #250/R est:2000-3000
£4000 $7160 €5840 Clouds over the Grampians (76x120cm-30x47in) s.d.1979 board. 28-May-4 Lyon & Turnbull, Edinburgh #33/R est:2000-3000
£5500 $8635 €7975 Farm in Angus, Scotland (77x152cm-30x60in) board. 27-Aug-3 Sotheby's, London #1176/R est:3000-4000
Works on paper
£400 $756 €584 St. Cyrus (25x66cm-10x26in) pen ink W/C. 19-Feb-4 Lyon & Turnbull, Edinburgh #6
£620 $1035 €905 Catterline (25x46cm-10x18in) s.d.1960 W/C gouache pair. 16-Oct-3 Bonhams, Edinburgh #17
£1000 $1860 €1460 Farnell (18x40cm-7x16in) s.d.1971 W/C pen ink exhib. 4-Mar-4 Christie's, Kensington #213/R est:300-500

MORRISON, John Lowrie (1948-) British
£750 $1418 €1095 Lock keeper's cottage on the pond, Crianan canal (30x30cm-12x12in) s. 19-Feb-4 Lyon & Turnbull, Edinburgh #33

MORRISON, Kenneth MacIver (attrib) (fl.1900-1930) British
£260 $481 €380 Study of a bearded man (30x33cm-12x13in) s. 13-Feb-4 Halls, Shrewsbury #806

MORRISON, Robert Edward (1852-1925) British
£1850 $3404 €2701 Sultan's favourite (43x33cm-17x13in) s. 12-Jun-4 Dickins, Middle Claydon #47

MORRISON, William (19th C) American
£360 $576 €526 Reclining female nude (50x61cm-20x24in) s. indis.d. i.verso painted 1957. 16-Sep-3 Rosebery Fine Art, London #438/R

MORRISSEAU, Norval (1932-) Canadian
£633 $1058 €924 Untitled (47x69cm-19x27in) s.d.1974 acrylic. 17-Nov-3 Hodgins, Calgary #294/R est:2000-2500 (C.D 1400)
£676 $1149 €987 The story teller and artists (85x56cm-33x22in) s. with syllabics i.d.1978 verso acrylic. 21-Nov-3 Walker's, Ottawa #103/R (C.D 1500)
£679 $1133 €991 Shaman journey to Astral Plane (63x56cm-25x22in) s.i.d.1980 acrylic. 17-Nov-3 Hodgins, Calgary #126/R est:2000-2500 (C.D 1500)
£679 $1133 €991 Three planes of knowledge (74x41cm-29x16in) s.i.d.1980 acrylic. 17-Nov-3 Hodgins, Calgary #149/R est:2000-2500 (C.D 1500)
£785 $1421 €1146 Four direction 2-4 (79x51cm-31x20in) s. s.i.d.1979 verso acrylic. 18-Apr-4 Levis, Calgary #89/R est:2500-3000 (C.D 1900)
£905 $1511 €1321 Animal totem (65x58cm-26x23in) s.i.d.1976 acrylic. 17-Nov-3 Hodgins, Calgary #383/R est:2000-2500 (C.D 2000)
£1322 $2393 €1930 Devouring watercat (90x90cm-35x35in) s. s.i.d.1970 verso acrylic prov. 18-Apr-4 Levis, Calgary #88/R est:2500-3000 (C.D 3200)
£1600 $2928 €2336 Untitled (113x69cm-44x27in) s. tempera. 3-Jun-4 Heffel, Vancouver #41/R est:2000-3000 (C.D 4000)
£1697 $2834 €2478 Untitled (69x165cm-27x65in) s.d.1973 acrylic. 17-Nov-3 Hodgins, Calgary #296/R est:4000-5000 (C.D 3750)
£2489 $3907 €3609 Unity of spirit and nature (135x102cm-53x40in) s.i.verso prov. 30-Aug-3 Heffel, Vancouver #20 est:3500-4500 (C.D 5500)

MORRO-HENZE, Ingfried Paul (1925-1972) German

£401	$750	€585	Ammersee (58x119cm-23x47in) s. 25-Feb-4 Dallas Auction Gallery, Dallas #239/R
£472	$850	€689	Still life with flowers (79x69cm-31x27in) s. 23-Jan-4 Freeman, Philadelphia #152/R

MORROCCO, Alberto (1917-1998) British

£6000	$10380	€8760	Beach at Rosas (35x46cm-14x18in) s. board. 11-Dec-3 Lyon & Turnbull, Edinburgh #59a/R est:4000-6000
£7000	$12810	€10220	Beach, Aderdeen (40x55cm-16x22in) s. canvasboard. 8-Apr-4 Bonhams, Edinburgh #47/R est:4000-6000
£7800	$14274	€11388	Aberdeenshire beach scene (51x74cm-20x29in) s.d.1948. 8-Apr-4 Bonhams, Edinburgh #48/R est:7000-10000
£11000	$19690	€16060	Summer afternoon (71x57cm-28x22in) s.d.83. 28-May-4 Lyon & Turnbull, Edinburgh #74/R est:10000-15000
£11500	$19550	€16790	White still life with blue lamp (56x51cm-22x20in) s.d.83. 30-Oct-3 Christie's, London #226/R est:4000-6000
£12000	$20400	€17520	Sunflower (49x41cm-19x16in) s.d.79 exhib. 30-Oct-3 Christie's, London #227/R est:3000-5000
Prints			
£18000	$32220	€26280	Still life on a white table (61x66cm-24x26in) s.d.88. 28-May-4 Lyon & Turnbull, Edinburgh #72/R est:18000-25000
Works on paper			
£480	$883	€701	Gathering maize (38x49cm-15x19in) s.d.58 chl. 29-Mar-4 Thomson Roddick & Medcalf, Edinburgh #254/R

MORROCCO, Léon (1942-) Australian

Works on paper			
£537	$914	€784	Rooftops and still life (109x129cm-43x51in) s.d.86 gouache W/C pastel. 29-Oct-3 Lawson Menzies, Sydney #161/R est:1500-2500 (A.D 1300)
£720	$1318	€1051	Boats at Marsaxlokk (40x50cm-16x20in) s.i.d.1994 mixed media. 8-Apr-4 Bonhams, Edinburgh #10/R
£920	$1619	€1343	Interior with two children (59x58cm-23x23in) s.d.1978 pastel. 20-May-4 Bonhams, Edinburgh #351
£1240	$2293	€1810	Studio interior with five birds (75x209cm-30x82in) s.d.88 gouache prov. 10-Mar-4 Deutscher-Menzies, Melbourne #335/R est:3500-5500 (A.D 3000)
£1301	$2042	€1886	Untitled, still life with fruit (111x75cm-44x30in) s.d.1985 gouache pastel prov.exhib.lit. 27-Aug-3 Christie's, Sydney #695/R est:2000-4000 (A.D 3200)
£4000	$7240	€5840	Still life with tropical birds and fruit (150x99cm-59x39in) s.d.1889-90 W/C chk pastel paper on board. 19-Apr-4 Sotheby's, London #149/R est:3000-5000

MORROW, Claudine (1931-) American

£559	$900	€816	Shepherd boy (58x51cm-23x20in) 22-Aug-3 Altermann Galleries, Santa Fe #48

MORSE, E E (19th C) American

£663	$1200	€968	Still life of red and white currants with leaves on vines in brass pot (38x76cm-15x30in) s. 2-Apr-4 Eldred, East Dennis #1024/R

MORSE, Eleanor Ecob (1837-1921) American

£559	$1000	€816	Chicks (13x16cm-5x6in) s. board. 14-May-4 Skinner, Boston #107/R

MORSE, F B (19th C) American

Works on paper			
£811	$1500	€1184	Steady as she goes (66x86cm-26x34in) s. pastel. 12-Mar-4 Jackson's, Cedar Falls #776/R est:1500-2500

MORSE, Jonathan Bradley (1834-1898) American

£579	$950	€845	Coastal scene with distant boats (43x66cm-17x26in) s. prov. 31-May-3 Brunk, Ashville #579/R

MORSE, N E (19th C) ?

£2006	$3250	€2929	Three chicks eating wild raspberries (20x30cm-8x12in) s. board. 1-Aug-3 North East Auctions, Portsmouth #271/R

MORSE, Samuel F B (1791-1872) American

£4420	$8000	€6453	Portrait of Mary Rutherford Clarkson (33x26cm-13x10in) panel prov. 31-Mar-4 Sotheby's, New York #77/R est:8000-12000
£5723	$9500	€8356	Huguenot Couple, Mr and Mrs Samuel Thurston Charleston (91x71cm-36x28in) pair. 4-Oct-3 Neal Auction Company, New Orleans #358/R est:4000-6000
£9945	$18000	€14520	Portrait of Catherine Helena Jay (33x27cm-13x11in) s.d.1835 verso panel prov. 31-Mar-4 Sotheby's, New York #75/R est:8000-12000

MORSE, Samuel F B (attrib) (1791-1872) American

£2824	$4800	€4123	Portrait of a gentleman, possibly Christopher Hughes (64x51cm-25x20in) prov. 22-Nov-3 Jackson's, Cedar Falls #96/R est:3000-5000
£3333	$6000	€4866	USS Niagara laying Atlantic cable (64x76cm-25x30in) prov. 24-Apr-4 Freeman, Philadelphia #71/R est:6000-8000

MORSING, Ivar (1919-) Swedish

£664	$1129	€950	Composition (61x38cm-24x15in) s.d.47. 29-Nov-3 Bukowskis, Helsinki #332/R
£1511	$2568	€2206	Woman selling fish (100x95cm-39x37in) s. 5-Nov-3 AB Stockholms Auktionsverk #726/R est:20000-25000 (S.KR 20000)

MORTEL, Jan (1650-1719) Dutch

£8054	$14819	€12000	Still life with grapes, peaches and greengages (38x31cm-15x12in) s.d.1716 panel. 24-Mar-4 Dorotheum, Vienna #135/R est:12000-18000

MORTELMANS, Frans (1865-c.1936) Belgian

£1793	$3317	€2600	Composition aux fruits et a la bouteille de vine blanc (56x46cm-22x18in) s. 16-Feb-4 Horta, Bruxelles #462 est:1200-1500
£2361	$3754	€3400	Still life with peaches (35x48cm-14x19in) s. 15-Sep-3 Bernaerts, Antwerp #728/R est:4500-5000
£12000	$21480	€18000	Blue vase with roses (70x40cm-28x16in) s. 15-May-4 De Vuyst, Lokeren #429/R est:16000-18000

MORTENSEN, J (?) Danish?

£287	$465	€416	Fisherman Hendrik Kortemann mending nets (58x74cm-23x29in) indis.sig. 4-Aug-3 Rasmussen, Vejle #456/R (D.KR 3000)

MORTENSEN, Richard (1910-1994) Danish

£376	$677	€549	Composition (76x56cm-30x22in) s.d.30-VI-89. 24-Apr-4 Rasmussen, Havnen #4196 (D.KR 4200)
£6381	$11487	€9316	Saltsjo (46x62cm-18x24in) s.i.d.1949 verso. 26-Apr-4 Bukowskis, Stockholm #235/R est:30000-35000 (S.KR 88000)
£7526	$12794	€10988	Room - composition (52x40cm-20x16in) s. stretcher prov.exhib.lit. 26-Nov-3 Kunsthallen, Copenhagen #47/R est:85000 (D.KR 80000)
£7614	$13706	€11116	Djuvnas (46x61cm-18x24in) s.i.d.1949 verso. 26-Apr-4 Bukowskis, Stockholm #236/R est:40000-50000 (S.KR 105000)
£8123	$14946	€11860	Composition (100x120cm-39x47in) s.d.1938 stretcher lit. 29-Mar-4 Rasmussen, Copenhagen #111/R est:100000 (D.KR 90000)
£8451	$14113	€12338	Marie Ahrenberg. Marie (100x80cm-39x31in) init.d.8 IX 1956 verso prov.lit. 7-Oct-3 Rasmussen, Copenhagen #87/R est:120000-150000 (D.KR 90000)
£15343	$28231	€22401	Composition - Opus 7 (73x92cm-29x36in) init.d.1948 verso exhib.lit. 29-Mar-4 Rasmussen, Copenhagen #3/R est:125000-150000 (D.KR 170000)
£18779	$31362	€27417	The sunny side (90x68cm-35x27in) s.d.48 verso prov. 7-Oct-3 Rasmussen, Copenhagen #89/R est:200000-250000 (D.KR 200000)
£20758	$38818	€30307	Presence de l'insolite (81x100cm-32x39in) init.i.d.1958 verso exhib.lit. 25-Feb-4 Kunsthallen, Copenhagen #29/R est:125000 (D.KR 230000)
£30686	$56462	€44802	Composition - Opus 7 (92x73cm-36x29in) i.verso prov.exhib.lit. 29-Mar-4 Rasmussen, Copenhagen #6/R est:125000-150000 (D.KR 340000)
£46931	$86354	€68519	Aleria - composition (197x130cm-78x51in) s.i.d.1960 stretcher prov.exhib.lit. 29-Mar-4 Rasmussen, Copenhagen #129/R est:500000-600000 (D.KR 520000)
Sculpture			
£1354	$2491	€1977	Relief No.III (100x70cm-39x28in) s. black white cut wood exec.c.1962. 29-Mar-4 Rasmussen, Copenhagen #438/R est:18000-20000 (D.KR 15000)
£1758	$3112	€2567	Ominenda - composition (102x83cm-40x33in) polychrome painted wood relief exhib.prov. 27-Apr-4 AB Stockholms Auktionsverk #1167/R est:20000-25000 (S.KR 24000)
£1805	$3321	€2635	Untitled (100x70cm-39x28in) s.d.1962 painted wood relief. 29-Mar-4 Rasmussen, Copenhagen #383/R est:15000 (D.KR 20000)
Works on paper			
£318	$532	€464	Composition with fantasy animal (19x28cm-7x11in) init. Indian ink W/C. 25-Oct-3 Rasmussen, Havnen #4030/R (D.KR 3400)
£469	$784	€685	Composition (43x57cm-17x22in) s.d.18 IX 48 Indian ink. 7-Oct-3 Rasmussen, Copenhagen #207 (D.KR 5000)
£508	$914	€742	Purple collage (76x56cm-30x22in) s.d.6-V-91 collage. 26-Apr-4 Bukowskis, Stockholm #243a/R (S.KR 7000)
£516	$862	€753	Composition (48x62cm-19x24in) s.d.18 IX 48 Indian ink lit.prov. 7-Oct-3 Rasmussen, Copenhagen #208/R (D.KR 5500)
£948	$1744	€1384	Composition (50x64cm-20x25in) s.d.28-V-59 gouache pencil prov. 29-Mar-4 Rasmussen, Copenhagen #371/R (D.KR 10500)

MORTEO, Ettore (1874-1939) Italian

£2536	$4159	€3500	Seascape. San Giacomo. Piccapietra Gate. View in Val Polcevera (36x28cm-14x11in) s. i.verso board four. 27-May-3 Finarte Semenzato, Milan #114/R est:1000-1200

MORTIER, Antoine (1908-1998) Belgian

£8000	$14640	€12000	Le partage (153x205cm-60x81in) s. d.1974 verso exhib. 7-Jun-4 Palais de Beaux Arts, Brussels #189/R est:12000-18000
Works on paper			
£594	$993	€850	Composition (26x35cm-10x14in) s.d.58 Indian ink. 13-Oct-3 Horta, Bruxelles #280
£1208	$2138	€1800	Nu (150x100cm-59x39in) s. chl paper on canvas. 27-Apr-4 Campo, Vlaamse Kaai #523 est:2000-2500
£2000	$3660	€3000	Composition (55x37cm-22x15in) s.d.51 gouache prov. 7-Jun-4 Palais de Beaux Arts, Brussels #136/R est:2000-3000
£4333	$7930	€6500	Composition (89x63cm-35x25in) s.d.56 gouache. 7-Jun-4 Palais de Beaux Arts, Brussels #342/R est:2500-3500

MORTIMER, Alexander (fl.1885-1895) British

£550	$919	€803	Scottish headland (61x106cm-24x42in) s.d.98. 12-Nov-3 Sotheby's, Olympia #68/R

MORTIMER, Geoffrey (1895-1986) British

£310	$499	€450	Gypsy trotting a horse by their caravans (18x25cm-7x10in) init. 15-Aug-3 Keys, Aylsham #568/R

MORTIMER, Geoffrey (attrib) (1895-1986) British

£270	$451	€394	Travellers (51x69cm-20x27in) bears false sig. after Sir Alfred J Munnings. 14-Oct-3 Bonhams, Ipswich #301

MORTIMER, John Hamilton (1740-1779) British

Works on paper			
£1800	$3330	€2628	Study relating the Drake Family (18x24cm-7x9in) pen ink wash. 10-Mar-4 Sotheby's, Olympia #25/R est:2000-3000

MORTIMER, Lewis (20th C) British

Works on paper			
£250	$418	€365	Horse and cart (30x36cm-12x14in) s. W/C. 14-Oct-3 David Lay, Penzance #502

£280 $484 €409 The Wharf, St Ives (24x34cm-9x13in) s. W/C. 11-Dec-3 Lane, Penzance #138
£310 $555 €453 St Ives (35x25cm-14x10in) s. W/C. 11-May-4 Dreweatt Neate, Newbury #453/R
£330 $531 €482 Dunsford village (25x36cm-10x14in) s. W/C. 14-Aug-3 Rendalls, Ashburton #1601

MORTON, Alastair (1910-1963) British
£260 $478 €380 Design for rug (40x65cm-16x26in) tempera i.verso panel prov. 23-Mar-4 Rosebery Fine Art, London #915

MORTON, Andrew (attrib) (1802-1845) British
£2200 $3894 €3212 Portrait of J Morris Esq sitting at his desk (124x99cm-49x39in) 28-Apr-4 Halls, Shrewsbury #551/R est:2000-3000

MORTON, Christina (20th C) American
£307 $500 €448 Woman with shawl (81x66cm-32x26in) s. 24-Sep-3 Doyle, New York #63
£2180 $3750 €3183 West Indian women on a dock (80x105cm-31x41in) s. 3-Dec-3 Doyle, New York #195/R est:3000-4000

MORTON, Constance (attrib) (c.1905-1992) British
£280 $442 €409 Evening harbour scene, probably Polperro (50x60cm-20x24in) s. 23-Jul-3 Hampton & Littlewood, Exeter #435/R

MORTON, Gary (1951-) American
Works on paper
£1676 $3000 €2447 Running out of rope fast (38x56cm-15x22in) gouache board. 15-May-4 Altermann Galleries, Santa Fe #110/R

MORTON, R (19th C) British
£2186 $4000 €3192 Duckwing. Prize game cock (43x53cm-17x21in) one s.d.1869 i.verso pair prov. 7-Apr-4 Sotheby's, New York #84/R est:2000-3000

MORTON, Ree (1936-) American
Works on paper
£1389 $2500 €2028 Untitled (14x10cm-6x4in) s.d.1970 graphite. 24-Apr-4 David Rago, Lambertville #263/R est:100-200
£1556 $2800 €2272 Untitled (10x16cm-4x6in) s.d.1968 col pencil. 24-Apr-4 David Rago, Lambertville #264/R est:100-200
£1944 $3500 €2838 Untitled (28x39cm-11x15in) chl W/C gouache. 24-Apr-4 David Rago, Lambertville #266/R est:250-500
£2500 $4500 €3650 Untitled. two s.d.1969 one s.d.1970 two s.d.1971 graphite one oil pastel 5. 24-Apr-4 David Rago, Lambertville #267/R est:300-600

MORTON, Thomas Corsan (1859-1928) British
£580 $916 €847 Figures on a road in a mountainous landscape (72x91cm-28x36in) d.1897 s.verso. 6-Sep-3 Shapes, Edinburgh #341/R
£1900 $2983 €2755 Shaded pasture (35x38cm-14x15in) s.d.1886. 27-Aug-3 Sotheby's, London #1028/R est:1000-1500
£2600 $4706 €3796 Woodland path at dusk. Homeward load (41x51cm-16x20in) one s.d.1900 one s. 19-Apr-4 Sotheby's, London #40/R est:2000-3000
£6400 $11712 €9344 Daffodils (26x20cm-10x8in) s.d.1888 panel. 8-Apr-4 Bonhams, Edinburgh #183/R est:800-1200

MORTON-JOHNSON, Francis (1878-1931) French
£503 $936 €750 Nature morte, Paris (50x65cm-20x26in) s.i.d.1909. 7-Mar-4 Livinec, Gaudcheau & Jezequel, Rennes #66
£839 $1401 €1200 Garden (38x46cm-15x18in) s. panel. 7-Oct-3 Livinec, Gaudcheau & Jezequel, Rennes #135/R
£979 $1635 €1400 Chaumiere (38x46cm-15x18in) s. panel. 7-Oct-3 Livinec, Gaudcheau & Jezequel, Rennes #136/R
£1511 $2478 €2100 Champs Elysees (38x46cm-15x18in) s. panel. 3-Jun-3 Livinec, Gaudcheau & Jezequel, Rennes #106/R
£2194 $3599 €3050 Fleurs, lilas (64x50cm-25x20in) s. cardboard. 3-Jun-3 Livinec, Gaudcheau & Jezequel, Rennes #105/R

MORVAN, Jean Jacques (1928-) French
£452 $769 €660 Le couple (92x65cm-36x26in) s.d.60. 19-Nov-3 Fischer, Luzern #226/R (S.FR 1000)
£592 $1089 €900 Vague en Bretagne (100x196cm-39x77in) s. i.d.1962 verso. 28-Jun-4 Joron-Derem, Paris #234

MORY, Louis (20th C) ?
£1135 $1895 €1600 Beaute orientale dans un interieur (100x80cm-39x31in) s.d.1940 panel. 16-Jun-3 Gros & Delettrez, Paris #570 est:1700-2500

MORZENTI, Natale (19th C) Italian
£3623 $5942 €5000 Card players (90x115cm-35x45in) 27-May-3 Finarte Semenzato, Milan #52/R est:5000-6000

MOSBACHER, Alois (1954-) Austrian
£909 $1564 €1300 Stones (122x100cm-48x39in) painted 1984 prov. 4-Dec-3 Van Ham, Cologne #335/R
£6711 $11879 €10000 Red cliff (180x130cm-71x51in) mono.d. lit. 28-Apr-4 Wiener Kunst Auktionen, Vienna #252/R est:10000-14000
£8333 $14167 €12000 Head (195x150cm-77x59in) s.d.83 jute exhib.lit. 28-Oct-3 Wiener Kunst Auktionen, Vienna #291/R est:12000-18000
Works on paper
£317 $555 €450 Hand in hand (61x42cm-24x17in) s. gouache. 19-Dec-3 Dorotheum, Vienna #369/R
£379 $694 €550 Figure seated in landscape (42x61cm-17x24in) s.d.82 gouache. 27-Jan-4 Dorotheum, Vienna #248/R
£423 $739 €600 Gardener 1 (49x35cm-19x14in) s.d.83 pencil W/C. 19-Dec-3 Dorotheum, Vienna #367/R
£805 $1490 €1200 Untitled (64x49cm-25x19in) s.d.83 mixed media. 9-Mar-4 Dorotheum, Vienna #205/R

MOSCONI, Lodovico (1928-) Italian
£345 $576 €500 Little Ordalia (39x51cm-15x20in) s. painted 1966. 17-Nov-3 Sant Agostino, Torino #151/R
£414 $691 €600 Untitled (80x60cm-31x24in) s.d.1962 s.d.verso. 17-Nov-3 Sant Agostino, Torino #162/R

MOSEBEKK, Olav (1910-2001) Norwegian
£407 $748 €611 Lovers (50x70cm-20x28in) s. 14-Jun-4 Blomqvist, Lysaker #1271/R (N.KR 5000)
Works on paper
£489 $876 €714 Seated woman (82x58cm-32x23in) s.indis.d.1953 chl. 25-May-4 Grev Wedels Plass, Oslo #110/R (N.KR 6000)

MOSELEY, R (?) American
£659 $1100 €962 Adobe with chili peppers (41x51cm-16x20in) 18-Oct-3 David Dike, Dallas #325/R

MOSELEY, R S (fl.1862-1893) British
£2000 $3400 €2920 Guide dog (34x40cm-13x16in) s.d.1867 board. 27-Nov-3 Christie's, Kensington #317/R est:2000-3000
£2210 $4000 €3227 Study of head of the celebrated wire haired terrier, Go Bank (20x25cm-8x10in) s.i.d.02 i.verso. 30-Mar-4 Bonhams & Butterfields, San Francisco #137/R est:1200-1800

MOSELEY, Richard S (fl.1862-1893) British
Works on paper
£850 $1556 €1241 Prize Pomeranian (19x26cm-7x10in) s.d.1879 W/C. 7-Apr-4 Dreweatt Neate, Newbury #36

MOSENGEL, Adolf (1837-1885) German
£849 $1494 €1240 Landscape (21x36cm-8x14in) s. 23-May-4 Agra, Warsaw #39/R (P.Z 6000)
£1208 $2211 €1800 View of Lake Grundel (70x117cm-28x46in) s. i.verso stretcher panel. 9-Jul-4 Dawo, Saarbrucken #46/R est:1800

MOSER, Frank H (1886-1964) American
£326 $600 €476 Late fall (30x41cm-12x16in) s.i.d. 1943 s.verso canvas on board. 25-Mar-4 Doyle, New York #46
£516 $950 €753 House in winter (41x51cm-16x20in) s. canvas on board. 25-Mar-4 Doyle, New York #49/R
£543 $1000 €793 Sand dunes, Provincetown, Massachusetts (23x30cm-9x12in) s.i.d.August 1936 s.verso canvas on board. 25-Mar-4 Doyle, New York #47/R est:800-1200
£924 $1700 €1349 View of the valley (41x51cm-16x20in) canvas on board. 25-Mar-4 Doyle, New York #48/R est:800-1200

MOSER, Julius (attrib) (1808-?) German
£1119 $1924 €1600 Man kneeling surrounded by other figures (77x108cm-30x43in) i.d.1874. 5-Dec-3 Michael Zeller, Lindau #734/R est:1500

MOSER, Karl (younger) (1873-1939) Austrian
£6993 $11888 €10000 Dairymaid (55x61cm-22x24in) s.d.05. 27-Nov-3 Dorotheum, Linz #433/R est:2400-3000
Prints
£3000 $5400 €4500 Tyrolean peasant girl (38x26cm-15x10in) s.i.d.1922 col woodcut. 21-Apr-4 Dorotheum, Vienna #9/R est:2400-3000

MOSER, Kolo (1868-1918) Austrian
£2797 $4755 €4000 Part of the forest (28x34cm-11x13in) mono. board prov. 28-Nov-3 Wiener Kunst Auktionen, Vienna #554/R est:4000-12000
£4545 $7727 €6500 Portrait of a young lady (22x28cm-9x11in) prov. 28-Nov-3 Wiener Kunst Auktionen, Vienna #555/R est:1500-3000
£4861 $8264 €7000 Landscape (33x28cm-13x11in) board lit. 28-Oct-3 Wiener Kunst Auktionen, Vienna #55/R est:4000-10000
£6000 $10920 €8760 Wooded hill (27x34cm-11x13in) s. board prov. 15-Jun-4 Sotheby's, London #60/R est:6000-8000
£10738 $19007 €16000 Karl Moll in chair (75x98cm-30x39in) 28-Apr-4 Wiener Kunst Auktionen, Vienna #103/R est:10000-20000
£15385 $26154 €22000 Two figures (34x28cm-13x11in) mono. board prov. 28-Nov-3 Wiener Kunst Auktionen, Vienna #558/R est:5000-12000
£22000 $40040 €32120 Wooded landscape (46x58cm-18x23in) s. prov. 15-Jun-4 Sotheby's, London #62/R est:15000-25000
£23077 $39231 €33000 Nude (32x32cm-13x13in) prov. 28-Nov-3 Wiener Kunst Auktionen, Vienna #556/R est:3000-15000
£27972 $47552 €40000 Landscape (29x33cm-11x13in) canvas on board prov. 28-Nov-3 Wiener Kunst Auktionen, Vienna #559/R est:7000-30000
£35000 $63700 €51100 Weiblicher Akt (34x28cm-13x11in) init. board prov. 3-Feb-4 Christie's, London #177/R est:8000-12000
£40000 $72800 €58400 Bluhende Blumen am Gartenzaun (100x100cm-39x39in) s. prov. 3-Feb-4 Christie's, London #173/R est:10000-15000
£46980 $84094 €70000 The source - lying in a grotto (37x50cm-15x20in) mono. prov. 25-May-4 Dorotheum, Vienna #10/R est:22000-30000
£48000 $87360 €70080 Weiblicher Akt mit blauem Schal (100x50cm-39x20in) s.d.1913 prov. 3-Feb-4 Christie's, London #174/R est:20000-30000
£48000 $87360 €70080 Landschaft bei Semmering (36x48cm-14x19in) canvasboard prov. 3-Feb-4 Christie's, London #176/R est:15000-20000
£65000 $118300 €94900 Geranien (100x100cm-39x39in) indis.s.d. s.i. stretcher prov. 3-Feb-4 Christie's, London #172/R est:15000-20000
£92486 $160000 €135030 Standing nude with blue robe (100x50cm-39x20in) mono. prov.exhib.lit. 11-Dec-3 Sotheby's, New York #168/R est:100000-150000

£150000 $273000 €219000 Die drei Grazien (100x100cm-39x39in) mono. prov. 3-Feb-4 Christie's, London #175/R est:80000-120000
Works on paper
£448 $820 €650 Ditz (16x9cm-6x4in) i.d.Juli 1914 chk W/C. 27-Jan-4 Dorotheum, Vienna #4/R
£1119 $1902 €1600 Ex libris for Fritz Waerndorfer (14x14cm-6x6in) s. s. verso Indian ink lit. 27-Nov-3 Wiener Kunst Auktionen, Vienna #267/R est:1600-2000
£1517 $2777 €2200 Girl in flower meadow (24x19cm-9x7in) d.30.6.12 col chk. 27-Jan-4 Dorotheum, Vienna #1/R est:1200-1800
£4138 $6910 €6000 Sketch for room arrangement (32x48cm-13x19in) pencil lit. 12-Nov-3 Dorotheum, Vienna #42/R est:6000-7000
£4196 $7133 €6000 God and angel (22x20cm-9x8in) mixed media prov. 28-Nov-3 Wiener Kunst Auktionen, Vienna #557/R est:2000-10000

MOSER, Lida (20th C) American
Photographs
£1693 $3200 €2472 From a window on Central Park West (18x20cm-7x8in) s.i.d.1955 gelatin silver print. 17-Feb-4 Christie's, Rockefeller NY #208/R est:1500-2000

MOSER, Nikolaus (1956-) Austrian
£1034 $1893 €1500 Untitled (41x41cm-16x16in) s.d.2000 verso. 27-Jan-4 Dorotheum, Vienna #261/R est:1500-2000
£1049 $1783 €1500 Untitled (50x50cm-20x20in) s.d.93 verso. 26-Nov-3 Dorotheum, Vienna #326/R est:1500-2000
£2345 $4291 €3400 Untitled (130x130cm-51x51in) s.d.1996 verso. 27-Jan-4 Dorotheum, Vienna #271/R est:2800-5000
£2517 $4280 €3600 Untitled (120x120cm-47x47in) s.d.1995 verso. 26-Nov-3 Dorotheum, Vienna #344/R est:3600-5000

MOSER, Olga (19/20th C) German?
£1300 $2457 €1898 Ancient artifacts, books and a candlestick on draped table (90x110cm-35x43in) i. 19-Feb-4 Christie's, Kensington #299/R est:1500-2000

MOSER, Richard (1874-?) Austrian
Works on paper
£371 $637 €530 Church interior (47x37cm-19x15in) s.i.d.1917 W/C. 5-Dec-3 Michael Zeller, Lindau #735/R
£800 $1440 €1200 Figures by a gateway, Vienna (25x18cm-10x7in) s.i.d.1909 pencil W/C htd white. 21-Apr-4 Christie's, Amsterdam #59/R
£1172 $1946 €1700 Backyard in old Vienna (26x19cm-10x7in) s.d.1929 W/C. 30-Sep-3 Dorotheum, Vienna #289/R est:1200-1400
£1379 $2290 €2000 Flowers in backyard in old Vienna (28x22cm-11x9in) s.d.1918 W/C. 30-Sep-3 Dorotheum, Vienna #290/R est:1200-15000
£4362 $7809 €6500 Vienna, in the courtyard (29x20cm-11x8in) s.i.d.1915 W/C lit. 27-May-4 Hassfurther, Vienna #62/R est:4000-6000

MOSER, Wilfried (1914-1997) Swiss
£860 $1462 €1256 Les coconel (26x30cm-10x12in) s.i. oilstick paper. 22-Nov-3 Burkhard, Luzern #10/R (S.FR 1900)
£950 $1615 €1387 Study for a sculpture (35x26cm-14x10in) d.4/11/69 oilstick paper. 22-Nov-3 Burkhard, Luzern #9/R (S.FR 2100)
£1026 $1815 €1498 Sarai (41x27cm-16x11in) s. prov. 27-Apr-4 AB Stockholms Auktionsverk #1192/R (S.KR 14000)
£3275 $5862 €4782 Composition (73x92cm-29x36in) s.d.1955. 26-May-4 Sotheby's, Zurich #149/R est:6000-8000 (S.FR 7500)
£4072 $7045 €5945 Voyage au bout de la nuit (73x91cm-29x36in) s. paper on canvas. 9-Dec-3 Sotheby's, Zurich #130/R est:7000-9000 (S.FR 9000)
Sculpture
£13453 $21928 €19641 Sculpture (37x21x11cm-15x8x4in) synthetic. 29-Sep-3 Christie's, Zurich #102/R est:10000-15000 (S.FR 30000)
Works on paper
£655 $1172 €956 Composition (31x37cm-12x15in) s. mixed media. 26-May-4 Sotheby's, Zurich #154/R (S.FR 1500)
£780 $1302 €1131 Charcuterie (20x26cm-8x10in) s. col chks. 19-Jun-3 Kornfeld, Bern #740 est:2000 (S.FR 1700)

MOSES, Anna Mary Robertson (Grandma) (1860-1961) American
£12784 $22500 €18665 July harvest time (25x36cm-10x14in) s. board painted 1945 prov.lit. 19-May-4 Sotheby's, New York #190/R est:15000-25000
£17442 $30000 €25465 Winter landscape (25x30cm-10x12in) s. masonite prov. 3-Dec-3 Sotheby's, New York #169/R est:15000-25000
£17442 $30000 €25465 Springtime landscape (25x30cm-10x12in) s. masonite prov. 3-Dec-3 Sotheby's, New York #170/R est:12000-18000
£20349 $35000 €29710 Belvedere (56x67cm-22x26in) s.i.d.1890 tempera masonite prov.lit. 4-Dec-3 Christie's, Rockefeller NY #105/R est:40000-60000
£22754 $38000 €33221 Come on Old Topsy (46x56cm-18x22in) s. d.Feb. 16 1948 verso prov. 23-Oct-3 Shannon's, Milford #104/R est:30000-50000
£28409 $50000 €41477 Old Oaken Bucket (45x60cm-18x24in) s. masonite prov.lit. 18-May-4 Christie's, Rockefeller NY #147/R est:40000-60000

MOSES, Ed (1926-) American
£3297 $6000 €4814 Untitled (152x122cm-60x48in) init.d.81-85 panel prov. 29-Jun-4 Sotheby's, New York #570/R est:8000-12000
£3297 $6000 €4814 Untitled (203x168cm-80x66in) s.verso oil dispersion paint prov. 29-Jun-4 Sotheby's, New York #591/R est:8000-12000
£6486 $12000 €9470 Untitled (168x198cm-66x78in) init.d.87 verso acrylic asphaltum prov.exhib. 12-Feb-4 Sotheby's, New York #294/R est:3000-4000
Works on paper
£1135 $2100 €1657 Untitled (71x56cm-28x22in) ink prov. 13-Jul-4 Christie's, Rockefeller NY #48/R est:1000-1500
£1902 $3500 €2853 Untitled (140x157cm-55x62in) encaustic exec.c.1973 prov. 10-Jun-4 Phillips, New York #581/R est:3500-4500

MOSES, Forrest K (1893-1974) American
£1796 $3000 €2622 School Recess (46x61cm-18x24in) s.d.1971 masonite. 23-Oct-3 Shannon's, Milford #219/R est:3000-5000

MOSES, Forrest Lee (jnr) (1934) American
£223 $400 €326 Untitled no.310. s. 13-May-4 Dallas Auction Gallery, Dallas #24/R
£307 $550 €448 Untitled no.534 (122x168cm-48x66in) 13-May-4 Dallas Auction Gallery, Dallas #303/R
£1536 $2750 €2243 Rock. i. 13-May-4 Dallas Auction Gallery, Dallas #127/R est:1500-2500
£2095 $3750 €3059 Shenandoah no.3. i. 13-May-4 Dallas Auction Gallery, Dallas #192/R est:2000-4000
£2374 $4250 €3466 Shenandoah no.2. i. 13-May-4 Dallas Auction Gallery, Dallas #280/R est:2000-4000

MOSES, Jacqueline (20th C) American
£301 $550 €452 Turmoil (127x127cm-50x50in) 10-Jul-4 Hindman, Chicago #358/R

MOSHER, Kirsten (20th C) ?
Works on paper
£699 $1189 €1000 Border control (38x30cm-15x12in) s. dr exhib. 27-Nov-3 Calmels Cohen, Paris #103/R

MOSKOVITZ OF SAFED, Shalom (1885-1980) Israeli
£2596 $4750 €3790 Jacob and his property (49x34cm-19x13in) s. tempera on paper. 1-Jun-4 Ben-Ami, Tel Aviv #4902/R est:5000-6000

MOSKOWITZ, Ira (1912-1985) American
£1988 $3200 €2902 Taos Indian deer dance (102x127cm-40x50in) 22-Aug-3 Altermann Galleries, Santa Fe #203

MOSLER, Henry (1841-1920) American
£279 $475 €407 Kitchen chores, interior genre scene (36x29cm-14x11in) s.d.1913. 21-Nov-3 Skinner, Boston #278/R
£994 $1800 €1451 View of the Venetian Lagoon at dusk (18x27cm-7x11in) s.d.92 panel. 30-Mar-4 Christie's, Rockefeller NY #135/R est:800-1200
£2286 $4000 €3338 Thinking of the absent ones (96x129cm-38x51in) s. 19-Dec-3 Sotheby's, New York #1108/R est:4000-6000

MOSLEY, William Edwin (19/20th C) British?
Works on paper
£760 $1368 €1110 Three children playing by a stream (26x19cm-10x7in) s.d.1913 pencil W/C htd white. 22-Apr-4 Mellors & Kirk, Nottingham #1040/R

MOSMAN, William (c.1700-1771) British
£2469 $4000 €3605 Portrait of Eupheme Erskine Boswell (84x69cm-33x27in) s.d.1742. 2-Aug-3 Neal Auction Company, New Orleans #234/R est:4000-6000

MOSNER, Ricardo (1948-) Argentinian
Works on paper
£600 $1092 €900 Trainer (30x20cm-12x8in) s.i. mixed media exec.1988 prov. 2-Jul-4 Binoche, Paris #1/R

MOSQUERA, Gustava (20th C) Ecuadorian
£240 $400 €350 Fruit and horses (41x61cm-16x24in) s.d. acrylic. 11-Oct-3 Nadeau, Windsor #68/R

MOSQUERA, Luis (1899-1987) Spanish
£2483 $4121 €3600 Still life with coal (42x50cm-17x20in) s.d.1940 lit. 30-Sep-3 Ansorena, Madrid #100/R est:3600
£2685 $4805 €4000 Still life with onions (26x34cm-10x13in) s. 25-May-4 Durán, Madrid #105/R est:900
£4795 $8151 €7000 Vase with roses (80x60cm-31x24in) s. board lit. 4-Nov-3 Ansorena, Madrid #92/R est:6000

MOSS, Charles Eugène (1860-1901) Canadian
£804 $1382 €1174 Harvest time (45x76cm-18x30in) s. 2-Dec-3 Joyner Waddington, Toronto #488 est:2000-2500 (C.D 1800)

MOSS, Henry William (fl.1885-1938) Irish
£2042 $3268 €2900 Watering place (51x61cm-20x24in) s.d.1913 exhib. 16-Sep-3 Whyte's, Dublin #163/R est:2000-3000

MOSS, Irene (20th C) American
£853 $1500 €1245 Focus 9 (127x127cm-50x50in) acrylic painted 1969 prov. 23-May-4 Hindman, Chicago #1000/R est:1500-2500

MOSS, Rod (1948-) Australian
Works on paper
£909 $1682 €1327 Charles Creek Horse Yard (121x277cm-48x109in) i.d.1995 stretcher graphite synthetic polymer paper on canvas dip. 15-Mar-4 Sotheby's, Melbourne #125 est:2000-4000 (A.D 2200)

MOSS, Sidney Dennant (1884-1946) British
£480 $888 €701 An English lane (50x67cm-20x26in) s.d.36. 16-Feb-4 Bonhams, Bath #133

MOSSA, Alexis (1844-1926) French
Works on paper
£333 $603 €500 Carnaval de Nice (12x20cm-5x8in) W/C exec. 1875. 30-Mar-4 Gioffredo, Nice #145/R

MOSSA, Giovanni Maria (1896-1973) Italian
£814 $1400 €1188 Ladies in the field (43x61cm-17x24in) s. 7-Dec-3 Grogan, Boston #22/R

MOSSA, Gustave Adolf (1883-1971) French
£507 $907 €750 Une maison a la campagne (30x44cm-12x17in) s. paper on cardboard. 7-May-4 Millon & Associes, Paris #69
£507 $907 €750 Paysage (30x44cm-12x17in) s. paper on cardboard. 7-May-4 Millon & Associes, Paris #71
Works on paper
£267 $483 €400 Belgica (45x26cm-18x10in) i. ink black crayon. 30-Mar-4 Rossini, Paris #824/R
£450 $765 €657 Loge (15x18cm-6x7in) st.sig. W/C pen ink over print. 18-Nov-3 Sotheby's, London #394/R
£553 $1002 €830 La revue des folies ye-ye (20x26cm-8x10in) studio.st ink W/C. 30-Mar-4 Gioffredo, Nice #362
£900 $1530 €1314 Colombine et Polichinel (18x17cm-7x7in) st.sig. W/C pen ink over print. 18-Nov-3 Sotheby's, London #391/R
£1600 $2720 €2336 Femme et faune (30x19cm-12x7in) s.i.d.1914 W/C pen ink gouache over pencil. 18-Nov-3 Sotheby's, London #370/R
£1600 $2720 €2336 Visions de la guerre (41x27cm-16x11in) s.d.1918 W/C pencil gouache htd gold lit. 18-Nov-3 Sotheby's, London #387/R
£1800 $3060 €2628 Couple endormi (29x19cm-11x7in) s.d.1914 W/C gouache ink pen over pencil. 18-Nov-3 Sotheby's, London #371/R
£1800 $3060 €2628 Junon (20x12cm-8x5in) s.i.d.MCMIV W/C pen ink over pencil prov.lit. 18-Nov-3 Sotheby's, London #390/R
£1800 $3060 €2628 Venus et Vulcain (37x21cm-15x8in) s.i.d.MCMIV W/C gouache pen ink over pencil. 18-Nov-3 Sotheby's, London #389/R
£2500 $4250 €3650 Pasiphae (20x36cm-8x14in) s.i.d.MCMVII W/C pen ink over pencil prov.lit. 18-Nov-3 Sotheby's, London #382/R
£2500 $4250 €3650 Sebastien martyr (44x30cm-17x12in) s.d.MCMVII W/C pen ink gouache over pencil prov.lit. 18-Nov-3 Sotheby's, London #384/R
£3000 $5100 €4380 Putiphar (19x37cm-7x15in) s.i.d.MCMIV W/C pen ink over pencil prov.lit. 18-Nov-3 Sotheby's, London #385/R
£3468 $6000 €5063 La mort d'adonis (27x46cm-11x18in) s.i. pencil W/C. 11-Dec-3 Sotheby's, New York #180/R est:6000-8000
£3600 $6120 €5256 Errante (37x22cm-15x9in) i. W/C ink pen over pencil. 18-Nov-3 Sotheby's, London #364/R
£3600 $6120 €5256 Dogaresse (48x30cm-19x12in) s.d.1911 W/C pen ink over pencil. 18-Nov-3 Sotheby's, London #363/R
£4800 $8160 €7008 Gorgone (30x46cm-12x18in) s.d.1917 W/C pen ink gouache over pencil lit. 18-Nov-3 Sotheby's, London #381/R
£6300 $10710 €9198 Fin de Danae (53x31cm-21x12in) s.i. pen ink W/C gouache over pencil prov.exhib. 18-Nov-3 Sotheby's, London #360/R
£6300 $10710 €9198 Resurrection (53x32cm-21x13in) s.i.d.MCMVII W/C pen ink gouache prov.exhib.lit. 18-Nov-3 Sotheby's, London #376/R
£6300 $10710 €9198 Vice (46x31cm-18x12in) s.i.d.MCMVII W/C pen ink over pencil prov.exhib.lit. 18-Nov-3 Sotheby's, London #386/R
£6500 $11050 €9490 Manon (46x30cm-18x12in) s.i.d.MCMVII pen ink W/C htd gouache gold prov.exhib.lit. 18-Nov-3 Sotheby's, London #365/R
£6800 $11560 €9928 Union (46x28cm-18x11in) s.i.d.1913 W/C gouache pen ink wash over pencil prov.exhib.lit. 18-Nov-3 Sotheby's, London #362/R
£7000 $11900 €10220 Dans la penombre (36x28cm-14x11in) s.i.d.1914 W/C gouache pen ink htd gold over pencil prov.lit. 18-Nov-3 Sotheby's, London #361/R
£7000 $11900 €10220 Loge (32x42cm-13x17in) s. W/C pen ink gouache over pencil prov.lit. 18-Nov-3 Sotheby's, London #393/R
£7200 $12240 €10512 Oedipus et le shinx (46x27cm-18x11in) s.i.d.1909 W/C pen ink gouache. 18-Nov-3 Sotheby's, London #379/R
£7500 $12750 €10950 Suzanne et les vieillards (37x56cm-15x22in) s.i.d.MCMVI W/C pen ink gouache over pencil prov.exhib.lit. 18-Nov-3 Sotheby's, London #359/R
£7500 $12750 €10950 Vierge aux lys rouges (48x29cm-19x11in) s.i.d.MCMVII W/C pen ink pencil gouache. 18-Nov-3 Sotheby's, London #374/R
£8000 $13600 €11680 Leda (49x30cm-19x12in) s.i.d.MCMVII W/C pen ink wash over pencil. 18-Nov-3 Sotheby's, London #368/R
£8000 $13600 €11680 Gretchen dans la cathedrale (29x46cm-11x18in) s.i.d.1913 W/C pen ink gouache. 18-Nov-3 Sotheby's, London #378/R
£8000 $13600 €11680 Perseus (48x29cm-19x11in) s.i.d.MCMVII W/C pen ink gouache over pencil prov.lit. 18-Nov-3 Sotheby's, London #380/R
£9500 $16150 €13870 Salome (49x30cm-19x12in) s.i.d.1908 W/C pen ink wash gouache over pencil prov.lit. 18-Nov-3 Sotheby's, London #358/R
£11000 $18700 €16060 Roses, lys et colombes (30x46cm-12x18in) s.i.d.1913 W/C brush pen ink over pencil lit. 18-Nov-3 Sotheby's, London #283/R
£13000 $22100 €18980 Guillaume et la Sarazine (40x27cm-16x11in) s.d.1913 W/C gouache pen ink over pencil prov.lit. 18-Nov-3 Sotheby's, London #367/R
£14000 $23800 €20440 Faust au jardine de Gretchen (46x27cm-18x11in) s.i.d.1913 W/C pen ink gouache over pencil prov.exhib.lit. 18-Nov-3 Sotheby's, London #366/R
£15000 $25500 €21900 Sphynges (48x35cm-19x14in) s.i.d.MCMVI W/C pencil pen ink gouache prov.exhib.lit. 18-Nov-3 Sotheby's, London #375/R

MOSSCHER, Jacob van (16/17th C) Dutch
£10056 $18000 €14682 River landscape with figures fishing in the distance (34x45cm-13x18in) s. panel. 27-May-4 Sotheby's, New York #108/R est:20000-30000

MOSSEL, Julius (1871-?) German
£818 $1300 €1194 Golden Buddha (74x84cm-29x33in) s. 12-Sep-3 Skinner, Boston #329/R

MOSSELVELD, Jos (1942-) Dutch
£294 $499 €420 Groot root (100x122cm-39x48in) s.d.99 panel. 24-Nov-3 Glerum, Amsterdam #235/R

MOSSET, Olivier (1944-) Swiss
£2867 $5246 €4300 Untitled - monochrome vert (61x61cm-24x24in) s.d.1980 dispersion oil acrylic. 4-Jun-4 Lempertz, Koln #315/R est:2600
£5333 $9813 €8000 Penta (210x200cm-83x79in) acrylic painted 1987 prov. 8-Jun-4 Artcurial Briest, Paris #281/R est:8000-10000
£5369 $9503 €8000 Untitled (96x96cm-38x38in) acrylic painted c.1970. 28-Apr-4 Artcurial Briest, Paris #380/R est:8000-10000
£6597 $10424 €9500 Untitled (100x100cm-39x39in) s.verso prov. 27-Apr-3 Versailles Encheres #114
£7333 $13493 €11000 Untitled (100x100cm-39x39in) s. verso acrylic painted c.1970 prov.lit. 8-Jun-4 Artcurial Briest, Paris #279/R est:8000-12000
£7333 $13493 €11000 Composition (100x100cm-39x39in) s. verso acrylic painted c.1970 prov.lit. 8-Jun-4 Artcurial Briest, Paris #280/R est:8000-12000
£7747 $13402 €11000 Untitled (100x100cm-39x39in) s.d.70 verso acrylic exhib. 9-Dec-3 Artcurial Briest, Paris #429/R est:8000-12000
£9028 $14896 €13000 Sans titre, O (100x100cm-39x39in) acrylic paint prov. 2-Jul-3 Cornette de St.Cyr, Paris #182/R est:10000-12000
£9731 $17905 €14500 Untitled (100x100cm-39x39in) acrylic painted 1970. 29-Mar-4 Cornette de St.Cyr, Paris #35/R est:12000-15000

MOSSMER, Raimund (1813-1874) Austrian
Works on paper
£604 $1111 €900 Hinterstoder (32x47cm-13x19in) s.d.1870 W/C. 26-Mar-4 Dorotheum, Vienna #218/R
£1141 $2099 €1700 Modling (17x27cm-7x11in) s. W/C. 26-Mar-4 Dorotheum, Vienna #181/R est:1600-1800

MOST, Ludwig August (1807-1883) German
£10423 $18656 €14800 Getting dressed for the first church visit (52x63cm-20x25in) s.d.1853 lit. 8-Jan-4 Allgauer, Kempten #2470/R est:7000

MOSTAERT, Gillis (elder) (1534-1598) Flemish
£2333 $4177 €3500 Fowler and wife (17x14cm-7x6in) panel. 17-May-4 Glerum, Amsterdam #59/R est:4000-6000

MOSTAERT, Jan (attrib) (1475-1555) Dutch
£39474 $72632 €60000 Portrait de gentilhomme en buste tenant fleur (49x34cm-19x13in) panel prov.exhib.lit. 24-Jun-4 Christie's, Paris #7/R est:30000-40000

MOSTAERT, Jan (circle) (1475-1555) Dutch
£5556 $10000 €8112 Christ in limbo blessing the Virgin (11x9cm-4x4in) panel prov. 23-Jan-4 Christie's, Rockefeller NY #111/R est:2000-3000

MOSTBOCK, Karl (1921-) Austrian
£350 $594 €500 Landscape (53x67cm-21x26in) s.d.1948 board. 27-Nov-3 Dorotheum, Linz #458/R

MOSTL, Alois (1843-?) Austrian
£755 $1200 €1102 Horn player (44x35cm-17x14in) s.d.1865. 12-Sep-3 Skinner, Boston #221/R

MOSTYN OWEN, Frances (c.1810-?) British
£1900 $3458 €2774 Madonna and Child (44x33cm-17x13in) i.d.1844 after Federico Barocci. 21-Jun-4 Christie's, London #59/R est:800-1200
£2400 $4368 €3504 Salome with the head of John the Baptist (74x96cm-29x38in) after Guido Reni. 21-Jun-4 Christie's, London #60/R est:3000-4000
£3200 $5824 €4672 Lovers (56x75cm-22x30in) i. after Dossi Dossi. 21-Jun-4 Christie's, London #58/R est:2000-3000

MOSTYN, T (1864-1930) British
£1250 $2163 €1825 Lane to the Sea (39x59cm-15x23in) s. 10-Dec-3 Rupert Toovey, Partridge Green #110/R est:1200-1800

MOSTYN, Tom (1864-1930) British
£320 $534 €467 Haystacks (28x39cm-11x15in) s. 16-Oct-3 Christie's, Kensington #237
£800 $1376 €1168 Two children by a lake in a farmyard (40x55cm-16x22in) s. 3-Dec-3 Christie's, Kensington #499/R
£800 $1432 €1168 Spring (51x69cm-20x27in) s. 26-May-4 Sotheby's, Olympia #112/R
£900 $1638 €1314 Figures in a garden (50x60cm-20x24in) 15-Jun-4 Bonhams, Knightsbridge #6/R
£1200 $2004 €1752 Garden and woodland scene (100x103cm-39x41in) 27-Jun-3 Bigwood, Stratford on Avon #314 est:1200-1500
£1400 $2338 €2044 Enchanted garden (51x68cm-20x27in) s. 16-Oct-3 Christie's, Kensington #384/R est:1500-2000
£2500 $4475 €3650 Portrait of a seated girl, wearing a turquoise dress, vase of flower on a table (91x71cm-36x28in) s. 27-May-4 Christie's, Kensington #111/R est:3000-4000
£3200 $5056 €4640 Portrait of a lady in a cream dress and bonnet (79x66cm-31x26in) s. oval. 4-Sep-3 Christie's, Kensington #74/R est:2000-3000
£3500 $5530 €5075 Portrait of a lady in a green dress, holding a parasol (76x66cm-30x26in) s. oval. 4-Sep-3 Christie's, Kensington #72/R est:2000-3000
£3600 $6696 €5256 Opera (51x69cm-20x27in) s. 4-Mar-4 Christie's, Kensington #655/R est:800-1200
£5000 $9300 €7300 In perpetuum, Lo-Ki (51x69cm-20x27in) s.i.d.1924. 4-Mar-4 Christie's, Kensington #654/R est:2000-3000
£7800 $13962 €11388 Dartmouth (76x102cm-30x40in) s. prov. 27-May-4 Christie's, Kensington #236/R est:4000-6000
£22000 $40920 €32120 Golden island (178x269cm-70x106in) s. 4-Mar-4 Christie's, Kensington #656/R est:4000-6000
£30000 $47400 €43500 Flower market (127x178cm-50x70in) s.d.1920/21. 4-Sep-3 Christie's, Kensington #299/R est:7000-10000
£34000 $53720 €49300 Portrait of a lady in a green and gold dress (102x86cm-40x34in) s. 4-Sep-3 Christie's, Kensington #71/R est:3000-5000
Works on paper
£1000 $1720 €1460 Children playing in a village street (28x44cm-11x17in) s.d.1903 pencil W/C htd white. 4-Dec-3 Mellors & Kirk, Nottingham #844/R est:1000-1500

MOSWITZER, Gerhard (1940-) Austrian
Sculpture
£2394 $4190 €3400 A 31-68, from the King series (47cm-19in) mono. num.2/12 welded metal. 19-Dec-3 Dorotheum, Vienna #242/R est:2000-3200

MOTA Y MORALES, Vicente (19/20th C) Spanish
£290 $475 €400 Bodegon (28x35cm-11x14in) s. 27-May-3 Durán, Madrid #34/R
£290 $475 €400 Still life (28x35cm-11x14in) s. 27-May-3 Durán, Madrid #35/R
£317 $548 €450 Landscape with goats (23x32cm-9x13in) s. board. 10-Dec-3 Castellana, Madrid #230/R

MOTE, George William (1832-1909) British
£567 $1037 €850 English summer landscape with sheep (41x61cm-16x24in) s. 5-Jun-4 Arnold, Frankfurt #680/R
£854 $1400 €1238 Hindhead, Surrey, mountain vista landscape with figures (61x91cm-24x36in) s. canvas over board. 4-Jun-3 Alderfer's, Hatfield #247/R est:1200-1500
£919 $1700 €1342 Extensive country landscape with cattle and a cottage farm (61x91cm-24x36in) s.d.1878. 17-Jul-4 New Orleans Auction, New Orleans #235/R est:2500-4000
£2700 $4644 €3942 Feeding the chickens (55x77cm-22x30in) s.d.1866. 4-Dec-3 Mellors & Kirk, Nottingham #929/R est:2500-3500

MOTHERSOLE, Jessie (fl.1901-1914) British
Works on paper
£480 $802 €701 Angelic inspiration (72x52cm-28x20in) s.d.1913 W/C. 14-Oct-3 Bonhams, Knightsbridge #153/R

MOTHERWELL, Robert (1915-1991) American
£16760 $30000 €24470 Drunk with turpentine (56x76cm-22x30in) s.d.June 79 paper prov.exhib. 13-May-4 Sotheby's, New York #200/R est:20000-30000
£28443 $47500 €41527 Gauloises with scarlet no 1 (51x41cm-20x16in) init.d.72 s.i.d.19 June 1972 verso acrylic collage board prov. 13-Nov-3 Sotheby's, New York #188/R est:20000-30000
£33520 $60000 €48939 Gypsy collage 4 (107x71cm-42x28in) init.d.82 acrylic collage board on cardboard prov.exhib.lit. 13-May-4 Sotheby's, New York #204/R est:30000-40000
£38922 $65000 €56826 Bust of Stravinsky (122x91cm-48x36in) init.d.75 i.verso acrylic paper collage canvas on panel prov. 13-Nov-3 Sotheby's, New York #246/R est:30000-40000
£44693 $80000 €65252 Baltic Sea bride II (122x91cm-48x36in) s.d.20 March 74 acrylic paper collage Upsom board prov.exhib.lit. 13-May-4 Sotheby's, New York #205/R est:40000-60000
£47486 $85000 €69330 Elegy for the Spanish Republic XXX (20x25cm-8x10in) s.i.d.1953 verso canvasboard prov. 13-May-4 Sotheby's, New York #111/R est:50000-70000
£94972 $170000 €138659 Bete Noire (203x126cm-80x50in) s.d.73 s.i.d.1 Dec 73 verso acrylic prov. 13-May-4 Sotheby's, New York #195/R est:120000-180000
Prints
£1519 $2750 €2218 From Africa Suite (103x72cm-41x28in) init.num.52/150 black cream silkscreen. 19-Apr-4 Bonhams & Butterfields, San Francisco #285/R est:800-1200
£1622 $3000 €2368 America-La France variations II (106x65cm-42x26in) s.num.X/XVIII col lithograph collage. 12-Feb-4 Christie's, Rockefeller NY #149/R est:2500-3500
£1765 $3000 €2577 Monster (104x80cm-41x31in) init. lithograph. 31-Oct-3 Sotheby's, New York #679/R
£1765 $3000 €2577 Saint Michael I (160x65cm-63x26in) init. screenprint lithograph monoprint. 31-Oct-3 Sotheby's, New York #683/R
£1765 $3000 €2577 America-La France (122x78cm-48x31in) s. col lithograph collage. 31-Oct-3 Sotheby's, New York #692/R
£1765 $3000 €2577 America-La France (116x74cm-46x29in) s. col lithograph collage. 31-Oct-3 Sotheby's, New York #691/R
£1765 $3000 €2577 America-La France (133x92cm-52x36in) s. col lithograph collage. 31-Oct-3 Sotheby's, New York #696/R
£1765 $3000 €2577 America-La France (117x79cm-46x31in) s. col lithograph collage. 31-Oct-3 Sotheby's, New York #694/R
£1765 $3000 €2577 Blackened sun (104x75cm-41x30in) s. etching aquatint. 4-Nov-3 Christie's, Rockefeller NY #313/R est:2500-3500
£1836 $3250 €2681 Automatism a (65x53cm-26x21in) s. num.55/100 lithograph. 30-Apr-4 Sotheby's, New York #400 est:3000-4000
£1840 $3000 €2686 America-La France Variations VII (134x91cm-53x36in) s. num.apxx/xx col lithograph collage exec 1983-4. 24-Sep-3 Christie's, Rockefeller NY #312/R est:2000-3000
£1892 $3500 €2762 America-La France variations III (122x78cm-48x31in) s.num.XX/XX col lithograph collage. 12-Feb-4 Christie's, Rockefeller NY #150/R est:2000-3000
£1912 $3250 €2792 Barcelona elegy to the Spanish republic (54x70cm-21x28in) s. col etching aquatint. 31-Oct-3 Sotheby's, New York #707/R
£1977 $3500 €2886 Sirens I (37x47cm-15x19in) init.i. lithograph. 30-Apr-4 Sotheby's, New York #418/R est:3000-4000
£1977 $3500 €2886 Three forms (30x60cm-12x24in) init. num.36/50 quatint etching. 30-Apr-4 Sotheby's, New York #419/R est:4000-6000
£2119 $3750 €3094 Hermitage (102x72cm-40x28in) s. num.191/200 col lithograph screenprint. 30-Apr-4 Sotheby's, New York #401/R est:3500-4500
£2119 $3750 €3094 Summer sign (45x59cm-18x23in) init.i. col carborundum print. 30-Apr-4 Sotheby's, New York #420/R est:3000-4000
£2147 $3500 €3135 Dance (49x78cm-19x31in) s. num.13/30 etching aquatint on TH Saunders exec 1978. 24-Sep-3 Christie's, Rockefeller NY #308/R est:1500-2000
£2206 $3750 €3221 America-La France (118x82cm-46x32in) s. col lithograph collage. 31-Oct-3 Sotheby's, New York #693/R
£2246 $3750 €3279 Yellow flight (25x58cm-10x23in) s.num.12/45 etching aquatint. 11-Nov-3 Doyle, New York #342/R est:3000-4000
£2260 $4000 €3300 La guerra II (80x113cm-31x44in) s. num.43/48 beige black lithograph. 30-Apr-4 Sotheby's, New York #404/R est:2500-3500
£2260 $4000 €3300 On the wing (118x77cm-46x30in) i. col lithograph. 30-Apr-4 Sotheby's, New York #415/R est:4000-6000
£2270 $4200 €3314 Green studio (13x30cm-5x12in) s.num.13/50 black green etching aquatint. 12-Feb-4 Christie's, Rockefeller NY #154/R est:2000-3000
£2324 $4300 €3393 Razor's edge (41x51cm-16x20in) s.d.1985 aquatint lift-ground etching. 17-Jul-4 Outer Cape Auctions, Provincetown #22/R
£2353 $4000 €3435 America (134x91cm-53x36in) s. col lithograph collage. 4-Nov-3 Christie's, Rockefeller NY #312/R est:3000-5000
£2432 $4500 €3551 America-La France variations V (117x78cm-46x31in) s.num.28/60 col lithograph collage. 12-Feb-4 Christie's, Rockefeller NY #151/R est:2500-3500
£2432 $4500 €3551 America-La France variations VI (117x80cm-46x31in) s.num.30/60 col lithograph collage. 12-Feb-4 Christie's, Rockefeller NY #152/R est:2500-3500
£2542 $4500 €3711 Game of chance (59x42cm-23x17in) s.i. col aquatint lithograph. 30-Apr-4 Sotheby's, New York #416/R est:4500-5500
£2577 $4200 €3762 On the Wing (119x77cm-47x30in) s. num.30/70 col lithograph collage Arches cover exec 1983-4. 24-Sep-3 Christie's, Rockefeller NY #314/R est:4000-5000
£2647 $4500 €3865 Untitled (66x50cm-26x20in) s. monotype lithograph. 31-Oct-3 Sotheby's, New York #682/R
£2647 $4500 €3865 Black cathedral (170x163cm-67x64in) init. col lithograph exec.1991. 4-Nov-3 Christie's, Rockefeller NY #315/R est:5000-7000
£2684 $4750 €3919 Elegy study (64x96cm-25x38in) init. num.84/98 lithograph. 30-Apr-4 Sotheby's, New York #403/R est:3500-4500
£2794 $4750 €4079 Game of chance (59x42cm-23x17in) s. aquatint lithograph. 31-Oct-3 Sotheby's, New York #700/R
£2794 $4750 €4079 Hollow man's cave (80x101cm-31x40in) init. col lithograph. 31-Oct-3 Sotheby's, New York #705/R
£2825 $5000 €4125 Put out all flags (30x50cm-12x20in) s. num.10/50 red black etching aquatint. 30-Apr-4 Sotheby's, New York #406 est:5000-7000
£2941 $5000 €4294 Delos (92x59cm-36x23in) init. col lithograph. 31-Oct-3 Sotheby's, New York #706/R
£2941 $5000 €4294 Australia (64x76cm-25x30in) s. col aquatint. 4-Nov-3 Christie's, Rockefeller NY #311/R est:2000-3000
£2973 $5500 €4341 Game of chance (27x41cm-11x16in) s.num.XIII col aquatint lithograph collage hand col. 12-Feb-4 Christie's, Rockefeller NY #155/R est:5000-7000
£3067 $5000 €4478 Red Queen (80x63cm-31x25in) init. num.24/40 etching col aquatint exec 1989. 24-Sep-3 Christie's, Rockefeller NY #315/R est:5000-7000
£3107 $5500 €4536 Signs on copper (45x60cm-18x24in) init.i. aquatint etching. 30-Apr-4 Sotheby's, New York #407/R est:6000-8000
£3107 $5500 €4536 Black cathedral (170x119cm-67x47in) init. num.39/40 col lithograph. 30-Apr-4 Sotheby's, New York #421/R est:5000-7000
£3107 $5500 €4536 Delos (92x59cm-36x23in) init. num.35/40 col lithograph. 30-Apr-4 Sotheby's, New York #422/R est:5000-7000
£3235 $5500 €4723 Lament for Lorca (101x143cm-40x56in) init. lit. 31-Oct-3 Sotheby's, New York #687/R
£3235 $5500 €4723 Game of chance (88x70cm-35x28in) s. aquatint lithograph collage. 4-Nov-3 Christie's, Rockefeller NY #314/R est:5000-7000
£3672 $6500 €5361 Red sea I (60x50cm-24x20in) s.num.84/100 red black aquatint. 28-Apr-4 Christie's, Rockefeller NY #372/R est:5000-7000
£3672 $6500 €5361 America la France variations (118x81cm-46x32in) s.i. col lithograph. 30-Apr-4 Sotheby's, New York #409/R est:5000-7000
£4118 $7000 €6012 Put out all flags (30x50cm-12x20in) s. etching aquatint. 31-Oct-3 Sotheby's, New York #686/R
£4237 $7500 €6186 Black mountain (45x60cm-18x24in) s.num.23/32 col etching aquatint. 28-Apr-4 Christie's, Rockefeller NY #374/R est:5000-7000
£4412 $7500 €6442 Black cathedral (170x119cm-67x47in) s. col lithograph. 31-Oct-3 Sotheby's, New York #704/R
£4706 $8000 €6871 Elegy study I (100x155cm-39x61in) s. col lithograph. 31-Oct-3 Sotheby's, New York #701/R
£5650 $10000 €8249 At the edge (95x47cm-37x19in) s.num.23/34 col etching aquatint. 28-Apr-4 Christie's, Rockefeller NY #375/R est:6000-9000
£5932 $10500 €8661 Three figures (141x101cm-56x40in) s.num.9/80 col lithograph. 28-Apr-4 Christie's, Rockefeller NY #377/R est:8000-10000
£6765 $11500 €9877 Gestures IV (50x40cm-20x16in) s. aquatint etching. 31-Oct-3 Sotheby's, New York #681/R
£7647 $13000 €11165 Black for Mozart (163x104cm-64x41in) s. col lithograph collage. 31-Oct-3 Sotheby's, New York #703/R
£8824 $15000 €12883 Redness of red (61x41cm-24x16in) s. col lithograph screenprint collage. 31-Oct-3 Sotheby's, New York #698/R
£13529 $23000 €19752 Personnage (12x17cm-5x7in) s. engraving. 31-Oct-3 Sotheby's, New York #678/R
£13559 $24000 €19796 Octavio paz suite (84x70cm-33x28in) init. num.15/50 lithograph portfolio. 30-Apr-4 Sotheby's, New York #417/R est:18000-22000
£23529 $40000 €34352 Burning elegy (108x136cm-43x54in) init. col lithograph. 31-Oct-3 Sotheby's, New York #702/R
Works on paper
£5307 $9500 €7748 Open Study 12 (56x77cm-22x30in) init.d.68 chl acrylic prov.exhib. 13-May-4 Sotheby's, New York #199/R est:10000-15000
£5988 $10000 €8742 Untitled, no 23 (60x48cm-24x19in) init.d.66 ink prov.exhib. 13-Nov-3 Sotheby's, New York #187/R est:10000-15000
£20000 $36800 €29200 Untitled (18x24cm-7x9in) init. pencil gouache card exec c.1960 prov.lit. 24-Jun-4 Sotheby's, London #251/R est:6000-8000
£39877 $65000 €58220 Three personages shot (29x35cm-11x14in) s.d.12 June 1944 ink wash sepia gouache W/C prov.exhib. 23-Sep-3 Christie's, Rockefeller NY #18/R est:12000-18000

MOTLEY, David (fl.1898) British
£290 $528 €423 Mountainous stream with an arched bridge (61x91cm-24x36in) s. 29-Jun-4 Capes Dunn, Manchester #760
£761 $1400 €1111 Landscape with sheep (46x81cm-18x32in) s. prov. 27-Jun-4 Hindman, Chicago #795/R est:1200-1800

MOTSWAI, Tommy (1963-) South African
Works on paper
£578 $1035 €844 Wrestlers (48x68cm-19x27in) s.d.1986 pastel. 31-May-4 Stephan Welz, Johannesburg #580/R (SA.R 7000)
£690 $1152 €1007 Wrestlers (48x68cm-19x27in) s.d.1986 pastel. 20-Oct-3 Stephan Welz, Johannesburg #372/R est:10000-14000 (SA.R 8000)

MOTT, George Henry (?) British
£420 $664 €613 Portrait of the ballerina, Svetlana Beriosova (60x50cm-24x20in) 25-Apr-3 Bigwood, Stratford on Avon #279/R

MOTT, Jean de la (attrib) (?) ?
£400 $632 €584 Landscape with cart horses travelling through open countryside (65x100cm-26x39in) 27-Apr-3 Wilkinson, Doncaster #285/R

MOTT, Laura (19/20th C) British
Works on paper
£280 $515 €409 Head and shoulders study of a young lady, Amy, wearing a white dress (50x42cm-20x17in) s.d.1899 gouache exhib. 26-Mar-4 Bigwood, Stratford on Avon #311/R

MOTTA, Raffaellino (attrib) (1550-1578) Italian
Works on paper
£2158 $3453 €3000 Woman holding heart (26x15cm-10x6in) i. pen W/C. 14-May-3 Finarte Semenzato, Milan #488/R est:1000-1500

MOTTARD VAN MARCKE, Leonie (1862-1936) Belgian
£1049 $1783 €1500 Borde de riviere fleuri (57x40cm-22x16in) s. 1-Dec-3 Palais de Beaux Arts, Brussels #101/R est:1500-2000

MOTTEZ, Victor (1809-1897) French
Works on paper
£559 $1000 €816 Portrait of a young gentleman sitting in his library (48x43cm-19x17in) W/C gouache. 19-Mar-4 Aspire, Cleveland #119 est:1000-1500

MOTTI, Giuseppe (1908-1988) Italian
£369 $683 €550 Rice girl (35x50cm-14x20in) s. 13-Mar-4 Meeting Art, Vercelli #495
£436 $807 €650 Hills (50x60cm-20x24in) s. s.i.d.1970 verso. 13-Mar-4 Meeting Art, Vercelli #170

MOTTINO, Francis (?) Italian
£560 $1058 €818 Venetian view of the Punta Della Dogana with figures and gondolas (34x54cm-13x21in) mono. 18-Feb-4 Rupert Toovey, Partridge Green #45/R

MOTTOLA, Giuseppe (18th C) Italian
£2411 $4027 €3400 River landscape with herd and sheperds (76x130cm-30x51in) s.d.1729. 14-Oct-3 Finarte Semenzato, Rome #262/R est:3000-4000

MOTTRAM, Charles Sim (fl.1880-1919) British
£850 $1352 €1241 Fisherfolk hauling nets on a beach (38x43cm-15x17in) s. 9-Sep-3 Peter Francis, Wales #26/R
Works on paper
£203 $340 €296 Fishing boats at dawn (24x42cm-9x17in) s. W/C. 17-Nov-3 Waddingtons, Toronto #48/R (C.D 450)
£300 $561 €438 Out going tide (54x32cm-21x13in) s. W/C. 26-Feb-4 Lane, Penzance #256
£480 $883 €701 On the beach, Lelant, Cornwall (35x66cm-14x26in) s. W/C. 22-Jun-4 Bonhams, Knightsbridge #47/R
£920 $1647 €1343 Fishing fleet off St. Michael's Mount, Cornwall (28x48cm-11x19in) s. W/C. 16-Mar-4 Bonhams, Leeds #618
£1300 $2366 €1898 The fishing fleet heading out to sea (28x47cm-11x19in) s. pencil W/C htd white. 1-Jul-4 Christie's, Kensington #310/R est:800-1200

MOTTU, Luc-Henri (1815-1859) Swiss
Works on paper
£526 $879 €768 Chateau de Chillon (11x17cm-4x7in) s. gouache. 16-Nov-3 Koller, Geneva #1225 (S.FR 1200)
£1009 $1685 €1473 Vue du Mont-Blanc (11x17cm-4x7in) s. gouache. 16-Nov-3 Koller, Geneva #1226 est:900-1200 (S.FR 2300)

MOUALLA, Fikret (1903-1967) Turkish
£1316 $2421 €2000 Nature morte aux fruits (25x22cm-10x9in) s.d.52 canvas on panel. 28-Jun-4 Rossini, Paris #88/R est:2000-2500
£2254 $3628 €3200 Nature morte a l'aubergine (20x34cm-8x13in) s.d.1951 paper. 22-Aug-3 Deauville, France #13/R est:2500-3000
Works on paper
£382 $638 €550 Trois poissons (18x20cm-7x8in) s.d.1957 gouache. 25-Oct-3 Cornette de St.Cyr, Paris #531
£671 $1248 €1000 Cruche et fruits (11x21cm-4x8in) s. gouache. 3-Mar-4 Tajan, Paris #164
£1259 $2102 €1800 Fruits (18x24cm-7x9in) s.d.54 gouache. 25-Jun-3 Blanchet, Paris #66/R
£3356 $6242 €5000 Personnages des Rues (32x52cm-13x20in) s.d.59 gouache. 3-Mar-4 Tajan, Paris #163/R est:2000-3000
£5000 $8650 €7300 Personnages sur fond bleu (32x54cm-13x21in) s.d.61 gouache. 11-Dec-3 Christie's, Kensington #175/R est:5000-7000
£5000 $9050 €7300 Au bar (33x55cm-13x22in) s. gouache. 1-Apr-4 Christie's, Kensington #122/R est:4000-6000
£6000 $10860 €8760 Personnages sur fond bleu (33x54cm-13x21in) s. gouache. 1-Apr-4 Christie's, Kensington #126/R est:4000-6000
£7000 $12110 €10220 Foule avec ballon (33x55cm-13x22in) s. gouache. 11-Dec-3 Christie's, Kensington #185/R est:5000-7000
£7692 $12846 €11000 Scene du rue (53x68cm-21x27in) s.d.1951 W/C gouache. 25-Jun-3 Maigret, Paris #46/R est:5000-7000
£9155 $14739 €13000 Chez le coiffeur (54x38cm-21x15in) s.d.1952 gouache. 22-Aug-3 Deauville, France #10/R est:12000-15000
£10000 $18300 €15000 Promeneurs a Paris (32x53cm-13x21in) s. gouache. 6-Jun-4 Anaf, Lyon #445/R est:12000-15000
£11000 $19910 €16060 Brasserie (55x67cm-22x26in) s. gouache. 1-Apr-4 Christie's, Kensington #131/R est:6000-8000
£12081 $22470 €18000 Scene de bar (50x61cm-20x24in) s.d.59 gouache. 2-Mar-4 Artcurial Briest, Paris #101/R est:8000-10000
£14000 $24220 €20440 Musiciens (53x63cm-21x25in) s. gouache. 11-Dec-3 Christie's, Kensington #180/R est:6000-8000
£14500 $25085 €21170 Personnage sur fond bleu (53x63cm-21x25in) s. gouache. 11-Dec-3 Christie's, Kensington #199/R est:6000-8000
£16500 $29865 €24090 Musiciens sur fond rouge (55x74cm-22x29in) s. gouache. 1-Apr-4 Christie's, Kensington #132/R est:6000-8000

MOUCHERON, Frederic de (1633-1686) Dutch
£4500 $7785 €6570 Extensive river landscape with goatherd playing a pipe and peasants (59x54cm-23x21in) s. 12-Dec-3 Christie's, Kensington #80/R est:5000-7000
£5517 $9159 €8000 Mountainous landscape with ruins and travellers (75x61cm-30x24in) s. 1-Oct-3 Dorotheum, Vienna #132/R est:8000-12000
£6000 $10740 €9000 Landscape with figures (58x81cm-23x32in) s. 17-May-4 Finarte Semenzato, Rome #20/R est:7000-8000
Works on paper
£425 $722 €620 Travellers in an extensive landscape (18x29cm-7x11in) black chk pen wash. 5-Nov-3 Christie's, Amsterdam #114/R

MOUCHERON, Frederic de (attrib) (1633-1686) Dutch
£2587 $4399 €3700 Les deux pecheurs au bord de la riviere (72x89cm-28x35in) bears sig. 26-Nov-3 Daguerre, Paris #57/R est:3000-4000
£3691 $6792 €5500 Wooded landscape with water (78x101cm-31x40in) 27-Mar-4 Geble, Radolfzell #751/R est:5000

MOUCHERON, Isaac de (1667-1744) Dutch
£19737 $36316 €30000 View of the terrace of a classical palace (74x102cm-29x40in) s. 25-Jun-4 Piasa, Paris #10/R est:12000-15000
£23448 $39159 €34000 Wooded landscape with classical ruins (51x68cm-20x27in) s. lit. 12-Nov-3 Sotheby's, Milan #108/R est:35000-45000
Works on paper
£629 $1051 €900 Fontaine du Bernin dans les jardins de la villa Montalto (33x23cm-13x9in) pen brown ink grey wash. 27-Jun-3 Millon & Associes, Paris #10
£2055 $3493 €3000 Classical gateway with a man and his dog at a fountain, port and mountains beyond (25x18cm-10x7in) chk pen ink wash W/C framing lines prov.lit. 5-Nov-3 Christie's, Amsterdam #122/R est:3000-4000
£3169 $5546 €4500 Un paysage avec un temple ionique et une fontaine (18x12cm-7x5in) black chk pen brown ink W/C prov. 17-Dec-3 Christie's, Paris #31/R est:5000-7000
£7432 $13081 €11000 Wooded river landscape with bathers (20x32cm-8x13in) s.d. pen black ink grey wash prov.exhib.lit. 19-May-4 Sotheby's, Amsterdam #92/R est:5500-6500
£11034 $18428 €16000 Landscape with palace. Coastal landscape (20x30cm-8x12in) pen ink W/C pair lit. 12-Nov-3 Sotheby's, Milan #109/R est:7000-10000

MOUCHERON, Isaac de (attrib) (1667-1744) Dutch
£1916 $3200 €2797 Pastoral valley scene (76x91cm-30x36in) 19-Oct-3 Susanin's, Chicago #6053/R est:3000-5000
Works on paper
£1556 $2800 €2272 Classical landscape with two women by a Roman sarcophagus (20x15cm-8x6in) s. chk pen ink sold with 2 attrib L Gadbois and P A Robart prov. 22-Jan-4 Christie's, Rockefeller NY #266/R est:1500-2000

MOUCHOT, Louis (19th C) French
£567 $948 €800 Echoppe au Caire (25x19cm-10x7in) s.i. panel. 16-Jun-3 Gros & Delettrez, Paris #134/R

MOUCHOT, Louis Hippolyte (1846-1893) French
£608 $1089 €900 Brother cellar master tasting wine from the bottle (35x26cm-14x10in) s. panel prov. 6-May-4 Michael Zeller, Lindau #792/R
£1527 $2779 €2229 Portrait of a lady (33x24cm-13x9in) s. board. 16-Jun-4 Deutscher-Menzies, Melbourne #431/R est:2000-3000 (A.D 4000)

MOUDARRES, Fateh (1922-) Syrian
£442 $805 €650 Fille en verte (50x34cm-20x13in) s.d.61 acrylic oil. 3-Feb-4 Sigalas, Stuttgart #565/R
Works on paper
£1007 $1782 €1500 Deux personnages (21x17cm-8x7in) s.d.1960 mixed media incisions gilt sheet. 28-Apr-4 Artcurial Briest, Paris #329a est:200-300

MOUGIN, A (?) French
Sculpture
£1538 $2646 €2200 Ecureuil rongeant une noisette (18cm-7in) s.st.f.A. Mougin brown pat bronze. 8-Dec-3 Horta, Bruxelles #86 est:2000-3000

MOULD, Nigel C (20th C) British
Works on paper
£248 $450 €362 Study of a boxer (48x39cm-19x15in) s.d.56 pastel. 30-Mar-4 Bonhams & Butterfields, San Francisco #122/R

MOULIGNON, Leopold de (1821-1897) French
£479 $800 €699 Duck and hare (53x104cm-21x41in) s. oval. 20-Jun-3 Freeman, Philadelphia #228/R

MOULIN, Felix Jacques Antoine (19th C) French?
Photographs
£1444 $2600 €2108 Photographer's daughter and baby (21x15cm-8x6in) salt print executed c.1853. 22-Apr-4 Phillips, New York #99/R est:4000-6000
£3056 $5500 €4462 Woman in front of a mirror. stereo daguerreotype. 22-Apr-4 Phillips, New York #92/R est:6000-8000

MOULIN, Hippolyte (1832-1884) French
Sculpture
£8400 $15288 €12600 Un secret d'en haut (100cm-39in) green brown pat. bronze marble base. 20-Jun-4 Wilkinson, Doncaster #18 est:8000-12000

MOULINET, Antoine Edouard Joseph (1833-1891) French
£3200 $5536 €4672 Chef and clerk (22x14cm-9x6in) s. board pair. 12-Dec-3 Bracketts, Tunbridge Wells #868 est:1000-1500

MOULINNEUF, Étienne (18th C) French
£6643 $11427 €9500 Still life with thermometer, pen, inkstand andcalendar (75x62cm-30x24in) s. 2-Dec-3 Sotheby's, Milan #90/R est:7000-10000

MOULINNEUF, Étienne (18th C) French
£2632 $4842 €4000 Nature morte aux carrelets et coquillages (25x40cm-10x16in) panel. 25-Jun-4 Piasa, Paris #135/R est:4000-6000

MOULLIN, Louis (1817-?) French
Works on paper
£1538 $2646 €2200 Peintre partant sur le motif dans la grande rue de Barbizon (19x26cm-7x10in) s.i.d.5 avril 1866 W/C. 7-Dec-3 Osenat, Fontainebleau #112

MOULLION, Alfred (1832-1886) French
£1733 $3189 €2600 Jardinier dans un paysage de campagne (80x150cm-31x59in) s.d.1878. 8-Jun-4 Livinec, Gaudcheau & Jezequel, Rennes #137/R
£2200 $3982 €3300 Vue panoramique (49x81cm-19x32in) s.d.1882. 30-Mar-4 Rossini, Paris #1030/R est:1200-1800

MOULTON, Frank B (1847-1932) American
£347 $600 €507 Cows at pasture (36x56cm-14x22in) s. 13-Dec-3 Charlton Hall, Columbia #80/R

MOULTRAY, James Douglas (fl.1860-1880s) British
£373 $600 €545 Road to the village (23x30cm-9x12in) s.i. on stretcher. 24-Feb-3 O'Gallerie, Oregon #899/R
£4200 $6762 €6090 Deer in a highland glen (50x75cm-20x30in) s. 21-Aug-3 Bonhams, Edinburgh #1073/R est:3000-4000

MOULY, Marcel (1920-) French
£706 $1200 €1031 L'Isle aux tresors (58x30cm-23x12in) s.d.1960 i.d.verso prov. 22-Nov-3 Jackson's, Cedar Falls #409/R est:300-500
£2533 $4560 €3800 Venise jour et nuit (73x73cm-29x29in) s.d.1959 s.i.d.verso. 24-Apr-4 Cornette de St.Cyr, Paris #663/R est:3000

MOUNCEY, William (1852-1901) British
£700 $1169 €1022 Landscape near Kirkcudbright (58x48cm-23x19in) 13-Nov-3 Bonhams, Edinburgh #396
£1300 $2171 €1898 Closing day (50x60cm-20x24in) s. i.on stretcher. 16-Oct-3 Bonhams, Edinburgh #199 est:800-1200
£1800 $3348 €2628 Figure in a wooded river landscape (51x61cm-20x24in) s. 4-Mar-4 Christie's, Kensington #75/R est:2000-3000

MOUNT, Rita (1888-1967) Canadian
£938 $1613 €1369 On the St Lawrence (22x27cm-9x11in) s.d.1924 canvas on board. 2-Dec-3 Joyner Waddington, Toronto #420 est:1500-1800 (C.D 2100)
£1480 $2708 €2161 Mount Rainier, Washington (22x27cm-9x11in) s. canvasboard. 1-Jun-4 Joyner Waddington, Toronto #380/R est:1000-1200 (C.D 3700)
£1786 $3071 €2608 Beached boats in a fishing village (24x27cm-9x11in) s. board prov. 2-Dec-3 Joyner Waddington, Toronto #441 est:1200-1500 (C.D 4000)
£2000 $3660 €2920 White clouds, Gaspe (22x27cm-9x11in) s. canvasboard. 1-Jun-4 Joyner Waddington, Toronto #211/R est:2500-3000 (C.D 5000)
£9000 $15030 €13140 Winters day in old Montreal (62x70cm-24x28in) s. prov.exhib. 14-Oct-3 Sotheby's, London #218/R est:2000-3000
Works on paper
£242 $445 €353 Portrait of a young girl (41x34cm-16x13in) s. chl. 9-Jun-4 Walker's, Ottawa #148/R (C.D 600)

MOUNTFORT, Arnold (1873-1942) American/British
£429 $686 €622 Torbay (20x36cm-8x14in) s. i. stretcher. 15-May-3 Stuker, Bern #1402/R (S.FR 900)

MOUQUE, A (19th C) French
£692 $1191 €1010 Pastoral landscape (30x36cm-12x14in) s.d.1838 panel. 2-Dec-3 Bukowskis, Stockholm #275/R (S.KR 9000)

MOURANT, Elise (?) ?
£277 $496 €404 Irish fisherwoman on the quay (32x41cm-13x16in) s.i.verso board prov. 12-May-4 Dunbar Sloane, Wellington #3/R (NZ.D 800)
£346 $619 €505 Houses and railway (26x34cm-10x13in) s. board. 11-May-4 Peter Webb, Auckland #160/R est:500-800 (NZ.D 1000)

MOURIER, Claude (1930-) French
£296 $545 €450 Jardin fleuri (46x55cm-18x22in) s. 22-Jun-4 Chassaing Rivet, Toulouse #323

MOUSSON, Jozef Teodor (1887-1946) Czechoslovakian
£1236 $2298 €1805 Zelny trh in Michalovce (59x74cm-23x29in) s.i. 6-Mar-4 Dorotheum, Prague #74/R est:60000-90000 (C.KR 60000)

MOVALLI, Charles (1945-) American
£351 $650 €512 Winter on Cape Ann (51x61cm-20x24in) s. acrylic. 18-Jul-4 William Jenack, New York #119

MOWBRAY, Henry Siddons (1858-1928) American
£5298 $9695 €8000 La presentation (92x71cm-36x28in) s.d.1889. 9-Apr-4 Claude Aguttes, Neuilly #140 est:2000-3000

MOY, Seong (1921-) American
£468 $750 €683 Four winds (112x91cm-44x36in) s. 17-May-3 Bunte, Elgin #673
£563 $900 €822 Twilight meeting on the beach (61x76cm-24x30in) s.d.1955 masonite on board. 17-May-3 Bunte, Elgin #1315 est:400-600

MOYA Y CALVO, Victor (1884-1972) Spanish
£1931 $3225 €2800 Valencian florist (91x75cm-36x30in) s.d.1929. 17-Nov-3 Durán, Madrid #129/R est:2800
£2414 $4031 €3500 Flowers in Valencia (91x75cm-36x30in) s.d.1929. 17-Nov-3 Durán, Madrid #128/R est:2800

MOYA, Antonio (20th C) Venezuelan
Works on paper
£714 $1300 €1071 First world (105x125cm-41x49in) s. mixed media panel exec.1993. 21-Jun-4 Subastas Odalys, Caracas #98

MOYA, Patrick (1955-) French
£795 $1446 €1200 Canon Moya (73x60cm-29x24in) s.d.2002 acrylic. 18-Jun-4 Charbonneaux, Paris #163/R
£1678 $3087 €2500 L'oiseau (97x103cm-38x41in) s.d.02 peinture. 28-Mar-4 Anaf, Lyon #195/R est:2500-3000

MOYANO (1929-1965) Belgian?
£268 $475 €400 Composition (80x116cm-31x46in) s. d.1963 verso. 27-Apr-4 Campo, Vlaamse Kaai #527

MOYANO, Louis (1907-) ?
£433 $793 €650 Milliers de mots (116x81cm-46x32in) s.d.1963 verso prov. 7-Jun-4 Palais de Beaux Arts, Brussels #137/R
£467 $854 €700 Composition (65x92cm-26x36in) s.d.61 verso prov. 7-Jun-4 Palais de Beaux Arts, Brussels #138

MOYER, Marvin (1905-) American
£1497 $2500 €2186 Abstraction (69x53cm-27x21in) masonite. 18-Oct-3 David Dike, Dallas #250/R est:3000-5000

MOYERS, John (1958-) American
£1037 $1670 €1514 Sioux drummer (30x41cm-12x16in) s. s.i. verso board. 20-Aug-3 James Julia, Fairfield #664/R est:2000-4000
£5294 $9000 €7729 Donkey (71x56cm-28x22in) oil on linen. 1-Nov-3 Altermann Galleries, Santa Fe #177
£5307 $9500 €7748 Mexican saddle (102x76cm-40x30in) board. 15-May-4 Altermann Galleries, Santa Fe #9/R
£7059 $12000 €10306 Across the Taos valley (76x102cm-30x40in) 1-Nov-3 Altermann Galleries, Santa Fe #1a
£7059 $12000 €10306 Winter passage (76x102cm-30x40in) 1-Nov-3 Altermann Galleries, Santa Fe #17
£12032 $22500 €17567 Winter trail (102x152cm-40x60in) s. 24-Jul-4 Coeur d'Alene, Hayden #191/R est:30000-50000
£12291 $22000 €17945 Trails of his ancestors (122x86cm-48x34in) 15-May-4 Altermann Galleries, Santa Fe #12/R
Sculpture
£471 $800 €688 Whiteman's headdress (23cm-9in) bronze. 1-Nov-3 Altermann Galleries, Santa Fe #18

MOYERS, Terri Kelly (1953-) American
£2647 $4500 €3865 Yes, Virginia (51x41cm-20x16in) 1-Nov-3 Altermann Galleries, Santa Fe #197

MOYERS, William (1916-1976) American
£1553 $2500 €2252 Taking a count (41x51cm-16x20in) 22-Aug-3 Altermann Galleries, Santa Fe #95
£3416 $5500 €4953 Not fit for women or children (20x24cm-8x9in) 22-Aug-3 Altermann Galleries, Santa Fe #128
£4749 $8500 €6934 Strawberry roan (51x61cm-20x24in) 15-May-4 Altermann Galleries, Santa Fe #123/R
Sculpture
£765 $1300 €1117 Spring (33x33x25cm-13x13x10in) s.d.1973 num.6/30 bronze st.f. prov. 1-Nov-3 Santa Fe Art, Santa Fe #178/R est:1500-2500
£882 $1500 €1288 Loser buys the drinks (30x46x25cm-12x18x10in) s.d.1971 num.6/30 bronze st.f. prov. 1-Nov-3 Santa Fe Art, Santa Fe #177/R est:2000-3000
£1118 $1800 €1621 Spring (36x30x36cm-14x12x14in) bronze. 22-Aug-3 Altermann Galleries, Santa Fe #64
Works on paper
£497 $800 €721 Riding a tough one (16x12cm-6x5in) W/C. 22-Aug-3 Altermann Galleries, Santa Fe #130
£2765 $4700 €4037 Not much of a cow horse (56x74cm-22x29in) W/C. 1-Nov-3 Altermann Galleries, Santa Fe #116

MOYNAN, Richard Thomas (1856-1906) British
£4698 $8409 €7000 Woman wearing a plumed hat (75x55cm-30x22in) s.d.1888. 26-May-4 James Adam, Dublin #25/R est:7000-10000
£16667 $28333 €24000 The Little Grandmother (91x44cm-36x17in) s.d.1893. 28-Oct-3 Mealy's, Castlecomer #475

MOYNE, Jacques le (c.1533-1588) French
Works on paper
£3333 $6000 €4866 Study of an apple blossom (17x14cm-7x6in) W/C gouache over black chk. 21-Jan-4 Sotheby's, New York #49/R est:6000-8000
£6389 $11500 €9328 Sheet studies of flowers, liverwort, two pasque (15x19cm-6x7in) i. W/C gouache over black chk. 21-Jan-4 Sotheby's, New York #50/R est:10000-15000
£7778 $14000 €11356 Sheet studies of flowers, two narcissi and a lady's smock (14x17cm-6x7in) i. W/C gouache over black chk. 21-Jan-4 Sotheby's, New York #47/R est:8000-12000

£9444 $17000 €13788 Study of an orange lily and an iris (19x13cm-7x5in) i. W/C gouache over black chk. 21-Jan-4 Sotheby's, New York #46/R est:10000-15000
£10000 $18000 €14600 Sheet of studies of flowers, two double daisies, four primroses (16x21cm-6x8in) W/C gouache over black chk. 21-Jan-4 Sotheby's, New York #38/R est:18000-22000
£10000 $18000 €14600 Study of a yellowhammer (11x18cm-4x7in) W/C gouache over black chk. 21-Jan-4 Sotheby's, New York #48/R est:7000-9000
£11667 $21000 €17034 Sheet studies with two gillyflowers and a peacock butterfly (15x18cm-6x7in) W/C gouache over black chk. 21-Jan-4 Sotheby's, New York #39/R est:15000-20000
£15278 $27500 €22306 Kingfisher on a branch (11x18cm-4x7in) W/C gouache over black chk. 21-Jan-4 Sotheby's, New York #33/R est:10000-15000
£16667 $30000 €24334 Sheet of studies of flowers, German iris and three violets (20x14cm-8x6in) i. W/C gouache over black chk. 21-Jan-4 Sotheby's, New York #35/R est:30000-40000
£16667 $30000 €24334 Sheet studies with grasshopper, spider, ladybird (16x21cm-6x8in) W/C g, over black chk. 21-Jan-4 Sotheby's, New York #42/R est:20000-30000
£18056 $32500 €26362 Sheet of studies with a swallow and a double gilliflower (12x18cm-5x7in) W/C gouache over black chk. 21-Jan-4 Sotheby's, New York #31/R est:15000-20000
£18056 $32500 €26362 Sheet of studies of flowers, borage, French rose and two wild irises (21x15cm-8x6in) i. W/C gouache over chk. 21-Jan-4 Sotheby's, New York #37/R est:30000-40000
£22222 $40000 €32444 Sheet of studies of flowers, peony, Spanish iris and a wild geranium (19x15cm-7x6in) i. W/C gouache over black chk. 21-Jan-4 Sotheby's, New York #36/R est:40000-60000
£22222 $40000 €32444 Sheet studies with two day lilies and a caterpillar (16x20cm-6x8in) i. W/C gouache over black chk. 21-Jan-4 Sotheby's, New York #45/R est:10000-15000
£33333 $60000 €48666 Sheet of flowers, two opium poppies, lily and love-in-a-mist (17x21cm-7x8in) i. W/C gouache pen ink. 21-Jan-4 Sotheby's, New York #30/R est:60000-80000
£36111 $65000 €52722 Sheet studies with French roses and an oxeye daisy (21x16cm-8x6in) W/C gouache over black chk. 21-Jan-4 Sotheby's, New York #43/R est:20000-30000
£38889 $70000 €56778 Sheet studies of flowers, two corn poppies, corn cockle and a cornflower (21x16cm-8x6in) i. W/C gouache over black chk. 21-Jan-4 Sotheby's, New York #44/R est:25000-35000
£47222 $85000 €68944 Sheet studies of flowers and insects (16x19cm-6x7in) i. W/C gouache htd white. 21-Jan-4 Sotheby's, New York #29/R est:50000-70000
£52778 $95000 €77056 Sheet of studies of flowers and admiral butterfly (17x20cm-7x8in) W/C gouache htd white. 21-Jan-4 Sotheby's, New York #34/R est:50000-70000
£55556 $100000 €81112 Sheet of studies with five clove pinks (14x21cm-6x8in) W/C gouache over black chk. 21-Jan-4 Sotheby's, New York #32/R est:50000-70000
£66667 $120000 €97334 Sheet studies of fruits, apples, chestnuts and medlars (15x20cm-6x8in) W/C gouache over black chk. 21-Jan-4 Sotheby's, New York #40/R est:20000-30000

MOYNE, Jacques le (attrib) (c.1533-1588) French
Works on paper
£2778 $5000 €4056 Study of a melon with a slice cut out (22x14cm-9x6in) W/C gouache over black chk. 21-Jan-4 Sotheby's, New York #52/R est:4000-6000
£3889 $7000 €5678 Two bunches of grapes, one white one black (18x14cm-7x6in) W/C gouache over black chk. 21-Jan-4 Sotheby's, New York #54/R est:5000-7000
£4722 $8500 €6894 Study of a jay (14x22cm-6x9in) W/C gouache over black chk. 21-Jan-4 Sotheby's, New York #55/R est:4000-6000
£6111 $11000 €8922 Study of a cucumber, with its leaves (17x24cm-7x9in). g. over black chk. 21-Jan-4 Sotheby's, New York #51/R est:4000-6000
£8333 $15000 €12166 Various study of walnuts (21x15cm-8x6in) W/C gouache htd white over black chk. 21-Jan-4 Sotheby's, New York #53/R est:6000-8000

MOYNIHAN, Rodrigo (1910-) British
£360 $673 €526 Portrait of the artist's grand-daughter (46x35cm-18x14in) s.d.85. 24-Feb-4 Bonhams, Knowle #138
£700 $1253 €1022 Fishermen, Deal (23x28cm-9x11in) board prov. 14-May-4 Christie's, Kensington #537/R

MOYSE, Edouard (1827-?) French
Works on paper
£1517 $2731 €2200 Jeune femme d'Afrique du NOrd (44x35cm-17x14in) s. pastel. 21-Jan-4 Tajan, Paris #113/R est:2000-3000

MOZART, Anton (attrib) (1573-1625) German
£845 $1462 €1200 Elegant figures in Renaissance castle park (25x33cm-10x13in) i. copper. 11-Dec-3 Dr Fritz Nagel, Stuttgart #471/R

MOZERT, Zoe (1904-1993) American
Works on paper
£6376 $11413 €9500 Beauty by night (90x77cm-35x30in) s. pastel cardboard. 27-May-4 Sotheby's, Paris #121/R est:2000-3000

MOZIN, Charles Louis (1806-1862) French
£903 $1563 €1318 Coastal landscape with vessel and figures (36x51cm-14x20in) s. 15-Dec-3 Lilla Bukowskis, Stockholm #792 (S.KR 11500)
£1184 $2179 €1800 Le chemin des herbages (24x32cm-9x13in) s. cardboard. 22-Jun-4 Calmels Cohen, Paris #39/R est:1200-1500
£1513 $2785 €2300 La vallee d'Auge, la Dives (24x32cm-9x13in) s. cardboard. 22-Jun-4 Calmels Cohen, Paris #38/R est:1200-1500
£2021 $3172 €2950 Bateau dans la tempete (31x51cm-12x20in) s. 20-Apr-3 Deauville, France #99/R est:3000-3500
£3125 $5219 €4500 Barque en vent arriere (19x24cm-7x9in) s. i.verso panel. 23-Oct-3 Credit Municipal, Paris #57 est:1500-2000
£4503 $8196 €6800 Voiliers dans la tempete (47x59cm-19x23in) s. 18-Jun-4 Piasa, Paris #48 est:2000-3000
£5208 $8698 €7500 Barque de pecheurs et trois mats (28x41cm-11x16in) s. panel. 23-Oct-3 Credit Municipal, Paris #58/R est:3000-3500
Works on paper
£567 $1026 €850 La sortie du port (14x22cm-6x9in) s.d.1828 brown ink wash exhib. 30-Mar-4 Rossini, Paris #1032
£634 $1096 €900 Vue d'un port anime en Normandie (19x27cm-7x11in) s. W/C traces blk crayon. 10-Dec-3 Piasa, Paris #82
£1888 $3153 €2700 Port (33x51cm-13x20in) graphite dr htd gouache. 27-Jun-3 Doutrebente, Paris #37/R

MOZINA, Livio (1941-) Italian
£284 $474 €400 Case in Carso (19x24cm-7x9in) s. 21-Jun-3 Stadion, Trieste #184/R

MOZLEY, Charles (1914-1991) British
Works on paper
£550 $1001 €803 Paris restaurant (32x24cm-13x9in) s.d.73 gouache. 1-Jul-4 Christie's, Kensington #29/R
£1200 $2220 €1752 Mon oncle (32x41cm-13x16in) s.i.d.73 W/C ink gouache. 11-Feb-4 Sotheby's, Olympia #217/R est:400-600
£2300 $3657 €3358 Mobile policemen use Shell (53x95cm-21x37in) pen ink W/C board sold with another by the same hand lit. 10-Sep-3 Sotheby's, Olympia #80/R est:1000-1500

MOZOS, Pedro (1915-1983) Spanish
£345 $576 €500 Ballet (62x45cm-24x18in) s. chl dr. 17-Nov-3 Durán, Madrid #82/R

MRKUSICH, Milan (1925-) New Zealander
£3731 $6455 €5447 Painting indigo (77x92cm-30x36in) s.i.d.1969 verso. 9-Dec-3 Peter Webb, Auckland #135/R est:12000-18000 (NZ.D 10000)
£4478 $7746 €6538 Blue area (42x33cm-17x13in) s.d.1974 i.d.1974 verso acrylic. 9-Dec-3 Peter Webb, Auckland #54/R est:12000-18000 (NZ.D 12000)
£5357 $9696 €7821 Arcs and lines on grey - diamond (227x227cm-89x89in) s.d.1983 verso acrylic. 30-Mar-4 Peter Webb, Auckland #58/R est:15000-20000 (NZ.D 15000)
£5639 $9586 €8233 Four circles dark (60x41cm-24x16in) s.d.1977 verso acrylic paper prov. 27-Nov-3 International Art Centre, Auckland #79/R est:15000-25000 (NZ.D 15000)
£8571 $15771 €12514 Small emblem (46x46cm-18x18in) s.d.1965 board. 25-Mar-4 International Art Centre, Auckland #55/R est:15000-25000 (NZ.D 24000)
£20522 $35504 €29962 Composition (42x72cm-17x28in) s.d.1958 canvasboard. 9-Dec-3 Peter Webb, Auckland #70/R est:55000-70000 (NZ.D 55000)
£22727 $41364 €33181 Painting III. s.i.d.1972 verso acrylic. 29-Jun-4 Peter Webb, Auckland #42/R est:75000-95000 (NZ.D 65000)
£30686 $50018 €44802 Blue achromatic (160x122cm-63x48in) s.i.d.1980 verso acrylic customwood. 23-Sep-3 Peter Webb, Auckland #77/R est:45000-65000 (NZ.D 85000)
Works on paper
£5714 $10514 €8342 Achromatic dark with red (53x42cm-21x17in) s.d.1982 verso col pencil wax crayon. 25-Mar-4 International Art Centre, Auckland #77/R est:15000-22000 (NZ.D 16000)

MTHETHWA, Zwelethu (1960-) American?
Photographs
£5028 $9000 €7341 Untitled, reclining figure with coat. Untitled, girl in green skirt (96x127cm-38x50in) chromogenic print UV plexiglass edition 2 of 3 pair prov.exhib. 12-May-4 Christie's, Rockefeller NY #461/R est:10000-15000

MUBIN, Orhon (1924-1981) Turkish
£260 $465 €380 Untitled (30x15cm-12x6in) s.d.1956 verso. 16-Mar-4 Bonhams, Knightsbridge #122
£333 $543 €480 Composition (100x80cm-39x31in) s. 29-Sep-3 Charbonneaux, Paris #263
£360 $644 €526 Abstract Study (61x38cm-24x15in) s. 16-Mar-4 Bonhams, Knightsbridge #121/R
£567 $1043 €850 Composition (72x92cm-28x36in) s. 11-Jun-4 Pierre Berge, Paris #45

MUCCHI-VIGNOLI, Anton Maria (1871-1945) Italian
Works on paper
£467 $840 €700 Susa Valley (22x28cm-9x11in) pencil exec.1907 lit. 21-Apr-4 Finarte Semenzato, Milan #604/R

MUCCINI, Marcello (1926-1978) Italian
£1409 $2621 €2100 Waiting (120x80cm-47x31in) s. 4-Mar-4 Babuino, Rome #468 est:800-1200

MUCHA, A (1860-1939) Czechoslovakian
Prints
£18000 $32940 €27000 La topaz, l'emeraude, l'amethyste, le rubis (65x28cm-26x11in) s.i. polychrome lithograph exec. 1900 four lit. 7-Jun-4 Sotheby's, Amsterdam #1/R est:20000-30000

MUCHA, Alphonse (1860-1939) Czechoslovakian
£3497 $5944 €5000 Landscape in Bohm (16x27cm-6x11in) s. board. 29-Nov-3 Villa Grisebach, Berlin #109/R est:5000-7000
£29412 $50000 €42942 Solitude (61x35cm-24x14in) s. 29-Oct-3 Christie's, Rockefeller NY #49/R est:25000-35000
Prints
£1635 $2600 €2387 Spring (97x48cm-38x19in) s. lithograph. 14-Sep-3 Susanin's, Chicago #6002/R est:2000-4000
£2901 $5221 €4235 Biscuits lefavre-utile (60x43cm-24x17in) col lithograph lit. 26-Apr-4 Bukowskis, Stockholm #405/R est:50000-60000 (S.KR 40000)
£2980 $5424 €4500 Medee (207x77cm-81x30in) i. lithograph. 15-Jun-4 Christie's, Amsterdam #360/R est:5000-8000
£3243 $6000 €4735 Sarah Bernhardt, American tour (191x72cm-75x28in) lithograph. 11-Mar-4 Sotheby's, New York #109/R est:4000-6000
£3243 $6000 €4735 Sarah Bernhardt in the role of Princess Lointaine (69x50cm-27x20in) chromolithograph. 11-Mar-4 Sotheby's, New York #114/R est:5000-8000
£3357 $5706 €4800 Eclat du jour (35x103cm-14x41in) col lithograph panel. 28-Nov-3 Tajan, Paris #346/R est:4000
£3481 $6265 €5082 Job (52x39cm-20x15in) col lithograph lit. 26-Apr-4 Bukowskis, Stockholm #404/R est:60000-70000 (S.KR 48000)

£3514 $6500 €5130 Job cigarette papers (142x94cm-56x37in) lithograph. 11-Mar-4 Sotheby's, New York #110/R est:5000-8000
£3784 $7000 €5525 Fall (102x53cm-40x21in) s. col lithograph exec.c.1896. 9-Mar-4 Christie's, Rockefeller NY #235/R est:8000-10000
£3784 $7000 €5525 Job cigarette papers (142x94cm-56x37in) lithograph. 11-Mar-4 Sotheby's, New York #111/R est:6000-9000
£4061 $7310 €5929 F. Champenois imprime (64x47cm-25x19in) col lithograph lit. 26-Apr-4 Bukowskis, Stockholm #406/R est:40000-50000 (S.KR 56000)
£4351 $7832 €6352 Job (153x102cm-60x40in) col. lithograph lit. 26-Apr-4 Bukowskis, Stockholm #407/R est:30000-40000 (S.KR 60000)
£4595 $8500 €6709 Les calendriers des saisons (42x59cm-17x23in) lithograph metalic ink. 11-Mar-4 Sotheby's, New York #112/R est:8000-12000
£4595 $8500 €6709 Biscuits lefevre-utile (60x43cm-24x17in) chromolithograph. 11-Mar-4 Sotheby's, New York #113/R est:3000-5000
£4865 $9000 €7103 Leslie Carter (202x70cm-80x28in) col lithograph. 11-Mar-4 Sotheby's, New York #108/R est:7000-10000
£5946 $11000 €8681 Biscuits lefevre-utile (62x44cm-24x17in) s. col lithograph exec.c.1897. 9-Mar-4 Christie's, Rockefeller NY #232/R est:5500-7500
£6780 $12000 €9899 Benedictine de l'Abbaye de Fecamp (206x76cm-81x30in) col lithograph two sheets. 28-Apr-4 Christie's, Rockefeller NY #108/R est:12000-15000
£22703 $42000 €33146 Poetry, dance, painting and music (58x38cm-23x15in) s.d.98 col lithograph set of four prov. 9-Mar-4 Christie's, Rockefeller NY #234/R est:30000-50000

Works on paper
£483 $806 €700 Woman in a chair (18x15cm-7x6in) pencil board prov. 13-Nov-3 Neumeister, Munich #407/R
£1536 $2612 €2243 Horse (25x20cm-10x8in) s. wash ink white lead. 29-Nov-3 Dorotheum, Prague #145/R est:70000-100000 (C.KR 70000)
£1647 $2750 €2405 Studies of women (41x34cm-16x13in) blue pencil over pencil card prov. 7-Oct-3 Sotheby's, New York #248 est:2000-3000
£2000 $3620 €3000 Jeune femme pensive (23x14cm-9x6in) s. W/C gouache. 31-Mar-4 Sotheby's, Paris #121/R est:1200-1500
£2333 $4293 €3500 Portrait d'une fille sur le quai (36x27cm-14x11in) s. W/C gouache. 11-Jun-4 Claude Aguttes, Neuilly #98/R est:3000-4000
£2500 $4175 €3650 Mother and child (32x23cm-13x9in) s. chl htd white prov. 12-Nov-3 Sotheby's, Olympia #224/R est:1000-1500
£2973 $5500 €4341 Girl with an oil lamp (44x30cm-17x12in) s. col crayon gouache. 11-Mar-4 Sotheby's, New York #107/R est:5000-7000
£3495 $6500 €5103 Diploma design for Charles University, Prague (33x29cm-13x11in) s. brush ink htd white. 2-Mar-4 Swann Galleries, New York #464/R est:8000-12000
£4533 $8205 €6800 L'artiste dans son atelier (24x15cm-9x6in) s. W/C gouache. 31-Mar-4 Sotheby's, Paris #122/R est:1500-2000
£7514 $13000 €10970 Four times of day (81x19cm-32x7in) W/C over pencil four on one sheet. 11-Dec-3 Sotheby's, New York #178/R est:8000-12000

MUCHA, Willy (c.1920-) French
£320 $592 €467 Les fillets au Sechage (24x35cm-9x14in) s. i.verso board. 15-Jan-4 Christie's, Kensington #972
£350 $651 €511 Filets au Sechage (23x31cm-9x12in) s. panel prov. 7-Mar-4 Lots Road Auctions, London #350

Works on paper
£314 $541 €450 Regate a collioure (40x60cm-16x24in) s.i. Indian ink. 3-Dec-3 Tajan, Paris #138
£345 $638 €500 Collioure (44x55cm-17x22in) s. gouache. 16-Feb-4 Giraudeau, Tours #27

MUCKE DOF, Carl (19th C) ?
£1241 $2297 €1800 Fillette et ses chatons (45x38cm-18x15in) s. panel. 16-Feb-4 Horta, Bruxelles #500 est:1000-1500

MUCKE, Carl Emil (1847-1923) German
£1457 $2652 €2200 An unwanted visitor (17x23cm-7x9in) s. panel. 21-Jun-4 Dorotheum, Vienna #104/R est:1800-2200
£1958 $3329 €2800 Genre scene - Dutch girl with dog and cat (35x27cm-14x11in) s. 20-Nov-3 Van Ham, Cologne #1750/R est:1200

MUCKLEY, Louis Fairfax (fl.1887-1901) British
Works on paper
£1700 $3145 €2482 Landscape with sheep (34x49cm-13x19in) s.d.1900 W/C. 9-Mar-4 Bonhams, New Bond Street #133/R est:1000-1500

MUCKLEY, William Jabez (1837-1905) British
£460 $860 €672 Oranges and blossom on a table (47x56cm-19x22in) s. 24-Feb-4 Bonhams, Knowle #84

MUDGE, Alfred (fl.1862-1877) British
£55000 $93500 €80300 Terrace at Richmond (92x170cm-36x67in) s.d.1883 prov. 27-Nov-3 Sotheby's, London #382/R est:40000-60000

MUDJIDELL, Joseph (20th C) Australian
Works on paper
£667 $1193 €974 Miropula (100x50cm-39x20in) synthetic polymer paint canvas exec 1992 prov. 25-May-4 Lawson Menzies, Sydney #133/R (A.D 1700)

MUEHLEMANN, Kathy (1950-) American
£1222 $2200 €1784 Untitled (22x16cm-9x6in) s.verso. 24-Apr-4 David Rago, Lambertville #271/R

Works on paper
£1167 $2100 €1704 Nocturn with moons. Nitya Saktis. Hypnotic flight. Dance of Diana. Polar. one s.i.d.1980 verso W/C 4 s.i.d.verso graphite five. 24-Apr-4 David Rago, Lambertville #270/R est:250-500

MUEHLHAUS, Daniel (1907-1981) Dutch
£267 $477 €400 Varied still life with stone bottle and bowl of fruit (60x73cm-24x29in) s.d.38. 11-May-4 Vendu Notarishuis, Rotterdam #223/R
£276 $461 €400 City view with flower stall (50x40cm-20x16in) s. 11-Nov-3 Vendu Notarishuis, Rotterdam #577/R

MUELLER, Howard (20th C) American
£3429 $6000 €5006 Illustrations to Ian Fleming's Man with the Golden Gun (89x58cm-35x23in) one board other canvas two exec April July 1965 lit. 17-Dec-3 Christie's, Rockefeller NY #78/R est:6000-8000

Works on paper
£571 $1000 €834 Horsing them in with Hemingway (60x81cm-24x32in) chl W/C paper on illus board exec 1965. 17-Dec-3 Christie's, Rockefeller NY #20/R
£800 $1400 €1168 Hemingway (48x65cm-19x26in) ink pencil W/C exec 1957. 17-Dec-3 Christie's, Rockefeller NY #21/R

MUELLER, Stephen (1947-) American
£769 $1323 €1100 Drawing (127x122cm-50x48in) s.verso lit. 3-Dec-3 Stadion, Trieste #1130/R

MUELLER-TOSA, Heinz (1943-) Swiss
£495 $852 €723 Untitled (60x59cm-24x23in) s.d.1969 verso acrylic. 8-Dec-3 Philippe Schuler, Zurich #3351 (S.FR 1100)

MUENIER, Jules Alexis (1863-1942) French
£274 $466 €400 Etude de bergers (40x40cm-16x16in) st.sig. cardboard. 6-Nov-3 Rabourdin & Choppin de Janvry, Paris #12
£274 $466 €400 Paysage au lac (22x13cm-9x5in) s.d.1882 panel. 6-Nov-3 Rabourdin & Choppin de Janvry, Paris #19/R
£274 $466 €400 Paysage de campagne (16x22cm-6x9in) st.sig.verso panel. 6-Nov-3 Rabourdin & Choppin de Janvry, Paris #34
£274 $466 €400 Paysan sur un chemin (14x23cm-6x9in) i. st.sig.verso panel. 6-Nov-3 Rabourdin & Choppin de Janvry, Paris #51
£274 $466 €400 Les grands arbres (65x50cm-26x20in) st.sig. 6-Nov-3 Rabourdin & Choppin de Janvry, Paris #54
£274 $466 €400 Femme dans sa chambre (65x54cm-26x21in) st.sig. cardboard. 6-Nov-3 Rabourdin & Choppin de Janvry, Paris #65/R
£274 $466 €400 Portrait d'une elegante (22x16cm-9x6in) st.sig. panel. 6-Nov-3 Rabourdin & Choppin de Janvry, Paris #73/R
£274 $466 €400 Bords de riviere (41x33cm-16x13in) st.sig. panel. 6-Nov-3 Rabourdin & Choppin de Janvry, Paris #79
£274 $466 €400 Paysage d'Italie (41x33cm-16x13in) st.sig. panel. 6-Nov-3 Rabourdin & Choppin de Janvry, Paris #87
£274 $466 €400 Paysage aux grands arbres (61x50cm-24x20in) st.sig. cardboard. 6-Nov-3 Rabourdin & Choppin de Janvry, Paris #102
£308 $524 €450 L'ouvrier au repos (17x34cm-7x13in) st.sig.i. 6-Nov-3 Rabourdin & Choppin de Janvry, Paris #1
£308 $524 €450 Portrait d'une dame (73x60cm-29x24in) s.d.1826. 6-Nov-3 Rabourdin & Choppin de Janvry, Paris #63
£308 $524 €450 Le lac Leman (41x33cm-16x13in) s. panel. 6-Nov-3 Rabourdin & Choppin de Janvry, Paris #77
£308 $524 €450 Fermette sous la neige (55x38cm-22x15in) st.sig. 6-Nov-3 Rabourdin & Choppin de Janvry, Paris #97/R
£342 $582 €500 Jeune fille assoupie (47x29cm-19x11in) painted on studio window pane. 6-Nov-3 Rabourdin & Choppin de Janvry, Paris #2
£342 $582 €500 Plan d'eau dans le sous-bois (57x65cm-22x26in) st.sig. 6-Nov-3 Rabourdin & Choppin de Janvry, Paris #62
£342 $582 €500 Le bouquet de roses blanches (47x33cm-19x13in) st.sig. 6-Nov-3 Rabourdin & Choppin de Janvry, Paris #98/R
£377 $640 €550 La bergerie (33x41cm-13x16in) st.sig. 6-Nov-3 Rabourdin & Choppin de Janvry, Paris #69
£377 $640 €550 Les moutons (38x55cm-15x22in) st.sig. 6-Nov-3 Rabourdin & Choppin de Janvry, Paris #70
£411 $699 €600 Bords de riviere (50x61cm-20x24in) st.sig. 6-Nov-3 Rabourdin & Choppin de Janvry, Paris #55
£411 $699 €600 La fermiere (33x23cm-13x9in) st.sig. 6-Nov-3 Rabourdin & Choppin de Janvry, Paris #71/R
£479 $815 €700 Le faucheur (37x40cm-15x16in) st.sig. 6-Nov-3 Rabourdin & Choppin de Janvry, Paris #11
£479 $815 €700 Portrait d'un enfant (22x17cm-9x7in) st.sig. 6-Nov-3 Rabourdin & Choppin de Janvry, Paris #81/R
£479 $815 €700 Etude d'un cabanon fleuri (38x56cm-15x22in) st.sig. 6-Nov-3 Rabourdin & Choppin de Janvry, Paris #88/R
£479 $815 €700 Scene pastorale (55x66cm-22x26in) st.sig. 6-Nov-3 Rabourdin & Choppin de Janvry, Paris #92/R
£544 $974 €800 Etude de berger vu de trois-quarts et de dos (41x36cm-16x14in) cardboard studio st. 22-Mar-4 E & Eve, Paris #51/R
£548 $932 €800 Bord de riviere (60x73cm-24x29in) st.sig. 6-Nov-3 Rabourdin & Choppin de Janvry, Paris #60
£582 $990 €850 La belle fermiere (22x16cm-9x6in) st.sig. panel. 6-Nov-3 Rabourdin & Choppin de Janvry, Paris #80
£685 $1164 €1000 Portrait d'un ami peintre (17x10cm-7x4in) st.sig.verso panel. 6-Nov-3 Rabourdin & Choppin de Janvry, Paris #30/R
£685 $1164 €1000 Paysage aux grands arbres (55x35cm-22x14in) st.sig. 6-Nov-3 Rabourdin & Choppin de Janvry, Paris #84/R
£685 $1164 €1000 Bouquet de fleurs (61x50cm-24x20in) st.sig. 6-Nov-3 Rabourdin & Choppin de Janvry, Paris #96/R
£685 $1164 €1000 Scene pastorale (50x61cm-20x24in) s. 6-Nov-3 Rabourdin & Choppin de Janvry, Paris #107/R
£822 $1397 €1200 Le presbytere (65x54cm-26x21in) st.sig. 6-Nov-3 Rabourdin & Choppin de Janvry, Paris #91/R
£822 $1397 €1200 Paysage d'un jeune homme a la barbe (59x37cm-23x15in) s.d.1887. 6-Nov-3 Rabourdin & Choppin de Janvry, Paris #95/R
£822 $1397 €1200 Portrait du pere de l'artiste, le poete Alexis Muenier (35x29cm-14x11in) st.sig. 6-Nov-3 Rabourdin & Choppin de Janvry, Paris #101
£959 $1630 €1400 Nature morte aux fruits (54x43cm-21x17in) s. oval. 6-Nov-3 Rabourdin & Choppin de Janvry, Paris #76/R
£959 $1630 €1400 Jeune homme au chapeau (61x50cm-24x20in) st.sig. 6-Nov-3 Rabourdin & Choppin de Janvry, Paris #104/R
£959 $1630 €1400 Le chemin du village (46x38cm-18x15in) s. panel. 6-Nov-3 Rabourdin & Choppin de Janvry, Paris #113/R
£1027 $1747 €1500 La lavandiere (50x54cm-20x21in) st.sig. 6-Nov-3 Rabourdin & Choppin de Janvry, Paris #61/R est:1000-1200
£1027 $1747 €1500 Nature morte aux fruits (46x38cm-18x15in) s. 6-Nov-3 Rabourdin & Choppin de Janvry, Paris #83/R est:400-500
£1027 $1747 €1500 Pecheur et paysanne (50x60cm-20x24in) s.d.1938. 6-Nov-3 Rabourdin & Choppin de Janvry, Paris #110/R est:2500-3000

£1062	$1805	€1550	Voilier (15x22cm-6x9in) i.d. st.sig.verso panel. 6-Nov-3 Rabourdin & Choppin de Janvry, Paris #49 est:400-600
£1096	$1863	€1600	Couple a la barque (41x32cm-16x13in) st.sig. 6-Nov-3 Rabourdin & Choppin de Janvry, Paris #20/R est:500-600
£1096	$1863	€1600	Le faucheur (37x31cm-15x12in) st.sig. 6-Nov-3 Rabourdin & Choppin de Janvry, Paris #43/R est:1200-1500
£1199	$2038	€1750	Fillette aux fruits (41x33cm-16x13in) st.sig. 6-Nov-3 Rabourdin & Choppin de Janvry, Paris #82/R est:600-800
£1233	$2096	€1800	Village de Franche-Comte (65x54cm-26x21in) s. 6-Nov-3 Rabourdin & Choppin de Janvry, Paris #28/R est:1500-2000
£1233	$2096	€1800	La vase de roses (54x43cm-21x17in) s. oval. 6-Nov-3 Rabourdin & Choppin de Janvry, Paris #75/R est:2500-3000
£1233	$2096	€1800	Fillette a la rose (40x30cm-16x12in) s.d.1928 oval. 6-Nov-3 Rabourdin & Choppin de Janvry, Paris #112/R est:2500-3000
£1301	$2212	€1900	Bord de rivage Mediterraneen (54x65cm-21x26in) s. 6-Nov-3 Rabourdin & Choppin de Janvry, Paris #90/R est:800-1000
£1541	$2620	€2250	Eclairage dans le cellier (68x57cm-27x22in) st.sig. 6-Nov-3 Rabourdin & Choppin de Janvry, Paris #58 est:400-500
£1712	$2911	€2500	Jeune fille dans un paysage (33x41cm-13x16in) st.sig. panel. 6-Nov-3 Rabourdin & Choppin de Janvry, Paris #37/R est:600-700
£1712	$2911	€2500	Reflets sur la riviere (65x54cm-26x21in) st.sig. 6-Nov-3 Rabourdin & Choppin de Janvry, Paris #57/R est:1800-2000
£1712	$2911	€2500	Barque sur la riviere (45x55cm-18x22in) s.d.1938. 6-Nov-3 Rabourdin & Choppin de Janvry, Paris #59 est:800-1000
£1712	$2911	€2500	Le retour des champs (60x47cm-24x19in) st.sig. 6-Nov-3 Rabourdin & Choppin de Janvry, Paris #67/R est:1600-2000
£1747	$2969	€2550	Le retour a la ferme (46x40cm-18x16in) s. panel. 6-Nov-3 Rabourdin & Choppin de Janvry, Paris #111/R est:2000-2500
£1849	$3144	€2700	Le moissonneur (40x31cm-16x12in) st.sig. panel. 6-Nov-3 Rabourdin & Choppin de Janvry, Paris #114/R est:2000-2500
£1854	$3375	€2800	Paysage de neige (54x66cm-21x26in) s. 20-Jun-4 Salle des ventes Pillet, Lyon la Foret #28/R est:1500-1800
£1918	$3260	€2800	Bucherons sur le rivage (60x54cm-24x21in) s. 6-Nov-3 Rabourdin & Choppin de Janvry, Paris #109/R est:800-1000
£2055	$3493	€3000	La petite paysanne (50x60cm-20x24in) st.sig. panel. 6-Nov-3 Rabourdin & Choppin de Janvry, Paris #108/R est:800-1000
£2123	$3610	€3100	Etude d'un cure (60x71cm-24x28in) st.sig. 6-Nov-3 Rabourdin & Choppin de Janvry, Paris #89/R est:1500-1800
£2260	$3842	€3300	Le reveil (55x65cm-22x26in) st.sig. 6-Nov-3 Rabourdin & Choppin de Janvry, Paris #106/R est:800-1000
£2877	$4890	€4200	Etude de nu academique, effet de contre jour (80x55cm-31x22in) st.sig. 6-Nov-3 Rabourdin & Choppin de Janvry, Paris #24 est:200-300
£3129	$5601	€4600	Le retour de la peche (37x45cm-15x18in) s. 22-Mar-4 E & Eve, Paris #52/R
£3493	$5938	€5100	Portrait de monsieur le Marechal Foch (92x60cm-36x24in) s.d.1919. 6-Nov-3 Rabourdin & Choppin de Janvry, Paris #116/R est:4000-6000
£3562	$6055	€5200	Le peintre Dagnan Bouveret a Alger (14x10cm-6x4in) s.i.d.1888 panel. 6-Nov-3 Rabourdin & Choppin de Janvry, Paris #10/R est:500-600
£5822	$9897	€8500	Portrait du peintre Carl von Stetten (10x9cm-4x4in) i.d.1884 st.sig.verso panel. 6-Nov-3 Rabourdin & Choppin de Janvry, Paris #29/R est:300-400

MUGGERIDGE, Marianne (?) New Zealander?

£1091	$1713	€1582	From Willis St, mid afternoon, late summer (70x79cm-28x31in) s.i.d.2001. 27-Aug-3 Dunbar Sloane, Wellington #55/R est:3000-5000 (NZ.D 3000)
£1384	$2478	€2021	Kaponga (121x137cm-48x54in) 12-May-4 Dunbar Sloane, Wellington #138/R est:4000-7000 (NZ.D 4000)

MUGHAL SCHOOL (16th C) Asian

Works on paper

£55000	$97350	€80300	Khwaja Umar, escaping at night from the camp of Murzuq (68x52cm-27x20in) i. i.verso gouache gold cotton album leaf exec.c.1570 prov.lit. 28-Apr-4 Sotheby's, London #54/R est:60000-80000
£70000	$123900	€102200	Member of the Barmakid Family offering gifts to the Caliph (24x16cm-9x6in) i.verso gouache htd gold text exec.c.1595-1600 prov. 28-Apr-4 Sotheby's, London #55/R est:70000-100000

MUGHAL SCHOOL (17th C) Asian

Miniatures

£6000	$10320	€8760	Prince in a garden. Lady (18x13cm-7x5in) s.d.1628 lacquered rec. mirror case style of Manohar. 2-Dec-3 Gorringes, Lewes #2206/R est:6000-8000

MUGHAL SCHOOL (18th C) Asian

Works on paper

£6000	$10740	€8760	Blue jay (47x29cm-19x11in) i. W/C bodycol pen ink exec.c.1760. 13-May-4 Sotheby's, London #30/R est:6000-8000
£6000	$10740	€8760	Blackbellied finch lark in grassland (47x29cm-19x11in) i. W/C bodycol pen ink exec.c.1760. 13-May-4 Sotheby's, London #32/R est:6000-8000
£6000	$10740	€8760	Male wedgetailed green pigeon on a branch (47x29cm-19x11in) i. W/C bodycol pen ink exec.c.1760. 13-May-4 Sotheby's, London #34/R est:6000-8000
£7000	$12530	€10220	Male shikra, on a perch (47x29cm-19x11in) i. W/C bodycol pen ink exec.c.1760. 13-May-4 Sotheby's, London #28/R est:7000-9000
£7000	$12530	€10220	Male black partridge in a landscape (46x28cm-18x11in) i. W/C bodycol pen ink exec.c.1760. 13-May-4 Sotheby's, London #31/R est:7000-9000
£7000	$12530	€10220	Dove, possibly the rufous turtle dove on a branch (47x29cm-19x11in) i. W/C bodycol pen ink exec.c.1760. 13-May-4 Sotheby's, London #33/R est:6000-8000
£9000	$16110	€13140	Golden plover, on a riverbank (47x29cm-19x11in) i. W/C bodycol pen ink exec.c.1760. 13-May-4 Sotheby's, London #29/R est:7000-9000

MUHL, Otto (1924-) Russian

£319	$533	€450	Head (37x27cm-15x11in) s.d.8.12.85 acrylic prov. 14-Oct-3 Dorotheum, Vienna #270/R
£420	$722	€600	Nude (28x42cm-11x17in) s.d. oil crayon. 4-Dec-3 Dorotheum, Graz #159/R
£493	$863	€700	Female nude sitting (43x30cm-17x12in) mono.d.91 oilstick paper. 19-Dec-3 Dorotheum, Vienna #381/R
£667	$1227	€1000	Nude (30x40cm-12x16in) mono.d.17.8.82 oil chk. 9-Jun-4 Dorotheum, Salzburg #861/R
£800	$1440	€1200	Vincent van Gogh (122x86cm-48x34in) s.d.89 acrylic. 21-Apr-4 Dorotheum, Vienna #294/R
£800	$1440	€1200	Vincent van Gogh (122x86cm-48x34in) s.d.89 acrylic. 21-Apr-4 Dorotheum, Vienna #295/R
£1342	$2483	€2000	Vincent van Gogh (122x86cm-48x34in) s.d.89 acrylic. 9-Mar-4 Dorotheum, Vienna #191/R est:2000-3000
£1611	$2980	€2400	Vincent van Gogh (122x86cm-48x34in) s.d.89 zrylic. 9-Mar-4 Dorotheum, Vienna #192/R est:2000-3000
£4698	$8691	€7000	Indian (140x120cm-55x47in) s.i.d.23.5.85 acrylic jute. 9-Mar-4 Dorotheum, Vienna #236 est:8000-12000
£7383	$13215	€11000	Lenin (150x140cm-59x55in) s.i.d.2.4.85 prov. 25-May-4 Dorotheum, Vienna #374/R est:12000-15000
£12587	$21399	€18000	Still life II (130x150cm-51x59in) s.d.4.10.86 acrylic prov. 26-Nov-3 Dorotheum, Vienna #97/R est:19000-23000

Works on paper

£280	$481	€400	Loving couple (28x19cm-11x7in) s.d. ink. 4-Dec-3 Dorotheum, Graz #158
£290	$484	€420	Head (44x30cm-17x12in) s.d.85 W/C oilstick. 13-Nov-3 Neumeister, Munich #588
£319	$533	€450	Lovers (30x21cm-12x8in) s.d.2.IX.83 W/C. 16-Oct-3 Dorotheum, Salzburg #919/R
£333	$600	€500	Lohengrin's swan (43x61cm-17x24in) mono.d.83.6.17 Indian ink W/C. 21-Apr-4 Dorotheum, Vienna #272
£420	$713	€600	Lovers (28x20cm-11x8in) d.23.9.83 W/C. 19-Nov-3 Dorotheum, Klagenfurt #60/R
£423	$701	€600	Man with owl (28x42cm-11x17in) s.d.2.9.85 pencil w/C. 12-Jun-3 Dorotheum, Graz #112/R
£423	$701	€600	Woman (29x20cm-11x8in) s.d.12.9.85 W/C col chk. 12-Jun-3 Dorotheum, Graz #113/R
£423	$701	€600	Fat man (20x29cm-8x11in) s.d.20.10.83 Indian ink W/C. 12-Jun-3 Dorotheum, Graz #114/R
£426	$711	€600	Nude on hands and knees (30x44cm-12x17in) mono.d.27.3.82 oil chk prov. 14-Oct-3 Dorotheum, Vienna #261/R
£503	$901	€750	Nose penis (22x33cm-9x13in) s.d.4.12.85 pencil w/C. 27-May-4 Dorotheum, Graz #108/R
£524	$902	€750	Loving couple (20x28cm-8x11in) s.d. ink W/C. 4-Dec-3 Dorotheum, Graz #73/R
£552	$921	€800	Pair (30x44cm-12x17in) s.d.85 mixed media. 13-Nov-3 Neumeister, Munich #587
£570	$1021	€850	Messing about by the lake (28x42cm-11x17in) s.d.7/8.12.85 pencil W/C. 27-May-4 Dorotheum, Graz #109/R
£570	$1021	€850	Lovers in purple (20x28cm-8x11in) s.d.22.9.83 mixed media. 27-May-4 Dorotheum, Graz #193/R
£638	$1141	€950	Penis carrier (36x51cm-14x20in) s.d.13.12.85 pencil W/C. 27-May-4 Dorotheum, Graz #110/R
£676	$1189	€1000	Woman in red dancing (28x19cm-11x7in) d.26.3.83 W/C. 19-May-4 Dorotheum, Klagenfurt #51/R
£780	$1303	€1100	Lovers (20x29cm-8x11in) s.d.22.IX.83 Indian ink W/C. 16-Oct-3 Dorotheum, Salzburg #920/R
£1399	$2378	€2000	Untitled (58x79cm-23x31in) s.d.1984 mixed media. 28-Nov-3 Wiener Kunst Auktionen, Vienna #643/R est:2500-4000

MUHL, Roger (1929-) French

£497	$900	€726	Marche (110x119cm-43x47in) s. 18-Apr-4 Bonhams & Butterfields, Los Angeles #7067 est:500-700
£660	$1089	€950	Nature morte a la bouteille (50x53cm-20x21in) s. 3-Jul-3 Claude Aguttes, Neuilly #131
£694	$1160	€1000	Bretagne (19x24cm-7x9in) s. i.verso. 21-Oct-3 Christie's, Paris #167/R
£707	$1300	€1032	Paris, Cours la Reine (25x41cm-10x16in) s. prov. 25-Jun-4 Freeman, Philadelphia #261/R est:500-800
£718	$1300	€1048	Dance Balinaise (110x119cm-43x47in) s. 18-Apr-4 Bonhams & Butterfields, Los Angeles #7068 est:500-700
£909	$1563	€1300	La rose (27x19cm-11x7in) s. 3-Dec-3 Tajan, Paris #429 est:300-500
£1322	$2247	€1930	Paysage de neige (50x65cm-20x26in) s. 5-Nov-3 Dobiaschofsky, Bern #826/R est:2800 (S.FR 3000)
£1977	$3500	€2886	Bouquet jaune (119x110cm-47x43in) s. prov. 2-May-4 Bonhams & Butterfields, Los Angeles #3016a/R est:3000-5000
£2116	$4000	€3089	Marche Indonesien (100x109cm-39x43in) s. 22-Feb-4 Bonhams & Butterfields, Los Angeles #7076 est:500-700
£2378	$4042	€3400	Les rochers (24x33cm-9x13in) s. 24-Nov-3 Boscher, Cherbourg #795 est:2000-3000
£2703	$5000	€3946	Nature morte blanche (63x81cm-25x32in) s. i.verso prov. 12-Feb-4 Sotheby's, New York #317/R est:3000-5000
£2740	$4658	€4000	Nu assis (80x85cm-31x33in) s. 9-Nov-3 Eric Pillon, Calais #274/R
£3297	$6000	€4814	Fenetre ouvert (150x160cm-59x63in) s. painted 1990 prov.exhib. 29-Jun-4 Sotheby's, New York #363/R est:7000-10000
£3571	$6500	€5214	Les toits roses (60x64cm-24x25in) s. painted c.1990 prov. 29-Jun-4 Sotheby's, New York #370/R est:3000-5000

Works on paper

£350	$602	€500	Maison sous la neige (33x44cm-13x17in) s. gouache. 3-Dec-3 Tajan, Paris #94
£420	$722	€600	Bord de mer (44x55cm-17x22in) s. W/C. 3-Dec-3 Tajan, Paris #93

MUHLBECK, Joseph (1878-1948) German

£333	$603	€500	Summer idyll (10x18cm-4x7in) s. panel. 1-Apr-4 Van Ham, Cologne #1551
£959	$1630	€1400	Chiemsee (35x39cm-14x15in) s. 5-Nov-3 Hugo Ruef, Munich #1074/R
£972	$1604	€1400	Studies. s. board several. 3-Jul-3 Van Ham, Cologne #1366
£2400	$4344	€3600	Harvesting (18x25cm-7x10in) s. canvas on board. 1-Apr-4 Van Ham, Cologne #1553/R est:2200

MUHLBRECHT, Fritz (1880-?) German

£379	$694	€550	Evening storm over Munich (41x61cm-16x24in) s. s.d.1924 verso panel. 27-Jan-4 Dorotheum, Vienna #30/R

MUHLEN, Hermann (1886-1964) German

£2867	$5131	€4300	Bathers (101x110cm-40x43in) s.d. 14-May-4 Ketterer, Munich #63/R est:2800-3200
£3867	$6921	€5800	Still life with pumpkins (70x72cm-28x28in) s.d. 14-May-4 Ketterer, Munich #62/R est:2500-3000

MUHLENEN, Max von (1903-1971) Swiss
£493 $824 €720 Poplar trees in the Wallis (46x61cm-18x24in) s.d.41 s. verso. 24-Oct-3 Hans Widmer, St Gallen #124/R (S.FR 1100)
£776 $1389 €1133 Reclining female nude (51x75cm-20x30in) s.d.24 i. verso. 14-May-4 Dobiaschofsky, Bern #204/R est:3000 (S.FR 1800)
£1322 $2247 €1930 Chevaliers (88x98cm-35x39in) s.d.58 i. verso paper on board. 7-Nov-3 Dobiaschofsky, Bern #274/R est:4600 (S.FR 3000)
£1586 $2696 €2316 View from rose garden over Berne (70x95cm-28x37in) 7-Nov-3 Dobiaschofsky, Bern #273/R est:3600 (S.FR 3600)

MUHLENHAUPT, Kurt (1921-) German
£319 $521 €460 Herrmannstrasse (30x40cm-12x16in) mono.d.1984 i. stretcher. 27-Sep-3 Dannenberg, Berlin #600/R
£417 $679 €600 Pub corner in Kreuzberg (50x40cm-20x16in) mono.d.1985 s.i.d.1985 verso panel. 27-Sep-3 Dannenberg, Berlin #599/R
£490 $832 €700 Red goblin (48x38cm-19x15in) mono.d.1995 panel. 29-Nov-3 Bassenge, Berlin #7291
£1133 $2040 €1700 Goat (40x50cm-16x20in) mono.d. i. verso panel. 24-Apr-4 Dr Lehr, Berlin #319/R est:2400

MUHLHAN, Adolf (1886-?) German
£573 $986 €820 Sailing ship off Finkenwerder (72x100cm-28x39in) s. 4-Dec-3 Schopman, Hamburg #782/R
£1806 $2853 €2600 Hamburg harbour (70x105cm-28x41in) s. 6-Sep-3 Schopman, Hamburg #764/R est:2500

MUHLIG, Albert Ernst (1862-?) German
£331 $516 €490 Two poachers with dead deer, hunters with dog (24x26cm-9x10in) s. 28-Mar-3 Behringer, Furth #1121/R
£596 $1085 €900 Interior with peasant woman (28x28cm-11x11in) s.d.86 board on canvas. 21-Jun-4 Dorotheum, Vienna #322/R
Works on paper
£483 $801 €700 Winter in the mountains (13x21cm-5x8in) s.i. mixed media. 30-Sep-3 Dorotheum, Vienna #378/R

MUHLIG, Bernard (1829-1910) German
£537 $988 €800 Spring mountain (23x20cm-9x8in) s. board. 24-Mar-4 Hugo Ruef, Munich #1056/R
£1007 $1852 €1500 Children playing by village (18x24cm-7x9in) s. 25-Mar-4 Dr Fritz Nagel, Stuttgart #749/R est:900
£1074 $1997 €1600 Alpine landscape with a view of Wetterstein (21x26cm-8x10in) mono. 5-Mar-4 Wendl, Rudolstadt #3803/R est:1300
£1383 $2559 €2019 River with mountainous landscape (26x21cm-10x8in) 14-Mar-4 Agra, Warsaw #5/R (P.Z 10000)
£1457 $2652 €2200 Villa in the park in summer (37x58cm-15x23in) s. sold with two old postcards. 19-Jun-4 Bergmann, Erlangen #816 est:2200
Works on paper
£347 $549 €500 Bohemian village scene (41x30cm-16x12in) s. i.verso mixed media. 5-Sep-3 Wendl, Rudolstadt #3534/R

MUHLIG, Hugo (1854-1929) German
£800 $1456 €1200 Potato harvest (54x74cm-21x29in) s. 30-Jun-4 Neumeister, Munich #626/R
£1467 $2655 €2200 Behind the farmstead (49x35cm-19x14in) s. canvas on panel. 1-Apr-4 Van Ham, Cologne #1555/R est:1900
£2533 $4585 €3800 Fields by the Nierst, lower Rhine (23x26cm-9x10in) s. panel lit. 1-Apr-4 Van Ham, Cologne #1556/R est:3500
£2639 $4354 €3800 Peasant cart before old charcoal burner (27x45cm-11x18in) s. lit. 3-Jul-3 Van Ham, Cologne #1369/R est:5000
£3333 $6033 €5000 Ducks in summer meadow (25x21cm-10x8in) s. panel. 1-Apr-4 Van Ham, Cologne #1552/R est:2400
£7110 $11874 €10310 Winter woodland with hunters and dogs (24x32cm-9x13in) s. panel. 23-Jun-3 Philippe Schuler, Zurich #3536/R est:7000-9000 (S.FR 15500)
£9396 $16819 €14000 After the hunt (34x60cm-13x24in) s. 27-May-4 Dorotheum, Vienna #28/R est:9000-11000
£16107 $28832 €24000 Resting near a wintry battue (28x48cm-11x19in) s. panel. 27-May-4 Dorotheum, Vienna #70/R est:8000-12000
Works on paper
£483 $806 €700 Flower market (17x27cm-7x11in) W/C over pencil prov. study verso. 15-Nov-3 Lempertz, Koln #1524
£2615 $4498 €3818 Woman and sheep (25x34cm-10x13in) s. W/C. 3-Dec-3 AB Stockholms Auktionsverk #2641/R est:18000-20000 (S.KR 34000)

MUHLIG, Meno (1823-1873) German
£567 $948 €800 Two boys with horse and dog (37x45cm-15x18in) s. 17-Oct-3 Behringer, Furth #1531/R
£2027 $3628 €3000 Showmen resting (49x44cm-19x17in) lit. 8-May-4 Schloss Ahlden, Ahlden #753/R est:2400
£2113 $3655 €3000 Deer hunter (51x62cm-20x24in) s. 10-Dec-3 Dorotheum, Vienna #164/R est:3000-3400

MUHLSTOCK, Louis (1904-2001) Canadian
Works on paper
£472 $736 €684 Woman with pink shawl (37x25cm-15x10in) s. pastel chl. 26-Mar-3 Walker's, Ottawa #460/R est:600-800 (C.D 1100)
£901 $1532 €1315 Reclining nude woman (48x63cm-19x25in) s. col chk. 21-Nov-3 Walker's, Ottawa #109/R est:1200-1600 (C.D 2000)

MUHRMAN, Henry (1854-1916) American
Works on paper
£350 $637 €511 Domes and clock towers (46x35cm-18x14in) s.d.92 col chk. 1-Jul-4 Christie's, Kensington #215

MUIJSENBERG, Toon van den (1901-1967) Dutch
Works on paper
£340 $619 €500 Bavarian village (48x58cm-19x23in) s. gouache. 3-Feb-4 Christie's, Amsterdam #417
£612 $1114 €900 Woman in thorn, Limburg (46x54cm-18x21in) s. gouache. 3-Feb-4 Christie's, Amsterdam #365

MUIR, Bruce (1953-) Canadian
£778 $1276 €1136 Queen Charlotte Strait (132x178cm-52x70in) s. 28-May-3 Maynards, Vancouver #31 (C.D 1750)
£822 $1348 €1200 The rubbing beach (91x152cm-36x60in) s. 28-May-3 Maynards, Vancouver #32 (C.D 1850)

MUIR, James Nathan (1945-) American
Sculpture
£932 $1500 €1351 Whitworth sharpshooter (20cm-8in) num.24/30 bronze. 22-Aug-3 Altermann Galleries, Santa Fe #28
£932 $1500 €1351 Carried to safety (36x43cm-14x17in) bronze edition of 30. 22-Aug-3 Altermann Galleries, Santa Fe #29

MUIR, William (19th C) British
£290 $522 €423 Fishermen, Ailsa Craig in the distance (42x65cm-17x26in) s.d.1881. 22-Apr-4 Bonhams, Edinburgh #339

MUIRHEAD, David (1867-1930) British
£450 $819 €657 Driving sheep in an extensive landscape (30x45cm-12x18in) s. 1-Jul-4 Mellors & Kirk, Nottingham #848
£650 $1203 €949 Figures in an expansive landscape, mill beyond (51x76cm-20x30in) s. 15-Jan-4 Christie's, Kensington #786/R

MUIRHEAD, Lionel (fl.1870-1890) British
Works on paper
£3800 $6346 €5548 Ruins at Baalbec (23x33cm-9x13in) mono.i. W/C over pencil htd white. 14-Oct-3 Sotheby's, London #58/R est:2000-3000

MUJICA, Manuel Vicente (?) South American?
£305 $510 €445 Composition (42x33cm-17x13in) s. painted 1978. 19-Oct-3 Subastas Odalys, Caracas #88/R
£326 $600 €489 Flowers (57x48cm-22x19in) s. painted 1965. 27-Jun-4 Subastas Odalys, Caracas #2/R
£367 $675 €551 Still life (51x61cm-20x24in) s. painted 1968. 27-Jun-4 Subastas Odalys, Caracas #73/R
£449 $750 €656 Composition with two figures (60x50cm-24x20in) s. painted 1974. 19-Oct-3 Subastas Odalys, Caracas #48/R
£492 $885 €718 Flowers (56x46cm-22x18in) s. painted 1965. 25-Apr-4 Subastas Odalys, Caracas #71/R
£662 $1125 €967 Still life (61x74cm-24x29in) s. painted 1980. 23-Nov-3 Subastas Odalys, Caracas #137/R
£802 $1460 €1203 Interior with woman (92x73cm-36x29in) s. 21-Jun-4 Subastas Odalys, Caracas #42
£1030 $1875 €1545 Big still life (92x73cm-36x29in) s. painted 1960. 21-Jun-4 Subastas Odalys, Caracas #115/R
£1141 $1940 €1666 Interior with Eddy (100x80cm-39x31in) s. painted 1971-73. 23-Nov-3 Subastas Odalys, Caracas #88/R

MULAS, Franco (1938-) Italian
£483 $806 €700 Water and rocks (62x60cm-24x24in) s. s.i.d.1992 verso board. 13-Nov-3 Finarte Semenzato, Rome #234/R

MULAS, Ugo (1928-1973) Italian
£621 $1037 €900 Lovers (75x90cm-30x35in) s. painted 1960. 13-Nov-3 Finarte Semenzato, Rome #342

MULCAHY, Michael (1952-) Irish
£979 $1664 €1400 Vegetation (66x94cm-26x37in) s. prov. 25-Nov-3 De Veres Art Auctions, Dublin #201/R est:1500-2000
Works on paper
£629 $1070 €900 Glasshouse Mountain (56x76cm-22x30in) s.d.85 mixed media. 25-Nov-3 De Veres Art Auctions, Dublin #133/R
£671 $1188 €1000 Warrior's song 28 (41x30cm-16x12in) s.d.1989 verso mixed media prov.exhib. 27-Apr-4 Whyte's, Dublin #94/R

MULDER, Anne (1926-) Dutch
£367 $656 €550 Interior with mother and child (49x59cm-19x23in) s. 11-May-4 Vendu Notarishuis, Rotterdam #656/R

MULDER, Johan (19th C) Dutch
£483 $806 €700 Wood cutters by the forest pond (74x91cm-29x36in) s. 11-Nov-3 Vendu Notarishuis, Rotterdam #34/R

MULDERS, Jean (1913-) Belgian
£1867 $3435 €2800 Le vieil homme et son fidele ami (110x80cm-43x31in) s. 14-Jun-4 Gros & Delettrez, Paris #539/R est:1500-2300

MULDERS, Johannes (1899-1989) Dutch
£2397 $4075 €3500 View of village with children in the foreground (58x68cm-23x27in) s.d.1926. 5-Nov-3 Vendue Huis, Gravenhage #390/R est:4000-5000

MULDERS, Marc (1958-) Dutch
£4333 $7973 €6500 Lilies I (60x50cm-24x20in) s.i.d.94 verso prov. 8-Jun-4 Sotheby's, Amsterdam #312/R est:3000-5000

£4667	$8587	€7000	Lelies (90x130cm-35x51in) s.i.d.Feb 98 verso. 9-Jun-4 Christie's, Amsterdam #392/R est:4000-6000
£5333	$9813	€8000	Scarface III (240x130cm-94x51in) s.i.d.1999 verso. 9-Jun-4 Christie's, Amsterdam #390/R est:8000-12000
Works on paper			
£296	$545	€450	Salamander (76x56cm-30x22in) s.d.98 W/C. 28-Jun-4 Sotheby's, Amsterdam #195/R

MULERTT, Carel Eugene (1869-1915) American

£2568	$4750	€3749	Sewing by a sun filled window (79x107cm-31x42in) s. 10-Mar-4 Doyle, New York #39/R est:1500-2500
Works on paper			
£401	$750	€602	Woman and child at the beach (24x47cm-9x19in) s.d.1910 W/C. 25-Jul-4 Bonhams & Butterfields, San Francisco #6165/R

MULHAUPT, Frederick J (1871-1938) American

£1453	$2500	€2121	Ship in Harbour (18x13cm-7x5in) s. cigar box panel. 7-Dec-3 Freeman, Philadelphia #136 est:1500-2500
£1694	$3100	€2473	Englewood women's club (41x61cm-16x24in) s.d.1899. 31-Jan-4 South Bay, Long Island #116
£2391	$3850	€3491	Shoreline beach scene (23x23cm-9x9in) s. panel. 20-Aug-3 James Julia, Fairfield #1589/R est:3000-4000
£2616	$4500	€3819	Boating on a canal. River view and landscape (32x27cm-13x11in) s. canvasboard one double-sided pair. 3-Dec-3 Doyle, New York #218/R est:6000-8000
£2778	$4500	€4028	Misty morning at the dock (18x34cm-7x13in) s.d.10 board. 8-Aug-3 Barridorf, Portland #298/R est:2000-3000
£4144	$7500	€6050	Venus (26x35cm-10x14in) s.d.1910 panel prov. 31-Mar-4 Sotheby's, New York #54/R est:6000-8000

MULHOLLAND, Sydney A (19th C) British

Works on paper			
£280	$456	€409	Gondolas on the Grand Canal, Venice (44x69cm-17x27in) s. W/C. 24-Sep-3 Peter Wilson, Nantwich #92

MULIER, Pieter (elder) (1615-1670) Dutch

£16000	$27680	€23360	A Smalschip and a Man-of-War in choppy seas, other vessels beyond (29x37cm-11x15in) panel prov. 11-Dec-3 Sotheby's, London #140/R est:10000-15000

MULIER, Pieter (school) (17th C) Dutch

£9868	$18158	€15000	Italian landscape with trees and soldier resting by river (75x99cm-30x39in) 24-Jun-4 Dr Fritz Nagel, Stuttgart #594/R est:7000

MULIER, Pieter (younger) (1637-1701) Dutch

£3500	$6405	€5110	Shipping off a rocky coast in a storm (27x33cm-11x13in) 6-Jul-4 Sotheby's, Olympia #548/R est:4000-6000
£7895	$14526	€12000	Stormy seascape (145x190cm-57x75in) 22-Jun-4 Babuino, Rome #77/R est:8000-10000

MULIER, Pieter (younger-attrib) (1637-1701) Dutch

£3000	$5100	€4380	Flood (28x34cm-11x13in) oil paper on canvas prov. 29-Oct-3 Bonhams, New Bond Street #52/R est:3000-4000

MULLEN, Fritz (1814-1861) American/German

£304	$550	€444	Autumnal scene by the shore (41x51cm-16x20in) s.d.Nov 1901. 3-Apr-4 Neal Auction Company, New Orleans #832

MULLENER, Johann Karl (1768-1832) Swiss

Works on paper			
£1322	$2247	€1930	Landscapes (47x60cm-19x24in) W/C two. 7-Nov-3 Dobiaschofsky, Bern #8/R est:5000 (S.FR 3000)

MULLER, A (19/20th C) ?

£1528	$2490	€2200	Winter pleasures (43x58cm-17x23in) 29-Sep-3 Dr Fritz Nagel, Stuttgart #7164/R est:2000

MULLER, Adolf (19th C) Hungarian

£1736	$2830	€2500	Hungarian market (33x49cm-13x19in) s.i.d.1880 panel. 24-Sep-3 Neumeister, Munich #509/R est:1200

MULLER, Albert (1897-1926) Swiss

£1100	$1980	€1650	Bodensee (65x79cm-26x31in) s.d.1930. 26-Apr-4 Rieber, Stuttgart #1069/R est:1650
£1542	$2621	€2251	Rear view of nude (55x39cm-22x15in) s. prov.exhib.lit. 7-Nov-3 Dobiaschofsky, Bern #125/R est:7000 (S.FR 3500)
£1957	$3580	€2857	Wartenberg (27x36cm-11x14in) mono. board on canvas prov.exhib.lit. 7-Jun-4 Christie's, Zurich #82/R est:5000-7000 (S.FR 4500)
£5652	$10343	€8252	Landscape in moonlight (35x40cm-14x16in) prov.exhib.lit. 7-Jun-4 Christie's, Zurich #83/R est:15000-18000 (S.FR 13000)
£9441	$16049	€13500	Dream picture (89x71cm-35x28in) s. prov.exhib.lit. 29-Nov-3 Villa Grisebach, Berlin #181/R est:12000-15000
£100000	$183000	€146000	Extensive landscape (110x100cm-43x39in) s.d.25 prov.exhib.lit. 7-Jun-4 Christie's, Zurich #87/R est:200000-300000 (S.FR 230000)
Works on paper			
£271	$462	€396	Portrait sketch of woman (22x17cm-9x7in) Indian ink. 18-Nov-3 Hans Widmer, St Gallen #1156 (S.FR 600)
£271	$462	€396	On the train (18x22cm-7x9in) pencil. 18-Nov-3 Hans Widmer, St Gallen #1157/R (S.FR 600)
£271	$462	€396	Little Kaspar at the easel, E L Kirchner looking out of the window (22x17cm-9x7in) Indian ink sketch. 18-Nov-3 Hans Widmer, St Gallen #1159 (S.FR 600)
£317	$538	€463	Rear view of a standing nude (47x32cm-19x13in) chk chl exec. c.1925. 22-Nov-3 Burkhard, Luzern #65/R (S.FR 700)
£317	$538	€463	Sailing boat (17x22cm-7x9in) Indian ink sketch. 18-Nov-3 Hans Widmer, St Gallen #1158 (S.FR 700)
£522	$955	€762	Two figures. Figure and half-length portrait (21x17cm-8x7in) two. 4-Jun-4 Zofingen, Switzerland #2891 (S.FR 1200)
£524	$892	€750	Head of E L Kirchner (25x16cm-10x6in) Indian ink prov. 26-Nov-3 Lempertz, Koln #870/R
£543	$923	€793	Portrait of Anna Muller (21x17cm-8x7in) col chk pencil prov. 22-Nov-3 Burkhard, Luzern #68/R (S.FR 1200)
£543	$923	€793	The twins Kaspar and Judith (50x34cm-20x13in) chk chl. 22-Nov-3 Burkhard, Luzern #69/R (S.FR 1200)
£642	$1072	€931	Boccia player (21x17cm-8x7in) wax chk Indian ink sold with photos. 23-Jun-3 Philippe Schuler, Zurich #3267 (S.FR 1400)
£647	$1157	€945	Variety show in Dresden (17x21cm-7x8in) wax chk. 12-May-4 Dobiaschofsky, Bern #1858/R est:1800 (S.FR 1500)
£733	$1312	€1070	Village with church (17x22cm-7x9in) Indian ink oil chk. 12-May-4 Dobiaschofsky, Bern #1859/R est:1900 (S.FR 1700)
£776	$1389	€1133	Mountains (17x22cm-7x9in) wax chk. 14-May-4 Dobiaschofsky, Bern #221/R est:2000 (S.FR 1800)
£957	$1750	€1397	The artist's family in the mountains (17x21cm-7x8in) chk. 4-Jun-4 Zofingen, Switzerland #2892/R (S.FR 2200)
£1086	$1846	€1586	Untitled (24x17cm-9x7in) chl double-sided four. 25-Nov-3 Germann, Zurich #146/R est:1500-2000 (S.FR 2400)
£1092	$1987	€1594	Nude (33x32cm-13x13in) Indian ink. 17-Jun-4 Kornfeld, Bern #607 est:2000 (S.FR 2500)
£1130	$2069	€1650	Farmer working in the field with a wheelbarrow (50x34cm-20x13in) chl. 7-Jun-4 Christie's, Zurich #86/R est:3000-5000 (S.FR 2600)
£1310	$2384	€1913	Landscape in Tessin (25x31cm-10x12in) W/C double-sided. 17-Jun-4 Kornfeld, Bern #604 est:2500 (S.FR 3000)
£1397	$2543	€2040	Portrait of Ernst Ludwig Kirchner. Nude in room. Lovers. pencil ink W/C three. 17-Jun-4 Kornfeld, Bern #609 est:2000 (S.FR 3200)
£1739	$3183	€2539	Group of houses (23x27cm-9x11in) s. W/C over pencil prov. 7-Jun-4 Christie's, Zurich #84/R est:5000-8000 (S.FR 4000)
£2183	$3974	€3187	Tessin landscape (34x48cm-13x19in) col chk. 17-Jun-4 Kornfeld, Bern #605 est:6000 (S.FR 5000)
£2882	$5245	€4208	Trees in landscape (36x54cm-14x21in) W/C over pencil. 17-Jun-4 Kornfeld, Bern #606 est:6000 (S.FR 6600)
£3913	$7161	€5713	Girl sitting at a table (63x46cm-25x18in) s. wax crayon lit. 7-Jun-4 Christie's, Zurich #85/R est:10000-15000 (S.FR 9000)
£9955	$17222	€14534	Forest passage (49x35cm-19x14in) num.1252 W/C col pencil lit. 9-Dec-3 Sotheby's, Zurich #81/R est:18000-25000 (S.FR 22000)

MULLER, Alfredo (1869-1940) Italian

Works on paper			
£530	$964	€800	Village (30x38cm-12x15in) s. pencil. 21-Jun-4 Pandolfini, Florence #225

MULLER, Anton (19/20th C) American

£695	$1300	€1015	Winter landscapes (20x28cm-8x11in) s. board pair. 25-Feb-4 Dallas Auction Gallery, Dallas #396/R

MULLER, Anton (1853-1897) Austrian

£281	$450	€410	Child with geese (41x51cm-16x20in) s. 21-Sep-3 William Jenack, New York #264

MULLER, August (1836-1885) German

£567	$1020	€850	Young girl writing at table (32x26cm-13x10in) s.i. lit. 22-Apr-4 Allgauer, Kempten #3660/R

MULLER, C (?) ?

£1408	$2437	€2000	Hunter and girl in national costume in the Inn (23x17cm-9x7in) s. panel. 10-Dec-3 Dorotheum, Vienna #66/R est:1500-1800
£1537	$2750	€2244	The chemist (20x30cm-8x12in) s. 8-Jan-4 James Julia, Fairfield #676/R est:4000-6000
£3636	$6255	€5200	Reclining nude in a harem, resting while watched by a eunuch (31x39cm-12x15in) s.d.1840 i.d. stretcher. 3-Dec-3 Neumeister, Munich #680/R est:5500

MULLER, Carl (?) ?

Works on paper			
£369	$679	€550	Interior - red salon (47x37cm-19x15in) s.d.915 W/C. 26-Mar-4 Dorotheum, Vienna #348/R
£608	$1070	€900	Study (43x31cm-17x12in) chk prov. 22-May-4 Lempertz, Koln #1440/R
£1472	$2400	€2149	Der Michaelerplatz im Wien (23x28cm-9x11in) s.d.1903 gouache over pencil paper on board. 25-Sep-3 Christie's, Rockefeller NY #546/R est:2000-3000

MULLER, Carl Wilhelm (1839-1904) German

£2335	$4250	€3409	Venetian wedding (71x102cm-28x40in) s. 19-Jun-4 Jackson's, Cedar Falls #43/R est:3500-4500

MULLER, Charles Louis (1815-1892) French

£1034	$1717	€1500	Portrait de femme (148x114cm-58x45in) s. 2-Oct-3 Sotheby's, Paris #111/R
£3333	$6067	€5000	Spinner woman dressed in traditional Italian dress (70x50cm-28x20in) s.d.62 lit. 3-Jul-4 Geble, Radolfzell #418/R est:1200

MULLER, Charles Louis (attrib) (1815-1892) French

£299	$550	€437	Harem beauty (28x20cm-11x8in) s.d.1885. 25-Jun-4 Freeman, Philadelphia #134/R

MULLER, Christian Benjamin (1690-1758) German

Works on paper			
£546	$1000	€797	Baccahanale (20x28cm-8x11in) s.verso pen black ink wash gouache. 29-Jan-4 Swann Galleries, New York #293/R

MULLER, Crefeld (?) ?
Sculpture
£1600 $2768 €2336 Girl, standing nude, drinking from vessel (86cm-34in) st.sig. bronze marble base. 10-Dec-3 Hamptons Fine Art, Godalming #333/R est:1500-2000

MULLER, E (20th C) German
£838 $1542 €1257 Hygienia (170x115cm-67x45in) s. 14-Jun-4 Lilla Bukowskis, Stockholm #513/R (S.KR 11500)

MULLER, Edmund Gustavus (fl.1836-1871) British
£450 $828 €657 Windmill on a country lane with a shepherd driving a flock of sheep (20x39cm-8x15in) s.d.1850 panel. 8-Jun-4 Bonhams, Knightsbridge #165/R
£450 $842 €675 Making corn dollies at harvest time (29x44cm-11x17in) s. 26-Jul-4 Bonhams, Bath #69/R

MULLER, Eduard Josef (1851-1922) German
£403 $749 €600 Village at foot of fortress (86x115cm-34x45in) s. 6-Mar-4 Arnold, Frankfurt #796/R
£500 $915 €750 On the Nied (51x70cm-20x28in) s.i.d.10. 5-Jun-4 Arnold, Frankfurt #681/R

MULLER, Emma von (1859-1925) Austrian
£430 $731 €628 Two connoisseurs in wine cellar (24x31cm-9x12in) s.i. board. 28-Nov-3 Zofingen, Switzerland #2645 (S.FR 950)
£543 $869 €793 Girl's portrait (27x21cm-11x8in) s. panel. 16-Sep-3 Philippe Schuler, Zurich #3346 (S.FR 1200)
£671 $1228 €1000 Portrait of a young girl in national costume (27x21cm-11x8in) s. panel lit. 8-Jul-4 Allgauer, Kempten #2171/R
£905 $1538 €1321 Interior with spinner (30x22cm-12x9in) mono. panel. 1-Dec-3 Koller, Zurich #6473/R est:1500-2500 (S.FR 2000)
£1131 $1923 €1651 Young woman from the Vorarlbeg wearing hat (26x21cm-10x8in) s. board. 19-Nov-3 Fischer, Luzern #1156/R est:3500-4500 (S.FR 2500)
£1149 $2022 €1700 Happy girl with knitting (25x17cm-10x7in) s.d.1887 s. verso panel. 22-May-4 Lempertz, Koln #1569/R est:2000
£1250 $2063 €1800 Peasant girl (27x21cm-11x8in) s. board. 2-Jul-3 Neumeister, Munich #726/R est:1000
£4000 $7280 €6000 Girl playing zither (60x63cm-24x25in) s. 30-Jun-4 Neumeister, Munich #628/R est:5000

MULLER, Erich Martin (1888-1972) German
£625 $1019 €900 Passau cathedral (48x62cm-19x24in) s. board. 25-Sep-3 Neumeister, Munich #2827/R
£1332 $2078 €1945 Orchard with blossoming tree (72x74cm-28x29in) s.indis.d.1912. 30-Mar-3 Agra, Warsaw #37/R est:5000 (P.Z 8500)

MULLER, Ernst (1823-1875) German
£315 $526 €450 Wedding announcement (36x28cm-14x11in) s.d.1898. 26-Jun-3 Weidler, Nurnberg #307/R

MULLER, Ernst Emmanuel (1844-1915) German
£454 $785 €663 Vase of flowers (62x45cm-24x18in) s. cardboard painted c.1910. 14-Dec-3 Agra, Warsaw #71/R (P.Z 3000)

MULLER, Felix (1897-1977) German
£479 $748 €700 Village (48x61cm-19x24in) s. board. 10-Apr-3 Weidler, Nurnberg #4411
£1096 $1710 €1600 Portrait / self portrait (67x47cm-26x19in) s.d.1928 board. 10-Apr-3 Weidler, Nurnberg #4408/R
Works on paper
£479 $748 €700 Neunkirchen am Brand (53x76cm-21x30in) s.d.1956 chl col chk oil. 10-Apr-3 Weidler, Nurnberg #4409/R
£479 $748 €700 Violinist - self portrait (37x28cm-15x11in) s. pencil. 10-Apr-3 Weidler, Nurnberg #4412

MULLER, Frank Christian (1860-1938) American
£543 $1000 €793 Battleships engaged in battle (61x102cm-24x40in) s.d.1901. 9-Jun-4 Alderfer's, Hatfield #421/R est:800-1200

MULLER, Franz (1843-1929) German
£671 $1235 €1000 Pieta (21x29cm-8x11in) s. panel. 26-Mar-4 Bolland & Marotz, Bremen #566/R

MULLER, Franz Adolf Christian (1841-1903) Swiss
£1724 $3086 €2517 Chateau de Chillon on Lake Geneva (67x99cm-26x39in) one of pair. 14-May-4 Dobiaschofsky, Bern #63/R est:4500 (S.FR 4000)
£3017 $5401 €4405 Montreux with the Dents du Midi (65x104cm-26x41in) s.d.1900 one of pair. 14-May-4 Dobiaschofsky, Bern #61/R est:5000 (S.FR 7000)

MULLER, Friedrich Wilhelm (18/19th C) German
£952 $1705 €1390 Vierwaldstattersee (82x111cm-32x44in) s.d. 22-Mar-4 Philippe Schuler, Zurich #4421/R (S.FR 2200)

MULLER, Fritz (19th C) German
£320 $502 €464 Gypsy fiddler (60x49cm-24x19in) s.i. sold with three others by same hand. 28-Aug-3 Christie's, Kensington #56
£463 $750 €676 Gentleman reading the morning paper (23x18cm-9x7in) s. panel. 9-Aug-3 Auctions by the Bay, Alameda #1499/R
£470 $813 €686 Half length portrait of a bearded old man smoking a cheroot (29x23cm-11x9in) s. prov. 9-Dec-3 Bristol Auction Rooms #428/R
£494 $800 €721 Gentleman enjoying a beer (36x30cm-14x12in) s. panel. 9-Aug-3 Auctions by the Bay, Alameda #1498/R
£560 $1003 €818 Bedouins resting at Tolga Oasis (60x82cm-24x32in) mono.i i. verso. 12-May-4 Dobiaschofsky, Bern #819/R (S.FR 1300)

MULLER, G (?) ?
£1042 $1646 €1500 Bridge in Sachsen, Switzerland (55x81cm-22x32in) i. verso. 19-Sep-3 Schloss Ahlden, Ahlden #1457/R est:1400

MULLER, Gregor (attrib) (17th C) Austrian
Works on paper
£267 $491 €400 Saint Alois et Saint Stanislas (33x20cm-13x8in) i. pen brown ink grey wash. 11-Jun-4 Maigret, Paris #15/R

MULLER, Hans (?) German
£300 $501 €438 Still life of shellfish and fruit (60x81cm-24x32in) s. 20-Oct-3 Bonhams, Bath #36
£419 $750 €612 Mountain town (61x76cm-24x30in) s. 8-May-4 Susanin's, Chicago #6160/R
Sculpture
£950 $1530 €1378 Racing charioteer pulled by two horses backed by masonry (56cm-22in) s. brown pat. bronze. 13-Aug-3 Andrew Hartley, Ilkley #160/R

MULLER, Heinrich (1885-1960) Swiss
£655 $1192 €956 Red amaryllis in a glass vase (46x38cm-18x15in) s.d.1931. 16-Jun-4 Fischer, Luzern #2292/R (S.FR 1500)
£917 $1669 €1339 Still life with fruit and a model of a bird (34x45cm-13x18in) s.d.1936 cardboard. 16-Jun-4 Fischer, Luzern #2291/R (S.FR 2100)
£1174 $2148 €1714 Still life with clock (55x70cm-22x28in) s.d.1913 prov. 7-Jun-4 Christie's, Zurich #41/R est:2000-3000 (S.FR 2700)

MULLER, Heinrich (1903-1978) Swiss
£407 $692 €594 Still life with model ship (75x75cm-30x30in) s. 18-Nov-3 Hans Widmer, St Gallen #1160 (S.FR 900)

MULLER, Heinrich Edouard (1823-1853) German
£435 $713 €600 Landscape with girls tying flowers (21x34cm-8x13in) mono.d.21.Sept.1846 paper. 30-May-3 Bassenge, Berlin #7891
£1284 $2259 €1900 Traunstein on Traunsee (27x37cm-11x15in) d.i.Sept 1845 paper. 22-May-4 Lempertz, Koln #1441 est:800

MULLER, Heinz (1872-?) German
Sculpture
£963 $1599 €1406 Hunter with dog (42cm-17in) s. pat bronze. 15-Jun-3 Agra, Warsaw #37/R est:4000 (P.Z 6000)

MULLER, J (18th C) German
£11176 $19000 €16317 Castillo de Chapultepec (55x69cm-22x27in) s. painted c.1850 prov. 19-Nov-3 Sotheby's, New York #76/R est:10000-15000

MULLER, Jacques (1930-1997) Belgian
£667 $1213 €1000 Paris, Grands Boulevards (24x33cm-9x13in) s. 4-Jul-4 Eric Pillon, Calais #244/R
£671 $1242 €1000 Paris, Place de la Republique (24x33cm-9x13in) s. 14-Mar-4 Eric Pillon, Calais #256/R
£704 $1218 €1000 Paris, Grands Boulevards (24x33cm-9x13in) s. 14-Dec-3 Eric Pillon, Calais #218/R
£753 $1281 €1100 Paris, Grands Boulevards (23x32cm-9x13in) s. 9-Nov-3 Eric Pillon, Calais #228/R
£804 $1343 €1150 Paris, Champs-Elysees et Arc de Triomphe (24x33cm-9x13in) s. 29-Jun-3 Eric Pillon, Calais #243/R
£863 $1416 €1200 Place du Chatelet. s. 6-Jun-3 David Kahn, Paris #51

MULLER, Jan (1922-1958) American
£9341 $17000 €13638 Mountain path with horse and rider (91x76cm-36x30in) s.i.verso prov.exhib. 29-Jun-4 Sotheby's, New York #448/R est:7000-10000

MULLER, Jan Harmensz (c.1571-1628) Dutch
Prints
£8000 $14320 €12000 Bellona leading the royal army against the Turks (70x50cm-28x20in) copperplate after Bartholomaus Spranger. 13-May-4 Bassenge, Berlin #5234/R est:5500
£9441 $16049 €13500 Minerva and Mercury preparing Perseus for battle (57x40cm-22x16in) copperplate after Bartholomaus Spranger. 27-Nov-3 Bassenge, Berlin #5281/R est:6000
£13986 $23776 €20000 Bellona leading the royal troops against the Turks (35x51cm-14x20in) i. copperplate two. 21-Nov-3 Reiss & Sohn, Konigstein #109/R est:1000

MULLER, Johann Georg (1913-1986) German
£3497 $5944 €5000 Portrait (47x53cm-19x21in) s.d.66 i.d.66 verso tempera board. 29-Nov-3 Villa Grisebach, Berlin #347/R est:6000-8000
£10345 $17276 €15000 Still life with apples (60x72cm-24x28in) s.d.1978 board on canvas. 13-Nov-3 Neumeister, Munich #590/R est:15000-18000
£12667 $22673 €19000 Reclining figure (55x78cm-22x31in) s.d. i.d. verso board. 13-May-4 Neumeister, Munich #707/R est:18000-20000
£13333 $24400 €20000 Untitled - still life with chair (50x70cm-20x28in) s.d.56 board on canvas. 4-Jun-4 Lempertz, Koln #320/R est:15000
£24476 $41608 €35000 Morning (110x119cm-43x47in) s.d.67 prov.exhib. 29-Nov-3 Villa Grisebach, Berlin #344/R est:30000-40000
£73826 $132148 €110000 Palatina, evening after harvest (120x150cm-47x59in) s.d.1983 s.i.d. verso. 25-May-4 Dorotheum, Vienna #100/R est:45000-50000
Works on paper
£14667 $26987 €22000 Antares. Composition (120x90cm-47x35in) s.d.1970 i.verso mixed media canvas double-sided exhib. 12-Jun-4 Villa Grisebach, Berlin #403/R est:20000-25000

MULLER, Johann Marius Hartmann (1863-1945) Norwegian

£322	$588	€470	Archipelago (40x60cm-16x24in) s. 2-Feb-4 Blomqvist, Lysaker #1194/R (N.KR 4000)

MULLER, Josef Felix (1955-) Swiss

£679	$1154	€991	Untitled (37x50cm-15x20in) s.d.1987 verso prov.exhib. 25-Nov-3 Germann, Zurich #854 est:2000-2500 (S.FR 1500)
£814	$1385	€1188	Untitled (37x50cm-15x20in) s.d.1987 verso prov.exhib. 25-Nov-3 Germann, Zurich #853 est:2000-2500 (S.FR 1800)

MULLER, Judith (1923-1977) Swiss

£302	$540	€441	Untitled (18x22cm-7x9in) s. verso. 12-May-4 Dobiaschofsky, Bern #3786 (S.FR 700)

MULLER, Karl (1818-1893) German

£629	$1082	€900	Woman in an interior (30x39cm-12x15in) s.i. canvas on board. 7-Dec-3 Sotheby's, Amsterdam #664/R

MULLER, Karl Erich (1917-) German

£300	$540	€450	Autumn in Krollwitz (44x59cm-17x23in) s.i.d. i. verso board. 24-Apr-4 Dr Lehr, Berlin #329/R

MULLER, Leopold (19th C) German?

£1549	$2572	€2200	Dog with dead deer (55x71cm-22x28in) 16-Jun-3 Dorotheum, Vienna #65/R est:2000-2500

MULLER, Leopold (20th C) Belgian?

£433	$784	€650	Nature morte aux fleurs (61x45cm-24x18in) s. 30-Mar-4 Campo & Campo, Antwerp #188

MULLER, Leopold Carl (1834-1892) German

£350	$594	€500	Girl wearing hat (24x16cm-9x6in) i. verso oil sketch canvas on board. 20-Nov-3 Dorotheum, Salzburg #143/R
£470	$841	€700	Le beguinage a Bruges (90x75cm-35x30in) s. 25-May-4 Campo & Campo, Antwerp #172
£1944	$3306	€2800	Portrait of young woman (26x16cm-10x6in) st.sig. panel. 28-Oct-3 Dorotheum, Vienna #193/R est:1500-1700
£5500	$10010	€8030	Exotic beauty (28x20cm-11x8in) s. i.verso panel prov. 16-Jun-4 Christie's, Kensington #271/R est:4000-6000
£6711	$11879	€10000	Cairo street (81x61cm-32x24in) s. 28-Apr-4 Wiener Kunst Auktionen, Vienna #36/R est:5000-9000
£10000	$17000	€14600	Bedouin (60x34cm-24x13in) s. panel. 18-Nov-3 Sotheby's, London #341/R est:10000-15000
£16107	$28832	€24000	Water carriers (51x83cm-20x33in) s. panel lit. 27-May-4 Hassfurther, Vienna #63/R est:15000-25000
Works on paper			
£5816	$9712	€8200	Marche au Caire (29x45cm-11x18in) s. W/C gouache. 16-Jun-3 Gros & Delettrez, Paris #492/R est:8000-10000

MULLER, Leopold Carl (style) (1834-1892) German

£5960	$10848	€9000	Market in Cairo (138x218cm-54x86in) after the original in Belvedere, Vienna. 21-Jun-4 Dorotheum, Vienna #176/R est:3000-3600

MULLER, Leopold Carl and Marie (19th C) German

£1528	$2597	€2200	Portrait studies. s. canvas board three. 28-Oct-3 Dorotheum, Vienna #194/R est:1800-2000

MULLER, M (19th C) ?

£2055	$3493	€3000	La chasse au tigre (56x74cm-22x29in) s.i.d.1894. 5-Nov-3 Rabourdin & Choppin de Janvry, Paris #64/R est:3500-4000

MULLER, Max (1911-1991) Danish

£622	$1132	€933	Bell terrace, summer scene (37x48cm-15x19in) s.d.47. 19-Jun-4 Rasmussen, Havnen #4215/R (D.KR 7000)

MULLER, Mela (c.1887-?) Hungarian

Works on paper			
£467	$859	€700	Portrait of a young lady (64x78cm-25x31in) s. pastel. 11-Jun-4 Wendl, Rudolstadt #4186/R

MULLER, Moritz (snr) (1841-1899) German

£547	$980	€810	Deer fighting in the mountains (37x32cm-15x13in) s.d.1873. 8-May-4 Dawo, Saarbrucken #40/R
£570	$1044	€850	Fox with his prey in a winter landscape (27x34cm-11x13in) s.i.d.93 cardboard. 9-Jul-4 Dawo, Saarbrucken #59/R
£1200	$2148	€1800	Successful hunt (50x65cm-20x26in) s.i. lit. 14-May-4 Schloss Ahlden, Ahlden #2893/R est:1400

MULLER, Moritz Karl Friedrich (1807-1865) German

£1528	$2490	€2200	Painter with young peasant girl inside mountain hut (34x28cm-13x11in) mono. panel. 24-Sep-3 Neumeister, Munich #510/R est:2000
£2667	$4853	€4000	Two peasant girls listening to boy playing flute by fire in evening (62x53cm-24x21in) s. bears d.1858. 30-Jun-4 Neumeister, Munich #627/R est:5000

MULLER, Morten (1828-1911) Norwegian

£569	$1047	€854	Woman in landscape (11x19cm-4x7in) s. panel. 14-Jun-4 Blomqvist, Lysaker #1270/R (N.KR 7000)
£1733	$3155	€2600	Mountainous landscape with stream (56x98cm-22x39in) s. 1-Jul-4 Van Ham, Cologne #1517 est:1000
£2402	$4299	€3507	Mountain landscape, Romsdalen, Norway (40x58cm-16x23in) s/ i.stretcher. 22-Mar-4 Blomqvist, Oslo #340/R est:40000-50000 (N.KR 30000)
£3672	$6132	€5361	Horses and man by woodland lake (58x79cm-23x31in) s.d.60. 13-Oct-3 Blomqvist, Oslo #282/R est:45000-55000 (N.KR 43000)
£4441	$7416	€6484	On a road along the water (67x90cm-26x35in) s.d.1853. 13-Oct-3 Blomqvist, Oslo #281/R est:60000-80000 (N.KR 52000)

MULLER, Morten (attrib) (1828-1911) Norwegian

£436	$803	€650	Fallen tree (40x54cm-16x21in) s. 25-Mar-4 Hagelstam, Helsinki #1049

MULLER, Otto (1874-1930) German

£195804	$336783	€280000	Dancer with veil (120x90cm-47x35in) s. prov.exhib.lit. 5-Dec-3 Ketterer, Munich #40/R est:280000-350000
Prints			
£2183	$3974	€3187	Mother with child. s.i. lithograph. 17-Jun-4 Kornfeld, Bern #598 est:6000 (S.FR 5000)
£2657	$4571	€3800	Stream (39x28cm-15x11in) s.i. lithograph one of 8 prov. 5-Dec-3 Ketterer, Munich #56/R est:5000-7000
£2667	$4907	€4000	Girl between two leaves (28x37cm-11x15in) s. woodcut. 10-Jun-4 Hauswedell & Nolte, Hamburg #509/R est:5000
£2667	$4907	€4000	Two crouching female nudes (29x40cm-11x16in) s. lithograph exec. 1921-22. 11-Jun-4 Villa Grisebach, Berlin #1542/R est:7000-9000
£2685	$4940	€4000	Girl between two leafy plants (28x37cm-11x15in) s. woodcut. 26-Mar-4 Ketterer, Hamburg #570/R est:4000-6000
£2797	$4755	€4000	Russian house with sunflowers (29x40cm-11x16in) s. lithograph. 29-Nov-3 Villa Grisebach, Berlin #149/R est:4000-6000
£2937	$5052	€4200	Three girls in profile (29x39cm-11x15in) s. lithograph. 2-Dec-3 Hauswedell & Nolte, Hamburg #452/R est:5000
£3125	$5219	€4500	Schmiedeberg station (26x38cm-10x15in) s.i. lithograph prov. 24-Oct-3 Ketterer, Hamburg #483/R est:5000-6000
£3636	$6255	€5200	Three girls in profile (29x39cm-11x15in) s. lithograph. 2-Dec-3 Hauswedell & Nolte, Hamburg #453/R est:6000
£3667	$6563	€5500	Seated figure (30x21cm-12x8in) s. lithograph. 15-May-4 Bassenge, Berlin #7051/R est:7000
£3893	$7162	€5800	Mother and child 2 (26x19cm-10x7in) s.i. lithograph. 26-Mar-4 Ketterer, Hamburg #571/R est:3000-4000
£4000	$7360	€6000	Polish family (26x19cm-10x7in) s. W/C col chks on lithograph. 10-Jun-4 Hauswedell & Nolte, Hamburg #504/R est:8000
£4000	$7320	€6000	Circus couple (26x19cm-10x7in) mono. lithograph. 5-Jun-4 Lempertz, Koln #895/R est:5800
£4196	$7217	€6000	Two girls with hand mirror II (42x31cm-17x12in) s. lithograph. 2-Dec-3 Hauswedell & Nolte, Hamburg #450/R est:8000
£4196	$7133	€6000	Schmiedeberg station (26x38cm-10x15in) s. lithograph. 29-Nov-3 Bassenge, Berlin #6919/R est:8000
£4362	$8027	€6500	Girl sitting on shore (37x26cm-15x10in) s. lithograph. 26-Mar-4 Ketterer, Hamburg #572/R est:6000-8000
£4452	$7568	€6500	Wooded landscape. lithograph. 6-Nov-3 Piasa, Paris #141/R
£4469	$8000	€6525	Selbstbildnis nacht rechts (39x30cm-15x12in) s. lithograph. 6-May-4 Swann Galleries, New York #536/R est:10000-15000
£4545	$7727	€6500	Two girls standing, one sitting (40x30cm-16x12in) s. lithograph. 26-Nov-3 Lempertz, Koln #874/R est:7000-9000
£5022	$9140	€7332	Two seated girls. s.i. lithograph. 17-Jun-4 Kornfeld, Bern #603/R est:12500 (S.FR 11500)
£5235	$9632	€7800	Two girls standing and one sitting (39x30cm-15x12in) s. lithograph prov. 26-Mar-4 Ketterer, Hamburg #573/R est:7000-8000
£5333	$9547	€8000	Two seated girls 2 (29x39cm-11x15in) s. lithograph prov. 14-May-4 Ketterer, Munich #165/R est:6000-7000
£5594	$9622	€8000	Girl on couch - 3 (25x36cm-10x14in) s. lithograph. 2-Dec-3 Hauswedell & Nolte, Hamburg #451/R est:10000
£5594	$9510	€8000	Girls by woodland pond (33x27cm-13x11in) s. lithograph. 29-Nov-3 Bassenge, Berlin #6918/R est:6000
£5677	$10332	€8288	Girl between leaves. s. woodcut. 17-Jun-4 Kornfeld, Bern #597/R est:15000 (S.FR 13000)
£6154	$10585	€8800	Two girls seated on sofa (21x27cm-8x11in) s. W/C lithograph. 2-Dec-3 Hauswedell & Nolte, Hamburg #448/R est:6000
£6643	$11427	€9500	Two girls by water (28x37cm-11x15in) s. lithograph. 2-Dec-3 Hauswedell & Nolte, Hamburg #455/R est:10000
£6711	$12349	€10000	Two bathers by stream (25x17cm-10x7in) s. lithograph. 26-Mar-4 Ketterer, Hamburg #575/R est:10000-12000
£7333	$13493	€11000	Half portrait of two girls (43x33cm-17x13in) mono. lithograph one of 60 exec. 1920. 11-Jun-4 Villa Grisebach, Berlin #1543/R est:8000-10000
£8000	$14640	€12000	Two girls in dunes - one lying, one sitting (29x39cm-11x15in) s. col lithograph. 5-Jun-4 Lempertz, Koln #897/R est:13000
£8667	$15687	€13000	Three girls by tree - standing, one seated and one bathing (26x19cm-10x7in) s.i. lithograph. 2-Apr-4 Winterberg, Heidelberg #1373/R est:15400
£9396	$16819	€14000	Five girls by forest pond (50x38cm-20x15in) s. lithograph. 25-May-4 Karl & Faber, Munich #425/R est:16000-18000
£12587	$21650	€18000	Finding Moses (29x39cm-11x15in) s. col lithograph. 2-Dec-3 Hauswedell & Nolte, Hamburg #456/R est:16000
£16107	$28832	€24000	Five yellow nudes by water (33x42cm-13x17in) mono. col lithograph. 25-May-4 Karl & Faber, Munich #417/R est:26000-28000
£16667	$29833	€25000	Mother and child 2 (26x19cm-10x7in) s.i. i. verso lithograph W/C prov. 14-May-4 Ketterer, Munich #156/R est:24000-28000
£26667	$49067	€40000	Gypsy Madonna (70x50cm-28x20in) s. col lithograph W/C. 10-Jun-4 Hauswedell & Nolte, Hamburg #507/R est:48000
Works on paper			
£4167	$6958	€6000	Seated girl (37x28cm-15x11in) mono. Indian ink brush prov. 24-Oct-3 Ketterer, Hamburg #481/R est:6000-7000
£4667	$8587	€7000	Bathers and rowing boats (23x21cm-9x8in) s. col chk W/C pencil exec. c.1911 prov.exhib. 12-Jun-4 Villa Grisebach, Berlin #215/R est:8000-10000
£18182	$31273	€26000	Gypsy family (50x68cm-20x27in) s. col chk lit. 2-Dec-3 Hauswedell & Nolte, Hamburg #447/R est:25000

MULLER, Paul Jakob (1894-1982) Swiss

£286	$457	€415	Portrait of old bearded man (30x30cm-12x12in) s. board. 15-May-3 Stuker, Bern #1432 (S.FR 600)
£330	$562	€482	Card players (30x39cm-12x15in) s. i.d.1966 verso board. 5-Nov-3 Dobiaschofsky, Bern #3660 (S.FR 750)
£345	$617	€504	Diogenes looking for someone (70x48cm-28x19in) s. 12-May-4 Dobiaschofsky, Bern #851/R (S.FR 800)
£474	$849	€692	Foundry (97x130cm-38x51in) s. i.d.1955 verso. 12-May-4 Dobiaschofsky, Bern #850/R (S.FR 1100)
£517	$926	€755	Young ballet dancer (60x43cm-24x17in) s. panel. 12-May-4 Dobiaschofsky, Bern #3824/R (S.FR 1200)

£647 $1157 €945 Nude in front of mirror (84x55cm-33x22in) s. i. verso. 14-May-4 Dobiaschofsky, Bern #214/R est:1600 (S.FR 1500)

MULLER, Paul Lothar (1869-?) German
£275 $506 €410 Lonely poet (21x16cm-8x6in) s.d.28 panel. 27-Mar-4 Dannenberg, Berlin #602/R
£1250 $2000 €1825 Mainbrucke in Wurzburg (71x91cm-28x36in) s. s.i.verso board. 19-Sep-3 Freeman, Philadelphia #70 est:2000-3000

MULLER, Peter Paul (1853-?) German
£317 $507 €463 River landscape (30x47cm-12x19in) s. 16-Sep-3 Philippe Schuler, Zurich #5465 (S.FR 700)
£423 $731 €600 Sunny winter day (50x70cm-20x28in) s. 10-Dec-3 Hugo Ruef, Munich #2465/R
£611 $1008 €880 Cows by stream (70x89cm-28x35in) 7-Jul-3 Dr Fritz Nagel, Stuttgart #7083
£3642 $6666 €5500 Moonrise over extensive landscape with birch trees (121x140cm-48x55in) s. 8-Apr-4 Dorotheum, Vienna #57/R est:3600-4000

MULLER, Richard (1874-1954) Austrian
£324 $571 €480 Village street (49x49cm-19x19in) lit. 21-May-4 Mehlis, Plauen #15153/R
Works on paper
£400 $720 €600 Artist (12x32cm-5x13in) s.d. graphite board. 24-Apr-4 Dr Lehr, Berlin #332/R
£467 $840 €700 Anteater (24x34cm-9x13in) s.d. graphite board. 24-Apr-4 Dr Lehr, Berlin #331/R
£600 $1098 €900 Female nude (34x57cm-13x22in) s.d.11.09.1925 chl htd white chk. 5-Jun-4 Lempertz, Koln #899/R
£2500 $4175 €3600 Lillian Sanderson/Rich Muller (48x38cm-19x15in) s. chk. 25-Oct-3 Dr Lehr, Berlin #358/R est:3000

MULLER, Rosa (19th C) German
£799 $1318 €1150 Stream in the forest (46x61cm-18x24in) s. 3-Jul-3 Dr Fritz Nagel, Stuttgart #504/R
£1831 $3168 €2600 Idyll at forest stream with washerwomen (46x61cm-18x24in) s. 10-Dec-3 Dorotheum, Vienna #34/R est:3000-3800
Works on paper
£480 $888 €701 Watermill with sheep on a track in the foreground (41x61cm-16x24in) s.d.1894 W/C bodycol. 11-Mar-4 Duke & Son, Dorchester #111

MULLER, Rudolph (1802-1885) Swiss
Works on paper
£441 $749 €644 Southern Italian coast (36x53cm-14x21in) s. w/C over pencil. 7-Nov-3 Dobiaschofsky, Bern #15/R (S.FR 1000)
£467 $840 €700 Village in Greece (15x22cm-6x9in) s. W/C. 25-Apr-4 Chenu & Scrive, Lyon #63
£573 $974 €837 Landscape in southern Italy (30x45cm-12x18in) s. W/C over pencil. 7-Nov-3 Dobiaschofsky, Bern #17/R (S.FR 1300)
£952 $1705 €1400 Vue d'Olevano, pres de Rome (42x55cm-17x22in) s. graphite W/C. 18-Mar-4 Christie's, Paris #325/R
£1041 $1769 €1520 Lago di Como (43x60cm-17x24in) s.d.1853 W/C. 28-Nov-3 Zofingen, Switzerland #2479/R est:4000 (S.FR 2300)
£1300 $2080 €1898 View of Rome (49x68cm-19x27in) s.i.d.1842 W/C over pencil htd gum arabic scratching out. 16-Sep-3 Bonhams, Knowle #57 est:500-700

MULLER, Rudolph Gustav (1858-1888) German
£5298 $9642 €8000 Jeunes femmes pres d'une fontaine (76x100cm-30x39in) s. 18-Jun-4 Piasa, Paris #46/R est:8000-10000

MULLER, Tamara (1975-) Dutch?
£1910 $3017 €2750 Big girl, little girl (170x75cm-67x30in) 26-Apr-3 Auction Maastricht #9/R est:3500-5500

MULLER, Walter Emil (1896-1983) Swiss
£638 $1066 €900 Still life with cakes (21x27cm-8x11in) s. 16-Oct-3 Dorotheum, Salzburg #644/R

MULLER, William James (1812-1845) British
£250 $462 €365 Study of plants and rocks (18x27cm-7x11in) canvas on panel. 10-Mar-4 Sotheby's, Olympia #54/R
£400 $704 €584 Setting the trap (46x61cm-18x24in) s.d.1845. 19-May-4 Christie's, Kensington #619
£680 $1244 €993 Burning of the New Gaol with St. Paul's. Bedminster during the Bristol riots of 1831 (13x22cm-5x9in) oil on paper. 6-Apr-4 Bristol Auction Rooms #496/R
£1000 $1850 €1460 Dutch pond (27x39cm-11x15in) s. panel. 13-Jan-4 Bonhams, Knightsbridge #149/R est:1000-1500
£1200 $1896 €1740 Sunrise over downland (14x32cm-6x13in) oil paper on canvas prov. 4-Sep-3 Christie's, Kensington #121/R est:500-800
£1800 $3006 €2628 Figures in a town square, North Africa (31x46cm-12x18in) s. panel exhib. 14-Oct-3 Sotheby's, London #107/R est:2000-3000
Works on paper
£250 $450 €365 Snowdon Horseshoe with bridge (23x30cm-9x12in) s. 24-Apr-4 Rogers Jones, Clwyd #117
£390 $616 €566 Brook in Clifton Woods (33x48cm-13x19in) W/C exec.c.1840. 27-Apr-3 Desmond Judd, Cranbrook #1076
£390 $616 €566 Path through Clifton Woods (33x48cm-13x19in) W/C exec.c.1840. 27-Apr-3 Desmond Judd, Cranbrook #1077
£400 $728 €584 A windmill in an extensive landscape (34x51cm-13x20in) s. pencil W/C htd white. 1-Jul-4 Christie's, Kensington #98/R
£600 $1002 €876 Street scene, Venice (22x29cm-9x11in) pencil W/C prov. 16-Oct-3 Christie's, Kensington #55/R
£620 $1141 €905 View of a rocky stream. s.d.1844 W/C. 23-Mar-4 Bonhams, Knightsbridge #200/R
£700 $1295 €1022 Harbour at Rhodes (21x34cm-8x13in) W/C bodycol. 9-Mar-4 Bonhams, Knightsbridge #71/R
£820 $1369 €1197 Rocky wooded river scene (32x50cm-13x20in) s.d.1838 W/C bodycol. 14-Oct-3 Bearnes, Exeter #341/R
£900 $1665 €1314 Whitchurch, near Bristol (25x35cm-10x14in) W/C pencil prov. 10-Mar-4 Sotheby's, Olympia #140/R est:1000-1500
£900 $1665 €1314 Eastern covered market (19x26cm-7x10in) indis.sig. W/C prov. 14-Jul-4 Sotheby's, Olympia #49/R
£1000 $1670 €1460 Staffordshire mill (32x51cm-13x20in) i. pencil W/C. 16-Oct-3 Christie's, Kensington #119/R est:1000-1500
£1600 $2672 €2336 Tivoli (23x18cm-9x7in) pencil W/C prov.exhib.lit. 16-Oct-3 Christie's, Kensington #60/R est:1000-1500
£1900 $3401 €2774 A view from the Parthenon (35x24cm-14x9in) init.i.d.1838 W/C pencil prov. 11-May-4 Bonhams, New Bond Street #13/R est:500-800
£7000 $12880 €10220 Rialto Bridge, Venice (45x75cm-18x30in) s. W/C over pencil htd bodycol prov.exhib. 26-Mar-4 Sotheby's, London #89/R est:8000-12000

MULLER, William James (attrib) (1812-1845) British
£340 $541 €496 Sole Survivor (25x41cm-10x16in) board. 12-Sep-3 Richardson & Smith, Whitby #370
£350 $630 €511 Enchanted garden (22x34cm-9x13in) board. 21-Jan-4 Sotheby's, Olympia #311/R
£516 $950 €753 View near Colchester (30x46cm-12x18in) 25-Mar-4 Doyle, New York #50/R
£1253 $2294 €1829 Harbour town on the English coast (26x38cm-10x15in) s. 9-Jun-4 Rasmussen, Copenhagen #1838/R est:8000-10000 (D.KR 14000)

MULLER, Willy (1889-1953) Swiss
£339 $577 €495 Hudelmoos near Muolen (45x50cm-18x20in) s. s.i. stretcher. 18-Nov-3 Hans Widmer, St Gallen #1164 (S.FR 750)

MULLER, Wout (1946-2000) Dutch
Sculpture
£1049 $1783 €1500 Wagon (40cm-16in) welded metal bronze copper lead wood exhib. 25-Nov-3 Christie's, Amsterdam #149/R est:700-900

MULLER-BAUMGARTEN, Carl (1879-1946) German
£319 $533 €450 Wine tasting (45x33cm-18x13in) s. board. 16-Oct-3 Dorotheum, Salzburg #598/R
£625 $1044 €900 Fishing in Chiemsee landscape (29x45cm-11x18in) s. lit. 25-Oct-3 Bergmann, Erlangen #924/R
£1127 $1870 €1600 Chiemsee landscape (66x100cm-26x39in) s. 16-Jun-3 Dorotheum, Vienna #80/R est:1400-1600

MULLER-BRITTNAU, Willy (1938-) Swiss
£628 $1048 €917 Autumn (50x120cm-20x47in) s.d.58 i. verso. 24-Oct-3 Hans Widmer, St Gallen #59/R (S.FR 1400)
£786 $1446 €1148 Nr 60/66 (94x69cm-37x27in) s.i.d.verso. 14-Jun-4 Philippe Schuler, Zurich #4227/R (S.FR 1800)
£1280 $2100 €1869 Number 66/67 (71x71cm-28x28in) s.i.verso diagonal painted 1967 diagonal prov. 28-May-3 Sotheby's, Amsterdam #168/R est:1200-1500
£2183 $4017 €3187 Untitled (120x150cm-47x59in) s.d.1964 verso. 8-Jun-4 Germann, Zurich #66/R est:6000-8000 (S.FR 5000)
£3057 $5624 €4463 Untitled (110x220cm-43x87in) s.d.1970 verso acrylic. 8-Jun-4 Germann, Zurich #50/R est:7000-10000 (S.FR 7000)
£6114 $11249 €8926 Untitled (120x120cm-47x47in) s.d.1976 verso acrylic prov. 8-Jun-4 Germann, Zurich #53/R est:6000-8000 (S.FR 14000)

MULLER-CASSEL, Adolf Leonhard (1864-?) German
£1007 $1883 €1500 Beach scene (69x77cm-27x30in) s.d.1909. 24-Feb-4 Dorotheum, Vienna #147/R est:2000-2300

MULLER-CORNELIUS, Ludwig (1864-1946) German
£272 $495 €400 Horse drawn cart outside farmstead (16x24cm-6x9in) s. panel. 4-Feb-4 Neumeister, Munich #733/R
£345 $576 €500 Post coach outside guest house (15x19cm-6x7in) s. panel. 9-Jul-3 Hugo Ruef, Munich #149
£451 $713 €650 Post coach in mountain village street (15x20cm-6x8in) s. panel. 6-Sep-3 Arnold, Frankfurt #627/R
£604 $1111 €900 Horse drawn carriage (8x11cm-3x4in) s. panel. 24-Mar-4 Hugo Ruef, Munich #1058
£694 $1132 €1000 Hay harvest with Watzmann beyond (11x9cm-4x4in) s. panel. 25-Sep-3 Neumeister, Munich #2831/R
£764 $1260 €1100 Post coach to Tolz (22x32cm-9x13in) s. panel. 2-Jul-3 Neumeister, Munich #727/R
£769 $1308 €1100 Hay harvest in pre-Alps (8x16cm-3x6in) s. panel. 20-Nov-3 Van Ham, Cologne #1753
£822 $1397 €1200 Post coach outside guest house (12x16cm-5x6in) s. panel. 5-Nov-3 Hugo Ruef, Munich #1071/R
£1189 $1985 €1700 Hay harvest (8x17cm-3x7in) s. panel lit. 27-Jun-3 Auktionhaus Georg Rehm, Augsburg #8133/R est:2400

MULLER-GOSSEN, Franz (1871-1946) German
£431 $719 €629 Sunset over Elben (55x49cm-22x19in) s. 25-Oct-3 Rasmussen, Havnen #2502 (D.KR 4600)
£839 $1427 €1200 Sailing boats at harbour entrance (100x81cm-39x32in) s. 20-Nov-3 Van Ham, Cologne #1754

MULLER-GRANTZOW, Adolf (19th C) German
£603 $1080 €880 Female nude with vines (50x37cm-20x15in) s. 12-May-4 Dobiaschofsky, Bern #821/R (S.FR 1400)

MULLER-KAEMPFF, Paul (1861-1941) German
£405 $714 €600 Heath landscape with croft at night (67x42cm-26x17in) s. lit. 21-May-4 Mehlis, Plauen #15154/R
£559 $951 €800 Roses (60x70cm-24x28in) s. 20-Nov-3 Van Ham, Cologne #1755
£671 $1188 €1000 Moor landscape in evening (45x56cm-18x22in) s.d. 30-Apr-4 Dr Fritz Nagel, Stuttgart #358/R

£1154 $1985 €1650 Autumn woodland scene (80x120cm-31x47in) s. 6-Dec-3 Hans Stahl, Toestorf #77/R est:1400
£1538 $2646 €2200 Fisherman's cottage on the dunes at Ahrenshooper (50x70cm-20x28in) 5-Dec-3 Bolland & Marotz, Bremen #611/R est:1300
£1736 $2743 €2500 Hamburg (85x130cm-33x51in) s.d.1915. 6-Sep-3 Schopman, Hamburg #766/R est:2800
£3125 $5094 €4500 Fishing huts in spring (80x120cm-31x47in) s. 26-Sep-3 Bolland & Marotz, Bremen #583/R est:4900
£4636 $8437 €7000 River landscape with house (80x120cm-31x47in) s. 18-Jun-4 Bolland & Marotz, Bremen #701/R est:7500

MULLER-KURZWELLY, Konrad Alexander (1855-1914) German
£733 $1327 €1100 Woodland pond in the evening (70x10cm-28x4in) s. 1-Apr-4 Van Ham, Cologne #1557
£759 $1403 €1100 Evening landscape (64x74cm-25x29in) s. 14-Feb-4 Hans Stahl, Hamburg #67/R
£1119 $1924 €1600 Dutch landscape with windmill (38x58cm-15x23in) s. i. stretcher. 3-Dec-3 Neumeister, Munich #686/R est:1400
£1445 $2398 €2110 Landscape with lake (71x101cm-28x40in) s. painted c.1900. 15-Jun-3 Agra, Warsaw #27/R est:7000 (P.Z 9000)

MULLER-LANDAU, Rolf (1903-1956) Austrian
£1611 $2980 €2400 Marguerites (75x66cm-30x26in) s.i. verso mono. 9-Mar-4 Dorotheum, Vienna #62/R est:4000-6000

MULLER-LANDECK, Fritz (1865-1942) German
£784 $1223 €1145 Winter landscape (60x91cm-24x36in) s. painted c.1910. 30-Mar-3 Agra, Warsaw #49/R (P.Z 5000)

MULLER-LINGKE, Albert (1844-?) German
£363 $566 €530 Girl's portrait (14x10cm-6x4in) s. panel. 10-Apr-3 Weidler, Nurnberg #311/R
£450 $765 €657 Full stein (50x36cm-20x14in) s. 1-Dec-3 Bonhams, Bath #143/R
£980 $1754 €1450 Village with figures and animals on winter evening (109x83cm-43x33in) s. 6-May-4 Michael Zeller, Lindau #794/R
£1078 $2005 €1574 Winter landscape with travelling musicians (93x69cm-37x27in) s. 2-Mar-4 Rasmussen, Copenhagen #1322/R est:12000-15000 (D.KR 12000)

MULLER-LINOW, Bruno (1909-1997) German
Works on paper
£533 $965 €800 Still life (35x44cm-14x17in) mono. s.i. verso W/C bodycol. 2-Apr-4 Winterberg, Heidelberg #1392/R

MULLER-MUNSTER, Franz (1867-?) German
£716 $1311 €1045 The angel and Saint Peter (40x31cm-16x12in) s. panel prov. 9-Jun-4 Rasmussen, Copenhagen #1539/R (D.KR 8000)

MULLER-SCHEESEL, Ernst (1863-1936) German
£867 $1569 €1300 Summer idyll (49x59cm-19x23in) s. 1-Apr-4 Van Ham, Cologne #1558/R

MULLER-SCHONHAUSEN, A (1838-?) German
£3605 $6200 €5263 In the picture gallery (64x53cm-25x21in) s. masonite. 6-Dec-3 Neal Auction Company, New Orleans #422/R est:2500-3500
£3800 $6916 €5548 In the picture gallery (63x54cm-25x21in) s. board prov.lit. 16-Jun-4 Christie's, Kensington #162/R est:6000-8000

MULLER-SCHWABEN, Fritz (1879-1957) German
£351 $650 €512 Floral still life (64x51cm-25x20in) s. panel. 15-Jul-4 Sotheby's, New York #28/R

MULLER-URY, Adolf (1862-?) American
£692 $1100 €1010 Portrait of woman in profile (33x23cm-13x9in) s. canvas on board. 12-Sep-3 Skinner, Boston #357/R

MULLER-WERLAU, Peter Paul (1864-1945) German
£400 $724 €600 Waves breaking on southern Italian coast (60x80cm-24x31in) s. 1-Apr-4 Van Ham, Cologne #1559

MULLER-WISCHIN, Anton (1865-1949) German
£596 $1085 €900 Still life with grapes and lemons (32x38cm-13x15in) s. cardboard. 16-Jun-4 Hugo Ruef, Munich #1045/R
£1361 $2435 €2000 Still life with tea doll (73x57cm-29x22in) s.d.1917. 17-Mar-4 Neumeister, Munich #548/R est:2500

MULLER-WISCHIN, Anton (attrib) (1865-1949) German
£303 $542 €430 Tree landscape during a thunder storm (31x60cm-12x24in) indis.s. i.verso board lit. 8-Jan-4 Allgauer, Kempten #2473/R

MULLEY, Oskar (1891-1949) Austrian
£552 $921 €800 Farmstead (35x50cm-14x20in) s. board. 9-Jul-3 Hugo Ruef, Munich #151
£629 $1070 €900 Landscape with trees (40x50cm-16x20in) s.d.45. 20-Nov-3 Weidler, Nurnberg #313/R
£633 $1134 €950 View over the lake (64x36cm-25x14in) s. panel. 14-May-4 Behringer, Furth #1583/R
£637 $981 €1000 Konigsee and Teufelshorner (34x22cm-13x9in) s.i. tempera. 4-Sep-2 Schopman, Hamburg #97/R
£1348 $2250 €1900 Still water (24x33cm-9x13in) s. i. verso board. 14-Oct-3 Dorotheum, Vienna #116/R est:1200-1600
£1712 $2911 €2500 Autumn landscape (40x64cm-16x25in) s. board. 5-Nov-3 Hugo Ruef, Munich #1069 est:2500
£2098 $3566 €3000 Near Garmisch (60x78cm-24x31in) s. fibreboard. 28-Nov-3 Wiener Kunst Auktionen, Vienna #469/R est:3000-5000
£2585 $4627 €3800 Farmstead in the mountains (34x50cm-13x20in) i. paper on board prov. 17-Mar-4 Neumeister, Munich #550/R est:4000
£3056 $4981 €4400 Kufstein fortress in evening light (80x120cm-31x47in) s.i. 25-Sep-3 Dr Fritz Nagel, Stuttgart #1382/R est:2000
£3357 $5773 €4800 Chapel high in the mountains (54x62cm-21x24in) s.i. board. 3-Dec-3 Neumeister, Munich #688/R est:3500
£3611 $5958 €5200 Mountain shrine lit by the sun (75x92cm-30x36in) s/. 3-Jul-3 Dr Fritz Nagel, Stuttgart #508/R est:4000
£3691 $6534 €5500 Landscape with village (28x33cm-11x13in) s.d.20 bears i. verso paper. 28-Apr-4 Wiener Kunst Auktionen, Vienna #83/R est:4000-7000
£5245 $9021 €7500 Mountain village (80x130cm-31x51in) s. 3-Dec-3 Neumeister, Munich #687/R est:8000
£5310 $9824 €7700 Farmstead in the high mountains (108x145cm-43x57in) s.i. 12-Feb-4 Weidler, Nurnberg #331/R est:7000
£6250 $10188 €9000 Chapel in mountain landscape (109x200cm-43x79in) s.i. 25-Sep-3 Dr Fritz Nagel, Stuttgart #1383/R est:6500
£6711 $11879 €10000 Old Inn bridge in Kufstein (63x67cm-25x26in) s.i. oil chk board. 28-Apr-4 Wiener Kunst Auktionen, Vienna #82/R est:6000-10000
£6849 $10685 €10000 High mountain farmstead (73x120cm-29x47in) s. 10-Apr-3 Weidler, Nurnberg #300/R est:4500
£12587 $21399 €18000 Mountain village (83x110cm-33x43in) s. prov. 26-Nov-3 Dorotheum, Vienna #160/R est:18000-22000
Works on paper
£2096 $3815 €3060 Mountain landscape in early spring (42x47cm-17x19in) s.d.20 mixed media. 16-Jun-4 Fischer, Luzern #2660/R est:4000-5000 (S.FR 4800)

MULLHOLLAND, St John (19th C) British
£1750 $3133 €2555 Fishing boats off a jetty (59x105cm-23x41in) s. 17-Mar-4 Bonhams, Chester #373/R est:1000-1500
£2000 $3740 €2920 Santa Maria della Salute, from the Grand Canal, Venice (77x126cm-30x50in) s. 24-Feb-4 Bonhams, Knowle #66 est:400-600

MULLI, Rudolf (1882-1962) Swiss
£270 $465 €394 Landscape (55x85cm-22x33in) s.d.1931. 8-Dec-3 Philippe Schuler, Zurich #5945 (S.FR 600)

MULLICAN, Lee (1919-1998) American
£4908 $8000 €7166 Untitled (127x76cm-50x30in) s.d.1951 verso prov. 23-Sep-3 Christie's, Rockefeller NY #58/R est:10000-15000
Works on paper
£359 $600 €524 Abstract (41x34cm-16x13in) s.d.1976 W/C. 19-Oct-3 Bonhams & Butterfields, Los Angeles #7063

MULLICAN, Matt (1951-) American
Sculpture
£833 $1500 €1216 Sign flag (33x59cm-13x23in) s. cotton duck applique prov. 24-Apr-4 David Rago, Lambertville #430/R est:1500-2500

MULLNER, Joseph (1879-1968) Austrian
Sculpture
£2767 $4953 €4040 Head of a Gorgon (25cm-10in) s.d.1918 bronze prov. 15-May-4 Christie's, Sydney #190/R est:2000-3000 (A.D 7000)

MULLOCK, James Flewitt (1818-1892) British
£13000 $22100 €18980 Sir Charles Morgan at the Castelton Ploughing match (61x76cm-24x30in) lit. 18-Nov-3 Sotheby's, Olympia #40/R est:3000-5000

MULNIER, Jean Baptiste Ferdinand (attrib) (1757-1836) French
£4196 $7007 €6000 Accord Parfait (29x23cm-11x9in) panel. 30-Jun-3 Bailly Pommery, Paris #71/R est:6000-8000

MULOCK, Frederick C (1888-1932) British
£280 $476 €409 Portrait of a lady seated on a garden bench (51x76cm-20x30in) 19-Nov-3 Tennants, Leyburn #1148
£700 $1260 €1022 Portrait of a girl wearing a tartan shawl (36x40cm-14x16in) mono. board. 21-Apr-4 Tennants, Leyburn #1212
£800 $1440 €1168 Study of a lady, seated wearing period costume (76x30cm-30x12in) mono.indis.d.1926. 21-Apr-4 Tennants, Leyburn #1213
£1700 $2839 €2482 Hidden door (183x111cm-72x44in) 12-Nov-3 Sotheby's, Olympia #82/R est:1200-1800

MULREADY, Augustus E (fl.1863-1905) British
£480 $893 €701 London flower girl (51x28cm-20x11in) 7-Mar-4 Paul Beighton, Rotherham #497/R
£900 $1611 €1314 London flower girl standing beneath poster for the Lyric Theatre (48x29cm-19x11in) s.i. s.d.1897 verso. 17-May-4 David Duggleby, Scarborough #620/R
£3500 $5530 €5075 Fisherman's daughter (53x43cm-21x17in) s. s.i.verso. 4-Sep-3 Christie's, Kensington #261/R est:3000-5000

MULREADY, William (1786-1863) British
£398 $700 €581 Young woman with a hat holding a baby, with young girl and boy (20x18cm-8x7in) s.verso board. 20-May-4 American Auctioneer #475002/R
£800 $1336 €1168 Young musician (15x12cm-6x5in) s.d.1846 board. 13-Nov-3 Christie's, Kensington #328/R
£2000 $3580 €2920 Portrait of a lady, in a landscape (112x87cm-44x34in) 14-May-4 Christie's, Kensington #312/R est:2000-3000
£3200 $5440 €4672 Self portrait (12x10cm-5x4in) panel. 27-Nov-3 Sotheby's, London #158/R est:3000-4000
Works on paper
£1500 $2685 €2190 Shepherd with his flock on a track, a river beyond (25x34cm-10x13in) black white chk. 14-May-4 Christie's, London #128/R est:1500-2000

MULTRUS, Josef (19/20th C) Austrian?
£438 $727 €639 Artist's mother and sister in Zizkov apartment (31x35cm-12x14in) s. board. 4-Oct-3 Dorotheum, Prague #138/R est:20000-30000 (C.KR 20000)

MULVAD, Emma (1838-1903) Danish
£537 $983 €784 Roses and other flowers on ledge (22x31cm-9x12in) indis sig.d.1860 panel. 9-Jun-4 Rasmussen, Copenhagen #1867/R (D.KR 6000)

MULVANY, George Francis (1809-1869) Irish
£1000 $1790 €1460 Portrait of Michael Kelly (71x91cm-28x36in) 14-May-4 Christie's, Kensington #304/R est:1000-1500

MULVANY, John (attrib) (1844-1906) American
£1788 $3200 €2610 The scouts of the Yellowstone (64x76cm-25x30in) 11-Jan-4 William Jenack, New York #157 est:1000-1500

MULVANY, Thomas James (1779-1845) British
£2000 $3440 €2920 The Devil's Punchbowl, Killarney, looking towards the Glen of the Horse (52x68cm-20x27in) 4-Dec-3 Mellors & Kirk, Nottingham #944/R est:2000-2500

MULVEY, Matilda (1882-c.1947) British
£360 $637 €526 Violets and anemones (40x51cm-16x20in) s. 27-Apr-4 Bonhams, Knightsbridge #125/R

MUMFORD, Elizabeth (20th C) American
£4938 $8000 €7209 Mermaids just want to have fun (26x31cm-10x12in) s. 31-Jul-3 Eldred, East Dennis #985/R est:7000-9000

MUMMA, Eddie (1908-1986) American
£254 $425 €371 Face and hands in orange (43x36cm-17x14in) paint board. 15-Nov-3 Slotin Folk Art, Buford #293/R
£719 $1200 €1050 Green eyes (36x25cm-14x10in) paint board. 15-Nov-3 Slotin Folk Art, Buford #294/R

MUMMERT, Sallie (1888-1938) American
£1497 $2500 €2186 Floral still life (81x86cm-32x34in) 18-Oct-3 David Dike, Dallas #162/R est:2500-5000

MUMPRECHT, Walter Rudolf (1918-) Swiss
£3744 $6366 €5466 Que chaque heure du jour te soit amie (105x105cm-41x41in) mono.d.22 mai 1977 s.i. verso. 7-Nov-3 Dobiaschofsky, Bern #239/R est:8500 (S.FR 8500)
Works on paper
£374 $637 €546 Femme nue (30x21cm-12x8in) mono.d.74 Indian ink col crayon double-sided. 5-Nov-3 Dobiaschofsky, Bern #1792/R (S.FR 850)
£1121 $2006 €1637 Joie amour vie espoire (24x30cm-9x12in) s.d.71 Indian ink W/C. 14-May-4 Dobiaschofsky, Bern #279/R est:1500 (S.FR 2600)

MUNAKATA, Shiko (1903-1975) Japanese
Prints
£1687 $2800 €2446 Fish and flower and female Buddha (30x23cm-12x9in) s.d. woodcut edition of 250. 14-Jun-3 Rachel Davis, Shaker Heights #111/R est:2500-3500
£1695 $3000 €2475 Hawk woman (40x31cm-16x12in) s.d.1958 num.20/200 woodcut. 30-Apr-4 Sotheby's, New York #166/R est:4000-6000
£1765 $3000 €2577 Two fanciful birds (81x64cm-32x25in) s.i. hand col sumizuri-e. 4-Nov-3 Bonhams & Butterfields, San Francisco #3043/R est:3000-5000
£1807 $3000 €2620 Gauatama and Godhisattvas (23x33cm-9x13in) s.d. woodcut edition of 250. 14-Jun-3 Rachel Davis, Shaker Heights #112/R est:3000-4000
£1923 $3500 €2808 Fish and flower and female Buddha (33x20cm-13x8in) s.d.1957 woodcut. 19-Jun-4 Rachel Davis, Shaker Heights #22 est:3000-5000
£2059 $3500 €3006 Goddess (40x51cm-16x20in) mono. woodcut. 31-Oct-3 Sotheby's, New York #345/R
£2059 $3500 €3006 Women embodying the main Buddhist Sutras (76x107cm-30x42in) s.i.d.1958 sumizuri-e. 4-Nov-3 Bonhams & Butterfields, San Francisco #3039/R est:4000-6000
£3529 $6000 €5152 Seated goddess with poem (107x140cm-42x55in) s.i. hand col sumizuri-e. 4-Nov-3 Bonhams & Butterfields, San Francisco #3042/R est:6000-8000
£5000 $8950 €7300 Chicago no Onna (42x31cm-17x12in) s.d.1962 woodblock. 6-May-4 Sotheby's, London #27/R est:3000-4000
£9040 $16000 €13198 Subhuti, Master of the Immaterial (92x29cm-36x11in) s. woodcut. 28-Apr-4 Christie's, Rockefeller NY #109/R est:10000-15000
£14689 $26000 €21446 Portrait of a Goddess (25x19cm-10x7in) s. col hand col woodcut exec.c.1965. 28-Apr-4 Christie's, Rockefeller NY #110/R est:28000-32000
Works on paper
£2065 $3800 €3015 Seimyochiin (27x24cm-11x9in) s. ink. 23-Mar-4 Christie's, Rockefeller NY #131/R est:2000-3000
£5435 $8913 €7500 Seated goddess (39x29cm-15x11in) st.sig W/C. 27-May-3 Sotheby's, Amsterdam #325/R est:4000-5000

MUNARI, Bruno (1907-1998) Italian
£1879 $3364 €2800 Unreadable writing (119x43cm-47x17in) s.i.d.1975 acrylic paper on card. 25-May-4 Sotheby's, Milan #161/R est:400
£1879 $3495 €2800 Space (85x118cm-33x46in) board. 4-Mar-4 Babuino, Rome #432 est:2500-3000
Works on paper
£306 $548 €450 Avida dollars (55x49cm-22x19in) s.i.d.1991 felt-tip pen. 16-Mar-4 Finarte Semenzato, Milan #195
£699 $1189 €1000 Love (33x42cm-13x17in) pencil felt-tip pen. 26-Nov-3 Pandolfini, Florence #473/R
£786 $1446 €1148 Ricostruzione teoretica di un oggetto immaginario (69x69cm-27x27in) s.i.d.1971 Indian ink pencil collage exhib. 8-Jun-4 Germann, Zurich #845 (S.FR 1800)
£966 $1545 €1400 Negative, positive, curved (45x45cm-18x18in) s.verso collage wood panel. 13-Mar-3 Galleria Pace, Milan #41/R est:1550-2000
£966 $1612 €1400 Negative-positive sketch (30x30cm-12x12in) s.i.d.1988 collage card. 17-Nov-3 Sant Agostino, Torino #146/R
£1469 $2497 €2100 Untitled (21x26cm-8x10in) s.d.1951 W/C. 26-Nov-3 Pandolfini, Florence #472/R est:1350-1450

MUNARI, Cristoforo (1667-1720) Italian
£57343 $98629 €82000 Nature morte aux citrons de Sorrento, pommes, porcelain, livre et vase (48x71cm-19x28in) prov. 8-Dec-3 Rossini, Paris #46/R est:12000-15000
£97315 $181980 €145000 Still life with violin, jug, watermelon and grapes (95x74cm-37x29in) prov.exhib.lit. 25-Feb-4 Porro, Milan #84/R est:145000
£124138 $207310 €180000 Still life with pewter jug, watermelon and grapes (95x74cm-37x29in) prov.exhib.lit. 15-Nov-3 Porro, Milan #246/R est:145000

MUNCASTER, Claude (1903-1974) British
£300 $501 €438 Tarn Hows (70x77cm-28x30in) s.d.1952 i.verso board. 11-Nov-3 Rosebery Fine Art, London #1028
£400 $728 €584 Tarns How (70x77cm-28x30in) s.d.1952 board. 15-Jun-4 Bonhams, Knightsbridge #41/R
£500 $880 €730 Study of skies over Duncton Down (12x18cm-5x7in) s. i.verso board. 19-May-4 Rupert Toovey, Partridge Green #132/R
Works on paper
£320 $554 €467 March morning above Byworth, Sussex (26x37cm-10x15in) s.i.d.1934 s.verso W/C. 10-Dec-3 Bonhams, Bury St Edmunds #533/R
£320 $592 €467 HMS Milford (20x28cm-8x11in) s.d.1946. 9-Mar-4 Gorringes, Lewes #2070
£500 $885 €730 View of Nunster Lovell (38x58cm-15x23in) s. W/C. 27-Apr-4 Bonhams, Knightsbridge #278/R
£550 $1007 €803 Rotherhithe (23x36cm-9x14in) s.d.1925 W/C. 27-Jan-4 Bonhams, Knightsbridge #188/R

MUNCH, Anna E (1876-1960) Danish
£300 $500 €438 Figure in an interior (59x79cm-23x31in) s.d.1911. 26-Oct-3 Bonhams & Butterfields, San Francisco #6471/R
£327 $517 €474 Four Italian women by well (36x47cm-14x19in) s. 2-Sep-3 Rasmussen, Copenhagen #1939/R (D.KR 3500)

MUNCH, Axel (20th C) Danish?
£1469 $2351 €2130 Houses in Gudhjelm (42x83cm-17x33in) init.i. 17-Sep-3 Kunsthallen, Copenhagen #244/R est:6000 (D.KR 15500)

MUNCH, Constanze (fl.1890s) German?
Works on paper
£805 $1482 €1200 Cherry blossom in oriental vase (72x29cm-28x11in) s.d.1891 W/C. 26-Mar-4 Dorotheum, Vienna #334/R
£805 $1482 €1200 Still life with oleander in dish (53x74cm-21x29in) s.d.8/8 1891 W/C. 26-Mar-4 Dorotheum, Vienna #335/R

MUNCH, Edvard (1863-1944) Norwegian
£8130 $14878 €11870 Horse and cart on road (19x15cm-7x6in) s. paper on panel exec.c.1881. 7-Jun-4 Blomqvist, Oslo #370/R est:125000-150000 (N.KR 100000)
£370000 $677100 €540200 Promenade des Anglais, Nice (65x107cm-26x42in) s.d.1891 prov.exhib.lit. 2-Feb-4 Christie's, London #7/R est:350000-450000
Prints
£1882 $3200 €2748 Cally Monrad (39x27cm-15x11in) s. col lithograph. 6-Nov-3 Swann Galleries, New York #660/R est:4000-6000
£2000 $3680 €3000 Portrait of a woman's head (28x21cm-11x8in) s. drypoint one of 22. 12-Jun-4 Villa Grisebach, Berlin #119/R est:3000-4000
£2082 $3726 €3040 Alfa and Omega (25x46cm-10x18in) s. lithograph printed in black exec.c.1908-09. 22-Mar-4 Blomqvist, Oslo #380/R est:25000-30000 (N.KR 26000)
£2129 $3663 €3108 The dead mother and the child (32x48cm-13x19in) etching drypoint prov. 8-Dec-3 Blomqvist, Oslo #502/R est:40000-50000 (N.KR 25000)
£2300 $3910 €3358 Berlin girl (64x51cm-25x20in) col lithograph exec.1906. 1-Dec-3 Bonhams, New Bond Street #263/R est:2500-3000
£2322 $4156 €3390 Omega and the pig (32x46cm-13x18in) s. lithograph printed in black exec.c.1908-109. 22-Mar-4 Blomqvist, Oslo #383/R est:24000-28000 (N.KR 29000)
£2477 $4136 €3616 The seducer (44x63cm-17x25in) s. lithograph printed in black. 13-Oct-3 Blomqvist, Oslo #361/R est:35000-45000 (N.KR 29000)
£2562 $4586 €3741 Idyll (44x37cm-17x15in) s. lithograph printed in black. 22-Mar-4 Blomqvist, Oslo #379/R est:35000-45000 (N.KR 32000)
£2566 $4363 €3746 The cloud (26x50cm-10x20in) s.d.1908-09 lithograph printed in black. 19-Nov-3 Grev Wedels Plass, Oslo #5/R est:20000-30000 (N.KR 30000)
£2652 $4508 €3872 Man with horse II (37x61cm-15x24in) s.i.d.1915 intaglio print printed in black. 19-Nov-3 Grev Wedels Plass, Oslo #18/R est:30000-40000 (N.KR 31000)
£2994 $5090 €4371 Life (33x39cm-13x15in) s.i.d.1915 intaglio print printed in black. 19-Nov-3 Grev Wedels Plass, Oslo #9/R est:40000-60000 (N.KR 35000)
£3089 $5654 €4510 Omega's flight (47x63cm-19x25in) s. lithograph printed in black exec.c.1908-09. 7-Jun-4 Blomqvist, Oslo #402/R est:35000-40000 (N.KR 38000)
£3107 $5500 €4536 Old man praying (47x34cm-19x13in) black yellow woodcut. 30-Apr-4 Sotheby's, New York #167/R est:6000-8000
£3165 $5381 €4621 Architect Henrik Bull (33x34cm-13x13in) s.d.1928 lithograph printed in black. 19-Nov-3 Grev Wedels Plass, Oslo #22/R est:15000-20000 (N.KR 37000)
£3610 $6643 €5271 Theatre program from Per Gynt without text - Solveig and Per Gynt's mother (25x30cm-10x12in) s.d.96 lithograph lit. 29-Mar-4 Rasmussen, Copenhagen #48/R est:50000-75000 (D.KR 40000)
£3683 $6592 €5377 Portrait of Hans Jaeger III (38x32cm-15x13in) lithograph printed in black exec.1943-44. 22-Mar-4 Blomqvist, Oslo #374/R est:45000-55000 (N.KR 46000)
£3800 $6536 €5548 Alley (24x26cm-9x10in) s.d.97 lithograph prov. 2-Dec-3 Christie's, London #224/R est:3000-5000
£3849 $6544 €5620 Lion lying down II (35x45cm-14x18in) s.d.1920 lithograph printed in black. 19-Nov-3 Grev Wedels Plass, Oslo #1/R est:30000-40000 (N.KR 45000)
£3902 $7141 €5697 Alfa's despair (42x34cm-17x13in) s. lithograph printed in black exec.c.1908-09. 7-Jun-4 Blomqvist, Oslo #404/R est:40000-50000 (N.KR 48000)
£3902 $7141 €5697 Self-portrait with beard (42x61cm-17x24in) lithograph printed in black. 7-Jun-4 Blomqvist, Oslo #405/R est:40000-60000 (N.KR 48000)
£4000 $7280 €5840 Louise and Else Heyerdahl (50x67cm-20x26in) s.num17 lithograph prov. 30-Jun-4 Christie's, London #284/R est:1800-2200
£4200 $7644 €6132 Girl at the window (22x16cm-9x6in) i. drypoint sold with a lithograph by Paul Klee. 1-Jul-4 Sotheby's, London #231/R est:4000-5000
£4600 $7911 €6716 A Bohemian wedding (34x50cm-13x20in) s. lithograph printed in black exec.c.1929-30. 8-Dec-3 Blomqvist, Oslo #500/R est:40000-60000 (N.KR 54000)

£4706 $8000 €6871 Die frauen und das gerippe (31x43cm-12x17in) s. drypoint. 6-Nov-3 Swann Galleries, New York #658/R est:6000-9000
£4804 $8599 €7014 Moonrise (21x43cm-8x17in) lithograph printed in black exec.c.1908-09. 22-Mar-4 Blomqvist, Oslo #376/R est:40000-60000 (N.KR 60000)
£5500 $9460 €8030 Woman bathing (32x22cm-13x9in) s.i. etching drypoint prov. 2-Dec-3 Christie's, London #225/R est:6000-8000
£5594 $9510 €8000 The flower of love (64x40cm-25x16in) s. lithograph. 26-Nov-3 Dorotheum, Vienna #1/R est:6000-6500
£5667 $10427 €8500 In front of the house (17x19cm-7x7in) s.i. woodcut. 10-Jun-4 Hauswedell & Nolte, Hamburg #516/R est:8000
£6042 $10272 €8821 Model resting - rehende frau, halbakt (58x46cm-23x18in) s. lithograph exec.c.1919-20 lit. 4-Nov-3 Bukowskis, Stockholm #425/R est:100000-120000 (S.KR 80000)
£8500 $14620 €12410 August Strindberg (60x46cm-24x18in) s. lithograph prov. 2-Dec-3 Christie's, London #230/R est:6000-8000
£8741 $15035 €12500 Violin concert (47x53cm-19x21in) s. lithograph. 2-Dec-3 Hauswedell & Nolte, Hamburg #459/R est:15000
£9410 $15997 €13739 Death and the woman (23x17cm-9x7in) s. intaglio print printed in black. 19-Nov-3 Grev Wedels Plass, Oslo #20/R est:150000-200000 (N.KR 110000)
£10000 $18200 €14600 Jealousy II (46x56cm-18x22in) s.num7 lithograph. 30-Jun-4 Christie's, London #277/R est:10000-15000
£10000 $18200 €14600 Attraction (47x35cm-19x14in) s. lithograph prov. 30-Jun-4 Christie's, London #279/R est:30000-50000
£11000 $20020 €16060 Sin (70x40cm-28x16in) s. lithograph prov. 30-Jun-4 Christie's, London #278/R est:12000-18000
£12000 $22080 €18000 Attraction I (46x35cm-18x14in) s. lithograph. 11-Jun-4 Villa Grisebach, Berlin #1527/R est:18000-24000
£15000 $25800 €21900 Woman (45x59cm-18x23in) s. lithograph prov. 2-Dec-3 Christie's, London #229/R est:15000-25000
£15398 $26176 €22481 Separation II (41x64cm-16x25in) lithograph printed in greyish blue. 19-Nov-3 Grev Wedels Plass, Oslo #24/R est:150000-200000 (N.KR 180000)
£15819 $28000 €23096 Selbsportrat (46x32cm-18x13in) s. lithograph. 28-Apr-4 Christie's, Rockefeller NY #111/R est:25000-35000
£16225 $27096 €23689 Self-portrait II (46x32cm-18x13in) lithograph printed in black exec.1895. 13-Oct-3 Blomqvist, Oslo #359/R est:160000-180000 (N.KR 190000)
£16681 $28358 €24354 The day after the night before (19x27cm-7x11in) s.d.1894 intaglio print printed in black. 19-Nov-3 Grev Wedels Plass, Oslo #11/R est:250000-300000 (N.KR 195000)
£17109 $29085 €24979 Washing clothes on the shore (33x46cm-13x18in) s.d.1903 woodcut printed in black and red. 19-Nov-3 Grev Wedels Plass, Oslo #8/R est:150000-200000 (N.KR 200000)
£18000 $30960 €26280 Woman II (30x34cm-12x13in) etching aquatint prov. 2-Dec-3 Christie's, London #228/R est:20000-30000
£18000 $32760 €26280 Alpha and Omega. lithograph 20 vignettes 2 complete series. 1-Jul-4 Sotheby's, London #230/R est:20000-25000
£20000 $36800 €30000 Eva Mudocci and the brooch (60x46cm-24x18in) s. lithograph. 11-Jun-4 Villa Grisebach, Berlin #1528/R est:20000-30000
£20530 $34902 €29974 Jealousy I (33x46cm-13x18in) s.d.1896 lithograph printed in black. 19-Nov-3 Grev Wedels Plass, Oslo #2/R est:200000-300000 (N.KR 240000)
£25000 $43000 €36500 Alpha and Omega (47x63cm-19x25in) s. lithograph set of 18 prov. 2-Dec-3 Christie's, London #238/R est:25000-35000
£25663 $43627 €37468 The sick child I (36x27cm-14x11in) s. intaglio print printed in black. 19-Nov-3 Grev Wedels Plass, Oslo #12/R est:300000-400000 (N.KR 300000)
£26173 $48159 €38213 Attraction (44x34cm-17x13in) s. etching with drypoint lit. 29-Mar-4 Rasmussen, Copenhagen #49/R est:100000 (D.KR 290000)
£30568 $55633 €44629 The heart (25x19cm-10x7in) i. col woodcut conceived 1898-99 exec. 1913. 18-Jun-4 Kornfeld, Bern #120/R est:50000 (S.FR 70000)
£56000 $101920 €81760 Melancholy (38x45cm-15x18in) s.i. black grey woodcut. 30-Jun-4 Christie's, London #281/R est:25000-35000
£60000 $109200 €87600 Sick child (42x56cm-17x22in) s.d.97 red mustard yellow lithograph. 30-Jun-4 Christie's, London #280/R est:60000-80000
£72052 $131135 €105196 Young girl on a bridge (50x42cm-20x17in) i. woodcut exec. 1918. 18-Jun-4 Kornfeld, Bern #121/R est:175000 (S.FR 165000)
£125000 $215000 €182500 Girls on the bridge (50x43cm-20x17in) woodcut lithograph. 2-Dec-3 Christie's, London #235/R est:120000-180000
£130000 $223600 €189800 Girls on the bridge (50x42cm-20x17in) s. col lithograph woodcut. 4-Dec-3 Sotheby's, London #180/R est:120000-180000

Works on paper
£10000 $18200 €14600 Nude couple (27x41cm-11x16in) i.verso chl exec.c.1912-15 prov. 4-Feb-4 Sotheby's, London #429/R est:12000-15000
£22000 $40480 €32120 On the bridge (13x11cm-5x4in) init. brush blue ink exec 1920 prov. 24-Jun-4 Christie's, London #378/R est:15000-20000
£350000 $637000 €511000 Vampire (27x37cm-11x15in) W/C pastel card exec.c.1893-96 prov.exhib.lit. 4-Feb-4 Sotheby's, London #424/R est:200000-300000

MUNCH, Hanspeter (1940-) German
£719 $1180 €1000 Untitled (61x50cm-24x20in) s.i.d. verso. 4-Jun-3 Ketterer, Hamburg #700/R

MUNCY, Percy W (20th C) American
£640 $1100 €934 Carnations (27x37cm-11x15in) s.d.1920 panel. 3-Dec-3 Doyle, New York #223/R est:2000-3000

MUND, Hugo (1892-1962) Hungarian
£685 $1240 €1000 Market place (37x49cm-15x19in) s. oil on card. 16-Apr-4 Mu Terem Galeria, Budapest #33/R (H.F 260000)
£977 $1622 €1426 Still life (60x50cm-24x20in) s. 4-Oct-3 Kieselbach, Budapest #175/R (H.F 360000)

Works on paper
£1001 $1812 €1461 Nude (55x85cm-22x33in) s. 16-Apr-4 Mu Terem Galeria, Budapest #56/R (H.F 380000)

MUNDARAY, Ismael (1952-) Venezuelan
£436 $750 €637 Still life (60x80cm-24x31in) s. painted 1998. 7-Dec-3 Subastas Odalys, Caracas #126/R
£484 $760 €707 Still life (60x80cm-24x31in) s. acrylic. 23-Nov-2 Subastas Odalys, Caracas #6/R

MUNDELL, John (1818-1875) British
£550 $1012 €803 Shipping in coastal waters (25x36cm-10x14in) s. 8-Jun-4 Bonhams, Knightsbridge #157/R
£600 $1104 €876 Figure on a woodland track (31x25cm-12x10in) s. panel. 8-Jun-4 Bonhams, Knightsbridge #256/R
£1150 $1829 €1668 Fishing smacks and other shipping off the south coast (18x51cm-7x20in) s. wood panel painted c.1860. 23-Mar-3 Desmond Judd, Cranbrook #1056

MUNDT, Caroline Emilie (1849-1922) Danish
£403 $737 €588 Still life of potted plants and budgie on window ledge (61x46cm-24x18in) s.d.1919. 9-Jun-4 Rasmussen, Copenhagen #1887/R (D.KR 4500)
£431 $698 €625 Road to the marshes at Kokkedal (23x47cm-9x19in) s.d.98. 4-Aug-3 Rasmussen, Vejle #323/R (D.KR 4500)
£531 $967 €775 Still life of wild flowers (45x32cm-18x13in) s.d.1917. 7-Feb-4 Rasmussen, Havnen #2237 (D.KR 5800)
£985 $1802 €1438 Wild flowers (45x32cm-18x13in) s.d.1917 exhib. 9-Jun-4 Rasmussen, Copenhagen #1869/R (D.KR 11000)

MUNDUWALAWALA, Ginger Riley (c.1937-) Australian

Works on paper
£2344 $4383 €3516 Untitled (51x72cm-20x28in) s. synthetic polymer paint prov. 26-Jul-4 Sotheby's, Melbourne #282/R est:7000-10000 (A.D 6000)
£3049 $4817 €4421 Untitled, Limmen Bight country (107x128cm-42x50in) synthetic polymer paint canvas prov. 28-Jul-3 Sotheby's, Paddington #373/R est:7000-10000 (A.D 7500)
£5285 $8350 €7663 Untitled (82x107cm-32x42in) synthetic polymer paint canvas prov. 28-Jul-3 Sotheby's, Paddington #119/R est:10000-15000 (A.D 13000)
£8130 $12846 €11789 Limmen Bight river (143x148cm-56x58in) synthetic polymer paint linen prov. 28-Jul-3 Sotheby's, Paddington #208/R est:20000-30000 (A.D 20000)
£8537 $13488 €12379 Untitled, Limmen Bight country (100x100cm-39x39in) i.d.30/11/93 verso synthetic polymer paint linen prov. 28-Jul-3 Sotheby's, Paddington #122/R est:20000-30000 (A.D 21000)
£9766 $18262 €14649 Four archers (91x127cm-36x50in) d.1990 verso synthetic polymer paint canvas prov. 26-Jul-4 Sotheby's, Melbourne #147/R est:30000-50000 (A.D 25000)
£17969 $33602 €26954 Limmen Bight country (123x172cm-48x68in) s.d.1990 verso synthetic polymer paint canvas prov. 26-Jul-4 Sotheby's, Melbourne #149/R est:35000-45000 (A.D 46000)

MUNEYASHI (19th C) Japanese

Sculpture
£8389 $15436 €12500 Carp (57cm-22in) s. carved iron. 24-Mar-4 Joron-Derem, Paris #287/R est:10000-12000

MUNG-MUNG, Patrick (fl.1990s) Australian

Works on paper
£1860 $3161 €2716 Untitled 2001 (100x140cm-39x55in) synthetic polymer paint natural earth pigment prov. 29-Oct-3 Lawson Menzies, Sydney #54/R est:2500-5000 (A.D 4500)

MUNGATOPI, Deaf Tommy (attrib) (?-1985) Australian

Works on paper
£1406 $2630 €2109 Pukumani designs (77x31cm-30x12in) earth pigments eucalyptus bark exec.c.1962 prov. 26-Jul-4 Sotheby's, Melbourne #225/R est:5000-7000 (A.D 3600)

MUNGER, Gilbert (1837-1903) American
£400 $744 €584 Landscape view near Bourron (34x45cm-13x18in) s. panel. 2-Mar-4 Bearnes, Exeter #423
£1200 $2124 €1752 Bacino San Marco, Venice. San Giorgio Maggiore (18x25cm-7x10in) s. one d.1882 board pair. 27-Apr-4 Bonhams, New Bond Street #107/R est:600-800
£2800 $5152 €4088 Cattle grazing (37x46cm-15x18in) s. panel. 25-Mar-4 Christie's, Kensington #26/R est:2000-3000
£3000 $5520 €4380 By the river (29x46cm-11x18in) s. panel. 25-Mar-4 Christie's, Kensington #27/R est:2000-3000

MUNGER, Rudolf (1862-1929) Swiss

Works on paper
£1565 $2864 €2285 Sowing and reaping (48x31cm-19x12in) s.d.1915 ink W/C two. 4-Jun-4 Zofingen, Switzerland #2897/R est:2000 (S.FR 3600)

MUNIER, Émile (1810-1895) French
£17647 $30000 €25765 Teasing the doves (46x28cm-18x11in) s.d.1895 prov. 29-Oct-3 Christie's, Rockefeller NY #127/R est:15000-20000
£36111 $65000 €52722 Portrait de Marie Louise (45x53cm-18x21in) s.d.1879. 23-Apr-4 Sotheby's, New York #52/R est:50000-70000
£52000 $94640 €75920 En penitence (94x64cm-37x25in) s.d.1879 prov.exhib. 15-Jun-4 Sotheby's, London #191/R est:20000-30000
£77586 $142759 €113276 Broken vase (93x62cm-37x24in) s. 26-Mar-4 Koller, Zurich #3113/R est:15000-20000 (S.FR 180000)

Works on paper
£3500 $6475 €5110 New Arrival (48x39cm-19x15in) s. chl chk. 10-Mar-4 Sotheby's, Olympia #270/R est:3000-5000

MUNILLA, Felix (1885-1958) Spanish
£267 $483 €400 Dusk on the lake (17x26cm-7x10in) s. board. 30-Mar-4 Segre, Madrid #24/R

MUNIZ, Vik (1961-) Brazilian
£5000 $9200 €7300 Torso - after Frantisek Dritikol (58x49cm-23x19in) s.i.d.1997 num.1/10 verso gelatin silver print prov. 24-Jun-4 Sotheby's, London #323/R est:5000-7000

Photographs
£2235 $4000 €3263 Picasso touching jellyfish (51x41cm-20x16in) s.i.d.1994 num. of 5 gelatin silver print prov. 14-May-4 Phillips, New York #342/R est:6000-8000
£2235 $4000 €3263 Teddy bear, pictures of wire (50x40cm-20x16in) s.i.d.1995 num. of 5 gelatin silver print prov.lit. 14-May-4 Phillips, New York #343/R est:6000-8000

£3000 $5460 €4380 Bowl (57x47cm-22x19in) s.i.d.1998 num.Ap 2/3 verso gelatin silver print prov. 4-Feb-4 Sotheby's, Olympia #76/R est:3000-5000
£3293 $5500 €4808 The white shirt (38x38cm-15x15in) s.i.d.1994 num.3/5 sepia toned gelatin silver print prov. 17-Oct-3 Phillips, New York #51/R est:3000-5000
£3867 $7115 €5800 Eleven thousand yards (51x61cm-20x24in) silver gelatin print exec.1999 prov.exhib.lit. 10-Jun-4 Christie's, Paris #93/R est:4800-6500
£4891 $9000 €7141 Still after Cindy Sherman, pictures of ink (76x102cm-30x40in) cibachrome numbered of five prov. 10-Jun-4 Phillips, New York #403/R est:10000-15000
£5587 $10000 €8157 For he's a jolly good fellow (133x170cm-52x67in) cibachrome edition of three prov. 14-May-4 Phillips, New York #325/R est:12000-18000
£5988 $10000 €8742 Self Portrait - Pictures of Soil (61x51cm-24x20in) cibachrome print on foamcore exec 1997 prov.exhib. 12-Nov-3 Christie's, Rockefeller NY #552/R est:10000-15000
£5988 $10000 €8742 Milk drop (65x52cm-26x20in) s.i.d.1997 cibachrome mounted on aluminum prov. 14-Nov-3 Phillips, New York #211/R est:10000-15000
£7200 $13248 €10512 Sacred Lodovica - after Bernini (111x149cm-44x59in) s.i.d.1997 num.AP 1/3 verso cibachrome print prov. 24-Jun-4 Sotheby's, London #320/R est:8000-12000
£7500 $12525 €10950 Monster (156x126cm-61x50in) cibachrome print exec 2000 prov. 21-Oct-3 Sotheby's, London #322/R est:6000-8000
£7821 $14000 €11419 Orchestra, pictures of chocolate (170x123cm-67x48in) cibachrome print aluminum edition of 3 prov. 12-May-4 Christie's, Rockefeller NY #456/R est:15000-20000
£8380 $15000 €12235 Boys of Carnival (152x122cm-60x48in) cibachrome exec.1998 prov.exhib. 26-May-4 Sotheby's, New York #169a/R est:15000-20000
£8383 $14000 €12239 After Claude Monet, from pictures of colour (189x280cm-74x110in) s.d.2001 num.3 chromogenic col print one of three prov.exhib.lit. 17-Oct-3 Phillips, New York #199/R est:15000-25000
£8982 $15000 €13114 Milk drop, after Dr Harold Edgarton (154x120cm-61x47in) c-print exhib. 13-Nov-3 Sotheby's, New York #454/R est:15000-20000
£9000 $15030 €13140 Angelica (101x81cm-40x32in) cibachrome print edition of 5. 22-Oct-3 Christie's, London #162/R est:6000-8000
£9155 $15838 €13000 Professeur (155x122cm-61x48in) num.3/3 cibachrome prov.exhib. 9-Dec-3 Artcurial Briest, Paris #447/R est:12000-15000
£9444 $17000 €13788 Still (125x166cm-49x65in) s.d. cibachrome print after Cindy Sherman prov.exhib. 23-Apr-4 Phillips, New York #97/R est:15000-20000
£9497 $17000 €13866 Milk drop, pictures of chocolate (102x76cm-40x30in) cibachrome print after Dr Harold Edgerton prov.exhib. 12-May-4 Christie's, Rockefeller NY #457/R est:10000-15000
£9581 $16000 €13988 After Yves Klein, from pictures of colour (228x189cm-90x74in) s.d.2001 num.3 chromogenic col print one of three prov.exhib.lit. 17-Oct-3 Phillips, New York #200/R est:15000-25000
£10056 $18000 €14682 Picture of holes (60x51cm-24x20in) s.i.d.1997 num.6/10 verso gelatin silver print 5 parts prov.lit. 13-May-4 Sotheby's, New York #405/R est:15000-20000
£10615 $19000 €15498 Babe - From pictures of chocolate (102x152cm-40x60in) cibachrome print two parts exec 1998 prov.lit. 13-May-4 Sotheby's, New York #406/R est:15000-20000
£10778 $18000 €15736 Migrant Mother after D Lange (165x122cm-65x48in) cibachrome print exec 2000 prov. 12-Nov-3 Christie's, Rockefeller NY #548/R est:15000-20000
£12000 $21840 €17520 Teacher (87x75cm-34x30in) s.i.d.1999 cibachrome print prov. 6-Feb-4 Sotheby's, London #274/R est:10000-15000
£13408 $24000 €19576 Untitled Balloon and Brick. s.i.d.89 num.17 gelatin silver print two parts rubber cord prov. 13-May-4 Sotheby's, New York #403/R est:3000-5000
£14525 $26000 €21207 Raft of the Medusa, pictures of chocolate (113x176cm-44x69in) cibachrome print diptych edition 2 of 3 prov.lit. 12-May-4 Christie's, Rockefeller NY #454/R est:20000-30000
£14970 $25000 €21856 After Van Gogh, from pictures of colour (248x189cm-98x74in) s.d.2001 num.3 chromogenic col print one of three prov.exhib.lit. 17-Oct-3 Phillips, New York #198/R est:15000-25000
£16168 $27000 €23605 After Mark Rothko, from pictures of colour (251x189cm-99x74in) s.d.2001 num.3 chromogenic col print one of three prov.exhib.lit. 17-Oct-3 Phillips, New York #201/R est:15000-25000
£19461 $32500 €28413 Mao (89x72cm-35x28in) c-print after Warhol prov. 13-Nov-3 Sotheby's, New York #523/R est:20000-30000
£19553 $35000 €28547 Las Meninas, pictures of chocolate (152x114cm-60x45in) col coupler print Cintra edition 2 of 3 after Velazquez prov. 12-May-4 Christie's, Rockefeller NY #455/R est:20000-30000
£20950 $37500 €30587 Reader (102x79cm-40x31in) cibachrome print exec 2002 edn of 3 after Fragonard prov. 13-May-4 Sotheby's, New York #394/R est:15000-20000
£20958 $35000 €30599 After Richard Serra (170x122cm-67x48in) cibachrome print mounted Cintra exec 2000 prov. 12-Nov-3 Christie's, Rockefeller NY #547/R est:22000-28000
£22156 $37000 €32348 Chuck, from pictures of colour (235x188cm-93x74in) s.d.2001 num.3 chromogenic col print one of three prov.exhib.lit. 17-Oct-3 Phillips, New York #202/R est:15000-25000
£27545 $46000 €40216 After Gerhard Richter, from pictures of colour (275x189cm-108x74in) s.d.2001 num.3 chromogenic col print one of three prov.exhib.lit. 17-Oct-3 Phillips, New York #203/R est:15000-25000
£28000 $51520 €40880 Double Mona Lisa - Peanut butter and jelly (119x155cm-47x61in) s.i.d.1999 cibachrome print prov.exhib. 24-Jun-4 Sotheby's, London #112/R est:15000-20000
£29940 $50000 €43712 Liz, cayenne, black pepper, curry, chili pepper (100x100cm-39x39in) c-print four prov.lit. 13-Nov-3 Sotheby's, New York #455/R est:50000-70000
£32222 $58000 €47044 Bloody Marilyn (145x125cm-57x49in) s.verso cibachrome print mounted on aluminum prov. 23-Apr-4 Phillips, New York #13/R est:25000-35000
£38922 $65000 €56826 Action photo (152x121cm-60x48in) s.d.1997 num.3/3 verso c-print prov. 13-Nov-3 Sotheby's, New York #483/R est:40000-60000
£43000 $79120 €62780 Liz - Cayenne, black pepper, curry, chilli pepper (93x93cm-37x37in) s.i.d.1999 cibachrome print mounted aluminium four parts prov.lit. 24-Jun-4 Sotheby's, London #113/R est:25000-35000

Prints
£6145 $11000 €8972 Nadia (76x96cm-30x38in) s.i.d.2000 dye destruction print edn of 5 prov.lit. 13-May-4 Sotheby's, New York #339/R est:8000-10000

Sculpture
£8380 $15000 €12235 Clown skull (30x20x23cm-12x8x9in) init.d.90.3 num.AP cast plastic prov. 13-May-4 Sotheby's, New York #417/R est:15000-20000

MUNKACSI, Martin (1896-1963) Hungarian

Photographs
£2000 $3680 €3000 Children running into the sea, Liberia (32x26cm-13x10in) i. verso silver gelatin lit.exhib. 10-Jun-4 Villa Grisebach, Berlin #1232/R est:700-900
£2096 $3500 €3060 Peignoir with dove (23x29cm-9x11in) studio st.verso photo. 17-Oct-3 Sotheby's, New York #243/R est:5000-8000

MUNKACSY, Mihaly Lieb (1844-1900) Hungarian

£24795 $42896 €36201 Lady with a Golden Medaillon (26x20cm-10x8in) panel painted 1871. 12-Dec-3 Kieselbach, Budapest #218/R (H.F 9500000)
£95018 $157730 €138726 Resting lady (87x116cm-34x46in) panel. 4-Oct-3 Kieselbach, Budapest #141/R (H.F 35000000)
£197608 $357670 €288508 Two families (140x105cm-55x41in) s. 16-Apr-4 Mu Terem Galeria, Budapest #110/R (H.F 75000000)
£344118 $585000 €502412 Two families (106x150cm-42x59in) s.d.1880 panel prov.exhib.lit. 29-Oct-3 Christie's, Rockefeller NY #29/R est:300000-400000
£525000 $955500 €766500 By the stream (119x91cm-47x36in) s. painted c.1885 prov.lit. 15-Jun-4 Sotheby's, London #47/R est:120000-180000

Works on paper
£537 $988 €800 Christ before Pilate (21x17cm-8x7in) s. pencil. 26-Mar-4 Dorotheum, Vienna #130/R
£1007 $1852 €1500 Oriental figure (19x15cm-7x6in) s. pencil. 26-Mar-4 Dorotheum, Vienna #132/R est:1400-1600
£2318 $4219 €3500 Young Hungarian country girl (60x23cm-24x9in) s. pastel canvas. 19-Jun-4 Dannenberg, Berlin #598/R est:3500

MUNKACSY, Mihaly Lieb (attrib) (1844-1900) Hungarian

£2657 $4571 €3800 Portrait of old woman (32x24cm-13x9in) 5-Dec-3 Michael Zeller, Lindau #739/R est:3200
£3294 $5600 €4809 Woodland path with figures (36x25cm-14x10in) s. 22-Nov-3 Jackson's, Cedar Falls #14/R est:750-1000

MUNKARA, Benedict (20th C) Australian

Sculpture
£3418 $6392 €5127 Untitled, bird (52cm-20in) earth pigments ironwood exec.c.1973 prov. 26-Jul-4 Sotheby's, Melbourne #51/R est:4000-6000 (A.D 8750)

MUNN, George Frederick (1852-1907) British

£1286 $2250 €1878 Still life with fan (28x38cm-11x15in) s.d.1890 s.i.d.1890 verso board. 19-Dec-3 Sotheby's, New York #1099/R est:2500-3500

MUNNICH, Heinz (19/20th C) German

£268 $491 €400 In rose garden in the Dolomites (70x80cm-28x31in) s.i.verso lit. 8-Jul-4 Allgauer, Kempten #2176/R

MUNNIK, Henk (1912-1997) Dutch

£280 $481 €400 Japanese doll (50x40cm-20x16in) s. 8-Dec-3 Glerum, Amsterdam #94/R
£280 $481 €400 Composition (24x34cm-9x13in) s. panel. 8-Dec-3 Glerum, Amsterdam #174/R
£385 $662 €550 Sailing boats (40x50cm-16x20in) s. i.verso board. 8-Dec-3 Glerum, Amsterdam #215/R
£959 $1630 €1400 Still life with bottles (50x60cm-20x24in) s. prov. 5-Nov-3 Vendue Huis, Gravenhage #407/R

Works on paper
£280 $481 €400 Composition (39x49cm-15x19in) s. mixed media. 8-Dec-3 Glerum, Amsterdam #162/R
£280 $481 €400 Composition (100x60cm-39x24in) s. d.74 verso mixed media canvas. 8-Dec-3 Glerum, Amsterdam #183/R
£350 $601 €500 Nocturne II (50x40cm-20x16in) s. d.92 verso mixed media. 8-Dec-3 Glerum, Amsterdam #168/R

MUNNINGER, Ludwig (20th C) German

£1069 $1700 €1561 Winter mountain landscape with two figures overlooking a cliff (76x102cm-30x40in) s. 13-Sep-3 Selkirks, St. Louis #495 est:800-1200
£1445 $2500 €2110 Winter mountain scene with family (76x102cm-30x40in) 12-Dec-3 Du Mouchelle, Detroit #2012/R est:1800-2500

MUNNINGHOFF, Xeno (1873-1944) Dutch

£395 $726 €600 Birch trees (36x55cm-14x22in) s. canvas on panel. 28-Jun-4 Sotheby's, Amsterdam #142/R
£414 $691 €600 Farmer on a sandy path (34x52cm-13x20in) s. 11-Nov-3 Vendu Notarishuis, Rotterdam #87

MUNNINGS (1878-1959) British

£1275 $2346 €1900 Horse fair (50x60cm-20x24in) canvas on board. 23-Mar-4 Mealy's, Castlecomer #1147/R est:700-900

MUNNINGS, Sir Alfred (1878-1959) British

£2235 $4000 €3263 Barnyard ox (25x36cm-10x14in) s. 8-May-4 Susanin's, Chicago #6134/R est:6000-8000
£2600 $4810 €3796 Tree study at Holmcote, Exmoor (30x41cm-12x16in) s.i. i.verso board prov. 11-Mar-4 Duke & Son, Dorchester #195/R est:1500-2500
£6200 $10540 €9052 Portrait of Colonel Harry Egerton Norton (77x53cm-30x21in) s. 19-Nov-3 Tennants, Leyburn #1171/R est:3500-4500
£7000 $12320 €10220 Tree study at Holmecote, Exmoor (30x41cm-12x16in) panel prov. 21-May-4 Christie's, London #59/R est:7000-10000
£8000 $13760 €11680 Winter landscape (24x32cm-9x13in) s.d.1902 s.i.on stretcher prov. 2-Dec-3 Bonhams, New Bond Street #24/R est:8000-12000
£8000 $14080 €11680 Landscape - Study of a pond. Study of a mountainous landscape (25x34cm-10x13in) panel double-sided prov. 21-May-4 Christie's, London #19/R est:10000-15000
£12849 $23000 €18760 Blenheim groom cinching a girth (30x25cm-12x10in) s.verso prov. 27-May-4 Sotheby's, New York #295/R est:15000-20000
£15500 $27280 €22630 Cloud studies (40x51cm-16x20in) canvasboard prov. 21-May-4 Christie's, London #55/R est:8000-12000
£16000 $27520 €23360 Exmoor ponies, studies no. 15 (17x25cm-7x10in) s. board prov.exhib. 3-Dec-3 Sotheby's, London #64/R est:12000-15000
£16000 $28160 €23360 Suffolk landscape (41x51cm-16x20in) panel prov. 21-May-4 Christie's, London #54/R est:10000-15000

£16279 $28000 €23767 Anarchist (35x46cm-14x18in) painted 1943 prov.exhib. 5-Dec-3 Christie's, Rockefeller NY #119/R est:15000-20000
£16760 $30000 €24470 Artist painting near Lamorna (25x36cm-10x14in) panel prov. 27-May-4 Sotheby's, New York #298/R est:30000-50000
£22093 $38000 €32256 Withypool landscape, Exmoor (51x61cm-20x24in) s. panel painted 1940-44 prov. 5-Dec-3 Christie's, Rockefeller NY #120/R est:25000-35000
£24000 $41280 €35040 Huntsman (51x26cm-20x10in) s.d.1914 prov. 2-Dec-3 Bonhams, New Bond Street #26/R est:25000-30000
£40000 $70400 €58400 Porlock Hill (51x61cm-20x24in) s.i. prov. 21-May-4 Christie's, London #18/R est:18000-25000
£40000 $70400 €58400 Jerry (51x61cm-20x24in) s.i.d.1914 prov. 21-May-4 Christie's, London #21/R est:30000-50000
£40000 $70400 €58400 Gypsy encampment (51x61cm-20x24in) s. prov. 21-May-4 Christie's, London #57/R est:40000-60000
£45000 $77400 €65700 Exmoor ponies, Study no 12 (17x25cm-7x10in) s. init.verso board prov.exhib. 3-Dec-3 Sotheby's, London #65/R est:12000-15000
£46512 $80000 €67908 Autumn, Sir John Shelley's Park, Hampshire (64x77cm-25x30in) s. painted 1913 prov.exhib. 5-Dec-3 Christie's, Rockefeller NY #137/R est:100000-150000
£60000 $109200 €87600 Study for Lord Astor with his mares (30x51cm-12x20in) s. board prov.exhib. 1-Jul-4 Sotheby's, London #26/R est:60000-80000
£156977 $270000 €229186 Second set (35x71cm-14x28in) s. panel painted c.1943 prov.exhib. 5-Dec-3 Christie's, Rockefeller NY #117/R est:100000-150000
£162791 $280000 €237675 Study for going to the start (25x35cm-10x14in) s. i.verso panel painted 1945-46 prov.exhib. 5-Dec-3 Christie's, Rockefeller NY #132/R est:100000-150000
£167598 $300000 €244693 Autumn sunshine (63x76cm-25x30in) s. 27-May-4 Sotheby's, New York #297/R est:300000-500000
£190000 $334400 €277400 A Summer evening Cliveden (30x51cm-12x20in) s. board prov.exhib. 21-May-4 Christie's, London #23/R est:120000-180000
£215000 $378400 €313900 Sydney Tucker, Huntsman of the Devon and Somerset crossing Withycombe ford (51x61cm-20x24in) s.d.1919. 21-May-4 Christie's, London #67/R est:120000-180000
£350000 $616000 €511000 Horse fair in Ireland (51x61cm-20x24in) s.i. prov. 21-May-4 Christie's, London #73/R est:250000-400000
£350000 $640500 €511000 Evening (58x73cm-23x29in) s.d.1910 prov.exhib. 2-Jun-4 Sotheby's, London #5/R est:400000-600000
£363129 $650000 €530168 The winner (52x62cm-20x24in) s. painted c.1910 prov.exhib.lit. 5-May-4 Sotheby's, New York #32/R est:500000-700000
£385000 $700700 €562100 Newmarket CHeveley (30x66cm-12x26in) s.i.d.1937 board prov.exhib. 1-Jul-4 Sotheby's, London #25/R est:120000-150000
£418994 $750000 €611731 Leaving the paddock at Epsom Downs (65x76cm-26x30in) s. prov.exhib.lit. 5-May-4 Sotheby's, New York #33/R est:600000-800000
£446927 $800000 €652513 Before the start (36x71cm-14x28in) s. prov.exhib.lit. 5-May-4 Sotheby's, New York #31/R est:500000-700000
£544693 $975000 €795252 Afternoon ride (51x61cm-20x24in) s. 27-May-4 Sotheby's, New York #299/R est:1000000-1500000
£980000 $1783600 €1430800 Creme Brulee (71x92cm-28x36in) s. prov.exhib. 1-Jul-4 Sotheby's, London #24/R est:1000000-1500000
£1350000 $2295000 €1971000 Early morning on the Manton Downs (76x101cm-30x40in) s. prov.exhib.lit. 27-Nov-3 Sotheby's, London #35/R est:100000-1500000
£3910615 $7000000 €5709498 The Red Prince Mare (102x152cm-40x60in) s. painted 1921 prov.exhib.lit. 5-May-4 Sotheby's, New York #30/R est:4000000-6000000
Works on paper
£520 $957 €759 Flowers (15x11cm-6x4in) one i.d.1893 one i.d.1890 W/C pencil sketch verso two. 24-Jun-4 Olivers, Sudbury #118/R
£550 $875 €803 Design for a menu card (24x36cm-9x14in) init.i. pencil. 10-Sep-3 Sotheby's, Olympia #122/R
£574 $930 €838 Ascot before the races, Royal Enclosure (9x12cm-4x5in) s.i. pencil prov. 30-Jul-3 Goodman, Sydney #192/R (A.D 1400)
£600 $966 €870 Sketch of a race horse (15x23cm-6x9in) init. dr. 15-Aug-3 Keys, Aylsham #654
£850 $1369 €1233 Show jumper clearing a fence (15x20cm-6x8in) init. pencil sketch. 15-Aug-3 Keys, Aylsham #656/R
£850 $1445 €1241 What ho' (14x11cm-6x4in) s.i. pencil prov. 27-Nov-3 Christie's, Kensington #39/R
£1000 $1810 €1460 Lead off from Castle House (18x25cm-7x10in) s.i. pencil. 16-Apr-4 Keys, Aylsham #632/R est:1200-1500
£1100 $2057 €1650 Study for the Riding Lesson (20x15cm-8x6in) s. chl col chk. 22-Jul-4 Dominic Winter, Swindon #332/R est:1000-1500
£1230 $1992 €1796 Hurst Park (10x12cm-4x5in) s.i. pencil prov. 30-Jul-3 Goodman, Sydney #191/R est:1000-1500 (A.D 3000)
£1600 $2752 €2336 Poster design for Caleys, Norwich (48x38cm-19x15in) W/C bodycol. 5-Dec-3 Keys, Aylsham #560 est:1500-2000
£1844 $2988 €2692 Lewes, 1955 going out (14x15cm-6x6in) s.i. pencil prov. 30-Jul-3 Goodman, Sydney #193/R est:1200-2000 (A.D 4500)
£2000 $3520 €2920 96 Degrees - increasing to 100 (20x25cm-8x10in) s.d.1924 pencil. 21-May-4 Christie's, London #66/R est:2500-3500
£2700 $4968 €3942 Rushed off home in a cowd sweat. Got howd on him and lugged him home. Found him in bed (9x13cm-4x5in) i. pen ink set of five different sizes prov. 10-Jun-4 Christie's, Kensington #141/R est:3000-5000
£2907 $5000 €4244 Rufus and Ajm at dinner (13x17cm-5x7in) i. pencil headed writing paper. 5-Dec-3 Christie's, Rockefeller NY #115/R est:3000-5000
£2994 $5000 €4371 Figures (15x11cm-6x4in) s. pen ink pair prov. 20-Oct-3 Sotheby's, New York #504/R est:5000-7000
£3100 $4991 €4495 Sketch of race horse with handler (18x23cm-7x9in) s. pencil dr. 15-Aug-3 Keys, Aylsham #655 est:500-600
£3200 $5440 €4672 Self portrait at an easel (29x23cm-11x9in) s. pen ink. 27-Nov-3 Christie's, Kensington #37/R est:2000-3000
£5814 $10000 €8488 Bay hunter in a stable (24x36cm-9x14in) pencil crayon W/C prov. 5-Dec-3 Christie's, Rockefeller NY #118/R est:7000-10000
£10000 $17600 €14600 Dainty Dame (27x35cm-11x14in) s.d.1905 pencil chl W/C bodycol. 21-May-4 Christie's, London #58/R est:7000-10000
£10465 $18000 €15279 Boer War (36x47cm-14x19in) s.d.1907 brown wash exhib. 5-Dec-3 Christie's, Rockefeller NY #112/R est:7000-10000
£16500 $29040 €24090 History of a Cycling tour. And what it brought about. Showing how fortune favours the brave (36x25cm-14x10in) s.i. ink W/C bodycol three prov. 21-May-4 Christie's, London #70/R est:5000-8000
£69767 $120000 €101860 Spinney in the hollow (48x52cm-19x20in) s.d.1912 W/C bodycol exhib. 5-Dec-3 Christie's, Rockefeller NY #110/R est:120000-180000
£80000 $140800 €116800 Flash of Scarlet (51x67cm-20x26in) s. W/C bodycol exec 1907 prov.exhib. 21-May-4 Christie's, London #71/R est:100000-150000
£86000 $157380 €125560 Horse fair (32x45cm-13x18in) s.d.1905 W/C gouache pencil. 2-Jun-4 Sotheby's, London #1/R est:80000-120000
£145000 $246500 €211700 Taking the fence (49x67cm-19x26in) s.d.1906 W/C gouache. 19-Nov-3 Sotheby's, Olympia #74/R est:70000-100000

MUNNINGS, Sir Alfred (attrib) (1878-1959) British
Works on paper
£300 $543 €438 Study of hands (18x20cm-7x8in) bears sig pencil. 16-Apr-4 Keys, Aylsham #686

MUNNO, Giovanni di (20th C) ?
£323 $530 €472 Avila (33x46cm-13x18in) s. painted 1973. 1-Jun-3 Subastas Odalys, Caracas #14
£563 $940 €822 Beach (38x46cm-15x18in) s. painted 1972. 13-Jul-3 Subastas Odalys, Caracas #16/R
£581 $970 €848 Dusk in La Guaira (33x24cm-13x9in) s. painted 1973. 13-Jul-3 Subastas Odalys, Caracas #112/R
£599 $1000 €875 La Guaira Street (55x46cm-22x18in) s. painted 1970. 13-Jul-3 Subastas Odalys, Caracas #85/R
£599 $1000 €875 Landscape in Caurimare (77x66cm-30x26in) s. painted 1970. 13-Jul-3 Subastas Odalys, Caracas #113
£749 $1250 €1094 Landscape in Caracas (46x55cm-18x22in) s. painted 1972. 13-Jul-3 Subastas Odalys, Caracas #47/R
£1035 $1925 €1511 View from the top (46x55cm-18x22in) s. painted 1973. 14-Mar-4 Subastas Odalys, Caracas #76/R

MUNNS, John Bernard (1869-1942) British
£400 $740 €584 Portrait of a gentleman, in a flat cap (91x61cm-36x24in) s. 13-Jan-4 Bonhams, Knightsbridge #293/R
£503 $800 €734 Portrait of a seated girl (43x33cm-17x13in) s. board. 14-Sep-3 Susanin's, Chicago #6055/R

MUNOZ BARBERAN, Manuel (1921-) Spanish
£1655 $2748 €2400 Masks (65x54cm-26x21in) s. s.i.d.1974 verso board. 1-Oct-3 Ansorena, Madrid #562/R est:2000

MUNOZ MELGOSA, Jose Maria (1897-?) Spanish
£1342 $2403 €2000 Choir boy (42x20cm-17x8in) s. 25-May-4 Durán, Madrid #43/R est:800

MUNOZ MONTORO, Gregorio (1906-1978) Spanish
Works on paper
£330 $544 €475 Fishermen (41x31cm-16x12in) s. mixed media. 2-Jul-3 Ansorena, Madrid #835/R

MUNOZ RUBIO, Ramon (19th C) Spanish
£805 $1498 €1200 Spanish beauty (27x16cm-11x6in) s. board. 2-Mar-4 Ansorena, Madrid #143/R
£12676 $21930 €18000 Strolling in the park (75x40cm-30x16in) s. pair. 15-Dec-3 Ansorena, Madrid #38/R est:18000

MUNOZ Y CUESTA, Domingo (1850-1912) Spanish
£3819 $6226 €5500 Fight in the inn (38x46cm-15x18in) s. 23-Sep-3 Durán, Madrid #194/R
£4027 $7530 €6000 Fight in the inn (38x46cm-15x18in) s.i. 24-Feb-4 Durán, Madrid #227/R est:2500
Works on paper
£486 $792 €700 Boy (23x15cm-9x6in) s. W/C. 23-Sep-3 Durán, Madrid #25/R

MUNOZ Y LUCENA, Tomas (1860-1943) Spanish
£4276 $7740 €6500 Payment with goods (58x63cm-23x25in) s. 14-Apr-4 Ansorena, Madrid #162/R est:6500
£8889 $16000 €12978 La floriste aux Folies-Bergere (119x70cm-47x28in) s.d.1886. 23-Apr-4 Sotheby's, New York #110/R est:18000-25000
Works on paper
£1141 $2122 €1700 Gallant scene in the park (38x68cm-15x27in) s. W/C. 2-Mar-4 Ansorena, Madrid #355/R est:1500

MUNOZ, Ana Maria (1947-) Spanish
£839 $1401 €1200 Garden (62x81cm-24x32in) s. board. 30-Jun-3 Ansorena, Madrid #398/R

MUNOZ, Bartolome Mongrell (1890-1038) Spanish
£694 $1132 €1000 Valencian cottages (43x67cm-17x26in) s.d.1936. 23-Sep-3 Durán, Madrid #34/R

MUNOZ, Godofredo Ortega (1905-1982) Spanish
£1562 $2547 €2250 Parisian woman (50x40cm-20x16in) s. prov. 23-Sep-3 Durán, Madrid #112/R
£18056 $29792 €26000 Landscape with trunks (44x32cm-17x13in) s. cardboard. 2-Jul-3 Ansorena, Madrid #855/R est:24000

MUNOZ, Juan (1953-2001) Spanish
£5978 $11000 €8967 Untitled (23x10cm-9x4in) s. oil acrylic plastic prov. 10-Jun-4 Phillips, New York #624/R est:5000-7000
£24000 $44160 €35040 Raincoat drawing - attic of my family (150x150cm-59x59in) oilstick painted 1994 prov.exhib. 25-Jun-4 Christie's, London #254/R est:8000-12000
Sculpture
£17964 $30000 €26227 Window shutter (143x104x5cm-56x41x2in) steel bronze prov. 13-Nov-3 Sotheby's, New York #144/R est:15000-20000
£18000 $33120 €26280 Untitled - pasa a mano (145cm-57in) wood metal supports executed 1987 prov.exhib. 25-Jun-4 Christie's, London #251/R est:18000-22000
£22455 $37500 €32784 Painted dragons (162x70x40cm-64x28x16in) oil bronze wood base pair prov.exhib. 13-Nov-3 Sotheby's, New York #586/R est:20000-30000
£30000 $55200 €43800 La pieza de la Rane (122x101x44cm-48x40x17in) iron executed 1987 prov. 25-Jun-4 Christie's, London #257/R est:30000-50000

£50000 $91000 €73000 Fortuna's dreamer (73x43x60cm-29x17x24in) mixed media resin wood executed 2000 prov. 4-Feb-4 Christie's, London #31/R est:40000-60000
£55000 $101200 €80300 Perfect balcony (86x88x44cm-34x35x17in) welded steel with switchblade executed 1988 prov.lit. 24-Jun-4 Christie's, London #29/R est:40000-60000
£55866 $100000 €81564 Sarah with blue dress (195x100x100cm-77x39x39in) acrylic polyester resin mirror exec 1996 prov.exhib. 11-May-4 Christie's, Rockefeller NY #61/R est:150000-200000
£58659 $105000 €85642 Untitled - figure (67x45x45cm-26x18x18in) cast bronze wooden base executed c.1990 prov.exhib. 13-May-4 Phillips, New York #57/R est:40000-60000
£95808 $160000 €139880 Looking sideways (127x103x46cm-50x41x18in) oil on polyester resin wood executed 1996-97 prov. 13-Nov-3 Phillips, New York #34/R est:100000-150000
£106145 $190000 €154972 Balcony with two figures (150x51x28cm-59x20x11in) terracotta bronze three parts exec 1992 prov. 13-May-4 Sotheby's, New York #351/R est:100000-150000
£106145 $190000 €154972 Ballerina (193x56x56cm-76x22x22in) bronze polished copper base on ceramic tiles wood base exec 1990. 13-May-4 Sotheby's, New York #374/R est:180000-250000

Works on paper
£8000 $14720 €11680 Untitled (101x72cm-40x28in) s.d.92 verso wax pastel prov. 25-Jun-4 Christie's, London #252/R est:8000-12000

MUNOZ, Lucio (1929-1998) Spanish
Prints
£2222 $3667 €3200 Untitled (98x74cm-39x29in) s.d.83 engraving. 2-Jul-3 Ansorena, Madrid #936/R

Works on paper
£2431 $4010 €3500 Untitled (58x49cm-23x19in) s. mixed media paper on canvas. 2-Jul-3 Ansorena, Madrid #884/R
£4545 $7727 €6500 Silencio No 3 (60x59cm-24x23in) s.d.1968 verso panel. 29-Nov-3 Arnold, Frankfurt #397/R est:6000
£21127 $36549 €30000 Night composition (114x146cm-45x57in) s.d.1975 s.i.d.verso mixed media board. 15-Dec-3 Ansorena, Madrid #981/R est:30000

MUNOZ-BOQUERA, Albert (1925-) Spanish
£603 $977 €850 Mallorca (61x82cm-24x32in) s. s.i.verso. 20-May-3 Ansorena, Madrid #204/R

MUNOZ-DEGRAIN, Antoine (1843-1924) French
£1655 $2748 €2400 Landscape with trunk (22x29cm-9x11in) s. board. 30-Sep-3 Ansorena, Madrid #107/R est:2000
£3448 $6207 €5000 Grove (17x27cm-7x11in) s. board. 26-Jan-4 Durán, Madrid #157/R est:5000
£4027 $7208 €6000 Penafiel Castle (39x50cm-15x20in) s. 25-May-4 Durán, Madrid #146/R est:6000
£5517 $9931 €8000 Windmills (57x71cm-22x28in) s. 26-Jan-4 Durán, Madrid #166/R est:8000
£5517 $9931 €8000 Venice (27x17cm-11x7in) s. board. 26-Jan-4 Durán, Madrid #165/R est:8000
£6944 $11319 €10000 Landscape with peak covered in snow (75x100cm-30x39in) s. lit. 23-Sep-3 Durán, Madrid #183/R est:7500

Works on paper
£267 $483 €400 Landscape (26x51cm-10x20in) s.d.1891 W/C. 30-Mar-4 Segre, Madrid #8/R

MUNOZ-VERA, Guillermo (1949-) Chilean
Works on paper
£922 $1494 €1300 Desnudos academicos (47x32cm-19x13in) s.d.1985 pencil htd white. 20-May-3 Ansorena, Madrid #420/R
£11034 $18428 €16000 Inaki, flute player (200x96cm-79x38in) s.d.1998 crayon graphite pastel wash paper on board lit. 17-Nov-3 Durán, Madrid #227/R est:16000

MUNRO, Alexander (attrib) (1825-1871) British
Sculpture
£22000 $39380 €32120 Figure of the fountain nymph (213cm-84in) white marble executed c.1865. 25-May-4 Sotheby's, Billingshurst #373/R est:10000-15000

MUNRO, B (19th C) ?
£424 $721 €619 Mountain landscape with cattle, Scotland (61x91cm-24x36in) s. 10-Nov-3 Rasmussen, Vejle #493 (D.KR 4600)

MUNRO, Daniel (19th C) British
£320 $566 €467 New scholars (31x25cm-12x10in) s. panel. 27-Apr-4 Bonhams, Knowle #82

MUNRO, Hugh (1873-1928) British
£2200 $3542 €3190 Sketching by the river (29x39cm-11x15in) s. 21-Aug-3 Bonhams, Edinburgh #1216/R est:800-1200

MUNROE, Sarah Sewell (1870-1946) American
£3438 $5500 €5019 Lady with peacock (94x61cm-37x24in) s. indis d. board. 20-Sep-3 Sloans & Kenyon, Bethesda #1189/R est:4000-6000

MUNSCH, Leopold (attrib) (1826-1888) Austrian
Works on paper
£2113 $3380 €3000 Studies of a country house (41x66cm-16x26in) s. W/C pair prov. 22-Sep-3 Sotheby's, Amsterdam #139/R est:1500-2500

MUNSELL, William A O (1866-?) American
£1099 $2000 €1605 Russian woman reading (46x36cm-18x14in) s. board. 15-Jun-4 John Moran, Pasadena #109 est:2000-3000

MUNSTER, Mia (1898-1970) German
Works on paper
£396 $725 €590 Gentleman and ladies wearing elegant clothes (37x27cm-15x11in) s. W/C pencil. 9-Jul-4 Dawo, Saarbrucken #141/R
£406 $690 €580 Couple in bedroom (35x26cm-14x10in) s.d. 21-Nov-3 Reiss & Sohn, Konigstein #485/R
£416 $761 €620 Southern coastal scene with sailing boats and figures (23x32cm-9x13in) s. W/C. 9-Jul-4 Dawo, Saarbrucken #139/R
£453 $829 €675 Three riders in conversation standing in front of a horse (32x27cm-13x11in) s. W/C pencil. 9-Jul-4 Dawo, Saarbrucken #140/R
£503 $921 €750 Southern landscape (28x39cm-11x15in) s. W/C pencil. 9-Jul-4 Dawo, Saarbrucken #138/R

MUNSTERHJELM, Ali (1873-1944) Finnish
£599 $958 €850 Red cottage (63x77cm-25x30in) s.d.1915. 18-Sep-3 Hagelstam, Helsinki #877
£600 $1074 €900 Aura river (43x75cm-17x30in) s. 15-May-4 Hagelstam, Helsinki #167/R
£600 $1104 €900 Farm buildings (36x49cm-14x19in) s. 9-Jun-4 Bukowskis, Helsinki #488/R
£633 $1165 €950 Old wooden house in Aabo (40x50cm-16x20in) s. 9-Jun-4 Bukowskis, Helsinki #489/R
£640 $1178 €960 Shipwreck (48x77cm-19x30in) s. 9-Jun-4 Bukowskis, Helsinki #486/R
£775 $1239 €1100 Lojo Church (88x203cm-35x80in) 21-Sep-3 Bukowskis, Helsinki #399/R
£775 $1239 €1100 Boat by shore (48x64cm-19x25in) s. 18-Sep-3 Hagelstam, Helsinki #876
£800 $1472 €1200 Summer's day (46x60cm-18x24in) s. 9-Jun-4 Bukowskis, Helsinki #487/R
£805 $1498 €1200 The bay (51x66cm-20x26in) s. 7-Mar-4 Bukowskis, Helsinki #384/R
£972 $1624 €1400 House in the country (50x68cm-20x27in) s. 26-Oct-3 Bukowskis, Helsinki #421/R
£1007 $1852 €1500 Tavastehus (47x81cm-19x32in) s. 25-Mar-4 Hagelstam, Helsinki #1004 est:2000
£1056 $1690 €1500 Old country road (52x67cm-20x26in) s. 21-Sep-3 Bukowskis, Helsinki #400/R est:1800
£1409 $2621 €2100 Landscape from Aura river (44x62cm-17x24in) s. 7-Mar-4 Bukowskis, Helsinki #383/R est:2000
£1462 $2514 €2135 Town by water (50x65cm-20x26in) s. 7-Dec-3 Uppsala Auktionskammare, Uppsala #262/R est:8000-10000 (S.KR 19000)
£1554 $2782 €2300 Aura river (65x103cm-26x41in) s. 8-May-4 Bukowskis, Helsinki #43/R est:3500-4500
£1736 $2899 €2500 In the harbour (50x66cm-20x26in) s. 26-Oct-3 Bukowskis, Helsinki #422/R est:1700
£1818 $3091 €2600 Rome (22x48cm-9x19in) s. 29-Nov-3 Bukowskis, Helsinki #72/R est:1500-2000
£1959 $3507 €2900 In the harbour (46x80cm-18x31in) s. 8-May-4 Bukowskis, Helsinki #29/R est:2000-2500
£2098 $3566 €3000 View from Aura river (50x67cm-20x26in) s. 29-Nov-3 Bukowskis, Helsinki #119/R est:3000-3500
£2168 $3685 €3100 Winter scene from Aura river (50x67cm-20x26in) s. 29-Nov-3 Bukowskis, Helsinki #47/R est:2000-2500

MUNSTERHJELM, Hjalmar (1840-1905) Finnish
£3776 $6420 €5400 Evening fishing (11x25cm-4x10in) s. canvas on board. 29-Nov-3 Bukowskis, Helsinki #123/R est:5000-6000
£3803 $6579 €5400 Miinas cottage (32x54cm-13x21in) i.d.1878. 13-Dec-3 Hagelstam, Helsinki #89/R est:10000
£5541 $9918 €8200 Summer evening in Tavastland (17x34cm-7x13in) s. canvas on board. 8-May-4 Bukowskis, Helsinki #140/R est:4500-5500
£6757 $12095 €10000 The jetty in Barosund (12x24cm-5x9in) s. i.verso board. 8-May-4 Bukowskis, Helsinki #76/R est:10000-12000
£10140 $17238 €14500 Summer landscape (38x55cm-15x22in) s. 29-Nov-3 Bukowskis, Helsinki #160/R est:12000-15000
£10211 $17665 €14500 Spring landscape, Tavastland (35x25cm-14x10in) s. canvas on board. 13-Dec-3 Hagelstam, Helsinki #86/R est:15000
£11000 $19690 €16500 Sunset in the outer skerries (29x46cm-11x18in) s. 15-May-4 Hagelstam, Helsinki #79/R est:12000
£12000 $21600 €18000 Bay of Lake Roine, Finland (52x80cm-20x31in) s.d.72. 21-Apr-4 Christie's, Amsterdam #171/R est:20000-30000
£22535 $38986 €32000 Lake landscape, Chiemsee (45x76cm-18x30in) s.d.1864. 13-Dec-3 Hagelstam, Helsinki #88/R est:25000
£34965 $59441 €50000 Windy autumn day at sea (55x80cm-22x31in) s.d.1876. 29-Nov-3 Bukowskis, Helsinki #139/R est:50000-60000

MUNTANE MUNS, Luis (1899-1987) Spanish
£950 $1511 €1378 Portrait of a lady with a yellow parasol (41x27cm-16x11in) s. board. 9-Sep-3 Bonhams, Knightsbridge #211/R
£1000 $1570 €1450 Florista (89x129cm-35x51in) s. i.verso. 28-Aug-3 Christie's, Kensington #64/R est:600-800
£1408 $2465 €2000 Romantic lady (37x24cm-15x9in) s. board. 16-Dec-3 Durán, Madrid #123/R

MUNTEAN, Markus and ROSENBLUM, Adi (1962-) Austrian/Israeli
£4500 $8190 €6570 Untitled (30x40cm-12x16in) acrylic pencil two painted 2000 prov.exhib. 5-Feb-4 Christie's, London #216/R est:3000-4000
£7263 $13000 €10604 Untitled (178x158cm-70x62in) s.d.99 verso acrylic prov. 12-May-4 Christie's, Rockefeller NY #340/R est:12000-18000
£15642 $28000 €22837 Untitled, sometimes you get (200x250cm-79x98in) s.d.01 verso acrylic prov.lit. 14-May-4 Phillips, New York #140/R est:15000-20000

MUNTER, David Heinrich (1816-1879) German
£1336 $2271 €1910 Herders with cattle at ford (60x77cm-24x30in) s. 20-Nov-3 Van Ham, Cologne #1763/R est:2800

MUNTER, Gabriele (1877-1962) German
£8000 $14320 €12000 Landscape near Murnau (15x23cm-6x9in) i. verso pencil board prov. 14-May-4 Ketterer, Munich #131/R est:12000-18000

£9333 $16707 €14000 Still life with jug, dish, brush and cap (37x49cm-15x19in) s.d. verso board prov. 14-May-4 Ketterer, Munich #130/R est:18000-24000
£10490 $17832 €15000 Still life of flowers (63x45cm-25x18in) mono.i. oil on pencil prov. 29-Nov-3 Villa Grisebach, Berlin #243/R est:14000-18000
£14000 $25620 €21000 Church in village (54x37cm-21x15in) paper prov. 5-Jun-4 Lempertz, Koln #901/R est:20000-22000
£14667 $26840 €22000 Dahlias and roses in brown jug (62x45cm-24x18in) mono.i. paper prov. 5-Jun-4 Lempertz, Koln #902/R est:20000-22000
£16000 $29120 €23360 Blumenstilleben (35x27cm-14x11in) s.d.1935 board prov. 3-Feb-4 Christie's, London #214/R est:12000-16000
£28000 $51520 €42000 Easter still life, primroses and Easter eggs (35x27cm-14x11in) s. paintboard prov.exhib. 11-Jun-4 Villa Grisebach, Berlin #57/R est:40000-60000
£29333 $52507 €44000 Man between hayricks (41x33cm-16x13in) board prov. 14-May-4 Ketterer, Munich #171/R est:28000-34000
£29371 $49930 €42000 Advent flowers (3x25cm-1x10in) board prov. 26-Nov-3 Lempertz, Koln #875/R est:40000
£33333 $61333 €50000 Narrow street in Pisogne (61x46cm-24x18in) 10-Jun-4 Hauswedell & Nolte, Hamburg #510/R est:50000
£50000 $91000 €73000 Landschaft am Staffelsee. Blumenstilleben (32x44cm-13x17in) s.d.1931 board double-sided prov. 3-Feb-4 Christie's, London #215/R est:30000-40000
£85000 $154700 €124100 Beach at Bornholm (36x46cm-14x18in) s.d.5.VIII 19 canvasboard prov.exhib. 3-Feb-4 Sotheby's, London #22/R est:50000-70000
£93333 $171733 €140000 Flowers, delphinium and capuchin (55x46cm-22x18in) s.d.1952 i.verso prov. 11-Jun-4 Villa Grisebach, Berlin #45/R est:90000-120000
£116667 $213500 €175000 Dungheap, Murnau (33x41cm-13x16in) s.i.d.27.VIII.08 i. verso board prov.exhib.lit. 5-Jun-4 Lempertz, Koln #900/R est:160000-180000
£133333 $238667 €200000 Painting (69x48cm-27x19in) board prov. 14-May-4 Ketterer, Munich #147/R est:200000-300000
£146853 $249650 €210000 Landscape in March II - landscape with solitary farmstead (56x34cm-22x13in) prov. 28-Nov-3 Villa Grisebach, Berlin #40/R est:150000-200000
£170588 $290000 €249058 Gartentoerl (33x45cm-13x18in) s. board painted 1912 prov.exhib. 5-Nov-3 Christie's, Rockefeller NY #252/R est:100000-150000

Prints

£2587 $4399 €3700 M Vernot (20x18cm-8x7in) s.i. col woodcut. 29-Nov-3 Villa Grisebach, Berlin #638/R est:2000-3000

Works on paper

£8042 $13671 €11500 Zinnia in blue vase (31x23cm-12x9in) s. Indian ink brush. 29-Nov-3 Villa Grisebach, Berlin #214/R est:5000-7000
£8515 $15498 €12432 Flowers in glass vase (61x45cm-24x18in) mono. W/C. 17-Jun-4 Kornfeld, Bern #618 est:8000 (S.FR 19500)
£29000 $52780 €42340 Landscape (43x53cm-17x21in) s.i. gouache W/C exec 1955 prov. 5-Feb-4 Christie's, London #359/R est:15000-20000

MUNTHE, Gerhard Peter Franz Vilhelm (1849-1929) Norwegian

£1874 $3223 €2736 Winter landscape, Markerudporten in fog (38x48cm-15x19in) s.d.1906 i.stretcher exhib. 8-Dec-3 Blomqvist, Oslo #433/R est:20000-25000 (N.KR 22000)
£4804 $8599 €7014 The milkmaid, possibly Torda Bjelle (68x55cm-27x22in) s.i.d.1890. 28-May-4 Uppsala Auktionskammare, Uppsala #155/R est:80000-100000 (S.KR 65000)
£6814 $11721 €9948 The steamboat Ferdesmanden near ferry stop, Mjosa (50x85cm-20x33in) s.i.d.75 prov.lit. 8-Dec-3 Blomqvist, Oslo #463/R est:120000-150000 (N.KR 80000)
£17036 $29302 €24873 The suitors (75x93cm-30x37in) s.d.1893 prov.lit. 8-Dec-3 Blomqvist, Oslo #410/R est:120000-150000 (N.KR 200000)

MUNTHE, Ludvig (1841-1896) Norwegian

£1552 $2778 €2266 Peasants brining in the last harvest (41x32cm-16x13in) s. 13-May-4 Stuker, Bern #262/R est:4000-5000 (S.FR 3600)
£2198 $4000 €3209 Evening on the beach with figure seated (35x90cm-14x35in) s.d.71. 7-Feb-4 Rasmussen, Havnen #2201/R est:20000-30000 (D.KR 24000)
£2733 $4564 €3990 Atmosphere - landscape (56x47cm-22x19in) s. 13-Oct-3 Blomqvist, Oslo #283/R est:40000-50000 (N.KR 32000)
£2797 $4755 €4000 Fisherwomen returning from harbour in winter (66x49cm-26x19in) s.d.90 panel. 20-Nov-3 Van Ham, Cologne #1765/R est:3200
£3145 $5000 €4592 Pasture (66x109cm-26x43in) s. 12-Sep-3 Skinner, Boston #244/R est:12000
£3203 $5733 €4676 Children tobogganing near the edge of river (83x110cm-33x43in) s.d.96. 22-Mar-4 Blomqvist, Oslo #332/R est:55000-65000 (N.KR 40000)
£3691 $6607 €5500 Evening time (95x77cm-37x30in) s.d.88. 27-May-4 Dorotheum, Vienna #212/R est:5000-6000

MUNTHE-NORSTEDT, Anna (1854-1936) Swedish

£702 $1257 €1025 Still life of carnations in a vase (21x10cm-8x4in) s. canvas on panel. 26-May-4 AB Stockholms Auktionsverk #2179/R (S.KR 9500)
£962 $1654 €1405 Still life of flowers and apples (28x37cm-11x15in) s.d.1928 panel. 3-Dec-3 AB Stockholms Auktionsverk #2383/R (S.KR 12500)
£982 $1699 €1434 Father Christmas's helper (17x18cm-7x7in) s. panel. 15-Dec-3 Lilla Bukowskis, Stockholm #1073 (S.KR 12500)
£1239 $2230 €1809 Still life (17x14cm-7x6in) s. panel. 26-Jan-4 Lilla Bukowskis, Stockholm #656 est:10000-12000 (S.KR 16500)
£2365 $4234 €3453 Still life of summer flowers (55x33cm-22x13in) s.i.d.6 Juni 1929. 26-May-4 AB Stockholms Auktionsverk #2283/R est:15000-20000 (S.KR 32000)
£3030 $5424 €4424 From the home of Reinhold Norstedt (65x44cm-26x17in) s. 25-May-4 Bukowskis, Stockholm #44/R est:15000-20000 (S.KR 41000)

MUNTZ-ADAMS, Josephine (1861-1950) Australian

£552 $861 €800 Corotesque (14x22cm-6x9in) s. canvas on board exhib. 1-Aug-2 Joel, Victoria #146 est:1500-2500 (A.D 1600)
£1012 $1630 €1478 New friend (60x40cm-24x16in) s. canvas board. 13-Oct-3 Joel, Victoria #296 est:3000-4000 (A.D 2500)
£1021 $1736 €1491 Portrait of a girl (25x18cm-10x7in) s.d.1903. 26-Nov-3 Deutscher-Menzies, Melbourne #268/R (A.D 2400)

MUNUNGGURR, Marrnyula (1964-) Australian

Works on paper

£2344 $4383 €3516 If you love me love me safely (110x57cm-43x22in) bears name.verso earth pigments eucalyptus bark. 26-Jul-4 Sotheby's, Melbourne #304/R est:3000-5000 (A.D 6000)

MUNZER, Adolf (1870-1952) German

£743 $1159 €1100 Genoveva and son in wood with deer (54x64cm-21x25in) s. d.8.Sept.1920 verso. 28-Mar-3 Behringer, Furth #1185/R
£4375 $7131 €6300 Boy on beach (78x95cm-31x37in) s. 19-Jul-3 Berlinghof, Heidelberg #244 est:800

MUONA, Eeli (20th C) Finnish

Works on paper

£282 $451 €400 Flowers (75x54cm-30x21in) s.d.1944 W/C. 18-Sep-3 Hagelstam, Helsinki #956/R

MUR, J (?) ?

£1208 $2162 €1800 Judith holding Holofernes' head (125x106cm-49x42in) s. prov. 25-May-4 Durán, Madrid #117/R est:1800

MURA, Francesco de (attrib) (1696-1782) Italian

£5493 $9503 €7800 Annunciation (120x98cm-47x39in) 14-Dec-3 Finarte, Venice #133/R est:9000-10000

MURA, Francesco de (circle) (1696-1782) Italian

£8278 $15149 €12500 Les enfants aux oiseux (95x117cm-37x46in) 7-Apr-4 Libert, Castor, Paris #11/R est:2000-4000

MURADO, Antonio (20th C) Spanish

£1056 $1849 €1500 Untitled (76x61cm-30x24in) s.i.d.1998 verso prov. 16-Dec-3 Segre, Madrid #198/R est:1800
£1224 $2229 €1800 Untitled (76x61cm-30x24in) s.i.d.1997 verso exhib.lit. 3-Feb-4 Segre, Madrid #228/R est:1500

MURAKAMI, Takashi (1962-) Japanese

£7186 $12000 €10492 Minyulu (50x64cm-20x25in) s.d.97 acrylic prov. 14-Nov-3 Phillips, New York #106/R est:15000-20000
£10778 $18000 €15736 Untitled, mushroom dob (15x15cm-6x6in) s.d.02 verso acrylic wood panel prov. 13-Nov-3 Sotheby's, New York #476/R est:6000-8000
£11976 $20000 €17485 Physical na kibun (120x170cm-47x67in) acrylic silkscreen ink canvas on panel prov.exhib. 13-Nov-3 Sotheby's, New York #441/R est:30000-40000
£12291 $22000 €17945 Peach milk (50x65cm-20x26in) s.d.98 acrylic canvas on panel prov. 12-May-4 Christie's, Rockefeller NY #304/R est:20000-30000
£15569 $26000 €22731 Blue Milk (50x65cm-20x26in) s.d.1998 verso acrylic linen on panel prov. 12-Nov-3 Christie's, Rockefeller NY #501/R est:15000-20000
£22346 $40000 €32625 Tokun (34x34cm-13x13in) s.d.1995 verso acrylic canvas on masonite prov.lit. 12-May-4 Christie's, Rockefeller NY #308/R est:35000-45000
£25000 $46000 €36500 Kiki (40x40cm-16x16in) s.d.verso acrylic prov. 25-Jun-4 Christie's, London #281/R est:25000-35000
£25140 $45000 €36704 Dob (51x72cm-20x28in) s.i.d.97 verso acrylic prov. 12-May-4 Christie's, Rockefeller NY #309/R est:50000-70000
£26816 $48000 €39151 Chaos (40x40cm-16x16in) s.d.1998 verso acrylic canvas on panel prov.exhib. 12-May-4 Christie's, Rockefeller NY #307/R est:35000-45000
£27607 $45000 €40306 Mr DOB DNA (41x41cm-16x16in) s.d.98 verso acrylic canvas on board prov.exhib. 23-Sep-3 Christie's, Rockefeller NY #86/R est:20000-25000
£29940 $50000 €43712 Cosmos (34x34cm-13x13in) s.d.98 verso acrylic wood prov. 13-Nov-3 Sotheby's, New York #478/R est:25000-35000
£33742 $55000 €49263 Mushroom painting no 5 (41x41cm-16x16in) s.d.00 acrylic canvas on panel prov.exhib. 23-Sep-3 Christie's, Rockefeller NY #87/R est:20000-25000
£39106 $70000 €57095 Chaos (40x40cm-16x16in) s.d.98'99 verso acrylic canvas on panel prov.exhib. 12-May-4 Christie's, Rockefeller NY #306/R est:35000-45000
£50279 $90000 €73407 Cosmos (34x34cm-13x13in) s.d.1996 acrylic five panels prov.exhib. 12-May-4 Christie's, Rockefeller NY #303/R est:100000-150000
£59880 $100000 €87425 Hoyoyo (41x41cm-16x16in) s.d.98 acrylic prov.exhib. 13-Nov-3 Sotheby's, New York #442/R est:35000-45000
£75000 $138000 €109500 N Cha (60x60cm-24x24in) acrylic canvas on wood panel painted 2001 prov.exhib. 24-Jun-4 Sotheby's, London #138/R est:50000-70000
£100000 $182000 €146000 Pink Summer (70x100cm-28x39in) s.d.98 verso acrylic canvas on wood panel prov.exhib.lit. 5-Feb-4 Sotheby's, London #51/R est:100000-150000
£125749 $210000 €183594 Forest of DOB (100x100cm-39x39in) s.d.1995 verso acrylic canvas on panel prov.exhib.lit. 12-Nov-3 Christie's, Rockefeller NY #561/R est:100000-150000
£128492 $230000 €187598 Cosmos (61x61cm-24x24in) s.d.98 99 verso acrylic canvas on panel three parts prov. 13-May-4 Sotheby's, New York #310/R est:250000-350000
£131737 $220000 €192336 Po and Ku surrealism - Pink (279x243cm-110x96in) s.d.99 acrylic canvas on panel triptych prov.exhib. 12-Nov-3 Christie's, Rockefeller NY #557/R est:200000-300000
£251397 $450000 €367040 In the Deep DOB - Yellow/Green/Pink/Aqua Blue/Purple (70x100cm-28x39in) st.sig. acrylic 5 panels painted 1999 prov.exhib. 11-May-4 Christie's, Rockefeller NY #8/R est:200000-300000
£263473 $440000 €384671 Nega mushroom (180x142cm-71x56in) s.i. verso acrylic painted 2000 prov. 12-Nov-3 Sotheby's, New York #33/R est:150000-200000
£307263 $550000 €448604 Flower ball (250x250cm-98x98in) s.d.2002 verso acrylic canvas on board round prov.exhib. 12-May-4 Sotheby's, New York #3/R est:250000-350000
£329341 $550000 €480838 Lost child returned by myself (203x203cm-80x80in) s.d.01 acrylic canvas on panel prov. 11-Nov-3 Christie's, Rockefeller NY #7/R est:200000-300000

Prints

£2147 $3800 €3135 And then and then and then and then and then, red (40x40cm-16x16in) s.d.1999 num.18/50 verso col screenprint. 28-Apr-4 Christie's, Rockefeller NY #381/R est:4000-5000
£2712 $4800 €3960 Hiropon (106x75cm-42x30in) s.d.1994 num.10/15 col screenprint. 28-Apr-4 Christie's, Rockefeller NY #378/R est:5000-7000

Sculpture

£3500 $6265 €5110 Oval, figure seated on a cosmos ball. cd music composes player. 6-May-4 Sotheby's, London #82/R est:3800-4500
£4167 $6875 €6000 Project Ko2 (52x15x14cm-20x6x6in) paint resin one of 200 prov. 2-Jul-3 Cornette de St.Cyr, Paris #177/R est:3000-4000
£5085 $9000 €7424 Coco (52cm-20in) painted molded resin oil multiple edition of 200. 28-Apr-4 Christie's, Rockefeller NY #379/R est:5000-7000
£5500 $10120 €8030 Coco (52x24x14cm-20x9x6in) oil moulded resin edition of 200. 24-Jun-4 Sotheby's, Olympia #432/R est:4000-6000
£7500 $13800 €10950 Coco - project K02 (51cm-20in) painted resin executed 1999 prov. 25-Jun-4 Christie's, London #285/R est:7000-9000
£7500 $13800 €10950 Project Ko2 - Perfect edition (51x20x18cm-20x8x7in) painted resin exec 1999 edn 24/200 prov. 24-Jun-4 Sotheby's, London #136/R est:4000-6000

£8667 $15947 €13000 Project KO2 (51x20x18cm-20x8x7in) painted resin num.36/200 prov. 8-Jun-4 Artcurial Briest, Paris #288/R est:10000-15000
£8939 $16000 €13051 Yamori-ni-hi (70x45x12cm-28x18x5in) s.d.1991 verso resin iron Tamiya military figures Plexiglas prov. 14-May-4 Phillips, New York #345/R est:5000-7000
£9497 $17000 €13866 Coco - Project KO2 - Parfect Edition - Parco version (52x24x15cm-20x9x6in) oil moulded resin exec 1999 edn 1/200 prov. 13-May-4 Sotheby's, New York #302/R est:6000-8000
£16467 $27500 €24042 Coco, project KO2/parfect edition/parco version (52x24x15cm-20x9x6in) oil molded resin edition 1 of 200 prov. 13-Nov-3 Sotheby's, New York #426/R est:4000-6000
£20670 $37000 €30178 Dob's march (235x305x180cm-93x120x71in) vinyl chloride and helium executed 1994 prov.exhib.lit. 13-May-4 Phillips, New York #50/R est:40000-60000
Works on paper
£3631 $6500 €5301 DOB (22x30cm-9x12in) s.d.2001 prov. 14-May-4 Phillips, New York #336/R est:4000-6000
£8380 $15000 €12235 Untitled (8x15cm-3x6in) s.d.98 ink gouache paperboard prov. pair. 13-May-4 Sotheby's, New York #301/R est:8000-12000
£8380 $15000 €12235 Untitled (8x38cm-3x15in) s.d.98 ink gouache paperboard pair prov. 13-May-4 Sotheby's, New York #303/R est:8000-12000

MURANT, Emanuel (attrib) (1622-1700) Dutch
£909 $1518 €1300 Farmhouse in a landscape (25x32cm-10x13in) panel. 30-Jun-3 Sotheby's, Amsterdam #33
£2793 $4664 €4050 Personnage sous le porche (10x13cm-4x5in) panel. 14-Nov-3 Drouot Estimations, Paris #31/R est:4000-6000

MURATON, E (19th C) French
£3600 $6444 €5256 La convoitise (40x61cm-16x24in) s. 22-Mar-4 Bonhams & Brooks, Norfolk #266/R est:600-800

MURATON, Euphemie (1840-?) French
£1700 $2890 €2482 Still life with peaches in a basket (38x46cm-15x18in) s. 19-Nov-3 Bonhams, New Bond Street #125/R est:1500-2000

MURAVYOV, Count Vladimir Leonidovich (1861-1915) Russian
£36486 $65311 €54000 In the forest (100x63cm-39x25in) s.d.1908 oil tempera. 8-May-4 Bukowskis, Helsinki #420/R est:10000-15000
£56000 $95200 €81760 Capercaillie in winter (99x142cm-39x56in) s.d.1912. 19-Nov-3 Sotheby's, London #73/R est:25000-35000
Works on paper
£15000 $26850 €21900 Forest at dawn with ducks in flight (95x65cm-37x26in) s. gouache on card. 26-May-4 Sotheby's, London #71/R est:15000-20000

MURCH, Arthur (1902-1990) Australian
£697 $1129 €1018 Afternoon light (34x44cm-13x17in) s. board. 30-Jul-3 Goodman, Sydney #111/R (A.D 1700)
£851 $1472 €1242 Old mission house, Hermmansburg (45x60cm-18x24in) s. i.verso masonite board. 10-Dec-3 Shapiro, Sydney #7 (A.D 2000)
£909 $1545 €1327 Headland (31x32cm-12x13in) s.d.36 board. 29-Oct-3 Lawson Menzies, Sydney #100/R est:2500-4500 (A.D 2200)
£977 $1826 €1466 Mother and child (36x28cm-14x11in) s. board. 20-Jul-4 Goodman, Sydney #117/R (A.D 2500)
£988 $1788 €1442 Untitled - young girl (33x18cm-13x7in) prov.exhib. 30-Mar-4 Lawson Menzies, Sydney #99/R est:3000-5000 (A.D 2400)
£1488 $2752 €2172 Bathers (49x39cm-19x15in) s. board. 10-Mar-4 Deutscher-Menzies, Melbourne #466/R est:3000-5000 (A.D 3600)
£1967 $3108 €2872 Nude with cat (40x30cm-16x12in) s. board. 2-Sep-3 Deutscher-Menzies, Melbourne #289/R est:3000-5000 (A.D 4800)
£2686 $4969 €3922 Squirrel (48x68cm-19x27in) s. prov.exhib. 10-Mar-4 Deutscher-Menzies, Melbourne #61/R est:6000-8000 (A.D 6500)
Works on paper
£496 $843 €724 Reclining nude (30x53cm-12x21in) s. pastel chk. 29-Oct-3 Lawson Menzies, Sydney #133/R est:900-1200 (A.D 1200)

MURCH, Henry (fl.1850-1851) British
£2200 $3784 €3212 Near Paestum, Greece (33x51cm-13x20in) init.d.1854. 4-Dec-3 Christie's, Kensington #74/R est:1500-2000

MURCH, Walter (1907-1967) American/Canadian
£15625 $27500 €22813 Fragments (51x76cm-20x30in) s. canvas on masonite painted 1962 prov.exhib.lit. 19-May-4 Sotheby's, New York #158/R est:20000-30000
Works on paper
£2647 $4500 €3865 Measures of time (30x38cm-12x15in) s.d.1948 pencil. 9-Nov-3 Wright, Chicago #188 est:5000-7000

MURER, Albert (?) ?
Sculpture
£1678 $2803 €2400 Cuddles (33x31cm-13x12in) s. wood. 10-Oct-3 Stadion, Trieste #794/R est:2200-3200

MURER, Augusto (1922-1985) Italian
Sculpture
£2158 $3540 €3000 Female nude (32cm-13in) bronze. 5-Jun-3 Adma, Formigine #435 est:3300-3500
Works on paper
£1439 $2360 €2000 Chair and cloth (65x48cm-26x19in) mixed media. 5-Jun-3 Adma, Formigine #519 est:2200-2400

MURER, Christoph (1558-1614) Swiss
Prints
£2797 $4755 €4000 Lot and his daughters (26x33cm-10x13in) etching. 27-Nov-3 Bassenge, Berlin #5172/R est:4000

MURER, Heinrich (1774-1822) Swiss
£952 $1705 €1390 Lake landscape with ferry and figures (34x41cm-13x16in) s.d. panel. 22-Mar-4 Philippe Schuler, Zurich #4347/R est:2000-2600 (S.FR 2200)

MURGIA DE CASTRO, Ovidio (1871-1900) Spanish
£3262 $5285 €4600 Landscape with mountain in the background (16x24cm-6x9in) s. panel. 20-May-3 Ansorena, Madrid #192/R est:2000

MURILLO BRACHO, Jose Maria (1827-1882) Spanish
£3947 $7263 €6000 Vase of flowers (54x41cm-21x16in) s. 22-Jun-4 Durán, Madrid #135/R est:2250
£4762 $8667 €7000 Still life of fruit (70x49cm-28x19in) s. board. 3-Feb-4 Segre, Madrid #95/R est:3500

MURILLO, Bartolome Esteban (1618-1682) Spanish
Works on paper
£31944 $57500 €46638 Mystic marriage of St. Catherine. Virgin and Child appearing to a Franciscan Friar (13x10cm-5x4in) s.i. pen ink wash double-sided prov.exhib.lit. 21-Jan-4 Sotheby's, New York #76/R est:35000-45000

MURILLO, Bartolome Esteban (attrib) (1618-1682) Spanish
£1667 $3000 €2434 Untitled, young Christ (74x61cm-29x24in) exhib. 26-Apr-4 Schrager Galleries, Milwaukee #1442/R
£18310 $30394 €26000 Le Christ en croix (60x39cm-24x15in) 11-Jun-3 Delorme & Bocage, Paris #8/R est:20000-30000
Works on paper
£884 $1583 €1300 La Sainte Famille avec Saint Jean Baptiste dans un paysage (12x13cm-5x5in) black chk pen brown ink grey wash. 18-Mar-4 Christie's, Paris #225/R

MURILLO, Bartolome Esteban (circle) (1618-1682) Spanish
£5278 $9500 €7706 Girl with cabbage (82x65cm-32x26in) 21-Jan-4 Doyle, New York #50/R est:6000-8000

MURILLO, Bartolome Esteban (studio) (1618-1682) Spanish
£19000 $32870 €27740 Sleeping Christ Child (64x84cm-25x33in) prov.exhib.lit. 11-Dec-3 Sotheby's, London #178/R est:15000-20000

MURILLO, Salvador (19/20th C) Latin American
£1800 $3294 €2700 Trees by the river (22x32cm-9x13in) s.d.1892 pair. 6-Jun-4 Osenat, Fontainebleau #270 est:3000-3500

MURIN, Wilmos (?) ?
£664 $1109 €950 Roses in a vase (80x60cm-31x24in) 10-Oct-3 Stadion, Trieste #79/R

MURNOT, Felix (1924-) ?
£315 $535 €450 Marine (22x25cm-9x10in) s. panel. 24-Nov-3 Boscher, Cherbourg #717
£327 $584 €480 Voiliers sortant du port (15x23cm-6x9in) s. paper. 18-Mar-4 Peschetau-Badin Godeau & Leroy, Paris #90
£354 $633 €520 Voiliers a Deauville (17x21cm-7x8in) s. board. 18-Mar-4 Peschetau-Badin Godeau & Leroy, Paris #93

MUROWUNA, Lorenz (c.1900-?) Dutch?
£559 $951 €800 Berlin at night (80x120cm-31x47in) s. 20-Nov-3 Van Ham, Cologne #1724
£567 $1015 €828 Berlin, Dom mit Friedrichsbrucke, evening (70x120cm-28x47in) s.d.1930. 12-Jan-4 Rasmussen, Vejle #418/R (D.KR 6000)

MURPHY, Ada Clifford (19/20th C) American
Works on paper
£249 $450 €364 Side view of an old house (26x17cm-10x7in) s. W/C. 18-Apr-4 Bonhams & Butterfields, Los Angeles #7014

MURPHY, Denis Brownell (1763-1842) Irish
Miniatures
£4000 $6800 €5840 Adam Duncan (8cm-3in) i.d.1804 enamel octagonal prov.exhib.lit. 18-Nov-3 Bonhams, New Bond Street #174/R est:3000-5000

MURPHY, Frank (20th C) Irish
Works on paper
£320 $586 €467 Cottage, Donegal (23x28cm-9x11in) s. W/C. 2-Jun-4 John Ross, Belfast #97

MURPHY, Genevieve E (19th C) American
£503 $800 €734 Sheep grazing in a pasture (51x61cm-20x24in) s. 13-Sep-3 Selkirks, St. Louis #52

MURPHY, Herman Dudley (1867-1945) American
£237 $425 €346 Hazy skies (32x50cm-13x20in) estate st.verso. 14-May-4 Skinner, Boston #150/R
£280 $500 €409 Winter view (21x26cm-8x10in) estate st.verso canvasboard. 14-May-4 Skinner, Boston #222/R

£484	$900	€707	Still life with white porcelain (32x24cm-13x9in) panel. 5-Mar-4 Skinner, Boston #374/R
£484	$900	€707	Hot springs (30x40cm-12x16in) s. s.i.d.1913 verso canvasboard. 5-Mar-4 Skinner, Boston #478/R
£535	$850	€781	Distant trees (30x40cm-12x16in) s. board. 12-Sep-3 Skinner, Boston #420/R
£950	$1700	€1387	Cottage (25x35cm-10x14in) estate st.verso canvasboard. 14-May-4 Skinner, Boston #160/R est:2000-3000
£4839	$9000	€7065	Casa blanca, San Juan - White house (73x91cm-29x36in) s. prov.exhib. 5-Mar-4 Skinner, Boston #520/R est:500-700
Works on paper			
£480	$850	€701	Barn and wheat field (18x20cm-7x8in) mono. W/C pastel. 2-May-4 Van Blarcom, South Natick #46
£1006	$1800	€1469	Venice (20x28cm-8x11in) mono.i.d.94 W/C graphite gouache. 14-May-4 Skinner, Boston #149/R est:1000-1500

MURPHY, J Francis (1853-1921) American

£469	$750	€685	Figure in a landscape (25x30cm-10x12in) s. board. 21-Sep-3 William Jenack, New York #388
£667	$1200	€974	Autumn landscape (25x34cm-10x13in) s. panel. 24-Apr-4 Weschler, Washington #601/R
£1195	$1900	€1745	Forest scene with workers (20x25cm-8x10in) s. 14-Sep-3 Susanin's, Chicago #6161/R est:400-600
£1229	$2200	€1794	Sunset (22x28cm-9x11in) s. board. 14-May-4 Skinner, Boston #70/R est:1000-1500
£2273	$4000	€3319	Catskill sunset (30x41cm-12x16in) s. canvas on board prov. 3-Jan-4 Collins, Maine #42/R est:2500-3500
£2600	$4602	€3796	Woodland at dusk (41x61cm-16x24in) s. 27-Apr-4 Bonhams, New Bond Street #113/R est:1500-2000
£2624	$4750	€3831	House on a knoll (30x48cm-12x19in) s.d.1849. 31-Mar-4 Sotheby's, New York #90/R est:4000-6000
£3200	$5664	€4672	Woodland clearing (36x48cm-14x19in) s.d.88. 27-Apr-4 Bonhams, New Bond Street #117/R est:1500-2000
£3302	$5250	€4821	Cows watering (26x41cm-10x16in) s.d.77. 12-Sep-3 Skinner, Boston #265/R
£3468	$6000	€5063	October Afternoon (36x48cm-14x19in) s.d.1907 prov. 10-Dec-3 Bonhams & Butterfields, San Francisco #6025/R est:7000-10000
£5367	$9500	€7836	Autumn (61x91cm-24x36in) s. i. stretcher prov. 28-Apr-4 Christie's, Los Angeles #10/R est:10000-15000
£11176	$19000	€16317	Summer afternoon (61x92cm-24x36in) s.d.1910. 30-Oct-3 Phillips, New York #56/R est:10000-15000
Works on paper			
£331	$600	€483	Autumn river landscape (43x53cm-17x21in) W/C. 16-Apr-4 Du Mouchelle, Detroit #2145/R
£1975	$3200	€2864	Landscape (28x36cm-11x14in) s. W/C. 8-Aug-3 Barridorf, Portland #274/R est:3000-5000

MURPHY, J Francis (attrib) (1853-1921) American

£520	$900	€759	Autumn landscape (25x36cm-10x14in) s. 10-Dec-3 Alderfer's, Hatfield #330 est:1000-1200

MURPHY, Jack Roland (20th C) American

Works on paper			
£233	$375	€340	High and dry (33x53cm-13x21in) s. W/C. 20-Aug-3 James Julia, Fairfield #1800/R

MURPHY, John (20th C) Irish

Works on paper			
£3500	$6510	€5110	Man is not a bird (78x64cm-31x25in) pen ink board postcard. 8-Mar-4 Christie's, London #12

MURPHY, Mabel C (20th C) American

£228	$425	€333	Sand dunes, California (20x25cm-8x10in) s.i.d.1949 verso board. 7-Mar-4 Treadway Gallery, Cincinnati #594/R

MURPHY, Martin (1949-) British

£347	$627	€520	Winter morning (61x61cm-24x24in) s. acrylic. 30-Mar-4 De Veres Art Auctions, Dublin #237

MURPHY, Nelly Littlehale (1867-1941) American

Works on paper			
£531	$950	€775	Cats school (44x32cm-17x13in) init. pen ink W/C board pair. 14-May-4 Skinner, Boston #219/R
£615	$1100	€898	Seasons (32x14cm-13x6in) init. pen ink W/C board three. 14-May-4 Skinner, Boston #388/R
£944	$1500	€1378	Peonies I (58x58cm-23x23in) s. W/C. 12-Sep-3 Skinner, Boston #342/R est:1500-3000

MURPHY, Noel (?) Irish?

Works on paper			
£400	$664	€584	Demolition day (15x20cm-6x8in) s.d.90 W/C. 1-Oct-3 John Ross, Belfast #76
£1800	$3348	€2628	Figure study (96x30cm-38x12in) s.d.2002 verso chl. 3-Mar-4 John Ross, Belfast #153 est:1800-2000

MURPHY, Sandy (1956-) British

£320	$550	€467	Jug with wild flowers (30x30cm-12x12in) s. board. 3-Dec-3 Christie's, Kensington #720
£600	$1032	€876	Michaelmas daisies (38x41cm-15x16in) s. board. 3-Dec-3 Christie's, Kensington #717/R
£800	$1336	€1168	Jug of wild flowers (27x27cm-11x11in) s. board. 16-Oct-3 Christie's, Kensington #678/R

MURPHY, William (20th C) Irish

£533	$960	€800	Rashers Tierney, Strumpet City (70x60cm-28x24in) s.d.90 board. 20-Apr-4 James Adam, Dublin #95/R

MURRAY, Alexander Henry Hallom (1854-1934) British

Works on paper			
£350	$655	€525	Venice with figures (18x25cm-7x10in) s.i. W/C. 21-Jul-4 John Nicholson, Haslemere #56
£500	$920	€730	Benares, India (27x18cm-11x7in) s.i. pencil W/C. 25-Mar-4 Christie's, Kensington #64/R

MURRAY, Andrew (1917-1998) South African

£958	$1600	€1399	Untitled (56x68cm-22x27in) s.d.73. 20-Oct-3 Sotheby's, New York #80/R est:1500-2500
£1008	$1825	€1472	Cape town cat (45x27cm-18x11in) s. board. 30-Mar-4 Stephan Welz, Johannesburg #517/R est:5000-8000 (SA.R 12000)
£2096	$3500	€3060	Untitled (71x90cm-28x35in) s. 20-Oct-3 Sotheby's, New York #81/R est:1500-2500

MURRAY, Doctor John (1809-1898) British

Photographs			
£1556	$2800	€2272	Gateway fort, Agra (37x46cm-15x18in) waxed paper negative prov. 22-Apr-4 Phillips, New York #183/R est:4000-6000
£2500	$4500	€3650	Simla, 1865 (39x49cm-15x19in) waxed paper negative prov. 22-Apr-4 Phillips, New York #6/R est:7000-10000
£5000	$9000	€7300	View of the King's Tower from the south (39x44cm-15x17in) albumen print prov. 22-Apr-4 Phillips, New York #185/R est:9000-12000

MURRAY, Eileen (1885-1962) British

£360	$673	€526	River landscape with castle ruins on a hill (9x12cm-4x5in) panel. 25-Feb-4 Mallams, Oxford #118/R
£800	$1312	€1168	Woman with scarf (76x61cm-30x24in) s. 4-Jun-3 John Ross, Belfast #162

MURRAY, Elizabeth (1940-) American

£14371	$24000	€20982	Tug (141x138cm-56x54in) s.i.d.1978 verso prov. 12-Nov-3 Christie's, Rockefeller NY #632/R est:25000-35000
£20950	$37500	€30587	Clock (256x19cm-101x7in) shaped canvas painted 1992 prov. 13-May-4 Sotheby's, New York #458/R est:30000-40000

MURRAY, Frank (1848-1915) British

£360	$644	€526	Mother, infant and children in woodland (30x20cm-12x8in) indis.s. 17-Mar-4 Bonhams, Chester #372

MURRAY, George S (fl.1850-1899) British

£4200	$7770	€6132	Stable interior at Glenapp Castle, with a groom, two horses and a dog (75x126cm-30x50in) s. painted c.1880 prov. 11-Feb-4 Cheffins, Cambridge #415/R est:3000-5000

MURRAY, H (fl.1850-1860) British

Works on paper			
£605	$1113	€883	Run to Earth (29x44cm-11x17in) s. W/C. 14-Jun-4 Waddingtons, Toronto #82/R est:800-1000 (C.D 1500)
£1242	$2000	€1813	Rough crossing. Finding the scent (30x46cm-12x18in) s. W/C gouache paper on board pair. 14-Jan-4 Christie's, Rockefeller NY #77/R est:2000-3000

MURRAY, John (1942-) American/Irish

£946	$1665	€1400	Desire II (215x161cm-85x63in) d.1985 s.i.verso acrylic. 18-May-4 Galerie Moderne, Brussels #154/R

MURRAY, John R (20th C) American

£1351	$2500	€1972	Doorway (161x119cm-63x47in) s. acrylic exec c.1980. 12-Feb-4 Sotheby's, New York #250/R est:2500-3500

MURRAY, John Reid (1861-1906) British

£1100	$1969	€1606	Barges on the Scheldt (28x45cm-11x18in) indis sig.i. panel. 26-May-4 Sotheby's, Olympia #245/R est:1000-1500

MURRAY, Sir David (1849-1933) British

£203	$340	€296	Autumn in the Glen (36x45cm-14x18in) s.d.1933 panel. 17-Nov-3 Waddingtons, Toronto #143/R (C.D 450)
£300	$516	€438	Children fishing from a stone bridge (38x43cm-15x17in) s.d.1928. 5-Dec-3 Keys, Aylsham #649
£523	$900	€764	Home by the river (46x61cm-18x24in) s. 7-Dec-3 Susanin's, Chicago #6064/R
£934	$1700	€1364	Trysting place (76x51cm-30x20in) s. 19-Jun-4 Jackson's, Cedar Falls #48/R est:800-1200
£950	$1796	€1387	Figures walking on a beach (25x33cm-10x13in) s.d.08. 19-Feb-4 Lyon & Turnbull, Edinburgh #42
£1765	$3000	€2577	Landscape with figures harvesting and a fisherman preparing his line on a bridge (46x62cm-18x24in) s.d.95. 19-Nov-3 Bonhams & Butterfields, San Francisco #149/R
£2300	$4117	€3358	Swan lake (31x41cm-12x16in) 26-May-4 Sotheby's, Olympia #235/R est:2000-3000
£3400	$6154	€4964	Apple blossom (46x43cm-18x17in) s.d.81. 19-Apr-4 Sotheby's, London #90/R est:2000-3000

MURRAY, Sir David (attrib) (1849-1933) British

£1200	$2040	€1752	View of the tees (111x161cm-44x63in) canvas on board. 18-Nov-3 Bonhams, Leeds #229 est:1500-2000

MURRAY, T (1663-1734) British
£2300 $4255 €3358 Portrait of the packet ship, Britannia leaving harbour (46x64cm-18x25in) s.d.1847. 10-Feb-4 David Lay, Penzance #566/R est:2000-3000

MURRAY, Thomas (attrib) (1663-1734) British
£13000 $22100 €18980 Portrait of a young boy holding a bow and a quiver of arrows, spaniel at his side (76x63cm-30x25in) 25-Nov-3 Christie's, London #14/R est:8000-12000

MURRAY, William Grant (1877-1950) British
£400 $732 €584 Rural mountainous landscape (18x33cm-7x13in) s.d.1922 i.verso. 7-Apr-4 Gardiner & Houlgate, Bath #183/R

MURRIE, Desmond (?) ?
£250 $415 €365 Final furlong (30x38cm-12x15in) s. board. 1-Oct-3 John Ross, Belfast #13
£250 $430 €365 Race to the line (30x35cm-12x14in) s. board. 3-Dec-3 John Ross, Belfast #238
£260 $426 €380 Full gallop (30x35cm-12x14in) s. board. 4-Jun-3 John Ross, Belfast #243
£280 $521 €409 Close cluster (23x30cm-9x12in) s. board. 3-Mar-4 John Ross, Belfast #144
£300 $492 €438 Break for the finish (25x30cm-10x12in) s. board. 4-Jun-3 John Ross, Belfast #6
£300 $498 €438 Break for the finish (30x35cm-12x14in) s. board. 1-Oct-3 John Ross, Belfast #250
£300 $558 €438 Final furlong (30x30cm-12x12in) s. board. 3-Mar-4 John Ross, Belfast #51
£320 $595 €467 Out in front (35x28cm-14x11in) s. board. 3-Mar-4 John Ross, Belfast #85
£350 $602 €511 Closely packed (35x40cm-14x16in) s. board. 3-Dec-3 John Ross, Belfast #92
£400 $656 €584 Race to the line (45x66cm-18x26in) s. board. 4-Jun-3 John Ross, Belfast #39
£400 $688 €584 Out in front (61x50cm-24x20in) s. board. 3-Dec-3 John Ross, Belfast #197
£400 $744 €584 At the off (53x58cm-21x23in) s. board. 3-Mar-4 John Ross, Belfast #131
£450 $824 €657 Break for the finish (50x61cm-20x24in) s. board. 2-Jun-4 John Ross, Belfast #120
£580 $1079 €847 Break for the finish (53x61cm-21x24in) s. board. 3-Mar-4 John Ross, Belfast #58
£600 $996 €876 Three horse race (61x61cm-24x24in) s. board. 1-Oct-3 John Ross, Belfast #92
£620 $1135 €905 Full gallop (50x61cm-20x24in) s. board. 2-Jun-4 John Ross, Belfast #48
£650 $1118 €949 Two horse race (61x61cm-24x24in) s. board. 3-Dec-3 John Ross, Belfast #47

MURRUMURRU, Dick Nguleingulei (1920-1988) Australian
Works on paper
£276 $437 €400 Ungadaitja, fish trap (116x52cm-46x20in) earth pigments eucalyptus bark exec.c.1981 prov. 28-Jul-3 Sotheby's, Paddington #352 (A.D 680)
£528 $835 €766 Two goannas, kawalan-kurrh. Kangaroo, wolerak (58x32cm-23x13in) earth pigments eucalyptus bark exec.c. 1970 pair prov. 28-Jul-3 Sotheby's, Paddington #541 est:1000-2000 (A.D 1300)
£625 $1169 €938 Kangaroo (33x56cm-13x22in) earth pigments eucalyptus bark exec.c.1975 prov. 26-Jul-4 Sotheby's, Melbourne #542/R (A.D 1600)
£1016 $1899 €1524 Echidna (38x64cm-15x25in) earth pigments eucalyptus bark exec.c.1980 prov. 26-Jul-4 Sotheby's, Melbourne #544/R (A.D 2600)
£1172 $2191 €1758 Rainbow serpent, Ngalyod and the lightning spirit, Namarrkon (62x40cm-24x16in) name.i.verso earth pigments eucalyptus bark exec.c.1975 prov. 26-Jul-4 Sotheby's, Melbourne #541/R est:2000-3000 (A.D 3000)
£1250 $2338 €1875 Two freshwater fish (28x50cm-11x20in) earth pigments eucalyptus bark exec.c.1973 prov. 26-Jul-4 Sotheby's, Melbourne #288/R est:1200-1800 (A.D 3200)
£1382 $2184 €2004 Kangaroo (94x64cm-37x25in) i.verso earth pigments eucalyptus bark exec.c.1975 prov. 28-Jul-3 Sotheby's, Paddington #461/R est:4000-6000 (A.D 3400)

MURRUWARR, Yuwun Yuwun (1928-) Australian
Works on paper
£447 $707 €653 Legendary emu (95x61cm-37x24in) earth pigments eucalyptus bark exec.c.1968 prov.exhib.lit. 28-Jul-3 Sotheby's, Paddington #259 (A.D 1100)

MURRY, J B (?) American?
Works on paper
£444 $800 €648 Buried spirits releasing (43x36cm-17x14in) marker W/C. 24-Apr-4 Slotin Folk Art, Buford #364/R
£667 $1200 €974 Spirit heads (71x56cm-28x22in) marker W/C on poster. 24-Apr-4 Slotin Folk Art, Buford #365/R est:1000-3000
£1557 $2600 €2273 Single figure with hands (74x64cm-29x25in) marker W/C prov. 15-Nov-3 Slotin Folk Art, Buford #204/R est:1000-3000
£1611 $2900 €2352 Spirits (56x71cm-22x28in) ink marker on poster prov. 24-Apr-4 Slotin Folk Art, Buford #366/R est:3000-5000
£2083 $3750 €3041 Calendar with spirit writing (61x46cm-24x18in) marker paint on poster prov. 24-Apr-4 Slotin Folk Art, Buford #363/R est:4000-6000

MURSHIDABAD SCHOOL (18th C) Indian
Works on paper
£5000 $8850 €7300 Alivardi Khan and Hadji Mahmud, seated on a terrace (35x25cm-14x10in) i. gouache htd gold. 27-Apr-4 Christie's, London #129/R est:4000-6000

MURTIC, Edo (1921-) Yugoslavian
£795 $1400 €1161 Germination (130x193cm-51x76in) s. exhib. 22-May-4 Selkirks, St. Louis #792

MURU, Selwyn (20th C) New Zealander
£571 $1051 €834 Cityscape (53x67cm-21x26in) s. board. 25-Mar-4 International Art Centre, Auckland #52/R (NZ.D 1600)

MUS, Italo (1892-1967) Italian
£1119 $1869 €1600 Landscape in Aosta Valley (24x30cm-9x12in) s. board. 26-Jun-3 Sant Agostino, Torino #78/R est:1000
£1773 $2961 €2500 Sunset (24x34cm-9x13in) s. cardboard. 20-Oct-3 Sant Agostino, Torino #158/R
£2069 $3434 €3000 Bread oven (30x24cm-12x9in) s. board. 1-Oct-3 Della Rocca, Turin #223/R
£4362 $7721 €6500 Saint Vincent (50x60cm-20x24in) s. board. 1-May-4 Meeting Art, Vercelli #364 est:5000

MUSANTE, Francesco (1950-) Italian
£310 $518 €450 Moon thieves (40x10cm-16x4in) s.i. masonite. 13-Nov-3 Galleria Pace, Milan #21/R
£448 $717 €650 Butterflies tamer (30x30cm-12x12in) s.d.1964 board. 13-Mar-3 Galleria Pace, Milan #40/R
£580 $951 €800 Balance (50x9cm-20x4in) s. mixed media board. 29-May-3 Galleria Pace, Milan #78/R
£933 $1717 €1400 Little theatre (50x50cm-20x20in) s. acrylic board painted 1992. 12-Jun-4 Meeting Art, Vercelli #911/R
Works on paper
£342 $582 €500 Waiting the falling stars (15x40cm-6x16in) s. mixed media board. 7-Nov-3 Galleria Rosenberg, Milan #147/R
£533 $965 €800 Last train at night (30x30cm-12x12in) s. mixed media panel. 2-Apr-4 Farsetti, Prato #222
£616 $1010 €850 Pencil tamer (35x25cm-14x10in) s. mixed media board. 29-May-3 Galleria Pace, Milan #42/R
£655 $1048 €950 Frizzi and Frazzi weighing kind Miss Degas (40x50cm-16x20in) s.d.1967 mixed media board. 13-Mar-3 Galleria Pace, Milan #6/R
£800 $1472 €1200 Night in Vienna (60x60cm-24x24in) s. mixed media board. 12-Jun-4 Meeting Art, Vercelli #239/R
£805 $1490 €1200 Oceans were born like that (35x25cm-14x10in) s. mixed media board. 13-Mar-4 Meeting Art, Vercelli #464
£867 $1595 €1300 Lost encounters island (50x40cm-20x16in) s.i. mixed media board. 12-Jun-4 Meeting Art, Vercelli #544/R

MUSAVVIR, Muin (circle) (17th C) Persian
Works on paper
£5000 $8850 €7300 Dervish (26x16cm-10x6in) s. gouache htd gold. 27-Apr-4 Christie's, London #78/R est:5000-8000

MUSCHAMP, F Sydney (1851-1929) British
£260 $447 €380 Portrait of a lady in panelled interior (43x25cm-17x10in) s. 5-Dec-3 Keys, Aylsham #337
£1400 $2646 €2044 The milkmaid (13x20cm-5x8in) s. 23-Feb-4 David Duggleby, Scarborough #680/R est:1500-2500
£1892 $3500 €2762 Conway Valley, N Wales (76x132cm-30x52in) 12-Mar-4 Du Mouchelle, Detroit #2083/R est:3000-5000
£2000 $3340 €2920 Recital (49x75cm-19x30in) s. 11-Nov-3 Bonhams, Knightsbridge #230/R est:2000-3000
Works on paper
£920 $1472 €1343 Latest News (25x36cm-10x14in) s. W/C. 16-Sep-3 Gorringes, Bexhill #1585/R

MUSCHAMP, Francis (fl.1865-1885) British
£750 $1253 €1095 Fairy glen (45x35cm-18x14in) s.d.1875. 12-Nov-3 Sotheby's, Olympia #42/R

MUSFELD, Ernst Max (1900-1964) Swiss
Works on paper
£321 $536 €465 Vineyard (27x36cm-11x14in) s.d. W/C. 23-Jun-3 Philippe Schuler, Zurich #3268 (S.FR 700)
£352 $599 €514 Birch trees near Besazio (36x48cm-14x19in) s.d.1955 i. verso W/C. 5-Nov-3 Dobiaschofsky, Bern #3626 (S.FR 800)

MUSGRAVE, Harry (fl.1884-1910) British
£526 $953 €800 Sailing boat at sea (46x77cm-18x30in) s. 14-Apr-4 Ansorena, Madrid #23/R

MUSI, Agostino dei (1490-1540) Italian
Prints
£6333 $11337 €9500 La carcasse (30x64cm-12x25in) coperplate. 13-May-4 Bassenge, Berlin #5332/R est:6000

MUSIALOWICZ, Henryk (1914-) Polish
Works on paper
£261 $477 €381 Composition (66x49cm-26x19in) s. i.d.1945 verso mixed media. 4-Jun-4 Zofingen, Switzerland #2494 (S.FR 600)
£508 $920 €742 Composition (73x58cm-29x23in) s.d.1979 Indian ink oil acrylic. 4-Apr-4 Agra, Warsaw #65/R (P.Z 3600)

MUSIARI, Elso (20th C) Italian
£374 $595 €550 Hilly landscape with peasant woman and dog (40x50cm-16x20in) s. i. verso. 28-Feb-3 Altus, Berlin #464

MUSIC, Zoran (1909-) Italian
£4000 $6680 €5840 Terre dalmate (50x65cm-20x26in) s.d.1959 tempera on butten. 22-Oct-3 Bonhams, New Bond Street #78/R est:4000-5000

£7000 $12880 €10220 Canale della Giudecca (33x41cm-13x16in) s.d.80 s.i.d. verso prov. 24-Jun-4 Sotheby's, London #201/R est:5000-7000
£8099 $13444 €11500 Saint Mark's Square (27x22cm-11x9in) tempera W/C lit. 11-Jun-3 Finarte Semenzato, Milan #633/R
£9091 $15455 €13000 Landscape (32x41cm-13x16in) s.d.79 prov. 25-Nov-3 Sotheby's, Milan #206/R est:4000-6000
£12162 $21405 €18000 Tuesday market (38x46cm-15x18in) s. s.i.d.1954 verso prov. 24-May-4 Christie's, Milan #197/R est:18000-24000
£16107 $28832 €24000 Landscape (73x92cm-29x36in) prov. 25-May-4 Sotheby's, Milan #71/R est:22000
£21622 $38054 €32000 We are the last ones (60x50cm-24x20in) s.d.74 s.i.d.verso acrylic prov. 24-May-4 Christie's, Milan #172/R est:15000-20000
£24476 $41608 €35000 Composition (50x100cm-20x39in) s.d.1957 s.d.verso prov. 24-Nov-3 Christie's, Milan #320/R est:40000-60000
£27211 $48708 €40000 Nous ne sommes pas les derniers (73x92cm-29x36in) s.d.70 s.i.verso acrylic. 21-Mar-4 Calmels Cohen, Paris #180/R est:20000-30000
£34965 $59441 €50000 Landscape around Siena (53x81cm-21x32in) s.d.1951 s.i.verso prov.exhib. 25-Nov-3 Sotheby's, Milan #210/R est:25000-35000
£45000 $81900 €65700 Motivo dalmata (34x30cm-13x12in) s.d.1950 s.i.d.1950 verso. 6-Feb-4 Sotheby's, London #157/R est:20000-30000
£52000 $86840 €75920 Lotta di cavalli (45x64cm-18x25in) s. s.d.1949 stretcher prov. 21-Oct-3 Christie's, London #5/R est:30000-50000
£111732 $200000 €163129 Cavalli che passano (72x100cm-28x39in) s.d.1951 s.i.d.verso. 5-May-4 Christie's, Rockefeller NY #326/R est:180000-220000

Works on paper
£350 $602 €500 Portrait d'homme (20x13cm-8x5in) s.d.1995 black felt pen. 3-Dec-3 Tajan, Paris #440/R
£759 $1267 €1100 Landscape (21x29cm-8x11in) s.d.62 col crayon. 14-Nov-3 Farsetti, Prato #281/R
£828 $1382 €1200 Little horses (17x23cm-7x9in) i. col crayon on brochure. 14-Nov-3 Farsetti, Prato #283/R
£897 $1497 €1300 Little horses (18x20cm-7x8in) s.d.1967 col crayon dr. 14-Nov-3 Farsetti, Prato #282/R
£1014 $1784 €1500 Landscape (21x29cm-8x11in) s.d.1981 pencil. 22-May-4 Galleria Pananti, Florence #404/R est:1200-1500
£1048 $1928 €1530 We are not the last (10x13cm-4x5in) bears i. verso Indian ink biro. 8-Jun-4 Germann, Zurich #846 (S.FR 2400)
£1103 $1843 €1600 Landscape (12x9cm-5x4in) s.i.d.1967 col crayon dr. 14-Nov-3 Farsetti, Prato #280/R est:1600-1900
£1259 $2140 €1800 Vue de Venise (22x28cm-9x11in) s.d.1980 col crayon prov. 25-Nov-3 Tajan, Paris #36/R est:1500-2000
£1800 $3222 €2700 Cortina (24x32cm-9x13in) s. pastel. 12-May-4 Stadion, Trieste #630/R est:1200-1600
£2000 $3600 €3000 Port de Venise (20x29cm-8x11in) s.d.1982 ink wash exhib. 25-Apr-4 Versailles Encheres #104 est:3000-4000
£2013 $3705 €3000 Canale della Giudecca (13x24cm-5x9in) s.d.9-8-80 pencil col pen prov. 26-Mar-4 Ketterer, Hamburg #576/R est:3500-4000
£2254 $3741 €3200 Paysage rocheux (23x32cm-9x13in) s.d.1979 gouache. 13-Jun-3 Hauswedell & Nolte, Hamburg #777/R est:3000
£2414 $4031 €3500 Landscape (38x57cm-15x22in) s.d.67 pastel gouache paper on canvas. 14-Nov-3 Farsetti, Prato #289/R est:3200-3700
£2533 $4610 €3698 Composition (38x56cm-15x22in) s.d.64 i. verso pastel. 17-Jun-4 Kornfeld, Bern #619 est:5000 (S.FR 5800)
£2550 $4565 €3800 Landscape (38x56cm-15x22in) s.d.65 verso pastel prov. 25-May-4 Sotheby's, Milan #69/R est:3000
£2657 $4517 €3800 Landscape (32x49cm-13x19in) s.d.69 gouache prov. 25-Nov-3 Sotheby's, Milan #208/R est:2000-3000
£2685 $4805 €4000 Landscape (38x56cm-15x22in) s.d.65 pastel prov. 25-May-4 Sotheby's, Milan #68/R est:3000
£2800 $5096 €4088 Self portrait (67x48cm-26x19in) s.d.1998 brown wash chl. 21-Jun-4 Bonhams, New Bond Street #48/R est:2800-3500
£2937 $4993 €4200 Landscape (38x55cm-15x22in) s.d.64 s.i.d.verso pastel prov. 25-Nov-3 Sotheby's, Milan #209 est:2000-3000
£2953 $5286 €4400 Landscape with black hill (44x54cm-17x21in) s.d.76 chl card prov. 25-May-4 Sotheby's, Milan #74/R est:1500
£3357 $5706 €4800 Landscape (37x56cm-15x22in) s.d.64 s.d.verso pastel prov. 25-Nov-3 Sotheby's, Milan #207/R est:2000-3000
£3521 $5845 €5000 Dalmatian lands (47x66cm-19x26in) s. mixed media. 11-Jun-3 Finarte Semenzato, Milan #625/R est:6500
£3691 $6607 €5500 Landscape with brown hill. Landscape (21x32cm-8x13in) one s.d.76 col pencil prov. two. 25-May-4 Sotheby's, Milan #73/R est:3000
£4094 $7534 €6100 Composition (43x63cm-17x25in) s.d.1958 pastel gouache. 29-Mar-4 Cornette de St.Cyr, Paris #19/R est:6000-7000
£4200 $7644 €6132 Natura morta (26x41cm-10x16in) s.d.85 s.i.d.1985 verso gouache paper on board prov. 6-Feb-4 Sotheby's, London #156/R est:4000-6000
£4333 $7973 €6500 Dalmatian hill (45x63cm-18x25in) s.d.1958 mixed media paper on canvas. 11-Jun-4 Farsetti, Prato #351/R est:6200-7200
£5046 $8427 €7317 Composition (55x75cm-22x30in) s.d.62 W/C. 19-Jun-3 Kornfeld, Bern #769/R est:12500 (S.FR 11000)
£5705 $10211 €8500 Landscapes (19x29cm-7x11in) s.d.1980 W/C two. 25-May-4 Sotheby's, Milan #70/R est:2000

MUSIN, Auguste (1852-1920) Belgian

£437 $795 €638 Dutch river landscape (11x21cm-4x8in) s. panel. 16-Jun-4 Fischer, Luzern #2297 (S.FR 1000)
£524 $954 €765 Flemish canal landscape (8x6cm-3x2in) s. panel. 16-Jun-4 Fischer, Luzern #2296 (S.FR 1200)
£690 $1234 €1007 Sailing boat (21x15cm-8x6in) s. board. 13-May-4 Stuker, Bern #264 est:1800-2300 (S.FR 1600)
£700 $1281 €1022 Sailing ship (49x64cm-19x25in) s. 7-Jul-4 Cheffins, Cambridge #21/R
£862 $1543 €1259 Sailing boats off Dutch coast (16x24cm-6x9in) s. board. 13-May-4 Stuker, Bern #263/R est:1800-2300 (S.FR 2000)
£2000 $3200 €2920 Le Bassin des Pecheurs, Ostende (30x24cm-12x9in) s. panel. 16-Sep-3 Bonhams, New Bond Street #58/R est:1000-1500
£2432 $4500 €3551 La find d'un beau jour sur Le Zuyder Zee en Holland (40x70cm-16x28in) s. 10-Feb-4 Christie's, Rockefeller NY #230/R est:5000-7000
£2552 $4721 €3700 Port anime (40x60cm-16x24in) s. canvas on panel. 13-Jan-4 Vanderkindere, Brussels #60 est:1800-2500
£2953 $5463 €4400 Travaux au bateau de peche (27x20cm-11x8in) s. panel. 15-Mar-4 Horta, Bruxelles #164/R est:4000-6000
£3974 $7232 €6000 Marine (53x76cm-21x30in) s. 15-Jun-4 Vanderkindere, Brussels #145/R est:6000-8000
£4333 $7973 €6500 Journee d'automne sur le Zuiderzee (51x77cm-20x30in) s. 14-Jun-4 Horta, Bruxelles #100/R est:7000-9000
£5634 $9746 €8000 Seascape with fishing boats (150x100cm-59x39in) s. 13-Dec-3 De Vuyst, Lokeren #531/R est:8000-9000
£27778 $44167 €40000 Tower of London (87x160cm-34x63in) s. 15-Sep-3 Horta, Bruxelles #189/R est:40000-50000

MUSIN, François Etienne (1820-1888) Belgian

£833 $1325 €1200 Bateaux en pleine mer (27x35cm-11x14in) s.d.1848 panel. 9-Sep-3 Palais de Beaux Arts, Brussels #257/R
£1736 $2830 €2500 Coast in storm (80x105cm-31x41in) s.d.1883. 24-Sep-3 Neumeister, Munich #512/R est:6000
£2113 $3655 €3000 Bathing vehicle in Ostend (21x30cm-8x12in) canvas on canvas. 10-Dec-3 Dorotheum, Vienna #128/R est:4500-5000
£2207 $4083 €3200 Ancienne digue de mer a Ostende (44x119cm-17x47in) s. 16-Feb-4 Horta, Bruxelles #196/R est:6000-8000
£2349 $4205 €3500 Binnenvaren in woelige zee (30x58cm-12x23in) s. 25-May-4 Campo & Campo, Antwerp #174/R est:4000-6000
£2778 $4417 €4000 Naufrage (22x50cm-9x20in) s.i. panel. 9-Sep-3 Vanderkindere, Brussels #60/R
£2797 $4755 €4000 Pecheurs et bateaux en bord de mer (25x41cm-10x16in) s. panel. 18-Nov-3 Vanderkindere, Brussels #132 est:1500-2000
£3200 $5120 €4672 French shipping off the coast in a light breeze (41x74cm-16x29in) s. panel. 16-Sep-3 Bonhams, New Bond Street #63/R est:2000-3000
£4000 $6800 €5840 View near Hastings (42x77cm-17x30in) s. i.verso. 19-Nov-3 Bonhams, New Bond Street #1/R est:5000-7000
£4000 $7200 €6000 Midst a naval battle, Dutch fighting the Danes and the Swedes (114x177cm-45x70in) s. 20-Apr-4 Sotheby's, Amsterdam #91/R est:8000-12000
£5200 $8840 €7592 Off the French coast (51x98cm-20x39in) s. 28-Oct-3 Henry Adams, Chichester #441/R est:5000-7000
£6174 $11423 €9200 L'arrivee de la barque par gros temps, grace a un feu cotier et naufrage (29x41cm-11x16in) one s. panel pair. 15-Mar-4 Horta, Bruxelles #163/R est:3000-5000
£9091 $15636 €13000 Les deux navires, L'Erbus et Le Terror (42x74cm-17x29in) s. i.verso panel. 8-Dec-3 Horta, Bruxelles #161/R est:15000-18000
£9333 $16893 €14000 Le dechargement des navires (51x82cm-20x32in) s. 30-Mar-4 Campo, Vlaamse Kaai #121/R est:10000-12000
£10417 $17396 €15000 L'approche d'un orage, plage de la panne (68x124cm-27x49in) s. 21-Oct-3 Sotheby's, Amsterdam #186/R est:15000-20000
£11892 $22000 €17362 Shipping becalmed in Calais harbour (54x79cm-21x31in) s. prov. 10-Feb-4 Christie's, Rockefeller NY #234/R est:12000-18000
£12000 $22080 €17520 Une plage (76x102cm-30x40in) s. i.verso. 23-Mar-4 Bonhams, New Bond Street #5/R est:2000-4000
£13986 $24056 €20000 Pecheurs ostendais au large de Douvres (57x79cm-22x31in) s. 8-Dec-3 Horta, Bruxelles #160/R est:22000-24000
£18493 $31438 €27000 Arrivee du trois-mats (40x73cm-16x29in) s. panel. 10-Nov-3 Horta, Bruxelles #164
£23776 $40895 €34000 Pecheurs par gros temps (68x125cm-27x49in) s. 8-Dec-3 Horta, Bruxelles #159/R est:35000-40000

Works on paper
£3125 $5219 €4500 Voiliers dans le chenal (30x48cm-12x19in) s. W/C. 21-Oct-3 Campo, Vlaamse Kaai #513/R est:1000-1500

MUSIN, Maurice (1939-) Belgian

£336 $594 €500 Maternite (70x70cm-28x28in) s.d.1967 panel. 27-Apr-4 Campo, Vlaamse Kaai #530
£493 $853 €700 Les vergers (80x98cm-31x39in) s.d.1967 panel. 10-Dec-3 Hotel des Ventes Mosan, Brussels #278
£567 $948 €800 Tete doree (38x46cm-15x18in) s. panel. 15-Oct-3 Hotel des Ventes Mosan, Brussels #250

MUSITELLI, Giulio Vito (1901-1990) Italian

£811 $1427 €1200 Attilia (50x40cm-20x16in) s.d.57. 19-May-4 Il Ponte, Milan #1092

MUSS-ARNOLT, Gustav (1858-1927) American

£3400 $6188 €4964 Pointers working in a wood (41x55cm-16x22in) s. 1-Jul-4 Mellors & Kirk, Nottingham #814/R est:1000-1400

MUSSA, Patrick (1880-?) French

£364 $618 €520 Procession a Locronan (46x55cm-18x22in) s. exhib. 24-Nov-3 Boscher, Cherbourg #850/R

MUSSCHER, Michiel van (1645-1705) Dutch

£2013 $3705 €3000 Portrait of Dutch family on palace terrace (81x99cm-32x39in) prov. 24-Mar-4 Dorotheum, Vienna #400/R est:2000-5000
£3333 $5267 €4800 Doctor's visit (28x21cm-11x8in) s. panel. 2-Sep-3 Christie's, Amsterdam #127/R est:2500-3500

MUSSCHER, Michiel van (attrib) (1645-1705) Dutch

£1900 $3477 €2774 Portrait of artist smoking pipe (34x28cm-13x11in) 9-Jul-4 Christie's, Kensington #61/R est:2000-3000

MUSSINO, Giorgio (19th C) Italian

£738 $1307 €1100 Study (16x30cm-6x12in) s.d.1894 board. 1-May-4 Meeting Art, Vercelli #11

MUSSO, Carlo (1907-1968) Italian

£340 $609 €500 Lanzo valleys (25x30cm-10x12in) s. cardboard. 22-Mar-4 Sant Agostino, Torino #52/R
£521 $885 €750 Vase of flowers (50x40cm-20x16in) s. 1-Nov-3 Meeting Art, Vercelli #81/R
£903 $1535 €1300 Coming storm (49x59cm-19x23in) s. cardboard. 1-Nov-3 Meeting Art, Vercelli #206/R
£972 $1653 €1400 Cottages (33x42cm-13x17in) s.d.1955 cardboard. 1-Nov-3 Meeting Art, Vercelli #429/R
£1074 $1901 €1600 Landscape covered in snow (40x50cm-16x20in) s. board. 1-May-4 Meeting Art, Vercelli #102 est:1500
£1267 $2331 €1900 Last snow (50x60cm-20x24in) s. cardboard. 14-Jun-4 Sant Agostino, Torino #297/R est:1500-2000
£1458 $2479 €2100 Autumn by Corio Canavese (50x70cm-20x28in) s. i.verso cardboard. 1-Nov-3 Meeting Art, Vercelli #436/R est:1500
£1477 $2613 €2200 Snow in Cartman Valley (40x50cm-16x20in) s. masonite. 1-May-4 Meeting Art, Vercelli #222 est:2000

£2000 $3680 €3000 Savona harbour (65x75cm-26x30in) s. 14-Jun-4 Sant Agostino, Torino #287/R est:3000-3500
Works on paper
£1354 $2302 €1950 Seascape (27x40cm-11x16in) s.d.1954 mixed media card. 1-Nov-3 Meeting Art, Vercelli #315/R est:750

MUSSOLINI, Romano (1927-) Italian
£272 $495 €400 Clown (70x50cm-28x20in) s. 6-Feb-4 Galleria Rosenberg, Milan #122/R
£342 $582 €500 Untitled (50x60cm-20x24in) s. 7-Nov-3 Galleria Rosenberg, Milan #91/R

MUSTONEN, Yrjo (?-1900) Finnish
£326 $545 €470 Country idyll (65x80cm-26x31in) s.d.78. 26-Oct-3 Bukowskis, Helsinki #425/R

MUTCH, Tom (20th C) New Zealander
£290 $467 €423 Opito Bay from Matapawa Road (30x41cm-12x16in) s.d.1994 board. 12-Aug-3 Peter Webb, Auckland #55/R (NZ.D 800)
£1107 $1982 €1616 Nikau with tree spirit and dogs over New Plymouth (98x101cm-39x40in) s.d.1985 verso hardboard. 11-May-4 Peter Webb, Auckland #124/R est:2500-4500 (NZ.D 3200)

MUTER, Mela (1886-1967) French
£4363 $8115 €6500 Portrait d'Ambroise Vollard (91x88cm-36x35in) s. 3-Mar-4 Tajan, Paris #125/R est:4000-6000
£4605 $8474 €7000 Fort Saint-Andre (60x74cm-24x29in) s. 25-Jun-4 Millon & Associes, Paris #165/R est:4000-6000
£5132 $9442 €7800 Jardin a Saint-Tropez (73x91cm-29x36in) s. 25-Jun-4 Millon & Associes, Paris #166/R est:3000-4000
£5556 $9056 €8000 Harvest landscape (50x62cm-20x24in) mono.d.1907 i. verso prov. 27-Sep-3 Dr Fritz Nagel, Stuttgart #9581/R est:3000
£6040 $10691 €9000 Nature morte aux legumes (81x81cm-32x32in) 27-Apr-4 Campo & Campo, Antwerp #174/R est:7000-10000
£13245 $24106 €20000 Nature morte avec legumes et bouteille d'huile (80x80cm-31x31in) prov.exhib. 16-Jun-4 Claude Boisgirard, Paris #116/R est:20000-22000
£16598 $30705 €24233 Village scene (83x89cm-33x35in) 14-Mar-4 Agra, Warsaw #74/R (P.Z 120000)
Works on paper
£1379 $2290 €2000 Jeune fille au bureau (45x35cm-18x14in) s. W/C. 1-Oct-3 Millon & Associes, Paris #18/R

MUTHESIUS, Eckart (1904-1989) German
Works on paper
£3779 $6500 €5517 Designs for the Maharaja of Indore's Manik Bagh Palace (19x28cm-7x11in) i. pencil two different sizes. 8-Dec-3 Phillips, New York #106/R est:4000-6000

MUTI, Rutilio (1904-1995) Italian
£280 $507 €420 Countryside (24x35cm-9x14in) s. board. 2-Apr-4 Farsetti, Prato #524
£288 $472 €400 Landscape. board. 10-Jun-3 Pandolfini, Florence #268
£317 $549 €450 Snowfall in Vicchio (15x25cm-6x10in) s. s.i.d.verso board. 9-Dec-3 Pandolfini, Florence #265
£845 $1462 €1200 Herd coming back (50x60cm-20x24in) s. 9-Dec-3 Pandolfini, Florence #416/R

MUTJI, Michael (c.1940-2002) Australian
Works on paper
£1098 $1965 €1603 Milpinlilli (120x80cm-47x31in) synthetic polymer paint canvas 1998 prov. 25-May-4 Lawson Menzies, Sydney #136/R est:3000-4000 (A.D 2800)

MUTRIE, Annie Feray (1826-1893) British
£2200 $3960 €3212 Still life of eggs in a basket. Still life of apples in a basket (30x39cm-12x15in) i. pair. 21-Apr-4 Tennants, Leyburn #1209 est:1200-1400

MUTRIE, Martha Darley (1824-1885) British
£9600 $17280 €14016 Still life of flower with a vase, nautilus shell and gold china upon a marble shelf (48x80cm-19x31in) init. 22-Apr-4 Lawrence, Crewkerne #919/R est:6000-8000

MUTTI, Adolfo (1893-?) Italian
£652 $1193 €952 Landscape (50x65cm-20x26in) s.i.d.1932 verso prov. 4-Jun-4 Zofingen, Switzerland #2495 (S.FR 1500)

MUTZE, Carl (20th C) American
£1863 $3000 €2720 Fox hunt (91x122cm-36x48in) s. 14-Jan-4 Christie's, Rockefeller NY #61/R est:4000-6000

MUTZNER, Sammys (1869-1958) Rumanian
Works on paper
£496 $815 €724 Two women (46x31cm-18x12in) s. mixed media exec.1919. 1-Jun-3 Subastas Odalys, Caracas #74

MUTZNER, Samuel (1886-?) Rumanian
£833 $1492 €1250 Vue de la Cote d'Azur (50x61cm-20x24in) s.d.36 canvas on cardboard. 11-May-4 Vanderkindere, Brussels #28
£1000 $1810 €1500 Sunny bazaar in Kairouan - Tunisia (37x58cm-15x23in) s.i.d.1921 canvas on board. 3-Apr-4 Hans Stahl, Hamburg #61/R est:1500

MUUKKA, Elias (1853-1938) Finnish
£537 $999 €800 The farmer (52x35cm-20x14in) s.d.12. 7-Mar-4 Bukowskis, Helsinki #391/R
£694 $1160 €1000 Winter's day (26x51cm-10x20in) s.d.1927. 26-Oct-3 Bukowskis, Helsinki #428/R
£880 $1408 €1250 Landscape (40x61cm-16x24in) s.d.1917. 18-Sep-3 Hagelstam, Helsinki #1041
£903 $1508 €1300 Summer's day (32x44cm-13x17in) s.d.1934. 26-Oct-3 Bukowskis, Helsinki #426/R
£1014 $1814 €1500 Landscape from Savolax (37x54cm-15x21in) s. 8-May-4 Bukowskis, Helsinki #65/R est:1700-2000
£1197 $1915 €1700 Forest road (48x39cm-19x15in) s.d.27. 21-Sep-3 Bukowskis, Helsinki #404/R est:2000
£1333 $2387 €2000 Silver birch (49x30cm-19x12in) s. board. 15-May-4 Hagelstam, Helsinki #83/R est:2000
£1338 $2141 €1900 Landscape (38x55cm-15x22in) s.d.1915. 18-Sep-3 Hagelstam, Helsinki #835/R est:1500
£1408 $2254 €2000 Moonlight (38x32cm-15x13in) s.d.04. 21-Sep-3 Bukowskis, Helsinki #403/R est:2000
£1538 $2615 €2200 Meadow by the water (30x39cm-12x15in) s.d.03. 29-Nov-3 Bukowskis, Helsinki #217/R est:1800-2000
£1748 $2972 €2500 Evening fishing (43x30cm-17x12in) s.d.96. 29-Nov-3 Bukowskis, Helsinki #145/R est:2500-3000
£2238 $3804 €3200 Solitary rower (33x62cm-13x24in) s.d.1907 exhib. 29-Nov-3 Bukowskis, Helsinki #138/R est:3000-3500
£3099 $5361 €4400 In the sauna (38x52cm-15x20in) s.d.1913. 13-Dec-3 Hagelstam, Helsinki #142/R est:3000
£3867 $6921 €5800 Child on shore (36x57cm-14x22in) s.d.1887. 15-May-4 Hagelstam, Helsinki #82/R est:5000
£4000 $7160 €6000 Horse and carriage (34x56cm-13x22in) s.d.1877. 15-May-4 Hagelstam, Helsinki #87/R est:5000
£4392 $7861 €6500 Washing day (35x56cm-14x22in) s.d.1882. 8-May-4 Bukowskis, Helsinki #32/R est:6000-8000

MUUSARI, Janne (1886-1966) Finnish
£300 $552 €450 Dark water (39x63cm-15x25in) s.d.1921. 9-Jun-4 Bukowskis, Helsinki #492/R

MUXART, Jaime (1922-) Spanish
£1034 $1862 €1500 Couple (96x70cm-38x28in) s. 26-Jan-4 Durán, Madrid #102/R est:1500

MUYDEN, Alfred van (1818-1898) Swiss
£559 $934 €800 Lecture de la lettre (24x32cm-9x13in) s.d.1865. 29-Jun-3 Eric Pillon, Calais #61/R
£661 $1123 €965 The farewell (67x84cm-26x33in) s.d.1863. 5-Nov-3 Dobiaschofsky, Bern #833/R (S.FR 1500)
£1711 $2857 €2498 Famille de paysans (24x34cm-9x13in) s.d.1878. 16-Nov-3 Koller, Geneva #1204/R est:1000-2000 (S.FR 3900)
£1834 $3338 €2678 Monks on a south-facing terrace (42x71cm-17x28in) s.d.1870 panel. 16-Jun-4 Fischer, Luzern #1276/R est:5000-6000 (S.FR 4200)
£3017 $5401 €4405 Italian peasants in field (35x49cm-14x19in) s.i.d.1853. 14-May-4 Dobiaschofsky, Bern #74/R est:7500 (S.FR 7000)
Works on paper
£543 $923 €793 Madame Eynard Lullin dans la bibliotheque (34x25cm-13x10in) i. verso W/C. 28-Nov-3 Zofingen, Switzerland #2476/R (S.FR 1200)
£1572 $2861 €2295 Monk on a donkey meeting two market ladies (16x19cm-6x7in) s.d.1849 W/C. 16-Jun-4 Fischer, Luzern #2801/R est:1300-1500 (S.FR 3600)

MUYDEN, Charles Henri van (1860-1936) Swiss
£1586 $2696 €2316 Woman from Wallis havesting wheat (30x30cm-12x12in) s.i. canvas on panel. 5-Nov-3 Dobiaschofsky, Bern #831/R est:1200 (S.FR 3600)
£1957 $3580 €2857 Fileuse au Rouet, Saviese (45x55cm-18x22in) s.i. prov. 5-Jun-4 Galerie du Rhone, Sion #555/R est:3500-4500 (S.FR 4500)
£12844 $21450 €18624 Repas champetre au couchant (71x127cm-28x50in) s.d. prov. 21-Jun-3 Galerie du Rhone, Sion #473/R est:25000-35000 (S.FR 28000)

MUYDEN, Evert Louis van (1853-1922) Swiss
Works on paper
£264 $449 €385 Cow herder (67x84cm-26x33in) s.d.1863. 5-Nov-3 Dobiaschofsky, Bern #832/R (S.FR 600)

MUYLDER, An de (?) Belgian?
£367 $671 €550 Paysage surrealiste (100x100cm-39x39in) s. 7-Jun-4 Palais de Beaux Arts, Brussels #171

MUYLDER, Pierre Willy de (1921-) Belgian
£586 $1084 €850 La visite de prelat (62x50cm-24x20in) s. 19-Jan-4 Horta, Bruxelles #448

MUZIANO, Girolamo (1528-1592) Italian
£15000 $27450 €21900 Assumption of the Virgin (154x107cm-61x42in) prov. 8-Jul-4 Sotheby's, London #155/R est:15000-20000
Works on paper
£22222 $40000 €32444 Rocky gorge with mill (32x21cm-13x8in) black chk pen brown ink wash prov.exhib. 22-Jan-4 Christie's, Rockefeller NY #10/R est:40000-60000

MUZIANO, Girolamo and RUBENS, Sir Peter Paul (attrib) (16/17th C) Italian/Flemish
Works on paper
£56338 $98592 €80000 L'entree du Christ a Jerusalem (23x31cm-9x12in) indis.i. black chk pen brown ink wash prov. 17-Dec-3 Christie's, Paris #3/R est:60000-80000

MUZIKA, Frantisek (1900-1974) Czechoslovakian
£949 $1671 €1424 Pear (7x13cm-3x5in) init.d.42 cardboard. 22-May-4 Dorotheum, Prague #171/R est:10000-15000 (C.KR 45000)

MUZZIOLI, Giovanni (1854-1894) Italian

£1719	$2751	€2510	Young woman with fan (23x19cm-9x7in) s. 16-Sep-3 Philippe Schuler, Zurich #3347/R est:3000-5000 (S.FR 3800)
£2878	$4719	€4000	Reclining woman on lion skin (35x45cm-14x18in) s. prov. 10-Jun-3 Pandolfini, Florence #102/R est:4500-5000
£27397	$46575	€40000	Roman scene (158x95cm-62x37in) 7-Nov-3 Tuttarte, Modena #851

MY, Hieronymus van der (1687-1761) Dutch

£986	$1706	€1400	Portrait of elegant shipowner (3x2cm-1x1in) enamel. 13-Dec-3 Lempertz, Koln #35/R

MYERS, Bernard (1925-) British

£380	$692	€555	Still life with blue coffee pot (54x74cm-21x29in) s. oil pastel. 15-Jun-4 Bonhams, Knightsbridge #179/R

MYERS, Ethel (1881-1960) American

Sculpture

£3529	$6000	€5152	Florence Reed (31cm-12in) s.num.6 bronze. 30-Oct-3 Phillips, New York #70/R est:4000-6000
£3529	$6000	€5152	Vaudeville (36cm-14in) s.num.10 bronze. 30-Oct-3 Phillips, New York #72/R est:6000-8000

MYERS, Frank Harmon (1899-1956) American

£519	$950	€758	Crashing waves (41x51cm-16x20in) painted c.1930. 5-Jun-4 Treadway Gallery, Cincinnati #636/R
£2310	$4250	€3373	Crashing waves (77x97cm-30x38in) s. prov. 8-Jun-4 Bonhams & Butterfields, San Francisco #4234/R est:7000-10000

Works on paper

£1509	$2400	€2203	Chess match (20x21cm-8x8in) s.d.42 gouache. 12-Sep-3 Skinner, Boston #380/R

MYERS, Harry (1886-1961) American

£369	$650	€539	Girl with parasol (41x51cm-16x20in) init. s.verso board painted c.1960. 23-May-4 Treadway Gallery, Cincinnati #634/R
£625	$1100	€913	Dancer (41x30cm-16x12in) init. s.verso board painted c.1960. 23-May-4 Treadway Gallery, Cincinnati #627/R
£625	$1100	€913	Ballet dancer (41x30cm-16x12in) init. s.verso painted c.1960 board. 23-May-4 Treadway Gallery, Cincinnati #628/R

MYERS, Jerome (1867-1940) American

£4360	$7500	€6366	East side market (32x40cm-13x16in) s.d.1937 i.stretcher prov. 3-Dec-3 Doyle, New York #283/R est:10000-15000
£6704	$12000	€9788	Street vendor (20x24cm-8x9in) s. prov. 6-May-4 Shannon's, Milford #133/R est:12000-18000

Works on paper

£233	$415	€340	Summer sailing. Lady (18x23cm-7x9in) s. pastel double-sided. 8-Jan-4 James Julia, Fairfield #818a/R
£432	$700	€626	Listening in the park (17x19cm-7x7in) s. dr. prov. 8-Aug-3 Barridorf, Portland #314/R

MYERS, Joyce (20th C) American

£410	$750	€615	Plus one (150x178cm-59x70in) 10-Jul-4 Hindman, Chicago #364/R

MYGATT, Robertson K (1861-1919) American

£520	$915	€759	Setting sun (26x36cm-10x14in) s.d.1915 board. 18-May-4 Bonhams, Knightsbridge #84/R

MYJAK, Adam (1947-) Polish

Sculpture

£847	$1534	€1271	Figurine (42cm-17in) polished pat bronze. 4-Apr-4 Agra, Warsaw #12/R (P.Z 6000)

MYLES, John (19th C) British

£920	$1711	€1343	Medicine time (51x37cm-20x15in) s.d.1872. 4-Mar-4 Christie's, Kensington #603/R

MYLES, W Scott (1830-1911) British

£304	$492	€444	Seascape with sailing vessels off a pier (31x53cm-12x21in) s. 9-Aug-3 Hindemae, Ullerslev #258/R (D.KR 3200)
£320	$589	€467	Harvest time (35x45cm-14x18in) s. 10-Jun-4 Lyon & Turnbull, Edinburgh #135
£750	$1403	€1095	Cattle on a path by a river (40x30cm-16x12in) s.d.93. 21-Jul-4 Lyon & Turnbull, Edinburgh #137/R

MYN, Francis van der (1719-1783) Dutch

£3800	$7106	€5548	Portrait of a lady, holding flowers, in a landscape (76x62cm-30x24in) init. oval prov. 27-Feb-4 Christie's, Kensington #42/R est:700-1000

MYN, Francis van der (attrib) (1719-1783) Dutch

£2800	$5040	€4088	Portrait of Madame Morehead (125x99cm-49x39in) 21-Jan-4 Sotheby's, Olympia #14/R est:2000-3000

MYNTTI, Eemu (1890-1943) Finnish

£667	$1227	€1000	The red-haired (54x42cm-21x17in) s. 9-Jun-4 Bukowskis, Helsinki #493/R
£839	$1560	€1250	The singer (46x38cm-18x15in) s. 7-Mar-4 Bukowskis, Helsinki #392/R
£845	$1352	€1200	Still life (58x50cm-23x20in) s. 18-Sep-3 Hagelstam, Helsinki #842

MYR, Louis Marcel (1893-1964) French

£816	$1461	€1200	Combat de boxe (81x65cm-32x26in) 21-Mar-4 Rossini, Paris #250/R

MYRAH, Newman (1921-) Canadian

£514	$950	€750	Bison on a grassy plateau (46x61cm-18x24in) s. 19-Jan-4 O'Gallerie, Oregon #114/R
£719	$1200	€1050	Time out (61x76cm-24x30in) s. 27-Oct-3 O'Gallerie, Oregon #92/R est:1800-2500
£765	$1300	€1117	Brahma bull rider with pick up rider in the background (41x51cm-16x20in) d. prov. 1-Dec-3 O'Gallerie, Oregon #162/R est:800-1200
£1069	$1700	€1561	Taking his leave (46x61cm-18x24in) s. 5-May-3 O'Gallerie, Oregon #130/R est:2000-3000
£1195	$1900	€1745	Buffalo (46x61cm-18x24in) s. 5-May-3 O'Gallerie, Oregon #92/R est:1800-2500
£1195	$1900	€1745	Time out, mounted cowboy lighting up (61x76cm-24x30in) s.d.69. 5-May-3 O'Gallerie, Oregon #754/R est:3500-4500
£1415	$2250	€2066	Gathering strays in the Badlands (56x71cm-22x28in) s. i.verso. 5-May-3 O'Gallerie, Oregon #784/R est:2750-3750
£3476	$6500	€5075	First out (61x91cm-24x36in) s. 24-Jul-4 Coeur d'Alene, Hayden #258/R est:6000-9000

MYRBACH-RHEINFELD, Felicien von (1853-1940) Austrian

£310	$536	€440	Napoleon (41x32cm-16x13in) s. board. 15-Dec-3 Ansorena, Madrid #371/R

Works on paper

£1611	$2964	€2400	Funeral procession of EH Albrech, Field Marshall (14x18cm-6x7in) mono. W/C. 26-Mar-4 Dorotheum, Vienna #330/R est:600-700

MYSTKOWSKI, Czeslaw (1898-1938) Polish

£6250	$10438	€9125	Two Balinese girls on the beach (69x562cm-27x221in) s. board. 12-Oct-3 Sotheby's, Singapore #8/R est:18000-25000 (S.D 18000)
£6536	$11830	€9543	Girl with cigarette (53x42cm-21x17in) s.d.1937 panel. 4-Apr-4 Sotheby's, Singapore #9/R est:12000-15000 (S.D 20000)

Works on paper

£340	$609	€500	Taking a rest from wood gathering (67x57cm-26x22in) W/C exhib. 16-Mar-4 Christie's, Amsterdam #70

MYTENS, Daniel (elder) (1590-1648) Dutch

£47222	$85000	€68944	Portrait of Frederik Hendrik, Prince of Orange (206x122cm-81x48in) prov.lit. 23-Jan-4 Christie's, Rockefeller NY #58/R est:100000-150000

MYTENS, Daniel (style) (17th C) Dutch

£5700	$9690	€8322	Portrait of Christopher Cresacre More (56x44cm-22x17in) panel. 27-Nov-3 Sotheby's, London #113/R est:3000-5000

MYTENS, Isack (1602-1666) Dutch

£7534	$12808	€11000	Elegant couple playing a theorbo-lute and a lute with a boy singing (130x170cm-51x67in) s.d.i65 prov. 4-Nov-3 Sotheby's, Amsterdam #15/R est:15000-20000

MYTENS, Jan (1614-1670) Dutch

£8000	$13600	€11680	Group portrait of a family in a landscape (100x94cm-39x37in) tranferred from panel prov. 29-Oct-3 Christie's, London #31/R est:8000-12000
£25000	$45500	€36500	Portrait of a boy traditionally said to be Charles Lennox Duke of Richmond (128x90cm-50x35in) s.i. prov. 1-Jul-4 Sotheby's, London #110 est:30000-40000

MYTENS, Martin I (attrib) (1648-1736) Dutch

£1477	$2717	€2200	Noble youth wearing wig (78x62cm-31x24in) lit. 25-Mar-4 Karlheinz Kaupp, Staufen #2285/R est:2200

MYTENS, Martin II (1695-1770) Swedish

£7009	$11075	€10163	Portrait of a Princess (94x77cm-37x30in) 2-Sep-3 Rasmussen, Copenhagen #1587/R est:75000 (D.KR 75000)
£11409	$20993	€17000	Portrait of Louis Charles I (120x90cm-47x35in) prov. 24-Mar-4 Dorotheum, Vienna #216/R est:16000-24000

Works on paper

£338	$595	€500	Line of waggons with castle beyond (22x31cm-9x12in) s. pen wash prov. 22-May-4 Lempertz, Koln #1317

MYTENS, Martin II (attrib) (1695-1770) Swedish

£2069	$3704	€3021	Portraits of Johan J Falck and his wife Maria (89x73cm-35x29in) i.verso oval pair. 25-May-4 Bukowskis, Stockholm #406/R est:35000-40000 (S.KR 28000)
£3231	$5557	€4717	Portrait of Queen Maria Theresa of Austria (236x122cm-93x48in) 3-Dec-3 AB Stockholms Auktionsverk #2335/R est:35000-40000 (S.KR 42000)
£10738	$19758	€16000	Portrait of Archduchess Maria Anna (87x69cm-34x27in) prov. 24-Mar-4 Dorotheum, Vienna #211/R est:6000-8000

MYTENS, Martin II (studio) (1695-1770) Swedish

£6711	$12349	€10000	Empress Maria Theresa as Crown Princess (70x56cm-28x22in) exhib.lit.prov. 24-Mar-4 Dorotheum, Vienna #213/R est:5000-7000

MYTTEIS, Victor (1874-1936) Hungarian

£805	$1442	€1200	Landscape near Mariatrost (30x34cm-12x13in) s.d.1924 board. 27-May-4 Dorotheum, Graz #50/R

MZIMBA, Velaphi (1959-) South African
Works on paper
£429 $769 €626 Ubuntu (70x99cm-28x39in) s.d.95 mixed media prov. 31-May-4 Stephan Welz, Johannesburg #378 (SA.R 5200)

N F (?) ?
£8200 $14432 €11972 Falcon on a gloved hand (63x45cm-25x18in) init.d.1674. 18-May-4 Woolley & Wallis, Salisbury #122/R est:1000-1500

NAAGER, Franz (1870-1942) German
£521 $823 €750 Venice Laguna (84x163cm-33x64in) s.d.1922. 5-Sep-3 Wendl, Rudolstadt #3537/R
£544 $974 €800 Venice - Festa del Redentore (105x120cm-41x47in) s.d.22.7.39. 17-Mar-4 Neumeister, Munich #552/R
£671 $1235 €1000 Carnival in Venice (96x120cm-38x47in) s.d.23. 24-Mar-4 Hugo Ruef, Munich #1244/R

NABAA, Nazir (1938-) Syrian
£3800 $6726 €5548 Nude with fruit head dress (108x78cm-43x31in) s.d.1989. 29-Apr-4 Bonhams, New Bond Street #577/R est:3000-5000

NABEGEYO, Billinjara (c.1913-?) Australian
Works on paper
£2148 $4018 €3222 Lumahlumah the fisherman (136x65cm-54x26in) earth pigments eucalyptus bark exec.c.1975 prov. 26-Jul-4 Sotheby's, Melbourne #293/R est:4000-6000 (A.D 5500)

NABINGER, Dollie (1905-1988) American
£2545 $4250 €3716 Springtime, Texas (64x76cm-25x30in) 18-Oct-3 David Dike, Dallas #211/R est:3000-6000

NABOKOV, Vladimir (1899-1977) American?
Works on paper
£8571 $15000 €12514 Rabbithead logo in the form of a butterfly (15x18cm-6x7in) pencil pastel exec 1976. 17-Dec-3 Christie's, Rockefeller NY #261/R est:15000-20000

NABRAVIN, J (19th C) ?
£1342 $2470 €2000 Visiting the stables (46x37cm-18x15in) s. 24-Mar-4 Finarte Semenzato, Rome #2/R est:5000-6000

NABULAYA, Jack (1928-) Australian
Works on paper
£691 $1092 €1002 Djinaurnya (94x27cm-37x11in) earth pigments eucalyptus bark prov. 28-Jul-3 Sotheby's, Paddington #451/R est:1200-1800 (A.D 1700)
£976 $1541 €1415 Djinawurnya (118x41cm-46x16in) earth pigments eucalyptus bark prov. 28-Jul-3 Sotheby's, Paddington #450/R est:2500-3500 (A.D 2400)

NACH, David (20th C) ?
Works on paper
£389 $650 €568 Ash dome (140x100cm-55x39in) i. pastel. 19-Oct-3 Bonhams & Butterfields, Los Angeles #7094

NACHTMANN, Franz Xaver (1799-1846) German
Works on paper
£1497 $2679 €2200 Une femme cueillant une rose sur une terrasse donnant sur la mer (26x21cm-10x8in) s. graphite pen brown ink W/C gouache htd gold mica. 18-Mar-4 Christie's, Paris #329/R est:3000-5000

NACK, Kenneth (1923-) American
£941 $1600 €1374 Untitled (33x41cm-13x16in) s.d.1948. 9-Nov-3 Wright, Chicago #260 est:2000-3000

NACKAERTS, Frans (1884-?) Belgian
£600 $1074 €900 Children playing (32x35cm-13x14in) s.d.05. 15-May-4 De Vuyst, Lokeren #233/R
£704 $1218 €1000 Dimanche, pres de la chapelle (68x80cm-27x31in) s. 9-Dec-3 Campo, Vlaamse Kaai #366/R
Works on paper
£451 $736 €650 View of Amsterdam (48x60cm-19x24in) s. pastel. 29-Sep-3 Sotheby's, Amsterdam #174/R

NACKE, Carl (1876-?) German
Sculpture
£1119 $1902 €1600 Centaur and fauns (40cm-16in) i. pat.bronze. 25-Nov-3 Dorotheum, Vienna #363/R est:1200-1500

NADAL FARRERAS, Carlos (1918-1998) Spanish?
Works on paper
£680 $1218 €1000 Bench and fruit bowl (23x14cm-9x6in) s. gouache. 22-Mar-4 Durán, Madrid #87/R
£897 $1614 €1300 Town (31x45cm-12x18in) s. W/C. 26-Jan-4 Durán, Madrid #94/R
£966 $1738 €1400 Square (31x45cm-12x18in) s. W/C. 26-Jan-4 Durán, Madrid #95/R
£1310 $2359 €1900 Urban view (33x43cm-13x17in) s. gouache. 26-Jan-4 Durán, Madrid #136/R est:1600

NADAL, Carlos (1917-1998) Spanish
£1701 $3095 €2500 Albeat beach (32x36cm-13x14in) s.d.74 oil ink board. 3-Feb-4 Segre, Madrid #167/R est:2300
£3092 $5597 €4700 Beach on the North Sea (42x27cm-17x11in) s. s.i.verso paper on canvas. 14-Apr-4 Ansorena, Madrid #290/R
£3261 $5348 €4500 Urban landscape (33x41cm-13x16in) s. 27-May-3 Durán, Madrid #285/R est:3000
£3767 $6404 €5500 Beach scene (50x65cm-20x26in) s.d.80. 4-Nov-3 Ansorena, Madrid #929/R est:5500
£4000 $6360 €5800 Village avec eglise (38x46cm-15x18in) s. s.i.d.78 verso oil paper on canvas. 11-Sep-3 Christie's, Kensington #156/R est:4000-6000
£4000 $6680 €5840 Quadros al museo (33x41cm-13x16in) s. s.verso oil paper on canvas prov. 21-Oct-3 Sotheby's, London #136/R est:4000-6000
£4167 $6875 €6000 Promenade (38x47cm-15x19in) s. s.i.d.1999 verso paper on canvas. 2-Jul-3 Ansorena, Madrid #875/R
£4700 $7849 €6862 Le port (41x33cm-16x13in) s. oil paper on canavs. 21-Oct-3 Sotheby's, London #137/R est:4000-6000
£6600 $11880 €9636 Sainte-Adrese, France (50x61cm-20x24in) s. s.i.d.24.7.73 verso. 20-Jan-4 Bonhams, Knightsbridge #248/R est:3000-5000
£8000 $14480 €11680 Village (61x81cm-24x32in) s. board. 1-Apr-4 Christie's, Kensington #145/R est:3000-4000
£8500 $15470 €12410 Le village (54x65cm-21x26in) s.d.80 s.i.d.verso prov. 4-Feb-4 Sotheby's, London #321/R est:6000-8000
£8511 $13787 €12000 Interior (60x73cm-24x29in) s.d.76 s.i.d.verso. 20-May-3 Ansorena, Madrid #323/R est:11000
£9333 $16987 €14000 Station (60x73cm-24x29in) s.d.1982 s.i.d. verso prov. 29-Jun-4 Segre, Madrid #111/R est:9500
£10000 $16700 €14600 Paysage Normand (54x65cm-21x26in) s. s.i.verso prov.exhib. 22-Oct-3 Sotheby's, Olympia #117/R est:5000-7000
£11000 $20020 €16060 Venise Basilique Saint Marc (73x92cm-29x36in) s.d.76 s.i.d.verso prov. 4-Feb-4 Sotheby's, London #320/R est:9000-12000
£11000 $20240 €16060 Marine gris (42x55cm-17x22in) s.d.82 s.i. verso. 22-Jun-4 Sotheby's, London #315/R est:8000-12000
£11500 $21160 €16790 Saint Tropez (27x35cm-11x14in) s. i.verso oil paper on canvas prov. 24-Mar-4 Sotheby's, Olympia #96/R est:5000-7000
£13000 $23920 €18980 L'Opera (61x50cm-24x20in) s. s.i.d.1981 verso paper on canvas prov. 23-Jun-4 Christie's, London #180/R est:15000-20000
£14000 $25760 €20440 Composition (81x100cm-32x39in) s. i.d.1983 verso. 22-Jun-4 Sotheby's, London #316/R est:18000-25000
£15000 $27600 €21900 Salon de Babette (50x61cm-20x24in) s. s.i.d.78 verso paper on canvas. 22-Jun-4 Sotheby's, London #314/R est:8000-12000
£17000 $30940 €24820 La repeche (53x64cm-21x25in) s. s.i.verso oil paper on canvas prov. 4-Feb-4 Sotheby's, London #247/R est:8000-12000
£19500 $35490 €28470 Les trois villages (54x65cm-21x26in) s.d.88 s.i.d.verso studio stamp verso oil paper on canvas. 3-Feb-4 Christie's, London #223/R est:12000-18000
£26000 $47320 €37960 Bord de l'eau a Bougival (54x65cm-21x26in) s.d.83 s.i.d.verso. 3-Feb-4 Christie's, London #222/R est:15000-20000
Works on paper
£461 $770 €650 Landscape (29x20cm-11x8in) s. gouache. 23-Jun-3 Durán, Madrid #662/R
£700 $1211 €1022 La plage (16x21cm-6x8in) s.d.87 gouache. 11-Dec-3 Christie's, Kensington #187/R
£1399 $2336 €2000 Urban view (32x43cm-13x17in) s. gouache. 30-Jun-3 Ansorena, Madrid #114/R
£1725 $2761 €2450 Aiguadolc harbour (33x46cm-13x18in) s.d.1976 gouache ink. 16-Sep-3 Segre, Madrid #110/R
£3500 $6335 €5110 Scene de tauromachie (50x64cm-20x25in) brush black ink gouache. 1-Apr-4 Christie's, Kensington #142/R est:800-1200
£15000 $27150 €21900 Chateau (79x102cm-31x40in) gouache exec.c.1953 sold with a letter. 1-Apr-4 Christie's, Kensington #149/R est:5000-7000

NADAL, Carlos (attrib) (1917-1998) Spanish
£625 $1131 €950 Verbena (48x78cm-19x31in) board. 14-Apr-4 Ansorena, Madrid #302/R
£1277 $2068 €1800 Verbena (49x80cm-19x31in) panel. 20-May-3 Ansorena, Madrid #190/R est:1800

NADAL, Guillem (20th C) ?
£1351 $2378 €2000 Untitled - Still life (130x195cm-51x77in) s.i.d.1987 verso exhib.lit. 18-May-4 Segre, Madrid #243/R est:1800
£1769 $3219 €2600 Water reflections (195x157cm-77x62in) s.i.d.1987 verso oil collage. 3-Feb-4 Segre, Madrid #324/R est:900

NADALINI, Louis E (1927-1995) American
£217 $400 €317 Malescope (185x94cm-73x37in) s.i. verso acrylic wood construction. 27-Jun-4 Bonhams & Butterfields, San Francisco #3857/R
£222 $400 €324 Myoptic painting (162x125cm-64x49in) s.i.d.1965-1977 verso acrylic wood. 25-Apr-4 Bonhams & Butterfields, San Francisco #5596/R

NADELMAN, Elie (1882-1946) American/Polish
Sculpture
£1765 $3000 €2577 Dancing woman (23cm-9in) painted plaster. 30-Oct-3 Phillips, New York #71/R est:3000-5000
£4012 $6500 €5817 Girl with thorn in her foot (18cm-7in) ceramic prov. 8-Aug-3 Barridorf, Portland #277/R est:4500-6500
£4624 $8000 €6751 Head (25cm-10in) s. i.verso brown pat bronze incl marble base prov. 10-Dec-3 Bonhams & Butterfields, San Francisco #6077/R est:10000-15000
£6704 $12000 €9788 Two circus woman (38x18cm-15x7in) terracotta prov.lit. 16-May-4 Wright, Chicago #141/R est:10000-15000
£10227 $18000 €14931 Portrait of Gerrish H Milliken (61cm-24in) s. verso marble incl green marble base exec c.1918 lit. 18-May-4 Christie's, Rockefeller NY #145/R est:20000-30000
£113636 $200000 €165909 Standing male nude (69cm-27in) i.f.F Costenoble Paris brown pat bronze prov. 19-May-4 Sotheby's, New York #163/R est:60000-90000
Works on paper
£938 $1500 €1369 Female head (13x11cm-5x4in) artist st. pencil laid paper exec.c.1915-20. 18-Sep-3 Swann Galleries, New York #464/R est:1000-1500

£4118 $7000 €6012 Male head study (28x20cm-11x8in) ink pencil prov. executed c.1921. 9-Nov-3 Wright, Chicago #110 est:3000-5000

NADITCH, Vladimir (20th C) Russian
£2000 $3580 €2920 Birch trees by the pond (38x46cm-15x18in) 26-May-4 Sotheby's, Olympia #399/R est:2000-3000

NADJAMERREK, Lofty Nabarrayal (1926-) Australian
Works on paper
£2246 $4200 €3369 Barrmundi (40x104cm-16x41in) earth pigments eucalyptus bark prov. 26-Jul-4 Sotheby's, Melbourne #286/R est:3000-5000 (A.D 5750)
£2637 $4931 €3956 Creatures of the sacred Maraian ceremony (100x153cm-39x60in) earth pigments prov. 26-Jul-4 Sotheby's, Melbourne #287/R est:7000-10000 (A.D 6750)

NADLER, Robert (1858-?) Hungarian
£333 $557 €486 Terefere a mosasnal (40x53cm-16x21in) s. panel. 12-Oct-3 Uppsala Auktionskammare, Uppsala #427 (S.KR 4300)
£352 $609 €500 Playing on the beach (25x41cm-10x16in) s. card on canvas. 9-Dec-3 Pandolfini, Florence #367/R
£580 $1049 €847 Waterside idyll (25x41cm-10x16in) s. canvas on card. 16-Apr-4 Mu Terem Galeria, Budapest #19/R (H.F 220000)
£940 $1738 €1400 View of Venice (60x80cm-24x31in) s.i. 15-Mar-4 Sotheby's, Amsterdam #165/R est:800-1200

NADORP, Johann Theodor (1761-1802) German
£833 $1317 €1200 Portrait of a gentleman (87x63cm-34x25in) i. oval. 5-Sep-3 Wendl, Rudolstadt #3539/R

NAEF, Erika (20th C) Swiss?
£281 $504 €410 Winter (15x21cm-6x8in) s. panel. 22-Mar-4 Philippe Schuler, Zurich #6074 (S.FR 650)

NAEF, Hermann (1892-1964) Swiss
£1176 $2000 €1717 Bodeli - (21cm-8in circular) mono. s.i. verso. 18-Nov-3 Hans Widmer, St Gallen #1254 est:1500-3000 (S.FR 2600)

NAEGELE, Alfons (20th C) ?
£671 $1235 €1000 Chrysanthemums in vase (100x90cm-39x35in) s. lit. 25-Mar-4 Karlheinz Kaupp, Staufen #2635/R

NAEKE, Gustav Heinrich (1786-1835) German
Works on paper
£633 $1134 €950 Inner courtyard of Palazzo deallaa Cancelleria (18x12cm-7x5in) pencil. 13-May-4 Bassenge, Berlin #5621

NAFTEL, Isabel (fl.1862-1891) British
£800 $1448 €1168 Portrait of a Victorian beauty (33x23cm-13x9in) s.d.1875. 1-Apr-4 Martel Maides, Guernsey #219
Works on paper
£700 $1309 €1022 Three travellers (30x43cm-12x17in) s.d.1854 W/C. 22-Jul-4 Martel Maides, Guernsey #207/R
£1700 $2890 €2482 Woman carrying a pail outside a cottage surrounded by doves and poultry (33x25cm-13x10in) s.d.1889 W/C bodycol. 30-Oct-3 Duke & Son, Dorchester #90/R est:300-600
£1765 $3000 €2577 Portrait of Miss Slade dressed as Cinderella (56x46cm-22x18in) s.d.1864 pencil W/C htd white. 19-Nov-3 Bonhams & Butterfields, San Francisco #146/R

NAFTEL, Maud (1856-1890) British
Works on paper
£400 $748 €584 Still life with pelagoniums (13x20cm-5x8in) s. W/C. 22-Jul-4 Martel Maides, Guernsey #203/R

NAFTEL, Paul Jacob (1817-1891) British
Works on paper
£280 $504 €409 Sailing boats off the shore (9x15cm-4x6in) W/C over pencil bodycol. 21-Jan-4 Sotheby's, Olympia #161/R
£700 $1260 €1022 Cattle grazing in water (12x35cm-5x14in) init.indis.d.1863 pencil W/C htd white prov. 21-Apr-4 Tennants, Leyburn #1032
£750 $1388 €1095 Snowy mountain pass (33x52cm-13x20in) pencil W/C gouache sold with W/C by W Leighton Leitch two prov. 10-Mar-4 Sotheby's, Olympia #148/R
£800 $1376 €1168 Glen Falloch, Head of Loch Lomond (23x49cm-9x19in) mono.d.1866 W/C htd white prov. 4-Dec-3 Bonhams, Edinburgh #96
£920 $1536 €1343 Lismore Castle. Lismore. Figures on a bridge (48x32cm-19x13in) s. W/C over pencil three. 20-Oct-3 Bonhams, Bath #61
£929 $1700 €1394 Ships in a harbour (20x30cm-8x12in) s. pen ink. 29-Jul-4 Eldred, East Dennis #482/R est:1200-1400
£1200 $2160 €1752 River scene in the Lake District (14x23cm-6x9in) s.d.1871 pencil W/C. 21-Apr-4 Tennants, Leyburn #1031/R est:1000-1200
£1450 $2465 €2117 Mountain stream at dusk (32x23cm-13x9in) init. W/C. 25-Nov-3 Martel Maides, Guernsey #198/R est:500-700
£1700 $3128 €2482 Loading the hay cart (42x80cm-17x31in) pencil W/C bodycol. 25-Mar-4 Christie's, Kensington #203/R est:600-800

NAGARE, Masayuki (1923-) Japanese
Sculpture
£2027 $3750 €2959 Windstone (30x89x35cm-12x35x14in) red granite two parts exec 1972. 12-Feb-4 Sotheby's, New York #160/R est:6000-8000

NAGASAWA, Hidetoshi (1940-) Japanese
Sculpture
£2238 $3804 €3200 Ofir's gold (2x7x3cm-1x3x1in) gold exec.1972 in 2 parts prov.exhib. 24-Nov-3 Christie's, Milan #211/R est:250-350

NAGEL, Andres (1947-) Spanish
£6993 $11678 €10000 Pareja de baile (98x137cm-39x54in) s. acrylic sand collage carton on panel. 24-Jun-3 Segre, Madrid #163/R est:4500
Works on paper
£563 $986 €800 Bulls (42x30cm-17x12in) s.d.1972 gouache ink. 16-Dec-3 Segre, Madrid #196/R

NAGEL, Hanna (1907-1974) German
Works on paper
£355 $592 €500 Lovers (30x22cm-12x9in) s. Indian ink. 14-Oct-3 Dorotheum, Vienna #128/R
£1200 $2172 €1800 Marionette (32x16cm-13x6in) s. Indian ink pen brush. 2-Apr-4 Winterberg, Heidelberg #1401/R est:2400
£2098 $3566 €3000 Porter (39x24cm-15x9in) i. graphite chk. 29-Nov-3 Villa Grisebach, Berlin #185/R est:3000-4000

NAGEL, Hans (1926-1978) German
Works on paper
£352 $609 €500 Start of November - horse chestnuts (60x88cm-24x35in) s.i.d.1974 pencil. 13-Dec-3 Lempertz, Koln #171/R

NAGEL, Johann Friedrich (1765-1825) German
£3333 $6000 €4866 Figures ice skating on a frozen lake (96x122cm-38x48in) s. 22-Apr-4 Christie's, Rockefeller NY #23/R est:10000-15000

NAGEL, Otto (1894-1967) German
Works on paper
£315 $541 €450 At Leopold Square (34x25cm-13x10in) s.d.34 chl pencil. 6-Dec-3 Dannenberg, Berlin #815/R
£369 $679 €550 Spare on Mullerstrasse (24x37cm-9x15in) s.d.33 wax. 27-Mar-4 Dannenberg, Berlin #603/R
£1333 $2387 €2000 House entrances in Friedrichsgracht II (43x63cm-17x25in) s. pastel. 15-May-4 Bassenge, Berlin #7062/R est:3000

NAGEL, Patrick (1945-1984) American
£1714 $3000 €2502 Playboy Advisor (44x28cm-17x11in) a. gouache ink board three painted c.1975. 17-Dec-3 Christie's, Rockefeller NY #256/R est:3000-5000
Works on paper
£1714 $3000 €2502 Untitled (76x61cm-30x24in) gouache ink pastel board exec 1982. 17-Dec-3 Christie's, Rockefeller NY #270/R est:4000-6000
£2000 $3500 €2920 Untitled (76x61cm-30x24in) gouache ink pastel board exec 1985. 17-Dec-3 Christie's, Rockefeller NY #284/R est:4000-6000
£2286 $4000 €3338 Untitled (76x61cm-30x24in) gouache ink pastel board exec 1985. 17-Dec-3 Christie's, Rockefeller NY #295/R est:4000-6000

NAGEL, Peter (1941-) German
£1512 $2707 €2208 Entwurf fur ein Goethe-Denkmal (100x130cm-39x51in) s.d.67 acrylic oil. 12-Jan-4 Rasmussen, Vejle #649/R est:15000-20000 (D.KR 16000)

NAGEL, Wilhelm (1866-1945) German
£333 $603 €500 Swabian Alps on sunny winter day (49x78cm-19x31in) s. lit. 1-Apr-4 Frank Peege, Freiburg #1165/R
£556 $928 €800 Schwetzing Castle park (85x107cm-33x42in) s. board. 22-Oct-3 Neumeister, Munich #736/R
£615 $1058 €880 Ripe corn (38x52cm-15x20in) s. i. verso board. 5-Dec-3 Michael Zeller, Lindau #740/R
Works on paper
£699 $1168 €1000 Old Rhine landscape (83x108cm-33x43in) W/C bodycol over chk. 10-Oct-3 Winterberg, Heidelberg #1728

NAGELE, Reinhold (1884-1972) German
£1181 $1924 €1700 Sketch for church window (31x21cm-12x8in) s.d.1953 i. verso tempera. 25-Sep-3 Dr Fritz Nagel, Stuttgart #1387/R est:1800
£3169 $5482 €4500 Arosa (31x42cm-12x17in) s.i.d.1933 tempera paper. 11-Dec-3 Dr Fritz Nagel, Stuttgart #536/R est:1900
£19444 $31694 €28000 Stuttgart at night (16x31cm-6x12in) s.d.1925 tempera board. 25-Sep-3 Dr Fritz Nagel, Stuttgart #1386/R est:29000
Works on paper
£1467 $2655 €2200 Still life of flowers (44x36cm-17x14in) s.i.d.1934 lit. 1-Apr-4 Frank Peege, Freiburg #1256/R est:3000

NAGELI, Heinrich (1841-1937) Swiss
£281 $504 €410 Storm gathering over landscape with trees (61x50cm-24x20in) s. 22-Mar-4 Philippe Schuler, Zurich #4350 (S.FR 650)
£480 $884 €701 Manegg ruins with Zurichsee beyond (65x81cm-26x32in) s.d. 14-Jun-4 Philippe Schuler, Zurich #4228/R (S.FR 1100)

NAGL, C (19th C) ?
£2657 $4517 €3800 Girl with dog (144x111cm-57x44in) s.d.46. 24-Nov-3 Dorotheum, Vienna #33/R est:4500-5000

NAGL, Walter (1939-) Austrian
£533 $981 €800 Hotting village street (60x50cm-24x20in) s. 9-Jun-4 Dorotheum, Salzburg #711/R

£851 $1421 €1200 Still life with pepper and lemon (54x45cm-21x18in) s.d.90. 16-Oct-3 Dorotheum, Salzburg #732/R

NAGLER, Edith Kroger van (1895-1986) American
£313 $500 €457 Hilly landscape (41x61cm-16x24in) s. 20-Sep-3 Nadeau, Windsor #232

NAGLER, Fred (1891-1983) American
£424 $750 €619 Modernist crucifixion of Christ (76x102cm-30x40in) s.d.1944 stretcher vignette. 1-May-4 Thomaston Place, Thomaston #839/R

NAGOMARA, Albert (c.1926-) Australian
Works on paper
£1855 $3470 €2783 Nguntalpi (119x85cm-47x33in) bears name.verso synthetic polymer paint canvas prov.exhib. 26-Jul-4 Sotheby's, Melbourne #87/R est:5000-8000 (A.D 4750)

NAGORNOV, Vladislav (1974-) Russian
£250 $448 €365 Etude of a girl with ear-rings (41x33cm-16x13in) s. 5-May-4 John Nicholson, Haslemere #184
£400 $700 €584 Nude on the pink background (33x41cm-13x16in) s. 17-Dec-3 John Nicholson, Haslemere #21/R
£400 $748 €600 By the window (50x35cm-20x14in) s. 21-Jul-4 John Nicholson, Haslemere #450/R
£450 $788 €657 Nadya (41x33cm-16x13in) s. 17-Dec-3 John Nicholson, Haslemere #22/R
£500 $815 €730 Shepherds (46x33cm-18x13in) s. 28-Sep-3 John Nicholson, Haslemere #136
£537 $961 €800 Nude (33x46cm-13x18in) s. 25-May-4 Durán, Madrid #726/R
£550 $897 €803 Nude (33x55cm-13x22in) s. after Joaquin Sorolla. 28-Sep-3 John Nicholson, Haslemere #26
£550 $897 €803 Nude with flower (46x61cm-18x24in) s. 28-Sep-3 John Nicholson, Haslemere #86/R
£550 $919 €803 Girl with a bouquet (33x46cm-13x18in) s. 13-Jul-3 John Nicholson, Haslemere #105/R
£556 $883 €800 Oriental music (58x42cm-23x17in) s. 29-Apr-3 Durán, Madrid #809/R
£600 $1074 €876 Spring (50x40cm-20x16in) s. 5-May-4 John Nicholson, Haslemere #48/R
£600 $1122 €900 Sleeping model (27x46cm-11x18in) s. 21-Jul-4 John Nicholson, Haslemere #458/R
£750 $1343 €1095 Girl with berries (46x33cm-18x13in) s. after William Adolphe Bouguereau. 5-May-4 John Nicholson, Haslemere #183
£797 $1307 €1100 Mirandose al espejo (61x46cm-24x18in) s. 27-May-3 Durán, Madrid #778/R

NAGY, Anity (1896-1975) Hungarian
£709 $1184 €1000 Market day (40x50cm-16x20in) s. oil mixed media panel. 16-Oct-3 Dorotheum, Salzburg #656/R

NAGY, Ernest de (1906-1944) American
£782 $1400 €1142 Untitled neighbourhood scene (56x71cm-22x28in) s. 21-Mar-4 Hindman, Chicago #842/R est:800-1200

NAGY, Ernoi (1881-1951) Hungarian?
£382 $638 €550 Goosemaid (40x30cm-16x12in) s. lit. 25-Oct-3 Bergmann, Erlangen #968/R

NAGY, Gabor (1945-) Canadian
£223 $379 €326 Pansies and roses (61x51cm-24x20in) s. i.d.1994 verso. 6-Nov-3 Heffel, Vancouver #88/R (C.D 500)
£226 $378 €330 Evening ferry from Levis (40x50cm-16x20in) s.i.d.1989 board. 17-Nov-3 Hodgins, Calgary #336/R (C.D 500)
£246 $417 €359 Anemones (61x51cm-24x20in) s. i.d.1994 verso. 6-Nov-3 Heffel, Vancouver #87/R (C.D 550)
£310 $561 €453 Portrait of Lydia (75x57cm-30x22in) s.d.1985 oil on paper prov. 18-Apr-4 Levis, Calgary #520/R (C.D 750)
£357 $614 €521 Dutch speciality (30x40cm-12x16in) s. 2-Dec-3 Joyner Waddington, Toronto #366/R (C.D 800)
£400 $732 €584 Flowers in a red vase (75x60cm-30x24in) 1-Jun-4 Hodgins, Calgary #53/R (C.D 1000)
£1200 $2196 €1752 Surface distraction (80x200cm-31x79in) s.i.d.2000. 1-Jun-4 Hodgins, Calgary #76/R est:3000-4000 (C.D 3000)

NAGY, Imre (1893-1976) Hungarian
£3162 $5723 €4617 At the window (92x70cm-36x28in) s. 16-Apr-4 Mu Terem Galeria, Budapest #148/R (H.F 1200000)
£4216 $7630 €6155 Riverscape (100x190cm-39x75in) s. 16-Apr-4 Mu Terem Galeria, Budapest #34/R (H.F 1600000)

NAGY, Istvan (1873-1937) Hungarian
Works on paper
£1054 $1908 €1539 Self portrait (22x28cm-9x11in) s. pastel. 16-Apr-4 Mu Terem Galeria, Budapest #8/R (H.F 400000)
£1303 $2163 €1902 Portrait of a man (41x31cm-16x12in) s. pastel. 4-Oct-3 Kieselbach, Budapest #78/R (H.F 480000)
£1697 $2935 €2478 Snow-covered rooftops (30x40cm-12x16in) s. pastel. 12-Dec-3 Kieselbach, Budapest #191/R (H.F 650000)
£2088 $3612 €3048 Portrait of an elderly man (68x50cm-27x20in) s. pastel. 12-Dec-3 Kieselbach, Budapest #91/R (H.F 800000)

NAGY, Oszkar (1883-1965) Hungarian
£1107 $2003 €1616 Saint Stephan tower in Nagybanya (60x78cm-24x31in) 16-Apr-4 Mu Terem Galeria, Budapest #63/R (H.F 420000)
£1305 $2258 €1905 Banks of the Zazar in Nagybanya (40x80cm-16x31in) s. 12-Dec-3 Kieselbach, Budapest #102/R (H.F 500000)
£1449 $2623 €2116 Forest leaves offering shadow (89x104cm-35x41in) s. 16-Apr-4 Mu Terem Galeria, Budapest #61/R (H.F 550000)
£1900 $3155 €2774 Street in Nagybanya (44x64cm-17x25in) s. 4-Oct-3 Kieselbach, Budapest #13/R (H.F 700000)
£2871 $4967 €4192 Nagybanya landscape (62x65cm-24x26in) s. 12-Dec-3 Kieselbach, Budapest #80/R (H.F 1100000)
£2871 $4967 €4192 Istvan Tower in Nagybanya (70x100cm-28x39in) s. 12-Dec-3 Kieselbach, Budapest #146/R (H.F 1100000)
£3952 $7153 €5770 Forest leaves offering shadow (89x104cm-35x41in) s. 16-Apr-4 Mu Terem Galeria, Budapest #60/R (H.F 1500000)
£4479 $8107 €6539 Sunshine above the manor in Nagybanya (55x58cm-22x23in) s. 16-Apr-4 Mu Terem Galeria, Budapest #151/R (H.F 1700000)
£4887 $8112 €7135 Grove in Nagybanya (74x89cm-29x35in) s. 4-Oct-3 Kieselbach, Budapest #95/R (H.F 1800000)

NAGY, Vilmos (1874-1953) Hungarian
£280 $515 €420 Young child eating cherries (50x39cm-20x15in) s. 11-Jun-4 Wendl, Rudolstadt #4190/R
£355 $592 €500 Elegant scene (77x94cm-30x37in) s. 14-Oct-3 Dorotheum, Vienna #59/R

NAGY, Zsigmond (1872-?) Hungarian
£481 $851 €702 In the window of the studio in Paris (73x60cm-29x24in) s. 28-Apr-4 Kieselbach, Budapest #16/R (H.F 180000)
£526 $968 €800 Big house in Soto del Barco (31x40cm-12x16in) s. cardboard. 22-Jun-4 Durán, Madrid #39/R

NAHL, Johann August (younger) (1752-1825) German
Works on paper
£1485 $2702 €2228 Alpine landscape with beech trees and woman sitting (46x67cm-18x26in) i. brush sepia over pen sepia ink. 17-Jun-4 Kornfeld, Bern #41/R est:1000 (S.FR 3400)

NAIDA, Dmitri (1969-) Russian
£336 $617 €500 Still life of roses (50x50cm-20x20in) s. 24-Mar-4 Hugo Ruef, Munich #1245
£403 $741 €600 Still life of roses and apples (60x50cm-24x20in) s. 24-Mar-4 Hugo Ruef, Munich #1246
£671 $1235 €1000 Still life of flowers and fruit (70x100cm-28x39in) s. 24-Mar-4 Hugo Ruef, Munich #1247

NAIDITCH, Vladimir (1903-1980) Russian
£600 $1074 €900 Landscape (73x60cm-29x24in) s. 17-May-4 Chayette & Cheval, Paris #143
£629 $1070 €900 Paysage (50x60cm-20x24in) s. 27-Nov-3 Calmels Cohen, Paris #55
£671 $1242 €1000 Lisa au piano (65x49cm-26x19in) s. canvas on cardboard. 15-Mar-4 Claude Boisgirard, Paris #83
£805 $1490 €1200 Nu dans un fauteuil (81x65cm-32x26in) s. 15-Mar-4 Claude Boisgirard, Paris #82

NAIGEON, Jean Claude (attrib) (1753-1832) French
Works on paper
£437 $795 €638 Portrait of Claudine Naigeon (13x9cm-5x4in) s.d.1772 pencil. 16-Jun-4 Fischer, Luzern #2535/R (S.FR 1000)

NAIRN, Cecilia (1791-1857) British
Works on paper
£1800 $3222 €2628 On the Dargle, Co Wicklow (20x33cm-8x13in) pencil W/C prov. 14-May-4 Christie's, London #61/R est:700-1000

NAIRN, James (20th C) New Zealander
£3636 $5709 €5309 Wellington harbour from above Sydney and Hill Street (26x44cm-10x17in) board. 27-Aug-3 Dunbar Sloane, Wellington #20/R est:6500-9500 (NZ.D 10000)

NAIRN, James (attrib) (20th C) New Zealander
Works on paper
£329 $588 €480 Haystacks (18x34cm-7x13in) W/C. 12-May-4 Dunbar Sloane, Wellington #380 (NZ.D 950)

NAIRN, James McLachlan (1859-1904) British
Works on paper
£451 $718 €658 Somes Island, Wellington Harbour (21x28cm-8x11in) s.i.d.1897 W/C. 1-May-3 Dunbar Sloane, Wellington #107 est:2000-3000 (NZ.D 1300)

NAISH, John George (1824-1905) British
Works on paper
£550 $990 €803 Evening red, near Lydford, Dartmoor (16x25cm-6x10in) W/C over pencil bodycol. 21-Jan-4 Sotheby's, Olympia #180/R

NAISH, William (c.1767-1800) British
Miniatures
£1600 $2944 €2336 Joseph Badeley, wearing brown coat (8cm-3in) gold frame. 24-Jun-4 Bonhams, New Bond Street #113/R est:1000-1500
£3000 $5100 €4380 Gentleman with brown coat and black collar (7cm-3in) gold frame oval. 18-Nov-3 Bonhams, New Bond Street #115/R est:1500-2500

NAIVEU, Matthys (attrib) (1647-1721) Dutch
£3800 $6460 €5548 Lady pouring wine at a casement (39x32cm-15x13in) canvas on panel. 31-Oct-3 Christie's, Kensington #67/R est:3000-5000

£6711 $12349 €10000 Young woman at window pouring wine into silver tazza (39x32cm-15x13in) canvas on panel. 24-Mar-4 Dorotheum, Vienna #113/R est:9000-12000

NAKAGAWA, Naoto (20th C) Japanese
£5278 $9500 €7706 Over the table (70x56cm-28x22in) i.d.1967-68 s.i.d.verso acrylic. 24-Apr-4 David Rago, Lambertville #280/R est:200-400
Works on paper
£1167 $2100 €1704 Inside of the case. Still life in progress (13x11cm-5x4in) one s.i.d.1967 graphite col pencil one s.i.d.1966 verso oil two. 24-Apr-4 David Rago, Lambertville #279/R est:200-400
£5556 $10000 €8112 Timepiece. Untitled (22x29cm-9x11in) one s.i.d.1970 graphite one s.d.1978 chl two. 24-Apr-4 David Rago, Lambertville #278/R est:300-600

NAKAMARRA, Angela Lee (c.1968-) Australian
Works on paper
£332 $621 €498 Katjamarra (61x90cm-24x35in) bears name.verso synthetic polymer paint canvas prov. 26-Jul-4 Sotheby's, Melbourne #446/R (A.D 850)

NAKAMARRA, Queenie McKenzie (c.1930-1998) Australian
Works on paper
£1020 $1825 €1489 Balankerr Country (60x43cm-24x17in) i. verso earth pigments Belgian linen prov. 25-May-4 Lawson Menzies, Sydney #1/R est:2500-4000 (A.D 2600)
£1804 $3229 €2634 Bow River Place (61x51cm-24x20in) natural earth pigments canvas exec 1995. 25-May-4 Lawson Menzies, Sydney #27/R est:5000-7000 (A.D 4600)
£2157 $3861 €3149 Dalwyn Country (51x61cm-20x24in) natural earth pigments canvas exec 1995. 25-May-4 Lawson Menzies, Sydney #26/R est:5000-7000 (A.D 5500)
£3137 $5616 €4580 Horso Creek Killing Place (76x102cm-30x40in) s. verso ocres canvas exec 1995. 25-May-4 Lawson Menzies, Sydney #156/R est:10000-12000 (A.D 8000)
£31373 $56157 €45805 Limestone Hills, Texas (180x121cm-71x48in) natural earth pigments linen exec 1994. 25-May-4 Lawson Menzies, Sydney #39/R est:60000-80000 (A.D 80000)

NAKAMURA, Kazuo (1926-2002) Canadian/Japanese
£2008 $3735 €2932 Solitude 2 (71x55cm-28x22in) s.d.1972 linen prov. 4-Mar-4 Heffel, Vancouver #29/R est:2000-3000 (C.D 5000)
£2222 $3844 €3244 Northern landscape treed hillside in snow (91x112cm-36x44in) s.d.1971 verso. 9-Dec-3 Maynards, Vancouver #256 est:2500-3000 (C.D 5000)
£2455 $4223 €3584 Solitude (67x72cm-26x28in) s. painted 1974. 2-Dec-3 Joyner Waddington, Toronto #72/R est:3000-5000 (C.D 5500)
£2642 $4730 €3857 Space time dimension (48x61cm-19x24in) s.d.1970 i.stretcher prov. 31-May-4 Sotheby's, Toronto #92/R est:5000-7000 (C.D 6500)
£3427 $6306 €5003 Abstract composition in blue (47x61cm-19x24in) s. board prov.exhib. 9-Jun-4 Walker's, Ottawa #166/R est:1500-2500 (C.D 8500)

NAKAMURA, Nakiko (20th C) Japanese?
£639 $1041 €920 Untitled (61x61cm-24x24in) s.i.d.2001 verso canvas on board prov.exhib. 23-Sep-3 De Veres Art Auctions, Dublin #227/R

NAKAMURA, Setsuya (1905-) Japanese
£1333 $2400 €1946 Family portrait (118x90cm-46x35in) s.d.1946. 24-Apr-4 Weschler, Washington #583/R est:3000-5000

NAKHALOV, Boris (1925-) Russian
£270 $491 €394 Still life with Russian dishes (79x58cm-31x23in) s. painted 1972. 20-Jun-4 Lots Road Auctions, London #371/R

NAKIAN, Reuben (1897-1986) American
Sculpture
£898 $1500 €1311 Untitled (28x28cm 11x11in) s. terracotta bronze glaze. 25-Oct-3 David Rago, Lambertville #679 est:600-900
£1081 $2000 €1578 Woodland nymph and goat (42x48cm-17x19in) s.d.78 num.2/7 brown pat bronze st.f.Renaisance Art. 12-Feb-4 Sotheby's, New York #158/R est:1500-2000
£1486 $2750 €2170 Nymph and Goat (46x36cm-18x14in) s.d.1978 num.6/7 brown pat bronze st.f.Renaissance Art. 12-Feb-4 Sotheby's, New York #159/R est:1500-2000
£2162 $4000 €3157 Leda and the Swan (23x25x21cm-9x10x8in) sig.d.1963 num.1/12 black brown pat bronze prov. 12-Feb-4 Sotheby's, New York #183/R est:1500-2000
Works on paper
£503 $900 €734 Nymphs and goats (56x28cm-22x11in) s. ink wash prov.lit. 16-May-4 Wright, Chicago #342/R
£543 $1000 €793 Duchess of Alba (38x41cm-15x16in) s. brush india ink. 10-Jun-4 Swann Galleries, New York #181/R

NAKKEN, Willem Carel (1835-1926) Dutch
£461 $834 €700 Portrait of a horse (22x29cm-9x11in) init. panel. 19-Apr-4 Glerum, Amsterdam #76/R
£590 $933 €850 Brown horse (21x27cm-8x11in) init. cardboard. 2-Sep-3 Christie's, Amsterdam #171/R
£1057 $1797 €1543 Apple seller (50x61cm-20x24in) s. 5-Nov-3 Dobiaschofsky, Bern #835/R est:4800 (S.FR 2400)
£1301 $2212 €1900 Farmer with horse and cart (22x32cm-9x13in) s. panel. 5-Nov-3 Vendue Huis, Gravenhage #239/R est:1000-1500
£1467 $2669 €2200 Head of a horse (25x20cm-10x8in) s.d.1866 panel. 1-Jul-4 Christie's, Amsterdam #583/R est:1500-2000
£3191 $5330 €4500 Persian horse with dogs and figure (28x37cm-11x15in) s.d.56 panel. 20-Oct-3 Glerum, Amsterdam #28/R est:4500-5500
£3401 $6190 €5000 Peasants in a sunlit farmyard (43x75cm-17x30in) s. 3-Feb-4 Christie's, Amsterdam #119/R est:4000-6000
£4333 $7887 €6500 Chat-botte met snip en snoek- Horse and dog in a stable (34x45cm-13x18in) s.d.1865 i.stretcher. 1-Jul-4 Christie's, Amsterdam #582/R est:2500-3500
£4762 $8667 €7000 At the end of the harvest day (22x40cm-9x16in) s.d.77. 3-Feb-4 Christie's, Amsterdam #116/R est:3000-5000
£7600 $13908 €11096 Harvest scene with peasants loading a haycart (33x53cm-13x21in) s.d.94. 7-Apr-4 Woolley & Wallis, Salisbury #263/R est:3000-5000
Works on paper
£279 $500 €407 Stable scene (56x74cm-22x29in) s. W/C board. 21-Mar-4 Jeffery Burchard, Florida #10/R
£300 $546 €450 Horse in the meadow (23x27cm-9x11in) s. W/C. 30-Jun-4 Vendue Huis, Gravenhage #23/R
£420 $769 €613 Returning from the hunt (29x41cm-11x16in) s. W/C. 28-Jan-4 Hampton & Littlewood, Exeter #383/R

NALBANDIAN, Dmitri A (1906-1993) Russian
£3128 $5600 €4567 Yerevan, Lenin Square (60x69cm-24x27in) canvas on cardboard painted 1972. 29-May-4 Shishkin Gallery, Moscow #39/R est:6000-8000
£3687 $6600 €5383 The herd (50x80cm-20x31in) painted 1975. 29-May-4 Shishkin Gallery, Moscow #38/R est:8000-10000
£4167 $7500 €6084 Mstersky Castle (52x73cm-20x29in) oil on plywood. 24-Apr-4 Shishkin Gallery, Moscow #39/R est:8000-9000
Works on paper
£815 $1500 €1190 Portrait of Stalin (30x23cm-12x9in) pencil painted 1949. 27-Mar-4 Shishkin Gallery, Moscow #52/R est:4000-5000

NALDINI, Giovan Battista (attrib) (1537-1591) Italian
£10563 $17007 €15000 Crucifixion of Jesus with Maddalena at the foot of the cross (41x29cm-16x11in) 8-May-3 Farsetti, Prato #398/R est:18000-22000
£26846 $49396 €40000 Madonna and Child with Saints (60x45cm-24x18in) board. 24-Mar-4 Finarte Semenzato, Rome #98/R est:14000

NALECZ, Halima (1917-) British
£450 $824 €657 Little bit of love (108x154cm-43x61in) 7-Apr-4 Dreweatt Neate, Newbury #116

NALIWAJKO, Jan (1938-) Lithuanian
£1147 $1904 €1675 Portrait (81x51cm-32x20in) painted 1964. 2-Oct-3 Agra, Warsaw #26/R est:500 (P.Z 7500)
Works on paper
£244 $449 €366 Composition (75x58cm-30x23in) s, collage mixed media. 14-Jun-4 Blomqvist, Lysaker #1278 (N.KR 3000)

NALL (20th C) ?
Works on paper
£14388 $23597 €20000 Blue iris (100x80cm-39x31in) mixed media. 6-Jun-3 Chochon-Barre & Allardi, Paris #79/R est:8000-9000
£19424 $31856 €27000 Security blanket (111x95cm-44x37in) mixed media. 6-Jun-3 Chochon-Barre & Allardi, Paris #80/R est:10000-12000

NALLARD, Louis (1918-) French
£272 $495 €400 Le guerite (40x45cm-16x18in) s. board painted 1999 prov. 3-Feb-4 Christie's, Amsterdam #638
£490 $832 €700 Le chemin de fer (90x100cm-35x39in) s. prov. 29-Nov-3 Neret-Minet, Paris #155/R
£1189 $2045 €1700 Composition (40x37cm-16x15in) s. board prov. 2-Dec-3 Sotheby's, Amsterdam #206/R est:1000-1500

NAM GREB (19/20th C) Austrian
Sculpture
£1800 $3222 €2628 Female Persian lion tamer (27x27cm-11x11in) s. pat enamel bronze onyx dish. 13-May-4 Christie's, Kensington #253/R est:2000-3000

NAM GREB (after) (19/20th C) Austrian
Sculpture
£4670 $8500 €7005 The love nest (33cm-13in) i. bronze st.f. Bergman prov. 16-Jun-4 Sotheby's, New York #278/R est:4000-6000

NAM KWAN (1911-1990) Korean
£2500 $4475 €3650 Untitled (47x19cm-19x7in) s.d.65 i.verso. 6-May-4 Sotheby's, London #96/R est:3000-4000
£2800 $5012 €4088 Le soleil mourant (59x42cm-23x17in) s.i.d.58. 6-May-4 Sotheby's, London #97/R est:3000-5000
£3000 $5370 €4380 Untitled (47x19cm-19x7in) s. i.verso. 6-May-4 Sotheby's, London #94/R est:3000-4000
£3400 $6086 €4964 Line formation (47x19cm-19x7in) s. i.d.64 verso. 6-May-4 Sotheby's, London #95/R est:3000-4000

NAM, Jacques (1881-1974) French
£8649 $16000 €12628 Untitled (70cm-28in) mono. coromandel technique lacquer wood panel. 9-Mar-4 Christie's, Rockefeller NY #395/R est:8000-10000
Sculpture
£2113 $3655 €3000 Trois lapins (16x31x18cm-6x12x7in) s.num.1/8 brown pat bronze exec.c.1920-1925 st.f.Landowski prov. 13-Dec-3 Martinot & Savignat, Pontoise #55/R est:3000-3500
Works on paper
£296 $512 €420 Deux lions (17x21cm-7x8in) s.i. gouache exec.c.1930 prov. 13-Dec-3 Martinot & Savignat, Pontoise #43/R
£387 $670 €550 Jaguar couche (16x31cm-6x12in) s. black crayon htd W/C exec.c.1929-1930 prov. 13-Dec-3 Martinot & Savignat, Pontoise #41/R
£423 $731 €600 Hibou sur une branche (45x33cm-18x13in) s. chl sanguine exec.c.1920-1930 prov. 13-Dec-3 Martinot & Savignat, Pontoise #36
£528 $914 €750 Singe et chat (33x46cm-13x18in) s. chl htd W/C. 13-Dec-3 Martinot & Savignat, Pontoise #37/R
£528 $914 €750 Panthere mouchetee (21x31cm-8x12in) s. ink W/C exec.c.1925/1930 prov. 13-Dec-3 Martinot & Savignat, Pontoise #39/R
£528 $914 €750 Tigre couche (13x18cm-5x7in) s. chl pen htd pencil exec.c.1915-1920 prov. 13-Dec-3 Martinot & Savignat, Pontoise #49

£634 $1096 €900 Panthere noire (47x68cm-19x27in) s. mixed media exec.c.1930 prov. 13-Dec-3 Martinot & Savignat, Pontoise #46/R

NAMATJIRA, Albert (1902-1959) Australian

£2041 $3755 €2980 Woomera. s. hand painted sold with a photo. 29-Mar-4 Goodman, Sydney #179/R est:5000-7000 (A.D 5000)
£2734 $5113 €4101 Untitled, ceremonial designs (15x45cm-6x18in) i. pokerwork mulga wood exec.c.1935 prov. 26-Jul-4 Sotheby's, Melbourne #134/R est:2000-4000 (A.D 7000)

Sculpture

£3659 $5780 €5306 Painted spearthrower (75cm-30in) s.i. hardwood W/C twine peg resin. 28-Jul-3 Sotheby's, Paddington #321/R est:4000-6000 (A.D 9000)

Works on paper

£2290 $4168 €3343 Landscape (22x34cm-9x13in) s. W/C. 16-Jun-4 Deutscher-Menzies, Melbourne #262/R est:10000-15000 (A.D 6000)
£2479 $4388 €3619 Central Australian landscape (19x35cm-7x14in) s. W/C. 3-May-4 Christie's, Melbourne #122/R est:8000-12000 (A.D 6000)
£3239 $5215 €4729 Inland landscape (27x38cm-11x15in) s. W/C prov. 25-Aug-3 Sotheby's, Paddington #218/R est:8000-12000 (A.D 8000)
£3512 $6498 €5128 MacDonnell Ranges (25x35cm-10x14in) s. W/C. 10-Mar-4 Deutscher-Menzies, Melbourne #284/R est:8000-12000 (A.D 8500)
£3906 $7305 €5859 Untitled, Central Australian landscape (12x64cm-5x25in) W/C Arrernte spear thrower hardwood spinifex resin sinew prov. 26-Jul-4 Sotheby's, Melbourne #132/R est:5000-7000 (A.D 10000)
£4043 $6872 €5903 Arrernte Aranda language group (25x36cm-10x14in) s. W/C prov. 26-Nov-3 Deutscher-Menzies, Melbourne #124/R est:7000-9000 (A.D 9500)
£4201 $6805 €6133 Landscape with Orange Hill (25x36cm-10x14in) s. W/C. 30-Jul-3 Goodman, Sydney #122/R est:9000-12000 (A.D 10250)
£4490 $8261 €6555 Glen Helen gorge (35x25cm-14x10in) s. s.i.verso W/C. 29-Mar-4 Goodman, Sydney #177/R est:10000-15000 (A.D 11000)
£4580 $8336 €6687 Ghost gum, Mt. Sonder area (25x37cm-10x15in) s. W/C prov. 16-Jun-4 Deutscher-Menzies, Melbourne #261/R est:12000-15000 (A.D 12000)
£4675 $8368 €6826 Majestic hills (23x34cm-9x13in) s. prov. 4-May-4 Sotheby's, Melbourne #173/R est:12000-14000 (A.D 11500)
£4688 $8766 €7032 Untitled, Central Australian landscape (25x36cm-10x14in) s. W/C prov. 26-Jul-4 Sotheby's, Melbourne #136/R est:8000-12000 (A.D 12000)
£4878 $8732 €7122 Palm Valley (25x37cm-10x15in) s. W/C exec c.1952 prov. 10-May-4 Joel, Victoria #362/R est:12000-16000 (A.D 12000)
£5085 $8644 €7424 Central Australian landscape (25x35cm-10x14in) s. W/C. 24-Nov-3 Sotheby's, Melbourne #203/R est:12000-15000 (A.D 12000)
£5957 $10128 €8697 Arrente Aranda language group (30x45cm-12x18in) s. W/C prov. 26-Nov-3 Deutscher-Menzies, Melbourne #123/R est:12000-15000 (A.D 14000)
£6144 $10445 €8970 Haast's Bluff (36x53cm-14x21in) s. W/C. 24-Nov-3 Sotheby's, Melbourne #248/R est:7000-10000 (A.D 14500)
£6250 $11688 €9375 Untitled, Central Australian landscape (26x35cm-10x14in) s. W/C exec.c.1955 prov. 26-Jul-4 Sotheby's, Melbourne #135/R est:10000-15000 (A.D 16000)
£6531 $12016 €9535 Chewings Ranges, Stanley Chasm (25x36cm-10x14in) s. s.i.verso W/C. 29-Mar-4 Goodman, Sydney #180/R est:17000-22000 (A.D 16000)
£6612 $11240 €9654 Morning, McDonald Ranges (25x35cm-10x14in) s. W/C prov. 29-Oct-3 Lawson Menzies, Sydney #88/R est:12000-15000 (A.D 16000)
£6641 $12418 €9962 Oonapoona, Honey Ant Place, Karanyi, Central Mount Wedge (24x35cm-9x14in) s. W/C. 20-Jul-4 Goodman, Sydney #107/R est:20000-25000 (A.D 17000)
£7025 $11942 €10257 Wall of the Hammersley Gorge (37x27cm-15x11in) s. W/C executed c.1939. 29-Oct-3 Lawson Menzies, Sydney #89/R est:12000-15000 (A.D 17000)
£7025 $12434 €10257 Ghost gum, Central Australia (35x25cm-14x10in) s. W/C prov. 3-May-4 Christie's, Melbourne #118/R est:8000-12000 (A.D 17000)
£7059 $12635 €10306 Macdonnell Ranges (27x38cm-11x15in) s.d.1940 W/C prov. 25-May-4 Lawson Menzies, Sydney #107/R est:10000-12000 (A.D 18000)
£7347 $13518 €10727 Mountain ranges (24x34cm-9x13in) s. W/C. 29-Mar-4 Goodman, Sydney #15/R est:18000-22000 (A.D 18000)
£7347 $13518 €10727 Landscape (25x35cm-10x14in) s. W/C. 29-Mar-4 Goodman, Sydney #178/R est:18000-22000 (A.D 18000)
£7813 $14609 €11720 Ghost gum (25x35cm-10x14in) s. W/C prov. 20-Jul-4 Goodman, Sydney #12/R est:12000-18000 (A.D 20000)
£9504 $16822 €13876 Central Australian landscape (25x35cm-10x14in) s. W/C exec.c.1946 prov. 3-May-4 Christie's, Melbourne #236/R est:8000-12000 (A.D 23000)
£10331 $19112 €15083 Central Australian landscape with ghost gum (25x36cm-10x14in) s. W/C. 10-Mar-4 Deutscher-Menzies, Melbourne #169/R est:15000-20000 (A.D 25000)
£11983 $22169 €17495 Glen Helen (35x53cm-14x21in) s. i.verso W/C prov. 10-Mar-4 Deutscher-Menzies, Melbourne #121/R est:25000-35000 (A.D 29000)
£12033 $20095 €18050 First Gorge Glen Helen (35x25cm-14x10in) s. W/C i.verso. 27-Oct-3 Goodman, Sydney #45/R est:14000-18000 (A.D 29000)
£12295 $19426 €17951 Ghost gums (38x37cm-15x15in) s. W/C prov.exhib. 2-Sep-3 Deutscher-Menzies, Melbourne #71/R est:18000-24000 (A.D 30000)
£12810 $21777 €18703 Alice Springs landscape (23x34cm-9x13in) s. W/C executed c.1955 prov. 29-Oct-3 Lawson Menzies, Sydney #18/R est:15000-20000 (A.D 31000)
£14228 $25467 €20773 Ghost gums in the Ranges (34x48cm-13x19in) s. bears i.verso W/C prov. 4-May-4 Sotheby's, Melbourne #53/R est:25000-30000 (A.D 35000)
£15102 $27788 €22049 White ghost gum landscape (26x36cm-10x14in) s. W/C prov. 29-Mar-4 Goodman, Sydney #150/R est:25000-30000 (A.D 37000)
£15574 $24607 €22738 Central Australian landscape with ghost gum (26x36cm-10x14in) s. W/C prov. 2-Sep-3 Deutscher-Menzies, Melbourne #72/R est:20000-30000 (A.D 38000)
£15702 $29050 €22925 Sweeping MacDonnell Ranges (35x52cm-14x20in) s. W/C executed c.1950-54 prov.exhib. 10-Mar-4 Deutscher-Menzies, Melbourne #21/R est:20000-30000 (A.D 38000)

NAMATJIRA, Enos (1920-1966) Australian

Works on paper

£303 $552 €442 Landscape (16x24cm-6x9in) W/C. 5-Feb-4 Joel, Victoria #23 (A.D 725)

NAMATJIRA, Ewald (1930-1984) Australian

Works on paper

£244 $383 €354 Untitled desert landscape with gum (35x49cm-14x19in) s. W/C. 26-Aug-3 Lawson Menzies, Sydney #113/R (A.D 600)
£285 $447 €413 Untitled - McDonnell Ranges (37x48cm-15x19in) s. W/C. 26-Aug-3 Lawson Menzies, Sydney #111 (A.D 700)
£292 $534 €438 Central Australia (35x52cm-14x20in) W/C. 3-Jun-4 Joel, Victoria #257 (A.D 750)
£350 $641 €525 Central Australia. W/C. 3-Jun-4 Joel, Victoria #361/R (A.D 900)
£386 $606 €560 Untitled - landscape (30x48cm-12x19in) s. i.verso W/C. 26-Aug-3 Lawson Menzies, Sydney #112 est:600-800 (A.D 950)
£392 $702 €572 Central Australian landscape (25x35cm-10x14in) s. W/C. 25-May-4 Lawson Menzies, Sydney #115/R (A.D 1000)
£496 $917 €724 Central Australian landscape (30x51cm-12x20in) s. W/C. 10-Mar-4 Deutscher-Menzies, Melbourne #572/R est:400-800 (A.D 1200)
£826 $1405 €1239 Australian landscape (26x36cm-10x14in) s. W/C. 28-Oct-3 Goodman, Sydney #272/R (A.D 2000)

NAMATJIRA, Gabriel (1941-1969) Australian

Works on paper

£286 $517 €418 Central Australian landscape (24x33cm-9x13in) s. mixed media. 4-Apr-4 International Art Centre, Auckland #323/R (NZ.D 800)

NAMATJIRA, Keith (1938-1977) Australian

Works on paper

£335 $609 €489 Central Australia (24x35cm-9x14in) s. 5-Feb-4 Joel, Victoria #7 (A.D 800)

NAMCHEONG (19th C) Chinese

£1000 $1700 €1460 Nine stag pagoda at Whampoa Anchorage, Pearl River (51x37cm-20x15in) 4-Nov-3 Bonhams, New Bond Street #28/R est:1000-1500

NAMINGHA, Dan (1950-) American

£1765 $3000 €2577 Night formation (71x53cm-28x21in) s.d.1984 acrylic collage prov. 1-Nov-3 Santa Fe Art, Santa Fe #67/R est:2000-4000
£2794 $4750 €4079 Spirit gathering (102x132cm-40x52in) s.d.1983 i.verso acrylic prov. 1-Nov-3 Santa Fe Art, Santa Fe #66/R est:2000-4000
£3533 $6500 €5158 Abstraction of a Mesa at sunset (150x175cm-59x69in) acrylic. 24-Jun-4 Sotheby's, New York #202/R est:8000-12000

NAMOK, Rosella (1979-) Australian

Works on paper

£1406 $2630 €2109 Stinging rain, Old Site (130x90cm-51x35in) i.verso synthetic polymer canvas exec. 2002 prov. 21-Jul-4 Shapiro, Sydney #120/R est:4500-6000 (A.D 3600)
£1484 $2776 €2226 Camping at Old Site (122x85cm-48x33in) i.verso synthetic polymer canvas exec. 2002 prov. 21-Jul-4 Shapiro, Sydney #123/R est:4000-6000 (A.D 3800)
£4688 $8766 €7032 Para Street, Para Way (125x92cm-49x36in) s.i.d.2001 synthetic polymer paint canvas prov. 26-Jul-4 Sotheby's, Melbourne #114/R est:12000-18000 (A.D 12000)

NAMPAJINPA, Jean (1956-) Australian

£688 $1170 €1004 Fire dreaming (120x120cm-47x47in) s.i.verso acrylic. 4-Nov-3 Peter Webb, Auckland #79/R est:1000-2000 (NZ.D 1900)

NAMPIJINPA, Alice (1925-) Australian

Works on paper

£671 $1060 €980 Untitled (135x81cm-53x32in) i.verso synthetic polymer paint linen prov. 28-Jul-3 Sotheby's, Paddington #380 est:1500-2500 (A.D 1650)

NAMPIJINPA, Maureen Turner (1952-) Australian

£335 $609 €489 Fire dreaming. acrylic. 5-Feb-4 Joel, Victoria #207 (A.D 800)

NAMPITJIMPA, Colleen (c.1953-) Australian

Works on paper

£863 $1544 €1260 Sandhills West to Kintore (90x60cm-35x24in) synthetic polymer paint linen exec 2000. 25-May-4 Lawson Menzies, Sydney #97/R (A.D 2200)

NAMPITJIN, Eubena (c.1930-) Australian

Works on paper

£2033 $3211 €2948 Maniboro (91x61cm-36x24in) i.verso synthetic polymer paint linen prov. 28-Jul-3 Sotheby's, Paddington #404/R est:5000-8000 (A.D 5000)
£2134 $3372 €3094 Untitled (92x61cm-36x24in) i.verso synthetic polymer paint linen prov. 28-Jul-3 Sotheby's, Paddington #216/R est:5000-7000 (A.D 5250)
£2344 $4383 €3516 Wiritji kinu rockhole (75x50cm-30x20in) synthetic polymer paint linen prov. 26-Jul-4 Sotheby's, Melbourne #447/R est:5000-7000 (A.D 6000)
£2846 $4496 €4127 Taritjirri rockhole (100x50cm-39x20in) i.verso synthetic polymer paint canvas prov. 28-Jul-3 Sotheby's, Paddington #215/R est:7000-10000 (A.D 7000)
£6198 $11467 €9049 Wilba (150x75cm-59x30in) synthetic polymer executed 1999 prov. 15-Mar-4 Sotheby's, Melbourne #3/R est:8000-12000 (A.D 15000)
£8594 $16070 €12891 Kinyu (180x120cm-71x47in) i.verso synthetic polymer linen exec. 2002 prov. 21-Jul-4 Shapiro, Sydney #42/R est:20000-30000 (A.D 22000)
£9756 $15415 €14146 Tjilla (180x120cm-71x47in) i.verso synthetic polymer paint linen prov.exhib. 28-Jul-3 Sotheby's, Paddington #217/R est:12000-18000 (A.D 24000)
£17188 $32141 €25782 Wantaru/yintarnyu (100x75cm-39x30in) bears name.verso synthetic polymer paint canvas prov.exhib.lit. 26-Jul-4 Sotheby's, Melbourne #63/R est:15000-20000 (A.D 44000)
£27344 $51133 €41016 Ikara (180x120cm-71x47in) bears name.verso synthetic polymer paint canvas prov.exhib.lit. 26-Jul-4 Sotheby's, Melbourne #75/R est:40000-60000 (A.D 70000)

NAMPITJIN, Millie Skeen (1932-) Australian

Works on paper

£1563 $2922 €2345 Lightning at Kameradda (90x60cm-35x24in) synthetic polymer paint linen prov. 26-Jul-4 Sotheby's, Melbourne #474 est:4000-6000 (A.D 4000)
£2734 $5113 €4101 Lirwaddi (100x76cm-39x30in) bears name.verso synthetic polymer paint canvas prov.exhib. 26-Jul-4 Sotheby's, Melbourne #83/R est:7000-10000 (A.D 7000)
£2734 $5113 €4101 Narajilpiro (100x50cm-39x20in) bears name.verso synthetic polymer paint canvas prov.exhib.lit. 26-Jul-4 Sotheby's, Melbourne #84/R est:7000-10000 (A.D 7000)

NAMPITJINPA, Inyuwa (c.1922-1999) Australian
Works on paper
£1057 $1670 €1533 Pukunya (105x27cm-41x11in) i.verso synthetic polymer paint linen prov. 28-Jul-3 Sotheby's, Paddington #390/R est:2500-3500 (A.D 2600)
£4472 $7065 €6529 Pukanya (91x91cm-36x36in) i.verso synthetic polymer paint linen prov. 28-Jul-3 Sotheby's, Paddington #277/R est:10000-15000 (A.D 11000)

NAMPITJINPA, Kayi Kayi (c.1946-) Australian
Works on paper
£661 $1223 €965 Wirrulnga waterhole site (91x46cm-36x18in) synthetic polymer prov. 15-Mar-4 Sotheby's, Melbourne #33 est:2000-4000 (A.D 1600)
£1484 $2776 €2226 Untitled (122x122cm-48x48in) bears name.verso synthetic polymer paint linen prov. 26-Jul-4 Sotheby's, Melbourne #502/R est:3000-5000 (A.D 3800)

NAMPITJINPA, Nyurapayai (20th C) Australian
Works on paper
£1057 $1670 €1533 Untitled (91x91cm-36x36in) i.verso synthetic polymer paint linen prov. 28-Jul-3 Sotheby's, Paddington #400/R est:2000-4000 (A.D 2600)
£1563 $2922 €2345 Yumarra (137x122cm-54x48in) bears name.verso synthetic polymer paint linen prov. 26-Jul-4 Sotheby's, Melbourne #504/R est:5000-8000 (A.D 4000)

NAMUR, Émile (1852-1908) Belgian
Sculpture
£14500 $26100 €21170 La cigale (93cm-37in) s.i. white marble lit. 21-Apr-4 Sotheby's, London #142/R est:12000-18000

NANALA, Winnefred (1964-) Australian
Works on paper
£392 $702 €572 Kunakulu (120x80cm-47x31in) synthetic polymer paint canvas exec 2002. 25-May-4 Lawson Menzies, Sydney #131/R est:1500-2000 (A.D 1000)

NANGALA, Ningie (1934-) Australian
Works on paper
£469 $877 €704 Untitled (89x60cm-35x24in) i.verso synthetic polymer canvas exec. 1994 prov. 21-Jul-4 Shapiro, Sydney #105/R (A.D 1200)
£813 $1285 €1179 Marlu, kangaroo dreaming (120x81cm-47x32in) i.verso synthetic polymer paint linen prov. 28-Jul-3 Sotheby's, Paddington #407 est:2000-4000 (A.D 2000)
£1094 $2045 €1641 Bush potato (100x73cm-39x29in) bears name.verso synthetic polymer paint canvas prov.exhib. 26-Jul-4 Sotheby's, Melbourne #443/R (A.D 2800)
£2745 $4914 €4008 Kurppi (91x61cm-36x24in) synthetic polymer paint canvas exec 1989 prov. 25-May-4 Lawson Menzies, Sydney #140/R est:5000-7000 (A.D 7000)

NANGERONI, Carlo (1922-) American
£1197 $2095 €1700 Mutation (100x100cm-39x39in) s.i.d.1971 acrylic. 16-Dec-3 Finarte Semenzato, Milan #18 est:500-600
£1888 $3210 €2700 Diffusion (111x111cm-44x44in) s.d.93 verso acrylic exhib.lit. 28-Nov-3 Farsetti, Prato #139/R est:2700-3200

NANI, Giacomo (1701-1770) Italian
£10067 $18725 €15000 Still lives of fruit (17x24cm-7x9in) set of 8. 2-Mar-4 Ansorena, Madrid #282/R est:20000

NANKIVELL, Frank Arthur (1869-1959) American
£838 $1500 €1223 Clam diggers (23x25cm-9x10in) prov. 26-May-4 Doyle, New York #59/R est:1000-1500

NANNINGA, Jaap (1904-1962) Dutch
£820 $1500 €1230 Portrait of a clown (58x41cm-23x16in) s.d.1947. 9-Jul-4 Du Mouchelle, Detroit #2091/R est:2000-2500
£1084 $1810 €1550 Ardennes (40x49cm-16x19in) s.i.d.59 paper prov. 30-Jun-3 Sotheby's, Amsterdam #491/R
£10667 $19627 €16000 Untitled (50x70cm-20x28in) s.d.61 prov.exhib. 8-Jun-4 Sotheby's, Amsterdam #77/R est:12000-15000
Works on paper
£1678 $2853 €2400 Abstract Composition (50x64cm-20x25in) chl gouache. 25-Nov-3 Christie's, Amsterdam #66/R est:3000-5000
£1739 $2852 €2400 Still life with lemons (36x45cm-14x18in) s.d.53 gouache prov.lit. 27-May-3 Sotheby's, Amsterdam #531/R est:2000-2500
£2800 $5152 €4200 King on a white horse (40x29cm-16x11in) s.d.47 gouache pastel. 9-Jun-4 Christie's, Amsterdam #124/R est:5000-7000
£3467 $6379 €5200 Sombre (323x37cm-127x15in) s.d.61 gouache prov.exhib.lit. 8-Jun-4 Sotheby's, Amsterdam #258/R est:4000-6000
£6000 $11040 €9000 Untitled (42x56cm-17x22in) s. gouache wax crayon exec. c.1959-1961 prov. 9-Jun-4 Christie's, Amsterdam #150/R est:3500-4500

NANNINI, Raphael (fl.1870-1895) Italian
Sculpture
£3000 $5370 €4380 Cossack on horseback (53x56cm-21x22in) s. ivory bronze marble base. 17-Mar-4 John Nicholson, Haslemere #238/R est:3000-4000

NANREFF, Claude (1908-) Dutch?
Works on paper
£2657 $4571 €3800 Procession (37x40cm-15x16in) s.i. W/C. 2-Dec-3 Sotheby's, Amsterdam #207/R est:500-700

NANSEN, Fridtjof (1861-1930) Norwegian
Works on paper
£490 $832 €700 Figure before Northern Lights (30x42cm-12x17in) s. gouache W/C board. 21-Nov-3 Reiss & Sohn, Konigstein #490/R

NANTENBO, Nakahara (1839-1925) Japanese
Works on paper
£455 $782 €650 Horse (128x33cm-50x13in) s.i. ink hanging scroll. 5-Dec-3 Lempertz, Koln #781/R

NANTES, Hugo (?) South American
£240 $400 €350 Coastal scene (98x79cm-39x31in) s. 7-Oct-3 Galeria y Remates, Montevideo #96
£324 $550 €473 Church (141x91cm-56x36in) s. 25-Nov-3 Galeria y Remates, Montevideo #102/R
£353 $650 €515 Trains (100x80cm-39x31in) s. acrylic. 22-Jun-4 Galeria y Remates, Montevideo #168/R

NANTEUIL, Robert (1623-1678) French
Prints
£2133 $3840 €3200 Louis XIV (68x59cm-27x23in) engraving. 22-Apr-4 Christie's, Paris #515/R est:800-1200

NAPALJARRI, Biddy Rockman (20th C) Australian
Works on paper
£703 $1195 €1026 Munekiyi - sugarbag, wild honey (120x172cm-47x68in) synthetic polymer paint on canvas. 29-Oct-3 Lawson Menzies, Sydney #80/R est:2000-2500 (A.D 1700)

NAPALTJARRI, Linda Syddick (1941-) Australian
Works on paper
£553 $957 €807 Ascension (120x120cm-47x47in) i.verso synthetic polymer paint linen prov. 10-Dec-3 Shapiro, Sydney #204 (A.D 1300)

NAPALTJARRI, Mary Markati (c.1926-) Australian
Works on paper
£2148 $4018 €3222 Mangkai (100x74cm-39x29in) bears name.verso synthetic polymer paint canvas prov. 26-Jul-4 Sotheby's, Melbourne #82/R est:5000-7000 (A.D 5500)
£4297 $8035 €6446 Yuparilpa (120x60cm-47x24in) bears name.verso synthetic polymer paint canvas prov. 26-Jul-4 Sotheby's, Melbourne #81/R est:7000-10000 (A.D 11000)

NAPALTJARRI, Milliga (c.1920-1993) Australian
Works on paper
£8594 $16070 €12891 Pururrungu (91x61cm-36x24in) bears name.verso synthetic polymer paint canvas prov.exhib. 26-Jul-4 Sotheby's, Melbourne #66/R est:12000-18000 (A.D 22000)
£11719 $21914 €17579 Kulkarta (91x61cm-36x24in) bears name.verso synthetic polymer paint canvas prov.exhib. 26-Jul-4 Sotheby's, Melbourne #67/R est:12000-18000 (A.D 30000)

NAPALTJARRI, Tjunkiya (20th C) Australian
Works on paper
£549 $983 €802 Women's Ceremony at Umari (91x46cm-36x18in) synthetic polymer paint canvas exec 1998 prov. 25-May-4 Lawson Menzies, Sydney #95/R (A.D 1400)
£627 $1123 €915 Women's Dreaming at Umari (91x91cm-36x36in) synthetic polymer paint canvas exec 2001. 25-May-4 Lawson Menzies, Sydney #77/R (A.D 1600)
£671 $1060 €973 Untitled (107x28cm-42x11in) i.verso synthetic polymer paint linen prov. 28-Jul-3 Sotheby's, Paddington #389/R est:1500-2500 (A.D 1650)

NAPALTJARRI, Wintjiya (20th C) Australian
Works on paper
£471 $842 €688 Women's dreaming at Watanuma (91x61cm-36x24in) synthetic polymer paint canvas exec 1998. 25-May-4 Lawson Menzies, Sydney #76/R (A.D 1200)
£508 $950 €762 Women at Watanuma (107x28cm-42x11in) bears name.verso synthetic polymer paint canvas prov. 26-Jul-4 Sotheby's, Melbourne #486/R (A.D 1300)
£625 $1169 €938 Claypan site of Watanuma (107x28cm-42x11in) bears name.verso synthetic polymer paint canvas. 26-Jul-4 Sotheby's, Melbourne #487/R (A.D 1600)

NAPANANGKA, Freda (c.1935-) Australian
Works on paper
£938 $1753 €1407 Yukupalli (90x60cm-35x24in) bears name.verso synthetic polymer paint canvas prov.exhib.lit. 26-Jul-4 Sotheby's, Melbourne #433/R (A.D 2400)

NAPANANGKA, Lucy Yukenbarri (1932-2003) Australian
Works on paper
£392 $702 €572 Winpupula Rockhole (75x50cm-30x20in) synthetic polymer paint canvas exec 1999 prov. 25-May-4 Lawson Menzies, Sydney #128/R (A.D 1000)
£935 $1477 €1356 Nanangka (89x60cm-35x24in) i.verso synthetic polymer paint canvas prov. 28-Jul-3 Sotheby's, Paddington #493 est:2000-3000 (A.D 2300)
£1569 $2808 €2291 Marpu Rock Hole (120x80cm-47x31in) synthetic polymer paint canvas exec 1995 prov. 25-May-4 Lawson Menzies, Sydney #123/R est:4500-5500 (A.D 4000)
£1953 $3652 €2930 Tjalinya (90x61cm-35x24in) bears name.verso synthetic polymer paint canvas prov.exhib. 26-Jul-4 Sotheby's, Melbourne #427/R est:5000-8000 (A.D 5000)

NAPANANGKA, Makinti (c.1930-) Australian
Works on paper
£527 $986 €791 Untitled (87x28cm-34x11in) i.verso synthetic polymer linen exec. 2001 prov.exhib. 21-Jul-4 Shapiro, Sydney #79/R (A.D 1350)
£627 $1123 €915 Kungka Kutjarr - Two women (61x55cm-24x22in) synthetic polymer paint canvas. 25-May-4 Lawson Menzies, Sydney #75/R est:1200-1500 (A.D 1600)

£703 $1315 €1055 Untitled (61x30cm-24x12in) i.verso synthetic polymer linen exec. 1996 prov. 21-Jul-4 Shapiro, Sydney #92/R (A.D 1800)
£1020 $1825 €1489 Kungka Jutjarra - Two women - Hair string (91x91cm-36x36in) synthetic polymer paint Belgian linen exec 2002. 25-May-4 Lawson Menzies, Sydney #16/R est:3500-4500 (A.D 2600)
£1064 $1841 €1553 Untitled, designs associated with the rockhole site of Lupulnga (91x61cm-36x24in) i.verso synthetic polymer paint linen prov. 10-Dec-3 Shapiro, Sydney #173/R est:3000-5000 (A.D 2500)
£1445 $2703 €2168 Untitled (122x61cm-48x24in) i.verso synthetic polymer linen exec. 2000 prov.exhib. 21-Jul-4 Shapiro, Sydney #77/R est:3500-5000 (A.D 3700)
£1961 $3510 €2863 Women's Hair String Ceremony (153x93cm-60x37in) synthetic polymer paint linen prov. 25-May-4 Lawson Menzies, Sydney #73/R est:6000-8000 (A.D 5000)

NAPANANGKA, Mati Bridget Mudjidell (c.1935-) Australian
Works on paper
£938 $1753 €1407 Kuna kula soak water (73x50cm-29x20in) i.verso synthetic polymer canvas exec. 2000 prov. 21-Jul-4 Shapiro, Sydney #102/R (A.D 2400)
£1953 $3652 €2930 Talapunta (100x50cm-39x20in) bears name.verso synthetic polymer paint canvas prov. 26-Jul-4 Sotheby's, Melbourne #437/R est:2000-3000 (A.D 5000)

NAPANANGKA, Minnie (c.1934-) Australian
Works on paper
£664 $1242 €996 Tjangirikakurlangu (100x76cm-39x30in) bears name.verso synthetic polymer paint canvas prov. 26-Jul-4 Sotheby's, Melbourne #440/R (A.D 1700)

NAPANANGKA, Nancy Naninurra (1936-) Australian
Works on paper
£510 $913 €745 Mina Mina (60x45cm-24x18in) synthetic polymer paint canvas exec 2001 prov. 25-May-4 Lawson Menzies, Sydney #119/R (A.D 1300)
£742 $1388 €1113 Tjalkirri (100x50cm-39x20in) bears name.verso synthetic polymer paint canvas prov. 26-Jul-4 Sotheby's, Melbourne #430/R (A.D 1900)

NAPANANGKA, Ningura (c.1938-) Australian
Works on paper
£1098 $1734 €1603 Untitled, wirrulnga (122x91cm-48x36in) i.verso synthetic polymer paint linen prov. 28-Jul-3 Sotheby's, Paddington #402/R est:3000-5000 (A.D 2700)

NAPANANGKA, Pirrmangka (1945-2001) Australian
Works on paper
£1220 $1927 €1769 Untitled (61x55cm-24x22in) i.verso synthetic polymer paint linen prov. 28-Jul-3 Sotheby's, Paddington #403/R est:2000-3000 (A.D 3000)
£1563 $2922 €2345 Untitled (91x46cm-36x18in) bears name.verso synthetic polymer paint linen prov. 26-Jul-4 Sotheby's, Melbourne #490/R est:4000-6000 (A.D 4000)
£1619 $2607 €2364 Travel design (91x91cm-36x36in) synthetic polymer on linen. 13-Oct-3 Joel, Victoria #418/R est:4000-6000 (A.D 4000)
£2266 $4237 €3399 Untitled (168x46cm-66x18in) bears name.verso synthetic polymer paint linen prov. 26-Jul-4 Sotheby's, Melbourne #489/R est:6000-8000 (A.D 5800)

NAPANANGKA, Warlangkara (c.1946-) Australian
Works on paper
£813 $1285 €1179 Untitled (91x61cm-36x24in) i.verso synthetic polymer paint linen. 28-Jul-3 Sotheby's, Paddington #401/R est:2000-3000 (A.D 2000)
£3922 $7020 €5726 Old Woman Dreaming (153x122cm-60x48in) synthetic polymer paint canvas exec 2002. 25-May-4 Lawson Menzies, Sydney #74a/R est:10000-12000 (A.D 10000)
£5273 $9861 €7910 Untitled (183x122cm-72x48in) i.verso synthetic polymer linen exec. 2003 prov. 21-Jul-4 Shapiro, Sydney #76/R est:10000-15000 (A.D 13500)
£6641 $12418 €9962 Travels of Kutungka Napanangka (137x122cm-54x48in) bears name.verso synthetic polymer paint linen prov. 26-Jul-4 Sotheby's, Melbourne #190/R est:15000-20000 (A.D 17000)

NAPANGARDI, Dorothy (c.1956-) Australian
Works on paper
£10938 $20453 €16407 Karntakurlangu Jukurrpa, salt on Mina Mina (122x122cm-48x48in) s.verso synthetic polymer paint linen two panesl prov.exhib. 26-Jul-4 Sotheby's, Melbourne #240/R est:30000-40000 (A.D 28000)
£14118 $25271 €20612 Karntakurlangu Tjukurpa - Women's Dreaming (121x173cm-48x68in) synthetic polymer paint linen exec 2000 prov. 25-May-4 Lawson Menzies, Sydney #198/R est:30000-40000 (A.D 36000)
£18750 $35063 €28125 Karntakurlangu jukurrpa (122x198cm-48x78in) s. synthetic polymer paint linen prov.exhib.lit. 26-Jul-4 Sotheby's, Melbourne #185/R est:50000-70000 (A.D 48000)
£42969 $80352 €64454 Karntakurlangu (122x152cm-48x60in) synthetic polymer paint prov.exhib.lit. 26-Jul-4 Sotheby's, Melbourne #113/R est:40000-60000 (A.D 110000)

NAPANGARDI, Maggie Watson (c.1925-) Australian
Works on paper
£2734 $5113 €4101 Yarla manu wanakiji jukurrpa, bush potato and bush tomato dreaming (91x91cm-36x36in) bears name.verso synthetic polymer paint linen prov. 26-Jul-4 Sotheby's, Melbourne #469/R est:8000-12000 (A.D 7000)
£4492 $8400 €6738 Ngalyipi, snake vine, Jukurrpa (122x76cm-48x30in) i.verso synthetic polymer linen exec. 1999 prov. 21-Jul-4 Shapiro, Sydney #91/R est:12000-18000 (A.D 11500)

NAPANGARDI, Polly Watson (c.1930-) Australian
Works on paper
£1176 $2106 €1717 Mala Jukurrpa (103x105cm-41x41in) synthetic polymer paint linen exec 1989 prov. 25-May-4 Lawson Menzies, Sydney #209/R est:3000-5000 (A.D 3000)

NAPANGARTI, Balba (c.1926-) Australian
Works on paper
£391 $730 €587 Tarfil (99x49cm-39x19in) bears name.verso synthetic polymer paint canvas prov.exhib. 26-Jul-4 Sotheby's, Melbourne #442/R (A.D 1000)

NAPANGARTI, Nita Kuniyangka (c.1930-) Australian
£1707 $2680 €2475 Warlupararra, artist's country (100x75cm-39x30in) i.verso synthetic polymer paint canvas prov. 26-Aug-3 Christie's, Sydney #243 est:2000-3000 (A.D 4200)

NAPANGATI, Bye Bye (c.1935-) Australian
Works on paper
£586 $1096 €879 Untitled (90x60cm-35x24in) i.verso synthetic polymer canvas exec.1995 prov. 21-Jul-4 Shapiro, Sydney #107/R est:1500-2500 (A.D 1500)
£1020 $1825 €1489 Yunpa (120x80cm-47x31in) synthetic polymer paint canvas exec 2003 prov. 25-May-4 Lawson Menzies, Sydney #125/R est:3000-5000 (A.D 2600)
£1176 $2106 €1717 Pulkabardu (120x80cm-47x31in) synthetic polymer paint canvas exec 1999 prov. 25-May-4 Lawson Menzies, Sydney #118/R est:3500-4500 (A.D 3000)
£1797 $3360 €2696 Marnawee (120x80cm-47x31in) i.verso synthetic polymer linen exec. 2003 prov. 21-Jul-4 Shapiro, Sydney #104/R est:4000-6000 (A.D 4600)
£3711 $6939 €5567 Warnpuparta (100x76cm-39x30in) bears name.verso synthetic polymer paint canvas prov.lit. 26-Jul-4 Sotheby's, Melbourne #73/R est:10000-15000 (A.D 9500)
£7031 $13148 €10547 Tjurnpul (100x75cm-39x30in) bears name.verso synthetic polymer paint canvas prov.exhib.lit. 26-Jul-4 Sotheby's, Melbourne #72/R est:10000-15000 (A.D 18000)

NAPANGATI, Nanyuma (20th C) Australian
£648 $1043 €946 Marraprinti rockhole, 2000 (137x122cm-54x48in) acrylic. 13-Oct-3 Joel, Victoria #436 est:1500-2000 (A.D 1600)

NAPANGATI, Pansy (c.1948-) Australian
£588 $1053 €858 Two women dreaming (76x120cm-30x47in) painted 1990 prov. 25-May-4 Lawson Menzies, Sydney #89/R est:2500-3500 (A.D 1500)
Works on paper
£784 $1404 €1145 Water Dreaming Luritja - Walpiri (182x60cm-72x24in) s. verso synthetic polymer paint linen exec 1996 prov. 25-May-4 Lawson Menzies, Sydney #90/R est:2500-3500 (A.D 2000)
£1745 $3019 €2548 Untitled, hailstone dreaming at the site of Ilpilli (122x122cm-48x48in) i.verso synthetic polymer paint linen prov. 10-Dec-3 Shapiro, Sydney #212/R est:4000-6000 (A.D 4100)

NAPANGATI, Susie Bootja Bootja (c.1932-2003) Australian
£2353 $4212 €3435 Kaningarra near the Canning Stock Route (120x90cm-47x35in) painted 1998 prov. 25-May-4 Lawson Menzies, Sydney #120/R est:5000-7000 (A.D 6000)
Works on paper
£1172 $2191 €1758 Kaningarra (90x120cm-35x47in) bears name.verso synthetic polymer paint canvas prov.exhib. 26-Jul-4 Sotheby's, Melbourne #445/R est:3000-4000 (A.D 3000)
£1172 $2191 €1758 Wirrinpar near the Canning Stock Route (90x60cm-35x24in) synthetic polymer paint linen prov. 26-Jul-4 Sotheby's, Melbourne #475 est:3000-4000 (A.D 3000)
£1797 $3360 €2696 Kaningala, in the great sandy desert (91x61cm-36x24in) i.verso synthetic polymer linen exec. 1996 prov.exhib. 21-Jul-4 Shapiro, Sydney #101/R est:5000-7000 (A.D 4600)
£14118 $25271 €20612 Waterhole, Jurtal Country (120x80cm-47x31in) synthetic polymer paint canvas exec 2000 prov.exhib. 25-May-4 Lawson Menzies, Sydney #9/R est:8000-10000 (A.D 36000)

NAPARRULA, Lorna (20th C) Australian
£700 $1204 €1022 Possum dreaming (51x61cm-20x24in) i. acrylic canvas on board pair. 2-Dec-3 Sotheby's, Olympia #369/R

NAPOLI, Giuseppe (20th C) Italian
£514 $950 €750 Ritratto de Bernald (38x28cm-15x11in) s.d.1956 s.i.d.verso panel on board prov. 10-Mar-4 Doyle, New York #63/R

NAPPER, John (1916-) British
£1500 $2385 €2190 Intruder (34x59cm-13x23in) s.i. 10-Sep-3 Sotheby's, Olympia #219/R est:1500-2000
Works on paper
£550 $968 €803 Fast food (35x27cm-14x11in) mono.d.1989 W/C. 19-May-4 Sotheby's, Olympia #276/R
£1200 $2160 €1752 Still life no.2 (29x43cm-11x17in) s.d.1986 W/C. 20-Jan-4 Bonhams, Knightsbridge #17/R est:300-500

NAPPI, Rudy (20th C) American
£1074 $1922 €1600 Pin-up (42x30cm-17x12in) s. 27-May-4 Sotheby's, Paris #146/R est:1500-2000

NAPS, Jevgeni (19th C) Russian
Sculpture
£1818 $3091 €2600 Hunter with his hawk on horseback (31cm-12in) s. bronze. 29-Nov-3 Bukowskis, Helsinki #427/R est:1200-1500

NAPURRULA, Marlee (c.1930-) Australian

Works on paper			
£325	$514	€471	Kungkayunti (72x104cm-28x41in) synthetic polymer paint prov.exhib.lit. 28-Jul-3 Sotheby's, Paddington #391 (A.D 800)
£392	$702	€572	Flowers at Awalki (76x56cm-30x22in) synthetic polymer paint exec 2001 prov. 25-May-4 Lawson Menzies, Sydney #103/R (A.D 1000)
£1255	$2246	€1832	Flowers at Awalka (71x76cm-28x30in) synthetic polymer paint canvas exec 2000 prov. 25-May-4 Lawson Menzies, Sydney #100/R est:4000-5000 (A.D 3200)

NAPURRULA, Mitjili (c.1930-) Australian

Works on paper			
£1176	$2106	€1717	Wadyia Trees (67x122cm-26x48in) synthetic polymer paint linen exec 2002. 25-May-4 Lawson Menzies, Sydney #105/R est:2000-3000 (A.D 3000)

NAPURRULA, Narpula Scobie (c.1958-) Australian

Works on paper			
£1545	$2425	€2256	Dreamtime string weaving (183x121cm-72x48in) synthetic polymer paint canvas prov. 26-Aug-3 Christie's, Sydney #254/R est:3000-5000 (A.D 3800)

NAPURRULA, Ningara (c.1938-) Australian

Works on paper			
£1961	$3510	€2863	Women's Ceremonial Site (164x121cm-65x48in) synthetic polymer paint linen exec 2002 prov. 25-May-4 Lawson Menzies, Sydney #82/R est:4000-6000 (A.D 5000)
£2969	$5552	€4454	Untitled (122x152cm-48x60in) bears name.verso synthetic polymer paint canvas prov. 26-Jul-4 Sotheby's, Melbourne #266/R est:8000-12000 (A.D 7600)

NAPURRULA, Rosie Nanyuma (c.1940-) Australian

Works on paper			
£1875	$3506	€2813	Yunpa (50x101cm-20x40in) bears name.verso synthetic polymer paint canvas prov.lit. 26-Jul-4 Sotheby's, Melbourne #439/R est:3000-5000 (A.D 4800)
£2734	$5113	€4101	Larkar (91x61cm-36x24in) bears name.verso synthetic polymer paint canvas prov.lit. 26-Jul-4 Sotheby's, Melbourne #425/R est:4000-6000 (A.D 7000)

NAPURRULA, Tjarmia Samuels (c.1941-) Australian

Works on paper			
£313	$584	€468	Tjarma Plain (90x60cm-35x24in) i.verso synthetic polymer canvas exec. 1999 prov. 21-Jul-4 Shapiro, Sydney #112/R (A.D 800)

NAPURULLA, Peggy (1935-) Australian

Works on paper			
£784	$1404	€1145	Possum dreaming (76x122cm-30x48in) synthetic polymer paint linen. 25-May-4 Lawson Menzies, Sydney #11/R (A.D 2000)

NAQASH, Ali (19th C) Persian

£1678	$2803	€2400	Tribal wedding ceremony (28x34cm-11x13in) s.i. 30-Jun-3 Ansorena, Madrid #209/R est:2400

NARA, Yoshimoto (1959-) American

£6486	$12000	€9470	Debuneko - Fat Cat (31x41cm-12x16in) s.i.d.95 verso prov. 12-Feb-4 Sotheby's, New York #338/R est:8000-12000
£18000	$32760	€26280	Duckling, the Tannenbaum Ambassador (120x110cm-47x43in) s.i.d.96 acrylic prov.exhib. 5-Feb-4 Christie's, London #235/R est:20000-30000
£20000	$33400	€29200	Chick the Embassador No. 4. Chick the Embassador No. 3 (50x40cm-20x16in) both s.i.d.93 verso acrylic prov. pair. 21-Oct-3 Sotheby's, London #310/R est:20000-30000
£20950	$37500	€30587	Puppy (51x36cm-20x14in) acrylic paper painted 2000 prov. 13-May-4 Sotheby's, New York #304/R est:15000-20000
£22346	$40000	€32625	Remember your childhood days (55x41cm-22x16in) s.i.d.95 verso acrylic prov. 13-May-4 Sotheby's, New York #309/R est:35000-45000
£26536	$47500	€38743	Already we have no future - but we have to create (29x42cm-11x17in) s.i.d.95 acrylic paper collage paper prov. 13-May-4 Sotheby's, New York #312/R est:12000-18000
£28743	$48000	€41965	Your Guardian Beast (57x54cm-22x21in) s.i.d.97 verso acrylic prov. 12-Nov-3 Christie's, Rockefeller NY #560/R est:20000-30000
£31902	$52000	€46577	Night cat (59x50cm-23x20in) init.i.d.99 verso acrylic prov. 23-Sep-3 Christie's, Rockefeller NY #85/R est:12000-18000
£40000	$73600	€58400	Kitty in a puddle (60x40cm-24x16in) i.d.99 overlap acrylic on cotton prov. 25-Jun-4 Christie's, London #286/R est:20000-30000
£53892	$90000	€78682	Sprout the ambassador (180x180cm-71x71in) s.d.17 Marz 01 overlap acrylic fiberglass exhib. 13-Nov-3 Sotheby's, New York #428/R est:80000-120000
£55866	$100000	€81564	This is how to become an adult (100x100cm-39x39in) s.i.d.95 96 verso acrylic prov. 14-May-4 Phillips, New York #136/R est:80000-120000
£59880	$100000	€87425	Youth (120x110cm-47x43in) s.i.d.2000 verso prov. 13-Nov-3 Sotheby's, New York #474/R est:40000-60000
£94972	$170000	€138659	Blue sheep (122x112cm-48x44in) acrylic cotton exec 1999 prov.exhib.lit. 12-May-4 Sotheby's, New York #2/R est:100000-150000
Sculpture			
£2500	$4475	€3650	Dod (10x16x6cm-4x6x2in) i.d.85 cubic wood stand painted wood box in two parts. 6-May-4 Sotheby's, London #81/R est:2600-3000
£5500	$9185	€8030	Doberman (30x9x75cm-12x4x30in) s.d.87 verso acrylic col pencil crayon carved wood. 21-Oct-3 Sotheby's, London #307/R est:3000-4000
£6145	$11000	€8972	Little Pilgrim - Night walking (28x18x18cm-11x7x7in) s.d.2002 num.16/20 acrylic fibreglass. 13-May-4 Sotheby's, New York #311/R est:3000-4000
£7542	$13500	€11011	Untitled, puppy head (13x11x11cm-5x4x4in) s.d.00 num.7/8 verso acrylic cast composite. 12-May-4 Christie's, Rockefeller NY #312/R est:15000-20000
£10056	$18000	€14682	Untitled, bunny head (10x11x8cm-4x4x3in) s.d.98 acrylic cast composite gauze prov.lit. 12-May-4 Christie's, Rockefeller NY #311/R est:20000-30000
£16000	$29120	€23360	Bunny head (11x13x9cm-4x5x4in) init.d.98 num.W-2 verso acrylic cast composite gauze prov. 6-Feb-4 Sotheby's, London #268/R est:6000-8000
£29940	$50000	€43712	Little pilgrim, night walking (72x46x43cm-28x18x17in) fiberglass, acrylic cloth cotton edition 1 of 10 series of 25. 13-Nov-3 Sotheby's, New York #427/R est:18000-25000
£39106	$70000	€57095	Untitled (101x56x46cm-40x22x18in) s.d.95 num.AP verso acrylic cast composite prov. 12-May-4 Christie's, Rockefeller NY #310/R est:50000-70000
£65868	$110000	€96167	Little Pilgrims - night walking (72x50x42cm-28x20x17in) fibreglass cotton cloth acrylic paint five prov.exhib.lit. 11-Nov-3 Christie's, Rockefeller NY #1/R est:100000-150000
Works on paper			
£824	$1500	€1203	Guitar wolf from Japan (23x31cm-9x12in) s.d.96 pencil crayon W/C. 29-Jun-4 Sotheby's, New York #624/R est:2000-3000
£2400	$4296	€3504	Welcome to fight (30x42cm-12x17in) s.d.95 drawing. 6-May-4 Sotheby's, London #76/R est:2500-3000
£2747	$5000	€4011	Scarecrow (30x21cm-12x8in) s.i.d.95 pencil col crayon. 29-Jun-4 Sotheby's, New York #617/R est:3000-4000
£3022	$5500	€4412	Attack to the rotten world! (24x30cm-9x12in) s.d.95 fiber tip pen. 29-Jun-4 Sotheby's, New York #620/R est:3000-4000
£3352	$6000	€4894	With her treasure on a cloud (31x23cm-12x9in) s.i.d.97 W/C ink col pencil prov. 13-May-4 Sotheby's, New York #308/R est:5000-7000
£4190	$7500	€6117	Untitled (29x22cm-11x9in) s.d.97 col pencil felt tip pen prov. 14-May-4 Phillips, New York #335/R est:6000-8000
£4362	$7721	€6500	Fliessband a go go (23x26cm-9x10in) s. verso col crayon black paper. 28-Apr-4 Artcurial Briest, Paris #439/R est:3000-4000
£5988	$10000	€8742	Living day (29x20cm-11x8in) s.d.97 ink gouache pencil col crayon prov. 13-Nov-3 Sotheby's, New York #425/R est:5000-7000
£7362	$12000	€10749	You may dream (44x28cm-17x11in) s.i.d.1998 W/C prov. 23-Sep-3 Christie's, Rockefeller NY #88/R est:3000-5000
£15642	$28000	€22837	Little star message (30x23cm-12x9in) init.d.2000 verso col pencil prov. 12-May-4 Christie's, Rockefeller NY #302/R est:15000-20000

NARA, Yoshitomo (20th C) American

Works on paper			
£16000	$29120	€23360	Girl (52x50cm-20x20in) wax crayons paper on cardboard prov. 5-Feb-4 Christie's, London #236/R est:6000-8000

NARANJO, Eduardo (1944-) Spanish

£8276	$13821	€12000	Man (146x98cm-57x39in) s. exhib. 17-Nov-3 Durán, Madrid #225/R est:12000
£16779	$31376	€25000	Dead bird (60x53cm-24x21in) s.d.1988 lit. 24-Feb-4 Durán, Madrid #257/R est:25000
£20833	$34375	€30000	Male nude (150x98cm-59x39in) s. 2-Jul-3 Ansorena, Madrid #858a/R est:30000
Works on paper			
£2685	$4752	€4000	Paternity (22x16cm-9x6in) s.d.77 W/C. 27-Apr-4 Durán, Madrid #102/R est:3000

NARAY, Aurel (1883-1948) Hungarian

£302	$559	€450	Pious maiden (68x48cm-27x19in) s. 15-Mar-4 Sotheby's, Amsterdam #175/R
£312	$550	€456	Young woman seated in flowered dress (81x60cm-32x24in) s. 23-May-4 Bonhams & Butterfields, Los Angeles #7038/R
£329	$605	€500	Angel watching over (67x55cm-26x22in) s. 28-Jun-4 Sotheby's, Amsterdam #94/R
£329	$605	€500	Mother and child (100x74cm-39x29in) s. 28-Jun-4 Sotheby's, Amsterdam #110/R
£521	$849	€750	Little children playing at the waterside (80x61cm-31x24in) s. 29-Sep-3 Sotheby's, Amsterdam #221/R
£523	$968	€780	Little girl (70x50cm-28x20in) 15-Mar-4 Sotheby's, Amsterdam #174/R
£556	$906	€800	Flower still life with roses (70x55cm-28x22in) s. 29-Sep-3 Sotheby's, Amsterdam #214
£729	$1188	€1050	Sleeping time (67x56cm-26x22in) s. 29-Sep-3 Sotheby's, Amsterdam #222/R

NARBONA BELTRAN, Francisco (1860-1926) Spanish

£612	$1096	€900	Flowers (60x30cm-24x12in) s. 22-Mar-4 Durán, Madrid #45/R
£612	$1096	€900	Flowers (60x30cm-24x12in) s. 22-Mar-4 Durán, Madrid #44/R

NARDI, Enrico (1864-1947) Italian

Works on paper			
£634	$1096	€900	Venice (32x55cm-13x22in) s. W/C card. 11-Dec-3 Christie's, Rome #81/R
£850	$1445	€1241	Sunset on the coast (30x63cm-12x25in) s. W/C. 4-Nov-3 Bonhams, New Bond Street #12/R
£987	$1816	€1500	View of Saint Peter's from the Gianicolo (35x53cm-14x21in) s. W/C. 22-Jun-4 Babuino, Rome #403/R est:800-1200
£1250	$2300	€1900	Seashore at sunset (30x63cm-12x25in) s. W/C. 22-Jun-4 Babuino, Rome #405/R est:700-900
£2000	$3640	€2920	In the Roman Campagna (36x53cm-14x21in) s. pencil W/C pair. 1-Jul-4 Christie's, Kensington #363 est:400-600

NARDI, François (1861-1936) French

Works on paper			
£543	$923	€793	Marseilles harbour (16x22cm-6x9in) s. WC oval. 19-Nov-3 Fischer, Luzern #2482/R (S.FR 1200)

NARDI, J (?) ?

£2500	$4550	€3650	Venetian lagoon (39x55cm-15x22in) s. 16-Jun-4 Christie's, Kensington #92/R est:3000-5000

NARDINI, Didino (1890-1953) South American

£1587	$3000	€2317	Golden winter (140x170cm-55x67in) s.d.1928 exhib. 22-Feb-4 Galeria y Remates, Montevideo #162/R est:4500

NARJARURUBI (1927-) Australian
Works on paper
£1057 $1670 €1543 Barramundi (42x105cm-17x41in) earth pigments eucalyptus bark exec.c.1978 prov. 28-Jul-3 Sotheby's, Paddington #347/R est:1500-2500 (A.D 2600)

NARJOT, Ernest (1826-1898) American
£1879 $3250 €2743 Portrait of Mrs John B R Cooper (69x56cm-27x22in) s.d.1888 prov. 10-Dec-3 Bonhams & Butterfields, San Francisco #6138/R est:4000-6000
£5435 $10000 €7935 The escape (68x108cm-27x43in) s.d.1886 prov. 8-Jun-4 Bonhams & Butterfields, San Francisco #4162/R est:15000-20000

NARVAEZ PATINO, Manuel (1945-) Spanish
£671 $1255 €1000 I saw it (38x46cm-15x18in) s. s.i.verso. 24-Feb-4 Durán, Madrid #37/R
£1377 $2258 €1900 Tierras del Tio Chori (38x46cm-15x18in) s. s.i.verso exhib. 27-May-3 Durán, Madrid #136/R est:1800

NARVAEZ, Francisco (1905-1982) Venezuelan
£645 $1000 €942 Figure (23x15cm-9x6in) s. mixed media masonite. 29-Sep-2 Subastas Odalys, Caracas #48/R
£1698 $3125 €2479 Seascape (41x41cm-16x16in) s. 28-Mar-4 Subastas Odalys, Caracas #65/R
£2256 $4060 €3294 Flowers (50x40cm-20x16in) s. 25-Apr-4 Subastas Odalys, Caracas #8/R
Sculpture
£4377 $7310 €6390 Bust (40x20x13cm-16x8x5in) s. num.2/8 bronze. 13-Jul-3 Subastas Odalys, Caracas #89/R est:10000
£5448 $9915 €8172 Bust (52x18x16cm-20x7x6in) s. num.1/8 pat bronze. 21-Jun-4 Subastas Odalys, Caracas #46/R est:12000
£6409 $11665 €9614 Bust (23x74x13cm-9x29x5in) s. num.3/8 pat bronze. 21-Jun-4 Subastas Odalys, Caracas #88/R est:15000
£29779 $50625 €43477 Figure (102x45x12cm-40x18x5in) bronze. 23-Nov-3 Subastas Odalys, Caracas #156/R est:40000
Works on paper
£258 $400 €377 Untitled (18x16cm-7x6in) s. mixed media masonite. 29-Sep-2 Subastas Odalys, Caracas #32/R
£511 $950 €746 Face (17x14cm-7x6in) s. pastel. 14-Mar-4 Subastas Odalys, Caracas #105
£1497 $2500 €2186 Landscape (47x63cm-19x25in) s. pastel. 13-Jul-3 Subastas Odalys, Caracas #64

NASH, David (1945-) British
Sculpture
£1700 $2924 €2482 Crack and warp stack (49cm-19in) s.i.d.1988 num.214 1/3 silver birch prov. 3-Dec-3 Sotheby's, London #81/R est:1400-1800
£1733 $3103 €2600 Composition (54x25cm-21x10in) s.d.2000 wood. 15-May-4 De Vuyst, Lokeren #234/R est:2000-3000
£1800 $3096 €2628 Descending vessels (205cm-81in) yew tripartite exec 1987 prov. 3-Dec-3 Sotheby's, London #80/R est:2500-3500

NASH, Eustace (1886-?) British
£400 $680 €584 Building the rick, a breezy day (39x46cm-15x18in) s. board. 26-Nov-3 Hamptons Fine Art, Godalming #129

NASH, Frederick (1782-1856) British
Works on paper
£244 $383 €356 Study for the painting The Wreck (17x25cm-7x10in) s. W/C. 1-Sep-3 Shapiro, Sydney #384b/R (A.D 600)
£450 $819 €657 Kensington Garden (13x18cm-5x7in) prov. 16-Jun-4 John Nicholson, Haslemere #643/R
£480 $859 €701 Study for the wreck (17x24cm-7x9in) W/C. 26-May-4 Sotheby's, Olympia #43/R

NASH, John (1893-1977) British
£2500 $4325 €3650 Woodland path (58x83cm-23x33in) s. 11-Dec-3 Lyon & Turnbull, Edinburgh #105/R est:3000-5000
£40000 $72800 €58400 Norfolk coast (51x76cm-20x30in) s. prov.exhib. 15-Jun-4 Bonhams, New Bond Street #59/R est:15000-20000
Works on paper
£400 $728 €584 Funckia Sieboldu, Plantain lily (33x27cm-13x11in) s.i. prov.exhib. pencil. 1-Jul-4 Christie's, Kensington #152/R
£500 $795 €730 Sunlit farmyard (40x55cm-16x22in) s. W/C. 10-Sep-3 Sotheby's, Olympia #144/R
£850 $1547 €1241 Winter trees in Suffolk (38x54cm-15x21in) studio st.verso pencil wash. 15-Jun-4 Bonhams, Knightsbridge #10/R
£950 $1729 €1387 A prospect of flowers (20x14cm-8x6in) pen ink. 15-Jun-4 Bonhams, New Bond Street #56/R
£1100 $2024 €1606 Valley below Stoke by Nayland (9x13cm-4x5in) s. W/C pencil prov. 11-Jun-4 Keys, Aylsham #464/R est:1000-1500
£1200 $2208 €1752 Cornfield, Wiston (13x17cm-5x7in) s. W/C pencil prov. 11-Jun-4 Keys, Aylsham #468 est:1200-1500
£1250 $2300 €1825 Disused gravel pit, Cornwall (12x19cm-5x7in) s.d.74 W/C prov. 11-Jun-4 Keys, Aylsham #466 est:1000-1500
£1300 $2392 €1898 Waterfall, Wales (9x13cm-4x5in) s. W/C pencil prov. 11-Jun-4 Keys, Aylsham #463 est:1000-1500
£1300 $2392 €1898 Giant sprinkler, Batley (11x20cm-4x8in) s. W/C pencil prov. 11-Jun-4 Keys, Aylsham #465/R est:1000-1500
£1500 $2580 €2190 Avenue (38x54cm-15x21in) s.d.1934 i.verso W/C pencil. 2-Dec-3 Bonhams, New Bond Street #62/R est:1500-2000
£2000 $3680 €2920 Ivyed trees in avenue, Cornwall (14x19cm-6x7in) s.d.1975 W/C prov. 11-Jun-4 Keys, Aylsham #469/R est:1500-2000
£3400 $6256 €4964 Old lock gate, Warmingford (12x20cm-5x8in) s.d.1930-40 W/C prov. 11-Jun-4 Keys, Aylsham #467/R est:1200-1500
£5800 $9976 €8468 Winter evening, Wormingford (39x52cm-15x20in) s. W/C exhib. 2-Dec-3 Bonhams, New Bond Street #64/R est:2000-3000

NASH, Joseph (1808-1878) British
Works on paper
£350 $637 €511 A church interior (33x40cm-13x16in) s.d.1833 pencil W/C htd white. 1-Jul-4 Christie's, Kensington #292
£550 $1007 €803 Fisherman on a bank before a windmill (24x35cm-9x14in) s.d.1835 W/C. 7-Apr-4 Bonhams, Bury St Edmunds #375
£1050 $1680 €1533 Bay window in the hall, Speke, Lancashire (299x41cm-118x16in) s.d.1844 W/C over pencil htd bodycol. 16-Sep-3 Bonhams, Knowle #59/R est:800-1200
£1400 $2548 €2044 The oak room at Broughton Castle near Banbury, Oxfordshire (34x48cm-13x19in) s.d.1889 pencil W/C bodycol. 1-Jul-4 Christie's, Kensington #258/R est:1200-1800
£6500 $11960 €9490 Opening of the Crystal Palace, Sydenham, by Queen Victoria on 10th June 1854 (39x52cm-15x20in) W/C bodycol over pencil. 26-Mar-4 Sotheby's, London #141/R est:4000-6000

NASH, Paul (1889-1946) British
£10000 $18300 €14600 Severn Bore near Pimlico Sands (30x41cm-12x16in) s. 7-Apr-4 Gardiner & Houlgate, Bath #62/R est:1000-2000
£55000 $100650 €80300 End of the steps (51x61cm-20x24in) s.d.1922 s.overlap prov.exhib.lit. 4-Jun-4 Christie's, London #35/R est:30000-50000
£80000 $146400 €116800 Autumn landscape (76x56cm-30x22in) prov.exhib.lit. 4-Jun-4 Christie's, London #34/R est:30000-50000
Works on paper
£332 $527 €485 View of town (49x65cm-19x26in) s. ink W/C. 29-Apr-3 Louis Morton, Mexico #79/R (M.P 5500)
£950 $1587 €1387 Hills (11x19cm-4x7in) pencil blue green chk prov. 22-Oct-3 Cheffins, Cambridge #483
£1400 $2562 €2044 Coastal landscape (28x39cm-11x15in) pencil W/C sold with two others. 4-Jun-4 Christie's, London #38/R est:1500-2500
£1600 $2752 €2336 Path through the wood (35x27cm-14x11in) s. pencil W/C. 2-Dec-3 Bonhams, New Bond Street #65/R est:1200-1800
£2400 $4128 €3504 Landscape with pines (37x55cm-15x22in) s. pencil col crayon. 3-Dec-3 Christie's, Kensington #611/R est:1200-1800
£2400 $4128 €3504 Meeting place (12x16cm-5x6in) pencil. 2-Dec-3 Bonhams, New Bond Street #63/R est:1000-1500
£2600 $4758 €3796 Landscape of the Toad's Mouth Rock (18x25cm-7x10in) i. pencil crayon W/C executed 1943 prov. 4-Jun-4 Christie's, London #37/R est:3000-5000
£9800 $17542 €14308 Landscape at Rye (37x55cm-15x22in) s. W/C pencil. 16-Mar-4 Bonhams, New Bond Street #47/R est:1500-2500
£12000 $21960 €17520 Landscape of the Wittenham Clumps (16x25cm-6x10in) s. pencil col chk W/C executed 1946 prov.exhib.lit. 4-Jun-4 Christie's, London #36/R est:5000-8000

NASH, Thomas (1891-1968) British
Works on paper
£3500 $5600 €5110 The bathers (36x25cm-14x10in) s. gouache. 17-Sep-3 Brightwells, Leominster #880/R est:500-800

NASH, Willard Ayer (1898-1943) American
£726 $1300 €1060 Western homestead in mountain valley (23x28cm-9x11in) s. board. 8-Jan-4 James Julia, Fairfield #1010/R

NASHAR (1928-1994) Indonesian
£2083 $3479 €3041 Abstract (140x140cm-55x55in) s.d.12-Nop-1978. 12-Oct-3 Sotheby's, Singapore #178/R est:8000-10000 (S.D 6000)

NASIRUN (1965-) Indonesian
£694 $1160 €1013 Mystical figure (69x69cm-27x27in) s.d.94. 12-Oct-3 Sotheby's, Singapore #185/R est:2000-3000 (S.D 2000)
£1087 $1685 €1587 Fertility goddess (60x90cm-24x35in) s.d.94 s.i.d.1994 verso. 6-Oct-2 Sotheby's, Singapore #182/R est:3000-4000 (S.D 3000)
£2366 $3785 €3454 Petruk bagong garene berpangkat (145x90cm-57x35in) s.d.2001 s.i.d.2001 verso. 18-May-3 Sotheby's, Singapore #190/R est:4000-6000 (S.D 6600)

NASJAH, Damin (20th C) Indonesian?
£679 $1154 €991 Indonesians on beach (33x100cm-13x39in) s.d.69. 19-Nov-3 Fischer, Luzern #2231/R (S.FR 1500)

NASMYTH, Alexander (1758-1840) British
£683 $1100 €997 Untitled, landscape with lake and distant mountains (46x61cm-18x24in) 15-Aug-3 Du Mouchelle, Detroit #54/R
£1900 $3496 €2774 Woodland with cottages, figure and cattle (47x65cm-19x26in) s. prov. 29-Mar-4 Thomson Roddick & Medcalf, Edinburgh #210 est:2000-3000
£2771 $4600 €4046 Lincluden Abbey (30x43cm-12x17in) s. board. 4-Oct-3 Neal Auction Company, New Orleans #49 est:3000-5000
£3500 $5950 €5110 Family picnic in front of Loch Leven Castle, Kinross (22x31cm-9x12in) s. i.verso panel prov. 27-Nov-3 Sotheby's, London #181/R est:4000-6000
£4000 $7160 €5840 St Anthony's Chapel, Arthur's Seat (28x40cm-11x16in) panel. 28-May-4 Lyon & Turnbull, Edinburgh #23/R est:2000-3000
£8725 $15617 €13000 Paysage de montagne (70x90cm-28x35in) 25-May-4 Campo & Campo, Antwerp #175/R est:3000-5000
£9500 $17765 €13870 Loch Achray in the Trossachs (45x61cm-18x24in) s. prov. 22-Jul-4 Tennants, Leyburn #788/R est:3000-4000
£12000 $20400 €17520 View of the Sisters of Glencoe with figures and livestock on a bridge (92x68cm-36x27in) s. prov. 30-Oct-3 Christie's, London #2/R est:15000-20000
£26000 $44200 €37960 View of Loch Tay with Kenmore Church and bridge (88x121cm-35x48in) init.d.1810 prov.exhib.lit. 30-Oct-3 Christie's, London #4/R est:20000-30000

NASMYTH, Alexander (attrib) (1758-1840) British
£524 $965 €765 Peasant and his horse resting in rural landscape (10x15cm-4x6in) panel. 14-Jun-4 Waddingtons, Toronto #186/R est:700-900 (C.D 1300)
£544 $990 €800 Romantic landscape (22x29cm-9x11in) i.verso. 3-Feb-4 Segre, Madrid #25/R

NASMYTH, Charlotte (attrib) (1804-1884) British
£260 $478 €380 Cottage in a landscape (3x42cm-1x17in) 8-Jun-4 Bonhams, Knightsbridge #114

NASMYTH, James (1808-1890) British
£2200 $4026 €3212 Portrait of Robert Burns (46x35cm-18x14in) s.i.verso oval panel. 8-Jul-4 Sotheby's, London #69/R est:2000-3000
Works on paper
£300 $501 €438 Penshurst, Kent, a figure on a track (21x30cm-8x12in) s.i.verso W/C pastel. 14-Oct-3 Bearnes, Exeter #343/R

NASMYTH, James (attrib) (1808-1890) British
£350 $595 €511 Evening landscape with cattle and sheep near a sandy quarry (63x76cm-25x30in) indis.sig.indis.d. 1-Dec-3 Bonhams, Bath #105

NASMYTH, Jane (attrib) (1788-1867) British
£1000 $1670 €1460 Figure in a landscape with a village beyond (40x62cm-16x24in) 7-Oct-3 Bonhams, Knightsbridge #169/R est:1000-1500

NASMYTH, Patrick (1787-1831) British
£620 $980 €905 Figures in a landscape (22x29cm-9x11in) s.d.1815. 3-Sep-3 Bonhams, Bury St Edmunds #424/R
£720 $1274 €1051 Shipping at anchor, with figures and cottages on the shore (17x27cm-7x11in) s. 27-Apr-4 Henry Adams, Chichester #702/R
£766 $1302 €1118 Rural cottage with two figures on a road (25x34cm-10x13in) canvas on panel prov. 23-Nov-3 Levis, Calgary #209/R (C.D 1700)
£1100 $2013 €1606 Figures on a path (29x26cm-11x10in) s.d.1824 board. 6-Jun-4 Lots Road Auctions, London #365 est:800-1500
£1171 $1991 €1710 Conversation on the bridge (30x41cm-12x16in) s. prov. 23-Nov-3 Levis, Calgary #207/R est:3000-4000 (C.D 2600)
£1171 $1991 €1710 Couple walking in a wooded lane (24x29cm-9x11in) s.d.1816 panel prov. 23-Nov-3 Levis, Calgary #208/R est:3000-3500 (C.D 2600)
£2000 $3340 €2920 Figures by farm buildings in a landscape (25x30cm-10x12in) s. panel. 26-Jun-3 Greenslade Hunt, Taunton #511/R est:1500-2500
£3000 $5370 €4380 Landscape, with wood cutter before a hut in a wooded area (25x38cm-10x15in) s. panel prov. 5-May-4 John Nicholson, Haslemere #552/R est:2500-5000
£5200 $8840 €7592 Distant view of Edinburgh from the South-west (46x61cm-18x24in) 30-Oct-3 Christie's, London #12/R est:3000-5000
£6790 $11000 €9846 Laundry day (38x46cm-15x18in) s.d.1824 board. 8-Aug-3 Barridorf, Portland #161/R est:10000-15000
£8000 $14560 €11680 View of Addington, Surrey with the Shirley Mills beyond (69x89cm-27x35in) s. prov.lit. 1-Jul-4 Sotheby's, London #140/R est:8000-12000
£9000 $15300 €13140 Wooded river landscape with a figure on a path (51x74cm-20x29in) s.d.1828 panel prov. 30-Oct-3 Christie's, London #24/R est:8000-12000

NASMYTH, Patrick (attrib) (1787-1831) British
£305 $546 €445 Old oak (23x25cm-9x10in) i. 4-May-4 Ritchie, Toronto #32/R (C.D 750)
£565 $1039 €825 Goat herders resting at a waterfall in extensive landscape (35x46cm-14x18in) bears sig panel. 14-Jun-4 Waddingtons, Toronto #191/R est:1500-2500 (C.D 1400)
£3000 $5370 €4380 Figures crossing a gorge with approaching storm beyond (46x61cm-18x24in) with sig. 27-May-4 Christie's, Kensington #117/R est:3000-5000

NASON, Gertrude (1890-1969) American
£1075 $2000 €1570 Female nude study (76x55cm-30x22in) s. 5-Mar-4 Skinner, Boston #369/R est:1800-2000
£6177 $10500 €9018 Four o'clock (101x91cm-40x36in) s. prov. 21-Nov-3 Skinner, Boston #398/R est:15000-25000

NASON, Kathryn (1892-1976) American
£221 $375 €323 Still life (48x41cm-19x16in) s. en grisaille. 21-Nov-3 Skinner, Boston #381/R

NASON, Pieter (1612-1688) Dutch
£17000 $31110 €24820 Portrait of Friedrich Wilhelm, Elector of Brandenburg (119x94cm-47x37in) s.d.1666 lit. 8-Jul-4 Sotheby's, London #209/R est:7000-10000

NASON, Pieter (attrib) (1612-1688) Dutch
£600 $1074 €876 Portrait of Dudley Colley wearing lace collar and black tunic, seated half-length (84x71cm-33x28in) 4-May-4 Gorringes, Bexhill #1404

NASON, Thomas Willoughby (1889-1971) American
Works on paper
£503 $800 €734 View of the countryside with farmhouse (34x49cm-13x19in) s. pastel. 13-Sep-3 Weschler, Washington #767/R

NASS, Willi (1899-1966) German
£1533 $2775 €2300 Girl's head, cubist (52x36cm-20x14in) s.d.1937 board lit. 3-Apr-4 Hans Stahl, Hamburg #172/R est:2500

NAST, Thomas (1840-1902) American
£4624 $8000 €6751 Father Christmas in a winter landscape (15x23cm-6x9in) s.d.1860. 13-Dec-3 Weschler, Washington #543 est:300-500
Works on paper
£353 $600 €515 Put that garland where it will do the most good (28x25cm-11x10in) pen ink on board. 18-Nov-3 Doyle, New York #26
£958 $1600 €1399 Selfportraits (15x10cm-6x4in) s.i. one d.1896 one d.1882 pen ink pair. 15-Nov-3 Illustration House, New York #38/R est:1500-2500
£1196 $2200 €1746 The New Hay-Pauncefote Treaty (58x38cm-23x15in) s.i.d.Dec 1901 brush oil ink grisaille board. 10-Jun-4 Swann Galleries, New York #180a/R est:3000-5000

NASTAPOKA, Abraham (1900-1981) North American
Sculpture
£3604 $6126 €5262 Woman holding a kamik (46cm-18in) i. mottled dark soapstone. 3-Nov-3 Waddingtons, Toronto #146/R est:7000-9000 (C.D 8000)

NAT, Willem Hendrik van der (1864-1929) Dutch
£296 $545 €450 Farm house in a landscape (27x40cm-11x16in) s.d.06 canvas on board. 28-Jun-4 Sotheby's, Amsterdam #124/R
£987 $1786 €1500 Farm near Noordwijkerhout (24x38cm-9x15in) s. board exhib. 19-Apr-4 Glerum, Amsterdam #133/R est:1000-1500
£1370 $2329 €2000 Farmhouse in winter (25x41cm-10x16in) s. marouflé. 5-Nov-3 Vendue Huis, Gravenhage #230/R est:2000-3000
£2276 $3641 €3300 Sheep looking over fence (32x42cm-13x17in) s.d.20. 12-Mar-3 Auction Maastricht #1038
Works on paper
£987 $1816 €1500 Feeding chickens (30x47cm-12x19in) s. W/C. 28-Jun-4 Sotheby's, Amsterdam #32/R est:1500-2000

NATALI, Fausto Maria (?) Italian
Sculpture
£24648 $42641 €35000 Cleopatra's death (157cm-62in) marble sold withbase. 9-Dec-3 Pandolfini, Florence #281/R est:35000-38000

NATALI, Renato (1883-1979) Italian
£704 $1232 €1000 Tuscan countryside (30x40cm-12x16in) s. s.i.verso board. 17-Dec-3 Il Ponte, Milan #1196
£728 $1326 €1100 Figures (28x18cm-11x7in) s. board. 17-Jun-4 Galleria Pananti, Florence #505/R
£816 $1362 €1150 Harbour (18x38cm-7x15in) s. 17-Jun-3 Finarte Semenzato, Milan #5
£867 $1595 €1300 Venice (40x30cm-16x12in) s. board. 11-Jun-4 Farsetti, Prato #405/R
£867 $1595 €1300 Seascape (20x30cm-8x12in) s. board. 11-Jun-4 Farsetti, Prato #480/R
£1007 $1782 €1500 Peasant woman with dogs (50x35cm-20x14in) s. board. 1-May-4 Meeting Art, Vercelli #183 est:1500
£1088 $1948 €1600 Serenade (30x39cm-12x15in) s. s.verso cardboard. 22-Mar-4 Sant Agostino, Torino #466/R est:2000
£1208 $2247 €1800 Women at fountain (50x40cm-20x16in) s. s.verso. 4-Mar-4 Babuino, Rome #58
£1267 $2293 €1900 Seascape (11x19cm-4x7in) s. board. 2-Apr-4 Farsetti, Prato #429/R est:1800-2000
£1400 $2576 €2100 Lady riding (23x15cm-9x6in) s. panel. 10-Jun-4 Christie's, Rome #167/R est:800-1200
£1400 $2576 €2100 Figures in costume (16x29cm-6x11in) s. panel. 10-Jun-4 Christie's, Rome #168/R est:800-1200
£1408 $2437 €2000 Vase of roses (39x50cm-15x20in) s. s.i.verso. 10-Dec-3 Sotheby's, Milan #126/R est:2000-4000
£1479 $2558 €2100 Tuscan peasant women (68x49cm-27x19in) s. 9-Dec-3 Finarte Semenzato, Milan #15 est:2000-3000
£1586 $2649 €2300 Livorno harbour (22x30cm-9x12in) s. board. 14-Nov-3 Farsetti, Prato #472/R est:2100-2400
£1600 $2896 €2400 Fight (35x50cm-14x20in) s. s.i.verso board. 2-Apr-4 Farsetti, Prato #405/R est:1500-2000
£1600 $2880 €2400 Horses running in southern landscape (50x70cm-20x28in) s. panel lit. 22-Apr-4 Allgauer, Kempten #3667/R est:1500
£1600 $2944 €2400 Jockeys (23x15cm-9x6in) s. panel. 10-Jun-4 Christie's, Rome #169/R est:800-1200
£1690 $2806 €2400 Antignano (40x60cm-16x24in) s. 13-Jun-3 Farsetti, Prato #551/R
£1806 $3069 €2600 Moonlight (50x70cm-20x28in) s. board. 1-Nov-3 Meeting Art, Vercelli #437/R est:2000
£1867 $3435 €2800 Back from hunting (38x59cm-15x23in) s. board. 11-Jun-4 Farsetti, Prato #471/R est:2800-3200
£2069 $3455 €3000 Barberini Square, Rome (34x50cm-13x20in) s. board. 14-Nov-3 Farsetti, Prato #587/R est:3000-3500
£2133 $3925 €3200 Lazzaretto (20x24cm-8x9in) s. board. 11-Jun-4 Farsetti, Prato #514/R est:2400-2800
£2200 $4048 €3300 Woodcutters (50x39cm-20x15in) s. s.i.verso board. 11-Jun-4 Farsetti, Prato #451/R est:3000-3600
£2267 $4171 €3400 Rural street (35x50cm-14x20in) s. board. 11-Jun-4 Farsetti, Prato #472/R est:2900-3300
£2400 $4344 €3600 Old caves, Livorno (49x70cm-19x28in) s. s.i.verso board. 2-Apr-4 Farsetti, Prato #503/R est:1500-1800
£2400 $4416 €3600 View of Livorno (36x27cm-14x11in) s. panel. 10-Jun-4 Christie's, Rome #172/R est:1500-2000
£2600 $4706 €3900 Night scene (38x29cm-15x11in) s. board. 2-Apr-4 Farsetti, Prato #481/R est:2900-3300
£2819 $5271 €4200 Boar hunting (80x100cm-31x39in) masonite. 26-Feb-4 Cambi, Genoa #490/R est:3000-3500
£2819 $4989 €4200 Antignano (40x60cm-16x24in) s. s.i.verso lit. 1-May-4 Meeting Art, Vercelli #318 est:1500
£3000 $5520 €4500 Women at the door (40x34cm-16x13in) s. board. 11-Jun-4 Farsetti, Prato #575/R est:4500-5500
£3333 $6133 €5000 Seascape and figures (50x70cm-20x28in) s. board. 11-Jun-4 Farsetti, Prato #580/R est:5000-6000
£3667 $6747 €5500 Flower market (44x90cm-17x35in) s. cardboard. 8-Jun-4 Sotheby's, Milan #45/R est:2500-3500
£4000 $7240 €6000 Farmers at dusk (44x68cm-17x27in) s. board. 2-Apr-4 Farsetti, Prato #480/R est:5500-6500
£4079 $7505 €6200 Livorno Fortress. Pozzolani. Newsagent's (24x90cm-9x35in) s.i. board three in one frame. 23-Jun-4 Finarte Semenzato, Rome #117/R est:6000-8000
£4895 $8322 €7000 Sunset (70x100cm-28x39in) 19-Nov-3 Cambi, Genoa #417/R est:7000-8000
£5282 $9137 €7500 Fight (60x77cm-24x30in) s. board. 9-Dec-3 Pandolfini, Florence #381/R est:5000-5500
£5493 $9503 €7800 Rest during hunt (47x57cm-19x22in) s. 11-Dec-3 Christie's, Rome #106/R est:4000-6000
£5667 $10427 €8500 Sunset on the harbour (27x41cm-11x16in) s..si.verso painted 1949 exhib. 8-Jun-4 Sotheby's, Milan #98/R est:8000-12000
£10145 $16638 €14000 Party (52x88cm-20x35in) s. board. 27-May-3 Finarte Semenzato, Milan #94/R est:8000-9000

Works on paper
£497 $904 €750 Square in Livorno (21x17cm-8x7in) s. chl. 21-Jun-4 Pandolfini, Florence #240

NATHAN, Annette (?) American?
£424 $750 €619 Portrait of a young girl (48x38cm-19x15in) indis.s. 1-May-4 Susanin's, Chicago #5039/R

NATHAN, Arturo (1891-1944) Italian
£17333 $31027 €26000 Fantasy landscape (66x90cm-26x35in) s.d.1936 board prov.exhib.lit. 12-May-4 Stadion, Trieste #800/R est:22000-26000

NATHAN, Ian (1954-) British
£350 $627 €511 Bull elephant (61x51cm-24x20in) s. 18-Mar-4 Christie's, Kensington #698/R

NATIVI, Gualtiero (1921-1997) Italian
£1087 $1783 €1500 Untitled (35x25cm-14x10in) s. s.d.1981 verso tempera paper on canvas. 29-May-3 Galleria Pace, Milan #28/R
£1342 $2483 €2000 Relationship (50x70cm-20x28in) s. s.d.1994 verso acrylic. 13-Mar-4 Meeting Art, Vercelli #74 est:2000
£1342 $2403 €2000 Untitled (100x72cm-39x28in) s. tempera acrylic painted 1992. 30-May-4 Meeting Art, Vercelli #3 est:2000
£1389 $2194 €2000 Grandonio's memories (80x60cm-31x24in) acrylic painted 1998. 6-Sep-3 Meeting Art, Vercelli #600 est:2000
£1408 $2338 €2000 Colloquio (90x60cm-35x24in) s. s.d.1980 verso acrylic tempera. 14-Jun-3 Meeting Art, Vercelli #71/R est:2000
£1957 $3209 €2700 Untitled (112x91cm-44x36in) s. i.d.1980 verso acrylic mixed media. 30-May-3 Farsetti, Prato #51/R
£2029 $3328 €2800 Ambush (100x80cm-39x31in) s. tempera painted 1991. 29-May-3 Galleria Pace, Milan #132/R est:4000
£2517 $4280 €3600 Sound wall (80x120cm-31x47in) s. s.d.1962-63 exhib. 26-Nov-3 Pandolfini, Florence #46/R est:5000-5200
£4082 $7306 €6000 Untitled (45x80cm-18x31in) s. tempera paper on canvas exhib.lit. 22-Mar-4 Sant Agostino, Torino #561/R est:8000

NATKIN, Robert (1930-) American
£1323 $2250 €1932 Berne series no.490 (110x89cm-43x35in) s. acrylic on paper prov. 9-Nov-3 Bonhams & Butterfields, Los Angeles #4088/R est:3000-5000
£1500 $2385 €2175 Untitled (47x35cm-19x14in) s.d.62. 11-Sep-3 Christie's, Kensington #214/R est:400-600
£1796 $3000 €2622 Untitled, abstract (84x84cm-33x33in) s.d.1981. 25-Oct-3 David Rago, Lambertville #157 est:800-1200
£2973 $5500 €4341 Untitled (249x102cm-98x40in) s.verso acrylic. 12-Feb-4 Sotheby's, New York #125/R est:3000-5000
£3293 $5500 €4808 Intimate lighting series (214x86cm-84x34in) s. acrylic prov. 7-Oct-3 Sotheby's, New York #357 est:3000-4000
£3514 $6500 €5130 Hitchcock Series (91x122cm-36x48in) s.d.1984 acrylic. 12-Feb-4 Sotheby's, New York #267/R est:3000-4000
£3533 $6500 €5158 Abstract composition (107x152cm-42x60in) s. acrylic. 27-Jun-4 Freeman, Philadelphia #148/R est:2500-4000
£3571 $6500 €5214 Intimate lighting (122x66cm-48x26in) s. acrylic painted 1972 prov. 29-Jun-4 Sotheby's, New York #483/R est:3000-5000
£3631 $6500 €5301 Bath-apollo series (135x175cm-53x69in) s. acrylic prov. 6-May-4 Doyle, New York #117/R est:3000-5000
£4651 $8000 €6790 Prude's fall - hommage to Alfred Hitchcock (223x244cm-88x96in) s. acrylic painted 1982 prov.exhib. 3-Dec-3 Doyle, New York #52 est:5000-7000
£4706 $8000 €6871 Berne no.672 (160x229cm-63x90in) s acrylic prov. 9-Nov-3 Wright, Chicago #403 est:9000-12000
£7568 $14000 €11049 Bern Series (96x120cm-38x47in) s. acrylic. 12-Feb-4 Sotheby's, New York #263/R est:10000-15000
£8242 $15000 €12033 Intimate lighting series (213x335cm-84x132in) s. acrylic painted 1980 prov. 29-Jun-4 Sotheby's, New York #535/R est:8000-12000
Works on paper
£598 $1100 €873 Abstract composition (58x46cm-23x18in) s.d.1967 acrylic W/C board. 10-Jun-4 Swann Galleries, New York #184/R
£824 $1400 €1203 Untitled (46x53cm-18x21in) s.d.1963 W/C. 9-Nov-3 Wright, Chicago #402 est:1500-2000

NATO, Olivier de (1968-) French?
£333 $597 €500 Sur le rivage (50x60cm-20x24in) s. 16-May-4 MonsAntic, Maisieres #391

NATOIRE, Charles-Joseph (1700-1777) French
£51020 $91327 €75000 Diane et Acteon (80x60cm-31x24in) lit. 19-Mar-4 Oger, Dumont, Paris #36/R est:80000-100000
Works on paper
£1311 $2400 €1914 Portrait of a young gentleman (46x36cm-18x14in) indis.i.verso black chk card stock. 29-Jan-4 Swann Galleries, New York #217/R est:3000-5000
£2000 $3660 €2920 Sancho Panza pursued by cooks trying to shave his beard (25x22cm-10x9in) i. black white chk pen ink wash prov. 6-Jul-4 Christie's, London #127/R est:2000-3000
£2318 $4219 €3500 La toilette de Venus (15x19cm-6x7in) black crayon white chk prov. 16-Jun-4 Piasa, Paris #125/R est:2500-3000
£2600 $4758 €3796 Adoration of the shepherds (27x20cm-11x8in) black chk pen ink htd white and a study by another hand. 6-Jul-4 Christie's, London #126/R est:3000-5000
£4082 $7306 €6000 Jeune homme enlevant une femme, une autre femme a leurs pieds (48x31cm-19x12in) sanguine. 17-Mar-4 Tajan, Paris #38/R est:6000
£6463 $11568 €9500 Etude d'homme nu, assis (50x41cm-20x16in) sanguine estompe htd white chk prov. 19-Mar-4 Piasa, Paris #54/R est:6000
£8844 $15830 €13000 Etude our Psyche et reprises de la main (37x25cm-15x10in) col crayon beige paper prov. 17-Mar-4 Tajan, Paris #42/R est:12000-15000
£10000 $18000 €14600 Study of a partly draped female figure, seated amongst rocks (29x23cm-11x9in) init. black white chk prov. 21-Jan-4 Sotheby's, New York #107/R est:8000-12000
£12676 $22183 €18000 Le triomphe d'Amphitrite (18x26cm-7x10in) black chk pen grey ink wash prov. 17-Dec-3 Christie's, Paris #58/R est:10000-15000
£19000 $34770 €27740 Orpheus charmong the animals and the nymphs (32x42cm-13x17in) s. black chk pen ink W/C htd white. 6-Jul-4 Christie's, London #125/R est:7000-10000

NATON, Avraham (1906-1959) Israeli
Works on paper
£601 $1100 €877 Woman by the window (37x24cm-15x9in) s. mixed media. 1-Jun-4 Ben-Ami, Tel Aviv #4854/R est:1500-2000

NATTES, John Claude (1765-1822) British
Works on paper
£300 $540 €438 Swiss lake (29x46cm-11x18in) i.mount W/C black chk. 20-Apr-4 Sotheby's, Olympia #131/R

NATTES, John Claude (attrib) (1765-1822) British
Works on paper
£1700 $3060 €2482 View at Horsham, Sussex (24x36cm-9x14in) W/C. 22-Apr-4 Charles Ross, Woburn #243/R est:300-500

NATTIER, J M (1685-1766) French
£311 $566 €467 Young woman with blue flowers in her hair (80x65cm-31x26in) 19-Jun-4 Rasmussen, Havnen #2122 (D.KR 3500)

NATTIER, Jean Marc (1685-1766) French
Works on paper
£1412 $2400 €2062 Three soldiers playing cards (29x29cm-11x11in) chk prov. 25-Nov-3 Christie's, Rockefeller NY #501/R est:2000-3000

NATTIER, Jean Marc (attrib) (1685-1766) French
£4620 $8500 €6745 Portrait of of Mlle de Sambreval (119x97cm-47x38in) 9-Jun-4 Doyle, New York #3094/R est:7000-9000
Works on paper
£4698 $8644 €7000 Portrait of young lady as Diana (42x37cm-17x15in) pastel paper on board prov. 24-Mar-4 Dorotheum, Vienna #291/R est:4000-6000

NATTIER, Jean-Baptiste (elder) (1678-1726) French
£30201 $55570 €45000 Judgement of Paris (34x43cm-13x17in) copper lit. 24-Mar-4 Dorotheum, Vienna #301/R est:15000-20000

NATTINO, Vittorio (1890-1971) Italian
£671 $1255 €1000 Peasant man along the river (55x70cm-22x28in) board. 26-Feb-4 Cambi, Genoa #428/R
£1074 $2008 €1600 Choppy sea in Pegli (50x70cm-20x28in) board. 26-Feb-4 Cambi, Genoa #511/R est:500-600

NATTONIER, Henri (19th C) French
£750 $1320 €1095 Swordsmith's workshop (24x29cm-9x11in) s. bears i. verso. 18-May-4 Fellows & Sons, Birmingham #72

NATTRESS, George (fl.1866-1888) British
Works on paper
£750 $1343 €1095 Rosslyn Chapel with the Apprentice Pillar (40x28cm-16x11in) s. W/C. 28-May-4 Lyon & Turnbull, Edinburgh #57
£900 $1422 €1314 Lausanne, Lake of Geneva (23x48cm-9x19in) s. i.backing board W/C. 3-Sep-3 Wingetts, Wrexham #323/R

NAUDE, Hugo (1869-1941) South African
£1345 $2434 €1964 Sand dunes near a rocky outcrop (25x35cm-10x14in) s. board. 30-Mar-4 Stephan Welz, Johannesburg #456/R est:14000-18000 (SA.R 16000)
£1652 $2956 €2412 Groot river, South Africa (24x34cm-9x13in) s. board. 31-May-4 Stephan Welz, Johannesburg #485/R est:12000-16000 (SA.R 20000)
£1724 $2879 €2517 Worcester Valley (18x29cm-7x11in) s. s.i.verso board. 20-Oct-3 Stephan Welz, Johannesburg #331/R est:16000-20000 (SA.R 20000)
£1817 $3252 €2653 Breaking waves with seagulls (22x28cm-9x11in) s. board i.verso. 31-May-4 Stephan Welz, Johannesburg #546/R est:8000-12000 (SA.R 22000)
£1849 $3346 €2700 Mountainous landscape (24x19cm-9x7in) s. board. 30-Mar-4 Stephan Welz, Johannesburg #446/R est:10000-15000 (SA.R 22000)
£2069 $3455 €3021 Worcester mountains (24x34cm-9x13in) s. board. 20-Oct-3 Stephan Welz, Johannesburg #334/R est:20000-30000 (SA.R 24000)
£2185 $3955 €3190 Sunlit mountains seen from Brandvlei (19x24cm-7x9in) s. board. 30-Mar-4 Stephan Welz, Johannesburg #447/R est:16000-20000 (SA.R 26000)
£2241 $3743 €3272 Table Mountain from Milnerton (18x28cm-7x11in) s. canvasboard. 20-Oct-3 Stephan Welz, Johannesburg #328/R est:15000-20000 (SA.R 26000)
£2586 $4319 €3776 Lagoon and mountains (19x27cm-7x11in) s. i.verso board. 20-Oct-3 Stephan Welz, Johannesburg #335/R est:20000-25000 (SA.R 30000)
£2735 $4650 €3993 Near Caledon (21x28cm-8x11in) board. 4-Nov-3 Stephan Welz, Johannesburg #621/R est:12000-18000 (SA.R 32000)
£2890 $5173 €4219 Drakensberg under snow (22x26cm-9x10in) s. board. 31-May-4 Stephan Welz, Johannesburg #535/R est:15000-20000 (SA.R 35000)
£4701 $7991 €6863 Namaqualand landscape (24x34cm-9x13in) s. panel. 4-Nov-3 Stephan Welz, Johannesburg #622/R est:60000-90000 (SA.R 55000)
£11207 $18716 €16362 Namaqualand in spring (24x34cm-9x13in) s. canvasboard. 20-Oct-3 Stephan Welz, Johannesburg #313/R est:80000-120000 (SA.R 130000)
£14286 $25857 €20858 Springtime in Namaualand (29x44cm-11x17in) s. panel. 30-Mar-4 Stephan Welz, Johannesburg #466/R est:90000-120000 (SA.R 170000)
£15517 $25914 €22655 Namaqualand in spring (34x43cm-13x17in) s. board. 20-Oct-3 Stephan Welz, Johannesburg #312/R est:100000-120000 (SA.R 180000)

NAUDET, Thomas Charles (1773-1810) French
Works on paper
£600 $1098 €876 Three peasants women and a child. Peasant family with a mother and child seated on donkey (9x15cm-4x6in) i. brown ink W/C over pencil pair. 7-Jul-4 Bonhams, Knightsbridge #16/R

NAUEN, Heinrich (1880-1941) German
£1174 $2161 €1750 By the sea (48x57cm-19x22in) s. i. verso W/C tempera. 26-Mar-4 Karrenbauer, Konstanz #1753/R est:2000
£4605 $8474 €7000 Jug containing white blossom (59x49cm-23x19in) s.d.25 tempera. 26-Jun-4 Karrenbauer, Konstanz #1753/R est:5800
£8333 $13583 €12000 Girl in blue dress with cow (151x107cm-59x42in) s. prov.exhib. 27-Sep-3 Dr Fritz Nagel, Stuttgart #9590/R est:25000
Works on paper
£433 $776 €650 Shepherd with flock (16x28cm-6x11in) s.d.1897/98 gouache Indian ink W/C board prov. 15-May-4 Van Ham, Cologne #811
£600 $1074 €900 Storm over sea (22x28cm-9x11in) s. W/C paper on board. 15-May-4 Van Ham, Cologne #810

NAUER, Adolph (1893-1966) German
£503 $926 €750 Holy men buying art (75x80cm-30x31in) s. 24-Mar-4 Hugo Ruef, Munich #1060
£828 $1382 €1200 Clerics burying artefacts (56x72cm-22x28in) s. 9-Jul-3 Hugo Ruef, Munich #156/R

NAUER, Ludwig (1888-1965) German
£274 $427 €400 Men round table (63x79cm-25x31in) s. 10-Apr-3 Weidler, Nurnberg #6540

NAUJOKS, Heino (1937-) German
Works on paper
£345 $576 €500 Untitled (31x44cm-12x17in) s.d.1975 mixed media collage board. 13-Nov-3 Neumeister, Munich #591/R

NAUMAN, Bruce (1941-) American
Photographs
£7263 $13000 €10604 Untitled (61x51cm-24x20in) s.d.1987 num. of 12 col photo prov. 14-May-4 Phillips, New York #252/R est:10000-15000
Prints
£2778 $5000 €4056 Normal desires (24x35cm-9x14in) s.d.1973 num.24/50 lithograph. 24-Apr-4 David Rago, Lambertville #442/R est:1000-2000
Sculpture
£26946 $45000 €39341 Double poke in the eye II (61x91x16cm-24x36x6in) s. neon tubing clear glass tubing suspension supports prov. 14-Nov-3 Phillips, New York #172/R est:50000-70000
£28443 $47500 €41527 Double poke in the eye II (61x91x23cm-24x36x9in) neon tubing aluminum monolith edition 28 of 40 prov.exhib.lit. 13-Nov-3 Sotheby's, New York #486/R est:40000-60000
£167665 $280000 €244791 Eat war (14x79x5cm-6x31x2in) neon tubing clear glass executed 1986 prov.exhib.lit. 12-Nov-3 Sotheby's, New York #65/R est:300000-400000
£508982 $850000 €743114 Wheels and suspended double pyramid (273x273x273cm-107x107x107in) Cor-Ten steel exec 1978 num 2 from edn of 3 prov.exhib.lit. 11-Nov-3 Christie's, Rockefeller NY #59/R est:350000-450000
Works on paper
£9581 $16000 €13988 Untitled (56x76cm-22x30in) s.d.87 graphite prov. 14-Nov-3 Phillips, New York #173/R est:20000-30000
£95808 $160000 €139880 Hanged man (201x107cm-79x42in) s.i.d.85 W/C pencil prov.exhib. 12-Nov-3 Sotheby's, New York #51/R est:150000-200000

NAUMANN, Karl Georg (1827-1902) German
£1048 $1928 €1530 Couple playing cards (47x43cm-19x17in) s. 14-Jun-4 Philippe Schuler, Zurich #4316/R est:3500-4000 (S.FR 2400)

NAUR, Albert (1889-1973) Danish
£281 $469 €410 Green landscape (67x88cm-26x35in) s.d.55. 25-Oct-3 Rasmussen, Havnen #4257 (D.KR 3000)
£293 $533 €428 Field landscape (50x66cm-20x26in) s. prov. 7-Feb-4 Rasmussen, Havnen #4018 (D.KR 3200)
£304 $517 €444 Interior scene with the actors Ib Schonberg and Else Skobo (50x62cm-20x24in) s. 10-Nov-3 Rasmussen, Vejle #656/R (D.KR 3300)
£330 $600 €482 Portrait of Margot Lander (122x90cm-48x35in) s.i.d.50 prov. 7-Feb-4 Rasmussen, Havnen #4011/R (D.KR 3600)
£332 $531 €485 Autumn landscape with corn stooks (53x59cm-21x23in) s.d.22. 22-Sep-3 Rasmussen, Vejle #607/R (D.KR 3500)
£332 $597 €485 Still life of flowers (65x53cm-26x21in) s.d.55. 24-Apr-4 Rasmussen, Havnen #4219 (D.KR 3700)
£378 $677 €552 Still life of flowers (85x102cm-33x40in) s.d.1929 prov. 12-Jan-4 Rasmussen, Vejle #546 (D.KR 4000)
£389 $622 €568 Country road through green landscape (70x101cm-28x40in) s.d.55. 22-Sep-3 Rasmussen, Vejle #603/R (D.KR 4100)
£397 $711 €580 Landscape (74x92cm-29x36in) s. 12-Jan-4 Rasmussen, Vejle #662 (D.KR 4200)
£458 $833 €669 Portrait of seated female nude (77x85cm-30x33in) s.d.1920 prov. 7-Feb-4 Rasmussen, Havnen #4007/R (D.KR 5000)
£478 $775 €693 Still life of flowers in copper pot on table (100x125cm-39x49in) s.d.44. 4-Aug-3 Rasmussen, Vejle #604/R (D.KR 5000)
£595 $1083 €869 Field landscape From the Garden of Eden. s. two prov. 7-Feb-4 Rasmussen, Havnen #4031/R (D.KR 6500)
£641 $1167 €936 Scene's from Garden of Eden. s. pair. 7-Feb-4 Rasmussen, Havnen #4015/R (D.KR 7000)

NAUWELAERTS, Georges (19/20th C) ?
£944 $1605 €1350 Vieille femme assise devant la cheminee (56x71cm-22x28in) s. 18-Nov-3 Vanderkindere, Brussels #19

NAUWENS, Jozef (1830-1886) Belgian
£548 $932 €800 Laveuse. s.d.1883. 4-Nov-3 Servarts Themis, Bruxelles #602
£1027 $1747 €1500 Accesoires (41x32cm-16x13in) s.d.1874 s.i.verso panel. 10-Nov-3 Horta, Bruxelles #353
£1700 $3111 €2550 Composition with copper jug (54x41cm-21x16in) s.d.1875 panel. 6-Jun-4 Osenat, Fontainebleau #223/R est:3000-3500

NAVA, Hector (1875-1940) ?
£1500 $2700 €2190 Girls in Venice (89x100cm-35x39in) s.d.919. 21-Jan-4 Sotheby's, Olympia #509/R est:1500-2000

NAVALON, Mirou (1955-) French
Works on paper
£274 $466 €400 La mise en jeu (42x57cm-17x22in) pastel. 7-Nov-3 Coutau Begarie, Paris #146

NAVARRA, Pietro (17/18th C) Italian
£10345 $17276 €15000 Composition aux raisins, grenades et figues sur fond de paysage (47x66cm-19x26in) 17-Nov-3 Delorme & Bocage, Paris #52/R est:15000-20000

NAVARRO BALDEWEG, Juan (1939-) Spanish
£1690 $2958 €2400 In the studio (33x41cm-13x16in) s.d.1988 verso prov. 16-Dec-3 Segre, Madrid #162/R est:1400

NAVARRO LLORENS, Jose (1867-1923) Spanish
£3000 $5100 €4380 Beached boats (38x61cm-15x24in) s. 18-Nov-3 Sotheby's, London #227/R
£5396 $8849 €7500 Jeune enfant au portail (20x29cm-8x11in) s. panel. 6-Jun-3 Chochon-Barre & Allardi, Paris #82/R est:4500-5000
£14685 $24524 €21000 Mountainous landscape with shelter (80x120cm-31x47in) s. 30-Jun-3 Ansorena, Madrid #352/R est:21000
£19000 $32300 €27740 Market in Tetuan (29x48cm-11x19in) s.d.98 prov. 18-Nov-3 Sotheby's, London #201/R
£24823 $40213 €35000 Zoco arabe (29x49cm-11x19in) s.d.96. 20-May-3 Ansorena, Madrid #161/R est:30000
£53191 $86170 €75000 Naufragio (161x259cm-63x102in) 20-May-3 Ansorena, Madrid #93/R est:75000
Works on paper
£7200 $12024 €10512 Red apple (52x68cm-20x27in) s. W/C. 12-Nov-3 Sotheby's, Olympia #205/R est:5000-7000

NAVARRO PRUNA, Carmen (20th C) Spanish
Works on paper
£312 $506 €440 La espera (48x33cm-19x13in) s. pastel. 20-May-3 Ansorena, Madrid #455/R

NAVARRO, Enrique (1924-1997) Spanish
£559 $934 €800 Arlequin (55x46cm-22x18in) s. 30-Jun-3 Ansorena, Madrid #311/R

NAVARRO, J Elizalde (1924-1999) Philippino
£5556 $9278 €8112 Seasons four (84x122cm-33x48in) s.d.11.15.96 acrylic. 12-Oct-3 Sotheby's, Singapore #58/R est:8000-15000 (S.D 16000)
£6882 $11011 €10048 Honey, there are no escalators going to heaven (123x113cm-48x44in) s.i.d.7.28.97. 18-May-3 Sotheby's, Singapore #89/R est:10000-18000 (S.D 19200)
£7190 $13013 €10497 Beginning of the end, almost (89x134cm-35x53in) s.i.d.2.15.91 s.i.d.verso. 4-Apr-4 Sotheby's, Singapore #113/R est:15000-20000 (S.D 22000)

NAVARRO, Jose (attrib) (19th C) Spanish
£451 $736 €650 Boy on the beach (20x31cm-8x12in) canvas on cardboard. 23-Sep-3 Durán, Madrid #575/R

NAVARRO, Miquel (1945-) Spanish
Works on paper
£405 $714 €600 Untitled (30x20cm-12x8in) s.d.1979 ink dr prov. 18-May-4 Segre, Madrid #130/R
£405 $714 €600 Untitled (30x20cm-12x8in) s.d.1978 ink dr prov. 18-May-4 Segre, Madrid #131/R
£533 $971 €800 Retrato de Aurelio (41x29cm-16x11in) s.d.2002 ink drawing. 29-Jun-4 Segre, Madrid #159/R

NAVARRO, Pascual (1923-1985) Venezuelan
Works on paper
£297 $505 €434 Head (20x15cm-8x6in) s. chl exec.1945. 23-Nov-3 Subastas Odalys, Caracas #11

NAVE, Royston (1886-1931) American
Works on paper
£240 $400 €350 Mexican hut (23x30cm-9x12in) W/C. 18-Oct-3 David Dike, Dallas #219/R
£240 $400 €350 Oxen and cart (23x30cm-9x12in) W/C. 18-Oct-3 David Dike, Dallas #220/R

NAVELLIER, Edouard (1865-1944) French
Sculpture
£4490 $7139 €6600 Rhinoceros de l'Inde (20x38cm-8x15in) s. pat bronze. 23-Mar-3 Salle des ventes Pillet, Lyon la Foret #166

NAVEZ, François Joseph (1787-1869) Belgian

£1409 $2465 €2000 Etude de tetes d'hommes barbus (39x64cm-15x25in) 18-Dec-3 Tajan, Paris #125/R
£4196 $7133 €6000 Portrait du Vicomte Alberic du Bus des Gisignies (76x62cm-30x24in) s.d.1840 lit. 21-Nov-3 Coutau Begarie, Paris #108/R est:6000-8000
Works on paper
£759 $1403 €1100 Self portrait (50x40cm-20x16in) mono. pastel. 19-Jan-4 Horta, Bruxelles #275

NAVEZ, Léon (1900-1967) Belgian

£405 $726 €600 Composition au cactus (50x58cm-20x23in) s. 10-May-4 Horta, Bruxelles #24
£586 $1084 €850 Femme pensive a la fenetre (39x31cm-15x12in) s. panel. 13-Jan-4 Vanderkindere, Brussels #4
£1389 $2319 €2000 Contours du jardin (60x73cm-24x29in) s. 21-Oct-3 Campo & Campo, Antwerp #227/R est:3000
£3784 $7151 €5600 Enfant au caban (100x80cm-39x31in) s. 17-Feb-4 Vanderkindere, Brussels #121 est:1250-1500

NAVIASKY, Philip (1894-1983) British

£260 $442 €380 Portrait of a seated girl in a red hat (74x62cm-29x24in) s. board. 18-Nov-3 Bonhams, Leeds #139
£320 $582 €467 Winter landscape with farm buildings (48x63cm-19x25in) s. 15-Jun-4 Bonhams, Leeds #58/R
£420 $714 €613 Still life of anemones in a vase (39x49cm-15x19in) s. board. 18-Nov-3 Bonhams, Leeds #143
£420 $714 €613 Spanish courtyard with figures (49x59cm-19x23in) s. 18-Nov-3 Bonhams, Leeds #144
£480 $859 €701 Portrait of a young lady (69x58cm-27x23in) s. canvasboard. 6-May-4 Biddle & Webb, Birmingham #936
£640 $1088 €934 Mulatto (74x62cm-29x24in) s. 18-Nov-3 Bonhams, Leeds #140
£700 $1295 €1022 The green dress (114cm-45in) s. 12-Feb-4 Andrew Hartley, Ilkley #884/R
£820 $1394 €1197 Self portrait (74x61cm-29x24in) board. 18-Nov-3 Bonhams, Leeds #137
£820 $1394 €1197 Self portrait (58x44cm-23x17in) s. canvasboard. 18-Nov-3 Bonhams, Leeds #141
£900 $1611 €1314 St. Tropez (37x44cm-15x17in) s.i.verso board. 16-Mar-4 Bonhams, Leeds #581/R
£1000 $1790 €1460 Galway Connemara woman, knitting (61x52cm-24x20in) s. 14-May-4 Christie's, Kensington #317/R est:600-800
Works on paper
£280 $476 €409 Portrait of the artist's daughter seated, wearing a red shirt (49x36cm-19x14in) s.d.1925 chl pastel. 18-Nov-3 Bonhams, Leeds #138

NAVLET, Gustave Andre (1832-?) French

Sculpture
£3200 $5440 €4672 Jeune berger assis (85cm-33in) s.d.1865 pat bronze. 28-Oct-3 Sotheby's, London #68/R est:2500-3500

NAVLET, Joseph (1821-1889) French

£8333 $15000 €12166 Arrival of the infantry (52x88cm-20x35in) s. 22-Apr-4 Christie's, Rockefeller NY #156/R est:18000-25000
Works on paper
£1007 $1612 €1400 Jeune femme recevant dans son boudoir. Jeune femme ecrivant une lettre et recevant du monde (43x27cm-17x11in) both s. W/C gouache pair. 16-May-3 Tajan, Paris #165 est:1200-1500
£1385 $2382 €2022 Napoleon au milieu de ses troupes (27x45cm-11x18in) s. W/C. 3-Dec-3 AB Stockholms Auktionsverk #2632/R est:18000-20000 (S.KR 18000)
£1608 $2766 €2300 Scene d'orgie dans une maison close (27x35cm-11x14in) i.verso gouache. 8-Dec-3 Piasa, Paris #32/R est:1600-1800

NAVOZOV, Vassily Ivanovich (1862-1919) Russian

£7400 $12580 €10804 Travellers in a Georgian landscape (80x106cm-31x42in) s.d.1917. 19-Nov-3 Sotheby's, London #23/R est:8000-12000

NAVRATIL, Walter (1950-) Austrian

£1748 $2972 €2500 Flight of the fly (59x49cm-23x19in) s.i.d.1970 verso. 28-Nov-3 Wiener Kunst Auktionen, Vienna #646/R est:2500-5000
£2098 $3566 €3000 Orang-Utan (100x80cm-39x31in) s.d. 28-Nov-3 Wiener Kunst Auktionen, Vienna #654/R est:4000-6000
£2797 $4755 €4000 Orang-Utan (100x80cm-39x31in) 28-Nov-3 Wiener Kunst Auktionen, Vienna #655/R est:4000-6000

NAWARA, Lucille (20th C) American

£437 $800 €656 Ledge (117x102cm-46x40in) 10-Jul-4 Hindman, Chicago #367/R
£492 $900 €738 Umpachene II (76x91cm-30x36in) 10-Jul-4 Hindman, Chicago #368/R est:300-500

NAY, Ernst Wilhelm (1902-1968) German

£49296 $85282 €70000 Improvisation (61x73cm-24x29in) s.d.56 s. verso s.i.d.1956 stretcher lit.exhib. 13-Dec-3 Lempertz, Koln #172/R est:50000-70000
£50000 $92000 €75000 Sicily blue (125x90cm-49x35in) s.d.59 s.i.d.verso stretcher exhib.lit. 11-Jun-4 Villa Grisebach, Berlin #1605/R est:80000-120000
£53333 $98133 €80000 Figurale, gamma (70x70cm-28x28in) s.d.1950 s.i. on stretcher prov.exhib. 11-Jun-4 Villa Grisebach, Berlin #73/R est:80000-100000
£68531 $116504 €98000 Bird people and others (59x72cm-23x28in) s.d.45 panel. 29-Nov-3 Bassenge, Berlin #6924/R est:75000
£73427 $124825 €105000 Crossing (110x100cm-43x39in) s.d.64 s.i.d.1964 stretcher prov.exhib.lit. 27-Nov-3 Lempertz, Koln #297/R est:100000-110000
£76667 $141067 €115000 Composition (100x120cm-39x47in) s.d.52 s.i.d.verso stretcher exhib.lit. 11-Jun-4 Villa Grisebach, Berlin #1604/R est:100000-150000
£80000 $147200 €120000 Pink and turquoise (100x81cm-39x32in) s.d.59 s.i.d.verso prov.exhib. 11-Jun-4 Villa Grisebach, Berlin #74/R est:120000-150000
£120000 $220800 €180000 With bright yellow (100x120cm-39x47in) s.d.1953 s.i.d. stretcher. 10-Jun-4 Hauswedell & Nolte, Hamburg #517/R est:180000
£139860 $237762 €200000 Black stroke (100x161cm-39x63in) s.d.55 s.i.d. stretcher prov. 28-Nov-3 Villa Grisebach, Berlin #82/R est:200000-250000
Prints
£2517 $4330 €3600 Coloured aquatint 1957 - 4 (33x45cm-13x18in) s. col aquatint. 2-Dec-3 Hauswedell & Nolte, Hamburg #462/R est:3000
£2550 $4693 €3800 Red out of blue (5x47cm-2x19in) s.i.d. col lithograph. 26-Mar-4 Ketterer, Hamburg #580/R est:3000-3500
£2550 $4693 €3800 Dominant blue (57x48cm-22x19in) s.i.d. col lithograph. 26-Mar-4 Ketterer, Hamburg #581/R est:3000-3500
Works on paper
£800 $1472 €1200 Reclining female nude (38x59cm-15x23in) s.d.1929 pen ink brush over pencil. 12-Jun-4 Villa Grisebach, Berlin #807/R
£1748 $2972 €2500 Leda (28x25cm-11x10in) s.d.49 d.9/VII/49 verso double-sided. 29-Nov-3 Bassenge, Berlin #6925/R est:2500
£2028 $3448 €2900 Fishermen fishing (47x63cm-19x25in) s.d.36 pen. 27-Nov-3 Lempertz, Koln #298/R est:3000
£2153 $3595 €3100 Baltic fishermen with boat (48x63cm-19x25in) s.d. Indian ink brush. 25-Oct-3 Dr Lehr, Berlin #367/R est:3500
£4000 $7360 €6000 Composition (50x57cm-20x22in) s.d.49 i.verso graphite W/C. 11-Jun-4 Villa Grisebach, Berlin #1603/R est:4000-6000
£4895 $8420 €7000 Composition (49x62cm-19x24in) s.d.1954 ink cardboard. 4-Dec-3 Van Ham, Cologne #346/R est:7000
£10000 $18200 €14600 Untitled (42x60cm-17x24in) s.d.60 W/C prov.exhib. 5-Feb-4 Christie's, London #120/R est:8000-12000
£12587 $21650 €18000 Black orbit of star (42x60cm-17x24in) s.d.1955 W/C brown Indian ink opaque white prov. 5-Dec-3 Ketterer, Munich #144/R est:18000-25000
£16667 $30500 €25000 Composition (14x21cm-6x8in) s.d.50 gouache W/C bodycol prov. 4-Jun-4 Lempertz, Koln #323/R est:25000
£17333 $31027 €26000 Blue fruit harvest (21x28cm-8x11in) s.d. gouache board. 15-May-4 Bassenge, Berlin #7063/R est:25000
£17333 $31893 €26000 Untitled (42x60cm-17x24in) s.d.63 W/C prov.exhib. 11-Jun-4 Villa Grisebach, Berlin #67/R est:25000-35000
£23077 $39692 €33000 Composition (60x42cm-24x17in) s.d.1964 W/C. 2-Dec-3 Hauswedell & Nolte, Hamburg #461/R est:18000

NAYAR, Ved (1933-) Indian

Works on paper
£1359 $2500 €1984 Untitled (56x45cm-22x18in) s.d.86 pencil black ink. 24-Mar-4 Sotheby's, New York #185/R est:2500-3500

NAYLOR, Marie J (fl.1883-1904) British

£380 $692 €555 Portrait of a young woman (50x39cm-20x15in) s. 1-Jul-4 Mellors & Kirk, Nottingham #783

NAZARI, Nazario (attrib) (1724-?) Italian

£7222 $13000 €10544 Portrait of Venetian Senator, standing by a table (235x158cm-93x62in) prov. 22-Jan-4 Sotheby's, New York #252a/R est:20000-30000

NAZON, François-Henri (1821-1902) French

£620 $1147 €905 Beach scene at dusk (24x38cm-9x15in) s. 10-Mar-4 Sotheby's, Olympia #242/R

NAZZARI, Bartolommeo (1699-1758) Italian

Works on paper
£650 $1125 €949 Portraits of ecclesiastics in cartouches (29x21cm-11x8in) black white chk pair prov.lit. 12-Dec-3 Christie's, Kensington #354/R

NEAL, James (1918-) British

£380 $608 €551 Still life with teapots (5x13cm-2x5in) s. board. 16-Sep-3 Bonhams, Knightsbridge #95
£450 $720 €653 Egypt (11x7cm-4x3in) s. panel. 16-Sep-3 Bonhams, Knightsbridge #1/R
£480 $768 €696 Marine (9x11cm-4x4in) s. board. 16-Sep-3 Bonhams, Knightsbridge #94
£700 $1295 €1022 Egypt (28x16cm-11x6in) s. board on panel. 11-Feb-4 Sotheby's, Olympia #205/R

NEALE, E and SEVERN, Walter (19th C) British

£1150 $2070 €1679 Day before the Glorious Twelth (61x97cm-24x38in) s.i. W/C scratching out. 21-Apr-4 Christie's, Kensington #181/R est:1000-1500

NEALE, Edward (19/20th C) British

Works on paper
£250 $463 €365 Grouse in a snow storm (10x15cm-4x6in) s.d.1970 W/C. 13-Feb-4 Keys, Aylsham #554

NEALE, George Hall (fl.1883-1935) British

£260 $481 €380 Portrait of Thomas Hughes (133x103cm-52x41in) s. 13-Jan-4 Bonhams, Knightsbridge #9
£750 $1358 €1095 Dinham Bridge, Ludlow (36x43cm-14x17in) board. 31-Mar-4 Brightwells, Leominster #960/R
£1050 $1943 €1533 Cottage interior with woman taking tea (42x52cm-17x20in) s.d.92. 14-Jul-4 Bonhams, Chester #333/R est:1000-1500

NEALE, John (20th C) British

£195 $350 €285 Sunlight and shadows at Pin Mill on the Thames (38x61cm-15x24in) s. masonite. 14-May-4 Skinner, Boston #257/R

NEALE, Maud Hall (fl.1889-1940) British

£250 $403 €363 Mountainous landscape with trees in the foreground (99x74cm-39x29in) s. 13-Aug-3 Andrew Hartley, Ilkley #816
£300 $546 €438 Lake District landscape (27x43cm-11x17in) s. 5-Feb-4 Mellors & Kirk, Nottingham #549
£1700 $2703 €2465 Portrait of Mrs McLaren (101x75cm-40x30in) s. 9-Sep-3 Bonhams, Knightsbridge #171/R est:800-1200

NEAPOLITAN SCHOOL (14th C) Italian

Works on paper
£15385 $25692 €22000 Francescan monk (170x85cm-67x33in) fresco. 7-Oct-3 Pandolfini, Florence #544 est:23000-25000

NEAPOLITAN SCHOOL (17th C) Italian

£3333 $6000 €4866 Saint Peter (50x36cm-20x14in) 21-Jan-4 Sotheby's, New York #90/R est:10000-15000
£6133 $11163 €9200 Battle scene (135x160cm-53x63in) 4-Jul-4 Finarte, Venice #22/R est:9000-12000
£6944 $11806 €10000 Harvest (79x103cm-31x41in) 28-Oct-3 Il Ponte, Milan #382/R
£6993 $11678 €10000 Portrait of young man with cat (43x36cm-17x14in) after Caravaggio. 7-Oct-3 Pandolfini, Florence #570/R est:10000-12000
£7333 $13127 €11000 Christ and the adulterer (122x152cm-48x60in) 17-May-4 Finarte Semenzato, Rome #108/R est:11000-13000
£7667 $13723 €11500 Allegory of Vanity (122x174cm-48x69in) 12-May-4 Finarte Semenzato, Milan #17/R est:8000-12000
£7801 $13028 €11000 Allegory of the World (102x170cm-40x67in) 23-Jun-3 Finarte Semenzato, Rome #178/R
£8000 $13840 €11680 Crucifixion of Saint Peter (176x129cm-69x51in) 12-Dec-3 Christie's, Kensington #221/R est:8000-12000
£8000 $14640 €11680 Portrait of man (46x35cm-18x14in) exhib.lit. 8-Jul-4 Sotheby's, London #207/R est:3000-5000
£8152 $15000 €11902 Still life with basket of mixed flowers, assorted fruits, urn and guinea pigs (96x109cm-38x43in) 27-Jun-4 Freeman, Philadelphia #1/R est:4000-8000
£8392 $14434 €12000 Ecce Homo (134x96cm-53x38in) 2-Dec-3 Sotheby's, Milan #102/R est:12000-16000
£10000 $17000 €14400 Moses and the rock (109x91cm-43x36in) 28-Oct-3 Il Ponte, Milan #381/R
£10067 $18523 €15000 Philosopher (103x79cm-41x31in) init. 29-Mar-4 Pandolfini, Florence #775/R est:18000
£14444 $26000 €21088 Isaac blessing Esau (113x182cm-44x72in) 23-Jan-4 Christie's, Rockefeller NY #131/R est:7000-10000
£15333 $27447 €23000 Still lives of fruit (117x82cm-46x32in) pair exhib.lit. 17-May-4 Finarte Semenzato, Rome #55/R est:24000-26000
£16667 $30000 €24334 Barber (147x113cm-58x44in) 23-Jan-4 Christie's, Rockefeller NY #6/R est:4000-6000
£19444 $35000 €28388 Judith with the head of Holofernes (13x13cm-5x5in) copper. 22-Jan-4 Sotheby's, New York #18/R est:25000-35000
£19444 $35000 €28388 Still life with a blue and yellow macaw perched atop of a watermelon. Still life cockatoo and fruit (84x133cm-33x52in) pair. 22-Jan-4 Sotheby's, New York #260/R est:40000-60000
£22378 $37371 €32000 Saint Peter (128x98cm-50x39in) 7-Oct-3 Pandolfini, Florence #621/R est:40000-50000
£22819 $40846 €34000 Peaches, fruit and pumpkin. Apricots, cherries and figs (73x96cm-29x38in) pair. 26-May-4 Porro, Milan #39/R est:40000-50000
£25698 $46000 €37519 Tobit applying fish gall to his father's sightless eyes (104x122cm-41x48in) 11-May-4 Roland's, New York #473290/R
£27778 $50000 €40556 Three angels appearing to Abraham (113x181cm-44x71in) 23-Jan-4 Christie's, Rockefeller NY #130/R est:8000-12000
£75000 $137250 €109500 Hercules and Antaeus (234x92cm-92x36in) prov. 6-Jul-4 Sotheby's, Olympia #499/R est:8000-12000
£78014 $130283 €110000 Saint Jerome (167x188cm-66x74in) 15-Oct-3 Finarte Semenzato, Rome #148/R est:60000

NEAPOLITAN SCHOOL (18th C) Italian

£4631 $8521 €6900 Madonna and Child with angel (62x47cm-24x19in) oval. 24-Mar-4 Finarte Semenzato, Rome #176/R est:3500
£4730 $8324 €7000 Portrait of queen (135x97cm-53x38in) 18-May-4 Sotheby's, Milan #171/R est:7000-10000
£5000 $9150 €7300 Madonna and Child (15x12cm-6x5in) 6-Jul-4 Sotheby's, Olympia #517/R est:5000-7000
£5913 $10584 €8633 Portrait of gentleman wearing red (77x61cm-30x24in) 25-May-4 Bukowskis, Stockholm #515/R est:40000-50000 (S.KR 80000)
£7194 $11799 €10000 Still life with apples, figs, pear, grapes and pots (75x102cm-30x40in) 4-Jun-3 Sotheby's, Milan #95/R est:12000-15000
£8630 $14671 €12600 Martyrdom (165x135cm-65x53in) 4-Nov-3 Ansorena, Madrid #41/R est:12600
£11972 $20951 €17000 Holy Family (120x139cm-47x55in) 17-Dec-3 Christie's, Rome #497/R est:15000-20000
£12838 $22595 €19000 Portrait of soldier (86x71cm-34x28in) 18-May-4 Sotheby's, Milan #474/R est:7000-10000
£15541 $27351 €23000 Portrait of Maddalena Rospigliosi (74x61cm-29x24in) i.d.verso. 18-May-4 Sotheby's, Milan #501/R est:7000-10000
£17731 $29610 €25000 Pele-mele au jeu de l'oie et jeux de societe Italiens (77x51cm-30x20in) 17-Oct-3 Tajan, Paris #22/R est:10000-12000
£18667 $33413 €28000 Still lives with flowers and dead game (150x60cm-59x24in) pair exhib.lit. 17-May-4 Finarte Semenzato, Rome #100/R est:32000-35000
£27465 $45592 €39000 Celebrating in a villa (216x555cm-85x219in) in ten parts. 11-Jul-3 Finarte, Venice #392/R est:40000-50000
£100000 $183000 €146000 Still life with shell and pears (49x106cm-19x42in) prov. 8-Jul-4 Sotheby's, London #322/R est:15000-20000

Sculpture
£8451 $13521 €12000 Saint Michael (27cm-11in) bronze. 21-Sep-3 Finarte, Venice #339/R
£10811 $19027 €16000 Archangel Saint Michael and the DEvil (18cm-7in) pat bronze. 18-May-4 Sotheby's, Milan #434/R est:8000-12000

Works on paper
£1972 $3411 €2800 Peasants and fishermen in Pozzuoli Bay (30x46cm-12x18in) W/C. 10-Dec-3 Finarte Semenzato, Rome #149/R est:3000-4000

NEAPOLITAN SCHOOL (19th C) Italian

£8609 $15669 €13000 Teti leaving Achilles with Chiron (105x144cm-41x57in) 16-Jun-4 Christie's, Rome #499/R est:10000-12800

Sculpture
£24823 $41454 €35000 Apollus (158cm-62in) bronze. 15-Oct-3 Finarte Semenzato, Rome #136/R

Works on paper
£5352 $9259 €7600 French Navy (27x36cm-11x14in) gouache. 10-Dec-3 Finarte Semenzato, Rome #155/R est:3000-3500

NEAVE, David (fl.1903-1936) British

£280 $501 €409 Girl with a hat (67x54cm-26x21in) panel. 17-Mar-4 Rupert Toovey, Partridge Green #72

NEBBIA, Cesare (attrib) (1536-1614) Italian

Works on paper
£1319 $2400 €1926 Pope baptising a crowd through a gated window (26x23cm-10x9in) pen brown ink brown wash squared in red chk. 4-Feb-4 Christie's, Rockefeller NY #121/R est:2000-3000
£1633 $2922 €2400 Ange a la mandoline (13x8cm-5x3in) brown pen grey wash graphite. 17-Mar-4 Maigret, Paris #47 est:600-800

NEBEKER, Bill (1942-) American

Sculpture
£1117 $2000 €1631 I ride the wild colts (53cm-21in) bronze edn of 25. 15-May-4 Altermann Galleries, Santa Fe #125/R
£1242 $2000 €1801 Flowers for my wagon widow (66cm-26in) bronze edition of 25. 22-Aug-3 Altermann Galleries, Santa Fe #27
£1242 $2000 €1801 Down from the stronghold (41cm-16in) bronze edition of 25. 22-Aug-3 Altermann Galleries, Santa Fe #56
£4190 $7500 €6117 Leaving a legacy (51cm-20in) bronze edn of 25. 15-May-4 Altermann Galleries, Santa Fe #11/R
£4190 $7500 €6117 If horses could talk (43cm-17in) bronze edn of 25. 15-May-4 Altermann Galleries, Santa Fe #165/R

NEBEL, Carl (1865-?) German

Works on paper
£2318 $4219 €3500 Extensive Mexican landscape (22x34cm-9x13in) s.d.1837 W/C. 19-Jun-4 Bergmann, Erlangen #751 est:3500

NEBEL, Friedrich Joseph Adolf (1818-1892) German

£915 $1584 €1300 Portrait of a lady. Portrait of a gentleman (108x83cm-43x33in) s. one d.78 one d.1872. 10-Dec-3 Christie's, Amsterdam #178
£1972 $3411 €2800 Sweet siblings (69x52cm-27x20in) s.d.1875. 10-Dec-3 Christie's, Amsterdam #177/R est:1000-1500
£4636 $8437 €7000 Portrait of Ludwig van Beethoven (99x78cm-39x31in) s.d.1859. 16-Jun-4 Dorotheum, Vienna #149/R est:9000-12000

NEBEL, Otto (1892-1975) German

£1238 $1981 €1795 Femme a sa fenetre (39x31cm-15x12in) collage paper board panel rattan. 15-May-3 Stuker, Bern #1414 est:1600-2000 (S.FR 2600)

Works on paper
£330 $562 €482 Man's head (11x8cm-4x3in) s.d.1935 bodycol. 5-Nov-3 Dobiaschofsky, Bern #1805 (S.FR 750)
£366 $656 €534 Uplift (33x20cm-13x8in) s.i.d.193 mixed media. 12-May-4 Dobiaschofsky, Bern #1888/R (S.FR 850)
£431 $772 €629 Elements (24x9cm-9x4in) s.d.1951 bodycol paper collage. 12-May-4 Dobiaschofsky, Bern #1880/R (S.FR 1000)
£948 $1697 €1384 After 70 winters (43x29cm-17x11in) s.i.d.1963 gouache. 13-May-4 Stuker, Bern #266/R est:2500-3000 (S.FR 2200)
£2183 $4017 €3187 Composition (23x33cm-9x13in) s.d.1966 collage. 8-Jun-4 Germann, Zurich #24/R est:4000-4500 (S.FR 5000)
£2715 $4534 €3964 N 507 - intervention (41x26cm-16x10in) s.i.d. 2 Oktober 1937 gouache prov. 24-Jun-3 Germann, Zurich #91/R est:6000-7000 (S.FR 6000)
£2715 $4615 €3964 Muntelier N 312A (24x31cm-9x12in) s.d.1933 gouache Indian ink grattage. 25-Nov-3 Germann, Zurich #59/R est:5000-7000 (S.FR 6000)

NEBOLSIN, Anatoly Alexeyevich (1928-) Russian

£498 $831 €727 Olga (80x120cm-31x47in) s.i.d.1969 verso prov. 17-Nov-3 Waddingtons, Toronto #290/R (C.D 1100)

NECHAEVA, V A (1920-1992) Russian

£245 $450 €358 At the Oka River (16x27cm-6x11in) painted 1950. 27-Mar-4 Shishkin Gallery, Moscow #93/R
£326 $600 €476 Dusk (19x29cm-7x11in) canvas on cardboard painted 1950's. 27-Mar-4 Shishkin Gallery, Moscow #91/R

NECHVATAL, Dennis (1948-) American

£273 $500 €399 Landscape no.1 (56x66cm-22x26in) 10-Jul-4 Hindman, Chicago #369/R
£601 $1100 €877 Space no.2 (56x66cm-22x26in) 10-Jul-4 Hindman, Chicago #370/R est:200-400

NECK, Jan van (1635-1714) Dutch

£12000 $21600 €17520 Bacchanal with nymphs, satyrs and putti before a herm (70x58cm-28x23in) s.d.1676. 23-Apr-4 Christie's, Kensington #113/R est:8000-12000

NECKERMANN, Marlene (20th C) German

£345 $576 €500 Seated female nude (130x130cm-51x51in) s. verso. 9-Jul-3 Hugo Ruef, Munich #359

NEDDEAU, Donald Frederick Price (1913-1998) Canadian
£1071 $1843 €1564 Country Fair (65x80cm-26x31in) s. exhib. 2-Dec-3 Joyner Waddington, Toronto #358/R est:3000-4000 (C.D 2400)

NEDER, Johann Michael (1807-1882) Austrian
£2416 $4325 €3600 A bull and a cow (34x42cm-13x17in) s.d.1837 board. 27-May-4 Dorotheum, Vienna #197/R est:3600-4500
£5594 $9510 €8000 Father visiting daughter (30x23cm-12x9in) s. board on panel. 24-Nov-3 Dorotheum, Vienna #69/R est:8000-10000

NEEBE, Minnie Harms (1873-1946) American
£795 $1400 €1161 Still life (66x56cm-26x22in) s. painted c.1920. 23-May-4 Treadway Gallery, Cincinnati #576/R

NEEDHAM, Arthur (?) British?
£350 $595 €511 Highland loch scene with mountains above (51x76cm-20x30in) s. 5-Nov-3 John Nicholson, Haslemere #593

NEEFFS, Pieter (elder) (1578-1658) Flemish
£2500 $4525 €3800 Cathedral interior (18x21cm-7x8in) board. 14-Apr-4 Ansorena, Madrid #149/R est:3800
£9500 $17100 €13870 Church interior with figures and dogs (54x69cm-21x27in) s. 21-Apr-4 Bonhams, New Bond Street #1/R est:5000-7000
£15789 $29053 €24000 Church interior (7x10cm-3x4in) s. copper octagonal. 24-Jun-4 Christie's, Paris #16/R est:5000-7000
£20270 $35676 €30000 Church interior by night a priest and other figures by torchlight (53x80cm-21x31in) s. panel. 18-May-4 Sotheby's, Amsterdam #44/R est:12000-18000
£55000 $99000 €80300 Interior of a cathedral with elegant company, a service in progress in a side altar (42x59cm-17x23in) s.i. panel. 21-Apr-4 Christie's, London #4/R est:15000-25000
£66207 $110566 €96000 Many people in Cathedral in Antwerp (41x61cm-16x24in) s. panel. 11-Nov-3 Vendu Notarishuis, Rotterdam #100/R est:10000-15000

NEEFFS, Pieter (elder-attrib) (1578-1658) Flemish
£3974 $7232 €6000 View of the interior of the so-called Cathedral of Antwerp (39x46cm-15x18in) panel prov. 16-Jun-4 Dorotheum, Vienna #81/R est:7000-10000

NEEFFS, Pieter (younger) (1620-1675) Flemish
£36000 $65880 €52560 Cathedral interior (48x64cm-19x25in) s.d.1648 panel prov. 8-Jul-4 Sotheby's, London #285/R est:15000-20000

NEEFFS, Pieter (younger-attrib) (1620-1675) Flemish
£6500 $11830 €9490 Architectural fantasy with Saint Peter imprisoned (25x21cm-10x8in) indis sig. 21-Jun-4 Christie's, London #244/R est:8000-12000

NEEL, Alice (1900-1984) American
£14535 $25000 €21221 Fugs (127x76cm-50x30in) s.d.66 prov. 3-Dec-3 Doyle, New York #62/R est:30000-40000
£41916 $70000 €61197 Portrait of George (78x58cm-31x23in) s. painted c.1967 prov. 13-Nov-3 Sotheby's, New York #221/R est:50000-70000

NEELMEYER, Ludwig (1814-1870) German
£800 $1456 €1200 Returning home after the hunt (35x43cm-14x17in) s.d.1842 board. 30-Jun-4 Neumeister, Munich #632/R

NEER, Aert van der (1603-1677) Dutch
£12086 $22117 €17646 Village on fire at night (32x45cm-13x18in) panel. 9-Jun-4 Rasmussen, Copenhagen #1520/R est:50000-75000 (D.KR 135000)
£23973 $40753 €35000 Moonlit river landscape with fishermen repairing their nets (42x56cm-17x22in) mono. panel prov.exhib.lit. 4-Nov-3 Sotheby's, Amsterdam #54/R est:25000-35000
£24138 $40069 €35000 Summer landscape with travellers (55x79cm-22x31in) board. 30-Sep-3 Ansorena, Madrid #47/R est:35000
£30000 $51900 €43800 Wooded landscape with peasants conversing on a road by a cottage (22x32cm-9x13in) mono. panel prov. 10-Dec-3 Christie's, London #28/R est:30000-50000
£37162 $65405 €55000 Extensive river landscape by moonlight with fishermen and cows in the foreground (109x150cm-43x59in) mono. prov.exhib.lit. 18-May-4 Sotheby's, Amsterdam #18/R est:30000-40000

NEER, Aert van der (attrib) (1603-1677) Dutch
£4196 $7133 €6000 Moonlit landscape (40x62cm-16x24in) mono. lit. 28-Nov-3 Schloss Ahlden, Ahlden #1383/R est:6500

NEER, Eglon Hendrik van der (1634-1703) Dutch
£6849 $11644 €10000 Family portrait of a gentleman, his wife and their four children (135x120cm-53x47in) prov.exhib.lit. 4-Nov-3 Sotheby's, Amsterdam #18/R est:10000-15000

NEER, Eglon Hendrik van der (attrib) (1634-1703) Dutch
£1987 $3616 €3000 Venus et Adonis (27x23cm-11x9in) panel. 15-Jun-4 Galerie Moderne, Brussels #221/R est:3000-4000

NEER, Eglon Hendrik van der (circle) (1634-1703) Dutch
£6500 $11895 €9490 Card palyers (27x23cm-11x9in) panel. 8-Jul-4 Sotheby's, London #272/R est:6000-8000

NEERVOORT, Jan (1863-1940) Belgian
£671 $1188 €1000 Paysan a la ferme (65x82cm-26x32in) s. 27-Apr-4 Campo, Vlaamse Kaai #534/R
£1408 $2437 €2000 Bourgeois interior with lady, dog and parrot (44x52cm-17x20in) s. panel. 15-Dec-3 Bernaerts, Antwerp #71/R est:2000-2500

NEESON, John R (1948-) Australian
£310 $573 €453 Mirror 2 (121x182cm-48x72in) s.d.1989 prov. 15-Mar-4 Sotheby's, Melbourne #170 (A.D 750)

NEFF, Edith (20th C) American
£313 $500 €457 Self portrait (112x150cm-44x59in) s. 19-Sep-3 Freeman, Philadelphia #125
£438 $700 €639 Pony ride (140x178cm-55x70in) s. 19-Sep-3 Freeman, Philadelphia #169/R
£469 $750 €685 Figures at a park bench (137x160cm-54x63in) s. 19-Sep-3 Freeman, Philadelphia #66
£594 $950 €867 Construction workers (140x183cm-55x72in) s. 19-Sep-3 Freeman, Philadelphia #199/R
Works on paper
£497 $900 €726 Tree shadows on a sidewalk (58x79cm-23x31in) s. pastel. 2-Apr-4 Freeman, Philadelphia #136/R

NEFFLEN, Paul (fl.1855-1865) American?
£1413 $2600 €2063 Still life with fruit, silver compote and decanter (61x93cm-24x37in) s. 27-Jun-4 Freeman, Philadelphia #80/R est:3000-5000

NEFKENS, Martinus Jacobus (1866-1941) Dutch
£296 $536 €450 Still life of flowers (50x40cm-20x16in) s. 19-Apr-4 Glerum, Amsterdam #148/R
£621 $1037 €900 Landscape with sand cart (46x57cm-18x22in) s. 11-Nov-3 Vendu Notarishuis, Rotterdam #186

NEGRET, Edgar (1920-) Colombian
Sculpture
£915 $1665 €1373 Butterfly (36x41x41cm-14x16x16in) s. num.5/60 painted iron exec.1997. 21-Jun-4 Subastas Odalys, Caracas #181
£938 $1500 €1369 Sol (46cm-18in) s.d.1985 num.29/30 red painted metal. 20-Sep-3 Sloans & Kenyon, Bethesda #652a/R est:1750-2250

NEGRI, A (?) ?
£903 $1535 €1300 Path in the wood (48x65cm-19x26in) s. cardboard. 28-Oct-3 Il Ponte, Milan #104 est:1200-1500

NEGRI, Mario (1916-) Italian
Sculpture
£703 $1300 €1026 Torsetto Accoccolato (21x11x11cm-8x4x4in) st.s. num.4/6 brown pat bronze prov. 12-Feb-4 Sotheby's, New York #174/R est:1800-2200
£887 $1632 €1295 Madre in attera (28cm-11in) s.num.3/3 bronze. 14-Jun-4 Waddingtons, Toronto #339/R est:3000-3500 (C.D 2200)
£1027 $1900 €1499 Piccolo Torso Nero (23cm-9in) st.num.5/6 black pat bronze prov. 12-Feb-4 Sotheby's, New York #143/R est:1500-2000
£1176 $2200 €1717 Small caryatid (32cm-13in) st.init. st.sig. num.6/6 verso bronze prov. 25-Feb-4 Christie's, Rockefeller NY #90/R est:3000-5000
£1216 $2250 €1775 Figura Distesa (20x9x18cm-8x4x7in) mono. num.2/6 brown pat bronze exec 1975 prov. 12-Feb-4 Sotheby's, New York #146/R est:2000-3000
£1923 $3500 €2808 Colonna del piccolo coro (61x36x37cm-24x14x15in) mono.num.3/3 brown pat. bronze executed c.1975 prov. 29-Jun-4 Sotheby's, New York #312/R est:5000-7000
£5435 $8913 €7500 Fairy (61x25x14cm-24x10x6in) init. bronze prov.lit. 27-May-3 Sotheby's, Milan #97/R est:1000-1500

NEGRI, Pietro (c.1591-1661) Italian
£22667 $40573 €34000 Achille and Lycomedes' daughters (148x91cm-58x36in) lit. 17-May-4 Finarte Semenzato, Rome #122/R est:40000-45000

NEGRI, Pietro (circle) (c.1591-1661) Italian
£16667 $27833 €24000 Judith (61x54cm-24x21in) 22-Oct-3 Finarte Semenzato, Milan #34/R est:8000-12000

NEGRONI, Pietro (attrib) (1503-1565) Italian
£5578 $9985 €8200 Dormition de la Vierge (38x74cm-15x29in) panel prov. 19-Mar-4 Beaussant & Lefèvre, Paris #44/R est:4000-5000

NEHER, Caspar (20th C) German
£755 $1200 €1102 Landscape (43x30cm-17x12in) s. board. 14-Sep-3 Susanin's, Chicago #6099/R

NEHER, Joseph Anton (1776-1832) German
£1810 $2896 €2643 Rheinfall (43x61cm-17x24in) s.d.1830 verso. 16-Sep-3 Philippe Schuler, Zurich #3348 est:2500-3000 (S.FR 4000)

NEIDHARDT, Paul G (1873-?) German
£733 $1320 €1100 Wooded autumn landscape in Thuringen (42x62cm-17x24in) s. board. 24-Apr-4 Dr Lehr, Berlin #346/R

NEIF, Arifien (1955-) Javanese
£784 $1420 €1145 Still life (32x27cm-13x11in) s.d.88. 3-Apr-4 Glerum, Singapore #1/R est:3000-4000 (S.D 2400)
£1307 $2366 €1908 Wanita and Bunga (50x45cm-20x18in) s.d.95. 3-Apr-4 Glerum, Singapore #38/R est:4400-5400 (S.D 4000)
£2471 $4127 €3608 If you really love me, let me know (70x60cm-28x24in) s.d.2001 acrylic. 26-Oct-3 Christie's, Hong Kong #78/R est:28000-35000 (HK.D 32000)
£2941 $5324 €4294 I wish you love (60x70cm-24x28in) s.d.2002 i.d.2002 verso. 3-Apr-4 Glerum, Singapore #37/R est:6000-7000 (S.D 9000)
£5792 $9672 €8456 Ballroom, 1994 (73x61cm-29x24in) s.d.94 acrylic lit. 26-Oct-3 Christie's, Hong Kong #77/R est:28000-35000 (HK.D 75000)
£8535 $15363 €12461 Dancing (180x100cm-71x39in) s.d.95 prov.lit. 25-Apr-4 Christie's, Hong Kong #572/R est:130000-200000 (HK.D 120000)

NEILAND, Brendan (1941-) British
£703 $1300 €1026 Tolmer Square II (77x99cm-30x39in) acrylic painted 1981 prov. 12-Feb-4 Sotheby's, New York #296/R est:1800-2200

NEILL, Henry Echlin (1888-1981) British
Works on paper
£300 $537 €438 Rapho, Co Conegal (27x37cm-11x15in) s. pencil W/C pen ink. 14-May-4 Christie's, Kensington #308

NEILLOT, Louis (1898-1973) French
£1343 $2497 €2000 Paris, La Seine (60x73cm-24x29in) s. 3-Mar-4 Tajan, Paris #102 est:2000-3000
£2013 $3745 €3000 Gravieres, Bourbonnais (50x61cm-20x24in) s. lit. 2-Mar-4 Artcurial Briest, Paris #238/R est:2500-3000
£2778 $4639 €4000 Vase de fleurs (61x50cm-24x20in) s. 21-Oct-3 Artcurial Briest, Paris #212/R est:2500-3500
£3143 $5847 €4685 La carriere abandonnee (73x92cm-29x36in) s. painted c.1964 prov.lit. 2-Mar-4 Artcurial Briest, Paris #237/R est:3500-4000

NEILSON, Harry B (fl.1895-1900) British
Works on paper
£1600 $2912 €2336 Day with the Royal Reynardshire Hunt in the first light (48x64cm-19x25in) s.d.1920 black ink W/C wash. 29-Jun-4 Beeston Castle Salerooms, Tarporley #402/R est:500-800
£2600 $4732 €3796 Day with the Royal Reynardshire Hunt going to the meet (48x64cm-19x25in) s.d.1920 black ink W/C wash. 29-Jun-4 Beeston Castle Salerooms, Tarporley #401/R est:500-800

NEILSON, Raymond Perry Rodgers (1881-1964) American
£625 $1000 €913 Gentleman of the turf, Ralph Beaver Strassburger (91x76cm-36x30in) s.d.34. 19-Sep-3 Freeman, Philadelphia #196/R est:400-600

NEIMAN, Leroy (1926-) American
£12500 $22000 €18250 Jazz players (56x86cm-22x34in) s.d.61. 23-May-4 Hindman, Chicago #979/R est:5000-7000
£14857 $26000 €21691 Superbowl XI - Miami and Dallas (60x83cm-24x33in) s. enamel board painted 1972 exhib. 17-Dec-3 Christie's, Rockefeller NY #213/R est:8000-10000
£21714 $38000 €31702 Girgaglia Yacht Race (91x110cm-36x43in) s. i.verso enamel printed paper map painted 1966. 17-Dec-3 Christie's, Rockefeller NY #157/R est:4000-6000
£24000 $42000 €35040 Painting a playmate (91x61cm-36x24in) s.d.60 enamel board exhib.lit. 17-Dec-3 Christie's, Rockefeller NY #58/R est:10000-15000
£25714 $45000 €37542 Bacchanal/ Milton Berle's 50th Birthday Party (88x121cm-35x48in) s.d.58 s.i.d.verso enamel board. 17-Dec-3 Christie's, Rockefeller NY #26/R est:8000-12000
£28571 $50000 €41714 Hialeah Race Course (97x153cm-38x60in) s. painted 1959. 17-Dec-3 Christie's, Rockefeller NY #25/R est:8000-12000
£40000 $70000 €58400 Auction at Sotheby's - From Man at his Leisure (66x91cm-26x36in) s. i.verso enamel printed paper collage board painted 1972. 17-Dec-3 Christie's, Rockefeller NY #226/R est:15000-20000
£51429 $90000 €75086 Le Mans - from Man at his Leisure (91x122cm-36x48in) s. enamel board painted 1969. 17-Dec-3 Christie's, Rockefeller NY #160/R est:20000-30000
Works on paper
£1006 $1800 €1469 Start to twist (70x51cm-28x20in) s. mixed media. 21-Mar-4 Bonhams & Butterfields, Los Angeles #7374a/R est:2000-3000
£1250 $2200 €1825 Stan Kenton (36x28cm-14x11in) s.i.d.1959 W/C. 23-May-4 Treadway Gallery, Cincinnati #722/R est:600-800
£1396 $2500 €2038 Brian Epstein with the Beatles in the background (74x53cm-29x21in) s. mixed media. 21-Mar-4 Bonhams & Butterfields, Los Angeles #7373a/R est:2000-3000
£1396 $2500 €2038 Roulette table II (41x53cm-16x21in) s. mixed media. 21-Mar-4 Bonhams & Butterfields, Los Angeles #7374/R est:2000-3000
£1420 $2500 €2073 Stillman's gym (33x25cm-13x10in) s. dr exec.c.1959. 23-May-4 Treadway Gallery, Cincinnati #726/R est:600-800
£1676 $3000 €2447 Janoree bullabulue (58x41cm-23x16in) s. mixed media. 21-Mar-4 Bonhams & Butterfields, Los Angeles #7375/R est:2000-3000
£1705 $3000 €2489 Paris cafe (33x56cm-13x22in) s. dr exec.c.1959. 23-May-4 Treadway Gallery, Cincinnati #723/R est:600-800
£1705 $3000 €2489 SS United States (36x58cm-14x23in) s.d.1968 ink. 23-May-4 Treadway Gallery, Cincinnati #724/R est:600-800
£1847 $3250 €2697 Max Roach (33x28cm-13x11in) s.i.d.1957 pastel pencil. 23-May-4 Treadway Gallery, Cincinnati #725/R est:600-800
£3143 $5500 €4589 Femlin (22x37cm-9x15in) one s. ink gouache exec Oct 1969. 17-Dec-3 Christie's, Rockefeller NY #84/R est:3000-4000
£3911 $7000 €5710 Bunny Tracey loves her tail (62x48cm-24x19in) s. mixed media. 21-Mar-4 Bonhams & Butterfields, Los Angeles #7375a/R est:2000-3000
£4000 $7000 €5840 Femlin (31x19cm-12x7in) one s. ink pencil two exec March 1970. 17-Dec-3 Christie's, Rockefeller NY #85/R est:3000-4000
£4000 $7000 €5840 Femlin (41x32cm-16x13in) one s. ink board two exec Nov 1969. 17-Dec-3 Christie's, Rockefeller NY #83/R est:3000-4000
£4286 $7500 €6258 Femlin (28x35cm-11x14in) one s. ink gouache two exec Dec 1967. 17-Dec-3 Christie's, Rockefeller NY #87/R est:3000-4000
£5714 $10000 €8342 Backstage at the Lido (65x79cm-26x31in) s.i. chl paper on board exec Dec 1964 exhib.lit. 17-Dec-3 Christie's, Rockefeller NY #168/R est:2000-30000
£6286 $11000 €9178 Femlins (36x19cm-14x7in) ink gouache three exec June 1963. 17-Dec-3 Christie's, Rockefeller NY #86/R est:3000-4000
£7429 $13000 €10846 The Not Nice guy (53x44cm-21x17in) s. chl gouache board exec May 1957. 17-Dec-3 Christie's, Rockefeller NY #48/R est:20000-30000
£12571 $22000 €18354 French Riviera - Cannes Beauty Contest (60x77cm-24x30in) i.d.1960 pencil paper on board. 17-Dec-3 Christie's, Rockefeller NY #169/R est:2000-3000
£16000 $28000 €23360 New York Playboy club (73x58cm-29x23in) W/C pencil exec March 1965. 17-Dec-3 Christie's, Rockefeller NY #51/R est:2000-3000
£17143 $30000 €25029 Bird (61x48cm-24x19in) s. ink gouache exec 1967. 17-Dec-3 Christie's, Rockefeller NY #10/R est:6000-8000

NEIRMAN, Leonardo M (1932-) American/Mexican
£745 $1200 €1088 Cosmic flame (46x53cm-18x21in) s.d.1963 acrylic board. 22-Feb-3 Bunte, Elgin #1189
£1366 $2200 €1994 Untitled (119x89cm-47x35in) s. acrylic masonite. 22-Feb-3 Bunte, Elgin #1189a est:2000-3000

NEITHARDT, Johann Matthias (1816-1886) Swiss
Works on paper
£818 $1358 €1186 Rheinfall (36x48cm-14x19in) s. W/C. 13-Jun-3 Zofingen, Switzerland #2370/R est:2500 (S.FR 1800)

NEJAD, Mehmed (1923-1994) Turkish
£375 $625 €548 White composition (27x35cm-11x14in) s.d.957. 25-Oct-3 Rasmussen, Havnen #4002 (D.KR 4000)

NEJEDLY, Otakar (1883-1957) Czechoslovakian
£1313 $2180 €1917 River (68x103cm-27x41in) s. 4-Oct-3 Dorotheum, Prague #31/R est:60000-90000 (C.KR 60000)
£1853 $3447 €2705 Funeral (53x63cm-21x25in) s. 6-Mar-4 Dorotheum, Prague #59/R est:90000-140000 (C.KR 90000)
£2845 $4723 €4154 Pathway in Jilove (95x114cm-37x45in) s. oil tempera. 4-Oct-3 Dorotheum, Prague #132/R est:90000-150000 (C.KR 130000)
£2953 $5197 €4430 Ceylon (40x51cm-16x20in) s. 22-May-4 Dorotheum, Prague #55/R est:120000-180000 (C.KR 140000)
£8755 $14533 €12782 From Ceylon (65x75cm-26x30in) s.d.1909. 4-Oct-3 Dorotheum, Prague #20/R est:200000-300000 (C.KR 400000)

NEL, Karel Anthony (1955-) South African?
Works on paper
£9083 $16259 €13261 Shore beyond (202x106cm-80x42in) s.i.d.92 mixed media bonded fibre. 31-May-4 Stephan Welz, Johannesburg #552/R est:50000-70000 (SA.R 110000)

NELAN, Charles (1854-1904) American
Works on paper
£699 $1300 €1021 Bottled. Will he escape Levi P Morton for President. Crop of 1896 (56x43cm-22x17in) s. ink over pencil three. 6-Mar-4 North East Auctions, Portsmouth #517

NELIMARKKA, Eero (1891-1977) Finnish
£403 $749 €600 Winter's day (40x69cm-16x27in) s.d.64. 7-Mar-4 Bukowskis, Helsinki #406/R
£483 $889 €720 Landscape (28x40cm-11x16in) s. 25-Mar-4 Hagelstam, Helsinki #836
£531 $966 €780 Southern landscape (49x45cm-19x18in) s.d.1955. 8-Feb-4 Bukowskis, Helsinki #409/R
£549 $879 €780 Landscape (39x48cm-15x19in) s. 18-Sep-3 Hagelstam, Helsinki #964
£563 $901 €800 Winter in the forest (40x41cm-16x16in) s.d.1933. 21-Sep-3 Bukowskis, Helsinki #407/R
£563 $901 €800 Interior (24x33cm-9x13in) s.d.1926. 18-Sep-3 Hagelstam, Helsinki #772
£694 $1160 €1000 Landscape (45x50cm-18x20in) s.d.1931. 23-Oct-3 Hagelstam, Helsinki #845
£694 $1160 €1000 Landscape (38x47cm-15x19in) s.d.1952. 23-Oct-3 Hagelstam, Helsinki #945/R
£704 $1127 €1000 Field landscape (46x60cm-18x24in) s.d.1973. 18-Sep-3 Hagelstam, Helsinki #810
£775 $1239 €1100 Winter landscape (31x65cm-12x26in) s.d.1942. 18-Sep-3 Hagelstam, Helsinki #811/R
£800 $1472 €1200 Field landscape (47x56cm-19x22in) s.d.1950. 9-Jun-4 Bukowskis, Helsinki #499/R
£805 $1498 €1200 Yellow flowers (55x46cm-22x18in) s.d.1937. 7-Mar-4 Bukowskis, Helsinki #401/R
£833 $1392 €1200 River landscape in autumn (46x65cm-18x26in) s.d.1940. 23-Oct-3 Hagelstam, Helsinki #861/R
£833 $1392 €1200 Solitary pine tree (39x46cm-15x18in) s.d.1929. 26-Oct-3 Bukowskis, Helsinki #433/R
£845 $1352 €1200 Landscape (46x82cm-18x32in) s.d.1974. 18-Sep-3 Hagelstam, Helsinki #954
£872 $1605 €1300 Landscape (46x56cm-18x22in) s.d.1937. 25-Mar-4 Hagelstam, Helsinki #1029
£872 $1623 €1300 Fjord landscape (33x57cm-13x22in) s.d.1933. 7-Mar-4 Bukowskis, Helsinki #405/R est:1000
£915 $1465 €1300 In the studio (66x56cm-26x22in) s.d.1947. 18-Sep-3 Hagelstam, Helsinki #812/R
£940 $1748 €1400 Winter landscape (46x87cm-18x34in) s.d.1937. 7-Mar-4 Bukowskis, Helsinki #404/R
£986 $1647 €1420 Winter landscape with houses on the plain (48x82cm-19x32in) s.d.1941. 23-Oct-3 Hagelstam, Helsinki #860/R
£1007 $1852 €1500 Landscape from Muonio (103x40cm-41x16in) s.d.1944. 25-Mar-4 Hagelstam, Helsinki #953 est:1200
£1021 $1634 €1450 Winter (46x86cm-18x34in) s. 18-Sep-3 Hagelstam, Helsinki #944
£1042 $1740 €1500 River landscape (46x73cm-18x29in) s.d.1930. 23-Oct-3 Hagelstam, Helsinki #961/R est:1600
£1049 $1783 €1500 Paris (44x64cm-17x25in) s.d.1920 board exhib. 29-Nov-3 Bukowskis, Helsinki #69/R est:1600-1800
£1119 $1902 €1600 The meeting (38x46cm-15x18in) s. exhib. 29-Nov-3 Bukowskis, Helsinki #148/R est:2000-2200
£1127 $1803 €1600 Winter landscape (47x70cm-19x28in) s.d.1962. 21-Sep-3 Bukowskis, Helsinki #406/R est:1200
£1141 $1825 €1620 Winter landscape (46x88cm-18x35in) s. 18-Sep-3 Hagelstam, Helsinki #942/R est:1500
£1216 $2177 €1800 Landscape (55x65cm-22x26in) s.d.1952. 8-May-4 Bukowskis, Helsinki #46/R est:1500-1800
£1469 $2497 €2100 Landscape from Alavus (46x87cm-18x34in) s.d.1943. 29-Nov-3 Bukowskis, Helsinki #216/R est:1500-2000
£2109 $3838 €3100 Winter's day (90x125cm-35x49in) s. 8-Feb-4 Bukowskis, Helsinki #411/R est:2500
£2267 $4171 €3400 East Bothnian girl (55x46cm-22x18in) s.d.1917. 9-Jun-4 Bukowskis, Helsinki #500/R est:1000

NELIMARKKA, Tuomas (1925-1997) Finnish
£349 $642 €520 Winter landscape (38x68cm-15x27in) s.d.1966. 25-Mar-4 Hagelstam, Helsinki #1057

NELL, William (20th C) American
£659 $1200 €962 Tabletop still life with white pitcher (46x53cm-18x21in) s. 7-Feb-4 Sloans & Kenyon, Bethesda #1295/R

NELLENS, Roger (1937-) Belgian
£1067 $1909 €1600 Mouvement immobile (170x80cm-67x31in) i.verso. 15-May-4 De Vuyst, Lokeren #236 est:1000-1100
£1232 $2132 €1750 Composition (125x105cm-49x41in) s.i.d.1976 verso. 13-Dec-3 De Vuyst, Lokeren #246/R est:1700-2000

NELLIS, Emile (?) ?
£671 $1235 €1000 La contrariete (43x34cm-17x13in) s.d.80 panel. 28-Mar-4 Anaf, Lyon #216/R

NELLIUS, Martinus (fl.1670-1706) Dutch
£4000 $7320 €5840 Still life of a peeled lemon in a roemer, apple, paper and oyster on a ledge (21x18cm-8x7in) s. panel prov. 6-Jul-4 Sotheby's, Olympia #554/R est:4000-6000
£7200 $12456 €10512 Still life of an orange and two medlars upon a ledge (23x18cm-9x7in) s. panel prov. 9-Dec-3 Sotheby's, Olympia #339/R est:4000-6000
£7500 $13275 €10950 Still life of a vase of summer flowers and insects (29x23cm-11x9in) s. panel. 27-Apr-4 Henry Adams, Chichester #680/R est:1000-1500
£8667 $15773 €13000 Coupe de fruits (50x40cm-20x16in) s. 30-Jun-4 Pierre Berge, Paris #38/R est:15000-20000

NELLY (1899-1998) Turkish
Photographs
£5000 $8800 €7300 Athens (16x22cm-6x9in) s. gelatin silver print. 19-May-4 Christie's, London #157/R est:6000-8000
£5500 $10065 €8030 Dancer Nikolska in the Parthenon (17x22cm-7x9in) i. silver bromide print card. 8-Jul-4 Sotheby's, London #416/R est:4000-6000

NELSON, A (18th C) British
Sculpture
£1678 $2887 €2400 Fantasia (68cm-27in) s.st.f.Luppen bronze. 3-Dec-3 Palais de Beaux Arts, Brussels #885/R est:2000-2500

NELSON, Charles M (20th C) American
£324 $600 €473 Inness like landscape with figures (51x71cm-20x28in) s. 24-Jan-4 Jeffery Burchard, Florida #72/R

NELSON, Ernest Bruce (1888-1952) American
£69364 $120000 €101271 Pacific coastline on a clear day (61x76cm-24x30in) s. prov. 10-Dec-3 Bonhams & Butterfields, San Francisco #6197/R est:80000-120000

NELSON, George Laurence (1887-1978) American
£409 $650 €597 Daffodils and Lilies (36x25cm-14x10in) s. canvasboard. 10-Sep-3 Alderfer's, Hatfield #317
£640 $1100 €934 Sea shell with June flowers (62x75cm-24x30in) s. i.verso. 3-Dec-3 Doyle, New York #228/R est:2000-3000
£707 $1300 €1032 Globe amaranths. Spring bouquet (25x20cm-10x8in) s. canvasboard pair painted oval exhib. 23-Jun-4 Doyle, New York #5057/R est:600-800
£872 $1500 €1273 Springtime (60x75cm-24x30in) s. board. 3-Dec-3 Doyle, New York #227/R est:2000-3000
£1453 $2500 €2121 Foxglove with still life (50x60cm-20x24in) s.d.38 prov. 3-Dec-3 Doyle, New York #226/R est:2000-3000
£2235 $4000 €3263 Central Park (38x28cm-15x11in) s. board. 26-May-4 Doyle, New York #133/R est:1500-2000

NELSON, Jan (1955-) Australian
£1626 $2553 €2358 Synecdoche (121x182cm-48x72in) s.i.d.1987 stretcher. 27-Aug-3 Christie's, Sydney #672/R est:3000-5000 (A.D 4000)

NELSON, Joan (1958-) American
£3892 $6500 €5682 Untitled, no 113 (53x48cm-21x19in) s.d.1986 verso oil wax wood prov. 13-Nov-3 Sotheby's, New York #599/R est:10000-15000
Works on paper
£1757 $3250 €2565 Dirt Road (69x61cm-27x24in) s.d.1985 verso mixed media masonite. 12-Feb-4 Sotheby's, New York #280/R est:4000-6000

NELSON, John McKerdy (1825-1881) Australian/British
Works on paper
£287 $453 €419 You Yangs from German Town (18x27cm-7x11in) init.i.d.15 April 1879 pencil. 2-Sep-3 Deutscher-Menzies, Melbourne #263/R (A.D 700)
£656 $1036 €958 Queenscliff (18x27cm-7x11in) init.i.d.21 Jan 1879 pencil two. 2-Sep-3 Deutscher-Menzies, Melbourne #261/R est:1800-2400 (A.D 1600)

NELSON, Kim (1958-) Australian
£535 $969 €781 First flight II choices (64x83cm-25x33in) mono.i.d. oil wash pencil conte. 31-Mar-4 Goodman, Sydney #376/R (A.D 1300)
£1224 $2253 €1787 Firmament IV (80x160cm-31x63in) mono. 29-Mar-4 Goodman, Sydney #63/R est:2500-4500 (A.D 3000)

NELSON, Leonard L (1912-1993) American
£1397 $2500 €2040 Untitled (30x41cm-12x16in) s.d.1942. 16-May-4 Wright, Chicago #222/R est:3000-4000

NELSON, Michael Tjakamarra (1949-) Australian
Works on paper
£5078 $9496 €7617 Kangaroo story at Wantapi (224x212cm-88x83in) bears name.verso synthetic polymer paint linen prov.lit. 26-Jul-4 Sotheby's, Melbourne #265/R est:12000-18000 (A.D 13000)
£5469 $10227 €8204 Mikilangu (122x182cm-48x72in) bears name.verso synthetic polymer paint canvas prov. 26-Jul-4 Sotheby's, Melbourne #264/R est:12000-18000 (A.D 14000)

NELSON, Paddy Jupurrula (c.1919-) Australian
Works on paper
£781 $1461 €1172 Karrku jukurrpa (61x45cm-24x18in) bears name.i.verso synthetic polymer paint canvasboard prov. 26-Jul-4 Sotheby's, Melbourne #414/R est:1500-2000 (A.D 2000)
£2744 $4335 €3979 Untitled (67x93cm-26x37in) i.verso synthetic polymer paint canvas prov. 28-Jul-3 Sotheby's, Paddington #419/R est:3000-5000 (A.D 6750)
£5078 $9496 €7617 Wati jukurrpa (137x53cm-54x21in) bears name.i.verso synthetic polymer paint canvas prov. 26-Jul-4 Sotheby's, Melbourne #419/R est:6000-8000 (A.D 13000)

NELSON, Robert Lyn (20th C) American
£1341 $2400 €1958 Underwater. s.i. oil acrylic. 13-May-4 Dallas Auction Gallery, Dallas #130/R est:8000-10000
£1536 $2750 €2243 Under sea song. s.i. 13-May-4 Dallas Auction Gallery, Dallas #245/R est:10000-15000
£5028 $9000 €7341 Gracefully deep near Wanna. s.i. acrylic. 13-May-4 Dallas Auction Gallery, Dallas #306/R est:8000-12000

NELSON, Roger Laux (1945-) American
£710 $1300 €1037 Study for Rocket tree (66x97cm-26x38in) oil on paper. 10-Jul-4 Hindman, Chicago #373/R est:800-1200
£765 $1400 €1117 Study for coming up (48x69cm-19x27in) oil on paper. 10-Jul-4 Hindman, Chicago #372/R est:700-900

NEME, Clarel (1926-) Uruguayan
£294 $500 €429 Portrait (55x46cm-22x18in) s. 20-Nov-3 Galeria y Remates, Montevideo #134/R
£449 $750 €656 Fat woman (73x60cm-29x24in) s. 7-Oct-3 Galeria y Remates, Montevideo #89/R
£455 $800 €664 Lorry with brides and grooms (35x28cm-14x11in) s. 5-Jan-4 Galeria y Remates, Montevideo #2
£1087 $2000 €1587 Chaparron (130x97cm-51x38in) s.d.1963. 22-Jun-4 Galeria y Remates, Montevideo #96/R est:2500-3000
Works on paper
£529 $1000 €772 Park (56x78cm-22x31in) s. mixed media cardboard. 22-Feb-4 Galeria y Remates, Montevideo #128/R

NEMECEK, Vaclav (1877-1959) Czechoslovakian
£422 $742 €633 Hennery in Podoli (74x109cm-29x43in) cardboard exhib. 22-May-4 Dorotheum, Prague #140/R est:12000-18000 (C.KR 20000)

NEMES, Endre (1909-1985) Hungarian
£653 $1175 €980 Cafe interior (55x80cm-22x31in) s. 25-Apr-4 Goteborg Auktionsverk, Sweden #361/R (S.KR 9000)
£1060 $1928 €1600 Composition with two figures (41x33cm-16x13in) s. panel. 15-Jun-4 Rossini, Paris #182/R est:1000-1500
£2198 $3890 €3209 Study for A surprise meeting (60x41cm-24x16in) s. tempera panel exhib.prov. 27-Apr-4 AB Stockholms Auktionsverk #775/R est:40000-45000 (S.KR 30000)
£4396 $7780 €6418 The road to the old house (133x193cm-52x76in) s.d.1970 acrylic oil tempera exhib.lit. 27-Apr-4 AB Stockholms Auktionsverk #880/R est:60000-80000 (S.KR 60000)
£4909 $8346 €7167 Composition in blue (234x164cm-92x65in) s. 5-Nov-3 AB Stockholms Auktionsverk #730/R est:50000-60000 (S.KR 65000)
Works on paper
£399 $718 €583 Yellow and red (41x47cm-16x19in) s.i.d.63 mixed media exhib. 26-Apr-4 Bukowskis, Stockholm #203/R (S.KR 5500)
£400 $716 €584 Silent Fall (40x47cm-16x19in) s.d.1965 mixed media collage prov. 16-Mar-4 Bonhams, Knightsbridge #127/R
£747 $1323 €1091 Difficult to know (31x24cm-12x9in) s.d.1967 collage tempera exhib.lit. 27-Apr-4 AB Stockholms Auktionsverk #777/R (S.KR 10200)
£750 $1350 €1095 Abstract (54x65cm-21x26in) s.d.1962 mixed media canvas prov. 20-Jan-4 Bonhams, Knightsbridge #174/R
£1360 $2311 €1986 Round of honour (50x64cm-20x25in) s.d.1967 collage tempera exhib. 5-Nov-3 AB Stockholms Auktionsverk #728/R est:20000-25000 (S.KR 18000)
£1832 $3242 €2675 Jungle picture (160x130cm-63x51in) s.d.63 mixed media canvas exhib. 27-Apr-4 AB Stockholms Auktionsverk #882/R est:25000-30000 (S.KR 25000)

NEMES-LAMPERTH, Jozsef (1891-1924) Hungarian
Works on paper
£1212 $2194 €1770 Belfry of Spytkowice (40x28cm-16x11in) s. pencil. 16-Apr-4 Mu Terem Galeria, Budapest #12/R (H.F 460000)

NEMETHY, Albert (1920-) American
£348 $550 €508 Portrait of gaffrigged yacht with two figures (15x20cm-6x8in) s. board. 6-Sep-3 Brunk, Ashville #679
£405 $700 €591 Streamship with paddle wheel flying American flag (13x25cm-5x10in) s. board. 10-Dec-3 Alderfer's, Hatfield #411
£973 $1800 €1421 Castle Garden, New York (71x91cm-28x36in) s.i.d.1845 stretcher. 15-Jul-4 Sotheby's, New York #111/R est:2000-3000
£1087 $1750 €1587 Sidewheeler, Highlander (46x76cm-18x30in) init. prov. 20-Aug-3 James Julia, Fairfield #835/R est:1500-2500
£1215 $2200 €1774 Sidewheeler Metamora. Ship portraits (53x76cm-21x30in) s. prov. 16-Apr-4 James Julia, Fairfield #688/R est:1500-2500
£1685 $2715 €2460 Sidewheeler, Metamora (53x76cm-21x30in) s. prov. 20-Aug-3 James Julia, Fairfield #836/R est:2000-3000

NEMETHY, George (20th C) American
£299 $475 €437 Three mast sailing sloop (28x23cm-11x9in) mono. board. 9-Mar-3 William Jenack, New York #366

NEMOURS, Aurelie (1910-) French
£2414 $4466 €3500 Come (22x22cm-9x9in) s.i.d.1978 verso. 13-Feb-4 Charbonneaux, Paris #104/R est:1000-1500
£10490 $17517 €15000 Polyptique V, quatuor (80x80cm-31x31in) s.i.d.1988 verso four together prov.lit. 11-Oct-3 Cornette de St.Cyr, Paris #4/R est:10000-12000
£11538 $19269 €16500 La vierge (65x46cm-26x18in) s.d.1969 verso prov.exhib. 11-Oct-3 Cornette de St.Cyr, Paris #74/R est:15000-18000

NEMUKHIN, Vladimir (1925-) Russian
Works on paper
£10000 $17900 €14600 Composition with playing card (120x100cm-47x39in) s.d.83-85 mixed media on canvas. 26-May-4 Sotheby's, London #318/R est:10000-15000

NEO-CLASSICAL SCHOOL
Sculpture
£5298 $9643 €8000 Deux lutteurs (49x61cm-19x24in) marble. 16-Jun-4 Tajan, Paris #200/R est:8000-12000
£8389 $15688 €12500 Young bather (160cm-63in) white marble. 29-Feb-4 Finarte, Venice #55/R est:14000-18000
£8389 $15436 €12500 Ancient warrior (51cm-20in) marble wooden base. 29-Mar-4 Pandolfini, Florence #801/R est:7600

NEOCLASSICAL SCHOOL (18th C)
Sculpture
£5120 $8500 €7475 Sybil (142x41x33cm-56x16x13in) marble grey composite ionic column. 4-Oct-3 Neal Auction Company, New Orleans #258/R est:5000-7000

NEOGRADY, Antal (1861-1942) Hungarian
£417 $658 €600 Hungarian country garden (19x31cm-7x12in) s. panel. 6-Sep-3 Schopman, Hamburg #814/R
£496 $829 €700 Hunter (60x80cm-24x31in) s. 14-Oct-3 Dorotheum, Vienna #61/R
£635 $1150 €927 Washer women (61x79cm-24x31in) s. 18-Apr-4 Jeffery Burchard, Florida #145/R
£1420 $2500 €2073 Peasant woman in a landscape (51x61cm-20x24in) s. painted c.1930. 23-May-4 Treadway Gallery, Cincinnati #530/R est:1000-2000
Works on paper
£426 $711 €600 Farmstead (37x46cm-15x18in) s. W/C. 14-Oct-3 Dorotheum, Vienna #46/R

NEOGRADY, Laszlo (1896-1962) Hungarian
£286 $487 €418 Hunter in snowy wood (60x79cm-24x31in) s. 5-Nov-3 Dobiaschofsky, Bern #837 (S.FR 650)
£330 $600 €482 River landscape with girl and geese (33x43cm-13x17in) s. board. 19-Jun-4 Jeffery Burchard, Florida #70
£389 $650 €568 Landscape with mountains (36x51cm-14x20in) s. 19-Oct-3 William Jenack, New York #395
£458 $792 €650 Girl in front of a flower garden (25x35cm-10x14in) s. board. 10-Dec-3 Dorotheum, Vienna #163/R
£467 $850 €682 Portrait of Matador pedro Basauri-Pedrucho (79x119cm-31x47in) s.i.indis.d. prov. 19-Jun-4 Jackson's, Cedar Falls #263/R
£469 $750 €685 Autumnal forest landscape with stream (58x79cm-23x31in) s. 20-Sep-3 Jeffery Burchard, Florida #37/R
£525 $950 €767 Village stream (61x79cm-24x31in) s. 18-Apr-4 Jeffery Burchard, Florida #143/R
£600 $1104 €900 Summer lake landscape with women on field path (60x80cm-24x31in) s. 9-Jun-4 Dorotheum, Salzburg #594/R
£611 $1100 €892 River in a snow-covered landscape (61x91cm-24x36in) s. 25-Jan-4 Bonhams & Butterfields, San Francisco #3579/R
£625 $1044 €900 Goosemaid with flock by stream (50x40cm-20x16in) s. 22-Oct-3 Neumeister, Munich #737/R
£750 $1200 €1095 Winter mountain landscape (61x76cm-24x30in) s. prov. 21-Sep-3 William Jenack, New York #24
£795 $1446 €1200 Landscape with stream and blossoming trees (80x100cm-31x39in) s. 21-Jun-4 Dorotheum, Vienna #24/R
£820 $1435 €1197 Cattle watering at a wooded brook (56x79cm-22x31in) s. 19-Dec-3 Mallams, Oxford #258/R
£927 $1697 €1400 Country idyll (21x34cm-8x13in) s. board. 8-Apr-4 Dorotheum, Vienna #198/R
£1000 $1590 €1450 Figures and chickens in a farmyard. Young girl in a courtyard (51x71cm-20x28in) s. pair. 9-Sep-3 Bonhams, Knightsbridge #70/R est:1000-1500
£1049 $1752 €1500 Young woman in cornfield with flowers in spring (25x38cm-10x15in) s. 9-Oct-3 Michael Zeller, Lindau #703/R
£1058 $2000 €1545 River landscape with cows and female figure (58x79cm-23x31in) s. 21-Feb-4 Jeffery Burchard, Florida #36/R
£1145 $1947 €1672 Mediterranean coast (100x149cm-39x59in) s. 5-Nov-3 Dobiaschofsky, Bern #836/R est:2600 (S.FR 2600)
£1180 $1900 €1723 Village and landscape (61x76cm-24x30in) 15-Aug-3 Du Mouchelle, Detroit #2009/R est:1500-1800
£1242 $2000 €1813 Winter scene with river (61x76cm-24x30in) s. 20-Aug-3 James Julia, Fairfield #1079/R est:2500-3500
£1398 $2250 €2041 Winter fantasy (61x76cm-24x30in) 15-Aug-3 Du Mouchelle, Detroit #2008/R est:1500-1800
£1456 $2300 €2126 Winter woodland scene with stream (61x91cm-24x36in) s. 6-Sep-3 Brunk, Ashville #430

NEOGRADY, Miklos (20th C) Hungarian
£275 $500 €402 Mountainous winter landscape (91x61cm-36x24in) s. 19-Jun-4 Jackson's, Cedar Falls #253/R

NEPO, Ernst (1895-1971) Austrian
£11409 $20423 €17000 Portrait of young man (106x88cm-42x35in) s.d.1931 prov. 25-May-4 Dorotheum, Vienna #40/R est:13000-18000
£16107 $28832 €24000 Still life with gladioli and wooden cube (90x66cm-35x26in) s.d.1944. 25-May-4 Dorotheum, Vienna #195/R est:24000-30000

NEPOTE, Alexander (1913-1986) American
Works on paper
£398 $700 €581 Two in transition (135x112cm-53x44in) s. mixed media board exec.c.1960. 23-May-4 Treadway Gallery, Cincinnati #743/R
£1796 $3000 €2622 Industrial scene (54x74cm-21x29in) s. pencil W/C. 26-Oct-3 Bonhams & Butterfields, San Francisco #6537/R
£2245 $3750 €3278 Bay view with shipyard in the foreground (54x74cm-21x29in) s. pencil W/C. 26-Oct-3 Bonhams & Butterfields, San Francisco #6536/R

NEPPEL, Heinrich (1874-1936) German
£259 $463 €378 Evening river landscape (25x44cm-10x17in) s. panel. 12-May-4 Dobiaschofsky, Bern #826/R (S.FR 600)

NERDRUM, Odd (1944-) Norwegian
£31868 $58000 €46527 Man with a woman's head (159x121cm-63x48in) s.d.1994 s.d.overlap oil on linen prov.exhib. 29-Jun-4 Sotheby's, New York #614/R est:30000-40000
Prints
£2039 $3650 €2977 Baby (51x72cm-20x28in) s.num.23/100 lithograph. 25-May-4 Grev Wedels Plass, Oslo #104/R est:30000 (N.KR 25000)
£5220 $9344 €7621 Dawn (64x92cm-25x36in) s.num.45/45 lithograph. 25-May-4 Grev Wedels Plass, Oslo #105/R est:100000 (N.KR 64000)
Works on paper
£804 $1471 €1174 Vietnam always FNL (99x71cm-39x28in) s. i.verso chl W/C prov. 2-Feb-4 Blomqvist, Lysaker #1196/R est:40000 (N.KR 10000)

NEREE TOT BABBERICH, Christophe Karel Henri de (1880-1909) Dutch
Works on paper
£559 $934 €800 Expectation (35x23cm-14x9in) ink exhib. 30-Jun-3 Sotheby's, Amsterdam #216

NERENZ, Wilhelm (1804-1871) German
Works on paper
£2657 $4517 €3800 Resting Italian peasant family (21x33cm-8x13in) s.d.1847 pen Indian ink brush. 27-Nov-3 Bassenge, Berlin #5624 est:4500

NERI, Manuel (1930-) American
£2353 $4000 €3435 Wooden arms (30x23cm-12x9in) s.i.d.84 oil graphite prov. 9-Nov-3 Bonhams & Butterfields, Los Angeles #4065/R est:5000-7000
Works on paper
£960 $1700 €1402 From Couple of Girls Series, study III, study IV (91x61cm-36x24in) s.verso graphite gouache pair. 2-May-4 Bonhams & Butterfields, Los Angeles #3068/R est:2000-3000

NERI, Paul (1910-1966) Italian?
£1544 $2856 €2300 Casbah de Zaouia de Tahanaout, Maroc (38x46cm-15x18in) s. 15-Mar-4 Gros & Delettrez, Paris #30/R est:1500-2500
£1678 $3104 €2500 La Casbah d'Ayachi (45x94cm-18x37in) s.i. 15-Mar-4 Gros & Delettrez, Paris #29/R est:2500-3500
£3000 $5520 €4500 Fantasia a Marrakech (50x100cm-20x39in) s.i. 14-Jun-4 Gros & Delettrez, Paris #245/R est:4000-5000
Works on paper
£671 $1242 €1000 Vue du Port de Rabat (31x45cm-12x18in) s. gouache. 15-Mar-4 Gros & Delettrez, Paris #31/R

NERI, Stefano Gaetano (18th C) Italian
£3297 $6000 €4814 Madonna and Child (62x51cm-24x20in) canvas on masonite. 29-Jun-4 Sotheby's, New York #42/R est:6000-8000

NERLI, Marchese Girolamo Ballatti (1860-1926) Italian
£13060 $22593 €19068 Maori children bathing in hot pools, Rotorua (34x24cm-13x9in) s. board. 9-Dec-3 Peter Webb, Auckland #78/R est:35000-45000 (NZ.D 35000)
£15574 $24607 €22738 Rotten Row, Hyde Park, London (25x32cm-10x13in) s. board pair prov. 2-Sep-3 Deutscher-Menzies, Melbourne #41/R est:30000-40000 (A.D 38000)

NERLI, Rolf (20th C) Norwegian
£322 $588 €470 Regatta (100x73cm-39x29in) s. painted c.1986-87. 2-Feb-4 Blomqvist, Lysaker #1198/R (N.KR 4000)

NERLICH, Georg (1893-?) German
£1867 $3341 €2800 Waterlilies (60x80cm-24x31in) s. i.d. stretcher. 15-May-4 Bassenge, Berlin #7066/R est:3000
Works on paper
£1467 $2625 €2200 Wood (54x44cm-21x17in) s.d. i. verso W/C. 14-May-4 Ketterer, Munich #64/R est:1200-1800

NERLY, Friedrich (19th C) Italian/Austrian
£7328 $13483 €10699 Doges Palace in morning mist (47x61cm-19x24in) 26-Mar-4 Koller, Zurich #3119/R est:15000-20000 (S.FR 17000)
£42361 $69049 €61000 Grand Canal, Venice with gondolas and boats (60x82cm-24x32in) s.i. verso i. verso lit. 27-Sep-3 Dannenberg, Berlin #604/R est:10000
£108000 $196560 €157680 Venice with the Dogenpalace and Isola di San Georgio Maggiore (60x96cm-24x38in) s.d.1841 prov. 15-Jun-4 Sotheby's, London #8/R est:20000-30000

Works on paper
£267 $480 €400 Gondolas in Venice (22x23cm-9x9in) s.d. W/c pencil. 24-Apr-4 Reiss & Sohn, Konigstein #5534/R
£455 $759 €650 Church of St Zeno Maggiore in Verona (42x26cm-17x10in) s.i. pencil. 10-Oct-3 Winterberg, Heidelberg #711/R
£1477 $2717 €2200 Syracuse (20x31cm-8x12in) i. W/C. 26-Mar-4 Ketterer, Hamburg #202/R est:1100-1300
£1690 $2806 €2400 Venezia, gondole e vele a S Marco. Venezia, gondole a Rialto (30x50cm-12x20in) s. W/C cardboard two. 11-Jun-3 Christie's, Rome #27/R est:2300-2800

NERLY, Friedrich (elder) (1807-1878) Italian/Austrian
Works on paper
£397 $723 €600 Gondola in the Laguna, Venice (13x17cm-5x7in) s.d.1855 i.verso W/C. 18-Jun-4 Bolland & Marotz, Bremen #707

NERLY, Friedrich (younger) (1824-1919) Italian
Works on paper
£467 $835 €700 Monte Circello in Bay of Terracina (15x23cm-6x9in) s.d. W/C. 13-May-4 Bassenge, Berlin #5625/R

NERMAN, Einar (1888-1983) Swedish
£275 $443 €402 Still life of flowers with yellow background (35x26cm-14x10in) s.d.55 panel exhib. 25-Aug-3 Lilla Bukowskis, Stockholm #511 (S.KR 3600)
£382 $615 €558 Still life of wild flowers (50x61cm-20x24in) s.d.75. 25-Aug-3 Lilla Bukowskis, Stockholm #512 (S.KR 5000)
£407 $728 €594 My father is resting (41x31cm-16x12in) s.d.09. 28-May-4 Uppsala Auktionskammare, Uppsala #202 (S.KR 5500)

NERONE, Dino (19/20th C) ?
£265 $475 €387 Winter skirmish (46x102cm-18x40in) s. painted c.1900. 10-Jan-4 Harvey Clar, Oakland #1155

NERRIMAH, Jimmy (c.1930-) Australian
Works on paper
£1098 $1965 €1603 Jilarrkujarra (90x60cm-35x24in) synthetic polymer paint canvas exec 2001 prov. 25-May-4 Lawson Menzies, Sydney #121/R est:4000-5000 (A.D 2800)
£2539 $4748 €3809 Walpa jila (102x92cm-40x36in) i.d.2001 verso synthetic polymer paint canvas prov.exhib. 26-Jul-4 Sotheby's, Melbourne #255/R est:7000-10000 (A.D 6500)

NERUD, Josef Karl (1900-1982) German
£470 $864 €700 Lower Bavarian landscape (64x90cm-25x35in) panel. 24-Mar-4 Hugo Ruef, Munich #1249
£867 $1595 €1300 View from Monchsberg of old town of Salzburg (47x35cm-19x14in) i. verso tempera. 9-Jun-4 Dorotheum, Salzburg #637/R
Works on paper
£1333 $2387 €2000 Landscape with bridge (33x55cm-13x22in) s.d. W/C col Indian ink prov. 14-May-4 Ketterer, Munich #66/R est:1200-1600
£1600 $2864 €2400 Reclining woman (30x47cm-12x19in) s.i.d. W/C gouache prov. 14-May-4 Ketterer, Munich #65/R est:1200-1600

NERY, Ishmael (1900-1934) Brazilian
Works on paper
£3297 $5835 €4946 Lovers (15x23cm-6x9in) s. W/C. 27-Apr-4 Bolsa de Arte, Rio de Janeiro #69/R (B.R 18000)
£7326 $12967 €10989 The boss (27x18cm-11x7in) s. W/C. 27-Apr-4 Bolsa de Arte, Rio de Janeiro #70/R (B.R 40000)

NES, Adi (1966-) Israeli
Photographs
£10056 $18000 €14682 Untitled, Soldiers series (90x90cm-35x35in) s.num.AP1 verso c-print exhib. 18-Mar-4 Sotheby's, New York #80/R est:6000-8000

NESBITT, Fannie M (fl.1881-1885) British
£2400 $3984 €3504 Resting shepherd (46x30cm-18x12in) s.i. 1-Oct-3 Sotheby's, Olympia #121/R est:1500-2000

NESBITT, John (1831-1904) British
£1100 $2046 €1606 Across the Sound (61x96cm-24x38in) s. 4-Mar-4 Christie's, Kensington #132/R est:600-800
£2994 $5000 €4371 View of the Bass Rock (61x91cm-24x36in) s.d.1884. 16-Nov-3 CRN Auctions, Cambridge #43/R

NESBITT, Lowell (1933-1993) American
£604 $1100 €882 White elephant (64x80cm-25x31in) s.i.d.1981 verso prov. 7-Feb-4 Sloans & Kenyon, Bethesda #1230/R
£694 $1200 €1013 1820 No Carolina Stairs (152x122cm-60x48in) i.d.66 verso oil en grisaille. 13-Dec-3 Weschler, Washington #592
£800 $1472 €1168 Two electric lilies (76x46cm-30x18in) s.i.d.74 verso. 24-Jun-4 Sotheby's, Olympia #482/R
£949 $1500 €1386 Pink lily (30x30cm-12x12in) 7-Sep-3 Treadway Gallery, Cincinnati #760/R est:1000-2000
£1622 $3000 €2368 II - Rosa Hybrida (127x91cm-50x36in) s. i.verso painted 1976 prov. 12-Feb-4 Sotheby's, New York #121/R est:4000-6000
£1622 $3000 €2368 Three pink roses (127x91cm-50x36in) s. i.verso painted 1977. 12-Feb-4 Sotheby's, New York #122/R est:4000-6000
£1648 $3000 €2406 Chairs from two spaces (60x60cm-24x24in) s.i.d.1968 verso. 7-Feb-4 Sloans & Kenyon, Bethesda #1231/R est:2000-3000
£1786 $3250 €2608 Yellow rose (90x90cm-35x35in) s.i.d.73 verso prov. 7-Feb-4 Sloans & Kenyon, Bethesda #1232/R est:3000-4000
£1923 $3500 €2808 Stairs (127x87cm-50x34in) s.d.65 i.verso prov. 29-Jun-4 Sotheby's, New York #437/R est:1500-2500
£2344 $3750 €3422 Manhattan (122x137cm-48x54in) s.i.verso. 20-Sep-3 Sloans & Kenyon, Bethesda #994/R est:4500-6500
£2813 $4500 €4107 Ten lemons on blue (165x229cm-65x90in) s.i.d.78 verso prov. 20-Sep-3 Sloans & Kenyon, Bethesda #997/R est:1500-2000
£3750 $6000 €5475 Electric tulip II (213x152cm-84x60in) s.i.d.80 verso prov. 20-Sep-3 Sloans & Kenyon, Bethesda #993/R est:1500-2000
£5000 $8000 €7300 Pink iris (122x122cm-48x48in) s.i.d.86 verso. 20-Sep-3 Sloans & Kenyon, Bethesda #990/R est:2000-2500
Works on paper
£600 $1092 €876 Tulip Dance (75x59cm-30x23in) s.d.1973 pencil chl prov. 4-Feb-4 Sotheby's, Olympia #208/R
£604 $1100 €882 Fruit on a quilt (40x60cm-16x24in) s.d.1989 col pencil pastel. 7-Feb-4 Sloans & Kenyon, Bethesda #1229/R
£688 $1100 €1004 Elephant (102x152cm-40x60in) s.d.1988 verso col pencil. 20-Sep-3 Sloans & Kenyon, Bethesda #995/R est:800-1200
£875 $1400 €1278 Iris II (76x61cm-30x24in) s.d.1989 pencil W/C. 20-Sep-3 Sloans & Kenyon, Bethesda #988/R est:600-800
£938 $1500 €1369 Iris (76x61cm-30x24in) s.d.1989 pencil W/C. 20-Sep-3 Sloans & Kenyon, Bethesda #987/R est:600-800
£1125 $1800 €1643 Electric iris (102x152cm-40x60in) s.d.1980 pencil chl. 20-Sep-3 Sloans & Kenyon, Bethesda #989/R est:600-800

NESCH, Rolf (1893-1975) Norwegian
£839 $1401 €1200 Portrait of Friedel Rolphs (55x41cm-22x16in) s. i. verso. 28-Jun-3 Dannenberg, Berlin #743/R
£51444 $94657 €75108 Saint Sebastian (65x138cm-26x54in) s. metal print monotype in colour triptych executed 1941 lit. 29-Mar-4 Rasmussen, Copenhagen #47/R est:300000-500000 (D.KR 570000)
Prints
£2245 $3727 €3255 Seagull (44x54cm-17x21in) s. mixed print. 16-Jun-3 Blomqvist, Lysaker #1153/R est:12000-15000 (N.KR 26000)
£2333 $4293 €3500 Mask like face (44x40cm-17x16in) s.i. col metal print. 10-Jun-4 Hauswedell & Nolte, Hamburg #528/R est:3000
£2641 $4542 €3856 Pegasus (54x39cm-21x15in) s. col metal print exec.c.1968/69. 8-Dec-3 Blomqvist, Oslo #547/R est:20000-25000 (N.KR 31000)
£3497 $6014 €5000 Angel (54x44cm-21x17in) s.i.d.1967 col print. 2-Dec-3 Hauswedell & Nolte, Hamburg #469/R est:5000
£4277 $7271 €6244 From the Bird series (65x50cm-26x20in) s.i.d.2 juli 1969 col metal print. 19-Nov-3 Grev Wedels Plass, Oslo #113/R est:70000-90000 (N.KR 50000)
£4940 $8497 €7212 To fly - birds (57x47cm-22x19in) s.d.7 juli 1969 col metal print lit. 8-Dec-3 Blomqvist, Oslo #556/R est:65000-75000 (N.KR 58000)
£6814 $11721 €9948 To fly - birds (61x47cm-24x19in) s.d.14 august 1969 col metal print. 8-Dec-3 Blomqvist, Oslo #546/R est:70000-90000 (N.KR 80000)
£7692 $13231 €11000 Alster bridge (45x60cm-18x24in) s.i. col print. 2-Dec-3 Hauswedell & Nolte, Hamburg #466/R est:6000
£8007 $13772 €11690 To fly - birds (59x46cm-23x18in) s.d.12 august 1969 col metal print lit. 8-Dec-3 Blomqvist, Oslo #545/R est:70000-90000 (N.KR 94000)
£84543 $141187 €123433 Herring fishing (60x42cm-24x17in) s.i. col metal print aquatint each print two plates in 6 parts. 13-Oct-3 Blomqvist, Oslo #369/R est:800000-900000 (N.KR 990000)
Works on paper
£387 $623 €565 Muck conducting (27x19cm-11x7in) s. dr. 25-Aug-3 Blomqvist, Lysaker #1195/R (N.KR 4500)
£492 $905 €718 Fishing boats (42x58cm-17x23in) s. crayon. 29-Mar-4 Blomqvist, Lysaker #1215 (N.KR 6200)
£699 $1189 €1000 Three men by bed with female nude (25x34cm-10x13in) s.d. wash chl board. 21-Nov-3 Reiss & Sohn, Konigstein #492/R
£2000 $3680 €3000 Mountain landscape (50x65cm-20x26in) s.d.1924 W/C chl. 10-Jun-4 Hauswedell & Nolte, Hamburg #520/R est:2000
£2306 $3851 €3367 Women bathing (49x66cm-19x26in) s.d.39 pastel. 13-Oct-3 Blomqvist, Oslo #368/R est:18000-22000 (N.KR 27000)

NESEMANN, Enno (1861-1949) American
£412 $750 €618 Golden gate (30x46cm-12x18in) s.d.1919. 19-Jun-4 Harvey Clar, Oakland #2398

NESFIELD, William Andrews (1793-1881) British
Works on paper
£800 $1432 €1168 Dover. Ben Lomond (19x27cm-7x11in) s.i. W/C bodycol pair. 25-May-4 Bonhams, Knightsbridge #277/R

NESHAT, Shirin (1957-) American
Photographs
£1359 $2500 €1984 Tooba series (61x65cm-24x26in) c-print edition of 35. 10-Jun-4 Phillips, New York #426/R est:3000-4000
£1734 $3000 €2532 From Tooba series (61x66cm-24x26in) s.i.d.2002 num.35 c-print mounted on plexiglas prov. 10-Dec-3 Phillips, New York #665/R est:3000-4000
£2200 $4048 €3212 Untitled, Toba (39x48cm-15x19in) s.i.d.2002 num.34/35 verso cibachrome print plexiglas prov. 24-Jun-4 Sotheby's, Olympia #628/R est:1800-2500
£2601 $4500 €3797 Rapture series (56x75cm-22x30in) s.i.d.1999 verso num.35 c-print prov. 10-Dec-3 Phillips, New York #664/R est:3000-5000
£2793 $5000 €4078 Rapture series, women in line (28x60cm-11x24in) s.i.d.1999 verso gelatin silver print prov. 14-May-4 Phillips, New York #174/R est:7000-9000
£3200 $5344 €4672 Untitled, rapture (50x60cm-20x24in) s.num.1 verso gelatin silver print prov.exhib. 22-Oct-3 Christie's, London #109/R est:3000-5000
£3593 $6000 €5246 Untitled - possessed series (52x66cm-20x26in) s.i.d.2001 num.10 cibachrome prov.lit. 14-Nov-3 Phillips, New York #246/R est:8000-12000
£4895 $8322 €7000 Untitled, from the 'Rapture' series (39x58cm-15x23in) s.i.d. verso gelatin silver gelatin. 27-Nov-3 Villa Grisebach, Berlin #1326/R est:5000-7000
£5500 $9185 €8030 Rapture - series (41x59cm-16x23in) s.i.d.1999 num.6/10 verso colour photograph prov. 21-Oct-3 Sotheby's, London #321/R est:4000-6000
£6587 $11000 €9617 Untitled, from the Rapture series (51x61cm-20x24in) gelatin silver print edition of 10 prov. 13-Nov-3 Sotheby's, New York #500/R est:10000-15000
£7000 $12740 €10220 Grace under duty (35x28cm-14x11in) s.i.d.1994 num.7-10 gelatin silver print ink prov.lit. 5-Feb-4 Christie's, London #212/R est:5000-7000
£7784 $13000 €11365 Untitled, from the Rapture series (51x61cm-20x24in) s.i.d.1999 num.5/10 verso gelatin silver print prov.lit. 13-Nov-3 Sotheby's, New York #499/R est:6000-8000
£7784 $13000 €11365 Speechless (35x27cm-14x11in) s.verso num.4/10 gelatin silver print exec.1996 prov.lit. 17-Oct-3 Phillips, New York #288/R est:8000-12000

£7821 $14000 €11419 Untitled Rapture series (49x61cm-19x24in) s. num.8/10 verso gelatin silver print exec 1999 prov.exhib. 13-May-4 Sotheby's, New York #368/R est:10000-15000
£8500 $15640 €12410 Stripped (34x22cm-13x9in) s.i.d.1995 num 8/10 verso gelatin silver print prov.lit. 24-Jun-4 Sotheby's, London #110/R est:7000-9000
£10000 $18400 €14600 All demons flee (99x127cm-39x50in) s.i.d.1996 num.2/3 gelatin silver print prov. 25-Jun-4 Christie's, London #233/R est:10000-15000
£10180 $17000 €14863 Untitled, Rapture series (117x178cm-46x70in) s.d.1999 num.1 verso gelatin silver print prov.exhib. 13-Nov-3 Sotheby's, New York #420/R est:20000-30000
£10500 $19110 €15330 Mystified (101x147cm-40x58in) s.i.d.1997 gelatin silver print prov. 5-Feb-4 Christie's, London #207/R est:8000-10000
£11000 $20240 €16060 Mystified (22x34cm-9x13in) s.i.d.1997 num 1/10 verso gelatin silver print prov. 24-Jun-4 Sotheby's, London #109/R est:7000-9000
£12000 $21840 €17520 Rapture series (110x176cm-43x69in) s.i.d.1999 num. AP 1 verso gelatin silver print prov.exhib.lit. 6-Feb-4 Sotheby's, London #273/R est:15000-20000
£12291 $22000 €17945 Untitled Rapture series (49x61cm-19x24in) s.i.d.1999 num.AP verso gelatin silver print prov.exhib. 13-May-4 Sotheby's, New York #369/R est:10000-15000
£13408 $24000 €19576 Moon song (94x35cm-37x14in) s.verso ink gelatin silver print edition of 3 prov.lit. 12-May-4 Christie's, Rockefeller NY #361/R est:20000-30000
£14525 $26000 €21207 Soliloquy, figure in front of steps (119x159cm-47x63in) s.i.d.1999 num. of five verso gelatin silver print prov.lit. 14-May-4 Phillips, New York #201/R est:25000-35000
£15642 $28000 €22837 Fervor, crowd from back, woman looking over her shoulder (169x119cm-67x47in) s.i.d.1999 num. of five verso prov.lit. 14-May-4 Phillips, New York #200/R est:25000-35000
£17000 $28390 €24820 Fervor (119x152cm-47x60in) s.i.d.1999 num.5/5 verso prov. 22-Oct-3 Christie's, London #143/R est:12000-16000
£17964 $30000 €26227 Untitled, Rapture series (117x178cm-46x70in) s.i.d.1999 num.1 verso gelatin silver print prov.exhib. 13-Nov-3 Sotheby's, New York #421/R est:20000-30000
£19162 $32000 €27977 Veilded women in three arches (102x193cm-40x76in) s.i.d.1999 num.5 gelatin silver print prov.lit. 14-Nov-3 Phillips, New York #207/R est:20000-30000
£19500 $35880 €28470 Untitled - from women of Allah (36x28cm-14x11in) s.i.d.1996 num.5/10 gelatin silver print ink prov.lit. 25-Jun-4 Christie's, London #232/R est:8000-12000
£20000 $36800 €29200 Unveiling (34x23cm-13x9in) s.i.d.1993 num.3/10 verso col inks on gelatin silver print prov.lit. 24-Jun-4 Sotheby's, London #322/R est:6000-8000
£20958 $35000 €30599 Identified - Women of Allah Series (141x100cm-56x39in) s.i.num.d.1995 verso pen ink on gelatin silver print prov.exhib. 12-Nov-3 Christie's, Rockefeller NY #550/R est:25000-35000
£21229 $38000 €30994 Grace under duty (119x85cm-47x33in) s.i.d.1994 num.1/3 verso ink gelatin silver print prov.lit. 12-May-4 Christie's, Rockefeller NY #360/R est:25000-35000
£22000 $40040 €32120 Stories of Martyrdom (97x147cm-38x58in) s. gelatin silver print ink exec 1993 prov.lit. 5-Feb-4 Christie's, London #209/R est:20000-30000

Prints
£2446 $4500 €3571 Rapture series (39x41cm-15x16in) s.i.d.1999 num.35 verso digital inkjet print prov. 10-Jun-4 Phillips, New York #423/R est:4000-6000

Works on paper
£14000 $25480 €20440 Offered eyes (35x28cm-14x11in) s.i.d.1993 verso ink gelatin silver print prov.lit. 6-Feb-4 Sotheby's, London #271/R est:5000-7000
£14525 $26000 €21207 Offered eyes - from women of Allah series (25x20cm-10x8in) s.d.1993 num.2/10 verso ink on gelatin silver print exhib.lit. 13-May-4 Sotheby's, New York #370/R est:15000-20000
£17000 $30940 €24820 Speechless (35x28cm-14x11in) s.i.d.1996 verso ink gelatin silver print prov.lit. 6-Feb-4 Sotheby's, London #272/R est:7000-10000

NESJAR, Carl (1920-) Norwegian
£957 $1655 €1397 Coastal landscape II (57x112cm-22x44in) s.verso panel. 13-Dec-3 Blomqvist, Lysaker #1260 (N.KR 11000)

NESPOLO, Ugo (1941-) Italian
£643 $1029 €930 Towards war (18x24cm-7x9in) s. s.i.verso acrylic wood. 13-Mar-3 Galleria Pace, Milan #15/R
£699 $1203 €1000 Game (44x30cm-17x12in) s. tempera card. 3-Dec-3 Stadion, Trieste #988/R
£986 $1637 €1400 Faccia di cuore (24x18cm-9x7in) s. s.i.verso acrylic wood. 14-Jun-3 Meeting Art, Vercelli #542/R
£1000 $1840 €1500 Neo-classical (50x35cm-20x14in) s. acrylic cardboard. 12-Jun-4 Meeting Art, Vercelli #358/R est:1000
£1074 $1922 €1600 Expressionism (40x30cm-16x12in) s. i.verso acrylic board. 28-May-4 Farsetti, Prato #203/R est:1600-1900
£1181 $1865 €1700 Works (34x42cm-13x17in) acrylic cardboard on panel. 6-Sep-3 Meeting Art, Vercelli #673 est:1500
£1200 $2208 €1800 Summer time (30x40cm-12x16in) s. acrylic panel. 11-Jun-4 Farsetti, Prato #57/R est:1900
£1200 $2208 €1800 Jonico (40x30cm-16x12in) s. acrylic panel. 11-Jun-4 Farsetti, Prato #204/R est:1600-1900
£1216 $2141 €1800 Picasso style (30x40cm-12x16in) s. i.verso acrylic board. 22-May-4 Galleria Pananti, Florence #342/R est:1800-2000
£1517 $2428 €2200 Town and Country (30x40cm-12x16in) s. acrylic on wood. 13-Mar-3 Galleria Pace, Milan #135/R est:2700-3500
£1736 $2743 €2500 Quotations (70x50cm-28x20in) acrylic panel. 6-Sep-3 Meeting Art, Vercelli #739
£2933 $5397 €4400 Chez Jourdain (100x70cm-39x28in) s. acrylic on wood. 12-Jun-4 Meeting Art, Vercelli #743/R est:4000
£4483 $7486 €6500 Roller coaster (70x100cm-28x39in) s.i.verso acrylic panel. 17-Nov-3 Sant Agostino, Torino #142/R est:5500-6500

Works on paper
£278 $506 €420 Chair (29x20cm-11x8in) s. felt-tip pen. 17-Jun-4 Galleria Pananti, Florence #423/R
£1049 $1783 €1500 Untitled (101x72cm-40x28in) s. col threads cardboard. 24-Nov-3 Christie's, Milan #61/R est:1500-2000
£1067 $1920 €1600 Berlin by night (50x70cm-20x28in) s.i. pastel card on board. 22-Apr-4 Finarte Semenzato, Rome #104/R est:1600-1800
£2200 $3982 €3300 MGT (70x50cm-28x20in) s. s.i.verso acrylic board. 2-Apr-4 Farsetti, Prato #305/R est:2600-2900

NESSI, Marie Lucie (1900-1992) French
£260 $416 €380 Table and chairs in a garden (46x55cm-18x22in) s. 16-Sep-3 Rosebery Fine Art, London #472/R

NESSIM, Suzanne (1944-) Swedish
£2266 $3852 €3308 Swimmer and dancing dog (180x140cm-71x55in) s.d.84. 5-Nov-3 AB Stockholms Auktionsverk #933/R est:12000-15000 (S.KR 30000)

NESTE, Alfred van (1874-1969) Belgian
£302 $535 €450 Vieille gloire (50x60cm-20x24in) s.d.1945 panel. 27-Apr-4 Campo, Vlaamse Kaai #632
£306 $557 €450 Vue d'un village (38x48cm-15x19in) 9-Feb-4 Amberes, Antwerp #299
£347 $580 €500 Riviere a Verrelande (60x90cm-24x35in) s. panel. 21-Oct-3 Campo, Vlaamse Kaai #600
£552 $1021 €800 Vase fleuri de mimosas (66x49cm-26x19in) s. 16-Feb-4 Horta, Bruxelles #317
£625 $994 €900 Vue de Bruges (80x70cm-31x28in) s. 9-Sep-3 Palais de Beaux Arts, Brussels #284
£1745 $3089 €2600 Canal scene, Bruges (100x125cm-39x49in) s.d.1923. 27-Apr-4 Campo & Campo, Antwerp #254/R est:2000-3000

NESTEL, Hermann (1858-?) German
£6000 $10800 €9000 Bordighera (65x95cm-26x37in) s.d.1899. 26-Apr-4 Rieber, Stuttgart #950/R est:3500

NESTEROV (20th C) Russian
£5333 $9707 €8000 Rowing boat on the lake (23x31cm-9x12in) s.i.d.1919 verso cardboard. 3-Jul-4 Geble, Radolfzell #420/R est:1400

NESTEROV, Igor (1961-) Russian
£336 $628 €500 Still life with white roses (41x33cm-16x13in) s. 24-Feb-4 Durán, Madrid #733/R

NESTEROV, Mikhail Vasilievich (1862-1942) Russian
£11000 $19360 €16060 St Barbara (20x16cm-8x6in) s.i.d.1921 verso board. 18-May-4 Bonhams, Knightsbridge #76/R est:1500-2000
£500000 $895000 €730000 Na Zemlye pokoi, peace on Earth (102x66cm-40x26in) s.d.1912 prov.exhib.lit. 26-May-4 Sotheby's, London #110/R est:500000-700000

NESTEROV, Mikhail Vasilievich (attrib) (1862-1942) Russian
£4829 $8500 €7050 In the convent (43x33cm-17x13in) bears sig. 18-May-4 Bonhams & Butterfields, San Francisco #83/R est:4000-6000

NESTLER-LAUX, Marie (1852-?) German
£1133 $2074 €1700 Still life with grapes and robin. Still life with fish and onions (46x83cm-18x33in) s. pair. 5-Jun-4 Arnold, Frankfurt #685/R est:300

NESWABDA, Gerhard (20th C) German
£378 $700 €567 Wheatfield and lavender (30x41cm-12x16in) s. 14-Jan-4 Dallas Auction Gallery, Dallas #184/R
£865 $1600 €1298 Wheatfield poppies (69x79cm-27x31in) s.i. 14-Jan-4 Dallas Auction Gallery, Dallas #485/R est:1500-2500
£1892 $3500 €2838 Floral landscape. s. 14-Jul-4 Dallas Auction Gallery, Dallas #475/R est:3000-5000

NETHER, Heinrich (c.1760-?) French
Works on paper
£1233 $2096 €1800 Landscape with shepherds and peasants (27x35cm-11x14in) s. gouache. 6-Nov-3 Tajan, Paris #97/R est:2000

NETHERLANDISH SCHOOL, 16th C
£7000 $11900 €10220 Portrait of a gentleman waering a brown coat, red cap holing a quill (47x27cm-19x11in) panel arched top prov. 30-Oct-3 Sotheby's, Olympia #91/R est:4000-6000
£7500 $13500 €10950 Man playing a flute, wearing red jacket and hat (46x38cm-18x15in) panel. 20-Apr-4 Sotheby's, Olympia #247/R est:4000-6000
£7800 $13494 €11388 Crucifixion. Mary Magdalene. Saint John the Baptist and Saint Sebastian (111x155cm-44x61in) panel triptych. 9-Dec-3 Sotheby's, Olympia #300/R est:6000-8000
£35616 $60548 €52000 Christ on the cross with the Virgin Mary Magdalene and other figures (57x47cm-22x19in) panel. 4-Nov-3 Sotheby's, Amsterdam #44/R est:15000-20000

NETHERLANDISH SCHOOL, 17th C
£7000 $11620 €10220 Portrait of a young lady, wearing a black dress with garland of flowers in her hair (61x41cm-24x16in) panel. 30-Sep-3 Sotheby's, London #63/R est:8000-12000
£8000 $14960 €11680 Portrait of Isabella of Portugal (64x49cm-25x19in) i. feigned oval painted c.1600. 27-Feb-4 Christie's, Kensington #13/R est:2000-3000

NETHERLANDISH SCHOOL, 18th C
£18000 $31140 €26280 Parkland scenes (200x81cm-79x32in) set of four prov. 9-Dec-3 Sotheby's, Olympia #442/R est:15000-20000

NETHERWOOD, Arthur (1864-1930) British
£450 $842 €657 Coastal scene with man and horse and cart near sand dunes (61x91cm-24x36in) s. 22-Jul-4 Tennants, Leyburn #810

Works on paper
£400 $748 €584 The valley of Chamonix with Mont Blanc in the distance (35x47cm-14x19in) s.i. pencil W/C. 22-Jul-4 Tennants, Leyburn #663
£1100 $1870 €1606 Polperro harbour (58x93cm-23x37in) s. pencil W/C sold with press cutting. 19-Nov-3 Tennants, Leyburn #991a/R est:1000-1500

NETO, Ernesto (1964-) Brazilian
£4200 $7728 €6132 Untitled (35x25cm-14x10in) init.d.93 paraffin thread lead on paper prov.exhib. 25-Jun-4 Christie's, London #258/R est:3000-5000

Sculpture
£5000 $9200 €7300 Untitled (10x30x5cm-4x12x2in) polyamide lime executed 1995 prov. 25-Jun-4 Christie's, London #259/R est:5000-7000

£8982 $15000 €13114 Suspense 5 (264x274x56cm-104x108x22in) aluminum polyamide nails template prov.exhib. 13-Nov-3 Sotheby's, New York #471/R est:20000-30000
£9333 $17173 €14000 Puff (91x23x15cm-36x9x6in) stocking saffron exec.1997 prov.exhib.lit. 10-Jun-4 Christie's, Paris #98/R est:6500-9500
£9412 $16000 €13742 Life crawl. polyamide cotton nylon sand exec. 2000 prov.exhib. 18-Nov-3 Christie's, Rockefeller NY #1/R est:15000-20000

NETSCHER (?) Dutch
£3800 $5966 €5510 Portrait of a lady, in an elegant interior (48x36cm-19x14in) indis.sig.indis.d.16 wood panel. 15-Dec-2 Desmond Judd, Cranbrook #824

NETSCHER, Caspar (1639-1684) Dutch
£2961 $5447 €4500 Portrait of Princess by fountain (48x38cm-19x15in) prov. 25-Jun-4 Piasa, Paris #26/R est:6000-8000
£3425 $5822 €5000 Portrait of a lady, seated, wearing pearl jewellery, in a park setting (52x42cm-20x17in) s.d.1683 canvas laid down prov.lit. 4-Nov-3 Sotheby's, Amsterdam #38/R est:6000-8000
£7240 $11584 €10570 Portrait of nobleman (47x38cm-19x15in) s. 19-Sep-3 Koller, Zurich #3040/R est:16000-22000 (S.FR 16000)
£12000 $21840 €18000 Portrait of elegant woman as shepherdess (35x28cm-14x11in) mono. panel prov. 30-Jun-4 Neumeister, Munich #471/R est:7000
£52000 $93600 €75920 Portrait of Suzanna Huygens, an evening landscape beyond (45x35cm-18x14in) s.d.1669 panel prov.exhib.lit. 22-Apr-4 Sotheby's, London #42/R est:30000-40000

Miniatures
£15500 $27900 €22630 Lady, in a dress with gold embroidered bodice (16cm-6in) s. oil copper gilded carved wood frame oval exhib.lit. 22-Apr-4 Bonhams, New Bond Street #13/R est:4000-6000

NETSCHER, Caspar (attrib) (1639-1684) Dutch
£2349 $4322 €3500 Countess Shrewsbury (49x40cm-19x16in) 26-Mar-4 Bolland & Marotz, Bremen #460b/R est:4500
£3493 $6428 €5100 Portrait of nobleman (53x45cm-21x18in) prov. 14-Jun-4 Philippe Schuler, Zurich #4317/R est:7000-9000 (S.FR 8000)
£8000 $14400 €12000 Portrait of a Maltese nobleman (80x60cm-31x24in) 22-Apr-4 Weidler, Nurnberg #321/R est:4500

Works on paper
£476 $852 €700 La melancolie (21x27cm-8x11in) pen brown ink wash black crayon. 19-Mar-4 Piasa, Paris #38

NETSCHER, Constantyn (1668-1723) Dutch
£1987 $3616 €3000 Portrait of an elegant lady wearing a pearl necklace (49x39cm-19x15in) 16-Jun-4 Dorotheum, Vienna #113/R est:4000-6000
£2000 $3600 €2920 Portrait of a lady seated in an interior, wearing a blue silk dress with a pink silk shawl (69x50cm-27x20in) s.d.1701. 20-Apr-4 Sotheby's, Olympia #239/R est:2000-3000

NETSCHER, Constantyn (attrib) (1668-1723) Dutch
£1701 $3095 €2500 Portrait d'un jeune fumeur vu a mi-jambes (46x37cm-18x15in) 8-Feb-4 Anaf, Lyon #250/R est:2500-3000
£3179 $5817 €4800 Portrait d'un jeune garcon et de sa soeur dans une fenetre (48x39cm-19x15in) 7-Apr-4 Libert, Castor, Paris #30/R est:4000-6000
£6623 $12053 €10000 Group portrait of five aristocratic children playing with a billy goat (113x90cm-44x35in) prov. 16-Jun-4 Dorotheum, Vienna #88/R est:10000-15000

NETTER, Benjamin (1811-1881) French
£979 $1684 €1400 Paysanne a l'oree du bois (46x55cm-18x22in) s. 7-Dec-3 Osenat, Fontainebleau #244

NEUBAUER, Frederick August (1855-?) American
£13000 $22360 €18980 Birth of Venus (121x71cm-48x28in) s.d.111.93. 3-Dec-3 Christie's, London #52/R est:15000-20000

NEUBERGER, Ferdinand (attrib) (17th C) German
Sculpture
£5800 $10614 €8468 Equestrian battle scene (8x15cm-3x6in) red wax lit. 9-Jul-4 Sotheby's, London #47/R est:3000-5000

NEUBERT, Ludwig (1846-1892) German
£636 $1082 €910 Beach party with figures (18x53cm-7x21in) s. lit. 28-Nov-3 Schloss Ahlden, Ahlden #1487/R
£5000 $9350 €7300 Dutch canal scene at dusk (60x100cm-24x39in) s. 21-Jul-4 Lyon & Turnbull, Edinburgh #125/R est:3000-5000

NEUBOCK, Max (1893-1960) Austrian
£1528 $2490 €2200 Still life with flowers (54x43cm-21x17in) s. panel. 25-Sep-3 Dorotheum, Graz #18/R est:1000
£2013 $3604 €3000 Landscape with stream (70x60cm-28x24in) s. 27-May-4 Dorotheum, Graz #51/R est:3000

Works on paper
£604 $1081 €900 Portrait of southern woman with jug (64x57cm-25x22in) s. col chk. 27-May-4 Dorotheum, Graz #195/R

NEUBRAND, Otto (1911-1975) German
£281 $477 €410 River landscape (51x61cm-20x24in) s.d.1954 pavatex. 19-Nov-3 Fischer, Luzern #2232/R (S.FR 620)
£577 $924 €820 Old shepherd (33x39cm-13x15in) s. board. 18-Sep-3 Rieber, Stuttgart #991

NEUBURGER, Elie (1891-?) Dutch
£451 $713 €650 View of the Oude Schans, Amsterdam, in winter (74x100cm-29x39in) s.d.1942 exhib. 2-Sep-3 Christie's, Amsterdam #357

NEUENSCHWANDER, Albert (1902-1984) Swiss
£308 $524 €450 Still life with lemons on plate (32x46cm-13x18in) s.d.45. 5-Nov-3 Dobiaschofsky, Bern #3629/R (S.FR 700)
£586 $1007 €856 Spring landscape (60x81cm-24x32in) s.d.1979. 8-Dec-3 Philippe Schuler, Zurich #5948 (S.FR 1300)
£588 $1000 €858 Flowers (120x90cm-47x35in) s. 25-Nov-3 Germann, Zurich #858 (S.FR 1300)
£1762 $2996 €2573 Hartlisberg in the morning (84x110cm-33x43in) s. bears d. 7-Nov-3 Dobiaschofsky, Bern #76/R est:6000 (S.FR 4000)

NEUFCHATEL, Nicolas (style) (1527-1590) Flemish
£5500 $9900 €8030 Portrait of a gentleman wearing black coat and holding a pair of gloves and sword (89x63cm-35x25in) panel. 20-Apr-4 Sotheby's, Olympia #231/R est:3000-5000

NEUGEBAUER, Josef (1810-1895) Austrian
£1268 $2193 €1800 Portrait of a boy, probably Prince Ludwig Hoenlohe (52x42cm-20x17in) s.d.1874 canvas on board. 10-Dec-3 Dorotheum, Vienna #127/R est:1800-2000

NEUHAUS, Eugen (1879-1963) American
£2206 $3750 €3221 Study of trees (46x61cm-18x24in) s. 20-Nov-3 Auctions by the Bay, Alameda #1084/R

Works on paper
£466 $750 €676 Still life with daisies. s. mixed media. 23-Aug-3 Harvey Clar, Oakland #1378

NEUHAUS, Fritz (1852-?) German
£565 $1039 €825 Flirtation (56x75cm-22x30in) s. 14-Jun-4 Waddingtons, Toronto #301/R est:1500-2500 (C.D 1400)

NEUHAUS, Fritz Berthold (1882-?) German
£1200 $2184 €1800 Young woman wearing traditional Greek attire, leading a horse (120x181cm-47x71in) s. 1-Jul-4 Van Ham, Cologne #1528/R est:2400

NEUHAUS, Robert R (20th C) American
£447 $800 €653 View of a small industrial town (46x61cm-18x24in) init. 8-May-4 Auctions by the Bay, Alameda #494/R

NEUHAUS, Werner (1897-1934) Swiss
£278 $473 €406 Boy's portrait (29x23cm-11x9in) s. i. verso pastel. 28-Nov-3 Zofingen, Switzerland #3100 (S.FR 615)
£690 $1234 €1007 Peasant boy (51x49cm-20x19in) panel. 14-May-4 Dobiaschofsky, Bern #147/R est:2600 (S.FR 1600)
£2707 $4928 €3952 Houses (74x68cm-29x27in) 17-Jun-4 Kornfeld, Bern #624/R est:6000 (S.FR 6200)
£4128 $6894 €5986 Landscape with red rider (79x52cm-31x20in) i. verso canvas on pavatex. 19-Jun-3 Kornfeld, Bern #775 est:10000 (S.FR 9000)
£6193 $10342 €8980 Wood (68x55cm-27x22in) i. verso. 19-Jun-3 Kornfeld, Bern #777/R est:10000 (S.FR 13500)

Works on paper
£699 $1272 €1021 Autumn wood (43x32cm-17x13in) pastel. 17-Jun-4 Kornfeld, Bern #626 est:2000 (S.FR 1600)
£742 $1351 €1083 Landscape with pine trees (37x25cm-15x10in) s.d.28 pastel. 17-Jun-4 Kornfeld, Bern #625 est:2000 (S.FR 1700)
£4072 $6923 €5945 Davos mountain landscape (55x42cm-22x17in) s.d.1926 gouache chk. 25-Nov-3 Germann, Zurich #122/R est:7500-9500 (S.FR 9000)

NEUHOF, Walthere Joseph (attrib) (1904-1984) Dutch
£280 $467 €400 Winter landscape (60x90cm-24x35in) s. 10-Oct-3 Vendue Huis, Gravenhage #864

NEUHUYS, Albert (1844-1914) Dutch
£680 $1238 €1000 Haringvliet, Rotterdam (40x50cm-16x20in) s. board old with W/C by same hand. 3-Feb-4 Christie's, Amsterdam #374 est:800-1200
£1136 $2000 €1659 Mother and Child (53x64cm-21x25in) painted 1904 prov. 23-May-4 Hindman, Chicago #25/R est:2000-4000
£2036 $3400 €2973 Untitled woman reading in interior (59x49cm-23x19in) s. prov. 17-Nov-3 Hodgins, Calgary #309/R est:6000-8000 (C.D 4500)
£4000 $7200 €6000 Family meal (75x101cm-30x40in) s. painted c.1890 prov.exhib. 21-Apr-4 Christie's, Amsterdam #161/R est:6000-8000

Works on paper
£1678 $2803 €2400 Mother's little helper (53x35cm-21x14in) s.d.94 W/C. 30-Jun-3 Sotheby's, Amsterdam #117/R
£4861 $8264 €7000 Combing the wool (69x51cm-27x20in) s.d.79 W/C htd white prov. 28-Oct-3 Christie's, Amsterdam #147/R est:5000-7000

NEUHUYS, Joseph Hendrikus (1841-1889) Dutch
£521 $849 €750 Boat in a river landscape (50x31cm-20x12in) s. 29-Sep-3 Sotheby's, Amsterdam #86

NEUJEAN, Nat (1923-) Belgian
Sculpture
£4167 $6625 €6000 Standing female nude (59x72cm-23x28in) st.f. Fonderia d'arte/De Andreis green pat bronze. 15-Sep-3 Bernaerts, Antwerp #780/R est:2500-3000

NEUMAN, Robert S (1926-) American
Works on paper
£1154 $2100 €1685 Un Caja (102x71cm-40x28in) s.i.d.1960 verso mixed media canvas. 19-Jun-4 Skinner, Boston #378 est:100-150

NEUMANN, Carl (1833-1891) Danish

£320	$582	€480	Coastal landscape with view towards Kronborg (25x32cm-10x13in) init.d.76. 19-Jun-4 Rasmussen, Havnen #2307/R (D.KR 3600)
£379	$607	€553	Coastal landscape with cliffs (23x36cm-9x14in) s. 22-Sep-3 Rasmussen, Vejle #292/R (D.KR 4000)
£448	$819	€654	Fishermen in Kattegat (40x65cm-16x26in) prov. 9-Jun-4 Rasmussen, Copenhagen #1782/R (D.KR 5000)
£449	$836	€656	Study of a fisherman (36x22cm-14x9in) s.d.1860. 2-Mar-4 Rasmussen, Copenhagen #1361 (D.KR 5000)
£537	$983	€784	Seascape with sailing vessels in Sundet (27x53cm-11x21in) s. 9-Jun-4 Rasmussen, Copenhagen #1764/R (D.KR 6000)
£627	$1129	€915	Evening with fisherman and family by boat (30x46cm-12x18in) s.d.1857. 24-Apr-4 Rasmussen, Havnen #2255 (D.KR 7000)
£756	$1308	€1104	Warm summer's day in the desert (25x32cm-10x13in) s. 9-Dec-3 Rasmussen, Copenhagen #1683/R (D.KR 8000)
£809	$1504	€1181	Seascape with boats (15x20cm-6x8in) init. panel. 2-Mar-4 Rasmussen, Copenhagen #1410 (D.KR 9000)
£1465	$2667	€2139	Evening at Koldinghus with figure in rowing boat (46x61cm-18x24in) init.d.76. 7-Feb-4 Rasmussen, Havnen #2005/R est:10000 (D.KR 16000)
£1850	$3145	€2701	Portrait of a woman (74x53cm-29x21in) s. 5-Nov-3 Dobiaschofsky, Bern #838/R est:5500 (S.FR 4200)
£4942	$9191	€7215	Sailing ship off Kronborg (93x144cm-37x57in) s.d.1873. 2-Mar-4 Rasmussen, Copenhagen #1228/R est:60000-80000 (D.KR 55000)
£5263	$8526	€7631	Summer's day on the beach at Fanoe with boats, figures, oxen and cart (34x48cm-13x19in) s. 4-Aug-3 Rasmussen, Vejle #3/R est:50000 (D.KR 55000)
£8000	$13600	€11680	Acropolis (70x136cm-28x54in) s.d.75 metal prov. 18-Nov-3 Sotheby's, London #77/R est:8000-12000
£11191	$20479	€16339	Evening off Copenhagen (80x138cm-31x54in) s.d.1885. 9-Jun-4 Rasmussen, Copenhagen #1453/R est:50000-75000 (D.KR 125000)

NEUMANN, Ernst (1907-1955) Canadian

Works on paper

£407	$639	€594	Portrait d'homme (15x11cm-6x4in) mono. crayon. 26-Aug-3 Iegor de Saint Hippolyte, Montreal #124 (C.D 900)
£452	$710	€660	Pere de l'artiste (23x16cm-9x6in) s.d.31 chl. 26-Aug-3 Iegor de Saint Hippolyte, Montreal #122 (C.D 1000)

NEUMANN, Fritz (1881-?) German

£397	$723	€600	Three riders (60x44cm-24x17in) s. cardboard. 17-Jun-4 Frank Peege, Freiburg #1176
£1267	$2305	€1900	Cossacks riding wildly along riverbank (60x80cm-24x31in) s.i. 30-Jun-4 Neumeister, Munich #633/R

NEUMANN, Hartmut (1954-) German

£315	$541	€450	Figure (100x46cm-39x18in) s.d.85 paper on canvas. 5-Dec-3 Bolland & Marotz, Bremen #854

NEUMANN, Johan (1860-1940) Danish

£287	$465	€416	Seascape with ships off Kronborg (44x65cm-17x26in) s. 4-Aug-3 Rasmussen, Vejle #41 (D.KR 3000)
£301	$512	€439	Seascape with Kronborg in background (27x42cm-11x17in) s. 29-Nov-3 Rasmussen, Havnen #2143 (D.KR 3200)
£303	$485	€442	Coastal landscape with figures and sailing vessels (42x66cm-17x26in) s. 22-Sep-3 Rasmussen, Vejle #300/R (D.KR 3200)
£313	$573	€457	From Kronborg Point, evening (55x82cm-22x32in) s. 9-Jun-4 Rasmussen, Copenhagen #1830/R (D.KR 3500)
£318	$532	€464	Seascape with off Kronborg (29x36cm-11x14in) s. 25-Oct-3 Rasmussen, Havnen #2507 (D.KR 3400)
£412	$750	€602	Seascape with sailing vessels (45x66cm-18x26in) s. 7-Feb-4 Rasmussen, Havnen #2268 (D.KR 4500)
£417	$696	€600	Copenhagen seascape (31x54cm-12x21in) s. 24-Oct-3 Ketterer, Hamburg #21/R
£582	$1048	€850	Seascape with vessels in a calm off Kronborg (64x95cm-25x37in) s. 24-Apr-4 Rasmussen, Havnen #2009 (D.KR 6500)
£756	$1308	€1104	Seascape with busy traffic off Kronborg (75x115cm-30x45in) s.d.1894. 9-Dec-3 Rasmussen, Copenhagen #1462/R (D.KR 8000)
£843	$1407	€1231	Boats off the coast near Kronborg (67x99cm-26x39in) s.d.1930. 25-Oct-3 Rasmussen, Havnen #2066/R (D.KR 9000)
£1014	$1724	€1480	Summer afternoon in Gilleleje Harbour (68x98cm-27x39in) s. 10-Nov-3 Rasmussen, Vejle #271/R (D.KR 11000)
£1985	$3434	€2898	The battle at Koge Bay, 1677 (48x73cm-19x29in) s. 9-Dec-3 Rasmussen, Copenhagen #1460/R est:5000-7000 (D.KR 21000)

NEUMANN, Max (1949-) German

Works on paper

£300	$552	€450	Often (40x30cm-16x12in) i.d.87 chl. 12-Jun-4 Villa Grisebach, Berlin #811/R
£386	$711	€580	Greater confusion (33x23cm-13x9in) s.d.1980 mixed media. 12-Jun-4 Villa Grisebach, Berlin #809/R
£500	$920	€750	Untitled (36x24cm-14x9in) s.d.87 gouache green paper. 12-Jun-4 Villa Grisebach, Berlin #810/R
£1042	$1740	€1500	Untitled (64x80cm-25x31in) s.d.April 1981 mixed media. 25-Oct-3 Dr Lehr, Berlin #369/R est:2000
£1538	$2615	€2200	Untitled (60x60cm-24x24in) s.d.Sept 79 s.d. verso gouache graphite bodycol paper on canvas. 27-Nov-3 Lempertz, Koln #304/R est:2200

NEUMANN, Robert von (1888-1976) American

£500	$900	€730	Door Country fishing boat leaving pier (41x51cm-16x20in) s. panel. 26-Jan-4 Schrager Galleries, Milwaukee #1451

NEUMANN, S (19th C) ?

£338	$615	€507	Rowing boat and sailing vessel (80x69cm-31x27in) s.d.85. 19-Jun-4 Rasmussen, Havnen #2165 (D.KR 3800)

NEUMANS, Alphonse (19th C) British

£1800	$3060	€2628	Scarborough by moonlight. Scarborough harbour, Grand Hotel in distance (13x30cm-5x12in) s.d.1875 board pair. 19-Nov-3 Tennants, Leyburn #1038/R est:1500-2000

NEUQUELMAN, Lucien (1909-1988) French

£400	$716	€600	Promenade au lac d'Annecy (35x27cm-14x11in) s. s.i.verso. 17-May-4 Chayette & Cheval, Paris #153
£5000	$9100	€7500	La Seine pres d'Herblay (54x65cm-21x26in) s. i.verso prov. 29-Jun-4 Sotheby's, Paris #17/R est:2000-3000

NEURDENBURG, Christoffel (1817-1906) German

£1041	$1697	€1500	Girl in an interior (54x42cm-21x17in) s.d.1839. 29-Sep-3 Sotheby's, Amsterdam #25/R

NEUSCH, Edwin J (20th C) American

£269	$500	€393	Old country road (41x51cm-16x20in) s. 3-Mar-4 Alderfer's, Hatfield #354
£269	$500	€393	Still life with tulips and narcissi in white vase (46x36cm-18x14in) s. 3-Mar-4 Alderfer's, Hatfield #355/R
£435	$800	€635	Figures on boardwalk watching sailing vessels under way (30x41cm-12x16in) s. 9-Jun-4 Alderfer's, Hatfield #495
£462	$850	€675	Philadelphia street scene with colonial figures (41x51cm-16x20in) s. 9-Jun-4 Alderfer's, Hatfield #494
£538	$1000	€785	Feeding time, farm scene (41x51cm-16x20in) s. 3-Mar-4 Alderfer's, Hatfield #353/R est:400-600

NEUVILLE, Alphonse Marie de (1835-1885) French

£1958	$3329	€2800	Surprise au petit jour (104x156cm-41x61in) s.d.1877. 18-Nov-3 Galerie Moderne, Brussels #687/R est:2000-3000

NEUVONEN, Antti (1937-) Finnish

Sculpture

£1127	$1949	€1600	Playing with ribbons (51cm-20in) s.d.1976 bronze. 13-Dec-3 Hagelstam, Helsinki #15/R est:1200
£1329	$2259	€1900	Female figure (42cm-17in) s. bronze. 29-Nov-3 Bukowskis, Helsinki #237/R est:800-1000

NEUWIRTH, Arnulf (1912-) Austrian

£1389	$2264	€2000	Exodus (41x49cm-16x19in) s.d.71 s.i.d.71 verso canvas on novopan. 23-Sep-3 Wiener Kunst Auktionen, Vienna #139/R est:2000-3500

NEUZ, Richard (1894-1976) German

£300	$540	€450	Fishing boats (23x34cm-9x13in) mono.d.1946 board. 26-Apr-4 Rieber, Stuttgart #1256/R
£302	$535	€450	Composition (31x23cm-12x9in) mono.d. masonite. 30-Apr-4 Dr Fritz Nagel, Stuttgart #369/R
£403	$713	€600	Blue slice (37x54cm-15x21in) mono.d. s.i.d. verso masonite. 30-Apr-4 Dr Fritz Nagel, Stuttgart #370/R

NEVE, Cornelius de (attrib) (c.1612-1678) Flemish

£1500	$2745	€2190	Portrait of Thomas Marriott of Whitchurch (76x66cm-30x26in) i. 8-Jul-4 Sotheby's, London #218/R est:3000-4000

NEVE, Franciscus de (1606-1681) Belgian

£1854	$3375	€2800	Venus and Cupid (72x61cm-28x24in) i.verso. 16-Jun-4 Dorotheum, Vienna #371/R est:1000-1500

NEVELE, Nicolas van (16th C) Flemish

£2800	$5068	€4200	Portrait de jeune femme a la collerette (12x12cm-5x5in) s.d.1.5.8.8. panel round. 30-Mar-4 Millon & Associes, Paris #7 est:600-700

NEVELSON, Louise (1899-1988) American

Prints

£1796	$3000	€2622	Sky shadow (76x64cm-30x25in) s.i.d.1973 num.121/150 lead relief intaglio collage. 11-Nov-3 Doyle, New York #345/R est:2000-3000
£2174	$4000	€3174	Nightscape (69x76cm-27x30in) s.d.75 num.27 cast paper relief print. 28-Mar-4 Wright, Chicago #578/R est:700-900

Sculpture

£986	$1637	€1400	Night blossom (37x34x8cm-15x13x3in) init.num.71/100 painted wood. 11-Jun-3 Finarte Semenzato, Milan #671/R
£1836	$3250	€2681	Moon garden (81x55cm-32x22in) s.d.1976 num.71/75 black cast paper relief. 30-Apr-4 Sotheby's, New York #424/R est:3000-4000
£2119	$3750	€3094	Morning haze (85x116cm-33x46in) s.d.1978 num.75/125 white cast paper relief. 30-Apr-4 Sotheby's, New York #424a/R est:3000-4000
£3293	$5500	€4808	Untitled (14x19x32cm-6x7x13in) s. wood painted black executed 1966-67 prov. 11-Nov-3 Christie's, Rockefeller NY #155/R est:8000-12000
£3374	$5500	€4926	Voyage no II (45x18x7cm-18x7x3in) black painted wood prov. 23-Sep-3 Christie's, Rockefeller NY #13/R est:4000-6000
£4301	$8000	€6279	Seated figure (24x30cm-9x12in) s. wood prov. 5-Mar-4 Skinner, Boston #427/R est:8000-12000
£4301	$8000	€6279	Untitled (28x20x9cm-11x8x4in) painted wood box with interior. 2-Mar-4 Swann Galleries, New York #468/R est:5000-8000
£4945	$9000	€7220	Crypt XII (15x18x13cm-6x7x5in) i. painted wooden box executed 1966 prov. 29-Jun-4 Sotheby's, New York #421/R est:8000-12000
£5028	$9000	€7341	Untitled (30x36cm-12x14in) s. num.2/6 bronze. 16-May-4 Wright, Chicago #242/R est:10000-15000
£7647	$13000	€11165	Cryptic box no.64 (23x25cm-9x10in) painted wood construction prov. 9-Nov-3 Wright, Chicago #371 est:10000-15000
£9659	$17000	€14102	Sky City (127x38x13cm-50x15x5in) s. blk painted wood. 23-May-4 Hindman, Chicago #1098/R est:15000-20000
£10000	$17300	€14600	Diminishing reflection I (52x42cm-20x17in) black paint wood prov. 11-Dec-3 Christie's, Kensington #223/R est:5000-7000
£11892	$22000	€17362	Cryptic XXXVI (18x30x20cm-7x12x8in) painted wooden box hinged lid exec 1966 prov. 12-Feb-4 Sotheby's, New York #179/R est:5000-7000
£13836	$22000	€20201	Construction (78x30x25cm-31x12x10in) init. painted wood prov. 12-Sep-3 Skinner, Boston #547/R est:20000

£15569 $26000 €22731 Maquette for Monumental Sculpture XIV (63x36x34cm-25x14x13in) wood painted blk plastic base exec 1976 prov. 12-Nov-3 Christie's, Rockefeller NY #408/R est:18000-25000

£16760 $30000 €24470 Sky Gate's Curtain I (102x61x13cm-40x24x5in) wood painted black exec 1973 prov. 13-May-4 Sotheby's, New York #196/R est:20000-30000

£16779 $30034 €25000 End of the day XV (85x46x9cm-33x18x4in) painted wood exec.1972 prov. 25-May-4 Sotheby's, Milan #177/R est:6000-8000

£23333 $42933 €35000 Dark sound (190x103x27cm-75x41x11in) painted wood exec.1968 prov.exhib.lit. 14-Jun-4 Porro, Milan #57/R est:35000-45000

£24161 $43248 €36000 Colonne II (266cm-105in) painted wood prov.exhib. 26-May-4 Christie's, Paris #117/R est:15000-20000

£25140 $45000 €36704 Rain Garden VII (103x80x18cm-41x31x7in) wall relief wood painted black exec 1978 prov.exhib. 12-May-4 Christie's, Rockefeller NY #206/R est:40000-60000

£30675 $50000 €44786 Moon gardenscape I (122x193x23cm-48x76x9in) black painted wood prov.exhib. 23-Sep-3 Christie's, Rockefeller NY #32/R est:50000-70000

£33520 $60000 €48939 End of Day IX and end of Day XII (87x48x5cm-34x19x2in) blk painted wood constructions Formica frames two prov. 13-May-4 Sotheby's, New York #201/R est:25000-35000

£39106 $70000 €57095 Dream House XI (160x71x44cm-63x28x17in) wood painted black exec 1972 prov. 13-May-4 Sotheby's, New York #124/R est:40000-60000

£44910 $75000 €65569 Mirror - Shadow XVI (158x267x38cm-62x105x15in) wood painted blk exec 1985 prov.exhib. 12-Nov-3 Christie's, Rockefeller NY #411/R est:7000-90000

£44910 $75000 €65569 Reflection one (118x20x20cm-46x8x8in) s. painted wood prov.exhib. 13-Nov-3 Sotheby's, New York #248/R est:15000-20000

Works on paper

£1111 $1800 €1611 Two figures (48x33cm-19x13in) s. pencil dr. 8-Aug-3 Barridorf, Portland #306/R est:1200-1800

£1923 $3500 €2808 Series of an unknown cosmos LXXI (55x45cm-22x18in) s.d.79 wood paper collage prov.exhib. 29-Jun-4 Sotheby's, New York #524/R est:2000-3000

£5000 $8350 €7300 Untitled (142x114cm-56x45in) s.d.74 spray-paint cardboard wood collage panel prov. 21-Oct-3 Sotheby's, London #445/R est:5000-7000

£7500 $13800 €10950 Untitled (142x114cm-56x45in) s.d.74 spray paint cardboard wood collage panel prov. 24-Jun-4 Sotheby's, Olympia #573/R est:5000-7000

NEVIL, Edward (19th C) British

Works on paper

£680 $1108 €993 Continental street scenes of Couvain and Rheims (37x27cm-15x11in) pair W/C. 28-Sep-3 Wilkinson, Doncaster #308/R

NEVINSON, C R W (1889-1946) British

Prints

£2800 $4760 €4088 Le port (50x39cm-20x15in) s.d.1919 lithograph. 30-Oct-3 Christie's, Kensington #21/R est:3000-4000

£2800 $5096 €4088 Great War, Britains efforts and ideals, making aircraft, making the engine (41x30cm-16x12in) s.d.1917 num.53 lithograph edition of 200. 1-Jul-4 Sotheby's, London #238/R est:2500-3000

£3500 $5950 €5110 Workers (51x35cm-20x14in) s. lithograph. 30-Oct-3 Christie's, Kensington #23/R est:2000-2500

NEVINSON, Christopher Richard Wynne (1889-1946) British

£520 $972 €780 Vulcans Forge (48x59cm-19x23in) monochrome. 22-Jul-4 Dominic Winter, Swindon #333

£680 $1285 €993 Vulcan's forge (51x61cm-20x24in) oil en grisaille prov. 17-Feb-4 Rosebery Fine Art, London #586

£3800 $6346 €5548 Forest glade (102x76cm-40x30in) s. 16-Oct-3 Christie's, Kensington #646/R est:4000-6000

£5500 $9350 €8030 Goldfish - pisson d'or (50x75cm-20x30in) s. s.i.on stretcher painted c.1928 exhib. 21-Nov-3 Christie's, London #11/R est:6000-8000

£5500 $10065 €8030 River (46x61cm-18x24in) s. lit. 2-Jun-4 Sotheby's, London #27/R est:6000-8000

£7000 $11900 €10220 Easter (81x68cm-32x27in) s. exhib. 26-Nov-3 Sotheby's, Olympia #33/R est:3000-5000

£25000 $43000 €36500 Conciergerie (51x61cm-20x24in) s. prov.exhib. 3-Dec-3 Sotheby's, London #27/R est:10000-20000

£48000 $87360 €70080 Old Battersea power station (51x71cm-20x28in) s. prov. 15-Jun-4 Bonhams, New Bond Street #25/R est:25000-30000

Prints

£2300 $4187 €3450 Sinister Paris night. s.num.11 etching drypoint. 2-Jul-4 Bloomsbury, London #208/R est:2000-2500

£5500 $10011 €8250 Third avenue under the el-train (35x23cm-14x9in) s. etching drypoint edition of 75. 2-Jul-4 Bloomsbury, London #207/R est:3000-3500

Works on paper

£2400 $4392 €3504 La plage (28x44cm-11x17in) ink W/C bodycol prov.exhib. 4-Jun-4 Christie's, London #2/R est:3000-5000

NEW ENGLAND SCHOOL, American

£4938 $8000 €7209 Young man in black trimmed yellow vest and black jacket (76x56cm-30x22in) panel. 1-Aug-3 North East Auctions, Portsmouth #815/R

NEWACK, Thomas E (19th C) Irish

£550 $919 €803 Quiet snooze (46x61cm-18x24in) i.verso painted c.1880. 22-Jun-3 Desmond Judd, Cranbrook #1026

NEWBERY, Francis H (1855-1946) British

£3488 $6000 €5092 In the tavern (66x76cm-26x30in) s. 7-Dec-3 Freeman, Philadelphia #46 est:5000-8000

£6200 $11098 €9052 The mirror (75x46cm-30x18in) s. prov. 28-May-4 Lyon & Turnbull, Edinburgh #27/R est:1000-1500

NEWBURY, Albert Ernest (1891-1941) Australian

£506 $926 €759 Woodland pastoral. board. 3-Jun-4 Joel, Victoria #168/R (A.D 1300)

NEWCOMB, Mary (1922-) British

Works on paper

£700 $1211 €1022 Beached fishing boat, Burnham Overy Staithe (20x25cm-8x10in) i. W/C voer pencil sold with other W/C two. 10-Dec-3 Bonhams, Bury St Edmunds #508

£900 $1557 €1314 We float with the blue gourami (10x16cm-4x6in) i. pencil sold with five other studies. 10-Dec-3 Bonhams, Bury St Edmunds #505

£900 $1611 €1314 Young pigeon sees some white bread (9x21cm-4x8in) pencil W/C. 16-Mar-4 Bonhams, New Bond Street #90/R

£1000 $1790 €1460 Ewe looking back (16x22cm-6x9in) init. i.backboard pencil sold with another by the same hand. 16-Mar-4 Bonhams, New Bond Street #91/R est:1000-1500

£1000 $1790 €1460 Black Bess (20x19cm-8x7in) pencil W/C. 16-Mar-4 Bonhams, New Bond Street #92/R est:800-1000

£1100 $1903 €1606 Rooftops and weathervane, Bruges (13x11cm-5x4in) i.verso W/C over pencil sold with eight other studies. 10-Dec-3 Bonhams, Bury St Edmunds #502/R est:300-500

£1200 $2076 €1752 Swan by a fountain (18x20cm-7x8in) s.i.verso pencil sold with ten other studies. 10-Dec-3 Bonhams, Bury St Edmunds #507 est:300-400

£1250 $2163 €1825 Castle Cornet, Guernsey (25x20cm-10x8in) i.verso pencil sold with five other studies. 10-Dec-3 Bonhams, Bury St Edmunds #503 est:200-300

£1250 $2163 €1825 By the Dyke (12x20cm-5x8in) init. s.i.verso pencil wash sold with fourteen other studies. 10-Dec-3 Bonhams, Bury St Edmunds #504 est:400-600

£1400 $2422 €2044 Eck on Wiel, Holland - boats at anchor (20x24cm-8x9in) i.verso pencil crayon wash sold with two W/C three. 10-Dec-3 Bonhams, Bury St Edmunds #509/R est:500-700

£1400 $2506 €2044 Calves, June evening (12x14cm-5x6in) s.verso pencil W/C sold with another by the same hand. 16-Mar-4 Bonhams, New Bond Street #93/R est:1500-2000

£1500 $2685 €2190 Dorset horned polled ram and young ram (32x28cm-13x11in) init. s.i.verso pencil W/C. 16-Mar-4 Bonhams, New Bond Street #88/R est:1500-2000

£1800 $3222 €2628 River trip (21x29cm-8x11in) init. pencil W/C. 16-Mar-4 Bonhams, New Bond Street #87/R est:1500-2000

£1900 $3287 €2774 Spray Plane (14x21cm-6x8in) s.i.verso pencil crayon W/C sold with three W/C four. 10-Dec-3 Bonhams, Bury St Edmunds #510/R est:700-900

£1950 $3374 €2847 Sketches of a vessel at anchor, Calais (12x20cm-5x8in) i. pencil crayon sold with eight other studies. 10-Dec-3 Bonhams, Bury St Edmunds #506/R est:250-350

£2200 $3806 €3212 Tractor with rake (21x15cm-8x6in) pencil sold with eight other studies. 10-Dec-3 Bonhams, Bury St Edmunds #511/R est:250-350

£2800 $4816 €4088 Standing sheep (13x8cm-5x3in) s. pencil black ink pastel sold with two further studies. 3-Dec-3 Christie's, Kensington #741/R est:700-1000

£3600 $6228 €5256 Sheep by a gate (21x14cm-8x6in) init. s.verso pencil sold with sixteen studies of animals. 10-Dec-3 Bonhams, Bury St Edmunds #501 est:400-600

NEWCOMB, Rock (1945-) American

£5882 $10000 €8588 Ageless connection (91x61cm-36x24in) acrylic on board. 1-Nov-3 Altermann Galleries, Santa Fe #142

NEWCOMB, Tessa (1955-) British

£360 $601 €526 Morning bird (20x43cm-8x17in) init.d.99. 17-Oct-3 Keys, Aylsham #792

NEWCOMBE, Peter (20th C) British

£290 $458 €423 Rough sea on a moonlit night (63x103cm-25x41in) s.d.67 oil acrylic highlights board. 2-Sep-3 Gildings, Market Harborough #440

NEWEY, Harry Foster (1858-1933) British

£400 $740 €584 Winter landscape, the old mill, near Matloch. i.verso. 14-Jan-4 Brightwells, Leominster #855

NEWILI (c.1910-1993) Australian

Works on paper

£2439 $3854 €3561 Native dance (29x62cm-11x24in) earth pigments eucalyptus bark exec.c.1965 prov. 28-Jul-3 Sotheby's, Paddington #446/R est:2000-4000 (A.D 6000)

NEWKINGA, Jackie (1957-) North American

Sculpture

£901 $1532 €1315 Polar bears (10cm-4in) s. green soapstone. 3-Nov-3 Waddingtons, Toronto #600 est:400-600 (C.D 2000)

NEWMAN, Allen George (1875-1940) American

£347 $600 €507 Early days (20x25cm-8x10in) s. board. 10-Dec-3 Alderfer's, Hatfield #452/R

NEWMAN, Anna Mary (?-1930) American

£579 $950 €840 Brookville, Indiana (10x13cm-4x5in) s. canvas on board painted c.1910 prov. 7-Jun-3 Treadway Gallery, Cincinnati #1439

Works on paper

£2744 $4500 €3979 Pensive (36x26cm-14x10in) s. W/C paperboard exec.c.1910 prov. 7-Jun-3 Treadway Gallery, Cincinnati #1438 est:6000-8000

NEWMAN, Arnold (1918-) American

Photographs

£2222 $3778 €3200 Pablo Picasso (46x37cm-18x15in) s.i.d. gelatin silver lit. 31-Oct-3 Lempertz, Koln #252/R est:4000

£2361 $4014 €3400 Igor Strawinsky (25x47cm-10x19in) s.i.d. gelatin silver lit. 31-Oct-3 Lempertz, Koln #251/R est:3500

NEWMAN, Barnett (1905-1970) American

£13043 $24000 €19043 Untitled (15x10cm-6x4in) paper two. 10-Jun-4 Swann Galleries, New York #185/R est:5000-7000

£1976048 $3300000 €2885030 White fire I (122x152cm-48x60in) s.d.1954. 12-Nov-3 Sotheby's, New York #20/R est:3000000-4000000

Prints

£36723 $65000 €53616 Untitled (38x28cm-15x11in) s.d.1961 num.23/25 lithograph. 30-Apr-4 Sotheby's, New York #425/R est:60000-80000
£41176 $70000 €60117 Untitled (39x28cm-15x11in) s.d.1961 lithograph. 4-Nov-3 Christie's, Rockefeller NY #318/R est:40000-50000

NEWMAN, George A (19th C) American

£272 $500 €397 Autumn dusk (51x61cm-20x24in) s. 9-Jun-4 Alderfer's, Hatfield #497
£520 $900 €759 Covered bridge, Wissahickom at Chestnut Hill (41x51cm-16x20in) s. 10-Dec-3 Alderfer's, Hatfield #451/R est:800-1200

NEWMAN, George Adolph (20th C) American

£692 $1100 €1010 Just a Memory, Knights Bridge (25x36cm-10x14in) s. i.d.1958 verso canvasboard. 10-Sep-3 Alderfer's, Hatfield #376/R

NEWMAN, Harry W (1873-?) American

£3198 $5500 €4669 Winter afternoon (25x35cm-10x14in) s.d.05 prov. 3-Dec-3 Doyle, New York #243/R est:3000-5000

NEWMAN, Henry Roderick (c.1833-1918) American

Works on paper

£11173 $20000 €16313 Gateway of Philadelphus, Philae (26x17cm-10x7in) s.i.d.April 6 1892 W/C paperboard linen. 6-May-4 Shannon's, Milford #104/R est:20000-30000
£23256 $40000 €33954 Kom Ombo (66x43cm-26x17in) s.d.1895 W/C prov.exhib.lit. 3-Dec-3 Sotheby's, New York #121/R est:40000-60000

NEWMAN, John (1952-) American

Sculpture

£1189 $2200 €1736 Swayed by the Desire for the Middle (92x178x66cm-36x70x26in) wall relief brushed welded steel exec 1983 prov. 13-Jul-4 Christie's, Rockefeller NY #74/R est:3000-5000

NEWMAN, Joseph (1890-1979) American

£538 $1000 €785 Farm landscape with figures (41x51cm-16x20in) s. canvasboard. 3-Mar-4 Alderfer's, Hatfield #356/R est:1200-1800
£629 $1000 €918 Swimming Hole (30x41cm-12x16in) s. board. 10-Sep-3 Alderfer's, Hatfield #459/R
£699 $1300 €1021 Drydocked boats with river and buildings (41x51cm-16x20in) s. board. 3-Mar-4 Alderfer's, Hatfield #357/R est:1200-1800
£3459 $5500 €5050 Gott St., Rockport (64x76cm-25x30in) s. 10-Sep-3 Alderfer's, Hatfield #458/R est:6000-8000

NEWMAN, Louise (20th C) Irish?

Works on paper

£318 $579 €480 Different places II (46x46cm-18x18in) init. mixed media aluminium. 15-Jun-4 James Adam, Dublin #107/R
£411 $747 €620 Different places I (46x46cm-18x18in) init. mixed media aluminium. 15-Jun-4 James Adam, Dublin #106/R

NEWMAN, Marvin (1927-) American

Photographs

£1714 $3000 €2502 Playboy cover (33x22cm-13x9in) i. dye transfer print paper acetate overlay exec June 1962. 17-Dec-3 Christie's, Rockefeller NY #126/R est:2000-3000

NEWMAN, Robert Loftin (1827-1912) American

£1647 $2800 €2405 Bather by a stream (15x20cm-6x8in) init. 30-Oct-3 Phillips, New York #52/R est:800-1200
£3068 $5400 €4479 Harvest (18x25cm-7x10in) s. prov. 3-Jan-4 Collins, Maine #51/R est:700-900

NEWMANN, Eugene (1936-) American

£503 $900 €734 Figure and sequels (124x107cm-49x42in) i. 13-May-4 Dallas Auction Gallery, Dallas #194/R
£559 $1000 €816 Head. figure and bodies (142x191cm-56x75in) oil gesso acrylic chk on linen. 13-May-4 Dallas Auction Gallery, Dallas #58/R est:600-900

NEWMARCH, G B (19th C) British

£5000 $9300 €7300 Prize bull (71x89cm-28x35in) s.d.1820. 4-Mar-4 Christie's, Kensington #541/R est:3000-5000

NEWTON, Algernon (1880-1968) British

£520 $848 €759 No 3 The Haystack (61x51cm-24x20in) s.d.1914 i.verso. 24-Sep-3 Dreweatt Neate, Newbury #146/R
£2200 $4004 €3212 Landscape with three trees (60x90cm-24x35in) mono. 15-Jun-4 Bonhams, Knightsbridge #101/R est:800-1200
£2300 $4209 €3358 Evening (49x59cm-19x23in) mono.d.36 s.i.d. overlap. 8-Jul-4 Lawrence, Crewkerne #1660/R est:1500-2000
£5000 $8950 €7300 River landscape (61x91cm-24x36in) init. 16-Mar-4 Bonhams, New Bond Street #44/R est:1200-1800
£8000 $14320 €11680 Queens House, Greenwich (43x89cm-17x35in) mono.d.25 prov. 17-Mar-4 John Nicholson, Haslemere #722/R est:1500-2000

NEWTON, Harold (20th C) American

£1061 $1900 €1549 Florida highwaymen coastal scene (61x122cm-24x48in) s. board. 21-Mar-4 Jeffery Burchard, Florida #84/R

NEWTON, Helmut (1920-2004) German

£7292 $12396 €10500 Parlor games (45x45cm-18x18in) s.i.d. verso gelatin silver. 31-Oct-3 Lempertz, Koln #256/R est:8000-10000
£12153 $20660 €17500 Self portrait with wife and models (36x36cm-14x14in) s.i.d. verso gelatin silver lit. 31-Oct-3 Lempertz, Koln #254/R est:10000-12000

Photographs

£1829 $3200 €2670 Closed TV circuit, Beverley Hills (26x27cm-10x11in) gelatin silver print exec 1991 lit. 17-Dec-3 Christie's, Rockefeller NY #274/R est:3000-5000
£2096 $3500 €3060 Miami, Florida (16x24cm-6x9in) s.verso cibachrome print exec. 1978 prov.lit. 17-Oct-3 Phillips, New York #227/R est:3000-4000
£2156 $3600 €3148 Pere lachaise, Tomb of Talina (43x29cm-17x11in) s.i.d.1977 verso gelatin silver print prov.lit. 17-Oct-3 Phillips, New York #252/R est:3000-5000
£2286 $4000 €3338 Big nude in doorway (27x26cm-11x10in) gelatin silver print exec 1991. 17-Dec-3 Christie's, Rockefeller NY #283a/R est:3000-5000
£2297 $4112 €3400 Paloma Picasso (41x30cm-16x12in) s. verso silver gelatin lit. 8-May-4 Lempertz, Koln #218/R est:2500
£2400 $4200 €3504 Nastassia Kinski (50x37cm-20x15in) i.d.verso dye transfer print exec 1983. 17-Dec-3 Christie's, Rockefeller NY #264/R est:2000-3000
£2754 $4516 €3800 Audition (40x30cm-16x12in) s.verso silver print exec.c.1980. 2-Jun-3 Tajan, Paris #199 est:2000-3000
£3378 $6047 €5000 Vivane F, Hotel Volney, New York 1972 (36x24cm-14x9in) s. verso silver gelatin. 8-May-4 Lempertz, Koln #217/R est:2500
£3429 $6000 €5006 Nastassia Kinski (24x16cm-9x6in) gelatin silver print two exec 1983 lit. 17-Dec-3 Christie's, Rockefeller NY #266/R est:3000-4000
£3429 $6000 €5006 Couple reflected in mirror (26x26cm-10x10in) gelatin silver print exec 1989. 17-Dec-3 Christie's, Rockefeller NY #306/R est:3000-5000
£3955 $7000 €5774 Givenchy and Blgari, French Vogue, Paris (36x24cm-14x9in) s.num.14 verso photo printed 1984. 28-Apr-4 Sotheby's, New York #224/R est:5000-7000
£4000 $7000 €5840 American Playboy (26x27cm-10x11in) gelatin silver print exec 1991 lit. 17-Dec-3 Christie's, Rockefeller NY #273/R est:3000-5000
£4286 $7500 €6258 Nastassia Kinski (16x24cm-6x9in) gelatin silver print exec 1983. 17-Dec-3 Christie's, Rockefeller NY #265/R est:2000-3000
£4444 $8000 €6488 Fashion study for queen magazine (61x50cm-24x20in) s.i.d.1966 gelatin silver print prov.lit. 23-Apr-4 Phillips, New York #133/R est:8000-12000
£4571 $8000 €6674 Roberta Vasquez and Ava Fabian (34x26cm-13x10in) gelatin silver print exec 1987. 17-Dec-3 Christie's, Rockefeller NY #282/R est:3000-5000
£5500 $9680 €8030 Woman novelist (37x24cm-15x9in) s.i. num.1/5 verso cibachrome print. 19-May-4 Christie's, London #196/R est:5000-7000
£5714 $10000 €8342 Barbara Edwards and Helmut Newton (26x26cm-10x10in) gelatin silver print exec 1987 two lit. 17-Dec-3 Christie's, Rockefeller NY #301/R est:3000-5000
£6286 $11000 €9178 Hugh Hefner's projection room, Beverley Hills (27x27cm-11x11in) i.d.1986 verso gelatin silver print lit. 17-Dec-3 Christie's, Rockefeller NY #272/R est:3000-5000
£6587 $11000 €9617 Hotel room, Place de la Republique, Paris (36x24cm-14x9in) s.verso gelatin silver print exec.1976 prov. 20-Oct-3 Christie's, Rockefeller NY #48/R est:8000-10000
£6857 $12000 €10011 Nudes through doorway (26x26cm-10x10in) gelatin silver print exec 1991. 17-Dec-3 Christie's, Rockefeller NY #307/R est:3000-5000
£7429 $13000 €10846 Kimberly McArthur (26x26cm-10x10in) i.d.1987 num.2/5 verso gelatin silver print lit. 17-Dec-3 Christie's, Rockefeller NY #300/R est:3000-5000
£8000 $14000 €11680 American Playboy, Beverly Hills (32x26cm-13x10in) gelatin silver print exec 1991 lit. 17-Dec-3 Christie's, Rockefeller NY #308/R est:3000-5000
£8333 $15000 €12166 Jenny Kapitan in my studio (61x50cm-24x20in) s.i.d.1978 verso gelatin silver print prov. 23-Apr-4 Phillips, New York #27/R est:15000-20000
£9605 $17000 €14023 Woman examining man, Saint Tropez (58x38cm-23x15in) s.i.d.1975 num.7/10 photo printed later. 28-Apr-4 Sotheby's, New York #223/R est:10000-15000
£11111 $20000 €16222 Brescia, Italy, midday (58x49cm-23x19in) s.i.d.1981 gelatin silver print two. 23-Apr-4 Phillips, New York #111/R est:20000-30000
£12153 $20660 €17500 Two playmates (48x47cm-19x19in) s.i.d. verso gelatin silver lit. 31-Oct-3 Lempertz, Koln #255/R est:14000-16000
£12571 $22000 €18354 Kirstin Bell (24x16cm-9x6in) st.verso gelatin silver print three exec 1976. 17-Dec-3 Christie's, Rockefeller NY #257/R est:3000-5000
£13333 $24000 €19466 Nude descending staircase (61x50cm-24x20in) s.i.d.1981 gelatin silver print prov. 23-Apr-4 Phillips, New York #26/R est:15000-20000
£18079 $32000 €26395 Domestic nudes, 1993 (46x37cm-18x15in) s.i.d.1994 num.9/15 gelatin silver print set of five lit. 27-Apr-4 Christie's, Rockefeller NY #370/R est:12000-18000
£19209 $34000 €28045 Rue Aubriot, fashion model and nude (59x39cm-23x15in) s.i.d.1975 num.6/10 verso photo printed later lit. 27-Apr-4 Sotheby's, New York #36/R est:20000-30000
£53672 $95000 €78361 Sie kommen, dressed. Sie kommen, naked (31x27cm-12x11in) s.i.d.1981 verso one num.22/75 verso photo pair. 27-Apr-4 Sotheby's, New York #34/R est:15000-25000
£87571 $155000 €127854 Panoramic nude with gun, Villa d'Este, Como, 1989 (150x49cm-59x19in) s.i.d.1989 verso gelatin silver print. 27-Apr-4 Christie's, Rockefeller NY #371/R est:40000-60000

NEWTON, Kenneth (20th C) British

£1100 $1980 €1606 Still life, old barrel and cobs of corn (51x56cm-20x22in) s. 20-Apr-4 Canterbury Auctions, UK #141/R est:1500-2000

NEWTON, Lilias Torrance (1896-1980) Canadian

£447 $800 €653 Maude Ferguson (40x30cm-16x12in) s. board. 27-May-4 Heffel, Vancouver #136 (C.D 1100)
£1464 $2489 €2137 Portrait of a girl (41x30cm-16x12in) s.i.d.1973 verso prov. 18-Nov-3 Sotheby's, Toronto #50/R est:4000-6000 (C.D 3250)
£10811 $18378 €15784 Solange (51x41cm-20x16in) s. s.verso on stretcher prov.lit. 18-Nov-3 Sotheby's, Toronto #145/R est:8000-10000 (C.D 24000)

NEWTON, Richard (c.1777-1798) British

£26950 $45007 €38000 Les gardiens du haras (153x122cm-60x48in) s.i.d.1889. 16-Jun-3 Gros & Delettrez, Paris #54/R est:25000-35000

NEWTON, Richard (jnr) (20th C) British?

£1215 $2200 €1774 Portrait of the championship harness horse Nala (71x91cm-28x36in) s.d.1919. 2-Apr-4 Eldred, East Dennis #67/R est:1200-1800

NEWTON, Sir William John (1785-1869) British

Miniatures

£2300 $4232 €3358 Henry Hake Seward (7cm-3in) s.d.1817 set in red leather case. 24-Jun-4 Bonhams, New Bond Street #167/R est:800-1200

NEY, Lancelot (1900-1965) Hungarian

£284 $475 €415 Paris (41x33cm-16x13in) s. 11-Oct-3 Auctions by the Bay, Alameda #1657/R

NEY, Lloyd Raymond (1893-1964) American
£376 $650 €549 Sunflower (71x56cm-28x22in) s.d.1959 verso masonite. 10-Dec-3 Alderfer's, Hatfield #485
£2514 $4500 €3670 Newhope modernist abstract (76x76cm-30x30in) s.d.55. 26-May-4 Doyle, New York #164/R est:5000-7000
Works on paper
£245 $450 €358 New hope (30x48cm-12x19in) s.d.1963 W/C ink. 11-Jun-4 David Rago, Lambertville #130/R
£396 $650 €574 View of African American figures seated in yard (41x56cm-16x22in) s.d.33 W/C ink. 4-Jun-3 Alderfer's, Hatfield #319
£1524 $2500 €2210 Abstract composition with triangles and spheres (33x33cm-13x13in) s.d.Oct 18 1951 W/C. 4-Jun-3 Alderfer's, Hatfield #318/R est:2000-3000
£1630 $3000 €2380 Geometric abstraction (36x51cm-14x20in) s.d.1946 i.verso W/C. 11-Jun-4 David Rago, Lambertville #185/R est:1200-1600

NEY, Maria A (1849-1915) American
Works on paper
£414 $750 €604 Beach at la Jolla, California (25x41cm-10x16in) s. W/C. 16-Apr-4 James Julia, Fairfield #736/R

NEYA, P (20th C) Uruguayan?
£235 $400 €343 Saxon elector (70x58cm-28x23in) 20-Nov-3 Galeria y Remates, Montevideo #1/R

NEYLAND, Harry A (1877-1958) American
£382 $650 €558 Floral still life in pink (25x30cm-10x12in) s. 21-Nov-3 Skinner, Boston #418/R
£1118 $1800 €1632 Forsythia (30x23cm-12x9in) s. i. stretcher. 20-Aug-3 James Julia, Fairfield #1359a/R est:2000-2500
£2174 $3500 €3174 The lone gate Apple Dore Island, Isle of Shoals, NH (30x46cm-12x18in) s. i. stretcher. 20-Aug-3 James Julia, Fairfield #1359/R est:4000-6000

NEYMARK, Gustave (1850-?) French
£391 $700 €571 Charging Cossacks (23x28cm-9x11in) s. board prov. 21-Mar-4 Hindman, Chicago #782/R

NEYN, Pieter de (1597-1639) Dutch
£3103 $5152 €4500 Dune landscape with village and peasants (30x40cm-12x16in) bears sig. panel oval. 1-Oct-3 Dorotheum, Vienna #134/R est:6000-8000
£3800 $6460 €5548 Wooded river landscape with a shepherd, sheep and a goat on a track (37x57cm-15x22in) panel. 29-Oct-3 Bonhams, New Bond Street #20/R est:4000-6000
£8108 $14270 €12000 River landscape with ferry (39x60cm-15x24in) panel. 22-May-4 Lempertz, Koln #1105/R est:9000
£8380 $15000 €12235 Figures resting in field by haystacks (37x51cm-15x20in) mono. panel. 27-May-4 Sotheby's, New York #28/R est:10000-15000
£17333 $31027 €26000 Wooded landscape with huntsman, dogs and peasants (39x67cm-15x26in) init.d.1629 prov.lit. 17-May-4 Christie's, Amsterdam #76/R est:12000-16000

NEYRAC, Guy de (20th C) French
Works on paper
£223 $400 €326 Herald Square, New York (30x41cm-12x16in) s. W/C. 12-May-4 South Bay, Long Island #473401/R
£249 $450 €364 Paris street scene (43x58cm-17x23in) s. W/C. 14-Apr-4 Dallas Auction Gallery, Dallas #275b
£359 $650 €524 Place des Voges (43x58cm-17x23in) s. W/C. 14-Apr-4 Dallas Auction Gallery, Dallas #275/R

NEYT, Bernard (1825-1880) Belgian
£2533 $4560 €3800 Church interior with figures in prayer (66x54cm-26x21in) s.d.1859 panel. 21-Apr-4 Christie's, Amsterdam #187/R est:4000-6000
£2533 $4560 €3800 Figures in Canterbury Cathedral (66x54cm-26x21in) s.i.d.1869. 20-Apr-4 Sotheby's, Amsterdam #37/R est:4000-6000

NEYTS, Gillis (1623-1687) Flemish
Works on paper
£1622 $2854 €2400 Landscape with windmills and distant view of Antwerp (8x13cm-3x5in) s. pen brown ink grey wash. 19-May-4 Sotheby's, Amsterdam #40/R est:1500-2000
£7770 $13676 €11500 Study of an old tree (23x18cm-9x7in) mono. pen brown ink prov.exhib. 19-May-4 Sotheby's, Amsterdam #47/R est:5500-7000

NEYTS, Gillis (attrib) (1623-1687) Flemish
Works on paper
£973 $1791 €1450 Paysage (12x18cm-5x7in) bistre pen. 24-Mar-4 Claude Boisgirard, Paris #4/R

NEZZO, Luciano (1856-?) Italian
£27000 $45090 €39420 Thief (127x157cm-50x62in) s. 12-Nov-3 Sotheby's, Olympia #229/R est:12000-18000

NG ENG TENG (1934-2001) Singaporean
Sculpture
£1144 $2070 €1670 Girl (33cm-13in) s.d.1961 clay. 3-Apr-4 Glerum, Singapore #14/R est:4000-5000 (S.D 3500)

NGALE, Gracie Morton (20th C) Australian?
£325 $511 €475 Untitled (124x64cm-49x25in) acrylic. 26-Aug-3 Lawson Menzies, Sydney #314 (A.D 800)

NGAN, Guy (20th C) New Zealander
£1391 $2365 €2031 Equilibrium (122x122cm-48x48in) s. acrylic on board. 26-Nov-3 Dunbar Sloane, Wellington #84/R est:2000-4000 (NZ.D 3700)
£1410 $2397 €2059 Orange and brown chief (122x122cm-48x48in) s.d.1971 oil paint and polyurethane. 26-Nov-3 Dunbar Sloane, Wellington #87/R est:2000-4000 (NZ.D 3750)
£1974 $3355 €2882 Untitled (120x182cm-47x72in) s.d.1969 board. 26-Nov-3 Dunbar Sloane, Wellington #86/R est:3000-6000 (NZ.D 5250)
£2076 $3716 €3031 Blue structure no.1 (122x122cm-48x48in) s.d.1974. 12-May-4 Dunbar Sloane, Wellington #67/R est:4000-8000 (NZ.D 6000)
£2595 $4645 €3789 Suspended animation no.4 (60x136cm-24x54in) s.d.74 board. 12-May-4 Dunbar Sloane, Wellington #68/R est:2500-5000 (NZ.D 7500)
£3008 $5113 €4392 Untitled (122x171cm-48x67in) s.d.1973 board. 26-Nov-3 Dunbar Sloane, Wellington #85/R est:3000-6000 (NZ.D 8000)
Sculpture
£1557 $2787 €2273 Three peaks (40x23x28cm-16x9x11in) bronze. 12-May-4 Dunbar Sloane, Wellington #69/R est:5000-10000 (NZ.D 4500)
£1730 $3097 €2526 Untitled wooden anchor form (28x21x21cm-11x8x8in) recycled kauri. 12-May-4 Dunbar Sloane, Wellington #70/R est:3000-6000 (NZ.D 5000)

NGANJMIRA, Bobby Barrdjaray (1915-1992) Australian
Works on paper
£575 $1046 €840 Four freshwater bream (71x29cm-28x11in) natural pigments on bark prov. 1-Jul-4 Joel, Victoria #242/R (A.D 1500)
£1328 $2484 €1992 Lumahlumah the giant with dilly bags (119x41cm-47x16in) earth pigments eucalyptus bark prov. 26-Jul-4 Sotheby's, Melbourne #404/R est:4000-6000 (A.D 3400)
£2148 $4018 €3222 Legend of Nimbuwah Rock (69x33cm-27x13in) bears name.i.d.1968 verso earth pigments eucalyptus bark prov. 26-Jul-4 Sotheby's, Melbourne #239/R est:8000-12000 (A.D 5500)
£2148 $4018 €3222 Lumahlumah the giant with dilly bags (162x58cm-64x23in) bears name.d.1988 verso earth pigments eucalyptus bark prov. 26-Jul-4 Sotheby's, Melbourne #403/R est:7000-10000 (A.D 5500)

NGANJMIRRA, Jimmy Nakkurridjdjilmi (1917-1982) Australian
Works on paper
£650 $1028 €949 Rainbow serpent (116x51cm-46x20in) i.verso earth pigments eucalyptus bark prov. 28-Jul-3 Sotheby's, Paddington #459/R est:1000-1500 (A.D 1600)

NGANTUNG, Henk (1921-1991) Indonesian
£654 $1183 €955 Serimpi dancer (28x22cm-11x9in) panel exhib.lit. 4-Apr-4 Sotheby's, Singapore #159/R est:2000-3000 (S.D 2000)

NGARLA, Glory (20th C) Australian
£747 $1247 €1121 Bush plum (122x90cm-48x35in) i.verso acrylic. 27-Oct-3 Goodman, Sydney #48/R (A.D 1800)
£1224 $2253 €1787 Bush plum (120x180cm-47x71in) i.verso acrylic linen. 29-Mar-4 Goodman, Sydney #37/R est:4000-6000 (A.D 3000)
Works on paper
£1176 $2106 €1717 Bush Plum (180x120cm-71x47in) synthetic polymer paint canvas exec 2002 prov. 25-May-4 Lawson Menzies, Sydney #225/R est:8000-10000 (A.D 3000)

NGATANE, Ephraim (1938-1971) South African
£431 $720 €629 Soccer players (29x29cm-11x11in) s. board. 20-Oct-3 Stephan Welz, Johannesburg #613 est:4000-6000 (SA.R 5000)
£1800 $3276 €2628 Gum Boot dancers (61x76cm-24x30in) s. 5-Feb-4 Gorringes, Worthing #446 est:100-150
Works on paper
£345 $576 €504 Dancers (74x54cm-29x21in) s.d.69 mixed media. 20-Oct-3 Stephan Welz, Johannesburg #631 est:3000-4000 (SA.R 4000)
£396 $709 €578 Conversation (57x43cm-22x17in) s. mixed media. 31-May-4 Stephan Welz, Johannesburg #372 (SA.R 4800)
£1552 $2591 €2266 Street with a coal vendor (57x75cm-22x30in) s.d.68 mixed media on board. 20-Oct-3 Stephan Welz, Johannesburg #343/R est:8000-12000 (SA.R 18000)
£4542 $8130 €6631 Man reading with his family (74x59cm-29x23in) s. mixed media board. 31-May-4 Stephan Welz, Johannesburg #600/R est:20000-30000 (SA.R 55000)

N'GUYEN ANH (1914-2000) Vietnamese
£3673 $6576 €5400 Pecheurs sur la plage a Long-Hai (61x78cm-24x31in) s.d.1942 panel. 21-Mar-4 St-Germain-en-Laye Encheres #134/R est:3000-4000

NGUYEN CAT TUONG (1912-) Vietnamese
Works on paper
£24510 $44363 €35785 Mother and child (74x38cm-29x15in) s.d.1940 ink gouache on silk. 4-Apr-4 Sotheby's, Singapore #50/R est:18000-25000 (S.D 75000)

NGUYEN DINH DUNG (20th C) Vietnamese
£514 $873 €750 Jeune femme a la table (46x41cm-18x16in) s.d.83 silk. 4-Nov-3 Adjug'art, Brest #35/R

NGUYEN GIA TRI (1908-1993) Vietnamese
£19097 $31892 €27882 Women (80x60cm-31x24in) s. lacquer panel prov.exhib.lit. 12-Oct-3 Sotheby's, Singapore #95/R est:55000-65000 (S.D 55000)
Works on paper
£805 $1442 €1200 Untitled (44x51cm-17x20in) ink pastel. 27-May-4 Beaussant & Lefèvre, Paris #288/R
£853 $1536 €1245 Dragon (18x24cm-7x9in) s. mixed media prov. 25-Apr-4 Christie's, Hong Kong #531/R est:15000-25000 (HK.D 12000)
£980 $1775 €1431 Procession (39x30cm-15x12in) s. mixed media. 4-Apr-4 Sotheby's, Singapore #83/R est:3000-4000 (S.D 3000)
£1275 $2283 €1900 Untitled (22x17cm-9x7in) ink pastel. 27-May-4 Beaussant & Lefèvre, Paris #292 est:300-350
£2685 $4805 €4000 Untitled (150x120cm-59x47in) gouache chl diptych. 27-May-4 Beaussant & Lefèvre, Paris #289 est:2000-3000

N'GUYEN PHAN CHANH (1892-1984) Vietnamese
£58824 $106471 €85883 Girl combing hair (65x50cm-26x20in) s.i.d.1933 silk on board exhib.lit. 4-Apr-4 Sotheby's, Singapore #68/R est:150000-200000 (S.D 180000)
Works on paper
£19355 $30968 €28258 Woman in the rice fields (55x37cm-22x15in) s.d.1936 gouache ink silk. 18-May-3 Sotheby's, Singapore #106/R est:50000-60000 (S.D 54000)
£35172 $58738 €51000 Jeu des cases gagnantes (65x89cm-26x35in) s. gouache silk exec.c.1930. 14-Nov-3 Piasa, Paris #302/R est:12000-15000

NGUYEN PHUOC (1943-) Vietnamese
£6536 $11830 €9543 Friendly chat (82x76cm-32x30in) s.d.03. 4-Apr-4 Sotheby's, Singapore #193/R est:12000-15000 (S.D 20000)

NGUYEN SANG (1923-1988) Vietnamese
£2778 $4639 €4056 Mot Cot Pagoda, Hanoi (61x86cm-24x34in) s. painted c.1943 prov. 12-Oct-3 Sotheby's, Singapore #93/R est:8000-10000 (S.D 8000)

NGUYEN THANH HOA (1965-) Vietnamese
£719 $1301 €1050 Still life with oil lamp (62x72cm-24x28in) 3-Apr-4 Glerum, Singapore #89/R est:2700-3700 (S.D 2200)

NGUYEN TIEN CHUNG (1914-1976) Vietnamese
Works on paper
£2014 $3363 €2940 Pigeon (16x23cm-6x9in) s.d.70 ink W/C. 12-Oct-3 Sotheby's, Singapore #113/R est:2500-3500 (S.D 5800)

NGUYEN TRUNG (1940-) Vietnamese
£1806 $3015 €2637 Girl holding lotus flower (100x100cm-39x39in) s.d.91. 12-Oct-3 Sotheby's, Singapore #114/R est:5500-7500 (S.D 5200)
£2174 $3370 €3174 Portrait of a girl (100x100cm-39x39in) s.d.92. 6-Oct-2 Sotheby's, Singapore #101/R est:5500-7500 (S.D 6000)
£2355 $3650 €3438 Girl with lotus (100x100cm-39x39in) s.d.91. 6-Oct-2 Sotheby's, Singapore #102/R est:5500-7500 (S.D 6500)
£2796 $4473 €4082 Seated girl (100x100cm-39x39in) s.d.91. 18-May-3 Sotheby's, Singapore #114/R est:5500-7500 (S.D 7800)
£3431 $6211 €5009 Girl on hammock (100x100cm-39x39in) s.d.92. 4-Apr-4 Sotheby's, Singapore #192/R est:6000-8000 (S.D 10500)

NGUYEN TU NGHIEM (1922-) Vietnamese
£5161 $8258 €7535 Ancient dance (50x80cm-20x31in) s.d.66 lacquer. 18-May-3 Sotheby's, Singapore #124/R est:12000-15000 (S.D 14400)
£5797 $8986 €8464 Ancient dance (63x81cm-25x32in) s.d.74 lacquer. 6-Oct-2 Sotheby's, Singapore #99/R est:12000-15000 (S.D 16000)

NGUYEN XUAN VIET (1949-) Vietnamese
£3011 $4817 €4396 Market place (84x122cm-33x48in) s.d.97 lacquer. 18-May-3 Sotheby's, Singapore #125/R est:7000-9000 (S.D 8400)

NGUYEN, Patricia (20th C) Canadian
£226 $378 €330 Pour un soir (60x45cm-24x18in) s.i. 17-Nov-3 Hodgins, Calgary #27/R (C.D 500)

NGUYEN, Rosa (1960-) ?
Sculpture
£1300 $2366 €1898 Recumbent cow (67x100cm-26x39in) painted glazed terracotta. 4-Feb-4 Sotheby's, Olympia #101/R est:400-600

NGWENYA, Malangatana (1936-) Mozambican
£215 $400 €314 The night club (121x90cm-48x35in) s.d.63 board. 5-Mar-4 Skinner, Boston #601/R

NHLENGETHWA, Sam (1955-) South African
Works on paper
£743 $1330 €1085 Germiston station - platform 13 (20x29cm-8x11in) s.d.85 collage pen chl. 31-May-4 Stephan Welz, Johannesburg #352 (SA.R 9000)

NI ZAN (attrib) (1301-1374) Chinese
Works on paper
£17070 $30725 €24922 Pavilion in a sparse landscape (74x39cm-29x15in) s.i. hanging scroll ink prov. 26-Apr-4 Christie's, Hong Kong #948/R est:120000-150000 (HK.D 240000)

NIALSON, Eric (20th C) ?
£994 $1600 €1451 Shipping off the coast (61x91cm-24x36in) s. 14-Jan-4 Christie's, Rockefeller NY #43/R est:1000-1500

NIBBRIG, Ferdinand Hart (1866-1915) Dutch
£2721 $4952 €4000 Dame met blauwe hoed - lady with blue hat (60x50cm-24x20in) s. painted c.1914 prov.exhib. 3-Feb-4 Christie's, Amsterdam #416/R est:6000-8000
£22667 $41707 €34000 Korenvelden in Zuid-Limburg (46x80cm-18x31in) s.d.1905 i.verso prov.exhib.lit. 8-Jun-4 Sotheby's, Amsterdam #7/R est:50000-70000
£26667 $49067 €40000 Girl and a goat, Laren (42x42cm-17x17in) s.d.03. 9-Jun-4 Christie's, Amsterdam #218/R est:20000-30000
Works on paper
£5667 $10427 €8500 Johanne Hart Nibbrig-Moltzer and her sons in the garden of their house (32x36cm-13x14in) s. pencil col crayon exhib. 9-Jun-4 Christie's, Amsterdam #33/R est:4000-6000

NIBBS, Richard Henry (1816-1893) British
£420 $760 €613 Jetty with fishing boats (24x39cm-9x15in) s. 30-Mar-4 David Duggleby, Scarborough #190/R
£550 $1023 €803 Morning after a gale (76x115cm-30x45in) s. 2-Mar-4 Bearnes, Exeter #412/R
£2000 $3700 €2920 Brigantine, Shoreham harbour (25x40cm-10x16in) s. 14-Jul-4 Sotheby's, Olympia #70/R est:1000-1500
£2400 $4464 €3504 Gilding up the estuary, Holland (41x74cm-16x29in) s.i. 4-Mar-4 Christie's, Kensington #505/R est:1500-2000
Works on paper
£280 $451 €406 Two masted vessel and other shipping off a coast (23x38cm-9x15in) s.d.1851 W/C. 15-Aug-3 Keys, Aylsham #483/R
£280 $476 €409 Paddle tug of the London and Thames steam Co. (33x51cm-13x20in) W/C. 30-Oct-3 Duke & Son, Dorchester #88
£350 $641 €511 Up with the tide (30x46cm-12x18in) s.d.1865 W/C over pencil. 6-Jul-4 Peter Wilson, Nantwich #45/R
£350 $641 €511 Greenwich Hospital (39x58cm-15x23in) s. W/C over pencil htd bodycol. 6-Jul-4 Peter Wilson, Nantwich #46/R
£650 $1047 €943 Sussex town of Hailsham with figures conversing in street (25x36cm-10x14in) i.verso W/C exec.c.1860-1802. 23-Feb-3 Desmond Judd, Cranbrook #1044
£850 $1556 €1241 Portsmouth Harbour (50x75cm-20x30in) s. W/C over pencil htd white. 6-Jul-4 Bearnes, Exeter #410/R
£2400 $4536 €3504 Towing out of Port (49x74cm-19x29in) s.i. W/C htd white. 17-Feb-4 Bonhams, New Bond Street #28/R est:1000-1500

NIBLETT, Gary (1943-) American
£1176 $2000 €1717 Women of Golondrinas (28x36cm-11x14in) s.d.87 prov. 1-Nov-3 Santa Fe Art, Santa Fe #50/R est:3000-4000
£2793 $5000 €4078 Beneath Old Baldy (46x61cm-18x24in) 15-May-4 Altermann Galleries, Santa Fe #117/R
£3529 $6000 €5152 Taos night (41x51cm-16x20in) s.d.79 masonite panel. 1-Nov-3 Santa Fe Art, Santa Fe #85/R est:6000-8000

NICE, Christiaan (?) South African?
£429 $769 €626 Children playing on the rocks (29x39cm-11x15in) s.d.85 canvas on board. 31-May-4 Stephan Welz, Johannesburg #239 (SA.R 5200)

NICE, Don (1932-) American
Works on paper
£722 $1300 €1054 South, spring. North, winter. West, summer (45x45cm-18x18in) pencil W/C three prov. 25-Apr-4 Bonhams & Butterfields, San Francisco #5568/R est:2000-4000
£773 $1400 €1129 Picture within a picture, painted frame (99x58cm-39x23in) W/C. 16-Apr-4 American Auctioneer #294/R

NICHOLAS, Darcy (20th C) New Zealander
£2536 $4109 €3677 Rongoue Roa (5x67cm-2x26in) s.d.1985. 31-Jul-3 International Art Centre, Auckland #89/R est:8000-11000 (NZ.D 7000)
Works on paper
£692 $1239 €1010 Last carving (75x56cm-30x22in) s. mixed media. 12-May-4 Dunbar Sloane, Wellington #128 est:2000-4000 (NZ.D 2000)

NICHOLAS, Hilda Emma Rix (1884-1961) Australian
£3830 $6510 €5592 Algerian (50x61cm-20x24in) mono. i.on stretcher. 26-Nov-3 Deutscher-Menzies, Melbourne #125/R est:10000-15000 (A.D 9000)
£5372 $9938 €7843 Cottage garden, Etaples, France (61x50cm-24x20in) s. painted c.1920 prov. 10-Mar-4 Deutscher-Menzies, Melbourne #101/R est:14000-18000 (A.D 13000)
Works on paper
£1220 $2183 €1781 Arab Market scene (37x27cm-15x11in) s. conte. 10-May-4 Joel, Victoria #226 est:1500-2500 (A.D 3000)

NICHOLAS, Thomas Andrew (1934-) American
£511 $950 €746 River torrent (30x25cm-12x10in) s. board prov. 5-Mar-4 Skinner, Boston #434/R
£753 $1400 €1099 The mountain village (30x17cm-12x7in) s. board prov. 5-Mar-4 Skinner, Boston #431/R est:500-700
£824 $1400 €1203 Quiet canal, Venice (36x25cm-14x10in) s. prov. 21-Nov-3 Skinner, Boston #520/R est:400-600
£1452 $2700 €2120 Mousehole Harbour, Cornwall, England (25x35cm-10x14in) s. i.verso prov. 5-Mar-4 Skinner, Boston #505/R est:700-900

NICHOLAS, Thomas M (jnr) (1963-) American
£900 $1450 €1314 Mount Desert landscape (51x61cm-20x24in) s. 20-Aug-3 James Julia, Fairfield #1667/R est:1500-2000

NICHOLL, Andrew (1804-1886) British
£750 $1230 €1095 Church by the woods (33x50cm-13x20in) s.d.1863. 4-Jun-3 John Ross, Belfast #69
Works on paper
£280 $482 €409 Rosshire (25x35cm-10x14in) s. W/C exec.1850. 3-Dec-3 John Ross, Belfast #129
£333 $603 €500 Waterloo Bridge, Clifden, Connemara (20x32cm-8x13in) W/C. 31-Mar-4 James Adam, Dublin #21/R
£423 $731 €600 River landscape (39x28cm-15x11in) s. W/C. 10-Dec-3 Bonhams & James Adam, Dublin #21/R
£507 $958 €750 Foxglove (30x23cm-12x9in) s.i. W/C prov. 17-Feb-4 Whyte's, Dublin #164
£600 $1098 €876 Carrickfergus (25x33cm-10x13in) s. W/C. 2-Jun-4 John Ross, Belfast #95
£671 $1188 €1000 Cattle in bogland, with a rain shower approaching (14x23cm-6x9in) s. W/C sgraffito prov. 27-Apr-4 Whyte's, Dublin #214/R
£750 $1350 €1095 Waterloo Bridge, Cliften (19x32cm-7x13in) i. W/C over pencil. 21-Jan-4 Sotheby's, Olympia #141/R
£811 $1532 €1200 Study of wild birds (24x36cm-9x14in) i.verso W/C over pencil prov. 17-Feb-4 Whyte's, Dublin #162/R est:1500-2000

£850 $1556 €1241 Study of three elephants (30x43cm-12x17in) s. W/C. 2-Jun-4 John Ross, Belfast #126
£900 $1665 €1314 Shipping at sunset on the Indian ocean (26x36cm-10x14in) W/C. 10-Mar-4 Sotheby's, Olympia #156/R est:1000-1500
£900 $1665 €1314 Sunset over the Indian ocean (25x35cm-10x14in) i.d.1849 verso W/C htd stopping out scratching out. 10-Mar-4 Sotheby's, Olympia #157/R est:1000-1500
£900 $1611 €1314 Kenbane Castle, Co Antrim (19x29cm-7x11in) i.indis.d. W/C. 14-May-4 Christie's, London #136/R
£1049 $1783 €1500 Study of cattle after Cuyp at Dulwich College. Study of sheep (20x30cm-8x12in) one i.d.1832 verso one i.verso pen ink pair prov. 18-Nov-3 Whyte's, Dublin #113/R
£1119 $1902 €1600 Cattle in Hyde Park (22x34cm-9x13in) two i.d.1845 W/C over pencil three studies prov. 18-Nov-3 Whyte's, Dublin #111/R
£1141 $2019 €1700 Landscape with Procris and Cephalus (36x50cm-14x20in) i.d.3rd July verso W/C bodycol sgraffito after Claude prov. 27-Apr-4 Whyte's, Dublin #131/R est:1500-2000
£1208 $2138 €1800 Distant view of Glengariff Castle, Glengariff harbour, mountains beyond (18x29cm-7x11in) i. W/C pair prov. 27-Apr-4 Whyte's, Dublin #215/R est:2000-3000
£1800 $3186 €2628 Elephants browsing amongst water lilies (49x72cm-19x28in) s. W/C bodycol. 27-Apr-4 Bonhams, New Bond Street #45/R est:700-1000
£1800 $3222 €2628 Steamer off Staffa (33x51cm-13x20in) s. pencil W/C scratching out. 14-May-4 Christie's, London #20/R est:2000-3000
£1831 $3168 €2600 Ruins of the Abbey and Round Tower, Devenish Island, Lough Erne (33x51cm-13x20in) s. W/C. 10-Dec-3 Bonhams & James Adam, Dublin #23/R est:2000-3000
£2200 $3982 €3300 Duck shotting (31x51cm-12x20in) s. W/C prov. 31-Mar-4 James Adam, Dublin #22/R est:2500-3500
£2400 $4296 €3504 Giant's Eye, Causeway Head (17x26cm-7x10in) s.d.1859 pencil W/C bodycol scratching out. 14-May-4 Christie's, London #134/R est:2500-3500
£2600 $4654 €3796 Trees on a riverbank with cattle grazing nearby (49x71cm-19x28in) pencil W/C scratching out prov. 14-May-4 Christie's, London #82/R est:3000-5000
£3000 $5370 €4380 Carrick-a-rede, Co Antrim (32x42cm-13x17in) s. pencil W/C gum arabic scratching out prov. 14-May-4 Christie's, London #21/R est:2000-3000
£3000 $5370 €4380 The Giant's Causeway, Co Antrim (35x53cm-14x21in) s. pencil pen ink W/C gum arabic htd white scratching out prov. 14-May-4 Christie's, London #81/R est:3000-5000
£3200 $5728 €4672 Pigeon Cave, Co Donegal (22x32cm-9x13in) s. pencil W/C gum arabic scratching out. 14-May-4 Christie's, London #132/R est:3500-4500
£3800 $6802 €5548 The Giant's Causeway, Co Antrim (24x33cm-9x13in) s. pencil W/C htd bodycol scratching out. 14-May-4 Christie's, London #133/R est:3000-5000
£4500 $8235 €6570 Wild flowers, Ceylon (30x48cm-12x19in) s. W/C. 2-Jun-4 John Ross, Belfast #153 est:7000-8000
£5000 $8950 €7300 Glenarm, Co Antrim (34x50cm-13x20in) pencil W/C gum arabic scratching out. 14-May-4 Christie's, London #131/R est:6000-8000
£6000 $10740 €8760 Poppies, buttercups and daisies (30x49cm-12x19in) pen brown ink W/C gum arabic htd bodycol scratching out prov. 14-May-4 Christie's, London #18/R est:7000-10000
£6000 $10740 €8760 Pleaskin Head, Co Antrim (41x66cm-16x26in) s. pencil W/C gum arabic htd bodycol scratching out. 14-May-4 Christie's, London #129/R est:7000-10000
£6000 $10740 €8760 Carrickfergus Castle (33x51cm-13x20in) s. pencil W/C gum arabic scratching out. 14-May-4 Christie's, London #130/R est:7000-10000
£8099 $12958 €11500 Bank of wild flowers with Dunstaffnage Castle beyond (36x51cm-14x20in) s. W/C bodycol sgraffito. 16-Sep-3 Whyte's, Dublin #99/R est:10000-15000
£11972 $19155 €17000 Poppies, ox-eye daisies and other flowers, with a view of Londonderry (34x52cm-13x20in) s. W/C gum arabic sgraffito. 16-Sep-3 Whyte's, Dublin #98/R est:15000-20000

NICHOLL, Andrew (attrib) (1804-1886) British
Works on paper
£1200 $2148 €1752 View in Ceylon (24x30cm-9x12in) s. pencil W/C scratching out. 14-May-4 Christie's, London #27/R est:400-600

NICHOLL, William (1794-1840) British
Works on paper
£1074 $1901 €1600 Dawn over Carlingford Louch (25x41cm-10x16in) i.verso W/C bodycol sgraffito prov. 27-Apr-4 Whyte's, Dublin #137/R est:1000-1500
£1900 $3401 €2774 On the Lagan from Annadale, Co Antrim (22x31cm-9x12in) i.verso pencil W/C gum arabic scratching out. 14-May-4 Christie's, London #60/R est:1000-1500
£2819 $4989 €4200 Topographical landscapes. one s. three i. W/C bodycol sgraffito 26 folio prov. 27-Apr-4 Whyte's, Dublin #132/R est:3000-4000

NICHOLLS, Bertram (1883-1974) British
£280 $440 €406 Figures by a sunlit ruin (51x60cm-20x24in) s.d.1949. 28-Aug-3 Christie's, Kensington #313
£380 $673 €555 Sussex landscape (31x41cm-12x16in) s. 27-Apr-4 Bonhams, Knightsbridge #124/R
£800 $1480 €1168 View of Windsor from Eton (38x76cm-15x30in) s.d.1946. 17-Jul-4 Bonhams, Knightsbridge #203/R
Works on paper
£380 $673 €555 Conversation piece (33x41cm-13x16in) s. W/C prov. 28-Apr-4 Halls, Shrewsbury #486/R

NICHOLLS, Burr H (1848-1915) American
£520 $900 €759 Stable interior with chickens (25x30cm-10x12in) s.verso board. 10-Dec-3 Alderfer's, Hatfield #332 est:600-800
£1734 $3000 €2532 Horse-drawn cart on a country lane (51x66cm-20x26in) s. prov. 10-Dec-3 Bonhams & Butterfields, San Francisco #6044/R est:3000-5000

NICHOLLS, Charles Wynne (1831-1903) British
£1700 $2839 €2482 Eastern beauty (20x16cm-8x6in) i. 13-Nov-3 Christie's, Kensington #257/R est:600-8000

NICHOLLS, George F (1885-1937) British
Works on paper
£620 $973 €905 Broadway Cotswold cottage. Chipping Campden (31x22cm-12x9in) s. one i. W/C pair. 17-Apr-3 Bruton Knowles, Cheltenham #62

NICHOLLS, John E (fl.1922-1955) British
£1755 $3230 €2562 Peonies (65x50cm-26x20in) s.d.47 i.verso board prov. 29-Mar-4 Goodman, Sydney #133/R est:2000-3000 (A.D 4300)

NICHOLLS, Michael (1960-) Australian
£288 $521 €420 Untitled (130x59cm-51x23in) init.d.MN. 30-Mar-4 Lawson Menzies, Sydney #8 (A.D 700)
£494 $894 €721 Let's drink to the smoke (183x150cm-72x59in) s.i.verso. 30-Mar-4 Lawson Menzies, Sydney #60 est:1500-2500 (A.D 1200)
£535 $968 €781 Bucks night out (172x122cm-68x48in) init.verso oil canvas strips on canvas. 30-Mar-4 Lawson Menzies, Sydney #66 est:1500-2500 (A.D 1300)
£1235 $2235 €1803 Untitled (38x52cm-15x20in) acrylic. 30-Mar-4 Lawson Menzies, Sydney #39 est:800-1000 (A.D 3000)
£2429 $3911 €3546 Devil's Banquet (152x183cm-60x72in) d.87 bears i.verso prov. 25-Aug-3 Sotheby's, Paddington #232/R est:6000-8000 (A.D 6000)
Works on paper
£247 $447 €361 Lovers lane (38x38cm-15x15in) init.d.1986 gouache. 30-Mar-4 Lawson Menzies, Sydney #62 est:400-600 (A.D 600)
£267 $484 €390 Headache 1986 (58x78cm-23x31in) gouache. 30-Mar-4 Lawson Menzies, Sydney #55 (A.D 650)
£267 $484 €390 Untitled (40x51cm-16x20in) s.d.85 mixed media oil pastel gouache sawdust. 30-Mar-4 Lawson Menzies, Sydney #65 (A.D 650)
£288 $521 €420 Untitled (46x53cm-18x21in) s. pastel. 30-Mar-4 Lawson Menzies, Sydney #3/R (A.D 700)
£412 $745 €602 Nightmare in Melbourne (56x76cm-22x30in) s.d.86 gouache. 30-Mar-4 Lawson Menzies, Sydney #28 est:400-600 (A.D 1000)
£453 $819 €661 Ned Kelly's tits (54x39cm-21x15in) init.d.86 gouache. 30-Mar-4 Lawson Menzies, Sydney #43 est:400-600 (A.D 1100)

NICHOLLS, Rhoda Holmes (1854-1938) American
£1890 $3250 €2759 Summer Idyll (30x45cm-12x18in) s. prov.exhib. 3-Dec-3 Doyle, New York #222/R est:4000-6000
Works on paper
£247 $400 €361 Island Gloucester Mass, from mothers piazza in the province house, Hawthorne Inn (25x36cm-10x14in) s. W/C. 9-Aug-3 Auctions by the Bay, Alameda #1488/R

NICHOLS, Dale (1904-1995) American
£595 $1100 €869 Caribbean scene (51x61cm-20x24in) s.d.1964. 13-Mar-4 DeFina, Austinburg #596/R
£5308 $9500 €7750 Western winter (61x91cm-24x36in) s.d.1985 i.verso prov. 6-May-4 Shannon's, Milford #28/R est:6000-8000
£9581 $16000 €13988 Laundry Day (61x76cm-24x30in) s. prov. 23-Oct-3 Shannon's, Milford #48/R est:12000-18000
£9827 $17000 €14347 Long Shadows on the farm, Nebraska (51x76cm-20x30in) s.d.1966 prov. 10-Dec-3 Bonhams & Butterfields, San Francisco #6049/R est:20000-30000
£16766 $28000 €24478 Coming home (71x76cm-28x30in) s.d.1939. 9-Oct-3 Christie's, Rockefeller NY #117/R est:7000-10000

NICHOLS, Frederick (20th C) American
£2210 $4000 €3315 Tree lined creek (122x180cm-48x71in) 16-Apr-4 American Auctioneer #295/R

NICHOLS, H (20th C) American
£1509 $2700 €2203 Harbour view, hazy morning (46x66cm-18x26in) 14-May-4 Skinner, Boston #129/R est:2000-4000

NICHOLS, Henry Hobart (1869-1962) American
£1235 $2000 €1791 Hills in winter (41x50cm-16x20in) s. board. 8-Aug-3 Barridorf, Portland #293/R est:3000-5000
£1304 $2100 €1904 Winter in Rockport (61x76cm-24x30in) s. 20-Aug-3 James Julia, Fairfield #1300/R est:3000-5000

NICHOLS, John (1899-1963) American
£240 $400 €350 Abstract composition (137x66cm-54x26in) indis.sig. canvas on board. 25-Oct-3 David Rago, Lambertville #1011

NICHOLS, Pauline Wright (1889-1983) American
£519 $950 €758 Plantation home (38x28cm-15x11in) canvasboard. 5-Jun-4 Neal Auction Company, New Orleans #408

NICHOLS, Perry (1911-1992) American
£1078 $1800 €1574 Nudes (71x41cm-28x16in) panel. 18-Oct-3 David Dike, Dallas #186/R est:2000-4000

NICHOLS, Spencer B (1875-1950) American
£598 $1100 €873 Kent, landscape with village (30x41cm-12x16in) s. board. 9-Jun-4 Alderfer's, Hatfield #424 est:300-400

NICHOLSON, Ben (1894-1982) British
£850 $1573 €1241 Diamond jug with cup (25x29cm-10x11in) i.verso board prov. 10-Mar-4 Cheffins, Cambridge #48/R
£7059 $12000 €10306 Glass with 5 Facets (26x35cm-10x14in) s.d.73 verso oil wash pencil paper prov. 5-Nov-3 Christie's, Rockefeller NY #154/R est:15000-20000
£9396 $16819 €14000 Gythian Theatre (52x68cm-20x27in) s.i.d.72 verso oil wash pencil paper on masonite prov.exhib.lit. 25-May-4 Dorotheum, Vienna #93/R est:14000-18000
£11173 $20000 €16313 Sept 58 - Ronco 69 (43x50cm-17x20in) s.i. verso oil pencil paper on artist board prov. 6-May-4 Sotheby's, New York #363/R est:18000-25000
£11173 $20000 €16313 Still life (43x37cm-17x15in) s.d.1965 verso oil wash pen ink paper prov.exhib. 6-May-4 Sotheby's, New York #369/R est:20000-25000
£19580 $33287 €28000 Untitled (49x36cm-19x14in) s.d.1968 oil pencil exhib. 29-Nov-3 Villa Grisebach, Berlin #339/R est:24000-28000
£29694 $54638 €43353 June 1960 - Stone goblet (41x19cm-16x7in) s.i.d. verso oil pencil relief on painted pavatex prov.exhib.lit. 8-Jun-4 Germann, Zurich #69/R est:30000-40000 (S.FR 68000)

£32000	$58880	€46720	Granite - green - yellow (43x43cm-17x17in) s.i. verso board on prepared board painted 1963 prov.exhib. 22-Jun-4 Sotheby's, London #202/R est:30000-40000
£35000	$63700	€51100	Off Cascais (63x51cm-25x20in) s.d.1966 verso oil gesso carved relief prov. 3-Feb-4 Christie's, London #281/R est:35000-45000
£38000	$65360	€55480	April 1956 (40x35cm-16x14in) s.i.d.1956 verso carved board. 3-Dec-3 Sotheby's, London #59/R est:40000-60000
£42177	$75497	€62000	Suspended yellow (61x53cm-24x21in) s.i.d.55 verso oil pencil cardboard masonite prov. 16-Mar-4 Finarte Semenzato, Milan #432/R est:90000
£43000	$79120	€62780	Composition (60x30cm-24x12in) s.d.1958 verso oil W/C pencil paper on board prov. 22-Jun-4 Sotheby's, London #513/R est:20000-30000
£72000	$131760	€105120	July 13-49 (31x41cm-12x16in) s.i.d.49 canvasboard prov.exhib.lit. 2-Jun-4 Sotheby's, London #61a/R est:60000-80000
£72000	$131760	€105120	Nov 1960 - Chalcedon (69x59cm-27x23in) s.i.d.Nov 1960 verso carved board on masonite prov.exhib. 4-Jun-4 Christie's, London #128/R est:40000-60000
£90000	$153000	€131400	1970 - Sienese landscape (72x176cm-28x69in) s.i.d.1970 canvasboard exhib.lit. 21-Nov-3 Christie's, London #183/R est:70000-100000
£90000	$163800	€131400	March 59 kos variation on a theme (53x36cm-21x14in) s.i.verso oil pencil relief on board painted 1959 exhib.lit. 4-Feb-4 Sotheby's, London #286/R est:30000-40000
£98000	$178360	€143080	November (63x50cm-25x20in) indis.s.d.Nov 25-46 oil pencil prov.exhib.lit. 3-Feb-4 Christie's, London #280/R est:100000-150000
£98000	$180320	€143080	Menalon with off green (89x51cm-35x20in) s.i. verso oil pencil wooden relief on board prov.exhib.lit. 22-Jun-4 Sotheby's, London #200/R est:50000-70000

Prints

£2059	$3500	€3006	Olympia fragment (32x37cm-13x15in) s.d.1965 et. 4-Nov-3 Christie's, Rockefeller NY #142/R est:4500-5500
£2400	$4392	€3504	Pewter (21x15cm-8x6in) s.i.d.1967 tone etching. 3-Jun-4 Christie's, Kensington #135/R est:1500-2000
£4200	$7644	€6132	Goblets forms (33x31cm-13x12in) s.d.1967 num.37/50 etching sold with another etching. 1-Jul-4 Sotheby's, London #235/R est:3500-4500
£20524	$37354	€29965	Profiles (26x18cm-10x7in) mono.d.1933 linocut. 17-Jun-4 Kornfeld, Bern #628/R est:3000 (S.FR 47000)

Sculpture

£52239	$90373	€76269	Stone and dark mauve (44x43cm-17x17in) s.i.d.1965 verso wood relief prov.exhib. 9-Dec-3 Peter Webb, Auckland #87/R est:90000-120000 (NZ.D 140000)

Works on paper

£2700	$4941	€3942	Kite (17x10cm-7x4in) s.i.verso pen ink W/C prov. 2-Jun-4 Sotheby's, London #124/R est:3000-4000
£4200	$7014	€6132	Variation 1, paros with moon (13x26cm-5x10in) s.i.d.66-67 verso gouache pen brush ink. 16-Oct-3 Christie's, Kensington #666/R est:3000-5000
£4310	$7716	€6293	Jug and bowl (34x52cm-13x20in) s.i.d.July 62 verso pencil. 12-May-4 Dobiaschofsky, Bern #829/R est:14000 (S.FR 10000)
£4600	$7682	€6716	Euboca (35x19cm-14x7in) s.i.d.68 verso pencil prov. 16-Oct-3 Christie's, Kensington #668/R est:4000-6000
£5000	$8600	€7300	Bottle, sun and moon composition (20x15cm-8x6in) init. pen ink prov. 5-Dec-3 Keys, Aylsham #478/R est:5000-7000
£5500	$9460	€8030	April 1981 (39x20cm-15x8in) ink wash prov. 2-Dec-3 Bonhams, New Bond Street #156/R est:4500-6500
£13000	$23660	€18980	Feb 64 (47x44cm-19x17in) s.i.verso W/C pencil paper on board exec.1964 prov.exhib. 4-Feb-4 Sotheby's, London #513/R est:6000-8000
£18000	$32760	€26280	Goblets with red (37x42cm-15x17in) s.i.d.1967 verso gouache pencil pen ink wash prov. 5-Feb-4 Christie's, London #355/R est:15000-20000
£19500	$35490	€28470	March 63 (60x50cm-24x20in) s.i.d.63 verso pencil wash paper on artist mount prov.exhib. 5-Feb-4 Christie's, London #356/R est:12000-18000
£20000	$36400	€29200	Maggiore (42x27cm-17x11in) gouache pen ink paper on board exec.1979 prov.exhib.lit. 4-Feb-4 Sotheby's, London #514/R est:20000-30000
£32000	$57280	€46720	St Ives, full moon behind cloud (67x56cm-26x22in) s.i.d.Oct. 15-51 backboard pencil prov.exhib. 16-Mar-4 Bonhams, New Bond Street #77/R est:10000-15000
£34000	$61880	€49640	Composition (40x31cm-16x12in) s.d.1938 verso pencil gouache card prov. 4-Feb-4 Sotheby's, London #511/R est:6000-8000
£36000	$60120	€52560	Cornwall, painting (23x23cm-9x9in) s.verso gouache on board prov. 14-Oct-3 David Lay, Penzance #600/R est:12000-15000

NICHOLSON, Charles W (1886-1965) American

£396	$650	€578	Along the California coast (46x69cm-18x27in) s. 8-Feb-3 Auctions by the Bay, Alameda #343/R

NICHOLSON, Francis (1753-1844) British

Works on paper

£250	$418	€365	Cascade in Cottendale, the head of Wensleydale (35x48cm-14x19in) pen brown ink W/C. 16-Oct-3 Christie's, Kensington #122/R
£260	$406	€377	Travellers conversing, Cader Idris beyond (23x33cm-9x13in) i.verso W/C exec.c.1780-1820. 20-Oct-2 Desmond Judd, Cranbrook #822
£300	$549	€438	Stone Byre Lin, a fall on the Clyde near Lanark (52x43cm-20x17in) W/C. 6-Apr-4 Bonhams, Chester #874
£400	$756	€584	South view of Bolton Abbey, Yorkshire (16x27cm-6x11in) W/C. 23-Feb-4 David Duggleby, Scarborough #615/R
£450	$828	€657	Stormy seas below a ruined castle (45x59cm-18x23in) W/C lit. 23-Mar-4 Anderson & Garland, Newcastle #310/R
£800	$1304	€1160	Horses and cart on a beach (23x32cm-9x13in) W/C. 23-Sep-3 Bonhams, Knightsbridge #54/R
£4400	$7480	€6424	Rudding House, Yorkshire (29x41cm-11x16in) W/C pencil. 4-Nov-3 Bonhams, New Bond Street #23/R est:2000-3000
£4600	$7820	€6716	Temple of Flora, Stourhead, Wiltshire (40x54cm-16x21in) W/C prov. 4-Nov-3 Bonhams, New Bond Street #25/R est:5000-8000
£5500	$9350	€8030	Pantheon, Stourhead, Wiltshire (39x54cm-15x21in) W/C prov. 4-Nov-3 Bonhams, New Bond Street #24/R est:6000-9000

NICHOLSON, Francis (attrib) (1753-1844) British

Works on paper

£280	$515	€409	River scene with angler (27x50cm-11x20in) W/C. 23-Jun-4 Bonhams, Bury St Edmunds #305
£300	$525	€438	Upland landscape with river cascading through a rocky gorge (33x46cm-13x18in) W/C. 16-Dec-3 Capes Dunn, Manchester #776
£671	$1188	€1000	Bulloch Castle, Dalkey, County Dublin (28x36cm-11x14in) i. W/C pencil. 27-Apr-4 Whyte's, Dublin #136/R

NICHOLSON, George W (1832-1912) American

£497	$900	€726	North African coastal scene with figures at foreground (25x33cm-10x13in) s. 3-Apr-4 Nadeau, Windsor #233/R
£670	$1200	€1126	Rural landscape (25x36cm-10x14in) 20-Mar-4 Pook & Pook, Downington #290/R
£914	$1700	€1334	Untitled (30x41cm-12x16in) board. 6-Mar-4 Page, Batavia #24
£1000	$1800	€1460	Coming storm (25x30cm-10x12in) s. 23-Jan-4 Freeman, Philadelphia #284/R est:600-1000
£1105	$2000	€1613	Dim north African interior with seated figure (28x38cm-11x15in) s. 3-Apr-4 Nadeau, Windsor #108/R est:1500-2500
£4268	$7000	€6189	Landscape with boats, figures on a road, and distant village (61x107cm-24x42in) s. prov. 31-May-3 Brunk, Ashville #537/R est:5000-10000

NICHOLSON, Jean (20th C) American

£363	$625	€530	Ducks near a pond and a passing rooster (51x61cm-20x24in) s. 6-Dec-3 Selkirks, St. Louis #227

NICHOLSON, John H (1911-1988) British

Works on paper

£260	$447	€380	Isle of Man steam packet ship ramming a German submarine (10x18cm-4x7in) W/C. 5-Dec-3 Chrystals Auctions, Isle of Man #224/R
£260	$468	€380	Large fishing boats anchored beside buildings (12x22cm-5x9in) s.d.1934 pencil W/C. 21-Apr-4 Tennants, Leyburn #942
£260	$465	€380	View from the summit of Cronk-ny-Chree Lhaa (38x56cm-15x22in) s. W/C. 7-May-4 Chrystals Auctions, Isle of Man #325
£340	$568	€496	Gravel pit (28x36cm-11x14in) s. W/C ink. 20-Jun-3 Chrystals Auctions, Isle of Man #211
£340	$585	€496	SS Peveril, Douglas harbour (41x61cm-16x24in) s. col chk. 5-Dec-3 Chrystals Auctions, Isle of Man #250/R
£360	$601	€526	Tynwald Hill (20x28cm-8x11in) s.i.verso W/C. 20-Jun-3 Chrystals Auctions, Isle of Man #187
£360	$601	€526	King William College (30x46cm-12x18in) s. col chks. 20-Jun-3 Chrystals Auctions, Isle of Man #286
£360	$644	€526	Castletown harbour (33x48cm-13x19in) s. W/C. 7-May-4 Chrystals Auctions, Isle of Man #326
£420	$701	€613	Castletown harbour (20x28cm-8x11in) s. W/C. 20-Jun-3 Chrystals Auctions, Isle of Man #195/R
£450	$752	€657	Ballaugh Curraghs (38x56cm-15x22in) s.i.verso col chks. 20-Jun-3 Chrystals Auctions, Isle of Man #285
£460	$768	€672	Two Biplanes at Ronaldsway (15x23cm-6x9in) s.d.1941 W/C. 20-Jun-3 Chrystals Auctions, Isle of Man #197/R
£520	$868	€759	Port Erin. Langnes (15x23cm-6x9in) s.d.1947 W/C two. 20-Jun-3 Chrystals Auctions, Isle of Man #203/R

NICHOLSON, John Millar (fl.1877-1888) British

£450	$806	€657	Sulby (30x46cm-12x18in) s.d.1889 panel. 7-May-4 Chrystals Auctions, Isle of Man #294
£800	$1376	€1168	Water mill, West Baldwin (46x74cm-18x29in) init. 5-Dec-3 Chrystals Auctions, Isle of Man #222/R

Works on paper

£950	$1634	€1387	Cathedral, Bruges (64x43cm-25x17in) init.d.1872 W/C. 5-Dec-3 Chrystals Auctions, Isle of Man #223

NICHOLSON, Kate (1929-) British

£1950	$3257	€2847	Tuscan landscape with Camponile (70x90cm-28x35in) prov. 14-Oct-3 Bearnes, Exeter #415/R est:1200-1800

NICHOLSON, Lillie May (1884-1964) American

£1058	$2000	€1545	Fishing boats - Monterey, Calif (41x30cm-16x12in) i. verso board. 17-Feb-4 John Moran, Pasadena #24/R est:1500-2500
£2174	$4000	€3174	Six fishing boats at anchor with Mount Toro beyond (30x40cm-12x16in) s. board prov.exhib.lit. 8-Jun-4 Bonhams & Butterfields, San Francisco #4296/R est:3000-5000

NICHOLSON, Peter Walker (1856-1885) British

Works on paper

£10000	$17000	€14600	Burning weeds (63x103cm-25x41in) s.d.84 pencil W/C bodycol scratching out exhib. 30-Oct-3 Christie's, London #62/R est:10000-15000

NICHOLSON, Sir William (1872-1949) British

£1350	$2322	€1971	Fife Coast, Kinghorn Bay (15x35cm-6x14in) s. prov. 4-Dec-3 Bonhams, Edinburgh #74 est:500-800
£6000	$10200	€8760	Landscape with farmhouse (20x25cm-8x10in) init. panel prov.exhib.lit. 21-Nov-3 Christie's, London #50/R est:6000-8000
£22000	$37840	€32120	Meadows (33x41cm-13x16in) init. canvasboard. 3-Dec-3 Sotheby's, London #15/R est:12000-18000
£24000	$41280	€35040	Ciboure Harbour (37x46cm-15x18in) panel painted 1939 prov.lit. 3-Dec-3 Sotheby's, London #14/R est:10000-15000
£24000	$42960	€35040	Three boats (32x41cm-13x16in) s. canvasboard prov.exhib. 16-Mar-4 Bonhams, New Bond Street #1/R est:10000-15000
£37000	$62900	€54020	Downland landscape (55x61cm-22x24in) s.d.1912 prov.exhib.lit. 21-Nov-3 Christie's, London #51/R est:30000-50000
£46196	$85000	€67446	Mending the nets (33x41cm-13x16in) i. canvasboard lit. 10-Jun-4 Sotheby's, New York #128/R est:20000-30000

Works on paper

£950	$1577	€1387	Two designs for the Rakes Progress (27x19cm-11x7in) init. crayon pencil pen ink two. 1-Oct-3 Woolley & Wallis, Salisbury #132/R

NICHOLSON, Winifred (1893-1981) British

£4300	$7181	€6278	Rustle of dried grass (76x30cm-30x12in) s.i.d.1967 prov. 14-Oct-3 Bearnes, Exeter #417/R est:4000-6000
£8000	$14800	€11680	Rustle of dried grass (76x30cm-30x12in) s.i.d.1967 stretcher prov. 11-Feb-4 Sotheby's, Olympia #248/R est:7000-10000
£9200	$17204	€13432	Restronguet (55x81cm-22x32in) s.d.1928 verso. 21-Jul-4 Bonhams, New Bond Street #187/R est:3000-5000
£12000	$20640	€17520	Witches garden (50x39cm-20x15in) board scratching out. 2-Dec-3 Bonhams, New Bond Street #155/R est:12000-18000

£15000 $27450 €21900 Aegean coast line (37x68cm-15x27in) i.d.1962 panel prov. 4-Jun-4 Christie's, London #55/R est:6000-8000
£26000 $47580 €37960 Pike Hill (51x76cm-20x30in) s.i.d.1972 prov. 4-Jun-4 Christie's, London #54/R est:12000-18000
Works on paper
£1650 $2756 €2409 Sacred Hill (28x49cm-11x19in) i.d.1970 mixed media prov. 14-Oct-3 Bearnes, Exeter #416/R est:1000-1500

NICKEL, Hans (1916-1986) German
£267 $480 €400 Horse drawn wood cart (70x100cm-28x39in) s. 26-Apr-4 Rieber, Stuttgart #1147/R
£302 $553 €450 Farmer with foal and two horses at the drinking trough (81x71cm-32x28in) s. 8-Jul-4 Allgauer, Kempten #2180/R
£403 $737 €600 Two horses with feeding vehicle and with foal (60x71cm-24x28in) s. lit. 8-Jul-4 Allgauer, Kempten #2179/R
£423 $676 €600 Flowers (70x60cm-28x24in) s. 18-Sep-3 Rieber, Stuttgart #1330
£445 $757 €650 Peasant ploughing (70x80cm-28x31in) s. 5-Nov-3 Hugo Ruef, Munich #1077

NICKERSON, Reginald E (1915-) American
£838 $1500 €1223 American ship, Mary D Lane (56x71cm-22x28in) a. 16-May-4 CRN Auctions, Cambridge #55/R
£949 $1500 €1386 Two masted schooner Lewis A Edwards (56x71cm-22x28in) s. 25-Jul-3 Eldred, East Dennis #323/R est:2000-3000
£1456 $2300 €2126 Three masted schooner Robert Morgan (61x97cm-24x38in) s. 25-Jul-3 Eldred, East Dennis #322/R est:3000-4000

NICKLE, Lawrence (?) Canadian
£301 $561 €439 King Mountain, Algoma (61x51cm-24x20in) s. board. 2-Mar-4 Ritchie, Toronto #138/R (C.D 750)

NICKLIN, Tim (20th C) Kenyan
Sculpture
£1027 $1747 €1500 Antilope (42cm-17in) s.d.1988 pat.bronze. 5-Nov-3 Hugo Ruef, Munich #2165 est:1500
£1918 $3260 €2800 Defending the herd (35x75cm-14x30in) s.d.1983 pat.bronze wood socle. 5-Nov-3 Hugo Ruef, Munich #2164/R est:2800

NICKOL, Adolf (1824-1905) German
£1039 $1860 €1517 Loaded donkeys with dogs on pass (69x116cm-27x46in) s. 22-Mar-4 Philippe Schuler, Zurich #4422/R est:3000-4000 (S.FR 2400)
£3000 $5400 €4500 Mountain landscape (58x79cm-23x31in) s. 26-Apr-4 Rieber, Stuttgart #1249/R est:6500

NICKOLLS, Trevor (1949-) Australian
Works on paper
£2148 $4018 €3222 Dreamtime travel (75x66cm-30x26in) init. synthetic polymer paint canvas prov. 26-Jul-4 Sotheby's, Melbourne #143/R est:7000-10000 (A.D 5500)
£2539 $4748 €3809 Machinetime blues (76x60cm-30x24in) s.d.1989 verso synthetic polymer paint canvas prov. 26-Jul-4 Sotheby's, Melbourne #140/R est:7000-10000 (A.D 6500)
£2539 $4748 €3809 Face the machinetime (76x61cm-30x24in) s.d.1989 verso synthetic polymer paint canvas prov. 26-Jul-4 Sotheby's, Melbourne #141/R est:7000-10000 (A.D 6500)
£2846 $4496 €4127 Untitled, waterholes and trees (122x61cm-48x24in) i.d.1981 verso synthetic polymer paint canvas prov. 28-Jul-3 Sotheby's, Paddington #193/R est:7000-10000 (A.D 7000)
£4297 $8035 €6446 Machinetime head (91x76cm-36x30in) synthetic polymer paint canvas prov.exhib.lit. 26-Jul-4 Sotheby's, Melbourne #142/R est:10000-15000 (A.D 11000)

NICOL, Erskine (1825-1904) British
£2500 $4475 €3650 St Patrick's Day (28x23cm-11x9in) board prov. 14-May-4 Christie's, London #140/R est:3000-5000
£3073 $5500 €4487 Sanitary operation (59x48cm-23x19in) init.d.1849 board on panel painted oval. 6-May-4 Doyle, New York #45/R est:3000-5000
£3600 $6552 €5256 Noon day rest (23x43cm-9x17in) s.d.1853. 1-Jul-4 Mellors & Kirk, Nottingham #793/R est:2000-4000
£6338 $10141 €9000 Three children playing at marching soldiers (53x43cm-21x17in) s.d.1861. 16-Sep-3 Whyte's, Dublin #100/R est:6000-8000
£16500 $27390 €24090 Waiting for an answer (45x66cm-18x26in) s.d.1862. 1-Oct-3 John Ross, Belfast #147 est:12000-15000
Works on paper
£400 $728 €584 Raiders (22x31cm-9x12in) s. pencil W/C htd white. 1-Jul-4 Mellors & Kirk, Nottingham #708
£423 $731 €600 Outward bound (11x7cm-4x3in) s.d.52 W/C. 10-Dec-3 Bonhams & James Adam, Dublin #28/R
£570 $1021 €850 Peeling potatoes (38x28cm-15x11in) mono.d.1849 pencil W/C htd white. 26-May-4 James Adam, Dublin #28/R
£805 $1442 €1200 Farmyard scene with a child (35x45cm-14x18in) s.d.1856 W/C. 31-May-4 Hamilton Osborne King, Dublin #174/R
£1181 $1924 €1700 Man and a pig by a wall (10x16cm-4x6in) mono.d.54 monochrome wash. 24-Sep-3 James Adam, Dublin #2/R est:500-800
£2254 $3606 €3200 Salmon fishing (51x33cm-20x13in) s.d.1893 W/C prov. 16-Sep-3 Whyte's, Dublin #111/R est:2500-3500

NICOL, Erskine (attrib) (1825-1904) British
£520 $952 €759 Reveller (27x22cm-11x9in) board. 8-Apr-4 Bonhams, Edinburgh #158

NICOL, J M (19/20th C) French
£356 $581 €520 Coastal landscape (38x53cm-15x21in) s. 27-Sep-3 Rasmussen, Havnen #2295 (D.KR 3800)

NICOL, John (20th C) New Zealander?
£321 $591 €469 Evening palm (85x96cm-33x38in) s.d.1991 verso acrylic MDF. 25-Mar-4 International Art Centre, Auckland #89/R (NZ.D 900)

NICOL, John Watson (?-1926) British
£400 $664 €584 Portrait of an elderly fisherman wearing a sou'wester (23x18cm-9x7in) s.d.1891 board. 10-Jun-3 Canterbury Auctions, UK #97/R
£733 $1224 €1070 Man with a flute (60x44cm-24x17in) s.d.1882. 20-Oct-3 Stephan Welz, Johannesburg #199/R est:8000-12000 (SA.R 8500)
£900 $1611 €1314 Solo serenade (61x46cm-24x18in) s. 27-May-4 Christie's, Kensington #311/R
£7800 $14118 €11388 Highlander (51x41cm-20x16in) s.d.1895. 19-Apr-4 Sotheby's, London #12/R est:3000-4000

NICOLA DA CAMPIONE, Alberto di (fl.1393-1404) Italian
Sculpture
£80986 $134437 €115000 Madonna and Child enthroned (72x30x40cm-28x12x16in) wood lit. 11-Jun-3 Semenzato, Florence #4/R est:150000-180000

NICOLA, Francesco de (1882-1958) Italian
£1127 $1870 €1600 La collana di perle (55x40cm-22x16in) s. board. 11-Jun-3 Christie's, Rome #44 est:1500-2000
Works on paper
£845 $1462 €1200 Young woman (50x35cm-20x14in) s. chl pastel. 11-Dec-3 Christie's, Rome #61/R

NICOLAI, Carsten (1965-) ?
£4348 $8000 €6348 Prototype telefunken L169 (260x199cm-102x78in) s.i.d.2000 verso oil polyester prov. 10-Jun-4 Phillips, New York #445/R est:10000-15000
£8380 $15000 €12235 Prototype telefunken L16 plus 6 (260x200cm-102x79in) oil polyester prov. 14-May-4 Phillips, New York #132/R est:10000-15000

NICOLAI, Paul (1876-1948) ?
£1049 $1804 €1500 Lecture de la lettre (32x41cm-13x16in) s. panel. 8-Dec-3 Tajan, Paris #303/R est:1500-1800
£2349 $4346 €3500 Marche dans la campagne en Algerie (54x65cm-21x26in) s. 15-Mar-4 Gros & Delettrez, Paris #154/R est:3000-3500

NICOLAISEN, Peter (1894-1989) Danish
£276 $470 €403 Landscape from Schakenborg Palace (42x67cm-17x26in) init. 10-Nov-3 Rasmussen, Vejle #563 (D.KR 3000)
£284 $455 €415 Flowers in a jug (100x90cm-39x35in) init. 22-Sep-3 Rasmussen, Vejle #687 (D.KR 3000)
£290 $518 €423 Still life of flowers (44x50cm-17x20in) init. 10-May-4 Rasmussen, Vejle #548 (D.KR 3200)
£326 $583 €476 Landscape (48x100cm-19x39in) init. 10-May-4 Rasmussen, Vejle #544/R (D.KR 3600)
£350 $595 €511 Landscape from Schackenborg (57x67cm-22x26in) init. 10-Nov-3 Rasmussen, Vejle #564 (D.KR 3800)
£359 $643 €524 Landscape from Schackenborg (96x94cm-38x37in) init. 12-Jan-4 Rasmussen, Vejle #306 (D.KR 3800)

NICOLAS, Joep (1897-?) Dutch
£1467 $2684 €2200 Highwaymen (62x51cm-24x20in) s. panel. 7-Jun-4 Glerum, Amsterdam #340/R est:3000-4000

NICOLAS, Marie (19th C) French
Works on paper
£250 $460 €365 Portrait of a girl in a pink dress (46x37cm-18x15in) s.d.1934 prov. 23-Mar-4 Rosebery Fine Art, London #894

NICOLAUS, Martin (1870-1945) German
£263 $484 €400 Landscape in the Hegau region (60x82cm-24x32in) s.d.38. 26-Jun-4 Karrenbauer, Konstanz #1754
£690 $1104 €980 Pavilion in Stuttgart vineyards (27x32cm-11x13in) s.d.1858. 18-Sep-3 Rieber, Stuttgart #857

NICOLAYSEN, Lyder Wentzel (1821-1898) Norwegian
£643 $1177 €939 Coastal landscape with boats (34x54cm-13x21in) s. panel. 2-Feb-4 Blomqvist, Lysaker #1208/R (N.KR 8000)

NICOLELLO, Edoardo (1871-1948) Italian
£267 $491 €400 Val Tournance (40x28cm-16x11in) s. board. 8-Jun-4 Della Rocca, Turin #298/R

NICOLI, Carlo (1850-?) Italian
Sculpture
£1400 $2548 €2044 Standing blacksmith allegorical of work (95cm-37in) s.i. brown pat bronze. 15-Jun-4 Sotheby's, Olympia #134/R est:1500-2000

NICOLI, Claudio (1958-) Italian
Sculpture
£1224 $2044 €1750 Horse and rider (30x41x13cm-12x16x5in) s.i.d.1998 num.2/2 bronze. 26-Jun-3 Sant Agostino, Torino #277/R est:1800
£1333 $2453 €2000 Jumping horse (27cm-11in) s.d.1997 num.2/2 bronze. 14-Jun-4 Sant Agostino, Torino #378/R est:1500-2000
£2759 $4607 €4000 Nude with plait (83x34x27cm-33x13x11in) s.d.199 bronze. 17-Nov-3 Sant Agostino, Torino #235/R est:4000-5000

NICOLIE, Josephus Christianus (1791-1854) Belgian
£1800 $3240 €2628 Interior of Saint Jacobs Church, Antwerp (32x39cm-13x15in) s.d.1822 i.verso panel. 23-Apr-4 Christie's, Kensington #120/R est:2000-3000

NICOLINI, Aldo (1934-) Italian

£333 $613 €500 Papillon, l'esprit de mon ame (100x100cm-39x39in) s.verso oil enamel lit. 12-Jun-4 Meeting Art, Vercelli #440/R

NICOLL, Archibald Frank (1886-1953) New Zealander

£346 $619 €505 Canterbury hay stacks, end of winter (29x38cm-11x15in) s. paintd c. 1930. 12-May-4 Dunbar Sloane, Wellington #199 est:1500-3000 (NZ.D 1000)
£362 $583 €529 Street scene (28x39cm-11x15in) s. board. 20-Aug-3 Dunbar Sloane, Auckland #64/R est:3000-5000 (NZ.D 1000)
£551 $1031 €804 Road through landscape (29x39cm-11x15in) s. 24-Feb-4 Peter Webb, Auckland #54/R (NZ.D 1500)
£714 $1314 €1042 Snowfall, Canterbury (29x39cm-11x15in) s. 25-Mar-4 International Art Centre, Auckland #82/R (NZ.D 2000)
£714 $1314 €1042 Dutch village (35x45cm-14x18in) s. 25-Mar-4 International Art Centre, Auckland #114/R (NZ.D 2000)

Works on paper
£311 $557 €454 Oriental Bay parade (26x28cm-10x11in) s. W/C. 12-May-4 Dunbar Sloane, Wellington #201 (NZ.D 900)
£429 $776 €626 Boat sheds, Titahi Bay (18x24cm-7x9in) s. W/C. 4-Apr-4 International Art Centre, Auckland #213/R (NZ.D 1200)
£551 $1031 €804 Cairo street scene (20x27cm-8x11in) s.i. W/C. 24-Feb-4 Peter Webb, Auckland #46/R (NZ.D 1500)

NICOLL, James McLaren (1892-1986) Canadian

Works on paper
£238 $397 €347 Bowness Street car (18x23cm-7x9in) pencil prov. 17-Nov-3 Hodgins, Calgary #202/R (C.D 525)
£249 $416 €364 Untitled - hillside (23x30cm-9x12in) s. W/C. 17-Nov-3 Hodgins, Calgary #287/R (C.D 550)

NICOLL, Marion Florence (1909-1985) Canadian

Works on paper
£440 $805 €642 Still life (31x39cm-12x15in) s.d.1930 W/C. 1-Jun-4 Hodgins, Calgary #55/R (C.D 1100)

NICOLL, Meriel (20th C) Irish

£403 $721 €600 Still life in blues (33x41cm-13x16in) s. 31-May-4 Hamilton Osborne King, Dublin #52/R

NICOLLE, Émile Frederic (1830-1894) French

£6500 $10855 €9490 The John Hasbrouck in port at Rouen (65x81cm-26x32in) s.d.1877. 12-Nov-3 Sotheby's, Olympia #183/R est:3000-5000

NICOLLE, Ernest Philippe (19th C) French

£440 $734 €620 Tailleur de pierres dans un paysage (61x50cm-24x20in) s.d.1886. 17-Oct-3 Renaud, Paris #55

NICOLLE, Victor Jean (1754-1826) French

£7667 $13953 €11500 Vue du Pantheon. Vues du Chateau Saint-Ange. Vue de la Baie de Naples (7cm-3in circular) W/C dr five in one frame. 30-Jun-4 Pierre Berge, Paris #1/R est:8000-12000

Works on paper
£323 $518 €450 View of the Church of Saint Pierre in Venice (16x21cm-6x8in) i. blk crayon pen brown ink. 16-May-3 Tajan, Paris #60
£408 $731 €600 Vue de Pont des Senateurs, dit Ponterotto situe sur le Tibre a Rome (7x7cm-3x3in) W/C pen brown ink round. 17-Mar-4 Tajan, Paris #79
£600 $1038 €876 Interior of a gothic monastery seen through an arch (17x12cm-7x5in) s. pen brown ink W/C prov. 12-Dec-3 Christie's, Kensington #466/R
£612 $1096 €900 Vue de la Collone Antoinine a Rome (8x6cm-3x2in) pen black ink grey wash W/C. 17-Mar-4 Tajan, Paris #78
£616 $1048 €900 Vues de ruines (16x12cm-6x5in) pen ink pair. 6-Nov-3 Tajan, Paris #90
£822 $1397 €1200 Vue du Forum a Rome (16x11cm-6x4in) s.i. pen ink W/C. 6-Nov-3 Tajan, Paris #87
£884 $1583 €1300 Vue du Colisee a Rome. Vue d'une rue de Rome (7x7cm-3x3in) W/C pen brown grey wash round pair. 17-Mar-4 Tajan, Paris #80 est:1500
£915 $1584 €1300 Personnages dans les ruines (13x17cm-5x7in) brown ink pen brown wash. 10-Dec-3 Piasa, Paris #63/R
£1119 $1924 €1600 Homme passant sous une arche (8x6cm-3x2in) i. pen ink wash W/C. 8-Dec-3 Christie's, Paris #27/R est:800-1200
£1400 $2422 €2044 Sailors hauling a boat up a beach, a tower beyond (25x33cm-10x13in) s. black lead pen brown ink W/C. 12-Dec-3 Christie's, Kensington #465/R est:1500-2000
£1639 $3000 €2393 Column of Marcus Aurelius (25x18cm-10x7in) pen brown ink wash over pencil card stock. 29-Jan-4 Swann Galleries, New York #246/R est:1500-2500
£1967 $3600 €2872 Theater of Marcellus (18x26cm-7x10in) pen brown ink wash over pencil card stock. 29-Jan-4 Swann Galleries, New York #243/R est:1500-2500
£2041 $3653 €3000 Rome vue du Tibre avec le chateau Saint-Ange (20x31cm-8x12in) s. i.verso W/C pen brown ink. 19-Mar-4 Piasa, Paris #67/R est:3000
£2077 $3800 €3032 Porto di Repetta (18x25cm-7x10in) pen brown ink wash over pencil card stock. 29-Jan-4 Swann Galleries, New York #245/R est:1500-2500
£2585 $4627 €3800 Paysage anime (6x9cm-2x4in) ink. 22-Mar-4 Digard, Paris #15/R est:4000-6000
£2721 $4871 €4000 Paysage (6x9cm-2x4in) ink wash. 22-Mar-4 Digard, Paris #16/R est:4000-6000
£2721 $4871 €4000 Vue de la place du palais public, et de l'eglise St Jean Baptiste a Bologne (6x9cm-2x4in) s.i.verso W/C pen brown ink pair. 19-Mar-4 Piasa, Paris #68/R est:2000
£2732 $5000 €3989 Arch of Septimius Severus (18x25cm-7x10in) pen brown ink wash over pencil card stock. 29-Jan-4 Swann Galleries, New York #244/R est:1500-2500
£3061 $5480 €4500 La fontaine de l'Aqua Felice a Rome (17x30cm-7x12in) s. pen brown ink col wash W/C prov. 18-Mar-4 Christie's, Paris #129/R est:5000-8000
£3265 $5845 €4800 Vue du chateau de Valencay (25x37cm-10x15in) s.d.1788 W/C pen brown ink prov. 19-Mar-4 Piasa, Paris #70/R est:5000-7000
£3401 $6088 €5000 Views of Venice (8x13cm-3x5in) s.i.verso pen brown ink W/C pair. 19-Mar-4 Piasa, Paris #69/R est:5000-6000
£5442 $9741 €8000 Vue d'une arche du Colisee a Rome, un homme au premier plan (17x25cm-7x10in) graphite pen brown ink wash W/C. 18-Mar-4 Christie's, Paris #130/R est:3000-5000
£7042 $12183 €10000 Vue de la fontaine de Trevise. Vue du Forum (13x19cm-5x7in) W/C pair. 15-Dec-3 Bailly Pommery, Paris #30/R est:6000
£9864 $17656 €14500 Le club de Patriotes de Toulon (23x44cm-9x17in) s.d.1793 W/C pen black ink. 19-Mar-4 Piasa, Paris #71/R est:15000-20000

NICOLLE, Victor Jean (attrib) (1754-1826) French

Works on paper
£470 $864 €700 Paysage dans des ruines Romaines (40x30cm-16x12in) bears sig. pierre noire. 24-Mar-4 Claude Boisgirard, Paris #14/R

NICOT, François (20th C) French

£300 $531 €438 Mediterranean moorings (43x60cm-17x24in) s. board. 27-Apr-4 Bearnes, Exeter #612
£300 $531 €438 Boats in a Venetian backwater (37x54cm-15x21in) s. board. 27-Apr-4 Bearnes, Exeter #611
£872 $1614 €1300 Devant les remparts de meknes (32x41cm-13x16in) s. panel. 15-Mar-4 Gros & Delettrez, Paris #219/R

NICZKY, Edouard (1850-1919) German

£453 $816 €680 Portrait of young woman (72x92cm-28x36in) s.d.78 panel lit. 22-Apr-4 Allgauer, Kempten #3669/R

NIDO Y NAVAS, Antonio (19th C) Spanish

£290 $521 €420 Gypsy (24x17cm-9x7in) s.d.79 board. 26-Jan-4 Ansorena, Madrid #267/R

NIDZGORSKI, Adam (20th C) ?

Works on paper
£336 $571 €480 Untitled (42x29cm-17x11in) mono. china ink. 29-Nov-3 Neret-Minet, Paris #230
£367 $664 €550 Sans titre (35x31cm-14x12in) mono. mixed media tissue. 3-Apr-4 Neret-Minet, Paris #117/R
£385 $654 €550 Untitled (47x46cm-19x18in) mono. china ink. 29-Nov-3 Neret-Minet, Paris #150

NIE OU (1948-) Chinese

Works on paper
£4633 $7737 €6764 Village life (68x126cm-27x50in) s.i.d.1992 ink col. 27-Oct-3 Sotheby's, Hong Kong #376/R est:60000-80000 (HK.D 60000)

NIEBLA, Jose (1945-) Spanish

£676 $1189 €1000 Plan for flag 50 (100x100cm-39x39in) s.d.1975 acrylic prov.lit. 18-May-4 Segre, Madrid #269/R
£884 $1610 €1300 Take-away A (165x145cm-65x57in) s.d.1984. 3-Feb-4 Segre, Madrid #224/R

NIEDERER, Traugott Walter Eugen (1881-1957) German

£271 $462 €396 Engadin flowers (46x64cm-18x25in) s.d.23. 19-Nov-3 Fischer, Luzern #2233/R (S.FR 600)

NIEDERHAUSERN, François Louis Fritz de (1828-1888) Swiss

£328 $603 €479 Dog with dead pheasant (55x46cm-22x18in) s. 14-Jun-4 Philippe Schuler, Zurich #4229/R (S.FR 750)
£560 $1003 €818 In the barn (38x55cm-15x22in) s. 12-May-4 Dobiaschofsky, Bern #830/R (S.FR 1300)

NIEDERMAYR, Walter (1952-) German?

Photographs
£4333 $7973 €6500 Gardeccia IV (212x133cm-83x52in) col photo two forming diptych exec 1996 prov. 8-Jun-4 Artcurial Briest, Paris #291/R est:6000-8000
£5000 $8350 €7300 Marmolada punta rocca IV (98x125cm-39x49in) s.i.d.1994 num.3/6 verso c-print pair prov. 22-Oct-3 Christie's, London #113/R est:3000-4000
£8000 $14560 €11680 Ghiacciaio della Marmolada II (77x98cm-30x39in) s.i.d.1995 num.2/6 verso chibrome print 9 parts prov. 6-Feb-4 Sotheby's, London #281/R est:8000-12000

NIEDMANN, August Heinrich (1826-1910) German

£1800 $3330 €2628 Story for the baby (88x73cm-35x29in) s.i.d.1873. 14-Jul-4 Christie's, Kensington #856/R est:2000-3000
£7042 $11268 €10000 Children playing blind man's bluff (76x86cm-30x34in) s. 19-Sep-3 Sigalas, Stuttgart #407/R est:12000

NIEKERK, Maurits (1871-1940) Dutch

£1633 $2971 €2400 Roses in a jug (41x33cm-16x13in) s. canvas on panel. 3-Feb-4 Christie's, Amsterdam #294/R est:2000-3000
£9333 $16800 €14000 Jeune garcon a la fenetre (140x107cm-55x42in) s.i.d.1915 i.stretcher. 21-Apr-4 Christie's, Amsterdam #153/R est:7000-9000

NIELSEN, Alsing (20th C) Danish

£843 $1407 €1231 Model study on blue (55x39cm-22x15in) 25-Oct-3 Rasmussen, Havnen #4171 (D.KR 9000)

NIELSEN, Amaldus Clarin (1838-1932) Norwegian

£3263 $5840 €4764 Landscape from Hobdeheien near Mandal (31x54cm-12x21in) s.d.1922 s.i.d.stretcher. 25-May-4 Grev Wedels Plass, Oslo #44/R est:40000-60000 (N.KR 40000)
£3407 $5860 €4974 Archipelago (33x50cm-13x20in) s.d.1922. 8-Dec-3 Blomqvist, Oslo #401/R est:20000-25000 (N.KR 40000)
£4514 $7132 €6500 Evening harmony in Norway (116x183cm-46x72in) s.d.1890. 2-Sep-3 Christie's, Amsterdam #318/R est:4000-6000

£5710	$10220	€8337	Fjord landscape, calm summer's day (49x85cm-19x33in) s. i.stretcher. 25-May-4 Grev Wedels Plass, Oslo #45/R est:70000-90000 (N.KR 70000)
£10976	$20085	€16025	Landscape from Lindesnaes (105x182cm-41x72in) s.d.1904 i.stretcher exhib. 7-Jun-4 Blomqvist, Oslo #309/R est:150000-180000 (N.KR 135000)
£13821	$25293	€20179	Outside Hardanger (60x108cm-24x43in) s.d.1897 i.stretcher. 7-Jun-4 Blomqvist, Oslo #340/R est:140000-160000 (N.KR 170000)

NIELSEN, Arthur (1883-1946) Danish

£357	$650	€521	Road to the farm (51x66cm-20x26in) s. 19-Jun-4 Jackson's, Cedar Falls #63/R

NIELSEN, Christian Vilhelm (1833-1910) Danish

£327	$517	€474	Young girl (80x47cm-31x19in) mono.d.99. 2-Sep-3 Rasmussen, Copenhagen #1923 (D.KR 3500)

NIELSEN, Eivind (1864-1939) Norwegian

£482	$805	€704	Interior scene with woman and flower (54x36cm-21x14in) s. 20-Oct-3 Blomqvist, Lysaker #1215 (N.KR 5600)

NIELSEN, Ejnar (1872-1956) Danish

£301	$512	€439	Lofoten (33x42cm-13x17in) mono.d.1947. 29-Nov-3 Rasmussen, Havnen #4355 (D.KR 3200)
£687	$1250	€1003	Landscape from Gjern (35x41cm-14x16in) mono. panel. 7-Feb-4 Rasmussen, Havnen #2261 (D.KR 7500)

NIELSEN, H C (19th C) Danish

£582	$1065	€850	Still life of fruit and basket of flowers (44x55cm-17x22in) s. 7-Jun-4 Museumsbygningen, Copenhagen #46/R (D.KR 6500)

NIELSEN, Jais (1885-1961) Danish

£751	$1254	€1096	The market with pump, Moret (46x55cm-18x22in) s.i.d.25 prov. 7-Oct-3 Rasmussen, Copenhagen #334/R (D.KR 8000)
£1596	$2666	€2330	Many figures (662x88cm-261x35in) s.d.09 canvas on masonite. 7-Oct-3 Rasmussen, Copenhagen #147/R est:20000-25000 (D.KR 17000)
Works on paper			
£1264	$2325	€1845	The Lotus boy (43x35cm-17x14in) s. gouache artist's board exec.c.1918-19 prov. 29-Mar-4 Rasmussen, Copenhagen #179/R est:15000-20000 (D.KR 14000)

NIELSEN, Johan (1835-1912) Norwegian

£5133	$8725	€7494	Thunder storm, Ny-Hellesund (48x70cm-19x28in) init. i.d.1869 verso canvas on panel. 19-Nov-3 Grev Wedels Plass, Oslo #50/R est:40000-60000 (N.KR 60000)

NIELSEN, K (20th C) Danish

Works on paper			
£2817	$4704	€4113	Symbolic scene with flower borders (33x33cm-13x13in) s. gouache pencil Indian ink gold silver painted c.1913 prov. 7-Oct-3 Rasmussen, Copenhagen #135/R est:25000 (D.KR 30000)

NIELSEN, Kai (1882-1924) Danish

Sculpture			
£1264	$2325	€1845	Elegant lady rubbing camphorated spirits on her hips (28cm-11in) i. pat plaster exec.c.1908-09 lit. 29-Mar-4 Rasmussen, Copenhagen #461/R est:7000-10000 (D.KR 14000)
£3610	$6643	€5271	Prince Paris seated on the back of a panther (29cm-11in) s.num.7 pat.bronze. 29-Mar-4 Rasmussen, Copenhagen #39/R est:15000-20000 (D.KR 40000)
£8123	$15190	€11860	Head of the boxer Dick Nelson (50cm-20in) s.d.1918 white masonite. 25-Feb-4 Kunsthallen, Copenhagen #224/R est:30000 (D.KR 90000)

NIELSEN, Kay (1886-1957) Danish

£297	$481	€431	Rape of the Sabine Women (74x82cm-29x32in) s. 4-Aug-3 Rasmussen, Vejle #551 (D.KR 3100)
£853	$1365	€1245	Self-portrait (39x31cm-15x12in) init.i.d.04. 22-Sep-3 Rasmussen, Vejle #36 (D.KR 9000)

NIELSEN, Kehnet (1947-) Danish

£318	$532	€464	Figure composition (60x51cm-24x20in) s.d.1985 verso. 25-Oct-3 Rasmussen, Havnen #4296/R (D.KR 3400)
£1014	$1724	€1480	Composition (82x71cm-32x28in) s.d.1999 verso. 10-Nov-3 Rasmussen, Vejle #615/R (D.KR 11000)
£1408	$2352	€2056	Duino II (150x120cm-59x47in) s.d.1987 verso. 7-Oct-3 Rasmussen, Copenhagen #157/R est:15000 (D.KR 15000)
£1715	$3207	€2504	Composition (150x120cm-59x47in) s.d.1993 oil W/C paper exhib. 25-Feb-4 Kunsthallen, Copenhagen #134/R est:15000 (D.KR 19000)
£1925	$3215	€2811	Rain - composition (120x100cm-47x39in) s.d.1997 verso. 7-Oct-3 Rasmussen, Copenhagen #176/R est:15000-18000 (D.KR 20500)
£1986	$3653	€2900	Virgil - composition (100x73cm-39x29in) s.d.1995 verso exhib. 29-Mar-4 Rasmussen, Copenhagen #344/R est:15000-20000 (D.KR 22000)
£2708	$4982	€3954	Composition (100x73cm-39x29in) s.d.1995 verso exhib. 29-Mar-4 Rasmussen, Copenhagen #346/R est:15000-20000 (D.KR 30000)
£2844	$4550	€4124	Composition (190x160cm-75x63in) s.d.1987 verso. 17-Sep-3 Kunsthallen, Copenhagen #101/R est:30000 (D.KR 30000)

NIELSEN, Knud (1916-) Danish

£403	$726	€588	Composition (60x73cm-24x29in) s.d.58 verso. 24-Apr-4 Rasmussen, Havnen #4233/R (D.KR 4500)
£422	$687	€616	Composition (73x60cm-29x24in) s.d.62 verso. 27-Sep-3 Rasmussen, Havnen #4081 (D.KR 4500)
£493	$887	€720	C-105-8 (54x81cm-21x32in) s.d.56 verso. 24-Apr-4 Rasmussen, Havnen #4241/R (D.KR 5500)
£543	$972	€793	Composition (81x100cm-32x39in) s.d.58-59 verso. 10-May-4 Rasmussen, Vejle #621 (D.KR 6000)
£567	$1015	€828	Composition (30x80cm-12x31in) s.d.88 acrylic W/C. 12-Jan-4 Rasmussen, Vejle #595/R (D.KR 6000)
£751	$1254	€1096	Figure composition (55x43cm-22x17in) s.d.90 paper on canvas. 7-Oct-3 Rasmussen, Copenhagen #50/R (D.KR 8000)
£813	$1318	€1179	Composition with figures (65x50cm-26x20in) s. 4-Aug-3 Rasmussen, Vejle #543/R (D.KR 8500)
£860	$1539	€1256	Romantic composition (65x50cm-26x20in) s. s.d.78 verso. 10-May-4 Rasmussen, Vejle #616/R (D.KR 9500)
£861	$1395	€1248	Green composition (81x60cm-32x24in) s.d.1960 verso. 4-Aug-3 Rasmussen, Vejle #542/R (D.KR 9000)
£1033	$1725	€1508	Composition (81x65cm-32x26in) s.d.65. 7-Oct-3 Rasmussen, Copenhagen #65/R (D.KR 11000)
£1127	$1882	€1645	Composition (54x46cm-21x18in) s.d.47 verso. 7-Oct-3 Rasmussen, Copenhagen #5/R est:12000 (D.KR 12000)
£1254	$2258	€1831	Composition (97x130cm-38x51in) s.d.56 verso. 24-Apr-4 Rasmussen, Havnen #4238/R est:8000 (D.KR 14000)
Works on paper			
£378	$677	€552	Composition (30x22cm-12x9in) W/C crayon. 12-Jan-4 Rasmussen, Vejle #594/R (D.KR 4000)
£948	$1744	€1384	Figure composition (55x46cm-22x18in) s. s.d.80 verso. 29-Mar-4 Rasmussen, Copenhagen #366 (D.KR 10500)

NIELSEN, Niels (1917-1989) Danish

£282	$480	€412	Summer landscape, Roskilde fjord (62x82cm-24x32in) s. 29-Nov-3 Rasmussen, Havnen #4058 (D.KR 3000)
£284	$518	€426	Winter landscape (62x84cm-24x33in) s.d.60. 19-Jun-4 Rasmussen, Havnen #4109 (D.KR 3200)
£320	$582	€480	Coastal landscape (58x79cm-23x31in) s. 19-Jun-4 Rasmussen, Havnen #4108 (D.KR 3600)
£496	$928	€724	Landscape (62x81cm-24x32in) s. 25-Feb-4 Kunsthallen, Copenhagen #220 (D.KR 5500)

NIELSEN, Otto (1877-?) Danish

£366	$667	€534	View of Slotskirken and Gammel Strand (68x89cm-27x35in) s.d.1910. 7-Feb-4 Rasmussen, Havnen #2227 (D.KR 4000)

NIELSEN, Peter (1873-1965) American/Danish

£2335	$4250	€3409	Cottages in California coastal (64x76cm-25x30in) s. 15-Jun-4 John Moran, Pasadena #47 est:2000-3000

NIELSEN, Poul (1920-1998) Danish

£298	$468	€435	Portrait of girl (28x36cm-11x14in) mono. 30-Aug-3 Rasmussen, Havnen #4182/R (D.KR 3200)
£322	$516	€470	Portrait of girl (90x60cm-35x24in) mono.d.54. 22-Sep-3 Rasmussen, Vejle #625/R (D.KR 3400)
£366	$667	€534	Interior scene with the artist's wife and their daughter (50x60cm-20x24in) mono.d.65. 7-Feb-4 Rasmussen, Havnen #4002/R (D.KR 4000)
£378	$677	€552	Town scene, Karlebo (70x80cm-28x31in) mono. 12-Jan-4 Rasmussen, Vejle #479 (D.KR 4000)
£385	$700	€562	Portrait of the artist's daughter (30x40cm-12x16in) mono. 7-Feb-4 Rasmussen, Havnen #4004 (D.KR 4200)
£387	$658	€565	Flowers on window ledge (81x65cm-32x26in) mono. 10-Nov-3 Rasmussen, Vejle #675/R (D.KR 4200)
£550	$880	€803	Street scene with houses (60x40cm-24x16in) mono.i.d.60. 22-Sep-3 Rasmussen, Vejle #604/R (D.KR 5800)
£582	$1048	€850	Interior scene with girl reading (88x73cm-35x29in) mono.d.55. 24-Apr-4 Rasmussen, Havnen #4231 (D.KR 6500)
£588	$1053	€858	Still life of flowers, fruit and jug on table (63x85cm-25x33in) init.d.52. 10-May-4 Rasmussen, Vejle #625/R (D.KR 6500)
£590	$1003	€861	Still life of flowers and fruit on table (40x30cm-16x12in) mono. 10-Nov-3 Rasmussen, Vejle #677/R (D.KR 6400)
£633	$1134	€924	Interior scene with girl and potted plant (40x73cm-16x29in) mono.d.59. 10-May-4 Rasmussen, Vejle #648/R (D.KR 7000)
£676	$1251	€987	Still life on table (60x50cm-24x20in) mono. 15-Mar-4 Rasmussen, Vejle #646/R (D.KR 7500)
£679	$1215	€991	Interior scene with girl (50x60cm-20x24in) mono. 10-May-4 Rasmussen, Vejle #649/R (D.KR 7500)
£766	$1240	€1111	Town scene from Bornholm, sea in background (50x60cm-20x24in) mono. 4-Aug-3 Rasmussen, Vejle #669/R (D.KR 8000)
£829	$1410	€1210	Landscape from Allinge, Bornholm (40x76cm-16x30in) mono. 10-Nov-3 Rasmussen, Vejle #701/R (D.KR 9000)
£995	$1782	€1453	Two girls playing (80x70cm-31x28in) init. 10-May-4 Rasmussen, Vejle #647/R (D.KR 11000)

NIELSEN, Sarus (1897-1973) Danish?

£675	$1100	€986	Woman dancing (100x89cm-39x35in) s.d.1956. 28-Sep-3 Hindemae, Ullerslev #236/R (D.KR 7200)

NIELSEN, Solo (20th C) Danish

£357	$608	€521	Landscape with dog sleighs, Eastern Greenland (32x42cm-13x17in) s. 29-Nov-3 Rasmussen, Havnen #2284 (D.KR 3800)
£470	$800	€686	The Royal ship arriving, Good Hope 1921 (65x97cm-26x38in) s. 29-Nov-3 Rasmussen, Havnen #2283/R (D.KR 5000)

NIEMAN, Leroy (1921-) American

£40984	$75000	€59837	1970 America's Cup defence - Intrepid vs Gretel I (245x122cm-96x48in) s.d.71 masonite prov. 29-Jul-4 Christie's, Rockefeller NY #314/R est:40000-50000

NIEMANN, Edmund John (1813-1876) British

£217	$400	€317	Landscape with barn (30x41cm-12x16in) s.d.57. 27-Jun-4 Bonhams & Butterfields, San Francisco #3806/R
£458	$760	€650	Mountain landscape with anglers (29x46cm-11x18in) s. panel. 16-Jun-3 Dorotheum, Vienna #51/R
£500	$830	€730	Angler by waterfall in a wooded river landscape (15x22cm-6x9in) s. board. 6-Oct-3 David Duggleby, Scarborough #190/R
£500	$905	€730	Landscape with figures near a windmill (16x41cm-6x16in) s.d.1948 board. 30-Mar-4 Sworder & Son, Bishops Stortford #507/R
£552	$1000	€806	Landscape with Newwark cathedral (20x48cm-8x19in) s.i. 3-Apr-4 Neal Auction Company, New Orleans #984/R est:800-1200
£600	$1056	€876	Transporting the catch (36x46cm-14x18in) s.d.186. 19-May-4 Christie's, Kensington #572/R

£706 $1300 €1031 River Avon (61x107cm-24x42in) s. prov. 13-Jun-4 Bonhams & Butterfields, Los Angeles #7008/R est:2500-3500
£1000 $1860 €1460 Low tide (20x27cm-8x11in) s. 4-Mar-4 Christie's, Kensington #559/R est:800-1200
£1196 $2200 €1746 Kirby Malzeard on Moors York (30x46cm-12x18in) s. prov. 27-Jun-4 Hindman, Chicago #793/R est:2000-3000
£1300 $2366 €1898 Extensive wooded landscape (29x54cm-11x21in) s.d.1863 i.stretcher. 1-Jul-4 Mellors & Kirk, Nottingham #834 est:1000-1400
£1333 $2427 €2000 Elevated view of an extensive summer landscape (55x91cm-22x36in) s.indis.i. 1-Jul-4 Van Ham, Cologne #1536 est:700
£1350 $2133 €1958 Windsor and Eton from the Thames (33x51cm-13x20in) board. 4-Sep-3 Christie's, Kensington #111/R est:1500-2000
£1497 $2500 €2186 River near Pegwell Castle. s. 18-Oct-3 Harvey Clar, Oakland #1488
£1600 $2944 €2336 Harvest time, Hampstead (26x36cm-10x14in) s.i.d.1864. 11-Jun-4 Christie's, London #134/R est:1200-1800
£1848 $3400 €2698 Ludford Bridge on the Teme (51x76cm-20x30in) s. prov. 27-Jun-4 Hindman, Chicago #792/R est:2000-3000
£1902 $3082 €2758 North Bardon Tower (74x125cm-29x49in) s.i. 31-Jul-3 International Art Centre, Auckland #150/R est:3000-5000 (NZ.D 5250)
£2035 $3500 €2971 Fishermen by a dam (79x58cm-31x23in) s.d.1853. 7-Dec-3 Freeman, Philadelphia #37 est:2500-4000
£2400 $3984 €3504 Fisherman by a watermill (51x40cm-20x16in) s.d.61. 1-Oct-3 Sotheby's, Olympia #122/R est:2500-3500
£2500 $4100 €3650 Storm in the Channel, with sail and steam (43x74cm-17x29in) s.d.55-60. 29-May-3 Neales, Nottingham #783/R est:2500-3500

NIEMANN, Edmund John (attrib) (1813-1876) British
£500 $795 €725 Country river landscape with figures in a boat (51x76cm-20x30in) 9-Sep-3 Bonhams, Knightsbridge #268/R
£847 $1600 €1237 Pastoral landscape with large tree, cows and figure by a stream (46x64cm-18x25in) 23-Feb-4 Winter Associates, Plainville #98/R est:600-900
£2700 $4941 €3942 Windsor Castle from the river (150x124cm-59x49in) 8-Jul-4 Duke & Son, Dorchester #194/R

NIEMANN, Edward H (fl.1863-1887) British
£250 $448 €365 Returning from market (25x36cm-10x14in) s.d.Jun 1863. 27-May-4 Christie's, Kensington #173/R
£270 $494 €394 View of Paul's Cray Common, Kent (27x43cm-11x17in) s.d.68. 27-Jan-4 Holloways, Banbury #371
£300 $528 €438 Figure on a river bank at dusk (20x30cm-8x12in) s. board. 19-May-4 Christie's, Kensington #520/R
£400 $692 €584 River Wharfe and woodland (23x30cm-9x12in) s. 11-Dec-3 Ewbank, Send #406
£650 $1086 €949 Old Hampstead (16x25cm-6x10in) s. board. 20-Oct-3 Bonhams, Bath #207
£700 $1190 €1022 On a shore at low tide (22x27cm-9x11in) s. 26-Nov-3 Hamptons Fine Art, Godalming #161/R
£800 $1336 €1168 Richmond, Yorkshire (51x76cm-20x30in) s.i. 12-Nov-3 Sotheby's, Olympia #72/R
£900 $1593 €1314 Near Birk Crags, Yorkshire (56x97cm-22x38in) s. 29-Apr-4 Gorringes, Lewes #2524
£950 $1587 €1387 Darley bridge (51x76cm-20x30in) s.i. 12-Nov-3 Sotheby's, Olympia #44/R
£1397 $2250 €2040 River Nidd, Yorkshire England landscapes (23x51cm-9x20in) s. pair. 20-Aug-3 James Julia, Fairfield #529/R est:2500-3500
£1800 $3330 €2628 Extensive country landscape with cottages in the distance (56x92cm-22x36in) s. 13-Jan-4 Bonhams, Knightsbridge #342/R est:2000-3000
£1900 $3496 €2774 Driving cattle and sheep on a woodland path, a valley beyond (30x47cm-12x19in) s. panel. 23-Mar-4 Bonhams, New Bond Street #58/R est:2000-3000

NIEMANN, Eva (20th C) German?
£490 $832 €700 Composition in reds (200x150cm-79x59in) s.d.1991 tempera. 29-Nov-3 Arnold, Frankfurt #400/R

NIEMANN, Hendrik Christiaan (1941-) South African
£289 $517 €422 Head of a boy (36x29cm-14x11in) s.d.2003 board. 31-May-4 Stephan Welz, Johannesburg #311 (SA.R 3500)

NIEMEYER, Adelbert (1867-1923) German
£909 $1545 €1300 The Garden (80x60cm-31x24in) s.d.23 lit. 28-Nov-3 Schloss Ahlden, Ahlden #1539/R

NIEMEYER-HOLSTEIN, Otto (1896-1984) German
£667 $1200 €1000 Harbour town (42x56cm-17x22in) mono.i.d.12.09.58 board. 24-Apr-4 Dr Lehr, Berlin #349/R
£694 $1160 €1000 Portrait study of Robby (22x15cm-9x6in) mono.d. i. verso. 25-Oct-3 Dr Lehr, Berlin #370/R
£867 $1560 €1300 Angler in the mist (28x33cm-11x13in) mono. i. verso canvas on board. 23-Apr-4 Altus, Berlin #549/R

NIERMAN, Leonardo (1932-) Mexican
£329 $550 €480 Estruendo (30x41cm-12x16in) s. board. 25-Oct-3 Susanin's, Chicago #5008/R
£389 $700 €568 Bird in flight (56x38cm-22x15in) s. masonite. 20-Apr-4 Arthur James, Florida #117/R
£500 $900 €730 Composition (41x58cm-16x23in) s.d.69 masonite. 20-Jan-4 Arthur James, Florida #127
£508 $950 €742 Cosmic meditation (58x79cm-23x31in) s.d.65 i.verso. 29-Feb-4 Grogan, Boston #94
£556 $1000 €812 Malbic flight (76x56cm-30x22in) s. i.verso masonite. 20-Apr-4 Arthur James, Florida #115/R est:600-900
£559 $900 €816 Biblical fire (58x38cm-23x15in) acrylic masonite. 15-Aug-3 Du Mouchelle, Detroit #2122/R
£643 $1074 €932 Influencia lunar (40x60cm-16x24in) s. acrylic masonite. 24-Jun-3 Louis Morton, Mexico #397/R (M.P 11200)
£659 $1100 €962 Bird of paradise (58x41cm-23x16in) s. board. 25-Oct-3 Susanin's, Chicago #5011/R est:200-400
£667 $1200 €974 Meteor shower (58x79cm-23x31in) s.d.68 masonite. 20-Jan-4 Arthur James, Florida #128
£667 $1200 €974 Composition (58x79cm-23x31in) s.d.68 masonite. 20-Jan-4 Arthur James, Florida #129
£667 $1200 €974 City at night (58x76cm-23x30in) s.d.65 masonite prov. 20-Apr-4 Arthur James, Florida #116/R est:700-1000
£889 $1600 €1298 Prismatic City (60x80cm-24x31in) s.d.67 i. verso masonite. 24-Apr-4 Weschler, Washington #648/R est:1200-1800
£973 $1800 €1421 Cosmic reach (91x61cm-36x24in) s.d.67 board. 17-Jul-4 Susanin's, Chicago #5046/R est:1000-1500
£984 $1800 €1437 Dream (41x61cm-16x24in) s. board sold with book. 5-Jun-4 Susanin's, Chicago #5129/R est:600-800
£1000 $1600 €1460 Untitled abstract (41x61cm-16x24in) s. acrylic masonite board painted c.1973. 20-Sep-3 Bunte, Elgin #1292 est:600-800
£2344 $3750 €3422 Bird fury (122x91cm-48x36in) s. acrylic masonite board. 20-Sep-3 Bunte, Elgin #1293 est:2500-3500
Works on paper
£297 $550 €434 City lights (41x61cm-16x24in) s. mixed media. 17-Jan-4 Susanin's, Chicago #113/R

NIESIOLOWSKI, Tymon (1882-1966) Polish
£1525 $2531 €2227 Still life with kettle and moonlight (81x60cm-32x24in) s.d.57. 15-Jun-3 Agra, Warsaw #25/R est:7000 (P.Z 9500)

NIESSEN, Johannes (1821-1910) German
£556 $906 €800 Portrait of young girl with poppies (60x50cm-24x20in) s.d.1877. 24-Sep-3 Neumeister, Munich #514

NIETO, Anselmo Miguel (1881-1964) Spanish
£1184 $2179 €1800 Portrait of young female hunter (50x40cm-20x16in) s. 22-Jun-4 Durán, Madrid #601/R est:1500

NIETO, Rodolfo (1936-1988) Mexican
£1972 $3411 €2800 Composition (60x73cm-24x29in) s. s.d.Julio 65 verso prov. 14-Dec-3 Versailles Encheres #32/R est:3000-4000
Works on paper
£348 $550 €508 Oaxacan girl. s. 26-Jul-3 Harvey Clar, Oakland #1222
£376 $700 €549 Oaxacan girl (46x33cm-18x13in) s. crayon. 6-Mar-4 Harvey Clar, Oakland #1228
£1471 $2500 €2148 Composicion - Composition (48x63cm-19x25in) s. gouache exec. 1965 prov. 18-Nov-3 Christie's, Rockefeller NY #139/R est:4000-6000

NIETSCHE, Paul (1885-1950) British
£347 $549 €500 Forest lake (50x50cm-20x20in) s.d.23. 2-Sep-3 Christie's, Amsterdam #422/R
£1300 $2236 €1898 County Down farm (50x61cm-20x24in) s.d.37 board. 3-Dec-3 John Ross, Belfast #159 est:1200-1500
£2676 $4282 €3800 Dahlais (51x61cm-20x24in) s.d.1946 board. 16-Sep-3 Whyte's, Dublin #179/R est:4000-5000
£2800 $4592 €4088 Road to Greencastle (50x61cm-20x24in) s.d.47 board. 4-Jun-3 John Ross, Belfast #161 est:2000
£3000 $5370 €4380 Red poppies (51x61cm-20x24in) s.d.45 board. 14-May-4 Christie's, Kensington #392/R est:3000-5000
£6000 $10020 €8760 Still life chrysanthemums, melon and a jug (51x41cm-20x16in) s.d.29. 20-Jun-3 Chrystals Auctions, Isle of Man #228 est:5500-6500
£6224 $10580 €8900 View of a church, lake and hills through trees (51x61cm-20x24in) s.d.1936 board. 18-Nov-3 Whyte's, Dublin #179/R est:1500-2000
Works on paper
£400 $664 €584 Female portrait (50x43cm-20x17in) s.d.1946 pastel. 1-Oct-3 John Ross, Belfast #252

NIEUWENHOVEN, Willem van (1879-1973) Dutch
£250 $400 €365 At his easel (30x25cm-12x10in) s. 19-Sep-3 Freeman, Philadelphia #195/R
£380 $703 €555 Portrait of a man lighting a pipe (52x42cm-20x17in) s. board. 10-Feb-4 Bonhams, Knightsbridge #2
£667 $1193 €1000 Old man with stick and pipe (39x29cm-15x11in) s. panel. 11-May-4 Vendu Notarishuis, Rotterdam #274/R
£1599 $2750 €2335 Sewing by a window (51x40cm-20x16in) 3-Dec-3 Doyle, New York #111/R est:4000-6000

NIEUWENHUIJS, Constant (1920-) Dutch
Works on paper
£8721 $15000 €12733 New Babylon (61x76cm-24x30in) s.d.1969 W/C pastel. 7-Dec-3 Treadway Gallery, Cincinnati #646/R est:15000-25000

NIEUWENHUIS, Jacques Emile Edouard (1840-?) Belgian
£9929 $16582 €14000 Prise de Strasbourg par le Roi et Richelieu (113x172cm-44x68in) s.d.1869. 19-Oct-3 Anaf, Lyon #221/R est:15000-20000

NIEUWENHUIS, Theodorus Wilhelmus (1866-1951) Dutch
Works on paper
£1892 $3330 €2800 Designs for a vignette, one with the letter K, one with the letter E (7x12cm-3x5in) one init. pen black ink 2 sold with two vignettes exhib.lit. 19-May-4 Sotheby's, Amsterdam #375/R est:1400-1600

NIEUWERKERKE, Comte de Alfred-Emilien (1811-1892) French
Sculpture
£8000 $14400 €11680 Death of the Duke of Clarence (59x61cm-23x24in) s.d.1858 brown pat bronze st.f.Susse prov.lit. 21-Apr-4 Sotheby's, London #59/R est:8000-12000

NIEWEG, Jaap (1877-1955) Dutch
£526 $968 €800 Portrait of a man (60x50cm-24x20in) s.d.1925. 28-Jun-4 Sotheby's, Amsterdam #145/R

£526	$968	€800	Forest landscape (60x50cm-24x20in) s.d.44. 28-Jun-4 Sotheby's, Amsterdam #147/R
£685	$1164	€1000	Still life of flowers (59x49cm-23x19in) mono.d.1939. 5-Nov-3 Vendue Huis, Gravenhage #341
£979	$1684	€1400	Still life (80x90cm-31x35in) s.d.1920 prov. 2-Dec-3 Sotheby's, Amsterdam #238/R est:1500-2000
£2098	$3503	€3000	A tree (60x45cm-24x18in) s.d.1915. 30-Jun-3 Sotheby's, Amsterdam #230/R
£2550	$4718	€3800	Horse in an orchard (61x90cm-24x35in) s.d. 15-Mar-4 Sotheby's, Amsterdam #151/R est:1500-2000
£3200	$5888	€4800	Summer landscape (35x50cm-14x20in) init. d.1907. 8-Jun-4 Sotheby's, Amsterdam #175/R est:4500-5500
£3819	$6035	€5500	Landscape with pollard willows (80x60cm-31x24in) init.d.1922 prov. 2-Sep-3 Christie's, Amsterdam #396/R est:3000-5000

NIFTERIK, Gustaaf van (1886-1954) Dutch

£884	$1610	€1300	Mountain village (64x81cm-25x32in) s. 3-Feb-4 Christie's, Amsterdam #518a est:500-700

NIGG, Joseph (attrib) (1782-1863) Austrian

£3191	$5330	€4500	Vases of flowers (59x45cm-23x18in) tempera paper pair. 23-Jun-3 Finarte Semenzato, Rome #162/R

NIGHTINGALE, Basil (1864-1940) British

£1000	$1840	€1460	Portrait of a hunter (45x60cm-18x24in) s.d.1896. 29-Mar-4 Bonhams, Bath #94/R est:1200-1800
Works on paper			
£320	$566	€467	Tally ho! (35x54cm-14x21in) s.d.1924 i.verso black white chk. 27-Apr-4 Bonhams, Knowle #45
£380	$695	€555	Breaking cover (39x58cm-15x23in) s.d.1882 W/C. 8-Apr-4 Christie's, Kensington #116
£400	$680	€584	Incident with the Pytchley (23x23cm-9x9in) s.i.d.1886 oval. 19-Nov-3 Sotheby's, Olympia #65/R
£500	$835	€730	Pals!, British bulldog being cuddled by the artist's infant grandson (35x53cm-14x21in) s.i.d.1914 W/C. 27-Jun-3 Bigwood, Stratford on Avon #303/R
£600	$1098	€876	On furlough (36x54cm-14x21in) s.i.d.1919 W/C htd white. 28-Jul-4 Bonhams, Knightsbridge #127/R
£750	$1290	€1095	Critical moment! (36x54cm-14x21in) s.i. W/C gouache pencil. 3-Dec-3 Bonhams, Knightsbridge #159/R
£800	$1472	€1168	Lord Lonsdale jumping the Great Dalby Brook (63x96cm-25x38in) s.i. pencil W/C bodycol. 10-Jun-4 Christie's, Kensington #133/R
£1800	$3096	€2628	Crime. Thief's end. Musical honours. Retribution (46x56cm-18x22in) s.i.d. W/C htd set of four. 3-Dec-3 Bonhams, Knightsbridge #156/R est:1500-2000
£2209	$3800	€3225	Not the way to cultivate the friendship of the master (37x50cm-15x20in) s.i.d.1893 pencil pen ink col chk paper on card. 5-Dec-3 Christie's, Rockefeller NY #61/R est:2500-3500
£3867	$7000	€5646	Celebrated Belvoir Gambler by Wethergate, Gratitude (54x72cm-21x28in) s.i. black chk W/C. 30-Mar-4 Bonhams & Butterfields, San Francisco #72/R est:2200-3300

NIGHTINGALE, Leonard Charles (19/20th C) British

£24000	$44880	€35040	The garden gate (91x71cm-36x28in) init. 22-Jul-4 Tennants, Leyburn #904/R est:10000-15000

NIGHTINGALE, Robert (1815-1895) British

£1150	$2116	€1679	Groom with two hunters and dogs (86x112cm-34x44in) i.verso oil on card. 23-Jun-4 Bonhams, Bury St Edmunds #380/R est:1200-1800

NIGRO, Adolfo (1942-) Argentinian

£824	$1500	€1203	River (14x20cm-6x8in) s.d.95 acrylic. 5-Jul-4 Arroyo, Buenos Aires #102/R est:1300
£989	$1800	€1444	Moon and horizon (14x9cm-6x4in) s. s.d.1926 verso acrylic cardboard. 29-Jun-4 Arroyo, Buenos Aires #2/R est:800
£1657	$3000	€2419	Water and night (32x41cm-13x16in) acrylic paper. 30-Mar-4 Arroyo, Buenos Aires #96
£2363	$4300	€3450	Sea rythms (40x50cm-16x20in) s.d.89 acrylic paper. 5-Jul-4 Arroyo, Buenos Aires #88/R est:4300
£16484	$30000	€24067	Fruit from the coast (80x100cm-31x39in) s. s.i.d.1986 verso. 29-Jun-4 Arroyo, Buenos Aires #96/R est:28000
£16940	$31000	€24732	Net (150x150cm-59x59in) 1-Jun-4 Arroyo, Buenos Aires #64
£21229	$38000	€30994	Coastal shapes (100x120cm-39x47in) s.d.92 s.i.d.verso lit. 4-May-4 Arroyo, Buenos Aires #72/R est:22000
£23204	$42000	€33878	Green moon (120x120cm-47x47in) 30-Mar-4 Arroyo, Buenos Aires #72
Works on paper			
£994	$1750	€1451	Water memories (47x62cm-19x24in) s.i.d. W/C prov. 5-Jan-4 Galeria y Remates, Montevideo #22/R est:2800-3500
£1154	$2100	€1685	Earth rythms (28x36cm-11x14in) s.d.00 i.d.verso mixed media. 5-Jul-4 Arroyo, Buenos Aires #103/R est:1700
£1676	$3000	€2447	Clam pickers (19x28cm-7x11in) s.d.83 s.i.d.verso ink. 4-May-4 Arroyo, Buenos Aires #60/R est:800
£2637	$4800	€3850	Sea rhythms (32x47cm-13x19in) s.d.89 ink pair. 29-Jun-4 Arroyo, Buenos Aires #73/R est:2000

NIGRO, Jan (1920-) ?

£725	$1167	€1059	Miss silk II (80x56cm-31x22in) s.d.97 oil pastel on paper. 20-Aug-3 Dunbar Sloane, Auckland #89 est:2000-3000 (NZ.D 2000)
Works on paper			
£286	$517	€418	Encounter Haast Bridge 1 (26x44cm-10x17in) s. mixed media. 4-Apr-4 International Art Centre, Auckland #257/R (NZ.D 800)
£564	$959	€823	Nude (60x66cm-24x26in) s.d.1999 pastel. 27-Nov-3 International Art Centre, Auckland #2/R (NZ.D 1500)
£868	$1380	€1267	Female nude, Sara (60x54cm-24x21in) s.d.1997 pastel acrylic. 1-May-3 Dunbar Sloane, Wellington #81 est:2500-3500 (NZ.D 2500)
£893	$1643	€1304	Dancer (58x37cm-23x15in) s.d.1973 pencil. 25-Mar-4 International Art Centre, Auckland #99/R (NZ.D 2500)

NIGRO, Mario (1917-1992) Italian

£755	$1284	€1102	Diagonale azzurra - fondo rosso (70x27cm-28x11in) s.d.80 tempera prov. 5-Nov-3 AB Stockholms Auktionsverk #952/R (S.KR 10000)
£755	$1284	€1102	Diagonale blu - fondo grigio (70x27cm-28x11in) s.d.80 tempera prov. 5-Nov-3 AB Stockholms Auktionsverk #953/R (S.KR 10000)
£1361	$2435	€2000	Simultaneous vibration (72x50cm-28x20in) s. tempera. 16-Mar-4 Finarte Semenzato, Milan #430/R est:2500
£1471	$2500	€2148	Palude (71x97cm-28x38in) s.d.1959 s.i.d.verso. 9-Nov-3 Wright, Chicago #303 est:3000-4000
£3691	$6607	€5500	Thought (81x81cm-32x32in) s. i.verso acrylic painted 1975. 25-May-4 Sotheby's, Milan #136/R est:4000
£4196	$7133	€6000	Untitled (31x31cm-12x12in) i.verso acrylic. 20-Nov-3 Finarte Semenzato, Milan #19/R est:6000-6500
£4577	$7599	€6500	From total space (64x54cm-25x21in) s.i.d.1965 verso acrylic prov. 11-Jun-3 Finarte Semenzato, Milan #561/R
£4710	$7725	€6500	Paintings (135x105cm-53x41in) s.i.verso painted 1989. 29-May-3 Galleria Pace, Milan #102/R est:11000
£5435	$8913	€7500	Untitled (60x50cm-24x20in) s. s.verso prov. 27-May-3 Sotheby's, Milan #204/R est:4000-6000
£6993	$11888	€10000	I will never give up (72x72cm-28x28in) s.i.verso tempera painted 1973. 28-Nov-3 Farsetti, Prato #268/R est:10000-12000
£7667	$14107	€11500	FRom the space (60x50cm-24x20in) s.i.verso prov. 8-Jun-4 Finarte Semenzato, Milan #356/R est:10000-12000
£13103	$21883	€19000	Total space 12 (55x75cm-22x30in) s.i.d.1953 verso. 13-Nov-3 Galleria Pace, Milan #110/R est:26000
£13986	$23776	€20000	Contrasting patterns (65x85cm-26x33in) s.d.52 s.i.d.verso prov.exhib.lit. 24-Nov-3 Christie's, Milan #265/R est:20000-30000
Works on paper			
£420	$701	€600	Untitled (50x67cm-20x26in) s. W/C. 26-Jun-3 Sant Agostino, Torino #232/R

NIIZUMA, Minoru (1930-) Japanese

Sculpture			
£1117	$2000	€1631	Untitled - candles (13x35x10cm-5x14x4in) black marble prov. 6-May-4 Doyle, New York #119/R est:2500-3500
£1676	$3000	€2447	UMA - unicorn (139cm-55in) s. black marble on wood pedestal. 6-May-4 Doyle, New York #89/R est:4000-6000

NIJINSKY, Waslav (1890-1950) Russian

£4865	$9000	€7103	Mask (25x20cm-10x8in) mono. oil W/C prov.exhib. 12-Feb-4 Sotheby's, New York #65/R est:4000-6000

NIJINSKY, Waslav and RICHARD-WILLM, Pierre (20th C) Russian?

Sculpture			
£6111	$10389	€8800	Danseur dans Scheherazade (24cm-9in) init.d.1914 brown wax black marble socle. 30-Oct-3 Artus Associes, Paris #77/R est:1200-1500

NIJLAND, Dirk (1881-1955) Dutch

£411	$699	€600	Rotterdam harbour (113x72cm-44x28in) s.verso paper. 5-Nov-3 Vendue Huis, Gravenhage #370/R
£544	$990	€800	Dutch water landscape (23x32cm-9x13in) mono. canvas on board. 3-Feb-4 Christie's, Amsterdam #524
£959	$1630	€1400	Fishing port with the ship, Goede Verwachting (80x96cm-31x38in) mono. 5-Nov-3 Vendue Huis, Gravenhage #369/R
£1020	$1857	€1500	Seascape with two seagulls (34x45cm-13x18in) init. prov. 3-Feb-4 Christie's, Amsterdam #415/R est:2000-3000
£3472	$5486	€5000	Lente - spring (45x60cm-18x24in) mono.i. i.verso. 2-Sep-3 Christie's, Amsterdam #382/R est:3000-5000

NIJMEGEN, Dionys van (1705-1789) Dutch

Works on paper			
£1486	$2616	€2200	Four heads of Putti (21x28cm-8x11in) s. W/C black chk exhib. 19-May-4 Sotheby's, Amsterdam #240/R est:1200-1800

NIKANOROV, Eduardo (1951-) Russian?

£461	$834	€700	Eve (48x31cm-19x12in) init. paper on cardboard. 14-Apr-4 Ansorena, Madrid #293/R

NIKEL, Lea (1918-) Israeli

£1497	$2500	€2186	Untitled (46x38cm-18x15in) s.d.85. 7-Oct-3 Sotheby's, New York #355 est:2500-3500
£1511	$2750	€2206	Abstract (48x48cm-19x19in) s.d.87 s.d.verso. 29-Jun-4 Sotheby's, New York #576/R est:2000-3000
£2260	$4000	€3300	Composition (45x55cm-18x22in) s. painted c.1952. 1-May-4 Ben-Ami, Tel Aviv #4794/R est:3000-4000
£2514	$4500	€3670	Untitled (46x33cm-18x13in) s.d.67. 18-Mar-4 Sotheby's, New York #38/R est:3000-4000
£4217	$7000	€6157	Untitled (60x46cm-24x18in) s. prov. 2-Oct-3 Christie's, Tel Aviv #114/R est:8000-12000
£6704	$12000	€9788	Untitled (132x137cm-52x54in) s.d.88 acrylic. 18-Mar-4 Sotheby's, New York #41/R est:15000-20000
£7263	$13000	€10604	Untitled (116x81cm-46x32in) s.d.82. 18-Mar-4 Sotheby's, New York #50/R est:8000-10000

NIKODEM, Artur (1870-1940) Austrian

£1974	$3632	€3000	Book shelves (47x63cm-19x25in) 22-Jun-4 Wiener Kunst Auktionen, Vienna #66/R est:3000
£8725	$15443	€13000	Landscape (50x54cm-20x21in) s.d.1923 s.d. verso. 28-Apr-4 Wiener Kunst Auktionen, Vienna #88/R est:10000-20000
£27972	$47552	€40000	First spring evening - Sistrans (74x76cm-29x30in) s.d.1913 s.i.d.1913 stretcher prov. 26-Nov-3 Dorotheum, Vienna #26/R est:18000-26000

NIKOLAEV, Y S (1899-1978) Russian

£223	$400	€326	Larisa's portrait (70x50cm-28x20in) painted 1947. 29-May-4 Shishkin Gallery, Moscow #76/R
£531	$950	€775	Earth decree (34x59cm-13x23in) painted 1947 sketch. 29-May-4 Shishkin Gallery, Moscow #75/R

NILES, William J (attrib) (19/20th C) American

£430	$800	€628	Morning (50x76cm-20x30in) 5-Mar-4 Skinner, Boston #287/R

NILOUSS, Piotr Alexandrovitch (1869-1943) Russian

£537	$993	€800	Jardin de Luxembourg (24x35cm-9x14in) s. panel. 15-Mar-4 Claude Boisgirard, Paris #84/R
£1020	$1827	€1500	Paysage (28x34cm-11x13in) s. board. 19-Mar-4 Millon & Associes, Paris #82b est:1500-1800
£1241	$2073	€1800	Paysage II (29x33cm-11x13in) s. cardboard. 17-Nov-3 Claude Boisgirard, Paris #69 est:1800-2000
£14000	$25060	€20440	Still life with tomatoes (38x46cm-15x18in) s. 26-May-4 Sotheby's, London #198a est:6000-8000
Works on paper			
£1986	$3138	€2800	Night stroll. s. gouache. 24-Jul-3 Claude Boisgirard, Paris #68

NILSEN, Ulf Roger (1950-) Norwegian

£317	$584	€463	Hands tied behind his back (80x66cm-31x26in) s. panel. 29-Mar-4 Blomqvist, Lysaker #1219/R (N.KR 4000)
Works on paper			
£523	$956	€764	Maria's head. Rose (62x48cm-24x19in) s. pastel two exec.c.1996-97 exhib. 2-Feb-4 Blomqvist, Lysaker #1210/R (N.KR 6500)

NILSON, Johann Esaias (1721-1788) German

Works on paper			
£250	$450	€365	Design for a portrait cartouche (22x16cm-9x6in) red chk. 21-Jan-4 Doyle, New York #4
£1747	$3179	€2551	Travellers and figures resting in front of a town, with a pair fishing (21x30cm-8x12in) bodycol W/C htd bodycol prov. 17-Jun-4 Kornfeld, Bern #42/R est:3000 (S.FR 4000)

NILSON, Karl Gustaf (1942-) Swedish

£508	$914	€762	Geometric composition (70x70cm-28x28in) s.d.1987 acrylic. 25-Apr-4 Goteborg Auktionsverk, Sweden #304/R (S.KR 7000)
£733	$1297	€1070	La Maison (65x81cm-26x32in) s.d.1970. 27-Apr-4 AB Stockholms Auktionsverk #1038/R (S.KR 10000)
£982	$1669	€1434	Starry sky (102cm-40in circular) s.d.1996 exhib. 4-Nov-3 Bukowskis, Stockholm #289/R (S.KR 13000)
£1284	$2183	€1875	Composition with circles and squares (81x130cm-32x51in) s.d.85 prov. 5-Nov-3 AB Stockholms Auktionsverk #786/R est:18000-20000 (S.KR 17000)
Works on paper			
£352	$566	€514	Composition (54x110cm-21x43in) s.d.1989 panel mixed media. 25-Aug-3 Lilla Bukowskis, Stockholm #72 (S.KR 4600)
£491	$835	€717	Growing (49x49cm-19x19in) s.d.1990 polychrome stones. 5-Nov-3 AB Stockholms Auktionsverk #833/R (S.KR 6500)

NILSON, Severin (1846-1918) Swedish

£517	$926	€755	Idyll in the skerries (23x31cm-9x12in) s. panel. 26-May-4 AB Stockholms Auktionsverk #2113/R (S.KR 7000)
£576	$939	€841	Coastal landscape (31x69cm-12x27in) s. canvas on panel. 29-Sep-3 Lilla Bukowskis, Stockholm #690 (S.KR 7500)
£665	$1191	€971	Landscape at dusk (41x67cm-16x26in) s. panel. 28-May-4 Uppsala Auktionskammare, Uppsala #213/R (S.KR 9000)
£703	$1132	€1026	Summer's day in the country (40x71cm-16x28in) s. 25-Aug-3 Lilla Bukowskis, Stockholm #410 (S.KR 9200)
£841	$1354	€1228	Lake landscape with sailing boat and house (43x75cm-17x30in) s. 25-Aug-3 Lilla Bukowskis, Stockholm #128 (S.KR 11000)
£864	$1495	€1261	Swedish summer night (75x100cm-30x39in) s. 15-Dec-3 Lilla Bukowskis, Stockholm #566 (S.KR 11000)
£887	$1588	€1295	Still life of vegetables and bird (49x68cm-19x27in) s. panel. 28-May-4 Uppsala Auktionskammare, Uppsala #191/R (S.KR 12000)
£961	$1720	€1403	Coastal landscape at dusk (31x70cm-12x28in) s. panel. 26-May-4 AB Stockholms Auktionsverk #2339/R (S.KR 13000)
£1035	$1852	€1511	The road to the sea (16x12cm-6x5in) init.d.96 panel. 26-May-4 AB Stockholms Auktionsverk #2168/R (S.KR 14000)
£1231	$2117	€1797	En plein air (24x18cm-9x7in) s. panel. 3-Dec-3 AB Stockholms Auktionsverk #2304/R est:18000-20000 (S.KR 16000)
£1231	$2117	€1797	Chickens in from of cottage (85x65cm-33x26in) s. 7-Dec-3 Uppsala Auktionskammare, Uppsala #133/R est:12000-15000 (S.KR 16000)
£1231	$2117	€1797	Tarn by woodland meadow (53x80cm-21x31in) s. panel. 7-Dec-3 Uppsala Auktionskammare, Uppsala #186/R est:10000-12000 (S.KR 16000)
£1269	$2183	€1853	Coastal landscape from Gullmarsfjord, Bohuslan (33x77cm-13x30in) s. 3-Dec-3 AB Stockholms Auktionsverk #2307/R est:10000-12000 (S.KR 16500)
£1462	$2514	€2135	Woman by small red house (88x66cm-35x26in) s. 7-Dec-3 Uppsala Auktionskammare, Uppsala #130/R est:12000-15000 (S.KR 19000)
£1532	$2650	€2237	Harvesting time (68x100cm-27x39in) s. 15-Dec-3 Lilla Bukowskis, Stockholm #491 est:15000-18000 (S.KR 19500)
£1615	$2778	€2358	Winter evening near Huddinge (40x70cm-16x28in) indis.sig.d.1910. 3-Dec-3 AB Stockholms Auktionsverk #2302/R est:12000-15000 (S.KR 21000)
£1923	$3308	€2808	Summer landscape with farm by the coast (60x88cm-24x35in) s. panel. 3-Dec-3 AB Stockholms Auktionsverk #2409/R est:25000-30000 (S.KR 25000)
£2538	$4366	€3705	Man fishing from rowing boat (24x18cm-9x7in) panel. 7-Dec-3 Uppsala Auktionskammare, Uppsala #129/R est:20000-25000 (S.KR 33000)
£5000	$8600	€7300	Children picking berries in forest (51x68cm-20x27in) s. 3-Dec-3 AB Stockholms Auktionsverk #2267/R est:80000-100000 (S.KR 65000)

NILSSON, Algot (1898-1993) Swedish

£559	$951	€800	Amazone of Malmoe (28x41cm-11x16in) 18-Nov-3 Cambi, Genoa #348/R

NILSSON, Axel (1889-1981) Swedish

£984	$1810	€1476	Foaming seas (46x65cm-18x26in) s. 14-Jun-4 Lilla Bukowskis, Stockholm #54 (S.KR 13500)
£1172	$2075	€1711	Still life of green dish (74x60cm-29x24in) s. 27-Apr-4 AB Stockholms Auktionsverk #893/R est:20000-25000 (S.KR 16000)
£1282	$2269	€1872	Landscape from Jarvso (24x35cm-9x14in) s. panel. 27-Apr-4 AB Stockholms Auktionsverk #809/R est:20000-25000 (S.KR 17500)
£1378	$2480	€2012	The white mountain in snow (73x54cm-29x21in) s. 26-Apr-4 Bukowskis, Stockholm #180/R est:18000-20000 (S.KR 19000)
£1885	$3394	€2752	Factory buildings, Kungsholmen (32x43cm-13x17in) s.d.1929 panel prov.exhib.lit. 26-Apr-4 Bukowskis, Stockholm #21/R est:30000-40000 (S.KR 26000)
£3626	$6526	€5294	Venetian canal scene (54x36cm-21x14in) s. canvas on panel painted c.1922-24 lit. 26-Apr-4 Bukowskis, Stockholm #182/R est:40000-50000 (S.KR 50000)
£4061	$7310	€5929	Italian landscape, Roviano (46x58cm-18x23in) s.d.1923 prov.lit. 26-Apr-4 Bukowskis, Stockholm #17/R est:40000-50000 (S.KR 56000)
£23205	$41769	€33879	The blue saloon, Smedsudden. Sketch of the custom's house, Smedsudden (39x50cm-15x20in) s.i.d.1920 panel double-sided prov.exhib.lit. 26-Apr-4 Bukowskis, Stockholm #22/R est:125000-150000 (S.KR 320000)

NILSSON, Gladys (1940-) American

£440	$800	€642	Terrarium (14x18cm-6x7in) s.d.1980 i.verso acrylic prov. 7-Feb-4 Sloans & Kenyon, Bethesda #866/R

NILSSON, Lars (1956-) Swedish

Works on paper			
£393	$668	€574	Bacchus (69x49cm-27x19in) s.d.88-89 verso mixed media canvas on panel. 4-Nov-3 Bukowskis, Stockholm #636/R (S.KR 5200)

NILSSON, Mats (1920-) Swedish

£616	$1109	€899	Eriksdalsundet (47x35cm-19x14in) s.d.59. 26-Apr-4 Bukowskis, Stockholm #589/R (S.KR 8500)

NILSSON, Nils (1901-1949) Swedish

£355	$635	€518	Man seated on sofa (58x40cm-23x16in) mono. panel. 28-May-4 Uppsala Auktionskammare, Uppsala #340 (S.KR 4800)
£407	$728	€594	Self-portrait with green background (50x35cm-20x14in) mono.indis.d.21. 28-May-4 Uppsala Auktionskammare, Uppsala #322 (S.KR 5500)
£1026	$1815	€1498	Young model (80x66cm-31x26in) st.init. exhib. 27-Apr-4 AB Stockholms Auktionsverk #889/R (S.KR 14000)
£1133	$1926	€1654	Self-portrait with palette (82x65cm-32x26in) init. painted c.1929 exhib.lit. 5-Nov-3 AB Stockholms Auktionsverk #854/R est:25000-30000 (S.KR 15000)
£1319	$2334	€1926	Towards the sea (65x81cm-26x32in) init. exhib. 27-Apr-4 AB Stockholms Auktionsverk #888/R est:15000-20000 (S.KR 18000)
£1978	$3501	€2888	At the dinner table (97x119cm-38x47in) init. panel lit. 27-Apr-4 AB Stockholms Auktionsverk #886/R est:40000-50000 (S.KR 27000)
£2115	$3595	€3088	View of town (35x36cm-14x14in) init. panel. 4-Nov-3 Bukowskis, Stockholm #186/R est:20000-25000 (S.KR 28000)

NILSSON, Olof (1868-1956) Swedish

£306	$492	€447	Winter landscape (47x61cm-19x24in) s.d.1946 panel. 25-Aug-3 Lilla Bukowskis, Stockholm #531 (S.KR 4000)

NILSSON, Vera (1888-1979) Swedish

£1166	$2146	€1749	Cleaning fish, Herron (34x47cm-13x19in) init. paper on cardboard. 14-Jun-4 Lilla Bukowskis, Stockholm #113 est:20000-25000 (S.KR 16000)
£1511	$2568	€2206	Moonlit landscape (28x36cm-11x14in) init.d.32 exhib.prov. 5-Nov-3 AB Stockholms Auktionsverk #671/R est:20000-25000 (S.KR 20000)
£1586	$2696	€2316	The blue tree, Oland (33x41cm-13x16in) init. panel. 4-Nov-3 Bukowskis, Stockholm #133/R est:15000-20000 (S.KR 21000)
£1888	$3210	€2756	Landscape, Raplinge, Oland (54x72cm-21x28in) init. painted c.1934. 5-Nov-3 AB Stockholms Auktionsverk #669/R est:25000-30000 (S.KR 25000)
Works on paper			
£586	$1037	€856	On the balcony (24x19cm-9x7in) s.i.d.1924 pencil lit. 27-Apr-4 AB Stockholms Auktionsverk #754/R (S.KR 8000)

NIMIER, Pierre (1917-) French

£1007	$1862	€1500	Alger et ses environs (22x33cm-9x13in) s. 15-Mar-4 Gros & Delettrez, Paris #213/R est:1500-2500

NIMMO, John Jules (1830-?) French

Miniatures			
£1700	$3043	€2482	Young boy, in lace bordered blue dress (6cm-2in) s.d.1868 ormolu easel frame. 25-May-4 Christie's, London #167/R est:600-800

NIMMO, Louise Everett (1899-1959) American

£809	$1400	€1181	Still life with hibiscus blossoms (61x51cm-24x20in) s. 10-Dec-3 Bonhams & Butterfields, San Francisco #6273/R est:3000-5000

NIMOCZEWSKI, Helmut (20th C) ?

£367	$675	€550	A la queue Leu-Leu (42x56cm-17x22in) s.d.92 col crayon ball pen felt pen lit. 9-Jun-4 Artcurial Briest, Paris #384

NIN, Buck (20th C) ?

£1504	$2556	€2196	Through the mists of time (90x59cm-35x23in) s. acrylic board. 27-Nov-3 International Art Centre, Auckland #16/R est:4500-6500 (NZ.D 4000)
£2068	$3515	€3019	Untitled (58x137cm-23x54in) s. board. 27-Nov-3 International Art Centre, Auckland #86/R est:10000-15000 (NZ.D 5500)

NINAS, Paul (1903-1964) American

Works on paper			
£1506	$2500	€2199	New Orleans Dock (28x43cm-11x17in) s. pencil. 4-Oct-3 Neal Auction Company, New Orleans #577/R est:2500-4000
£3039	$5500	€4437	Louisiana swamp scene (58x89cm-23x35in) s. W/C gouache. 3-Apr-4 Neal Auction Company, New Orleans #560/R est:5000-7000

NINHAM, Henry (1793-1874) British
£1200 $1992 €1752 Cinder Oven, Norwich (25x33cm-10x13in) board. 1-Oct-3 Sotheby's, Olympia #14/R est:1200-1800

NINNES, Bernard (1899-1971) British
£600 $1002 €876 St. Ives Harbour (51x61cm-20x24in) s. 14-Oct-3 David Lay, Penzance #597

NINO, Carmelo (20th C) South American
£494 $780 €721 Untitled (48x39cm-19x15in) s. 27-Apr-3 Subastas Odalys, Caracas #15
£7869 $14165 €11489 Untitled (150x150cm-59x59in) s. painted 1998. 25-Apr-4 Subastas Odalys, Caracas #27/R est:15000

NIRO, Robert de (20th C) American
Works on paper
£444 $800 €648 Boy in striped shirt (74x60cm-29x24in) s.d.1975 colour pastels cream wove paper. 22-Jan-4 Swann Galleries, New York #219

NISBET, Ethel C (fl.1882-1916) British
Works on paper
£1150 $2116 €1679 Cornish garden (23x34cm-9x13in) s. W/C. 23-Mar-4 Bonhams, Knightsbridge #290/R est:300-500

NISBET, Henriette (20th C) American
£245 $450 €358 Asters in a slip glass (51x38cm-20x15in) mono. masonite. 25-Jun-4 Freeman, Philadelphia #177/R

NISBET, Pollock (1848-1922) British
£340 $619 €496 Sands near Bass Rock (23x36cm-9x14in) s. 16-Jun-4 Andrew Hartley, Ilkley #1077
£400 $728 €584 Street in Tunis, with figures and camel (34x24cm-13x9in) s. 15-Jun-4 Bonhams, Oxford #107
£535 $850 €781 Landscape with beached boat (91x61cm-36x24in) s.indis.d. 13-Sep-3 Weschler, Washington #671/R

NISBET, Robert Buchan (1857-1942) British
Works on paper
£260 $465 €380 Comrie Scotland, Canal Lock - Moonlight (18x23cm-7x9in) init. W/C. 17-Mar-4 Bonhams, Chester #369

NISBET, Robert H (1879-1961) American
£1384 $2200 €2021 Thaw, So Kent, Connecticut (41x51cm-16x20in) s. i.verso masonite. 13-Sep-3 Weschler, Washington #756/R est:2000-3000
£3593 $6000 €5246 Connecticut winter landscape (71x91cm-28x36in) s. masonite prov. 23-Oct-3 Shannon's, Milford #178/R est:6000-8000

NISBET, Tom (1909-2001) Irish
£320 $512 €464 Evening river scene (60x50cm-24x20in) 17-Sep-3 James Thompson, Kirby Lonsdale #119
£1974 $3632 €3000 St Stephen's Green (73x88cm-29x35in) s. board. 22-Jun-4 De Veres Art Auctions, Dublin #167/R est:3000-4000
£2098 $3566 €3000 Female nude study (28x33cm-11x13in) 25-Nov-3 De Veres Art Auctions, Dublin #178/R est:3000-4000
£2797 $4755 €4000 Brendan Behan in McDaids pub (64x51cm-25x20in) s. i.verso board. 25-Nov-3 De Veres Art Auctions, Dublin #176/R est:4000-6000
Works on paper
£263 $484 €400 Canal side study (26x36cm-10x14in) s.i.verso W/C. 22-Jun-4 De Veres Art Auctions, Dublin #158
£296 $545 €450 Autumn at Huband Bridge (26x36cm-10x14in) s.i.verso W/C. 22-Jun-4 De Veres Art Auctions, Dublin #159
£347 $627 €520 Autumn, St Columba's College, Rathfarnham (27x37cm-11x15in) s. W/C. 31-Mar-4 James Adam, Dublin #160/R
£400 $744 €584 Evening, Grand Canal, Dublin (31x37cm-12x15in) s. W/C. 2-Mar-4 Bearnes, Exeter #387/R

NISEN, Jean Baptiste (1819-1885) Belgian
£578 $1035 €850 L'Italienne (34x23cm-13x9in) s.d.1844 panel. 17-Mar-4 Hotel des Ventes Mosan, Brussels #95
£5594 $9510 €8000 Deux belles Romaines et un enfant aux raisins (91x75cm-36x30in) s.d.1848 oval. 18-Nov-3 Vanderkindere, Brussels #190/R est:4000-6000

NISEUS, Gustav Adolf (1836-1900) German
£2293 $3531 €3600 New discovery (58x70cm-23x28in) s.d.1861 i. stretcher. 4-Sep-2 Schopman, Hamburg #38/R est:1600

NISHIZAWA, Luis (1926-) Mexican
Works on paper
£1491 $2729 €2177 Landscape with cattle (35x55cm-14x22in) s. ink. 27-Jan-4 Louis Morton, Mexico #198/R est:14000-35000 (M.P 30000)
£2898 $4926 €4231 Landscape (45x59cm-18x23in) s. ink. 30-Oct-3 Louis Morton, Mexico #57/R est:60000-65000 (M.P 55000)

NISIO, Arthur (1906-1974) German/Brazilian
£1701 $3044 €2500 Snowy village landscape (60x80cm-24x31in) s.d.1932. 20-Mar-4 Bergmann, Erlangen #1122 est:2500

NISS, Thorvald (1842-1905) Danish
£316 $591 €461 Dunes at Skagen (20x32cm-8x13in) mono. i.d.1877 verso canvas on panel. 25-Feb-4 Kunsthallen, Copenhagen #545/R (D.KR 3500)
£360 $576 €526 Woodland landscape with lake (43x61cm-17x24in) mono.d.898 i.verso. 22-Sep-3 Rasmussen, Vejle #334/R (D.KR 3800)
£403 $726 €588 Coastal landscape with fishermen by their boats (24x37cm-9x15in) mono.d.1873. 24-Apr-4 Rasmussen, Havnen #2142/R (D.KR 4500)
£452 $810 €660 Wooded landscape with lake (58x83cm-23x33in) 10-May-4 Rasmussen, Vejle #107/R (D.KR 5000)
£541 $849 €790 Autumn landscape with man walking (89x74cm-35x29in) mono.d.1881. 30-Aug-3 Rasmussen, Havnen #2020 (D.KR 5800)
£809 $1504 €1181 Autumn in Dyrehaven (86x68cm-34x27in) mono. 2-Mar-4 Rasmussen, Copenhagen #1240/R (D.KR 9000)
£898 $1671 €1311 Autumn landscape with man and wheel-barrow (88x72cm-35x28in) s.i.d.1879. 2-Mar-4 Rasmussen, Copenhagen #1343/R (D.KR 10000)
£1172 $2169 €1711 Coastal landscape with wave break (53x71cm-21x28in) mono. 15-Mar-4 Rasmussen, Vejle #187/R est:5000-6000 (D.KR 13000)
£1707 $3175 €2492 Landscape from Arildsleje, sunset (68x98cm-27x39in) mono.d.1902. 2-Mar-4 Rasmussen, Copenhagen #1216/R est:10000-12000 (D.KR 19000)
£4492 $8356 €6558 Autumn day by Fure Lake (95x134cm-37x53in) mono.d.1890 exhib. 2-Mar-4 Rasmussen, Copenhagen #1233/R est:25000-35000 (D.KR 50000)

NISSL, Rudolf (1870-1955) Austrian
£1467 $2640 €2200 Nude woman (51x72cm-20x28in) s. i. verso. 21-Apr-4 Neumeister, Munich #2695/R est:1500
£6944 $11597 €10000 Young woman reading (64x61cm-25x24in) s. d.1907 verso lit. 25-Oct-3 Bergmann, Erlangen #952/R

NISSLE, Fritz (20th C) German
£1233 $2096 €1800 Children sledging (41x31cm-16x12in) s.d.1919 board. 8-Nov-3 Hans Stahl, Toestorf #46/R est:1800

NITKOWISI, Stani (1949-2001) ?
£3944 $6349 €5600 Jardin suspendu (73x60cm-29x24in) s.i.d.1982 verso. 11-May-3 Versailles Encheres #230 est:250-300

NITSCH, Hermann (1938-) Austrian
£2238 $3804 €3200 Untitled (56x63cm-22x25in) s.d.1986 verso paper on canvas. 26-Nov-3 Dorotheum, Vienna #303/R est:1800-2200
£3103 $5679 €4500 Shaken picture (66x59cm-26x23in) s.d.1998. 27-Jan-4 Dorotheum, Vienna #268/R est:3600-5000
£4196 $7133 €6000 Untitled (100x80cm-39x31in) s.i.d.2000 verso. 27-Nov-3 Dorotheum, Linz #527/R est:7000-9000
£4196 $7133 €6000 Untitled (91x160cm-36x63in) s.d.1984 verso sprayed acrylic paper on canvas prov. 27-Nov-3 Lempertz, Koln #307/R est:6000
£4577 $7919 €6500 Splash picture (105x80cm-41x31in) s.d.1983 stretcher. 13-Dec-3 Lempertz, Koln #173/R est:3500
£10738 $19221 €16000 Untitled (120x216cm-47x85in) s.d.1985 verso prov. 25-May-4 Dorotheum, Vienna #394/R est:13000-16000
£13889 $23611 €20000 Shaken picture, red-blue (200x160cm-79x63in) s.d.2000 verso acrylic mixed media jute exhib.lit. 28-Oct-3 Wiener Kunst Auktionen, Vienna #251/R est:15000-27000
£32000 $58880 €46720 Kreuzwegstation XIX (200x300cm-79x118in) s.d.1989 s.i.d.verso oil burlap and wood prov. 25-Jun-4 Christie's, London #214/R est:30000-50000
Works on paper
£1448 $2419 €2100 Untitled (99x146cm-39x57in) s.i.d.1987 mixed media. 13-Nov-3 Neumeister, Munich #594/R est:4000-4500
£2069 $3455 €3000 Untitled (98x161cm-39x63in) s.d.1987 mixed media. 13-Nov-3 Neumeister, Munich #595/R est:4000-4500
£2797 $4755 €4000 Chasuble (110x64cm-43x25in) blood priest's clothing. 26-Nov-3 Dorotheum, Vienna #95/R est:4000-6000

NITSCH, Richard (1866-1945) German
£310 $518 €450 Portrait of woman in traditional costume (18x14cm-7x6in) s. bears i. verso panel lit. 10-Jul-3 Allgauer, Kempten #2623/R
£310 $518 €450 Musician (18x14cm-7x6in) s. i. verso panel. 10-Jul-3 Allgauer, Kempten #2624/R

NITSCH, Richard (attrib) (1866-1945) German
£629 $1070 €900 Portrait of peasant in costume reading (18x13cm-7x5in) s. panel. 20-Nov-3 Van Ham, Cologne #1782

NITSCHKE, Detlev (1935-) German
£537 $950 €800 At the beach (20x15cm-8x6in) s. 30-Apr-4 Auktionhaus Georg Rehm, Augsburg #8081
£2119 $3878 €3200 Flowermarket before Karlskirche in Vienna (21x31cm-8x12in) s. canvas on panel. 8-Apr-4 Dorotheum, Vienna #173/R est:3500-4000

NITTIS, Giuseppe de (1846-1884) Italian
£14000 $25480 €20440 Forest scene with horses (77x46cm-30x18in) s. lit. 15-Jun-4 Sotheby's, London #169/R est:5000-7000
£16107 $28832 €24000 Painter Rossano creating (24x17cm-9x7in) s. cardboard lit. 25-May-4 Finarte Semenzato, Milan #194/R est:20000-25000
Works on paper
£559 $951 €800 Study of heads (15x20cm-6x8in) pencil. 19-Nov-3 Finarte Semenzato, Milan #529/R
£2817 $4873 €4000 Black woman (50x36cm-20x14in) s. pastel card prov.lit. 11-Dec-3 Christie's, Rome #135/R est:4000-6000
£4930 $8528 €7000 Portrait of Jules de Goncourt (73x53cm-29x21in) s.i. pastel card. 11-Dec-3 Christie's, Rome #136/R est:8000-12000
£58824 $100000 €85883 Nude with red stockings (81x99cm-32x39in) s.d.79 pastel canvas lit. 29-Oct-3 Christie's, Rockefeller NY #215/R est:70000-90000

NIVELT, Roger (1899-1962) French
£1049 $1752 €1500 P. d'enfant (43x36cm-17x14in) s.i.d.1929. 7-Oct-3 Livinec, Gaudcheau & Jezequel, Rennes #103/R
£2797 $4671 €4000 Dakar (49x37cm-19x15in) s.i.d.1928 panel. 7-Oct-3 Livinec, Gaudcheau & Jezequel, Rennes #102/R

Works on paper
£612 $1096 €900 Homme et enfant d'Afrique (53x39cm-21x15in) s. pastel lit. 21-Mar-4 St-Germain-en-Laye Encheres #100/R
£629 $1051 €900 Couple d'africains (53x39cm-21x15in) studio st. crayon dr. 7-Oct-3 Livinec, Gaudcheau & Jezequel, Rennes #104

NIVEN, Barbara (20th C) British
£300 $561 €438 Portrait of Mrs M Maitland (45x35cm-18x14in) s. 25-Feb-4 British Auctioneer #181/R

NIVIAKSIAK (1918-1959) North American
Sculpture
£2027 $3446 €2959 Inuit man (36cm-14in) mottled grey soapstone exec.c.1955. 3-Nov-3 Waddingtons, Toronto #311/R est:5000-7000 (C.D 4500)
£12613 $21441 €18415 Inuit mother with her child on her shoulders (30cm-12in) mottled grey soapstone exec.c.1955. 3-Nov-3 Waddingtons, Toronto #310/R est:5000-7000 (C.D 28000)
Works on paper
£450 $766 €657 Sled and seal cached on snow blocks (30x61cm-12x24in) skin stencil. 3-Nov-3 Waddingtons, Toronto #287/R (C.D 1000)
£901 $1532 €1315 Hunter with bear (38x29cm-15x11in) stencil. 3-Nov-3 Waddingtons, Toronto #263/R est:2000-2500 (C.D 2000)

NIVISON, Angus (1953-) Australian
£453 $819 €661 Trickle, Stoney Creek (213x137cm-84x54in) 30-Mar-4 Lawson Menzies, Sydney #194/R est:500-800 (A.D 1100)

NIXON, Francis Russell (1803-1879) British
Works on paper
£1028 $1840 €1542 Tasman's Island and Cape Pillar (18x29cm-7x11in) i.d.July 13 1846 W/C. 17-May-4 Sotheby's, Melbourne #570 est:400-600 (A.D 2600)

NIXON, James (c.1741-1812) British
Miniatures
£7500 $13500 €10950 Lady in white robes with pink underdress (8cm-3in) init. gold frame oval exhib. 22-Apr-4 Bonhams, New Bond Street #113/R est:6000-8000

NIXON, James (attrib) (c.1741-1812) British
Miniatures
£1400 $2520 €2044 Lady wearing white fichu (6cm-2in) diamond gold frame oval exhib. 22-Apr-4 Bonhams, New Bond Street #105/R est:1200-1800

NIXON, John (1949-) Australian
£1021 $1736 €1491 Untitled (66x66cm-26x26in) hessian prov. 26-Nov-3 Deutscher-Menzies, Melbourne #211/R (A.D 2400)
Works on paper
£909 $1682 €1327 Self portrait (76x62cm-30x24in) s.verso s.stretcher verso synthetic polymer. 10-Mar-4 Deutscher-Menzies, Melbourne #239/R est:2500-3000 (A.D 2200)
£1082 $1709 €1580 Untitled (71x56cm-28x22in) synthetic polymer. 2-Sep-3 Deutscher-Menzies, Melbourne #186/R est:3000-4000 (A.D 2640)

NIXON, John (1760-1818) British
Works on paper
£550 $985 €803 Coastal landscape with figures pushing a boat from the shore (18x23cm-7x9in) init.d.1791 grey ink W/C prov. 14-May-4 Christie's, London #76/R est:600-800
£1000 $1790 €1460 First entrance to the Giant's Causeway (11x18cm-4x7in) init.i.d.1785 pencil black ink W/C prov. 14-May-4 Christie's, London #77/R est:600-800
£1000 $1790 €1460 First sketch of the Wicklow girl. Vendor of Faulkner's journal. Mother, child and cat (26x20cm-10x8in) one s.i.d.1757 two init.i.d.1785 pencil ink W/C three prov. 14-May-4 Christie's, London #79/R est:1200-1800
£1300 $2327 €1898 Blarney Castle, Co Cork (11x18cm-4x7in) init.i.d.1792 pencil grey ink W/C prov. 14-May-4 Christie's, London #78/R est:1000-1500
£1400 $2506 €2044 Rostrevor (20x28cm-8x11in) init.i.d.1791 pencil grey ink W/C prov. 14-May-4 Christie's, London #73/R est:1500-2000
£1600 $2864 €2336 The Linen Hall, Belfast (19x28cm-7x11in) s.d.1790 i.verso pencil grey ink W/C prov. 14-May-4 Christie's, London #75/R est:1500-2000
£2000 $3580 €2920 The Giant's Causeway (19x31cm-7x12in) init.i.d.1790 pencil black ink W/C prov. 14-May-4 Christie's, London #74/R est:1500-2000
£5500 $9845 €8030 A Margate Hoy unloading her cargo (42x62cm-17x24in) s.indis.d. pencil black ink W/C prov.exhib. 14-May-4 Christie's, London #101/R est:4000-6000
£7500 $13425 €10950 Busy street in Dublin (48x67cm-19x26in) s.d.1810 W/C over pencil. 13-May-4 Sotheby's, London #7/R est:8000-12000

NIXON, Kay (1895-1988) British
Works on paper
£460 $810 €672 Cat and bird amongst foliage (28x31cm-11x12in) s. W/C htd white. 21-May-4 Bracketts, Tunbridge Wells #253/R
£540 $950 €788 Kingfisher and frogs in a pond scene (29x35cm-11x14in) s. W/C htd white. 21-May-4 Bracketts, Tunbridge Wells #252/R

NOA, J D Riviero (attrib) (20th C) Brazilian
£549 $1000 €802 Town scene (24x20cm-9x8in) s. 7-Feb-4 Sloans & Kenyon, Bethesda #1225/R

NOACK, Astrid (1888-?) Swedish?
Sculpture
£1878 $3136 €2742 Female head (28cm-11in) brown pat.bronze. 7-Oct-3 Rasmussen, Copenhagen #348/R est:15000 (D.KR 20000)

NOACK, August (1822-1905) German
£4967 $9040 €7500 The Merchant of Venice (96x78cm-38x31in) s.d.1860. 16-Jun-4 Hugo Ruef, Munich #1050/R est:4500

NOACK, H (fl.1920s) German
Sculpture
£3352 $6000 €4894 Standing male youth (30cm-12in) s. bronze exec. c.1920. 11-Jan-4 William Jenack, New York #304 est:300-500

NOAILLES, Anna Elisabeth de (1876-1933) French
Works on paper
£1200 $2172 €1800 Untitled (24x48cm-9x19in) s.d.1928 pastel. 1-Apr-4 Piasa, Paris #269/R est:1000-1200

NOAILLY, Francisque (1855-1942) French?
£559 $900 €816 Arabs on horseback (81x33cm-32x13in) s. painted c.1895. 22-Feb-3 Bunte, Elgin #1295
£733 $1327 €1100 Plage pres d'Alger (43x61cm-17x24in) s. cardboard. 5-Apr-4 Marie & Robert, Paris #99
£851 $1421 €1200 Fileuse dans un interieur a Bou-Saada (22x18cm-9x7in) s. i.verso cardboard. 16-Jun-3 Gros & Delettrez, Paris #252
£2685 $4966 €4000 Ruelle animee a Felden, Kabylie (54x37cm-21x15in) s. 15-Mar-4 Gros & Delettrez, Paris #61/R est:4000-5000
£3000 $5520 €4500 Le Port d'Alger (32x55cm-13x22in) s.i.d.1894. 11-Jun-4 Claude Aguttes, Neuilly #130/R est:5000-7000

NOAIN, Javier (20th C) Spanish
Works on paper
£1207 $2016 €1750 Yaphiel (150x150cm-59x59in) s.i.d.91 verso mixed media. 11-Nov-3 Castellana, Madrid #158/R est:1500

NOAKE, Edward (fl.c.1910) British
£320 $576 €467 Peasants with cattle gathering seaweed on the beach (29x59cm-11x23in) s. 22-Apr-4 Lawrence, Crewkerne #922

NOAKES, Frederick (20th C) British
Works on paper
£320 $592 €467 Siesta time, Seville, Spain (30x47cm-12x19in) s. W/C. 13-Feb-4 Sworder & Son, Bishops Stortford #146/R

NOALLY, Francisque (?) ?
£1477 $2732 €2200 Porteuse d'eau dans le desert (46x55cm-18x22in) s. 15-Mar-4 Horta, Bruxelles #29 est:600-800

NOBBE, Erwin (19/20th C) ?
£1028 $1624 €1491 Schwere Wolken aus Nordwest, Fanoe (70x100cm-28x39in) s.i.d.1913. 2-Sep-3 Rasmussen, Copenhagen #1774/R (D.KR 11000)

NOBBE, Jacob (1850-1919) Danish
£709 $1270 €1050 Woman and man (101x71cm-40x28in) s.d.1906 pair. 8-May-4 Hans Stahl, Toestorf #74/R

NOBBE, Walter (1941-) Dutch?
£434 $686 €625 Lemon and pear (24x30cm-9x12in) s.d.2002 verso. 26-Apr-3 Auction Maastricht #3/R

NOBELE, Henri de (c.1820-1870) Belgian
£350 $594 €500 Portrait de Theodore, frere de Jacqueline van Overloop (82x68cm-32x27in) s. 1-Dec-3 Millon & Associes, Paris #96

NOBILE, Mimmo (1955-) Italian
£1933 $3499 €2900 Corn (80x120cm-31x47in) s.i.d.1992. 2-Apr-4 Farsetti, Prato #244 est:2100-2400

NOBLE, J (19/20th C) British
£424 $708 €615 Old barrels at the entranceway (38x28cm-15x11in) s.d.1878. 17-Jun-3 Pinneys, Montreal #70 (C.D 950)
£1200 $2040 €1752 Portrait of a little girl standing in a garden (38x32cm-15x13in) s.i.d.1840 verso. 19-Nov-3 Tennants, Leyburn #1150/R est:500-600

NOBLE, James (1919-1989) British
£420 $764 €613 Whisky chaser (25x20cm-10x8in) s. 15-Jun-4 Bonhams, Knightsbridge #90/R
£440 $761 €642 Roses and Stocks in a glass vase (25x20cm-10x8in) s. prov. 11-Dec-3 Neales, Nottingham #659/R
£520 $946 €759 Freshly picked roses in a glass vase (25x20cm-10x8in) s. 15-Jun-4 Bonhams, Knightsbridge #93/R
£600 $1020 €876 Christmas roses (35x46cm-14x18in) s. i.on overlap. 29-Oct-3 Bonhams, Chester #464
£620 $980 €905 Still life study of apples on a bench (24x30cm-9x12in) s. 2-Sep-3 Gildings, Market Harborough #427/R
£700 $1204 €1022 Mimosa (30x41cm-12x16in) s. 2-Dec-3 Gorringes, Lewes #2529/R
£1000 $1700 €1460 Still life of Christmas rose, primrose, bluebells and magnolia (25x20cm-10x8in) s. prov.exhib. 19-Nov-3 Tennants, Leyburn #1226 est:1000-1200
£1000 $1630 €1460 Spring flowers (24x19cm-9x7in) s. 25-Sep-3 Mellors & Kirk, Nottingham #779/R est:1000-1400

NOBLE, James Campbell (1846-1913) British
£600 $1098 €876 Dutch waterway (40x29cm-16x11in) bears sig. 8-Apr-4 Bonhams, Edinburgh #90
£620 $1035 €905 Sheep grazing in the lowlands (45x60cm-18x24in) s. 19-Jun-3 Bonhams, Edinburgh #327
£900 $1548 €1314 Summer (44x34cm-17x13in) s. 4-Dec-3 Mellors & Kirk, Nottingham #951/R
£1200 $2148 €1752 Signal of distress (77x91cm-30x36in) s. 26-May-4 Sotheby's, Olympia #234/R est:1500-2000
£1450 $2422 €2117 Vessels at Barwyk (45x60cm-18x24in) s. i.overlap. 13-Nov-3 Bonhams, Edinburgh #316 est:1500-2000
£1563 $2609 €2266 Haymaking (46x76cm-18x30in) s.d.83 i.verso. 17-Jun-3 Pinneys, Montreal #57 est:1500-2500 (C.D 3500)
£1800 $3096 €2628 Harvesting, possibly Dirleton Castle behind (46x77cm-18x30in) s.d.83. 4-Dec-3 Bonhams, Edinburgh #55/R est:2000-3000
£2000 $3140 €2900 Open gate (35x25cm-14x10in) i.verso board. 27-Aug-3 Sotheby's, London #1074/R est:1500-2000
£2000 $3620 €2920 Coldingham Bay (61x112cm-24x44in) 19-Apr-4 Sotheby's, London #27/R est:2500-3000
£3000 $4710 €4350 Dutch village with windmills (72x93cm-28x37in) s. 27-Aug-3 Sotheby's, London #1125/R est:3000-4000

NOBLE, Jill (1962-) Australian
£329 $596 €480 Red head (30x20cm-12x8in) init.d.89 s.i.verso acrylic on paper. 30-Mar-4 Lawson Menzies, Sydney #38/R (A.D 800)
£741 $1341 €1082 No.24 (92x90cm-36x35in) s.verso oil on wood. 30-Mar-4 Lawson Menzies, Sydney #68/R est:1500-2500 (A.D 1800)
£972 $1564 €1419 Stnding figure (185x104cm-73x41in) cardboard prov. 25-Aug-3 Sotheby's, Paddington #269/R est:2000-4000 (A.D 2400)
£1235 $2235 €1803 The lovers (122x112cm-48x44in) s. 30-Mar-4 Lawson Menzies, Sydney #74/R est:3000-5000 (A.D 3000)
£1423 $2233 €2063 Robert's house and the research station (122x168cm-48x66in) s.d.92 s.i.d.92 verso acrylic prov. 27-Aug-3 Christie's, Sydney #800/R est:2000-3000 (A.D 3500)
£2881 $5214 €4206 Boats I (92x127cm-36x50in) s.d.89 exhib. 30-Mar-4 Lawson Menzies, Sydney #2/R est:3000-5000 (A.D 7000)
£3846 $6192 €5615 Homage to Chagall (162x118cm-64x46in) s. prov.exhib. 25-Aug-3 Sotheby's, Paddington #280/R est:5000-7000 (A.D 9500)
Works on paper
£412 $745 €602 Self portrait with Lucy (68x50cm-27x20in) s.d.89 s.i.d.verso gouache on canvas. 30-Mar-4 Lawson Menzies, Sydney #26 est:600-1000 (A.D 1000)
£453 $819 €661 Pond in the valley (37x56cm-15x22in) init. s.i.d.88 verso gouache. 30-Mar-4 Lawson Menzies, Sydney #13 est:400-600 (A.D 1100)
£1152 $2086 €1682 Portrait of a woman (29x20cm-11x8in) gouache. 30-Mar-4 Lawson Menzies, Sydney #37/R est:600-800 (A.D 2800)

NOBLE, John (1874-1935) American
£750 $1380 €1125 Sporting dogs and game (48x76cm-19x30in) s. 23-Jun-4 Byrne's, Chester #692/R

NOBLE, John Sargeant (1848-1896) British
£1600 $2864 €2336 Waiting for the gun (19x29cm-7x11in) s. panel. 26-May-4 Sotheby's, Olympia #110/R est:800-1200
£2200 $4070 €3212 Otter hunt, hounds amongst reeds (22x32cm-9x13in) s. 11-Mar-4 Morphets, Harrogate #290/R est:1500-1800
£4200 $7686 €6132 Portrait of a horse and two dogs in a stable (42x54cm-17x21in) s.indis.d. 5-Jun-4 Windibank, Dorking #371 est:2000-3000
£5200 $9620 €7592 Waiting for the guns (24x40cm-9x16in) s.d.1889 panel. 11-Mar-4 Morphets, Harrogate #291/R est:2000-2500

NOBLE, Matthew (1818-1876) British
Sculpture
£1900 $3515 €2774 Bust of Robert Bently Todd (75cm-30in) i.verso marble marble socle. 13-Jan-4 Woolley & Wallis, Salisbury #258/R est:1000-1500
£2711 $4500 €3958 Alexandra, Princess of Wales (76x48x28cm-30x19x11in) s.d.1867 i.verso marble. 4-Oct-3 Neal Auction Company, New Orleans #257/R est:2500-3500

NOBLE, Richard Pratchett (fl.1830-1861) British
Works on paper
£280 $442 €406 Farmstead (28x49cm-11x19in) W/C over chl. 3-Sep-3 Bonhams, Bury St Edmunds #354

NOBLE, Robert (1857-1917) British
£403 $742 €588 Early morning (25x32cm-10x13in) s.d.98 board prov. 14-Jun-4 Waddingtons, Toronto #187/R est:1000-1500 (C.D 1000)
£500 $790 €725 Spring (23x33cm-9x13in) s. board. 4-Sep-3 Christie's, Kensington #174/R
£600 $1104 €876 Extensive landscape with a cornfield (30x51cm-12x20in) s.i. 8-Jun-4 Bonhams, Knightsbridge #148/R
£700 $1127 €1015 East Linton (11x22cm-4x9in) s. panel prov. 21-Aug-3 Bonhams, Edinburgh #1010/R
£980 $1578 €1421 Apple blossom (24x32cm-9x13in) s. panel prov.exhib. 21-Aug-3 Bonhams, Edinburgh #1177
£3800 $7068 €5548 Willows (51x61cm-20x24in) s.d.96. 4-Mar-4 Christie's, Kensington #142/R est:1500-2000
£5200 $9672 €7592 Meeting of the Tay and the Earn (69x89cm-27x35in) s. 4-Mar-4 Christie's, Kensington #143/R est:3000-5000

NOBLE, Robert Heysham (fl.1821-1860) British
Works on paper
£363 $650 €530 Beckenham, rural Kentish scene with sheep grazing (20x15cm-8x6in) s.d.1854 W/C. 18-Mar-4 Richard Opfer, Timonium #224/R

NOBLE, Thomas Satterwhite (1835-1907) American
£4286 $7500 €6258 View across Gravesend Bay to Seagate (36x46cm-14x18in) s.d.1905 prov. 19-Dec-3 Sotheby's, New York #1069/R est:8000-12000

NOBLE, Tim and WEBSTER, Sue (20th C) American
Sculpture
£38000 $69160 €55480 Vicious (79x239x10cm-31x94x4in) ninety eight pink fairground reflector caps lightbulbs two parts. 4-Feb-4 Christie's, London #3/R est:30000-50000
£49162 $88000 €71777 Excessive sensual indulgence (190x90x25cm-75x35x10in) multicolor light fixtures, caps spray paint prov.exhib.lit. 13-May-4 Phillips, New York #2/R est:70000-90000
£65000 $119600 €94900 Golden showers (158x122x7cm-62x48x3in) 293 multi coloured light fittings fairground reflector cap painted. 23-Jun-4 Sotheby's, London #1/R est:40000-60000
£111732 $200000 €163129 Sweet smell of excess (118x98x4cm-46x39x2in) 162 light fittings with bulbs and caps exec 1998 prov. 12-May-4 Sotheby's, New York #1/R est:100000-150000
£111732 $200000 €163129 Dollar (183x122x25cm-72x48x10in) reflector caps lamps holders brass edition 4 of 5 prov.exhib. 12-May-4 Christie's, Rockefeller NY #346/R est:40000-60000
£113772 $190000 €166107 Wasted youth (134x210x66cm-53x83x26in) miscellany of styrofoam cardboard plastic executed 2000 prov. 13-Nov-3 Phillips, New York #7/R est:100000-150000

NOBLE, William P (19th C) ?
£291 $500 €425 What are the wild waves saying? (36x25cm-14x10in) s.d.1869 s.i.d.verso. 2-Dec-3 Christie's, Rockefeller NY #102/R

NOBUSADA, Eiseisai (19th C) Japanese
Works on paper
£7609 $14000 €11109 Tiger and leopards in a bamboo grove (70x226cm-28x89in) ink gold six panel screen pair. 23-Mar-4 Christie's, Rockefeller NY #86/R est:5000-7000

NOCI, Arturo (1875-1953) Italian
£1974 $3632 €3000 Portrait of man (101x99cm-40x39in) s.d.1912. 23-Jun-4 Finarte Semenzato, Rome #100/R est:3000-4000

NOCK, Leo F (20th C) American
Sculpture
£1029 $1750 €1502 Cowboy on a bucking bronco (48x36x20cm-19x14x8in) s.d.1907 bronze prov. 1-Nov-3 Santa Fe Art, Santa Fe #176/R est:2500-3500

NOCKEN, Wilhelm Theodor (1830-1905) German
£1153 $2098 €1683 Landscape with trees in the foreground and mountains in the distance (67x96cm-26x38in) s. 20-Jun-4 Agra, Warsaw #34/R (P.Z 8000)
£1361 $2435 €2000 Romantic landscape (97x125cm-38x49in) s. lit. 20-Mar-4 Bergmann, Erlangen #1100 est:2000

NOCKOLDS, Roy (1911-1979) British
£3200 $5088 €4672 Two spitfires (91x152cm-36x60in) s.d.1966. 10-Sep-3 Sotheby's, Olympia #220/R est:1200-1800
Works on paper
£4500 $8280 €6570 Old No. 7 at le Mans 1927 (55x40cm-22x16in) mixed media. 25-Jun-4 Bonhams, New Bond Street #611 est:1500-2000

NOE, Luis Felipe (1933-) Argentinian
Works on paper
£13966 $25000 €20390 Pictorial exorcism (195x130cm-77x51in) s. s.i.d.1989 verso mixed media on canvas. 4-May-4 Arroyo, Buenos Aires #80/R est:24000

NOEH, Anna T (1926-) Canadian
£260 $476 €380 Mother and child, Arctic Bay (20x25cm-8x10in) s.i.d.1988 acrylic panel prov. 1-Jun-4 Hodgins, Calgary #30/R (C.D 650)

NOEL, Alexandre Jean (1752-1834) French
Works on paper
£274 $465 €400 Vue presumee du Port de Malaga (22x37cm-9x15in) s. i. wash W/C. 6-Nov-3 Tajan, Paris #140
£1944 $3500 €2838 Shipping off the coast of Gibraltar (13x31cm-5x12in) s. bodycol. 22-Jan-4 Christie's, Rockefeller NY #238/R est:3000-5000
£2432 $4281 €3600 Moonlit southern sea harbour (54x71cm-21x28in) s. gouache prov. 22-May-4 Lempertz, Koln #1330/R est:4000
£2676 $4683 €3800 Navire pres de cote rocheuse (69x99cm-27x39in) gouache. 17-Dec-3 Piasa, Paris #88/R est:3000-4000
£3028 $5239 €4300 Marine - navire de haut bord pris dans une tempete (60x95cm-24x37in) s. gouache. 10-Dec-3 Piasa, Paris #86/R est:4500

NOEL, Alexandre Jean (attrib) (1752-1834) French
£1560 $2606 €2200 Pecheurs a l'epuisette (223x184cm-88x72in) 15-Oct-3 Neret-Minet, Paris #28/R
Works on paper
£633 $1165 €950 Philosophe et jeune fille devant le tombeau d'un roi (47x55cm-19x22in) gouache. 11-Jun-4 Maigret, Paris #31
£927 $1687 €1400 Personnages dans la tempete, une ville dans le lointain (29x47cm-11x19in) s. gouache. 16-Jun-4 Piasa, Paris #216

NOEL, Georges (1924-) French
£537 $999 €800 Untitled (60x73cm-24x29in) s. d.1958 verso. 3-Mar-4 Tajan, Paris #221
£1329 $2285 €1900 Mer etale (65x50cm-26x20in) s.d.96 s.i.d.verso oil sand. 2-Dec-3 Sotheby's, Amsterdam #335/R est:1000-1500
£2431 $4059 €3500 Composition (143x105cm-56x41in) s.d.1961. 21-Oct-3 Artcurial Briest, Paris #400/R est:3000-4000
£3264 $5157 €4700 Palimpseste (73x116cm-29x46in) s.d.1960 oil grattage. 27-Apr-3 Versailles Encheres #26

Works on paper

£385	$654	€550	Porte magique (35x27cm-14x11in) s.d.1964 s.i.d.1964 verso mixed media panel. 27-Nov-3 Millon & Associes, Paris #255
£493	$908	€750	Composition (48x65cm-19x26in) s. mixed media paper on canvas. 28-Jun-4 Joron-Derem, Paris #212
£537	$988	€800	Composition (48x65cm-19x26in) s. mixed media paper on canvas. 24-Mar-4 Joron-Derem, Paris #177
£805	$1490	€1200	Composition (51x66cm-20x26in) s. mixed media paper on canvas. 15-Mar-4 Blanchet, Paris #177/R
£1200	$2076	€1752	Purple velvet (55x74cm-22x29in) s.d.1986 verso i.stretcher sand mixed media canvas. 11-Dec-3 Christie's, Kensington #254/R est:1500-2000
£2238	$3804	€3200	Porte magique (145x114cm-57x45in) s.d.1964 s.i.d.1964 verso mixed media panel. 27-Nov-3 Millon & Associes, Paris #254/R est:4500-6000
£2308	$3923	€3300	Totem (116x89cm-46x35in) s.d.1962 s.i.d.aout 62 verso mixed media prov.exhib. 28-Nov-3 Blanchet, Paris #221/R est:3000-4000
£2448	$4161	€3500	Codice tres decisif (100x65cm-39x26in) s.d.1961 i.d.verso mixed media prov.exhib. 28-Nov-3 Blanchet, Paris #219/R est:3000-4000
£3239	$5604	€4600	Sable pale (50x65cm-20x26in) s. s.i.d.1951 verso mixed media paper on canvas. 13-Dec-3 Lempertz, Koln #174/R est:2000
£3893	$6890	€5800	Palimpseste blue Egyptien (130x97cm-51x38in) s.d.1964 mixed media grattage incisions paper on canvas prov. 28-Apr-4 Artcurial Briest, Paris #275a/R est:4000-5000
£5500	$9515	€8030	Tick-tack play (190x190cm-75x75in) s.d.1989 s.i.d.1989 verso sand mixed media canvas. 11-Dec-3 Christie's, Kensington #246/R est:4000-6000

NOEL, John Bates (fl.1893-1909) British

£280	$448	€409	Lake scene with sailing vessels (51x74cm-20x29in) s.d.1923. 15-May-3 Mitchells, Cockermouth #1016
£300	$510	€438	Woman with ducks on a track beside a river (51x76cm-20x30in) s.d.1900. 30-Oct-3 Duke & Son, Dorchester #189
£320	$592	€467	Fisherwives with their catch on a beach (25x33cm-10x13in) s.d.1907. 9-Mar-4 Peter Francis, Wales #10/R
£368	$600	€537	Job of the gum slave, Sutton Park (61x46cm-24x18in) s.d.1898. 19-Jul-3 Susanin's, Chicago #5002
£460	$768	€672	On Ripple Common (24x34cm-9x13in) s. s.i.verso. 14-Oct-3 Bearnes, Exeter #370/R
£500	$885	€730	Perry Bar Birmingham with two figures passing over a stone bridge (40x60cm-16x24in) s.d.1895. 30-Apr-4 Bigwood, Stratford on Avon #353/R
£650	$1170	€949	Woodland scene, two children on a woodland path (20x25cm-8x10in) s.i.d.1891. 21-Apr-4 Tennants, Leyburn #1124
£739	$1323	€1079	The Grant Llyn, Lledv Valley (61x91cm-24x36in) s. d.1897 verso. 26-May-4 AB Stockholms Auktionsverk #2410/R (S.KR 10000)
£800	$1480	€1168	Near Llanbedr, North Wales (34x45cm-13x18in) s.i.verso. 13-Jan-4 Bonhams, Knightsbridge #39/R

Works on paper

£260	$432	€380	On Welland Common (25x36cm-10x14in) s. W/C. 2-Oct-3 Mitchells, Cockermouth #837/R
£270	$451	€394	Crossing the moor, the old road to Capel Curig (36x52cm-14x20in) s.d.1907 W/C bodycol. 20-Oct-3 Bonhams, Bath #112
£290	$502	€423	Peasant family cutting wood by a river (36x51cm-14x20in) s. W/C. 14-Dec-3 Desmond Judd, Cranbrook #1048
£340	$568	€496	Near Malvern (26x35cm-10x14in) s. s.i.verso W/C. 14-Oct-3 Bearnes, Exeter #315/R
£500	$835	€730	Figures on a moorland track approaching a stream (36x51cm-14x20in) s.d.1907 W/C pair. 8-Oct-3 Halls, Shrewsbury #101/R

NOEL, John Bates (attrib) (fl.1893-1909) British

£417	$750	€609	Gypsy encampment (25x36cm-10x14in) s. i.verso. 24-Jan-4 Skinner, Boston #390

NOEL, Jules (1815-1881) French

£800	$1480	€1168	Bretagne (38x54cm-15x21in) s.i. 15-Jan-4 Christie's, Kensington #941/R
£1166	$2146	€1749	Seascape (38x28cm-15x11in) s. 14-Jun-4 Lilla Bukowskis, Stockholm #520/R est:20000-25000 (S.KR 16000)
£1351	$2378	€2000	View of Mosque (27x20cm-11x8in) s. panel. 22-May-4 Lempertz, Koln #1572 est:800
£1591	$2641	€2307	Marine (39x59cm-15x23in) s. 13-Jun-3 Zofingen, Switzerland #2372/R est:4500 (S.FR 3500)
£1974	$3296	€2882	Scene de rue a Morlaix (50x32cm-20x13in) s.d.1869. 16-Nov-3 Koller, Geneva #1259/R est:3000-5000 (S.FR 4500)
£2000	$3400	€2920	At anchor (27x35cm-11x14in) s.d.72 panel pair. 19-Nov-3 Christie's, Kensington #566/R
£2069	$3703	€3021	Fishing boat on beach (46x37cm-18x15in) s. panel prov. 12-May-4 Dobiaschofsky, Bern #833/R est:4500 (S.FR 4800)
£2270	$3790	€3200	L'arrivee des pecheurs (18x36cm-7x14in) mono. panel. 23-Jun-3 Ribeyre & Baron, Paris #41/R est:750-1200
£2624	$4199	€3831	Ships by lighthouse (40x55cm-16x22in) s. 19-Sep-3 Koller, Zurich #3088/R est:6000-9000 (S.FR 5800)
£2986	$4987	€4300	Debarquement sur un rivage Oriental (36x56cm-14x22in) s.d.1879. 22-Oct-3 Ribeyre & Baron, Paris #10/R est:3500-5000
£3121	$5211	€4400	Les lavandieres en Bretagne (38x27cm-15x11in) s.d.1869. 20-Jun-3 Drouot Estimations, Paris #68 est:3000-5000
£3147	$5413	€4500	Paturage dans le Morbihan (32x46cm-13x18in) s.d.58. 7-Dec-3 Osenat, Fontainebleau #162 est:4500-5000
£3497	$6014	€5000	Le passage du gue (25x55cm-10x22in) s.d.1874. 7-Dec-3 Osenat, Fontainebleau #170 est:5000-6000
£3846	$6615	€5500	Bateaux de pecheurs par gros temps (38x53cm-15x21in) s.d.1869. 7-Dec-3 Osenat, Fontainebleau #163
£4400	$7920	€6424	Summer fete held in the grounds of a large house (21x37cm-8x15in) s.i.d.1850. 25-Apr-4 Wilkinson, Doncaster #285
£4545	$7818	€6500	Chemin au bord de la riviere de Quimperle (27x41cm-11x16in) s. 7-Dec-3 Osenat, Fontainebleau #164
£4667	$8540	€7000	Arrivee a Hennebon (26x37cm-10x15in) s. 6-Jun-4 Osenat, Fontainebleau #60a/R est:5500-6000
£5000	$9150	€7500	Promenade a barque (38x27cm-15x11in) s. lit. 6-Jun-4 Osenat, Fontainebleau #147/R est:8000-10000
£5106	$8528	€7200	Procession de l'Assomption a Hennebont (54x38cm-21x15in) s.i.d.1871. 20-Jun-3 Drouot Estimations, Paris #69 est:4500-6000
£5455	$9382	€7800	Les lanvadieres en Bretagne (38x27cm-15x11in) s.d.1869. 7-Dec-3 Osenat, Fontainebleau #165 est:6000-7000
£5800	$10556	€8468	Le port de Brest (71x97cm-28x38in) s.i.d.1840 prov. 16-Jun-4 Bonhams, New Bond Street #94/R est:4000-6000
£5882	$9412	€8588	Treport (37x54cm-15x21in) s. canvas on panel. 19-Sep-3 Koller, Zurich #3085/R est:14000-20000 (S.FR 13000)
£6884	$11290	€9500	Bateaux de peche pres de la jetee (27x38cm-11x15in) s.d.1866. 11-May-3 Osenat, Fontainebleau #159/R est:10000-12000
£7333	$13420	€11000	Tempete. Temps calme (29x40cm-11x16in) s.d.1846 pair. 6-Jun-4 Rouillac, Vendome #23
£7483	$11898	€11000	Return of the fishermen (45x36cm-18x14in) s.d.1871. 23-Mar-3 Mercier & Cie, Lille #253/R est:12000-15000
£8252	$14193	€11800	Promenade en barque au chateau de Fontainebleau (47x26cm-19x10in) s. i.verso. 7-Dec-3 Osenat, Fontainebleau #166 est:10000-12000
£9667	$17497	€14500	Le port de Saint-Goustan, Auray (24x47cm-9x19in) s. 5-Apr-4 Deburaux, Boulogne #84/R est:5000-5500
£12667	$23307	€19000	Vue de Constantinople (70x97cm-28x38in) s.d.1841. 14-Jun-4 Cornette de St.Cyr, Paris #49/R est:20000-30000

Works on paper

£280	$481	€400	Village de pecheurs (10x18cm-4x7in) s. W/C. 7-Dec-3 Osenat, Fontainebleau #167
£288	$460	€400	Barque dans un paysages (24x37cm-9x15in) s.d.1860 chl htd white gouache. 16-May-3 Tajan, Paris #167
£362	$594	€500	Le bac, le passeur (15x23cm-6x9in) s.d.1864 graphite. 11-May-3 Osenat, Fontainebleau #5
£420	$722	€600	Paysage d'hiver (16x25cm-6x10in) s. W/C. 7-Dec-3 Osenat, Fontainebleau #169
£423	$739	€600	Personnages devant la chaumiere (19x40cm-7x16in) s. chl. 21-Dec-3 Thierry & Lannon, Brest #450
£423	$731	€600	Leaving for fishing (27x36cm-11x14in) s.d.1865. 10-Dec-3 Finarte Semenzato, Rome #178/R
£775	$1387	€1100	Le troupeau (69x54cm-27x21in) s.d.1855 pencil. 11-Jan-4 Rouillac, Vendome #74b
£845	$1462	€1200	Soleil couchant sur une ville d'Orient (17x30cm-7x12in) s. W/C. 12-Dec-3 Renaud, Paris #76/R
£1733	$3137	€2600	Bateaux sur la greve (30x44cm-12x17in) s.d.1869 W/C. 1-Apr-4 Credit Municipal, Paris #25/R est:1800-2300

NOEL, Jules Alexandre (1752-1828) French

Works on paper

£5986	$9937	€8500	Marine animee sur une cote (44x73cm-17x29in) gouache pastel. 16-Jun-3 E & Eve, Paris #41/R

NOELANDERS, Gaston (1910-) Belgian

£300	$540	€450	Bourgeois interior with white roses and books (100x130cm-39x51in) s. 26-Apr-4 Bernaerts, Antwerp #634/R

NOELQUI, Quintavalle (20th C) Italian

£349	$636	€510	Seated female nude (40x35cm-16x14in) s.d.954. 16-Jun-4 Fischer, Luzern #2300/R (S.FR 800)

NOELSMITH, Thomas (fl.1889-1900) British

Works on paper

£400	$652	€584	Hampshire village scene with figures before an inn (24x34cm-9x13in) s. W/C. 24-Sep-3 Peter Wilson, Nantwich #114
£800	$1312	€1168	Boating trip (62x37cm-24x15in) s. W/C htd white. 3-Jun-3 Fellows & Sons, Birmingham #109/R

NOERR, Julius (1827-1897) German

£329	$605	€500	The rest (21x27cm-8x11in) s. panel. 22-Jun-4 Wiener Kunst Auktionen, Vienna #179/R
£2064	$3447	€2993	Chatting in the meadow (42x32cm-17x13in) s.d.76 panel. 23-Jun-3 Philippe Schuler, Zurich #3538/R est:4000-6000 (S.FR 4500)
£2098	$3608	€3000	Two children talking to a horse rider at the spring (25x20cm-10x8in) s.d.91. 3-Dec-3 Neumeister, Munich #694/R est:2200
£2448	$4210	€3500	Riders and vehicles on the fens (32x54cm-13x21in) s. canvas on canvas prov. 5-Dec-3 Ketterer, Munich #7/R est:4000-6000
£2517	$4280	€3600	After the hunt (40x62cm-16x24in) s.d.882. 24-Nov-3 Dorotheum, Vienna #158/R est:3500-4000
£6294	$10825	€9000	Haying on the shore of a lake (68x115cm-27x45in) s.d.1886. 3-Dec-3 Neumeister, Munich #693/R est:6000
£8333	$13583	€12000	Fishing family on shore of Fraueninsel (21x33cm-8x13in) s.d.1876 panel. 24-Sep-3 Neumeister, Munich #516/R est:12000

NOGARI, Giuseppe (1699-1763) Italian

£2685	$5020	€4000	Writer (60x46cm-24x18in) 29-Feb-4 Finarte, Venice #16/R est:4000-5000
£2703	$4757	€4000	Archimedes (4x50cm-2x20in) prov. 22-May-4 Lempertz, Koln #1110/R est:8000
£3000	$5100	€4380	Philosopher (58x46cm-23x18in) 29-Oct-3 Bonhams, New Bond Street #116/R est:3000-4000
£4500	$8100	€6570	An old lady in a brown dress with a brown headscarf holding a rosary (62x48cm-24x19in) 21-Apr-4 Bonhams, New Bond Street #106/R est:2000-3000
£6040	$11114	€9000	Portrait of man writing letter (58x46cm-23x18in) 24-Mar-4 Dorotheum, Vienna #7/R est:12000-15000
£21477	$38013	€32000	Portrait of girl with tambourine. Portrait of boy with flute (60x45cm-24x18in) pair. 27-Apr-4 Porro, Milan #297/R est:25000

Works on paper

£3500	$6405	€5110	Portrait of a man in a white stock (34x32cm-13x13in) black white chk. 6-Jul-4 Christie's, London #76/R est:2500-3500

NOGUCHI, Isamu (1904-1988) American

Sculpture

£59880	$100000	€87425	Seen and unseen (16x70x66cm-6x28x26in) bronze two parts prov.exhib.lit. 13-Nov-3 Sotheby's, New York #109/R est:50000-70000
£65868	$110000	€96167	Messenger (199x41x56cm-78x16x22in) stainless steel prov.exhib.lit. 13-Nov-3 Sotheby's, New York #256/R est:80000-120000

NOGUE MASSO, Jose (1880-1973) Spanish

£379	$683	€550	Mountainous landscape (57x76cm-22x30in) s. 26-Jan-4 Durán, Madrid #21/R

£612	$1096	€900	Landscape (60x81cm-24x32in) s. 22-Mar-4 Durán, Madrid #35/R

NOGUEIRA LIMA, Mauricio (1930-) Brazilian

£8425	$15418	€12638	Composition (65x81cm-26x32in) s.d.1958 i.verso. 6-Jul-4 Bolsa de Arte, Rio de Janeiro #164/R (B.R 46000)

NOIR, Ernest (1864-1931) French

£276	$450	€403	Girl in forest (46x33cm-18x13in) s.i.d.96 prov.exhib. 24-Sep-3 Doyle, New York #64

NOIRE, Maxime (1861-1927) French

£537	$993	€800	L'oued du sud Algerien (35x80cm-14x31in) s. 15-Mar-4 Gros & Delettrez, Paris #130
£667	$1207	€1000	Crepuscule dans les Aures (39x60cm-15x24in) s. 30-Mar-4 Gioffredo, Nice #346
£667	$1220	€1000	Paysage du Sud-Algerien (46x27cm-18x11in) s. 3-Jun-4 Tajan, Paris #301
£927	$1687	€1400	Aloes devant le minaret (73x51cm-29x20in) s.d.1889. 19-Jun-4 Binoche, Orleans #41
£1667	$2633	€2400	Le reveil du Douar (32x45cm-13x18in) s. 25-Apr-3 Etude de Provence, Marseille #181 est:2000-2500
£2098	$3608	€3000	Village du sud Algerien (36x82cm-14x32in) s. 8-Dec-3 Tajan, Paris #306/R est:1800-2300
£2448	$4210	€3500	Campement au bord de l'oued (45x134cm-18x53in) s. 8-Dec-3 Tajan, Paris #307/R est:2000-2500
£2837	$4738	€4000	Soleil couchant dans une vallee de l'Atlas (42x132cm-17x52in) s. 16-Jun-3 Gros & Delettrez, Paris #454/R est:2000-3000

NOIROT, Émile (1853-1924) French

£567	$1020	€850	Coup de vent d'est aux trayas (55x81cm-22x32in) s.d.1913 s.i.d.verso. 26-Apr-4 Tajan, Paris #95
£1000	$1800	€1500	Un soir (16x24cm-6x9in) s.d.1910 i.verso cardboard. 20-Apr-4 Chenu & Scrive, Lyon #131/R est:1200-1500
£1000	$1800	€1500	L'etang (24x35cm-9x14in) s.d.1903. 20-Apr-4 Chenu & Scrive, Lyon #132/R est:600-800
£1467	$2669	€2200	Mer a Saint-Brieuc (61x50cm-24x20in) s.d.85 s.i.d.verso. 29-Jun-4 Chenu & Scrive, Lyon #139/R

NOJECHOWIZ, Noe (1929-) Argentinian

£1209	$2200	€1765	Children's corner (36x26cm-14x10in) s.d.1978 paper. 5-Jul-4 Arroyo, Buenos Aires #79/R est:2000
£1319	$2400	€1926	Memory (35x26cm-14x10in) s.d.78 paper. 5-Jul-4 Arroyo, Buenos Aires #89/R est:2000
£2210	$4000	€3227	Surrealist composition (56x40cm-22x16in) 30-Mar-4 Arroyo, Buenos Aires #23

NOLAN, James (1929-) British

£764	$1245	€1100	Still life, Espanol (51x71cm-20x28in) s. 23-Sep-3 De Veres Art Auctions, Dublin #150/R

NOLAN, Sidney (1917-1992) Australian

£400	$720	€584	Flowers (30x25cm-12x10in) card. 20-Jan-4 Bonhams, Knightsbridge #286/R
£950	$1701	€1387	Australian flowers (28x24cm-11x9in) s.i.d.1992 oil on paper. 11-May-4 Sotheby's, Olympia #602/R
£1098	$1965	€1603	Moonboy (25x30cm-10x12in) paper. 4-May-4 Sotheby's, Melbourne #299 est:1500-2500 (A.D 2700)
£1220	$1915	€1769	Landscape (30x25cm-12x10in) s. i.verso ripolin paper. 26-Aug-3 Christie's, Sydney #315 est:2000-3000 (A.D 3000)
£1277	$2170	€1864	Leaf study (30x24cm-12x9in) s. ripolin paper. 25-Nov-3 Christie's, Melbourne #211/R est:3000-5000 (A.D 3000)
£1277	$2170	€1864	Leaf study (29x24cm-11x9in) s. ripolin paper. 25-Nov-3 Christie's, Melbourne #268 est:3000-5000 (A.D 3000)
£1319	$2243	€1926	Study for Shakespeare's Sonnet (30x25cm-12x10in) s.d.6 July 69 ripolin paper. 26-Nov-3 Deutscher-Menzies, Melbourne #235/R est:1000-2000 (A.D 3100)
£1362	$2315	€1989	Wild flowers (30x25cm-12x10in) init. paper on board prov. 25-Nov-3 Christie's, Melbourne #277/R est:3000-4000 (A.D 3200)
£1600	$2864	€2336	Flowers (25x30cm-10x12in) s.d.67 i.verso board. 11-May-4 Sotheby's, Olympia #601/R est:800-1200
£1626	$2553	€2358	Native flowers (30x25cm-12x10in) s.d.24 June 69 verso ripolin paper. 26-Aug-3 Christie's, Sydney #208 est:2000-3000 (A.D 4000)
£1626	$2553	€2358	Figure (30x25cm-12x10in) s. s.i.d.1968 verso ripolin paper. 26-Aug-3 Christie's, Sydney #313 est:2000-3000 (A.D 4000)
£1700	$2924	€2482	Landscape (49x73cm-19x29in) riploin. 2-Dec-3 Bonhams, New Bond Street #161/R est:1000-1500
£1702	$2945	€2485	Untitled, Greek scene (26x31cm-10x12in) s. board prov. 10-Dec-3 Shapiro, Sydney #6 est:4000-6000 (A.D 4000)
£1707	$2680	€2475	Camel (30x25cm-12x10in) s. s.d.1 June 63 verso ripolin paper. 26-Aug-3 Christie's, Sydney #221 est:2000-3000 (A.D 4200)
£1736	$3211	€2535	Head (30x25cm-12x10in) init.d.13.3.56 verso oil on paper prov. 10-Mar-4 Deutscher-Menzies, Melbourne #369/R est:3500-5500 (A.D 4200)
£1800	$3096	€2628	Prehistoric animals (63x51cm-25x20in) s. ripolin prov. 2-Dec-3 Bonhams, New Bond Street #162/R est:2000-3000
£1859	$3291	€2714	Landscape (49x75cm-19x30in) s. ripolin paper on board. 3-May-4 Christie's, Melbourne #203/R est:5000-6000 (A.D 4500)
£1859	$3291	€2714	Flower studies (30x25cm-12x10in) s. one d.23 June 69 one d.24 June 69 verso ripolin pair. 3-May-4 Christie's, Melbourne #207 est:4000-6000 (A.D 4500)
£1859	$3291	€2714	White man and New Guinea girl (26x30cm-10x12in) s. s.i.d.26 April 1967 verso ripolin. 3-May-4 Christie's, Melbourne #402/R est:3000-4000 (A.D 4500)
£1983	$3511	€2895	Leda and the Swan (30x25cm-12x10in) init. ripolin. 3-May-4 Christie's, Melbourne #204/R est:4000-6000 (A.D 4800)
£2000	$3440	€2920	Convict and landscape (24x29cm-9x11in) s. ripolin. 2-Dec-3 Bonhams, New Bond Street #159/R est:1500-2000
£2128	$3617	€3107	Head (20x16cm-8x6in) s.d.55 ripolin paper on board prov. 25-Nov-3 Christie's, Melbourne #214/R est:5000-7000 (A.D 5000)
£2479	$4215	€3619	Untitled (30x37cm-12x15in) s. board painted c.1955. 29-Oct-3 Lawson Menzies, Sydney #147/R est:4000-6000 (A.D 6000)
£2553	$4340	€3727	Spanish boy (28x23cm-11x9in) s.i.d.52 ripolin paper on cardboard prov. 25-Nov-3 Christie's, Melbourne #130/R est:5000-7000 (A.D 6000)
£2686	$4754	€3922	Central Australia (49x75cm-19x30in) s. ripolin paper on board prov. 3-May-4 Christie's, Melbourne #406/R est:6000-8000 (A.D 6500)
£2800	$5180	€4088	Mother and child in a landscape (52x76cm-20x30in) s. ripolin wax crayon painted 1967. 11-Mar-4 Christie's, Kensington #213/R est:2000-3000
£3300	$5808	€4818	Kelly walking on water (75x51cm-30x20in) mono.verso oil wax paper prov. 18-May-4 Woolley & Wallis, Salisbury #48/R est:4000-6000
£3846	$6192	€5615	Bathers (120x90cm-47x35in) ripolin enamel on composition board painted 1975 prov. 25-Aug-3 Sotheby's, Paddington #207/R est:8000-12000 (A.D 9500)
£4049	$6518	€5912	Head with crucifix (120x120cm-47x47in) s.d.1.3.64 composition board prov. 25-Aug-3 Sotheby's, Paddington #205/R est:5000-8000 (A.D 10000)
£4065	$6382	€5894	Explorer (52x75cm-20x30in) s. ripolin pastel paper on board prov. 26-Aug-3 Christie's, Sydney #352/R est:7000-9000 (A.D 10000)
£4251	$6844	€6206	Bather (120x90cm-47x35in) ripolin enamel composition board painted 1975 prov.exhib. 25-Aug-3 Sotheby's, Paddington #202/R est:12000-18000 (A.D 10500)
£4453	$7170	€6501	Bather (120x90cm-47x35in) ripolin enamel composition board painted 1975 prov. 25-Aug-3 Sotheby's, Paddington #206/R est:10000-15000 (A.D 11000)
£4453	$7170	€6501	Head, with red hair (120x120cm-47x47in) d.24.5.64 verso composition board prov. 25-Aug-3 Sotheby's, Paddington #210/R est:10000-15000 (A.D 11000)
£4681	$7957	€6834	Ledge (91x122cm-36x48in) s.i.d.1985 composition board. 26-Nov-3 Deutscher-Menzies, Melbourne #90/R est:12000-18000 (A.D 11000)
£4858	$7822	€7093	Two bathers as lovers (120x90cm-47x35in) ripolin enamel composition board painted 1975 prov.exhib. 25-Aug-3 Sotheby's, Paddington #209/R est:10000-15000 (A.D 12000)
£5106	$8681	€7455	Burke and Camel (51x62cm-20x24in) s. composition board. 26-Nov-3 Deutscher-Menzies, Melbourne #10/R est:14000-18000 (A.D 12000)
£5106	$8681	€7455	Burke and Camels (63x51cm-25x20in) s. composition board. 26-Nov-3 Deutscher-Menzies, Melbourne #37b/R est:14000-18000 (A.D 12000)
£5344	$9725	€7802	Gorilla (122x119cm-48x47in) init. board prov.exhib. 16-Jun-4 Deutscher-Menzies, Melbourne #147/R est:16000-24000 (A.D 14000)
£5668	$9126	€8275	Rimbaud (120x90cm-47x35in) s.i.d.1980 verso synthetic polymer paint composition board prov. 25-Aug-3 Sotheby's, Paddington #204/R est:8000-12000 (A.D 14000)
£5691	$10187	€8309	Cactus (59x49cm-23x19in) s. oil Ripolin enamel board prov. 4-May-4 Sotheby's, Melbourne #304/R est:10000-15000 (A.D 14000)
£5957	$10128	€8697	New Guinea warrior (51x75cm-20x30in) s. board. 26-Nov-3 Deutscher-Menzies, Melbourne #94/R est:1000-15000 (A.D 14000)
£6478	$10429	€9458	African figure (150x120cm-59x47in) init. composition board prov. 25-Aug-3 Sotheby's, Paddington #212/R est:15000-25000 (A.D 16000)
£6809	$11574	€9941	Bald Native Head (122x91cm-48x36in) init. d.27/12/62 verso composition board prov. 26-Nov-3 Deutscher-Menzies, Melbourne #61/R est:10000-15000 (A.D 16000)
£6911	$10850	€10021	Central Australia (90x120cm-35x47in) s. s.i.verso board prov. 27-Aug-3 Christie's, Sydney #500/R est:12000-18000 (A.D 17000)
£7000	$12040	€10220	Kelly at night (29x24cm-11x9in) s. ripolin prov. 2-Dec-3 Bonhams, New Bond Street #160/R est:1500-2000
£7025	$12434	€10257	Dancing figure (43x51cm-17x20in) s.d.1942 hessian board prov. 3-May-4 Christie's, Melbourne #152/R est:18000-25000 (A.D 17000)
£7317	$11488	€10610	Figure in a landscape (51x76cm-20x30in) s. oil paper on board. 26-Aug-3 Christie's, Sydney #201/R est:12000-15000 (A.D 18000)
£7692	$12385	€11230	Monkey (150x120cm-59x47in) composition board prov. 25-Aug-3 Sotheby's, Paddington #197/R est:12000-18000 (A.D 19000)
£8130	$14553	€11870	Landscape (90x120cm-35x47in) s. s.i.d.1981 verso composition board prov.exhib.lit. 4-May-4 Sotheby's, Melbourne #61/R est:20000-30000 (A.D 20000)
£8130	$14553	€11870	Explorer, Antarctica (120x120cm-47x47in) s.verso composition board. 4-May-4 Sotheby's, Melbourne #278/R est:20000-30000 (A.D 20000)
£8333	$13083	€12083	Kelly and figure (63x51cm-25x20in) init. ripolin paper prov. 26-Aug-3 Christie's, Sydney #206/R est:10000-15000 (A.D 20500)
£8502	$13688	€12413	Elephant (120x150cm-47x59in) init. composition board prov. 25-Aug-3 Sotheby's, Paddington #198/R est:25000-35000 (A.D 21000)
£8502	$13688	€12413	Antarctica (120x120cm-47x47in) s.d.12 Sept 1964 s.i.d.verso prov. 25-Aug-3 Sotheby's, Paddington #200/R est:20000-30000 (A.D 21000)
£9160	$16672	€13374	Kelly in the forest (76x52cm-30x20in) s. oil paper on board prov. 16-Jun-4 Deutscher-Menzies, Melbourne #17/R est:18000-25000 (A.D 24000)
£9160	$16672	€13374	Kelly on horse (51x75cm-20x30in) s. ripolin paper on board prov.exhib. 16-Jun-4 Deutscher-Menzies, Melbourne #18/R est:18000-25000 (A.D 24000)
£9312	$14992	€13596	Antarctica (122x122cm-48x48in) s.d.27 Aug 1964 composition board prov. 25-Aug-3 Sotheby's, Paddington #201/R est:18000-25000 (A.D 23000)
£9312	$14992	€13596	African figure (150x120cm-59x47in) init. composition board prov. 25-Aug-3 Sotheby's, Paddington #211/R est:14000-18000 (A.D 23000)
£9350	$16736	€13651	Ned Kelly in a landscape (25x30cm-10x12in) s.d.67 mixed media paper on board prov. 4-May-4 Sotheby's, Melbourne #233/R est:12000-18000 (A.D 23000)
£9717	$15644	€14187	Antarctica (120x120cm-47x47in) s.d.1964 verso composition board prov. 25-Aug-3 Sotheby's, Paddington #203/R est:20000-30000 (A.D 24000)
£9917	$17554	€14479	Figures on horseback (52x63cm-20x25in) s. ripolin. 3-May-4 Christie's, Melbourne #126/R est:10000-15000 (A.D 24000)
£10526	$16947	€15368	Ram (120x150cm-47x59in) init. composition board prov. 25-Aug-3 Sotheby's, Paddington #199/R est:12000-18000 (A.D 26000)
£12195	$21829	€17805	Central Australian landscape (90x90cm-35x35in) s.d.6 Oct 69 i.verso composition prov. 4-May-4 Sotheby's, Melbourne #44/R est:25000-35000 (A.D 30000)
£18595	$32913	€27149	Crucifixion (90x120cm-35x47in) init.d.56 ripolin enamel board prov. 3-May-4 Christie's, Melbourne #143/R est:45000-55000 (A.D 45000)
£19835	$36694	€28959	Portrait of a woman (77x63cm-30x25in) s. s.i.d.1945 verso ripolin board prov. 10-Mar-4 Deutscher-Menzies, Melbourne #82/R est:40000-50000 (A.D 48000)
£20325	$36382	€29675	Sand hills near Birdsville (90x120cm-35x47in) s.d.53 i.verso prov. 4-May-4 Sotheby's, Melbourne #71/R est:50000-70000 (A.D 50000)
£34553	$61850	€50447	Elephant and lily pool (120x150cm-47x59in) s.d.63 composition board prov. 4-May-4 Sotheby's, Melbourne #19/R est:45000-60000 (A.D 85000)
£37190	$65826	€54297	Gallipoli soldier (122x121cm-48x48in) init. i.verso ripolin board prov. 3-May-4 Christie's, Melbourne #27/R est:60000-80000 (A.D 90000)
£105691	$189187	€154309	Kelly and Drought (90x120cm-35x47in) init.d.6-4-57 prov.exhib.lit. 4-May-4 Sotheby's, Melbourne #70/R est:240000-280000 (A.D 260000)

Prints

£1859	$3291	€2714	Ned Kelly (54x70cm-21x28in) s.num.25/60 col screenprint. 3-May-4 Christie's, Melbourne #357/R est:3000-5000 (A.D 4500)
£1983	$3511	€2895	Trial (54x70cm-21x28in) s.num.25/60 col screenprint. 3-May-4 Christie's, Melbourne #358/R est:3000-5000 (A.D 4800)
£2439	$3829	€3537	Siege (47x63cm-19x25in) s.num.27/60 col photolithograph. 27-Aug-3 Christie's, Sydney #757/R est:1800-2500 (A.D 6000)

Works on paper

£426	$766	€622	Landscape VII (52x63cm-20x25in) s. helizarin dye. 23-Jan-4 Lawson Menzies, Sydney #2173 (A.D 1000)
£550	$1018	€803	Portrait of Ned Kelly (28x23cm-11x9in) i.d.1967 brush black ink. 9-Mar-4 Gorringes, Lewes #2126
£584	$1068	€876	Untitled. s. ink wash. 3-Jun-4 Joel, Victoria #149/R (A.D 1500)
£732	$1310	€1069	Moonboy (25x30cm-10x12in) orange pencil oil. 4-May-4 Sotheby's, Melbourne #296 (A.D 1800)

£826	$1529	€1206	Outback (24x30cm-9x12in) s.i. mixed media. 10-Mar-4 Deutscher-Menzies, Melbourne #350/R est:3000-5000 (A.D 2000)
£894	$1601	€1305	Ram caught in flood (30x21cm-12x8in) bears init. col crayon rubbing. 4-May-4 Sotheby's, Melbourne #292/R (A.D 2200)
£950	$1672	€1387	Warrior (30x25cm-12x10in) mixed media. 19-May-4 Sotheby's, Olympia #316/R
£1069	$1945	€1561	Jungle flower (30x25cm-12x10in) init. mixed media prov. 16-Jun-4 Deutscher-Menzies, Melbourne #342/R est:3000-5000 (A.D 2800)
£1148	$1813	€1676	The cathedral (29x24cm-11x9in) init. ink enamel glass. 2-Sep-3 Deutscher-Menzies, Melbourne #281/R est:3000-5000 (A.D 2800)
£1374	$2378	€2006	China (25x30cm-10x12in) mixed media board exec.c.1978. 10-Dec-3 Shapiro, Sydney #30 est:4000-5000 (A.D 3230)
£1374	$2501	€2006	Bull (25x29cm-10x11in) init.d.56 verso mixed media. 16-Jun-4 Deutscher-Menzies, Melbourne #341/R est:4000-6000 (A.D 3600)
£1545	$2765	€2256	Gallipoli swimmer (25x30cm-10x12in) d.1955 W/C. 4-May-4 Sotheby's, Melbourne #293/R est:3000-5000 (A.D 3800)
£1653	$3058	€2413	Ball game, Greece (24x29cm-9x11in) s.d.1956 mixed media. 10-Mar-4 Deutscher-Menzies, Melbourne #222/R est:4500-6500 (A.D 4000)
£1653	$3058	€2413	Anzac inferno I (55x75cm-22x30in) s.i.d.82 pastel. 10-Mar-4 Deutscher-Menzies, Melbourne #273/R est:4500-6500 (A.D 4000)
£1695	$2881	€2475	Kelly and Bird (30x25cm-12x10in) wax crayon relief rubbing exhib. 24-Nov-3 Sotheby's, Melbourne #89/R est:4000-6000 (A.D 4000)
£1707	$3056	€2492	Head of Christ (40x37cm-16x15in) s. mixed media prov. 4-May-4 Sotheby's, Melbourne #263/R est:4000-6000 (A.D 4200)
£1822	$2933	€2660	Bird and man (75x60cm-30x24in) s. s.i.verso mixed media. 13-Oct-3 Joel, Victoria #312 est:4000-6000 (A.D 4500)
£2033	$3191	€2948	Trial (47x63cm-19x25in) s.num.27/60 col photolithograph. 27-Aug-3 Christie's, Sydney #739/R est:2000-3000 (A.D 5000)
£2034	$3458	€2970	Landscape (25x30cm-10x12in) s. mixed media board. 24-Nov-3 Sotheby's, Melbourne #174/R est:4000-6000 (A.D 4800)
£2119	$3602	€3094	Landscape (20x25cm-8x10in) s.d.52 mixed media. 24-Nov-3 Sotheby's, Melbourne #106/R est:2000-4000 (A.D 5000)
£2236	$4002	€3265	Kelly and gun (17x13cm-7x5in) crayon. 4-May-4 Sotheby's, Melbourne #297/R est:4000-6000 (A.D 5500)
£2459	$3984	€3590	Figure in landscape (20x30cm-8x12in) init. mixed media. 30-Jul-3 Goodman, Sydney #30/R est:5000-7000 (A.D 6000)
£2481	$4515	€3622	Leda and Swan (30x25cm-12x10in) s. mixed media. 16-Jun-4 Deutscher-Menzies, Melbourne #96/R est:7000-9000 (A.D 6500)
£2553	$4340	€3727	Figure in outback landscape (24x29cm-9x11in) s. mixed media prov. 26-Nov-3 Deutscher-Menzies, Melbourne #151/R est:4500-6500 (A.D 6000)
£2686	$4969	€3922	Ostrich (30x25cm-12x10in) init. i.d.Feb 7th 57 mixed media prov. 10-Mar-4 Deutscher-Menzies, Melbourne #289/R est:3500-5500 (A.D 6500)
£2966	$5042	€4330	Yellow moon, Samson and Dalila (61x76cm-24x30in) s.i.verso mixed media exec 1981 prov. 24-Nov-3 Sotheby's, Melbourne #130/R est:7000-9000 (A.D 7000)
£2966	$5042	€4330	Samson et Dalila (61x76cm-24x30in) s.i.verso mixed media exec 1981 prov. 24-Nov-3 Sotheby's, Melbourne #133/R est:7000-9000 (A.D 7000)
£3099	$5269	€4525	Bird in flight (30x25cm-12x10in) s. mixed media prov. 29-Oct-3 Lawson Menzies, Sydney #123/R est:5000-7000 (A.D 7500)
£3192	$5426	€4660	Swimmer 1962 (47x63cm-19x25in) init. mixed media prov. 26-Nov-3 Deutscher-Menzies, Melbourne #119/R est:6500-8500 (A.D 7500)
£3252	$5821	€4748	Four men in a canoe - New Guinea (51x76cm-20x30in) s. mixed media paper on board. 4-May-4 Sotheby's, Melbourne #257/R est:8000-12000 (A.D 8000)
£3279	$5311	€4787	Hydra (25x30cm-10x12in) s. mixed media board. 30-Jul-3 Goodman, Sydney #33/R est:8000-10000 (A.D 8000)
£3390	$5763	€4949	Bird with mammal (76x61cm-30x24in) s. d.5 Aug 84 verso prov. 24-Nov-3 Sotheby's, Melbourne #121/R est:7000-9000 (A.D 8000)
£3435	$6252	€5015	Figure and swan in the landscape (51x75cm-20x30in) s. mixed media on board executed c.1964. 16-Jun-4 Deutscher-Menzies, Melbourne #178/R est:10000-15000 (A.D 9000)
£3455	$6185	€5044	Landscape and figure (51x85cm-20x33in) s. bears i.verso mixed media paper on board. 4-May-4 Sotheby's, Melbourne #323/R est:10000-15000 (A.D 8500)
£3512	$6498	€5128	Gallipoli (61x49cm-24x19in) s. mixed media executed c.1965 prov. 10-Mar-4 Deutscher-Menzies, Melbourne #208/R est:7000-9000 (A.D 8500)
£3602	$6123	€5259	Bird over a desert landscape (63x52cm-25x20in) mixed media exec c.1984 prov. 24-Nov-3 Sotheby's, Melbourne #123/R est:6000-9000 (A.D 8500)
£3602	$6123	€5259	Bird, man and gun (76x61cm-30x24in) s. s.i.verso mixed media exec c.1982 prov. 24-Nov-3 Sotheby's, Melbourne #128/R est:7000-9000 (A.D 8500)
£3814	$6483	€5568	Upside down bird and insect (76x61cm-30x24in) s. d.4 Aug 84 verso mixed media prov. 24-Nov-3 Sotheby's, Melbourne #127/R est:7000-9000 (A.D 9000)
£3814	$6483	€5568	Bird with figure on a column (76x61cm-30x24in) s. d.5 Aug 84 verso mixed media prov. 24-Nov-3 Sotheby's, Melbourne #129/R est:8000-10000 (A.D 9000)
£3814	$6483	€5568	Nightmare and four humming birds (76x61cm-30x24in) s. s.i.verso mixed media exec c.1982 prov. 24-Nov-3 Sotheby's, Melbourne #131/R est:8000-12000 (A.D 9000)
£4132	$7025	€6033	Parrot on a branch (30x25cm-12x10in) s. mixed media prov. 29-Oct-3 Lawson Menzies, Sydney #124/R est:5000-7000 (A.D 10000)
£4237	$7203	€6186	Bird in flight (76x61cm-30x24in) s.d.31 May 1982 i.verso mixed media prov. 24-Nov-3 Sotheby's, Melbourne #118/R est:8000-10000 (A.D 10000)
£4237	$7203	€6186	Aboriginal man and bird (76x61cm-30x24in) s. s.i.d.1982 verso mixed media prov. 24-Nov-3 Sotheby's, Melbourne #120/R est:10000-12000 (A.D 10000)
£4237	$7203	€6186	Bird and Convict (76x61cm-30x24in) s. s.i.d.May 1982 verso mixed media prov. 24-Nov-3 Sotheby's, Melbourne #122/R est:10000-12000 (A.D 10000)
£4237	$7203	€6186	Plumed Parrot (76x61cm-30x24in) mixed media exec c.1982 prov. 24-Nov-3 Sotheby's, Melbourne #124/R est:8000-10000 (A.D 10000)
£4237	$7203	€6186	Bird and plant (76x61cm-30x24in) s. s.d.3 Aug 84 verso mixed media prov. 24-Nov-3 Sotheby's, Melbourne #126/R est:10000-12000 (A.D 10000)
£4449	$7564	€6496	Lotus Pool, Samson et Dalila (61x76cm-24x30in) s.i.verso mixed media exec 1981 prov. 24-Nov-3 Sotheby's, Melbourne #117/R est:7000-9000 (A.D 10500)
£4472	$8004	€6529	Central Australian landscape (51x75cm-20x30in) s. mixed media exec c.1967 prov. 4-May-4 Sotheby's, Melbourne #226/R est:10000-15000 (A.D 11000)
£4661	$7924	€6805	Five birds with figure and column (76x61cm-30x24in) mixed media painted c.1982 prov. 24-Nov-3 Sotheby's, Melbourne #115/R est:6000-9000 (A.D 11000)
£4661	$7924	€6805	Desert landscape - The mountains of Sorex - Act II, Gauz No.9 (61x76cm-24x30in) s.i.verso exec 1981 mixed media prov.exhib. 24-Nov-3 Sotheby's, Melbourne #116/R est:8000-12000 (A.D 11000)
£4661	$7924	€6805	Display (63x51cm-25x20in) s.d.2.12.63 mixed media prov. 24-Nov-3 Sotheby's, Melbourne #134/R est:8000-12000 (A.D 11000)
£4752	$8079	€6938	Landscape (52x76cm-20x30in) s.d.15.7.66 fabric dye crayon on card prov. 29-Oct-3 Lawson Menzies, Sydney #125/R est:8000-12000 (A.D 11500)
£4878	$8732	€7122	Elephant (51x63cm-20x25in) s. mixed media. 4-May-4 Sotheby's, Melbourne #109/R est:10000-15000 (A.D 12000)
£5165	$9556	€7541	Kelly (24x30cm-9x12in) s.d.21.12.54 ink prov. 10-Mar-4 Deutscher-Menzies, Melbourne #370/R est:3500-5500 (A.D 12500)
£5508	$9364	€8042	Humming bird with flower (76x61cm-30x24in) s. mixed media prov. 24-Nov-3 Sotheby's, Melbourne #119/R est:10000-12000 (A.D 13000)
£5508	$9364	€8042	Bird and exotic flower (76x61cm-30x24in) s. s.d.3 Aug 84 verso mixed media prov. 24-Nov-3 Sotheby's, Melbourne #125/R est:10000-12000 (A.D 13000)
£5632	$10250	€8223	Glenrowan, wounded Kelly nocturne (60x75cm-24x30in) s. s.i.d.1981 mixed media. 16-Jun-4 Deutscher-Menzies, Melbourne #140/R est:18000-24000 (A.D 14755)
£5785	$9835	€8446	Figure in the landscape (52x76cm-20x30in) s. fabric dye wax crayon on card executed c.1966 prov. 29-Oct-3 Lawson Menzies, Sydney #11/R est:10000-15000 (A.D 14000)
£5785	$10702	€8446	Antarctica 1964 (58x73cm-23x29in) synthetic polymer on board prov. 10-Mar-4 Deutscher-Menzies, Melbourne #50/R est:15000-20000 (A.D 14000)
£5932	$10085	€8661	Figure, Burke and Wills expedition (50x76cm-20x30in) s. d.7 Dec 67 verso mixed media prov. 24-Nov-3 Sotheby's, Melbourne #168/R est:12000-18000 (A.D 14000)
£6198	$10537	€9049	Central Australia (51x75cm-20x30in) s. mixed media on card. 29-Oct-3 Lawson Menzies, Sydney #160/R est:12000-18000 (A.D 15000)
£6504	$11642	€9496	Man on horse (51x74cm-20x29in) s. mixed media paper on board. 4-May-4 Sotheby's, Melbourne #208/R est:10000-15000 (A.D 16000)
£6780	$11525	€9899	Display II (63x51cm-25x20in) s.i.d.6th Dec 1963 mixed media prov. 24-Nov-3 Sotheby's, Melbourne #113/R est:10000-12000 (A.D 16000)
£6911	$12370	€10090	Ned Kelly on horse (24x30cm-9x12in) s.d.67 mixed media. 4-May-4 Sotheby's, Melbourne #111/R est:10000-15000 (A.D 17000)
£7692	$12385	€11230	Man and bird (58x74cm-23x29in) s. mixed media board prov.exhib. 25-Aug-3 Sotheby's, Paddington #174/R est:15000-18000 (A.D 19000)
£8051	$13686	€11754	Ram in thicket- Samson and Dalila - Act III. Scene I (61x76cm-24x30in) i. d.1981 verso mixed media prov.exhib. 24-Nov-3 Sotheby's, Melbourne #114/R est:12000-18000 (A.D 19000)
£12214	$22229	€17832	Wild beast (61x51cm-24x20in) s. mixed media executed c.1952 prov. 16-Jun-4 Deutscher-Menzies, Melbourne #141/R est:18000-24000 (A.D 32000)
£12245	$22531	€17878	Yellow cross (152x122cm-60x48in) s. synthetic polymer paint masonite prov. 29-Mar-4 Goodman, Sydney #94/R est:30000-50000 (A.D 30000)
£12397	$22934	€18100	Kelly and clouds (63x51cm-25x20in) s. mixed media on board. 10-Mar-4 Deutscher-Menzies, Melbourne #73/R est:15000-25000 (A.D 30000)
£34413	$55405	€50243	Siege and burning at Glenrown (297x451cm-117x178in) s. woven wool tapestry prov. 25-Aug-3 Sotheby's, Paddington #101/R est:50000-80000 (A.D 85000)

NOLAND, Cady (1956-) American

Sculpture

£32934	$55000	€48084	Chainsaw cut cowboy head with car lock (236x127x1cm-93x50x0in) aluminum cut-out lock garter cowboy hat assemblage prov. 13-Nov-3 Sotheby's, New York #531/R est:10000-15000

NOLAND, Kenneth (1924-) American

£7263	$13000	€10604	Untitled (213x178cm-84x70in) s.d.1956 verso acrylic prov. 20-Mar-4 Sloans & Kenyon, Bethesda #1206/R est:10000-15000
£13966	$25000	€20390	Mountaineer (58x229cm-23x90in) s.i.d.1981 acrylic prov.exhib. 13-May-4 Sotheby's, New York #198/R est:10000-15000
£18405	$30000	€26871	Rose wide (52x237cm-20x93in) s.i.d.1965 verso acrylic prov. 23-Sep-3 Christie's, Rockefeller NY #113/R est:12000-18000
£22455	$37500	€32784	Level out (39x236cm-15x93in) s.i.d.1967 verso prov. 13-Nov-3 Sotheby's, New York #232/R est:15000-20000
£38922	$65000	€56826	Trans south (117x360cm-46x142in) s.i.d.1968 verso acrylic prov.exhib. 13-Nov-3 Sotheby's, New York #230/R est:30000-40000
£44693	$80000	€65252	Untitled (176x176cm-69x69in) s.i.d.1960 verso prov. 13-May-4 Sotheby's, New York #166/R est:80000-120000
£47904	$80000	€69940	Trans Flux (258x411cm-102x162in) s.i.d.1963 acrylic prov.exhib. 12-Nov-3 Christie's, Rockefeller NY #353/R est:100000-150000
£191617	$320000	€279761	Bess (114x114cm-45x45in) s.i.d.1962 verso acrylic prov.exhib. 13-Nov-3 Sotheby's, New York #112/R est:100000-150000

Prints

£1647	$2750	€2405	Quartet no 1 (31x107cm-12x42in) num.22/35 print varnish. 21-Oct-3 Bonhams & Butterfields, San Francisco #1377/R
£2206	$3750	€3221	Project (81x53cm-32x21in) s. lithograph monoprint paper pulp. 31-Oct-3 Sotheby's, New York #710/R
£2647	$4500	€3865	Horizontal stripes (128x91cm-50x36in) s.d.1978 pressed paper pulp. 31-Oct-3 Sotheby's, New York #711/R
£5495	$10000	€8023	Twin planes (15x147cm-6x58in) silkscreen on canvas. 19-Jun-4 Du Mouchelle, Detroit #3174/R est:1000-1800

NOLDE, Emil (1867-1956) German

£6993	$11888	€10000	Hamburg: ship in dock (31x40cm-12x16in) s.i. etching. 29-Nov-3 Bassenge, Berlin #6930/R est:12000
£19580	$33287	€28000	Large mill (51x34cm-20x13in) s.i. col lithograph. 29-Nov-3 Bassenge, Berlin #6930a/R est:30000
£26573	$45175	€38000	Evening marshland with farmstead and tree (23x34cm-9x13in) s. W/C Indian ink prov.exhib. 26-Nov-3 Lempertz, Koln #882/R est:40000-50000
£130000	$239200	€189800	Stilleben mit Orangen und gelbe Blumen - Still life with oranges and yellow flowers (65x77cm-26x30in) s.i. stretcher painted 1911 prov.lit. 23-Jun-4 Christie's, London #172/R est:120000-180000
£200000	$366000	€292000	Seascape with horses (73x88cm-29x35in) s. s.i.on stretcher painted 1911 prov.exhib.lit. 2-Feb-4 Christie's, London #30/R est:200000-300000
£339367	$576923	€750000	Flower garden (74x88cm-29x35in) s.d.1915 lit. 25-Nov-3 Pierre Berge, Paris #14/R est:300000-350000
£380000	$691600	€554800	Phlox and white dahlias (88x73cm-35x29in) s. s.i.verso b. painted 1940 prov.exhib.lit. 3-Feb-4 Sotheby's, London #21/R est:400000-600000
£917031	$1668996	€1338865	Two female priests (100x86cm-39x34in) s. s.i.verso stretcher painted 1912 prov.exhib.lit. 18-Jun-4 Kornfeld, Bern #122/R (S.FR 2100000)

Prints

£1613	$3000	€2355	Bildnis (19x15cm-7x6in) s.d.1906 num.20 etching drypoint. 2-Mar-4 Swann Galleries, New York #470/R est:3500-5000
£1730	$3200	€2526	Stehende Frau (17x5cm-7x2in) s.i. lithograph edition of 20. 12-Feb-4 Christie's, Rockefeller NY #349/R est:2500-3500
£1836	$3250	€2681	Aegypterin II (15x10cm-6x4in) s.i. woodcut. 30-Apr-4 Sotheby's, New York #168/R est:3000-5000
£2000	$3640	€2920	Der asthet (31x24cm-12x9in) s. etching aquatint. 1-Jul-4 Sotheby's, London #240/R est:2000-3000
£2098	$3608	€3000	Lady standing (18x6cm-7x2in) s. lithograph exec. 1911. 4-Dec-3 Van Ham, Cologne #356/R est:2800
£2098	$3566	€3000	Lausbuben - two boys (23x16cm-9x6in) s. etching aquatint prov. 29-Nov-3 Villa Grisebach, Berlin #156/R est:3500-4500

£2151 $4000 €3140 Christus und die sunderin (30x25cm-12x10in) s. etching. 2-Mar-4 Swann Galleries, New York #471/R est:5000-8000
£2238 $3804 €3200 Horse market (15x19cm-6x7in) s.d. etching. 29-Nov-3 Bassenge, Berlin #6929/R est:3000
£2294 $3830 €3326 Man and woman. s.i. etching drypoint. 19-Jun-3 Kornfeld, Bern #785 est:6000 (S.FR 5000)
£2374 $3894 €3300 Conversation (15x19cm-6x7in) s.i.d. etching. 4-Jun-3 Ketterer, Hamburg #718/R est:2800-3500
£2431 $4059 €3500 Portrait (19x15cm-7x6in) s.i.d. etching. 24-Oct-3 Ketterer, Hamburg #486/R est:3500-4500
£2500 $4550 €3650 Heimat (31x45cm-12x18in) s. green etching. 1-Jul-4 Sotheby's, London #242/R est:3000-5000
£2941 $5000 €4294 Dancers (26x21cm-10x8in) s. etching. 31-Oct-3 Sotheby's, New York #348/R
£2941 $5000 €4294 Figures (24x32cm-9x13in) s. etching aquatint. 31-Oct-3 Sotheby's, New York #349/R
£2953 $5286 €4400 Fishing boats (21x15cm-8x6in) s. woodcut. 25-May-4 Karl & Faber, Munich #464/R est:4000
£3057 $5563 €4463 Retreating fighters. s.i. woodcut. 17-Jun-4 Kornfeld, Bern #631/R est:10000 (S.FR 7000)
£3357 $5773 €4800 Ring o' roses (22x26cm-9x10in) s. etching. 2-Dec-3 Hauswedell & Nolte, Hamburg #476/R est:7000
£3497 $5944 €5000 Young couple (32x25cm-13x10in) s. etching brush scratching. 29-Nov-3 Villa Grisebach, Berlin #157/R est:5000-7000
£3500 $6020 €5110 Tanzerin (15x11cm-6x4in) s.i. num.9 lithograph prov. 2-Dec-3 Christie's, London #246/R est:2000-3000
£3620 $6045 €5285 Dusterer mannerkopf (43x34cm-17x13in) s.i. lithograph. 16-Oct-3 Waddingtons, Toronto #166/R est:5000-7000 (C.D 8000)
£3624 $6668 €5400 Yachtsman and steam (41x31cm-16x12in) i. etching. 26-Mar-4 Karrenbauer, Konstanz #1573/R est:3000
£3947 $7263 €6000 Dealer (60x40cm-24x16in) s.i. col lithograph exec. 1913. 26-Jun-4 Karrenbauer, Konstanz #1617 est:2000
£4000 $6880 €5840 Sturm (16x19cm-6x7in) s.d.1906 woodcut. 2-Dec-3 Christie's, London #247/R est:4000-6000
£4000 $7360 €6000 Double portrait (31x23cm-12x9in) s. woodcut. 10-Jun-4 Hauswedell & Nolte, Hamburg #547/R est:8000
£4367 $7948 €6376 Self portrait. s.i. drypoint. 17-Jun-4 Kornfeld, Bern #638/R est:12500 (S.FR 10000)
£4698 $8785 €7000 Hamburg (30x40cm-12x16in) s. woodcut. 28-Feb-4 Quittenbaum, Hamburg #77/R est:13000
£5000 $8600 €7300 Freihafen Hamburg (38x47cm-15x19in) s.i. woodcut. 4-Dec-3 Sotheby's, London #179/R est:5000-7000
£5000 $9100 €7300 Doppelbildnis (32x23cm-13x9in) s.num.66 woodcut relief edition of 150. 1-Jul-4 Sotheby's, London #241/R est:6000-8000
£5333 $9813 €8000 Hamburg, Katharinenkirche (41x31cm-16x12in) s.i. etching. 10-Jun-4 Hauswedell & Nolte, Hamburg #539/R est:10000
£5588 $9500 €8158 Der tod als tanzerin (21x26cm-8x10in) s. etching aquatint. 6-Nov-3 Swann Galleries, New York #664/R est:10000-15000
£6550 $11921 €9563 In the morning. s.d.07 etching. 17-Jun-4 Kornfeld, Bern #634/R est:17500 (S.FR 15000)
£6667 $11933 €10000 Nude with arms raised (47x31cm-19x12in) s. etching drypoint. 14-May-4 Ketterer, Munich #161/R est:10000-12000
£6704 $12000 €9788 Dusterer mannerkopf (61x43cm-24x17in) s.i. color lithograph. 6-May-4 Swann Galleries, New York #537/R est:10000-15000
£8667 $15513 €13000 Woman's head III (30x23cm-12x9in) s.i. woodcut. 15-May-4 Dr Sturies, Dusseldorf #134/R
£8824 $15000 €12883 Frau N, Frau Ada Nolde (23x19cm-9x7in) s.i. drypoint. 6-Nov-3 Swann Galleries, New York #663/R est:8000-12000
£10000 $17200 €14600 Diskussion (79x57cm-31x22in) s.i. lithograph prov. 2-Dec-3 Christie's, London #243/R est:10000-15000
£10764 $17545 €15500 Large windmill (59x42cm-23x17in) s.i. col lithograph prov. 27-Sep-3 Dr Fritz Nagel, Stuttgart #9592/R est:20000
£12000 $21960 €18000 Cows resting (62x81cm-24x32in) s.i. col lithograph. 5-Jun-4 Lempertz, Koln #913/R est:16000
£12587 $21399 €18000 Flirtation (31x23cm-12x9in) s.i. woodcut board prov. 28-Nov-3 Villa Grisebach, Berlin #24/R est:14000-18000
£13333 $23867 €20000 Girl kneeling (30x22cm-12x9in) s.i. drypoint etching. 13-May-4 Neumeister, Munich #446/R est:15000-17000
£13986 $24056 €20000 Large mill (50x33cm-20x13in) s. num.2 col lithograph one of 14 exec.1907/15 prov. 5-Dec-3 Ketterer, Munich #50/R est:20000-25000
£14000 $24080 €20440 Prophet (32x23cm-13x9in) s.i. woodcut prov. 2-Dec-3 Christie's, London #249/R est:15000-20000
£17467 $31790 €25502 Prophet (32x22cm-13x9in) s.i. woodcut exec. 1912. 18-Jun-4 Kornfeld, Bern #123/R est:40000 (S.FR 40000)
£22000 $40480 €33000 Kneeling girl (31x23cm-12x9in) s. drypoint etching one of two prov. 11-Jun-4 Villa Grisebach, Berlin #17/R est:24000-28000
£27000 $46440 €39420 Junge Danin (68x57cm-27x22in) lithograph prov. 2-Dec-3 Christie's, London #242/R est:20000-30000
£62937 $108252 €90000 Dancer (53x69cm-21x27in) s. col lithograph one of 6 prov. 5-Dec-3 Ketterer, Munich #58/R est:100000-150000

Sculpture
£12000 $21480 €18000 Bearded man (24x5x2cm-9x2x1in) s. bronze. 15-May-4 Dr Sturies, Dusseldorf #133/R

Works on paper
£5882 $10000 €8588 Schlepper mit rauch, Hamburg (32x39cm-13x15in) s. brush ink executed c.1910. 9-Nov-3 Bonhams & Butterfields, Los Angeles #4002/R
£6500 $11765 €9490 Kopf (21x27cm-8x11in) s. brush blue ink. 1-Apr-4 Christie's, Kensington #44/R est:3000-4000
£7333 $13420 €11000 Woman in profile (33x48cm-13x19in) s. W/C. 5-Jun-4 Lempertz, Koln #907/R est:10000-11000
£7432 $13304 €11000 Elegant couple (31x20cm-12x8in) s. Indian ink brush pen. 6-May-4 Michael Zeller, Lindau #801 est:11000
£8235 $14000 €12023 Ballroom, Cospeda (21x26cm-8x10in) s.d.08 pen feather ink exec 1908 prov. 6-Nov-3 Sotheby's, New York #224/R est:8000-12000
£11888 $20210 €17000 Madonna with red hyacinth (27x23cm-11x9in) s. W/C prov. 29-Nov-3 Villa Grisebach, Berlin #158/R est:25000-30000
£12081 $21624 €18000 Yellow and red fish (36x47cm-14x19in) s. W/C lit.exhib.prov. 25-May-4 Karl & Faber, Munich #462/R est:30000-35000
£13087 $23426 €19500 Couple sitting in cafe (31x21cm-12x8in) s. Indian brush wash. 25-May-4 Karl & Faber, Munich #463/R est:22000-25000
£13333 $24533 €20000 Chinese junk (27x31cm-11x12in) s. W/C exec. c.1913 prov. 12-Jun-4 Villa Grisebach, Berlin #213/R est:20000-25000
£14706 $25000 €21471 Die Alhambra (35x47cm-14x19in) s. W/C Japan paper exec 1921. 6-Nov-3 Sotheby's, New York #223a/R est:20000-30000
£16779 $30034 €25000 Two heads (17x11cm-7x4in) s. W/C pencil. 25-May-4 Dorotheum, Vienna #45/R est:25000-35000
£19333 $35573 €29000 Portrait of a girl's head (35x27cm-14x11in) s. W/C ink exec. c.1918-19 prov. 12-Jun-4 Villa Grisebach, Berlin #167/R est:25000-30000
£20000 $36800 €30000 Steamer on green sea (18x27cm-7x11in) s. W/C bodycol. 10-Jun-4 Hauswedell & Nolte, Hamburg #532/R est:45000
£22000 $39820 €32120 Frauenkopf, mit kurzem Haar (36x28cm-14x11in) s. W/C exec.c.1918/19. 1-Apr-4 Christie's, Kensington #43/R est:10000-15000
£23333 $42933 €35000 Head of a young South Sea islander (48x35cm-19x14in) s. W/C India ink paper on silk linen prov. 11-Jun-4 Villa Grisebach, Berlin #19/R est:35000-45000
£25175 $42797 €36000 South Sea islander (48x33cm-19x13in) s.i. W/C brush paper on board prov. 28-Nov-3 Villa Grisebach, Berlin #33/R est:40000-60000
£26667 $49067 €40000 Coastal landscape with fishing boat (35x48cm-14x19in) s. W/C India ink prov.exhib. 11-Jun-4 Villa Grisebach, Berlin #29/R est:40000-60000
£28671 $49315 €41000 Farmhouse under high clouds (15x14cm-6x6in) s. W/C gouache prov. 5-Dec-3 Ketterer, Munich #87/R est:40000-60000
£29371 $50517 €42000 Sea view with sailing boat (13x16cm-5x6in) s. W/C prov. 5-Dec-3 Ketterer, Munich #76/R est:40000-50000
£30667 $54893 €46000 Red poppy and yellow flower (19x14cm-7x6in) s. w/C gouache prov. 14-May-4 Ketterer, Munich #202/R est:40000-50000
£31034 $51828 €45000 Children playing (35x48cm-14x19in) s. W/C prov. 13-Nov-3 Neumeister, Munich #414/R est:40000-50000
£32000 $57280 €48000 Two women's heads (35x49cm-14x19in) s. W/C brush drawing prov. 14-May-4 Ketterer, Munich #172/R est:40000-50000
£35000 $63700 €51100 Bildnis einer frau in gruner bluse - Portrait of a woman in a green blouse (46x34cm-18x13in) s. W/C exec.c.1920-25 prov.exhib. 4-Feb-4 Sotheby's, London #537/R est:30000-40000
£40000 $73600 €60000 Sailing boats on canal (45x31cm-18x12in) s. W/C. 10-Jun-4 Hauswedell & Nolte, Hamburg #530/R est:70000
£40559 $68951 €58000 Bathers (35x47cm-14x19in) s. W/C Indian ink brush prov. 26-Nov-3 Lempertz, Koln #881/R est:50000
£41176 $70000 €60117 Head of a South Pacific Girl (40x32cm-16x13in) s. W/C ink buff paper exec c.1918-19 prov.exhib. 6-Nov-3 Sotheby's, New York #225/R est:70000-90000
£41958 $71329 €60000 Portrait of a woman (39x30cm-15x12in) s. W/C Indian ink brush prov. 28-Nov-3 Villa Grisebach, Berlin #39/R est:80000-100000
£43333 $79733 €65000 Red and yellow tulips (23x35cm-9x14in) s. W/C prov. 11-Jun-4 Villa Grisebach, Berlin #27/R est:60000-80000
£50000 $92000 €73000 Blumenstilleben mit Paradiesvogelblume (34x47cm-13x19in) s. W/C Japan paper exec c.1925 prov. 24-Jun-4 Christie's, London #338/R est:50000-70000
£50350 $85594 €72000 Anenomes and other flowers (47x39cm-19x15in) W/C prov. 28-Nov-3 Villa Grisebach, Berlin #36/R est:80000-100000
£52941 $90000 €77294 Pfingstrosen (47x35cm-19x14in) s. W/C Japan paper prov. 5-Nov-3 Christie's, Rockefeller NY #124/R est:60000-80000
£56667 $101433 €85000 Summer flowers (35x47cm-14x19in) s. W/C tempera prov.exhib. 14-May-4 Ketterer, Munich #195/R est:80000-100000
£58042 $99832 €83000 Red haired woman and man (17x18cm-7x7in) s. W/C gouache over pen ink prov. 5-Dec-3 Ketterer, Munich #89/R est:90000-120000
£65000 $118300 €94900 Man and two women (25x21cm-10x8in) s. W/C Japan paper exec 1938-1945 prov. 5-Feb-4 Christie's, London #363/R est:18000-20000
£65000 $118300 €94900 Marsh landscape with cloud reflection (34x47cm-13x19in) s. W/C executed c.1925. 3-Feb-4 Sotheby's, London #20/R est:40000-60000
£72414 $120931 €105000 Friesen farm (34x46cm-13x18in) s. W/C prov. 13-Nov-3 Neumeister, Munich #413/R est:50000-60000
£74000 $136160 €111000 Sunflowers and dahlias (47x32cm-19x13in) s. W/C exec. c.1952-55 prov. 11-Jun-4 Villa Grisebach, Berlin #1541/R est:50000-70000
£80420 $136713 €115000 Steamer at sea (22x27cm-9x11in) s. W/C prov. 28-Nov-3 Villa Grisebach, Berlin #34/R est:70000-90000
£83333 $149167 €125000 Yellow and blue irises (45x34cm-18x13in) s. w/C prov. 14-May-4 Ketterer, Munich #164/R est:80000-100000
£144366 $249754 €205000 Young couple (62x50cm-24x20in) s.i. Indian ink brush col lithograph print lit. 13-Dec-3 Lempertz, Koln #175/R est:140000-150000

NOLDE, Emil (attrib) (1867-1956) German

Works on paper
£357 $596 €521 Seascape with sailing vessel (27x27cm-11x11in) s.d.37 W/C Indian ink. 7-Oct-3 Rasmussen, Copenhagen #352 (D.KR 3800)

NOLET, Didier (20th C) American

£301 $550 €452 First step (157x79cm-62x31in) 10-Jul-4 Hindman, Chicago #377/R

Works on paper
£355 $650 €533 Chemin forestier (91x91cm-36x36in) gouache. 10-Jul-4 Hindman, Chicago #378/R

NOLKEN, Franz (attrib) (1884-1918) German

Works on paper
£470 $864 €700 Seated nude (21x17cm-8x7in) s. i. verso Indian ink wash over pencil. 26-Mar-4 Ketterer, Hamburg #1066/R

NOLL, Alexandre (1890-1970) French

Sculpture
£1576 $2900 €2301 Untitled (5x18x8cm-2x7x3in) carved ebony prov. 28-Mar-4 Wright, Chicago #253/R est:3000-5000
£3145 $5000 €4592 Untitled (20x13x8cm-8x5x3in) s. ebony prov. 14-Sep-3 Wright, Chicago #300/R est:5000-7000
£9730 $18000 €14206 Untitled (36cm-14in) s. ebony exec.c.1950. 9-Mar-4 Christie's, Rockefeller NY #480/R est:18000-24000
£13448 $24610 €19500 Untitled (33cm-13in) s. ebony socle exec.c.1945. 2-Feb-4 Cornette de St.Cyr, Paris #44/R est:10000-14000
£20231 $35000 €29537 Sculpture (54cm-21in) s.d.1968 ebony prov. 13-Dec-3 Sotheby's, New York #631/R est:20000-30000
£21676 $37500 €31647 Sculpture (49cm-19in) s. ebony prov. 13-Dec-3 Sotheby's, New York #630/R est:20000-30000
£31792 $55000 €46416 Masque sculpture (89cm-35in) s.d.1965 ebony prov.exhib. 13-Dec-3 Sotheby's, New York #632/R est:50000-70000

NOLLE, James (20th C) ?

£345 $638 €500 Vase et bouquet (41x31cm-16x12in) s. 16-Feb-4 Giraudeau, Tours #94

NOLLE, Lambert (19th C) French

£7042 $11690 €10000 Vue de la rue du Jour et St Eustache a Paris (65x54cm-26x21in) s.d.1837. 16-Jun-3 E & Eve, Paris #59/R

NOLLEKENS, Joseph (after) (1737-1823) British
Sculpture
£4200 $7140 €6132 Charles James Fox (47cm-19in) i. marble. 28-Oct-3 Sotheby's, London #85/R est:2000-3000

NOLLET, J H (19/20th C) Belgian
£1119 $1902 €1600 Paysage hivernal aux patineurs (80x120cm-31x47in) s. 18-Nov-3 Vanderkindere, Brussels #47 est:750-1250

NOLLET, Paul (1911-1996) Belgian
£780 $1303 €1100 Adam et Eve (170x120cm-67x47in) s.d.7 panel. 15-Oct-3 Hotel des Ventes Mosan, Brussels #282

NOLTE, H (?) ?
Sculpture
£1208 $2247 €1800 Nude lady sitting on elk (48cm-19in) s. bronze black marble base. 4-Mar-4 Auction Maastricht #159/R est:1500-2000

NOLTEE, Cornelis (1903-1967) Dutch
£263 $484 €400 A country walk (30x40cm-12x16in) s. 22-Jun-4 Christie's, Amsterdam #272/R
£445 $757 €650 View of Bruges (60x50cm-24x20in) s. 5-Nov-3 Vendue Huis, Gravenhage #196/R
£461 $847 €700 Haystacks by a farm in summer (35x50cm-14x20in) s. 22-Jun-4 Christie's, Amsterdam #304/R
£490 $842 €700 Narcissus in ginger pot (38x28cm-15x11in) s. maroufle. 8-Dec-3 Glerum, Amsterdam #312/R
£510 $929 €750 Passing the farmhouse (40x60cm-16x24in) s. 3-Feb-4 Christie's, Amsterdam #187
£590 $962 €850 Dune landscape (17x23cm-7x9in) s. panel. 29-Sep-3 Sotheby's, Amsterdam #234/R
£685 $1164 €1000 Self portrait with colourful tie (97x57cm-38x22in) s.d.1951 exhib. 5-Nov-3 Vendue Huis, Gravenhage #198/R
£833 $1358 €1200 View of houses (23x30cm-9x12in) s. 29-Sep-3 Sotheby's, Amsterdam #228/R
£855 $1574 €1300 Autumn in Amsterdam (50x35cm-20x14in) s. 22-Jun-4 Christie's, Amsterdam #248/R
£1020 $1857 €1500 Harvesting the land (50x78cm-20x31in) s. 3-Feb-4 Christie's, Amsterdam #250/R est:1200-1600
£1088 $1981 €1600 Street fun on a summer's day (41x61cm-16x24in) s. 3-Feb-4 Christie's, Amsterdam #217/R est:1000-1500
£1088 $1981 €1600 Peasants in a kitchen interior (60x80cm-24x31in) s. prov. 3-Feb-4 Christie's, Amsterdam #259 est:1500-2000
£1316 $2421 €2000 A studio still life (89x80cm-35x31in) s. 22-Jun-4 Christie's, Amsterdam #290/R est:1500-2000
£1379 $2303 €2000 Street with figures and horse and carriage (49x59cm-19x23in) s. 11-Nov-3 Vendu Notarishuis, Rotterdam #167/R est:2000-2500
£1806 $2943 €2600 Street scene with figures (40x30cm-16x12in) s. 29-Sep-3 Sotheby's, Amsterdam #217/R
£1905 $3467 €2800 Figures in a street (40x30cm-16x12in) s. 3-Feb-4 Christie's, Amsterdam #227 est:600-800
£2238 $3849 €3200 Flat-bottom boats on the Brouwer canal in Amsterdam (59x98cm-23x39in) s. 8-Dec-3 Glerum, Amsterdam #124a/R est:2500-3500
Works on paper
£1316 $2421 €2000 A rainy evening in a town (24x36cm-9x14in) s. W/C bodycol. 22-Jun-4 Christie's, Amsterdam #174/R est:400-600

NOME, François de (1593-c.1640) French
£9220 $15397 €13000 Palazzo in un giardino immaginario (51x60cm-20x24in) prov.lit. 18-Jun-3 Christie's, Rome #456/R est:14000-18000

NOME, François de (style) (1593 c.1640) French
£8451 $14620 €12000 Ruins with figures (91x124cm-36x49in) 12-Dec-3 Raboudin & Choppin de Janvry, Paris #17/R est:13000-15000

NOMELLINI, Plinio (1866-1943) Italian
£8273 $13568 €11500 Playing on the beach (29x39cm-11x15in) s. board. 10-Jun-3 Pandolfini, Florence #370/R est:8000-10000
£12590 $20647 €17500 Portrait of girl (56x72cm-22x28in) s. 10-Jun-3 Pandolfini, Florence #375/R est:18000-20000
£16197 $28021 €23000 Hunting (88x119cm-35x47in) s. exhib. 9-Dec-3 Pandolfini, Florence #113/R est:10000-12000
£19928 $32681 €27500 Wild Elba (63x77cm-25x30in) s. exhib. 27-May-3 Finarte Semenzato, Milan #80/R est:30000-35000
£56338 $97465 €80000 Pirate ship (188x100cm-74x39in) s. canvas on board lit. 11-Dec-3 Christie's, Rome #186/R est:60000-90000
£62667 $115307 €94000 Blue vortex (138x100cm-54x39in) s. prov.exhib. 8-Jun-4 Sotheby's, Milan #107/R est:80000-100000
Works on paper
£1589 $2893 €2400 Seascape (17x25cm-7x10in) s. pastel lit. 17-Jun-4 Galleria Pananti, Florence #116/R est:3000-3200

NONAS, Richard (1936-) American
Works on paper
£361 $650 €527 Untitled (9x12cm-4x5in) s.i.d.1974 chl. 24-Apr-4 David Rago, Lambertville #211/R

NONELL Y MONTURIOL, Isidro (1873-1911) Spanish
Works on paper
£816 $1362 €1150 Study of portrait (17x12cm-7x5in) dr lit. 20-Oct-3 Durán, Madrid #70/R

NONGAH, Bobyin (20th C) Australian
Works on paper
£352 $657 €528 Kunmanggur, the creator snake (24x63cm-9x25in) earth pigments eucalyptus bark exec.c.1963 prov. 26-Jul-4 Sotheby's, Melbourne #296/R (A.D 900)
£430 $804 €645 Kunmanggur, the creator snake (21x54cm-8x21in) earth pigments eucalyptus bark prov. 26-Jul-4 Sotheby's, Melbourne #298/R (A.D 1100)
£469 $877 €704 Figure and kunmanggur, creator snake (63x21cm-25x8in) earth pigments eucalyptus bark exec.c.1965 prov. 26-Jul-4 Sotheby's, Melbourne #520/R (A.D 1200)
£664 $1242 €996 Kunmanggur, the creator snake (24x70cm-9x28in) earth pigments eucalyptus bark exec.c.1963 prov. 26-Jul-4 Sotheby's, Melbourne #297/R (A.D 1700)

NONN, Carl (1876-1949) German
£533 $965 €800 Nonnenwerth (40x50cm-16x20in) s. 1-Apr-4 Van Ham, Cologne #1577
£733 $1335 €1100 On the banks of the Rhine (60x70cm-24x28in) s. s.i.verso. 1-Jul-4 Van Ham, Cologne #1538
£1000 $1810 €1500 Summer landscape (32x41cm-13x16in) s.d.44 board. 1-Apr-4 Van Ham, Cologne #1576/R est:1500
£1119 $1924 €1600 Country landscape with flowering trees (46x50cm-18x20in) s. i.verso. 6-Dec-3 Hans Stahl, Toestorf #20/R est:800
£1200 $2184 €1800 Landscape with a lake (46x65cm-18x26in) s. s.i.verso. 1-Jul-4 Van Ham, Cologne #1537/R est:1200
£1399 $2378 €2000 Mehlen valley near Prum in the Eifel (50x60cm-20x24in) s. 20-Nov-3 Van Ham, Cologne #1784/R est:2200

NONNENBRUCH, Max (1857-1922) German
£1389 $2264 €2000 Evening prayer (110x81cm-43x32in) s.d.1904. 25-Sep-3 Neumeister, Munich #2837/R est:1000

NONNIA, R (?) French
Sculpture
£2400 $3912 €3504 Coquette (30cm-12in) ivory golden brown pat bronze onyx plinth Cast.f.Paris. 28-Sep-3 Wilkinson, Doncaster #33/R

NONNOTTE, Donat (1708-1785) French
£2587 $4399 €3700 Portrait presume de Louis-Francois Anne de Villeroy Duc de Retz (80x64cm-31x25in) 30-Nov-3 Anaf, Lyon #188/R est:3000-3500
£2993 $5358 €4400 Portrait de Madame de Brosse, fille de Monsieur Briasson echevin lyonnais (91x73cm-36x29in) s.d.1758. 19-Mar-4 Oger, Dumont, Paris #38/R est:4000-6000

NONO, Luigi (1850-1918) Italian
£7333 $13493 €11000 Portrait of the artist's sister Luigia (23x16cm-9x6in) s.i.d.1875 board prov. 8-Jun-4 Sotheby's, Milan #125/R est:4000-6000
£14493 $23768 €20000 Santa Maria Gloriosa dei Frari, Venice (103x67cm-41x26in) s.d.1874 i.verso. 27-May-3 Il Ponte, Milan #977/R est:30000
£23611 $42500 €34472 Il funerale di un bambino - A boy's funeral (90x63cm-35x25in) mono. 23-Apr-4 Sotheby's, New York #85/R est:40000-60000
£87248 $156175 €130000 Shy lover (85x45cm-33x18in) s.d.1885 lit. 25-May-4 Finarte Semenzato, Milan #217/R est:90000-110000

NOOIGER, Jacob de (?) Dutch?
£300 $510 €438 Leopard (51x79cm-20x31in) s.d.1977. 30-Oct-3 Chrystals Auctions, Isle of Man #269
£340 $578 €496 Lioness and cubs (48x79cm-19x31in) s. 30-Oct-3 Chrystals Auctions, Isle of Man #270

NOOMS, Reinier (1623-1667) Dutch
£5921 $10895 €9000 Warships setting off from Fort Rammenkens, Vlissingen (61x101cm-24x40in) mono. 24-Jun-4 Dr Fritz Nagel, Stuttgart #614/R est:6000

NOOMS, Reinier (attrib) (1623-1667) Dutch
£600 $1020 €876 English man-o'war (16x21cm-6x8in) panel. 19-Nov-3 Christie's, Kensington #444/R

NOORDE, Cornelis van (1731-1795) Dutch
Works on paper
£1181 $1948 €1700 River landscape with figures and cattle (21x32cm-8x13in) mon.d.1776 W/C. 3-Jul-3 Van Ham, Cologne #1004/R

NOORDHOF, Els (20th C) New Zealander
Works on paper
£319 $590 €466 Girl by the window (40x60cm-16x24in) s.d.1983 pastel. 13-Jul-4 Watson's, Christchurch #26/R (NZ.D 900)

NOORDIJK, Willem Frederik (1887-1970) Dutch
£210 $375 €307 Beach view (30x41cm-12x16in) s. 14-May-4 Skinner, Boston #305/R
£420 $713 €600 Kolkje (65x43cm-26x17in) s. 24-Nov-3 Glerum, Amsterdam #65/R

NOORT, Adam van (studio) (16/17th C) Flemish
£21000 $37800 €30660 Christ at the marriage feast at Cana (68x190cm-27x75in) panel prov. 22-Apr-4 Sotheby's, London #44/R est:8000-12000

NOORT, Adrianus Cornelis van (1914-2003) Dutch
£300 $540 €450 Animated beach view at Zandvoort (40x50cm-16x20in) s. panel. 26-Apr-4 Bernaerts, Antwerp #980/R
£451 $736 €650 Mills in bulb fields (30x40cm-12x16in) s. panel. 29-Sep-3 Sotheby's, Amsterdam #347/R
£521 $849 €750 Children playing on the beach (40x30cm-16x12in) s. panel. 29-Sep-3 Sotheby's, Amsterdam #348/R

£667 $1213 €1000 On the beach on the Dutch coast (30x40cm-12x16in) s. panel. 1-Jul-4 Van Ham, Cologne #1539
£867 $1551 €1300 Bulb-field near Heemstede (69x99cm-27x39in) s. 11-May-4 Vendu Notarishuis, Rotterdam #89/R
£898 $1607 €1311 Coastal landscape with many figures (50x70cm-20x28in) s. 12-Jan-4 Rasmussen, Vejle #361/R (D.KR 9500)

NOORT, Lambert van (attrib) (c.1520-1571) Dutch
£6579 $12105 €10000 St Joseph and St Peter brought before the High Priest (33x25cm-13x10in) panel. 24-Jun-4 Dr Fritz Nagel, Stuttgart #583/R est:17000

NOOTEBOOM, Jacobus Hendricus Johannes (1811-1878) Dutch
£1122 $2009 €1650 Figures on the ice near a ruin (42x50cm-17x20in) d.1841. 17-Mar-4 De Zwann, Amsterdam #4548/R est:1000-2000
£2933 $5309 €4400 Dutch coast (41x55cm-16x22in) s.d.1846. 1-Apr-4 Van Ham, Cologne #1578/R est:3600

NORAMIES, Kaj (1918-1976) Finnish
Sculpture
£1047 $1875 €1550 This is what's left (18cm-7in) s.d.73 bronze. 8-May-4 Bukowskis, Helsinki #23/R est:600-800
£1182 $2117 €1750 Morning jobs (29cm-11in) s.d.72 bronze. 8-May-4 Bukowskis, Helsinki #17/R est:1000-1200
£1538 $2615 €2200 The first steps (22cm-9in) s.d.62 bronze. 29-Nov-3 Bukowskis, Helsinki #8/R est:1000-1200

NORBERTO (1927-) Italian
£1793 $2994 €2600 Night scene (30x20cm-12x8in) s. board. 13-Nov-3 Finarte Semenzato, Rome #320 est:2000-2400
£1800 $3240 €2700 Structure (18x13cm-7x5in) s. board. 22-Apr-4 Finarte Semenzato, Rome #160 est:1000-1200
£2345 $3916 €3400 Structure (18x13cm-7x5in) s. board. 13-Nov-3 Finarte Semenzato, Rome #321 est:1500-1700
Works on paper
£2667 $4800 €4000 Wind (60x40cm-24x16in) s. mixed media on canvas. 22-Apr-4 Finarte Semenzato, Rome #165/R est:3800-4200

NORBLIN DE LA GOURDAINE, Jean Pierre (1745-1830) French
Works on paper
£492 $900 €718 Landscape with figures and livestock on a river bank (12x20cm-5x8in) brush blue ink wash gouache. 29-Jan-4 Swann Galleries, New York #241/R
£719 $1151 €1000 Ancient historical scene (25x25cm-10x10in) pen ink grey wash traces of blk crayon. 16-May-3 Tajan, Paris #62
£993 $1808 €1500 La marchande de marrons (11x17cm-4x7in) W/C gouache. 16-Jun-4 Piasa, Paris #126/R est:1500-2000

NORBLIN DE LA GOURDAINE, Jean Pierre (attrib) (1745-1830) French
£1005 $1900 €1467 Fete Champetre (10x8cm-4x3in) panel oval. 23-Feb-4 Winter Associates, Plainville #169/R est:2000-2500

NORBLIN DE LA GOURDAINE, Sebastien Louis Guillaume (1796-1884) French
£2345 $3916 €3400 Destruction d'Herculanum, en l'an 79, par l'eruption du Vesuve (66x87cm-26x34in) s.d. exhib. 17-Nov-3 Tajan, Paris #13/R est:3000-4000
Works on paper
£867 $1569 €1300 Vue de Tivoli (32x43cm-13x17in) s.i.d.1827 pen brown grey wash. 31-Mar-4 Sotheby's, Paris #115/R est:600-900

NORBURY, Richard (1815-1886) British
£460 $754 €672 Extensive loch scene with figures and dog (76x127cm-30x50in) s. 6-Jun-3 Biddle & Webb, Birmingham #236

NORDBERG, Olle (1905-1986) Swedish
£259 $463 €378 Spring again (72x60cm-28x24in) s.d.67. 28-May-4 Uppsala Auktionskammare, Uppsala #303 (S.KR 3500)
£550 $951 €803 Woman in garden (27x35cm-11x14in) s.d.66 canvas on panel. 15-Dec-3 Lilla Bukowskis, Stockholm #454 (S.KR 7000)

NORDEN, Gerald (1912-2000) British
£300 $531 €438 Postal pieces (29x40cm-11x16in) s. board. 27-Apr-4 Henry Adams, Chichester #738

NORDENBERG, Bengt (1822-1902) Swedish
£568 $1000 €829 Interior scene (48x66cm-19x26in) s. 28-May-4 Aspire, Cleveland #15/R est:1200-1500
£615 $1058 €898 Studio interior (30x54cm-12x21in) init.d.1915. 3-Dec-3 AB Stockholms Auktionsverk #2352/R (S.KR 8000)
£665 $1191 €971 Boy wearing sailor's uniform (23x17cm-9x7in) init. 26-May-4 AB Stockholms Auktionsverk #2219/R (S.KR 9000)
£1382 $2350 €2018 Swedish fjord landscape with figures in rowing boat (71x60cm-28x24in) s. 10-Nov-3 Rasmussen, Vejle #368/R est:18000-20000 (D.KR 15000)
£1774 $3175 €2590 Cottage interior with visiting fortune teller (35x46cm-14x18in) init. 25-May-4 Bukowskis, Stockholm #129/R est:20000-25000 (S.KR 24000)
£1848 $3307 €2698 Cottage interior with woman embroidering and children playing (32x41cm-13x16in) s. 26-May-4 AB Stockholms Auktionsverk #2189/R est:25000-30000 (S.KR 25000)
£3077 $5292 €4492 Visiting a cottage in Halland (47x40cm-19x16in) s.d.77 lit. 2-Dec-3 Bukowskis, Stockholm #70/R est:20000-25000 (S.KR 40000)
£3326 $5953 €4856 Mid-summer Night (61x80cm-24x31in) s.d.1860. 25-May-4 Bukowskis, Stockholm #127/R est:50000-60000 (S.KR 45000)
£3353 $6169 €5030 On the way to church (68x58cm-27x23in) s.d.1876. 14-Jun-4 Lilla Bukowskis, Stockholm #719 est:30000-35000 (S.KR 46000)
£3846 $6615 €5615 The journey in winter (30x40cm-12x16in) s.d.1882. 2-Dec-3 Bukowskis, Stockholm #179/R est:35000-40000 (S.KR 50000)
£4769 $8203 €6963 In the vestry (82x120cm-32x47in) s.d.1864. 2-Dec-3 Bukowskis, Stockholm #120/R est:70000-90000 (S.KR 62000)
£11923 $20508 €17408 After the christening (85x105cm-33x41in) s.d.1868. 3-Dec-3 AB Stockholms Auktionsverk #2329/R est:150000-175000 (S.KR 155000)
£19586 $35059 €28596 Home coming of the old soldier (86x110cm-34x43in) s.d.1855. 25-May-4 Bukowskis, Stockholm #130/R est:100000-125000 (S.KR 265000)

NORDENBERG, Bengt (attrib) (1822-1902) Swedish
£2538 $4569 €3807 Genre scene with boy playing flute to two girls and goats (38x45cm-15x18in) init. 25-Apr-4 Goteborg Auktionsverk, Sweden #215/R est:30000 (S.KR 35000)

NORDENBERG, Hendrick (1857-1928) Swedish
£805 $1482 €1200 Woman sewing (58x42cm-23x17in) s. 27-Mar-4 L & B, Essen #171/R
£1154 $1985 €1685 Interior scene with man (65x49cm-26x19in) s. 2-Dec-3 Bukowskis, Stockholm #65/R est:20000-25000 (S.KR 15000)
£1615 $2778 €2358 Interior scene with woman sewing (61x50cm-24x20in) s. 2-Dec-3 Bukowskis, Stockholm #176/R est:15000-18000 (S.KR 21000)
£1996 $3572 €2914 Interior scene with woman reading (63x49cm-25x19in) s. 26-May-4 AB Stockholms Auktionsverk #2209/R est:12000-15000 (S.KR 27000)
£5077 $8732 €7412 Interior scene with woman sewing (67x47cm-26x19in) s/. 2-Dec-3 Bukowskis, Stockholm #66/R est:20000-25000 (S.KR 66000)
Works on paper
£995 $1692 €1453 Young woman sitting sewing (41x28cm-16x11in) s.i.d.21/3 94 Indian ink wash htd white. 19-Nov-3 Fischer, Luzern #2483/R est:300-400 (S.FR 2200)

NORDENSKIOLD, Gerda (1913-1999) Swedish
£586 $1037 €856 Concrete composition (55x46cm-22x18in) init. s.d.1993 verso. 27-Apr-4 AB Stockholms Auktionsverk #827/R (S.KR 8000)

NORDFELDT, B J O (1878-1955) American
Works on paper
£552 $900 €806 Farm (25x36cm-10x14in) s. pastel. 19-Jul-3 Outer Cape Auctions, Provincetown #125/R

NORDFELDT, Bror Julius Olsson (1878-1955) American
£2310 $4250 €3373 Lady in a white dress reading a book in an interior (67x99cm-26x39in) prov. 8-Jun-4 Bonhams & Butterfields, San Francisco #4074/R est:3000-5000
£4491 $7500 €6557 Yellow tablecloth (91x107cm-36x42in) s. prov.exhib.lit. 7-Oct-3 Sotheby's, New York #213 est:8000-12000
£8671 $15000 €12660 Barrier Rocks No. 2 (76x102cm-30x40in) painted 1954 prov. 10-Dec-3 Bonhams & Butterfields, San Francisco #6061/R est:10000-15000
£8824 $15000 €12883 Moonrise (67x86cm-26x34in) s. s.i.verso. 30-Oct-3 Phillips, New York #79/R est:15000-25000
Prints
£4118 $7000 €6012 Branch (28x20cm-11x8in) col woodcut. 31-Oct-3 Sotheby's, New York #194/R

NORDGREN, Anna (1847-1916) Swedish
£630 $1027 €920 Country idyll (61x91cm-24x36in) s.d.1893. 29-Sep-3 Lilla Bukowskis, Stockholm #247 (S.KR 8200)
£950 $1682 €1387 Enjoying the sunshine (18x251cm-7x99in) s. panel. 28-Apr-4 Halls, Shrewsbury #495/R
£979 $1664 €1400 Ducks on water by farm (61x91cm-24x36in) s.d.1892. 29-Nov-3 Bukowskis, Helsinki #375/R
£1552 $2778 €2266 Girls on the beach (76x101cm-30x40in) s. 26-May-4 AB Stockholms Auktionsverk #2152/R est:20000-25000 (S.KR 21000)

NORDGREN, Axel (1828-1888) Swedish
£559 $962 €800 Coastal scene by full moon (67x110cm-26x43in) s. 6-Dec-3 Quittenbaum, Hamburg #38/R
£875 $1609 €1313 Coastal landscape in winter (48x85cm-19x33in) s. 14-Jun-4 Lilla Bukowskis, Stockholm #845 (S.KR 12000)
£1154 $1985 €1685 Fishing village in winter (41x78cm-16x31in) s. 2-Dec-3 Bukowskis, Stockholm #181/R est:20000-25000 (S.KR 15000)
£1342 $2470 €2000 Coast in evening (100x80cm-39x31in) s.d.1884 canvas on panel. 27-Mar-4 L & B, Essen #172/R est:1500
£3497 $5944 €5000 Fishermen by stream, landscape from Varmland (107x71cm-42x28in) s. 29-Nov-3 Bukowskis, Helsinki #379/R est:5000-7000

NORDHAUSEN, August Henry (1901-) American
£710 $1300 €1037 Seated nude (56x46cm-22x18in) s. 31-Jan-4 South Bay, Long Island #118

NORDIN, Alice (1871-1948) Swedish
Sculpture
£1462 $2514 €2135 Seated girl (46cm-18in) s.d.1911 white marble. 2-Dec-3 Bukowskis, Stockholm #236/R est:20000-25000 (S.KR 19000)

NORDIN, Ann-Marie (1955-) Swedish
Works on paper
£277 $510 €416 Seated model (186x109cm-73x43in) s. crayon chl. 14-Jun-4 Lilla Bukowskis, Stockholm #548 (S.KR 3800)

NORDLIEN, Olaf (1864-1919) Norwegian
£250 $418 €365 Wooded landscape (70x102cm-28x40in) s. 17-Nov-3 Blomqvist, Lysaker #1235 (N.KR 3000)

NORDLING, Adolf (1840-1888) Swedish
£2752 $4431 €4018 Sailing vessel on stormy seas (160x222cm-63x87in) s.d.70. 25-Aug-3 Lilla Bukowskis, Stockholm #162 est:20000-25000 (S.KR 36000)

NORDMANN, Germaine (20th C) French

£319	$533	€450	Dans le port (150x116cm-59x46in) s. 14-Oct-3 Millon & Associes, Paris #199
£355	$592	€500	Souffleur deverre (60x80cm-24x31in) s. 14-Oct-3 Millon & Associes, Paris #163
£532	$888	€750	Baigneuses (100x82cm-39x32in) s. 14-Oct-3 Millon & Associes, Paris #180/R
£603	$1007	€850	Union et paix (130x97cm-51x38in) s. 14-Oct-3 Millon & Associes, Paris #196/R

NORDSTRAND, Nathalie Johnson (20th C) American

£315	$500	€460	Summer swans, Boston Public Gardens (56x76cm-22x30in) s. 12-Sep-3 Skinner, Boston #430/R

NORDSTROM, Jockum (1963-) Swedish

£1360	$2311	€1986	Birds (30x42cm-12x17in) s.d.1996 verso panel. 5-Nov-3 AB Stockholms Auktionsverk #1020/R est:12000-15000 (S.KR 18000)
£2393	$4307	€3494	Playing football by the sea (93x95cm-37x37in) s.d.90 verso prov. 26-Apr-4 Bukowskis, Stockholm #483/R est:50000-60000 (S.KR 33000)
£3097	$5264	€4522	Untitled (180x120cm-71x47in) s.d.1990 verso. 4-Nov-3 Bukowskis, Stockholm #633/R est:35000-40000 (S.KR 41000)
£4714	$8484	€6882	Carambole (105x106cm-41x42in) s.d.92 verso panel exhib. 26-Apr-4 Bukowskis, Stockholm #484/R est:50000-60000 (S.KR 65000)
£7326	$12967	€10696	Happy New Year 1993 (81x112cm-32x44in) s.d.93 verso. 27-Apr-4 AB Stockholms Auktionsverk #913/R est:40000-45000 (S.KR 100000)

NORDSTROM, Karl (1855-1923) Swedish

£591	$1058	€863	Girl with bouquet of flowers (31x28cm-12x11in) init.d.1918 canvas on panel. 26-May-4 AB Stockholms Auktionsverk #2199/R (S.KR 8000)
£1382	$2253	€2018	Northern landscape (88x150cm-35x59in) s. 29-Sep-3 Lilla Bukowskis, Stockholm #339 est:20000-25000 (S.KR 18000)
£2000	$3440	€2920	Field landscape, Tjorn (70x77cm-28x30in) init. 2-Dec-3 Bukowskis, Stockholm #188/R est:20000-25000 (S.KR 26000)
£2000	$3440	€2920	View of Stockholm with the river (24x35cm-9x14in) init. 3-Dec-3 AB Stockholms Auktionsverk #2295/R est:25000-30000 (S.KR 26000)
£2231	$3837	€3257	Street, Montmartre (24x18cm-9x7in) s.d.81 panel exhib. 2-Dec-3 Bukowskis, Stockholm #84/R est:10000-12000 (S.KR 29000)
£8869	$15876	€12949	Grondals beach with children bathing (60x75cm-24x30in) init.d.1919. 25-May-4 Bukowskis, Stockholm #118/R est:60000-80000 (S.KR 120000)
£19956	$35721	€29136	The mills in the Visby area (73x100cm-29x39in) s.i.d.89 prov.exhib.lit. 28-May-4 Uppsala Auktionskammare, Uppsala #152/R est:150000-200000 (S.KR 270000)

Prints

£3178	$5689	€4640	Landscape, Bohuslan (85x120cm-33x47in) s. exhib. 25-May-4 Bukowskis, Stockholm #220/R est:50000-60000 (S.KR 43000)

Works on paper

£887	$1588	€1295	Evening landscape outside Varberg (46x60cm-18x24in) mono.indis.d.94 mixed media. 28-May-4 Uppsala Auktionskammare, Uppsala #231 (S.KR 12000)

NORDSTROM, Lars Gunnar (1924-) Finnish

£336	$617	€500	Blue green composition (35x25cm-14x10in) s.d.1965 tempera. 25-Mar-4 Hagelstam, Helsinki #928
£3239	$5604	€4600	Composition (47x60cm-19x24in) s.d.1958 tempera. 13-Dec-3 Hagelstam, Helsinki #190/R est:3000

Works on paper

£566	$978	€826	Geometric composition in black, green and white (35x21cm-14x8in) mixed media. 15-Dec-3 Lilla Bukowskis, Stockholm #659/R (S.KR 7200)

NORDT, Maxwell (?) ?

£537	$961	€800	Fjiord (60x80cm-24x31in) s. 25-May-4 Durán, Madrid #171/R

NOREAU, Francine (20th C) American

£315	$536	€460	Spring bouquet (61x49cm-24x19in) s. s.i.verso. 23-Nov-3 Levis, Calgary #524/R (C.D 700)

NORIE, Orlando (1832-1901) British

Works on paper

£260	$468	€380	Charge (18x28cm-7x11in) s. W/C htd white. 23-Apr-4 Charterhouse, Sherborne #705/R
£270	$432	€394	Mounted officer of 3rd Dragoon guards (20x16cm-8x6in) s. W/C htd bodycol. 16-Sep-3 Bonhams, Knowle #75
£300	$537	€438	Officer of the Royal Horse Artillery upon horseback in landscape (23x19cm-9x7in) s. W/C. 20-Mar-4 Lacy Scott, Bury St.Edmunds #482
£310	$518	€453	Royal Horse Artillery (23x19cm-9x7in) s. W/C pencil. 16-Oct-3 Lawrence, Crewkerne #638
£350	$595	€511	Officer on horseback (39x28cm-15x11in) s. W/C. 4-Nov-3 Rowley Fine Art, Newmarket #387
£360	$612	€526	Cavalry officer riding into battle (19x14cm-7x6in) s. W/C. 25-Nov-3 Bonhams, Knightsbridge #184/R
£360	$637	€526	Guards resting in an encampment (32x45cm-13x18in) s. W/C. 27-Apr-4 Bonhams, Knowle #40
£400	$680	€584	Soldiers resting beside woods (20x30cm-8x12in) s. W/C. 4-Nov-3 Rowley Fine Art, Newmarket #388
£470	$855	€686	The 12th Regiment of the Prince of Wales's Royal Lancers (41x32cm-16x13in) s. pencil W/C htd white prov. 1-Jul-4 Christie's, Kensington #242/R
£550	$1012	€803	Household brigade at exercises near Brookwood (33x50cm-13x20in) s. W/C exec.c.1885. 29-Mar-4 Thomson Roddick & Medcalf, Edinburgh #229
£750	$1275	€1095	Officer of the 2nd Dragoons passing a sentry on duty (38x27cm-15x11in) s. W/C. 4-Nov-3 Rowley Fine Art, Newmarket #383/R
£750	$1275	€1095	Officer of the 2nd Dragoons dismounted and in conversation (56x39cm-22x15in) s. W/C. 4-Nov-3 Rowley Fine Art, Newmarket #385/R
£800	$1360	€1168	Guards officers on horseback (39x38cm-15x15in) s. W/C. 4-Nov-3 Rowley Fine Art, Newmarket #386/R
£850	$1445	€1241	Guards officer on horseback reading a dispatch outside barracks (44x37cm-17x15in) s. W/C. 4-Nov-3 Rowley Fine Art, Newmarket #384/R
£887	$1569	€1295	Seventh Hussar's battle scene (40x71cm-16x28in) s. W/C. 28-Apr-4 Dunbar Sloane, Auckland #52/R (NZ.D 2500)
£900	$1467	€1314	Napoleonic soldiers on horseback. Soldier on horseback with scouts (28x41cm-11x16in) s. W/C pair. 23-Sep-3 John Nicholson, Haslemere #111/R
£900	$1530	€1314	Troop of soldiers on horseback passing down a lane (20x31cm-8x12in) s. W/C. 4-Nov-3 Rowley Fine Art, Newmarket #382/R
£1150	$1955	€1679	Royal Horse Artillery at the gallop and preparing to fire (19x29cm-7x11in) s. W/C over pencil pair. 1-Dec-3 Bonhams, Bath #69/R est:1000-1500
£1300	$2392	€1898	Parade of cavalry of various regiments watched by an officer (55x99cm-22x39in) s. W/C. 8-Jun-4 Bonhams, New Bond Street #60/R est:1000-1500
£1800	$3330	€2628	The Yorkshire Yeomanry at the charge (35x59cm-14x23in) s. W/C. 11-Feb-4 Cheffins, Cambridge #390/R est:1200-1500
£7200	$12240	€10512	Scenes during the Battle Of Balaklava (31x44cm-12x17in) s. W/C over pencil set of four. 27-Nov-3 Sotheby's, London #309/R est:6000-8000

NORLDAM, Federico (20th C) Latin American

£574	$952	€832	Bag of oranges (40x104cm-16x41in) s.d.1998. 12-Jun-3 Louis Morton, Mexico #106/R est:2000-3000 (M.P 10000)

NORLING, Barry (20th C) American

Sculpture

£1173	$1900	€1713	If the buck stops here (183x33x66cm-72x13x26in) hollow copper. 26-Jul-3 Thomaston Place, Thomaston #643/R

NORMAN, Dorothy (1905-) American

Photographs

£2797	$4755	€4000	Church, Waquoit, Mass. VI (7x9cm-3x4in) silver gelatin lit.exhib. 27-Nov-3 Villa Grisebach, Berlin #1331/R est:4000-5000

NORMAN, Edmund (?) New Zealander?

Works on paper

£692	$1239	€1010	Mt. Cook and Hooker Glaciers (23x39cm-9x15in) s.i. W/C pencil. 12-May-4 Dunbar Sloane, Wellington #198/R est:2000-3000 (NZ.D 2000)

NORMAN, George Parsons (1840-1914) British

Works on paper

£520	$962	€759	Figures amongst poppies at the edge of a field, Norfolk (36x25cm-14x10in) one s. W/C pair. 13-Feb-4 Keys, Aylsham #537

NORMAN, Knut (1896-1977) Swedish

£259	$432	€378	From Svolvaer (62x81cm-24x32in) s. 17-Nov-3 Blomqvist, Lysaker #1237 (N.KR 3100)
£273	$500	€399	Untitled (48x58cm-19x23in) s. 31-Jul-4 Sloans & Kenyon, Bethesda #268/R

NORMAN, Percy (?) British?

£480	$888	€701	Moorland road in East Norfolk (49x75cm-19x30in) s. 14-Jul-4 Bonhams, Chester #457

NORMANN, A (1848-1918) Norwegian

£4667	$8447	€7000	Fjord landscape (110x150cm-43x59in) i. 2-Apr-4 Dr Fritz Nagel, Leipzig #3916/R est:6000

NORMANN, Adelsteen (1848-1918) Norwegian

£400	$736	€600	Fjord landscape (35x50cm-14x20in) mono.d.97. 11-Jun-4 Wendl, Rudolstadt #4198/R
£700	$1295	€1022	Fjord landscape (65x95cm-26x37in) s. 9-Mar-4 Bonhams, Knightsbridge #238/R
£776	$1389	€1133	Unloading the catch (32x46cm-13x18in) s. panel. 26-May-4 AB Stockholms Auktionsverk #2430/R (S.KR 10500)
£1167	$2112	€1750	Norwegian bay lit by morning sun (36x53cm-14x21in) s. canvas on board. 3-Apr-4 Hans Stahl, Hamburg #62/R est:1400
£1500	$2505	€2190	Norwegian fjord (24x34cm-9x13in) s. canvas on board. 8-Oct-3 Christie's, Kensington #799/R est:1000-1500
£1888	$3210	€2700	On the Lofoten (51x70cm-20x28in) s. 20-Nov-3 Van Ham, Cologne #1785/R est:2000
£2994	$5090	€4371	Fjord landscape with steam boat (40x60cm-16x24in) s. 19-Nov-3 Grev Wedels Plass, Oslo #57/R est:30000-40000 (N.KR 35000)
£3112	$5477	€4544	Fijord (48x68cm-19x27in) s. board. 23-May-4 Agra, Warsaw #18/R (P.Z 22000)
£3147	$5350	€4500	Norwegian fjord with fishing village (43x72cm-17x28in) s. 20-Nov-3 Dorotheum, Salzburg #188/R est:2800-4000
£3217	$5469	€4600	Fjord in summer (64x104cm-25x41in) s. 22-Nov-3 Arnold, Frankfurt #602/R est:1600
£3414	$6350	€4984	Evening landscape in Norwegian fjord (72x100cm-28x39in) s. 2-Mar-4 Rasmussen, Copenhagen #1217/R est:50000-75000 (D.KR 38000)
£3500	$6475	€5110	Fishing in a fjord (53x84cm-21x33in) s. 14-Jul-4 Sotheby's, Olympia #212/R est:4000-6000
£3557	$6545	€5300	Norwegian fjord (60x96cm-24x38in) s. 26-Mar-4 Ketterer, Hamburg #204/R est:5000-6000
£3718	$6060	€5428	Norwegian fjord (62x100cm-24x39in) s. 17-Jul-3 Naón & Cia, Buenos Aires #19/R
£4027	$7490	€6000	Mountain lake with sailing boat on sunny autumn day (105x158cm-41x62in) s. 6-Mar-4 Arnold, Frankfurt #812/R est:4000
£4615	$7938	€6738	Norwegian fjord landscape with fishermen (54x85cm-21x33in) s. 3-Dec-3 AB Stockholms Auktionsverk #2590/R est:50000-60000 (S.KR 60000)
£4769	$8203	€6963	Fjord landscape with fishing village (78x104cm-31x41in) s. 3-Dec-3 AB Stockholms Auktionsverk #2626/R est:60000-80000 (S.KR 62000)
£6333	$11463	€9500	Boat and figures by glacier on Lofoten (63x95cm-25x37in) s. 1-Apr-4 Van Ham, Cologne #1579/R est:8200
£7089	$12689	€10350	Norwegian skerries with boats, women and children (60x96cm-24x38in) s.i. 12-Jan-4 Rasmussen, Vejle #400/R est:50000 (D.KR 75000)
£8000	$13760	€11680	Trollfjorden, Norway (71x105cm-28x41in) s. 3-Dec-3 Christie's, London #85/R est:8000-12000
£9000	$15300	€13140	Boating on fjord (72x100cm-28x39in) s. 18-Nov-3 Sotheby's, London #354/R
£11000	$20020	€16060	Boats on a Norwegian fjord (62x94cm-24x37in) s. 5-Feb-4 Mellors & Kirk, Nottingham #571/R est:8000-12000

NORMANN, Christine (19th C) Danish
£5000 $8350 €7200 Still life with asparagus (55x70cm-22x28in) s.d. 24-Oct-3 Ketterer, Hamburg #92/R est:7500-8000

NORMANN, Emil Wilhelm (1798-1881) Danish
£222 $400 €324 Young girl with a rake (36x28cm-14x11in) s. board. 23-Jan-4 Freeman, Philadelphia #233a/R

NORMANN, Emma (1871-1954) Norwegian
£470 $812 €686 Fjord landscape (27x35cm-11x14in) s. panel. 13-Dec-3 Blomqvist, Lysaker #1265/R (N.KR 5400)
£730 $1277 €1066 Farm by fjord on the west side of Norway (31x40cm-12x16in) s/ panel. 16-Dec-3 Grev Wedels Plass, Oslo #206/R (N.KR 8500)
£854 $1571 €1281 Village by fjord on the west coast of Norway (60x80cm-24x31in) s. panel. 14-Jun-4 Blomqvist, Lysaker #1284/R (N.KR 10500)
£1000 $1820 €1460 Flower pickers at a Norwegian fjord (65x90cm-26x35in) s.d.1918. 16-Jun-4 Christie's, Kensington #191/R est:1000-1500
£1333 $2413 €2000 Summer idyll (72x52cm-28x20in) s.d. 1-Apr-4 Van Ham, Cologne #1594/R est:2200
£1533 $2745 €2300 Girl in fjord landscape (80x120cm-31x47in) s.d.1919 lit. 14-May-4 Schloss Ahlden, Ahlden #2844/R est:2300

NORREGAARD, Asta (1853-1933) Norwegian
£20392 $36501 €29772 French kitchen interior (59x73cm-23x29in) s.d.1881 lit. 25-May-4 Grev Wedels Plass, Oslo #33/R est:300000 (N.KR 250000)

NORRETRANDERS, Johannes (1871-1957) Danish
£378 $691 €552 Apple tree (110x90cm-43x35in) s. 2-Feb-4 Blomqvist, Lysaker #1222/R (N.KR 4700)

NORRIE, Susan (1953-) Australian
£455 $841 €664 Equivalence (30x30cm-12x12in) s. i.d.92 verso. 10-Mar-4 Deutscher-Menzies, Melbourne #140/R est:1200-1500 (A.D 1100)
£1277 $2170 €1864 ACC Series, BB (38x38cm-15x15in) s.d.88 verso prov. 25-Nov-3 Christie's, Melbourne #110/R est:3000-4000 (A.D 3000)
£4065 $6382 €5894 Wreath, from the determined installation (69cm-27in circular) board prov.exhib. 26-Aug-3 Christie's, Sydney #57/R est:10000-15000 (A.D 10000)
£6098 $9573 €8842 Untitled collection (152x122cm-60x48in) s.i.d.93 verso diptych prov. 26-Aug-3 Christie's, Sydney #110/R est:10000-15000 (A.D 15000)
Works on paper
£732 $1149 €1061 Untitled (18x12cm-7x5in) oil gouache board. 26-Aug-3 Christie's, Sydney #240/R est:1500-2000 (A.D 1800)
£1707 $2680 €2475 Tinman's makeover. Different colour (16x18cm-6x7in) i. s.i.d.2002 verso W/C gouache pair. 26-Aug-3 Christie's, Sydney #232/R est:3000-5000 (A.D 4200)

NORRINGTON, Claire (1969-) British
Sculpture
£1100 $1936 €1606 Rearing bull (40x30cm-16x12in) mono. num.3/9 bronze. 18-May-4 Woolley & Wallis, Salisbury #350/R est:1200-1800
£1600 $2816 €2336 Charging bull (30x46cm-12x18in) mono. num.9/9 bronze. 18-May-4 Woolley & Wallis, Salisbury #351/R est:1200-1800
Works on paper
£520 $915 €759 Hanging around, a red-ruffed lemur (68x48cm-27x19in) s. chl conte. 18-May-4 Woolley & Wallis, Salisbury #229a/R
£550 $968 €803 Snorting bull (55x75cm-22x30in) s. pencil mixed media. 18-May-4 Woolley & Wallis, Salisbury #228/R

NORRIS, Joe (1924-) Canadian
£960 $1757 €1402 Lower Prospect (44x59cm-17x23in) s. board. 1-Jun-4 Joyner Waddington, Toronto #298/R est:3000-4000 (C.D 2400)
£1525 $2729 €2227 Two moose and lake with loons (61x91cm-24x36in) s. plywood prov.exhib. 31-May-4 Sotheby's, Toronto #48/R est:3000-5000 (C.D 3750)
£1626 $2911 €2374 Rita MacNeil on Cape Breton Island (35x45cm-14x18in) s.d.1987 panel prov. 27-May-4 Heffel, Vancouver #219/R est:4000-5000 (C.D 4000)

NORRMAN, Gunnar (1912-) Swedish
Works on paper
£352 $609 €500 La jetee (47x60cm-19x24in) s.d.1979 black crayon. 10-Dec-3 Rossini, Paris #24

NORRMAN, Herman (1864-1906) Swedish
£2500 $4000 €3650 Portrait of Mr Sutherland (127x109cm-50x43in) s.d.82. 20-Sep-3 Jeffery Burchard, Florida #100/R

NORSELIUS, Erik (1874-1956) Swedish
£451 $745 €650 In Brittany (39x46cm-15x18in) s.d.30. 3-Jul-3 Van Ham, Cologne #1391

NORTH AMERICAN SCHOOL, 19th C
£5000 $8850 €7300 St. Ann's Episcopal church, Brooklyn Heights, New York (66x98cm-26x39in) canvas on board prov. 27-Apr-4 Bonhams, New Bond Street #116/R est:5000-8000

NORTH GERMAN SCHOOL, 16th C
£10884 $19483 €16000 Christ on the cross (100x126cm-39x50in) panel. 17-Mar-4 Neumeister, Munich #371/R est:18000

NORTH ITALIAN SCHOOL, 15th C
£5500 $9900 €8030 Portrait of a gentleman wearing black (29x24cm-11x9in) 20-Apr-4 Sotheby's, Olympia #225/R est:2500-4000

NORTH ITALIAN SCHOOL, 16th C
£5694 $8997 €8200 Christ on the cross with St Hieronymus, Anthony and Francis of Assisi (102x77cm-40x30in) panel. 19-Sep-3 Schloss Ahlden, Ahlden #1416/R est:8500
£12195 $21829 €17805 The Holy Family (74x53cm-29x21in) canvas on panel. 25-May-4 Bukowskis, Stockholm #421/R est:60000-80000 (S.KR 165000)
£13423 $24698 €20000 Bust of man in landscape (28x22cm-11x9in) panel. 24-Mar-4 Dorotheum, Vienna #46/R est:12000-15000
£17000 $29410 €24820 Portrait of a young girl wearing a red dress standing with her nurse-maid (102x89cm-40x35in) 11-Dec-3 Sotheby's, London #187/R est:12000-18000
Works on paper
£3889 $7000 €5678 Classical warrior crowned with an eagle (40x26cm-16x10in) black chk pen brown ink wash. 22-Jan-4 Christie's, Rockefeller NY #2/R est:5000-7000

NORTH ITALIAN SCHOOL, 17th C
£6291 $11450 €9500 Saint Sebastian looked after by charitable women (132x201cm-52x79in) 16-Jun-4 Christie's, Rome #503/R est:12000-18000
£7500 $12750 €10950 Portrait of a young noble girl, attended by two pages (108x122cm-43x48in) i. 30-Oct-3 Sotheby's, Olympia #97/R est:8000-12000
£8200 $14760 €11972 Stormy seascape with ships being wrecked off a rocky coast with mercury and cupid and other figures (89x127cm-35x50in) prov. 20-Apr-4 Sotheby's, Olympia #377/R est:7000-10000
£9859 $17056 €14000 Bullfight on idealised Venetian square (330x78cm-130x31in) 11-Dec-3 Dr Fritz Nagel, Stuttgart #422/R est:19000
£11000 $20130 €16060 Portrait of young lady holding fan (74x62cm-29x24in) 8-Jul-4 Sotheby's, London #296/R est:6000-8000
Sculpture
£13000 $22100 €18980 Dancing seraphs (88x85cm-35x33in) painted wood pair. 28-Oct-3 Sotheby's, London #29/R

NORTH ITALIAN SCHOOL, 18th C
£6500 $11700 €9490 Still life of grapes in a basket, with lemons, peaches, figs, cherries and a watermelon (57x75cm-22x30in) 20-Apr-4 Sotheby's, Olympia #359/R est:2500-3500
£6500 $11895 €9490 Young lady with a cat (73x60cm-29x24in) 7-Jul-4 Bonhams, New Bond Street #91/R est:3000-4000
£7063 $12007 €10100 Wood with shepherds (95x128cm-37x50in) 1-Dec-3 Babuino, Rome #150/R est:4000-6000
£23179 $42417 €35000 Marine, paysage et scenes d'architecture (75x95cm-30x37in) four. 7-Apr-4 Doutrebente, Paris #16/R est:8000-10000
£25000 $45750 €36500 Allegorical subject (157x183cm-62x72in) 8-Jul-4 Sotheby's, London #163/R est:25000-35000
Sculpture
£101351 $178378 €150000 Lady (157cm-62in) i.d.1735 marble sold with base prov. 18-May-4 Sotheby's, Milan #490/R est:25000-40000

NORTH ITALIAN SCHOOL, 19th C
£30000 $54900 €43800 Landscape with buildings (73x95cm-29x37in) tempera set of 4. 8-Jul-4 Sotheby's, London #345/R est:30000-40000

NORTH, John William (1842-1924) British
£4600 $8418 €6716 Summer in a Western wood (54x75cm-21x30in) init.d.1907 prov.exhib. 3-Jun-4 Christie's, London #11/R est:5000-7000
Works on paper
£2600 $4758 €3796 October wood (33x48cm-13x19in) s.d.1903 pencil W/C gum arabic scratching out prov. 3-Jun-4 Christie's, London #14/R est:3000-5000
£2800 $5124 €4088 Spring in a Western orchard (46x31cm-18x12in) init. indist.i.d.1899 W/C touches bodycol scratching prov.exhib. 3-Jun-4 Christie's, London #12/R est:2500-3500
£3000 $5490 €4380 The wood-reeve's daughter (57x41cm-22x16in) s.d.1901-2 pencil W/C gum arabic scratching out prov.exhib. 3-Jun-4 Christie's, London #16/R est:4000-6000
£5000 $9150 €7300 Imprisonment (65x94cm-26x37in) init.d.1876-7 W/C gum arabic bodycol scratching out prov.exhib. 3-Jun-4 Christie's, London #13/R est:6000-10000

NORTH, Marianne (1830-1890) British
£400 $736 €584 Royal Botanic Gardens- Kew (18x23cm-7x9in) panel. 12-Jun-4 Dickins, Middle Claydon #57

NORTHAM, Pitt (19th C) British
Works on paper
£299 $500 €437 Clipper ship (41x61cm-16x24in) W/C. 16-Nov-3 CRN Auctions, Cambridge #32/R

NORTHCOTE, James (1746-1831) British
£407 $680 €594 Fisherman on an east coast shoreline (15x46cm-6x18in) s.d.93. 17-Nov-3 Waddingtons, Toronto #3/R (C.D 900)
£552 $1000 €806 Landscape and figures (25x20cm-10x8in) board. 3-Apr-4 South Bay, Long Island #166
£800 $1456 €1168 Portrait of Gentleman wearing a white stock and dark jacket (65x62cm-26x24in) s.d.1807. 16-Jun-4 Rupert Toovey, Partridge Green #75/R
£1099 $2000 €1605 Portrait of Captain Edward Brace (77x63cm-30x25in) s.d.1814. 29-Jun-4 Sotheby's, New York #51/R est:5000-7000
£1198 $2000 €1749 Portrait of a gentleman (76x63cm-30x25in) 7-Oct-3 Sotheby's, New York #46/R est:2000-3000
£2335 $4250 €3409 Portrait of Sir Joshua Reynolds (73x65cm-29x26in) canvas on panel. 29-Jun-4 Sotheby's, New York #55/R est:4000-6000
£10556 $19000 €15412 Return of the gleaners (195x149cm-77x59in) prov. 23-Jan-4 Christie's, Rockefeller NY #138/R est:20000-30000
£28000 $51520 €40880 Tiger hunting (191x214cm-75x84in) s. prov.exhib.lit. 26-Mar-4 Sotheby's, London #46/R est:30000-40000
£46000 $76360 €67160 Portrait of Lieutenant George Dyer wearing 1768 uniform of the Corps of Marines (74x61cm-29x24in) i.stretcher painted oval prov.exhib.lit. 30-Sep-3 Sotheby's, London #181/R est:30000-40000

NORTHCOTE, James (attrib) (1746-1831) British
£800 $1432 €1168 Portrait of a gentleman in a black jacket and white cravat (74x61cm-29x24in) 27-May-4 Christie's, Kensington #104/R

NORTHMANN, Hans (1883-?) German
£459 $706 €720 Hamburg harbour (67x80cm-26x31in) s. 4-Sep-2 Schopman, Hamburg #261/R

NORTHUP, George (20th C) American
Sculpture
£2690 $4250 €3901 Noontime covey (74cm-29in) bronze. 26-Jul-3 Coeur d'Alene, Hayden #218/R est:3500-4500
£3209 $6000 €4685 Green drake day lamp (69x69x36cm-27x27x14in) bronze. 24-Jul-4 Coeur d'Alene, Hayden #257/R est:6000-8000

NORTON, Benjamin Cam (1835-1900) British
£1400 $2324 €2044 Chestnut hunter in a stable (51x61cm-20x24in) s.d.1879. 1-Oct-3 Woolley & Wallis, Salisbury #304/R est:600-800
£8500 $15640 €12410 Primrose II with Charles Wood up (82x107cm-32x42in) s.i.d.1883 i.verso. 23-Mar-4 Bonhams, New Bond Street #36/R est:6000-8000

NORTON, Crandall (1920-) American
Works on paper
£1374 $2500 €2006 Irvine Lake (36x53cm-14x21in) s.d.62 W/C. 15-Jun-4 John Moran, Pasadena #85 est:1000-1500

NORTON, Helen (1961-) Australian
£496 $917 €724 Mount Hart man visits silent grove (91x122cm-36x48in) s.d.94 i.verso. 10-Mar-4 Deutscher-Menzies, Melbourne #559/R est:1000-1500 (A.D 1200)
£1417 $2281 €2069 Forgiving prayer (90x120cm-35x47in) s.d.99. 13-Oct-3 Joel, Victoria #409/R est:2500-3500 (A.D 3500)

NORTON, Jim C (1953-) American
£2174 $3500 €3174 Ahead of the storm (24x18cm-9x7in) 22-Aug-3 Altermann Galleries, Santa Fe #133
£3294 $5600 €4809 Two in a circle (48x58cm-19x23in) board. 1-Nov-3 Altermann Galleries, Santa Fe #101
£3294 $5600 €4809 Gathering on 6666s (43x58cm-17x23in) board. 1-Nov-3 Altermann Galleries, Santa Fe #102
£6471 $11000 €9448 Cheyenne dog soldier (58x43cm-23x17in) 1-Nov-3 Altermann Galleries, Santa Fe #104
£7263 $13000 €10604 Trail home (81x61cm-32x24in) 15-May-4 Altermann Galleries, Santa Fe #1/R
£10588 $18000 €15458 Cheyenne at sunset (71x102cm-28x40in) 1-Nov-3 Altermann Galleries, Santa Fe #103

NORTON, Louis Doyle (1867-?) American
Works on paper
£430 $800 €628 The marshes, sunrise (22x32cm-9x13in) s. pastel paper on board. 5-Mar-4 Skinner, Boston #453/R

NORTON, William Edward (1843-1916) American
£1397 $2250 €2040 Sailing - Maine coast (20x36cm-8x14in) s. 20-Aug-3 James Julia, Fairfield #912/R est:2000-3000
£1497 $2500 €2186 Burning boat (23x33cm-9x13in) 23-Oct-3 Shannon's, Milford #199/R est:2500-3500
£3495 $6500 €5103 Full sails (35x27cm-14x11in) s.d.74. 5-Mar-4 Skinner, Boston #316/R est:2000-4000
£6790 $11000 €9846 Harbour scene (51x76cm-20x30in) s. 8-Aug-3 Barridorf, Portland #77/R est:12000-15000
£9000 $16110 €13140 Barque under sail and running down Channel (122x165cm-48x65in) s. prov.exhib. 26-May-4 Christie's, Kensington #746/R est:6000-8000
Works on paper
£400 $736 €584 Fisherfolk on the beach (43x58cm-17x23in) s. W/C. 8-Jun-4 Gorringes, Lewes #2169

NORTWICK, C K van (20th C) American
£276 $500 €403 New England winter scene (28x46cm-11x18in) s. board. 18-Apr-4 Jeffery Burchard, Florida #133/R

NORWELL, Graham Noble (1901-1967) Canadian
£205 $334 €299 Winter fairyland (30x41cm-12x16in) canvasboard. 23-Sep-3 Ritchie, Toronto #133/R (C.D 450)
£565 $1039 €825 Gatineau Hills in winter (40x61cm-16x24in) s. 9-Jun-4 Walker's, Ottawa #23/R (C.D 1400)
Works on paper
£262 $482 €383 Percy Rock, Quebec (36x47cm-14x19in) s. W/C. 9-Jun-4 Walker's, Ottawa #102/R (C.D 650)
£267 $461 €390 Autumn, Laurentians (33x51cm-13x20in) s. W/C. 9-Dec-3 Maynards, Vancouver #206a (C.D 600)
£268 $447 €389 Sunrise fresh snowfall (46x56cm-18x22in) s.d.1924 pastel. 17-Jun-3 Pinneys, Montreal #148 (C.D 600)
£290 $485 €421 Farmhouse in winter (48x61cm-19x24in) s.d.1923 pastel. 17-Jun-3 Pinneys, Montreal #185 (C.D 650)
£893 $1536 €1304 Cabin in winter (46x61cm-18x24in) s.d.23 pastel. 2-Dec-3 Joyner Waddington, Toronto #158/R est:1800-2200 (C.D 2000)

NOTER, David de (1825-1875) Belgian
£2734 $5113 €4101 Still life (35x29cm-14x11in) s.d.56 panel prov. 20-Jul-4 Goodman, Sydney #89/R est:6000-8000 (A.D 7000)
£3741 $6697 €5500 Bouquet de fleurs avec des oranges sur un entablement (54x65cm-21x26in) s. 19-Mar-4 Millon & Associes, Paris #36/R est:3500-4000
£12000 $21600 €18000 Nature morte aux fruits (75x60cm-30x24in) s. 20-Apr-4 Galerie Moderne, Brussels #394/R est:20000-26000
£14205 $25000 €20739 Elegant lady in an interior with two King Charles Spaniels at her feet (67x53cm-26x21in) s.d.52 panel. 18-May-4 Bonhams & Butterfields, San Francisco #68/R est:20000-30000
Works on paper
£1200 $2196 €1800 Promeneurs a Tlemcen (28x21cm-11x8in) s. W/C. 3-Jun-4 Tajan, Paris #230/R est:1500-1800

NOTER, Jean Baptiste Andre de (1787-1855) Belgian
Works on paper
£1329 $2259 €1900 Vues a Malines (14x19cm-6x7in) s. pen W/C three. 1-Dec-3 Palais de Beaux Arts, Brussels #243 est:2000-3000

NOTER, Pierre François de (1779-1843) Belgian
£733 $1313 €1100 Cour d'abbaye animee (37x29cm-15x11in) s.indis.d.1821 panel. 11-May-4 Vanderkindere, Brussels #53

NOTERMAN, Emmanuel (1808-1863) Flemish
£500 $895 €750 Chiens couches (29x36cm-11x14in) s. panel. 11-May-4 Vanderkindere, Brussels #13

NOTERMAN, Emmanuel (attrib) (1808-1863) Flemish
£1528 $2490 €2200 Young woman and daughter selling flowers (55x73cm-22x29in) s.d.1841 panel. 25-Sep-3 Dr Fritz Nagel, Stuttgart #1389/R est:2300

NOTERMAN, Zacharias (1820-1890) German
£1000 $1820 €1500 Circus dog (19x24cm-7x9in) s. panel double-sided. 3-Jul-4 Badum, Bamberg #227/R est:1500
£1818 $3091 €2600 Deux chiens de cirque (65x79cm-26x31in) s. 1-Dec-3 Palais de Beaux Arts, Brussels #105/R est:7000-10000
£3586 $5953 €5200 Bonne aventure (53x66cm-21x26in) s. panel. 2-Oct-3 Sotheby's, Paris #92/R
£4392 $7730 €6500 Singes savants dans un cabaret (74x93cm-29x37in) s. 18-May-4 Galerie Moderne, Brussels #168/R est:5000-7000
£9184 $14602 €13500 Cirque ambulant (85x72cm-33x28in) s. 23-Mar-3 Mercier & Cie, Lille #241/R est:9000-10000

NOTT, Raymond (1888-1948) American
Works on paper
£375 $600 €548 Mountain landscape (122x170cm-48x67in) s. pastel. 18-May-3 Auctions by the Bay, Alameda #1091/R

NOTTINGHAM, Robert A (jnr) (fl.1853-1875) British
Works on paper
£750 $1253 €1095 Figure beside a waterfall. Figures beside river rapids (55x84cm-22x33in) s.d.1868 W/C pair. 20-Oct-3 Bonhams, Bath #119

NOURNEY, Maria (1856-1923) Dutch
£582 $990 €850 Still life with flowers and currants (51x39cm-20x15in) s.d.1885. 5-Nov-3 Vendue Huis, Gravenhage #80a
£651 $1106 €950 Still life of flowers (51x39cm-20x15in) s.d.1885. 5-Nov-3 Vendue Huis, Gravenhage #80/R

NOURSE, Elizabeth (1859-1938) American
Works on paper
£964 $1600 €1398 Italian gardens (20x30cm-8x12in) s.d. W/C. 14-Jun-3 Rachel Davis, Shaker Heights #424/R est:1000-2000
£2439 $4000 €3537 French soldiers memorial (23x18cm-9x7in) s.d.1914 and Sept 1915 W/C. 7-Jun-3 Treadway Gallery, Cincinnati #1324 est:4000-6000

NOURY, Gaston (1866-?) French
Works on paper
£638 $1186 €950 La cour de ferme (27x43cm-11x17in) s.d.1902 pastel. 7-Mar-4 Lesieur & Le Bars, Le Havre #110

NOUVEAU, Germain Bernard Marie (1851-1920) French
£533 $976 €800 Rue fortifiee (22x16cm-9x6in) s. d.25 aout 1870 verso cardboard. 6-Jun-4 Anaf, Lyon #461/R
£533 $976 €800 Personnages a la porte de la ville (22x16cm-9x6in) s. d.aout 1870 verso cardboard. 6-Jun-4 Anaf, Lyon #462/R

NOUVEAU, Henri (1901-1959) Rumanian
£544 $975 €800 Improvisation (49x32cm-19x13in) mono.d.1955 mono.i.d.verso paint paper. 21-Mar-4 Calmels Cohen, Paris #4/R
£2238 $3804 €3200 Geometrie poetique (30x44cm-12x17in) mono.d.1941 oil paper prov. 23-Nov-3 Cornette de St.Cyr, Paris #241/R est:600-800
£3176 $5590 €4700 Composition (30x45cm-12x18in) mono.d.1949 prov. 18-May-4 Tajan, Paris #23/R est:4500-5000
Works on paper
£315 $535 €450 Poissons, nizza. mono.d.10/III/36 gouache prov.exhib. 23-Nov-3 Cornette de St.Cyr, Paris #240
£878 $1572 €1300 Improvisation (46x31cm-18x12in) mono.d.1953 gouache. 4-May-4 Calmels Cohen, Paris #182/R est:1000-1500
£1259 $2140 €1800 Improvisation (50x32cm-20x13in) mono.d. s.i.d.19/IV.55 verso gouache collage. 23-Nov-3 Cornette de St.Cyr, Paris #242/R est:400-500
£1933 $3538 €2900 Arbuste lumineux (48x34cm-19x13in) d.1946 s.i.d.verso mixed media prov. 6-Jun-4 Anaf, Lyon #463/R est:3000-4000

NOVAK, I (19th C) ?
£1854 $3375 €2800 Aeneas in the Underworld (95x125cm-37x49in) s.i. 16-Jun-4 Dorotheum, Vienna #248/R est:2000-3000

NOVATI, Cesare Calchi (1858-1939) Italian
£2333 $4293 €3500 Still life with cherries and flowers (92x122cm-36x48in) s. 8-Jun-4 Sotheby's, Milan #105/R est:1500-2500

NOVATI, Marco (1895-1975) Italian
£490 $842 €700 Portrait of the Earl Ugo Viarelli (55x66cm-22x26in) s. 3-Dec-3 Stadion, Trieste #1126
£541 $1022 €800 Peacock (127x99cm-50x39in) s.d.1920. 20-Feb-4 Stadion, Trieste #563/R
£874 $1503 €1250 Peacock (128x100cm-50x39in) s.d.1920. 3-Dec-3 Stadion, Trieste #1059/R

NOVELLI, Francesco (1767-1836) Italian
Works on paper
£833 $1358 €1200 Italian market (9x13cm-4x5in) W/C htd gold. 24-Sep-3 Neumeister, Munich #289/R

NOVELLI, Gastone (1925-1968) Italian
£18116 $29710 €25000 Doe (50x50cm-20x20in) s. s.i.d.61 verso prov. 27-May-3 Sotheby's, Milan #269/R est:22000-28000
£23649 $41622 €35000 Maintenant (45x60cm-18x24in) s.i.d.62 verso oil pencil. 24-May-4 Christie's, Milan #307/R est:35000-45000
£31469 $53497 €45000 Girl dreaming in pink bed (80x99cm-31x39in) s.i.d.1965 acrylic pencil. 28-Nov-3 Farsetti, Prato #367/R est:45000-50000
£43624 $78087 €65000 Dans le plis (65x100cm-26x39in) s. i.d.61 verso oil pencil pastel exhib.lit. 25-May-4 Sotheby's, Milan #293/R est:60000-80000
£55000 $91850 €80300 Il mito della condanna (135x135cm-53x53in) s.i.d.63 verso prov.exhib.lit. 21-Oct-3 Christie's, London #27/R est:55000-65000
£140940 $252282 €210000 Dictionary (200x200cm-79x79in) s.d.64 s.i.d.verso oil pencil. 25-May-4 Sotheby's, Milan #279/R est:140000-180000
Works on paper
£3000 $5520 €4500 Sunset in November (35x49cm-14x19in) s.i.d.1963 pastel pencil prov. 14-Jun-4 Porro, Milan #39/R est:4500-6000
£3020 $5406 €4500 Great maze (49x71cm-19x28in) s.i.d.67 pencil pen prov. 25-May-4 Sotheby's, Milan #154/R est:6000
£3333 $6133 €5000 Untitled (33x48cm-13x19in) s.d.1966 mixed media masonite. 8-Jun-4 Finarte Semenzato, Milan #441/R est:5000-6000
£5034 $9312 €7500 Untitled (50x70cm-20x28in) s.d.1960 pencil W/C. 11-Mar-4 Galleria Pace, Milan #139/R est:8500-12000
£5245 $8916 €7500 Alphabet 4 (48x66cm-19x26in) s.i.d.62 ink pastel pencil prov. 24-Nov-3 Christie's, Milan #147/R est:7500-8500
£9790 $16643 €14000 Untitled (70x100cm-28x39in) s.d.62 ink pastel prov. 24-Nov-3 Christie's, Milan #145/R est:11500-13500
£10067 $18020 €15000 Untitled (69x99cm-27x39in) s.d.1960 mixed media. 30-May-4 Meeting Art, Vercelli #25 est:10000
£16084 $27343 €23000 Earth is protecting us (35x50cm-14x20in) s.d.62 s.i.d.verso hydropaint on canvas. 28-Nov-3 Farsetti, Prato #168/R est:20000-24000

NOVELLI, Pietro (1603-1647) Italian
£48611 $79236 €70000 La Madonna del Carmine (165x126cm-65x50in) prov. 25-Sep-3 Dr Fritz Nagel, Stuttgart #1217/R

NOVELLI, Pietro Antonio (1729-1804) Italian
Works on paper
£328 $600 €479 St John at the crucifixion of Christ (28x19cm-11x7in) i. pen brown ink wash over pencil. 29-Jan-4 Swann Galleries, New York #131/R
£600 $1038 €876 Orlando Furioso (13x9cm-5x4in) s.i. pen black ink grey. 12-Dec-3 Christie's, Kensington #374/R
£816 $1461 €1200 L'Assomption de la Vierge entouree d'anges musiciens (28x22cm-11x9in) black chk pen black ink col wash prov. 18-Mar-4 Christie's, Paris #49/R
£833 $1500 €1216 Faun with grapes and a cup (39x21cm-15x8in) pencil. 21-Jan-4 Sotheby's, New York #28/R est:1500-2500
£890 $1513 €1300 Madonna and Child (20x14cm-8x6in) pen ink wash. 6-Nov-3 Tajan, Paris #43/R
£900 $1557 €1314 Immaculate Madonna (40x30cm-16x12in) pen black ink brush brown wash over black chk. 9-Dec-3 Bonhams, Knightsbridge #68/R
£2000 $3660 €2920 Two groups of putti at play (19x24cm-7x9in) red chk. 8-Jul-4 Sotheby's, London #114/R est:2000-3000
£2381 $4262 €3500 Une jeune femme a mi-corps portant un panier de fruits (22x18cm-9x7in) black chk pen brown ink wash. 18-Mar-4 Christie's, Paris #50/R est:1500-2000
£4218 $7550 €6200 Une jeune femme lavant du linge (38x29cm-15x11in) i. pen black ink grey wash prov. 18-Mar-4 Christie's, Paris #48/R est:4000-6000

NOVELLI, Sebastiano (attrib) (1853-1916) Italian
£3500 $5600 €5110 Sull'Canale Grande, Venezia (63x79cm-25x31in) 18-Sep-3 Christie's, Kensington #72/R est:3500-4500

NOVICE, William (fl.1809-1833) British
£600 $1116 €876 Portrait of a gentleman in a black and brown waistcoat (48x37cm-19x15in) s. panel. 4-Mar-4 Christie's, Kensington #349/R
£1342 $2470 €2000 Horse and dog in extensive landscape (63x76cm-25x30in) s.d.38. 24-Mar-4 Hugo Ruef, Munich #1062 est:2000

NOVO, Stefano (1862-1902) Italian
£500 $860 €730 Mother and children in the nursery (23x18cm-9x7in) s.d.86 board. 5-Dec-3 Chrystals Auctions, Isle of Man #212/R
£650 $1190 €949 Mother with children in an interior (15x18cm-6x7in) s.d.81 panel. 28-Jan-4 Mallams, Oxford #508
£7746 $13556 €11000 La marchande de fleurs (86x59cm-34x23in) s. 16-Dec-3 Claude Aguttes, Neuilly #107/R est:10000-12000

NOVOA, Glexis (1964-) Cuban
£838 $1500 €1223 Tiger on branch. Jaguar on branch (30x25cm-12x10in) s.d.1971 panel pair. 20-Mar-4 Selkirks, St. Louis #167 est:500-700

NOVOA, Gustavo (1941-) Chilean
£7059 $12000 €10306 Virtual forest (91x91cm-36x36in) s. s.i.d.2000 verso acrylic prov. 19-Nov-3 Sotheby's, New York #181/R est:10000-15000

NOVOA, Leopoldo (1929-) Uruguayan
£2083 $3542 €3000 Space and vertical (81x65cm-32x26in) s.i.d.1982 verso acrylic sand collage canvas on board. 28-Oct-3 Segre, Madrid #194/R est:2400

NOVOPACKY, Johann (1821-1908) Austrian
Works on paper
£325 $582 €475 Winter in the square (28x49cm-11x19in) s.d.1878 W/C. 4-May-4 Ritchie, Toronto #99/R (C.D 800)

NOVOPACKY, Johann (attrib) (1821-1908) Austrian
£350 $601 €500 Thatched cottage with figures on summer day (12x16cm-5x6in) board. 5-Dec-3 Michael Zeller, Lindau #743/R

NOVOTNY, Elmer L (1909-1997) American
£1243 $2300 €1815 Summer sports, fishing, sailing and golf (191x107cm-75x42in) one s.d.96 panel tryptich. 13-Mar-4 DeFina, Austinburg #597/R est:2000-3000

NOVROS, David (1941-) American
£1528 $2750 €2231 Untitled (272x89cm-107x35in) diptych two pieces. 24-Apr-4 Du Mouchelle, Detroit #3227/R est:2000-4000
Works on paper
£611 $1100 €892 Untitled (30x22cm-12x9in) d.March 16 1967 W/C pair. 24-Apr-4 David Rago, Lambertville #284/R

NOWACK, Hans (1866-1918) Austrian
£315 $535 €450 Street in Hall, Tyrol with blacksmith (31x40cm-12x16in) s.d.1916 board. 20-Nov-3 Dorotheum, Salzburg #200/R

NOWAK, Anton (1865-1932) Austrian
£4043 $6751 €5700 Market in the old square, Prague (126x140cm-50x55in) s.d.1909. 14-Oct-3 Finarte Semenzato, Milan #140/R est:8000

NOWAK, Ernst (1853-1919) Austrian
£1060 $1939 €1600 The connoisseur (26x20cm-10x8in) s. panel. 8-Apr-4 Dorotheum, Vienna #7 est:2000-2400

NOWAK, Franz (19/20th C) Austrian
£1913 $3500 €2793 Still life of grapes and pomegranates. Still lifes (8x8cm-3x3in) s. board set of four. 3-Jun-4 Christie's, Rockefeller NY #1145/R est:1000-1500

NOWAK, Hans (1922-) German
£625 $987 €900 Still life of flowers with jug (80x70cm-31x28in) s. 19-Sep-3 Schloss Ahlden, Ahlden #1674/R

NOWAK, Miryam (20th C) Polish
£268 $494 €400 Wedding journey (33x50cm-13x20in) bears sig.d.1952 board. 25-Mar-4 Karlheinz Kaupp, Staufen #2642/R

NOWAK, Otto (1874-1945) Austrian
Works on paper
£403 $741 €600 Lilienfeld monastery garden (25x34cm-10x13in) s.i.d.1913 verso W/C exhib. 26-Mar-4 Dorotheum, Vienna #329/R

NOWAKOWSKI, Aleksander (1872-1935) Polish
£694 $1132 €1000 Mountainous river landscape in winter (24x32cm-9x13in) s.cyrillic board. 26-Sep-3 Bolland & Marotz, Bremen #587/R

NOWAKOWSKI, Wojceich (20th C) Canadian
£339 $567 €495 Untitled - classical still life (60x50cm-24x20in) s.d.1989 prov. 17-Nov-3 Hodgins, Calgary #397/R (C.D 750)

NOWELL, Annie C (19th C) American
Works on paper
£240 $400 €350 Girl holding her hat (56x33cm-22x13in) s.d.85 W/C. 16-Nov-3 CRN Auctions, Cambridge #16/R

NOWELL, Arthur Trevithan (1862-1940) British
£24000 $44160 €35040 Captives (101x126cm-40x50in) s.i.d.1887 prov.exhib.lit. 23-Mar-4 Bonhams, New Bond Street #73/R est:20000-30000

NOWEY, Adolf (1835-?) British?
£260 $478 €380 Animals in a barn (25x38cm-10x15in) s. panel. 8-Jun-4 Bonhams, Knightsbridge #295/R

NOWOSIELSKI, Jerzy (1923-) Polish
£1204 $2155 €1758 Ship (45x65cm-18x26in) painted 1947. 6-May-4 Agra, Warsaw #63/R (P.Z 8500)
£2976 $5119 €4345 Abstract (39x53cm-15x21in) s.d.1957 verso board. 4-Dec-3 Agra, Warsaw #7/R est:20000 (P.Z 20000)
£4237 $7669 €6186 Abstract (50x70cm-20x28in) s.d.1984. 4-Apr-4 Agra, Warsaw #44/R (P.Z 30000)

£4828	$8062	€7000	Portrait of a seated girl (98x65cm-39x26in) 16-Nov-3 Agra, Warsaw #25/R est:4000
£7589	$13054	€11080	Male nude (75x60cm-30x24in) s.verso. 4-Dec-3 Agra, Warsaw #22/R est:30000 (P.Z 51000)
£7925	$14424	€11571	Seated female nude (65x50cm-26x20in) s.d.1958. 20-Jun-4 Agra, Warsaw #35/R (P.Z 55000)
£8051	$14572	€11754	Composition (73x50cm-29x20in) s.d.1981. 4-Apr-4 Agra, Warsaw #14/R (P.Z 57000)
£8276	$13821	€12000	Green landscape (60x80cm-24x31in) s.d.1985 verso. 16-Nov-3 Agra, Warsaw #17/R est:7000
£9174	$15229	€13394	Figure sitting before a table with glasses (60x73cm-24x29in) painted 1974. 2-Oct-3 Agra, Warsaw #15/R est:30000 (P.Z 60000)
£11161	$19196	€16295	Car papers (30x60cm-12x24in) s.i.d.1965 verso panel. 4-Dec-3 Agra, Warsaw #12 R est:40000 (P.Z 75000)
£15581	$27890	€22748	Figure (124x80cm-49x31in) painted 1989. 6-May-4 Agra, Warsaw #7/R est:50000 (P.Z 110000)
£15850	$28847	€23141	Composition (100x70cm-39x28in) s.d.1980. 20-Jun-4 Agra, Warsaw #37/R (P.Z 110000)
£18732	$34092	€27349	Bikini clad woman (80x100cm-31x39in) s.d.1971. 20-Jun-4 Agra, Warsaw #39/R (P.Z 130000)
£19878	$32997	€29022	Woman in an interior scene (60x80cm-24x31in) painted 1965. 2-Oct-3 Agra, Warsaw #40/R est:40000 (P.Z 130000)
£25517	$42614	€37000	Portraits of strangers (100x80cm-39x31in) s.d.1978 verso. 16-Nov-3 Agra, Warsaw #11/R est:10000

Works on paper

£298	$512	€435	Woman with red hat (20x14cm-8x6in) W/C exec.1945. 4-Dec-3 Agra, Warsaw #21/R (P.Z 2000)
£524	$938	€765	Two women (24x34cm-9x13in) Chinese ink W/C. 6-May-4 Agra, Warsaw #62/R (P.Z 3700)
£688	$1148	€1004	Castle (17x13cm-7x5in) s. W/C pencil. 15-Oct-3 Agra, Warsaw #17/R (P.Z 4400)
£706	$1278	€1031	Gymnast (42x30cm-17x12in) gouache exec 1955. 4-Apr-4 Agra, Warsaw #58/R (P.Z 5000)
£729	$1254	€1064	Having a wash (28x21cm-11x8in) pencil exec.1955. 4-Dec-3 Agra, Warsaw #33/R (P.Z 4900)
£897	$1497	€1300	Kneeling female nude (32x22cm-13x9in) s.d.1962 pen. 16-Nov-3 Agra, Warsaw #95/R
£917	$1523	€1339	Cat (38x29cm-15x11in) pen exec.1980. 2-Oct-3 Agra, Warsaw #1/R est:3000 (P.Z 6000)
£921	$1648	€1345	Couple (34x24cm-13x9in) wax board. 6-May-4 Agra, Warsaw #6/R (P.Z 6500)
£992	$1775	€1448	Portrait from behind (34x25cm-13x10in) Chinese ink W/C. 6-May-4 Agra, Warsaw #5/R (P.Z 7000)
£1034	$1728	€1500	Woman (33x19cm-13x7in) gouache chk pencil ink pen exec. 1950. 16-Nov-3 Agra, Warsaw #42/R est:1000
£1682	$2792	€2456	Wearing high heels (34x24cm-13x9in) W/C exec.1959. 2-Oct-3 Agra, Warsaw #13/R est:5000 (P.Z 11000)
£1682	$2792	€2456	Still life (31x26cm-12x10in) gouache cardboard. 2-Oct-3 Agra, Warsaw #74/R est:8000 (P.Z 11000)
£1729	$3147	€2524	Seated female nude (49x32cm-19x13in) s.d.97 India ink pen. 20-Jun-4 Agra, Warsaw #36/R (P.Z 12000)
£1835	$3046	€2679	Working on the railroad (24x34cm-9x13in) pastel W/C exec.1948. 2-Oct-3 Agra, Warsaw #38/R est:8000 (P.Z 12000)
£2119	$3835	€3094	Woman (34x24cm-13x9in) s.d.47 Indian ink W. 4-Apr-4 Agra, Warsaw #62/R (P.Z 15000)
£2141	$3554	€3126	Composition (29x47cm-11x19in) W/C exec.1983. 2-Oct-3 Agra, Warsaw #67/R est:10000 (P.Z 14000)
£17655	$31956	€25776	Composition with figure (90x80cm-35x31in) s.d.1976 polymer paint. 4-Apr-4 Agra, Warsaw #11/R (P.Z 125000)

NOYER, Denis Paul (20th C) French

£398	$700	€581	Cafe Chinois (69x89cm-27x35in) s. 23-May-4 Hindman, Chicago #984/R

NOYER, Philippe (1917-1985) French

£300	$501	€438	La fontaine au pigeons (63x51cm-25x20in) s. 14-Oct-3 Sotheby's, London #518
£389	$700	€568	Portrait of a girl. s.d.68 acrylic. 24-Jan-4 Susanin's, Chicago #5050/R
£543	$1000	€793	Girls at the piano (99x81cm-39x32in) s. 27-Jun-4 Hindman, Chicago #910/R est:1000-1500
£699	$1300	€1021	Two children with a pony (91x60cm-36x24in) s.d.49 prov. 3-Mar-4 Christie's, Rockefeller NY #64/R est:1500-2000
£779	$1300	€1137	Portrait of a girl (100x49cm-39x19in) s.d.59. 19-Oct-3 Bonhams & Butterfields, Los Angeles #7025 est:800-1200
£1183	$2200	€1727	Girl taking tea on a rooftop (54x64cm-21x25in) s.i.d.1951. 3-Mar-4 Christie's, Rockefeller NY #62/R est:1500-2000
£1364	$2400	€1991	Le pecheur bleu (61x71cm-24x28in) s.d.1966 i. 18-May-4 Arthur James, Florida #155/R est:1200-1800

Works on paper

£1000	$1670	€1460	Flower girls (110x64cm-43x25in) s. W/C pair. 14-Oct-3 Sotheby's, London #517/R est:400-600

NOYES, George L (1864-1954) Canadian

£1796	$3000	€2622	Massachusetts pond landscape (33x38cm-13x15in) s. 16-Nov-3 CRN Auctions, Cambridge #60/R
£2950	$4750	€4307	Chateau de Tremouille (36x41cm-14x16in) s. board prov. 20-Aug-3 James Julia, Fairfield #1447/R est:3000-5000
£3294	$5500	€4809	Stone Wall (30x41cm-12x16in) s. board prov. 23-Oct-3 Shannon's, Milford #253/R est:2000-3000
£3632	$6500	€5303	Winter landscape Millis, Mass (33x38cm-13x15in) s.i.d.1915 verso board. 6-May-4 Shannon's, Milford #31/R est:3000-5000
£4268	$7000	€6189	North African landscape (33x46cm-13x18in) s.i. 31-May-3 Brunk, Ashville #587/R est:3000-6000
£5028	$9000	€7341	Les Lavoirs, Paris (36x41cm-14x16in) s.i.verso canvas on panel prov. 6-May-4 Shannon's, Milford #30/R est:6000-8000
£5495	$10000	€8023	Still life with copper covered pot, whale oil lamp and porcelain (61x51cm-24x20in) s.d.1910 prov.exhib. 15-Jun-4 John Moran, Pasadena #104 est:5000-7500
£7784	$13000	€11365	Gloucester fishing boats (46x61cm-18x24in) s. canvasboard. 7-Oct-3 Sotheby's, New York #185 est:12000-18000
£10180	$17000	€14863	Mckinnley Homestead (64x76cm-25x30in) s. prov. 23-Oct-3 Shannon's, Milford #112/R est:10000-15000

NOYES, George L (attrib) (1864-1954) Canadian

£419	$750	€612	Floral still lifes (51x39cm-20x15in) double-sided board. 14-May-4 Skinner, Boston #380/R

NOZAL, Alexandre (1852-1929) French

£364	$663	€550	Bord de riviere (22x35cm-9x14in) s.i. 16-Jun-4 Renaud, Paris #30
£1100	$2035	€1606	Village in a sunlit landscape (46x61cm-18x24in) s. 15-Jan-4 Christie's, Kensington #794/R est:700-1000
£1409	$2621	€2100	Etang a Villeneuve (27x41cm-11x16in) s.d.1900. 7-Mar-4 Lesieur & Le Bars, Le Havre #111
£1469	$2526	€2100	Vaches en Normandie (55x74cm-22x29in) s. 5-Dec-3 Maigret, Paris #98/R est:1000-1200
£2013	$3685	€3000	Seine au Bas-Meudon (73x105cm-29x41in) s.i. 7-Jul-4 Artcurial Briest, Paris #85 est:2500-3500

Works on paper

£789	$1429	€1200	Bord de mer (42x50cm-17x20in) s. W/C gouache. 19-Apr-4 Boscher, Cherbourg #898/R

NUCKEL, Otto (1888-1956) German

£1528	$2551	€2200	Village in the pre Alps (83x59cm-33x23in) s. canvas on panel. 24-Oct-3 Ketterer, Hamburg #487/R est:2500-3500
£4977	$7964	€7266	Schutzmann (100x75cm-39x30in) s. s.i.d.1928 stretcher exhib.prov. 16-Sep-3 Philippe Schuler, Zurich #3368/R est:8000-12000 (S.FR 11000)

Works on paper

£336	$617	€500	News (31x24cm-12x9in) s. chk pencil. 26-Mar-4 Venator & Hansten, Koln #1812/R
£369	$679	€550	Forty winks (33x27cm-13x11in) s. chk wash. 26-Mar-4 Venator & Hansten, Koln #1813/R

NUDERSCHER, Frank (1880-1959) American

£767	$1250	€1112	Riverside winter landscape, probably Arcadia (71x86cm-28x34in) s. 20-Jul-3 Jeffery Burchard, Florida #73
£1307	$2300	€1908	Antonio, Missouri (51x61cm-20x24in) s. i.verso masonite. 22-May-4 Selkirks, St. Louis #616/R est:1000-1400

NUESCH, Johann Jakob (1845-1895) Swiss

£1121	$1872	€1637	Schloss Grunenstein with view of Rhine valley (24x34cm-9x13in) s. 24-Oct-3 Hans Widmer, St Gallen #39/R est:2500-5500 (S.FR 2500)

NUILAALIK, Josiah (1928-) North American

Sculpture

£1532	$2604	€2237	Flying bear/shaman (46cm-18in) s. marbled green soapstone. 3-Nov-3 Waddingtons, Toronto #733/R est:3000-4000 (C.D 3400)

NUMANS, Auguste (1823-?) Belgian

£400	$716	€600	Interieur anime (50x34cm-20x13in) s. 11-May-4 Vanderkindere, Brussels #83
£582	$990	€850	Port mediterraneen (55x67cm-22x26in) s. 10-Nov-3 Horta, Bruxelles #428
£1000	$1800	€1500	Ruelle Italienne animee (65x55cm-26x22in) s. 20-Apr-4 Galerie Moderne, Brussels #369/R est:1000-1500

NUMBULMOORE, Charlie (c.1907-1971) Australian

Works on paper

£6250	$11688	€9375	Wanjina (61x26cm-24x10in) earth pigments slate prov. 26-Jul-4 Sotheby's, Melbourne #17/R est:12000-18000 (A.D 16000)
£6504	$10276	€9431	Wanjina (42x20cm-17x8in) i.verso earth pigments slate exec.c.1970 prov. 28-Jul-3 Sotheby's, Paddington #76/R est:8000-12000 (A.D 16000)
£12397	$21074	€18100	Ngarinyin, Gibb River, WA - two spotted Wandjina (78x60cm-31x24in) natural earth pigments on cardboard executed c.1960 prov. 29-Oct-3 Lawson Menzies, Sydney #33/R est:25000-35000 (A.D 30000)
£16406	$30680	€24609	Wanjina (62x38cm-24x15in) earth pigments exhib. prov. 26-Jul-4 Sotheby's, Melbourne #18/R est:40000-60000 (A.D 42000)
£18293	$28902	€26525	Wanjina (57x37cm-22x15in) earth pigments eucalyptus bark prov. 28-Jul-3 Sotheby's, Paddington #75/R est:20000-30000 (A.D 45000)
£20325	$32114	€29471	Wanjina (55x37cm-22x15in) earth pigments eucalyptus bark prov. 28-Jul-3 Sotheby's, Paddington #74/R est:20000-30000 (A.D 50000)

NUMERS, Fredrik Adolf (1745-1792) Swedish

Works on paper

£451	$844	€658	Swedish farmers harvesting (31x45cm-12x18in) i. pen W/C. 25-Feb-4 Museumsbygningen, Copenhagen #141/R (D.KR 5000)

NUNA, Sharky (1918-1979) North American

Sculpture

£1802	$3063	€2631	Inuit mother with her children (62cm-24in) marbled green soapstone exec.c.1975. 3-Nov-3 Waddingtons, Toronto #319/R est:4000-6000 (C.D 4000)

NUNAMAKER, Alfred R (20th C) American

£2717	$5000	€3967	New Hope - late autumn (20x25cm-8x10in) s.i.verso board. 11-Jun-4 David Rago, Lambertville #258/R est:9000-12000
£8696	$16000	€12696	Pennsylvania landscape (36x36cm-14x14in) s.i. 11-Jun-4 David Rago, Lambertville #351/R est:6000-9000

NUNAMAKER, Kenneth R (1890-1957) American

£2989	$5500	€4364	Center Bridge (10x13cm-4x5in) init.i. artist st. verso board. 27-Jun-4 Freeman, Philadelphia #194/R est:3000-5000
£4717	$7500	€6887	House beside tree-lined road (20x25cm-8x10in) s. 10-Sep-3 Alderfer's, Hatfield #377/R est:6000-8000
£13587	$25000	€19837	Winter panorama (36x107cm-14x42in) s. prov. 27-Jun-4 Freeman, Philadelphia #211/R est:8000-12000

£40761 $75000 €59511 Old Home, Bucks Country PA (36x36cm-14x14in) s. s.i. verso. 27-Jun-4 Freeman, Philadelphia #214/R est:12000-18000
£65217 $120000 €95217 Tony's Place (56x61cm-22x24in) s. i.artist.st.verso prov. 27-Jun-4 Freeman, Philadelphia #177/R est:15000-25000
£65217 $120000 €95217 Winter sunlight (91x91cm-36x36in) s. i. verso. 27-Jun-4 Freeman, Philadelphia #188/R est:25000-40000

NUNAN, Shona (1959-) Australian
Sculpture
£1702 $2894 €2485 Female form (91cm-36in) bronze edn 4/6 exec 1987 prov. 26-Nov-3 Deutscher-Menzies, Melbourne #162/R est:3000-5000 (A.D 4000)

NUNEZ DE CELIS, Francisco (1919-1996) Spanish
Works on paper
£276 $458 €400 View of village (47x64cm-19x25in) s. mixed media. 1-Oct-3 Ansorena, Madrid #493/R

NUNEZ DE VILLAVICENCIO, Pedro (attrib) (1644-1700) Spanish
£1129 $2100 €1648 Bishop distributing alms to the poor (50x40cm-20x16in) s.d.1665. 5-Mar-4 Skinner, Boston #208/R est:800-1200

NUNEZ DEL PRADO, Marina (1911-1995) Bolivian
Sculpture
£5587 $10000 €8157 Flowers of the Andes (62x42x36cm-24x17x14in) s. glazed terracotta wooden base exec.c.1945 prov. 26-May-4 Sotheby's, New York #90/R est:10000-15000

NUNEZ LOSADA, Francisco (attrib) (1889-1973) Spanish
£636 $1100 €929 Dutch figures on shore (41x61cm-16x24in) s. 13-Dec-3 Charlton Hall, Columbia #610/R est:700-1000

NUNGARRAYI, Maggie Hargraves (c.1930-) Australian
Works on paper
£745 $1334 €1088 Woman Karnta dreaming (122x91cm-48x36in) synthetic polymer paint canvas exec 1994 prov. 25-May-4 Lawson Menzies, Sydney #200/R (A.D 1900)

NUNGORAYI, Munkja (c.1930-) Australian
Works on paper
£2539 $4748 €3809 Littari (91x61cm-36x24in) bears name.verso synthetic polymer paint canvas prov.lit. 26-Jul-4 Sotheby's, Melbourne #426/R est:3000-5000 (A.D 6500)

NUNGURRAYAI, Muntja (c.1930-) Australian
Works on paper
£1797 $3360 €2696 Paltjukujara (91x61cm-36x24in) i.verso synthetic polymer linen exec. 1996 prov.exhib. 21-Jul-4 Shapiro, Sydney #96/R est:5000-7000 (A.D 4600)

NUNGURRAYI, Ena Gimme (1953-1992) Australian
Works on paper
£4297 $8035 €6446 Talinyu (100x50cm-39x20in) bears name.verso synthetic polymer paint canvas prov.exhib.lit. 26-Jul-4 Sotheby's, Melbourne #64/R est:10000-15000 (A.D 11000)
£14063 $26297 €21095 Lilpuwu (99x76cm-39x30in) bears name.verso synthetic polymer paint canvas prov.exhib.lit. 26-Jul-4 Sotheby's, Melbourne #65/R est:20000-30000 (A.D 36000)

NUNGURRAYI, Gabriella Possum (1932-) Australian
£2553 $4340 €3727 Milky Way dreaming (142x178cm-56x70in) with sig. verso synthetic polymer paint canvas. 25-Nov-3 Christie's, Melbourne #287/R est:4500-6000 (A.D 6000)
Works on paper
£2266 $4237 €3399 Grandmother's country, Central Mount Wedge (118x183cm-46x72in) i.verso synthetic polymer canvas exec. 2001 prov. 21-Jul-4 Shapiro, Sydney #68/R est:5000-7000 (A.D 5800)

NUNGURRAYI, Jeannie Egan (20th C) Australian
Works on paper
£785 $1335 €1146 Puurda jukurrpa - bush potato dreaming (185x124cm-73x49in) synthetic polymer paint on canvas. 29-Oct-3 Lawson Menzies, Sydney #79/R est:2000-2500 (A.D 1900)

NUNGURRAYI, Lorraine Granites (20th C) Australian
Works on paper
£784 $1404 €1145 Karnta, Women's dreaming (91x129cm-36x51in) synthetic polymer paint canvas exec c.1995 prov. 25-May-4 Lawson Menzies, Sydney #210/R (A.D 2000)

NUNGURRAYI, Naata (1932-) Australian
Works on paper
£1020 $1825 €1489 Marrapinti (91x46cm-36x18in) synthetic polymer paint linen exec 2002 prov. 25-May-4 Lawson Menzies, Sydney #17/R est:3000-4500 (A.D 2600)
£1777 $3324 €2688 Untitled (123x152cm-48x60in) i.verso synthetic polymer linen exec. 2003 prov. 21-Jul-4 Shapiro, Sydney #55/R est:6000-8000 (A.D 4550)
£2539 $4748 €3809 Senior women camped at the rockhole site of Marrapinti (91x62cm-36x24in) bears name.verso synthetic polymer paint linen prov. 26-Jul-4 Sotheby's, Melbourne #188/R est:5000-7000 (A.D 6500)
£4314 $7722 €6298 Marrapinti (154x183cm-61x72in) synthetic polymer paint linen exec 2003 prov. 25-May-4 Lawson Menzies, Sydney #51/R est:13000-18000 (A.D 11000)

NUNGURRAYI, Nancy (c.1935-) Australian
Works on paper
£772 $1220 €1127 Untitled (107x28cm-42x11in) i.verso synthetic polymer paint linen prov. 28-Jul-3 Sotheby's, Paddington #388/R est:1500-2500 (A.D 1900)
£1172 $2191 €1758 Karrilwara (91x91cm-36x36in) bears name.verso synthetic polymer paint linen prov. 26-Jul-4 Sotheby's, Melbourne #503/R est:2000-3000 (A.D 3000)
£1882 $3369 €2748 Marrapinti (91x91cm-36x36in) synthetic polymer paint linen exec 1999 prov. 25-May-4 Lawson Menzies, Sydney #19/R est:3000-4000 (A.D 4800)

NUNGURRAYI, Nora Wompi (c.1935-) Australian
Works on paper
£332 $621 €498 Tjartajirra (75x49cm-30x19in) bears name.verso synthetic polymer paint canvas prov.exhib. 26-Jul-4 Sotheby's, Melbourne #441/R (A.D 850)

NUNZIANTE, Antonio (1956-) Italian
£1550 $2852 €2325 Composition (30x40cm-12x16in) s. s.i.verso. 12-Jun-4 Meeting Art, Vercelli #159/R est:500
£1733 $3189 €2600 Silent presence (50x60cm-20x24in) s. painted 1995. 12-Jun-4 Meeting Art, Vercelli #376/R est:1000
£2081 $3849 €3100 Still life (50x70cm-20x28in) s.d.1977. 13-Mar-4 Meeting Art, Vercelli #449 est:1000
£2467 $4539 €3700 Ballerina (70x50cm-28x20in) s. s.verso. 12-Jun-4 Meeting Art, Vercelli #3628/R est:1500
£3933 $7237 €5900 Atelier at sunset (100x70cm-39x28in) s. s.d.2002 verso. 12-Jun-4 Meeting Art, Vercelli #982/R est:2500

NUNZIO (1954-) American
£6294 $10699 €9000 Shaking (81x141cm-32x56in) s.i.d.1989 verso prov. 25-Nov-3 Sotheby's, Milan #257/R est:8000-10000
Sculpture
£2200 $4048 €3300 Untitled (46x26x8cm-18x10x3in) s.i.d.1994 verso burnt wood. 12-Jun-4 Meeting Art, Vercelli #503/R est:3000
£2759 $4607 €4000 Untitled (45x57cm-18x22in) s.d.1991 verso iron wood. 13-Nov-3 Finarte Semenzato, Rome #478/R est:3800-4500
£3356 $6007 €5000 Halt (86x21x5cm-34x8x2in) burnt wood exec.1988. 30-May-4 Meeting Art, Vercelli #8 est:5000
Works on paper
£1007 $1862 €1500 Untitled (51x35cm-20x14in) s.d.2003 chl lead board. 13-Mar-4 Meeting Art, Vercelli #106

NUPEN, Kjell (1955-) Norwegian
£1217 $2106 €1777 Waterfall on the west coast of Norway (65x54cm-26x21in) s. 13-Dec-3 Blomqvist, Lysaker #1275/R est:18000-22000 (N.KR 14000)
£1533 $2637 €2238 Composition (76x56cm-30x22in) init.d.1985 paper. 8-Dec-3 Blomqvist, Oslo #581/R est:18000-22000 (N.KR 18000)
£1537 $2567 €2244 Momment (42x63cm-17x25in) s.i.d.1986 verso. 13-Oct-3 Blomqvist, Oslo #324/R est:15000-20000 (N.KR 18000)
£1793 $2995 €2618 Sketch for landscape (80x62cm-31x24in) s. s.i.d.1983-1985 verso. 13-Oct-3 Blomqvist, Oslo #330/R est:20000-25000 (N.KR 21000)
£4259 $7325 €6218 Landscape sign (109x79cm-43x31in) init. s.i.d.1989 verso. 8-Dec-3 Blomqvist, Oslo #572/R est:60000-80000 (N.KR 50000)
£5963 $10256 €8706 Restored landscape (109x79cm-43x31in) s. s.i.d.1989 verso. 8-Dec-3 Blomqvist, Oslo #576/R est:50000-70000 (N.KR 70000)
£9350 $17110 €13651 Sentimental journey B -1985/86 (200x108cm-79x43in) init. i.d.1985/86 verso. 7-Jun-4 Blomqvist, Oslo #455/R est:150000-180000 (N.KR 115000)
Works on paper
£2733 $4564 €3990 Figure (100x73cm-39x29in) s. mixed media canvas. 13-Oct-3 Blomqvist, Oslo #335/R est:20000-25000 (N.KR 32000)

NURSEY, Rev Perry (fl.1815-1839) British
£2600 $4654 €3796 Seckford Hall Lodge with workers returning from the fields (34x43cm-13x17in) 22-Mar-4 Bonhams & Brooks, Norfolk #230/R est:400-600

NUSE, Roy Cleveland (1885-?) American
£11628 $20000 €16977 Old Shet, Rushland Quarry, winter (30x41cm-12x16in) mono. board prov. 7-Dec-3 Freeman, Philadelphia #194 est:20000-30000
£21739 $40000 €31739 Quarry - Autumn (30x41cm-12x16in) canvas laid down prov. 27-Jun-4 Freeman, Philadelphia #200/R est:25000-40000
£38043 $70000 €55543 Landscape with mill building on riverbank (64x76cm-25x30in) s.d.44. 9-Jun-4 Alderfer's, Hatfield #498 est:30000-50000
£152174 $280000 €222174 Three boys at the sheephole (91x76cm-36x30in) prov. 27-Jun-4 Freeman, Philadelphia #193/R est:70000-100000

NUSS, Fritz (20th C) German?
Sculpture
£1611 $2851 €2400 Mother with child (64cm-25in) s.d. verso brown pat.bronze. 30-Apr-4 Dr Fritz Nagel, Stuttgart #910/R est:2400

NUSS, Karl Ulrich (1943-) German
Sculpture
£1400 $2520 €2100 House altar (43cm-17in) s.d.1977 bronze Cast.Strassacker Sussen. 26-Apr-4 Rieber, Stuttgart #2213/R est:1800

NUSSBAUM, Jacob (1873-1936) German
Works on paper
£2400 $4392 €3600 View over River Main to cathedral (39x29cm-15x11in) s.d.23 pastel. 5-Jun-4 Arnold, Frankfurt #686/R est:300

NUSSBAUMER, Paul (1934-) Swiss
Works on paper
£655 $1192 €956 Eva (39x39cm-15x15in) s.d.87 ink tempera. 16-Jun-4 Fischer, Luzern #2804/R (S.FR 1500)

NUSSI, Arnaldo (1906-) Italian
£507 $832 €700 Mountainous landscape (31x40cm-12x16in) s. board. 27-May-3 Finarte Semenzato, Milan #117/R

NUSSIO, Oscar (1899-1976) Swiss
£216 $387 €315 Coastline near Bogliasco (27x35cm-11x14in) s.d. panel. 22-Mar-4 Philippe Schuler, Zurich #6039 (S.FR 500)
£298 $498 €432 In the meadows (60x50cm-24x20in) s.d.1965 masonite. 23-Jun-3 Philippe Schuler, Zurich #8451 (S.FR 650)
£346 $620 €505 Winter landscape near Ardez (44x60cm-17x24in) s.d. 22-Mar-4 Philippe Schuler, Zurich #6040 (S.FR 800)
£609 $1114 €889 Piz Nuna and Lai Pitschen (32x42cm-13x17in) s.i.d.1927 verso panel. 4-Jun-4 Zofingen, Switzerland #2899 (S.FR 1400)

NUSSLEIN, Heinrich (1879-?) German
£1342 $2403 €2000 Venus (36x29cm-14x11in) i. oil. 25-May-4 Dorotheum, Vienna #329/R est:2000-2600

NUTI, Enrico (19th C) Italian
£336 $594 €500 Public school (20x29cm-8x11in) s. i.verso board. 1-May-4 Meeting Art, Vercelli #276
£537 $950 €800 Countryside around Arezzo (19x29cm-7x11in) s. i.verso board. 1-May-4 Meeting Art, Vercelli #286
£728 $1326 €1100 View of harbour with sailing boats (70x98cm-28x39in) s. board. 21-Jun-4 Pandolfini, Florence #157

NUTT, Elizabeth Styring (1870-1946) British
£2600 $4134 €3796 Fishing boat in a mountainous moonlit estuary (48x74cm-19x29in) s.d.1931 exhib. 12-Sep-3 Gardiner & Houlgate, Bath #152/R est:150-250
£2800 $4452 €4088 Moorland stream (64x76cm-25x30in) s.d.1932 sold with a book. 12-Sep-3 Gardiner & Houlgate, Bath #151/R est:200-400
£4800 $7632 €7008 Where sunshine falls (71x91cm-28x36in) s.d.1924 i.verso sold with two books. 12-Sep-3 Gardiner & Houlgate, Bath #140/R est:400-800

NUTTER, William Henry (1821-1872) British
Works on paper
£320 $544 €467 Brother's water, a Lakeland vignette (13x17cm-5x7in) init.i.d.1846 W/C. 24-Nov-3 Tiffin King & Nicholson, Carlisle #204/R
£500 $915 €730 The entrance to Carlisle Castle with troops crossing the bridge over the moat (12x8cm-5x3in) W/C. 7-Jun-4 Cumbria Auction Rooms, Carlisle #225/R
£850 $1420 €1241 Country promenade (23x36cm-9x14in) s.d.1861 W/C. 13-Nov-3 Bonhams, Edinburgh #379

NUTTING, Iain (1961-) British
Sculpture
£1100 $1936 €1606 Spider monkey (160cm-63in) scrap metal. 18-May-4 Woolley & Wallis, Salisbury #385/R est:600-800
£1800 $3168 €2628 Reclining figure (35x71cm-14x28in) bronze one of 8. 18-May-4 Woolley & Wallis, Salisbury #380/R est:1200-1800
£2300 $4048 €3358 Gorilla (147cm-58in) 18-May-4 Woolley & Wallis, Salisbury #384/R est:1000-1500

NUVOLONE, Giuseppe (1619-1703) Italian
£4500 $7785 €6570 Saint John the Evangelist (55x42cm-22x17in) s.verso. 10-Dec-3 Bonhams, New Bond Street #113/R est:5000-7000
£7500 $13725 €10950 Madonna and Child (80x66cm-31x26in) 6-Jul-4 Sotheby's, Olympia #511/R est:4000-6000
£12000 $20760 €17520 Christ and the woman taken in adultery (126x102cm-50x40in) prov. 11-Dec-3 Sotheby's, London #196/R est:12000-18000

NUVOLONE, Giuseppe (attrib) (1619-1703) Italian
£5333 $9760 €8000 Venus and putto in landscape (32x43cm-13x17in) board. 1-Jun-4 Sotheby's, Milan #168/R est:6000-8000

NUVOLONE, Panfilo (c.1581-1651) Italian
£48993 $91617 €73000 Dish with peaches (19x30cm-7x12in) board. 25-Feb-4 Porro, Milan #82/R est:73000

NUYTTENS, Josef Pierre (1885-?) American/Belgian
£290 $510 €423 Stable scene with a blacksmith and other figures (69x5cm-27x2in) s. 28-May-4 Aspire, Cleveland #52/R

NUZZI, Mario (1603-1673) Italian
£18440 $30794 €26000 Basket of flowers (34x50cm-13x20in) 23-Jun-3 Finarte Semenzato, Rome #185/R est:28000
£26000 $46800 €37960 Still life of flowers in a stone urn on a pedestal (66x51cm-26x20in) prov. 22-Apr-4 Sotheby's, London #110/R est:15000-20000
£52349 $97893 €78000 Vases of flowers (67x49cm-26x19in) pair. 25-Feb-4 Porro, Milan #11/R est:78000
£62069 $103655 €90000 Vase with flowers (66x50cm-26x20in) 15-Nov-3 Porro, Milan #221/R est:50000

NUZZI, Mario (attrib) (1603-1673) Italian
£1130 $2000 €1650 Still life with flowers in a bronze urn (46x36cm-18x14in) 2-May-4 Bonhams & Butterfields, San Francisco #1003/R est:3000-5000
£8741 $15035 €12500 Bouquet de fleurs sur entablement (64x45cm-25x18in) 8-Dec-3 Claude Aguttes, Neuilly #24/R est:8000-10000

NUZZI, Mario (style) (1603-1673) Italian
£14085 $24648 €20000 Daffodils and other flowers in metal urn (100x75cm-39x30in) 17-Dec-3 Christie's, Rome #475/R est:10000-12000

NYANKAPITI and PANKALYIRRI (20th C) Australian
Sculpture
£31250 $58438 €46875 Jijigarrgaly, spirit being of lake disappointment (93x18cm-37x7in) mulga wood prov. 26-Jul-4 Sotheby's, Melbourne #13/R est:40000-60000 (A.D 80000)

NYBERG, Frans (1882-1962) Finnish
Works on paper
£272 $495 €400 Still life (54x74cm-21x29in) s.d.1943 W/C. 8-Feb-4 Bukowskis, Helsinki #415/R

NYBOE, Friis (1869-1929) Danish
£280 $439 €409 Woman at piano seen from behind (52x45cm-20x18in) s. 30-Aug-3 Rasmussen, Havnen #2285/R (D.KR 3000)
£287 $516 €419 Breakers (90x120cm-35x47in) s. 24-Apr-4 Rasmussen, Havnen #2099 (D.KR 3200)
£300 $500 €438 Sunshine on Skagen Strand (87x112cm-34x44in) s.i. 25-Oct-3 Rasmussen, Havnen #2261 (D.KR 3200)
£317 $497 €463 Interior scene with girl playing piano (32x39cm-13x15in) s. 30-Aug-3 Rasmussen, Havnen #2283 (D.KR 3400)
£320 $544 €467 Interior scene with small girl standing by table (45x45cm-18x18in) s. 29-Nov-3 Rasmussen, Havnen #2319 (D.KR 3400)
£395 $672 €577 Interior scene with woman (39x31cm-15x12in) s. 29-Nov-3 Rasmussen, Havnen #2049 (D.KR 4200)
£561 $886 €813 Interior scene with grand piano, evening (52x39cm-20x15in) s. 2-Sep-3 Rasmussen, Copenhagen #1966/R (D.KR 6000)

NYBORG, Asle (1966-) Norwegian
£861 $1437 €1257 Small girl's world (200x120cm-79x47in) s. 20-Oct-3 Blomqvist, Lysaker #1232 (N.KR 10000)
£2050 $3423 €2993 We are all gonna go to heaven (200x121cm-79x48in) s.d.1998 i.verso lit. 13-Oct-3 Blomqvist, Oslo #336/R est:20000-24000 (N.KR 24000)

NYBORG, Peter (1937-) Danish
£271 $506 €396 Cult figures (81x100cm-32x39in) s.d.67. 25-Feb-4 Kunsthallen, Copenhagen #103 (D.KR 3000)
£1625 $2989 €2373 Ninetinine faces I - orange composition (200x200cm-79x79in) 29-Mar-4 Rasmussen, Copenhagen #362/R est:15000-18000 (D.KR 18000)

NYE, Edgar (1879-1943) American
£278 $500 €406 Industrial scene (71x84cm-28x33in) s. 24-Apr-4 Weschler, Washington #644/R
£306 $550 €447 Beach with skeleton (94x101cm-37x40in) s.d.39. 24-Apr-4 Weschler, Washington #645/R
£409 $650 €597 Harbour scene with sailboats (61x86cm-24x34in) s. 13-Sep-3 Weschler, Washington #775/R
£419 $750 €612 Bridge and mountain (84x71cm-33x28in) s. 7-May-4 Sloans & Kenyon, Bethesda #1697/R
£598 $950 €873 Farmer's portrait (71x61cm-28x24in) s. board. 13-Sep-3 Weschler, Washington #776/R
£629 $1000 €918 Gertrude (84x72cm-33x28in) s.d.34 i.verso. 13-Sep-3 Weschler, Washington #774/R
£1125 $1800 €1643 The C and O Canal (94x107cm-37x42in) 20-Sep-3 Sloans & Kenyon, Bethesda #1187/R est:2000-2250
Works on paper
£250 $450 €365 Sculptor with muses (47x62cm-19x24in) s. W/C. 24-Apr-4 Weschler, Washington #643/R

NYFELLER, Albert (1883-1969) German
£348 $637 €508 View of the Lotschenlucke from Kippel (40x46cm-16x18in) s.d.25 i.verso. 4-Jun-4 Zofingen, Switzerland #2901/R (S.FR 800)

NYGAARD, Olav (20th C) Norwegian
£397 $730 €580 Blue winter (80x100cm-31x39in) s. 29-Mar-4 Blomqvist, Lysaker #1233 (N.KR 5000)

NYGREN, Arvid (19/20th C) American
£309 $500 €451 Autumn landscape with reflective lake (46x61cm-18x24in) s.d.1913 board. 9-Aug-3 Auctions by the Bay, Alameda #1544/R

NYILASY, Sandor (1873-?) Hungarian
£685 $1240 €1000 Brides (35x25cm-14x10in) s. oil on wood. 16-Apr-4 Mu Terem Galeria, Budapest #160/R (H.F 260000)
£5796 $10492 €8462 Waterside afternoon (65x54cm-26x21in) s. 16-Apr-4 Mu Terem Galeria, Budapest #109/R (H.F 2200000)

NYL-FROSCH, Marie (1857-1914) German
£1049 $1804 €1500 Still life with peonies and a butterfly (36x54cm-14x21in) s.i.d.89. 3-Dec-3 Neumeister, Munich #696/R est:1300
£2606 $4508 €3700 Bunch of roses in a vase (86x63cm-34x25in) s. 10-Dec-3 Hugo Ruef, Munich #2469/R est:1000

NYMAN, Bjorn (1934-) Swedish
£268 $499 €400 Still life XII (27x32cm-11x13in) s. d.1977 verso. 7-Mar-4 Bukowskis, Helsinki #410/R
£423 $676 €600 Hibiscus III (39x31cm-15x12in) s.d.1981 acrylic oil. 21-Sep-3 Bukowskis, Helsinki #415/R

£423 $676 €600 Rosa Maria (25x33cm-10x13in) s.d.1981 acrylic oil. 21-Sep-3 Bukowskis, Helsinki #416/R
£559 $951 €800 Broken flight (49x64cm-19x25in) s.d.1976 oil acrylic exhib. 29-Nov-3 Bukowskis, Helsinki #36/R
£1099 $1945 €1605 Still life of pewter dish (45x65cm-18x26in) s.d.1977 panel exhib. 27-Apr-4 AB Stockholms Auktionsverk #1172/R est:10000-12000 (S.KR 15000)

NYMAN, Olle (1909-1999) Swedish
£725 $1305 €1059 Still life of teapot (50x60cm-20x24in) s.d.52 exhib.prov. 26-Apr-4 Bukowskis, Stockholm #187/R (S.KR 10000)
£798 $1436 €1165 Southern townscape with figures (39x47cm-15x19in) s.indis.d. 26-Apr-4 Bukowskis, Stockholm #186/R (S.KR 11000)
£1172 $2075 €1711 Woman in profile (65x54cm-26x21in) s.i. 27-Apr-4 AB Stockholms Auktionsverk #794/R est:6000-8000 (S.KR 16000)
Sculpture
£1450 $2611 €2117 Russian Empress (36cm-14in) s.d.89 stone collage. 26-Apr-4 Bukowskis, Stockholm #273/R est:10000-12000 (S.KR 20000)
£1478 $2646 €2158 Figure (38cm-15in) s.d.89 stone collage ceramic shell. 28-May-4 Uppsala Auktionskammare, Uppsala #408/R est:15000-20000 (S.KR 20000)
Works on paper
£346 $595 €505 Man at garden table (98x82cm-39x32in) s. gouache. 7-Dec-3 Uppsala Auktionskammare, Uppsala #284/R (S.KR 4500)
£1099 $1945 €1605 Abstract landscape (74x95cm-29x37in) s. gouache. 27-Apr-4 AB Stockholms Auktionsverk #725/R est:12000-15000 (S.KR 15000)

NYMEGEN, Elias van (1667-1755) Dutch
Works on paper
£800 $1432 €1200 Queen receiving news whilst dressing (21x18cm-8x7in) s. pen wash. 13-May-4 Bassenge, Berlin #5445

NYROP, Borge (1881-1948) Danish
£240 $400 €348 Horses and farmer with children in a field (84x112cm-33x44in) 8-Jul-3 Douglas, South Deerfield #6
£1127 $2085 €1645 Summer landscape with girls making flower garlands, Denmark (137x155cm-54x61in) s.d.1927. 15-Mar-4 Rasmussen, Vejle #438/R est:10000-12000 (D.KR 12500)

NYS, Carl (1858-?) Belgian
£1150 $2093 €1725 Still life with vase of anemones and a side lamp (41x33cm-16x13in) panel. 20-Jun-4 Wilkinson, Doncaster #332 est:800-1200

NYS, Francis (1863-1900) Belgian
£900 $1665 €1314 Pres de la voie ferree (43x62cm-17x24in) s. 14-Jul-4 Sotheby's, Olympia #276/R

NYSTROM, Jenny (1854-1946) Swedish
£1728 $2990 €2523 Boy picking apples (27x22cm-11x9in) s.d.1940. 15-Dec-3 Lilla Bukowskis, Stockholm #440 est:8000-10000 (S.KR 22000)
£1774 $3175 €2590 Spanish lady (102x75cm-40x30in) s.d.1889. 28-May-4 Uppsala Auktionskammare, Uppsala #158/R est:30000-40000 (S.KR 24000)
£3400 $6086 €4964 The steps to the hallway in full bloom (75x52cm-30x20in) s.d.1917. 28-May-4 Uppsala Auktionskammare, Uppsala #162/R est:30000-40000 (S.KR 46000)
Works on paper
£377 $652 €550 The wine party, Skogsboda (14x21cm-6x8in) s. Indian ink wash htd white. 15-Dec-3 Lilla Bukowskis, Stockholm #652 (S.KR 4800)
£443 $794 €647 Two young girls meeting old woman on path (21x31cm-8x12in) mono. mixed media. 28-May-4 Uppsala Auktionskammare, Uppsala #160 (S.KR 6000)
£492 $801 €718 Catching crayfish (21x14cm-8x6in) s. Indian ink wash htd white illustration. 29-Sep-3 Lilla Bukowskis, Stockholm #318 (S.KR 6400)
£517 $926 €755 Flirting (17x11cm-7x4in) s.d.1902 Indian ink wash grisaille. 26-May-4 AB Stockholms Auktionsverk #2301/R (S.KR 7000)
£517 $926 €755 Fork in the road (16x11cm-6x4in) s.d.1902 Indian ink wash en grisaille. 26-May-4 AB Stockholms Auktionsverk #2302/R (S.KR 7000)
£550 $886 €803 Three generations (23x22cm-9x9in) s. Indian ink htd white. 25-Aug-3 Lilla Bukowskis, Stockholm #337 (S.KR 7200)
£765 $1408 €1148 Girl with rake (56x38cm-22x15in) s.i.d.1885 chl. 14-Jun-4 Lilla Bukowskis, Stockholm #82 (S.KR 10500)
£887 $1588 €1295 Sailing party (22x26cm-9x10in) mono. mixed media. 28-May-4 Uppsala Auktionskammare, Uppsala #146/R (S.KR 12000)
£1220 $2183 €1781 Girl with rose (25x19cm-10x7in) s. mixed media. 28-May-4 Uppsala Auktionskammare, Uppsala #145/R est:12000-15000 (S.KR 16500)
£1231 $2117 €1797 Christmas celebration of the family of pigs (17x26cm-7x10in) s. W/C. 3-Dec-3 AB Stockholms Auktionsverk #2479/R est:12000-15000 (S.KR 16000)
£1256 $2249 €1834 Girl by Christmas tree (9cm-4in circular) s. W/C. 25-May-4 Bukowskis, Stockholm #136/R est:12000-15000 (S.KR 17000)
£1478 $2646 €2158 Baby boy with daffodill (19x15cm-7x6in) s.i. W/C prov. 26-May-4 AB Stockholms Auktionsverk #2101/R est:20000-25000 (S.KR 20000)
£1615 $2778 €2358 Christmas angel (23x14cm-9x6in) s. W/C study. 2-Dec-3 Bukowskis, Stockholm #38/R est:12000-15000 (S.KR 21000)
£2042 $3533 €2981 Youth's Christmas roses (44x32cm-17x13in) s. W/C. 15-Dec-3 Lilla Bukowskis, Stockholm #69 est:25000-30000 (S.KR 26000)
£2143 $3837 €3129 Boy with cockerel in cage (27x17cm-11x7in) s. W/C. 28-May-4 Uppsala Auktionskammare, Uppsala #144/R est:20000-25000 (S.KR 29000)
£2513 $4498 €3669 Girl with apples at Christmas (24x15cm-9x6in) s. W/C. 26-May-4 AB Stockholms Auktionsverk #2329/R est:30000-35000 (S.KR 34000)
£2692 $4631 €3930 Boy with ABS book (22x13cm-9x5in) s. gouache W/C exec.c.1910. 2-Dec-3 Bukowskis, Stockholm #41/R est:25000-30000 (S.KR 35000)
£2769 $4763 €4043 Gnome and pig (25x16cm-10x6in) s. W/C study. 2-Dec-3 Bukowskis, Stockholm #37/R est:12000-15000 (S.KR 36000)
£2809 $5027 €4101 Boy with red hat and cuckoo-clock (15x12cm-6x5in) s. W/C oval. 25-May-4 Bukowskis, Stockholm #135/R est:20000-25000 (S.KR 38000)
£2846 $4895 €4155 Delivering Christmas presents (23x15cm-9x6in) s. W/C. 2-Dec-3 Bukowskis, Stockholm #39/R est:15000-20000 (S.KR 37000)
£3695 $6615 €5395 Welcomming the spring - idyllic farmhouse scene (38x83cm-15x33in) s. W/C. 26-May-4 AB Stockholms Auktionsverk #2102/R est:30000-35000 (S.KR 50000)
£5543 $9922 €8093 Washing in summer (22x36cm-9x14in) s. W/C. 25-May-4 Bukowskis, Stockholm #138/R est:50000-60000 (S.KR 75000)

NYUMI, Elizabeth (1947-) Australian
Works on paper
£1057 $1670 €1533 Gathering food near Kiwirrkura (99x51cm-39x20in) synthetic polymer paint canvas prov. 28-Jul-3 Sotheby's, Paddington #546 est:1500-2500 (A.D 2600)
£7617 $14244 €11426 Minjalli, near Kiwirrkurra (180x120cm-71x47in) i.verso synthetic polymer linen exec. 1999 prov. 21-Jul-4 Shapiro, Sydney #89/R est:7000-9000 (A.D 19500)

OAKES, H F (fl.1841-1847) British?
£1100 $2024 €1606 Interior, possibly the old curiosity shop (44x62cm-17x24in) s.i.verso. 8-Jun-4 Bonhams, Knightsbridge #321/R est:800-1200

OAKES, John Wright (1820-1887) British
£397 $719 €580 Morning in the Bay of Uri, Lake Lucerne (39x72cm-15x28in) s. 1-Apr-4 Heffel, Vancouver #114/R (C.D 950)
£610 $1092 €891 Afternoon on the Devonshire Coast (31x40cm-12x16in) s. i.verso board. 27-May-4 Christie's, Kensington #227/R
£960 $1766 €1402 Near Southall with figures in a cornfield beyond a river (28x46cm-11x18in) s.d.1875. 8-Jun-4 Lawrences, Bletchingley #1409
£2200 $3674 €3212 Peel Castle (88x127cm-35x50in) 17-Nov-3 Trembath Welch, Great Dunmow #510/R est:4000-6000
£13000 $23920 €18980 Peel Castle, Isle of man (89x130cm-35x51in) s. prov. 11-Jun-4 Christie's, London #153/R est:7000-10000

OAKES, John Wright (attrib) (1820-1887) British
£251 $450 €366 Cumberland landscape with figures (45x56cm-18x22in) bears sig. 21-Mar-4 Bonhams & Butterfields, Los Angeles #7364/R
Works on paper
£250 $425 €365 Posford Beck, Wharfedale (49x35cm-19x14in) bears sig.indis.d.1878 pencil W/C. 19-Nov-3 Tennants, Leyburn #985

OAKES, Wilbur L (1876-1934) American
£1471 $2500 €2148 Cloudy day (41x51cm-16x20in) s.d.12 prov. 18-Nov-3 John Moran, Pasadena #197 est:1500-2500

OAKLEY, Charles (1925-) British
£242 $445 €353 Balthaus box (24x28cm-9x11in) s.i.d.Feb 89 verso oil mixed media on canvas. 14-Jun-4 Waddingtons, Toronto #111/R (C.D 600)
£500 $915 €730 Worn rocks, Pelmore Head (50x101cm-20x40in) s.verso board. 2-Jun-4 John Ross, Belfast #131
£806 $1484 €1177 Fragments of memory - a Cumbrian interior (48x76cm-19x30in) s.d.88 s.i.d.verso panel. 14-Jun-4 Waddingtons, Toronto #119/R est:1000-1500 (C.D 2000)
Works on paper
£320 $550 €467 Flight path riot (91x91cm-36x36in) s.verso mixed media. 3-Dec-3 John Ross, Belfast #237

OAKLEY, George (?) Irish?
£302 $541 €450 Farmland (35x45cm-14x18in) s. 31-May-4 Hamilton Osborne King, Dublin #84/R

OAKLEY, Octavius (1800-1867) British
Works on paper
£940 $1729 €1400 Gypsy woman (31x25cm-12x10in) s. W/C oval. 26-Mar-4 Dorotheum, Vienna #209/R
£1000 $1870 €1460 New trick (29x23cm-11x9in) W/C. 22-Jul-4 Martel Maides, Guernsey #199/R est:800-1000

OAKLEY, Violet (1874-1961) American
£2717 $5000 €3967 Thy God bringeth thee into a good land (100x121cm-39x48in) i. oil paint over printed base prov. 27-Jun-4 Freeman, Philadelphia #159/R est:800-1200
£3533 $6500 €5158 Madonna of the Miracle (76x51cm-30x20in) s. exhib. 27-Jun-4 Freeman, Philadelphia #160/R est:3000-5000
£4891 $9000 €7141 Burning the books at Oxford (137x68cm-54x27in) i. oil paint over printed base prov. 27-Jun-4 Freeman, Philadelphia #158/R est:1500-2500
£7609 $14000 €11109 Penn's vision (65x138cm-26x54in) i. oil paint over printed base prov. 27-Jun-4 Freeman, Philadelphia #157/R est:3000-5000

OATES, Bennett (1928-) British
£2200 $3476 €3212 Irises and Hollyhocks (60x50cm-24x20in) s.d.82 panel. 2-Sep-3 Gildings, Market Harborough #429/R est:2000-3000
£2400 $4224 €3504 Still life of hollyhocks and peonies (66x76cm-26x30in) s.d.72. 18-May-4 Bonhams, Knightsbridge #3/R est:1000-1500
£3000 $4740 €4380 Hollyhocks, peonies and lilies on a marble ledge (52x41cm-20x16in) s.d.79 panel. 2-Sep-3 Gildings, Market Harborough #428/R est:2000-3000
£3400 $5372 €4964 Hollyhocks, peony and orchid (59x49cm-23x19in) s.d.77 panel. 2-Sep-3 Gildings, Market Harborough #430/R est:2000-3000

OBATA, Chiura (1885-1975) American
Works on paper
£269 $500 €393 Large waterfall amid autumn foliage (180x46cm-71x18in) ink col silk hanging scroll. 6-Mar-4 Harvey Clar, Oakland #1232
£300 $500 €438 Wild oats (46x32cm-18x13in) s.d.April 1963 W/C. 26-Oct-3 Bonhams & Butterfields, San Francisco #6528/R

OBEL, Niels (20th C) Danish
£373 $679 €560 Composition (130x118cm-51x46in) prov. 19-Jun-4 Rasmussen, Havnen #4119/R (D.KR 4200)

OBER, Hermann (?) ?
£355 $592 €500 Light blue in the centre (32x24cm-13x9in) s.d.80 masonite. 16-Oct-3 Dorotheum, Salzburg #724/R

£390 $651 €550 Moving landscape (47x68cm-19x27in) mono.d.79 masonite. 16-Oct-3 Dorotheum, Salzburg #723/R

OBERBERGER, Josef (1905-1994) German
Works on paper
£268 $481 €400 Young woman on Whit Monday (61x43cm-24x17in) s.i.d.1975 pen W/C. 25-May-4 Karl & Faber, Munich #476/R

OBERG, Josef (1890-1967) Swedish
£378 $642 €552 Flowers and river trout (56x49cm-22x19in) s.d.1945 exhib. 5-Nov-3 AB Stockholms Auktionsverk #863/R (S.KR 5000)

OBERG, Ralph E (1950-) American
£8021 $15000 €11711 HRH the King of the Yukon (107x127cm-42x50in) s. board prov. 24-Jul-4 Coeur d'Alene, Hayden #193/R est:12000-18000

OBERHUBER, Oswald (1931-) Austrian
Works on paper
£600 $1104 €900 Flowers (56x38cm-22x15in) s.d.81 mixed media newspaper. 9-Jun-4 Dorotheum, Salzburg #698/R
£709 $1184 €1000 Couple (37x53cm-15x21in) d.82 pencil col pen. 14-Oct-3 Dorotheum, Vienna #259/R

OBERLANDER, Adolf (1845-1923) German
£625 $1019 €900 St George fighting the dragon (38x67cm-15x26in) s. 24-Sep-3 Neumeister, Munich #517/R

OBERMAN, Anthony (1781-1845) Dutch
£4333 $7843 €6500 On the Eise (62x85cm-24x33in) s.d.1836. 1-Apr-4 Van Ham, Cologne #1581/R est:7000

OBERMUELLNER, Adolf (1833-1898) Austrian
£451 $767 €650 Mill near in Grein, upper Austria (26x21cm-10x8in) s.d.1882 i. verso. 28-Oct-3 Dorotheum, Vienna #221
£1972 $3411 €2800 Fishermen at edge of the lake (65x55cm-26x22in) s.d.1878. 10-Dec-3 Dorotheum, Vienna #94 est:3200-3600

OBERTEUFFER, George (1878-1940) American
£1308 $2250 €1910 Paris, impression of the past (37x52cm-15x20in) s. i.stretcher. 3-Dec-3 Doyle, New York #188/R est:4000-6000
£3198 $5500 €4669 Paris from the Seine (45x52cm-18x20in) s. 3-Dec-3 Doyle, New York #187/R est:6000-8000
£5135 $9500 €7497 Farm in winter (65x81cm-26x32in) s. painted c.1910 prov. 11-Mar-4 Christie's, Rockefeller NY #53/R est:7000-10000

OBIOLS DELGADO, Mariano (19th C) Spanish
£845 $1479 €1200 Riders (13x45cm-5x18in) s. board. 16-Dec-3 Segre, Madrid #73/R

O'BRADY, Gertrude (1901-) American
£233 $400 €340 Ecole Technique de Photographie et Cinematographie (25x36cm-10x14in) s.d.1948 panel. 7-Dec-3 William Jenack, New York #352
£2446 $4500 €3571 Row of shops (33x56cm-13x22in) s.d.1939. 10-Jun-4 Sotheby's, New York #230/R est:3000-5000

OBREGON, Alejandro (1920-1992) Colombian
£4571 $8000 €6674 Barracuda (36x44cm-14x17in) panel prov. 19-Dec-3 Sotheby's, New York #1184/R est:10000-15000
£5667 $10427 €8500 Detail of an ocean (31x40cm-12x16in) s. s.i.d.1987 verso panel prov. 9-Jun-4 Artcurial Briest, Paris #442/R est:4500-6000
£13333 $24533 €20000 Mar de Leva (70x91cm-28x36in) s.i.d.83 verso panel prov. 9-Jun-4 Artcurial Briest, Paris #441/R est:10000-15000

O'BRIEN, Dermod (1865-1945) British
£1748 $2972 €2500 Coastal landscape (25x34cm-10x13in) 25-Nov-3 De Veres Art Auctions, Dublin #107/R est:2500-3500
£3217 $5469 €4600 Portrait of a model, thought to be Emily Scobel (61x46cm-24x18in) studio st. exhib. 18-Nov-3 Whyte's, Dublin #53/R est:2000-3000
£4500 $8055 €6570 Howth from Bull Island (38x46cm-15x18in) s. 14-May-4 Christie's, London #206/R est:4500-6500
£5667 $10257 €8500 Milking time (63x76cm-25x30in) s.d.1922. 30-Mar-4 De Veres Art Auctions, Dublin #76/R est:9000-12000
£19580 $33287 €28000 Heading the Stooks (76x101cm-30x40in) s. exhib. 25-Nov-3 De Veres Art Auctions, Dublin #73/R est:14000-18000

O'BRIEN, George (1821-1888) Australian/Irish
Works on paper
£498 $832 €747 Logan Park, Mt Cargill in the background (29x43cm-11x17in) s. W/C. 27-Oct-3 Goodman, Sydney #121/R (A.D 1200)

O'BRIEN, Geraldine (1922-) Irish
£400 $728 €584 Vase of pink roses (35x26cm-14x10in) s.d.56 canvas on board. 15-Jun-4 Bonhams, Knightsbridge #46/R
£400 $728 €584 Still life of lilies, delphiniums and other flowers by a sunlit window (65x91cm-26x36in) s. 15-Jun-4 Bonhams, Oxford #87/R

O'BRIEN, John (1834-1904) British
£336 $571 €480 Country church (23x28cm-9x11in) s. board. 18-Nov-3 Mealy's, Castlecomer #1406
£350 $594 €500 Port Salon Golf Course, Co Donegal (29x49cm-11x19in) board. 18-Nov-3 Mealy's, Castlecomer #1376/R

O'BRIEN, Justin Maurice (1917-1996) Australian
£6883 $11081 €10049 Baptism of Christ (54x23cm-21x9in) s. card prov. 25-Aug-3 Sotheby's, Paddington #178/R est:14000-18000 (A.D 17000)
£12146 $19555 €17733 Before the storm, Skyros (40x49cm-16x19in) s. canvas on board prov. 25-Aug-3 Sotheby's, Paddington #167/R est:30000-40000 (A.D 30000)
£16260 $29106 €23740 Net menders (68x48cm-27x19in) s. painted 1965 prov.lit. 4-May-4 Sotheby's, Melbourne #69/R est:30000-40000 (A.D 40000)
£16406 $30680 €24609 The draped chair (60x51cm-24x20in) s. canvas on board painted 1972 prov. 21-Jul-4 Shapiro, Sydney #154/R est:25000-35000 (A.D 42000)
Works on paper
£1102 $1873 €1609 Boy's fishing (36x49cm-14x19in) s. W/C prov. 24-Nov-3 Sotheby's, Melbourne #179/R est:3000-5000 (A.D 2600)
£1702 $2894 €2485 The kiss of Judas (46x33cm-18x13in) indis.sig. ink W/C pencil prov. 25-Nov-3 Christie's, Melbourne #118/R est:5000-7000 (A.D 4000)

O'BRIEN, Ken (20th C) Irish
£265 $482 €400 Clifden (39x49cm-15x19in) s.d.2002. 15-Jun-4 James Adam, Dublin #231/R

O'BRIEN, Kitty Wilmer (1910-1982) British
£1000 $1810 €1500 Dublin by night (56x69cm-22x27in) s. board. 30-Mar-4 De Veres Art Auctions, Dublin #125/R est:1500-2000
£2500 $4725 €3700 Winetavern Street and wood quay from Christchurch Olace, Dublin (29x70cm-11x28in) s. board. 17-Feb-4 Whyte's, Dublin #3/R est:3000-4000
Works on paper
£1250 $2037 €1800 Figures by the Mall, Westport (25x34cm-10x13in) gouache prov. 24-Sep-3 James Adam, Dublin #146/R est:1500-2500
£2083 $3396 €3000 Westport Street scene with figures (38x60cm-15x24in) s. gouache. 24-Sep-3 James Adam, Dublin #79a/R est:3000-5000
£2162 $4086 €3200 Westport quay (25x64cm-10x25in) s. gouache on board exhib. 17-Feb-4 Whyte's, Dublin #108/R est:3000-4000

O'BRIEN, Lucius Richard (1832-1899) Canadian
£2823 $5194 €4122 Sailing on a sunny day (28x47cm-11x19in) s.d.1895 board. 9-Jun-4 Walker's, Ottawa #114/R est:1500-2500 (C.D 7000)
Works on paper
£446 $768 €651 Country landscape with cow and farmer (24x34cm-9x13in) s. W/C. 2-Dec-3 Joyner Waddington, Toronto #446 (C.D 1000)
£522 $971 €762 Canoeing on the lake (18x25cm-7x10in) s.d.1885 W/C. 2-Mar-4 Ritchie, Toronto #46/R (C.D 1300)
£864 $1408 €1261 On the Severn (29x22cm-11x9in) s.d.78 i.verso W/C. 23-Sep-3 Ritchie, Toronto #64/R est:1000-1500 (C.D 1900)
£893 $1536 €1304 Pastoral landscape with stream (24x35cm-9x14in) s.d.1891 W/C. 2-Dec-3 Joyner Waddington, Toronto #301/R est:3000-3500 (C.D 2000)
£1016 $1819 €1483 Riverside cottage (34x57cm-13x22in) s.d.1892 W/C prov. 27-May-4 Heffel, Vancouver #95/R est:3000-4000 (C.D 2500)
£1111 $1844 €1622 Herring boats becalmed (17x27cm-7x11in) s.d.1885 s.i.verso W/C prov. 5-Oct-3 Levis, Calgary #78a/R est:2500-3000 (C.D 2500)
£1440 $2635 €2102 Falls of Kakabekka, Lake Superior (27x44cm-11x17in) W/C lit. 1-Jun-4 Joyner Waddington, Toronto #140/R est:3000-4000 (C.D 3600)
£1802 $3063 €2631 Deer by the water's edge (36x54cm-14x21in) s.d.1890 W/C prov. 27-Nov-3 Heffel, Vancouver #21/R est:2000-3000 (C.D 4000)
£1900 $3477 €2774 Loggers by the rapids (24x37cm-9x15in) s. W/C. 1-Jun-4 Joyner Waddington, Toronto #204/R est:3000-4000 (C.D 4750)
£2027 $3446 €2959 Boats drawn up on the river bank (36x57cm-14x22in) s.d.1893 W/C prov. 27-Nov-3 Heffel, Vancouver #22/R est:2000-3000 (C.D 4500)
£3455 $6185 €5044 Cape Gaspe (52x34cm-20x13in) s.i.d.1882 W/C prov.lit. 27-May-4 Heffel, Vancouver #170/R est:4000-6000 (C.D 8500)

OBROVSKY, Jacub (1882-1949) Czechoslovakian
£1067 $1941 €1600 Autoportrait (25x15cm-10x6in) s. canvas on panel. 5-Jul-4 Le Mouel, Paris #33/R est:1500-2000

OCAMPO, Galo (1913-1985) Philippino
£4902 $8873 €7157 Un headquarters, New York (94x71cm-37x28in) s. 4-Apr-4 Sotheby's, Singapore #117/R est:15000-20000 (S.D 15000)

OCAMPO, Isidoro (1902-) Mexican
Works on paper
£181 $288 €264 Carnival scene (65x50cm-26x20in) init.d.1980 col pencil. 29-Apr-3 Louis Morton, Mexico #144/R (M.P 3000)

OCAMPO, Manuel (1965-) ?
£3784 $7000 €5525 Ospital san Lucas (206x220cm-81x87in) s.i.d.1991 verso prov. 12-Feb-4 Sotheby's, New York #327/R est:7000-9000
£5946 $11000 €8681 Todos Caeran (243x305cm-96x120in) s.i.d.1991 verso two parts prov. 12-Feb-4 Sotheby's, New York #328/R est:8000-10000

OCHIAI, Tam (1967-) American?
£5587 $10000 €8157 Canele (147x96cm-58x38in) acrylic col pencil prov.lit. 12-May-4 Christie's, Rockefeller NY #465/R est:12000-15000

OCHOA Y MADRAZO, Raphael de (1858-?) Spanish
£1103 $2041 €1600 Le chapeau bleu (70x42cm-28x17in) s.i.d.1884 panel. 11-Feb-4 Beaussant & Lefèvre, Paris #195 est:600-800
£7095 $12701 €10359 Interior scene with young woman resting on sofa (54x88cm-21x35in) s. panel. 28-May-4 Uppsala Auktionskammare, Uppsala #126/R est:10000-12000 (S.KR 96000)
£8235 $14000 €12023 The letter (37x46cm-15x18in) s. panel. 28-Oct-3 Sotheby's, New York #147/R est:10000-15000

OCHOA, Francisco (20th C) Mexican?
£211 $335 €308 Party (59x89cm-23x35in) s.d.1987. 29-Apr-3 Louis Morton, Mexico #143/R (M.P 3500)
£229 $364 €334 Religious scene (59x50cm-23x20in) s.d.1988. 29-Apr-3 Louis Morton, Mexico #48/R (M.P 3800)
£229 $364 €334 Untitled (46x81cm-18x32in) s.d.1988. 29-Apr-3 Louis Morton, Mexico #72/R (M.P 3800)
£229 $364 €334 Saint George and the dragon (50x60cm-20x24in) s.d.1987. 29-Apr-3 Louis Morton, Mexico #156/R (M.P 3800)

OCHS, Jacques (1883-1971) French
£265 $482 €400 Mere et enfant (50x60cm-20x24in) d.45. 15-Jun-4 Galerie Moderne, Brussels #175
£1370 $2329 €2000 Jeune femme nue et admirateurs (90x72cm-35x28in) s.d.1960 panel. 10-Nov-3 Horta, Bruxelles #66

OCHTERVELT, Jacob (1635-?) Dutch
£3514 $6500 €5130 Visit to a lady. s.i. panel. 14-Jan-4 Dallas Auction Gallery, Dallas #462/R est:6000-10000
£11667 $21000 €17034 Musical party in an interior (84x67cm-33x26in) prov.lit. 23-Jan-4 Christie's, Rockefeller NY #147/R est:15000-20000

OCHTMAN, Dorothy (1892-1971) American
£4167 $7500 €6084 Persian vases (76x64cm-30x25in) prov. 25-Jan-4 Hindman, Chicago #1044/R est:5000-7000

OCHTMAN, Leonard (1854-1934) American
£414 $750 €604 Autumn landscape with stream (25x18cm-10x7in) s. panel. 3-Apr-4 Nadeau, Windsor #139
£1173 $2100 €1713 Road to village (56x71cm-22x28in) bears sig. 8-Jan-4 James Julia, Fairfield #764b/R est:4000-6000
£1374 $2500 €2006 Spring landscape (41x56cm-16x22in) s. prov. 15-Jun-4 John Moran, Pasadena #171 est:2000-3000
£3537 $5800 €5129 Connecticut hills (61x76cm-24x30in) i.verso prov.exhib. 31-May-3 Brunk, Ashville #334/R est:3000-5000
£3631 $6500 €5447 June (76x102cm-30x40in) s.d.1913. 16-May-4 Abell, Los Angeles #398/R
£4749 $8500 €7124 Moonlit harbour (61x71cm-24x28in) s.d.1912 board. 16-May-4 Abell, Los Angeles #399/R
£9581 $16000 €13988 Connecticut hills (61x76cm-24x30in) s.d.1912 prov.exhib. 23-Oct-3 Shannon's, Milford #111/R est:12000-18000

OCHTMAN, Leonard (attrib) (1854-1934) American
£1037 $1700 €1504 Landscape with pond in the foreground (41x56cm-16x22in) bears sig.verso prov. 31-May-3 Brunk, Ashville #335/R est:1500-2500

OCIEPKA, Teofil (1891-1978) Polish
£333 $613 €500 Forest clearing with blossoming bushes (35x50cm-14x20in) s.d.1964. 11-Jun-4 Wendl, Rudolstadt #4201/R
£595 $1024 €869 Fir tree with roughnecks (70x50cm-28x20in) s.i.d.1958. 4-Dec-3 Agra, Warsaw #16/R (P.Z 4000)

OCKEL, Eduard (1834-1910) German
£671 $1235 €1000 Rocky coast with figures and horses (35x65cm-14x26in) s. lit. 25-Mar-4 Karlheinz Kaupp, Staufen #2643/R

OCKERT, Carl Friedrich (1825-1899) German
£390 $651 €566 Forest clearing with pond and pheasants (15x27cm-6x11in) s. panel. 23-Jun-3 Philippe Schuler, Zurich #3539/R (S.FR 850)
£733 $1342 €1100 Fox finds a hare (25x33cm-10x13in) s. 5-Jun-4 Arnold, Frankfurt #687

O'COLMAIN, Seamus (1925-1990) Irish
£559 $1029 €850 Ally ally o (23x29cm-9x11in) s.i. s.d.1979 verso board prov. 22-Jun-4 De Veres Art Auctions, Dublin #221/R
£600 $1098 €876 Dublin doorway (30x35cm-12x14in) s.d.1965 verso board. 2-Jun-4 John Ross, Belfast #53
£671 $1201 €1000 Dublin street scene (45x60cm-18x24in) s. board. 31-May-4 Hamilton Osborne King, Dublin #100/R
£738 $1321 €1100 Portrait of the artist's wife (90x70cm-35x28in) s. board. 31-May-4 Hamilton Osborne King, Dublin #12/R
£1020 $1876 €1550 Old Dublin street (59x64cm-23x25in) board. 22-Jun-4 De Veres Art Auctions, Dublin #222/R est:1500-2000
Works on paper
£403 $721 €600 Marine Pool number five (50x63cm-20x25in) s. mixed media board. 31-May-4 Hamilton Osborne King, Dublin #3/R

OCON Y RIVAS, Emilio (1848-1904) Spanish
£690 $1241 €1000 Beached boats (9x14cm-4x6in) s. board. 26-Jan-4 Durán, Madrid #227/R
£3125 $5094 €4500 Sailing boats in a bay (19x32cm-7x13in) s.d.1874 board. 23-Sep-3 Durán, Madrid #172/R est:2750

O'CONNELL, John (20th C) Irish?
£320 $525 €467 Female nude study (58x28cm-23x11in) s. board. 4-Jun-3 John Ross, Belfast #56
£360 $659 €526 Bogland towards Muckish (50x76cm-20x30in) s. board. 2-Jun-4 John Ross, Belfast #67
£500 $915 €730 Female nude study (61x45cm-24x18in) s. board. 2-Jun-4 John Ross, Belfast #30

O'CONNELL, Madame Frederique Emile Auguste (1823-1885) German
£559 $951 €800 Venus et putti (22x26cm-9x10in) bears sig.d.1851 panel. 20-Nov-3 Gioffredo, Nice #25/R

O'CONNOR, Declan (1957-) Irish
£464 $844 €700 Clowns (51x60cm-20x24in) s.d.03 board. 15-Jun-4 James Adam, Dublin #200/R
£464 $844 €700 Returning home (74x98cm-29x39in) s.d.03 board. 15-Jun-4 James Adam, Dublin #201/R
£533 $960 €800 In the paddock (87x113cm-34x44in) s.d.03 board. 20-Apr-4 James Adam, Dublin #66/R
£867 $1560 €1300 Larger than life (102x72cm-40x28in) s.d.04 canvasboard. 20-Apr-4 James Adam, Dublin #65/R

O'CONNOR, J A (1792-1841) British
£1150 $2093 €1679 Figures in an wooded landscape (28x38cm-11x15in) s. panel. 16-Jun-4 Andrew Hartley, Ilkley #1062/R est:1500-2000

O'CONNOR, James (1945-) Irish
£1141 $2019 €1700 Untitled (38x56cm-15x22in) s.d.1985 alkyd collage prov. 27-Apr-4 Whyte's, Dublin #97/R est:1000-1500

O'CONNOR, James Arthur (1792-1841) British
£2000 $3220 €2900 Figure on a woodland path (20x23cm-8x9in) s.d.1830. 13-Aug-3 Andrew Hartley, Ilkley #842/R est:2000-3000
£3100 $4991 €4495 Three figures in an extensive wooded landscape (28x38cm-11x15in) s. 15-Aug-3 Keys, Aylsham #679/R est:2750-3500
£4605 $8474 €7000 County Wicklow landscape with figures chatting on a path (19x24cm-7x9in) board. 22-Jun-4 Mealy's, Castlecomer #789/R est:7000-11000
£6500 $11635 €9490 Mountainous river landscape with figures on a path in the foreground (22x30cm-9x12in) s.indis.d. 14-May-4 Christie's, London #126/R est:4000-6000
£7821 $14000 €11419 Wooded landscape with figures on path (45x62cm-18x24in) s.d.1826 prov. 27-May-4 Sotheby's, New York #225/R est:15000-20000
£9500 $17005 €13870 Two boys fishing in a landscape (36x48cm-14x19in) s. 13-May-4 Sotheby's, London #2/R est:6000-8000
£10000 $18100 €15000 Figures by a lake in a wooded landscape (22x17cm-9x7in) s. board. 31-Mar-4 James Adam, Dublin #7/R est:10000-15000
£10738 $19221 €16000 Travellers in a landscape (37x51cm-15x20in) s. 26-May-4 James Adam, Dublin #9/R est:12500-18500
£12676 $21930 €18000 Landscape views with figures and donkey (12x11cm-5x4in) one s. three init. two d.1832 board set of four. 10-Dec-3 Bonhams & James Adam, Dublin #6/R est:9000-12000
£28000 $50120 €40880 Mountainous river landscape with a figure with a wagon and horses at a ford (71x91cm-28x36in) s.d.1832 prov.exhib.lit. 14-May-4 Christie's, London #111/R est:30000-50000
£36000 $64440 €52560 View on the Shannon, with figures in a rowing boat (41x46cm-16x18in) s.d.1828 prov.exhib. 14-May-4 Christie's, London #6/R est:20000-30000

O'CONNOR, John (1830-1889) British
£600 $1062 €876 Track at Ardee (76x61cm-30x24in) s. 27-Apr-4 Bonhams, Knightsbridge #161
£700 $1274 €1022 December Flood (61x76cm-24x30in) s. prov. 1-Jul-4 Christie's, Kensington #257
Works on paper
£290 $537 €423 Hawthorn by wet lane (30x40cm-12x16in) s. pen ink W/C. 13-Feb-4 Sworder & Son, Bishops Stortford #29/R
£300 $555 €438 View on Dartmoor (56x76cm-22x30in) s. pencil pen ink W/C. 13-Feb-4 Sworder & Son, Bishops Stortford #32/R
£350 $648 €511 Autumn Garden (46x37cm-18x15in) s. pencil pen ink W/C. 13-Feb-4 Sworder & Son, Bishops Stortford #28/R
£400 $740 €584 Blue window and valley (45x50cm-18x20in) s. W/C. 13-Feb-4 Sworder & Son, Bishops Stortford #31
£420 $777 €613 Rain from South West, a river landscape (56x72cm-22x28in) s.i. pencil pen ink W/C. 13-Feb-4 Sworder & Son, Bishops Stortford #33/R
£600 $1110 €876 Dry stone wall, Dartmoor (56x76cm-22x30in) s. pencil pen ink W/C. 13-Feb-4 Sworder & Son, Bishops Stortford #34/R

O'CONNOR, Kathleen (1886-1968) British/New Zealander
£4255 $7234 €6212 Three working women resting in the Luxemberg Gardens (22x32cm-9x13in) init. i.verso board prov. 25-Nov-3 Christie's, Melbourne #100/R est:10000-15000 (A.D 10000)

O'CONNOR, Sean (20th C) Irish
£223 $373 €323 Colleen Bawn Rock, Killarney (41x51cm-16x20in) s. board painted c.1958. 17-Jun-3 Pinneys, Montreal #30 (C.D 500)
£223 $373 €323 Brickeen Bridge, Killarney (41x51cm-16x20in) s. board. 17-Jun-3 Pinneys, Montreal #31 (C.D 500)
Works on paper
£309 $553 €460 Brickeen Bridge, Killarney (25x35cm-10x14in) s. W/C prov. 26-May-4 James Adam, Dublin #194/R

O'CONNOR, Victor G (1918-) Australian
£383 $651 €559 Friends (45x61cm-18x24in) s. prov. 26-Nov-3 Deutscher-Menzies, Melbourne #238/R (A.D 900)
£1626 $2553 €2358 Procession (74x100cm-29x39in) s. 26-Aug-3 Christie's, Sydney #302/R est:4000-6000 (A.D 4000)

O'CONOR, Roderic (1860-1940) Irish
£14000 $25060 €20440 Sketch of a nude, half-length (41x30cm-16x12in) s. board painted c.1923-6 prov.lit. 14-May-4 Christie's, London #180/R est:15000-20000
£18000 $32220 €26280 Mixed flowers in a vase (36x31cm-14x12in) studio st. painted c.1923-26 prov.lit. 14-May-4 Christie's, London #185/R est:18000-25000
£38000 $68020 €55480 Fleurs sur une chaise (46x54cm-18x21in) s.d.1919 s.i.verso board prov.exhib. 13-May-4 Sotheby's, London #80/R est:20000-30000
£43662 $75535 €62000 Nude on a couch (55x66cm-22x26in) studio st.verso. 10-Dec-3 Bonhams & James Adam, Dublin #131/R est:60000-80000
£50000 $89500 €73000 Head of a Breton boy (30x34cm-12x13in) studio st. verso board prov.exhib.lit. 13-May-4 Sotheby's, London #58/R est:50000-70000

£50350 $85594 €72000 A Breton fisherman (81x60cm-32x24in) prov.lit. studio st. 18-Nov-3 Whyte's, Dublin #51/R est:60000-80000
£60000 $107400 €87600 Nature Morte (45x53cm-18x21in) Studio st. on backboard board prov.exhib. 13-May-4 Sotheby's, London #39/R est:60000-80000
£200000 $358000 €292000 The bathers (74x91cm-29x36in) s. studio st. verso prov.exhib.lit. 14-May-4 Christie's, London #187/R est:200000-300000
£260000 $465400 €379600 Autumn landscape (54x65cm-21x26in) s. prov.exhib. 14-May-4 Christie's, London #183/R est:180000-250000
Works on paper
£5800 $10382 €8468 Breton girl (29x19cm-11x7in) black ink exec.c.1892-94 prov.exhib.lit. 14-May-4 Christie's, London #98/R est:3000-5000
£22000 $39380 €32120 Road with trees (53x42cm-21x17in) studio st. black ink wash prov.exhib.lit. 13-May-4 Sotheby's, London #14/R est:10000-15000

ODAZZI, Giovanni (attrib) (1663-1731) Italian
£5319 $8883 €7500 Sant'Anna con la Vergine bambina. Estasi di una Santa domenicana (27x27cm-11x11in) copper round two prov. 18-Jun-3 Christie's, Rome #307/R est:8000-12000

ODDE, Knud (1955-) Danish
£341 $613 €498 Figure composition with woman (78x60cm-31x24in) s.d.90. 24-Apr-4 Rasmussen, Havnen #4247 (D.KR 3800)
£357 $608 €521 Composition (46x64cm-18x25in) s. acrylic gouache. 26-Nov-3 Kunsthallen, Copenhagen #133 (D.KR 3800)
£469 $784 €685 Singer with microphone (62x49cm-24x19in) s.d.2000 acrylic paper prov. 7-Oct-3 Rasmussen, Copenhagen #295 (D.KR 5000)
£4242 $7805 €6193 Sunbathers diary (195x340cm-77x134in) s.d.98 acrylic paper prov.exhib.lit. 29-Mar-4 Rasmussen, Copenhagen #387/R est:40000 (D.KR 47000)

ODDONE, Max (1974-) Italian
£369 $683 €550 Painting to invest (120x80cm-47x31in) s.i. s.i.d.2003 verso oil enamel collage. 13-Mar-4 Meeting Art, Vercelli #323

O'DEA, Michael (1958-) Irish
£592 $1089 €900 Clea standing (81x56cm-32x22in) s.d.1990 acrylic. 22-Jun-4 De Veres Art Auctions, Dublin #32/R
£1678 $2853 €2400 Robbie, Bewley's Cafe, Dublin (51x51cm-20x20in) mono.d.1988. 18-Nov-3 Whyte's, Dublin #148/R est:1500-1800

ODEGAARD, Hans (1876-1943) Norwegian
£1348 $2332 €1968 Landscape (89x79cm-35x31in) s. exhib. 13-Dec-3 Blomqvist, Lysaker #1414/R est:12000-15000 (N.KR 15500)

ODEKERKEN, Willem van (?-1677) Dutch
£2685 $4940 €4000 Woman in the kitchen (103x89cm-41x35in) s. 26-Mar-4 Daguerre, Paris #53/R est:4000-5000

ODELMARK, F W (1849-1937) Swedish
Works on paper
£353 $612 €515 Alhambra (53x41cm-21x16in) s. W/C. 15-Dec-3 Lilla Bukowskis, Stockholm #650 (S.KR 4500)

ODELMARK, Frans Wilhelm (1849-1937) Swedish
£330 $595 €482 Interior scene with house gnome (26x32cm-10x13in) s.i. 26-Jan-4 Lilla Bukowskis, Stockholm #659 (S.KR 4400)
£500 $860 €730 Monk in wine cellar (68x50cm-27x20in) s. 7-Dec-3 Uppsala Auktionskammare, Uppsala #163 (S.KR 6500)
£518 $897 €756 Venetian canal view (53x41cm-21x16in) s.i.d.1882. 15-Dec-3 Lilla Bukowskis, Stockholm #420 (S.KR 6600)
£768 $1252 €1121 Dinner for the Cardinal (84x63cm-33x25in) s. 29-Sep-3 Lilla Bukowskis, Stockholm #134 (S.KR 10000)
£826 $1486 €1206 In the monastery cellar (70x83cm-28x33in) s. 26-Jan-4 Lilla Bukowskis, Stockholm #635 (S.KR 11000)
£846 $1455 €1235 Farm yard, Djurgardsstaden, Stockholm (90x68cm-35x27in) s. 7-Dec-3 Uppsala Auktionskammare, Uppsala #168/R (S.KR 11000)
£960 $1565 €1402 Farm in Skanor, Skaane (90x70cm-35x28in) s/. 29-Sep-3 Lilla Bukowskis, Stockholm #825 (S.KR 12500)
£1231 $2117 €1797 Street scene, Regeringsgatan, Stockholm (69x49cm-27x19in) s. 7-Dec-3 Uppsala Auktionskammare, Uppsala #167/R est:10000-12000 (S.KR 16000)
£1300 $2093 €1898 Procession by monastery garden (71x95cm-28x37in) s.d.1892. 25-Aug-3 Lilla Bukowskis, Stockholm #130 est:12000-15000 (S.KR 17000)
£1478 $2646 €2158 Palazzo Ducale, Venice (104x80cm-41x31in) s. 26-May-4 AB Stockholms Auktionsverk #2205/R est:25000-30000 (S.KR 20000)
£1922 $3440 €2806 Testing the wine (70x90cm-28x35in) s. 26-May-4 AB Stockholms Auktionsverk #2352/R est:15000-18000 (S.KR 26000)
£2462 $4234 €3595 Bazaar street (111x67cm-44x26in) s.d.1896. 2-Dec-3 Bukowskis, Stockholm #100/R est:20000-25000 (S.KR 32000)
£4878 $8732 €7122 Palace interior (100x63cm-39x25in) s. 25-May-4 Bukowskis, Stockholm #164/R est:70000-80000 (S.KR 66000)
£7243 $12965 €10575 Oriental interior (130x80cm-51x31in) s. 25-May-4 Bukowskis, Stockholm #165/R est:70000-80000 (S.KR 98000)
£7391 $13230 €10791 Palace courtyard with woman from the harem (127x76cm-50x30in) s.d.1889. 26-May-4 AB Stockholms Auktionsverk #2147/R est:60000-80000 (S.KR 100000)
£16000 $29120 €23360 Courtyard in Alhambra (130x88cm-51x35in) s.i.d.1889 prov. 15-Jun-4 Sotheby's, London #118/R est:8000-12000
Works on paper
£254 $457 €381 Palace court yard with men smoking (54x34cm-21x13in) s.i. W/C htd white. 25-Apr-4 Goteborg Auktionsverk, Sweden #212/R (S.KR 3500)
£299 $516 €437 By the monastery well (54x39cm-21x15in) s.indis.d.1899 W/C. 15-Dec-3 Lilla Bukowskis, Stockholm #450 (S.KR 3800)
£355 $640 €533 Palace court yard with figures (56x42cm-22x17in) s. W/C htd white. 25-Apr-4 Goteborg Auktionsverk, Sweden #211/R (S.KR 4900)
£430 $701 €628 Kornhams Square (59x41cm-23x16in) s. pastel. 29-Sep-3 Lilla Bukowskis, Stockholm #683 (S.KR 5600)
£1077 $1852 €1572 Street scene, Cairo (89x54cm-35x21in) s. pastel. 3-Dec-3 AB Stockholms Auktionsverk #2382/R (S.KR 14000)

ODENA, Isidro (1910-) Spanish
£350 $584 €500 Landscape (73x92cm-29x36in) s. 30-Jun-3 Ansorena, Madrid #259/R

ODENBACH, Marcel (1953-) French?
Works on paper
£1267 $2318 €1900 Untitled (33x47cm-13x19in) s.d.7.4.80 pencil on gouache two prov. 4-Jun-4 Lempertz, Koln #331/R est:1800

ODEVAERE, Joseph Denis (1778-1830) Belgian
Works on paper
£317 $555 €450 Le peintre Louis David dans son atelier. s. dr. 16-Dec-3 Galerie Moderne, Brussels #681

ODIER, Jacques (1853-1930) Swiss
£611 $1038 €892 La Loirs a St Maurice sur (46x60cm-18x24in) i. verso. 28-Nov-3 Zofingen, Switzerland #3104/R (S.FR 1350)

ODIERNO, Guido (1913-) Italian
£250 $400 €365 Capri (69x99cm-27x39in) s. painted 1963. 20-Sep-3 Bunte, Elgin #1443
£268 $500 €402 View of a fountain under shady trees (38x49cm-15x19in) s.i. 25-Jul-4 Bonhams & Butterfields, San Francisco #6058/R
£293 $497 €428 Shores of Capri (69x98cm-27x39in) s. 21-Nov-3 Walker's, Ottawa #235/R (C.D 650)
£300 $528 €438 Seascape (59x115cm-23x45in) s. 19-May-4 John Bellman, Billingshurst #1829
£343 $550 €501 Capri coastal scene (30x61cm-12x24in) s. 17-May-3 Bunte, Elgin #1258
£426 $711 €600 Wonder cave in Capri (60x50cm-24x20in) s.i. 20-Oct-3 Sant Agostino, Torino #89/R
£450 $774 €657 Fishing boats at sunset at Sestri Levante (67x97cm-26x38in) s. 3-Dec-3 Cheffins, Cambridge #629/R
£659 $1200 €962 Capri at sunset (102x71cm-40x28in) s. 19-Jun-4 Jackson's, Cedar Falls #254/R
£800 $1472 €1200 Seascape (32x35cm-13x14in) s.i. board prov. 14-Jun-4 Sant Agostino, Torino #146/R
£800 $1432 €1200 Seascape in Capri (70x103cm-28x41in) s. 12-May-4 Stadion, Trieste #656/R
£850 $1573 €1241 Capri coast at dusk (61x91cm-24x36in) s. 15-Jan-4 Christie's, Kensington #953/R

ODIN, Blanche (1865-?) French
Works on paper
£576 $921 €800 Still life of a book and an anemone (21x24cm-8x9in) s. W/C oval. 16-May-3 Tajan, Paris #168
£652 $1070 €900 Un oeillet (27x13cm-11x5in) s. W/C. 11-May-3 Osenat, Fontainebleau #176
£704 $1232 €1000 Vase de fleurs (20x26cm-8x10in) s. W/C. 21-Dec-3 Thierry & Lannon, Brest #67 est:700-800
£739 $1294 €1050 Nature morte a la theiere (15x19cm-6x7in) s. W/C. 21-Dec-3 Thierry & Lannon, Brest #240
£872 $1605 €1300 Vase d'oeillets (27x33cm-11x13in) s. W/C. 28-Mar-4 Anaf, Lyon #217

O'DONNELL, Simon (20th C) Irish
£400 $720 €600 Volta Picture Theatre (34x42cm-13x17in) s.d.04 board. 20-Apr-4 James Adam, Dublin #198/R
£530 $964 €800 The casino (29x37cm-11x15in) s.d.03 board. 15-Jun-4 James Adam, Dublin #70/R

O'DOWD, Gwen (?) ?
£1711 $3147 €2600 Spaces 10 (79x56cm-31x22in) paper prov. 22-Jun-4 De Veres Art Auctions, Dublin #33/R est:2500-3500

O'DUILAING, Sean (20th C) Irish
£265 $482 €400 Landscape with woman sitting beneath trees (25x29cm-10x11in) s.d.32 board. 15-Jun-4 James Adam, Dublin #207/R

OECHSLIN, Arnold (1885-1969) Swiss
£362 $615 €529 Rhine landscape (60x80cm-24x31in) s.d.1924. 19-Nov-3 Fischer, Luzern #2235/R (S.FR 800)

OECONOMOU, Georgios (c.1850-?) Greek
£20000 $35800 €29200 Girl with flowers (90x50cm-35x20in) s.d.1896. 11-May-4 Bonhams, New Bond Street #21/R est:20000-30000

OEDER, Georg (1846-1931) German
£1933 $3499 €2900 Autumn (46x62cm-18x24in) s. 1-Apr-4 Van Ham, Cologne #1582/R est:3000

OEHLEN, Albert (1954-) German
£3467 $6344 €5200 Untitled (76x55cm-30x22in) s.d.85 paper collage silicon. 4-Jun-4 Lempertz, Koln #333/R est:2000
£5944 $10224 €8500 Untitled (59x49cm-23x19in) prov. 5-Dec-3 Ketterer, Munich #173/R est:3500-4500
£8333 $15250 €12500 Beach scene (55x55cm-22x22in) s.i.d.93/99 verso material. 4-Jun-4 Lempertz, Koln #332/R est:4000
£36872 $66000 €53833 Picture and eye (235x343cm-93x135in) s.i.d.96/00 verso prov. 14-May-4 Phillips, New York #205/R est:20000-30000

OEHLEN, Markus (1956-) German
£1007 $1852 €1500 Untitled (105x89cm-41x35in) s.d. oil chk varnish monotype on dispersion Indian ink oil chk. 26-Mar-4 Ketterer, Hamburg #584/R est:2000-3000

OEHLER, Bernice (1881-?) American
Works on paper
£250 $400 €365 Explosive flame (33x20cm-13x8in) s. gouache exhib. 21-Sep-3 William Jenack, New York #256

OEHLER, Christoph Friedrich (1881-1964) German
£273 $453 €396 Gandria (56x42cm-22x17in) s.mono.i.d.1929 verso. 13-Jun-3 Zofingen, Switzerland #2971 (S.FR 600)
£441 $749 €644 Lake Thun with Niesen (50x60cm-20x24in) mono. s.i.d.1938 verso. 5-Nov-3 Dobiaschofsky, Bern #841/R (S.FR 1000)

OEHLSCHLAGER, Mario (younger) (1920-1990) German
£280 $481 €400 Sailing ship at sea (54x65cm-21x26in) s.i.d.1979 verso board. 4-Dec-3 Schopman, Hamburg #777/R

OEHME, Carl Gustav (1817-1881) German?
Photographs
£4056 $6895 €5800 Group portrait of three men. i. verso daguerreotype prov.lit. 28-Nov-3 Bassenge, Berlin #4028/R est:2500

OEHME, Ernst Ferdinand (1797-1855) German
Works on paper
£1223 $2225 €1786 Grasses on sand by sea (13x20cm-5x8in) W/C over pencil prov.exhib. 17-Jun-4 Kornfeld, Bern #45/R est:1500 (S.FR 2800)
£1700 $2941 €2482 Schloss Colditz, Saxony, seen through trees (20x28cm-8x11in) indis.i. black lead pen grey ink wash W/C sold with another. 12-Dec-3 Christie's, Kensington #560/R est:700-1000
£4585 $8345 €6694 Landscape with lake and trees (12x21cm-5x8in) W/C prov.exhib. 17-Jun-4 Kornfeld, Bern #44/R est:3000 (S.FR 10500)
£5677 $10332 €8288 Scots pine trees in the clouds (21x20cm-8x8in) W/C over pencil prov.exhib. 17-Jun-4 Kornfeld, Bern #43/R est:1500 (S.FR 13000)

OEHME, Ernst Ferdinand (attrib) (1797-1855) German
Works on paper
£765 $1400 €1117 Alpine landscape (24x38cm-9x15in) W/C over pencil. 29-Jan-4 Swann Galleries, New York #324/R

OEHME, Erwin (1831-1907) German
Works on paper
£611 $1113 €892 Mill (24x24cm-9x9in) s. W/C prov. 17-Jun-4 Kornfeld, Bern #46/R (S.FR 1400)

OEHME, Hanns (1890-1955) German
£549 $879 €780 Dr Th Bohle (100x80cm-39x31in) s.d.1929. 18-Sep-3 Rieber, Stuttgart #993/R

OEHMICHEN, Hugo (1843-1933) German
£1007 $1852 €1500 Portrait of young boy (26x20cm-10x8in) s. panel. 24-Mar-4 Hugo Ruef, Munich #1063 est:1400
£1007 $1852 €1500 Small girl lying on red carpet (38x50cm-15x20in) s. 27-Mar-4 Geble, Radolfzell #754/R est:1500
£1528 $2490 €2200 Boy with tablet (50x34cm-20x13in) s. one of pair. 24-Sep-3 Neumeister, Munich #519/R est:1500
£2066 $3844 €3016 The small apple thief (64x46cm-25x18in) s. 2-Mar-4 Rasmussen, Copenhagen #1578/R est:10000 (D.KR 23000)
£2083 $3396 €3000 Small girl with cat (50x35cm-20x14in) s. one of pair. 24-Sep-3 Neumeister, Munich #518/R est:1500
£3333 $6000 €4866 Sharpening the quill (57x43cm-22x17in) s. 21-Jan-4 Sotheby's, New York #249/R est:3000-5000
£27149 $46154 €39638 Day for paying taxes (65x92cm-26x36in) s prov.lit. 19-Nov-3 Fischer, Luzern #1153/R est:65000-80000 (S.FR 60000)

OEHRING, Hedwig (1855-?) German
£397 $727 €600 Three kittens under umbrella (16x24cm-6x9in) s.i. panel. 8-Apr-4 Dorotheum, Vienna #283/R

OELZE, Richard (1900-1980) German
Works on paper
£2018 $3371 €2926 Tree study (20x14cm-8x6in) s.d.27 pencil wash prov.exhib. 19-Jun-3 Kornfeld, Bern #796/R est:3000 (S.FR 4400)
£8000 $14560 €11680 Farnlandschaft (25x26cm-10x10in) s. gouache blk paper exec 1935 prov. 5-Feb-4 Christie's, London #395/R est:3000-5000

OEPTS, Willem Anthonie (1904-1988) Dutch
£2222 $3622 €3200 View of a Mediterranean village (35x45cm-14x18in) s.d.56. 29-Sep-3 Sotheby's, Amsterdam #359/R
£2430 $3961 €3500 Moroccan view (30x40cm-12x16in) s.d.47. 29-Sep-3 Sotheby's, Amsterdam #361/R
£9333 $17173 €14000 Southern France (41x33cm-16x13in) s.d.51. 8-Jun-4 Sotheby's, Amsterdam #13/R est:8000-14000

OER, Theobald Reinhold von (1807-1885) German
Works on paper
£733 $1313 €1100 Three girls by front steps (14x17cm-6x7in) mono.d. W/C. 13-May-4 Bassenge, Berlin #5627/R

OERDER, F (1866-1944) Dutch
£4762 $8667 €7000 Begonia (50x60cm-20x24in) s. 3-Feb-4 Christie's, Amsterdam #289/R est:3000-5000

OERDER, Frans (1866-1944) Dutch
£362 $605 €529 Extensive landscape (42x63cm-17x25in) s. chl. 20-Oct-3 Stephan Welz, Johannesburg #528 est:2000-3000 (SA.R 4200)
£560 $936 €818 Cows and chickens in a stable (42x69cm-17x27in) s. 20-Oct-3 Stephan Welz, Johannesburg #263 est:7000-10000 (SA.R 6500)
£1034 $1728 €1510 Figures tending a new orchard (28x52cm-11x20in) s. 20-Oct-3 Stephan Welz, Johannesburg #256/R est:10000-15000 (SA.R 12000)
£1333 $2440 €2000 Orange azaleas in a vase (50x60cm-20x24in) s. 7-Jun-4 Glerum, Amsterdam #6/R est:2000-3000
£1724 $2879 €2517 Still life of flowers in a vase (54x62cm-21x24in) s. 20-Oct-3 Stephan Welz, Johannesburg #267/R est:18000-24000 (SA.R 20000)
£2657 $4438 €3800 Woman in a flower garden (130x87cm-51x34in) s. 30-Jun-3 Sotheby's, Amsterdam #245/R
£2890 $5173 €4219 Sleeping child (21x17cm-8x7in) s. 31-May-4 Stephan Welz, Johannesburg #544/R est:7000-10000 (SA.R 35000)
£3017 $5039 €4405 Poinsettias (58x72cm-23x28in) s. 20-Oct-3 Stephan Welz, Johannesburg #278/R est:25000-35000 (SA.R 35000)
£3468 $6208 €5063 Woodcutters resting (28x47cm-11x19in) s. board. 31-May-4 Stephan Welz, Johannesburg #584/R est:8000-12000 (SA.R 42000)
£4741 $7918 €6922 Three young men in an interior (17x24cm-7x9in) s.d.1896. 20-Oct-3 Stephan Welz, Johannesburg #270/R est:15000-20000 (SA.R 55000)
£6207 $10366 €9062 Still life of gloxynia (59x89cm-23x35in) s. 20-Oct-3 Stephan Welz, Johannesburg #274/R est:30000-40000 (SA.R 72000)
£6724 $11229 €9817 Leisure hours (87x67cm-34x26in) s. painted c.1900. 20-Oct-3 Stephan Welz, Johannesburg #276/R est:40000-60000 (SA.R 78000)
£26424 $47300 €38579 Interior of a boer house (44x59cm-17x23in) s.d.96. 31-May-4 Stephan Welz, Johannesburg #602/R est:50000-70000 (SA.R 320000)
Works on paper
£410 $697 €599 Genet (18x25cm-7x10in) s.i.d.4.9.03 pencil htd. 4-Nov-3 Stephan Welz, Johannesburg #352 est:2000-4000 (SA.R 4800)

OESCH, Albert Sebastian (1893-1920) Swiss
Works on paper
£856 $1472 €1250 Interior scene of a stage with a performing clown (25x40cm-10x16in) s.d.1916 pastel chk. 8-Dec-3 Philippe Schuler, Zurich #3217/R (S.FR 1900)
£1719 $2923 €2510 Girl in Ascona (36x30cm-14x12in) s.d.1918 pastel. 25-Nov-3 Germann, Zurich #861 est:1000-1500 (S.FR 3800)
£1839 $3070 €2685 Portrait of Appenzell peasant wearing cap (25x21cm-10x8in) s.i.d.1918 pastel chk. 24-Oct-3 Hans Widmer, St Gallen #112/R est:1800-3500 (S.FR 4100)

OESER, Adam Friedrich (1717-1799) German
£22069 $36634 €32000 Portrait of Emperor Charles Albert VII (243x125cm-96x49in) 1-Oct-3 Dorotheum, Vienna #216/R est:12000-18000

OESER, Adam Friedrich (attrib) (1717-1799) German
£4605 $8474 €7000 Allegorical scene with woman in mourning (47x66cm-19x26in) pair. 24-Jun-4 Dr Fritz Nagel, Stuttgart #673/R est:1800

OESTERITZ, Alfred (1876-1904) German
£1181 $1972 €1700 Untitled - landscape with chapel (68x62cm-27x24in) s.i. board. 25-Oct-3 Dr Lehr, Berlin #373/R est:1500

OESTERLE, Wilhelm (1876-1928) German
£278 $453 €400 Nude shepherd with three female nudes (50x64cm-20x25in) s.d.16 panel. 27-Sep-3 Dannenberg, Berlin #605/R

OESTERLEY, Carl August Heinrich Ferdinand (1839-1930) German
£267 $477 €400 Fjord landscape (32x58cm-13x23in) s.d.1892 lit. 14-May-4 Schloss Ahlden, Ahlden #2851/R
£278 $439 €400 Fjord landscape (33x50cm-13x20in) s. board. 5-Sep-3 Wendl, Rudolstadt #3555/R

OESTERLEY, Marie (1842-1916) German
£1342 $2510 €2000 Woodland stream (50x40cm-20x16in) s. 24-Feb-4 Dorotheum, Vienna #220/R est:2200-2600

OFFEL-LEVY, Shmuel (1884-1966) Israeli
£387 $700 €565 Portrait of a young girl (61x39cm-24x15in) s. painted 1930's. 1-Apr-4 Ben-Ami, Tel Aviv #4766/R
£829 $1500 €1210 Figures on the road to Meyron Mountain (94x75cm-37x30in) s. painted 1940's. 1-Apr-4 Ben-Ami, Tel Aviv #4764/R est:2000-3000

OFFER, Frank Rawlings (1847-1932) British
£600 $978 €876 Coastal cottage scene with figures on a path (24x40cm-9x16in) s. panel pair. 24-Sep-3 Peter Wilson, Nantwich #41
£720 $1174 €1051 River landscape with cottage and figures on a bank. Figures gathering firewood before castle ruins (25x40cm-10x16in) s. panel pair. 24-Sep-3 Peter Wilson, Nantwich #42

OFFRESSON, Jean Michel (?) French
Works on paper
£267 $477 €400 Sur le quai a Douarnenez (46x55cm-18x22in) s. pastel. 16-May-4 Renault-Aubry, Pontivy #481

OFFTERDINGER, Carl (attrib) (1829-1889) German
£2778 $4583 €4000 Queen Elisabeth I of England holding quill (151x103cm-59x41in) i. verso. 3-Jul-3 Dr Fritz Nagel, Stuttgart #506/R est:2500

OFILI, Chris (1968-) British

Works on paper

£700	$1274	€1022	Self portrait (20x14cm-8x6in) s.i.d.89 col pencil prov. 21-Jun-4 Bonhams, New Bond Street #142/R
£2246	$3750	€3279	Untitled, profile of bearded man (24x15cm-9x6in) init.d.99 verso W/C pencil. 7-Oct-3 Sotheby's, New York #392 est:3000-5000
£2346	$4200	€3425	Untitled (24x16cm-9x6in) s.verso W/C grahpite exec.c.1999 prov. 14-May-4 Phillips, New York #346/R est:2000-3000
£2432	$4500	€3551	Untitled (24x16cm-9x6in) W/C over pencil exec 1998. 12-Feb-4 Sotheby's, New York #330/R est:4000-6000
£2800	$5068	€4088	Untitled (29x21cm-11x8in) pencil executed c.1999 prov. 1-Apr-4 Christie's, Kensington #349/R est:3000-5000
£2994	$5000	€4371	Untitled (24x15cm-9x6in) s.d.99 W/C graphite prov. 14-Nov-3 Phillips, New York #260/R est:5000-7000
£4000	$7280	€5840	Untitled (24x15cm-9x6in) s.d.1998 verso W/C pencil prov.exhib. 6-Feb-4 Sotheby's, London #113/R est:4000-6000
£4000	$7280	€5840	Untitled (24x16cm-9x6in) s.d.1998 verso W/C pencil prov.exhib. 6-Feb-4 Sotheby's, London #114/R est:4000-6000
£4000	$7280	€5840	Untitled (24x15cm-9x6in) s.d.98 verso W/C pencil prov. 6-Feb-4 Sotheby's, London #267/R est:4000-6000
£4000	$7360	€5840	Untitled (24x15cm-9x6in) W/C pencil two executed c.2000 prov. 25-Jun-4 Christie's, London #247/R est:4000-6000
£4000	$7360	€5840	Untitled (24x15cm-9x6in) W/C pencil exec c.1998 prov. 24-Jun-4 Sotheby's, London #299/R est:4000-6000
£4000	$7360	€5840	Untitled (24x15cm-9x6in) s.d.98 verso W/C pencil prov. 24-Jun-4 Sotheby's, London #300/R est:4000-6000
£5028	$9000	€7341	Untitled (24x16cm-9x6in) s.d.2001 verso W/C prov. 13-May-4 Sotheby's, New York #307/R est:6000-8000
£5307	$9500	€7748	Untitled (23x15cm-9x6in) s.d.2000 verso W/C graphite diptych prov. 12-May-4 Christie's, Rockefeller NY #343/R est:8000-12000
£6000	$10020	€8760	Untitled (24x16cm-9x6in) s. d.99 verso W/C pencil prov. 21-Oct-3 Sotheby's, London #309/R est:3000-4000
£6287	$10500	€9179	Untitled - women (32x20cm-13x8in) s.d.99 W/C graphite two prov. 14-Nov-3 Phillips, New York #261/R est:10000-15000
£6500	$10855	€9490	Untitled (24x16cm-9x6in) W/C pencil prov. 22-Oct-3 Christie's, London #122/R est:3000-5000
£7186	$12000	€10492	Untitled (24x16cm-9x6in) s.d.2000 verso W/C pencil prov. 13-Nov-3 Sotheby's, New York #429/R est:5000-7000
£8000	$14720	€11680	Untitled (24x16cm-9x6in) s.d.2001 verso pencil W/C prov. 24-Jun-4 Sotheby's, London #134/R est:4000-6000
£9000	$15030	€13140	Untitled (24x15cm-9x6in) s. d.98 verso W/C pencil prov. 21-Oct-3 Sotheby's, London #300/R est:3000-4000
£12000	$21840	€17520	Untitled (24x15cm-9x6in) s.d.99 verso W/C pencil two prov. 5-Feb-4 Christie's, London #224/R est:7000-9000
£12500	$20875	€18250	Untitled (24x15cm-9x6in) s. d.2000 verso W/C pencil prov. 21-Oct-3 Sotheby's, London #301/R est:3000-4000

OGDEN, Frederick D (19th C) American

£511	$900	€746	Restless sky, landscape with trees and stream (61x91cm-24x36in) s. 21-May-4 North East Auctions, Portsmouth #270
£813	$1300	€1187	Singing stream (61x91cm-24x36in) s. s.i.verso. 20-Sep-3 Jeffery Burchard, Florida #54/R

OGGIONO, Marco (attrib) (1470-1530) Italian

£16667	$30000	€24334	Madonna and Child in a landscape (62x43cm-24x17in) panel. 22-Jan-4 Sotheby's, New York #190/R est:30000-40000

OGILVIE, John Clinton (1838-1900) American

£344	$550	€502	In the valley of Lauterbrunnen, Switzerland (43x61cm-17x24in) s.d.1882 s.i.d.verso. 18-May-3 Auctions by the Bay, Alameda #1035/R
£1029	$1800	€1502	Port in choppy seas (89x137cm-35x54in) s. 19-Dec-3 Sotheby's, New York #1085/R est:2000-4000
£1934	$3500	€2824	Valley landscape (28x41cm-11x16in) s. 16-Apr-4 James Julia, Fairfield #621/R est:5000-7000

OGILVIE, Llly (20th C) British?

£450	$752	€657	Peter the Bedlington, canine portrait (45x34cm-18x13in) s.i.d.1928 verso. 13-Nov-3 Bonhams, Edinburgh #398

OGLE, Mark (?) American

£294	$500	€429	Elk by a river, autumn (16x30cm-6x12in) s. board prov. 21-Nov-3 Skinner, Boston #338/R

O'GORMAN, Lance (fl.1970s) New Zealander

£321	$582	€469	Far from the madding crown, Northland (44x60cm-17x24in) s. board. 4-Apr-4 International Art Centre, Auckland #256/R (NZ.D 900)
£393	$711	€574	Tologa Bay, East Coast Gisbourne (44x60cm-17x24in) s. board. 4-Apr-4 International Art Centre, Auckland #269/R (NZ.D 1100)

OGUISS, Takanari (1901-1986) Japanese

£3810	$6095	€5525	Interior courtyard (61x50cm-24x20in) s. 15-May-3 Stuker, Bern #1423 est:5000-7000 (S.FR 8000)
£7018	$12912	€10246	Still life with ham (50x61cm-20x24in) s.d.34 prov. 23-Jun-4 Koller, Zurich #3151/R est:15000-20000 (S.FR 16000)
£7207	$12396	€10522	Self portrait (35x26cm-14x10in) s.i. panel prov. 2-Dec-3 Koller, Zurich #3054/R est:15000-25000 (S.FR 16000)
£12324	$21321	€17500	Burano, Italy (23x33cm-9x13in) s. panel. 9-Dec-3 Artcurial Briest, Paris #179/R est:8000-12000
£14085	$24648	€20000	Venise (46x54cm-18x21in) s. 18-Dec-3 Cornette de St.Cyr, Paris #4/R est:18000-22000
£15642	$28000	€22837	Burano, Venise (25x33cm-10x13in) s. panel painted 1957. 5-May-4 Christie's, Rockefeller NY #278/R est:22000-28000
£17000	$31280	€25500	Pont a Venise (35x27cm-14x11in) s. 9-Jun-4 Beaussant & Lefèvre, Paris #201/R est:9000-10000
£17117	$29441	€24991	Parisian bridge (26x35cm-10x14in) s. panel prov. 2-Dec-3 Koller, Zurich #3058/R est:30000-40000 (S.FR 38000)
£21000	$38640	€30660	Neige a gonesse (54x73cm-21x29in) s. i.verso painted 1958 exhib. 24-Mar-4 Sotheby's, Olympia #48/R est:10000-12000
£25000	$42500	€36500	Cour fleurie (61x51cm-24x20in) s. painted August 1950. 6-Nov-3 Sotheby's, New York #336/R est:25000-35000
£30000	$50100	€43800	Place rondeau, Carouge (60x76cm-24x30in) s. i.verso painted 1939 prov. 21-Oct-3 Sotheby's, London #88/R est:35000-45000
£34286	$54857	€49715	Rue du Faub St Martin (73x60cm-29x24in) s. i. verso. 15-May-3 Stuker, Bern #1422/R est:15000-18000 (S.FR 72000)
£41899	$75000	€61173	Samaritaine - rue de la Reynie (73x60cm-29x24in) s. painted c.1968 prov. 6-May-4 Sotheby's, New York #447/R est:50000-70000
£42793	$73604	€62478	Pont des trois arcs, Cannaregio - Venice (65x90cm-26x35in) s. i. verso prov. 2-Dec-3 Koller, Zurich #3056/R est:80000-120000 (S.FR 95000)
£78212	$140000	€114190	Hotel du Cantal (92x65cm-36x26in) s.i.verso painted 1936 prov.lit. 5-May-4 Christie's, Rockefeller NY #288/R est:140000-180000
£85586	$147207	€124956	Hotel du Cantal (92x64cm-36x25in) s. prov.lit. 2-Dec-3 Koller, Zurich #3055/R est:100000-200000 (S.FR 190000)
£94118	$160000	€137412	Rue du Faubourg Saint-Martin, Paris (73x60cm-29x24in) s.i.verso. 5-Nov-3 Christie's, Rockefeller NY #357/R est:70000-90000

Works on paper

£2517	$4580	€3800	Montmartre (70x88cm-28x35in) s. india ink. 16-Jun-4 Claude Boisgirard, Paris #121 est:500-800

O'HAGAN, Peter (20th C) New Zealander

Works on paper

£1071	$1971	€1564	Waiting in the spring rain, Giverney (75x53cm-30x21in) s. mixed media. 25-Mar-4 International Art Centre, Auckland #126/R est:2800-3800 (NZ.D 3000)

O'HALLORAN, James (1955-) Irish

£413	$748	€620	Autumn colours St Stephen's Green (51x33cm-20x13in) s.i. s.verso board. 30-Mar-4 De Veres Art Auctions, Dublin #183
£447	$823	€680	Girl in interior (31x26cm-12x10in) s. board. 22-Jun-4 De Veres Art Auctions, Dublin #193/R
£769	$1308	€1100	Brass bed, interior (34x45cm-13x18in) s.i.verso board. 18-Nov-3 Mealy's, Castlecomer #1397/R
£1259	$2140	€1800	Brass bed, morning light (51x61cm-20x24in) s. board exhib. 18-Nov-3 Whyte's, Dublin #210/R est:1800-2200

O'HARA, Frank and RIVERS, Larry (20th C) American

Prints

£14118	$24000	€20612	Stones (57x69cm-22x27in) s.i. lithograph set of 12. 4-Nov-3 Christie's, Rockefeller NY #338/R est:25000-35000

O'HARA, Helen (fl.1881-1908) British

Works on paper

£1000	$1790	€1460	Path by the brook (24x35cm-9x14in) mono.d.1891 pencil W/C. 14-May-4 Christie's, Kensington #329a est:1200-1800
£1477	$2643	€2200	Coastal scene with distant boat (38x54cm-15x21in) mono. W/C. 26-May-4 James Adam, Dublin #39/R est:2000-3000

OHASHI, Yutaka (1923-) American/Japanese

£973	$1800	€1460	White I (124x91cm-49x36in) s. s.i.d.1959 verso prov. 14-Jul-4 American Auctioneer #490401/R est:1000-1500

OHL, Fritz (1904-1976) Dutch

£1027	$1747	€1500	Chinese junk (89x69cm-35x27in) s. 5-Nov-3 Vendue Huis, Gravenhage #547/R est:1500-2000
£1042	$1740	€1521	Fishing boat (70x50cm-28x20in) s. 12-Oct-3 Sotheby's, Singapore #2/R est:3000-4000 (S.D 3000)
£1233	$2096	€1800	Two figures by a tree (55x48cm-22x19in) s. 5-Nov-3 Vendue Huis, Gravenhage #543/R est:1500-2000
£1258	$2290	€1900	Flamboyant (70x90cm-28x35in) s. board. 18-Jun-4 Bolland & Marotz, Bremen #942/R est:2800
£1449	$2246	€2116	Boat (40x50cm-16x20in) s. 6-Oct-2 Sotheby's, Singapore #50/R est:3000-4000 (S.D 4000)
£1562	$2609	€2281	Boat (70x60cm-28x24in) s. board. 12-Oct-3 Sotheby's, Singapore #1/R est:4000-6000 (S.D 4500)
£1562	$2609	€2281	Under a flamboyan (61x91cm-24x36in) s. 12-Oct-3 Sotheby's, Singapore #47/R est:5000-7000 (S.D 4500)
£1720	$2753	€2511	Boats (61x91cm-24x36in) s. 18-May-3 Sotheby's, Singapore #43/R est:4000-6000 (S.D 4800)
£2134	$3841	€3116	Chines junk with cargo (90x70cm-35x28in) s. 25-Apr-4 Christie's, Hong Kong #503/R est:20000-30000 (HK.D 30000)
£2355	$3650	€3438	Boat (76x61cm-30x24in) s. 6-Oct-2 Sotheby's, Singapore #49/R est:5000-7000 (S.D 6500)
£2536	$3931	€3703	Landscape (76x116cm-30x46in) s. 6-Oct-2 Sotheby's, Singapore #31/R est:7000-9000 (S.D 7000)
£2778	$4639	€4056	Ngaben (74x106cm-29x42in) s. board. 12-Oct-3 Sotheby's, Singapore #37/R est:8000-10000 (S.D 8000)
£2796	$4473	€4082	Balinese girl (47x35cm-19x14in) s. board. 18-May-3 Sotheby's, Singapore #6/R est:2000-3000 (S.D 7800)
£3226	$5161	€4710	Boat (61x91cm-24x36in) s. 18-May-3 Sotheby's, Singapore #44/R est:4000-6000 (S.D 9000)

OHLSEN, Jeppe Madsen (1891-1948) Danish

£287	$465	€416	Wooded landscape with large trees (40x34cm-16x13in) s. 4-Aug-3 Rasmussen, Vejle #653/R (D.KR 3000)
£526	$853	€763	Landscape from Snoghoi (47x58cm-19x23in) s. i.stretcher. 4-Aug-3 Rasmussen, Vejle #651/R (D.KR 5500)
£676	$1251	€987	Still life of poppies in vase (46x36cm-18x14in) s.d.1921. 15-Mar-4 Rasmussen, Vejle #645/R (D.KR 7500)
£995	$1782	€1453	Still life of glass, jug and apples (38x45cm-15x18in) s. 10-May-4 Rasmussen, Vejle #539/R (D.KR 11000)
£1448	$2592	€2114	Figures by thatched houses (41x47cm-16x19in) s. 10-May-4 Rasmussen, Vejle #538/R est:15000 (D.KR 16000)
£2805	$5022	€4095	The old watch house in Christiansfeld (54x68cm-21x27in) s. exhib. 10-May-4 Rasmussen, Vejle #537/R est:40000 (D.KR 31000)

OHLSEN, Theodor (1855-1913) German

£1259	$2165	€1800	Camels by the lake (36x67cm-14x26in) s. 3-Dec-3 Stadion, Trieste #1102/R est:2000-3000
£1500	$2760	€2190	Woman in a South American sugar plantation (67x40cm-26x16in) s. board prov. 25-Mar-4 Christie's, Kensington #61/R est:1500-2000

£13966 $25000 €20390 View of Valparaiso harbour (151x88cm-59x35in) s.i.d.91. 26-May-4 Sotheby's, New York #76/R est:30000-40000

OHLSON, Alfred (1868-1940) Swedish

Sculpture

£2462 $4234 €3595 St George and the Dragon (44cm-17in) s.d.1911 silver after Bernt Notke incl.stone socle two. 3-Dec-3 AB Stockholms Auktionsverk #2518/R est:15000-18000 (S.KR 32000)

OHM, August (1943-) German

Works on paper

£338 $605 €500 Lovers (44x32cm-17x13in) s.d.79 pen sepia board. 8-May-4 Hans Stahl, Toestorf #77/R
£638 $1066 €900 Ship in Munkmarsch (64x49cm-25x19in) s. gouache mixed media. 21-Jun-3 Hans Stahl, Hamburg #108/R

OHM, Wilhelm (1905-1965) German

£1600 $2928 €2400 Musician and dancer (52x71cm-20x28in) i. verso tempera prov. 5-Jun-4 Lempertz, Koln #915/R est:2500

Works on paper

£2400 $4296 €3600 Two women (40x33cm-16x13in) mono.d. pencil board prov.lit. 14-May-4 Ketterer, Munich #67/R est:1600-2000

OHMAYER, Max (1903-) German

£350 $584 €500 Cows (48x58cm-19x23in) s. 26-Jun-3 Weidler, Nurnberg #4534/R

OHMERT, Paul Hans (1890-1960) German?

£313 $509 €450 Still life of vegetables with mushrooms and asparagus (65x75cm-26x30in) s. 25-Sep-3 Neumeister, Munich #2841

OHRLING, Eva (20th C) Danish

£469 $878 €685 Composition (190x140cm-75x55in) 25-Feb-4 Kunsthallen, Copenhagen #184 (D.KR 5200)

OHTAKE, Tomie (1917-) Brazilian

£6227 $11022 €9341 Untitled (70x70cm-28x28in) s.d.1983 i.verso. 27-Apr-4 Bolsa de Arte, Rio de Janeiro #134/R (B.R 34000)
£12821 $22692 €19232 Red on a white background (50x70cm-20x28in) s. 27-Apr-4 Bolsa de Arte, Rio de Janeiro #126/R (B.R 70000)

OINONEN, Mikko (1883-1956) Finnish

£338 $541 €480 White house (40x29cm-16x11in) s. 18-Sep-3 Hagelstam, Helsinki #971/R
£369 $679 €550 Water-lilies (50x60cm-20x24in) s. 25-Mar-4 Hagelstam, Helsinki #1083
£369 $679 €550 Landscape (46x55cm-18x22in) s.d.1956. 25-Mar-4 Hagelstam, Helsinki #954
£507 $811 €720 Red cottage (54x65cm-21x26in) s. 18-Sep-3 Hagelstam, Helsinki #859/R
£535 $856 €760 Landscape (54x65cm-21x26in) s. 18-Sep-3 Hagelstam, Helsinki #968/R
£608 $1089 €900 Poppies in a vase (65x54cm-26x21in) s.d.1930. 8-May-4 Bukowskis, Helsinki #61/R
£658 $1210 €980 Peonies in a garden (65x80cm-26x31in) s. 25-Mar-4 Hagelstam, Helsinki #904
£764 $1276 €1100 Lake landscape (36x45cm-14x18in) s.d.1922. 26-Oct-3 Bukowskis, Helsinki #446/R
£940 $1729 €1400 Nude (80x45cm-31x18in) s.d.1908. 25-Mar-4 Hagelstam, Helsinki #992
£1076 $1798 €1550 Lilac bushes (56x67cm-22x26in) s.d.1913. 26-Oct-3 Bukowskis, Helsinki #447/R est:1000
£1127 $1803 €1600 Paris (65x84cm-26x33in) s. 18-Sep-3 Hagelstam, Helsinki #765/R est:1800
£1678 $2853 €2400 Autumn landscape (86x105cm-34x41in) s.d.1922. 29-Nov-3 Bukowskis, Helsinki #134/R est:2500-2800
£2095 $3749 €3100 Parisian view (49x61cm-19x24in) s.i.d.09. 8-May-4 Bukowskis, Helsinki #203/R est:1300-1600

OITICICA, Helio (1937-1980) Brazilian

Works on paper

£9158 $16209 €13737 Abstract (40x40cm-16x16in) gouache mixed media. 27-Apr-4 Bolsa de Arte, Rio de Janeiro #96/R (B.R 50000)
£15934 $29159 €23901 Blockade (37x40cm-15x16in) s.d.1958 i.verso gouache cardboard. 6-Jul-4 Bolsa de Arte, Rio de Janeiro #102/R (B.R 87000)

OJA, Onni (1909-) Finnish

£833 $1392 €1200 Woodland tarn, Karhumaki (33x40cm-13x16in) s. 26-Oct-3 Bukowskis, Helsinki #449/R
£872 $1605 €1300 Still life (41x33cm-16x13in) s. 25-Mar-4 Hagelstam, Helsinki #822
£1007 $1852 €1500 Summer's day in Vihtis (27x41cm-11x16in) s. d.1981 verso. 25-Mar-4 Hagelstam, Helsinki #905 est:1000
£1007 $1872 €1500 Men building (33x45cm-13x18in) s.d.45. 7-Mar-4 Bukowskis, Helsinki #414/R est:1000
£1056 $1690 €1500 Amaryllis (65x50cm-26x20in) s. 21-Sep-3 Bukowskis, Helsinki #417/R est:700
£1156 $2105 €1700 House in Ilomants (27x41cm-11x16in) s. 8-Feb-4 Bukowskis, Helsinki #420/R est:1300
£1275 $2372 €1900 Landscape from Miehikkala (27x41cm-11x16in) s. 7-Mar-4 Bukowskis, Helsinki #412/R est:1500
£1275 $2372 €1900 View of Hattula through studio window (27x41cm-11x16in) s. 7-Mar-4 Bukowskis, Helsinki #413/R est:1200
£1275 $2372 €1900 Landscape from Ria in Vichtis (27x41cm-11x16in) s. 7-Mar-4 Bukowskis, Helsinki #415/R est:1500
£1285 $2145 €1850 Village (38x61cm-15x24in) s.d.1977. 23-Oct-3 Hagelstam, Helsinki #830/R est:2000
£1342 $2470 €2000 Lappo river (54x81cm-21x32in) s.d.1980. 25-Mar-4 Hagelstam, Helsinki #1026 est:1300
£1544 $2840 €2300 Spring landscape with old apple tree (40x65cm-16x26in) s. 25-Mar-4 Hagelstam, Helsinki #863/R est:1500
£1667 $2783 €2400 Still life (55x81cm-22x32in) s. 23-Oct-3 Hagelstam, Helsinki #990 est:2500
£1892 $3386 €2800 Landscape from Tammela (54x81cm-21x32in) s. 8-May-4 Bukowskis, Helsinki #45/R est:2300-2600
£1944 $3247 €2800 Tavastehus (55x81cm-22x32in) s. 23-Oct-3 Hagelstam, Helsinki #1020 est:1500
£2432 $4354 €3600 By Invid river (54x81cm-21x32in) s. 8-May-4 Bukowskis, Helsinki #30/R est:3000-4000
£2448 $4161 €3500 Day in June, Saksala (54x81cm-21x32in) s. 29-Nov-3 Bukowskis, Helsinki #91/R est:3000-3500
£2867 $4874 €4100 Winter landscape from Vichtis (60x81cm-24x32in) s. 29-Nov-3 Bukowskis, Helsinki #70/R est:3500-3800

OJEDA, Froylan (1932-1991) Mexican

£844 $1342 €1232 Beached boats and figures (94x74cm-37x29in) s. 29-Apr-3 Louis Morton, Mexico #102/R est:22000-26000 (M.P 14000)

OJEN, Evert Marinus van (1888-1964) Dutch

Photographs

£3497 $5944 €5000 Van Nelle factory, Rotterdam (15x22cm-6x9in) i. verso silver gelatin lit.exhib. 27-Nov-3 Villa Grisebach, Berlin #1332/R est:5000-7000

OKADA, Minoru (20th C) Japanese?

£300 $546 €450 Bouquet d'iris (54x65cm-21x26in) s. s.d.1931 verso. 29-Jun-4 Chenu & Scrive, Lyon #140/R

OKASHY, Avshalom (1916-1980) Israeli

£492 $900 €718 Composition (45x34cm-18x13in) s.d.1965 s.verso. 1-Jun-4 Ben-Ami, Tel Aviv #4889/R est:1200-1600

Works on paper

£442 $800 €645 Figures in Acre (50x70cm-20x28in) s. gouache exec. 1960's. 1-Apr-4 Ben-Ami, Tel Aviv #4749/R

O'KEEFE, Alfred Henry (1858-1941) Australian

£1022 $1758 €1492 Tessa (43x36cm-17x14in) board. 7-Dec-3 International Art Centre, Auckland #284 (NZ.D 2750)

O'KEEFFE, Georgia (1887-1986) American

£188953 $325000 €275871 Petunias in oval no.2 (41x33cm-16x13in) board painted 1924 prov.exhib.lit. 3-Dec-3 Sotheby's, New York #57/R est:300000-400000
£255682 $450000 €373296 Sunset, Long Island (25x36cm-10x14in) canvasboard painted 1939 prov.exhib.lit. 19-May-4 Sotheby's, New York #121/R est:400000-600000
£494186 $850000 €721512 Cannas (42x26cm-17x10in) linen on board painted 1919 prov.exhib.lit. 4-Dec-3 Christie's, Rockefeller NY #112/R est:500000-700000
£930233 $1600000 €1358140 Birch and pine trees, pink (91x56cm-36x22in) s.i.d.1925 prov.exhib.lit. 4-Dec-3 Christie's, Rockefeller NY #88/R est:1200000-1800000

Works on paper

£63953 $110000 €93371 Flowers (24x18cm-9x7in) pastel executed 1923 prov.exhib. 3-Dec-3 Sotheby's, New York #66/R est:80000-120000

O'KELLY, A (1853-1929) Irish

£1538 $2615 €2200 Busy Breton street scene with figures (34x27cm-13x11in) bears sig. board. 18-Nov-3 Mealy's, Castlecomer #1400a/R est:2000-3000

O'KELLY, Aloysius (1853-1929) Irish

£3803 $6085 €5400 Country churchyard with memorial cross (36x51cm-14x20in) s. canvas on board. 16-Sep-3 Whyte's, Dublin #160/R est:4000-6000
£5307 $9500 €7748 Arab horsemen (43x51cm-17x20in) s. 6-May-4 Doyle, New York #46/R est:2500-3500
£5594 $9510 €8000 Male study. Woodland river (46x38cm-18x15in) double-sided prov.exhib. 18-Nov-3 Whyte's, Dublin #56/R est:8000-10000
£6200 $11160 €9052 Skirmish, scouts surprised (41x53cm-16x21in) s. 21-Jan-4 Sotheby's, Olympia #290/R est:3000-5000
£10490 $17832 €15000 Entering the gate (51x36cm-20x14in) s. 18-Nov-3 Whyte's, Dublin #52/R est:10000-12000
£10738 $19221 €16000 View of a lake through trees (128x102cm-50x40in) s. 26-May-4 James Adam, Dublin #30/R est:6000-8000
£12752 $22570 €19000 Market place, Tangier (32x37cm-13x15in) s.i. prov.exhib. 27-Apr-4 Whyte's, Dublin #126/R est:12000-15000
£23000 $41170 €33580 Portrait of a Breton child (24x20cm-9x8in) s. 14-May-4 Christie's, London #162/R est:6000-10000

Works on paper

£3378 $6385 €5000 Ladies land league (28x23cm-11x9in) s. gouache board grisaille pencil. 17-Feb-4 Whyte's, Dublin #156/R est:1500-2000

OKINCZYC, Andrzej (1949-) Polish

£538 $963 €785 Composition (68x81cm-27x32in) tempera paper. 6-May-4 Agra, Warsaw #26/R (P.Z 3800)
£1379 $2303 €2000 In the bathroom (62x23cm-24x9in) s.d.1979 verso oil tempera board. 16-Nov-3 Agra, Warsaw #16/R est:500

OKNER, Gunnar (1920-) Swedish

£378 $642 €552 September (39x38cm-15x15in) s.d.96 verso. 5-Nov-3 AB Stockholms Auktionsverk #957/R (S.KR 5000)
£1208 $2054 €1764 February light (92x89cm-36x35in) s.d.95-96 verso. 5-Nov-3 AB Stockholms Auktionsverk #946/R est:8000-10000 (S.KR 16000)

OKULICK, John (1947-) American
Sculpture
£1317 $2200 €1923 Ceremonial box (35x35x7cm-14x14x3in) wood rope twigs executed 1977 prov. 11-Nov-3 Christie's, Rockefeller NY #157/R est:300-500

OKUN, Edward (1872-1945) Polish
£895 $1638 €1307 Portrait of an artist with long dark hair and brown shirt (48x40cm-19x16in) s.i.d.1898 canvas on cardboard. 7-Jun-4 Museumsbygningen, Copenhagen #163/R (D.KR 10000)
£6270 $9781 €9154 Concert (50x40cm-20x16in) s. canvasboard painted c.1911. 30-Mar-3 Agra, Warsaw #9/R est:40000 (P.Z 40000)

OKX, Kees (1939-) Dutch
£467 $845 €700 Entre soir et matin (60x81cm-24x32in) s. 3-Apr-4 Neret-Minet, Paris #184/R
£500 $905 €750 Fenetre sur l'infini (92x60cm-36x24in) s. 3-Apr-4 Neret-Minet, Paris #96/R
£664 $1129 €950 L'habit du paysage (65x54cm-26x21in) s. 29-Nov-3 Neret-Minet, Paris #180/R
Works on paper
£699 $1189 €1000 Poesinage (100x70cm-39x28in) s. mixed media canvas. 29-Nov-3 Neret-Minet, Paris #106/R

OLAFSSON, Sigurjon (1908-1982) Icelandic
Sculpture
£2166 $3986 €3162 Ingi T Larussom, Memorial (106cm-42in) wood copper exec.c.1974-75 exhib.lit. 29-Mar-4 Rasmussen, Copenhagen #234/R est:30000 (D.KR 24000)

OLAFSSON, Trygvi (1940-) Icelandic
£1408 $2352 €2056 Empty - red composition (180x120cm-71x47in) mono.d.89. 7-Oct-3 Rasmussen, Copenhagen #234/R est:15000-18000 (D.KR 15000)

OLAIO, Pedro (younger) (1930-) Portuguese
£671 $1201 €1000 Fishing boats by the coast (29x40cm-11x16in) s. board. 31-May-4 Cabral Moncada Leiloes, Lisbon #236
£1007 $1802 €1500 Dusk, seascape (73x60cm-29x24in) s. board. 31-May-4 Cabral Moncada Leiloes, Lisbon #228/R est:1500-2250

OLALDE, Gaston (1925-2003) Uruguayan
£1359 $2500 €1984 Still life (51x57cm-20x22in) s.d.51 s.i.d.verso cardboard. 22-Jun-4 Galeria y Remates, Montevideo #112/R est:3000-4000

OLARIA, Frederico (1849-1898) French
£1408 $2254 €2000 Dog and puppies (113x78cm-44x31in) s. 16-Sep-3 Segre, Madrid #76/R

OLAUSSON, Lennart (1944-) Swedish
£435 $783 €653 Boy in landscape (55x46cm-22x18in) s.d.78 panel. 25-Apr-4 Goteborg Auktionsverk, Sweden #374/R (S.KR 6000)

OLBERT, V (?) ?
£1951 $3063 €2848 Now I can read too (63x79cm-25x31in) s. i.verso. 1-Sep-3 Shapiro, Sydney #351/R est:5000-7000 (A.D 4800)
£2195 $3446 €3205 Untitled, busy cobbler (63x79cm-25x31in) s. i.verso. 1-Sep-3 Shapiro, Sydney #352/R est:5000-7000 (A.D 5400)

OLBINSKI, Rafal (1945-) Polish
Works on paper
£586 $979 €850 Ballerina, her tutu serving as a coffee table (68x53cm-27x21in) s. black chk. 16-Nov-3 Agra, Warsaw #24/R

OLD MASTER SCHOOL, 18th C
£9929 $16085 €14000 Asiatic see battle (76x113cm-30x44in) 23-May-3 Karlheinz Kaupp, Staufen #1722/R est:2500

OLDE, Hans (1855-1917) German
£2793 $5000 €4690 Winter landscape (71x102cm-28x40in) s.d.1891. 20-Mar-4 Pook & Pook, Downington #390 est:1000-1500

OLDEMAN, Rudolf Hendrik (1901-1964) Dutch
£271 $462 €396 Still life of flowers with nest (61x50cm-24x20in) s. 1-Dec-3 Koller, Zurich #6478 (S.FR 600)

OLDENBURG, Claes (1929-) American
Prints
£2000 $3400 €2920 Miniature soft drum set (25x48cm-10x19in) init.num.103/200 screenprint. 21-Nov-3 Swann Galleries, New York #143/R est:3000-5000
£5491 $9500 €8017 Chicago stuffed with numbers, Tyler 477 C01 (97x66cm-38x26in) s.num. col lithograph edition of 85 prov. 15-Dec-3 Hindman, Chicago #128/R est:2000-4000
Sculpture
£1057 $1798 €1543 Cripsbread (9x16cm-4x6in) s.i. iron lit. 4-Nov-3 Bukowskis, Stockholm #565/R est:8000-10000 (S.KR 14000)
£1734 $3000 €2532 Green pill (5x15cm-2x6in) d.77 num.15/33 enamel cast aluminum plexiglass stand. 15-Dec-3 Hindman, Chicago #127/R est:2500-5000
£1800 $2988 €2628 Baked potato (24x12cm-9x5in) init.num.36/75 paint cast resin ceramic plate. 6-Oct-3 Sotheby's, London #280/R est:1800-2600
£2059 $3500 €3006 Soft drum set (28x48x35cm-11x19x14in) init. num.78/200 screenprint spray paint rope wood. 4-Nov-3 Christie's, Rockefeller NY #320/R est:2000-3000
£2414 $4345 €3500 Tea bag (100x70x5cm-39x28x2in) s.num.112/125 verso vinyl felt photo cardboard plexiglas prov.lit. 25-Jan-4 Cornette de St.Cyr, Paris #488 est:3500-5000
£3235 $5500 €4723 Fire plug souvenir (20x20x15cm-8x8x6in) init. cast plaster acrylic. 4-Nov-3 Christie's, Rockefeller NY #319/R est:4000-6000
£4237 $7500 €6186 Tilting neon cocktail (47x16x18cm-19x6x7in) init.i. num.23/50 stainless steel plastic wood. 30-Apr-4 Sotheby's, New York #428/R est:3500-4500
£4800 $8736 €7008 Miniature soft drum set (28x53x40cm-11x21x16in) init.num.186/200 multiple silkscreen canvas drum set wood box. 1-Jul-4 Sotheby's, London #428/R est:2500-3500
£12752 $22826 €19000 Wall paper biscuit (21x21cm-8x8in) s.i.d.1966 verso plaster casein prov. 26-May-4 Christie's, Paris #92/R est:10000-15000
£14371 $24000 €20982 Soft Inverted Q (46x46x33cm-18x18x13in) init.d.76 num.7/12 cast resin prov.lit. 12-Nov-3 Christie's, Rockefeller NY #406/R est:20000-30000
£14970 $25000 €21856 Soft inverted Q (45x53x336cm-18x21x132in) init.d.76 num.6-12 verso cast resin. 13-Nov-3 Sotheby's, New York #292/R est:12000-18000
£39106 $70000 €57095 Profile airflow, gemini 178 (84x165cm-33x65in) s.i.d.69 num.58/75 polyurethane over col lithograph prov. 7-May-4 Sloans & Kenyon, Bethesda #1761/R est:60000-80000
£41916 $70000 €61197 String bean (452x16cm-178x6in) suede vinyl wood steel case epoxy beans prov.exhib. 13-Nov-3 Sotheby's, New York #115/R est:70000-90000
£726257 $1300000 €1060335 Sewing machine (118x161cm-46x63in) init.d.61 muslin plaster wire enamel paint prov.exhib.lit. 12-May-4 Sotheby's, New York #34/R est:500000-700000
Works on paper
£3593 $6000 €5246 Proposal for a giant balloon in the form of cornflakes and banana slices (20x24cm-8x9in) init.d.69 pencil col pencil prov. 13-Nov-3 Sotheby's, New York #205/R est:6000-8000
£3988 $6500 €5822 Erotic monument for NYC (28x22cm-11x9in) init.i.d.66 W/C pencil prov. 23-Sep-3 Christie's, Rockefeller NY #90/R est:8000-12000
£4790 $8000 €6993 New/old school (28x21cm-11x8in) s.i.d.3/69 ballpoint pen notepad paper on paper prov. 13-Nov-3 Sotheby's, New York #114/R est:5500-7500
£12973 $24000 €18941 Soft Fan (33x46cm-13x18in) init.i.d.65 crayon W/C prov. 12-Feb-4 Sotheby's, New York #100/R est:15000-20000
£16000 $29120 €23360 Giant balloon in shape of screw (74x59cm-29x23in) s.d.73 pencil chl W/C prov. 30-Jun-4 Christie's, Kensington #164/R est:9000-12000

OLDENHAVE, Arnoldus (1905-?) Dutch
£1769 $3219 €2600 De dam, Amsterdam (65x110cm-26x43in) s. 3-Feb-4 Christie's, Amsterdam #336/R est:800-1200

OLDEROCK, Max (1895-1972) German
£268 $494 €400 Composition (49x78cm-19x31in) panel. 26-Mar-4 Bolland & Marotz, Bremen #689/R
£486 $792 €700 Composition (55x105cm-22x41in) s.d.1962 masonite. 27-Sep-3 Dr Fritz Nagel, Stuttgart #9310/R
£1200 $2184 €1800 The water spirit (51x127cm-20x50in) board lit. 3-Jul-4 Badum, Bamberg #163/R est:2400

OLDERT, Johan (1912-1984) South African?
£248 $443 €362 Swellendam Way, Cape Province (34x50cm-13x20in) s. board. 31-May-4 Stephan Welz, Johannesburg #137 (SA.R 3000)
£289 $517 €422 Grobelaars Plek, Kaap (29x42cm-11x17in) s. board. 31-May-4 Stephan Welz, Johannesburg #162 (SA.R 3500)
£314 $562 €458 Blue gum trees (44x60cm-17x24in) canvas on board. 31-May-4 Stephan Welz, Johannesburg #192 (SA.R 3800)
£330 $591 €482 Extensive landscape with blue gums and a dirt road (49x75cm-19x30in) s. board. 31-May-4 Stephan Welz, Johannesburg #194 (SA.R 4000)
£345 $576 €504 Road and blue gum trees (60x90cm-24x35in) s. canvas on board. 20-Oct-3 Stephan Welz, Johannesburg #891 est:3000-5000 (SA.R 4000)

OLDEWELT, Ferdinand Gustaaf Willem (1857-1935) Dutch
£1122 $2009 €1650 Poppies (40x64cm-16x25in) 17-Mar-4 De Zwann, Amsterdam #4520/R est:1700-2000

OLDFIELD, Fred (20th C) American
£688 $1100 €1004 Hunting cabin in the Goat Wilderness area (61x91cm-24x36in) s. 22-Sep-3 O'Gallerie, Oregon #794/R est:2000-3000

OLDS, Elizabeth (?) British
Works on paper
£245 $450 €358 New Hampshire (20x28cm-8x11in) s.i.d.1930 brush ink wash. 10-Jun-4 Swann Galleries, New York #186/R
£489 $900 €714 Gulls at the shore (38x53cm-15x21in) s.d.1955 gouache. 10-Jun-4 Swann Galleries, New York #188/R
£978 $1800 €1428 Adoration of the Masters 2 (30x43cm-12x17in) s.d.1940 brush ink wash gouache card exhib. 10-Jun-4 Swann Galleries, New York #187/R est:800-1200

OLEFFE, Auguste (1867-1931) Belgian
£1164 $1979 €1700 Vase de fleurs (50x40cm-20x16in) s.d.1910 d.verso. 10-Nov-3 Horta, Bruxelles #369
£2000 $3540 €2920 Lady in an interior (70x48cm-28x19in) s. 29-Apr-4 Christie's, Kensington #198/R est:2000-3000

OLEINIK, N and PROKOPOV, E (20th C) Russian
Sculpture
£30000 $53700 €45000 Group of cyclists (180x366cm-71x144in) green brown pat. bronze. 25-May-4 Sotheby's, Billingshurst #387/R est:30000-50000

OLEJNIK, Janka (1887-1954) Hungarian
£1317 $2384 €1923 Houses on the riverside (58x49cm-23x19in) s. 16-Apr-4 Mu Terem Galeria, Budapest #21/R (H.F 500000)

OLGAARD, Hans (20th C) Danish?
£303 $485 €442 Bathing girls (65x80cm-26x31in) mono. 22-Sep-3 Rasmussen, Vejle #577/R (D.KR 3200)
£431 $719 €629 Autumn scene with figures by haystack (66x66cm-26x26in) init. 25-Oct-3 Rasmussen, Havnen #4277 (D.KR 4600)
£447 $702 €653 Figures in woodland (109x89cm-43x35in) s.verso. 30-Aug-3 Rasmussen, Havnen #4140/R (D.KR 4800)

OLGIATI, Rodolfo (1887-1930) Swiss
£1000 $1830 €1460 Country landscape with group of houses and church steeple (24x40cm-9x16in) s.i.verso. 4-Jun-4 Zofingen, Switzerland #2907/R (S.FR 2300)

OLGYAI, Ferenc (1872-1939) Hungarian
£403 $640 €580 Landscape with track (31x46cm-12x18in) s. panel. 13-Sep-3 Quittenbaum, Hamburg #79/R
£486 $773 €700 Landscape with cows (74x97cm-29x38in) s. 13-Sep-3 Quittenbaum, Hamburg #80/R

OLGYAI, Viktor (1870-1929) Hungarian
£604 $1100 €882 Winter landscape (74x99cm-29x39in) s. 19-Jun-4 Charlton Hall, Columbia #187/R
£2405 $4257 €3511 Evening in the farm (123x150cm-48x59in) s. 28-Apr-4 Kieselbach, Budapest #94/R (H.F 900000)

OLHOLM, Jorn (1937-) Danish
£271 $500 €396 Composition (92x120cm-36x47in) mono. i.verso. 15-Mar-4 Rasmussen, Vejle #525/R (D.KR 3000)

OLINSKY, Ivan G (1878-1962) American
£7182 $13000 €10486 Marguerite (51x41cm-20x16in) s.d.1914 prov. 31-Mar-4 Sotheby's, New York #134/R est:8000-12000

OLINSKY, Tosca (?) ?
£270 $500 €394 Still life of flowers and fruit (36x46cm-14x18in) s. masonite. 13-Mar-4 DeFina, Austinburg #516/R
£297 $550 €434 Silver dollars in a vase (41x30cm-16x12in) s. 13-Mar-4 DeFina, Austinburg #521/R
£1006 $1800 €1469 Still life with woldflowers (76x63cm-30x25in) s. 14-May-4 Skinner, Boston #349/R est:1500-2500

OLIS, Jan (1610-1676) Dutch
£2000 $3680 €3000 Portrait d'homme (19x14cm-7x6in) mono. panel. 9-Jun-4 Oger, Dumont, Paris #32/R est:3000-4000

OLIS, Jan (attrib) (1610-1676) Dutch
£839 $1427 €1200 Soldiers and peasants playing in tavern (12x14cm-5x6in) panel prov. 20-Nov-3 Dorotheum, Salzburg #101/R
£21333 $38187 €32000 Portrait of a young man wearing a feathered velvet cap (75x61cm-30x24in) mono. panel oval prov.exhib. 17-May-4 Christie's, Amsterdam #12/R est:6000-8000

OLITSKI, Jules (1922-) American/Russian
£5500 $9185 €8030 Taurus Rift - 6 (188x132cm-74x52in) s.i.d.1975 verso acrylic prov.lit. 21-Oct-3 Sotheby's, London #361/R est:2000-3000
£7362 $12000 €10749 Dokosleeve I (229x147cm-90x58in) s.i.d.1974 verso acrylic prov.exhib. 23-Sep-3 Christie's, Rockefeller NY #40/R est:8000-12000
£17964 $30000 €26227 Prince Patutsky's blue laugh (122x66cm-48x26in) s.i.d.1963 verso prov. 13-Nov-3 Sotheby's, New York #184/R est:15000-20000

OLIVA, Eugenio (19/20th C) Spanish
Works on paper
£903 $1435 €1300 El ensayo (50x33cm-20x13in) s. W/C. 29-Apr-3 Durán, Madrid #757/R

OLIVA, Frederic (19th C) Italian
£662 $1205 €1000 Young girl (82x50cm-32x20in) s. 21-Jun-4 Dorotheum, Vienna #144/R

OLIVARES VELENCIAGA, Juan Benito (1909-) Spanish
£282 $487 €400 Village near Alava (62x80cm-24x31in) s. 15-Dec-3 Ansorena, Madrid #149/R
£414 $687 €600 Village in Alava (62x80cm-24x31in) s. 1-Oct-3 Ansorena, Madrid #714/R
£548 $932 €800 Harbour (47x56cm-19x22in) s. 4-Nov-3 Ansorena, Madrid #336/R
£582 $990 €850 Cargo boats (47x56cm-19x22in) s. 4-Nov-3 Ansorena, Madrid #415/R

OLIVARES, Gustavo (19th C) Spanish
£330 $538 €475 Favourable wind (28x21cm-11x8in) cardboard. 23-Sep-3 Durán, Madrid #173/R
Works on paper
£345 $621 €500 Ships (50x66cm-20x26in) s.d.1921 col dr. 26-Jan-4 Durán, Madrid #221/R
£347 $566 €500 Sailing boat in storm (32x30cm-13x12in) W/C. 23-Sep-3 Durán, Madrid #174/R

OLIVARES, Juan (1973-) Spanish
£367 $667 €550 Untitled (100x70cm-39x28in) s.d.2000 oil acrylic paper prov. 29-Jun-4 Segre, Madrid #265/R
£500 $905 €750 Untitled (100x70cm-39x28in) s.d.2000 oil acrylic prov. 30-Mar-4 Segre, Madrid #170/R

OLIVE DES MARTIGUES, Henri (1898-1980) French
£2098 $3566 €3000 Port Mediterraneen (38x55cm-15x22in) s.d.1921. 27-Nov-3 Millon & Associes, Paris #206/R est:2000-2500

OLIVE, Ceferi (1907-1995) Spanish
Works on paper
£338 $592 €480 Seascape (31x45cm-12x18in) s.d.MCMLXIX W/C. 16-Dec-3 Segre, Madrid #289/R
£1042 $1771 €1500 Locomotive (50x64cm-20x25in) s.d.MCMLXXXIII W/C. 28-Oct-3 Segre, Madrid #333/R

OLIVE, Jean Baptiste (1848-1936) French
£2098 $3608 €3000 Voiliers dans la conche (22x41cm-9x16in) s.i. 2-Dec-3 Claude Aguttes, Neuilly #50 est:3000-4000
£2148 $3952 €3200 Barque de peche (44x30cm-17x12in) s.d.1873 canvas on cardboard. 29-Mar-4 Rieunier, Paris #56/R est:4000-5000
£2238 $3804 €3200 Paysage boise (26x34cm-10x13in) s.i. panel. 28-Nov-3 Drouot Estimations, Paris #145/R
£6522 $11935 €9522 Littoral mediterraneen (26x42cm-10x17in) s.d.15 aout 1874 panel prov. 5-Jun-4 Galerie du Rhone, Sion #533/R est:7000-9000 (S.FR 15000)
£7333 $13347 €11000 Plage a maree basse (45x73cm-18x29in) s. 4-Jul-4 Eric Pillon, Calais #91/R
£7718 $14201 €11500 Marseille, la corniche (31x40cm-12x16in) s. panel. 29-Mar-4 Rieunier, Paris #35/R est:3000-4000
£12667 $23180 €19000 Nature morte aux grenades (46x56cm-18x22in) s. lit. 6-Jun-4 Anaf, Lyon #147/R est:20000-25000
£16225 $29692 €24500 Le cabanon (50x73cm-20x29in) s. prov. 9-Apr-4 Claude Aguttes, Neuilly #80/R est:25000-30000

OLIVE, Jean Baptiste (attrib) (1848-1936) French
£3394 $5769 €4955 Beach at low tide (46x73cm-18x29in) s.d.8. Octobre 1875 canvas on panel. 19-Nov-3 Fischer, Luzern #2237/R est:1500-1800 (S.FR 7500)

OLIVECRONA, Emilie Eliza (1858-1902) Swedish
£747 $1247 €1121 Woman reading (66x49cm-26x19in) s.d.1885. 27-Oct-3 Goodman, Sydney #228/R (A.D 1800)

OLIVEIRA, Nathan (1928-) American
£6780 $12000 €9899 Yellow portrait (137x137cm-54x54in) s.d.65/99 prov.exhib. 2-May-4 Bonhams & Butterfields, Los Angeles #3070/R est:15000-20000
£23529 $40000 €34352 Swiss site 1 (244x198cm-96x78in) s.d.79. 9-Nov-3 Bonhams & Butterfields, Los Angeles #4064/R est:50000-70000
Prints
£1933 $3500 €2822 Running woman (30x22cm-12x9in) s.i.d.1973 monotype. 19-Apr-4 Bonhams & Butterfields, San Francisco #292/R est:1500-2500
Works on paper
£1323 $2250 €1932 Untitled - figure study (30x23cm-12x9in) s.d.60 W/C ink. 9-Nov-3 Bonhams & Butterfields, Los Angeles #4063/R est:4000-6000
£2401 $4250 €3505 Standing female nude (25x20cm-10x8in) s.d.65 W/C ink. 2-May-4 Bonhams & Butterfields, Los Angeles #3069/R est:3000-5000
£5882 $10000 €8588 Seated man on a branch (31x24cm-12x9in) s.d.59 s.i.d.verso mixed media prov. 9-Nov-3 Bonhams & Butterfields, Los Angeles #4062/R est:7000-9000

OLIVER Y AZNAR, Mariano (1863-1927) Spanish
£638 $1186 €950 Tram (16x32cm-6x13in) s. paper. 2-Mar-4 Ansorena, Madrid #207/R

OLIVER, Alfred (fl.1886-1921) British
£280 $515 €409 Solitude (62x76cm-24x30in) s. 8-Jun-4 Bonhams, Knightsbridge #147/R

OLIVER, Clark (19th C) American
£3179 $5500 €4641 Small boat off the coast (23x30cm-9x12in) s.d.78. 10-Dec-3 Bonhams & Butterfields, San Francisco #6011/R est:2500-3500

OLIVER, Frederick W (1876-1963) American
£376 $700 €549 Rockport (35x45cm-14x18in) s. canvasboard. 5-Mar-4 Skinner, Boston #535/R

OLIVER, Isaac (c.1550-1617) British
Miniatures
£22000 $39600 €32120 Gentleman, traditionally called Robert Devereux (4cm-2in) vellum enamel frame oval prov.exhib.lit. 22-Apr-4 Bonhams, New Bond Street #2/R est:15000-25000
£30000 $54000 €43800 Gentleman, with fair hair and beard, in a black doublet (5cm-2in) vellum bone wood frame oval exhib.lit. 22-Apr-4 Bonhams, New Bond Street #3/R est:15000-25000
Works on paper
£11111 $20000 €16222 Annunciation (18x11cm-7x4in) black chk pen brown ink grey wash. 22-Jan-4 Christie's, Rockefeller NY #81/R est:10000-15000
£13000 $22100 €18980 St Jerome reading (11x9cm-4x4in) i. pen brown ink grey wash prov. 20-Nov-3 Christie's, London #1/R est:3500-4500

OLIVER, Peter (1594-1648) British
£260 $465 €380 Sunday (61x61cm-24x24in) s. board. 14-May-4 Christie's, Kensington #611
£400 $728 €584 Still life with lamp (53x72cm-21x28in) board. 1-Jul-4 Christie's, Kensington #371/R
£1300 $2392 €1898 Oyster catchers in flight over a rocky shore line (41x61cm-16x24in) s.d.73. 11-Jun-4 Halls, Shrewsbury #710 est:200-300

Miniatures
£60000 $108000 €87600 Lady Dorothy Percy, Countess of Leicester (5cm-2in) mono. i.verso vellum card silver frame oval prov.exhib.lit. 22-Apr-4 Bonhams, New Bond Street #4/R est:40000-60000

OLIVER, Richard Aldworth (1811-1889) New Zealander
£409 $703 €597 Two young Maori women (35x25cm-14x10in) W/C. 3-Dec-3 Dunbar Sloane, Auckland #75/R (NZ.D 1100)
Works on paper
£297 $512 €434 Wooden bridge above a waterfall (26x25cm-10x10in) W/C. 3-Dec-3 Dunbar Sloane, Auckland #81 (NZ.D 800)
£595 $1023 €869 Young Maori (25x36cm-10x14in) W/C. 3-Dec-3 Dunbar Sloane, Auckland #72/R (NZ.D 1600)
£595 $1023 €869 Maori girl wearing a red cloak (33x25cm-13x10in) W/C. 3-Dec-3 Dunbar Sloane, Auckland #73/R (NZ.D 1600)
£632 $1087 €923 Port Nicholson, Wellington (27x37cm-11x15in) W/C. 3-Dec-3 Dunbar Sloane, Auckland #76/R (NZ.D 1700)
£632 $1087 €923 Lizzy a Maori girl (35x25cm-14x10in) W/C. 3-Dec-3 Dunbar Sloane, Auckland #82 (NZ.D 1700)
£706 $1215 €1031 Maori girl wearing a cloak (36x25cm-14x10in) W/C. 3-Dec-3 Dunbar Sloane, Auckland #79/R (NZ.D 1900)
£743 $1279 €1085 Maori mother and child (36x26cm-14x10in) W/C. 3-Dec-3 Dunbar Sloane, Auckland #80/R est:3000-5000 (NZ.D 2000)
£781 $1343 €1140 Maori Canoe, East Coast (25x37cm-10x15in) W/C. 3-Dec-3 Dunbar Sloane, Auckland #83 (NZ.D 2100)
£929 $1599 €1356 On the road with pack horse, Hutt (37x26cm-15x10in) W/C. 3-Dec-3 Dunbar Sloane, Auckland #71/R (NZ.D 2500)
£1301 $2238 €1899 Te Rehe, Maori Chief at Akaroa (31x23cm-12x9in) W/C. 3-Dec-3 Dunbar Sloane, Auckland #78 est:4500-6000 (NZ.D 3500)
£4461 $7673 €6513 Inside the Stockade (27x37cm-11x15in) W/C exec c.1850. 3-Dec-3 Dunbar Sloane, Auckland #70/R est:5500-7000 (NZ.D 12000)

OLIVER, Thomas (1979-) British
£500 $850 €730 J-class yachts Endeavour and Yankee (35x61cm-14x24in) s.d.03. 19-Nov-3 Christie's, Kensington #414/R
£800 $1432 €1168 American three-masted racing schooner Atlantic powering to windward (61x91cm-24x36in) s.d.04. 26-May-4 Christie's, Kensington #511/R
£850 $1522 €1241 Velsheda and Endeavour during the America's Cup Jubilee 2001 (61x91cm-24x36in) s.d.2002. 26-May-4 Christie's, Kensington #510/R
£1000 $1700 €1460 J-class yachts Endeavour, Yankee and Velsheda (61x91cm-24x36in) s.d.03. 19-Nov-3 Christie's, Kensington #415/R est:800-1200
£1000 $1700 €1460 Big class yachts, Vigilant, Britannia and Satanita (61x91cm-24x36in) s.d.03. 19-Nov-3 Christie's, Kensington #413/R est:1000-1500

OLIVER, William (1805-1853) British
£2032 $3250 €2967 Bathing beauty (76x51cm-30x20in) s. painted c.1850. 20-Sep-3 Bunte, Elgin #1453 est:600-800

OLIVER, William (fl.1865-1897) British
£5600 $9520 €8176 Birds nest (41x31cm-16x12in) s.d.1879. 29-Oct-3 Bonhams, Chester #510/R est:2500-3500
£10000 $18200 €14600 Mediterranean beauties (77x112cm-30x44in) s. 1-Jul-4 Sotheby's, London #331/R est:10000-15000

OLIVERO, Matteo (1879-1932) Italian
£3667 $6747 €5500 Snow in Saluzzo (25x26cm-10x10in) s. s.i.verso cardboard exhib.lit. 14-Jun-4 Sant Agostino, Torino #326/R est:6000-8000
£17007 $30442 €25000 Sunset (72x90cm-28x35in) s.d.1914. 22-Mar-4 Sant Agostino, Torino #241/R est:35000
£27586 $45793 €40000 Street in Pagno (69x76cm-27x30in) s. lit. 1-Oct-3 Della Rocca, Turin #115/R est:35000-40000

OLIVETTI, Ercole (1874-1941) Italian
£1042 $1771 €1500 Dusk in the village (55x45cm-22x18in) init.d.1904. 1-Nov-3 Meeting Art, Vercelli #358/R est:500

OLIVETTI, Eva (20th C) ?
£345 $576 €500 Untitled (33x41cm-13x16in) s. cardboard. 11-Nov-3 Castellana, Madrid #217/R

OLIVIER, Ferdinand (1873-1957) French
Works on paper
£364 $663 €550 Southern Italian coastal scene (19x32cm-7x13in) d.1869 verso pencil. 18-Jun-4 Bolland & Marotz, Bremen #558/R

OLIVIER, Friedrich (1791-1859) German
Works on paper
£1747 $3179 €2551 Homecoming of the lost son (16x12cm-6x5in) i. pencil pen ink prov.lit. 17-Jun-4 Kornfeld, Bern #47/R est:5000 (S.FR 4000)
£2009 $3656 €2933 Compassionate Samaritan (16x12cm-6x5in) i. pencil pen ink prov. 17-Jun-4 Kornfeld, Bern #48/R est:5000 (S.FR 4600)

OLIVIER, Heinrich von (attrib) (1783-1848) German
£2162 $3805 €3200 Scene from the crusades (53x39cm-21x15in) 22-May-4 Lempertz, Koln #1575/R est:3000-4000

OLIVIER, Herbert Arnould (1861-1952) British
£2000 $3720 €2920 Passion flower (152x91cm-60x36in) s. s.i.on stretcher exhib.lit. 4-Mar-4 Christie's, Kensington #653/R est:3000-5000

OLIVIER, Michel Barthelemy (attrib) (1712-1784) French
£11842 $21789 €18000 Arrivee de Marie-Clotilde de Bourbon (48x74cm-19x29in) panel prov. 24-Jun-4 Christie's, Paris #114/R est:30000-40000

OLIVIER, Pierre David (attrib) (18th C) French
Works on paper
£531 $950 €775 Battle scene with triumphant angel (30x23cm-12x9in) pen ink drawing. 20-Mar-4 Sloans & Kenyon, Bethesda #1146/R

OLIVIER-CYR (?) French?
Sculpture
£3217 $5533 €4600 Media (35x22x22cm-14x9x9in) s.num.1/8 bronze. 7-Dec-3 Feletin, Province #84

OLIVIERI, Claudio (1934-) Italian
£667 $1227 €1000 Wise mind (60x80cm-24x31in) s.i.d.1989 verso. 12-Jun-4 Meeting Art, Vercelli #841/R
£671 $1242 €1000 Pointed (60x80cm-24x31in) s.i.d.1989 verso. 13-Mar-4 Meeting Art, Vercelli #96
£867 $1595 €1300 Untitled (80x100cm-31x39in) s.d.1971 verso. 10-Jun-4 Galleria Pace, Milan #56/R
£1076 $1701 €1550 Blue shadow (101x76cm-40x30in) 6-Sep-3 Meeting Art, Vercelli #312
£1208 $2162 €1800 Aedus (61x81cm-24x32in) s.i.d.1990 verso. 30-May-4 Meeting Art, Vercelli #27 est:1000

OLLEROS Y QUINTANA, Blas (1851-1919) Italian
£838 $1500 €1223 Marina (19x32cm-7x13in) s. panel. 6-May-4 Doyle, New York #50/R est:2000-3000

OLLERS, Edvin (1888-1959) Swedish
£322 $557 €470 Southern landscape (46x38cm-18x15in) s. 15-Dec-3 Lilla Bukowskis, Stockholm #456 (S.KR 4100)

OLLEY, Margaret Hannah (1923-) Australian
£1138 $1787 €1650 Three natives (44x64cm-17x25in) s.d.68 board prov. 26-Aug-3 Christie's, Sydney #391 est:3000-5000 (A.D 2800)
£2979 $5064 €4349 Pears (20x45cm-8x18in) s. board prov. 25-Nov-3 Christie's, Melbourne #217/R est:3000-5000 (A.D 7000)
£3306 $6116 €4827 Star guest house (23x29cm-9x11in) s.d.44 W/C gouache pen ink prov. 10-Mar-4 Deutscher-Menzies, Melbourne #332/R est:3500-5000 (A.D 8000)
£6198 $10971 €9049 Two sisters (95x120cm-37x47in) s.d.62 board. 3-May-4 Christie's, Melbourne #105/R est:18000-25000 (A.D 15000)
£7025 $11942 €10257 Still life with mushrooms (52x44cm-20x17in) s. board prov. 29-Oct-3 Lawson Menzies, Sydney #21/R est:18000-22000 (A.D 17000)
£7438 $13165 €10859 Bottles and grapes (52x45cm-20x18in) s. board prov. 3-May-4 Christie's, Melbourne #144/R est:20000-30000 (A.D 18000)
£9091 $16818 €13273 Calendulas and fruit (47x58cm-19x23in) s. board prov.exhib. 10-Mar-4 Deutscher-Menzies, Melbourne #13/R est:25000-35000 (A.D 22000)
£12146 $19555 €17733 Still life with marigolds and oranges (64x43cm-25x17in) s.d.67 composition board. 25-Aug-3 Sotheby's, Paddington #154/R est:30000-40000 (A.D 30000)
£12195 $19146 €17683 Still life with apples (60x72cm-24x28in) s. board prov.exhib. 27-Aug-3 Christie's, Sydney #529/R est:28000-35000 (A.D 30000)
£14980 $24117 €21871 Summer flowers and cherries (100x74cm-39x29in) s.d.65 composition board prov. 25-Aug-3 Sotheby's, Paddington #168/R est:40000-60000 (A.D 37000)
£17021 $28936 €24851 Blue kitchen dresser (75x59cm-30x23in) s. board painted c.1989 prov. 25-Nov-3 Christie's, Melbourne #3/R est:35000-50000 (A.D 40000)
£17557 $31954 €25633 Calendulas (76x61cm-30x24in) s.d.67 s.verso board prov. 16-Jun-4 Deutscher-Menzies, Melbourne #64/R est:30000-40000 (A.D 46000)
£19084 $34733 €27863 Cliveas and mandarins (61x76cm-24x30in) s. i.verso board. 16-Jun-4 Deutscher-Menzies, Melbourne #15/R est:40000-60000 (A.D 50000)
£19592 $36049 €28604 Mandarins on a blue cloth (76x101cm-30x40in) s.d.65 i.verso board prov. 29-Mar-4 Goodman, Sydney #1/R est:45000-65000 (A.D 48000)
£20492 $32377 €29918 Still life with pears and cyclamen (60x75cm-24x30in) s. board prov. 2-Sep-3 Deutscher-Menzies, Melbourne #76/R est:38000-50000 (A.D 50000)
£20661 $36570 €30165 Cornflowers and interior (75x75cm-30x30in) s. board prov. 3-May-4 Christie's, Melbourne #11/R est:50000-60000 (A.D 50000)
£21277 $36170 €31064 Garden Room interior (62x76cm-24x30in) s. composition board prov. 26-Nov-3 Deutscher-Menzies, Melbourne #18/R est:50000-70000 (A.D 50000)
£22358 $35102 €32419 Still life (100x75cm-39x30in) s.d.63 board prov. 26-Aug-3 Christie's, Sydney #5/R est:40000-60000 (A.D 55000)
£24390 $38293 €35366 Floral still life, tiger lilies (75x59cm-30x23in) s.d.69 board. 26-Aug-3 Christie's, Sydney #12/R est:40000-60000 (A.D 60000)
£26860 $49690 €39216 Harbour view, bottlebrush and kelim (76x106cm-30x42in) s. painted c.1999 board exhib. 10-Mar-4 Deutscher-Menzies, Melbourne #29/R est:65000-85000 (A.D 65000)
Works on paper
£337 $620 €492 Kuka Kuka, Goroka show (18x12cm-7x5in) s. gouache. 28-Jun-4 Australian Art Auctions, Sydney #75 (A.D 900)
£1016 $1899 €1524 Fishermans wharf (43x53cm-17x21in) s.d.60 s.i.d.verso W/C. 20-Jul-4 Goodman, Sydney #132/R est:1800-2500 (A.D 2600)
£1527 $2779 €2229 Venice (39x52cm-15x20in) i.d.1951 W/C pen ink prov. 16-Jun-4 Deutscher-Menzies, Melbourne #318/R est:4500-5500 (A.D 4000)
£2686 $4969 €3922 Point Piper Lane (39x49cm-15x19in) s.d.64 W/C ink gouache prov. 10-Mar-4 Deutscher-Menzies, Melbourne #505/R est:1000-1500 (A.D 6500)

OLLGAARD, Hans (1911-1969) Danish
£316 $581 €461 Couple walking in evening (93x105cm-37x41in) s. 29-Mar-4 Rasmussen, Copenhagen #547 (D.KR 3500)
£496 $913 €724 Autumn scene with figures by hay stook (66x66cm-26x26in) init. 29-Mar-4 Rasmussen, Copenhagen #470/R (D.KR 5500)

OLLILA, Yrjo (1887-1932) Finnish
£423 $676 €600 Landscape (55x65cm-22x26in) s. 18-Sep-3 Hagelstam, Helsinki #841
£625 $1044 €900 View from Marly near Paris (46x56cm-18x22in) s.d.1926. 26-Oct-3 Bukowskis, Helsinki #451/R
£1014 $1814 €1500 Weeping birch (64x46cm-25x18in) s.d.1929 prov. 8-May-4 Bukowskis, Helsinki #38/R est:1500-1800

£1014 $1814 €1500 Coastal landscape from Sodern (55x66cm-22x26in) s.d.1920 board. 8-May-4 Bukowskis, Helsinki #116/R est:1500-1800
£1689 $3024 €2500 View of Florence (33x48cm-13x19in) s.i.d.1914. 8-May-4 Bukowskis, Helsinki #81/R est:1000-1500
£2400 $4296 €3600 Church goers by Raumo church (46x34cm-18x13in) s. lit. 15-May-4 Hagelstam, Helsinki #152/R est:3000
£3357 $5706 €4800 Reflections in woodland tarn (102x80cm-40x31in) s.d.1919. 29-Nov-3 Bukowskis, Helsinki #133/R est:4000-4500
£10490 $17832 €15000 Fishermen on the Seine (53x80cm-21x31in) s.d.08. 29-Nov-3 Bukowskis, Helsinki #48/R est:4000-5000
Works on paper
£1000 $1790 €1500 Women bathing (34x26cm-13x10in) s.d.1915 W/C. 15-May-4 Hagelstam, Helsinki #154/R est:600

OLLIVARY, Anette (20th C) French
£350 $616 €511 Les petits Tigrae (41x27cm-16x11in) prov. 19-May-4 Christie's, Kensington #744/R

OLMEDO, Cristobal (1957-) Spanish
£436 $816 €650 Life (25x25cm-10x10in) s.d.03 board. 24-Feb-4 Durán, Madrid #39/R
£563 $986 €800 November (120x61cm-47x24in) s.d.91 oil acrylic board exhib. 16-Dec-3 Durán, Madrid #57/R
£599 $1048 €850 Paint tins (122x82cm-48x32in) s. oil acrylic board. 16-Dec-3 Durán, Madrid #53/R

OLMEDO, Onib (1937-1996) Philippino
Works on paper
£1290 $2065 €1883 Still life (70x56cm-28x22in) s.d.92 mixed media. 18-May-3 Sotheby's, Singapore #94/R est:4000-6000 (S.D 3600)

OLOFSSON, Pierre (1921-1996) Swedish
Works on paper
£378 $642 €552 Playful movement (9x30cm-4x12in) s. mixed media. 5-Nov-3 AB Stockholms Auktionsverk #780/R (S.KR 5000)
£491 $835 €717 Sports hall, Sundsvall (8x80cm-3x31in) s. gouache wax painted c.1965-66 prov. 5-Nov-3 AB Stockholms Auktionsverk #779/R (S.KR 6500)
£755 $1284 €1102 Composition (38x44cm-15x17in) s. mixed media. 5-Nov-3 AB Stockholms Auktionsverk #789/R (S.KR 10000)
£869 $1477 €1269 Black abstract (29x21cm-11x8in) s. mixed media. 4-Nov-3 Bukowskis, Stockholm #230/R (S.KR 11500)
£1088 $1958 €1588 Untitled (12x110cm-5x43in) s. mixed media. 26-Apr-4 Bukowskis, Stockholm #224/R est:12000-15000 (S.KR 15000)
£2344 $4149 €3422 Rock-rose (54x99cm-21x39in) s. coracolla panel. 27-Apr-4 AB Stockholms Auktionsverk #756/R est:30000-40000 (S.KR 32000)

OLOMUTZ, Wenzel von (fl.1481-1497) German
Prints
£1700 $3060 €2550 Man of Sorrow (19x15cm-7x6in) init. burin. 21-Apr-4 Finarte Semenzato, Milan #422/R est:2800-3000

OLOVSON, Gudmar (1936-) Swedish
Sculpture
£1414 $2545 €2064 Les deux Arbres (31cm-12in) s. dark pat.bronze Cast Valsuani cire perdue stone socle. 26-Apr-4 Bukowskis, Stockholm #266/R est:10000-12000 (S.KR 19500)
£5740 $9758 €8380 Femme oiseau blessee (50cm-20in) s.num.1/10 green pat.bronze Cast Valsuani cire perdue lit. 4-Nov-3 Bukowskis, Stockholm #79a/R est:40000-45000 (S.KR 76000)

OLRIK, Balder (1966-) Danish
£1444 $2657 €2108 Figure composition with umbrellas (120x150cm-47x59in) s. s.d.86 verso. 29-Mar-4 Rasmussen, Copenhagen #321/R est:18000 (D.KR 16000)
Works on paper
£3249 $5978 €4744 Landscape I (150x121cm-59x48in) s.d.92 verso mixed media canvas. 29-Mar-4 Rasmussen, Copenhagen #386/R est:20000-25000 (D.KR 36000)

OLSANSKY, Klement (c.1909-1963) Canadian
£193 $301 €280 Icebound freighter (51x61cm-20x24in) s. board. 26-Mar-3 Walker's, Ottawa #428/R (C.D 450)

OLSEN, Alfred (1854-1932) Danish
£320 $544 €467 View of Gammel Strand (31x42cm-12x17in) s.i.d.1892. 29-Nov-3 Rasmussen, Havnen #2188 (D.KR 3400)
£356 $647 €534 Seascape off a coast (63x130cm-25x51in) s. 19-Jun-4 Rasmussen, Havnen #2225 (D.KR 4000)
£452 $768 €660 Veterans at Helgoland - old boat at anchor - 1864 (48x85cm-19x33in) s/d/24. 29-Nov-3 Rasmussen, Havnen #2129/R (D.KR 4800)
£945 $1692 €1380 From Copenhagen Harbour (48x85cm-19x33in) s.d.84. 12-Jan-4 Rasmussen, Vejle #37/R (D.KR 10000)

OLSEN, Carl (1818-1878) Danish
£728 $1326 €1100 The steamship Veile out on the lake in the evening light (45x79cm-18x31in) s.d.1868. 18-Jun-4 Bolland & Marotz, Bremen #711/R
£748 $1181 €1085 Sailing vessels at sea (26x35cm-10x14in) 2-Sep-3 Rasmussen, Copenhagen #1637/R (D.KR 8000)
£806 $1474 €1177 Sailing vessels at sunset, Mediterranean (24x33cm-9x13in) s.d.60. 9-Jun-4 Rasmussen, Copenhagen #1837/R (D.KR 9000)
£870 $1583 €1270 Seascape with sailing vessels in rough seas (25x33cm-10x13in) s. 7-Feb-4 Rasmussen, Havnen #2124/R (D.KR 9500)
£2617 $4135 €3795 Three master passing a lighthouse in the English Channel (106x163cm-42x64in) s.indis.d. 2-Sep-3 Rasmussen, Copenhagen #1576/R est:30000 (D.KR 28000)

OLSEN, Chr Benjamin (1873-1935) Danish
£276 $470 €403 Gronsund (21x29cm-8x11in) s.d.1920. 10-Nov-3 Rasmussen, Vejle #285/R (D.KR 3000)
£276 $470 €403 Ship's portrait of Tordenskjold firing salute (23x40cm-9x16in) s. 10-Nov-3 Rasmussen, Vejle #313/R (D.KR 3000)
£284 $455 €415 Seascape with view toward Espergaerde (28x35cm-11x14in) s.i.d.1918. 22-Sep-3 Rasmussen, Vejle #268 (D.KR 3000)
£287 $516 €419 Coastal landscape near Gilleleje (34x48cm-13x19in) s. 24-Apr-4 Rasmussen, Havnen #2120/R (D.KR 3200)
£295 $501 €431 Sailing vessel off Lyngs Odde (28x39cm-11x15in) s. 10-Nov-3 Rasmussen, Vejle #284 (D.KR 3200)
£295 $501 €431 Entrance to a fjord (23x41cm-9x16in) s.d.1923 exhib. 10-Nov-3 Rasmussen, Vejle #286 (D.KR 3200)
£295 $501 €431 By the Norwegian coast, Skagerak (27x44cm-11x17in) s. 10-Nov-3 Rasmussen, Vejle #306 (D.KR 3200)
£295 $501 €431 Two large sailing ship with full sails (25x42cm-10x17in) s.i.d.29/5 29. 10-Nov-3 Rasmussen, Vejle #314/R (D.KR 3200)
£326 $583 €476 Seascape with sailing vessels (21x29cm-8x11in) s.d.1913. 10-May-4 Rasmussen, Vejle #350/R (D.KR 3600)
£326 $583 €476 Seascape with vessels (26x36cm-10x14in) s. 10-May-4 Rasmussen, Vejle #352/R (D.KR 3600)
£332 $564 €485 View from the sea (24x40cm-9x16in) s.d.16/6 1926. 10-Nov-3 Rasmussen, Vejle #294 (D.KR 3600)
£350 $595 €511 Blue sky by the coast of Gibraltar (18x29cm-7x11in) s.i.d.11/5-29. 10-Nov-3 Rasmussen, Vejle #295 (D.KR 3800)
£369 $627 €539 The ship Niels Juel by Troldekonefiguren, Faeroe Islands (27x40cm-11x16in) s. 10-Nov-3 Rasmussen, Vejle #311/R (D.KR 4000)
£369 $627 €539 Ships' portrait of Niels Juel and Fylla (26x41cm-10x16in) s. 10-Nov-3 Rasmussen, Vejle #312/R (D.KR 4000)
£380 $615 €555 Sailing vessel in a calm (15x12cm-6x5in) s. panel. 9-Aug-3 Hindemae, Ullerslev #255/R (D.KR 4000)
£412 $688 €602 Seascape with sailing vessel passing lighthouse (45x65cm-18x26in) s.i. 25-Oct-3 Rasmussen, Havnen #2521/R (D.KR 4400)
£421 $704 €615 Two masted schooner (37x57cm-15x22in) s.d.1925. 25-Oct-3 Rasmussen, Havnen #2642 (D.KR 4500)
£447 $702 €653 Seascape with sailing vessel (49x39cm-19x15in) s,. 30-Aug-3 Rasmussen, Havnen #2069 (D.KR 4800)
£449 $836 €656 Fishing boats leaving harbour (36x57cm-14x22in) s. 2-Mar-4 Rasmussen, Copenhagen #1450/R (D.KR 5000)
£471 $842 €688 Greek armoured vessel Sara at Copenhagen (41x55cm-16x22in) s.d.1902. 10-May-4 Rasmussen, Vejle #353/R (D.KR 5200)
£473 $818 €691 Sailing boats on the Mediterranean (37x57cm-15x22in) s. 9-Dec-3 Rasmussen, Copenhagen #1464/R (D.KR 5000)
£507 $862 €740 Many vessels off a large town (28x42cm-11x17in) s. 10-Nov-3 Rasmussen, Vejle #308/R (D.KR 5500)
£507 $862 €740 Seascape off rocky coast (70x99cm-28x39in) s. 10-Nov-3 Rasmussen, Vejle #315/R (D.KR 5500)
£514 $812 €745 Fishing boats at sea (30x35cm-12x14in) s. 2-Sep-3 Rasmussen, Copenhagen #1650/R (D.KR 5500)
£674 $1126 €984 Seascape with vessel (43x48cm-17x19in) s. 25-Oct-3 Rasmussen, Havnen #2611/R (D.KR 7200)
£749 $1251 €1094 Seascape with sailing vessel and steamship (60x90cm-24x35in) s. 25-Oct-3 Rasmussen, Havnen #2503/R (D.KR 8000)
£769 $1377 €1123 An old frigate south of Kullen (44x54cm-17x21in) s. 10-May-4 Rasmussen, Vejle #378/R (D.KR 8500)
£783 $1332 €1143 Seascape with Danish sailing vessels off the coast (33x45cm-13x18in) s.d.1918. 10-Nov-3 Rasmussen, Vejle #310/R (D.KR 8500)
£841 $1329 €1219 Three master off Kronborg (32x38cm-13x15in) s.d.1902. 2-Sep-3 Rasmussen, Copenhagen #1655/R (D.KR 9000)
£850 $1556 €1241 Seascape with sailing boats in fresh breeze (37x58cm-15x23in) s. 9-Jun-4 Rasmussen, Copenhagen #1826/R (D.KR 9500)
£851 $1523 €1242 Three master sailing ship (70x100cm-28x39in) s.d.1913. 12-Jan-4 Rasmussen, Vejle #13/R (D.KR 9000)
£895 $1638 €1307 Seascape with sailing vessels in a fresh breeze (70x100cm-28x39in) s.d.1913. 9-Jun-4 Rasmussen, Copenhagen #1766/R (D.KR 10000)
£1134 $2030 €1656 Seascape with the ship Chr J Kampann off Kronborg (70x110cm-28x43in) s.d.1923. 12-Jan-4 Rasmussen, Vejle #14/R est:8000-10000 (D.KR 12000)
£1215 $1920 €1762 Two master and small boats at sea, sunset (50x41cm-20x16in) s. 2-Sep-3 Rasmussen, Copenhagen #1652/R est:6000-8000 (D.KR 13000)
£1229 $2126 €1794 Three master in rough seas on a rainy day (70x100cm-28x39in) s. 9-Dec-3 Rasmussen, Copenhagen #1491/R est:6000 (D.KR 13000)
£1229 $2199 €1794 Sailing ship at sunset (51x70cm-20x28in) s.indis.d. 12-Jan-4 Rasmussen, Vejle #15/R est:5000 (D.KR 13000)
£1264 $2111 €1845 Seascape with sailing ship off town harbour (45x75cm-18x30in) s.d.1939. 25-Oct-3 Rasmussen, Havnen #2528/R est:6000-8000 (D.KR 13500)
£1522 $2785 €2222 Sailing vessels at entrance to Copenhagen Harbour (65x100cm-26x39in) s.d.1915. 9-Jun-4 Rasmussen, Copenhagen #1797/R est:10000-15000 (D.KR 17000)

OLSEN, Einar (1876-1950) Danish
£392 $636 €568 Interior scene with woman arranging flowers (50x38cm-20x15in) init.d.1909. 4-Aug-3 Rasmussen, Vejle #94/R (D.KR 4100)
Works on paper
£362 $648 €529 Ship's portrait of the steamer Hroptatyr (17x23cm-7x9in) s.d.1910 pen W/C. 10-May-4 Rasmussen, Vejle #362/R (D.KR 4000)

OLSEN, Gert E (20th C) American
Sculpture
£2486 $4600 €3729 Polar bears (160cm-63in) s. granite marble base. 17-Jul-4 Susanin's, Chicago #5005/R est:150-250

OLSEN, Gudmund (1913-1985) Danish
£282 $480 €412 Herstedvester, evening (76x78cm-30x31in) s.d.1945 verso. 29-Nov-3 Rasmussen, Havnen #4092 (D.KR 3000)
£358 $645 €523 Winter landscape, evening (125x120cm-49x47in) s.i.d.46 verso. 24-Apr-4 Rasmussen, Havnen #4039/R (D.KR 4000)
£993 $1827 €1450 Mother and child in Sondermarken, winter (45x60cm-18x24in) s. 29-Mar-4 Rasmussen, Copenhagen #508/R (D.KR 11000)
£1173 $2159 €1713 Ziwara - blue composition (89x116cm-35x46in) s.d.1973 verso. 29-Mar-4 Rasmussen, Copenhagen #40/R est:8000-10000 (D.KR 13000)

OLSEN, John (1928-) Australian
£2801 $4677 €4202 Water birds, Coorong (23x13cm-9x5in) s.d.71-72 verso board. 27-Oct-3 Goodman, Sydney #82/R est:4000-6000 (A.D 6750)

£4681 $7957 €6834 Landscape 1985 (30x40cm-12x16in) init. prov. 26-Nov-3 Deutscher-Menzies, Melbourne #95/R est:12000-16000 (A.D 11000)
£4959 $9174 €7240 River and landscape (30x38cm-12x15in) s.d.03 board prov. 10-Mar-4 Deutscher-Menzies, Melbourne #124/R est:15000-20000 (A.D 12000)
£6489 $11809 €9474 Night sky at Rydal (46x36cm-18x14in) s.d.94 prov. 16-Jun-4 Deutscher-Menzies, Melbourne #165/R est:18000-24000 (A.D 17000)
£12766 $21702 €18638 Hawkesbury Country (77x56cm-30x22in) s.d.72 canvas-paper on composition board prov.exhib. 26-Nov-3 Deutscher-Menzies, Melbourne #4/R est:20000-30000 (A.D 30000)
£24793 $45868 €36198 Dust stom over Clarendon (91x101cm-36x40in) s. painted c.1982 prov. 10-Mar-4 Deutscher-Menzies, Melbourne #71/R est:55000-65000 (A.D 60000)
£37190 $63223 €54297 Rydal landscape (136x152cm-54x60in) s.d.92 prov. 29-Oct-3 Lawson Menzies, Sydney #38/R est:100000-120000 (A.D 90000)
£40486 $65182 €59110 Village square (150x136cm-59x54in) s.d.1991. 25-Aug-3 Sotheby's, Paddington #127/R est:100000-140000 (A.D 100000)
£40650 $72764 €59349 Brown landscape (123x153cm-48x60in) s.d.90 bears i.verso prov. 4-May-4 Sotheby's, Melbourne #41/R est:100000-150000 (A.D 100000)
£42553 $72340 €62127 Figures descending Spanish steps (137x152cm-54x60in) init. painted 1986 prov.exhib. 26-Nov-3 Deutscher-Menzies, Melbourne #24/R est:120000-160000 (A.D 100000)
£54656 $87996 €79798 Slices of South Head (181x121cm-71x48in) s.d.69 composition board exhib. 25-Aug-3 Sotheby's, Paddington #173/R est:140000-180000 (A.D 135000)
£59574 $101277 €86978 How rivers run (198x259cm-78x102in) s. s.i.stretcher verso painted 1986 prov. 26-Nov-3 Deutscher-Menzies, Melbourne #21/R est:150000-200000 (A.D 140000)
£64886 $118092 €94734 Spring in the Beaut Country (152x167cm-60x66in) s.d.82-87 prov. 16-Jun-4 Deutscher-Menzies, Melbourne #72/R est:180000-240000 (A.D 170000)
£86066 $139426 €125656 The Spanish kitchen (180x490cm-71x193in) board diptych prov.exhib. 30-Jul-3 Goodman, Sydney #51/R est:190000-250000 (A.D 210000)
£123967 $229339 €180992 Broken egg and summer landscape (197x228cm-78x90in) s.d.86 prov.exhib. 10-Mar-4 Deutscher-Menzies, Melbourne #32/R est:340000-400000 (A.D 300000)
£179688 $336016 €269532 Seaport, entrance into the City of Opportunity (185x214cm-73x84in) s.d.64 i.stretcher. 20-Jul-4 Goodman, Sydney #58/R est:250000-350000 (A.D 460000)

Prints

£2114 $3319 €2509 Laughing frog (64x50cm-25x20in) s.i.d.1977 num.72/90 etching. 27-Aug-3 Christie's, Sydney #501 est:2000-3000 (A.D 5200)
£2254 $3562 €3291 Sticking your neck out (40x38cm-16x15in) s.i.d.92 col lithograph. 2-Sep-3 Deutscher-Menzies, Melbourne #229/R est:1800-2400 (A.D 5500)
£2863 $5210 €4180 Giraffes and Mt. Kenya (90x62cm-35x24in) s.i.d.1980 col lithograph. 16-Jun-4 Deutscher-Menzies, Melbourne #459/R est:5000-7000 (A.D 7500)

Works on paper

£372 $688 €543 No good boy o (15x10cm-6x4in) init. pen ink. 10-Mar-4 Deutscher-Menzies, Melbourne #451 (A.D 900)
£483 $753 €700 Pelican (34x21cm-13x8in) s. ink. 1-Aug-2 Joel, Victoria #222 est:1200-1500 (A.D 1400)
£533 $842 €778 Earth hold (19x29cm-7x11in) init.i.d.79 pen prov. 2-Sep-3 Deutscher-Menzies, Melbourne #282 est:900-1200 (A.D 1300)
£772 $1444 €1127 Kingfisher (27x28cm-11x11in) init.i. ink. 24-Feb-4 Peter Webb, Auckland #188/R (NZ.D 2100)
£847 $1441 €1237 Lake Eyre, The edge of the void (120x80cm-47x31in) s.i.d.75 mixed media paper on board. 24-Nov-3 Sotheby's, Melbourne #247 (A.D 2000)
£1619 $2607 €2364 Ostrich (51x68cm-20x27in) W/C prov. 25-Aug-3 Sotheby's, Paddington #480 est:4000-6000 (A.D 4000)
£1653 $3058 €2413 Man with his pink cat (19x25cm-7x10in) s. W/C pastel. 10-Mar-4 Deutscher-Menzies, Melbourne #338/R est:2500-3500 (A.D 4000)
£1781 $2868 €2600 Honeyeater and Grevillea (24x15cm-9x6in) s.i. crayon prov. 25-Aug-3 Sotheby's, Paddington #397/R est:4000-6000 (A.D 4400)
£1943 $3129 €2837 Platypus (71x51cm-28x20in) W/C prov. 25-Aug-3 Sotheby's, Paddington #289 est:4000-6000 (A.D 4800)
£2066 $3822 €3016 Cat drinking milk (38x53cm-15x21in) s.d.86 W/C. 10-Mar-4 Deutscher-Menzies, Melbourne #125/R est:6000-8000 (A.D 5000)
£2227 $3585 €3251 Cat 'n' mouse (24x15cm-9x6in) s.i. prov. 25-Aug-3 Sotheby's, Paddington #370 est:4000-6000 (A.D 5500)
£2236 $4002 €3265 Finding of the possum (54x64cm-21x25in) init.i.d.71 ink pastel. 10-May-4 Joel, Victoria #345 est:4500-6000 (A.D 5500)
£2429 $3911 €3546 Frog and Dragonfly (24x15cm-9x6in) s.i. crayon prov. 25-Aug-3 Sotheby's, Paddington #260/R est:4000-6000 (A.D 6000)
£2468 $4195 €3603 Egret (40x29cm-16x11in) init.d.83 gouache W/C. 26-Nov-3 Deutscher-Menzies, Melbourne #228/R est:3000-5000 (A.D 5800)
£2930 $4630 €4278 Frogs and stork (36x33cm-14x13in) s. W/C pastel. 2-Sep-3 Deutscher-Menzies, Melbourne #253/R est:4000-6000 (A.D 7150)
£3265 $6008 €4767 Frog (50x40cm-20x16in) s.d.78 W/C gouache prov. 29-Mar-4 Goodman, Sydney #79/R est:8000-12000 (A.D 8000)
£3719 $6880 €5430 Improvisation on a shell, Sydney Opera house (54x69cm-21x27in) s.i.d.1973 W/C pen ink. 10-Mar-4 Deutscher-Menzies, Melbourne #182/R est:12000-15000 (A.D 9000)
£3817 $6947 €5573 Ruined homestead (55x75cm-22x30in) s. W/C prov.exhib. 16-Jun-4 Deutscher-Menzies, Melbourne #31/R est:15000-20000 (A.D 10000)
£4082 $7510 €5960 Cat (76x56cm-30x22in) s. s.i.d.80 verso W/C pastel prov. 29-Mar-4 Goodman, Sydney #72/R est:10000-15000 (A.D 10000)
£6107 $11115 €8916 Honey possum in spring 2003 (72x49cm-28x19in) s.i.d.03 W/C pastel. 16-Jun-4 Deutscher-Menzies, Melbourne #14/R est:18000-25000 (A.D 16000)
£7692 $12385 €11230 Jumping frog (37x40cm-15x16in) s. W/C paper on board. 25-Aug-3 Sotheby's, Paddington #128/R est:15000-20000 (A.D 19000)
£8085 $13744 €11804 Swimmer surrounded by a second landscape (58x78cm-23x31in) s. gouache W/C exec 1985 prov.exhib. 26-Nov-3 Deutscher-Menzies, Melbourne #91/R est:20000-25000 (A.D 19000)
£10569 $16593 €15325 Petals (56x75cm-22x30in) s. W/C pastel prov. 26-Aug-3 Christie's, Sydney #51/R est:25000-30000 (A.D 26000)
£10569 $16593 €15325 Landscape with echidna (60x80cm-24x31in) s.i. W/C pastel sold with photos of the artist prov. 26-Aug-3 Christie's, Sydney #92/R est:20000-30000 (A.D 26000)
£10569 $18919 €15431 Cats drinking milk (75x54cm-30x21in) s.i. W/C crayon prov. 4-May-4 Sotheby's, Melbourne #56/R est:22000-28000 (A.D 26000)
£13636 $23182 €19909 View of the River Glen (82x77cm-32x30in) s.d.78 mixed media prov. 29-Oct-3 Lawson Menzies, Sydney #27/R est:25000-30000 (A.D 33000)
£14575 $23466 €21280 Rhino (92x97cm-36x38in) s.i.d.90 W/C pastel. 25-Aug-3 Sotheby's, Paddington #115/R est:30000-50000 (A.D 36000)
£18595 $32913 €27149 Young giraffe (96x70cm-38x28in) s.i. W/C pastel prov. 3-May-4 Christie's, Melbourne #4/R est:30000-40000 (A.D 45000)
£20426 $34723 €29822 People attached to an animal (98x132cm-39x52in) s.d.86 W/C pastel gouache prov. 26-Nov-3 Deutscher-Menzies, Melbourne #37/R est:50000-70000 (A.D 48000)
£20661 $38223 €30165 Pond life (174x95cm-69x37in) init. W/C pastel executed c.1980 prov. 10-Mar-4 Deutscher-Menzies, Melbourne #78/R est:45000-65000 (A.D 50000)
£23404 $39787 €34170 Wet Season (98x95cm-39x37in) s.i.d.94 W/C pastel prov. 26-Nov-3 Deutscher-Menzies, Melbourne #8/R est:45000-55000 (A.D 55000)
£36885 $58279 €53852 Honey possum and river (190x99cm-75x39in) s.i. W/C pastel exhib. 2-Sep-3 Deutscher-Menzies, Melbourne #58/R est:60000-80000 (A.D 90000)
£49587 $91736 €72397 Cuisine of the sun (95x95cm-37x37in) s.i. W/C in four parts prov. 10-Mar-4 Deutscher-Menzies, Melbourne #39/R est:160000-200000 (A.D 120000)

OLSEN, Kjell Erik Killi (1952-) Norwegian

£1708 $2852 €2494 Nude (80x80cm-31x31in) s.d.2001 verso. 13-Oct-3 Blomqvist, Oslo #337/R est:25000-35000 (N.KR 20000)

OLSEN, Maria (1945-) New Zealander

Works on paper

£346 $619 €505 Untitled (120x90cm-47x35in) s.d.1980 pastel. 11-May-4 Peter Webb, Auckland #96/R est:1000-1500 (NZ.D 1000)
£368 $688 €537 Nature study (91x122cm-36x48in) i.d.1994 wax medium canvas. 24-Feb-4 Peter Webb, Auckland #111/R (NZ.D 1000)

OLSEN, Otto (1905-1966) Danish

£269 $484 €393 Young woman on steps (88x65cm-35x26in) s.d.65. 24-Apr-4 Rasmussen, Havnen #4013 (D.KR 3000)
£305 $548 €445 Winter landscape from Holmens Canal (62x80cm-24x31in) s. 24-Apr-4 Rasmussen, Havnen #2287 (D.KR 3400)

OLSEN, William Skotte (1945-) Danish

£458 $833 €669 Composition with figures, houses and bird (60x80cm-24x31in) init. d.1984-87 verso. 7-Feb-4 Rasmussen, Havnen #4161 (D.KR 5000)
£564 $960 €823 Figures, bird and houses (64x81cm-25x32in) s.d.1979. 29-Nov-3 Rasmussen, Havnen #4174 (D.KR 6000)
£578 $1052 €867 Figure composition (22x27cm-9x11in) 19-Jun-4 Rasmussen, Havnen #4270 (D.KR 6500)
£578 $1052 €867 Guitar player (30x35cm-12x14in) init.d.1965. 19-Jun-4 Rasmussen, Havnen #4273 (D.KR 6500)
£595 $1083 €869 Composition of red figure on black background (120x100cm-47x39in) init.d.78. 7-Feb-4 Rasmussen, Havnen #4143/R (D.KR 6500)
£778 $1417 €1136 Figure composition (20x65cm-8x26in) init. d.1967 and 82 verso furniture panel. 7-Feb-4 Rasmussen, Havnen #4148 (D.KR 8500)
£870 $1583 €1270 Two portraits. Bird composition. three. 7-Feb-4 Rasmussen, Havnen #4153 (D.KR 9500)
£916 $1667 €1337 Figure composition (65x45cm-26x18in) init. d.1979 verso. 7-Feb-4 Rasmussen, Havnen #4159 (D.KR 10000)
£1083 $2025 €1581 Figures in landscape (54x73cm-21x29in) s.stretcher. 25-Feb-4 Kunsthallen, Copenhagen #14/R est:5000 (D.KR 12000)
£1099 $2000 €1605 Composition (23x20cm-9x8in) 7-Feb-4 Rasmussen, Havnen #4160 est:1500 (D.KR 12000)
£1244 $2265 €1866 Front cover on a LP - Green Grass, Hasse William, 1969/1970 (31x31cm-12x12in) init.d.73 cardboard prov. 19-Jun-4 Rasmussen, Havnen #4267/R est:5000 (D.KR 14000)
£1956 $3559 €2934 Figure composition (60x70cm-24x28in) init.d.68. 19-Jun-4 Rasmussen, Havnen #4268/R est:12000 (D.KR 22000)
£3136 $5645 €4579 Saint Augustin. s.d.68 exhib. 24-Apr-4 Rasmussen, Havnen #4105/R est:4000 (D.KR 35000)

Works on paper

£433 $810 €632 Figures in landscape (57x77cm-22x30in) init. W/C. 25-Feb-4 Kunsthallen, Copenhagen #65 (D.KR 4800)

OLSOMMER, Charles Clos (1883-1966) Swiss

£1532 $2634 €2237 Summer in Veyras (38x38cm-15x15in) 8-Dec-3 Philippe Schuler, Zurich #3352/R est:3000-3500 (S.FR 3400)
£1719 $2923 €2510 Etude de femme (35x33cm-14x13in) board. 19-Nov-3 Fischer, Luzern #1284/R est:4000-6000 (S.FR 3800)
£2826 $5172 €4126 Chagrin d'enfant (42x56cm-17x22in) s. mixed media cardboard exec. c.1925 prov.lit. 5-Jun-4 Galerie du Rhone, Sion #554/R est:7000-9000 (S.FR 6500)

Works on paper

£522 $955 €762 Village valaisan (25x18cm-10x7in) s. W/C. 5-Jun-4 Galerie du Rhone, Sion #372 (S.FR 1200)
£746 $1245 €1089 Portrait de dame (21x29cm-8x11in) s. pastel. 16-Nov-3 Koller, Geneva #1294/R (S.FR 1700)
£1207 $2160 €1762 Petit joueur de flute (36x29cm-14x11in) s. i. verso bodycol. 14-May-4 Dobiaschofsky, Bern #157/R est:3500 (S.FR 2800)
£1538 $2615 €2245 Quand je pense a mon village (29x29cm-11x11in) s. i. verso W/C pastel. 19-Nov-3 Fischer, Luzern #2654/R est:3400-3600 (S.FR 3400)
£12156 $20300 €17626 Anniviarde au missel (48x35cm-19x14in) s.d. mixed media prov. 21-Jun-3 Galerie du Rhone, Sion #476/R est:20000-25000 (S.FR 26500)

OLSON, Axel (1899-1986) Swedish

£269 $463 €393 Surrealistic head (19x16cm-7x6in) s. d.1960 verso panel. 7-Dec-3 Uppsala Auktionskammare, Uppsala #223 (S.KR 3500)
£580 $1044 €870 Poem (17x34cm-7x13in) s. panel. 25-Apr-4 Goteborg Auktionsverk, Sweden #314/R (S.KR 8000)
£599 $976 €875 White beach (14x48cm-6x19in) s. panel. 29-Sep-3 Lilla Bukowskis, Stockholm #508 (S.KR 7800)
£616 $1109 €899 Our daily bread (25x34cm-10x13in) s.d.49. 26-Apr-4 Bukowskis, Stockholm #160/R (S.KR 8500)
£657 $1059 €959 The street (46x33cm-18x13in) s. 25-Aug-3 Lilla Bukowskis, Stockholm #748 (S.KR 8600)
£870 $1566 €1270 The hand and the ball (50x62cm-20x24in) s. 26-Apr-4 Bukowskis, Stockholm #161/R (S.KR 12000)
£923 $1588 €1348 Glass verandah (39x25cm-15x10in) s. panel. 7-Dec-3 Uppsala Auktionskammare, Uppsala #272/R (S.KR 12000)
£979 $1576 €1429 Table for two (55x30cm-22x12in) s. 25-Aug-3 Lilla Bukowskis, Stockholm #157 (S.KR 12800)
£1026 $1815 €1498 Girl towards the window (41x33cm-16x13in) s. 27-Apr-4 AB Stockholms Auktionsverk #739/R (S.KR 14000)
£1032 $1662 €1507 Light shore (24x33cm-9x13in) s.d.42 panel. 25-Aug-3 Lilla Bukowskis, Stockholm #981 (S.KR 13500)
£1057 $1798 €1543 Street scene, Paris (24x35cm-9x14in) s.i. panel. 5-Nov-3 AB Stockholms Auktionsverk #748/R est:15000-18000 (S.KR 14000)
£1060 $1835 €1548 Green composition with head (22x26cm-9x10in) s. panel. 15-Dec-3 Lilla Bukowskis, Stockholm #250 (S.KR 13500)
£1077 $1852 €1572 Crab fishing in the harbour (26x75cm-10x30in) s. 7-Dec-3 Uppsala Auktionskammare, Uppsala #269/R (S.KR 14000)

£1261 $2031 €1841 The blue liana (24x33cm-9x13in) s.indis.d. panel. 25-Aug-3 Lilla Bukowskis, Stockholm #759 est:10000-12000 (S.KR 16500)
£1305 $2350 €1905 Female figure by wall (33x49cm-13x19in) s. 26-Apr-4 Bukowskis, Stockholm #76/R est:20000-25000 (S.KR 18000)
£1435 $2440 €2095 Siesta (22x70cm-9x28in) s.d.49 canvas on panel. 4-Nov-3 Bukowskis, Stockholm #143/R est:20000-25000 (S.KR 19000)
£1774 $3175 €2590 From Grotvik's harbour (39x55cm-15x22in) s. 28-May-4 Uppsala Auktionskammare, Uppsala #308/R est:15000-18000 (S.KR 24000)
£1964 $3338 €2867 Selling birds in France (22x90cm-9x35in) s. 5-Nov-3 AB Stockholms Auktionsverk #761/R est:28000-30000 (S.KR 26000)
£1964 $3338 €2867 Landscape from Haverdal (46x61cm-18x24in) s.i. 4-Nov-3 Bukowskis, Stockholm #44/R est:30000-35000 (S.KR 26000)
£2492 $4237 €3638 Wreck on shore (35x70cm-14x28in) s. 5-Nov-3 AB Stockholms Auktionsverk #648/R est:30000-35000 (S.KR 33000)
£2946 $5008 €4301 The bay in summer (33x41cm-13x16in) s.d.45. 5-Nov-3 AB Stockholms Auktionsverk #675/R est:25000-30000 (S.KR 39000)
£5076 $9137 €7411 The eye (116x89cm-46x35in) s.d.74 exhib.lit. 26-Apr-4 Bukowskis, Stockholm #162/R est:70000-80000 (S.KR 70000)
£13595 $23112 €19849 The park (40x57cm-16x22in) s.d.32 i.verso canvas on panel. 4-Nov-3 Bukowskis, Stockholm #48a/R est:100000-125000 (S.KR 180000)
£18127 $30816 €26465 Fiesole - Italian landscape with buildings (125x105cm-49x41in) s.d.1931. 5-Nov-3 AB Stockholms Auktionsverk #856/R est:250000-300000 (S.KR 240000)
Works on paper
£363 $653 €530 Das Geheimnis der Himmel (15x12cm-6x5in) s.i.d.22 mixed media. 26-Apr-4 Bukowskis, Stockholm #161a/R (S.KR 5000)

OLSON, Bengt (1930-) Swedish
£348 $627 €522 Landscape (33x24cm-13x9in) S. 25-Apr-4 Goteborg Auktionsverk, Sweden #372/R (S.KR 4800)

OLSON, Carl (1864-1940) Swedish
£2209 $3600 €3225 Sunset over North Carolina stream (97x137cm-38x54in) s.d.1916. 27-Sep-3 Charlton Hall, Columbia #113/R est:800-1200

OLSON, Eric H (1909-1996) Swedish
£604 $1027 €882 Composition (38x46cm-15x18in) s.verso tempera. 5-Nov-3 AB Stockholms Auktionsverk #788/R (S.KR 8000)
Sculpture
£1662 $2825 €2427 Optochromie (44cm-17in) s. 4-Nov-3 Bukowskis, Stockholm #254/R est:20000-25000 (S.KR 22000)
£2491 $4409 €3637 Optochromi (32cm-13in) s. glass filter plexiglass. 27-Apr-4 AB Stockholms Auktionsverk #834/R est:25000-30000 (S.KR 34000)
£3004 $5316 €4386 Optochromi (41cm-16in) s. glass filter plexiglass. 27-Apr-4 AB Stockholms Auktionsverk #835/R est:30000-35000 (S.KR 41000)

OLSON, Erik (1901-1986) Swedish
£534 $924 €780 Ascension Day (38x46cm-15x18in) s.d.1959 panel. 15-Dec-3 Lilla Bukowskis, Stockholm #180 (S.KR 6800)
£923 $1588 €1348 Composition with female figure (27x34cm-11x13in) s.d.1961 panel. 7-Dec-3 Uppsala Auktionskammare, Uppsala #274/R (S.KR 12000)
£1269 $2284 €1853 Summer landscape with hay drying (16x24cm-6x9in) s.d.40 panel prov. 26-Apr-4 Bukowskis, Stockholm #13/R est:12000-15000 (S.KR 17500)
£1269 $2284 €1853 Hermit's description (21x49cm-8x19in) s.i.d.1925 lit. 26-Apr-4 Bukowskis, Stockholm #67/R est:15000-20000 (S.KR 17500)
£1300 $2093 €1898 Stone quarry (34x50cm-13x20in) s.d.45 panel. 25-Aug-3 Lilla Bukowskis, Stockholm #757 est:15000-18000 (S.KR 17000)
£1322 $2247 €1930 Field landscape (16x23cm-6x9in) s.d.40 panel. 4-Nov-3 Bukowskis, Stockholm #51/R est:12000-15000 (S.KR 17500)
£1342 $2415 €1959 Towards the water (25x28cm-10x11in) init.d.17 canvas on panel. 26-Apr-4 Bukowskis, Stockholm #68/R est:12000-15000 (S.KR 18500)
£1414 $2545 €2121 Market scene (31x40cm-12x16in) s.d.1944 cardboard. 25-Apr-4 Goteborg Auktionsverk, Sweden #340/R est:25000 (S.KR 19500)
£1586 $2696 €2316 The clouds are breaking (46x54cm-18x21in) s.d.46 panel. 4-Nov-3 Bukowskis, Stockholm #43/R est:30000-40000 (S.KR 21000)
£1662 $2825 €2427 Assisi - Portiuncula and Saint Francis (34x55cm-13x22in) s.d.1950. 4-Nov-3 Bukowskis, Stockholm #142/R est:25000-30000 (S.KR 22000)
£2103 $3785 €3070 People are always on the move (30x70cm-12x28in) s.d.1965. 26-Apr-4 Bukowskis, Stockholm #152/R est:20000-25000 (S.KR 29000)
£2248 $4046 €3282 The observer - the poet (33x29cm-13x11in) s.d.1970 panel prov. 26-Apr-4 Bukowskis, Stockholm #82/R est:10000-15000 (S.KR 31000)
£2756 $4960 €4024 Open windows (30x39cm-12x15in) s.d.47 cardboard. 26-Apr-4 Bukowskis, Stockholm #12/R est:30000-40000 (S.KR 38000)
£5801 $10442 €8469 Human figure (54x73cm-21x29in) s.d.1936 prov. 26-Apr-4 Bukowskis, Stockholm #74/R est:100000-125000 (S.KR 80000)
£7252 $13053 €10588 Italian soldiers (40x28cm-16x11in) s.d.24 panel lit. 26-Apr-4 Bukowskis, Stockholm #70/R est:60000-80000 (S.KR 100000)
£8308 $14124 €12130 Sails on the beach (38x62cm-15x24in) s.d.1935. 4-Nov-3 Bukowskis, Stockholm #46/R est:80000-100000 (S.KR 110000)
£10989 $19451 €16044 Surrealistic figure composition (58x36cm-23x14in) s.d.1937 panel. 27-Apr-4 AB Stockholms Auktionsverk #646/R est:175000-200000 (S.KR 150000)
£15861 $26964 €23157 Corrida de Toros (14x23cm-6x9in) s.i.d.1930 lit. 5-Nov-3 AB Stockholms Auktionsverk #677/R est:100000-120000 (S.KR 210000)
Works on paper
£437 $805 €656 Composition (49x100cm-19x39in) s.d.1962 gouache. 14-Jun-4 Lilla Bukowskis, Stockholm #697 (S.KR 6000)
£620 $1140 €930 Bishop Brynolf from Skara (41x33cm-16x13in) s.d.1953 mixed media. 14-Jun-4 Lilla Bukowskis, Stockholm #1085 (S.KR 8500)
£700 $1287 €1050 The old farm (37x46cm-15x18in) s.d.1942 mixed media. 14-Jun-4 Lilla Bukowskis, Stockholm #48/R (S.KR 9600)

OLSON, George Wallace (1876-1938) American
£1250 $2000 €1825 Mountain landscape (61x76cm-24x30in) s. 17-May-3 Bunte, Elgin #1257 est:2500-3500

OLSON, J Olaf (1894-1979) American
£2695 $4500 €3935 Mediterranean Boats (71x91cm-28x36in) s. prov. 23-Oct-3 Shannon's, Milford #44/R est:3000-5000

OLSSON, Julius (1864-1942) British
£620 $1153 €905 Black rock off Falmouth (45x60cm-18x24in) s. 2-Mar-4 Bearnes, Exeter #424/R
£850 $1471 €1241 After the storm, rainbow over the sea (34x43cm-13x17in) s. 11-Dec-3 Lane, Penzance #184
£1100 $1947 €1606 Vessels at sea (46x61cm-18x24in) s. 29-Apr-4 Christie's, Kensington #225/R est:800-1200
£1200 $2244 €1752 Moonlit seascape (43x58cm-17x23in) 24-Feb-4 Tayler & Fletcher, Cheltenham #5
£1200 $2244 €1752 Coastal scene with waves breaking onto rocks (51x61cm-20x24in) s. 22-Jul-4 Tennants, Leyburn #805 est:1200-1400
£1613 $2968 €2355 Sunlit coast (35x46cm-14x18in) s. panel prov. 14-Jun-4 Waddingtons, Toronto #149/R est:1600-1800 (C.D 4000)
£1800 $3222 €2628 Coast at dusk (35x46cm-14x18in) s. panel. 26-May-4 Christie's, Kensington #731/R est:1500-2500
£1800 $3294 €2628 Waves crashing on a Cornish headland (45x61cm-18x24in) s. 3-Jun-4 Lane, Penzance #311 est:1800-2500
£1900 $3173 €2755 Sunlit sea, Seaford (33x43cm-13x17in) 22-Jun-3 Desmond Judd, Cranbrook #1053
£2600 $4498 €3796 Waves breaking on a deserted rocky coast (137x184cm-54x72in) i.stretcher. 11-Dec-3 Lyon & Turnbull, Edinburgh #71/R est:2000-3000
£3500 $6405 €5110 Setting sun above breaking waves (59x75cm-23x30in) s. 3-Jun-4 Lane, Penzance #15 est:2000-4000
£3800 $6574 €5548 Passing shower (106x164cm-42x65in) s.i. 11-Dec-3 Lyon & Turnbull, Edinburgh #70/R est:2000-3000
£4200 $7686 €6132 Moonlight over breaking waves (46x61cm-18x24in) s. 3-Jun-4 Lane, Penzance #140/R est:3000-3500

OLSSON, Wilgot (1906-1990) Swedish
£290 $522 €435 Man with guitar (50x60cm-20x24in) s. 25-Apr-4 Goteborg Auktionsverk, Sweden #410/R (S.KR 4000)

OLSSON-HAGALUND, Olle (1904-1972) Swedish
£1057 $1798 €1543 Coastal landscape, Nynashamn (26x30cm-10x12in) s.d.33 canvas on board. 4-Nov-3 Bukowskis, Stockholm #126/R (S.KR 14000)
£4381 $7447 €6396 The crayfish feast (19x22cm-7x9in) s. panel. 4-Nov-3 Bukowskis, Stockholm #10/R est:40000-50000 (S.KR 58000)
£4834 $8218 €7058 Girl with hat (32x27cm-13x11in) s. panel. 4-Nov-3 Bukowskis, Stockholm #6/R est:30000-40000 (S.KR 64000)
£5287 $8988 €7719 The dairy shop in Hagalund (36x40cm-14x16in) s. cardboard prov. 4-Nov-3 Bukowskis, Stockholm #125/R est:80000-100000 (S.KR 70000)
£6135 $10981 €8957 Moving house in Hagalund (47x55cm-19x22in) s. panel exhib. 28-May-4 Uppsala Auktionskammare, Uppsala #279/R est:80000-100000 (S.KR 83000)
£21148 $35952 €30876 The red fence, Hagalund (46x55cm-18x22in) s. exhib.prov. 5-Nov-3 AB Stockholms Auktionsverk #773/R est:280000-300000 (S.KR 280000)
£22659 $38520 €33082 Sailor's inn in Gdynia (65x57cm-26x22in) s. lot. 5-Nov-3 AB Stockholms Auktionsverk #843/R est:300000-350000 (S.KR 300000)
£30211 $51360 €44108 Girl with plaster churches (90x80cm-35x31in) s. painted 1943 exhib.lit. 4-Nov-3 Bukowskis, Stockholm #121/R est:400000-450000 (S.KR 400000)
£35165 $62242 €51341 The yellow twist cake (76x91cm-30x36in) s. exhib. 27-Apr-4 AB Stockholms Auktionsverk #674/R est:300000-350000 (S.KR 480000)
£100073 $180131 €146107 Spring day by the bridge in Djurgaarden with many figures (56x62cm-22x24in) s.d.44 exhib.lit. 26-Apr-4 Bukowskis, Stockholm #131/R est:700000-900000 (S.KR 1380000)
Works on paper
£375 $676 €548 Seascape (19x25cm-7x10in) s.d.29 W/C. 26-Jan-4 Lilla Bukowskis, Stockholm #607 (S.KR 5000)
£2271 $4020 €3316 Norreborg, Hven (48x49cm-19x19in) s. gouache exhib. 27-Apr-4 AB Stockholms Auktionsverk #846/R est:40000-50000 (S.KR 31000)
£2756 $4960 €4024 Street scene, Strandvagen (22x17cm-9x7in) s. W/C. 26-Apr-4 Bukowskis, Stockholm #127/R est:35000-40000 (S.KR 38000)
£2828 $5091 €4129 Twilight, Hagalund (42x55cm-17x22in) s. W/C. 26-Apr-4 Bukowskis, Stockholm #126/R est:50000-60000 (S.KR 39000)
£2901 $5221 €4235 Harbour in Normandy (24x33cm-9x13in) s. mixed media. 26-Apr-4 Bukowskis, Stockholm #2/R est:40000-50000 (S.KR 40000)
£18315 $32418 €26740 Molin's fountain, The Royal Gardens (65x65cm-26x26in) s.d.34 gouache prov.exhib.lit. 27-Apr-4 AB Stockholms Auktionsverk #718/R est:150000-175000 (S.KR 250000)

OLSTED, Peter (1824-1887) Danish
£2507 $4587 €3660 Large stones by fjord (64x85cm-25x33in) s.d.1853 prov. 9-Jun-4 Rasmussen, Copenhagen #1689/R est:30000-40000 (D.KR 28000)
£2836 $4905 €4141 Summer landscape from Oresund with the Danish flag (72x115cm-28x45in) s.d.1877 prov. 9-Dec-3 Rasmussen, Copenhagen #1390/R est:30000-40000 (D.KR 30000)

OLSZEWSKI, Karl Ewald (1884-?) Rumanian
£1049 $1804 €1500 Grey geese landing on the beach (75x120cm-30x47in) s. 5-Dec-3 Bolland & Marotz, Bremen #744/R est:1600
Works on paper
£611 $966 €880 Sea eagle chasing cranes over sea (52x72cm-20x28in) s. W/C. 6-Sep-3 Schopman, Hamburg #816/R

OLTMANNS, Willi (1905-1979) German
£1722 $3134 €2600 Fields in August (65x80cm-26x31in) s. i.d.12 August 71 verso board. 18-Jun-4 Bolland & Marotz, Bremen #373/R est:3500

OLUND-HANSEN, Edvard (1887-1979) Danish
£271 $500 €396 Interior scene with woman in front of window (68x65cm-27x26in) mono. 15-Mar-4 Rasmussen, Vejle #413/R (D.KR 3000)
£7089 $12264 €10350 Summer, Bornholm - family enjoying a warm summer's day (110x135cm-43x53in) mono.d.22 exhib. 9-Dec-3 Rasmussen, Copenhagen #1425/R est:75000 (D.KR 75000)

O'LYNCH OF TOWN, Karl (1869-1942) German
£548 $932 €800 Old house at dusk (41x52cm-16x20in) s. canvas on board. 8-Nov-3 Hans Stahl, Toestorf #14/R

£633 $1140 €950 Castle on southern coast (35x33cm-14x13in) s. board. 26-Apr-4 Rieber, Stuttgart #847/R
£733 $1320 €1100 Quayside with fishing boat (30x39cm-12x15in) board. 22-Apr-4 Dorotheum, Graz #21
£1067 $1963 €1600 Ferry in Frickenhausen am Main (5x66cm-2x26in) s. 9-Jun-4 Dorotheum, Salzburg #542/R est:2800-3400
£1181 $2007 €1700 Horse and cart on beach (114x140cm-45x55in) s. 28-Oct-3 Dorotheum, Vienna #233/R est:1500-2000
£1408 $2338 €2000 Near Berwang (50x64cm-20x25in) s. i. verso. 12-Jun-3 Dorotheum, Graz #36/R est:2000
£1562 $2750 €2281 Waves breaking on the cliffs (105x135cm-41x53in) s. 18-May-4 Bonhams & Butterfields, San Francisco #108/R est:3000-5000
£1944 $3169 €2800 Rocky sea coast (111x165cm-44x65in) s. 24-Sep-3 Neumeister, Munich #22/R est:2800
£2500 $4250 €3600 By the cliffs (77x100cm-30x39in) s. i. verso. 28-Oct-3 Dorotheum, Vienna #176/R est:2600-2800

OLYSLAGER, Jan (1926-) Dutch
£1389 $2194 €2000 Untitled (50x80cm-20x31in) s.d.1969. 26-Apr-3 Auction Maastricht #167/R est:3000-4000

O'MALLEY, Jane (1944-) Irish
£500 $910 €730 Still life by the sea, St. Ives (20x20cm-8x8in) s.d.1988 i.verso oil on card. 15-Jun-4 David Lay, Penzance #575
£650 $1164 €949 January painting (76x51cm-30x20in) s. oil acrylic mixed media board. 14-May-4 Christie's, Kensington #404/R
Works on paper
£1399 $2378 €2000 Hedge flowers in the studio, St Ives (64x51cm-25x20in) s.i.d.1985 gouache board. 18-Nov-3 Whyte's, Dublin #226/R est:1500-2000

O'MALLEY, Tony (1913-2003) British/Irish
£2500 $4175 €3650 October, 1988 (15x30cm-6x12in) init. i.d.1989 verso board after Lanzarote. 14-Oct-3 David Lay, Penzance #570/R est:1500-2000
£2685 $4752 €4000 Wood in County Wexford (48x51cm-19x20in) board painted c.1956-1960 prov. 27-Apr-4 Whyte's, Dublin #31/R est:3000-5000
£2817 $4507 €4000 Interior study with artist's reflection (48x27cm-19x11in) board prov. 16-Sep-3 Whyte's, Dublin #194/R est:3000-4000
£4196 $7133 €6000 Morning light (51x37cm-20x15in) s.i.d.November 78 oil on paper. 25-Nov-3 De Veres Art Auctions, Dublin #142/R est:6000-8000
£4459 $8428 €6600 October 1988 after Lanzarote (15x30cm-6x12in) init.i.d.1 June 1989 board. 17-Feb-4 Whyte's, Dublin #84/R est:6000-8000
£5000 $8350 €7300 Autumn (51x74cm-20x29in) init. board. 14-Oct-3 David Lay, Penzance #30/R est:4000-5000
£5000 $8950 €7300 Orzola (63x51cm-25x20in) init.i.d.26/10/88 acrylic collage pastel exhib. 14-May-4 Christie's, Kensington #469/R est:3000-5000
£5369 $9503 €8000 Night patio (46x36cm-18x14in) s.i.d.1975 verso. 27-Apr-4 Whyte's, Dublin #96/R est:8000-10000
£5500 $9185 €8030 Bahamas Collage II (56x28cm-22x11in) init.d.1983 i.verso acrylic on paper. 14-Oct-3 David Lay, Penzance #567/R est:4000-5000
£6000 $10920 €8760 Bahamas cottage no 1 (56x36cm-22x14in) mono.d.1/86 acrylic paper prov. 16-Jun-4 John Nicholson, Haslemere #702/R est:2000-3000
£7042 $12183 €10000 Entrance to the orchard, Ashgrove, Fethard-on-sea (80x54cm-31x21in) init.d.1959 s.i.d.verso board. 10-Dec-3 Bonhams & James Adam, Dublin #88/R est:10000-15000
£7133 $12126 €10200 Houses in winter (36x45cm-14x18in) init. board. 25-Nov-3 De Veres Art Auctions, Dublin #90/R est:6000-8000
£7832 $13315 €11200 St. Martins Moths (74x23cm-29x9in) init. i.d.Oct 1985 verso board. 25-Nov-3 De Veres Art Auctions, Dublin #110/R est:10000-15000
£8000 $14320 €11680 Spanish place, Yaiza, Good Friday (91x61cm-36x24in) s.i.d.24/3/89 verso board exhib. 14-May-4 Christie's, Kensington #470/R est:4000-6000
£26174 $46852 €39000 Three shadows, Nassau Bahamas (122x91cm-48x36in) init. i.verso board. 26-May-4 James Adam, Dublin #80/R est:40000-50000
Works on paper
£650 $1203 €949 Untitled (18x13cm-7x5in) s.d.1967 mixed media. 10-Feb-4 David Lay, Penzance #128
£900 $1584 €1314 Landscape with goat (31x20cm-12x8in) inidis.i. d.Dec 1965 pastel scratching out. 18-May-4 Bonhams, Knightsbridge #28
£1200 $2112 €1752 Farm buildings with trees (22x30cm-9x12in) indis.i.d. pastel scratching out. 18-May-4 Bonhams, Knightsbridge #66/R est:400-600
£1338 $2141 €1900 October morning, Grange, Fethard-on-Sea (17x25cm-7x10in) s.d.October 1959 s.i.verso W/C gouache prov. 16-Sep-3 Whyte's, Dublin #151/R est:2000-3000
£1408 $2437 €2000 Wexford landscapes (11x16cm-4x6in) mixed media two framed as one. 10-Dec-3 Bonhams & James Adam, Dublin #86/R est:2000-3000
£1500 $2730 €2190 Storm, Porthmeor (20x25cm-8x10in) s.d.69 gouache. 15-Jun-4 David Lay, Penzance #621 est:1500-2500
£1892 $3576 €2800 February collage, 1974 (25x18cm-10x7in) init.d.1974 mixed media. 17-Feb-4 Whyte's, Dublin #102/R est:2000-3000
£2013 $3564 €3000 Backyard, winter (28x41cm-11x16in) s. W/C gouache pencil exec.c.1950 prov. 27-Apr-4 Whyte's, Dublin #6/R est:2000-3000
£2100 $3885 €3066 Bird (18x25cm-7x10in) s.d.3/75 mixed media. 10-Feb-4 David Lay, Penzance #463 est:1200-1800
£2500 $4075 €3600 St Martins (42x29cm-17x11in) init.i.d.3/74 gouache. 23-Sep-3 De Veres Art Auctions, Dublin #236/R est:3500-4500
£2727 $4636 €3900 February (18x26cm-7x10in) s.d.1974 gouache pen. 25-Nov-3 De Veres Art Auctions, Dublin #112/R est:4000-6000
£2797 $4755 €4000 Autumn sea panel (97x10cm-38x4in) init.d.5.87 s.i.d.verso mixed media. 25-Nov-3 De Veres Art Auctions, Dublin #100c est:4000-6000
£2819 $4989 €4200 Alan and Valerie's window, Rosewall (23x28cm-9x11in) s.i.d.November 1968 gouache board exhib. 27-Apr-4 Whyte's, Dublin #82/R est:4000-5000
£3000 $5370 €4380 St Martin's (42x29cm-17x11in) init.i.d.3/74 s.i.d.1974 verso pencil gouache. 14-May-4 Christie's, Kensington #471/R est:1500-2500
£3000 $5460 €4380 Winter (28x30cm-11x12in) s.i.d.1986 mixed media collage. 15-Jun-4 David Lay, Penzance #620/R est:3000-4000
£3378 $6385 €5000 Farm buildings, County Wexford, 1950s (38x48cm-15x19in) gouache on board prov. 17-Feb-4 Whyte's, Dublin #42/R est:3000-4000
£3662 $5859 €5200 Nassau, Bahamas (22x28cm-9x11in) init.d.January 1975 gouache sand board. 16-Sep-3 Whyte's, Dublin #49/R est:6000-7000
£3667 $6637 €5500 Myself at the window in the evening (26x17cm-10x7in) init.i.d.9/72 mixed media. 30-Mar-4 De Veres Art Auctions, Dublin #87/R est:4000-5000
£4196 $7133 €6000 Winter arklow (30x47cm-12x19in) s.i.d.Feb 1956 mixed media. 25-Nov-3 De Veres Art Auctions, Dublin #91/R est:6000-8000
£5282 $8451 €7500 Table top still life with house plant (33x41cm-13x16in) s. gouache board exec.c.1956-60 prov. 16-Sep-3 Whyte's, Dublin #4/R est:2000-3000
£5467 $9895 €8200 Clare Island, sheep skulls (41x48cm-16x19in) s.i. mixed media. 30-Mar-4 De Veres Art Auctions, Dublin #166/R est:8000-10000
£9000 $15030 €13140 Red nocturne (61x122cm-24x48in) init. s.i.verso mixed media. 14-Oct-3 David Lay, Penzance #566/R est:8000-12000

OMAN, Valentin (1935-) Austrian
Works on paper
£315 $535 €450 Untitled (29x20cm-11x8in) s.d.87 mixed media. 19-Nov-3 Dorotheum, Klagenfurt #64
£315 $535 €450 Sattnitz (23x32cm-9x13in) s.d.85 mixed media. 19-Nov-3 Dorotheum, Klagenfurt #65

OMEENYO, Fiona (1981-) Australian
Works on paper
£1641 $3068 €2462 Night hunting (187x121cm-74x48in) s.d.2002 i.verso synthetic polymer canvas prov. 21-Jul-4 Shapiro, Sydney #124/R est:4000-6000 (A.D 4200)
£1680 $3141 €2520 Windy night (90x125cm-35x49in) s.d.2003 i.verso synthetic polymer canvas prov. 21-Jul-4 Shapiro, Sydney #121/R est:4000-6000 (A.D 4300)

OMEGNA, Filippo (1881-1948) Italian
£278 $472 €400 Farms (34x24cm-13x9in) s. cardboard. 1-Nov-3 Meeting Art, Vercelli #300

OMICCIOLI, Giovanni (1901-1975) Italian
£241 $449 €360 House (30x40cm-12x16in) s. board painted 1974. 4-Mar-4 Babuino, Rome #137
£500 $920 €750 Fish (30x40cm-12x16in) s. cardboard. 12-Jun-4 Meeting Art, Vercelli #555/R
£533 $965 €800 Hut and trees (36x51cm-14x20in) s. cardboard. 2-Apr-4 Farsetti, Prato #275
£550 $1023 €820 Bunch of flowers (41x27cm-16x11in) s. lit. 4-Mar-4 Babuino, Rome #375
£590 $1098 €880 Vase de fleurs (22x21cm-9x8in) s. card on canvas. 4-Mar-4 Babuino, Rome #31
£671 $1242 €1000 Flowers in blue vase (40x30cm-16x12in) s. cardboard on canvas. 13-Mar-4 Meeting Art, Vercelli #465
£767 $1411 €1150 Hut in Passoscuro (30x40cm-12x16in) s. 12-Jun-4 Meeting Art, Vercelli #158/R
£795 $1446 €1200 Fregene (35x50cm-14x20in) s. s.i.d.1968 verso cardboard. 17-Jun-4 Galleria Pananti, Florence #409/R
£828 $1382 €1200 Landscape with hut. Wild flowers (25x35cm-10x14in) s.verso one oil cardboard on canvas one tempera cardboard two. 13-Nov-3 Finarte Semenzato, Rome #272
£933 $1717 €1400 Landscape (37x52cm-15x20in) s. s.verso cardboard. 10-Jun-4 Galleria Pace, Milan #64/R
£1034 $1728 €1500 Landscape (17x33cm-7x13in) s. card. 13-Nov-3 Galleria Pace, Milan #128/R est:2200
£1049 $1783 €1500 Scales in Fiumicino (25x35cm-10x14in) s. s.i.d.1963 verso. 24-Nov-3 Christie's, Milan #108
£1056 $1754 €1500 Capanna a Passoscuro (40x50cm-16x20in) s. 14-Jun-3 Meeting Art, Vercelli #459/R est:1500
£1067 $1963 €1600 Landscape (36x51cm-14x20in) s. s.d.1970 verso cardboard. 10-Jun-4 Galleria Pace, Milan #170/R est:2800
£1329 $2259 €1900 Hut and boat. Face of woman (20x30cm-8x12in) s.s.verso cardboard one by E Treccani two. 24-Nov-3 Christie's, Milan #91 est:1200-1800
£1333 $2400 €2000 Football match (36x29cm-14x11in) s. card on masonite. 22-Apr-4 Finarte Semenzato, Rome #167/R est:1800-2200
£1733 $3120 €2600 Fish (31x51cm-12x20in) s.verso board. 22-Apr-4 Finarte Semenzato, Rome #162/R est:1600-1800
Works on paper
£268 $499 €400 Scilla (22x36cm-9x14in) s.d.1960 pastel paper on canvas. 4-Mar-4 Babuino, Rome #462
£1200 $2208 €1800 Landscape (35x50cm-14x20in) i.verso pastel cardboard. 8-Jun-4 Finarte Semenzato, Milan #200 est:1400-1600

OMLOR, Pete (1947-) American
£455 $800 €664 Ohr-pink (183x183cm-72x72in) acrylic. 22-May-4 Selkirks, St. Louis #618/R

OMMEGANCK, B P (1755-1826) Flemish
£1399 $2378 €2000 Berger dans un paysage (28x35cm-11x14in) panel. 1-Dec-3 Amberes, Antwerp #333a/R

OMMEGANCK, Balthasar Paul (1755-1826) Flemish
£721 $1240 €1053 Landscape with sheep and goats (25x32cm-10x13in) s.d.1798 panel. 8-Dec-3 Philippe Schuler, Zurich #5877 (S.FR 1600)
£900 $1611 €1314 Cattle in open landscape (30x37cm-12x15in) s.d.1780 panel. 22-Mar-4 Bonhams & Brooks, Norfolk #283/R
£1000 $1630 €1460 Landscape with a shepherd and his flock at sunset (40x49cm-16x19in) s.d.1799 panel. 26-Sep-3 Christie's, Kensington #160/R est:1000-1500
£1477 $2600 €2156 Wooded landscape with cattle, sheep and goat grazing by a river (42x56cm-17x22in) s.i.d.1807 panel prov. 18-May-4 Bonhams & Butterfields, San Francisco #30/R est:3000-5000
£1538 $2646 €2200 Berger avec son troupeau (39x44cm-15x17in) s. panel. 2-Dec-3 Campo & Campo, Antwerp #250/R est:2000-3000
£1656 $3013 €2500 Goats in a mountain landscape (25x32cm-10x13in) s.d.1798 panel. 21-Jun-4 Dorotheum, Vienna #131/R est:2500-2800
£1667 $2633 €2400 Sheep by river (31x41cm-12x16in) i. verso panel lit. 19-Sep-3 Schloss Ahlden, Ahlden #1511/R est:2800
£1761 $3046 €2500 Bull and sheep in meadow landscape (43x52cm-17x20in) panel. 10-Dec-3 Hugo Ruef, Munich #2373/R est:2500
£1800 $3222 €2700 Trois moutons (33x35cm-13x14in) s. panel. 11-May-4 Vanderkindere, Brussels #205/R est:3000-5000
£1900 $3458 €2774 Figure with sheep before a watering hole (38x53cm-15x21in) 3-Feb-4 Lawrences, Bletchingley #159715 est:2000-3000
£2207 $4083 €3200 Troupeau dans la clairiere (81x64cm-32x25in) s. 19-Jan-4 Horta, Bruxelles #208 est:3000-4000
£9091 $15455 €13000 Couple de bergers et leur troupeau au bord de la mare (70x88cm-28x35in) s. 18-Nov-3 Vanderkindere, Brussels #26/R est:6000-8000

OMMEGANCK, Balthasar Paul (attrib) (1755-1826) Flemish
£738 $1358 €1100 Girl milking and cattle grazing in summer landscape with river (26x33cm-10x13in) panel. 27-Mar-4 L & B, Essen #175/R

ONDERDONK, Julian (1882-1922) American
£1923 $3308 €2808 Late afternoon (15x23cm-6x9in) s. s.i.d.1908 verso panel. 3-Dec-3 AB Stockholms Auktionsverk #2554/R est:30000-40000 (S.KR 25000)
£2994 $5000 €4371 Texas morning (18x10cm-7x4in) s. canvas on board. 23-Oct-3 Shannon's, Milford #37/R est:3000-5000
£3297 $6000 €4814 Winter landscape (15x23cm-6x9in) s. i.d.1909 verso panel prov. 15-Jun-4 John Moran, Pasadena #167 est:6000-8000
£4571 $8000 €6674 Night, Highbridge, NY City. Misty evening (15x23cm-6x9in) s. s.i.d.1909 verso two. 19-Dec-3 Sotheby's, New York #1094/R est:8000-12000
£13174 $22000 €19234 Milkweed (30x41cm-12x16in) 18-Oct-3 David Dike, Dallas #228/R est:20000-30000
£15569 $26000 €22731 Morning on the Pond (41x61cm-16x24in) s. prov. 23-Oct-3 Shannon's, Milford #36/R est:12000-18000
£25815 $47500 €37690 Blue bonnets, sunny morning, San Antonio, Texas (30x40cm-12x16in) s. i.verso painted 1914 prov. 8-Jun-4 Bonhams & Butterfields, San Francisco #4130/R est:20000-30000
£83333 $135000 €120833 Blue bonnets at twilight, North of San Antonio, Texas (65x76cm-26x30in) s. prov. 8-Aug-3 Barridorf, Portland #257/R est:60000-90000

ONDERDONK, Robert Jenkins (1853-1917) American
£13772 $23000 €20107 Market at Cuernavaca, Mexico (20x28cm-8x11in) board. 18-Oct-3 David Dike, Dallas #206/R est:10000-20000

O'NEIL, Horton (20th C) American
Works on paper
£243 $450 €355 Portrait of a lady (46x46cm-18x18in) bears sig. i. verso conte crayon after Constantine Guys. 15-Jul-4 Sotheby's, New York #117

O'NEILL, Daniel (1920-1974) British
£3356 $5940 €5000 The Grotto (51x61cm-20x24in) s. board prov. 27-Apr-4 Whyte's, Dublin #80/R est:5000-7000
£3490 $6247 €5200 Tide can wait (32x35cm-13x14in) s.i.verso board. 26-May-4 James Adam, Dublin #133/R est:3500-4500
£4000 $6640 €5840 Night alone is with me, self portrait (35x30cm-14x12in) board. 1-Oct-3 John Ross, Belfast #152 est:6000-8000
£5986 $10356 €8500 Seascape (40x51cm-16x20in) s. prov. 10-Dec-3 Bonhams & James Adam, Dublin #129/R est:9000-12000
£6500 $11635 €9490 Tomorrow perhaps (51x76cm-20x30in) s. i.verso board prov. 14-May-4 Christie's, London #91/R est:6000-8000
£6579 $12105 €10000 The pianist (61x46cm-24x18in) s. 22-Jun-4 De Veres Art Auctions, Dublin #60/R est:10000-15000
£8108 $15324 €12000 Bathers (23x36cm-9x14in) s. board exhib. 17-Feb-4 Whyte's, Dublin #113/R est:12000-15000
£9211 $16947 €14000 Landscape (45x60cm-18x24in) s.i.verso board prov. 22-Jun-4 De Veres Art Auctions, Dublin #43/R est:15000-20000
£9396 $16631 €14000 Night sky (46x36cm-18x14in) s. i.verso prov. 27-Apr-4 Whyte's, Dublin #76/R est:15000-20000
£9859 $17056 €14000 Scalligstown, Co Donegal (36x53cm-14x21in) board. 10-Dec-3 Bonhams & James Adam, Dublin #101/R est:12000-16000
£10000 $17900 €14600 Landscape with figure (40x61cm-16x24in) board prov. 13-May-4 Sotheby's, London #83/R est:10000-15000
£14085 $22535 €20000 Bride (53x42cm-21x17in) s. panel prov.exhib. 16-Sep-3 Whyte's, Dublin #66/R est:20000-30000
£14789 $25585 €21000 Lake (46x61cm-18x24in) s. board. 10-Dec-3 Bonhams & James Adam, Dublin #85/R est:15000-20000
£16000 $28640 €23360 Studio interior (51x61cm-20x24in) s. board prov. 13-May-4 Sotheby's, London #103/R est:10000-15000
£16667 $27167 €24000 Landscape with three figures (63x51cm-25x20in) s.i.verso board prov. 24-Sep-3 James Adam, Dublin #45/R est:25000-30000
£16779 $30034 €25000 Two girls and a boy (30x40cm-12x16in) s. i.verso board prov. 26-May-4 James Adam, Dublin #57/R est:25000-35000
£17500 $32375 €25550 Girl with a ruff collar (60x50cm-24x20in) s. board. 13-Feb-4 Sworder & Son, Bishops Stortford #1/R est:2000-3000
£18000 $32580 €27000 Young man with a rose (51x41cm-20x16in) s. board prov. 30-Mar-4 De Veres Art Auctions, Dublin #109f/R est:9000-12000
£18500 $33855 €27010 Flower sellers (61x50cm-24x20in) s. board. 2-Jun-4 John Ross, Belfast #144 est:20000-25000
£19444 $31694 €28000 Going to Mass (46x61cm-18x24in) s.i.verso board. 24-Sep-3 James Adam, Dublin #68/R est:25000-35000
£19718 $31549 €28000 Backyards, Downpatrick (51x61cm-20x24in) s. board exhib. 16-Sep-3 Whyte's, Dublin #32/R est:20000-30000
£20134 $36040 €30000 Seated girl (60x45cm-24x18in) s. board. 26-May-4 James Adam, Dublin #71/R est:30000-40000
£20270 $38311 €30000 Western family (51x66cm-20x26in) s. 17-Feb-4 Whyte's, Dublin #44/R est:30000-40000
£25503 $45141 €38000 The lake (46x61cm-18x24in) s. i.verso board. 27-Apr-4 Whyte's, Dublin #72/R est:25000-35000
£26056 $45077 €37000 Studio interior (35x50cm-14x20in) s. exhib. 10-Dec-3 Bonhams & James Adam, Dublin #110/R est:25000-35000
£32215 $57664 €48000 Head (50x40cm-20x16in) s.i.verso board prov. 26-May-4 James Adam, Dublin #120/R est:25000-35000
£33557 $60067 €50000 Wise men (53x64cm-21x25in) s. i. verso board. 31-May-4 Hamilton Osborne King, Dublin #177/R est:50000-70000
Works on paper
£1150 $1886 €1679 Dun Angus Fort, Aran (15x76cm-6x30in) s. mixed media. 4-Jun-3 John Ross, Belfast #32
£2098 $3566 €3000 Mother and child (53x43cm-21x17in) pencil. 18-Nov-3 Whyte's, Dublin #134/R est:1000-1500

O'NEILL, George Bernard (1828-1917) Irish
£1200 $2208 €1752 Children playing a garden beneath a spreading beech tree (14x10cm-6x4in) s. panel. 11-Jun-4 Keys, Aylsham #623/R est:1500-2000
£1800 $2844 €2610 Father's return (35x46cm-14x18in) indis sig. panel. 4-Sep-3 Christie's, Kensington #302/R est:2000-3000
£2600 $4108 €3770 Platter man (20x15cm-8x6in) s.d.1863 wood panel. 17-Nov-2 Desmond Judd, Cranbrook #801
£8000 $14320 €11680 Little angler (30x24cm-12x9in) s. 26-May-4 Sotheby's, Olympia #139/R est:5000-7000
£8500 $14450 €12410 Hide and seek (39x30cm-15x12in) s. panel. 19-Nov-3 Bonhams, New Bond Street #68/R est:6000-8000
£10000 $18400 €14600 Ill-prepared (33x39cm-13x15in) s. 23-Mar-4 Bonhams, New Bond Street #52/R est:10000-15000
£40000 $73600 €58400 Market day, the arrival of the hippodrome (84x137cm-33x54in) init. s.i.verso exhib.lit. 11-Jun-4 Christie's, London #136/R est:25000-35000

O'NEILL, George Bernard (attrib) (1828-1917) Irish
£850 $1530 €1241 Children playing in an interior (28x34cm-11x13in) panel. 22-Apr-4 Mellors & Kirk, Nottingham #1112

O'NEILL, Geraldine (20th C) Irish
£643 $1094 €920 Still life assorted cakes (41x33cm-16x13in) s.verso. 25-Nov-3 De Veres Art Auctions, Dublin #59/R est:900-1200
£1250 $2300 €1900 Rose wallpaper (57x77cm-22x30in) s.d.01 i.verso. 22-Jun-4 De Veres Art Auctions, Dublin #87a/R est:2000-3000
£2378 $4042 €3400 Studio still life (78x58cm-31x23in) s. 25-Nov-3 De Veres Art Auctions, Dublin #115/R est:1800-2200
£2933 $5309 €4400 Crowded table (76x56cm-30x22in) s. 30-Mar-4 De Veres Art Auctions, Dublin #9/R est:2000-3000

O'NEILL, Henry Nelson (1817-1880) British
£8500 $14450 €12410 Two extremes - the pre Raphaelite (48x39cm-19x15in) s.d.1856 exhib.lit. 25-Nov-3 Christie's, London #184/R est:8000-12000
Works on paper
£1879 $3364 €2800 Resting (16x12cm-6x5in) W/C htd white. 26-May-4 James Adam, Dublin #4/R est:2500-3500

O'NEILL, Liam (20th C) Irish
£3099 $5423 €4400 An Sherdan (76x102cm-30x40in) s. 16-Dec-3 James Adam, Dublin #216/R est:1000-1500

O'NEILL, Mark (1963-) Irish?
£694 $1132 €1000 Estuary at low tide (26x34cm-10x13in) s.d.1991 canvas board. 24-Sep-3 James Adam, Dublin #136/R est:1000-1500
£921 $1695 €1400 Male study (38x38cm-15x15in) s. board. 22-Jun-4 De Veres Art Auctions, Dublin #194/R
£1867 $3379 €2800 Denise, nude study (61x51cm-24x20in) s.d.2003 oil paper. 31-Mar-4 James Adam, Dublin #92/R est:3000-4000
£2533 $4585 €3800 Long summer shade (44x88cm-17x35in) s.d.2002 board. 31-Mar-4 James Adam, Dublin #93/R est:4000-5000
£2535 $4386 €3600 Italian connection (26x39cm-10x15in) s.d.1999 board exhib. 10-Dec-3 Bonhams & James Adam, Dublin #124/R est:2500-3500
£2685 $4805 €4000 Back garden light (30x42cm-12x17in) s.d.2001 board. 31-May-4 Hamilton Osborne King, Dublin #148/R est:4000-5000
£2685 $4805 €4000 Free range green (30x35cm-12x14in) s.d.2002 board. 31-May-4 Hamilton Osborne King, Dublin #149/R est:3000-4000
£2819 $4989 €4200 Sheep in a yard (56x79cm-22x31in) s.d.2001 board. 27-Apr-4 Whyte's, Dublin #60/R est:3500-4500
£2838 $5364 €4200 Bullock (41x51cm-16x20in) s.d.2002 board. 17-Feb-4 Whyte's, Dublin #238/R est:3000-4000
£2933 $5309 €4400 Little Piebald Blue (27x57cm-11x22in) s.d.1999 board prov. 30-Mar-4 De Veres Art Auctions, Dublin #28/R est:3000-4000
£3378 $6385 €5000 Feeding foal (46x64cm-18x25in) s.d.2001 board exhib. 17-Feb-4 Whyte's, Dublin #237/R est:4000-5000
£5503 $9741 €8200 Porter's Pride, interior, County Louth (64x76cm-25x30in) s.d.2002 board. 27-Apr-4 Whyte's, Dublin #241/R est:5000-7000
£6014 $10224 €8600 Peonie, interior of a country house in County Laois (51x76cm-20x30in) s.d.1995 canvas on board. 18-Nov-3 Whyte's, Dublin #48/R est:4000-5000
£6081 $11493 €9000 Tartan chair (94x48cm-37x19in) s.d.2001 board. 17-Feb-4 Whyte's, Dublin #186/R est:4000-5000

O'NEILL, Michael (20th C) Irish?
£671 $1201 €1000 Irises (60x40cm-24x16in) s. board. 31-May-4 Hamilton Osborne King, Dublin #50/R

O'NEILL, Niall (1952-) Irish
Sculpture
£1678 $2853 €2400 Viking (58cm-23in) st.mono. phosphor bronze black marble plinth. 18-Nov-3 Whyte's, Dublin #227/R est:2000-3000

O'NEILL, Rose (1875-1944) American
Works on paper
£1117 $2000 €1631 Kewpies and miss Susan (43x36cm-17x14in) s. pen ink. 15-May-4 Illustration House, New York #52/R est:2500-3500

O'NEILL, Terry (1938-) British
Photographs
£2600 $4420 €3796 Jean Shrimpton at a doll's hospital, London (50x41cm-20x16in) s. silver print card exec.1964 printed later. 19-Nov-3 Sotheby's, Olympia #231/R est:600-800

ONETTI, Luigi (1876-1968) Italian
£3972 $6633 €5600 Monferrato towards Pomaro (92x132cm-36x52in) s.d.1958 masonite. 20-Oct-3 Sant Agostino, Torino #311/R est:6000-8000

ONG BOON KONG (20th C) Taiwanese
Works on paper
£223 $400 €326 Tiger in a landscape (74x46cm-29x18in) W/C. 15-May-4 Jeffery Burchard, Florida #252
£251 $450 €366 Tiger taking a drink (135x74cm-53x29in) W/C. 15-May-4 Jeffery Burchard, Florida #251

ONG KIM SENG (1945-) Singaporean
Works on paper
£2083 $3479 €3041 Chinatown Scene (56x75cm-22x30in) s.d.80 W/C. 12-Oct-3 Sotheby's, Singapore #72/R est:3000-5000 (S.D 6000)

ONG, Jimmy (1964-) Singaporean
Works on paper
£2951 $4929 €4308 Loving couple (128x72cm-50x28in) s.d.2001 chl. 12-Oct-3 Sotheby's, Singapore #197/R est:8000-15000 (S.D 8500)
£3299 $5509 €4817 Figures (31x23cm-12x9in) chl nine. 12-Oct-3 Sotheby's, Singapore #198/R est:5000-7000 (S.D 9500)

ONGANIA, Umberto (19th C) Italian
Works on paper
£270 $486 €394 View of Venice waterfront (20x38cm-8x15in) W/C. 21-Apr-4 Brightwells, Leominster #677
£360 $601 €526 St. Marks Square, Venice (19x30cm-7x12in) s. W/C. 14-Oct-3 Bonhams, Knightsbridge #170/R
£380 $699 €555 Venice St Mark's Square with gondolas before (23x41cm-9x16in) s. W/C. 12-Jun-4 Dickins, Middle Claydon #24
£550 $1018 €803 View of the bridge of Sighs. View over the lagoon (17x29cm-7x11in) s. W/C pair. 9-Mar-4 Bonhams, Knightsbridge #23/R

ONGENAE, Joseph (1921-1993) Belgian
£933 $1708 €1400 Lampe a petrole sur une table (110x85cm-43x33in) mono.d.46 cardboard prov. 7-Jun-4 Palais de Beaux Arts, Brussels #140/R
£3129 $5601 €4600 Vedanta, no 1 (53x98cm-21x39in) s.verso panel. 17-Mar-4 De Zwann, Amsterdam #4750/R est:800-1200
£4710 $7725 €6500 Boogie woogie number 3 (100x70cm-39x28in) s.i.d.1962 verso board. 27-May-3 Sotheby's, Amsterdam #455/R est:3000-5000

ONGONIA, Umberto (19th C) Italian
Works on paper
£216 $400 €315 Gondola ride (41x28cm-16x11in) s. W/C. 13-Mar-4 Susanin's, Chicago #6197/R

ONI PINELL, Antonio (20th C) Spanish
£336 $594 €500 San Salvador (21x26cm-8x10in) s.d.1947 s.i.d.verso board. 27-Apr-4 Durán, Madrid #94/R

ONKEN, Karl (1846-1934) German
£280 $481 €400 Sailing boat by seashore (19x29cm-7x11in) s. canvas on board. 4-Dec-3 Dorotheum, Graz #26/R

ONLEY, Toni (1928-) Canadian
£379 $645 €553 Vargas Island (51x61cm-20x24in) s. board prov. 6-Nov-3 Heffel, Vancouver #92/R (C.D 850)
£405 $689 €591 Stranded (50x65cm-20x26in) s. i.d.1972 verso board prov. 27-Nov-3 Heffel, Vancouver #172 (C.D 900)
£679 $1133 €991 White cloud (50x64cm-20x25in) s.i. acrylic on panel. 17-Nov-3 Hodgins, Calgary #83/R est:1750-2250 (C.D 1500)
£811 $1378 €1184 Rain squall, Harrison Lake, BC (76x102cm-30x40in) s.d.1982. 19-Nov-3 Maynards, Vancouver #69 est:1500-1800 (C.D 1800)
£813 $1455 €1187 Cumulus nimbus (50x63cm-20x25in) s. i.d.1974 verso panel prov. 6-May-4 Heffel, Vancouver #106/R est:1500-2500 (C.D 2000)
£930 $1692 €1358 Boundary Pass from East Point, Saturna Island BC (20x24cm-8x9in) s.i.d.1980 board. 5-Feb-4 Heffel, Vancouver #56/R est:1000-1500 (C.D 2250)
£982 $1689 €1434 Glacial boulders, Savary island B C (75x100cm-30x39in) s. 2-Dec-3 Joyner Waddington, Toronto #41/R est:2500-3000 (C.D 2200)
£1161 $1996 €1695 Mount Baker across Juan de Fuca Strait (75x100cm-30x39in) s.d.1984. 2-Dec-3 Joyner Waddington, Toronto #8/R est:2500-3000 (C.D 2600)
Works on paper
£244 $455 €356 Lodi Tombs, Delhi (30x39cm-12x15in) s.i.d.December 30 1982 W/C. 2-Mar-4 Ritchie, Toronto #153/R (C.D 610)
£248 $421 €362 Old Farm, Yoshino-Hama Shodo Shimo, Japan (29x38cm-11x15in) s.indis.d. W/C prov. 23-Nov-3 Levis, Calgary #527/R (C.D 550)
£402 $683 €587 Macdonald Peak, Chilliwack Lake, BC (29x39cm-11x15in) s.i.d.1981 W/C. 6-Nov-3 Heffel, Vancouver #91/R (C.D 900)
£491 $845 €717 Bald Mountain B C (27x36cm-11x14in) s.i. 2-Dec-3 Joyner Waddington, Toronto #471 (C.D 1100)

ONNES, Harm Henrick Kamerlingh (1893-1985) Dutch
£486 $768 €700 Portrait of Jonkvrouwe de Brauw (63x56cm-25x22in) mono.d.46. 2-Sep-3 Christie's, Amsterdam #411
£600 $1074 €900 Little house at Terschelling (26x35cm-10x14in) mono.d.71. 11-May-4 Vendu Notarishuis, Rotterdam #129
£694 $1097 €1000 In the cafe (38x32cm-15x13in) mono. board. 2-Sep-3 Christie's, Amsterdam #402/R est:1200-1600
£1319 $2085 €1900 Rocking-horse (50x38cm-20x15in) mono.d.73 board. 2-Sep-3 Christie's, Amsterdam #433/R est:1500-2000
£1469 $2526 €2100 View of window from garden (58x45cm-23x18in) s.d.70 exhib. 4-Dec-3 Vendue Huis, Gravenhage #1033
£1469 $2526 €2100 View of window from garden (58x45cm-23x18in) s.d.70 prov.exhib. 3-Dec-3 Auction Maastricht #1033/R est:2000-2500
£1645 $3026 €2500 Garden picture (37x27cm-15x11in) mono.d.46 s.i.verso plywood prov. 22-Jun-4 Christie's, Amsterdam #605/R est:2500-3500
£2029 $3328 €2800 Villa in The Hague (35x51cm-14x20in) s.d.39 canvas on board prov. 27-May-3 Sotheby's, Amsterdam #340/R est:3000-5000
£2378 $4090 €3400 Doing business on the sea (38x49cm-15x19in) s.d.1970 board. 8-Dec-3 Glerum, Amsterdam #347/R est:2000-2500
£2536 $4159 €3500 Small barn (30x45cm-12x18in) s.d.42 board. 27-May-3 Sotheby's, Amsterdam #341/R est:2500-3500
£2639 $4169 €3800 Spider in the flower garden (57x70cm-22x28in) mono.d.78. 2-Sep-3 Christie's, Amsterdam #425/R est:1000-1500
£2800 $5124 €4200 Shelter (27x33cm-11x13in) init.d.78 board prov. 7-Jun-4 Glerum, Amsterdam #13/R est:2500-3500
£3333 $5467 €4600 The station (25x40cm-10x16in) s.d.44 panel. 27-May-3 Sotheby's, Amsterdam #338/R est:3000-5000
£4452 $7568 €6500 Stage performance (44x52cm-17x20in) mono.d.67. 5-Nov-3 Vendue Huis, Gravenhage #469/R est:5000-7000
£5000 $9200 €7500 Regen - rain (36x47cm-14x19in) mono.d.16 s.i.verso. 9-Jun-4 Christie's, Amsterdam #215/R est:6000-8000
Works on paper
£350 $601 €500 Restaurant in Voorschoten (22x29cm-9x11in) s.d.1970 W/C. 8-Dec-3 Glerum, Amsterdam #340/R
£1042 $1646 €1500 Pas op, mijn kopje thee! (21x14cm-8x6in) mono.d.80 W/C felt tip ballpoint. 2-Sep-3 Christie's, Amsterdam #409a est:500-700
£1389 $2194 €2000 In the rain. Strolling family (21x30cm-8x12in) mono.d.80 black chk col crayons W/C pen two. 2-Sep-3 Christie's, Amsterdam #407 est:1000-1500
£2083 $3292 €3000 Enjoying retirement. Woman drinking tea (20x29cm-8x11in) W/C pencil two. 2-Sep-3 Christie's, Amsterdam #409/R est:1000-1500
£4082 $7429 €6000 At the Karel Appel exhibition in Museum Boymans van Beuningen (24x23cm-9x9in) mono.d.82 pencil W/C sold with 16 others by same hand prov. 3-Feb-4 Christie's, Amsterdam #634/R est:700-900

ONNES, Menso Kamerlingh (1860-1925) Dutch
£5903 $9326 €8500 Blooming hawthorn tree (52x69cm-20x27in) bears sig prov.exhib.lit. 2-Sep-3 Christie's, Amsterdam #231/R est:3000-5000
Works on paper
£680 $1238 €1000 Blue irises in a glass vase (59x40cm-23x16in) s. pencil W/C htd white. 3-Feb-4 Christie's, Amsterdam #155 est:600-800

ONOFRI, Crescenzio (circle) (1632-1698) Italian
£5114 $9000 €7466 Extensive landscape with figures in the foreground (114x84cm-45x33in) 18-May-4 Bonhams & Butterfields, San Francisco #10/R est:6000-8000

ONSAGER, Soren (1878-1946) Norwegian
£1387 $2482 €2025 Court yard in the south (69x62cm-27x24in) s. 25-May-4 Grev Wedels Plass, Oslo #73/R est:20000-30000 (N.KR 17000)
£3263 $5840 €4764 Portrait of girl. Wooded landscape with snow (72x51cm-28x20in) s. double-sided. 25-May-4 Grev Wedels Plass, Oslo #72/R est:20000-30000 (N.KR 40000)

ONSLOW-FORD, Edward (1852-1901) British
Sculpture
£5800 $10672 €8468 Linos (77cm-30in) s. brown pat. bronze prov.lit. 11-Jun-4 Christie's, London #79/R est:5000-8000

ONSLOW-FORD, Gordon (1912-2003) British
£11173 $20000 €16313 Travellers (91x76cm-36x30in) s.i.d.3-75 verso acrylic prov. 13-May-4 Sotheby's, New York #128/R est:20000-30000
£18644 $33000 €27220 Untitled (81x127cm-32x50in) s.d.1959-50 verso Parles paint prov. 2-May-4 Bonhams & Butterfields, Los Angeles #3085/R est:10000-15000
Works on paper
£647 $1100 €945 Untitled (38x30cm-15x12in) s.d.1959 gouache W/C. 9-Nov-3 Wright, Chicago #302 est:300-500

ONSTAD, Albert Bernhard (1895-1981) Swedish
£566 $963 €826 The pink carnation (45x34cm-18x13in) s.d.23. 5-Nov-3 AB Stockholms Auktionsverk #679/R (S.KR 7500)
£604 $1027 €882 The pink houses, Stockholm (41x33cm-16x13in) s.d.1919 verso. 5-Nov-3 AB Stockholms Auktionsverk #680/R (S.KR 8000)
£718 $1220 €1048 Demi-monde (40x32cm-16x13in) init. 5-Nov-3 AB Stockholms Auktionsverk #678/R (S.KR 9500)

ONTANI, Luigi (1943-) Italian
Photographs
£3893 $6968 €5800 Fishermen (30x21cm-12x8in) s.i.verso col photograph exec.1998. 28-May-4 Farsetti, Prato #243/R est:5000-6000
Works on paper
£1448 $2317 €2100 Always standing (48x36cm-19x14in) s.i.verso Indian ink W/C exec 1994 prov. 13-Mar-3 Galleria Pace, Milan #62/R est:2800-3600
£2215 $3964 €3300 Mountain cricket (48x36cm-19x14in) s.i.d.1999 Chinese ink W/C. 28-May-4 Farsetti, Prato #64/R est:1700-2200
£3378 $5946 €5000 Framed wishes (130x92cm-51x36in) s.i.d.86 verso ink W/C. 24-May-4 Christie's, Milan #145/R est:5000-7000
£3623 $5942 €5000 Atlas (25cm-10in circular) s.verso W/C Chinese ink. 27-May-3 Sotheby's, Milan #109 est:1300-1800
£4196 $7133 €6000 Saint Christophorus' treasure (109x67cm-43x26in) s.i.verso W/C exhib. 25-Nov-3 Sotheby's, Milan #150/R est:5000-6000
£11224 $20092 €16500 Prestantin (233x149cm-92x59in) s.i.d.89 W/C Chinese ink. 16-Mar-4 Finarte Semenzato, Milan #463/R est:12000
£12752 $22826 €19000 Tip, Tap, Top (130cm-51in circular) s.i.d.1999 verso Chinese ink W/C lit. 28-May-4 Farsetti, Prato #361/R est:7800-8800
£13043 $21391 €18000 Bertoldo, Bertoldino e Cacasenno (50x50cm-20x20in) s. Chinese ink W/C exec.1982 in 10 parts prov.exhib. 27-May-3 Sotheby's, Milan #207/R est:20000-30000

ONUS, Lin (1948-1996) Australian
£3512 $6498 €5128 Reflective pool (40x51cm-16x20in) s. canvas on board. 10-Mar-4 Deutscher-Menzies, Melbourne #119/R est:9000-14000 (A.D 8500)
Works on paper
£5410 $8548 €7899 Goannas and eucalyptus trunks (49x37cm-19x15in) s. synthetic polymer board. 2-Sep-3 Deutscher-Menzies, Melbourne #141/R est:6000-9000 (A.D 13200)
£21875 $40906 €32813 Nininyi guyi, little fish (51x167cm-20x66in) synthetic polymer paint canvas prov.exhib. 26-Jul-4 Sotheby's, Melbourne #138/R est:40000-60000 (A.D 56000)
£24390 $38537 €35366 Frogs on waterlillies (91x122cm-36x48in) s. synthetic polymer paint canvas prov. 28-Jul-3 Sotheby's, Paddington #194/R est:35000-50000 (A.D 60000)

£59574 $101277 €86978 Yorta Yorta language group Reflections, Barmah Forest (182x182cm-72x72in) s. synthetic polymer paint canvas exec 1996 prov. 26-Nov-3 Deutscher-Menzies, Melbourne #26/R est:80000-100000 (A.D 140000)
£59574 $101277 €86978 Yorta Yorta Language group - Dawn at Barmah Forest (182x182cm-72x72in) s. s.i.stretcher verso synthetic polymer paint exec 1996 prov. 26-Nov-3 Deutscher-Menzies, Melbourne #27/R est:80000-100000 (A.D 140000)

OOMS, Karel (1845-1900) Belgian
£4861 $8264 €7000 Last Meal (101x165cm-40x65in) s.i.d.1873. 28-Oct-3 Christie's, Amsterdam #54/R est:6000-8000

OONARK, Jessie (1906-1985) North American
Prints
£3153 $5360 €4603 Tattooed faces (57x28cm-22x11in) num.24/50 stonecut. 3-Nov-3 Waddingtons, Toronto #277/R est:2500-3500 (C.D 7000)
Works on paper
£495 $842 €723 Young woman (33x51cm-13x20in) stencil. 3-Nov-3 Waddingtons, Toronto #303/R (C.D 1100)
£1577 $2680 €2302 Kudloopudooaluk (56x75cm-22x30in) stencil. 3-Nov-3 Waddingtons, Toronto #537/R est:700-1000 (C.D 3500)

OORSCHOT, Dorus van (1910-1989) Dutch
£685 $1164 €1000 Roses in white vase (78x58cm-31x23in) s. 5-Nov-3 Vendue Huis, Gravenhage #306/R

OOST, Jacques van (17th C) Belgian
£22535 $39437 €32000 Portrait de gentilhomme au manteau rouge (64x79cm-25x31in) s.d.1666. 18-Dec-3 Tajan, Paris #32/R est:25000-30000
£165000 $297000 €240900 Interior with soldiers cheating at cards (58x97cm-23x38in) s.d.1634 prov.lit. 22-Apr-4 Sotheby's, London #30/R est:50000-70000

OOST, Jacques van (elder-attrib) (1601-1671) Belgian
£5379 $9952 €7800 Portrait de Jacob van Oost la jeune (19x14cm-7x6in) panel. 13-Jan-4 Vanderkindere, Brussels #40 est:2500-4000

OOSTEN, Izaack van (1613-1661) Flemish
£4027 $7208 €6000 Personnages et betail dans un paysage avec chateau (26x35cm-10x14in) panel. 25-May-4 Palais de Beaux Arts, Brussels #92/R est:8000-12000
£28169 $46761 €40000 Paysage flamand avec une route passant pres d'un petit chateau (27x36cm-11x14in) mono. panel. 13-Jun-3 Ferri, Paris #59/R est:40000-45000

OOSTEN, Izaack van (attrib) (1613-1661) Flemish
£7000 $12110 €10220 Country house with elegant company playing music and cavorting (99x111cm-39x44in) 12-Dec-3 Christie's, Kensington #71/R est:6000-8000

OOSTENGA, Thomas Teekes (1812-1865) Dutch
£780 $1303 €1100 Visitor to the poulterer (42x37cm-17x15in) s. panel. 20-Oct-3 Glerum, Amsterdam #35/R

OOSTERLYNCK, Jean (1915-1995) Belgian
£940 $1738 €1400 Portrait with birds (100x80cm-39x31in) s.d.76. 13-Mar-4 De Vuyst, Lokeren #250
£1000 $1790 €1500 Composition with figures (72x80cm-28x31in) s.d.77. 15-May-4 De Vuyst, Lokeren #239/R est:1500-1700

OOSTERWYCK, Maria van (1630-1693) Dutch
£17000 $29410 €24820 Poppy, a snowball, pinks and yellow roses and other flowers, and insects (40x32cm-16x13in) s. panel prov. 10-Dec-3 Christie's, London #33/R est:20000-30000

OPALKA, Roman (1931-) Polish
£3172 $5298 €4600 Abstract (100x70cm-39x28in) s.d.59. 16-Nov-3 Agra, Warsaw #33/R est:2000
£4167 $7167 €6084 Composition (229x59cm-90x23in) s.i. exec.1984. 4-Dec-3 Agra, Warsaw #5/R est:12000 (P.Z 28000)
£65000 $119600 €94900 1965/1 Detail 407817-434714 (194x135cm-76x53in) acrylic prov.exhib. 24-Jun-4 Sotheby's, London #143/R est:25000-35000
£81006 $145000 €118269 OPALKA 1965 1-8, 1044019-1063435, DETAIL (196x143cm-77x56in) s.i.d.1965 verso prov.exhib. 14-May-4 Phillips, New York #255/R est:50000-70000
Works on paper
£282 $511 €412 Mother and child (100x73cm-39x29in) s.d.1953 chl. 4-Apr-4 Agra, Warsaw #6/R (P.Z 2000)
£623 $1116 €910 Composition (64x50cm-25x20in) mixed media exec.1970. 6-May-4 Agra, Warsaw #8/R (P.Z 4400)
£664 $1202 €969 Self-portrait (127x100cm-50x39in) s.d.1954 gouache. 4-Apr-4 Agra, Warsaw #30/R (P.Z 4700)
£34637 $62000 €50570 Various (33x24cm-13x9in) ink five prov. 14-May-4 Phillips, New York #254/R est:10000-15000

OPDAHL, Ornulf (1944-) Norwegian
£852 $1363 €1235 Glazier 2000 (30x30cm-12x12in) s. 22-Sep-3 Blomqvist, Lysaker #1235/R (N.KR 10000)
£976 $1785 €1425 The mountain Sula (27x53cm-11x21in) s. s.i.d.1996 verso. 7-Jun-4 Blomqvist, Oslo #458/R (N.KR 12000)
£1022 $1758 €1492 Study (24x27cm-9x11in) s.i.d.99 verso sold with smaller landscape. 8-Dec-3 Blomqvist, Oslo #560/R (N.KR 12000)
£1793 $2995 €2618 Composition (91x100cm-36x39in) S.D.1974. 13-Oct-3 Blomqvist, Oslo #341/R est:18000-22000 (N.KR 21000)
£1951 $3571 €2848 Coastal landscape (50x50cm-20x20in) s.d.1997 i.verso exhib.lit. 7-Jun-4 Blomqvist, Oslo #454/R est:20000-25000 (N.KR 24000)
£2470 $4249 €3606 Distant mountains (61x65cm-24x26in) s.i.d.1997 verso. 8-Dec-3 Blomqvist, Oslo #566/R est:20000-30000 (N.KR 29000)
£3181 $5694 €4644 Sarcophagus (70x90cm-28x35in) s.d.77 i.stretcher. 25-May-4 Grev Wedels Plass, Oslo #119/R est:30000-40000 (N.KR 39000)
Works on paper
£413 $665 €603 Flowers and butterflies (38x31cm-15x12in) s. mixed media. 25-Aug-3 Blomqvist, Lysaker #1211/R (N.KR 4800)
£413 $665 €603 Butterflies (32x39cm-13x15in) s. gouache panel. 25-Aug-3 Blomqvist, Lysaker #1212/R (N.KR 4800)

OPDENHOFF, George Willem (1807-1873) Dutch
£2128 $3553 €3000 Fishing boats in the harbour mouth (22x32cm-9x13in) panel. 20-Oct-3 Glerum, Amsterdam #26/R est:2500-3000
£3200 $5760 €4800 Sailing vessels in choppy water (43x63cm-17x25in) s. 20-Apr-4 Sotheby's, Amsterdam #33/R est:4000-6000
£3448 $5517 €5000 Rowboat and ships (48x68cm-19x27in) s. 12-Mar-3 Auction Maastricht #1124
£4082 $7429 €6000 Shipping activity in a river estuary (71x98cm-28x39in) with sig. 3-Feb-4 Christie's, Amsterdam #89/R est:6000-8000
£4667 $8400 €7000 Shipping in an estuary (17x23cm-7x9in) s. panel. 20-Apr-4 Sotheby's, Amsterdam #45/R est:4000-6000
£4667 $8447 €7000 Shipwreck in stormy sea (67x92cm-26x36in) s. 1-Apr-4 Van Ham, Cologne #1590/R est:8000
£7333 $13200 €11000 Unloading the catch (70x98cm-28x39in) s. 21-Apr-4 Christie's, Amsterdam #67/R est:8000-12000
£7333 $13200 €11000 A calm, busy day near a coast (36x53cm-14x21in) s. panel. 21-Apr-4 Christie's, Amsterdam #212/R est:8000-12000
£9333 $16800 €14000 French coastal scene with fishermen working at dusk (71x97cm-28x38in) s.d.1863. 21-Apr-4 Christie's, Amsterdam #32/R est:7000-9000
£10417 $16979 €15000 Fishing boats and sailing ship off Dutch beach (85x118cm-33x46in) s. 26-Sep-3 Bolland & Marotz, Bremen #588/R est:5500
£12162 $21405 €18000 Ships off coast in calm seas. Storm off the coast (47x67cm-19x26in) s. two prov. 22-May-4 Lempertz, Koln #1576/R est:12000-15000
£12925 $23136 €19000 Marine (71x98cm-28x39in) s. 17-Mar-4 Hotel des Ventes Mosan, Brussels #101 est:12000-15000
£15172 $28069 €22000 Depart des pecheurs au lever du soleil. Le retour des pecheurs au coucher du soleil (70x97cm-28x38in) both s. one d.1863 pair. 19-Jan-4 Horta, Bruxelles #109/R est:13000-15000

OPHEY, Walter (1882-1930) German
£2333 $4177 €3500 Landscape (51x64cm-20x25in) s. lit. 15-May-4 Van Ham, Cologne #816/R est:2800
Works on paper
£333 $597 €500 Still life with pot plant (30x44cm-12x17in) s. col chk prov. 13-May-4 Neumeister, Munich #448/R

OPHIR, Gilad (1957-) Israeli
Photographs
£3073 $5500 €4487 Shooting targets, Necropolis series (120x150cm-47x59in) s.d.1997 num.3/5 silver print. 18-Mar-4 Sotheby's, New York #79/R est:3000-5000

OPIE, Edward (1810-1894) British
£3000 $5010 €4380 Portrait of the Baxter brothers of Bedford with their dog (119x94cm-47x37in) s.d.1866. 13-Nov-3 Christie's, Kensington #47/R est:3000-5000

OPIE, J (1761-1807) British
£3618 $6658 €5500 Portrait of Ladu Stanhope wearing gold necklace over a lace blouse (75x62cm-30x24in) 22-Jun-4 Mealy's, Castlecomer #372/R est:2800-3500

OPIE, John (1761-1807) British
£1100 $1749 €1606 Harriet Wright of Mapperley (75x62cm-30x24in) i. 9-Sep-3 Bamfords, Derby #1143/R
£4200 $7770 €6132 Portrait of a gentleman, possibly the artist himself (57x47cm-22x19in) 13-Jan-4 Bonhams, Knightsbridge #97/R est:1800-2500
£7200 $13248 €10512 Shepherd boy (126x95cm-50x37in) exhib. 26-Mar-4 Sotheby's, London #27/R est:5000-7000
£8200 $13038 €11890 Portrait of Colonel John Henderson (76x63cm-30x25in) s.i. 9-Sep-3 Sworder & Son, Bishops Stortford #405/R est:4000-6000

OPIE, John (attrib) (1761-1807) British
£420 $777 €613 Portrait of the Rev Frederick Barnwell (74x61cm-29x24in) 14-Jan-4 Lawrence, Crewkerne #1388/R
£900 $1674 €1314 Adoration of the Magi (46x57cm-18x22in) with sig.i.d.1795. 4-Mar-4 Christie's, Kensington #577/R
£7000 $12600 €10220 Portrait of a young lady seated, wearing a cream dress (76x63cm-30x25in) 21-Apr-4 Tennants, Leyburn #1095/R est:3000-5000
Works on paper
£2517 $4505 €3700 La boutique du chausseur (26x22cm-10x9in) W/C pen black ink. 19-Mar-4 Piasa, Paris #108/R est:2000-2500

OPIE, John (studio) (1761-1807) British
£5500 $9350 €8030 Portrait of the Hon Charles James Foc (125x99cm-49x39in) 27-Nov-3 Sotheby's, London #162/R est:6000-8000

OPIE, Julian (1958-) British
£45000 $82800 €65700 Kate Moss (193x151cm-76x59in) acrylic stretched vinyl painted 2001 prov. 24-Jun-4 Sotheby's, London #122/R est:10000-15000
Photographs
£1739 $3200 €2539 Veronique, state agent nr 3 (89x70cm-35x28in) s.verso c-print wood prov. 10-Jun-4 Phillips, New York #547/R est:2000-3000
£1902 $3500 €2777 Francois, schoolboy (89x70cm-35x28in) s.verso c-print wood prov. 10-Jun-4 Phillips, New York #537/R est:2000-3000
£2337 $4300 €3412 Maho, gallery director no 2 (89x70cm-35x28in) s.verso c-print wood prov. 10-Jun-4 Phillips, New York #545/R est:2000-3000
£2446 $4500 €3571 Fiona, artist nr 4 (89x70cm-35x28in) s.verso c-print wood prov. 10-Jun-4 Phillips, New York #353/R est:2000-3000

Sculpture
£2000 $3620 €2920 In the study (140x105x61cm-55x41x24in) painted metal installation executed 1984. 1-Apr-4 Christie's, Kensington #303/R est:2000-3000

OPISSO, Alfredo (1907-1980) Spanish
£780 $1303 €1100 Flowers (92x73cm-36x29in) s. 20-Oct-3 Durán, Madrid #50/R
Works on paper
£789 $1429 €1200 Market (31x24cm-12x9in) s.d.1967 pastel. 14-Apr-4 Ansorena, Madrid #399/R

OPISSO, Ricardo (1880-1966) Spanish
Works on paper
£738 $1321 €1100 Conversation (21x26cm-8x10in) s. ink dr. 25-May-4 Durán, Madrid #130/R
£872 $1562 €1300 Woman at piano (38x27cm-15x11in) s. ink dr. 25-May-4 Durán, Madrid #125/R
£1831 $2930 €2600 Toulouse-Lautrec with a lady in a bar (45x33cm-18x13in) s. col crayon dr prov. 16-Sep-3 Segre, Madrid #107/R est:2000
£2759 $4966 €4000 Scene with women (16x22cm-6x9in) s.d.1900 dr set of 6. 26-Jan-4 Durán, Madrid #154/R est:4000

OPITZ, Franz Karl (1916-1998) Swiss
£371 $683 €542 Magliasina waterfall near Curio (60x50cm-24x20in) s.d. i. verso board. 14-Jun-4 Philippe Schuler, Zurich #4230 (S.FR 850)
£385 $654 €562 On the Thur (33x45cm-13x18in) s.d.41. 19-Nov-3 Fischer, Luzern #2238/R (S.FR 850)
£390 $697 €569 Early spring landscape (50x73cm-20x29in) s.d. 22-Mar-4 Philippe Schuler, Zurich #4351 (S.FR 900)

OPITZ, Georg Emanuel (1775-1841) German
Works on paper
£900 $1665 €1314 The witches celebration (29x34cm-11x13in) s. pen ink W/C. 9-Mar-4 Bonhams, New Bond Street #15/R
£967 $1750 €1450 Officers receiving two elegant women at camp (35x27cm-14x11in) W/C Indian ink. 2-Apr-4 Winterberg, Heidelberg #501/R
£5500 $9845 €8030 Tending to the horse (24x28cm-9x11in) s. W/C over pencil. 26-May-4 Sotheby's, London #5/R est:3000-5000

OPITZ, Georg Emanuel (attrib) (1775-1841) German
Works on paper
£550 $935 €803 Interesting market stall (38x30cm-15x12in) s. W/C sold with unsigned companion. 1-Dec-3 Bonhams, Bath #84/R

OPPEL, Lisel (1897-1960) German
£604 $1111 €900 Aster bouquet (48x25cm-19x10in) s.d.1947 canvas on board. 26-Mar-4 Bolland & Marotz, Bremen #364/R

OPPENHEIM, Alfred Nathaniel (1873-1953) German
£1867 $3416 €2800 At the mill stream, Unterfranken (45x66cm-18x26in) mono.d.1905 i.verso. 5-Jun-4 Arnold, Frankfurt #689/R est:800

OPPENHEIM, Dennis (1938-) American
£1944 $3500 €2838 Project detail intervention for university of Alaska (39x50cm-15x20in) s.d.1983 oil chl paper. 24-Apr-4 David Rago, Lambertville #391/R est:2000-4000
£2797 $4755 €4000 Proposal for kitchen table (97x127cm-38x50in) s.d.1981 acrylic col ck pencil board prov. 26-Nov-3 Dorotheum, Vienna #297/R est:4000-6000
£5000 $9100 €7300 Polarities (75x101cm-30x40in) s.d.1972 paper photographic collage on board. 4-Feb-4 Sotheby's, Olympia #12/R est:1500-2000
Photographs
£5500 $10010 €8030 Wishing the mountains madness (152x180cm-60x71in) s.d.1977 col photo printed map text on board four parts. 4-Feb-4 Sotheby's, Olympia #14/R est:3000-4000
Sculpture
£5000 $9100 €7300 Untitled (51x51x51cm-20x20x20in) s.d.1963 base painted metal. 4-Feb-4 Sotheby's, Olympia #168/R est:2500-3500
Works on paper
£405 $700 €591 Saturn up-draft, project for ARC Paris (97x77cm-38x30in) graphite prov. 10-Dec-3 Phillips, New York #461/R
£725 $1188 €1000 A way station for launching an obsolete power, project for PSI, NYC (98x127cm-39x50in) s.i.d.1979 ink pastel. 27-May-3 Sotheby's, Amsterdam #576/R
£1389 $2320 €2000 Launching structure no. 12 (95x125cm-37x49in) s.i.d.1981 mixed media paper prov. 21-Oct-3 Artcurial Briest, Paris #634a/R est:1500-2000
£3243 $6000 €4735 Study for Upper cut (206x264cm-81x104in) s.d.1992 col pencil oil wash four sheets paper prov. 12-Feb-4 Sotheby's, New York #345/R est:4000-6000
£4200 $7728 €6132 Star skid (41x238cm-16x94in) s.d.1977 mixed media col photos map board 3 parts prov. 24-Jun-4 Sotheby's, Olympia #465/R est:2000-3000
£5000 $9100 €7300 Annual rings (101x76cm-40x30in) s.d.1968 paper collage on board. 4-Feb-4 Sotheby's, Olympia #13/R est:1500-2000
£5800 $10672 €8468 Poison (240x98cm-94x39in) s.d.1977 mixed media photos maps board 10 parts sold with photos. 24-Jun-4 Sotheby's, Olympia #464/R est:3000-4000
£7000 $11690 €10220 Study for cutting tools, two electric drill, saw blades, masks (127x97cm-50x38in) s.i.d.1989 pastel chl silver paint prov. 22-Oct-3 Christie's, London #84/R est:4000-6000
£7500 $13650 €10950 Indirect hit/crossfire (151x101cm-59x40in) s.d.1974 gouache felt tip pen col photos collage card prov. 6-Feb-4 Sotheby's, London #124/R est:3000-4000
£8000 $14720 €11680 Time line, USA/Canada (101x75cm-40x30in) s.d.1968 mixed media collage offset lithograph map board prov. 24-Jun-4 Sotheby's, Olympia #470/R est:4000-5000

OPPENHEIM, Guido (1862-1942) Luxembourger
£1316 $2421 €2000 Stream in the woods (65x91cm-26x36in) s. 22-Jun-4 Palais de Beaux Arts, Brussels #76/R est:500-700

OPPENHEIM, Meret (1913-1986) Swiss
£5240 $9537 €7650 Winter landscape (34x48cm-13x19in) mono.d.49 board. 17-Jun-4 Kornfeld, Bern #645/R est:10000 (S.FR 12000)
£15934 $29000 €23264 Grosser bewolkter himmel uber kontinenten - cloudy sky over the Continents (110x210cm-43x83in) init.d.64 init.d.verso exhib. 29-Jun-4 Sotheby's, New York #449/R est:15000-20000
Works on paper
£229 $411 €334 Man walking left (30x21cm-12x8in) s.i.d. mixed media lit. 22-Mar-4 Philippe Schuler, Zurich #4203 (S.FR 530)
£1293 $2315 €1888 Oiseau preliminaire (42x59cm-17x23in) mono.d.54 W/C chk. 14-May-4 Dobiaschofsky, Bern #274/R est:3800 (S.FR 3000)
£1674 $2846 €2444 Figure humaine (20x20cm-8x8in) s.d.1970 s.i.verso collage spraypaint. 22-Nov-3 Burkhard, Luzern #32/R est:2000-2500 (S.FR 3700)
£1810 $3023 €2643 Diana on magpie hunt (20x29cm-8x11in) s.d.1939 gouache prov.lit. 24-Jun-3 Germann, Zurich #150/R est:4000-5000 (S.FR 4000)
£4587 $7661 €6651 Sun on beach with eggs (23x30cm-9x12in) gouache col chks. 19-Jun-3 Kornfeld, Bern #799 est:10000 (S.FR 10000)

OPPENHEIM, Moritz Daniel (1800-1882) German
£1038 $1900 €1515 Landscape (28x21cm-11x8in) estate st.verso oil paper on cardboard prov. 1-Feb-4 Ben-Ami, Tel Aviv #4655/R est:1500-2000
Works on paper
£782 $1400 €1142 Jewish girl (14x9cm-6x4in) pencil. 18-Mar-4 Sotheby's, New York #251/R est:2000-3000
£1536 $2750 €2243 New Judaism (22x17cm-9x7in) pencil ink. 18-Mar-4 Sotheby's, New York #252/R est:2000-3000

OPPENHEIM, Ville (20th C) ?
£753 $1279 €1099 Interior scene with gentleman reading (97x85cm-38x33in) mono.d.15. 29-Nov-3 Rasmussen, Havnen #4433 (D.KR 8000)

OPPENHEIM, Yves (1948-) French
£3169 $5546 €4500 Paysage no 18 (200x150cm-79x59in) exhib. 18-Dec-3 Cornette de St.Cyr, Paris #143/R est:5000-6000
Works on paper
£704 $1232 €1000 Paysages (100x113cm-39x44in) crayon exhib. 18-Dec-3 Cornette de St.Cyr, Paris #144/R

OPPENHEIMER, Charles (1875-1961) British
Works on paper
£500 $800 €730 River landscape (39x59cm-15x23in) s. W/C. 18-Sep-3 Bonhams, Edinburgh #360

OPPENHEIMER, Joel (20th C) American
£232 $425 €348 Homage to El Greco (86x127cm-34x50in) 10-Jul-4 Hindman, Chicago #388/R

OPPENHEIMER, Josef (1876-1966) German
£1256 $2249 €1834 Portrait of woman (49x40cm-19x16in) s.d.1901. 26-May-4 AB Stockholms Auktionsverk #2457/R est:25000-30000 (S.KR 17000)
£2200 $3938 €3212 Still life of flowers (69x57cm-27x22in) s.d.28. 16-Mar-4 Bonhams, New Bond Street #28/R est:1000-1500
£2800 $5012 €4088 Portrait of a lady, in a hat (69x56cm-27x22in) s. 16-Mar-4 Bonhams, New Bond Street #27/R est:2000-3000

OPPENHEIMER, Max (1885-1954) Austrian
£9790 $16643 €14000 Daily life: ashtray (21x24cm-8x9in) s. lit. 25-Nov-3 Hassfurther, Vienna #61/R est:10000-12000
£12081 $21383 €18000 Still life with radishes (32x45cm-13x18in) s. exhib.lit. 28-Apr-4 Wiener Kunst Auktionen, Vienna #115/R est:18000-28000
£58000 $96860 €84680 Vienna string quartet (74x98cm-29x39in) s. board. 22-Oct-3 Bonhams, New Bond Street #34/R est:20000-30000
£65000 $119600 €94900 Quartet (71x97cm-28x38in) s.d.1939 prov. 24-Mar-4 Sotheby's, Olympia #56/R est:10000-15000
£67114 $118792 €100000 Violin, hands, notes (40x81cm-16x32in) s. lit. 28-Apr-4 Wiener Kunst Auktionen, Vienna #116/R est:70000-140000

OPPENOORTH, Willem (1847-1905) Dutch
£329 $595 €500 Soir d'ete sur la riviere (71x100cm-28x39in) s. 19-Apr-4 Glerum, Amsterdam #224/R
Works on paper
£471 $800 €688 Farm landscape (53x38cm-21x15in) s. W/C. 22-Nov-3 Jackson's, Cedar Falls #15/R

OPPERMANN, Wolfgang (20th C) German
Works on paper
£385 $654 €550 Animal motor sport (64x84cm-25x33in) s.d.1980 W/C pastel. 29-Nov-3 Arnold, Frankfurt #409/R

OPPI, Ubaldo (1889-1942) Italian
£45638 $81691 €68000 Armer's son (127x93cm-50x37in) s.d.1925 prov.exhib.lit. 25-May-4 Sotheby's, Milan #240/R est:55000-65000
Works on paper
£662 $1205 €1000 Portrait of man (47x37cm-19x15in) sanguine. 17-Jun-4 Galleria Pananti, Florence #486/R
£933 $1717 €1400 Head of boy (20x17cm-8x7in) s.d.1914 Chinese ink lit. 8-Jun-4 Finarte Semenzato, Milan #204/R est:1200-1400
£1689 $2973 €2500 View of mountain (50x40cm-20x16in) graphite. 22-May-4 Galleria Pananti, Florence #329/R est:2500-3000

OPPLER, Ernst (1867-1929) German
£336 $608 €491 Women outside a building (80x64cm-31x25in) s. 30-Mar-4 Stephan Welz, Johannesburg #413 est:4000-6000 (SA.R 4000)

OPPO, Cipriano Efisio (1891-1962) Italian
£13986 $23776 €20000 Suburbs (61x50cm-24x20in) s.d.1913. 29-Nov-3 Farsetti, Prato #521/R est:25000-28000

OPSOMER, Isidore (1878-1967) Belgian
£3333 $6000 €5000 Zierikzee, Hollande (108x160cm-43x63in) s. 26-Apr-4 Bernaerts, Antwerp #281/R est:5000-6000
£4196 $7133 €6000 Still life with grapes (50x62cm-20x24in) s. painted c.1946 exhib. 25-Nov-3 Christie's, Amsterdam #215/R est:6000-8000

OPSTAL, Jasper Jacob van (c.1654-1717) Flemish
Works on paper
£1027 $1747 €1500 Roundel design, with bacchus surrounded by putti (21cm-8in circular) pen brown ink over black chk. 4-Nov-3 Sotheby's, Amsterdam #48/R est:1500-2000

OQUTAQ, Sheokjuk (1920-1982) North American
Sculpture
£901 $1532 €1315 Loon (23cm-9in) mottled dark soapstone exec.c.1968. 3-Nov-3 Waddingtons, Toronto #328/R est:2000-2500 (C.D 2000)
£1081 $1838 €1578 Mother owl and her young (23cm-9in) s. mottled green soapstone. 3-Nov-3 Waddingtons, Toronto #321/R est:2500-3500 (C.D 2400)

ORACZEWSKI, Jozef Krzysztof (1951-) Polish
Works on paper
£216 $393 €315 Postac lezaca (105x180cm-41x71in) s.d.2000 collage acrylic canvas. 20-Jun-4 Agra, Warsaw #38/R (P.Z 1500)
£634 $1154 €926 Postac lezaca II (105x180cm-41x71in) s.d.2000 collage acrylic canvas. 20-Jun-4 Agra, Warsaw #40/R (P.Z 4400)

ORAM, Ann (1956-) British
Works on paper
£1000 $1700 €1460 Spring flowers (99x108cm-39x43in) s.d.94 pencil W/C htd white. 4-Nov-3 Dreweatt Neate, Newbury #62/R est:300-500

ORAMAS, Alirio (1924-) Venezuelan
£1169 $1905 €1707 Untitled (115x88cm-45x35in) s. painted 1986. 20-Jul-3 Subastas Odalys, Caracas #88
Works on paper
£524 $965 €786 Untitled (25x34cm-10x13in) s. mixed media cardboard. 27-Jun-4 Subastas Odalys, Caracas #102/R

ORANGE, Maurice Henri (1868-1916) French
Works on paper
£388 $694 €566 Jeune garde (29x22cm-11x9in) s.i.d.1812 pen W/C. 13-May-4 Stuker, Bern #9518/R (S.FR 900)
£524 $892 €750 Tirailleur en tenue de campagne (22x14cm-9x6in) s.i. W/C. 1-Dec-3 Coutau Begarie, Paris #156/R

ORANT, Marthe (1874-1953) French
£855 $1574 €1300 Jeune mere et son enfant (55x37cm-22x15in) s. cardboard. 25-Jun-4 Millon & Associes, Paris #239
£2098 $3608 €3000 Fleurs a leur fenetre (76x105cm-30x41in) s. oil on cardboad prov. 2-Dec-3 Sotheby's, Amsterdam #223/R est:3000-4000
Works on paper
£526 $968 €800 L'atelier (104x73cm-41x29in) s. mixed media paper on panel. 28-Jun-4 Joron-Derem, Paris #96

ORAZI, Manuel (1860-1934) French
£10000 $18000 €14600 Hot chocolate (146x70cm-57x28in) mono. 23-Apr-4 Sotheby's, New York #109/R est:20000-30000

ORBAN, Desiderius (1884-1986) Hungarian
£1021 $1736 €1491 Valley Road (45x60cm-18x24in) s. 26-Nov-3 Deutscher-Menzies, Melbourne #244/R (A.D 2400)
£1700 $2738 €2482 Red roofs (44x59cm-17x23in) s.d.1932 prov. 25-Aug-3 Sotheby's, Paddington #339/R est:3000-5000 (A.D 4200)
£3952 $7153 €5770 Detail of a villa (60x50cm-24x20in) s. 16-Apr-4 Mu Terem Galeria, Budapest #134/R (H.F 1500000)
£9086 $16081 €13266 Nude (54x34cm-21x13in) s. painted c.1911. 28-Apr-4 Kieselbach, Budapest #64/R (H.F 3400000)
£20042 $35474 €29261 French landscape (66x82cm-26x32in) s. 28-Apr-4 Kieselbach, Budapest #76/R (H.F 7500000)

ORBITOWSKI, Janusz (1940-) Polish
£238 $410 €347 Untitled, 2/75 (100x80cm-39x31in) s.d.1975 verso canvas on panel. 4-Dec-3 Agra, Warsaw #29/R (P.Z 1600)
Works on paper
£345 $576 €500 7/74 (100x100cm-39x39in) s.i.d.1974 verso collage oil board. 16-Nov-3 Agra, Warsaw #5/R

ORCAGNA (c.1308-1368) Italian
£172535 $286408 €245000 Christ blessing (51x42cm-20x17in) tempera gold board. 11-Jun-3 Semenzato, Florence #19/R est:280000-320000
£172535 $286408 €245000 Saint Peter (48x36cm-19x14in) tempera gold board. 11-Jun-3 Semenzato, Florence #20/R est:280000-320000

ORCHARD, Colin (1935-) British
£620 $1091 €905 Sunrise, Venice (40x40cm-16x16in) mono. 18-May-4 Woolley & Wallis, Salisbury #26/R

ORCHARDSON, Charles M Q (?-1917) British
£700 $1169 €1022 Sketch from Hungerford bridge (35x46cm-14x18in) init.i.d.1900 prov. 13-Nov-3 Christie's, Kensington #171/R

ORCHARDSON, Sir William Quiller (1832-1910) British
£1100 $1738 €1606 Cottage interior with rustic table before heath (35x53cm-14x21in) mono. 6-Sep-3 Shapes, Edinburgh #347/R est:800-1200
£5978 $11000 €8728 Market girl from the Lido (58x102cm-23x40in) s. exhib. 26-Jun-4 Sloans & Kenyon, Bethesda #1076/R est:15000-18000
£28000 $50680 €40880 Venetian fruit seller (82x119cm-32x47in) s.d.1874 exhib.lit. 19-Apr-4 Sotheby's, London #8/R est:30000-50000

ORCHART, Stanley (?) ?
£520 $962 €759 Chelveston Hunts (58x68cm-23x27in) s.i.d.May 1973 canvasboard. 13-Feb-4 Sworder & Son, Bishops Stortford #76/R

ORDAZ, Luis (1912-1976) Venezuelan
£258 $400 €377 Landscape (61x86cm-24x34in) s. cardboard. 29-Sep-2 Subastas Odalys, Caracas #106
£573 $900 €837 Still life (50x60cm-20x24in) s. 23-Nov-2 Subastas Odalys, Caracas #34/R

ORDONEZ, Sylvia (1956-) Mexican
£1714 $3000 €2502 Retrato (58x53cm-23x21in) s. 19-Dec-3 Sotheby's, New York #1212/R est:4000-6000
£1810 $3077 €2643 Casas y plazas (110x90cm-43x35in) s.d.1987 s.i.d. verso prov. 25-Nov-3 Germann, Zurich #80/R est:5000-7000 (S.FR 4000)
£2715 $4615 €3964 Amanecer, Atardecer y anocher del pueblo (175x145cm-69x57in) s.d.1987 s.i.d. verso prov. 25-Nov-3 Germann, Zurich #79/R est:8000-12000 (S.FR 6000)
£4310 $7716 €6293 Amanecer, atardecer y anochecer del pueblo (171x145cm-67x57in) s.d.87 i. verso prov. 12-May-4 Dobiaschofsky, Bern #838/R est:14000 (S.FR 10000)

ORDWAY, Alfred (1819-1897) American
£838 $1500 €1223 Old Orchard Beach (23x36cm-9x14in) init. board painted c.1876 prov. 26-May-4 Doyle, New York #36/R est:2000-3000

O'REILLY, Myra (20th C) Irish
£855 $1574 €1300 Parting (84x61cm-33x24in) s.d.2003 three. 22-Jun-4 De Veres Art Auctions, Dublin #218

O'REILLY, Patrick (20th C) Irish
Sculpture
£2000 $3580 €2920 Pegasus bear (30cm-12in) mono.d.2002 num.1/1 dark brown pat bronze bronze marble base. 13-May-4 Sotheby's, London #115/R
£2368 $4358 €3600 Horse (49x61cm-19x24in) s. num.1/1 bronze. 22-Jun-4 De Veres Art Auctions, Dublin #143/R est:3000-4000
£3636 $6182 €5200 Bear with bucket 2 (24cm-9in) bronze. 25-Nov-3 De Veres Art Auctions, Dublin #226/R est:2000-3000

O'REILLY, Rosemary (20th C) Irish
£320 $576 €480 Colliemore harbour (31x39cm-12x15in) s. 20-Apr-4 James Adam, Dublin #101/R

ORELL, Argio (1884-1942) Italian
£2333 $4177 €3500 Model with red shirt (90x80cm-35x31in) s.d.1938 s.d.verso. 12-May-4 Stadion, Trieste #637/R est:2500-3500

ORELLANA, A (19th C) ?
Works on paper
£685 $1164 €1000 Chalco lagoon (19x25cm-7x10in) s.d.1891 W/C. 29-Oct-3 Louis Morton, Mexico #40/R est:8000-10000 (M.P 13000)

ORELLANA, Gaston (1933-) Chilean
£634 $1014 €900 Boy running (99x81cm-39x32in) s.d.1975 s.i.d.verso. 16-Sep-3 Segre, Madrid #256/R

ORFEI, Orfeo (1836-1915) Italian
£1594 $2614 €2200 Travelling player (28x15cm-11x6in) s.d.1872 board. 27-May-3 Finarte Semenzato, Milan #121/R
£7000 $11900 €10220 New shoes (44x55cm-17x22in) s. 19-Nov-3 Bonhams, New Bond Street #86/R est:4000-6000

ORGAN, Bryan (1935-) British
£2200 $3960 €3212 Lilies against a blue background (140x126cm-55x50in) s.d.1977. 20-Jan-4 Bonhams, Knightsbridge #249/R est:1000-1500
Works on paper
£250 $400 €365 Sketch for portrait of Malcolm Muggeridge (64x50cm-25x20in) s.i.d.1965 chl gouache. 16-Sep-3 Rosebery Fine Art, London #574
£480 $864 €701 Study of Prince Charles (64x38cm-25x15in) s.i.d.July 1980 pencil. 20-Jan-4 Bonhams, Knightsbridge #198/R
£480 $845 €701 Dame Margot Fonteyn (17x18cm-7x7in) s.d.1967 pencil acrylic board. 18-May-4 Bonhams, Knightsbridge #207/R

ORGAN, Elizabeth (20th C) British

£320 $534 €467 Abstract still life with cup and saucer, brandy decanter and fruit on table (75x49cm-30x19in) s.d.1963 board. 21-Oct-3 Gildings, Market Harborough #504

ORI, Luciano (1928-) Italian

Works on paper

£433 $784 €650 Motorway, prelude 3 (70x50cm-28x20in) s.d.80 collage card on masonite exhib.lit. 2-Apr-4 Farsetti, Prato #64/R

ORIACH, Xavier (1922-) ?

£417 $696 €600 Sans titre (115x73cm-45x29in) s. acrylic wood prov. 25-Oct-3 Cornette de St.Cyr, Paris #441

ORIANI, Pippo (1909-1972) Italian

£867 $1595 €1300 Human presence in primitive landscape (30x45cm-12x18in) s.d.1965. 14-Jun-4 Sant Agostino, Torino #169/R
£1000 $1840 €1500 Muse (32x42cm-13x17in) s. encaustic graphite cardboard lit. 12-Jun-4 Meeting Art, Vercelli #963/R est:1500
£1020 $1827 €1500 Spatial itinerary (50x60cm-20x24in) s. 22-Mar-4 Sant Agostino, Torino #458/R est:1600
£1133 $2085 €1700 Still life of fruit with guitar (60x80cm-24x31in) s. 14-Jun-4 Sant Agostino, Torino #170/R est:2000
£1133 $2085 €1700 Spatial composition (50x70cm-20x28in) s. 14-Jun-4 Sant Agostino, Torino #404/R est:1500-2000
£1333 $2453 €2000 Spatial conquest (50x60cm-20x24in) s. s.i.verso. 14-Jun-4 Sant Agostino, Torino #371/R est:1500-2000
£1745 $3228 €2600 Lazy woman (50x60cm-20x24in) s. 13-Mar-4 Meeting Art, Vercelli #211 est:1500
£2552 $4261 €3700 Structures (120x60cm-47x24in) s.d.1963. 17-Nov-3 Sant Agostino, Torino #98/R est:3500-4500
£2937 $4905 €4200 Structure and presence (50x120cm-20x47in) s.d.1962. 26-Jun-3 Sant Agostino, Torino #217/R est:3000-4000
£2958 $5117 €4200 Formal patterns (50x40cm-20x16in) s.d.30 prov. 9-Dec-3 Pandolfini, Florence #141 est:2000-2500
£3077 $5138 €4400 Totem and trees VI (120x50cm-47x20in) s.d.1962. 26-Jun-3 Sant Agostino, Torino #218/R est:3000-4000
£6294 $10699 €9000 Landscape (70x105cm-28x41in) s. i.verso. 20-Nov-3 Finarte Semenzato, Milan #8/R est:9000-10000
£13333 $24000 €20000 Simultaneita' organica (100x70cm-39x28in) s. painted 1931 exhib.lit. 22-Apr-4 Finarte Semenzato, Rome #338/R est:16000-18000

Works on paper

£533 $981 €800 Still life (50x65cm-20x26in) s. encaustic card on cardboard. 11-Jun-4 Farsetti, Prato #134/R
£839 $1427 €1200 Masks (32x44cm-13x17in) s. encaustic cardboard prov. 24-Nov-3 Christie's, Milan #70 est:1200-1800
£1014 $1784 €1500 Harlequin (44x32cm-17x13in) s. encaustic graphite cardboard. 22-May-4 Galleria Pananti, Florence #344/R est:1500-1800
£1056 $1754 €1500 Arlequin (50x65cm-20x26in) s. encaustic. 11-Jun-3 Finarte Semenzato, Milan #588/R
£1439 $2360 €2000 Female nude (50x65cm-20x26in) encaustic cardboard. 5-Jun-3 Adma, Formigine #941 est:2000-2200
£2467 $4539 €3700 Woman with red dress (60x50cm-24x20in) s. graphite cardboard. 12-Jun-4 Meeting Art, Vercelli #722/R est:1000
£3733 $6869 €5600 Reading (60x50cm-24x20in) s. graffiti cardboard. 12-Jun-4 Meeting Art, Vercelli #357/R est:1000

ORIENTAL SCHOOL, 18th C

Works on paper

£8000 $14640 €11680 Lively scene outside Tao Li's studio set on a river bank (92x159cm-36x63in) ink. 7-Apr-4 Sotheby's, Olympia #343/R est:400-600

ORIX, Bill (1900-1983) Belgian

£436 $807 €650 Mindscape (89x116cm-35x46in) s. s.i.d.56 verso oil sand. 13-Mar-4 De Vuyst, Lokeren #251

ORKIN, Ruth (1921-1985) American

Photographs

£1796 $3000 €2622 Central Park South from Sheep Meadow N.Y.C (22x34cm-9x13in) s.i.d.1956 s.verso silver print. 21-Oct-3 Swann Galleries, New York #244/R est:2500-3500
£3114 $5200 €4546 American girl in Italy (30x46cm-12x18in) with sig.i.d.1951 silver print. 21-Oct-3 Swann Galleries, New York #243/R est:3500-4500
£3593 $6000 €5246 MGM messenger girls (16x24cm-6x9in) i. gelatin silver print lit. 20-Oct-3 Christie's, Rockefeller NY #128/R est:6000-8000
£5000 $9000 €7300 Robert Capa in Paris cafe (32x20cm-13x8in) i.verso gelatin silver print. 24-Apr-4 Phillips, New York #28/R est:2000-3000
£6780 $12000 €9899 American girl in Italy, Florence (30x47cm-12x19in) s.i.d. gelatin silver print. 27-Apr-4 Christie's, Rockefeller NY #231/R est:7000-9000
£7186 $12000 €10492 American girl in Florence, Italy (30x45cm-12x18in) s.i. s.i.d.1951 verso gelatin silver print printed later. 20-Oct-3 Christie's, Rockefeller NY #127/R est:7000-9000

ORLAI, Soma Samuel (1822-1880) Hungarian

£1581 $2861 €2308 Girl portrait (70x55cm-28x22in) 16-Apr-4 Mu Terem Galeria, Budapest #50/R (H.F 600000)

ORLANDI, Nazzarreno (1861-?) Italian

£5634 $9746 €8000 Army kitchen (54x79cm-21x31in) s. 10-Dec-3 Sotheby's, Milan #91/R est:7800-8200

ORLANDINI, A (20th C) French

Sculpture

£3846 $6423 €5500 Jeune femme assise en amazone sur un cheval marin, tenant un poisson (39x60cm-15x24in) s.d.50 biscuit st.f.Sevres. 24-Jun-3 Millon & Associes, Paris #166/R est:5000-6000

ORLEY, Barend van (circle) (c.1492-1542) Flemish

£10067 $18523 €15000 Crucifixion of Christ (114x83cm-45x33in) panel arched top prov. 24-Mar-4 Dorotheum, Vienna #111/R est:8000-14000
£17568 $30919 €26000 Virgin and child under a canopy, canopy, together with the Archangel Michael (128x89cm-50x35in) panel prov.exhib. 18-May-4 Sotheby's, Amsterdam #35/R est:20000-30000

ORLEY, Richard van (1663-1732) Flemish

Works on paper

£662 $1205 €1000 The procession of Christ through Jerusalem (32x37cm-13x15in) s. pen prov. 18-Jun-4 Bolland & Marotz, Bremen #468/R

ORLEY, Richard van (attrib) (1663-1732) Flemish

Works on paper

£667 $1200 €974 Leda with Castor and Pollux beside Eurotas, Jupiter up above (17x23cm-7x9in) i. bodycol. 22-Jan-4 Christie's, Rockefeller NY #236/R

ORLIK, Emil (1870-1932) Czechoslovakian

£3497 $5944 €5000 Still life of flowers (67x54cm-26x21in) s.d.19 panel prov. 29-Nov-3 Villa Grisebach, Berlin #129/R est:5000-7000
£6643 $11294 €9500 Nude with mask (44x84cm-17x33in) s. prov.exhib.lit. 29-Nov-3 Villa Grisebach, Berlin #141/R est:8000-10000

Prints

£2235 $3800 €3263 Still life (48x54cm-19x21in) s. col woodcut exec.1908. 4-Nov-3 Christie's, Rockefeller NY #143/R est:4500-5500

Works on paper

£307 $552 €460 Street scene (20x12cm-8x5in) s.d. pencil. 24-Apr-4 Dr Lehr, Berlin #358/R
£438 $727 €639 Mulatto nude (31x11cm-12x4in) s. pencil. 4-Oct-3 Dorotheum, Prague #265/R est:10000-16000 (C.KR 20000)
£629 $1083 €900 Portrait of young woman (29x24cm-11x9in) s. pencil col pen chl. 2-Dec-3 Hauswedell & Nolte, Hamburg #485/R
£667 $1227 €1000 Breta Walker (25x20cm-10x8in) i. black red chk. 12-Jun-4 Villa Grisebach, Berlin #625/R
£800 $1472 €1200 Portrait of a girl (39x28cm-15x11in) s.d.31 pencil col chk. 12-Jun-4 Villa Grisebach, Berlin #626/R
£922 $1457 €1300 Portrait of Bernhard Pankok (32x25cm-13x10in) s. prov. 22-Jul-3 Sigalas, Stuttgart #330/R
£1000 $1820 €1460 Portrait of a young lady (42x33cm-17x13in) s. chl red chk wash. 21-Jun-4 Bonhams, New Bond Street #10/R est:1000-1500
£1189 $2021 €1700 Orthodox Jew (48x30cm-19x12in) s.d.01 graphite chk. 26-Nov-3 Lempertz, Koln #887/R est:800
£1958 $3368 €2800 Luxor (30x21cm-12x8in) s.d.1912 col chk. 2-Dec-3 Hauswedell & Nolte, Hamburg #484/R est:1000

ORLIK, Emil and ROLLINS, Charlotte (20th C) Czechoslovakian/German

Prints

£2797 $4755 €4000 Still life with fruit and gold pheasant (43x48cm-17x19in) s. col woodcut gouache. 29-Nov-3 Villa Grisebach, Berlin #140/R est:3000-4000

ORLINSKI, Andrew (20th C) ?

£1202 $2200 €1755 Russo-Swedish war of (80x109cm-31x43in) 29-Jul-4 Christie's, Rockefeller NY #226/R est:3000-5000

ORLOFF, Alexander (1899-1979) Polish

£599 $958 €850 Flower meadow (29x47cm-11x19in) s. 21-Sep-3 Bukowskis, Helsinki #518/R
£671 $1228 €1000 Composition (85x124cm-33x49in) s.d.1961 panel. 7-Jul-4 Artcurial Briest, Paris #316 est:1000-1500
£738 $1358 €1100 Autumn landscape (56x41cm-22x16in) s. 25-Mar-4 Hagelstam, Helsinki #890
£1000 $1810 €1500 Composition (85x125cm-33x49in) s.d.61 panel. 1-Apr-4 Credit Municipal, Paris #68 est:1500-2000
£5828 $10607 €8800 Un couple (79x64cm-31x25in) s. double-sided. 16-Jun-4 Claude Boisgirard, Paris #123/R est:2500-3000

Works on paper

£1000 $1810 €1500 Composition (118x36cm-46x14in) s.d.62 mixed media isorel. 1-Apr-4 Credit Municipal, Paris #67 est:1200-1500

ORLOFF, Chana (1878-1968) French

£236 $425 €345 Untitled, interior (20x28cm-8x11in) s.indis.d.55 oil W/C pencil. 23-Jan-4 Freeman, Philadelphia #203/R
£262 $475 €383 Untitled (25x20cm-10x8in) s.d.56 two. 2-Apr-4 Freeman, Philadelphia #62
£306 $550 €447 Abstract (25x18cm-10x7in) s. oil mixed media board. 23-Jan-4 Freeman, Philadelphia #264/R
£333 $600 €486 Black-white (28x20cm-11x8in) s. acrylic board. 23-Jan-4 Freeman, Philadelphia #215/R
£465 $800 €679 Abstract (28x18cm-11x7in) s. s.i.d.1956 verso oil mixed media card prov. 7-Dec-3 Freeman, Philadelphia #59
£531 $950 €775 Composition (28x15cm-11x6in) s. board. 20-Mar-4 Sloans & Kenyon, Bethesda #1158/R
£559 $1000 €816 Composition (28x20cm-11x8in) s. 20-Mar-4 Sloans & Kenyon, Bethesda #1159/R

Sculpture

£10564 $17113 €15000 La petite Suzy (76cm-30in) s.num.2/8 black pat bronze st.f.Susse prov.exhib.lit. 5-Aug-3 Tajan, Paris #27/R est:16000-18000
£30120 $50000 €43975 Torse (123cm-48in) s.d.1912 num.3/8 brown pat bronze st.f.Susse Fondeur lit. 2-Oct-3 Christie's, Tel Aviv #21/R est:50000-70000

ORLOFF, F (19th C) Russian
£3000 $5460 €4380 Running from the wolves (15x31cm-6x12in) s. panel. 16-Jun-4 Christie's, Kensington #211/R est:3000-5000

ORLOFF, Ivan Petrovitch (attrib) (1815-1861) Russian
£1444 $2700 €2108 Winter landscapes with troika, Russia (15x31cm-6x12in) s. panel pair. 25-Feb-4 Museumsbygningen, Copenhagen #146/R est:6000-8000 (D.KR 16000)

ORLOFF, J (18th C) Russian
£1100 $1727 €1595 Fending off the wolves. Troika ride (16x31cm-6x12in) s. panel pair. 28-Aug-3 Christie's, Kensington #83/R est:600-800

ORLOV, A (19/20th C) Russian
£1438 $2674 €2099 Summer landscape from the outskirts of wood (30x46cm-12x18in) s. 2-Mar-4 Rasmussen, Copenhagen #1324/R est:4000 (D.KR 16000)

ORLOV, Nikolai Vasilievich (1863-1924) Russian
£1141 $2099 €1700 Le traineau sur la neige (31x54cm-12x21in) s. 29-Mar-4 Rieunier, Paris #34/R est:1500-2000

ORLOVSKI, Boris Ivanovitch (1796-1837) Russian
Sculpture
£3252 $5821 €4748 General field marshal Michail Kutuzov-Smolensk (50cm-20in) dark pat.bronze incl. marble base. 25-May-4 Bukowskis, Stockholm #307a/R est:20000-25000 (S.KR 44000)

ORLOVSKI, Hans (1894-?) German
£417 $679 €600 Hyacinthes (33x55cm-13x22in) s. i. verso oil mixed media panel. 26-Sep-3 Bolland & Marotz, Bremen #796/R
£3333 $5967 €5000 Female nude (54x46cm-21x18in) s.d. panel prov. 14-May-4 Ketterer, Munich #69/R est:5000-7000

ORLOWSKI, Alexander (1777-1832) Polish
£6649 $12367 €9708 Highly spirited soldier and monk on horsebacks (22x26cm-9x10in) mono.d.1813. 2-Mar-4 Rasmussen, Copenhagen #1625/R est:5000 (D.KR 74000)
Works on paper
£2096 $3500 €3060 Two Jews quarrelling (26x20cm-10x8in) mono. pencil brush wash cardboard sold with a lithograph prov.lit. 21-Oct-3 Christie's, Rockefeller NY #88 est:3000-5000
£15385 $24000 € Cossacks (50x40cm-20x16in) s.d.1831 ink. 11-Apr-3 Christie's, Rockefeller NY #5/R est:10000-12000
£16000 $28640 €23360 Cossack patrol (40x56cm-16x22in) W/C. 26-May-4 Sotheby's, London #4/R est:6000-8000

ORLOWSKI, Vladimir (1842-1914) Russian
£3077 $5231 €4400 Boats at low tide (25x36cm-10x14in) s. board. 29-Nov-3 Bukowskis, Helsinki #403/R est:1200-1600
£4266 $7337 €6100 Tree lined avenue on summer day (35x44cm-14x17in) s. 5-Dec-3 Michael Zeller, Lindau #749/R est:850
£8108 $14514 €12000 River landscape in evening (61x87cm-24x34in) s. 6-May-4 Michael Zeller, Lindau #804/R est:850
£62667 $112173 €94000 Landscape from Ukraine with cattle by river bank (55x159cm-22x63in) s. 15-May-4 Hagelstam, Helsinki #37/R est:18000

ORMAOLEA, Jose Antonio (1912-1984) Spanish
£5035 $8408 €7200 Guernica bridge (60x81cm-24x32in) s. s.i.d.73 verso. 30-Jun-3 Ansorena, Madrid #342/R est:7200

ORNATI, Mario (1887-1955) Italian
£690 $1234 €1007 Il Lago Maggiore visto da Bre (60x79cm-24x31in) s. i. verso panel exhib. 12-May-4 Dobiaschofsky, Bern #841/R est:1500 (S.FR 1600)

ORNSTEIN, Jacob Arthur (1907-) American
Works on paper
£272 $500 €397 Tabletop still life (46x56cm-18x22in) s.d.44 W/C. 25-Jun-4 Freeman, Philadelphia #87/R

OROQUIETA, Famuceno Bonifacio (1901-?) Argentinian
£391 $700 €571 Dusk (40x50cm-16x20in) s.d.48 board. 4-May-4 Arroyo, Buenos Aires #2/R
£1209 $2200 €1765 River landscape (50x70cm-20x28in) s. board. 5-Jul-4 Arroyo, Buenos Aires #47/R est:1000
£3315 $6000 €4840 Conducting the boat (120x150cm-47x59in) 30-Mar-4 Arroyo, Buenos Aires #100

OROZCO, Gabriel (1962-) Mexican
Photographs
£2989 $5500 €4364 Ladrillos en varillas, wire holding bricks (40x51cm-16x20in) s.i.d.1993 num.verso cibachrome prov. 10-Jun-4 Phillips, New York #500/R est:3500-4500
£3400 $6154 €4964 Migration (40x50cm-16x20in) s.i.d.1993 num.4/5 cibachrome prov. 1-Apr-4 Christie's, Kensington #334/R est:2000-3000
£5978 $11000 €8728 Spaleta derritida, melted popsicle (47x31cm-19x12in) s.verso cibachrome prov. 10-Jun-4 Phillips, New York #497/R est:3000-5000
£6135 $10000 €8957 Perro Durmiendo, sleeping dog (36x28cm-14x11in) s.i.d.1990 verso cibachrome print. 23-Sep-3 Christie's, Rockefeller NY #172/R est:2000-3000
£10667 $19627 €16000 Evasive action (200x93cm-79x37in) num.3/3 photoshop image plastic prov. 8-Jun-4 Artcurial Briest, Paris #294/R est:12000-15000

OROZCO, Jose Clemente (1883-1949) Mexican
£2778 $5000 €4056 Sophisticated lady (36x25cm-14x10in) 24-Apr-4 Du Mouchelle, Detroit #3229/R est:5000-8000
£116279 $200000 €169767 Who is next (64x46cm-25x18in) s.prov.exhib. 7-Dec-3 Susanin's, Chicago #6008/R est:50000-70000
£276471 $470000 €403648 Prometeo (90x105cm-35x41in) s. masonite painted 1944 prov.exhib.lit. 19-Nov-3 Sotheby's, New York #7/R est:300000-350000
£480000 $883200 €720000 Cellar (65x80cm-26x31in) s.d.1941 prov.exhib. 10-Jun-4 Christie's, Paris #16/R est:570000-730000
Prints
£3352 $6000 €4894 Revolution (30x40cm-12x16in) s.num.9/100 lithograph. 6-May-4 Swann Galleries, New York #540/R est:5000-8000
Works on paper
£216 $400 €315 Hands (53x71cm-21x28in) s. pen ink. 13-Mar-4 Susanin's, Chicago #6028/R
£972 $1750 €1419 Kneeling figure (43x58cm-17x23in) chl. 24-Apr-4 Du Mouchelle, Detroit #3231/R est:1500-2500
£972 $1750 €1419 Two nudes (30x46cm-12x18in) ink. 24-Apr-4 Du Mouchelle, Detroit #3233/R est:2000-4000
£8889 $16000 €12978 Girls dancing (18x30cm-7x12in) W/C. 24-Apr-4 Du Mouchelle, Detroit #3230/R est:3000-5000
£35294 $60000 €51529 Guerreros, espanoles e indios (35x52cm-14x20in) s. gouache exec. c.1945. 18-Nov-3 Christie's, Rockefeller NY #52/R est:70000-90000

OROZCO, Lara (20th C) Mexican?
£500 $900 €730 Mother and child (61x91cm-24x36in) board. 24-Apr-4 Du Mouchelle, Detroit #3235/R

OROZCO, Trino (1915-) Venezuelan
£235 $405 €343 Turbio Valley (60x80cm-24x31in) s. painted 1975. 7-Dec-3 Subastas Odalys, Caracas #164
£258 $400 €377 Landscape (34x44cm-13x17in) s. panel. 29-Sep-2 Subastas Odalys, Caracas #42/R
£258 $480 €377 Sunday Mass (50x60cm-20x24in) s. painted 1976. 14-Mar-4 Subastas Odalys, Caracas #24/R
£260 $435 €380 Seascape (48x62cm-19x24in) s. 19-Oct-3 Subastas Odalys, Caracas #40
£263 $440 €384 Untitled (43x57cm-17x22in) s. painted 1945. 13-Jul-3 Subastas Odalys, Caracas #46/R
£269 $495 €393 Untitled (43x63cm-17x25in) s. 28-Mar-4 Subastas Odalys, Caracas #78/R
£269 $495 €393 Path (61x78cm-24x31in) s. painted 1968. 28-Mar-4 Subastas Odalys, Caracas #18/R
£272 $435 €397 Untitled (65x45cm-26x18in) s. 21-Sep-3 Subastas Odalys, Caracas #29
£272 $435 €397 Wood on the beach (60x80cm-24x31in) s. painted 1970. 21-Sep-3 Subastas Odalys, Caracas #69
£281 $470 €410 Gran bucare (65x76cm-26x30in) s. painted 1971. 19-Oct-3 Subastas Odalys, Caracas #23
£286 $520 €429 Old (65x84cm-26x33in) s. painted 1969. 21-Jun-4 Subastas Odalys, Caracas #136
£291 $500 €425 Bucare (62x80cm-24x31in) s. painted 1980. 7-Dec-3 Subastas Odalys, Caracas #26
£323 $500 €472 Banana trees in the jungle (76x66cm-30x26in) s. 29-Sep-2 Subastas Odalys, Caracas #107
£374 $625 €546 Seascape (43x58cm-17x23in) s. 19-Oct-3 Subastas Odalys, Caracas #67/R
£413 $690 €603 Church La Pastora (56x45cm-22x18in) s. 13-Jul-3 Subastas Odalys, Caracas #6/R
£419 $650 €612 Tree (60x80cm-24x31in) s. 29-Sep-2 Subastas Odalys, Caracas #74
£452 $700 €660 Village (70x85cm-28x33in) s. painted 1969. 3-Nov-2 Subastas Odalys, Caracas #26
£644 $1095 €940 Still life (50x67cm-20x26in) s. 23-Nov-3 Subastas Odalys, Caracas #107/R
£809 $1375 €1181 Untitled (59x80cm-23x31in) s. 23-Nov-3 Subastas Odalys, Caracas #26

OROZDOVA, Elena (1960-) Russian
£310 $518 €450 Winter in Russia (30x60cm-12x24in) s. 17-Nov-3 Durán, Madrid #674/R
£532 $888 €750 Ice-skating (25x55cm-10x22in) s. 20-Oct-3 Durán, Madrid #716/R

ORPEN, Bea (1913-1980) British
Works on paper
£500 $815 €720 Cruit Island, Co Donegal (34x49cm-13x19in) s.i. s.verso gouache. 23-Sep-3 De Veres Art Auctions, Dublin #166
£671 $1201 €1000 Donkeys on the lakeshore (17x24cm-7x9in) s. gouache prov. 26-May-4 James Adam, Dublin #195/R est:800-1200
£1477 $2613 €2200 St Peter's Place, Drogheda (23x18cm-9x7in) s. i.verso W/C prov.exhib. 27-Apr-4 Whyte's, Dublin #105/R est:800-1000

ORPEN, R O K (19th C) ?
Works on paper
£480 $859 €701 Queen Ann's state bedroom at Raynham (91x71cm-36x28in) mono.d.1847 W/C. 22-Mar-4 Bonhams & Brooks, Norfolk #168/R

ORPEN, Sir William (1878-1931) Irish
£18000 $32220 €26280 View of Montmartre, Paris; cloud over Montmartre (40x61cm-16x24in) s. prov.lit. 13-May-4 Sotheby's, London #34/R est:20000-30000
£20000 $35800 €29200 Portrait of Sir Alexander Henderson (127x102cm-50x40in) s. 16-Mar-4 Bonhams, New Bond Street #17/R est:20000-25000
£22000 $37400 €32120 Investiture of King Manoel of Portugal as knight of the garter at Windsor Castle (63x76cm-25x30in) s.i. painted 1910. 21-Nov-3 Christie's, London #140/R est:8000-12000
Works on paper
£350 $648 €511 Study of a child (36x20cm-14x8in) pencil prov. 10-Feb-4 David Lay, Penzance #399

£450 $806 €657 Study of a gentleman (20x15cm-8x6in) s.i.d.1928 pen brown ink. 14-May-4 Christie's, Kensington #327/R
£500 $795 €730 Two male head studies (21x17cm-8x7in) pencil. 10-Sep-3 Sotheby's, Olympia #130/R
£500 $935 €750 Self portrait (9x11cm-4x4in) s.i.d.1925 pen ink. 22-Jul-4 Dominic Winter, Swindon #203/R
£1200 $2124 €1752 Portrait of Lee Hankey (20x15cm-8x6in) s. pencil drawing prov. 28-Apr-4 Halls, Shrewsbury #483/R est:500-700
£1974 $3632 €3000 Vattetot study (22x28cm-9x11in) pen wash prov.exhib.lit. 22-Jun-4 De Veres Art Auctions, Dublin #55/R est:3000-5000
£2685 $4752 €4000 Portrait of Grace Westray (32x25cm-13x10in) sanguine conte crayon rag paper. 27-Apr-4 Whyte's, Dublin #53/R est:5000-7000
£3400 $6086 €4964 Seated semi-nude girl. Head study (32x25cm-13x10in) pencil red chk black wash double-sided prov.exhib. 14-May-4 Christie's, London #197/R est:2500-3500
£3497 $5944 €5000 The fancy dress ball of Cany (25x20cm-10x8in) i. pen ink prov. 18-Nov-3 Whyte's, Dublin #54/R est:4000-5000
£3500 $6265 €5110 Mother and child (27x37cm-11x15in) s.d.03 pencil black ink exhib. 14-May-4 Christie's, Kensington #326/R est:3000-5000
£5369 $9503 €8000 Cany at the first (25x20cm-10x8in) i. pen ink prov. 27-Apr-4 Whyte's, Dublin #54/R est:4000-6000
£5500 $9845 €8030 Dancer tying her shoe (32x26cm-13x10in) s.d.1900 pencil pen ink red chk brown wash two prov.exhib. 14-May-4 Christie's, London #196/R est:3000-5000
£13000 $23270 €18980 The winner, the Champ (73x51cm-29x20in) s.i. pencil W/C white chk prov.exhib.lit. 13-May-4 Sotheby's, London #27/R est:10000-15000

ORPEN, Sir William (attrib) (1878-1931) Irish
Works on paper
£1379 $2303 €2013 Study of a lady with a fan. Study of a lady seated (26x20cm-10x8in) bears sig d.July 1894 pen ink pair. 20-Oct-3 Stephan Welz, Johannesburg #198/R est:4000-6000 (SA.R 16000)

ORR, Eric (20th C) American
Works on paper
£270 $450 €394 Aggies transmutation (38x58cm-15x23in) mixed media. 26-Oct-3 Bonhams & Butterfields, San Francisco #6602/R
£621 $1100 €907 You have had the experience, but missed the meaning (74x61cm-29x24in) s.i.d. mixed media board prov. 2-May-4 Bonhams & Butterfields, Los Angeles #3086/R
£2035 $3500 €2971 Night shift no.9 (74x61cm-29x24in) lead gold leaf oil linen on board prov. 3-Dec-3 Doyle, New York #81/R est:3000-5000

ORR, Joseph (1949-) American
£284 $500 €415 Chicken feed (23x30cm-9x12in) s.d.1986 acrylic masonite. 22-May-4 Selkirks, St. Louis #619
£284 $500 €415 Rural winter scene (23x30cm-9x12in) s.d.1985 acrylic masonite. 22-May-4 Selkirks, St. Louis #620/R
£284 $500 €415 Artist painting by river (30x23cm-12x9in) s.d.1985 acrylic masonite. 22-May-4 Selkirks, St. Louis #621
£1087 $2000 €1587 Used car lot (61x76cm-24x30in) s.d.1978 board. 26-Jun-4 Selkirks, St. Louis #147/R est:2500-3500

ORR, Monro Scott (1874-?) British
Works on paper
£280 $442 €409 African with a cockerel in a coop (18x25cm-7x10in) s. W/C. 3-Sep-3 Bonhams, Bury St Edmunds #371

ORR, Stewart (1872-1944) British
Works on paper
£380 $654 €555 Iona (28x34cm-11x13in) s. W/C. 6-Dec-3 Shapes, Edinburgh #400

ORRENTE, Pedro (attrib) (1570-1644) Spanish
Works on paper
£993 $1808 €1500 Le bon Samaritain (12x16cm-5x6in) pen ink wash prov. 16-Jun-4 Piasa, Paris #25/R est:1200-1500

ORROCK, James (1829-1913) British
£1100 $2002 €1606 Warkworth Castle (29x44cm-11x17in) s.indis.d.1895. 15-Jun-4 Bonhams, Leeds #124/R
Works on paper
£360 $659 €526 Figures with cattle in an extensive landscape (48x73cm-19x29in) s.d.1895 W/C pencil scratching out htd. bodycol. 8-Jul-4 Lawrence, Crewkerne #1519
£400 $680 €584 Kegworth, cattle in the fields with loch and stone bridge (25x56cm-10x22in) s.i. 5-Nov-3 John Nicholson, Haslemere #491
£650 $1073 €949 Estuary scene with distant figures (28x46cm-11x18in) s. W/C. 3-Jul-3 Biddle & Webb, Birmingham #899
£700 $1169 €1022 On the Tees (33x50cm-13x20in) s.d.1877 W/C over pencil. 16-Oct-3 Lawrence, Crewkerne #648
£720 $1138 €1044 Cottages, Newton Linford (32x49cm-13x19in) s.i.d.1882 W/C. 3-Sep-3 Bonhams, Bury St Edmunds #324
£800 $1496 €1168 Conisburgh Castle, south Yorkshire with a figure on a barge on a river (23x34cm-9x13in) s.i. pencil W/C. 22-Jul-4 Tennants, Leyburn #750

ORSEL, Victor (1795-1850) French
Works on paper
£288 $472 €400 Study of apple tree (36x26cm-14x10in) pencil W/C. 10-Jun-3 Pandolfini, Florence #9/R
£490 $842 €700 Portrait de femme de profil (15x12cm-6x5in) mono. black crayon. 8-Dec-3 Piasa, Paris #42

ORSELLI, Arturo (19th C) Italian
£2108 $3500 €3078 Genre Courting scenes (41x30cm-16x12in) s. pair. 4-Oct-3 Neal Auction Company, New Orleans #300/R est:4000-6000
£5000 $9000 €7300 Rivals (102x76cm-40x30in) s. 22-Apr-4 Christie's, Rockefeller NY #230/R est:10000-15000

ORSI, Bernardino di (fl.1485-1522) Italian
£8511 $14213 €12000 San Sebastiano (44x27cm-17x11in) tempera panel. 17-Jun-3 Finarte Semenzato, Milan #620/R est:12000-15000

ORSI, Lelio (attrib) (1511-1587) Italian
Works on paper
£3265 $5845 €4800 Pelerins musiciens de Saint Jacques de Compostelle (12x26cm-5x10in) i. pen brown ink wash. 19-Mar-4 Piasa, Paris #6/R est:3000-4000

ORSINI, Robert (20th C) New Zealander?
£336 $581 €491 Cloudy sky above mountain range (52x61cm-20x24in) s. prov. 9-Dec-3 Peter Webb, Auckland #100/R (NZ.D 900)
Works on paper
£560 $968 €818 Wolves in the woods (66x46cm-26x18in) s.i.d.1986 gouache prov. 9-Dec-3 Peter Webb, Auckland #99/R (NZ.D 1500)

ORTEGA, Charles (1925-) ?
£333 $613 €500 Quai au crepuscule (24x34cm-9x13in) s. 8-Jun-4 Livinec, Gaudcheau & Jezequel, Rennes #130

ORTEGA, Hector (20th C) Venezuelan
£2273 $4000 €3319 America (91x117cm-36x46in) s.i. painted c.1960. 23-May-4 Treadway Gallery, Cincinnati #716/R est:5000-7000

ORTEGA, Jose (1880-1955) Spanish
£3191 $5330 €4500 Reverie dans la cour du palais (75x60cm-30x24in) s. 19-Oct-3 Rabourdin & Choppin de Janvry, Paris #109/R est:4500-5000
£3688 $6159 €5200 Danse au clair de lune (60x92cm-24x36in) s. 19-Oct-3 Rabourdin & Choppin de Janvry, Paris #31/R est:5500-6000

ORTEGA, Jose (1921-1991) Spanish
£345 $576 €500 Nuts (34x27cm-13x11in) s. s.i.d.1974 verso acrylic nut shells board. 17-Nov-3 Sant Agostino, Torino #149/R
£461 $747 €650 Andalusian scene (61x50cm-24x20in) s. panel. 20-May-3 Ansorena, Madrid #209/R
£767 $1411 €1150 Untitled (70x64cm-28x25in) s.d.1972 tempera card on board. 12-Jun-4 Meeting Art, Vercelli #413/R
£767 $1411 €1150 Mythological scene (63x69cm-25x27in) s.d.1972 tempera card on canvas. 12-Jun-4 Meeting Art, Vercelli #940/R
£1000 $1790 €1460 Portrait of a Spanish beauty in a yellow dress (99x71cm-39x28in) s. 7-May-4 Mallams, Oxford #324/R est:1000-1500
Works on paper
£1127 $1972 €1600 Untitled (51x53cm-20x21in) mixed media board exec.1980. 16-Dec-3 Finarte Semenzato, Milan #331/R est:1000-1200
£1361 $2435 €2000 Portrait of young woman from Dresden (90x65cm-35x26in) s.d.1972 s.i.verso mixed media paper on canvas prov. 16-Mar-4 Finarte Semenzato, Milan #472/R est:2000-2400

ORTEGA, Jose Benito (?) Spanish
£2083 $3292 €3000 Scene de danse dans la baie d'Alger. 25-Apr-3 Etude de Provence, Marseille #163 est:3000-4000

ORTEGA, Pascual (1839-1899) Spanish
£987 $1786 €1500 Figures (46x55cm-18x22in) s.d.1872. 14-Apr-4 Ansorena, Madrid #112/R est:1500
£2113 $3507 €3000 La semaine sainte a Seville (37x46cm-15x18in) s.d.1872 panel. 13-Jun-3 Renaud, Paris #40 est:4000-5000

ORTELLI, Gottardo (1938-) Italian
£533 $981 €800 Untitled (60x60cm-24x24in) s.verso acrylic prov. 8-Jun-4 Finarte Semenzato, Milan #205/R
£667 $1227 €1000 Untitled (100x90cm-39x35in) s.d.1989 verso. 12-Jun-4 Meeting Art, Vercelli #120/R

ORTH, Benjamin (1803-1875) German
£324 $580 €460 Portrait of a woman dressed in Biedermeier period clothing (39x29cm-15x11in) s.d.1846 lit. 8-Jan-4 Allgauer, Kempten #2475
£1420 $2500 €2073 Seaman's family (38x30cm-15x12in) s.d.1846 canvas laid down. 23-May-4 Treadway Gallery, Cincinnati #555/R est:2500-3500
£4698 $8644 €7000 Portrait d'homme a la veste noire. Portrait de femme (75x60cm-30x24in) s. one d.1860 one d.1861 oval pair. 24-Mar-4 Tajan, Paris #79/R est:5000-6000

ORTH, Peter (1904-1962) German?
£470 $864 €700 Horse of the Year 1959 (74x88cm-29x35in) s. 27-Mar-4 L & B, Essen #177/R

ORTH, Willy (1889-1976) American/German
£276 $500 €403 Still life with yellow flowers (91x76cm-36x30in) s. 18-Apr-4 Bonhams & Butterfields, Los Angeles #7023
£430 $800 €628 Still life (76x91cm-30x36in) s. board painted c.1930. 7-Mar-4 Treadway Gallery, Cincinnati #537/R
£1044 $1900 €1524 Atmospheric landscape (46x61cm-18x24in) s. board prov. 15-Jun-4 John Moran, Pasadena #116 est:1500-2000

ORTIZ DE ZARATE, Manuel (1886-1946) French
£280 $476 €400 Still life with tomatoes and eggs on a small plate (23x32cm-9x13in) s. 24-Nov-3 Glerum, Amsterdam #102/R

£769 $1308 €1100 Portrait presume de Madame de Waroquier (64x54cm-25x21in) prov. 23-Nov-3 Cornette de St.Cyr, Paris #245/R
£800 $1432 €1200 Composition aux fleurs et aux fruits (55x38cm-22x15in) s. cardboard. 16-May-4 Thierry & Lannon, Brest #166/R
£1126 $2060 €1700 Nature morte (61x50cm-24x20in) s. 9-Apr-4 Claude Aguttes, Neuilly #89 est:1000-1500
£1408 $2465 €2000 Composition aux fleurs et aux fruits (55x38cm-22x15in) s. board. 21-Dec-3 Thierry & Lannon, Brest #348/R est:1200-1500
£1469 $2497 €2100 Femme en buste (55x46cm-22x18in) s. 23-Nov-3 Cornette de St.Cyr, Paris #621/R est:800-1000
£1879 $3477 €2800 Cote Mediterraneenne (50x61cm-20x24in) s. 15-Mar-4 Blanchet, Paris #90/R est:2000-2500
£2657 $4517 €3800 Nature morte a l'intransigeant (30x50cm-12x20in) painted c.1911 prov.exhib. 23-Nov-3 Cornette de St.Cyr, Paris #244/R est:1200-1500
£3401 $5408 €5000 La Seine, pont de Paris (50x65cm-20x26in) s. 23-Mar-3 Mercier & Cie, Lille #278/R est:4000-5000
£6107 $11299 €9100 Nature morte (60x81cm-24x32in) s. 15-Mar-4 Claude Boisgirard, Paris #86/R est:2000-2500

ORTIZ DE ZARATE, Nicolas Martinez (1907-) Spanish
£6738 $10915 €9500 Still life with jug and fruit (73x92cm-29x36in) s. cloth. 20-May-3 Ansorena, Madrid #314/R est:6000
£9220 $14936 €13000 Siesta (102x150cm-40x59in) s.d.67. 20-May-3 Ansorena, Madrid #322/R est:13000

ORTIZ LOPEZ, Concepcion (19/20th C) Cuban
£436 $816 €650 Woman with still life of fruit (95x70cm-37x28in) s.d.1900. 24-Feb-4 Durán, Madrid #140/R

ORTIZ, Emilio (1936-) Mexican
Works on paper
£316 $503 €461 Two figures (49x68cm-19x27in) s. pastel. 29-Apr-3 Louis Morton, Mexico #95/R (M.P 5250)

ORTIZ, Manuel Angeles (1895-1984) Spanish
£590 $962 €850 Lake Mascardi, Argentina (20x31cm-8x12in) s. cardboard. 23-Sep-3 Durán, Madrid #130/R
£604 $1130 €900 Landscape near Mascardi Lake (16x24cm-6x9in) s. cardboard. 24-Feb-4 Durán, Madrid #129/R
£1667 $2750 €2400 Untitled (23x16cm-9x6in) s. 2-Jul-3 Ansorena, Madrid #1026/R
£3026 $5478 €4600 Landscape in Argentina (44x29cm-17x11in) s. 14-Apr-4 Ansorena, Madrid #55/R est:4600
Works on paper
£486 $773 €700 Tree (56x38cm-22x15in) s. col drawing. 29-Apr-3 Durán, Madrid #77/R
£493 $863 €700 Four heads (15x13cm-6x5in) s. felt-tip pen pencil col crayon. 16-Dec-3 Segre, Madrid #126/R
£537 $950 €800 Shapes (23x19cm-9x7in) s. mixed media. 27-Apr-4 Durán, Madrid #638/R
£634 $1109 €900 Seated woman (13x13cm-5x5in) s. pencil. 16-Dec-3 Segre, Madrid #128/R
£655 $1088 €950 Composition (19x23cm-7x9in) s. mixed media. 1-Oct-3 Ansorena, Madrid #551/R
£769 $1285 €1100 4 Cabenzas (16x15cm-6x6in) ball-point pen. 24-Jun-3 Segre, Madrid #176/R
£775 $1356 €1100 Dove (15x15cm-6x6in) s. collage. 16-Dec-3 Segre, Madrid #125/R
£845 $1479 €1200 Woman (30x19cm-12x7in) s. ink pencil. 16-Dec-3 Segre, Madrid #127/R
£1027 $1747 €1500 Village (40x40cm-16x16in) s. mixed media collage. 4-Nov-3 Ansorena, Madrid #892/R
£1056 $1849 €1500 Garden (31x24cm-12x9in) s. ink wash. 16-Dec-3 Segre, Madrid #124/R est:1200

ORTIZ-ECHAGUE, Antonio (1883-1942) Mexican
£7895 $14289 €12000 Garden in Granada (96x85cm-38x33in) s. 14-Apr-4 Ansorena, Madrid #57/R est:8000

ORTLIEB, Friedrich (1839-1909) German
£7059 $12000 €10306 New Year's eve at grandfather's (93x117cm-37x46in) s.d.1873. 29-Oct-3 Christie's, Rockefeller NY #32/R est:12000-18000

ORTMAN, George (1926-) American
£503 $900 €734 Red world (142x81cm-56x32in) s. acrylic canvas on wood prov. 16-May-4 Wright, Chicago #304/R

ORTMANS, François-Auguste (1827-1884) French
£2797 $4755 €4000 Canal landscape on the Ile de France (23x34cm-9x13in) s. panel. 20-Nov-3 Van Ham, Cologne #1789/R est:2000
£3179 $5500 €4641 Maisons along the riverbank (28x41cm-11x16in) s.d.1859 panel prov. 13-Dec-3 Sloans & Kenyon, Bethesda #793/R est:6000-8000

ORTNER, Rudolf (1912-) German
£475 $808 €694 B 87 27 (40x30cm-16x12in) s.i.d.1987 verso oil mixed media board exhib. 22-Nov-3 Burkhard, Luzern #48/R (S.FR 1050)
Works on paper
£403 $741 €600 Small pool (50x65cm-20x26in) mono.d. s.i. verso W/C gouache woodchip on masonite. 26-Mar-4 Ketterer, Hamburg #1074/R

ORTUNO, Roberto (1953-) Spanish
£1333 $2427 €2000 Patio andaluz (92x73cm-36x29in) s. painted c.1970 prov. 29-Jun-4 Segre, Madrid #238/R est:1800

ORTVAD, Erik (1917-) Danish
£287 $465 €416 Landscape with road by sea (62x73cm-24x29in) s. 4-Aug-3 Rasmussen, Vejle #588/R (D.KR 3000)
£559 $878 €816 Composition with figures (65x50cm-26x20in) s. d.januar 1935 verso oil on material. 30-Aug-3 Rasmussen, Havnen #4111/R (D.KR 6000)
£632 $1162 €923 Concrete composition (44x65cm-17x26in) s.d.1971 verso exhib. 29-Mar-4 Rasmussen, Copenhagen #131/R (D.KR 7000)
£1319 $2334 €1926 Kvaenjarp - composition (38x46cm-15x18in) s.d.1964 verso. 27-Apr-4 AB Stockholms Auktionsverk #1202/R est:12000-15000 (S.KR 18000)
Works on paper
£316 $591 €461 Composition (29x44cm-11x17in) W/C. 25-Feb-4 Kunsthallen, Copenhagen #116 (D.KR 3500)

O'RYAN, Fergus (1911-1989) Irish
£282 $451 €400 Angel Alley, Dublin (64x43cm-25x17in) s. indis.i.verso board. 16-Sep-3 Whyte's, Dublin #126/R
£303 $557 €460 The canal near Sallins (23x35cm-9x14in) s. canvasboard. 22-Jun-4 De Veres Art Auctions, Dublin #48/R
£313 $509 €450 On the Maigue, nr Adare (28x37cm-11x15in) s. canvasboard. 23-Sep-3 De Veres Art Auctions, Dublin #145
£493 $908 €750 Annamoe River, County Wicklow (24x30cm-9x12in) s. canvasboard. 22-Jun-4 De Veres Art Auctions, Dublin #49/R
£667 $1207 €1000 Dogs Bay, Connemara (38x56cm-15x22in) s. 30-Mar-4 De Veres Art Auctions, Dublin #215/R
£800 $1448 €1200 Pool on the Maigue, near Adare (32x41cm-13x16in) board. 31-Mar-4 James Adam, Dublin #48/R
£800 $1448 €1200 Street scene, Sainte Maxime (36x46cm-14x18in) s. i.verso board. 30-Mar-4 De Veres Art Auctions, Dublin #35/R
£805 $1442 €1200 Conil, Cadiz (26x38cm-10x15in) s.i. board. 31-May-4 Hamilton Osborne King, Dublin #127/R
£855 $1574 €1300 St Stephen's Green, at the Grafton Street Gate (30x40cm-12x16in) s. canvasboard. 22-Jun-4 De Veres Art Auctions, Dublin #7/R
£874 $1486 €1250 Preparing nets (20x28cm-8x11in) s. i.verso canvas on board. 18-Nov-3 Whyte's, Dublin #29/R
£921 $1695 €1400 Canal at Leeson Street Bridge (29x38cm-11x15in) s.i.verso canvasboard. 22-Jun-4 De Veres Art Auctions, Dublin #124/R
£1007 $1802 €1500 Santorini, Greece (24x34cm-9x13in) s.i. board. 26-May-4 James Adam, Dublin #105/R est:1600-2000
£1007 $1802 €1500 Pink bridge, autumn (23x50cm-9x20in) s. board. 26-May-4 James Adam, Dublin #139/R est:1000-1500
£1053 $1937 €1600 Dublin street scene (31x40cm-12x16in) s. canvasboard. 22-Jun-4 De Veres Art Auctions, Dublin #229/R est:900-1200
£1053 $1937 €1600 Dun Laoghaire and Howth from the mountains (25x56cm-10x22in) 22-Jun-4 Mealy's, Castlecomer #737/R est:1500-1700
£1056 $1690 €1500 Brown pool, Glendalough river (41x51cm-16x20in) s. i.verso board. 16-Sep-3 Whyte's, Dublin #183/R est:1200-1500
£1329 $2259 €1900 Convoy Woollen Mill, Donegal (47x55cm-19x22in) s. board. 18-Nov-3 Whyte's, Dublin #177/R est:2000-3000
£1690 $2704 €2400 Bridge and river, Wicklow (38x46cm-15x18in) s. board. 16-Sep-3 Whyte's, Dublin #187/R est:1500-2000
£1745 $3123 €2600 Mediterranean port (35x44cm-14x17in) s. board. 26-May-4 James Adam, Dublin #106/R est:1500-2500
£2148 $3844 €3200 Christ Church Dublin and the Houses of Wine Tavern Street (40x48cm-16x19in) s. i. verso. 31-May-4 Hamilton Osborne King, Dublin #122/R est:2500-3500
£2297 $4342 €3400 Millicent, County Kildare (51x61cm-20x24in) s. board exhib. 17-Feb-4 Whyte's, Dublin #220/R est:2000-3000
£2937 $4993 €4200 Smith and Pearson steelworkers on the Liffey Quays, Dublin (57x72cm-22x28in) s. board. 18-Nov-3 Whyte's, Dublin #25/R est:3500-4500
£3067 $5551 €4600 Avonmore river, Co Wicklow (46x68cm-18x27in) s. board. 31-Mar-4 James Adam, Dublin #118/R est:2000-3000
£3221 $5766 €4800 Andalucian village (37x46cm-15x18in) s. board. 26-May-4 James Adam, Dublin #192/R est:2000-3000
£3239 $5183 €4600 St Patrick's Park, Bride Street, Dublin (53x64cm-21x25in) s. board. 16-Sep-3 Whyte's, Dublin #127/R est:3000-4000
£5000 $8150 €7200 Crampton Court, Dame Street (91x71cm-36x28in) s. board. 24-Sep-3 James Adam, Dublin #127/R est:3000-5000
£8389 $14849 €12500 Christ Church, Dublin (81x152cm-32x60in) s. i.verso board prov.exhib. 27-Apr-4 Whyte's, Dublin #106/R est:8000-10000
Works on paper
£517 $925 €770 On the Seine (27x37cm-11x15in) s. W/C. 26-May-4 James Adam, Dublin #130/R
£694 $1132 €1000 Donegal views (23x31cm-9x12in) s. i.verso W/C pair. 28-Sep-3 Hamilton Osborne King, Dublin #245 est:600-800

OS, Georgius Jacobus Johannes van (1782-1861) Dutch
£1600 $2896 €2400 Still life of flowers (35x27cm-14x11in) i. 2-Apr-4 Dr Fritz Nagel, Leipzig #3966/R est:600
£1863 $3000 €2720 Flowers in vase (46x36cm-18x14in) s. verso. 20-Aug-3 James Julia, Fairfield #699/R est:3000-5000
£3448 $5724 €5000 Still life with dead game and fruit (81x65cm-32x26in) 30-Sep-3 Ansorena, Madrid #25/R est:5000
£4861 $8264 €7000 Partridge, prunes, grapes, walnuts and flowers on a ledge (10x16cm-4x6in) s. panel. 28-Oct-3 Christie's, Amsterdam #208/R est:5000-7000
Works on paper
£493 $908 €750 Fruits and flowers on a ledge (63x46cm-25x18in) s. pencil W/C htd white prov. 22-Jun-4 Christie's, Amsterdam #2/R
£3819 $6493 €5500 Partridge, prunes, peaches, grapes and flowers in vase on a ledge (40x30cm-16x12in) s.d.1845 W/C col chks bodycol htd white. 28-Oct-3 Christie's, Amsterdam #3/R est:6000-8000

OS, Jan van (1744-1808) Dutch
£10067 $18523 €15000 Frigate flying Dutch flag and other ships in stormy seas (47x60cm-19x24in) s. 25-Mar-4 Dr Fritz Nagel, Stuttgart #610/R est:2500

OS, Jan van (attrib) (1744-1808) Dutch
£4600 $8280 €6716 Dutch shipping in calm coastal waters (50x65cm-20x26in) 20-Apr-4 Sotheby's, Olympia #274/R est:3500-4500

OS, Jan van (circle) (1744-1808) Dutch
£4918 $9000 €7180 Still life with flowers and insects (69x51cm-27x20in) bears sig. 5-Jun-4 Neal Auction Company, New Orleans #484/R est:15000-18000

OS, Jan van (studio) (1744-1808) Dutch
£7986 $13576 €11500 Terracotta vase representing Bacchus, flowers and insects (40x32cm-16x13in) board. 28-Oct-3 Il Ponte, Milan #380/R est:13000-14000

OS, Jan van (style) (1744-1808) Dutch
£17400 $30102 €25404 Still life with roses and other flowers in a glass vase, birds nest on a stone ledge (35x26cm-14x10in) bears sig panel prov. 9-Dec-3 Sotheby's, Olympia #408/R est:4000-6000

OS, Maria Margrita van (1780-1862) Dutch
£2200 $4004 €3300 Still life with peaches, grapes and wine glass (18x31cm-7x12in) s. panel. 30-Jun-4 Neumeister, Munich #638/R est:3000
Works on paper
£1014 $1784 €1500 Butterfly (22x30cm-9x12in) s. W/C gouache black chk prov. 19-May-4 Sotheby's, Amsterdam #286/R est:500-700

OS, Ph van (?) ?
£933 $1717 €1400 Deux chevaux et un chien a la barriere (18x24cm-7x9in) s. panel. 14-Jun-4 Horta, Bruxelles #313

OS, Pieter Gerardus van (1776-1839) Dutch
£1389 $2194 €2000 Cattle in a meadow (39x31cm-15x12in) s. panel. 2-Sep-3 Christie's, Amsterdam #150/R est:2000-3000
£2667 $4800 €4000 Shepherd and his flock. Cattle in a meadow (20x23cm-8x9in) s.d.1817 panel pair. 20-Apr-4 Sotheby's, Amsterdam #46/R est:4000-6000
Works on paper
£273 $500 €399 Landscape with cows resting (22x30cm-9x12in) init. brush brown ink wash over pencil. 29-Jan-4 Swann Galleries, New York #198/R
£483 $869 €700 Le repos du troupeau (32x41cm-13x16in) s.d.1838 W/C. 26-Jan-4 Gros & Delettrez, Paris #14
£850 $1530 €1241 Drovers with sheep, goats and cattle in an Italianate landscape (41x52cm-16x20in) s.d.1808 W/C prov. 21-Apr-4 Cheffins, Cambridge #454/R

OS, Tony van (1886-1945) Belgian
£845 $1462 €1200 Matinee de Septembre, Anvers (90x111cm-35x44in) s. 13-Dec-3 De Vuyst, Lokeren #361
£1533 $2760 €2300 River landscape with moored sloops and farmhouse (103x140cm-41x55in) s. 26-Apr-4 Bernaerts, Antwerp #290/R est:1250-1500

OS, van (attrib) (18th C) Dutch
£9000 $16200 €13140 Still life - mixed garden flowers in a vase (76x56cm-30x22in) prov. 20-Apr-4 Clarke Gammon, Guildford #20/R est:3000-5000

OS-DELHEZ, Hendrik van (1880-1976) Dutch
£867 $1586 €1300 Montmartre (28x38cm-11x15in) s.i. 7-Jun-4 Glerum, Amsterdam #21/R

OSA, Lars (1860-1958) Norwegian
£3098 $5174 €4523 Musicians in the open-hearth room (67x53cm-26x21in) s. 20-Oct-3 Blomqvist, Lysaker #1234/R est:25000-30000 (N.KR 36000)

OSANNE (1934-) French?
Works on paper
£268 $481 €400 Petit week-end (38x46cm-15x18in) s. mixed media on canvas. 30-May-4 Eric Pillon, Calais #312/R

OSBERT, Alphonse (1857-1939) French
Works on paper
£1467 $2699 €2200 Nocturne ou melancolie (41x30cm-16x12in) s. crayon chl rounded top. 11-Jun-4 Claude Aguttes, Neuilly #58/R est:1500-2000
£1667 $3067 €2500 Lyrisme (28x35cm-11x14in) chl htd white chk rounded top. 11-Jun-4 Claude Aguttes, Neuilly #59/R est:2000-3000

OSBORN, Emily Mary (1834-?) British
Works on paper
£650 $1183 €949 Rural scene with a watermill, barges, moored boats and a village inn (74x36cm-29x14in) s. W/C. 3-Feb-4 Gorringes, Bexhill #946/R

OSBORN, Emily Mary (attrib) (1834-?) British
£604 $1111 €900 Cows grazing (51x76cm-20x30in) s.d.1885. 26-Mar-4 Bolland & Marotz, Bremen #570/R

OSBORN, Suzan (20th C) American
£471 $800 €688 Idle afternoon in the Catmint (28x35cm-11x14in) s.d.03. 21-Nov-3 Skinner, Boston #92/R

OSBORNE, Dennis Henry (1919-) British
£263 $484 €400 Still life with vase and apple (36x31cm-14x12in) s. prov. 22-Jun-4 De Veres Art Auctions, Dublin #214/R
£347 $545 €500 Bridge Street Lisburn (77x29cm-30x11in) s. board. 26-Aug-3 James Adam, Dublin #29/R

OSBORNE, Elizabeth (20th C) American
£756 $1300 €1104 Flowers for J L (51x61cm-20x24in) s. painted 1962 prov. 7-Dec-3 Freeman, Philadelphia #212

OSBORNE, James (1940-1992) British
Sculpture
£900 $1638 €1314 Leopard negotiating a tree trunk. s.d.92 brown pat bronze wood socle. 15-Jun-4 Sotheby's, Olympia #70/R est:1000-1500

OSBORNE, Walter (1859-1903) Irish
£10667 $19307 €16000 Cottage garden, Antwerp (30x12cm-12x5in) board prov. 31-Mar-4 James Adam, Dublin #104/R est:10000-15000
£14085 $24366 €20000 Study of a village (18x25cm-7x10in) s.i.d.1901 canvasboard. 10-Dec-3 Bonhams & James Adam, Dublin #60/R est:20000-25000
£19580 $33287 €28000 Flemish homestead (27x17cm-11x7in) init. board. 25-Nov-3 De Veres Art Auctions, Dublin #50/R est:25000-35000
£23026 $42368 €35000 The end of the day (40x31cm-16x12in) s. board prov. 22-Jun-4 De Veres Art Auctions, Dublin #42/R est:35000-50000
£300000 $537000 €438000 A new arrival (46x36cm-18x14in) s. painted 1885. 14-May-4 Christie's, London #179/R est:300000-500000
Works on paper
£750 $1343 €1095 Sarah Purser (12x11cm-5x4in) pencil prov. 14-May-4 Christie's, London #32/R
£1250 $2238 €1825 Lady with spectacles (18x13cm-7x5in) pencil prov. 14-May-4 Christie's, London #33/R est:800-1200
£2800 $5012 €4088 Study for Milking Time in St Marnock's Byre (19x25cm-7x10in) i. pencil prov. 14-May-4 Christie's, London #35/R est:2000-3000
£3600 $6444 €5256 Sketch for Cherry Ripe (33x24cm-13x9in) pencil prov.exhib.lit. 14-May-4 Christie's, London #34/R est:4000-6000
£3873 $6701 €5500 Portrait of Lydia May Montgomery (33x24cm-13x9in) s. pastel. 10-Dec-3 Bonhams & James Adam, Dublin #29/R est:3000-5000
£12238 $20804 €17500 Portrait of Aubrey lane (69x42cm-27x17in) s.d.1891 pastel prov. 25-Nov-3 De Veres Art Auctions, Dublin #97/R est:10000-15000

OSBORNE, William (1823-1901) Irish
£2817 $4507 €4000 Pepita (51x66cm-20x26in) mono. 16-Sep-3 Whyte's, Dublin #109/R est:4000-6000
£4336 $7371 €6200 Terrier (44x37cm-17x15in) mono. prov. 25-Nov-3 De Veres Art Auctions, Dublin #62/R est:4000-6000
£10563 $18275 €15000 Bay hunter, saddled, outside a stable (49x63cm-19x25in) s.d.1867 verso. 10-Dec-3 Bonhams & James Adam, Dublin #18/R est:15000-20000

OSCARSSON, Bernhard (1894-1971) Swedish
£733 $1297 €1070 The water carrier (81x54cm-32x21in) s.d.1956. 27-Apr-4 AB Stockholms Auktionsverk #727/R (S.KR 10000)
£3533 $5759 €5158 The Central yard plans (34x47cm-13x19in) s.d.1932 cardboard. 29-Sep-3 Lilla Bukowskis, Stockholm #451 est:8000-10000 (S.KR 46000)

OSGOOD, Charles (1809-1890) American
£389 $700 €568 Portrait of a lady, said to be Sarah Shepard Cooke Cushing (74x61cm-29x24in) oval. 23-Jan-4 Freeman, Philadelphia #182/R

OSGOOD, Harry Haviland (1875-?) American
£233 $400 €340 Late summer day. s. board painted c.1925. 7-Dec-3 Treadway Gallery, Cincinnati #546/R

OSGOOD, Ruth (?-1977) American
£331 $600 €483 Picnic on the rocks (51x64cm-20x25in) s. 16-Apr-4 James Julia, Fairfield #629/R

O'SHEA, John (1876-1956) American
Works on paper
£707 $1300 €1032 Crashing surf (44x54cm-17x21in) s. pencil W/C prov. 8-Jun-4 Bonhams & Butterfields, San Francisco #4235/R est:2000-3000

OSHIN, Maruyama (1790-1838) Japanese
Works on paper
£1400 $2338 €2030 Dragonfly and Plants (92x27cm-36x11in) s. ink paper silk hanging scrolls four. 18-Jun-3 Christie's, London #292 est:1800-2000

OSHIVER, Harry J (1888-1974) American/Russian
Works on paper
£419 $700 €612 Standing male figure (99x56cm-39x22in) s.d.1917 pastel. 20-Jun-3 Freeman, Philadelphia #42/R

OSHUITOQ, Anirnik (1902-1983) Canadian
Works on paper
£315 $536 €460 Man and woman (48x63cm-19x25in) stencil. 3-Nov-3 Waddingtons, Toronto #276/R (C.D 700)

O'SICKEY, Joseph B (1918-) American
£346 $550 €502 Untitled (8x102cm-3x40in) s. d.1953 verso. 12-Sep-3 Aspire, Cleveland #108

OSIPOW, Paul (1937-) Finnish
£270 $484 €400 Composition (42x50cm-17x20in) s.d.72 paper. 8-May-4 Bukowskis, Helsinki #289/R
£867 $1551 €1300 Composition (121x81cm-48x32in) s.d.1989 acrylic. 15-May-4 Hagelstam, Helsinki #232/R
£1056 $1827 €1500 Composition (120x80cm-47x31in) s. d.1989 verso. 13-Dec-3 Hagelstam, Helsinki #189/R est:1000

OSLER, Emanuel Victor (1860-?) Austrian
£811 $1451 €1200 Plattensee shore (62x95cm-24x37in) s. 6-May-4 Michael Zeller, Lindau #807/R

OSNAGHI, Josefine (fl.1890-1920) Austrian
£667 $1200 €1000 Tea with cherries (20x26cm-8x10in) s. panel prov. 21-Apr-4 Christie's, Amsterdam #24/R

OSORIO LUQUE, Antonio (1913-) Argentinian
£495 $900 €723 Coming back (30x40cm-12x16in) s.i.d.1970. 5-Jul-4 Arroyo, Buenos Aires #26/R
£782 $1400 €1142 Landscape near Quebrada (40x50cm-16x20in) 11-May-4 Arroyo, Buenos Aires #66

OSORIO, Signe (20th C) Portuguese?
Works on paper
£268 $481 €400 Interior with chair and chest of drawers (36x28cm-14x11in) s.d.1940 W/C. 31-May-4 Cabral Moncada Leiloes, Lisbon #383/R

OSPINA ORTIZ, Juan Carlos (20th C) Spanish
£3276 $5471 €4750 Fruit II (60x70cm-24x28in) s. 11-Nov-3 Castellana, Madrid #124/R est:4500

OSPINA, Nadin (1960-) Colombian
Sculpture
£8235 $14000 €12023 Jugador de pelota (55x41x25cm-22x16x10in) inscribed sig.d.2001 num.1/7 brown pat. bronze exhib. 19-Nov-3 Sotheby's, New York #55/R est:10000-15000

OSSA, Wilhelm (20th C) American?
£539 $900 €787 The bar (119x58cm-47x23in) s. polychrome exhib. 25-Oct-3 David Rago, Lambertville #383/R

OSSANI, Alessandro (fl.1857-1888) British
£1200 $2220 €1752 Little harvest girl (81x59cm-32x23in) s.d.1872. 13-Jan-4 Bonhams, Knightsbridge #34/R est:500-800

OSSLUND, Helmer (1866-1938) Swedish
£385 $662 €562 Landscape (46x61cm-18x24in) s. greaseproof paper on panel. 3-Dec-3 AB Stockholms Auktionsverk #2245/R (S.KR 5000)
£471 $815 €688 Winter landscape with buildings (16x28cm-6x11in) s.d.99 canvas on panel. 15-Dec-3 Lilla Bukowskis, Stockholm #472 (S.KR 6000)
£480 $860 €701 Mountain landscape in autumn colours (26x35cm-10x14in) s. greaseproof paper. 28-May-4 Uppsala Auktionskammare, Uppsala #170/R (S.KR 6500)
£500 $860 €730 Landscape with buildings (22x27cm-9x11in) s. greaseproof paper on panel. 7-Dec-3 Uppsala Auktionskammare, Uppsala #170/R (S.KR 6500)
£566 $978 €826 Docksta farmer (33x41cm-13x16in) s. paper on canvas on cardboard exhib. 15-Dec-3 Lilla Bukowskis, Stockholm #455/R (S.KR 7200)
£615 $1058 €898 Summer in Nordland (22x32cm-9x13in) s. greaseproof paper on cardboard. 2-Dec-3 Bukowskis, Stockholm #113/R (S.KR 8000)
£721 $1297 €1053 Alpine landscape (26x38cm-10x15in) s. greaseproof paper on cardboard. 26-Jan-4 Lilla Bukowskis, Stockholm #140 (S.KR 9600)
£938 $1689 €1369 Landscape from Raggforsen, Medelpad (43x32cm-17x13in) s. greaseproof paper on cardboard. 26-Jan-4 Lilla Bukowskis, Stockholm #423 (S.KR 12500)
£1020 $1878 €1530 Landscape from Moja (31x50cm-12x20in) s. greaseproof paper on cardboard. 14-Jun-4 Lilla Bukowskis, Stockholm #348 (S.KR 14000)
£1276 $2297 €1863 Common hepatica (24x19cm-9x7in) s.d.31. 26-Jan-4 Lilla Bukowskis, Stockholm #775 est:10000-12000 (S.KR 17000)
£1404 $2514 €2050 Summer landscape (57x33cm-22x13in) s. paper. 26-May-4 AB Stockholms Auktionsverk #2343/R est:15000-18000 (S.KR 19000)
£1423 $2448 €2078 From Gymnasiet in Harnosand with trees in autumn colours (43x60cm-17x24in) s. panel. 3-Dec-3 AB Stockholms Auktionsverk #2471/R est:12000-15000 (S.KR 18500)
£1462 $2514 €2135 River landscape (38x73cm-15x29in) s. greaseproof paper on board. 2-Dec-3 Bukowskis, Stockholm #105/R est:20000-25000 (S.KR 19000)
£1615 $2778 €2358 Landscape, Lapporten (27x46cm-11x18in) s canvas on board. 2-Dec-3 Bukowskis, Stockholm #114a/R est:15000-20000 (S.KR 21000)
£2077 $3572 €3032 Northern landscape with blue mountains (39x49cm-15x19in) s. panel. 3-Dec-3 AB Stockholms Auktionsverk #2293/R est:25000-30000 (S.KR 27000)
£2624 $4697 €3831 Autumn landscape, Angermanland (22x34cm-9x13in) s. greaseproof paper on cardboard. 25-May-4 Bukowskis, Stockholm #87/R est:25000-30000 (S.KR 35500)
£2735 $4895 €3993 Autumn landscape from Abisko (34x65cm-13x26in) s. greaseproof paper on panel painted c.1925. 25-May-4 Bukowskis, Stockholm #82/R est:25000-30000 (S.KR 37000)
£2846 $4895 €4155 Sunset in Aadalen (30x41cm-12x16in) s. cardboard. 2-Dec-3 Bukowskis, Stockholm #106/R est:20000-25000 (S.KR 37000)
£2846 $4895 €4155 View from Ringkallen (36x63cm-14x25in) s. greaseproof paper on canvas. 2-Dec-3 Bukowskis, Stockholm #114/R est:25000-30000 (S.KR 37000)
£2956 $5292 €4316 Salmon fishing (42x86cm-17x34in) cardboard. 25-May-4 Bukowskis, Stockholm #228/R est:100000-125000 (S.KR 40000)
£3104 $5557 €4532 Coastal landscape, Angermanland (34x43cm-13x17in) s. greaseproof paper on cardboard painted c.1927. 25-May-4 Bukowskis, Stockholm #88/R est:25000-30000 (S.KR 42000)
£3231 $5557 €4717 Reindeer Mountain, Aare (51x86cm-20x34in) s. greaseproof paper on board. 2-Dec-3 Bukowskis, Stockholm #104/R est:35000-40000 (S.KR 42000)
£3252 $5821 €4748 Breakers (35x61cm-14x24in) s. greaseproof paper on panel. 25-May-4 Bukowskis, Stockholm #81/R est:25000-30000 (S.KR 44000)
£3538 $6086 €5165 Landscape, Porjus (57x82cm-22x32in) s. greaseproof paper on board. 2-Dec-3 Bukowskis, Stockholm #112/R est:60000-80000 (S.KR 46000)
£3548 $6350 €5180 Mountain landscape with reindeer (49x81cm-19x32in) s. tempera cardboard on cloth. 25-May-4 Bukowskis, Stockholm #86/R est:30000-40000 (S.KR 48000)
£4287 $7673 €6259 Approaching storm, bay of Genoa (39x70cm-15x28in) s. greaseproof paper on panel exhib.lit. 25-May-4 Bukowskis, Stockholm #83/R est:35000-40000 (S.KR 58000)
£4615 $7938 €6738 Winter at Stora Sjofallet (36x77cm-14x30in) s. greaseproof paper on panel. 2-Dec-3 Bukowskis, Stockholm #103/R est:50000-60000 (S.KR 60000)
£10717 $19183 €15647 Spring day by the river (59x81cm-23x32in) s. panel. 25-May-4 Bukowskis, Stockholm #94/R est:120000-140000 (S.KR 145000)
£11086 $19845 €16186 Northern river landscape (38x68cm-15x27in) s. panel. 26-May-4 AB Stockholms Auktionsverk #2347/R est:75000-100000 (S.KR 150000)
£12500 $22750 €18250 Lake Sjofallet in winter (49x82cm-19x32in) indis.s. paper on board prov.exhib.lit. 15-Jun-4 Sotheby's, London #323/R est:12000-18000
£12934 $23152 €18884 Landscape from Slugga, Suorva (42x68cm-17x27in) s. canvas on cardboard. 25-May-4 Bukowskis, Stockholm #201/R est:100000-125000 (S.KR 175000)
£15891 $28444 €23201 Landscape from Slugga, Suorva (67x115cm-26x45in) s. 25-May-4 Bukowskis, Stockholm #90/R est:250000-300000 (S.KR 215000)
£30769 $52923 €44923 View from Ringkallen, Aangermanland (52x101cm-20x40in) s. greaseproof paper on panel. 2-Dec-3 Bukowskis, Stockholm #107/R est:250000-300000 (S.KR 400000)
Works on paper
£480 $860 €701 Landscape with red houses (28x51cm-11x20in) s. gouache. 28-May-4 Uppsala Auktionskammare, Uppsala #188 (S.KR 6500)
£688 $1108 €1004 Northern landscape, autumn (34x50cm-13x20in) s. W/C. 25-Aug-3 Lilla Bukowskis, Stockholm #123 (S.KR 9000)
£923 $1588 €1348 Northern landscape with cottage, winter (38x55cm-15x22in) s. gouache. 3-Dec-3 AB Stockholms Auktionsverk #2238/R (S.KR 12000)
£3923 $6748 €5728 Northern landscape, summer (39x87cm-15x34in) s. gouache. 3-Dec-3 AB Stockholms Auktionsverk #2279/R est:12000-15000 (S.KR 51000)
£18477 $33075 €26976 Autumn by Klocka, Jamtland (42x68cm-17x27in) s.d.1905 gouache prov.exhib.lit. 25-May-4 Bukowskis, Stockholm #85/R est:175000-200000 (S.KR 250000)

OSSOLA, Giancarlo (1935-) Italian
£333 $613 €500 Contamination (35x25cm-14x10in) s.i.d.1990 verso. 12-Jun-4 Meeting Art, Vercelli #325/R

OSSWALD, Eugen (1879-1960) German
£382 $623 €550 Ox and horse pulling plough (26x34cm-10x13in) s. panel. 25-Sep-3 Dr Fritz Nagel, Stuttgart #1391/R
£433 $797 €650 Chamois in a mountain landscape (41x52cm-16x20in) s. 11-Jun-4 Wendl, Rudolstadt #4205/R
£667 $1200 €1000 At the finish (40x52cm-16x20in) s. 26-Apr-4 Rieber, Stuttgart #1255/R

OSSWALD, Fritz (1878-1966) Swiss
£282 $451 €400 Abula pass (70x78cm-28x31in) s. i. verso panel lit. 19-Sep-3 Karlheinz Kaupp, Staufen #2066/R
£414 $713 €604 On the banks of the Elbe (47x57cm-19x22in) s. i.verso board. 8-Dec-3 Philippe Schuler, Zurich #5949 (S.FR 920)
£633 $1077 €924 Autumn sunshine (63x76cm-25x30in) s.d.16. 28-Nov-3 Falk & Falk, Zurich #413 (S.FR 1400)
£1101 $1839 €1596 Spring day in park near Zurichberg (86x111cm-34x44in) s.d.1905. 23-Jun-3 Philippe Schuler, Zurich #3409 (S.FR 2400)
£2333 $4177 €3500 Palace garden in winter (42x56cm-17x22in) s. s.i.d.1916 verso board. 14-May-4 Von Zezschwitz, Munich #377/R est:3000

OSSWALD, Hilda (19/20th C) German?
£483 $806 €700 Snail rider (25x16cm-10x6in) s. i. verso masonite. 15-Nov-3 Von Zezschwitz, Munich #47/R

OSSWALD, Karl (1925-1972) German
Works on paper
£461 $847 €700 Landscape in the Hegau region (55x75cm-22x30in) s. W/C. 26-Jun-4 Karrenbauer, Konstanz #1757
£671 $1235 €1000 Garden full of blossoming fruit trees (57x75cm-22x30in) s. mixed media lit. 26-Mar-4 Karrenbauer, Konstanz #1754

OSSWALD-TOPPI, Margherita (1897-1971) Italian
£396 $674 €578 Bouquet of dried flowers (46x35cm-18x14in) s. board. 5-Nov-3 Dobiaschofsky, Bern #842/R (S.FR 900)
£437 $803 €638 Still life with sunflowers (53x67cm-21x26in) s. board. 8-Jun-4 Germann, Zurich #851 (S.FR 1000)
£611 $1125 €892 Still life (53x70cm-21x28in) s. panel. 8-Jun-4 Germann, Zurich #850 (S.FR 1400)
£749 $1273 €1094 Young girl (70x56cm-28x22in) s. board. 7-Nov-3 Dobiaschofsky, Bern #172/R (S.FR 1700)
£1013 $1722 €1479 Two flower girls (79x41cm-31x16in) s. board. 7-Nov-3 Dobiaschofsky, Bern #171/R est:3600 (S.FR 2300)
£1336 $2392 €1951 Girl in pink dress (96x59cm-38x23in) s. board. 14-May-4 Dobiaschofsky, Bern #192/R est:3800 (S.FR 3100)

OST, Alfred (1884-1945) Belgian
Works on paper
£268 $491 €400 Untitled (28x35cm-11x14in) mono.d.1923 W/C exhib. 8-Jul-4 Campo, Vlaamse Kaai #220
£300 $537 €450 The walk (25x17cm-10x7in) d.43 wash Indian ink. 15-May-4 De Vuyst, Lokeren #242
£350 $584 €500 The dance (36x27cm-14x11in) mono.i.d.XII Indian ink. 11-Oct-3 De Vuyst, Lokeren #273
£373 $646 €530 The road to Antwerp (28x36cm-11x14in) s.d.23 wash Indian ink. 13-Dec-3 De Vuyst, Lokeren #254
£387 $670 €550 Figures (24x24cm-9x9in) mono. Chinese ink. 15-Dec-3 Bernaerts, Antwerp #1493/R
£433 $776 €650 On the way (24x32cm-9x13in) s. Indian ink. 15-May-4 De Vuyst, Lokeren #241
£455 $759 €650 Female flower (35x28cm-14x11in) mono.d.XXXVIII W/C Indian ink. 11-Oct-3 De Vuyst, Lokeren #272
£458 $792 €650 Calvarie (15x11cm-6x4in) mono. W/C exhib. 13-Dec-3 De Vuyst, Lokeren #251
£567 $1014 €850 Peace messenger (27x35cm-11x14in) s.i.d.39 W/C. 15-May-4 De Vuyst, Lokeren #240
£594 $993 €850 Lime trees, Hoogstraten (27x35cm-11x14in) mono.d.XXXX W/C Indian ink. 11-Oct-3 De Vuyst, Lokeren #271

OSTADE, Adriaen van (1610-1684) Dutch

£14500 $24650 €21170 Peasants drinking in an interior (28x23cm-11x9in) panel prov. 29-Oct-3 Christie's, London #30/R est:10000-15000
£19310 $32055 €28000 Peasant family in barn (17x21cm-7x8in) prov. panel. 1-Oct-3 Dorotheum, Vienna #89/R est:20000-30000

Prints

£2200 $3784 €3212 Knifegrinder (8x7cm-3x3in) etching exec.c.1682 prov. 4-Dec-3 Sotheby's, London #63/R est:2000-3000
£2533 $4535 €3800 Saying Grace (16x13cm-6x5in) etching. 13-May-4 Bassenge, Berlin #5245/R est:2400
£2700 $4644 €3942 Quacksalver (15x12cm-6x5in) etching. 4-Dec-3 Sotheby's, London #67/R est:3000-5000
£2700 $4644 €3942 Hunchbacked fiddler (16x11cm-6x4in) etching exec.c.1654 prov. 4-Dec-3 Sotheby's, London #68/R est:3000-5000
£2800 $4816 €4088 Peasants' quarrel (13x14cm-5x6in) etching prov. 4-Dec-3 Sotheby's, London #52/R est:2000-3000
£2800 $4816 €4088 Barn (16x19cm-6x7in) etching prov. 4-Dec-3 Sotheby's, London #55/R est:2000-3000
£3500 $6020 €5110 Fiddler and the hurdy-gurdy boy (15x13cm-6x5in) etching exec.c.1660 prov. 4-Dec-3 Sotheby's, London #69/R est:4000-6000
£3800 $6536 €5548 Mother with two children (9x7cm-4x3in) etching exec.c.1675 prov. 4-Dec-3 Sotheby's, London #48/R est:1500-2000
£4000 $6880 €5840 Village romance (16x12cm-6x5in) etching exec.c.1667. 4-Dec-3 Sotheby's, London #46/R est:2000-3000
£4000 $6880 €5840 The doll (10x9cm-4x4in) etching sold with another etching. 4-Dec-3 Sotheby's, London #50/R est:2500-3500
£4500 $7740 €6570 Breakfast (20x26cm-8x10in) etching exec.c.1664. 4-Dec-3 Sotheby's, London #73/R est:5000-7000
£4800 $8256 €7008 Woman spinning (14x17cm-6x7in) etching prov. 4-Dec-3 Sotheby's, London #60/R est:1800-2200
£5200 $8944 €7592 Pigkillers (12x12cm-5x5in) etching prov. 4-Dec-3 Sotheby's, London #65/R est:4000-6000
£5500 $9460 €8030 Singers (24x19cm-9x7in) etching exec.c.1667 prov. 4-Dec-3 Sotheby's, London #53/R est:2500-3500
£6500 $11180 €9490 Organ grinder (11x9cm-4x4in) etching prov. 4-Dec-3 Sotheby's, London #45/R est:5000-7000
£6500 $11180 €9490 Man and woman conversing (9x8cm-4x3in) etching exec.c.1673 prov. 4-Dec-3 Sotheby's, London #47/R est:3000-4000
£6500 $11180 €9490 Painter (23x17cm-9x7in) etching exec.c.1667 prov. 4-Dec-3 Sotheby's, London #61/R est:2000-3000
£13000 $22360 €18980 Family (18x16cm-7x6in) etching prov. 4-Dec-3 Sotheby's, London #70/R est:10000-15000
£13500 $23220 €19710 Anglers (11x16cm-4x6in) etching exec.c.1653. 4-Dec-3 Sotheby's, London #59/R est:5000-8000
£16000 $27520 €23360 Dance under the trellis (13x17cm-5x7in) etching exec.c.1652 prov. 4-Dec-3 Sotheby's, London #71/R est:8000-12000
£18500 $31820 €27010 Fair (12x23cm-5x9in) etching exec.c.1660 prov. 4-Dec-3 Sotheby's, London #72/R est:10000-15000

Works on paper

£3378 $5946 €5000 Standing peasant with his hand in his pocket (6x3cm-2x1in) pen grey ink W/C prov.lit. 19-May-4 Sotheby's, Amsterdam #76/R est:5000-7000
£10811 $19027 €16000 Peasants fighting in an inn (15x28cm-6x11in) pen brown ink wash black chk prov.exhib.lit. 19-May-4 Sotheby's, Amsterdam #75/R est:10000-15000

OSTADE, Adriaen van (attrib) (1610-1684) Dutch

£2270 $3790 €3200 Interieur d'auberge anime (43x55cm-17x22in) panel. 14-Oct-3 Vanderkindere, Brussels #20

OSTADE, Isaac van (1621-1649) Dutch

£15000 $27450 €21900 Interior with peasants playing cards (18x18cm-7x7in) s.i. panel prov.exhib.lit. 8-Jul-4 Sotheby's, London #130/R est:20000-30000
£67123 $114110 €98000 Winter landscape with skaters, children playing on the ice, near a bridge (41x48cm-16x19in) s. panel prov.exhib. 4-Nov-3 Sotheby's, Amsterdam #72/R est:20000-30000

OSTERGAARD, Niels (1924-1974) Danish

£406 $747 €593 Room and landscape (114x162cm-45x64in) init.d.67 verso exhib. 29-Mar-4 Rasmussen, Copenhagen #487/R (D.KR 4500)

OSTERIDER, Adolf A (1924-) Austrian

Works on paper

£420 $722 €600 House on the southern coast (59x42cm-23x17in) s. W/C. 4-Dec-3 Dorotheum, Graz #75/R

OSTERLIN, Anders (1926-) Swedish

£373 $679 €560 Composition (92x89cm-36x35in) 19-Jun-4 Rasmussen, Havnen #4069 (D.KR 4200)

OSTERLIND, Allan (1855-1938) Swedish

£538 $926 €785 Summer landscape from the island Brehat, France (39x46cm-15x18in) s. cardboard. 3-Dec-3 AB Stockholms Auktionsverk #2314/R (S.KR 7000)
£538 $926 €785 Portrait of Rabbi Louis Imhoff (62x50cm-24x20in) s.i.d.1886. 3-Dec-3 AB Stockholms Auktionsverk #2406/R (S.KR 7000)

Works on paper

£461 $847 €700 Autour de l'enfant (85x60cm-33x24in) s. W/C paper on canvas. 28-Jun-4 Joron-Derem, Paris #98
£493 $908 €750 Scene intime (85x60cm-33x24in) s. W/C paper on canvas. 28-Jun-4 Joron-Derem, Paris #97/R

OSTERLIND, Anders (1887-1960) French

£265 $482 €400 Fonceau-Charente (38x46cm-15x18in) s. 18-Jun-4 Piasa, Paris #141
£699 $1168 €1000 Roque Haute, Aix-en-Provence (116x87cm-46x34in) s.d.1958. 30-Jun-3 Bailly Pommery, Paris #113/R
£704 $1218 €1000 Arbres et maison en bord de route (54x65cm-21x26in) s.d.1954 verso. 10-Dec-3 Rossini, Paris #99
£805 $1506 €1200 Tempete sur la chaumiere (80x100cm-31x39in) s. 24-Feb-4 Thierry & Lannon, Brest #331/R
£1197 $2071 €1700 Chemin a l'oree du village (60x73cm-24x29in) 12-Dec-3 Piasa, Paris #127 est:2000-3000

OSTERMAN, Bernhard (1870-1938) ?

£1532 $2650 €2237 Joran Persson captured in King Erik XIV's state-room (235x325cm-93x128in) s. prov. 15-Dec-3 Lilla Bukowskis, Stockholm #900 est:25000 (S.KR 19500)

OSTERMAN, Elvine (1908-1997) Swedish

£1595 $2872 €2393 Coastal landscape with bay (91x96cm-36x38in) s. 25-Apr-4 Goteborg Auktionsverk, Sweden #353/R est:18000 (S.KR 22000)
£2568 $4366 €3749 Sailing boats on a summer morning (77x100cm-30x39in) s. 5-Nov-3 AB Stockholms Auktionsverk #804/R est:10000-12000 (S.KR 34000)

OSTERSETZER, Carl (1865-1914) Austrian

£638 $1129 €950 Shoemaker drinking schnaps (48x31cm-19x12in) s. bears d.04 panel. 28-Apr-4 Schopman, Hamburg #511/R
£667 $1213 €1000 Portrait of a young woman (26x20cm-10x8in) s.d.1904 panel. 1-Jul-4 Van Ham, Cologne #1546
£694 $1132 €1000 Portrait of a Jewish man (19x14cm-7x6in) s. 23-Sep-3 Wiener Kunst Auktionen, Vienna #10/R
£833 $1317 €1200 Cellar master tasting the wine (48x31cm-19x12in) bears sig. panel. 6-Sep-3 Arnold, Frankfurt #634/R
£867 $1577 €1300 Wine tasting (53x42cm-21x17in) s.d.1905 panel. 1-Jul-4 Van Ham, Cologne #1545/R
£1067 $1963 €1600 Le joueur de violon dans une auberge (47x31cm-19x12in) s. panel. 14-Jun-4 Horta, Bruxelles #56 est:1500-2000
£2484 $4000 €3627 Counting up his money (32x25cm-13x10in) s.d.90 panel. 14-Jan-4 Christie's, Rockefeller NY #7/R est:800-1200
£2778 $4722 €4000 Card trick (54x68cm-21x27in) s. 28-Oct-3 Dorotheum, Vienna #161/R est:3200-3800
£2993 $5358 €4400 Chess game (55x85cm-22x33in) s. 17-Mar-4 Neumeister, Munich #560/R est:2000

OSTERWALD, George (1803-1884) German

Works on paper

£1067 $1909 €1600 Southern park (74x105cm-29x41in) s. lit. 14-May-4 Schloss Ahlden, Ahlden #2779/R est:1600

OSTHAUS, Edmund H (1858-1928) American

£4651 $8000 €6790 Hounds on a scent (69x89cm-27x35in) prov. 5-Dec-3 Christie's, Rockefeller NY #56/R est:15000-20000
£6522 $12000 €9522 Cows resting (122x184cm-48x72in) s. prov.exhib. 8-Jun-4 Bonhams & Butterfields, San Francisco #4023/R est:10000-15000
£22727 $40000 €33181 Setter and her puppies (91x66cm-36x26in) s. 19-May-4 Sotheby's, New York #94/R est:25000-35000

Works on paper

£299 $500 €437 Landscape with tree (41x41cm-16x16in) s.d.1888 W/C. 20-Jun-3 Freeman, Philadelphia #84/R
£449 $750 €656 Forest interior with stream (38x61cm-15x24in) s. W/C. 20-Jun-3 Freeman, Philadelphia #52/R
£2162 $4000 €3157 The tiger hunt (46x84cm-18x33in) s. W/C htd white. 10-Feb-4 Doyle, New York #205/R est:4000-6000
£4190 $7500 €6117 Father and son with setters (25x30cm-10x12in) s. W/C. 8-May-4 Susanin's, Chicago #6089/R est:8000-10000
£5523 $9500 €8064 English setters pointing (39x54cm-15x21in) s. W/C bodycol paper on card. 5-Dec-3 Christie's, Rockefeller NY #57/R est:12000-18000
£26163 $45000 €38198 English setters at a stream (67x100cm-26x39in) s. W/C bodycol. 5-Dec-3 Christie's, Rockefeller NY #93/R est:40000-60000

OSTLIHN, Barbro (1930-1995) Swedish

£1511 $2568 €2206 Brooklyn Bridge I (46x51cm-18x20in) s.d.63 exhib.prov. 5-Nov-3 AB Stockholms Auktionsverk #914/R est:25000-30000 (S.KR 20000)
£1978 $3501 €2888 Man-hole-cover (104x115cm-41x45in) s.d.1962 prov.exhib.lit. 27-Apr-4 AB Stockholms Auktionsverk #1145/R est:40000-50000 (S.KR 27000)
£2930 $5187 €4278 229 Water Street (100x212cm-39x83in) s.d.1964 prov.exhib.lit. 27-Apr-4 AB Stockholms Auktionsverk #975/R est:30000-40000 (S.KR 40000)
£3021 $5136 €4411 17th William Street (143x178cm-56x70in) s.d.67 exhib.prov. 5-Nov-3 AB Stockholms Auktionsverk #911/R est:50000-70000 (S.KR 40000)
£3223 $5705 €4706 20 Fulton Street (167x176cm-66x69in) s.d.1967 exhib.prov. 27-Apr-4 AB Stockholms Auktionsverk #994/R est:50000-60000 (S.KR 44000)
£3297 $5835 €4814 261 Fifth Avenue (120x50cm-47x20in) s.d.68 exhib.lit. 27-Apr-4 AB Stockholms Auktionsverk #993/R est:20000-30000 (S.KR 45000)
£4154 $7062 €6065 10th Street Wall - even China (178x153cm-70x60in) s.d.74 prov.exhib.lit. 5-Nov-3 AB Stockholms Auktionsverk #912/R est:40000-60000 (S.KR 55000)
£5287 $8988 €7719 New York Steam Company (178x117cm-70x46in) s.d.62 prov.exhib.lit. 5-Nov-3 AB Stockholms Auktionsverk #909/R est:60000-70000 (S.KR 70000)
£5287 $8988 €7719 Brooklyn Bridge II (209x127cm-82x50in) s.d.1963 prov.exhib.lit. 5-Nov-3 AB Stockholms Auktionsverk #913/R est:70000-80000 (S.KR 70000)
£24924 $42372 €36389 Erik's house - Lego (225x144cm-89x57in) s.d.1965 prov.exhib.lit. 5-Nov-3 AB Stockholms Auktionsverk #908/R est:100000-125000 (S.KR 330000)
£27190 $46224 €39697 The Cold War (45x107cm-18x42in) s.d.69 diptych pair prov.exhib.lit. 5-Nov-3 AB Stockholms Auktionsverk #907/R est:50000-70000 (S.KR 360000)

OSUITOK, Ipeelee (1922-) North American

Sculpture

£3378 $5743 €4932 Inuit hunter fighting off a musk ox (51cm-20in) mottled grey soapstone. 3-Nov-3 Waddingtons, Toronto #120/R est:8000-12000 (C.D 7500)

O'SULLIVAN, Sean (1906-1964) British

£2568 $4853 €3800 Gardens with view of a neoclassical temple (51x61cm-20x24in) s. board. 17-Feb-4 Whyte's, Dublin #221/R est:3000-4000

Works on paper

£361 $589 €520 Head of a Celtic Warrior (11x11cm-4x4in) s.d.1927 pen ink. 24-Sep-3 James Adam, Dublin #115/R
£436 $781 €650 Study of a man (40x34cm-16x13in) s.d.1935 pastel. 31-May-4 Hamilton Osborne King, Dublin #117/R

£638 $1141 €950 Study of a boy (52x40cm-20x16in) s.d. 1936 pastel. 31-May-4 Hamilton Osborne King, Dublin #116/R

OSUNA, Justo (20th C) Venezuelan?
Works on paper
£383 $625 €559 Circular still life with flowers (90x120cm-35x47in) s. mixed media on canvas exec.1994. 20-Jul-3 Subastas Odalys, Caracas #91

OSUNA, Manuel (19th C) Spanish
£839 $1401 €1200 Landscapes with figures (51x33cm-20x13in) s.d.1917-1918 pair. 30-Jun-3 Ansorena, Madrid #237/R
£1103 $1832 €1600 Woman amongst flowers (72x52cm-28x20in) s. 30-Sep-3 Ansorena, Madrid #114/R est:1600
Works on paper
£336 $614 €500 Couple (66x33cm-26x13in) s.d.1914 W/C. 12-Jul-4 Durán, Madrid #47/R
£369 $676 €550 Fisherwomen (65x33cm-26x13in) s. W/C. 12-Jul-4 Durán, Madrid #46/R

OSVER, Arthur (20th C) American
£765 $1300 €1117 Flight (36x41cm-14x16in) s. painted c.1965. 7-Nov-3 Selkirks, St. Louis #508/R
£1497 $2500 €2186 Stream jet (91x115cm-36x45in) s.d.46 s.i.d.Dec/1946 verso prov.exhib.lit. 7-Oct-3 Sotheby's, New York #237 est:2000-4000

OSWALD, C W (fl.1892) British
£480 $763 €701 Highland cattle on the banks of a loch (51x38cm-20x15in) s. 12-Sep-3 Halls, Shrewsbury #734
£540 $902 €788 Highland cattle in a landscape. Highland cattle by the lochside (51x76cm-20x30in) s. pair. 24-Jun-3 Bonhams, Chester #921
£750 $1275 €1095 Winter landscape with figure loading timber onto a cart (41x31cm-16x12in) s. 19-Nov-3 Tennants, Leyburn #1062

OSWALD, Charles W (19th C) British
£1000 $1790 €1460 Cattle watering in a loch landscape (46x81cm-18x32in) s. pair. 27-May-4 Christie's, Kensington #204/R est:1000-1500

OSWALD, John H (1843-1895) British
£420 $672 €613 Crossing the sands (13x22cm-5x9in) s.i. board. 15-May-3 Bonhams, Edinburgh #332
£520 $832 €759 Paris, a grey day (12x21cm-5x8in) s. 15-May-3 Bonhams, Edinburgh #331
Works on paper
£280 $448 €409 After the gale (30x53cm-12x21in) s.i. 16-Sep-3 Capes Dunn, Manchester #843/R

OTEIZA, Jorge de (1908-2003) Spanish
Sculpture
£1748 $2920 €2500 Carlos III y la Ilustracion 1788-1988 (13x13cm-5x5in) s. num.12/50 i.d.1988 verso bronze exhib. 24-Jun-3 Segre, Madrid #141/R est:2500

OTERO ABELEDO LAXEIRO, Jose (1908-1996) Spanish
£5705 $10611 €8500 Shapes (70x70cm-28x28in) s. 2-Mar-4 Ansorena, Madrid #857/R est:8500
£10383 $19000 €15159 Madonna and Child (45x35cm-18x14in) cardboard on canvas. 1-Jun-4 Arroyo, Buenos Aires #48
Works on paper
£272 $495 €400 Couple (15x9cm-6x4in) s. ink dr. 3-Feb-4 Segre, Madrid #179/R
£282 $451 €400 Peasant with stick (13x10cm-5x4in) s. ink. 16-Sep-3 Segre, Madrid #276/R
£284 $499 €420 Portrait in profile (24x16cm-9x6in) s. pencil dr. 18-May-4 Segre, Madrid #116/R
£284 $499 €420 Portrait in profile (24x17cm-9x7in) s. pencil dr. 18-May-4 Segre, Madrid #117/R
£295 $481 €425 Figures (33x47cm-13x19in) s. Indian ink board. 16-Jul-3 Durán, Madrid #85/R
£302 $541 €450 Forms (12x19cm-5x7in) s. ink dr. 25-May-4 Durán, Madrid #613/R
£304 $535 €450 Accumulation (16x24cm-6x9in) s. ink wash dr. 18-May-4 Segre, Madrid #118/R
£313 $516 €450 Untitled (21x17cm-8x7in) s.d.1967 ink dr. 2-Jul-3 Ansorena, Madrid #906/R
£313 $570 €460 Figure (15x10cm-6x4in) s. ink dr. 3-Feb-4 Segre, Madrid #177/R
£315 $526 €450 Couple (14x9cm-6x4in) dr. 30-Jun-3 Ansorena, Madrid #125/R
£320 $582 €470 Nude (14x21cm-6x8in) s. ink wash dr. 3-Feb-4 Segre, Madrid #176/R
£326 $535 €450 Nude (33x27cm-13x11in) s. gouache. 27-May-3 Durán, Madrid #686/R
£333 $607 €500 Retrato de perfil (23x16cm-9x6in) s. ink. 29-Jun-4 Segre, Madrid #117/R
£333 $607 €500 Mujer sentada con la luna (15x10cm-6x4in) s. ink wash. 29-Jun-4 Segre, Madrid #118/R
£342 $582 €500 Face (20x16cm-8x6in) s. wash. 4-Nov-3 Ansorena, Madrid #197/R
£345 $552 €490 Peasant family (24x17cm-9x7in) s. pencil. 16-Sep-3 Segre, Madrid #279/R
£379 $683 €550 Old woman (23x17cm-9x7in) s. dr. 26-Jan-4 Durán, Madrid #101/R
£385 $642 €550 Hombre de perfil (24x17cm-9x7in) s. gouache. 24-Jun-3 Segre, Madrid #208/R
£387 $620 €550 Portrait and children (13x10cm-5x4in) s. ink card. 16-Sep-3 Segre, Madrid #278/R
£387 $678 €550 Head of man (21x14cm-8x6in) s.d.1953 dr. 16-Dec-3 Durán, Madrid #672/R
£400 $728 €600 Mujer cubista (29x18cm-11x7in) s. ink drawing. 29-Jun-4 Segre, Madrid #119/R
£423 $676 €600 Man with hat (13x9cm-5x4in) s. ink. 16-Sep-3 Segre, Madrid #277/R
£433 $789 €650 El Baile (10x15cm-4x6in) s. W/C ink wash. 29-Jun-4 Segre, Madrid #116/R
£439 $773 €650 Peasant woman (38x26cm-15x10in) s. pencil dr. 18-May-4 Segre, Madrid #119/R
£458 $801 €650 Composition (23x27cm-9x11in) s. mixed media. 16-Dec-3 Durán, Madrid #611/R
£493 $863 €700 Composition (20x30cm-8x12in) s. mixed media. 16-Dec-3 Durán, Madrid #612/R
£805 $1498 €1200 Figures. Composition (33x24cm-13x9in) s.d.1986 wash double-sided. 2-Mar-4 Ansorena, Madrid #356/R
£986 $1577 €1400 Untitled (51x36cm-20x14in) s. W/C wash. 16-Sep-3 Segre, Madrid #171/R
£986 $1706 €1400 Composition with faces (73x50cm-29x20in) s.d.66 wash. 15-Dec-3 Ansorena, Madrid #987/R
£1172 $2110 €1700 Nude (23x16cm-9x6in) s. gouache. 26-Jan-4 Durán, Madrid #100/R est:600

OTERO BESTERIO, Francisco (1933-1994) Spanish
Sculpture
£3691 $6866 €5500 Face (48cm-19in) s. stone sold with base. 2-Mar-4 Ansorena, Madrid #750/R est:5500
£4113 $6664 €5800 Rostro (48cm-19in) s. base stone. 20-May-3 Ansorena, Madrid #808/R

OTERO, Alejandro (1921-1990) Venezuelan
Sculpture
£24818 $42190 €36234 Nude (70x36x40cm-28x14x16in) s.verso bronze exec.1942. 23-Nov-3 Subastas Odalys, Caracas #133/R est:40000
Works on paper
£253 $400 €369 Dimensions (28x21cm-11x8in) s. mixed media exec.1987. 1-Dec-2 Subastas Odalys, Caracas #71
£528 $845 €771 Untitled (30x30cm-12x12in) s. pastel. 16-Mar-3 Subastas Odalys, Caracas #80/R
£1290 $2000 €1883 Untitled (56x59cm-22x23in) s. mixed media. 3-Nov-2 Subastas Odalys, Caracas #106/R est:2000

OTERO, Carlos (1886-1977) Venezuelan
£764 $1405 €1115 Andorra la belle (46x38cm-18x15in) s. panel painted 1966. 28-Mar-4 Subastas Odalys, Caracas #5
£1012 $1690 €1478 Dovelan (33x46cm-13x18in) s. painted 1924. 13-Jul-3 Subastas Odalys, Caracas #75/R
£1204 $2240 €1758 Cumana' (41x33cm-16x13in) s. masonite painted 1945. 14-Mar-4 Subastas Odalys, Caracas #83/R
£1690 $3075 €2535 Untitled (68x97cm-27x38in) s. painted 1959. 21-Jun-4 Subastas Odalys, Caracas #4/R
Works on paper
£363 $675 €530 Untitled (47x61cm-19x24in) s. mixed media. 14-Mar-4 Subastas Odalys, Caracas #104

OTERO, Juan (?) Argentinian?
£503 $900 €734 Golden field (30x40cm-12x16in) cardboard. 11-May-4 Arroyo, Buenos Aires #67
£559 $1000 €816 White jug (39x50cm-15x20in) cardboard. 11-May-4 Arroyo, Buenos Aires #68

OTHONEOS, Nicholaos (1877-1950) Greek
£2800 $4900 €4088 Goats (21x31cm-8x12in) init. cardboard. 16-Dec-3 Bonhams, New Bond Street #86/R est:1500-2000
£6000 $10200 €8760 Feeding goats (84x66cm-33x26in) init. 18-Nov-3 Sotheby's, London #85/R est:6000-8000

OTIS, Bass (attrib) (1784-1861) American
£1913 $3500 €2793 Portrait of a mother holding child, said to be Sra Wattson and daughter Fannie Watson (91x76cm-36x30in) 10-Apr-4 Brunk, Ashville #602/R est:1000-2000

OTIS, George Demont (1877-1962) American
£1078 $1800 €1574 Row of rural homes with figures (13x18cm-5x7in) s. oil on paperboard. 12-Jul-3 Auctions by the Bay, Alameda #407/R
£1630 $3000 €2380 Rainbow Valley (50x66cm-20x26in) s.indis.i. 8-Jun-4 Bonhams & Butterfields, San Francisco #4261/R est:4000-6000
£2206 $3750 €3221 Field of yellow (61x76cm-24x30in) s. i.verso masonite prov. 18-Nov-3 John Moran, Pasadena #77 est:5000-7000
£2513 $4750 €3669 Cows in eucalyptus landscape, Santa Monica Hills (30x41cm-12x16in) s. i. verso canvasboard prov. 17-Feb-4 John Moran, Pasadena #171/R est:1500-2500
£2673 $4250 €3903 China camp, Marin Country (51x61cm-20x24in) s. i.verso masonite. 23-Mar-3 Auctions by the Bay, Alameda #865/R
£2794 $4750 €4079 Boathouse and harbour (41x51cm-16x20in) s. 18-Nov-3 John Moran, Pasadena #25 est:5000-7000
£2890 $5000 €4219 Spanish school of St Anthony (25x33cm-10x13in) board prov. 10-Dec-3 Bonhams & Butterfields, San Francisco #6222/R est:2000-3000
£3293 $5500 €4808 Landscape at morning (51x61cm-20x24in) masonite. 18-Oct-3 David Dike, Dallas #276/R est:4000-6000
£3892 $6500 €5682 Snow capped mountains (76x91cm-30x36in) s. prov. 23-Oct-3 Shannon's, Milford #212/R est:6000-8000
£4396 $8000 €6418 Sycamores and cabin in summer landscape (61x76cm-24x30in) s. prov. 15-Jun-4 John Moran, Pasadena #150b est:6000-8000
£5291 $10000 €7725 Golden Glory of the Desert (61x76cm-24x30in) s. i. stretcher prov. 17-Feb-4 John Moran, Pasadena #101a/R est:4000-6000
£5820 $11000 €8497 Mountain landscape - Sweet June (61x76cm-24x30in) s. i. stretcher prov. 17-Feb-4 John Moran, Pasadena #72/R est:6000-8000
£8092 $14000 €11814 Desert Palms (76x102cm-30x40in) s. painted 1930 prov. 10-Dec-3 Bonhams & Butterfields, San Francisco #6329/R est:15000-20000

O'TOOLE, Michael (1963-) Canadian
£600 $1098 €876 Porto Venere (101x91cm-40x36in) acrylic prov. 3-Jun-4 Heffel, Vancouver #42/R (C.D 1500)

OTSU-E (18th C) Chinese
Works on paper
£479 $815 €700 Oni Nenbutsu with umbrella, gong and book (24x15cm-9x6in) Indian ink col hanging scroll. 8-Nov-3 Dr Fritz Nagel, Stuttgart #1918/R

OTT, Jerry (1947-) American
£3046 $5482 €4447 Toy room (195x244cm-77x96in) s.d.1974 acrylic. 26-Apr-4 Bukowskis, Stockholm #574/R est:18000-20000 (S.KR 42000)

OTT, Johann Nepomuk (1804-1870) Swiss
£2028 $3488 €2900 Country landscape with village, church and mountains in distance (48x67cm-19x26in) s. indis.d. 3-Dec-3 Neumeister, Munich #699/R est:3800

OTT, Johann Nepomuk (attrib) (1804-1870) Swiss
£1181 $1865 €1700 Partenkirchen with Zugspitze (48x67cm-19x26in) i. stretcher. 6-Sep-3 Schopman, Hamburg #691/R est:1000

OTTAVIANI, Giovanni (1735-1808) Italian
Prints
£31206 $52113 €44000 Raphael's columns. col eau forte after Savorelli set of 10. 15-Oct-3 Sotheby's, Paris #143/R est:12000-18000

OTTE, William Louis (1871-1957) American
£3293 $5500 €4808 Cypress, Monterrey Coast, California (25x30cm-10x12in) s. i.verso canvasboard prov. 7-Oct-3 Sotheby's, New York #197 est:3000-5000
Works on paper
£899 $1700 €1313 Foothill landscape (10x13cm-4x5in) s.d.16 pastel board. 17-Feb-4 John Moran, Pasadena #2/R est:1000-2000
£3779 $6500 €5517 Eucalyptus trees at twilight, Santa Barbara (53x69cm-21x27in) s. s.i.verso pastel prov. 7-Dec-3 Freeman, Philadelphia #122 est:4000-6000

OTTEN-ROSIER, Berthe (1885-1973) Belgian
£533 $960 €800 Baby (26x21cm-10x8in) s. cardboard. 26-Apr-4 Bernaerts, Antwerp #437/R

OTTENFELD, Rudolf Ritter von (1856-1913) Italian
£1646 $2799 €2403 Praying Arab (25x18cm-10x7in) s.d.879 panel. 29-Nov-3 Dorotheum, Prague #34/R est:50000-80000 (C.KR 75000)
£3800 $6802 €5548 The Italian Alps (60x43cm-24x17in) s.d. panel. 28-May-4 Lyon & Turnbull, Edinburgh #49/R est:1000-1500
£3975 $7195 €5804 Eastern market place (55x81cm-22x32in) s.i.d.1885 prov.lit. 1-Apr-4 Heffel, Vancouver #106/R est:10000-15000 (C.D 9500)
£6000 $10020 €8760 An Egyptian merchant's stall (38x49cm-15x19in) s.i.d.91 panel. 14-Oct-3 Sotheby's, London #40/R est:6000-9000

OTTER, Thomas (attrib) (fl.1850-1880) American
£578 $1000 €844 Lower Godshalk Mill (41x61cm-16x24in) painted c.1880. 10-Dec-3 Alderfer's, Hatfield #448/R est:800-1200

OTTERNESS, Tom (1952-) American
Sculpture
£3243 $6000 €4735 Fish plate - knife - fork (25x28x6cm-10x11x2in) s.d.1986 num.1/5 brown pat bronze 3 parts prov. 12-Feb-4 Sotheby's, New York #211/R est:2500-3500
£3293 $5500 €4808 Girl with turtle. s.d.90 num.2/3 green pat bronze. 7-Oct-3 Sotheby's, New York #382 est:5000-7000
£3514 $6500 €5130 Foot (23cm-9in) s.d.1992 num.2/9 brown pat bronze. 12-Feb-4 Sotheby's, New York #241/R est:1200-1800

OTTERSON, Joel (20th C) American
Sculpture
£811 $1500 €1184 Nonfound - unfound (258cm-102in) mixed media incl plumbing parts. 12-Feb-4 Sotheby's, New York #272/R est:2500-3500

OTTERSTEDT, Alexander (1848-1909) Russian
£559 $1029 €850 Ecce-Homo-Head (57x46cm-22x18in) s. 25-Jun-4 Michael Zeller, Lindau #528/R

OTTESEN, Johannes (1875-1936) Danish
£544 $886 €794 Interior scene with girl (53x45cm-21x18in) s.d.1920. 27-Sep-3 Rasmussen, Havnen #2090 (D.KR 5800)
£1000 $1850 €1460 Good book (51x44cm-20x17in) s.d.20. 14-Jul-4 Sotheby's, Olympia #255/R est:1500-2000
£1087 $1880 €1587 Interior scene with girl reading by window (53x45cm-21x18in) s.d.20. 9-Dec-3 Rasmussen, Copenhagen #1572/R (D.KR 11500)

OTTESEN, Otto Didrik (1816-1892) Danish
£291 $500 €425 Pink roses (22x17cm-9x7in) st.init.d.1866 paper on canvas prov. 2-Dec-3 Christie's, Rockefeller NY #58/R
£403 $737 €588 Still life of flowers in glass vase (33x27cm-13x11in) s. 9-Jun-4 Rasmussen, Copenhagen #1859/R (D.KR 4500)
£1000 $1850 €1460 Still life with pineapple, strawberries and grapes (32x43cm-13x17in) s.d.1837 panel. 10-Mar-4 Sotheby's, Olympia #291/R est:2000-3000
£1258 $2340 €1837 Sulsted church in Wendsyssl, farm with animals in foreground (26x51cm-10x20in) s.d.1866 i.verso. 2-Mar-4 Rasmussen, Copenhagen #1617/R est:15000 (D.KR 14000)
£2686 $4915 €3922 Pineapple, grapes and strawberries on pewter dish (33x43cm-13x17in) s.d.1851. 9-Jun-4 Rasmussen, Copenhagen #1882/R est:30000-35000 (D.KR 30000)
£5391 $10027 €7871 Violets and other wild flowers on woodland ground (40x48cm-16x19in) s.d.1863 exhib. 2-Mar-4 Rasmussen, Copenhagen #1259/R est:60000-80000 (D.KR 60000)
Works on paper
£843 $1407 €1231 Marble relief surrounded by garland of roses (22cm-9in circular) i.verso W/C gouache. 25-Oct-3 Rasmussen, Havnen #2103/R (D.KR 9000)

OTTESEN, Otto Didrik (attrib) (1816-1892) Danish
£5500 $8800 €7975 Camelias (34x30cm-13x12in) 18-Sep-3 Christie's, Kensington #33/R est:2000-3000

OTTEVAERE, Henri (1870-1940) Belgian
£306 $486 €440 Les dunes (45x65cm-18x26in) s.d.1912. 9-Sep-3 Palais de Beaux Arts, Brussels #258
£313 $522 €450 Dunes (45x64cm-18x25in) s. 21-Oct-3 Galerie Moderne, Brussels #357/R
£483 $893 €700 Coucher de soleil sur le mer du Nord (60x101cm-24x40in) s.d.1939. 19-Jan-4 Horta, Bruxelles #488
£933 $1671 €1400 L'inculpe (81x65cm-32x26in) s.d.1917. 11-May-4 Vanderkindere, Brussels #40/R

OTTEWELL, Benjamin John (fl.1885-1930) British
Works on paper
£280 $515 €409 Beeches, East Burnham (44x59cm-17x23in) s. W/C. 23-Mar-4 Bonhams, Knightsbridge #80/R
£320 $573 €467 Rural landscape in summer (35x53cm-14x21in) s.d.1894 W/C. 25-May-4 Bonhams, Knightsbridge #273/R

OTTIN, Henri (20th C) French
£430 $731 €628 Still life with flowers (65x54cm-26x21in) s. 28-Nov-3 Zofingen, Switzerland #2654 (S.FR 950)

OTTIN, Leon Auguste (c.1839-?) French
£517 $926 €755 Boy sitting on beach (21x32cm-8x13in) s.d.75 panel. 13-May-4 Stuker, Bern #276/R (S.FR 1200)

OTTINGER, George Martin (1833-1917) American
£2542 $4500 €3711 Mountain grandeur. The rabbit hunt (26x55cm-10x22in) one init. two. 28-Apr-4 Christie's, Los Angeles #42/R est:5000-7000

OTTINI, Pasquale (attrib) (1580-1630) Italian
£7747 $13557 €11000 Ecce homo (27x36cm-11x14in) slate. 18-Dec-3 Tajan, Paris #2/R est:8000-12000
£11921 $21695 €18000 Flight to Egypt. Circumcision (26x33cm-10x13in) on slate octagonal double-sided. 16-Jun-4 Christie's, Rome #430/R est:10000-15000

OTTMANN, Henri (1877-1927) French
£789 $1453 €1200 Rue de village (31x25cm-12x10in) s. board. 28-Jun-4 Joron-Derem, Paris #113
£1007 $1862 €1500 Grande allee en foret (60x73cm-24x29in) s. 14-Mar-4 Eric Pillon, Calais #178/R
£1208 $2247 €1800 Chez la modiste (74x93cm-29x37in) s. 3-Mar-4 Tajan, Paris #50 est:1700-2000
£2817 $4873 €4000 Nature morte (38x55cm-15x22in) s. s.verso lit. 9-Dec-3 Artcurial Briest, Paris #260/R est:3000-4000
£3289 $6053 €5000 Verger (83x102cm-33x40in) s. 28-Jun-4 Joron-Derem, Paris #112/R est:5000-6000
Works on paper
£203 $350 €296 Woman feeding a caged bird on Bastille day (23x18cm-9x7in) s. W/C. 6-Dec-3 Neal Auction Company, New Orleans #441
£629 $1145 €950 Jardin public (43x47cm-17x19in) s. pastel. 15-Jun-4 Blanchet, Paris #154/R
£1849 $2903 €2700 Femme a la nappe jaune (48x62cm-19x24in) s. pastel. 20-Apr-3 Deauville, France #22/R est:1500-1800

OTTO, Alfred (1873-1953) German
£839 $1443 €1200 Loisachtal in winter (60x80cm-24x31in) s. 5-Dec-3 Michael Zeller, Lindau #751/R

OTTO, Carl (1830-1902) German
£724 $1332 €1100 Portrait of elegant woman in light blue dress (65x51cm-26x20in) s. i. stretcher. 24-Jun-4 Dr Fritz Nagel, Stuttgart #737/R
£724 $1332 €1100 Portrait of elegant woman in pink dress (65x51cm-26x20in) s. bears i. stretcher. 24-Jun-4 Dr Fritz Nagel, Stuttgart #738/R
£1399 $2378 €2000 Nature morte au homard et aux huitres (61x80cm-24x31in) s. 18-Nov-3 Vanderkindere, Brussels #51 est:1500-2000

OTTO, Ernst (1807-1847) German
£556 $928 €800 Stags fighting (80x125cm-31x49in) 24-Oct-3 Ketterer, Hamburg #64/R

OTTO, Rudolf (1887-) German
£507 $907 €750 View of Meissen over River Elbe (80x100cm-31x39in) s. 6-May-4 Michael Zeller, Lindau #809/R

OTTO, Walt (1895-1963) American
£2235 $4000 €3263 Nude woman at water's edge (91x76cm-36x30in) s. 15-May-4 Illustration House, New York #123/R est:5000-8000

OUAKNINE, Marc Alain (1957-) French
£1399 $2378 €2000 Jerusalem (68x48cm-27x19in) s. oil paper. 27-Nov-3 Calmels Cohen, Paris #126/R est:700-1000
Works on paper
£909 $1545 €1300 Hommage a Pythagore (48x68cm-19x27in) s. ink acrylic. 27-Nov-3 Calmels Cohen, Paris #124/R

OUATTARA (20th C) American?
£1250 $2088 €1800 Sans titre (195x237cm-77x93in) 21-Oct-3 Artcurial Briest, Paris #630 est:3000-4000

OUBORG, Piet (1893-1956) Dutch
£10669 $19203 €15577 Two standing women (57x43cm-22x17in) prov.lit. 25-Apr-4 Christie's, Hong Kong #512/R est:160000-200000 (HK.D 150000)
Works on paper
£315 $541 €450 Composition (12x17cm-5x7in) s.verso mixed media. 8-Dec-3 Glerum, Amsterdam #195/R
£1049 $1783 €1500 Composition (25x33cm-10x13in) d.1947 blk ink sold with blk ink drawing same hand two prov. 25-Nov-3 Christie's, Amsterdam #62/R est:1000-1500
£2238 $3849 €3200 Figuren tussen roependen (48x63cm-19x25in) i.verso gouache ink executed c.1948. 2-Dec-3 Sotheby's, Amsterdam #127/R est:5000-7000

OUBOTER, Rudolf de Bruin (1894-1983) Dutch
Works on paper
£524 $902 €750 Cactus flower (26x18cm-10x7in) s.d.1940 W/C prov. 8-Dec-3 Glerum, Amsterdam #294/R

OUDART, Paul Louis and TRAVIES, Edouard (19th C) French
Works on paper
£2069 $3455 €3000 Various animals. s. one indis.d.183 one d.1835 W/C gouache crayon 3 sheets 1 mount. 13-Nov-3 Binoche, Paris #35/R est:3000

OUDENHOVEN, Joseph van (19th C) Flemish
£276 $461 €400 Paysage collineux anime d'un berger aux vaches. mono. 17-Nov-3 Bernaerts, Antwerp #286

OUDERRA, Pierre van der (1841-1915) Belgian
£12414 $20607 €18000 Scene orientale avec sept figures (96x129cm-38x51in) 6-Oct-3 Amberes, Antwerp #276/R
£26667 $48000 €38934 In the dressing room (90x109cm-35x43in) s.i.d.1902. 22-Apr-4 Christie's, Rockefeller NY #244/R est:30000-50000

OUDINET, G (18th C) ?
Works on paper
£7823 $14003 €11500 Vue de la maison et du jardin de Monsieur David (26x51cm-10x20in) s.d.1782 pen W/C prov.exhib. 19-Mar-4 Beaussant & Lefèvre, Paris #26/R est:8000-10000

OUDINOT, Achille (1820-1891) Flemish
£531 $950 €775 Autumn pasture with grazing flock (23x36cm-9x14in) s. panel. 14-May-4 Skinner, Boston #21/R
£3357 $5773 €4800 Jeune femme dans la foret (46x38cm-18x15in) s. 7-Dec-3 Osenat, Fontainebleau #111

OUDOT, Georges (1928-) French
Sculpture
£1141 $2122 €1700 Tete de femme pensive (23cm-9in) num.2/8 brown green pat bronze Cast E Godard. 7-Mar-4 Lesieur & Le Bars, Le Havre #212
£1242 $2309 €1850 Femme drapee (40cm-16in) num.2/8 brown pat bronze marble base Cast Godard. 7-Mar-4 Lesieur & Le Bars, Le Havre #211
£1987 $3616 €3000 Tete de Minerve (40cm-16in) s.i. bronze. 19-Jun-4 Gerard, Besancon #141
Works on paper
£1119 $1924 €1600 La pensee (73x47cm-29x19in) s. pastel prov. 2-Dec-3 Sotheby's, Amsterdam #214/R est:1000-1500

OUDOT, Roland (1897-1981) French
£240 $400 €350 Jeune fille blonde (27x22cm-11x9in) s. prov. 7-Oct-3 Sotheby's, New York #293
£313 $522 €450 Rose (27x19cm-11x7in) s. prov. 21-Oct-3 Christie's, Paris #174/R
£355 $592 €500 La ferme (24x33cm-9x13in) s. 19-Jun-3 Millon & Associes, Paris #235
£359 $600 €524 Moisson en Ile de France (26x40cm-10x16in) s. ink W/C prov. 7-Oct-3 Sotheby's, New York #299
£530 $970 €800 Paysage (19x24cm-7x9in) s. panel. 7-Apr-4 Piasa, Paris #157
£539 $900 €787 Moroccan street scene (58x30cm-23x12in) s. masonite. 16-Nov-3 CRN Auctions, Cambridge #30/R
£541 $1000 €790 Harbour scene (38x46cm-15x18in) 13-Feb-4 Du Mouchelle, Detroit #2145/R
£634 $1096 €900 Vse de roses (27x19cm-11x7in) s. 14-Dec-3 Eric Pillon, Calais #121/R
£652 $1193 €952 Nature morte au homard (54x38cm-21x15in) s. 4-Jun-4 Zofingen, Switzerland #2499/R (S.FR 1500)
£658 $1211 €1000 Paysage au chateau d'eau (60x81cm-24x32in) s. 28-Jun-4 Joron-Derem, Paris #169
£694 $1160 €1000 Nature morte au violon (24x28cm-9x11in) s. 21-Oct-3 Christie's, Paris #175/R
£696 $1273 €1016 Village in an extensive landscape (27x41cm-11x16in) s. prov. 4-Jun-4 Zofingen, Switzerland #2498/R (S.FR 1600)
£739 $1279 €1050 Trois roses blanches (32x23cm-13x9in) s. 10-Dec-3 Ferri, Paris #79
£769 $1323 €1100 Nature morte aux fruits (32x45cm-13x18in) s. 3-Dec-3 Oger, Dumont, Paris #25
£944 $1624 €1350 La ferme (38x55cm-15x22in) s. oil paper on canvas. 3-Dec-3 Beaussant & Lefèvre, Paris #65/R
£1224 $2192 €1800 Paysage aux oliviers (60x73cm-24x29in) s. prov. 19-Mar-4 Oger, Dumont, Paris #16/R est:2000-3000
£1259 $2140 €1800 De modele Judith (55x46cm-22x18in) s. 29-Nov-3 Bukowskis, Helsinki #342/R est:2000-2500
£1313 $2100 €1917 Saint Tropez (51x64cm-20x25in) s. i.verso. 17-May-3 Bunte, Elgin #1277 est:3000-5000
£1334 $2400 €2000 Femme en buste (46x33cm-18x13in) bears sig. paper on canvas. 26-Apr-4 Tajan, Paris #167/R est:2000-2500
£1342 $2483 €2000 Vase de roses blanches (33x24cm-13x9in) s. 14-Mar-4 Eric Pillon, Calais #156/R
£1589 $2972 €2400 Jeune femme a la poire (80x59cm-31x23in) s. 20-Jul-4 Gioffredo, Nice #6/R
£1645 $3026 €2500 Sur la route de Lindos (60x81cm-24x32in) s. 22-Jun-4 Ribeyre & Baron, Paris #69/R est:2500-3500
£1652 $3023 €2412 Village street on a summer's day (64x81cm-25x32in) s. 4-Jun-4 Zofingen, Switzerland #2497/R est:4500 (S.FR 3800)
£1656 $3013 €2500 Le verger (65x81cm-26x32in) s. 18-Jun-4 Piasa, Paris #162 est:1500-2000
£1879 $3495 €2800 Route a Mouries dans les Alpilles (54x821cm-21x323in) s. 3-Mar-4 Tajan, Paris #161 est:2000-3000
£1987 $3715 €3000 Barques a maree basse (74x93cm-29x37in) s. 20-Jul-4 Gioffredo, Nice #12/R
£2013 $3745 €3000 La route au pigeonnier (65x91cm-26x36in) s. 3-Mar-4 Ferri, Paris #344 est:3000-3500
£2013 $3745 €3000 Barques a Mikonos (50x73cm-20x29in) s. prov. 3-Mar-4 Ferri, Paris #359 est:3500-4000
£2632 $4842 €4000 Planches a Deauville (54x81cm-21x32in) s. 22-Jun-4 Ribeyre & Baron, Paris #70/R est:4000-5000
£3472 $5799 €5000 Village de Provence (81x116cm-32x46in) s. exhib. 21-Oct-3 Christie's, Paris #169/R est:2500-3500
£3800 $6916 €5700 Chemin borde d'arbres en Provence (60x81cm-24x32in) s. 4-Jul-4 Eric Pillon, Calais #195/R
£7383 $13215 €11000 Paysage d'Arcadie (81x100cm-32x39in) s. s.i.verso prov. 26-May-4 Christie's, Paris #37/R est:6000-8000
Works on paper
£299 $500 €437 Les banderilles (31x42cm-12x17in) s. ink W/C crayon varnish prov. 7-Oct-3 Sotheby's, New York #295
£347 $580 €500 La tour (25x32cm-10x13in) s. W/C india ink. 21-Oct-3 Christie's, Paris #113/R
£405 $750 €591 Scene de theatre (33x51cm-13x20in) s. ink W/C prov. 15-Jul-4 Sotheby's, New York #98
£451 $754 €650 Venise (25x33cm-10x13in) s.i. ink ink wash prov. 21-Oct-3 Christie's, Paris #112/R
£493 $853 €700 Le palais Saint-Marc (23x31cm-9x12in) s. W/C. 10-Dec-3 Ferri, Paris #78

OUDRY, Jacques-Charles (1720-1778) French
£3289 $6053 €5000 Paysage avec moulin et pecheurs (10x14cm-4x6in) i.d.1767 verso copper. 25-Jun-4 Doutrebente, Paris #11/R est:5000-6000
Works on paper
£319 $533 €450 Etude d'arbre et ferme. s. pierre noire prov. 15-Oct-3 Sotheby's, Paris #135/R

OUDRY, Jacques-Charles (attrib) (1720-1778) French
£3400 $6086 €4964 Hunting still life with birds (48x59cm-19x23in) 25-May-4 Bukowskis, Stockholm #487/R est:35000-40000 (S.KR 46000)

OUDRY, Jean Baptiste (1686-1755) French
£3056 $5500 €4462 Duck with two barbels at the edge of a pond (65x81cm-26x32in) with sig.d.1726 prov. 23-Jan-4 Christie's, Rockefeller NY #3/R est:10000-15000
£4895 $8322 €7000 Portrait du Marquis de Brancas, enfant (91x73cm-36x29in) s.d.1711 prov.lit. 1-Dec-3 Millon & Associes, Paris #13a est:8000-10000
£230265 $423688 €350000 Levrier surveillant trophee de chasse (131x114cm-52x45in) s.d.1731 prov. 24-Jun-4 Tajan, Paris #53/R est:400000-600000
Works on paper
£1126 $2049 €1700 Portrait presume de Anne Louise de Noailles, marquise de Louvois et Courtenjaux (15x13cm-6x5in) pen ink wash. 16-Jun-4 Piasa, Paris #123 est:1800-2000
£1958 $3329 €2800 Sleeping dogs. chk six. 27-Nov-3 Bassenge, Berlin #5485/R est:1200
£2415 $4250 €3526 View of a bear from behind (27x42cm-11x17in) black white chk prov.exhib.lit. 19-May-4 Doyle, New York #6026/R est:8000-12000
£5000 $9000 €7300 Figures playing games (28x39cm-11x15in) s.d.1728 black white chk prov.exhib.lit. 22-Jan-4 Christie's, Rockefeller NY #91/R est:10000-15000
£14444 $26000 €21088 Hare looking back (28x42cm-11x17in) s. black white chk prov. 22-Jan-4 Christie's, Rockefeller NY #90/R est:8000-12000
£16822 $26579 €24392 Birds fighting (26x46cm-10x18in) s.d.1749 pencil W/C wash. 2-Sep-3 Rasmussen, Copenhagen #2032/R est:25000 (D.KR 180000)
£25850 $46272 €38000 Tigre couche dans un paysage (30x40cm-12x16in) s. pierre noire htd white prov.lit. 19-Mar-4 Beaussant & Lefèvre, Paris #36/R est:30000
£73944 $122746 €105000 Le blaireau (26x42cm-10x17in) i. col crayon. 13-Jun-3 Ferri, Paris #37/R est:8000-10000

OUDRY, Jean Baptiste (attrib) (1686-1755) French
£1972 $3411 €2800 Daim attaque par une meute (51x38cm-20x15in) panel. 10-Dec-3 Ferri, Paris #11/R est:2600-3000

OUDRY, Jean Baptiste (circle) (1686-1755) French
£5636 $9862 €8000 Paysage de torrent anime de chasseurs (161x141cm-63x56in) 18-Dec-3 Tajan, Paris #43/R est:8000-12000

OUDRY, Jean Baptiste (studio) (1686-1755) French
£3823 $6500 €5582 Romantic landscape with ducks by a fountain (91x74cm-36x29in) bears sig.d.1747. 19-Nov-3 Bonhams & Butterfields, San Francisco #33/R
£42764 $78686 €65000 Chien a l'affut de perdrix (131x114cm-52x45in) bears sig prov. 24-Jun-4 Tajan, Paris #54/R est:60000-80000

OUDRY, Jean Baptiste (style) (1686-1755) French
£7200 $12456 €10512 Wooded landscape with gentlemen on horses hunting (112x93cm-44x37in) 9-Dec-3 Sotheby's, Olympia #443/R est:5000-7000

OULESS, Catherina (1879-?) British
£700 $1204 €1022 Sent to bed (30x23cm-12x9in) s.d.1942 canvasboard. 3-Dec-3 Bonhams, Knightsbridge #61/R
£860 $1591 €1256 Portrait of an officer in uniform (126x75cm-50x30in) s.d.1917. 14-Jan-4 Lawrence, Crewkerne #1424

OULESS, Philip J (1817-1885) British
£20000 $37800 €29200 Jersey-St.Malo paddle steamer Superb outward bound from St Helier (41x66cm-16x26in) s.d.1850. 17-Feb-4 Bonhams, New Bond Street #79/R est:8000-12000

OULTON, Therese (1953-) British
£2300 $3841 €3358 Song of deceit (234x213cm-92x84in) s.i.d.April 1988 verso. 21-Oct-3 Bonhams, Knightsbridge #214/R est:2000-3000
£2500 $4300 €3650 Inward bound (217x167cm-85x66in) s.i.d.1985. 2-Dec-3 Bonhams, New Bond Street #170/R est:2500-3500
£2800 $5096 €4088 Cross purposes (238x214cm-94x84in) s.i.d.1983 verso prov. 1-Jul-4 Christie's, Kensington #386/R est:3000-5000

OURSLER, Tony (1957-) American
£2027 $3568 €3000 Rumour mill (76x56cm-30x22in) s.d.2002 verso oil tempera ink pencil card prov. 24-May-4 Christie's, Milan #69/R est:3000-4000
Sculpture
£8333 $13750 €12000 More blood (25x25cm-10x10in) installation video plaster glove prov. 2-Jul-3 Cornette de St.Cyr, Paris #110/R est:12000-15000

OUSEY, Buckley (1851-1889) British
£1150 $2116 €1679 Bringing in the catch, Conway Castle beyond (39x83cm-15x33in) s.d.1888. 8-Jun-4 Bonhams, Knightsbridge #350b/R est:800-1200

OUSLEY, William (1866-1953) American
£617 $1000 €901 Scene at Choupique (43x84cm-17x33in) s. s.i.d.1929 verso. 2-Aug-3 Neal Auction Company, New Orleans #416/R est:1500-2500
£783 $1300 €1143 Calcasieu River, Louisiana (41x71cm-16x28in) s. 4-Oct-3 Neal Auction Company, New Orleans #587/R est:1500-2000
£802 $1500 €1171 Louisiana landscape (51x94cm-20x37in) s. 25-Feb-4 Dallas Auction Gallery, Dallas #113/R est:1500-2500
£879 $1600 €1283 Louisiana Landscape (61x36cm-24x14in) s.i. 7-Feb-4 Neal Auction Company, New Orleans #776/R est:2000-4000
£984 $1800 €1437 Old tree of Ousley's landing at Bagdad, Louisiana (51x30cm-20x12in) s.i.d.1934 board. 5-Jun-4 Neal Auction Company, New Orleans #414/R est:2000-3000
£984 $1800 €1437 Evangeline oak at St. Martinville, La (30x48cm-12x19in) s.i. i.verso board. 5-Jun-4 Neal Auction Company, New Orleans #415/R est:2000-3000
£1099 $2000 €1605 West Fork of Calcasieu River, Louisiana no 212 (48x84cm-19x33in) s.i. 7-Feb-4 Neal Auction Company, New Orleans #775/R est:2000-3000
£1374 $2500 €2006 West fork of the Calcasieu River S W No 492, the mist (46x89cm-18x35in) s.i. s.i.d.1930 verso. 7-Feb-4 Neal Auction Company, New Orleans #783/R est:2500-3500
£1728 $2800 €2523 Red buds of Louisiana (30x69cm-12x27in) s. s.i.verso masonite. 2-Aug-3 Neal Auction Company, New Orleans #417/R est:2000-3000

OUTENDAG, Egbert (1914-1998) Canadian
£200 $366 €292 Clematis (35x27cm-14x11in) s. board prov. 3-Jun-4 Heffel, Vancouver #43/R (C.D 500)

OUTER, Nestor (1865-1923) Belgian
£417 $663 €600 Bateaux de peche en Mer du Nord (37x53cm-15x21in) s.d.1922. 15-Sep-3 Horta, Bruxelles #243
Works on paper
£265 $482 €400 La neige. s.d.1910 W/C. 15-Jun-4 Galerie Moderne, Brussels #104
£728 $1326 €1100 La Vire pres de Chenois (55x37cm-22x15in) s.d.1910 W/C. 15-Jun-4 Galerie Moderne, Brussels #139
£789 $1453 €1200 Village a Midi (36x55cm-14x22in) s.i.d.1906 W/C. 22-Jun-4 Palais de Beaux Arts, Brussels #293/R
£1447 $2620 €2200 A l'ombre, sous El Roslane (34x48cm-13x19in) s.d.1893 W/C. 19-Apr-4 Horta, Bruxelles #201 est:1000-1200

OUTERBRIDGE, Paul (jnr) (1896-1958) American
Photographs
£1587 $3000 €2317 Untitled (12x9cm-5x4in) gelatin silver print executed c.1924. 17-Feb-4 Christie's, Rockefeller NY #91/R est:8000-10000
£2373 $4200 €3465 Paula (21x15cm-8x6in) platinum print executed 1923-24. 27-Apr-4 Christie's, Rockefeller NY #257/R est:6000-8000
£2910 $5500 €4249 Coffee advertisment (28x38cm-11x15in) carbro print. 17-Feb-4 Christie's, Rockefeller NY #90/R est:7000-9000
£3390 $6000 €4949 Semi nude with fur wrap (34x23cm-13x9in) gelatin silver print executed c.1931 lit. 27-Apr-4 Christie's, Rockefeller NY #256/R est:8000-10000
£3593 $6000 €5246 Scrubbing the hull (42x32cm-17x13in) estate st.num.810 verso col carbro print exec.c.1937 prov. 17-Oct-3 Sotheby's, New York #184/R est:5000-7000
£3968 $7500 €5793 Paula at her vanity (20x14cm-8x6in) platinum print. 17-Feb-4 Christie's, Rockefeller NY #88/R est:6000-8000
£4192 $7000 €6120 Seashell abstraction (11x8cm-4x3in) bleached toned photo exec.c.1928 prov. 17-Oct-3 Sotheby's, New York #183/R est:8000-12000
£5000 $8800 €7300 Fan and pearl necklace (10x10cm-4x4in) s.d. platinum print prov. 19-May-4 Christie's, London #184/R est:5000-7000
£5291 $10000 €7725 Avocados (14x22cm-6x9in) gelatin silver print executed c.1936. 17-Feb-4 Christie's, Rockefeller NY #89/R est:8000-10000
£7910 $14000 €11549 Piano, 1926 (23x18cm-9x7in) s.d. i.verso gelatin silver print prov.lit. 27-Apr-4 Christie's, Rockefeller NY #41/R est:10000-15000
£9040 $16000 €13198 Untitled - beach equipment (37x30cm-15x12in) color carbro print prov.lit. 27-Apr-4 Christie's, Rockefeller NY #259/R est:12000-18000
£11299 $20000 €16497 Still life, cheese and crackers (12x9cm-5x4in) i. platinum print lit. 27-Apr-4 Christie's, Rockefeller NY #39/R est:15000-20000
£16949 $30000 €24746 Nude with a drape of green material (53x23cm-21x9in) estate st.num.823 verso col carbro print exec.c.1937 prov. 28-Apr-4 Sotheby's, New York #169/R est:15000-20000
£22754 $38000 €33221 Seated nude (42x30cm-17x12in) estate st.num.733 verso col carbro print exec.c.1937 prov.exhib. 17-Oct-3 Sotheby's, New York #151/R est:20000-30000
£77844 $130000 €113652 Standing nude with chair (17x11cm-7x4in) platinum print exec.c.1924 prov.exhib.lit. 20-Oct-3 Christie's, Rockefeller NY #126/R est:60000-80000
Works on paper
£2098 $3608 €3000 Composition (35x25cm-14x10in) s.d.1934 ink. 4-Dec-3 Van Ham, Cologne #263/R est:4000

OUTHWAITE, Ida Rentoul (1888-1960) Australian
Works on paper
£934 $1709 €1401 Catching birds. ink. 3-Jun-4 Joel, Victoria #163/R (A.D 2400)
£1829 $3274 €2670 May I have this dance (24x19cm-9x7in) init. W/C. 10-May-4 Joel, Victoria #212a est:5000-6000 (A.D 4500)
£2273 $4022 €3319 Asleep (39x29cm-15x11in) s. ink gouache exec.c.1916 prov.exhib. 3-May-4 Christie's, Melbourne #302/R est:6000-8000 (A.D 5500)
£2340 $3979 €3416 Elves and fairies (45x32cm-18x13in) s. W/C gouache ink exhib.prov. 25-Nov-3 Christie's, Melbourne #102/R est:5000-7000 (A.D 5500)
£3846 $6192 €5615 Miss Lizzie gave her message very politely (26x20cm-10x8in) init.i. W/C pen. 13-Oct-3 Joel, Victoria #283/R est:6000-8000 (A.D 9500)
£3846 $6192 €5615 Willy wagtail and the kookaburra (25x20cm-10x8in) init. W/C ink. 13-Oct-3 Joel, Victoria #287/R est:6000-8000 (A.D 9500)
£3846 $6192 €5615 I would learn to talk said the parrot (25x20cm-10x8in) init.i. W/C bodycol ink. 13-Oct-3 Joel, Victoria #288/R est:6000-8000 (A.D 9500)
£4453 $7170 €6501 Guests went into conference (26x20cm-10x8in) init.i. W/C pen. 13-Oct-3 Joel, Victoria #281/R est:6000-8000 (A.D 11000)
£4858 $7822 €7093 Echidna performs (26x20cm-10x8in) init.i. W/C bodycol ink. 13-Oct-3 Joel, Victoria #282/R est:6000-8000 (A.D 12000)
£4858 $7822 €7093 One day her special little playmate came into the forest to look for her (25x20cm-10x8in) init.i. W/C ink. 13-Oct-3 Joel, Victoria #285/R est:6000-8000 (A.D 12000)
£5061 $8148 €7389 Wishing pool (25x20cm-10x8in) init.i. W/C ink. 13-Oct-3 Joel, Victoria #3284/R est:6000-8000 (A.D 12500)
£5061 $8148 €7389 Winter fairy came in the snow (25x21cm-10x8in) init.i. W/C ink bodycol. 13-Oct-3 Joel, Victoria #286/R est:6000-8000 (A.D 12500)
£6478 $10429 €9458 Lyre bird's dance (25x20cm-10x8in) init. W/C bodycol ink. 13-Oct-3 Joel, Victoria #280/R est:6000-8000 (A.D 16000)

OUTIN, Pierre (1840-1899) French
£20000 $36400 €29200 Quiet moment (82x65cm-32x26in) s. 17-Jun-4 Christie's, London #104/R est:20000-30000

OUTKIN, Nicolai Ivanovitch (1780-1868) Russian
Works on paper
£347 $566 €500 Portraits of woman and man (18x14cm-7x6in) s.d.1808 chk pencil htd white two. 25-Sep-3 Neumeister, Munich #301/R

OUTKINE, Petr Savitch (1877-1934) Russian
£1007 $1862 €1500 Paysage d'automne (21x29cm-8x11in) s. canvas on cardboard. 15-Mar-4 Claude Boisgirard, Paris #88 est:1500-2000

OUVRIE, Justin (1806-1879) French
£567 $1026 €850 Eglise en Bretagne (20x14cm-8x6in) s.d.1836 panel. 5-Apr-4 Deburaux, Boulogne #39
£567 $1026 €850 Cathedrale de Chartres. 5-Apr-4 Deburaux, Boulogne #39b
£897 $1659 €1300 Le palais rose (11x19cm-4x7in) s.d.1858 panel. 11-Feb-4 Beaussant & Lefèvre, Paris #194/R
£1867 $3379 €2800 Ville au bord du lac (22x38cm-9x15in) s. 5-Apr-4 Deburaux, Boulogne #25 est:5000-5500
£2133 $3861 €3200 Canal de Ryswick, La Haye (13x17cm-5x7in) s. panel. 5-Apr-4 Deburaux, Boulogne #20 est:5500-6000
£2269 $3857 €3313 Canal en Hollande (26x41cm-10x16in) s. bears d.1839 panel. 5-Nov-3 Dobiaschofsky, Bern #848/R est:12000 (S.FR 5150)
£2333 $4223 €3500 Aix les Bains (30x48cm-12x19in) s. 5-Apr-4 Deburaux, Boulogne #28 est:5500-6000
£2667 $4827 €4000 Paysage (32x24cm-13x9in) s.i.d.1853 panel. 5-Apr-4 Deburaux, Boulogne #12 est:6000-6500
£2667 $4827 €4000 Paysage (32x40cm-13x16in) s. panel. 5-Apr-4 Deburaux, Boulogne #18 est:5000-7000
£2667 $4827 €4000 Paysage au moulin (32x43cm-13x17in) s. panel. 5-Apr-4 Deburaux, Boulogne #29 est:6000-6500
£3000 $5430 €4500 La promenade au bord de la riviere (24x32cm-9x13in) s.d.1833 panel. 5-Apr-4 Deburaux, Boulogne #6 est:5800-6000
£3067 $5551 €4600 Chateau d'Heidelberg (27x40cm-11x16in) s. panel. 5-Apr-4 Deburaux, Boulogne #13/R est:6000-6500
£3125 $5219 €4500 Citadelle en bord de mer (17x22cm-7x9in) s.d.1871 panel. 22-Oct-3 Ribeyre & Baron, Paris #28/R est:1000-1500
£3125 $5219 €4500 Chateau au bord de l'Aar (14x24cm-6x9in) s.d.1871 panel. 22-Oct-3 Ribeyre & Baron, Paris #29/R est:1000-1500
£3333 $6033 €5000 Canal anime en Hollande (13x18cm-5x7in) s. panel. 5-Apr-4 Deburaux, Boulogne #19 est:6500-7000
£3400 $6154 €5100 Place animee (41x32cm-16x13in) s.d.1861 panel. 5-Apr-4 Deburaux, Boulogne #27/R est:5000-5500
£3667 $6637 €5500 Marche aux herbes, Amsterdam (33x41cm-13x16in) s.i. 5-Apr-4 Deburaux, Boulogne #16 est:6500-7000
£3667 $6747 €5500 Paysage (28x40cm-11x16in) s. panel prov. 9-Jun-4 Oger, Dumont, Paris #69/R est:3000-4000
£4667 $8540 €7000 Canal en Hollande (26x41cm-10x16in) s. panel. 6-Jun-4 Osenat, Fontainebleau #182/R est:6000-6500
£5000 $9050 €7500 Village au bord de la riviere (24x33cm-9x13in) s.i.d.1839. 5-Apr-4 Deburaux, Boulogne #8/R est:6500-7000
£5000 $9050 €7500 Lac de montagne anime de barques (26x40cm-10x16in) s. panel. 5-Apr-4 Deburaux, Boulogne #22 est:5500-6000
£5333 $9653 €8000 Londres (27x41cm-11x16in) s. 5-Apr-4 Deburaux, Boulogne #30/R est:6200-6500

£5600 $10136 €8400 Bord de riviere dans la ville (41x61cm-16x24in) s. panel. 5-Apr-4 Deburaux, Boulogne #4/R est:6000-6500
£6667 $12067 €10000 Bruges, canal anime (29x41cm-11x16in) s. panel. 5-Apr-4 Deburaux, Boulogne #10/R est:6500-7000
Works on paper
£267 $483 €400 Eglise au bord d'un lac (19x14cm-7x6in) s. W/C. 5-Apr-4 Deburaux, Boulogne #5
£267 $483 €400 Bruges (23x29cm-9x11in) i. graphite. 5-Apr-4 Deburaux, Boulogne #32
£300 $543 €450 Ville pres de Mayenne (13x22cm-5x9in) s. W/C. 5-Apr-4 Deburaux, Boulogne #38
£333 $603 €500 Place de village (9x13cm-4x5in) s.i.d.1839 W/C. 5-Apr-4 Deburaux, Boulogne #2
£333 $603 €500 Ville au bord du lac (21x35cm-8x14in) s.i. W/C. 5-Apr-4 Deburaux, Boulogne #44
£367 $664 €550 Chateau au bord d'une riviere (14x21cm-6x8in) s.d.1864 W/C. 5-Apr-4 Deburaux, Boulogne #37
£400 $724 €600 Eglise au bord du lac (14x19cm-6x7in) s.d.1866 W/C. 5-Apr-4 Deburaux, Boulogne #35
£467 $845 €700 Paysage de Suisse (12x21cm-5x8in) s.d.1863 W/C. 5-Apr-4 Deburaux, Boulogne #15
£467 $845 €700 Moulin au bord de l'eau (14x23cm-6x9in) s.i. W/C. 5-Apr-4 Deburaux, Boulogne #36
£467 $845 €700 Rue animee pres de la cathedrale (26x18cm-10x7in) s.i. W/C. 5-Apr-4 Deburaux, Boulogne #40
£533 $965 €800 Tour au bord du lac (21x29cm-8x11in) s. W/C. 5-Apr-4 Deburaux, Boulogne #1
£533 $965 €800 Village au bord du lac (6x15cm-2x6in) s.i. W/C. 5-Apr-4 Deburaux, Boulogne #23
£667 $1207 €1000 Paysage de Hollande, canal anime (22x28cm-9x11in) s. W/C. 5-Apr-4 Deburaux, Boulogne #7
£667 $1207 €1000 Vue d'Amsterdam (18x24cm-7x9in) s.d.1865 W/C. 5-Apr-4 Deburaux, Boulogne #21
£733 $1327 €1100 Le vieux pont Savigliano (21x27cm-8x11in) s.d.1834 wash. 5-Apr-4 Deburaux, Boulogne #11
£867 $1569 €1300 Canal a Bruges (23x33cm-9x13in) s.i. W/C. 5-Apr-4 Deburaux, Boulogne #43
£1127 $1825 €1600 Village autrichien au pied d'un lac (13x13cm-5x5in) s. W/C. 11-Aug-3 Boscher, Cherbourg #718 est:2000-3000
£1157 $2070 €1700 Vue d'une eglise gothique dans un ville traversee par un fleuve (15x21cm-6x8in) s. W/C gouache pen brown ink. 17-Mar-4 Tajan, Paris #107/R est:1500
£1259 $2102 €1800 Treves-sur-Moselle (22x30cm-9x12in) s.i. W/C. 29-Jun-3 Eric Pillon, Calais #3/R
£1316 $2421 €2000 Bateaux sur la greve (14x23cm-6x9in) s.i. W/C. 25-Jun-4 Daguerre, Paris #154 est:300-500
£1497 $2380 €2200 Barques entrant dans le port de Dordrecht (14x21cm-6x8in) s. W/C. 23-Mar-3 Mercier & Cie, Lille #226/R est:1800-2200
£1497 $2380 €2200 Animation au bord du lac (16x23cm-6x9in) s.d.1839 W/C. 23-Mar-3 Mercier & Cie, Lille #228/R est:1800-2200
£2333 $4223 €3500 Falaise d'Etretat (12x19cm-5x7in) s.i.d.1866 W/C gouache. 5-Apr-4 Deburaux, Boulogne #45/R est:600-650

OUWATER, Isaak (1750-1793) Dutch
£7308 $12643 €10670 Hostelry to the vaulting deer by the St Michael Well (36x56cm-14x22in) board. 12-Dec-3 Kieselbach, Budapest #200/R (H.F 2800000)
£44521 $75685 €65000 Brouwersgracht and the Liynbaansgracht, Amsterdam, with the rope maker, t'Fortuin and the Bullebak (40x56cm-16x22in) s.d.1786 copper prov.exhib. 5-Nov-3 Christie's, Amsterdam #65/R est:60000-80000
£50000 $86500 €73000 Ouderkerk, near Amsterdam, view from the west bank of the river Amstel (56x77cm-22x30in) s.d.1779. 11-Dec-3 Sotheby's, London #72/R est:30000-50000

OVADYAHU, Samuel (1892-1963) Israeli
£1148 $2100 €1676 Sea and Old Jaffa (23x40cm-9x16in) s. canvas on board. 1-Jun-4 Ben-Ami, Tel Aviv #4859/R est:2500-3500
£1148 $2100 €1676 Still life with a vase of flowers (60x48cm-24x19in) s. board prov. 1-Jun-4 Ben-Ami, Tel Aviv #4864/R est:2500-3500

OVENDEN, Graham (1943-) British
£1900 $3458 €2774 Kate (29x21cm-11x8in) s.d.97 verso board. 1-Jul-4 Christie's, Kensington #245/R est:1500-2000

OVENS, Jurgen (attrib) (1623-1678) German
£1200 $2040 €1752 Portrait of a gentleman in a brown coat (64x52cm-25x20in) 31-Oct-3 Christie's, Kensington #56/R est:1500-2000

OVERBECK, Fritz (1869-1909) German
£979 $1684 €1400 Beach (44x65cm-17x26in) s. board. 2-Dec-3 Hauswedell & Nolte, Hamburg #500/R
£1259 $2165 €1800 Sea (37x46cm-15x18in) s. board. 2-Dec-3 Hauswedell & Nolte, Hamburg #498/R est:1800
£1399 $2406 €2000 Clouds over sea (36x46cm-14x18in) s. board. 2-Dec-3 Hauswedell & Nolte, Hamburg #499/R est:1800
£4895 $8420 €7000 Sun streaming through the forest at Weyerberg (54x70cm-21x28in) 5-Dec-3 Bolland & Marotz, Bremen #392/R est:4500
£5629 $10245 €8500 Landscape with trees (58x46cm-23x18in) s.d.11/7/98 board. 18-Jun-4 Bolland & Marotz, Bremen #375/R est:7600

OVERBECK, Johann Friedrich (1789-1869) German
£30667 $55813 €46000 Portrait of a young woman from Rome (71x57cm-28x22in) panel painted c.1817-18 prov.lit. 1-Jul-4 Van Ham, Cologne #1548/R est:12000
Works on paper
£1100 $1980 €1606 Wooded landscape with figures, cottage and distant mountains (21x29cm-8x11in) s. pen black ink grey wash black chk. 20-Apr-4 Sotheby's, Olympia #188/R est:1400-1800

OVERBEEK, Gijsbertus Johannes van (1882-1947) Dutch
£333 $597 €500 View of Hillegonda Church in Hillegersberg (44x54cm-17x21in) s.d.1907. 11-May-4 Vendu Notarishuis, Rotterdam #44/R
£570 $1055 €850 Farmer ploughing the fields (60x81cm-24x32in) s. 15-Mar-4 Sotheby's, Amsterdam #158/R est:1000-1500
£655 $1094 €950 Caravan on Rotterdam quay (59x99cm-23x39in) s. 11-Nov-3 Vendu Notarishuis, Rotterdam #185/R
£690 $1152 €1000 Caravan on the Veer quay (58x98cm-23x39in) s. 11-Nov-3 Vendu Notarishuis, Rotterdam #52
£805 $1490 €1200 Horse and carriage (60x100cm-24x39in) s. 15-Mar-4 Sotheby's, Amsterdam #274 est:800-1200
£1293 $2352 €1900 On the quay of the Nieuwe Haven, Rotterdam (58x99cm-23x39in) s. 3-Feb-4 Christie's, Amsterdam #373 est:1500-2000

OVERBEEK, Leendert (1752-1815) Dutch
Works on paper
£267 $485 €400 Paysage anime (31x38cm-12x15in) pen ink wash. 5-Jul-4 Neret-Minet, Paris #12

OVERBEEK, Olaf Cleofas van (1946-) Dutch
£1184 $2179 €1800 Still life with apples (30x23cm-12x9in) s.d.81. 28-Jun-4 Sotheby's, Amsterdam #218/R est:800-1200

OVERBY, Robert (1935-1993) American
Sculpture
£5215 $8500 €7614 Untitled, two door cabinet (95x99x5cm-37x39x2in) latex rubber prov. 23-Sep-3 Christie's, Rockefeller NY #64/R est:10000-15000

OVERLAND, Arnulf (1889-1968) Norwegian
£365 $632 €533 Landscape (45x56cm-18x22in) s. 13-Dec-3 Blomqvist, Lysaker #1416 (N.KR 4200)

OVERLAND, Tom Erik (20th C) Norwegian
£739 $1279 €1079 Woman with her eyes shut (90x85cm-35x33in) s. 13-Dec-3 Blomqvist, Lysaker #1417 (N.KR 8500)

OVERMANS, Thys (1928-) Dutch
£350 $601 €500 Great white clouds (75x85cm-30x33in) s.d.1952 panel. 8-Dec-3 Glerum, Amsterdam #231/R
£350 $601 €500 Landscape with poppies (70x100cm-28x39in) s.d.1991. 8-Dec-3 Glerum, Amsterdam #408/R
£455 $782 €650 Landscape (95x90cm-37x35in) s.d.54. 8-Dec-3 Glerum, Amsterdam #246/R

OVERPECK, Ray (20th C) American
£598 $1100 €873 Cafferty Road, Point Pleasant (30x41cm-12x16in) s. canvasboard. 9-Jun-4 Alderfer's, Hatfield #501/R est:800-1200
£629 $1000 €918 Gatekeeper's House (51x61cm-20x24in) s. board. 10-Sep-3 Alderfer's, Hatfield #389/R est:800-1200
£809 $1400 €1181 Winter splendor (41x51cm-16x20in) s. board. 10-Dec-3 Alderfer's, Hatfield #435/R est:2000-3000
£1445 $2500 €2110 Miller's house, Hereford, winter landscape (51x61cm-20x24in) s. board. 10-Dec-3 Alderfer's, Hatfield #436/R est:2000-2500
£1572 $2500 €2295 Hagersville (61x76cm-24x30in) s. 10-Sep-3 Alderfer's, Hatfield #388/R est:1500-2000
£1630 $3000 €2380 Bend in the road (51x61cm-20x24in) s. 9-Jun-4 Alderfer's, Hatfield #500/R est:2000-3000
£2285 $4250 €3336 Quiet village (46x61cm-18x24in) s. board. 3-Mar-4 Alderfer's, Hatfield #416/R est:2000-3000

OVERSTRAETEN, War van (1891-1981) Belgian
£276 $500 €420 La femme en noir (65x54cm-26x21in) s.d.61 s.i.d.verso. 19-Apr-4 Horta, Bruxelles #338
£333 $530 €480 Amandiers en fleurs (46x60cm-18x24in) s.i.verso. 15-Sep-3 Horta, Bruxelles #329
£382 $638 €550 Femme assise (80x66cm-31x26in) s.d.1960 verso. 21-Oct-3 Campo, Vlaamse Kaai #602

OVSYANNIKOV, Sergey Osipovich (1880-?) Russian
Works on paper
£338 $605 €500 View from St Petersburg (16x11cm-6x4in) s.d.1896 W/C. 8-May-4 Bukowskis, Helsinki #414/R
£811 $1451 €1200 House in the south (21x27cm-8x11in) s. W/C. 8-May-4 Bukowskis, Helsinki #418/R

OVTCHINNIKOV, Vladimir (1941-) Russian
£10000 $17900 €14600 Death of Orpheus. Angles in the wood (64cm-25in circular) s.d.86-87 pair. 26-May-4 Sotheby's, London #322/R est:5000-7000

OVTCHINNIKOV, Vladimir (1911-1978) Russian
£327 $594 €480 Travaux d'hiver. s. 8-Feb-4 Lesieur & Le Bars, Le Havre #151

OWEN, Bill (1942-) American
£4706 $8000 €6871 Joshua (30x41cm-12x16in) 1-Nov-3 Altermann Galleries, Santa Fe #16
£11765 $20000 €17177 Few strays (61x76cm-24x30in) 1-Nov-3 Altermann Galleries, Santa Fe #77
£14706 $25000 €21471 Admiration (58x84cm-23x33in) 1-Nov-3 Altermann Galleries, Santa Fe #75
Sculpture
£978 $1750 €1428 Cutting horse (53cm-21in) s.d.1978 num.14/20 bronze wood base. 20-Mar-4 Selkirks, St. Louis #187/R est:2500-3000
£1765 $3000 €2577 Takin the jerk (36cm-14in) bronze. 1-Nov-3 Altermann Galleries, Santa Fe #78

Works on paper
£435 $700 €631 Cowboy portrait (9x7cm-4x3in) chl. 22-Aug-3 Altermann Galleries, Santa Fe #118

OWEN, Joel (20th C) British
£270 $451 €394 Crofter's cottage, Loch Etive (50x75cm-20x30in) s.d.1926 i.verso. 20-Oct-3 Bonhams, Bath #79
£279 $490 €407 Untitled landscape (48x74cm-19x29in) s. board painted c.1928. 3-Jan-4 Outer Cape Auctions, Provincetown #47/R
£420 $769 €613 Extensive Highland landscape with cattle watering (59x90cm-23x35in) s.d.1889. 6-Apr-4 Bonhams, Chester #934
£500 $925 €730 Family group in a wooded lane with cottages (28x48cm-11x19in) s. 13-Feb-4 Keys, Aylsham #649/R
£2431 $4132 €3500 Mountainous river landscape (75x80cm-30x31in) s.d. pair. 28-Oct-3 Mealy's, Castlecomer #473

OWEN, Robert Emmett (1878-1957) American
£535 $850 €781 Hillside cottages (38x31cm-15x12in) s. 12-Sep-3 Skinner, Boston #442/R
£765 $1400 €1117 Polygiest (76x102cm-30x40in) s.i.verso. 7-Jun-4 O'Gallerie, Oregon #194 est:2500-3500
£884 $1600 €1291 Red mill (43x56cm-17x22in) s. board. 16-Apr-4 James Julia, Fairfield #789/R est:1000-2000
£1576 $2820 €2301 Old sawmill above Plymouth, NH (30x41cm-12x16in) s. i.verso board. 8-Jan-4 James Julia, Fairfield #764c/R est:2500-3000
£1818 $3200 €2654 Country Road, Autumn (43x48cm-17x19in) s. prov. 23-May-4 Hindman, Chicago #150/R est:3000-5000
£2130 $3450 €3089 Winter scene with pine trees at the edge of a snowy field (48x58cm-19x23in) s. painted c.1910. 26-Jul-3 Thomaston Place, Thomaston #71
£2130 $3450 €3089 Roadside Colonial homes in a mountain valley (43x48cm-17x19in) s. painted c.1950 pair. 26-Jul-3 Thomaston Place, Thomaston #72/R
£2180 $3750 €3183 Covered bridge at Conway, Massachusetts (40x50cm-16x20in) s. i.stretcher. 3-Dec-3 Doyle, New York #217/R est:2500-3500
£3975 $6400 €5804 Themajestic oak (51x64cm-20x25in) s. 20-Aug-3 James Julia, Fairfield #1329/R est:5000-7000

OWEN, Samuel (1768-1857) British
Works on paper
£302 $562 €450 Warship and freighter at sea (25x32cm-10x13in) bears sig.d.1795 W/C wash pencil. 6-Mar-4 Arnold, Frankfurt #815/R
£750 $1388 €1095 Harbour scene (14x11cm-6x4in) s.d.1824 W/C. 10-Mar-4 Sotheby's, Olympia #130/R
£750 $1343 €1095 Fishing boat heading out to sea in a heavy swell (14x20cm-6x8in) s. prov. W/C scratching out. 26-May-4 Christie's, Kensington #382/R
£900 $1530 €1314 Dutch tjalk in heavy offshore swell with larger vessels beyond (16x22cm-6x9in) W/C prov. 4-Nov-3 Bonhams, New Bond Street #29/R
£1400 $2590 €2044 Harbour scenes (15x12cm-6x5in) one s. W/C pair. 14-Jul-4 Sotheby's, Olympia #38/R est:500-700
£1500 $2550 €2190 Unloading the catch (24x21cm-9x8in) s. pencil W/C. 19-Nov-3 Christie's, Kensington #318/R
£1600 $2560 €2336 French pilot cutter heading out to an arriving merchantman (19x27cm-7x11in) s. W/C htd white. 16-Sep-3 Bonhams, New Bond Street #4/R est:1500-2000

OWEN, William (attrib) (1769-1825) British
Works on paper
£235 $400 €343 Portrait of The Honorable James O'Neil (76x64cm-30x25in) pastel. 31-Oct-3 North East Auctions, Portsmouth #1794

OWENS, Laura (1970-) American
£41899 $75000 €61173 Untitled (300x246cm-118x97in) oil acrylic prov. 14-May-4 Phillips, New York #143/R est:50000-70000

OXENAAR, Tourette (20th C) Dutch
£400 $732 €600 Mother with three children on the beach (30x40cm-12x16in) s.d.76. 7-Jun-4 Glerum, Amsterdam #337/R

OXTOBY, David (1938-) British
£500 $935 €730 Ray Charles blowing the bagpipes (48x36cm-19x14in) s. board prov. 24-Feb-4 Canterbury Auctions, UK #164/R
Works on paper
£462 $800 €675 That's the way it was and is (37x51cm-15x20in) pencil. 11-Dec-3 Sotheby's, New York #220/R

OYEN, Wenche (1946-) Norwegian
Works on paper
£531 $978 €775 King Lear at the National Theatre (81x101cm-32x40in) s. pastel. 29-Mar-4 Blomqvist, Lysaker #1368 (N.KR 6700)

OYENS, David (1842-1902) Flemish
£748 $1362 €1100 Modest interior (17x26cm-7x10in) s.d.1892 canvas on panel. 3-Feb-4 Christie's, Amsterdam #157 est:700-900
£1250 $2125 €1800 Jolly fellow (24x17cm-9x7in) s. panel. 28-Oct-3 Christie's, Amsterdam #167/R est:2000-3000
£3200 $5728 €4800 Le voyageur (30x36cm-12x14in) s.d.1884 lit. 15-May-4 De Vuyst, Lokeren #427/R est:2400-3000
£4167 $7083 €6000 Visiting the artist's studio (48x37cm-19x15in) s.d.74. 28-Oct-3 Christie's, Amsterdam #166/R est:6000-8000

OYENS, Pierre (1842-1894) Flemish
£1000 $1820 €1460 Study of a seated gentleman (50x36cm-20x14in) s. 16-Jun-4 Christie's, Kensington #222/R est:1000-1500
Works on paper
£592 $1089 €900 L'Emigrant: a traveller resting (28x34cm-11x13in) s.d.87 pencil W/C. 22-Jun-4 Christie's, Amsterdam #163/R

OYENS, Pierre (attrib) (1842-1894) Flemish
£267 $477 €400 Portrait de dame (46x38cm-18x15in) 11-May-4 Vanderkindere, Brussels #584

OYSTON, George (c.1860-?) British
Works on paper
£260 $476 €380 Sheep in a lane (22x51cm-9x20in) s. W/C. 7-Apr-4 Woolley & Wallis, Salisbury #51/R
£270 $427 €392 Ducks by pond in rural landscape (36x23cm-14x9in) s. W/C exec.c.1890. 27-Apr-3 Desmond Judd, Cranbrook #1046
£270 $427 €392 Anglers by river in rural landscape (36x23cm-14x9in) s. exec.c.1890. 27-Apr-3 Desmond Judd, Cranbrook #1047
£280 $442 €409 Sheep and figures on a track with distant coastal scene (28x46cm-11x18in) s.d.1916 W/C. 23-Jul-3 Hampton & Littlewood, Exeter #413/R
£300 $546 €438 Sheep and figure on a country lane (23x51cm-9x20in) s. W/C. 16-Jun-4 Andrew Hartley, Ilkley #1001
£330 $551 €482 Figures and sheep on path by rural hamlet (23x76cm-9x30in) s. W/C exec 1890. 19-Oct-3 Desmond Judd, Cranbrook #1030
£370 $618 €540 Figures and sheep on path by rural hamlet (23x76cm-9x30in) s. W/C. 16-Nov-3 Desmond Judd, Cranbrook #1092
£780 $1420 €1139 Shepherdess and three sheep in a lane (32x48cm-13x19in) s. W/C. 3-Feb-4 Sworder & Son, Bishops Stortford #254/R
£820 $1509 €1197 Geese by a river. Figure on a rural lane (69x49cm-27x19in) s. W/C pair. 22-Jun-4 Bonhams, Knightsbridge #11/R
£1500 $2700 €2190 River landscape with sheep grazing on bank to foreground (28x46cm-11x18in) s.d.1815 W/C. 20-Apr-4 Canterbury Auctions, UK #167 est:250-350

OZANNE, Nicolas Marie (1728-1811) French
Works on paper
£1565 $2801 €2300 Les fondeurs de canons (21x24cm-8x9in) mono.d.1765 pen black ink grey wash black pencil prov. 19-Mar-4 Piasa, Paris #89/R est:1500

OZANNE, Nicolas Marie (attrib) (1728-1811) French
Works on paper
£2800 $5068 €4200 Vue de Mont Saint Michel (14x22cm-6x9in) pen black ink grey wash. 30-Mar-4 Rossini, Paris #86/R est:800-1200

OZENFANT, Amedee (1886-1966) French
£1469 $2497 €2100 La vague (54x81cm-21x32in) s.d.56. 18-Nov-3 Pierre Berge, Paris #44/R est:2000-3000
£5500 $10010 €8030 Trois yachts (46x55cm-18x22in) s. painted 1959 prov.exhib. 4-Feb-4 Sotheby's, London #289/R est:6000-8000
£58000 $105560 €84680 Sisteron (117x97cm-46x38in) s. painted 1918-27 prov. 4-Feb-4 Sotheby's, London #285/R est:40000-60000
Works on paper
£1000 $1730 €1460 Etude pour maternite no 2 (25x21cm-10x8in) d.1940 pencil prov. 11-Dec-3 Christie's, Kensington #129/R est:1200-1800
£9500 $15865 €13870 Nature morte aux carafes (49x69cm-19x27in) s.d.25 pencil prov. 21-Oct-3 Sotheby's, London #52/R est:2500-3500

OZERI, Yigal (1958-) Israeli
£15363 $27500 €22430 Blue dress (166x126cm-65x50in) s.i.d.1998 verso prov. 18-Mar-4 Sotheby's, New York #70/R est:10000-15000

OZERNY, Michail (20th C) Irish?
£292 $458 €420 Silence (38x58cm-15x23in) s. 26-Aug-3 James Adam, Dublin #174/R

PAAL, Ladislas de (1846-1879) Hungarian
£58789 $104056 €85832 Forest in Barbizon (49x65cm-19x26in) s.d.77. 28-Apr-4 Kieselbach, Budapest #81/R (H.F 22000000)

PAALEN, Wolfgang (1905-1959) Austrian
£3133 $5765 €4700 Untitled (65x36cm-26x14in) s.i.d.25 III 45 parchment on wood. 11-Jun-4 Pierre Berge, Paris #51 est:5000-6000
£3400 $6256 €4964 Composition (62x40cm-24x16in) init. oil on paper painted 1954 prov. 24-Mar-4 Sotheby's, Olympia #129/R est:3000-5000
£9000 $16470 €13140 Composition (33x53cm-13x21in) s.d.34 verso oil black pen canvas on cork prov. 2-Feb-4 Christie's, London #95/R est:5000-8000
£13000 $23790 €18980 Composition (27x46cm-11x18in) s.d.35 prov.lit. 2-Feb-4 Christie's, London #93/R est:10000-15000

PAATELA, Oskari (1888-1952) Finnish
£805 $1482 €1200 Bacchus (80x116cm-31x46in) s.d.1913. 25-Mar-4 Hagelstam, Helsinki #943

PAAUWE, Deborah (1972-) Australian
Photographs
£1822 $2933 €2660 Midnight autograph (119x119cm-47x47in) C-type photograph from edn of 6 prov. 25-Aug-3 Sotheby's, Paddington #253/R est:2500-4000 (A.D 4500)
£2114 $3784 €3086 Candy Girl (120x120cm-47x47in) s. C-type photograph edn 6/6. 4-May-4 Sotheby's, Melbourne #98/R est:4000-6000 (A.D 5200)
£2236 $4002 €3265 Lime Dreams (120x120cm-47x47in) C-type photograph exec c.2002. 4-May-4 Sotheby's, Melbourne #192/R est:4000-6000 (A.D 5500)
£2328 $3748 €3399 Candy Heart (119x119cm-47x47in) s. C-type photograph prov. 25-Aug-3 Sotheby's, Paddington #252/R est:2500-4000 (A.D 5750)

PABLO, Julio de (1917-) Spanish
£414 $745 €600 Untitled (46x38cm-18x15in) s. s.i.verso. 26-Jan-4 Ansorena, Madrid #924/R

PABLO, Maximo de (1930-) Spanish

£414	$691	€600	Landscape (50x80cm-20x31in) s. 17-Nov-3 Durán, Madrid #238/R
£1181	$1924	€1700	Cat (81x100cm-32x39in) s. 23-Sep-3 Durán, Madrid #216/R est:1600
£1310	$2188	€1900	Still life with cock (81x65cm-32x26in) s. 17-Nov-3 Durán, Madrid #231/R est:1800
£1379	$2303	€2000	Goat (84x61cm-33x24in) s. 17-Nov-3 Durán, Madrid #230/R est:1900
£1408	$2465	€2000	Still life with cock (89x117cm-35x46in) s. exhib. 16-Dec-3 Durán, Madrid #200/R est:1900
£1585	$2773	€2250	Bull (110x150cm-43x59in) s. s.verso. 16-Dec-3 Durán, Madrid #201/R
£1736	$2830	€2500	Still life with coffee pot (73x100cm-29x39in) s. 23-Sep-3 Durán, Madrid #217/R est:2000

PABST, Johannes Cornelis (1853-?) Dutch

Works on paper

£347	$573	€500	Peasant woman outside Dutch village in the dunes (31x48cm-12x19in) s. gouache board. 3-Jul-3 Van Ham, Cologne #1399

PACANOWSKA, Felicia (1915-2002) Polish

£699	$1189	€1000	Paysage anime (44x60cm-17x24in) s. wood. 27-Nov-3 Calmels Cohen, Paris #59/R

PACE, Stephen (1918-) American

£1965	$3400	€2869	Artist's studio, early morning (178x114cm-70x45in) s. 15-Dec-3 Hindman, Chicago #109/R est:3000-4000
£4261	$7500	€6221	Num 401, abstract composition in primary colours (239x183cm-94x72in) 22-May-4 Selkirks, St. Louis #623/R est:2500-3000

Works on paper

£578	$1000	€844	Down view of the artists house (69x81cm-27x32in) s. W/C. 15-Dec-3 Hindman, Chicago #108/R
£636	$1100	€929	Maine dining room no 1 (69x81cm-27x32in) s. W/C. 15-Dec-3 Hindman, Chicago #107/R

PACENZA, Onofrio (1904-1971) Argentinian

£710	$1300	€1037	Pompei ruins (33x26cm-13x10in) cardboard. 1-Jun-4 Arroyo, Buenos Aires #2
£7692	$14000	€11230	Chile Street in San Telmo (34x44cm-13x17in) s. s.i.verso cardboard. 29-Jun-4 Arroyo, Buenos Aires #102/R est:6000
£16484	$30000	€24067	Suburbs (52x58cm-20x23in) s. board exhib.lit. 29-Jun-4 Arroyo, Buenos Aires #88/R est:12000

PACHECO REINA, Joaquin (1934-) Spanish

£1053	$1905	€1600	Metaphysical landscape (92x73cm-36x29in) s. 14-Apr-4 Ansorena, Madrid #288/R est:1600

PACHECO, Fernando Castro (1918-) South American

£3911	$7000	€5710	Two women (80x76cm-31x30in) s. prov. 26-May-4 Sotheby's, New York #93/R est:10000-15000

PACHT, Wilhelm (1843-1912) Danish

£1172	$2015	€1711	Street scene, Skindergade with figures and horse and cart (24x20cm-9x8in) s. 3-Dec-3 Museumsbygningen, Copenhagen #114/R est:4000-6000 (D.KR 12500)

PACHTA, Josef (1902-) Austrian

£496	$829	€700	In the pleasure house (49x68cm-19x27in) s. s.d.1965 verso canvas on masonite. 14-Oct-3 Dorotheum, Vienna #213/R

PACINI, Santi (1735-1790) Italian

Works on paper

£1429	$2600	€2086	Cleansing of the Temple (39x27cm-15x11in) s.i. pencil chl paper on paper. 4-Feb-4 Christie's, Rockefeller NY #122/R est:2000-3000

PACKARD, Ann (20th C) American

£284	$525	€415	Untitled, landscape (13x18cm-5x7in) s. board. 17-Jul-4 Outer Cape Auctions, Provincetown #68/R
£382	$650	€558	Untitled, landscape (18x13cm-7x5in) s. board. 9-Nov-3 Outer Cape Auctions, Provincetown #90/R
£399	$650	€583	Untitled - landscape (20x25cm-8x10in) s. board. 19-Jul-3 Outer Cape Auctions, Provincetown #69/R
£486	$900	€710	Still life with fruit (30x30cm-12x12in) s. 17-Jul-4 Outer Cape Auctions, Provincetown #83/R
£3182	$5600	€4646	Landscape (91x152cm-36x60in) s. painted c.1983. 3-Jan-4 Outer Cape Auctions, Provincetown #70/R

PACKARD, Cynthia (20th C) American

£405	$750	€591	Mom (122x91cm-48x36in) s.d.1984. 17-Jul-4 Outer Cape Auctions, Provincetown #40/R
£429	$700	€626	Lusting sun (91x102cm-36x40in) s. 19-Jul-3 Outer Cape Auctions, Provincetown #60/R

PACKARD, Emmy Lou (1914-) American

Works on paper

£359	$600	€521	Electric transmission lines (62x135cm-24x53in) s. W/C gouache. 13-Jul-3 Butterfields, San Francisco #2062/R

PACKER, Richard G (?-1998) American

£243	$450	€355	Summer, Concord, Massachusetts (61x91cm-24x36in) s. board. 13-Mar-4 Susanin's, Chicago #6111/R
£378	$700	€552	San Marco, Venice (61x91cm-24x36in) s. masonite. 13-Mar-4 Susanin's, Chicago #6113/R

PACOR, Giovanni (1943-) Italian

£464	$844	€700	Celebrating on the quay, Trieste (70x90cm-28x35in) s. 18-Jun-4 Stadion, Trieste #325/R
£629	$1145	€950	Celebrating in Unita' Square (70x90cm-28x35in) s. 18-Jun-4 Stadion, Trieste #326/R

PADAMSEE, Akbar (1928-) Indian

£3533	$6500	€5158	Houses (41x33cm-16x13in) s.d.63 exhib. 25-Mar-4 Christie's, Rockefeller NY #207/R est:6000-8000
£8696	$16000	€12696	Nude (107x71cm-42x28in) s.d.2001 acrylic. 24-Mar-4 Sotheby's, New York #200/R est:18000-22000
£13043	$24000	€19043	Christ (80x45cm-31x18in) s. board. 25-Mar-4 Christie's, Rockefeller NY #208/R est:24000-28000
£32006	$57610	€46729	Head (120x60cm-47x24in) s.d.65. 25-Apr-4 Christie's, Hong Kong #599/R est:100000-130000 (HK.D 450000)

Works on paper

£1280	$2304	€1869	Nude (50x36cm-20x14in) s.d.2002 W/C. 25-Apr-4 Christie's, Hong Kong #601/R est:20000-25000 (HK.D 18000)
£1630	$3000	€2380	Untitled (56x38cm-22x15in) s.d.96 chl. 24-Mar-4 Sotheby's, New York #198/R est:4000-6000

PADILLA, Cayetano (19th C) Mexican

£1895	$3430	€2767	Holy Heart (83x61cm-33x24in) s.d.1845. 31-Mar-4 Louis Morton, Mexico #94/R est:40000-50000 (M.P 38000)

PADILLA, Juan (1906-1980) Spanish

£922	$1494	€1300	Still life with flowers and fruit (82x115cm-32x45in) S. 20-May-3 Ansorena, Madrid #67/R

PADOVANO, Anthony John (1933-) American

Sculpture

£838	$1500	€1223	Maquette for bridge number 2 (18x20cm-7x8in) st.sig.i.d.1969. 16-May-4 Wright, Chicago #416/R est:700-900

PADUA SCHOOL (14th C) Italian

£361111	$650000	€527222	Madonna and Child with Saints (77x97cm-30x38in) tempera panel triptych painted c.1335. 22-Jan-4 Sotheby's, New York #13/R est:400000-600000

PADUA, Paul Matthias (1903-1981) Austrian

£2080	$3723	€3120	Nude girl with flowers (76x60cm-30x24in) s.d. 13-May-4 Neumeister, Munich #450/R est:3500-4000
£3667	$6563	€5500	Woman wearing yellow hat (75x61cm-30x24in) s. 13-May-4 Neumeister, Munich #451/R est:5000-5500
£30000	$54600	€45000	Garmisch peasant couple (87x82cm-34x32in) s.d.1927 board. 30-Jun-4 Neumeister, Munich #639/R est:25000

PADWICK, Philip Hugh (1876-1958) British

£320	$592	€467	Sussex landscape (61x91cm-24x36in) s. 13-Jan-4 Bonhams, Knightsbridge #134/R

PAEDE, Paul (1868-1929) German

£436	$798	€650	Portrait of a girl (41x35cm-16x14in) s. board oval lit. 8-Jul-4 Allgauer, Kempten #2185/R
£694	$1132	€1000	Female nude in salon (31x18cm-12x7in) s. board. 25-Sep-3 Neumeister, Munich #2844
£1182	$1962	€1714	Bathers in woodland pond (54x75cm-21x30in) s.i. lit. 13-Jun-3 Zofingen, Switzerland #2508/R est:3500 (S.FR 2600)
£1316	$2421	€2000	Reclining female nude (65x80cm-26x31in) s.i. 24-Jun-4 Dr Fritz Nagel, Stuttgart #747/R est:1000
£1931	$3225	€2800	Reclining female nude (42x58cm-17x23in) s. board. 9-Jul-3 Hugo Ruef, Munich #164/R est:700
£2667	$4853	€4000	Afternoon coffee in the garden (78x122cm-31x48in) s. 30-Jun-4 Neumeister, Munich #640/R est:2800
£10490	$17832	€15000	Bachantal party (119x182cm-47x72in) s.d.19. 20-Nov-3 Van Ham, Cologne #1791/R est:10000

PAEFFGEN, C O (20th C) German

£867	$1586	€1300	Untitled (40x30cm-16x12in) mono.d.1994 acrylic on box lit. 4-Jun-4 Lempertz, Koln #340/R
£3000	$5490	€4500	Untitled - bird (50x61cm-20x24in) mono.d.96 acrylic photocanvas on cotton. 4-Jun-4 Lempertz, Koln #341/R est:4600

PAEFFGEN, Claes Otto (20th C) German

£671	$1188	€1000	Rouge et noir (110x65cm-43x26in) s.i.d. acrylic panel. 30-Apr-4 Dr Fritz Nagel, Stuttgart #380/R
£940	$1663	€1400	Untitled (140x110cm-55x43in) mono.d verso. 30-Apr-4 Dr Fritz Nagel, Stuttgart #920/R
£1887	$3057	€2755	Tass tee (47x57cm-19x22in) s.i.d.1977 verso acrylic photo canvas. 24-May-3 Burkhard, Luzern #167/R est:4500-5500 (S.FR 4000)
£2075	$3362	€3030	Troubadour (74x40cm-29x16in) s.i.d.1977 verso acrylic photo canvas. 24-May-3 Burkhard, Luzern #168/R est:4500-5500 (S.FR 4400)

Works on paper

£350	$594	€500	So high hang the cherries (31x24cm-12x9in) mono.d.82 W/C chk pencil. 29-Nov-3 Villa Grisebach, Berlin #863/R

PAERELS, Willem (1878-1962) Belgian/Dutch

£1216	$2177	€1800	View of harbour (58x78cm-23x31in) 10-May-4 Amberes, Antwerp #297
£1933	$3461	€2900	Le port de Saint-Tropez (40x49cm-16x19in) s. paper exhib. 15-May-4 De Vuyst, Lokeren #243/R est:2000-2500

£2899 $4754 €4000 Station (50x60cm-20x24in) s. prov. 27-May-3 Sotheby's, Amsterdam #488/R est:4000-6000
£3623 $5942 €5000 Collioure beach (50x40cm-20x16in) s. prov. 27-May-3 Sotheby's, Amsterdam #489/R est:5000-7000
£4710 $7725 €6500 Ostend Beach (40x50cm-16x20in) s. prov. 27-May-3 Sotheby's, Amsterdam #487/R est:5000-7000
£6376 $11795 €9500 Vieux quartier de Marseille (100x80cm-39x31in) s. lit. 13-Mar-4 De Vuyst, Lokeren #472/R est:8000-10000
£7895 $14526 €12000 Vue portuaire avec voiliers (72x74cm-28x29in) s.d.20. 22-Jun-4 Palais de Beaux Arts, Brussels #294/R est:8000-12000
£24000 $44160 €36000 Harbour of Blankenberge (71x74cm-28x29in) s. prov. 9-Jun-4 Christie's, Amsterdam #101/R est:10000-15000
Works on paper
£574 $1085 €850 Etudes de personnages (20x13cm-8x5in) bears studio st. chl pastel col crayon. 17-Feb-4 Vanderkindere, Brussels #17
£909 $1564 €1300 River landscape. Two nudes (36x45cm-14x18in) s. pastel double-sided. 2-Dec-3 Sotheby's, Amsterdam #246/R est:1200-1500

PAESCHKE, Paul (1875-1943) German
£629 $1070 €900 Still life with grapes (40x50cm-16x20in) s. i.d.1937 verso. 22-Nov-3 Arnold, Frankfurt #603/R
Works on paper
£629 $1051 €900 Changing the guard in Berlin (26x33cm-10x13in) s. i. verso mixed media board. 9-Oct-3 Michael Zeller, Lindau #713/R

PAETZ, Otto (1914-) German
£521 $823 €750 Village street (42x60cm-17x24in) s.i.d.1946 board. 5-Sep-3 Wendl, Rudolstadt #3558/R

PAEZ DEL NOGAL, Jose (1923-) Venezuelan
Works on paper
£424 $780 €636 Tropical X-rays (150x100cm-59x39in) s. dr. 27-Jun-4 Subastas Odalys, Caracas #5

PAEZ VILARO, Carlos (20th C) Argentinian?
£1117 $2000 €1631 Abstract (60x81cm-24x32in) 11-May-4 Arroyo, Buenos Aires #69

PAEZ VILARO, Jorge (1922-) Uruguayan
£529 $1000 €772 Abstract landscape (60x80cm-24x31in) s. 22-Feb-4 Galeria y Remates, Montevideo #123/R
£568 $1000 €829 Beach (73x87cm-29x34in) s. 5-Jan-4 Galeria y Remates, Montevideo #20/R
£625 $1100 €913 Canteen (100x81cm-39x32in) s. 5-Jan-4 Galeria y Remates, Montevideo #19/R
£741 $1400 €1082 Cigalle (50x70cm-20x28in) s. 22-Feb-4 Galeria y Remates, Montevideo #121/R
£1193 $2100 €1742 Punta del Este harbour (61x82cm-24x32in) s. s.i.d.1978 verso. 5-Jan-4 Galeria y Remates, Montevideo #21/R est:1000-1500
Sculpture
£881 $1550 €1286 Birds (183x276cm-72x109in) s.d.64 painted wood in 3 parts. 5-Jan-4 Galeria y Remates, Montevideo #123/R est:3000-4000

PAGADOR, Fernando (1950-) Spanish
£295 $481 €425 Apple (55x46cm-22x18in) s.d.84. 16-Jul-3 Durán, Madrid #91/R

PAGAN, Luigi (1907-1980) Italian
£297 $550 €434 Canal Vena (30x41cm-12x16in) s. panel prov. 15-Jul-4 Sotheby's, New York #90
£661 $1123 €965 Venice (29x40cm-11x16in) i.d.1952 verso panel. 5-Nov-3 Dobiaschofsky, Bern #3654 (S.FR 1500)

PAGAN, Luigi (attrib) (1907-1980) Italian
£1067 $1920 €1600 Market scene in Venice (80x60cm-31x24in) i. verso panel lit. 22-Apr-4 Allgauer, Kempten #3671 est:900

PAGANI, Carla (1907-) Italian
£1333 $2453 €2000 Departure (95x141cm-37x56in) s. 8-Jun-4 Della Rocca, Turin #328/R est:150-250

PAGANI, Gregorio (1558-1605) Italian
£36879 $59745 €52000 Moses and the Rock (217x288cm-85x113in) 21-May-3 Babuino, Rome #36/R
Works on paper
£4722 $8500 €6894 Study of the head and shoulders of a woman. Drapery study (21x17cm-8x7in) pen ink chk double-sided prov.exhib. 21-Jan-4 Sotheby's, New York #27/R est:6000-8000

PAGANI, Gregorio (circle) (1558-1605) Italian
£45638 $83973 €68000 Bathseba bathing (228x160cm-90x63in) bears sig. 25-Mar-4 Dr Fritz Nagel, Stuttgart #638/R est:4000

PAGANI, Luigi (19th C) Italian
Sculpture
£164706 $280000 €240471 Nelusko. Selika (98cm-39in) s.i.d.1871 marble pat bronze pair exhib.lit. 28-Oct-3 Christie's, Rockefeller NY #170/R est:60000-90000

PAGANI, Paolo (attrib) (1661-1716) Italian
£6579 $12105 €10000 Liberation of Saint Peter (107x84cm-42x33in) 24-Jun-4 Tajan, Paris #38/R est:10000-12000

PAGANO, Michele (1697-1732) Italian
£6338 $11092 €9000 Three travellers by stream. Travellers in landscape (93cm-37in circular) pair. 17-Dec-3 Christie's, Rome #467/R est:8000-10000

PAGE, Dennis (1926-) British
Works on paper
£680 $1197 €993 Elevenses, Florians. Sitting and thinking (19x24cm-7x9in) s. ink wash two. 18-May-4 Woolley & Wallis, Salisbury #291/R

PAGE, Edward A (1850-1928) American
£235 $400 €343 Cottage (15x22cm-6x9in) s. board prov. 21-Nov-3 Skinner, Boston #448/R
£346 $550 €505 Maine (25x29cm-10x11in) s. canvas on board prov. 12-Sep-3 Skinner, Boston #494/R
£409 $650 €597 Mountainous landscape (45x51cm-18x20in) s.d.1922 prov. 12-Sep-3 Skinner, Boston #392/R
£441 $750 €644 Fishing shack interior (15x23cm-6x9in) s. board prov. 21-Nov-3 Skinner, Boston #530/R
£472 $750 €689 Boats ashore (13x18cm-5x7in) s. canvas on board prov. 12-Sep-3 Skinner, Boston #514/R
£597 $950 €872 Fisherman (23x15cm-9x6in) board prov. 12-Sep-3 Skinner, Boston #516/R
£870 $1400 €1270 The flats in Essex looking out to haystacks (18x23cm-7x9in) s. board. 20-Aug-3 James Julia, Fairfield #1662/R est:1500-2500
£941 $1600 €1374 On the wharf, fishing shack interior (25x36cm-10x14in) s. prov. 21-Nov-3 Skinner, Boston #533/R est:600-800
£2514 $4500 €3670 Beached dories, Lynn, Massachusetts (30x46cm-12x18in) s. prov. 14-May-4 Skinner, Boston #125/R est:1500-2500

PAGE, Evelyn (1899-?) New Zealander
£2364 $3711 €3428 Still life with flowers (29x22cm-11x9in) s. canvas on board. 27-Aug-3 Dunbar Sloane, Wellington #48/R est:8000-12000 (NZ.D 6500)
£2422 $4336 €3536 Last of the country, Waikanae (22x34cm-9x13in) s. board. 12-May-4 Dunbar Sloane, Wellington #45/R est:12000-20000 (NZ.D 7000)
£5776 $9415 €8433 Queenstown (26x44cm-10x17in) s. board exhib. 23-Sep-3 Peter Webb, Auckland #35/R est:15000-20000 (NZ.D 16000)
£6391 $10865 €9331 Norwich Quay, Lyttelton (36x30cm-14x12in) s. board. 27-Nov-3 International Art Centre, Auckland #57/R est:15000-20000 (NZ.D 17000)
£7273 $11418 €10546 Still life and fruit (33x41cm-13x16in) s.i.d.March 1960 verso canvas on board exhib. 27-Aug-3 Dunbar Sloane, Wellington #18/R est:15000-25000 (NZ.D 20000)
£20000 $31400 €29000 Admiral Byrd's flagship and sailors playing (41x53cm-16x21in) s.d.1947 canvasboard exhib. 27-Aug-3 Dunbar Sloane, Wellington #34/R est:55000-65000 (NZ.D 55000)
Works on paper
£545 $856 €790 Portrait of Dennis Glover (33x24cm-13x9in) s. pencil. 27-Aug-3 Dunbar Sloane, Wellington #110 (NZ.D 1500)

PAGE, Evelyn (attrib) (1899-?) New Zealander
£977 $1662 €1426 Veryan Clare, aged 6 at Governors Bay 1941 (29x24cm-11x9in) board prov. 26-Nov-3 Dunbar Sloane, Wellington #35/R est:3000-6000 (NZ.D 2600)

PAGE, Henry Maurice (fl.1878-1890) British
£520 $957 €759 Punt on a river backwater with cottage in distance (15x11cm-6x4in) s. 11-Jun-4 Keys, Aylsham #658
£1477 $2717 €2200 Woodland scene, mid winter with figures working (76x127cm-30x50in) s.d.1889. 23-Mar-4 Mealy's, Castlecomer #911/R est:700-1100

PAGE, John R (19th C) British?
£810 $1450 €1183 Bull portrait, Earl of Clifton 35370 at 4 yrs (41x61cm-16x24in) s.i.d.1883 verso. 8-Jan-4 James Julia, Fairfield #842/R est:2500-4000

PAGE, Robert (attrib) (fl.1881-1890) British
£469 $750 €685 Cows in a stable (51x51cm-20x20in) 20-Sep-3 Sloans & Kenyon, Bethesda #139/R

PAGE, Robin (1932-) British
Sculpture
£1000 $1790 €1500 Axe and cloud (80x76x13cm-31x30x5in) wood oil on canvas plexiglas. 13-May-4 Neumeister, Munich #728/R est:1200-1500

PAGE, Willard J (20th C) American
£247 $450 €371 Colorado autumn (28x20cm-11x8in) init. board. 20-Jun-4 Charlton Hall, Columbia #566/R

PAGENKOPF, Ursula (20th C) Canadian/German
£339 $567 €495 Hockey night in Canada (30x40cm-12x16in) s.i.d.2003 acrylic. 17-Nov-3 Hodgins, Calgary #103/R (C.D 750)

PAGES, Aimee (1803-1886) French
£3154 $5867 €4700 Portrait d'homme (56x46cm-22x18in) s.d.1830. 8-Mar-4 Artcurial Briest, Paris #30/R est:1500

PAGES, Bernard (1940-) French?
Sculpture
£6711 $12013 €10000 Composition (155x70x90cm-61x28x35in) brick stone. 26-May-4 Christie's, Paris #112/R est:8000-12000
£10667 $19733 €16000 Chapiteau bleu (180x150x145cm-71x59x57in) stone tar col pebbles exec.1986 prov. 18-Jul-4 Sotheby's, Paris #164/R est:10000-15000

PAGES, Irene (20th C) French
£662 $1238 €1000 Bouquet de fleurs sur entablement aux fruits (81x100cm-32x39in) s. i.verso. 20-Jul-4 Gioffredo, Nice #1/R

PAGES, Jules Eugene (1867-1946) American
£1630 $3000 €2380 Man and children walking along a dock (17x22cm-7x9in) s. canvasboard prov. 8-Jun-4 Bonhams & Butterfields, San Francisco #4203/R est:3000-5000
£2312 $4000 €3376 Sailing ships in the harbour (28x36cm-11x14in) s. board. 10-Dec-3 Bonhams & Butterfields, San Francisco #6017/R est:5000-7000
£6522 $12000 €9522 An afternoon at Dournez (54x65cm-21x26in) s. 8-Jun-4 Bonhams & Butterfields, San Francisco #4257/R est:12000-18000
£7609 $14000 €11109 View of Notre-Dame, Paris (48x61cm-19x24in) s. prov. 8-Jun-4 Bonhams & Butterfields, San Francisco #4256/R est:10000-15000

PAGES, Jules François (1833-1910) American
£5026 $9500 €7338 Church at Moret (61x51cm-24x20in) s. 17-Feb-4 John Moran, Pasadena #68/R est:5500-7500

PAGES, Mariano (20th C) Argentinian
Sculpture
£2011 $3600 €2936 Nude (38cm-15in) s. pat bronze. 4-May-4 Arroyo, Buenos Aires #31/R est:1400
£3825 $7000 €5585 Nude (61cm-24in) bronze. 1-Jun-4 Arroyo, Buenos Aires #37
£6704 $12000 €9788 Nude (40x73cm-16x29in) s. pat bronze marble base. 4-May-4 Arroyo, Buenos Aires #36/R est:12000

PAGET, Germain (1817-1884) French
£4503 $8241 €6800 Les petits delinquants (41x33cm-16x13in) s. exhib. 9-Apr-4 Claude Aguttes, Neuilly #23/R est:5000-6000

PAGGI, Giovanni Battista (1554-1627) Italian
£5200 $8840 €7592 Holy family (70x54cm-28x21in) s.d.1614. 30-Oct-3 Sotheby's, Olympia #109/R est:3000-4000
Works on paper
£4000 $7320 €5840 Madonna in glory adored by Saints Bernard, Lucy, Catherine and George (31x21cm-12x8in) pen brown ink over blk chk buff paper prov.exhib. 8-Jul-4 Sotheby's, London #96/R est:4000-6000

PAGLIACCI, Aldo (1913-) Italian
£240 $400 €350 Festive dance (41x33cm-16x13in) s.d. board. 19-Oct-3 Susanin's, Chicago #6037/R
£268 $499 €400 Man (40x30cm-16x12in) s.d.1974. 4-Mar-4 Babuino, Rome #393
£438 $700 €639 Surrealist figures in a courtyard (41x64cm-16x25in) s.d.56 tempera board. 21-Sep-3 William Jenack, New York #328

PAGLIACCI, Mirko (1959-) Swiss
£302 $559 €450 Top model (25x35cm-10x14in) s.i.verso enamel pigment. 13-Mar-4 Meeting Art, Vercelli #250
£369 $683 €550 Top model (35x25cm-14x10in) s.i.verso enamel acrylic. 13-Mar-4 Meeting Art, Vercelli #546
£570 $1055 €850 Top model (50x70cm-20x28in) s.i.verso enamel acrylic. 13-Mar-4 Meeting Art, Vercelli #156
Works on paper
£537 $993 €800 Top model (50x70cm-20x28in) s.i.verso mixed media on canvas. 13-Mar-4 Meeting Art, Vercelli #445
£915 $1520 €1300 Archeologie notturne - Cairo (60x90cm-24x35in) s.i.verso pigment acrylic enamel cibachrome sand canvas. 14-Jun-3 Meeting Art, Vercelli #521/R
£1127 $1870 €1600 Oasi telematica (60x80cm-24x31in) s.i.verso sand pigment canvas. 14-Jun-3 Meeting Art, Vercelli #450/R est:1000

PAGLIANI, Inigio (1911-1991) Italian
£685 $1164 €1000 Meloni Street (60x50cm-24x20in) s. 7-Nov-3 Tuttarte, Modena #692

PAGLIANO, Eleuterio (1826-1903) Italian
£667 $1207 €1000 Portrait of young woman (63x52cm-25x20in) 30-Mar-4 Babuino, Rome #297/R
£1479 $2455 €2100 Young woman (52x32cm-20x13in) s. i.verso prov. 11-Jun-3 Christie's, Rome #184/R est:2000-3000
Works on paper
£530 $964 €800 Woman with fan (42x28cm-17x11in) s. wax crayon lead. 17-Jun-4 Finarte Semenzato, Milan #293/R
£1172 $1946 €1700 Gentleman reading (32x21cm-13x8in) s. W/C. 1-Oct-3 Della Rocca, Turin #30/R

PAGLIANO, Eleuterio (attrib) (1826-1903) Italian
£670 $1152 €978 Homage to the poet (22x30cm-9x12in) bears sig. panel. 2-Dec-3 Ritchie, Toronto #114/R (C.D 1500)

PAGNUELO, Francoise (20th C) Canadian?
£223 $415 €326 Cote de Liesse (25x35cm-10x14in) i.Mai 1938 verso board. 2-Mar-4 Ritchie, Toronto #131/R (C.D 555)

PAGOWSKA, Teresa (1926-) Russian
£917 $1523 €1339 Chair (50x50cm-20x20in) acrylic. 2-Oct-3 Agra, Warsaw #14/R est:2000 (P.Z 6000)
£6356 $11504 €9280 Erotica (139x130cm-55x51in) s.d.1992 tempera acrylic. 4-Apr-4 Agra, Warsaw #7/R (P.Z 45000)

PAGUENAUD, Jean-Louis (1876-1952) French
£1867 $3416 €2800 Tranquille derriere le Mausolee (60x73cm-24x29in) s. 3-Jun-4 Tajan, Paris #300/R est:1200-1800
Works on paper
£400 $725 €584 Coastal view of town (36x51cm-14x20in) s. W/C. 16-Apr-4 James Julia, Fairfield #926/R

PAHL, Manfred (1900-1994) German
£296 $473 €420 Portrait of young woman (73x50cm-29x20in) i.d.1943 verso. 18-Sep-3 Rieber, Stuttgart #1172
£336 $594 €500 Heath courtyard (37x51cm-15x20in) s.i.d. verso board. 30-Apr-4 Dr Fritz Nagel, Stuttgart #911/R
£352 $563 €500 Portrait of young woman (60x42cm-24x17in) i.d.1943 verso. 18-Sep-3 Rieber, Stuttgart #1160

PAHR-IVERSEN, Kjell (1937-) Norwegian
£528 $972 €792 Bienevue au jaune XI (73x52cm-29x20in) s. 14-Jun-4 Blomqvist, Lysaker #1297 (N.KR 6500)
£813 $1488 €1187 Yellow and red composition (55x38cm-22x15in) s.d.94 verso. 7-Jun-4 Blomqvist, Oslo #470/R (N.KR 10000)
£1626 $2976 €2374 Yellow composition (116x116cm-46x46in) s. 7-Jun-4 Blomqvist, Oslo #468/R est:25000-30000 (N.KR 20000)
£3203 $5733 €4676 The new Jerusalem II (230x140cm-91x55in) s. s.i.d.1989 verso. 22-Mar-4 Blomqvist, Oslo #655/R est:30000-35000 (N.KR 40000)
£3683 $6592 €5377 Composition (170x120cm-67x47in) s. 22-Mar-4 Blomqvist, Oslo #632/R est:30000-35000 (N.KR 46000)
Works on paper
£254 $467 €371 Actor putting on makeup (70x46cm-28x18in) s. chl. 29-Mar-4 Blomqvist, Lysaker #1236 (N.KR 3200)
£289 $530 €422 Composition (63x77cm-25x30in) s. mixed media. 2-Feb-4 Blomqvist, Lysaker #1224/R (N.KR 3600)

PAICE, George (1854-1925) British
£260 $442 €380 Boxer dog Joe, seated outside a green kennel (30x21cm-12x8in) s.i.d.98 board. 4-Nov-3 Rowley Fine Art, Newmarket #348/R
£260 $442 €380 Goldflake, chestnut hunter in a landscape (23x30cm-9x12in) s.i.d. board. 30-Oct-3 Duke & Son, Dorchester #215
£325 $517 €475 Horse in an open landscape. 9-Sep-3 Rowley Fine Art, Newmarket #419
£420 $769 €613 Portrait of a bay hunter in a stable (23x30cm-9x12in) s.d.88. 6-Apr-4 Bonhams, Knightsbridge #120/R
£430 $688 €628 Bay hunter and dog, in a field (25x30cm-10x12in) s.d.85. 16-Sep-3 Bonhams, Knowle #96
£450 $806 €657 Horse and dog in a meadow (24x29cm-9x11in) s.d.85. 11-May-4 Bonhams, Knightsbridge #41/R
£480 $802 €701 Baby, portrait of a horse in a stable (35x46cm-14x18in) s.i. 11-Nov-3 Bonhams, Knightsbridge #36/R
£480 $773 €701 Calves in an orchard (36x46cm-14x18in) mono. 12-Aug-3 Canterbury Auctions, UK #166
£500 $835 €730 Portrait of horse (33x43cm-13x17in) s.d.21. 17-Oct-3 Keys, Aylsham #708
£500 $850 €730 Bay hunter in a stable (23x30cm-9x12in) s.d.88. 27-Nov-3 Christie's, Kensington #114/R
£500 $925 €730 Portrait of a horse, thought to be Ontario, in a stable (22x30cm-9x12in) s.d.87 board. 10-Feb-4 Bonhams, Knightsbridge #157/R
£500 $930 €730 Tom, a grey stallion (22x29cm-9x11in) s.i. board. 2-Mar-4 Bearnes, Exeter #419/R
£500 $865 €730 Alexander, study of a hunter (33x43cm-13x17in) s.d. 9-Dec-3 Clarke Gammon, Guildford #46
£524 $892 €750 Study of chestnut horse in a stable, Templemore (14x18cm-6x7in) s.d.03. 18-Nov-3 Mealy's, Castlecomer #1271/R
£550 $858 €803 Portrait of the charger Beltenebrosa of the XII Lancers, in a landscape (35x45cm-14x18in) s.i.d.98. 28-Mar-3 Greenslade Hunt, Taunton #502/R
£550 $990 €803 Midge, a study of a terrier (29x21cm-11x8in) s.d.22 i.verso canvasboard. 21-Apr-4 Tennants, Leyburn #1195
£600 $1074 €876 Saddled bay hunter in a stable with a goat (51x68cm-20x27in) s.d.84. 18-Mar-4 Christie's, Kensington #483/R
£700 $1288 €1022 Sit T Gallway's Leinster in a stable (30x46cm-12x18in) s.i. 10-Jun-4 Christie's, Kensington #183/R
£850 $1607 €1241 Jenny a bay hunter in a landscape (52x69cm-20x27in) s.i.d.15. 19-Feb-4 Christie's, Kensington #321/R
£900 $1656 €1314 Opera, chestnut mare with a foal (51x68cm-20x27in) s.i. 10-Jun-4 Christie's, Kensington #187/R
£1657 $3000 €2419 Priceless, by Belvoir Vanquisher out of Pensive (34x44cm-13x17in) s.d.99. 30-Mar-4 Bonhams & Butterfields, San Francisco #66/R est:1800-2800
£1800 $3060 €2628 Mabruk and Bourton, hunters (35x45cm-14x18in) s.i.d.00 pair. 1-Dec-3 Bonhams, Bath #123/R est:1000-1500
£1800 $3222 €2628 Dutch Oven and Mercury, one with huntsman up, one holding his horse (51x66cm-20x26in) s.d.92. 5-May-4 John Nicholson, Haslemere #592 est:2000
£2500 $4250 €3650 Over the ditch (67x79cm-26x31in) s. 27-Nov-3 Christie's, Kensington #41/R est:2000-3000

PAIER, Theodor (19th C) German
£366 $656 €534 Landscape with horse drawn cart (52x79cm-20x31in) s. 12-May-4 Dobiaschofsky, Bern #843/R (S.FR 850)

PAIK, Nam June (1932-) American/Korean
Sculpture
£1200 $2184 €1800 Composition aux 45 tours et cassette (43cm-17in) s. num.1/9 mixed media. 5-Jul-4 Neret-Minet, Paris #70/R est:500
£3333 $6067 €5000 Deux robots. 5-Jul-4 Neret-Minet, Paris #71 est:200-300
£4476 $7608 €6400 Untitled (80x76x28cm-31x30x11in) s.d.84 TV artificial plants bulbs. 27-Nov-3 Lempertz, Koln #314/R est:6000
£10615 $19000 €15498 Nude (48x58x30cm-19x23x12in) s.d.97 marble laserdiscs televisions laserdisc players prov. 14-May-4 Phillips, New York #355/R est:12000-18000
£11000 $18370 €16060 Casablanca in red and green (262x178x23cm-103x70x9in) s.d.88 silkscreen print acrylic wood metal plastic canvas. 22-Oct-3 Christie's, London #76/R est:8000-12000

£12000 $21840 €17520 Hydra - Budda. masks televisions video tapes violin sand exhib. 5-Feb-4 Christie's, London #196/R est:15000-20000
£21000 $38220 €30660 Paintings is not art (107x194x101cm-42x76x40in) s.d.88 TV chairs gold paint monitors video player prov.exhib.lit. 6-Feb-4 Sotheby's, London #231/R est:15000-20000
£52000 $95680 €78000 Robespierre (300x200x50cm-118x79x20in) television sets nine various objects exec 1989 prov.exhib.lit. 8-Jun-4 Artcurial Briest, Paris #237/R est:70000-90000
Works on paper
£1700 $3043 €2482 Untitled (36x43cm-14x17in) s.d.98 crayon. 6-May-4 Sotheby's, London #89/R est:1600-2000
£48951 $81748 €70000 TV Beuys, Bogie (244x214cm-96x84in) s. mixed media moniteurs videos prov.exhib. 11-Oct-3 Cornette de St.Cyr, Paris #21/R est:60000-80000

PAIL, Edouard (1851-1916) French
£420 $722 €600 Village pres de Corbigny (24x30cm-9x12in) s. board. 5-Dec-3 Maigret, Paris #19
£420 $722 €600 Cours d'eau dans la Nievre (23x32cm-9x13in) s. board. 5-Dec-3 Maigret, Paris #20/R
£634 $1052 €900 Bord de riviere en ete (24x39cm-9x15in) s. panel. 15-Jun-3 Peron, Melun #113
£680 $1218 €1000 Troupeau de mouton (33x41cm-13x16in) s. 19-Mar-4 Millon & Associes, Paris #43
£700 $1295 €1022 Lakeland landscape with heather (30x35cm-12x14in) s. 14-Jul-4 Christie's, Kensington #955/R
£938 $1500 €1369 Summer landscape (53x43cm-21x17in) s. 21-Sep-3 Grogan, Boston #29/R
£1242 $2000 €1813 Tending the hens (46x55cm-18x22in) s. prov. 14-Jan-4 Christie's, Rockefeller NY #16/R est:3000-5000

PAILES, Isaac (1895-1978) French
£315 $526 €450 Triste clown (27x22cm-11x9in) s. 29-Jun-3 Feletin, Province #115
£1656 $3013 €2500 Saint-Paul-de-Vence (60x73cm-24x29in) s. 16-Jun-4 Claude Boisgirard, Paris #127/R est:1000-1500

PAILHES, Fred (1902-1991) French
£369 $687 €550 Les trois amis sous les ponts de Paris (33x50cm-13x20in) s. felt. 7-Mar-4 Lesieur & Le Bars, Le Havre #114
£420 $722 €600 Le cafe du Port (60x73cm-24x29in) s.d.60 isorel. 7-Dec-3 Lesieur & Le Bars, Le Havre #238
£503 $936 €750 L'entree du port du Havre (46x55cm-18x22in) s. panel. 7-Mar-4 Lesieur & Le Bars, Le Havre #113
£1448 $2419 €2100 Animation au Havre (73x92cm-29x36in) s.i.d.1933. 11-Nov-3 Lesieur & Le Bars, Le Havre #132
Works on paper
£448 $749 €650 Vieille rue a Honfleur (67x47cm-26x19in) s. gouache. 11-Nov-3 Lesieur & Le Bars, Le Havre #86
£586 $979 €850 Quai Notre-Dame (48x61cm-19x24in) s.i. gouache. 11-Nov-3 Lesieur & Le Bars, Le Havre #131
£690 $1152 €1000 Vieux cafe a Saint-Francois (46x61cm-18x24in) s.d.1958 gouache. 11-Nov-3 Lesieur & Le Bars, Le Havre #85
£839 $1560 €1250 La joyeuse viree (45x58cm-18x23in) s. W/C. 7-Mar-4 Lesieur & Le Bars, Le Havre #112

PAILLARD, Henri (1844-1912) French
£3478 $5704 €4800 Le retour des pecheurs aux sables d'Olonne (90x151cm-35x59in) s.d.84. 11-May-3 Osenat, Fontainebleau #166/R est:3500-4000

PAILLARD, Victor (19th C) ?
Sculpture
£3451 $5728 €4900 Statue of Moliere, seated in a chair (44cm-17in) s. dark pat. bronze. 11-Jun-3 Sotheby's, Amsterdam #338/R est:5500-6500

PAILLER, Henri (1876-1954) French
£282 $487 €400 Soleil couchant (38x55cm-15x22in) s. 13-Dec-3 Martinot & Savignat, Pontoise #163
£303 $524 €430 Montagne de Die, le matine - Drome (50x65cm-20x26in) s. 13-Dec-3 Martinot & Savignat, Pontoise #169
£366 $634 €520 Le clocher du village, Centre (73x60cm-29x24in) s. 13-Dec-3 Martinot & Savignat, Pontoise #179
£394 $682 €560 Veilles maisons a Saint Come (53x64cm-21x25in) s. 13-Dec-3 Martinot & Savignat, Pontoise #174
£408 $707 €580 Vallee de la Seine au printemps (61x46cm-24x18in) s. 13-Dec-3 Martinot & Savignat, Pontoise #157
£423 $731 €600 Paysage de montagne au Ruisseau (50x65cm-20x26in) s. 13-Dec-3 Martinot & Savignat, Pontoise #158/R
£458 $792 €650 Village de la vallee de la Seine (61x46cm-24x18in) s. 13-Dec-3 Martinot & Savignat, Pontoise #156
£458 $792 €650 Pommiers en fleurs, vallee de la Seine (75x54cm-30x21in) s. 13-Dec-3 Martinot & Savignat, Pontoise #159
£563 $975 €800 Brume matinale, vallee de la Seine (54x73cm-21x29in) s. 13-Dec-3 Martinot & Savignat, Pontoise #160
£599 $1036 €850 Effet de soleil (60x73cm-24x29in) s. 13-Dec-3 Martinot & Savignat, Pontoise #161
£1007 $1862 €1500 Paysage de la Creuse (46x61cm-18x24in) s. 14-Mar-4 St-Germain-en-Laye Encheres #105/R
£1200 $2184 €1800 Vieux pont a Annet-sur-Marne (39x56cm-15x22in) s. 4-Jul-4 Eric Pillon, Calais #212/R
£1678 $3104 €2500 Effet rose sur Crozant (60x73cm-24x29in) s. 14-Mar-4 St-Germain-en-Laye Encheres #102/R est:2000

PAILLET, Charles (1871-1937) French
Sculpture
£1184 $2179 €1800 Les deux amis (26x61x28cm-10x24x11in) st.f. Barbedienne pat bronze marble base. 25-Jun-4 Daguerre, Paris #257/R est:1800-2200
£2000 $3400 €2920 Deux amis (13x33cm-5x13in) s.st.f.Barbedienne pat bronze. 28-Oct-3 Sotheby's, London #167/R
£2500 $3975 €3650 Two alsatians, one standing, one seated (56x69cm-22x27in) s. bronze. 1-May-3 John Nicholson, Haslemere #292/R est:2000-3000
£11500 $21045 €16790 Deux amis (27x61cm-11x24in) s.st.f.Barbedienne pat bronze lit. 9-Jul-4 Sotheby's, London #127/R est:6000

PAILLOT, C (?) French?
Sculpture
£2838 $5080 €4200 Cerf et biche (59cm-23in) s. brown pat bronze marble socle. 10-May-4 Horta, Bruxelles #42/R est:1800-2200

PAILOS, Manuel (1917-) Uruguayan
£500 $905 €750 Composition (25x25cm-10x10in) s. acrylic paper on board prov.lit. 30-Mar-4 Segre, Madrid #140/R
£838 $1400 €1223 Composition (30x25cm-12x10in) s. cardboard. 7-Oct-3 Galeria y Remates, Montevideo #63/R
£1463 $2400 €2136 Composition (55x80cm-22x31in) s.d.62 cardboard. 3-Jun-3 Galeria y Remates, Montevideo #72
£2118 $3600 €3092 Red fish (53x61cm-21x24in) s. 25-Nov-3 Galeria y Remates, Montevideo #55/R
£3750 $6600 €5475 Still life (77x67cm-30x26in) s. 5-Jan-4 Galeria y Remates, Montevideo #51/R est:7000-8000
£5682 $10000 €8296 Composition D (160x111cm-63x44in) s.d.88 oil collage. 5-Jan-4 Galeria y Remates, Montevideo #99/R est:13000-15000
£6098 $10000 €8903 Composition (120x80cm-47x31in) s. s.d.90 verso oil sand fabric. 3-Jun-3 Galeria y Remates, Montevideo #71
£9497 $17000 €13866 Two figures (97x114cm-38x45in) s.d.58 tempera board exhib. 26-May-4 Sotheby's, New York #106/R est:10000-15000
Works on paper
£426 $750 €622 Faces (27x18cm-11x7in) s.d.67 mixed media. 5-Jan-4 Galeria y Remates, Montevideo #101/R
£483 $850 €705 Cathedral (38x28cm-15x11in) s.i.d.1969 ink W/C. 5-Jan-4 Galeria y Remates, Montevideo #100/R
£488 $800 €712 Bathers (25x25cm-10x10in) s. ink W/C on canvas prov. 3-Jun-3 Galeria y Remates, Montevideo #38
£635 $1200 €927 Composition with sun (25x25cm-10x10in) s. mixed media on canvas. 22-Feb-4 Galeria y Remates, Montevideo #141/R
£637 $1000 €930 Cup and fruit (34x26cm-13x10in) s. ink wash. 23-Nov-2 Subastas Odalys, Caracas #25
£739 $1300 €1079 Woman (25x19cm-10x7in) s.d.65 mixed media. 5-Jan-4 Galeria y Remates, Montevideo #102/R
£824 $1400 €1203 Fish and barrels (26x26cm-10x10in) s. encaustic on canvas. 25-Nov-3 Galeria y Remates, Montevideo #56/R
£1402 $2300 €2047 Adventures (57x47cm-22x19in) s. ink W/C. 3-Jun-3 Galeria y Remates, Montevideo #73
£1522 $2800 €2222 Composition (54x44cm-21x17in) s.d.97 encaustic. 22-Jun-4 Galeria y Remates, Montevideo #101/R est:3000-4000
£1761 $3100 €2571 Composition (43x34cm-17x13in) s. ink W/C. 5-Jan-4 Galeria y Remates, Montevideo #53/R est:2000-3000
£2000 $3400 €2920 Boats (76x66cm-30x26in) s.d.88 encaustic on canvas. 25-Nov-3 Galeria y Remates, Montevideo #54/R
£7059 $12000 €10306 Adventures (110x90cm-43x35in) s.d.90 encaustic on canvas. 25-Nov-3 Galeria y Remates, Montevideo #53/R

PAINE, Roxy (1966-) American
Sculpture
£838 $1500 €1223 No 15, RF (25x25cm-10x10in) s.i.verso prov. 16-May-4 Wright, Chicago #434/R est:700-900

PAIVINEN, Kathy (20th C) American
Works on paper
£479 $800 €699 Airedales (51x71cm-20x28in) s. W/C. 11-Oct-3 Nadeau, Windsor #204/R

PAIZS-GOEBEL, Jeno (1899-1944) Hungarian
Works on paper
£992 $1716 €1448 Spring in the Garden in Szentendre (46x55cm-18x22in) s.d.41 W/C. 12-Dec-3 Kieselbach, Budapest #137/R (H.F 380000)
£2172 $3605 €3171 Bunch of flowers in the window (58x42cm-23x17in) s.d.936 W/C. 4-Oct-3 Kieselbach, Budapest #52/R (H.F 800000)

PAJER-GARTEGEN, Robert (1866-1944) Austrian
£533 $955 €800 Sunbathing (28x37cm-11x15in) mono. 13-May-4 Dorotheum, Linz #479/R

PAJETTA, Guido (1898-1987) Italian
£2245 $4018 €3300 Soldier and childminder (73x61cm-29x24in) s.d.57. 16-Mar-4 Finarte Semenzato, Milan #199/R est:1900
£2245 $4018 €3300 Woman in profile (79x59cm-31x23in) s. 16-Mar-4 Finarte Semenzato, Milan #296/R est:2200
£2449 $4384 €3600 Pipe smoker (80x60cm-31x24in) s.d.76. 16-Mar-4 Finarte Semenzato, Milan #297/R est:2200
£3007 $5112 €4300 Reclining figures (38x33cm-15x13in) s.d.1932. 20-Nov-3 Finarte Semenzato, Milan #119/R est:4000-4500
£3472 $5486 €5000 Riders (91x76cm-36x30in) painted 1962. 6-Sep-3 Meeting Art, Vercelli #473a est:3000
£6803 $12177 €10000 Bathers (97x130cm-38x51in) s.d.1933. 16-Mar-4 Finarte Semenzato, Milan #330/R est:4700

PAJETTA, Pietro (1845-1911) Italian
£22535 $38986 €32000 Peasant and cow (43x34cm-17x13in) s.d.1880. 10-Dec-3 Sotheby's, Milan #83/R est:12000-18000

PAJOL, Charles (1812-1891) Russian
Prints
£10256 $16000 € Russian Military (62cm-24in) lithograph 46. 11-Apr-3 Christie's, Rockefeller NY #4/R est:6000-8000

PAJOT, Émile Paul (1870-1930) French
Miniatures
£703 $1300 €1026 Untitled, sailing ship on choppy waters (43x58cm-17x23in) W/C gouache. 12-Mar-4 Du Mouchelle, Detroit #271/R

PAJOT, Gilbert (?) French
Works on paper
£1724 $3155 €2500 Le Ketch, Lilas d'Avril (38x53cm-15x21in) s.i. W/C gouache. 31-Jan-4 Neret-Minet, Paris #128/R est:3000-3500
£1806 $3015 €2600 Marine scenes (45x58cm-18x23in) s.i. W/C gouache pair. 26-Oct-3 Lesieur & Le Bars, Le Havre #58
£2621 $4796 €3800 Le dundee thonier, Le Doux Zephir (37x53cm-15x21in) s. W/C gouache. 31-Jan-4 Neret-Minet, Paris #129/R est:3000-3500

PAJOU, Augustin (1730-1809) French
Works on paper
£2381 $4262 €3500 Pyrrhus presente a Glaucias (57x80cm-22x31in) s.i. graphite pen grey ink wash prov.exhib.lit. 18-Mar-4 Christie's, Paris #140/R est:3000-5000
£2740 $4657 €4000 Venus mere de l'amour courtois (26x39cm-10x15in) s.d.1780 crayon chk. 6-Nov-3 Tajan, Paris #57/R

PAKENHAM, Jack (?) British
£280 $465 €409 Journey painting (30x35cm-12x14in) s.d.71 board. 1-Oct-3 John Ross, Belfast #26
£300 $558 €438 Winter hill (25x35cm-10x14in) s. 3-Mar-4 John Ross, Belfast #29
£340 $585 €496 Connemara landscape (30x30cm-12x12in) s.d.1998 board. 3-Dec-3 John Ross, Belfast #84
£380 $707 €555 Landscape, Murcia (61x61cm-24x24in) s.d.83 verso board. 3-Mar-4 John Ross, Belfast #229
£420 $769 €613 Dolmen Shore (50x61cm-20x24in) s. board. 2-Jun-4 John Ross, Belfast #51
£600 $1032 €876 Winter Lough (50x61cm-20x24in) s. board. 3-Dec-3 John Ross, Belfast #208
Works on paper
£320 $550 €467 Swanage summer (66x91cm-26x36in) mixed media. 3-Dec-3 John Ross, Belfast #126

PAL, Fried (1914-) Hungarian
£245 $450 €358 Runaway, cowboy with lariat on a pony chasing black steer (61x76cm-24x30in) s. 29-Mar-4 O'Gallerie, Oregon #130/R
£313 $500 €457 Elegant lady in white gown (102x76cm-40x30in) s. 21-Sep-3 Grogan, Boston #57/R
£464 $850 €696 Two ballerinas (61x91cm-24x36in) 9-Jul-4 Du Mouchelle, Detroit #1018/R
£562 $939 €815 Reclining nude (79x59cm-31x23in) s. 30-Jun-3 Australian Art Auctions, Sydney #103 (A.D 1400)
£588 $1000 €858 Ballerina in a blue dress (71x61cm-28x24in) s. prov. 18-Nov-3 John Moran, Pasadena #151
£699 $1300 €1021 Portrait of a woman in purple evening gown (71x56cm-28x22in) s. 3-Mar-4 Alderfer's, Hatfield #317/R est:800-1200
£982 $1600 €1434 Portrait of a woman on a Paris street (76x64cm-30x25in) s. 27-Sep-3 Charlton Hall, Columbia #103/R est:2000-3000
£1159 $1900 €1681 Portrait of an opera singer in a blue dress (76x64cm-30x25in) s. 4-Jun-3 Alderfer's, Hatfield #253/R est:1200-1800
£1374 $2500 €2006 Spanish Dancer (89x69cm-35x27in) s. canvasboard. 7-Feb-4 Neal Auction Company, New Orleans #973/R est:3000-4000
£1415 $2250 €2066 Girl with oxen on beach (76x102cm-30x40in) s. 10-Sep-3 Alderfer's, Hatfield #463/R est:2000-3000
£1421 $2600 €2075 Three ballerinas (76x61cm-30x24in) s.i. 5-Jun-4 Neal Auction Company, New Orleans #903/R est:2500-3500
£2100 $3885 €3066 Monique (61x76cm-24x30in) s. sold with another by the same hand. 14-Jul-4 Sotheby's, Olympia #286/R est:2500-3000

PALACIOS TARDEZ, Pascual (1920-1994) Spanish
£284 $474 €400 Landscape (27x35cm-11x14in) s. 23-Jun-3 Durán, Madrid #1266

PALACIOS, Alirio (1944-) Venezuelan
Works on paper
£1688 $2870 €2464 Untitled (110x106cm-43x42in) s. mixed media. 23-Nov-3 Subastas Odalys, Caracas #142
£8380 $15000 €12235 Horse (140x150cm-55x59in) s.d.99 s.i.d.verso pigment wood. 26-May-4 Sotheby's, New York #158/R est:18000-22000
£8492 $15625 €12738 Study after Remington (170x175cm-67x69in) s. pigment ink paper on canvas. 27-Jun-4 Subastas Odalys, Caracas #80/R
£11912 $20250 €17392 In memoriam (150x112cm-59x44in) s. mixed media card exec.1982. 23-Nov-3 Subastas Odalys, Caracas #132 est:20000

PALACIOS, Joaquin Vaquero (1900-1998) Spanish
£5369 $9611 €8000 Woman putting wheat to dry (45x37cm-18x15in) s. cardboard. 25-May-4 Durán, Madrid #207/R est:3000
£9155 $16021 €13000 Landscape (66x81cm-26x32in) s.i. painted c.925. 16-Dec-3 Segre, Madrid #101/R est:12000
Works on paper
£369 $661 €550 Study of horses (27x20cm-11x8in) s.i.d.1930 dr lit. 25-May-4 Durán, Madrid #93/R

PALACIOS, Luisa (1938-) Venezuelan
£647 $1165 €945 Untitled (65x55cm-26x22in) s. 25-Apr-4 Subastas Odalys, Caracas #22/R

PALADINO, Mimmo (1948-) Italian
£2378 $4090 €3400 Selvatico (27x25cm-11x10in) s.i.d.1978 verso. 2-Dec-3 Sotheby's, Amsterdam #192/R est:2000-3000
£7292 $11521 €10500 Untitled (102x72cm-40x28in) oil pastel cardboard painted 1989. 6-Sep-3 Meeting Art, Vercelli #612 est:8000
£8333 $15333 €12166 Untitled (59x77cm-23x30in) s. oil acrylic plaster. 23-Jun-4 Koller, Zurich #3133/R est:2500-3800 (S.FR 19000)
£8500 $15640 €12410 Untitled (73x103cm-29x41in) oil wax crayon pastel card prov. 24-Jun-4 Sotheby's, London #296/R est:8000-12000
£11000 $20020 €16060 Untitled (150x99cm-59x39in) s.d.1982 verso oil pastel. 5-Feb-4 Christie's, London #140/R est:10000-15000
£11173 $20000 €16313 Untitled (56x77cm-22x30in) oil acrylic gouache exec 1982 prov. 13-May-4 Sotheby's, New York #428/R est:12000-15000
£25449 $42500 €37156 Le cinque eta dell'oro IV (211x150cm-83x59in) s.i.d.1986 verso oil gold leaf plaster wood prov. 13-Nov-3 Sotheby's, New York #552/R est:40000-60000
£30000 $54600 €43800 Rosso (110x154cm-43x61in) init.d.1982 s.d.verso prov. 5-Feb-4 Christie's, London #136/R est:2500-35000
£32000 $58240 €46720 Puttura Fantasma (184x368cm-72x145in) s.i.d.1980-81 oil tempera paper wool plaster triptych prov. 5-Feb-4 Christie's, London #143/R est:22000-28000
£32895 $60526 €48027 Composition with large figure (103x73cm-41x29in) s.verso oil crayon chl collage prov. 23-Jun-4 Koller, Zurich #3134/R est:4000-5500 (S.FR 75000)
£55000 $91850 €80300 Passion room (200x200cm-79x79in) s.i.d.1986 verso prov. 20-Oct-3 Sotheby's, London #44/R est:60000
Prints
£2238 $3804 €3200 Untitled (66x49cm-26x19in) s.i.d.1984 num.10/12 drypoint aquatint prov. 25-Nov-3 Sotheby's, Milan #147/R est:1200-1500
£6992 $12027 €10000 Extemporisation (136x206cm-54x81in) s.num.1/1 monotype ink sand etching. 3-Dec-3 Sotheby's, Amsterdam #395/R est:10000-15000
Sculpture
£8383 $14000 €12239 Untitled (118x51x39cm-46x20x15in) s.d.1988 verso brown pat bronze prov. 13-Nov-3 Sotheby's, New York #557/R est:10000-15000
£11976 $20000 €17485 Untitled (62x47x29cm-24x19x11in) s.d.1987 num.1/3 green brown pat bronze prov. 13-Nov-3 Sotheby's, New York #541/R est:20000-30000
£16000 $29120 €23360 Carro (63x60x58cm-25x24x23in) incised sig.d.1986 blk pat bronze st.f.Giacomo Napoli lit. 5-Feb-4 Christie's, London #141/R est:16000-22000
£18000 $30060 €26280 Carriage (71x61x60cm-28x24x24in) s.d.1986 num.6/6 bronze prov.lit. 20-Oct-3 Sotheby's, London #47/R est:20000
£19461 $32500 €28413 Fluid dream (216x86x53cm-85x34x21in) s.d.1986 num.2/3 brown pat bronze st.f.Fonderia de Giacomo prov. 13-Nov-3 Sotheby's, New York #555/R est:30000-40000
£22346 $40000 €32625 Fluid dream (216x48x74cm-85x19x29in) s.d.1985 num.III st.f.Giacomo green pat bronze prov. 13-May-4 Sotheby's, New York #444/R est:15000-20000
£33333 $61333 €50000 Untitled (127x76x32cm-50x30x13in) s.d.1987 verso mixed media canvas prov.exhib. 8-Jun-4 Artcurial Briest, Paris #254/R est:50000-60000
£50279 $90000 €73407 Untitled - Fountain (210x192x76cm-83x76x30in) s.d.1987 num.2/3 st.f.Giacomo Napoli bronze prov. 13-May-4 Sotheby's, New York #442/R est:60000-80000
£58667 $108533 €88000 Untitled (212x197x77cm-83x78x30in) s.st.f.Di Giacomo d.1987 num.1/3 bronze prov. 18-Jul-4 Sotheby's, Paris #169/R est:60000-80000
Works on paper
£362 $605 €529 Tre pescatori minacciati da una stella cometa (29x38cm-11x15in) s.i.d.1981 verso pencil exhib.lit. 24-Jun-3 Germann, Zurich #52/R (S.FR 800)
£362 $605 €529 Tre pescatori minacciati da una cometa (24x34cm-9x13in) s.i.d.1981 pencil gold bronze. 24-Jun-3 Germann, Zurich #54 (S.FR 800)
£407 $680 €594 Senza ragione (24x34cm-9x13in) s.i.d.1980 verso pencil Ink prov.exhib.lit. 24-Jun-3 Germann, Zurich #56 (S.FR 900)
£600 $1080 €900 Untitled (31x52cm-12x20in) s.d. verso Indian ink. 24-Apr-4 Reiss & Sohn, Konigstein #5820/R
£700 $1211 €1022 Untitled (21x28cm-8x11in) s.indis.i.d.1978 verso pen black ink. 11-Dec-3 Christie's, Kensington #243/R
£1200 $2076 €1752 Legni bruciati (24x32cm-9x13in) i.d.1979 init.verso ballpoint pen red ink wax crayon prov. 11-Dec-3 Christie's, Kensington #252/R est:1000-1500
£1400 $2534 €2044 Alle prime luci dell'alba (34x49cm-13x19in) s.i.d.1980 verso pencil col pencil W/C. 1-Apr-4 Christie's, Kensington #232/R est:800-1200
£1730 $3200 €2526 Untitled (29x41cm-11x16in) s.d.1984 verso pencil oil pastel W/C prov. 13-Jul-4 Christie's, Rockefeller NY #69/R est:2000-3000
£1879 $3477 €2800 Figure (31x23cm-12x9in) pencil. 11-Mar-4 Galleria Pace, Milan #133/R est:3300-4300
£1974 $3632 €2882 Untitled (48x68cm-19x27in) s.verso pencil oil crayon. 23-Jun-4 Koller, Zurich #3113 est:2200-3500 (S.FR 4500)
£2365 $4234 €3500 Santa Lucia (24x32cm-9x13in) mono.d.1974-94 crayon chl exhib. 4-May-4 Calmels Cohen, Paris #239/R est:4000-5000
£2797 $4755 €4000 Untitled (30x40cm-12x16in) s.verso pencil W/C. 24-Nov-3 Christie's, Milan #143/R est:4000-6000
£2817 $4704 €4113 Figure composition (34x49cm-13x19in) init.d.1983 gouache pencil gold paint collage. 7-Oct-3 Rasmussen, Copenhagen #105/R est:25000-30000 (D.KR 30000)
£3289 $6053 €4802 Untitled (75x100cm-30x39in) s.verso mixed media. 23-Jun-4 Koller, Zurich #3138/R est:5000-7000 (S.FR 7500)
£3728 $6860 €5443 Untitled (48x65cm-19x26in) s.d.80 W/C bodycol pencil prov. 23-Jun-4 Koller, Zurich #3114/R est:1800-2800 (S.FR 8500)
£3947 $7263 €5763 Untitled (48x66cm-19x26in) s. mixed media collage prov. 23-Jun-4 Koller, Zurich #3115/R est:2000-3000 (S.FR 9000)
£4762 $8524 €7000 Un (49x69cm-19x27in).s.d.1982 v. mm. 16-Mar-4 Finarte Semenzato, Milan #409/R est:9000
£5071 $8772 €7200 Untitled (48cm-19in circular) mono.d.83 mixed media prov. 9-Dec-3 Artcurial Briest, Paris #425/R est:3000-4000
£7000 $12880 €10220 Untitled (158x108cm-62x43in) s.d.1989 verso mixed media canvas prov. 24-Jun-4 Sotheby's, Olympia #586/R est:5000-7000
£8000 $14720 €11680 Untitled (158x108cm-62x43in) s.d.1989 verso mixed media canvas prov. 24-Jun-4 Sotheby's, Olympia #587/R est:5000-7000
£8054 $14899 €12000 Untitled (109x79cm-43x31in) s.d.2000 verso cardboard plaster collage mixed media net lit. 13-Mar-4 Meeting Art, Vercelli #126 est:10000
£10870 $17826 €15000 Bach (76x57cm-30x22in) s.i.d.1997 mixed media. 30-May-3 Farsetti, Prato #311/R
£13408 $24000 €19576 Untitled (77x56cm-30x22in) pastel chl white chk exec 1982 prov. 13-May-4 Sotheby's, New York #427/R est:14000-18000

PALAMEDES, Anthonie (1601-1673) Dutch
£2432 $4281 €3600 In the guardroom (23x31cm-9x12in) s. panel prov. 22-May-4 Lempertz, Koln #1114/R est:4000

£2806 $4601 €3900 Fumeurs et musiciens dans un taverne (23x30cm-9x12in) s. panel. 6-Jun-3 Drouot Estimations, Paris #23/R est:3000-4000
£2897 $4837 €4200 Portrait of woman (71x61cm-28x24in) panel. 15-Nov-3 Lempertz, Koln #1115/R est:6000
£3000 $5460 €4500 Elegant figures making merry (42x53cm-17x21in) panel prov. 30-Jun-4 Neumeister, Munich #478/R est:3000
£4500 $7785 €6570 Elegant company making music in an interior (35x44cm-14x17in) panel. 10-Dec-3 Bonhams, New Bond Street #1/R est:3000-5000
£4730 $8324 €7000 Officer blowing a trumpet standing in a window with a balcony (38x31cm-15x12in) s. panel prov. 18-May-4 Sotheby's, Amsterdam #10/R est:8000-12000
£7432 $13081 €11000 Portrait of a lady in rich lace robe (100x80cm-39x31in) s.d.1666. 24-May-4 Bernaerts, Antwerp #170/R est:11000-13000

PALAMEDES, Anthonie (attrib) (1601-1673) Dutch
£739 $1300 €1079 Birth of the Virgin (18x66cm-7x26in) 19-May-4 Doyle, New York #6099
£2979 $4706 €4200 Interior with two people making music (31x25cm-12x10in) panel. 25-Jul-3 Altus, Berlin #545/R est:3300
£3500 $6300 €5110 Banquet (60x93cm-24x37in) indis.init. panel. 23-Apr-4 Christie's, Kensington #43/R est:4000-6000

PALAMEDES, Palamedesz (17th C) Dutch
£14667 $26253 €22000 Cavalry skirmishes, with fallen soldier, and with fallen horse (37x50cm-15x20in) one indis.sig.d.1637 one s. panel oval pair prov. 17-May-4 Christie's, Amsterdam #9/R est:4000-6000

PALANTI, Giuseppe (1881-1946) Italian
£1594 $2614 €2200 Portrait of woman (68x53cm-27x21in) s. oval. 27-May-3 Il Ponte, Milan #938/R est:1200
£2886 $5310 €4300 Houses in the lagoon (53x44cm-21x17in) s. board. 24-Mar-4 Il Ponte, Milan #535/R est:2000

PALASSO, Pablo (1954-) Dominican
£7000 $12880 €10500 America, coffee seller (101x76cm-40x30in) s. acrylic crayon painted c.2000 prov. 10-Jun-4 Christie's, Paris #71/R est:9500-12000

PALATKO, D (?) Russian
£608 $1089 €900 Verdant landscape (25x36cm-10x14in) s. 8-May-4 Bukowskis, Helsinki #417/R

PALAZZI, Bernardino (1907-1987) Italian
£2448 $4210 €3500 Mara resting (49x67cm-19x26in) s. i.verso board. 3-Dec-3 Stadion, Trieste #1005/R est:1000-1500

PALAZZOLO, Carl (20th C) ?
£278 $500 €406 Untitled (30x22cm-12x9in) acrylic. 24-Apr-4 David Rago, Lambertville #300/R

PALDI, Israel (1892-1979) Israeli
£264 $450 €385 Abstract (61x48cm-24x19in) s. oil mixed media painted 1960's. 1-Dec-3 Ben-Ami, Tel Aviv #4347/R

PALENCIA, Benjamin (1894-1980) Spanish
£828 $1382 €1200 Plan for boat (52x62cm-20x24in) s. paper. 17-Nov-3 Durán, Madrid #108/R
£1141 $2088 €1700 Peasants (35x50cm-14x20in) s. paper. 12-Jul-4 Durán, Madrid #99/R est:1700
£1184 $2179 €1800 Peasants resting (36x50cm-14x20in) s. paper. 22-Jun-4 Durán, Madrid #164/R est:1600
£1510 $2673 €2250 Vase of flowers (48x34cm-19x13in) s. paper. 27-Apr-4 Durán, Madrid #173/R est:2200
£1724 $3103 €2500 Ox and cart (36x50cm-14x20in) s. 26-Jan-4 Durán, Madrid #150/R est:2300
£8451 $14789 €12000 Landscape with poppies (24x31cm-9x12in) s.d.68 cardboard lit. 16-Dec-3 Durán, Madrid #192/R est:12000
£9220 $15397 €13000 Landscape (40x50cm-16x20in) s.d.54. 20-Oct-3 Durán, Madrid #119/R
£9929 $16085 €14000 Sea landscape (36x50cm-14x20in) s. 20-May-3 Ansorena, Madrid #158/R est:14000
£13423 $25101 €20000 Mountainous landscape with stream (88x76cm-35x30in) s.d.1943. 24-Feb-4 Durán, Madrid #254/R est:18000
£15541 $27351 €23000 Landscape in Castilla with fields and trees (40x50cm-16x20in) s.d.1954 s.verso. 18-May-4 Segre, Madrid #297/R est:21000
£45775 $79190 €65000 Pena Negra (98x75cm-39x30in) s. 10-Dec-3 Castellana, Madrid #274/R est:35000
Works on paper
£467 $845 €700 Study of flowers (20x15cm-8x6in) s.d.1967 ink dr. 30-Mar-4 Segre, Madrid #266/R
£467 $845 €700 Pastoral scene (20x24cm-8x9in) s. ink dr. 30-Mar-4 Segre, Madrid #343/R
£642 $1130 €950 Boy (31x21cm-12x8in) pencil col pastel dr exec.c.1920. 18-May-4 Segre, Madrid #341/R
£655 $1088 €950 Landscape (32x45cm-13x18in) s. felt-tip pen. 1-Oct-3 Ansorena, Madrid #476/R
£660 $1075 €950 Search (49x33cm-19x13in) s. felt-tip pen dr. 23-Sep-3 Durán, Madrid #134/R
£664 $1109 €950 Trees (50x32cm-20x13in) s. ink dr. 30-Jun-3 Ansorena, Madrid #118/R
£704 $1127 €1000 Anglers by boat (32x23cm-13x9in) s.d.1971 felt-tip pen dr. 16-Sep-3 Segre, Madrid #281/R
£738 $1321 €1100 Boys (36x47cm-14x19in) s. pencil dr. 25-May-4 Durán, Madrid #44/R
£748 $1339 €1100 Study of dogs (50x35cm-20x14in) s. ink dr. 22-Mar-4 Durán, Madrid #70/R
£753 $1281 €1100 Landscape (55x41cm-22x16in) s. felt-tip pen. 4-Nov-3 Ansorena, Madrid #190/R
£769 $1285 €1100 Dance (24x32cm-9x13in) s.d.1930 wax crayon. 30-Jun-3 Ansorena, Madrid #144/R
£800 $1448 €1200 Peasant family (30x21cm-12x8in) s.d.1972 ink dr. 30-Mar-4 Segre, Madrid #131/R
£805 $1426 €1200 Man (49x37cm-19x15in) s. ink dr. 27-Apr-4 Durán, Madrid #641/R
£839 $1560 €1250 Boy (35x48cm-14x19in) s. ink dr. 2-Mar-4 Ansorena, Madrid #330/R
£845 $1479 €1200 Landscape (32x45cm-13x18in) s. felt-tip pen dr. 16-Dec-3 Durán, Madrid #665/R
£867 $1569 €1300 Vase of flowers (29x22cm-11x9in) s.d.1977 wax crayon prov. 30-Mar-4 Segre, Madrid #139/R
£884 $1583 €1300 In the cafe (38x26cm-15x10in) s. ink dr. 22-Mar-4 Durán, Madrid #159/R
£903 $1472 €1300 Woman with guitar (48x37cm-19x15in) s. drawing Indian ink. 16-Jul-3 Durán, Madrid #39/R
£903 $1472 €1300 Landscape of La Mancha (32x45cm-13x18in) s. felt tip pen drawing. 16-Jul-3 Durán, Madrid #127/R
£915 $1602 €1300 Pasture (20x30cm-8x12in) s.d.1961 Chinese ink dr. 16-Dec-3 Durán, Madrid #84/R
£915 $1602 €1300 Sierra Nevada, Granada (24x31cm-9x12in) s.i.d.1960 felt-tip pen ink wash. 16-Dec-3 Segre, Madrid #256/R
£972 $1546 €1400 Woman (48x38cm-19x15in) s. Indian ink double-sided. 29-Apr-3 Durán, Madrid #81/R
£1135 $1895 €1600 View of El Escorial (41x55cm-16x22in) s. felt tip pen drawing. 23-Jun-3 Durán, Madrid #181/R est:1600
£1172 $1958 €1700 Landscape (32x50cm-13x20in) s. felt-tip pen dr. 17-Nov-3 Durán, Madrid #90/R est:950
£1208 $2259 €1800 Landscape in Villafranca (53x37cm-21x15in) s. felt-tip pen dr. 24-Feb-4 Durán, Madrid #197/R est:1100
£1233 $2096 €1800 Vase of flowers (50x34cm-20x13in) s. sanguine. 4-Nov-3 Ansorena, Madrid #193/R est:1800
£1379 $2483 €2000 Figure (43x33cm-17x13in) s. gouache. 26-Jan-4 Durán, Madrid #123/R est:1200
£1678 $3070 €2500 Boy with doll (49x38cm-19x15in) s. ink dr. 12-Jul-4 Durán, Madrid #102/R est:1100
£2517 $4204 €3600 Ninos de Vallecas (39x28cm-15x11in) s. W/C prov. 24-Jun-3 Segre, Madrid #113/R est:3200
£3267 $5945 €4900 Figura surrealista (34x22cm-13x9in) s.d.1932 ink drawing. 29-Jun-4 Segre, Madrid #115/R est:1900

PALERMO, Blinky (1943-1977) German
Works on paper
£845 $1403 €1200 Objects (20x16cm-8x6in) pencil. 13-Jun-3 Hauswedell & Nolte, Hamburg #783

PALET BATISTE, Juan (1911-) Spanish
£423 $731 €600 Urban view (40x50cm-16x20in) s. 15-Dec-3 Ansorena, Madrid #271/R

PALEZIEUX, Edmond de (1850-1924) Swiss
£390 $651 €566 Coastal landscape with approaching storm (61x73cm-24x29in) s.d.1903. 23-Jun-3 Philippe Schuler, Zurich #3410 (S.FR 850)
£1101 $1872 €1607 Funerailes d'un capucin (100x141cm-39x56in) s. 5-Nov-3 Dobiaschofsky, Bern #850/R est:3500 (S.FR 2500)

PALEZIEUX, Gerard (1919-) Swiss
£1357 $2348 €1981 Paysage (19x33cm-7x13in) s.d.54 board. 12-Dec-3 Galerie du Rhone, Sion #572/R est:2500-3500 (S.FR 3000)
£2036 $3523 €2973 Nature morte aux noix (30x17cm-12x7in) s. panel prov. 12-Dec-3 Galerie du Rhone, Sion #664/R est:5000-7000 (S.FR 4500)
Works on paper
£1584 $2740 €2313 Filets (18x19cm-7x7in) mono. W/C exhib. 12-Dec-3 Galerie du Rhone, Sion #571/R est:3000-4000 (S.FR 3500)

PALIN, Arthur (20th C) British
£260 $471 €380 Fishing off Whitby (23x34cm-9x13in) mono. board. 30-Mar-4 David Duggleby, Scarborough #21/R

PALIN, William Mainwaring (1862-1947) British
£2800 $5096 €4088 Green walk - parkland with views across lakes (76x102cm-30x40in) s. 16-Jun-4 Brightwells, Leominster #932/R est:2000-3000
£5913 $10584 €8633 Summer landscape with children picking berries (102x130cm-40x51in) s. 25-May-4 Bukowskis, Stockholm #361/R est:25000-30000 (S.KR 80000)

PALIWODA, Ambrozi (20th C) ?
£968 $1800 €1413 Still life with flowers in a vase (56x46cm-22x18in) s.d.29 sold with oil photo drawing by other artists four. 3-Mar-4 Christie's, Rockefeller NY #58/R est:700-900

PALIZZI, Filippo (1818-1899) Italian
£599 $1000 €875 Landscape (18x28cm-7x11in) i.verso board. 20-Jun-3 Freeman, Philadelphia #149/R
£1972 $3411 €2800 Study of donkey (18x18cm-7x7in) s. paper. 10-Dec-3 Finarte Semenzato, Rome #159/R est:3000-4000
£2635 $4717 €3900 Young with goats in mountainous landscape (66x45cm-26x18in) s.d.1888. 8-May-4 Hans Stahl, Toestorf #30/R est:3000
£3670 $6128 €5322 Cattle woman with child (26x39cm-10x15in) s.d.1856. 23-Jun-3 Philippe Schuler, Zurich #3540/R est:6000-8000 (S.FR 8000)
£6711 $12013 €10000 Little peasant (46x34cm-18x13in) i. 25-May-4 Finarte Semenzato, Milan #222/R est:10000-12000
£8000 $13760 €11680 Un asino e i suoi amici (157x124cm-62x49in) s. 4-Dec-3 Christie's, Kensington #38/R est:8000-12000
£10690 $17852 €15500 Little shepherd (28x22cm-11x9in) init. 14-Nov-3 Farsetti, Prato #542/R est:15000-18000
£80537 $148188 €120000 Trip to Sorrento (80x116cm-31x46in) s.d.1845. 24-Mar-4 Finarte Semenzato, Rome #14/R est:125000-150000
Works on paper
£1533 $2745 €2300 Donkey and books (21x29cm-8x11in) s.d.1844 W/C pencil card. 13-May-4 Babuino, Rome #407 est:400-600
£4225 $7310 €6000 Goats feeding (26x38cm-10x15in) s.d.870 W/C. 11-Dec-3 Christie's, Rome #182/R est:5000-8000

PALIZZI, Giuseppe (1812-1888) Italian

£1405 $2249 €2037 Pack ass and chickens (45x38cm-18x15in) s. 22-Sep-3 Blomqvist, Lysaker #1236/R est:15000-20000 (N.KR 16500)
£2000 $3320 €2920 Goat and its kid (22x16cm-9x6in) s. studio st.stretcher. 1-Oct-3 Sotheby's, Olympia #267/R est:2000-3000
£49296 $81831 €70000 Il temporale (100x177cm-39x70in) s.d.1864. 11-Jun-3 Christie's, Rome #249/R est:75000-90000

Works on paper

£338 $605 €500 Etudes de chevres (21x27cm-8x11in) s.d.71 chl htd pastel. 5-May-4 Coutau Begarie, Paris #31/R

PALIZZI, Nicola (attrib) (1820-1870) Italian

£2908 $4856 €4100 Labour under the Vesuvius (32x49cm-13x19in) s. 14-Oct-3 Finarte Semenzato, Milan #142/R est:5000
£3067 $5489 €4600 Seascape in Pescara (35x51cm-14x20in) s.i.verso board lit. 13-May-4 Babuino, Rome #318/R est:2000-3000

PALKA, Witold (1928-) Polish

£379 $633 €550 Model in yellow dress on the catwalk (60x50cm-24x20in) s.d.2003. 16-Nov-3 Agra, Warsaw #84/R

PALLA, F (?) Italian?

Sculpture

£24324 $45000 €35513 Dancing figures (155cm-61in) white marble pair after Canova. 13-Jul-4 Christie's, Rockefeller NY #1021/R est:30000-50000

PALLANDT, Charlotte van (1898-1997) Dutch

Sculpture

£1812 $2971 €2500 Standing nude with drape (20cm-8in) mono.num.III bronze three of six prov.lit. 27-May-3 Sotheby's, Amsterdam #369/R est:1000-1500
£2333 $4293 €3500 Nude (12cm-5in) dark brown pat bronze conceived 1943 one of ten prov.lit. 9-Jun-4 Christie's, Amsterdam #264/R est:3500-5000
£3147 $5413 €4500 Portrait of Roland Holst (30cm-12in) i. bronze executed 1963 lit. 2-Dec-3 Sotheby's, Amsterdam #289/R est:3000-4000
£6884 $11290 €9500 Torso (67cm-26in) mono.d.1940 wood one of one prov. 27-May-3 Sotheby's, Amsterdam #370/R est:4500-5500
£11333 $20853 €17000 Grote staande met voet vooruit (63cm-25in) s.st.f.Brummen grey pat bronze conceived 1955 one of ten prov.lit. 9-Jun-4 Christie's, Amsterdam #267/R est:12000-16000
£13333 $24533 €20000 Zittende figuur (61x59x48cm-24x23x19in) mono. rosso di Alicante stone base exec. 1996 unique prov.lit. 9-Jun-4 Christie's, Amsterdam #271/R est:20000-30000

Works on paper

£523 $963 €780 Nude woman standing (60x42cm-24x17in) s.d.1941 chl. 29-Mar-4 Glerum, Amsterdam #79

PALLARES MOYA, Jordi (1962-) Spanish

£336 $561 €480 Cuna (65x50cm-26x20in) s.d.1990 d.i.verso prov. 24-Jun-3 Segre, Madrid #177/R

PALLARES Y ALLUSTANTE, Joaquin (1853-1935) Spanish

£690 $1241 €1000 Admiring the statue of Diana (17x14cm-7x6in) s. board. 26-Jan-4 Durán, Madrid #199/R
£1127 $1949 €1600 In the park (33x24cm-13x9in) s. board. 15-Dec-3 Ansorena, Madrid #288/R est:1200
£1849 $3144 €2700 Paris, Rue Royale (16x18cm-6x7in) s. panel. 9-Nov-3 Eric Pillon, Calais #55/R
£2762 $5000 €4033 Parc Monceau (36x51cm-14x20in) s.i. 30-Mar-4 Christie's, Rockefeller NY #104/R est:5000-7000
£3889 $7000 €5678 Elegantes sur le quai (35x27cm-14x11in) s. panel. 22-Apr-4 Christie's, Rockefeller NY #179/R est:8000-12000
£3889 $7000 €5678 Ladies crossing the street (35x27cm-14x11in) indis.sig. panel. 22-Apr-4 Christie's, Rockefeller NY #180/R est:8000-12000
£4233 $7280 €6180 Scenes in Paris (30x41cm-12x16in) s. pair. 3-Dec-3 Naón & Cia, Buenos Aires #79/R est:6500-7500

PALLETA, Karl (1898-1970) German

£486 $812 €700 Artist's lives (40x50cm-16x20in) i. verso. 25-Oct-3 Dr Lehr, Berlin #384/R

PALLIER, Raymond (19/20th C) French

£483 $801 €700 Nu (74x100cm-29x39in) s. 1-Oct-3 Millon & Associes, Paris #59

PALLIERE, Armand Julien (1784-1862) French

£1278 $2250 €1866 Boy with marionette (48x36cm-19x14in) s.d.1810. 19-May-4 Doyle, New York #6083/R est:4000-6000

PALLIERE, Jean Léon (1823-1887) Brazilian/French

Works on paper

£284 $509 €415 Whaler - Divisando Trombas Marinas (8x14cm-3x6in) i.d.1861 pencil prov. 10-May-4 Joel, Victoria #311 (A.D 700)
£2118 $3600 €3092 Montevideo (17x23cm-7x9in) s. ink W/C. 25-Nov-3 Galeria y Remates, Montevideo #172/R
£4706 $8000 €6871 Caravan (23x46cm-9x18in) s. W/C on board prov. 19-Nov-3 Sotheby's, New York #82/R est:10000-15000
£8258 $13460 €12057 Street in Buenos Aires (172x231cm-68x91in) s. Chinese ink prov. 17-Jul-3 Naón & Cia, Buenos Aires #8/R

PALLMANN, Gotz (1908-1966) German

£4054 $7257 €6000 Berlin Schlossplatz (52x61cm-20x24in) s. panel lit. 8-May-4 Schloss Ahlden, Ahlden #818/R est:6500

Works on paper

£310 $496 €440 Seine shore with Notre Dame (28x41cm-11x16in) s. W/C. 18-Sep-3 Rieber, Stuttgart #842

PALLMANN, Kurt (1886-?) German

£350 $594 €500 Danzig harbour (55x54cm-22x21in) s. 21-Nov-3 Reiss & Sohn, Konigstein #25/R

PALLUT, Pierre (1918-) French

£238 $426 €347 Still life with melon (81x60cm-32x24in) s. 22-Mar-4 Philippe Schuler, Zurich #6178 (S.FR 550)

PALM, Anna (1859-1924) Swedish

Works on paper

£378 $654 €552 Figures in front of the Danish pavilion in Paris 1900 (52x49cm-20x19in) s.i.d.1900 W/C pencil. 9-Dec-3 Rasmussen, Copenhagen #1746/R (D.KR 4000)
£390 $703 €569 Boats in the channel (13x18cm-5x7in) s. W/C. 26-Jan-4 Lilla Bukowskis, Stockholm #590 (S.KR 5200)
£443 $794 €647 Sailing vessels on river the Stockholm in background (6x10cm-2x4in) s. W/C. 26-May-4 AB Stockholms Auktionsverk #2299/R (S.KR 6000)
£685 $1261 €1028 Seascape near Capri (45x68cm-18x27in) s. W/C. 14-Jun-4 Lilla Bukowskis, Stockholm #240 (S.KR 9400)
£885 $1522 €1292 Sailing boats in the outer skerries (18x31cm-7x12in) s. W/C. 3-Dec-3 AB Stockholms Auktionsverk #2444/R (S.KR 11500)
£961 $1720 €1403 Fishing boats, Skagen (21x37cm-8x15in) s. W/C. 26-May-4 AB Stockholms Auktionsverk #2300/R (S.KR 13000)
£1109 $1984 €1619 The Danish Pavillion in Paris, year 1900 (52x50cm-20x20in) s.i.d.1900 W/C. 25-May-4 Bukowskis, Stockholm #102/R est:20000-25000 (S.KR 15000)
£1231 $2117 €1797 Stockholm Palace (22x33cm-9x13in) s. W/C. 7-Dec-3 Uppsala Auktionskammare, Uppsala #150/R est:20000-30000 (S.KR 16000)
£1231 $2117 €1797 The old Opera House (21x27cm-8x11in) s. W/C. 7-Dec-3 Uppsala Auktionskammare, Uppsala #151/R est:20000-30000 (S.KR 16000)
£1269 $2183 €1853 The French - couple in horse carriage (19x28cm-7x11in) s. W/C. 2-Dec-3 Bukowskis, Stockholm #17/R est:8000-10000 (S.KR 16500)
£1330 $2381 €1942 View towards the gunpowder tower (13x24cm-5x9in) s.i. W/C. 25-May-4 Bukowskis, Stockholm #217/R est:10000-12000 (S.KR 18000)
£1346 $2315 €1965 Vessels on the Stockholm river (31x46cm-12x18in) s.i.d.1887 W/C. 2-Dec-3 Bukowskis, Stockholm #20/R est:20000-25000 (S.KR 17500)
£1346 $2315 €1965 Stockholm from Maelaren (13x22cm-5x9in) s. W/C. 2-Dec-3 Bukowskis, Stockholm #22/R est:12000-14000 (S.KR 17500)
£1404 $2514 €2050 View of Skeppsbron (10x14cm-4x6in) s.i. W/C. 25-May-4 Bukowskis, Stockholm #9/R est:8000-10000 (S.KR 19000)
£1462 $2514 €2135 View of Kastellholmen, Stockholm (13x22cm-5x9in) s. W/C. 2-Dec-3 Bukowskis, Stockholm #21/R est:12000-14000 (S.KR 19000)
£1552 $2778 €2266 Emperor Wilhelm II's visit to Stockholm 1888 (22x45cm-9x18in) s. W/C prov. 26-May-4 AB Stockholms Auktionsverk #2327/R est:20000-25000 (S.KR 21000)
£1615 $2778 €2358 The English - woman in horse carriage (19x27cm-7x11in) s. W/C. 2-Dec-3 Bukowskis, Stockholm #18/R est:8000-10000 (S.KR 21000)
£1615 $2778 €2358 Moonlight over the boats (51x68cm-20x27in) s. W/C. 2-Dec-3 Bukowskis, Stockholm #101a/R est:18000-20000 (S.KR 21000)
£1626 $2911 €2374 Boats by Stockholm's Palace (8x11cm-3x4in) s. W/C. 25-May-4 Bukowskis, Stockholm #10/R est:12000-15000 (S.KR 22000)
£1846 $3175 €2695 View across Visby (35x76cm-14x30in) s.i.d.1891 W/C. 3-Dec-3 AB Stockholms Auktionsverk #2287/R est:30000-40000 (S.KR 24000)
£1922 $3440 €2806 Hunting party (45x52cm-18x20in) s. gouache. 28-May-4 Uppsala Auktionskammare, Uppsala #149/R est:18000-20000 (S.KR 26000)
£2291 $4101 €3345 View towards Stockholm's Palace (5x17cm-2x7in) s.i. W/C. 25-May-4 Bukowskis, Stockholm #8/R est:12000-15000 (S.KR 31000)
£2308 $3969 €3370 Boats in Stockholm harbour (49x36cm-19x14in) s.i.d.1889 W/C. 2-Dec-3 Bukowskis, Stockholm #101/R est:40000-45000 (S.KR 30000)
£2400 $4440 €3504 Palais Royal, Stockholm (8x26cm-3x10in) s.i. W/C pair. 10-Mar-4 Sotheby's, Olympia #253/R est:800-1200
£3548 $6350 €5180 View towards Stockholm's Palace (9x27cm-4x11in) s.i. W/C. 25-May-4 Bukowskis, Stockholm #7/R est:20000-25000 (S.KR 48000)
£5322 $9525 €7770 View across the river to the Royal Palace, Stockholm (23x66cm-9x26in) s. W/C. 28-May-4 Uppsala Auktionskammare, Uppsala #148/R est:40000-50000 (S.KR 72000)
£10000 $17200 €14600 From the Grand Hotel, Stockholm (34x128cm-13x50in) s.i.d.1890 W/C. 2-Dec-3 Bukowskis, Stockholm #19/R est:100000-125000 (S.KR 130000)
£12308 $21169 €17970 View towards Stockholm Palace from Blasieholmen (55x95cm-22x37in) s. W/C. 2-Dec-3 Bukowskis, Stockholm #179c/R est:80000-100000 (S.KR 160000)

PALM, Brian (20th C) Irish?

Works on paper

£667 $1200 €1000 Winter (50x59cm-20x23in) s. mixed media. 20-Apr-4 James Adam, Dublin #16/R

PALM, Gustaf Wilhelm (1810-1890) Swedish

£462 $794 €675 Cottage in the mountains (21x28cm-8x11in) s.d.58. 3-Dec-3 AB Stockholms Auktionsverk #2398/R (S.KR 6000)
£538 $926 €785 Klara Norra Kyrkogata, Stockholm (24x16cm-9x6in) s.d.86 panel. 3-Dec-3 AB Stockholms Auktionsverk #2403/R (S.KR 7000)
£846 $1455 €1235 Evening landscape, Herron in Stockholm's skerries (34x45cm-13x18in) s.d.1886 prov.lit. 2-Dec-3 Bukowskis, Stockholm #187/R (S.KR 11000)
£887 $1588 €1295 Landscape from Waddo Canal (41x51cm-16x20in) s.d.1883. 26-May-4 AB Stockholms Auktionsverk #2187/R (S.KR 12000)
£2069 $3704 €3021 View of Mantorp Manor (35x54cm-14x21in) s.d.1879 lit. 26-May-4 AB Stockholms Auktionsverk #2239/R est:30000-35000 (S.KR 28000)
£6704 $12000 €9788 Entrance to the garden in Villa Borghese, Rome (33x46cm-13x18in) i.d.1844 paper on canvas prov.exhib. 27-May-4 Sotheby's, New York #98/R est:8000-12000
£10000 $17200 €14600 Italian landscape (40x62cm-16x24in) init.i.d.11 October 1844 canvas on panel exhib.prov. 2-Dec-3 Bukowskis, Stockholm #62b/R est:18000-20000 (S.KR 130000)

Works on paper

£420 $701 €600 Genazzano (25x36cm-10x14in) init. pencil. 24-Jun-3 Finarte Semenzato, Rome #4/R
£448 $747 €640 Olevano (42x28cm-17x11in) init. pencil. 24-Jun-3 Finarte Semenzato, Rome #3/R

PALM, Gustaf Wilhelm (attrib) (1810-1890) Swedish
£31538 $54246 €46045 The Forum in Rome (145x200cm-57x79in) 2-Dec-3 Bukowskis, Stockholm #319/R est:100000-150000 (S.KR 410000)

PALM, Torsten (1875-1934) Swedish
£513 $908 €749 Town scene from Pau (33x24cm-13x9in) s.i.d.31 panel prov.exhib.lit. 27-Apr-4 AB Stockholms Auktionsverk #699/R (S.KR 7000)

PALMA, Jacopo (16/17th C) Italian
Works on paper
£1972 $3155 €2800 Sketch of Christ being taken down from the cross (9x12cm-4x5in) wash over chl lit. 19-Sep-3 Karlheinz Kaupp, Staufen #1878/R est:100

PALMA, Jacopo (attrib) (16/17th C) Italian
£1931 $3206 €2800 Arrest of Christ (27x21cm-11x8in) copper prov.exhib. 1-Oct-3 Dorotheum, Vienna #302/R est:2000-3000

PALMA, Jacopo (il Giovane) (1544-1628) Italian
Works on paper
£524 $902 €750 Holy person entering into heaven (21x15cm-8x6in) brown pen double-sided. 5-Dec-3 Bolland & Marotz, Bremen #465/R
£993 $1808 €1500 Holy men (95x50cm-37x20in) sanguine pair. 16-Jun-4 Christie's, Rome #460/R est:1500-2000
£3000 $5490 €4380 Seven heads with self portrait and portrait of Adriana Negretti. Two heads (26x14cm-10x6in) pen ink double-sided. 6-Jul-4 Christie's, London #21/R est:1500-2000
£3401 $6088 €5000 Un groupe de personnages sur un nuage. Une scene de massacre (20x17cm-8x7in) red chk pen brown ink wash double-sided prov. 18-Mar-4 Christie's, Paris #8/R est:6000-8000

PALMA, Jacopo (il Giovane-attrib) (1544-1628) Italian
Works on paper
£1156 $2070 €1700 L'Assomption de la Vierge (39x21cm-15x8in) i. pen brown ink wash htd white prov. 18-Mar-4 Christie's, Paris #10/R est:800-1200

PALMA, Jacopo (il Vecchio) (1480-1528) Italian
£31034 $51828 €45000 Mythical marriage of St Katherine (47x40cm-19x16in) panel prov. 15-Nov-3 Lempertz, Koln #1116/R est:45000-50000

PALMAROLA ROMEU, Ramon (1877-?) Spanish
£1773 $2961 €2500 Female portrait with Toledo in the background (102x98cm-40x39in) s. 23-Jun-3 Durán, Madrid #176/R est:2500

PALMAROLI Y GONZALEZ, Vicente (1834-1896) Spanish
£9231 $15415 €13200 Strolling in Madrid (24x45cm-9x18in) s. 30-Jun-3 Ansorena, Madrid #353/R est:12000
£13380 $23415 €19000 Hiding the toys (45x34cm-18x13in) s. board. 16-Dec-3 Durán, Madrid #212/R est:18000

PALMAROLI, Vicente (?) Spanish
Works on paper
£417 $679 €600 Young woman on swing (44x32cm-17x13in) s. dr. 23-Sep-3 Durán, Madrid #655/R

PALMEIRO, Jose (1903-1984) Spanish
£263 $484 €400 Vase of flowers (32x22cm-13x9in) s. cardboard. 22-Jun-4 Durán, Madrid #65/R
£350 $601 €500 Portrait (92x73cm-36x29in) s.d.40. 3-Dec-3 Beaussant & Lefèvre, Paris #70
£369 $653 €550 Coastal landscape (24x33cm-9x13in) s. cardboard. 27-Apr-4 Durán, Madrid #182/R
£382 $660 €558 Still life of flowers (55x46cm-22x18in) s.d.51. 15-Dec-3 Galeria y Remates, Montevideo #94/R
£411 $699 €600 Vase of flowers (44x35cm-17x14in) s. paper. 4-Nov-3 Ansorena, Madrid #79/R
£559 $950 €816 Still life (36x54cm-14x21in) s. cardboard. 20-Nov-3 Galeria y Remates, Montevideo #50/R
£600 $1074 €900 Bouquet de fleurs (41x24cm-16x9in) s. 16-May-4 Lombrail & Teucquam, Paris #163/R
£629 $1083 €900 La locomotive (50x65cm-20x26in) s. prov. 3-Dec-3 Beaussant & Lefèvre, Paris #69/R
£805 $1506 €1200 View of Montmartre (52x65cm-20x26in) s. cardboard. 24-Feb-4 Durán, Madrid #185/R
£828 $1382 €1200 Jeune femme au chemisier rouge (65x50cm-26x20in) s. 17-Nov-3 Claude Boisgirard, Paris #71/R
£1007 $1873 €1500 Bouquet de fleurs (73x59cm-29x23in) s. 3-Mar-4 Tajan, Paris #152 est:1500-2000
£1020 $1857 €1500 Vase with flowers (60x50cm-24x20in) s. 3-Feb-4 Segre, Madrid #358/R est:1500
£1074 $1997 €1600 Grand bouquet (73x60cm-29x24in) s. 3-Mar-4 Tajan, Paris #155155/R est:1500-2000
£1074 $1997 €1600 Seashore (50x68cm-20x27in) s. cardboard. 2-Mar-4 Ansorena, Madrid #117/R est:1600
£1138 $1889 €1650 View of Paris (43x58cm-17x23in) s. paper on board. 1-Oct-3 Ansorena, Madrid #594/R est:1350
£1150 $2024 €1679 Antibes (59x72cm-23x28in) 19-May-4 Dreweatt Neate, Newbury #51/R est:850-950
£1200 $2076 €1752 Vase of summer flowers (73x60cm-29x24in) s.d.34. 11-Dec-3 Christie's, Kensington #68/R est:1500-2000
£1232 $2020 €1700 Paysage du Lot (73x92cm-29x36in) s.d.79 i.verso. 27-May-3 Durán, Madrid #103/R est:1400
£1241 $2234 €1800 Dreaming (73x60cm-29x24in) s. 26-Jan-4 Durán, Madrid #119/R est:1600
£1259 $2102 €1800 Marina (38x55cm-15x22in) s. 24-Jun-3 Segre, Madrid #214/R est:1300
£1342 $2376 €2000 Vase of flowers (70x44cm-28x17in) s. board. 27-Apr-4 Durán, Madrid #76/R
£1348 $2250 €1900 Rincon de Montmartre (52x65cm-20x26in) s.d.28 board. 23-Jun-3 Durán, Madrid #139/R est:1800
£1377 $2258 €1900 Woman with a lamp (81x65cm-32x26in) s.d.1950 i.d.verso. 27-May-3 Durán, Madrid #104/R est:1500
£1377 $2258 €1900 Flowers (92x73cm-36x29in) s. 27-May-3 Durán, Madrid #275/R est:1900
£2041 $3245 €3000 Marchande de fleurs, Paris (74x92cm-29x36in) s. 21-Mar-3 Bailly Pommery, Paris #116/R
£2113 $3697 €3000 Reflections (73x61cm-29x24in) s.d.1961 i.verso. 16-Dec-3 Segre, Madrid #271/R est:2400
£2254 $3944 €3200 Boats in harbour (64x44cm-25x17in) s. 16-Dec-3 Segre, Madrid #273/R est:2400
£2685 $4805 €4000 Nature morte (46x61cm-18x24in) s. s.i.d.79 verso. 25-May-4 Chambelland & Giafferi, Paris #72/R est:4000-6000
Works on paper
£326 $529 €460 Jug and fruit (49x36cm-19x14in) s.i.d.1953 wax crayon. 20-May-3 Ansorena, Madrid #457/R
£379 $630 €550 Tree (58x45cm-23x18in) s. mixed media. 1-Oct-3 Ansorena, Madrid #481/R

PALMER, A H (1911-1985) British
£323 $600 €472 Dahlias in copper pot (61x51cm-24x20in) mono. panel. 7-Mar-4 William Jenack, New York #355

PALMER, Adelaide (1851-1938) American
£307 $550 €448 Birch lined path to the woods (46x30cm-18x12in) s.d.1915. 14-May-4 Skinner, Boston #58/R est:500-700
£1706 $2900 €2491 Still life with oranges (46x76cm-18x30in) s.d,1899. 21-Nov-3 Skinner, Boston #301/R est:1500-2500

PALMER, Alfred (1877-1951) British
£280 $512 €409 Still life with flowers (40x28cm-16x11in) s. board. 7-Apr-4 Dreweatt Neate, Newbury #117/R
£1700 $2822 €2482 Figures by a lake (51x61cm-20x24in) s. panel. 1-Oct-3 Woolley & Wallis, Salisbury #269/R est:800-1200

PALMER, Erastus Dow (1817-1904) American
Sculpture
£1676 $3000 €2447 Sleeping angels (12cm-5in) marble prov. 6-May-4 Shannon's, Milford #113/R est:3000-5000

PALMER, Franklin (1912-1990) Canadian
£331 $598 €483 Harbor (30x41cm-12x16in) s. s.i.verso. 18-Apr-4 Levis, Calgary #530/R (C.D 800)
£493 $814 €715 Night harbour (82x100cm-32x39in) s. exhib. 3-Jul-3 Heffel, Vancouver #25/R (C.D 1100)
Works on paper
£339 $567 €495 Foothills (34x49cm-13x19in) W/C. 17-Nov-3 Hodgins, Calgary #198/R (C.D 750)

PALMER, Harry Sutton (1854-1933) British
Works on paper
£250 $418 €365 Seberga, village (22x15cm-9x6in) d.28 pencil W/C. 11-Oct-3 Shapes, Edinburgh #304
£300 $543 €438 Valley of the wharfe (26x36cm-10x14in) s. W/C exec.c.1909 prov. 4-Apr-4 Lots Road Auctions, London #354/R
£600 $1032 €876 Lake District (25x34cm-10x13in) s. pencil W/C. 3-Dec-3 Christie's, Kensington #136/R
£720 $1303 €1051 Bit of Amberley, Sussex (34x24cm-13x9in) s.d.84 W/C. 30-Mar-4 Sworder & Son, Bishops Stortford #531/R
£850 $1530 €1241 On the Wharfe (23x34cm-9x13in) s.d.81 pencil W/C prov. 21-Apr-4 Tennants, Leyburn #1049
£950 $1739 €1387 Middle Eastern landscape (22x34cm-9x13in) s. W/C. 28-Jan-4 Dreweatt Neate, Newbury #27/R
£1100 $2013 €1650 Arundel Castle (35x53cm-14x21in) s. W/C. 27-Jul-4 Henry Adams, Chichester #395/R est:1000-1500
£1150 $2105 €1679 Distant view of Arundel Castle, Sussex (36x53cm-14x21in) s. pencil W/C prov. 27-Jan-4 Holloways, Banbury #330/R est:1000-1500
£1300 $2236 €1898 Castle Crag, St John's, near Keswick (34x46cm-13x18in) s.d.1880 pencil W/C htd white. 4-Dec-3 Mellors & Kirk, Nottingham #843/R est:1400-1600
£1550 $2774 €2263 Ben Cruachan, Dalmally (66x102cm-26x40in) s. W/C. 26-May-4 Sotheby's, Olympia #121/R est:1500-2000
£1650 $2805 €2409 Thirlmere looking towards Saddleback (33x52cm-13x20in) s. i.mount W/C. 25-Nov-3 Bonhams, Knowle #174 est:700-900
£1900 $3268 €2774 Near Arley, on the Severn (53x35cm-21x14in) s. pencil W/C. 3-Dec-3 Christie's, Kensington #133/R est:800-1200
£3000 $5100 €4380 Spring, Leith Hills, Surrey (53x38cm-21x15in) s.i. pencil W/C htd white scrathcing out prov. 20-Nov-3 Christie's, London #100/R est:3000-5000
£3200 $5440 €4672 Perfect peace (64x39cm-25x15in) s.d.1881 pencil W/C scratching out prov. 20-Nov-3 Christie's, London #101/R est:2500-3500

PALMER, Herbert Sidney (1881-1970) Canadian
£361 $672 €527 King O'Connor (47x56cm-19x22in) s. canvas on board. 2-Mar-4 Ritchie, Toronto #114/R (C.D 900)
£545 $889 €796 Country road (37x44cm-15x17in) s. canvasboard. 23-Sep-3 Ritchie, Toronto #75/R est:1500-2000 (C.D 1200)
£772 $1383 €1127 In the dell (35x43cm-14x17in) s. i.verso board. 27-May-4 Heffel, Vancouver #159/R est:2000-2500 (C.D 1900)
£901 $1532 €1315 Country farm (26x33cm-10x13in) s. 27-Nov-3 Heffel, Vancouver #35/R est:2000-3000 (C.D 2000)
£1000 $1830 €1460 Road to Maple Lake (26x34cm-10x13in) s. canvas on board. 1-Jun-4 Joyner Waddington, Toronto #308/R est:1000-1500 (C.D 2500)
£1161 $1996 €1695 Mountain Road, Autumn (50x40cm-20x16in) s. board. 2-Dec-3 Joyner Waddington, Toronto #226/R est:2000-2500 (C.D 2600)

£2000 $3660 €2920 Rocky pasture (50x60cm-20x24in) s. prov. 1-Jun-4 Joyner Waddington, Toronto #131/R est:3500-4500 (C.D 5000)
£2009 $3455 €2933 Ranger's Outpost (40x50cm-16x20in) s. 2-Dec-3 Joyner Waddington, Toronto #222/R est:3500-4000 (C.D 4500)
£2054 $3532 €2999 Haliburton Hills (65x75cm-26x30in) s. 2-Dec-3 Joyner Waddington, Toronto #1/R est:3000-4000 (C.D 4600)
£2902 $4991 €4237 Across Lake Kashag (60x75cm-24x30in) s. exhib. 2-Dec-3 Joyner Waddington, Toronto #23/R est:3000-4000 (C.D 6500)

PALMER, J (19th C) British
£2297 $4112 €3400 Bite of the snake (120x100cm-47x39in) s. lit. 8-May-4 Schloss Ahlden, Ahlden #672/R est:3000

PALMER, James Lynwood (1868-1941) British
£600 $1020 €876 Sketch of a dark brown horse (36x46cm-14x18in) 19-Nov-3 Sotheby's, Olympia #100/R
£750 $1275 €1095 Dark brown horse with Star (46x61cm-18x24in) i. 19-Nov-3 Sotheby's, Olympia #93/R
£750 $1275 €1095 Grey horse (46x61cm-18x24in) i. 19-Nov-3 Sotheby's, Olympia #109/R
£850 $1445 €1241 Dark brown horse (46x61cm-18x24in) 19-Nov-3 Sotheby's, Olympia #91/R
£900 $1530 €1314 Bay horse (75x84cm-30x33in) 19-Nov-3 Sotheby's, Olympia #88/R
£900 $1530 €1314 Sketch of Valour (46x61cm-18x24in) i. 19-Nov-3 Sotheby's, Olympia #92/R
£900 $1530 €1314 Bay horse (36x46cm-14x18in) 19-Nov-3 Sotheby's, Olympia #108/R
£1000 $1700 €1460 Sketches of horses (41x51cm-16x20in) three. 19-Nov-3 Sotheby's, Olympia #98/R est:300-500
£1200 $2040 €1752 Brown horse (46x56cm-18x22in) 19-Nov-3 Sotheby's, Olympia #89/R est:500-700
£1200 $2040 €1752 Saddled horses (30x40cm-12x16in) pair. 19-Nov-3 Sotheby's, Olympia #94/R est:300-500
£1300 $2210 €1898 Sketch in the stable of Minoru (36x46cm-14x18in) s.i. 19-Nov-3 Sotheby's, Olympia #87/R est:600-800
£1300 $2210 €1898 Dark brown horse (36x51cm-14x20in) 19-Nov-3 Sotheby's, Olympia #99/R est:500-700
£1400 $2380 €2044 Sketches of horses (51x66cm-20x26in) three. 19-Nov-3 Sotheby's, Olympia #96/R est:800-1200
£1500 $2550 €2190 Sketches of horses (30x35cm-12x14in) three. 19-Nov-3 Sotheby's, Olympia #95/R est:500-700
£1900 $3230 €2774 Phar lap (52x71cm-20x28in) s.i. chl. 19-Nov-3 Sotheby's, Olympia #107/R est:1000-1200
£2000 $3400 €2920 Kellsboro Jack (51x61cm-20x24in) i.stretcher. 19-Nov-3 Sotheby's, Olympia #90/R est:400-600
£2400 $4080 €3504 Sketches of horses (61x43cm-24x17in) three. 19-Nov-3 Sotheby's, Olympia #103/R est:800-1200
£2800 $4760 €4088 Black horse trotting (45x52cm-18x20in) 19-Nov-3 Sotheby's, Olympia #97/R est:500-700
£5137 $8733 €7500 Horse in the countryside (92x104cm-36x41in) s.d.1924. 6-Nov-3 Sotheby's, Paris #143/R est:2500-3500
£48000 $87360 €70080 Jock Whitney's Easter Hero and Sir Lindsay (94x153cm-37x60in) s.d.1930 prov.lit. 1-Jul-4 Sotheby's, London #27/R est:30000-40000
Works on paper
£330 $561 €482 Horse's head (28x36cm-11x14in) s.d.1929 chl. 19-Nov-3 Sotheby's, Olympia #104/R
£750 $1380 €1095 Over the jump. Early morning exercise (22x31cm-9x12in) s.d.1890 pencil W/C htd white pair. 10-Jun-4 Christie's, Kensington #166/R

PALMER, Pauline (1867-1938) American
£1857 $3250 €2711 The sun hat (34x27cm-13x11in) s. board. 19-Dec-3 Sotheby's, New York #1112/R est:2500-3500
£4192 $7000 €6120 Cape Cod, Street (23x33cm-9x13in) s. prov. 23-Oct-3 Shannon's, Milford #83/R est:6000-8000
Works on paper
£251 $450 €366 Autumn landscape with corn stacks (25x33cm-10x13in) s. W/C. 8-May-4 Susanin's, Chicago #6067/R

PALMER, Samuel (1805-1881) British
Prints
£2200 $3740 €3212 Early ploughman (18x25cm-7x10in) s. etching. 30-Oct-3 Christie's, Kensington #24/R est:1500-2500
Works on paper
£26000 $44200 €37960 Broken Bridge (40x50cm-16x20in) s. pencil W/C htd bodycol gum arabic scratching out prov.exhib.li. 20-Nov-3 Christie's, London #59/R est:30000-50000

PALMER, Simon (20th C) British
Works on paper
£449 $750 €656 His master's silence (36x53cm-14x21in) s. W/C. 15-Nov-3 Sloans & Kenyon, Bethesda #107/R
£3000 $5160 €4380 Waiting the weekend (57x53cm-22x21in) s.i. W/C bodycol pen black ink exhib. 3-Dec-3 Christie's, Kensington #685/R est:1000-1500
£4000 $6880 €5840 Contractor man, tractor, tractorman (71x48cm-28x19in) s.i. W/C bodycol pen black ink exhib. 3-Dec-3 Christie's, Kensington #687/R est:1000-1500
£5500 $10175 €8030 Paramour (38x38cm-15x15in) s.i. W/C bodycol. 11-Mar-4 Christie's, Kensington #278/R est:1500-2000

PALMER, Stanley (1936-) New Zealander
£3214 $5914 €4692 Northland (54x110cm-21x43in) s.d.2001 canvasboard. 25-Mar-4 International Art Centre, Auckland #48/R est:5500-7500 (NZ.D 9000)

PALMER, Walter L (1854-1932) American
£2060 $3750 €3008 Winter landscape (20x20cm-8x8in) s. board. 15-Jun-4 John Moran, Pasadena #23 est:2500-3500
£12500 $20000 €18250 Snowy stream in winter light (76x61cm-30x24in) s. board lit. 20-Sep-3 Sloans & Kenyon, Bethesda #1195/R est:25000-30000
£23464 $42000 €34257 Hudson River sunset (18x12cm-7x5in) s. board. 6-May-4 Shannon's, Milford #120/R est:20000-30000
£34431 $57500 €50269 Late afternoon (64x76cm-25x30in) s. 14-Nov-3 Aspire, Cleveland #38 est:20000-40000
Works on paper
£2500 $4000 €3650 Landscape with central figure (33x46cm-13x18in) s.i.d.1884 pastel. 20-Sep-3 Pook & Pook, Downington #314/R est:2000-4000
£4891 $9000 €7141 Winter landscape (51x41cm-20x16in) gouache. 28-Mar-4 Carlsen Gallery, Greenville #611/R
£5028 $9000 €7341 Back from church in winter (48x36cm-19x14in) s. W/C prov. 6-May-4 Shannon's, Milford #59/R est:6000-8000

PALMER, William C (1906-1987) American
£500 $800 €730 Zero afternoon (41x51cm-16x20in) s.d.1960 canvas on board. 20-Sep-3 Bunte, Elgin #1259

PALMER, Wyn (?) American?
£882 $1500 €1323 Portrait of lady (56x46cm-22x18in) s. 29-Nov-3 Carlsen Gallery, Greenville #361/R

PALMERO DE GREGORIO, Alfredo (1901-1991) Spanish
£306 $519 €440 Notre-Dame (42x31cm-17x12in) s. 28-Oct-3 Segre, Madrid #32/R
£451 $767 €650 Street in Paris (42x31cm-17x12in) s. 28-Oct-3 Segre, Madrid #329/R
£1418 $2369 €2000 Tuileries, Paris (89x115cm-35x45in) s. 20-Oct-3 Durán, Madrid #86/R
£2431 $4010 €3500 Untitled (73x92cm-29x36in) s.i.d.3. 3-Jul-3 Claude Aguttes, Neuilly #136a est:4000-5000

PALMERO, Maestro (1901-1991) Spanish
£1538 $2569 €2200 Wild horses (65x131cm-26x52in) s. 30-Jun-3 Ansorena, Madrid #441/R

PALMEZZANO, Marco (1458-1539) Italian
£8380 $15000 €12235 Madonna and Child with the Infant Saint John (65x52cm-26x20in) s. panel prov. 27-May-4 Sotheby's, New York #6a/R est:20000-30000

PALMIE, Charles (1863-1911) German
£738 $1366 €1100 Trees on river shore (35x45cm-14x18in) s. 9-Mar-4 Dorotheum, Vienna #18/R est:1800-2500
£4828 $8062 €7000 Torbole (73x83cm-29x33in) s.i.d.1910. 13-Nov-3 Neumeister, Munich #417/R est:5000-5500

PALMIERI, Pietro Giacomo (?-c.1819) Italian
Works on paper
£924 $1654 €1349 Italian landscape with buildings and ruins (30x43cm-12x17in) s. Indian ink wash. 25-May-4 Bukowskis, Stockholm #553/R (S.KR 12500)

PALMORE, Tom (1944-) American
£2570 $4600 €3752 Guana (163x183cm-64x72in) acrylic. 8-May-4 Susanin's, Chicago #6047/R est:5000-7000

PALMU, Jan (1945-1995) Finnish
£423 $786 €630 Still life (20x29cm-8x11in) s. 7-Mar-4 Bukowskis, Helsinki #417/R

PALMU, Juhani (1944-) Finnish
£352 $563 €500 The thoughtful (40x20cm-16x8in) s/. 21-Sep-3 Bukowskis, Helsinki #425/R
£470 $864 €700 Barns at dusk (40x65cm-16x26in) s. 25-Mar-4 Hagelstam, Helsinki #1023/R
£490 $891 €720 Winter in the country (35x60cm-14x24in) s.d.81. 8-Feb-4 Bukowskis, Helsinki #423/R
£537 $999 €800 Winter in town (28x48cm-11x19in) s. 7-Mar-4 Bukowskis, Helsinki #420/R
£671 $1248 €1000 Evening dusk (46x65cm-18x26in) s.d.81. 7-Mar-4 Bukowskis, Helsinki #418/R
£685 $1273 €1020 Evening light (35x60cm-14x24in) s. 7-Mar-4 Bukowskis, Helsinki #419/R
£915 $1465 €1300 Road in Satakunda (50x65cm-20x26in) s. 21-Sep-3 Bukowskis, Helsinki #424/R
£986 $1577 €1400 Winter night in Ilmajoki (50x65cm-20x26in) s. 21-Sep-3 Bukowskis, Helsinki #426/R

PALONEN, Sinikka (1948-) Finnish
£347 $580 €500 In spite of everything, it's not true (150x100cm-59x39in) s.d.88 acrylic. 26-Oct-3 Bukowskis, Helsinki #452/R

PALTRINIERI, Oreste (1873-?) Italian
£1074 $1976 €1600 Around Viareggio (19x24cm-7x9in) s. painted 1939. 27-Mar-4 Farsetti, Prato #307 est:650

PALTRONIERI, Pietro (attrib) (1673-1741) Italian
£8681 $14497 €12500 Scenes de caprices architecturaux animes de personnages (88x166cm-35x65in) pair curved top. 25-Oct-3 Binoche, Orleans #61
£13333 $24400 €20000 River landscape with ruins and figures (204x215cm-80x85in) tempera. 1-Jun-4 Sotheby's, Milan #176/R est:20000-30000
£13966 $25000 €20390 Capicci with figures and ruins (147x156cm-58x61in) tempera set of 3 prov. 27-May-4 Sotheby's, New York #55/R est:25000-35000
£28000 $51240 €42000 Landscape with ruins and figures (204x238cm-80x94in) tempera. 1-Jun-4 Sotheby's, Milan #175/R est:30000-40000

PALUCHA, Jacek (1966-) Polish
£253 $435 €369 Couple on a motorcycle (33x46cm-13x18in) s.d.98. 4-Dec-3 Agra, Warsaw #11/R (P.Z 1700)
£657 $1091 €959 Fat man smoking with cottage in background (46x33cm-18x13in) painted 1998. 2-Oct-3 Agra, Warsaw #60/R (P.Z 4300)

PALUE, Pierre (1920-) French
£395 $714 €600 Maree basse (38x46cm-15x18in) s. i.verso. 19-Apr-4 Boscher, Cherbourg #732/R

PALUMBO, Alphonse (?) ?
£331 $600 €483 Sunday picnic (92x81cm-36x32in) s. 18-Apr-4 Bonhams & Butterfields, Los Angeles #7000
£599 $1000 €869 Man on horseback with children and dogs (74x89cm-29x35in) 8-Jul-3 Douglas, South Deerfield #1

PALUMBO, Eduardo (1932-) Italian
£333 $613 €500 Nature from colour and sign from nature (50x70cm-20x28in) s.i.d.1987 verso vinyl. 12-Jun-4 Meeting Art, Vercelli #453/R
£352 $585 €500 Vento d'Egitto (30x24cm-12x9in) s.i.d.2001 verso vinyl canvas. 14-Jun-3 Meeting Art, Vercelli #53/R
£369 $683 €550 Amazement (50x70cm-20x28in) s.i.d.2001 verso vinyl. 13-Mar-4 Meeting Art, Vercelli #24

PALUMBO, Michele (1874-?) Italian
£805 $1506 €1200 Portrait of Neapolitan girl (28x17cm-11x7in) s.i. panel. 24-Feb-4 Dorotheum, Vienna #255/R

PALUMBO, Onofrio (17th C) Italian
£26490 $48212 €40000 Allegory of Charity (128x155cm-50x61in) 16-Jun-4 Christie's, Rome #508/R est:40000-60000

PAMBERGER, Ferdinand (1873-1956) Austrian
Works on paper
£347 $566 €500 Donawitz (70x50cm-28x20in) s.i. i.verso chk. 23-Sep-3 Wiener Kunst Auktionen, Vienna #105/R
£738 $1321 €1100 Graz mausoleum (70x52cm-28x20in) s. mixed media board. 27-May-4 Dorotheum, Graz #197

PAMBOUJIAN, Gerard (1941-) French
£828 $1374 €1200 Les demoiselles de Versailles (65x56cm-26x22in) s. 5-Oct-3 Lombrail & Teucquam, Paris #422
£2238 $3849 €3200 Clair obscur (73x54cm-29x21in) s. 7-Dec-3 Feletin, Province #108

PAMPALONI, Luigi (1791-1847) Italian
Sculpture
£9000 $16110 €13500 The Infant Saint John (96cm-38in) s. white marble. 17-May-4 Finarte Semenzato, Rome #195/R est:8000-9000
£14500 $26535 €21170 Young girl with dove (65cm-26in) s. marble lit. 9-Jul-4 Sotheby's, London #109/R est:6000-8000

PAN TIANSHOU (1897-1971) Chinese
Works on paper
£15444 $25792 €22548 Chicks (67x36cm-26x14in) s.i.d.1962 ink col hanging scroll. 27-Oct-3 Sotheby's, Hong Kong #250/R est:160000-200000 (HK.D 200000)
£25605 $46088 €37383 Cat on a rock (96x44cm-38x17in) s. ink col hanging scroll. 26-Apr-4 Sotheby's, Hong Kong #637/R est:180000-220000 (HK.D 360000)

PAN YULIANG (1899-1977) Chinese
Prints
£3600 $6444 €5256 Woman and cat (31x48cm-12x19in) s. hand col lithograph. 6-May-4 Sotheby's, London #113/R est:2000-2500

PAN ZHIWAN and XU GU (19th C) Chinese
Works on paper
£8535 $15363 €12461 Squirrel and calligraphy (70x28cm-28x11in) s.i. ink col hanging scrolls set of three. 25-Apr-4 Christie's, Hong Kong #77/R est:150000-200000 (HK.D 120000)

PAN, Abel (20th C) Israeli
Works on paper
£14094 $26215 €21000 Petite chevriere (73x66cm-29x26in) s. pastel. 3-Mar-4 Tajan, Paris #154/R est:4000-6000

PAN, Antonio (1937-2001) Spanish
£276 $461 €400 Playing on the beach (32x31cm-13x12in) s. board. 17-Nov-3 Durán, Madrid #1210/R
£352 $616 €500 The horse game (55x46cm-22x18in) s.d.2000 s.i.d.verso. 16-Dec-3 Durán, Madrid #1187/R
£379 $633 €550 On the beach (43x48cm-17x19in) s. s.d.2000 verso board. 17-Nov-3 Durán, Madrid #640/R

PANABAKER, Frank S (1904-1992) Canadian
£610 $1091 €891 Cable Beach, Nassau (54x69cm-21x27in) s. s.i.d.1939 verso. 6-May-4 Heffel, Vancouver #107/R (C.D 1500)
£676 $1149 €987 Wharf at Holy Loach, Scotland (30x38cm-12x15in) s. i.verso board. 21-Nov-3 Walker's, Ottawa #61/R (C.D 1500)
£763 $1419 €1114 Quiet stream near Denbigh (41x51cm-16x20in) s. masonite prov. 2-Mar-4 Ritchie, Toronto #110/R est:1500-2000 (C.D 1900)
£901 $1532 €1315 Ontario Road, June (40x50cm-16x20in) s. i.verso prov. 27-Nov-3 Heffel, Vancouver #93/R est:2000-3000 (C.D 2000)
£1364 $2223 €1991 Shoreline (41x51cm-16x20in) s. masonite. 23-Sep-3 Ritchie, Toronto #88/R est:3000-5000 (C.D 3000)
£1802 $3063 €2631 Sugar shack (50x61cm-20x24in) s. painted c.1940. 27-Nov-3 Heffel, Vancouver #146/R est:2500-3500 (C.D 4000)

PANAMARENKO (1940-) Belgian
£805 $1426 €1200 Untitled (21x27cm-8x11in) pencil felt pen biro prov. 30-Apr-4 Dr Fritz Nagel, Stuttgart #918/R
Sculpture
£1333 $2453 €2000 Accelerator (5x20x21cm-2x8x8in) s. num.23/50 wood copper iron magnet exec 1979 lit. 8-Jun-4 Sotheby's, Amsterdam #142/R est:2800-3300
£3667 $6710 €5500 Big paradox (115x48x35cm-45x19x14in) s. num.16/25 silver wood cloth fishing rod lit. 7-Jun-4 Palais de Beaux Arts, Brussels #379/R est:6000-8000
£4000 $7320 €6000 Thermo photovoltaic energy converter (13x65x32cm-5x26x13in) s. num.24/25 wood paint plexiglass electric motor lit. 7-Jun-4 Palais de Beaux Arts, Brussels #378/R est:6000-8000
£4667 $8587 €7000 Meganeudon (15x36x12cm-6x14x5in) s.d.73 num.1/50 iron PVC wood other objects in perspex prov.lit. 8-Jun-4 Sotheby's, Amsterdam #139/R est:8000-10000
£5000 $9200 €7500 Encarsia-Formosa (21x40x13cm-8x16x5in) i. num.AP IX/X copper iron PVC elec motor batteries lit. 8-Jun-4 Sotheby's, Amsterdam #141/R est:7500-9000
Works on paper
£2621 $4717 €3800 Etude pour une machine volante (30x23cm-12x9in) s.d.1977 ink graphite. 25-Jan-4 Cornette de St.Cyr, Paris #500 est:4000-6000
£3467 $6240 €5200 Liften. Schroef en machinen de villegastr.31/3600 Berchem/Antw (26x34cm-10x13in) s. pencil two in one frame. 26-Apr-4 Bernaerts, Antwerp #563/R est:5000-6000

PANCETTI, Jose (c.1902-1958) Brazilian
£7143 $12643 €10715 Mother and daughters (31x23cm-12x9in) s.d.1949. 27-Apr-4 Bolsa de Arte, Rio de Janeiro #66/R (B.R 39000)
£40293 $71319 €60440 The navy (46x65cm-18x26in) s.d.1952 i.verso. 27-Apr-4 Bolsa de Arte, Rio de Janeiro #14/R (B.R 220000)

PANCHERI, Gino (1905-1943) Italian
£2797 $4755 €4000 School (40x75cm-16x30in) tempera card. 20-Nov-3 Finarte Semenzato, Milan #124/R est:3000-3500

PANCHINE, Youri (?) Russian?
£340 $619 €500 Bouquet rouge. s. 8-Feb-4 Lesieur & Le Bars, Le Havre #36

PANCHOUNETTE, Presence (20th C) French
£694 $1097 €1000 Monochrome jaune (23x33cm-9x13in) mono. s.i.d.1987 verso prov. 27-Apr-3 Versailles Encheres #116

PANCKOUCKE, Ernestine (1784-1860) French
Works on paper
£20000 $37000 €29200 Still life of flowers (95x70cm-37x28in) s.d.1829 W/C vellum. 15-Jul-4 Bonhams, New Bond Street #41/R est:20000-30000

PANCOAST, Clara C (1873-1959) American
£1198 $2000 €1749 Landscape (41x51cm-16x20in) canvasboard. 18-Oct-3 David Dike, Dallas #90/R est:2000-4000

PANCOAST, Henry Boller (1876-?) American
£1875 $3000 €2738 Summer landscape with lane leading to houses by a river (61x76cm-24x30in) s. prov. 20-Sep-3 Pook & Pook, Downington #350/R est:1500-2000
£15000 $24000 €21900 Summer wooded landscape with a mill reflected in the water (71x84cm-28x33in) s. prov. 20-Sep-3 Pook & Pook, Downington #310/R est:7000-9000

PANCOAST, Morris Hall (1877-?) American
£667 $1200 €974 Clearing skies (20x25cm-8x10in) s. board. 20-Jan-4 Arthur James, Florida #680
£722 $1300 €1054 Village houses (20x25cm-8x10in) s. board. 20-Jan-4 Arthur James, Florida #679
£944 $1700 €1378 Coastal scene (30x41cm-12x16in) s. 20-Jan-4 Arthur James, Florida #678
£1258 $2000 €1837 Landscape with horses (20x25cm-8x10in) s. board. 10-Sep-3 Alderfer's, Hatfield #345/R est:1500-1800
£2222 $4000 €3244 Winding road (71x81cm-28x32in) s. 20-Jan-4 Arthur James, Florida #747
£3333 $6000 €4866 Harbour scene (46x56cm-18x22in) s. 20-Jan-4 Arthur James, Florida #681

PANCRAZI, Luca (1961-) Italian
£4577 $8011 €6500 Motorway (55x80cm-22x31in) acrylic. 16-Dec-3 Finarte Semenzato, Milan #288/R est:5800-6800

PANDE KETUT TAMAN (1970-) Indonesian
£2237 $3578 €3266 Bunga tanah (140x140cm-55x55in) s.i.d.2002. 18-May-3 Sotheby's, Singapore #188/R est:4000-6000 (S.D 6240)

PANDIANI, Giesserei (fl.1875-1910) Italian
Sculpture
£1111 $1811 €1600 Galant scene (26x49x17cm-10x19x7in) brown pat.bronze. 25-Sep-3 Neumeister, Munich #185/R est:1400

PANE, Gina (1939-1999) Italian
Photographs
£3624 $6487 €5400 Escalade sanglante (50x57cm-20x22in) s.d.71 verso black/white photograph prov. 25-May-4 Sotheby's, Milan #215/R est:3000-3500
£6294 $10699 €9000 Psyche (78x118cm-31x46in) s.i.d.1974 num.2/2 prov. 25-Nov-3 Sotheby's, Milan #259/R est:10000-15000

PANEK, Jerzy (1918-2001) Polish
Works on paper
£353 $639 €515 Self portrait (38x27cm-15x11in) s.d.1987 pastel. 4-Apr-4 Agra, Warsaw #61/R (P.Z 2500)

PANERAI, Ruggero (1862-1923) Italian
£1754 $2930 €2561 Vache (25x32cm-10x13in) s. cardboard. 16-Nov-3 Koller, Geneva #1231/R est:2500-4500 (S.FR 4000)
£3974 $7232 €6000 Herd resting (70x99cm-28x39in) s. i.verso. 21-Jun-4 Pandolfini, Florence #152/R est:7000-9000
£4667 $8447 €7000 Mother and cub (49x63cm-19x25in) s. 2-Apr-4 Farsetti, Prato #563/R est:6000-7000

PANG JIUN (1936-) Chinese
£3912 $7041 €5712 Pink orchard (65x53cm-26x21in) s.d.2003. 25-Apr-4 Christie's, Hong Kong #751/R est:55000-75000 (HK.D 55000)
£6757 $12162 €9865 Wu town (72x60cm-28x24in) s.d.2003. 25-Apr-4 Christie's, Hong Kong #746/R est:70000-110000 (HK.D 95000)
£8494 $14185 €12401 Bridge of scholar (72x60cm-28x24in) s.d.2003. 26-Oct-3 Christie's, Hong Kong #107/R est:70000-110000 (HK.D 110000)

PANG XUNQIN (1906-1985) Chinese
£34749 $58031 €50734 Azalea (60x45cm-24x18in) s.d.1979 s.d.verso board. 26-Oct-3 Christie's, Hong Kong #122/R est:400000-500000 (HK.D 450000)

PANGNARK, John (1920-1980) North American
Sculpture
£785 $1413 €1146 Inuit figure (13cm-5in) s. grey soapstone. 26-Apr-4 Waddingtons, Toronto #618/R est:600-900 (C.D 1900)
£811 $1378 €1184 Inuk (18cm-7in) mottled grey soapstone. 3-Nov-3 Waddingtons, Toronto #382/R est:1000-1500 (C.D 1800)
£1171 $1991 €1710 Inuit woman (16cm-6in) s. mottled grey soapstone. 3-Nov-3 Waddingtons, Toronto #365/R est:1500-2000 (C.D 2600)
£1261 $2144 €1841 Inuit mother and her child (15cm-6in) mottled dark soapstone. 3-Nov-3 Waddingtons, Toronto #377/R est:1500-2500 (C.D 2800)

PANIARAS, Costas (1934-) Greek
£1200 $2040 €1752 Untitled (261x125cm-103x49in) s. oil plastic. 18-Nov-3 Sotheby's, London #110/R est:1200-1800

PANICEV, Dimitri (20th C) Italian
£1034 $1717 €1500 At the mirror (116x93cm-46x37in) s.d.53. 1-Oct-3 Della Rocca, Turin #280/R est:1500-2000

PANIKER, K C S (1911-1977) Indian?
£9239 $17000 €13489 Words and symbols (69x87cm-27x34in) s.d.68 i.verso. 24-Mar-4 Sotheby's, New York #197/R est:2500-3500

PANINI, Francesco (attrib) (18th C) Italian
£15625 $26562 €22500 Interior of Saint Peter's (160x130cm-63x51in) 29-Oct-3 Il Ponte, Milan #580/R est:18000-22000

PANINI, Giovanni Paolo (1691-1765) Italian
£9333 $16707 €14000 Capriccio with figures (73x100cm-29x39in) 17-May-4 Finarte Semenzato, Rome #117/R est:12000-15000
£14894 $24872 €21000 San Pietro apostolo battezza il centurione Cornelio (98x74cm-39x29in) painted with studio. 18-Jun-3 Christie's, Rome #434/R est:8000-10000
£33333 $60000 €48666 Capriccio of classical buildings by a pool (93x93cm-37x37in) mono. prov.lit. 23-Jan-4 Christie's, Rockefeller NY #86/R est:60000-80000
£67114 $118792 €100000 Capriccio with apostle preaching (58x88cm-23x35in) init. 27-Apr-4 Porro, Milan #319/R est:100000
£80000 $146400 €120000 View of Titus Arch (73x94cm-29x37in) bears sig. lit. 1-Jun-4 Sotheby's, Milan #169/R est:80000-120000
£95000 $164350 €138700 Classical landscape with the judgement of Midas (49x65cm-19x26in) prov.lit. 10-Dec-3 Christie's, London #115/R est:70000-100000
£139860 $240559 €200000 View of Rome (80x112cm-31x44in) init. lit. 2-Dec-3 Sotheby's, Milan #126/R est:150000-200000
£2100000 $3843000 €3066000 Interior of Saint Peter's, Rome. Interior of San Paolo fuori le Mura, Rome (75x103cm-30x41in) s.d.MDCCXXXXI pair prov.exhib.lit. 7-Jul-4 Christie's, London #106/R est:1500000-2500000
Works on paper
£34615 $59538 €50538 Paysage de ruines antiques avec personnages (23x36cm-9x14in) Indian ink wash prov. 3-Dec-3 AB Stockholms Auktionsverk #2657/R est:80000-100000 (S.KR 450000)

PANINI, Giovanni Paolo (circle) (1691-1765) Italian
£38462 $66154 €56155 Roman landscape with ruins and figures (125x93cm-49x37in) oval prov. 2-Dec-3 Bukowskis, Stockholm #423/R est:200000-250000 (S.KR 500000)

PANINI, Giovanni Paolo (school) (1691-1765) Italian
£4335 $7500 €6329 Sacrificial lamb amid a capriccio of ruins (94x76cm-37x30in) 13-Dec-3 Weschler, Washington #507 est:2000-3000

PANINI, Giovanni Paolo (studio) (1691-1765) Italian
£10345 $17276 €15000 Archeologist (49x66cm-19x26in) lit. 12-Nov-3 Sotheby's, Milan #154/R est:10000-15000
£26000 $47580 €37960 Capriccio with Belisarius and soldiers among ruins (64x100cm-25x39in) 8-Jul-4 Sotheby's, London #180/R est:30000-40000
£51799 $84950 €72000 View of Florentine and Greek ruins (45x82cm-18x32in) 4-Jun-3 Sotheby's, Milan #136/R est:18000-22000

PANINI, Giovanni Paolo (style) (1691-1765) Italian
£7500 $12450 €10950 Capriccio of Roman ruins including Arch of Titus and the Statue of Achilles (85x101cm-33x40in) 30-Sep-3 Sotheby's, London #268/R est:6000-8000
£8500 $15300 €12410 Capriccio of Roman ruins with soldiers and other figures (97x72cm-38x28in) 23-Apr-4 Christie's, Kensington #269/R est:3000-5000
£11842 $21789 €18000 Extensive landscape with figures and sheep under a classical ruin (137x142cm-54x56in) 22-Jun-4 Mealy's, Castlecomer #362/R est:4000-6000
£25175 $42042 €36000 Church interior (173x196cm-68x77in) 7-Oct-3 Pandolfini, Florence #607/R est:35000-40000
£40000 $73200 €58400 Pantheon interior, Rome (93x85cm-37x33in) i. prov. 9-Jul-4 Christie's, Kensington #198/R est:10000-15000

PANITZSCH, Robert (1879-1949) German/Danish
£267 $485 €401 Interior scene with a Buddha and paintings in a hall (60x50cm-24x20in) s.d.1923. 19-Jun-4 Rasmussen, Havnen #2250/R (D.KR 3000)
£328 $535 €479 Harbour scene with steamer with Danish flag (56x66cm-22x26in) s.d.39. 27-Sep-3 Rasmussen, Havnen #2153/R (D.KR 3500)
£369 $627 €539 Harbour scene with fishing vessels and figures (42x65cm-17x26in) s.d.1905. 10-Nov-3 Rasmussen, Vejle #270/R (D.KR 4000)
£398 $637 €581 Evening idyll with family by lamplight (66x86cm-26x34in) s.d.28. 22-Sep-3 Rasmussen, Vejle #44/R (D.KR 4200)
£421 $664 €610 Blue painted sitting room with paintings in wall (66x79cm-26x31in) s. panel. 2-Sep-3 Rasmussen, Copenhagen #1965/R (D.KR 4500)
£421 $704 €615 Sunshine in the sitting room (60x72cm-24x28in) s.d.31. 25-Oct-3 Rasmussen, Havnen #2031 (D.KR 4500)
£541 $876 €790 Interior scene with grand piano (60x51cm-24x20in) s.d.31.7. 9-Aug-3 Hindemae, Ullerslev #129/R (D.KR 5700)
£588 $1000 €858 Morgenstemning ved louisekilde i Sorgentri Park (49x69cm-19x27in) s.d.1929. 21-Nov-3 Skinner, Boston #524/R est:1800-2200
£794 $1255 €1151 Girl writing a letter in sunny sitting room (68x62cm-27x24in) s. 2-Sep-3 Rasmussen, Copenhagen #1968/R (D.KR 8500)
£805 $1426 €1200 Biedermeier interior (75x100cm-30x39in) s.d.29. 28-Apr-4 Schopman, Hamburg #569/R
£1134 $2030 €1656 Interior scene with girl from the Art Museum, Copenhagen (66x81cm-26x32in) s.d.1920. 12-Jan-4 Rasmussen, Vejle #317/R est:12000-15000 (D.KR 12000)

PANKIEWICZ, Jozef (1866-1940) Polish
£9077 $15703 €13252 Grove of pine trees with sea in background (64x53cm-25x21in) s. painted 1921. 14-Dec-3 Agra, Warsaw #74/R est:40000 (P.Z 60000)

PANKOK, Bernhard (1872-1943) German
£1888 $3248 €2700 Still life with flowers (52x43cm-20x17in) s.d.1937. 4-Dec-3 Van Ham, Cologne #370/R est:4200

PANKOK, Otto (1893-1966) German
£1014 $1814 €1500 Girl's portrait (42x47cm-17x19in) board study verso lit. 8-May-4 Schloss Ahlden, Ahlden #828/R est:1800
Works on paper
£2000 $3660 €3000 Self portrait (45x34cm-18x13in) mono.d.41 chl. 5-Jun-4 Lempertz, Koln #916/R est:2500
£3357 $5706 €4800 Landscape with donkey cart (899x118cm-354x46in) s.d.26 chl. 26-Nov-3 Lempertz, Koln #890/R est:7000

PANN, Abel (1883-1963) Israeli/Latvian
£4698 $8315 €7000 Petite fille a la robe verte (29x21cm-11x8in) s. canvasboard painted c.1912. 27-Apr-4 Artcurial Briest, Paris #149/R est:8000-10000
£9639 $16000 €14073 Self portrait (92x73cm-36x29in) s.d.1909. 2-Oct-3 Christie's, Tel Aviv #13/R est:10000-15000
Works on paper
£4469 $8000 €6525 Expulsion from Eden (56x42cm-22x17in) s.i.d.1950 i.verso pastel on board. 18-Mar-4 Sotheby's, New York #233/R est:8000-12000
£5120 $8500 €7475 Abel (64x48cm-25x19in) s. pastel paper on board. 2-Oct-3 Christie's, Tel Aviv #3/R est:9000-12000
£7667 $14107 €11500 Etude pour le sacrifice d'Abraham (46x61cm-18x24in) s.i. pastel. 13-Jun-4 Lombrail & Teucquam, Paris #109/R
£10615 $19000 €15498 Return, return o shulamit (47x62cm-19x24in) s.i. pastel on board. 18-Mar-4 Sotheby's, New York #232/R est:10000-15000
£15333 $28213 €23000 Le jeune roi David (48x31cm-19x12in) s. pastel exec. c.1952. 8-Jun-4 Artcurial Briest, Paris #127/R est:25000-30000

PANN, Abel (attrib) (1883-1963) Israeli/Latvian
Works on paper
£377 $640 €550 Abduction (37x53cm-15x21in) pastel. 5-Nov-3 Vendue Huis, Gravenhage #393/R

PANNETT, Richard (20th C) British
Works on paper
£400 $740 €584 Flamenco dancer (35x24cm-14x9in) s. W/C bodycol. 14-Jul-4 Christie's, Kensington #1107

PANNKA, Claude (1928-1972) Australian
Works on paper
£314 $562 €458 Untitled (37x35cm-15x14in) s. i. verso W/C. 25-May-4 Lawson Menzies, Sydney #111/R (A.D 800)

PANSER-FLECK-RABENSTEINER, Wilma (1890-1945) Austrian
Works on paper
£300 $540 €450 Trees by village (33x23cm-13x9in) s.d.1916 W/C. 22-Apr-4 Dorotheum, Graz #67/R

PANSINI, Edoardo (1886-1968) Italian
£1049 $1783 €1500 Cardinals playing chess (39x54cm-15x21in) s. i.verso. 28-Nov-3 Wendl, Rudolstadt #4131/R est:1400

PANTALEON, Theodoros (1945-) Greek
£2400 $4296 €3504 Surrealist landscape (12x17cm-5x7in) s. panel. 11-May-4 Bonhams, New Bond Street #120/R est:1500-2000
£7800 $13962 €11388 Female figure in a surrealist landscape (50x40cm-20x16in) s.d.93 exhib. 11-May-4 Bonhams, New Bond Street #117/R est:6500-8500
£9200 $16100 €13432 Girl in surrealistic landscapes (50x35cm-20x14in) s. panel. 16-Dec-3 Bonhams, New Bond Street #143/R est:6000-8000
Works on paper
£1100 $1969 €1606 Image (41x33cm-16x13in) s. W/C. 11-May-4 Bonhams, New Bond Street #130/R est:500-700
£1500 $2625 €2190 Girl in profile (33x24cm-13x9in) s. W/C pair. 16-Dec-3 Bonhams, New Bond Street #148/R est:1500-2000

PANTAZIS, Pericles (1849-1884) Greek
£4196 $7217 €6000 Sous-bois (46x33cm-18x13in) 8-Dec-3 Horta, Bruxelles #73 est:3000-4000
£6000 $10200 €8760 Still life with fish and vegetables (54x63cm-21x25in) prov. 18-Nov-3 Sotheby's, London #12/R est:4000-6000
£6000 $10200 €8760 By the stream (28x42cm-11x17in) prov. 18-Nov-3 Sotheby's, London #26/R est:2000-3000
£11000 $19690 €16060 Portrait of a boy (35x27cm-14x11in) s. 10-May-4 Sotheby's, Olympia #5/R est:6000-8000
£18000 $32220 €26280 Village sous la neige, vallee de la Meuse (31x41cm-12x16in) prov.exhib. 11-May-4 Bonhams, New Bond Street #35/R est:20000-30000
£60000 $102000 €87600 Winter (70x50cm-28x20in) s. prov.exhib.lit. 18-Nov-3 Sotheby's, London #22/R est:60000-80000
£115000 $205850 €167900 Le phare de Marseille (72x112cm-28x44in) s. prov.exhib.lit. 11-May-4 Bonhams, New Bond Street #31/R est:100000-150000

PANTAZOPOULOS, Epaminondas (1874-1961) Greek
£500 $875 €730 Sea view (30x43cm-12x17in) s. panel. 16-Dec-3 Bonhams, New Bond Street #58/R

PANTOJA DE LA CRUZ (style) (1551-1608) Spanish
£6500 $11050 €9490 Portrait of a gentleman in armour with the order of the Golden Fleece (202x104cm-80x41in) 29-Oct-3 Bonhams, New Bond Street #55/R est:7000-10000

PANTON, Lawrence Arthur Colley (1894-1954) Canadian
£420 $769 €609 Forest clearing (32x40cm-13x16in) s. canvas on board. 1-Jun-4 Joyner Waddington, Toronto #315/R (C.D 1050)
£484 $890 €707 Rock forms, Cape Breton (32x40cm-13x16in) s. i.verso board prov. 9-Jun-4 Walker's, Ottawa #91/R (C.D 1200)
£536 $921 €783 Landscape with rolling hills (25x30cm-10x12in) s. board. 2-Dec-3 Joyner Waddington, Toronto #512 (C.D 1200)
£650 $1164 €949 Don Valley Farm, York country, Ontario (25x30cm-10x12in) s.i.d.1946 verso panel prov. 6-May-4 Heffel, Vancouver #108/R (C.D 1600)

PANTORBA, Bernardino de (1896-1990) Spanish
£789 $1429 €1200 Village street (28x38cm-11x15in) s. board. 14-Apr-4 Ansorena, Madrid #32/R

PANUSKA, Jaroslav (1872-1958) Czechoslovakian
£288 $536 €420 Summer landscape (23x32cm-9x13in) s. board. 6-Mar-4 Dorotheum, Prague #99 est:14000-21000 (C.KR 14000)
£316 $557 €474 Landscape (25x33cm-10x13in) s.d.1919 paper on cardboard. 22-May-4 Dorotheum, Prague #130/R est:15000-23000 (C.KR 15000)
£438 $727 €639 Winter landscape with European bison (50x65cm-20x26in) s. 4-Oct-3 Dorotheum, Prague #63/R est:20000-30000 (C.KR 20000)
£453 $843 €661 Summer landscape (49x65cm-19x26in) s. board. 6-Mar-4 Dorotheum, Prague #98/R est:22000-34000 (C.KR 22000)
£458 $801 €650 Summer landscape (49x64cm-19x25in) s. board. 19-Dec-3 Dorotheum, Vienna #130/R
£535 $996 €781 Scarecrow (35x50cm-14x20in) s. panel exhib. 6-Mar-4 Dorotheum, Prague #96/R est:26000-38000 (C.KR 26000)
£717 $1262 €1076 Summer landscape before a storm (49x86cm-19x34in) s. cardboard. 22-May-4 Dorotheum, Prague #67/R est:26000-38000 (C.KR 34000)
£1371 $2413 €2057 Flooded brook (64x49cm-25x19in) s. cardboard. 22-May-4 Dorotheum, Prague #59/R est:30000-45000 (C.KR 65000)

PANZA, Giovanni (1894-1989) Italian
£400 $732 €584 Girl on the beach, Naples (20x28cm-8x11in) s. board. 7-Apr-4 Gardiner & Houlgate, Bath #333/R
£493 $853 €700 Face of girl (24x18cm-9x7in) s. paper on cardboard. 10-Dec-3 Sotheby's, Milan #137
£608 $949 €900 Girl (18x13cm-7x5in) board. 30-Mar-3 Adma, Formigine #348/R
£915 $1584 €1300 Peasant woman with jug (32x25cm-13x10in) board. 11-Dec-3 Christie's, Rome #53/R
£1014 $1581 €1500 Pulcinella (30x24cm-12x9in) board. 30-Mar-3 Adma, Formigine #381 est:1500-1600
£1176 $1882 €1717 Tristezza (50x40cm-20x16in) s. panel. 16-Sep-3 Philippe Schuler, Zurich #3369/R est:3000-4000 (S.FR 2600)
£1554 $2424 €2300 Children (26x20cm-10x8in) board. 30-Mar-3 Adma, Formigine #414
£1579 $2905 €2400 Girl at well (40x30cm-16x12in) s. board. 23-Jun-4 Finarte Semenzato, Rome #76/R est:2000-2200
£1579 $2905 €2400 Bathers (28x30cm-11x12in) s. board. 23-Jun-4 Finarte Semenzato, Rome #80/R est:2500-2800
£1645 $3026 €2500 Girl on the grass (24x30cm-9x12in) s. board. 23-Jun-4 Finarte Semenzato, Rome #78/R est:1400-1500
£1972 $3411 €2800 Little violinist (50x57cm-20x22in) s. 11-Dec-3 Christie's, Rome #55/R est:2000-3000
£2113 $3655 €3000 Boats and fishermen in Ischia (50x70cm-20x28in) s.d.31. 11-Dec-3 Christie's, Rome #86/R est:1800-2500

PAOLETTI, Antonio (1834-1912) Italian
£247 $450 €361 Accordion player (23x21cm-9x8in) s. 7-Feb-4 Sloans & Kenyon, Bethesda #885/R
£6500 $11830 €9490 Italian fruit seller (56x81cm-22x32in) s.i. 15-Jun-4 Capes Dunn, Manchester #756/R
£6667 $12267 €10000 Poor children (59x43cm-23x17in) s.i. 8-Jun-4 Sotheby's, Milan #132/R est:8000-12000
£7059 $12000 €10306 Feeding the pigeons (46x66cm-18x26in) s.i. canvas wrapped around board prov. 28-Oct-3 Sotheby's, New York #142/R est:15000-20000
£8725 $16054 €13000 Venise, petit pecheur Place Saint Marc (34x24cm-13x9in) s.i. panel. 28-Mar-4 Anaf, Lyon #219/R est:13000-15000
£12000 $21840 €17520 Bird seller (50x76cm-20x30in) s. 16-Jun-4 Christie's, Kensington #99/R est:8000-12000
£16667 $30000 €24334 Young musicians in Piazza San Marco, Venice (49x70cm-19x28in) s.i. 22-Apr-4 Christie's, Rockefeller NY #225/R est:20000-30000
Works on paper
£469 $750 €685 Boy fishing (20x36cm-8x14in) s. W/C. 21-Sep-3 Grogan, Boston #26/R
£578 $1000 €844 Boy fishing (20x38cm-8x15in) s. W/C. 12-Dec-3 Du Mouchelle, Detroit #2532/R

PAOLETTI, Rodolfo (1866-1940) Italian
£347 $590 €500 Venice (40x30cm-16x12in) s. board. 1-Nov-3 Meeting Art, Vercelli #69/R
£369 $690 €550 Canal in Venice (60x50cm-24x20in) board. 26-Feb-4 Cambi, Genoa #515/R
£521 $885 €750 Shepherdess and goat (40x30cm-16x12in) s. board. 1-Nov-3 Meeting Art, Vercelli #317/R
£556 $944 €800 Evening in Venice (37x45cm-15x18in) s. board. 1-Nov-3 Meeting Art, Vercelli #219/R
£563 $975 €800 Venice (60x74cm-24x29in) s. board. 10-Dec-3 Sotheby's, Milan #9/R
£600 $1074 €900 Entrance to the villa (50x40cm-20x16in) s. board. 12-May-4 Stadion, Trieste #732/R
£638 $1066 €900 Venetian scene (71x48cm-28x19in) s. board. 14-Oct-3 Finarte Semenzato, Milan #129/R
£833 $1417 €1200 Scene in Venice (48x38cm-19x15in) s. board. 1-Nov-3 Meeting Art, Vercelli #319/R
£1189 $1985 €1700 Night harmony in Venice (78x58cm-31x23in) s. s.i.verso board. 24-Jun-3 Finarte Semenzato, Rome #158/R
£1389 $2361 €2000 Gondola, Venice (80x60cm-31x24in) s. board. 1-Nov-3 Meeting Art, Vercelli #399/R est:1500
£10000 $18400 €15000 Duomo Square, Milan (142x269cm-56x106in) s.i.d.06 prov. 8-Jun-4 Sotheby's, Milan #90/R est:12000-18000

PAOLI, Bruno (1915-) Italian
£290 $484 €420 Model and painter (40x30cm-16x12in) s. s.i.verso. 14-Nov-3 Farsetti, Prato #457
£867 $1595 €1300 Cristina (40x30cm-16x12in) s. s.i.verso. 12-Jun-4 Meeting Art, Vercelli #976/R

PAOLILLO, Luigi (1864-?) Italian
£800 $1432 €1200 Fishing boats (18x35cm-7x14in) s. board. 13-May-4 Babuino, Rome #359
£2151 $4000 €3140 Amalfi by the setting sun (71x91cm-28x36in) s. i.verso. 5-Mar-4 Skinner, Boston #326/R est:1500-2500

PAOLINI, Giulio (1940-) Italian
Sculpture
£30726 $55000 €44860 Intervallo (129x50x30cm-51x20x12in) two plaster bust wooden pedestal executed 1986. 13-May-4 Phillips, New York #39/R est:80000-120000
Works on paper
£2207 $3686 €3200 Untitled (19x18cm-7x7in) s.d.1975 verso collage prov. 13-Nov-3 Finarte Semenzato, Rome #183/R est:3000-4000
£2637 $4668 €3850 Sunset (20x20cm-8x8in) s.d.1974 verso collage prov. 27-Apr-4 AB Stockholms Auktionsverk #926/R est:3000-4000 (S.KR 36000)
£2817 $4930 €4000 Untitled (70x50cm-28x20in) s.d.1990 verso collage card. 16-Dec-3 Finarte Semenzato, Milan #213/R est:3800-4200
£4348 $7130 €6000 Untitled (35x50cm-14x20in) s.d.1975 verso collage. 30-May-3 Farsetti, Prato #351/R
£4362 $7809 €6500 Hermaphrodite (49x70cm-19x28in) s.d.1982 verso collage exhib. 26-May-4 Christie's, Paris #130/R est:1500-2000
£4362 $7809 €6500 Cleopatra (49x70cm-19x28in) s.d.982 verso collage exhib. 26-May-4 Christie's, Paris #128/R est:1500-2000
£4545 $7727 €6500 Rue du Regard (70x100cm-28x39in) s.i.d.1991 verso pencil collage card prov.exhib. 25-Nov-3 Sotheby's, Milan #157/R est:7000-9000
£5034 $9010 €7500 Paetus et Avia (49x70cm-19x28in) s.d.1982 verso collage. 26-May-4 Christie's, Paris #131/R
£5034 $9010 €7500 Narcissus (49x70cm-19x28in) s.d.982 verso collage exhib. 26-May-4 Christie's, Paris #129/R est:1500-2000
£6040 $10812 €9000 Untitled (58x45cm-23x18in) s.d.1964 collage prov.lit. 25-May-4 Sotheby's, Milan #284/R est:8000-10000
£9396 $16819 €14000 Untitled (40x40cm-16x16in) s.d.1975 pencil collage prov. 25-May-4 Sotheby's, Milan #285/R est:10000-15000
£11486 $20216 €17000 Clio (60x50cm-24x20in) s.i.d.80 verso collage pencil ink. 24-May-4 Christie's, Milan #247/R est:18000-25000
£20000 $33400 €29200 Ennesima, appunti per la descrizione di sette tele datate 1973 (45x211cm-18x83in) one s.i.d.1973 stretcher graphite canvas 7 prov. 21-Oct-3 Christie's, London #58/R est:20000-30000
£25362 $41594 €35000 Diapason (107x100cm-42x39in) s.i.d.1979-80 on stretcher pencil on canvas on metal prov. 27-May-3 Sotheby's, Milan #289/R est:30000-35000
£35000 $58450 €51100 Quadrante (41x180cm-16x71in) one s.i.d.1975 stretcher 2 folded canvas 1 graphite 3 prov.exhib. 21-Oct-3 Christie's, London #56/R est:35000-45000

PAOLINI, Pietro (1603-1681) Italian
£40426 $65489 €57000 Young player (97x160cm-38x63in) 21-May-3 Babuino, Rome #41/R
£60284 $97660 €85000 Young woman playing violin (105x161cm-41x63in) 21-May-3 Babuino, Rome #18/R
£77181 $144329 €115000 Girl with basket of fruit (77x117cm-30x46in) lit. 25-Feb-4 Porro, Milan #89/R est:115000
£88652 $143617 €125000 Concert (105x160cm-41x63in) 21-May-3 Babuino, Rome #17/R
£220000 $380600 €321200 Portrait of a boy, head and shoulders (41x33cm-16x13in) i. verso stretcher prov.lit. 11-Dec-3 Sotheby's, London #21/R est:80000-120000

PAOLOZZI, Eduardo (1924-) British
Sculpture
£925 $1600 €1351 Ety (41cm-16in) i. chromed steel prov. 15-Dec-3 Hindman, Chicago #46/R est:2000-4000
£3198 $5500 €4669 Crash Head (38cm-15in) s. num.7-10 burnished bronze steel chain exec 1970 prov. 7-Dec-3 Freeman, Philadelphia #48 est:5000-8000
£8589 $14000 €12540 Study for large head (57x34x26cm-22x13x10in) s.d.Nov 1957 gold pat bronze edition of 2 st.f.Susse prov.exhib. 23-Sep-3 Christie's, Rockefeller NY #2/R est:7000-9000
£13497 $22000 €19706 Standing figure (78x25x13cm-31x10x5in) gold brown pat bronze exec.c.1957 prov. 23-Sep-3 Christie's, Rockefeller NY #3/R est:6000-8000
£30000 $51600 €43800 Little King (142cm-56in) artist st.d.57 mottled green brown pat bronze prov. 3-Dec-3 Sotheby's, London #74/R est:14000-18000
Works on paper
£1700 $3094 €2482 Composition (25x35cm-10x14in) s.d.1968 pen black ink sold with two pencil composition studies. 30-Jun-4 Christie's, Kensington #42/R est:1000-1500
£2400 $4368 €3504 Abstract composition (29x23cm-11x9in) s.d.1967 pencil pen black ink crayon. 30-Jun-4 Christie's, Kensington #41/R est:1500-2000
£2800 $5096 €4088 Automobile figure (51x31cm-20x12in) s.d.1957 W/C lithographic base prov. 30-Jun-4 Christie's, Kensington #6/R est:800-1200
£9000 $16470 €13140 Sammelmappe (32x23cm-13x9in) s. collage set of 10. 2-Jun-4 Sotheby's, London #70/R est:10000-15000

PAON, Jean Baptiste le (c.1736-1785) French
Works on paper
£265 $482 €400 Une femme partant en promenade avec son page, conversant avec un soldat (33x48cm-13x19in) s.d.1770 pen ink wash black crayon. 16-Jun-4 Piasa, Paris #118
£2105 $3874 €3200 Cheval a l'arret piaffant (26x33cm-10x13in) bears sig sanguine pierre noire htd white. 23-Jun-4 Sotheby's, Paris #28/R est:2000-3000

PAP, Emil (1884-?) Hungarian
£750 $1275 €1095 Flower girl (79x60cm-31x24in) s. 6-Nov-3 Christie's, Kensington #834/R

PAP, Gyala (1899-1984) Hungarian
Photographs
£6250 $10625 €9000 Untitled (12x16cm-5x6in) gelatin silver. 31-Oct-3 Lempertz, Koln #260/R est:2000

PAPADIMITRIOU, Efthimios (1895-1958) Greek
£1600 $2864 €2336 Composition (40x50cm-16x20in) s.d.53 oil pastel paper on canvas. 11-May-4 Bonhams, New Bond Street #96/R est:600-800

PAPADOPOULOS, Epaminondas (1922-) Greek
£7000 $12530 €10220 Nu de Carina (93x72cm-37x28in) s. i. stretcher oil pastel exhib. 11-May-4 Bonhams, New Bond Street #95/R est:7000-9000
£7600 $13300 €11096 Figure avec fruit (131x97cm-52x38in) oil pastel painted c.1965 exhib. 16-Dec-3 Bonhams, New Bond Street #114/R est:6000-8000
£8000 $14320 €11680 Ballade de Villon (73x92cm-29x36in) s. exhib. 10-May-4 Sotheby's, Olympia #31/R est:8000-12000

PAPAGEORGIOU, Michail (1896-1987) Greek
£1000 $1750 €1460 At the horse races (70x50cm-28x20in) s. cardboard. 16-Dec-3 Bonhams, New Bond Street #89/R est:800-1200
£1000 $1790 €1460 Two friends (80x60cm-31x24in) s. 11-May-4 Bonhams, New Bond Street #45/R est:1000-1500

PAPALOUCAS, Spyros (1892-1957) Greek
£40000 $71600 €58400 Mountain village (34x28cm-13x11in) s. board. 10-May-4 Sotheby's, Olympia #26/R est:18000-25000

PAPALUCA, L (20th C) Italian
Works on paper
£3200 $5440 €4672 Sunbeam (43x67cm-17x26in) s.i. bodycol. 19-Nov-3 Christie's, Kensington #363/R

PAPALUCA, Louis (1890-1934) Italian
£801 $1450 €1169 Ship portrait of the Exeter (61x81cm-24x32in) s. 16-Apr-4 James Julia, Fairfield #689/R est:1500-2000
Works on paper
£780 $1303 €1139 The M Y Crusader (40x68cm-16x27in) s.i. gouache. 23-Oct-3 Honiton Galleries, Honiton #485/R
£1050 $1911 €1533 S.Y. Sapphire R.Y.S steaming in the Bay of Naples (38x69cm-15x27in) s.i. bodycol. 15-Jun-4 David Lay, Penzance #465/R est:500-700
£1500 $2505 €2190 Sayonara N.Y.Y.C, American cruiser in the Bay of Naples (41x62cm-16x24in) s.i. gouache pair. 21-Oct-3 Sworder & Son, Bishops Stortford #300/R est:1500-2000
£2000 $3700 €2920 Sy Albion R.T.Y.C, shop portrait off Naples in stormy seas (85x59cm-33x23in) s. gouache pair. 17-Jul-4 Bonhams, Knightsbridge #191/R est:2000-3000

PAPAPETROU, Polixeni (20th C) Australian
Photographs
£2066 $3512 €3016 Olympia and Alice dreaming by the riverbank (105x105cm-41x41in) s.verso type C photograph. 29-Oct-3 Lawson Menzies, Sydney #48/R est:2500-4000 (A.D 5000)
£2119 $3602 €3094 Flying cards (105x105cm-41x41in) s.i.d.2003 verso C-type photograph edn 4/6 prov. 24-Nov-3 Sotheby's, Melbourne #72/R est:2500-4000 (A.D 5000)

PAPART, Max (1911-1994) French
£267 $483 €400 La Sainte Victoire (54x75cm-21x30in) s. 30-Mar-4 Gioffredo, Nice #343
£417 $696 €600 Certaine solitude (22x17cm-9x7in) s. wood. 21-Oct-3 Artcurial Briest, Paris #325
£762 $1219 €1105 Still life of fruit (33x41cm-13x16in) s. s.d.53 verso. 15-May-3 Stuker, Bern #1436 (S.FR 1600)
£911 $1676 €1367 Coloured world mystery (80x80cm-31x31in) s. 14-Jun-4 Lilla Bukowskis, Stockholm #580 (S.KR 12500)
£1000 $1790 €1500 Definition sacrale (54x64cm-21x25in) s.d.59. 15-May-4 Van Ham, Cologne #820/R est:2000
£1100 $1947 €1606 Lady and roses (63x53cm-25x21in) s. s.d.1985-86 verso. 27-Apr-4 Bonhams, Knightsbridge #193/R est:800-1200
£1275 $2346 €1900 Composition (46x55cm-18x22in) s. painted c.1960. 24-Mar-4 Joron-Derem, Paris #195/R est:3000-4000
£1275 $2346 €1900 Alouette (61x50cm-24x20in) s. s.i.d.1973 verso. 24-Mar-4 Joron-Derem, Paris #196 est:3000-4000
£2400 $4392 €3504 Couple conjugal au bord de la Mer (80x80cm-31x31in) s. i.d.66 verso. 28-Jan-4 Dreweatt Neate, Newbury #110/R est:600-800
Sculpture
£1197 $2154 €1748 Humanite (38cm-15in) s.num.6/8 bronze Cast Guyot. 26-Apr-4 Bukowskis, Stockholm #287/R est:10000-12000 (S.KR 16500)
£5594 $9510 €8000 Homme (128cm-50in) s.num.I/IV bronze. 29-Nov-3 Bukowskis, Helsinki #311/R est:8000-10000
Works on paper
£278 $464 €400 Cirque II (31x50cm-12x20in) s.d.51 s.i.d.verso ink drawing ink wash. 21-Oct-3 Artcurial Briest, Paris #331
£282 $454 €400 Untitled (60x47cm-24x19in) s. collage. 11-May-3 Versailles Encheres #140
£312 $521 €450 Never fails (37x31cm-15x12in) s. collage. 21-Oct-3 Artcurial Briest, Paris #330
£462 $800 €675 Echiquer. s. s.i.d.1976 verso gouache collage prov. 10-Dec-3 Phillips, New York #411/R
£465 $800 €679 Espace IV (46x38cm-18x15in) s. s.i.verso mixed media collage prov. 7-Dec-3 Freeman, Philadelphia #57
£521 $869 €750 Jeune fille au plat bleu (38x49cm-15x19in) s.d.3.56 pastel lead pencil. 21-Oct-3 Artcurial Briest, Paris #334
£534 $960 €800 Composition (65x50cm-26x20in) s.d.1983 collage isorel. 26-Apr-4 Tajan, Paris #223
£594 $1010 €850 Jeune fille de profil (14x18cm-6x7in) s.d.69 mixed media collage. 20-Nov-3 Gioffredo, Nice #169
£724 $1332 €1100 Untitled (38x44cm-15x17in) s. mixed media collage. 27-Jun-4 Versailles Encheres #4
£833 $1392 €1200 Portrait d'homme avec noeud papillon (51x65cm-20x26in) s. collage. 25-Oct-3 Cornette de St.Cyr, Paris #776
£881 $1498 €1286 Abstract composition (65x54cm-26x21in) s.d.LX i. verso mixed media collage canvas. 5-Nov-3 Dobiaschofsky, Bern #853/R (S.FR 2000)
£940 $1729 €1400 Scotch (64x50cm-25x20in) s. d.1963 verso mixed media collage board. 24-Mar-4 Joron-Derem, Paris #197
£993 $1658 €1400 Composition (49x65cm-19x26in) s.d.60 mixed media collage. 15-Oct-3 Claude Aguttes, Neuilly #9
£1300 $2067 €1885 Sans titre (50x65cm-20x26in) s.i.d.11.58 chk collage. 11-Sep-3 Christie's, Kensington #178/R est:800-1200

PAPAS, John (1942-) New Zealander
£1028 $1820 €1501 Tell me of other cities other lands (121x80cm-48x31in) s.d.1990 oil earthenware. 28-Apr-4 Dunbar Sloane, Auckland #82/R (NZ.D 2900)
Works on paper
£308 $496 €450 Winter fruits (121x120cm-48x47in) s.d.1986 s.i.verso mixed media. 12-Aug-3 Peter Webb, Auckland #199 (NZ.D 850)

PAPAUSCHEK, Ignaz (1864-?) Austrian
£361 $650 €527 Ducks along a streambank (53x79cm-21x31in) s.d.1899. 23-Jan-4 Freeman, Philadelphia #148/R

PAPAZOFF, Georges (1894-1972) Bulgarian
£280 $476 €400 Exposition de maquettes et de costumes (80x100cm-31x39in) s. 23-Nov-3 Cornette de St.Cyr, Paris #250
£769 $1308 €1100 La tribu (27x35cm-11x14in) painted c.1928 prov. 23-Nov-3 Cornette de St.Cyr, Paris #248/R
£909 $1545 €1300 Poisson lune (31x43cm-12x17in) s. s.i.verso painted c.1950 prov. 23-Nov-3 Cornette de St.Cyr, Paris #252/R
£979 $1664 €1400 Paysage de Dordogne (27x35cm-11x14in) s. painted c.1930-35 prov. 23-Nov-3 Cornette de St.Cyr, Paris #249
£1200 $2196 €1800 Chiens de cirque (89x116cm-35x46in) d.1970 prov. 3-Jun-4 E & Eve, Paris #83/R est:1000-1200
£1316 $2421 €2000 Grands et petits poissons (33x46cm-13x18in) s. i.d.1962 verso. 28-Jun-4 Joron-Derem, Paris #145/R est:2300-2800
£1748 $2972 €2500 Formes se detachant de la terre (41x33cm-16x13in) s. painted c.1935-40 prov. 23-Nov-3 Cornette de St.Cyr, Paris #254/R est:600-800
£2308 $3923 €3300 Trois personnages a l'etoile filante (114x144cm-45x57in) s. 23-Nov-3 Cornette de St.Cyr, Paris #260/R est:800-1000
£2381 $4262 €3500 Composition (41x33cm-16x13in) s. 19-Mar-4 Millon & Associes, Paris #215/R est:4000-5000
£2667 $4853 €4000 Avions sur fond bleu (50x61cm-20x24in) s. 5-Jul-4 Le Mouel, Paris #47/R est:4500-6000
£3521 $6092 €5000 Signaux de la plage (73x92cm-29x36in) s. prov.exhib. 10-Dec-3 Rossini, Paris #100/R
£4755 $8084 €6800 Personnages magiques (27x41cm-11x16in) s. painted c.1927 prov. 23-Nov-3 Cornette de St.Cyr, Paris #253/R est:300-400
Works on paper
£315 $535 €450 L'atelier de l'artiste (13x14cm-5x6in) s. W/C prov. 23-Nov-3 Cornette de St.Cyr, Paris #265

£385 $654 €550 Eclatement (35x25cm-14x10in) s. gouache cardboard exec.c.1925 prov. 23-Nov-3 Cornette de St.Cyr, Paris #256

PAPE, Eduard (1817-1905) German
£1656 $3013 €2500 Coastal landscape with grazing cows and figures (84x126cm-33x50in) s. 18-Jun-4 Bolland & Marotz, Bremen #713/R est:3800

PAPE, Eric (1870-1938) American
£250 $425 €365 His home and studio (28x38cm-11x15in) estate st.verso board. 9-Nov-3 Outer Cape Auctions, Provincetown #31/R

PAPE, Frank Cheyne (1878-1972) American
Works on paper
£1100 $2013 €1606 James Branch Cabell's Jurgen, mediaeval fantasy world (25x18cm-10x7in) pen ink grey wash four. 7-Apr-4 Woolley & Wallis, Salisbury #160/R est:500-700

PAPE, Friedrich Eduard (1817-1905) German
£800 $1472 €1200 Mill in Canton Vaud, Switzerland (14x23cm-6x9in) s.insis.i. panel. 11-Jun-4 Wendl, Rudolstadt #4214/R

PAPE, Jean Constant (1865-1920) French
£364 $663 €550 Paysage champetre (46x61cm-18x24in) s. 20-Jun-4 Salle des ventes Pillet, Lyon la Foret #33/R

PAPELEN, Victor de (1810-1881) French
£1739 $2852 €2400 Paysage en ete a Aix-en-Provence (32x51cm-13x20in) s. panel painted c.1875. 11-May-3 Osenat, Fontainebleau #227 est:2800-3000

PAPENDRECHT, Jan Hoynck van (1858-1933) Dutch
Works on paper
£1413 $2600 €2063 Figures at leisure (20x20cm-8x8in) s. ink W/C five. 25-Jun-4 Freeman, Philadelphia #77/R est:1500-2500

PAPETTI, Alessandro (1958-) Italian
£1933 $3557 €2900 Untitled (60x60cm-24x24in) s.d.1989. 12-Jun-4 Meeting Art, Vercelli #244/R est:2500
£4295 $7689 €6400 Bay (75x54cm-30x21in) s. 30-May-4 Meeting Art, Vercelli #58 est:4000
£5034 $9312 €7500 Seated figure (100x50cm-39x20in) s.d.1985. 13-Mar-4 Meeting Art, Vercelli #521 est:5000
£5570 $10305 €8300 Interior with sofa (130x100cm-51x39in) s.d.1987. 13-Mar-4 Meeting Art, Vercelli #277 est:5000
£5986 $10475 €8500 Nude (95x130cm-37x51in) s. 16-Dec-3 Finarte Semenzato, Milan #227/R
£9333 $17173 €14000 Suspended figure (87x162cm-34x64in) s.d.2004 triptych. 12-Jun-4 Meeting Art, Vercelli #10000/R est:10000
Works on paper
£4667 $8587 €7000 Interior (140x100cm-55x39in) s.d.1993 mixed media card on canvas. 8-Jun-4 Finarte Semenzato, Milan #388/R est:7000-8000
£4762 $8524 €7000 Study interior (140x100cm-55x39in) s.d.91 mixed media card. 16-Mar-4 Finarte Semenzato, Milan #380/R est:6800-7000

PAPETY, Dominique Louis (1815-1849) French
Works on paper
£367 $664 €550 Bas-relief au guerrier Greç (32x18cm-13x7in) s. W/C exhib. 30-Mar-4 Rossini, Paris #828
£600 $1086 €900 Maternite, Rome (27x21cm-11x8in) s.i.d.1843 W/C. 30-Mar-4 Rossini, Paris #825/R

PAPETY, Dominique Louis (attrib) (1815-1849) French
£267 $483 €400 Etude de tete executee a Rome (46x38cm-18x15in) 30-Mar-4 Rossini, Paris #826
£400 $724 €600 Tete de femme de profil (16x15cm-6x6in) canvas on cardboard. 30-Mar-4 Rossini, Paris #827
Works on paper
£273 $497 €410 Jugurtha (35x25cm-14x10in) crayon. 5-Jul-4 Neret-Minet, Paris #26

PAPIALUK, Josie Pamiutu (1918-) North American
Works on paper
£475 $856 €713 Untitled (33x51cm-13x20in) felt tip dr. two. 26-Apr-4 Waddingtons, Toronto #471/R est:200-300 (C.D 1150)

PAPINI, Emilio (?) Italian
£496 $829 €700 View of Ponte Vecchio with Bardi Street (29x20cm-11x8in) s. tempera paper. 14-Oct-3 Finarte Semenzato, Milan #73/R

PAPP, Emile (20th C) Hungarian
£656 $1200 €958 Woman with flowers (81x61cm-32x24in) s. 5-Jun-4 Treadway Gallery, Cincinnati #555/R est:1500-2500

PAPPERITZ, Fritz Georg (1846-1918) German
£338 $595 €500 Standing nymph - female nude in water (47x62cm-19x24in) s. i. verso. 21-May-4 Mehlis, Plauen #15166/R
£2465 $4264 €3500 Venice, lute and song in Renaissance dress (40x30cm-16x12in) s. panel. 10-Dec-3 Christie's, Amsterdam #686/R est:4000-6000
£3057 $5563 €4463 Amazone (140x95cm-55x37in) s. 16-Jun-4 Fischer, Luzern #1225/R est:7500-8500 (S.FR 7000)

PAPSDORF, Frederick (1887-?) American
£245 $450 €358 Landscape with mushrooms (25x20cm-10x8in) s.d.1970 sold with dr. 26-Jun-4 Susanin's, Chicago #6030/R
£373 $600 €545 Pink asters (30x25cm-12x10in) s.d.1969. 22-Feb-3 Bunte, Elgin #1162

PAQUIER-SARRASIN, Joanny (1847-1909) French
Works on paper
£533 $960 €800 Jeunne femme, torse nu (50x35cm-20x14in) s. pastel. 20-Apr-4 Chenu & Scrive, Lyon #134/R

PAQUIN, Pauline (1952-) Canadian
£800 $1464 €1168 Au Mont-Tremblant (37x75cm-15x30in) s. acrylic. 1-Jun-4 Joyner Waddington, Toronto #256/R est:1500-2000 (C.D 2000)

PAQUOT, Maurice (20th C) French
£467 $835 €700 Bord de Seine (38x55cm-15x22in) 16-May-4 Osenat, Fontainebleau #98

PARACHINI, Achille (1888-1970) Italian
£333 $613 €500 Landscape (26x37cm-10x15in) s.d.1921. 14-Jun-4 Sant Agostino, Torino #145/R

PARADA FUSTEL, Ramon (1871-1902) Spanish
£12081 $22470 €18000 Boy on rocking horse (92x73cm-36x29in) s.d.1893. 2-Mar-4 Ansorena, Madrid #41/R est:3000

PARADIES, Herman Cornelis Adolf (1883-1966) Dutch
£474 $857 €720 View of Old Delft (80x60cm-31x24in) s. 19-Apr-4 Glerum, Amsterdam #154/R
Works on paper
£1067 $1909 €1600 View of old harbour with Lion Bridge of Rotterdam (38x49cm-15x19in) W/C. 11-May-4 Vendu Notarishuis, Rotterdam #65/R est:1500-2000
£1118 $2024 €1700 Canal of Schiedam, possibly (38x76cm-15x30in) s. W/C. 19-Apr-4 Glerum, Amsterdam #261/R est:1000-1200
£1467 $2625 €2200 Town scene with dray and many figures (49x69cm-19x27in) s. W/C. 11-May-4 Vendu Notarishuis, Rotterdam #81/R est:2000-2500
£1600 $2752 €2336 Amsterdam (48x66cm-19x26in) s. W/C. 4-Dec-3 Christie's, Kensington #196/R est:1500-2000

PARADISE, Philip Herschel (1905-1997) American
£275 $500 €402 Portrait of Johan Birnie (86x71cm-34x28in) s. prov. 15-Jun-4 John Moran, Pasadena #179
Works on paper
£5495 $10000 €8023 Horses in farm scene. Sailboats in channel (38x56cm-15x22in) s. W/C double-sided prov. 15-Jun-4 John Moran, Pasadena #132a est:2000-3000

PARANT, Jean Luc (20th C) French
£733 $1320 €1100 Rode oliphant (85x128cm-33x50in) s.d.1991 verso mixed media panel. 24-Apr-4 Cornette de St.Cyr, Paris #668/R

PARAVANO, Dino (1935-) South African
£328 $547 €479 Yellow roses (17x22cm-7x9in) s. canvas on board. 20-Oct-3 Stephan Welz, Johannesburg #909 est:1400-1800 (SA.R 3800)
£336 $608 €491 Cock fight (59x44cm-23x17in) s. i.verso board. 30-Mar-4 Stephan Welz, Johannesburg #495 est:3000-5000 (SA.R 4000)
£396 $709 €578 Cape cottage near a lake (49x75cm-19x30in) s. board. 31-May-4 Stephan Welz, Johannesburg #160 (SA.R 4800)
£462 $837 €675 Brown hooded kingfisher on a perch (50x39cm-20x15in) s.d.1974. 30-Mar-4 Stephan Welz, Johannesburg #240 est:2000-3000 (SA.R 5500)
£505 $929 €737 Still life of roses (45x59cm-18x23in) board. 8-Jun-4 Dales, Durban #3 (SA.R 6000)
£560 $936 €818 Still life of roses (50x34cm-20x13in) s. canvas on board. 20-Oct-3 Stephan Welz, Johannesburg #901 est:2000-3000 (SA.R 6500)
£619 $1109 €904 Street scene with Cape Dutch houses (60x44cm-24x17in) s. canvas on board. 31-May-4 Stephan Welz, Johannesburg #155 (SA.R 7500)
£619 $1109 €904 Noordhoek, Cape Province (50x75cm-20x30in) s. i.verso canvas on board. 31-May-4 Stephan Welz, Johannesburg #166 (SA.R 7500)
£630 $1141 €920 Yellow and red flowers (44x60cm-17x24in) s. board. 30-Mar-4 Stephan Welz, Johannesburg #260 est:2500-4000 (SA.R 7500)
£647 $1080 €945 Extensive landscape with cattle (50x75cm-20x30in) s. canvas on board. 20-Oct-3 Stephan Welz, Johannesburg #890 est:3000-5000 (SA.R 7500)
£726 $1235 €1060 Three proteas in a brass bowl (44x59cm-17x23in) s. canvas on board. 4-Nov-3 Stephan Welz, Johannesburg #709 est:2500-3000 (SA.R 8500)
£798 $1445 €1165 White roses (34x49cm-13x19in) s. i.verso board. 30-Mar-4 Stephan Welz, Johannesburg #261 est:2500-3500 (SA.R 9500)
£991 $1656 €1447 Going fishing, Vleesbaai (50x75cm-20x30in) s. canvas on board. 20-Oct-3 Stephan Welz, Johannesburg #892 est:3000-5000 (SA.R 11500)
£1008 $1825 €1472 Launching the trek boat, fish hoek (43x58cm-17x23in) s. i.verso board. 30-Mar-4 Stephan Welz, Johannesburg #183/R est:2500-4000 (SA.R 12000)
£1008 $1825 €1472 Fishermen at Buffels Bay, C Peninsula (45x60cm-18x24in) s. i.verso board. 30-Mar-4 Stephan Welz, Johannesburg #189 est:2000-3000 (SA.R 12000)
£1026 $1744 €1498 White roses in a stoneware jug (49x63cm-19x25in) s. board. 4-Nov-3 Stephan Welz, Johannesburg #710 est:2500-3500 (SA.R 12000)
£1429 $2586 €2086 Near East London (49x75cm-19x30in) s. i.verso board. 30-Mar-4 Stephan Welz, Johannesburg #480 est:3000-5000 (SA.R 17000)
Works on paper
£826 $1478 €1206 Fishermen (51x72cm-20x28in) s.d.80 pastel. 31-May-4 Stephan Welz, Johannesburg #252 (SA.R 10000)

PARAYRE, Henry Ernest (1883-?) French
Sculpture
£4196 $7133 €6000 Reclining female nude (27x34x14cm-11x13x6in) s. brown pat bronze. 19-Nov-3 Tajan, Paris #123/R est:5000-6000

PARC, Julio le (1928-) Argentinian
£1412 $2400 €2062 Modulation 739 (80x80cm-31x31in) s.verso. 25-Nov-3 Galeria y Remates, Montevideo #193/R
£1554 $2782 €2300 Untitled (40x50cm-16x20in) s. acrylic plexiglas. 4-May-4 Calmels Cohen, Paris #248/R est:2500-3000
£1620 $2689 €2300 Modulation 876 (46x33cm-18x13in) s. i.d.1986 verso acrylic. 11-Jun-3 Finarte Semenzato, Milan #574/R
£1959 $3449 €2900 Chemistry (33x46cm-13x18in) s.i.d.1988 verso acrylic. 22-May-4 Galleria Pananti, Florence #321/R est:3000-3200
£4667 $8587 €7000 Modulation (97x130cm-38x51in) s.i.d.1990 verso acrylic. 12-Jun-4 Meeting Art, Vercelli #128/R est:5000
Sculpture
£1103 $1986 €1600 Caisson cinetique (54x41x20cm-21x16x8in) illuminated crate four interchangeable boards exec. 1967 prov. 25-Jan-4 Cornette de St.Cyr, Paris #391/R est:300-400
£2308 $3854 €3300 Composition cinetique (120x120x12cm-47x47x5in) painted wood steel prov. 29-Jun-3 Versailles Encheres #200
Works on paper
£450 $850 €657 Composition (30x30cm-12x12in) s.d.1970 mixed media. 22-Feb-4 Galeria y Remates, Montevideo #20
£478 $860 €698 Untitled (41x41cm-16x16in) s.verso mixed media. 25-Apr-4 Subastas Odalys, Caracas #120
£489 $900 €714 Optical composition (30x30cm-12x12in) s.d.1970 verso mixed media. 22-Jun-4 Galeria y Remates, Montevideo #152/R

PARDI, Gian Franco (1933-) Italian
£403 $745 €600 Untitled (35x50cm-14x20in) s.i.verso painted 1989. 11-Mar-4 Galleria Pace, Milan #8
£497 $829 €720 Composition (68x58cm-27x23in) s.d.1986 exhib. 13-Nov-3 Galleria Pace, Milan #32/R
£600 $1104 €900 Mask (35x25cm-14x10in) s. cardboard prov. 10-Jun-4 Galleria Pace, Milan #55/R
£1333 $2453 €2000 Architecture (100x100cm-39x39in) s.i.d.93 oil wire. 8-Jun-4 Finarte Semenzato, Milan #208/R est:1800-2200
£1477 $2643 €2200 Architecture (102x50cm-40x20in) s. i.d.73 verso acrylic string steel prov. 25-May-4 Sotheby's, Milan #145/R est:1500

PARDI, Justin Anthony (1898-1951) American
£250 $400 €365 Bouquet of zinnias (61x51cm-24x20in) s. 20-Sep-3 Sloans & Kenyon, Bethesda #634/R

PARDINAS, Jose (19th C) Spanish
£1389 $2361 €2000 Immaculate (92x71cm-36x28in) s. after Murillo. 28-Oct-3 Segre, Madrid #69/R est:700

PARDO GALINDO, Victoriano (1918-) Spanish
£1241 $2234 €1800 Female nude (23x31cm-9x12in) s. board. 26-Jan-4 Ansorena, Madrid #243/R est:1800

PARDO, Jorge (1963-) German
£59880 $100000 €87425 Untitled (250x400cm-98x157in) acrylic painted 1999 prov.exhib.lit. 13-Nov-3 Phillips, New York #35/R est:30000-40000
Works on paper
£2275 $3800 €3322 Untitled 8 (91x60cm-36x24in) pantone on vellum executed 1998 prov. 14-Nov-3 Phillips, New York #220/R est:4000-6000
£2515 $4200 €3672 Untitled 5 (91x60cm-36x24in) pantone on vellum executed 1998 prov. 14-Nov-3 Phillips, New York #217/R est:4000-6000
£2515 $4200 €3672 Untitled 9 (91x60cm-36x24in) pantone on vellum executed 1998 prov. 14-Nov-3 Phillips, New York #221/R est:4000-6000
£2682 $4800 €3916 Untitled (129x54cm-51x21in) ink vellum prov. 14-May-4 Phillips, New York #334/R est:4000-6000

PARDO, Mercedes (1922-) South American
£3407 $5860 €4974 Stage 4 (130x130cm-51x51in) s. painted 1970. 7-Dec-3 Subastas Odalys, Caracas #177 est:6500
£6947 $11810 €10143 Measurable space (124x124cm-49x49in) s.verso. 23-Nov-3 Subastas Odalys, Caracas #100/R est:12500

PARDON, James (attrib) (fl.1800-1850) British
£6000 $10020 €8760 Portrait of Captain Adolphus Bayard of the 15th Hussars mounted on his charger (65x59cm-26x23in) 14-Oct-3 Sotheby's, London #492/R est:3000-4000

PAREDES, Vicenta de (1857-1903) Spanish
£1325 $2411 €2000 Scene galante (22x15cm-9x6in) s. panel. 18-Jun-4 Piasa, Paris #72/R est:2800-3000
£1678 $3121 €2500 Cardinal's visit (60x85cm-24x33in) s. board. 2-Mar-4 Ansorena, Madrid #36/R est:2500
£2246 $4178 €3279 In the library - gentlemen reading (35x27cm-14x11in) s. 2-Mar-4 Rasmussen, Copenhagen #1643/R est:25000 (D.KR 25000)
£6164 $10479 €9000 Courtly meeting (46x55cm-18x22in) s. 4-Nov-3 Ansorena, Madrid #145/R est:9000
£11000 $18920 €16060 Square near the Stock Exchange, Paris (46x38cm-18x15in) s.i. 3-Dec-3 Christie's, London #54/R est:12000-16000

PAREDES, Vicente Garcia de (1845-1903) Spanish
£2160 $3500 €3132 Reading a story (35x27cm-14x11in) s. 8-Aug-3 Barridorf, Portland #100/R est:4000-6000
£2536 $4159 €3500 Velada andaluza (64x81cm-25x32in) s. 27-May-3 Durán, Madrid #112/R est:3000
£3356 $6275 €5000 Andalucian dance (64x81cm-25x32in) s. 24-Feb-4 Durán, Madrid #208/R est:3250
£7000 $11900 €10220 Music room (32x53cm-13x21in) s. prov. 18-Nov-3 Sotheby's, London #266/R

PARELLE, Marc-Antoine (attrib) (fl.1766-1774) French
Works on paper
£822 $1397 €1200 Jeune palefrenier (41x31cm-16x12in) pierre noire stump. 5-Nov-3 Beaussant & Lefèvre, Paris #17

PARENT, Léon (1869-?) French
£1513 $2784 €2300 Pont Neuf a Paris (65x81cm-26x32in) s.d.1926. 28-Jun-4 Joron-Derem, Paris #167/R est:2500-3000

PARENT, Mimi (1925-) Canadian
Sculpture
£3061 $5480 €4500 Untitled (46x41x15cm-18x16x6in) s.d.98 various objects tissue in wooden box. 21-Mar-4 Calmels Cohen, Paris #87/R est:2000-3000

PARENT, Roger (1881-1963) French
£658 $1211 €1000 Grands nus dans un paysage (175x100cm-69x39in) s.d.1960 prov. 22-Jun-4 Palais de Beaux Arts, Brussels #295
£2128 $3553 €3000 Les baigneuses (80x100cm-31x39in) s. 17-Jun-3 Galerie Moderne, Brussels #351 est:2600-3600
£4667 $8587 €7000 Petite fille a la poupee (151x130cm-59x51in) s.d.1918 lit. 8-Jun-4 Artcurial Briest, Paris #177/R est:5000-7000
Works on paper
£319 $533 €450 Couple. s.d.1966 wash. 17-Jun-3 Galerie Moderne, Brussels #131/R

PAREROULTJA, Edwin (1918-1986) Australian
Works on paper
£285 $447 €413 Untitled - landscape (18x28cm-7x11in) s. W/C. 26-Aug-3 Lawson Menzies, Sydney #110 (A.D 700)
£703 $1195 €1026 Palm Valley with Initation stone (38x54cm-15x21in) s. W/C. 29-Oct-3 Lawson Menzies, Sydney #86/R est:800-1200 (A.D 1700)

PAREROULTJA, Otto (1914-1973) Australian
Works on paper
£351 $650 €512 Central Australian landscape (32x26cm-13x10in) s. W/C. 10-Mar-4 Deutscher-Menzies, Melbourne #575/R (A.D 850)
£687 $1250 €1003 Aranda Country (28x38cm-11x15in) s. W/C exhib. 16-Jun-4 Deutscher-Menzies, Melbourne #377/R est:2000-3000 (A.D 1800)
£687 $1250 €1003 Australian landscape (19x34cm-7x13in) s. W/C. 16-Jun-4 Deutscher-Menzies, Melbourne #384/R est:2000-3000 (A.D 1800)
£703 $1315 €1055 Untitled, Central Australian landscape (36x27cm-14x11in) indis.sig. W/C pencil exec.c.1960 prov. 26-Jul-4 Sotheby's, Melbourne #517/R (A.D 1800)
£728 $1325 €1063 Billabong reflections (36x53cm-14x21in) W/C. 1-Jul-4 Joel, Victoria #273/R (A.D 1900)
£785 $1452 €1146 Central Australian landscape (26x42cm-10x17in) s. W/C. 10-Mar-4 Deutscher-Menzies, Melbourne #574/R est:1200-1500 (A.D 1900)
£826 $1405 €1206 Central Australian landscape (26x36cm-10x14in) s. W/C. 29-Oct-3 Lawson Menzies, Sydney #87/R est:700-900 (A.D 2000)
£840 $1528 €1226 Symbolic rhythm - James Range (32x49cm-13x19in) s. W/C. 16-Jun-4 Deutscher-Menzies, Melbourne #378/R est:2000-3000 (A.D 2200)
£1412 $2527 €2062 Untitled (27x38cm-11x15in) s. i.verso W/C. 25-May-4 Lawson Menzies, Sydney #110/R est:1000-1500 (A.D 3600)
£1484 $2776 €2226 Untitled, Central Australian landscape (28x43cm-11x17in) s.d.3.8.61 verso W/C pencil board. 26-Jul-4 Sotheby's, Melbourne #518/R est:4000-6000 (A.D 3800)
£1758 $3287 €2637 Untitled, Central Australian landscape (36x54cm-14x21in) s. W/C exec.c.1956 prov. 26-Jul-4 Sotheby's, Melbourne #137/R est:7000-10000 (A.D 4500)
£8130 $12846 €11789 Central Australian landscape (53x71cm-21x28in) s. W/C exec.c.1956 prov. 28-Jul-3 Sotheby's, Paddington #320/R est:7000-10000 (A.D 20000)

PARESCE, Renato (1886-1937) Italian
£4000 $7360 €6000 Woman at window (45x29cm-18x11in) tempera paper on card painted 1933. 11-Jun-4 Farsetti, Prato #346/R est:5200-6200
£5797 $9507 €8000 Landscape (22x33cm-9x13in) s.d.1910 paper exhib.lit. 31-May-3 Farsetti, Prato #633/R est:5000-7000
£7112 $12731 €10384 Summer garden (59x72cm-23x28in) s.d.XXI. 12-May-4 Dobiaschofsky, Bern #852/R est:13000 (S.FR 16500)
£11888 $20210 €17000 Landscape (60x73cm-24x29in) s.d.29 prov. 25-Nov-3 Sotheby's, Milan #190/R est:15000-20000
£14765 $26430 €22000 Still life (21x35cm-8x14in) s.d.XVIII s.i.d.verso. 29-May-4 Farsetti, Prato #446/R est:12000-15000
£14978 $25463 €21868 Paesaggio marino (65x81cm-26x32in) s.d.31. 5-Nov-3 Dobiaschofsky, Bern #854/R est:22000 (S.FR 34000)
£27273 $46364 €39000 Landscape (60x71cm-24x28in) s.d.23 lit. 29-Nov-3 Farsetti, Prato #512/R est:25000-30000
£29530 $52859 €44000 Statue and stairs (91x65cm-36x26in) s.d.31 prov. 25-May-4 Sotheby's, Milan #239/R est:25000-35000
£35570 $63671 €53000 Still life (40x50cm-16x20in) painted 1921 lit. 29-May-4 Farsetti, Prato #498/R est:35000-45000
£55405 $97514 €82000 Window (65x81cm-26x32in) s.d.31. 24-May-4 Christie's, Milan #319/R est:40000-60000
Works on paper
£1333 $2453 €2000 Still life (22x33cm-9x13in) s.d.1922 pencil. 11-Jun-4 Farsetti, Prato #336/R est:1100-1400
£2133 $3925 €3200 Waiting (33x23cm-13x9in) Chinese ink exec.1932. 11-Jun-4 Farsetti, Prato #342/R est:3200-4200
£2133 $3925 €3200 View of garden (43x29cm-17x11in) s. W/C exec.1918. 11-Jun-4 Farsetti, Prato #341/R est:3200-4200
£2133 $3925 €3200 Still life (23x31cm-9x12in) s.d.XXV W/C paper on card. 11-Jun-4 Farsetti, Prato #340/R est:3200-4200
£2467 $4539 €3700 Still life (46x30cm-18x12in) W/C Chinese ink exec.1926. 11-Jun-4 Farsetti, Prato #339/R est:3200-4200

£6800	$11356	€9928	Visone metafisica (48x31cm-19x12in) s.d.32 gouache pencil htd white on card. 22-Oct-3 Bonhams, New Bond Street #53/R est:1500-2000
£7500	$12525	€10950	Landscape with shooting star (31x24cm-12x9in) s.d.33 gouache htd white on card sold with 9 other painting by sa. 22-Oct-3 Bonhams, New Bond Street #54/R est:1500-2000
£8000	$13360	€11680	Metaphysical interior (48x31cm-19x12in) gouache paper on card sold with 12 other by same hand. 22-Oct-3 Bonhams, New Bond Street #52/R est:1500-2000
£9000	$15030	€13140	Two figures within an interior, the sea beyond (31x24cm-12x9in) s.d.31 gouache on card sold with 9 other works by same hand. 22-Oct-3 Bonhams, New Bond Street #55/R est:1500-2000

PARET Y ALCAZAR, Luis (circle) (1746-1799) Spanish

£8333	$15000	€12166	Still life of fruit (64x51cm-25x20in) 22-Jan-4 Sotheby's, New York #244/R est:12000-15000

PARIGI, Giulio (1571-1635) Italian

Works on paper

£395	$726	€600	Head of young man (10x9cm-4x4in) pen ink W/C over pencil. 22-Jun-4 Sotheby's, Milan #2

PARIN, Gino (1876-1944) Italian

£769	$1323	€1100	Portrait of lady (53x40cm-21x16in) s. board. 3-Dec-3 Stadion, Trieste #1032/R
£1467	$2625	€2200	Model (27x21cm-11x8in) s. canvas on board. 12-May-4 Stadion, Trieste #783/R est:1500-2000
£2333	$4177	€3500	Launch (42x68cm-17x27in) s.d.1919 cardboard. 12-May-4 Stadion, Trieste #683/R est:3000-4000

Works on paper

£861	$1567	€1300	Posing (63x48cm-25x19in) s.d.1919 col chk. 18-Jun-4 Stadion, Trieste #119/R

PARIS, Camille Adrien (1834-1901) French

£1000	$1600	€1460	River landscape (50x65cm-20x26in) s. 18-Sep-3 Christie's, Kensington #21/R est:1200-1800

PARIS, Enrico T de (1960-) Italian

Works on paper

£420	$701	€600	In the light (40x30cm-16x12in) s.i.d.1997 verso mixed media on canvas. 26-Jun-3 Sant Agostino, Torino #316/R

PARIS, Harold (1925-1979) American

Sculpture

£1055	$1900	€1540	Untitled (25x38cm-10x15in) s. polychrome bronze wooden base. 25-Apr-4 Bonhams & Butterfields, San Francisco #5639/R est:1500-2500
£3248	$5750	€4742	Mem shields (23x27cm-9x11in) s.i. bronze 3 pieces wood base sold with another bronze sculpture. 2-May-4 Bonhams & Butterfields, Los Angeles #3047/R est:2000-3000

PARIS, Pierre-Adrien (attrib) (1745-1819) French

Works on paper

£240	$407	€350	Fontaine (21x15cm-8x6in) crayon. 6-Nov-3 Tajan, Paris #71
£816	$1461	€1200	Vue d'une villa Italienne en ruine (14x20cm-6x8in) black pencil. 19-Mar-4 Piasa, Paris #99

PARIS, Roland (1894-?) French

Sculpture

£1034	$1728	€1500	Mephisto (35cm-14in) s. bronze ivory. 14-Nov-3 Von Zezschwitz, Munich #808/R est:1100

PARISH, Thomas (1933-) American

£273	$500	€399	Coastal road west (196x117cm-77x46in) 10-Jul-4 Hindman, Chicago #393/R
£294	$500	€429	City limits (91x102cm-36x40in) s. prov. 9-Nov-3 Wright, Chicago #407

PARISOD, Charles (20th C) Swiss

£317	$538	€463	Extensive country landscape (33x24cm-13x9in) s. 28-Nov-3 Zofingen, Switzerland #3112 (S.FR 700)
£431	$772	€629	Landscape (36x67cm-14x26in) s. 13-May-4 Stuker, Bern #755 (S.FR 1000)
£455	$755	€660	Mountain vineyards by Lake Geneva (26x50cm-10x20in) s.d.1922. 13-Jun-3 Zofingen, Switzerland #2975 (S.FR 1000)

PARIZEAU, Philippe-Louis (attrib) (1740-1801) French

Works on paper

£284	$517	€415	Study of a seated figure, side angle and from the back (11x18cm-4x7in) red chk prov. 16-Jun-4 Fischer, Luzern #2538 (S.FR 650)

PARK SOO KEUN (1914-1965) Korean

Works on paper

£597826	$1100000	€872826	Seated woman and jar (65x53cm-26x21in) s. i.verso mixed media on canvas prov. 23-Mar-4 Christie's, Rockefeller NY #357/R est:400000-500000

PARK, David (1911-1960) American

Works on paper

£7595	$12000	€11089	Figure study (89x58cm-35x23in) s.d.1955 gouache W/C. 7-Sep-3 Treadway Gallery, Cincinnati #755/R est:10000-15000

PARK, H Morley (fl.1884-1895) British

£1900	$3230	€2774	Lowing herd winds slowly o'er there (61x91cm-24x36in) s. 19-Nov-3 Tennants, Leyburn #1111/R est:1200-1500

PARK, James Chalmers (1858-?) British

Works on paper

£360	$648	€526	Study of a terrier (35x27cm-14x11in) s. W/C prov. 21-Apr-4 Tennants, Leyburn #980

PARK, John Anthony (1880-1962) British

£320	$554	€467	Waves breaking against the Cornish coast (36x48cm-14x19in) s. board. 11-Dec-3 Lane, Penzance #206
£380	$703	€555	Figures beside cottages (15x23cm-6x9in) s.d.1915 board. 10-Feb-4 David Lay, Penzance #496
£480	$874	€701	Waves breaking on a Cornish beach (19x27cm-7x11in) s. canvasboard. 5-Feb-4 Mellors & Kirk, Nottingham #518
£520	$972	€759	Welsh mountain stream with bridge crossing to a mill (32x40cm-13x16in) s. panel. 26-Feb-4 Lane, Penzance #298
£750	$1365	€1095	St. Ives coast (51x61cm-20x24in) s. 15-Jun-4 David Lay, Penzance #334
£850	$1530	€1241	Shallow river (33x41cm-13x16in) s. board. 20-Jan-4 Bonhams, Knightsbridge #285/R
£1000	$1870	€1500	Silvery day, Porthmeor, St Ives (50x60cm-20x24in) s. i.verso plywood. 26-Jul-4 Bonhams, Bath #39/R est:1500-2000
£1200	$2064	€1752	St John's in the Field's, St Ives (32x41cm-13x16in) s. 3-Dec-3 Christie's, Kensington #473/R est:1500-2000
£1300	$2171	€1898	Harbour at Concarneau (38x46cm-15x18in) s. 16-Oct-3 Christie's, Kensington #394/R est:1500-2000
£1700	$3094	€2482	Red sails, Concarneau (20x25cm-8x10in) s. board. 15-Jun-4 David Lay, Penzance #340/R est:1500-1800
£1800	$3096	€2628	Yachts off the Cornish coast (32x41cm-13x16in) s. board. 3-Dec-3 Christie's, Kensington #471/R est:2000-3000
£1800	$3222	€2628	St Ives street scene (45x34cm-18x13in) s. board prov. 7-Jan-4 George Kidner, Lymington #200/R est:1500-2500
£1800	$3276	€2628	Down along St. Ives (33x41cm-13x16in) s. board. 15-Jun-4 David Lay, Penzance #342/R est:1800-2400
£2000	$3320	€2920	A corner of the harbour (33x40cm-13x16in) s. board. 2-Oct-3 Lane, Penzance #30/R est:2000-3000
£2200	$3498	€3212	Fish Street, St Ives (46x35cm-18x14in) s. panel. 10-Sep-3 Sotheby's, Olympia #204/R est:1000-1500
£2200	$4070	€3212	Continental harbour scene (47x59cm-19x23in) s. 11-Feb-4 Sotheby's, Olympia #123/R est:2500-3500
£2500	$4075	€3625	Brittany harbour (39x50cm-15x20in) s. 23-Sep-3 Bonhams, Leeds #175/R est:2500-3500
£2600	$4342	€3796	Little farm, St Ives (33x41cm-13x16in) s. s.i.verso board. 16-Oct-3 Christie's, Kensington #393/R est:2000-3000
£3000	$5610	€4380	Back lane St Ives (44x34cm-17x13in) s. board. 26-Feb-4 Lane, Penzance #90/R est:3000-3500
£3600	$6228	€5256	The harbour, St Ives (31x39cm-12x15in) s. board. 11-Dec-3 Lane, Penzance #70/R est:2500-3000
£4171	$6673	€6090	Harbour scene with beached boats and many figures (30x40cm-12x16in) s. 22-Sep-3 Rasmussen, Vejle #320/R est:15000-20000 (D.KR 44000)
£5500	$10175	€8030	Harbour, St. Ives (36x46cm-14x18in) s. board prov. 11-Mar-4 Christie's, Kensington #70/R est:4000-6000
£11413	$21000	€16663	Iron bridge, winter (119x124cm-47x49in) s. 27-Jun-4 Freeman, Philadelphia #56/R est:8000-12000

PARK, John Anthony (attrib) (1880-1962) British

£500	$910	€730	Hillside cottage (30x41cm-12x16in) board. 15-Jun-4 David Lay, Penzance #132
£2500	$4500	€3650	Venice (33x40cm-13x16in) bears sig. board. 21-Apr-4 John Bellman, Billingshurst #1762/R est:400-600

PARK, Stephen (1953-) British

£580	$1067	€847	Cheetah cubs (28x40cm-11x16in) s. board. 23-Jun-4 Cheffins, Cambridge #531/R

PARK, Stuart (1862-1933) British

£450	$824	€657	A cottage (25x34cm-10x13in) s. canvas on board. 29-Jan-4 Bonhams, Edinburgh #323
£500	$945	€730	Still life of roses (31x45cm-12x18in) s. 19-Feb-4 Lyon & Turnbull, Edinburgh #17
£900	$1548	€1314	Dead finch and books (18x30cm-7x12in) mono.d.86 prov. 4-Dec-3 Bonhams, Edinburgh #84
£1000	$1860	€1460	Red roses (29x60cm-11x24in) s. 4-Mar-4 Christie's, Kensington #191/R est:1000-1500
£1200	$2232	€1752	White and red roses (30x46cm-12x18in) s. 4-Mar-4 Christie's, Kensington #190/R est:1000-1500
£1500	$2415	€2175	Wild roses (39x39cm-15x15in) s. prov. 21-Aug-3 Bonhams, Edinburgh #1045/R est:1500-2500
£1500	$2835	€2190	Still life of red and white roses (56x46cm-22x18in) s. 19-Feb-4 Lyon & Turnbull, Edinburgh #124/R est:1000-1500
£1700	$2737	€2465	Pink rose (50x75cm-20x30in) s. oval. 21-Aug-3 Bonhams, Edinburgh #1141 est:1000-1500
£1700	$2890	€2482	Red and white roses (37x48cm-15x19in) s. 30-Oct-3 Christie's, London #132/R est:1000-1500
£1900	$3059	€2755	Pink roses (37x29cm-15x11in) s. 21-Aug-3 Bonhams, Edinburgh #1072/R est:1000-1500
£1900	$3173	€2774	Pink roses (60x50cm-24x20in) s. oval. 16-Oct-3 Bonhams, Edinburgh #149/R est:1500-2000
£2000	$3140	€2900	Red and yellow roses (63x38cm-25x15in) s. oval. 27-Aug-3 Sotheby's, London #1053/R est:2500-3000
£2400	$4008	€3504	Still life with flowers in a vase (51x41cm-20x16in) s.d.09. 16-Oct-3 Christie's, Kensington #369/R est:1200-1800
£2400	$4080	€3504	Pink roses (47x47cm-19x19in) s. 30-Oct-3 Christie's, London #158/R est:2000-3000

£2400 $4080 €3504 Still life with wild roses (31x38cm-12x15in) s. 26-Nov-3 Sotheby's, Olympia #40/R est:2000-3000
£2500 $3925 €3625 Still life of roses in a glass vase (61x76cm-24x30in) s. 27-Aug-3 Sotheby's, London #1051/R est:3000-4000
£2500 $4175 €3650 Pink roses (48cm-19in circular) s. 16-Oct-3 Bonhams, Edinburgh #152 est:1500-2000
£2700 $4941 €3942 Still life of pink roses (50x75cm-20x30in) s. canvas on board. 8-Apr-4 Bonhams, Edinburgh #106/R est:1000-1500
£2800 $4760 €4088 Still life of flowers (36x36cm-14x14in) s. 26-Nov-3 Sotheby's, Olympia #41/R est:2000-3000
£3692 $6351 €5390 Still life of roses (76x62cm-30x24in) s/. 2-Dec-3 Bukowskis, Stockholm #290/R est:25000-30000 (S.KR 48000)
£3800 $5966 €5510 Red and white roses (60x49cm-24x19in) s. prov. 27-Aug-3 Sotheby's, London #1048/R est:2500-3500
£4200 $6594 €6090 Pink roses (52x41cm-20x16in) s. oval. 27-Aug-3 Sotheby's, London #1049/R est:2500-3000
£8200 $13940 €11972 Dendrobium orchids (41x51cm-16x20in) s. 30-Oct-3 Christie's, London #133/R est:4000-6000
£15500 $26350 €22630 Yellow and pink roses (46x76cm-18x30in) mono.d.1888. 30-Oct-3 Christie's, London #131/R est:7000-10000
£19000 $30590 €27550 Roses (45x65cm-18x26in) mono.d.1889 prov. 21-Aug-3 Bonhams, Edinburgh #1195/R est:8000-12000
£26000 $47060 €37960 Yellow, pink and white roses (46x76cm-18x30in) mono. 19-Apr-4 Sotheby's, London #84/R est:22000-30000

PARK, Stuart (style) (1862-1933) British
£18000 $31680 €26280 Still life of flowers (44x74cm-17x29in) 18-May-4 Patersons, Paisley #534

PARKER, A G (20th C) New Zealander
£725 $1167 €1059 Castle Point race meeting (50x70cm-20x28in) s. board. 20-Aug-3 Peter Webb, Auckland #2061 (NZ.D 2000)

PARKER, Bill (1922-) American
£265 $482 €400 grisaille (61x50cm-24x20in) s.i.d.58 verso. 18-Jun-4 Charbonneaux, Paris #185
£298 $542 €450 Composition 71 (54x65cm-21x26in) mono.d.58. 18-Jun-4 Charbonneaux, Paris #184
£331 $603 €500 Nature morte 12 (61x46cm-24x18in) s.d.56. 18-Jun-4 Charbonneaux, Paris #186
£430 $783 €650 Composition 55 (60x73cm-24x29in) s.d.54. 18-Jun-4 Charbonneaux, Paris #183

PARKER, C (fl.1829) British
£3800 $6954 €5548 Trompe L'Oeil of sporting accessories (51x60cm-20x24in) 28-Jul-4 Bonhams, Knightsbridge #103/R

PARKER, Colin Ross (1941-) Australian
£262 $482 €383 Stormy distance (30x30cm-12x12in) s. board. 28-Jun-4 Australian Art Auctions, Sydney #11 (A.D 700)
£262 $482 €383 Queensland light (30x30cm-12x12in) s. board. 28-Jun-4 Australian Art Auctions, Sydney #145 (A.D 700)
£455 $841 €664 Sydney Harbour (35x44cm-14x17in) s. board. 10-Mar-4 Deutscher-Menzies, Melbourne #497/R est:1400-2200 (A.D 1100)
£488 $766 €708 Geologists camp, Birdsville Track country (118x126cm-46x50in) s. s.i.verso board prov.exhib. 27-Aug-3 Christie's, Sydney #737/R (A.D 1200)
£599 $1103 €875 Corner Hotel, Longreach (91x142cm-36x56in) s. board. 28-Jun-4 Australian Art Auctions, Sydney #111 (A.D 1600)
£1240 $2293 €1810 At Milparinka, Western NSW (88x118cm-35x46in) s. i.verso board. 10-Mar-4 Deutscher-Menzies, Melbourne #560/R est:2000-2600 (A.D 3000)

PARKER, Ed (20th C) American
£240 $400 €350 Garden angel (36x46cm-14x18in) s. acrylic on barnwood. 11-Oct-3 Nadeau, Windsor #67/R

PARKER, Erik (1968-) American
£4358 $7800 €6363 Too much pressur (91x61cm-36x24in) s.i.d.2002 overlap oil acrylic col pencil marker pen ink prov. 14-May-4 Phillips, New York #139/R est:8000-12000

PARKER, George Waller (1888-1957) American
£435 $800 €635 Stream in winter (58x71cm-23x28in) s. 25-Jun-4 Freeman, Philadelphia #156/R

PARKER, Henry H (1858-1930) British
£1105 $1900 €1613 Near Bisham, on Thames (30x43cm-12x17in) s. i.verso. 7-Dec-3 Hindman, Chicago #733/R est:2000-3000
£1300 $2301 €1898 Evening (27x35cm-11x14in) s. s.i.verso board. 27-Apr-4 Bonhams, Knowle #106 est:500-800
£1413 $2600 €2063 Cows by a river (25x64cm-10x25in) s. 27-Jun-4 Hindman, Chicago #788/R est:3000-5000
£1667 $3000 €2434 River Stort-Harlow (28x43cm-11x17in) s. s.i.verso. 26-Apr-4 Schrager Galleries, Milwaukee #1458/R
£1806 $2853 €2600 Cows by stream (112x86cm-44x34in) s. 19-Sep-3 Schloss Ahlden, Ahlden #1486/R est:2800
£2200 $3652 €3212 Haymaking (38x63cm-15x25in) s. 1-Oct-3 Sotheby's, Olympia #81/R est:2000-3000
£2200 $3938 €3212 Near Great Marlow on Thames (30x46cm-12x18in) s. s.i.verso. 26-May-4 Sotheby's, Olympia #129/R est:2000-3000
£2800 $4676 €4088 Chertsey on Thames (61x90cm-24x35in) s. canvas on board prov. 13-Nov-3 Christie's, Kensington #109/R est:3000-5000
£3000 $5520 €4380 At Hindhead, Surrey (30x45cm-12x18in) s. s.i.verso. 29-Mar-4 Bonhams, Bath #63/R est:2000-3000
£3200 $5920 €4672 Lledr river at Bettws-y-Coed, North Wales (51x76cm-20x30in) s. s.i.verso. 13-Jan-4 Bonhams, Knightsbridge #181/R est:3000-5000
£3226 $5935 €4710 On the banks of the Thames near Marlow (62x91cm-24x36in) s. s.i.verso. 14-Jun-4 Waddingtons, Toronto #158/R est:8000-12000 (C.D 8000)
£3300 $5247 €4785 Mole, Dorking, Surrey (51x76cm-20x30in) s. s.i.verso. 9-Sep-3 Bonhams, Knightsbridge #306/R est:3000-5000
£3400 $5780 €4964 Severn, Bridgnorth, Shropshire (43x33cm-17x13in) s. i.verso prov. 19-Nov-3 Tennants, Leyburn #1067/R est:1800-2200
£3400 $6188 €4964 Figures harvesting in a hillside field (25x33cm-10x13in) s. 20-Jun-4 Lawrences, Bletchingley #1407 est:3000-5000
£3500 $5950 €5110 Thames at Pangbourne (61x93cm-24x37in) s. s.verso. 25-Nov-3 Christie's, London #105/R est:4000-6000
£3500 $5950 €5110 Fishing party, with haymakers beyond (49x75cm-19x30in) s. 25-Nov-3 Christie's, London #107/R est:4000-6000
£3620 $6045 €5285 Cattle watering on a riverbank (39x59cm-15x23in) s. 17-Nov-3 Waddingtons, Toronto #121/R est:5000-6000 (C.D 8000)
£3779 $6500 €5517 Haymaking by the coast (51x76cm-20x30in) s. 7-Dec-3 Freeman, Philadelphia #42 est:4000-6000
£3800 $6992 €5548 Thames at Pangbourne (50x75cm-20x30in) s. i.verso. 29-Mar-4 Bonhams, Bath #69/R est:4000-6000
£3800 $6916 €5548 View of the Thames at Marlow with harvesters working in a field (23x30cm-9x12in) s. s.i.verso. 20-Jun-4 Lawrences, Bletchingley #1406 est:3000-5000
£4000 $7360 €5840 Pangbourne, Berkshire cattle watering by a footbridge (49x74cm-19x29in) s. 11-Jun-4 Christie's, London #175/R est:4000-6000
£5200 $8216 €7540 Figures and cattle resting on a river bank in a wooded valley (49x74cm-19x29in) s. 2-Sep-3 Bonhams, Oxford #72/R est:300-500
£5600 $9352 €8176 On the Lledr Valley (61x91cm-24x36in) s. 14-Oct-3 Bearnes, Exeter #357/R est:4000-6000
Works on paper
£500 $860 €730 Near Leith Hill, Surrey (36x54cm-14x21in) s. pencil W/C. 3-Dec-3 Christie's, Kensington #112/R
£500 $860 €730 River Wey near Ripley, Surrey (38x56cm-15x22in) s. 2-Dec-3 Peter Francis, Wales #65/R
£800 $1472 €1168 Haymaking (10x13cm-4x5in) s. W/C. 11-Jun-4 Keys, Aylsham #416/R

PARKER, Henry Perlee (1795-1873) British
£300 $549 €438 Portrait of a lawyer seated, holding a magnifying glass (41x34cm-16x13in) s. indis d.1870. 6-Jul-4 Bonhams, Knightsbridge #49/R
£320 $605 €467 Rest from studies (41x36cm-16x14in) s.i.d.18.0. 19-Feb-4 Christie's, Kensington #16/R
£12000 $21600 €17520 Hell's kitchen (19x48cm-7x19in) prov. 21-Apr-4 Cheffins, Cambridge #493/R est:10000-15000
Works on paper
£500 $895 €730 An oyster seller, street scene with figures (33x23cm-13x9in) s.d. W/C. 7-May-4 Christopher Matthews, Yorkshire #324

PARKER, Henry Perlee (attrib) (1795-1873) British
Works on paper
£270 $440 €394 Cullercoats morning: sketch from nature (25x34cm-10x13in) i.d.1833 W/C exhib. 23-Sep-3 Anderson & Garland, Newcastle #246

PARKER, John (?) New Zealander?
£1504 $2556 €2196 Lemon light (121x121cm-48x48in) s.d.2001. 26-Nov-3 Dunbar Sloane, Wellington #38/R est:6000-9000 (NZ.D 4000)
£2500 $4525 €3650 Plane song (182x120cm-72x47in) s.i.d.1990. 30-Mar-4 Peter Webb, Auckland #160/R est:8000-12000 (NZ.D 7000)
£3008 $5113 €4392 Plain song, Hymns to light, Dusk autumn (182x121cm-72x48in) s.d.1999. 26-Nov-3 Dunbar Sloane, Wellington #37/R est:8000-11000 (NZ.D 8000)
Works on paper
£450 $832 €657 River bend (26x35cm-10x14in) s.d.83 W/C. 10-Mar-4 Sotheby's, Olympia #73/R
£1800 $3330 €2628 Robn (32x40cm-13x16in) s.d.76 W/C. 10-Mar-4 Sotheby's, Olympia #168/R est:2000-3000

PARKER, John Adams (1827-1906) American
£5689 $9500 €8306 Mountain landscape (25x46cm-10x18in) mono. 23-Oct-3 Shannon's, Milford #93/R est:6000-8000

PARKER, Lawton S (1868-1954) American
£1589 $2750 €2320 Spring landscape, Santa Barbara (29x36cm-11x14in) s. i.verso canvasboard prov. 10-Dec-3 Bonhams & Butterfields, San Francisco #6233/R est:3000-5000
Works on paper
£269 $500 €393 Redhead (15x23cm-6x9in) W/C executed c.1900. 7-Mar-4 Treadway Gallery, Cincinnati #508/R
£316 $500 €461 Blanche (28x18cm-11x7in) W/C. 7-Sep-3 Treadway Gallery, Cincinnati #604/R
£348 $550 €508 Redhead (15x23cm-6x9in) W/C. 7-Sep-3 Treadway Gallery, Cincinnati #607/R
£647 $1100 €945 Reclining woman (36x46cm-14x18in) s. graphite. 18-Nov-3 John Moran, Pasadena #26

PARKER, Olivia (1941-) American
Photographs
£7784 $13000 €11365 Ephemera. s.i.d.num.2 gelatin silver print 10 folio clamshell box. 20-Oct-3 Christie's, Rockefeller NY #245/R est:6000-8000

PARKER, Ray (1922-1990) American
£933 $1717 €1400 Untitled (25x23cm-10x9in) s.i.d. verso acrylic. 11-Jun-4 Hauswedell & Nolte, Hamburg #1456/R

PARKER, Ron (1942-) Canadian
£455 $823 €664 Rhododendron (30x23cm-12x9in) s.d.1996 s.i.d.verso acrylic hard board prov. 18-Apr-4 Levis, Calgary #91/R est:1500-2000 (C.D 1100)
£2695 $4500 €3935 Grizzlies in the falls (61x122cm-24x48in) s.d. acrylic. 11-Oct-3 Nadeau, Windsor #107/R est:5000-8000

PARKER, William (1946-) Canadian
£331 $598 €483 Thunderhead and canola field (41x51cm-16x20in) s. s.i.d.2002 verso prov. 18-Apr-4 Levis, Calgary #92/R (C.D 800)
£901 $1532 €1315 Summer light (61x45cm-24x18in) s.i.d.Feb 8 1988 verso board. 27-Nov-3 Heffel, Vancouver #175/R est:1800-2200 (C.D 2000)

PARKHURST, Thomas (1853-1923) American
£2168 $3750 €3165 Opal Sea, Carmel, California (76x76cm-30x30in) s.d.1917 canvas on board. 10-Dec-3 Bonhams & Butterfields, San Francisco #6205/R est:3000-5000

PARKINSON, George Leighton (19th C) British?
£340 $541 €496 Courting couple, in 18th century dress, walking in a woodland of silver birch (28x24cm-11x9in) s.d.1885 verso. 9-Sep-3 Bamfords, Derby #1171/R

PARKINSON, Norman (1913-1990) British
Photographs
£2000 $3660 €2920 Le touquet, fashion study, Simpson's Suits (61x50cm-24x20in) s.i.d.1939 printed later platinum print edition 3/25 prov. 8-Jul-4 Sotheby's, London #471/R est:2000-3000
£2200 $4026 €3212 Fashion study, Jill Kennington (50x37cm-20x15in) silver print exec.c.1960. 8-Jul-4 Sotheby's, London #474/R est:1500-2000
£2200 $4026 €3212 Fashion study, Jean Patchett wearing a Jean Desses evening dress (60x56cm-24x22in) s.d.1950 printed later col print. 8-Jul-4 Sotheby's, London #477/R est:1000-1500
£5200 $8840 €7592 Apollonia von Ravenstein at the Crane Beach Hotel, Barbados (61x61cm-24x24in) s.verso col print exec.July 1973 lit. 19-Nov-3 Sotheby's, Olympia #197/R est:2000-3000
£12000 $20400 €17520 Jerry Hall, Russia (51x41cm-20x16in) s.d.75 i.d.verso col print pair. 19-Nov-3 Sotheby's, Olympia #198/R est:8000-12000

PARKMAN, Alfred Edward (1852-?) British
Works on paper
£280 $482 €409 Transcept looking N, York (43x25cm-17x10in) s.d.1918. 2-Dec-3 Peter Francis, Wales #61
£300 $552 €438 Artist's easel by a watermill (59x44cm-23x17in) s.d.1888 W/C. 14-Jun-4 Bonhams, Bath #112
£330 $591 €482 Oystermouth Church (26x44cm-10x17in) s.d.1920 W/C. 17-Mar-4 Anthemion, Cardiff #374
£550 $1012 €803 Pennard Castle (23x46cm-9x18in) s.d.1909 W/C. 8-Jun-4 Peter Francis, Wales #54
£550 $974 €803 Mumbles lighthouse near Swansea (23x46cm-9x18in) s.d.1910 W/C. 27-Apr-4 Peter Francis, Wales #42/R
£850 $1445 €1241 Worm's Head (43x61cm-17x24in) s.i.d.1917 W/C. 18-Nov-3 Sotheby's, Olympia #11/R
£1800 $3060 €2628 Pennard Castle (27x47cm-11x19in) s.d.1918 W/C set of 5. 18-Nov-3 Sotheby's, Olympia #25/R est:400-600

PARKMAN, Ernest (1856-1921) British
Works on paper
£360 $659 €526 Chepstow Arch, Chepstow, Monmouthshire (30x48cm-12x19in) s. W/C. 28-Jan-4 Wintertons, Lichfield #362

PARKS, Charles Cropper (1922-) American
Sculpture
£815 $1500 €1190 Seated man with book (76cm-30in) i.d.70 brown pat. bronze. 25-Jun-4 Freeman, Philadelphia #207/R est:2000-3000

PARKS, Eric Vernon (1948-) American
Sculpture
£815 $1500 €1190 Standing female nude (79cm-31in) s. num.2/5 brown pat. bronze incl. marble base. 25-Jun-4 Freeman, Philadelphia #206/R est:1000-1500

PARKS, Gordon (1912-) American
Photographs
£2515 $4200 €3672 Paris fashions, modelling evening gowns from the French collection (40x49cm-16x19in) gelatin silver print exec. 1949 prov.lit. 17-Oct-3 Phillips, New York #222/R est:3000-5000

PARMENTIER, Pol (20th C) Belgian
£268 $494 €400 Nature morte avec vase de jonquilles et mimosas (50x60cm-20x24in) mono. 23-Mar-4 Galerie Moderne, Brussels #220/R

PARMIGGIANI, Claudio (1943-) Italian
£6711 $12013 €10000 Composition for MOndrian (115x80cm-45x31in) s.d.1974 verso oil assemblage prov. 25-May-4 Sotheby's, Milan #283/R est:6000-8000
£42000 $70140 €61320 Tele filosofica. s.i.d.1977 verso gold leaf canvas white marble 4 prov.exhib.lit. 21-Oct-3 Christie's, London #68/R est:15000-20000
Photographs
£1905 $3410 €2800 Allocation (74x59cm-29x23in) s.d.1972 cibachrome. 16-Mar-4 Finarte Semenzato, Milan #200/R est:1200
Prints
£3020 $5406 €4500 Untitled (45x30cm-18x12in) s. s.i.d.1966 verso print prov. 25-May-4 Sotheby's, Milan #158a/R est:3000
Sculpture
£32168 $54685 €46000 Night (37x37x21cm-15x15x8in) s.d.64 verso plaster fabric oil wood exhib. 25-Nov-3 Sotheby's, Milan #241/R est:25000-30000
Works on paper
£1800 $3312 €2700 Men (67x47cm-26x19in) s. mixed media collage exec.1972. 8-Jun-4 Finarte Semenzato, Milan #453/R est:2000-2500

PARONE, Francesco (?-1634) Italian
Works on paper
£391 $700 €571 Entombment of Christ (36x33cm-14x13in) s. graphite chl. 20-Mar-4 Sloans & Kenyon, Bethesda #1147/R

PARPAN, Ferdinand (1902-) French
Sculpture
£3800 $6992 €5548 Le chat allonge (16x46cm-6x18in) mono.num.II/V bronze. 24-Jun-4 Sotheby's, Olympia #523/R est:1500-2000
£6936 $12000 €10127 Guitarist (97cm-38in) num.1/8 bronze st.f.Blanchet lit. 12-Dec-3 Sotheby's, New York #466/R est:4000-6000
£6936 $12000 €10127 Accordion player (76cm-30in) num.8/8 bronze st.f.Blanchet lit. 12-Dec-3 Sotheby's, New York #467/R est:4000-6000
£7514 $13000 €10970 Trumpeter (77cm-30in) num.7/8 bronze lit. 12-Dec-3 Sotheby's, New York #465/R est:4000-6000
£9827 $17000 €14347 Bear (32cm-13in) num.1/8 bronze st.f.Blanchet lit. 12-Dec-3 Sotheby's, New York #468/R est:5000-7000
£16185 $28000 €23630 Elephant (46cm-18in) s.d.num5/8 bronze st.f.Blanchet prov.lit. 13-Dec-3 Sotheby's, New York #629/R est:6000-8000

PARR (1893-1969) North American
Prints
£1667 $2833 €2434 Men and walrus (76x51cm-30x20in) num.20/50 stonecut. 3-Nov-3 Waddingtons, Toronto #269/R est:2000-3000 (C.D 3700)
£2546 $4328 €3717 My people (76x43cm-30x17in) num.23/50 stonecut. 3-Nov-3 Waddingtons, Toronto #284/R est:3000-5000 (C.D 5650)
Works on paper
£1441 $2450 €2104 Untitled (43x46cm-17x18in) pencil. 3-Nov-3 Waddingtons, Toronto #216/R est:2500-3000 (C.D 3200)
£1622 $2757 €2368 Untitled (46x61cm-18x24in) s. col crayon. 3-Nov-3 Waddingtons, Toronto #208/R est:2000-3000 (C.D 3600)
£1892 $3216 €2762 Untitled (48x46cm-19x18in) pencil. 3-Nov-3 Waddingtons, Toronto #212/R est:2000-3000 (C.D 4200)
£2008 $3735 €2932 Untitled (34x41cm-13x16in) sig.syllabics i.verso graphite prov. 2-Mar-4 Ritchie, Toronto #210/R est:2000-3000 (C.D 5000)

PARR, Frederick (fl.1880-1912) British
Works on paper
£310 $527 €453 Penzance from Newlyn (52x36cm-20x14in) s. W/C. 28-Oct-3 Bearnes, Exeter #738
£350 $595 €511 Harbour wall (24x34cm-9x13in) s. W/C. 28-Oct-3 Bearnes, Exeter #698

PARR, Mike (1945-) Australian
Works on paper
£620 $1054 €905 Untitled 1989 (112x71cm-44x28in) s. ink W/C. 29-Oct-3 Lawson Menzies, Sydney #150/R est:2500-3500 (A.D 1500)
£620 $1054 €905 Fissure (106x75cm-42x30in) s. pastel acrylic. 29-Oct-3 Lawson Menzies, Sydney #175/R est:2500-3500 (A.D 1500)

PARR, Nuna (1949-) North American
Sculpture
£1261 $2144 €1841 Joyful walrus with tusks (56cm-22in) marbled green soapstone. 3-Nov-3 Waddingtons, Toronto #107/R est:2500-3500 (C.D 2800)
£2027 $3446 €2959 Dancing bear (53x30x22cm-21x12x9in) s. green serpentine stone prov. 27-Nov-3 Heffel, Vancouver #140/R est:5000-7000 (C.D 4500)

PARR, Samuel (fl.1888-1890) British
£588 $1100 €858 Ashover Church yard (38x25cm-15x10in) s. board painted c.1902. 25-Feb-4 Dallas Auction Gallery, Dallas #127/R

PARRA, Gines (1895-1960) Spanish
£972 $1546 €1400 Woman (24x18cm-9x7in) s. panel. 29-Apr-3 Durán, Madrid #109/R
£1000 $1840 €1500 Seated female nude (22x16cm-9x6in) s. paper on board prov. 8-Jun-4 Sotheby's, Amsterdam #52/R est:2000-3000
£1133 $2063 €1700 Compotier aux figues et aux bananes (27x41cm-11x16in) s. d.1944 verso. 30-Jun-4 Delvaux, Paris #60 est:500-700
£1910 $3113 €2750 Maternity (46x38cm-18x15in) s. 23-Sep-3 Durán, Madrid #56/R
£2000 $3680 €3000 Figures (26x35cm-10x14in) s. board prov. 8-Jun-4 Sotheby's, Amsterdam #51/R est:2500-3500
£2055 $3493 €3000 Flowers (44x44cm-17x17in) s. board. 4-Nov-3 Ansorena, Madrid #939/R est:2800
£2300 $4209 €3358 Figures, perhaps angels, in a garden (64x79cm-25x31in) s.d.55 prov. 27-Jan-4 Holloways, Banbury #359 est:800-1200
£2303 $4237 €3500 Landscape (70x50cm-28x20in) s. 22-Jun-4 Durán, Madrid #659/R est:3500
£2414 $4345 €3500 Still life (31x40cm-12x16in) s. 26-Jan-4 Durán, Madrid #141/R est:2500
£2465 $4264 €3500 Urban landscape (37x29cm-15x11in) s. cardboard. 15-Dec-3 Ansorena, Madrid #304/R est:3500
£2847 $4698 €4100 Grey flowers (73x38cm-29x15in) s. cardboard. 2-Jul-3 Ansorena, Madrid #850/R
£2979 $4826 €4200 Landscape with trees (36x48cm-14x19in) s. board. 20-May-3 Ansorena, Madrid #311/R est:4200
£3448 $5724 €5000 The Seine, Paris (40x54cm-16x21in) s. canvas on cardboard. 30-Sep-3 Ansorena, Madrid #94/R est:4800
£3691 $6534 €5500 Townscape with river (48x61cm-19x24in) s. board. 27-Apr-4 Durán, Madrid #174/R est:5500
£3704 $6000 €5371 Untitled (55x47cm-22x19in) s. 8-Aug-3 Barridorf, Portland #38/R est:2000-3000
£4085 $7066 €5800 Town and river (46x61cm-18x24in) s. board. 15-Dec-3 Ansorena, Madrid #310/R est:5800

£4333	$7973	€6500	Ile de Noirmoutier,Vande (50x60cm-20x24in) s.d.48 s.i.d. verso board prov.lit. 8-Jun-4 Sotheby's, Amsterdam #49/R est:3500-4500
£5172	$8638	€7500	Still life with mandolin (81x61cm-32x24in) s. 17-Nov-3 Durán, Madrid #117/R est:7000
Works on paper			
£520	$921	€775	Woman (24x15cm-9x6in) s. ink dr. 27-Apr-4 Durán, Madrid #633/R
£552	$993	€800	Couple (18x25cm-7x10in) s. wax crayon. 26-Jan-4 Ansorena, Madrid #311/R
£590	$962	€850	Figure (30x30cm-12x12in) s. dr. 23-Sep-3 Durán, Madrid #32/R
£820	$1501	€1197	Naked figures (47x30cm-19x12in) s. chk pen ink grey wash prov. 27-Jan-4 Holloways, Banbury #323
£966	$1738	€1400	Woman (35x25cm-14x10in) s. mixed media. 26-Jan-4 Durán, Madrid #127/R
£1206	$2013	€1700	Head of woman (50x36cm-20x14in) s. mixed media card. 20-Oct-3 Durán, Madrid #188/R

PARRA, Jose Felipe (1824-?) Spanish

£685	$1164	€1000	Still life with fruit (30x41cm-12x16in) s. 4-Nov-3 Ansorena, Madrid #90/R
£738	$1321	€1100	Still life with peaches (35x54cm-14x21in) s. 25-May-4 Durán, Madrid #174/R
£940	$1682	€1400	Still life with pears (36x59cm-14x23in) s. 25-May-4 Durán, Madrid #175/R
£1103	$1832	€1600	Still life with turkey (130x73cm-51x29in) s. 30-Sep-3 Ansorena, Madrid #23/R est:1600

PARRA, Miguel (1784-1846) Spanish

£32895	$60526	€50000	Still lives with flowers (117x90cm-46x35in) s.d.1844 pair. 25-Jun-4 Piasa, Paris #42/R est:12000-15000

PARRA, Yobel (20th C) ?

£253	$400	€369	Table and objects (112x102cm-44x40in) s. painted 2002. 1-Dec-2 Subastas Odalys, Caracas #26
£261	$470	€381	Untitled (130x104cm-51x41in) s. acrylic painted 2003. 25-Apr-4 Subastas Odalys, Caracas #80/R
£272	$495	€408	Untitled (100x130cm-39x51in) s. painted 1999. 21-Jun-4 Subastas Odalys, Caracas #89
£272	$495	€408	Untitled (100x135cm-39x53in) s. acrylic painted 1998. 21-Jun-4 Subastas Odalys, Caracas #125
£272	$495	€408	Untitled (100x130cm-39x51in) s. acrylic painted 1998. 21-Jun-4 Subastas Odalys, Caracas #130
£273	$470	€399	Untitled (102x38cm-40x15in) s. painted 1998. 7-Dec-3 Subastas Odalys, Caracas #58
£275	$495	€402	Untitled (104x130cm-41x51in) s. acrylic painted 2003. 25-Apr-4 Subastas Odalys, Caracas #109
£276	$470	€403	Untitled (93x125cm-37x49in) painted 2002. 23-Nov-3 Subastas Odalys, Caracas #37
£282	$460	€412	Untitled (143x134cm-56x53in) s. painted 2002. 28-Sep-3 Subastas Odalys, Caracas #12/R
£283	$520	€413	Untitled (135x132cm-53x52in) s. acrylic painted 2003. 28-Mar-4 Subastas Odalys, Caracas #19
£299	$500	€437	Untitled (93x124cm-37x49in) s. painted 2002. 19-Oct-3 Subastas Odalys, Caracas #28/R
£313	$575	€470	Untitled (130x105cm-51x41in) s. acrylic painted 2003. 27-Jun-4 Subastas Odalys, Caracas #54/R
£320	$550	€467	Untitled (100x50cm-39x20in) s. painted 2002. 7-Dec-3 Subastas Odalys, Caracas #73/R
£326	$600	€489	Untitled (130x103cm-51x41in) s. acrylic painted 2002. 27-Jun-4 Subastas Odalys, Caracas #49
£333	$600	€486	Untitled (94x123cm-37x48in) s. painted 2002. 25-Apr-4 Subastas Odalys, Caracas #58
£335	$520	€489	Untitled (95x125cm-37x49in) s. 3-Nov-2 Subastas Odalys, Caracas #117
£340	$625	€496	Blue table (89x130cm-35x51in) s. acrylic painted 2001. 28-Mar-4 Subastas Odalys, Caracas #37/R
£340	$625	€510	Untitled (135x130cm-53x51in) s. acrylic painted 2003. 27-Jun-4 Subastas Odalys, Caracas #69/R
£340	$625	€510	Untitled (105x135cm-41x53in) s. acrylic painted 2003. 27-Jun-4 Subastas Odalys, Caracas #122/R
£343	$625	€515	Untitled (95x133cm-37x52in) s. acrylic painted 2002. 21-Jun-4 Subastas Odalys, Caracas #81
£353	$650	€515	Untitled (135x105cm-53x41in) s. acrylic painted 2003. 28-Mar-4 Subastas Odalys, Caracas #63
£363	$625	€530	Untitled (125x121cm-49x48in) s. painted 2003. 7-Dec-3 Subastas Odalys, Caracas #101/R
£374	$680	€561	Untitled (134x109cm-53x43in) s. acrylic painted 2003. 21-Jun-4 Subastas Odalys, Caracas #25/R
£381	$655	€556	Untitled (124x95cm-49x37in) s. painted 2002. 7-Dec-3 Subastas Odalys, Caracas #52
£381	$655	€556	Untitled (123x104cm-48x41in) s. painted 2002. 7-Dec-3 Subastas Odalys, Caracas #88/R
£387	$705	€581	Untitled (104x130cm-41x51in) s. painted 2003. 21-Jun-4 Subastas Odalys, Caracas #18/R
£394	$610	€575	Untitled (143x103cm-56x41in) s. painted 2002. 3-Nov-2 Subastas Odalys, Caracas #13/R
£419	$720	€612	Untitled (105x136cm-41x54in) s. painted 2003. 7-Dec-3 Subastas Odalys, Caracas #121/R
£419	$780	€612	Untitled (155x94cm-61x37in) s. painted 2002. 14-Mar-4 Subastas Odalys, Caracas #91/R
£459	$780	€670	Untitled (107x138cm-42x54in) painted 1998. 23-Nov-3 Subastas Odalys, Caracas #48/R
£564	$970	€823	Untitled (130x130cm-51x51in) s. painted 2003. 7-Dec-3 Subastas Odalys, Caracas #112/R
£624	$1060	€911	Untitled (102x138cm-40x54in) s. painted 1998. 23-Nov-3 Subastas Odalys, Caracas #74
£659	$1200	€989	Untitled (155x93cm-61x37in) s. acrylic painted 2002. 21-Jun-4 Subastas Odalys, Caracas #109/R
£784	$1310	€1145	Untitled (95x126cm-37x50in) s. painted 2003. 19-Oct-3 Subastas Odalys, Caracas #125/R
Works on paper			
£419	$780	€612	Yellow wood (94x122cm-37x48in) s. mixed media on canvas exec.2002. 14-Mar-4 Subastas Odalys, Caracas #107

PARRAMON, Luis (20th C) ?

£274	$466	€400	Venice (55x46cm-22x18in) s. s.verso. 4-Nov-3 Ansorena, Madrid #325/R

PARRATT, Denis (?) ?

Works on paper			
£260	$447	€380	Rainswept Road, Connemara (36x56cm-14x22in) W/C. 5-Dec-3 Chrystals Auctions, Isle of Man #299e

PARREIRAS (19/20th C) Brazilian?

£2747	$4863	€4121	Country scene with houses (33x55cm-13x22in) s.d.1912. 27-Apr-4 Bolsa de Arte, Rio de Janeiro #20/R (B.R 15000)

PARREIRAS, Antonio (1860-1937) Brazilian

£1832	$3242	€2748	View of Rio de Janeiro from Niteroi (15x38cm-6x15in) s.i.d.13 mar 1894. 27-Apr-4 Bolsa de Arte, Rio de Janeiro #6/R (B.R 10000)
£3663	$6484	€5495	Autumn landscape (46x65cm-18x26in) s.d.1910. 27-Apr-4 Bolsa de Arte, Rio de Janeiro #21/R (B.R 20000)

PARREIRAS, Edgard (20th C) Brazilian?

£1300	$2302	€1950	Landscape with a cottage (22x32cm-9x13in) s.d.1922 panel. 27-Apr-4 Bolsa de Arte, Rio de Janeiro #22/R (B.R 7100)

PARRES, Alberto (1953-) Italian

£302	$559	€450	Fundamental 2 (50x50cm-20x20in) s.d.2003 acrylic. 13-Mar-4 Meeting Art, Vercelli #372
£336	$621	€500	Italian night (60x75cm-24x30in) s.i.d.2003 acrylic. 13-Mar-4 Meeting Art, Vercelli #34
£352	$585	€500	Spirale Forte (40x50cm-16x20in) s.i.d.2001 acrylic. 14-Jun-3 Meeting Art, Vercelli #91/R
£528	$877	€750	Notturno Italiano (60x75cm-24x30in) s.i.d.2003 verso acrylic. 14-Jun-3 Meeting Art, Vercelli #295/R

PARRIS, Edmond Thomas (1793-1873) British

£900	$1530	€1314	On the road to the fishing lake (35x46cm-14x18in) s.d.1862 s.i.d.verso board. 18-Nov-3 Sotheby's, Olympia #179/R

PARRISH, Maxfield (1870-1966) American

£170455	$300000	€248864	Romance - Aucassin seeks for Nicolette (66x46cm-26x18in) s. i.verso paper over panel prov.lit. 19-May-4 Sotheby's, New York #174/R est:150000-250000
£204545	$360000	€298636	Autumn woods (91x56cm-36x22in) s.d.1927 i.verso panel prov. 19-May-4 Sotheby's, New York #175/R est:150000-250000
Works on paper			
£33520	$60000	€48939	Seated man eating bread (5x23cm-2x9in) init. pen ink chl lit. 15-May-4 Illustration House, New York #77/R est:20000-30000
£99432	$175000	€145171	Duchess - Apartments are beyond - said the old man (69x49cm-27x19in) init. gouache pencil illustration board prov.lit. 18-May-4 Christie's, Rockefeller NY #153/R est:40000-60000

PARRISH, Stephen (1846-1938) American

£726	$1300	€1060	Coastline (23x30cm-9x12in) s. board. 7-May-4 Sloans & Kenyon, Bethesda #1708/R

PARROCEL, Charles (1688-1752) French

£15278	$24903	€22000	Cavalry battle in evening light (105x160cm-41x63in) 25-Sep-3 Dr Fritz Nagel, Stuttgart #1222/R
Works on paper			
£2162	$3805	€3200	Cavalry battle (14x42cm-6x17in) bears i. brush brown ink grey wash prov.exhib.lit. 19-May-4 Sotheby's, Amsterdam #139/R est:2200-2800
£3288	$5589	€4800	Battle scenes (10x11cm-4x4in) one s. pen ink wash pair. 6-Nov-3 Tajan, Paris #23/R

PARROCEL, Charles (attrib) (1688-1752) French

Works on paper			
£420	$722	€600	Chasse aux lions (22x37cm-9x15in) crayon sanguine. 5-Dec-3 Gros & Delettrez, Paris #2
£497	$904	€750	Etude de jeune homme (37x26cm-15x10in) pierre noire htd white. 15-Jun-4 Artcurial Briest, Paris #227/R
£599	$1048	€850	Un cavalier portant un tricorne dans un paysage (20x16cm-8x6in) pen grey ink wash prov. 17-Dec-3 Christie's, Paris #51/R

PARROCEL, Charles (circle) (1688-1752) French

£5960	$10848	€9000	Prince Karl of Lothringen taking back the town from the Turks (120x170cm-47x67in) 16-Jun-4 Hugo Ruef, Munich #880/R est:2500

PARROCEL, Étienne (1696-1776) French

Works on paper			
£350	$606	€511	Studies of a hand holding a letter and holding a box (23x17cm-9x7in) col chk. 12-Dec-3 Christie's, Kensington #440
£397	$723	€600	Academie d'homme assis. Academie d'homme debout (33x46cm-13x18in) i. sanguine htd white chk double-sided. 16-Jun-4 Piasa, Paris #133
£3605	$6454	€5300	Etudes de mains. graphite sanguine five. 17-Mar-4 Maigret, Paris #81/R est:2500-3000

PARROCEL, Étienne (attrib) (1696-1776) French

£397	$723	€600	Vierge de l'Immaculee Conception entouree de saints (60x32cm-24x13in) 15-Jun-4 Claude Aguttes, Neuilly #8/R

Works on paper

£816	$1461	€1200	Saint Antoine en Priere. Etudes de mains (27x18cm-11x7in) blk crayon white chk beige paper double-sided. 17-Mar-4 Tajan, Paris #40/R

PARROCEL, Jacques Ignace (1667-1722) French

£12000	$21960	€17520	Battle scene with cavalry fleeing. Aftermath of battle (82x119cm-32x47in) i.d.1706 verso pair. 8-Jul-4 Sotheby's, London #295/R est:15000-20000
Works on paper			
£1530	$2800	€2234	Jupiter and Io (26x22cm-10x9in) i. black white chalk prov. 3-Jun-4 Christie's, Rockefeller NY #1291/R est:2000-3000
£2177	$3897	€3200	Une jeune femme assise, jouant du luth, une fille chantant (16x12cm-6x5in) s.d.1769 black chk pen brown ink double-sided. 18-Mar-4 Christie's, Paris #255/R est:600-800

PARROCEL, Jacques Ignace (attrib) (1667-1722) French

£1316	$2421	€2000	Conversion de Saint-Paul (64x80cm-25x31in) 25-Jun-4 Piasa, Paris #107/R est:2500-3000
Works on paper			
£884	$1583	€1300	La mort d'Abel (37x28cm-15x11in) graphite pen brown ink yellow wash. 17-Mar-4 Maigret, Paris #40/R

PARROCEL, Joseph (1646-1704) French

£3846	$6423	€5500	Battle scenes (32x47cm-13x19in) pair. 30-Jun-3 Ansorena, Madrid #365/R
£4027	$7410	€6000	Attaque de brigands dans un clairiere (46x64cm-18x25in) prov. 24-Mar-4 Tajan, Paris #109/R est:4000-6000
Works on paper			
£749	$1340	€1100	Scene de chasse a courre (9x16cm-4x6in) pen brown ink grey wash. 17-Mar-4 Tajan, Paris #36/R

PARROCEL, Joseph (attrib) (1646-1704) French

£3873	$6779	€5500	Scenes de chocs de cavalerie (31x59cm-12x23in) pair. 18-Dec-3 Tajan, Paris #37/R est:4000-6000

PARROCEL, Joseph François (1704-1781) French

Works on paper			
£530	$964	€800	Putto musicien (18x22cm-7x9in) black crayon white chk. 16-Jun-4 Piasa, Paris #124
£642	$1130	€950	Two seated women, one with her arm resting on a basket (26x32cm-10x13in) bears i.verso black white chk. 19-May-4 Sotheby's, Amsterdam #153/R

PARROT, Philippe (1831-1894) French

£600	$942	€870	Artist's model (66x36cm-26x14in) s. 28-Aug-3 Christie's, Kensington #254/R

PARROT, William Samuel (1844-1915) American

£579	$950	€845	Mt. Rainer (36x18cm-14x7in) board prov. 9-Jun-3 O'Gallerie, Oregon #873/R
£1630	$3000	€2380	Mt Hood at sunset (36x51cm-14x20in) painted c.1890 prov. 29-Mar-4 O'Gallerie, Oregon #778/R est:4000-6000

PARROTT, Samuel (1797-1876) British

£300	$549	€438	Warwick Castle with anglers and figures strolling by the river (53x89cm-21x35in) s.i.d.1851 canvas on board. 10-Jun-4 Neales, Nottingham #608

PARROTT, William (1813-1869) British

£4790	$8000	€6993	Mt. Hood at sunset (30x41cm-12x16in) s. 27-Oct-3 O'Gallerie, Oregon #740/R est:3000-5000

PARROW, Karin (1900-1986) Swedish

£665	$1191	€971	Lovers (65x55cm-26x22in) s. 28-May-4 Uppsala Auktionskammare, Uppsala #290/R (S.KR 9000)
£906	$1541	€1323	Horses in summer meadow (50x65cm-20x26in) s. 5-Nov-3 AB Stockholms Auktionsverk #872/R (S.KR 12000)
£906	$1541	€1323	Cliffs and sea (41x33cm-16x13in) s. 4-Nov-3 Bukowskis, Stockholm #31/R (S.KR 12000)
£906	$1632	€1359	Figure in landscape (58x69cm-23x27in) s. 25-Apr-4 Goteborg Auktionsverk, Sweden #347/R (S.KR 12500)
£1051	$1892	€1534	Music by the sea (83x64cm-33x25in) s. 26-Jan-4 Lilla Bukowskis, Stockholm #600 (S.KR 14000)
£1586	$2696	€2316	Fruit and vase (54x65cm-21x26in) s. 4-Nov-3 Bukowskis, Stockholm #28/R est:25000-30000 (S.KR 21000)
£1586	$2696	€2316	Towards the ocean (53x37cm-21x15in) s.d.1941. 4-Nov-3 Bukowskis, Stockholm #29/R est:12000-15000 (S.KR 21000)
£2417	$4109	€3529	View with fishing boat (51x65cm-20x26in) s. 5-Nov-3 AB Stockholms Auktionsverk #735/R est:20000-25000 (S.KR 32000)
£2719	$4622	€3970	By the window (69x67cm-27x26in) s. 4-Nov-3 Bukowskis, Stockholm #33/R est:30000-35000 (S.KR 36000)
£2946	$5008	€4301	Summer evening by the sea (54x65cm-21x26in) s. 4-Nov-3 Bukowskis, Stockholm #30/R est:25000-30000 (S.KR 39000)
£3172	$5393	€4631	Newspaper boys. Sketch of the sea (71x72cm-28x28in) init. double-sided. 4-Nov-3 Bukowskis, Stockholm #32/R est:40000-45000 (S.KR 42000)

PARRY, David (1942-) British

Works on paper			
£400	$732	€584	Otter in the snow (35x51cm-14x20in) s. W/C. 3-Jun-4 Lane, Penzance #86

PARRY, David H (fl.1891-1895) British

Works on paper			
£500	$835	€730	French curassiers (36x51cm-14x20in) s. W/C. 14-Oct-3 Bonhams, Knightsbridge #167/R

PARRY, David Henry (snr) and Joseph (19th C) British

£700	$1120	€1022	Portrait (23x18cm-9x7in) 19-May-3 Bruton Knowles, Cheltenham #239/R

PARRY, Ian (1947-) Australian

£284	$446	€415	Queenscliff (91x106cm-36x42in) s.d.95 i.d.June 1985 verso board prov. 27-Aug-3 Christie's, Sydney #607 (A.D 700)
£310	$573	€453	Point Lonsdale (122x122cm-48x48in) s.d.91 si.d.verso prov. 15-Mar-4 Sotheby's, Melbourne #185/R (A.D 750)

PARSHALL, Dewitt (1864-1956) American

£14550	$27500	€21243	Panoramic landscape - Lookout Rock, Yosemite (142x99cm-56x39in) s.d.1892 prov. 17-Feb-4 John Moran, Pasadena #95b/R est:20000-30000

PARSHALL, Douglas (1899-1990) American

£1359	$2500	€1984	Beach scene (30x40cm-12x16in) s. i.verso canvasboard prov. 8-Jun-4 Bonhams & Butterfields, San Francisco #4362/R est:2000-4000
£1879	$3250	€2743	Beach Scene no 2 (53x84cm-21x33in) s. i.stretcher. 10-Dec-3 Bonhams & Butterfields, San Francisco #6296/R est:3000-5000
Works on paper			
£543	$1000	€793	Young man with horses (36x53cm-14x21in) s. W/C. 13-Jun-4 Bonhams & Butterfields, Los Angeles #7035/R est:1500-2500

PARSON, Del (1948-) American

£1366	$2200	€1994	Indian women with child (61x76cm-24x30in) 22-Aug-3 Altermann Galleries, Santa Fe #47

PARSONS, Alfred William (1847-1920) British

£500	$800	€730	Fallen tree in a wooded river landscape beneath stormy skies (25x61cm-10x24in) s.d.1879. 16-Sep-3 Rosebery Fine Art, London #395/R
£650	$1105	€949	At the mouth of a cave (23x33cm-9x13in) s.d.1877 sold with a landscape by another hand. 6-Nov-3 Christie's, Kensington #792/R
£1500	$2400	€2190	Summer weather, Falmouth harbour (16x22cm-6x9in) s.d.95 i.verso. 16-Sep-3 Bonhams, New Bond Street #29/R est:1500-2000
Works on paper			
£360	$598	€526	A view in the Lake District (19x27cm-7x11in) s. W/C. 13-Jun-3 Jacobs & Hunt, Petersfield #200/R
£400	$668	€584	Garden landscape (24x36cm-9x14in) s. W/C. 14-Oct-3 Bonhams, Knightsbridge #181/R
£450	$819	€657	Old arbutus - Langland Bay in South Wales (26x36cm-10x14in) s. W/C. 21-Jun-4 Bonhams, Bath #344

PARSONS, Arthur Wilde (1854-1931) British

£340	$568	€496	Near Kings Norton (50x76cm-20x30in) s.d.95 i.on stretcher. 16-Oct-3 Lawrence, Crewkerne #737
£450	$833	€657	Figures on a beach (30x46cm-12x18in) s.d.1901. 10-Feb-4 David Lay, Penzance #112
£820	$1394	€1197	In the harbour, Newquay (40x60cm-16x24in) s.d.1914 i.verso. 1-Dec-3 Bonhams, Bath #131/R
£1050	$1922	€1533	Figures on a beach (30x46cm-12x18in) s.d.1901. 3-Jun-4 Lane, Penzance #319 est:1000-1200
£7500	$13425	€10950	Towing out the tramp (99x152cm-39x60in) s.d.1906. 26-May-4 Christie's, Kensington #720/R est:2000-3000
Works on paper			
£250	$425	€365	Guidecca, Venice (34x52cm-13x20in) s.d.1925 W/C over pencil. 4-Nov-3 Bristol Auction Rooms #564/R
£280	$476	€409	Beached paddle steamer and other shipping in an estuary (36x53cm-14x21in) s.d.1925 W/C bodycol. 30-Oct-3 Duke & Son, Dorchester #44/R
£340	$609	€496	Regency gothic country house (37x55cm-15x22in) s.d.92 W/C bodycol. 11-May-4 Dreweatt Neate, Newbury #449/R
£380	$600	€551	Lock keeper's rest (39x60cm-15x24in) s.d.94 W/C. 2-Sep-3 Bristol Auction Rooms #570/R
£400	$732	€584	Plymouth fishing boat, grey weather (25x38cm-10x15in) s.d.1908 W/C htd white. 8-Jul-4 Lawrence, Crewkerne #1530/R
£580	$1056	€847	Landscape with figures fishing beside a canal (50x76cm-20x30in) s.d.93 W/C. 17-Jun-4 Clevedon Sale Rooms #1026
£2500	$4550	€3650	Bristol Docks (50x75cm-20x30in) s.d.96 W/C. 21-Jun-4 Bonhams, Bath #454/R est:2000-3000

PARSONS, Beatrice (1870-1955) British

Works on paper			
£590	$1003	€850	Study of a marble statue Galatea with doves in the garden (35x24cm-14x9in) s. W/C. 28-Oct-3 Mealy's, Castlecomer #219/R
£598	$1100	€873	Cottage in spring (36x25cm-14x10in) s. W/C. 23-Mar-4 Arthur James, Florida #12/R est:1200-1600
£800	$1376	€1168	Mountains near Turin (18x25cm-7x10in) s. pencil W/C prov. 3-Dec-3 Christie's, Kensington #196/R
£840	$1512	€1226	Hillbrough Garden, Overstrad Hall (20x28cm-8x11in) s. W/C exec. 1924. 25-Jan-4 Desmond Judd, Cranbrook #1025
£1000	$1670	€1460	Mediterranean garden (25x17cm-10x7in) s. pencil W/C. 16-Oct-3 Christie's, Kensington #192/R est:1000-1500
£1000	$1850	€1460	Rose bower (28x22cm-11x9in) s. W/C. 9-Mar-4 Bonhams, New Bond Street #107/R est:1200-1800
£1250	$2163	€1825	Valley in Spring from a sunny road (30x24cm-12x9in) s. W/C. 9-Dec-3 Bonhams, Oxford #59/R est:600-900
£1250	$2088	€1825	Delphiniums in a Hertfordshire garden (38x28cm-15x11in) W/C. 22-Oct-3 Halls, Shrewsbury #10 est:600-800
£1300	$2379	€1898	Continental Garden (18x25cm-7x10in) s. W/C. 28-Jan-4 Dreweatt Neate, Newbury #32/R est:300-500
£1500	$2700	€2190	Foreign Office (25x35cm-10x14in) s.i. W/C. 21-Jan-4 Sotheby's, Olympia #234/R est:1500-2000
£1500	$2775	€2190	Climbing roses (17x25cm-7x10in) s. W/C. 14-Jul-4 Sotheby's, Olympia #129/R est:800-1200

£1650	$3003	€2409	Queen Mary's rose garden (22x30cm-9x12in) s. W/C. 29-Jun-4 Bonhams, Knowle #39 est:600-800
£1900	$3173	€2774	Ridge Lane, Watford (23x29cm-9x11in) s.i. pencil W/C. 16-Oct-3 Christie's, Kensington #187/R est:1500-2000
£2000	$3460	€2920	Lilies, the Water Garden, The Pleasance, Overstrand (14x18cm-6x7in) s. W/C. 11-Dec-3 Olivers, Sudbury #122/R est:1500-1800
£2000	$3660	€2920	Lady Hilborough's Garden, Overstrand Hall, Norfolk (22x28cm-9x11in) s. i.d.1924 verso pencil W/C htd bodycol. 3-Jun-4 Christie's, London #186/R est:1800-2500
£2200	$4070	€3212	Summer garden (29x22cm-11x9in) s. W/C. 9-Mar-4 Bonhams, New Bond Street #105/R est:2500-3000
£2200	$4048	€3212	Mediterranean garden (18x25cm-7x10in) pencil W/C. 25-Mar-4 Christie's, Kensington #112/R est:1500-2000
£2500	$4175	€3650	Apple orchard in full bloom (28x40cm-11x16in) s. W/C. 16-Oct-3 Christie's, Kensington #193/R est:2500-3500
£2600	$4810	€3796	Summer garden (24x28cm-9x11in) s. W/C sold with another W/C by the same hand. 14-Jul-4 Sotheby's, Olympia #130/R est:1000-1500
£2700	$5049	€3942	Rose garden, Buxted Rectory, Sussex (10x8cm-4x3in) s. W/C. 24-Feb-4 Canterbury Auctions, UK #199/R est:600-800
£2800	$5180	€4088	Rose arbour (29x22cm-11x9in) s. W/C. 9-Mar-4 Bonhams, New Bond Street #104/R est:3000-4000
£7000	$11900	€10220	London garden in August (33x46cm-13x18in) s. W/C htd white. 27-Nov-3 Sotheby's, London #408/R est:7000-10000

PARSONS, Betty (1900-1982) American

Sculpture			
£1222	$2200	€1784	Block house (18x7x10cm-7x3x4in) s.i. painted wood nails exec.c.1970. 24-Apr-4 David Rago, Lambertville #304/R est:400-800
Works on paper			
£353	$600	€515	Untitled - music box (13x13cm-5x5in) s. gouache crayon. 9-Nov-3 Wright, Chicago #346

PARSONS, Edith Baretto (1878-1956) American

Sculpture			
£5988	$10000	€8742	Frog baby (60cm-24in) s.st.f.Gorham green brown pat bronze lit. 9-Oct-3 Christie's, Rockefeller NY #37/R est:10000-15000
£9341	$17000	€13638	Frog baby (102cm-40in) s. weathered pat bronze. 20-Jun-4 Charlton Hall, Columbia #620/R est:15000-25000
£15988	$27500	€23342	Frog baby - fountain (100cm-39in) i. weathered brown pat. bronze. 3-Dec-3 Sotheby's, New York #39/R est:15000-25000
£24709	$42500	€36075	Duck baby (107cm-42in) i. weathered green pat. bronze. 3-Dec-3 Sotheby's, New York #38/R est:20000-30000

PARSONS, George W (?) British

£1500	$2580	€2190	Stapenhill on the Trent (79x117cm-31x46in) s. 5-Dec-3 Keys, Aylsham #663 est:1500-2000

PARSONS, John F (fl.1850-1898) British

£850	$1420	€1241	Guard dog (86x71cm-34x28in) s.d.88. 12-Nov-3 Sotheby's, Olympia #96/R

PARSONS, Margaret (?) American

£300	$468	€438	Eric, facial study of a young boy with fair curls and wearing a rufflette collar (31x24cm-12x9in) mono. 28-Mar-3 Bigwood, Stratford on Avon #413/R

PARSONS, Marion Randall (1878-1953) American

£1099	$2000	€1605	School house and grave yard (61x51cm-24x20in) init. board prov. 15-Jun-4 John Moran, Pasadena #143 est:2000-3000

PARSONS, Max (19/20th C) British?

£260	$432	€380	Clipper at full sail (46x55cm-18x22in) s. 1-Oct-3 Bonhams, Knightsbridge #136
£260	$434	€380	Ships at sea in full sail (51x61cm-20x24in) s. board. 28-Jun-3 Hogben, Folkstone #195
£265	$500	€387	Harbour with frigates (30x46cm-12x18in) s. panel. 21-Feb-4 Weschler, Washington #255

PARSONS, Orrin Sheldon (1866-1943) American

£1117	$2000	€1631	On the edge of the swamp (81x61cm-32x24in) s. i.stretcher. 26-May-4 Doyle, New York #68/R est:3000-5000
£8235	$14000	€12023	Adobes in panoramic southwest landscape (24x32cm-9x13in) s. wood panel prov. 18-Nov-3 John Moran, Pasadena #116b est:15000-20000

PARSONS, Sheldon (?) American?

£3529	$6000	€5152	Taos pueblo (41x51cm-16x20in) s. masonite panel prov. 1-Nov-3 Santa Fe Art, Santa Fe #198/R est:7000-12000
£4076	$7500	€5951	Mid afternoon shadows and a pueblo (40x50cm-16x20in) s. board. 8-Jun-4 Bonhams & Butterfields, San Francisco #4128/R est:3000-5000

PARTENHEIMER, Jurgen (1947-) German

£5667	$10370	€8500	Canto II (115x90cm-45x35in) mono.i.d.89.11 s.i.d. stretcher oil shellack graphite paper. 4-Jun-4 Lempertz, Koln #345/R est:8000
£7333	$13420	€11000	Tension (152x122cm-60x48in) mono. s.i.d.1990 stretcher oil shellack graphite paper. 4-Jun-4 Lempertz, Koln #346/R est:10000
Works on paper			
£400	$732	€600	Untitled - songs and other lies (18x14cm-7x6in) mono.d.96 gouache paper collage lit. 4-Jun-4 Lempertz, Koln #348/R
£699	$1189	€1000	Untitled - 90.53 (28x21cm-11x8in) mono.i.d.90 pencil Indian ink chl paper collage board. 27-Nov-3 Lempertz, Koln #324/R
£699	$1189	€1000	Untitled - 90.39 (28x21cm-11x8in) mono.i.d.90 mixed media pencil board. 27-Nov-3 Lempertz, Koln #325/R
£1000	$1830	€1500	Untitled (78x69cm-31x27in) mono.d.96 varnish plastic. 4-Jun-4 Lempertz, Koln #349/R est:1500
£1379	$2303	€2000	Amoitie (39x26cm-15x10in) mono.d.89 mixed media collage. 13-Nov-3 Neumeister, Munich #603/R est:1800-2000

PARTHENIS, Constantine (1878-1967) Greek

Works on paper			
£950	$1701	€1387	Landscape (27x38cm-11x15in) s.i. pen ink prov. 10-May-4 Sotheby's, Olympia #124/R
£1200	$2040	€1752	Sincerity (29x21cm-11x8in) s.i. ink pencil prov.exhib. 18-Nov-3 Sotheby's, London #101/R est:1200-1800
£1400	$2380	€2044	La nuit me regarde (23x21cm-9x8in) init.i. pen ink prov. 18-Nov-3 Sotheby's, London #100/R est:1000-1500
£2200	$3740	€3212	Angel. Orpheus. Woman with jug (17x18cm-7x7in) s.i. pen ink set of 3 prov. 18-Nov-3 Sotheby's, London #102/R est:1800-2000
£2400	$4080	€3504	Bather (45x29cm-18x11in) init. pencil chk prov. 18-Nov-3 Sotheby's, London #104/R est:1500-2000

PARTINGTON, John H E (1843-1899) British

£1109	$1984	€1619	Interior scene with man reading newspaper (67x51cm-26x20in) s. 25-May-4 Bukowskis, Stockholm #359/R est:20000-25000 (S.KR 15000)
Works on paper			
£550	$1012	€803	Young boy fishing by a pond, with houses beyond (30x46cm-12x18in) s.d.1877 W/C. 10-Jun-4 Morphets, Harrogate #539/R

PARTON, Arthur (1842-1914) American

£793	$1300	€1150	After the harvest (33x51cm-13x20in) s. 4-Jun-3 Alderfer's, Hatfield #268/R
£1372	$2250	€1989	Cows crossing stream (41x61cm-16x24in) s. 4-Jun-3 Alderfer's, Hatfield #267/R est:2000-4000
£1635	$2600	€2387	Ships in a harbour (28x24cm-11x9in) s.indis.i. 13-Sep-3 Weschler, Washington #760/R est:800-1200
£1887	$3000	€2755	Water edge (46x61cm-18x24in) s. 12-Sep-3 Skinner, Boston #267/R
£2654	$4750	€3875	Open landscape with running stream (56x71cm-22x28in) s. 14-May-4 Skinner, Boston #159/R est:4500-6500
£2973	$5500	€4341	Landscape (84x107cm-33x42in) 13-Feb-4 Du Mouchelle, Detroit #2108/R est:3000-4000
£3294	$5500	€4809	Apple blossoms (61x91cm-24x36in) s. prov. 23-Oct-3 Shannon's, Milford #234/R est:5000-7000
£4012	$6500	€5817	Spring brook and pasture, Arkville, new York (36x51cm-14x20in) s. board. 8-Aug-3 Barridorf, Portland #133/R est:6000-9000
£4670	$8500	€6818	Landscape with lake (59x91cm-23x36in) s. 29-Jun-4 Sotheby's, New York #219/R est:3000-5000
£5249	$9500	€7664	September morning in the Catskills (66x91cm-26x36in) s. 31-Mar-4 Sotheby's, New York #69/R est:7000-10000
£9259	$15000	€13426	On the banks of the Hudson River (51x91cm-20x36in) s. 8-Aug-3 Barridorf, Portland #66/R est:10000-15000

PARTON, Ernest (1845-1933) British

£280	$512	€409	Figure beside a river (22x34cm-9x13in) s. board. 9-Jul-4 Dreweatt Neate, Newbury #399/R
£420	$769	€613	Summer woodland landscape (25x35cm-10x14in) panel. 9-Jul-4 Dreweatt Neate, Newbury #396/R
£420	$769	€613	Water landscape with lake in the distance (23x30cm-9x12in) s. 9-Jul-4 Dreweatt Neate, Newbury #402/R
£757	$1400	€1105	Fall landscape. 18-Jan-4 Carlsen Gallery, Greenville #535/R
£815	$1500	€1190	Catskill stream (102x71cm-40x28in) s. 27-Jun-4 Freeman, Philadelphia #111/R est:4000-6000
£958	$1600	€1399	House beside a lake (15x27cm-6x11in) i.verso board. 26-Oct-3 Bonhams & Butterfields, San Francisco #6494/R
£1150	$2116	€1679	Backwater (58x80cm-23x31in) s. 29-Mar-4 Bonhams, Bath #74/R est:800-1200
£1384	$2200	€2021	Sunrise on a river (23x37cm-9x15in) s. board. 13-Sep-3 Weschler, Washington #754/R est:3000-4000
£2523	$3987	€3658	A pool on the Medway, Kent, England (109x143cm-43x56in) s. 2-Sep-3 Rasmussen, Copenhagen #1754/R est:15000 (D.KR 27000)
£4595	$8500	€6709	Landscape with pond and poplars (75x114cm-30x45in) s. canvas on board prov. 11-Mar-4 Christie's, Rockefeller NY #20/R est:10000-15000
£5294	$9000	€7729	Extensive landscape (107x142cm-42x56in) 29-Nov-3 Carlsen Gallery, Greenville #633/R
£7821	$14000	€11419	Field of wildflowers (10x14cm-4x6in) s. board. 6-May-4 Shannon's, Milford #93/R est:8000-12000
£8200	$13694	€11972	Pool on the Medway (137x213cm-54x84in) s. exhib. 7-Oct-3 Bonhams, Knightsbridge #287/R est:3000-5000

PARTOS, Paul (1943-) Australian

£1619	$2607	€2364	Untitled (71x56cm-28x22in) s.d.1987 verso oil graphite. 25-Aug-3 Sotheby's, Paddington #228/R est:400-6000 (A.D 4000)
£2893	$5351	€4224	Table painting V (51x46cm-20x18in) s.i.d.94 prov. 10-Mar-4 Deutscher-Menzies, Melbourne #266/R est:6500-8500 (A.D 7000)
£2979	$5064	€4349	Untitled (76x57cm-30x22in) s.d.79 oil W/C. 26-Nov-3 Deutscher-Menzies, Melbourne #76/R est:4000-5000 (A.D 7000)
£3435	$6252	€5015	Calendar painting (106x96cm-42x38in) s. i.d.1987 verso. 16-Jun-4 Deutscher-Menzies, Melbourne #7/R est:10000-15000 (A.D 9000)
Works on paper			
£1157	$2140	€1689	Untitled (39x29cm-15x11in) s. synthetic polymer paint on etching. 10-Mar-4 Deutscher-Menzies, Melbourne #140a/R est:1500-2000 (A.D 2800)

PARTRIDGE, Beatrice (1867-1963) New Zealander

£376	$639	€549	Otira Gorge landscape (64x76cm-25x30in) s. 27-Nov-3 International Art Centre, Auckland #163/R (NZ.D 1000)

PARTRIDGE, Bernard (1861-1945) British

Works on paper			
£300	$489	€438	Study of a golfer in mid-swing (24x19cm-9x7in) s.d.Sept 1820 pencil headed paper. 24-Sep-3 Dreweatt Neate, Newbury #52

PARTRIDGE, E (?) British

£1100	$1837	€1606	Children playing in rural surroundings (40x60cm-16x24in) pair. 11-Nov-3 John Taylors, Louth #380

PARTRIDGE, Edward (19/20th C) British
£360 $659 €526 Old farm buildings, near Meridan, Warwickshire (39x59cm-15x23in) s. i.verso. 8-Jul-4 Lawrence, Crewkerne #1650
£560 $1002 €818 Windermere. Lune scene (15x30cm-6x12in) s. pair. 13-May-4 Mitchells, Cockermouth #1011/R
£1100 $1749 €1595 On the Lledr, north Wales, with cattle crossing a bridge (34x49cm-13x19in) s.d.1878 pair. 12-Sep-3 ELR Auctions, Sheffield #311/R est:500-700

PARTRIDGE, Frederick Henry (?) British
Works on paper
£280 $515 €409 Brancaster Marsh (26x72cm-10x28in) s.i.d.1908 W/C. 14-Jun-4 Bonhams, Bath #136

PARTRIDGE, H T (19/20th C) British
£769 $1308 €1100 Chestnut hunter in a stable (46x61cm-18x24in) 18-Nov-3 Mealy's, Castlecomer #1035/R

PARTRIDGE, Henry T (19/20th C) British
£1678 $2853 €2400 Chestnut hunter in a stable, Goldsmith Maid. Horse in a stable (46x61cm-18x24in) s.d.94 pair. 18-Nov-3 Mealy's, Castlecomer #1036/R est:1200-1800

PARTRIDGE, John (1790-1872) British
£720 $1346 €1080 Robert Seymour Nash, a portrait (38x31cm-15x12in) i.d.1839 verso panel. 26-Jul-4 Bonhams, Bath #47/R

PARTURIER, Marcel (1901-1976) French
£263 $484 €400 Les baux (33x41cm-13x16in) d.1938 cardboard. 23-Jun-4 Maigret, Paris #111
£263 $484 €400 Dock a Anvers (19x24cm-7x9in) s. i.d.1932 verso panel. 23-Jun-4 Maigret, Paris #135
£263 $484 €400 Canal de Zubrugge (16x24cm-6x9in) s.d.1932 panel. 23-Jun-4 Maigret, Paris #157
£296 $545 €450 Saint Medard (32x41cm-13x16in) s. panel. 23-Jun-4 Maigret, Paris #124/R
£296 $545 €450 Etude en Tunisie (16x24cm-6x9in) d.1921 cardboard. 23-Jun-4 Maigret, Paris #142
£296 $545 €450 Port breton (19x24cm-7x9in) s.d.1925 panel. 23-Jun-4 Maigret, Paris #143
£315 $526 €450 Tunisie (24x33cm-9x13in) s. cardboard. 25-Jun-3 Maigret, Paris #95
£350 $601 €500 Le Loing a Nemours (46x55cm-18x22in) s. i.verso. 3-Dec-3 Beaussant & Lefèvre, Paris #71/R
£362 $666 €550 Bateaux docks a Anvers (19x24cm-7x9in) s. i.d.1932 verso panel. 23-Jun-4 Maigret, Paris #136
£362 $666 €550 La pointe du Raz (19x24cm-7x9in) s. i.verso panel exec. c.1968. 23-Jun-4 Maigret, Paris #147/R
£385 $642 €550 Les alpilles (27x35cm-11x14in) s. cardboard. 25-Jun-3 Maigret, Paris #93
£395 $726 €600 Voiliers au pont de Douarnenez (19x24cm-7x9in) s. i.verso panel exec. c.1930. 23-Jun-4 Maigret, Paris #140
£395 $726 €600 Anvers (19x24cm-7x9in) s. panel. 23-Jun-4 Maigret, Paris #148/R
£395 $726 €600 Tunisie (16x24cm-6x9in) d.1921 cardboard. 23-Jun-4 Maigret, Paris #155
£428 $787 €650 Aben Morgat (60x73cm-24x29in) s. 23-Jun-4 Maigret, Paris #116
£428 $787 €650 Tunisie (60x73cm-24x29in) s.1921 cardboard. 23-Jun-4 Maigret, Paris #117
£428 $787 €650 Tunisie (24x33cm-9x13in) d.1924 cardboard. 23-Jun-4 Maigret, Paris #121
£428 $787 €650 Thoniers a quai (19x24cm-7x9in) s. i.verso panel exec. c.1920. 23-Jun-4 Maigret, Paris #137
£428 $787 €650 Tunisie (24x33cm-9x13in) d.1924 cardboard. 23-Jun-4 Maigret, Paris #152/R
£434 $724 €620 Notre Dame de Paris (43x11cm-17x4in) s. cardboard. 25-Jun-3 Maigret, Paris #92/R
£461 $847 €700 Tunisie (24x33cm-9x13in) d.1924 panel. 23-Jun-4 Maigret, Paris #115
£461 $847 €700 Concarneau (22x27cm-9x11in) s.d.1936 panel. 23-Jun-4 Maigret, Paris #144
£493 $908 €750 Port de Douarnenez (19x27cm-7x11in) s.d.1925 panel. 23-Jun-4 Maigret, Paris #153
£526 $968 €800 Chemin dans les Alpilles (82x115cm-32x45in) s. 23-Jun-4 Maigret, Paris #150/R
£559 $1029 €850 Tunisie (16x24cm-6x9in) d.1921 cardboard. 23-Jun-4 Maigret, Paris #151/R
£573 $958 €820 Saint Paul de Vence (27x35cm-11x14in) s.d.1940 panel. 25-Jun-3 Maigret, Paris #91
£810 $1401 €1150 Nu allonge (46x31cm-18x12in) s. 10-Dec-3 Millon & Associes, Paris #81a
£1172 $2169 €1700 Bateaux sur la Somme (46x65cm-18x26in) s. s.i.verso. 11-Feb-4 Beaussant & Lefèvre, Paris #202/R est:700-900
£2013 $3604 €3000 Peniches (65x81cm-26x32in) s. 30-May-4 Eric Pillon, Calais #64/R
£2013 $3604 €3000 Voiliers sur le Zuiderzee (65x81cm-26x32in) s. i.verso. 30-May-4 Eric Pillon, Calais #63/R
£2042 $3533 €2900 Rhu a Douarnenez (46x55cm-18x22in) s. 14-Dec-3 Eric Pillon, Calais #192/R

PARYS, Louis van (?-1896) French
Works on paper
£1408 $2465 €2000 Elegants sur le pont (42x26cm-17x10in) s. W/C cardboard. 16-Dec-3 Claude Aguttes, Neuilly #94/R est:1000-2000

PARZINGER, Tommi (20th C) American
£1657 $3000 €2419 Do Ki instigates the blind hoedum to kill his silent brother Baldun no.97 (145x119cm-57x47in) 3-Apr-4 David Rago, Lambertville #186/R est:2500-3000

PARZINI, Luigi (1925-1998) Italian
£336 $601 €500 Grey shape over red (100x92cm-39x36in) s.d.61 verso prov. 25-May-4 Sotheby's, Milan #92/R

PASCAL (19th C) French
Sculpture
£3624 $6741 €5400 Three putti with grapevines (50x58cm-20x23in) s. ba. green marble base. 4-Mar-4 Auction Maastricht #151/R est:3000-4000

PASCAL, François Michel (1810-1882) French
Sculpture
£12000 $21720 €18000 Groupe representant les enfants d'Edouard (158cm-62in) s. white marble incl. wooden base exhib.lit. 31-Mar-4 Sotheby's, Paris #245/R est:18000-25000

PASCAL, P (20th C) French
£4545 $7727 €6500 Canal a Venise (48x63cm-19x25in) s. 28-Nov-3 Drouot Estimations, Paris #144/R est:2300-3000

PASCAL, P B (19th C) ?
Works on paper
£865 $1600 €1263 Nomads (46x66cm-18x26in) s.d.1900 gouache. 13-Mar-4 Susanin's, Chicago #6167/R est:800-1200

PASCAL, Paul (1832-1903) French
Works on paper
£349 $600 €510 Sunset landscape of Arabs on camels and on foot leading flock of sheep (38x56cm-15x22in) s. gouache board. 6-Dec-3 Pook & Pook, Downington #542
£426 $711 €600 Scene orientaliste (11x14cm-4x6in) s.d.1875 gouache. 15-Oct-3 Neret-Minet, Paris #6/R
£520 $900 €759 Arabs on camel in oasis desert at sunset (36x56cm-14x22in) s.d.1901 gouache board. 13-Dec-3 Sloans & Kenyon, Bethesda #530/R
£534 $976 €800 Scene de campement (20x28cm-8x11in) s.d.1888 gouache. 3-Jun-4 Tajan, Paris #303
£556 $1000 €812 North African coastline with fishermen at dawn (19x27cm-7x11in) s.d.1879 W/C bodycol. 22-Jan-4 Christie's, Rockefeller NY #243/R
£775 $1340 €1100 Campement de bedouins au soleil couchant (26x38cm-10x15in) s.d.1881 W/C gouache. 10-Dec-3 Piasa, Paris #130 est:1000
£878 $1572 €1300 L'arrivee a l'oasis (21x28cm-8x11in) s.d.1888 gouache. 10-May-4 Horta, Bruxelles #504
£979 $1684 €1400 Halte des chameliers en Egypte (41x28cm-16x11in) s. W/C. 5-Dec-3 Chochon-Barre & Allardi, Paris #135/R
£1319 $2400 €1926 Encampment along the Nile (30x43cm-12x17in) s.d.1901 gouache board. 19-Jun-4 Jackson's, Cedar Falls #65/R est:750-1000
£2083 $3479 €3000 Danse du ventre (32x44cm-13x17in) s. gouache. 25-Oct-3 Dianous, Marseille #399
£2450 $4484 €3700 Vue d'une ile et le village (7x11cm-3x4in) s. W/C pair. 9-Apr-4 Claude Aguttes, Neuilly #124/R est:1200-1500

PASCAL, Paul (attrib) (1832-1903) French
Works on paper
£237 $425 €346 Bedouins herding sheep in the desert (20x43cm-8x17in) gouache. 7-May-4 Sloans & Kenyon, Bethesda #1104/R

PASCALI, Pino (1935-1968) Italian
£1739 $2852 €2400 Totem (25x15cm-10x6in) board painted 1965. 27-May-3 Sotheby's, Milan #111/R est:3000-4000
£2899 $4754 €4000 Letters (26x34cm-10x13in) oil mixed media board painted 1962. 27-May-3 Sotheby's, Milan #113/R est:3500-4000
£11189 $19021 €16000 Ship (71x79cm-28x31in) s.d.64 board. 24-Nov-3 Christie's, Milan #186/R est:20000-30000
Sculpture
£480000 $801600 €700800 Quattro trofei di caccia (340x166x75cm-134x65x30in) canvas plywood four pieces prov.exhib.lit. 21-Oct-3 Christie's, London #51/R est:350000-550000
£1400000 $2338000 €2044000 Cannone semovente (251x340x246cm-99x134x97in) wood scrap metal wheels prov.exhib.lit. 21-Oct-3 Christie's, London #52/R est:500000-700000
Works on paper
£533 $981 €800 Rude (20x26cm-8x10in) graphite exec.1964. 12-Jun-4 Meeting Art, Vercelli #431/R
£563 $1025 €850 Killer (21x28cm-8x11in) mixed media cardboard. 17-Jun-4 Galleria Pananti, Florence #435/R
£629 $1145 €950 Indian (22x14cm-9x6in) mixed media exec.1963. 17-Jun-4 Galleria Pananti, Florence #26/R
£1067 $1920 €1600 Totem (34x23cm-13x9in) ink tempera prov. 22-Apr-4 Finarte Semenzato, Rome #99/R est:1600-1800
£1156 $2070 €1700 Tristan and Isotta (24x34cm-9x13in) s.d.1960 mixed media collage. 16-Mar-4 Finarte Semenzato, Milan #398/R est:2200
£1156 $2070 €1700 Explosion (23x33cm-9x13in) s.d.1959 Chinese ink W/C. 16-Mar-4 Finarte Semenzato, Milan #399/R est:2200
£1208 $2162 €1800 Autumn (25x33cm-10x13in) mixed media over photograph on card exec.1965. 25-May-4 Sotheby's, Milan #188/R est:2200
£1389 $2194 €2000 Hawaii women (22x28cm-9x11in) graphite. 6-Sep-3 Meeting Art, Vercelli #292 est:2000
£1486 $2616 €2200 Notes (26x38cm-10x15in) pen pencil ink pastel exec.1964. 24-May-4 Christie's, Milan #63/R est:2500-3500
£1622 $2854 €2400 Cossak (25x35cm-10x14in) ink pastel collage paper on card exec.1963. 24-May-4 Christie's, Milan #61/R est:1800-2500
£1678 $3003 €2500 Warriors (31x25cm-12x10in) mixed media card exec.1964. 25-May-4 Sotheby's, Milan #187/R est:2500
£1818 $3091 €2600 Notes (28x22cm-11x9in) pastel col pencil pen ink. 25-Nov-3 Sotheby's, Milan #59/R est:2000-3000
£2027 $3568 €3000 Parrot (34x25cm-13x10in) mixed media exec.1963. 22-May-4 Galleria Pananti, Florence #375/R est:3200-3500
£2448 $4161 €3500 An hour with Saul Steinberg (18x28cm-7x11in) mixed media exhib. 24-Nov-3 Christie's, Milan #41/R est:2200-3000
£9790 $16643 €14000 New York (26x69cm-10x27in) mixed media collage card. 25-Nov-3 Sotheby's, Milan #58/R est:5000-6000

PASCAREL, Charles (20th C) French?
£486 $812 €700 Present (129x97cm-51x38in) s.d.10/84 i.verso acrylic. 21-Oct-3 Artcurial Briest, Paris #669

PASCH, Johan (elder) (1706-1769) Swedish
£6652 $11907 €9712 Composition with bird and jug (105x131cm-41x52in) or possibly style of overdoor prov.lit. 25-May-4 Bukowskis, Stockholm #413/R est:90000-100000 (S.KR 90000)

PASCH, Lorens (elder-attrib) (1702-1776) Swedish
£1152 $1878 €1682 Portrait of lady wearing light grey outfit (57x46cm-22x18in) 29-Sep-3 Lilla Bukowskis, Stockholm #35 est:18000-20000 (S.KR 15000)

PASCH, Lorens (younger) (1733-1805) Swedish
£1996 $3572 €2914 Portrait of gentleman wearing Swedish costume (66x52cm-26x20in) 25-May-4 Bukowskis, Stockholm #411/R est:20000-25000 (S.KR 27000)
£14231 $24477 €20777 Portrait of King Gustav Vasa dressed in black (98x77cm-39x30in) prov.lit. 3-Dec-3 AB Stockholms Auktionsverk #2349/R est:80000-100000 (S.KR 185000)

PASCH, Lorens (younger-attrib) (1733-1805) Swedish
£4231 $7277 €6177 Portrait of a noble lady (67x53cm-26x21in) oval exhib. 3-Dec-3 AB Stockholms Auktionsverk #2347/R est:35000-40000 (S.KR 55000)

PASCH, Ulrika (1735-1796) Swedish
£1700 $3043 €2482 Portrait of young man (64x50cm-25x20in) s.d.1776. 26-May-4 AB Stockholms Auktionsverk #2259/R est:18000-20000 (S.KR 23000)
£2769 $4763 €4043 Crown Prince Gustaf III (20x15cm-8x6in) s. panel. 2-Dec-3 Bukowskis, Stockholm #309/R est:15000-20000 (S.KR 36000)
£3400 $6086 €4964 Jonas Ekengren and his wife Christina (52x42cm-20x17in) pair lit. 25-May-4 Bukowskis, Stockholm #412/R est:40000-50000 (S.KR 46000)
£11826 $21168 €17266 Portrait of Gabriel Thimothaeus Lutkeman (56x45cm-22x18in) s. prov. 28-May-4 Uppsala Auktionskammare, Uppsala #74/R est:40000-50000 (S.KR 160000)

PASCHEN, Peter (1873-?) German
£569 $894 €820 Warnemund ship (49x59cm-19x23in) s. s.i.d.1912 verso board. 30-Aug-3 Hans Stahl, Toestorf #59/R

PASCHETTA, Mario (1949-) Italian
£268 $497 €400 Seascape (30x30cm-12x12in) s.i.verso oil pigment. 13-Mar-4 Meeting Art, Vercelli #232
£333 $613 €500 Valdichiana (100x50cm-39x20in) s.i.d.2001 verso. 12-Jun-4 Meeting Art, Vercelli #306/R
£342 $633 €510 Tuscany landscape (30x30cm-12x12in) s.i.verso oil pigment painted 2002. 13-Mar-4 Meeting Art, Vercelli #532
£367 $675 €550 Tuscany composition (48x54cm-19x21in) s.i.d.2000 verso oil pigment canvas on board. 12-Jun-4 Meeting Art, Vercelli #560/R
£367 $675 €550 Black and red landscape (40x30cm-16x12in) s. oil pigment painted 2002. 12-Jun-4 Meeting Art, Vercelli #731
£367 $675 €550 Landscape (54x44cm-21x17in) s.i.d.2000 verso oil pigment. 12-Jun-4 Meeting Art, Vercelli #872
£369 $683 €550 Night scene (50x50cm-20x20in) s.i.d.1999 verso oil pigment. 13-Mar-4 Meeting Art, Vercelli #545
£387 $643 €550 Sun and Sea (90x50cm-35x20in) s.i.d.1999 verso oil enamel earth canvas. 14-Jun-3 Meeting Art, Vercelli #506
£436 $807 €650 Landscape in Siena (60x40cm-24x16in) s.i.d.2000 verso oil pigment. 13-Mar-4 Meeting Art, Vercelli #254
£500 $920 €750 Lido degli Scacchi, Italy (72x92cm-28x36in) s.i.verso oil pigment in 15 parts. 12-Jun-4 Meeting Art, Vercelli #692/R
£503 $931 €750 North Sea (60x120cm-24x47in) s.i.verso oil pigment. 13-Mar-4 Meeting Art, Vercelli #273
£528 $877 €750 Apuane, I Blocchi (100x90cm-39x35in) s.i.d.2000 verso oil enamel earth. 14-Jun-3 Meeting Art, Vercelli #620/R
£563 $935 €800 Lavanda (120x50cm-47x20in) s.i.d.1999 verso oil mortar earth. 14-Jun-3 Meeting Art, Vercelli #129/R
£599 $994 €850 Sun (120x70cm-47x28in) s.i.verso oil enamel earth canvas. 14-Jun-3 Meeting Art, Vercelli #460/R
£1342 $2483 €2000 Mediterranean beach (80x120cm-31x47in) s.i.verso oil pigment painted 2002. 13-Mar-4 Meeting Art, Vercelli #484 est:1000
Works on paper
£1310 $2188 €1900 Storm in Val di Chiana (80x80cm-31x31in) i.d.2000 verso pigment earth exhib.lit. 14-Nov-3 Farsetti, Prato #99/R est:1800-2200

PASCHINGER, Anton (19th C) Austrian
£6993 $11888 €10000 Still life of flowers (79x63cm-31x25in) s.d.55. 24-Nov-3 Dorotheum, Vienna #65/R est:12000-15000

PASCHKE, Ed (1939-) American
£4088 $6500 €5968 Two faces of Robin (71x56cm-28x22in) s.verso. 14-Sep-3 Susanin's, Chicago #6126/R est:8000-10000
£6286 $11000 €9178 Playboy's 40th Anniversary Logo (53x39cm-21x15in) s. a. shaped foamcore on linen exec 1993 exhib. 17-Dec-3 Christie's, Rockefeller NY #297/R est:4000-6000
£7558 $13000 €11035 Blue hats (97x152cm-38x60in) painted c.1976. 7-Dec-3 Treadway Gallery, Cincinnati #635/R est:15000-20000
£13408 $24000 €19576 Jacke-O (203x254cm-80x100in) s.d.85 acrylic prov. 13-May-4 Sotheby's, New York #477/R est:20000-30000
£16000 $28000 €23360 Saint Gloria and the Troll (102x56cm-40x22in) each s.d.74 acrylic four separate panels exhib.lit. 17-Dec-3 Christie's, Rockefeller NY #205/R est:20000-30000
Works on paper
£857 $1500 €1251 White House (74x52cm-29x20in) paper mylar collage over col pencils ink on board exec 1971. 17-Dec-3 Christie's, Rockefeller NY #221/R est:2000-3000
£2171 $3800 €3170 Queen Dido (60x30cm-24x12in) chl pastel exec May 1962. 17-Dec-3 Christie's, Rockefeller NY #167/R est:2000-3000

PASCHKE, Willibald (1888-?) Polish
£417 $696 €600 Castle by lake (70x60cm-28x24in) s. 25-Oct-3 Dr Lehr, Berlin #385/R

PASCIN (1885-1930) American/Bulgarian
Works on paper
£296 $545 €450 Femme nu assise (28x18cm-11x7in) s. studio st. lead pencil. 28-Jun-4 Joron-Derem, Paris #78
£369 $653 €550 Nu assis et etude de nu. Femmes causant (23x18cm-9x7in) st.sig. lead pencil htd. ink double-sided. 27-Apr-4 Artcurial Briest, Paris #110
£634 $1096 €900 Promeneuses en Afrique du Nord (20x31cm-8x12in) ink crayon. 14-Dec-3 St-Germain-en-Laye Encheres #73/R
£694 $1159 €1000 Deux femmes (42x35cm-17x14in) st.sig. ink drawing. 21-Oct-3 Artcurial Briest, Paris #281/R
£694 $1159 €1000 Portrait de femme (20x16cm-8x6in) st.sig. studio st. ink drawing. 21-Oct-3 Artcurial Briest, Paris #284/R
£694 $1159 €1000 Paysage, maisons et charette (17x21cm-7x8in) st.sig. lead pencil. 21-Oct-3 Artcurial Briest, Paris #290/R
£764 $1276 €1100 Table tournante (25x33cm-10x13in) st.sig studio st. ink lead pencil. 21-Oct-3 Artcurial Briest, Paris #282

PASCIN, Jules (1885-1930) American/Bulgarian
£3067 $5000 €4478 Venus et cupidon (21x30cm-8x12in) st.sig. oil paper on canvas lit. 25-Sep-3 Christie's, Rockefeller NY #509/R est:5000-7000
£10056 $18000 €14682 Femme assise (63x55cm-25x22in) s. oil pencil board prov. 6-May-4 Sotheby's, New York #447a/R est:20000-30000
£12000 $22080 €17520 Rite Barber (107x77cm-42x30in) indis.s.i.d.1923 prov.exhib.lit. 22-Jun-4 Sotheby's, London #284/R est:15000-20000
£14525 $26000 €21207 Personages a Cuba (65x54cm-26x21in) s. painted 1917 prov.lit. 5-May-4 Christie's, Rockefeller NY #285/R est:30000-40000
£22346 $40000 €32625 Nu a la tenture (53x63cm-21x25in) s. painted 1914 prov.lit. 5-May-4 Christie's, Rockefeller NY #281/R est:50000-70000
£23000 $42320 €33580 Jeune femme endormie (61x46cm-24x18in) s. 24-Mar-4 Sotheby's, Olympia #57/R est:25000-35000
£25000 $45500 €36500 Portrait d'Hermine David. Portrait de jeune fille (65x50cm-26x20in) double-sided. 3-Feb-4 Christie's, London #257/R est:25000-35000
£25140 $45000 €36704 Hermine enrose. Personnages Cubains (76x89cm-30x35in) st.sig.i.d.1918 double-sided prov.lit. 6-May-4 Sotheby's, New York #462/R est:50000-70000
£27933 $50000 €40782 Nu aux bras derriere la tete (56x51cm-22x20in) i.d.1920 verso lit. 18-Mar-4 Sotheby's, New York #95/R est:50000-70000
£30882 $52500 €45088 Fillette assise dans un fauteuil (81x65cm-32x26in) s. painted 1925 prov.lit. 6-Nov-3 Sotheby's, New York #340/R est:40000-70000
£33520 $60000 €48939 Hermine David (65x54cm-26x21in) s. i.d.1917 verso prov.lit. 18-Mar-4 Sotheby's, New York #94/R est:50000-70000
Works on paper
£267 $477 €400 Nu feminin (27x20cm-11x8in) s.d.1908 crayon. 17-May-4 Chayette & Cheval, Paris #106
£268 $494 €400 Femme au chapeau (17x11cm-7x4in) st.sig. lead pencil. 24-Mar-4 Joron-Derem, Paris #40
£280 $501 €420 Nu feminin assis (27x20cm-11x8in) s. crayon. 17-May-4 Chayette & Cheval, Paris #107
£296 $545 €450 Couple (16x20cm-6x8in) s. studio st. lead pencil. 28-Jun-4 Joron-Derem, Paris #81
£296 $545 €450 Pose (26x21cm-10x8in) s. studio st. lead pencil exec 1921 prov. 28-Jun-4 Joron-Derem, Paris #86
£298 $545 €450 Passant et femmes dans la rue (32x23cm-13x9in) s. bears studio st. pen W/C. 7-Apr-4 Piasa, Paris #203
£298 $545 €450 Two women (31x25cm-12x10in) s. bears studio st. pen W/C. 7-Apr-4 Piasa, Paris #204
£298 $545 €450 Modele agenouille (27x17cm-11x7in) bears st.sig. studio st. blk crayon. 7-Apr-4 Piasa, Paris #205
£302 $559 €450 Femme au tabouret (30x35cm-12x14in) st.sig. pen Indian ink. 15-Mar-4 Blanchet, Paris #113
£302 $556 €450 Pudique (30x23cm-12x9in) st.sig. lead pencil. 24-Mar-4 Joron-Derem, Paris #38
£303 $557 €460 Jeune homme (26x20cm-10x8in) s. studio st. wax crayon prov. 28-Jun-4 Joron-Derem, Paris #85
£320 $573 €480 Joueur de tambour (42x26cm-17x10in) studio st. chl. 17-May-4 Chayette & Cheval, Paris #109
£323 $600 €472 L'artiste et modele (31x23cm-12x9in) brush ink. 2-Mar-4 Swann Galleries, New York #479/R
£326 $600 €476 Seated female nude (30x23cm-12x9in) st.sig. ink graphite. 25-Jun-4 Freeman, Philadelphia #13/R
£329 $605 €500 Nu assis (32x20cm-13x8in) s. studio st. lead pencil. 28-Jun-4 Joron-Derem, Paris #83
£336 $628 €500 Nu (30x16cm-12x6in) s. pencil. 29-Feb-4 Versailles Encheres #174
£336 $628 €500 Deux femmes (25x19cm-10x7in) s. pencil. 29-Feb-4 Versailles Encheres #176
£336 $628 €500 Femme nue (28x16cm-11x6in) s. pencil. 29-Feb-4 Versailles Encheres #177
£336 $621 €500 Quatre personnages (12x19cm-5x7in) st.sig. graphite. 15-Mar-4 Blanchet, Paris #114
£350 $601 €500 Two girls (18x14cm-7x6in) i. on stretcher W/C pen oval. 5-Dec-3 Bolland & Marotz, Bremen #747/R
£362 $666 €550 Etude de nu allonge (19x25cm-7x10in) s. studio st. lead pencil double-sided. 28-Jun-4 Joron-Derem, Paris #82
£369 $687 €550 La fuite, Paris (31x31cm-12x12in) st.sig.i.d.1927 ink estompe. 2-Mar-4 Artcurial Briest, Paris #61
£369 $690 €550 Femme dans un paysage (26x20cm-10x8in) s. ink wash. 29-Feb-4 Versailles Encheres #173/R
£369 $690 €550 Femme nue (23x17cm-9x7in) s. pencil. 29-Feb-4 Versailles Encheres #175
£369 $653 €550 Marie et Guy (27x21cm-11x8in) st.sig.i.d.1921 ink wash. 28-Apr-4 Charbonneaux, Paris #208
£379 $630 €550 Nu assis (20x25cm-8x10in) st.sig. pen Indian ink wax crayon. 30-Sep-3 Blanchet, Paris #301/R
£382 $623 €550 Figure. s. ink. 23-Sep-3 Galerie Moderne, Brussels #814/R
£382 $702 €580 Nu d'atelier (27x20cm-11x8in) s. studio st. lead pencil prov. 28-Jun-4 Joron-Derem, Paris #87
£414 $745 €600 Femmes (21x26cm-8x10in) studio st. ink. 25-Jan-4 Chayette & Cheval, Paris #130
£414 $745 €600 Female nude. Two female nudes (21x19cm-8x7in) studio st. lead pencil double-sided. 25-Jan-4 Chayette & Cheval, Paris #131
£430 $800 €628 Etude de figures (23x39cm-9x15in) d.Feb 4 1924 pen ink. 2-Mar-4 Swann Galleries, New York #474/R

£461	$847	€700	Scene intime (22x13cm-9x5in) s. lead pencil. 28-Jun-4 Joron-Derem, Paris #80
£466	$840	€700	Nu debout et etude de personnages et de chien (30x19cm-12x7in) st.sig. black crayon. 26-Apr-4 Tajan, Paris #73
£470	$864	€700	Louise (20x14cm-8x6in) bears studio st. lead pencil. 24-Mar-4 Joron-Derem, Paris #36/R
£470	$841	€700	Nu debout (30x19cm-12x7in) st.sig. graphite dr. 30-May-4 Eric Pillon, Calais #165/R
£470	$841	€700	Femme a l'ombrelle (20x19cm-8x7in) st.sig. Chinese ink dr. 30-May-4 Eric Pillon, Calais #164/R
£470	$841	€700	Jeune femme au chapeau (30x20cm-12x8in) st.sig. chl dr. 30-May-4 Eric Pillon, Calais #163/R
£470	$841	€700	Nu a genoux (28x21cm-11x8in) st.sig. graphite dr. 30-May-4 Eric Pillon, Calais #176/R
£470	$841	€700	Portrait de jeunes filles (19x12cm-7x5in) st.sig. graphite dr. 30-May-4 Eric Pillon, Calais #175/R
£470	$841	€700	Nu debout de dos (30x19cm-12x7in) st.sig. graphite dr. 30-May-4 Eric Pillon, Calais #174/R
£470	$841	€700	Conversation (13x20cm-5x8in) st.sig. chl dr prov. 30-May-4 Eric Pillon, Calais #178/R
£470	$841	€700	Nu (30x23cm-12x9in) st.sig. chl Chinese ink dr. 30-May-4 Eric Pillon, Calais #179/R
£470	$841	€700	Caleche (47x58cm-19x23in) st.sig. Chinese ink wash dr. 30-May-4 Eric Pillon, Calais #180/R
£470	$841	€700	Nu debout (30x18cm-12x7in) st.sig. graphite dr. 30-May-4 Eric Pillon, Calais #177/R
£470	$841	€700	Femmes et angelot (44x53cm-17x21in) st.sig. graphite dr prov. 30-May-4 Eric Pillon, Calais #171/R
£470	$841	€700	Sur la scene (26x35cm-10x14in) st.sig. chl dr. 30-May-4 Eric Pillon, Calais #170/R
£470	$841	€700	Repas champetre (20x24cm-8x9in) st.sig. Chinese ink dr. 30-May-4 Eric Pillon, Calais #169/R
£470	$841	€700	Militaires (14x21cm-6x8in) s. W/C chl prov. 30-May-4 Eric Pillon, Calais #172/R
£470	$841	€700	Chevaux et cabanes sur la dune (22x28cm-9x11in) st.sig. Chinese ink dr prov. 30-May-4 Eric Pillon, Calais #181/R
£517	$859	€750	Nu debout les bras leves (30x19cm-12x7in) st.sig. ball point pen W/C. 30-Sep-3 Blanchet, Paris #300/R
£528	$946	€771	Marchands de poissons (16x13cm-6x5in) s.i. graphite ink. 4-May-4 Ritchie, Toronto #70/R est:1000-1500 (C.D 1300)
£530	$964	€800	Nu academique de dos (27x18cm-11x7in) st.sig. crayon exec. 1908 prov. 18-Jun-4 Charbonneaux, Paris #110/R
£532	$888	€750	Modele de dos jambe gauche levee (29x20cm-11x8in) st.sig. pencil. 12-Oct-3 St-Germain-en-Laye Encheres #185/R
£537	$961	€800	Nu debout (30x22cm-12x9in) st.sig. chl dr double-sided. 30-May-4 Eric Pillon, Calais #161/R
£537	$983	€800	Scene animee au cheval (21x18cm-8x7in) s. W/C Indian ink. 7-Jul-4 Artcurial Briest, Paris #131
£537	$983	€800	Seated nude (22x19cm-9x7in) st.sig.i.d.1905 lead pencil drawing. 7-Jul-4 Artcurial Briest, Paris #134
£552	$993	€800	Personages (12x24cm-5x9in) studio st. ink. 25-Jan-4 Chayette & Cheval, Paris #133
£570	$1021	€850	Nu debout (23x19cm-9x7in) st.sig. chl dr. 30-May-4 Eric Pillon, Calais #160/R
£570	$1050	€850	Beau moustachu (32x24cm-13x9in) st.sig. lead pencil. 24-Mar-4 Joron-Derem, Paris #39
£570	$1021	€850	Modele nu (22x28cm-9x11in) st.sig. chl dr. 30-May-4 Eric Pillon, Calais #162/R
£586	$1084	€850	Academie (24x16cm-9x6in) st.sig.i.d.1909 pencil prov. 13-Feb-4 Charbonneaux, Paris #62
£591	$1100	€863	Rebecca (37x48cm-15x19in) s. chl cardstock. 2-Mar-4 Swann Galleries, New York #476/R est:2000-3000
£591	$1100	€863	Deux nus couchees (43x32cm-17x13in) s. chl cardstock. 2-Mar-4 Swann Galleries, New York #477/R est:2000-3000
£600	$954	€870	Deux personnages (15x17cm-6x7in) s. pencil pen ink paper on card. 11-Sep-3 Christie's, Kensington #30/R
£600	$1086	€876	Au jardin botanique (17x21cm-7x8in) st.sig. pencil exec.c.1916-1917. 1-Apr-4 Christie's, Kensington #20/R
£604	$1111	€900	Hermine David et jeune femme (21x18cm-8x7in) s. chk. 26-Mar-4 Ketterer, Hamburg #589/R
£625	$1150	€950	Pensive (19x13cm-7x5in) s. was crayon prov. 28-Jun-4 Joron-Derem, Paris #798/R
£629	$1151	€950	Bord de mer (20x25cm-8x10in) chl htd wash. 7-Apr-4 Doutrebente, Paris #57/R
£645	$1200	€942	Femme assise (43x32cm-17x13in) s. chl cardstock. 2-Mar-4 Swann Galleries, New York #475/R est:2000-3000
£671	$1201	€1000	Femme a sa toilette (40x43cm-16x17in) s. crayon prov. 26-May-4 Christie's, Paris #60/R
£671	$1201	€1000	Nu assis tet penchee (31x23cm-12x9in) st.sig. graphite Chinese ink dr. 30-May-4 Eric Pillon, Calais #159/R
£724	$1332	€1100	Mile et une nuits (37x27cm-15x11in) s. studio st. lead pencil prov. 28-Jun-4 Joron-Derem, Paris #84
£845	$1462	€1200	L'homme au chapeau (25x34cm-10x13in) s.st.sig. indian ink. 14-Dec-3 Rabourdin & Choppin de Janvry, Paris #52
£938	$1500	€1369	Femme et deux hommes (26x35cm-10x14in) s. W/C. 18-Sep-3 Swann Galleries, New York #478/R est:2000-3000
£938	$1500	€1369	Trois femmes (26x18cm-10x7in) s. W/C. 18-Sep-3 Swann Galleries, New York #479/R est:2000-3000
£950	$1701	€1387	Femme et fleurs (19x15cm-7x6in) s. mixed media. 20-Mar-4 Lacy Scott, Bury St.Edmunds #469/R
£952	$1686	€1390	La famille (20x31cm-8x12in) s. W/C Indian ink. 27-Apr-4 AB Stockholms Auktionsverk #1234/R (S.KR 13000)
£1056	$1828	€1500	Jeune fille au tambourin (33x22cm-13x9in) studio st. graphite dr prov. 9-Dec-3 Artcurial Briest, Paris #183/R est:1500-2000
£1074	$1922	€1600	Summer landscape (19x29cm-7x11in) studio st. W/C prov. 30-May-4 Eric Pillon, Calais #173/R
£1075	$2000	€1570	Paysage avec figures (24x41cm-9x16in) s. W/C brush ink. 2-Mar-4 Swann Galleries, New York #480/R est:2000-3000
£1259	$2140	€1800	Au bistrot (23x31cm-9x12in) s. W/C. 27-Nov-3 Calmels Cohen, Paris #38/R est:1500-1800
£1313	$2100	€1917	Trois femmes dans une bourdelle (34x23cm-13x9in) s. pencil. 18-Sep-3 Swann Galleries, New York #477/R est:2000-3000
£1469	$2452	€2100	Les poivrottes (47x63cm-19x25in) st.sig. ink dr lit. 25-Jun-3 Rabourdin & Choppin de Janvry, Paris #63/R est:2300-2600
£1469	$2452	€2100	La plage, Tunisie (46x61cm-18x24in) st.sig. ink crayon. 25-Jun-3 Rabourdin & Choppin de Janvry, Paris #64/R est:2300-2500
£1469	$2452	€2100	L'orchestre (49x64cm-19x25in) st.sig. ink exec.c.1929. 25-Jun-3 Rabourdin & Choppin de Janvry, Paris #65/R est:2300-2500
£1600	$2544	€2320	Scene de harem (19x34cm-7x13in) atelier st. pencil ink. 11-Sep-3 Christie's, Kensington #29/R est:2000-3000
£1762	$2996	€2573	Trois jeunes filles (25x25cm-10x10in) s. W/C Indian ink prov.lit. 5-Nov-3 Dobiaschofsky, Bern #855/R est:4000 (S.FR 4000)
£1796	$3000	€2622	Study of a reclining nude (44x28cm-17x11in) estate st. pencil. 19-Oct-3 Bonhams & Butterfields, Los Angeles #7074/R est:800-1200
£1931	$3225	€2800	Le modele. Nu assis (23x31cm-9x12in) s. crayon wash W/C double-sided lit. 17-Nov-3 Claude Boisgirard, Paris #74 est:3000-3500
£1935	$3600	€2825	La papollon et les dormeuses. Les Amazones (13x20cm-5x8in) s. pen ink pair. 2-Mar-4 Swann Galleries, New York #481/R est:1500-2500
£2081	$3724	€3100	Trois graces (34x45cm-13x18in) s. chl dr prov. 30-May-4 Eric Pillon, Calais #168/R
£2610	$4750	€3811	Le grande Germaine (63x48cm-25x19in) st.sig. pencil chl prov.exhib. 29-Jun-4 Sotheby's, New York #332/R est:4000-6000
£2657	$4517	€3800	Deux femmes (48x34cm-19x13in) s. ink double-sided. 27-Nov-3 Calmels Cohen, Paris #49/R est:3000-4000
£2685	$4805	€4000	Enfant prodigue (46x60cm-18x24in) s.i. W/C. 30-May-4 Eric Pillon, Calais #167/R
£3356	$6208	€5000	PER KROGH a l'accordeon (27x21cm-11x8in) st.sig. Indian ink wash. 15-Mar-4 Blanchet, Paris #110/R est:2000-2500
£3486	$5822	€5055	Men and women at shop counter (15x15cm-6x6in) s. Indian ink. 19-Jun-3 Kornfeld, Bern #805/R est:4000 (S.FR 7600)
£4196	$7133	€6000	Scene de maison close (17x23cm-7x9in) s. W/C graphite. 27-Nov-3 Millon & Associes, Paris #63/R est:6000-7500
£5500	$9185	€8030	L'enfant prodigue (35x51cm-14x20in) st.sig. W/C gouache pen ink executed 1928 prov. 21-Oct-3 Sotheby's, London #114/R est:6000-8000
£9036	$15000	€13193	Fillette au chapeau (38x30cm-15x12in) s.studio st. W/C pencil prov. 2-Oct-3 Christie's, Tel Aviv #27/R est:14000-18000

PASCIUTI, Antonio (1937-) Italian

£336	$621	€500	Flowers of Murgia (30x40cm-12x16in) s. s.i.verso. 13-Mar-4 Meeting Art, Vercelli #145
£500	$920	€750	Rural path (40x60cm-16x24in) s. s.i.verso. 12-Jun-4 Meeting Art, Vercelli #565/R
£671	$1242	€1000	Looking for mushrooms on the Murgia (40x50cm-16x20in) s. s.i.verso. 13-Mar-4 Meeting Art, Vercelli #474
£704	$1169	€1000	Interno di Sera (40x50cm-16x20in) s. s.i.verso. 14-Jun-3 Meeting Art, Vercelli #194/R
£1056	$1754	€1500	Alberi in fiore (50x70cm-20x28in) s. s.i.verso. 14-Jun-3 Meeting Art, Vercelli #488/R est:1500

PASCUA CAMARA, Lorenzo (1937-) Spanish

£604	$1081	€900	Procession (37x51cm-15x20in) s.d.1990 board. 25-May-4 Durán, Madrid #167/R
£1074	$1922	€1600	Still life with books and gun (40x50cm-16x20in) s. board. 25-May-4 Durán, Madrid #166/R est:1200

PASCUAL DUCE, Antonio (20th C) Spanish

£567	$919	€800	Still life with orange and glasses (27x22cm-11x9in) s. panel. 20-May-3 Ansorena, Madrid #69/R

PASCUAL MONTURIOL, Eduardo (1882-?) Spanish

£326	$600	€476	Fishermen (49x63cm-19x25in) s.d.1922. 22-Jun-4 Galeria y Remates, Montevideo #43/R

PASCUAL, Felix (1893-?) Spanish

£414	$687	€600	Harbour workers (44x54cm-17x21in) s. 1-Oct-3 Ansorena, Madrid #781/R

PASINELLI, Lorenzo (1629-1700) Italian

£3000	$5490	€4380	Putti making music (31cm-12in circular) en brunaille prov. 7-Jul-4 Bonhams, New Bond Street #59/R est:5000-7000
£44444	$80000	€64888	Sybil inspired by putto (152x114cm-60x45in) prov.exhib.lit. 22-Jan-4 Sotheby's, New York #82/R est:100000-150000

PASINELLI, Lorenzo (attrib) (1629-1700) Italian

£3061	$5480	€4500	Lucrece (79x53cm-31x21in) canvas on panel. 19-Mar-4 Ribeyre & Baron, Paris #58/R est:4000-6000

PASINI, Alberto (1826-1899) Italian

£4469	$8000	€6525	The meeting (18x33cm-7x13in) s. 8-Jan-4 James Julia, Fairfield #524/R est:8000-12000
£11667	$21467	€17500	Bab el Nasr, Cairo (40x32cm-16x13in) s. prov.lit. 8-Jun-4 Della Rocca, Turin #360/R est:16000-20000
£12931	$23147	€18879	Oriental riders (76x115cm-30x45in) s.d.891. 12-May-4 Dobiaschofsky, Bern #854/R est:60000 (S.FR 30000)
£13287	$22853	€19000	Attaque d'une ville fortifiee (27x46cm-11x18in) s.d.1864 prov. 8-Dec-3 Tajan, Paris #315/R est:13000-18000
£18056	$32500	€26362	On the Grand Canal, Venice (27x35cm-11x14in) s.d.1881 lit. 23-Apr-4 Sotheby's, New York #78/R est:15000-20000

Works on paper

£769	$1308	€1100	Arab market (19x26cm-7x10in) s. ink card. 19-Nov-3 Finarte Semenzato, Milan #519/R
£8451	$14789	€12000	Le jour du marche (40x32cm-16x13in) s.d.1878 W/C. 16-Dec-3 Claude Aguttes, Neuilly #79/R est:10000-12000
£11620	$20335	€16500	Rue animee (40x32cm-16x13in) s.d.1878 W/C. 16-Dec-3 Claude Aguttes, Neuilly #77/R est:10000-15000
£12676	$22183	€18000	L'entree du marche a Istanbul (35x49cm-14x19in) s.d.1870 W/C. 16-Dec-3 Claude Aguttes, Neuilly #78/R est:10000-15000
£12676	$22183	€18000	Les marchands de ceramiques (52x48cm-20x19in) s.d.1872 W/C. 16-Dec-3 Claude Aguttes, Neuilly #80/R est:10000-15000

PASINI, L (20th C) ?

£1844	$2987	€2600	Squadriglia di aerosiluranti sopra la flotta (92x123cm-36x48in) s. 22-May-3 Stadion, Trieste #347/R est:4000-5000

PASINI, Lazzaro (1861-1949) Italian

£222	$369	€324	Untitled, market day (34x23cm-13x9in) s. canvasboard. 5-Oct-3 Levis, Calgary #86/R (C.D 500)

£600 $1098 €876 Fishermen off a Neapolitan coastal town (29x44cm-11x17in) 8-Apr-4 Christie's, Kensington #163/R
£1208 $2223 €1800 Grazzano Visconti (44x58cm-17x23in) s.d.1943 board. 24-Mar-4 Il Ponte, Milan #649/R est:600
£1208 $2162 €1800 Restoring a church (79x60cm-31x24in) s.d.1932 board. 25-May-4 Finarte Semenzato, Milan #53/R est:1800-2200
£2270 $3790 €3200 Notre-Dame, Paris (60x80cm-24x31in) s.d.1926 board double-sided. 14-Oct-3 Finarte Semenzato, Milan #200/R est:5000

PASINI, Ludwig (1832-1903) Austrian
Works on paper
£1848 $3307 €2698 Palace interior (50x36cm-20x14in) s.d.1862 W/C. 26-May-4 AB Stockholms Auktionsverk #2464/R est:25000-30000 (S.KR 25000)
£2175 $3916 €3263 Eine Prioggiotin - woman praying (59x43cm-23x17in) s.i.d.1871 W/C. 25-Apr-4 Goteborg Auktionsverk, Sweden #202/R est:8000 (S.KR 30000)
£3800 $6954 €5548 Interior of the Basilica of Santa Maria Maggiore, Rome (50x70cm-20x28in) s.i.d.1867 pencil W/C scratching out. 6-Jul-4 Christie's, London #204/R est:4000-6000

PASKELL, William (1866-1951) American
£440 $700 €642 Landscape with tree-lined lake and distant mountains (30x48cm-12x19in) s. 10-Sep-3 Alderfer's, Hatfield #302
£541 $1000 €790 Fisherman's Haven, Rockport, Mass (51x64cm-20x25in) s. i.verso. 24-Jan-4 Jeffery Burchard, Florida #46/R
Works on paper
£195 $350 €285 River view, sunset (24x74cm-9x29in) s. W/C paper on board. 14-May-4 Skinner, Boston #68/R
£225 $425 €329 Shoreline scene with boats (23x36cm-9x14in) s. W/C. 21-Feb-4 Jeffery Burchard, Florida #58/R

PASKELL, William (attrib) (1866-1951) American
£221 $400 €323 Sundown at the harbor (38x48cm-15x19in) s. 16-Apr-4 James Julia, Fairfield #852c/R

PASMORE, Daniel (19th C) British
£3800 $7030 €5548 Cavalier in love. Toast to a beauty (45x35cm-18x14in) s.d.1867 pair. 14-Jul-4 Sotheby's, Olympia #67/R est:3000-5000

PASMORE, Frederick George (jnr-attrib) (fl.1875-1884) British
£400 $680 €584 Children feeding hens beside a stone barn (30x45cm-12x18in) board. 19-Nov-3 Tennants, Leyburn #1245

PASMORE, John F (1820-1871) British
£1013 $1723 €1479 Preparing to saddle up (51x66cm-20x26in) s.d.1851. 21-Nov-3 Walker's, Ottawa #256/R est:2500-3500 (C.D 2250)
£1088 $1981 €1600 Feeding the cat (36x45cm-14x18in) s. 8-Feb-4 Bukowskis, Helsinki #500/R est:1000
£5200 $9620 €7592 Shepherdess with sheep, cockerel, ducks and hens in a barn (62x75cm-24x30in) 11-Feb-4 Cheffins, Cambridge #418/R est:4000-5000

PASMORE, Victor (1908-1998) British
£7500 $12975 €10950 Linear images no IV (41x41cm-16x16in) oil gravure board prov.lit. 11-Dec-3 Lyon & Turnbull, Edinburgh #25/R est:4000-6000
£10738 $19221 €16000 Linear image 1 (40x40cm-16x16in) init. s.d.1971 verso oil engraving board prov. 25-May-4 Sotheby's, Milan #174/R est:5000-6000
£12000 $20400 €17520 Black image - the pistol shot (91x183cm-36x72in) init. canvas on panel painted 1977 prov.exhib.lit. 21-Nov-3 Christie's, London #184/R est:12000-18000
£30000 $54900 €43800 Still life with jug of zinnias and green ladder back chair (53x43cm-21x17in) init. board sketch verso. 28-Jul-4 Mallams, Oxford #286/R est:12000-15000
Prints
£4200 $7728 €6132 Sleeping shepherd, early morning (31x30cm-12x12in) s.d.1952 linocut. 28-Jun-4 Bonhams, New Bond Street #221/R est:300-500
Works on paper
£5000 $9250 €7300 Black development D (41x41cm-16x16in) init.d.76 pencil oil paper on board. 11-Mar-4 Christie's, Kensington #370/R est:4000-6000
£10200 $17952 €14892 Three images (244x152cm-96x60in) init. tapestry. 19-May-4 Sotheby's, Olympia #329/R est:2500-3500

PASMORE, Victor (attrib) (1908-1998) British
Works on paper
£340 $622 €510 Landscape with ploughed fields (20x30cm-8x12in) pen ink. 28-Jul-4 Mallams, Oxford #273/R

PASPOUR, Louis (?) ?
£1050 $1712 €1533 Sailing boats (18x23cm-7x9in) s. board. 23-Sep-3 John Nicholson, Haslemere #288

PASQUA, Philippe (1965-) French
Works on paper
£1000 $1800 €1500 Untitled (200x130cm-79x51in) s.d.1996 mixed media on canvas. 24-Apr-4 Cornette de St.Cyr, Paris #673 est:1500-2000
£1733 $3120 €2600 Untitled (150x205cm-59x81in) s.d.1997 mixed media on canvas. 24-Apr-4 Cornette de St.Cyr, Paris #672 est:2000-3000

PASQUE, Aubin (1903-1981) Belgian
£578 $1035 €850 Les somnambules (81x105cm-32x41in) s.d.1931 i.d.verso. 17-Mar-4 Hotel des Ventes Mosan, Brussels #109

PASQUIER, Aulde (?) Italian?
Works on paper
£504 $826 €700 Pieta' (82x65cm-32x26in) s.i. pencil after Michelangelo. 10-Jun-3 Pandolfini, Florence #45/R

PASQUIER, Louis du (18th C) Swiss
£559 $900 €811 Still life of ceramic vessels on an oriental rug (28x43cm-11x17in) s. sold with handkerchief. 17-Aug-3 Jeffery Burchard, Florida #16

PASQUIER, Noel (20th C) French
Works on paper
£3020 $5346 €4500 Pourquoi pas (50x50cm-20x20in) s. mixed media canvas. 29-Apr-4 Claude Aguttes, Neuilly #201/R est:4500-4800

PASS, Izreal Abramovich (1868-?) Russian
£24324 $43541 €36000 On the way to the masquerade (112x137cm-44x54in) s.d.1904. 8-May-4 Bukowskis, Helsinki #462/R est:8000-10000

PASSAGE, Comte Arthur Marie Gabriel du (1838-1909) French
Sculpture
£1735 $3105 €2550 Deux chiens jouant avec un piege a rat (14x27cm-6x11in) s. brown pat. bronze. 21-Mar-4 Muizon & Le Coent, Paris #67/R

PASSAGLIA, Augusto (1838-1918) Italian
Sculpture
£3000 $5460 €4380 Masaniello (63cm-25in) s.i. white marble. 15-Jun-4 Sotheby's, Olympia #123/R est:2000-3000

PASSANI, Decimo (?) Italian
Sculpture
£993 $1808 €1500 Mother and children (24x30cm-9x12in) s. terracotta. 21-Jun-4 Pandolfini, Florence #268/R est:1600-1800
£1151 $1888 €1600 Waiting on the quay (43cm-17in) bears sig terracotta. 10-Jun-3 Pandolfini, Florence #185/R est:800-900

PASSANI, Italo Amerigo (20th C) Italian
£563 $975 €800 Rags. Masterpiece (32x46cm-13x18in) s. chl pastel two. 9-Dec-3 Pandolfini, Florence #183/R est:800-900
Works on paper
£986 $1706 €1400 Everybody in overalls. Clearance (43x37cm-17x15in) s. pencil two. 9-Dec-3 Pandolfini, Florence #182 est:900-1000

PASSANISE, Gary (20th C) American
Works on paper
£398 $700 €581 Abstract composition (135x58cm-53x23in) s. mixed media six sheets. 22-May-4 Selkirks, St. Louis #626/R

PASSAROTTI, Bartolomeo (1529-1592) Italian
£7263 $13000 €10604 Holy Family with Saint Elizabeth and the INfant Saint John (29x22cm-11x9in) copper prov. 27-May-4 Sotheby's, New York #6/R est:10000-15000
£181208 $324362 €270000 Allegory of the Senses (111x77cm-44x30in) 26-May-4 Porro, Milan #25/R est:250000-300000
Works on paper
£4722 $8500 €6894 Nude seen from behind holding a sword and shield (28x18cm-11x7in) i. pen brown ink prov. 22-Jan-4 Christie's, Rockefeller NY #18/R est:6000-8000

PASSAROTTI, Bartolomeo (attrib) (1529-1592) Italian
£782 $1400 €1142 St. Francis Assisi (43x43cm-17x17in) board exhib. 8-May-4 Susanin's, Chicago #6157/R est:1500-2500

PASSAURO, Edmondo (1893-1969) Italian
£280 $481 €400 Jeune femme nue de dos (70x60cm-28x24in) s. panel sold with monographie of the artist. 8-Dec-3 Horta, Bruxelles #504
£298 $542 €450 Woman (43x36cm-17x14in) s. cardboard. 18-Jun-4 Stadion, Trieste #415
£2533 $4535 €3800 Dream (50x67cm-20x26in) s. cardboard. 12-May-4 Stadion, Trieste #812/R est:1800-2200

PASSERI, Giuseppe (1654-1714) Italian
Works on paper
£1100 $1903 €1606 Female figure clasping her hands to her chest (25x16cm-10x6in) red chk pen brown ink prov. 12-Dec-3 Christie's, Kensington #370/R est:700-1000
£2500 $4500 €3650 Christ preaching outside Jerusalem (23x19cm-9x7in) red chk pen ink wash prov. 21-Jan-4 Sotheby's, New York #77/R est:3000-5000
£5592 $10289 €8500 Historical scene with King Louis IX of France (22x17cm-9x7in) pen ink W/C sanguine prov. 22-Jun-4 Sotheby's, Milan #10/R est:3000-4000

PASSET, Gerard (20th C) French
£206 $350 €301 La route (51x51cm-20x20in) s.d.63 s.verso prov. 22-Nov-3 Jackson's, Cedar Falls #397/R
£300 $540 €438 French landscape with church (60x74cm-24x29in) s. s.i.verso. 20-Jan-4 Bonhams, Knightsbridge #48
£350 $630 €511 On the banks of the river (76x192cm-30x76in) s. 20-Jan-4 Bonhams, Knightsbridge #47
£400 $708 €584 Road through the village (46x55cm-18x22in) s. 27-Apr-4 Bonhams, Knightsbridge #209/R
£541 $919 €790 La Seine (51x61cm-20x24in) s. s.i.verso prov. 21-Nov-3 Walker's, Ottawa #221/R (C.D 1200)

PASSEY, Charles H (fl.1870-1885) British
£400 $732 €584 Country landscape with figure working in a hayfield (52x42cm-20x17in) s. 6-Apr-4 Bonhams, Knightsbridge #20
£600 $1098 €876 Dorking, Surrey - lambs in a country lane (69x89cm-27x35in) s.d.1895 s.i.d. verso. 6-Jul-4 Bearnes, Exeter #514
£695 $1300 €1015 Lane, Gomshall, Surrey (61x51cm-24x20in) s. i.verso. 29-Feb-4 Bonhams & Butterfields, San Francisco #4526 est:1000-1500
£700 $1169 €1022 Harvesting (91x71cm-36x28in) s. 13-Nov-3 Christie's, Kensington #134/R
£1134 $2053 €1656 Wharfedale Valley, Yorkshire (60x101cm-24x40in) s. s.i.verso. 30-Mar-4 Stephan Welz, Johannesburg #402/R est:7000-10000 (SA.R 13500)
£1200 $2232 €1752 Returning home (71x91cm-28x36in) s.d.1893. 4-Mar-4 Christie's, Kensington #460/R est:600-800
£4200 $6972 €6132 Harvestime. Flock of sheep (91x71cm-36x28in) both s. pair. 1-Oct-3 Sotheby's, Olympia #128/R est:1500-2500

PASSEY, Charles H (attrib) (fl.1870-1885) British
£280 $515 €409 Harvest landscape (61x107cm-24x42in) 8-Jun-4 Bonhams, Chester #915/R

PASSIGLI, Carlo (1881-1953) Italian
£265 $482 €400 Shepherd (25x39cm-10x15in) s. card. 21-Jun-4 Pandolfini, Florence #198/R
£397 $723 €600 Seascape at sunset (25x35cm-10x14in) s. card. 21-Jun-4 Pandolfini, Florence #214/R
£493 $818 €700 Tuscan countryside (18x25cm-7x10in) cardboard. 13-Jun-3 Farsetti, Prato #416
£634 $1096 €900 Farm (37x30cm-15x12in) board. 9-Dec-3 Pandolfini, Florence #379/R
£719 $1180 €1000 Labour (29x50cm-11x20in) s. board. 10-Jun-3 Pandolfini, Florence #277/R
£733 $1327 €1100 Cascine Square (51x57cm-20x22in) s. cardboard. 2-Apr-4 Farsetti, Prato #438
£795 $1446 €1200 Sailing boats at sunset (25x36cm-10x14in) s. card. 21-Jun-4 Pandolfini, Florence #181
£800 $1448 €1200 Farm (51x42cm-20x17in) s. board. 2-Apr-4 Farsetti, Prato #502/R
£966 $1612 €1400 Mower (25x37cm-10x15in) s. cardboard. 14-Nov-3 Farsetti, Prato #578/R
£993 $1808 €1500 Seascape with sailing boats (50x70cm-20x28in) s. board. 21-Jun-4 Pandolfini, Florence #206/R est:1600-1800
£1172 $1958 €1700 Santo Spirito Square, Florence (37x29cm-15x11in) s.d.945 cardboard. 14-Nov-3 Farsetti, Prato #448/R est:1300-1900
£1890 $3250 €2759 First bloom (55x75cm-22x30in) s. 3-Dec-3 Doyle, New York #124/R est:3000-5000

PASSINI, Johann Nepomuk (1798-1874) Austrian
£1067 $1941 €1600 Poacher surprised by hunter (79x63cm-31x25in) s. 30-Jun-4 Neumeister, Munich #641/R

PASSINI, Rita Margarete (1882-1976) Austrian
£1678 $2887 €2400 Sunlit magnolia tree (86x72cm-34x28in) s. 5-Dec-3 Michael Zeller, Lindau #754/R est:1600

PASSMORE, John Richard (1904-1984) Australian
£1735 $3192 €2533 Nothing takes them back to this (39x46cm-15x18in) init. i.verso board prov. 29-Mar-4 Goodman, Sydney #51/R est:4000-6000 (A.D 4250)
£2049 $3320 €2992 Interior with figures (31x40cm-12x16in) init. board. 30-Jul-3 Goodman, Sydney #163/R est:5000-7000 (A.D 5000)
£4580 $8336 €6687 Two figures (40x31cm-16x12in) init. oil paper on board. 16-Jun-4 Deutscher-Menzies, Melbourne #166/R est:12000-15000 (A.D 12000)
£20492 $33197 €29918 Boy bathers (72x92cm-28x36in) exhib. 30-Jul-3 Goodman, Sydney #80/R est:50000-70000 (A.D 50000)

PASTEGA, Luigi (1858-1927) Italian
£1291 $2350 €1885 Beauty at fountain (58x38cm-23x15in) s. 7-Feb-4 Sloans & Kenyon, Bethesda #1278/R est:3000-5000
£1884 $3090 €2600 View of Venice with figures (15x22cm-6x9in) s. board. 27-May-3 Il Ponte, Milan #924
£5667 $10257 €8500 Courtship (118x89cm-46x35in) s. 30-Mar-4 Babuino, Rome #335/R est:5000
£13000 $23660 €18980 Mischievous pet (59x80cm-23x31in) s.d.1890. 17-Jun-4 Christie's, London #87/R est:10000-15000
£32000 $58880 €48000 Nosy woemn (40x55cm-16x22in) s. 8-Jun-4 Sotheby's, Milan #110/R est:20000-30000

PASTERNAK, Alexandre (19th C) Russian
£793 $1348 €1158 Boyarin (44x28cm-17x11in) mono. 5-Nov-3 Dobiaschofsky, Bern #857/R (S.FR 1800)

PASTERNAK, Leonid Ossipowitsch (1862-1945) Russian
£25641 $40000 € Portrait of a woman (88x73cm-35x29in) s.d.1893. 11-Apr-3 Christie's, Rockefeller NY #33/R est:60000-90000
Works on paper
£479 $800 €699 Interior with child studying (54x43cm-21x17in) s. col pencil pastel. 21-Oct-3 Christie's, Rockefeller NY #107
£2800 $4760 €4200 Portrait of Ilia Iakovlevich Ginsburg (32x24cm-13x9in) s.d.1905 pastel chl. 25-Nov-3 Christie's, London #169/R est:2000-3000

PASTINA, Ed (19th C) Italian
£960 $1700 €1402 Italian landscape with lake and town beyond (71x97cm-28x38in) s.d.1857. 2-May-4 Bonhams & Butterfields, San Francisco #1027/R est:2000-3000

PASTIS, E T (19th C) French
£5923 $10188 €8648 L'orquestre d'enfants (110x125cm-43x49in) s. pair. 3-Dec-3 AB Stockholms Auktionsverk #2573/R est:60000-80000 (S.KR 77000)

PASTOR CALPENA, Vicente (1918-1993) Spanish
£855 $1574 €1300 Angel Street, Madrid (38x46cm-15x18in) s. s.i.verso board. 22-Jun-4 Durán, Madrid #170/R
£1974 $3572 €3000 Angel Street, Madrid (38x46cm-15x18in) board. 14-Apr-4 Ansorena, Madrid #174/R est:1300
Works on paper
£537 $1004 €800 Village (43x59cm-17x23in) s. W/C. 24-Feb-4 Durán, Madrid #123/R
£833 $1358 €1200 Village (56x87cm-22x34in) s. W/C. 23-Sep-3 Durán, Madrid #38/R
£855 $1574 €1300 Guadalupe Square (50x64cm-20x25in) s.d.1958 W/C. 22-Jun-4 Durán, Madrid #92/R
£1020 $1827 €1500 Landscape covered in snow (69x100cm-27x39in) s. W/C. 22-Mar-4 Durán, Madrid #603/R est:1500
£1184 $2179 €1800 View of village (54x76cm-21x30in) s.d.1968 W/C. 22-Jun-4 Durán, Madrid #127/R est:1800
£1510 $2673 €2250 Village (37x55cm-15x22in) s. W/C. 27-Apr-4 Durán, Madrid #20/R est:650

PASTOR, Gilbert (1932-) French
£400 $720 €600 Fillette (55x43cm-22x17in) s. panel. 20-Apr-4 Chenu & Scrive, Lyon #135/R
£933 $1680 €1400 La chambre (80x120cm-31x47in) s. panel. 20-Apr-4 Chenu & Scrive, Lyon #136/R

PASTORE, Giuseppina (20th C) Italian
Works on paper
£233 $429 €350 Lettre au Pape (35x50cm-14x20in) d.1992-97 verso crayon felt pen prov. 9-Jun-4 Artcurial Briest, Paris #409

PASTORE, Margherita Pastore (19th C) British?
£350 $616 €511 Cherry picker (46x35cm-18x14in) s. i.verso. 19-May-4 Christie's, Kensington #686/R

PASTORIO, Ezio (1911-) Italian
£533 $981 €800 Station (41x51cm-16x20in) s. 12-Jun-4 Meeting Art, Vercelli #583/R

PASTOUKHOFF, Boris (1894-1974) Russian
£1800 $3222 €2628 Vase of flowers (65x54cm-26x21in) s.d.1959. 26-May-4 Sotheby's, Olympia #471/R est:1800-2500

PASTOUR, Louis (1876-1948) French
£563 $975 €800 Soleil de pluie, Sospel (38x46cm-15x18in) s. i.d.1941 verso panel. 13-Dec-3 Martinot & Savignat, Pontoise #261
£567 $1020 €850 Village anime. Vue de Cannes (23x15cm-9x6in) s.i.d.Juillet 1931 cardboard double-sided. 20-Apr-4 Chenu & Scrive, Lyon #137/R
£600 $1086 €900 Vieux pont (35x46cm-14x18in) s. board. 1-Apr-4 Credit Municipal, Paris #84
£850 $1590 €1241 Mediterranean coastal town (60x45cm-24x18in) s. i.verso. 21-Jul-4 Bonhams, New Bond Street #182/R
£1074 $1900 €1600 Voile rouge (50x60cm-20x24in) s. 30-Apr-4 Tajan, Paris #218/R est:1500-2000

PASZTHORY, Baron A (19/20th C) ?
£1000 $1840 €1460 Portrait of a beautiful young lady wearing a pale blue chiffon headscarf (52x34cm-20x13in) s. 8-Jun-4 Bonhams, Knightsbridge #339b/R est:800-1200

PATA, Cherubino (1827-1899) French
£733 $1327 €1100 Village au bord de l'eau (22x35cm-9x14in) s. exhib. 30-Mar-4 Rossini, Paris #287/R
£986 $1706 €1400 Sous-bois (64x80cm-25x31in) 9-Dec-3 Chambelland & Giafferi, Paris #107/R
£2000 $3640 €2920 Le bief pres du moulin (65x81cm-26x32in) bears sig prov.exhib. 16-Jun-4 Bonhams, New Bond Street #87/R est:2000-3000

PATAKY VON SOSPATAK, Laszlo (1857-1912) Hungarian
£804 $1342 €1174 Peasant wagon crossing a flooded marsh (66x114cm-26x45in) s. 17-Jun-3 Maynards, Vancouver #304 est:2000-3000 (C.D 1800)
£2000 $3640 €3000 Young shepherdess knitting while watching her sheep in Hungary (59x112cm-23x44in) s. 1-Jul-4 Van Ham, Cologne #1550/R est:3500
£2539 $4493 €3707 Courting (50x41cm-20x16in) s. 28-Apr-4 Kieselbach, Budapest #22/R (H.F 950000)
£2579 $4281 €3765 Coach with horses (63x112cm-25x44in) s. 4-Oct-3 Kieselbach, Budapest #193/R (H.F 950000)
£2685 $4805 €4000 Shepherdess (58x100cm-23x39in) s. 27-May-4 Dorotheum, Vienna #6/R est:4000-5000
£6850 $12399 €10001 Market (54x73cm-21x29in) s. 16-Apr-4 Mu Terem Galeria, Budapest #38/R (H.F 2600000)

PATAKY, Maria (19/20th C) German?
£600 $1092 €900 Kaiser Wilhelm wearing traditonal attire (130x80cm-51x31in) s.d.1905. 1-Jul-4 Van Ham, Cologne #1549

PATCH, Thomas (1720-1782) British
£65957 $106851 €93000 Vista del Canal Grande desde el Rialto (75x130cm-30x51in) 20-May-3 Ansorena, Madrid #96/R est:93000

PATEK, Ludwig (1837-?) Austrian
£563 $975 €800 The application: schoolboy with rucksack (51x35cm-20x14in) s. canvas on canvas. 10-Dec-3 Hugo Ruef, Munich #2471/R
£1107 $2047 €1616 Young boy waving his hand (52x36cm-20x14in) 14-Mar-4 Agra, Warsaw #2/R (P.Z 8000)

PATEL, Antoine Pierre (younger) (1648-1707) French
Works on paper
£3056 $5500 €4462 Classical temple by the sea with two figures in the foreground (16x27cm-6x11in) s.d.1695 bodycol vellum. 22-Jan-4 Christie's, Rockefeller NY #226/R est:7000-10000
£4110 $6986 €6000 Paysage anime (20x27cm-8x11in) s.d.1699 gouache. 6-Nov-3 Tajan, Paris #34/R
£4110 $6986 €6000 Paysage anime (19x26cm-7x10in) s.d.1699 gouache. 6-Nov-3 Tajan, Paris #33/R
£4636 $8437 €7000 Le Christ et la Samaritaine dans un paysage (13x22cm-5x9in) gouache. 16-Jun-4 Piasa, Paris #110/R est:7000-8000

PATEL, Antoine Pierre (younger-attrib) (1648-1707) French
£1329 $2285 €1900 Paysage (18x31cm-7x12in) cardboard. 8-Dec-3 Cornette de St.Cyr, Paris #48/R est:1500-2000
£3158 $5811 €4800 Promeneurs et paysans au bord de lac (23x33cm-9x13in) paper on panel. 25-Jun-4 Piasa, Paris #100/R est:4000-6000
£3873 $6779 €5500 Scenes pastorales dans la campagne Romaine (26cm-10in circular) panel pair. 18-Dec-3 Tajan, Paris #36/R est:4000-6000

PATEL, Antoine Pierre (younger-circle) (1648-1707) French
£5000 $9150 €7300 Classical wooded landscape (48x61cm-19x24in) copper prov. 9-Jul-4 Christie's, Kensington #102/R est:5000-7000

PATELLIERE, Amedee de la (1890-1932) French
£1189 $2045 €1700 Nature morte aux pommes et au coffret (24x30cm-9x12in) d.21 oil paper. 5-Dec-3 Chochon-Barre & Allardi, Paris #36 est:1800-2000
£1723 $3084 €2550 Scene champetre (38x46cm-15x18in) s. 5-May-4 Coutau Begarie, Paris #64/R est:2000-2500
£2098 $3608 €3000 Le peintre et son modele (39x46cm-15x18in) s. exhib. 5-Dec-3 Chochon-Barre & Allardi, Paris #34/R est:3000-3500
£2168 $3729 €3100 La tentation de Saint Antoine (61x46cm-24x18in) mono. 5-Dec-3 Chochon-Barre & Allardi, Paris #64 est:3000-3500
£3497 $5944 €5000 Baigneuses a l'etang bleu (46x55cm-18x22in) s. 21-Nov-3 Lombrail & Teucquam, Paris #151/R est:6000-8000
Works on paper
£268 $499 €400 Belle-Ile, au bord de la mer (23x30cm-9x12in) s.i.d.1922 W/C pastel pencil. 2-Mar-4 Artcurial Briest, Paris #44
£331 $603 €500 Sieste champetre (52x73cm-20x29in) s.d.1925 chl. 18-Jun-4 Charbonneaux, Paris #99
£490 $842 €700 Une vache (30x34cm-12x13in) s. graphite. 5-Dec-3 Chochon-Barre & Allardi, Paris #48
£629 $1083 €900 Femme dormant les bras leves (25x19cm-10x7in) s.d.1922 graphite. 5-Dec-3 Chochon-Barre & Allardi, Paris #45
£839 $1443 €1200 Paysage vallonne (35x45cm-14x18in) s.d.1922 col crayon. 5-Dec-3 Chochon-Barre & Allardi, Paris #44/R
£986 $1706 €1400 Jeune femme nue (43x55cm-17x22in) s.d.1912 graphite dr. 9-Dec-3 Artcurial Briest, Paris #200 est:1000-1500
£1189 $2045 €1700 Chevaux et personnages, scene de la conversion de Saint Paul (48x63cm-19x25in) conte crayon. 5-Dec-3 Chochon-Barre & Allardi, Paris #42 est:2000-2500
£1189 $2045 €1700 Baigneuses sous les arbres (26x28cm-10x11in) st.sig. gouache. 5-Dec-3 Chochon-Barre & Allardi, Paris #59/R est:2000-2500

PATENIER, Joachim (circle) (1485-1524) Flemish
£10265 $18682 €15500 Saint Christophe (39x58cm-15x23in) panel. 21-Jun-4 Tajan, Paris #33/R est:4000-6000
£26667 $48800 €40000 Saint Jerome praying (42x59cm-17x23in) board. 1-Jun-4 Sotheby's, Milan #47/R est:12000-16000

PATENIER, Joachim (style) (1485-1524) Flemish
£8333 $15000 €12166 Landscape with the Peniten Saint Jerome (37x49cm-15x19in) panel prov.exhib. 22-Jan-4 Sotheby's, New York #131/R est:20000-30000
£20423 $35739 €29000 Saint Christophe (45x36cm-18x14in) panel. 19-Dec-3 Delvaux, Paris #79/R est:8000-10000

PATER, Jean Baptiste (1695-1736) French
£1067 $1941 €1600 Elegant company in a park landscape (24x18cm-9x7in) board. 1-Jul-4 Van Ham, Cologne #1151/R est:1800
Works on paper
£680 $1218 €1000 Jeune femme tenant un verre dans sa main gauche (22x14cm-9x6in) sanguine. 19-Mar-4 Piasa, Paris #31
£6000 $10980 €8760 Seated gallant. Study of wheel (17x19cm-7x7in) red chk prov.exhib. 8-Jul-4 Sotheby's, London #125/R est:7000-9000
£15556 $28000 €22712 Reclining woman looking down to the left (15x21cm-6x8in) red chk prov. 22-Jan-4 Christie's, Rockefeller NY #98/R est:7000-10000

PATER, Jean Baptiste (attrib) (1695-1736) French
£6897 $11448 €10000 Les amants heureux (32x40cm-13x16in) 1-Oct-3 Dorotheum, Vienna #207/R est:10000-15000

PATERSON, Caroline (1856-1911) British
Works on paper
£1700 $3043 €2482 Sharing the bread (24x23cm-9x9in) init. W/C. 26-May-4 Sotheby's, Olympia #174/R est:1000-1500
£2200 $3938 €3212 Feeding time (24x23cm-9x9in) init. W/C. 26-May-4 Sotheby's, Olympia #176/R est:1000-1500
£2400 $4296 €3504 Get well soon (24x23cm-9x9in) init. W/C. 26-May-4 Sotheby's, Olympia #175/R est:1000-1500
£2600 $4654 €3796 Offering (24x23cm-9x9in) init. W/C. 26-May-4 Sotheby's, Olympia #173/R est:1000-1500
£2700 $4590 €3942 Captured unawares (23x20cm-9x8in) s. W/C. 27-Nov-3 Sotheby's, London #341/R est:2000-3000
£3000 $5520 €4380 A secret store (40x32cm-16x13in) s. W/C. 10-Jun-4 Lyon & Turnbull, Edinburgh #122 est:300-500
£12000 $22080 €17520 Cat's cradle (39x34cm-15x13in) s. W/C exhib.lit. 8-Jun-4 Bonhams, New Bond Street #77/R est:12000-18000

PATERSON, Emily Murray (1855-1934) British
Works on paper
£275 $501 €402 Venice (25x36cm-10x14in) s. W/C. 4-Feb-4 John Nicholson, Haslemere #33/R
£400 $748 €584 Sand dunes (8x11cm-3x4in) s W/C bodycol. 25-Feb-4 Mallams, Oxford #131/R
£400 $732 €584 Lagoon, Venice (24x35cm-9x14in) s. W/C. 31-Jan-4 Shapes, Edinburgh #361
£420 $722 €613 Venice (27x37cm-11x15in) s. W/C. 6-Dec-3 Shapes, Edinburgh #431
£550 $1012 €803 Sailing ship becalmed by moonlight (22x19cm-9x7in) s. W/C. 11-Jun-4 Keys, Aylsham #444
£750 $1275 €1095 Venice (29x39cm-11x15in) s. W/C. 26-Nov-3 Hamptons Fine Art, Godalming #85

PATERSON, James (1854-1932) British
£300 $477 €438 Figures in a Mediterranean courtyard (44x37cm-17x15in) s. board. 9-Sep-3 Bonhams, Knightsbridge #249/R
£1700 $3111 €2482 Solway (26x34cm-10x13in) with sig. s.verso canvasboard prov. 8-Apr-4 Bonhams, Edinburgh #181/R est:1800-2500
£1800 $3114 €2628 Moffat Mill (51x61cm-20x24in) s. s.i.verso. 11-Dec-3 Lyon & Turnbull, Edinburgh #2/R est:1500-2000
£3200 $5024 €4640 Landscape at moniave (37x58cm-15x23in) s.i.d.1891. 27-Aug-3 Sotheby's, London #1020/R est:2000-3000
Works on paper
£280 $482 €409 Continental town square (28x23cm-11x9in) s. W/C. 4-Dec-3 Bonhams, Edinburgh #3
£1900 $2983 €2755 Place Saint Sauveur, Dinan, early spring (26x17cm-10x7in) s.i. i.verso W/C. 27-Aug-3 Sotheby's, London #1036/R est:1000-1500
£2200 $3454 €3190 Old houses on the Rance, Port of Dinan (25x17cm-10x7in) s.d. W/C. 27-Aug-3 Sotheby's, London #1037/R est:1000-1500
£2300 $4163 €3358 Still life with roses (33x24cm-13x9in) s.i.d.1889 W/C. 19-Apr-4 Sotheby's, London #50/R est:1500-2000
£2400 $4344 €3504 Borderland (59x77cm-23x30in) s.i.d.1896 W/C exhib. 19-Apr-4 Sotheby's, London #34/R est:1500-2000
£4200 $7602 €6132 Dumfriesshire meadow, Kirkconnel (23x32cm-9x13in) s.i.d.1892 W/C. 19-Apr-4 Sotheby's, London #36/R est:1500-2000

PATERSON, James (attrib) (1854-1932) British
Works on paper
£900 $1413 €1305 On the Seine, Paris (36x26cm-14x10in) W/C prov. 27-Aug-3 Sotheby's, London #1038/R

PATERSON, John Ford (1851-1912) Australian
£405 $652 €591 River bank at sunset (34x24cm-13x9in) board. 13-Oct-3 Joel, Victoria #442 est:1000-1500 (A.D 1000)
£1362 $2315 €1989 Old red bluff, Point Ormond (15x31cm-6x12in) s.d.1896 board. 26-Nov-3 Deutscher-Menzies, Melbourne #131a/R est:3000-5000 (A.D 3200)

PATERSON, Rueben (20th C) New Zealander
Works on paper
£2068 $3515 €3019 Show us ya glit (110x110cm-43x43in) s.i.d.2003 verso glitter dust canvas. 27-Nov-3 International Art Centre, Auckland #9/R est:5500-6500 (NZ.D 5500)

PATERSON, Tom (fl.early 1900`s) British
Works on paper
£300 $549 €438 Girls playing on an Ayrshire beach (25x35cm-10x14in) s. W/C. 8-Apr-4 Bonhams, Edinburgh #150
£360 $590 €526 Happy hours on the sand dunes (33x24cm-13x9in) s. i.verso W/C. 3-Jun-3 Fellows & Sons, Birmingham #105/R

PATERSON, Viola (1899-1981) British
£3800 $6840 €5548 Mediterranean farm, near the sea (53x64cm-21x25in) s. prov.exhib.lit. 21-Apr-4 Cheffins, Cambridge #519/R est:1500-2000

PATERSSON, Benjamin (c.1748-1815) Swedish
Prints
£3000 $5460 €4380 Vue de la Grande Parade au Palais de L'Empereur Alexandre (52x73cm-20x29in) hand col etching. 1-Jul-4 Sotheby's, London #100/R est:3000-4000
Works on paper
£11154 $19185 €16285 Le grand theatre Imperial. Facade du chateau St Michel, St Petersbourg (50x68cm-20x27in) s.d.1806 1807 W/C pair. 7-Dec-3 Uppsala Auktionskammare, Uppsala #64/R est:60000-80000 (S.KR 145000)

PATINO, Anton (1957-) Spanish
£2113 $3697 €3000 Mask (80x65cm-31x26in) s.i.d.1984 verso acrylic. 16-Dec-3 Durán, Madrid #101/R est:3000
£2465 $3944 €3500 Black tide (198x97cm-78x38in) s.d.1988 verso oil mixed media prov.exhib. 16-Sep-3 Segre, Madrid #168a/R est:4500
£2740 $4658 €4000 Head (85x112cm-33x44in) sid.1986 verso. 4-Nov-3 Ansorena, Madrid #907/R est:4000
£2759 $4579 €4000 Mask (81x65cm-32x26in) s.i.d.1984 verso. 1-Oct-3 Ansorena, Madrid #580/R est:4000
£2937 $4905 €4200 A Coroza (162x130cm-64x51in) s. s.i.d.1985 verso oil acrylic prov. 24-Jun-3 Segre, Madrid #160/R est:5400
£8333 $13750 €12000 Crowned tower (195x270cm-77x106in) s.i.d.1983 verso. 2-Jul-3 Ansorena, Madrid #858c/R est:12000

PATKO, Karoly (1895-1941) Hungarian
£5000 $9100 €7300 Factory yard (62x75cm-24x30in) s. num.15 verso tempera panel painted 1920's prov.exhib. 15-Jun-4 Sotheby's, London #76/R est:5000-7000
£6500 $11830 €9490 Loading the carts (62x75cm-24x30in) s. num.14 verso tempera panel painted 1931 prov.exhib. 15-Jun-4 Sotheby's, London #75/R est:5000-7000
£10859 $18026 €15854 Remorse (60x49cm-24x19in) s.d.923. 4-Oct-3 Kieselbach, Budapest #203/R (H.F 4000000)
£11000 $20020 €16060 Still life with bread (50x61cm-20x24in) s. indis.num.28 verso tempera panel painted 1929 prov.exhib. 15-Jun-4 Sotheby's, London #77/R est:10000-15000
£13000 $23660 €18980 Still life with paintbrushes and spatula (71x75cm-28x30in) s. num.29 verso tempera panel painted 1923 prov.exhib. 15-Jun-4 Sotheby's, London #74/R est:12000-18000
£69478 $122976 €101438 Grape harvesting (115x126cm-45x50in) s. 28-Apr-4 Kieselbach, Budapest #92/R (H.F 26000000)
£100121 $181219 €146177 Adam and Eve (130x115cm-51x45in) 16-Apr-4 Mu Terem Galeria, Budapest #35/R (H.F 38000000)
Works on paper
£1449 $2623 €2116 Watering (48x66cm-19x26in) s. pastel. 16-Apr-4 Mu Terem Galeria, Budapest #13/R (H.F 550000)

PATON, Frank (1856-1909) British
£700 $1113 €1022 Portrait of a tabby cat (21x21cm-8x8in) s.d.1880 round. 18-Mar-3 Anderson & Garland, Newcastle #201/R
£800 $1336 €1168 Evening Star, portrait of a horse (30x41cm-12x16in) 21-Oct-3 Gorringes, Lewes #2029/R
£1008 $1855 €1472 Buchley (51x61cm-20x24in) s.d.1891 i.stretcher. 14-Jun-4 Waddingtons, Toronto #116/R est:1500-2000 (C.D 2500)
£14500 $26680 €21170 First (61x51cm-24x20in) s.d.1891 prov. 10-Jun-4 Christie's, Kensington #365/R est:7000-10000
Works on paper
£280 $512 €409 Grey horse in a woodland landscape (24x32cm-9x13in) s.d.1901 pencil W/C htd white. 8-Apr-4 Christie's, Kensington #149
£350 $641 €511 Ben, a chestnut horse (34x48cm-13x19in) s.i.d.1903 W/C htd white. 8-Apr-4 Christie's, Kensington #121
£380 $680 €555 Tethered donkey (12x14cm-5x6in) init. ink. 25-May-4 Bonhams, Knightsbridge #25/R
£390 $608 €569 Portrait of the Irish race horse Gary Owen (33x45cm-13x18in) s.i.d.1898 W/C. 28-Mar-3 Greenslade Hunt, Taunton #494
£600 $1098 €876 Promising litter (46x71cm-18x28in) s. 27-Jan-4 Gorringes, Lewes #1563/R
£620 $1110 €905 Study of a rabbit (48x35cm-19x14in) s.d.1900 W/C gouache. 26-May-4 Sotheby's, Olympia #119/R
£872 $1605 €1300 Driven partridge (56x77cm-22x30in) s.d.1897 W/C. 29-Mar-4 Glerum, Amsterdam #148
£2000 $3400 €2920 Three kittens in a barn (35x51cm-14x20in) s.d.1903 W/C htd bodycol. 4-Nov-3 Bonhams, New Bond Street #151/R est:2000-3000

PATON, Fraser (?) British?
Works on paper
£420 $773 €613 View of Glasgow from the surrounding countryside (48x86cm-19x34in) s. W/C. 23-Mar-4 Anderson & Garland, Newcastle #128

PATON, Richard (attrib) (1717-1791) British
£980 $1548 €1421 Action in the West Indies off Cap Francois (18x50cm-7x20in) panel. 24-Jul-3 Lawrence, Crewkerne #914/R

PATON, Sir Joseph Noel (1821-1901) British
£450 $711 €653 Christ in the garden of Gethsemane (24x32cm-9x13in) mono.d.1870. 4-Sep-3 Christie's, Kensington #227/R
£1645 $3026 €2500 Interior scene with gentlemen playing chess (25x30cm-10x12in) s.d.72 panel. 25-Jun-4 Michael Zeller, Lindau #623/R est:2500
£2000 $3140 €2900 Study of a young girl's head (20cm-8in circular) mono. panel. 27-Aug-3 Sotheby's, London #905/R est:2000-3000
£2000 $3320 €2920 The Vision (24x31cm-9x12in) 1-Oct-3 Sotheby's, Olympia #171/R est:2000-3000
£2000 $3440 €2920 Historical scene with Charles I of England (71x92cm-28x36in) 2-Dec-3 Bukowskis, Stockholm #288/R est:30000-40000 (S.KR 26000)
£3360 $6014 €4906 Valley of the Shadow of Death (29x18cm-11x7in) mono.d.1866 prov. 15-May-4 Christie's, Sydney #121/R est:5000-7000 (A.D 8500)
£5000 $7850 €7250 Valley of the shadow of Death (25x39cm-10x15in) mono. i.on stretcher exhib. 27-Aug-3 Sotheby's, London #906/R est:5000-7000
£13873 $24000 €20255 Adversary - where their worm dieth not, fire is not quenched (38x21cm-15x8in) mono.d.1878 prov.exhib.lit. 11-Dec-3 Sotheby's, New York #110/R est:12000-18000
£30000 $54300 €43800 Pursuit of pleasure - vision of human life (25x40cm-10x16in) mono. board arched top prov.exhib. 19-Apr-4 Sotheby's, London #1/R est:20000-30000
£38000 $64600 €55480 Mors Janua Vitae - death the gateway to life (17x74cm-7x29in) mono.d.66 prov.exhib.lit. 26-Nov-3 Christie's, London #12/R est:50000-80000
Works on paper
£3600 $5976 €5256 Paolo and Francesca (31x18cm-12x7in) W/C. 1-Oct-3 Sotheby's, Olympia #174/R est:1000-1500

PATON, Waller Hugh (1828-1895) British
Works on paper
£340 $643 €496 The Dhulochan Banffshire (22x35cm-9x14in) s.i.d.1864 W/C. 23-Feb-4 David Duggleby, Scarborough #656/R
£500 $835 €730 Anglers on the banks of a river (24x35cm-9x14in) s.i.d.12th August 1882 pencil W/C bodycol. 16-Oct-3 Christie's, Kensington #116/R
£520 $972 €759 Moorland view with castle. init. W/C. 22-Jul-4 Bonhams, Edinburgh #334
£550 $990 €803 Killiecrankie (24x34cm-9x13in) s.i.d.1877 pencil W/C htd white shaped top. 21-Apr-4 Tennants, Leyburn #1036
£560 $1025 €818 An east coast fishing village (18x34cm-7x13in) s.d.28th August 1878 W/C gouache arched top. 8-Apr-4 Bonhams, Edinburgh #153
£720 $1325 €1051 Near Forres (10x20cm-4x8in) init.d.1972 W/C. 10-Jun-4 Lyon & Turnbull, Edinburgh #113
£800 $1496 €1168 Kyleakin, Skye (8x13cm-3x5in) s.d.11 July 1866 W/C. 25-Feb-4 Mallams, Oxford #130/R
£800 $1432 €1168 Dollar (25x35cm-10x14in) s.i.d.1988 W/C. 28-May-4 Lyon & Turnbull, Edinburgh #79
£800 $1472 €1168 Arran (26x37cm-10x15in) s.i.d.1864 W/C. 10-Jun-4 Lyon & Turnbull, Edinburgh #25
£820 $1419 €1197 At Hastings (21x51cm-8x20in) mono.i.d.15th October 1862 W/C htd gouache. 10-Dec-3 Rupert Toovey, Partridge Green #50/R
£950 $1777 €1387 Skeabost, Skye (10x24cm-4x9in) s.i.d.1886 W/C arched top. 21-Jul-4 Lyon & Turnbull, Edinburgh #119/R
£1000 $1840 €1460 Keswick (17x25cm-7x10in) mono.i.d.1867 arched top. 10-Jun-4 Lyon & Turnbull, Edinburgh #90 est:300-500
£1100 $2057 €1606 Evening at North Connel (24x36cm-9x14in) s.i.d.1880 W/C arched top. 21-Jul-4 Lyon & Turnbull, Edinburgh #118/R est:300-500
£1464 $2488 €2137 Lochside hamlet (32x51cm-13x20in) s.i.d.1875 prov. 21-Nov-3 Walker's, Ottawa #243/R est:1000-1500 (C.D 3250)

PATOUX, Émile (1893-1985) Belgian
£621 $1148 €900 Jeune femme nue aux colombes (100x68cm-39x27in) s. 19-Jan-4 Horta, Bruxelles #464
£1197 $2071 €1700 Jeune fille assise au jardin (85x70cm-33x28in) s. 9-Dec-3 Vanderkindere, Brussels #58 est:375-625

PATRIARCA, Amato (1945-) Italian
£333 $613 €500 Bus (35x35cm-14x14in) s. i.verso acrylic painted 2003. 12-Jun-4 Meeting Art, Vercelli #164/R
£333 $613 €500 Town (40x30cm-16x12in) s. acrylic painted 2003. 12-Jun-4 Meeting Art, Vercelli #542/R
£403 $745 €600 Icecream (50x70cm-20x28in) s. i.verso. 13-Mar-4 Meeting Art, Vercelli #519
£533 $981 €800 Eros (60x40cm-24x16in) s. acrylic painted 2003. 12-Jun-4 Meeting Art, Vercelli #535/R
£775 $1286 €1100 Mercato (60x60cm-24x24in) s. i.verso painted 2002. 14-Jun-3 Meeting Art, Vercelli #441/R
£1351 $2378 €2000 Bus (60x90cm-24x35in) s. acrylic painted 2003. 22-May-4 Galleria Pananti, Florence #356/R est:1500-2000

PATRICALAKIS, Faidon (1935-) Greek
£2800 $5012 €4088 Two figures (60x50cm-24x20in) s. 10-May-4 Sotheby's, Olympia #38/R est:1500-2000

PATRICK, James McIntosh (1907-1998) British
£3400 $6358 €4964 Flocklone, Casse of Gowrie (44x33cm-17x13in) s.d.39. 21-Jul-4 Bonhams, New Bond Street #163/R est:4000-6000
£9000 $16740 €13140 Autumn afternoon (63x76cm-25x30in) s. 4-Mar-4 Christie's, Kensington #220/R est:7000-10000
£10000 $16700 €14600 Spring ploughing, Carse of Gowrie (71x91cm-28x36in) s. prov. 16-Oct-3 Bonhams, Edinburgh #48/R est:8000-12000
£11000 $20460 €16060 Road from sunnyhall, Lundy, Angus (51x61cm-20x24in) s.d.50 s.i.verso. 4-Mar-4 Christie's, Kensington #219/R est:10000-15000
£13000 $20410 €18850 Breezy day, Carse of Gowrie (63x76cm-25x30in) s. 27-Aug-3 Sotheby's, London #1172/R est:15000-20000
£22000 $34540 €31900 River Tay from Kinfauns (63x75cm-25x30in) s. prov.exhib. 27-Aug-3 Sotheby's, London #1173/R est:20000-30000
Works on paper
£500 $930 €730 View of a bridge (19x23cm-7x9in) s.d.1925 pencil W/C. 4-Mar-4 Christie's, Kensington #221
£650 $1196 €949 June morning Capua (23x28cm-9x11in) s.i. W/C prov. 10-Jun-4 Lyon & Turnbull, Edinburgh #17
£700 $1288 €1022 Kingoody on the Tay (28x46cm-11x18in) s. W/C. 10-Jun-4 Lyon & Turnbull, Edinburgh #16
£700 $1288 €1022 The crest of the hill near Duntrune (36x55cm-14x22in) s. W/C. 10-Jun-4 Lyon & Turnbull, Edinburgh #79
£700 $1288 €1022 Den of Fowlis, Carse of Gowrie (38x56cm-15x22in) s. pen ink W/C. 10-Jun-4 Lyon & Turnbull, Edinburgh #119
£900 $1656 €1314 Volturno's Banks near Capua (23x28cm-9x11in) W/C prov. 10-Jun-4 Lyon & Turnbull, Edinburgh #19
£1200 $2208 €1752 The suspension bridge, Edzell (20x38cm-8x15in) s.i. W/C prov. 10-Jun-4 Lyon & Turnbull, Edinburgh #18
£1400 $2408 €2044 Fallaws and craigowl, Angus (36x52cm-14x20in) s. W/C prov. 4-Dec-3 Bonhams, Edinburgh #27/R est:1500-2000
£1600 $2576 €2320 Fowlis village (27x38cm-11x15in) s. W/C. 21-Aug-3 Bonhams, Edinburgh #1194 est:1500-2000
£2800 $4844 €4088 Landscape with trees (37x55cm-15x22in) s. W/C. 11-Dec-3 Lyon & Turnbull, Edinburgh #10a/R est:1500-2000

PATRICK, John Douglas (1863-1937) American
£212 $400 €310 Portrait (51x43cm-20x17in) s.d.1913 canvas on board. 21-Feb-4 Susanin's, Chicago #5025/R

PATRIGNANI, Carlo (1869-1947) Italian
£1309 $2316 €1950 Mountain village with figure (62x46cm-24x18in) s.verso board. 1-May-4 Meeting Art, Vercelli #376 est:500

PATRIX, Michel (1917-) French
£296 $545 €450 Baigneuses (38x55cm-15x22in) s. i. verso. 28-Jun-4 Joron-Derem, Paris #243

PATROIS, Isidore (1815-1884) French
£950 $1701 €1387 Young girl in an interior holding a book (25x20cm-10x8in) s.d.56. 5-May-4 John Nicholson, Haslemere #557

PATRU, Émile (20th C) French?
£526 $879 €768 Les voiliers (37x29cm-15x11in) s. 16-Nov-3 Koller, Geneva #1201 (S.FR 1200)

PATRYARCHA, Anna (1950-) Polish
£311 $562 €454 Boat scene (64x64cm-25x25in) s. 4-Apr-4 Agra, Warsaw #95/R (P.Z 2200)

PATTEIN, Cesar (1850-1931) French
£1348 $2250 €1900 Les petits barbouilleurs (34x46cm-13x18in) s. 12-Oct-3 St-Germain-en-Laye Encheres #40/R est:2000-2500
£2032 $3250 €2967 Landscape with children holding birds (56x66cm-22x26in) s. painted c.1925. 20-Sep-3 Bunte, Elgin #1418 est:4000-6000
£7000 $12040 €10220 Country meeting (63x81cm-25x32in) s.d.1908. 4-Dec-3 Christie's, Kensington #139/R est:7000-10000
£12222 $22000 €17844 Flower gril (73x49cm-29x19in) s. 22-Apr-4 Christie's, Rockefeller NY #142/R est:15000-20000

PATTEN, William (jnr) (?-1843) British
£800 $1416 €1168 Portrait of a gentleman wearing black coat. Portrait of a lady wearing a lace bonnet (91x71cm-36x28in) s.d.1839 two. 28-Apr-4 Halls, Shrewsbury #547/R

PATTERSON, Ambrose McCarthy (1877-1966) American
£2569 $4188 €3700 Les roses tremieres (46x55cm-18x22in) s. 18-Jul-3 Feletin, Province #104

PATTERSON, Howard Ashman (1891-?) American
£578 $1000 €844 Colorado Mountains (23x28cm-9x11in) s. board. 13-Dec-3 Charlton Hall, Columbia #548/R est:600-900

PATTERSON, Margaret (20th C) American
£1220 $2000 €1769 Impressionist landscape of hillside village (38x46cm-15x18in) s.d.1912 board. 4-Jun-3 Alderfer's, Hatfield #276/R est:1000-1500
Prints
£1720 $3200 €2511 Main street, Nantucket (18x27cm-7x11in) s.i. col woodcut. 2-Mar-4 Swann Galleries, New York #482/R est:1500-2500
£2374 $4250 €3466 Spring in Italy (20x28cm-8x11in) s.i. col woodcut. 20-Mar-4 Rachel Davis, Shaker Heights #261/R est:1500-2500
£2793 $5000 €4078 Coast cedars (18x28cm-7x11in) s.i. col woodcut. 20-Mar-4 Rachel Davis, Shaker Heights #260/R est:1500-2500
Works on paper
£598 $1100 €873 Landscape with tress and river (43x36cm-17x14in) s. gouache board. 10-Jun-4 Swann Galleries, New York #189/R

PATTERSON, Margaret Jordan (1867-1950) American
Works on paper
£441 $700 €644 Mountainlaurel (38x27cm-15x11in) s.d.1897 W/C gouache. 12-Sep-3 Skinner, Boston #339/R
£497 $900 €726 San Luis Obispo, Lisbon (45x30cm-18x12in) s.d.1909 gouache. 31-Mar-4 Sotheby's, New York #32/R
£950 $1700 €1387 Cypresses (33x24cm-13x9in) s. W/C gouache paperboard. 14-May-4 Skinner, Boston #199/R est:1800-2200

PATTERSON, Margaret Jordan (attrib) (1867-1950) American
£494 $800 €721 Landscape (36x43cm-14x17in) 31-Jul-3 Eldred, East Dennis #840/R

PATTERSON, Neil (1947-) Canadian
£537 $972 €784 Moonlight hillside (61x76cm-24x30in) s. i.verso hard board prov. 18-Apr-4 Levis, Calgary #93/R est:1500-2000 (C.D 1300)
£560 $1025 €818 Red flowers (45x60cm-18x24in) s.i. board. 1-Jun-4 Hodgins, Calgary #267/R (C.D 1400)
£588 $982 €858 Mountain flowers (45x60cm-18x24in) s.i. board. 17-Nov-3 Hodgins, Calgary #56/R est:1250-1750 (C.D 1300)
£600 $1098 €876 Sunset camp (60x90cm-24x35in) s.i. 1-Jun-4 Hodgins, Calgary #308/R (C.D 1500)
£1160 $2123 €1694 Fall cabin (60x75cm-24x30in) s.i. board. 1-Jun-4 Hodgins, Calgary #263/R est:2000-2500 (C.D 2900)
£1357 $2267 €1981 Upper Waterfowl Lake (90x120cm-35x47in) s.i. 17-Nov-3 Hodgins, Calgary #136/R est:3000-4000 (C.D 3000)

PATTISON, Abbott Lawrence (1916-) American
Sculpture
£1176 $2000 €1717 Untitled - reclining figure (15x36cm-6x14in) init. carved marble prov. 9-Nov-3 Wright, Chicago #373 est:2000-3000

PATTISON, Robert J (1838-1903) American
£898 $1500 €1311 Road to the village (48x71cm-19x28in) init.d.1860 prov. 23-Oct-3 Shannon's, Milford #261/R est:3000-5000
Works on paper
£736 $1200 €1075 New York Harbour (25x51cm-10x20in) s. W/C. 24-Sep-3 Jackson's, Cedar Falls #761/R

PATTON, Eric (?) Irish?
£493 $863 €700 City evening (60x50cm-24x20in) s. 16-Dec-3 James Adam, Dublin #98/R

PATTY, William Arthur (1884-1960) American
£1190 $2250 €1737 Fishing boats (43x58cm-17x23in) s. s.i. stretcher. 17-Feb-4 John Moran, Pasadena #174/R est:1000-1500

PATURSSON, Trondur (20th C) Danish
£722 $1350 €1054 Composition (104x75cm-41x30in) s.d.85. 25-Feb-4 Kunsthallen, Copenhagen #141a/R (D.KR 8000)

PATZELT, Andreas (1896-1980) Austrian
£403 $737 €600 Portrait of a lady from Vienna (52x41cm-20x16in) s. panel. 9-Jul-4 Dawo, Saarbrucken #86/R
£537 $983 €800 Portrait of a lady from Vienna (80x70cm-31x28in) s. 9-Jul-4 Dawo, Saarbrucken #85/R

PATZIG, Otto (1822-1885) German
£795 $1446 €1200 Biedermeier portraits (109x84cm-43x33in) s.d.1855 two lit. 19-Jun-4 Bergmann, Erlangen #796

PAU, Jan de (attrib) (17th C) German
Works on paper
£417 $688 €600 Golgotha (27x41cm-11x16in) W/C. 3-Jul-3 Van Ham, Cologne #1006

PAUELSEN, Erik (1749-1790) Danish
£945 $1635 €1380 Man being pulled by his nose (75x60cm-30x24in) 9-Dec-3 Rasmussen, Copenhagen #1612/R (D.KR 10000)
£1218 $2096 €1778 Portrait of a noble lady (63x50cm-25x20in) s. 2-Dec-3 Kunsthallen, Copenhagen #545/R est:15000 (D.KR 13000)
£2336 $3692 €3387 Portrait of Count Conrad Holck (96x78cm-38x31in) 2-Sep-3 Rasmussen, Copenhagen #1585/R est:25000 (D.KR 25000)
£2516 $4679 €3673 Portraits of Abraham Schneider and his with Elisabeth (79x62cm-31x24in) pair. 2-Mar-4 Rasmussen, Copenhagen #1459/R est:30000-40000 (D.KR 28000)

PAUELSEN, Erik (attrib) (1749-1790) Danish
£872 $1421 €1273 Portrait of a noble lady with blue dress (77x52cm-30x20in) 27-Sep-3 Rasmussen, Havnen #2084/R (D.KR 9300)

PAUL, Art (1925-) American
Works on paper
£1029 $1800 €1502 Artwork for the July cover of Playboy 1954 (51x37cm-20x15in) ink gouache illus board exec 1954. 17-Dec-3 Christie's, Rockefeller NY #5/R est:1000-1500

PAUL, Bea (20th C) American
Works on paper
£1714 $3000 €2502 Assemblage for the October 1956 cover of Playboy (48x42cm-19x17in) printed paper felt fabric paper collage exec 1956. 17-Dec-3 Christie's, Rockefeller NY #9/R est:2000-3000
£1714 $3000 €2502 Original Mr Playboy rabbit from January 1965 Playboy cover (25cm-10in) fabric paper accessories shaped board on cardboard. 17-Dec-3 Christie's, Rockefeller NY #127/R est:2500-3500
£2000 $3500 €2920 Mr Playboy Rabbit (15cm-6in) fabric paper paper accessories shaped board exec 1958. 17-Dec-3 Christie's, Rockefeller NY #3/R est:800-1200
£2286 $4000 €3338 Assemblage for the August 1957 cover of Playboy (59x46cm-23x18in) printed paper fabric collage acrylic panel exec 1957. 17-Dec-3 Christie's, Rockefeller NY #4/R est:2000-3000
£2286 $4000 €3338 Original Mr Playboy rabbit (23cm-9in) fabric paper plastic metal shaped plastic on board exec 1974. 17-Dec-3 Christie's, Rockefeller NY #220/R est:800-1200

PAUL, John (19th C) British
£700 $1169 €1022 Portrait of the cavalry mount King Victor standing in a courtyard (46x61cm-18x24in) s.d.1885. 14-Oct-3 David Lay, Penzance #386/R
£744 $1376 €1086 Phinea's party (183x168cm-72x66in) s.d.1990 i.verso. 15-Mar-4 Sotheby's, Melbourne #180 est:800-1200 (A.D 1800)
£1700 $2890 €2482 Dark chestnut hunter in a stable (49x59cm-19x23in) pair. 29-Oct-3 Bonhams, Chester #516 est:1500-2000
£3200 $5440 €4672 Groom leading two cobs out of a stable (61x74cm-24x29in) 27-Nov-3 Christie's, Kensington #95/R est:3000-5000
£5000 $8500 €7300 View of old London Bridge (43x63cm-17x25in) 27-Nov-3 Sotheby's, London #198/R est:4000-6000
£7200 $12240 €10512 View of old Northumerland House (56x76cm-22x30in) prov. 27-Nov-3 Sotheby's, London #197/R est:5000-7000
£7500 $13725 €10950 Cheyne Walk, London (76x127cm-30x50in) s. 7-Jul-4 Bonhams, New Bond Street #128/R est:3000-5000
£13000 $21710 €18980 Lambeth Palace (78x128cm-31x50in) 7-Oct-3 Bonhams, Knightsbridge #88/R est:12000-18000
£14000 $23380 €20440 Westminster bridge. Tower of London (73x125cm-29x49in) pair. 7-Oct-3 Bonhams, Knightsbridge #87/R est:12000-18000

PAUL, John (attrib) (19th C) British
£5500 $9900 €8030 Horesguards parade from St. James's Park. The Mall from Buckingham House (61x91cm-24x36in) pair prov. 21-Jan-4 Sotheby's, Olympia #85/R est:6000-8000

PAUL, Joseph (1804-1887) British
£350 $620 €511 Wooded river landscape with figures in rowing boat (36x46cm-14x18in) 1-May-4 Hamptons Fine Art, Godalming #38
£750 $1193 €1088 Tavern by a stream (48x66cm-19x26in) 9-Sep-3 Bonhams, Knightsbridge #71/R

PAUL, Léon Eugene (1889-1953) French
£733 $1349 €1100 L'enfant a la cuiller (27x35cm-11x14in) s. 9-Jun-4 Beaussant & Lefèvre, Paris #192/R

PAUL, Maurice (1889-1965) Dutch
£350 $594 €500 Ladies strolling on a pier (40x50cm-16x20in) s. 24-Nov-3 Glerum, Amsterdam #34/R
£350 $594 €500 Fishing boats on Ostend quay (50x60cm-20x24in) s. 24-Nov-3 Glerum, Amsterdam #38/R
£385 $654 €550 Le retour des pecheurs (40x50cm-16x20in) s. 24-Nov-3 Glerum, Amsterdam #35/R
£455 $773 €650 Moored boats in Menton (34x41cm-13x16in) s. 24-Nov-3 Glerum, Amsterdam #33/R
£461 $847 €700 Moored fishing boats, Oostende (54x65cm-21x26in) s. 22-Jun-4 Christie's, Amsterdam #130/R

£490 $832 €700 Town square in Brussels (49x59cm-19x23in) 24-Nov-3 Glerum, Amsterdam #43/R

PAUL, Peter (1943-) ?
£378 $642 €552 Dunkl Freitag - from Stortorget (55x46cm-22x18in) s.d.77 acrylic. 5-Nov-3 AB Stockholms Auktionsverk #1162/R (S.KR 5000)

PAUL, Sir John Dean (style) (1775-1852) British
£9500 $15010 €13775 Old Westminster Bridge, with the abbey beyond (46x66cm-18x26in) 4-Sep-3 Christie's, Kensington #87/R est:2000-3000

PAUL, Tim (1950-) Canadian
Sculpture
£625 $1063 €913 Moon eclipse, super natural god (49x44x8cm-19x17x3in) s.i.d.1992 verso painted wood. 6-Nov-3 Heffel, Vancouver #93/R est:1500-2500 (C.D 1400)

PAULHARDT, Siegfried (20th C) German
£387 $670 €550 Abstract composition (105x166cm-41x65in) s.d.71. 12-Dec-3 Berlinghof, Heidelberg #1109/R

PAULI, Georg (1855-1935) Swedish
£369 $601 €539 Landscape from Visby (26x42cm-10x17in) s. canvas on panel exhib.prov. 29-Sep-3 Lilla Bukowskis, Stockholm #14 (S.KR 4800)
£385 $662 €562 The pine trees - landscape with evening sun (47x57cm-19x22in) s.d.1897 panel. 7-Dec-3 Uppsala Auktionskammare, Uppsala #162 (S.KR 5000)
£423 $728 €618 Southern town scene (50x60cm-20x24in) mono. s. verso. 7-Dec-3 Uppsala Auktionskammare, Uppsala #195 (S.KR 5500)
£614 $1002 €896 Impressive evening scene (33x41cm-13x16in) s. 29-Sep-3 Lilla Bukowskis, Stockholm #475 (S.KR 8000)
£641 $1180 €962 On the way to the bath (27x21cm-11x8in) s. panel. 14-Jun-4 Lilla Bukowskis, Stockholm #269 (S.KR 8800)
£998 $1627 €1457 Portrait of the artist's wife Hanna (78x60cm-31x24in) s. s.d.33/34 verso. 29-Sep-3 Lilla Bukowskis, Stockholm #375 (S.KR 13000)
£1035 $1852 €1511 Interior from Brunkebergstorg 24 (31x27cm-12x11in) s/d/1887 panel. 25-May-4 Bukowskis, Stockholm #43/R (S.KR 14000)
£1183 $2117 €1727 After the bath (87x61cm-34x24in) mono,. 28-May-4 Uppsala Auktionskammare, Uppsala #269/R est:10000-12000 (S.KR 16000)
£2190 $3724 €3197 Pegasus and Orpheus (50x50cm-20x20in) s.d.1917 verso. 5-Nov-3 AB Stockholms Auktionsverk #760/R est:12000-15000 (S.KR 29000)
£2462 $4234 €3595 View from window in Paris (46x55cm-18x22in) s. d.1883 verso. 3-Dec-3 AB Stockholms Auktionsverk #2274/R est:40000-50000 (S.KR 32000)
£3400 $6086 €4964 Young man on beach (41x67cm-16x26in) mono.d.17. 25-May-4 Bukowskis, Stockholm #234/R est:15000-20000 (S.KR 46000)
£4930 $7887 €7000 Classical interior with female nude and lyre player (53x79cm-21x31in) s.d.1904 lit. 19-Sep-3 Karlheinz Kaupp, Staufen #2116/R est:1200
£14231 $24477 €20777 The trip in the gondola (46x54cm-18x21in) s. painted c.1880. 3-Dec-3 AB Stockholms Auktionsverk #2354/R est:200000-250000 (S.KR 185000)
Works on paper
£439 $821 €641 Reclining woman by dam (20x45cm-8x18in) s.i. dr. 29-Feb-4 Uppsala Auktionskammare, Uppsala #303 (S.KR 6000)
£476 $890 €695 Reading the newspaper (48x38cm-19x15in) s. W/C. 29-Feb-4 Uppsala Auktionskammare, Uppsala #69 (S.KR 6500)
£659 $1232 €962 Mod (116x122cm-46x48in) mono.d.1912 mixed media. 29-Feb-4 Uppsala Auktionskammare, Uppsala #400 (S.KR 9000)
£776 $1389 €1133 Study for the painting - French confirmation candidate (50x37cm-20x15in) s.d.1889 W/C. 25-May-4 Bukowskis, Stockholm #18/R (S.KR 10500)

PAULI, Hanna (1864-1940) Swedish
£437 $805 €656 Studio interior (41x32cm-16x13in) s.d.88 prov. 14-Jun-4 Lilla Bukowskis, Stockholm #243 (S.KR 6000)
£739 $1323 €1079 Portrait of a friend - Richard Bergh (35x25cm-14x10in) s.d.1890 study. 26-May-4 AB Stockholms Auktionsverk #2177/R (S.KR 10000)
£776 $1389 €1133 Coastal landscape with sailing boats at anchor (45x69cm-18x27in) s. 26-May-4 AB Stockholms Auktionsverk #2098/R (S.KR 10500)
£1035 $1852 €1511 Portrait of a friend - Betty (42x28cm-17x11in) s.d.1890 study. 26-May-4 AB Stockholms Auktionsverk #2178/R (S.KR 14000)
£2385 $4102 €3482 Lady wearing pink dress on a beach in Gotland (29x45cm-11x18in) s.i.d.1892 prov. 2-Dec-3 Bukowskis, Stockholm #83/R est:12000-15000 (S.KR 31000)
£20769 $35723 €30323 Portrait of the actress Ellen Hartman (103x66cm-41x26in) s. painted c.1888 exhib. 3-Dec-3 AB Stockholms Auktionsverk #2397/R est:100000-150000 (S.KR 270000)

PAULI, Hanna (attrib) (1864-1940) Swedish
£471 $815 €688 The club Handicrafts Friends (48x63cm-19x25in) i. verso sketch. 15-Dec-3 Lilla Bukowskis, Stockholm #444 (S.KR 6000)

PAULIDES, Hendrik (1892-1967) Dutch
Works on paper
£13889 $23194 €20278 Javanese Dancer (150x100cm-59x39in) mono.d.26 chl lit. 12-Oct-3 Sotheby's, Singapore #15/R est:40000-60000 (S.D 40000)
£27027 $48649 €39459 Gender player (100x92cm-39x36in) s.i.d.1930 mixed media. 25-Apr-4 Christie's, Hong Kong #509/R est:160000-240000 (HK.D 380000)

PAULIN, Paul (19/20th C) French
£282 $468 €400 Portrait de jeune fille (65x51cm-26x20in) 15-Jun-3 Teitgen, Nancy #88

PAULMAN, J (19th C) British
£268 $499 €400 By the camp-fire (30x41cm-12x16in) s. 7-Mar-4 Bukowskis, Helsinki #505/R

PAULMAN, Joseph (19th C) British
£275 $500 €402 After the rain (30x41cm-12x16in) s. 29-Jun-4 Sotheby's, New York #147/R
£550 $990 €803 The end of the day, timber wagon with figures passing a pond at sunset (30x40cm-12x16in) s. 21-Apr-4 Tennants, Leyburn #1121
£1500 $2340 €2175 Victorian harvest scene with mounted figure and field worker (41x61cm-16x24in) s. painted c.1880. 20-Oct-2 Desmond Judd, Cranbrook #809
£2600 $4654 €3796 Fishing from the bridge. Retriever (30x40cm-12x16in) s. pair. 27-May-4 Christie's, Kensington #195/R est:1000-1500

PAULSEN, Fritz (1838-1898) German
£1053 $1937 €1600 Portrait of an elegant lady wearing a white evening dress (155x97cm-61x38in) s.d.1891. 22-Jun-4 Christie's, Amsterdam #80/R est:1000-2000

PAULSEN, Ingwer (attrib) (1883-1943) German
£520 $931 €770 Warft (62x77cm-24x30in) bears mono. board. 8-May-4 Hans Stahl, Toestorf #81/R

PAULSEN, Julius (1860-1940) Danish
£284 $491 €415 Self-portrait (80x67cm-31x26in) s. 9-Dec-3 Rasmussen, Copenhagen #1653/R (D.KR 3000)
£342 $553 €499 Heath landscape (36x50cm-14x20in) init. 9-Aug-3 Hindemae, Ullerslev #74/R (D.KR 3600)
£391 $615 €571 Wooded landscape in evening (36x32cm-14x13in) init.d.98 panel. 30-Aug-3 Rasmussen, Havnen #2290 (D.KR 4200)
£561 $886 €813 Female model on sofa (50x39cm-20x15in) init.d.31. 2-Sep-3 Rasmussen, Copenhagen #1956/R (D.KR 6000)
£588 $940 €858 Study of female nude (26x33cm-10x13in) init. 22-Sep-3 Rasmussen, Vejle #34/R (D.KR 6200)
£613 $1134 €895 Young woman seen from behind (44x33cm-17x13in) init. 15-Mar-4 Rasmussen, Vejle #306/R (D.KR 6800)
£676 $1251 €987 Reclining female nude seen from behind (42x56cm-17x22in) init. 15-Mar-4 Rasmussen, Vejle #305/R (D.KR 7500)
£724 $1296 €1057 Wooded landscape with lake in moonlight (27x30cm-11x12in) s.d.97. 10-May-4 Rasmussen, Vejle #146/R (D.KR 8000)
£935 $1477 €1356 Field landscape with trees in background (54x64cm-21x25in) init.d.29. 2-Sep-3 Rasmussen, Copenhagen #1656/R (D.KR 10000)
£947 $1752 €1383 Coastal landscape from Tisvilde (68x78cm-27x31in) s.d.1915 exhib. 15-Mar-4 Rasmussen, Vejle #307/R (D.KR 10500)
£957 $1550 €1388 Reclining nude (56x76cm-22x30in) init. 4-Aug-3 Rasmussen, Vejle #72/R (D.KR 10000)
£1043 $1668 €1523 Nude woman with book seated on bed (54x41cm-21x16in) init. 22-Sep-3 Rasmussen, Vejle #32/R (D.KR 11000)
£1137 $1820 €1660 Self-portrait (55x46cm-22x18in) s. 22-Sep-3 Rasmussen, Vejle #33/R est:10000-12000 (D.KR 12000)
£2150 $3396 €3118 Reclining fishermen on green sofa (38x55cm-15x22in) init.d.1912. 2-Sep-3 Rasmussen, Copenhagen #1972/R est:10000 (D.KR 23000)
£3480 $6333 €5081 Interior scene with female nude (52x52cm-20x20in) s.d.09. 7-Feb-4 Rasmussen, Havnen #2066/R est:20000-25000 (D.KR 38000)
£13084 $20673 €18972 Adam and Eve (148x153cm-58x60in) s.i.d.1893. 2-Sep-3 Rasmussen, Copenhagen #1554/R est:50000-75000 (D.KR 140000)

PAULUCCI, Enrico (1901-1999) Italian
£500 $920 €750 The Po in Turin (20x30cm-8x12in) s. s.verso. 12-Jun-4 Meeting Art, Vercelli #557/R
£694 $1097 €1000 Sailing boats at Tigullio (20x30cm-8x12in) 6-Sep-3 Meeting Art, Vercelli #726
£700 $1288 €1050 Seashore with three sailing boats (18x24cm-7x9in) s. s.verso. 12-Jun-4 Meeting Art, Vercelli #295/R
£1000 $1800 €1500 Sailing boats (35x50cm-14x20in) s. painted 1970 prov. 22-Apr-4 Finarte Semenzato, Rome #129/R est:1600-1800
£2000 $3620 €3000 Little harbour (45x55cm-18x22in) s. s.i.d.1971 verso. 2-Apr-4 Farsetti, Prato #210/R est:2100-2400
£2069 $3455 €3000 Countryside in Forio (35x50cm-14x20in) s. i.on stretcher. 17-Nov-3 Sant Agostino, Torino #114/R est:4000
£2759 $4607 €4000 Venice, San Giorgio (31x40cm-12x16in) s.d.1932 tempera card. 17-Nov-3 Sant Agostino, Torino #199/R est:3000-3500
£3034 $5068 €4400 Zoagli, terrace (40x50cm-16x20in) s. s.i.d.1957 verso. 17-Nov-3 Sant Agostino, Torino #201/R est:3500-4500
£3103 $5183 €4500 Seascape (34x55cm-13x22in) s.d.1933. 17-Nov-3 Sant Agostino, Torino #200/R est:3000-4000
£3103 $5183 €4500 At the window (50x40cm-20x16in) s. 17-Nov-3 Sant Agostino, Torino #214/R est:3500-4500
£3357 $5606 €4800 Boat on the lake (33x46cm-13x18in) s.d.1942. 26-Jun-3 Sant Agostino, Torino #246/R est:4000-5000
£3448 $5759 €5000 In the park (45x60cm-18x24in) s.d.1932 tempera card. 17-Nov-3 Sant Agostino, Torino #197/R est:3000-3500
£3448 $5759 €5000 Harbour in Liguria (50x60cm-20x24in) s. s.verso. 17-Nov-3 Sant Agostino, Torino #215/R est:5000-7000
£3741 $6697 €5500 Landscape near Susa (55x75cm-22x30in) s. s.i.d.1964 verso. 22-Mar-4 Sant Agostino, Torino #518/R est:8000
£4362 $7809 €6500 Rapallo (46x55cm-18x22in) s.i. exhib.lit. 30-May-4 Meeting Art, Vercelli #83 est:5000
£4545 $7591 €6500 Still life with figs and grapes (32x46cm-13x18in) s.d.1945. 26-Jun-3 Sant Agostino, Torino #245/R est:5000-6000
£4895 $8175 €7000 At sea (65x90cm-26x35in) s. s.i.d.1964 verso. 26-Jun-3 Sant Agostino, Torino #248/R est:5000-6000
£5594 $9510 €8000 Still life (91x75cm-36x30in) s.d.47. 25-Nov-3 Sotheby's, Milan #31/R est:3000-4000
£8276 $13821 €12000 Sailing boats (65x100cm-26x39in) s.d.1951 exhib.lit. 17-Nov-3 Sant Agostino, Torino #216/R est:9000-12000
Works on paper
£352 $585 €500 San Pantaleo (23x34cm-9x13in) s.i. pastel. 14-Jun-3 Meeting Art, Vercelli #168
£364 $663 €550 Seascape (38x32cm-15x13in) s. mixed media. 17-Jun-4 Galleria Pananti, Florence #181/R
£483 $806 €700 Village in Liguria (23x32cm-9x13in) s. pastel. 17-Nov-3 Sant Agostino, Torino #116/R
£537 $993 €800 Langa (26x36cm-10x14in) s. gouache. 13-Mar-4 Meeting Art, Vercelli #163
£667 $1227 €1000 For Garcia Lorca (35x50cm-14x20in) s. mixed media. 10-Jun-4 Galleria Pace, Milan #65/R
£828 $1382 €1200 Dunes (35x50cm-14x20in) s. wash paper on canvas. 17-Nov-3 Sant Agostino, Torino #117/R
£900 $1656 €1350 Seascape (31x48cm-12x19in) s. gouache. 12-Jun-4 Meeting Art, Vercelli #687/R
£900 $1656 €1350 Red cloud (35x49cm-14x19in) s. gouache lit. 12-Jun-4 Meeting Art, Vercelli #943/R

£1200 $2208 €1800 Boats (47x65cm-19x26in) s.d.1958 mixed media. 14-Jun-4 Sant Agostino, Torino #176/R est:1200-1600
£1200 $2208 €1800 Beached boats (34x47cm-13x19in) s. W/C. 10-Jun-4 Galleria Pace, Milan #143/R est:3500
£1241 $2073 €1800 Boats in harbour (35x50cm-14x20in) s. gouache paper on canvas. 17-Nov-3 Sant Agostino, Torino #115/R est:2000
£1310 $2097 €1900 Little bay (48x65cm-19x26in) s. W/C paper on canvas. 13-Mar-3 Galleria Pace, Milan #71/R est:2200-3000
£1528 $2414 €2200 Landscape in the Langhe (46x66cm-18x26in) gouache card on canvas. 6-Sep-3 Meeting Art, Vercelli #414 est:2000
£1667 $3067 €2500 Tigullio Bay (30x37cm-12x15in) s.d.1929 gouache. 12-Jun-4 Meeting Art, Vercelli #249/R est:1000
£3172 $5298 €4600 Landscape in Liguria (45x60cm-18x24in) s.d.1938 gouache. 17-Nov-3 Sant Agostino, Torino #198/R est:3300-3800

PAULUS, Leon (19th C) ?
£547 $984 €820 Stream in Engadin (96x73cm-38x29in) s. 26-Apr-4 Rieber, Stuttgart #893/R

PAULUS, Pierre (1881-1959) Belgian
£912 $1724 €1350 La Sambre industrielle (33x41cm-13x16in) s. panel. 17-Feb-4 Vanderkindere, Brussels #125
£2384 $4339 €3600 Bord de Sambre industriel a Charleroi (50x60cm-20x24in) s. 15-Jun-4 Vanderkindere, Brussels #25 est:4000-6000
£2740 $4658 €4000 Coucher de soleil sur les hauts fourneaux (40x50cm-16x20in) s. 10-Nov-3 Horta, Bruxelles #67/R est:4000-6000
£4054 $7257 €6000 Paysage industriel (60x50cm-24x20in) s. 10-May-4 Horta, Bruxelles #113/R est:7000-9000
£4138 $7655 €6000 Retour au charbonnage au bord de la Sambre (65x81cm-26x32in) s. 16-Feb-4 Horta, Bruxelles #176 est:7000-9000
£4306 $6846 €6200 Paysage de neige (50x65cm-20x26in) s. sold with a book exhib. 15-Sep-3 Horta, Bruxelles #92 est:5000-6000
£5634 $9746 €8000 Maternite (110x100cm-43x39in) s. 9-Dec-3 Vanderkindere, Brussels #95 est:8000-10000
£6250 $9938 €9000 Charbonnage a Wasmes (49x67cm-19x26in) s.i. s.verso panel. 15-Sep-3 Horta, Bruxelles #91/R est:8000-12000

PAULUZZI, Daniel (1866-1956) Austrian
£1867 $3360 €2800 Journey to cemetery (44x60cm-17x24in) s. 22-Apr-4 Dorotheum, Graz #23/R est:900
Works on paper
£500 $900 €750 Composition (26x44cm-10x17in) s.d.1900 pencil. 22-Apr-4 Dorotheum, Graz #117

PAULUZZI, Daniel (attrib) (1866-1956) Austrian
£282 $468 €400 Figures in park (25x19cm-10x7in) canvas on board. 12-Jun-3 Dorotheum, Graz #43/R

PAULY, Franz (1837-1913) German
£473 $832 €700 Boathouse on Vierwaldstatter See (46x40cm-18x16in) s.d.1882. 22-May-4 Lempertz, Koln #1579/R

PAUNZEN, Arthur (1890-) Austrian
£287 $513 €430 Nude (35x28cm-14x11in) s.d.1919 col pen. 15-May-4 Van Ham, Cologne #821/R

PAUR, Jaroslav (1918-) Czechoslovakian
£591 $1039 €887 Cathedral (73x54cm-29x21in) s.d.62. 22-May-4 Dorotheum, Prague #173/R est:28000-45000 (C.KR 28000)
£878 $1493 €1282 Black town (39x56cm-15x22in) s.d.64. 29-Nov-3 Dorotheum, Prague #99/R est:18000-27000 (C.KR 40000)
£1313 $2180 €1917 City (54x73cm-21x29in) s.d.65. 4-Oct-3 Dorotheum, Prague #126/R est:26000-40000 (C.KR 60000)

PAUSER, Sergius (1896-?) Austrian
£8054 $14416 €12000 Peonies (50x40cm-20x16in) s. board. 25-May-4 Dorotheum, Vienna #38/R est:10000-13000
£8392 $14266 €12000 Still life with flowers (73x60cm-29x24in) s. 26-Nov-3 Dorotheum, Vienna #161/R est:13000-20000
Works on paper
£2483 $4445 €3700 Waldhofer, Ybbs, Ybbsitzer Street (34x49cm-13x19in) s.i.d.1943 W/C board. 27-May-4 Hassfurther, Vienna #64/R est:3000-3700
£4196 $7133 €6000 Promenade in Monte Carlo (34x49cm-13x19in) s.i. W/C gouache. 26-Nov-3 Dorotheum, Vienna #143/R est:6000-7000

PAUSINGER, Clemens von (1855-1936) German
Works on paper
£1140 $1893 €1664 Lady in a hat with fur collar (95x63cm-37x25in) s.d.1917 pastel canvas on cardboard. 4-Oct-3 Kieselbach, Budapest #178/R (H.F 420000)

PAUSINGER, Franz von (1839-1915) German
£479 $815 €700 White brown bull (40x56cm-16x22in) mono.i.d.Dec 1880 lit. 6-Nov-3 Allgauer, Kempten #3530/R
£961 $1691 €1403 Deer in forest clearing (72x76cm-28x30in) s. prov. 22-May-4 Galerie Gloggner, Luzern #109/R est:1200-1500 (S.FR 2200)
£2649 $4821 €4000 The hunting party returning home with their bounty (120x177cm-47x70in) s. 16-Jun-4 Hugo Ruef, Munich #1057/R est:1500
Works on paper
£6338 $10141 €9000 Studies of a stag (133x89cm-52x35in) one s.d.1889 one s.i.d.1895 chl paper on canvas pair prov. 22-Sep-3 Sotheby's, Amsterdam #348/R est:1000-1500

PAUSINGER, Helene Paula von (19/20th C) Austrian
£1678 $3003 €2500 Scene from a castle garden, possibly Mirabell Gardens in Salzburg (45x58cm-18x23in) s. board. 27-May-4 Dorotheum, Vienna #88/R est:3000-3200

PAUSINGER, Helene von (1891-1956) Austrian
£306 $550 €447 Flower garden (46x58cm-18x23in) s. board. 23-Jan-4 Freeman, Philadelphia #120/R

PAUTROT, Ferdinand (1832-1874) French
Sculpture
£1208 $2259 €1800 Perdrix (34cm-13in) brown pat bronze. 1-Mar-4 Coutau Begarie, Paris #229/R est:1800-2000
£1500 $2700 €2190 Pair of ducks (43x36cm-17x14in) incised sig. bronze. 24-Apr-4 Skinner, Boston #274/R est:1000-1200
£1765 $3000 €2577 Pair of pheasants (33cm-13in) s. pat bronze. 28-Oct-3 Christie's, Rockefeller NY #244/R
£2118 $3750 €3092 Setter with a bird (30cm-12in) i. brown pat. bronze. 2-May-4 Grogan, Boston #52/R
£2260 $4000 €3300 Pheasants with three chicks. s.d.1870 bronze pair. 1-May-4 Thomaston Place, Thomaston #102/R
£2400 $4080 €3504 Cockerel with lizard (20x23cm-8x9in) s. pat bronze. 28-Oct-3 Sotheby's, London #159/R
£4000 $7200 €5840 Seated retriever with a hare and brace of pheasant (46x46cm-18x18in) s. golden brown pat bronze. 21-Apr-4 Sotheby's, London #73/R est:4000-6000

PAUTROT, Ferdinand (attrib) (1832-1874) French
Sculpture
£993 $1818 €1500 Pheasant (57cm-22in) bears sig dark brown pat. bronze. 6-Apr-4 Sotheby's, Olympia #147/R est:1500-2000

PAUW, Gabriel de (1924-2000) Belgian
£352 $609 €500 Paysage (90x105cm-35x41in) s. 9-Dec-3 Campo, Vlaamse Kaai #617

PAUW, Jef de (1888-1930) Belgian
£400 $724 €600 Paysage hivernal (39x49cm-15x19in) s. panel. 30-Mar-4 Palais de Beaux Arts, Brussels #504
£655 $1212 €950 Portrait de l'epouse de l'artiste (58x46cm-23x18in) s. 19-Jan-4 Horta, Bruxelles #390
£769 $1323 €1100 Rue enneigee (50x60cm-20x24in) s. 8-Dec-3 Horta, Bruxelles #462
£2933 $5251 €4400 Morning mist (100x70cm-39x28in) s. 15-May-4 De Vuyst, Lokeren #100/R est:2200-2400
£6849 $11644 €10000 Rue a Drogenbos (100x125cm-39x49in) s. 10-Nov-3 Horta, Bruxelles #124/R
Works on paper
£1028 $1717 €1450 Autoportrait (60x48cm-24x19in) s. W/C. 17-Jun-3 Vanderkindere, Brussels #231

PAUW, Paul de (1910-1961) Belgian
£2000 $3680 €3000 Portrait d'Africain (54x34cm-21x13in) s. 14-Jun-4 Gros & Delettrez, Paris #288/R est:3000-4000

PAUW, René de (1887-1946) Belgian
£272 $487 €400 Elegante assise (46x37cm-18x15in) s. panel. 16-Mar-4 Vanderkindere, Brussels #291
£604 $1117 €900 Pecheur conversant avec une jeune femme (76x76cm-30x30in) s. panel. 15-Mar-4 Horta, Bruxelles #437
£3472 $5903 €5000 Finishing the ship model (124x124cm-49x49in) s. plywood. 28-Oct-3 Christie's, Amsterdam #149/R est:5000-7000

PAUWELS, Henri Joseph (1903-1983) Belgian
£300 $552 €438 Venice (68x99cm-27x39in) s. 28-Mar-4 Lots Road Auctions, London #368
£317 $548 €450 Scene de rue Orientale (74x101cm-29x40in) s. 9-Dec-3 Campo, Vlaamse Kaai #382
£330 $561 €482 In port (60x100cm-24x39in) s. 2-Nov-3 Lots Road Auctions, London #350
£367 $664 €550 La rade d'Anvers (100x135cm-39x53in) s. 30-Mar-4 Campo, Vlaamse Kaai #137
£420 $777 €613 Boats in a harbour (70x100cm-28x39in) s. 9-Mar-4 Bonhams, Knightsbridge #150/R
£878 $1572 €1300 Le port d'Anvers anime (65x95cm-26x37in) s. 10-May-4 Horta, Bruxelles #465
£1000 $1850 €1460 Rotterdam harbour scene (102x150cm-40x59in) s. 9-Mar-4 Bonhams, Knightsbridge #191/R est:1000-1500

PAUWELS, Jos (1818-1876) Belgian
£336 $621 €500 Table fleurie (50x70cm-20x28in) s. 15-Mar-4 Horta, Bruxelles #481
£350 $550 €508 Tea and cherries in an oriental garden (64x100cm-25x39in) s. 28-Aug-3 Christie's, Kensington #327/R
£350 $595 €511 Pears and plums in the garden (61x80cm-24x31in) s. canvas on board. 6-Nov-3 Christie's, Kensington #893/R
£369 $683 €550 Le the au jardin (54x70cm-21x28in) s. panel. 15-Mar-4 Horta, Bruxelles #482
£379 $702 €550 Table de gouter au jardin (50x70cm-20x28in) s. cardboard. 16-Feb-4 Horta, Bruxelles #298
£380 $680 €555 Fishing fleet in harbour (40x51cm-16x20in) s. panel. 18-Mar-4 Christie's, Kensington #661/R
£400 $680 €584 Fruit course before the fountain (70x81cm-28x32in) s. 6-Nov-3 Christie's, Kensington #897/R
£400 $716 €584 Reading in the shade (39x46cm-15x18in) s. board. 18-Mar-4 Christie's, Kensington #672/R
£403 $721 €600 Nu dans un interieur (50x60cm-20x24in) s. 25-May-4 Campo & Campo, Antwerp #220
£417 $658 €600 Enjoying the garden (50x70cm-20x28in) s. 2-Sep-3 Christie's, Amsterdam #416
£420 $752 €613 Refreshments by lamplight (71x71cm-28x28in) s. board. 18-Mar-4 Christie's, Kensington #660/R

£420 $752 €613 Elegant woman sitting on a table under a parasol (61x77cm-24x30in) s. board. 18-Mar-4 Christie's, Kensington #664/R
£420 $752 €613 Playtime (54x66cm-21x26in) s. 18-Mar-4 Christie's, Kensington #670
£420 $752 €613 Afternoon siesta (53x59cm-21x23in) s. 18-Mar-4 Christie's, Kensington #671/R
£461 $834 €700 Elegante devant la Tour Eiffel (72x100cm-28x39in) s. panel. 19-Apr-4 Horta, Bruxelles #281
£470 $841 €700 En visite. Interieur (60x75cm-24x30in) s. panel double-sided. 25-May-4 Campo & Campo, Antwerp #224
£500 $850 €730 Fruit course in the shade (65x80cm-26x31in) s. 6-Nov-3 Christie's, Kensington #894/R
£520 $931 €759 Summer reflections (45x72cm-18x28in) s. board. 18-Mar-4 Christie's, Kensington #665/R
£556 $878 €800 Tea in the garden with a dog in the background (60x80cm-24x31in) s. 2-Sep-3 Christie's, Amsterdam #414/R
£556 $928 €800 Petit-dejeuner devant le lac (50x66cm-20x26in) s. 21-Oct-3 Campo & Campo, Antwerp #240
£600 $942 €870 After a good meal (60x75cm-24x30in) s. 28-Aug-3 Christie's, Kensington #322/R
£600 $1074 €876 Observation point (56x74cm-22x29in) s. board. 18-Mar-4 Christie's, Kensington #666/R
£600 $1110 €876 In the cafe (80x100cm-31x39in) s. 14-Jul-4 Sotheby's, Olympia #288/R
£600 $1110 €876 On the terrace (61x91cm-24x36in) s. 14-Jul-4 Sotheby's, Olympia #289/R
£600 $1110 €876 In the boudoir (70x82cm-28x32in) s. 14-Jul-4 Sotheby's, Olympia #290/R
£604 $1081 €900 Nu dans un interieur (50x62cm-20x24in) s. 25-May-4 Campo & Campo, Antwerp #221
£621 $1148 €900 Le lac d'amour (76x74cm-30x29in) s. cardboard. 16-Feb-4 Horta, Bruxelles #299
£625 $987 €900 Fruitful lunch (60x80cm-24x31in) s. 2-Sep-3 Christie's, Amsterdam #413/R
£650 $1021 €943 Afternoon tea with a good read (60x69cm-24x27in) s. board. 28-Aug-3 Christie's, Kensington #323/R
£650 $1170 €949 Teddy bear's picnic (50x70cm-20x28in) s. 21-Jan-4 Sotheby's, Olympia #531/R
£650 $1170 €949 Thirsty kitten (60x70cm-24x28in) s. 21-Jan-4 Sotheby's, Olympia #533/R
£650 $1164 €949 Supper by lamplight (56x73cm-22x29in) s. board. 18-Mar-4 Christie's, Kensington #656/R
£650 $1164 €949 Tea in the garden, mid-summer (51x71cm-20x28in) s. 18-Mar-4 Christie's, Kensington #662/R
£658 $1191 €1000 Au jardin (52x64cm-20x25in) s. panel. 19-Apr-4 Horta, Bruxelles #283
£694 $1097 €1000 Table with tea and wine in the garden (50x80cm-20x31in) s. 2-Sep-3 Christie's, Amsterdam #415/R est:700-900
£694 $1160 €1000 Quai Vert a Bruges (53x77cm-21x30in) s. 21-Oct-3 Campo & Campo, Antwerp #239
£700 $1253 €1022 Elegant woman seated at a cafe by the Eiffel Tower (43x55cm-17x22in) s. 18-Mar-4 Christie's, Kensington #659/R
£700 $1253 €1022 Reflections on a backwater (46x56cm-18x22in) s. 18-Mar-4 Christie's, Kensington #668/R
£704 $1232 €1000 Le jardin (50x70cm-20x28in) s. panel. 16-Dec-3 Galerie Moderne, Brussels #795
£724 $1340 €1050 La partie de tennis (56x76cm-22x30in) s. cardboard. 16-Feb-4 Horta, Bruxelles #300
£738 $1321 €1100 Nu (50x60cm-20x24in) s. 25-May-4 Campo & Campo, Antwerp #219
£750 $1178 €1088 Summer refreshments (63x89cm-25x35in) s. 28-Aug-3 Christie's, Kensington #326/R
£764 $1276 €1100 Interior (61x80cm-24x31in) s. 21-Oct-3 Campo & Campo, Antwerp #238
£800 $1256 €1160 Refreshments by the bloom (67x85cm-26x33in) s. board. 28-Aug-3 Christie's, Kensington #325/R
£805 $1442 €1200 Dame au jardin (60x75cm-24x30in) s. 25-May-4 Campo & Campo, Antwerp #222/R
£850 $1522 €1241 Picking cherries (51x71cm-20x28in) s. board. 18-Mar-4 Christie's, Kensington #667/R
£900 $1503 €1314 Lover's punt (60x80cm-24x31in) s. 12-Nov-3 Sotheby's, Olympia #222/R
£950 $1492 €1378 Proposal (56x77cm-22x30in) s. board. 28-Aug-3 Christie's, Kensington #324/R
£1074 $1922 €1600 Dame au jardin (71x100cm-28x39in) s. 25-May-4 Campo & Campo, Antwerp #218 est:1000-1500
£1300 $2158 €1898 Al fresco (68x89cm-27x35in) s. 1-Oct-3 Sotheby's, Olympia #302/R est:600-800
£1400 $2198 €2030 Refreshments before the lake (63x80cm-25x31in) s. 28-Aug-3 Christie's, Kensington #328/R est:500-700
£1800 $2988 €2628 Afternoon nap (51x95cm-20x37in) s. board. 1-Oct-3 Sotheby's, Olympia #304/R est:600-800
£3400 $5644 €4964 Best friends (61x76cm-24x30in) s. 1-Oct-3 Sotheby's, Olympia #303/R est:600-800

PAVAN, Angelo (1893-1945) Italian
£1736 $2951 €2500 Red curtain (40x31cm-16x12in) s. s.i.verso board. 1-Nov-3 Meeting Art, Vercelli #304/R est:2500
£2568 $4519 €3800 Building site in Chioggia (45x65cm-18x26in) s. board. 19-May-4 Il Ponte, Milan #580 est:2600-2800

PAVANEL, Augusto (1940-) Italian
Works on paper
£2953 $5434 €4400 Nu, Africa (160x125cm-63x49in) s.i.d.1993 verso dry pastel tempera. 24-Mar-4 Binoche, Paris #112/R est:1500-1800

PAVEC, Georges (19th C) French
£1200 $2208 €1752 Dressing for dinner (82x45cm-32x18in) s.d.17. 25-Mar-4 Christie's, Kensington #43/R est:1200-1500

PAVESI, Pietro (19th C) Italian
Works on paper
£688 $1100 €1004 Scene of a little girl bringing fruit to her mother (53x36cm-21x14in) s.d.1877 W/C. 20-Sep-3 Pook & Pook, Downington #184/R
£1389 $2264 €2000 Three clergymen at table (52x71cm-20x28in) s. W/C htd white. 25-Sep-3 Dr Fritz Nagel, Stuttgart #1158/R est:1500
£2013 $3705 €3000 Afternoon tea with the cardinals (76x52cm-30x20in) s. W/C. 23-Mar-4 Mealy's, Castlecomer #1096/R est:4000-6000

PAVI, Fosco (?) Italian?
£232 $422 €350 Still life with fish and vegetables (65x80cm-26x31in) s. 21-Jun-4 Pandolfini, Florence #253/R

PAVIL, Elie Anatole (1873-1948) French
£420 $722 €600 Le bassin des Tuileries (46x61cm-18x24in) s. 8-Dec-3 Cornette de St.Cyr, Paris #63
£428 $787 €650 Rue des Poissonniers a Paris (32x24cm-13x9in) panel. 25-Jun-4 Millon & Associes, Paris #62
£433 $797 €650 Un jardin a Marrakech (20x27cm-8x11in) s. cardboard. 14-Jun-4 Gros & Delettrez, Paris #234/R
£570 $1044 €850 Cigale, avant le lever du rideau (22x27cm-9x11in) s. board painted 1912 prov. 7-Jul-4 Artcurial Briest, Paris #94
£600 $1104 €900 Au cafe (15x22cm-6x9in) s. panel. 9-Jun-4 Beaussant & Lefèvre, Paris #198/R
£862 $1431 €1250 Peniche a quai (54x73cm-21x29in) st.sig. 5-Oct-3 Lombrail & Teucquam, Paris #307
£872 $1614 €1300 Paysage Normand (33x43cm-13x17in) s. panel. 15-Mar-4 Claude Boisgirard, Paris #92
£987 $1816 €1500 Sailing boats on a river bank (60x81cm-24x32in) s.indis.i. 22-Jun-4 Christie's, Amsterdam #526/R est:1800-2200
£1409 $2269 €2100 Les bouquinistes quai des grands augustins (27x35cm-11x14in) s. i.verso. 23-Feb-3 St-Germain-en-Laye Encheres #80/R est:2200-2500
£1477 $2732 €2200 Ville au bord d'une fleuve (38x55cm-15x22in) s. 15-Mar-4 Claude Boisgirard, Paris #90/R est:2200-2500
£1600 $2896 €2400 Paris, une place (50x65cm-20x26in) s. 2-Apr-4 Rossini, Paris #63/R est:1800-2200
£1700 $3128 €2482 La loge (22x27cm-9x11in) s.d.1916 i.verso board prov. 24-Mar-4 Sotheby's, Olympia #61/R est:700-900
£2069 $3434 €3000 Piece d'eau au Parc Monceau (60x73cm-24x29in) s. 1-Oct-3 Millon & Associes, Paris #168/R
£2349 $3782 €3500 L'ancien cirque Medrano a Montmartre (50x65cm-20x26in) s. d.1933 verso. 23-Feb-3 St-Germain-en-Laye Encheres #84/R est:2200-2500
£2483 $4594 €3700 Rue a Montmartre (61x50cm-24x20in) s. painted 1924. 14-Mar-4 Eric Pillon, Calais #110/R

PAVIOT, Louis Claude (19/20th C) French
Works on paper
£267 $480 €400 Avant le bain (46x35cm-18x14in) s. W/C col crayon. 20-Apr-4 Chenu & Scrive, Lyon #138/R

PAVLOS (1930-) Greek
Sculpture
£1818 $3091 €2600 Chemise (46x29cm-18x11in) s.verso poster paper plexiglas box. 27-Nov-3 Calmels Cohen, Paris #67/R est:1800-2200
£2113 $3655 €3000 Bar ombre (44x69x14cm-17x27x6in) s.d.1997 posters under plexiglass prov. 9-Dec-3 Artcurial Briest, Paris #537/R est:3000-4000
£2465 $4265 €3500 Bar (47x51x20cm-19x20x8in) s.d.19976 poster under plexiglass prov. 9-Dec-3 Artcurial Briest, Paris #538/R est:2800-3200
£2819 $5187 €4200 Still life (44x34x20cm-17x13x8in) s.d.1996 posters cut shaped panel plexiglass. 29-Mar-4 Cornette de St.Cyr, Paris #81/R est:3500-4500
£6993 $11888 €10000 Affiches massicotees (162x130x6cm-64x51x2in) s.i. verso collage on canvas. 27-Nov-3 Lempertz, Koln #326/R est:10000
£8000 $13600 €11680 Two columns (290x60cm-114x24in) plexiglass paper prov.exhib.lit. pair. 18-Nov-3 Sotheby's, London #51/R est:8000-12000
Works on paper
£8000 $13600 €11680 Six tyres (105x140cm-41x55in) plexiglass paper. 18-Nov-3 Sotheby's, London #50/R est:5000-7000
£8667 $15860 €13000 Arbre (176x273cm-69x107in) stripe collage on canvas prov. 4-Jun-4 Lempertz, Koln #351/R est:12000-15000

PAVLOVSKY, Vladmir (1884-1944) American
£860 $1600 €1256 On the lake (66x106cm-26x42in) s. s.i.d.1937 verso. 5-Mar-4 Skinner, Boston #550/R est:300-500
£881 $1400 €1286 Peacock and hen (84x102cm-33x40in) s. 12-Sep-3 Skinner, Boston #344/R
£1955 $3500 €2854 Sunday in the hills (86x102cm-34x40in) s. exhib. 8-Jan-4 James Julia, Fairfield #726/R est:3000-5000
£3955 $7000 €5774 Harbour in winter (25x30cm-10x12in) s. 2-May-4 Bonhams & Butterfields, San Francisco #1096/R est:3000-5000
Works on paper
£252 $400 €368 Bridge (38x48cm-15x19in) s. W/C. 12-Sep-3 Skinner, Boston #450/R
£282 $500 €412 Waves crashing on rocky shore (14x20cm-6x8in) s. pencil W/C. 2-May-4 Bonhams & Butterfields, San Francisco #1097/R
£363 $650 €530 Landscape view (38x56cm-15x22in) s. W/C. 14-May-4 Skinner, Boston #181/R
£755 $1200 €1102 Fantasy landscape (31x67cm-12x26in) s. gouache triptych. 12-Sep-3 Skinner, Boston #533/R
£791 $1400 €1155 Figures raising the sails on a fishing boat in a harbour (17x23cm-7x9in) s. pencil W/C. 2-May-4 Bonhams & Butterfields, San Francisco #1102/R est:800-1200

PAVOLA, C (19th C) Italian?
£1216 $2141 €1800 Gondoliers on the Grand Canal (68x98cm-27x39in) s. 19-May-4 James Adam, Dublin #48/R est:2000-4000

PAVY, E (19/20th C) French
£670 $1200 €978 Coastal Scene (10x18cm-4x7in) painted c.1900. 9-Jan-4 Du Mouchelle, Detroit #2286/R

PAVY, Eugène (19th C) French
£300 $543 €438 Street scene with figures gathered together resting before arched doorway (28x48cm-11x19in) s.d.1885 board. 3-Apr-4 Shapes, Edinburgh #432/R
£2700 $4779 €3942 Successful hunt (558x71cm-220x28in) s. 27-Apr-4 Bonhams, New Bond Street #69/R est:3000-5000
Works on paper
£310 $533 €453 Alger (28x20cm-11x8in) s.d.1886 W/C. 5-Dec-3 Keys, Aylsham #405

PAWLA, Frederick Alexander (1876-1964) American
£1766 $3250 €2578 Sunny afternoon (71x91cm-28x36in) s. s.i.verso prov.exhib. 25-Jun-4 Freeman, Philadelphia #137/R est:800-1200

PAWLAK, Wlodzimierz (1957-) Polish
£1034 $1728 €1500 Portrait of Rysard Grzyb (88x69cm-35x27in) s.i.d.1984 verso acrylic. 16-Nov-3 Agra, Warsaw #51/R est:500
£1376 $2284 €2009 Fifteen, fifteen, thirty (130x117cm-51x46in) 2-Oct-3 Agra, Warsaw #68/R est:4000 (P.Z 9000)
£1554 $2812 €2269 Composition (130x160cm-51x63in) s.d.1988. 4-Apr-4 Agra, Warsaw #20/R (P.Z 11000)
£1793 $2994 €2600 European culture (134x190cm-53x75in) s. s.i.d.1988 verso. 16-Nov-3 Agra, Warsaw #87/R est:1000

PAWLE, John (1915-) British
£360 $576 €526 Wife and mistress (24x22cm-9x9in) s. 19-May-3 Bruton Knowles, Cheltenham #246
£2500 $4625 €3650 Mougins (64x64cm-25x25in) s. board. 13-Feb-4 Sworder & Son, Bishops Stortford #2114/R est:2800-3000
£2800 $5180 €4088 Lourmarin (61x71cm-24x28in) s. 13-Feb-4 Sworder & Son, Bishops Stortford #115/R est:2500-3000
£3000 $5550 €4380 House in the trees, Bonnieux (65x65cm-26x26in) s. 13-Feb-4 Sworder & Son, Bishops Stortford #116/R est:2500-3000

PAWLOWITZ, Alex (1884-1955) Austrian
£1748 $3007 €2500 Portrait of the artist's life wearing Japanese kimono (190x66cm-75x26in) s.d.1946 i. verso. 5-Dec-3 Michael Zeller, Lindau #755/R est:1800

PAXSON, Edgar S (1852-1919) American
£9626 $18000 €14054 Evening (25x30cm-10x12in) s. 24-Jul-4 Coeur d'Alene, Hayden #136/R est:8000-12000
£13174 $22000 €19234 Springtime hunt (76x46cm-30x18in) s.d.1914. 9-Oct-3 Christie's, Rockefeller NY #85/R est:20000-30000
£26738 $50000 €39037 Chief Charlo (56x46cm-22x18in) s.d.1910 prov. 24-Jul-4 Coeur d'Alene, Hayden #172/R est:30000-50000
Works on paper
£1844 $3300 €2692 Indian portrait (25x20cm-10x8in) W/C. 15-May-4 Altermann Galleries, Santa Fe #70/R
£2395 $4000 €3497 Flathead (34x24cm-13x9in) s.d.1909 W/C pencil prov. 9-Oct-3 Christie's, Rockefeller NY #83/R est:6000-8000
£5348 $10000 €7808 Young Charlo (33x25cm-13x10in) s.d.1917 W/C prov.lit. 24-Jul-4 Coeur d'Alene, Hayden #50/R est:10000-15000
£9626 $18000 €14054 Indian warrior (36x20cm-14x8in) s.d.1902 W/C prov. 24-Jul-4 Coeur d'Alene, Hayden #137/R est:10000-15000
£21390 $40000 €31229 Scouting party (33x48cm-13x19in) s.d.1905 gouache prov. 24-Jul-4 Coeur d'Alene, Hayden #51/R est:20000-30000

PAXTON, William McGregor (1869-1941) American
£11050 $20000 €16133 French landscape (56x68cm-22x27in) s. painted c.1890-93. 31-Mar-4 Sotheby's, New York #44/R est:20000-30000
Works on paper
£588 $1000 €858 Portrait of Mrs Charles Tobin (23x18cm-9x7in) s.d.1935 crayon. 21-Nov-3 Skinner, Boston #397/R est:800-1200

PAYA, Emilio (1935-) Spanish
£272 $487 €400 Canal in Venice (50x60cm-20x24in) s. 22-Mar-4 Durán, Madrid #618/R

PAYEN, G (19th C) French
£2600 $4732 €3796 Elegants sur les grands boulevards (56x38cm-22x15in) s. 16-Jun-4 Christie's, Kensington #261/R est:2000-3000
Works on paper
£1479 $2381 €2100 Le cercle du jeu de polo a Bagatelle, Bois de Boulogne (45x55cm-18x22in) s.i.d.1909 wash gouache. 6-May-3 Coutau Begarie, Paris #35 est:800-1200

PAYER, Julius von (1842-1915) Austrian
£3497 $5944 €5000 Captured in perpetual ice (67x130cm-26x51in) s.d.98. 28-Nov-3 Wiener Kunst Auktionen, Vienna #453/R est:5000-10000

PAYETTE, Jacques (1951-) Canadian
£4018 $6911 €5866 Couple (167x225cm-66x89in) s.d.1985 acrylic col pencil prov. 2-Dec-3 Joyner Waddington, Toronto #164/R est:7000-9000 (C.D 9000)

PAYNE, Albert Henry (attrib) (1812-1902) British
£870 $1426 €1200 Landscape with cows (44x63cm-17x25in) s.d.1840. 27-May-3 Finarte Semenzato, Milan #113/R est:600-700

PAYNE, Ann (attrib) (20th C) British?
Works on paper
£360 $569 €526 Study in solitude (57x43cm-22x17in) s.verso pastels. 24-Jul-3 Lawrence, Crewkerne #879

PAYNE, Charles Johnson (1884-1967) British
Prints
£3500 $5950 €5110 I would bring such fishes back (51x53cm-20x21in) s. hand col exec.c.1934. 25-Nov-3 Bonhams, Knowle #59/R est:1500-2500
£3500 $6195 €5110 Irish point to point (54x75cm-21x30in) i. print hand col W/C. 27-Apr-4 Bonhams, Knowle #12/R est:3000-5000
Works on paper
£380 $646 €555 Office of the 11th Prince Albert's Own Hussars (31x25cm-12x10in) s.i. pencil W/C bodycol. 25-Nov-3 Bonhams, Knowle #2
£680 $1224 €993 Soldier in mess kit (30x17cm-12x7in) s. W/C gouache. 21-Jan-4 Sotheby's, Olympia #264/R
£1100 $2002 €1606 Sketch of a jockey being thrown from his mount, happy landings (24x32cm-9x13in) init. monochrome pastel W/C bodycol. 17-Jun-4 Clevedon Sale Rooms #1008/R est:750-1000
£1500 $2775 €2190 Indian lancer (20x23cm-8x9in) s. pencil pen htd white pair. 11-Mar-4 Duke & Son, Dorchester #55/R est:600-1000
£1500 $2700 €2190 The Warwickshire Yeomanry Cavalry (29x18cm-11x7in) s.i. pencil W/C gouache htd white. 21-Apr-4 Tennants, Leyburn #989/R est:1500-1700
£1700 $2686 €2482 I don't know whose dam column I'm in (35x29cm-14x11in) s.i. W/C over pencil. 23-Jul-3 Hampton & Littlewood, Exeter #390/R est:600-800
£1700 $3060 €2482 Study of an officer in military uniform, holding sword in left hand (29x18cm-11x7in) s.i. pencil W/C gouache htd white. 21-Apr-4 Tennants, Leyburn #988/R est:1500-1700
£2300 $3634 €3335 Polo player on a pony, probably Col Edward Brown (31x29cm-12x11in) s. W/C pencil prov. 24-Jul-3 Lawrence, Crewkerne #868/R est:500-700
£3400 $5780 €4964 Right man on the wrong oss (28x28cm-11x11in) s.i. chl W/C htd white. 27-Nov-3 Christie's, Kensington #38/R est:2000-3000
£3800 $6460 €5548 Old horse looks strong and well, Micky (22x29cm-9x11in) s. W/C bodycol. 19-Nov-3 Sotheby's, Olympia #72/R est:4000-6000
£3800 $6460 €5548 Wrong man on the right oss (32x32cm-13x13in) s.i. pencil W/C htd white. 27-Nov-3 Christie's, Kensington #36/R est:2000-3000
£4000 $7320 €5840 Sport in the Shiney (19x25cm-7x10in) s.i. pen ink W/C prov. 7-Apr-4 Woolley & Wallis, Salisbury #84/R est:4000-6000
£6000 $10020 €8760 Thrusters (35x80cm-14x31in) s.i. W/C pencil. 16-Oct-3 Lawrence, Crewkerne #696/R
£7500 $12975 €10950 Cottesmore, fourteen various character studies (36x48cm-14x19in) s. pen ink W/C htd white. 9-Dec-3 Clarke Gammon, Guildford #31/R est:2000-3000
£8800 $14696 €12848 Roadsters (35x80cm-14x31in) s.i. W/C pencil. 16-Oct-3 Lawrence, Crewkerne #695/R
£9400 $14852 €13630 Hogany tops - a rum un to follow (37x30cm-15x12in) s.i. W/C pencil prov. 24-Jul-3 Lawrence, Crewkerne #869/R est:2000-3000
£16279 $28000 €23767 Glad trong that goes laughing along (32x91cm-13x36in) s.i. pencil pen ink W/C gouache hw/ paper on card. 5-Dec-3 Christie's, Rockefeller NY #131/R est:8000-12000

PAYNE, David (19th C) British
£311 $538 €454 Changing pasture (25x41cm-10x16in) s. i.d.1877 verso. 9-Dec-3 Maynards, Vancouver #129 (C.D 700)
£800 $1456 €1168 River landscape with figures, horse and cart (51x76cm-20x30in) i.verso. 30-Jun-4 Neal & Fletcher, Woodbridge #254

PAYNE, Edgar (1882-1947) American
£2647 $4500 €3865 Autumn landscape (23x30cm-9x12in) s. board. 18-Nov-3 John Moran, Pasadena #71 est:5000-7000
£3911 $7000 €5710 Western hillside (33x46cm-13x18in) s. masonite prov. 6-May-4 Shannon's, Milford #44/R est:3000-5000
£6349 $12000 €9270 High Sierras landscape (30x30cm-12x12in) board prov. 17-Feb-4 John Moran, Pasadena #19a/R est:10000-14000
£6593 $12000 €9626 Boats at Chiogga (25x33cm-10x13in) s. canvas on board. 15-Jun-4 John Moran, Pasadena #30 est:10000-15000
£7065 $13000 €10315 The San Gabriel mountains, late afternoon. Ocean study (30x40cm-12x16in) s. board double-sided prov. 8-Jun-4 Bonhams & Butterfields, San Francisco #4281/R est:10000-15000
£9827 $17000 €14347 Fishing boats (27x31cm-11x12in) s. canvasboard prov. 10-Dec-3 Bonhams & Butterfields, San Francisco #6251/R est:12000-15000
£14365 $26000 €20973 Landscape (46x51cm-18x20in) prov. 31-Mar-4 Sotheby's, New York #108/R est:12000-18000
£14706 $25000 €21471 Kearsarge Peaks, Inyo Co, Calif (41x51cm-16x20in) s. i.verso prov. 18-Nov-3 John Moran, Pasadena #47 est:25000-30000
£19841 $37500 €28968 San Gabriel Valley (51x61cm-20x24in) s. i. verso prov. 17-Feb-4 John Moran, Pasadena #110a/R est:30000-40000
£23352 $42500 €34094 Desert Mesa, Monument Valley, Utah (41x51cm-16x20in) s. i.verso prov. 15-Jun-4 John Moran, Pasadena #48a est:25000-35000
£24528 $39000 €35811 California landscape (51x66cm-20x26in) s. i.verso. 13-Sep-3 Selkirks, St. Louis #54/R est:35000-40000
£27456 $47500 €40086 Tuna boats, Brittany (64x77cm-25x30in) s. i.stretcher. 10-Dec-3 Bonhams & Butterfields, San Francisco #6198/R est:40000-60000
£29101 $55000 €42487 Brittany harbour (61x71cm-24x28in) s. prov. 17-Feb-4 John Moran, Pasadena #44/R est:40000-60000
£29891 $55000 €43641 Brittany boats. Red sails (50x61cm-20x24in) s. double-sided prov. 8-Jun-4 Bonhams & Butterfields, San Francisco #4271/R est:25000-35000
£31792 $55000 €46416 Summit Lake (71x86cm-28x34in) s. prov. 10-Dec-3 Bonhams & Butterfields, San Francisco #6201/R est:65000-85000
£60440 $110000 €88242 Fishermen of Concarneau (74x74cm-29x29in) s. prov. 15-Jun-4 John Moran, Pasadena #48 est:50000-70000
Works on paper
£894 $1600 €1305 River landscape (23x38cm-9x15in) s. W/C. 8-May-4 Susanin's, Chicago #6071/R est:500-700
£2245 $3750 €3278 Boats in a harbour (20x26cm-8x10in) s. pencil. 26-Oct-3 Bonhams & Butterfields, San Francisco #6506/R
£3533 $6500 €5158 Brittany boats in a harbour (29x28cm-11x11in) s. pencil. 8-Jun-4 Bonhams & Butterfields, San Francisco #4321/R est:3000-5000

PAYNE, Elsie Palmer (1884-1971) American
£714 $1300 €1042 Seated nude (23x18cm-9x7in) s. canvasboard prov. 15-Jun-4 John Moran, Pasadena #191

PAYNE, Frances Mallalieu (1885-1975) Australian
£393 $617 €574 Child reading (35x21cm-14x8in) s.d.1922 panel. 24-Nov-2 Goodman, Sydney #59/R est:600-1000 (A.D 1100)
£2996 $5093 €4374 Girl reading by the window. Paris street scene (35x20cm-14x8in) s. board double-sided. 29-Oct-3 Lawson Menzies, Sydney #91/R est:3500-5000 (A.D 7250)

PAYNE, Gordon Eastcott (1891-1983) Canadian
£252 $400 €368 Eastern point light (14x19cm-6x7in) s. i.verso board. 12-Sep-3 Skinner, Boston #505/R
£267 $437 €390 Gloucester fishing boats (56x66cm-22x26in) s. 28-May-3 Maynards, Vancouver #23 (C.D 600)
£1333 $2213 €1946 Down the hill (51x61cm-20x24in) s.d.1932 exhib. 5-Oct-3 Levis, Calgary #87/R est:3500-4000 (C.D 3000)

PAYNE, Harry (19/20th C) British
Works on paper
£900 $1593 €1314 An officer Bombay horse artillery. An officer Madras horse artillery (26x21cm-10x8in) s.i.d.1846-49 W/C bodycol pair. 27-Apr-4 Bonhams, New Bond Street #37

PAYNE, Henry Albert (1868-1940) British
Works on paper
£800 $1336 €1168 Norwegian fjord (20x23cm-8x9in) s.d.1915 pencil W/C. 16-Oct-3 Christie's, Kensington #183/R

PAYNE, Hilma (20th C) American
£376 $700 €549 Water lilies (28x36cm-11x14in) s.d.1939 board. 7-Mar-4 Treadway Gallery, Cincinnati #599/R

PAYNE, William (1760-1830) British
£420 $701 €613 Fetching water across a wooden footbridge (25x43cm-10x17in) s. 20-Oct-3 Bonhams, Bath #181
Works on paper
£210 $375 €307 Marine near Plymouth (20x30cm-8x12in) s. W/C paperboard prov. 14-May-4 Skinner, Boston #137/R
£380 $695 €555 The ferry, Bay of Naples (19x30cm-7x12in) s.d.1817 W/C prov. 7-Apr-4 Woolley & Wallis, Salisbury #181/R
£400 $668 €584 Gaff ridden cutter in a coastal inlet, Devon (0x16cm-0x6in) pencil W/C. 16-Oct-3 Christie's, Kensington #34/R
£450 $824 €657 Fishermen on a river bank (17x27cm-7x11in) W/C ink. 7-Apr-4 Woolley & Wallis, Salisbury #180/R
£460 $768 €672 View of Torbay (17x29cm-7x11in) W/C pencil. 16-Oct-3 Lawrence, Crewkerne #627/R
£500 $850 €730 Slate Quarry at Crabtree, Axminster (15x20cm-6x8in) s. W/C ink. 29-Oct-3 Hampton & Littlewood, Exeter #493/R
£550 $1012 €803 Outside the cottage (8x6cm-3x2in) s. W/C. 23-Mar-4 Bonhams, Knightsbridge #207/R
£610 $1049 €891 River estuary view with figures and boats (13x15cm-5x6in) s. W/C. 5-Dec-3 Keys, Aylsham #416/R
£700 $1190 €1022 Horse drawn carriage (42x57cm-17x22in) pencil W/C gum arabic htd bodycol. prov. 20-Nov-3 Christie's, London #85/R
£1050 $1953 €1533 Mount Edgcumbe, Plymouth, seen across the water (37x55cm-15x22in) s.d.1793 W/C lit. 2-Mar-4 Bearnes, Exeter #312/R est:400-600
£1700 $2890 €2482 Panoramic view of the river Tiber (25x39cm-10x15in) s.d.1818 W/C. 4-Nov-3 Bonhams, New Bond Street #63/R est:1200-1800
£2000 $3680 €2920 Wood river landscape with figures on a path. By a castle, near an estuary (30x44cm-12x17in) W/C pair. 24-Mar-4 Hamptons Fine Art, Godalming #264/R
£3500 $6020 €5110 Horses grazing in a rural landscape with castle ruins beyond (29x39cm-11x15in) s. pencil grey ink W/C. 3-Dec-3 Christie's, Kensington #9/R est:800-1200

PAYNE, William (attrib) (1760-1830) British
£1000 $1800 €1460 Estuary scene in Devon with a man and three donkeys approaching a church (27cm-11in circular) panel. 21-Apr-4 Tennants, Leyburn #1082 est:1000-1500

PAYNTER, Catherine (1949-) ?
£302 $504 €441 Cloete's cafe, port St. John's (79x99cm-31x39in) s. i.d.1981 verso. 20-Oct-3 Stephan Welz, Johannesburg #785 est:4000-6000 (SA.R 3500)
£908 $1626 €1326 Still life of mangoes and strelitzias in a bowl (100x80cm-39x31in) s. 31-May-4 Stephan Welz, Johannesburg #510/R (SA.R 11000)
£991 $1774 €1447 Still life of flowers and monkeys (98x78cm-39x31in) s. 31-May-4 Stephan Welz, Johannesburg #509/R (SA.R 12000)

PAYTON, Edward William (1859-1944) New Zealander
£870 $1409 €1262 At Okere Falls, Rotorua (91x60cm-36x24in) s.d.1912. 31-Jul-3 International Art Centre, Auckland #135/R est:1500-2500 (NZ.D 2400)

PAYZANT, Charles (1898-1980) American/Canadian
Works on paper
£1984 $3750 €2897 Fishing boats at rest in harbour (28x38cm-11x15in) s. W/C prov. 17-Feb-4 John Moran, Pasadena #138a/R est:2000-3000

PAZZAGLI, Aldo (1902-?) Italian
£483 $806 €700 Villa (24x70cm-9x28in) s. s.i.verso cardboard. 14-Nov-3 Farsetti, Prato #425

PEACE, John (?) British
£280 $445 €409 Plaza, Tynemouth (25x35cm-10x14in) s.d.91. 18-Mar-3 Anderson & Garland, Newcastle #330
£310 $493 €453 Levelled ground at the site of the Montague Pit, Lemington, Newcastle (27x41cm-11x16in) s.d.61 board. 18-Mar-3 Anderson & Garland, Newcastle #423

PEACH, Henry (attrib) (fl.1894-1928) British
£400 $732 €584 Chasing the pheasant (31x40cm-12x16in) 6-Apr-4 Bonhams, Knightsbridge #135/R

PEACOCK, George (fl.1875-1900) Australian
£328 $518 €479 Evening stroll (31x45cm-12x18in) s. exhib. 2-Sep-3 Deutscher-Menzies, Melbourne #208/R (A.D 800)

PEACOCK, George Edward (1806-1890) Australian
£14876 $27521 €21719 Views of Sydney and the harbour, New South Wales (14x20cm-6x8in) s.d.1847-48 board pair prov. 10-Mar-4 Deutscher-Menzies, Melbourne #162/R est:16000-22000 (A.D 36000)

PEAK, Bob (1928-1992) American
£1173 $2100 €1713 Boxing match (76x102cm-30x40in) s. lit. 15-May-4 Illustration House, New York #19/R est:2000-4000
£8380 $15000 €12235 Squadron of helicopters passing in front of a setting sun, Apocalypse Now (102x76cm-40x30in) s. 15-May-4 Illustration House, New York #1/R est:7000-10000
Works on paper
£428 $800 €625 Gary Cooper and Audrey Hepburn (53x36cm-21x14in) s. chl. 26-Feb-4 Illustration House, New York #135

PEAKE, Fabian (1942-) British
£800 $1480 €1168 Surrealist Dream (183x244cm-72x96in) mono.d.72. 13-Feb-4 Sworder & Son, Bishops Stortford #50/R

PEAKE, Kathleen (fl.1904-1906) British
£1350 $2133 €1958 Portrait of a young girl in a white dress, holding a puppy (51x41cm-20x16in) s. 4-Sep-3 Christie's, Kensington #80/R est:700-1000

PEAKE, Mervyn (1911-1968) British
Works on paper
£1250 $2125 €1825 Workmen repairing the roof of Sark Mill (26x36cm-10x14in) s.i.d.1950 crayon. 25-Nov-3 Martel Maides, Guernsey #173/R est:400-500
£2000 $3440 €2920 Where are you going to my pretty maid (25x18cm-10x7in) s. black ink W/C prov.lit. 3-Dec-3 Christie's, Kensington #271/R est:2000-3000

PEAKE, Robert (circle) (16/17th C) British
£13000 $23270 €18980 Portrait of Robert Dudley, Earl of Leicester (113x81cm-44x32in) i. panel. 22-Mar-4 Bonhams & Brooks, Norfolk #330/R est:8000-12000

PEAKE, Robert (elder-attrib) (?-1626) British
£70000 $119000 €102200 Portrait of a lady said to be Elizabeth Throckmorton (198x96cm-78x38in) 27-Nov-3 Sotheby's, London #126/R est:30000-50000

PEALE, Anna Claypoole (attrib) (1791-1878) American
Miniatures
£3352 $6000 €4894 Portrait of Constance Thibault Dunn of Philadelphia (8x5cm-3x2in) oil oval exec. c.1830. 20-Mar-4 Pook & Pook, Downington #447/R est:800-1200

PEALE, Charles Willson (1741-1827) American
£3125000 $5500000 €4562500 George Washington (127x102cm-50x40in) painted c.1780-82 prov.lit. 18-May-4 Christie's, Rockefeller NY #18/R est:2500000-4000000
Miniatures
£1136 $2000 €1659 Portrait of James Clypole (5x5cm-2x2in) init. W/C on ivory with lock of hair. 21-May-4 Pook & Pook, Downington #247/R est:5000-8000
Works on paper
£587 $1050 €857 Samuel Smith, hero of the Battle of Mud Fort (13x18cm-5x7in) s.d.10 June 1777 by Samuel Smith ink laid paper. 18-Mar-4 Richard Opfer, Timonium #44/R

PEALE, James (elder) (1749-1831) American
Miniatures
£13408 $24000 €22512 Portrait of Hester Craig Green (8cm-3in) mono.d.1790 panel oval with lock of hair. 20-Mar-4 Pook & Pook, Downington #444/R est:3000-5000

PEALE, Margaretta Angelica (1795-1882) American
£17663 $32500 €25788 Still life with peaches (24x33cm-9x13in) s.d.1865 prov. 8-Jun-4 Bonhams & Butterfields, San Francisco #4013/R est:7000-10000

PEALE, R (?) American
£2733 $5002 €4100 Engines (38x46cm-15x18in) s.d.1821 prov. 6-Jun-4 Rouillac, Vendome #31

PEALE, Rembrandt (1778-1860) American
£904 $1600 €1320 Portrait of an elderly woman (61x51cm-24x20in) s.d.1855. 27-Apr-4 Doyle, New York #12a/R est:3000-5000
£1676 $3000 €2447 Portrait of a young woman (22x18cm-9x7in) s.i. panel oval after Greuze prov. 6-May-4 Shannon's, Milford #112/R est:3000-5000
£4520 $8000 €6599 Portrait of Ethel Hazleton of Boston (76x63cm-30x25in) s. painted c.1820's prov. 28-Apr-4 Christie's, Los Angeles #66/R est:10000-15000
£96257 $180000 €140535 Portrait of George Washington (94x76cm-37x30in) prov. 24-Jul-4 Coeur d'Alene, Hayden #63/R est:100000-200000
£159091 $280000 €232273 Portrait of George Washington (76x64cm-30x25in) s. prov.lit. 19-May-4 Sotheby's, New York #76/R est:150000-250000

PEALE, Rembrandt (attrib) (1778-1860) American
£2610 $4750 €3811 Portrait of General Elijah Clarke (77x64cm-30x25in) prov. 29-Jun-4 Sotheby's, New York #186/R est:2000-4000

£218580 $400000 €319127 Portrait of George Washington (127x102cm-50x40in) masonite. 6-Jun-4 Skinner, Boston #95/R est:12000-18000

PEAN, René (1875-1956) French
Works on paper
£367 $656 €550 Jeune fille au turban (40x32cm-16x13in) s. W/C gouache. 16-May-4 other European Auctioneer #59
£972 $1564 €1419 In the atelier - looking through the folio (54x45cm-21x18in) s. pastel. 13-Oct-3 Joel, Victoria #257 est:1000-2000 (A.D 2400)

PEARCE, Bryan (1929-) British
£1300 $2366 €1898 St. Ives church (53x76cm-21x30in) s. board. 15-Jun-4 David Lay, Penzance #624/R est:1500-2500
£3100 $5642 €4526 St. Ives school of painting (38x56cm-15x22in) s.d.1957 verso board. 15-Jun-4 David Lay, Penzance #114/R est:1200-1800
Works on paper
£500 $835 €730 Fishing boats (36x51cm-14x20in) s. ink pencil. 14-Oct-3 David Lay, Penzance #164
£500 $830 €730 The Chapel on the island, St Ives (19x33cm-7x13in) s. ink over pencil prov. 2-Oct-3 Lane, Penzance #307
£750 $1388 €1095 Fishing boat (35x51cm-14x20in) s. pencil. 11-Mar-4 Christie's, Kensington #354/R
£820 $1369 €1197 Vase of flowers (33x20cm-13x8in) s. W/C. 14-Oct-3 David Lay, Penzance #163/R

PEARCE, Charles Sprague (1851-1914) American
£3892 $6500 €5682 Contadina (32x41cm-13x16in) s.d.76. 9-Oct-3 Christie's, Rockefeller NY #18/R est:8000-12000
£8642 $14000 €12531 Young peasant girl (55x46cm-22x18in) prov. 8-Aug-3 Barridorf, Portland #117/R est:12000-18000
£19231 $35000 €28077 La bourasque (56x46cm-22x18in) s.i. indis i.d.1905 stretcher. 29-Jun-4 Sotheby's, New York #301/R est:8000-12000
Works on paper
£300 $516 €438 Study of a palazzo, Venice (42x30cm-17x12in) init.d.11 pencil black ink W/C. 3-Dec-3 Christie's, Kensington #106/R

PEARLSTEIN, Philip (1924-) American
Works on paper
£1059 $1800 €1546 Two nudes (43x36cm-17x14in) s.d.1964 pencil. 9-Nov-3 Wright, Chicago #412 est:1500-2000
£1073 $1900 €1567 Seated nude (49x61cm-19x24in) s.d.1970 W/C prov. 2-May-4 Bonhams & Butterfields, Los Angeles #3059/R est:1500-2500
£1511 $2750 €2206 Female nude reclining on sofa (48x61cm-19x24in) s.d.1971 pencil prov. 29-Jun-4 Sotheby's, New York #541/R est:1000-1500

PEARS, Charles (1873-1958) British
£420 $777 €613 Towing in a wind-jammer at dusk (51x76cm-20x30in) s. 10-Feb-4 Bonhams, Knightsbridge #120/R
£700 $1288 €1022 Fire over London (38x64cm-15x25in) s. oil on card. 8-Jun-4 Gorringes, Lewes #2101
£909 $1564 €1300 Wind on the English Channel (72x92cm-28x36in) s. 3-Dec-3 Stadion, Trieste #1162/R
£1200 $2004 €1752 Swedish barquentine in Studland Bay (79x112cm-31x44in) s. 14-Oct-3 David Lay, Penzance #596 est:1000-1500
£1800 $3402 €2628 Moonlit Barque (101x127cm-40x50in) s. exhib. 17-Feb-4 Bonhams, New Bond Street #34/R est:2000-3000
£2432 $4500 €3551 Convoy, winter (38x57cm-15x22in) s. canvasboard. 10-Feb-4 Christie's, Rockefeller NY #141/R est:5000-7000
£3784 $7000 €5525 Convoy off Falmouth at dusk (80x128cm-31x50in) s. 10-Feb-4 Christie's, Rockefeller NY #139/R est:8000-12000

PEARS, Dion (20th C) British?
£185 $300 €268 Rolls Royce Silver Ghost (91x71cm-36x28in) 1-Aug-3 Bonhams & Butterfields, San Francisco #801/R
£300 $531 €438 Monte Carlo rally (61x76cm-24x30in) s. 29-Apr-4 Gorringes, Lewes #2516

PEARSON, Alan (20th C) New Zealander?
£865 $1548 €1263 Roman variation (58x58cm-23x23in) i. s.d.1976-77 verso board. 11-May-4 Peter Webb, Auckland #59/R est:3500-4500 (NZ.D 2500)
£1000 $1810 €1460 Yellow still life (60x60cm-24x24in) s.i.verso board. 30-Mar-4 Peter Webb, Auckland #182/R est:3500-4500 (NZ.D 2800)

PEARSON, Augusta (19th C) British
Works on paper
£400 $740 €584 Victorian sitting room (24x35cm-9x14in) s.d.1858 W/C bodycol. 9-Mar-4 Bonhams, Knightsbridge #31/R

PEARSON, Cornelius (1805-1891) British
Works on paper
£280 $501 €409 On the river Torridge, near Bideford, Devon (21x41cm-8x16in) s.d.1870 W/C. 25-May-4 Bonhams, Knightsbridge #7/R
£300 $552 €438 Cattle watering at dusk (17x47cm-7x19in) s.d.1863 pencil W/C. 25-Mar-4 Christie's, Kensington #141/R
£340 $568 €496 Cattle watering in English river landscape (20x41cm-8x16in) s.d.1872 W/C. 19-Oct-3 Desmond Judd, Cranbrook #1070
£400 $728 €584 Lakeland scene with cattle watering (33x51cm-13x20in) s.d.1889 W/C. 16-Jun-4 Andrew Hartley, Ilkley #951
£550 $1029 €803 Lakeland scene with a painter sketching beside a rock (30x47cm-12x19in) s.d.1853 pencil W/C scratching out htd white. 22-Jul-4 Tennants, Leyburn #729
£700 $1190 €1022 Lakeland landscape with mother and child, and sheep grazing (28x54cm-11x21in) s.d.1869 pencil W/C. 19-Nov-3 Tennants, Leyburn #993
£1000 $1800 €1460 Wood stream (32x50cm-13x20in) s.d.1857 W/C stopping out gum arabic. 22-Apr-4 Mellors & Kirk, Nottingham #1039/R est:800-1200
£10000 $15700 €14500 Cattle resting at Loch Lomond. Loch Rannoch, Perthshire (35x72cm-14x28in) s.i.d.1871 W/C pair. 27-Aug-3 Sotheby's, London #984/R est:6000-8000

PEARSON, Cornelius and WAINEWRIGHT, Thomas Francis (19th C) British
Works on paper
£1900 $3477 €2774 Cattle and sheep before a loch (36x71cm-14x28in) s.d.1872 W/C. 27-Jan-4 Bonhams, Knightsbridge #160/R est:1000-1500

PEARSON, Harry John (1872-1933) British
£440 $730 €642 Portrait of a girl with a teddy bear leaning against a wall (39x32cm-15x13in) s. panel. 1-Oct-3 Woolley & Wallis, Salisbury #339/R

PEARSON, Henry (1914-) American
Sculpture
£1899 $3400 €2773 Lime tree bower (66x61x61cm-26x24x24in) prov.exhib. 16-May-4 Wright, Chicago #359/R est:700-900
Works on paper
£299 $550 €437 Square II (18x18cm-7x7in) sd.1959 pen ink. 13-Jun-4 Bonhams & Butterfields, Los Angeles #7056/R

PEARSON, Kathleen Margaret (1898-1961) British
£650 $1216 €975 Autumn (51x61cm-20x24in) s. 21-Jul-4 John Nicholson, Haslemere #138

PEARSON, Marguerite S (1898-1978) American
£430 $800 €628 Still life with white and yellow roses (20x25cm-8x10in) s. canvasboard prov. 5-Mar-4 Skinner, Boston #367/R
£1000 $1700 €1460 Floral still lifes (25x20cm-10x8in) s.i. i.verso pair prov. 21-Nov-3 Skinner, Boston #379/R est:1500-2000
£1519 $2750 €2218 Still life of flowers in a silver urn (76x63cm-30x25in) s. 31-Mar-4 Sotheby's, New York #169/R est:2000-4000
£1863 $3000 €2720 Arrangement with summer flowers (56x71cm-22x28in) s. 20-Aug-3 James Julia, Fairfield #1323/R est:3000-5000
£3409 $6000 €4977 Woman in an interior (61x74cm-24x29in) s. 23-May-4 Hindman, Chicago #168/R est:6000-8000

PEARSON, Peter (20th C) Irish
£382 $623 €550 Liffey gasometer (41x58cm-16x23in) s.d.1983 i.verso board. 23-Sep-3 De Veres Art Auctions, Dublin #185

PEARSON, Robert (?-1891) American
£1400 $2212 €2030 Rustic achievement (76x127cm-30x50in) s. 4-Sep-3 Christie's, Kensington #158/R est:800-1200
£2096 $3500 €3060 Ship at sea (51x76cm-20x30in) s.indis.d.18. 16-Nov-3 CRN Auctions, Cambridge #58/R

PEARSON, William Henry (19/20th C) British
Works on paper
£300 $555 €438 Greenwich (30x48cm-12x19in) s. 9-Mar-4 Gorringes, Lewes #2143
£300 $531 €438 The Lower Pool (26x67cm-10x26in) s.i. W/C. 28-Apr-4 Hampton & Littlewood, Exeter #524/R
£320 $550 €467 Fishing boat returning to port (33x53cm-13x21in) s.d.19 W/C. 2-Dec-3 Gorringes, Lewes #2520
£700 $1204 €1022 Wind rising. Below the Nore (41x66cm-16x26in) s.d.14 W/C pair. 2-Dec-3 Gorringes, Lewes #2519

PEART, John (1945-) Australian
£267 $484 €390 Scenario (36x57cm-14x22in) s. i.d.1992-93 verso oil acrylic. 30-Mar-4 Lawson Menzies, Sydney #77 (A.D 650)
£350 $633 €511 Untitled (117x32cm-46x13in) s.d.1978 verso. 30-Mar-4 Lawson Menzies, Sydney #133 est:800-1000 (A.D 850)
£2099 $3821 €3065 Slip'n n slid'n (203x152cm-80x60in) s. i.d.1972 prov. 16-Jun-4 Deutscher-Menzies, Melbourne #361/R est:4000-6000 (A.D 5500)
£4527 $8193 €6609 Bezerker (347x169cm-137x67in) i. s.d.1971 verso. 30-Mar-4 Lawson Menzies, Sydney #141/R est:5000-8000 (A.D 11000)
£5285 $8297 €7663 Light and shade (170x289cm-67x114in) s.i.d.1989 verso acrylic prov.exhib. 27-Aug-3 Christie's, Sydney #620/R est:10000-15000 (A.D 13000)
Works on paper
£656 $1036 €958 Kokugaku (49x179cm-19x70in) i. verso synthetic polymer prov. 2-Sep-3 Deutscher-Menzies, Melbourne #342/R est:1500-2500 (A.D 1600)
£5957 $10306 €8697 Ravenna (170x366cm-67x144in) synthetic polymer paint. 10-Dec-3 Shapiro, Sydney #102 est:8000-12000 (A.D 14000)

PEASE, Lute (1869-1963) American
£248 $400 €362 Summer landscape with tranquil pond (56x71cm-22x28in) s. 18-Aug-3 O'Gallerie, Oregon #748/R

PEAT, Thomas (fl.1791-1805) British
£3300 $5610 €4818 Portrait of a young girl in a white dress holding a blue sash (80x60cm-31x24in) sold with a portrait by follower of Sir Godfrey Kneller. 26-Nov-3 Hamptons Fine Art, Godalming #184/R est:600-800

PEAT, Wilbur David (1898-?) American
£223 $400 €326 Rural landscape with farm houses in a meadow clearing (46x56cm-18x22in) with sig. 21-Mar-4 Jeffery Burchard, Florida #53a
£279 $500 €407 Urban landscape through the trees, possibly Central Park (41x30cm-16x12in) mono. board. 21-Mar-4 Jeffery Burchard, Florida #53/R

PEBBLES, Frank M (1839-1928) American
£269 $450 €393 Cyprus trees on the shoreline. s. 18-Oct-3 Harvey Clar, Oakland #1285

PECH, Gabriel Edouard Baptiste (1854-1930) French
Sculpture
£1500 $2550 €2190 Bust of young boy (34cm-13in) s.st.f.Susse pat bronze marble base. 28-Oct-3 Sotheby's, London #199/R

PECHAM, Georg (c.1568-1604) German
Works on paper
£300 $549 €438 Birth of Adonis (15x25cm-6x10in) pen ink grey wash black framing lines. 7-Jul-4 Bonhams, Knightsbridge #88/R

PECHAUBES, Eugène (1890-1967) French
£300 $552 €450 Chasse a courre (46x55cm-18x22in) s. 8-Jun-4 Livinec, Gaudcheau & Jezequel, Rennes #140
£333 $603 €500 Scene de venerie (61x50cm-24x20in) s.d.1913. 2-Apr-4 Coutau Begarie, Paris #163/R
£855 $1548 €1300 Chevaux de labour (46x55cm-18x22in) s. 19-Apr-4 Boscher, Cherbourg #711/R
£1222 $2200 €1784 Longchamps (38x56cm-15x22in) s. 23-Jan-4 Freeman, Philadelphia #231/R est:500-800
£1333 $2453 €2000 L'Empereur Napoleon sur le champ de bataille (50x100cm-20x39in) s. 9-Jun-4 Oger, Dumont, Paris #70/R est:2300-2800
£1454 $2428 €2050 Fantasia (46x55cm-18x22in) s. isorel panel. 19-Oct-3 Peron, Melun #317
£1712 $2688 €2500 Course de chevaux (33x92cm-13x36in) s.i.d.1965. 20-Apr-3 Deauville, France #63/R est:2000-2500
Works on paper
£360 $634 €526 Polo players (30x41cm-12x16in) s. pencil W/C. 19-May-4 Dreweatt Neate, Newbury #41
£750 $1380 €1095 Polo players pursuing a chukka (30x41cm-12x16in) s. mixed media. 12-Jun-4 Dickins, Middle Claydon #63
£1958 $3329 €2800 Head to head. Fine chucka (19x22cm-7x9in) s. crayon W/C wash pair. 18-Nov-3 Mealy's, Castlecomer #992/R est:2500-3200

PECHE, Dagobert (1887-1923) Austrian
Works on paper
£400 $720 €584 Study for a roundel (10x10cm-4x4in) init.d.10 ink pencil. 21-Apr-4 Lyon & Turnbull, Edinburgh #237/R

PECHEUX, Laurent (1729-1821) French
£25352 $43859 €36000 Char de Cybele. Venus demandant a Vulcain des armes pour Enee (125x184cm-49x72in) one s.d.1807 one s.d1804 pair. 10-Dec-3 Beaussant & Lefèvre, Paris #33/R est:40000-60000

PECHMANN, Carl Heinrich von (1826-1905) German
£2817 $4873 €4000 Mountain landscape by moonlight (90x160cm-35x63in) mono.d.1879. 10-Dec-3 Dorotheum, Vienna #16/R est:4500-5500

PECHSTEIN, Max (1881-1955) German
£2400 $4392 €3600 Man using scythe (37x30cm-15x12in) mono.d.1928 oil chk prov. 5-Jun-4 Lempertz, Koln #920/R est:3000-4000
£18056 $30153 €26000 Burial of revolution victims II (30x36cm-12x14in) s. board. 25-Oct-3 Dr Lehr, Berlin #390/R est:25000
£26000 $47840 €39000 Fishing boats (30x35cm-12x14in) s.d.1917 i.verso cardboard prov. 12-Jun-4 Villa Grisebach, Berlin #217/R est:20000-30000
£36036 $61982 €52613 Sunflowers (80x70cm-31x28in) s. i. verso prov. 2-Dec-3 Koller, Zurich #3074/R est:80000-120000 (S.FR 80000)
£42000 $76440 €61320 Still life with flowering plant (99x70cm-39x28in) mono.d.1913 prov.exhib. 3-Feb-4 Sotheby's, London #27/R est:40000-60000
£69930 $118881 €100000 Grey day (80x100cm-31x39in) s. s.i.d.21 1922 verso prov. 28-Nov-3 Villa Grisebach, Berlin #46/R est:120000-140000
£80000 $143200 €120000 Yucca with twig (100x80cm-39x31in) s.d. prov. 14-May-4 Ketterer, Munich #175/R est:120000-150000
£100671 $185235 €150000 Punt (80x70cm-31x28in) mono.d.1919 i. verso. 26-Mar-4 Bolland & Marotz, Bremen #690/R est:195000
£105000 $191100 €153300 Italian church, Convent of San Gimignano (70x80cm-28x31in) mono.d.1914 prov.exhib. 3-Feb-4 Sotheby's, London #15/R est:120000-150000
£105000 $191100 €153300 Two nudes in a forest (99x70cm-39x28in) mono.d.1912 prov.exhib. 3-Feb-4 Sotheby's, London #26/R est:80000-120000
£220000 $404800 €321200 Still life (38x46cm-15x18in) init.d.09 board prov. 22-Jun-4 Christie's, London #41/R est:120000-160000
£300699 $511189 €430000 Reclining female nude with cat (55x60cm-22x24in) mono.d.09 prov.lit. 26-Nov-3 Lempertz, Koln #891/R est:400000-450000
£530726 $950000 €774860 Boy on a sofa (70x79cm-28x31in) s.d.1910 prov.exhib. 6-May-4 Sotheby's, New York #135/R est:700000-900000
Prints
£2000 $3660 €2920 Tanzerin (18x13cm-7x5in) s.i.d.1923 woodcut. 3-Jun-4 Christie's, Kensington #136/R est:3000-4000
£2098 $3608 €3000 Bathers III (34x40cm-13x16in) s.d.1912 woodcut. 2-Dec-3 Hauswedell & Nolte, Hamburg #513/R est:4000
£2667 $4773 €4000 Italian landscape (24x33cm-9x13in) s.i.d.07 woodcut. 14-May-4 Ketterer, Munich #158/R est:4000-4500
£2727 $4636 €3900 Cutters in harbour. s.d.23 woodcut prov. 26-Nov-3 Lempertz, Koln #901/R est:3800
£2797 $4811 €4000 Kneeling nude with dish (37x30cm-15x12in) mono.i. woodcut. 2-Dec-3 Hauswedell & Nolte, Hamburg #514/R est:5000
£3776 $6495 €5400 Blonde girl I (43x32cm-17x13in) s.i.d.1908 bears mono. col lithograph. 2-Dec-3 Hauswedell & Nolte, Hamburg #511/R est:3500
£3846 $6538 €5500 Two women talking (40x32cm-16x13in) s.d. col woodcut. 26-Nov-3 Lempertz, Koln #900/R est:6000-8000
£3846 $6538 €5500 Swiss man smoking (49x40cm-19x16in) s. col woodcut. 26-Nov-3 Lempertz, Koln #904/R est:5500
£4000 $7360 €6000 Two different languages (40x32cm-16x13in) s.d.1920 col woodcut. 12-Jun-4 Villa Grisebach, Berlin #206/R est:6000-8000
£5000 $9200 €7500 Fishermen talking (40x49cm-16x19in) s. col woodcut. 10-Jun-4 Hauswedell & Nolte, Hamburg #565/R est:9000
£5667 $10427 €8500 Female nude (38x28cm-15x11in) s.i.d.1911 col lithograph. 10-Jun-4 Hauswedell & Nolte, Hamburg #559/R est:10000
£5874 $10103 €8400 Swiss man smoking (50x40cm-20x16in) s.i.d.1923 col woodcut. 2-Dec-3 Hauswedell & Nolte, Hamburg #522/R est:10000
£5874 $10103 €8400 Dancer in mirror (49x40cm-19x16in) s. col woodcut. 2-Dec-3 Hauswedell & Nolte, Hamburg #523/R est:12000
£6667 $11933 €10000 The dance (43x32cm-17x13in) s.i.d. lithograph W/C prov. 14-May-4 Ketterer, Munich #142/R est:10000-15000
£9091 $15455 €13000 Sailors chatting (40x50cm-16x20in) s. col woodcut. 29-Nov-3 Villa Grisebach, Berlin #167/R est:8000-10000
Works on paper
£733 $1349 €1100 Fishermen and boat (12x19cm-5x7in) mono.d. col chk. 10-Jun-4 Hauswedell & Nolte, Hamburg #556/R
£1000 $1840 €1500 Head of fisherman (21x15cm-8x6in) mono.d.1911 grey brush pen over pencil prov. 12-Jun-4 Villa Grisebach, Berlin #631/R est:1200-1500
£1133 $2085 €1700 Bather (14x22cm-6x9in) mono. pen ink prov. 12-Jun-4 Villa Grisebach, Berlin #630/R est:1500-2000
£1200 $2160 €1800 Coastal landscape with fishing boat (19x14cm-7x6in) mono.d. col chk graphite brush. 24-Apr-4 Dr Lehr, Berlin #373/R est:1800
£1259 $2140 €1800 Bathers (24x17cm-9x7in) mono.d.1910 pen over pencil. 29-Nov-3 Bassenge, Berlin #6944/R est:2500
£1333 $2453 €2000 Female nude sitting (17x17cm-7x7in) mono. pen ink board double-sided prov. 12-Jun-4 Villa Grisebach, Berlin #629/R est:2000-3000
£1667 $3067 €2500 Study of a dance (17x21cm-7x8in) mono.d.1912 pink wax crayon chl prov. 12-Jun-4 Villa Grisebach, Berlin #188/R est:3000-4000
£1667 $3067 €2500 Bathers (26x36cm-10x14in) mono.d. ink prov. 12-Jun-4 Villa Grisebach, Berlin #192/R est:3000-4000
£1958 $3270 €2800 Baltic beach with fishing boats (29x40cm-11x16in) s. chl. 11-Oct-3 Hans Stahl, Hamburg #198/R est:1800
£2000 $3680 €3000 Ballet scene (20x16cm-8x6in) mono.d.1912 col wax crayon ink chl prov. 12-Jun-4 Villa Grisebach, Berlin #185/R est:4000-5000
£2000 $3680 €3000 Seated woman propping her head up (34x30cm-13x12in) mono. ink exec. c.1912 prov. 12-Jun-4 Villa Grisebach, Berlin #193/R est:4000-5000
£2133 $3925 €3200 Five boys at the beach (22x28cm-9x11in) s. pen ink prov. 12-Jun-4 Villa Grisebach, Berlin #632/R est:2500-3000
£2378 $4042 €3400 Eel fishermen on Garder lake in Hinterpommern (28x37cm-11x15in) mono.d.1929 Indian ink pen brush. 29-Nov-3 Villa Grisebach, Berlin #168/R est:3500-4500
£2500 $4325 €3650 Akt (20x16cm-8x6in) init. pen black ink prov. 11-Dec-3 Christie's, Kensington #75/R est:1500-2000
£2667 $4907 €4000 Theatre scene (16x21cm-6x8in) mono.d.1912 W/C ink prov. 12-Jun-4 Villa Grisebach, Berlin #186/R est:5000-7000
£2667 $4907 €4000 Left-hand view of a seated woman (28x22cm-11x9in) ink wash exec. c.1910 prov. 12-Jun-4 Villa Grisebach, Berlin #190/R est:5000-7000
£2667 $4907 €4000 Two nudes in front of a mirror (21x27cm-8x11in) mono.d.09 ink lit. 12-Jun-4 Villa Grisebach, Berlin #208/R est:4000-5000
£2667 $4907 €4000 Stormy seas (44x57cm-17x22in) s.d.1927 ink prov.exhib.lit. 12-Jun-4 Villa Grisebach, Berlin #216/R est:6000-8000
£2700 $5050 €3942 Landscape (25x33cm-10x13in) init.d.1913 ink gouache prov. 1-Mar-4 Ben-Ami, Tel Aviv #4681/R est:4000-6000
£2797 $4755 €4000 Two nudes bathing (29x40cm-11x16in) s.d.1911 chk. 29-Nov-3 Villa Grisebach, Berlin #175/R est:4000-6000
£3067 $5643 €4600 Dancing couple (19x16cm-7x6in) mono.d.1912 col wax crayon chl prov. 12-Jun-4 Villa Grisebach, Berlin #187/R est:3000-4000
£3333 $5967 €5000 Dune landscape with house (64x50cm-25x20in) s.d.1919 W/C pencil. 15-May-4 Van Ham, Cologne #822/R est:10000
£3472 $5799 €5000 Female portrait (28x22cm-11x9in) mono.d. W/C prov. 24-Oct-3 Ketterer, Hamburg #489/R est:5000-7000
£3472 $5799 €5000 Dance (20x22cm-8x9in) i. W/C. 24-Oct-3 Ketterer, Hamburg #490/R est:5000-6000
£3867 $7115 €5800 Couple dancing together (21x16cm-8x6in) mono.d.1912 W/C pen chl prov. 12-Jun-4 Villa Grisebach, Berlin #184/R est:5000-7000
£4000 $7160 €6000 Landscape with grazing sheep beneath trees (14x9cm-6x4in) i. verso Indian ink W/C prov. 14-May-4 Ketterer, Munich #152/R est:6000-8000
£4317 $7079 €6000 Seated woman wearing hat (40x27cm-16x11in) mono.d. Indian ink prov. 4-Jun-3 Ketterer, Hamburg #737/R est:6000-7000
£4333 $7973 €6500 Roadworkers (14x19cm-6x7in) mono.d.1911 W/C ink pencil prov. 12-Jun-4 Villa Grisebach, Berlin #183/R est:6000-8000
£4333 $7973 €6500 Dancing couple (10x13cm-4x5in) col wax crayon ink prov. 12-Jun-4 Villa Grisebach, Berlin #191/R est:7000-9000
£4514 $7538 €6500 Head of Baltic fisherman (60x43cm-24x17in) s.d. Indian ink brush prov. 24-Oct-3 Ketterer, Hamburg #491/R est:7000-9000
£4545 $7818 €6500 Fishermen III (52x75cm-20x30in) s.d.1920 i.verso ink W/C pencil. 4-Dec-3 Van Ham, Cologne #371/R est:6500
£4651 $8000 €6790 Herbsttag (48x64cm-19x25in) s.d.1922 i.verso W/C gouache pencil prov. 3-Dec-3 Doyle, New York #70/R est:8000-12000
£5594 $9510 €8000 Two female nudes on beach (27x37cm-11x15in) mono.i.d.1920 pencil. 26-Nov-3 Lempertz, Koln #893/R est:8000-10000
£5814 $10000 €8488 Nachmittag (49x58cm-19x23in) s.i.d.1922 i.verso W/C pencil prov. 3-Dec-3 Doyle, New York #69/R est:12000-18000
£7333 $13127 €11000 Fishermen with boats on beach (26x33cm-10x13in) s. W/C chk stylographic pen ink prov. 14-May-4 Ketterer, Munich #168/R est:7000-9000
£8000 $13360 €11680 Wald - forest (65x52cm-26x20in) s.d.1934 W/C brush ink prov. 21-Oct-3 Sotheby's, London #106/R est:8000-12000
£8000 $13840 €11680 Schlafende. Woman's head (39x54cm-15x21in) s.d.1917 pencil chl W/C double-sided prov. 11-Dec-3 Christie's, Kensington #74/R est:8000-12000
£9333 $17173 €14000 Spring dance (16x23cm-6x9in) mono.d.1917 W/C ink pencil prov. 12-Jun-4 Villa Grisebach, Berlin #189/R est:7000-9000
£9500 $17290 €13870 Kopf eines fischers mit pfeife - Fisherman with pipe (58x45cm-23x18in) init.d.1913 brush ink prov. 4-Feb-4 Sotheby's, London #548/R est:10000-20000
£9667 $17787 €14500 Bathers (16x19cm-6x7in) mono. W/C blue chk exec. c.1910 prov. 12-Jun-4 Villa Grisebach, Berlin #181/R est:7000-9000
£9790 $16839 €14000 House with garden (64x48cm-25x19in) s.d.1922 W/C over black chk prov. 5-Dec-3 Ketterer, Munich #83/R est:14000-18000
£10000 $16700 €14600 Kuhe auf der weide - cows in the meadow (47x58cm-19x23in) s.d.1921 gouache. 21-Oct-3 Sotheby's, London #107/R est:12000-16000
£10000 $18200 €14600 Vier Manner im Ruderboot (27x37cm-11x15in) init.d.1920 chl wash prov. 5-Feb-4 Christie's, London #378/R est:7000-10000
£11333 $20740 €17000 Evening (59x73cm-23x29in) mono.d.32 s.i. verso gouache prov. 5-Jun-4 Lempertz, Koln #921/R est:18000-22000
£13333 $23867 €20000 Reclining female nude (36x49cm-14x19in) s.i. W/C pencil board prov. 14-May-4 Ketterer, Munich #150/R est:15000-20000
£13333 $24400 €20000 Bathers (38x53cm-15x21in) s.d.1911 gouache board prov. 5-Jun-4 Lempertz, Koln #9119/R est:20000-25000
£14667 $26987 €22000 Cakewalk dancer (16x13cm-6x5in) mono. W/C ink pencil exec. c.1910 prov. 12-Jun-4 Villa Grisebach, Berlin #182/R est:7000-9000

£16000 $29120 €23360 Stehende Frau mit Facher (64x48cm-25x19in) init.i.d.1914 W/C pencil prov. 5-Feb-4 Christie's, London #361/R est:8000-12000
£22000 $40040 €32120 Three nude women (43x56cm-17x22in) s.d.1911 gouache wax crayon yellow paper prov. 5-Feb-4 Christie's, London #362/R est:18000-25000
£30726 $55000 €44860 Village street in Liba with church (49x66cm-19x26in) s.d.1922 i.verso W/C pencil card prov. 6-May-4 Sotheby's, New York #324/R est:20000-30000

PECHSTEIN, Max (attrib) (1881-1955) German
Works on paper
£1050 $1900 €1533 Female nude (18x25cm-7x10in) mono. W/C blk ink exec. 1912. 19-Apr-4 Daniel Cooney, Brooklyn #469179/R

PECK, H Hamlin (?) American?
£347 $600 €507 Military figures with horses and canon (38x30cm-15x12in) s.d.96. 10-Dec-3 Alderfer's, Hatfield #328

PECK, Sheldon (1797-1868) American
£27027 $50000 €39459 Portrait of a boy in green suit (62x53cm-24x21in) panel painted c.1828 prov.exhib.lit. 16-Jan-4 Sotheby's, New York #12/R est:50000-80000

PECK, Sheldon (attrib) (1797-1868) American
£2160 $3500 €3154 New England folk portrait of man in brown vest (71x56cm-28x22in) 1-Aug-3 North East Auctions, Portsmouth #688/R

PECRUS, Charles (1826-1907) French
£927 $1697 €1400 Le violoncelliste (22x15cm-9x6in) s.d.1868 panel. 9-Apr-4 Claude Aguttes, Neuilly #50/R
£927 $1688 €1400 Paysage pastoral (23x32cm-9x13in) s. panel. 21-Jun-4 Tajan, Paris #155 est:600-800
£1678 $3121 €2500 Marine (35x44cm-14x17in) s. 7-Mar-4 Lesieur & Le Bars, Le Havre #117
£1988 $3500 €2902 Love letter (56x45cm-22x18in) s. panel. 18-May-4 Bonhams & Butterfields, San Francisco #124/R est:4000-6000
£2185 $3977 €3300 La joueuse de mandoline (43x34cm-17x13in) s. panel. 16-Jun-4 Renaud, Paris #32/R est:400-500
£2333 $4200 €3500 Literary diversion (32x24cm-13x9in) s. panel. 21-Apr-4 Christie's, Amsterdam #27/R est:4000-6000
£3151 $4947 €4600 Barques de peche (23x13cm-9x5in) s. lit. 20-Apr-3 Deauville, France #97/R est:3000-4000
£3265 $5192 €4800 The piano lesson (34x27cm-13x11in) s. panel. 23-Mar-3 Mercier & Cie, Lille #209/R est:4500-5000
£3826 $7115 €5700 Voiliers (38x55cm-15x22in) s. 7-Mar-4 Lesieur & Le Bars, Le Havre #116
£3873 $6236 €5500 Port de Trouville (25x40cm-10x16in) panel. 22-Aug-3 Deauville, France #40/R est:5000-6000
£3973 $6237 €5800 Dechargement de bois au Havre (38x46cm-15x18in) s. 20-Apr-3 Deauville, France #98/R est:6000-7000
£4899 $9113 €7300 Voiliers dans le port du Havre (38x46cm-15x18in) s. 7-Mar-4 Lesieur & Le Bars, Le Havre #115/R

PECSI-PILCH, Dezso (1888-1949) Hungarian
£1900 $3155 €2774 Restaurant by the lakeside (47x60cm-19x24in) s. 4-Oct-3 Kieselbach, Budapest #2/R (H.F 700000)
£3132 $5418 €4573 Woman in blue-red scarf (99x74cm-39x29in) s.d.930. 12-Dec-3 Kieselbach, Budapest #153/R (H.F 1200000)
£4437 $7676 €6478 Pucunic (123x95cm-48x37in) s. 12-Dec-3 Kieselbach, Budapest #40/R (H.F 1700000)

PECZELY, Anton (1891-?) Hungarian
£275 $500 €402 Three women sewing (24x30cm-9x12in) s. 7-Feb-4 Sloans & Kenyon, Bethesda #886/R
£347 $549 €500 Antiques dealer (30x41cm-12x16in) s. 6-Sep-3 Schopman, Hamburg #817/R
£629 $1051 €900 Arabs playing chess (60x80cm-24x31in) 10-Oct-3 Stadion, Trieste #125/R

PEDDER, John (1850-1929) British
Works on paper
£280 $501 €409 Cattle on a village green (18x26cm-7x10in) s. W/C bodycol. 25-May-4 Bonhams, Knightsbridge #278/R

PEDEMONTE, Adan (1896-1976) Argentinian
£385 $700 €562 CHuirch in Cordoba (14x20cm-6x8in) s. cardboard. 5-Jul-4 Arroyo, Buenos Aires #71/R
£5464 $10000 €7977 Landscape (101x99cm-40x39in) 1-Jun-4 Arroyo, Buenos Aires #88

PEDERSEN, Andreas (19/20th C) ?
£649 $1200 €948 Crucifixion (155x244cm-61x96in) s. 12-Mar-4 Jackson's, Cedar Falls #1028/R est:250-500

PEDERSEN, Carl-Henning (1913-1993) Danish
£6585 $11195 €9614 Blue figure in room with animals (70x80cm-28x31in) s.d.1943 verso. 26-Nov-3 Kunsthallen, Copenhagen #43/R est:100000 (D.KR 70000)
£6635 $10616 €9621 From the wood (61x81cm-24x32in) s.i.d.1978-79. 17-Sep-3 Kunsthallen, Copenhagen #4/R est:75000 (D.KR 70000)
£13146 $21953 €19193 Figure with stars in blue (102x82cm-40x32in) s.i.d.Juni 2000. 7-Oct-3 Rasmussen, Copenhagen #60/R est:125000-150000 (D.KR 140000)
£18779 $31362 €27417 The day today - and the day yesterday (124x104cm-49x41in) s.i.d.1988. 7-Oct-3 Rasmussen, Copenhagen #40/R est:200000 (D.KR 200000)
£30047 $50178 €43869 La Dame et la Licorne (124x104cm-49x41in) s.d.1984 verso. 7-Oct-3 Rasmussen, Copenhagen #49/R est:250000 (D.KR 320000)
Sculpture
£1502 $2509 €2193 The man from the ocean (23cm-9in) init.num.6/20 green pat.bronze incl.marble socle. 7-Oct-3 Rasmussen, Copenhagen #34/R est:10000-12000 (D.KR 16000)
Works on paper
£629 $1000 €918 Central spot. Funny horse (33x46cm-13x18in) s.d.77 ink gouache pair prov. 10-Sep-3 Sotheby's, New York #158/R
£812 $1519 €1186 Fantasy animal. W/C exec.c.1941 prov. 25-Feb-4 Kunsthallen, Copenhagen #9/R (D.KR 9000)
£903 $1661 €1318 Birds (31x43cm-12x17in) init.d.44 crayon pencil prov. 29-Mar-4 Rasmussen, Copenhagen #398/R (D.KR 10000)
£909 $1518 €1300 Untitled (50x40cm-20x16in) s.d.1967 W/C ink. 30-Jun-3 Sotheby's, Amsterdam #355/R
£1221 $2038 €1783 Figure composition (27x40cm-11x16in) init.d.46 prov. 7-Oct-3 Rasmussen, Copenhagen #55/R est:10000-12000 (D.KR 13000)
£1315 $2195 €1920 Heaven's birds (39x52cm-15x20in) init.i.d.1984 W/C Indian ink. 7-Oct-3 Rasmussen, Copenhagen #68/R est:18000 (D.KR 14000)
£1418 $2538 €2070 Sunset II (31x42cm-12x17in) s.d.1950 pastel. 12-Jan-4 Rasmussen, Vejle #567/R est:20000 (D.KR 15000)
£1512 $2707 €2208 Composition with mask and bird (47x36cm-19x14in) init.d.1953 W/C. 12-Jan-4 Rasmussen, Vejle #565/R est:8000-12000 (D.KR 16000)
£1596 $2666 €2330 Yellow seabird, Greece (39x51cm-15x20in) init.d.1951 exhib.prov. 7-Oct-3 Rasmussen, Copenhagen #72/R est:25000 (D.KR 17000)
£2352 $3998 €3434 The blue bird - Myconos (52x40cm-20x16in) init.d.1958 W/C. 26-Nov-3 Kunsthallen, Copenhagen #2/R est:25000 (D.KR 25000)
£2822 $4798 €4120 Greek mountain village - Olympos (40x51cm-16x20in) init.d.1951 W/C. 26-Nov-3 Kunsthallen, Copenhagen #6/R est:40000 (D.KR 30000)
£3005 $5018 €4387 Figure composition with horse, figures and birds (32x40cm-13x16in) W/C on back of wallpaper. 7-Oct-3 Rasmussen, Copenhagen #51/R est:15000-20000 (D.KR 32000)
£3286 $5488 €4798 Figure composition with sun and moon (52x66cm-20x26in) init.i.d.1986 W/C Indian ink prov. 7-Oct-3 Rasmussen, Copenhagen #26/R est:30000 (D.KR 35000)
£3568 $5959 €5209 Female star (77x55cm-30x22in) init.i.d.1977 W/C Indian ink. 7-Oct-3 Rasmussen, Copenhagen #70/R est:30000 (D.KR 38000)

PEDERSEN, Erland (19/20th C) Scandinavian
£244 $449 €366 Small, but with one bone, large, but without (28x42cm-11x17in) s. panel. 14-Jun-4 Blomqvist, Lysaker #1298/R (N.KR 3000)

PEDERSEN, Finn (1944-) Danish
£300 $500 €438 Frustrated woman (100x81cm-39x32in) s.d.72. 25-Oct-3 Rasmussen, Havnen #4015 (D.KR 3200)
£369 $627 €539 Blue dorn (100x81cm-39x32in) s. verso. 10-Nov-3 Rasmussen, Vejle #569/R (D.KR 4000)
£369 $627 €539 Hommage Lord Nelson (100x81cm-39x32in) s.verso. 10-Nov-3 Rasmussen, Vejle #571/R (D.KR 4000)
£699 $1189 €1000 Untitled (104x85cm-41x33in) s. acrylic. 25-Nov-3 Christie's, Amsterdam #81/R
£700 $1288 €1022 Frustreret/kvinde (100x81cm-39x32in) s.d.73 i.stretcher. 24-Jun-4 Sotheby's, Olympia #529/R
£789 $1453 €1200 My heritage (116x89cm-46x35in) s. s.i.d.2000 verso. 22-Jun-4 Christie's, Amsterdam #380/R
£884 $1610 €1300 Vosner i kosmos (110x90cm-43x35in) s. s.i.verso. 3-Feb-4 Christie's, Amsterdam #563/R est:1000-1500
£1200 $2184 €1752 Eathquik (81x101cm-32x40in) s.d.84 s.i.d.84 verso. 4-Feb-4 Sotheby's, Olympia #187/R est:800-1200

PEDERSEN, Hugo Vilfred (1870-1959) Danish
£281 $458 €410 Study of a camel (49x44cm-19x17in) s. canvas on panel. 27-Sep-3 Rasmussen, Havnen #2067/R (D.KR 3000)
£285 $461 €416 From the river Ganges in India (37x49cm-15x19in) s. 9-Aug-3 Hindemae, Ullerslev #35/R (D.KR 3000)
£374 $591 €542 Portrait of a Singaleser, Colombo, Ceylon (27x40cm-11x16in) s. lit. 3-Sep-3 Museumsbygningen, Copenhagen #179 (D.KR 4000)
£374 $591 €542 Sunlight through window (55x80cm-22x31in) s. 2-Sep-3 Rasmussen, Copenhagen #1747/R (D.KR 4000)
£379 $607 €550 Oriental street scene (39x55cm-15x22in) s.i.d.1901 exhib. 17-Sep-3 Kunsthallen, Copenhagen #448/R (D.KR 4000)
£379 $607 €550 From Java (37x31cm-15x12in) s. 17-Sep-3 Kunsthallen, Copenhagen #458 (D.KR 4000)
£380 $615 €555 Greek mythological scene with Andromeda (56x31cm-22x12in) s. 9-Aug-3 Hindemae, Ullerslev #177/R (D.KR 4000)
£449 $836 €656 Kiliputti Mantapam Temple passage, Mandura, Southern India (75x56cm-30x22in) s. prov. 2-Mar-4 Rasmussen, Copenhagen #1481 (D.KR 5000)
£474 $758 €687 By a Buddhist temple (49x59cm-19x23in) s. exhib. 17-Sep-3 Kunsthallen, Copenhagen #450/R (D.KR 5000)
£774 $1239 €1130 Man fighting a tiger (100x140cm-39x55in) s. 18-May-3 Sotheby's, Singapore #27/R (S.D 2160)
£905 $1620 €1321 Asian town scene with temples (100x63cm-39x25in) s. 10-May-4 Rasmussen, Vejle #502/R (D.KR 10000)
£1438 $2674 €2099 Two Indians and their camels by the Taj Mahal in Agra (72x98cm-28x39in) s. prov. 2-Mar-4 Rasmussen, Copenhagen #1376/R est:12000 (D.KR 16000)
£1880 $3440 €2745 From Liseleje. Cabins, Sumatra. Portrait of H H T Soesoehoenan. s. three prov. 9-Jun-4 Rasmussen, Copenhagen #1531/R est:10000 (D.KR 21000)

PEDERSEN, Jens Peder (1859-1949) Danish
£340 $609 €496 Landscape with stones and wild flowers (47x68cm-19x27in) s. 12-Jan-4 Rasmussen, Vejle #88/R (D.KR 3600)
£459 $744 €666 Wooded landscape in spring (47x69cm-19x27in) 4-Aug-3 Rasmussen, Vejle #372 (D.KR 4800)

PEDERSEN, Thorolf (1858-1942) Danish
£437 $805 €656 Seascape (45x65cm-18x26in) s. 14-Jun-4 Lilla Bukowskis, Stockholm #744/R (S.KR 6000)

PEDERSEN, Viggo (1854-1926) Danish
£267 $485 €401 Coastal landscape from Tisvilde (24x46cm-9x18in) s.i. panel. 19-Jun-4 Rasmussen, Havnen #2054/R (D.KR 3000)
£276 $470 €403 Summer in the garden (78x92cm-31x36in) s/. 10-Nov-3 Rasmussen, Vejle #116/R (D.KR 3000)
£287 $516 €419 Interior scene with dinner table (50x41cm-20x16in) s.d.1907. 24-Apr-4 Rasmussen, Havnen #2333/R (D.KR 3200)
£292 $496 €426 Autumn day by woodland lake (47x51cm-19x20in) s. panel. 29-Nov-3 Rasmussen, Havnen #2299 (D.KR 3100)
£307 $567 €448 Sunset over the sea (34x48cm-13x19in) s.d.1904. 15-Mar-4 Rasmussen, Vejle #428 (D.KR 3400)

£307 $567 €448 Summer landscape with cattle and sheep (22x36cm-9x14in) s/d/1886. 15-Mar-4 Rasmussen, Vejle #451/R (D.KR 3400)
£313 $573 €457 Tall trees by the water (38x55cm-15x22in) s. 9-Jun-4 Rasmussen, Copenhagen #1729 (D.KR 3500)
£316 $591 €461 Cattle grazing near thatched farmhouse (18x24cm-7x9in) s.i.d.August 1885. 25-Feb-4 Museumsbygningen, Copenhagen #191 (D.KR 3500)
£335 $543 €486 Evening glow over hilly landscape (38x50cm-15x20in) s.d.1892. 4-Aug-3 Rasmussen, Vejle #447 (D.KR 3500)
£373 $605 €541 Landscape with houses by road (38x50cm-15x20in) s.d.1915 panel. 4-Aug-3 Rasmussen, Vejle #319/R (D.KR 3900)
£425 $761 €621 Summer landscape, Denmark (74x86cm-29x34in) s.d.1887 prov. 12-Jan-4 Rasmussen, Vejle #131/R (D.KR 4500)
£448 $819 €654 Sunset over the sea, Haga (58x72cm-23x28in) s. exhib. 9-Jun-4 Rasmussen, Copenhagen #1652/R (D.KR 5000)
£466 $839 €680 Evening on the beach at Tisvildeleje (29x73cm-11x29in) s.d.1904 verso panel. 24-Apr-4 Rasmussen, Havnen #2003/R (D.KR 5200)
£494 $919 €721 Girl and chickens in front of farmhouse (28x48cm-11x19in) s. 2-Mar-4 Rasmussen, Copenhagen #1610 (D.KR 5500)
£537 $983 €784 Landscape from Sora with Italian woman and donkey (54x37cm-21x15in) s.i.d.1884. 9-Jun-4 Rasmussen, Copenhagen #1706/R (D.KR 6000)
£539 $1003 €787 Calves in the shade of a walnut tree behind the farm (39x60cm-15x24in) s.i.d.1881. 2-Mar-4 Rasmussen, Copenhagen #1381/R (D.KR 6000)
£673 $1063 €976 Hilly landscape with lambs, Skramstrup (55x46cm-22x18in) s. 3-Sep-3 Museumsbygningen, Copenhagen #182 (D.KR 7200)
£699 $1097 €1021 Figures in field landscape (35x44cm-14x17in) init.d.22.9.1892. 30-Aug-3 Rasmussen, Havnen #2059/R (D.KR 7500)
£721 $1335 €1053 View of Tisvilde (48x74cm-19x29in) s.i.d.1904. 15-Mar-4 Rasmussen, Vejle #298/R (D.KR 8000)
£1078 $2005 €1574 Girl wearing white head scarf picking something from the grass (25x32cm-10x13in) s.i.d.1887. 2-Mar-4 Rasmussen, Copenhagen #1589/R est:12000 (D.KR 12000)
£1121 $1772 €1625 Danish summer landscape with corn fields (19x41cm-7x16in) s.d.1879. 3-Sep-3 Museumsbygningen, Copenhagen #190/R est:12000 (D.KR 12000)
£1164 $2130 €1699 Interior scene with the artist's wife (31x40cm-12x16in) s. 9-Jun-4 Rasmussen, Copenhagen #1953/R est:8000-10000 (D.KR 13000)
£1340 $2170 €1943 Two girls looking at flowers on the outskirts of village (46x64cm-18x25in) s. 4-Aug-3 Rasmussen, Vejle #285/R est:15000 (D.KR 14000)
£2156 $4011 €3148 Old farm in winter sunshine (67x81cm-26x32in) s.i.d.9.3.1911 exhib. 2-Mar-4 Rasmussen, Copenhagen #1655/R est:25000 (D.KR 24000)
£2430 $3839 €3524 Cliffs by the sea, Tisvilde (123x151cm-48x59in) s.d.1901 exhib. 2-Sep-3 Rasmussen, Copenhagen #1759/R est:30000 (D.KR 26000)
£2686 $4915 €3922 Italian women on terrace in Sora (37x60cm-15x24in) s. panel prov. 9-Jun-4 Rasmussen, Copenhagen #1920/R est:30000-40000 (D.KR 30000)
£2871 $4651 €4163 Farm yard with girl feeding chickens in winter (44x67cm-17x26in) s. 4-Aug-3 Rasmussen, Vejle #357/R est:40000 (D.KR 30000)
Works on paper
£537 $983 €784 The road to Kajemose (65x105cm-26x41in) s. d.1895-1907 pastel. 9-Jun-4 Rasmussen, Copenhagen #1721/R (D.KR 6000)

PEDERSEN, Vilhelm (1820-1859) Danish
£394 $642 €575 Farm and figures by the coast (26x37cm-10x15in) s. 28-Sep-3 Hindemae, Ullerslev #54/R (D.KR 4200)
£1348 $2507 €1968 Father building house of cards, mother and children watching (47x43cm-19x17in) s. 2-Mar-4 Rasmussen, Copenhagen #1530/R est:15000 (D.KR 15000)
£1890 $3270 €2759 Horses carrying post by country inn (31x47cm-12x19in) i.verso. 9-Dec-3 Rasmussen, Copenhagen #1579/R est:10000-15000 (D.KR 20000)

PEDERZOLI, Samuele (1968-) Italian
£267 $491 €400 Anna (100x100cm-39x39in) s.d.2004 verso. 12-Jun-4 Meeting Art, Vercelli #951

PEDON, Bartolomeo (1665-1732) Italian
£20000 $35800 €30000 Stormy seascapes (61x92cm-24x36in) pair. 12-May-4 Finarte Semenzato, Milan #55/R est:35000-45000

PEDRAZA OSTOS, Jose (1888-1937) Spanish
Works on paper
£382 $607 €550 Pueblo (59x76cm-23x30in) s. 29-Apr-3 Durán, Madrid #746/R

PEDRAZA, Jorge (1962-) Spanish
£285 $533 €425 Landscape in Murcia (55x46cm-22x18in) s. s.i.d.2003 verso board. 24-Feb-4 Durán, Madrid #42/R

PEDRETTI, Gian (1926-) Swiss
Works on paper
£413 $756 €603 Figures (75x75cm-30x30in) s.d.1970 verso mixed media sand canvas prov. 4-Jun-4 Zofingen, Switzerland #2913 (S.FR 950)

PEDRETTI, Turo (1896-1964) Swiss
£3211 $5362 €4656 Large artichokes (75x74cm-30x29in) s. i.d.1960 verso. 23-Jun-3 Philippe Schuler, Zurich #3413 est:7000-9000 (S.FR 7000)
£3670 $6128 €5322 Hunting spoils in Elsace (84x105cm-33x41in) s.d. i. verso. 23-Jun-3 Philippe Schuler, Zurich #3412 est:9000-12000 (S.FR 8000)
£3812 $6213 €5566 Winter (61x75cm-24x30in) s.d.55 s.i.d. verso masonite. 29-Sep-3 Christie's, Zurich #70/R est:7000-9000 (S.FR 8500)
£4803 $8598 €7012 Botta Maria, storm (61x75cm-24x30in) s.d.1957 s.i.d.1957 verso prov.lit. 26-May-4 Sotheby's, Zurich #65/R est:15000-20000 (S.FR 11000)
£7623 $12731 €11130 Celerina with Piz Margna (60x74cm-24x29in) s.d.45 canvas on masonite. 24-Oct-3 Hans Widmer, St Gallen #64/R est:7500-12000 (S.FR 17000)
£10860 $18787 €15856 Winter scene with footpath (70x75cm-28x30in) s. prov.lit. 9-Dec-3 Sotheby's, Zurich #104/R est:24000-28000 (S.FR 24000)
£11312 $19570 €16516 View through old larches (85x85cm-33x33in) s.d.1956 s.i.d.1956 exhib.lit. 9-Dec-3 Sotheby's, Zurich #80/R est:25000-30000 (S.FR 25000)
Works on paper
£814 $1409 €1188 Palugletscher (4x32cm-2x13in) mono. s.i. on mount. 9-Dec-3 Sotheby's, Zurich #95/R est:1800-2500 (S.FR 1800)

PEDRICK, Frederick T (fl.1915-16) British
Works on paper
£660 $1102 €964 Barbican, Plymouth (29x39cm-11x15in) s. W/C htd white. 14-Oct-3 Bearnes, Exeter #346

PEDRINI, Domenico (1728-1800) Italian
Works on paper
£2111 $3800 €3082 Elevation and ground plan with subsidiary studies of a capital and altar (59x43cm-23x17in) i. pen brown ink grey wash. 22-Jan-4 Christie's, Rockefeller NY #79/R est:3000-5000

PEDROSO, Joao (1825-1890) Portuguese
£10067 $18020 €15000 Seascapes (24x31cm-9x12in) s. pair. 31-May-4 Cabral Moncada Leiloes, Lisbon #86/R est:12000-18000

PEEBLES, Don (1922-) New Zealander
£870 $1400 €1270 Untitled - green blue (167x175cm-66x69in) s.d.1987 verso acrylic. 20-Aug-3 Dunbar Sloane, Auckland #62 est:1800-2400 (NZ.D 2400)
£1071 $1939 €1564 Relief painting (60x64cm-24x25in) s.i.d.1977-78 acrylic canvas on wood. 30-Mar-4 Peter Webb, Auckland #145/R est:3500-5000 (NZ.D 3000)
£1224 $2227 €1787 Ascending (60x33cm-24x13in) i.d.1997 verso acrylic pencil paper on board. 29-Jun-4 Peter Webb, Auckland #185/R est:3000-5000 (NZ.D 3500)
Works on paper
£277 $496 €404 Wellington (19x27cm-7x11in) s.i.d.79 mixed media. 12-May-4 Dunbar Sloane, Wellington #216 (NZ.D 800)

PEEBLES, Roy B (1899-1957) American
£206 $350 €301 October (51x56cm-20x22in) s. 21-Nov-3 Skinner, Boston #441/R

PEEL, James (1811-1906) British
£300 $477 €438 On the Tyne at Elswick (19x29cm-7x11in) s.i.d.1845 verso exhib. 18-Mar-3 Anderson & Garland, Newcastle #533
£650 $1170 €949 Lakeland landscape with cattle, a river and mountains (40x66cm-16x26in) s. indis.i.verso. 21-Apr-4 Tennants, Leyburn #1171
£700 $1302 €1022 Figures on a riverside path, Beddgelert, North Wales (41x66cm-16x26in) s. 4-Mar-4 Christie's, Kensington #455/R
£750 $1373 €1095 Travellers on the path in an extensive mountainous landscape (41x66cm-16x26in) s.d.1875. 7-Apr-4 Bonhams, Bury St Edmunds #465
£855 $1565 €1248 Fisherwoman and her donkey on a coastal path (51x76cm-20x30in) s. 8-Apr-4 Christie's, Kensington #150/R
£988 $1700 €1442 Surrey Village (41x66cm-16x26in) s. 7-Dec-3 Freeman, Philadelphia #34 est:1500-2500
£1200 $2004 €1752 Drover with cattle (43x64cm-17x25in) mono. 17-Oct-3 Keys, Aylsham #713
£1200 $2148 €1752 Cattle grazing in a landscape (30x46cm-12x18in) s. 27-May-4 Christie's, Kensington #185/R est:500-700
£1250 $2250 €1825 Peasant girl with donkey above a jetty, sailing craft beyond (51x76cm-20x30in) s. 25-Jan-4 Desmond Judd, Cranbrook #1066
£2200 $3674 €3212 Pershore mill stream. Path to the brook (48x73cm-19x29in) s. pair. 16-Oct-3 Lawrence, Crewkerne #739/R

PEEL, James (attrib) (1811-1906) British
£1300 $2093 €1885 Landscape with anglers in a meandering river, with sheep grazing (44x64cm-17x25in) 13-Aug-3 Rupert Toovey, Partridge Green #3/R est:800-1200

PEEL, Paul (1861-1892) Canadian
£15244 $27287 €22256 Woman with spinning wheel (54x43cm-21x17in) s.d.1883. 27-May-4 Heffel, Vancouver #78/R est:25000-30000 (C.D 37500)
£26000 $47580 €37960 Portrait of Gloria Roberts (76x57cm-30x22in) s.d.1889 prov. 1-Jun-4 Joyner Waddington, Toronto #90/R est:30000-35000 (C.D 65000)
£27517 $50631 €41000 Wood nymph resting on tree trunk (90x61cm-35x24in) s.i.d.1888. 25-Mar-4 Dr Fritz Nagel, Stuttgart #748/R est:12000
£49550 $84234 €72343 Dancing doll (67x50cm-26x20in) s.d.1892 prov.exhib. 18-Nov-3 Sotheby's, Toronto #61/R est:90000-110000 (C.D 110000)
£65041 $116423 €94960 Pont aven I (85x56cm-33x22in) s.i.d.1881 prov.exhib.lit. 31-May-4 Sotheby's, Toronto #111/R est:80000-120000 (C.D 160000)

PEELE, James (1847-1905) Australian
£348 $644 €508 Point Lonsdale, Port Melbourne (30x45cm-12x18in) s.d.1905 board. 9-Mar-4 Watson's, Christchurch #169 est:2000-2500 (NZ.D 950)
£414 $703 €604 Evening sunset (40x60cm-16x24in) s.d.1897. 27-Nov-3 International Art Centre, Auckland #158/R (NZ.D 1100)
£670 $1086 €972 Preservation inlet (31x46cm-12x18in) s.d.1902 board. 31-Jul-3 International Art Centre, Auckland #196/R est:1600-2200 (NZ.D 1850)
£1268 $2042 €1851 Mitre Peak (75x105cm-30x41in) s.d.1889. 20-Aug-3 Dunbar Sloane, Auckland #123/R est:3500-4500 (NZ.D 3500)
£1417 $2281 €2069 Nancy Sound (48x74cm-19x29in) s.d.1898. 13-Oct-3 Joel, Victoria #448 est:3000-3500 (A.D 3500)
£3623 $5870 €5253 Lower Otira Gorge (90x125cm-35x49in) s. 31-Jul-3 International Art Centre, Auckland #64/R est:8000-12000 (NZ.D 10000)
Works on paper
£1091 $1713 €1582 Otira gorge (51x33cm-20x13in) s.d.1881 W/C. 27-Aug-3 Dunbar Sloane, Wellington #70/R est:4000-6000 (NZ.D 3000)

PEELE, John Thomas (1822-1897) British
£2400 $4008 €3504 Reading lesson (89x74cm-35x29in) 13-Nov-3 Christie's, Kensington #271/R est:2000-3000
£2439 $4000 €3537 Children reading (89x74cm-35x29in) s.verso painted c.1875. 7-Jun-3 Treadway Gallery, Cincinnati #1322 est:4000-6000
£5682 $10000 €8296 Children and kid (71x94cm-28x37in) s. i.verso canvas on panel. 18-May-4 Sotheby's, New York #30/R est:6000-8000

PEEPLES, Nina (1897-1979) American
Works on paper
£419 $700 €612 Three girls with kittens (76x56cm-30x22in) 18-Oct-3 David Dike, Dallas #153/R

PEERDT, Ernst te (1852-1932) German
£533 $971 €800 Fishing boats drawn up on the beach (56x43cm-22x17in) s.i.d.1910 panel. 1-Jul-4 Van Ham, Cologne #1551/R

PEERLESS, Tom (19/20th C) Australian
Works on paper
£276 $430 €400 Southern lake scene (32x51cm-13x20in) s. W/C. 1-Aug-2 Joel, Victoria #325 (A.D 800)
£345 $538 €500 High mountain stream (42x60cm-17x24in) s. W/C. 1-Aug-2 Joel, Victoria #339 est:1500-2000 (A.D 1000)

PEETERS, Bonaventura I (1614-1652) Flemish
£4000 $7320 €5840 English shipping in choppy seas (19x25cm-7x10in) panel. 7-Jul-4 Bonhams, New Bond Street #24/R est:4000-6000
£4000 $7240 €6000 Scene de port italien (39x59cm-15x23in) panel. 4-Apr-4 St-Germain-en-Laye Encheres #2/R est:5000-6000
£6338 $10965 €9000 Marine (119x170cm-47x67in) s. 10-Dec-3 Maigret, Paris #50/R est:12000-15000
£9500 $17385 €13870 Shipping in choppy waters off promontory (36x55cm-14x22in) s.d.1636 panel. 8-Jul-4 Sotheby's, London #288/R est:7000-10000
£17808 $30274 €26000 View of a southern coast with wounded Turkish soldiers in rowing boats (51x85cm-20x33in) s.d.1652 panel prov. 4-Nov-3 Sotheby's, Amsterdam #63/R est:15000-25000
£19014 $33275 €27000 Naval battle (79x117cm-31x46in) s.d.1633. 16-Dec-3 Segre, Madrid #45/R est:39000
£30667 $55813 €46000 Dutch ship near Brazilian coast (43x37cm-17x15in) panel prov.lit. 29-Jun-4 Sotheby's, Paris #39/R est:12000-18000
£52778 $95000 €77056 An estuary with loggers at a northern trading post (42x71cm-17x28in) s.d.1636 panel prov. 23-Jan-4 Christie's, Rockefeller NY #26/R est:40000-60000

PEETERS, Bonaventura I (attrib) (1614-1652) Flemish
£6000 $10380 €8760 Dutch whaling ships in the North Atlantic off the coast of Iceland (119x186cm-47x73in) 10-Dec-3 Bonhams, New Bond Street #122/R est:6000-8000

PEETERS, Clara (style) (1594-1657) Flemish
£6200 $10540 €9052 Still life of roses, lilies and other flowers in an urn, upon a stone ledge (48x38cm-19x15in) panel. 30-Oct-3 Sotheby's, Olympia #2/R est:4000-6000

PEETERS, Gillis (1612-1653) Flemish
£4741 $8724 €6922 Landscape (56x79cm-22x31in) s.d.1649. 26-Mar-4 Koller, Zurich #3029/R est:10000-15000 (S.FR 11000)
£34000 $61200 €49640 Estuary scene, with boats before a fortified house (117x200cm-46x79in) s. prov.lit. 22-Apr-4 Sotheby's, London #85/R est:30000-50000

PEETERS, Gillis (attrib) (1612-1653) Flemish
£2254 $3899 €3200 Le regal des chiens a l'entree d'un village (48x41cm-19x16in) panel. 10-Dec-3 Maigret, Paris #58/R est:2000-3000

PEETERS, Henk (1937-) Dutch
Works on paper
£699 $1189 €1000 Untitled (40x40cm-16x16in) feathers on canvas exec 1999. 25-Nov-3 Christie's, Amsterdam #317/R
£3333 $6133 €5000 61-26 (80x75cm-31x30in) s.i.d.61 verso s.i.d. stretcher mixed media. 8-Jun-4 Sotheby's, Amsterdam #103/R est:6000-8000

PEETERS, Jan (1624-1680) Flemish
Works on paper
£2740 $4658 €4000 View of Aelst (10x31cm-4x12in) i. pen brown ink grey wash exhib. 4-Nov-3 Sotheby's, Amsterdam #45/R est:4000-6000
£10959 $18630 €16000 View of Macon (10x30cm-4x12in) i. pen brown ink grey wash exhib. 4-Nov-3 Sotheby's, Amsterdam #44/R est:4000-6000

PEETERS, Jozef (1895-1960) Belgian
Works on paper
£490 $832 €700 Portrait d'homme (18x19cm-7x7in) mono. graphite prov. 23-Nov-3 Cornette de St.Cyr, Paris #270/R

PEGOT-OGIER, Jean Bertrand (1877-1915) French
£1056 $1849 €1500 Sechage des filets au Pouldu (18x18cm-7x7in) s.i. board. 21-Dec-3 Thierry & Lannon, Brest #185 est:1000-1200
£1338 $2342 €1900 Conversation et bolee de cidre entre jeunes Bretons (24x31cm-9x12in) board. 21-Dec-3 Thierry & Lannon, Brest #190 est:1800-2200
£1338 $2342 €1900 Route jaune vers le bourg (62x30cm-24x12in) canvas on board. 21-Dec-3 Thierry & Lannon, Brest #350 est:600-800
£1399 $2406 €2000 Two women and a young girl in the field under the trees (22x28cm-9x11in) s. cardboard. 6-Dec-3 Hans Stahl, Toestorf #58/R est:2500
£1867 $3341 €2800 La Laita et la lande de sable au Pouldu (50x80cm-20x31in) 16-May-4 Thierry & Lannon, Brest #353 est:1200-1500
£1888 $3153 €2700 Cote bretonne (33x41cm-13x16in) mono. cardboard. 29-Jun-3 St-Germain-en-Laye Encheres #10/R
£2148 $3995 €3200 Repas de fete en Bretagne, region du Pouldu (33x46cm-13x18in) s. board. 3-Mar-4 Tajan, Paris #30/R est:3000-4000
£2676 $4683 €3800 Elegante de dos - l'onglier (46x35cm-18x14in) s.i.d.1915. 21-Dec-3 Thierry & Lannon, Brest #187b/R est:2000-2500
£3217 $5372 €4600 Paysanne aux champs (27x35cm-11x14in) s. 7-Oct-3 Livinec, Gaudcheau & Jezequel, Rennes #123/R
£3400 $6086 €5100 Jeune femme et enfants dans un jardin (44x35cm-17x14in) s.i. cardboard. 16-May-4 Thierry & Lannon, Brest #167/R est:2000-2500
£4085 $7148 €5800 Femme attendant le bac au Pouldu (42x29cm-17x11in) s. board. 21-Dec-3 Thierry & Lannon, Brest #189/R est:2000-2200
£4225 $7394 €6000 Deux femmes assises au pied d'un arbre au bord du Blavet (61x50cm-24x20in) s.d.1913. 21-Dec-3 Thierry & Lannon, Brest #186 est:3200-3500
£4366 $7641 €6200 Grande soeur ou jeux d'enfants (100x73cm-39x29in) s. canvas laid down. 21-Dec-3 Thierry & Lannon, Brest #191 est:6000-7000
£4503 $8421 €6800 La danse bretonne (95x29cm-37x11in) s. 24-Jul-4 Thierry & Lannon, Brest #245/R est:5000-6000
£4820 $7905 €6700 Marche a Hennebont (33x41cm-13x16in) s. 3-Jun-3 Livinec, Gaudcheau & Jezequel, Rennes #66/R
£7042 $12324 €10000 Doelan, retour de peche, animation (40x56cm-16x22in) s. board. 21-Dec-3 Thierry & Lannon, Brest #187/R est:5500-6500
£7183 $12570 €10200 Marine, le Pouldu face a la Laita (58x77cm-23x30in) s.i.verso. 21-Dec-3 Thierry & Lannon, Brest #188/R est:8000-9000
Works on paper
£367 $656 €550 Breton a la barriere (43x25cm-17x10in) s.i. chl. 16-May-4 Thierry & Lannon, Brest #404
£599 $1048 €850 Portrait de jeune femme en coiffe sur fond de marine (22x20cm-9x8in) s. chl htd W/C. 21-Dec-3 Thierry & Lannon, Brest #118
£599 $1048 €850 Jeune femme et son enfant pres de la barque (22x29cm-9x11in) s. chl htd W/C. 21-Dec-3 Thierry & Lannon, Brest #119
£733 $1313 €1100 Jour de marche, jeune Bretonne aux deux paniers (31x18cm-12x7in) s. chl col crayon. 16-May-4 Thierry & Lannon, Brest #72
£795 $1486 €1200 Paysage a la chapelle dans les arbres (32x25cm-13x10in) s. W/C. 24-Jul-4 Thierry & Lannon, Brest #75
£1197 $2095 €1700 Chapelle St Philibert a Doelan (26x42cm-10x17in) s.i.d.1913 W/C gouache. 21-Dec-3 Thierry & Lannon, Brest #68 est:1500-1600
£1333 $2387 €2000 La chapelle de Moelan (23x31cm-9x12in) s.i.d.13 W/C. 16-May-4 Thierry & Lannon, Brest #71 est:1500-1600

PEGRAM, Henry Alfred (1863-1937) British
Sculpture
£3000 $5460 €4380 Figure of Harry Vardon, holding his club in full swing (31cm-12in) s.i. brown pat. bronze. 29-Jun-4 Bonhams, Knightsbridge #265/R est:3000-4000
£3200 $5824 €4672 Portrait relief of the artist Charles W Wyllie (67x60cm-26x24in) i.d.1904 brown pat bronze oak. 15-Jun-4 Sotheby's, Olympia #79/R est:2000-3000
£9200 $16836 €13432 Ignis Fatuus (53x53cm-21x21in) s.d.1889 pat bronze lit. 9-Jul-4 Sotheby's, London #162/R est:6000-8000

PEGURIER, Auguste (1856-1936) French
£568 $1000 €829 Harbour scene with fishing boat (61x53cm-24x21in) s. 21-May-4 North East Auctions, Portsmouth #1061

PEHRMANN, H (19/20th C) ?
£1229 $2126 €1794 Still life of grapes and melon on table, uninvited guest helping himself to grapes (89x64cm-35x25in) s. 9-Dec-3 Rasmussen, Copenhagen #1635/R est:10000 (D.KR 13000)

PEHRSON, Karl Axel (1921-) Swedish
£604 $1027 €882 Composition with vegetation (41x29cm-16x11in) s.d.57. 5-Nov-3 AB Stockholms Auktionsverk #828/R (S.KR 8000)
£1057 $1945 €1586 Landscape near Onoba (58x39cm-23x15in) s. 14-Jun-4 Lilla Bukowskis, Stockholm #527 est:15000-20000 (S.KR 14500)
£1093 $2012 €1640 The sculpture near Lecri (39x58cm-15x23in) s. 14-Jun-4 Lilla Bukowskis, Stockholm #528 est:15000-20000 (S.KR 15000)
£1099 $1945 €1605 Iniana (65x54cm-26x21in) s. acrylic. 27-Apr-4 AB Stockholms Auktionsverk #826/R est:15000-18000 (S.KR 15000)
£1154 $1985 €1685 White yejla - fantasy flowers in landscape (65x54cm-26x21in) s. acrylic. 7-Dec-3 Uppsala Auktionskammare, Uppsala #288/R est:15000-18000 (S.KR 15000)
£1511 $2568 €2206 Still life (50x61cm-20x24in) s.d.1947 panel. 4-Nov-3 Bukowskis, Stockholm #225/R est:25000-30000 (S.KR 20000)
£1769 $3043 €2583 Dingola - fantasy flowers in landscape (60x72cm-24x28in) s. acrylic. 7-Dec-3 Uppsala Auktionskammare, Uppsala #289/R est:20000-25000 (S.KR 23000)
£2266 $3852 €3308 Unknown flora (60x71cm-24x28in) s. 5-Nov-3 AB Stockholms Auktionsverk #827/R est:30000-35000 (S.KR 30000)
£3021 $5136 €4411 Tortoise track (48x65cm-19x26in) s. acrylic. 5-Nov-3 AB Stockholms Auktionsverk #812/R est:18000-20000 (S.KR 40000)
£3046 $5482 €4447 Lago Amlapalasi (41x65cm-16x26in) s. 26-Apr-4 Bukowskis, Stockholm #234/R est:35000-40000 (S.KR 42000)
£11240 $20232 €16410 Lianknut near Iatsu - fantasy landscape (130x210cm-51x83in) s. 26-Apr-4 Bukowskis, Stockholm #221/R est:200000-250000 (S.KR 155000)
Works on paper
£566 $963 €826 Study black (18x14cm-7x6in) s.d.1949 Indian ink pencil chk prov. 4-Nov-3 Bukowskis, Stockholm #224/R (S.KR 7500)

PEIDRO, Miguel (20th C) Spanish
£829 $1500 €1210 View of a meadow (64x81cm-25x32in) s. 3-Apr-4 Charlton Hall, Columbia #103/R est:1000-1500

PEIFFER-WATENPHUL, Max (1896-1976) German
£1477 $2717 €2200 Flowers in blue vase with butterfly (38x33cm-15x13in) s.d.1936 W/C pencil gouache. 26-Mar-4 Bolland & Marotz, Bremen #691/R est:1600
£14667 $26987 €22000 Still life with two vases of flowers (62x86cm-24x34in) mono.i. painted 1949 exhib. 11-Jun-4 Villa Grisebach, Berlin #1580/R est:15000-20000
£20979 $35664 €30000 Vase with summer flowers (64x46cm-25x18in) s.d.33 prov. 29-Nov-3 Villa Grisebach, Berlin #257/R est:28000-32000
£30201 $53456 €45000 Still life with field flowers and corn (80x100cm-31x39in) s.d.1934/35 lit. 28-Apr-4 Wiener Kunst Auktionen, Vienna #117/R est:45000-90000
Works on paper
£805 $1442 €1200 Still life with fruit (8x18cm-3x7in) mono. pencil W/C exhib. 25-May-4 Karl & Faber, Munich #485/R
£839 $1427 €1200 Still life (10x23cm-4x9in) mono. W/C. 29-Nov-3 Villa Grisebach, Berlin #865/R est:1400-1600
£3000 $5400 €4500 Terrace (33x48cm-13x19in) mono.d.36 and 52 W/C on pencil. 24-Apr-4 Reiss & Sohn, Konigstein #5686/R est:8000

£4267 $7851 €6400 Colourful bouquet of flowers (44x31cm-17x12in) s.d.42 W/C pencil. 11-Jun-4 Villa Grisebach, Berlin #1579/R est:3000-4000
£5263 $9684 €8000 Landscape at Ischia with two tall pine trees (32x48cm-13x19in) s.d.61 pencil W/C lit. 25-Jun-4 Von Zezschwitz, Munich #315/R est:9600
£8667 $15513 €13000 House on Ischia (26x48cm-10x19in) mono.d.55 i. verso W/C on pencil prov. 13-May-4 Neumeister, Munich #455/R est:8000-8500

PEINADO, Francisco (1941-) Spanish
£3310 $5296 €4700 Interior (60x65cm-24x26in) s.d.1981 prov. 16-Sep-3 Segre, Madrid #145/R

PEINADO, Joaquin (1898-1975) Spanish
£3986 $6536 €5500 Still life (35x27cm-14x11in) s. 27-May-3 Durán, Madrid #143/R est:2000
£11409 $21221 €17000 Still life (46x38cm-18x15in) s.d.54. 2-Mar-4 Ansorena, Madrid #856/R est:8000
£12319 $20203 €17000 Cubic still life (59x72cm-23x28in) s.d.51. 27-May-3 Durán, Madrid #274/R est:9000
Works on paper
£387 $670 €550 Cogners, 14 July (27x21cm-11x8in) i.d.1957 pencil dr. 15-Dec-3 Ansorena, Madrid #197/R
£503 $941 €750 Skyscrapers (28x38cm-11x15in) s.d.71 dr. 24-Feb-4 Durán, Madrid #1196/R
£524 $876 €750 Horse (27x21cm-11x8in) d.57 pencil dr. 30-Jun-3 Ansorena, Madrid #143/R
£528 $914 €750 Stags (31x23cm-12x9in) dr. 15-Dec-3 Ansorena, Madrid #187/R
£805 $1506 €1200 Still life (26x35cm-10x14in) pastel. 24-Feb-4 Durán, Madrid #670/R
£828 $1374 €1200 Broom (73x80cm-29x31in) s.d.1973 pen dr. 1-Oct-3 Ansorena, Madrid #479/R
£870 $1426 €1200 Female portrait (35x26cm-14x10in) s.d.juin 47 drawing. 27-May-3 Durán, Madrid #90/R
£2267 $4125 €3400 Still life with grapes (31x24cm-12x9in) s.d.1940. 30-Jun-4 Delvaux, Paris #52 est:800-1000
£2667 $4827 €4000 Still life with jug and grapes (40x31cm-16x12in) s.d.1940 W/C. 30-Mar-4 Segre, Madrid #133/R est:2500

PEINER, Werner (1897-1981) German
£567 $1014 €850 Landscape (49x69cm-19x27in) s.d.49 paper on panel. 15-May-4 Van Ham, Cologne #825/R
£1200 $2160 €1800 Eifel landscape (50x70cm-20x28in) s.d. oil board on masonite. 24-Apr-4 Reiss & Sohn, Konigstein #5687/R est:1200
£3706 $6375 €5300 Still life with orchids and cacti (50x40cm-20x16in) s.d.1920. 4-Dec-3 Van Ham, Cologne #376/R est:1000

PEINS, Albert (20th C) ?
£474 $769 €692 Seascape with German U-boat U-25 (35x49cm-14x19in) s. panel. 9-Aug-3 Hindemae, Ullerslev #232/R (D.KR 5000)

PEINTE, Henri (1845-1912) French
Sculpture
£1312 $2191 €1850 Orphee endormant Cerbere (29cm-11in) s.st.f.Siot gilt pat bronze sold with alabaster socle. 19-Oct-3 Peron, Melun #354
£1399 $2378 €2000 Orpheus in the Underworld (91cm-36in) i. bronze Cast.Siot-Decauville Paris. 20-Nov-3 Van Ham, Cologne #1254/R est:300

PEINTNER, Elmar (1954-) Austrian
Works on paper
£333 $613 €500 Still life with doll, branch and wall (35x21cm-14x8in) s.d.1987 pencil egg tempera. 9-Jun-4 Dorotheum, Salzburg #789/R
£467 $859 €700 Still life with doll, toy umbrella and autumn sunflowers (34x20cm-13x8in) s.i.d.87 pencil W/C. 9-Jun-4 Dorotheum, Salzburg #793/R
£467 $859 €700 Large doll wearing hat (38x26cm-15x10in) s. i. verso pencil W/C. 9-Jun-4 Dorotheum, Salzburg #796/R
£467 $859 €700 Standing doll and child ballet (33x27cm-13x11in) s.i.d.1989 pencil W/C. 9-Jun-4 Dorotheum, Salzburg #790/R
£496 $829 €700 Flowers in vase (27x38cm-11x15in) s. pencil W/C. 16-Oct-3 Dorotheum, Salzburg #925/R
£533 $981 €800 Seated doll with basket and teddy bear (38x27cm-15x11in) s.i.d.93 pencil egg tempera. 9-Jun-4 Dorotheum, Salzburg #794/R
£709 $1184 €1000 Clowns making music (35x26cm-14x10in) s.d.1990 pencil egg tempera. 16-Oct-3 Dorotheum, Salzburg #969/R
£780 $1303 €1100 Ballet dancer and marionettes (37x27cm-15x11in) s. pencil W/C egg tempera. 16-Oct-3 Dorotheum, Salzburg #926/R
£1067 $1963 €1600 Rooms, sheep and clown (27x34cm-11x13in) s.i.d.1990 pencil egg tempera. 9-Jun-4 Dorotheum, Salzburg #792/R est:2000-2600

PEINTNER, Max (1937-) Austrian
Works on paper
£1049 $1783 €1500 Vibrations on the bridge (22x40cm-9x16in) mono.i.d.1978 mixed media. 28-Nov-3 Wiener Kunst Auktionen, Vienna #659/R est:1500-2500

PEIPERS, Eugène Friedrich (1805-1885) German
Works on paper
£709 $1149 €1000 Idar Oberstein (23x28cm-9x11in) mono.i.d.1864. 23-May-3 Paul Kieffer, Pforzhiem #4736

PEIRCE, Augustus Baker (1840-1919) Australian
£1943 $3129 €2837 Robert Chirnside and the Melbourne Hunt Club (65x91cm-26x36in) s.d.1882 prov. 25-Aug-3 Sotheby's, Paddington #484/R est:3000-5000 (A.D 4800)

PEIRCE, Waldo (1884-1970) American
£391 $700 €571 Blue bowl, red beans (30x46cm-12x18in) s.d.62. 8-Jan-4 James Julia, Fairfield #858/R
£682 $1200 €996 Webber Merideth's house (64x76cm-25x30in) s.d.1948 prov. 3-Jan-4 Collins, Maine #21/R
£760 $1360 €1110 Still life of fruit (30x46cm-12x18in) s.d.62 s.d.verso. 8-Jan-4 James Julia, Fairfield #857/R est:500-1000
£829 $1500 €1210 Old witch doctor (61x51cm-24x20in) i. 16-Apr-4 James Julia, Fairfield #804/R est:800-1200
£1118 $1800 €1632 The lady of the sea (51x41cm-20x16in) init.i. init.d. verso board prov. 20-Aug-3 James Julia, Fairfield #1432/R est:1500-2500
£1167 $1875 €1704 Flowers 1961 (61x76cm-24x30in) i. verso prov. 20-Aug-3 James Julia, Fairfield #1433/R est:1500-2500
£1242 $2000 €1813 Father in his temple (51x41cm-20x16in) s.i.d.February 15th 29 verso prov. 20-Aug-3 James Julia, Fairfield #1430/R est:2500-4000
£1313 $2350 €1917 Ruby's siesta (79x109cm-31x43in) s.d.45 s.i.d.verso. 8-Jan-4 James Julia, Fairfield #856/R est:1500-2500
£1397 $2250 €2040 Jack Nickolaus winning the Masters (66x119cm-26x47in) s.i. s.i. verso prov. 20-Aug-3 James Julia, Fairfield #1431/R est:2500-4000
£1975 $3200 €2864 Picnic table (65x80cm-26x31in) s.i. prov. 8-Aug-3 Barridorf, Portland #197/R est:3000-5000
£2096 $3500 €3060 Still life with flowers by the sea (71x61cm-28x24in) init.d.57 s.d.57 verso. 7-Oct-3 Sotheby's, New York #240 est:2500-3500
£2273 $4000 €3319 String quartet (64x76cm-25x30in) s.d.1947 prov. 3-Jan-4 Collins, Maine #24/R est:2500-3500
£2639 $4250 €3853 Halloween, Searsport 47 (119x66cm-47x26in) s. s.i. verso prov. 20-Aug-3 James Julia, Fairfield #1429/R est:5000-8000
£5114 $9000 €7466 Outboard motor of the Gulf Stream (51x61cm-20x24in) init.d.1932 prov. 3-Jan-4 Collins, Maine #22/R est:2500-3500
£7407 $12000 €10740 De cirque (102x83cm-40x33in) s.i. i.d.1933 verso prov. 8-Aug-3 Barridorf, Portland #215/R est:12000-18000
Works on paper
£617 $1000 €895 Still life (34x27cm-13x11in) s.d.65 W/C prov. 8-Aug-3 Barridorf, Portland #324/R est:900-1200
£663 $1200 €968 Grim reapers of the Penobscot (28x35cm-11x14in) i.d.11 Nov 1939 W/C pencil prov. 31-Mar-4 Sotheby's, New York #140/R
£1705 $3000 €2489 Haircut by the sea (58x46cm-23x18in) W/C board. 3-Jan-4 Collins, Maine #23/R est:1200-1600

PEIRE, Luc (1916-1994) Belgian
£979 $1635 €1400 Nzamba (42x29cm-17x11in) s.verso paper lit. 11-Oct-3 De Vuyst, Lokeren #285/R
£3472 $5799 €5000 Temple, 855 (54x65cm-21x26in) s.d.1971. 21-Oct-3 Campo, Vlaamse Kaai #517/R est:4000-6000

PEISER, Kurt (1887-1962) Belgian
£280 $481 €400 Homme au chapeau (21x15cm-8x6in) s. cardboard. 2-Dec-3 Campo & Campo, Antwerp #299
£423 $731 €600 Portrait da dame (24x17cm-9x7in) s. panel. 9-Dec-3 Campo, Vlaamse Kaai #385
£426 $711 €600 Panier de poissons (80x60cm-31x24in) s. 17-Jun-3 Galerie Moderne, Brussels #338
£517 $957 €750 Cheminees en Branant (26x33cm-10x13in) s. 19-Jan-4 Horta, Bruxelles #439
£733 $1313 €1100 L'estacade (30x40cm-12x16in) s. canvas on panel. 11-May-4 Vanderkindere, Brussels #163
£734 $1226 €1050 Brabancons atteles (24x34cm-9x13in) s. 13-Oct-3 Horta, Bruxelles #303
£833 $1392 €1200 Enfants sous un arbre (34x54cm-13x21in) s. 21-Oct-3 Campo & Campo, Antwerp #242
£2098 $3566 €3000 Mere et enfant dans les dunes (27x65cm-11x26in) s. panel. 18-Nov-3 Galerie Moderne, Brussels #709/R est:1000-1500
£2568 $4596 €3800 Pecheurs sur la digue (80x60cm-31x24in) s. 10-May-4 Horta, Bruxelles #172/R est:3000-4000

PEITHNER VON LICHTENFELS, Eduard (1833-1913) Austrian
£1852 $3000 €2685 Farm in an extensive landscape (49x63cm-19x25in) s. panel. 8-Aug-3 Barridorf, Portland #339/R est:3000-5000
Works on paper
£470 $864 €700 Durnstein cemetery (48x37cm-19x15in) s.i. pen Indian ink W/C paper on board. 26-Mar-4 Dorotheum, Vienna #191/R
£738 $1358 €1100 Castle and house in Durnstein (35x48cm-14x19in) s.i.d.1888 pen Indian ink W/C paper on board. 26-Mar-4 Dorotheum, Vienna #215/R

PEIXOTTO, George da Maduro (1862-1937) American
£2747 $5000 €4011 Lady of Lyon (201x119cm-79x47in) s.d.1882. 7-Feb-4 Neal Auction Company, New Orleans #112/R est:4000-6000
£6849 $11644 €10000 Portrait de la pianiste Marie Roger Miclas (145x188cm-57x74in) s.d.1893. 9-Nov-3 Eric Pillon, Calais #51/R

PEIZEL, Bart (1887-1974) Dutch
£336 $561 €480 Flower still life (82x60cm-32x24in) 30-Jun-3 Sotheby's, Amsterdam #253
£839 $1427 €1200 Portrait of Freddy Barvoet (79x60cm-31x24in) s.d.1921. 24-Nov-3 Glerum, Amsterdam #627/R

PEKARY, Istvan (1905-1981) Hungarian
£4008 $7095 €5852 Snow covered village (60x100cm-24x39in) s.d.1963. 28-Apr-4 Kieselbach, Budapest #106/R (H.F 1500000)

PEKEK, Djoko (1938-) Javanese
£2941 $5324 €4294 Ketoprak (65x75cm-26x30in) s.d.12 Dec 1997 i.v. 4-Apr-4 Sotheby's, Singapore #169/R est:6000-8000 (S.D 9000)
£4086 $6538 €5966 Ketoprak (75x65cm-30x26in) s.d.2000. 18-May-3 Sotheby's, Singapore #174/R est:9000-12000 (S.D 11400)
£13072 $23660 €19085 Parangtritis (95x131cm-37x52in) s.d.1980. 3-Apr-4 Glerum, Singapore #45/R est:34000-44000 (S.D 40000)
£21622 $36108 €31568 Kuda lumping (93x132cm-37x52in) s.d.6/XII-1989. 26-Oct-3 Christie's, Hong Kong #89/R est:55000-75000 (HK.D 280000)

PEKEL, Herman (1956-) Australian
£766 $1302 €1118 Victoria Hotel (100x66cm-39x26in) s. board. 26-Nov-3 Deutscher-Menzies, Melbourne #188/R est:2000-3000 (A.D 1800)

PELAEZ, Amelia (1897-1968) Cuban
£3161 $5374 €4615 Untitled (24x30cm-9x12in) init.d.1967. 30-Oct-3 Louis Morton, Mexico #98/R est:65000-75000 (M.P 60000)
£33333 $61333 €50000 Vase of flowers (152x49cm-60x19in) s.d.67 prov. 10-Jun-4 Christie's, Paris #34/R est:65000-80000
£64706 $110000 €94471 Vitral (75x53cm-30x21in) s.d.64. 18-Nov-3 Christie's, Rockefeller NY #45/R est:120000-140000
Works on paper
£2000 $3460 €2920 Woman holding a parrot (69x49cm-27x19in) init.d.63 W/C prov. 10-Dec-3 Edgar Horn, Eastbourne #279/R est:2000-2500
£5826 $9905 €8506 Untitled (51x30cm-20x12in) s. wash cardboard. 23-Nov-3 Subastas Odalys, Caracas #154 est:5000

PELAEZ, Angeles (1942-) Spanish
£369 $690 €550 Expressionist influence (54x81cm-21x32in) s. 24-Feb-4 Durán, Madrid #43/R

PELAEZ, Juan (1881-1937) Argentinian
£1173 $2100 €1713 Path to the Fair (68x88cm-27x35in) s. 4-May-4 Arroyo, Buenos Aires #88/R est:1800

PELAEZ, Mariano (1920-) Spanish
£278 $442 €400 Maternidad (35x27cm-14x11in) s. 29-Apr-3 Durán, Madrid #111/R
£470 $860 €700 We have lost already (81x65cm-32x26in) s. 12-Jul-4 Durán, Madrid #139/R
£660 $1075 €950 Twilight (65x81cm-26x32in) s. 23-Sep-3 Durán, Madrid #117/R
£724 $1303 €1050 In the car (81x100cm-32x39in) s. 26-Jan-4 Ansorena, Madrid #909/R
£775 $1239 €1100 Me too (71x100cm-28x39in) s. 16-Sep-3 Segre, Madrid #182/R
£839 $1401 €1200 Mirando la flor (65x81cm-26x32in) s. 24-Jun-3 Segre, Madrid #201/R
£851 $1421 €1200 Nobody can (100x81cm-39x32in) s. 20-Oct-3 Durán, Madrid #73/R
£951 $1645 €1350 Souvenirs (83x117cm-33x46in) s. 15-Dec-3 Ansorena, Madrid #1034/R

PELAYO FERNANDEZ, Eduardo (c.1850-?) Spanish
£1402 $2215 €2033 Interior scene with a Spanish couple (40x26cm-16x10in) s. 2-Sep-3 Rasmussen, Copenhagen #1708/R est:15000-20000 (D.KR 15000)
£3986 $6536 €5500 Hombres de guerra saludando a un hombre de paz (32x49cm-13x19in) s.d.1889 panel. 27-May-3 Durán, Madrid #109/R est:3000

PELAYO, Orlando (1920-1990) Spanish
£694 $1160 €1000 Jeune homme (43x30cm-17x12in) s. panel. 25-Oct-3 Cornette de St.Cyr, Paris #537
£699 $1189 €1000 Mujet (27x35cm-11x14in) s. 20-Nov-3 Claude Aguttes, Neuilly #267
£1469 $2452 €2100 Infant (65x50cm-26x20in) s. s.i.verso prov. 29-Jun-3 Versailles Encheres #21/R
£1597 $2668 €2300 Scene de tauromachie (46x64cm-18x25in) s. 21-Oct-3 Artcurial Briest, Paris #343 est:1000-1200
£2013 $3685 €3000 Torro de Corrida (54x65cm-21x26in) s. isorel panel. 7-Jul-4 Artcurial Briest, Paris #150/R est:3000-4000
£2819 $5271 €4200 Femme sur en ane (65x50cm-26x20in) s. 29-Feb-4 Versailles Encheres #178/R est:2500-3000
£5674 $9475 €8000 Iberian II (50x65cm-20x26in) s. s.i.d.1988 verso. 20-Oct-3 Durán, Madrid #113/R
£6122 $10959 €9000 Portugaise (50x50cm-20x20in) s.d.68 s.i.d.verso lit. 22-Mar-4 Durán, Madrid #128/R est:8000
£6463 $11762 €9500 Dream (80x80cm-31x31in) s. s.i.verso prov.exhib.lit. 3-Feb-4 Segre, Madrid #173/R est:8000
Works on paper
£349 $653 €520 Portrait d'Albert Camus (26x20cm-10x8in) s.d.1955 ink. 29-Feb-4 Versailles Encheres #180
£439 $830 €650 Composition abstraite (48x64cm-19x25in) s. pastel. 21-Feb-4 Cornette de St.Cyr, Paris #366
£477 $891 €710 Composition (13x13cm-5x5in) s. gouache. 29-Feb-4 Versailles Encheres #179
£828 $1374 €1200 Composition (33x25cm-13x10in) s. W/C. 1-Oct-3 Ansorena, Madrid #556/R
£851 $1379 €1200 Untitled (45x60cm-18x24in) s. wax crayon. 20-May-3 Ansorena, Madrid #344/R
£1510 $2673 €2250 Figures (52x73cm-20x29in) s. gouache. 27-Apr-4 Durán, Madrid #172/R

PELGROM, Jacobus (1811-1861) Dutch
£1200 $2196 €1800 Southern ford near ruined aqueduct with peasant woman and cattle (28x43cm-11x17in) s. panel. 5-Jun-4 Arnold, Frankfurt #693/R est:1000
£2105 $3874 €3200 Figures by a bridge in an extensive river landscape at dusk (61x126cm-24x50in) s.d.1845. 22-Jun-4 Christie's, Amsterdam #23/R est:3000-5000

PELHAM, James III (1840-1906) British
£811 $1500 €1217 Pastoral landscapes with cattle (18x30cm-7x12in) one bears mono. board pair. 17-Jul-4 New Orleans Auction, New Orleans #297/R est:1200-1800

PELHAM, Peter (1697-1751) American/British
Prints
£4012 $6500 €5858 Cottonus Matherus. mezzotint engraving oval lit. 1-Aug-3 North East Auctions, Portsmouth #397/R est:4000-6000

PELHAM, Thomas Kent (fl.1860-1891) British
£2349 $4205 €3500 The Spanish Rose (76x63cm-30x25in) s.d.1873. 27-May-4 Dorotheum, Vienna #121/R est:3500-4000

PELISSIER-PEZOLT, Agnes (1901-1997) Swiss
£271 $462 €396 Easter bouquet (35x27cm-14x11in) s. masonite. 28-Nov-3 Zofingen, Switzerland #3113 (S.FR 600)
£304 $557 €444 Still life with flowers (37x46cm-15x18in) s.d.1958 verso panel. 4-Jun-4 Zofingen, Switzerland #2927 (S.FR 700)
£318 $528 €461 Still life with apples (28x38cm-11x15in) masonite. 13-Jun-3 Zofingen, Switzerland #2976 (S.FR 700)

PELL, Ella Ferris (1846-1922) American
£470 $850 €686 Northern Gate to the Hudson Highlands (25x38cm-10x15in) s.d.1917 board. 18-Apr-4 Jeffery Burchard, Florida #70/R

PELLAN, Alfred (1906-1988) Canadian
£901 $1532 €1315 Abstract composition (19x33cm-7x13in) s.verso prov.lit. 21-Nov-3 Walker's, Ottawa #125/R est:2000-3000 (C.D 2000)
£10400 $19032 €15184 Lac des Deux-Montagnes (42x57cm-17x22in) s.d.41 prov.lit. 1-Jun-4 Joyner Waddington, Toronto #18/R est:15000-20000 (C.D 26000)
£12162 $20676 €17757 Oasis (46x16cm-18x6in) s.d.68 s.i.d.1968 verso oil silica cardboard on wood prov. 18-Nov-3 Sotheby's, Toronto #76/R est:15000-20000 (C.D 27000)
£12387 $21059 €18085 Terrasse de cafe (21x32cm-8x13in) s. i.verso prov. 18-Nov-3 Sotheby's, Toronto #135/R est:25000-30000 (C.D 27500)
£14640 $24887 €21374 Les ombelles (46x28cm-18x11in) s.d.66 s.i.d.1966 verso oil silica cardboard on wood prov. 18-Nov-3 Sotheby's, Toronto #129/R est:25000-35000 (C.D 32500)
£23214 $39929 €33892 Monde invisible (70x25cm-28x10in) s.d.61 panel prov.lit. 2-Dec-3 Joyner Waddington, Toronto #56/R est:30000-40000 (C.D 52000)
Works on paper
£320 $586 €467 L'est du Canada (19x31cm-7x12in) s. gouache card lit. 1-Jun-4 Joyner Waddington, Toronto #483 (C.D 800)
£3982 $6252 €5814 Bailler l'infini (29x23cm-11x9in) s. i.verso mixed media board. 26-Aug-3 Iegor de Saint Hippolyte, Montreal #130 (C.D 8800)
£5285 $9459 €7716 Les Graces (33x25cm-13x10in) s.d.74 i.verso Chinese ink W/C prov. 31-May-4 Sotheby's, Toronto #67/R est:10000-15000 (C.D 13000)
£5285 $9459 €7716 Folies bergeres (33x24cm-13x9in) s.d.73 i.verso Chinese ink W/C. 31-May-4 Sotheby's, Toronto #68/R est:10000-15000 (C.D 13000)

PELLAR, Hanns (1886-?) Austrian
£420 $713 €600 Elegant scene at Castle park gates (62x56cm-24x22in) s. board. 20-Nov-3 Van Ham, Cologne #1795

PELLARIZ, Jesus (?) Spanish?
£530 $991 €800 Port of Barcelona. panel. 20-Jul-4 other European Auctioneer #134

PELLE, John Thomas (19th C) British
£409 $650 €597 Meeting (51x41cm-20x16in) s. board. 14-Sep-3 Susanin's, Chicago #6086/R

PELLEGRIN, Honore (1800-1870) French
Works on paper
£1300 $2418 €1898 Brig Ver of Sunderland, Captain George Hall entering the port of Marseilles (46x59cm-18x23in) s.d.1851 verso W/C. 4-Mar-4 Clevedon Sale Rooms #145 est:300-450
£1500 $2790 €2190 Brig Phobus of Newport, Captain George Hall, entering Marseilles Jan 1848 (44x58cm-17x23in) s.d.1848 W/C. 4-Mar-4 Clevedon Sale Rooms #144/R est:400-600
£2292 $3827 €3300 Brick la Marie Anne. s.i. W/C. 25-Oct-3 Dianous, Marseille #418
£2980 $5454 €4500 Privince de Constantine, Trois mats (44x60cm-17x24in) s.i.d.1868 W/C two. 7-Apr-4 Piasa, Paris #24b est:5000-7000

PELLEGRIN, Louis Antonin Victor (1836-1884) French
£1631 $2724 €2300 Portrait de femme a la robe noire (136x105cm-54x41in) s.d.1865. 15-Oct-3 Neret-Minet, Paris #31

PELLEGRINI, Alfred Heinrich (1881-1958) Swiss
£1181 $1924 €1700 Anemones (37x45cm-15x18in) s. i.verso board. 27-Sep-3 Dr Fritz Nagel, Stuttgart #9607/R est:1500
£2402 $4371 €3507 Two lying nudes with a fan (31x42cm-12x17in) mono. cardboard painted 1911. 16-Jun-4 Fischer, Luzern #1326/R est:6000-8000 (S.FR 5500)
£2863 $4868 €4180 Brusata verso - a la Ca (45x56cm-18x22in) mono.d.46 i. verso board. 7-Nov-3 Dobiaschofsky, Bern #173/R est:9000 (S.FR 6500)
£3696 $6763 €5396 If it brightens up, in Grund Grindelwald (56x73cm-22x29in) mono.d.50 s.i.d.1950 verso canvas on board prov.exhib. 7-Jun-4 Christie's, Zurich #114/R est:5000-7000 (S.FR 8500)
£5677 $10162 €8288 Persuasion (98x120cm-39x47in) s. exhib.lit. 26-May-4 Sotheby's, Zurich #101/R est:25000-30000 (S.FR 13000)
Works on paper
£181 $308 €264 Lake Geneva with Mont Blanc (28x37cm-11x15in) mono.d.IV 45 pencil. 18-Nov-3 Hans Widmer, St Gallen #1170 (S.FR 400)
£1092 $1954 €1594 Self portrait (33x24cm-13x9in) mono. i.d.1917 verso gouache exhib.lit. 26-May-4 Sotheby's, Zurich #125/R est:2500-3500 (S.FR 2500)

PELLEGRINI, Alfred Heinrich (attrib) (1881-1958) Swiss
£490 $817 €700 Girls with sledge (70x48cm-28x19in) mono. stretcher. 11-Oct-3 Hans Stahl, Hamburg #26/R

PELLEGRINI, Carlo (1839-1889) Italian
Works on paper
£500 $830 €730 Marquis (30x17cm-12x7in) s.i. W/C. 1-Oct-3 Woolley & Wallis, Salisbury #135/R

PELLEGRINI, Carlo (1866-1937) Swiss
£764 $1299 €1100 Landscape covered in snow (50x70cm-20x28in) s. tempera cardboard oval. 1-Nov-3 Meeting Art, Vercelli #275

PELLEGRINI, Giovanni Antonio (1675-1741) Italian
£55479 $94315 €81000 Euterpe (66x56cm-26x22in) prov.lit. 9-Nov-3 Finarte, Venice #105/R est:45000-60000

PELLEGRINI, Giovanni Antonio (attrib) (1675-1741) Italian
£1397 $2543 €2040 Abigail kneeling before King David (63x76cm-25x30in) prov. 16-Jun-4 Fischer, Luzern #1059/R est:3000-4500 (S.FR 3200)
Works on paper
£719 $1180 €1000 Scene de mariage (37x47cm-15x19in) pen grey wash gouache. 6-Jun-3 Maigret, Paris #60

PELLEGRINI, Giovanni Antonio (circle) (1675-1741) Italian
£32000 $55360 €46720 Bozetto for a wall panel (26x19cm-10x7in) oil paper on panel. 12-Dec-3 Christie's, Kensington #244/R est:2000-3000

PELLEGRINI, Giovanni Antonio (style) (1675-1741) Italian
£13103 $21883 €19000 Venus with putto and dove (76x64cm-30x25in) 12-Nov-3 Sotheby's, Milan #127/R est:8000-12000

PELLEGRINI, Riccardo (1863-1934) Italian
£2174 $3565 €3000 Autumn sun (60x90cm-24x35in) s. s.i.verso. 27-May-3 Finarte Semenzato, Milan #49/R
£2340 $3909 €3300 Resting high (65x121cm-26x48in) s. 14-Oct-3 Finarte Semenzato, Milan #119/R
£3472 $5903 €5000 Mosque interior (45x34cm-18x13in) s. 1-Nov-3 Meeting Art, Vercelli #421/R est:5000
Works on paper
£1690 $2924 €2400 Praying (41x37cm-16x15in) s.d.1907 mixed media card. 10-Dec-3 Sotheby's, Milan #99/R est:1000-2000
£2083 $3542 €3000 Carnival (46x63cm-18x25in) s.i. mixed media paper on card. 1-Nov-3 Meeting Art, Vercelli #234/R est:3000
£2394 $4142 €3400 Milan Exhibition (40x57cm-16x22in) s.d.1906 pencil W/C lead. 10-Dec-3 Finarte Semenzato, Rome #182/R est:1300-1500

PELLET, Alphonse (19th C) French
£3000 $5520 €4380 Moment of reverie in the harem (65x81cm-26x32in) s. 25-Mar-4 Christie's, Kensington #220/R est:3000-5000

PELLETIER (?) French
£833 $1500 €1216 Washerwoman at a river's edge (50x63cm-20x25in) s. canvasboard. 24-Apr-4 Weschler, Washington #559/R est:1200-1800

PELLETIER, Auguste (fl.1800-1847) French
Works on paper
£1655 $2764 €2400 Grimpar enfume (52x39cm-20x15in) s. W/C gouache black crayon. 13-Nov-3 Binoche, Paris #77/R est:3000
£1724 $2879 €2500 Huppe d'Europe (51x38cm-20x15in) W/C gouache black crayon. 13-Nov-3 Binoche, Paris #72/R est:3000-4000
£1724 $2879 €2500 Couroucou orange, jeune (52x39cm-20x15in) s. W/C gouache black crayon. 13-Nov-3 Binoche, Paris #79/R est:3000-5000
£1931 $3225 €2800 Variete du guepier de Savigny (52x38cm-20x15in) W/C gouache black crayon. 13-Nov-3 Binoche, Paris #76/R est:3000-5000
£2069 $3455 €3000 Guepier de perse (52x39cm-20x15in) W/C gouache varnish black pencil. 13-Nov-3 Binoche, Paris #87/R est:3000-4000
£2966 $4952 €4300 Guepier Bonelli (52x39cm-20x15in) W/C gouache black crayon. 13-Nov-3 Binoche, Paris #68/R est:3000-5000
£4138 $6910 €6000 Grimpar des cabosses (52x39cm-20x15in) W/C gouache black pencil. 13-Nov-3 Binoche, Paris #81/R est:3000

PELLETIER, Leonce (?) French
£245 $450 €358 Fleurs (43x33cm-17x13in) s.d.1940. 26-Jun-4 Selkirks, St. Louis #429/R
£769 $1285 €1100 Environs de Nice (51x61cm-20x24in) s.i.d.1905. 29-Jun-3 St-Germain-en-Laye Encheres #7/R

PELLETIER, Pierre-Jacques (1869-1931) French
£1800 $2880 €2610 French coastal landscape (33x60cm-13x24in) s. 18-Sep-3 Christie's, Kensington #112/R est:2000-3000
£2980 $5424 €4500 Normandy coast (38x55cm-15x22in) s. i.verso paper on canvas. 21-Jun-4 Dorotheum, Vienna #30/R est:3400-4000

PELLICCIOTTI, Tito (1872-1943) Italian
£333 $613 €500 Dunkey and sheep in the stable (17x25cm-7x10in) s. cardboard prov. 10-Jun-4 Christie's, Rome #11
£474 $849 €692 Peasant with donkey in stable (16x25cm-6x10in) s. panel. 12-May-4 Dobiaschofsky, Bern #857/R (S.FR 1100)
£563 $975 €800 Cows at pasture (20x40cm-8x16in) s. cardboard. 11-Dec-3 Christie's, Rome #58
£667 $1227 €1000 In the stable (16x19cm-6x7in) s. board. 8-Jun-4 Sotheby's, Milan #68/R
£750 $1418 €1095 Waif in rags (29x12cm-11x5in) s. panel. 19-Feb-4 Christie's, Kensington #80/R
£946 $1665 €1400 Coastal landscape with cart and peasants (26x52cm-10x20in) s. board. 19-May-4 Il Ponte, Milan #676 est:1200-1300
£1832 $3242 €2748 Stable interior with animals (50x73cm-20x29in) s. 27-Apr-4 Bolsa de Arte, Rio de Janeiro #24/R (B.R 10000)
£1867 $3435 €2800 Camels and figures (28x62cm-11x24in) s. 10-Jun-4 Christie's, Rome #102/R est:1500-2000
£4225 $7310 €6000 Shepherdess and sheep (50x69cm-20x27in) s. 9-Dec-3 Finarte Semenzato, Milan #51/R est:5000

PELLICER Y ROUVIERE, Carlos (1865-?) Spanish
£1918 $3260 €2800 Roman woman (110x70cm-43x28in) s. 4-Nov-3 Ansorena, Madrid #62/R est:2800

PELLICER, Rafael (1906-1963) Spanish
£2586 $4655 €3750 Paper birds (39x32cm-15x13in) s. board. 26-Jan-4 Durán, Madrid #120/R

PELLICONE, William (20th C) American
£552 $1000 €806 Sunset, farm and figure (28x36cm-11x14in) 16-Apr-4 American Auctioneer #304/R
£552 $1000 €806 Young woman sewing (56x46cm-22x18in) acrylic under oil board. 16-Apr-4 American Auctioneer #305/R

PELLIS, Giovanni Napoleone (1888-1962) Italian
£1434 $2466 €2050 Flowers in bronze vase (45x65cm-18x26in) s. oil mixed media cardboard on concrete. 3-Dec-3 Stadion, Trieste #969/R est:2000-3000

PELLIZZA DA VOLPEDO, Giuseppe (1868-1907) Italian
£24823 $41454 €35000 Study of female head (39x30cm-15x12in) i.verso. 14-Oct-3 Finarte Semenzato, Milan #194/R est:60000
£208054 $389060 €310000 Valley in Volpedo (61x88cm-24x35in) prov.exhib.lit. 25-Feb-4 Porro, Milan #33/R
Works on paper
£671 $1188 €1000 Nude (11x23cm-4x9in) pen ink lit. 1-May-4 Meeting Art, Vercelli #146
£1354 $2302 €1950 Study of nude (11x23cm-4x9in) s. Chinese ink double-sided. 1-Nov-3 Meeting Art, Vercelli #30/R est:750
£5634 $9746 €8000 Self-portrait (15x12cm-6x5in) d.1887 Chinese ink prov.lit. 10-Dec-3 Sotheby's, Milan #138/R est:4000-6000

PELLONI, Tino (1895-1981) Italian
£473 $738 €700 View of church (36x30cm-14x12in) 30-Mar-3 Adma, Formigine #1163
£541 $843 €800 Vase of flowers (52x34cm-20x13in) 30-Mar-3 Adma, Formigine #584
Works on paper
£333 $610 €500 Houses in Burano (35x28cm-14x11in) W/C exec.1953. 4-Jun-4 Tuttarte, Modena #245

PELNSO, F (?) ?
£3000 $5490 €4500 Le jeu de la main chaude. Le jeu de gobelets (31x19cm-12x7in) panel pair. 5-Jun-4 Gros & Delettrez, Paris #67/R est:2000-3000

PELOUSE, Léon Germain (1838-1891) French
£336 $624 €500 Procession de la Saint-Jean a Vetheuil (20x15cm-8x6in) s.d.30 juin 1872 panel. 3-Mar-4 Ferri, Paris #373/R
£436 $811 €650 L'Eglise du Faouet (14x19cm-6x7in) s. panel. 3-Mar-4 Ferri, Paris #376
£470 $874 €700 Portrait d'homme a la barbe blanche (14x14cm-6x6in) panel. 3-Mar-4 Ferri, Paris #378
£738 $1373 €1100 En foret (46x65cm-18x26in) s. 3-Mar-4 Ferri, Paris #370
£772 $1436 €1150 Sur le plateau de Bretagne, route d'Huelgoat (14x23cm-6x9in) s. i.verso panel. 3-Mar-4 Ferri, Paris #377
£805 $1498 €1200 Rocher en bord de mer (32x55cm-13x22in) 3-Mar-4 Ferri, Paris #368/R
£872 $1623 €1300 Charbonniers au bord du Doubs (39x55cm-15x22in) s. 3-Mar-4 Ferri, Paris #371/R
£900 $1611 €1314 Haystacks (37x56cm-15x22in) s. panel. 26-May-4 Sotheby's, Olympia #273/R est:1000-1500
£1007 $1872 €1500 Vue de Poigny (46x65cm-18x26in) s. 3-Mar-4 Ferri, Paris #367/R est:2000-3000
£1007 $1872 €1500 Rue du vieil Anvers (28x19cm-11x7in) s.i. panel. 3-Mar-4 Ferri, Paris #375 est:600-900
£1256 $2097 €1834 Landscape with farmstead in evening (49x80cm-19x31in) s. panel. 24-Oct-3 Hans Widmer, St Gallen #98/R est:1400-3500 (S.FR 2800)
£1342 $2497 €2000 Maree basse a Grandchamp, Calvados (20x30cm-8x12in) s. panel. 3-Mar-4 Ferri, Paris #372/R est:600-900
£1549 $2680 €2200 Bord de riviere a la fabrique (65x46cm-26x18in) s. 10-Dec-3 Rossini, Paris #101/R
£1549 $2680 €2200 Au coin de Cernay en Janvier (74x48cm-29x19in) s. 14-Dec-3 St-Germain-en-Laye Encheres #46/R est:2000-3000
£2060 $3750 €3008 Approaching storm (89x117cm-35x46in) s. 29-Jun-4 Sotheby's, New York #75/R est:6000-8000
£2324 $3858 €3300 L'entree du verger (80x110cm-31x43in) s. 15-Jun-3 Muizon & Le Coent, Paris #38
£2333 $4270 €3500 Cueillette des champignons en foret (54x40cm-21x16in) s. 6-Jun-4 Osenat, Fontainebleau #264/R est:5000-5500
£2349 $4369 €3500 Coucher de soleil a Honfleur (36x57cm-14x22in) s. 3-Mar-4 Ferri, Paris #369/R est:1500-2000
£2517 $4330 €3600 Paysage pres d'un ruisseau (46x65cm-18x26in) s. 7-Dec-3 Osenat, Fontainebleau #95 est:2500-3000
£2536 $4159 €3500 Ruisseau dans le Doubs (56x38cm-22x15in) s. i.verso. 11-May-3 Osenat, Fontainebleau #226/R est:5000-5500
£4789 $7949 €6800 Mare aux herons (66x91cm-26x36in) s. 15-Jun-3 Peron, Melun #137
£10556 $19000 €15412 Les fagoteurs a Fontainbleau (65x92cm-26x36in) s. 23-Apr-4 Sotheby's, New York #156/R est:8000-12000

PELS LEUSDEN, Betty (19/20th C) German
£274 $466 €400 Garden (32x25cm-13x10in) s. panel. 5-Nov-3 Hugo Ruef, Munich #1078

PELS, Albert (1910-1998) American
£243 $450 €355 Waiting room (28x36cm-11x14in) s. canvas on masonite. 13-Mar-4 DeFina, Austinburg #970/R
£820 $1500 €1197 Bar (30x41cm-12x16in) s. canvasboard. 5-Jun-4 Treadway Gallery, Cincinnati #736/R est:2000-3000
£852 $1500 €1244 Tango (36x46cm-14x18in) s. canvasboard painted c.1940. 23-May-4 Treadway Gallery, Cincinnati #714/R est:1400-1800
£1022 $1900 €1492 Young girl and wealthy benefactor (36x46cm-14x18in) s. painted c.1940. 7-Mar-4 Treadway Gallery, Cincinnati #648/R est:2500-3500
£2112 $3400 €3084 Express train (51x64cm-20x25in) s. 20-Aug-3 James Julia, Fairfield #1565/R est:2000-3000

PELTONEN, Jarkko (1947-) Finnish
£296 $473 €420 Still life of flowers (61x46cm-24x18in) s.d.1990. 21-Sep-3 Bukowskis, Helsinki #427/R

PELUSO, Francesco (1836-?) Italian
£806 $1500 €1177 The serenade (32x19cm-13x7in) s. panel. 5-Mar-4 Skinner, Boston #228/R est:1500-2000
£1389 $2500 €2028 Small disagreement (26x45cm-10x18in) s. panel. 21-Jan-4 Sotheby's, New York #169/R est:3000-5000
£1744 $3000 €2546 Learning to read (32x19cm-13x7in) s. panel. 3-Dec-3 Doyle, New York #116a/R est:3000-5000

PELUZZI, Eso (1894-1985) Italian
£694 $1181 €1000 Rue Hautefeville, Paris (24x18cm-9x7in) s. board. 1-Nov-3 Meeting Art, Vercelli #71/R
£1189 $2021 €1700 Self-portrait (30x25cm-12x10in) cardboard. 19-Nov-3 Cambi, Genoa #396/R est:1500-1800
£1620 $2835 €2300 Morning in Moltrasio (50x70cm-20x28in) s. masonite. 17-Dec-3 Il Ponte, Milan #1086 est:2000-2500
£4762 $8524 €7000 Drawings and violins (50x40cm-20x16in) s.d.1977 board prov.lit. 22-Mar-4 Sant Agostino, Torino #519/R est:4500-5500
Works on paper
£347 $590 €500 Bardonecchia (17x24cm-7x9in) s. mixed media. 1-Nov-3 Meeting Art, Vercelli #36

PELVO, Paavo (1947-) Finnish
£507 $907 €750 A snob (92x116cm-36x46in) s.d.87. 8-May-4 Bukowskis, Helsinki #287/R

PEMBA, George Mnyalaza Milwa (1912-2001) South African
£714 $1293 €1042 Citizen of New Brighton (55x45cm-22x18in) s.d.1990 i.d.verso board. 30-Mar-4 Stephan Welz, Johannesburg #488/R est:6000-9000 (SA.R 8500)
£2241 $3743 €3272 Granny Zibi (55x40cm-22x16in) s.d.83 board. 20-Oct-3 Stephan Welz, Johannesburg #290/R est:7000-10000 (SA.R 26000)
£2521 $4563 €3681 Warrior (36x29cm-14x11in) s.d.55 board. 30-Mar-4 Stephan Welz, Johannesburg #492/R est:18000-24000 (SA.R 30000)
£3276 $5471 €4783 Young boy reading (41x55cm-16x22in) s.d.89. 20-Oct-3 Stephan Welz, Johannesburg #323/R est:18000-24000 (SA.R 38000)
£3448 $5759 €5034 View from New Bright (30x38cm-12x15in) s.d.81 board. 20-Oct-3 Stephan Welz, Johannesburg #300/R est:25000-30000 (SA.R 40000)
£3800 $6346 €5548 Women and children (49x39cm-19x15in) s. board. 14-Oct-3 Sotheby's, London #126/R est:2000-3000
£7432 $13303 €10851 Pensioners (43x60cm-17x24in) s.d.85 i.verso board prov. 31-May-4 Stephan Welz, Johannesburg #598/R est:40000-60000 (SA.R 90000)
£9083 $16259 €13261 Three musicians (44x59cm-17x23in) s.d.70 canvasboard. 31-May-4 Stephan Welz, Johannesburg #597/R est:40000-60000 (SA.R 110000)
Works on paper
£362 $605 €529 Selby msimang typing a column for Ilanga (27x34cm-11x13in) s.d.82 pen ink. 20-Oct-3 Stephan Welz, Johannesburg #590 est:1500-2000 (SA.R 4200)
£462 $837 €675 Construction of the flyover, Port Elizabeth (21x32cm-8x13in) s.d.80 pencil W/C. 30-Mar-4 Stephan Welz, Johannesburg #502 est:5000-7000 (SA.R 5500)
£4310 $7198 €6293 Young boy with a bowl and spoon (36x26cm-14x10in) s.d.29/10/47 W/C. 20-Oct-3 Stephan Welz, Johannesburg #291/R est:25000-35000 (SA.R 50000)

PEMBERTON, Muriel (1909-1993) British
Works on paper
£480 $874 €701 Portrait (73x52cm-29x20in) s. crayon. 4-Feb-4 Sotheby's, Olympia #138/R

PENA TEJEDO, Antonio de la (1936-) Spanish
£329 $605 €500 Lagoon, Castilla (30x72cm-12x28in) s.d.68 board. 22-Jun-4 Durán, Madrid #171/R

PENA Y MUNOZ, Maximino (1863-1940) Spanish
£606 $951 €885 Portrait of young woman (55x40cm-22x16in) s. 30-Aug-3 Rasmussen, Havnen #2088/R (D.KR 6500)
Works on paper
£1103 $1843 €1600 Landscape (34x49cm-13x19in) s. pastel. 17-Nov-3 Durán, Madrid #163/R est:1000
£2517 $4505 €3750 Young man (70x114cm-28x45in) s. pastel. 25-May-4 Durán, Madrid #218/R est:3500

PENA, Angel (1949-) Venezuelan
£452 $700 €660 Untitled (83x57cm-33x22in) s. 29-Sep-2 Subastas Odalys, Caracas #92/R
£1029 $1750 €1502 Woman and full moon (90x120cm-35x47in) s. acrylic painted 1994. 23-Nov-3 Subastas Odalys, Caracas #109/R
£1258 $2290 €1887 Teens (110x130cm-43x51in) s. acrylic painted. 21-Jun-4 Subastas Odalys, Caracas #55/R

PENA, Feliciano (20th C) Mexican?
£498 $846 €727 Los volcanes desde el Cantil (45x61cm-18x24in) s.d.1979 canvas on panel prov. 25-Nov-3 Germann, Zurich #81/R (S.FR 1100)
£498 $846 €727 Paisaje de Valle de Bravo (55x80cm-22x31in) s.d.1979 prov. 25-Nov-3 Germann, Zurich #82/R (S.FR 1100)

PENA, Maximino (?) Spanish
Works on paper
£805 $1506 €1200 Still life (40x56cm-16x22in) s. 24-Feb-4 Durán, Madrid #195/R
£828 $1382 €1200 Landscape (34x49cm-13x19in) s. pastel. 17-Nov-3 Durán, Madrid #164/R

PENA, Miguel (1951-) Spanish
£743 $1308 €1100 Untitled (96x44cm-38x17in) s.d.1982 canvas on board prov. 18-May-4 Segre, Madrid #270/R

PENA, Tonita (1895-1949) American
Works on paper
£272 $500 €397 Pueblo dancers (25x18cm-10x7in) s. gouache on board pair. 14-Jun-4 Bonhams & Butterfields, San Francisco #1114/R
£815 $1500 €1190 Pueblo dance scene (30x43cm-12x17in) s. gouache on board. 14-Jun-4 Bonhams & Butterfields, San Francisco #1113/R est:2000-3000

PENAGOS ZALABARDO, Rafael de (1889-1954) Spanish
Works on paper
£313 $509 €450 Classical Spanish costume (16x15cm-6x6in) s. mixed media. 23-Sep-3 Durán, Madrid #626/R
£326 $535 €450 Dancer (15x13cm-6x5in) s. mixed media. 27-May-3 Durán, Madrid #729/R
£855 $1574 €1300 Waiting for a call (58x43cm-23x17in) s. dr W/C. 22-Jun-4 Durán, Madrid #30/R
£855 $1574 €1300 In a bar (58x43cm-23x17in) s. dr W/C. 22-Jun-4 Durán, Madrid #29/R

PENALBA, Alicia (1918-1982) Argentinian
Sculpture
£3200 $5888 €4672 Totem d'amour (88cm-35in) resin sold with marble base exec.c.1960 prov. 24-Jun-4 Sotheby's, Olympia #553/R est:2000-3000
£7000 $12880 €10220 Totem d'amour (85cm-33in) s.num.1/6 bronze st.f.Susse exec.c.1960 prov. 24-Jun-4 Sotheby's, Olympia #554/R est:2000-3000
£7639 $12069 €11000 Mistral (44x38x28cm-17x15x11in) s. num.1/7 green pat bronze marble base Cast Valsuani prov.lit. 27-Apr-3 Versailles Encheres #106
£7692 $14000 €11230 Le double (43cm-17in) sig.num.2/6 brown pat. bronze stone base cast 1959 prov. 29-Jun-4 Sotheby's, New York #431/R est:8000-12000
£22346 $40000 €32625 Cathedral (167x46x41cm-66x18x16in) st.sig. num.2/3 pat bronze prov. 26-May-4 Sotheby's, New York #118/R est:20000-25000

PENALBA, Rodrigo (1908-1979) Nicaraguan
£316 $524 €458 Revelacion de San Juan de la Cruz (64x57cm-25x22in) s.d.1946 wood. 12-Jun-3 Louis Morton, Mexico #147 est:2500-3000 (M.P 5500)
£803 $1333 €1164 Pareja en espera (92x61cm-36x24in) s.d.1996 board. 12-Jun-3 Louis Morton, Mexico #110/R est:3000-3500 (M.P 14000)
£975 $1619 €1414 Rostro de mujer (60x56cm-24x22in) s.d.1970 triplay. 12-Jun-3 Louis Morton, Mexico #111/R est:4000-5000 (M.P 17000)
£1033 $1714 €1498 Mi hermana Maria Augusta de Maja (88x66cm-35x26in) s.d.1947. 12-Jun-3 Louis Morton, Mexico #122/R est:3000-4000 (M.P 18000)
Works on paper
£275 $457 €399 Maternidad con sandias (75x55cm-30x22in) s.d.1957 mixed media wood. 12-Jun-3 Louis Morton, Mexico #94/R est:2500-3000 (M.P 4800)
£861 $1429 €1248 Announciation (51x41cm-20x16in) s.d.1969 mixed media. 12-Jun-3 Louis Morton, Mexico #142/R est:2000-2500 (M.P 15000)

PENAULT, Wilf (20th C) Canadian
£586 $995 €856 One way (114x145cm-45x57in) s.d.1979 verso acrylic. 19-Nov-3 Maynards, Vancouver #50 est:600-800 (C.D 1300)

PENCK, A R (1939-) German
£2183 $3624 €3100 Sendero luminoso I (30x40cm-12x16in) s. i. verso acrylic. 13-Jun-3 Hauswedell & Nolte, Hamburg #784/R est:4500
£2691 $4493 €3929 Untitled (50x45cm-20x18in) s. acrylic pvc. 24-Oct-3 Hans Widmer, St Gallen #115/R est:6000-11000 (S.FR 6000)
£3883 $6873 €5669 Standart TX SV (35x27cm-14x11in) s. s.verso. 27-Apr-4 AB Stockholms Auktionsverk #1211/R est:35000-45000 (S.KR 53000)
£4667 $8353 €7000 Pentagon emblem R (59x50cm-23x20in) s. s.i. stretcher acrylic prov. 14-May-4 Ketterer, Munich #295/R est:7000-9000
£5986 $10356 €8500 Y (100x100cm-39x39in) mono. s.i.d.1976 verso acrylic prov. 13-Dec-3 Lempertz, Koln #342/R est:8000
£6667 $12200 €10000 Charly (100x80cm-39x31in) s. i.d.1993 stretcher acrylic. 4-Jun-4 Lempertz, Koln #353/R est:10000
£8392 $14266 €12000 Order and consequence (130x160cm-51x63in) s. acrylic on serigraph on canvas. 27-Nov-3 Lempertz, Koln #328/R est:12000-15000
£9333 $17173 €14000 A man and Jupiter, half-man half-lion (100x79cm-39x31in) s. s.i.verso acrylic painted c.1998. 12-Jun-4 Villa Grisebach, Berlin #417/R est:7000-9000
£9790 $16839 €14000 Untitled (100x130cm-39x51in) s.i.d.1977 acrylic pair prov. 5-Dec-3 Ketterer, Munich #170/R est:14000-18000
£14667 $26987 €22000 Fight (98x130cm-39x51in) s.d.83 i. verso acrylic prov. 8-Jun-4 Artcurial Briest, Paris #253/R est:25000-30000
£16000 $26720 €23360 Situation (260x350cm-102x138in) dispersion painted 1982 prov.exhib. 21-Oct-3 Sotheby's, London #429/R est:8000-12000
£16667 $30500 €25000 Charly (80x100cm-31x39in) s. i.d.1992 stretcher acrylic. 4-Jun-4 Lempertz, Koln #352/R est:10000

£19632 $32000 €28663 Der jager (200x250cm-79x98in) s. acrylic prov. 23-Sep-3 Christie's, Rockefeller NY #149/R est:18000-25000
£26000 $47840 €37960 Situation - large problem (260x350cm-102x138in) dispersion exec 1982 prov.exhib. 24-Jun-4 Sotheby's, London #295/R est:8000-10000
£50000 $92500 €75000 Was system wird (250x330cm-98x130in) acrylic painted 1982 lit. 18-Jul-4 Sotheby's, Paris #226/R est:40000-60000
Sculpture
£1042 $1740 €1500 Object (9x22x8cm-4x9x3in) s.i. dark brown pat.bronze marble socle. 24-Oct-3 Ketterer, Hamburg #494/R est:1500-2000
£2667 $4773 €4000 Untitled (59x10x10cm-23x4x4in) i. bronze. 15-May-4 Van Ham, Cologne #829/R est:4500
£7333 $13493 €11000 Standard, model 36 (29x37x25cm-11x15x10in) i. cardboard collage newspaper exec. 1971 prov. 12-Jun-4 Villa Grisebach, Berlin #415a/R est:2500-3500
Works on paper
£271 $453 €396 Synthetics (41x58cm-16x23in) s.i.d.1979 verso felt pen. 24-Jun-3 Germann, Zurich #135 (S.FR 600)
£271 $453 €396 Synthetics (58x41cm-23x16in) s.i.d.1979 verso feltpen. 24-Jun-3 Germann, Zurich #136/R (S.FR 600)
£271 $453 €396 Synthetics (58x41cm-23x16in) s.i.d.1979 verso felt pen. 24-Jun-3 Germann, Zurich #137 (S.FR 600)
£271 $453 €396 Synthetics (41x58cm-16x23in) s.i.d.1979 verso felt pen. 24-Jun-3 Germann, Zurich #138/R (S.FR 600)
£271 $453 €396 Synthetics (58x41cm-23x16in) s. verso felt pen. 24-Jun-3 Germann, Zurich #139/R (S.FR 600)
£430 $731 €628 Eye composition (38x28cm-15x11in) s. W/C on etching. 25-Nov-3 Germann, Zurich #566 (S.FR 950)
£433 $780 €650 Untitled - woman's head (38x29cm-15x11in) s. graphite oil board. 24-Apr-4 Dr Lehr, Berlin #374/R
£452 $756 €660 Synthetics (41x58cm-16x23in) s. verso felt pen. 24-Jun-3 Germann, Zurich #134 (S.FR 1000)
£500 $895 €750 Synthetics (41x59cm-16x23in) s.i.d.79 verso col pen. 15-May-4 Van Ham, Cologne #828/R
£867 $1586 €1300 Man and eagle 9 (30x21cm-12x8in) s. i. verso Indian ink col chk. 4-Jun-4 Lempertz, Koln #356/R
£1007 $1652 €1400 Woman's head (38x28cm-15x11in) s. chl. 4-Jun-3 Ketterer, Hamburg #746/R
£1067 $1952 €1600 Syntetics (59x42cm-23x17in) s.i.d.79 verso feltpen. 4-Jun-4 Lempertz, Koln #355/R est:1500
£1469 $2526 €2100 Composition (30x42cm-12x17in) s. W/C. 3-Dec-3 Hauswedell & Nolte, Hamburg #941/R est:2800
£1678 $2853 €2400 Untitled - seated female nude (59x43cm-23x17in) s. graphite W/C. 27-Nov-3 Lempertz, Koln #330/R est:2400
£2000 $3680 €2920 Untitled (21x28cm-8x11in) gouache oil exhib. 24-Jun-4 Sotheby's, Olympia #580/R est:2000-3000
£2000 $3680 €2920 Untitled (20x29cm-8x11in) W/C gouache exhib. 24-Jun-4 Sotheby's, Olympia #581/R est:2000-3000
£3333 $6100 €5000 Climbing down II (57x77cm-22x30in) s. i. verso W/C Indian ink. 4-Jun-4 Lempertz, Koln #358/R est:4800
£3497 $5944 €5000 Untitled (54x80cm-21x31in) s. Indian ink carpenter's pencil board. 27-Nov-3 Lempertz, Koln #329/R est:3000-4000
£3944 $6901 €5600 Erzeugung (48x36cm-19x14in) s. wax pastel prov. 18-Dec-3 Cornette de St.Cyr, Paris #152/R est:4000-5000
£4336 $7241 €6200 Untitled (52x84cm-20x33in) mono. gouache prov. 29-Jun-3 Versailles Encheres #222/R
£5644 $9595 €8240 Composition (59x88cm-23x35in) s. gouache W/C crayon prov. 26-Nov-3 Kunsthallen, Copenhagen #134/R est:60000 (D.KR 60000)
£23776 $40895 €34000 Split of R-problems 2 (147x147cm-58x58in) s.i.verso synthetic resin prov. 5-Dec-3 Ketterer, Munich #175/R est:30000-40000

PENCREACH, Stephane (1970-) French?
£2013 $3564 €3000 Ad Augusta per Angusta (195x130cm-77x51in) acrylic mixed media painted 2002 prov.exhib. 28-Apr-4 Artcurial Briest, Paris #442/R est:4500-5000

PENDER, Jack (1918-1998) British
£400 $740 €584 Two fishing boats (25x38cm-10x15in) s. board. 10-Feb-4 David Lay, Penzance #363
£400 $704 €584 Christ and the fishermen (60x91cm-24x36in) s. board. 18-May-4 Rosebery Fine Art, London #816
£1000 $1830 €1460 Beached boat (34x25cm-13x10in) s. board. 3-Jun-4 Lane, Penzance #120/R est:1200-1400
£1500 $2595 €2190 Newlyn fishing boats at anchor (49x60cm-19x24in) s. 11-Dec-3 Lane, Penzance #195/R est:800-1200
£1500 $2490 €2190 Newlyn old harbour (60x73cm-24x29in) s. board. 2-Oct-3 Lane, Penzance #147 est:700-900
£2600 $4602 €3796 Fisherman's square (23x51cm-9x20in) s. board. 27-Apr-4 Bonhams, Knightsbridge #280 est:400-600
Works on paper
£250 $418 €365 Tom Bawcock's Eve (48x61cm-19x24in) s. mixed media. 14-Oct-3 David Lay, Penzance #18

PENDERGAST, N B (19/20th C) ?
£829 $1500 €1210 Pitcher plant (33x28cm-13x11in) s. i.verso painted c.1910 prov. 31-Mar-4 Sotheby's, New York #38/R est:1000-1500

PENDL, Erwin (1875-1945) Austrian
Works on paper
£633 $1165 €950 Dorothegasse in Vienna (32x19cm-13x7in) s.i.d.Juni 1934 i. verso W/C. 9-Jun-4 Dorotheum, Salzburg #850/R
£738 $1358 €1100 Vienna (12x10cm-5x4in) s. grisaille W/C. 26-Mar-4 Dorotheum, Vienna #279/R
£915 $1584 €1300 View of Graben in Vienna (40x35cm-16x14in) s.d.1896 W/C paper on board. 10-Dec-3 Dorotheum, Vienna #154/R

PENDL, Erwin (attrib) (1875-1945) Austrian
Works on paper
£483 $801 €700 Vienna, Donau canal (22x32cm-9x13in) W/C. 30-Sep-3 Dorotheum, Vienna #293/R

PENE DU BOIS, Guy (1884-1958) American
£719 $1200 €1050 By the river (25x36cm-10x14in) s.i. canvasboard. 23-Oct-3 Shannon's, Milford #251/R
£4749 $8500 €6934 Woman in green jacket, Marion Bouche (51x41cm-20x16in) s.d.39 i.stretcher prov. 26-May-4 Doyle, New York #101/R est:3000-4000
£7065 $13000 €10315 Portrait of a young woman (51x38cm-20x15in) panel prov. 8-Jun-4 Bonhams & Butterfields, San Francisco #4111/R est:4000-6000
£8383 $14000 €12239 Girls and a dog wading (41x30cm-16x12in) s.d.34 prov. 23-Oct-3 Shannon's, Milford #134/R est:15000-25000
£9392 $17000 €13712 Sonia (41x30cm-16x12in) s.d.34 prov. 31-Mar-4 Sotheby's, New York #126/R est:10000-15000
£21307 $37500 €31108 In memoriam of Giorgione (41x51cm-16x20in) s.i. 19-May-4 Sotheby's, New York #186/R est:15000-25000
Works on paper
£1286 $2250 €1878 Coney Island (26x18cm-10x7in) s.d.36 pencil. 19-Dec-3 Sotheby's, New York #1010/R est:1500-2500

PENEL, Jules (1833-?) French
Works on paper
£510 $913 €750 L'interieur de Saint-Pierre a Rome (43x60cm-17x24in) s.i. graphite pen black ink col wash after Giovanni Paolo Panini. 18-Mar-4 Christie's, Paris #300/R

PENET, Lucien Francois (1834-1901) French
£364 $667 €550 Nature morte au jambon et au livre (54x65cm-21x26in) s.d.1877. 7-Apr-4 Piasa, Paris #47

PENFIELD, Edward (1866-1925) American
Works on paper
£1677 $2800 €2448 Franklin arriving in Philadelphia (30x43cm-12x17in) s. pen ink W/C exec.c.1923. 15-Nov-3 Illustration House, New York #9/R est:3000-4000

PENFOLD, Frank C (1849-1920) American
£707 $1300 €1032 Portrait of sleeping bearded man seated before wall posted with French handbill (53x38cm-21x15in) s. 9-Jun-4 Alderfer's, Hatfield #382 est:400-600

PENGUILLY-LHARIDON, Octave (1811-1870) French
£13667 $24737 €20500 Paysage aux Rochers, Rouges (94x150cm-37x59in) s.d.1861 lit. 30-Mar-4 Rossini, Paris #260/R est:4000-6000

PENHALL, Ross (1959-) Canadian
£4065 $7276 €5935 Curved wall, corner lot (61x177cm-24x70in) s. s.i.d.2000 verso prov. 27-May-4 Heffel, Vancouver #183/R est:10000-12000 (C.D 10000)

PENKOAT, Pierre (1945-) French
£319 $533 €450 Composition (30x40cm-12x16in) s. cardboard. 19-Oct-3 Charbonneaux, Paris #116
£423 $685 €600 Portrait of a smoker (41x33cm-16x13in) s. 11-Aug-3 Boscher, Cherbourg #857/R
£872 $1544 €1300 Guitare souple (80x30cm-31x12in) s. panel. 29-Apr-4 Claude Aguttes, Neuilly #103
Works on paper
£428 $787 €650 Composition (88x53cm-35x21in) s. collage chl. 25-Jun-4 Millon & Associes, Paris #266
£436 $772 €650 Composition au masque (75x41cm-30x16in) s. gouache. 28-Apr-4 Charbonneaux, Paris #209
£490 $832 €700 Nature morte au tabouret rouge (46x31cm-18x12in) s. gouache. 20-Nov-3 Claude Aguttes, Neuilly #173/R
£621 $1148 €900 Modele aux bras croises (46x38cm-18x15in) s. gouache. 13-Feb-4 Charbonneaux, Paris #65

PENLEY, Aaron Edwin (1807-1870) British
Works on paper
£700 $1239 €1022 Ruins at Bergama, Turkey (28x44cm-11x17in) s.d.1851 W/C. 27-Apr-4 Bonhams, New Bond Street #49

PENLEY, Edwin A (fl.1853-1890) British
Works on paper
£300 $477 €438 On the Lledr (20x43cm-8x17in) s.d.1883 W/C. 9-Sep-3 Gorringes, Lewes #1986
£300 $537 €438 Head of Loch Lomond (24x49cm-9x19in) s.d.1879 W/C htd white. 25-May-4 Bonhams, Knightsbridge #9/R
£350 $637 €511 After the battle (30x48cm-12x19in) s.d.1855 pencil W/C htd white gum arabic. 1-Jul-4 Christie's, Kensington #224/R
£420 $668 €613 Loch Awe (23x46cm-9x18in) s.d.1882 W/C. 9-Sep-3 Gorringes, Lewes #1985

PENN, Irving (1917-) American
Photographs
£1693 $3200 €2472 Max Ernst and wife Dorothea Tanning (23x20cm-9x8in) ferrotype silver print. 17-Feb-4 Swann Galleries, New York #72/R est:4000-6000
£1916 $3200 €2797 Marcel Duchamp, New York (24x19cm-9x7in) s.i.d.1948/1984 gelatin silver print one of 20 lit. 20-Oct-3 Christie's, Rockefeller NY #72/R est:3000-5000
£2200 $3872 €3212 Birds bones (49x29cm-19x11in) s.i.d.1980-81 num.11/32 platinum palladium print. 18-May-4 Bonhams, New Bond Street #518/R est:2000-3000
£2373 $4200 €3465 Brown bear (49x59cm-19x23in) s.i.d.1986 gelatin silver print prov.exhib. 27-Apr-4 Christie's, Rockefeller NY #168/R est:4000-6000
£2395 $4000 €3497 American Ballet Theater (19x24cm-7x9in) with sig. silver contact print. 21-Oct-3 Swann Galleries, New York #215/R est:5000-7000
£2600 $4420 €3796 Telegraphiste, Paris (48x36cm-19x14in) s.i.d.July 1976 num.20/22 verso platinum-palladium print. 19-Nov-3 Sotheby's, Olympia #77/R est:2000-3000
£2600 $4576 €3796 Rudolf Nureyev (35x35cm-14x14in) vintage gelatin silver print. 18-May-4 Bonhams, New Bond Street #519/R est:3000-4000

£2825 $5000 €4125 Roe deer, 1986 (48x59cm-19x23in) s.i.d.1986 gelatin silver print prov.exhib. 27-Apr-4 Christie's, Rockefeller NY #166/R est:5000-7000
£3593 $6000 €5246 Nude 55 (40x39cm-16x15in) s. i.verso photo 1 of 23 prov. 17-Oct-3 Sotheby's, New York #248/R est:5000-7000
£3593 $6000 €5246 Egg seller with his son (20x19cm-8x7in) s.i. gelatin silver print exec.1948 one of seven lit. 17-Oct-3 Phillips, New York #73/R est:8000-12000
£3672 $6500 €5361 Warthog, 1986 (48x60cm-19x24in) s.i.d.1986 gelatin silver print prov.exhib. 27-Apr-4 Christie's, Rockefeller NY #167/R est:4000-6000
£3955 $7000 €5774 Barnett Newman (40x39cm-16x15in) s.i.d.1966 num.1/20 platinum-palladium print printed 1977. 28-Apr-4 Sotheby's, New York #219/R est:8000-12000
£4491 $7500 €6557 Optician's window, New York (28x27cm-11x11in) s.i.d.1939 gelatin silver print lit. 17-Oct-3 Phillips, New York #61/R est:4000-6000
£4667 $8587 €7000 Balenciaga (32x26cm-13x10in) i. s.i. verso silver gelatin lit.exhib. 10-Jun-4 Villa Grisebach, Berlin #1237/R est:7000-8000
£4790 $8000 €6993 Camel pack, New York (25x21cm-10x8in) s.i.d.1975 num.63 verso platinum-palladium print one of 68 lit. 17-Oct-3 Phillips, New York #102/R est:10000-15000
£5090 $8500 €7431 Nude 119 (39x38cm-15x15in) s.i.d.1949-50 verso photo 1 of 13 prov. 17-Oct-3 Sotheby's, New York #247/R est:5000-7000
£5090 $8500 €7431 Gorilla, female, Prague, from Cranium Architecture (48x59cm-19x23in) s.i.d.1986 gelatin silver print one of 8 prov.exhib. 20-Oct-3 Christie's, Rockefeller NY #210/R est:8000-10000
£5090 $8500 €7431 Lion, three quarter view, Prague, from Cranium Architecture (48x59cm-19x23in) s.i.d.1986 gelatin silver print one of 19 prov.exhib.lit. 20-Oct-3 Christie's, Rockefeller NY #211/R est:6000-8000
£5367 $9500 €7836 Issey Miyake design with black fan, New York (55x46cm-22x18in) s.i.d.1987 dye transfer print. 27-Apr-4 Christie's, Rockefeller NY #327/R est:7000-9000
£5988 $10000 €8742 Parade (29x46cm-11x18in) s.i.d.1980 num.4/16 i.verso platinum-palladium aluminum. 17-Oct-3 Sotheby's, New York #251/R est:7000-10000
£6111 $11000 €8922 Cigarette 42 (63x56cm-25x22in) s.verso platinum palladium print prov.lit. 23-Apr-4 Phillips, New York #251/R est:7000-10000
£6215 $11000 €9074 Man with pink face (53x49cm-21x19in) s.i.d.1970 num.29/50 platinum-palladium print printed 1980. 28-Apr-4 Sotheby's, New York #222/R est:6000-9000
£6287 $10500 €9179 Three Dahomey girls, one reclining (50x49cm-20x19in) num.26/35 platinum-palladium print aluminium prov.lit. 17-Oct-3 Phillips, New York #236/R est:7000-10000
£6349 $12000 €9270 Cigarette no.69 (60x48cm-24x19in) s.i.d.1974 num.32/46 platinum palladium print on aluminum. 17-Feb-4 Christie's, Rockefeller NY #258/R est:10000-15000
£6780 $12000 €9899 Five Okapa warriors, New Guinea, 1970 (50x50cm-20x20in) s.i.d. num.26/35 platinum palladium print prov.lit. 27-Apr-4 Christie's, Rockefeller NY #337/R est:10000-15000
£7910 $14000 €11549 Optician's window (34x24cm-13x9in) s.i.d.1983 gelatin silver print prov.exhib.lit. 27-Apr-4 Christie's, Rockefeller NY #222/R est:8000-12000
£8475 $15000 €12374 Nubile young beauty of Diamare, Cameroon (49x49cm-19x19in) s.i.d.1974 num.20/40 platinum-palladium print printed 1980. 28-Apr-4 Sotheby's, New York #221/R est:10000-15000
£8475 $15000 €12374 Fish made of fish, New York, 1939 (27x50cm-11x20in) s.i.d. num.7/40 prov.lit. 27-Apr-4 Christie's, Rockefeller NY #169/R est:10000-15000
£8982 $15000 €13114 Cocoa-coloured Balenciaga dress, Lisa Fonssagrives-Penn (49x49cm-19x19in) s.i.num.4/50 platinum-palladium print exec.1950 prov. 17-Oct-3 Sotheby's, New York #242/R est:8000-12000
£9040 $16000 €13198 Truman Capote (40x39cm-16x15in) s.i.d.1965 num.20/20 platinum palladium print. 27-Apr-4 Christie's, Rockefeller NY #326/R est:7000-9000
£9581 $16000 €13988 Pablo Picasso at La Californie, Cannes (49x49cm-19x19in) s.d.1957 num.31/45 platinum-palladium print aluminum lit. 20-Oct-3 Christie's, Rockefeller NY #207/R est:15000-20000
£10180 $17000 €14863 Cigarette no 69 (58x47cm-23x19in) s.d.1972/1974 num.45/46 verso platinum-palladium print prov.lit. 20-Oct-3 Christie's, Rockefeller NY #52/R est:10000-15000
£11976 $20000 €17485 Girl behind bottle (47x45cm-19x18in) s.i.d.1949 num.10/33 platinum-palladium print printed later. 17-Oct-3 Sotheby's, New York #241/R est:25000-35000
£11976 $20000 €17485 Two Guedras (53x43cm-21x17in) s.i.d.1974 num.4/40 i.verso platinum-palladium print prov. 17-Oct-3 Sotheby's, New York #245/R est:20000-30000
£13000 $22880 €18980 Two guedras, Morocco (53x43cm-21x17in) s. platinum print lit. 19-May-4 Christie's, London #194/R est:8000-12000
£13559 $24000 €19796 Nude 150, 1949-50 (46x44cm-18x17in) s.i.d. num.16/57 platinum palladium print prov.lit. 27-Apr-4 Christie's, Rockefeller NY #171/R est:30000-50000
£15569 $26000 €22731 Twelve of the most photographed models of the period (33x40cm-13x16in) s.i.d.1947 gelatin silver print board prov.lit. 17-Oct-3 Phillips, New York #55/R est:20000-30000
£20380 $37500 €29755 Portraits of Spencer Tracy (23x15cm-9x6in) s.d.1948 verso gelatin silver print two. 10-Jun-4 Sotheby's, New York #459/R est:3000-5000
£23333 $42000 €34066 Girl drinking, Mary Jane Russell, New York (41x49cm-16x19in) s.i.d.1996 i.verso gelatin silver print prov.lit. 23-Apr-4 Phillips, New York #22/R est:25000-35000
£23729 $42000 €34644 Girl in bed on telephone, Jean Patchett (50x40cm-20x16in) s.i.d.1949 verso photo edition of 19 prov.lit. 27-Apr-4 Sotheby's, New York #33/R est:20000-30000
£29940 $50000 €43712 After dinner games, New York, from Service to the Trade (100x79cm-39x31in) s.i.d.1949 dye-transfer print aluminum one of 13 prov.lit. 20-Oct-3 Christie's, Rockefeller NY #212/R est:25000-35000

Prints
£13000 $22880 €18980 Woman with roses (49x37cm-19x15in) s. gelatin silver print lit. 19-May-4 Christie's, London #195/R est:7000-9000

Works on paper
£7910 $14000 €11549 Lisa Fonssagrives (8x7cm-3x3in) i.verso platinum-palladium print assemblage printed later prov. 28-Apr-4 Sotheby's, New York #220/R est:5000-7000

PENN, William Charles (1877-1968) British
£250 $458 €365 Still life, glitter (60x50cm-24x20in) s. 7-Jun-4 Cumbria Auction Rooms, Carlisle #246/R
£300 $501 €438 Spring flowers in a blue vase (54x44cm-21x17in) s. 21-Oct-3 Bonhams, Knightsbridge #193/R
£560 $1025 €818 Still life, giant mushroom (53x42cm-21x17in) s. board. 7-Jun-4 Cumbria Auction Rooms, Carlisle #247/R
£2686 $4754 €3922 Sitting in the sun (49x39cm-19x15in) s.d.1919. 3-May-4 Lawson Menzies, Sydney #410/R est:6000-8000 (A.D 6500)
£6500 $11050 €9490 Picnic (51x61cm-20x24in) s.d.1921 prov.lit. 21-Nov-3 Christie's, London #126/R est:4000-6000

PENNACHINI, Domenico (1860-?) Italian
£2762 $5000 €4033 Dance of spring (54x75cm-21x30in) s.i. 30-Mar-4 Christie's, Rockefeller NY #72/R est:4000-6000

Works on paper
£500 $835 €730 Woodland romance (35x50cm-14x20in) s. W/C. 16-Oct-3 Lawrence, Crewkerne #635/R

PENNAMEN, Guy (1932-) French
£298 $557 €450 Ste Anne la Palud (55x46cm-22x18in) s. 24-Jul-4 Thierry & Lannon, Brest #281

PENNASILICO, Giuseppe (1861-1940) Italian
£600 $1086 €900 View of San Sebastianello Street in Rome (29x24cm-11x9in) s. 30-Mar-4 Babuino, Rome #402
£724 $1332 €1100 Wild flowers (61x37cm-24x15in) s. 23-Jun-4 Finarte Semenzato, Rome #94/R
£1408 $2437 €2000 Labour (37x63cm-15x25in) s.i. 10-Dec-3 Sotheby's, Milan #84/R est:1500-2500
£4196 $7217 €6000 Woman reading (35x50cm-14x20in) s. canvas on cardboard. 3-Dec-3 Stadion, Trieste #980/R est:2000-3000

PENNAZIO, Augusto (1877-?) Italian
£1277 $2132 €1800 Mountainous landscape (77x93cm-30x37in) s.d.1916. 20-Oct-3 Sant Agostino, Torino #257/R est:1800-2200

PENNE, Arnovl T (19th C) British
£1800 $3006 €2628 Precipice walk, Dollelly, north Wales (71x91cm-28x36in) s.d.98 s.i.d.2/5/98 verso. 13-Nov-3 Christie's, Kensington #193/R est:1000-1500

PENNE, Olivier de (1831-1897) French
£877 $1465 €1280 Chiens de chasse (43x36cm-17x14in) s. 16-Nov-3 Koller, Geneva #1263 (S.FR 2000)
£2471 $4200 €3608 Dogs waiting (26x37cm-10x15in) 25-Nov-3 Galeria y Remates, Montevideo #187/R
£2517 $4280 €3600 Hunter taking a break (27x22cm-11x9in) s. panel. 24-Nov-3 Dorotheum, Vienna #186/R est:4000-4500
£3467 $6275 €5200 Hunting dogs round campfire (40x27cm-16x11in) s. panel. 1-Apr-4 Van Ham, Cologne #1597/R est:6000
£3624 $6741 €5400 Deux chiens (46x61cm-18x24in) s. 3-Mar-4 Ferri, Paris #144/R est:4000-5000
£4503 $8196 €6800 Six chiens de chasse au relais (26x21cm-10x8in) s. panel. 19-Jun-4 St-Germain-en-Laye Encheres #56/R est:7000-8000
£15294 $26000 €22329 Boar chase (145x129cm-57x51in) s. exhib. 28-Oct-3 Sotheby's, New York #171/R est:30000-40000

Works on paper
£559 $962 €800 Chiens poursuivant un lapin (18x25cm-7x10in) s. graphite W/C. 7-Dec-3 Osenat, Fontainebleau #196
£839 $1443 €1200 Chiens de chasse au relais (14x20cm-6x8in) s. black ink. 7-Dec-3 Osenat, Fontainebleau #195
£1176 $2000 €1717 Pack of hounds (47x32cm-19x13in) s. W/C graphite gouache. 21-Nov-3 Skinner, Boston #128/R est:600-800
£1678 $2853 €2400 Hallali du sanglier (31x47cm-12x19in) wash. 20-Nov-3 Millon & Associes, Paris #114/R
£2105 $3874 €3200 Chiens hardes (30x45cm-12x18in) s. W/C. 23-Jun-4 Maigret, Paris #18/R est:2000-3000
£2319 $3803 €3200 Panoramique d'un relais de chasse courre (21x61cm-8x24in) s. W/C fan shaped. 11-May-3 Osenat, Fontainebleau #149/R est:3000-4000
£3310 $5498 €4700 Curee (34x48cm-13x19in) s. W/C. 15-Jun-3 Peron, Melun #55
£13706 $23301 €19600 Sanglier au ferme et chiens dans la neige (43x28cm-17x11in) s. W/C. 20-Nov-3 Millon & Associes, Paris #115/R

PENNELL, Harry (19th C) British
£700 $1169 €1022 Mooring on the river (61x102cm-24x40in) s. 12-Nov-3 Sotheby's, Olympia #127/R
£756 $1300 €1104 River landscape with boat (58x99cm-23x39in) s.i. painted c.1910. 7-Dec-3 Treadway Gallery, Cincinnati #493/R
£800 $1336 €1168 River mooring (61x101cm-24x40in) s. 12-Nov-3 Sotheby's, Olympia #120/R
£1161 $1996 €1695 Penryhn Castle, North Wales (41x61cm-16x24in) s.i.verso prov. 2-Dec-3 Ritchie, Toronto #72/R est:2000-3000 (C.D 2600)
£1600 $2672 €2336 Continental river landscape at sunset (91x71cm-36x28in) s. s.indis.i.verso. 7-Oct-3 Bonhams, Knightsbridge #161/R est:700-1000

PENNI, Giovanni Francesco (1488-1528) Italian
Works on paper
£5000 $9150 €7300 Hercules kneeling before a snake (17x16cm-7x6in) i. pen ink lit. 6-Jul-4 Christie's, London #6/R est:4000-6000

PENNI, Giovanni Francesco (attrib) (1488-1528) Italian
£7394 $12940 €10500 Madonna and Child (86x62cm-34x24in) board. 17-Dec-3 Christie's, Rome #450/R est:8000-12000

PENNINGTON, George (20th C) British
Works on paper
£260 $434 €377 Mullion Cove (24x34cm-9x13in) mono. W/C bodycol. 17-Jun-3 Rosebery Fine Art, London #570/R

PENNINGTON, George Farquhar (1872-1961) British
£310 $515 €453 Boats on the hard at Cadgwith Cove, Cornwall (36x48cm-14x19in) s. board. 2-Oct-3 Lane, Penzance #47

PENNOYER, Albert Shelton (1888-1957) American
£284 $500 €415 Covered bridge (61x74cm-24x29in) s. painted c.1930. 23-May-4 Treadway Gallery, Cincinnati #584/R

£314 $500 €458 Portrait of Spanish woman wearing yellow blouse and red flowers in her hair (76x102cm-30x40in) s. 10-Sep-3 Alderfer's, Hatfield #296/R
£373 $600 €545 Steam engine travelling through mountain landscape (41x30cm-16x12in) s. board painted c.1930's. 22-Feb-3 Bunte, Elgin #1219
£745 $1200 €1088 Steam engine travelling through winter landscape (30x41cm-12x16in) s. canvas on board painted c.1930's. 22-Feb-3 Bunte, Elgin #1220
£1879 $3250 €2743 Hour of the siesta, Ronda (63x76cm-25x30in) s.i.verso prov.exhib. 10-Dec-3 Bonhams & Butterfields, San Francisco #6107/R est:5000-7000

PENNY, Evan (1953-) Canadian
Sculpture
£4065 $7276 €5935 Janet (67x30x20cm-26x12x8in) s.i.d.1980-1981 num.2/2 epoxy resin prov. 27-May-4 Heffel, Vancouver #76/R est:10000-12000 (C.D 10000)

PENNY, L (?) British?
£1250 $2150 €1825 Lady playing a church organ with man looking on, preraphaelite style (81x48cm-32x19in) s. 3-Dec-3 Brightwells, Leominster #1218/R est:800-1200

PENNY, William Daniel (1834-1924) British
£750 $1275 €1095 Shipping scene (22x27cm-9x11in) panel. 18-Nov-3 Bonhams, Leeds #183
Works on paper
£1138 $2083 €1661 The barque Daghild (45x69cm-18x27in) s.i.d.1907 mixed media. 7-Jun-4 Blomqvist, Oslo #256/R est:18000-22000 (N.KR 14000)

PENONE, Giuseppe (1947-) Italian
Works on paper
£2489 $4156 €3634 Untitled (71x56cm-28x22in) s.d.1975 plaster collage biro. 24-Jun-3 Germann, Zurich #83/R est:3500-4500 (S.FR 5500)

PENOT, Albert Joseph (19th C) French
£413 $756 €603 La lecture du soir (32x24cm-13x9in) s. cardboard. 4-Jun-4 Zofingen, Switzerland #2500 (S.FR 950)

PENOT, Jean Vallette (1710-1777) French
£11111 $20000 €16222 Tromple l'oeil with a basket of cherries on a table engraving tacked up a wall (64x52cm-25x20in) 22-Jan-4 Sotheby's, New York #226/R est:20000-30000

PENRAAT, Maria (?) French
£483 $883 €700 Le port de Collioure au matin (46x55cm-18x22in) s. 1-Feb-4 Feletin, Province #144

PENROSE, Sir Roland (1900-1984) British
Works on paper
£296 $545 €450 Very Jolly Roger (26x20cm-10x8in) s.i. ink col crayon prov. 28-Jun-4 Joron-Derem, Paris #149

PENSTONE, Constance (19th C) British
Works on paper
£571 $1034 €834 Two Malay flower sellers (52x38cm-20x15in) s. pencil W/C. 30-Mar-4 Stephan Welz, Johannesburg #201 est:1500-2000 (SA.R 6800)

PENWARDEN, Walter (?) American?
£251 $475 €366 Desert wash (41x61cm-16x24in) s. panel. 22-Feb-4 Bonhams & Butterfields, Los Angeles #7005

PEPLOE, Denis (1914-1993) British
£720 $1318 €1051 Church in the cornfield (33x41cm-13x16in) s. board. 8-Apr-4 Bonhams, Edinburgh #7/R
£750 $1343 €1095 Paps of Jura (22x27cm-9x11in) s. panel. 28-May-4 Lyon & Turnbull, Edinburgh #26
£2500 $4250 €3650 Sunlit street, Southern Spain (61x45cm-24x18in) s. 30-Oct-3 Christie's, London #198/R est:3000-5000

PEPLOE, Samuel John (1871-1935) British
£6000 $9420 €8700 Landscape with haystacks (16x23cm-6x9in) i.verso panel prov. 27-Aug-3 Sotheby's, London #1198/R est:6000-8000
£13000 $20930 €18850 The milkmaid (25x25cm-10x10in) s. panel painted c.1896 prov. 21-Aug-3 Bonhams, Edinburgh #1032/R est:7000-10000
£30000 $51600 €43800 Iona (37x45cm-15x18in) s. panel prov.exhib. 4-Dec-3 Bonhams, Edinburgh #38/R est:25000-35000
£42000 $71400 €61320 Rough Day, Iona (48x58cm-19x23in) s. prov.exhib. 30-Oct-3 Christie's, London #160/R est:30000-50000
£45000 $77850 €65700 Luxembourg Gardens, Paris (34x26cm-13x10in) s.verso board prov.lit. 11-Dec-3 Lyon & Turnbull, Edinburgh #115/R est:20000-30000
£68841 $110833 €100508 Green hat (59x49cm-23x19in) s. board. 20-Aug-3 Dunbar Sloane, Auckland #28/R est:125000-160000 (NZ.D 190000)
£75000 $117750 €108750 Still life with a jug and a bowl of apples (45x41cm-18x16in) s. prov. 27-Aug-3 Sotheby's, London #1199/R est:70000-100000
£85000 $136850 €123250 Still life of fruit, comport and pink rose (37x45cm-15x18in) s. prov. 21-Aug-3 Bonhams, Edinburgh #1107/R est:50000-80000
£85000 $144500 €124100 Marigolds in a jug (51x41cm-20x16in) s. life study of table-top verso double-sided prov.exhib. 30-Oct-3 Christie's, London #159/R est:100000-150000
£230000 $416300 €335800 Still life of pink and red roses in a Chinese vase (64x64cm-25x25in) s. prov. 19-Apr-4 Sotheby's, London #69/R est:200000-250000
Works on paper
£520 $957 €759 Someone's fainted, a group of figures (19x25cm-7x10in) init. black conte. 29-Mar-4 Thomson Roddick & Medcalf, Edinburgh #220

PEPPER, Beverly (1924-) American
Sculpture
£1018 $1700 €1486 Untitled - maquette (4x13cm-2x5in) s.d.66 painted metal. 11-Nov-3 Christie's, Rockefeller NY #159/R est:1000-1500
£1098 $1900 €1603 Lopez de Vega (56cm-22in) s.i. painted cor-ten steel prov. 15-Dec-3 Hindman, Chicago #45/R est:2000-4000
£1117 $2000 €1631 Abstract form (50x68x18cm-20x27x7in) walnut lacquered metal prov. 6-May-4 Doyle, New York #88/R est:3000-5000
£1816 $3250 €2651 Untitled (15x23x29cm-6x9x11in) s.d.1971 num.4/6 polished steel. 4-May-4 Doyle, New York #239/R est:1000-1500
£4491 $7500 €6557 Untitled (27x193x91cm-11x76x36in) s.d.70 varnished steel prov. 12-Nov-3 Christie's, Rockefeller NY #409/R est:5000-7000
Works on paper
£1027 $1900 €1499 Untitled (28x21cm-11x8in) first s.d.79 chl ink sold with two others three prov. 13-Jul-4 Christie's, Rockefeller NY #131/R est:800-1200
£1081 $2000 €1578 Untitled (99x69cm-39x27in) s.d.89 chl ink. 13-Jul-4 Christie's, Rockefeller NY #132/R est:1000-1500

PEPPER, George Douglas (1903-1962) Canadian
£800 $1464 €1168 Fast water at Kananaskis (38x45cm-15x18in) s.i. board exhib. 1-Jun-4 Hodgins, Calgary #136/R est:2250-2750 (C.D 2000)
£1351 $2297 €1972 Spring break-up, Gouffre River, PQ (25x30cm-10x12in) s. s.i.verso sketch verso prov. 23-Nov-3 Levis, Calgary #101/R est:3500-4500 (C.D 3000)
£4955 $8423 €7234 Evening, St Hilarion (31x37cm-12x15in) s.d.33 board prov.exhib. 18-Nov-3 Sotheby's, Toronto #7/R est:4000-6000 (C.D 11000)
Works on paper
£223 $384 €326 Road to recovery (9x42cm-4x17in) W/C. 2-Dec-3 Joyner Waddington, Toronto #517 (C.D 500)

PEPPER, J H (19th C) ?
£1550 $2589 €2263 Emperor, Lieutenant C W Bell's 2nd Charger XV Hussars (41x56cm-16x22in) s.d.1857. 16-Nov-3 Desmond Judd, Cranbrook #1057

PEPPERCORN, Arthur Douglas (1847-1924) British
£552 $1000 €806 Landscape (25x46cm-10x18in) s. 18-Apr-4 Bonhams & Butterfields, Los Angeles #7037 est:600-800
£600 $948 €870 Windy estuary (76x127cm-30x50in) s. 4-Sep-3 Christie's, Kensington #160/R

PEPYN, Marten (attrib) (1575-1642) Flemish
£3642 $6629 €5500 Saint Cosme et Saint Damien (58x86cm-23x34in) panel. 21-Jun-4 Tajan, Paris #32/R est:4000-6000

PERAHIM, Jules (20th C) French
£671 $1228 €1000 Un mutant (92x73cm-36x29in) s.d.75 s.i.d. verso acrylic. 7-Jul-4 Artcurial Briest, Paris #320
£839 $1427 €1200 Lumiere physique (56x56cm-22x22in) s.d.1967 panel prov. 23-Nov-3 Cornette de St.Cyr, Paris #268/R
£979 $1664 €1400 Objets a toucher (65x81cm-26x32in) s. i.verso prov.lit. 23-Nov-3 Cornette de St.Cyr, Paris #267/R
Works on paper
£268 $491 €400 Composition (47x65cm-19x26in) s.d.74 gouache col crayons. 7-Jul-4 Artcurial Briest, Paris #319
£350 $594 €500 Oiseaux (50cm-20in circular) s. W/C prov. 23-Nov-3 Cornette de St.Cyr, Paris #269

PERAIRE, Paul Emmanuel (1829-1893) French
£1133 $2074 €1700 Loing a Moret (38x61cm-15x24in) s. 6-Jun-4 Osenat, Fontainebleau #143/R est:2000-2500
£1241 $2073 €1800 Fagotiere et son enfant au bord de la riviere (51x70cm-20x28in) s. 17-Nov-3 Tajan, Paris #62/R est:2200-2400
£1629 $2720 €2378 River landscape with mill (35x68cm-14x27in) s. 24-Jun-3 Germann, Zurich #162 est:3000-4000 (S.FR 3600)

PERALTA DEL CAMPO, Francisco (1837-1897) Spanish
£563 $1025 €850 Spanish scene with rider and gypsy musician in a village street (25x33cm-10x13in) s. panel. 19-Jun-4 Bergmann, Erlangen #882

PERALTA, Pedro (1961-) Uruguayan
£335 $550 €489 Lupin comes back to find a moon of honey (81x100cm-32x39in) s. s.i.verso acrylic. 3-Jun-3 Galeria y Remates, Montevideo #56

PERAUX, Lionel (1871-?) French
Works on paper
£278 $464 €400 Roccoco scene (29x23cm-11x9in) s. W/C gouache board. 24-Oct-3 Ketterer, Hamburg #204/R

PERBANDT, Carl von (1832-1911) American
£2168 $3750 €3165 Cows watering at a pond in an extensive landscape (51x91cm-20x36in) s. prov. 10-Dec-3 Bonhams & Butterfields, San Francisco #6159/R est:3500-4500

PERBOYRE, Paul Emile Léon (c.1826-1907) French
£2695 $5013 €3935 Charge de Curraissers a Lena (52x65cm-20x26in) s. 2-Mar-4 Rasmussen, Copenhagen #1504/R est:30000-40000 (D.KR 30000)
£3073 $5500 €4487 Back from the hunt (38x46cm-15x18in) s. 8-Jan-4 James Julia, Fairfield #417/R est:4000-5000

PERCEVAL, Celia (1949-) Australian
£2290 $4168 €3343 Forest pond (122x111cm-48x44in) s. painted c.1983. 16-Jun-4 Deutscher-Menzies, Melbourne #307/R est:4500-6000 (A.D 6000)

£2479 $4587 €3619 View across Hicks Point in Croajingalong National Park (91x122cm-36x48in) s. i.verso board. 10-Mar-4 Deutscher-Menzies, Melbourne #489/R est:2000-5000 (A.D 6000)
£2893 $5120 €4224 Black boys on the Sinclair Bay Track, Queensland (91x121cm-36x48in) s. board prov. 3-May-4 Christie's, Melbourne #311/R est:4000-8000 (A.D 7000)

PERCEVAL, Don Louis (1908-1979) American
£2096 $3500 €3060 California Yosemite National Park (56x41cm-22x16in) board. 18-Oct-3 David Dike, Dallas #203/R est:2000-4000
£2353 $4000 €3435 Hopiland (56x41cm-22x16in) s.i. tempera paper board prov. 1-Nov-3 Santa Fe Art, Santa Fe #69/R est:5000-10000
£2844 $4750 €4152 Navajo Country (56x41cm-22x16in) board. 18-Oct-3 David Dike, Dallas #205/R est:2000-4000
£2941 $5000 €4294 Sunset over the Sonora Desert (56x41cm-22x16in) s. tempera paper board prov. 1-Nov-3 Santa Fe Art, Santa Fe #71/R est:5000-10000
£3529 $6000 €5152 Navajo Country (56x41cm-22x16in) s. tempera paper board prov. 1-Nov-3 Santa Fe Art, Santa Fe #70/R est:5000-10000

PERCEVAL, John (1923-2000) Australian
£418 $762 €610 Untitled (20x28cm-8x11in) prov. 5-Feb-4 Joel, Victoria #192 (A.D 1000)
£909 $1609 €1327 Mother playing with Remus II (54x77cm-21x30in) s.i.d.69 oil paper prov. 3-May-4 Christie's, Melbourne #336/R est:2500-4000 (A.D 2200)
£1094 $2045 €1641 Cow beside a pont at sunset (25x35cm-10x14in) s.d.58 i.verso oil paper pair. 20-Jul-4 Goodman, Sydney #60/R est:3000-5000 (A.D 2800)
£1417 $2281 €2069 Untitled (101x80cm-40x31in) init.d.85. 13-Oct-3 Joel, Victoria #358 est:3500-4500 (A.D 3500)
£2290 $4168 €3343 Woman knitting (71x56cm-28x22in) s. s.i.verso canvas on board painted c.1949 pencil. 16-Jun-4 Deutscher-Menzies, Melbourne #34/R est:6000-9000 (A.D 6000)
£2290 $4168 €3343 Portrait of Laurie Beck (61x47cm-24x19in) s.d.49 canvas on board exhib. 16-Jun-4 Deutscher-Menzies, Melbourne #222/R est:6000-9000 (A.D 6000)
£2766 $4702 €4038 Portrait of Tessa (35x25cm-14x10in) s.d.53 canvas on board. 26-Nov-3 Deutscher-Menzies, Melbourne #118/R est:6000-8000 (A.D 6500)
£2834 $4563 €4138 Standing nude (68x42cm-27x17in) s.d.67 paper on board exhib. 25-Aug-3 Sotheby's, Paddington #344/R est:5000-7000 (A.D 7000)
£3719 $6880 €5430 Wheatfield with sickle farmer and scarecrow (42x51cm-17x20in) s. canvas on board. 10-Mar-4 Deutscher-Menzies, Melbourne #279/R est:10000-15000 (A.D 9000)
£5372 $9938 €7843 Angel Kathy crawling (40x51cm-16x20in) s. s.i.d.64 verso. 10-Mar-4 Deutscher-Menzies, Melbourne #16/R est:15000-25000 (A.D 13000)
£5691 $10187 €8309 Bermagui backwater (49x60cm-19x24in) s.d.66 s.i.d.verso oil mixed media composition board. 4-May-4 Sotheby's, Melbourne #185/R est:14000-18000 (A.D 14000)
£6356 $10805 €9280 Mother playing with Romelus and Remus (49x60cm-19x24in) s.d.65 s.i.verso canvas on board prov.exhib. 24-Nov-3 Sotheby's, Melbourne #45/R est:15000-20000 (A.D 15000)
£6612 $11240 €9654 Grandmother in the wheatfields 1988 (50x60cm-20x24in) s.i.verso. 29-Oct-3 Lawson Menzies, Sydney #24/R est:20000-30000 (A.D 16000)
£6612 $11240 €9654 Pair of monks (50x60cm-20x24in) s. s.i.verso. 29-Oct-3 Lawson Menzies, Sydney #109/R est:20000-30000 (A.D 16000)
£13934 $22016 €20344 Gaffney's Creek (91x122cm-36x48in) s. s.i.d. verso prov. 2-Sep-3 Deutscher-Menzies, Melbourne #98/R est:35000-45000 (A.D 34000)
£15702 $26694 €22925 Hide and seek (90x120cm-35x47in) s. i.verso oil leaves on canvas. 29-Oct-3 Lawson Menzies, Sydney #42/R est:40000-60000 (A.D 38000)
£16393 $25902 €23934 Tug boat and tug boat, Williamstown (91x122cm-36x48in) s. s.i.d.89-90 verso prov. 2-Sep-3 Deutscher-Menzies, Melbourne #68/R est:40000-60000 (A.D 40000)
£16393 $25902 €23934 White light at Wiliamstown (91x122cm-36x48in) s. s.i.d.88 verso prov.exhib. 2-Sep-3 Deutscher-Menzies, Melbourne #93/R est:40000-60000 (A.D 40000)
£19835 $35107 €28959 Casuarina Sands (90x100cm-35x39in) s.d.65 s.i.d.Oct 1965 verso prov. 3-May-4 Christie's, Melbourne #10/R est:40000-50000 (A.D 48000)
£24793 $45868 €36198 Resue at Gibraltar, near Canberra (86x101cm-34x40in) s.d.66 prov.exhib. 10-Mar-4 Deutscher-Menzies, Melbourne #38/R est:70000-90000 (A.D 60000)
£35124 $59711 €51281 Fisherman sights Williamstown (80x101cm-31x40in) s. i.verso. 29-Oct-3 Lawson Menzies, Sydney #40/R est:60000-70000 (A.D 85000)
£35270 $58900 €52905 Primeval forests You Yangs (91x121cm-36x48in) s.d.56 board. 27-Oct-3 Goodman, Sydney #66/R est:160000-200000 (A.D 85000)
£51653 $87810 €75413 Richmond landscape (74x91cm-29x36in) s.d.44 exhib. 29-Oct-3 Lawson Menzies, Sydney #34/R est:140000-180000 (A.D 125000)
Works on paper
£268 $488 €391 Roman Catholics. d.June 44 pencil. 1-Jul-4 Joel, Victoria #317/R (A.D 700)
£345 $538 €500 Flower lady (21x15cm-8x6in) init.d.87 pencil. 1-Aug-2 Joel, Victoria #168 est:1000-1500 (A.D 1000)
£351 $650 €512 Bee sting (21x15cm-8x6in) s.i.verso pencil. 10-Mar-4 Deutscher-Menzies, Melbourne #277 (A.D 850)
£379 $591 €550 Insects as decoration (21x16cm-8x6in) init.d.64 pencil. 1-Aug-2 Joel, Victoria #352 est:1000-1500 (A.D 1100)
£430 $804 €645 Woman knitting with bee (21x16cm-8x6in) s. pencil sold with another. 21-Jul-4 Shapiro, Sydney #152 (A.D 1100)
£486 $782 €710 Self portrait (47x36cm-19x14in) s. pencil. 13-Oct-3 Joel, Victoria #376 est:1000-1500 (A.D 1200)
£486 $782 €710 Boab trees (26x37cm-10x15in) init.d.90 col pastel. 13-Oct-3 Joel, Victoria #415 est:900-1200 (A.D 1200)
£552 $861 €800 American angel landing on the moon (26x18cm-10x7in) s.i.d.67 pencil. 1-Aug-2 Joel, Victoria #173 est:1500-2500 (A.D 1600)
£625 $1169 €938 The warning (38x48cm-15x19in) s.i. ink wash. 21-Jul-4 Shapiro, Sydney #151/R (A.D 1600)
£936 $1591 €1367 Bird (55x76cm-22x30in) s.d.83 W/C. 26-Nov-3 Deutscher-Menzies, Melbourne #229/R (A.D 2200)
£992 $1806 €1448 Dance (36x54cm-14x21in) s. pencil. 16-Jun-4 Deutscher-Menzies, Melbourne #376/R est:2800-3500 (A.D 2600)
£1362 $2315 €1989 Portrait of Fred Williams (54x73cm-21x29in) s. felt tip pen graphite. 26-Nov-3 Deutscher-Menzies, Melbourne #234/R est:4000-5000 (A.D 3200)
£1527 $2779 €2229 Dancing in Carlton with cat (25x29cm-10x11in) s.d.March 44 ink prov.exhib. 16-Jun-4 Deutscher-Menzies, Melbourne #33/R est:4000-6000 (A.D 4000)

PERCEVAL, Matthew (1945-) Australian
£276 $498 €403 Aroona Valley (60x90cm-24x35in) s. board. 23-Jan-4 Lawson Menzies, Sydney #2118/R (A.D 650)
£392 $695 €572 Poppies (66x73cm-26x29in) board prov. 3-May-4 Christie's, Melbourne #304 (A.D 950)
£392 $695 €572 Autumn landscape (50x65cm-20x26in) s. prov. 3-May-4 Christie's, Melbourne #383/R (A.D 950)
£1025 $1660 €1497 Moored fishing boat (67x90cm-26x35in) s. board. 30-Jul-3 Goodman, Sydney #9/R (A.D 2500)
£2152 $3486 €3142 Boats waiting offshore (151x120cm-59x47in) s. 30-Jul-3 Goodman, Sydney #57/R est:2000-3000 (A.D 5250)

PERCEVAL, Tessa (1946-) Australian
£1763 $2945 €2645 Orchard in spring (49x62cm-19x24in) s.d.1972. 27-Oct-3 Goodman, Sydney #161/R est:1000-1500 (A.D 4250)

PERCIER, Charles (1764-1838) French
Works on paper
£1338 $2315 €1900 Etudes. W/C dr several in one frame. 15-Dec-3 Bailly Pommery, Paris #29 est:600-900
£2303 $4237 €3500 Composition d'antiques (41x29cm-16x11in) pierre noire pen ink wash W/C. 23-Jun-4 Sotheby's, Paris #39/R est:4000-6000
£3289 $6053 €5000 Fontaine (40x29cm-16x11in) pierre noire pen ink wash W/C. 23-Jun-4 Sotheby's, Paris #41/R est:4000-6000

PERCIVAL, Bessie (fl.1885-1891) British
£2143 $3837 €3129 Southern woman by well (128x77cm-50x30in) s. 25-May-4 Bukowskis, Stockholm #355/R est:30000-40000 (S.KR 29000)

PERCIVAL, Harold (1868-1914) British
Works on paper
£300 $510 €438 Hermione (48x68cm-19x27in) s.d.1896 pen ink W/C htd white. 19-Nov-3 Christie's, Kensington #366

PERCY, Arthur (1886-1976) Swedish
£346 $595 €505 Wild country, Oland (38x45cm-15x18in) s.d.31. 7-Dec-3 Uppsala Auktionskammare, Uppsala #244 (S.KR 4500)
£769 $1323 €1123 Still life of sunflowers (59x66cm-23x26in) s.d.17. 7-Dec-3 Uppsala Auktionskammare, Uppsala #234/R (S.KR 10000)
£1586 $2696 €2316 Woman nursing baby (36x30cm-14x12in) s.d.1914. 5-Nov-3 AB Stockholms Auktionsverk #687/R est:20000-25000 (S.KR 21000)
£1769 $3043 €2583 Still life of flowers in vase (80x53cm-31x21in) s.d.1969. 7-Dec-3 Uppsala Auktionskammare, Uppsala #219/R est:18000-20000 (S.KR 23000)
£2039 $3467 €2977 Still life of fruit (41x33cm-16x13in) s.d.15. 4-Nov-3 Bukowskis, Stockholm #1/R est:25000-30000 (S.KR 27000)
£2231 $3837 €3257 Red flowers - Still life of flowers with blue background (45x54cm-18x21in) s.d.1938 panel exhib. 7-Dec-3 Uppsala Auktionskammare, Uppsala #231/R est:30000-40000 (S.KR 29000)
£4305 $7319 €6285 Ceres - girl with basket of fruit and sheaf of corn (68x48cm-27x19in) s.d.1916. 5-Nov-3 AB Stockholms Auktionsverk #686/R est:50000-60000 (S.KR 57000)
Works on paper
£623 $1102 €910 Still life of flowers (43x33cm-17x13in) s.d.41 W/C. 27-Apr-4 AB Stockholms Auktionsverk #898/R (S.KR 8500)

PERCY, Herbert Sidney (fl.1880-1903) British
£300 $549 €438 At the village pump (60x34cm-24x13in) s. 6-Jul-4 Bearnes, Exeter #487/R
£440 $708 €642 Rural landscape with two cattle on track, river and thatched cottage beyond (13x20cm-5x8in) s. panel. 12-Aug-3 Canterbury Auctions, UK #167
£500 $790 €725 Path through the fields (61x30cm-24x12in) s. 4-Sep-3 Christie's, Kensington #304/R
£591 $1100 €863 Landscape with hay cart (33x38cm-13x15in) s. board. 7-Mar-4 William Jenack, New York #311 est:1000-1500
£1150 $1817 €1668 Summer's rest (46x31cm-18x12in) s. 4-Sep-3 Christie's, Kensington #257/R est:2000-3000

PERCY, Lady Elizabeth Susan (?-1847) British
Works on paper
£260 $478 €380 Villa Pescatore from Villa Muti, Piombino (17x45cm-7x18in) i.d.June 14 1833 W/C. 23-Jun-4 Bonhams, Bury St Edmunds #325

PERCY, Samuel (1750-1820) British
Miniatures
£5000 $8500 €7300 Ludivina, Lady Stuart Menteith (15cm-6in) gilt frame oval prov.lit. 18-Nov-3 Bonhams, New Bond Street #7/R est:1200-1800

PERCY, Sidney Richard (1821-1886) British
£2335 $4250 €3409 Llyn y Ddinas, North Wales (23x37cm-9x15in) s. 29-Jun-4 Sotheby's, New York #146/R est:4000-6000
£4000 $7360 €5840 Retreating tide (15x23cm-6x9in) board. 11-Jun-4 Christie's, London #97/R est:3000-5000
£4500 $8370 €6570 Cattle watering in a mountainous landscape (38x59cm-15x23in) s.d.1854. 4-Mar-4 Christie's, Kensington #527/R est:5000-8000
£5000 $9200 €7300 Highland cattle in a mountainous landscape (15x23cm-6x9in) board. 11-Jun-4 Christie's, London #96/R est:4000-6000
£10500 $17850 €15330 Derwent Water, with young boy and girl at the roadside (46x64cm-18x25in) s.d.1885. 5-Nov-3 John Nicholson, Haslemere #592/R est:5000-6000
£14500 $22910 €21025 Penmaen Pool, near Dolgelly (61x91cm-24x36in) s.d.1884 prov. 4-Sep-3 Christie's, Kensington #185/R est:7000-10000
£15000 $25500 €21900 Gypsy camp (92x145cm-36x57in) s. 19-Nov-3 Bonhams, New Bond Street #19/R est:20000-30000
£16000 $27200 €23360 Glen Dochart, Perthshire (61x91cm-24x36in) s.d.1885 i.stretcher prov. 30-Oct-3 Christie's, London #94/R est:15000-20000
£18500 $33670 €27010 Landscape with cattle watering (61x96cm-24x38in) s.d.1872. 16-Jun-4 Bonhams, New Bond Street #39/R est:12000-18000
£18895 $32500 €27587 On the Thames near Medmenham (96x152cm-38x60in) s.d.1847. 3-Dec-3 Doyle, New York #97/R est:60000-90000
£25000 $42500 €36500 On the Mawddach, North Wales (61x103cm-24x41in) s.d.1873 prov. 25-Nov-3 Christie's, London #135/R est:20000-30000

£45000 $82800 €65700 Mountain landscape with figures and cattle by a lake (61x98cm-24x39in) s.d.64. 11-Jun-4 Christie's, London #98/R est:30000-40000
Photographs
£1667 $3000 €2434 Gypsy girls (16x14cm-6x6in) albumen print lit. 22-Apr-4 Phillips, New York #83/R est:4000-6000

PERCY, Sidney Richard (attrib) (1821-1886) British
£900 $1638 €1314 Highland river landscape with cattle at the waters edge (30x46cm-12x18in) 4-Feb-4 John Nicholson, Haslemere #115/R

PERCY, William (1820-1903) British
Works on paper
£4054 $7662 €6000 Bogland scene with cattle (18x46cm-7x18in) s. W/C. 17-Feb-4 Whyte's, Dublin #121/R est:5000-7000

PERDOMO, Felix (1956-) Venezuelan
£261 $470 €381 Untitled (69x65cm-27x26in) s. painted 2003. 25-Apr-4 Subastas Odalys, Caracas #29
£500 $860 €730 Untitled (60x73cm-24x29in) s. painted 2000. 7-Dec-3 Subastas Odalys, Caracas #74/R
£537 $875 €784 Untitled (93x67cm-37x26in) s. painted 1999. 20-Jul-3 Subastas Odalys, Caracas #138
£578 $1040 €844 Untitled (87x147cm-34x58in) s. 25-Apr-4 Subastas Odalys, Caracas #3
£603 $1085 €880 Untitled (57x70cm-22x28in) s. painted 2004. 25-Apr-4 Subastas Odalys, Caracas #55/R
£665 $1050 €971 Untitled (98x79cm-39x31in) s. painted 2001. 1-Dec-2 Subastas Odalys, Caracas #105
£707 $1300 €1032 Untitled (125x140cm-49x55in) s. painted 1998. 28-Mar-4 Subastas Odalys, Caracas #85/R
£727 $1250 €1061 Untitled (45x138cm-18x54in) s. painted 2000. 7-Dec-3 Subastas Odalys, Caracas #82/R
£857 $1560 €1286 Middle side (74x66cm-29x26in) s. painted 2003. 21-Jun-4 Subastas Odalys, Caracas #71/R
£887 $1615 €1331 Untitled (44x131cm-17x52in) s. painted 2001. 21-Jun-4 Subastas Odalys, Caracas #11
£900 $1530 €1314 Untitled (145x96cm-57x38in) s. painted 200. 23-Nov-3 Subastas Odalys, Caracas #62/R
£1270 $2185 €1854 Untitled (100x154cm-39x61in) s. 7-Dec-3 Subastas Odalys, Caracas #144
£1613 $2500 €2355 Untitled (106x178cm-42x70in) s. 3-Nov-2 Subastas Odalys, Caracas #48/R
£1717 $3125 €2576 Untitled (85x157cm-33x62in) s. painted 2002. 21-Jun-4 Subastas Odalys, Caracas #101
£1911 $3000 €2790 Untitled (130x195cm-51x77in) s. 23-Nov-2 Subastas Odalys, Caracas #48
£2258 $3500 €3297 Untitled (156x137cm-61x54in) s. 29-Sep-2 Subastas Odalys, Caracas #53/R
£2582 $4390 €3770 Untitled (155x160cm-61x63in) s. painted 2000. 23-Nov-3 Subastas Odalys, Caracas #6/R
Sculpture
£433 $780 €632 Figure (95x17x27cm-37x7x11in) iron. 25-Apr-4 Subastas Odalys, Caracas #106
£1885 $3205 €2752 Untitled (108x110x57cm-43x43x22in) s.verso painted iron. 23-Nov-3 Subastas Odalys, Caracas #116
Works on paper
£519 $935 €758 Untitled (99x81cm-39x32in) s. mixed media on canvas exec.1987. 25-Apr-4 Subastas Odalys, Caracas #18
£565 $1040 €825 Untitled (52x75cm-20x30in) s. mixed media on canvas exec.2003. 28-Mar-4 Subastas Odalys, Caracas #124
£565 $1040 €825 Untitled (56x70cm-22x28in) s. mixed media on canvas exec.2000. 28-Mar-4 Subastas Odalys, Caracas #115
£595 $1095 €893 Untitled (52x74cm-20x29in) s. mixed media exec.2003. 27-Jun-4 Subastas Odalys, Caracas #12/R
£736 $1355 €1075 Untitled (45x140cm-18x55in) s. mixed media on canvas. 28-Mar-4 Subastas Odalys, Caracas #94
£793 $1460 €1190 Untitled (70x65cm-28x26in) s. mixed media on canvas exec.2003. 27-Jun-4 Subastas Odalys, Caracas #51/R
£1389 $2500 €2028 Untitled (85x157cm-33x62in) s. mixed media on canvas exec.2003. 25-Apr-4 Subastas Odalys, Caracas #93/R
£2546 $4685 €3819 Untitled (169x150cm-67x59in) s. mixed media on canvas exec.1994. 27-Jun-4 Subastas Odalys, Caracas #91/R

PERDRAUT, Charles (19/20th C) French?
£2685 $4966 €4000 Echappee sur Tunis (46x64cm-18x25in) s. 15-Mar-4 Gros & Delettrez, Paris #147/R est:4000-6000

PEREA Y ROJAS, Alfredo (1839-1895) Spanish
Works on paper
£423 $739 €600 Strolling in the garden (32x23cm-13x9in) s.d.1877 W/C. 16-Dec-3 Segre, Madrid #1/R

PEREHUDOFF, Rebecca (1953-) Canadian
Works on paper
£241 $448 €352 Rose garden (73x104cm-29x41in) s.d.1991 W/C prov. 4-Mar-4 Heffel, Vancouver #35/R (C.D 600)

PEREHUDOFF, William (1919-) Canadian
£556 $961 €812 Okena no.17 (102x163cm-40x64in) s.d.1974 verso acrylic. 9-Dec-3 Maynards, Vancouver #246a est:1800-2000 (C.D 1250)

PEREIRA, Ezequiel (1868-1943) Portuguese
£1544 $2763 €2300 Valdevez, houses and trees (12x18cm-5x7in) s.d.1901 panel. 31-May-4 Cabral Moncada Leiloes, Lisbon #85/R est:2000-3000

PEREIRA, F V (20th C) Philippino
£1812 $2971 €2500 Young filipinos playing (50x40cm-20x16in) s.d.1957 canvas on board. 27-May-3 Durán, Madrid #101/R est:1000

PEREIRA, Joan (1921-) American
£245 $400 €358 Herman's store (51x61cm-20x24in) s. acrylic. 19-Jul-3 Outer Cape Auctions, Provincetown #25/R

PEREIRA, Jose (20th C) Cuban
£556 $928 €800 Composition (94x74cm-37x29in) s.d.1974. 21-Oct-3 Campo, Vlaamse Kaai #520

PEREJAUME (1957-) Spanish
£1761 $3081 €2500 Garrumbau (60x73cm-24x29in) s.d.1978 prov. 16-Dec-3 Segre, Madrid #183/R est:2500

PERELLE, Gabriel (attrib) (1603-1677) French
Works on paper
£263 $484 €400 Vue de monuments de Rome (13x21cm-5x8in) i. pen ink. 22-Jun-4 Calmels Cohen, Paris #13

PERELLON, Celedonio (1926-) Spanish
£621 $1117 €900 Nude with white tights (15x38cm-6x15in) s. board. 26-Jan-4 Ansorena, Madrid #258/R
Works on paper
£922 $1494 €1300 Sinfonia inacabada (49x33cm-19x13in) s. pencil chl. 20-May-3 Ansorena, Madrid #419/R

PERELMAN, Victor (1892-1967) Russian
£1222 $2200 €1784 Head of a boy (39x31cm-15x12in) 24-Apr-4 Shishkin Gallery, Moscow #18/R est:1500-2500
£1944 $3500 €2838 Sudzhonka, Kuzbass (45x72cm-18x28in) 24-Apr-4 Shishkin Gallery, Moscow #17/R est:5000-6000
£2500 $4500 €3650 Woman at the sofa (31x38cm-12x15in) oil on paper. 24-Apr-4 Shishkin Gallery, Moscow #16/R est:4000-5000

PERETTI, Achille (1857-1923) American
£4972 $9000 €7259 Rooster and chickens in the barn (30x41cm-12x16in) s. 3-Apr-4 Neal Auction Company, New Orleans #417/R est:4000-6000

PERETZ, David (1906-) French
£700 $1169 €1022 Still life with melon (46x55cm-18x22in) s.d.55. 22-Oct-3 Sotheby's, Olympia #93/R

PEREZ CELIS (1939-) Argentinian
£1156 $2000 €1688 Genesis (132x158cm-52x62in) prov. 10-Dec-3 Phillips, New York #574/R est:5000-7000
£1913 $3500 €2793 Landscape (60x50cm-24x20in) 1-Jun-4 Arroyo, Buenos Aires #7
£2118 $3600 €3092 Human relationships (122x90cm-48x35in) s.d.1989. 25-Nov-3 Galeria y Remates, Montevideo #194/R
£2308 $4200 €3370 Penetrations (53x65cm-21x26in) s.d.1981. 5-Jul-4 Arroyo, Buenos Aires #69/R est:2000
£3204 $5800 €4678 Untitled (100x60cm-39x24in) 30-Mar-4 Arroyo, Buenos Aires #24
Works on paper
£3352 $6000 €4894 Untitled (109x72cm-43x28in) mixed media. 11-May-4 Arroyo, Buenos Aires #70

PEREZ DE LA ROCHA, Roger (1949-) Nicaraguan
£275 $457 €399 Three women (98x98cm-39x39in) s.d.1998. 12-Jun-3 Louis Morton, Mexico #205 est:1100-1300 (M.P 4800)
£430 $714 €624 Ruben Dario mozuelo. Ruben Dario catrin (70x54cm-28x21in) d.1994 two. 12-Jun-3 Louis Morton, Mexico #67 est:1200-1400 (M.P 7500)
Works on paper
£373 $619 €541 Two nudes (120x80cm-47x31in) d.1996 mixed media canvas. 12-Jun-3 Louis Morton, Mexico #178/R est:1200-1400 (M.P 6500)

PEREZ DE LA ROCHA, Roger and VANEGAS, Leonel (20th C) Nicaraguan
Works on paper
£459 $762 €666 La vieja Managua (219x122cm-86x48in) s.d.1977 mixed media triplay. 12-Jun-3 Louis Morton, Mexico #92/R est:2700-3000 (M.P 8000)

PEREZ DE VILLAAMIL, Genaro (1807-1854) Spanish
£12000 $20400 €17520 Romantic landscape (58x68cm-23x27in) panel prov. 18-Nov-3 Sotheby's, London #237/R
£18000 $30600 €26280 Alcala de Guadaira Castle (50x68cm-20x27in) panel prov. 18-Nov-3 Sotheby's, London #236/R
Works on paper
£828 $1490 €1200 View of Malaga (23x38cm-9x15in) s. dr. 26-Jan-4 Durán, Madrid #200/R
£1014 $1664 €1400 Aldea (21x24cm-8x9in) s. drawing. 27-May-3 Durán, Madrid #97/R
£1512 $2600 €2208 Santa Maria del Funchal, Madeira (30x40cm-12x16in) i. pencil W/C bodycol. 2-Dec-3 Christie's, Rockefeller NY #154/R est:1000-1500

PEREZ DIEZ, Jose Luis (1931-) Spanish
£839 $1401 €1200 Fishing boats in Bilbao (22x27cm-9x11in) s. s.verso cardboard. 30-Jun-3 Ansorena, Madrid #221/R

PEREZ GIL, Jose (1918-1998) Spanish
£282 $493 €400 Urban landscape (17x13cm-7x5in) s. board. 16-Dec-3 Durán, Madrid #552/R
£669 $1070 €950 White walls (18x25cm-7x10in) s.d.1972 s.i.d.verso board el. 16-Sep-3 Segre, Madrid #121/R
£1690 $2704 €2400 View of La Golecha (46x81cm-18x32in) s.d.1972 s.i.d.verso. 16-Sep-3 Segre, Madrid #116/R

PEREZ MARTINEZ, Tomas (1911-) Spanish
£329 $605 €500 Montblanch, Tarragona (50x62cm-20x24in) s. 22-Jun-4 Durán, Madrid #585/R

PEREZ RUBIO, Antonio (1822-1888) Spanish
£897 $1488 €1300 Church interior (18x26cm-7x10in) s. board. 1-Oct-3 Ansorena, Madrid #741/R

PEREZ RUBIO, Timoteo (1886-1977) Spanish
£1268 $2218 €1800 Landscape (17x24cm-7x9in) s. cardboard. 16-Dec-3 Durán, Madrid #83/R est:1000

PEREZ VEGA, Angel (20th C) Argentinian
£377 $640 €550 Picking grapes (100x61cm-39x24in) s. board. 4-Nov-3 Ansorena, Madrid #880/R

PEREZ VILLALTA, Guillermo (1948-) Spanish
£9459 $16649 €14000 Sun entering a hoose with a draught (140x110cm-55x43in) s.d.1978 acrylic exhib.lit. 18-May-4 Segre, Madrid #127/R est:14000
Works on paper
£1200 $2172 €1800 Water. Fire (18x13cm-7x5in) s.d.1987 wash ink 2 in one frame. 30-Mar-4 Segre, Madrid #368/R est:1800
£1497 $2724 €2200 Verbena surrealista (73x43cm-29x17in) s.i.d.1981 col crayon pencil. 3-Feb-4 Segre, Madrid #377/R est:1500
£1933 $3499 €2900 Constant movement (36x102cm-14x40in) s.i.d.1975 pencil dr exhib.lit. 30-Mar-4 Segre, Madrid #162/R est:2900

PEREZ Y VILLAGROSSA, Mariano Alonso (1857-1930) Spanish
£2685 $4966 €4000 Incroyables au marche aux fleurs (34x27cm-13x11in) s. panel. 14-Mar-4 Eric Pillon, Calais #1/R
£7241 $12021 €10500 Market (61x73cm-24x29in) s. 30-Sep-3 Ansorena, Madrid #87/R est:10500
Works on paper
£329 $595 €500 Gallant scene (38x28cm-15x11in) s. W/C. 14-Apr-4 Ansorena, Madrid #382/R

PEREZ, Alonzo (fl.1893-1914) Spanish
£1860 $3200 €2716 Flirt (56x41cm-22x16in) s. panel. 2-Dec-3 Christie's, Rockefeller NY #57/R est:4000-6000
£2800 $5152 €4088 Amorous approach (23x12cm-9x5in) s. 11-Jun-4 Keys, Aylsham #640/R est:3000-4000
£6818 $12000 €9954 Two town crier (61x49cm-24x19in) s. panel. 18-May-4 Bonhams & Butterfields, San Francisco #55/R est:12000-18000
£11111 $20000 €16222 Proposal (53x65cm-21x26in) s. panel. 22-Apr-4 Christie's, Rockefeller NY #238/R est:25000-35000
£16000 $29120 €23360 Entertainer at Les Halles, Paris (80x100cm-31x39in) s. panel. 17-Jun-4 Christie's, London #97/R est:10000-15000
Works on paper
£300 $561 €438 Waiting for the wine (33x23cm-13x9in) s. W/C. 22-Jul-4 Mallams, Cheltenham #443

PEREZ, Augusto (1929-2000) Italian
Sculpture
£3147 $5350 €4500 Head of boy (37cm-15in) s.d.67 bronze. 29-Nov-3 Farsetti, Prato #447/R est:3000-4000
£4336 $7371 €6200 Untitled (50x70x42cm-20x28x17in) s. num.1/2 bronze. 29-Nov-3 Farsetti, Prato #446/R est:6000-7000

PEREZ, Carlos (1853-1929) Spanish
£1333 $2453 €2000 Neapolitan soldiers in front of the barracks (44x55cm-17x22in) s. panel painted c.1860. 11-Jun-4 Wendl, Rudolstadt #4217/R est:880

PEREZ, J G (19th C) Spanish
£1300 $2119 €1898 Lake scene with figures and cow at waters edge, village in distance (25x38cm-10x15in) s. 23-Sep-3 John Nicholson, Haslemere #259 est:1500-3000

PEREZ, Javier (1969-) Spanish
Sculpture
£1408 $2465 €2000 Dialogue (110x180x60cm-43x71x24in) leather fibre exec 1996. 18-Dec-3 Cornette de St.Cyr, Paris #184/R est:1200-1500

PEREZ, Josef Antonio (19th C) Spanish
Works on paper
£601 $1100 €877 Calligraphic portrait of Ferdinand VII, King of Spain, on horseback (60x43cm-24x17in) i. pen black ink pencil. 29-Jan-4 Swann Galleries, New York #345/R

PEREZ, Manuel (20th C) South American
£368 $600 €537 Arcade I (100x150cm-39x59in) s. painted 1990. 20-Jul-3 Subastas Odalys, Caracas #163
£1288 $2345 €1932 This will be my house (135x190cm-53x75in) s. painted 1993. 21-Jun-4 Subastas Odalys, Caracas #83/R

PEREZ, Raphael (1938-) Swiss/Venezuelan
£271 $462 €396 Framentation chromatique n. 002/a (185x150cm-73x59in) acrylic panel. 25-Nov-3 Germann, Zurich #863 (S.FR 600)
£271 $462 €396 Fragmentation chromatique n. 002/b (150x180cm-59x71in) acrylic panel. 25-Nov-3 Germann, Zurich #864 (S.FR 600)
£271 $462 €396 Fragmentation chromatique n. 001/b (185x150cm-73x59in) acrylic panel. 25-Nov-3 Germann, Zurich #865 (S.FR 600)
£452 $769 €660 Fragmentation chromatique n. 19 (160x100cm-63x39in) acrylic panel. 25-Nov-3 Germann, Zurich #866 (S.FR 1000)
£2838 $5223 €4143 Espacios geometricos (104x90cm-41x35in) s.i.d. verso acrylic canvas on panel. 8-Jun-4 Germann, Zurich #52/R est:4000-6000 (S.FR 6500)
Sculpture
£3057 $5624 €4463 Espacios geometricos (105x43x9cm-41x17x4in) s.i.d. verso acrylic canvas on panel. 8-Jun-4 Germann, Zurich #60/R est:3000-4000 (S.FR 7000)

PEREZ, Régulo (1929-) Bolivian
£495 $910 €723 Untitled (50x70cm-20x28in) s. painted 1976. 28-Mar-4 Subastas Odalys, Caracas #84/R
£563 $940 €822 Flower (52x38cm-20x15in) s. acrylic painted 1981. 13-Jul-3 Subastas Odalys, Caracas #31/R
£802 $1460 €1203 Eagle nest (72x86cm-28x34in) s. acrylic painted 1976. 21-Jun-4 Subastas Odalys, Caracas #58/R

PEREZ-OJEDA, Luz (20th C) ?
Works on paper
£267 $483 €400 Carre de ciel (65x92cm-26x36in) s. mixed media canvas. 3-Apr-4 Neret-Minet, Paris #143/R
£300 $543 €450 Erosion (65x100cm-26x39in) s. mixed media. 3-Apr-4 Neret-Minet, Paris #76/R
£315 $535 €450 Cielo azul - blue sky (60x40cm-24x16in) s. mixed media panel. 29-Nov-3 Neret-Minet, Paris #194/R
£350 $594 €500 Piece of sky (65x91cm-26x36in) s. mixed media canvas. 29-Nov-3 Neret-Minet, Paris #143/R

PERFALL, Erich Freiherr von (1882-1961) German
£280 $515 €420 Boats on the water, evening (53x70cm-21x28in) s. 11-Jun-4 Wendl, Rudolstadt #4218/R
£350 $601 €500 Rhine landscape with boats at anchor (60x70cm-24x28in) s. 5-Dec-3 Michael Zeller, Lindau #759/R
£533 $971 €800 Snow-covered hilly landscape in early spring (60x70cm-24x28in) s. 1-Jul-4 Van Ham, Cologne #1552

PERGOLESI, Michelangelo (attrib) (18th C) Italian
Works on paper
£3279 $6000 €4787 Untitled, exotic animals and birds with Roman scenes (70x53cm-28x21in) gouache W/C panel oval exec.c.1780. 7-Apr-4 Sotheby's, New York #154/R est:8000-12000

PERIDANI, Carlo (20th C) Italian
£683 $1100 €997 Grand Marina, Capri (61x76cm-24x30in) s. s.i.verso. 17-Aug-3 Jeffery Burchard, Florida #75a

PERIER, Marc Francois (attrib) (18th C) French
£1867 $3397 €2800 Castle interior scene with a nobleman's family (122x100cm-48x39in) lit. 3-Jul-4 Badum, Bamberg #115/R est:2200

PERIES, Ivan (1921-1988) Indian
£3000 $5010 €4380 Nude standing in water, moonlit (51x41cm-20x16in) s.d.1947. 14-Oct-3 Sotheby's, London #139/R est:3000-5000
£4000 $6680 €5840 Figures by a tree with houses beyond (102x76cm-40x30in) 14-Oct-3 Sotheby's, London #134/R est:3000-5000
£4000 $6680 €5840 Nude standing by a tree (51x41cm-20x16in) 14-Oct-3 Sotheby's, London #136/R est:4000-6000
£4800 $8016 €7008 Portrait of a girl (40x28cm-16x11in) board. 14-Oct-3 Sotheby's, London #135/R est:3000-5000
£9000 $15030 €13140 Fishing village, Dehiwela, Ceylon (62x86cm-24x34in) oil on gesso panel. 14-Oct-3 Sotheby's, London #138/R est:4000-6000
£11000 $18370 €16060 Nude reclining (35x46cm-14x18in) s. 14-Oct-3 Sotheby's, London #137/R est:3000-5000

PERIGAL, Arthur (jnr) (1816-1884) British
£280 $448 €409 Nook on Loch (20x33cm-8x13in) s.d.1880 i.verso board. 16-Sep-3 Gorringes, Bexhill #1647/R
£700 $1281 €1022 Nook in Loch Awe (24x36cm-9x14in) s. s.i.d.1880 verso board. 8-Apr-4 Bonhams, Edinburgh #107 est:700-900
£1000 $1760 €1460 Trout Beck (23x36cm-9x14in) s.d.1865 i.verso board. 20-May-4 Gardiner & Houlgate, Bath #482/R est:1000-1400
£6500 $12090 €9490 On the Tweed at Nesbitt (67x107cm-26x42in) s.d.1866 prov. 4-Mar-4 Christie's, Kensington #72/R est:8000-12000
Works on paper
£350 $662 €511 Bay of Naples (14x24cm-6x9in) s.i.d.1875 W/C. 19-Feb-4 Lyon & Turnbull, Edinburgh #54
£380 $646 €555 View of Cader Idris (30x46cm-12x18in) s.i.d.1842 pencil W/C htd white. 6-Nov-3 Christie's, Kensington #1021/R
£480 $797 €701 On the Banffshire Coast (23x38cm-9x15in) s.d.Sept 1877 W/C. 4-Oct-3 Finan Watkins & Co, Mere #135

PERIGNON, Alexis Nicolas (elder) (1726-1782) French
Works on paper
£979 $1664 €1400 Figures in village street (10x16cm-4x6in) mono. W/C over pen. 27-Nov-3 Bassenge, Berlin #5486/R

PERIGRINI, Kate Macready (1839-1929) British?

£360	$590	€526	Portrait of an Italian peasant girl, head and shoulders (25x18cm-10x7in) init. canvas on artist board. 29-May-3 Neales, Nottingham #834/R

PERILLI, Achille (1927-) Italian

£543	$891	€750	Warm inside (25x32cm-10x13in) i.d.1992 tempera paper. 29-May-3 Galleria Pace, Milan #51/R
£940	$1738	€1400	Rodia (20x20cm-8x8in) s.d.2002 s.i.d.verso. 11-Mar-4 Galleria Pace, Milan #16/R est:1700-2200
£1379	$2207	€2000	First model (50x50cm-20x20in) s. s.i.verso painted 2000. 13-Mar-3 Galleria Pace, Milan #96/R est:2500-3300
£1594	$2614	€2200	Filets invisibles (50x50cm-20x20in) s.d.2001. 29-May-3 Galleria Pace, Milan #33/R est:2500-3200
£2245	$4018	€3300	Untitled (50x50cm-20x20in) s.d.1977. 22-Mar-4 Sant Agostino, Torino #563/R
£4027	$7369	€6000	Mystique Luciferienne (100x81cm-39x32in) s.i.d.1970 verso prov. 7-Jul-4 Artcurial Briest, Paris #321 est:4000-5000
£5667	$10427	€8500	Bitter sophism (65x80cm-26x31in) s.d.72 mixed media on canvas sold with oil by Roberto Crippa. 8-Jun-4 Finarte Semenzato, Milan #313/R est:7000-9000
£8333	$13167	€12000	Good soul of Gertrude Stein (93x73cm-37x29in) painted 1956. 6-Sep-3 Meeting Art, Vercelli #591 est:10000
£12081	$21624	€18000	Ruthless (50x75cm-20x30in) s.d.1957 enamel tempera exhib.lit. 30-May-4 Meeting Art, Vercelli #21 est:12000
£12414	$20731	€18000	Bene Kasimir (160x160cm-63x63in) s.d.1967. 17-Nov-3 Sant Agostino, Torino #292/R est:18000-22000

Works on paper

£467	$859	€700	Philosopher (24x31cm-9x12in) s.i.d.1993 W/C card. 8-Jun-4 Finarte Semenzato, Milan #212/R
£845	$1403	€1200	Verglas (20x20cm-8x8in) s.d.2000 s.i.d.verso mixed media canvas. 14-Jun-3 Meeting Art, Vercelli #45/R
£1133	$2085	€1700	Limb (20x20cm-8x8in) s.d.2000 mixed media on canvas. 12-Jun-4 Meeting Art, Vercelli #499/R est:1500
£1197	$1987	€1700	Punti fermi e Debolezze (57x78cm-22x31in) s.i.d.1990 W/C. 14-Jun-3 Meeting Art, Vercelli #518/R est:1500
£1389	$2194	€2000	We are on our own (50x50cm-20x20in) mixed media on canvas. 6-Sep-3 Meeting Art, Vercelli #308 est:2000
£1867	$3435	€2800	Accumulation (50x50cm-20x20in) s.d.2001 mixed media on canvas lit. 10-Jun-4 Galleria Pace, Milan #53/R est:4000
£2113	$3507	€3000	Lo spostamento dal centro (50x40cm-20x16in) s.d.1971 mixed media canvas. 14-Jun-3 Meeting Art, Vercelli #582/R est:3000
£2148	$3973	€3200	Delice (50x50cm-20x20in) s.d.2000 mixed media on canvas. 13-Mar-4 Meeting Art, Vercelli #390 est:2000
£2667	$4907	€4000	Black bird flying (65x81cm-26x32in) s.d.1990 mixed media on canvas. 12-Jun-4 Meeting Art, Vercelli #385/R est:4000
£2685	$4966	€4000	Square's wings (65x81cm-26x32in) s.d.1989 mixed media. 13-Mar-4 Meeting Art, Vercelli #119
£3099	$5144	€4400	La conoscenza oscena (65x81cm-26x32in) s.d.1989 s.i.d.verso mixed media. 14-Jun-3 Meeting Art, Vercelli #111/R est:4000
£3472	$5486	€5000	Untitled (70x100cm-28x39in) pastel tempera. 6-Sep-3 Meeting Art, Vercelli #551 est:5000
£3793	$6334	€5500	Abstract 3 (70x100cm-28x39in) s.d.59 mixed media collage paper on canvas. 13-Nov-3 Finarte Semenzato, Rome #340/R est:7000-8000
£4225	$7014	€6000	Composition (98x69cm-39x27in) s.d.62 mixed media cardboard. 11-Jun-3 Finarte Semenzato, Milan #605/R
£4348	$7130	€6000	Exciting relax (55x35cm-22x14in) s.d.66 mixed media on canvas. 30-May-3 Farsetti, Prato #280/R
£4348	$7130	€6000	Eclectic career (89x116cm-35x46in) s.d.71 hydropaint acrylic on canvas. 30-May-3 Farsetti, Prato #461/R

PERIN, Yvonne (1905-1967) Belgian

£694	$1104	€1000	Mere et enfant (120x100cm-47x39in) s.d.35. 9-Sep-3 Palais de Beaux Arts, Brussels #259/R

PERIN-SALBREUX, Lie Louis (1753-1817) French

Miniatures

£4800	$8592	€7008	Young lady in a forest, wearing orange striped silk dress (7cm-3in) s. gilt metal frame ribbon tie surmount. 25-May-4 Christie's, London #107/R est:3000-5000
£9000	$15570	€13140	Young lady (5cm-2in) gold frame oval. 9-Dec-3 Christie's, London #60/R est:2000-3000

PERINCIOLI, Marcel (1911-) Swiss

Sculpture

£1552	$2778	€2266	Untitled (17cm-7in) pat.bronze. 13-May-4 Stuker, Bern #6762/R est:3500-4500 (S.FR 3600)

PERINDANI, Carlo (1899-?) Italian

£333	$597	€500	Street in Capri (37x34cm-15x13in) s. board. 12-May-4 Stadion, Trieste #757/R
£423	$756	€600	Houses on Capri (37x100cm-15x39in) s. canvas on board lit. 8-Jan-4 Allgauer, Kempten #2479/R

PERIS ARAGO, Jose (1907-) Spanish

Works on paper

£738	$1381	€1100	Village houses (51x72cm-20x28in) s. W/C. 24-Feb-4 Durán, Madrid #112/R

PERIS MARCO, Vicente (1943-) Spanish

£537	$1004	€800	Composition (35x50cm-14x20in) s.d.1987 paper. 24-Feb-4 Durán, Madrid #1132/R

PERIZI, Nino (1917-) Italian

£315	$541	€450	Sailing boats in the bay (39x56cm-15x22in) s. tempera paper. 3-Dec-3 Stadion, Trieste #953/R
£833	$1492	€1250	Changing (99x149cm-39x59in) s. 12-May-4 Stadion, Trieste #767 est:1000-1500

PERJONS, Per Hilding (1911-1998) Swedish

£349	$583	€510	Still life of pot (49x60cm-19x24in) s.d.52. 12-Oct-3 Uppsala Auktionskammare, Uppsala #580 (S.KR 4500)
£476	$890	€695	Still life of grapes and china (65x85cm-26x33in) s.d.51. 29-Feb-4 Uppsala Auktionskammare, Uppsala #62 (S.KR 6500)

PERKINS, Christopher (1891-1968) British

£620	$1035	€905	Continental river (51x61cm-20x24in) s.d.1936. 14-Oct-3 David Lay, Penzance #336
£1805	$2942	€2635	Annette Stiver (38x28cm-15x11in) s.d.1938 verso. 23-Sep-3 Peter Webb, Auckland #122/R est:3500-5000 (NZ.D 5000)

Works on paper

£952	$1703	€1390	Portrait of a young woman (29x23cm-11x9in) init. conte executed c.1940. 12-May-4 Dunbar Sloane, Wellington #47/R est:3000-5000 (NZ.D 2750)

PERKINS, Frederick Stanton (1832-1899) American

£3971	$6750	€5798	Still life of green apples spilling out of a tipped basket (23x41cm-9x16in) s. 21-Nov-3 Eldred, East Dennis #868/R est:500-1000

PERKINS, Granville (1830-1895) American

£438	$700	€639	Coastal scene (25x46cm-10x18in) s. board. 21-Sep-3 Grogan, Boston #91/R
£1934	$3500	€2824	Seaside chores (30x46cm-12x18in) s. canvas on masonite. 31-Mar-4 Sotheby's, New York #95/R est:3000-5000
£4190	$7500	€6117	Marsh hay (25x41cm-10x16in) s.d.1890 prov. 6-May-4 Shannon's, Milford #167/R est:5000-7000
£5587	$10000	€8157	Off Sandy Hook (66x91cm-26x36in) s.d.1889. 6-May-4 Shannon's, Milford #40/R est:8000-12000

Works on paper

£411	$650	€600	Passaic Falls (76x53cm-30x21in) s. W/C. 6-Apr-3 William Jenack, New York #24
£479	$800	€699	Shipping off the Florida coast (38x56cm-15x22in) s. W/C. 29-Jun-3 William Jenack, New York #73

PERKINS, Mary Smyth (1875-1931) American

£500	$945	€730	Waves breaking on a deserted beach. Figures outside a colleges (40x50cm-16x20in) s. pair. 19-Feb-4 Lyon & Turnbull, Edinburgh #129

PERKINS, Parker S (19/20th C) American

£269	$500	€393	Ocean view (25x33cm-10x13in) s.d.99.1.1 canvasboard. 5-Mar-4 Skinner, Boston #546/R

PERKINS, Ruth Ma (20th C) American

£333	$600	€486	Auction today (81x69cm-32x27in) acrylic painted c.1980 prov.exhib. 24-Apr-4 Slotin Folk Art, Buford #264/R

PERKINSON, Tom (1940-) American

£1765	$3300	€2577	Flag day (102x76cm-40x30in) s. 28-Feb-4 William A Smith, Plainfield #108/R

PERKO, Anton (1833-1905) Austrian

£400	$688	€584	Secret harbour (15x22cm-6x9in) s.d.1873 panel. 2-Dec-3 Sotheby's, London #52/R

PERKOIS, Jacobus (1756-1804) Dutch

Works on paper

£839	$1443	€1200	L'agreable conversation au march (26x19cm-10x7in) s.d.1796 W/C. 3-Dec-3 Palais de Beaux Arts, Brussels #610/R

PERKUHN, Edwin (1861-1943) German

£1200	$2184	€1800	Elks in an extensive landscape (76x107cm-30x42in) indis.s. lit. 1-Jul-4 Van Ham, Cologne #1553 est:1800

PERL, Karl (1876-?) Austrian

Sculpture

£4500	$8235	€6570	Figure of a dancer (48cm-19in) s. bronze ivory polychrome. 3-Jun-4 Sotheby's, Olympia #254/R est:5000-6000

PERL, Thomas (1962-) German

£263	$484	€400	In the mine (150x100cm-59x39in) s.d.87 acrylic ink. 25-Jun-4 Von Zezschwitz, Munich #377/R
£263	$484	€400	In the mine (150x100cm-59x39in) s.d.87 acrylic ink. 25-Jun-4 Von Zezschwitz, Munich #379/R

PERLBERG, Friedrich (1848-1921) German

Works on paper

£754	$1281	€1100	View of fountain (55x41cm-22x16in) s.d.1880 W/C over crayon. 6-Nov-3 Tajan, Paris #245

PERLMUTTER, Isaac (1866-1932) Czechoslovakian

£909	$1608	€1327	Felka and the high Tatra mountains (15x24cm-6x9in) s. panel. 28-Apr-4 Kieselbach, Budapest #174c (H.F 340000)
£1054	$1908	€1539	Vegetable market (19x24cm-7x9in) s. 16-Apr-4 Mu Terem Galeria, Budapest #32/R (H.F 400000)
£1470	$2601	€2146	Lady by the piano (31x29cm-12x11in) s. cardboard. 28-Apr-4 Kieselbach, Budapest #174a/R (H.F 550000)
£1493	$2479	€2180	Italian port (20x27cm-8x11in) s. panel. 4-Oct-3 Kieselbach, Budapest #6/R (H.F 550000)

£1958 $3386 €2859 Snow covered street (18x24cm-7x9in) s.d.1914 panel. 12-Dec-3 Kieselbach, Budapest #11/R (H.F 750000)
£5344 $9460 €7802 Woman in a room (41x37cm-16x15in) s. cardboard. 28-Apr-4 Kieselbach, Budapest #195/R (H.F 2000000)
£5973 $9914 €8721 Girl in a sunny garden (63x51cm-25x20in) s. 4-Oct-3 Kieselbach, Budapest #32/R (H.F 2200000)
Works on paper
£1871 $3311 €2732 Lady in a hat (40x30cm-16x12in) s.d.931 pastel. 28-Apr-4 Kieselbach, Budapest #9/R (H.F 700000)

PERLMUTTER, Jack (1920-) American
£444 $800 €648 Florist (76x61cm-30x24in) s. masonite. 23-Jan-4 Freeman, Philadelphia #122/R

PERLMUTTER, Stella (20th C) American
£305 $500 €442 In the garden (76x102cm-30x40in) s. painted c.1960. 7-Jun-3 Treadway Gallery, Cincinnati #1520

PERLMUTTER, Zoltan (20th C) Israeli
Works on paper
£414 $745 €600 Musicians (34x49cm-13x19in) s.d.1968 chl. 21-Jan-4 Tajan, Paris #122
£483 $869 €700 Orchestra (35x53cm-14x21in) s.d.1968 chl. 21-Jan-4 Tajan, Paris #123

PERLROTT-CSABA, Vilmos (1880-1955) Hungarian
£1629 $2704 €2378 Still life (69x50cm-27x20in) cardboard. 4-Oct-3 Kieselbach, Budapest #157/R (H.F 600000)
£3162 $5723 €4617 Still life with jug (50x50cm-20x20in) s. tempera on carton. 16-Apr-4 Mu Terem Galeria, Budapest #150/R (H.F 1200000)
£3162 $5723 €4617 Flower still life (72x51cm-28x20in) s. oil on card. 16-Apr-4 Mu Terem Galeria, Budapest #189/R (H.F 1200000)
£5796 $10492 €8462 Le cahier d'art (77x57cm-30x22in) s. tempera pastel. 16-Apr-4 Mu Terem Galeria, Budapest #28/R (H.F 2200000)
£6787 $11266 €9909 Yellow dressed model in landscape in Kecskemet (65x45cm-26x18in) cardboard painted c.1910. 4-Oct-3 Kieselbach, Budapest #202/R (H.F 2500000)
£8017 $14190 €11705 Kecskemet (72x64cm-28x25in) s. painted early 1910's. 28-Apr-4 Kieselbach, Budapest #177/R (H.F 3000000)
£10000 $18200 €14600 Still life with flowers and apples (67x54cm-26x21in) s. tempera paper prov. 15-Jun-4 Sotheby's, London #64/R est:8000-12000
£10859 $18026 €15854 Nagybanya (46x53cm-18x21in) s. 4-Oct-3 Kieselbach, Budapest #76/R (H.F 4000000)
£11066 $20030 €16156 Self portrait with Zifferr (80x59cm-31x23in) s. 16-Apr-4 Mu Terem Galeria, Budapest #68/R (H.F 4200000)
£13174 $23845 €19234 Parisian scene, Notre Dame (50x60cm-20x24in) s. 16-Apr-4 Mu Terem Galeria, Budapest #136/R (H.F 5000000)
£17126 $30998 €25004 Yellow room (92x72cm-36x28in) s. 16-Apr-4 Mu Terem Galeria, Budapest #66/R (H.F 6500000)

PERMAN, Louise E (1854-1921) British
£800 $1336 €1168 Still life of a vase of carnations (53x43cm-21x17in) s. 18-Jun-3 John Nicholson, Haslemere #612
£1900 $3439 €2774 White and pink carnations (56x45cm-22x18in) s. prov. 19-Apr-4 Sotheby's, London #88/R est:2500-3000
£3000 $5160 €4380 Yellow roses (46x77cm-18x30in) s. 4-Dec-3 Bonhams, Edinburgh #57/R est:1500-2000
£3600 $6120 €5256 White roses and Violets (61x51cm-24x20in) s. prov.exhib. 30-Oct-3 Christie's, London #153/R est:3000-5000
£4800 $8976 €7008 Still life of yellow roses (60x40cm-24x16in) s. 21-Jul-4 Lyon & Turnbull, Edinburgh #122/R est:2000-3000
£8000 $12560 €11600 Still life with white and pink roses (51x61cm-20x24in) s. 27-Aug-3 Sotheby's, London #1060/R est:5000-7000

PERMEKE, Constant (1886-1952) Belgian
£3667 $6563 €5500 Seascape (65x75cm-26x30in) s. prov. 15-May-4 De Vuyst, Lokeren #568/R est:8000-9500
£4514 $7177 €6500 Mer du Nord (55x75cm-22x30in) s. 15-Sep-3 Horta, Bruxelles #94/R est:8000-12000
£5594 $9510 €8000 Landscape with houses (50x60cm-20x24in) s. 25-Nov-3 Christie's, Amsterdam #202/R est:8000-12000
£5903 $9858 €8500 Paysage au soleil jaune et orange (65x75cm-26x30in) s. 21-Oct-3 Campo & Campo, Antwerp #243/R est:5000-6000
£8803 $15229 €12500 Summer in Jabbeke (60x80cm-24x31in) s. 13-Dec-3 De Vuyst, Lokeren #482/R est:13000-15000
£9091 $15636 €13000 Winterlandscape (55x80cm-22x31in) s. prov.exhib. 2-Dec-3 Sotheby's, Amsterdam #51/R est:15000-20000
£10000 $17900 €15000 Draught horse (50x70cm-20x28in) s. exhib. 15-May-4 De Vuyst, Lokeren #474/R est:16000-20000
£10490 $17832 €15000 Barques dans le bassin d'Ostende (45x62cm-18x24in) s. painted 1912 exhib.lit. 29-Nov-3 Farsetti, Prato #542/R est:10000
£13043 $21391 €18000 Winter landscape (50x70cm-20x28in) s. prov. 27-May-3 Sotheby's, Amsterdam #330/R est:10000-12000
£13287 $22587 €19000 Landscape with red-roofed farm (60x90cm-24x35in) s. 25-Nov-3 Christie's, Amsterdam #209/R est:15000-20000
£33333 $55667 €48000 Winter landscape (69x100cm-27x39in) s. 21-Oct-3 Campo & Campo, Antwerp #244/R est:60000-80000
£192029 $314928 €265000 Rower from Scheldt (96x77cm-38x30in) s.d.1921 prov. 27-May-3 Sotheby's, Amsterdam #335/R est:20000-30000
Works on paper
£352 $609 €500 Two women with child (23x22cm-9x9in) s. ink wash. 15-Dec-3 Bernaerts, Antwerp #1513/R
£738 $1373 €1100 Reclining nude (26x42cm-10x17in) s. sepia. 4-Mar-4 Auction Maastricht #1093/R est:1000-1500
£4196 $7133 €6000 Drinking farmer (24x18cm-9x7in) s. pencil. 25-Nov-3 Christie's, Amsterdam #214/R est:6000-8000
£5123 $8299 €7480 Nude (147x101cm-58x40in) s.d.42 chl pastel prov. 30-Jul-3 Goodman, Sydney #185/R est:15000-20000 (A.D 12500)
£6711 $11879 €10000 Nu de dos (120x82cm-47x32in) s. dr. 27-Apr-4 Campo, Vlaamse Kaai #550/R est:7500-7800

PERMEKE, John (20th C) Belgian?
£319 $533 €450 Portrait de femme (80x65cm-31x26in) s. panel. 17-Jun-3 Galerie Moderne, Brussels #254

PERMEKE, Paul (1918-1990) Belgian
£309 $574 €460 Landscape at sunset (25x35cm-10x14in) panel. 8-Mar-4 Bernaerts, Antwerp #865
£338 $595 €500 Champ de ble (50x70cm-20x28in) s. panel. 18-May-4 Galerie Moderne, Brussels #283/R
£369 $687 €550 City garden (52x48cm-20x19in) s. panel. 8-Mar-4 Bernaerts, Antwerp #869
£380 $692 €555 Stormy sky over yellow fields (50x70cm-20x28in) s. 15-Jun-4 Bonhams, Knightsbridge #175/R
£385 $642 €550 Seascape (40x50cm-16x20in) s. 11-Oct-3 De Vuyst, Lokeren #289
£385 $642 €550 Farm in the snow (40x50cm-16x20in) s. 11-Oct-3 De Vuyst, Lokeren #290
£524 $892 €750 Coin d'atelier (70x53cm-28x21in) s.d.57 oil paper. 1-Dec-3 Palais de Beaux Arts, Brussels #297
£556 $928 €800 Paysage d'hiver (70x100cm-28x39in) s. 21-Oct-3 Campo, Vlaamse Kaai #519
£563 $975 €800 Port de peche anime (60x90cm-24x35in) s. 9-Dec-3 Vanderkindere, Brussels #84
£604 $1117 €900 Old attic (60x80cm-24x31in) s. exhib. 13-Mar-4 De Vuyst, Lokeren #258
£608 $1089 €900 Les forains (45x54cm-18x21in) s. panel. 10-May-4 Horta, Bruxelles #67
£667 $1220 €1000 Hommage to Van Ieperen (49x78cm-19x31in) s. 7-Jun-4 Glerum, Amsterdam #132/R
£775 $1340 €1100 Seascape with sunset (50x70cm-20x28in) s. 13-Dec-3 De Vuyst, Lokeren #258
£851 $1421 €1200 Chaumiere en hiver (100x120cm-39x47in) s. 17-Jun-3 Galerie Moderne, Brussels #382
£890 $1514 €1300 Forains avant l'orage (40x50cm-16x20in) s. panel. 10-Nov-3 Horta, Bruxelles #419
£915 $1584 €1300 Sunset on the North Sea (70x100cm-28x39in) s. 13-Dec-3 De Vuyst, Lokeren #257
£1049 $1752 €1500 Jeune femme nue se levant (80x100cm-31x39in) s. 13-Oct-3 Horta, Bruxelles #194 est:1500-1800
£1389 $2319 €2000 Ciel nuageux (121x101cm-48x40in) s.d.1970. 21-Oct-3 Campo & Campo, Antwerp #245 est:1750-2250
£1600 $2928 €2400 Marine au coucher du soleil (80x150cm-31x59in) s.d.78. 7-Jun-4 Palais de Beaux Arts, Brussels #90/R est:2500-3500

PERNES, Leo (?-1960) ?
£278 $520 €420 Le port de Concarneau (50x61cm-20x24in) 24-Jul-4 Thierry & Lannon, Brest #399
£333 $607 €500 Chalutiers dans le port (39x31cm-15x12in) s. panel. 4-Jul-4 Eric Pillon, Calais #204/R
£759 $1403 €1100 Port de peche (46x61cm-18x24in) s. 16-Feb-4 Giraudeau, Tours #98
£782 $1244 €1150 Pecheur a Saint-Cado (50x100cm-20x39in) s. 18-Mar-3 Adjug'art, Brest #121
£816 $1298 €1200 Sortie de messe a Notre-Dame de Tronoen (65x81cm-26x32in) s. 18-Mar-3 Adjug'art, Brest #122

PERNET, Jean Henry Alexandre (1763-?) French
Works on paper
£704 $1218 €1000 Soldats dans des ruines antiques (34x25cm-13x10in) i.d.1776 black crayon. 12-Dec-3 Renaud, Paris #51
£1026 $1868 €1550 Personnages dans les ruines (11x17cm-4x7in) one s. W/C pen black ink pair. 16-Jun-4 Piasa, Paris #127/R est:1500
£4762 $7571 €7000 Projet de theatre (42x55cm-17x22in) s. pen ink wash. 21-Mar-3 Bailly Pommery, Paris #45

PERNOT, François Alexandre (1793-1865) French
£450 $774 €657 Stalls at a market (43x32cm-17x13in) panel. 2-Dec-3 Kunsthallen, Copenhagen #515 (D.KR 4800)

PEROTTI, Edoardo (1824-1870) Italian
£280 $467 €400 Swiss landscape (27x22cm-11x9in) s.d.1857. 26-Jun-3 Sant Agostino, Torino #29/R

PEROUSE, Mario (?) ?
£1389 $2292 €2000 Soleil d'hiver aux Ballais (39x54cm-15x21in) s. i.verso cardboard. 3-Jul-3 Claude Aguttes, Neuilly #138 est:450

PERRACHON, Andre (1827-1909) French
£1192 $2181 €1800 Bouquet de roses (65x54cm-26x21in) s. 9-Apr-4 Claude Aguttes, Neuilly #38/R est:1500-2000

PERRAUDIN, Paul (1907-1993) French
Works on paper
£338 $585 €480 Voiliers (34x40cm-13x16in) s.d.69 W/C gouache. 13-Dec-3 Touati, Paris #148

PERRAULT, Léon (1832-1908) French
£6490 $11877 €9800 Autoportrait (41x32cm-16x13in) prov. 9-Apr-4 Claude Aguttes, Neuilly #44/R est:6000-8000
£7186 $12000 €10492 Girl with grapes (46x38cm-18x15in) s.d.68. 7-Oct-3 Sotheby's, New York #155 est:10000-15000
£8000 $13760 €11680 Her favourite pet (56x46cm-22x18in) s.d.67. 3-Dec-3 Christie's, London #46/R est:10000-15000
£8889 $16000 €12978 Italian girl (55x46cm-22x18in) s.d.77. 22-Apr-4 Christie's, Rockefeller NY #130/R est:10000-15000
£11111 $20000 €16222 Petite fille au bouquet de fleurs (55x46cm-22x18in) s.d.1896 prov. 23-Apr-4 Sotheby's, New York #162/R est:18000-25000

£26490 $48477 €40000 Jeune fille a la fenetre (59x47cm-23x19in) s.d.1901 prov. 9-Apr-4 Claude Aguttes, Neuilly #45/R est:15000-20000
£27152 $49689 €41000 Apres le bain (199x90cm-78x35in) s. prov. 9-Apr-4 Claude Aguttes, Neuilly #46/R est:25000-30000

PERRAULT, Marie (1874-?) American
Prints
£2147 $3500 €3135 Evening (46x40cm-18x16in) s.i.num.9/10 col woodcut. 24-Sep-3 Christie's, Rockefeller NY #16/R est:2000-3000
£2147 $3500 €3135 Wild flowers (46x40cm-18x16in) s.i.num.17/100 col woodcut. 24-Sep-3 Christie's, Rockefeller NY #17/R est:1200-1800

PERRAULT, Wilf (1947-) Canadian
£1423 $2547 €2078 Early spring in Saskatoon (143x91cm-56x36in) s.d.1976 prov. 6-May-4 Heffel, Vancouver #109/R est:2500-3500 (C.D 3500)

PERRE, Henri (?) Canadian?
Works on paper
£362 $605 €529 Summer landscape with lake reflections (33x50cm-13x20in) s.d.1899 W/C. 17-Nov-3 Hodgins, Calgary #362 (C.D 800)

PERREL, Aime (?) ?
£604 $1130 €900 Gallant scene (23x33cm-9x13in) board. 26-Feb-4 Cambi, Genoa #429/R

PERRENOT, Rene Vincent (c.1780-1910) French
Works on paper
£6111 $11000 €8922 Emperor Napoleon I at Tilsit, with Tsar Alexander I and others (23x31cm-9x12in) s. black lead pen brown ink col wash exec.c.1810 prov. 22-Jan-4 Christie's, Rockefeller NY #132/R est:4000-6000

PERRET (?) ?
£4255 $7106 €6000 Village anime au bord de l'eau. Paysage anime pres du chateau (92x73cm-36x29in) s. oval pair. 19-Oct-3 Anaf, Lyon #225/R est:6000-7000

PERRET, Aime (1847-1927) French
£2207 $4083 €3200 Young peasant couple talking in evening landscape (45x56cm-18x22in) s.d.90. 14-Feb-4 Hans Stahl, Hamburg #71/R est:4800
£3911 $7000 €5710 Harvesters (53x66cm-21x26in) s. prov. 6-May-4 Shannon's, Milford #196/R est:6000-8000
Works on paper
£862 $1543 €1259 Breton christening (36x47cm-14x19in) s. W/C. 12-May-4 Dobiaschofsky, Bern #861/R est:1600 (S.FR 2000)

PERRETT, Galen Joseph (1875-1949) American
£1285 $2300 €1876 View of Rockport (20x15cm-8x6in) s.d.34 board. 16-May-4 CRN Auctions, Cambridge #35/R

PERRETT, J D (1859-1937) New Zealander
Works on paper
£964 $1774 €1407 Lake Te Anau (27x70cm-11x28in) s. pastel. 25-Mar-4 International Art Centre, Auckland #117/R est:2000-3000 (NZ.D 2700)

PERRETT, John Douglas (1859-1937) New Zealander
£692 $1239 €1010 Winter dusk across the snow clad hills (54x72cm-21x28in) s. 11-May-4 Watson's, Christchurch #114/R (NZ.D 2000)
Works on paper
£277 $496 €404 Lake scene with sailing vessel (23x66cm-9x26in) s. pastel. 11-May-4 Peter Webb, Auckland #158/R (NZ.D 800)

PERRI, Frank (20th C) American
£215 $400 €314 Nudes by the lake (51x71cm-20x28in) s. board. 7-Mar-4 Treadway Gallery, Cincinnati #666/R
£228 $425 €333 Sisters (76x61cm-30x24in) s.verso painted c.1940. 7-Mar-4 Treadway Gallery, Cincinnati #651/R
£232 $425 €339 Mother and her child (61x76cm-24x30in) s.verso painted c.1950. 5-Jun-4 Treadway Gallery, Cincinnati #755/R
£259 $425 €376 Mexican landscape (76x64cm-30x25in) s.verso painted c.1940. 7-Jun-3 Treadway Gallery, Cincinnati #1483
£274 $450 €397 Climbing a tree (76x51cm-30x20in) s.verso painted c.1940. 7-Jun-3 Treadway Gallery, Cincinnati #1480
£276 $475 €403 Garden lawn (46x61cm-18x24in) s. board painted c.1940. 7-Dec-3 Treadway Gallery, Cincinnati #688/R
£349 $600 €510 Still life with apples (13x30cm-5x12in) s. canvas on board painted c.1940. 7-Dec-3 Treadway Gallery, Cincinnati #669/R
£378 $650 €552 Indian women weaving (18x23cm-7x9in) s. board painted c.1940. 7-Dec-3 Treadway Gallery, Cincinnati #691/R
£511 $900 €746 Mexican scene (102x61cm-40x24in) s. painted c.1940. 23-May-4 Treadway Gallery, Cincinnati #623/R
Works on paper
£262 $450 €383 Airplane wing worker (25x15cm-10x6in) s. mixed media exec.c.1945. 7-Dec-3 Treadway Gallery, Cincinnati #662/R

PERRIE, Bertha Eversfield (1868-1921) American
£1377 $2300 €2010 Seaside lane (56x46cm-22x18in) s. 15-Nov-3 Sloans & Kenyon, Bethesda #117/R est:700-900

PERRIER, François (1584-1650) French
£10556 $19000 €15412 Sacrificial scene (141x131cm-56x52in) exhib.lit. 23-Jan-4 Christie's, Rockefeller NY #10/R est:15000-20000
Works on paper
£22535 $39437 €32000 Un procession de nereides et de centaures de mer avec putti (14x31cm-6x12in) col chk pen brown ink wash prov. 17-Dec-3 Christie's, Paris #33/R est:30000-50000

PERRIGARD, Hal Ross (1891-1960) Canadian
£191 $355 €279 Melting snow, Laurentians (30x41cm-12x16in) s. canvasboard. 2-Mar-4 Ritchie, Toronto #115/R (C.D 475)
£300 $489 €438 Farmhouse by the firs, winter (20x25cm-8x10in) s. board. 23-Sep-3 John Nicholson, Haslemere #247
£379 $634 €550 Old grist mill, near Vercheres, P.Q (30x41cm-12x16in) s. i.verso board. 17-Jun-3 Pinneys, Montreal #150a (C.D 850)
£714 $1229 €1042 Dark Firs - Springtime - Eastern Townships, Quebec (40x50cm-16x20in) s. canvasboard. 2-Dec-3 Joyner Waddington, Toronto #411 (C.D 1600)
£721 $1225 €1053 Farmhouse by the Firs, Winter (20x25cm-8x10in) s. s.i.verso board prov. 21-Nov-3 Walker's, Ottawa #1/R (C.D 1600)
£868 $1571 €1267 Morning in the harbour (15x22cm-6x9in) s.i.verso prov. panel. 18-Apr-4 Levis, Calgary #94/R est:1800-2200 (C.D 2100)
£893 $1536 €1304 New England springtime - Vermont (45x60cm-18x24in) s. board. 2-Dec-3 Joyner Waddington, Toronto #233/R est:2500-3000 (C.D 2000)
£1532 $2604 €2237 Old French Canadian house, St Pierre (30x41cm-12x16in) s. board prov. 23-Nov-3 Levis, Calgary #104/R est:900-1200 (C.D 3400)

PERRIN, Alfred Feyen (fl.1860-1911) British
£260 $481 €380 Penmaenbach from the Glen (51x76cm-20x30in) s.d.1879 s.i.d. verso. 14-Jul-4 Bonhams, Chester #328
£380 $703 €555 Happy days (97x71cm-38x28in) s. s.i. verso. 14-Jul-4 Bonhams, Chester #329

PERRIN, John W (fl.1884-1909) British
£680 $1231 €993 Study of gooseberries and lemons in and by a basket (18x28cm-7x11in) s. 16-Apr-4 Keys, Aylsham #787/R

PERRIN, Philippe (1964-) French
Sculpture
£4054 $7135 €6000 Les Menottes. s.d.1998 num.2/3 steel handcuffs lit. 18-May-4 Tajan, Paris #189/R est:6000-8000
£10667 $19733 €16000 Uzi (64x311x214cm-25x122x84in) painted stainless steel exec.1997 prov.exhib. 18-Jul-4 Sotheby's, Paris #181/R est:10000-15000
£12667 $23433 €19000 Poing americain (237x297x35cm-93x117x14in) s. stainless steel exec.1992 prov. 18-Jul-4 Sotheby's, Paris #182/R est:8000-12000
£12667 $23433 €19000 Couteau (300cm-118in) stainless steel exec.1994 prov.exhib. 18-Jul-4 Sotheby's, Paris #180/R est:10000-15000
Works on paper
£676 $1189 €1000 Nigeria (76x56cm-30x22in) s.i.d.1983 1999 felt col crayons ink prov. 18-May-4 Tajan, Paris #190/R

PERRIN, Sidney (?) British
Works on paper
£250 $463 €365 West Country winter landscape (36x54cm-14x21in) s. W/C. 16-Feb-4 Bonhams, Bath #12

PERRIN-MAXENCE, Henri (1872-1944) French
£1611 $2996 €2400 Maison rouge dans le verdure a Crozant (38x46cm-15x18in) s. 3-Mar-4 Tajan, Paris #46/R est:2500-3000

PERRINE, Van Dearing (1869-1955) American
£3073 $5500 €4487 Ring of the moon (66x89cm-26x35in) prov. 26-May-4 Doyle, New York #100/R est:7000-9000
£5814 $10000 €8488 Coasting firewood down (87x105cm-34x41in) prov. 3-Dec-3 Doyle, New York #219/R est:8000-12000

PERRON, Charles Clement Francis (1893-1958) French
£500 $830 €730 Still life with jar of jam and pears (38x55cm-15x22in) s. prov. 1-Oct-3 George Kidner, Lymington #184/R
£839 $1427 €1200 Bouquet de roses (38x46cm-15x18in) s. panel. 27-Nov-3 Millon & Associes, Paris #213
£867 $1577 €1300 Interieur en Bretagne (46x55cm-18x22in) s. 4-Jul-4 Eric Pillon, Calais #4/R
£1400 $2646 €2044 Nature mort with pears and conkers (38x55cm-15x22in) s. 19-Feb-4 Christie's, Kensington #276/R est:1000-1500
£2667 $4773 €4000 Sous-bois en automne (170x100cm-67x39in) s.d.1923. 16-May-4 Thierry & Lannon, Brest #168/R est:5000-6000
Works on paper
£333 $613 €500 Etang dans un sous-bois (40x32cm-16x13in) s. W/C. 8-Jun-4 Livinec, Gaudcheau & Jezequel, Rennes #50

PERRON, Charles Theodore (1862-1934) French
Sculpture
£915 $1602 €1300 Eclipse (36cm-14in) s. pewter vase Cast Petizon. 16-Dec-3 Artcurial Briest, Paris #111/R est:1500-2200

PERRONEAU, Jean Baptiste (1715-1783) French
Works on paper
£7237 $13316 €11000 Portrait presume de Monsieur de Laval, maitre a danser des enfants du roi (58x48cm-23x19in) pastel prov.exhib.lit. 23-Jun-4 Sotheby's, Paris #14/R est:12000-15000

PERRONEAU, Jean Baptiste (attrib) (1715-1783) French
Works on paper
£367 $660 €550 Portrait de femme (66x54cm-26x21in) pastel. 20-Apr-4 Galerie Moderne, Brussels #355/R

PERRONEAU, Jean Baptiste (style) (1715-1783) French
Works on paper
£22000 $37400 €32120 Portrait of a gentleman, head and shoulders (58x48cm-23x19in) bears sig. bears d. pastel. 28-Oct-3 Henry Adams, Chichester #388/R est:1000-1500

PERROT, Adolphe (1818-1887) French
£1800 $3294 €2628 Venetian canal with river traffic. Continental street scene (32x23cm-13x9in) s. panel pair. 8-Apr-4 Christie's, Kensington #175/R est:2000-3000

PERROT, Ferdinand (1808-1841) French
Works on paper
£800 $1360 €1168 Passengers disembarking (28x42cm-11x17in) s.d.1834 pencil w bodycol pair. 19-Nov-3 Christie's, Kensington #328/R

PERROT, Maurice (1892-?) French
£308 $529 €450 La Seine et i'll de Medon (19x27cm-7x11in) s. i.verso panel. 3-Dec-3 AB Stockholms Auktionsverk #2649/R (S.KR 4000)

PERRY, Arthur W (fl.1908-1939) British
Works on paper
£330 $545 €482 The Haven Cliff, Seaton (17x37cm-7x15in) s. W/C. 4-Jul-3 Honiton Galleries, Honiton #53/R
£400 $736 €584 Chickens in the street, Seaton, Devon (18x27cm-7x11in) s. W/C. 23-Mar-4 Bonhams, Knightsbridge #209/R
£620 $1135 €905 Fishing boats pulled up on a beach with an extensive coastal landscape (56x79cm-22x31in) s. W/C. 8-Jul-4 Duke & Son, Dorchester #73/R

PERRY, Enoch Wood (1831-1915) American
£472 $750 €689 Woodland path (30x22cm-12x9in) s.d.1909 prov. 12-Sep-3 Skinner, Boston #448/R
£566 $900 €826 Pan (40x31cm-16x12in) s.i.d.1905 canvas on board prov. 12-Sep-3 Skinner, Boston #347/R
£1856 $3100 €2710 Reading tea leaves (36x43cm-14x17in) s.d.1884. 19-Oct-3 William Jenack, New York #237 est:5000-8000

PERRY, Enoch Wood (attrib) (1831-1915) American
£1630 $3000 €2380 Hidden bird's nest (35x50cm-14x20in) 8-Jun-4 Bonhams & Butterfields, San Francisco #4031/R est:3000-5000

PERRY, Grace (20th C) American
Works on paper
£244 $400 €354 Mother and daughter (19x25cm-7x10in) s. pastel exec.c.1925. 7-Jun-3 Treadway Gallery, Cincinnati #1444

PERRY, Grayson (1960-) British
Sculpture
£6000 $11040 €8760 Western art in the form of a Saki bottle (34x26x29cm-13x10x11in) i. painted on glazed earthenware exec 1992 prov. 24-Jun-4 Sotheby's, London #125/R est:6000-8000
£15000 $27600 €21900 Scenes from Hello Magazine (54x25x25cm-21x10x10in) i. painted on glazed earthenware exec 1996 prov.exhib. 24-Jun-4 Sotheby's, London #117/R est:15000-20000
£15000 $27600 €21900 Essex landscape (37x33x30cm-15x13x12in) i. painted on glazed earthenware exec c.1994 prov. 24-Jun-4 Sotheby's, London #118/R est:15000-20000
£26000 $47840 €37960 Earth goddess (43x27x27cm-17x11x11in) i. glazed earthenware executed c.1996 prov. 23-Jun-4 Sotheby's, London #39/R est:15000-20000

PERRY, Lilla Cabot (1848-1933) American
£1889 $3400 €2758 Autumn sketch (36x43cm-14x17in) prov. 24-Apr-4 Weschler, Washington #599/R est:3000-5000
£5000 $9050 €7500 Washerwomen on rivershore in early spring (38x46cm-15x18in) s. 1-Apr-4 Van Ham, Cologne #1599/R est:7000
£55866 $100000 €81564 Portrait of a girl in a red bonnet (69x53cm-27x21in) 8-Jan-4 James Julia, Fairfield #100/R

PERRY, Raymond (20th C) American
£4420 $8000 €6453 From the studio window, Brooklyn (56x86cm-22x34in) s.d.17 prov. 31-Mar-4 Sotheby's, New York #125/R est:8000-12000

PERRY, Roy (1935-1993) British
£320 $586 €467 Thames barges off Greenwich (30x46cm-12x18in) s. card. 28-Jul-4 Mallams, Oxford #381
£380 $684 €555 Surrey farm in winter (51x66cm-20x26in) s. board. 20-Jan-4 Bonhams, Knightsbridge #177/R
£750 $1253 €1095 Pool of London, with the Tower beyond (45x68cm-18x27in) s. acrylic board. 8-Oct-3 Christie's, Kensington #758/R
£2200 $3674 €3212 Upper pool from Tower Bridge (76x97cm-30x38in) s. acrylic. 8-Oct-3 Christie's, Kensington #754/R est:2000-3000
Works on paper
£250 $448 €365 Country house by a stream (36x53cm-14x21in) s. gouache. 7-May-4 Mallams, Oxford #202/R
£750 $1253 €1095 Dutch eel boats off Billingsgate. Moorings off Limehouse (25x37cm-10x15in) s. bodycol pair. 8-Oct-3 Christie's, Kensington #755/R
£1500 $2505 €2190 Barge repairs. Tower Bridge from Wapping (69x89cm-27x35in) s. bodycol pair. 8-Oct-3 Christie's, Kensington #759 est:1000-1500

PERRYMAN, Norman (20th C) British?
£1600 $2864 €2336 Jeremy Menuhin plays beach with father at the Gstaad festival (73x116cm-29x46in) s.d.66 s.d.stretcher. 11-May-4 Sotheby's, Olympia #560/R est:700-900

PERSAC, Marie Adrien (1823-1873) American/French
Works on paper
£18895 $32500 €27587 Boat on the Mississippi (29x42cm-11x17in) s. gouache prov. 3-Dec-3 Sotheby's, New York #99/R est:12000-18000
£27616 $47500 €40319 View of Cincinnati (27x44cm-11x17in) s. W/C gouache prov. 3-Dec-3 Sotheby's, New York #100/R est:12000-18000

PERSEUS, Edward (1841-1890) Swedish
£364 $671 €546 Portrait of Isabella Boklund (60x46cm-24x18in) s.d.1877 verso oval. 14-Jun-4 Lilla Bukowskis, Stockholm #179 (S.KR 5000)

PERSIAN SCHOOL, 16th C
Works on paper
£10000 $17700 €14600 Two lovers (15x10cm-6x4in) gouache htd gold script album page exec.c.1530-1550. 28-Apr-4 Sotheby's, London #36/R est:10000-15000
£14000 $24780 €20440 Rustam kiling the White Div (29x20cm-11x8in) gouache htd gold text manuscript leaf exec.c.1565. 28-Apr-4 Sotheby's, London #37/R est:7000-10000

PERSOGLI, L (19th C) ?
£2439 $4366 €3561 Party in the wine cellar (73x98cm-29x39in) s. 25-May-4 Bukowskis, Stockholm #349/R est:25000-30000 (S.KR 33000)

PERSOGLIA, Franz von (1852-1912) Austrian
£3200 $5792 €4800 Music session (59x80cm-23x31in) s. 1-Apr-4 Van Ham, Cologne #1600/R est:4000
£4514 $7674 €6500 Musical diversion (68x105cm-27x41in) s. 28-Oct-3 Christie's, Amsterdam #55/R est:7000-9000

PERSON, Henri (1876-1926) French
£1215 $2200 €1774 Bateaux pres de St. Tropez (22x35cm-9x14in) canvasboard prov. 30-Mar-4 Christie's, Rockefeller NY #103/R est:2000-3000
£1225 $2230 €1850 La Chapelle Sainte Anne a Saint Tropez (32x46cm-13x18in) s. panel. 17-Jun-4 Marie & Robert, Paris #62 est:1200-1500
£1678 $3070 €2500 Saint-Tropez, Le Golfe vue du Chemin de la Citadelle (38x46cm-15x18in) st.sig. painted c.1916 lit. 7-Jul-4 Artcurial Briest, Paris #93 est:2500-3500
£1691 $2773 €2350 Paysage (65x81cm-26x32in) s. 3-Jun-3 Livinec, Gaudcheau & Jezequel, Rennes #104/R
£2685 $4913 €4000 Vue de Saint-Tropez (41x55cm-16x22in) st.sig. board painted c.1916 lit. 7-Jul-4 Artcurial Briest, Paris #92/R est:2500-3500
Works on paper
£1538 $2615 €2200 Le vieux port (30x4cm-12x2in) s. W/C chl. 27-Nov-3 Millon & Associes, Paris #14/R est:1500-2000

PERSONS, Timothy (20th C) Finnish
Works on paper
£1119 $1902 €1600 Balance (64x90cm-25x35in) s.d.96 mixed media. 29-Nov-3 Bukowskis, Helsinki #235/R est:1000-1300

PERSSON, Folke (1905-1964) Swedish
£725 $1305 €1088 Summer in the skerries with sailing boats (50x60cm-20x24in) s. 25-Apr-4 Goteborg Auktionsverk, Sweden #390/R (S.KR 10000)
£870 $1566 €1305 Gothenburg Harbour (61x72cm-24x28in) s. panel. 25-Apr-4 Goteborg Auktionsverk, Sweden #348/R (S.KR 12000)

PERSSON, Peter Adolf (1862-1914) Swedish
£443 $794 €647 Sailing boat near rocky coast (47x69cm-19x27in) s. 28-May-4 Uppsala Auktionskammare, Uppsala #122 (S.KR 6000)

PERSSON, Ragnar (1905-1993) Swedish
£331 $569 €483 At the kitchen table (19x24cm-7x9in) mono. i.verso panel. 7-Dec-3 Uppsala Auktionskammare, Uppsala #256 (S.KR 4300)
£423 $728 €618 Dancing on the jetty (20x27cm-8x11in) mono. s.verso panel. 7-Dec-3 Uppsala Auktionskammare, Uppsala #243 (S.KR 5500)
£480 $860 €701 In the park (28x35cm-11x14in) mono. s.verso. 28-May-4 Uppsala Auktionskammare, Uppsala #209 (S.KR 6500)
£517 $926 €755 At the market (28x37cm-11x15in) mono. s.verso panel. 28-May-4 Uppsala Auktionskammare, Uppsala #298 (S.KR 7000)
£538 $926 €785 Girl wearing garland of flowers (41x32cm-16x13in) mono. 7-Dec-3 Uppsala Auktionskammare, Uppsala #279/R (S.KR 7000)
£583 $1073 €875 By the window (27x35cm-11x14in) init. panel. 14-Jun-4 Lilla Bukowskis, Stockholm #631 (S.KR 8000)
£591 $1058 €863 Couple dancing (39x46cm-15x18in) mono. s.verso. 28-May-4 Uppsala Auktionskammare, Uppsala #296/R (S.KR 8000)
£604 $1027 €882 Interior (27x35cm-11x14in) init. panel. 5-Nov-3 AB Stockholms Auktionsverk #868/R (S.KR 8000)
£612 $985 €894 Composition with figures (24x33cm-9x13in) s. 25-Aug-3 Lilla Bukowskis, Stockholm #452 (S.KR 8000)
£776 $1389 €1133 Town scene with many figures (46x55cm-18x22in) mono. s.verso. 28-May-4 Uppsala Auktionskammare, Uppsala #300/R (S.KR 10500)
£788 $1419 €1150 Home from market (33x41cm-13x16in) s. panel. 26-Jan-4 Lilla Bukowskis, Stockholm #386 (S.KR 10500)
£846 $1455 €1235 Town view with figures (45x37cm-18x15in) mono. s. verso. 7-Dec-3 Uppsala Auktionskammare, Uppsala #224 (S.KR 11000)
£846 $1455 €1235 Reading the paper (33x41cm-13x16in) mono.d.46. 7-Dec-3 Uppsala Auktionskammare, Uppsala #282/R (S.KR 11000)

£943 $1631 €1377 Composition with figures (33x41cm-13x16in) s. s.verso. 15-Dec-3 Lilla Bukowskis, Stockholm #535 (S.KR 12000)
£952 $1686 €1390 The carpenter's workshop (38x46cm-15x18in) init. panel. 27-Apr-4 AB Stockholms Auktionsverk #723/R est:15000-18000 (S.KR 13000)
£961 $1720 €1403 From an inn (47x55cm-19x22in) mono. s.d.79 verso. 28-May-4 Uppsala Auktionskammare, Uppsala #297/R (S.KR 13000)
£982 $1669 €1434 In the living-room (33x41cm-13x16in) init. s.verso. 4-Nov-3 Bukowskis, Stockholm #156a/R (S.KR 13000)
£1231 $2117 €1797 In the farm-hands' quarters (46x55cm-18x22in) mono. s.verso panel. 7-Dec-3 Uppsala Auktionskammare, Uppsala #281/R est:12000-15000 (S.KR 16000)
£1314 $2365 €1918 The workshop (46x55cm-18x22in) s. panel. 26-Jan-4 Lilla Bukowskis, Stockholm #254 est:18000-20000 (S.KR 17500)
£1360 $2311 €1986 Old men on park bench (38x46cm-15x18in) init. 5-Nov-3 AB Stockholms Auktionsverk #866/R est:20000-25000 (S.KR 18000)
£1385 $2382 €2022 Washing day (62x81cm-24x32in) mono. 7-Dec-3 Uppsala Auktionskammare, Uppsala #280/R est:12000-15000 (S.KR 18000)
£1462 $2514 €2135 Meditation - horse and carriage with figures (46x55cm-18x22in) mono. s.verso. 7-Dec-3 Uppsala Auktionskammare, Uppsala #283/R est:15000-18000 (S.KR 19000)
£1813 $3082 €2647 Auction of the farm (33x46cm-13x18in) init. 5-Nov-3 AB Stockholms Auktionsverk #871/R est:12000-15000 (S.KR 24000)
£1885 $3394 €2752 Street life (46x38cm-18x15in) init. 26-Apr-4 Bukowskis, Stockholm #194/R est:22000-25000 (S.KR 26000)

PERTZ, Anna J (fl.1880-1911) British
£700 $1295 €1022 The Lady of Shalott (80x64cm-31x25in) prov. 11-Feb-4 Cheffins, Cambridge #447/R
£700 $1295 €1022 Portrait of a lady (57x42cm-22x17in) mono.d.1886 prov. 11-Feb-4 Cheffins, Cambridge #452/R

PERUGIA, Vinicio (1947-) Italian
£480 $883 €720 Secret source (40x30cm-16x12in) s.d.2002 s.i.d.verso acrylic. 12-Jun-4 Meeting Art, Vercelli #173/R
£933 $1717 €1400 Stones resting (60x80cm-24x31in) s. s.i.d.2002 verso acrylic. 12-Jun-4 Meeting Art, Vercelli #599/R

PERUGINI, Kate (1838-1929) British
Miniatures
£2000 $3660 €2920 Portrait of Charles Dickens (10x7cm-4x3in) silver plated frame oval. 8-Jul-4 Sotheby's, London #102/R est:1500-2000
Works on paper
£1700 $3111 €2482 Carlo Perugini painting his picture of the artist in A Labour of Love (17x25cm-7x10in) s. W/C. 8-Jul-4 Sotheby's, London #105/R est:1000-1500

PERUVIAN SCHOOL, 17th C
£7895 $14289 €12000 Archangel Saint Michael (151x102cm-59x40in) 14-Apr-4 Ansorena, Madrid #130/R est:5000

PERUZZI, Osvaldo (1907-) Italian
£690 $1152 €1000 Painting (45x50cm-18x20in) s.d.75 s.i.d.verso. 13-Nov-3 Finarte Semenzato, Rome #324/R

PERUZZINI, Antonio Francesco (1668-?) Italian
£4225 $7014 €6000 Landscape with travellers and washerwomen (108x88cm-43x35in) painted with circle lit. 11-Jul-3 Finarte, Venice #542/R est:4000-5000
£7000 $12600 €10220 Wooded landscape with a capuchin friar adoring the cross (77x57cm-30x22in) oval made up. 21-Apr-4 Christie's, London #99/R est:7000-10000

PERUZZINI, Antonio Francesco (attrib) (1668-?) Italian
£5278 $9500 €7706 Saint Jerome in the Wilderness (122x95cm-48x37in) 21-Jan-4 Sotheby's, New York #117/R est:6000-8000
£6897 $11448 €10000 Peasants in wooded landscape (74x58cm-29x23in) prov. 1-Oct-3 Dorotheum, Vienna #31/R est:10000-15000
£12414 $20607 €18000 Wooded landscape with figures (69x85cm-27x33in) 1-Oct-3 Dorotheum, Vienna #35/R est:18000-25000

PERUZZINI, Giovanni (1629-1694) Italian
£5000 $8950 €7500 Putti in landscape (73x97cm-29x38in) 17-May-4 Finarte Semenzato, Rome #73/R est:5000-6000

PESATORI, Elie (1923-) Italian
£300 $540 €450 Martina Franca (65x48cm-26x19in) 25-Apr-4 Daniel Herry, Beaune #120
£600 $1080 €900 L'orient (68x86cm-27x34in) 25-Apr-4 Daniel Herry, Beaune #121

PESCE, Gaetano (1939-) Italian
Sculpture
£3667 $6783 €5500 UP5 Woman and UP6 (94x110x106cm-37x43x42in) foam felt exec.2000 prov. 18-Jul-4 Sotheby's, Paris #194/R est:1000-1500
£4500 $8190 €6570 Il piede (82x170x61cm-32x67x24in) lacquered polyurethane foam lit. 30-Jun-4 Christie's, Kensington #153/R est:4000-6000
Works on paper
£1093 $2000 €1596 Untitled, pencil num 259, fish design (46x226cm-18x89in) pencil col resin exhib. 6-Jun-4 Wright, Chicago #404/R est:1000-1500

PESCHCKE-KOEDT, Matthias (1885-1949) Danish
Works on paper
£1040 $1799 €1518 Flowering rhododendrons and lilacs in a garden (83x72cm-33x28in) init.d.1918 gouache. 9-Dec-3 Rasmussen, Copenhagen #1585/R (D.KR 11000)

PESCHKA, Anton (1885-1940) Austrian
£417 $679 €600 Potschmuhle in Krumau (40x50cm-16x20in) s.d.1933 i.verso board. 23-Sep-3 Wiener Kunst Auktionen, Vienna #58/R
£2797 $4755 €4000 Street in the Vienna Woods (53x79cm-21x31in) s.d.1931 i.verso. 28-Nov-3 Wiener Kunst Auktionen, Vienna #479/R est:4000-7000
Works on paper
£280 $481 €400 Female nude seated (47x31cm-19x12in) chl. 4-Dec-3 Dorotheum, Graz #160
£704 $1232 €1000 Winter landscape (34x49cm-13x19in) s.indis.d. chk W/C. 19-Dec-3 Dorotheum, Vienna #112/R
£2345 $4291 €3400 Female nude (30x46cm-12x18in) s.d.1922 pencil W/C sold with another. 27-Jan-4 Dorotheum, Vienna #48/R est:1100-1500

PESCHKA, Anton (attrib) (1885-1940) Austrian
£851 $1421 €1200 Flowers (53x42cm-21x17in) i. bears d. board. 14-Oct-3 Dorotheum, Vienna #66/R

PESCHKE, Christian (1946-) German
£1479 $2366 €2100 Woman (80x60cm-31x24in) s. panel. 19-Sep-3 Sigalas, Stuttgart #339/R est:2200
£1608 $2734 €2300 Boats moored on the coast at the foot of some red hills (72x53cm-28x21in) s. panel. 29-Nov-3 Sigalas, Stuttgart #699/R est:2500
£1831 $2930 €2600 Landscape with tree lined road (80x70cm-31x28in) s. board. 19-Sep-3 Sigalas, Stuttgart #340/R est:2500
Sculpture
£1806 $2853 €2600 Reclining nude (24cm-9in) s. gilded bronze. 19-Sep-3 Schloss Ahlden, Ahlden #772/R est:2800
£2361 $3731 €3400 Dancing nude (34cm-13in) gilded bronze. 19-Sep-3 Schloss Ahlden, Ahlden #771/R est:2200
£6667 $11933 €10000 Female nude (138cm-54in) green pat.bronze marble socle. 14-May-4 Schloss Ahlden, Ahlden #2003/R est:9500
Works on paper
£559 $951 €800 Seated woman wearing a hat (50x34cm-20x13in) s.d.96 pastel. 29-Nov-3 Sigalas, Stuttgart #698/R

PESCI, Girolamo (1684-1759) Italian
£23000 $39100 €33580 Rebecca at the well (43x34cm-17x13in) s. panel prov. 29-Oct-3 Christie's, London #70/R est:15000-20000

PESCI, Giuseppe (18th C) Italian
£5333 $9760 €8000 Cock, cherries and flowers in landscape. Hen and flowers in landscape (63x95cm-25x37in) pair. 1-Jun-4 Sotheby's, Milan #55/R est:8000-12000

PESCINA, Aurelio (20th C) Mexican
£496 $913 €724 Tianguis (50x50cm-20x20in) s.d.1935. 25-Mar-4 Louis Morton, Mexico #79/R (M.P 10000)

PESKE, Geza (1859-1934) Hungarian
£988 $1700 €1442 Young boy and goose (99x79cm-39x31in) s. 6-Dec-3 Selkirks, St. Louis #656/R est:2000-3000
£1581 $2861 €2308 Spring in Bodajk (130x101cm-51x40in) s. 16-Apr-4 Mu Terem Galeria, Budapest #161/R (H.F 600000)
£1800 $3276 €2628 Refreshments at playtime (30x25cm-12x10in) s. 16-Jun-4 Christie's, Kensington #213/R est:1800-2200
£1818 $3036 €2600 Boy with snowballs in winter wood (100x75cm-39x30in) s. 9-Oct-3 Michael Zeller, Lindau #718/R est:2600

PESKE, Jean (1870-1949) French
£795 $1446 €1200 Mere et enfant dans le jardin (33x24cm-13x9in) s. panel. 16-Jun-4 Claude Boisgirard, Paris #130/R
£952 $1705 €1400 Still life with fish (33x45cm-13x18in) s. 19-Mar-4 Millon & Associes, Paris #114
£967 $1730 €1450 Bords du ruisseau (37x46cm-15x18in) s. s.i.verso panel exhib. 17-May-4 Chayette & Cheval, Paris #198
£1162 $2010 €1650 Raisins et coupe (35x27cm-14x11in) s. cardboard. 15-Dec-3 Marc Kohn, Paris #99/R est:1500-2000
£2028 $3448 €2900 Deux chevaux tirant une charrue sous les arbres (74x99cm-29x39in) s. cardboard prov. 24-Nov-3 E & Eve, Paris #169/R est:2000-3000
£2980 $5454 €4500 Sous-bois (130x158cm-51x62in) s. 7-Apr-4 Piasa, Paris #141/R est:4000-6000
£4400 $8052 €6600 Parc d'Alonville (114x146cm-45x57in) s. i.on stretcher prov. 3-Jun-4 E & Eve, Paris #95 est:2500-3000
£4698 $8691 €7000 Personnages sur le chemin dans la campagne (81x117cm-32x46in) s. prov.exhib. 15-Mar-4 Claude Boisgirard, Paris #95/R est:7000-8000
£4967 $9040 €7500 La Pointe de Gouron (81x116cm-32x46in) s. i.verso. 16-Jun-4 Claude Boisgirard, Paris #132/R est:10000-11000
Works on paper
£604 $1124 €900 L'Automne (62x47cm-24x19in) s. mixed media. 3-Mar-4 Tajan, Paris #118/R est:1000-1500

PESNE, Antoine (attrib) (1683-1757) French
£2500 $4600 €3800 Portrait d'homme en buste (82x66cm-32x26in) 25-Jun-4 Piasa, Paris #105/R est:2000-3000
£3000 $5190 €4380 Portraits of Frederick II the Great and Queen Elizabeth Christine of Prussia (19x15cm-7x6in) 12-Dec-3 Christie's, Kensington #155/R est:2000-3000
£3571 $6500 €5214 Portrait of Princess Poniatowska (81x68cm-32x27in) oval. 29-Jun-4 Sotheby's, New York #56/R est:4000-6000
£3691 $6792 €5500 Portrait of Friedrich II as young officer (160x113cm-63x44in) 27-Mar-4 Dannenberg, Berlin #605/R est:3000
£6040 $11114 €9000 L'enlevement d'Europe Diane au bain (12x18cm-5x7in) pair. 24-Mar-4 Tajan, Paris #128 est:1500-2000

PESU, Daniel Johannes (attrib) (1891-1956) Finnish
£436 $803 €650 Sordavala (45x58cm-18x23in) s.d.1930. 25-Mar-4 Hagelstam, Helsinki #852

PETAZZI, Elio (1912-1998) Italian

£370	$629	€540	Nude at mirror (60x120cm-24x47in) s. 7-Nov-3 Tuttarte, Modena #793
£1027	$1747	€1500	Little concert (100x120cm-39x47in) s. 7-Nov-3 Tuttarte, Modena #799 est:1500-2000

PETEL, Georg (after) (c.1593-1634) German

Sculpture

£5800	$10034	€8468	St Jerome (29cm-11in) wax stepped base lit. 12-Dec-3 Sotheby's, London #165/R est:5000-8000

PETER, Emanuel (1799-1873) Austrian

Miniatures

£1800	$3114	€2628	Young lady (10cm-4in) s. gilt-metal frame oval. 9-Dec-3 Christie's, London #240/R est:1500-2500
£4800	$8400	€7008	Lady with elaborately coiled hair wearing large lace cap with pink bows (9cm-4in) rectangular giltwood composition frame. 18-Dec-3 Sotheby's, Olympia #22/R est:5000-6000

Works on paper

£759	$1259	€1100	Portrait of young woman in brown velvet jacket (11x8cm-4x3in) s. W/C oval. 30-Sep-3 Dorotheum, Vienna #397/R
£8966	$14883	€13000	Portrait of Countess Leonie Potocka (11x9cm-4x4in) s. W/C ivory. 30-Sep-3 Dorotheum, Vienna #394/R est:10000-15000

PETER, Maria (1904-?) Hungarian

£3132	$5418	€4573	Nude in the studio (100x81cm-39x32in) s. 12-Dec-3 Kieselbach, Budapest #22/R (H.F 1200000)

PETER, Victor (1840-1918) French

Sculpture

£1000	$1700	€1460	Head of lion (15x8cm-6x3in) s. pat bronze. 28-Oct-3 Sotheby's, London #113/R

PETER, William (19th C) American

£483	$850	€705	Wooded landscape with fisherman (23x30cm-9x12in) s. sold with another. 21-May-4 Pook & Pook, Downington #232

PETERDI, Gabor (1915-) American/Hungarian

£500	$800	€730	West II (61x46cm-24x18in) s.d.1961 s.i.d.verso prov. 20-Sep-3 Sloans & Kenyon, Bethesda #1186/R

PETERELLE, Adolphe (1874-1947) French

£276	$436	€400	Visage (41x24cm-16x9in) s. 6-Apr-3 Salle des ventes Pillet, Lyon la Foret #602
£345	$545	€500	Baigneuse assise (73x50cm-29x20in) s. 6-Apr-3 Salle des ventes Pillet, Lyon la Foret #600
£414	$654	€600	Femme assise (55x38cm-22x15in) s. 6-Apr-3 Salle des ventes Pillet, Lyon la Foret #603
£420	$713	€600	La rue (35x27cm-14x11in) s. 28-Nov-3 Blanchet, Paris #73
£420	$713	€600	Saint Louis (55x46cm-22x18in) s. i.verso. 28-Nov-3 Blanchet, Paris #75
£559	$951	€800	L'assemblee (55x46cm-22x18in) s. 28-Nov-3 Blanchet, Paris #77/R
£629	$1070	€900	Fleurs (73x54cm-29x21in) s. 28-Nov-3 Blanchet, Paris #74/R
£690	$1090	€1000	Portrait de femme (39x29cm-15x11in) s. cardboard. 6-Apr-3 Salle des ventes Pillet, Lyon la Foret #606
£699	$1189	€1000	Les charettes (65x92cm-26x36in) s. 28-Nov-3 Blanchet, Paris #76/R
£839	$1427	€1200	Mere et enfant (65x54cm-26x21in) s. 28-Nov-3 Blanchet, Paris #80/R
£1184	$2143	€1800	Le village (50x61cm-20x24in) s. 16-Apr-4 Pierre Berge, Paris #7/R est:2000-3000
£1189	$2021	€1700	Les cavaliers (81x60cm-32x24in) s. 28-Nov-3 Blanchet, Paris #79/R est:1500-2000
£1469	$2497	€2100	Paysage (61x50cm-24x20in) s. 28-Nov-3 Blanchet, Paris #72/R est:1000-1200

PETERS, Anna (1843-1926) German

£743	$1330	€1100	Sunlit flowers (26x22cm-10x9in) canvas on board oval. 6-May-4 Michael Zeller, Lindau #812/R
£833	$1375	€1200	Cabbage in bloom (13x17cm-5x7in) s. canvas on board. 3-Jul-3 Dr Fritz Nagel, Stuttgart #513/R
£855	$1574	€1300	Jug of flowers (46x30cm-18x12in) 28-Jun-4 Dr Fritz Nagel, Stuttgart #7013/R
£1316	$2421	€2000	Bunch of flowers lying on a stone pillar (62x42cm-24x17in) 28-Jun-4 Dr Fritz Nagel, Stuttgart #7021/R est:1500
£1458	$2304	€2100	Still life (32x24cm-13x9in) s. board lit. 19-Sep-3 Schloss Ahlden, Ahlden #1629/R est:2800
£1533	$2760	€2300	Flowers in vase (46x38cm-18x15in) s. 26-Apr-4 Rieber, Stuttgart #802/R est:3800
£1600	$2912	€2400	Still life with flowers (40x54cm-16x21in) s. 1-Jul-4 Van Ham, Cologne #1554/R est:2200
£2055	$3493	€3000	Flowers (28x48cm-11x19in) s. canvas on board lit. 6-Nov-3 Allgauer, Kempten #3531/R est:3700
£3333	$6000	€5000	Still life with pansies and fruit (28x48cm-11x19in) s. 26-Apr-4 Rieber, Stuttgart #1292/R est:5950
£3403	$5547	€4900	Still life of meadow flowers (47x36cm-19x14in) s. 24-Sep-3 Neumeister, Munich #525/R est:3000
£3521	$5634	€5000	Daisies in basket (53x42cm-21x17in) s.d.1920 board. 18-Sep-3 Rieber, Stuttgart #913/R est:5800
£4605	$8474	€7000	Arrangement of yellow and pink roses (22x34cm-9x13in) s. board. 24-Jun-4 Dr Fritz Nagel, Stuttgart #740/R est:6900
£5556	$9278	€8000	Sunflowers (64x80cm-25x31in) s. 24-Oct-3 Ketterer, Hamburg #93/R est:9000-12000

Works on paper

£1056	$1690	€1500	Swabian Alb with view of the Teck (21x30cm-8x12in) s. W/C. 18-Sep-3 Rieber, Stuttgart #1175/R est:1800

PETERS, Carl W (1897-1980) American

£538	$1000	€785	Genesee Valley park (36x43cm-14x17in) 6-Mar-4 Page, Batavia #91
£2038	$3750	€2975	Harbour side shack (51x61cm-20x24in) 27-Jun-4 Freeman, Philadelphia #120/R est:2500-4000
£2654	$4750	€3875	Gloucester (41x51cm-16x20in) s.i.verso canvasboard. 6-May-4 Shannon's, Milford #1/R est:3000-5000
£2688	$5000	€3924	Autumn (51x61cm-20x24in) s. 6-Mar-4 Page, Batavia #146
£3073	$5500	€4487	Rocks and sea, Gloucester (51x61cm-20x24in) s. s.i.verso. 6-May-4 Shannon's, Milford #222/R est:4000-6000
£3977	$7000	€5806	Sugar maples (51x61cm-20x24in) s. 3-Jan-4 Collins, Maine #7/R est:2000-3000
£4469	$8000	€6525	Fairport farm (74x99cm-29x39in) prov. 6-May-4 Shannon's, Milford #48/R est:8000-12000
£5308	$9500	€7750	View of Gloucester Haroubr (51x61cm-20x24in) s. panelr. 6-May-4 Shannon's, Milford #47/R est:7000-9000
£6587	$11000	€9617	Winter landscape with stream (61x76cm-24x30in) s. 23-Oct-3 Shannon's, Milford #238/R est:4000-6000
£8140	$14000	€11884	Lanesville (62x75cm-24x30in) s. i.verso prov.exhib. 3-Dec-3 Doyle, New York #230/R est:8000-12000

PETERS, Charles Rollo (1862-1928) American

£909	$1700	€1327	Street scene, Katwijk Ann Zee, Holland (41x33cm-16x13in) s.i.d.1884. 29-Feb-4 Bonhams & Butterfields, San Francisco #4537 est:1000-1500
£1136	$2000	€1659	Forest interior (31x41cm-12x16in) s.i.d.1901 panel prov. 23-May-4 Bonhams & Butterfields, San Francisco #6606/R
£2038	$3750	€2975	View of Alcatraz with fishing boats in the foreground (26x43cm-10x17in) s.d.1885 panel prov. 8-Jun-4 Bonhams & Butterfields, San Francisco #4158/R est:3000-5000
£5780	$10000	€8439	Casa Orgega, Monterey (41x61cm-16x24in) s. prov. 10-Dec-3 Bonhams & Butterfields, San Francisco #6172/R est:6000-8000

PETERS, Hugo (1911-) German

Works on paper

£671	$1201	€1000	Boats on shore (29x38cm-11x15in) mono.d. mixed media. 25-May-4 Karl & Faber, Munich #490/R

PETERS, Leslie H (1916-) American?

£1203	$2250	€1756	Looking into the valley (46x61cm-18x24in) s.d.1964 prov. 24-Jul-4 Coeur d'Alene, Hayden #112/R est:1500-2500

PETERS, Matthew William (1742-1814) British

£763	$1297	€1114	Mrs Robert Grimshaw (73x63cm-29x25in) i.verso prov. 24-Nov-3 Sotheby's, Melbourne #304/R (A.D 1800)

PETERS, Nikolai (1766-1825) Danish

Works on paper

£671	$1235	€1000	Fish on line (24x25cm-9x10in) s. gouache. 26-Mar-4 Dorotheum, Vienna #108/R

PETERS, Otto (1858-1908) Austrian

£2254	$3741	€3200	Country scene (89x119cm-35x47in) s.d.89. 16-Jun-3 Dorotheum, Vienna #156/R est:3500-4000

PETERS, Pieter Francis (1818-1903) Dutch

£1389	$2264	€2000	Farmstead in trees by river (56x79cm-22x31in) s. 25-Sep-3 Dr Fritz Nagel, Stuttgart #1394/R est:3900
£3020	$5557	€4500	After the storm (21x26cm-8x10in) s.d.1850 panel. 25-Mar-4 Dr Fritz Nagel, Stuttgart #756/R est:3900

PETERS, Pietronella (1848-1924) German

£3020	$5557	€4500	Summer idyll (45x32cm-18x13in) canvas on panel. 25-Mar-4 Dr Fritz Nagel, Stuttgart #755/R est:3600
£3919	$7015	€5800	Two girls showing cat its reflection in mirror (46x31cm-18x12in) s. canvas on board. 6-May-4 Michael Zeller, Lindau #814/R est:5000

PETERS, Udo (1884-1964) German

£1074	$1901	€1600	Walk in north German spring landscape (50x70cm-20x28in) s.d. board prov. 30-Apr-4 Dr Fritz Nagel, Stuttgart #915/R est:3000
£1208	$2138	€1800	Canal on the moor (50x70cm-20x28in) s. board prov. 30-Apr-4 Dr Fritz Nagel, Stuttgart #914/R est:3500
£1342	$2470	€2000	Landscape (49x69cm-19x27in) s. masonite. 26-Mar-4 Ketterer, Hamburg #592/R est:2500-3000
£1944	$3169	€2800	Spring in Worpswede (47x60cm-19x24in) s. board on panel. 26-Sep-3 Bolland & Marotz, Bremen #358/R est:3200
£1944	$3169	€2800	Evening sun on moorland peat (50x70cm-20x28in) s. board. 26-Sep-3 Bolland & Marotz, Bremen #359/R est:3200
£1987	$3616	€3000	Road through the woods (55x70cm-22x28in) s.d.57 board. 18-Jun-4 Bolland & Marotz, Bremen #378/R est:3300
£2098	$3608	€3000	Hay making near Worpswede (50x69cm-20x27in) s. board. 5-Dec-3 Bolland & Marotz, Bremen #393/R est:3000
£2318	$4219	€3500	Boats on the River Hamme (48x60cm-19x24in) s. board. 18-Jun-4 Bolland & Marotz, Bremen #377/R est:3800
£2384	$4339	€3600	Forest road (60x73cm-24x29in) s.d.30 i.verso board. 18-Jun-4 Bolland & Marotz, Bremen #376/R est:4900
£2917	$4754	€4200	Sunny birch avenue near Worpswede (50x70cm-20x28in) s. board. 26-Sep-3 Bolland & Marotz, Bremen #357/R est:4400
£3221	$6024	€4800	Peat moorland (55x70cm-22x28in) s. 28-Feb-4 Bolland & Marotz, Bremen #283/R est:4500

£3758 $7028 €5600 Birch trees and children by moorland canal (48x60cm-19x24in) s. board. 28-Feb-4 Bolland & Marotz, Bremen #282/R est:6500

PETERS, Wilhelm Otto (1851-1935) Norwegian

£386 $676 €564 Rowing boat and boat houses (45x58cm-18x23in) s. 16-Dec-3 Grev Wedels Plass, Oslo #208/R (N.KR 4500)
£601 $1052 €877 Man seated on the shore (66x87cm-26x34in) s/d/09. 16-Dec-3 Grev Wedels Plass, Oslo #207/R (N.KR 7000)
£2135 $3565 €3117 Girls and goats in rowing boat (90x144cm-35x57in) s.d.1913. 13-Oct-3 Blomqvist, Oslo #295/R est:25000-30000 (N.KR 25000)

Works on paper
£2516 $4679 €3673 From Skagen Sonderstrand with Michael Ancher and two fishermen (11x15cm-4x6in) i. W/C pencil htd white. 2-Mar-4 Rasmussen, Copenhagen #1628/R est:12000 (D.KR 28000)

PETERSEN, Albert (1875-1957) Danish

£851 $1523 €1242 Nude female reclining on bed (34x52cm-13x20in) s.i.d.1913. 12-Jan-4 Rasmussen, Vejle #133/R (D.KR 9000)
£1075 $1935 €1570 Interior scene with two women at table (29x33cm-11x13in) s. 24-Apr-4 Rasmussen, Havnen #2265/R est:6000-8000 (D.KR 12000)

PETERSEN, Anna (1845-1910) Danish

£474 $758 €692 Interior scene with women, possibly Skagen (67x82cm-26x32in) init.d.88 exhib. 22-Sep-3 Rasmussen, Vejle #138/R (D.KR 5000)

PETERSEN, Armand (1891-1969) Swiss/French

Sculpture
£1379 $2303 €2000 Hare (14x17cm-6x7in) s.i. light brown pat.bronze Cast.Susse Freres, Paris. 15-Nov-3 Von Zezschwitz, Munich #76/R est:550

PETERSEN, Bob (20th C) American

£493 $853 €700 Legend series, Sentinel. s.i.d. 23 aout 75 acrylic paper prov. 15-Dec-3 Charbonneaux, Paris #254
£528 $914 €750 Legend series, Companion (189x184cm-74x72in) acrylic paper exec. 1975 prov. 15-Dec-3 Charbonneaux, Paris #253

PETERSEN, Edvard (1841-1911) Danish

£304 $492 €444 Hilly landscape with wooden bridge across waterway (37x58cm-15x23in) mono. 9-Aug-3 Hindemae, Ullerslev #81/R (D.KR 3200)
£425 $736 €621 Farmer with scythe and wooded box (66x43cm-26x17in) mono.d.1887. 9-Dec-3 Rasmussen, Copenhagen #1417/R (D.KR 4500)
£444 $809 €666 Autumn landscape with horse and cart (23x30cm-9x12in) init. 19-Jun-4 Rasmussen, Havnen #2282/R (D.KR 5000)
£448 $806 €654 Woman by river (26x37cm-10x15in) init. 24-Apr-4 Rasmussen, Havnen #2292 (D.KR 5000)
£496 $928 €724 Skraepper - greenery (20x32cm-8x13in) init. canvas on board. 25-Feb-4 Kunsthallen, Copenhagen #574/R (D.KR 5500)
£794 $1255 €1151 Canal view with mill, Holland (25x36cm-10x14in) mono. 2-Sep-3 Rasmussen, Copenhagen #1978/R (D.KR 8500)
£996 $1614 €1454 Italian mountain landscape with man on donkey, woman and child (40x58cm-16x23in) mono. 9-Aug-3 Hindemae, Ullerslev #45/R (D.KR 10500)
£1028 $1624 €1491 Guests strolling in the garden at Villa Borghese (37x59cm-15x23in) init. 2-Sep-3 Rasmussen, Copenhagen #1544/R (D.KR 11000)
£1323 $2289 €1932 Figures at Ponte Nomentina, Rome (20x30cm-8x12in) mono.i.d.1881 prov. 9-Dec-3 Rasmussen, Copenhagen #1354/R est:15000-20000 (D.KR 14000)
£5860 $10138 €8556 Roman fountain in Villa Borghese park (45x65cm-18x26in) mono. exhib.prov. 9-Dec-3 Rasmussen, Copenhagen #1353/R est:30000-40000 (D.KR 62000)
£10295 $18841 €15031 Young girl picking lilacs on a sunny day (81x60cm-32x24in) s.d.1910 prov. 9-Jun-4 Rasmussen, Copenhagen #1511/R est:125000-150000 (D.KR 115000)
£23445 $43372 €34230 From Villa Capucini in Rome (81x129cm-32x51in) mono.d.1879 exhib.prov. 15-Mar-4 Rasmussen, Vejle #24/R est:300000-400000 (D.KR 260000)

PETERSEN, Emmanuel Aage (1894-1948) Danish

£267 $485 €401 Seascape with sailing vessels (27x45cm-11x18in) init. 19-Jun-4 Rasmussen, Havnen #2148 (D.KR 3000)
£303 $485 €442 Landscape with polar bears, Greenland (18x24cm-7x9in) 22-Sep-3 Rasmussen, Vejle #374/R (D.KR 3200)
£317 $567 €463 Landscape from Greenland (34x48cm-13x19in) init. 10-May-4 Rasmussen, Vejle #234/R (D.KR 3500)
£332 $531 €485 Seascape with sailing vessels (51x58cm-20x23in) init. 22-Sep-3 Rasmussen, Vejle #215 (D.KR 3500)
£354 $556 €517 Seascape with sailing vessel (32x44cm-13x17in) init. 30-Aug-3 Rasmussen, Havnen #2061/R (D.KR 3800)
£356 $647 €534 Landscape from Greenland with figures by bonfire (41x50cm-16x20in) s.d.46. 19-Jun-4 Rasmussen, Havnen #2220 (D.KR 4000)
£361 $584 €527 Three masted schooner at sea (35x35cm-14x14in) mono.d.21. 9-Aug-3 Hindemae, Ullerslev #254/R (D.KR 3800)
£379 $701 €553 Greenland scene with hunters in kayak (28x36cm-11x14in) init. 15-Mar-4 Rasmussen, Vejle #293 (D.KR 4200)
£391 $615 €571 Several sailing vessels in Oresund (40x57cm-16x22in) s.d.1923. 30-Aug-3 Rasmussen, Havnen #2082 (D.KR 4200)
£397 $734 €580 Landscape with iceberg from Davis Straight (34x48cm-13x19in) s.d.1923. 15-Mar-4 Rasmussen, Vejle #295/R (D.KR 4400)
£407 $729 €594 Seascape with kayaks in summer, Greenland (42x32cm-17x13in) 10-May-4 Rasmussen, Vejle #236/R (D.KR 4500)
£422 $687 €616 Midnight sun at Ritenbenk (26x37cm-10x15in) init.i.d.24. 27-Sep-3 Rasmussen, Havnen #3047/R (D.KR 4500)
£448 $819 €654 Eskimo hunters (40x60cm-16x24in) s. 9-Jun-4 Rasmussen, Copenhagen #1776/R (D.KR 5000)
£450 $733 €657 Fjord landscape, Greenland (23x37cm-9x15in) init. panel. 27-Sep-3 Rasmussen, Havnen #3080 (D.KR 4800)
£469 $867 €685 Mountain landscape from Greenland with prisoners in kayak (42x67cm-17x26in) mono. 15-Mar-4 Rasmussen, Vejle #296/R (D.KR 5200)
£498 $891 €727 The icebreaker Vaedderen at work in winter (32x52cm-13x20in) init. 10-May-4 Rasmussen, Vejle #235/R (D.KR 5500)
£520 $931 €759 Seascape with sailing vessel (51x58cm-20x23in) init. 12-Jan-4 Rasmussen, Vejle #16/R (D.KR 5500)
£543 $972 €793 North of Sugartop (53x66cm-21x26in) s.i. 10-May-4 Rasmussen, Vejle #231/R (D.KR 6000)
£569 $910 €831 Landscape from Greenland with figures (22x44cm-9x17in) init. 22-Sep-3 Rasmussen, Vejle #377/R (D.KR 6000)
£599 $1018 €875 Coastal landscape with vessel, cabin and figures, Greenland (32x44cm-13x17in) s. 10-Nov-3 Rasmussen, Vejle #325/R (D.KR 6500)
£609 $993 €889 Landscape from Erik the Red's Island at East Greenland (50x75cm-20x30in) s.i.d.August 1932. 27-Sep-3 Rasmussen, Havnen #3081 (D.KR 6500)
£627 $1147 €915 Glazier, Greenland (70x100cm-28x39in) s. 9-Jun-4 Rasmussen, Copenhagen #1775/R (D.KR 7000)
£627 $1129 €915 Landscape with figures by cabins, Greenland (37x55cm-15x22in) init. 24-Apr-4 Rasmussen, Havnen #2269/R (D.KR 7000)
£645 $1161 €942 Fjord landscape with hunters and tents, Greenland (59x46cm-23x18in) init. 24-Apr-4 Rasmussen, Havnen #2060/R (D.KR 7200)
£656 $1069 €958 Evening by Holmen's Hills, Icefjord (49x63cm-19x25in) s.i. 27-Sep-3 Rasmussen, Havnen #3046/R (D.KR 7000)
£662 $1184 €967 Seascape from Julianehaabs fjord (31x44cm-12x17in) init. i.verso. 12-Jan-4 Rasmussen, Vejle #10/R (D.KR 7000)
£662 $1184 €967 Landscape from Greenland (26x40cm-10x16in) s.i.d.23. 12-Jan-4 Rasmussen, Vejle #12/R (D.KR 7000)
£670 $1085 €972 Coastal landscape with buildings, Greenland (52x70cm-20x28in) init. 4-Aug-3 Rasmussen, Vejle #55/R (D.KR 7000)
£679 $1215 €991 Landscape from a Greenland fjord (35x49cm-14x19in) init. 10-May-4 Rasmussen, Vejle #233/R (D.KR 7500)
£711 $1294 €1067 Summer landscape from Greenland (70x92cm-28x36in) s. exhib. 19-Jun-4 Rasmussen, Havnen #2227/R (D.KR 8000)
£718 $1163 €1041 Summer landscape (28x43cm-11x17in) init. 4-Aug-3 Rasmussen, Vejle #58 (D.KR 7500)
£721 $1335 €1053 Landscape from Greenland with figures and houses (38x53cm-15x21in) s. 15-Mar-4 Rasmussen, Vejle #297/R (D.KR 8000)
£750 $1222 €1095 Fjord landscape with Eskimos by cabins, Greenland (53x71cm-21x28in) s/. 27-Sep-3 Rasmussen, Havnen #3053/R (D.KR 8000)
£813 $1318 €1179 Coastal landscape, Greenland (52x70cm-20x28in) init. 4-Aug-3 Rasmussen, Vejle #57/R (D.KR 8500)
£860 $1539 €1256 Cruising vessel in South Greenland (32x50cm-13x20in) s. 10-May-4 Rasmussen, Vejle #232/R (D.KR 9500)
£898 $1607 €1311 Coastal landscape, Greenland (28x35cm-11x14in) i.verso. 12-Jan-4 Rasmussen, Vejle #23 (D.KR 9500)
£995 $1782 €1453 Coastal landscape from Greenland with kayak and figures (90x130cm-35x51in) s,. 10-May-4 Rasmussen, Vejle #239/R (D.KR 11000)
£1028 $1624 €1491 Sunset over icebergs, Greenland (68x99cm-27x39in) init. 2-Sep-3 Rasmussen, Copenhagen #1633/R (D.KR 11000)
£1074 $1966 €1568 Eskimos outside the cabins (52x70cm-20x28in) s. 9-Jun-4 Rasmussen, Copenhagen #1774/R est:12000 (D.KR 12000)
£1099 $2000 €1605 Fjord landscape with Norwegian vessel. Greenland (53x77cm-21x30in) s/d/22. 7-Feb-4 Rasmussen, Havnen #2044/R (D.KR 12000)
£1196 $1938 €1734 Hunters in kayaks, Greenland (45x60cm-18x24in) s. 4-Aug-3 Rasmussen, Vejle #56/R est:10000 (D.KR 12500)
£1198 $2037 €1749 Landscape with mother looking out to sea, Greenland (43x55cm-17x22in) s. 10-Nov-3 Rasmussen, Vejle #323/R est:6000 (D.KR 13000)
£1336 $2272 €1951 Summer's day by Kronprins Island (70x100cm-28x39in) s. 10-Nov-3 Rasmussen, Vejle #322/R est:15000 (D.KR 14500)
£1343 $2457 €1961 Midnight sun - Seal hunter leaving Disko Bay (51x70cm-20x28in) s. 9-Jun-4 Rasmussen, Copenhagen #1769/R est:15000 (D.KR 15000)
£1406 $2291 €2053 Inuit family with sleigh (70x100cm-28x39in) s. 27-Sep-3 Rasmussen, Havnen #3042/R est:6000-8000 (D.KR 15000)
£1448 $2592 €2114 The vessel Gertrud Rask among icebergs (70x101cm-28x40in) s. 10-May-4 Rasmussen, Vejle #240/R est:12000 (D.KR 16000)
£1500 $2444 €2190 Landscape from Greenland with Eskimo at foot of mountain (128x93cm-50x37in) s. panel prov. 27-Sep-3 Rasmussen, Havnen #3052/R est:20000 (D.KR 16000)
£1770 $2868 €2567 Coastal landscape with icebergs, Greenland (70x115cm-28x45in) s. 4-Aug-3 Rasmussen, Vejle #53/R est:10000 (D.KR 18500)
£1935 $3290 €2825 Midnight sun, Disko Bay with Inuits at campfire (101x140cm-40x55in) s. 10-Nov-3 Rasmussen, Vejle #321/R est:18000-20000 (D.KR 21000)
£1963 $3101 €2846 Floating ice along Disco Bay's coast, Greenland (68x99cm-27x39in) s. 2-Sep-3 Rasmussen, Copenhagen #1634/R est:6000 (D.KR 21000)
£1970 $3604 €2876 Midnight sun over Disco Bay (70x100cm-28x39in) s. 9-Jun-4 Rasmussen, Copenhagen #1773/R est:20000-25000 (D.KR 22000)
£2149 $3932 €3138 Eskimos in fjord landscape at sunset (65x101cm-26x40in) s. 9-Jun-4 Rasmussen, Copenhagen #1772/R est:20000-25000 (D.KR 24000)
£2488 $4031 €3608 Fjord landscape with boats and figures, Angmagssalik, Greenland (70x100cm-28x39in) s. 4-Aug-3 Rasmussen, Vejle #54/R est:15000-20000 (D.KR 26000)
£2686 $4915 €3922 Summer's day on a fjord, Greenland (111x141cm-44x56in) s. 9-Jun-4 Rasmussen, Copenhagen #1767/R est:20000-25000 (D.KR 30000)

PETERSEN, F (?) Scandinavian

Works on paper
£3521 $6092 €5000 The schooner Tetis (47x66cm-19x26in) s.d.1843 W/C gouache. 13-Dec-3 Hagelstam, Helsinki #56/R est:3000

PETERSEN, Gunther (1920-) German

£500 $905 €750 Mudflats near Rantum (60x80cm-24x31in) s. i. verso lit. 3-Apr-4 Hans Stahl, Hamburg #65/R
£733 $1327 €1100 Muscheltal near Hornum - Sylt (60x80cm-24x31in) s. i. verso. 3-Apr-4 Hans Stahl, Hamburg #64/R

PETERSEN, H E (19/20th C) Danish

£528 $972 €792 Calm day by the Danish coast (40x49cm-16x19in) s. panel. 14-Jun-4 Blomqvist, Lysaker #1300 (N.KR 6500)
£813 $1496 €1220 Calm day near Helsingor (45x57cm-18x22in) s. panel. 14-Jun-4 Blomqvist, Lysaker #1299/R (N.KR 10000)

PETERSEN, Hans Gyde (1862-1943) Danish

£860 $1539 €1256 Wooded landscape with lake and water-lilies (74x104cm-29x41in) s.d.1933. 10-May-4 Rasmussen, Vejle #99/R (D.KR 9500)

PETERSEN, Hans Ritter von (1850-1914) German

£903 $1426 €1300 Shipping in a harbour entrance (60x80cm-24x31in) s. 2-Sep-3 Christie's, Amsterdam #328/R est:1500-2000

PETERSEN, Hugo (19th C) Danish?

£267 $485 €400 Portrait of Harlequin (40x30cm-16x12in) s. canvas on panel. 1-Jul-4 Van Ham, Cologne #1555/R

PETERSEN, J (?) Danish?

Works on paper

£	$	€	Details
£1150	$1909	€1679	Nicholas of Newcastle (50x67cm-20x26in) i. W/C. 1-Oct-3 Bonhams, Knightsbridge #46/R est:300-500
£1600	$2896	€2336	Sailing vessel, Kingfisher of London (50x66cm-20x26in) s.i.d.1839 W/C. 16-Apr-4 Honiton Galleries, Honiton #639 est:200-400

PETERSEN, Jakob (1774-1854) Danish

£	$	€	Details
£1244	$2265	€1866	Ship's portrait of the frigate Betsy of Copenhagen (42x55cm-17x22in) s. 19-Jun-4 Rasmussen, Havnen #2289/R est:15000-20000 (D.KR 14000)
£2517	$4280	€3600	The Quay Side (55x76cm-22x30in) init.d. 18-Nov-3 Cambi, Genoa #427/R est:3500-4000
£2600	$4654	€3796	English brig Endimion of Whitby in the Sound off Cronborg Castle (54x72cm-21x28in) init.i.d.1838. 26-May-4 Christie's, Kensington #630/R est:2500-3000

Works on paper

£	$	€	Details
£1250	$1988	€1813	Ship's portrait, the Newcastle, Captain Ralph Henderson (50x66cm-20x26in) s.d.1839 W/C. 9-Sep-3 David Duggleby, Scarborough #99/R est:1000-2000
£1300	$2327	€1898	Brig of Minerva of Jersey (49x62cm-19x24in) s.i.d.1828 blk ink W/C. 26-May-4 Christie's, Kensington #393/R est:1200-1800
£1623	$3003	€2370	Ship's portrait of the brig Cara (48x62cm-19x24in) s.i.d.1851 pen W/C. 15-Mar-4 Rasmussen, Vejle #131/R est:20000-25000 (D.KR 18000)
£1797	$3342	€2624	Ship's portrait of the schooner Kirstine and Marie of Svendborg (45x61cm-18x24in) s.i. pen W/C. 2-Mar-4 Rasmussen, Copenhagen #1425/R est:25000-30000 (D.KR 20000)

PETERSEN, Lorenz (1803-1870) German

£	$	€	Details
£1685	$2815	€2460	Ship's portrait of the barque Jorgen Bech (47x64cm-19x25in) s.d.1855. 25-Oct-3 Rasmussen, Havnen #2644/R est:20000-30000 (D.KR 18000)
£3025	$5233	€4417	Tree-master with flag (45x65cm-18x26in) s.d.1850. 9-Dec-3 Rasmussen, Copenhagen #1222/R est:40000-50000 (D.KR 32000)

PETERSEN, Pavia (20th C) Danish

£	$	€	Details
£242	$445	€353	Greenland Inuit group settling an argument (42x58cm-17x23in) s.d.1939 s.i.d.verso panel prov. 14-Jun-4 Waddingtons, Toronto #207/R (C.D 600)

PETERSEN, Robert Storm (1882-1949) Danish

£	$	€	Details
£1223	$2079	€1786	Portrait of man with large mustache (23x30cm-9x12in) init. cardboard. 26-Nov-3 Kunsthallen, Copenhagen #327/R est:15000 (D.KR 13000)

Works on paper

£	$	€	Details
£395	$672	€577	Hostel for homeless (18x13cm-7x5in) init. Indian ink. 26-Nov-3 Kunsthallen, Copenhagen #325/R (D.KR 4200)
£423	$720	€618	Conversation between to gentlemen (16x13cm-6x5in) init. Indian ink. 26-Nov-3 Kunsthallen, Copenhagen #326 (D.KR 4500)
£440	$800	€642	Two men talking (28x23cm-11x9in) s.d.20 i.verso Indian ink. 7-Feb-4 Rasmussen, Havnen #4103 (D.KR 4800)
£504	$917	€736	Farm hand getting ready (33x39cm-13x15in) s. pen. 7-Feb-4 Rasmussen, Havnen #4198 (D.KR 5500)
£847	$1439	€1237	Father Christmas running away (16x22cm-6x9in) s. W/C. 26-Nov-3 Kunsthallen, Copenhagen #322/R (D.KR 9000)

PETERSEN, Roland (1926-) American

£	$	€	Details
£7910	$14000	€11549	Park figure in sunlight, a girl waiting in sunlight (60x102cm-24x40in) s.d.1971 s.i.verso. 2-May-4 Bonhams & Butterfields, Los Angeles #3073/R est:5000-7000
£11892	$22000	€17362	Figure in profile with fields (56x63cm-22x25in) s.d.62. 13-Jul-4 Christie's, Rockefeller NY #27/R est:6000-8000
£19553	$35000	€28547	Picnic (180x154cm-71x61in) s.d.60. 6-May-4 Doyle, New York #97/R est:30000-40000
£46512	$80000	€67908	Picnic scene (155x173cm-61x68in) s.d.63 prov. 3-Dec-3 Doyle, New York #67/R est:20000-30000

PETERSEN, Sophus (1837-1904) Danish

£	$	€	Details
£1172	$2169	€1711	Flowers on stone ledge (27x32cm-11x13in) s/. 15-Mar-4 Rasmussen, Vejle #213/R est:10000-15000 (D.KR 13000)
£1462	$2514	€2135	Still life of oranges (20x30cm-8x12in) s.d.1881. 3-Dec-3 AB Stockholms Auktionsverk #2570/R est:20000-25000 (S.KR 19000)
£4492	$8356	€6558	Oysters and wine (70x82cm-28x32in) s.d.1887 exhib. 2-Mar-4 Rasmussen, Copenhagen #1305/R est:50000-60000 (D.KR 50000)

PETERSEN, Thomas (20th C) American

£	$	€	Details
£688	$1300	€1004	Noank harbour (36x58cm-14x23in) s.d.1914. 21-Feb-4 Jeffery Burchard, Florida #66/R
£1529	$2600	€2232	Sailboat offshore (61x76cm-24x30in) s.i. 18-Nov-3 Doyle, New York #27 est:1000-1500

PETERSEN, Vilhelm (1812-1880) Danish

£	$	€	Details
£756	$1308	€1104	Thatched timber framed house by the coast (26x37cm-10x15in) i.verso. 9-Dec-3 Rasmussen, Copenhagen #1544/R (D.KR 8000)
£851	$1472	€1242	Evening glow (12x19cm-5x7in) painted c.1843 exhib. 9-Dec-3 Rasmussen, Copenhagen #1684/R (D.KR 9000)
£1134	$1962	€1656	Seascape with fishing boat in evening light (13x17cm-5x7in) d.24 Juli painted c.1847 exhib. 9-Dec-3 Rasmussen, Copenhagen #1478/R est:5000-7000 (D.KR 12000)
£1418	$2453	€2070	Landscape study with view of farm surrounded by trees (10x19cm-4x7in) d.30 Aug. 1843 exhib. 9-Dec-3 Rasmussen, Copenhagen #1499/R est:5000-7000 (D.KR 15000)
£1434	$2581	€2094	Italian view with steamer and sailing vessels (18x24cm-7x9in) init. paper on canvas. 24-Apr-4 Rasmussen, Havnen #2097/R est:6000-8000 (D.KR 16000)
£5623	$9672	€8210	Roman ruins (26x42cm-10x17in) indis.sig.d.21 Juni i.verso paper on canvas. 3-Dec-3 Museumsbygningen, Copenhagen #168/R est:60000-80000 (D.KR 60000)
£16068	$27798	€23459	The Tiber running through Rome (52x81cm-20x32in) mono.d.1857. 9-Dec-3 Rasmussen, Copenhagen #1239/R est:150000 (D.KR 170000)

Works on paper

£	$	€	Details
£281	$484	€410	Roman ruins (19x26cm-7x10in) init. pencil study. 3-Dec-3 Museumsbygningen, Copenhagen #169 (D.KR 3000)

PETERSEN, Vilhelm (attrib) (1812-1880) Danish

£	$	€	Details
£398	$637	€581	Coastal landscape with figures (19x27cm-7x11in) with sig. verso. 22-Sep-3 Rasmussen, Vejle #298/R (D.KR 4200)

PETERSEN, Walter (1862-1950) German

£	$	€	Details
£979	$1664	€1400	Portrait of Bismarck (106x87cm-42x34in) s. 20-Nov-3 Van Ham, Cologne #1796/R

PETERSEN, Wilhelm (1900-?) German

£	$	€	Details
£347	$549	€500	Northern Friesian farmstead in storm (71x95cm-28x37in) s.d.1945. 6-Sep-3 Schopman, Hamburg #768/R
£1806	$2853	€2600	Young woman in traditional dress (72x50cm-28x20in) s. 6-Sep-3 Schopman, Hamburg #767/R est:1000

PETERSEN, Willem (1925-) ?

£	$	€	Details
£688	$1100	€1004	Paris street scene (38x76cm-15x30in) s. board. 20-Sep-3 Sloans & Kenyon, Bethesda #149/R est:1000-1200

PETERSEN-FLENSBURG, Heinrich (1861-1908) German

£	$	€	Details
£1489	$2487	€2100	Sylt beach with fishermen and boats (38x51cm-15x20in) s. i.d.96 stretcher. 17-Oct-3 Behringer, Furth #1477/R est:500

PETERSON, Edgar J (19/20th C) American?

£	$	€	Details
£295	$475	€431	Harvesting wheat (13x25cm-5x10in) s.d.1909 board. 22-Feb-3 Bunte, Elgin #1229

PETERSON, Jane (1876-1965) American

£	$	€	Details
£1381	$2500	€2016	Purple and yellow orchids (23x23cm-9x9in) canvasboard. 16-Apr-4 Du Mouchelle, Detroit #2091/R est:1800-2500
£1436	$2600	€2097	Still life with flowers (66x51cm-26x20in) painted 1945. 19-Apr-4 Caddigan, Hanover #2/R
£1705	$3000	€2489	View of a bridge in France (46x61cm-18x24in) s. 18-May-4 Bonhams & Butterfields, San Francisco #169/R est:4000-6000
£1744	$3000	€2546	Harbour scene (41x51cm-16x20in) s. 7-Dec-3 Susanin's, Chicago #6089/R est:2000-4000
£1875	$3300	€2738	Venice boats, Italy (41x53cm-16x21in) s. oil graphite on board. 28-May-4 Aspire, Cleveland #25/R est:1000-2000
£4749	$8500	€6934	Still life with roses and candlesticks (76x102cm-30x40in) s. 6-May-4 Shannon's, Milford #169/R est:7000-9000
£7186	$12000	€10492	Zinnias in a vase (61x76cm-24x30in) s. prov. 23-Oct-3 Shannon's, Milford #23/R est:6000-8000

Works on paper

£	$	€	Details
£335	$600	€489	Cloud study, Rockport (25x36cm-10x14in) s. W/C gouache paperboard. 7-May-4 Sloans & Kenyon, Bethesda #1722/R
£497	$800	€726	Flowers from Hazlewood (28x20cm-11x8in) s. W/C. 20-Aug-3 James Julia, Fairfield #1652/R
£559	$1000	€816	Garden landscape (23x33cm-9x13in) s. W/C. 8-May-4 Susanin's, Chicago #6066/R est:500-700
£670	$1200	€978	Northwest coast (23x30cm-9x12in) W/C gouache paperboard prov. 14-May-4 Skinner, Boston #200/R
£1235	$2000	€1791	Outside a mosque (25x28cm-10x11in) W/C prov. 8-Aug-3 Barridorf, Portland #301/R est:1200-1800
£1398	$2600	€2041	Canadian Rockies (22x30cm-9x12in) s. W/C gouache paper on board prov. 5-Mar-4 Skinner, Boston #479/R est:1800-2200
£1398	$2600	€2041	Beach and blue sky (19x28cm-7x11in) W/C prov. 5-Mar-4 Skinner, Boston #575/R est:1800-2200
£1564	$2800	€2283	Quiet day (20x26cm-8x10in) W/C gouache paperboard prov. 14-May-4 Skinner, Boston #251/R est:2000-3000
£2717	$5000	€3967	Venetian sailing boats (29x30cm-11x12in) s. gouache crayon. 27-Jun-4 Freeman, Philadelphia #119/R est:4000-6000
£5114	$9000	€7466	At the beach. Beach umbrellas (19x25cm-7x10in) W/C gouache pencil paperboard two. 18-May-4 Christie's, Rockefeller NY #96/R est:10000-15000
£9497	$17000	€13866	Fishermen's shacks, Gloucester (43x58cm-17x23in) s. exec.c.1916/18 gouache prov. 6-May-4 Shannon's, Milford #79/R est:12000-18000
£14525	$26000	€21207	Orange sail, Venice (17x17cm-7x7in) s. gouache prov. 6-May-4 Shannon's, Milford #92/R est:20000-30000

PETERSSEN, Eilif (1852-1928) Norwegian

£	$	€	Details
£1223	$2190	€1786	From Falkensten Manor (47x62cm-19x24in) init.i. 25-May-4 Grev Wedels Plass, Oslo #49/R est:10000-20000 (N.KR 15000)
£1787	$3039	€2609	Landscape from Christiania (35x62cm-14x24in) s.d.91. 29-Nov-3 Rasmussen, Havnen #2026/R est:6000-8000 (D.KR 19000)
£5604	$10032	€8182	Orange trees (81x65cm-32x26in) s.i.d.20 i.stretcher exhib. 22-Mar-4 Blomqvist, Oslo #397/R est:45000-55000 (N.KR 70000)

PETERSSON, Axel (1868-1925) Swedish

Sculpture

£	$	€	Details
£1109	$1984	€1619	Ottenbyare - man standing (16x25cm-6x10in) carved wood. 26-May-4 AB Stockholms Auktionsverk #2224/R est:10000-12000 (S.KR 15000)
£1183	$2117	€1727	Finger pulling (25x42cm-10x17in) s. painted wood. 25-May-4 Bukowskis, Stockholm #278/R est:20000-25000 (S.KR 16000)
£1346	$2315	€1965	The caller - Olle (34cm-13in) s. painted wood. 2-Dec-3 Bukowskis, Stockholm #229/R est:12000-15000 (S.KR 17500)
£1500	$2580	€2190	Ottenbyare (19cm-7in) indis.sig. wood. 2-Dec-3 Bukowskis, Stockholm #227/R est:10000-15000 (S.KR 19500)
£4615	$7938	€6738	Enrolment of conscripts (34cm-13in) painted wood group of six. 2-Dec-3 Bukowskis, Stockholm #223/R est:60000-80000 (S.KR 60000)
£9978	$17860	€14568	The funeral (27cm-11in) s. painted wood nine. 25-May-4 Bukowskis, Stockholm #279/R est:100000-125000 (S.KR 135000)
£41390	$74087	€60429	At district court - or The boy who swore he's not the father of the child (29x51x79cm-11x20x31in) s. carved polychrome wood exec.c.1912 prov.exhib.lit. 26-May-4 AB Stockholms Auktionsverk #2221/R est:250000-300000 (S.KR 560000)

PETHER, Abraham (1756-1812) British

£650	$1040	€949	Moonlit scene with ruined abbey and figures (49x59cm-19x23in) 17-Sep-3 Bonhams, Brooks & Langlois, Jersey #55/R
£17000	$31280	€24820	Wooded river landscape, with a faggot gatherer on a bridge, cattle and sheep (104x135cm-41x53in) s.d.1792 prov. 11-Jun-4 Christie's, London #53/R est:8000-12000

PETHER, Abraham (attrib) (1756-1812) British

£550	$875	€803	Castle by moonlight with travellers watching by a river (48x58cm-19x23in) s. 10-Sep-3 Cheffins, Cambridge #521/R
£1250	$2025	€1813	Capriccio of a moonlit river landscape (65x77cm-26x30in) 30-Jul-3 Hamptons Fine Art, Godalming #278/R est:1000-1500

PETHER, Sebastian (1790-1844) British

£960	$1718	€1402	Travelers on a track, ruined castle beyond (45x66cm-18x26in) s. panel. 27-May-4 Christie's, Kensington #129/R
£4000	$7160	€5840	A riverside town by moonlight (24x32cm-9x13in) init. panel. 28-May-4 Lyon & Turnbull, Edinburgh #82/R est:4000-6000

PETHER, Sebastian (attrib) (1790-1844) British

£280	$518	€409	Figures by a camp fire in a moonlit river landscape (15x20cm-6x8in) 14-Jul-4 Christie's, Kensington #877/R
£500	$910	€730	Moonlit landscape with mountains, figures standing by a bonfire (46x61cm-18x24in) 29-Jun-4 Capes Dunn, Manchester #717/R

PETHER, William (c.1731-1821) British

Prints

£2200	$3960	€3212	Philospher giving a lecture on the orrery (48x58cm-19x23in) mezzotint after Joseph Wright of Derby. 22-Apr-4 Mellors & Kirk, Nottingham #967/R est:1500-2000

PETILLION, Jules (1845-1899) French

£658	$1211	€1000	Boulevard sous la neige (26x22cm-10x9in) s. 22-Jun-4 Ribeyre & Baron, Paris #47
£2000	$3640	€2920	Gossips on a village street (32x51cm-13x20in) s.i. 16-Jun-4 Christie's, Kensington #3/R est:2000-3000

PETION, Françoise (1944-) French

Works on paper

£280	$501	€420	Le coq (40x30cm-16x12in) s. pastel. 16-May-4 Thierry & Lannon, Brest #223
£296	$518	€420	Petite (30x15cm-12x6in) s. pastel. 21-Dec-3 Thierry & Lannon, Brest #405
£324	$567	€460	Reveuse (20x15cm-8x6in) s. pastel. 21-Dec-3 Thierry & Lannon, Brest #410
£331	$619	€500	Les causeuses (32x25cm-13x10in) s. pastel. 24-Jul-4 Thierry & Lannon, Brest #285
£352	$616	€500	Jeune Breton assis (19x24cm-7x9in) s. pastel. 21-Dec-3 Thierry & Lannon, Brest #409
£387	$678	€550	Petite danseuse (22x12cm-9x5in) s. pastel. 21-Dec-3 Thierry & Lannon, Brest #404
£387	$678	€550	Sur scene (33x41cm-13x16in) s. pastel. 21-Dec-3 Thierry & Lannon, Brest #408
£762	$1424	€1150	En famille, Plougastel (40x30cm-16x12in) s. pastel. 24-Jul-4 Thierry & Lannon, Brest #286/R

PETIT, August (19/20th C) French

£556	$928	€800	Portrait d'homme. Portrait de femme (66x54cm-26x21in) one s.d.1894 pair. 27-Oct-3 Giraudeau, Tours #39
£851	$1421	€1200	Still life with watermelons (54x65cm-21x26in) s.d.1904. 20-Oct-3 Duran, Madrid #126

PETIT, B (?) ?

£2465	$4264	€3500	Coast (90x89cm-35x35in) s. board. 15-Dec-3 Ansorena, Madrid #1016/R est:300

PETIT, Bernard le (?-1669) Dutch

Works on paper

£900	$1647	€1314	Moses and the burning bush. Lod ordering Aaron to go to the mountains. Moses kissing Aaron (9x11cm-4x4in) black chk pen ink set of three. 6-Jul-4 Christie's, London #102/R
£900	$1647	€1314	Esau selling his birthright to Jacob. Isaac and Abimelech (9x12cm-4x5in) black chk pen ink wash two. 6-Jul-4 Christie's, London #110/R
£1300	$2379	€1898	Moses hiding the body of the Egyptian in the sand. Seven daughters of Jethro by the well (10x12cm-4x5in) black chk pen ink two. 6-Jul-4 Christie's, London #101/R est:1500-2000
£2200	$4026	€3212	Midwives sparing the lives of the male infants (9x11cm-4x4in) black chk pen ink. 6-Jul-4 Christie's, London #99/R est:1500-2000
£2200	$4026	€3212	Rachel giving birth to Joseph. Judah and Tamar. Joseph taken captive. Joseph made steward of Egypt (9x11cm-4x4in) black chk pen ink wash set of four. 6-Jul-4 Christie's, London #111/R est:1500-2000
£2300	$4209	€3358	Plague of darkness (9x12cm-4x5in) black chk pen ink wash. 6-Jul-4 Christie's, London #103/R est:1000-1500
£2400	$4392	€3504	Sarah complaining of Ishmael. Departure of Hagar and Ishmael. Sacrifice of Abraham (9x12cm-4x5in) black chk pen ink wash corners cut set of four. 6-Jul-4 Christie's, London #108/R est:1500-2000
£2600	$4758	€3796	Joseph's feast. Joseph makes himself known. Joseph embracing Benjamin, Jacob travelling to Egypt (9x12cm-4x5in) black chk pen ink wash set of four. 6-Jul-4 Christie's, London #115/R est:1500-2000
£3000	$5490	€4380	Joseph retaining Simeon as a hostage. Joseph ordering food to be brought for his brother (9x12cm-4x5in) black chk pen ink wash two. 6-Jul-4 Christie's, London #114/R est:1500-2000
£3200	$5856	€4672	Jacob's ladder (9x11cm-4x4in) black chk pen ink wash. 6-Jul-4 Christie's, London #109/R est:800-1200
£4200	$7686	€6132	Hebrews camping in Elim (9x11cm-4x4in) black chk pen ink wash. 6-Jul-4 Christie's, London #105/R est:2000-3000
£4500	$8235	€6570	Calling of Abraham. Abraham and lot separate. Abraham and Melchizedek. Abraham refusing the goods (8x11cm-3x4in) black chk pen ink set of four. 6-Jul-4 Christie's, London #106/R est:1500-2000
£5000	$9150	€7300	Joseph's brother returning to Jacob (9x11cm-4x4in) black chk pen ink wash. 6-Jul-4 Christie's, London #113/R est:1500-2000
£5200	$9516	€7592	Three angels visiting Abraham, People of Sodom blinded by angels. Lot and his daughters. Abraham (8x11cm-3x4in) black chk pen ink set of four. 6-Jul-4 Christie's, London #107/R est:1500-2000
£6200	$11346	€9052	Crossing of the Red Sea (9x12cm-4x5in) black chk pen ink wash. 6-Jul-4 Christie's, London #104/R est:2000-3000
£6500	$11895	€9490	Joseph's brother unloading their sacks (9x11cm-4x4in) black chk pen ink wash. 6-Jul-4 Christie's, London #116/R est:1500-2000
£6800	$12444	€9928	Joseph and Potuphar's wife (9x12cm-4x5in) black chk pen ink wash. 6-Jul-4 Christie's, London #112/R est:2000-3000

PETIT, C (?) ?

£2800	$5152	€4088	Butter churn (67x57cm-26x22in) s.i. 25-Mar-4 Christie's, Kensington #74/R est:3000-5000

PETIT, Charles (19th C) French?

£950	$1748	€1387	Early morning, Coniston Lake and mountain (50x87cm-20x34in) mono.d.1879 i.verso. 8-Jun-4 Bonhams, Knightsbridge #196/R

PETIT, E (19/20th C) French

£4895	$8322	€7000	Epagneuls a l'arret levant des faisans (81x98cm-32x39in) s. 20-Nov-3 Millon & Associes, Paris #117/R

PETIT, Eugène (1839-1886) French

£800	$1360	€1168	On the point (38x46cm-15x18in) s. 27-Nov-3 Christie's, Kensington #426/R
£1173	$2100	€1713	English setter and a Gordon setter (46x56cm-18x22in) s. 16-May-4 CRN Auctions, Cambridge #17/R
£1900	$3458	€2774	Le chemin aux arbres et fleurs (67x95cm-26x37in) s. 16-Jun-4 Christie's, Kensington #11/R est:1500-2000
£3310	$5726	€4700	Bouquet (41x26cm-16x10in) s. panel. 10-Dec-3 Rossini, Paris #102/R
£6500	$11180	€9490	Chrysanthemums in a brass urn, and silver tray and jug on a table (96x132cm-38x52in) s.d.75. 4-Dec-3 Christie's, Kensington #94/R est:7000-10000

PETIT, Eugène Joseph (attrib) (1845-?) French

£420	$713	€600	Still life with fruit and knife (65x54cm-26x21in) i.d.1882 verso. 28-Nov-3 Wendl, Rudolstadt #4136/R

PETIT, Jacques (1925-) French

£248	$400	€360	Boats on the seine (42x48cm-17x19in) s. s.i.d.verso. 24-Aug-3 Bonhams & Butterfields, Los Angeles #7068

PETIT, Noel (19/20th C) ?

£458	$742	€650	Sheep (58x61cm-23x24in) s.i. panel. 11-Aug-3 Boscher, Cherbourg #825

PETIT, Pierre Joseph (1768-1825) French

£8505	$15564	€12417	Romantic Italian landscape with young shepherdess (65x92cm-26x36in) s.d.1806. 9-Jun-4 Rasmussen, Copenhagen #1558/R est:75000-100000 (D.KR 95000)
£38158	$70211	€58000	Vue du mole et du phare de Naples. Vue de la baie de Naples (54x82cm-21x32in) one s. pair. 24-Jun-4 Christie's, Paris #107/R est:35000-45000

PETITI, Filiberto (1845-1924) Italian

£387	$670	€550	Countryside (33x40cm-13x16in) s. board. 10-Dec-3 Finarte Semenzato, Rome #254/R
£772	$1366	€1150	Gran Sasso (24x29cm-9x11in) s.i. 1-May-4 Meeting Art, Vercelli #273
£1014	$1581	€1500	River in the woods (63x50cm-25x20in) cardboard. 30-Mar-3 Adma, Formigine #1136 est:1600
£2113	$3655	€3000	Mountainous landscape (80x103cm-31x41in) s. 10-Dec-3 Finarte Semenzato, Rome #266/R est:2000-2500
£4800	$8880	€7008	Mediterranean town (63x102cm-25x40in) s.i. 14-Jul-4 Sotheby's, Olympia #229/R est:3000-4000

PETITJEAN, E (1844-1925) French

£3288	$5589	€4800	Le port d'Audierne (46x65cm-18x26in) s. 9-Nov-3 Versailles Encheres #21/R est:6000-6500

PETITJEAN, Edmond (1844-1925) French

£600	$1002	€876	Steamer at sea in a squall (47x65cm-19x26in) s. 8-Oct-3 Christie's, Kensington #763
£894	$1627	€1350	Paysage vallonne (24x33cm-9x13in) s. metal. 19-Jun-4 Gerard, Besancon #99
£909	$1600	€1327	Le Pre (30x48cm-12x19in) board. 23-May-4 Hindman, Chicago #13/R est:1000-2000
£1469	$2452	€2100	Eclaircie sur la riviere (26x40cm-10x16in) paper on cardboard. 29-Jun-3 St-Germain-en-Laye Encheres #6/R
£1879	$3495	€2800	Pecheurs au bord de l'eau (44x29cm-17x11in) s. board. 3-Mar-4 Tajan, Paris #47/R est:2800-3000
£2083	$3396	€3000	Etude pour un port du Nord (45x65cm-18x26in) s. 26-Sep-3 Rabourdin & Choppin de Janvry, Paris #63/R est:3000-4000
£2500	$4500	€3650	Harbour view (38x46cm-15x18in) s. 21-Jan-4 Sotheby's, Olympia #422/R est:1800-2500
£2800	$4648	€4088	Chaussee de Charleroi (45x38cm-18x15in) s.i.stretcher. 1-Oct-3 Sotheby's, Olympia #287/R est:2000-3000

£3020 $5618 €4500 Rue de village en Vendee, Talmont (46x65cm-18x26in) s. 2-Mar-4 Artcurial Briest, Paris #120/R est:4000-5000
£3356 $6007 €5000 Ferme au bord de la riviere (60x81cm-24x32in) s. 26-May-4 Christie's, Paris #10/R est:5000-7000
£4600 $7636 €6716 Farmyard (46x65cm-18x26in) s. 1-Oct-3 Sotheby's, Olympia #281/R est:3000-4000
£5034 $8910 €7500 Queue d'etang (60x78cm-24x31in) s. 30-Apr-4 Tajan, Paris #151/R est:4000-5000
£5072 $8319 €7000 Venise (50x65cm-20x26in) s. carboard. 11-May-3 Osenat, Fontainebleau #165/R est:6000-6500
£5245 $9021 €7500 L'abri de pecheur pres de l'estuaire (50x84cm-20x33in) s. panel painted c.1880. 7-Dec-3 Osenat, Fontainebleau #192 est:7000-8000
£5308 $9500 €7750 Village lane (46x79cm-18x31in) s. prov. 6-May-4 Shannon's, Milford #23/R est:7000-9000
£5556 $10000 €8112 Harbor view (46x68cm-18x27in) s. prov. 23-Apr-4 Sotheby's, New York #213/R est:18000-25000
£6111 $11000 €8922 Vue d'un port (46x65cm-18x26in) s. 22-Apr-4 Christie's, Rockefeller NY #175/R est:12000-18000
£6704 $12000 €9788 Riverside activities (46x79cm-18x31in) s. prov. 6-May-4 Shannon's, Milford #22/R est:7000-9000

PETITJEAN, Hippolyte (1854-1929) French
£400 $704 €584 Paysage de campagne (17x22cm-7x9in) studio st. prov. 19-May-4 Dreweatt Neate, Newbury #85/R
£567 $1043 €850 Les meules (13x22cm-5x9in) bears studio st. cardboard. 14-Jun-4 Tajan, Paris #28/R
£900 $1638 €1314 Paysage a l'oree du bois (14x23cm-6x9in) studio st. board. 21-Jun-4 Bonhams, New Bond Street #4/R
£1049 $1804 €1500 Cour de ferme maconnaise (46x35cm-18x14in) s.d.97. 3-Dec-3 Oger, Dumont, Paris #28/R est:1200-1500
£1250 $2088 €1800 Paysage marin (21x36cm-8x14in) mono. canvas on board. 24-Oct-3 Ketterer, Hamburg #94/R est:1800-2000
£1400 $2548 €2044 Nature morte aux fruits (22x33cm-9x13in) studio st. canvasboard prov. 21-Jun-4 Bonhams, New Bond Street #2/R est:1000-1500
£1500 $2505 €2190 Paysage rural (23x34cm-9x13in) s. board executed c.1908 prov. 22-Oct-3 Bonhams, New Bond Street #18/R est:1500-2000
£1678 $3121 €2500 Nu au bord d'un lac (28x39cm-11x15in) s. panel. 2-Mar-4 Artcurial Briest, Paris #133/R est:2500-3500
£3169 $5546 €4500 Vision (48x37cm-19x15in) st.mono. i.verso panel painted c.1896. 19-Dec-3 Delvaux, Paris #20/R est:4000-6000
£3743 $7000 €5465 Trois femmes (22x27cm-9x11in) st.mono. board prov. 25-Feb-4 Christie's, Rockefeller NY #17/R est:2500-3500
£4000 $6360 €5800 Femme allongee (14x23cm-6x9in) mono. board. 11-Sep-3 Christie's, Kensington #16/R est:3000-4000
£6500 $10855 €9490 Bord de L'Oise (33x46cm-13x18in) s. 21-Oct-3 Sotheby's, London #24/R est:7000-9000
£6500 $11765 €9490 Vision (50x38cm-20x15in) mono. canvas on board prov. 1-Apr-4 Christie's, Kensington #8/R est:5000-7000
£7500 $12975 €10950 Paysage aux trois femmes (34x76cm-13x30in) s. 11-Dec-3 Christie's, Kensington #13/R est:8000-12000
Works on paper
£387 $692 €580 Muses dans les bois (50x37cm-20x15in) crayon. 16-May-4 Thierry & Lannon, Brest #405
£800 $1336 €1168 Portrait of a woman (46x31cm-18x12in) studio st.d.1911 chl prov. 22-Oct-3 Sotheby's, Olympia #17/R
£1049 $1783 €1500 Paysage (30x47cm-12x19in) s. sanguine. 27-Nov-3 Calmels Cohen, Paris #50/R est:800-1200
£3000 $5430 €4380 Notre Dame (48x32cm-19x13in) mono. W/C exec.c.1896 prov. 1-Apr-4 Christie's, Kensington #14/R est:3000-5000

PETITOT, Jean (jnr) (1653-1699) French
Miniatures
£5800 $9860 €8468 Lady wearing loose white chemise and yellow ribbon (3cm-1in) s.d.1697 enamel gilt frame oval. 18-Nov-3 Bonhams, New Bond Street #34/R est:2000-3000

PETITOT, Jean (snr) (1607-1691) French
Miniatures
£2200 $3740 €3212 Louis XIV (3cm-1in) enamel oval. 18-Nov-3 Bonhams, New Bond Street #32/R est:1000-1500
£19000 $32870 €27740 Portrait of Henri de la Tour D'Auvergne (3cm-1in) gilt metal mount translucent blue enameled border. 12-Dec-3 Sotheby's, London #46/R est:8000-12000

PETITOT, Jean (snr-attrib) (1607-1691) French
Miniatures
£2483 $4146 €3600 Marquise de Maintenon (3x3cm-1x1in) enamel oval in rectangular gilt frame lit. 14-Nov-3 Lempertz, Koln #523/R est:4000

PETITPAS, Sophie (20th C) French
Works on paper
£1867 $3416 €2800 Drapeau americain (92x150cm-36x59in) mixed media collage. 6-Jun-4 Anaf, Lyon #469/R est:4000-4500
£2432 $4597 €3600 Drapeau Americain (136x155cm-54x61in) s.verso mixed media flag. 21-Feb-4 Cornette de St.Cyr, Paris #368/R est:3000-4000

PETITPIERRE, Petra (1905-1959) Swiss
£259 $463 €378 Petites feuilles - little leaves (14x20cm-6x8in) s.d.1942 i. stretcher. 12-May-4 Dobiaschofsky, Bern #3842 (S.FR 600)
£290 $522 €423 Houses on a rocky outcrop overlooking a bay (30x36cm-12x14in) s.d.1930 board. 24-Jan-4 British Auctioneer #265/R
£345 $617 €504 Ruins (42x72cm-17x28in) s.d.1945 i. verso. 12-May-4 Dobiaschofsky, Bern #864/R (S.FR 800)
£431 $772 €629 Observation (57x47cm-22x19in) s.i.d.1943 gouache col chk. 12-May-4 Dobiaschofsky, Bern #863/R (S.FR 1000)

PETLEY, Roy (1951-) British
£380 $692 €555 River landscape with boat (48x70cm-19x28in) s. board. 15-Jun-4 Bonhams, Knightsbridge #181/R
£1200 $2160 €1752 Still life with rose (40x61cm-16x24in) s. board prov. 20-Jan-4 Bonhams, Knightsbridge #288/R est:1000-2000
£1200 $2040 €1752 Park in summer (50x81cm-20x32in) s.d.85 board. 26-Nov-3 Sotheby's, Olympia #65/R est:400-600
£1750 $3028 €2555 Female standing in a summer garden (58x38cm-23x15in) s. 14-Dec-3 Desmond Judd, Cranbrook #1056
£2133 $3861 €3200 Market Place, Bridgetown (49x74cm-19x29in) s. board prov. 31-Mar-4 James Adam, Dublin #131/R est:2500-3500
Works on paper
£260 $478 €380 Portrait of a lady (11x7cm-4x3in) s.d.85 pastel. 11-Jun-4 Keys, Aylsham #536
£420 $773 €613 Portrait of a partially nude lady (20x13cm-8x5in) s. crayon. 11-Jun-4 Keys, Aylsham #533
£750 $1290 €1095 Portrait of a semi-nude lady seated (48x33cm-19x13in) s. red chk. 5-Dec-3 Keys, Aylsham #460

PETLEY-JONES, Llewellyn (1908-1986) Canadian
£225 $383 €329 Albany Street, Marlyebone, London (27x40cm-11x16in) s.d.1954 s.i.verso prov. 27-Nov-3 Heffel, Vancouver #122 (C.D 500)
£280 $482 €409 Still life of roses in a vase (53x44cm-21x17in) s.d.71 board. 2-Dec-3 Sworder & Son, Bishops Stortford #494/R
£296 $482 €432 Boulevard Montparnasse, night (27x34cm-11x13in) s.i.verso prov. 23-Sep-3 Ritchie, Toronto #167 (C.D 650)
£300 $480 €438 Autumn on the Thames at Richmond (35x43cm-14x17in) s.d.57 s.i.verso. 18-Sep-3 Bonhams, Edinburgh #383
£330 $525 €479 Still life of roses in a vase (53x44cm-21x17in) s.d.71 board. 9-Sep-3 Sworder & Son, Bishops Stortford #419/R
£333 $547 €486 White caps - Whytecliffe, Horseshoe Bay (66x79cm-26x31in) s.d.52. 28-May-3 Maynards, Vancouver #39 (C.D 750)
£488 $873 €712 Self portrait (34x26cm-13x10in) s.d.1954 i.verso. 27-May-4 Heffel, Vancouver #161/R (C.D 1200)
£528 $946 €771 View from Butte, Montmartre (45x61cm-18x24in) s.d.1956 i.d.verso prov. 27-May-4 Heffel, Vancouver #12 (C.D 1300)
£1126 $1914 €1644 Hotel des Voyageurs, Paris (72x92cm-28x36in) s.d.55 s.i.verso prov. 18-Nov-3 Sotheby's, Toronto #41/R est:2000-2500 (C.D 2500)

PETRASSI, Luigi (1868-1948) Italian
£400 $736 €600 Village with stream (39x30cm-15x12in) s. 10-Jun-4 Christie's, Rome #33
£490 $817 €700 Landscape (25x55cm-10x22in) s. cardboard. 24-Jun-3 Finarte Semenzato, Rome #75
£1061 $1900 €1549 River scene with a boat (60x90cm-24x35in) s. 21-Mar-4 Bonhams & Butterfields, Los Angeles #7125/R est:1000-1500

PETRE, Mike (20th C) New Zealander
Works on paper
£714 $1314 €1042 Field study 11 (45x45cm-18x18in) s.d.2002 mixed media. 25-Mar-4 International Art Centre, Auckland #94/R (NZ.D 2000)
£959 $1630 €1400 Field study 6 (45x45cm-18x18in) s. mixed media. 27-Nov-3 International Art Centre, Auckland #35/R (NZ.D 2550)

PETRELLA DA BOLOGNA, Vittorio (1886-1951) Italian
£524 $876 €750 Old houses in Sanremo (37x27cm-15x11in) s. i.verso board. 26-Jun-3 Sant Agostino, Torino #108/R
£872 $1544 €1300 Torre Pellice (27x37cm-11x15in) s. s.i.verso board. 1-May-4 Meeting Art, Vercelli #401

PETRI, Erik (1880-?) Norwegian
£328 $545 €476 Memories from the summer of 1923, Filtvedt (39x50cm-15x20in) s. 16-Jun-3 Blomqvist, Lysaker #1175 (N.KR 3800)

PETRI, Svante (1944-) Swedish
£283 $509 €425 Coastal landscape (60x85cm-24x33in) s. 25-Apr-4 Goteborg Auktionsverk, Sweden #414/R (S.KR 3900)

PETRICCA, L (19th C) Italian
Works on paper
£900 $1611 €1314 Reader (50x73cm-20x29in) s. W/C. 26-May-4 Sotheby's, Olympia #290/R est:1000-1500

PETRICH, Ernst (1878-?) German
£315 $526 €450 Landscape with boat (40x53cm-16x21in) s. lit. 27-Jun-3 Auktionhaus Georg Rehm, Augsburg #8150/R

PETRIDES, Konrad (1863-1943) Austrian
£658 $1211 €1000 Mountain stream (73x54cm-29x21in) s. 22-Jun-4 Wiener Kunst Auktionen, Vienna #191/R

PETRILLI, Professor A (19th C) Italian
Sculpture
£934 $1700 €1364 Puti with musical instruments (61x71cm-24x28in) s. bronze. 8-Feb-4 William Jenack, New York #44/R est:1700

PETRINI, Giuseppe Antonio (1677-1758) Italian
Works on paper
£3611 $6500 €5272 Prophet Isaiah looking up (45x31cm-18x12in) red chk. 22-Jan-4 Christie's, Rockefeller NY #76/R est:2000-2500

PETRINI, Giuseppe Antonio (attrib) (1677-1758) Italian
£1867 $3397 €2800 Saint Peter (99x81cm-39x32in) 30-Jun-4 Delvaux, Paris #143/R est:3000-4000

£2941 $5088 €4294 Tete d'apotre (65x49cm-26x19in) prov. 12-Dec-3 Galerie du Rhone, Sion #171/R est:7000-9000 (S.FR 6500)

PETROCELLI, Arturo (1856-?) Italian

£276 $475 €403 Portrait of a man with pipe (28x23cm-11x9in) s. 7-Dec-3 Hindman, Chicago #774/R

£280 $476 €409 Portrait of an elderly Italian lady in a pink dress (27x20cm-11x8in) s. vignette. 19-Nov-3 Tennants, Leyburn #1289

PETROCELLI, Arturo (attrib) (1856-?) Italian

£380 $646 €555 Interior scene with cavalier playing a mandolin, a girl nearby (63x50cm-25x20in) s. 19-Nov-3 Tennants, Leyburn #1239

£500 $925 €730 Two elderly buskers, seated on a bench (25x18cm-10x7in) s. 14-Jan-4 Brightwells, Leominster #914/R

PETROCELLI, Vincenzo Pasquale Angelo (1823-1896) Italian

£17450 $32107 €26000 Waiting for the Duke of Guisa (89x174cm-35x69in) s. 24-Mar-4 Finarte Semenzato, Rome #12/R est:25000-28000

PETROFF, Wladimir (20th C) French/Russian

£450 $833 €657 Mosque Sultan Ahmed, Constantinople (33x23cm-13x9in) s.d.1926 board. 14-Jul-4 Christie's, Kensington #1183

£690 $1234 €1007 In the Hagia Sophia (57x44cm-22x17in) s.i.d.1930 canvas on board. 12-May-4 Dobiaschofsky, Bern #865/R est:1500 (S.FR 1600)

£690 $1234 €1007 Osmans praying in Sultan Ahmed Mosque (57x45cm-22x18in) s.i.d.1930. 12-May-4 Dobiaschofsky, Bern #866/R est:1500 (S.FR 1600)

£958 $1600 €1399 Interior of Hagia Sofia, Istanbul (58x46cm-23x18in) s.i.d.1928. 15-Nov-3 Sloans & Kenyon, Bethesda #127/R est:600-800

£2800 $4480 €4060 Blue mosque. St Sophia, Istanbul (28x47cm-11x19in) s.i.d.1930 canvas on plywood pair. 18-Sep-3 Christie's, Kensington #132/R est:1000-1500

PETROS (1928-) Greek

£600 $1074 €876 Seveso (150x195cm-59x77in) i.d.86 verso. 10-May-4 Sotheby's, Olympia #95/R

£1200 $2040 €1752 Cernobil (147x193cm-58x76in) s.d.86 s.i.d. on stretcher. 18-Nov-3 Sotheby's, London #107/R est:600-800

PETROV-VODKIN, Kuzma (1878-1939) Russian

£1329 $2285 €1900 Priere dans la Mosquee Sultan Ahmed (46x29cm-18x11in) s.i. canvas on board. 8-Dec-3 Tajan, Paris #316/R est:1500-1800

£138889 $250000 €202778 Chaos, 1906 (97x129cm-38x51in) prov.exhib.lit. 23-Apr-4 Sotheby's, New York #63/R est:250000-350000

Works on paper

£599 $1000 €875 Standing female nude (27x24cm-11x9in) s. pencil. 21-Oct-3 Christie's, Rockefeller NY #104

PETROVA, Elena (1971-) Russian

£278 $453 €400 Still life (33x40cm-13x16in) s. 23-Sep-3 Durán, Madrid #665/R

PETROVICHEV, Piotr Ivanovich (1874-1947) Russian

£4469 $8000 €6525 Troitse-Sergieva lavra (35x53cm-14x21in) oil cardboard painted 1920-30. 29-May-4 Shishkin Gallery, Moscow #37/R est:10000-12000

£29301 $50690 €42779 Patterned porcelain and red roses on table (70x98cm-28x39in) s. prov. 9-Dec-3 Rasmussen, Copenhagen #1522/R est:30000-40000 (D.KR 310000)

PETROVITS, Ladislaus Eugen (1839-1907) Austrian

£642 $1200 €937 View of a village in winter (66x102cm-26x40in) s. 29-Feb-4 Bonhams & Butterfields, San Francisco #4519

£1987 $3636 €3000 Michaelerplatz with old theatre (80x60cm-31x24in) s.i. 8-Apr-4 Dorotheum, Vienna #168/R est:3200-3500

Works on paper

£493 $853 €700 View of Goisern (39x27cm-15x11in) s.d.1903 W/C. 10-Dec-3 Dorotheum, Vienna #156/R

£503 $926 €750 Old doorway with vines (30x18cm-12x7in) s.d.1899 W/C. 26-Mar-4 Dorotheum, Vienna #311/R

£805 $1482 €1200 Budapest bridge (29x40cm-11x16in) s. W/C. 26-Mar-4 Dorotheum, Vienna #259/R

PETROVSKY, Ivan (1913-) Hungarian

£1012 $1720 €1478 Figures (64x93cm-25x37in) s. cardboard. 23-Nov-3 Subastas Odalys, Caracas #160/R

£1290 $2000 €1883 Untitled (65x81cm-26x32in) s. 3-Nov-2 Subastas Odalys, Caracas #43/R

PETROVSUIE, Vasili (19/20th C) ?

£1267 $2268 €1850 Young woman with red hair surrounded by white lilies (60x42cm-24x17in) s.i.d.1898. 10-May-4 Rasmussen, Vejle #412/R est:20000-25000 (D.KR 14000)

PETRUOLO, Salvatore (1857-1946) Italian

£1074 $2008 €1600 Coastal view (22x42cm-9x17in) 26-Feb-4 Cambi, Genoa #435/R

£2254 $3741 €3200 Costiera amalfitana (33x61cm-13x24in) 11-Jun-3 Christie's, Rome #65/R est:2500-3500

£3667 $6637 €5500 Seascape with anglers (84x67cm-33x26in) s. 30-Mar-4 Babuino, Rome #372/R est:4000

£10563 $18275 €15000 Street on the Amalfi coast (56x95cm-22x37in) s. prov.lit. 11-Dec-3 Christie's, Rome #164/R est:15000-20000

Works on paper

£315 $526 €450 Seascape with boats (19x12cm-7x5in) s.i.d.1908 W/C. 24-Jun-3 Finarte Semenzato, Rome #60

£1972 $3411 €2800 Coastal landscape (64x49cm-25x19in) s.d.1940 W/C. 10-Dec-3 Finarte Semenzato, Rome #164/R est:3000-4000

PETRUS, Marco (1960-) Italian

£3873 $6778 €5500 Melegnano (80x120cm-31x47in) s.d.1993 board exhib. 16-Dec-3 Finarte Semenzato, Milan #254/R est:3300-3700

PETRY, Victor (1903-) American

Works on paper

£447 $800 €653 Laundry day (38x56cm-15x22in) s. W/C. 14-May-4 Skinner, Boston #196/R

PETRYKOWSKI, Janusz (1940-2004) Polish

£424 $767 €636 Ariel (130x160cm-51x63in) s.d.1999. 4-Apr-4 Agra, Warsaw #78/R (P.Z 3000)

PETTENKOFEN, August von (1822-1889) Austrian

£317 $548 €450 Homecoming farmer with hay wagon (13x20cm-5x8in) s. panel. 10-Dec-3 Hugo Ruef, Munich #2472/R

£993 $1658 €1400 Kiss (27x21cm-11x8in) s. panel. 14-Oct-3 Vanderkindere, Brussels #63

£1773 $2961 €2500 Hungarian market (16x31cm-6x12in) s. panel. 17-Oct-3 Berlinghof, Heidelberg #1088/R est:2000

£1986 $3316 €2800 Horse market (16x31cm-6x12in) s. panel. 17-Oct-3 Berlinghof, Heidelberg #1087/R est:2000

£3020 $5346 €4500 Girl (26x16cm-10x6in) panel prov. 28-Apr-4 Wiener Kunst Auktionen, Vienna #59/R est:4500-10000

£12081 $21383 €18000 Horse market (8x16cm-3x6in) s. panel prov. 28-Apr-4 Wiener Kunst Auktionen, Vienna #58/R est:15000-30000

£13423 $24027 €20000 Gypsy girl with child (19x28cm-7x11in) panel exhib. 27-May-4 Dorotheum, Vienna #191/R est:6000-7000

£18792 $33262 €28000 Szolnok Market with two oxen feeding from cart (19x24cm-7x9in) s. panel prov.lit.exhib. 28-Apr-4 Wiener Kunst Auktionen, Vienna #57/R est:15000-30000

£36913 $66074 €55000 Hungarian donkeys and cart (42x30cm-17x12in) s.d.58 panel. 27-May-4 Dorotheum, Vienna #213/R est:10000-12000

Works on paper

£2326 $4000 €3396 Hungarian figures (28x18cm-11x7in) s.d.54-59 W/C pair. 3-Dec-3 Doyle, New York #104/R est:2000-3000

PETTENKOFEN, August von (attrib) (1822-1889) Austrian

£1126 $2049 €1700 General farming scene (35x27cm-14x11in) mono. 19-Jun-4 Bergmann, Erlangen #765

£2980 $5454 €4500 Market day in Hungarian village (18x27cm-7x11in) s. bears i. verso panel. 8-Apr-4 Dorotheum, Vienna #209/R est:4500-5000

Works on paper

£733 $1313 €1100 Portraits of Kaiser Franz Joseph and his wife Elisabeth of Austria (39x33cm-15x13in) mono.d.1857 and Juni 860 W/C over pencil board oval two. 13-May-4 Bassenge, Berlin #5628/R

PETTER, Franz Xaver (1791-1866) Austrian

£4698 $8315 €7000 Vase of flowers on ledge with peaches and fly (38x31cm-15x12in) board. 2-May-4 Finarte, Venice #3/R est:6000-7000

£25000 $45500 €36500 Still life with roses, tulips and poppy (88x68cm-35x27in) panel prov.exhib. 15-Jun-4 Sotheby's, London #24/R est:20000-30000

£31250 $53125 €45000 Still life (82x61cm-32x24in) s.d.1816 panel. 28-Oct-3 Wiener Kunst Auktionen, Vienna #23/R est:35000-100000

PETTER, Franz Xaver (attrib) (1791-1866) Austrian

£1200 $2064 €1752 Grapes and peaches in a basket on a ledge (20x26cm-8x10in) panel. 4-Dec-3 Christie's, Kensington #84/R est:1500-2000

PETTER, Theodor (1822-1872) Austrian

£2013 $3604 €3000 Bunch of alpine flowers with edelweiss and alpine roses (70x55cm-28x22in) s. 27-May-4 Dorotheum, Vienna #99/R est:3200-3600

PETTERSEN, Arvid (1943-) Norwegian

Works on paper

£1319 $2334 €1926 Precious Mash, Lapis Lazult (200x89cm-79x35in) s. verso mixed media verso canvas prov. 27-Apr-4 AB Stockholms Auktionsverk #1082/R est:20000-25000 (S.KR 18000)

£3021 $5136 €4411 Corridor (250x200cm-98x79in) init.d.88 mixed media canvas exhib.lit. 5-Nov-3 AB Stockholms Auktionsverk #986/R est:25000-30000 (S.KR 40000)

PETTERSSON, Johan (1957-) Swedish

£440 $778 €642 SEL - composition (120x100cm-47x39in) s.d.90. 27-Apr-4 AB Stockholms Auktionsverk #992/R (S.KR 6000)

PETTERSSON, Jonas (1887-1952) Finnish

£465 $777 €679 Self-portrait (59x51cm-23x20in) s. 12-Oct-3 Uppsala Auktionskammare, Uppsala #545 (S.KR 6000)

PETTIBON, Raymond (1957-) American

Works on paper

£1500 $2760 €2190 Untitled (35x28cm-14x11in) s.d.1989 verso ink prov. 25-Jun-4 Christie's, London #244/R est:1500-2000

£2353 $4000 €3435 Untitled - vavoom (61x46cm-24x18in) s.d.1988 ink. 9-Nov-3 Wright, Chicago #459 est:1500-2000

£3000 $5460 €4380 What's left for the girl (35x28cm-14x11in) ink. 4-Feb-4 Sotheby's, Olympia #2/R est:1500-2000

£3846 $7000 €5615 Untitled (56x43cm-22x17in) ink wash two prov. 29-Jun-4 Sotheby's, New York #625/R est:3000-4000

£10615 $19000 €15498 Untitled, the first artist's (71x49cm-28x19in) ink col pencil W/C prov. 12-May-4 Christie's, Rockefeller NY #335/R est:12000-18000

£15642	$28000	€22837	Untitled (31x23cm-12x9in) s.d.verso pen ink exec.1984-2000 five prov.exhib. 14-May-4 Phillips, New York #111/R est:10000-15000
£32000	$58880	€46720	Untitled. ink W/C ten prov.lit. 24-Jun-4 Sotheby's, London #133/R est:20000-30000

PETTIBONE, Richard (1938-) American

£2267	$4171	€3400	Stella (6x5cm-2x2in) s.d. verso. 11-Jun-4 Hauswedell & Nolte, Hamburg #1472/R est:1500
£2400	$4416	€3600	Ingres,, Princess of Bruglie - 1853, right shoulder and face (9x9cm-4x4in) s.i.d. verso. 11-Jun-4 Hauswedell & Nolte, Hamburg #1474/R est:2500
£2533	$4661	€3800	Stella (6x6cm-2x2in) s.d. verso. 11-Jun-4 Hauswedell & Nolte, Hamburg #1471/R est:1500
£2800	$5152	€4200	Stella (6x6cm-2x2in) s.d. verso. 11-Jun-4 Hauswedell & Nolte, Hamburg #1473/R est:1500
£2933	$5397	€4400	Stella (6x6cm-2x2in) s.d. 11-Jun-4 Hauswedell & Nolte, Hamburg #1470/R est:1500
£3147	$5255	€4500	Andy Warhol, lavender disaster 1964 (10x10cm-4x4in) s.i.d.1969 verso. 11-Oct-3 De Vuyst, Lokeren #485/R est:5000-6000
£3200	$5824	€4672	Andy Warhol - Two Jackies (7x12cm-3x5in) s.i.d.1996 acrylic silkscreen inks. 4-Feb-4 Sotheby's, Olympia #146/R est:1500-2000
£3497	$5839	€5000	Train wreck and large stella (24x49cm-9x19in) s.i.verso. 11-Oct-3 De Vuyst, Lokeren #486/R est:5000-6000
£5245	$8759	€7500	Andy Warhol, Campbell's tomato soup can (13x10cm-5x4in) s.i.d.1968 verso. 11-Oct-3 De Vuyst, Lokeren #482/R est:7000-7500
£5245	$8759	€7500	Andy Warhol, Jackie 1964 (13x20cm-5x8in) s.i.d.1968 verso. 11-Oct-3 De Vuyst, Lokeren #483/R est:5000-6000
£5282	$9243	€7500	Train wreck and large Stella (24x29cm-9x11in) s.i.verso acrylic ink serigraph canvas. 18-Dec-3 Cornette de St.Cyr, Paris #130/R est:8000-12000
£5282	$9137	€7500	Andy Warhol, Elvis (20x10cm-8x4in) s.i.verso. 13-Dec-3 De Vuyst, Lokeren #502/R est:5000-7000
£5333	$9600	€8000	Andy Warhol, lavender disaster (10x10cm-4x4in) s.i.d.1969 acrylic ink. 24-Apr-4 Cornette de St.Cyr, Paris #677/R est:10000-12000
£5369	$9933	€8000	Andy Warhol, lavender disaster (13x17cm-5x7in) s.i.d.1969 verso. 13-Mar-4 De Vuyst, Lokeren #489/R est:7000-8000
£6145	$11000	€8972	Jasper Johns. Tennyson (26x16cm-10x6in) s.i.d.1965 prov. 13-May-4 Sotheby's, New York #143/R est:6000-8000
£6704	$12000	€9788	Mao (9x9cm-4x4in) s.d.1975 overlap acrylic silkscreen inks prov.exhib. 13-May-4 Sotheby's, New York #144/R est:6000-8000
£8383	$14000	€12239	After Johns, lightbulb, red (15x21cm-6x8in) s.d.1967 stretcher acrylic silkscreen ink prov.exhib. 13-Nov-3 Sotheby's, New York #196/R est:5000-7000
£8667	$15773	€13000	Wandy Warhol's soup can (13x10cm-5x4in) s.i.d.1969 acrylic ink serigraph on canvas prov. 29-Jun-4 Cornette de St.Cyr, Paris #114/R est:10000-12000
£10180	$17000	€14863	After Warhol, Liz (26x21cm-10x8in) s.d.1965 verso acrylic silkscreen ink prov.exhib. 13-Nov-3 Sotheby's, New York #197/R est:10000-15000
£10333	$18807	€15500	Frank Stella Yard II (8x23cm-3x9in) s.i.d.1968 acrylic prov. 29-Jun-4 Cornette de St.Cyr, Paris #115/R est:7000-8000
£12570	$22500	€18352	Blue Marilyn (6x5cm-2x2in) init.d.73 stretcher acrylic silkscreen inks prov.exhib. 13-May-4 Sotheby's, New York #145/R est:6000-8000
Prints			
£7667	$14107	€11500	Roy Lichtenstein's Rouen Cathedral (20x13cm-8x5in) s.i.d. verso col serigraph canvas. 11-Jun-4 Hauswedell & Nolte, Hamburg #1476/R est:3000
£14667	$26987	€22000	Andy Warhol's Mona Lisa (16x16cm-6x6in) s.i.d. col serigraph canvas. 11-Jun-4 Hauswedell & Nolte, Hamburg #1475/R est:2500
Sculpture			
£2800	$5152	€4200	Self portrait (7x11x4cm-3x4x2in) s.i.d. verso objects in box. 11-Jun-4 Hauswedell & Nolte, Hamburg #1469/R est:2500
£3784	$7000	€5525	Untitled - Periplum (231x47x24cm-91x19x9in) init.d.1995 painted wood two parts exec 1995. 12-Feb-4 Sotheby's, New York #236/R est:3000-4000
£4267	$7851	€6400	Splash (14x19x5cm-6x7x2in) s.d. verso objects in box. 11-Jun-4 Hauswedell & Nolte, Hamburg #1468/R est:3000
Works on paper			
£1453	$2600	€2121	Frame drawing number 8 (10x10cm-4x4in) s.d.1974 pencil ragboard prov. 16-May-4 Wright, Chicago #381/R est:1000-1500

PETTIE, John (1839-1893) British

£1500	$2355	€2175	Soldier polishing his breastplate (46x35cm-18x14in) s. 27-Aug-3 Sotheby's, London #925/R est:1500-2000

PETTINGALE, W E (19/20th C) British

£270	$424	€394	Litteover Hollow, with shepherd and flock (39x30cm-15x12in) s. 10-Dec-2 Bamfords, Derby #748

PETTINGALE, William (19/20th C) British

£260	$481	€380	Country river landscape with figures in the foreground (34x24cm-13x9in) s. 10-Feb-4 Bonhams, Knightsbridge #21

PETTIT, Grace Genoi (20th C) American

£2057	$3250	€3003	Farm scene with cows (51x71cm-20x28in) s.d.1933 canvas on board. 7-Sep-3 Treadway Gallery, Cincinnati #743/R est:600-800

PETTITT, Charles (19th C) British

£7000	$12880	€10220	Head of Derwntwater and Borrowdale from the Raven Crag near Barrow (38x61cm-15x24in) s. i.verso prov. 26-Mar-4 Sotheby's, London #63/R est:6000-8000

PETTITT, Edwin Alfred (1840-1912) British

£800	$1336	€1168	Cwm Dyli stream Snowdon, after a storm (91x102cm-36x40in) s.d.1879 i.verso. 21-Oct-3 Peter Francis, Wales #29

PETTITT, George (1831-1863) British

£5800	$10382	€8468	Children and their dogs outside a stone cottage, lake district hills beyond (140x99cm-55x39in) s.d.1860. 6-Jan-4 Gildings, Market Harborough #407/R est:4000-6000

PETTITT, Wilfred Stanley (1904-1978) British

£470	$808	€686	Willow and marsh (25x33cm-10x13in) s. 5-Dec-3 Keys, Aylsham #570
Works on paper			
£300	$543	€438	Cattle grazing and resting in Norfolk landscape (33x43cm-13x17in) s. gouache. 16-Apr-4 Keys, Aylsham #570/R

PETTORUTI, Emilio (1892-1971) Argentinian

Prints			
£1676	$3000	€2447	Light flying high (46x37cm-18x15in) s. num.48/125 lithograph. 4-May-4 Arroyo, Buenos Aires #103/R est:2400
Works on paper			
£2762	$5000	€4033	Arlequins (16x16cm-6x6in) ink. 30-Mar-4 Arroyo, Buenos Aires #44
£3094	$5600	€4517	Head of Arlequin (13x11cm-5x4in) ink. 30-Mar-4 Arroyo, Buenos Aires #45

PETTRICH, Ferdinand Friedrich August (1798-1872) German

Sculpture			
£4335	$7500	€6329	Portrait of Andrew Jackson (61cm-24in) marble. 13-Dec-3 Weschler, Washington #537 est:10000-15000

PETTS, John (?) British

£600	$1074	€876	Red Structure (58x41cm-23x16in) s.d.58 board exhib. 16-Mar-4 Bonhams, Knightsbridge #143
Works on paper			
£330	$548	€482	Pendine caves, coastal study (38x48cm-15x19in) s. mixed media. 2-Oct-3 Biddle & Webb, Birmingham #702

PETTY, George (1894-1975) American

Works on paper			
£4698	$8409	€7000	Transparency (42x26cm-17x10in) s. gouache crayon ink painted c.1950 lit. 27-May-4 Sotheby's, Paris #122/R est:5000-7000

PETUEL, Rudolf (1870-1937) German

£993	$1808	€1500	Female nude, rear view (40x16cm-16x6in) s. panel. 16-Jun-4 Hugo Ruef, Munich #1059/R est:800

PETYARRE, Anna (20th C) Australian

£332	$554	€498	Campsite gathering (54x91cm-21x36in) i. acrylic. 27-Oct-3 Goodman, Sydney #41/R (A.D 800)

PETYARRE, Gloria (1945-) Australian

Works on paper			
£511	$883	€746	Grass seed (60x90cm-24x35in) i.verso synthetic polymer paint linen oval. 10-Dec-3 Shapiro, Sydney #162/R (A.D 1200)
£1875	$3506	€2813	Mountain devil awelye (150x91cm-59x36in) bears name.verso synthetic polymer paint canvas prov. 26-Jul-4 Sotheby's, Melbourne #242/R est:5000-7000 (A.D 4800)
£1953	$3652	€2930	Untitled (152x91cm-60x36in) bears name.verso synthetic polymer paint canvas prov. 26-Jul-4 Sotheby's, Melbourne #241/R est:5000-7000 (A.D 5000)

PETYARRE, Gloria Tamerre (1940-) Australian

£1633	$3004	€2384	Bush medicine (122x91cm-48x36in) acrylic linen prov. 29-Mar-4 Goodman, Sydney #169/R est:4000-6000 (A.D 4000)
£4668	$7796	€7002	Bush medicine (180x123cm-71x48in) i.verso acrylic. 27-Oct-3 Goodman, Sydney #51/R est:8000-10000 (A.D 11250)
Works on paper			
£1020	$1825	€1489	Mountain Devil Lizard Dreaming (81x124cm-32x49in) synthetic polymer paint canvas exec 1990. 25-May-4 Lawson Menzies, Sydney #227/R est:6000-8000 (A.D 2600)
£1680	$3141	€2520	Untitled (90x75cm-35x30in) i.verso synthetic polymer canvas exec. 2001 prov. 21-Jul-4 Shapiro, Sydney #35/R est:3000-5000 (A.D 4300)
£1882	$3369	€2748	Bush medicine leaves (91x122cm-36x48in) synthetic polymer paint linen exec 1999. 25-May-4 Lawson Menzies, Sydney #218/R est:7000-9000 (A.D 4800)
£2128	$3617	€3107	Mountain devil dreaming (123x120cm-48x47in) with sig.i. verso synthetic polymer paint canvas prov. 25-Nov-3 Christie's, Melbourne #115/R est:5000-6000 (A.D 5000)
£2344	$4383	€3516	Bush medicine (122x92cm-48x36in) s.verso synthetic polymer linen exec. 2003 prov. 21-Jul-4 Shapiro, Sydney #56/R est:4000-6000 (A.D 6000)
£3125	$5844	€4688	Bush medicine (214x115cm-84x45in) i. synthetic polymer exec. 2002 prov. 21-Jul-4 Shapiro, Sydney #37/R est:5000-7000 (A.D 8000)
£11328	$21184	€16992	Untitled, leaves (185x420cm-73x165in) bears name.i.d.November 1998 synthetic polymer paint canvas prov. 26-Jul-4 Sotheby's, Melbourne #243/R est:30000-40000 (A.D 29000)

PETYARRE, June Bird (20th C) Australian

Works on paper			
£227	$400	€331	Untitled (91x61cm-36x24in) bears artist name d.1990 verso synthetic polymer linen board. 22-May-4 Selkirks, St. Louis #795/R

PETYARRE, Kathleen (c.1930-) Australian

Works on paper			
£2114	$3340	€3065	Artist's country (122x96cm-48x38in) i.verso synthetic polymer paint linen exec.c.1997 prov. 28-Jul-3 Sotheby's, Paddington #365/R est:5000-7000 (A.D 5200)
£2539	$4748	€3809	Untitled (122x92cm-48x36in) synthetic polymer paint linen prov. 26-Jul-4 Sotheby's, Melbourne #303/R est:8000-12000 (A.D 6500)

£2553	$4417	€3727	Bush seeds (120x90cm-47x35in) i.verso synthetic polymer paint linen prov. 10-Dec-3 Shapiro, Sydney #196 est:7000-9000 (A.D 6000)
£2734	$5113	€4101	Thorny devil dreaming (90x60cm-35x24in) bears name.verso synthetic polymer paint linen prov. 26-Jul-4 Sotheby's, Melbourne #472/R est:8000-12000 (A.D 7000)
£3125	$5844	€4688	Untitled (119x90cm-47x35in) synthetic polymer paint linen prov. 26-Jul-4 Sotheby's, Melbourne #470/R est:8000-12000 (A.D 8000)
£3125	$5844	€4688	Untitled (122x92cm-48x36in) bears name.verso synthetic polymer paint linen prov. 26-Jul-4 Sotheby's, Melbourne #476/R est:8000-12000 (A.D 8000)
£3223	$6026	€4835	Atnangkere, my country (92x92cm-36x36in) bears name.verso synthetic polymer paint linen prov. 26-Jul-4 Sotheby's, Melbourne #473/R est:10000-15000 (A.D 8250)
£5691	$8992	€8252	Artist's country (183x122cm-72x48in) i.verso synthetic polymer paint linen prov. 28-Jul-3 Sotheby's, Paddington #363/R est:6000-8000 (A.D 14000)
£8943	$14130	€12967	Atnangkere (122x91cm-48x36in) i.verso synthetic polymer paint linen prov. 28-Jul-3 Sotheby's, Paddington #364/R est:5000-7000 (A.D 22000)
£10938	$20453	€16407	Mountain devil lizard (137x137cm-54x54in) bears name.verso synthetic polymer paint linen prov. 26-Jul-4 Sotheby's, Melbourne #184/R est:18000-25000 (A.D 28000)
£13281	$24836	€19922	My country, hailstorm, bush seeds (122x153cm-48x60in) synthetic polymer paint linen prov.exhib. 26-Jul-4 Sotheby's, Melbourne #112/R est:20000-30000 (A.D 34000)
£14634	$23122	€21219	Atnangkere (91x91cm-36x36in) i.verso synthetic polymer paint linen prov. 28-Jul-3 Sotheby's, Paddington #361/R est:6000-8000 (A.D 36000)

PETYARRE, Nancy Kunoth (c.1938-) Australian

£1592	$2929	€2324	Mountain devil (115x193cm-45x76in) acrylic linen prov. 29-Mar-4 Goodman, Sydney #45/R est:4000-6000 (A.D 3900)

PETYARRE, Pansy (20th C) Australian

£247	$447	€361	Untitled (149x120cm-59x47in) acrylic. 30-Mar-4 Lawson Menzies, Sydney #273 (A.D 600)

PETZHOLDT, Fritz (1805-1838) Danish

£4253	$7358	€6209	Landscape from Malcesine at Lake Garda (33x52cm-13x20in) prov. 9-Dec-3 Rasmussen, Copenhagen #1245/R est:50000 (D.KR 45000)
£7089	$12264	€10350	Italian mountain landscape (39x49cm-15x19in) exhib.prov. 9-Dec-3 Rasmussen, Copenhagen #1250/R est:75000-100000 (D.KR 75000)

PEUCKER, Leopold (attrib) (fl.1790-1793) Czechoslovakian

Works on paper

£590	$962	€850	Idyllic Roman landscape with ruins (41x63cm-16x25in) W/C. 26-Sep-3 Bolland & Marotz, Bremen #475/R

PEURSE, Adam van (1814-?) Dutch

£1329	$2219	€1900	Chemin de campagne avec paysans et voyageurs (43x51cm-17x20in) s.d.1837. 7-Oct-3 Palais de Beaux Arts, Brussels #593 est:1700-2200

PEVERELLI, Cesare (1922-2000) Italian

£276	$461	€400	Paradisiens (24x35cm-9x14in) s. card. 17-Nov-3 Sant Agostino, Torino #72/R
£379	$633	€550	Tale in three parts (32x23cm-13x9in) s.i.d.1970 cardboard on canvas. 17-Nov-3 Sant Agostino, Torino #50/R
£537	$993	€800	Rituel, la tentation (100x81cm-39x32in) s. s.i.d.1989-90 verso prov. 13-Mar-4 De Vuyst, Lokeren #259
£800	$1472	€1200	Cane field (81x100cm-32x39in) s. painted 1970 prov. 8-Jun-4 Finarte Semenzato, Milan #214/R
£839	$1401	€1200	Champs de cannes (100x81cm-39x32in) s.i.d.1968 acrylic prov. 29-Jun-3 Versailles Encheres #220/R
£1000	$1800	€1500	Untitled (115x89cm-45x35in) s.verso painted 1960 exhib. 22-Apr-4 Finarte Semenzato, Rome #237/R est:3000-4000
£1000	$1840	€1500	Japanese (100x69cm-39x27in) 8-Jun-4 Finarte Semenzato, Milan #215/R est:1500-2000
£1034	$1728	€1500	Certainly the insect is the fairy tales pest (60x80cm-24x31in) painted 1954-55. 14-Nov-3 Farsetti, Prato #264 est:500-800
£1275	$2283	€1900	Untitled (50x70cm-20x28in) painted 1950 prov.exhib. 25-May-4 Sotheby's, Milan #84/R est:1500
£1333	$2453	€2000	Being (70x100cm-28x39in) painted 1956 prov. 8-Jun-4 Finarte Semenzato, Milan #213/R est:2000-2500
£1818	$3091	€2600	Untitled (70x100cm-28x39in) s.verso painted c.1950 exhib. 25-Nov-3 Sotheby's, Milan #51/R est:1500-2000

Works on paper

£563	$986	€800	Studio (74x51cm-29x20in) s.d.64 mixed media board. 16-Dec-3 Finarte Semenzato, Milan #327

PEVERNAGIE, Erik (1939-) Belgian

£2778	$4417	€4000	Stay with us, don't go away (100x80cm-39x31in) s. 15-Sep-3 Horta, Bruxelles #93 est:2500-3500
£3741	$6810	€5500	Not on the short list (100x80cm-39x31in) s. s.i.on stretcher oil sand. 3-Feb-4 Christie's, Amsterdam #646/R est:2000-3000
£3819	$6378	€5500	From behind the coulisse (100x80cm-39x31in) s.verso oil mixed media. 21-Oct-3 Campo & Campo, Antwerp #248/R est:5000-6000
£3893	$7162	€5800	She only needed a light (73x92cm-29x36in) i. stretcher acrylic sand metal prov. 26-Mar-4 Ketterer, Hamburg #593/R est:3000-3500
£3911	$7000	€5710	Just for a moment (60x46cm-24x18in) s. i.verso oil sand metal filing on canvas. 6-May-4 Doyle, New York #93/R est:1500-2500
£4167	$6958	€6000	Waiting for an email from Alaska (100x80cm-39x31in) s. 21-Oct-3 Campo, Vlaamse Kaai #521/R est:5000-6000
£4605	$8474	€7000	Fear of the white page (100x80cm-39x31in) s. s.i. on stretcher oil mixed media. 22-Jun-4 Christie's, Amsterdam #375/R est:1500-2000

Works on paper

£3356	$6208	€5000	Drunken sailor (10x80cm-4x31in) s. mixed media canvas. 13-Mar-4 De Vuyst, Lokeren #260/R est:5000-6000
£3500	$5950	€5110	Empty mirror (99x80cm-39x31in) s.i. mixed media canvas. 18-Nov-3 Bonhams, Knightsbridge #165/R est:2000-3000

PEVERNAGIE, Louis (1904-1970) Belgian

£1678	$2803	€2400	Nude (54x40cm-21x16in) s. paper. 11-Oct-3 De Vuyst, Lokeren #291/R est:2000-2200

PEVETZ, Georg (1893-1971) Austrian

£280	$476	€400	Children from Brittany (60x50cm-24x20in) s.d.1973 board. 19-Nov-3 Dorotheum, Klagenfurt #24
£559	$951	€800	Seated female nude (60x50cm-24x20in) s. board. 19-Nov-3 Dorotheum, Klagenfurt #23/R
£694	$1132	€1000	Gloriette in Schonbrunn (54x68cm-21x27in) s.i. masonite. 23-Sep-3 Wiener Kunst Auktionen, Vienna #130/R
£1133	$2040	€1700	Faakersee - swimming pool (55x78cm-22x31in) s.d.s.d.1933/1932. 21-Apr-4 Dorotheum, Vienna #108/R est:2000-3000

PEVSNER, Antoine (1886-1962) Russian

Works on paper

£486	$812	€700	Composition (23x26cm-9x10in) s. graphite. 25-Oct-3 Cornette de St.Cyr, Paris #778
£1119	$1902	€1600	Composition (31x21cm-12x8in) chl prov. 23-Nov-3 Cornette de St.Cyr, Paris #276/R est:200-300

PEYER, Heinrich (19th C) Austrian

£2098	$3566	€3000	Donau river shore with view of Pressburg (49x62cm-19x24in) s. 20-Nov-3 Dorotheum, Salzburg #128/R est:4000-5000

PEYNET, Raymond (1908-1998) French

Works on paper

£1134	$2040	€1700	Les amoureux au soleil (41x31cm-16x12in) s.d.57 crayon htd gouache. 26-Apr-4 Tajan, Paris #47 est:100-120

PEYNOT, Émile Edmond (1850-1932) French

Sculpture

£2000	$3660	€3000	L'Angelus (72cm-28in) s. golden brown pat bronze. 6-Jun-4 Anaf, Lyon #306/R est:3000-3200
£8276	$15310	€12000	Le marchand Tunisien (56cm-22in) i. col pat bronze. 16-Feb-4 Horta, Bruxelles #125/R est:11000-13000

PEYRAUD, Frank Charles (1858-1948) American

£467	$850	€682	Wooded landscape (41x51cm-16x20in) s.i.d.36 masonite. 15-Jun-4 John Moran, Pasadena #69
£1189	$2200	€1736	Western landscape (61x51cm-24x20in) s. 12-Mar-4 Jackson's, Cedar Falls #771/R est:1500-2000
£1203	$1900	€1756	Cornstalks (18x28cm-7x11in) s.d.1894 board. 7-Sep-3 Treadway Gallery, Cincinnati #614/R est:1000-1500
£2180	$3750	€3183	Autumn haystacks (51x66cm-20x26in) s. painted c.1910. 7-Dec-3 Treadway Gallery, Cincinnati #629/R est:2500-3500

PEYRE, Raphael (1872-1949) French

Sculpture

£4000	$6520	€5840	Three playful putti (55cm-22in) gold pat bronze green brown pat bronze base. 28-Sep-3 Wilkinson, Doncaster #43/R

PEYRISSAC, Jean (1895-1974) French

Works on paper

£270	$484	€400	Nu au sofa (27x38cm-11x15in) s. chl pastel. 10-May-4 Giraudeau, Tours #62
£490	$832	€700	Etude pour une sculpture (23x32cm-9x13in) s. chl prov. 23-Nov-3 Cornette de St.Cyr, Paris #275/R
£664	$1129	€950	Composition surrealiste (15x22cm-6x9in) gouache prov. 23-Nov-3 Cornette de St.Cyr, Paris #273
£769	$1308	€1100	Le gitan (46x31cm-18x12in) s.i. Indian ink. 23-Nov-3 Cornette de St.Cyr, Paris #274/R
£1469	$2497	€2100	Personnage surrealiste (48x31cm-19x12in) s. ink gouache exec.c.1930 prov. 23-Nov-3 Cornette de St.Cyr, Paris #272/R est:400-500

PEYRON, Jean François Pierre (1744-1814) French

Works on paper

£1020	$1827	€1500	Un groupe de figures se lamentant (18x26cm-7x10in) pen brown ink grey wash. 18-Mar-4 Christie's, Paris #272/R est:1500-2000

PEYRON, Jean François Pierre (attrib) (1744-1814) French

Works on paper

£300	$537	€450	Allegorie de l'Amour (31x20cm-12x8in) i. graphite. 11-May-4 Christie's, Paris #133/R

PEYRONNET, Dominique Paul (1872-1943) French

£2139	$4000	€3123	Nature morte avec ananas et oranges (46x55cm-18x22in) s. st.sig.verso. 25-Feb-4 Christie's, Rockefeller NY #7/R
£2941	$5500	€4294	Nature morte avec langouste (46x55cm-18x22in) s. 25-Feb-4 Christie's, Rockefeller NY #8/R est:4000-6000
£8556	$16000	€12492	Falaise (54x81cm-21x32in) s. exhib. 25-Feb-4 Christie's, Rockefeller NY #6/R est:10000-15000

PEYROTTE, Alexis (1699-1769) French

Works on paper

£458	$801	€650	Une mere assise avec son enfant (9x9cm-4x4in) i. black chk pen black ink prov. 17-Dec-3 Christie's, Paris #53/R

£2381 $4262 €3500 Deux singeries, la partie de cartes, et les politiques (30x39cm-12x15in) i. gouache pair. 18-Mar-4 Christie's, Paris #250/R est:2500-3500

PEYTON, Bertha S Menzler (1871-1950) American
£355 $650 €518 Desert landscape (20x25cm-8x10in) s. canvas on board painted c.1920. 5-Jun-4 Treadway Gallery, Cincinnati #657/R
£801 $1450 €1169 White flowers in blue vase (46x61cm-18x24in) s. 16-Apr-4 James Julia, Fairfield #867/R est:1800-2400

PEYTON, Elizabeth (1965-) American
£53892 $90000 €78682 Jarvis and Liam smoking (30x23cm-12x9in) s.i.d.1997 d.February 1997 overlap prov.exhib.lit. 13-Nov-3 Sotheby's, New York #448/R est:40000-60000
Works on paper
£4000 $7360 €5840 Ian Brown, stone roses (33x28cm-13x11in) s.i.d.1995 verso ink pencil prov. 25-Jun-4 Christie's, London #243/R est:3000-4000
£5215 $8500 €7614 Queen Elizabeth aged 16, after Benton (30x23cm-12x9in) s.i.d.1997 verso chl prov.exhib. 23-Sep-3 Christie's, Rockefeller NY #167/R est:4000-6000
£19553 $35000 €28547 Ludwig II dressed in Louis XIV costume (46x30cm-18x12in) s.i.d.1993 verso ink prov. 12-May-4 Christie's, Rockefeller NY #349/R est:10000-15000

PEZ, Aime (1808-1849) Belgian
£5944 $9927 €8500 Serenite familiale (50x60cm-20x24in) s.d.1839 panel. 13-Oct-3 Horta, Bruxelles #120/R est:8500-10000
£12162 $22986 €18000 L'anniversaire de mariage (70x83cm-28x33in) s.d.1841 panel. 17-Feb-4 Vanderkindere, Brussels #145/R est:15000-20000

PEZANT, Aymar (1846-1916) French
£1613 $3000 €2355 The cattle herd (43x54cm-17x21in) s. 5-Mar-4 Skinner, Boston #239/R est:1500-3000
£2353 $4000 €3435 Cows in a landscape (66x81cm-26x32in) s. 21-Nov-3 Eldred, East Dennis #804/R est:1500-1800

PEZOLT, Georg (1810-1878) Austrian
£2621 $4377 €3800 Sant Antonio, Padua (231x178cm-91x70in) s. lit. 12-Jul-3 Bergmann, Erlangen #650/R est:3800

PEZOUS, Jean (1815-1885) French
£552 $1021 €800 Le bivouac (14x27cm-6x11in) s.d.1850 panel. 11-Feb-4 Beaussant & Lefèvre, Paris #201/R

PEZZEY, August (snr) (1847-1915) Austrian
£323 $579 €472 Portrait of Michael Waldner (20x15cm-8x6in) s.d.1901 i. verso panel. 12-May-4 Dobiaschofsky, Bern #867/R (S.FR 750)

PEZZEY, Hans (1871-?) Austrian
£2448 $4210 €3500 Flower market in Zurich (46x50cm-18x20in) s.d.1915 i.verso board. 3-Dec-3 Neumeister, Munich #701/R est:2000

PEZZO, Lucio del (1933-) Italian
£304 $499 €420 Untitled (21x23cm-8x9in) s.d.1993 tempera cardboard. 29-May-3 Galleria Pace, Milan #2/R
£336 $621 €500 Green, pink and blue (24x18cm-9x7in) s.d.1980 acrylic collage board. 11-Mar-4 Galleria Pace, Milan #34/R
£433 $797 €650 Losange (50x66cm-20x26in) s.d.1983 acrylic collage. 10-Jun-4 Galleria Pace, Milan #4/R
£699 $1189 €1000 Alchimist (38x57cm-15x22in) s.i.d.1985 tempera W/C collage card. 24-Nov-3 Christie's, Milan #49/R
£1087 $1783 €1500 Composition (50x40cm-20x16in) s.d.1968 painted wood. 27-May-3 Sotheby's, Milan #56/R est:1000
£2069 $3310 €3000 Rocky pattern (70x100cm-28x39in) s. acrylic sand collage canvas on wood. 13-Mar-3 Galleria Pace, Milan #35/R est:3500-4500
£2349 $4205 €3500 Golden obelisk (75x60cm-30x24in) s.i.verso acrylic collge sand gold leaf board. 28-May-4 Farsetti, Prato #235/R est:3200-3400
£2416 $4470 €3600 Hand (70x100cm-28x39in) s. s.i.verso acrylic collage panel. 11-Mar-4 Galleria Pace, Milan #107/R est:4200-5200
£2416 $4325 €3600 Xango (130x110cm-51x43in) s. s.i.verso collage acrylic brass pigment on wood. 30-May-4 Meeting Art, Vercelli #30 est:3000
£8042 $13671 €11500 Great floor (202x136cm-80x54in) s. painted wood acrylic canvas on board prov. 25-Nov-3 Sotheby's, Milan #252/R est:6000-8000
Sculpture
£2400 $4416 €3600 Ten elements (72x52x7cm-28x20x3in) s. mixed media masonite exec.1983. 12-Jun-4 Meeting Art, Vercelli #832/R est:2500
£3041 $5351 €4500 Untitled (53x65x12cm-21x26x5in) s.d.61 s.d.verso painted wood mixed media board prov. 24-May-4 Christie's, Milan #90/R est:3000-4000
£15436 $27631 €23000 Venetian red (133x263cm-52x104in) s.d.1965 s.i.d.verso painted wood. 25-May-4 Sotheby's, Milan #200/R est:18000-25000
Works on paper
£242 $447 €360 Untitled (23x21cm-9x8in) s.d. collage mixed media card. 11-Mar-4 Galleria Pace, Milan #2/R
£267 $491 €400 Untitled (23x21cm-9x8in) s. mixed media collage card. 8-Jun-4 Finarte Semenzato, Milan #115/R
£269 $449 €390 Composition (23x21cm-9x8in) s. mixed media card prov. 13-Nov-3 Galleria Pace, Milan #82/R
£500 $920 €750 Untitled (70x100cm-28x39in) s. s.verso mixed media collage paper on canvas. 12-Jun-4 Meeting Art, Vercelli #679/R
£600 $1104 €900 Star (58x58cm-23x23in) s.i.verso collage acrylic card on panel. 8-Jun-4 Finarte Semenzato, Milan #117/R
£700 $1260 €1050 Six signes (40x26cm-16x10in) s. s.i.d.1972 verso collage gouache lit. 25-Apr-4 Versailles Encheres #184
£839 $1427 €1200 Untitled (37x57cm-15x22in) s. W/C tempera collage. 24-Nov-3 Christie's, Milan #48/R
£1467 $2699 €2200 Red (75x60cm-30x24in) s. s.i.verso mixed media board. 10-Jun-4 Galleria Pace, Milan #22/R est:3300
£1678 $3104 €2500 From the dep (75x60cm-30x24in) s. s.i.verso collage acrylic sand pigment gold leaf enamel board. 13-Mar-4 Meeting Art, Vercelli #376 est:2500
£3380 $5611 €4800 Xango (130x110cm-51x43in) s. s.i.verso collage acrylic gilded brass metallic pigment wood. 14-Jun-3 Meeting Art, Vercelli #356/R est:4000

PFAFF, Judy (1946-) American/British
Works on paper
£1374 $2500 €2006 Loaves and fishes no.9 (125x76cm-49x30in) mixed media adhesive plastics on mylar prov. 29-Jun-4 Sotheby's, New York #597/R est:3000-4000

PFAHLER, Karl Georg (1926-2002) German
£500 $900 €750 Untitled (26x25cm-10x10in) s.d. tempera board. 24-Apr-4 Reiss & Sohn, Konigstein #5823/R
£2587 $4399 €3700 Formative No 139 (24x30cm-9x12in) s.i.d.20.6.61 verso tempera. 27-Nov-3 Lempertz, Koln #338/R est:3000

PFANNSCHMIDT, Ernst (1868-1949) German
£295 $543 €440 Neapolitan altar in a church (61x78cm-24x31in) s.i.d.97 canvas on board. 27-Mar-4 Dannenberg, Berlin #606/R
£989 $1800 €1444 Angels mourning the crucified Christ (15x30cm-6x12in) s.d.1898 board. 19-Jun-4 Jackson's, Cedar Falls #79/R est:1500-2500

PFAU, Conrad (1885-?) German
£455 $759 €650 Still life of roses (49x42cm-19x17in) s. i. verso. 9-Oct-3 Michael Zeller, Lindau #722/R

PFEFFERKORN, Felix Samuel (1945-) German
£851 $1421 €1200 Liberty New York (100x50cm-39x20in) mono. si.d.1976 verso acrylic masonite. 16-Oct-3 Dorotheum, Salzburg #748/R

PFEFFERLE, Erwin (1880-1962) German
£268 $494 €400 River on sunny day (55x71cm-22x28in) s. panel lit. 25-Mar-4 Karlheinz Kaupp, Staufen #2648
£268 $494 €400 Sun on misty valley (56x71cm-22x28in) s. lit. 25-Mar-4 Karlheinz Kaupp, Staufen #2651/R

PFEIFER, Emil (20th C) ?
£474 $849 €692 Female nude (43x28cm-17x11in) s.d.1952 pavatex. 13-May-4 Stuker, Bern #282 (S.FR 1100)

PFEIFFER, Gordon (1899-1983) Canadian
£490 $840 €715 Dull day, near Bay St. Paul (22x27cm-9x11in) panel painted 1929. 2-Dec-3 Joyner Waddington, Toronto #267/R (C.D 1100)
£1867 $3229 €2726 Baie St Paul (29x33cm-11x13in) s.d.34 s.i.d.verso board. 9-Dec-3 Pinneys, Montreal #185 est:600-800 (C.D 4200)
Works on paper
£600 $1098 €876 Lac Ducharme (60x75cm-24x30in) s. painted 1975 prov. 1-Jun-4 Joyner Waddington, Toronto #331/R (C.D 1500)

PFEIFFER, Hans (20th C) ?
£268 $502 €400 Composition (76x57cm-30x22in) mono.d.1930 peinture prov. 29-Feb-4 Versailles Encheres #292

PFEIFFER, Harry R (1874-1960) American
£217 $400 €317 Landscape with green leafy tree (41x51cm-16x20in) s. 9-Jun-4 Alderfer's, Hatfield #448
£272 $480 €397 Luxembourg Gardens (61x51cm-24x20in) s. 3-Jan-4 Outer Cape Auctions, Provincetown #51a/R
£309 $500 €451 By the dock (25x23cm-10x9in) s. board. 31-Jul-3 Eldred, East Dennis #802/R
£2151 $4000 €3140 Spanish house, St Augustine. Distant harbour (60x50cm-24x20in) s. one i.verso two. 5-Mar-4 Skinner, Boston #562/R est:800-1200

PFEIFFER, Henri (1907-1952) German
Works on paper
£378 $642 €552 Composition (46x31cm-18x12in) init.d.29 i.verso W/C. 5-Nov-3 AB Stockholms Auktionsverk #1166/R (S.KR 5000)

PFEIFFER, Paul (1966-) American?
Photographs
£6000 $10020 €8760 Four horsemen of the Apocalypse 4 (150x119cm-59x47in) cibachrome print edition 3 of 6 prov.lit. 22-Oct-3 Christie's, London #155/R est:6000-8000
£6000 $10020 €8760 Four horsemen of the Apocalypse 2 (150x119cm-59x47in) cibachrome print edition 3 of 6 prov.lit. 22-Oct-3 Christie's, London #156/R est:6000-8000
Sculpture
£40000 $72800 €58400 Study for morning after the deluge (14x16x152cm-6x6x60in) s. digital video loop LCD monitor metal armateur prov.lit. 5-Feb-4 Sotheby's, London #48/R est:30000-40000

PFEIFFER, Wilhelm (1822-1891) German
£1892 $3386 €2800 Hunter resting with dog (58x46cm-23x18in) s. lit. 8-May-4 Dawo, Saarbrucken #41/R est:2400
£2819 $5187 €4200 La pause pendant la fenaison (46x70cm-18x28in) s.i. 28-Mar-4 Anaf, Lyon #220/R est:5000-6000

PFEILER, Maximilian (18th C) German
£12849 $23000 €18760 Still life of melons, grapes, peaches and other fruit in landscape (81x121cm-32x48in) 27-May-4 Sotheby's, New York #56/R est:20000-30000

PFEILER, Maximilian and TREVISANI, Francesco (studio) (17/18th C) German/Italian
£11400 $19722 €16644 Putti dancing and holding garland of flowers (117x157cm-46x62in) 9-Dec-3 Sotheby's, Olympia #404/R est:5000-7000

PFENNINGER, Heinrich (1749-1815) Swiss
£388 $694 €566 Portrait of Johann Jacob Faesy (55x44cm-22x17in) 12-May-4 Dobiaschofsky, Bern #868/R (S.FR 900)

PFISTER, Albert (1884-1978) Swiss
£603 $1080 €880 Portrait of young man wearing glasses (30x39cm-12x15in) s. board. 12-May-4 Dobiaschofsky, Bern #869/R (S.FR 1400)
£1345 $2247 €1964 Landscape with small village (61x73cm-24x29in) 24-Oct-3 Hans Widmer, St Gallen #86/R est:3000-4800 (S.FR 3000)
£2489 $4305 €3634 Spring landscape (45x62cm-18x24in) s.d.1975 board. 9-Dec-3 Sotheby's, Zurich #35/R est:5500-6500 (S.FR 5500)

PFISTER, Jean Jacques (1878-1949) American
£228 $425 €333 Cypress Point (36x30cm-14x12in) s.d.1919 canvasboard. 6-Mar-4 Harvey Clar, Oakland #1295
£440 $800 €642 Carmel cypress (102x61cm-40x24in) s.d.1919. 19-Jun-4 Harvey Clar, Oakland #2186

PFLIEGER, Karl (1854-1922) Austrian
£331 $606 €500 The examination (38x63cm-15x25in) s.d.1918 panel. 8-Apr-4 Dorotheum, Vienna #212/R
£1060 $1939 €1600 New building (26x18cm-10x7in) s.i.d.1909 verso panel. 8-Apr-4 Dorotheum, Vienna #252/R est:1000-1200

PFORR, Heinrich (1880-1970) German
£556 $906 €800 Portrait of boy in dark jacket (70x60cm-28x24in) s.d.1909. 25-Sep-3 Dr Fritz Nagel, Stuttgart #1397/R

PFORR, Johann Georg (1745-1798) German
£4698 $8644 €7000 Horse market outside village (38x53cm-15x21in) prov. 24-Mar-4 Dorotheum, Vienna #279/R est:8000-10000
Works on paper
£6550 $11921 €9563 Blacksmith by a well (30x45cm-12x18in) s.d.1786 pen brush grey wash. 17-Jun-4 Kornfeld, Bern #50/R est:10000 (S.FR 15000)

PFORTNER, Ulrich (1950-) German
£333 $603 €500 Two women lying on beach (80x126cm-31x50in) s.d.83 vers0. 1-Apr-4 Frank Peege, Freiburg #1168/R

PFRETZSCHNER, Norbert (1850-1927) Austrian
Sculpture
£8054 $14819 €12000 Nymphe on stag killing bear. s.i. pat.bronze. 26-Mar-4 Dorotheum, Vienna #609/R est:4000-5000

PFUND, Alois (1876-1946) Austrian
£470 $864 €700 Courtyard in southern Tyrol (60x80cm-24x31in) s.d.33 i. verso lit. 25-Mar-4 Karlheinz Kaupp, Staufen #2652/R
£507 $811 €720 Old mill near Brandberg, Zillertal (36x50cm-14x20in) s. board. 18-Sep-3 Rieber, Stuttgart #1135
£646 $1176 €950 Farmsteads in the high mountains (80x100cm-31x39in) s. 4-Feb-4 Neumeister, Munich #739

PFUND, Roger (1943-) Swiss
Works on paper
£655 $1205 €956 Woman's portrait (45x105cm-18x41in) s.d.1976 mixed media collage. 8-Jun-4 Germann, Zurich #855 (S.FR 1500)

PFYFFER VON ALTISHOVEN, Dom F M A (1731-?) Swiss
Works on paper
£961 $1748 €1403 Peasant scenes (50x51cm-20x20in) one mono.d.1793 W/C ink pair. 16-Jun-4 Fischer, Luzern #2808 (S.FR 2200)

PHAM VAN DON (1917-) Vietnamese
£2105 $3811 €3200 Along Bay (52x61cm-20x24in) i. lacquer. 16-Apr-4 Dorotheum, Vienna #312/R est:700-800

PHELAN, Charles T (1840-?) American
£435 $700 €635 Sheep in farmyard (33x43cm-13x17in) s. board. 20-Aug-3 James Julia, Fairfield #989/R
£516 $955 €774 Sheep grazing near a stream (38x48cm-15x19in) s.d.95. 14-Jul-4 American Auctioneer #490306/R
£1283 $2400 €1873 Sheep in meadow. Sheep and shepherd by a pond (51x66cm-20x26in) s. pair. 29-Feb-4 Grogan, Boston #40/R

PHELAN, Frank (1932-) Irish
£1467 $2655 €2200 Maenads (64x64cm-25x25in) s.i.d.02. 30-Mar-4 De Veres Art Auctions, Dublin #178/R est:900-1200

PHELPS, Richard (attrib) (18th C) British
£2800 $5236 €4088 Portrait of a young girl (127x104cm-50x41in) 22-Jul-4 Sotheby's, Olympia #397/R est:3000-5000

PHELPS, Rusty (20th C) American
Sculpture
£1294 $2200 €1889 Cowboy roping a wild horse (56x56x53cm-22x22x21in) s.d.80 num.19/20 bronze prov.lit. 1-Nov-3 Santa Fe Art, Santa Fe #90/R est:4500-6500

PHELPS, William Preston (1848-1923) American
£377 $600 €550 House beside a creek in an autumn landscape (25x30cm-10x12in) s.d.89. 13-Sep-3 Weschler, Washington #745/R
£852 $1500 €1244 Winter stream through the woods (33x48cm-13x19in) s. 3-Jan-4 Cobbs, Peterborough #64a/R
£1384 $2200 €2021 Cascading stream through a forest (36x51cm-14x20in) s. 13-Sep-3 Weschler, Washington #744/R est:2000-3000
£1705 $3000 €2489 Hunter with his dogs (33x48cm-13x19in) s. 3-Jan-4 Cobbs, Peterborough #64b/R
£3142 $5750 €4587 New Hampshire pasture (30x46cm-12x18in) s. prov. 10-Apr-4 Cobbs, Peterborough #107/R

PHIDIAS (?) ?
£408 $707 €580 Le Pont Neuf (66x81cm-26x32in) 10-Dec-3 Millon & Associes, Paris #103/R

PHILEMON, Jean Volcy (1956-1999) Haitian
£385 $700 €562 Two tigers under an orange tree (25x30cm-10x12in) s. 7-Feb-4 Sloans & Kenyon, Bethesda #287/R

PHILIP, John (?) British?
£500 $860 €730 Maiden meditation (29x23cm-11x9in) 6-Dec-3 Shapes, Edinburgh #414

PHILIPP, Robert (1895-1981) American
£255 $475 €372 Still life of grapes and apples (28x33cm-11x13in) s. 3-Mar-4 Alderfer's, Hatfield #361
£374 $700 €546 Girl with red vest (20x15cm-8x6in) s.verso. 25-Feb-4 Doyle, New York #70/R
£523 $900 €764 Young girl (30x25cm-12x10in) s. 7-Dec-3 Hindman, Chicago #865/R
£615 $1100 €898 Reclining nude female (20x38cm-8x15in) s. panel. 8-May-4 Susanin's, Chicago #6167/R est:1000-1500
£700 $1190 €1022 Young girl (44x36cm-17x14in) s. s.i.verso. 29-Oct-3 Bonhams, Chester #463
£782 $1305 €1142 Young girl sitting by the ocean (36x38cm-14x15in) s. 14-Nov-3 Aspire, Cleveland #96
£800 $1400 €1168 Maxwell Simpson 1919 at Cheffetz, Simpson Studio (58x43cm-23x17in) s. 16-Dec-3 Lincoln, Orange #481
£824 $1500 €1203 Cocktail time (35x28cm-14x11in) s. s.verso prov. 29-Jun-4 Sotheby's, New York #280/R est:2000-3000
£838 $1500 €1223 Still life with flowers and guitar (46x56cm-18x22in) s. 8-May-4 Susanin's, Chicago #6058/R est:1500-2400
£1104 $1800 €1612 Nude reading the newspaper (20x10cm-8x4in) s. canvas on masonite prov. 24-Sep-3 Doyle, New York #66/R est:1000-1500
£1118 $1800 €1632 Cocktail time (36x28cm-14x11in) s. 22-Feb-3 Bunte, Elgin #1207 est:400-600
£1258 $2000 €1837 Table for two. Portrait of a woman (30x36cm-12x14in) s. pair. 10-Sep-3 Sotheby's, New York #168/R est:2500-3500
£1676 $3000 €2447 Seated nude (30x36cm-12x14in) s. 26-May-4 Doyle, New York #114/R est:2000-3000
£1714 $3000 €2502 Still life (66x54cm-26x21in) s. s.i.verso. 19-Dec-3 Sotheby's, New York #1045/R est:2500-3500
£2060 $3750 €3008 Arranging flowers (56x46cm-22x18in) s. s.i.verso prov. 29-Jun-4 Sotheby's, New York #281/R est:4000-6000
£2329 $3750 €3400 Arranging flowers (56x46cm-22x18in) s. 22-Feb-3 Bunte, Elgin #1206 est:800-1200
£2344 $3750 €3422 My wife Rochelle (198x94cm-78x37in) s.d.1965 s.i.d.1952 verso. 20-Sep-3 Bunte, Elgin #1217 est:2500-3500
£2957 $5500 €4317 Nude resting (51x61cm-20x24in) s. 3-Mar-4 Christie's, Rockefeller NY #55/R est:2500-3500
£3073 $5500 €4487 Old Carnegie restaurant (28x74cm-11x29in) s. s.i.verso. 26-May-4 Doyle, New York #136/R est:3000-5000
£3714 $6500 €5422 My studio (76x101cm-30x40in) s.d.75 s.i.verso. 19-Dec-3 Sotheby's, New York #1058/R est:3000-5000
£4192 $7000 €6120 At the Cabaret (41x51cm-16x20in) s. prov. 23-Oct-3 Shannon's, Milford #133/R est:7000-9000
£8939 $16000 €13051 Dinner for three at the Old Carnegie restaurant (71x89cm-28x35in) s. prov. 26-May-4 Doyle, New York #137/R est:6000-8000
Works on paper
£462 $850 €675 Draped nude (51x64cm-20x25in) pastel. 23-Jun-4 Doyle, New York #5058/R
£581 $1000 €848 Girlfriends teatime (66x66cm-26x26in) s.i. pastel on masonite. 3-Dec-3 Doyle, New York #306/R est:2000-3000
£581 $1000 €848 Tea time sisters (53x66cm-21x26in) s. s.i.verso pastel gouache. 3-Dec-3 Doyle, New York #307/R est:2000-3000
£815 $1500 €1190 Coney Island Beach (43x56cm-17x22in) s. col pastel. 10-Jun-4 Swann Galleries, New York #192/R est:2000-3000

PHILIPPE, Charles (20th C) French?
£3521 $6092 €5000 Bassin de l'Amiraute, Alger (55x92cm-22x36in) s. 15-Dec-3 Gros & Delettrez, Paris #357/R est:4000-6000

PHILIPPE, P (19/20th C) French
Sculpture
£1100 $1969 €1606 Dancer (44cm-17in) s. cold painted. 13-May-4 Christie's, Kensington #340/R est:1200-1500
£1958 $3329 €2800 Danseuse. bronze. 30-Nov-3 Teitgen, Nancy #155d
£2917 $4871 €4200 Danseuse orientale (56cm-22in) pat bronze marble socle. 25-Oct-3 Dianous, Marseille #158

PHILIPPE, Paul (fl.1920-1929) French
Sculpture
£1111 $1756 €1600 Radha (36cm-14in) brown pat.bronze lit. 19-Sep-3 Schloss Ahlden, Ahlden #789/R est:1400
£1400 $2380 €2044 Female nude (40cm-16in) i. gilt bronze marble pedestal. 25-Nov-3 Sotheby's, Olympia #139/R est:1200-1800

£2321 $4177 €3389 Dancer (53cm-21in) s. pat.bronze ivory ex.1925. 26-Apr-4 Bukowskis, Stockholm #1372/R est:20000-25000 (S.KR 32000)
£2416 $4470 €3600 Danseuse Russe (56cm-22in) s.num. pat bronze marble base lit. 15-Mar-4 Horta, Bruxelles #112/R est:3500-4000
£2500 $4250 €3650 Le grand ecart respectueux - respectful splits (21x28cm-8x11in) s. bronze ivory black marble pedestal. 25-Nov-3 Sotheby's, Olympia #155/R est:1000-1500
£2685 $4966 €4000 Radha (56cm-22in) s.num. pat bronze marble base lit. 15-Mar-4 Horta, Bruxelles #111/R est:3500-4000
£2800 $5124 €4200 L'eveil (74cm-29in) pat bronze green marble base. 7-Jun-4 Palais de Beaux Arts, Brussels #281/R est:3000-4000
£3557 $6368 €5193 Reveil (71cm-28in) s.i. st.f.Goldscheider golden brown pat bronze prov. 15-May-4 Christie's, Sydney #194/R est:8000-12000 (A.D 9000)
£3586 $5989 €5200 Coquine (22x7cm-9x3in) s. ivory onyx socle. 14-Nov-3 Claude Boisgirard, Paris #32/R est:4000-4500
£4027 $7450 €6000 Danseuse (43x18cm-17x7in) s. ivory pat bronze onyx socle. 14-Mar-4 St-Germain-en-Laye Encheres #98/R est:4000-5000
£7092 $11844 €10000 Danseuse mauresque (43x18cm-17x7in) s. ivory gilt pat bronze jupe onyx piedouche. 19-Oct-3 St-Germain-en-Laye Encheres #47/R est:2000-2200
£10000 $15900 €14600 Dancer with turban (93cm-37in) bronze ivory. 9-Sep-3 Sotheby's, Olympia #377/R est:10000-12000

PHILIPPE, Paul (after) (fl.1920-1929) French
Sculpture
£3846 $7000 €5769 Radha (43cm-17in) i. bronze ivory onyx exec. c.1920. 16-Jun-4 Sotheby's, New York #234/R est:4000-5000
£6000 $10800 €8760 Pierette (38cm-15in) s. cold-painted bronze ivory. 22-Apr-4 Christie's, Kensington #536/R est:5000-6000

PHILIPPEAU, Karel Frans (1825-1897) Dutch
£993 $1658 €1400 Grape pickers (17x13cm-7x5in) s. panel. 20-Oct-3 Glerum, Amsterdam #62/R
£1267 $2154 €1850 Neapolitan musicians (32x27cm-13x11in) s.d.1863 panel. 28-Nov-3 Zofingen, Switzerland #2480/R est:2500 (S.FR 2800)
£1944 $3169 €2800 Southern family in landscape (18x25cm-7x10in) s. panel. 25-Sep-3 Dr Fritz Nagel, Stuttgart #1398/R est:2900
£2667 $4800 €4000 Lullaby (31x40cm-12x16in) s.d.1861 panel. 21-Apr-4 Christie's, Amsterdam #12/R est:3000-5000
£2800 $4760 €4088 At the fountain (27x40cm-11x16in) s. panel. 1-Dec-3 Bonhams, Bath #144/R est:3000-5000
£11000 $20240 €16060 Young danders (34x34cm-13x13in) s. panel pair prov. 25-Mar-4 Christie's, Kensington #69/R est:10000-15000

PHILIPPET, Léon (1843-1906) Belgian
£319 $533 €450 Paysage campagnard (42x60cm-17x24in) s. panel. 15-Oct-3 Hotel des Ventes Mosan, Brussels #115
£345 $638 €500 Communiante - orientaliste (56x46cm-22x18in) s. 19-Jan-4 Horta, Bruxelles #295

PHILIPPI, Waldemar (1828-1869) German
£1736 $2830 €2500 Bergerie (62x81cm-24x32in) d.1865. 29-Sep-3 Coutau Begarie, Paris #271/R est:2500-3000

PHILIPPOTEAUX, Henri Felix Emmanuel (1815-1884) French
£1259 $2140 €1800 Officier a cheval donnant la charge (32x22cm-13x9in) s. painted c.1870. 18-Nov-3 Vanderkindere, Brussels #64 est:1500-2500
Works on paper
£563 $975 €800 Etudes de drapes presumees pour le portrait du Duc d'Orleans (12x16cm-5x6in) pierre noire W/C two. 10-Dec-3 Maigret, Paris #14
£3521 $6092 €5000 Etudes pour le portrait de Duc d'Orleans (15x14cm-6x6in) pierre noire W/C two. 10-Dec-3 Maigret, Paris #13/R est:600-800

PHILIPPOTEAUX, Paul Dominique (1846-1923) American
£649 $1200 €948 Pyramids at sunset (25x33cm-10x13in) s. paper on card. 15-Jul-4 Sotheby's, New York #44
£7927 $13000 €11494 Civil war battle scene with union Cavalry (102x163cm-40x64in) s. prov. 31-May-4 Brunk, Ashville #639/R est:500-1000
£10588 $18000 €15458 Two horses with an Arab groom and a town beyond (55x75cm-22x30in) s.d.1889. 19-Nov-3 Bonhams & Butterfields, San Francisco #118/R
£21679 $37287 €31000 Scene de marche au Caire (87x71cm-34x28in) s. 8-Dec-3 Tajan, Paris #311/R est:22000-25000
£28000 $50960 €40880 Deux etalons avec un valet d'ecurie (75x54cm-30x21in) s.d.1889. 15-Jun-4 Sotheby's, London #139/R est:20000-30000

PHILIPS, Charles (attrib) (1708-1747) British
£3333 $6000 €4866 Portrait of a family (93x133cm-37x52in) 21-Jan-4 Sotheby's, New York #111/R est:6000-8000

PHILIPS, Charles (circle) (1708-1747) British
£6800 $11356 €9928 Portrait of a girl holding a bird in a landscape (76x63cm-30x25in) prov. 13-Nov-3 Christie's, Kensington #17/R est:2500-3500

PHILIPS, Gerald (20th C) British
£400 $748 €584 St Ives, Shore Shelter (23x35cm-9x14in) s.d.71 verso. 25-Feb-4 Mallams, Oxford #266/R

PHILIPS, Margot (1902-1988) New Zealander
£714 $1314 €1042 Looking down (21x70cm-8x28in) s.d.1972 canvasboard exhib. 25-Mar-4 International Art Centre, Auckland #41/R (NZ.D 2000)

PHILIPS, Richard (1681-1741) British
Works on paper
£2695 $4500 €3935 Valentino (49x55cm-19x22in) chl chk prov. 13-Nov-3 Sotheby's, New York #431/R est:5000-7000

PHILIPS-WEBER, Marie (19/20th C) German
£13333 $24000 €20000 Celebrating carnival in Munich, the Alte Rathaus in the background (125x67cm-49x26in) s. 21-Apr-4 Christie's, Amsterdam #175/R est:15000-20000

PHILIPSEN, Sally (1879-1936) Danish
£473 $846 €691 Landscape from Vejle Fjord (32x39cm-13x15in) s. 12-Jan-4 Rasmussen, Vejle #327 (D.KR 5000)

PHILIPSEN, Theodor (1840-1920) Danish
£474 $758 €687 Sheep by the roadside (36x48cm-14x19in) mono. exhib. 17-Sep-3 Kunsthallen, Copenhagen #469/R (D.KR 5000)
£1121 $1772 €1625 Three cows on country road (35x43cm-14x17in) mono. d.1877 verso. 2-Sep-3 Rasmussen, Copenhagen #1533/R est:15000-20000 (D.KR 12000)
£1402 $2215 €2033 Cattle at Saltholmen with sketched sheep or geese (28x38cm-11x15in) mono. 2-Sep-3 Rasmussen, Copenhagen #1601/R est:12000-15000 (D.KR 15000)
£2516 $4679 €3673 From the large watering place at Saltholm with cows, horses and geese (100x135cm-39x53in) mono.d.1911 exhib.prov. 2-Mar-4 Rasmussen, Copenhagen #1299/R est:30000-40000 (D.KR 28000)
£2624 $4277 €3831 Cows, calves and horses by lean-to shed, Saltholmen (41x59cm-16x23in) init.d.1897. 28-Sep-3 Hindemae, Ullerslev #37/R est:20000-25000 (D.KR 28000)
£2804 $4430 €4066 Damhuskroen with country road (50x61cm-20x24in) mono.d.1909 exhib.prov. 2-Sep-3 Rasmussen, Copenhagen #1615/R est:30000 (D.KR 30000)
£3214 $5560 €4692 Harvesters, Scheelenborg (25x39cm-10x15in) mono. prov. 9-Dec-3 Rasmussen, Copenhagen #1563/R est:10000-12000 (D.KR 34000)
£3581 $6553 €5228 Young cattle at Saltholm (81x123cm-32x48in) exhib.prov. 9-Jun-4 Rasmussen, Copenhagen #1468/R est:40000-60000 (D.KR 40000)
£7009 $11075 €10163 From Trommesalen, flock of lamb in enclosure with three calves (140x198cm-55x78in) init. painted c.1870-1873 exhib.prov. 2-Sep-3 Rasmussen, Copenhagen #1534/R est:75000-100000 (D.KR 75000)
Sculpture
£1977 $3677 €2886 Roman bull (40x50cm-16x20in) pat.bronze exec.c.1892. 2-Mar-4 Rasmussen, Copenhagen #1205/R est:20000-25000 (D.KR 22000)
Works on paper
£473 $846 €691 Field with cows (58x88cm-23x35in) pastel prov. 12-Jan-4 Rasmussen, Vejle #100/R (D.KR 5000)
£851 $1532 €1242 Bringing the calves home, Saltholm (62x90cm-24x35in) pastel. 24-Apr-4 Rasmussen, Havnen #2308/R (D.KR 9500)

PHILIPSON, Robin (1916-1992) British
£1300 $2171 €1898 Rainbow and rose window (39x39cm-15x15in) s. board. 16-Oct-3 Bonhams, Edinburgh #20/R est:1000-1500
£1500 $2745 €2190 Red interior (23x22cm-9x9in) board. 5-Jun-4 Shapes, Edinburgh #479 est:800-1200
£2400 $3864 €3480 In the presence of abstracts I (75x75cm-30x30in) s.d.1989 board. 21-Aug-3 Bonhams, Edinburgh #1205/R est:3000-5000
£2600 $4706 €3796 Odalisques resting I, blue (29x39cm-11x15in) s. board prov. 19-Apr-4 Sotheby's, London #164/R est:3000-4000
£2800 $4508 €4060 Two decanters (39x31cm-15x12in) s. prov. 21-Aug-3 Bonhams, Edinburgh #1202/R est:3000-5000
£3000 $4710 €4350 Crowing cock, blue (41x30cm-16x12in) s. panel prov. 27-Aug-3 Sotheby's, London #1154/R est:3000-4000
£3000 $4710 €4350 Waiting II (30x40cm-12x16in) oil acrylic paper on canvas. 27-Aug-3 Sotheby's, London #1164/R est:3000-4000
£4200 $6762 €6090 Presentation, study II (15x15cm-6x6in) s.verso board. 21-Aug-3 Bonhams, Edinburgh #1052/R est:1500-2000
£4600 $8418 €6716 Green apples (24x34cm-9x13in) s. canvasboard exhib. 8-Apr-4 Bonhams, Edinburgh #30a/R est:2500-4000
£6000 $10380 €8760 Still life with abstracts (76x91cm-30x36in) s.i.d.1989/90 verso board prov. 11-Dec-3 Lyon & Turnbull, Edinburgh #108/R est:6000-8000
£15000 $27150 €21900 Far away (92x132cm-36x52in) s.i. prov.exhib. 19-Apr-4 Sotheby's, London #165/R est:15000-20000
£20000 $36200 €29200 Cathedral interior, dark window with chandelier (213x107cm-84x42in) s. exhib. 19-Apr-4 Sotheby's, London #166/R est:20000-30000
Works on paper
£372 $665 €543 Threnody, condemned (10x12cm-4x5in) s. W/C collage exhib. 31-May-4 Stephan Welz, Johannesburg #453 (SA.R 4500)
£720 $1310 €1051 Black and white (17x17cm-7x7in) s. W/C. 3-Jul-4 Shapes, Edinburgh #429
£850 $1369 €1233 Odalisqe (17x17cm-7x7in) s. W/C. 21-Aug-3 Bonhams, Edinburgh #1206/R
£850 $1522 €1241 View of a lake from rooftops (37x55cm-15x22in) s.i.d.1979 verso W/C. 28-May-4 Lyon & Turnbull, Edinburgh #61
£1050 $1922 €1533 Night-time with reclining nude (23x30cm-9x12in) W/C exhib. 28-Jul-4 Mallams, Oxford #284/R est:1000-1500
£1400 $2548 €2044 Attaque-attaque (41x30cm-16x12in) s. mixed media oil on board. 3-Jul-4 Shapes, Edinburgh #430/R est:1000-1500
£1500 $2715 €2190 Reclining female nude (9x14cm-4x6in) W/C. 19-Apr-4 Sotheby's, London #167/R est:1500-2000
£2600 $4706 €3796 Repose, two female nudes (18x23cm-7x9in) s.i.d.1980 verso pastel. 19-Apr-4 Sotheby's, London #168/R est:2000-3000
£4000 $6440 €5800 Threnody-the cry (25x25cm-10x10in) s.d.70 W/C exhib. 21-Aug-3 Bonhams, Edinburgh #1053/R est:1000-1500
£5500 $9955 €8030 Interior with four nudes (48x65cm-19x26in) i. W/C pastel prov. 19-Apr-4 Sotheby's, London #163/R est:5000-7000

PHILLIP, John (1817-1867) British
£806 $1484 €1177 Portrait of Mortimer Clark with his dog (58x58cm-23x23in) i.d.1842 prov.exhib. 14-Jun-4 Waddingtons, Toronto #194/R est:2000-3000 (C.D 2000)
£1500 $2790 €2190 Portrait of Miss Florence Penison, wearing a white dress with pink ribbons (30x30cm-12x12in) s.d.1852 s.i.d.verso board. 4-Mar-4 Christie's, Kensington #359/R est:700-1000
Works on paper
£800 $1480 €1168 Portrait of a peasant girl (15x14cm-6x6in) pencil W/C gouache. 10-Mar-4 Sotheby's, Olympia #66/R
£1724 $3103 €2500 Letter (85x60cm-33x24in) init.d.1866 gouache wash. 26-Jan-4 Durán, Madrid #201/R est:2500

PHILLIPET, Leon (19th C) Belgian?
£1418 $2369 €2000 Scene de cabaret (55x100cm-22x39in) s.d.1882. 17-Jun-3 Galerie Moderne, Brussels #228/R est:2000-3000

PHILLIPP, Werner (1897-1982) American
£412 $700 €602 Santa Clara Hills (61x79cm-24x31in) s.d.1960. 22-Nov-3 Jackson's, Cedar Falls #77/R

PHILLIPS, Ammi (1787-1865) American
£1757 $3250 €2565 Portrait of a grey haired gentleman posed in federal (79x66cm-31x26in) painted c.1830. 15-Jan-4 Sotheby's, New York #309/R est:5000-7000
£3243 $6000 €4735 Grey haired gentleman. Lady holding a bible (58x93cm-23x37in) pair painted c.1845. 15-Jan-4 Sotheby's, New York #308/R est:6000-8000
£3243 $6000 €4735 Portrait of gentleman (84x69cm-33x27in) 18-Jan-4 Carlsen Gallery, Greenville #171/R
£5946 $11000 €8681 Portrait of the artist's cousin (81x69cm-32x27in) 18-Jan-4 Carlsen Gallery, Greenville #172/R
£6486 $12000 €9470 Portrait of a lady wearing an elaborate lace bonnet (78x66cm-31x26in) painted c.1830. 15-Jan-4 Sotheby's, New York #307/R est:5000-8000
£8951 $14500 €13068 Portraits of a couple (81x66cm-32x26in) pair. 1-Aug-3 North East Auctions, Portsmouth #816/R
£32609 $60000 €47609 Portraits (88x71cm-35x28in) i.verso pair. 22-Jun-4 Sotheby's, New York #178/R est:30000-60000
£37838 $70000 €55243 Portrait of young woman in white (108x92cm-43x36in) painted c.1836 prov.exhib.lit. 16-Jan-4 Sotheby's, New York #16/R est:40000-60000

PHILLIPS, Ammi (attrib) (1787-1865) American
£3175 $6000 €4636 Portrait of blue eyed man (76x64cm-30x25in) 22-Feb-4 Skinner, Boston #265/R est:6000-8000

PHILLIPS, Bert G (1868-1956) American
£20588 $35000 €30058 Gathering water at Taos pueblo (46x56cm-18x22in) s. prov.lit. 1-Nov-3 Santa Fe Art, Santa Fe #197/R est:40000-50000
£31285 $56000 €45676 Husking Corn - Taos Pueblo (30x41cm-12x16in) 15-May-4 Altermann Galleries, Santa Fe #60/R
Works on paper
£668 $1250 €975 Portrait of an Indian (23x13cm-9x5in) s.d.1952 chl prov. 24-Jul-4 Coeur d'Alene, Hayden #277/R est:1500-2500

PHILLIPS, C (19th C) British
£373 $600 €545 Grazing sheep in landscape (30x46cm-12x18in) s. 20-Aug-3 James Julia, Fairfield #1054/R

PHILLIPS, Charles Gustav Louis (1864-1944) British
£650 $1086 €949 Picadilly Circus, London (14x21cm-6x8in) s.i. 7-Oct-3 Bonhams, Knightsbridge #76/R

PHILLIPS, Duncan (1886-1966) American
£250 $400 €365 Uphill road (46x61cm-18x24in) i.verso. 20-Sep-3 Sloans & Kenyon, Bethesda #687/R
£344 $550 €502 Plums and a peach. Bouquet (36x46cm-14x18in) mono.i. two. 20-Sep-3 Sloans & Kenyon, Bethesda #966/R
£594 $950 €867 Winter wheat. Landscape with barn (25x36cm-10x14in) mono. s.i.verso two. 20-Sep-3 Sloans & Kenyon, Bethesda #688/R
£1000 $1600 €1460 Bouquet view of ocean (38x30cm-15x12in) mono. 20-Sep-3 Sloans & Kenyon, Bethesda #968/R est:400-600
£1063 $1700 €1552 That red roof. Barn (36x46cm-14x18in) mono.i.verso two. 20-Sep-3 Sloans & Kenyon, Bethesda #694/R est:400-600
£2188 $3500 €3194 Flowers in iron urn. Thirsty flowers (61x46cm-24x18in) mono.i.verso two. 20-Sep-3 Sloans & Kenyon, Bethesda #967/R est:400-600
£2188 $3500 €3194 Violin (41x51cm-16x20in) mono. 20-Sep-3 Sloans & Kenyon, Bethesda #669/R est:400-500
£2500 $4000 €3650 Forest fire (30x46cm-12x18in) mono. board. 20-Sep-3 Sloans & Kenyon, Bethesda #970/R est:400-600
£3125 $5000 €4563 Farm in valley (36x56cm-14x22in) mono. masonite. 20-Sep-3 Sloans & Kenyon, Bethesda #971/R est:400-600

PHILLIPS, Henry Louis (19/20th C) American
£1890 $3250 €2759 Still life with fruit and a bird's nest on a ledge (23x30cm-9x12in) prov. 7-Dec-3 Freeman, Philadelphia #109 est:1000-1500

PHILLIPS, James Grainger (1915-) Australian?
£909 $1682 €1327 Contract no.1, Sydney Opera House (79x180cm-31x71in) s. board exhib. 10-Mar-4 Deutscher-Menzies, Melbourne #579/R est:1200-1800 (A.D 2200)
Works on paper
£324 $521 €473 Contract no.1 - Sydney Opera House (77x179cm-30x70in) s. mixed media on board. 13-Oct-3 Joel, Victoria #391 (A.D 800)

PHILLIPS, Joel (1960-) American
£2353 $4000 €3435 Song of the cowboy (53x71cm-21x28in) egg tempera on board. 1-Nov-3 Altermann Galleries, Santa Fe #144
£2795 $4500 €4053 Winter gate (76x102cm-30x40in) 22-Aug-3 Altermann Galleries, Santa Fe #61
£3911 $7000 €5710 Song of the Golden Range (76x61cm-30x24in) egg tempera panel. 15-May-4 Altermann Galleries, Santa Fe #97/R

PHILLIPS, John Campbell (1873-1949) American
£520 $900 €759 Landscape with trees in spring and distant mountains (30x41cm-12x16in) s. board. 10-Dec-3 Alderfer's, Hatfield #371 est:900-1200

PHILLIPS, Marjorie Acker (1895-1985) American
£469 $750 €685 Swan boat, tidal basin (61x46cm-24x18in) board. 20-Sep-3 Sloans & Kenyon, Bethesda #965/R

PHILLIPS, Peter (1939-) British
£1268 $2193 €1800 Tiger-tiger (73x112cm-29x44in) s.i.d.1968 verso thermoforming. 14-Dec-3 Rabourdin & Choppin de Janvry, Paris #76/R est:1800-2000
£3200 $5824 €4672 Eagle (56x51cm-22x20in) s.d.Nov 63 verso. 30-Jun-4 Christie's, Kensington #13/R est:2000-3000
£7500 $13800 €10950 Chicken song (161x119cm-63x47in) s.i.d.1996 verso canvas on board prov.exhib. 24-Jun-4 Sotheby's, London #254/R est:5000-7000
Works on paper
£671 $1228 €1000 Mini-converter (36x28cm-14x11in) s.d.1973 i. verso mixed media canvas. 7-Jul-4 Artcurial Briest, Paris #322

PHILLIPS, Samuel George (c.1890-1965) American
£15244 $25000 €22256 Impressionist canal view (69x66cm-27x26in) s. 4-Jun-3 Alderfer's, Hatfield #366/R est:20000-25000

PHILLIPS, Thomas (1770-1845) British
£3000 $5400 €4380 Portrait of Catherine Sherwin-Gregory (74x62cm-29x24in) sold with portrait of husband attributed to Thomas Phillips. 21-Jan-4 Sotheby's, Olympia #56/R est:3000-5000
£4500 $8280 €6570 Portraits of John Balguy of Derwent Hall, Derbyshire and his wife, Barbara (76x64cm-30x25in) mono.d.1824 pair prov. 24-Jun-4 Ewbank, Send #535/R est:3000-5000
£23000 $38410 €33580 Portrait of Lieutenant John David Duval of the 27th Light Dragoons (126x100cm-50x39in) prov. 14-Oct-3 Sotheby's, London #467/R est:12000-18000

PHILLIPS, Thomas (attrib) (1770-1845) British
£1300 $2340 €1898 Portrait of Mary Cunliffe, Mrs Drummond Smith (141x111cm-56x44in) i. 21-Jan-4 Sotheby's, Olympia #41/R est:400-600
£1400 $2520 €2044 Portrait of a lady (99x74cm-39x29in) 21-Jan-4 Sotheby's, Olympia #54/R est:500-700
£3000 $5010 €4380 Portrait of an officer of the 11th Light Dragoons (74x60cm-29x24in) 14-Oct-3 Sotheby's, London #482/R est:3000-4000

PHILLIPS, Tom (1937-) British
Works on paper
£814 $1385 €1188 Harrison Birdwhistle (150x124cm-59x49in) s.d.1995 pastel. 25-Nov-3 Germann, Zurich #124/R est:2000-4000 (S.FR 1800)

PHILLIPS, Walter Joseph (1884-1963) American/Canadian
Prints
£1524 $2728 €2225 Morning (18x19cm-7x7in) s.i.d.1924 num.90/150 col woodcut prov.lit. 27-May-4 Heffel, Vancouver #24 est:1500-2000 (C.D 3750)
£1700 $3111 €2482 Norman Bay, Lake of the Woods (29x21cm-11x8in) s.i. num.3/50 col woodcut exec.1920. 1-Jun-4 Hodgins, Calgary #42/R est:3000-4000 (C.D 4250)
£1757 $2986 €2565 Hnausa (30x44cm-12x17in) s.i. col woodblock. 23-Nov-3 Levis, Calgary #112a/R est:4000-4500 (C.D 3900)
£1829 $3274 €2670 Simoom, British Columbia (17x27cm-7x11in) s.i. num.18/100 col woodcut exec.1935. 27-May-4 Heffel, Vancouver #2/R est:3000-4000 (C.D 4500)
£2846 $5093 €4155 Norman Bay, Lake of the Woods (29x21cm-11x8in) s. num.27/50 col woodcut exec.1920 prov.lit. 27-May-4 Heffel, Vancouver #5/R est:3000-4000 (C.D 7000)
£2928 $4977 €4275 Sharp's Dock, Pender Harbour (24x35cm-9x14in) s.i. num.1/100 col woodcut executed 1952 prov.exhib.lit. 27-Nov-3 Heffel, Vancouver #13/R est:6000-8000 (C.D 6500)
£7600 $13908 €11096 Karlukwees (26x31cm-10x12in) s.i. num.72/100 col woodcut exec. 1929 lit. 1-Jun-4 Hodgins, Calgary #60/R est:10000-15000 (C.D 19000)
Works on paper
£1200 $2196 €1752 Mt Odaray (21x24cm-8x9in) s.i. W/C exec. 1937. 1-Jun-4 Hodgins, Calgary #399/R est:4000-6000 (C.D 3000)
£3167 $5290 €4624 Untitled - mountain lake (36x53cm-14x21in) s.d.1948 W/C. 17-Nov-3 Hodgins, Calgary #380/R est:8000-10000 (C.D 7000)
£3348 $5692 €4888 Jack Pine, Lake of the woods (30x25cm-12x10in) s. W/C prov. 6-Nov-3 Heffel, Vancouver #94/R est:6000-8000 (C.D 7500)
£3455 $6185 €5044 Autumn leaves, lake of the woods (25x22cm-10x9in) s. i.verso W/C exec. c.1920 lit. 27-May-4 Heffel, Vancouver #1/R est:4000-6000 (C.D 8500)
£3455 $6185 €5044 Star Lake, Lake of the Woods (22x27cm-9x11in) s. i.verso W/C exec. c.1920 lit. 27-May-4 Heffel, Vancouver #3/R est:6000-8000 (C.D 8500)
£3455 $6185 €5044 Junction of the Red and Assiniboine rivers in Winnipeg (30x35cm-12x14in) s. d.1933 verso W/C prov. 27-May-4 Heffel, Vancouver #4/R est:3500-4500 (C.D 8500)
£22523 $38288 €32884 Wharf at Hnausa, Winnipeg (37x55cm-15x22in) s. W/C prov. 23-Nov-3 Levis, Calgary #105/R est:10000-12000 (C.D 50000)

PHILLOTT, Constance (1842-1931) British
Works on paper
£260 $476 €380 When I was dead my spirit turned to seek the much frequented house, I passed the door (29x53cm-11x21in) i.verso W/C. 27-Jan-4 Bonhams, Knightsbridge #157/R
£300 $471 €435 Roman maiden (32x19cm-13x7in) mono.d.1883 pencil W/C bodycol. 28-Aug-3 Christie's, Kensington #375/R

PHILP, James George (1816-1885) British
£3000 $5100 €4380 View of Falmouth from Pendennis Castle, Cornwall (44x59cm-17x23in) s. 27-Nov-3 Sotheby's, London #187/R est:4000-6000
Works on paper
£450 $810 €657 At the Mumbles, south Wales (17x44cm-7x17in) s. W/C over pencil bodycol. 21-Jan-4 Sotheby's, Olympia #163/R

PHILPOT, Glyn (1884-1937) British
£950 $1634 €1387 Seated Moroccan, 1934 (40x25cm-16x10in) W/C pen ink prov.exhib.lit. 2-Dec-3 Bonhams, New Bond Street #40/R
£2800 $5096 €4088 Study of a landscape (25x30cm-10x12in) exhib. 1-Jul-4 Christie's, Kensington #78/R est:2000-3000

£9000 $14940 €13140 Portrait of Martyn Coleman (109x73cm-43x29in) init. painted 1936 prov.exhib.lit. 30-Sep-3 Sotheby's, London #304/R est:10000-15000
£11000 $18260 €16060 Portrait of Lieutenant Aymes (122x68cm-48x27in) init. painted c.1912-15. 30-Sep-3 Sotheby's, London #22/R est:15000-20000
£22000 $40040 €32120 Repose on the flight to Egypt (75x116cm-30x46in) painted c.1922 prov.exhib.lit. 15-Jun-4 Bonhams, New Bond Street #37/R est:25000-30000
£26000 $44200 €37960 Reclining nude (105x162cm-41x64in) painted c.1935 prov. 21-Nov-3 Christie's, London #89/R est:25000-35000
£28000 $51240 €40880 Negro model in studio (76x63cm-30x25in) s. prov.exhib.lit. 2-Jun-4 Sotheby's, London #57/R est:20000-30000
Sculpture
£5000 $8950 €7300 Mask of Negro (45cm-18in) num.5/8 black pat bronze prov.lit. 16-Mar-4 Bonhams, New Bond Street #23/R est:4000-6000
£9000 $16110 €13140 Echo and Narcissus (57cm-22in) num.7/8 green pat bronze prov.lit. 16-Mar-4 Bonhams, New Bond Street #25/R est:4000-6000
£10500 $18795 €15330 Fragment of a figure (71cm-28in) num.5/8 silver pat bronze prov.lit. 16-Mar-4 Bonhams, New Bond Street #24/R est:4000-6000
£15000 $26850 €21900 Negro walking (84cm-33in) num.5/8 black pat bronze prov.lit. 16-Mar-4 Bonhams, New Bond Street #26/R est:6000-8000

PHIPPEN, George (1916-1966) American
£588 $1100 €858 New aquaintance (28x36cm-11x14in) s. painted c.1957. 25-Feb-4 Dallas Auction Gallery, Dallas #154/R
£2395 $4000 €3497 Water hole (41x51cm-16x20in) s. 16-Nov-3 Simpson's, Houston #346/R
£3824 $6500 €5583 Thanks (41x51cm-16x20in) s. prov. 1-Nov-3 Santa Fe Art, Santa Fe #235/R est:6000-8000
£5000 $8500 €7300 Sagebrush nightingale (61x76cm-24x30in) s. prov. 1-Nov-3 Santa Fe Art, Santa Fe #99/R est:8000-10000
£14118 $24000 €20612 A tie hard in a storm (71x91cm-28x36in) s.d.59 prov. 1-Nov-3 Santa Fe Art, Santa Fe #37/R est:10000-15000

PHIPPS, Richard (20th C) American
£300 $500 €438 Heraldic devices (140x203cm-55x80in) s.d.1982 verso acrylic. 19-Oct-3 Bonhams & Butterfields, Los Angeles #7081

PHOENIX, George (attrib) (1863-1935) British
£350 $585 €511 Portrait of a gentleman, in a black jacket holding a cane (61x41cm-24x16in) 13-Nov-3 Christie's, Kensington #61/R

PHYSIOC, Wray (20th C) ?
Works on paper
£321 $600 €469 Arab woman under the stars (18x15cm-7x6in) s. W/C. 25-Feb-4 Doyle, New York #51/R

PIACENZA, Carlo (1814-1887) Italian
£1333 $2453 €2000 Strolling in the mountains (36x47cm-14x19in) s.d.1861 board. 8-Jun-4 Sotheby's, Milan #50/R est:2000-4000

PIACENZA, Pietro (1879-1964) Italian
£694 $1181 €1000 Landscape with farmer (35x47cm-14x19in) 1-Nov-3 Meeting Art, Vercelli #256/R

PIACESI, Walter (1929-) Italian
£748 $1272 €1070 Confidences (40x50cm-16x20in) s.d.1972 board prov. 18-Nov-3 Babuino, Rome #286
£1056 $1754 €1500 Visita al museo (30x40cm-12x16in) s. s.i.verso panel. 14-Jun-3 Meeting Art, Vercelli #189/R est:1500
£1133 $2085 €1700 Admiring Gericault's lovers (30x40cm-12x16in) s. s.i.verso board. 12-Jun-4 Meeting Art, Vercelli #962/R est:1000
Works on paper
£400 $736 €600 Arcades in Florence (50x35cm-20x14in) s.i. mixed media cardboard. 12-Jun-4 Meeting Art, Vercelli #581/R

PIAN, Antonio de (1784-1851) Italian
£31081 $54703 €46000 City - building similar to Castello Estense in Ferrara (110x155cm-43x61in) s. prov. 22-May-4 Lempertz, Koln #1581/R est:12000

PIANA, Giuseppe Ferdinando (1864-1958) Italian
£1000 $1840 €1500 River landscape with boats (27x20cm-11x8in) s. cardboard prov. 10-Jun-4 Christie's, Rome #37 est:100-1500

PIANE, Giovanni Maria delle (1660-1745) Italian
£1268 $2193 €1800 Portrait d'homme a la fraise (115x91cm-45x36in) 15-Dec-3 Bailly Pommery, Paris #61/R est:1500-2000

PIANE, Giovanni Maria delle (attrib) (1660-1745) Italian
£3667 $6563 €5500 Portrait of lady (140x100cm-55x39in) 12-May-4 Finarte Semenzato, Milan #84/R est:5000-7000

PIANI, Silvio (1862-?) Italian
£2013 $3765 €3000 Extensive river landscape in the pre-Alps (51x68cm-20x27in) s.d.1883. 24-Feb-4 Dorotheum, Vienna #179/R est:4000-4500

PIANO, Vittorio (1882-1970) Italian
£503 $891 €750 Landscape at sunset (40x50cm-16x20in) s. board. 1-May-4 Meeting Art, Vercelli #49

PIANON, Alessandro (20th C) Italian
Sculpture
£1413 $2600 €2063 Pulcini - chicken (23x10x10cm-9x4x4in) glass copper. 28-Mar-4 Wright, Chicago #140/R est:1500-2000
£1630 $3000 €2380 Pulcini - chicken (28x10x15cm-11x4x6in) glass internal murrines copper. 28-Mar-4 Wright, Chicago #141/R est:1500-2000

PIASEZKI, Leszek (1928-) German
£805 $1490 €1200 Battle against the Turks (70x120cm-28x47in) s. 9-Mar-4 Dorotheum, Vienna #89/R

PIAT, E (19th C) French
Sculpture
£1351 $2500 €1972 Bacchus scene of four cherubs in chariots being pulled by a tiger (51x41cm-20x16in) s. bronze. 13-Mar-4 DeFina, Austinburg #545/R est:800-1200

PIAT, Frederic Eugène (1827-1903) French
Sculpture
£76667 $141067 €115000 Paire de sphinges ailees (148cm-58in) s.d.1873 white marble pair. 9-Jun-4 Le Roux & Morel, Paris #244/R est:30000

PIATOWSKI, Henryk (1853-1932) Polish
£276 $500 €403 City and port (17x23cm-7x9in) s. board. 1-Apr-4 Ben-Ami, Tel Aviv #4746/R

PIATTELLA, Oscar (1932-) Italian
£1611 $2883 €2400 Red wall (120x80cm-47x31in) s.d.59 oil sand prov. 25-May-4 Sotheby's, Milan #85/R est:1000
Works on paper
£725 $1188 €1000 Yellow wall (133x110cm-52x43in) s.d.59 s.i.d.verso mixed media sand on canvas. 27-May-3 Sotheby's, Milan #114
£739 $1300 €1079 Abstract composition on gold (107x145cm-42x57in) s.d.1959 verso mixed media. 22-May-4 Selkirks, St. Louis #796/R

PIATTI, Antonio (1875-1962) Italian
£1831 $3168 €2600 Riva degli Schiavoni (30x40cm-12x16in) s.d.1924 panel. 11-Dec-3 Christie's, Rome #155/R est:3200

PIATTI, Giulio (1816-1872) Italian
£497 $904 €750 Bather. Portrait of gypsy (38x46cm-15x18in) one on canvas one on card two. 21-Jun-4 Pandolfini, Florence #60
£4238 $7714 €6400 Paolo and Francesca (58x68cm-23x27in) 21-Jun-4 Pandolfini, Florence #70/R est:6200-6400

PIATTOLI, Giuseppe (fl.1785-1807) Italian
Works on paper
£850 $1471 €1241 Sacrifice of Iphigenia (47x68cm-19x27in) col chk col ink brown wash. 12-Dec-3 Christie's, Kensington #403/R

PIAUBERT, Jean (1900-2001) French
£500 $895 €750 Composition - offerte au ciel (46x68cm-18x27in) s. oil gouache board. 15-May-4 Van Ham, Cologne #832/R
£605 $1083 €883 Cycle spatial - geometric composition (33x46cm-13x18in) s. i.d.1951 verso. 12-Jan-4 Rasmussen, Vejle #686 (D.KR 6400)
£699 $1189 €1000 Le table des vents (27x46cm-11x18in) s.i. prov. 23-Nov-3 Cornette de St.Cyr, Paris #277/R
£1093 $2000 €1650 Young land's (96x153cm-38x60in) 9-Apr-4 Claude Aguttes, Neuilly #94/R est:1500-2000
£1208 $2138 €1800 Offerte au ciel (50x94cm-20x37in) s. d.1958 verso. 27-Apr-4 Campo & Campo, Antwerp #183 est:1200-1800
£1215 $2030 €1750 Cri du soir (112x145cm-44x57in) s. 25-Oct-3 Cornette de St.Cyr, Paris #779 est:2000-3000
Works on paper
£719 $1129 €1050 Composition au cercle (81x100cm-32x39in) s. paint sand. 20-Apr-3 Deauville, France #142
£833 $1533 €1250 Signe (156x97cm-61x38in) s. mixed media panel. 10-Jun-4 Camard, Paris #132/R
£940 $1719 €1400 Noir imprevu (100x81cm-39x32in) s.i.d.1989 verso pigment sable resin panel prov. 7-Jul-4 Artcurial Briest, Paris #323 est:1500-2000
£940 $1719 €1400 Dans l'espace et dans le temps (100x81cm-39x32in) s.i.d.1989 verso pigment sable resin panel prov. 7-Jul-4 Artcurial Briest, Paris #324 est:1500-2000

PIAZZA, A (?) Italian
Sculpture
£5245 $8759 €7500 Cupid (71cm-28in) s. marble. 29-Jun-3 Eric Pillon, Calais #25/R

PIAZZETTA, Giambattista (attrib) (1682-1754) Italian
£1130 $2069 €1650 La visione de San Gerolamo (64x48cm-25x19in) i.verso prov. 4-Jun-4 Zofingen, Switzerland #2363/R est:3000 (S.FR 2600)
£13245 $24106 €20000 Saint Jerome (97x82cm-38x32in) prov. 16-Jun-4 Dorotheum, Vienna #14/R est:20000-30000

PIAZZETTA, Giambattista (circle) (1682-1754) Italian
£7000 $12600 €10220 Standard bearer (45x35cm-18x14in) prov. 21-Apr-4 Christie's, London #97/R est:7000-10000

PIAZZETTA, Giambattista (style) (1682-1754) Italian
£26000 $47580 €37960 Saint Lucy with putti (190x137cm-75x54in) prov. 6-Jul-4 Sotheby's, Olympia #404/R est:8000-12000

PIAZZO, Pierangelo (1934-1997) Italian

£382	$649	€550	Old chestnut trees (70x50cm-28x20in) s. s.i.d.1970 verso. 1-Nov-3 Meeting Art, Vercelli #443/R

PIAZZONI, Gottardo (1872-1945) American/Swiss

£11905	$22500	€17381	Evening prayer (33x48cm-13x19in) s.d.01 s.i. verso prov. 17-Feb-4 John Moran, Pasadena #30/R est:7000-9000

PICABIA, Francis (1878-1953) French

£10000	$15900	€14500	La gitane (62x52cm-24x20in) board prov. 11-Sep-3 Christie's, Kensington #182/R est:10000-15000
£13699	$23288	€20000	Voiliers au port de Saint-Tropez (46x55cm-18x22in) s. 9-Nov-3 Eric Pillon, Calais #74/R
£13907	$25450	€21000	Canal a Ouistreham, temps gris (38x46cm-15x18in) s.d.1908 s.i.d.verso. 9-Apr-4 Bailly Pommery, Paris #82/R est:15000-20000
£14000	$25480	€20440	Portrait (46x37cm-18x15in) s. oil card on canvas painted 1942 prov. 4-Feb-4 Sotheby's, London #340/R est:15000-20000
£15385	$25693	€22000	La baie des Cannoubiers (54x65cm-21x26in) s.d.1904 exhib. 30-Jun-3 Artcurial Briest, Paris #721/R est:10000-12000
£17606	$30458	€25000	La baie de Saint-Tropez (81x100cm-32x39in) s. s.i.d.1942-43 verso stretcher. 9-Dec-3 Chambelland & Giafferi, Paris #110/R est:30000-40000
£20950	$37500	€30587	Composition (73x60cm-29x24in) s. s.i.d.1946 verso masonite prov.lit. 6-May-4 Sotheby's, New York #337/R est:40000-60000
£21333	$39467	€32000	Paysage provencal (49x39cm-19x15in) s. panel exhib. 18-Jul-4 Sotheby's, Paris #306/R est:25000-35000
£25000	$41750	€36500	Sans titre (61x50cm-24x20in) s. board painted c.1946 prov.exhib. 21-Oct-3 Sotheby's, London #79/R est:18000-25000
£26974	$49632	€41000	Paysanne au chale rouge (92x73cm-36x29in) s. i.verso prov.exhib. 27-Jun-4 Versailles Encheres #124/R est:25000-30000
£29333	$53973	€44000	Bords du Loing, Moret (54x65cm-21x26in) s.d.1904. 8-Jun-4 Artcurial Briest, Paris #137/R est:45000-50000
£30000	$55500	€45000	Lavandieres (92x73cm-36x29in) s. painted 1935 prov.exhib. 18-Jul-4 Sotheby's, Paris #307/R est:50000-70000
£33333	$60000	€50000	Femme a la plage (75x53cm-30x21in) s. cardboard prov.lit. 22-Apr-4 Finarte Semenzato, Rome #341/R est:50000-55000
£35294	$60000	€51529	Bords de l'Orne a Benouville (54x65cm-21x26in) s.d.1908 prov.lit. 6-Nov-3 Sotheby's, New York #156/R est:50000-70000
£38000	$69920	€55480	L'etreinte (75x58cm-30x23in) s. board painted c.1940-1943. 23-Jun-4 Christie's, London #256/R est:45000-65000
£40000	$71600	€60000	La cabine de bains (73x92cm-29x36in) s.d prov. 13-May-4 Neumeister, Munich #463/R est:30000-40000
£40000	$74000	€60000	Portrait d'Yvonne Printemps (76x53cm-30x21in) s. cardboard on panel exhib. 18-Jul-4 Sotheby's, Paris #309/R est:60000-80000
£42667	$78933	€64000	Portrait de femme (36x33cm-14x13in) s. cardboard on panel prov.exhib. 18-Jul-4 Sotheby's, Paris #310/R est:35000-45000
£44118	$75000	€64412	Peniches sur le Loing, effet du matin (50x73cm-20x29in) s.d.1904 exhib.lit. 6-Nov-3 Sotheby's, New York #143/R est:60000-80000
£45000	$82800	€65700	Effet d'automne (60x72cm-24x28in) s.d.1905 prov. 22-Jun-4 Sotheby's, London #128/R est:40000-60000
£50000	$92500	€75000	Landscape (54x63cm-21x25in) s.i.d.1910 prov.exhib.lit. 18-Jul-4 Sotheby's, Paris #301/R est:70000-90000
£69832	$125000	€101955	Sycomore (92x73cm-36x29in) s.i. prov. 5-May-4 Christie's, Rockefeller NY #305/R est:100000-150000
£73333	$135667	€110000	Nu de dos devant la mer (75x53cm-30x21in) s. cardboard prov.exhib.lit. 18-Jul-4 Sotheby's, Paris #305/R est:50000-70000
£85000	$154700	€124100	Ferme a la petite mare (73x92cm-29x36in) s.d.1907 prov.lit. 4-Feb-4 Sotheby's, London #209/R est:60000-80000
£100000	$185000	€150000	Calanques (75x105cm-30x41in) s. cardboard on panel prov.exhib.lit. 18-Jul-4 Sotheby's, Paris #304/R est:65000-85000
£136667	$252833	€205000	Elegant (106x77cm-42x30in) s. cardboard painted 1942-43 prov.exhib. 18-Jul-4 Sotheby's, Paris #308/R est:75000-100000
£441176	$750000	€644117	Dispar (151x96cm-59x38in) s.i. oil on plywood painted c.1929 prov.exhib.lit. 5-Nov-3 Sotheby's, New York #30/R est:700000-900000
Works on paper			
£390	$632	€550	Vue de Fuenterrabia, Espagne (33x26cm-13x10in) s.d.1907 black crayon. 24-May-3 Martinot & Savignat, Pontoise #18/R
£408	$750	€596	Portrait of a woman (23x18cm-9x7in) i. pencil sold with a letter. 27-Jun-4 Hindman, Chicago #918/R
£496	$804	€700	Femme chantant (25x18cm-10x7in) s. black crayon. 24-May-3 Martinot & Savignat, Pontoise #19/R
£599	$1000	€875	Le Reve Risque (41x30cm-16x12in) s. W/C. 11-Oct-3 Auctions by the Bay, Alameda #1717/R
£638	$1066	€900	Scene de corrida (19x20cm-7x8in) s. ink. 20-Jun-3 Drouot Estimations, Paris #149
£658	$1211	€1000	Female nude study (22x17cm-9x7in) s. pencil wash. 22-Jun-4 De Veres Art Auctions, Dublin #81/R
£795	$1446	€1200	Personnage au regard fixe (23x14cm-9x6in) s. crayon W/C. 15-Jun-4 Rossini, Paris #160/R
£906	$1694	€1350	L'ombre est plus belle que l'academie (41x31cm-16x12in) mono. chl prov. 29-Feb-4 Versailles Encheres #182
£1034	$1728	€1500	Profile (31x20cm-12x8in) s.i.d.1944 Chinese ink. 17-Nov-3 Sant Agostino, Torino #185/R
£1192	$2170	€1800	Femme au tableau (23x14cm-9x6in) s. crayon W/C. 15-Jun-4 Rossini, Paris #159/R est:1800-2500
£1206	$2013	€1700	Portrait d'homme (19x15cm-7x6in) s. ink graphite. 20-Jun-3 Drouot Estimations, Paris #150 est:800-1000
£1225	$2192	€1800	Untitled (30x23cm-12x9in) mono. crayon exec c.1945-46 double-sided. 21-Mar-4 Calmels Cohen, Paris #79 est:2000-3000
£1343	$2376	€2000	Tete de femme (30x19cm-12x7in) s. crayon exec c.1940. 27-Apr-4 Artcurial Briest, Paris #76/R est:2000-3000
£1818	$3036	€2600	Visage et femme (32x25cm-13x10in) s.d.1950 chl. 25-Jun-3 Digard, Paris #87/R est:1200-2300
£1879	$3326	€2800	Tete de femme (31x25cm-12x10in) s. lead pencil exec c.1939-1940. 27-Apr-4 Artcurial Briest, Paris #77 est:3000-4000
£1944	$3247	€2800	Femme assise (24x18cm-9x7in) s. crayon drawing exec c.1925-30 exhib. 21-Oct-3 Artcurial Briest, Paris #89/R est:3000-4000
£2028	$3448	€2900	Portrait de femme (21x18cm-8x7in) mono. pencil. 27-Nov-3 Millon & Associes, Paris #82/R est:1500-2000
£2083	$3479	€3000	Torero (19x15cm-7x6in) s. ink drawing. 21-Oct-3 Artcurial Briest, Paris #88/R est:3000-4000
£2333	$4293	€3500	Angel (32x26cm-13x10in) s.d.1950 pencil W/C prov.exhib. 9-Jun-4 Christie's, Amsterdam #19/R est:4000-6000
£2333	$4293	€3500	Nu (17x32cm-7x13in) s. ink wash prov. 14-Jun-4 Tajan, Paris #118/R est:1800-2500
£2632	$4842	€4000	Deux amies (25x35cm-10x14in) s. graphite. 22-Jun-4 Ribeyre & Baron, Paris #59/R est:1500-1800
£2778	$4639	€4000	Nu au sofa (28x23cm-11x9in) s. chl stumping prov. 21-Oct-3 Artcurial Briest, Paris #6/R est:4500-6000
£2778	$4639	€4000	Scene de Tauromachie ou corrida (18x19cm-7x7in) s. brown ink drawing exec c.1903. 21-Oct-3 Artcurial Briest, Paris #87/R est:3000-3500
£2817	$4873	€4000	Paysage (25x34cm-10x13in) s.d.1910 pastel. 12-Dec-3 Piasa, Paris #173/R est:4000-5000
£3113	$5665	€4700	Buste de femme (38x28cm-15x11in) s, chl. 20-Jun-4 Versailles Encheres #30/R est:2500-3000
£3287	$5587	€4700	Nu assis, les bras en arriere (26x20cm-10x8in) s. grey crayon. 28-Nov-3 Blanchet, Paris #107/R est:2500-3000
£3333	$5567	€4800	L'espagnole au voile (26x20cm-10x8in) s. lead pencil chl prov. 21-Oct-3 Artcurial Briest, Paris #8/R est:3500-4500
£3401	$5408	€5000	Espagnole a la coiffe (31x23cm-12x9in) s. crayon. 21-Mar-3 Bailly Pommery, Paris #107/R
£3467	$6275	€5200	Portrait en buste (23x16cm-9x6in) wax crayon Chinese ink dr. 1-Apr-4 Piasa, Paris #274/R est:2500-3000
£3497	$6014	€5000	Untitled. mono.i. ink seven one sheet. 6-Dec-3 Renaud, Paris #259/R
£4133	$7399	€6200	Untitled (18x14cm-7x6in) W/C. 15-May-4 Renaud, Paris #241/R
£4200	$7014	€6132	Saint Mammes, La Seine (26x33cm-10x13in) s.d.1906 chl lit. 21-Oct-3 Sotheby's, London #10/R est:4000-6000
£4500	$8280	€6570	Portrait (28x19cm-11x7in) init. pencil chl prov. 24-Mar-4 Sotheby's, Olympia #162/R est:2000-3000
£4800	$8832	€7008	Une Amie (59x44cm-23x17in) s.i. W/C brush ink pencil. 24-Mar-4 Sotheby's, Olympia #150/R est:3000-4000
£5000	$8950	€7500	Untitled (20x15cm-8x6in) s. dr. 15-May-4 Renaud, Paris #242/R
£6145	$11000	€8972	Paysage (26x34cm-10x13in) s.d.1910 pastel. 6-May-4 Sotheby's, New York #414/R est:10000-15000
£6333	$11653	€9500	Female nude (42x29cm-17x11in) s. gouache. 8-Jun-4 Finarte Semenzato, Milan #3323/R est:6500-7000
£6500	$11960	€9490	Portrait (33x20cm-13x8in) s. W/C pen brush ink pencil prov. 24-Mar-4 Sotheby's, Olympia #144/R est:6000-8000
£7000	$12740	€10220	Grand gala du Chateau de Mai (27x35cm-11x14in) s.i.d.1928 black crayon pencil W/C. 4-Feb-4 Sotheby's, London #497/R est:8000-10000
£8500	$15640	€12410	Deux danseuses Espagnoles (22x18cm-9x7in) s. s.i.d.17 Juin 1923 verso W/C brush ink pencil. 24-Mar-4 Sotheby's, Olympia #139/R est:7000-9000
£9167	$15309	€13200	L'espagnole a la mantille (41x27cm-16x11in) s. W/C chl prov. 21-Oct-3 Artcurial Briest, Paris #5/R est:9000-12000
£14000	$25760	€20440	Tete de Folle (55x44cm-22x17in) s.i.d.1921 pencil brush ink. 24-Mar-4 Sotheby's, Olympia #152/R est:3000-4000
£18156	$32500	€26508	Tete de femme (42x28cm-17x11in) s. W/C chl ink wash. 6-May-4 Sotheby's, New York #468/R est:20000-30000
£19581	$33679	€28000	Visages entrelaces (63x48cm-25x19in) s.d.1932 chl Chinese ink dr. 8-Dec-3 Artcurial Briest, Paris #33/R est:30000-40000
£20530	$37364	€31000	L'Espagnole (61x46cm-24x18in) s. W/C gouache black crayon exec. c.1925-1928. 18-Jun-4 Piasa, Paris #34/R est:25000-30000
£26667	$49333	€40000	Literature (23x18cm-9x7in) s.i. Chinese ink prov.exhib.lit. 18-Jul-4 Sotheby's, Paris #302/R est:30000-40000
£27333	$50567	€41000	Nez pointu (48x31cm-19x12in) s. W/C crayon prov.exhib. 18-Jul-4 Sotheby's, Paris #303/R est:40000-50000
£27972	$48112	€40000	Semele (64x50cm-25x20in) s.i. W/C over a study by Paul Gauguin prov. 4-Dec-3 Piasa, Paris #96/R est:15000-20000
£35374	$63320	€52000	Dom Juan Indochinois. s. W/C lead pencil prov. 19-Mar-4 Millon & Associes, Paris #120/R est:20000-30000
£90000	$163800	€131400	Transparence - le chat (106x76cm-42x30in) s. W/C g. brush ink executed c.1929 p. 3-Feb-4 Sotheby's, London #77/R est:90000-120000

PICARD, Louis (1861-1940) French

£1338	$2315	€1900	Portrait of a woman with back uncovered (75x63cm-30x25in) s. canvas on canvas. 12-Dec-3 Berlinghof, Heidelberg #1111/R est:230
£3500	$6020	€5110	Sleeping model (73x92cm-29x36in) s. 4-Dec-3 Christie's, Kensington #163/R est:4000-6000
£3500	$6020	€5110	Sleeping beauty (66x81cm-26x32in) s. 4-Dec-3 Christie's, Kensington #164/R est:4000-6000

PICARDET, L (?) ?

£1497	$2800	€2186	Flower seller (46x33cm-18x13in) s.d.1899. 25-Feb-4 Doyle, New York #117/R est:4000-6000

PICART LE DOUX (19/20th C) French

£599	$1036	€850	Portrait de femme (46x38cm-18x15in) s. 10-Dec-3 Millon & Associes, Paris #87/R

PICART LE DOUX, Charles (1881-1959) French

£280	$467	€400	Nude in the studio (81x60cm-32x24in) s.d.52 panel. 11-Oct-3 De Vuyst, Lokeren #292
£450	$824	€657	Vase of tulips (46x38cm-18x15in) s. board. 7-Apr-4 Woolley & Wallis, Salisbury #204/R
£470	$874	€700	Nu dans l'atelier (81x60cm-32x24in) s. panel prov. 3-Mar-4 Tajan, Paris #58
£470	$864	€700	Vue de la Sainte Victoire (89x130cm-35x51in) s. 24-Mar-4 Joron-Derem, Paris #68
£620	$1135	€905	Paysage (51x62cm-20x24in) s.d.58 board. 7-Apr-4 Woolley & Wallis, Salisbury #201/R
£667	$1213	€1000	Nu assis sur le fauteuil (55x46cm-22x18in) s. panel. 4-Jul-4 Eric Pillon, Calais #218/R
£855	$1574	€1300	Les oliviers en Provence (50x64cm-20x25in) s.d.1950 panel. 28-Jun-4 Rossini, Paris #84/R
£861	$1567	€1300	Pont suspendu (27x41cm-11x16in) s.d. 19-Jun-4 St-Germain-en-Laye Encheres #199/R
£1333	$2453	€2000	Femme pensive (72x58cm-28x23in) s.d.1905. 14-Jun-4 Tajan, Paris #111 est:2000-2500
£1958	$3329	€2800	La danseuse de Rumba (150x122cm-59x48in) s. s.i.d.1937 verso panel. 18-Nov-3 Pierre Berge, Paris #85/R est:2000-2500
Works on paper			
£403	$741	€600	Scene de Bistrot (27x36cm-11x14in) s. ink wash. 24-Mar-4 Joron-Derem, Paris #69
£403	$741	€600	Au Cafe (27x31cm-11x12in) s.d.1916 ink ink wash. 24-Mar-4 Joron-Derem, Paris #70

PICART LEDOUX, Jean (1902-1982) French
Works on paper
£278 $464 €400 Colombe (26x24cm-10x9in) s. gouache. 25-Oct-3 Cornette de St.Cyr, Paris #538

PICART, Bernard (1673-1733) French
Works on paper
£646 $1157 €950 L'amoureux presse. La declaration (10x7cm-4x3in) pen brown ink wash black crayon htd gouache 2 in one frame. 19-Mar-4 Piasa, Paris #77/R
£1081 $1903 €1600 Saint Paul bitten by an adder (14x21cm-6x8in) s.d.1698 pen black ink wash prov.exhib. 19-May-4 Sotheby's, Amsterdam #114/R est:600-800
£1761 $3081 €2500 Epoux guides par l'Amour vers l'Hymen et se dirigeant vers le lit nuptial (12x14cm-5x6in) s.i.d.1716 black chk pen grey ink wash prov. 17-Dec-3 Christie's, Paris #57/R est:2000-3000
£1800 $2988 €2628 Apollo and Diana killing the children of Niobbe (32x44cm-13x17in) W/C htd white after Raphael prov. 5-Oct-3 Lots Road Auctions, London #362 est:2000-3000
£2958 $5176 €4200 Histoire d'Alexandre de Charles Le Brun. pen brown ink grey wash seven prov. 17-Dec-3 Christie's, Paris #41/R est:2000-3000
£3041 $5351 €4500 Male nude, seated on a stone ledge (37x47cm-15x19in) s.d.1722 red chk prov.exhib. 19-May-4 Sotheby's, Amsterdam #140/R est:2000-3000

PICART, Jean Michel (studio) (1600-1682) Flemish
£9868 $18158 €15000 Bouquet de fleurs sur entablemnt drape (112x88cm-44x35in) 24-Jun-4 Christie's, Paris #29/R est:8000-12000

PICASSO (20th C) Spanish
Sculpture
£2434 $4600 €3554 Untitled (3x41x33cm-1x16x13in) i.num.71/100 white col glaze ceramic platter. 21-Feb-4 Brunk, Ashville #761/R est:1000-2000
£3007 $5112 €4300 Visage d'homme (31x30cm-12x12in) terre de faience square plaque edition of 50 exec.c.1968/69 lit. 20-Nov-3 Camard, Paris #134/R est:4000-5000
£3297 $5835 €4946 Profil de Jackeline (19x19cm-7x7in) painted ceramic plate one of 500. 27-Apr-4 Bolsa de Arte, Rio de Janeiro #45/R (B.R 18000)
£9341 $16533 €14012 Woman's face (39x31cm-15x12in) painted ceramic plate one of 400. 27-Apr-4 Bolsa de Arte, Rio de Janeiro #47/R (B.R 51000)

PICASSO, Pablo (1881-1973) Spanish
£6533 $12021 €9800 Atelier (35x40cm-14x16in) s.i. eau forte. 10-Jun-4 Piasa, Paris #183
£9928 $18267 €14495 Buste blanc sur noir (65x50cm-26x20in) s.num.3/50 lithograph executed 4 march 1949 prov.lit. 29-Mar-4 Rasmussen, Copenhagen #64/R est:40000-60000 (D.KR 110000)
£10989 $19451 €16044 Nu assis, de Profil (45x60cm-18x24in) s.num.18/50 lithograph lit. 27-Apr-4 AB Stockholms Auktionsverk #1348/R est:40000-50000 (S.KR 150000)
£28000 $51520 €40880 Selfportrait (15x11cm-6x4in) s. pen ink buff envelope exec 1915 prov.exhib.lit. 24-Jun-4 Christie's, London #406/R est:20000-30000
£60000 $109200 €87600 Notre Dame (10x18cm-4x7in) d.13.4.45 on stretcher prov.exhib. 4-Feb-4 Sotheby's, London #279/R est:60000-80000
£80000 $147200 €116800 Nature morte au compotier (22x27cm-9x11in) oil col crayon painted 1924 prov. 23-Jun-4 Christie's, London #238/R est:80000-120000
£110000 $202400 €160600 Pomme, verre et couteau (20x25cm-8x10in) s.d.23 oil sand prov.exhib.lit. 22-Jun-4 Sotheby's, London #182/R est:120000-180000
£167421 $284615 €370000 Tete de femme (22x14cm-9x6in) d.1926 verso lit. 25-Nov-3 Pierre Berge, Paris #20/R est:120000-150000
£170000 $312800 €248200 La conversation (13x22cm-5x9in) s. panel painted 1901 prov.exhib.lit. 23-Jun-4 Christie's, London #222/R est:200000-300000
£205882 $350000 €300588 Verre et pipe (22x27cm-9x11in) s.d.18 verso oil sand India ink on canvas prov.exhib.lit. 5-Nov-3 Sotheby's, New York #44/R est:250000-350000
£235294 $400000 €343529 Verre et fruits (39x46cm-15x18in) s.d.20 Juin 44 verso prov.exhib.lit. 5-Nov-3 Sotheby's, New York #53/R est:300000-500000
£250000 $455000 €365000 Notre-Dame (50x32cm-20x13in) d.44 paper on canvas prov.exhib.lit. 3-Feb-4 Sotheby's, London #52/R est:250000-300000
£256667 $469700 €385000 Paysage, vu de l'atelier de l'artiste (65x81cm-26x32in) s.d.27/4/67 i.verso lit. 7-Jun-4 Artcurial Briest, Paris #38/R est:400000-500000
£280420 $482322 €401000 Nature morte, verre et compotier aux fruits (34x46cm-13x18in) s.d.29-1-38 prov.lit. 3-Dec-3 Beaussant & Lefèvre, Paris #72/R est:250000-300000
£305882 $520000 €446588 Buste d'homme a la pipe (97x66cm-38x26in) s.d.27.2.69 oil corrugated cardboard on panel prov.exhib.lit. 5-Nov-3 Sotheby's, New York #58/R est:600000-800000
£379888 $680000 €554636 Portrait de jeune homme (27x18cm-11x7in) s.d.1915 panel prov.exhib.lit. 4-May-4 Christie's, Rockefeller NY #21/R est:400000-600000
£422535 $739437 €600000 Trois femmes a la fontaine (48x56cm-19x22in) s.d.21 prov.exhib.lit. 18-Dec-3 Tajan, Paris #34/R est:800000-1000000
£480000 $873600 €700800 Homme assis et centaure (81x100cm-32x39in) d.72 verso prov.lit. 3-Feb-4 Sotheby's, London #56/R est:500000-700000
£496644 $888993 €740000 Tete d'homme et nu assis (46x55cm-18x22in) s. painted 1964 lit. 29-May-4 Farsetti, Prato #534/R
£506667 $927200 €760000 Nature morte au crane et au pot (50x60cm-20x24in) s.d.15 Aut 43 d. verso prov.exhib.lit. 5-Jun-4 Lempertz, Koln #935/R est:500000-600000
£547486 $980000 €799330 Peintre au chapeau (73x60cm-29x24in) s. d.65 verso prov.exhib.lit. 6-May-4 Sotheby's, New York #107/R est:750000-1000000
£558659 $1000000 €815642 Dejeuner sur l'herbe (65x81cm-26x32in) s.d.61 i.d.verso prov.exhib.lit. 4-May-4 Christie's, Rockefeller NY #38/R est:1200000-1600000
£720000 $1310400 €1051200 Femme au chapeau assise (81x65cm-32x26in) s. d.62 verso prov.lit. 3-Feb-4 Sotheby's, London #51/R est:350000-450000
£735294 $1250000 €1073529 Le tremplin (100x81cm-39x32in) s.d.22.7.57 verso prov.lit. 5-Nov-3 Christie's, Rockefeller NY #349/R est:500000-700000
£800000 $1456000 €1168000 Monument tete de femme (65x54cm-26x21in) s.d.29 d.XXIX on stretcher prov.exhib.lit. 3-Feb-4 Sotheby's, London #74/R est:600000-800000
£840000 $1537200 €1226400 Dans l'arene (24x30cm-9x12in) s. oil gouache pastel card painted 1900 prov.exhib.lit. 2-Feb-4 Christie's, London #20/R est:400000-600000
£882353 $1500000 €1288235 Baigneuse (62x38cm-24x15in) s. painted 1909 prov.lit. 4-Nov-3 Christie's, Rockefeller NY #40/R est:2000000-3000000
£1005587 $1800000 €1468157 Bouteille de Malaga (46x55cm-18x22in) s. painted 1919 prov.exhib.lit. 4-May-4 Christie's, Rockefeller NY #26/R est:1800000-2500000
£1033520 $1850000 €1508939 Peintre et modele (73x116cm-29x46in) i.d.63 verso prov.exhib.lit. 4-May-4 Christie's, Rockefeller NY #37/R est:2000000-3000000
£1058824 $1800000 €1545883 Nu assis (146x114cm-57x45in) i.d.11.2.61 verso prov.exhib.lit. 5-Nov-3 Sotheby's, New York #34/R est:1250000-1750000
£1235294 $2100000 €1803529 La mandoliniste assise (38x24cm-15x9in) s.verso painted 1911 prov.exhib.lit. 5-Nov-3 Sotheby's, New York #39/R est:1200000-1600000
£1284916 $2300000 €1875977 Nature morte a la cafetiere (81x100cm-32x39in) s. painted 1947 prov.exhib.lit. 6-May-4 Sotheby's, New York #143/R est:1500000-2000000
£1340782 $2400000 €1957542 Femme assise dans un fauteuil (130x97cm-51x38in) d.62 verso prov.exhib.lit. 4-May-4 Christie's, Rockefeller NY #34/R est:2000000-3000000
£1600000 $2928000 €2336000 Guitare sur tapis rouge (87x116cm-34x46in) s.d.22 prov.exhib.lit. 2-Feb-4 Christie's, London #40/R est:1400000-1800000
£2000000 $3640000 €2920000 Carafe et plante de tomate (74x92cm-29x36in) s. d.44 verso prov.exhib.lit. 21-Jun-4 Sotheby's, London #54/R est:1800000-2500000
£2117647 $3600000 €3091765 Personnage a la pipe (130x97cm-51x38in) d.16.11.71 prov.exhib.lit. 5-Nov-3 Sotheby's, New York #29/R est:2000000-2500000
£2122905 $3800000 €3099441 Femme assise (116x89cm-46x35in) s.d.49 s.d.verso prov.exhib.lit. 6-May-4 Sotheby's, New York #141/R est:4000000-6000000
£2200000 $4004000 €3212000 Femme assise au chapeau de paille (65x54cm-26x21in) d.38 prov.lit. 3-Feb-4 Sotheby's, London #46/R est:2400000-3200000
£2200000 $4004000 €3212000 Mousquetaire et nu couche (130x162cm-51x64in) s.d.67 d.verso prov.lit. 3-Feb-4 Sotheby's, London #49/R est:1800000-2500000
£2500000 $4575000 €3650000 Buste de femme (73x60cm-29x24in) s.d.42 prov.exhib.lit. 2-Feb-4 Christie's, London #38/R est:2500000-3500000
£2764706 $4700000 €4036471 Femme endormie (46x46cm-18x18in) i.d.16.5.XXXII prov.lit. 5-Nov-3 Sotheby's, New York #26/R est:3000000-4000000
£3407821 $6100000 €4975419 Plante de tomate (91x72cm-36x28in) s. d.44 verso prov.exhib.lit. 5-May-4 Sotheby's, New York #27/R est:3000000-4000000
£4550000 $8281000 €6643000 Femme couchee a la meche blonde (130x162cm-51x64in) s.d.21 d.on stretcher prov.exhib.lit. 21-Jun-4 Sotheby's, London #50/R est:2000000-3000000
£5865922 $10500000 €8564246 Nu accroupi (146x114cm-57x45in) s. d.59 verso prov.exhib.lit. 6-May-4 Sotheby's, New York #105/R est:3000000-4000000
£7374302 $13200000 €10766481 Sauvetage (97x130cm-38x51in) s. painted 1932 prov.exhib.lit. 6-May-4 Sotheby's, New York #120/R est:10000000-15000000
£51955308 $93000000 €75854750 Garcon a la pipe (100x81cm-39x32in) s. painted 1905 prov.exhib.lit. 5-May-4 Sotheby's, New York #7/R
Photographs
£1867 $3435 €2800 Picasso en costume de torero (12x17cm-5x7in) s.i. black and white photograph prov. 8-Jun-4 Artcurial Briest, Paris #131/R est:3000-3500
Prints
£1519 $2750 €2218 Tete d'homme au bouc (18x14cm-7x6in) s.num.15/100 photolithograph. 19-Apr-4 Bonhams & Butterfields, San Francisco #204/R est:1500-2500
£1622 $3000 €2368 Susanne et les Vieillards (27x37cm-11x15in) s.num.21/50 etching aquatint. 12-Feb-4 Christie's, Rockefeller NY #364/R est:3000-4000
£1667 $2983 €2500 Couple (33x25cm-13x10in) eau forte lit. 12-May-4 Stadion, Trieste #631/R est:2200-3000
£1703 $3100 €2486 Modele contemplant un groupe sculpte (13x17cm-5x7in) s. etching edition of 260. 7-Feb-4 Sloans & Kenyon, Bethesda #1219/R est:3500-4500
£1720 $3200 €2511 Toros en vallauris (99x63cm-39x25in) s. col linoleum cut. 2-Mar-4 Swann Galleries, New York #501/R est:2000-3000
£1720 $3200 €2511 Toros vallauris 1958 (100x65cm-39x26in) col linoleum cut. 2-Mar-4 Swann Galleries, New York #503/R est:1200-1800
£1730 $3200 €2526 Television, course de chars a l'antique (31x41cm-12x16in) s.num.6/50 etching. 12-Feb-4 Christie's, Rockefeller NY #365/R est:4000-6000
£1730 $3200 €2526 Femme sur un char Romain, spectateurs Rembranesques, et gamines (32x39cm-13x15in) s.num.6/50 etching drypoint aquatint. 12-Feb-4 Christie's, Rockefeller NY #368/R est:4000-6000
£1732 $3100 €2529 Untitled, 347 Series (15x20cm-6x8in) s.d.Aug 18 1968 etching num.23/50. 11-Jan-4 William Jenack, New York #61 est:2000-2500
£1747 $3179 €2551 Nature morte au livre. s.i. lithograph. 17-Jun-4 Kornfeld, Bern #686 est:5000 (S.FR 4000)
£1786 $3250 €2608 Les repos du sculpteur III (13x17cm-5x7in) s. etching edition of 250. 7-Feb-4 Sloans & Kenyon, Bethesda #1218/R est:4500-5500
£1788 $3200 €2610 Femme nue couchee (5x16cm-2x6in) s. color lithograph. 6-May-4 Swann Galleries, New York #560/R est:2500-3500
£1796 $3000 €2622 Huit silhouettes (33x44cm-13x17in) s.num.18/50 lithograph. 21-Oct-3 Bonhams & Butterfields, San Francisco #1224/R
£1796 $3000 €2622 From Sable Mouvant (38x28cm-15x11in) s.num.3/7 aquatint. 21-Oct-3 Bonhams & Butterfields, San Francisco #1231/R
£1796 $3000 €2622 From Sable Mouvant (39x28cm-15x11in) s.num.3/7 aquatint. 21-Oct-3 Bonhams & Butterfields, San Francisco #1232/R
£1816 $3250 €2651 Peintre et son modele (23x30cm-9x12in) s. num.6/60 lithograph. 16-May-4 Wright, Chicago #189/R est:2000-3000
£1836 $3250 €2681 Deux hommes sculptes (25x18cm-10x7in) s. drypoint etching edition of 250. 1-May-4 Thomaston Place, Thomaston #822/R
£1840 $3000 €2686 Untitled (25x33cm-10x13in) s.num.142/250 etching. 28-Sep-3 Simpson's, Houston #210/R
£1867 $3435 €2800 La sauterelle (41x31cm-16x12in) s. aquatint etching exec. 1936 one of 47. 12-Jun-4 Villa Grisebach, Berlin #384/R est:3000-4000
£1875 $3000 €2738 Femme nue couchee (5x16cm-2x6in) s. col lithograph edition of 1000. 18-Sep-3 Swann Galleries, New York #507/R est:3000-5000
£1879 $3477 €2800 Untitled (44x54cm-17x21in) s. num.42/50 engraving. 11-Mar-4 Galleria Pace, Milan #29/R est:3200-3400
£1879 $3477 €2800 Gladiators (32x39cm-13x15in) s. num.31/50 engraving prov. 11-Mar-4 Galleria Pace, Milan #59/R est:2800-3400
£1892 $3500 €2762 Femme assise et femme de dos (28x20cm-11x8in) s. etching edition of 250. 12-Feb-4 Christie's, Rockefeller NY #353/R est:4000-6000
£1899 $3400 €2773 Le danes des faunes (41x52cm-16x20in) lithograph. 6-May-4 Swann Galleries, New York #558a/R est:2000-3000
£1912 $3250 €2792 Portrait de Max Jacob (20x15cm-8x6in) s. drypoint. 31-Oct-3 Sotheby's, New York #374
£1946 $3250 €2841 Madoura (10x20cm-4x8in) s.num.18/100 col linocut. 11-Nov-3 Doyle, New York #351/R est:2000-3000
£1955 $3500 €2854 Faune et chevre (20x11cm-8x4in) s.num.22/50 linocut. 4-May-4 Doyle, New York #241/R est:1500-2000
£1963 $3200 €2866 Affiche pour Vallauris Peinture et Lumiere X Anniversaire (75x62cm-30x24in) s. num.90/185 col linocut on Arches executed 1964. 24-Sep-3 Christie's, Rockefeller NY #134/R est:2000-3000
£1963 $3200 €2866 Combat de Gladiateurs (45x57cm-18x22in) st.sig.num.18/50 etching BFK Rives executed 1970. 24-Sep-3 Christie's, Rockefeller NY #137/R est:3000-3500
£1974 $3632 €3000 Untitled. s. num.31 engraving. 24-Jun-4 Credit Municipal, Paris #10/R est:3000-4000
£1977 $3500 €2886 Famille de Saltimbanques (18x25cm-7x10in) s. drypoint etching edition of 300. 1-May-4 Thomaston Place, Thomaston #825/R
£1977 $3500 €2886 Tauros en vallauris (63x53cm-25x21in) s. linoleum. 30-Apr-4 Sotheby's, New York #189/R est:2000-3000
£2000 $3200 €2920 Pigeon et ses petits (40x53cm-16x21in) s.num.40/50 lithograph. 18-Sep-3 Swann Galleries, New York #493/R est:2000-3000
£2000 $3400 €2920 Series 347 167 (13x9cm-5x4in) s.num.45/50 etching. 6-Nov-3 Swann Galleries, New York #696/R est:2500-3500
£2000 $3440 €2920 Sculpture d'une jeune homme a la coupe (26x19cm-10x7in) etching edition of 300. 4-Dec-3 Sotheby's, London #194/R est:2500-3500

£2000	$3620	€3000	Maternity (50x38cm-20x15in) s.d.1963 col lithograph. 2-Apr-4 Farsetti, Prato #340 est:1600-1900
£2000	$3580	€3000	Exposition 1958 Vallauris (64x53cm-25x21in) s.i. col linocut. 15-May-4 Dr Sturies, Dusseldorf #138/R
£2014	$3304	€2800	L'atelier de Cannes (44x32cm-17x13in) s.i.d. col lithograph. 4-Jun-3 Ketterer, Hamburg #764/R est:2000-2500
£2054	$3800	€2999	Cinesias et Myrrhine (22x15cm-9x6in) s. etching. 12-Feb-4 Christie's, Rockefeller NY #354/R est:2000-3000
£2054	$3800	€2999	Jeune couple, vieux couple, spectateur, avec un carrosse au fond (32x41cm-13x16in) s.num.6/50 mezzotint. 12-Feb-4 Christie's, Rockefeller NY #371/R est:3000-4000
£2054	$3800	€2999	Homme avec deux femmes nues (32x39cm-13x15in) s.num.6/50 mezzotint. 12-Feb-4 Christie's, Rockefeller NY #374/R est:3500-4500
£2054	$3800	€2999	Deux sculpteurs devant une statue (23x33cm-9x13in) s. etching. 12-Mar-4 Jackson's, Cedar Falls #908/R est:2000-3000
£2059	$3500	€3006	Pique I (50x65cm-20x26in) s. lithograph. 31-Oct-3 Sotheby's, New York #377
£2059	$3500	€3006	Television (45x56cm-18x22in) etching exec.1968. 4-Nov-3 Christie's, Rockefeller NY #181/R est:3000-4000
£2059	$3500	€3006	Cavalier (25x33cm-10x13in) s. num.33/50 aquatint exec.1968. 4-Nov-3 Christie's, Rockefeller NY #186/R est:3500-4500
£2069	$3455	€3000	Repos du sculpteur (27x19cm-11x7in) i. eau forte exec.1933 lit. 13-Nov-3 Finarte Semenzato, Rome #42/R est:1500-1800
£2069	$3455	€3000	Untitled (31x32cm-12x13in) s. num.15/50 eau forte. 13-Nov-3 Galleria Pace, Milan #109/R est:3300
£2072	$3750	€3025	Homme et femme (20x28cm-8x11in) s.num.19/250 etching. 19-Apr-4 Bonhams & Butterfields, San Francisco #196/R est:3000-5000
£2072	$3750	€3025	Jeu de la Corrida (57x76cm-22x30in) s.num.38/50 lithograph. 19-Apr-4 Bonhams & Butterfields, San Francisco #199/R est:2500-3500
£2072	$3750	€3025	Trois mouquetaires saluant une femme au lit (9x12cm-4x5in) s.num.40/50 etching aquatint. 19-Apr-4 Bonhams & Butterfields, San Francisco #203/R est:2000-3000
£2096	$3500	€3060	Series 347-261 (33x20cm-13x8in) s.num.17/50 etching. 21-Oct-3 Bonhams & Butterfields, San Francisco #1233/R
£2098	$3566	€3000	Raphael et la Fornanina XXII (15x20cm-6x8in) s.d.8.9.68 etching. 26-Nov-3 Dorotheum, Vienna #211/R est:2800-3000
£2098	$3608	€3000	Peintre et modele aux cheveux longs (38x28cm-15x11in) s.d.1964 aquatint etching. 2-Dec-3 Hauswedell & Nolte, Hamburg #535/R est:4500
£2098	$3608	€3000	Peintre debout a son chevalet, avec une modele (38x28cm-15x11in) s.d.1964 aquatint etching. 2-Dec-3 Hauswedell & Nolte, Hamburg #536/R est:4000
£2098	$3608	€3000	Sculpteur et sculpture (38x28cm-15x11in) s.d.1965 drypoint etching aquatint. 2-Dec-3 Hauswedell & Nolte, Hamburg #537/R est:4000
£2098	$3566	€3000	L'abreuvoir - chevaux au bain (12x19cm-5x7in) drypoint. 29-Nov-3 Villa Grisebach, Berlin #147/R est:3000-4000
£2100	$3486	€3066	Femmes d'Alger dans leur apartement (28x35cm-11x14in) lithograph one of five. 6-Oct-3 Sotheby's, London #115/R est:2000-2500
£2113	$3655	€3000	Don Quichotte et Sancho Panca (34x34cm-13x13in) s.num. lithograph edition of 50. 11-Dec-3 Piasa, Paris #124
£2113	$3655	€3000	La bonne aventure avec un curieux simiesque (21x15cm-8x6in) s. etching vellum edition of 72. 11-Dec-3 Piasa, Paris #133
£2118	$3600	€3092	L'etreinte II (30x37cm-12x15in) drypoint edition of 56. 6-Nov-3 Swann Galleries, New York #673/R est:4000-6000
£2118	$3600	€3092	Homme couche et femme accroupie (43x51cm-17x20in) s.num.5/50 lithograph. 6-Nov-3 Swann Galleries, New York #686/R est:4000-6000
£2118	$3600	€3092	Series 347 191 (15x21cm-6x8in) s.num.17/50 aquatint drypoint. 6-Nov-3 Swann Galleries, New York #697/R est:3000-5000
£2119	$3750	€3094	Le repos du sculpteur III (18x25cm-7x10in) s. drypoint etching edition of 300. 1-May-4 Thomaston Place, Thomaston #820/R
£2119	$3750	€3094	Exposition (64x53cm-25x21in) s.num.162/175 linoleum cut print. 30-Apr-4 Sotheby's, New York #190/R est:3000-4000
£2128	$3553	€3000	Raphael et la Fornarina XVI (15x20cm-6x8in) s.d.4.9.68 etching. 14-Oct-3 Dorotheum, Vienna #184/R est:2600-2800
£2133	$3925	€3200	La maison Tellier, filles entre elles (36x49cm-14x19in) st.sig. etching exec. 1971 one of 50. 11-Jun-4 Villa Grisebach, Berlin #1596/R est:2000-3000
£2147	$3500	€3135	Les Deux Saltimbanques (21x18cm-8x7in) etching edition of 250 executed 1905. 24-Sep-3 Christie's, Rockefeller NY #123/R est:2000-3000
£2147	$3800	€3135	Exposition Vallauris (64x53cm-25x21in) s.num.137/175 col linocut. 28-Apr-4 Christie's, Rockefeller NY #162/R est:2000-3000
£2147	$3800	€3135	Egyptien et femmes (21x27cm-8x11in) s.num.27/50 etching. 28-Apr-4 Christie's, Rockefeller NY #188/R est:3000-5000
£2147	$3800	€3135	Autoportrait dedouble, Maja au pigeon (23x32cm-9x13in) st.sig.num.27/50 etching drypoint. 28-Apr-4 Christie's, Rockefeller NY #190/R est:4500-5500
£2147	$3800	€3135	Tetes et figures emmelees (27x20cm-11x8in) s. etching edition of 250. 28-Apr-4 Christie's, Rockefeller NY #127/R est:2500-3500
£2156	$3600	€3148	Composition au vase de fleurs (50x66cm-20x26in) s.num.28/50 col lithograph. 21-Oct-3 Bonhams & Butterfields, San Francisco #1225/R
£2162	$3719	€3157	From: Dessins (30x25cm-12x10in) s. lithograph. 2-Dec-3 Koller, Zurich #3360/R est:2000-3000 (S.FR 4800)
£2162	$4000	€3157	Femme et enfant sur un char Romain, avec une ecuyere-acrobate (28x39cm-11x15in) s.num.6/50 drypoint. 12-Feb-4 Christie's, Rockefeller NY #369/R est:5000-7000
£2162	$4000	€3157	Homme frise se balancant, avec odalisques, putto, et Espagnol de profil (28x39cm-11x15in) s.num.6/50 aquatint. 12-Feb-4 Christie's, Rockefeller NY #372/R est:3500-4500
£2162	$4000	€3157	Peintre, modele au chapeau de paille, et gentilhomme (28x39cm-11x15in) s.num.6/50 etching. 12-Feb-4 Christie's, Rockefeller NY #379/R est:5000-7000
£2200	$3784	€3212	Sculptures et vase de fleurs (26x19cm-10x7in) etching edition of 300. 4-Dec-3 Sotheby's, London #184/R est:2000-3000
£2200	$3784	€3212	Rembrandt et deux femmes (28x20cm-11x8in) etching edition of 300. 4-Dec-3 Sotheby's, London #187/R est:2500-3000
£2200	$3784	€3212	Le repos de sculpteur devant une bacchanale au taureau (19x26cm-7x10in) etching edition of 300. 4-Dec-3 Sotheby's, London #190/R est:2500-3500
£2200	$3938	€3300	Bacchanale I (45x59cm-18x23in) s. lithograph. 15-May-4 Van Ham, Cologne #834/R est:3800
£2200	$4026	€3212	Personnages (33x22cm-13x9in) s.num.16/125 etching. 3-Jun-4 Christie's, Kensington #146/R est:2000-3000
£2200	$4004	€3212	Untitled, 156 series (23x30cm-9x12in) st.sig.num.43/50 etching. 1-Jul-4 Sotheby's, London #278/R est:2500-3500
£2200	$4004	€3300	Toros y toreros (37x27cm-15x11in) s.num.104 lithograph. 2-Jul-4 Bloomsbury, London #328/R est:1500-2000
£2211	$3957	€3250	Vallauris (80x65cm-31x26in) s. linocut prov. 22-Mar-4 Durán, Madrid #152/R est:3000
£2215	$4097	€3300	Figures (41x49cm-16x19in) s. num.19/50 engraving. 11-Mar-4 Galleria Pace, Milan #89/R est:4000-5200
£2215	$3920	€3300	Le peintre (97x73cm-38x29in) s.i. col offset lithograph. 30-Apr-4 Dr Fritz Nagel, Stuttgart #926/R est:1500
£2216	$4100	€3235	Femme aguichant un homme songeur (28x39cm-11x15in) s.num.6/50 etching. 12-Feb-4 Christie's, Rockefeller NY #375/R est:5000-7000
£2235	$3800	€3263	Bacchanale au hibou et au jeune homme masque (26x31cm-10x12in) s. etching. 6-Nov-3 Swann Galleries, New York #685/R est:5000-8000
£2235	$3800	€3263	Personnage assis et personnage couche (44x53cm-17x21in) s.num.5/50 lithograph. 6-Nov-3 Swann Galleries, New York #687/R est:3000-5000
£2238	$3737	€3200	La danse barbare (18x23cm-7x9in) drypoint etching. 10-Oct-3 Winterberg, Heidelberg #1805/R est:3800
£2238	$3849	€3200	Le faune (30x25cm-12x10in) s. col aquatint etching. 2-Dec-3 Hauswedell & Nolte, Hamburg #547/R est:1000
£2238	$3804	€3200	Eau forte et pointe seche 2 aout 19681 (31x31cm-12x12in) s. etching drypoint. 29-Nov-3 Bassenge, Berlin #6952/R est:3800
£2245	$3727	€3255	Peintre au travail (23x33cm-9x13in) s.num.16/50 aquatint drypoint. 16-Jun-3 Blomqvist, Lysaker #1176/R est:18000-20000 (N.KR 26000)
£2248	$4046	€3282	Untitled (20x27cm-8x11in) s.num.7/50 etching lit. 26-Apr-4 Bukowskis, Stockholm #436/R est:30000-35000 (S.KR 31000)
£2258	$4200	€3297	Nature mort au pot de gres (43x59cm-17x23in) s.num.26/50 lithograph. 2-Mar-4 Swann Galleries, New York #495/R est:4000-6000
£2260	$4000	€3300	Cape et epee (17x20cm-7x8in) s.num.27/50 aquatint. 28-Apr-4 Christie's, Rockefeller NY #170/R est:2500-3500
£2266	$3852	€3308	Homme et femme (19x28cm-7x11in) s.num.125/250 etching lit. 4-Nov-3 Bukowskis, Stockholm #433/R est:40000-45000 (S.KR 30000)
£2267	$4171	€3400	Fumeur avec un home (41x31cm-16x12in) s.d.1964 aquatint etching drypoint. 10-Jun-4 Hauswedell & Nolte, Hamburg #577/R est:4000
£2270	$4200	€3314	La toilette (27x21cm-11x8in) s.i.num.7/50 lithograph. 12-Feb-4 Christie's, Rockefeller NY #352/R est:4000-6000
£2271	$4133	€3316	Peintre et modele avec un noeud dans les cheveux. s.i. etching. 17-Jun-4 Kornfeld, Bern #661 est:6000 (S.FR 5200)
£2275	$3800	€3322	Le cirque (31x44cm-12x17in) s.num.37/50 lithograph. 11-Nov-3 Christie's, Rockefeller NY #161/R est:3000-5000
£2282	$4039	€3400	Verre et fleur. num.37/50 lithograph. 27-Apr-4 Campo & Campo, Antwerp #778
£2294	$3830	€3326	Charrette foraine conduite par un petit animal, avec nu et amour dans le ciel. s.i. drypoint. 19-Jun-3 Kornfeld, Bern #836 est:6000 (S.FR 5000)
£2294	$3830	€3326	Odalisque. s.i. aquatint drypoint. 19-Jun-3 Kornfeld, Bern #840 est:5000 (S.FR 5000)
£2294	$3830	€3326	Homme pensif chez une jeune femme. s.i. aquatint drypoint. 19-Jun-3 Kornfeld, Bern #843 est:6000 (S.FR 5000)
£2294	$3830	€3326	Degas, Celestine et trois filles. st.sig.i. etching. 19-Jun-3 Kornfeld, Bern #850 est:5000 (S.FR 5000)
£2314	$4212	€3378	Peintre en demi figure et modele assis en tailleur. s.i. aquatint etching schabeisen. 17-Jun-4 Kornfeld, Bern #664 est:4000 (S.FR 5300)
£2321	$4177	€3389	Taureau et cheval (19x28cm-7x11in) s.num.42/99 etching lit. 26-Apr-4 Bukowskis, Stockholm #415/R est:20000-25000 (S.KR 32000)
£2331	$3800	€3403	Affiche pour Toros en Vallauris (90x59cm-35x23in) s. num.112/200 col linocut wove paper. 24-Sep-3 Christie's, Rockefeller NY #129/R est:3500-4500
£2341	$3980	€3418	Venus Foreine (32x42cm-13x17in) s.num.28/50 etching drypoint prov.lit. 5-Nov-3 AB Stockholms Auktionsverk #1276/R est:35000-40000 (S.KR 31000)
£2345	$3916	€3400	Repos du sculpteur (19x27cm-7x11in) i. eau forte exec.1933 lit. 13-Nov-3 Finarte Semenzato, Rome #46/R est:1500-1800
£2353	$4000	€3435	Vieux roi (65x49cm-26x19in) s. lithograph. 31-Oct-3 Sotheby's, New York #376
£2366	$4400	€3454	Autre chose (10x5cm-4x2in) s. num.21/30 etching. 2-Mar-4 Swann Galleries, New York #500/R est:4000-6000
£2373	$4200	€3465	La Celestine (17x21cm-7x8in) s.num.27/50 etching aquatint. 28-Apr-4 Christie's, Rockefeller NY #171/R est:3000-5000
£2381	$4262	€3476	Tete sur fond noir (69x54cm-27x21in) s.i.d.53 lithograph. 22-Mar-4 Philippe Schuler, Zurich #4040/R est:1300-2000 (S.FR 5500)
£2381	$4262	€3500	Vallauris (73x61cm-29x24in) s. linocut prov. 22-Mar-4 Durán, Madrid #151/R est:3000
£2393	$4307	€3590	Heads and stone (50x63cm-20x25in) s.num.42/50 lithograph. 25-Apr-4 Goteborg Auktionsverk, Sweden #456/R est:40000 (S.KR 33000)
£2400	$4296	€3600	Nature morte au pot de gres (43x59cm-17x23in) s. lithograph. 15-May-4 Bassenge, Berlin #7102/R est:4000
£2400	$4368	€3504	Untitled, 347 series (10x16cm-4x6in) s.num.17/50 aquatint. 1-Jul-4 Sotheby's, London #275/R est:1500-2000
£2400	$4368	€3504	Untitled, 347 series (15x22cm-6x9in) s.num.17/50 aquatint. 1-Jul-4 Sotheby's, London #276/R est:2000-3000
£2400	$4416	€3600	Composition du a aout 1947 (33x49cm-13x19in) s. col lithograph one of 50. 12-Jun-4 Villa Grisebach, Berlin #818/R est:1400-1800
£2431	$4060	€3525	Portrait de Piero Crommelynck II. s.i. aquatint etching. 19-Jun-3 Kornfeld, Bern #827/R est:6000 (S.FR 5300)
£2448	$4161	€3500	Corrida (29x43cm-11x17in) s. lithograph. 29-Nov-3 Villa Grisebach, Berlin #875/R est:2000-2500
£2448	$4161	€3500	Char romain, avec ecuyere tombant, femme nue et spectateurs (32x39cm-13x15in) s. etching. 29-Nov-3 Villa Grisebach, Berlin #308a/R est:4000-6000
£2455	$4223	€3584	Football (51x73cm-20x29in) s.d.61 num.100/200 col lithograph. 2-Dec-3 Ritchie, Toronto #160/R est:5000-7000 (C.D 5500)
£2465	$4313	€3500	Taureau attaquant un cheval (17x23cm-7x9in) s. eau forte exec.1921 one of 102. 17-Dec-3 Il Ponte, Milan #1145/R est:2800-3000
£2465	$4264	€3500	Modele accoude sur un tableau (34x24cm-13x9in) s.num.11/50 engraving. 10-Dec-3 Millon & Associes, Paris #25/R est:2500-3000
£2466	$4438	€3600	Peintre travaillant (19x28cm-7x11in) s.num.42/99 etching lit. 26-Apr-4 Bukowskis, Stockholm #416/R est:20000-25000 (S.KR 34000)
£2471	$4200	€3608	Taureau attaquant un cheval (18x24cm-7x9in) s. etching. 6-Nov-3 Swann Galleries, New York #668/R est:5000-8000
£2471	$4200	€3608	Etreinte (45x55cm-18x22in) s. num.11/50 aquatint exec.1963. 4-Nov-3 Christie's, Rockefeller NY #174/R est:4000-6000
£2471	$4200	€3608	Quatre hommes en costume (58x45cm-23x18in) s. num.32/50 etching exec.1968. 4-Nov-3 Christie's, Rockefeller NY #179/R est:5000-7000
£2471	$4200	€3608	Celstine et fille (25x33cm-10x13in) s. num.27/50 aquatint exec.1968. 4-Nov-3 Christie's, Rockefeller NY #184/R est:5000-7000
£2473	$4600	€3611	Pirosmanachvili 1914 (16x10cm-6x4in) s. drypoint. 2-Mar-4 Swann Galleries, New York #510/R est:4000-6000
£2486	$4500	€3630	La toilette de la mere (23x18cm-9x7in) drypoint edition of 250. 19-Apr-4 Bonhams & Butterfields, San Francisco #194/R est:5000-7000
£2500	$4250	€3650	Femme chevre et nu (27x17cm-11x7in) s. etching. 31-Oct-3 Sotheby's, New York #392/R
£2500	$4250	€3650	Series 156: number 117 (37x49cm-15x19in) st.sig. drypoint. 31-Oct-3 Sotheby's, New York #394
£2500	$4300	€3650	Tete et profil (55x41cm-22x16in) s.num.26/50 aquatint etching. 4-Dec-3 Sotheby's, London #203/R est:3000-4000
£2500	$4550	€3650	Nature morte au livre (42x62cm-17x24in) lithograph. 30-Jun-4 Christie's, London #307/R est:2000-3000
£2513	$4498	€3669	Bacchanal (47x56cm-19x22in) s.num.241/250 aquatint etching. 28-May-4 Uppsala Auktionskammare, Uppsala #376/R est:30000-35000 (S.KR 34000)
£2517	$4330	€3600	La pose nue (53x37cm-21x15in) s.d.1954 lithograph. 2-Dec-3 Hauswedell & Nolte, Hamburg #542/R est:5000
£2533	$4661	€3800	La pique (43x56cm-17x22in) s.d.1959 lithograph. 10-Jun-4 Hauswedell & Nolte, Hamburg #583/R est:5000
£2542	$4500	€3711	Minotaure Vaincu (18x25cm-7x10in) s. drypoint etching edition of 300. 1-May-4 Thomaston Place, Thomaston #826/R

£2542	$4500	€3711	Jeune femme en liquette, faune et tete de bouc (21x15cm-8x6in) s.num.27/50 etching. 28-Apr-4 Christie's, Rockefeller NY #177/R est:2000-3000
£2581	$4800	€3768	Couple au bords de l'eau (7x12cm-3x5in) s. drypoint. 2-Mar-4 Swann Galleries, New York #492/R est:4000-6000
£2588	$4400	€3778	Profil I (15x12cm-6x5in) s. drypoint. 6-Nov-3 Swann Galleries, New York #669/R est:6000-9000
£2595	$4800	€3789	Quatre portefaix apportant a un gentilhomme (28x39cm-11x15in) s.num.47/50 etching. 12-Feb-4 Christie's, Rockefeller NY #378/R est:6000-8000
£2610	$4750	€3811	Repos du sculpteur devant un centaure (13x17cm-5x7in) s. etching edition of 250. 7-Feb-4 Sloans & Kenyon, Bethesda #1222/R est:4500-5000
£2610	$4750	€3811	Minotaure vaincu (13x17cm-5x7in) s. etching edition of 260. 7-Feb-4 Sloans & Kenyon, Bethesda #1223/R est:4000-6000
£2620	$4769	€3825	Femmes a leur toilette. s.i. etching drypoint. 17-Jun-4 Kornfeld, Bern #663 est:7500 (S.FR 6000)
£2621	$4377	€3800	Repos du sculpteur (19x27cm-7x11in) i. eau forte exec.1933 lit. 13-Nov-3 Finarte Semenzato, Rome #45/R est:1500-1800
£2647	$4500	€3865	Modele et peintre (27x37cm-11x15in) s. etching aquatint. 31-Oct-3 Sotheby's, New York #388
£2647	$4500	€3865	Chute d'Icare (36x49cm-14x19in) s. etching drypoint. 31-Oct-3 Sotheby's, New York #395
£2654	$4750	€3875	Artist in his studio. s.i. lithograph. 13-May-4 Dallas Auction Gallery, Dallas #323/R est:6000-8000
£2661	$4443	€3858	Peintre et modele au bandeau. s.i. aquatint. 19-Jun-3 Kornfeld, Bern #835 est:6000 (S.FR 5800)
£2667	$4907	€4000	Les saltimbanques (28x32cm-11x13in) drypoint exec. 1905 one of 250. 12-Jun-4 Villa Grisebach, Berlin #172/R est:4000-6000
£2682	$4800	€3916	Modele accoude sur un tableau (26x19cm-10x7in) etching. 6-May-4 Swann Galleries, New York #544/R est:3000-5000
£2703	$5000	€3946	Peintre longiline avec des femmes (41x48cm-16x19in) s.i. etching num.33/50 exec.1969. 17-Jul-4 Brunk, Ashville #652/R est:4000-8000
£2706	$4600	€3951	Le repos du sculpteur (19x27cm-7x11in) s. etching. 6-Nov-3 Swann Galleries, New York #671/R est:4000-6000
£2706	$4600	€3951	Le repos du sculpteur III (19x27cm-7x11in) s. etching edition of 260. 6-Nov-3 Swann Galleries, New York #672/R est:6000-9000
£2706	$4600	€3951	Fete de la patronne (50x66cm-20x26in) s. etching exec.1971. 4-Nov-3 Christie's, Rockefeller NY #189/R est:3500-4500
£2712	$4800	€3960	Jeune femme laissant tomber sa robe (21x15cm-8x6in) s.num.27/50 aquatint. 28-Apr-4 Christie's, Rockefeller NY #175/R est:3000-5000
£2752	$4596	€3990	La lecture. s.i. lithograph. 19-Jun-3 Kornfeld, Bern #857 est:12500 (S.FR 6000)
£2752	$4596	€3990	Portrait de Max Jacob. s.i. lithograph. 19-Jun-3 Kornfeld, Bern #864 est:5000 (S.FR 6000)
£2762	$5000	€4033	Portrait of Dora Maar au Collier (42x32cm-17x13in) st.sig.num.21/50 drypoint. 19-Apr-4 Bonhams & Butterfields, San Francisco #198/R est:4000-6000
£2796	$5200	€4082	Tete d'homme (12x8cm-5x3in) s. etching. 2-Mar-4 Swann Galleries, New York #493/R est:5000-8000
£2797	$4755	€4000	Don Quichotte (22x32cm-9x13in) s. num.36/50 aquatint lit. 24-Nov-3 Christie's, Milan #14/R
£2800	$4816	€4088	Minotaure, une coupe a la main, et jeune femme (19x26cm-7x10in) etching edition of 300. 4-Dec-3 Sotheby's, London #192/R est:3000-4000
£2800	$4816	€4088	Composition (61x32cm-24x13in) s.num.195/250 col lithograph. 2-Dec-3 Christie's, London #268/R est:1500-2500
£2800	$5152	€4200	Interior scene (22x28cm-9x11in) s. lithograph exec.1926. 10-Jun-4 Piasa, Paris #181/R
£2811	$5200	€4104	La coiffure (26x17cm-10x7in) s.num.7/50 lithograph. 12-Feb-4 Christie's, Rockefeller NY #351/R est:5000-7000
£2817	$4873	€4000	Femme au fauteuil et nu assis (57x45cm-22x18in) s. aquatint drypoint one of 69 exec. 1963. 14-Dec-3 Rabourdin & Choppin de Janvry, Paris #8/R est:4000-5000
£2824	$4800	€4123	Minotaure vaincu (19x27cm-7x11in) s. etching edition of 260. 6-Nov-3 Swann Galleries, New York #674/R est:5000-8000
£2824	$4800	€4123	Les banderilles (47x50cm-19x20in) s.num.19/50 lithograph. 6-Nov-3 Swann Galleries, New York #682/R est:4000-6000
£2824	$4800	€4123	Atelier (50x66cm-20x26in) s. num.40/50 etching aquatint exec.1966. 4-Nov-3 Christie's, Rockefeller NY #177/R est:6000-8000
£2824	$4800	€4123	Enlevement (49x45cm-19x18in) s. num.30/50 aquatint exec.1968. 4-Nov-3 Christie's, Rockefeller NY #188/R est:5000-7000
£2824	$4800	€4123	Homme et deux femmes (47x57cm-19x22in) s. aquatint exec.1968. 4-Nov-3 Christie's, Rockefeller NY #187/R est:1500-2500
£2825	$5000	€4125	Sculpteur, modeles et sculpture (18x25cm-7x10in) s. drypoint etching edition of 300. 1-May-4 Thomaston Place, Thomaston #821/R
£2825	$5000	€4125	Visiteur Rembranesque chez une courtisane colatre (31x41cm-12x16in) s.num.22/50 etching. 28-Apr-4 Christie's, Rockefeller NY #169/R est:6000-8000
£2825	$5000	€4125	Jacqueline, en Maja Nue, avec la celestine et deux Mousquetaires (18x23cm-7x9in) s.num.27/50 aquatint. 28-Apr-4 Christie's, Rockefeller NY #183/R est:4000-6000
£2825	$5000	€4125	Les deux femmes (33x44cm-13x17in) s.num.6/50 lithograph. 30-Apr-4 Sotheby's, New York #178/R est:7000-10000
£2828	$5091	€4129	Nature morte au verre et fleurs (50x65cm-20x26in) s.num.5/50 lithograph lit. 26-Apr-4 Bukowskis, Stockholm #423/R est:40000-50000 (S.KR 39000)
£2838	$5166	€4143	Tete de garcon. s.i. linocut. 17-Jun-4 Kornfeld, Bern #692 est:5000 (S.FR 6500)
£2838	$5166	€4143	Femme au voile, modele assis et tete de Rembrandt. etching. 17-Jun-4 Kornfeld, Bern #658 est:7500 (S.FR 6500)
£2888	$5314	€4216	Amours du Jupitre et de Seleme (31x22cm-12x9in) s. etching in black lit. 29-Mar-4 Rasmussen, Copenhagen #68/R est:20000-30000 (D.KR 32000)
£2905	$5200	€4241	Le peintre et son modele (23x33cm-9x13in) s.num.16/50 aquatint. 6-May-4 Swann Galleries, New York #560a/R est:4000-6000
£2941	$5000	€4294	Trois femmes nues pres de fenetre (37x29cm-15x11in) s. etching. 31-Oct-3 Sotheby's, New York #360/R
£2941	$5000	€4294	Deux femmes (38x27cm-15x11in) s. aquatint. 31-Oct-3 Sotheby's, New York #386
£2941	$5000	€4294	La colombe volant (54x60cm-21x24in) s.num.36/50 lithograph. 6-Nov-3 Swann Galleries, New York #683/R est:6000-9000
£2941	$5000	€4294	Jacqueline (55x38cm-22x15in) s.i. col lithograph. 6-Nov-3 Swann Galleries, New York #692/R est:3000-5000
£2941	$5000	€4294	Joueur de diaule (45x62cm-18x24in) s. num.28/50 etching aquatint exec.1966. 4-Nov-3 Christie's, Rockefeller NY #178/R est:6000-8000
£2946	$5008	€4301	Fumeur (42x32cm-17x13in) s.num.14/50 etching aquatint lit. 4-Nov-3 Bukowskis, Stockholm #443/R est:50000-60000 (S.KR 39000)
£2973	$5500	€4341	Dans l'atelier (22x32cm-9x13in) s.num.30/50 aquatint drypoint. 12-Feb-4 Christie's, Rockefeller NY #363/R est:3500-4500
£2973	$5500	€4341	En pensant a Goya, femmes en prison (32x39cm-13x15in) s.num.6/50 aquatint. 12-Feb-4 Christie's, Rockefeller NY #373/R est:5000-7000
£2973	$5500	€4341	Clin d'oil au bain truc femmes faisant la sieste au soleil (28x39cm-11x15in) s.num.6/50 etching. 12-Feb-4 Christie's, Rockefeller NY #376/R est:6000-8000
£3000	$5160	€4380	Sculpteur et trois danseuses sculptees (22x31cm-9x12in) etching edition of 300. 4-Dec-3 Sotheby's, London #193/R est:3500-4500
£3000	$5160	€4380	Noble dame (64x49cm-25x19in) s.num.18/50 lithograph. 4-Dec-3 Sotheby's, London #205/R est:4000-5000
£3000	$5520	€4500	Le danseur (64x53cm-25x21in) s.i.d.1965 col linocut. 10-Jun-4 Hauswedell & Nolte, Hamburg #587/R est:5000
£3038	$5500	€4435	Personnages masques et femme oiseau (25x35cm-10x14in) s. etching aquatint edition of 250. 19-Apr-4 Bonhams & Butterfields, San Francisco #197/R est:4500-5500
£3057	$5563	€4463	Deux femmes. s.i. aquatint. 17-Jun-4 Kornfeld, Bern #662 est:7500 (S.FR 7000)
£3057	$5563	€4463	Troupe d'acteurs. s.i. lithograph. 17-Jun-4 Kornfeld, Bern #687 est:7500 (S.FR 7000)
£3070	$5649	€4482	From Sable Mouvant (38x28cm-15x11in) s. aquatint dry point. 23-Jun-4 Koller, Zurich #3279/R est:4500-6000 (S.FR 7000)
£3107	$5500	€4536	Caricature du general de gaulle, et deux femmes (32x39cm-13x15in) s.num.25/50 aquatint drypoint. 28-Apr-4 Christie's, Rockefeller NY #167/R est:4000-6000
£3107	$5500	€4536	La sieste, deux femmes (15x21cm-6x8in) s.num.27/50 etching. 28-Apr-4 Christie's, Rockefeller NY #184/R est:3000-4000
£3107	$5500	€4536	Portrait de Vollard, IV (35x25cm-14x10in) s. etching edition of 250. 28-Apr-4 Christie's, Rockefeller NY #132/R est:3000-5000
£3107	$5500	€4536	Deux femmes accroupies (42x54cm-17x21in) s.num.3/50 lithograph. 30-Apr-4 Sotheby's, New York #182 est:3000-5000
£3107	$5500	€4536	Bacchanale II (50x66cm-20x26in) s.num.20/50 lithograph. 30-Apr-4 Sotheby's, New York #185/R est:3000-5000
£3133	$5734	€4700	Les deux saltimbanques (12x9cm-5x4in) etching. 5-Jun-4 Lempertz, Koln #936/R est:3000
£3176	$5400	€4637	Corrida (51x66cm-20x26in) s.num.16/50 col lithograph. 6-Nov-3 Swann Galleries, New York #689/R est:6000-9000
£3200	$5504	€4672	Le chandail brode (43x35cm-17x14in) s.num.13/50 lithograph. 2-Dec-3 Christie's, London #264/R est:2500-3500
£3200	$5824	€4672	Scene d'interieur (22x28cm-9x11in) lithograph. 30-Jun-4 Christie's, London #293/R est:3000-5000
£3200	$5888	€4800	Femmes au bain (27x19cm-11x7in) s. etching exec.1934 one of 260. 12-Jun-4 Villa Grisebach, Berlin #365/R est:5000-7000
£3200	$5824	€4672	Untitled, 347 series (45x56cm-18x22in) s.num.21/50 etching. 1-Jul-4 Sotheby's, London #274/R est:3000-4000
£3221	$5766	€4800	Nature morte a la charlotte (50x62cm-20x24in) s. 25-May-4 Karl & Faber, Munich #493/R est:6000
£3235	$5500	€4723	Femme assise et femme de dos (27x20cm-11x8in) s. etching. 31-Oct-3 Sotheby's, New York #361/R
£3235	$5500	€4723	Abreuvoir (32x42cm-13x17in) etching exec.1905. 4-Nov-3 Christie's, Rockefeller NY #145/R est:3000-5000
£3235	$5500	€4723	Hibou au crayon (65x50cm-26x20in) s. num.24/50 lithograph exec.1947. 4-Nov-3 Christie's, Rockefeller NY #157/R est:4500-5500
£3235	$5500	€4723	Nature morte a la bouteille (75x62cm-30x24in) s. col linocut exec.1962 prov. 4-Nov-3 Christie's, Rockefeller NY #172/R est:4000-6000
£3243	$6000	€4735	Jeune femme (40x30cm-16x12in) i.num.30/75 lithograph. 12-Feb-4 Christie's, Rockefeller NY #357/R est:4000-5000
£3243	$6000	€4735	Autour d'El Greco, portraits, avec modele etendu, et bonhomme (21x32cm-8x13in) s.num.6/50 etching drypoint aquatint. 12-Feb-4 Christie's, Rockefeller NY #367/R est:4000-6000
£3275	$5961	€4782	Combat de centaures. s.i. lithograph. 17-Jun-4 Kornfeld, Bern #691 est:6000 (S.FR 7500)
£3275	$5961	€4782	Deux clowns. s.i. col lithograph. 17-Jun-4 Kornfeld, Bern #688 est:7500 (S.FR 7500)
£3275	$5961	€4782	Le torero blesse. s.i. lithograph. 17-Jun-4 Kornfeld, Bern #689 est:7500 (S.FR 7500)
£3294	$5500	€4809	Le repos du sculpteur devant un nu a la draperie (28x19cm-11x7in) s. etching. 21-Oct-3 Bonhams & Butterfields, San Francisco #1221/R
£3315	$6000	€4840	La danse (18x23cm-7x9in) drypoint edition of 250. 19-Apr-4 Bonhams & Butterfields, San Francisco #195/R est:4000-6000
£3315	$6000	€4840	L'entreinte (53x64cm-21x25in) s.num.3/50 linocut. 19-Apr-4 Bonhams & Butterfields, San Francisco #200/R est:6000-8000
£3323	$5650	€4852	Toros vallauris (65x53cm-26x21in) s.num.103/195 col linocut lit. 4-Nov-3 Bukowskis, Stockholm #445/R est:40000-50000 (S.KR 44000)
£3333	$6133	€5000	Verre sous la lampe (35x27cm-14x11in) s.i. col linocut exec.1962. 10-Jun-4 Piasa, Paris #187
£3333	$6000	€5000	Sculpture de jeune homme (26x19cm-10x7in) s. d.1933 verso eau forte lit. 22-Apr-4 Finarte Semenzato, Rome #13/R est:1500-1800
£3333	$6133	€5000	La grande corrida (55x66cm-22x26in) s.d.1949 lithograph. 10-Jun-4 Hauswedell & Nolte, Hamburg #579/R est:5000
£3352	$6000	€4894	Vallauris 1956 toros (75x62cm-30x24in) s.acrylic color linocut. 6-May-4 Swann Galleries, New York #558/R est:4000-6000
£3356	$6007	€5000	Series 347: The erotic suite - L305 (28x35cm-11x14in) s.i.d.1968 etching. 25-May-4 Dorotheum, Vienna #239/R est:4000-5000
£3357	$5706	€4800	Baccanale I (45x59cm-18x23in) s. lithograph. 26-Nov-3 Lempertz, Koln #910/R est:4000
£3380	$5848	€4800	Untitled (49x63cm-19x25in) s. num.164/300 lithograph. 15-Dec-3 Ansorena, Madrid #402/R est:3500
£3390	$6000	€4949	La toilette (27x21cm-11x8in) s.num.4/50 lithograph. 28-Apr-4 Christie's, Rockefeller NY #115/R est:3000-5000
£3390	$6000	€4949	Echange de regards (15x21cm-6x8in) s.num.27/50 aquatint drypoint. 28-Apr-4 Christie's, Rockefeller NY #178/R est:2500-3500
£3390	$6000	€4949	Trois femmes nues pres d'une fenetre (36x28cm-14x11in) s. drypoint etching edition of 250. 1-May-4 Thomaston Place, Thomaston #828/R
£3390	$6000	€4949	Portrait de D H Kahnweiller, II (66x51cm-26x20in) s.num.12/50 lithograph. 28-Apr-4 Christie's, Rockefeller NY #151/R est:4000-6000
£3390	$6000	€4949	Grosse prostituee sur les genoux d'un barby (21x15cm-8x6in) s.num.27/50 etching. 28-Apr-4 Christie's, Rockefeller NY #173/R est:4000-6000
£3390	$6000	€4949	Homme Rembranesque a la pipe (21x15cm-8x6in) s.num.27/50 etching. 28-Apr-4 Christie's, Rockefeller NY #185/R est:3000-5000
£3390	$6000	€4949	347 series no.91 (16x20cm-6x8in) s.num.45/50 aquatint etching drypoint. 30-Apr-4 Sotheby's, New York #194/R est:3000-4000
£3394	$5430	€4955	Peintre et modele tricotant (19x28cm-7x11in) s. etching lit. 16-Sep-3 Philippe Schuler, Zurich #3047/R est:8000-10000 (S.FR 7500)
£3406	$6199	€4973	Scene mythologique: peut-etre la convoitise d'Agamemnon pour Briseis. s.i. etching. 17-Jun-4 Kornfeld, Bern #672 est:8000 (S.FR 7800)
£3493	$6358	€5100	Le sauvetage de la noyee. s.i. etching. 17-Jun-4 Kornfeld, Bern #655 est:7500 (S.FR 8000)
£3500	$6020	€5110	Minotaure aveugle guide par une fillette (22x31cm-9x12in) etching edition of 300. 4-Dec-3 Sotheby's, London #197/R est:2500-3500
£3500	$6020	€5110	Personnages et colombe (50x65cm-20x26in) s.num.7/50 lithograph. 2-Dec-3 Christie's, London #266/R est:2500-3500
£3500	$6370	€5110	Fleurs dans un vase (24x16cm-9x6in) lithograph. 30-Jun-4 Christie's, London #305/R est:2000-3000
£3500	$6370	€5110	Jardins a Vallauris (51x64cm-20x25in) lithograph. 30-Jun-4 Christie's, London #308/R est:2500-3500
£3500	$6370	€5110	Untitled, 347 series (42x32cm-17x13in) s.num.6/50 etching. 1-Jul-4 Sotheby's, London #255/R est:2500-3000
£3500	$6370	€5110	Balzac (68x52cm-27x20in) s.num.10/25 lithograph. 1-Jul-4 Sotheby's, London #258/R est:3000-3500

£3500	$6370	€5110	Le chef d'oeuvre inconnu, peintre chauve devant son chevalet (20x28cm-8x11in) s.num.55/99 etching. 1-Jul-4 Sotheby's, London #265/R est:4000-6000
£3514	$6500	€5130	Autour d'El Greco et de Rembrandt, portraits (22x32cm-9x13in) s.num.6/50 col etching aquatint. 12-Feb-4 Christie's, Rockefeller NY #366/R est:4000-6000
£3521	$6092	€5000	Etreinte III (42x57cm-17x22in) s.num. etching vellum edition of 72. 11-Dec-3 Piasa, Paris #128
£3529	$6000	€5152	Buste de femme au fichu, portrait de Dora Maar (26x22cm-10x9in) s. aquatint engraving burnishing. 6-Nov-3 Swann Galleries, New York #678/R est:8000-12000
£3529	$6000	€5152	Modele (44x34cm-17x13in) s. etching exec.1933. 4-Nov-3 Christie's, Rockefeller NY #148/R est:6000-8000
£3529	$6000	€5152	Couple et enfant (38x29cm-15x11in) s. num.40/150 etching exec.1923. 4-Nov-3 Christie's, Rockefeller NY #156/R est:4000-6000
£3546	$5922	€5000	Deux femmes (38x27cm-15x11in) s. drypoint aquatint vellum prov. 19-Oct-3 Anaf, Lyon #227/R est:5000-6000
£3591	$6500	€5243	Bacchanale (47x56cm-19x22in) s.num.14/30 col etching aquatint. 19-Apr-4 Bonhams & Butterfields, San Francisco #205/R est:5000-7000
£3591	$6500	€5243	David and Bethsabea (75x56cm-30x22in) lithograph. 30-Mar-4 Arroyo, Buenos Aires #57
£3604	$6198	€5262	Au bain (31x22cm-12x9in) s. etching. 2-Dec-3 Koller, Zurich #3368/R est:8000-12000 (S.FR 8000)
£3620	$6154	€5285	7 August 1968 (32x40cm-13x16in) s. num.48/50 prov. 22-Nov-3 Burkhard, Luzern #97/R est:4000-5000 (S.FR 8000)
£3626	$6526	€5294	Bacchanale I (44x59cm-17x23in) s.num.15/50 lithograph prov.lit. 26-Apr-4 Bukowskis, Stockholm #426/R est:35000-40000 (S.KR 50000)
£3663	$6484	€5348	Les deux Saltimbanques (12x9cm-5x4in) s. drypoint one of 250 lit. 27-Apr-4 AB Stockholms Auktionsverk #1346/R est:50000-60000 (S.KR 50000)
£3663	$6484	€5348	Modele nu et Sculptures - Suile Villard (38x30cm-15x12in) s.one of 250 etching lit. 27-Apr-4 AB Stockholms Auktionsverk #1347/R est:60000-70000 (S.KR 50000)
£3667	$6747	€5500	Etreinte VI (32x42cm-13x17in) s.i. drypoint aquatint. 10-Jun-4 Piasa, Paris #188
£3667	$6563	€5500	Peintre entre deux modeles (19x28cm-7x11in) s. drypoint etching. 15-May-4 Bassenge, Berlin #7097/R est:4800
£3667	$6563	€5500	Le peintre et son modele (23x33cm-9x13in) s. drypoint etching aquatint. 15-May-4 Bassenge, Berlin #7099/R est:4500
£3667	$6563	€5500	Dwarf dancer (57x32cm-22x13in) s.i. col offset prov. 14-May-4 Ketterer, Munich #294/R est:4000-5000
£3667	$6747	€5500	Sculptures representant Marie-Therese et la tete du sculpture (26x19cm-10x7in) s. etching exec. 1933 one of 260. 12-Jun-4 Villa Grisebach, Berlin #364/R est:4000-6000
£3672	$6500	€5361	Homme Rembranesque assis chez les filles (15x21cm-6x8in) s.num.27/50 aquatint. 28-Apr-4 Christie's, Rockefeller NY #181/R est:4000-6000
£3672	$6500	€5361	Portrait de Vollard, III (35x25cm-14x10in) s. aquatint edition of 250. 28-Apr-4 Christie's, Rockefeller NY #131/R est:4000-6000
£3672	$6500	€5361	Prostituee et reitre (21x15cm-8x6in) s.num.27/50 aquatint. 28-Apr-4 Christie's, Rockefeller NY #176/R est:4000-6000
£3672	$6500	€5361	Le viol sous la fenetre (28x19cm-11x7in) s. etching aquatint edition of 250. 28-Apr-4 Christie's, Rockefeller NY #124/R est:4000-6000
£3672	$6500	€5361	Femme nue assise et trois tetes (13x18cm-5x7in) bears sig. etching edition of 250. 28-Apr-4 Christie's, Rockefeller NY #128/R est:1000-6000
£3672	$6500	€5361	Don Quichotte, Sancho et un Mousquetaire regardant passer dulcinee (15x21cm-6x8in) s.num.27/50 aquatint. 28-Apr-4 Christie's, Rockefeller NY #180/R est:4000-6000
£3672	$6500	€5361	Peintre ou sculpteur pensant a une femme guerriere (21x15cm-8x6in) s.num.27/50 aquatint. 28-Apr-4 Christie's, Rockefeller NY #182/R est:4000-6000
£3672	$6500	€5361	347 series no.147 (60x85cm-24x33in) s.num.23/50 aquatint. 30-Apr-4 Sotheby's, New York #195/R est:4000-6000
£3681	$6000	€5374	La maison tellier (50x65cm-20x26in) st.sig.num.18/50 etching BFK Rives executed 1971. 24-Sep-3 Christie's, Rockefeller NY #145/R est:2000-3000
£3728	$6860	€5443	Dans l'atelier (40x57cm-16x22in) s. aquatint etching. 23-Jun-4 Koller, Zurich #3281/R est:3500-4500 (S.FR 8500)
£3761	$6282	€5453	Femme au divan avec une jeune fille et un vieillard. s.i. etching. 19-Jun-3 Kornfeld, Bern #838 est:10000 (S.FR 8200)
£3776	$6306	€5400	Colombe volant (47x54cm-19x21in) s.i.d.28.12.61 lithograph. 10-Oct-3 Winterberg, Heidelberg #1822/R est:6500
£3776	$6495	€5400	Minotaure mourant et jeune femme pitoyable (19x27cm-7x11in) s.d.1933 etching. 2-Dec-3 Hauswedell & Nolte, Hamburg #530/R est:6000
£3776	$6420	€5513	La chute d'icare (37x49cm-15x19in) s.num.113/125 etching lit. 4-Nov-3 Bukowskis, Stockholm #446/R est:50000-60000 (S.KR 50000)
£3800	$6536	€5548	Tete de femme (12x11cm-5x4in) s. lithograph. 2-Dec-3 Christie's, London #255/R est:4000-6000
£3800	$6916	€5548	Les deux Saltimbanques (12x9cm-5x4in) etching. 30-Jun-4 Christie's, London #292/R est:3000-5000
£3800	$6916	€5548	Toros en Vallauris (90x59cm-35x23in) s.num.97/200 col linocut. 1-Jul-4 Sotheby's, London #283/R est:2500-3000
£3824	$6500	€5583	Chef-d'oeuvre inconnu (19x28cm-7x11in) s. etching. 31-Oct-3 Sotheby's, New York #354/R
£3824	$6500	€5583	Peintre a la palette (64x53cm-25x21in) s. linoleum cut. 31-Oct-3 Sotheby's, New York #385/R
£3824	$6500	€5583	Series 347: number 290 (28x39cm-11x15in) s. etching. 31-Oct-3 Sotheby's, New York #391/R
£3824	$6500	€5583	Figure (66x50cm-26x20in) s. num.23/50 lithograph exec.1948. 4-Nov-3 Christie's, Rockefeller NY #158/R est:8000-10000
£3824	$6500	€5583	Sexe (57x65cm-22x26in) s. num.5/50 etching exec.1968. 4-Nov-3 Christie's, Rockefeller NY #185/R est:6000-8000
£3829	$6586	€5590	Sculpteur et son modele devant une fenetre (19x27cm-7x11in) s. etching. 2-Dec-3 Koller, Zurich #3369/R est:10000-15000 (S.FR 8500)
£3846	$7000	€5615	Trois femmes nues pres d'un fenetre (18x13cm-7x5in) s. etching edition of 250. 7-Feb-4 Sloans & Kenyon, Bethesda #1221/R est:5000-7000
£3899	$6511	€5654	Le grand hibou. s.i. lithograph. 19-Jun-3 Kornfeld, Bern #858 est:10000 (S.FR 8500)
£3911	$7000	€5710	Homme devoilant une femme (38x28cm-15x11in) s. etching. 20-Mar-4 Rachel Davis, Shaker Heights #434/R est:8000-12000
£3911	$7000	€5710	Sculptor and reclining model viewing sculpture of bull and two horses (18x25cm-7x10in) s.d.1933 etching. 16-May-4 Wright, Chicago #182/R est:7000-9000
£3911	$7000	€5710	Two sculptors, male and female model and sculpture (18x25cm-7x10in) s.d.1933 etching lit. 16-May-4 Wright, Chicago #183/R est:7000-9000
£3911	$7000	€5710	Les pauvres (23x18cm-9x7in) etching drypoint. 6-May-4 Swann Galleries, New York #542/R est:5000-8000
£3919	$7015	€5800	Untitled from Series 156 Num.18 (51x64cm-20x25in) s.num.20/50 etching lit. 8-May-4 Bukowskis, Helsinki #342/R est:5000-6500
£3930	$7153	€5738	Le chevalier et le page. s.i. lithograph. 17-Jun-4 Kornfeld, Bern #684 est:7500 (S.FR 9000)
£3947	$7263	€5763	From 347 gravures (31x41cm-12x16in) s. num.26/50 etching. 23-Jun-4 Koller, Zurich #3276/R est:4800-6000 (S.FR 9000)
£3955	$7000	€5774	Femme acrobate au maquillage paillete et spectateurs (18x22cm-7x9in) s.num.27/50 etching. 28-Apr-4 Christie's, Rockefeller NY #186/R est:4000-6000
£3955	$7000	€5774	Le festin (22x15cm-9x6in) s.num.150/47 etching. 30-Apr-4 Sotheby's, New York #176/R est:3000-5000
£3955	$7000	€5774	La collection de tableautin (56x76cm-22x30in) s.num.7/50 col lithograph. 30-Apr-4 Sotheby's, New York #183 est:3000-5000
£4000	$7160	€6000	La coiffure (26x17cm-10x7in) s. lithograph. 14-May-4 Ketterer, Munich #176/R est:5500-6500
£4000	$7280	€5840	Belle jeune femme a sa toilette revant qu'elle possede (37x50cm-15x20in) st.sig.num.47/50 etching. 21-Jun-4 Bonhams, New Bond Street #63/R est:4000-6000
£4061	$7310	€5929	Rembrandt a la palette (28x20cm-11x8in) s. etching lit. 26-Apr-4 Bukowskis, Stockholm #417/R est:40000-50000 (S.KR 56000)
£4118	$7000	€6012	Danse des faunes (40x52cm-16x20in) s. lithograph. 31-Oct-3 Sotheby's, New York #375/R
£4118	$7000	€6012	Deux modeles se regardant (28x20cm-11x8in) s. etching edition of 260. 6-Nov-3 Swann Galleries, New York #675/R est:8000-12000
£4118	$7000	€6012	Salome (66x51cm-26x20in) drypoint. 4-Nov-3 Christie's, Rockefeller NY #146/R est:7000-10000
£4118	$7000	€6012	Peintre et modele (45x56cm-18x22in) s. etching aquatint exec.1968. 4-Nov-3 Christie's, Rockefeller NY #182/R est:7000-9000
£4128	$6894	€5986	Composition. s.i. lithograph. 19-Jun-3 Kornfeld, Bern #859 est:7500 (S.FR 9000)
£4133	$7605	€6200	Visage (35x27cm-14x11in) s. linocut exec. 1962 one of 50. 12-Jun-4 Villa Grisebach, Berlin #372/R est:4000-6000
£4154	$7062	€6065	Les bleus de Barcelona (23x33cm-9x13in) s.num.41/75 etching aquatint lit. 5-Nov-3 AB Stockholms Auktionsverk #1275/R est:65000-70000 (S.KR 55000)
£4192	$7000	€6120	Troisieme affiche vallauris (29x35cm-11x14in) s.num.21/50 col lithograph. 11-Nov-3 Christie's, Rockefeller NY #162/R est:4000-5000
£4196	$7133	€6000	Vollard Suite - Repos du sculpteur III (19x27cm-7x11in) s. etching. 26-Nov-3 Dorotheum, Vienna #44/R est:6000-6500
£4196	$7217	€6000	Les picadors II (20x30cm-8x12in) s. aquatint etching. 2-Dec-3 Hauswedell & Nolte, Hamburg #534/R est:6500
£4200	$6972	€6132	Nu a la chaise (50x38cm-20x15in) s.num.30/50 col lithograph sold with another after Georges Braque. 6-Oct-3 Sotheby's, London #116/R est:2800-3200
£4200	$7140	€6132	Dancer (64x52cm-25x20in) s. num.13/200 linocut exec.1965. 1-Dec-3 Bonhams, New Bond Street #292/R est:2000-3000
£4200	$7224	€6132	La danse des bandrilles (50x65cm-20x26in) s.num.50/50 lithograph. 2-Dec-3 Christie's, London #265/R est:3000-5000
£4200	$7644	€6132	Minotaure vaincu (19x26cm-7x10in) etching. 30-Jun-4 Christie's, London #301/R est:4000-6000
£4200	$7644	€6132	Sable mouvant, Le Sculpteur (38x27cm-15x11in) s.num.44/50 aquatint drypoint. 1-Jul-4 Sotheby's, London #271/R est:2500-3500
£4200	$7644	€6132	Le modele (38x28cm-15x11in) s.num.42/50 aquatint etching. 1-Jul-4 Sotheby's, London #272/R est:2500-3000
£4237	$7500	€6186	Jeux de gladiateurs (15x21cm-6x8in) s.num.27/50 etching. 28-Apr-4 Christie's, Rockefeller NY #174/R est:3000-5000
£4237	$7500	€6186	Au cirque, acrobates, girafe, nageuses (31x42cm-12x17in) s.num.30/50 etching. 28-Apr-4 Christie's, Rockefeller NY #166/R est:5000-7000
£4237	$7500	€6186	Le repos de sculpteur devant un centaure et une femme (19x27cm-7x11in) s. etching edition of 250. 28-Apr-4 Christie's, Rockefeller NY #121/R est:6000-9000
£4237	$7500	€6186	Minotaure et femme derriere un rideau (19x26cm-7x10in) s. etching edition of 250. 28-Apr-4 Christie's, Rockefeller NY #126/R est:7000-9000
£4237	$7500	€6186	Nature morte au verre et fleurs (39x55cm-15x22in) s.num.29/50 lithograph. 28-Apr-4 Christie's, Rockefeller NY #139/R est:7000-9000
£4333	$7800	€6500	Tete d'histrion (74x60cm-29x24in) s. num.46/200 linocut. 24-Apr-4 Cornette de St.Cyr, Paris #222/R est:6000
£4412	$7500	€6442	Femme nue a la jambe pliee (31x22cm-12x9in) s. etching. 31-Oct-3 Sotheby's, New York #356/R
£4412	$7500	€6442	Le repos du sculpteur devant le jeune cavalier (19x27cm-7x11in) s. etching edition of 260. 6-Nov-3 Swann Galleries, New York #675a/R est:8000-12000
£4412	$7500	€6442	Les faunes et la centaauresse (50x65cm-20x26in) s.num.42/50 lithograph. 6-Nov-3 Swann Galleries, New York #680/R est:7000-10000
£4412	$7500	€6442	Jacqueline (48x30cm-19x12in) s.num.12/100 col lithograph. 6-Nov-3 Swann Galleries, New York #691/R est:10000-15000
£4412	$7500	€6442	Le picador II (20x26cm-8x10in) s.num.21/50 col lithograph. 6-Nov-3 Swann Galleries, New York #694/R est:8000-12000
£4412	$7500	€6442	Jeunesse (56x76cm-22x30in) lithograph exec.1950. 4-Nov-3 Christie's, Rockefeller NY #161/R est:10000-15000
£4420	$8000	€6453	Fumeur (60x43cm-24x17in) s.num.2/50 col soft ground etching. 19-Apr-4 Bonhams & Butterfields, San Francisco #201/R est:5000-7000
£4491	$7500	€6557	Modele et sculpture surrealiste (27x19cm-11x7in) s. etching edition of 250. 21-Oct-3 Bonhams & Butterfields, San Francisco #1222/R
£4500	$7515	€6570	Sculpteur et trois danseuses sculptees (22x31cm-9x12in) s. etching. 22-Oct-3 Bonhams, New Bond Street #57/R est:5000-7000
£4500	$7740	€6570	La pose habillee (53x38cm-21x15in) s.num.26/50 lithograph. 4-Dec-3 Sotheby's, London #209/R est:5000-7000
£4500	$7740	€6570	Dormeuses et sculptures (26x19cm-10x7in) s.num.30/50 etching. 2-Dec-3 Christie's, London #259/R est:5000-7000
£4500	$7740	€6570	Picasso, un dimi siecle de livers illustres (70x50cm-28x20in) s. offset lithograph two. 2-Dec-3 Christie's, London #267/R est:3000-5000
£4500	$8190	€6570	Untitled, 347 series (37x27cm-15x11in) s.num.20/50 aquatint etching. 1-Jul-4 Sotheby's, London #281/R est:3000-4000
£4513	$8303	€6589	Les Saltimbanques - artistes (32x36cm-13x14in) s.d.1905 drypoint etching printed 1913 lit. 29-Mar-4 Rasmussen, Copenhagen #75/R est:18000-20000 (D.KR 50000)
£4514	$7448	€6500	Untitled (30x50cm-12x20in) s. num.24/50 eau forte. 2-Jul-3 Ansorena, Madrid #877/R
£4520	$8000	€6599	Famille de Saltimbanques (19x27cm-7x11in) s. etching edition of 250. 28-Apr-4 Christie's, Rockefeller NY #120/R est:7000-9000
£4520	$8000	€6599	Sculpteur et son modele devant une fenetre (19x27cm-7x11in) s. etching. 30-Apr-4 Sotheby's, New York #172/R est:7000-9000
£4525	$7240	€6607	Minotaure une coupe a la main, et jeune femme (34x44cm-13x17in) s.i.d.1933 etching lit. 16-Sep-3 Philippe Schuler, Zurich #3046/R est:12000-15000 (S.FR 10000)
£4532	$7704	€6617	Modele nu et sculptures - Suite Vollard (38x30cm-15x12in) s. etching prov.lit. 5-Nov-3 AB Stockholms Auktionsverk #1272/R est:60000-80000 (S.KR 60000)
£4533	$8341	€6800	Franco's dream and lies (30x30cm-12x12in) i. eau forte aquatint. 10-Jun-4 Piasa, Paris #185
£4545	$7727	€6500	Deux sculpteurs devant une statue (34x44cm-13x17in) s. etching. 23-Nov-3 Cornette de St.Cyr, Paris #637/R est:5000-7000
£4577	$7919	€6500	Le danseur (74x62cm-29x24in) s. col lithograph lit. 13-Dec-3 Lempertz, Koln #177/R est:5500
£4587	$7661	€6651	Le modele nu. s.i. etching. 19-Jun-3 Kornfeld, Bern #813 est:12500 (S.FR 10000)
£4587	$7661	€6651	Tete de femme. s. lithograph. 19-Jun-3 Kornfeld, Bern #854 est:12500 (S.FR 10000)
£4667	$8587	€7000	Atelier (32x47cm-13x19in) eau forte aquatint drypoint. 10-Jun-4 Piasa, Paris #190/R
£4698	$8409	€7000	Atelier de Cannes (50x38cm-20x15in) s. lithograph. 25-May-4 Durán, Madrid #701/R est:3000
£4706	$8000	€6871	Repos du sculpteur (19x27cm-7x11in) s. etching. 31-Oct-3 Sotheby's, New York #357/R

£4706	$8000	€6871	Repos du sculpteur (19x27cm-7x11in) s. etching. 31-Oct-3 Sotheby's, New York #358/R
£4706	$8000	€6871	Rembrandt et deux femmes (45x34cm-18x13in) s. etching exec.1934. 4-Nov-3 Christie's, Rockefeller NY #152/R est:8000-12000
£4706	$8000	€6871	Circus (47x56cm-19x22in) s. num.10/50 aquatint drypoint exec.1968. 4-Nov-3 Christie's, Rockefeller NY #183/R est:5000-7000
£4790	$8000	€6993	Composition with two figures (23x29cm-9x11in) s.num.40/100 col pochoir. 11-Nov-3 Christie's, Rockefeller NY #163/R est:5000-8000
£4800	$8256	€7008	Sueno y mentira de franco, songes et mensonges de franco (37x48cm-15x19in) s.num.132/150 etching aquatint. 4-Dec-3 Sotheby's, London #207/R est:5000-6000
£4800	$8592	€7200	Deux femmes accroupies (42x55cm-17x22in) s.i.d.10.1.56 lithograph prov. 14-May-4 Ketterer, Munich #236/R est:5000-7000
£4800	$8736	€7008	Minotaure mourant (20x27cm-8x11in) s. etching edition of 300. 1-Jul-4 Sotheby's, London #273/R est:3000-4000
£4802	$8500	€7011	Nature morte au compotier (25x36cm-10x14in) lithograph pair. 28-Apr-4 Christie's, Rockefeller NY #136/R est:6000-8000
£4802	$8500	€7011	Peintre et modele tricotant (19x28cm-7x11in) s.num.97/99 etching. 28-Apr-4 Christie's, Rockefeller NY #116/R est:4000-6000
£4802	$8500	€7011	Sculpteur et deux tetes sculptees (27x19cm-11x7in) bears sig. etching edition of 250. 28-Apr-4 Christie's, Rockefeller NY #119/R est:6000-8000
£4802	$8500	€7011	Peintre a lavallieere dessinant son modele dans le cadre de la maison (50x63cm-20x25in) st.sig.num.34/50 etching. 28-Apr-4 Christie's, Rockefeller NY #191/R est:5000-8000
£4817	$8044	€6985	La famille du saltimbanque. s.i. lithograph. 19-Jun-3 Kornfeld, Bern #863 est:12500 (S.FR 10500)
£4817	$8044	€6985	La fille au chapeau. s.i. lithograph. 19-Jun-3 Kornfeld, Bern #868 est:12500 (S.FR 10500)
£5000	$8000	€7300	Femme au miroir (18x13cm-7x5in) s. drypoint. 18-Sep-3 Swann Galleries, New York #489/R est:8000-12000
£5000	$8500	€7300	Series 347: number 18 (37x27cm-15x11in) s. etching aquatint. 31-Oct-3 Sotheby's, New York #389/R
£5000	$8500	€7300	Circus (45x56cm-18x22in) s. num.30/50 etching exec.1968. 4-Nov-3 Christie's, Rockefeller NY #180/R est:5000-7000
£5000	$9100	€7300	Colombe volant (50x64cm-20x25in) lithograph. 30-Jun-4 Christie's, London #306/R est:2500-3500
£5000	$9200	€7500	Modele et sculpteur avec sa sculpture (27x19cm-11x7in) s. etching. 10-Jun-4 Hauswedell & Nolte, Hamburg #572/R est:10000
£5000	$9100	€7300	Deux buveurs Catalans (24x30cm-9x12in) s. etching edition of 300. 21-Jun-4 Bonhams, New Bond Street #64/R est:3000-4000
£5000	$9150	€7500	Sculpteur, modele couche et autoportrait en Hercule sculpte (27x19cm-11x7in) s. etching. 5-Jun-4 Lempertz, Koln #936a/R est:7000-8000
£5022	$9140	€7332	Femme nue assise. s. col linocut. 17-Jun-4 Kornfeld, Bern #693 est:10000 (S.FR 11500)
£5028	$9000	€7341	Deux sculpteurs devant une statue (22x31cm-9x12in) s. etching. 6-May-4 Swann Galleries, New York #544a/R est:5000-8000
£5067	$9323	€7600	Sculpteur et modele admirant une tete sculptee (27x19cm-11x7in) s.d.1933 etching. 10-Jun-4 Hauswedell & Nolte, Hamburg #574/R est:8000
£5070	$8417	€7200	Bacchanale (57x76cm-22x30in) s.num.42/50 black lithograph. 13-Jun-3 Calmels Cohen, Paris #52/R est:7000-7500
£5085	$9000	€7424	Notables Espagnols visitant une maison close ornee d'une armure (41x49cm-16x19in) s.num.29/50 etching. 28-Apr-4 Christie's, Rockefeller NY #172/R est:6000-8000
£5200	$9464	€7592	Modele et grande sculpture de dos (45x34cm-18x13in) s. etching edition of 300. 1-Jul-4 Sotheby's, London #247/R est:4000-6000
£5240	$9537	€7650	Le vol de la colombe. s.i. lithograph. 17-Jun-4 Kornfeld, Bern #683 est:7500 (S.FR 12000)
£5240	$9537	€7650	L'ecuyere et les clowns. s.i. lithograph. 17-Jun-4 Kornfeld, Bern #690 est:7500 (S.FR 12000)
£5294	$9000	€7729	Buste de femme (25x14cm-10x6in) etching aquatint drypoint. 31-Oct-3 Sotheby's, New York #366/R
£5294	$9000	€7729	Series 347: number 109 (29x35cm-11x14in) s. aquatint. 31-Oct-3 Sotheby's, New York #390/R
£5300	$9646	€7738	Le repas frugal (61x49cm-24x19in) etching. 30-Jun-4 Christie's, London #291/R est:2000-3000
£5307	$9500	€7748	Three nudes seated by a window with basket of flowers (36x28cm-14x11in) s.d.1933 etching lit. 16-May-4 Wright, Chicago #186/R est:7000-9000
£5333	$9813	€8000	La colombe en vol (54x71cm-21x28in) s. lithograph exec. 1950 one of 5. 12-Jun-4 Villa Grisebach, Berlin #375/R est:6000-8000
£5333	$9813	€8000	Etreinte II (42x57cm-17x22in) s. etching drypoint exec. 1963 one of 50. 11-Jun-4 Villa Grisebach, Berlin #1595/R est:3000-4000
£5367	$9500	€7836	Autour de La Celestine (32x42cm-13x17in) s.num.25/50 etching. 28-Apr-4 Christie's, Rockefeller NY #168/R est:4000-6000
£5367	$9500	€7836	L'enterrement du Compte d'Orgaz, d'apres Picasso (28x38cm-11x15in) s.num.22/50 etching aquatint. 28-Apr-4 Christie's, Rockefeller NY #179/R est:7000-9000
£5369	$9611	€8000	Peintre chauve devant son chevalet (20x28cm-8x11in) s. dryppoint etching. 25-May-4 Dorotheum, Vienna #43/R est:8000-8500
£5459	$9934	€7970	Minotaure aveugle guide dans la nuit par une petite fille au pigeon. etching. 17-Jun-4 Kornfeld, Bern #659/R est:10000 (S.FR 12500)
£5479	$9315	€8000	Nudes by the mirror (27x37cm-11x15in) s. num.34/50 aquatint drypoint. 4-Nov-3 Ansorena, Madrid #933/R est:5000
£5493	$9503	€7800	Peintre Neoclassique dans son atelier (43x57cm-17x22in) s.num. etching vellum edition of 72. 11-Dec-3 Piasa, Paris #129
£5493	$9503	€7800	Minotaure endormi contemple par une femme (45x34cm-18x13in) s. eau forte one of 260 exec. 1933. 14-Dec-3 Rabourdin & Choppin de Janvry, Paris #7/R est:3500-4000
£5500	$9460	€8030	La toilette de la mere (24x18cm-9x7in) etching drypoint. 2-Dec-3 Christie's, London #254/R est:4500-5500
£5500	$9460	€8030	Jacqueline au Cheveux flous (25x27cm-10x11in) s.num.40/50 linocut. 2-Dec-3 Christie's, London #270/R est:3500-4500
£5500	$10010	€8030	Sculpteur et son modele (19x26cm-7x10in) etching. 30-Jun-4 Christie's, London #296/R est:5000-7000
£5500	$10010	€8030	Au cabaret (24x30cm-9x12in) st.sig.num.7/50 etching. 1-Jul-4 Sotheby's, London #277/R est:5000-7000
£5505	$9193	€7982	Minotaure et jeune femme enlaces revant sous une fenetre. s. etching. 19-Jun-3 Kornfeld, Bern #819/R est:12500 (S.FR 12000)
£5505	$9193	€7982	Peintre neo-classique dans son atelier. s.i. etching. 19-Jun-3 Kornfeld, Bern #824/R est:10000 (S.FR 12000)
£5588	$9500	€8158	Femme nue assise (35x27cm-14x11in) s. linoleum cut. 31-Oct-3 Sotheby's, New York #384/R
£5650	$10000	€8249	Figure (64x50cm-25x20in) s.num.28/50 lithograph. 28-Apr-4 Christie's, Rockefeller NY #143/R est:8000-10000
£5650	$10000	€8249	Femme nue a la jambe pliee (31x22cm-12x9in) s. etching edition of 250. 28-Apr-4 Christie's, Rockefeller NY #117/R est:8000-12000
£5650	$10000	€8249	Femme torero, II (30x24cm-12x9in) s. etching edition of 250. 28-Apr-4 Christie's, Rockefeller NY #129/R est:10000-15000
£5650	$10000	€8249	Trois femmes nues pres d'une fenetre (36x29cm-14x11in) s. etching. 30-Apr-4 Sotheby's, New York #173/R est:6000-8000
£5650	$10000	€8249	Sculpteur et trois danseuses sculptees (22x31cm-9x12in) s. etching. 30-Apr-4 Sotheby's, New York #175/R est:8000-10000
£5677	$10332	€8288	Sculpteur songeant, modele aux cheveux nors et bol avec anenomes. etching. 17-Jun-4 Kornfeld, Bern #656 est:10000 (S.FR 13000)
£5702	$10491	€8325	Plantes aux Toritos (66x54cm-26x21in) s. num.26/50 col linocut. 23-Jun-4 Koller, Zurich #3278/R est:6000-8000 (S.FR 13000)
£5733	$10549	€8600	Deux femmes regardant une tete sculptee (27x15cm-11x6in) s.d.1933 etching. 10-Jun-4 Hauswedell & Nolte, Hamburg #573/R est:12000
£5800	$10556	€8468	Le repos du sculpteur devant le petit torse (19x27cm-7x11in) s. etching edition of 300. 1-Jul-4 Sotheby's, London #251/R est:3000-4000
£5856	$10072	€8550	Les mains liees, III (51x66cm-20x26in) s. lithograph. 2-Dec-3 Koller, Zurich #3362/R est:4000-6000 (S.FR 13000)
£5882	$10000	€8588	Sculpteur et modele (19x27cm-7x11in) s. etching. 31-Oct-3 Sotheby's, New York #359/R
£5882	$10000	€8588	Source (34x45cm-13x18in) s. num.24/100 drypoint exec.1921. 4-Nov-3 Christie's, Rockefeller NY #147/R est:6000-8000
£5882	$10000	€8588	Sculpteur et trois danseuses (34x45cm-13x18in) s. etching exec.1934. 4-Nov-3 Christie's, Rockefeller NY #153/R est:8000-10000
£5882	$10000	€8588	Minotaure endormi (34x45cm-13x18in) s. etching exec.1933. 4-Nov-3 Christie's, Rockefeller NY #149/R est:8000-12000
£5963	$9959	€8646	Crane de chevre sur la table. s.i. aquatint. 19-Jun-3 Kornfeld, Bern #823/R est:10000 (S.FR 13000)
£6000	$11040	€9000	Fumeur a la cigarette rouge (42x32cm-17x13in) col aquatint exec.1964. 10-Jun-4 Piasa, Paris #189
£6000	$11040	€9000	Marie Therese considerant son effigie surrealist sculptee (27x19cm-11x7in) s.d.1933 etching. 10-Jun-4 Hauswedell & Nolte, Hamburg #576/R est:8000
£6114	$11127	€8926	Tete de femme au chignon. s.i. lithograph. 17-Jun-4 Kornfeld, Bern #685 est:12500 (S.FR 14000)
£6193	$10342	€8980	Dormeuse et sculpture. s.i. etching. 19-Jun-3 Kornfeld, Bern #816 est:15000 (S.FR 13500)
£6200	$11284	€9052	Les Trois Graces II (47x33cm-19x13in) s.num.85/100 tone etching. 1-Jul-4 Sotheby's, London #245/R est:4000-6000
£6215	$11000	€9074	Sculpteur et son modele (19x27cm-7x11in) s. etching edition of 250. 28-Apr-4 Christie's, Rockefeller NY #122/R est:8000-10000
£6215	$11000	€9074	Fumeur (60x43cm-24x17in) s.num.15/50 col etching aquatint. 28-Apr-4 Christie's, Rockefeller NY #163/R est:8000-12000
£6215	$11000	€9074	Le repos du sculpteur (19x27cm-7x11in) s. etching edition of 250. 28-Apr-4 Christie's, Rockefeller NY #123/R est:9000-12000
£6215	$11000	€9074	Tete de femme, de profil (29x25cm-11x10in) drypoint edition of 250 printed 1913. 28-Apr-4 Christie's, Rockefeller NY #114/R est:7000-9000
£6227	$11022	€9091	Jacqueline au Mouchoir noir (64x48cm-25x19in) s.num.15/50 lithograph lit. 27-Apr-4 AB Stockholms Auktionsverk #1349/R est:80000-100000 (S.KR 85000)
£6294	$10699	€9000	Tete de jeune fille (27x21cm-11x8in) s. lithograph. 26-Nov-3 Lempertz, Koln #909/R est:7000
£6294	$10699	€9000	Venus et l'Amour (68x50cm-27x20in) lithograph wash pen exec.1949. 28-Nov-3 Tajan, Paris #355/R est:10000
£6333	$11653	€9500	Salome (40x34cm-16x13in) drypoint etching exec. 1905 one of 250. 12-Jun-4 Villa Grisebach, Berlin #173/R est:9000-12000
£6333	$11653	€9500	Petit nu assis au miroir (31x48cm-12x19in) s. lithograph exec. 1947 one of 5. 12-Jun-4 Villa Grisebach, Berlin #369/R est:6000-8000
£6344	$10785	€9262	Bacchanale au hibou (53x64cm-21x25in) s.num.32/50 col linocut lit. 4-Nov-3 Bukowskis, Stockholm #438/R est:80000-100000 (S.KR 84000)
£6471	$11000	€9448	Tete de femme (29x25cm-11x10in) drypoint lit. 31-Oct-3 Sotheby's, New York #351/R
£6471	$11000	€9448	Trois baigneuses (18x13cm-7x5in) s. drypoint. 31-Oct-3 Sotheby's, New York #353/R
£6471	$11000	€9448	Les demoiselles d'Avignon (50x47cm-20x19in) s.num.70/100 col lithograph exec.c.1955. 6-Nov-3 Swann Galleries, New York #701/R est:10000-15000
£6471	$11000	€9448	Pauvres (39x30cm-15x12in) etching exec.1905. 4-Nov-3 Christie's, Rockefeller NY #144/R est:5000-7000
£6471	$11000	€9448	Colombe (55x77cm-22x30in) s. num.111/200 col lithograph exec.1952. 4-Nov-3 Christie's, Rockefeller NY #162/R est:4000-6000
£6479	$11208	€9200	Bacchanale au hibou (53x64cm-21x25in) s.num. col engraving linoleum vellum edition of 81. 11-Dec-3 Piasa, Paris #125/R
£6500	$11830	€9490	La poule (56x70cm-22x28in) s.num.36/50 aquatint drypoint. 1-Jul-4 Sotheby's, London #263/R est:7000-9000
£6704	$12000	€9788	Sculpteur et trois danseuses sculptees (22x31cm-9x12in) s. etching. 6-May-4 Swann Galleries, New York #550/R est:10000-15000
£6780	$12000	€9899	Modele nu et sculptures (38x30cm-15x12in) s. etching edition of 250. 28-Apr-4 Christie's, Rockefeller NY #125/R est:8000-10000
£6780	$12000	€9899	Hibou a la chaise fond ocre (66x50cm-26x20in) s.num.39/50 black ochre lithograph. 28-Apr-4 Christie's, Rockefeller NY #137/R est:6000-8000
£6780	$12000	€9899	Colombe volant (50x65cm-20x26in) s.num.137/200 col lithograph. 28-Apr-4 Christie's, Rockefeller NY #147/R est:5000-7000
£6780	$12000	€9899	347 series no.70 (31x41cm-12x16in) s.num.43/50 etching. 30-Apr-4 Sotheby's, New York #193/R est:5000-7000
£6787	$11335	€9909	Composition (55x44cm-22x17in) s. etching. 27-Jun-3 Falk & Falk, Zurich #873/R est:24000 (S.FR 15000)
£6800	$12376	€9928	Le combat (45x67cm-18x26in) s.num.10/50 etching drypoint. 1-Jul-4 Sotheby's, London #252/R est:4000-6000
£6944	$11597	€10000	Manolo Huguet - poster for the Musee de Ceret (64x47cm-25x19in) s.i.d.15.7.57 lithograph. 24-Oct-3 Ketterer, Hamburg #502/R est:10000-12000
£6962	$12531	€10165	Les vendangeurs (53x64cm-21x25in) s.num.15/50 col linocut prov.lit. 26-Apr-4 Bukowskis, Stockholm #428/R est:80000-100000 (S.KR 96000)
£6983	$12500	€10195	Femme au miroir (17x13cm-7x5in) s.i. drypoint. 6-May-4 Swann Galleries, New York #543/R est:8000-12000
£6987	$12716	€10201	Scene bacchique au minotaure. s. etching. 17-Jun-4 Kornfeld, Bern #657 est:10000 (S.FR 16000)
£7000	$12740	€10220	Le viol (29x36cm-11x14in) etching. 30-Jun-4 Christie's, London #298/R est:4000-6000
£7000	$12740	€10220	Profil au fond noir (54x37cm-21x15in) s.num.4/50 lithograph. 1-Jul-4 Sotheby's, London #253/R est:8000-10000
£7059	$12000	€10306	Fumeur (79x58cm-31x23in) s. aquatint etching exec.1964. 4-Nov-3 Christie's, Rockefeller NY #175/R est:8000-12000
£7110	$11874	€10310	Figure. s.i. lithograph. 19-Jun-3 Kornfeld, Bern #860 est:15000 (S.FR 15500)
£7143	$13071	€10715	Le peintre et son modele (23x33cm-9x13in) s.d.18 nov 1963 aquatint. 6-Jul-4 Bolsa de Arte, Rio de Janeiro #104/R (B.R 39000)
£7220	$13285	€10541	Les trois baigneuses III (20x15cm-8x6in) s.num.87/200 etching exec.c.1922/23 lit. 29-Mar-4 Rasmussen, Copenhagen #69/R est:50000 (D.KR 80000)
£7237	$13099	€11000	Agamennon and Briseida (45x54cm-18x21in) s. eau forte one of 347 lit. 14-Apr-4 Ansorena, Madrid #351/R est:5500
£7263	$13000	€10604	Rembrandt et tetes de femme (14x21cm-6x8in) s. etching. 6-May-4 Swann Galleries, New York #547/R est:7000-10000
£7263	$13000	€10604	Rembrandt a la palette (28x20cm-11x8in) s. etching. 6-May-4 Swann Galleries, New York #548/R est:10000-15000
£7333	$13493	€11000	Etude de profils (73x55cm-29x22in) s. lithograph exec. 1948 one of 50. 12-Jun-4 Villa Grisebach, Berlin #366/R est:7000-9000
£7343	$12483	€10500	La danse des banderilles (48x64cm-19x25in) s. lithograph. 26-Nov-3 Lempertz, Koln #912/R est:8000

£7345	$13000	€10724	Le peintre et son modele (53x64cm-21x25in) s.num.89/160 linocut. 28-Apr-4 Christie's, Rockefeller NY #164/R est:6000-8000
£7345	$13000	€10724	David et Bethsabee (65x48cm-26x19in) s.num.39/50 lithograph. 28-Apr-4 Christie's, Rockefeller NY #144/R est:8000-12000
£7345	$13000	€10724	Homme barbu couronne (35x27cm-14x11in) s.num.17/50 col linocut. 28-Apr-4 Christie's, Rockefeller NY #160/R est:10000-15000
£7345	$13000	€10724	Sculpteur et modele admirant un tete sculptee (27x19cm-11x7in) s. etching edition of250. 28-Apr-4 Christie's, Rockefeller NY #118/R est:9000-12000
£7415	$12606	€10826	Figure (64x49cm-25x19in) s. lithograph exec 1948. 24-Nov-3 Sotheby's, Melbourne #278/R est:15000-20000 (A.D 17500)
£7489	$12731	€10934	Faune musicien Nr 5 (69x50cm-27x20in) s.i. lithograph. 5-Nov-3 Dobiaschofsky, Bern #1838/R est:7500 (S.FR 17000)
£7639	$12986	€11000	Femme nue a la source (53x64cm-21x25in) s. num.37/50 col print prov.exhib.lit. 28-Oct-3 Il Ponte, Milan #255/R
£7639	$12757	€11000	Minotaure amoureux d'une femme centaure (19x27cm-7x11in) s.i.d.23 mai XXIII etching. 24-Oct-3 Ketterer, Hamburg #500/R est:12000-15000
£7642	$13908	€11157	Deux femmes nues. s.i. etching. 17-Jun-4 Kornfeld, Bern #654 est:17500 (S.FR 17500)
£7647	$13000	€11165	Profil au fond noir (57x38cm-22x15in) s. lithograph. 31-Oct-3 Sotheby's, New York #367/R
£7647	$13000	€11165	Picador et cheval (64x53cm-25x21in) s. linoleum cut. 31-Oct-3 Sotheby's, New York #379/R
£7647	$13000	€11165	Buste au corsage a carreaux (56x44cm-22x17in) s.num.24/50 lithograph. 6-Nov-3 Swann Galleries, New York #690/R est:12000-18000
£7647	$13000	€11165	Femme au fauteuil (76x56cm-30x22in) i. lithograph exec.1948. 4-Nov-3 Christie's, Rockefeller NY #159/R est:20000-30000
£7667	$14107	€11500	Trois amies (42x30cm-17x12in) s.i. eau forte exec.1927. 10-Jun-4 Piasa, Paris #182
£7667	$14030	€11500	Faune souriant (65x54cm-26x21in) s. lithograph. 5-Jun-4 Lempertz, Koln #937/R est:10000-15000
£7671	$14116	€11200	Le depart (53x65cm-21x26in) s.d.51 num.4/50 lithograph in colour lit. 29-Mar-4 Rasmussen, Copenhagen #76/R est:50000 (D.KR 85000)
£7746	$13401	€11000	Fumeur a la cigarette verte (60x43cm-24x17in) s.num. col vernis mou vellum edition of 75. 11-Dec-3 Piasa, Paris #130/R
£7910	$14000	€11549	Figure composee (65x50cm-26x20in) s.num.12/50 lithograph. 28-Apr-4 Christie's, Rockefeller NY #146/R est:8000-12000
£7910	$14000	€11549	Sculpteur et modele agenouille (37x29cm-15x11in) s. etching. 30-Apr-4 Sotheby's, New York #174/R est:14000-18000
£7910	$14000	€11549	Venus et l'amour (70x51cm-28x20in) s.num.32/50 lithograph. 30-Apr-4 Sotheby's, New York #179/R est:8000-12000
£7986	$13576	€11500	Dejeuner sur l'herbe (53x64cm-21x25in) s. num.37/50 col lithograph prov.exhib.lit. 28-Oct-3 Il Ponte, Milan #252/R
£8000	$14560	€11680	Minotaure caressant une femme (29x37cm-11x15in) etching. 30-Jun-4 Christie's, London #299/R est:6000-8000
£8000	$14560	€11680	Jacqueline lisant (56x44cm-22x17in) s.num.29/50 lithograph. 1-Jul-4 Sotheby's, London #260/R est:5000-7000
£8042	$13832	€11500	Tete de femme,de profil (29x25cm-11x10in) drypoint etching. 2-Dec-3 Hauswedell & Nolte, Hamburg #528/R est:10000
£8235	$14000	€12023	Deux femmes regardant un modele (18x13cm-7x5in) s. etching drypoint. 31-Oct-3 Sotheby's, New York #352/R
£8235	$14000	€12023	Vase de fleurs (64x53cm-25x21in) s. linoleum cut. 31-Oct-3 Sotheby's, New York #380/R
£8297	$15100	€12114	Figure composee. s.i. lithograph. 17-Jun-4 Kornfeld, Bern #682 est:12500 (S.FR 19000)
£8392	$14266	€12000	Jacqueline de profil (69x50cm-27x20in) lithograph wash on zinc. 28-Nov-3 Tajan, Paris #354/R est:12000
£8475	$15000	€12374	Clin d'oeil au Bain Turc (28x39cm-11x15in) s.num.6/50 etching. 28-Apr-4 Christie's, Rockefeller NY #187/R est:8000-12000
£8475	$15000	€12374	Taureau aile contemple par quatre enfants (24x30cm-9x12in) bears sig. etching edition of 250. 28-Apr-4 Christie's, Rockefeller NY #130/R est:10000-15000
£8475	$15000	€12374	Danseurs ey musicien (53x64cm-21x25in) s.num.50/50 brown black linoleum. 30-Apr-4 Sotheby's, New York #186/R est:3000-5000
£8486	$14172	€12305	Jacqueline au bandeau III. s. col linocut. 19-Jun-3 Kornfeld, Bern #870/R est:16000 (S.FR 18500)
£8486	$14172	€12305	Dormeuse. s.i. col linocut. 19-Jun-3 Kornfeld, Bern #871/R est:17500 (S.FR 18500)
£8500	$15470	€12410	Sculpteur, femme assise (30x18cm-12x7in) drypoint. 30-Jun-4 Christie's, London #294/R est:7000-10000
£8500	$15470	€12410	Trois femmes nues et coupe d'anemones (37x30cm-15x12in) etching. 30-Jun-4 Christie's, London #297/R est:5000-7000
£8500	$15470	€12410	Femme nue devant une statue (45x34cm-18x13in) s. etching edition of 300. 1-Jul-4 Sotheby's, London #246/R est:5000-7000
£8500	$15470	€12410	Trois femme nues pres d'une fenetre (37x30cm-15x12in) indis.sig. etching edition of 300. 1-Jul-4 Sotheby's, London #259/R est:6000-8000
£8500	$15470	€12410	Deux femmes sur la plage (47x62cm-19x24in) s.num.6/50 lithograph. 1-Jul-4 Sotheby's, London #266/R est:8000-10000
£8515	$15498	€12432	Centaure et bacchante avec un faune. s.i. lithograph. 17-Jun-4 Kornfeld, Bern #680/R est:17500 (S.FR 19500)
£8667	$15947	€13000	Jeune garcon revant, les femmes (49x41cm-19x16in) s. aquatint drypoint exec. 1968 one of 50. 11-Jun-4 Villa Grisebach, Berlin #1597/R est:4000-6000
£8725	$15617	€13000	Deux nus assis (26x19cm-10x7in) s. drypoint etching. 25-May-4 Dorotheum, Vienna #42/R est:9300-9500
£8734	$15895	€12752	Jeune fille aux grands cheveux. s.i. lithograph. 17-Jun-4 Kornfeld, Bern #679 est:10000 (S.FR 20000)
£8824	$15000	€12883	Taureau aile (24x30cm-9x12in) s. etching. 31-Oct-3 Sotheby's, New York #363/R
£8824	$15000	€12883	Petit buste de femme (63x44cm-25x17in) s. num.44/50 col linocut. 4-Nov-3 Christie's, Rockefeller NY #169/R est:12000-16000
£8939	$16000	€13051	Rembrandt et femme au voile (28x20cm-11x8in) s. etching. 6-May-4 Swann Galleries, New York #549/R est:7000-10000
£8939	$16000	€13051	Deux femmes assises (25x28cm-10x11in) s. etching. 6-May-4 Swann Galleries, New York #552/R est:10000-15000
£9040	$16000	€13198	Bacchanale (52x64cm-20x25in) s.num.2/50 col linocut. 28-Apr-4 Christie's, Rockefeller NY #156/R est:8000-12000
£9333	$17173	€14000	Crane de chevre sur la table (51x66cm-20x26in) s. aquatint exec. 1953 one of 50. 12-Jun-4 Villa Grisebach, Berlin #374/R est:14000-18000
£9412	$16000	€13742	La Celestine (21x17cm-8x7in) etchings aquatints 35 of 66 edition of 350 album. 6-Nov-3 Swann Galleries, New York #698/R est:8000-12000
£9500	$16340	€13870	Portrait de Jacqueline (51x38cm-20x15in) s.num.65/100 offset lithograph. 2-Dec-3 Christie's, London #269/R est:5000-7000
£9500	$17290	€13870	Femmes se reposant (30x36cm-12x14in) drypoint. 30-Jun-4 Christie's, London #295/R est:7000-9000
£9581	$16000	€13988	Taureau aile contemple par quatre enfants (23x30cm-9x12in) s. etching edition of 250. 21-Oct-3 Bonhams & Butterfields, San Francisco #1223/R
£9605	$17000	€14023	Visteurs divins a l'atelier (49x64cm-19x25in) s.num.17/50 aquatint. 30-Apr-4 Sotheby's, New York #181/R est:12000-15000
£10000	$17000	€14600	Buste (66x50cm-26x20in) s. lithograph exec.1949. 4-Nov-3 Christie's, Rockefeller NY #160/R est:10000-15000
£10000	$17200	€14600	Quatre femmes nues et tere sculptee (22x31cm-9x12in) s. etching. 2-Dec-3 Christie's, London #257/R est:10000-15000
£10000	$17900	€15000	Homards et poissons (79x109cm-31x43in) s.i. lithograph. 15-May-4 Van Ham, Cologne #833/R est:8500
£10000	$18200	€14600	Buste de jeune fille (49x42cm-19x17in) lithograph. 30-Jun-4 Christie's, London #303/R est:5000-7000
£10169	$18000	€14847	Mere, danseur et musicien (64x53cm-25x21in) s.num.3/50 col linocut. 28-Apr-4 Christie's, Rockefeller NY #155/R est:12000-15000
£10169	$18000	€14847	Petit buste de femme (35x27cm-14x11in) s.num.38/50 col linocut. 28-Apr-4 Christie's, Rockefeller NY #159/R est:10000-12000
£10169	$18000	€14847	Nature morte avec musique (28x21cm-11x8in) s.num.3/100 col pochoir print. 30-Apr-4 Sotheby's, New York #197/R est:4000-6000
£10490	$18042	€15000	David et Bethsabee (65x49cm-26x19in) s.d.1947 lithograph. 2-Dec-3 Hauswedell & Nolte, Hamburg #539/R est:20000
£10490	$17832	€15000	Tete d'homme a la pipe (13x11cm-5x4in) s. etching. 29-Nov-3 Bassenge, Berlin #6949/R est:18000
£10563	$18275	€15000	Homme Barbu Couronne (35x27cm-14x11in) s.num. engraving linoleum vellum edition of 74. 11-Dec-3 Piasa, Paris #127/R
£10588	$18000	€15458	Italienne (65x50cm-26x20in) s. num.8/50 offset photolitograph exec.1953. 4-Nov-3 Christie's, Rockefeller NY #163/R est:20000-30000
£10588	$18000	€15458	Tete de femme (75x62cm-30x24in) s. num.38/50 col linocut exec.1959. 4-Nov-3 Christie's, Rockefeller NY #164/R est:22000-28000
£10725	$18233	€15659	Taureau aile contemple par quatre enfants - la suite Vollard (24x30cm-9x12in) s. etching lit. 4-Nov-3 Bukowskis, Stockholm #434/R est:120000-140000 (S.KR 142000)
£10734	$19000	€15672	Femme torero (50x69cm-20x27in) etching edition of 50 printed 1930. 28-Apr-4 Christie's, Rockefeller NY #133/R est:15000-20000
£10734	$19000	€15672	La Grande Corrida, avec femme torero (50x69cm-20x27in) etching edition of 50 printed 1939. 28-Apr-4 Christie's, Rockefeller NY #134/R est:20000-30000
£10917	$19869	€15939	Baigneuse debout, avec une cape. s.i. col linocut. 17-Jun-4 Kornfeld, Bern #694/R est:20000 (S.FR 25000)
£10965	$20175	€16009	Grande nature morte au Compotier (47x61cm-19x24in) s. num.4/50 lithograph. 23-Jun-4 Koller, Zurich #3280/R est:4500-6000 (S.FR 25000)
£11000	$18260	€16060	La dame a la collerette (62x44cm-24x17in) s.i. col linocut. 6-Oct-3 Sotheby's, London #113/R est:12000-18000
£11173	$20000	€16313	Le petit dessinateur (65x50cm-26x20in) s.num.40/50 color lithograph. 6-May-4 Swann Galleries, New York #556/R est:15000-20000
£11176	$19000	€16317	Quatre femmes nues (22x32cm-9x13in) s. etching. 31-Oct-3 Sotheby's, New York #362/R
£11176	$19000	€16317	Femme nue (62x75cm-24x30in) s. num.3/50 col linocut exec.1962. 4-Nov-3 Christie's, Rockefeller NY #171/R est:16000-20000
£11176	$19000	€16317	Bearded man (63x44cm-25x17in) s. col linocut exec.1962. 4-Nov-3 Christie's, Rockefeller NY #170/R est:16000-20000
£11354	$20664	€16577	Petit dejeuner sur l'herbe (35x27cm-14x11in) s.i. col lithograph exec. 1962 after Manet. 18-Jun-4 Kornfeld, Bern #3130/R est:25000 (S.FR 26000)
£11468	$19151	€16629	Olga et Paulo: La soupe - Maternite. s.i. etching. 19-Jun-3 Kornfeld, Bern #812/R est:20000 (S.FR 25000)
£11468	$19151	€16629	Marie-Therese, en vestale, veillant le minotaure endormi. s. etching. 19-Jun-3 Kornfeld, Bern #817/R est:17500 (S.FR 25000)
£11765	$20000	€17177	Avant la pique (62x75cm-24x30in) s. num.14/50 col linocut. 4-Nov-3 Christie's, Rockefeller NY #165/R est:15000-20000
£11927	$19917	€17294	Dans l'arene, jeune homme achevant le minotaure. s. etching. 19-Jun-3 Kornfeld, Bern #818/R est:15000 (S.FR 26000)
£11957	$22000	€17457	L'Espanole (61x43cm-24x17in) s.d.1962 col linocut. 26-Jun-4 Susanin's, Chicago #6066/R est:15000-20000
£12000	$19920	€17520	Danseurs et musicien (53x64cm-21x25in) s.num.32/50 col linocut. 6-Oct-3 Sotheby's, London #114/R est:10000-12000
£12000	$21840	€17520	Scene Bacchique au minotaur (29x36cm-11x14in) etching. 30-Jun-4 Christie's, London #300/R est:7000-9000
£12153	$20660	€17500	Apres la pique (53x64cm-21x25in) s. num.6/50 col lithograph prov.exhib.lit. 28-Oct-3 Il Ponte, Milan #253/R
£12353	$21000	€18035	Trois femmes au reveil (52x64cm-20x25in) s. linoleum cut. 31-Oct-3 Sotheby's, New York #382/R
£12429	$22000	€18146	Le dejeuner su l'Herbe (53x64cm-21x25in) s.num.12/50 col linocut. 28-Apr-4 Christie's, Rockefeller NY #161/R est:12000-15000
£12667	$23307	€19000	Homme barbu couronne de feuillage (35x27cm-14x11in) s. col linocut exec.1962. 10-Jun-4 Piasa, Paris #186/R
£12667	$23307	€19000	Picador et taureau (53x64cm-21x25in) s. col linocut. 10-Jun-4 Hauswedell & Nolte, Hamburg #584/R est:25000
£12712	$22500	€18560	L'Italienne (44x38cm-17x15in) s.num.44/50 lithograph. 30-Apr-4 Sotheby's, New York #180/R est:25000-30000
£12941	$22000	€18894	Stylized figure (66x50cm-26x20in) i. lithograph. 31-Oct-3 Sotheby's, New York #368/R
£12941	$22000	€18894	Stylized figure (66x50cm-26x20in) i. lithograph. 31-Oct-3 Sotheby's, New York #369/R
£12941	$22000	€18894	Pique (53x64cm-21x25in) s. linoleum cut. 31-Oct-3 Sotheby's, New York #378
£12941	$22000	€18894	Lysistrata (40x30cm-16x12in) s.i. etching aquatint album. 4-Nov-3 Christie's, Rockefeller NY #155/R est:12000-18000
£13100	$23843	€19126	Portrait de femme II (64x37cm-25x15in) s.i. lithograph exec. Dec 1955. 18-Jun-4 Kornfeld, Bern #127/R est:25000 (S.FR 30000)
£13287	$22853	€19000	Garcon et dormeuse a la chandelle (24x30cm-9x12in) s. etching aquatint copperplate. 2-Dec-3 Hauswedell & Nolte, Hamburg #531/R est:22000
£13333	$24533	€20000	Flutiste et danseurs aux cymbales (53x64cm-21x25in) s. linocut exec. 1959 one of 50. 11-Jun-4 Villa Grisebach, Berlin #1594/R est:12000-15000
£13500	$24570	€19710	Sueno y Mentira de Franco (59x40cm-23x16in) s.num.63/150 etchings aquatint two portfolio. 1-Jul-4 Sotheby's, London #256/R est:8000-10000
£13538	$24910	€19765	Grande nature morte au compotier (49x65cm-19x26in) s.num.8/50 etching executed 1947 lit. 29-Mar-4 Rasmussen, Copenhagen #70/R est:30000-40000 (D.KR 150000)
£13559	$24000	€19796	Tete de femme II (30x24cm-12x9in) aquatint. 30-Apr-4 Sotheby's, New York #191/R est:25000-35000
£13966	$25000	€20390	Minotaure une coupe a la main, et Jeune femme (19x27cm-7x11in) s. etching. 6-May-4 Swann Galleries, New York #545/R est:12000-18000
£13974	$25432	€20402	Jacqueline lisant (55x44cm-22x17in) s.i. lithograph exec. Dec 1957. 18-Jun-4 Kornfeld, Bern #128/R est:25000 (S.FR 32000)
£14000	$25480	€20440	Quatre femmes nues et tete sculptee (22x31cm-9x12in) etching. 30-Jun-4 Christie's, London #302/R est:10000-15000
£14525	$26000	€21207	Jeunesse (50x65cm-20x26in) s.num.9/50 lithograph. 6-May-4 Swann Galleries, New York #554/R est:35000-45000
£14689	$26000	€21446	Danseurs et musicien (55x64cm-22x25in) s. col linocut. 28-Apr-4 Christie's, Rockefeller NY #157/R est:12000-18000
£14789	$23662	€21000	Portrait de femme au chapeau a pompons et au corsage imprime (63x53cm-25x21in) col linocut. 19-Sep-3 Sigalas, Stuttgart #344/R est:9000
£14789	$25585	€21000	Pique - rouge et jaune (62x75cm-24x30in) s.i. col linocut lit. 13-Dec-3 Lempertz, Koln #176/R est:20000-25000
£15000	$27300	€21900	La femme au bandeau (35x27cm-14x11in) linocut. 30-Jun-4 Christie's, London #309/R est:8000-12000
£15000	$27300	€21900	Femme au corsage a fleurs (65x51cm-26x20in) s.num.34/50 lithograph. 1-Jul-4 Sotheby's, London #254/R est:10000-15000

£15734	$27063	€22500	Jeune femme surprenant le reflet d'une hirondelle dans son miroir (35x25cm-14x10in) s.i. etching vernis mou. 2-Dec-3 Hauswedell & Nolte, Hamburg #532/R est:25000
£15861	$26964	€23157	Tete de femme aux cheveux flous (61x45cm-24x18in) s.num.17/50 aquatint. 4-Nov-3 Bukowskis, Stockholm #435/R est:200000-250000 (S.KR 210000)
£15954	$28716	€23293	Bacchanale (53x64cm-21x25in) s.num.26/50 col linocut lit. 26-Apr-4 Bukowskis, Stockholm #427/R est:200000-225000 (S.KR 220000)
£16000	$29440	€24000	Buste de profil (64x50cm-25x20in) s. lithograph exec. 1957 one of 50. 11-Jun-4 Villa Grisebach, Berlin #1590/R est:15000-20000
£16000	$29120	€23360	Femme accroupie au bras leve (43x59cm-17x23in) s.num.38/50 lithograph. 1-Jul-4 Sotheby's, London #267/R est:10000-12000
£16216	$30000	€23675	Tete de femme (71x61cm-28x24in) s. col linocut edition of 50. 13-Mar-4 Susanin's, Chicago #6018/R est:30000-40000
£16384	$29000	€23921	Apres la pique (53x64cm-21x25in) s.num.38/50 col linocut. 28-Apr-4 Christie's, Rockefeller NY #153/R est:16000-20000
£16471	$28000	€24048	Minotaure (34x44cm-13x17in) s. etching exec.1933. 4-Nov-3 Christie's, Rockefeller NY #150/R est:20000-30000
£16949	$30000	€24746	Jeune homme couronne de feuillage (35x27cm-14x11in) s. black brown linoleum. 30-Apr-4 Sotheby's, New York #188/R est:22000-26000
£17000	$29240	€24820	Le peintre et da toile (63x64cm-25x25in) s.d.8.9.64 linocut. 2-Dec-3 Christie's, London #271/R est:18000-22000
£17000	$30940	€24820	David and Bethsabee (65x48cm-26x19in) s. lithograph. 1-Jul-4 Sotheby's, London #262/R est:14000-18000
£17514	$31000	€25570	Grand air (42x32cm-17x13in) i. etching. 30-Apr-4 Sotheby's, New York #177/R est:8000-12000
£17544	$32281	€25614	Picador and Torero (53x64cm-21x25in) s. num.20/50 col linocut. 23-Jun-4 Koller, Zurich #3277/R est:7000-9000 (S.FR 40000)
£17647	$30000	€25765	Femme au fauteuil 1 (76x56cm-30x22in) s. lithograph. 31-Oct-3 Sotheby's, New York #370/R
£18000	$33120	€27000	Femme assise et dormeuse (49x61cm-19x24in) s. lithograph exec. 1947. 11-Jun-4 Villa Grisebach, Berlin #1587/R est:15000-20000
£18079	$32000	€26395	Femme au collier (63x53cm-25x21in) s.num.26/50 col linocut. 28-Apr-4 Christie's, Rockefeller NY #154/R est:22000-28000
£19214	$34969	€28052	Grande tete de femme au chapeau (64x52cm-25x20in) s.i. col linocut exec.1962. 18-Jun-4 Kornfeld, Bern #131/R est:30000 (S.FR 44000)
£19333	$35573	€29000	Portrait de Francoise aux cheveux flous (61x45cm-24x18in) s. aquatint exec. 1947 one of 50. 11-Jun-4 Villa Grisebach, Berlin #1591/R est:18000-24000
£20000	$36400	€29200	Femme, assise et dormeuse (50x66cm-20x26in) s.num.6/50 black grey lithograph. 1-Jul-4 Sotheby's, London #264/R est:15000-20000
£20904	$37000	€30520	Tete de femme (64x53cm-25x21in) s.num.33/50 col linocut. 28-Apr-4 Christie's, Rockefeller NY #158/R est:30000-40000
£20979	$36084	€30000	Jacqueline de profil (72x51cm-28x20in) d.1958 lithograph. 2-Dec-3 Hauswedell & Nolte, Hamburg #544/R est:35000
£22028	$37448	€31500	Minotaure aveugle guide par Marie Therese au pigeon dans une nuit etoilee (25x35cm-10x14in) s. etching. 26-Nov-3 Lempertz, Koln #908/R est:30000-35000
£22667	$41707	€34000	Figure au corsage raye (65x50cm-26x20in) s. col lithograph one of 50 prov. 11-Jun-4 Villa Grisebach, Berlin #62/R est:20000-30000
£22905	$41000	€33441	Faun uncovering a woman (30x41cm-12x16in) aquatint. 14-May-4 Du Mouchelle, Detroit #2122/R est:35000-45000
£23333	$42933	€35000	La dormeuse (50x64cm-20x25in) s. lithograph one of 50 prov. 11-Jun-4 Villa Grisebach, Berlin #61/R est:15000-20000
£23333	$42933	€35000	Danae (27x35cm-11x14in) s. col linocut one of 50. 11-Jun-4 Villa Grisebach, Berlin #64/R est:30000-40000
£23529	$40000	€34352	Jacqueline lisant (75x62cm-30x24in) s. num.35/50 linocut exec.1964 prov. 4-Nov-3 Christie's, Rockefeller NY #176/R est:35000-45000
£24000	$44160	€36000	Pique II (53x64cm-21x25in) s. col lithograph one of 50 prov. 11-Jun-4 Villa Grisebach, Berlin #63/R est:25000-35000
£24667	$45387	€37000	Femme au fauteuil I (69x54cm-27x21in) s. lithograph exec. 1948-49 one of five. 11-Jun-4 Villa Grisebach, Berlin #1589/R est:25000-30000
£25000	$43000	€36500	Faune devoilant une femme (31x41cm-12x16in) s. etching aquatint edition of 300. 4-Dec-3 Sotheby's, London #202/R est:25000-35000
£25333	$46613	€38000	Portrait de Jacqueline accoudee (64x53cm-25x21in) s. linocut exec. 1959 one of 50. 11-Jun-4 Villa Grisebach, Berlin #1593/R est:25000-35000
£26471	$45000	€38648	Faune (34x45cm-13x18in) s. etching aquatint exec.1936. 4-Nov-3 Christie's, Rockefeller NY #154/R est:50000-70000
£26471	$45000	€38648	Tete de femme (75x62cm-30x24in) s. num.44/100 col linocut exec.1962. 4-Nov-3 Christie's, Rockefeller NY #167/R est:40000-60000
£26946	$45000	€39341	Tete de femme, portrait de Jacqueline de face II (65x83cm-26x33in) s.num.44/50 col linocut. 21-Oct-3 Bonhams & Butterfields, San Francisco #1230/R
£27076	$49819	€39531	Tete du jeune femme (63x47cm-25x19in) s.d.24 Juill 47 num.42/50 lithograph prov.lit. 29-Mar-4 Rasmussen, Copenhagen #72/R est:75000-100000 (D.KR 300000)
£27076	$49819	€39531	La barre d'appui - composition in four quarters (41x30cm-16x12in) s.num.3/18 sugar aquatint printed 1936 lit. 29-Mar-4 Rasmussen, Copenhagen #78/R est:100000 (D.KR 300000)
£30000	$54600	€43800	Faune devoilant une femme (32x41cm-13x16in) s. etching aquatint edition of 300. 21-Jun-4 Bonhams, New Bond Street #62/R est:30000-40000
£35294	$60000	€51529	Femme au chapeau (62x44cm-24x17in) s. col linocut exec.1963. 4-Nov-3 Christie's, Rockefeller NY #173/R est:70000-90000
£43668	$79476	€63755	La tauromaquia (35x50cm-14x20in) aquatint one copperplate drypoint album of 28 exec.1959. 18-Jun-4 Kornfeld, Bern #129/R est:30000 (S.FR 100000)
£45126	$83032	€65884	Femme au feuteuil - Le manteau polonais (76x56cm-30x22in) s.num.18/50 lithograph executed 16 Jan 1949 lit. 29-Mar-4 Rasmussen, Copenhagen #66/R est:100000-125000 (D.KR 500000)
£47059	$80000	€68706	Repas frugal (46x37cm-18x15in) drypoint lit. 31-Oct-3 Sotheby's, New York #350/R
£50000	$85000	€73000	Jacqueline (75x62cm-30x24in) s. linoleum cut Chinese ink. 31-Oct-3 Sotheby's, New York #381/R
£56000	$103040	€84000	L'Egyptienne (83x47cm-33x19in) s. aquatint exec. 1953 one of 50. 11-Jun-4 Villa Grisebach, Berlin #1592/R est:70000-90000
£59441	$101049	€85000	L'egyptienne - torse de femme (83x47cm-33x19in) s. aquatint prov. 28-Nov-3 Villa Grisebach, Berlin #78/R est:40000-60000
£113537	$206638	€165764	Portrait de Dora Maar II (29x23cm-11x9in) s.i. col aquatint drypoint exec. Mar-Apr 1939. 18-Jun-4 Kornfeld, Bern #126/R est:350000 (S.FR 260000)
£141243	$250000	€206215	Buste de femme d'apres Cranach le Jeune (65x53cm-26x21in) s.num.26/50 col linocut. 28-Apr-4 Christie's, Rockefeller NY #152/R est:250000-350000
£545852	$993450	€796944	La minotauromachie (49x69cm-19x27in) s. num.7/50 line etching copperplate exec. 1935. 18-Jun-4 Kornfeld, Bern #125/R est:600000 (S.FR 1250000)
£600000	$1092000	€876000	La suite vollard (33x44cm-13x17in) etchings, set of 100. 30-Jun-4 Christie's, London #313/R est:500000-700000
Sculpture			
£1111	$1922	€1622	Centaure et visage (25cm-10in) d.1953 num.46/125 ceramic. 9-Dec-3 Maynards, Vancouver #182a est:2500-3500 (C.D 2500)
£1176	$2000	€1717	Horloge a la langue (42x42cm-17x17in) faience. 31-Oct-3 Sotheby's, New York #427/R
£1176	$2000	€1717	Poisson (14x21cm-6x8in) p faience. 31-Oct-3 Sotheby's, New York #447
£1176	$2000	€1717	Yan visage (26cm-10in) painted faience. 31-Oct-3 Sotheby's, New York #441
£1471	$2500	€2148	Pique (40x40cm-16x16in) painted faience. 31-Oct-3 Sotheby's, New York #400/R
£1471	$2500	€2148	Centaure et visage (27cm-11in) painted faience. 31-Oct-3 Sotheby's, New York #408/R
£1471	$2500	€2148	Pichet (23cm-9in) faience. 31-Oct-3 Sotheby's, New York #420
£1618	$2750	€2362	Profil de Jacqueline (19x19cm-7x7in) painted faience. 31-Oct-3 Sotheby's, New York #432
£1618	$2750	€2362	Pichet aux oiseaux (22cm-9in) painted faience. 31-Oct-3 Sotheby's, New York #439
£1647	$2750	€2405	Dove at the dormer (30x38cm-12x15in) st.num.31/200 verso col terre de faience dish. 21-Oct-3 Bonhams & Butterfields, San Francisco #1236/R
£1695	$3000	€2475	Bearded yan (27cm-11in) st.num.150/300 verso col ceramic pitcher. 28-Apr-4 Christie's, Rockefeller NY #223/R est:2000-2500
£1695	$3000	€2475	Columbe sur lit de paille (31x38cm-12x15in) painted platter. 30-Apr-4 Sotheby's, New York #198 est:4000-6000
£1695	$3000	€2475	Centaure et visage (26cm-10in) num.76/125 partially glazed pitcher. 30-Apr-4 Sotheby's, New York #201/R est:3000-4000
£1730	$3200	€2526	Seized handled pitcher (19x31cm-7x12in) st.num.14/200 verso part glazed white col ceramic pitcher. 12-Feb-4 Christie's, Rockefeller NY #388/R est:2000-3000
£1748	$2972	€2500	Face (24x24cm-9x9in) ceramic tile. 26-Nov-3 Pandolfini, Florence #72/R est:1800-2000
£1765	$3000	€2577	Poisson (25x33cm-10x13in) painted faience. 31-Oct-3 Sotheby's, New York #403/R
£1765	$3000	€2577	Pichet espagnol (23cm-9in) painted faience. 31-Oct-3 Sotheby's, New York #421
£1765	$3000	€2577	Visage numero 202 (25x25cm-10x10in) painted faience. 31-Oct-3 Sotheby's, New York #440
£1808	$3200	€2640	Hands with fish (30x30cm-12x12in) st.num.26/250 verso part glazed col ceramic dish. 28-Apr-4 Christie's, Rockefeller NY #209/R est:3000-4000
£1812	$2971	€2500	Bullfight on black ground (31x39cm-12x15in) painted ceramic dish lit. 27-May-3 Il Ponte, Milan #547/R
£1836	$3250	€2681	Femme (31cm-12in) pitcher. 30-Apr-4 Sotheby's, New York #206/R est:3500-5500
£1840	$3000	€2686	Fish subject (11x19cm-4x7in) st. edition of 50 ceramic pitcher executed 1952. 24-Sep-3 Christie's, Rockefeller NY #157/R est:1200-1800
£1875	$3356	€2738	La Pique (38x38cm-15x15in) glazed terre de faience charger painted blue white. 22-Mar-4 Waddingtons, Toronto #507/R est:3000-4000 (C.D 4500)
£1912	$3250	€2792	Chouette visage de femme (29cm-11in) painted faience. 31-Oct-3 Sotheby's, New York #405/R
£1912	$3250	€2792	Mains au poisson (30x30cm-12x12in) painted faience. 31-Oct-3 Sotheby's, New York #414
£1912	$3250	€2792	Taureau (38x38cm-15x15in) painted faience. 31-Oct-3 Sotheby's, New York #433
£1957	$3209	€2700	Small owl (27x13cm-11x5in) painted ceramic jug. 27-May-3 Il Ponte, Milan #497/R
£1963	$3200	€2866	Woman's face (36x32cm-14x13in) st.verso num.44/200 terracotta plaque exec 1971. 24-Sep-3 Christie's, Rockefeller NY #163/R est:1200-1800
£1977	$3500	€2886	Tormented faun's face (42x42cm-17x17in) st.num.17/100 verso glazed col ceramic dish. 28-Apr-4 Christie's, Rockefeller NY #213/R est:3500-4500
£2000	$3180	€2900	Visage no.202 (25x25cm-10x10in) num.202.31/500 glazed plate conceived 1963 lit. 11-Sep-3 Christie's, Kensington #139/R est:1200-1800
£2000	$3340	€2920	Pase de cape (42x42cm-17x17in) st. num.38/50 painted glazed white plate conceived 1959. 22-Oct-3 Sotheby's, Olympia #77/R est:2500-3000
£2000	$3340	€2920	L'estocado (42x42cm-17x17in) st. num.38/50 painted glazed white plate conceived 1959. 22-Oct-3 Sotheby's, Olympia #79/R est:2500-3000
£2000	$3620	€2920	Vallauris (43x43cm-17x17in) st.i.d.1956 num.C103 ceramic plate lit. 1-Apr-4 Christie's, Kensington #95/R est:2000-3000
£2000	$3680	€3000	Cruchon hibou (27cm-11in) earthenware jug exec. 1955 st.f. Madoura lit. 10-Jun-4 Camard, Paris #108/R est:3000-3500
£2000	$3680	€3000	Woman faced wood owl (29cm-11in) i. painted ceramic vase exec. 1952 one of 300. 12-Jun-4 Villa Grisebach, Berlin #371/R est:3000-4000
£2059	$3500	€3006	Tete (30cm-12in) painted faience. 31-Oct-3 Sotheby's, New York #430
£2059	$3500	€3006	Visage (31cm-12in) painted faience. 31-Oct-3 Sotheby's, New York #446
£2059	$3500	€3006	Visage aux points (30cm-12in) num.175/350 faience. 31-Oct-3 Sotheby's, New York #445
£2098	$3608	€3000	Colombe (31x39cm-12x15in) st.sig. faience lit. 8-Dec-3 Christie's, Paris #88/R est:2000-2500
£2119	$3750	€3094	Chouette visage de femme (29cm-11in) num.79/100 brown black vase. 30-Apr-4 Sotheby's, New York #200/R est:4000-6000
£2119	$3750	€3094	Mains au poisson (30x30cm-12x12in) num.156/250 partially glazed platter. 30-Apr-4 Sotheby's, New York #203/R est:4000-6000
£2119	$3750	€3094	Cruchon hibou (25cm-10in) glazed painted pitcher. 30-Apr-4 Sotheby's, New York #205/R est:3000-4000
£2147	$3500	€3135	Flute player and Cavaliers (14x14cm-6x6in) st.verso num.63/100 white ceramic plate 1956. 24-Sep-3 Christie's, Rockefeller NY #161/R est:1500-2000
£2147	$3800	€3135	Heads (14x15cm-6x6in) st.verso col ceramic pitcher edition of 500. 28-Apr-4 Christie's, Rockefeller NY #214/R est:2000-3000
£2147	$3800	€3135	Young wood owl (25cm-10in) st.verso enamel col ceramic vase edition of 500. 28-Apr-4 Christie's, Rockefeller NY #201/R est:2500-3500
£2147	$3800	€3135	Centaur and face (26x22cm-10x9in) st.num.8/25 verso black paraffin red ceramic pitcher. 28-Apr-4 Christie's, Rockefeller NY #205/R est:2500-3500
£2200	$3498	€3190	Quatre visages (24cm-9in) num.80/300 glazed ceramic jug conceived 1959. 11-Sep-3 Christie's, Kensington #116/R est:1500-2000
£2200	$3498	€3190	Scene de tauromachie (45x45cm-18x18in) d.11.6.59 num.10/100 partially glazed ceramic plate. 11-Sep-3 Christie's, Kensington #124/R est:2000-3000
£2200	$3498	€3190	Visage no.127 (25x25cm-10x10in) num.130.285/500 glazed plate conceived 1963 lit. 11-Sep-3 Christie's, Kensington #138/R est:1200-1800
£2200	$3498	€3190	Visage (31cm-12in) ceramic jug conceived 1955 lit. 11-Sep-3 Christie's, Kensington #151/R est:1500-2000
£2200	$3674	€3212	Pichet grave gris (28cm-11in) st. ceramic pitcher painted partially glazed lit. 22-Oct-3 Bonhams, New Bond Street #66/R est:2000-3000
£2200	$3674	€3212	Hibou (24cm-9in) st. painted glazed white jug conceived 1954 edn of 500. 22-Oct-3 Sotheby's, Olympia #84/R est:800-1200
£2200	$3806	€3212	Cruchon hibou (28cm-11in) st. glazed ceramic jug edition of 500 conceived 1955 lit. 11-Dec-3 Christie's, Kensington #148/R est:2500-3500
£2200	$3938	€3212	Tete de faune (38x32cm-15x13in) verso num.33/300 ceramic painted plate. 16-Mar-4 Bonhams, Knightsbridge #146 est:2000-3000
£2200	$4048	€3212	Profil de Jacqueline (18x18cm-7x7in) st.i.verso partially glazed plaque. 24-Mar-4 Sotheby's, Olympia #116/R est:1000-1500
£2238	$3804	€3200	Dishevelled woman (26cm-10in) ceramic plate. 29-Nov-3 Villa Grisebach, Berlin #306/R est:3500-4500
£2250	$3600	€3285	Black and maroon owl (25x25cm-10x10in) i.num.131/150 verso glaze terre de faience plate. 18-Sep-3 Swann Galleries, New York #508/R est:3000-5000

£2252	$3874	€3288	Visage dans un oval (39cm-15in) ceramic plate. 2-Dec-3 Koller, Zurich #3364/R est:2400-3500 (S.FR 5000)
£2260	$4000	€3300	Visage no.197 (25x25cm-10x10in) i.num.370/500 painted plate. 30-Apr-4 Sotheby's, New York #211/R est:3000-4000
£2260	$4000	€3300	Chouette (31cm-12in) i.num.51/250 glazed painted vase. 30-Apr-4 Sotheby's, New York #212/R est:3000-5000
£2267	$4057	€3400	Goat's head in profile. ceramic plate. 14-May-4 Ketterer, Munich #230/R est:2000-3000
£2270	$4200	€3314	Wood owl (29cm-11in) i.num.113/500 part glazed white col ceramic vase. 12-Feb-4 Christie's, Rockefeller NY #393/R est:3000-4000
£2300	$3979	€3358	Visage aux cheveux boucles (31x31cm-12x12in) st.num.214/200 terracotta plaque conceived 1968-1969 lit. 11-Dec-3 Christie's, Kensington #156/R est:1500-2000
£2333	$4177	€3500	Yan pitcher (24cm-9in) ceramic jug. 14-May-4 Ketterer, Munich #228/R est:2500-3500
£2340	$3909	€3300	Pase de muleta (41x41cm-16x16in) st.d.1959 num.4/50 terracotta plate lit. 12-Oct-3 St-Germain-en-Laye Encheres #112/R est:3000-3500
£2378	$4042	€3400	Visage noir (25x25cm-10x10in) num.31/100 ceramic lit. 24-Nov-3 Christie's, Milan #204/R est:2500-3000
£2400	$4152	€3504	Femme (31cm-12in) st.num.13/100 ceramic vase conceived 1955 lit. 11-Dec-3 Christie's, Kensington #141/R est:2500-3500
£2448	$4210	€3500	Personnages dansant (38x31cm-15x12in) st.sig. faience lit. 8-Dec-3 Christie's, Paris #89/R est:2000-2500
£2448	$4210	€3500	Profil de Jacqueline (36x36cm-14x14in) st.sig. faience. 8-Dec-3 Christie's, Paris #87/R est:2500-3500
£2464	$4041	€3400	Woman (30x22cm-12x9in) painted ceramic vase lit. 27-May-3 Il Ponte, Milan #545/R
£2500	$3975	€3625	Femme (30cm-12in) st.num.64/100 ceramic pitcher conceived 1955 lit. 11-Sep-3 Christie's, Kensington #131/R est:1500-2000
£2500	$4250	€3650	Corrida (43x43cm-17x17in) painted faience. 31-Oct-3 Sotheby's, New York #407/R
£2500	$4250	€3650	Vase (32cm-13in) painted faience. 31-Oct-3 Sotheby's, New York #410/R
£2500	$4250	€3650	Chouette mate (27cm-11in) painted faience. 31-Oct-3 Sotheby's, New York #437
£2500	$4525	€3650	Visage no 144 (25x25cm-10x10in) st.num.144 glazed ceramic plate conceived 1963 lit. 1-Apr-4 Christie's, Kensington #111/R est:1500-2000
£2500	$4475	€3650	Chouette (30x30cm-12x12in) glazed painted terre de faience vase. 22-Mar-4 Waddingtons, Toronto #510/R (C.D 6000)
£2533	$4535	€3800	Paysage (31x39x4cm-12x15x2in) ceramic plate. 14-May-4 Ketterer, Munich #227/R est:3500-4500
£2533	$4535	€3800	Centaur. ceramic plate. 14-May-4 Ketterer, Munich #229/R est:3800-4800
£2542	$4500	€3711	Hibou noir perche (43x43cm-17x17in) num.24/100 black plate. 30-Apr-4 Sotheby's, New York #209/R est:3000-5000
£2600	$4134	€3770	Visage (42x42cm-17x17in) d.17.1.65 num.U106/6/100 ceramic plate. 11-Sep-3 Christie's, Kensington #149/R est:2200-2800
£2600	$4342	€3796	Femme (30cm-12in) st. painted partially glazed jug conceived 1955 edn 1 of 10. 22-Oct-3 Sotheby's, Olympia #69/R est:1800-2500
£2600	$4342	€3796	Chouette (30cm-12in) st.i. num.6/500 painted partially glazed vase conceived 1969. 22-Oct-3 Sotheby's, Olympia #86/R est:2500-3500
£2600	$4498	€3796	Colombe sur lit de paille (39cm-15in) st. glazed ceramic plate edition of 300 conceived 1949 lit. 11-Dec-3 Christie's, Kensington #145/R est:3000-5000
£2600	$4706	€3796	Visage no 125 (25x25cm-10x10in) st.num.125 glazed ceramic plate conceived 1963 lit. 1-Apr-4 Christie's, Kensington #112/R est:1000-1500
£2647	$4500	€3865	Lampe femme (35cm-14in) painted faience. 31-Oct-3 Sotheby's, New York #425/R
£2647	$4500	€3865	Bouteille (44cm-17in) faience. 31-Oct-3 Sotheby's, New York #423
£2657	$4517	€3800	Sce de tauromachie (42x42cm-17x17in) d.1959 num.40/100 faience lit. 25-Nov-3 Millon & Associes, Paris #140/R est:5000-6000
£2657	$4571	€3800	Centaure (42x42cm-17x17in) st.sig. terracotta lit. 8-Dec-3 Christie's, Paris #85/R est:2500-3500
£2667	$4613	€3894	Viasge de faune tourmente (43x43cm-17x17in) num.74/200 ceramic. 9-Dec-3 Maynards, Vancouver #182 est:6000-8000 (C.D 6000)
£2667	$4800	€4000	Faune cavalier (42x42cm-17x17in) ceramic exec.1956 lit. 22-Apr-4 Finarte Semenzato, Rome #352/R est:4000-4500
£2667	$4880	€4000	Visage geometrique. i. ceramic plate. 5-Jun-4 Lempertz, Koln #940/R est:3500
£2681	$4397	€3700	Woman's face (31x21cm-12x8in) painted ceramic jug lit. 27-May-3 Il Ponte, Milan #493/R est:3000
£2684	$4750	€3919	Paysage (42x42cm-17x17in) num.133/200 partially glazed platter. 30-Apr-4 Sotheby's, New York #202/R est:4000-6000
£2684	$4750	€3919	Taureau (37x37cm-15x15in) num.77/200 platter. 30-Apr-4 Sotheby's, New York #208/R est:4000-6000
£2712	$4800	€3960	Wood owl with spots (30cm-12in) st.verso enamel col ceramic vase edition of300. 28-Apr-4 Christie's, Rockefeller NY #200/R est:4000-5000
£2761	$4500	€4031	Cantaur (17x17cm-7x7in) st.verso edition of 100 ceramic dish executed 1956. 24-Sep-3 Christie's, Rockefeller NY #160/R est:3000-4000
£2793	$5000	€4078	Ceramic green corrida (30x36cm-12x14in) glazed terre de faience dish. 6-May-4 Swann Galleries, New York #553/R est:5000-8000
£2794	$4750	€4079	Pichet (30cm-12in) painted faience. 31-Oct-3 Sotheby's, New York #409/R
£2794	$4750	€4079	Chouette (27cm-11in) painted faience. 31-Oct-3 Sotheby's, New York #442
£2797	$4755	€4000	Wood owl (29cm-11in) ceramic vase. 29-Nov-3 Villa Grisebach, Berlin #307/R est:4000-5000
£2797	$4755	€4000	Woman (30cm-12in) ceramic vase. 29-Nov-3 Villa Grisebach, Berlin #308/R est:4000-5000
£2800	$4452	€4060	Grosse tete, profil droit (28cm-11in) st.num.50/50 white earthenware figure. 11-Sep-3 Christie's, Kensington #129/R est:2200-2800
£2800	$4452	€4060	Corrida sur fond noir (39cm-15in) st. glazed ceramic plate conceived 1953 lit. 11-Sep-3 Christie's, Kensington #137/R est:2500-3500
£2800	$4676	€4088	Chope visage (22cm-9in) st.i. num.289/300 painted glazed white jug conceived 1959. 22-Oct-3 Sotheby's, Olympia #82/R est:1000-1500
£2800	$5068	€4088	Chouette femme (32cm-13in) st. glazed ceramic vase edition of 500 conceived 1951 lit. 1-Apr-4 Christie's, Kensington #88/R est:3000-5000
£2800	$5068	€4088	Visage no 111 (25x25cm-10x10in) st.num.111 glazed ceramic plate conceived 1963 lit. 1-Apr-4 Christie's, Kensington #119/R est:1500-2000
£2800	$5152	€4088	Tete d;homme aux cheveux longs (31x31cm-12x12in) st.i.num.31/50 partially glazed terracotta tile. 24-Mar-4 Sotheby's, Olympia #109/R est:1800-2200
£2800	$5152	€4088	Visage au nez pince (25x25cm-10x10in) st.i.num.98/100 partially glazed plate. 24-Mar-4 Sotheby's, Olympia #114/R est:2000-3000
£2800	$5096	€4088	Pichet espagnol (22x11x24cm-9x4x9in) st.i.num.54/300 painted part glazed earthenware pitcher lit. 21-Jun-4 Bonhams, New Bond Street #60/R est:1500-2000
£2825	$5000	€4125	Visage au nez pince (25x25cm-10x10in) num.46/100 black grey plate. 30-Apr-4 Sotheby's, New York #210/R est:4000-6000
£2899	$4754	€4000	Spanish pitcher (20cm-8in) i.num.8/200 glazed white earthenware. 27-May-3 Sotheby's, Amsterdam #373/R est:1500-2000
£2917	$5221	€4259	Colombe sur lit de Paille (38x38cm-15x15in) i. edn 167/200 glazed terre de faience platter painted. 22-Mar-4 Waddingtons, Toronto #508/R est:3000-4000 (C.D 7000)
£2928	$5036	€4275	Goat's head (42cm-17in) ceramic plate. 2-Dec-3 Koller, Zurich #3366/R est:5000-7000 (S.FR 6500)
£2941	$5000	€4294	Tete d'homme (31x31cm-12x12in) painted faience. 31-Oct-3 Sotheby's, New York #443
£2971	$4872	€4100	Speckled black face (32x39cm-13x15in) ceramic dish lit. 27-May-3 Il Ponte, Milan #549/R
£2973	$5500	€4341	Woman faced wood owl (29x23cm-11x9in) i.num.214/300 glazed white ceramic col vase. 12-Feb-4 Christie's, Rockefeller NY #385/R est:4000-6000
£3000	$4770	€4350	Colombe a la lucarne (37cm-15in) num.52/200 partially glazed ceramic plate conceived 1949 lit. 11-Sep-3 Christie's, Kensington #117/R est:3000-4000
£3000	$4770	€4350	Personnages (26x26cm-10x10in) st.num.43/100 partially glazed ceramic plate. 11-Sep-3 Christie's, Kensington #119/R est:2000-3000
£3000	$4770	€4350	Scene de tauromachie (43x43cm-17x17in) partially glazed ceramic plate lit. 11-Sep-3 Christie's, Kensington #140/R est:3000-4000
£3000	$5190	€4380	Visage de femme Pomone (30x30cm-12x12in) st.num.13/50 glazed ceramic plate conceived 1968-1969 lit. 11-Dec-3 Christie's, Kensington #153/R est:3000-5000
£3000	$5190	€4380	Mains au poisson (32x32cm-13x13in) st. ceramic bowl edition of 100 conceived 1953 lit. 11-Dec-3 Christie's, Kensington #154/R est:2200-2800
£3000	$5460	€4380	Visage (31cm-12in) i.base painted partially glazed white earthenware pitcher. 4-Feb-4 Sotheby's, Olympia #99/R est:1800-2500
£3000	$5520	€4380	Visage no.130 (25x25cm-10x10in) i.num.120/500 partley glazed white plate. 24-Mar-4 Sotheby's, Olympia #98/R est:2000-3000
£3000	$5490	€4500	Chouette (29cm-11in) i. ceramic vase. 5-Jun-4 Lempertz, Koln #943/R est:5000-6000
£3043	$4991	€4200	Grey face (32x39cm-13x15in) painted ceramic plate lit. 27-May-3 Il Ponte, Milan #548/R
£3153	$5423	€4603	Owl (26cm-10in) ceramic jug. 2-Dec-3 Koller, Zurich #3367/R est:2000-3500 (S.FR 7000)
£3200	$5792	€4672	Colombe sur lit de paille (39cm-15in) st. glazed ceramic plate editio of 300 conceived 1949 lit. 1-Apr-4 Christie's, Kensington #101/R est:3000-4000
£3200	$5888	€4672	Visage no.202 (25x25cm-10x10in) i.num.76/200 painted glazed white earthenware plate. 24-Mar-4 Sotheby's, Olympia #97/R est:2000-3000
£3261	$5348	€4500	Engraved bottle (43x16cm-17x6in) painted ceramic vase lit. 27-May-3 Il Ponte, Milan #543/R
£3275	$5961	€4782	Poisson en bleu, jaune, vert et rouge, sur fond blanc (34x42cm-13x17in) ceramic oval. 17-Jun-4 Kornfeld, Bern #695 est:7500 (S.FR 7500)
£3300	$5511	€4818	Visage No 130 (25cm-10in) i. num.123/500 painted glazed white plate conceived 1963. 22-Oct-3 Sotheby's, Olympia #76/R est:2000-3000
£3315	$6000	€4840	Trefle, clover (4x5cm-2x2in) s.num.8/20 23 carat gold medallion. 19-Apr-4 Bonhams & Butterfields, San Francisco #213/R est:6000-8000
£3333	$5533	€4866	Petit buste de femme (33x25cm-13x10in) terracotta relief plaque. 2-Oct-3 Heffel, Vancouver #32 (C.D 7500)
£3333	$6133	€5000	Wood owl with spots (28cm-11in) i. painted ceramic vase exec. 1951 one of 300. 12-Jun-4 Villa Grisebach, Berlin #370/R est:3500-4500
£3357	$5706	€4800	Poisson (42x34cm-17x13in) ceramic plate. 26-Nov-3 Lempertz, Koln #915/R est:4000
£3374	$5500	€4926	Picador and bull (10x10cm-4x4in) st.verso num.6/100 blk ivory plate red pat exec 1959. 24-Sep-3 Christie's, Rockefeller NY #162/R est:3500-4500
£3390	$6000	€4949	Landscape (42x42cm-17x17in) st.i.num.180/200 part glazed col ceramic dish. 28-Apr-4 Christie's, Rockefeller NY #208/R est:4000-6000
£3390	$6000	€4949	Pitcher with vase (30x18cm-12x7in) st.num.137/500 verso part glazed col ceramic pitcher. 28-Apr-4 Christie's, Rockefeller NY #210/R est:5000-7000
£3497	$6014	€5000	Tete de chevre (32x51cm-13x20in) st.sig. faience lit. 8-Dec-3 Christie's, Paris #90/R est:2000-2500
£3514	$6500	€5130	Black and maroon owl (30x18cm-12x7in) i. glazed white col ceramic vase. 12-Feb-4 Christie's, Rockefeller NY #384/R est:4000-6000
£3529	$6000	€5152	Femme fleur (33cm-13in) glazed ceramic. 31-Oct-3 Sotheby's, New York #397/R
£3529	$6000	€5152	Bouquet (30x36cm-12x14in) painted faience. 31-Oct-3 Sotheby's, New York #424
£3529	$6000	€5152	Visage de femme (39x31cm-15x12in) painted faience. 31-Oct-3 Sotheby's, New York #415
£3600	$6012	€5256	Poisson fond noir (42cm-17in) st. painted partially glazed plate exec 1952 edn 1 of 100. 22-Oct-3 Sotheby's, Olympia #74/R est:2000-3000
£3631	$6500	€5301	Face with grid (41x41cm-16x16in) white earthenware clay dish. 20-Mar-4 Rachel Davis, Shaker Heights #435/R est:6000-9000
£3667	$6673	€5500	Visage geometrique aux traits (44x44cm-17x17in) painted terracotta paint lit. 30-Jun-4 Calmels Cohen, Paris #53/R est:4000-5000
£3672	$6500	€5361	Pase de muleta (42x42cm-17x17in) st.num.50/50 verso part glazed col ceramic dish. 28-Apr-4 Christie's, Rockefeller NY #219/R est:4000-6000
£3672	$6500	€5361	Pitcher with arums (31x18cm-12x7in) st.i.num.116/350 verso col glazed ceramic pitcher. 28-Apr-4 Christie's, Rockefeller NY #206/R est:4000-6000
£3672	$6500	€5361	Engraved bottle (43x17cm-17x7in) st.num.84/100 verso col enamel white ceramic vase. 28-Apr-4 Christie's, Rockefeller NY #212/R est:4000-5000
£3672	$6500	€5361	Cogida (42x42cm-17x17in) st.num.50/50 verso part glazed col ceramic dish. 28-Apr-4 Christie's, Rockefeller NY #220/R est:4000-6000
£3672	$6500	€5361	Arrastro (42x42cm-17x17in) st.num.50/50 part glazed col ceramic dish. 28-Apr-4 Christie's, Rockefeller NY #221/R est:4000-6000
£3672	$6500	€5361	Lampe femme (35cm-14in) num.181/200 painted blue white grey lamp. 30-Apr-4 Sotheby's, New York #207/R est:6000-8000
£3696	$6061	€5100	Goat's head in profile (31x51cm-12x20in) ceramic plate lit. 27-May-3 Il Ponte, Milan #546/R
£3778	$6271	€5516	Vallauris (42x42cm-17x17in) painted glazed ceramic plate. 2-Oct-3 Heffel, Vancouver #34 (C.D 8500)
£3800	$6042	€5510	Hibou mat (39cm-15in) st.num. ceramic plate conceived 1955 lit. 11-Sep-3 Christie's, Kensington #128/R est:3000-5000
£3800	$6042	€5510	Tete de chevre de profil (51cm-20in) st. ceramic plate conceived 1952 lit. 11-Sep-3 Christie's, Kensington #133/R est:3500-4500
£3800	$6042	€5510	Taureau dans l'arene (39cm-15in) num. glazed ceramic plate conceived 1948 lit. 11-Sep-3 Christie's, Kensington #136/R est:3000-4000
£3800	$6042	€5510	Tete de chevre de profil (51cm-20in) partially glazed ceramic plate conceived 1952 lit. 11-Sep-3 Christie's, Kensington #148/R est:3500-4500
£3800	$6574	€5548	Bouteille gravee (44cm-17in) st. glazed ceramic vase edition of 100 conceived 1954 lit. 11-Dec-3 Christie's, Kensington #137/R est:4000-6000
£3800	$6878	€5548	Pichet grave gris (28cm-11in) st. glazed ceramic vase edition of 500 conceived 1954 lit. 1-Apr-4 Christie's, Kensington #104/R est:3000-4000
£3800	$6992	€5548	Le barbu (31cm-12in) st.i. partially glazed pitcher. 24-Mar-4 Sotheby's, Olympia #112/R est:2000-3000
£3824	$6500	€5583	Pichet (29cm-11in) faience. 31-Oct-3 Sotheby's, New York #417
£3846	$6615	€5500	Visage dans un ovale (33x40cm-13x16in) st.sig. faience. 8-Dec-3 Christie's, Paris #91/R
£3933	$7237	€5900	La femme du barbu (39cm-15in) earthenware jug one of 500 exec. 1953 st.f. Madoura exhib.lit. 10-Jun-4 Camard, Paris #107/R est:6000-8000
£3955	$7000	€5774	Paseo (42x42cm-17x17in) st.num.50/50 verso part glazed col ceramic dish. 28-Apr-4 Christie's, Rockefeller NY #217/R est:4000-6000
£3955	$7000	€5774	Jacqueline's profile (20x19cm-8x7in) st.verso col ceramic plate edition of 500 pair. 28-Apr-4 Christie's, Rockefeller NY #216/R est:4000-5000

£4000	$6360	€5800	Chouette (29cm-11in) num.225/250 partially glazed ceramic vase. 11-Sep-3 Christie's, Kensington #121/R est:3000-5000
£4000	$6360	€5800	Tete de chevre de profil (41x41cm-16x16in) partially glazed ceramic plate conceived 1952 lit. 11-Sep-3 Christie's, Kensington #123/R est:4000-6000
£4000	$7240	€5840	Trefle (4x5cm-2x2in) s.num. metal medallion 23 carat edition of 20 conceived 1956. 1-Apr-4 Christie's, Kensington #85/R est:4000-6000
£4000	$7240	€5840	Hibou brillant (39cm-15in) st. ceramic plate edition of 450 conceived 1955 lit. 1-Apr-4 Christie's, Kensington #107/R est:3000-5000
£4000	$7160	€6000	Engraved bottle (43x16cm-17x6in) ceramic. 15-May-4 Van Ham, Cologne #838/R est:7500
£4118	$7000	€6012	Visage gris (40cm-16in) painted faience. 31-Oct-3 Sotheby's, New York #411/R
£4118	$7000	€6012	Visage de profil. painted faience. 31-Oct-3 Sotheby's, New York #412/R
£4118	$7000	€6012	Pichet (27cm-11in) faience. 31-Oct-3 Sotheby's, New York #422
£4118	$7000	€6012	Tete de femme (23cm-9in) faience. 31-Oct-3 Sotheby's, New York #418
£4118	$7000	€6012	Goat's head (32x52cm-13x20in) ceramic exec.1952. 4-Nov-3 Christie's, Rockefeller NY #191/R est:4000-6000
£4200	$6678	€6090	Profil de Jacqueline (36x36cm-14x14in) st.num.9/100 partially glazed terracotta plate conceived 1962. 11-Sep-3 Christie's, Kensington #127/R est:3000-5000
£4200	$6678	€6090	La source (30cm-12in) i.num.14/100 partially glazed ceramic jug conceived 1954. 11-Sep-3 Christie's, Kensington #135/R est:4000-6000
£4200	$6678	€6090	Tete de taureau (42x42cm-17x17in) partially glazed ceramic plate conceived c.1956 lit. 11-Sep-3 Christie's, Kensington #141/R est:3000-5000
£4200	$7014	€6132	Femme du barbu (37cm-15in) st.i. painted partially glazed jug conceived 1953 edn 1 of 500. 22-Oct-3 Sotheby's, Olympia #73/R est:2000-3000
£4200	$7602	€6132	Colombe brillante (39x39cm-15x15in) st. glazed ceramic plate edition of 400 conceived 1953 lit. 1-Apr-4 Christie's, Kensington #99/R est:4000-6000
£4200	$7602	€6132	Pichet au vase (30x30cm-12x12in) st.num.142/500 glazed ceramic pitcher conceived 1954 lit. 1-Apr-4 Christie's, Kensington #102/R est:3000-4000
£4200	$7728	€6132	Pichet gothique aux feuilles (28cm-11in) partley glazed pitcher. 24-Mar-4 Sotheby's, Olympia #104/R est:2500-3500
£4200	$7728	€6132	Femme du barbu (37cm-15in) st. partially glazed jug. 24-Mar-4 Sotheby's, Olympia #105/R est:2000-3000
£4200	$7728	€6132	Vase chouette (30cm-12in) st.i.num.499/500 partially glazed vase. 24-Mar-4 Sotheby's, Olympia #107/R est:4000-5000
£4237	$7500	€6186	Pase de cape (52x52cm-20x20in) st.num.50/50 verso part glazed col ceramic dish. 28-Apr-4 Christie's, Rockefeller NY #218/R est:4000-6000
£4237	$7500	€6186	Diaulos player (32x39cm-13x15in) st.i.num.61/200 verso glazed col ceramic dish. 28-Apr-4 Christie's, Rockefeller NY #198/R est:3500-4500
£4400	$7348	€6424	Cruchon hibou (27cm-11in) i. painted partially glazed jug conceived 1955 edn of 500. 22-Oct-3 Sotheby's, Olympia #68/R est:1000-1500
£4412	$7500	€6442	Lampe femme (35cm-14in) faience. 31-Oct-3 Sotheby's, New York #426/R
£4412	$7500	€6442	Arene (30cm-12in) painted faience. 31-Oct-3 Sotheby's, New York #436
£4500	$8280	€6570	Poisson blue (32x39cm-13x15in) st.i.num.39/200 partially glazed plate. 24-Mar-4 Sotheby's, Olympia #115/R est:3000-4000
£4545	$7818	€6500	Homme barbu (35cm-14in) st.sig. faience lit. 8-Dec-3 Christie's, Paris #92/R est:3000-5000
£4545	$7818	€6500	Visage de femme (39cm-15in) st.sig. terracotta lit. 8-Dec-3 Christie's, Paris #84/R est:3000-5000
£4800	$8688	€7008	Scene de tauromachie (42x42cm-17x17in) st.num.71/100 glazed ceramic plate conceived 1959 lit. 1-Apr-4 Christie's, Kensington #92/R est:2500-3500
£4800	$8832	€7200	Poisson fond noir (50cm-20in) s.verso col terre de faience oval plate edition of 100 lit. 14-Jun-4 Tajan, Paris #141/R est:6000-8000
£4802	$8500	€7011	Man's head with long hair (31x31cm-12x12in) st.i.num.34/100 verso part glazed red earthenware col plaque. 28-Apr-4 Christie's, Rockefeller NY #224/R est:3000-4000
£5000	$7950	€7250	Visage brun/bleu (39cm-15in) num.109/25/200 glazed ceramic plate conceived 1947 lit. 11-Sep-3 Christie's, Kensington #142/R est:2000-3000
£5000	$9050	€7300	Tete de chevre de profil (43x43cm-17x17in) st. glazed ceramic plate edition of 100 conceived 1952 lit. 1-Apr-4 Christie's, Kensington #96/R est:4000-6000
£5085	$9000	€7424	Vase with two hight handles (38x19cm-15x7in) st.verso col part glazed ceramic vase edition of 400. 28-Apr-4 Christie's, Rockefeller NY #202/R est:7000-9000
£5085	$9000	€7424	Vase deux anses (37cm-15in) partially glazed vase. 30-Apr-4 Sotheby's, New York #199 est:8000-10000
£5294	$9000	€7729	Visage aux taches (41x41cm-16x16in) silver. 31-Oct-3 Sotheby's, New York #429
£5500	$9515	€8030	Scene de tauromachie (42x42cm-17x17in) st.num.16/100 ceramic plate edition of 100 conceived 1959 lit. 11-Dec-3 Christie's, Kensington #146/R est:3000-5000
£5882	$10000	€8588	Pichet (32cm-13in) num.94/100 faience. 31-Oct-3 Sotheby's, New York #404/R
£5882	$10000	€8588	Jacqueline (42x42cm-17x17in) faience. 31-Oct-3 Sotheby's, New York #428/R
£5882	$10000	€8588	Visage aux yeux (34cm-13in) faience. 31-Oct-3 Sotheby's, New York #444
£5932	$10500	€8661	Wood owl (31x24cm-12x9in) st.i.num.183/350 part glazed col ceramic vase. 28-Apr-4 Christie's, Rockefeller NY #225/R est:5000-7000
£6000	$9540	€8700	Petit buste de femme (33x25cm-13x10in) num.109/100/100 terracotta tile conceived 1964. 11-Sep-3 Christie's, Kensington #113/R est:6000-8000
£6000	$9540	€8700	Jouer de diaule (39cm-15in) st.num.1108 50/200 glazed ceramic plate conceived 1947. 11-Sep-3 Christie's, Kensington #132/R est:4000-6000
£6000	$10860	€8760	Vallauris (42x42cm-17x17in) st.i.d.1956 num. glazed ceramic plate edition of 100 lit. 1-Apr-4 Christie's, Kensington #100/R est:5000-7000
£6215	$11000	€9074	Goat's head in profile (41x41cm-16x16in) st.num.65/100 verso part glazed col ceramic plate. 28-Apr-4 Christie's, Rockefeller NY #203/R est:5000-7000
£6232	$10220	€8600	Face with black nose (33x23cm-13x9in) painted ceramic jug lit. 27-May-3 Il Ponte, Milan #542/R est:4000
£6500	$10335	€9425	Visage de femme (39cm-15in) st. ceremic plate conceived 1953 lit. 11-Sep-3 Christie's, Kensington #126/R est:4000-6000
£6500	$11765	€9490	Femme du barbu (37cm-15in) st. glazed ceramic jug edition of 500 conceived 1953 lit. 1-Apr-4 Christie's, Kensington #84/R est:5000-7000
£6711	$12013	€10000	Poissons (5x5cm-2x2in) st.sig. num.1/20 gold. 26-May-4 Christie's, Paris #49/R est:4000-6000
£7000	$11130	€10150	Visage (41x41cm-16x16in) st.sig.num.7/20 continental white metal conceived 1957 lit. 11-Sep-3 Christie's, Kensington #110/R est:8000-12000
£7186	$12000	€10492	Plat raisin (24x32cm-9x13in) s.verso glazed terre de faience oval plate. 21-Oct-3 Bonhams & Butterfields, San Francisco #1235/R
£7500	$13800	€10950	Visage aux taches (41x41cm-16x16in) i. num.6/20 silver plate conceived 1956 lit. 22-Jun-4 Sotheby's, London #204/R est:6000-8000
£8000	$12720	€11600	Visage (42x42cm-17x17in) partially glazed ceramic plate conceived 1960 lit. 11-Sep-3 Christie's, Kensington #143/R est:5000-7000
£10588	$18000	€15458	Poissons (26cm-10in) painted faience. 31-Oct-3 Sotheby's, New York #401/R
£10695	$20000	€15615	Tete en forme d'horloge (42x42cm-17x17in) s. num.6/20 silver lit. 25-Feb-4 Christie's, Rockefeller NY #124/R est:20000-30000
£11000	$20240	€16060	Plate, colombe (17x22cm-7x9in) s.d.7Juin 54 painted glazed dish. 24-Mar-4 Sotheby's, Olympia #106/R est:6000-7000
£12000	$21720	€17520	Centaure (42x42cm-17x17in) s.num.1/20 verso continental white metal conceived 1957. 1-Apr-4 Christie's, Kensington #120/R est:12000-18000
£12333	$22693	€18500	Grande tete de femme au chapeau orne (60x50cm-24x20in) i.verso red ceramic tile exec. 1964 one of 50. 12-Jun-4 Villa Grisebach, Berlin #373/R est:10000-15000
£14124	$25000	€20621	Oiseaux et poissons (49cm-19in) num.6/25 vase. 30-Apr-4 Sotheby's, New York #204/R est:40000-60000
£14706	$25000	€21471	Vase (52cm-20in) painted faience. 31-Oct-3 Sotheby's, New York #434/R
£15000	$23850	€21750	Les danseurs (23x15cm-9x6in) s. partially glazed terracotta plaque executed 1957. 11-Sep-3 Christie's, Kensington #115/R est:15000-20000
£15000	$27300	€21900	Boite peinte (6x19x12cm-2x7x5in) papiers colles oil on wood executed 1914 prov. 4-Feb-4 Sotheby's, London #278/R est:15000-20000
£15882	$27000	€23188	Tripode (73cm-29in) painted faience. 31-Oct-3 Sotheby's, New York #402/R
£18000	$28620	€26100	Tarasque (35x34cm-14x13in) num.17/50 partially glazed ceramic conceived 1954. 11-Sep-3 Christie's, Kensington #112/R est:12000-18000
£18000	$31140	€26280	Visage dans un carre (42x42cm-17x17in) st.sig.num.18/20 verso Continental metal conceived 1957 box. 11-Dec-3 Christie's, Kensington #136/R est:15000-20000
£20588	$35000	€30058	Tete d'homme (30x25cm-12x10in) d.11.3.57 verso glazed ceramic prov.lit. 6-Nov-3 Sotheby's, New York #289/R est:35000-45000
£22000	$40040	€32120	Vallauris (42x42cm-17x17in) i.num.18/20 silver plate conceived 1956. 4-Feb-4 Sotheby's, London #329/R est:18000-25000
£22000	$40040	€32120	Nu accroupi (20x20cm-8x8in) d.16.3.56 s.verso painted ceramic tile prov. 4-Feb-4 Sotheby's, London #330/R est:18000-22000
£25000	$45500	€36500	Femme debout (20cm-8in) st.f.Valsuani num.9/10 brown pat bronze cire perdue prov.lit. 3-Feb-4 Christie's, London #203/R est:25000-35000
£26536	$47500	€38743	Joueur de cymbales (15cm-6in) st.sig. num.2009/1694 cast gold conceived 1960 prov.lit. 6-May-4 Sotheby's, New York #396/R est:30000-40000
£28000	$50960	€40880	Compotier au poisson (16x53cm-6x21in) s. num.1/2 st.f. Hugo silver exec. 1959 prov.exhib.lit. 3-Feb-4 Christie's, London #272/R est:25000-35000
£28000	$51520	€40880	Horloge a la langue (42x42cm-17x17in) i. num.7/20 silver plate lit. 22-Jun-4 Sotheby's, London #205/R est:15000-20000
£34000	$62560	€49640	Poisson (42x42cm-17x17in) i. num.3/20 silver plate lit. 22-Jun-4 Sotheby's, London #206/R est:18000-25000
£35294	$60000	€51529	Centaure aile au hibou (12cm-5in) num.12/12 brown pat bronze St.f.Valsuani prov.lit. 5-Nov-3 Christie's, Rockefeller NY #287/R est:60000-80000
£39000	$70590	€56940	Corrida et spectateurs (39x39cm-15x15in) st. ceramic plate prov. 1-Apr-4 Christie's, Kensington #87/R est:25000-35000
£41899	$75000	€61173	Femme debout (24cm-9in) num.5/10 st.f.Valsuani brown pat bronze prov.exhib.lit. 6-May-4 Sotheby's, New York #353/R est:40000-60000
£69832	$125000	€101955	Grande vase aux danseurs (70cm-28in) st.d.24 Juin 50 num.5 painted terracotta vase lit. 6-May-4 Sotheby's, New York #335/R est:60000-80000
£106145	$190000	€154972	Profil de Jacqueline (30x30cm-12x12in) s.d.26.3.56 i.verso glazed double-sided ceramic round prov. 6-May-4 Sotheby's, New York #380/R est:80000-120000
£126667	$230533	€190000	Tete de femme (12x8x8cm-5x3x3in) s.verso pat bronze Cast Godard lit. 2-Jul-4 Binoche, Paris #34/R est:200000-300000
£292576	$532489	€427161	Le fou arlequin (41x36x21cm-16x14x8in) s. bronze exec. 1905 prov. 18-Jun-4 Kornfeld, Bern #124/R est:750000 (S.FR 670000)
Works on paper			
£1064	$1777	€1500	Cartel de la exposicion (65x48cm-26x19in) s.d.10-6-59 poster. 23-Jun-3 Durán, Madrid #171/R est:1400
£3000	$4800	€4380	Deux mains (27x21cm-11x8in) s.i.d.48 pen ink. 18-Sep-3 Swann Galleries, New York #497/R est:5000-8000
£3000	$5490	€4500	Compositions (29x46cm-11x18in) i. wax crayon set of 4 prov. 6-Jun-4 Rouillac, Vendome #56
£3200	$5344	€4672	Tete de chevre (21x15cm-8x6in) s.i.d.30.7.57 blue wax crayon prov. 22-Oct-3 Sotheby's, Olympia #151/R est:3000-4000
£3800	$6992	€5548	Tete de Taureau (13x10cm-5x4in) s.i.d.13.5.56 pen ink prov. 24-Mar-4 Sotheby's, Olympia #146/R est:3000-4000
£4000	$7360	€5840	Pour minouche (22x18cm-9x7in) s.i. s.d.25.Oct 57 verso crayon pencil ballpoint pen. 24-Mar-4 Sotheby's, Olympia #148/R est:4000-6000
£4200	$7014	€6132	Sketch of a woman (20x22cm-8x9in) i.d.21.1.71 ballpoint pen prov. 22-Oct-3 Sotheby's, Olympia #157/R est:2500-3000
£4444	$8000	€6488	Petit Bouquet (30x41cm-12x16in) s. coloured felt-tip pen drawing exec 1958. 26-Jan-4 Schrager Galleries, Milwaukee #1283
£4800	$8016	€7008	Three nude women (9x30cm-4x12in) s.i.d.26.12.68 and 6.3.69 yellow ball-point prov. 22-Oct-3 Sotheby's, Olympia #155/R est:2500-3500
£5200	$9516	€7800	Colombe (13x13cm-5x5in) s. crayon graphite. 6-Jun-4 Rouillac, Vendome #57
£5511	$9920	€8046	Mask (30x22cm-12x9in) s. col chk. 26-Apr-4 Bukowskis, Stockholm #245a/R est:50000-60000 (S.KR 76000)
£5800	$9686	€8468	Erotic sketch (16x16cm-6x6in) s.i.d.12.9.68 brush ink prov. 22-Oct-3 Sotheby's, Olympia #154/R est:3000-4000
£6466	$11573	€9440	Man with girl (17x10cm-7x4in) ink paper board. 13-May-4 Stuker, Bern #283/R est:15000-20000 (S.FR 15000)
£6667	$12200	€10000	Portrait d'homme (17x12cm-7x5in) ink exec.1970. 6-Jun-4 Rouillac, Vendome #58
£6800	$12716	€10200	Smiling satyr (18x13cm-7x5in) s.i.d.56 crayon. 22-Jul-4 Dominic Winter, Swindon #338/R est:2000-3000
£7382	$13067	€11000	Colombe de la Paix (17x19cm-7x7in) s. blue crayon prov. 27-Apr-4 Artcurial Briest, Paris #104/R est:8000-12000
£8000	$13360	€11680	Poule (8x11cm-3x4in) s.verso col crayons cut-out paper exec 1945 prov. 22-Oct-3 Sotheby's, Olympia #153/R est:7000-9000
£8000	$14720	€11680	Le Taureau (23x17cm-9x7in) s.i.d.27.6.49 black crayon prov. 24-Mar-4 Sotheby's, Olympia #149/R est:5000-6000
£8000	$14720	€11680	Chevre (36x27cm-14x11in) s.i.d.1952 crayon prov. 22-Jun-4 Sotheby's, London #516/R est:9000-10000
£8042	$13832	€11500	Chevre (35x26cm-14x10in) s.i.d.1952 blue chk. 5-Dec-3 Ketterer, Munich #121/R est:5000-6000
£8308	$14124	€12130	Faun (9x14cm-4x6in) s. crayon. 5-Nov-3 AB Stockholms Auktionsverk #1092/R est:100000-150000 (S.KR 110000)
£8733	$15982	€13100	Guenon (25x17cm-10x7in) crayon graphite. 6-Jun-4 Rouillac, Vendome #59
£9000	$15030	€13140	Seated man (34x27cm-13x11in) s.i.d.19.3.73 red crayon prov. 22-Oct-3 Sotheby's, Olympia #158/R est:8000-10000
£9333	$17173	€14000	Le gros pied (31x23cm-12x9in) s.d.58 crayon prov. 14-Jun-4 Tajan, Paris #142/R est:13500-16000
£9375	$15657	€13500	Petit faune (22x16cm-9x6in) s.i.d.7.3.57 col crayon prov. 21-Oct-3 Artcurial Briest, Paris #10/R est:8000-10000
£10070	$16816	€14500	Peintre (24x15cm-9x6in) s. red crayon prov. 21-Oct-3 Artcurial Briest, Paris #9/R est:7000-9000
£10615	$19000	€15498	Reclining nude (20x28cm-8x11in) s.d.29/10/68 felt tip pen cardboard prov. 11-Jan-4 William Jenack, New York #210 est:20000-30000
£10615	$19000	€15498	A la Belle tomate (12x19cm-5x7in) s.i. pencil exec c.1900 prov. 6-May-4 Sotheby's, New York #299/R est:15000-20000

£10615	$19000	€15498	Frommage a la creme (19x12cm-7x5in) s.i. pencil brown pencil exec c.1900 prov. 6-May-4 Sotheby's, New York #300/R est:15000-20000
£11000	$20240	€16060	Tete de femme (12x8cm-5x3in) s.d.11.8.50 pencil. 24-Mar-4 Sotheby's, Olympia #147/R est:800-1200
£11000	$20240	€16060	Le roi (36x26cm-14x10in) s.i.d.71 pencil prov. 22-Jun-4 Sotheby's, London #518/R est:10000-15000
£12676	$22183	€18000	Mousquetaire (16x16cm-6x6in) s.i.d.12.9.68 felt pen col crayon prov. 16-Dec-3 Claude Aguttes, Neuilly #32/R est:20000-30000
£13500	$22545	€19710	Painter in his studio (16x16cm-6x6in) s.i.d.24.12.68 blue felt-tip pen prov. 22-Oct-3 Sotheby's, Olympia #156/R est:7000-9000
£14124	$25000	€20621	Bottle and guitar (14x10cm-6x4in) s. gouache prov.lit. 2-May-4 Bonhams & Butterfields, Los Angeles #3025/R est:50000-60000
£14584	$24355	€21000	Tete de Barbu (36x25cm-14x10in) s.i.d.4.2.68 col felt-tip pen. 21-Oct-3 Artcurial Briest, Paris #119/R est:22000-28000
£15343	$28231	€22401	Le taureau noir (50x66cm-20x26in) s.d.20.4.47 wash on zinc lit. 29-Mar-4 Rasmussen, Copenhagen #73/R est:35000 (D.KR 170000)
£18000	$32760	€26280	Une chambre a Menerbes (29x41cm-11x16in) pen ink exec 1945 prov. 5-Feb-4 Christie's, London #419/R est:20000-30000
£18000	$33120	€26280	Tete (26x21cm-10x8in) s.d.41 pen ink prov.lit. 22-Jun-4 Sotheby's, London #448/R est:20000-30000
£18792	$33262	€28000	Untitled (33x24cm-13x9in) s. wax col crayon. 29-Apr-4 Christie's, Paris #179/R est:15000-20000
£19553	$35000	€28547	L'artiste et son modele. s.i. pencil. 13-May-4 Dallas Auction Gallery, Dallas #278/R est:8000-12000
£20000	$36400	€29200	Portrait of a nude woman, bust length (12x13cm-5x5in) s. pencil exec 1916 prov.lit. 5-Feb-4 Christie's, London #408/R est:20000-30000
£20588	$35000	€30058	Femme a la guitare assise (30x20cm-12x8in) s. pencil exec 1914 prov.lit. 6-Nov-3 Sotheby's, New York #206/R est:20000-30000
£21148	$35952	€30876	Les Menines - Dona Isabel de Velasco (24x18cm-9x7in) s.d.4.8.60 crayon prov.lit. 5-Nov-3 AB Stockholms Auktionsverk #1091/R est:150000-200000 (S.KR 280000)
£21622	$40000	€31568	Deux combattants (12x18cm-5x7in) s.i.d.69 felt-tip pen prov.lit. 11-Feb-4 Sotheby's, New York #57/R est:20000-30000
£22000	$40040	€32120	Etude pour l'aubade , femme nue etendue (21x27cm-8x11in) d.41 black crayon prov.lit. 4-Feb-4 Sotheby's, London #468/R est:15000-20000
£22346	$40000	€32625	Portrait de femme. Deux femmes (17x11cm-7x4in) pen ink exec 1906 double-sided prov. 6-May-4 Sotheby's, New York #301/R est:40000-60000
£22346	$40000	€32625	Artiste et son modele (38x28cm-15x11in) s. col crayon prov. 6-May-4 Sotheby's, New York #397/R est:20000-30000
£22346	$40000	€32625	Tete d'homme (31x24cm-12x9in) d.10.12.71 pencil brush ink wash prov. 6-May-4 Sotheby's, New York #401/R est:40000-60000
£23529	$40000	€34352	Boxeur (16x11cm-6x4in) pen ink W/C exec c.1902-04 prov. 6-Nov-3 Sotheby's, New York #202/R est:50000-70000
£24000	$43680	€35040	Pigeon (35x28cm-14x11in) decoupage W/C black-paper exec.1936 prov. 4-Feb-4 Sotheby's, London #523/R est:10000-15000
£24000	$44160	€35040	Pour Henri Alberti (41x30cm-16x12in) s.i.d.57 col crayon prov. 22-Jun-4 Sotheby's, London #524/R est:8000-12000
£25000	$46000	€36500	Jeune fille qui ne dort pas (21x27cm-8x11in) s.i.d.20.mai41 pencil prov.lit. 24-Jun-4 Christie's, London #401/R est:18000-24000
£25140	$45000	€36704	Junyer in Majorca. s.i. crayon. 13-May-4 Dallas Auction Gallery, Dallas #298/R est:15000-20000
£30000	$55200	€43800	Couple (34x27cm-13x11in) d.73 col crayon pencil pen ink wash prov.exhib.lit. 22-Jun-4 Sotheby's, London #458/R est:30000-40000
£30667	$56733	€46000	Alphabet anthropomorphe (29x23cm-11x9in) s. graphite prov. 18-Jul-4 Sotheby's, Paris #300/R est:28000-35000
£30882	$52500	€45088	Etudes (22x34cm-9x13in) each d.21.F46 pencil graph paper four prov.exhib.lit. 6-Nov-3 Sotheby's, New York #303/R est:50000-70000
£31690	$51339	€45000	Buste de femme assise (32x25cm-13x10in) s.d.03/01/61 graphite dr prov.lit. 5-Aug-3 Tajan, Paris #28/R est:50000-70000
£35000	$58450	€51100	Nature morte a la pomme (18x12cm-7x5in) d.18 Novembre 45 verso papiers decoupes chl on card prov.exhib. 21-Oct-3 Sotheby's, London #61/R est:25000-35000
£35000	$64400	€51100	In the studio (35x26cm-14x10in) s.d.25.12.53 pen India ink prov.exhib.lit. 24-Jun-4 Christie's, London #409/R est:30000-40000
£36000	$66240	€52560	Faunes et femme (50x65cm-20x26in) s.d.46 ink paper on board prov.lit. 22-Jun-4 Sotheby's, London #464/R est:40000-60000
£36313	$65000	€53017	Nu avec deux personnages (37x52cm-15x20in) s.d.2.7.1967 ink wash prov.lit. 6-May-4 Sotheby's, New York #404/R est:70000-90000
£38000	$69920	€55480	Femme dans une salle de bain (25x23cm-10x9in) d.1920 verso pencil prov. 22-Jun-4 Sotheby's, London #445/R est:30000-40000
£38235	$65000	€55823	Tete de femme (32x25cm-13x10in) s.d.22.7.70 felt-tip pen prov.lit. 6-Nov-3 Sotheby's, New York #258/R est:50000-70000
£39106	$70000	€57095	Tete de femme (27x21cm-11x8in) d.24.9.65 pencil prov.exhib.lit.. 6-May-4 Sotheby's, New York #341/R est:80000-100000
£39130	$64174	€54000	Nu, homme assis et buste de vieille femme (32x49cm-13x19in) s. Indian ink executed 1970 lit. 31-May-3 Farsetti, Prato #717/R est:50000-60000
£40000	$72800	€58400	Woman and a man (32x49cm-13x19in) d.6.4.70 pen India ink brown felt-tip pen prov. 5-Feb-4 Christie's, London #424/R est:40000-60000
£41899	$75000	€61173	Tete de femme (41x50cm-16x20in) s. blue crayon prov. 5-May-4 Christie's, Rockefeller NY #141/R est:70000-90000
£41899	$75000	€61173	Tete de femme (27x21cm-11x8in) d.25.9.65 pencil prov.exhib. 6-May-4 Sotheby's, New York #343/R est:40000-60000
£42000	$76440	€61320	Head of a man (24x18cm-9x7in) s.d.11.4.70 felt tip pen board prov.lit. 5-Feb-4 Christie's, London #420/R est:40000-60000
£45000	$81900	€65700	Seated nude (27x37cm-11x15in) d.3.5.63 pencil prov.lit. 5-Feb-4 Christie's, London #405/R est:40000-60000
£45000	$81900	€65700	Dessinateur et modele (32x24cm-13x9in) s.d.54 pen brush ink prov.lit. 4-Feb-4 Sotheby's, London #524/R est:35000-45000
£45000	$82800	€65700	Two people (24x32cm-9x13in) d.28.1.54 col crayon prov.exhib. 24-Jun-4 Christie's, London #416/R est:45000-65000
£47059	$80000	€68706	Homme et femme nus debout (36x25cm-14x10in) s.d.31.1.69 col wax crayons pencil board prov.lit. 5-Nov-3 Christie's, Rockefeller NY #151/R est:70000-90000
£50000	$91000	€73000	Chien, coq et pierrot (32x49cm-13x19in) pen India ink exec 1970 prov. 5-Feb-4 Christie's, London #421/R est:50000-70000
£50000	$92000	€73000	Tete d'homme. Trois esquisses (35x30cm-14x12in) s.d.10.3.69 felt-tip pen board double-sided prov.exhib.lit. 24-Jun-4 Christie's, London #449/R est:40000-60000
£51471	$87500	€75148	Dejeuner (27x42cm-11x17in) s.d.26.7.61 col crayon lit. 6-Nov-3 Sotheby's, New York #292/R est:80000-120000
£53073	$95000	€77487	Tete de jeune fille au chapeau (27x21cm-11x8in) d.24.9.65 pencil col crayon prov.exhib.lit. 6-May-4 Sotheby's, New York #349/R est:80000-100000
£53073	$95000	€77487	Tete de femme (27x21cm-11x8in) d.25.9.65 pencil prov.exhib.lit. 6-May-4 Sotheby's, New York #350/R est:50000-70000
£53073	$95000	€77487	Femmes au bord de la mer (25x35cm-10x14in) s.d.24 novembre XXXII brush India ink ink wash prov.lit. 6-May-4 Sotheby's, New York #354/R est:30000-40000
£54412	$92500	€79442	Tete d'homme barbu (64x50cm-25x20in) s.d.11/10/65 W/C ink wash prov.lit. 6-Nov-3 Sotheby's, New York #312/R est:60000-80000
£55000	$100100	€80300	Tauromaquia Complete, o sea El Arte de Torear en Plaza (15x10cm-6x4in) pen ink gouache pencil wax crayons eight exec 1955 prov. 5-Feb-4 Christie's, London #414/R est:60000-80000
£55000	$101200	€80300	Combat de faune et centaure (50x65cm-20x26in) s. pen ink prov.lit. 22-Jun-4 Sotheby's, London #482/R est:60000-80000
£58824	$100000	€85883	Guitare et compotier sur une table carree (27x21cm-11x8in) s.d.26-11-20 pastel pencil prov.lit. 5-Nov-3 Christie's, Rockefeller NY #127/R est:100000-150000
£58824	$100000	€85883	Nu et profils (49x65cm-19x26in) s.d.9.3.67 pen brush ink wash prov.exhib.lit. 6-Nov-3 Sotheby's, New York #295/R est:100000-150000
£60000	$109200	€87600	Circus scene (46x105cm-18x41in) s.d.1969 pen ink prov.exhib.lit. 5-Feb-4 Christie's, London #410/R est:50000-70000
£60000	$109200	€87600	Nu debout et flutiste (53x64cm-21x25in) s.d.67 col crayon chl exhib.lit. 5-Feb-4 Christie's, London #416/R est:60000-80000
£60000	$110400	€87600	Etude pour Le Mort (43x51cm-17x20in) s. pastel brush India ink chl double-sided exec prov.exhib.lit. 24-Jun-4 Christie's, London #377/R est:60000-80000
£60000	$110400	€90000	Deux tetes (23x30cm-9x12in) s.d.1972 s.d.verso India ink pen cardboard prov.exhib. 11-Jun-4 Villa Grisebach, Berlin #72/R est:90000-120000
£61453	$110000	€89721	Portrait de femme aux ongles rouges (27x21cm-11x8in) d.24.9.65 pencil col crayon prov.exhib. 6-May-4 Sotheby's, New York #340/R est:60000-80000
£62000	$112840	€90520	Homme nu debout et trois tetes (61x49cm-24x19in) s.i.d.66 brown crayon pencil lit. 4-Feb-4 Sotheby's, London #510/R est:60000-80000
£67039	$120000	€97877	Pot et compotier avec fruits (35x25cm-14x10in) s. pencil exec 1919 prov.lit. 5-May-4 Christie's, Rockefeller NY #110/R est:80000-100000
£67039	$120000	€97877	Nues (29x48cm-11x19in) s.d.27.1.68.III pencil prov.lit. 6-May-4 Sotheby's, New York #398/R est:120000-180000
£68000	$123760	€99280	Bust of a man and nude woman (24x30cm-9x12in) s.d.2.6.69 wax crayon felt tip pen prov.lit. 5-Feb-4 Christie's, London #415/R est:40000-60000
£72000	$131040	€105120	L'enlevement (34x45cm-13x18in) s.d.XXXIII pen ink prov.exhib. 4-Feb-4 Sotheby's, London #492/R est:60000-80000
£75000	$138000	€109500	L'ane savant (24x32cm-9x13in) s.d.10.1.54 pen brush India ink prov.exhib.lit. 24-Jun-4 Christie's, London #414/R est:40000-60000
£78212	$140000	€114190	Tete de femme (27x21cm-11x8in) d.25.9.65 pencil prov.exhib.lit. 6-May-4 Sotheby's, New York #352/R est:40000-60000
£79412	$135000	€115942	Buste et tetes d'hommes (56x75cm-22x30in) s.d.24.8.67 brush ink ink wash double-sided prov.lit. 6-Nov-3 Sotheby's, New York #301/R est:100000-150000
£80000	$145600	€116800	Le sculpteur et la statue (23x29cm-9x11in) s.d.XXXIII pen ink wash prov. 4-Feb-4 Sotheby's, London #491/R est:45000-55000
£80000	$148000	€120000	Tete de faune (71x68cm-28x27in) s.d.1957 verso mosaic panel prov.exhib.lit. 18-Jul-4 Sotheby's, Paris #298/R est:100000-150000
£85000	$154700	€124100	Nu dansant et arlequin (17x22cm-7x9in) s.d.16.6.70 gouache W/C brush India ink prov.lit. 5-Feb-4 Christie's, London #403/R est:80000-120000
£85000	$156400	€124100	Tete de mousquetaire (63x47cm-25x19in) s.d.1.3.67 brush blk ink prov.exhib.lit. 24-Jun-4 Christie's, London #418/R est:90000-120000
£92000	$167440	€134320	Compotier sur un meuble (16x11cm-6x4in) s.i. verso gouache exec.1917-18 prov. 4-Feb-4 Sotheby's, London #464/R est:50000-70000
£94972	$170000	€138659	Buste de femme (42x27cm-17x11in) s.d.20.5.62 pencil crayon prov.lit. 6-May-4 Sotheby's, New York #329/R est:120000-160000
£95000	$172900	€138700	Etreinte (55x41cm-22x16in) s.d.72 col crayon green ballpoint pen prov.lit. 5-Feb-4 Christie's, London #417/R est:60000-80000
£97000	$176540	€141620	Buste de femme (75x56cm-30x22in) s.d.67 brush ink prov.exhib.lit. 4-Feb-4 Sotheby's, London #522/R est:60000-80000
£100000	$182000	€146000	Femme au manteau (34x23cm-13x9in) pencil exec 1919 prov.exhib.lit. 5-Feb-4 Christie's, London #401/R est:100000-150000
£100437	$184804	€146638	Tete d'homme (41x33cm-16x13in) s.d.1969 col feltpen prov.lit. 8-Jun-4 Germann, Zurich #26/R est:100000-130000 (S.FR 230000)
£105000	$193200	€153300	Nu couche (26x33cm-10x13in) s.d.70 col crayon card prov.exhib.lit. 22-Jun-4 Sotheby's, London #457/R est:60000-80000
£115000	$192050	€167900	Femme nue assise (49x61cm-19x24in) s.d.25.12.66 col crayons pencil prov.exhib.lit. 21-Oct-3 Sotheby's, London #62/R est:100000-150000
£120000	$218400	€175200	El clam de les verges (48x31cm-19x12in) s. chl exec.1900 prov.exhib.lit. 4-Feb-4 Sotheby's, London #423/R est:100000-150000
£125698	$225000	€183519	Tableau de famille (50x66cm-20x26in) d.16.10.62 col crayon over lithograph lit. 6-May-4 Sotheby's, New York #395/R est:250000-350000
£125698	$225000	€183519	L'Aubade (25x33cm-10x13in) s.d.14.6.70 col crayon col chk card prov.lit. 6-May-4 Sotheby's, New York #400/R est:220000-280000
£130000	$239200	€189800	Peintre (31x22cm-12x9in) s.d.70 s.i.d.verso col crayon over pencil card prov.exhib.lit. 22-Jun-4 Sotheby's, London #460/R est:120000-150000
£146000	$268640	€213160	Femme endormie (51x66cm-20x26in) s.d.52 brush ink prov.lit. 22-Jun-4 Sotheby's, London #490/R est:90000-120000
£152941	$260000	€223294	Mere et enfant (41x19cm-16x7in) s. chl prov.exhib. 5-Nov-3 Christie's, Rockefeller NY #113/R est:80000-120000
£195531	$350000	€285475	Guitare sur table (49x64cm-19x25in) chl exec.1912 prov.exhib.lit. 6-May-4 Sotheby's, New York #139/R est:350000-450000
£215000	$391300	€313900	Faune a moustache (66x50cm-26x20in) s. d.1946 verso gouache W/C brush India ink prov.lit. 5-Feb-4 Christie's, London #406/R est:120000-150000
£223529	$380000	€326352	Deux fumeurs - tetes (53x75cm-21x30in) s.d.5.6.64 col crayon pastel. 5-Nov-3 Sotheby's, New York #57/R est:300000-400000
£258684	$463045	€377679	Retour du Geurrier - scene mythologique (56x75cm-22x30in) s.d.31.8.67 pencil prov.exhib.lit. 25-May-4 Bukowskis, Stockholm #340a/R est:700000-900000 (S.KR 3500000)
£280000	$515200	€408800	Etude pour la coiffure (17x11cm-7x4in) s. chl exec.c.1905-06 prov. 22-Jun-4 Sotheby's, London #443/R est:120000-180000
£335294	$570000	€489529	Coucher de soleil (62x48cm-24x19in) s. gouache W/C paper on canvas painted 1908 prov.exhib.lit. 5-Nov-3 Christie's, Rockefeller NY #117/R est:350000-450000
£391061	$700000	€570949	Ballerina (45x32cm-18x13in) s. pastel paper on board exec.1901 prov.lit. 4-May-4 Christie's, Rockefeller NY #17/R est:500000-700000
£446927	$800000	€652513	Tete d'homme (62x48cm-24x19in) chl exec.1912 prov.exhib.lit. 4-May-4 Christie's, Rockefeller NY #23/R est:400000-600000
£446927	$800000	€652513	La famille (62x47cm-24x19in) s. pastel pencil exec.1919 prov.lit. 6-May-4 Sotheby's, New York #131/R est:1000000-1500000
£950000	$1738500	€1387000	Danseuse de cancan (42x31cm-17x12in) pastel exec.1901 prov.exhib.lit. 2-Feb-4 Christie's, London #8/R est:500000-700000
£1000000	$1820000	€1460000	Tete de femme (49x36cm-19x14in) s. gouache crayon pencil card exec.1906 prov.lit. 21-Jun-4 Sotheby's, London #20/R est:600000-800000
£5117647	$8700000	€7471765	Nu couche (97x130cm-38x51in) chl on canvas executed 1932 prov.exhib.lit. 5-Nov-3 Sotheby's, New York #23/R est:5000000-7000000

PICASSO, Pablo (after) (1881-1973) Spanish

£31638	$56000	€46191	Imaginary portraits (69x53cm-27x21in) col lithograph set of 29 album. 28-Apr-4 Christie's, Rockefeller NY #197/R est:15000-25000
Prints			
£1899	$3400	€2773	Musicien, danseur, chevre et oiseau (63x50cm-25x20in) s. lithograph. 6-May-4 Swann Galleries, New York #562/R est:2000-3000
£4118	$7000	€6012	Bacchanale (48x56cm-19x22in) s.num.177/250 aquatint exec.c.1960. 6-Nov-3 Swann Galleries, New York #702/R est:6000-9000
£4324	$8000	€6313	Cubist composition with table and open window (37x27cm-15x11in) s.i. col photogravure roulette drypoint exec.c.1920. 12-Feb-4 Christie's, Rockefeller NY #381/R est:4000-6000

£5500 $10065 €8030 Gueridon avec guitare et partition (27x21cm-11x8in) s.num.52/100 col pochoir exec.c.1920. 3-Jun-4 Christie's, Kensington #138/R est:2000-3000
£5587 $10000 €8157 Bouteille de rhum (60x49cm-24x19in) s.num.148/250 color collotype stencil. 6-May-4 Swann Galleries, New York #563/R est:8000-12000
£6000 $10920 €8760 Le homard (26x45cm-10x18in) aquatint. 30-Jun-4 Christie's, London #311/R est:4000-6000
£6500 $11830 €9490 Venus et l'amour (64x49cm-25x19in) photo lithograph. 30-Jun-4 Christie's, London #312/R est:3000-5000
£6704 $12000 €9788 Mere et enfant au fichu (57x46cm-22x18in) s. num.XLVII/LX offset color lithograph. 6-May-4 Swann Galleries, New York #564/R est:3000-5000
£8939 $16000 €13051 Cavalier (46x30cm-18x12in) s.num.221/300 color lithograph. 6-May-4 Swann Galleries, New York #563a/R est:3000-5000
£8939 $16000 €13051 L'attente (57x46cm-22x18in) s.num.10/60 offset color lithograph. 6-May-4 Swann Galleries, New York #565/R est:4000-6000
£9605 $17000 €14023 Bacchanale (47x56cm-19x22in) s.num.214/300 col etching aquatint exec.c.1955. 28-Apr-4 Christie's, Rockefeller NY #196/R est:7000-9000
£12994 $23000 €18971 Nature morte au crane (43x62cm-17x24in) s. col aquatint. 30-Apr-4 Sotheby's, New York #196/R est:8000-12000
£38000 $69160 €55480 Imaginary portraits (66x50cm-26x20in) num.A227/250 col lithographs 29. 1-Jul-4 Sotheby's, London #285/R est:8000-12000
Sculpture
£7362 $12000 €10749 Interieur rouge avec transatlantique blue (51x40cm-20x16in) s.num.35/300 aquatint wove paper. 24-Sep-3 Christie's, Rockefeller NY #164/R est:2000-3000

PICASSO, Pablo (attrib) (1881-1973) Spanish
Prints
£3380 $5848 €4800 La colombe (48x64cm-19x25in) s. col lithograph. 10-Dec-3 Rossini, Paris #27
£11189 $19021 €16000 La corrida (57x46cm-22x18in) s.num.109/200 col aquatint. 23-Nov-3 Cornette de St.Cyr, Paris #636/R est:11000-13000

PICASSO, Pablo (style) (1881-1973) Spanish
Prints
£2941 $4912 €4294 Harlequin, from 'Barcelona' (75x52cm-30x20in) s. col offset lithograph lit. 24-Jun-3 Germann, Zurich #554/R est:5000-6000 (S.FR 6500)

PICAULT, Claude E (?) ?
£1308 $2250 €1910 Summer landscape with pond (27x34cm-11x13in) s. panel. 3-Dec-3 Doyle, New York #96/R est:2500-3500

PICAULT, E (1839-1915) French
Sculpture
£2006 $3250 €2909 Egyptian figures. pat bronze pair. 10-Aug-3 Skinner, Bolton #527/R est:500-700

PICAULT, Émile (1839-1915) French
Sculpture
£860 $1600 €1256 Figure of town crier holding a scroll (61cm-24in) s. bronze. 3-Mar-4 Alderfer's, Hatfield #248/R est:1200-1800
£894 $1601 €1305 La mutualite (79cm-31in) incised sig. brown pat. bronze. 4-May-4 Ritchie, Toronto #112/R est:2000-4000 (C.D 2200)
£909 $1600 €1327 Whaler (54cm-21in) s. pat bronze. 22-May-4 Weschler, Washington #207 est:1000-1500
£1040 $1882 €1560 Magician (35cm-14in) s. pat bronze. 31-Mar-4 Segre, Madrid #600/R
£1141 $2042 €1700 Ad lumen (74cm-29in) pat bronze. 25-May-4 Palais de Beaux Arts, Brussels #100/R est:1800-2400
£1342 $2497 €2000 Allegorical group with tow figures (78cm-31in) s.i. brown pat.bronze. 8-Mar-4 Bernaerts, Antwerp #86/R est:1750-2000
£1888 $3248 €2700 Excelsior (70cm-28in) s. brown pat bronze. 3-Dec-3 Palais de Beaux Arts, Brussels #867/R est:2500-3500
£1974 $3632 €3000 Grands hommes sont les phares de l'humanite (92cm-36in) Carrare marble marble base. 28-Jun-4 Joron-Derem, Paris #262/R est:3000-3500
£2900 $5481 €4234 Bust of Ambroise Pare. s.i. brown pat bronze red marble base. 17-Feb-4 Sotheby's, Olympia #37/R est:2000-3000
£3061 $5571 €4500 Le porteur d'eau (67x28x28cm-26x11x11in) s.i. pat bronze lit. 8-Feb-4 Anaf, Lyon #52/R est:4500-5000
£3125 $5000 €4563 Vincere Avt Morior (89cm-35in) s. bronze. 20-Sep-3 Bunte, Elgin #1196 est:4000-6000
£3472 $6250 €5069 Victory (68cm-27in) i. brown pat. bronze. 21-Jan-4 Sotheby's, New York #228/R est:3000-5000
£12414 $20606 €18000 Persee et Pegase (100cm-39in) s.d.1888 brown pat bronze lit. 2-Oct-3 Sotheby's, Paris #16/R est:28000
£32353 $55000 €47235 Egyptian princess. Egyptian scribe (73cm-29in) s. gilt-bronze griotte bronze pair. 29-Oct-3 Christie's, Rockefeller NY #159/R est:60000-80000

PICCINARDI, Mauro (1735-1809) Italian
£16000 $28640 €24000 Venus and Adonis (140x109cm-55x43in) 12-May-4 Finarte Semenzato, Milan #69/R est:20000-30000

PICCININI, Patricia (1965-) Australian?
£511 $883 €746 Metope (40x40cm-16x16in) s.i.d.1991 stretcher prov. 10-Dec-3 Shapiro, Sydney #118/R (A.D 1200)
Photographs
£2439 $4366 €3561 Mountain from the Desert Riders series (80x80cm-31x31in) digital Lambda photograph edn 14/30 prov.exhib.lit. 4-May-4 Sotheby's, Melbourne #250/R est:7000-9000 (A.D 6000)
£2479 $4587 €3619 Waiting for Jennifer (80x80cm-31x31in) s.d.2000 type c colour photograph. 10-Mar-4 Deutscher-Menzies, Melbourne #19/R est:3000-5000 (A.D 6000)
£2479 $4388 €3619 Desert riders, plain from Autosphere series (79x80cm-31x31in) s.d.2000 num.27/30 C type col photo prov. 3-May-4 Christie's, Melbourne #40/R est:6000-8000 (A.D 6000)
£2479 $4388 €3619 Desert riders, mountains from Autosphere series (79x80cm-31x31in) s.d.2001 num.27/30 C type col photo prov. 3-May-4 Christie's, Melbourne #73/R est:6000-8000 (A.D 6000)
£3099 $5269 €4525 Waiting for Jennifer So2 (80x80cm-31x31in) s.d.2000 type C photograph. 29-Oct-3 Lawson Menzies, Sydney #49/R est:3000-5000 (A.D 7500)
£3719 $6322 €5430 Social studies So2 (80x80cm-31x31in) s.d.2000 type C photograph. 29-Oct-3 Lawson Menzies, Sydney #50/R est:3000-5000 (A.D 9000)
£3814 $6483 €5568 Desert riders (80x80cm-31x31in) s.d.2001 C-type photograph edn 4/30. 24-Nov-3 Sotheby's, Melbourne #65/R est:3500-5500 (A.D 9000)
£4025 $6843 €5877 Social studies (80x80cm-31x31in) s.d.2000 C-type photograph. 24-Nov-3 Sotheby's, Melbourne #63/R est:3500-5500 (A.D 9500)
£4132 $7314 €6033 Sacrifice from Your Time Starts Now series (130x130cm-51x51in) type C photo edition of 6 prov. 3-May-4 Christie's, Melbourne #32/R est:20000-30000 (A.D 10000)
£8537 $15280 €12464 Natural selection - Sandman series (103x184cm-41x72in) C-type photograph edn 6/30 exec 2002 prov.exhib.lit. 4-May-4 Sotheby's, Melbourne #62/R est:20000-30000 (A.D 21000)
£10169 $17288 €14847 Protein lattice subset - Blue landscape (80x80cm-31x31in) s.d.2000 num. C-type photo edn 2/6. 24-Nov-3 Sotheby's, Melbourne #37/R est:18000-28000 (A.D 24000)
£11064 $18809 €16153 First satisfied customer from Your time starts now series (95x94cm-37x37in) num.2 of 3 C-type photo exhib.prov. 25-Nov-3 Christie's, Melbourne #56/R est:25000-35000 (A.D 26000)
£11336 $18251 €16551 Protein Lattice subset - red landscape (80x80cm-31x31in) s.d.1997 C-type photograph edn 1/6. 25-Aug-3 Sotheby's, Paddington #226/R est:8000-12000 (A.D 28000)
£11336 $18251 €16551 Protein Lattic subset - Red body (80x80cm-31x31in) s.d.1997 C-type photograph edn 3/6. 25-Aug-3 Sotheby's, Paddington #227/R est:8000-12000 (A.D 28000)
£28602 $48623 €41759 Psychogeography (120x258cm-47x102in) s.d.99 digital C-type photograph edn of 8 prov.exhib. 24-Nov-3 Sotheby's, Melbourne #13/R est:70000-100000 (A.D 67500)
Works on paper
£891 $1434 €1301 Untitled (57x76cm-22x30in) s.verso ink. 25-Aug-3 Sotheby's, Paddington #233/R est:1500-2500 (A.D 2200)

PICCINNI, Antonio (1846-1920) Italian
Works on paper
£933 $1717 €1400 Drawings. s. pencil 9 in two frames. 8-Jun-4 Sotheby's, Milan #147/R
£1000 $1840 €1500 Man (40x27cm-16x11in) s. W/C. 11-Jun-4 Farsetti, Prato #548/R est:1300-1600

PICCINNI, Gennaro (1933-) Italian
£336 $624 €500 Harbour (40x60cm-16x24in) s. board. 4-Mar-4 Babuino, Rome #42
£1056 $1754 €1500 Galleria (74x95cm-29x37in) s.d.1961 panel. 14-Jun-3 Meeting Art, Vercelli #679/R est:1500
Works on paper
£500 $920 €750 Rome, Piazza di Spagna (70x50cm-28x20in) s. mixed media card. 12-Jun-4 Meeting Art, Vercelli #341/R
£500 $920 €750 Rome, Trevi Fountain (70x50cm-28x20in) s. mixed media card lit. 12-Jun-4 Meeting Art, Vercelli #339/R
£567 $1043 €850 Rome, Trinita' dei Monti (70x50cm-28x20in) s. mixed media card. 12-Jun-4 Meeting Art, Vercelli #340/R
£600 $1104 €900 Rome, Piazza Navona (70x50cm-28x20in) s. mixed media card lit. 12-Jun-4 Meeting Art, Vercelli #342/R

PICCIONI, Gino (1873-1941) Italian
Works on paper
£11268 $19493 €16000 On the beach (100x120cm-39x47in) s. pastel card. 11-Dec-3 Christie's, Rome #146/R est:17000-19000

PICCIRILLI, Attilio (1866-1945) American
Sculpture
£765 $1300 €1117 Female nude (22cm-9in) s.d.1933 brown pat. bronze i.f.Cellini. 21-Nov-3 Skinner, Boston #399/R est:1000-1500

PICCOLO, Richard (1943-) American
£438 $700 €639 La strada (58x74cm-23x29in) s.i. prov. 21-Sep-3 William Jenack, New York #375

PICELJ, Yvan (1924-) Croatian
£284 $500 €415 Num 34 composition (97x97cm-38x38in) oil linen. 22-May-4 Selkirks, St. Louis #797/R

PICHETTE, James (1920-1996) French
£461 $847 €700 Composition (38x46cm-15x18in) s.d.1962 s.d.verso prov. 27-Jun-4 Versailles Encheres #48/R
£986 $1706 €1400 Composition (27x35cm-11x14in) s.d.1954. 14-Dec-3 Versailles Encheres #22/R
£1119 $1902 €1600 Composition (22x16cm-9x6in) s. 27-Nov-3 Calmels Cohen, Paris #43/R est:1500-2000
£1678 $3121 €2500 Soleil levant (40x60cm-16x24in) s. painted 1955. 3-Mar-4 Tajan, Paris #132/R est:2500-3000
£3581 $6303 €5300 Rythmes portieres (81x100cm-32x39in) s.d.1953 s.i.d. verso prov.exhib. 18-May-4 Tajan, Paris #39/R est:5000-6000

PICHHADZE, Meir (1955-) Israeli
£1283 $2400 €1873 Bed in the landscape (40x50cm-16x20in) s.d.1996 verso. 1-Mar-4 Ben-Ami, Tel Aviv #4675/R est:3500-4500
£3382 $5750 €4938 Girl sleeping in the landscape (80x55cm-31x22in) s.d.1997 s.i.d.verso. 1-Dec-3 Ben-Ami, Tel Aviv #4324/R est:6000-8000

PICHLER, Walter (1936-) Austrian
Works on paper
£1399 $2378 €2000 Kleid mit aufgenahten Kontinenten (34x41cm-13x16in) mono. col dr sold with a catalogue. 1-Dec-3 Amberes, Antwerp #125
£1745 $3123 €2600 Torso (30x42cm-12x17in) s.i.d.5.8.1976 pencil. 25-May-4 Dorotheum, Vienna #359/R est:2200-2800
£1748 $2972 €2500 Untitled (30x47cm-12x19in) d.1973 mixed media. 28-Nov-3 Wiener Kunst Auktionen, Vienna #640/R est:2500-3500
£2797 $4755 €4000 St Martin (33x47cm-13x19in) mono.i.d.1973 mixed media. 28-Nov-3 Wiener Kunst Auktionen, Vienna #639/R est:3500-4500
£3020 $5346 €4500 Jerusalem (34x48cm-13x19in) s.i.d. pencil col pen. 28-Apr-4 Wiener Kunst Auktionen, Vienna #260/R est:3000-5000
£6944 $11806 €10000 The right view (27x35cm-11x14in) s.i.d.6.5.74 mixed media. 28-Oct-3 Wiener Kunst Auktionen, Vienna #254/R est:8000-12000

PICHOT, Ramon (1924-1996) Spanish
£3200 $5088 €4672 Barques a Cadaques (60x131cm-24x52in) s. exhib. 11-Sep-3 Christie's, Kensington #48/R est:2000-2500

PICK, Anton (1840-1905) Austrian
£2000 $3200 €2900 Figures boating in an Austrian lake landscape (54x74cm-21x29in) s. 18-Sep-3 Christie's, Kensington #60/R est:2000-3000

PICK, Rudolf (1865-1915) Austrian
Works on paper
£1283 $2270 €1873 Horse race (68x97cm-27x38in) s.d.97 W/C. 28-Apr-4 Kieselbach, Budapest #68/R (H.F 480000)

PICK, Seraphine (1964-) New Zealander
£903 $1471 €1318 Enigma (105x75cm-41x30in) s.d.1994 oil graphite pencil. 23-Sep-3 Peter Webb, Auckland #127/R (NZ.D 2500)
£1429 $2586 €2086 Chair, suitcase, bed (28x37cm-11x15in) s.d.1995 acrylic. 30-Mar-4 Peter Webb, Auckland #4/R est:3000-4000 (NZ.D 4000)
£4275 $7353 €6242 Project - Series 5 (40x175cm-16x69in) s.d.99 verso each panel linen 5 panels. 3-Dec-3 Dunbar Sloane, Auckland #46/R est:10000-15000 (NZ.D 11500)

PICKARD, Charles (19th C) British
Works on paper
£400 $728 €584 Portrait of Charles Syville Thomson (24x28cm-9x11in) s. W/C. 3-Feb-4 Sworder & Son, Bishops Stortford #249/R

PICKARD, Louise (c.1865-1928) British
£428 $727 €625 View of the Thames (43x53cm-17x21in) s.d.1912. 21-Nov-3 Walker's, Ottawa #223/R (C.D 950)
£520 $915 €759 Still life of a bowl of fruit. Madonna and child (77x63cm-30x25in) s. double-sided painted 1928 prov. 18-May-4 Bonhams, Knightsbridge #16/R

PICKARDT, Ernst (1876-1931) German
£1399 $2378 €2000 Goethe in Venice (135x98cm-53x39in) s.d.1921 lit. 28-Nov-3 Schloss Ahlden, Ahlden #1574/R est:1800
£2098 $3566 €3000 Jardin la Tonnelle (89x63cm-35x25in) s.d.1920. 24-Nov-3 E & Eve, Paris #173/R est:3000-3500

PICKENOY (17th C) Dutch
£28767 $48904 €42000 Portrait of a lady, said to be Alijdt Fransdr, Boon wearing a black velvet bodice (115x84cm-45x33in) i.d.1626 panel. 5-Nov-3 Christie's, Amsterdam #17/R est:30000-50000

PICKERING, Henry (fl.1740-1771) British
£600 $948 €870 Portrait of a lady seated in a blue dress (91x73cm-36x29in) s.d.1768. 4-Sep-3 Christie's, Kensington #29
£1786 $3250 €2608 Portrait of a lady in a blue dress (98x78cm-39x31in) s.d.1760. 29-Jun-4 Sotheby's, New York #52/R est:4000-6000
£6500 $11895 €9490 Portrait of lady (75x62cm-30x24in) lit. 8-Jul-4 Sotheby's, London #225/R est:3000-5000
£32000 $58880 €46720 Portrait of Margaret Smith, seated in a pink dress holding a garland, in landscape, sheep by her sid (102x130cm-40x51in) s.d.1762 prov. 11-Jun-4 Christie's, London #15/R est:15000-20000

PICKERING, Henry (attrib) (fl.1740-1771) British
£1500 $2685 €2190 Portrait of an officer of the 7th Dragoons (76x64cm-30x25in) 11-May-4 Sotheby's, Olympia #595/R est:1500-2000

PICKERING, Joseph Langsdale (1845-1912) British
£280 $465 €409 Lucernette (27x64cm-11x25in) s. 1-Oct-3 George Kidner, Lymington #166
£306 $550 €447 Stream through a forest (46x36cm-18x14in) s. 24-Apr-4 Weschler, Washington #544/R
£2400 $3792 €3480 Shadowed land (76x66cm-30x26in) indis sig. prov. 4-Sep-3 Christie's, Kensington #125/R est:2000-3000

PICKERSGILL, Frederick Richard (1820-1900) British
£1300 $2366 €1898 Young mother with child in a country landscape (36x51cm-14x20in) init. panel. 3-Feb-4 Sworder & Son, Bishops Stortford #295/R est:1500-2000
£10241 $17000 €14952 Samson and Delilah (102x152cm-40x60in) s.d.1857/58 canvas laid down. 4-Oct-3 Neal Auction Company, New Orleans #268/R est:12000-18000
Works on paper
£600 $1002 €876 Old Ramsgate harbour (9x16cm-4x6in) pencil W/C. 16-Oct-3 Christie's, Kensington #144/R
£5200 $9568 €7592 Dante and Beatrice (19x22cm-7x9in) W/C sold with a collection of items relating to the artist. 8-Jun-4 Bonhams, New Bond Street #62/R est:3000-5000

PICKHARDT, Carl E (jnr) (1908-) American
£440 $800 €642 Quiet land (61x86cm-24x34in) init. s.i.stretcher. 7-Feb-4 Sloans & Kenyon, Bethesda #1308/R

PICKNELL, William Lamb (1854-1897) American
£17442 $30000 €25465 Walk on a country path (75x91cm-30x36in) s. painted c.1890 prov. 3-Dec-3 Sotheby's, New York #16/R est:20000-30000

PICKVANCE, Ian Robert (20th C) British?
£600 $1020 €876 Summer kestrel (36x49cm-14x19in) s. 27-Nov-3 Christie's, Kensington #246a/R

PICOLO Y LOPEZ, Manuel (1850-1892) Spanish
Works on paper
£296 $545 €450 Gallant scene (25x19cm-10x7in) s. gouache. 22-Jun-4 Durán, Madrid #87/R

PICOT, Andre (20th C) French
£247 $400 €361 Les Champs Ellysees (28x41cm-11x16in) s. board. 2-Aug-3 Neal Auction Company, New Orleans #582

PICOT, Jean Claude (20th C) French?
£244 $450 €356 Temps couvert au Bretagne (46x61cm-18x24in) s.i. 9-Jun-4 Alderfer's, Hatfield #364

PICOU, Eugène (1831-?) French
£267 $491 €400 Jeune femme aux oiseaux (33x20cm-13x8in) s. panel. 10-Jun-4 Camard, Paris #3
£559 $934 €800 Bouquet de fleurs (46x55cm-18x22in) studio st.verso prov. 7-Oct-3 Livinec, Gaudcheau & Jezequel, Rennes #131

PICOU, Henri Pierre (1824-1895) French
£2841 $5000 €4148 Woman dressing for a costume ball (61x51cm-24x20in) s.d.73. 21-May-4 North East Auctions, Portsmouth #1439
£3700 $5846 €5402 Nymph with a pair of weighing scales. Nymph wreathed in may blossom (27x20cm-11x8in) panel pair. 27-Apr-3 Wilkinson, Doncaster #297/R
£4934 $9079 €7500 Hermes presentant Psyche a Venus (65x90cm-26x35in) s.d.1889. 24-Jun-4 Tajan, Paris #73/R est:6000-8000
£5200 $9308 €7592 Watching the goldfish (54x65cm-21x26in) s.d.1859. 26-May-4 Sotheby's, Olympia #292/R est:3000-5000
£7801 $13028 €11000 Les nymphes et l'amour (65x90cm-26x35in) s.d.1874. 19-Jun-3 Millon & Associes, Paris #150/R est:12000-15000
£8000 $14720 €12000 Le bain de la sultane (49x63cm-19x25in) s. 14-Jun-4 Gros & Delettrez, Paris #180/R est:10000-15000
£10000 $18000 €14600 Weighting cupid against a butterfly (82x61cm-32x24in) s. 22-Apr-4 Christie's, Rockefeller NY #126/R est:20000-30000
£10544 $18874 €15500 Femme Grecques au bain (62x81cm-24x32in) s.d.1872. 19-Mar-4 Ribeyre & Baron, Paris #62/R est:5000-7000
£13529 $23000 €19752 Ronde de Mail (101x75cm-40x30in) s.d.1873 st.verso prov. 28-Oct-3 Sotheby's, New York #46/R est:18000-25000

PICOUX, C (19/20th C) French?
£1133 $2051 €1700 Les ruines d'Arles (37x46cm-15x18in) s. cardboard exhib. 30-Mar-4 Rossini, Paris #1036 est:600-900

PICQUE, Charles (1799-1869) Belgian
£2621 $4377 €3800 Les mendiants (82x68cm-32x27in) s.d.1837. 17-Nov-3 Bernaerts, Antwerp #291 est:2000-2500

PIDDING, Henry James (1797-1864) British
£550 $1007 €803 War times (67x87cm-26x34in) s.d.1855. 6-Jul-4 Bonhams, Knightsbridge #76/R

PIECK, Anton (1895-1987) Dutch
Works on paper
£229 $383 €332 Nu dans la salle de bain (45x30cm-18x12in) s. W/C prov. 21-Jun-3 Galerie du Rhone, Sion #134/R (S.FR 500)
£336 $594 €500 Vues de villes. s. col crayon W/C two. 27-Apr-4 Campo & Campo, Antwerp #185/R

PIECK, Henri (1895-1972) Dutch
£578 $1052 €850 Portrait of a seated woman (120x80cm-47x31in) s.d.40. 3-Feb-4 Christie's, Amsterdam #472

PIEDMONTESE SCHOOL (16th C) Italian
£8000 $13600 €11680 Last supper (67x81cm-26x32in) panel. 30-Oct-3 Sotheby's, Olympia #12/R est:8000-12000

PIEDMONTESE SCHOOL (17th C) Italian
£9333 $17080 €14000 Casale under siege (118x168cm-46x66in) 1-Jun-4 Sotheby's, Milan #81/R est:5000-7000

PIEDMONTESE SCHOOL (18th C) Italian
£6000 $10740 €9000 Still life of flowers (122x96cm-48x38in) 12-May-4 Finarte Semenzato, Milan #50/R est:3000-4000

£22000 $37400 €32120 Building with a tower and figures climbing the staircase and other Mediterranean scenes (167x51cm-66x20in) set of four different sizes. 31-Oct-3 Christie's, Kensington #146a/R est:8000-12000
Sculpture
£23630 $40171 €34500 Chinese figures (66x24x22cm-26x9x9in) papier mache pair prov. 7-Nov-3 Finarte, Venice #149/R est:28000-35000

PIELER, Franz Xaver (1879-1952) Austrian
£979 $1635 €1400 Still life of flowers with insects (41x32cm-16x13in) s. panel. 27-Jun-3 Michael Zeller, Lindau #636/R
£1397 $2543 €2040 Still life (50x40cm-20x16in) s. 16-Jun-4 Fischer, Luzern #1242/R est:2000-3000 (S.FR 3200)
£1493 $2538 €2180 Still life of flowers (80x60cm-31x24in) s. 1-Dec-3 Koller, Zurich #6497 est:3500-4500 (S.FR 3300)
£1500 $2760 €2190 Roses in a glass vase, a landscape beyond (33x24cm-13x9in) s. board. 25-Mar-4 Christie's, Kensington #83/R est:1500-2000
£1549 $2680 €2200 Large still life of flowers with bird's nest (75x55cm-30x22in) s. masonite. 10-Dec-3 Dorotheum, Vienna #101/R est:2200-2400
£1854 $3393 €2800 Flowers in glass vase with butterfly (24x18cm-9x7in) s. panel. 8-Apr-4 Dorotheum, Vienna #9 est:2000-2400
£2800 $5012 €4200 Still life of flowers (39x29cm-15x11in) s. panel lit. 14-May-4 Schloss Ahlden, Ahlden #2799/R est:3000
£4366 $7554 €6200 Still life of flowers (30x24cm-12x9in) s. panel prov. 13-Dec-3 Lempertz, Koln #242/R est:3000
Works on paper
£1034 $1717 €1500 Meadow flowers (37x27cm-15x11in) s. gouache. 30-Sep-3 Dorotheum, Vienna #376/R est:1600-1800

PIEMONTI, Lorenzo (1935-) Italian
£500 $920 €750 Chromoplastic (30x30cm-12x12in) s. s.i.d.2003 verso acrylic board. 12-Jun-4 Meeting Art, Vercelli #441/R
£667 $1227 €1000 Metal and plastic (30x30cm-12x12in) s.i.d.1990 verso acrylic canvas on board lit. 12-Jun-4 Meeting Art, Vercelli #42/R
£1000 $1840 €1500 Contrasting forces (74x92cm-29x36in) s.i.d.1984 acrylic. 12-Jun-4 Meeting Art, Vercelli #476/R est:1500
£1000 $1840 €1500 Chromoplastic (60x60cm-24x24in) s.i. acrylic board wood. 12-Jun-4 Meeting Art, Vercelli #839/R est:1500

PIENE, Otto (1928-) German
£285 $510 €416 Parisian street scene (51x41cm-20x16in) s. 19-Mar-4 Aspire, Cleveland #57
£583 $956 €810 Bleeding planet (18x24cm-7x9in) s.i.d. verso acrylic soot. 4-Jun-3 Ketterer, Hamburg #771/R
£704 $1218 €1000 Untitled (96x68cm-38x27in) s.d.72 silver fire smoke board. 13-Dec-3 Lempertz, Koln #347/R
£1208 $2223 €1800 Composition (68x95cm-27x37in) s.d. oil soot on gouache board. 26-Mar-4 Ketterer, Hamburg #599/R est:1900-2500
£1208 $2223 €1800 Fire gouache on black (48x68cm-19x27in) oil soot gouache board. 26-Mar-4 Ketterer, Hamburg #600/R est:2000-2500
£1400 $2506 €2100 Untitled - fire picture (40x30cm-16x12in) s.i.d. verso. 15-May-4 Dr Sturies, Dusseldorf #140/R
£2098 $3566 €3000 Untitled (50x70cm-20x28in) s.d.66 fire gouache oil smoke fire board. 27-Nov-3 Lempertz, Koln #341/R est:3000-3500
£3357 $5706 €4800 Golden city (72x101cm-28x40in) s.i.d.57 86 90 oil smoke gold bronze board. 27-Nov-3 Lempertz, Koln #340/R est:6000
£6294 $10699 €9000 Autumn leaves (100x100cm-39x39in) s.i.d.92 verso s.i.d. stretcher oil smoke fire. 27-Nov-3 Lempertz, Koln #339/R est:10000-12000
£6643 $11427 €9500 Rasterbild (54x54cm-21x21in) s.d.1958-72 oil gold leaf nails panel prov. 2-Dec-3 Sotheby's, Amsterdam #176/R est:8000-12000
£10976 $18000 €16025 Doppel feuerblume (100x100cm-39x39in) s.i.d.1965 on stretcher prov.exhib. 28-May-3 Sotheby's, Amsterdam #37/R est:18000-22000
Prints
£2013 $3705 €3000 Composition jaune, verte, bleue et rouge (33x50cm-13x20in) s.i. col lithograph. 26-Mar-4 Ketterer, Hamburg #603/R est:2200-2500
£2550 $4693 €3800 Composition rouge, jaune et bleue (58x44cm-23x17in) s.i. col lithograph. 26-Mar-4 Ketterer, Hamburg #604/R est:2500-3000
£2550 $4693 €3800 Composition orange et verte (60x45cm-24x18in) s.i. col lithograph. 26-Mar-4 Ketterer, Hamburg #605/R est:3800-4300
Works on paper
£854 $1400 €1247 Rauchzeichnung no38 (7x15cm-3x6in) s.d.59 smoke residue red paper prov.exhib. 28-May-3 Sotheby's, Amsterdam #43/R
£933 $1671 €1400 Eye (61x86cm-24x34in) s.d. gouache. 15-May-4 Dr Sturies, Dusseldorf #139/R
£1220 $2000 €1781 Rauchzeichnung (51x28cm-20x11in) s.i.d.60 smoke residue gouache paper prov.exhib. 28-May-3 Sotheby's, Amsterdam #127/R est:2000-3000
£1400 $2506 €2100 Veil (48x67cm-19x26in) s.i.d. fire gouache. 15-May-4 Dr Sturies, Dusseldorf #141/R

PIENEMAN, Jan Willem (1779-1853) Dutch
£2800 $5012 €4088 Portrait of Richard Trench, 2nd Earl of Clancarty, three-quarter length (141x103cm-56x41in) s.d.1823 prov. 13-May-4 Sotheby's, London #6/R est:3000-5000

PIENEMAN, Nicolaas (elder) (1809-1860) Dutch
£1944 $3072 €2800 Rejoice in the return (135x126cm-53x50in) s. 2-Sep-3 Christie's, Amsterdam #163/R est:2000-3000
£2763 $5001 €4200 Portrait of Arriens, possibly a Colonel (26x20cm-10x8in) s.d.1848 panel. 19-Apr-4 Glerum, Amsterdam #29/R est:1000-1500

PIEPER, Christian (1843-?) German
£1806 $2979 €2600 Elegant woman at table in salon (65x47cm-26x19in) s. 3-Jul-3 Van Ham, Cologne #1403 est:600

PIEPER, Hermann (1909-1964) Swiss
£1727 $2867 €2504 Women (100x150cm-39x59in) board. 13-Jun-3 Zofingen, Switzerland #2980/R est:2500 (S.FR 3800)

PIEPER, Hugo J (20th C) American
Works on paper
£732 $1200 €1061 Corner tavern (64x43cm-25x17in) s. gouache exec.c.1955. 7-Jun-3 Treadway Gallery, Cincinnati #1494

PIEPHO, Karl Johann Nikolaus (1869-1920) German
£594 $950 €867 Landscape with tall trees (94x69cm-37x27in) 20-Sep-3 Sloans & Kenyon, Bethesda #150/R
Works on paper
£537 $988 €800 Three female nudes in extensive hilly landscape (69x116cm-27x46in) gouache. 27-Mar-4 Dannenberg, Berlin #608/R

PIERCE, A (19th C) Danish?
£280 $443 €406 Portrait of young woman (30x23cm-12x9in) init. 3-Sep-3 Museumsbygningen, Copenhagen #180 (D.KR 3000)

PIERCE, Anne Honsley (attrib) (1877-1951) American
£565 $1000 €825 Southern California spring meadows (69x86cm-27x34in) painted c.1910. 1-May-4 Thomaston Place, Thomaston #94/R

PIERCE, Charles Drew (19th C) American?
£339 $600 €495 Dignity and impudence, portrait of a boxer dog (15x10cm-6x4in) i.d.1884 verso panel. 1-May-4 Thomaston Place, Thomaston #482/R

PIERCE, Charles Franklin (1844-1920) American
£538 $850 €785 Early autumn landscape (30x41cm-12x16in) s. board. 7-Sep-3 Treadway Gallery, Cincinnati #638/R
£802 $1500 €1171 Landscape (43x53cm-17x21in) s. 25-Feb-4 Dallas Auction Gallery, Dallas #194/R est:1500-2500
£879 $1600 €1283 Cattle by the stream (46x61cm-18x24in) s. 19-Jun-4 Jeffery Burchard, Florida #133
£1023 $1800 €1494 Autumn landscape (28x112cm-11x44in) s.d.79. 3-Jan-4 Cobbs, Peterborough #168/R

PIERCE, Elijah (1892-1984) American
Sculpture
£833 $1500 €1216 Alligator (10x43cm-4x17in) s.d.1980 carved painted wood rhinestone eyes popsicle stick tongu. 24-Apr-4 Slotin Folk Art, Buford #272/R est:1000-2000
£4790 $8000 €6993 Couple kissing (48x38cm-19x15in) acrylic wood prov.lit. 15-Nov-3 Slotin Folk Art, Buford #143/R est:8000-12000
£10000 $18000 €14600 Mule that wouldn't move (41x64cm-16x25in) painted wood relief. 24-Apr-4 Slotin Folk Art, Buford #271/R est:4000-6000

PIERCY, Rob (20th C) British
Works on paper
£330 $538 €482 Corrugated sheep flap in a North Wales stream wall (28x18cm-11x7in) s. W/C. 27-Sep-3 Rogers Jones, Clwyd #60

PIERNEEF, Jacob Hendrik (1886-1957) South African
£2241 $3743 €3272 Mountain landscape (29x37cm-11x15in) s.d.21. 20-Oct-3 Stephan Welz, Johannesburg #283/R est:10000-15000 (SA.R 26000)
£3017 $5039 €4405 Mountain landscape (30x40cm-12x16in) s.d.45 board. 20-Oct-3 Stephan Welz, Johannesburg #296/R est:22000-28000 (SA.R 35000)
£3276 $5471 €4783 Hartebeespoort Dam, Vanaf Saart Jiesnek (27x36cm-11x14in) s.d.32 board. 20-Oct-3 Stephan Welz, Johannesburg #337/R est:20000-30000 (SA.R 38000)
£3793 $6334 €5538 Mountain landscape (30x40cm-12x16in) s. board. 20-Oct-3 Stephan Welz, Johannesburg #336/R est:20000-30000 (SA.R 44000)
£4274 $7265 €6240 Bushveld landscape with trees (40x55cm-16x22in) s.d.42. 4-Nov-3 Stephan Welz, Johannesburg #632/R est:50000-70000 (SA.R 50000)
£4741 $7918 €6922 Artist's house, De Waal Street, Pretoria (34x29cm-13x11in) prov. 20-Oct-3 Stephan Welz, Johannesburg #284/R est:20000-30000 (SA.R 55000)
£5128 $8718 €7487 Three Rondavels in a mountainous landscape (29x39cm-11x15in) s. board. 4-Nov-3 Stephan Welz, Johannesburg #685/R est:25000-35000 (SA.R 60000)
£5172 $8638 €7551 Helderberg (21x29cm-8x11in) s. panel. 20-Oct-3 Stephan Welz, Johannesburg #305/R est:25000-35000 (SA.R 60000)
£6838 $11624 €9983 Karoo by Hofmeyer, K.P (29x39cm-11x15in) s. s.i.verso board. 4-Nov-3 Stephan Welz, Johannesburg #617/R est:30000-40000 (SA.R 80000)
£6897 $11517 €10070 Tree trunk and clouds (38x54cm-15x21in) s.d.50 board. 20-Oct-3 Stephan Welz, Johannesburg #285/R est:60000-90000 (SA.R 80000)
£7845 $14042 €11454 Farm landscape (29x43cm-11x17in) s.d.1928 board. 31-May-4 Stephan Welz, Johannesburg #479/R est:30000-50000 (SA.R 95000)
£7845 $14042 €11454 Cape farmstead (29x39cm-11x15in) s.d.45 board prov. 31-May-4 Stephan Welz, Johannesburg #480/R est:40000-60000 (SA.R 95000)
£12069 $20155 €17621 Landscape, Potgietersrus (45x60cm-18x24in) painted c.1928 prov. 20-Oct-3 Stephan Welz, Johannesburg #281/R est:60000-90000 (SA.R 140000)
£12931 $21595 €18879 Karoo landscape with rain clouds (45x60cm-18x24in) s.d.45. 20-Oct-3 Stephan Welz, Johannesburg #314/R est:60000-90000 (SA.R 150000)
£13212 $23650 €19290 Small farmstead near a tree (39x49cm-15x19in) s.d.20. 31-May-4 Stephan Welz, Johannesburg #481/R est:80000-120000 (SA.R 160000)
£14559 $25041 €21256 Malutis at Ficksburg (50x63cm-20x25in) s.d.1929 board prov. 3-Dec-3 Stephan Welz, Johannesburg #34/R est:80000-120000 (SA.R 160000)
Works on paper
£248 $443 €362 Tree near a roadway (13x19cm-5x7in) studio st. pencil. 31-May-4 Stephan Welz, Johannesburg #189 (SA.R 3000)
£330 $591 €482 Extensive landscape with a tree (11x18cm-4x7in) studio st. W/C over pencil. 31-May-4 Stephan Welz, Johannesburg #191 (SA.R 4000)
£517 $864 €755 Landscape with trees (13x27cm-5x11in) s. pencil pastel. 20-Oct-3 Stephan Welz, Johannesburg #530 est:1800-2400 (SA.R 6000)
£630 $1141 €920 Matlala, Pietersburg (39x48cm-15x19in) s. pencil W/C. 30-Mar-4 Stephan Welz, Johannesburg #509/R est:3000-5000 (SA.R 7500)
£812 $1380 €1186 Landscape with willow trees (29x39cm-11x15in) s.d.1918 W/C gouache. 4-Nov-3 Stephan Welz, Johannesburg #629 est:4000-6000 (SA.R 9500)
£991 $1774 €1447 By Leydsdorp (36x43cm-14x17in) s.i.d.1945 W/C over pencil. 31-May-4 Stephan Welz, Johannesburg #493 (SA.R 12000)
£3448 $5759 €5034 Vermeulen Street, 1885 (41x52cm-16x20in) s.i.d.1912 pencil crayon. 20-Oct-3 Stephan Welz, Johannesburg #282/R est:12000-16000 (SA.R 40000)

£5862 $9790 €8559 Willow trees, Pienaar's River (38x53cm-15x21in) s.d.1928 casein. 20-Oct-3 Stephan Welz, Johannesburg #280/R est:30000-40000 (SA.R 68000)
£8190 $13677 €11957 Cottages, mountain beyond (21x29cm-8x11in) s. W/C casein. 20-Oct-3 Stephan Welz, Johannesburg #306/R est:25000-30000 (SA.R 95000)

PIEROT, Henri (19/20th C) ?
£403 $753 €600 Landscape (37x50cm-15x20in) 26-Feb-4 Cambi, Genoa #499/R

PIEROTTI, Giuseppe (19th C) Italian
£3056 $5500 €4462 Tabletop still life (63x81cm-25x32in) s.d.1870 pair. 24-Apr-4 Weschler, Washington #579/R est:3000-5000

PIERRAKOS, Alkis (1920-) ?
£417 $696 €600 Composition (65x46cm-26x18in) s. 21-Oct-3 Arcurial Briest, Paris #673
£2500 $4475 €3650 Plafond a l'italienne (73x91cm-29x36in) s.d.78 exhib. 11-May-4 Bonhams, New Bond Street #108/R est:2500-3500
£3500 $6125 €5110 Fenetre (92x66cm-36x26in) s.d.77 i.verso. 16-Dec-3 Bonhams, New Bond Street #132/R est:2000-3000
Works on paper
£940 $1738 €1400 Remparts sur l'ile (75x108cm-30x43in) s. Indian ink wash. 15-Mar-4 Blanchet, Paris #172/R

PIERRAT, Nicolas-Constant (1829-1910) French
£719 $1337 €1050 Still life of smoked herring, jug and onions on table (33x40cm-13x16in) s. 2-Mar-4 Rasmussen, Copenhagen #1567/R (D.KR 8000)

PIERRE and GILLES (20th C) French
Photographs
£10405 $18000 €15191 Gaspard Hauser-Stephen Butet (115x89cm-45x35in) painted photograph one of one prov. 10-Dec-3 Phillips, New York #579/R est:20000-30000
£11111 $20000 €16222 La toreador (83x74cm-33x29in) s.i.d.1985 verso hand painted chromogenic colour print prov.lit. 23-Apr-4 Phillips, New York #68/R est:20000-30000
£12849 $23000 €18760 Nina Hagen (95x95cm-37x37in) s.verso hand paintee col photo prov. 14-May-4 Phillips, New York #203/R est:12000-18000
£15000 $25050 €21900 Les plaisirs de la foret, Jiro (122x102cm-48x40in) s.i.d.96 verso handpainted photo prov. 22-Oct-3 Christie's, London #144/R est:15000-20000
£17877 $32000 €26100 Creatures, Siouxsie Sioux et Budgie (118x148cm-46x58in) s.i.d.97 verso hand painted col photo prov.exhib.lit. 14-May-4 Phillips, New York #202/R est:28000-32000
£40223 $72000 €58726 Autoportrait sans visage, Pierre et Gilles (140x115cm-55x45in) s.i.d.1999 s.verso hand painted c-prints aluminum 2 prov.exhib. 14-May-4 Phillips, New York #204/R est:30000-50000
£101796 $170000 €148622 La madone au ceur blesse - lio (168x130cm-66x51in) hand painted photograph executed 1991 prov.exhib.lit. 13-Nov-3 Phillips, New York #43/R est:40000-60000

PIERRE, Gustave René (1875-?) French
£284 $500 €415 Portrait of a girl (38x30cm-15x12in) s. 23-May-4 Hindman, Chicago #14/R

PIERRE, Jean Baptiste Marie (1713-1789) French
£4518 $7500 €6596 Temptation of Eve (49x58cm-19x23in) prov.exhib.lit. 30-Sep-3 Christie's, Rockefeller NY #390/R est:7000-10000
Works on paper
£2077 $3800 €3032 Seated male nude looking to the right (39x51cm-15x20in) red chk card stock. 29-Jan-4 Swann Galleries, New York #220/R est:3000-5000
£5000 $9150 €7300 Four head studies and a dog (27x38cm-11x15in) red chk touches blk chk. 8-Jul-4 Sotheby's, London #122/R est:2500-3500

PIERRE, Jean Baptiste Marie (attrib) (1713-1789) French
Works on paper
£263 $484 €400 Etude de tete de jeune femme (35x21cm-14x8in) sanguine. 25-Jun-4 Rossini, Paris #16
£824 $1400 €1203 Amorous couple (18x27cm-7x11in) chk prov. 25-Nov-3 Christie's, Rockefeller NY #500/R

PIERRI, Orlando (1913-1992) Argentinian
£1421 $2600 €2075 Composition (27x41cm-11x16in) 1-Jun-4 Arroyo, Buenos Aires #1
Works on paper
£279 $500 €407 Garden (40x33cm-16x13in) mixed media. 11-May-4 Arroyo, Buenos Aires #73

PIERSON, Christoffel (1631-1714) Dutch
£1042 $1646 €1500 Tavern scene with a man teasing a sleeping woman (26x36cm-10x14in) s.d.1680 i.verso. 2-Sep-3 Christie's, Amsterdam #122/R est:1500-2500

PIERSON, Jack (1960-) American
£7821 $14000 €11419 Around the well (244x185cm-96x73in) st.sig.i.d.2001 acrylic lacquer prov. 14-May-4 Phillips, New York #134/R est:15000-20000
Photographs
£2065 $3800 €3015 Gold suit (96x75cm-38x30in) c-print paperboard edition of 10 prov. 10-Jun-4 Phillips, New York #504/R est:3000-4000
£2667 $4773 €4000 Window (96x76cm-38x30in) d.95 num.7/10 photo. 12-May-4 Chochon-Barre & Allardi, Paris #50 est:1000-1500
£2700 $4509 €3942 Shells o rail, P-Town (96x74cm-38x29in) cibachrome print exec 1995 8 from edn of 10 prov. 21-Oct-3 Sotheby's, London #455/R est:2000-3000
Sculpture
£3800 $6346 €5548 Applause (28x64x17cm-11x25x7in) aluminium plexiglas lightbox edition of 35. 22-Oct-3 Christie's, London #177/R est:4000-6000
£22754 $38000 €33221 Frankie (99x254cm-39x100in) found metal plastic objects executed 1995. 14-Nov-3 Phillips, New York #110/R est:20000-30000
Works on paper
£21333 $38187 €32000 Jamais (35x27cm-14x11in) crayon photo sold with a sculpture. 12-May-4 Chochon-Barre & Allardi, Paris #51 est:500-600

PIET, Fernand (1869-1942) French
£537 $988 €800 Woman seated under a tree (31x20cm-12x8in) s.d.1905 board. 24-Mar-4 Joron-Derem, Paris #61
£1034 $1717 €1500 Mere, nounou et enfant au jardin (24x32cm-9x13in) studio st. cardboard. 2-Oct-3 Sotheby's, Paris #133/R
£1724 $2862 €2500 Mere et enfant au jardin (42x57cm-17x22in) studio st. cardboard. 2-Oct-3 Sotheby's, Paris #132/R

PIETERCELIE, Alfred (1879-1955) Belgian
£240 $400 €350 Poplar trees. s.d.1916 panel. 15-Nov-3 Harvey Clar, Oakland #1167
£307 $561 €460 Les immortelles (38x45cm-15x18in) s.d.1924. 7-Jun-4 Palais de Beaux Arts, Brussels #91
£385 $642 €550 La Senne a Ruisbroeck sous la neige (70x70cm-28x28in) s.d.1935. 13-Oct-3 Horta, Bruxelles #287
£507 $958 €750 Bouquet de fleurs (80x90cm-31x35in) s.d.1928. 17-Feb-4 Vanderkindere, Brussels #90
£733 $1342 €1100 Jardin au printemps (30x36cm-12x14in) s.d.1919 cardboard. 7-Jun-4 Palais de Beaux Arts, Brussels #282
£1000 $1810 €1500 Place de village au printemps (60x70cm-24x28in) s.d.1923. 30-Mar-4 Palais de Beaux Arts, Brussels #676 est:1500-2500

PIETERS, Dick (1941-) Dutch
£7246 $11884 €10000 Confrontation (13x12cm-5x5in) mono. panel three painted 1988 prov. 27-May-3 Sotheby's, Amsterdam #350/R est:6000-8000

PIETERS, Evert (1856-1932) Dutch
£245 $409 €350 Wooded landscape (78x49cm-31x19in) s. canvas on panel. 30-Jun-3 Sotheby's, Amsterdam #223/R
£420 $739 €613 Fishing boat at low tide (43x23cm-17x9in) s. board. 19-May-4 Christie's, Kensington #649/R
£556 $878 €800 Garden entrance (77x92cm-30x36in) s. canvas on board. 2-Sep-3 Christie's, Amsterdam #253
£1733 $3120 €2600 Shell fisher (50x36cm-20x14in) s. board. 20-Apr-4 Sotheby's, Amsterdam #120/R est:3000-5000
£1736 $2899 €2500 Happy mother (59x45cm-23x18in) board. 21-Oct-3 Sotheby's, Amsterdam #123/R est:3000-5000
£1884 $3202 €2750 Hunter in the woods (69x109cm-27x43in) s. 5-Nov-3 Vendue Huis, Gravenhage #210 est:2000-2500
£2098 $3503 €3000 The smoker (40x30cm-16x12in) s. panel. 30-Jun-3 Sotheby's, Amsterdam #86/R
£2800 $5180 €4088 Riding along the shore (35x28cm-14x11in) s. panel. 14-Jul-4 Sotheby's, Olympia #219/R est:2500-3500
£4491 $7500 €6557 Seated child peeling potatoes (61x51cm-24x20in) 17-Oct-3 Du Mouchelle, Detroit #2004/R est:5000-8000
£5208 $8854 €7500 Houseproud - caring for the crockery (93x61cm-37x24in) s. prov. 28-Oct-3 Christie's, Amsterdam #146/R est:8000-12000
£5208 $8698 €7500 Shellfisher on the beach (36x25cm-14x10in) s. panel. 21-Oct-3 Sotheby's, Amsterdam #101/R est:4000-6000
£6250 $10438 €9000 Children making flower crowns (40x60cm-16x24in) s. 21-Oct-3 Sotheby's, Amsterdam #106/R est:6000-8000
£6696 $11518 €9776 Domestic interior with children and mother at the table (66x51cm-26x20in) s. 2-Dec-3 Ritchie, Toronto #120/R est:6000-8000 (C.D 15000)
£8380 $15000 €12235 Maternal love (28x23cm-11x9in) s. prov. 6-May-4 Shannon's, Milford #105/R est:10000-15000

PIETERSZ, Pieters (1550-1611) Flemish
£9000 $16470 €13140 Last Supper (114x143cm-45x56in) panel prov. 8-Jul-4 Sotheby's, London #251/R est:10000-15000

PIETERSZEN, Abraham van der Wayen (1817-1880) Dutch
£8000 $14400 €12000 Dusk at the watermill in summer. Sportsmen on a frozen river at dusk (37x50cm-15x20in) one indis.sig.d.1869 one s.d.69 panel pair. 21-Apr-4 Christie's, Amsterdam #69/R est:12000-16000

PIETILA, Tuulikki (1917-) Finnish
£805 $1482 €1200 Landscape (35x40cm-14x16in) s.d.1953. 25-Mar-4 Hagelstam, Helsinki #832
Works on paper
£537 $999 €800 Cat (30x41cm-12x16in) s.d.1976 wash. 7-Mar-4 Bukowskis, Helsinki #424/R
£967 $1779 €1450 Fishermen (30x25cm-12x10in) s.d.1952 mixed media. 9-Jun-4 Bukowskis, Helsinki #520/R
£1133 $2085 €1700 View from Toledo (47x30cm-19x12in) s.i.d.1951 gouache. 9-Jun-4 Bukowskis, Helsinki #522/R est:250

PIETRO DA RIMINI (fl.c.1315-1335) Italian
£88889 $160000 €129778 Nativity (20x16cm-8x6in) tempera panel. 22-Jan-4 Sotheby's, New York #19/R est:140000-180000

PIETROSANTI, Gisella (20th C) Italian
£300 $510 €438 Bersaglio immobile (120x100cm-47x39in) s.i.d.6/2002 oil asphalt. 18-Nov-3 Bonhams, Knightsbridge #168

PIETTE, Ludovic (1826-1877) French
£1761 $3046 €2500 Personnage dans un verger (21x30cm-8x12in) s. panel. 14-Dec-3 Rabourdin & Choppin de Janvry, Paris #13/R est:2800-3000

Works on paper
£3901 $6319 €5500 Vue de Pontoise (26x52cm-10x20in) s. gouache. 24-May-3 Martinot & Savignat, Pontoise #173/R est:6000-7000

PIETZSCH, Richard (1872-1960) German
£417 $688 €600 Isar in flood (126x98cm-50x39in) s.d.1939 i. verso. 3-Jul-3 Neumeister, Munich #2893/R

PIGA, Bernard (1934-) French
£1333 $2440 €2000 La toilette (114x146cm-45x57in) s. 6-Jun-4 Anaf, Lyon #486/R est:2000-2500
Works on paper
£1000 $1790 €1500 Cavalier de manege (80x80cm-31x31in) mixed media. 16-May-4 Osenat, Fontainebleau #100/R est:1000-1500

PIGAGE, Werner von (1888-1959) German
£400 $724 €600 Meersburg on the Bodensee (80x71cm-31x28in) s.i.d. 2-Apr-4 Winterberg, Heidelberg #1497/R

PIGALLE (?) French
Sculpture
£3401 $6088 €5000 Amour jouant avec une colombe (44cm-17in) s. gilt brown pat bronze green marble socle style of Louis XVI. 16-Mar-4 Vanderkindere, Brussels #575/R est:1250-1750

PIGEM ROSET, Manel (1900-1960) British
£420 $701 €600 Paisaje (24x34cm-9x13in) s. panel. 24-Jun-3 Segre, Madrid #288/R

PIGEON, Maurice (1883-1944) French?
£1250 $2263 €1900 Maison fleurie (38x55cm-15x22in) s. i.verso. 19-Apr-4 Boscher, Cherbourg #750/R est:2000
Works on paper
£490 $842 €700 Lavoirs en bord de riviere (34x52cm-13x20in) s. pastel. 7-Dec-3 Livinec, Gaudcheau & Jezequel, Rennes #17
£1049 $1783 €1500 La Saire (49x64cm-19x25in) s. pastel. 24-Nov-3 Boscher, Cherbourg #734/R est:1500-1800
£1250 $2263 €1900 Lavoirs sur la Saire pres du Vast (34x52cm-13x20in) s. pastel. 19-Apr-4 Boscher, Cherbourg #751/R est:2000

PIGGOTT, Rosslynd (1958-) Australian
£537 $994 €784 Milk tears (40x61cm-16x24in) s.d.1994 i.verso linen. 15-Mar-4 Sotheby's, Melbourne #118 est:1500-2500 (A.D 1300)
£1545 $2425 €2240 Flow (121x76cm-48x30in) s.i.d.1991 verso oil gold leaf linen prov. 27-Aug-3 Christie's, Sydney #520/R est:5000-7000 (A.D 3800)
£1736 $3211 €2535 Two glasses and rain (91x66cm-36x26in) s.d.1995 i.verso linen on canvas prov. 15-Mar-4 Sotheby's, Melbourne #46/R est:2500-3500 (A.D 4200)
£1983 $3669 €2895 Bowl collecting rain (91x66cm-36x26in) s.i.d.1995 verso linen on canvas prov. 15-Mar-4 Sotheby's, Melbourne #40/R est:2500-3500 (A.D 4800)
£3926 $7262 €5732 Elongation I (60x213cm-24x84in) s.d.1989 i.verso linen on canvas prov. 15-Mar-4 Sotheby's, Melbourne #58/R est:6000-10000 (A.D 9500)
Works on paper
£351 $650 €512 High bed and empty pictures (75x56cm-30x22in) init.d.1995 i.verso W/C. 15-Mar-4 Sotheby's, Melbourne #59 est:1000-2000 (A.D 850)

PIGINO, Carlo (1943-) Italian
£268 $475 €400 Spring morning in Oropa (20x30cm-8x12in) s.i. cardboard on canvas. 1-May-4 Meeting Art, Vercelli #287
£268 $475 €400 Snowfall in Gressoney (50x60cm-20x24in) s.i. oil acrylic cardboard on canvas. 1-May-4 Meeting Art, Vercelli #398

PIGNATELLI, Ercole (1935-) Italian
£352 $616 €500 Fragments. Untitled (28x58cm-11x23in) s. s.i.verso acrylic two. 16-Dec-3 Finarte Semenzato, Milan #336/R
£367 $675 €550 Untitled (73x60cm-29x24in) s.d.1961 verso. 12-Jun-4 Meeting Art, Vercelli #815/R
£367 $675 €550 Untitled (73x60cm-29x24in) s.d.1961. 12-Jun-4 Meeting Art, Vercelli #810
£680 $1218 €1000 Villa and oranges. Woman with flowers (60x50cm-24x20in) s.i.d.1966 pair. 16-Mar-4 Finarte Semenzato, Milan #206/R
£733 $1349 €1100 Figure at balcony (50x60cm-20x24in) s. s.i.d.1961 verso. 12-Jun-4 Meeting Art, Vercelli #464/R
£1133 $2085 €1700 Solarium (80x100cm-31x39in) s. painted 1980. 8-Jun-4 Finarte Semenzato, Milan #217/R est:800-1000
£1267 $2331 €1900 Vase with nude and lemon tree (100x81cm-39x32in) s. painted 1982 exhib. 8-Jun-4 Finarte Semenzato, Milan #216/R est:800-1000
£1408 $2465 €2000 Composition (90x75cm-35x30in) s. board. 16-Dec-3 Finarte Semenzato, Milan #330/R est:1800-2200
£1409 $2607 €2100 Untitled (65x50cm-26x20in) s. canvas on masonite. 13-Mar-4 Meeting Art, Vercelli #216 est:500
£1467 $2699 €2200 Untitled (130x161cm-51x63in) s. 12-Jun-4 Meeting Art, Vercelli #86/R est:2000
£1931 $3225 €2800 Factory (65x50cm-26x20in) s.s.d.1980 verso. 13-Nov-3 Finarte Semenzato, Rome #248/R est:2400-2800
£2000 $3600 €3000 Landscape (50x64cm-20x25in) s. s.i.d.1988 verso. 22-Apr-4 Finarte Semenzato, Rome #187/R est:3000-3500
£2113 $3507 €3000 Still life (60x33cm-24x13in) s.d.1955. 11-Jun-3 Finarte Semenzato, Milan #545/R
£4755 $8084 €6800 Mirage (68x98cm-27x39in) s. s.i.verso. 28-Nov-3 Farsetti, Prato #58/R est:4600-5000
Works on paper
£517 $864 €750 Washing bridge (81x100cm-32x39in) s.d.1964 verso mixed media on canvas. 13-Nov-3 Galleria Pace, Milan #12/R
£517 $864 €750 Woman at window (50x40cm-20x16in) s.d.1958 mixed media on canvas. 13-Nov-3 Galleria Pace, Milan #59/R
£563 $986 €800 Sophisticated (89x116cm-35x46in) s.d.1965 s.i.d.verso. 16-Dec-3 Finarte Semenzato, Milan #328
£667 $1227 €1000 Solarium (30x30cm-12x12in) s. s.i.verso mixed media card. 10-Jun-4 Galleria Pace, Milan #3/R

PIGNATELLI, Luca (1962-) Italian
£2667 $4907 €4000 Little Aphrodites (43x31cm-17x12in) s.i.d.2001 verso. 8-Jun-4 Finarte Semenzato, Milan #460/R est:3500-4500
£2817 $4930 €4000 Train (50x40cm-20x16in) s.d.1999 verso. 16-Dec-3 Finarte Semenzato, Milan #226/R est:2300-2700
£2819 $5215 €4200 Plane and mountains (40x60cm-16x24in) s.i.d.2003 verso. 11-Mar-4 Galleria Pace, Milan #105/R est:4600-6000
£3356 $6208 €5000 New York (43x31cm-17x12in) s.i.d.2001 verso. 13-Mar-4 Meeting Art, Vercelli #252 est:2000
£3401 $6088 €5000 Little train (40x60cm-16x24in) s.i.d.2002 verso. 16-Mar-4 Finarte Semenzato, Milan #382/R est:5000
£3401 $6088 €5000 Aphrodites (43x31cm-17x12in) s.i.d.2002 verso. 16-Mar-4 Finarte Semenzato, Milan #383/R est:4500
£3741 $6697 €5500 New york, chimneys (60x40cm-24x16in) s.i.d.2002 verso. 16-Mar-4 Finarte Semenzato, Milan #381/R est:5000
£6690 $11708 €9500 New York (80x60cm-31x24in) s.i.d.2003 enamel acrylic. 16-Dec-3 Finarte Semenzato, Milan #256/R est:4500-5500
£7042 $12324 €10000 Horse (171x146cm-67x57in) s.i.d.2000 verso. 16-Dec-3 Finarte Semenzato, Milan #257/R est:9200
£9396 $16819 €14000 Untitled (190x100cm-75x39in) s.d.1999 acrylic. 28-May-4 Farsetti, Prato #320/R est:14000-16000
Works on paper
£1000 $1840 €1500 Mountains (31x43cm-12x17in) s.d.2002 mixed media paper on canvas. 12-Jun-4 Meeting Art, Vercelli #616/R est:1500
£1014 $1784 €1500 Milan, Sant'Ambrogio (31x43cm-12x17in) s.d.2002 verso mixed media paper on canvas. 22-May-4 Galleria Pananti, Florence #357/R est:1500-2000
£1014 $1784 €1500 Campo dei Miracoli (31x43cm-12x17in) s.d.2002 verso mixed media. 22-May-4 Galleria Pananti, Florence #359/R est:1500-2000
£1133 $2085 €1700 Wood (31x43cm-12x17in) s.i.d.2000 verso mixed media paper on canvas exhib.lit. 12-Jun-4 Meeting Art, Vercelli #796/R est:1500
£1200 $2208 €1800 New York (43x31cm-17x12in) s.i.d.2001 verso mixed media paper on canvas. 8-Jun-4 Finarte Semenzato, Milan #218/R est:1800-2000
£1267 $2331 €1900 New York (31x43cm-12x17in) s.i.verso mixed media paper on canvas exec.2000. 12-Jun-4 Meeting Art, Vercelli #248/R est:1500
£1275 $2283 €1900 Untitled (31x43cm-12x17in) s.i.d.2001 mixed media paper on canvas. 30-May-4 Meeting Art, Vercelli #15 est:1500
£1745 $3228 €2600 Rome 2001 (31x43cm-12x17in) s.i.verso mixed media paper on canvas painted 2000 lit. 13-Mar-4 Meeting Art, Vercelli #458 est:1500
£4014 $6663 €5700 Ricognizione (40x60cm-16x24in) s.i.d.2002 mixed media on hessian. 14-Jun-3 Meeting Art, Vercelli #302/R est:3000

PIGNOLAT, Pierre (1838-1913) Swiss
£2294 $3830 €3326 Swamp landscape (30x38cm-12x15in) board exhib. 19-Jun-3 Kornfeld, Bern #884/R est:2500 (S.FR 5000)

PIGNON, Edouard (1905-1993) French
£824 $1500 €1203 Rooster (41x33cm-16x13in) s.d.58. 29-Jun-4 Sotheby's, New York #345/R est:2500-3500
£1528 $2551 €2200 Bateaux a Ostende (26x35cm-10x14in) s.d.47 prov. 21-Oct-3 Artcurial Briest, Paris #637/R est:1500-2000
£1776 $3268 €2700 Bataille (38x60cm-15x24in) s.d.1963 prov. 27-Jun-4 Versailles Encheres #118/R est:3000-3500
£2000 $3680 €2920 Untitled (48x65cm-19x26in) s.d.61. 24-Jun-4 Sotheby's, Olympia #548/R est:2000-3000
£2649 $4821 €4000 Untitled (64x80cm-25x31in) s.d.1952. 15-Jun-4 Rossini, Paris #185/R est:4000-5000
£3020 $5618 €4500 La bataille bleue (50x61cm-20x24in) s.d.63. 3-Mar-4 Artcurial Briest, Paris #509/R est:4000-5000
£3222 $5702 €4800 Combat de coqs multicolores (60x81cm-24x32in) s.d.68 i.verso. 28-Apr-4 Artcurial Briest, Paris #292/R est:5000-7000
£4167 $6583 €6000 Petit bleu de la mer (60x81cm-24x32in) s.d.1980 prov. 27-Apr-3 Versailles Encheres #65
£6993 $12028 €10000 Les oliviers brules (130x195cm-51x77in) s.d.1957 prov.exhib. 3-Dec-3 Fraysse & Associes, Paris #105/R est:10000-12000
£7237 $13316 €11000 Combat de coqs (140x195cm-55x77in) s.d.1959 prov. 27-Jun-4 Versailles Encheres #115/R est:15000-18000
£12667 $23433 €19000 Rendez-vous d'Antibes (144x300cm-57x118in) s.d.82 paper on canvas exhib.lit. 18-Jul-4 Sotheby's, Paris #276/R est:15000-20000
£14706 $25000 €21471 Femme assise (116x89cm-46x35in) s.d.45 prov.exhib. 6-Nov-3 Sotheby's, New York #280/R est:30000-40000
Works on paper
£278 $439 €400 Untitled (30x40cm-12x16in) W/C. 6-Sep-3 Meeting Art, Vercelli #525
£397 $727 €600 Puvre peintre salue le docteur (36x24cm-14x9in) i. wax crayons wash. 7-Apr-4 Piasa, Paris #221
£403 $749 €600 Paysage du Midi (31x41cm-12x16in) s.d.35 W/C. 2-Mar-4 Artcurial Briest, Paris #82
£530 $970 €800 Nu au parasol rouge (36x45cm-14x18in) s.d.86 gouache. 7-Apr-4 Piasa, Paris #220
£544 $974 €800 Nu (32x41cm-13x16in) s.d.72 pencil. 16-Mar-4 Finarte Semenzato, Milan #207/R
£604 $1105 €900 Tete de guerrier (56x76cm-22x30in) s.d.68 W/C. 7-Jul-4 Artcurial Briest, Paris #61
£959 $1630 €1400 Combat de coqs (35x52cm-14x20in) s. pastel crayon exec.1961. 9-Nov-3 Eric Pillon, Calais #270/R
£1083 $1993 €1581 La voile rose (54x78cm-21x31in) s.d.48 W/C pencil study. 29-Mar-4 Rasmussen, Copenhagen #12/R est:10000-12000 (D.KR 12000)
£1622 $3000 €2368 Shoe Shop (48x63cm-19x25in) s.d.55 ink gouache. 12-Feb-4 Sotheby's, New York #55/R est:1500-2000
£1622 $3000 €2368 Harvest (48x63cm-19x25in) s.d.52 W/C. 12-Feb-4 Sotheby's, New York #54/R est:1500-2000
£1842 $3389 €2800 Ostende, La Barque Noire (40x60cm-16x24in) s.d.1948 W/C exhib. 28-Jun-4 Joron-Derem, Paris #170 est:2800-3000
£1879 $3458 €2800 Ostende, la barque noire (40x60cm-16x24in) s.d.1948 W/C exhib. 24-Mar-4 Joron-Derem, Paris #161 est:3000-3500

PIGNONI, Simone (1614-1698) Italian
£12222 $22000 €17844 Laban searching for the households idols (145x129cm-57x51in) prov. 22-Jan-4 Sotheby's, New York #43/R est:20000-30000
£56000 $100800 €81760 Tarquin and Lucretia (175x147cm-69x58in) i.stretcher. 22-Apr-4 Sotheby's, London #56/R est:30000-40000

PIGNONI, Simone (attrib) (1614-1698) Italian
£6250 $11500 €9500 Magdalene (78x63cm-31x25in) 22-Jun-4 Finarte Semenzato, Rome #295/R est:10000-12000
£30172 $55517 €44051 Susannah bathing (166x220cm-65x87in) 26-Mar-4 Koller, Zurich #3048/R est:20000-30000 (S.FR 70000)

PIGNONI, Simone and SCACCIATI, Andrea (17th C) Italian
£5000 $9000 €7300 Abduction of Proserpine (98x138cm-39x54in) 23-Jan-4 Christie's, Rockefeller NY #127/R est:10000-15000

PIGNOTTI, Lamberto (20th C) Italian
Works on paper
£979 $1664 €1400 Wild rage town (69x50cm-27x20in) s.i.d.1964 collage cardboard. 28-Nov-3 Farsetti, Prato #16

PIGOT, R St Leger (fl.1864-1871) British
£260 $465 €380 Game of draughts (29x34cm-11x13in) s.d.64. 11-May-4 Bonhams, Knightsbridge #220/R

PIGOTT, Charles (1863-c.1940) British
Works on paper
£300 $477 €435 Sheep grazing on the cliff top with Whitby beyond (25x35cm-10x14in) s. W/C. 9-Sep-3 David Duggleby, Scarborough #227
£310 $586 €453 Dore moor, Sheffield, with sheep (23x33cm-9x13in) s. 19-Feb-4 Grant, Worcester #393
£560 $963 €818 Edge of Eyam Moor. Burbage brook with sheep and hills (29x19cm-11x7in) s. W/C pair. 5-Dec-3 ELR Auctions, Sheffield #681/R
£1550 $2635 €2263 Sheep on Dore Moor (61x91cm-24x36in) s. W/C. 28-Oct-3 Lawrences, Bletchingley #1720

PIGOTT, Walter Henry (c.1810-1901) British
Works on paper
£280 $468 €409 Sheep and cattle on a hillside (33x48cm-13x19in) s.d.77 W/C. 9-Jul-3 Peter Wilson, Nantwich #70
£290 $499 €423 Padley wood, Grindleford. with a man riding a horse (51x34cm-20x13in) s.d.June 15 77 W/C. 5-Dec-3 ELR Auctions, Sheffield #683/R
£360 $619 €526 Sunset with sheep on the Derbyshire hills (27x40cm-11x16in) s.d.69 W/C. 5-Dec-3 ELR Auctions, Sheffield #676/R
£1400 $2254 €2030 Shepherd with sheep in landscape (48x84cm-19x33in) s.d.82 W/C. 15-Aug-3 Keys, Aylsham #539 est:1400-1800

PIGUENIT, William Charles (1836-1914) Australian
£1943 $3129 €2837 River Ouse, Tasmania (14x19cm-6x7in) s.d.1863 board prov. 25-Aug-3 Sotheby's, Paddington #483/R est:4000-6000 (A.D 4800)
£2966 $5042 €4330 Aboriginal fisheries - Barwon River, Brewarina (25x45cm-10x18in) s. bears i.verso painted c.1906 prov. 24-Nov-3 Sotheby's, Melbourne #254/R est:4000-6000 (A.D 7000)
£7724 $12126 €11200 Milking time, droving cattle (23x44cm-9x17in) s. board prov. 26-Aug-3 Christie's, Sydney #152/R est:15000-20000 (A.D 19000)
£9717 $15644 €14187 Derwent at sunrise from the Eastern side, Tasmania (60x90cm-24x35in) s.d.1902. 25-Aug-3 Sotheby's, Paddington #219/R est:25000-35000 (A.D 24000)
£20243 $32591 €29555 Northern lagoon New South Wales (76x128cm 30x50in) s. prov.exhib.lit. 25-Aug-3 Sotheby's, Paddington #223/R est:50000-70000 (A.D 50000)
Works on paper
£2282 $3811 €3423 Our camp on the snowy Riber, N S Wales (21x35cm-8x14in) s.i. W/C prov. 27-Oct-3 Goodman, Sydney #125/R est:3000-5000 (A.D 5500)

PIGUET, Gustave (1909-1976) Austrian
Sculpture
£3947 $7263 €5763 Runner (184x130cm-72x51in) s. st.f.Pastori natural pat bronze sold with base prov. 23-Jun-4 Koller, Zurich #3152/R est:4500-6000 (S.FR 9000)

PIGUET, Jean Louis (1944-) Swiss
£388 $694 €566 Landscape in southern France (40x34cm-16x13in) s.d.83 panel. 12-May-4 Dobiaschofsky, Bern #871/R (S.FR 900)
£733 $1312 €1070 Summer lily pond (96x145cm-38x57in) s.d.86. 12-May-4 Dobiaschofsky, Bern #870/R est:1600 (S.FR 1700)
£1121 $2006 €1637 View of harbour through window (110x80cm-43x31in) s.d.91. 14-May-4 Dobiaschofsky, Bern #282/R est:1800 (S.FR 2600)

PIGUET, Rodolphe (1840-1915) Swiss
£642 $1072 €931 Le petit chemin (24x18cm-9x7in) s. panel prov. 21-Jun-3 Galerie du Rhone, Sion #405 est:900-1200 (S.FR 1400)

PIGUET, Timothee (1840-1904) Swiss
£371 $676 €542 Lake Geneva (27x34cm-11x13in) s. cardboard. 16-Jun-4 Fischer, Luzern #2310 (S.FR 850)

PIKE, Jimmy (1940-) Australian
£2157 $3861 €3149 Beela (51x76cm-20x30in) oil stick crayon pencil exec 1983 prov. 25-May-4 Lawson Menzies, Sydney #13/R est:6000-8000 (A.D 5500)
Works on paper
£1328 $2484 €1992 Kurrkuminti-kurruminti (51x61cm-20x24in) s.i.verso synthetic polymer paint canvas exec.c.1990 prov. 26-Jul-4 Sotheby's, Melbourne #252/R est:3000-5000 (A.D 3400)
£1484 $2776 €2226 Paparta the Mirage Man (120x90cm-47x35in) s.i.d.1990 verso synthetic polymer canvas prov. 21-Jul-4 Shapiro, Sydney #64/R est:4000-6000 (A.D 3800)
£2745 $4914 €4008 Cityscape (55x75cm-22x30in) pen paper exec 1981 exhib. 25-May-4 Lawson Menzies, Sydney #10/R est:4000-6000 (A.D 7000)

PIKE, Leonard W (1887-1959) British
£600 $1020 €876 View of Worcester Cathedral on a Sunny day (51x43cm-20x17in) s.d. 30-Oct-3 Grant, Worcester #552/R

PIKE, Sidney (fl.1880-1901) British
£420 $777 €613 Sheep on a coastal path (30x50cm-12x20in) s. 13-Jan-4 Bonhams, Knightsbridge #138/R
£650 $1203 €949 Coastal landscapes at low tide (15x46cm-6x18in) s.d.01 pair. 9-Mar-4 Gorringes, Lewes #2139
£1398 $2600 €2041 Highland cattle by the shore (23x30cm-9x12in) s.d.1906 board. 6-Mar-4 North East Auctions, Portsmouth #1130/R
£2100 $3759 €3066 River landscapes with cattle and harvesters (19x38cm-7x15in) s. pair. 17-May-4 David Duggleby, Scarborough #600/R est:1500-2000
£2600 $4420 €3796 Lancing Old Mill. Whiff from the sea (30x51cm-12x20in) s.d.82 two. 30-Oct-3 Duke & Son, Dorchester #222/R est:800-1600

PIKE, William H (1846-1908) British
£7500 $12525 €10950 Polperro Harbour (102x153cm-40x60in) s.d.1888. 27-Oct-3 Robin Fenner, Tavistock #1021/R est:10000-15000
Works on paper
£400 $652 €584 Coastal town (29x48cm-11x19in) s.d.1874 W/C htd white. 25-Sep-3 Mellors & Kirk, Nottingham #720/R
£4000 $7400 €5840 Charlestown Harbour, Cornwall (53x91cm-21x36in) s.d.1883 W/C. 10-Feb-4 David Lay, Penzance #247/R est:4000-5000

PIKELNY, Robert (1904-) Polish
£265 $485 €400 Paysage (81x66cm-32x26in) s. isorel exhib. 7-Apr-4 Piasa, Paris #257

PIKESLEY, Richard (1951-) British
£260 $458 €380 Venetian cafe (16x29cm-6x11in) s. board. 18-May-4 Woolley & Wallis, Salisbury #12/R
£320 $563 €467 Window-shoppers, Venice (24x35cm-9x14in) s. board. 18-May-4 Woolley & Wallis, Salisbury #25/R
£320 $563 €467 Feeding waterfowl, Slimbridge (15x20cm-6x8in) s. board. 18-May-4 Woolley & Wallis, Salisbury #32/R
£320 $563 €467 Villandry (40x56cm-16x22in) s. 18-May-4 Woolley & Wallis, Salisbury #50/R
£420 $739 €613 Fishing boats and morning light (15x35cm-6x14in) s. board. 18-May-4 Woolley & Wallis, Salisbury #73/R
£500 $880 €730 Evening harbour, West Bay (21x28cm-8x11in) s. board. 18-May-4 Woolley & Wallis, Salisbury #27/R
£540 $950 €788 Lilies at Marrowbone (63x76cm-25x30in) s. 18-May-4 Woolley & Wallis, Salisbury #51/R
£560 $986 €818 Morning coffee, Madeira (25x32cm-10x13in) s. board. 18-May-4 Woolley & Wallis, Salisbury #22/R
£620 $1128 €905 Lyme Regis (25x30cm-10x12in) s. board. 21-Jun-4 Bonhams, Bath #413
£720 $1267 €1051 Lyme Regis (45x60cm-18x24in) s. 19-May-4 Sotheby's, Olympia #213/R
£740 $1302 €1080 Cyclist, Topsham Quay (40x45cm-16x18in) s. 18-May-4 Woolley & Wallis, Salisbury #89/R
£760 $1338 €1110 Night reflections (76x91cm-30x36in) s. 18-May-4 Woolley & Wallis, Salisbury #88/R
£820 $1443 €1197 Sky light and lamp light, West Bay harbour (51x91cm-20x36in) s. 18-May-4 Woolley & Wallis, Salisbury #71/R
£880 $1549 €1285 Under the trees, Venice (30x30cm-12x12in) s. 18-May-4 Woolley & Wallis, Salisbury #94/R
£880 $1602 €1285 West Bay, Dorset (60x75cm-24x30in) s. 21-Jun-4 Bonhams, Bath #414/R
£900 $1440 €1314 Seaside bathers (29x34cm-11x13in) s. 17-Sep-3 Bonhams, Brooks & Langlois, Jersey #63/R
£980 $1725 €1431 Flower-sellers and passers-by, Funchal (44x60cm-17x24in) s. prov. 18-May-4 Woolley & Wallis, Salisbury #58/R
£980 $1725 €1431 Sheep on the hill, Eggadon (73x61cm-29x24in) s. 18-May-4 Woolley & Wallis, Salisbury #127/R
£1050 $1848 €1533 Opium poppies and mirror (35x30cm-14x12in) s. board. 18-May-4 Woolley & Wallis, Salisbury #54/R est:400-600
£1250 $2200 €1825 Fish and chips twice, West Bay (51x86cm-20x34in) s. 18-May-4 Woolley & Wallis, Salisbury #72/R est:600-800
£1550 $2728 €2263 Piazetta and steamer, Venice (45x51cm-18x20in) s. prov. 18-May-4 Woolley & Wallis, Salisbury #79/R est:600-800
£1550 $2728 €2263 The white hat (59x87cm-23x34in) s. 18-May-4 Woolley & Wallis, Salisbury #95/R est:2000-3000
£1600 $2816 €2336 Lido and Campari (40x56cm-16x22in) s. 18-May-4 Woolley & Wallis, Salisbury #57/R est:600-800
£1900 $3344 €2774 Topsham Quay (76x91cm-30x36in) s. 18-May-4 Woolley & Wallis, Salisbury #93/R est:1500-2500
£4000 $7040 €5840 Evening tide (91x91cm-36x36in) 18-May-4 Woolley & Wallis, Salisbury #70/R est:1500-2500
Works on paper
£520 $915 €759 Font and pilgrims, Wells Cathedral (28x37cm-11x15in) s. W/C. 18-May-4 Woolley & Wallis, Salisbury #279/R

PILAEV, Porfiri Egorovich (1873-1911) Russian
£18000 $30600 €26280 Feeding the pigeons (75x55cm-30x22in) s.d.1906. 19-Nov-3 Sotheby's, London #11/R est:7000-9000

PILET, Léon (1839-1916) French
Sculpture
£1342 $2483 €2000 Puss in boots (68x29cm-27x11in) s. brown pat bronze. 13-Mar-4 De Vuyst, Lokeren #261/R est:2000-2600

PILICHOWSKI, Leopold (c.1864-1934) Polish
Works on paper
£272 $500 €397 Portrait of a man wearing a black cap (25x20cm-10x8in) pastel. 9-Jun-4 Alderfer's, Hatfield #336/R

PILKINGTON, George W (1879-1958) South African
£756 $1369 €1104 Farmhouse and windmill in an extensive landscape (29x39cm-11x15in) s. board. 30-Mar-4 Stephan Welz, Johannesburg #196 est:1400-1800 (SA.R 9000)

PILLEMENT, Jean (1728-1808) French
£7292 $12031 €10500 Le repos des bergers (52x66cm-20x26in) oval. 1-Jul-3 Lemoine & Ferrando, Paris #41/R est:12000-15000
£17606 $30810 €25000 Portrait de dos (25x17cm-10x7in) mono.d. paper exhib. 17-Dec-3 Piasa, Paris #93/R est:6000-8000
£32895 $60526 €50000 La halte des bergers au bord d'une riviere. Les blanchisseuses (57x79cm-22x31in) pair. 23-Jun-4 Millon & Associes, Paris #22/R est:50000-80000
£35462 $59221 €50000 Paysage Portuguais (71x97cm-28x38in) s. 17-Oct-3 Tajan, Paris #101/R est:35000-40000
Works on paper
£306 $548 €450 Trois etudes de personnages de dos. Etudes de personnages (5x10cm-2x4in) W/C pen black ink double-sided. 19-Mar-4 Piasa, Paris #55
£367 $656 €550 Paysage avec maison et deux figures (11x16cm-4x6in) chk. 11-May-4 Christie's, Paris #131/R
£616 $1048 €900 Couple de bergers (17x25cm-7x10in) s. crayon prov. 6-Nov-3 Tajan, Paris #79
£616 $1048 €900 Paysans au bord de torrent (18x28cm-7x11in) s. crayon prov. 6-Nov-3 Tajan, Paris #77
£685 $1164 €1000 Vue de village anime (15cm-6in circular) mono. crayon stump prov. 6-Nov-3 Tajan, Paris #98
£750 $1388 €1095 River landscape with figures loading a boat (185x285cm-73x112in) s.d.1792 black chk sold with a companion. 9-Mar-4 Bonhams, Knightsbridge #24/R
£822 $1397 €1200 Tour (11x28cm-4x11in) s.d.1792 crayon prov. 6-Nov-3 Tajan, Paris #80
£959 $1631 €1400 Couple de bergers au repos (17x24cm-7x9in) s. crayon prov. 6-Nov-3 Tajan, Paris #78
£959 $1631 €1400 Lavandieres (14x20cm-6x8in) s.d.1792 crayon prov. 6-Nov-3 Tajan, Paris #99
£993 $1688 €1450 Figures dans un paysage (16x23cm-6x9in) s.d.1791 pierre noire. 5-Nov-3 Beaussant & Lefèvre, Paris #10/R
£1096 $1863 €1600 Paysages animes (4x21cm-2x8in) i. crayon wash pair. 6-Nov-3 Tajan, Paris #81
£1233 $2096 €1800 Bergers dans paysage (14x20cm-6x8in) s.d.1792 crayon prov. 6-Nov-3 Tajan, Paris #102
£1370 $2329 €2000 Bergers gardant troupeau (23x39cm-9x15in) i.d.1804 crayon chk prov. 6-Nov-3 Tajan, Paris #84/R
£1507 $2561 €2200 Pecheurs et bergers (17x26cm-7x10in) s.d.1792 crayon prov. 6-Nov-3 Tajan, Paris #83/R
£1712 $2911 €2500 Chaumiere et pecheurs (15x22cm-6x9in) crayon stump prov. 6-Nov-3 Tajan, Paris #76/R
£1712 $2911 €2500 Pont dans un paysage anime (18x28cm-7x11in) s.d.1792 crayon prov. 6-Nov-3 Tajan, Paris #85/R
£1712 $2911 €2500 Pecheurs au bord de torrent (18x28cm-7x11in) s.d.1792 crayon prov. 6-Nov-3 Tajan, Paris #95/R
£1810 $3241 €2643 Aracadian landscape (15x20cm-6x8in) s.d.1789 wash silver pen. 13-May-4 Stuker, Bern #9190/R est:2500-3500 (S.FR 4200)
£1983 $3549 €2895 Arcadian landscape (16x21cm-6x8in) s.d.1789 wash silver pen. 13-May-4 Stuker, Bern #9191/R est:2500-3500 (S.FR 4600)
£2128 $3553 €3000 Paysage de campagne anime (48x59cm-19x23in) s.d.1804 pastel gouache en grisaille. 19-Oct-3 Anaf, Lyon #243/R est:3000-4000
£2368 $4358 €3600 Paysage de riviere au Portugal (29x37cm-11x15in) s. pastel. 25-Jun-4 Rossini, Paris #17/R est:4000-5000
£2740 $4657 €4000 Bergers sur pont (18x28cm-7x11in) s.d.1792 crayon stump prov. 6-Nov-3 Tajan, Paris #82/R
£7222 $13000 €10544 Landscape with a river and travelers (21x35cm-8x14in) s.d.1779 pastel. 21-Jan-4 Sotheby's, New York #115/R est:4500-6000
£18421 $33895 €28000 Figures sur quai au bord de la mer apres la tempete (60x90cm-24x35in) s.d.1782 gouache. 23-Jun-4 Sotheby's, Paris #22/R est:6000-8000

PILLEMENT, Jean (attrib) (1728-1808) French
£9333 $16707 €14000 Chinoiseries (116x52cm-46x20in) triptych. 11-May-4 Christie's, Paris #190/R est:8000-10000
£10526 $19368 €16000 Deux voyageurs dans un paysage (65x88cm-26x35in) 25-Jun-4 Piasa, Paris #51/R est:12000-15000
£24725 $45000 €36099 Chinoiserie procession of figures riding on elephants with temple beyond (70x84cm-28x33in) en verdaille. 17-Jun-4 Christie's, Rockefeller NY #49/R est:40000-60000
Works on paper
£1528 $2521 €2200 Landscape capricci (7x10cm-3x4in) i. gouache three. 3-Jul-3 Van Ham, Cologne #1007/R est:3000
£2115 $3595 €3088 Les pecheurs au bord du torrent (32x45cm-13x18in) i. verso gouache. 5-Nov-3 Dobiaschofsky, Bern #867/R est:6500 (S.FR 4800)

PILLET, Edgar (1912-1996) French
£867 $1551 €1300 Zanzi (130x81cm-51x32in) s. i.verso. 15-May-4 De Vuyst, Lokeren #252/R
£1056 $1827 €1500 Regardee a deux fois (81x60cm-32x24in) s. s.i.d.1951 verso prov. 14-Dec-3 Versailles Encheres #18 est:1500-1800
£1399 $2336 €2000 Eclipse (49x95cm-19x37in) s.d.1954. 29-Jun-3 Versailles Encheres #33/R

PILLHOFER, Josef (1921-) Austrian
Sculpture
£14094 $24946 €21000 Lugalesi (170cm-67in) mono. mono.i. pat.bronze. 28-Apr-4 Wiener Kunst Auktionen, Vienna #227/R est:15000-30000
£15278 $25972 €22000 Lugalesi (170cm-67in) mono.i. pat.bronze. 28-Oct-3 Wiener Kunst Auktionen, Vienna #234/R est:25000-45000
Works on paper
£306 $557 €450 Sculpture (50x32cm-20x13in) s.d.69 chl. 9-Feb-4 Dorotheum, Vienna #156

PILLOT, Lucien (19th C) French
£397 $723 €600 Arbres en automne (33x46cm-13x18in) s. masonite. 19-Jun-4 Gerard, Besancon #100

PILNY, Otto (1866-1936) Swiss
£786 $1431 €1148 Evening on the Nile (35x25cm-14x10in) s.i. 16-Jun-4 Fischer, Luzern #2311/R (S.FR 1800)
£1200 $2184 €1752 Flamingo Lake (60x100cm-24x39in) s.d.1910. 16-Jun-4 Christie's, Kensington #72/R est:1500-2000
£1810 $2896 €2643 Tented camp in Nile delta (54x73cm-21x29in) s.d.1902. 16-Sep-3 Philippe Schuler, Zurich #3249/R est:4000-5000 (S.FR 4000)
£2371 $4244 €3462 Arabian trader with naked female slave (66x57cm-26x22in) s. 12-May-4 Dobiaschofsky, Bern #872/R est:5000 (S.FR 5500)
£3000 $5160 €4380 At the oasis. At prayer (48x92cm-19x36in) s. one d.1920 pair. 4-Dec-3 Christie's, Kensington #232/R est:4000-6000
£4348 $7957 €6348 Village by an oasis (60x73cm-24x29in) s. 4-Jun-4 Zofingen, Switzerland #2917/R est:4000 (S.FR 10000)
£10000 $16700 €14600 Desert dance (75x94cm-30x37in) s.d.1908 prov. 14-Oct-3 Sotheby's, London #53/R est:12000-18000
£17500 $31850 €25550 Desert dance (121x180cm-48x71in) s.i. 17-Jun-4 Christie's, London #134/R est:20000-30000

PILOT, Robert Wakeham (1898-1967) Canadian
£2846 $5093 €4155 Quebec from Levis (18x24cm-7x9in) s.d.1928 panel. 31-May-4 Sotheby's, Toronto #101/R est:4000-6000 (C.D 7000)
£3049 $5457 €4452 View at Grand Manan Island (32x42cm-13x17in) s.d.35 panel prov. 31-May-4 Sotheby's, Toronto #55/R est:8000-12000 (C.D 7500)
£3153 $5360 €4603 Stream in winter (20x26cm-8x10in) s.d.1945 panel prov. 27-Nov-3 Heffel, Vancouver #101/R est:5000-7000 (C.D 7000)
£4065 $7276 €5935 Dufferin terrace (20x26cm-8x10in) s. panel prov. 31-May-4 Sotheby's, Toronto #100/R est:8000-10000 (C.D 10000)
£4955 $8423 €7234 Tuna Wharf, Wedgeport, NS (56x71cm-22x28in) s. 18-Nov-3 Sotheby's, Toronto #154/R est:12000-15000 (C.D 11000)
£6048 $11129 €8830 Summer, Venice (45x61cm-18x24in) s. s.i.d.57 prov. 9-Jun-4 Walker's, Ottawa #104/R est:15000-20000 (C.D 15000)
£6400 $11712 €9344 Quebec at nightfall (20x26cm-8x10in) s. board painted 1957 prov. 1-Jun-4 Joyner Waddington, Toronto #92/R est:12000-15000 (C.D 16000)
£8130 $14553 €11870 Winter in the country (36x46cm-14x18in) s. prov. 31-May-4 Sotheby's, Toronto #152/R est:18000-22000 (C.D 20000)
£10163 $18191 €14838 Melting ice, Lac Superieur (54x71cm-21x28in) s. prov.exhib. 31-May-4 Sotheby's, Toronto #138/R est:30000-40000 (C.D 25000)
£10400 $19032 €15184 Red Sleigh, winter (45x55cm-18x22in) s. 1-Jun-4 Joyner Waddington, Toronto #60/R est:25000-30000 (C.D 26000)
£14640 $24887 €21374 Quebec from Levis (48x61cm-19x24in) s. prov.lit. 18-Nov-3 Sotheby's, Toronto #45/R est:30000-40000 (C.D 32500)
£15179 $26107 €22161 Winter, Laurentians (40x50cm-16x20in) s. 2-Dec-3 Joyner Waddington, Toronto #20/R est:20000-25000 (C.D 34000)
£17600 $32208 €25696 Distant view of Baie St Paul (60x80cm-24x31in) s. prov. 1-Jun-4 Joyner Waddington, Toronto #78/R est:50000-60000 (C.D 44000)
£40000 $73200 €58400 Quebec in Winter (70x90cm-28x35in) s. painted c.1938 prov.lit. 1-Jun-4 Joyner Waddington, Toronto #58/R est:50000-70000 (C.D 100000)

PILOTY, Karl Theodor von (1824-1886) German
£2215 $3964 €3300 Head study of Metellus Cimber (46x36cm-18x14in) s.i. 25-May-4 Karl & Faber, Munich #120/R est:2000
Works on paper
£738 $1321 €1100 Wallenstein's train to Eger (16x22cm-6x9in) pencil wash lit. 25-May-4 Karl & Faber, Munich #121
£872 $1562 €1300 Composition sketches (50x54cm-20x21in) pencil wash lit.exhib. 25-May-4 Karl & Faber, Munich #122/R

PILS, Isidore (1813-1875) French
£2763 $5084 €4200 Etude de tete d'arabe (23x18cm-9x7in) s. 22-Jun-4 Ribeyre & Baron, Paris #40/R est:3000-4000
£2980 $5424 €4500 Portrait d'homme (28x24cm-11x9in) 18-Jun-4 Piasa, Paris #82/R est:5000-7000
Works on paper
£367 $664 €550 Etude de chevaux (32x55cm-13x22in) black crayon htd white. 30-Mar-4 Rossini, Paris #829
£828 $1507 €1250 Enfant debout en tenue d'ecolier (38x29cm-15x11in) s.d.1853 W/C gouache black crayon. 16-Jun-4 Piasa, Paris #219
£986 $1765 €1400 Soldat du 2eme regiment de chasseurs (34x23cm-13x9in) s. W/C gouache. 11-Jan-4 Rouillac, Vendome #76
£1409 $2607 €2100 Jeune Kabyle (23x19cm-9x7in) s. pen Indian ink. 15-Mar-4 Gros & Delettrez, Paris #178/R est:1500-2000
£2300 $4209 €3358 Louise Becq de Fouquieres painting a portrait at an easel (22x17cm-9x7in) pencil pen ink prov. 6-Jul-4 Christie's, London #198/R est:1000-1500

PILSBURY, Wilmot (1840-1908) British
Works on paper
£250 $418 €365 Calf (18x25cm-7x10in) s.d.1871 W/C. 17-Oct-3 Keys, Aylsham #264
£600 $1020 €876 Girl feeding ducks before a watermill in an autumnal landscape (30x43cm-12x17in) s.d.1898 W/C. 28-Oct-3 Lawrences, Bletchingley #1844
£1100 $1969 €1606 Farmyard with cart and ducks. Woodland stream with sheep grazing (20x27cm-8x11in) s.d.1904 W/C pair. 17-Mar-4 Bonhams, Chester #278 est:900-1200
£1700 $3060 €2482 Village pond with ducks, a ewe and her lambs nearby with thatched cottages (24x35cm-9x14in) s.d.1885 pencil W/C htd white prov. 21-Apr-4 Tennants, Leyburn #1038/R est:400-600

PILTAN, Marcelle (?-1938) South African
Works on paper
£256 $436 €374 Union buildings, Pretoria (42x29cm-17x11in) s. pastel. 4-Nov-3 Stephan Welz, Johannesburg #355 est:300-500 (SA.R 3000)

PILTZ, Otto (1846-1910) German
£2235 $4000 €3263 Evening thoughts (91x69cm-36x27in) s. 7-May-4 Sloans & Kenyon, Bethesda #1649/R est:3000-5000

PIMENOV, Anatoli (?) Russian?
£300 $501 €438 Wooded lake landscape (58x78cm-23x31in) s.d.94 s.i.d.verso. 9-Jul-3 Peter Wilson, Nantwich #39

PIMM, William Edwin (1863-1952) British
£2050 $3424 €2993 Young girl droving four cows (107x137cm-42x54in) 11-Nov-3 John Taylors, Louth #390

PIMONENKO, Nikolai Kornilovich (1862-1912) Russian
£2778 $4528 €4000 Young Ukrainian woman in traditional costume (76x100cm-30x39in) s.cyrillic d.1905. 26-Sep-3 Bolland & Marotz, Bremen #591/R est:1100
£55000 $98450 €80300 By the well (81x59cm-32x23in) s. exhib. 26-May-4 Sotheby's, London #99/R est:8000-12000

PINA, Alfredo (1887-1966) Italian
Sculpture
£1074 $1987 €1600 Bust of Beethoven (71cm-28in) s. terracotta. 14-Mar-4 St-Germain-en-Laye Encheres #145/R est:1500-1800
£1374 $2500 €2006 Banana seller (51cm-20in) s.st.f. black pat bronze. 19-Jun-4 Jackson's, Cedar Falls #112/R est:2000-3000
£1477 $2732 €2200 Bust of young man (40x36cm-16x14in) s.verso pat bronze. 14-Mar-4 St-Germain-en-Laye Encheres #149/R est:2000
£1549 $2680 €2200 Wagner (69cm-27in) s.d.1920 terracotta. 12-Dec-3 Piasa, Paris #171/R est:2800-3500
£2848 $5183 €4300 Beethoven (55cm-22in) pat bronze marble base. 15-Jun-4 Rossini, Paris #49/R est:4000-6000
£8500 $15300 €12410 Bust of Ludwig van Beethoven (78cm-31in) s.num.16 brown pat bronze verde antico socle st.f.A.G. lit. 21-Apr-4 Sotheby's, London #137/R est:7000-10000

PINACCI, Giuseppe (1642-1718) Italian
£14570 $26517 €22000 Battle in a harbour (118x168cm-46x66in) prov. 16-Jun-4 Christie's, Rome #511/R est:25000-30000
Works on paper
£612 $1096 €900 Un choc de cavaleri. Un choc de cavalerie, chevaux fuyant sur la gauche (20x30cm-8x12in) black chk grey wash htd white prov. 18-Mar-4 Christie's, Paris #229/R

PINAL, Fernand (1881-1958) French
£638 $1186 €950 Prunier fleuri a crouttes (35x40cm-14x16in) s.d.avril 1949 i.verso cardboard. 2-Mar-4 Artcurial Briest, Paris #126
£2326 $4000 €3396 Symphonie en bleue mineur (131x96cm-52x38in) s.d.1911 exhib. 2-Dec-3 Christie's, Rockefeller NY #34/R est:6000-8000
£17568 $32500 €25649 Cafe de Commerce et cathedrale, Meaux (61x50cm-24x20in) s.d.1913 s.i.d.on stretcher prov. 11-Feb-4 Sotheby's, New York #16/R est:7000-10000

PINALIS, P (19th C) Italian?
£3800 $6840 €5548 Still life with earthenware pots and dishes together on a table (123x146cm-48x57in) s.d.1852 prov. 20-Apr-4 Sotheby's, Olympia #388/R est:4000-6000

PINAZO MARTINEZ, Ignacio (1883-1970) Spanish
£2069 $3724 €3000 Still life with apples and copper jugs (63x82cm-25x32in) s. 26-Jan-4 Ansorena, Madrid #394/R est:1800

PINAZO MARTINEZ, Jose Ignacio (1879-1933) Spanish
£862 $1595 €1250 Flowers (26x17cm-10x7in) s.d.1900 board. 14-Jan-4 Castellana, Madrid #108/R
£4934 $8931 €7500 Vase of flowers (100x80cm-39x31in) s. 14-Apr-4 Ansorena, Madrid #76/R est:7000
Works on paper
£451 $767 €650 Mother and baby (17x13cm-7x5in) pencil double-sided. 28-Oct-3 Segre, Madrid #121/R

PINAZO, Ignacio (?) ?
Works on paper
£326 $555 €470 Baby (13x17cm-5x7in) pencil double-sided. 28-Oct-3 Segre, Madrid #107/R
£326 $555 €470 Neapolitan woman (17x13cm-7x5in) ink double-sided. 28-Oct-3 Segre, Madrid #114/R
£326 $555 €470 Study (16x12cm-6x5in) wax crayon. 28-Oct-3 Segre, Madrid #110/R
£326 $555 €470 Jose blowing bubbles (13x17cm-5x7in) pencil double-sided. 28-Oct-3 Segre, Madrid #115/R
£326 $555 €470 Interior with Teresa (12x15cm-5x6in) d.1873 pencil double-sided. 28-Oct-3 Segre, Madrid #120/R
£326 $555 €470 Maternity (17x13cm-7x5in) wax crayon double-sided. 28-Oct-3 Segre, Madrid #127/R
£326 $555 €470 Baby (12x17cm-5x7in) pencil double-sided. 28-Oct-3 Segre, Madrid #135/R
£347 $590 €500 Man and cart (16x12cm-6x5in) pencil dr double-sided. 28-Oct-3 Segre, Madrid #112/R
£451 $767 €650 Cat (16x12cm-6x5in) ink wax crayon double-sided. 28-Oct-3 Segre, Madrid #113/R
£451 $767 €650 Baby (13x17cm-5x7in) chl. 28-Oct-3 Segre, Madrid #118/R
£451 $767 €650 Jose at the piano (17x13cm-7x5in) pencil double-sided. 28-Oct-3 Segre, Madrid #125/R
£451 $767 €650 Baby playing (12x17cm-5x7in) d.1883 pencil. 28-Oct-3 Segre, Madrid #129/R
£451 $767 €650 Ignacito (12x17cm-5x7in) s.i.d.1883 chl pencil. 28-Oct-3 Segre, Madrid #140/R
£590 $1003 €850 Sleeping baby (12x17cm-5x7in) i. chl double-sided. 28-Oct-3 Segre, Madrid #126/R
£625 $1063 €900 Jose by curtain (17x12cm-7x5in) chl double-sided. 28-Oct-3 Segre, Madrid #109/R
£625 $1063 €900 Baby (13x17cm-5x7in) s. chl pencil double-sided. 28-Oct-3 Segre, Madrid #117/R
£694 $1181 €1000 Jose blowing bubbles (12x17cm-5x7in) chl ink double-sided. 28-Oct-3 Segre, Madrid #108/R
£694 $1181 €1000 Mother playing with baby (13x17cm-5x7in) chl pencil. 28-Oct-3 Segre, Madrid #122/R
£694 $1181 €1000 Jose (17x13cm-7x5in) pencil double-sided. 28-Oct-3 Segre, Madrid #123/R
£694 $1181 €1000 Baby during nappy change (12x17cm-5x7in) s.d.1884 pencil. 28-Oct-3 Segre, Madrid #139/R
£833 $1417 €1200 Jose blowing bubbles (13x17cm-5x7in) chl pencil dr double-sided. 28-Oct-3 Segre, Madrid #105/R

PINCEMIN, Geo (?) French?
Works on paper
£367 $675 €550 Tante Mimi (36x31cm-14x12in) s.i. dr. 8-Jun-4 Livinec, Gaudcheau & Jezequel, Rennes #110
£483 $899 €720 Vue de Saint Guenole. Pardon a Saint Guenole (35x22cm-14x9in) s.i. gouache chl pastel double-sided. 7-Mar-4 Livinec, Gaudcheau & Jezequel, Rennes #38

PINCEMIN, Jean-Pierre (1944-) French
£903 $1426 €1300 Untitled (28x27cm-11x11in) s.d.1999 acrylic cardboard. 27-Apr-3 Versailles Encheres #119
£1736 $2899 €2500 Composition (21x16cm-8x6in) s. board. 21-Oct-3 Artcurial Briest, Paris #585/R est:800-1000
£3846 $6423 €5500 1, 2, 3, 4, 5, 6, 7 (160x106cm-63x42in) oil paper on canvas prov. 11-Oct-3 Cornette de St.Cyr, Paris #78/R est:6000-8000
£7368 $13337 €11200 Untitled (164x130cm-65x51in) s.d.1976 verso prov. 19-Apr-4 Boscher, Cherbourg #721/R est:6000-8000
£8054 $14819 €12000 Untitled (160x123cm-63x48in) s.d.1993 verso acrylic paper on canvas. 24-Mar-4 Joron-Derem, Paris #148/R est:15000-18000
£9859 $17056 €14000 Untitled (250x200cm-98x79in) s.d.1984 verso acrylic prov. 9-Dec-3 Artcurial Briest, Paris #431/R est:15000-20000
£10067 $18020 €15000 Untitled (279x371cm-110x146in) acrylic painted 1973 exhib. 26-May-4 Christie's, Paris #96/R est:15000-20000
£11409 $20423 €17000 Untitled (313x507cm-123x200in) acrylic painted 1976. 26-May-4 Christie's, Paris #95/R est:18000-22000
£12081 $22228 €18000 Untitled (197x131cm-78x52in) s.d.1978 verso. 24-Mar-4 Joron-Derem, Paris #144/R est:25000-30000
£12667 $23307 €19000 Composition (130x162cm-51x64in) s.i.d.27 Aout 1978 verso acrylic paper on canvas prov. 8-Jun-4 Artcurial Briest, Paris #266/R est:15000-20000
£12800 $23296 €19200 Untitled (191x130cm-75x51in) s.d.1977 verso prov. 29-Jun-4 Cornette de St.Cyr, Paris #136/R est:15000-18000
£13423 $24698 €20000 Untitled (161x161cm-63x63in) s.verso painted 1988. 29-Mar-4 Cornette de St.Cyr, Paris #42/R est:15000-18000
£24476 $41609 €35000 Composition (200x160cm-79x63in) painted 1983. 19-Nov-3 Tajan, Paris #28/R est:40000-50000
£25874 $43210 €37000 Sans titre (280x260cm-110x102in) peinture prov. 11-Oct-3 Cornette de St.Cyr, Paris #16/R est:20000-25000
Works on paper
£571 $1061 €850 Composition (50x55cm-20x22in) s. ink. 3-Mar-4 Artcurial Briest, Paris #510
£1049 $1752 €1500 Carres colles (53x53cm-21x21in) s.d.1969 assemblage prov. 29-Jun-3 Versailles Encheres #202/R
£2550 $4693 €3800 Untitled (75x53cm-30x21in) s.d.1977 mixed media paper on canvas. 24-Mar-4 Joron-Derem, Paris #145 est:5000-7000
£3000 $5460 €4500 Untitled (52x75cm-20x30in) s.d.77 gouache graphite paper on canvas. 29-Jun-4 Cornette de St.Cyr, Paris #135/R est:3000-4000

PINCHART, Émile Auguste (1842-1924) French
£1091 $1811 €1582 Jeune femme tunesienne (55x40cm-22x16in) s.i. 13-Jun-3 Zofingen, Switzerland #2512/R est:2000 (S.FR 2400)
£1343 $2457 €1961 Young woman by a voliere (33x22cm-13x9in) s. 9-Jun-4 Rasmussen, Copenhagen #1942/R est:12000 (D.KR 15000)

PINCHON, Robert Antoine (1886-1943) French
£8219 $13973 €12000 Coucher de soleil (50x61cm-20x24in) s. 9-Nov-3 Eric Pillon, Calais #66/R
£8904 $15137 €13000 Vue de Rouen (54x92cm-21x36in) s. 9-Nov-3 Eric Pillon, Calais #65/R

PINCHON, S (19/20th C) French
£1900 $3534 €2774 Rider with a pony and dog by the shore (66x60cm-26x24in) s. 4-Mar-4 Christie's, London #410/R est:1000-1500

PINDER, Douglas H (?) British
Works on paper
£420 $701 €613 Trevelgue Head (71x51cm-28x20in) s. W/C. 13-Nov-3 Rendalls, Ashburton #1989

PINE, Theodore E (attrib) (1828-1905) American
£1967 $3600 €2872 Portrait of sister in Italianate landscape (97x99cm-38x39in) prov. 31-Jan-4 South Bay, Long Island #104

PINEDA-BUENO, Jose Antonio (1950-) Spanish
£444 $804 €675 House and garden (46x55cm-18x22in) s. s.verso. 14-Apr-4 Ansorena, Madrid #196/R

PINEDO, Émile (1840-1916) French
Sculpture
£1141 $1837 €1700 L'esclave (60cm-24in) s. brown pat bronze. 23-Feb-3 St-Germain-en-Laye Encheres #22/R est:1800-2000
£3649 $6531 €5400 Elegante nue se coiffant dans un miroir biseaute de style Regence (35cm-14in) s.i. s.verso col pat bronze st.f.Bronze Garanti. 10-May-4 Horta, Bruxelles #123/R est:3000-5000

PINEL DE GRANDCHAMP, Louis-Émile (1831-1894) French
£5334 $9761 €8000 Enfant et son ane (40x32cm-16x13in) s. panel lit. 3-Jun-4 Tajan, Paris #261/R est:8000-12000

PINELLI, Auguste de (1823-1890) French
£663 $1200 €968 Deathbed of a monk (99x130cm-39x51in) s. i.verso. 3-Apr-4 Neal Auction Company, New Orleans #819/R est:2000-4000

PINELLI, Bartolomeo (1781-1835) Italian
Works on paper
£611 $1113 €892 Romulus and Remus (18x27cm-7x11in) i. W/C on pen bister. 17-Jun-4 Kornfeld, Bern #82 (S.FR 1400)
£709 $1149 €1000 Famille paysanne aux alentours de ruines (19x27cm-7x11in) s.i. brown wash W/C black crayon. 21-May-3 Daguerre, Paris #97
£750 $1298 €1095 Four men playing boules. Serenaders singing to a girl at a window (22x30cm-9x12in) black chk pair. 12-Dec-3 Christie's, Kensington #414/R
£1645 $3026 €2500 Adam and Eve (36x26cm-14x10in) bears sig.d.1806 pen ink W/C over pencil. 22-Jun-4 Sotheby's, Milan #129/R est:2500-3500
£3056 $5500 €4462 Condemnation of the songs of Brutus (33x44cm-13x17in) pen ink wash prov. 21-Jan-4 Sotheby's, New York #129/R est:3000-4000
£5000 $8500 €7300 Various (20x16cm-8x6in) ten s. eleven i. W/C over pencil eleven prov. 26-Nov-3 Hamptons Fine Art, Godalming #42/R est:5000-7000

PINELLI, Pino (1938-) Italian
£267 $491 €400 Untitled (60x80cm-24x31in) s.d.1993 paint paper. 12-Jun-4 Meeting Art, Vercelli #813
£470 $869 €700 Composition (58x78cm-23x31in) s.d.1993 verso paint paper. 11-Mar-4 Galleria Pace, Milan #21/R
Works on paper
£467 $859 €700 Composition (59x80cm-23x31in) s.d.1993 verso mixed media. 10-Jun-4 Galleria Pace, Milan #2/R
£471 $772 €650 Painting on cardboard (60x78cm-24x31in) s.i.d.1993 verso mixed media cardboard. 29-May-3 Galleria Pace, Milan #44/R

PINGET, Robert (1919-1997) French
£300 $552 €450 Composition abstraite et colore (31x40cm-12x16in) s.d.1985 panel. 9-Jun-4 Piasa, Paris #201

PINGGERA, Heinz (1900-) Italian
£629 $1083 €900 Winter landscape with view of Dolomites (60x80cm-24x31in) s. 4-Dec-3 Dorotheum, Graz #28/R

PINHEIRO, Oswaldo (20th C) Portuguese
£2586 $4629 €3776 Les refugies (121x92cm-48x36in) s. prov. 17-May-4 Beurret, Zurich #43/R est:2000-3000 (S.FR 6000)
£3448 $6172 €5034 Parisian boulevard (33x41cm-13x16in) s. 17-May-4 Beurret, Zurich #42/R est:2000-3000 (S.FR 8000)

PINHY, John Charles (1860-1912) Canadian
£256 $442 €374 Young girl wearing a white shawl (17x14cm-7x6in) s. board. 9-Dec-3 Pinneys, Montreal #166 (C.D 575)

PINI, Alfredo (1958-) Italian?
£268 $497 €400 Along the road (100x80cm-39x31in) s. painted 2003. 13-Mar-4 Meeting Art, Vercelli #213
£333 $613 €500 Usual day (140x100cm-55x39in) s. s.d.2003 verso. 12-Jun-4 Meeting Art, Vercelli #346/R
£400 $736 €600 With joy (100x120cm-39x47in) s. board painted 2001 lit. 12-Jun-4 Meeting Art, Vercelli #214/R
£436 $807 €650 A thousand miles (100x100cm-39x39in) s. s.d.2002 verso. 13-Mar-4 Meeting Art, Vercelli #524

PINKER, Stanley (1924-) South African
£1073 $1922 €1567 Pastorale (29x23cm-11x9in) s. board. 31-May-4 Stephan Welz, Johannesburg #494/R (SA.R 13000)

PINKERTON, Hamilton (19th C) American
£216 $400 €315 Thatched hut by the shore (30x46cm-12x18in) s.d.1891. 13-Mar-4 DeFina, Austinburg #748/R

PINNEY, Jean (20th C) American
£240 $400 €350 Redwood Creek (61x46cm-24x18in) s. 11-Oct-3 Nadeau, Windsor #151/R

PINNOCK, Mary (20th C) Australian?
£947 $1713 €1383 Untitled (150x91cm-59x36in) s.d.2003. 31-Mar-4 Goodman, Sydney #422/R (A.D 2300)

PINO, Marco da (1525-1588) Italian
£27465 $44218 €39000 Sant'Orsola (76x61cm-30x24in) 8-May-3 Farsetti, Prato #689/R est:42000-52000

PINOLE Y RODRIGUEZ, Nicanor (1877-1978) Spanish
£2535 $4056 €3600 Landscape (28x36cm-11x14in) s. board. 16-Sep-3 Segre, Madrid #97/R
£2676 $4282 €3800 Landscape in the Asturias (28x36cm-11x14in) s. board. 16-Sep-3 Segre, Madrid #102/R est:2100
£2887 $4620 €4100 Travellers (36x28cm-14x11in) s. board. 16-Sep-3 Segre, Madrid #100/R est:2100
£4348 $7130 €6000 Austrian landscape (24x32cm-9x13in) s. panel. 27-May-3 Durán, Madrid #151/R est:2500
Works on paper
£1596 $2665 €2250 In the bar (42x50cm-17x20in) s. dr wash. 20-Oct-3 Durán, Madrid #93/R

PINOS, Juan (1862-1910) Spanish
£993 $1609 €1400 Fiesta in Catalan (34x42cm-13x17in) s. 20-May-3 Ansorena, Madrid #198/R
£1250 $2263 €1900 Celebrations in Cataluna (27x38cm-11x15in) s. cardboard. 14-Apr-4 Ansorena, Madrid #42/R est:1900
£1736 $2830 €2500 Catalunian celebration (34x42cm-13x17in) s. 23-Sep-3 Durán, Madrid #116/R est:1400
£2113 $3697 €3000 Catalunia celebrating (27x38cm-11x15in) s. canvas on cardboard. 16-Dec-3 Durán, Madrid #124/R

PINOT, Albert (1875-1962) Belgian
£284 $474 €400 Nature morte aux fleurs des champs (30x34cm-12x13in) s. panel. 17-Jun-3 Vanderkindere, Brussels #5
£345 $638 €500 L'etude (73x60cm-29x24in) s. 19-Jan-4 Horta, Bruxelles #391
£533 $955 €800 On the beach (38x48cm-15x19in) s. 11-May-4 Vendu Notarishuis, Rotterdam #254
£699 $1189 €1000 Eglise a Menton (65x55cm-26x22in) s. 18-Nov-3 Galerie Moderne, Brussels #884/R
£699 $1272 €1021 Au parc (39x55cm-15x22in) s. 16-Jun-4 Fischer, Luzern #2312/R (S.FR 1600)
£745 $1200 €1088 Still life of roses (41x30cm-16x12in) s. panel. 20-Aug-3 James Julia, Fairfield #987/R
£845 $1462 €1200 Vernon (46x65cm-18x26in) s.d.1929. 13-Dec-3 Martinot & Savignat, Pontoise #222
£2657 $4517 €3800 Elegante au chapeau (40x55cm-16x22in) s. 18-Nov-3 Galerie Moderne, Brussels #829/R est:600-800

PINTA, Amable Louis (1820-1888) French
£1399 $2406 €2000 Le peintre sur le motif (60x50cm-24x20in) s. 7-Dec-3 Osenat, Fontainebleau #219 est:2000-2500

PINTADO SEVILLA, Angel (1955-) Spanish
£355 $592 €500 Landscape (30x24cm-12x9in) s.d.98 canvas on board. 20-Oct-3 Durán, Madrid #22/R

PINTALDI, Cristiano (1970-) Italian
£2817 $4930 €4000 Wario (45x55cm-18x22in) s.i.d.1998 acrylic prov. 16-Dec-3 Finarte Semenzato, Milan #282/R est:4500-5500
£7500 $12525 €10950 Senza titolo (75x120cm-30x47in) s.d.00 verso acrylic prov. 21-Oct-3 Christie's, London #75/R est:6000-8000

PINTER, L (20th C) German
£4861 $7681 €7000 Rape of the Daighters of Leucippus (199x179cm-78x70in) s.d.1920 verso after Sir Peter Paul Rubens. 2-Sep-3 Christie's, Amsterdam #21/R est:3000-5000

PINTO, Angelo (1908-1994) American
£469 $750 €685 Circus performers (20x25cm-8x10in) s. panel. 19-Sep-3 Freeman, Philadelphia #63/R
£1372 $2250 €1989 Trapeze performers (30x38cm-12x15in) s.d.1934. 4-Jun-3 Alderfer's, Hatfield #322/R est:500-700

PINTO, Antonio Alves (19th C) Portuguese
Sculpture
£8000 $13840 €11680 Maternity (77x57x42cm-30x22x17in) s.i. white marble green marble base. 12-Dec-3 Sotheby's, London #247/R est:6000-8000

PINTO, Biagio (1911-1989) American
£250 $450 €365 Nude (28x20cm-11x8in) s.i.d.1970. 23-Jan-4 Freeman, Philadelphia #205/R
£872 $1500 €1273 Landscape with boats (20x25cm-8x10in) s. 7-Dec-3 Freeman, Philadelphia #203 est:300-500
Works on paper
£269 $450 €393 Portrait (36x28cm-14x11in) s. crayon. 20-Jun-3 Freeman, Philadelphia #27/R

PINTO, Jody (20th C) American
Works on paper
£250 $450 €365 Landscape with fingers-for Dani women (32x41cm-13x16in) W/C exhib. 24-Apr-4 David Rago, Lambertville #327/R
£1333 $2400 €1946 Portable death hut num 2. Portable death hut num 1. Black-balled landscape (19x24cm-7x9in) i. s.i.d.verso one d.1976 one d.1975 one s.i.d.1977 verso W/C 3. 24-Apr-4 David Rago, Lambertville #364/R est:400-800

PINTO, Mercedes Sofia (1940-1982) Spanish
£274 $466 €400 Arcades (61x92cm-24x36in) s.d.1974. 4-Nov-3 Ansorena, Madrid #875/R

£603 $977 €850 Ibicenas (57x36cm-22x14in) s. panel. 20-May-3 Ansorena, Madrid #371/R
£709 $1149 €1000 Loca de Cahillot (100x73cm-39x29in) s.d.67. 20-May-3 Ansorena, Madrid #290/R

PINTO, Octavio (1890-1941) Argentinian
£772 $1250 €1119 Cala Mallorquina (42x46cm-17x18in) s. board. 29-Jul-3 Galeria y Remates, Montevideo #135/R
£1510 $2763 €2250 Rainbow in Majorca (31x40cm-12x16in) s. cardboard. 12-Jul-4 Durán, Madrid #152/R est:2250
£11173 $20000 €16313 Garden in bloom (68x87cm-27x34in) s. 4-May-4 Arroyo, Buenos Aires #97/R est:6000

PINTO, Salvatore (?) ?
£581 $1000 €848 Tent and tower (30x38cm-12x15in) linen painted c.1931-33 prov. 7-Dec-3 Freeman, Philadelphia #206 est:1000-1500
£750 $1200 €1095 Two women in a North African interior (20x25cm-8x10in) s. 19-Sep-3 Freeman, Philadelphia #90/R est:1000-1500
£1047 $1800 €1529 Four figures under a canopy (51x61cm-20x24in) linen painted c.1931-33 prov. 7-Dec-3 Freeman, Philadelphia #183 est:1200-1800

PINTO-COELHO, Luis (1942-) Portuguese
£2329 $3959 €3400 Untitled (160x110cm-63x43in) s. 4-Nov-3 Ansorena, Madrid #930/R est:3000

PINTUCCI, Niccolo (1697-1770) Italian
£49655 $82924 €72000 Carriage race in Santa Maria Novella Square, Florence (146x228cm-57x90in) prov.exhib.lit. 15-Nov-3 Porro, Milan #243/R est:60000

PINTURICCHIO, Bernardino (1454-1513) Italian
£72222 $130000 €105444 Madonna and Child before landscape (49x37cm-19x15in) canvas on panel prov.lit. 22-Jan-4 Sotheby's, New York #44/R est:100000-150000

PINWELL, George John (1842-1875) British
Works on paper
£250 $455 €365 Portrait of a bearded man standing by a ladder in an apple orchard (38x28cm-15x11in) mono. W/C. 4-Feb-4 John Nicholson, Haslemere #52
£280 $445 €409 Study of a woman carrying washing (14x11cm-6x4in) init pencil W/C prov. 10-Sep-3 Cheffins, Cambridge #427/R

PIOLA, Domenico (17/18th C) Italian
Works on paper
£1088 $1948 €1600 Minerve (20x17cm-8x7in) pen brown ink brown wash blk crayon htd white gouache. 17-Mar-4 Tajan, Paris #10/R est:1000
£1800 $3294 €2628 Seated shepherd with a dog, study for a lunette (15x26cm-6x10in) i. black chk pen ink wash prov. 6-Jul-4 Christie's, London #63/R est:2000-3000
£2041 $3653 €3000 Le Triomphe de l'Eglise, un projet pour un plafond (28x41cm-11x16in) i. black chk pen black ink brown wash prov. 18-Mar-4 Christie's, Paris #22/R est:1800-2200
£2177 $3897 €3200 L'Assomption de la Vierge (33x22cm-13x9in) i.verso black chk pen brown ink wash prov. 18-Mar-4 Christie's, Paris #23/R est:2000-4000
£2381 $4262 €3500 L'Immaculee Conception entouree de putti avec Dieu-le-Pere (27x41cm-11x16in) i.verso black chk pen brown ink wash prov. 18-Mar-4 Christie's, Paris #21/R est:2000-4000
£6667 $12000 €9734 Putto striking a satyr bound to a tree, with women playing a tambourine (16x22cm-6x9in) i. black chk pen brown ink wash. 22-Jan-4 Christie's, Rockefeller NY #62/R est:3000-5000

PIOLA, Domenico (elder) (1627-1703) Italian
Works on paper
£1259 $2140 €1800 Allegory of Faith (13x16cm-5x6in) pen W/C pencil. 19-Nov-3 Finarte Semenzato, Milan #493/R est:1000-1500
£4334 $7887 €6500 Assumption of the Virgin (38x26cm-15x10in) pen ink wash prov. 30-Jun-4 Pierre Berge, Paris #12/R est:3000-4000
£5334 $9707 €8000 Scene from Saul's life (25x37cm-10x15in) pierre noire ink wash. 30-Jun-4 Pierre Berge, Paris #13/R est:5000-7000

PIOLA, Domenico (elder-attrib) (1627-1703) Italian
£7448 $12439 €10800 Saint Christopher holding the Infant (131x96cm-52x38in) 14-Nov-3 Marc Kohn, Paris #11/R est:10000-15000

PIOLA, Paolo Gerolamo (1666-1724) Italian
Works on paper
£546 $1000 €797 St John the Baptist pointing to Christ in the wilderness (30x22cm-12x9in) i.verso pen brown ink over pencil. 29-Jan-4 Swann Galleries, New York #96/R
£1325 $2411 €2000 Assumption. Tobiolo and the angel (27x20cm-11x8in) chk double-sided. 16-Jun-4 Christie's, Rome #450/R est:1500-2000

PIOMBANTI AMMANNATI, Giuseppe (1898-1996) Italian
£867 $1595 €1300 Study for portrait (48x57cm-19x22in) s.d.1951 verso tempera cardboard. 14-Jun-4 Sant Agostino, Torino #335/R
£1361 $2435 €2000 Florence and surroundings (100x70cm-39x28in) tempera paper on canvas prov. 22-Mar-4 Sant Agostino, Torino #512/R est:1500-2000
£1818 $3036 €2600 Villa Medici's gardens (73x52cm-29x20in) s.d.1954. 26-Jun-3 Sant Agostino, Torino #260/R est:2000-2500
Works on paper
£267 $491 €400 Seated man (47x33cm-19x13in) s. chl. 14-Jun-4 Sant Agostino, Torino #365/R

PIOMBO, Sebastiano del (1485-1547) Italian
Works on paper
£77778 $140000 €113556 Christ carrying the Cross (17x12cm-7x5in) i. black white chk prov.lit. 22-Jan-4 Christie's, Rockefeller NY #12/R est:100000-150000

PIOT, Adolphe (1850-1910) French
£650 $1118 €949 Still life of flowers (49x39cm-19x15in) s. 3-Dec-3 Cheffins, Cambridge #637
£2371 $4244 €3462 Portrait of young woman (83x59cm-33x23in) s. 12-May-4 Dobiaschofsky, Bern #873/R est:4000 (S.FR 5500)
£3000 $5460 €4380 Lost in thought (46x38cm-18x15in) s. 16-Jun-4 Christie's, Kensington #243/R est:3000-5000
£3333 $6000 €5000 Little girl reading (49x38cm-19x15in) s. 20-Apr-4 Sotheby's, Amsterdam #81/R est:5000-7000
£9302 $16000 €13581 Young beauty with roses (92x62cm-36x24in) s. 3-Dec-3 Doyle, New York #113/R est:8000-12000
£18919 $35000 €27622 Young peasant girl seated on a large stone in a forest clearing (117x76cm-46x30in) s.d.1870. 24-Jan-4 Jeffery Burchard, Florida #36/R est:10000-20000
£20833 $37500 €30416 Young woman carding wool (130x91cm-51x36in) s. 23-Apr-4 Sotheby's, New York #58/R est:15000-20000

PIOT, Eugene (19th C) French
Photographs
£3000 $5280 €4380 Parthenon from the Acropolis (23x33cm-9x13in) num.16 verso salt print lit. 19-May-4 Christie's, London #97/R est:4000-6000

PIOTROWSKI (20th C) ?
£5587 $10000 €8157 Russian wedding party (79x109cm-31x43in) s.i. 8-May-4 Susanin's, Chicago #6164/R est:12000-16000

PIOTROWSKI, Antoni (1853-1924) Polish
£1070 $2000 €1605 Cossack on horseback (42x32cm-17x13in) s.i.d.1883 panel. 25-Jul-4 Bonhams & Butterfields, San Francisco #6045/R est:2000-3000
£4702 $7335 €6865 Young girl leading a horse (52x42cm-20x17in) s.d.1885. 30-Mar-3 Agra, Warsaw #10/R est:30000 (P.Z 30000)

PIOTROWSKI, Jozef (20th C) Polish
£1119 $1869 €1600 Beer garden on summer evening (41x75cm-16x30in) s. 28-Jun-3 Bolland & Marotz, Bremen #721/R est:1300

PIOTROWSKI, Maksymiljan Antoni (1813-1875) Polish
£405 $714 €600 Conversation in bed (19x21cm-7x8in) mono.d.50 canvas on panel. 22-May-4 Lempertz, Koln #1583/R
£2247 $3730 €3281 Autumn (65x93cm-26x37in) s.d.1909. 15-Jun-3 Agra, Warsaw #20/R (P.Z 14000)

PIOVANO, Ferruccio (1890-1981) Italian
£320 $589 €480 San Martino Valley (27x35cm-11x14in) s.d.1947 cardboard. 8-Jun-4 Della Rocca, Turin #304
£369 $653 €550 Santa Marherita Ligure, morning (35x45cm-14x18in) s.d.1955 s.i.d.verso cardboard. 1-May-4 Meeting Art, Vercelli #379
£382 $649 €550 Landscape with snow (16x18cm-6x7in) s.d.1968 board. 1-Nov-3 Meeting Art, Vercelli #445
£433 $797 €650 The Po in Casale (30x40cm-12x16in) s. cardboard prov. 14-Jun-4 Sant Agostino, Torino #196/R

PIPAL, Viktor (1887-1971) Austrian
£694 $1132 €1000 Wiener Vorstadt (42x53cm-17x21in) s. 23-Sep-3 Wiener Kunst Auktionen, Vienna #50/R
£780 $1303 €1100 Donau canal in Nussdorf (48x61cm-19x24in) s. panel. 14-Oct-3 Dorotheum, Vienna #120/R
£1342 $2483 €2000 Menacing sky (48x61cm-19x24in) s. masonite. 9-Mar-4 Dorotheum, Vienna #91/R est:2200-3000
£1389 $2264 €2000 Semmering train (47x61cm-19x24in) s. 23-Sep-3 Wiener Kunst Auktionen, Vienna #51/R est:1500-3000
£1408 $2465 €2000 Gersthof (46x59cm-18x23in) s. canvas on masonite. 19-Dec-3 Dorotheum, Vienna #163/R est:2800-3600
Works on paper
£709 $1184 €1000 Nussdorf lock after 1945 (33x47cm-13x19in) s.i. verso W/C gouache. 14-Oct-3 Dorotheum, Vienna #142/R

PIPER, Edward (1938-1990) British
Works on paper
£470 $879 €686 Cap de Cavalleria, Menorca (54x74cm-21x29in) s.i.d.28 III 87 W/C pencil. 20-Jul-4 Dreweatt Neate, Newbury #198/R
£580 $1061 €847 Female nude draped over a bed examining her facial reflection (48x36cm-19x14in) s.d.8 II 82 col wash. 28-Jan-4 Mallams, Oxford #557/R

PIPER, Jane (20th C) British
£10326 $19000 €15076 Abstract composition (41x51cm-16x20in) s. verso. 27-Jun-4 Freeman, Philadelphia #218/R est:8000-12000
£11047 $19000 €16129 Still life (30x41cm-12x16in) board painted c.1941-43 prov.exhib. 7-Dec-3 Freeman, Philadelphia #225 est:2000-3000

PIPER, John (1903-1992) British
£300 $501 €438 Evening gorse (30x30cm-12x12in) s.d.2003 i.verso board. 14-Oct-3 David Lay, Penzance #538
£350 $637 €511 Evening farm (30x61cm-12x24in) board. 15-Jun-4 David Lay, Penzance #423
£600 $1122 €900 Still life (41x53cm-16x21in) s. 21-Jul-4 John Nicholson, Haslemere #114
£1167 $2100 €1704 Montagne Street (15x20cm-6x8in) s. masonite exhib. 23-Jan-4 Freeman, Philadelphia #115/R est:1000-1500

£2500	$4475	€3650	Montagne St Victoire (15x20cm-6x8in) s. canvas on board prov. 14-May-4 Christie's, Kensington #610/R est:2500-3500
£5200	$9516	€7592	Kernascleden Church (20x25cm-8x10in) painted 1961 exhib. 28-Jul-4 Mallams, Oxford #255/R est:2000-3000
£6000	$10320	€8760	Chateau de Vayrac (24x34cm-9x13in) s. board prov. 3-Dec-3 Christie's, Kensington #705/R est:5000-8000
£9500	$17385	€13870	Anemones in a yellow jug (110x86cm-43x34in) s. painted 1988 prov.exhib. 4-Jun-4 Christie's, London #111/R est:7000-10000
£11500	$21045	€16790	Slate quarry village (25x36cm-10x14in) s. board painted 1958. 28-Jul-4 Mallams, Oxford #256/R est:2000-3000
£14000	$25620	€20440	Niton, Isle of White (63x76cm-25x30in) s. exhib. 2-Jun-4 Sotheby's, London #76/R est:10000-15000
£15000	$25800	€21900	Barn at Ecchinswell (63x76cm-25x30in) s. s.i.verso canvas on board painted 1960 prov. 3-Dec-3 Sotheby's, London #54/R est:15000-20000
£15000	$27450	€21900	Pear tree and wall (122x91cm-48x36in) s. exhib. 2-Jun-4 Sotheby's, London #94/R est:12000-18000
£16000	$29280	€23360	Saint Dogwell's, Pembrokeshire (86x112cm-34x44in) s. painted 1984. 2-Jun-4 Sotheby's, London #86/R est:12000-18000
£16000	$29280	€23360	Fawley V (127x157cm-50x62in) s. oil sand on canvas prov.exhib. 4-Jun-4 Christie's, London #42/R est:10000-15000
£21875	$35000	€31938	City streets (91x122cm-36x48in) s. 20-Sep-3 Bunte, Elgin #1294 est:15000-25000
£65000	$118950	€94900	Llanthony Abbey (46x56cm-18x22in) s. s.i.d.1941 verso canvas on panel prov.exhib. 4-Jun-4 Christie's, London #39/R est:25000-35000
Prints			
£2500	$4250	€3650	Five gates of London (42x160cm-17x63in) s.i. silkscreen exec.1978. 1-Dec-3 Bonhams, New Bond Street #314/R est:1200-1800
Works on paper			
£480	$782	€701	Study for the Gas Board murals (13x8cm-5x3in) mixed media. 25-Sep-3 Gorringes, Worthing #745/R
£500	$860	€730	South West Region Electricity Buildings in Wandsworth (13x10cm-5x4in) mixed media. 2-Dec-3 Andrew Smith, Winchester #116
£784	$1404	€1145	Brittany landscape (20x31cm-8x12in) s. i.verso mixed media. 31-May-4 Stephan Welz, Johannesburg #454/R (SA.R 9500)
£800	$1336	€1168	Nevern Valley, Wales (24x33cm-9x13in) i. grey wash bodycol brush ink. 16-Oct-3 Christie's, Kensington #651/R
£800	$1272	€1168	Studies for the Gas Board murals (13x8cm-5x3in) mixed media. 9-Sep-3 Gorringes, Lewes #1968/R
£1050	$1922	€1533	Seascape with Island (16x30cm-6x12in) s. pastel W/C. 28-Jan-4 Dreweatt Neate, Newbury #10/R est:1000-1500
£1100	$1837	€1606	Portrait of a girl (34x28cm-13x11in) chl pen brush black ink. 16-Oct-3 Christie's, Kensington #642/R est:700-1000
£1200	$1908	€1752	Costume design for 1st Lieutenants Redburn and Ratcliff (55x38cm-22x15in) s.i. pencil ink gouache collage. 10-Sep-3 Sotheby's, Olympia #281/R est:700-900
£1300	$2067	€1898	Landscape with trees (20x30cm-8x12in) W/C pencil crayon. 10-Sep-3 Sotheby's, Olympia #274/R est:600-800
£1400	$2226	€2044	Alvingham (23x75cm-9x30in) i.d. pencil col chk. 10-Sep-3 Sotheby's, Olympia #275/R est:600-800
£1400	$2226	€2044	Chatillon sur Loire (20x30cm-8x12in) i. W/C pencil. 10-Sep-3 Sotheby's, Olympia #278/R est:600-800
£1400	$2338	€2044	Rocky coastline (24x33cm-9x13in) pen black ink crayon W/C. 16-Oct-3 Christie's, Kensington #648/R est:1200-1800
£1500	$2580	€2190	Rhydefudr (33x52cm-13x20in) s.i. pen ink W/C gouache prov. 2-Dec-3 Bonhams, New Bond Street #87/R est:1500-2000
£1600	$2544	€2336	Amberville (20x30cm-8x12in) i. W/C pencil crayon. 10-Sep-3 Sotheby's, Olympia #277/R est:600-800
£1700	$2703	€2482	Reclining nude (32x41cm-13x16in) s. brown crayon black ink wash. 10-Sep-3 Sotheby's, Olympia #280/R est:1500-2000
£1700	$2839	€2482	Little steepjay (22x35cm-9x14in) i.d.17 XI 75 pencil pastel. 16-Oct-3 Christie's, Kensington #640/R est:800-1200
£1700	$3145	€2482	Port Bene (21x33cm-8x13in) s.indis.i. pencil col crayon. 11-Feb-4 Sotheby's, Olympia #250/R est:1000-1500
£1700	$2805	€2482	Abstract sketch (15x18cm-6x7in) s. W/C. 1-Jul-3 Tayler & Fletcher, Cheltenham #4
£1800	$3276	€2628	Pitti Palace, Florence (8x21cm-3x8in) s. pencil W/C pen blk ink. 1-Jul-4 Christie's, Kensington #330/R est:2000-3000
£2000	$3520	€2920	Great Haseley (39x35cm-15x14in) s.i. pen ink col crayons. 19-May-4 Sotheby's, Olympia #260/R est:2000-3000
£2400	$4248	€3504	Quainton (34x52cm-13x20in) s.i.d.62 W/C gouache. 27-Apr-4 Bonhams, Knightsbridge #39/R est:1000-1500
£2400	$4368	€3504	Study for stain glass window at Tarville Church, Bucks (34x52cm-13x20in) s.i.d.1975 verso pen brush blk ink pastel W/C. 1-Jul-4 Christie's, Kensington #355/R est:1000-1500
£2600	$4420	€3796	Newhaven sunset (35x53cm-14x21in) s. ink W/C bodycol col crayon. 21-Nov-3 Christie's, London #4/R est:2500-3500
£2600	$4420	€3796	Parma (34x52cm-13x20in) s. W/C bodycol. 21-Nov-3 Christie's, London #6/R est:2500-3500
£2600	$4472	€3796	Porch at St. Regrier (53x34cm-21x13in) s. wax crayon ink wash gouache prov. 2-Dec-3 Bonhams, New Bond Street #84/R est:3000-5000
£2600	$4654	€3796	North Buckinghamshire (34x52cm-13x20in) s. W/C gouache wax resist prov. 16-Mar-4 Bonhams, New Bond Street #56/R est:2500-3500
£2800	$4816	€4088	Warminster, Northants (64x32cm-25x13in) s.i.d.7.iv.64 pen brush black ink crayon W/C. 3-Dec-3 Christie's, Kensington #707/R est:3000-4000
£2800	$5012	€4088	Stones and bones XV (27x37cm-11x15in) s. pencil pen brush black ink pastel collage prov.lit. 14-May-4 Christie's, Kensington #612/R est:3000-5000
£2800	$5096	€4088	Study for the East window at Nettlebed Church, Oxon (61x35cm-24x14in) s.i.d.1970 verso brush blk ink W/C. 1-Jul-4 Christie's, Kensington #354/R est:1000-1500
£3200	$5440	€4672	Broselini in December (34x52cm-13x20in) s.i. ink W/C bodycol col crayon. 21-Nov-3 Christie's, London #2/R est:2500-3500
£3200	$5920	€4672	Llyn Dinas, Gweynedd (9x25cm-4x10in) s.i. pen brush ink. 11-Mar-4 Christie's, Kensington #237/R est:600-800
£3300	$5907	€4818	Landscape in the Levant (36x51cm-14x20in) pen ink W/C. 18-Mar-4 Neales, Nottingham #699/R est:1800-2200
£3400	$5372	€4930	Old gate (55x70cm-22x28in) s.i. pencil pen ink W/C htd bodycol. 3-Sep-3 Bonhams, Bury St Edmunds #386/R est:2000-3000
£3500	$6265	€5110	Stones and bonex XVI (27x37cm-11x15in) s. pencil pen brush black ink pastel collage prov.lit. 14-May-4 Christie's, Kensington #609/R est:3000-5000
£3800	$6536	€5548	Capesthorne (39x57cm-15x22in) i.d.19 IV 77 W/C g, pastel prov. 2-Dec-3 Bonhams, New Bond Street #86/R est:3000-5000
£3800	$7030	€5548	Pembrokeshire landscape (38x55cm-15x22in) s. gouache W/C col crayon ink prov. 11-Feb-4 Sotheby's, Olympia #249/R est:2000-3000
£4000	$6800	€5840	San Lorenzo (26x37cm-10x15in) s.i. ink W/C bodycol. 21-Nov-3 Christie's, London #71/R est:1500-2500
£4129	$7391	€6028	Garn Fawr, Pembrokeshire (36x55cm-14x22in) s. i.verso pen ink col crayon brush in W/C. 31-May-4 Stephan Welz, Johannesburg #455/R est:20000-30000 (SA.R 50000)
£4400	$7920	€6424	Welsh Landscape (40x58cm-16x23in) s.i. indis.d. W/C black ink. 20-Jan-4 Bonhams, Knightsbridge #306/R est:2000-3000
£4800	$8304	€7008	Vezelay (74x94cm-29x37in) s.d.1968 gouache prov. 11-Dec-3 Lyon & Turnbull, Edinburgh #109/R est:3000-5000
£5000	$8950	€7300	Venetian facades (38x54cm-15x21in) s.i. pencil pen brush black ink W/C bodycol prov. 14-May-4 Christie's, Kensington #613/R est:3000-5000
£5500	$9350	€8030	Taillebourg (42x56cm-17x22in) s. ink W/C bodycol col crayon executed 1958 prov.exhib. 21-Nov-3 Christie's, London #1/R est:5000-7000
£5500	$9460	€8030	Study for Death in Venice (52x69cm-20x27in) s. pencil brush black ink pastel gouache. 3-Dec-3 Christie's, Kensington #708/R est:3000-4000
£5500	$10065	€8030	Fawley VIII (56x75cm-22x30in) s. gouache chk executed 1989 prov.exhib. 4-Jun-4 Christie's, London #43/R est:5000-8000
£6000	$9540	€8760	Meidrim (35x52cm-14x20in) s.i.d.23.3.67 W/C gouache. 10-Sep-3 Sotheby's, Olympia #282/R est:3000-4000
£6000	$10980	€8760	Field Road at Weston, Portland (34x52cm-13x20in) s. col ink W/C bodycol wax crayon executed 1954 prov.lit. 4-Jun-4 Christie's, London #40/R est:6000-8000
£6200	$10664	€9052	View of Portland Bill (18x22cm-7x9in) s.i. ink gouache wax resist prov. 2-Dec-3 Bonhams, New Bond Street #85/R est:1800-2500
£6200	$11098	€9052	Harvest Garn Fawn (35x53cm-14x21in) s. pencil W/C gouache wax resist. 16-Mar-4 Bonhams, New Bond Street #55/R est:2500-3500
£6200	$11470	€9052	Normandy farmhouse (27x36cm-11x14in) s. W/C gouache. 11-Mar-4 Christie's, Kensington #235/R est:3000-5000
£6500	$10855	€9490	The Life, Oundle School Chapel window (68x15cm-27x6in) s. pencil W/C bodycol prov. 16-Oct-3 Christie's, Kensington #565/R est:1500-2500
£6500	$12025	€9490	Bosherston, Pembroke (39x58cm-15x23in) s.i.d.1958 verso ink W/C gouache. 11-Feb-4 Sotheby's, Olympia #251/R est:3000-5000
£7000	$12530	€10220	Espira (57x74cm-22x29in) s. W/C pastel prov.exhib. 16-Mar-4 Bonhams, New Bond Street #57/R est:5000-7000
£7500	$11925	€10950	Shell guide to Oxford (38x28cm-15x11in) i. ink gouache wax twelve. 10-Sep-3 Sotheby's, Olympia #89/R est:1000-1500
£7500	$13425	€10950	Stroud Valley (58x80cm-23x31in) s. W/C gouache pencil wax resist. 16-Mar-4 Bonhams, New Bond Street #58/R est:5000-7000
£7500	$13875	€10950	Death of Actaeon (53x61cm-21x24in) s.i. s.verso pencil pen brush pastel W/C. 11-Mar-4 Christie's, Kensington #218/R est:3000-5000
£7800	$14196	€11388	Norman Church (55x75cm-22x30in) s. ink W/C pastel. 15-Jun-4 Bonhams, New Bond Street #65/R est:5000-7000
£8000	$13840	€11680	Caernarvon III (39x57cm-15x22in) s. W/C gouache chk pen ink prov. 11-Dec-3 Lyon & Turnbull, Edinburgh #16/R est:3000-5000
£8000	$14640	€11680	Old Rectory, great Snoring (38x56cm-15x22in) s.i.d.5.V.81 ink W/C bodycol col crayon prov. 4-Jun-4 Christie's, London #41/R est:3000-5000
£9000	$15300	€13140	Stour Valley (55x75cm-22x30in) s. i.verso ink W/C bodycol col crayon. 21-Nov-3 Christie's, London #3/R est:10000-15000
£10000	$18300	€14600	Royal Military Canal, Kent (37x56cm-15x22in) s.i.d.8 VII 81 ink W/C bodycol. 4-Jun-4 Christie's, London #44/R est:2500-3500
£11000	$18700	€16060	Tetbury (24x34cm-9x13in) s. ink W/C bodycol wax resist exhib. 21-Nov-3 Christie's, London #69/R est:4000-6000
£11000	$19360	€16060	Trawsallt, Cardiganshire (40x51cm-16x20in) s.d.1939 W/C monotype prov.exhib. 18-May-4 Woolley & Wallis, Salisbury #246/R est:3000-5000
£17000	$28900	€24820	Foliate heads (54x71cm-21x28in) s. ink col crayon W/C bodycol. 21-Nov-3 Christie's, London #70/R est:4000-6000

PIPON, Florence MacDonald (20th C) Canadian

£227	$411	€331	Evening glow, Peggy's Cove, Nova Scotia (25x30cm-10x12in) s.d.1929 board prov. 18-Apr-4 Levis, Calgary #535/R (C.D 550)

PIPPAL, Hans Robert (1915-1999) Austrian

£524	$876	€750	Venice, Saint Marco's Square (24x33cm-9x13in) s.d.1953. 10-Oct-3 Stadion, Trieste #522/R
£733	$1320	€1100	Room with balcony (24x14cm-9x6in) s. i. verso panel. 21-Apr-4 Dorotheum, Vienna #153/R
Works on paper			
£315	$568	€460	Still life of flowers (61x46cm-24x18in) s.d.1951 pastel. 26-Jan-4 Lilla Bukowskis, Stockholm #24 (S.KR 4200)
£567	$948	€800	Avenue in Schonbrunn (62x47cm-24x19in) s.i. pastel. 14-Oct-3 Dorotheum, Vienna #170/R
£1127	$1972	€1600	On the Danube in Vienna, Kahlenberg in the background (28x20cm-11x8in) s. pastel. 19-Dec-3 Dorotheum, Vienna #186/R est:900-1200

PIPPEL, Otto (1878-1960) German

£387	$670	€550	Mountain lake (106x98cm-42x39in) 15-Dec-3 Dr Fritz Nagel, Stuttgart #7097/R
£408	$731	€600	Alpine landscape with stream (48x36cm-19x14in) s. i. verso board. 18-Mar-4 Neumeister, Munich #2745/R
£458	$792	€650	Mountain landscape (48x60cm-19x24in) 15-Dec-3 Dr Fritz Nagel, Stuttgart #7042/R
£556	$906	€800	Ombretta and Sasso Vernale - King of the Dolomites (71x80cm-28x31in) s. 27-Sep-3 Dannenberg, Berlin #606/R
£559	$934	€800	Alpine landscape (45x42cm-18x17in) s. board. 30-Jun-3 Bloss, Merzhausen #1963/R
£694	$1146	€1000	Hunting party in autumn wood (49x60cm-19x24in) s. 3-Jul-3 Van Ham, Cologne #1405/R
£694	$1146	€1000	Summer's day on Starnberger See (42x47cm-17x19in) s. i. verso. 2-Jul-3 Neumeister, Munich #740/R
£733	$1320	€1100	Wilde Kaiser (61x51cm-24x20in) s. i. verso oil study board. 21-Apr-4 Neumeister, Munich #2698/R
£828	$1382	€1200	Flock of sheep returning home (35x28cm-14x11in) s. panel. 9-Jul-3 Hugo Ruef, Munich #170
£867	$1577	€1300	Konigssee (110x101cm-43x40in) s. 30-Jun-4 Neumeister, Munich #644/R
£867	$1577	€1300	Watzmann (80x70cm-31x28in) s. 30-Jun-4 Neumeister, Munich #645/R
£1000	$1820	€1500	Heathland with birch trees (66x86cm-26x34in) s. 30-Jun-4 Neumeister, Munich #642/R
£1000	$1830	€1500	German harvest (65x85cm-26x33in) s. 5-Jun-4 Arnold, Frankfurt #695/R est:3000
£1007	$1852	€1500	Tegernsee (89x96cm-35x38in) s. 26-Mar-4 Ketterer, Hamburg #205/R est:1500-1700
£1067	$1920	€1600	Spring on Pfeifferalm - Wetterstein mountains (48x61cm-19x24in) s. i. verso. 22-Apr-4 Allgauer, Kempten #3679/R est:1400
£1111	$1811	€1600	Lauterbrunnen valley in the Bernese Oberland (106x96cm-42x38in) s. i. stretcher. 25-Sep-3 Dr Fritz Nagel, Stuttgart #1390/R est:1400
£1119	$1902	€1600	Rose garden groupy (65x86cm-26x34in) s. 20-Nov-3 Van Ham, Cologne #1797 est:1400
£1127	$1949	€1600	View of Tegernsee (70x80cm-28x31in) s. 10-Dec-3 Hugo Ruef, Munich #2475/R est:1500

£1200 $2160 €1800 Mountain view (80x68cm-31x27in) s. 22-Apr-4 Weidler, Nurnberg #340/R est:1800
£1379 $2552 €2000 Walchensee (80x70cm-31x28in) s. 12-Feb-4 Weidler, Nurnberg #334/R
£1467 $2699 €2200 Moorland pond, Moosschweige (50x60cm-20x24in) s. 9-Jun-4 Dorotheum, Salzburg #710/R est:4400-6500
£1467 $2699 €2200 View from on high looking down towards the Rhine valley (62x50cm-24x20in) s. i.verso. 11-Jun-4 Wendl, Rudolstadt #4221/R est:2200
£1467 $2669 €2200 Hunters in wood (80x70cm-31x28in) s. 30-Jun-4 Neumeister, Munich #643/R
£1538 $2615 €2200 Gathering storm (80x105cm-31x41in) s. i. verso. 22-Nov-3 Arnold, Frankfurt #608/R est:1200
£1608 $2734 €2300 View of the Raintal (99x90cm-39x35in) s. i.d.1920 verso lit. 28-Nov-3 Schloss Ahlden, Ahlden #1538/R est:3200
£1678 $3087 €2500 Amsel song - early spring in Bavaria (108x101cm-43x40in) s. lit. 25-Mar-4 Karlheinz Kaupp, Staufen #2657/R est:2500
£1769 $3166 €2600 Castle with pond (96x106cm-38x42in) i. 17-Mar-4 Neumeister, Munich #565/R est:1500
£1806 $2979 €2600 Fosombrone, Toscana (33x51cm-13x20in) s. 2-Jul-3 Neumeister, Munich #741 est:1000
£1818 $3036 €2600 Sunny woodland path (52x62cm-20x24in) s. i. verso. 9-Oct-3 Michael Zeller, Lindau #724/R est:2600
£1818 $3091 €2600 Fishing boats in Chioggia near Venice (28x36cm-11x14in) 20-Nov-3 Dorotheum, Salzburg #201/R est:5200-8000
£2000 $3680 €3000 Late summer on Chiemsee (50x60cm-20x24in) s. 9-Jun-4 Dorotheum, Salzburg #707/R est:6000-9000
£2055 $3493 €3000 Cows on Chiemsee shore (79x97cm-31x38in) s. 5-Nov-3 Hugo Ruef, Munich #1081/R est:2500
£2128 $3553 €3000 Venice (62x72cm-24x28in) s. 14-Oct-3 Dorotheum, Vienna #122/R est:3600-5000
£2192 $3726 €3200 Lago Maggiore (42x46cm-17x18in) s. 5-Nov-3 Hugo Ruef, Munich #1080/R est:1200
£2206 $3750 €3221 Kabarett (60x50cm-24x20in) s. i.verso masonite. 19-Nov-3 Bonhams & Butterfields, San Francisco #169/R
£2517 $4280 €3600 Garden cafe on Starnberger See (18x25cm-7x10in) board. 20-Nov-3 Dorotheum, Salzburg #203/R est:6000-9000
£2552 $4721 €3700 Tegernsee in early spring (42x47cm-17x19in) s. s.i. verso. 14-Feb-4 Hans Stahl, Hamburg #74/R est:2000
£2632 $4842 €4000 Piazetta, view of San Giorgio (60x70cm-24x28in) 22-Jun-4 Wiener Kunst Auktionen, Vienna #81/R est:3000
£2833 $5157 €4250 Haymakers at work (81x70cm-32x28in) s. 3-Jul-4 Badum, Bamberg #52/R est:3800
£2836 $4905 €4141 Schwartzwaldtannem, Das Muntertahl (96x115cm-38x45in) s. 9-Dec-3 Rasmussen, Copenhagen #1429/R est:30000-35000 (D.KR 30000)
£3000 $5370 €4500 Havel landscape (71x81cm-28x32in) s. 15-May-4 Bassenge, Berlin #7104/R est:7000
£3200 $5760 €4800 Hunt (47x42cm-19x17in) s. 20-Apr-4 Sotheby's, Amsterdam #57/R est:2000-3000
£3843 $6880 €5611 Im Maxim Paris (24x29cm-9x11in) s. panel. 25-May-4 Bukowskis, Stockholm #366/R est:20000-25000 (S.KR 52000)
£4000 $7200 €6000 Recital (34x52cm-13x20in) s. board. 20-Apr-4 Sotheby's, Amsterdam #68/R est:6000-8000
£4000 $7160 €6000 Berlin street scene (60x80cm-24x31in) s. 13-May-4 Neumeister, Munich #468/R est:6000-8000
£5743 $10108 €8500 Venice (62x50cm-24x20in) s. panel. 22-May-4 Lempertz, Koln #1584/R est:6000
£6993 $11888 €10000 Monument on Unter den Linden avenue, Berlin (89x100cm-35x39in) s.d.1920. 29-Nov-3 Bassenge, Berlin #6954/R est:8000
£12000 $21840 €17520 Potsdamer Square, Berlin (42x47cm-17x19in) s. s.i.verso prov. 15-Jun-4 Sotheby's, London #57/R est:10000-15000
£24658 $41918 €36000 Tavern garden on Starnberg Lake (80x100cm-31x39in) s. s.i. verso. 8-Nov-3 Hans Stahl, Toestorf #15/R est:20000

PIPPEN, Steven (1960-) American
Photographs
£3892 $6500 €5682 Laundromat pictures - self portrait profile (30x40cm-12x16in) s. black white photograph set of four prov. 14-Nov-3 Phillips, New York #226/R est:8000-12000

PIPPIN, Horace (1888-1946) American
£79545 $140000 €116136 Den (51x61cm-20x24in) s. painted 1945 prov.exhib.lit. 18-May-4 Christie's, Rockefeller NY #148/R est:80000-120000

PIQTOUKUN, David Ruben (1950-) North American
Sculpture
£1351 $2297 €1972 Shaman/musk ox with horns (34cm-13in) s. marbled brown stone. 3-Nov-3 Waddingtons, Toronto #413/R est:2500-3000 (C.D 3000)

PIQUET, Pierre (1828-1878) French
£873 $1590 €1275 Bird's nest between pink roses (41x33cm-16x13in) s.d.1857 panel. 16-Jun-4 Fischer, Luzern #2313/R (S.FR 2000)

PIRA, Gioacchino la (19th C) Italian
£2817 $4873 €4000 Amalfi (61x43cm-24x17in) tempera card. 11-Dec-3 Christie's, Rome #134/R est:4500-5500
£3082 $5240 €4500 View of Ischia (51x71cm-20x28in) s.i. 6-Nov-3 Tajan, Paris #138/R est:2500-3000
Works on paper
£5592 $10289 €8500 View of Naples at night (35x46cm-14x18in) s.i. gouache. 22-Jun-4 Sotheby's, Milan #185/R est:6000-8000
£7237 $13316 €11000 View of Sorrento (39x60cm-15x24in) s. gouache. 22-Jun-4 Sotheby's, Milan #194/R est:11000-13000

PIRA, Gioacchino la (attrib) (19th C) Italian
Works on paper
£4605 $8474 €7000 View of Ischia and Procida (46x67cm-18x26in) gouache. 22-Jun-4 Sotheby's, Milan #153/R est:9000-11000

PIRA, la (19th C) Italian
Works on paper
£1831 $3168 €2600 Fishermen at sunset (43x63cm-17x25in) s. gouache. 10-Dec-3 Finarte Semenzato, Rome #157/R est:3000-3500
£6145 $11000 €8972 Naples and Pompeii views (42x61cm-17x24in) s.i. gouache paperboard four. 14-May-4 Skinner, Boston #24a/R est:1500-2000

PIRANDELLO, Fausto (1899-1975) Italian
£10490 $17832 €15000 Untitled (69x87cm-27x34in) s. s.verso cardboard on board prov. 24-Nov-3 Christie's, Milan #197/R est:20000-30000
£12081 $21624 €18000 Entrance of the villa (50x60cm-20x24in) s. board painted c.1939 exhib.lit. 29-May-4 Farsetti, Prato #548/R est:18000-22000
£28000 $46760 €40880 Natura morta con black and white (70x101cm-28x40in) s. board prov.lit. 21-Oct-3 Christie's, London #17/R est:30000-40000
£46000 $76820 €67160 Bagnanti. Tetti di Roma (65x61cm-26x24in) s. panel double-sided. 22-Oct-3 Bonhams, New Bond Street #33/R est:10000-15000
£68966 $115172 €100000 Mother (94x71cm-37x28in) s.d.1932 board exhib. 17-Nov-3 Sant Agostino, Torino #249/R est:100000-130000
Works on paper
£1310 $2188 €1900 Bathers (22x28cm-9x11in) s. wax crayon. 13-Nov-3 Finarte Semenzato, Rome #165 est:1800-2400
£2276 $3801 €3300 Rooftops in Rome (28x22cm-11x9in) W/C prov.exhib. 13-Nov-3 Finarte Semenzato, Rome #151/R est:1600-1800

PIRANESI, Giovan Battista (1720-1778) Italian
£322 $593 €480 Trajan column (54x40cm-21x16in) 29-Mar-4 Dr Fritz Nagel, Stuttgart #6561/R
Prints
£2682 $4800 €3916 Vesuta dell Anfiteatro flavio detto il Colosseo (50x71cm-20x28in) etching. 6-May-4 Swann Galleries, New York #160/R est:2500-3500
£2877 $4890 €4200 Grande Place. eau forte. 6-Nov-3 Piasa, Paris #15/R
£7000 $12040 €10220 Pier with chains (40x55cm-16x22in) etching. 4-Dec-3 Sotheby's, London #41/R est:3000-4000
Works on paper
£25850 $46272 €38000 Homme debout vu de dos (18x25cm-7x10in) d.1753 pen brown ink wash col print. 19-Mar-4 Piasa, Paris #48/R est:40000-50000

PIRE, Ferdinand (1943-) Belgian
£671 $1242 €1000 L'inconsolable (40x30cm-16x12in) s. s.i.verso. 13-Mar-4 De Vuyst, Lokeren #264
£699 $1168 €1000 Jeunes femmes nues (60x50cm-24x20in) s. triptych. 13-Oct-3 Horta, Bruxelles #32
£759 $1403 €1100 Jeunes femmes nues (60x50cm-24x20in) s. triptych. 19-Jan-4 Horta, Bruxelles #74
Works on paper
£867 $1551 €1300 A la plage (23x27cm-9x11in) s. eglomise. 15-May-4 De Vuyst, Lokeren #253

PIRE, Marcel (1913-1981) Belgian
£362 $655 €550 Bouquet printanier (100x90cm-39x35in) s. 19-Apr-4 Horta, Bruxelles #364
£533 $955 €800 Vase de roses (60x50cm-24x20in) s. 11-May-4 Vanderkindere, Brussels #166
£2045 $3600 €2986 View towards Place de la Courde, Paris (66x97cm-26x38in) s. prov. 23-May-4 Hindman, Chicago #65/R est:2000-4000

PIRE, Sophie (1858-1936) Belgian
£582 $990 €850 Jeu de chatons (65x80cm-26x31in) s. 10-Nov-3 Horta, Bruxelles #10

PIRENNE-KEPENNE, Victoire (1883-1932) Belgian
£430 $783 €650 Vue de la Meuse (50x60cm-20x24in) s.d.novembre 1924 panel. 16-Jun-4 Hotel des Ventes Mosan, Brussels #241

PIRES, Yves (1958-) French
Sculpture
£1879 $3439 €2800 Nu agenouille (42cm-17in) s. num.4/8 brown pat bronze st.f.Serralheiro. 7-Jul-4 Artcurial Briest, Paris #149 est:3000-4000
£2014 $3283 €2900 Seduction (35x18x22cm-14x7x9in) s.num.6/8 violace brown pat bronze Cast Paumelle. 18-Jul-3 Feletin, Province #85
£2028 $3488 €2900 Severine. s.num.8/8 brown pat bronze Cast Serralheiro. 7-Dec-3 Feletin, Province #83

PIRIE, Sir George (1863-1946) British
£4200 $6594 €6090 White cockerel (28x38cm-11x15in) s. panel. 27-Aug-3 Sotheby's, London #1091/R est:1200-1800
Works on paper
£400 $720 €584 Moorish pack horse (26x29cm-10x11in) s. pencil chl W/C oil board. 21-Jan-4 Sotheby's, Olympia #260/R

PIROLA, René (1879-1912) French
£4610 $7699 €6500 Tunisiennes allant a la mosquee (68x92cm-27x36in) s.i. canvas on panel. 16-Jun-3 Gros & Delettrez, Paris #487/R est:6000-8000

PIRON, Léon (1899-1962) Belgian
£2381 $3810 €3452 Nukerke (27x35cm-11x14in) s.i. pavatex. 15-May-3 Stuker, Bern #1444/R est:800-1000 (S.FR 5000)
£6000 $10860 €9000 Paysage de neige, Etikhove (72x80cm-28x31in) s. 30-Mar-4 Campo, Vlaamse Kaai #140/R est:7500-8500

PIROSKA, Fuszko (20th C) ?
£269 $425 €393 Woman reading a book (51x41cm-20x16in) s. 6-Sep-3 Brunk, Ashville #75

PIROUS, Abdul Djalil (1933-) Indonesian
£1812 $2808 €2646 Balinese boats (63x95cm-25x37in) s.d.60. 6-Oct-2 Sotheby's, Singapore #116/R est:5000-7000 (S.D 5000)
£2174 $3370 €3174 Self portrait (30x50cm-12x20in) s.d.64 sold with oils by Sumardjo, Sudiardjo three. 6-Oct-2 Sotheby's, Singapore #123/R est:6000-9000 (S.D 6000)
£2717 $4212 €3967 Ikan Karang (43x65cm-17x26in) s.d.63 board. 6-Oct-2 Sotheby's, Singapore #138/R est:4000-6000 (S.D 7500)

PIRSCH, Adolf (1858-1929) Austrian
£629 $1145 €950 Landscape in Holland (58x88cm-23x35in) 21-Jun-4 Dorotheum, Vienna #311/R
£845 $1462 €1200 Portrait of a lady (42x67cm-17x26in) 10-Dec-3 Dorotheum, Vienna #99/R
£1528 $2597 €2200 Portrait of Wilhelmina Helena Pauline von Oranien-Nassau (90x70cm-35x28in) 28-Oct-3 Dorotheum, Vienna #166/R est:2500-2800

PISA, Alberto (1864-1931) Italian
Works on paper
£563 $975 €800 Mussels (21x42cm-8x17in) s.i. W/C oval. 9-Dec-3 Pandolfini, Florence #189/R
£704 $1218 €1000 Sorrento (60x45cm-24x18in) s. W/C. 9-Dec-3 Pandolfini, Florence #184 est:850-900
£1700 $3128 €2482 Power of music (25x36cm-10x14in) s. W/C. 24-Mar-4 Hamptons Fine Art, Godalming #241/R

PISAN SCHOOL (14th C) Italian
£13000 $22100 €18980 Saint Jerome and Michael, the Crucifixion with the Magdalen at the foot of the cross above (79x47cm-31x19in) panel arched top painted integral frame. 29-Oct-3 Christie's, London #79/R est:7000-10000

PISANI, Giuseppe (1757-1839) Italian
Sculpture
£4605 $8474 €7000 Bust of Homer (56cm-22in) s.i.d.1796 white marble lit. 23-Jun-4 Sotheby's, Paris #105/R est:7000-9000

PISANI, Louis (18/19th C) Italian?
£276 $500 €403 Dante Alighieri and Beatrice (25x20cm-10x8in) s.i.verso board oval. 18-Apr-4 Jeffery Burchard, Florida #49/R
£339 $600 €495 Mater Dolorosa (33x28cm-13x11in) i.verso after Giovanni Battista Salvi. 2-May-4 Bonhams & Butterfields, San Francisco #1004/R
£1617 $3008 €2361 Le Cardinal d'Este presente Torquato Tasso au Duc de Ferrara et ses soeurs (112x145cm-44x57in) i.verso. 2-Mar-4 Rasmussen, Copenhagen #1476/R est:25000 (D.KR 18000)
£2336 $3692 €3387 Cardinal d'Este with Duke of Ferrara and his sisters (112x145cm-44x57in) i. 2-Sep-3 Rasmussen, Copenhagen #1833/R est:15000 (D.KR 25000)

PISANO, Giovanni (1875-1954) Italian
£503 $891 €750 Autumn is beginning (25x35cm-10x14in) s. cardboard. 1-May-4 Meeting Art, Vercelli #313
£503 $891 €750 Summer landscape (25x35cm-10x14in) s. board. 1-May-4 Meeting Art, Vercelli #428
£638 $1129 €950 Rainy summer (25x36cm-10x14in) s. board. 1-May-4 Meeting Art, Vercelli #375
£705 $1247 €1050 Lagoon (28x45cm-11x18in) s. board. 1-May-4 Meeting Art, Vercelli #220
£1208 $2138 €1800 Seascape (41x63cm-16x25in) s. cardboard. 1-May-4 Meeting Art, Vercelli #328 est:1500
£1389 $2361 €2000 Winter sunset (35x62cm-14x24in) s. 1-Nov-3 Meeting Art, Vercelli #126/R est:2000
£1611 $2851 €2400 Grey weather (24x34cm-9x13in) s. board. 1-May-4 Meeting Art, Vercelli #271 est:1000
£2013 $3564 €3000 Back from pasture at sunset (40x100cm-16x39in) s.d.1915. 1-May-4 Meeting Art, Vercelli #347 est:3000

PISANO, Gustavo (1877-?) Italian
£1000 $1760 €1460 Neapolitan street scene (44x30cm-17x12in) s. 19-May-4 Christie's, Kensington #729 est:1000-1500
£1100 $1947 €1606 Neapolitan street (28x16cm-11x6in) s.i. i.d.August 1909 verso panel. 29-Apr-4 Christie's, Kensington #212/R est:1200-1800

PISCHINGER, Carl (1823-1886) Austrian
£1806 $3069 €2600 Goats in extensive landscape (33x45cm-13x18in) s. 28-Oct-3 Dorotheum, Vienna #17/R est:2200-2500

PISECKI, Josef (1878-1954) Czechoslovakian
£316 $557 €474 Isle of Rab (51x60cm-20x24in) s. cardboard. 22-May-4 Dorotheum, Prague #78/R est:15000-23000 (C.KR 15000)
£759 $1336 €1139 View from Old Prague (48x58cm-19x23in) s. cardboard. 22-May-4 Dorotheum, Prague #77/R est:20000-30000 (C.KR 36000)

PISIS, Filippo de (1896-1956) Italian
£3846 $6538 €5500 Portrait (35x28cm-14x11in) canvas on cardboard. 25-Nov-3 Sotheby's, Milan #199/R est:5000-7000
£5405 $9514 €8000 Still life with lemons and asparagus (30x40cm-12x16in) s. cardboard on canvas painted 1950. 19-May-4 Il Ponte, Milan #1083 est:9000-10000
£5743 $10108 €8500 Still life with bottle (17x11cm-7x4in) board exhib. 24-May-4 Christie's, Milan #164/R est:7000-10000
£6000 $10800 €9000 Still life on the beach (20x35cm-8x14in) s. cardboard on canvas painted 1949. 22-Apr-4 Finarte Semenzato, Rome #299/R est:10000-12000
£9091 $15455 €13000 Vase of flowers (28x19cm-11x7in) s.d.27 cardboard. 20-Nov-3 Finarte Semenzato, Milan #183/R est:14000-18000
£9333 $16893 €14000 Landscape (26x19cm-10x7in) s.d.26 lit. 2-Apr-4 Farsetti, Prato #319/R est:14000-16000
£9420 $15449 €13000 Still life with flowers and a cup of coffee (52x41cm-20x16in) s. tempera paper on canvas. 31-May-3 Farsetti, Prato #608/R est:12500-14500
£9459 $16649 €14000 Vase of flowers (34x28cm-13x11in) s.d.1942. 22-May-4 Galleria Pananti, Florence #525/R est:12000-15000
£10563 $17535 €15000 Vase of flowers (62x38cm-24x15in) s. 11-Jun-3 Finarte Semenzato, Milan #649/R
£10915 $18120 €15500 Still life with bottle (36x30cm-14x12in) s.d.44 board exhib. 11-Jun-3 Finarte Semenzato, Milan #646/R est:16000
£11888 $20210 €17000 Flowers (40x30cm-16x12in) s.i.d.52 prov.lit. 25-Nov-3 Sotheby's, Milan #129/R est:18000-22000
£13986 $23776 €20000 Studio (55x20cm-22x8in) s.d.38 canvas on board exhib.lit. 29-Nov-3 Farsetti, Prato #506/R est:20000-25000
£14493 $23768 €20000 Landscape (50x60cm-20x24in) s.d.49 exhib.lit. 31-May-3 Farsetti, Prato #626/R est:16000-19000
£14765 $26430 €22000 Vase of flowers (50x40cm-20x16in) s.d.1943. 29-May-4 Farsetti, Prato #449/R est:20000-25000
£14865 $26162 €22000 Courtyard (65x46cm-26x18in) s. prov. 24-May-4 Christie's, Milan #171/R est:13000-16000
£16779 $30034 €25000 Farms with figures (40x50cm-16x20in) s.d.1950 cardboard on canvas lit. 30-May-4 Meeting Art, Vercelli #93 est:20000
£17000 $30430 €25500 Still life with pepper (50x71cm-20x28in) s.d.51 cardboard prov. 12-May-4 Stadion, Trieste #691/R est:18000-22000
£17483 $29720 €25000 Still life with sea (50x60cm-20x24in) s.d.46. 24-Nov-3 Christie's, Milan #276/R est:25000-30000
£19580 $33287 €28000 Seascape with shell (27x40cm-11x16in) s.d.30. 25-Nov-3 Sotheby's, Milan #188/R est:30000-40000
£20979 $35664 €30000 Still life with grapes and figs (42x55cm-17x22in) s.d.28 board prov.exhib. 24-Nov-3 Christie's, Milan #277/R est:35000-45000
£20979 $35664 €30000 Road (70x50cm-28x20in) s.d.42. 24-Nov-3 Christie's, Milan #315/R est:18000-24000
£21739 $35652 €30000 Bottle and green leaves (51x36cm-20x14in) s.d.25 cardboard prov.lit. 27-May-3 Sotheby's, Milan #220/R est:30000-40000
£21739 $35652 €30000 Via Margutta, spring morning (75x55cm-30x22in) s.d.43 cardboard on canvas prov. 27-May-3 Sotheby's, Milan #232/R est:35000-45000
£22378 $38042 €32000 View of Cortina (80x64cm-31x25in) s. painted 1931 exhib.lit. 29-Nov-3 Farsetti, Prato #541/R est:20000
£25175 $42797 €36000 Vase of flowers (74x50cm-29x20in) s.d.42. 24-Nov-3 Christie's, Milan #253/R est:20000-30000
£29730 $52324 €44000 Vase of flowers with shell (80x60cm-31x24in) s.d.40. 24-May-4 Christie's, Milan #315/R est:25000-30000
£32609 $53478 €45000 Roses and carnations (60x50cm-24x20in) s.d.41 prov.exhib.lit. 27-May-3 Sotheby's, Milan #225/R est:45000-50000
£34483 $57586 €50000 Villa Patrizi courtyard (70x50cm-28x20in) s.d.43 prov.exhib.lit. 13-Nov-3 Finarte Semenzato, Rome #456/R est:60000-70000
£37584 $67275 €56000 Roses (68x51cm-27x20in) s.d.1929. 29-May-4 Farsetti, Prato #509/R est:40000-50000
£38462 $65385 €55000 Quai Voltaire (73x50cm-29x20in) s.d.34 prov. 25-Nov-3 Sotheby's, Milan #192/R est:60000-80000
£39161 $66573 €56000 Still life of fruit and bottle of spirit (65x75cm-26x30in) s.d.43 lit. 29-Nov-3 Farsetti, Prato #510/R est:55000-65000
£43478 $71304 €60000 Vase of flowers in an interior (100x65cm-39x26in) s.d.46 exhib.lit. 31-May-3 Farsetti, Prato #734/R est:60000-70000
£44138 $73710 €64000 View of Milan (90x70cm-35x28in) s.d.1941. 17-Nov-3 Sant Agostino, Torino #261/R est:65000-80000
£48951 $83217 €70000 Venice (95x73cm-37x29in) s.d.45. 26-Nov-3 Pandolfini, Florence #29/R est:70000-90000
£50725 $83188 €70000 Natura morta in riva al mare (51x67cm-20x26in) s.d.30 verso board on panel lit. 31-May-3 Farsetti, Prato #736/R est:70000-80000
£52817 $92430 €75000 Spring in Paris (56x46cm-22x18in) s. painted 1928 prov.exhib.lit. 16-Dec-3 Porro, Milan #13/R est:90000-100000
£53691 $96107 €80000 Still life of flowers and mushrooms (50x65cm-20x26in) s.d.26 exhib.lit. 29-May-4 Farsetti, Prato #529/R est:60000-80000
£72464 $118841 €100000 Rue de Volontaires (55x45cm-22x18in) s. painted 1924 exhib.lit. 31-May-3 Farsetti, Prato #743/R est:90000-120000
£90909 $154545 €130000 Still life with wine bottle (57x68cm-22x27in) s.d.1923 paper on canvas exhib.lit. 29-Nov-3 Farsetti, Prato #514/R est:130000-150000
Works on paper
£308 $514 €440 Nude (27x21cm-11x8in) s. pencil exhib.lit. 26-Jun-3 Sant Agostino, Torino #169/R
£455 $759 €650 Nudes (27x20cm-11x8in) s. pencil exec.1937 exhib.lit. 26-Jun-3 Sant Agostino, Torino #170/R
£455 $759 €650 Study of nude (20x27cm-8x11in) s. pencil exhib.lit. 26-Jun-3 Sant Agostino, Torino #176/R
£552 $921 €800 Figure (27x20cm-11x8in) ink. 17-Nov-3 Sant Agostino, Torino #38/R
£1189 $2021 €1700 Portrait of sailor (24x17cm-9x7in) Chinese ink W/C. 19-Nov-3 Cambi, Genoa #443/R est:1000-1200
£1310 $2175 €1900 Boy wearing hat (28x19cm-11x7in) s.i.d.1942 ink W/C. 1-Oct-3 Della Rocca, Turin #61/R
£1667 $3067 €2500 Boy with cap (37x26cm-15x10in) s.d.1933 pencil W/C prov. 8-Jun-4 Finarte Semenzato, Milan #113/R est:1000-1200
£2113 $3507 €3000 Great minds on the beach (26x17cm-10x7in) s.i. ink W/C. 11-Jun-3 Finarte Semenzato, Milan #505/R
£3147 $5413 €4500 Still life of flowers and ink stand (50x34cm-20x13in) s.d.55 W/C paper on cardboard. 3-Dec-3 Stadion, Trieste #1066/R est:2000-3000
£3497 $6014 €5000 Rose in a vase (50x34cm-20x13in) s. W/C paper on cardboard. 3-Dec-3 Stadion, Trieste #1068/R est:2000-3000
£4730 $8324 €7000 Interior (65x45cm-26x18in) s.d.40 W/C tempera paper on canvas prov. 24-May-4 Christie's, Milan #224/R est:7000-10000
£6294 $10699 €9000 Still life of fruit and vegetables (28x38cm-11x15in) W/C Chinese ink. 26-Nov-3 Pandolfini, Florence #18/R est:9000-12000
£8054 $14416 €12000 Vase of flowers (67x48cm-26x19in) s. W/C paper on canvas exec.1942. 29-May-4 Farsetti, Prato #409/R est:12000-15000

PISSARRO, Camille (1830-1903) French
£12583 $22901 €19000 Femme ecrivant (11x16cm-4x6in) st.mono. canvas on cardboard. 15-Jun-4 Rossini, Paris #29/R est:12000-18000
£52174 $95478 €76174 Boulevard sous la neige, Paris (9x13cm-4x5in) mono. painted 1878-79 prov. 5-Jun-4 Galerie du Rhone, Sion #534/R est:50000-70000 (S.FR 120000)
£81379 $135090 €118000 Jardin a eragny (19x27cm-7x11in) s. 2-Oct-3 Sotheby's, Paris #140/R est:100000
£120000 $218400 €175200 Brouillard a eragny (33x41cm-13x16in) init. init.on stretcher painted 1890 prov. 4-Feb-4 Sotheby's, London #218/R est:70000-90000

£126126	$216937	€184144	Vetheuil (38x46cm-15x18in) s.d.1890. 2-Dec-3 Koller, Zurich #3046/R est:300000-500000 (S.FR 280000)
£139860	$237762	€200000	Lavandieres a Eragny (38x46cm-15x18in) mono. painted 1898 lit. 21-Nov-3 Lombrail & Teucquam, Paris #114/R est:150000-200000
£156425	$280000	€228381	Etude a Pontoise (56x46cm-22x18in) init. painted c.1878 prov.exhib.lit. 5-May-4 Christie's, Rockefeller NY #235/R est:280000-350000
£180000	$327600	€262800	Leveuses a Eragny (38x46cm-15x18in) st.init. painted c.1898 prov.lit. 3-Feb-4 Christie's, London #134/R est:200000-300000
£190000	$349600	€277400	Coucher de soleil, Bazincourt (38x55cm-15x22in) s.d.1892 prov.exhib.lit. 23-Jun-4 Christie's, London #105/R est:100000-150000
£270742	$492751	€395283	Paysage avec maisons blanches a droite (46x56cm-18x22in) s.d.1870. 18-Jun-4 Kornfeld, Bern #132/R est:250000 (S.FR 620000)
£333333	$613333	€486666	Rue de village (32x40cm-13x16in) s. painted c.1865 prov. 23-Jun-4 Koller, Zurich #3022/R est:350000-550000 (S.FR 760000)
£470588	$800000	€687058	Le chou pres de Pontoise (53x54cm-21x21in) s.d.1878 prov.lit. 4-Nov-3 Christie's, Rockefeller NY #11/R est:900000-1200000
£480000	$878400	€700800	Port a Rouen (50x61cm-20x24in) s.d.1896. 2-Feb-4 Christie's, London #14/R est:450000-650000
£558659	$1000000	€815642	Pommes en fleurs, temps gris, Eragny (60x73cm-24x29in) s.d.97 prov.exhib. 5-May-4 Sotheby's, New York #10/R est:900000-1200000
£558824	$950000	€815883	Laveuse a eragny (60x73cm-24x29in) s.d.1899 prov.exhib.lit. 4-Nov-3 Christie's, Rockefeller NY #16/R est:1000000-1500000
£580000	$1067200	€846800	Repos des moissonneurs, Montfoucault (46x55cm-18x22in) s.d.1875 prov.lit. 22-Jun-4 Christie's, London #7/R est:350000-450000
£588235	$1000000	€858823	Sarcleurs dans les champs, Pontoise (46x55cm-18x22in) s.d.1875 prov.exhib.lit. 5-Nov-3 Sotheby's, New York #2/R est:1000000-1500000
£1176471	$2000000	€1717648	Paysage a osny pres de L'Abreuvoir (72x92cm-28x36in) s.d.1883 prov.exhib.lit. 5-Nov-3 Sotheby's, New York #14/R est:2500000-3500000

Prints

£1676	$3000	€2447	Repos du dimanche dans le Bois (18x29cm-7x11in) etching drypoint. 6-May-4 Swann Galleries, New York #307/R est:2000-3000
£1720	$3200	€2511	Faneuses (20x13cm-8x5in) etching. 2-Mar-4 Swann Galleries, New York #520/R est:2000-3000
£1765	$3000	€2577	Marche aux legumes, a Pointoise (26x20cm-10x8in) init.num.5/46 etching drypoint. 6-Nov-3 Swann Galleries, New York #398/R est:1800-2200
£1899	$3400	€2773	Vieille rue a Rouen (12x12cm-5x5in) s.i. etching drypoint. 6-May-4 Swann Galleries, New York #305/R est:4000-6000
£2000	$3440	€2920	La charrue (37x28cm-15x11in) s. col lithograph. 4-Dec-3 Sotheby's, London #213/R est:2000-3000
£2432	$4500	€3551	Paysage a Osny (11x16cm-4x6in) s.num.20 etching. 12-Feb-4 Christie's, Rockefeller NY #394/R est:2500-3500
£3067	$5489	€4600	Femmes nues (21x29cm-8x11in) st.mono. lithograph. 13-May-4 Bassenge, Berlin #5632/R est:1500
£3800	$6536	€5548	Quai des Menetriers a Bruges (16x20cm-6x8in) s.i. etching aquatint. 4-Dec-3 Sotheby's, London #212/R est:3500-4000
£4237	$7500	€6186	Rud de Gros-Horlage, a Rouen (19x14cm-7x6in) s.i.num.7 etching laid paper. 28-Apr-4 Christie's, Rockefeller NY #226/R est:6000-8000
£4367	$7948	€6376	Eglise et ferme d'Eragny. i. col etching. 17-Jun-4 Kornfeld, Bern #702/R est:10000 (S.FR 10000)
£4500	$7740	€6570	Paysage en long (11x40cm-4x16in) aquatint prov. 2-Dec-3 Christie's, London #290/R est:5000-7000
£4533	$8341	€6800	Paysanne bechant (16x12cm-6x5in) s.i. eau forte exec.1890. 10-Jun-4 Piasa, Paris #192
£4800	$8832	€7200	Ile Lacroix (11x15cm-4x6in) i. eau forte aquatint exec.1887. 10-Jun-4 Piasa, Paris #191/R
£4895	$8420	€7000	Femme a la barriere (16x11cm-6x4in) i. etching. 2-Dec-3 Hauswedell & Nolte, Hamburg #549/R est:9000
£5963	$9959	€8646	Baigneuses - theorie de baigneuses. s.i. lithograph. 19-Jun-3 Kornfeld, Bern #886/R est:12000 (S.FR 13000)
£6000	$11040	€9000	Quai de Paris, a Rouen (18x17cm-7x7in) s.i. etching. 10-Jun-4 Hauswedell & Nolte, Hamburg #589/R est:12000
£8235	$14000	€12023	Rue Moliere, a Rouen (19x14cm-7x6in) s.i. col lithograph. 6-Nov-3 Swann Galleries, New York #400/R est:5000-8000

Works on paper

£1818	$3036	€2600	Paysanne (22x16cm-9x6in) mono. chl dr exhib. 29-Jun-3 Eric Pillon, Calais #112/R
£3800	$6992	€5548	Pages d'etudes (20x16cm-8x6in) init. ink pencil. 24-Mar-4 Sotheby's, Olympia #23/R est:4000-6000
£3892	$6500	€5682	View of trees and brook (23x17cm 9x7in) init.d.87 pencil prov.exhib. 7-Oct-3 Sotheby's, New York #250 est:4000-6000
£4803	$8742	€7012	L'enfant au bol (32x28cm-13x11in) mono. chk prov. 17-Jun-4 Kornfeld, Bern #701/R est:15000 (S.FR 11000)
£5000	$8000	€7300	Femme a la parapluie (22x13cm-9x5in) st.init.i. pencil col ink. 18-Sep-3 Swann Galleries, New York #523/R est:10000-15000
£5500	$9185	€8030	Landscape (12x20cm-5x8in) st.init. pastel prov. 22-Oct-3 Sotheby's, Olympia #9/R est:4000-6000
£5946	$11000	€8681	Femme en profil (30x24cm-12x9in) st.init. chl exec.1895 prov. 11-Feb-4 Sotheby's, New York #1/R est:12000-18000
£7042	$12324	€10000	Les coteaux et les collines autour d'Eragny (22x30cm-9x12in) s. pastel exec.c.1890 prov. 16-Dec-3 Claude Aguttes, Neuilly #4/R est:5000-7000
£8000	$14480	€11680	Deux femmes de la campagne (29x28cm-11x11in) init.d.1891 chl col pastel card prov. 1-Apr-4 Christie's, Kensington #3/R est:5000-7000
£12000	$20040	€17520	Rue de village, la Roche-Guyon (30x47cm-12x19in) s.i. pencil brush ink wash prov. 21-Oct-3 Sotheby's, London #14/R est:10000-15000
£12291	$22000	€17945	Market scene with groups of peasants (23x18cm-9x7in) s. col chk dr. prov. 11-Jan-4 William Jenack, New York #251 est:20000-30000
£15294	$26000	€22329	Paysanne (21x12cm-8x5in) init. W/C over blk Conte crayon prov. 5-Nov-3 Christie's, Rockefeller NY #26000/R est:14000-18000
£17000	$30940	€24820	Etude pour la moisson a Montfoucault (21x26cm-8x10in) s.d.1876 pastel chl prov. 4-Feb-4 Sotheby's, London #409/R est:20000-30000
£20000	$33400	€29000	Arbre a Eragny (22x28cm-9x11in) mono.d.91 pastel. 17-Nov-3 Delorme & Bocage, Paris #111/R est:10000-12000
£20950	$37500	€30587	Cavia - Eragny (16x23cm-6x9in) s.i.d.1886 W/C prov.exhib. 6-May-4 Sotheby's, New York #227/R est:15000-20000
£22346	$40000	€32625	Collines autour d'Eragny (23x31cm-9x12in) s. pastel. 6-May-4 Sotheby's, New York #218/R est:20000-30000
£27000	$49680	€39420	Marche a Gisors (23x18cm-9x7in) init. col crayons chl exec c.1885 prov. 24-Jun-4 Christie's, London #313/R est:18000-24000
£29412	$50000	€42942	Vachere (25x31cm-10x12in) s. gouache prov. 6-Nov-3 Sotheby's, New York #136/R est:50000-70000
£32000	$58240	€46720	Portrait d'Eugenie Estruc (32x24cm-13x9in) s.d.1876 pastel prov.exhib.lit. 4-Feb-4 Sotheby's, London #422/R est:35000-45000
£41899	$75000	€61173	Paysanne assise (46x33cm-18x13in) s. W/C chl buff paper prov. 5-May-4 Christie's, Rockefeller NY #104/R est:40000-60000
£99291	$165816	€140000	Paysage d'hiver a Eragny (53x65cm-21x26in) s.d.95 pastel prov.exhib.lit. 19-Jun-3 Millon & Associes, Paris #27/R
£105960	$192848	€160000	Carnet de croquis (20x27cm-8x11in) album double-sided exec. 1854. 18-Jun-4 Piasa, Paris #15/R est:120000-150000
£120000	$218400	€175200	Gardeuse d'oies (29x59cm-11x23in) s.d.1890 gouache silk prov.exhib.lit. 5-Feb-4 Christie's, London #316/R est:150000-250000
£170000	$311100	€248200	Gardienne d'oie (27x21cm-11x8in) s. gouache silk on canvas prov. 2-Feb-4 Christie's, London #1/R est:120000-160000
£176471	$300000	€257648	Paysannes causant, soleil couchant, Eragny (20x13cm-8x5in) s.d.1892 gouache pencil silf on board prov.lit. 4-Nov-3 Christie's, Rockefeller NY #1/R est:300000-400000
£195531	$350000	€285475	Pere Melon fendant du bois (32x25cm-13x10in) s.d.80 gouache on linen prov.exhib.lit. 6-May-4 Sotheby's, New York #122/R est:380000-450000

PISSARRO, Camille (attrib) (1830-1903) French

Works on paper

£257	$475	€375	Girl reading (28x18cm-11x7in) s. chalk. 13-Feb-4 David Rago, Lambertville #55/R

PISSARRO, Camille and THORNLEY, Georges W (19th C) French

Prints

£3631	$6500	€5301	La mi-careme a Paris (20x25cm-8x10in) lithograph. 6-May-4 Swann Galleries, New York #308/R est:5000-8000

PISSARRO, Claude (1935-) French

£1657	$3000	€2419	Promenade sur la Grive (18x23cm-7x9in) s.i. 19-Apr-4 Daniel Cooney, Brooklyn #469055/R
£2676	$4683	€3800	Le bouquet de Pablo (100x81cm-39x32in) s. s.i.verso. 19-Dec-3 Delvaux, Paris #60 est:3000-5000
£3911	$7000	€5710	Le park d'Urville (51x61cm-20x24in) s. s.i.verso. 8-May-4 Susanin's, Chicago #6162/R est:6000-8000
£6486	$12000	€9470	Winter landscape (54x63cm-21x25in) s. 12-Feb-4 Sotheby's, New York #32/R est:5000-7000
£7027	$13000	€10259	Summer landscape (58x74cm-23x29in) s. 12-Feb-4 Sotheby's, New York #31/R est:7000-10000

Works on paper

£2905	$5200	€4241	Trois jeunes commeres au sord de L'orne (23x36cm-9x14in) s. pastel. 20-Mar-4 Selkirks, St. Louis #529/R est:3200-4200
£3000	$5010	€4380	Le lac de monsouris (37x51cm-15x20in) s. pastel. 22-Oct-3 Bonhams, New Bond Street #15/R est:3000-5000
£3000	$5010	€4380	La plage a maree haute - Arromanches (37x51cm-15x20in) s. pastel. 22-Oct-3 Bonhams, New Bond Street #16/R est:3000-5000

PISSARRO, Felix (1874-1897) French

£1849	$3144	€2700	Vase de fleurs (72x59cm-28x23in) s.d.1964 panel. 6-Nov-3 Sotheby's, Paris #33/R est:300-400
£1986	$3377	€2900	Vase avec bouquet de roses (64x63cm-25x25in) s. panel. 6-Nov-3 Sotheby's, Paris #32/R est:300-400

PISSARRO, Lucien (1863-1944) British/French

£9000	$15300	€13140	Nightingale farm, Langham, Essex (33x46cm-13x18in) mono.d.34 prov.lit. 26-Nov-3 Hamptons Fine Art, Godalming #250/R est:6000-10000
£13907	$25311	€21000	Paysage a la frette (24x33cm-9x13in) s.i. panel. 18-Jun-4 Piasa, Paris #17/R est:6000-8000
£14000	$23800	€20440	Orchard, rivers bridge (65x53cm-26x21in) mono.d.1922 prov.exhib.lit. 21-Nov-3 Christie's, London #99/R est:10000-15000
£20000	$34000	€29200	St. Mary Church in the mist, East Knoyle (53x65cm-21x26in) mono.d.1917 prov.exhib.lit. 21-Nov-3 Christie's, London #96/R est:20000-30000
£23000	$39100	€33580	Rhododendrons, Hawkchurch (54x46cm-21x18in) mono.d.1936 i.on stretcher prov.exhib.lit. 21-Nov-3 Christie's, London #97/R est:20000-30000
£23551	$38152	€34149	Brookleton Yulgreave, August (52x43cm-20x17in) s.d.1928 prov.exhib. 31-Jul-3 International Art Centre, Auckland #53/R est:50000-75000 (NZ.D 65000)
£27000	$49410	€39420	Soleil couchant dans les pins, Le Brusq (46x38cm-18x15in) mono.d.1925 prov.exhib.lit. 2-Jun-4 Sotheby's, London #47/R est:25000-35000
£28986	$46957	€42030	Campagne orovida, Fenouils et Amandier (65x54cm-26x21in) s.d.1934 i.verso prov.exhib. 31-Jul-3 International Art Centre, Auckland #52/R est:80000-100000 (NZ.D 80000)
£38000	$69540	€55480	Le Lauron, Cotignac (53x63cm-21x25in) mono.d.1937 s.i.verso exhib. 4-Jun-4 Christie's, London #7/R est:20000-30000
£42000	$76860	€61320	Warren, Hawkchurch (54x65cm-21x26in) mono.d.1936 prov.exhib.lit. 2-Jun-4 Sotheby's, London #46/R est:25000-35000
£44000	$80520	€64240	Brook, sunny weather (56x46cm-22x18in) mono.d.1911 i.stretcher prov.exhib.lit. 4-Jun-4 Christie's, London #10/R est:20000-30000
£50000	$91500	€73000	Terraces, Bandol (45x54cm-18x21in) mono.d.1925 prov.lit. 2-Jun-4 Sotheby's, London #45/R est:50000-70000
£75000	$129000	€109500	An Essex Hall (61x73cm-24x29in) mono.d.1893 prov.exhib.lit. 3-Dec-3 Sotheby's, London #3/R est:25000-35000
£95000	$163400	€138700	Vue du Lavandou avec mer bleue (60x73cm-24x29in) mono.d.1923 prov.exhib.lit. 3-Dec-3 Sotheby's, London #12/R est:50000-70000
£125000	$227500	€182500	Le petit chaperon rouge (73x50cm-29x20in) mono.d.92 i. stretcher prov.exhib.lit. 15-Jun-4 Bonhams, New Bond Street #10/R est:120000-180000

Works on paper

£2200	$4026	€3212	Chaumont-en-vexin (16x25cm-6x10in) mono.i.d.1926 pencil W/C prov. 4-Jun-4 Christie's, London #9/R est:1500-2500
£2600	$4472	€3796	Church, Dartmouth (25x19cm-10x7in) mono.i.d.1922 W/C col crayon pen ink prov.exhib. 3-Dec-3 Christie's, Kensington #605/R est:1000-1500

PISSARRO, Lucien (attrib) (1863-1944) British/French

Works on paper

£250	$458	€365	Untitled (10x13cm-4x5in) pencil col crayon. 28-Jul-4 Mallams, Oxford #104/R
£800	$1480	€1168	In Kew Garden (25x20cm-10x8in) mono. 9-Mar-4 Gorringes, Lewes #2024

PISSARRO, Ludovic Rodo (1878-1952) French

£420	$722	€600	Portrait de femme (55x45cm-22x18in) s. 3-Dec-3 Fraysse & Associes, Paris #108/R

Works on paper

£263	$484	€400	Porte de Brancion (25x35cm-10x14in) i.d.5 fev 04 W/C. 23-Jun-4 Maigret, Paris #167
£263	$484	€400	Bords du Loiret (28x38cm-11x15in) s.d.1927 W/C. 23-Jun-4 Maigret, Paris #174/R
£276	$508	€420	Couple de danseurs (21x17cm-8x7in) mono.13 fev 1903 W/C. 23-Jun-4 Maigret, Paris #194
£296	$545	€450	Maison normande, Alencon (20x25cm-8x10in) s.i. W/C. 23-Jun-4 Maigret, Paris #206
£300	$519	€438	Les danseuses (21x29cm-8x11in) pencil pen ink. 11-Dec-3 Christie's, Kensington #31/R
£329	$605	€500	Montmartre, Rue Norvins (23x33cm-9x13in) s. W/C. 23-Jun-4 Maigret, Paris #169
£362	$666	€550	Bords de la lezarde (25x35cm-10x14in) s.i.d.20 septembre 1904 W/C. 23-Jun-4 Maigret, Paris #170
£362	$666	€550	Jeunes filles (32x26cm-13x10in) s.d.1905 ink W/C. 23-Jun-4 Maigret, Paris #181
£395	$726	€600	Paysage breton (26x34cm-10x13in) s. W/C. 23-Jun-4 Maigret, Paris #172
£395	$726	€600	Bateaux pecheurs bretons (28x38cm-11x15in) W/C. 23-Jun-4 Maigret, Paris #173/R
£395	$726	€600	Paysage de riviere (38x28cm-15x11in) W/C sketch verso. 23-Jun-4 Maigret, Paris #176
£395	$726	€600	Bord de riviere (24x32cm-9x13in) mono. W/C. 23-Jun-4 Maigret, Paris #177
£395	$726	€600	Concarneau, port breton (19x30cm-7x12in) W/C. 23-Jun-4 Maigret, Paris #200
£461	$847	€700	Rue de Mont Cenis (25x20cm-10x8in) s.i. W/C. 23-Jun-4 Maigret, Paris #203
£461	$847	€700	Deux jeunes femmes (25x19cm-10x7in) s. W/C. 23-Jun-4 Maigret, Paris #204/R
£461	$847	€700	Bateau (19x25cm-7x10in) W/C. 23-Jun-4 Maigret, Paris #201/R
£537	$993	€800	Paris, la Seine et Notre-Dame (27x37cm-11x15in) s. W/C. 14-Mar-4 Eric Pillon, Calais #129/R
£789	$1453	€1200	Elegantes. mono. ink W/C three. 23-Jun-4 Maigret, Paris #199
£822	$1513	€1250	Pont Neuf avec personnages (21x25cm-8x10in) s. W/C. 23-Jun-4 Maigret, Paris #211/R
£855	$1574	€1300	Elegantes. mono. W/C two. 23-Jun-4 Maigret, Paris #197
£855	$1574	€1300	Saint Germain des Pres (29x22cm-11x9in) W/C. 23-Jun-4 Maigret, Paris #210
£987	$1816	€1500	Elegante. Les anglais. s. one d.1902 one. i. ink W/C two. 23-Jun-4 Maigret, Paris #196 est:150-200
£1316	$2421	€2000	Brighton (23x29cm-9x11in) s.i. W/C exec. 1906. 23-Jun-4 Maigret, Paris #205/R est:500-600

PISSARRO, Orovida (1893-1968) British

£2200	$3674	€3212	Les cinq chats (61x51cm-24x20in) s.d.1958. 16-Oct-3 Christie's, Kensington #375/R est:2500-3500
Works on paper			
£320	$589	€467	Horses in a field (13x20cm-5x8in) mono.d.1909 W/C. 8-Jun-4 Gorringes, Lewes #2223
£440	$779	€642	Horse in a field (13x20cm-5x8in) mono.d.1909 W/C. 29-Apr-4 Gorringes, Lewes #2398

PISSARRO, Paul Émile (1884-1972) French

£903	$1490	€1300	Neige a Placy (25x33cm-10x13in) s. 3-Jul-3 Claude Aguttes, Neuilly #141
£1597	$2635	€2300	Paysage (54x63cm-21x25in) s. 3-Jul-3 Claude Aguttes, Neuilly #140 est:200-450
£1656	$3013	€2500	Sous bois (55x46cm-22x18in) s. 18-Jun-4 Piasa, Paris #158/R est:2500-3000
£2276	$3801	€3300	Ferme en Suisse Romande (45x59cm-18x23in) 12-Nov-3 Chassaing Rivet, Toulouse #133
£2819	$5215	€4200	Chaumiere sous la neige (54x65cm-21x26in) s. i.verso. 14-Mar-4 Eric Pillon, Calais #168/R
£3007	$5172	€4300	Roche a Bunel (65x54cm-26x21in) s. 5-Dec-3 Maigret, Paris #18/R est:1800-2200
£4027	$7490	€6000	Port de Dieppe (89x116cm-35x46in) s.d.1924. 3-Mar-4 Tajan, Paris #52 est:6000-8000
Works on paper			
£293	$531	€440	Pommiers en fleurs (24x32cm-9x13in) s. W/C. 30-Mar-4 Palais de Beaux Arts, Brussels #677
£852	$1500	€1244	Harbour (23x30cm-9x12in) s. pastel exec.c.1900. 23-May-4 Treadway Gallery, Cincinnati #593/R est:1500-2000
£1379	$2303	€2000	Voiliers (17x24cm-7x9in) s. pastel. 11-Nov-3 Lesieur & Le Bars, Le Havre #89
£2115	$3595	€3088	Landscape with two figures by lake (22x30cm-9x12in) s. pastel. 5-Nov-3 Dobiaschofsky, Bern #859/R est:6000 (S.FR 4800)

PISSARRO, Victor (1891-1937) Argentinian

Works on paper			
£726	$1300	€1060	Big farm (40x48cm-16x19in) W/C. 11-May-4 Arroyo, Buenos Aires #74

PISSIS, Noel Aime (c.1812-?) French

Works on paper			
£733	$1341	€1100	Landscape (18x25cm-7x10in) i. W/C. 6-Jul-4 Bolsa de Arte, Rio de Janeiro #55/R (B.R 4000)
£1374	$2431	€2061	Landscape with a cove (15x25cm-6x10in) mixed media. 27-Apr-4 Bolsa de Arte, Rio de Janeiro #9/R (B.R 7500)
£1557	$2755	€2336	Rio de Janeiro (20x27cm-8x11in) W/C. 27-Apr-4 Bolsa de Arte, Rio de Janeiro #8/R (B.R 8500)

PISTAUER, Josef Anton (1718-?) Austrian

£2517	$4330	€3600	St Nepomuk between putti on clouds (86x52cm-34x20in) s.d.1767. 5-Dec-3 Michael Zeller, Lindau #549/R est:1500

PISTOLETTO, Ettore Olivero (1898-1984) Italian

£267	$491	€400	Church in the valley (33x25cm-13x10in) s.d.1944 board. 8-Jun-4 Della Rocca, Turin #294/R
£302	$535	€450	Granny Angiolina's courtyard (25x30cm-10x12in) s. board. 1-May-4 Meeting Art, Vercelli #425
£400	$736	€600	Plants and flowers (50x40cm-20x16in) s.d.1954 board. 8-Jun-4 Della Rocca, Turin #292/R

PISTOLETTO, Michelangelo (1933-) Italian

£2215	$3964	€3300	Frattali (114x93cm-45x37in) s.i.d.1999-2000 verso acrylic on mirror. 28-May-4 Farsetti, Prato #245/R est:2600-2900
£2937	$4993	€4200	Frattali (120x77cm-47x30in) oil felt-tip pen on mirror exhib. 24-Nov-3 Christie's, Milan #178/R est:4000-6000
£3472	$5486	€5000	Frattoli (70x78cm-28x31in) mirror. 6-Sep-3 Meeting Art, Vercelli #594 est:5000
£83333	$136667	€115000	Girl with bag (150x120cm-59x47in) s.i.d.1960 verso paint on steel prov. 27-May-3 Sotheby's, Milan #285/R est:60000-70000
Prints			
£2027	$3568	€3000	Monkey (100x70cm-39x28in) s. num.119/200 verso serigraph exec.1972. 24-May-4 Christie's, Milan #14/R est:3000-4000
£2365	$4162	€3500	Self-portrait with Russian hat (100x70cm-39x28in) s. num.119/200 verso serigraph exec.1972. 24-May-4 Christie's, Milan #13/R est:3500-5000
£2517	$4280	€3600	Pegs (100x70cm-39x28in) s. num.6/200 serigraph exec.1972. 24-Nov-3 Christie's, Milan #17/R est:4000-6000
£2937	$4993	€4200	Pegs (100x70cm-39x28in) s. num.124/200 verso serigraph. 24-Nov-3 Christie's, Milan #6/R est:4000-6000
£3378	$5946	€5000	Pegs (100x70cm-39x28in) s. num.119/200 verso serigraph exec.1972. 24-May-4 Christie's, Milan #12 est:3500-5000
£8099	$13444	€11500	Peg (40x40cm-16x16in) s.i.d.1982 verso serigraph on steel. 13-Jun-3 Farsetti, Prato #321/R est:1500
£32168	$54685	€46000	Light blue sock (125x125cm-49x49in) s.i.d.1976 serigraph prov. 25-Nov-3 Sotheby's, Milan #246/R est:35000-45000
£45000	$75150	€65700	Nude with guitar (120x70cm-47x28in) s.i.d.1975 silkscreen on stainless steel prov. 20-Oct-3 Sotheby's, London #36/R est:45000
£55000	$91850	€80300	Ragazza che disegna (230x125cm-91x49in) s.i.d.1979 num.142 silkscreen stainless steel. 21-Oct-3 Christie's, London #53/R est:50000-70000
Works on paper			
£1497	$2679	€2200	Black sculpture (37x28cm-15x11in) i. chl exec.1984. 16-Mar-4 Finarte Semenzato, Milan #341/R est:2200
£1497	$2679	€2200	Study of figures (35x26cm-14x10in) s.d.1984 pencil chl lit. 16-Mar-4 Finarte Semenzato, Milan #340/R est:2200
£3034	$5068	€4400	Mirror without date (69x99cm-27x39in) s.i. mixed media. 17-Nov-3 Sant Agostino, Torino #286/R est:4000-5000

PISTOR, Wilhelm (19th C) German

£420	$713	€600	Woodland source (51x41cm-20x16in) s. 20-Nov-3 Van Ham, Cologne #1800/R

PISTORIUS, Eduard (1796-1862) German

£4844	$8671	€7072	Family on country outing (61x87cm-24x34in) s. 11-May-4 Watson's, Christchurch #44/R est:18000-25000 (NZ.D 14000)
£5903	$9622	€8500	Scene outside busy tavern in Rome (95x78cm-37x31in) s. 25-Sep-3 Dr Fritz Nagel, Stuttgart #1399/R est:3000

PISTORIUS, Johanna (1881-1965) German

£490	$842	€700	Roses on the window sill (49x59cm-19x23in) s.d.1923 board. 5-Dec-3 Bolland & Marotz, Bremen #750/R

PISTORIUS, Max (1894-1960) Austrian

£300	$540	€450	Lilac, tulips in white vase (67x54cm-26x21in) s. masonite. 21-Apr-4 Dorotheum, Vienna #140
£532	$888	€750	Teisenhoferhof, Weissenkirchen (49x39cm-19x15in) s. canvas on board. 14-Oct-3 Dorotheum, Vienna #118/R

PISTRE, Marcel (20th C) French?

£276	$497	€400	Composition (65x100cm-26x39in) s. d.1963 verso. 25-Jan-4 Chayette & Cheval, Paris #22
£276	$497	€400	Composition (40x74cm-16x29in) s. s.d.1963 verso. 25-Jan-4 Chayette & Cheval, Paris #24
£276	$497	€400	Composition (100x81cm-39x32in) s. panel painted c.1975. 25-Jan-4 Chayette & Cheval, Paris #72
£276	$497	€400	Composition (73x100cm-29x39in) s. panel painted c.1972-1976. 25-Jan-4 Chayette & Cheval, Paris #74
£276	$497	€400	Composition (81x100cm-32x39in) st.sig. panel painted 1978. 25-Jan-4 Chayette & Cheval, Paris #91
£290	$521	€420	Composition (60x80cm-24x31in) st.sig. d.1964 verso. 25-Jan-4 Chayette & Cheval, Paris #27
£310	$559	€450	Composition (73x100cm-29x39in) s. s.d.1973 verso. 25-Jan-4 Chayette & Cheval, Paris #52
£310	$559	€450	Composition (54x73cm-21x29in) s. d.1973 verso panel. 25-Jan-4 Chayette & Cheval, Paris #55
£310	$559	€450	Composition (81x100cm-32x39in) s. panel painted 1979. 25-Jan-4 Chayette & Cheval, Paris #95
£317	$571	€460	Premier abstrait (100x81cm-39x32in) st.sig i.d.1954 verso panel. 25-Jan-4 Chayette & Cheval, Paris #10
£331	$596	€480	Composition (60x73cm-24x29in) st.sig. painted 1966. 25-Jan-4 Chayette & Cheval, Paris #39
£345	$621	€500	Composition (73x100cm-29x39in) s. d.1973 verso panel. 25-Jan-4 Chayette & Cheval, Paris #54
£345	$621	€500	Composition (64x81cm-25x32in) st.sig. d.1978 verso panel. 25-Jan-4 Chayette & Cheval, Paris #88/R
£359	$646	€520	Composition (24x75cm-9x30in) s. d.1958 verso panel. 25-Jan-4 Chayette & Cheval, Paris #46
£379	$683	€550	Composition (73x100cm-29x39in) s. d.aout 1973 verso panel. 25-Jan-4 Chayette & Cheval, Paris #53
£414	$745	€600	Composition (53x72cm-21x28in) s. d.1972 verso panel exhib. 25-Jan-4 Chayette & Cheval, Paris #49
£448	$807	€650	Composition (73x58cm-29x23in) st.sig panel. 25-Jan-4 Chayette & Cheval, Paris #23

£448	$807	€650	Composition (65x100cm-26x39in) s. s.d.1963 verso. 25-Jan-4 Chayette & Cheval, Paris #25
£469	$844	€680	Composition (58x100cm-23x39in) s. d.1972 verso. 25-Jan-4 Chayette & Cheval, Paris #50
£517	$931	€750	Composition blue (72x92cm-28x36in) st.sig. panel painted c.1966-1967. 25-Jan-4 Chayette & Cheval, Paris #51
£607	$1092	€880	Composition (60x80cm-24x31in) s. d.1964 verso panel. 25-Jan-4 Chayette & Cheval, Paris #73b/R
£690	$1241	€1000	Composition (96x146cm-38x57in) s. d.1974 verso panel exhib. 25-Jan-4 Chayette & Cheval, Paris #62

PISTRUCCI, Benedetto (1784-1855) Italian
Sculpture
£60000 $110400 €90000 Lion's head, various portrait medallions of men, women and beasts (32cm-13in) i.d.1829 marble black marble plinth lit. 10-Jun-4 Christie's, London #76/R est:7000-10000

PITA, Gerardo (1950-) ?
Works on paper
£552 $1000 €806 Head and shoulders portrait of woman (41x61cm-16x24in) col pencil. 16-Apr-4 American Auctioneer #311/R

PITARD, Ferdinand (1850-1894) French
£467 $859 €700 Jeune Africaine fumant (24x35cm-9x14in) s.d.1890. 9-Jun-4 Beaussant & Lefèvre, Paris #197

PITCHER, Henrie (fl.c.1900-1910) British
£320 $595 €467 Scotsman (24x19cm-9x7in) s.d.06 oil on paper. 4-Mar-4 Christie's, Kensington #87/R

PITCHFORTH, Roland Vivian (1895-1982) British
Works on paper
£280 $493 €409 Rural landscape with hills to the distance and expansive sky (58x42cm-23x17in) s. W/C. 18-May-4 Fellows & Sons, Birmingham #141/R
£300 $528 €438 Boats approaching harbour (45x30cm-18x12in) s. W/C. 18-May-4 Fellows & Sons, Birmingham #140/R
£400 $728 €584 Plymouth (45x32cm-18x13in) s.d. pencil W/C. 1-Jul-4 Christie's, Kensington #123
£600 $1092 €876 Fishing in the Orkneys (43x57cm-17x22in) s. pencil W/C. 1-Jul-4 Christie's, Kensington #114/R
£750 $1193 €1095 Pendarn, Wales (41x54cm-16x21in) s. W/C sold with 2 others by the same hand. 10-Sep-3 Sotheby's, Olympia #145/R

PITL, Nicholas R (1932-2001) American
£216 $400 €315 Rainbow trout with royal coachman fly (15x20cm-6x8in) s.d.1981 i.verso acrylic W/C paper. 19-Jul-4 Schrager Galleries, Milwaukee #824/R

PITLOO, Antonio Sminck (1791-1837) Dutch
£13000 $23790 €18980 View of Italian coast near Posillipo (31x43cm-12x17in) s. 8-Jul-4 Sotheby's, London #344/R est:12000-18000
£15086 $27759 €22026 Landscapes (13x18cm-5x7in) s. tin four. 26-Mar-4 Koller, Zurich #3109/R est:7000-10000 (S.FR 35000)

PITOCCHI, Matteo de (17th C) Italian
£2837 $4738 €4000 Religeous scene (70x43cm-28x17in) 17-Jun-3 Finarte Semenzato, Milan #601/R est:4000-6000

PITOCCHI, Matteo de (attrib) (17th C) Italian
£1000 $1820 €1500 Inn interior (29x38cm-11x15in) 3-Jul-4 Finarte, Venice #188/R est:1400-1500

PITRA, Margot (?) ?
Sculpture
£2819 $5243 €4200 Don de soie (29x44x20cm-11x17x8in) s.num.2/8 green pat bronze. 7-Mar-4 Livinec, Gaudcheau & Jezequel, Rennes #94

PITT, Charles Peter (19/20th C) British
£222 $400 €324 Rue de Bac-Rouen (20x18cm-8x7in) s. canvas on board prov. 20-Apr-4 Arthur James, Florida #20/R

PITT, William (19th C) British
£270 $432 €394 Sunset from the swilgate, Tewkesbury (22x36cm-9x14in) s.i.d.1887. 16-Sep-3 Bonhams, Knowle #124
£300 $501 €438 Old farmhouse, Coverack, South Cornwall (18cm-7in circular) s.i.d.1856 board. 14-Oct-3 David Lay, Penzance #22
£680 $1088 €993 River road on the Severn, Tewkesbury (22x40cm-9x16in) s.i.d.1884. 16-Sep-3 Bonhams, Knowle #113
£782 $1400 €1142 Villagers on a country road in an extensive river landscape (43x61cm-17x24in) s.d.1851. 8-Jan-4 Doyle, New York #34/R
£880 $1646 €1285 Riverside village (47x61cm-19x24in) s.d.1849. 24-Feb-4 Bonhams, Knowle #48
£1100 $2013 €1606 Mill Bay, near Dartmouth, South Devon (30x46cm-12x18in) s.i.d.1856 verso. 7-Apr-4 Gardiner & Houlgate, Bath #315/R est:400-800
£1500 $2370 €2175 Old cottage, Bigbury, Devon (30x45cm-12x18in) init. s.i.verso board. 4-Sep-3 Christie's, Kensington #136/R est:2000-3000
£1550 $2883 €2263 Fishing boats on beach at Beer, South Devon (29x45cm-11x18in) mono.d.1860 s.i.d. verso. 2-Mar-4 Bearnes, Exeter #429/R est:500-700
£1650 $2805 €2409 Toney Stratford, Wilts (28x34cm-11x13in) mono.d.1878 s.i.d.1878 verso. 25-Nov-3 Bonhams, Knowle #216/R est:1200-1800
£2600 $4810 €3796 In the Salcombe river, Devon (34x65cm-13x26in) s.i.d.1871 verso. 10-Feb-4 Bonhams, Knightsbridge #343/R est:2000-3000
£5000 $8150 €7300 Old houses, Looe, Cornwall (60x100cm-24x39in) init.d.1860. 24-Sep-3 Peter Wilson, Nantwich #14

PITT, William (attrib) (19th C) British
£313 $500 €457 Coast scene, South Wales (23x41cm-9x16in) indis.sig.i.verso painted c.1870. 20-Sep-3 Bunte, Elgin #1419

PITTINO, Fred (1906-) Italian
£1364 $2345 €1950 Holy water bowl (40x50cm-16x20in) s. i.d.verso. 3-Dec-3 Stadion, Trieste #968/R est:1200-1600
£1818 $3127 €2600 La Salute, Venice (60x50cm-24x20in) s.d.49. 3-Dec-3 Stadion, Trieste #967/R est:1500-2000

PITTMAN, Hobson (c.1899-1972) American
£1279 $2200 €1867 Flowers with fern (61x51cm-24x20in) s. s.i.stretcher. 7-Dec-3 Freeman, Philadelphia #179 est:2000-3000
£2471 $4250 €3608 Vase of flowers (51x41cm-20x16in) s. 7-Dec-3 Freeman, Philadelphia #208 est:3000-5000
£15569 $26000 €22731 Buffet (81x114cm-32x45in) s. painted c.1948 prov.exhib.lit. 7-Oct-3 Sotheby's, New York #231 est:7000-10000
Works on paper
£449 $750 €656 On the beach, Avalon, New Jersey (20x28cm-8x11in) s.i.d.June 58 W/C pencil. 20-Jun-3 Freeman, Philadelphia #48/R
£1136 $2000 €1659 Still life, vase of flowers (48x64cm-19x25in) s.d.70 pastel. 18-May-4 Arthur James, Florida #50 est:2000-3000
£1250 $2200 €1825 Floral still life (48x64cm-19x25in) s. pastel. 18-May-4 Arthur James, Florida #52/R est:2000-3000
£1307 $2300 €1908 Flowers in two glass vase (64x48cm-25x19in) s.i. pastel. 18-May-4 Arthur James, Florida #51 est:2000-3000
£1630 $3000 €2380 Untitled bouquet (46x60cm-18x24in) s. pastel prov. 27-Jun-4 Freeman, Philadelphia #179/R est:2000-3000
£1816 $3250 €2651 Lilies (61x46cm-24x18in) s. pastel board prov. 26-May-4 Doyle, New York #110/R est:5000-7000

PITTMAN, Osmund (1874-1958) British
£900 $1530 €1314 Italianate hillside town (59x87cm-23x34in) init. 6-Nov-3 Christie's, Kensington #859/R

PITTO, Giacomo (1872-?) Italian
£580 $969 €847 At the market (46x66cm-18x26in) s. 22-Oct-3 Cheffins, Cambridge #540

PITTONI, Francesco (1654-1724) Italian
£27778 $47222 €40000 Loth e le figlie (150x160cm-59x63in) 28-Oct-3 Della Rocca, Turin #115/R est:40000-50000

PITTONI, Francesco and Giovanni Battista (younger) (17/18th C) Italian
£34028 $57847 €49000 Sanson e Dalila (270x210cm-106x83in) s.d. 28-Oct-3 Della Rocca, Turin #116/R est:50000-60000

PITTONI, Giovanni Battista (younger) (1687-1767) Italian
£17000 $30600 €24820 Finding of Moses. Moses and the burning bush (21x14cm-8x6in) canvas on panel arched top pair. 21-Apr-4 Christie's, London #98/R est:8000-12000
£40000 $73200 €58400 Continence of Scipio (67x85cm-26x33in) prov.exhib.lit. 7-Jul-4 Christie's, London #87/R est:30000-50000

PITTONI, Giovanni Battista (younger-attrib) (1687-1767) Italian
£7860 $14306 €11476 Elieser courting Rebecca on behalf of Isaac (69x94cm-27x37in) i.verso. 16-Jun-4 Fischer, Luzern #1058/R est:18000-24000 (S.FR 18000)

PITTONI, Giovanni Battista (younger-circle) (1687-1767) Italian
£5369 $9879 €8000 St John the Baptist preaching (71x102cm-28x40in) paper on canvas. 24-Mar-4 Dorotheum, Vienna #17/R est:8000-12000
£12000 $21600 €17520 Sacrifice of Jephthah'd daughter. Solomon and the Queen of Sheba (59x78cm-23x31in) pair shaped. 21-Apr-4 Christie's, London #101/R est:10000-15000

PITTS, Frederick (fl.1856-1882) British
£4500 $8055 €6570 Playtime (36x52cm-14x20in) s.d.1859. 27-May-4 Christie's, Kensington #295/R est:5000-7000

PITZ, Henry C (1895-1974) American
Works on paper
£428 $800 €625 Swordsman on horseback riding past fire-breathing dragon (30x43cm-12x17in) s. pen ink. 26-Feb-4 Illustration House, New York #136/R

PITZIANTI, Paola (20th C) Italian
£333 $613 €500 Woman (60x50cm-24x20in) s. exhib.lit. 8-Jun-4 Della Rocca, Turin #238/R

PITZNER, Max Joseph (1855-1912) German
£1119 $1924 €1600 Artillery riding on a path (18x24cm-7x9in) s.i. panel. 3-Dec-3 Neumeister, Munich #704/R est:1500
£1316 $2197 €1921 Meeting the post coach (17x25cm-7x10in) s.i. panel prov. 15-Nov-3 Galerie Gloggner, Luzern #90/R est:2000-2500 (S.FR 3000)

PIUMATI, Giovanni (1850-1915) Italian
£426 $711 €600 Civrari, Piano del Lago (37x55cm-15x22in) s.i.d.1899. 20-Oct-3 Sant Agostino, Torino #20/R
£1667 $3067 €2500 October in Colle San Giovanni (41x30cm-16x12in) init.d.1889 s.i.d.verso board. 14-Jun-4 Sant Agostino, Torino #155/R est:800-1000

PIVA, Gino (1889-?) French
£336 $594 €500 Seascape, boats (40x50cm-16x20in) s. cardboard. 1-May-4 Meeting Art, Vercelli #378

PIXE, Robert Bond (19th C) American
Works on paper
£449 $750 €656 Van Vorst homestead, Schenectady NY (18x30cm-7x12in) s.i.d.1852 W/C. 16-Nov-3 William Jenack, New York #289

PIZEON, Emily (?) ?
£420 $777 €613 Blowing bubbles (25x28cm-10x11in) i.verso board. 11-Mar-4 Duke & Son, Dorchester #189/R

PIZIO, Oreste (1879-1938) Italian
£1208 $2138 €1800 Herd at pasture (44x57cm-17x22in) s. 1-May-4 Meeting Art, Vercelli #324 est:1500
Works on paper
£503 $891 €750 Lady (65x50cm-26x20in) s. pastel cardboard. 1-May-4 Meeting Art, Vercelli #459

PIZZELLA, Edmond (1868-?) Italian
Works on paper
£1361 $2163 €2000 Portrait of a woman (73x54cm-29x21in) s. pastel paper on canvas. 23-Mar-3 Mercier & Cie, Lille #240 est:2200-2400
£14184 $23688 €20000 Beaute du harem (96x162cm-38x64in) s. mixed media. 16-Jun-3 Gros & Delettrez, Paris #104/R est:20000-30000

PIZZI CANNELLA, Piero (1955-) Italian
£3310 $5528 €4800 Salle du verre (81x60cm-32x24in) s.verso painted 1989. 13-Nov-3 Finarte Semenzato, Rome #483/R est:5000-6000
£4027 $7208 €6000 Little vases (60x120cm-24x47in) i. s.verso. 30-May-4 Meeting Art, Vercelli #51 est:6000
Works on paper
£541 $951 €800 Grand Hotel (42x29cm-17x11in) s.i. mixed media. 22-May-4 Galleria Pananti, Florence #351/R
£1133 $2085 €1700 Composition (35x50cm-14x20in) s.d.1990 mixed media. 12-Jun-4 Meeting Art, Vercelli #468/R est:1000
£1690 $2806 €2400 Rosso dell'ombra (37x50cm-15x20in) s.i.d.1992 gouache. 14-Jun-3 Meeting Art, Vercelli #96/R est:2000
£2933 $5397 €4400 Untitled (80x40cm-31x16in) s. mixed media board exec.1991 lit. 12-Jun-4 Meeting Art, Vercelli #117/R est:4000

PIZZICHINI, Carlo (1962-) Italian
Works on paper
£873 $1607 €1275 Ritmi (70x100cm-28x39in) s. mixed media paper on canvas. 8-Jun-4 Germann, Zurich #856/R (S.FR 2000)

PIZZINATO, Armando (1910-) Italian
£1549 $2572 €2200 Untitled (26x39cm-10x15in) s. 13-Jun-3 Farsetti, Prato #299/R
£1690 $2806 €2400 Canal in Venice (25x36cm-10x14in) s.d.1969. 13-Jun-3 Farsetti, Prato #60/R

PIZZIRANI, Guglielmo (1886-1971) Italian
£431 $772 €629 Alpine landscape with small huts (24x18cm-9x7in) s. i.d.1922 verso panel. 12-May-4 Dobiaschofsky, Bern #876/R (S.FR 1000)
£1078 $1929 €1574 Portrait of young woman (41x32cm-16x13in) s.d.1919. 12-May-4 Dobiaschofsky, Bern #875/R est:3000 (S.FR 2500)

PLA Y GALLARDO, Cecilio (1860-1934) Spanish
£638 $1066 €900 Portrait of a woman (44x42cm-17x17in) s.d.1905. 23-Jun-3 Durán, Madrid #89/R
£966 $1603 €1400 Study of trees (22x22cm-9x9in) board. 1-Oct-3 Ansorena, Madrid #735/R
£2632 $4842 €4000 Model (29x20cm-11x8in) s. board. 22-Jun-4 Durán, Madrid #114/R est:4000
£2958 $5176 €4200 Bridge (17x24cm-7x9in) s. cardboard. 16-Dec-3 Segre, Madrid #79/R est:3500
£4192 $7000 €6120 Stroll on the beach (15x25cm-6x10in) s.d.1915 panel exhib. 7-Oct-3 Sotheby's, New York #129 est:5000-7000
£4965 $8043 €7000 Sketch of San Isidro (32x45cm-13x18in) 20-May-3 Ansorena, Madrid #156/R est:7000
£8621 $15517 €12500 Landscape with trees (14x23cm-6x9in) s. 26-Jan-4 Ansorena, Madrid #201/R est:9000
£14184 $23688 €20000 Amazone (82x115cm-32x45in) s. prov.exhib.lit. 20-Oct-3 Durán, Madrid #219/R
£110345 $184276 €160000 Sunday on Valencia beach (48x72cm-19x28in) s. 17-Nov-3 Durán, Madrid #211/R est:18000
Works on paper
£458 $801 €650 Rabbits (11x12cm-4x5in) s. dr. 16-Dec-3 Durán, Madrid #61/R
£470 $841 €700 Female nude (30x20cm-12x8in) s. dr exhib. 25-May-4 Durán, Madrid #68/R
£507 $832 €700 Monserrat (11x19cm-4x7in) s.i.d.1894 drawing double-sided. 27-May-3 Durán, Madrid #63/R
£514 $873 €750 Monastery (11x20cm-4x8in) s. dr. 4-Nov-3 Ansorena, Madrid #183/R
£2685 $4993 €4000 Director (10x7cm-4x3in) s.i. chl dr. 2-Mar-4 Ansorena, Madrid #333/R est:400

PLA Y RUBIO, Alberto (1867-1929) Spanish
£845 $1479 €1200 Caravane (15x23cm-6x9in) s.i. board. 16-Dec-3 Durán, Madrid #90/R
£3241 $5834 €4700 Woman and baby in courtyard (75x60cm-30x24in) s. 26-Jan-4 Ansorena, Madrid #277/R est:4000
£4138 $7448 €6000 Beach scene (33x41cm-13x16in) s. board. 26-Jan-4 Durán, Madrid #161/R est:6000
£8276 $14897 €12000 Breakfast (75x60cm-30x24in) s. i.verso. 26-Jan-4 Durán, Madrid #171/R est:12000
£13768 $22580 €19000 Romeria en las afueras del pueblo (35x66cm-14x26in) s.d.909. 27-May-3 Durán, Madrid #265/R est:18000

PLAAT, Henri (1936-) Dutch
Works on paper
£385 $654 €550 Stone (45x23cm-18x9in) s.i.d.1968 W/C. 24-Nov-3 Glerum, Amsterdam #265/R

PLACE, Francis (1647-1728) British
Works on paper
£260 $475 €380 Studies of peasants in hats (13x17cm-5x7in) brush brown ink wash pencil. 29-Jan-4 Swann Galleries, New York #346/R

PLAES, David van der (1647-1704) Dutch
£21000 $38430 €30660 Portrait of collector in his study (64x52cm-25x20in) i. prov. 8-Jul-4 Sotheby's, London #275/R est:8000-12000

PLAGEMANN, Carl (1805-1868) Swedish
£1154 $1985 €1685 Eva Dorothea Fredrika Charlotta Plagemann (66x54cm-26x21in) i.d.1830 verso oval. 2-Dec-3 Bukowskis, Stockholm #320/R est:20000-25000 (S.KR 15000)

PLAGEMANN, Carl (attrib) (1805-1868) Swedish
£3695 $6615 €5395 Forget-me-not (129x100cm-51x39in) 26-May-4 AB Stockholms Auktionsverk #2267/R est:50000-60000 (S.KR 50000)

PLAGNOL, Serge (1951-) French
£466 $840 €700 Vert, rouge, orangee (46x38cm-18x15in) s. s.i.d.2003 verso. 26-Apr-4 Tajan, Paris #258
£800 $1472 €1200 Voix, visage de femme (147x115cm-58x45in) s. s.i.d.1993 verso prov. 14-Jun-4 Tajan, Paris #224

PLAKOTARIS, Costas (1902-1969) Greek
£13000 $23270 €18980 Shipyard on the island of Cos (86x121cm-34x48in) s.d.1964 hardboard exhib.lit. 11-May-4 Bonhams, New Bond Street #99/R est:4000-6000

PLAMONDON, Peter (20th C) American
£1613 $3000 €2355 White dishes (91x81cm-36x32in) init. s.d.1991 verso. 5-Mar-4 Skinner, Boston #615/R est:3000-5000

PLANAS DORIA, Francisco (1879-1955) Spanish
£493 $789 €700 Landscape near Tiana (51x65cm-20x26in) s. s.i.verso board. 16-Sep-3 Segre, Madrid #101/R
£592 $1023 €840 San Fruitos de Bages (50x70cm-20x28in) s. s.i.d.1937 verso board. 15-Dec-3 Ansorena, Madrid #279/R

PLANCKH, Viktor (1904-1941) Austrian
£1842 $3389 €2800 Still life of flowers (41x51cm-16x20in) s. 22-Jun-4 Wiener Kunst Auktionen, Vienna #207/R est:1200

PLANCKNER, Lonny von (1863-?) German
£552 $916 €800 Mountain landscape in winter (82x99cm-32x39in) s. 6-Oct-3 Bloss, Merzhausen #1225/R

PLANDING, Otto (1887-?) Canadian
£203 $344 €296 Autumn stream (46x76cm-18x30in) s. 21-Nov-3 Walker's, Ottawa #35/R (C.D 450)
£338 $574 €493 Logging, Laurentians (46x66cm-18x26in) s. board. 21-Nov-3 Walker's, Ottawa #34/R (C.D 750)

PLANER, Josef (20th C) Austrian
£1806 $3069 €2600 Still life of flowers and fruit (74x100cm-29x39in) s. 28-Oct-3 Dorotheum, Vienna #143/R est:2000-2300

PLANGG, Werner (20th C) Canadian
£600 $1098 €876 Bugling elk, Banff high country (75x100cm-30x39in) s.i. prov. 1-Jun-4 Hodgins, Calgary #297/R (C.D 1500)

PLANK, Josef (1815-1901) Austrian
£676 $1209 €1000 On the beach (60x80cm-24x31in) s. 8-May-4 Schloss Ahlden, Ahlden #801/R

PLANQUETTE, Felix (1873-1964) French
£559 $951 €800 Paysage aux vaches (52x73cm-20x29in) d.1900. 30-Nov-3 Teitgen, Nancy #121
£780 $1303 €1100 Vaches s'abreuvant au couchant (27x35cm-11x14in) s. panel. 19-Jun-3 Millon & Associes, Paris #184/R
£789 $1429 €1200 Vaches en bord de mer (19x24cm-7x9in) s. cardboard. 19-Apr-4 Boscher, Cherbourg #864/R
£1267 $2305 €1900 Derniers rayons (27x35cm-11x14in) s. panel. 5-Jul-4 Neret-Minet, Paris #41/R est:2000-3000
£1308 $2249 €1910 Vaches a l'etang, soleil couchant (27x34cm-11x13in) s. panel. 3-Dec-3 AB Stockholms Auktionsverk #2545/R est:12000-15000 (S.KR 17000)

£1469 $2497 €2100 Baie d'Ecalgrain (22x27cm-9x11in) s. panel. 24-Nov-3 Boscher, Cherbourg #759c est:1000-1200
£1538 $2615 €2200 Vieille ferme fortifiee a Cosqueville (21x27cm-8x11in) s. panel. 24-Nov-3 Boscher, Cherbourg #759b est:1500-2000
£1748 $2972 €2500 Le retour des vaches et des moutons (38x55cm-15x22in) s. 24-Nov-3 Boscher, Cherbourg #759/R est:2000-2500
£2174 $3565 €3000 Troupeau au Mont Saint Michel, coucher de soleil (21x27cm-8x11in) s. panel. 11-May-3 Osenat, Fontainebleau #193/R est:3500-3800
£2391 $3922 €3300 La laitiere (46x65cm-18x26in) s. 11-May-3 Osenat, Fontainebleau #196/R est:3800-4000
£3239 $5248 €4600 Vaches s'abreuvant (28x41cm-11x16in) s. panel. 11-Aug-3 Boscher, Cherbourg #713/R est:3000-4000

PLANSON, Andre (1898-1981) French
£805 $1506 €1200 L'ancien pont neuf a la ferte sous jouarre (38x46cm-15x18in) s. cardboard. 29-Feb-4 Osenat, Fontainebleau #220
£815 $1500 €1190 La marne (58x71cm-23x28in) s.d.59 exhib. 9-Jun-4 Doyle, New York #3096 est:1500-2000
£1200 $2208 €1800 Village de Lizy sur Ourcy (50x61cm-20x24in) s.d.53. 14-Jun-4 Tajan, Paris #105 est:2000-2400
£1418 $2369 €2000 Saint-Clair, le lavandou (50x65cm-20x26in) s. s.i.verso cardboard. 12-Oct-3 St-Germain-en-Laye Encheres #91/R est:2000-2500
£1600 $2928 €2400 La cote sauvage - Quiberon (29x61cm-11x24in) s.d.57 i. verso panel prov. 5-Jun-4 Lempertz, Koln #946/R est:2000
£1867 $3397 €2800 Paysage a Saint-Clair, pres du Lavandou (50x65cm-20x26in) s. panel. 4-Jul-4 Eric Pillon, Calais #199/R
£2000 $3600 €3000 Le modele dans l'atelier (81x60cm-32x24in) s. 26-Apr-4 Tajan, Paris #192 est:1500-2000
£3200 $5760 €4800 Femme aux gants noirs (73x92cm-29x36in) s.d.51 prov. 26-Apr-4 Tajan, Paris #193/R est:5000-7000
Works on paper
£268 $499 €400 Le concours de peche a la ferte (30x47cm-12x19in) s.i.d.29 W/C ink paper on cardboard. 2-Mar-4 Artcurial Briest, Paris #80
£1119 $1924 €1600 Female nude (63x49cm-25x19in) s.d.42 W/C Indian ink traces crayon. 2-Dec-3 Christie's, Paris #364/R est:1800-2200

PLANTAR, Jean Baptiste Louis (c.1790-1879) French
Works on paper
£704 $1218 €1000 Projet de cheminee avec un bas-relief en pendule (26x22cm-10x9in) i. W/C blk crayon. 10-Dec-3 Piasa, Paris #98

PLANTEY, Madeleine (19/20th C) French
£600 $1080 €900 Jeune fille a la fenetre (33x24cm-13x9in) s. cardboard. 20-Apr-4 Chenu & Scrive, Lyon #140/R

PLAPP, Jon (1938-) Australian
Works on paper
£248 $459 €362 Packed and released (91x61cm-36x24in) s.d.89 i.verso synthetic polymer. 15-Mar-4 Sotheby's, Melbourne #145 (A.D 600)
£248 $459 €362 Not touching because (91x61cm-36x24in) s.d.88 i.verso synthetic polymer. 15-Mar-4 Sotheby's, Melbourne #236 (A.D 600)
£269 $497 €393 Next door nobody (91x61cm-36x24in) s.d.89 i.verso synthetic polymer prov. 15-Mar-4 Sotheby's, Melbourne #238 (A.D 650)
£279 $516 €407 Take the train (91x61cm-36x24in) s.d.89 i.verso synthetic polymer prov. 15-Mar-4 Sotheby's, Melbourne #237 (A.D 675)
£279 $516 €407 Imperfect various things (91x61cm-36x24in) s.d.88 i.verso synthetic polymer prov. 15-Mar-4 Sotheby's, Melbourne #239 (A.D 675)
£351 $650 €512 We are together (122x122cm-48x48in) s.d.89 i.verso powder paint synthetic polymer prov. 15-Mar-4 Sotheby's, Melbourne #71 est:900-1200 (A.D 850)
£451 $712 €658 Teach us a new terror (121x121cm-48x48in) s.i.d.89 verso synthetic polymer. 2-Sep-3 Deutscher-Menzies, Melbourne #336/R (A.D 1100)

PLAS, Adrianus Marie van der (1899-?) Dutch
£828 $1382 €1200 City view with barges in the winter (78x88cm-31x35in) board. 11-Nov-3 Vendu Notarishuis, Rotterdam #47/R

PLAS, Lourentius (1828-1888) Dutch
£276 $500 €420 A sheep and a lamb in a Dutch landscape (21x29cm-8x11in) s.d.1869 panel. 19-Apr-4 Glerum, Amsterdam #75

PLAS, Nicholaas van der (1954-) Dutch
£533 $971 €800 Bulb field near Pan van Persyn (30x40cm-12x16in) s. panel. 30-Jun-4 Vendue Huis, Gravenhage #591
£600 $1074 €900 Beach scene with many figures (29x39cm-11x15in) s. panel. 11-May-4 Vendu Notarishuis, Rotterdam #163
£733 $1313 €1100 Beach near Katwijk (22x28cm-9x11in) s. panel. 11-May-4 Vendu Notarishuis, Rotterdam #162/R
£806 $1484 €1177 On the beach (30x39cm-12x15in) s. panel. 14-Jun-4 Waddingtons, Toronto #224/R est:1600-1800 (C.D 2000)
£814 $1360 €1188 Beach scene (12x17cm-5x7in) s. panel. 17-Nov-3 Waddingtons, Toronto #152/R est:800-1000 (C.D 1800)
£903 $1508 €1300 View of beach in Katwijk (30x40cm-12x16in) s. panel. 21-Oct-3 Campo & Campo, Antwerp #315
£905 $1511 €1321 On the beach (33x43cm-13x17in) s. panel. 17-Nov-3 Waddingtons, Toronto #159/R est:1800-2000 (C.D 2000)

PLAS, Nicole van der (1943-) Dutch?
£800 $1480 €1168 Day at the seaside (59x48cm-23x19in) s. board. 15-Jan-4 Christie's, Kensington #997/R

PLAS, Pieter (1810-1853) Dutch
£769 $1308 €1100 Two goats and horse in stable (26x41cm-10x16in) s. board. 20-Nov-3 Van Ham, Cologne #1801/R

PLASENCIA, Casto (1846-1890) Spanish
£6944 $11319 €10000 Greek slave (100x76cm-39x30in) s.d.1877. 23-Sep-3 Durán, Madrid #195/R est:6000

PLASKETT, Joe (1918-) Canadian
£691 $1237 €1009 Day lilies (52x66cm-20x26in) s.d.1960 i.verso board. 6-May-4 Heffel, Vancouver #113/R (C.D 1700)
£1016 $1819 €1483 Still life (72x72cm-28x28in) s.d.1971 prov. 27-May-4 Heffel, Vancouver #195/R est:3000-4000 (C.D 2500)
£1118 $2001 €1632 Portrait of Alvin Balkind (81x99cm-32x39in) s.d.1980 prov. 31-May-4 Sotheby's, Toronto #50/R est:3000-3500 (C.D 2750)
£1138 $2037 €1661 Anemones with bust (72x59cm-28x23in) s.d.1982 i.d.verso prov. 27-May-4 Heffel, Vancouver #193/R est:2000-3000 (C.D 2800)
£1760 $3221 €2570 Still life with yellow table (70x90cm-28x35in) s. 1-Jun-4 Joyner Waddington, Toronto #32/R est:3000-4000 (C.D 4400)
£1931 $3457 €2819 Docks in New Westminster, B.C from Patullo bridge (74x99cm-29x39in) s.d.1972 i.verso prov. 31-May-4 Sotheby's, Toronto #50a/R est:3000-3500 (C.D 4750)
£2027 $3446 €2959 Still life with daffodils and wine (58x89cm-23x35in) s.d.1977 prov. 21-Nov-3 Walker's, Ottawa #50/R est:2000-3000 (C.D 4500)
£2642 $4730 €3857 Table with teapot (89x115cm-35x45in) s.d.1979 prov. 31-May-4 Sotheby's, Toronto #52/R est:3000-5000 (C.D 6500)
Works on paper
£222 $384 €324 Pond and Poplars (49x63cm-19x25in) s.d.1978 pastel prov. 9-Dec-3 Pinneys, Montreal #187 (C.D 500)
£248 $421 €362 French landscape (48x63cm-19x25in) s.d.1961 pastel prov. 23-Nov-3 Levis, Calgary #536/R (C.D 550)
£255 $424 €372 Old bridge, Decize, Loire, France (60x65cm-24x26in) s.d.1979 pastel prov. 5-Oct-3 Levis, Calgary #285/R (C.D 575)

PLASKY, Eugène (1851-1905) Belgian
£2368 $4287 €3600 Floraison des cerisiers a Uccle (118x93cm-46x37in) s. 19-Apr-4 Horta, Bruxelles #113 est:4000-6000

PLASSAN, Antoine-Émile (1817-1903) French
£2254 $3741 €3200 Bateau lavoir (14x23cm-6x9in) s. panel. 15-Jun-3 Peron, Melun #146
£2586 $4629 €3776 The lovesick maid (38x47cm-15x19in) s. panel. 17-May-4 Beurret, Zurich #14/R est:5000-7000 (S.FR 6000)
£2800 $4816 €4088 Conversation over a cup of tea (33x24cm-13x9in) s.d.1854 panel. 4-Dec-3 Christie's, Kensington #149/R est:3000-5000
£3169 $5261 €4500 Toilette (20x13cm-8x5in) s. panel. 15-Jun-3 Peron, Melun #2

PLATE, Carl Olaf (1909-1977) Australian
£681 $1157 €994 Blue Monument (138x97cm-54x38in) s.d.65-67. 26-Nov-3 Deutscher-Menzies, Melbourne #246/R (A.D 1600)
Works on paper
£820 $1295 €1197 Untitled (97x97cm-38x38in) s.d.66 synthetic polymer prov. 2-Sep-3 Deutscher-Menzies, Melbourne #305/R est:2000-3000 (A.D 2000)

PLATERO, Mario (1942-) Uruguayan
£420 $713 €600 Rue de la Bucherie a Paris (61x46cm-24x18in) s.d.99. 28-Nov-3 Blanchet, Paris #171

PLATT, Charles Adams (1861-1933) American
£7317 $12000 €10610 Harbour scene with distant windmill (38x56cm-15x22in) s.d.83 prov. 31-May-3 Brunk, Ashville #180/R est:2000-4000

PLATT, John Edgar (1886-1967) British
Works on paper
£400 $692 €584 The Red Mizzen, Brixham trawler before a pier (25x22cm-10x9in) s. W/C prov. 11-Dec-3 Lane, Penzance #39

PLATT, John Edgar (attrib) (1886-1967) British
£450 $833 €657 Dry dock (66x102cm-26x40in) s.d.53. 15-Jan-4 Christie's, Kensington #1027/R

PLATTENBERG, Mathieu van (1608-1660) Flemish
£2649 $4821 €4000 Sailing boats in the storm (60x80cm-24x31in) 16-Jun-4 Christie's, Rome #424/R est:4000-6000
£9869 $18158 €15000 Stormy seascape (111x158cm-44x62in) 24-Jun-4 Tajan, Paris #28/R est:18000-22000

PLATTENBERG, Mathieu van (circle) (1608-1660) Flemish
£5903 $9858 €8500 Stormy seascape (106x167cm-42x66in) 22-Oct-3 Finarte Semenzato, Milan #16/R est:6000-8000

PLATTENSTEINER, Christian von (1806-1858) Austrian
£497 $909 €750 Southern landscape (34x49cm-13x19in) bears sig.d.1857. 8-Apr-4 Dorotheum, Vienna #8

PLATTNER, Hermann Georg (1909-1997) Swiss
£690 $1234 €1007 Hay's wharf (72x90cm-28x35in) s.d.62 i. verso. 14-May-4 Dobiaschofsky, Bern #257/R est:1600 (S.FR 1600)

PLATTNER, Karl (1919-1987) Austrian
£2500 $3975 €3625 Fisch (18x25cm-7x10in) init.d.57 board. 11-Sep-3 Christie's, Kensington #109/R est:1000-1500
£10738 $19221 €16000 Fence (24x67cm-9x26in) s.d.1961 cardboard. 25-May-4 Sotheby's, Milan #88/R est:2000
£14000 $25760 €21000 Beach in Rio (59x84cm-23x33in) s.d.1952. 8-Jun-4 Finarte Semenzato, Milan #353/R est:25000-28000
£18000 $33120 €27000 Figures (76x36cm-30x14in) s.d.1955-56 oil mixed media card prov. 8-Jun-4 Finarte Semenzato, Milan #351/R est:10000-12000

£24000 $44160 €36000 Women on the beach (96x160cm-38x63in) s.d.52-53 board prov.exhib. 8-Jun-4 Finarte Semenzato, Milan #355/R est:40000-45000
£24000 $44160 €36000 Suburbs of San Paulo (60x80cm-24x31in) s.d.1956-57 board prov. 8-Jun-4 Finarte Semenzato, Milan #354/R est:30000-35000
Works on paper
£1600 $2768 €2336 Zwei figuren (35x19cm-14x7in) s.d.57 pen black ink. 11-Dec-3 Christie's, Kensington #164/R est:800-1200
£8333 $15333 €12500 Mother and daughter with umbrella (49x25cm-19x10in) s.indis.d. mixed media prov. 8-Jun-4 Finarte Semenzato, Milan #352/R est:8000-9000

PLATTNER, Otto (1886-1951) Swiss?
£273 $453 €396 Four girls under blossoming fruit trees (32x36cm-13x14in) mono. board. 13-Jun-3 Zofingen, Switzerland #2981 (S.FR 600)
£588 $1000 €858 Storm in the Birsig valley (55x44cm-22x17in) mono. i.d.1929 verso. 28-Nov-3 Zofingen, Switzerland #3119 (S.FR 1300)
£818 $1358 €1186 Girl by wood with view of Schloss Birseck (70x100cm-28x39in) s. hessian. 13-Jun-3 Zofingen, Switzerland #2982 est:2500 (S.FR 1800)

PLATTS, J (?) ?
£717 $1290 €1047 Waiting for dinner (41x61cm-16x24in) s.i. 24-Apr-4 Rasmussen, Havnen #2152/R (D.KR 8000)

PLATZ, Ernst Heinrich (1867-1940) German
£480 $830 €701 Tyrolean landscape with cattle (25x40cm-10x16in) s. i.verso panel. 10-Dec-3 Rupert Toovey, Partridge Green #8/R

PLATZER, Johann Georg (1704-1761) Austrian
£26316 $48421 €40000 Self-worship at the well (32x47cm-13x19in) copper prov. 22-Jun-4 Wiener Kunst Auktionen, Vienna #4/R est:35000
£145000 $265350 €211700 Interior with elegant figures in masquerade costumes. Music party in the grounds of Italianate villa (24x36cm-9x14in) copper pair prov. 7-Jul-4 Sotheby's, London #53/R est:100000-150000

PLAZZOTTA, Enzo (1921-1981) Italian
Sculpture
£2200 $4004 €3212 Nureyev - 4th study (89x56x20cm-35x22x8in) num 2/9 bronze conceived 1969 lit. 1-Jul-4 Christie's, Kensington #156 est:2500-3000
£2200 $4004 €3212 Arabesque III - Nadia Nerina (76x71x19cm-30x28x7in) num.1/9 brown pat bronze conceived 1969 lit. 1-Jul-4 Christie's, Kensington #154 est:2500-3000
£2800 $4760 €4088 Joni - Crouching position (32cm-13in) st.base pat bronze. 18-Nov-3 Bonhams, Knightsbridge #170/R est:2500-3500

PLE, Henri Honore (1853-1922) French
Sculpture
£1600 $2912 €2400 Figure of David with the head of Goliath at his feet (63cm-25in) s. brown pat. bronze. 20-Jun-4 Wilkinson, Doncaster #23 est:2500-3500
£6667 $12000 €9734 Le Vainqueur (112cm-44in) s. bronze rec. base. 23-Apr-4 Christie's, Rockefeller NY #178/R est:15000-20000

PLEISSNER, Ogden M (1905-1983) American
£4144 $7500 €6050 Lake above Simpson Lake (20x25cm-8x10in) s. canvas on masonite prov. 31-Mar-4 Sotheby's, New York #106/R est:7000-10000
£4420 $8000 €6453 Simpson Lake, Dubois, Wyoming (20x25cm-8x10in) s. canvas on masonite prov. 31-Mar-4 Sotheby's, New York #104/R est:7000-10000
£8021 $15000 €11711 Peggy's Cove (30x41cm-12x16in) s. canvas on board prov. 24-Jul-4 Coeur d'Alene, Hayden #66/R est:8000-12000
£9091 $17000 €13273 Farm in October (30x41cm-12x16in) s. canvas on board prov. 24-Jul-4 Coeur d'Alene, Hayden #68/R est:7000-10000
£11364 $20000 €16591 Pont neuf, Paris (61x91cm-24x36in) s. prov. 18-May-4 Sotheby's, New York #213/R est:10000-15000
£14706 $27500 €21471 North of Rawlins (76x127cm-30x50in) s. prov. 24-Jul-4 Coeur d'Alene, Hayden #64/R est:20000-30000
Works on paper
£341 $600 €498 Fishing boat tied up at dock (48x28cm-19x11in) s. W/C. 3-Jan-4 Cobbs, Peterborough #134/R
£2353 $4000 €3435 October afternoon, Tuileries (36x51cm-14x20in) s. W/C. 21-Nov-3 Skinner, Boston #511/R est:4000-6000
£2419 $4500 €3532 Boatyard, Essex, Connecticut (38x56cm-15x22in) s. i.verso pencil W/C prov. 3-Mar-4 Christie's, Rockefeller NY #46/R est:3000-5000
£2514 $4500 €3670 Mettowee River. s. W/C. 31-May-4 William A Smith, Plainfield #116/R
£2516 $4000 €3673 Pont Saint-Michel (27x44cm-11x17in) s. W/C. 12-Sep-3 Skinner, Boston #468/R
£3209 $6000 €4685 Fishing boat, Sea Island, Georgia (15x23cm-6x9in) s. W/C prov. 24-Jul-4 Coeur d'Alene, Hayden #65/R est:4000-6000
£3226 $6000 €4710 Fishing boat in dry dock (38x56cm-15x22in) s. W/C pencil prov. 3-Mar-4 Christie's, Rockefeller NY #45/R est:3000-5000
£3824 $6500 €5583 Irish farm (19x27cm-7x11in) s. W/C. 21-Nov-3 Skinner, Boston #469/R est:6000-8000
£4545 $8500 €6636 Red and white grill (25x36cm-10x14in) W/C prov. 24-Jul-4 Coeur d'Alene, Hayden #67/R est:5000-8000
£4559 $7750 €6656 Adirondack trout stream (18x25cm-7x10in) s. W/C. 21-Nov-3 Skinner, Boston #350/R est:6000-8000
£10465 $18000 €15279 Late afternoon, the doctor's pool (40x55cm-16x22in) s. W/C htd white. 3-Dec-3 Doyle, New York #249/R est:15000-25000
£22727 $40000 €33181 Toward Torry Mountains, Wyoming (38x58cm-15x23in) s. W/C prov. 19-May-4 Sotheby's, New York #187/R est:20000-30000
£24022 $43000 €35072 Snipe shooting (43x69cm-17x27in) s. W/C. 8-Jan-4 James Julia, Fairfield #50/R est:20000-40000

PLENSA, Jaume (1955-) Spanish
£5986 $10475 €8500 Still life 22 (108x106cm-43x42in) s.d.1991 paint paper on board prov. 16-Dec-3 Segre, Madrid #165/R est:5000
£6757 $11892 €10000 Animal fantastique (150x430cm-59x169in) s.d.1984 oil gouache paper prov. 18-May-4 Tajan, Paris #134/R est:11000-12000

PLESSI, Fabrizio (1940-) Italian
£3041 $5351 €4500 Tinned clouds (80x100cm-31x39in) s.i.d.67. 24-May-4 Christie's, Milan #89/R est:3000-5000
Works on paper
£507 $832 €700 Untitled (37x25cm-15x10in) s.d.65 Chinese ink acrylic prov. 27-May-3 Sotheby's, Milan #169/R
£629 $1070 €900 Untitled - Cairo VHS (70x100cm-28x39in) s. gouache chk. 27-Nov-3 Lempertz, Koln #344/R
£629 $1070 €900 Untitled - La stanza vill'architetto studio per videoinstallazione (100x70cm-39x28in) s. gouache chk. 27-Nov-3 Lempertz, Koln #345/R
£1399 $2378 €2000 Ice series (50x70cm-20x28in) s.d.76 pencil pair prov. 24-Nov-3 Christie's, Milan #36/R est:1100-1300

PLESSIS, Enslin du (1894-1978) South African
£289 $517 €422 Still life of proteas (49x59cm-19x23in) s.d.58 board. 31-May-4 Stephan Welz, Johannesburg #174 (SA.R 3500)
£410 $697 €599 Pavilion, Alicante (46x55cm-18x22in) s.i. board. 4-Nov-3 Stephan Welz, Johannesburg #297 est:2000-3000 (SA.R 4800)
£470 $799 €686 Pont Corneille, Rouen (31x40cm-12x16in) s. i.verso panel exhib. 4-Nov-3 Stephan Welz, Johannesburg #291 est:2000-4000 (SA.R 5500)
£684 $1162 €999 Back view, Gieen Tiye (30x39cm-12x15in) s. panel. 4-Nov-3 Stephan Welz, Johannesburg #318 est:2000-3000 (SA.R 8000)
£1026 $1744 €1498 St Albans (29x39cm-11x15in) s. i.verso panel exhib. 4-Nov-3 Stephan Welz, Johannesburg #372 est:2000-3000 (SA.R 12000)

PLESSNER, Rudolf (1889-?) German
£898 $1553 €1311 The Strand, London (64x92cm-25x36in) s. 9-Dec-3 Rasmussen, Copenhagen #1666/R (D.KR 9500)

PLETKA, Paul (1946-) American
£5435 $10000 €7935 Indian wrapped in red blanket (30x34cm-12x13in) 24-Jun-4 Sotheby's, New York #173/R est:3000-5000

PLEUER, Hermann (1863-1911) German
£544 $990 €800 Snowy village at night (22x23cm-9x9in) mono.d.06 board. 3-Feb-4 Sigalas, Stuttgart #514/R
£3200 $5760 €4800 Stuttgart, north station (26x39cm-10x15in) 26-Apr-4 Rieber, Stuttgart #1293/R est:4800

PLEYSIER, Ary (1809-1879) Dutch
£600 $1074 €876 Congestion at the harbour mouth (20x25cm-8x10in) 26-May-4 Christie's, Kensington #665/R
£1600 $2880 €2400 Fishing in a calm (17x27cm-7x11in) s. panel. 20-Apr-4 Sotheby's, Amsterdam #28/R est:2000-3000

PLIMER, Andrew (1763-1837) British
Miniatures
£1081 $2000 €1578 Miss Vaughan (5x5cm-2x2in) oval. 12-Mar-4 Du Mouchelle, Detroit #2020/R est:1000-2000
£1100 $1837 €1606 Charles Cumberland wearing a blue coat (7cm-3in) gilt metal papier mache frame. 7-Oct-3 Bonhams, New Bond Street #127/R est:1000-1500
£1300 $2392 €1898 John Jackson, wearing a dark brown coat (7cm-3in) gold frame lock of hair split pearls on foiled blue glass. 24-Jun-4 Bonhams, New Bond Street #112/R est:800-1200
£1900 $3230 €2774 Lady (8cm-3in) oval prov. 18-Nov-3 Bonhams, New Bond Street #94/R est:2000-3000
£2000 $3400 €2920 Lady (6cm-2in) gold frame oval. 18-Nov-3 Bonhams, New Bond Street #92/R est:2000-3000
£2000 $3680 €2920 Lady wearing black dress with white fichu (6cm-2in) gilt metal mount. 24-Jun-4 Bonhams, New Bond Street #86/R est:1000-1500
£2432 $4500 €3551 Thomas Stracey (8x5cm-3x2in) exec.c.1800 oval. 12-Mar-4 Du Mouchelle, Detroit #2018/R est:1000-2000
£2600 $4784 €3796 Lady wearing mauve dress with white sleeves and fichu tied at her corsage (6cm-2in) init.d.1787 fishskin case. 24-Jun-4 Bonhams, New Bond Street #60/R est:800-1200
£2973 $5500 €4341 Portrait of a lady (8x5cm-3x2in) exec.c.1780 oval. 12-Mar-4 Du Mouchelle, Detroit #2017/R est:2000-3000
£3000 $5370 €4380 Young gentleman in a brown coat (5cm-2in) init.d.1787 silver gilt frame lock of hair prov. 25-May-4 Christie's, London #105/R est:1500-2500
£3200 $5440 €4672 John Manners (8cm-3in) gold frame oval. 18-Nov-3 Bonhams, New Bond Street #97/R est:1500-2000
£3400 $6120 €4964 Lady, probably Joanna Plimer (22x147cm-9x58in) s.d.1829 pencil W/C wood frame rec. prov.exhib.lit. 22-Apr-4 Bonhams, New Bond Street #146/R est:1000-1500
£3500 $6055 €5110 Young lady (6cm-2in) silver-gilt frame oval prov. 9-Dec-3 Christie's, London #106/R est:2500-3500
£4000 $7360 €5840 Lady, called Mrs Jenny Pigott (6cm-2in) gilt metal mount. 24-Jun-4 Bonhams, New Bond Street #88/R est:1500-2500
£4200 $7560 €6132 Lady, probably Louisa Plimer (20cm-8in) W/C crayon paper gilded rec. wood frame octagonal prov.exhib.lit. 22-Apr-4 Bonhams, New Bond Street #147/R est:1000-1500
£7568 $14000 €11049 Portrait of a boy (5x5cm-2x2in) exec.c.1775 oval. 12-Mar-4 Du Mouchelle, Detroit #2019/R est:1000-2000

PLIMER, Nathaniel (c.1751-c.1822) British
Miniatures
£1081 $2000 €1578 Sir John Skipworth (8x5cm-3x2in) exec.c.1790 oval. 12-Mar-4 Du Mouchelle, Detroit #2022/R est:1000-2000
£1100 $2024 €1606 Gentleman wearing a blue coat (7cm-3in) gold frame. 24-Jun-4 Bonhams, New Bond Street #103/R est:600-800
£1622 $3000 €2368 Lady Skipworth (8x5cm-3x2in) exec.c.1790 oval. 12-Mar-4 Du Mouchelle, Detroit #2023/R est:1000-2000
£2162 $4000 €3157 Portrait of a gentleman (8x5cm-3x2in) exec.c.1800 oval. 12-Mar-4 Du Mouchelle, Detroit #2021/R est:1000-2000
£2200 $4048 €3212 Portrait of a gentleman, believed to be Colonel Hastie (7cm-3in) W/C on ivory red leather case. 23-Jun-4 Bonhams, Bury St Edmunds #287/R est:600-800

£2500 $4500 €3650 Young officer (4cm-2in) s.d.1786 gold bracelet clasp mount oval exhib. 22-Apr-4 Bonhams, New Bond Street #37/R est:700-900

PLIMER, Nathaniel (attrib) (c.1751-c.1822) British
Miniatures
£1600 $2944 €2336 Gentleman wearing a brown coat (5cm-2in) gold frame. 24-Jun-4 Bonhams, New Bond Street #100/R est:500-700

PLINKE, August H (1855-1910) German
£448 $829 €650 Les trois garnements (44x28cm-17x11in) s. panel. 16-Feb-4 Horta, Bruxelles #501

PLISCHKE, Franz (19/20th C) Austrian
£294 $500 €429 Country life (61x122cm-24x48in) s.d.1909 triptych. 28-Nov-3 Zofingen, Switzerland #2660 (S.FR 650)

PLISSON, Henri (1908-) French
£1176 $2000 €1717 Extensive landscape with blooming hollyhocks in a garden by the sea (77x63cm-30x25in) s. 19-Nov-3 Bonhams & Butterfields, San Francisco #167/R

PLOG, Olga (1894-?) German
£294 $499 €420 Procession with children holding lanterns (27x31cm-11x12in) s. 28-Nov-3 Wendl, Rudolstadt #4139/R

PLOMTEUX, Leopold (1920-) Belgian
Works on paper
£293 $537 €440 Abstraction (29x41cm-11x16in) s.d.1949 mixed media. 7-Jun-4 Palais de Beaux Arts, Brussels #381
£320 $586 €480 Abstraction (31x47cm-12x19in) s.d.58 mixed media. 7-Jun-4 Palais de Beaux Arts, Brussels #382

PLOSKY, Jonas (1940-) British
£360 $637 €526 Study of pebbles and shells. s.d.1980 board. 27-Apr-4 Bonhams, Knightsbridge #55
£380 $654 €555 Shoreline, Dorset (41x58cm-16x23in) s. s.i.verso board. 3-Dec-3 Christie's, Kensington #677/R
£500 $910 €730 Quarry Homestead, Blaenau Ffeftiniog (63x51cm-25x20in) s. board painted 1979. 1-Jul-4 Christie's, Kensington #322/R
£550 $946 €803 Farmbuildings near Waunfawr (54x71cm-21x28in) s. s.i.verso board. 3-Dec-3 Christie's, Kensington #675/R
£550 $946 €803 Smallholding, Gwynedd (51x61cm-20x24in) s. s.i.verso board. 3-Dec-3 Christie's, Kensington #679/R
£650 $1183 €949 Carrying home the shopping, Blaenau Ffestiniog (51x63cm-20x25in) s. board. 1-Jul-4 Christie's, Kensington #323/R
£800 $1456 €1168 Remote farm, Gwynedd (41x58cm-16x23in) s. board. 1-Jul-4 Christie's, Kensington #321/R

PLOTEK, Leopold (1948-) Russian
£221 $411 €323 Untitled (244x183cm-96x72in) d.Sept 1978 verso. 2-Mar-4 Ritchie, Toronto #200/R (C.D 550)

PLUCKEBAUM, Carl (1880-1952) German
£594 $1010 €850 Young couple in love in spring meadow (34x24cm-13x9in) s. panel. 20-Nov-3 Van Ham, Cologne #1802

PLUCKEBAUM, Meta (1876-1945) German
£467 $845 €700 Still life with roses in stoneware vase (60x50cm-24x20in) s. board. 1-Apr-4 Van Ham, Cologne #1604

PLUIM, Rie (1913-) Dutch
£433 $793 €650 Paysage de Cagnes (54x45cm-21x18in) s.verso. 7-Jun-4 Glerum, Amsterdam #254/R

PLUM, Poul August (1815-1876) Danish
£341 $613 €498 Historical scene (27x21cm-11x8in) s. mahogany panel. 24-Apr-4 Rasmussen, Havnen #2137/R (D.KR 3800)
Works on paper
£316 $591 €461 Tropical cabins with figures (26x20cm-10x8in) W/C pencil. 25-Feb-4 Museumsbygningen, Copenhagen #181/R (D.KR 3500)

PLUMBE, John (jnr) (1809-1857) American
Photographs
£3293 $5500 €4808 Officer and the young lady seated by a window. st.sig. daguerreotype cased exec.c.1840. 17-Oct-3 Sotheby's, New York #68/R est:3000-5000

PLUMIER, Edmond Theodore (attrib) (1694-1733) Flemish
£2817 $4873 €4000 Portrait d'un gentilhomme (93x65cm-37x26in) prov. 9-Dec-3 Vanderkindere, Brussels #331 est:1750-2500

PLUMMER, Edwin (1802-1880) American
Works on paper
£9836 $18000 €14361 Portrait of Miss Stevens (13x8cm-5x3in) i.verso W/C pencil prov.lit. 6-Jun-4 Skinner, Boston #21/R est:8000-12000

PLUMMER, W H (1839-?) American
£2174 $3500 €3174 Fishing schooners in choppy waters (51x91cm-20x36in) s.d.1874. 14-Jan-4 Christie's, Rockefeller NY #45/R est:3000-5000

PLUMOT, Andre (1829-1906) Belgian
£600 $942 €870 Milkmaid before a farmstead (23x30cm-9x12in) s. canvas on panel. 28-Aug-3 Christie's, Kensington #86/R
£5369 $9826 €8000 Une belle sortie (66x102cm-26x40in) s.d.1901. 8-Jul-4 Campo, Vlaamse Kaai #221/R est:8000-10000
£10345 $17276 €15000 Farmstead (83x120cm-33x47in) s.d.1883 prov. 15-Nov-3 Lempertz, Koln #1676/R est:6000-8000

PLUSS, Franz (1922-) Swiss
£317 $507 €463 Winter landscape with trees (87x110cm-34x43in) s. board. 16-Sep-3 Philippe Schuler, Zurich #5633 (S.FR 700)

PLUVIOSE, D (20th C) Haitian
£874 $1600 €1276 Peasants (61x81cm-24x32in) s.i. board. 3-Jun-4 Christie's, Rockefeller NY #1127/R est:200-300

PLUYM, Carel van der (attrib) (1625-1677) Dutch
£2515 $4200 €3672 Man weighing gold (91x76cm-36x30in) 19-Oct-3 Susanin's, Chicago #6045/R est:4000-6000

PLUYMERS, Toon (1910-1967) Dutch
£400 $732 €600 View of Magere bridge in Amsterdam (45x55cm-18x22in) s.d.42. 7-Jun-4 Glerum, Amsterdam #61/R

PO, Giacomo del (1652-1726) Italian
Works on paper
£1300 $2340 €1898 Five studies for Hercules and the Hydra (17x18cm-7x7in) bears i. pen brown ink grey wash prov. 20-Apr-4 Sotheby's, Olympia #17/R est:800-1200

PO, Pietro del (circle) (1610-1692) Italian
£11000 $18700 €16060 Perseus and Andromeda (111x151cm-44x59in) 29-Oct-3 Christie's, London #85/R est:7000-10000

PO, Teresa del (?-1716) Italian
Works on paper
£3402 $6089 €5000 Sainte Famille et Saint Jean Baptiste (35x27cm-14x11in) gouache vellum on wood after Annibale Carracci. 17-Mar-4 Tajan, Paris #33/R est:5000-6000

POATE, R (19th C) ?
£8600 $14620 €12556 Sailor's return, Jack at home (81x114cm-32x45in) s. i.verso. 5-Nov-3 Rupert Toovey, Partridge Green #77/R est:5000-8000

POBBIATI, Mario (1887-1956) Italian
£282 $493 €400 Mountainous landscape (29x40cm-11x16in) s. board. 17-Dec-3 Il Ponte, Milan #814
£302 $541 €450 Old cottage (30x40cm-12x16in) init. board. 25-May-4 Finarte Semenzato, Milan #143/R
£302 $541 €450 Stream and cottages (29x40cm-11x16in) init. board. 25-May-4 Finarte Semenzato, Milan #141/R
£317 $555 €450 Mountainous landscape with village (29x40cm-11x16in) s. board. 17-Dec-3 Il Ponte, Milan #819
£791 $1298 €1100 Snow in Milan (35x52cm-14x20in) s. board. 10-Jun-3 Pandolfini, Florence #255/R
£1268 $2193 €1800 Party in the garden (101x131cm-40x52in) 14-Dec-3 Finarte, Venice #29/R est:1600-2000
£1987 $3616 €3000 Woman with hat and vase of flowers (120x90cm-47x35in) s. 17-Jun-4 Finarte Semenzato, Milan #326/R est:3000-4000

POCCETTI, Bernardino (1542-1612) Italian
Works on paper
£1000 $1800 €1500 Study of figure (39x22cm-15x9in) pencil. 21-Apr-4 Finarte Semenzato, Milan #539/R est:1000-1500
£9500 $17385 €13870 Fortitude holding a sword, seated and turning to the right (21x15cm-8x6in) black chk prov. 6-Jul-4 Christie's, London #15/R est:10000-15000

POCCI, Franz Graf von (1807-1876) German
Works on paper
£327 $594 €480 Landscape with fortress (25x19cm-10x7in) mono. i. verso. 4-Feb-4 Neumeister, Munich #607

POCHITONOV, Ivan Pavlovitch (1850-1923) Russian
£26000 $44200 €39000 Nesting boxes above flowering shrubs (13x9cm-5x4in) s. panel. 25-Nov-3 Christie's, London #146/R est:1500-2000

POCHVALSKI, Kazimierz (1855-1940) Polish
£450 $752 €657 Portrait of a lady (33x26cm-13x10in) s.d.1904 board. 7-Oct-3 Bonhams, Knightsbridge #151/R
£927 $1697 €1400 Portrait (35x26cm-14x10in) s.d.1904 board. 8-Apr-4 Dorotheum, Vienna #186/R

POCHVALSKI, Kazimierz (attrib) (1855-1940) Polish
£2685 $4966 €4000 Portrait of Theodor Herzl (109x75cm-43x30in) 9-Mar-4 Dorotheum, Vienna #1/R est:3000-5000

POCHWALSKI, Kasper (1899-1971) Polish
£1254 $1956 €1831 Girl with bow in her hair (76x58cm-30x23in) s.d.1949. 30-Mar-3 Agra, Warsaw #38/R est:8000 (P.Z 8000)

POCK, Alexander (1871-1950) Austrian
Works on paper
£503 $926 €750 Rider on white horse (18x22cm-7x9in) s.i.d.1931 W/C. 26-Mar-4 Dorotheum, Vienna #331/R

POCOCK, Henry Childe (1854-1934) British
£650 $1203 €949 Musical recital (31x26cm-12x10in) s. board. 9-Mar-4 Bonhams, Knightsbridge #301/R
Works on paper
£840 $1344 €1226 Musician, gentleman seated at a table playing a flute (28x20cm-11x8in) s. W/C. 16-Sep-3 Louis Taylor, Stoke on Trent #1053

POCOCK, Lexden L (1850-1919) British
Works on paper
£436 $685 €632 Outlaws wife (17x23cm-7x9in) s. W/C. 27-Aug-3 Dunbar Sloane, Wellington #79/R (NZ.D 1200)
£450 $833 €657 Charcoal burners daughter (35x51cm-14x20in) W/C. 16-Jul-4 Charterhouse, Sherborne #524/R
£460 $768 €672 Angel (40x17cm-16x7in) s. W/C. 12-Nov-3 Sotheby's, Olympia #121/R

POCOCK, Nicholas (1740-1821) British
£58000 $109620 €84680 Admiral Rodney's flagship Formidable early in the battle of the Saintes (61x107cm-24x42in) init.d.1784 exhib. 17-Feb-4 Bonhams, New Bond Street #78/R est:20000-30000
Works on paper
£650 $1196 €949 Droving cattle (60x83cm-24x33in) s.d.1786 W/C. 22-Jun-4 Bonhams, Knightsbridge #21/R
£950 $1748 €1387 Shipping on the Avon (39x59cm-15x23in) s. pencil W/C. 25-Mar-4 Christie's, Kensington #16/R
£1200 $2232 €1752 Battle between the British and French at Isle de Groix (41x61cm-16x24in) s.d.1812 W/C. 2-Mar-4 Bristol Auction Rooms #343/R est:500-700
£1241 $2272 €1800 Debarquement dans l'estuaire (27x37cm-11x15in) s.d.1783 W/C. 31-Jan-4 Neret-Minet, Paris #151/R est:1200-1500
£4000 $6400 €5840 Frigate under tow down the Avon Gorge in light winds (59x82cm-23x32in) s.d.1787 pen ink W/C. 16-Sep-3 Bonhams, New Bond Street #43/R est:2500-3000
£4800 $8976 €7008 Various views (24x36cm-9x14in) two s. one d.1790 one d.1812 W/C aquatint eight. 20-Jul-4 Dreweatt Neate, Newbury #183/R est:3500-5000

POCOCK, Nicholas (attrib) (1740-1821) British
Works on paper
£330 $617 €482 Loss of the Dutton, East Indiaman, Plymouth (40x59cm-16x23in) W/C. 20-Jul-4 Dreweatt Neate, Newbury #179/R
£1200 $2040 €1752 View of the river Mersey near Liverpool, with shipping (22x30cm-9x12in) W/C. 27-Nov-3 Clevedon Sale Rooms #176/R est:1200-1800

PODCHERNIKOFF, Alexis M (1886-1933) American/Russian
£380 $700 €555 Maiden with cherub and tambourine (119x53cm-47x21in) s.d.1912. 9-Jun-4 Doyle, New York #3061
£397 $750 €580 Landscape - Santa Inez Peak, Santa Barbara (18x23cm-7x9in) s. board. 17-Feb-4 John Moran, Pasadena #11/R
£882 $1500 €1288 Barn in landscape (23x30cm-9x12in) s. board. 18-Nov-3 John Moran, Pasadena #13b est:1500-2000
£899 $1700 €1313 Wooded atmospheric landscape (18x25cm-7x10in) s. canvasboard. 17-Feb-4 John Moran, Pasadena #6/R est:1500-2000
£899 $1700 €1313 Nocturnal coastal landscape (20x25cm-8x10in) s. prov. 17-Feb-4 John Moran, Pasadena #163/R est:1000-2000
£924 $1700 €1349 Desert in bloom at sunrise (55x91cm-22x36in) s. masonite. 8-Jun-4 Bonhams & Butterfields, San Francisco #4216/R est:3000-5000
£1099 $2000 €1605 Landscape in hazy morning light (30x23cm-12x9in) init. board. 15-Jun-4 John Moran, Pasadena #4 est:1500-2000
£1324 $2250 €1933 Cattle in landscape (48x56cm-19x22in) s. 18-Nov-3 John Moran, Pasadena #68a est:2500-3500
£1324 $2250 €1933 Cattle watering in wooded landscape (36x46cm-14x18in) s. 18-Nov-3 John Moran, Pasadena #189 est:1000-2000
£1494 $2750 €2181 Women picking flowers (71x91cm-28x36in) s. 8-Jun-4 Bonhams & Butterfields, San Francisco #4215/R est:4000-6000
£1511 $2750 €2206 Lake in a sunset landscape (30x46cm-12x18in) s. masonite prov. 15-Jun-4 John Moran, Pasadena #159 est:3000-4000
£1618 $2750 €2362 Eucalyptus trees in a landscape (28x20cm-11x8in) init. wood panel. 18-Nov-3 John Moran, Pasadena #13c est:1500-2000
£1720 $3250 €2511 Cattle in wooded landscape (48x56cm-19x22in) s. 17-Feb-4 John Moran, Pasadena #27a/R est:2500-3500
£1758 $3200 €2567 Dunes in bloom (53x43cm-21x17in) s. board. 19-Jun-4 Jackson's, Cedar Falls #4/R est:2000-3000
£1902 $3500 €2777 Carmel sand dunes, California (63x76cm-25x30in) s. i. stretcher. 8-Jun-4 Bonhams & Butterfields, San Francisco #4212/R est:4000-6000
£2038 $3750 €2975 Path in the moonlight (45x55cm-18x22in) s. 8-Jun-4 Bonhams & Butterfields, San Francisco #4217/R est:3000-5000
£2310 $4250 €3373 Cows in a glen (66x50cm-26x20in) s. 8-Jun-4 Bonhams & Butterfields, San Francisco #4342/R est:4000-6000
£3439 $6500 €5021 Figures and cattle watering in wooded landscape (71x91cm-28x36in) s. 17-Feb-4 John Moran, Pasadena #42/R est:3000-5000
£3571 $6500 €5214 Flower fields and oaks (61x91cm-24x36in) s. canvas. 15-Jun-4 John Moran, Pasadena #26 est:3500-5500
£3968 $7500 €5793 Mt Tamalpais, Cal (66x102cm-26x40in) s.i. prov. 17-Feb-4 John Moran, Pasadena #101/R est:6000-8000
£4118 $7000 €6012 Lake in sunset, wooded landscape (71x91cm-28x36in) s. 18-Nov-3 John Moran, Pasadena #35 est:5000-7500
£6667 $12000 €9734 In the forest (71x56cm-28x22in) s. 23-Apr-4 Sotheby's, New York #41/R est:12000-18000

PODESTA, Andrea (1620-1674) Italian
Works on paper
£2600 $4498 €3796 Studies of putti and children (21x16cm-8x6in) i.verso black chk pen brown ink double-sided prov. 12-Dec-3 Christie's, Kensington #359/R est:2000-3000

PODHRAZSKY, Stanislav (1921-) Czechoslovakian
£2408 $3996 €3516 Berounka River (32x45cm-13x18in) s.d. board. 4-Oct-3 Dorotheum, Prague #139/R est:15000-25000 (C.KR 110000)

PODKOWINSKI, Wladyslaw (1866-1895) Polish
Works on paper
£3210 $5329 €4687 Path through the woods (51x35cm-20x14in) W/C. 15-Jun-3 Agra, Warsaw #12/R est:14000 (P.Z 20000)

PODLIASKI, Yuri (1923-1987) Russian
£223 $400 €326 Tobolsk, view from the mountain (31x46cm-12x18in) cardboard painted 1966. 29-May-4 Shishkin Gallery, Moscow #81/R
£313 $560 €457 Sketch for war years (47x56cm-19x22in) oil paper painted 1971. 29-May-4 Shishkin Gallery, Moscow #78/R
£419 $750 €612 October, by the passage (42x60cm-17x24in) oil paper painted 1976 sketch. 29-May-4 Shishkin Gallery, Moscow #82/R
£419 $750 €612 Severobaikalsk's moorings (38x48cm-15x19in) oil paper painted 1978. 29-May-4 Shishkin Gallery, Moscow #83/R
£419 $750 €612 Cities are growing up in Siberia (41x50cm-16x20in) oil paper painted 1986. 29-May-4 Shishkin Gallery, Moscow #84/R
£1000 $1800 €1460 First greenery (27x32cm-11x13in) oil on cardboard. 24-Apr-4 Shishkin Gallery, Moscow #60/R est:2000-3000
£1006 $1800 €1469 Yacht club (32x46cm-13x18in) cardboard painted 1968. 29-May-4 Shishkin Gallery, Moscow #77/R est:2000-2500
£1444 $2600 €2108 Hard kilometers Bam (61x50cm-24x20in) oil on paper. 24-Apr-4 Shishkin Gallery, Moscow #63/R est:2000-2500
Works on paper
£503 $900 €734 Kremlin (33x48cm-13x19in) W/C painted 1964. 29-May-4 Shishkin Gallery, Moscow #80/R

PODWIL, Jerome (20th C) American
£241 $450 €352 Space ship with energy shield approaching planet (51x33cm-20x13in) s. board painted c.1970. 26-Feb-4 Illustration House, New York #138

POEL, Egbert van der (1621-1664) Dutch
£2447 $4087 €3500 The Adoration of the shepherds (58x64cm-23x25in) s. panel. 30-Jun-3 Sotheby's, Amsterdam #19/R
£2448 $4210 €3500 Scene aux flambeaux (49x41cm-19x16in) s. panel. 3-Dec-3 Oger, Dumont, Paris #106/R est:5000-7000
£2533 $4661 €3800 Night fire in a village (24x31cm-9x12in) board. 14-Jun-4 Sant Agostino, Torino #308/R est:1500-2000
£3087 $5681 €4600 Barn interior (49x64cm-19x25in) bears sig. panel. 25-Mar-4 Dr Fritz Nagel, Stuttgart #601/R est:4000
£3816 $7021 €5800 Scene d'incendie nocturne dans un village au bord d'un canal (32x39cm-13x15in) s. panel. 24-Jun-4 Claude Boisgirard, Paris #7/R est:7500-10000
£4000 $7320 €5840 Barn interior with a cottager and his horse (49x62cm-19x24in) s. panel. 6-Jul-4 Sotheby's, Olympia #534/R est:4000-6000
£4878 $8732 €7122 By the farmhouse (24x26cm-9x10in) s. panel. 28-May-4 Uppsala Auktionskammare, Uppsala #14/R est:40000-50000 (S.KR 66000)
£8000 $13840 €11680 Nocturnal scene with a cottage ablaze beside a canal (31x38cm-12x15in) s. panel. 11-Dec-3 Sotheby's, London #145/R est:8000-12000
£9589 $16301 €14000 Cottage with kitchen utensils, ducks and woman washing her laundry (28x75cm-11x30in) panel. 4-Nov-3 Sotheby's, Amsterdam #22/R est:12000-18000
£12000 $20760 €17520 Fire in a village at night (38x49cm-15x19in) s.d.1655 panel prov. 11-Dec-3 Sotheby's, London #144/R est:12000-16000
£15556 $28000 €22712 Kitchen maid cleaning fish before a farmhouse (58x82cm-23x32in) s. panel prov. 23-Jan-4 Christie's, Rockefeller NY #145/R est:25000-35000
£36913 $67919 €55000 Gunpowder explosion in Delft, 12th October 1654 (37x49cm-15x19in) s.d.1654 panel prov. 24-Mar-4 Dorotheum, Vienna #175/R est:20000-30000

POEL, Egbert van der (attrib) (1621-1664) Dutch
£1325 $2411 €2000 Scene de cour de ferme (53x65cm-21x26in) panel. 21-Jun-4 Tajan, Paris #65 est:2000-3000

POELENBURGH, Cornelis van (1586-1667) Dutch
£4000 $6800 €5840 Christ. Saint Perter. Saint John the Enangelist. Saint Luke and Mattew (13x11cm-5x4in) panel set of six. 29-Oct-3 Christie's, London #32/R est:6000-8000
£5200 $8840 €7592 Italianate landscape with a herdsman and cattle by ruins (21x17cm-8x7in) init. copper. 29-Oct-3 Christie's, London #33/R est:6000-8000
£5500 $9900 €8030 Departure of Abraham and Isaac (19x25cm-7x10in) panel prov.exhib. 23-Apr-4 Christie's, Kensington #38/R est:6000-8000
£12000 $21960 €17520 Landscape with the expulsion of Hagar and Ishmael (26x24cm-10x9in) init. copper. 8-Jul-4 Sotheby's, London #242/R est:12000-15000
£19444 $35000 €28388 Adoration of the Magi (42x31cm-17x12in) panel prov. 22-Jan-4 Sotheby's, New York #27/R est:30000-40000
Works on paper
£410 $750 €599 Italianate landscape (34x46cm-13x18in) red chk. 29-Jan-4 Swann Galleries, New York #159/R

POELENBURGH, Cornelis van (attrib) (1586-1667) Dutch
£1277 $2132 €1800 Assomption (46x35cm-18x14in) panel. 14-Oct-3 Vanderkindere, Brussels #124
£1399 $2406 €2000 Sheperdess wearing a yellow dress (24x18cm-9x7in) panel. 7-Dec-3 Sotheby's, Amsterdam #547/R
£2013 $3705 €3000 Portrait of young woman (120x94cm-47x37in) s.d.1629. 25-Mar-4 Dr Fritz Nagel, Stuttgart #617/R est:2500
£2127 $3615 €3105 Nymphs bathing in classical ruin (25x31cm-10x12in) panel. 19-Nov-3 Fischer, Luzern #1022/R est:5000-7000 (S.FR 4700)
£3774 $6000 €5510 Bacchus in a landscape with a satyr and putti (44x61cm-17x24in) indis.sig.d.1660 panel. 13-Sep-3 Weschler, Washington #700/R est:5000-7000
£8145 $13032 €11892 Ruin landscape with animals and figures (26x24cm-10x9in) mono. copper prov. 16-Sep-3 Philippe Schuler, Zurich #3350/R est:8000-12000 (S.FR 18000)
£11815 $20440 €17250 Celebration meal of the Gods (37x49cm-15x19in) panel. 9-Dec-3 Rasmussen, Copenhagen #1631/R est:80000-100000 (D.KR 125000)

POELL, Alfred (1867-1929) Austrian
£7986 $12618 €11500 Winter in the mountains (84x82cm-33x32in) s.d.27 lit. 19-Sep-3 Schloss Ahlden, Ahlden #1650/R est:6800

POELS, A (1903-1984) Belgian
Sculpture
£2381 $4262 €3500 Tijl Uylenspiegel et Reinaert De Vos (36x33cm-14x13in) cherry wood black marble socle. 22-Mar-4 Amberes, Antwerp #391/R

POELS, Albert (1903-1984) Belgian
Sculpture
£1042 $1740 €1500 Pere et fils (60cm-24in) s. wood. 21-Oct-3 Campo & Campo, Antwerp #251/R est:2000-2500

POEPPEL, Rudolph (1823-1889) German
£901 $1532 €1315 Village in the mountains (89x132cm-35x52in) s.i. prov. 21-Nov-3 Walker's, Ottawa #213/R est:3000-5000 (C.D 2000)

POEPPEL, Rudolph (attrib) (1823-1889) German
£1589 $2909 €2400 Castelbell near Latsch in Vintschgau (24x35cm-9x14in) bears sig. 8-Apr-4 Dorotheum, Vienna #255/R est:1800-2000

POERSON, Charles (1609-1667) French
£26000 $44980 €37960 Marriage at Cana (54x63cm-21x25in) s. 10-Dec-3 Christie's, London #65/R est:25000-35000

POERTZEL, Otto (1876-?) German
Sculpture
£830 $1535 €1212 Pair of pheasants (34x76cm-13x30in) bronze. 14-Mar-4 Agra, Warsaw #64/R (P.Z 6000)
£1600 $2864 €2400 Female nude (50cm-20in) i. gold pat.bronze. 13-May-4 Neumeister, Munich #214/R est:2200-2300
£2270 $3790 €3200 Amazone riding Centaur (48x64cm-19x25in) s. dark pat.bronze. 15-Oct-3 Dorotheum, Salzburg #479/R est:2000-3000
£2727 $4636 €3900 Standing male nude with eagle (114cm-45in) brown pat.bronze marble socle. 22-Nov-3 Arnold, Frankfurt #231/R est:900
£3620 $5792 €5285 Dancer wearing black dress with flowers (18cm-7in) s. bronze ivory. 19-Sep-3 Koller, Zurich #1295/R est:2500-3500 (S.FR 8000)
£5063 $8000 €7392 Equestrian group (56cm-22in) s. bronze ivory. 7-Sep-3 Treadway Gallery, Cincinnati #649/R est:10000-15000
£14000 $22260 €20440 Carnival couple (35cm-14in) s. bronze ivory. 9-Sep-3 Sotheby's, Olympia #373/R est:8000-12000

POERTZEL, Otto (after) (1876-?) German
Sculpture
£8791 $16000 €13187 Columbine and Pierrot (36cm-14in) i. bronze ivory black marble plinth st.f. Preiss prov. 16-Jun-4 Sotheby's, New York #239/R est:12000-15000

POESCHMANN, Rudolf (1878-1954) German
£600 $1092 €900 The river Elbe near Dresden (48x65cm-19x26in) s. 1-Jul-4 Van Ham, Cologne #1559/R

POETZELBERGER, Oswald (1893-1966) German
£352 $630 €500 Portrait of a young lady (75x60cm-30x24in) s. lit. 8-Jan-4 Allgauer, Kempten #2482/R
£1517 $2534 €2200 People in front of large mountains (110x86cm-43x34in) s. sack. 13-Nov-3 Neumeister, Munich #431/R est:1200-1500

POETZELBERGER, Robert (1856-1930) Austrian
£700 $1267 €1050 Hunting in the summer (30x32cm-12x13in) mono. board lit. 1-Apr-4 Frank Peege, Freiburg #1182/R
£6338 $10965 €9000 Horse racing on the Naples coastal road (45x92cm-18x36in) s.d.85. 10-Dec-3 Dorotheum, Vienna #134/R est:7000-9000

POETZSCH, Gustave (1870-?) Swiss
£219 $366 €320 Quai au bord du lac (54x65cm-21x26in) s. 16-Nov-3 Koller, Geneva #1239 (S.FR 500)

POFFE, Andre (1911-) Belgian
£517 $957 €750 Rue au clair de lune (54x67cm-21x26in) s. 16-Feb-4 Horta, Bruxelles #67
£676 $1209 €1000 Conversation avec le cycliste (60x70cm-24x28in) s. 10-May-4 Horta, Bruxelles #1

POGEDAIEFF, George (1899-1971) Russian
£1000 $1670 €1450 Scene de cafe (49x65cm-19x26in) s. panel. 17-Nov-3 Claude Boisgirard, Paris #79/R
£1500 $2685 €2190 Street in Vaucluse (46x38cm-18x15in) s. i.verso board. 26-May-4 Sotheby's, Olympia #486/R est:1800-2500
£1517 $2534 €2200 Nature morte aux peches (55x38cm-22x15in) s.d.1964. 17-Nov-3 Claude Boisgirard, Paris #77 est:800-1000
£2207 $3686 €3200 Nature morte aux tomates (54x65cm-21x26in) s.d.1962. 17-Nov-3 Claude Boisgirard, Paris #78 est:800-1000
£2667 $4800 €4000 Nature morte aux pasteques (57x43cm-22x17in) s. cardboard. 26-Apr-4 Tajan, Paris #179 est:1500-2000
£2800 $4760 €4088 Meuerbes - landscape (38x46cm-15x18in) s.d.60. 19-Nov-3 Sotheby's, London #123/R est:2000-3000
£3000 $5100 €4380 Village in the hillside (50x64cm-20x25in) s. board. 19-Nov-3 Sotheby's, London #124/R est:4000-6000
£4000 $6800 €6000 Landscape (50x65cm-20x26in) s. board. 25-Nov-3 Christie's, London #228/R est:4000-6000
£4800 $8160 €7008 South of France (46x33cm-18x13in) s.d.61. 19-Nov-3 Sotheby's, London #121/R est:3500-4500
£7000 $11900 €10220 Moored boats (100x73cm-39x29in) init.i.d.1928. 19-Nov-3 Sotheby's, London #232/R est:4000-6000
£8500 $14450 €12410 Boats in the harbour (72x92cm-28x36in) s.d.1926. 19-Nov-3 Sotheby's, London #233/R est:4000-6000
£9500 $17005 €13870 Card players (49x64cm-19x25in) s. i.verso board. 26-May-4 Sotheby's, London #229/R est:5000-7000
Prints
£1600 $2864 €2336 French village (24x33cm-9x13in) s.i.verso board. 26-May-4 Sotheby's, Olympia #416/R est:1200-1800
Works on paper
£1500 $2550 €2190 Caricature of Russian Nobility in the provinces (46x61cm-18x24in) s. gouache chl. 19-Nov-3 Sotheby's, London #195/R est:1500-2000
£2083 $3479 €3000 Le docteur, projet de costume (39x24cm-15x9in) s. mono.i. W/C lead pencil board. 21-Oct-3 Artcurial Briest, Paris #80/R est:3000-4000
£2800 $5012 €4088 Chief and his henchmen (46x60cm-18x24in) s. gouache. 26-May-4 Sotheby's, London #230/R est:3000-5000
£4000 $6800 €6000 Costume design for Chinese warrior (40x24cm-16x9in) mono. W/C silver. 25-Nov-3 Christie's, London #213/R est:4000-6000
£4200 $7140 €6132 Costume designs for three women, from the Life and Death of King John (35x40cm-14x16in) init. W/C htd gouache over pencil on paint gold paint. 19-Nov-3 Sotheby's, London #163/R est:200-3000
£4500 $7650 €6570 Costume designs for King John from The Life and Death of King John (34x43cm-13x17in) init. W/C gouache over pencil htd gold paint. 19-Nov-3 Sotheby's, London #164/R est:2000-3000
£4800 $8160 €7008 Costume design for Three warriors from The Life and Death of King John (34x46cm-13x18in) init. W/C gouache over pencil. 19-Nov-3 Sotheby's, London #165/R est:2000-3000
£5500 $9350 €8030 Costume design from The life and Death of King John (35x61cm-14x24in) init.W/C over pencil htd gold paint. 19-Nov-3 Sotheby's, London #162/R est:3000-4000
£12000 $20400 €17520 Four Boyars (47x72cm-19x28in) s. W/C gouache gold silver paint pencil. 19-Nov-3 Sotheby's, London #166/R est:3000-4000
£12000 $20400 €17520 Design for three Russian Brides (47x47cm-19x19in) s.i.d.192 W/C gouache silver paint pencil. 19-Nov-3 Sotheby's, London #167/R est:3000-4000
£15000 $25500 €22500 Theatrical design. s.i. pencil W/C gold silver. 25-Nov-3 Christie's, London #214/R est:8000-10000

POGGENBEEK, Geo (1853-1903) Dutch
£789 $1453 €1200 Cows in a meadow in spring, a church beyond (37x54cm-15x21in) st.studio panel. 22-Jun-4 Christie's, Amsterdam #102/R est:1200-1600
£816 $1486 €1200 Sunlit valley in France (32x46cm-13x18in) s. 3-Feb-4 Christie's, Amsterdam #136 est:1200-1600
£20833 $34792 €30000 Market day at the Nieuwmarkt, Amsterdam (54x76cm-21x30in) s. prov.lit. 21-Oct-3 Sotheby's, Amsterdam #146/R est:4000-6000
Works on paper
£391 $700 €571 Gated stream (46x30cm-18x12in) s. 8-Jan-4 James Julia, Fairfield #830/R
£1053 $1937 €1600 Farm in winter landscape (13x22cm-5x9in) s. W/C gouache. 28-Jun-4 Sotheby's, Amsterdam #42/R est:1000-1500
£2105 $3874 €3200 Cows in a meadow (29x50cm-11x20in) s. W/C bodycol exhib. 22-Jun-4 Christie's, Amsterdam #110/R est:3000-5000

POGGI, François (1838-1900) Swiss
£264 $449 €385 Summer river (34x27cm-13x11in) s. board. 5-Nov-3 Dobiaschofsky, Bern #869/R (S.FR 600)

POGGINI, Domenico (attrib) (1520-1590) Italian
Sculpture
£14094 $26215 €21000 Buste representant certainement Marie de Medicis (74cm-29in) white Carrare marble exec.c.1590. 5-Mar-4 Tajan, Paris #153/R est:10000-15000

POGLIA, Angelo (attrib) (1681-1747) Italian
£1000 $1870 €1460 Saint John the Baptist (45x35cm-18x14in) 27-Feb-4 Christie's, Kensington #202/R est:1200-1800

POGLIAGHI, Ludovico (1857-1950) Italian
£4930 $8528 €7000 Salve Regina (39x26cm-15x10in) s. 9-Dec-3 Pandolfini, Florence #203/R est:3200-3500

POGNA, Giuseppe (1845-1907) Italian
£315 $541 €450 Fishermen pulling the nets (21x34cm-8x13in) s. cardboard. 3-Dec-3 Stadion, Trieste #1124/R
£629 $1083 €900 Landscape (21x33cm-8x13in) s. cardboard. 3-Dec-3 Stadion, Trieste #1098/R
£733 $1313 €1100 Fishermen pulling the nets (23x43cm-9x17in) s. cardboard. 12-May-4 Stadion, Trieste #681/R
£1850 $3145 €2701 Summer landscape (64x97cm-25x38in) s. 5-Nov-3 Dobiaschofsky, Bern #870/R est:3800 (S.FR 4200)

POGREBINSKY, Alexander Petrovitch (20th C) Russian
£509 $850 €743 Still life of roses on white (81x61cm-32x24in) s. 14-Nov-3 Aspire, Cleveland #110
£852 $1500 €1244 Pink roses in silver antique vase (107x61cm-42x24in) s. 28-May-4 Aspire, Cleveland #42/R est:2000-4000
£1508 $2700 €2202 Single pink rose in a vase on a table (119x79cm-47x31in) s. 19-Mar-4 Aspire, Cleveland #25/R est:3000-4000
£1635 $2600 €2387 Still life with white flowers (58x53cm-23x21in) s. 12-Sep-3 Aspire, Cleveland #112 est:2500-5000
£3514 $6500 €5130 Landscape with teardrop shaped trees and sandy dunes (81x107cm-32x42in) s. 16-Jan-4 Aspire, Cleveland #85/R est:4000-8000

POGZEBA, Wolfgang (1936-) American
Works on paper
£310 $500 €453 Cows in summer (38x55cm-15x22in) s. pastel. 17-Aug-3 Bonhams & Butterfields, San Francisco #5812

POHARNOK, Zoltan (1905-) Hungarian
£1697 $2935 €2478 Painter with palette (93x70cm-37x28in) s. 12-Dec-3 Kieselbach, Budapest #214/R (H.F 650000)

POHL, Edward Henry (1874-1956) American
£1301 $2250 €1899 California desert, Coachella Valley (48x76cm-19x30in) s. 10-Dec-3 Bonhams & Butterfields, San Francisco #6333/R est:2000-3000

POHL, Erwin (1896-1958) Swiss/American
£1493 $2538 €2180 Jazz musician (58x47cm-23x19in) s. 28-Nov-3 Zofingen, Switzerland #3122/R est:4000 (S.FR 3300)

POHLE, Hermann (1831-1901) German
£814 $1385 €1188 Mountain landscape (93x134cm-37x53in) s.d.78. 1-Dec-3 Koller, Zurich #6556 est:2000-3000 (S.FR 1800)
£941 $1600 €1374 Rehe in wald lichtung (33x46cm-13x18in) s. board. 22-Nov-3 Jackson's, Cedar Falls #13b/R est:2000-2500

POHLE, Hermann Emil (jnr) (1863-1914) German
£3020 $5557 €4500 Landscape with woman carrying water by river (118x144cm-46x57in) s. 26-Mar-4 Bolland & Marotz, Bremen #574a/R est:5500

POHLE, Léon (1841-1908) German
£766 $1418 €1118 Portrait of young woman (55x45cm-22x18in) with sig.stretcher oval. 15-Mar-4 Rasmussen, Vejle #53/R (D.KR 8500)

POIGNANT, Lucien (20th C) French
£540 $853 €788 Chateau de Bordeau et Lac du Bourget (60x50cm-24x20in) s.i.verso panel. 23-Jul-3 Hampton & Littlewood, Exeter #439/R

POILPREZ, Isabelle (?) French?
Works on paper
£839 $1443 €1200 Flacon et bouchon. mixed media. 6-Dec-3 Teitgen, Nancy #18d

POINGDESTRE, Charles H (?-1905) British
£2000 $3700 €2920 Carrara marble quarry (64x71cm-25x28in) mono.d.1884. 13-Feb-4 Keys, Aylsham #656 est:1200-1500

POINT, Armand (1860-1932) French
£1678 $3104 €2500 Vallee rose en Creuse (65x81cm-26x32in) s. 14-Mar-4 St-Germain-en-Laye Encheres #106/R est:3000
£1987 $3636 €3000 Le village de Jassat en Auvergne (65x85cm-26x33in) s. 9-Apr-4 Claude Aguttes, Neuilly #29 est:2000-3000
£10067 $18523 €15000 Salome (82x117cm-32x46in) s. exhib. 24-Mar-4 Joron-Derem, Paris #236/R est:6000-8000
Works on paper
£1333 $2453 €2000 Scene mythologique (74x60cm-29x24in) s.d.1902 pastel canvas. 9-Jun-4 Oger, Dumont, Paris #71/R est:2000-3000
£3757 $6500 €5485 Symbolic figure (34x22cm-13x9in) init.d.09 W/C over pencil. 11-Dec-3 Sotheby's, New York #96/R est:3000-5000
£5780 $10000 €8439 Narcisse et Echo (78x115cm-31x45in) chl chk prov. 11-Dec-3 Sotheby's, New York #138/R est:10000-15000

POINTELIN, Auguste (1839-1933) French
Works on paper
£467 $845 €700 Foret dans le Jura (50x72cm-20x28in) s. pastel. 30-Mar-4 Rossini, Paris #1037

POINTNER, Rudolf (1907-1991) Austrian
Works on paper
£329 $605 €500 Die Witwe - The widow (33x47cm-13x19in) s.d.1977 s.i.d.verso W/C. 22-Jun-4 Wiener Kunst Auktionen, Vienna #440/R
£423 $701 €600 Untitled. s.d.1985 mixed media collage masonite double-sided. 12-Jun-3 Dorotheum, Graz #45/R
£461 $847 €700 Composition (49x67cm-19x26in) s.d.1971 s.i.verso W/C. 22-Jun-4 Wiener Kunst Auktionen, Vienna #439/R

POINTURIER, Étienne Charles (1809-1853) French
£1141 $2100 €1700 Nature morte de cuisine (72x48cm-28x19in) s.d.1835 i.verso panel. 24-Mar-4 Tajan, Paris #180 est:1500-2000

POIRET, Paul (1879-1944) French
£629 $1145 €950 Nature morte au bouquet de fleurs (73x60cm-29x24in) s. 18-Jun-4 Piasa, Paris #101

POIRIER, Annick (20th C) Canadian
£320 $586 €467 Summer flower (50x75cm-20x30in) s. acrylic. 1-Jun-4 Hodgins, Calgary #368/R (C.D 800)

POIRIER, Jacques (1942-) Canadian
£180 $329 €263 Rivage (30x50cm-12x20in) s. 1-Jun-4 Joyner Waddington, Toronto #524 (C.D 450)
£293 $497 €428 St Urbain (51x61cm-20x24in) s. s.i.verso. 23-Nov-3 Levis, Calgary #116/R (C.D 650)
£383 $705 €559 Houses in the valley, Laurentians (50x61cm-20x24in) s. i.verso. 9-Jun-4 Walker's, Ottawa #18/R (C.D 950)
£403 $742 €588 Autumn near Lake Fonctionnaires (50x61cm-20x24in) s. s.i.verso. 9-Jun-4 Walker's, Ottawa #33/R (C.D 1000)
£434 $785 €634 Brume hivernale (60x76cm-24x30in) s. s.i.verso. 18-Apr-4 Levis, Calgary #95/R est:1200-1500 (C.D 1050)
£473 $804 €691 La montagne de Lours, Parc des Grands Jardins (61x76cm-24x30in) s. s.i.verso prov. 23-Nov-3 Levis, Calgary #115/R (C.D 1050)
£491 $845 €717 Matine de brune (60x75cm-24x30in) s. 2-Dec-3 Joyner Waddington, Toronto #377/R (C.D 1100)
£533 $885 €778 Le grande rapide (61x76cm-24x30in) s. s.i.verso. 5-Oct-3 Levis, Calgary #93a/R (C.D 1200)
£804 $1382 €1174 Cascade (60x75cm-24x30in) s. 2-Dec-3 Joyner Waddington, Toronto #312/R est:1500-2000 (C.D 1800)
£1339 $2304 €1955 Sur le Promontoire (100x75cm-39x30in) s. 2-Dec-3 Joyner Waddington, Toronto #348/R est:1500-2000 (C.D 3000)

POIRSON, Maurice (1850-1882) French
£13309 $21827 €18500 Thoughts (76x121cm-30x48in) s. 10-Jun-3 Pandolfini, Florence #101/R est:16000-18000
£38732 $67782 €55000 Reverie au parc (121x95cm-48x37in) s. lit. 16-Dec-3 Claude Aguttes, Neuilly #100/R est:30000-40000
Works on paper
£2260 $4000 €3300 The rest, woman with hand fan reclining in a hammock. s.d.80 W/C. 1-May-4 Thomaston Place, Thomaston #106/R

POISSON, Pierre (18/19th C) French
Sculpture
£1418 $2298 €2000 Portrait de Claude, fils de l'artiste (39x20cm-15x8in) green brown pat bronze exec.c.1925. 24-May-3 Martinot & Savignat, Pontoise #91/R est:2000-2500

POITEVIN, Georges le (1912-1992) French
£1135 $1895 €1600 Touaregs (55x46cm-22x18in) s. lit. 16-Jun-3 Gros & Delettrez, Paris #275/R est:1500-1800

POITEVIN, Maurice le (20th C) French
£1589 $2510 €2304 Southern landscape with two bathing nymphs by waterway (172x200cm-68x79in) s.d.1928. 2-Sep-3 Rasmussen, Copenhagen #1703/R est:25000 (D.KR 17000)

POITRAS, Jane Ash (1951-) Canadian
£500 $815 €730 Tar blanket no.2 (46x61cm-18x24in) s.i.verso acrylic collage prov. 23-Sep-3 Ritchie, Toronto #185/R est:800-1200 (C.D 1100)
Works on paper
£670 $1152 €978 Navajo Shaman (90x60cm-35x24in) s.d.96 mixed media collage prov. 2-Dec-3 Joyner Waddington, Toronto #338/R (C.D 1500)
£676 $1149 €987 Millennium Metis (76x56cm-30x22in) s.i. mixed media. 21-Nov-3 Walker's, Ottawa #104/R (C.D 1500)
£714 $1229 €1042 Spirit Shaman (77x45cm-30x18in) s. mixed media board. 2-Dec-3 Joyner Waddington, Toronto #218/R (C.D 1600)
£732 $1310 €1069 Grandfather, grandfather sun shines (72x56cm-28x22in) s.i.d.1998 mixed media canvas prov. 27-May-4 Heffel, Vancouver #199/R est:2000-3000 (C.D 1800)
£800 $1464 €1168 Individual power (90x60cm-35x24in) s.i.d.1998 mixed media canvas prov. 1-Jun-4 Hodgins, Calgary #92/R est:3000-4000 (C.D 2000)
£905 $1511 €1321 Untitled - mother and child (60x50cm-24x20in) mixed media on canvas. 17-Nov-3 Hodgins, Calgary #36/R est:2250-2750 (C.D 2000)
£1040 $1903 €1518 Shy shaman (59x62cm-23x24in) s. board mixed media. 1-Jun-4 Joyner Waddington, Toronto #220/R est:4000-5000 (C.D 2600)
£1802 $3063 €2631 Bagman and Haida mask (81x61cm-32x24in) s.d.2003 mixed media canvas. 27-Nov-3 Heffel, Vancouver #137/R est:2000-3000 (C.D 4000)

POJANSKI, Stephen J (1923-1997) American?
Works on paper
£428 $800 €625 Happy couple in Oldsmobile Super 88 holiday sedan (18x41cm-7x16in) gouache en grisaille. 26-Feb-4 Illustration House, New York #139

POKARZHEVSKIY, P D (1889-1968) Russian
Works on paper
£246 $440 €359 Khirgizian woman portrait (50x44cm-20x17in) col pencil painted 1933. 29-May-4 Shishkin Gallery, Moscow #22/R

POKITONOV, Ivan (1850-1923) Russian
£28231 $50534 €41500 Reparation du mat (15x25cm-6x10in) s.i. panel. 19-Mar-4 Millon & Associes, Paris #96 est:800-1000
£30952 $55405 €45500 Paysage d'hiver (24x33cm-9x13in) s. board. 19-Mar-4 Millon & Associes, Paris #95/R est:800-1000

POKORNY, Michaela (1967-) Austrian
£733 $1349 €1100 Female nude - self portrait (120x50cm-47x20in) s.d.99 acrylic panel. 9-Jun-4 Dorotheum, Salzburg #703/R

POKUSHEVA, Elena (1956-) Russian
£300 $525 €438 Fisherboys (30x40cm-12x16in) s. 17-Dec-3 John Nicholson, Haslemere #28/R

POL, Arend van de (1886-1956) Dutch
£342 $582 €500 Landscape with shepherd (42x57cm-17x22in) s. 5-Nov-3 Vendue Huis, Gravenhage #233/R
£448 $749 €650 Cows watering (59x44cm-23x17in) s. 11-Nov-3 Vendu Notarishuis, Rotterdam #106/R

£526 $953 €800 Sheep in a polder landscape near a small river (60x44cm-24x17in) s. 19-Apr-4 Glerum, Amsterdam #199/R
£1127 $1803 €1600 Virgin with child, Dutch peasants (70x100cm-28x39in) s.d.1937 board triptych. 19-Sep-3 Sigalas, Stuttgart #345/R

POL, Louis van der (1896-1982) Dutch
£282 $487 €400 City scene (29x39cm-11x15in) s. panel. 12-Dec-3 Berlinghof, Heidelberg #1142
£426 $750 €622 Figures on a street (25x20cm-10x8in) s. board painted c.1930. 23-May-4 Treadway Gallery, Cincinnati #615/R
£438 $700 €639 Winter sky (38x152cm-15x60in) s. panel painted c.1970. 18-May-3 Auctions by the Bay, Alameda #1020/R
£541 $1000 €790 Soldier with lady (30x25cm-12x10in) panel. 12-Mar-4 Du Mouchelle, Detroit #2138/R
£1040 $1800 €1518 Figures digging on the beach (30x41cm-12x16in) 12-Dec-3 Du Mouchelle, Detroit #2084/R est:1800-2500
£1250 $2000 €1825 Street scenes. board pair. 19-Sep-3 Du Mouchelle, Detroit #2146/R est:2000-3000
Works on paper
£219 $400 €320 Ladies at the beach (23x38cm-9x15in) s. W/C gouache. 10-Apr-4 Auctions by the Bay, Alameda #1515/R

POL, Willem Jilts (1905-1988) Dutch
£1400 $2380 €2044 Two peasants boys with their herd (80x64cm-31x25in) s. 6-Nov-3 Christie's, Kensington #806 est:300-400
£1800 $3060 €2628 Day's catch (80x54cm-31x21in) s. 6-Nov-3 Christie's, Kensington #807 est:300-400
£3268 $5915 €4771 Boys with cattle (81x65cm-32x26in) s. 4-Apr-4 Sotheby's, Singapore #40/R est:4500-6500 (S.D 10000)

POLA, Paola (1942-) Italian
£522 $955 €762 View (100x60cm-39x24in) s.i.d.1973 verso. 4-Jun-4 Zofingen, Switzerland #2920 (S.FR 1200)

POLACCO, Ferruccio (20th C) Argentinian
Sculpture
£8380 $15000 €12235 Lovers (97cm-38in) s.d.1961 pat bronze. 4-May-4 Arroyo, Buenos Aires #37/R est:6000

POLACK, Salomon (1757-1839) British
Miniatures
£946 $1750 €1381 Portrait of a lady (8x8cm-3x3in) exec.c.1800 oval. 12-Mar-4 Du Mouchelle, Detroit #2028/R est:1000-2000
£1000 $1810 €1460 Portrait of a lady with black hair and lace dress (5x5cm-2x2in) s. gold locket frame. 15-Apr-4 Gorringes, Worthing #663/R est:1000-1500

POLAROLI, Adolfo (1862-1952) Italian
£694 $1181 €1000 View of Lake Maggiore (60x100cm-24x39in) s. lit. 1-Nov-3 Meeting Art, Vercelli #372

POLEDNE, Franz (1873-1932) Austrian
£470 $864 €700 Dining room (26x42cm-10x17in) s. W/C. 26-Mar-4 Dorotheum, Vienna #184/R
Works on paper
£1060 $1928 €1600 Room in Tratzberg Castle (22x33cm-9x13in) s. W/C. 17-Jun-4 Finarte Semenzato, Milan #335/R est:1500-2000
£1275 $2346 €1900 Interior with blue oven (22x15cm-9x6in) s. W/C. 26-Mar-4 Dorotheum, Vienna #349/R est:1200-1400
£1655 $2748 €2400 Michaelerplatz with Cafe Griensteidl (20x35cm-8x14in) s.i. W/C. 30-Sep-3 Dorotheum, Vienna #296/R est:3000-3500
£1931 $3206 €2800 Maria am Gestade (36x27cm-14x11in) s.d.02 W/C. 30-Sep-3 Dorotheum, Vienna #292/R est:3000-3500

POLENOV, Vassili (1844-1927) Russian
£1831 $3168 €2600 Autumnal winter landscape with walls and arch (40x57cm-16x22in) s. 12-Dec-3 Altus, Berlin #553/R est:3500
£280000 $476000 €408800 Landscape with well and cypress trees (132x82cm-52x32in) s.d.96 prov.exhib.lit. 19-Nov-3 Sotheby's, London #36/R est:180000-250000

POLEO, Hector (1918-) Venezuelan
£2629 $4470 €3838 Self-portrait (46x32cm-18x13in) s. 23-Nov-3 Subastas Odalys, Caracas #120/R est:3500
£10216 $17060 €14915 Elle a toujours les yeux ouverts (38x46cm-15x18in) s. painted 1967. 13-Jul-3 Subastas Odalys, Caracas #55/R est:12000
£43333 $79733 €65000 Hero (51x40cm-20x16in) s.d.48 lit. 10-Jun-4 Christie's, Paris #61/R est:65000-95000
Sculpture
£9118 $15500 €13312 Head (32x27x25cm-13x11x10in) s. num.2/7 bronze exec.1987. 23-Nov-3 Subastas Odalys, Caracas #150/R est:15000
Works on paper
£256 $410 €374 Untitled (19x17cm-7x7in) s. mixed media exec.1966. 21-Sep-3 Subastas Odalys, Caracas #19
£391 $625 €571 Figure (23x16cm-9x6in) s. graphite. 21-Sep-3 Subastas Odalys, Caracas #96
£456 $720 €666 Untitled (22x17cm-9x7in) s. graphite exhib. 1-Dec-2 Subastas Odalys, Caracas #94/R
£694 $1180 €1013 Untitled (19x16cm-7x6in) s. mixed media. 23-Nov-3 Subastas Odalys, Caracas #113
£1399 $2575 €2099 Landscape (16x10cm-6x4in) s. W/C. 27-Jun-4 Subastas Odalys, Caracas #126/R est:3000

POLESELLO, Rogelio (1939-) Argentinian
£2210 $4000 €3227 Network (51x51cm-20x20in) acrylic. 30-Mar-4 Arroyo, Buenos Aires #106
£3352 $6000 €4894 Untitled (100x100cm-39x39in) s.d.1973 verso. 4-May-4 Arroyo, Buenos Aires #15/R est:6000
£6630 $12000 €9680 Untitled (200x100cm-79x39in) acrylic. 30-Mar-4 Arroyo, Buenos Aires #94
Sculpture
£1923 $3500 €2808 Untitled (34x34cm-13x13in) s.d.68 plexiglas. 29-Jun-4 Arroyo, Buenos Aires #30/R est:3000

POLHAMUS, Melissa (1957-) American
Works on paper
£329 $550 €480 Canary bird (61x76cm-24x30in) W/C ink prov. 15-Nov-3 Slotin Folk Art, Buford #708/R

POLI, Fabio de (1947-) Italian
£331 $603 €500 Flying cards (80x100cm-31x39in) s. s.i.verso. 21-Jun-4 Pandolfini, Florence #464
£364 $663 €550 George (80x100cm-31x39in) s. s.i.verso acrylic. 21-Jun-4 Pandolfini, Florence #436/R
£1611 $2883 €2400 Florentine portrait (120x80cm-47x31in) s. vinyl painted 1999. 28-May-4 Farsetti, Prato #58/R est:1500-2000

POLI, Gherardo (1676-1739) Italian
£7447 $12436 €10500 Festa compestre con rovine classiche e castello (42x56cm-17x22in) prov.lit. 18-Jun-3 Christie's, Rome #457/R est:10000-15000
£7500 $13500 €10950 Seascape with vessels in choppy seas (58x108cm-23x43in) 20-Apr-4 Sotheby's, Olympia #380/R est:4000-6000

POLI, Gherardo and Giuseppe (18th C) Italian
£30201 $56477 €45000 Battles (91x142cm-36x56in) pair. 25-Feb-4 Porro, Milan #23/R est:40000

POLIAKOFF, Nicolas (1899-1976) Russian
£1342 $2470 €2000 Portrait de femme assise dans un fauteuil (92x65cm-36x26in) s.d.1926. 29-Mar-4 Rieunier, Paris #29/R est:1500-2000
£1987 $3616 €3000 Nu cubiste (92x60cm-36x24in) s. 16-Jun-4 Claude Boisgirard, Paris #134/R est:1000-1500
£2550 $4718 €3800 Nu devant le miroir (100x73cm-39x29in) s.d.1933. 15-Mar-4 Claude Boisgirard, Paris #97/R est:4000-5000
Works on paper
£397 $723 €600 Nu au repos (46x61cm-18x24in) chl. 16-Jun-4 Claude Boisgirard, Paris #133

POLIAKOFF, Serge (1906-1969) Russian
£26000 $47840 €37960 Composition (73x60cm-29x24in) s. exec 1968 prov. 24-Jun-4 Sotheby's, London #176/R est:30000-40000
£30282 $52993 €43000 Composition (27x35cm-11x14in) s. s.d.1966 verso prov. 16-Dec-3 Porro, Milan #31/R est:18000-22000
£31469 $53497 €45000 Composition rouge et rosee (60x73cm-24x29in) s. panel prov. 25-Nov-3 Tajan, Paris #8/R est:40000-50000
£32237 $59316 €49000 Composition (65x81cm-26x32in) s. prov.lit. 27-Jun-4 Versailles Encheres #104/R est:50000-60000
£34899 $62470 €52000 Composition abstraite (54x65cm-21x26in) init. s.verso prov.exhib. 25-May-4 Sotheby's, Milan #287/R est:35000-45000
£37118 $67555 €54192 Composition (130x97cm-51x38in) s.verso painted c.1952 prov.exhib. 18-Jun-4 Kornfeld, Bern #133/R est:100000 (S.FR 85000)
£38000 $69920 €55480 Untitled (65x54cm-26x21in) s. s.verso painted 1954-55. 25-Jun-4 Christie's, London #111/R est:30000-40000
£38028 $65788 €54000 Composition polychrome (61x50cm-24x20in) s.d.1946 s.i.d.verso prov.exhib.lit. 9-Dec-3 Artcurial Briest, Paris #417/R est:55000-65000
£42254 $73099 €60000 Composition (55x44cm-22x17in) mono.d.1964 s.verso. 14-Dec-3 Versailles Encheres #117/R est:50000-55000
£45000 $82800 €65700 Composition en rouge (99x80cm-39x31in) s. exec c.1963-64. 24-Jun-4 Sotheby's, London #170/R est:20000-30000
£45045 $77477 €65766 Monchrome (51x61cm-20x24in) s. panel prov.exhib. 2-Dec-3 Koller, Zurich #3079/R est:70000-85000 (S.FR 100000)
£52000 $93600 €78000 Composition (100x81cm-39x32in) s. painted 1961-66 prov.exhib.lit. 25-Apr-4 Versailles Encheres #112 est:80000-90000
£52326 $90000 €76396 Composition abstraite (89x116cm-35x46in) s. prov. 3-Dec-3 Doyle, New York #72/R est:90000-120000
£52402 $96419 €76507 Composition rouge, vert, blanc, jaune (81x65cm-32x26in) s. prov. 8-Jun-4 Germann, Zurich #19/R est:120000-150000 (S.FR 120000)
£58000 $106720 €84680 Composition lie de vin, grise, rouge et bleue (73x60cm-29x24in) s. s.d.1965 verso prov.exhib. 24-Jun-4 Sotheby's, London #185/R est:50000-60000
£75000 $138000 €109500 Composition jaune (89x116cm-35x46in) s. board painted 1958 prov.exhib.lit. 24-Jun-4 Christie's, London #14/R est:50000-70000
£77778 $128333 €112000 Composition (65x46cm-26x18in) s. prov.exhib. 2-Jul-3 Cornette de St.Cyr, Paris #7/R est:70000-90000
£80000 $145600 €116800 Composition abstraite (92x74cm-36x29in) s. burlap painted 1954 prov.exhib. 5-Feb-4 Christie's, London #113/R est:30000-50000
£80556 $132917 €116000 Composition (116x89cm-46x35in) s. 2-Jul-3 Cornette de St.Cyr, Paris #4/R est:130000-180000
£81119 $139524 €116000 Composition (130x89cm-51x35in) s. exhib. 4-Dec-3 Piasa, Paris #59/R est:120000-180000
£82517 $141930 €118000 Untitled (73x92cm-29x36in) s. prov.exhib. 2-Dec-3 Calmels Cohen, Paris #73/R est:80000-120000
£87500 $144375 €126000 Composition (116x89cm-46x35in) s. 2-Jul-3 Cornette de St.Cyr, Paris #5/R est:130000-180000
£90604 $162181 €135000 Composition (97x130cm-38x51in) s. painted 1959 prov.exhib. 26-May-4 Christie's, Paris #67/R est:120000-180000
£115385 $192692 €165000 Composition (81x60cm-32x24in) s.d.1954 prov.exhib.lit. 29-Jun-3 Versailles Encheres #99/R est:230000
£165000 $303600 €240900 Composition (116x89cm-46x35in) s.d.66 oil pigment prov. 25-Jun-4 Christie's, London #121/R est:120000-160000
£166667 $306667 €250000 Composition (162x130cm-64x51in) s. painted 1966 prov.exhib.lit. 8-Jun-4 Artcurial Briest, Paris #213/R est:280000-350000
£180000 $327600 €262800 Composition abstract (162x135cm-64x53in) s. burlap painted 1969 prov.exhib. 5-Feb-4 Christie's, London #124/R est:90000-120000
£224832 $413691 €335000 Composition mauve, violet et rose (89x116cm-35x46in) s. painted 1954 prov.exhib.lit. 29-Mar-4 Cornette de St.Cyr, Paris #8/R est:200000-300000

£312500	$575000	€475000	Composition rouge (116x89cm-46x35in) s. s.verso painted 1954 prov.exhib.lit. 27-Jun-4 Versailles Encheres #98/R est:300000-400000

Prints

£1659	$3020	€2422	Composition in grey, green and blue. s.i. col lithograph. 17-Jun-4 Kornfeld, Bern #706 est:4000 (S.FR 3800)
£1724	$2879	€2500	Composition en gris brun et jaune. s.num.42/75 etching aquatint zinc vellum. 9-Jul-3 Tajan, Paris #331 est:1500-2000
£1808	$3200	€2640	Composition, bleu, vert et rouge (42x64cm-17x25in) s.i.num.XV/XV col aquatint. 28-Apr-4 Christie's, Rockefeller NY #227/R est:3000-5000
£1942	$3186	€2700	Composition in blue, green and red (46x62cm-18x24in) s.i. col lithograph. 4-Jun-3 Ketterer, Hamburg #779/R est:3300-3600
£2000	$3580	€3000	Composition in blue, yellow and red (59x44cm-23x17in) s. col lithograph. 15-May-4 Van Ham, Cologne #844/R est:4000
£2000	$3580	€3000	Composition in grey, red and green (44x59cm-17x23in) s.i. col lithograph. 15-May-4 Dr Sturies, Dusseldorf #142/R
£2000	$3680	€3000	Composition in green and yellow (47x63cm-19x25in) s. col lithograph exec. 1966 one of 75. 12-Jun-4 Villa Grisebach, Berlin #390/R est:3000-4000
£2000	$3680	€3000	Composition in orange (45x60cm-18x24in) s. col lithograph exec. 1956 one of 95. 12-Jun-4 Villa Grisebach, Berlin #391/R est:4000-6000
£2000	$3680	€3000	Composition in blue and green (64x47cm-25x19in) s. col lithograph exec. 1962 one of 65. 12-Jun-4 Villa Grisebach, Berlin #393/R est:3000-4000
£2193	$4035	€3202	Composition in green (22x34cm-9x13in) s. num.23/75 aquatint etching. 23-Jun-4 Koller, Zurich #3283 est:1000-1800 (S.FR 5000)
£2193	$4035	€3202	Composition in blue, yellow and red (59x44cm-23x17in) s. lithograph. 23-Jun-4 Koller, Zurich #3285/R est:3500-5000 (S.FR 5000)
£2200	$3982	€3300	Composition (97x73cm-38x29in) col lithograph. 31-Mar-4 Tajan, Paris #291/R est:2500-2800
£2238	$3804	€3200	Composition grise (48x63cm-19x25in) s. col lithograph. 26-Nov-3 Lempertz, Koln #923/R est:3200
£2266	$3852	€3308	Composition verte, rouge et bleue (49x64cm-19x25in) s.num.46/75 col lithograph lit. 4-Nov-3 Bukowskis, Stockholm #449/R est:20000-30000 (S.KR 30000)
£2358	$4292	€3443	Composition in brown and red. s.i. aquatint burin. 17-Jun-4 Kornfeld, Bern #707 est:6000 (S.FR 5400)
£2467	$4440	€3700	Composition grise, rouge et jaune (56x76cm-22x30in) s. num.24/100 col lithograph. 24-Apr-4 Cornette de St.Cyr, Paris #245/R est:3000
£2533	$4661	€3800	Composition in red, yellow, grey and blue (57x44cm-22x17in) s. lithograph exec. 1959 one of 200. 12-Jun-4 Villa Grisebach, Berlin #392/R est:4000-5000
£2533	$4661	€3800	Composition orange et verte (60x45cm-24x18in) s. col lithograph. 11-Jun-4 Hauswedell & Nolte, Hamburg #1481/R est:3500
£2550	$4565	€3800	Composition in blue and yellow (63x48cm-25x19in) s.i. col lithograph. 25-May-4 Dorotheum, Vienna #237/R est:3800-4000
£2632	$4842	€3843	Composition in grey, green and blue (48x63cm-19x25in) s. num.XXXV/L lithograph. 23-Jun-4 Koller, Zurich #3287/R est:3000-4000 (S.FR 6000)
£2657	$4571	€3800	Composition rouge, grise et noire (64x49cm-25x19in) s. col lithograph one of 300. 5-Dec-3 Ketterer, Munich #142/R est:3800-4500
£2667	$4773	€4000	Composition in pink (45x60cm-18x24in) s. col lithograph. 15-May-4 Van Ham, Cologne #845/R est:4000
£2667	$4773	€4000	Composition in red, grey and black (64x49cm-25x19in) s. col lithograph. 15-May-4 Van Ham, Cologne #846/R est:2800
£2667	$4880	€4000	Composition grise, verte et bleue (49x63cm-19x25in) s. lithograph. 5-Jun-4 Lempertz, Koln #951/R est:3200
£2727	$4636	€3900	Composition bleue, jaune et rouge (61x47cm-24x19in) s. col lithograph. 26-Nov-3 Lempertz, Koln #922/R est:3500
£2795	$4751	€4081	Composition jaune rouge et bleue (63x47cm-25x19in) s.num.74/75 col lithograph lit. 5-Nov-3 AB Stockholms Auktionsverk #1280/R est:25000-30000 (S.KR 37000)
£3067	$5520	€4600	Composition rouge, verte et jaune (56x43cm-22x17in) s. num.2/50 col lithograph. 24-Apr-4 Cornette de St.Cyr, Paris #244/R est:4000
£3097	$5264	€4522	Composition bleue, rouge, verte et noire (32x24cm-13x9in) s.num.80/100 col etching aquatint lit. 5-Nov-3 AB Stockholms Auktionsverk #1279/R est:35000-40000 (S.KR 41000)
£3147	$5350	€4500	Composition in burgundy red and blue (47x64cm-19x25in) s. col lithograph. 29-Nov-3 Villa Grisebach, Berlin #321/R est:3000-4000
£3467	$6344	€5200	Composition rouge et verte (63x46cm-25x18in) s. col etching. 5-Jun-4 Lempertz, Koln #949/R est:5500
£3509	$6456	€5123	Composition in grey, blue and red (47x62cm-19x24in) s.i. aquatint engraving. 23-Jun-4 Koller, Zurich #3282/R est:6500-8000 (S.FR 8000)
£3600	$6624	€5400	Composition verte, orange et lie-de-vin (48x63cm-19x25in) s.i. col lithograph. 11-Jun-4 Hauswedell & Nolte, Hamburg #1482/R est:3500
£3800	$6916	€5548	Composition noire, jaune, bleue et rouge (47x64cm-19x25in) s.num.13/75 col aquatint. 1-Jul-4 Sotheby's, London #244/R est:2500-3000
£3846	$6538	€5500	Composition in green, orange and burgundy red (48x63cm-19x25in) s. col lithograph. 29-Nov-3 Villa Grisebach, Berlin #319/R est:3000-4000
£4000	$7360	€6000	Composition in yellow, red and blue (63x47cm-25x19in) s. col lithograph exec. 1966 one of 75. 12-Jun-4 Villa Grisebach, Berlin #386/R est:4000-5000
£4133	$7605	€6200	Composition in green, red and blue (49x63cm-19x25in) s. col lithograph exec. 1966 one of 75. 12-Jun-4 Villa Grisebach, Berlin #387/R est:4000-5000
£4196	$7133	€6000	Composition in blue, grey, red and yellow (47x63cm-19x25in) s. col lithograph. 29-Nov-3 Villa Grisebach, Berlin #318/R est:3000-4000
£4333	$7973	€6500	Composition in blue, yellow and red (61x47cm-24x19in) s. col lithograph exec. 1965 one of 75. 12-Jun-4 Villa Grisebach, Berlin #389/R est:5000-6000
£5245	$8916	€7500	Composition in grey (47x62cm-19x24in) s. col lithograph. 29-Nov-3 Villa Grisebach, Berlin #320/R est:3000-4000
£27273	$46909	€39000	Lithographs (63x80cm-25x31in) s. num.65/75 col lithograph portfolio of ten. 5-Dec-3 Ketterer, Munich #148/R est:30000-40000

Works on paper

£4130	$7559	€6030	Figure bleu (24x31cm-9x12in) s. gouache prov. 4-Jun-4 Zofingen, Switzerland #2504/R est:12000 (S.FR 9500)
£7000	$12740	€10220	Composition (24x28cm-9x11in) s. gouache prov. 4-Feb-4 Sotheby's, Olympia #172/R est:3000-4000
£10000	$18300	€15000	Composition rouge, noir, verte et bleue (24x32cm-9x13in) s. gouache prov. 5-Jun-4 Lempertz, Koln #947/R est:20000-25000
£11333	$20853	€17000	Untitled (36x28cm-14x11in) s. pastel. 12-Jun-4 Villa Grisebach, Berlin #388/R est:10000-12000
£11888	$20210	€17000	Composition (63x49cm-25x19in) s. gouache prov. 25-Nov-3 Tajan, Paris #7/R est:18000-20000
£12162	$21771	€18000	Untitled (61x46cm-24x18in) s. gouache prov. 4-May-4 Calmels Cohen, Paris #179/R est:15000-20000
£12414	$19862	€18000	Composition (33x24cm-13x9in) s. gouache. 13-Mar-3 Galleria Pace, Milan #137/R est:21000-26000
£13000	$23660	€19500	Composition bleu, rouge, noire (31x24cm-12x9in) s.d.1963 gouache. 5-Jul-4 Le Mouel, Paris #52/R est:18000-25000
£13287	$22853	€19000	Composition (64x38cm-25x15in) s. gouache kraft paper exec.c.1950-51. 3-Dec-3 Tajan, Paris #451/R est:15000-20000
£14085	$24366	€20000	Composition bleue et grise (46x61cm-18x24in) s. gouache paper on canvas prov. 9-Dec-3 Artcurial Briest, Paris #417b/R est:23000-28000
£15988	$27500	€23342	Composition abstraite (47x63cm-19x25in) s. gouache prov. 3-Dec-3 Doyle, New York #73/R est:15000-20000
£16000	$29440	€23360	Untitled (64x60cm-25x24in) s. gouache exec 1949 prov. 24-Jun-4 Sotheby's, London #179/R est:6000-8000
£16000	$29440	€23360	Composition a la forme rouge noir et blanc (48x53cm-19x21in) s. gouache exec 1968. 24-Jun-4 Sotheby's, London #181/R est:10000-15000
£16500	$30360	€24090	Composition abstraite (33x24cm-13x9in) s.d.1961 gouache paper on canvas prov. 25-Jun-4 Christie's, London #115/R est:8000-12000
£19000	$34580	€27740	Composition (47x61cm-19x24in) s. gouache pencil card prov.exhib. 6-Feb-4 Sotheby's, London #179/R est:12000-15000
£20015	$34026	€29222	Composition (46x62cm-18x24in) s. gouache exec.c.1956-57. 5-Nov-3 AB Stockholms Auktionsverk #1115/R est:175000-200000 (S.KR 265000)
£21127	$36549	€30000	Composition (54x39cm-21x15in) s. gouache paper on canvas lit. 14-Dec-3 Versailles Encheres #92/R est:30000-35000
£22523	$38739	€32884	Composition noir et rouge (47x62cm-19x24in) s. gouache prov. 2-Dec-3 Koller, Zurich #3081/R est:45000-60000 (S.FR 50000)
£22887	$39595	€32500	Composition (45x56cm-18x22in) s. gouache exec.c.1954-1955 lit. 14-Dec-3 Versailles Encheres #91/R est:30000-35000
£24000	$44160	€35040	Untitled (61x45cm-24x18in) s. W/C exec 1961 prov. 24-Jun-4 Sotheby's, London #167/R est:15000-20000
£26760	$46295	€38000	Composition (48x62cm-19x24in) s. gouache paper on canvas prov. 9-Dec-3 Artcurial Briest, Paris #417a/R est:23000-28000
£27083	$45229	€39000	Composition abstraite (65x50cm-26x20in) s. gouache exec. c.1966 prov.exhib. 21-Oct-3 Christie's, Paris #198/R est:20000-30000
£38000	$69920	€57000	Composition (64x50cm-25x20in) s. gouache brown paper exec.late 1950s prov. 11-Jun-4 Villa Grisebach, Berlin #71/R est:35000-45000

POLICASTRO, Enrique (1898-1971) Argentinian

Works on paper

£773	$1400	€1129	Landscape (24x30cm-9x12in) mixed media cardboard. 30-Mar-4 Arroyo, Buenos Aires #6
£2346	$4200	€3425	Beached (21x30cm-8x12in) s.d.54 mixed media. 4-May-4 Arroyo, Buenos Aires #9/R est:1200

POLIDORO DA CARAVAGGIO (1492-1543) Italian

Works on paper

£70000	$128100	€102200	Madonna and child (14x8cm-6x3in) red chalk. 8-Jul-4 Sotheby's, London #24/R est:50000-80000

POLITTI, Leo (1908-) American

Works on paper

£324	$600	€473	Mother and child with baby sleeping (38x34cm-15x13in) s. w/C. 18-Jan-4 Bonhams & Butterfields, Los Angeles #7006/R
£4651	$8000	€6790	Three women (56x36cm-22x14in) s.d.1937 W/C pencil. 7-Dec-3 Treadway Gallery, Cincinnati #701/R est:1500-2000

POLKE, Sigmar (1941-) German

£11792	$19104	€17216	Untitled (86x61cm-34x24in) s.d.67 i. verso gouache prov. 24-May-3 Burkhard, Luzern #165/R est:25000-30000 (S.FR 25000)
£19580	$33287	€28000	Untitled - Munster 1973 (100x70cm-39x28in) s.d.73 gouache. 27-Nov-3 Lempertz, Koln #346/R est:30000
£20950	$37500	€30587	Untitled (64x84cm-25x33in) s.d.71 acrylic photo emulsion paper prov. 13-May-4 Sotheby's, New York #422/R est:20000-30000
£32934	$55000	€48084	Evangelista and 900 MHz (198x149cm-78x59in) s.d.2000 acrylic ink paper prov.exhib. 12-Nov-3 Christie's, Rockefeller NY #385/R est:70000-90000
£37126	$62000	€54204	Untitled (91x142cm-36x56in) acrylic lacquer on fabric diptych painted 1983. 14-Nov-3 Phillips, New York #169/R est:60000-80000
£38922	$65000	€56826	Turns Inside Out, Emerald Green Cashmere Sweater (198x149cm-78x59in) s.d.2000 acrylic ink prov.exhib. 12-Nov-3 Christie's, Rockefeller NY #386/R est:70000-90000
£107784	$180000	€157365	Lungta - cheveux de vent (150x180cm-59x71in) s. s.d.85 overlap acrylic dispersion on fabric. 13-Nov-3 Phillips, New York #17/R est:150000-200000
£117318	$210000	€171284	Untitled (135x155cm-53x61in) s.d.98 acrylic resin fabric prov.lit. 12-May-4 Christie's, Rockefeller NY #190/R est:150000-200000
£131737	$220000	€192336	Streifenbild II (90x75cm-35x30in) s.d.68 verso prov.exhib. 12-Nov-3 Christie's, Rockefeller NY #388/R est:120000-160000

Prints

£3636	$6182	€5200	Friends I (46x59cm-18x23in) s.d. offset lithograph board. 27-Nov-3 Lempertz, Koln #347/R est:4000
£3846	$6538	€5500	Friends (46x59cm-18x23in) s.d. offset board. 29-Nov-3 Villa Grisebach, Berlin #357/R est:3000-4000
£6000	$10740	€9000	S.H. - or when do the spots count? (90x70cm-35x28in) s.i.d. col silkscreen prov. 14-May-4 Ketterer, Munich #292/R est:9000-12000

Works on paper

£867	$1551	€1300	Profile (9x7cm-4x3in) s. biro. 15-May-4 Dr Sturies, Dusseldorf #147/R
£1400	$2562	€2100	Untitled (21x15cm-8x6in) s.d.72 feltpen. 4-Jun-4 Lempertz, Koln #373/R est:1500
£2800	$5012	€4200	Just got ot him (21x15cm-8x6in) feltpen pencil W/C. 15-May-4 Dr Sturies, Dusseldorf #148/R
£3007	$5172	€4300	Peace on earth (25x18cm-10x7in) s.d.2000 col crayon. 4-Dec-3 Van Ham, Cologne #394/R est:2400
£3467	$6205	€5200	Untitled (21x15cm-8x6in) s.d. biro W/C. 15-May-4 Dr Sturies, Dusseldorf #144/R
£6000	$10740	€9000	Three hat models (30x21cm-12x8in) s.d. W/C Indian ink. 15-May-4 Dr Sturies, Dusseldorf #146/R
£6267	$11217	€9400	Taxi murder (30x21cm-12x8in) s.d. biro. 15-May-4 Dr Sturies, Dusseldorf #145/R
£6333	$11337	€9500	S-H or the love of things (100x70cm-39x28in) s.d. mixed media. 15-May-4 Van Ham, Cologne #848/R est:10000
£9000	$16470	€13500	Untitled - new, bunn with ears (29x21cm-11x8in) s.d.65 biro pencil. 4-Jun-4 Lempertz, Koln #367/R est:8000
£10667	$19520	€16000	Untitled (29x21cm-11x8in) s.d.67 W/C bodycol. 4-Jun-4 Lempertz, Koln #371/R est:10000
£12575	$21000	€18360	Untitled (100x70cm-39x28in) s.d.83 brush ink W/C graphite prov. 14-Nov-3 Phillips, New York #162/R est:25000-30000
£17000	$30940	€24820	Untitled (23x17cm-9x7in) s.verso ink paint gelatin silver print pair prov. 6-Feb-4 Sotheby's, London #130/R est:20000-30000
£22000	$40480	€32120	Untitled (96x64cm-38x25in) s.d.68 W/C prov. 25-Jun-4 Christie's, London #242/R est:15000-20000

£40000	$66800	€58400	Untitled (132x152cm-52x60in) s. s.d.94 verso spray paint resin fabric prov. 22-Oct-3 Christie's, London #102/R est:40000-60000
£51333	$93940	€77000	Composition (84x60cm-33x24in) s.i.d.67 W/C prov.exhib. 4-Jun-4 Lempertz, Koln #368/R est:35000-40000
£70000	$128800	€102200	Quetta (84x118cm-33x46in) s.i.d.94 W/C sliver marker pen gelatin silver print prov. 23-Jun-4 Sotheby's, London #16/R est:60000-80000

POLKINGHORN, George (1898-1967) American

£311	$500	€454	Mt Shasta, North Face (51x61cm-20x24in) s. s.i.verso on stretcher. 20-Jan-3 O'Gallerie, Oregon #131/R

POLLACK, Hans (1891-1968) Austrian

£467	$835	€700	Muhlviertel landscape (70x80cm-28x31in) s.d.1957 panel. 13-May-4 Dorotheum, Linz #474/R
£629	$1070	€900	Bunch of flowers (70x80cm-28x31in) s.d.1966 panel. 27-Nov-3 Dorotheum, Linz #464/R
£667	$1193	€1000	Muhlviertel - Schloss Altenhof (62x66cm-24x26in) s.d.1936 board. 13-May-4 Dorotheum, Linz #473/R

POLLAK, Leopold (1816-1880) Austrian

£1641	$2725	€2396	Sweet sleep (100x75cm-39x30in) s.i. 4-Oct-3 Dorotheum, Prague #81/R est:60000-90000 (C.KR 75000)

POLLAK, Sigismund (1837-1912) Hungarian

£4648	$8041	€6600	Martin Luther (192x147cm-76x58in) s.d.868. 9-Dec-3 Pandolfini, Florence #223/R est:6500-7500

POLLARD (18th C) American

£29412	$50000	€42942	Portrait of Anne Pattershall (152x64cm-60x25in) painted c.1720 prov.lit. 1-Nov-3 Skinner, Boston #100/R est:30000-50000

POLLARD, James (1797-1867) British

£12000	$21120	€17520	Walking up grouse (34x44cm-13x17in) 21-May-4 Christie's, London #76/R est:5000-8000
£28000	$51520	€40880	Partridge shoot (43x53cm-17x21in) s.d.1829. 10-Jun-4 Christie's, Kensington #392/R est:4000-6000
£41860	$72000	€61116	London to Hastings royal mail coach (76x104cm-30x41in) s. 5-Dec-3 Christie's, Rockefeller NY #31/R est:7000-10000

POLLARD, James (attrib) (1797-1867) British

£5800	$10556	€8468	Old Rowley Mile, portrait of a hose with riders (46x58cm-18x23in) prov. 4-Feb-4 John Nicholson, Haslemere #126/R est:2000-3000

POLLARD, James (circle) (1797-1867) British

£22000	$38720	€32120	Metropolitan cattle market, Copenhagen Fields, Islington (58x91cm-23x36in) 18-May-4 Woolley & Wallis, Salisbury #151/R est:3000-5000

POLLASTRINI, Enrico (attrib) (1817-1876) Italian

£504	$826	€700	Oriental scene (25x35cm-10x14in) i.verso metal. 10-Jun-3 Pandolfini, Florence #20/R

POLLENTINE, Alfred (fl.1861-1880) British

£340	$622	€496	Italian lakeside scene (29x24cm-11x9in) s. 7-Apr-4 Woolley & Wallis, Salisbury #309/R
£520	$900	€759	Venetian canal (25x46cm-10x18in) s.verso. 10-Dec-3 Alderfer's, Hatfield #297
£736	$1200	€1075	Dogana, Venice (25x36cm-10x14in) s. s.i.verso. 24-Sep-3 Doyle, New York #67/R est:1500-2000
£820	$1492	€1197	Coastal landscape with figures before fishing boats (40x60cm-16x24in) s. 3-Feb-4 Sworder & Son, Bishops Stortford #285/R
£1279	$2200	€1867	Bacino di San Marco (41x61cm-16x24in) s. 7-Dec-3 Freeman, Philadelphia #36 est:2000-3000
£1300	$2405	€1898	Grand Canal, Venice (46x35cm-18x14in) s. s.i.verso. 10-Feb-4 Bonhams, Knightsbridge #168/R est:1000-1500
£1600	$2512	€2320	Grand canal, Venice (41x61cm-16x24in) s. s.i.verso. 28-Aug-3 Christie's, Kensington #245/R est:1500-2000
£1600	$2864	€2336	Figures before an Italianate lake (76x127cm-30x50in) indis sig. 27-May-4 Christie's, Kensington #251/R est:1500-2000
£1615	$2778	€2358	After the storm - shipwreck (43x90cm-17x35in) s.indis.d. 7-Dec-3 Uppsala Auktionskammare, Uppsala #114/R est:12000-15000 (S.KR 21000)
£1800	$3060	€2628	On the Grand Canal, Venice (30x51cm-12x20in) s.d.83 pair. 18-Nov-3 Bonhams, Leeds #157/R est:1800-2500
£1800	$3348	€2628	St. Pietro Cantello, Venice (41x61cm-16x24in) s.d.85. 4-Mar-4 Christie's, Kensington #561/R est:1500-2000
£2200	$4114	€3212	Grand Canal, Venice (51x76cm-20x30in) s. i.verso. 24-Feb-4 Bonhams, Knowle #79/R est:2000-3000
£2400	$4368	€3504	Santa Maria della Salute (41x60cm-16x24in) s.d.90 i. verso. 29-Jun-4 Bonhams, Knowle #86 est:2000-3000
£2600	$4082	€3770	Dogana, Venice (41x61cm-16x24in) s. s.i.verso. 28-Aug-3 Christie's, Kensington #244/R est:1500-2000
£3012	$5000	€4398	San Giorgio Maggiore, Venice (51x76cm-20x30in) s. 30-Sep-3 Christie's, Rockefeller NY #442/R est:6000-8000
£3313	$5500	€4837	Rialto, Venice (61x51cm-24x20in) s. s.i.verso. 30-Sep-3 Christie's, Rockefeller NY #443/R est:6000-8000
£3500	$5845	€5110	Grand Canal, Venice. S Georgio Maggiore, Venice (41x61cm-16x24in) s. i.verso pair. 13-Nov-3 Christie's, Kensington #338/R est:4000-6000
£4196	$7217	€6000	Venice, the Grand Canal with S Maria della Salute in background (127x77cm-50x30in) s.d.86. 3-Dec-3 Neumeister, Munich #707/R est:4000
£4200	$7560	€6132	Grand Canal, Venice (77x127cm-30x50in) s.d.1869. 21-Jan-4 Sotheby's, Olympia #365/R est:1000-1500
£4800	$8592	€7008	Grand Canal, Venice (77x127cm-30x50in) s.d.1869. 26-May-4 Sotheby's, Olympia #154/R est:3000-4000
£9500	$17385	€13870	On the Grand Canal, Venice (77x127cm-30x50in) s. 6-Jul-4 Bonhams, Knightsbridge #204/R est:6000-9000

POLLET, Joseph (1897-1979) American

£380	$600	€555	Portrait of Collet's barn (51x61cm-20x24in) s.i. exhib. 27-Jul-3 William Jenack, New York #68

POLLET, Joseph Michel-Ange (1814-1870) French

Sculpture

£1389	$2194	€2000	Une heure de la nuit (33cm-13in) s. conceived 1850. 5-Sep-3 Wendl, Rudolstadt #1315/R est:1900
£2654	$4750	€3875	Une heure de la nuit (97cm-38in) s.st.f. green brown pat bronze. 20-Mar-4 Freeman, Philadelphia #769/R est:2000-3000

POLLET, Victor Florence (1811-1882) French

Works on paper

£480	$859	€701	At the well (42x34cm-17x13in) s. W/C. 25-May-4 Bonhams, Knightsbridge #196/R

POLLEY, Frederick (1875-1958) American

£494	$825	€721	Bethany Ridge (46x48cm-18x19in) s. i.verso board. 27-Oct-3 Schrager Galleries, Milwaukee #1431/R
£884	$1406	€1300	Cheval a l'ecurie (51x61cm-20x24in) s. 21-Mar-3 Bailly Pommery, Paris #115

POLLI, Felice (1793-1859) Italian

£335	$600	€489	Serenade (28x20cm-11x8in) s. 8-Jan-4 James Julia, Fairfield #993/R

POLLI, Luigi (19th C) Italian

Works on paper

£480	$859	€701	Elegant figures boarding a gondola (31x23cm-12x9in) s. W/C. 22-Mar-4 Bonhams & Brooks, Norfolk #108/R

POLLITT, Albert (fl.1889-1920) British

£700	$1113	€1022	Fishing smacks beached near a village (24x34cm-9x13in) s. 18-Mar-3 Anderson & Garland, Newcastle #289/R

Works on paper

£260	$476	€380	Autumn river scene in a rugged landscape (38x58cm-15x23in) s. W/C. 28-Jan-4 Hampton & Littlewood, Exeter #387/R
£280	$518	€409	Cornfield at Rouen (23x33cm-9x13in) s.d.1920 W/C. 11-Mar-4 Duke & Son, Dorchester #45/R
£320	$573	€467	Evening at Little Budworth, Cheshire (27x45cm-11x18in) s.d.1903 W/C. 17-Mar-4 Bonhams, Chester #237/R
£320	$582	€467	Busy shipping lane with a town in the background (28x45cm-11x18in) s.d.1912 W/C. 15-Jun-4 Bonhams, Oxford #31
£320	$586	€467	North Wales landscape with figures walking on a path (30x40cm-12x16in) s. indis.d. W/C over pencil. 6-Jul-4 Peter Wilson, Nantwich #58/R
£360	$659	€526	River landscape (35x25cm-14x10in) s.d.1916 W/C. 27-Jan-4 Bonhams, Knightsbridge #219/R
£400	$688	€584	Coastal scene with beached boats (28x43cm-11x17in) s.d.1918 W/C. 3-Dec-3 Andrew Hartley, Ilkley #1056/R
£440	$748	€642	Wooded landscape (35x55cm-14x22in) s.d.1900 W/C. 29-Oct-3 Bonhams, Chester #355
£460	$856	€672	Rural lane, wagon and figures (36x55cm-14x22in) s. W/C. 2-Mar-4 Bearnes, Exeter #346/R
£480	$898	€701	The River Lledr, North Wales. Bettws-y-Coed, North Wales (35x25cm-14x10in) s.d.1915 W/C pair prov. 22-Jul-4 Tennants, Leyburn #755
£500	$860	€730	Figures on path (58x36cm-23x14in) s.d.1848 W/C. 3-Dec-3 Andrew Hartley, Ilkley #1117
£540	$918	€788	Country landscape with cattle grazing (39x68cm-15x27in) s. indis d. W/C. 29-Oct-3 Bonhams, Chester #346
£540	$988	€788	Galway Bay, Ireland (57x86cm-22x34in) s. W/C. 6-Apr-4 Bonhams, Chester #896
£660	$1181	€964	Busy harbour scene (34x26cm-13x10in) s.d.1913 W/C. 17-Mar-4 Bonhams, Chester #233
£700	$1169	€1022	Sorting the day's catch (32x47cm-13x19in) s.d.1905 pencil W/C. 16-Oct-3 Christie's, Kensington #142/R

POLLOCK, Jackson (1912-1956) American

£5810056	$10400000	€8482682	Number 12 (79x57cm-31x22in) s.d.49 paper on masonite prov.exhib.lit. 11-May-4 Christie's, Rockefeller NY #17/R est:5000000-7000000

Prints

£1912	$3250	€2792	Untitled (58x74cm-23x29in) screenprint. 31-Oct-3 Sotheby's, New York #718/R
£1912	$3250	€2792	Untitled (58x74cm-23x29in) screenprint. 31-Oct-3 Sotheby's, New York #715/R
£2059	$3500	€3006	Untitled (74x58cm-29x23in) screenprint. 31-Oct-3 Sotheby's, New York #716/R
£2059	$3500	€3006	Untitled (58x74cm-23x29in) screenprint. 31-Oct-3 Sotheby's, New York #714/R
£2260	$4000	€3300	Greeting card (18x27cm-7x11in) i. red screenprint. 30-Apr-4 Sotheby's, New York #429/R est:4000-6000
£2647	$4500	€3865	Untitled (74x58cm-29x23in) screenprint. 31-Oct-3 Sotheby's, New York #717/R
£4802	$8500	€7011	Untitled (40x58cm-16x23in) s.d.1951 num.25/14 screenprint. 30-Apr-4 Sotheby's, New York #430/R est:8000-12000
£12429	$22000	€18146	Untitled (58x39cm-23x15in) s. screenprint laid down prov. 28-Apr-4 Christie's, Rockefeller NY #384/R est:18000-25000
£22353	$38000	€32635	Untitled (74x59cm-29x23in) s.d.1951 num.25/18 col screenprint. 4-Nov-3 Christie's, Rockefeller NY #322/R est:8000-12000

Works on paper

£28743	$48000	€41965	Untitled - Psychoanalytic Drawing (38x28cm-15x11in) col pencils exec 1939-40 prov.exhib.lit. 12-Nov-3 Christie's, Rockefeller NY #316/R est:25000-35000

POLLONERA, Carlo (c.1849-1923) Italian

£867	$1595	€1300	Cherry trees in bloom (22x40cm-9x16in) s. board. 8-Jun-4 Della Rocca, Turin #211/R
£1000	$1840	€1500	Mountainous landscape (23x36cm-9x14in) s.d.1897 board. 14-Jun-4 Sant Agostino, Torino #284/R est:1500-2000

£1000	$1840	€1500	Mountainous landscape (32x40cm-13x16in) cardboard. 8-Jun-4 Della Rocca, Turin #228/R est:1300-1700
£2013	$3564	€3000	Landscape (34x48cm-13x19in) s.d.1921 cardboard. 1-May-4 Meeting Art, Vercelli #111 est:3000
£2695	$4501	€3800	Rivarossa (38x46cm-15x18in) s. s.i.d.1906 verso cardboard. 20-Oct-3 Sant Agostino, Torino #271/R est:4500
£17361	$29514	€25000	Blooming in the park (50x65cm-20x26in) s. lit. 1-Nov-3 Meeting Art, Vercelli #340/R est:25000

POLLONI, Silvio (1888-1972) Italian

£333	$613	€500	Landscape along the Arno (30x40cm-12x16in) s. 11-Jun-4 Farsetti, Prato #407
£468	$767	€650	San Mezzano Garden (57x57cm-22x22in) s.d.1921. 10-Jun-3 Pandolfini, Florence #254/R
£816	$1486	€1200	Landscape (62x47cm-24x19in) s. painted 1943 lit. 6-Feb-4 Galleria Rosenberg, Milan #93/R
£863	$1416	€1200	Still life of fruit and guitar (85x112cm-33x44in) s.d.950. 10-Jun-3 Pandolfini, Florence #258/R est:900-1200

POLOSINA, Nataliya (1954-) Russian

£350	$585	€511	Still life with lilac (64x66cm-25x26in) s. 13-Jul-3 John Nicholson, Haslemere #9
£700	$1169	€1022	Glade with poppies (60x100cm-24x39in) s. 13-Jul-3 John Nicholson, Haslemere #87/R
£700	$1309	€1050	Poppies (58x69cm-23x27in) s. 21-Jul-4 John Nicholson, Haslemere #330/R

POLSKY, Cynthia (1939-) American

£1080	$1900	€1577	Corinth (213x183cm-84x72in) acrylic painted c.1970. 23-May-4 Treadway Gallery, Cincinnati #762/R est:1000-1500

POLUS, Otto (1889-?) German

£845	$1352	€1200	Berlin park (120x86cm-47x34in) s. panel. 19-Sep-3 Altus, Berlin #547/R

POLUSHENKO, A P (1911-) Russian

£272	$500	€397	Lakeside (50x70cm-20x28in) cardboard painted1973. 27-Mar-4 Shishkin Gallery, Moscow #48/R
£333	$600	€486	First snow (75x65cm-30x26in) oil on cardboard. 24-Apr-4 Shishkin Gallery, Moscow #82/R
£500	$900	€730	Before the storm (56x65cm-22x26in) oil on plywood. 24-Apr-4 Shishkin Gallery, Moscow #81/R
£505	$930	€737	Landscape (50x70cm-20x28in) cardboard painted1974. 27-Mar-4 Shishkin Gallery, Moscow #47/R
£556	$1000	€812	Evening street (49x69cm-19x27in) oil on cardboard. 24-Apr-4 Shishkin Gallery, Moscow #84/R est:2000-2500
£679	$1250	€991	Fisherman on the lake (60x50cm-24x20in) cardboard painted 1960's. 27-Mar-4 Shishkin Gallery, Moscow #46/R

POLVLIET, Barend (1869-?) Dutch

Works on paper

£280	$501	€420	Potato pickers (25x29cm-10x11in) s. W/C. 11-May-4 Vendu Notarishuis, Rotterdam #717/R

POLZER-HODITZ, Comte Arthur (1870-?) Austrian

£615	$1100	€898	Coastal rocks (55x74cm-22x29in) s. i.verso. 14-May-4 Skinner, Boston #256/R

POMA, Silvio (1840-1932) Italian

£900	$1665	€1314	Villa at Cerro (16x28cm-6x11in) s. panel. 14-Jul-4 Christie's, Kensington #1123/R
£1020	$1827	€1500	Mountain landscape with wayside chapel (15x22cm-6x9in) s. board. 17-Mar-4 Neumeister, Munich #567/R est:800
£3841	$6991	€5800	Pescate Lake, Lecco (50x35cm-20x14in) s. board. 17-Jun-4 Finarte Semenzato, Milan #269/R est:6000-7000
£3867	$7115	€5800	Breakfast on the lake (64x99cm-25x39in) s. 10-Jun-4 Christie's, Rome #158/R est:3500-5000

POMA, Silvio (attrib) (1840-1932) Italian

£1348	$2250	€1900	Lake landscape with boat and anglers (15x27cm-6x11in) s. canvas on board. 14-Oct-3 Finarte Semenzato, Milan #116 est:2500

POMEROY, Florence W (1889-1981) American

£409	$650	€597	Portrait of man wearing hat and coat, holding cigarette (61x51cm-24x20in) s. 10-Sep-3 Alderfer's, Hatfield #366

POMI, Alessandro (1890-1976) Italian

£1563	$2750	€2282	Reclining nude (36x48cm-14x19in) s. board prov. 22-May-4 Harvey Clar, Oakland #2436
£1611	$2964	€2400	Seated nude (54x40cm-21x16in) s. board. 24-Mar-4 Il Ponte, Milan #673/R est:400
£2685	$4940	€4000	Woman in aboat (60x50cm-24x20in) s. board. 24-Mar-4 Il Ponte, Milan #501/R est:700
£3356	$6007	€5000	Fishermen in the lagoon (86x65cm-34x26in) s. board. 25-May-4 Finarte Semenzato, Milan #176/R est:5000-6000
£3691	$6607	€5500	Boys on aboat (100x69cm-39x27in) s. cardboard. 25-May-4 Finarte Semenzato, Milan #175/R est:5000-6000

POMMEREULLE, Daniel (1937-) French

Works on paper

£1208	$2139	€1800	Untitled (150x270cm-59x106in) s.d.84-85 pastel. 28-Apr-4 Artcurial Briest, Paris #521 est:2000-3000

POMODORO, Arnaldo (1926-) Italian

Sculpture

£989	$1800	€1444	Untitled (6x5cm-2x2in) silver prov. 29-Jun-4 Sotheby's, New York #476/R est:1500-2000
£1141	$2111	€1700	Little disc (18x18cm-7x7in) s. bronze wood. 13-Mar-4 Meeting Art, Vercelli #40 est:1500
£1147	$1915	€1663	Untitled (18cm-7in) s.i. gold pat.bronze. 23-Jun-3 Philippe Schuler, Zurich #3118/R est:3500-4000 (S.FR 2500)
£1208	$2054	€1764	Senzo titula (14cm-6in) s.num.6/125 silver polished metal prov. 5-Nov-3 AB Stockholms Auktionsverk #1128/R est:10000-15000 (S.KR 16000)
£1351	$2378	€2000	Square (19x19x3cm-7x7x1in) s. num.36/150 bronze wood relief exec.1982. 19-May-4 Il Ponte, Milan #1157 est:1600-1800
£1379	$2207	€2000	Untitled (13x4x2cm-5x2x1in) s.d.1975 silver steel base edn 15/30. 13-Mar-3 Galleria Pace, Milan #90/R
£1757	$3092	€2600	Wheel (18cm-7in) s. pat bronze. 19-May-4 Il Ponte, Milan #1102 est:1800-2000
£1867	$3360	€2800	Little column (19cm-7in) s. num.15/120 steel. 22-Apr-4 Finarte Semenzato, Rome #46/R est:1000-1300
£2533	$4535	€3800	Immagine trasversale (103x72cm-41x28in) s.verso num.7/30 plaster wood. 15-May-4 De Vuyst, Lokeren #508/R est:4000-5000
£2747	$5000	€4011	Untitled (12cm-5in) s. silver prov. 29-Jun-4 Sotheby's, New York #475/R est:2500-3500
£3352	$6000	€4894	Untitled (18x29x8cm-7x11x3in) s. stainless steel bronze. 6-May-4 Doyle, New York #92/R est:6000-9000
£3357	$5706	€4800	Pyramid (17x17x3cm-7x7x1in) s. num.1/9 bronze. 25-Nov-3 Sotheby's, Milan #4/R est:2000-3000
£3497	$5944	€5000	Disk (14x14x5cm-6x6x2in) s. num.51/95 exec.1984. 25-Nov-3 Sotheby's, Milan #5/R est:1500-2000
£3497	$5944	€5000	Stone (10x6x5cm-4x2x2in) s. num.4/9 gilt bronze. 25-Nov-3 Sotheby's, Milan #3/R est:4000-6000
£3691	$6607	€5500	Disk (12x12x12cm-5x5x5in) s. num.24/50 bronze exec.1987. 25-May-4 Sotheby's, Milan #134/R est:3000
£3862	$6450	€5600	Untitled (28x28x4cm-11x11x2in) s. num.24/30 pat bronze. 13-Nov-3 Finarte Semenzato, Rome #279/R est:4500-5000
£5906	$10926	€8800	Sphere (15x15x15cm-6x6x6in) s. num.9/150 gilt bronze. 13-Mar-4 Meeting Art, Vercelli #406 est:8000
£6000	$11040	€9000	Composition (100x70x11cm-39x28x4in) s.d.1974 num.8/12 bronze aluminium prov. 9-Jun-4 Artcurial Briest, Paris #495/R est:6000-8000
£6215	$11000	€9074	Tavola dei Segni (38x38cm-15x15in) i.d.1958 mount silver pat bronze wood. 2-May-4 Bonhams & Butterfields, Los Angeles #3038/R est:6000-8000
£6711	$12013	€10000	Relief (33x25x8cm-13x10x3in) s.d.2002 num.1/3 pat bronze. 30-May-4 Meeting Art, Vercelli #10 est:8000
£8276	$13821	€12000	Sphere (14x14x14cm-6x6x6in) s. num.149/150 bronze. 13-Nov-3 Galleria Pace, Milan #101/R est:18000
£8392	$14266	€12000	Transversal square (27x28x5cm-11x11x2in) s.d.77 num.13/30 bronze sold with base. 25-Nov-3 Sotheby's, Milan #160/R est:8000-10000
£8803	$14613	€12500	Double relief (21x15x5cm-8x6x2in) s.d.1999 num.7/8 gilt bronze. 11-Jun-3 Finarte Semenzato, Milan #684/R est:18000
£10000	$18400	€15000	Letter (45x35cm-18x14in) s.i.d.1977 bronze. 11-Jun-4 Farsetti, Prato #314/R est:15000-17000
£12245	$21918	€18000	Composition (48x60cm-19x24in) s.i.60.02 PA. gilt bronze Altuglass base. 19-Mar-4 Millon & Associes, Paris #198/R est:7000-8000
£12840	$21828	€18746	Romboid No.1 (30cm-12in) s.i.d.64 gold pat.bronze exhib.prov. 4-Nov-3 Bukowskis, Stockholm #258/R est:50000-70000 (S.KR 170000)
£13986	$23776	€20000	Sign table (58x87cm-23x34in) bronze exec.1960. 20-Nov-3 Finarte Semenzato, Milan #191/R est:20000-25000
£16000	$29440	€24000	Study (53x34x15cm-21x13x6in) s.d.1961 bronze prov. 8-Jun-4 Finarte Semenzato, Milan #361/R est:22000-24000
£16467	$27500	€24042	Frammento (182x66x15cm-72x26x6in) pat bronze prov. 13-Nov-3 Sotheby's, New York #558/R est:40000-60000
£17450	$31235	€26000	Relief 8 (90x41cm-35x16in) s.d.60 num.02 gilt bronze prov. 25-May-4 Sotheby's, Milan #292/R est:18000-22000
£19580	$33287	€28000	Relief (31x161cm-12x63in) s.d.58-59 bronze. 25-Nov-3 Sotheby's, Milan #220/R est:30000-40000
£21477	$38443	€32000	Double radar (46x48x48cm-18x19x19in) s.d.1965 num.0/2 bronze lit. 25-May-4 Sotheby's, Milan #302/R est:35000-45000
£22000	$40480	€32120	Bassorrilievo (59x45x10cm-23x18x4in) s.d.60 num 02 gold pat bronze prov. 24-Jun-4 Sotheby's, London #225/R est:15000-20000
£24476	$41608	€35000	Kite (37x50x51cm-15x20x20in) s. num.2/6 bronze. 24-Nov-3 Christie's, Milan #228/R est:35000-40000
£35928	$60000	€52455	Asta cielare VI (212x38x35cm-83x15x14in) s.num.A.P. gold pat bronze prov. 13-Nov-3 Sotheby's, New York #551/R est:50000-70000
£39161	$66573	€56000	Sphere (28x25x25cm-11x10x10in) s.i. bronze plexiglas. 24-Nov-3 Christie's, Milan #229/R est:25000-30000
£42000	$70140	€61320	Porta d'Europa (89x123x53cm-35x48x21in) gold brown pat bronze metal edition 2 of 9 exec.c.1978 prov. 21-Oct-3 Christie's, London #44/R est:40000-60000
£50725	$83188	€70000	Rotating (60x60x60cm-24x24x24in) s.d.1966 bronze. 27-May-3 Sotheby's, Milan #270/R est:35000-40000
£111888	$190210	€160000	Sphere 10 (59x59x59cm-23x23x23in) s.d.66 num.2/2 bronze prov. 25-Nov-3 Sotheby's, Milan #234/R est:135000-150000
£154362	$276309	€230000	Sphere 3 (60x60x60cm-24x24x24in) bronze exec.1964 lit. 25-May-4 Sotheby's, Milan #274/R est:130000-180000

Works on paper

£3147	$5350	€4500	Untitled (35x55cm-14x22in) s.d.59 chl Chinese ink W/C. 25-Nov-3 Sotheby's, Milan #120 est:1500-2000

POMODORO, Gio (1930-2002) Italian

Sculpture

£1117	$2000	€1631	Abstraction (15x30cm-6x12in) s. with artist's insignia gold pat bronze. 7-May-4 Sloans & Kenyon, Bethesda #1241/R est:2000-4000
£1374	$2500	€2006	Bassorilievo (33x61x15cm-13x24x6in) bronze executed c.1955-58 prov. 29-Jun-4 Sotheby's, New York #511/R est:4000-6000
£1399	$2378	€2000	Growing (17x7cm-7x3in) s. num.5/9 silver exec.1960. 25-Nov-3 Sotheby's, Milan #7/R est:1500-2000
£2098	$3566	€3000	Untitled (42x17x9cm-17x7x4in) init. num.1/11 bronze. 24-Nov-3 Christie's, Milan #223/R est:3000-4000
£4698	$8409	€7000	Sun (60cm-24in) init.d.73 black marble exhib. 25-May-4 Sotheby's, Milan #135/R est:7000
£5493	$9118	€7800	Chatting with son (39x19x14cm-15x7x6in) st.sig. white marble exhib. 11-Jun-3 Finarte Semenzato, Milan #685/R
£6159	$10101	€8500	Tense surface (29x32x4cm-11x13x2in) init.d.62 num.III bronze. 27-May-3 Sotheby's, Milan #198/R est:8000-12000
£10067	$18020	€15000	T- vertical horizontal (116cm-46in) init. marble exhib. 25-May-4 Sotheby's, Milan #265/R est:13000-18000
£16667	$27333	€23000	Untitled (60x100x28cm-24x39x11in) init.d.59 num.2/3 bronze. 27-May-3 Sotheby's, Milan #274/R est:18000-22000

Works on paper
£315 $535 €450 Plan I (41x33cm-16x13in) s.i.d.73 felt-tip pen. 26-Nov-3 Pandolfini, Florence #148
£1690 $2806 €2400 Composition (70x99cm-28x39in) s.i.d.1959 verso mixed media paper on canvas. 14-Jun-3 Meeting Art, Vercelli #58/R est:2000

POMPA, Gaetano (1928-) Italian
£4138 $6910 €6000 Soldier. Captain (115x88cm-45x35in) s. s.i.d.1965 verso pair prov.exhib. 13-Nov-3 Finarte Semenzato, Rome #241/R est:5000-6000
Works on paper
£1216 $2141 €1800 Three grey paintings (45x70cm-18x28in) s.d.1961 s.i.d.on stretcher mixed media on canvas. 24-May-4 Christie's, Milan #98/R est:2000-3000

POMPON, François (1855-1933) French
Sculpture
£4899 $7888 €7300 Grand ours polaire (41cm-16in) s.st. sandstone pat. 23-Feb-3 St-Germain-en-Laye Encheres #104/R est:7000-7500
£5245 $8916 €7500 Truie (11x21x6cm-4x8x2in) s.st.f.Valsuani num.5/12 pat bronze. 25-Nov-3 Millon & Associes, Paris #47/R est:7000-8000
£5944 $10105 €8500 Panthere jouant (8x12x4cm-3x5x2in) s.st.f.Valsuani num.7/12 pat bronze. 25-Nov-3 Millon & Associes, Paris #41/R est:9000-12000
£6232 $10782 €8850 Condor (24x9cm-9x4in) s. black pat bronze lit. 13-Dec-3 Martinot & Savignat, Pontoise #102 est:10000-12000
£7092 $11489 €10000 Coq de girouette (47cm-19in) vert de gris pat copper exec.c.1908-1932 prov.lit. 24-May-3 Martinot & Savignat, Pontoise #94/R est:15000-18000
£7343 $12483 €10500 Ours blanc (21x40x10cm-8x16x4in) biscuit. 25-Nov-3 Millon & Associes, Paris #42/R est:5000-7000
£8099 $14173 €11500 Chouette (18cm-7in) s.st.f.Hebrard pat bronze lit. 18-Dec-3 Tajan, Paris #22/R est:7500-9000
£9028 $15076 €13000 Petit pelican (17cm-7in) s. num.1/12 black pat. bronze Cast Valsuani exec.c.1970 prov.lit. 21-Oct-3 Christie's, Paris #121/R est:14000-18000
£9790 $16350 €14000 Cerf bramant (21x21x10cm-8x8x4in) s.st.f.C Valsuani black pat bronze. 24-Jun-3 Millon & Associes, Paris #22/R est:15000-20000
£9790 $16643 €14000 Toy, le Boston terrier (19x20x9cm-7x8x4in) s.st.f.Valsuani pat bronze. 25-Nov-3 Millon & Associes, Paris #46/R est:15000-18000
£11888 $20210 €17000 Panthere noire (14x32x6cm-6x13x2in) s.st.f.Valsuani pat bronze. 25-Nov-3 Millon & Associes, Paris #45/R est:18000-22000
£12238 $20437 €17500 Pintade (20x23x10cm-8x9x4in) s.st.f.A.A. Hebrard black pat bronze. 24-Jun-3 Millon & Associes, Paris #23/R est:18000-22000
£12587 $21399 €18000 Grand duc (27x11x12cm-11x4x5in) s.st.f.Valsuani pat bronze. 25-Nov-3 Millon & Associes, Paris #48/R est:18000-22000
£12587 $21399 €18000 Panthere noire (13x37x5cm-5x15x2in) s.st.f.Valsuani pat bronze. 25-Nov-3 Millon & Associes, Paris #45a est:20000-25000
£13986 $23357 €20000 Canard (18x14x9cm-7x6x4in) s.st.f.C.Valsuani black pat bronze. 24-Jun-3 Millon & Associes, Paris #24/R est:10000-15000
£16779 $31209 €25000 Toy, Boston terrier (30x33x10cm-12x13x4in) s.num.16 black pat bronze st.f.C. Valsuani prov.lit. 2-Mar-4 Artcurial Briest, Paris #150/R est:15000-20000
£25532 $41362 €36000 Le perdreau rouge (26x9x15cm-10x4x6in) s.st.f.C.Valsuani red pat bronze prov.lit. 24-May-3 Martinot & Savignat, Pontoise #93/R est:35000-38000
£28188 $50457 €42000 Panthere noire, oreilles couchees (21x58cm-8x23in) s. black pat bronze cire exec. 1925 perdue st.f. Valsuani lit. 27-May-4 Tajan, Paris #27/R est:45000-50000
£56338 $97465 €80000 Ours blanc (24x45x11cm-9x18x4in) s. black pat bronze exec.c.1925 Cast C. Valsuani. 13-Dec-3 Martinot & Savignat, Pontoise #89/R est:79000-82000

PONC, Joan (1927-1984) Spanish
£14765 $27463 €22000 Surrealist still life (65x92cm-26x36in) s.d.64 verso. 2-Mar-4 Ansorena, Madrid #860/R est:22000
Works on paper
£2517 $4706 €3750 Composition (50x64cm-20x25in) s. W/C. 24-Feb-4 Durán, Madrid #74/R est:2000
£3793 $6334 €5500 Composition (50x70cm-20x28in) s. gouache. 17-Nov-3 Durán, Madrid #237/R est:2000
£4754 $7606 €6750 Hallucinations (50x65cm-20x26in) s. gouache wash. 16-Sep-3 Segre, Madrid #127/R est:9900

PONCE DE LEON, Angel (20th C) South American
£738 $1373 €1100 Hommage a Nicolas de Stael (73x92cm-29x36in) s.d.88 s.i.verso. 8-Mar-4 Rieunier, Paris #122

PONCE DE LEON, Fidelio (1896-1957) Cuban
£2113 $3697 €3000 White flowers (46x38cm-18x15in) s. prov. 16-Dec-3 Segre, Madrid #143/R est:4000
£2817 $4930 €4000 Two women (46x38cm-18x15in) s. prov. 16-Dec-3 Segre, Madrid #142/R est:4000

PONCE, Jorge (20th C) Argentinian
£2473 $4500 €3611 Sunny (100x100cm-39x39in) s.d.98 s.i.d.verso. 29-Jun-4 Arroyo, Buenos Aires #63/R est:4500

PONCEL, H V (19th C) ?
£2318 $4219 €3500 Portrait of Charles of England (105x135cm-41x53in) s.d.1885 after Van Dyck. 16-Jun-4 Christie's, Rome #417/R est:3000-4000

PONCELET, Thierry (1946-) Belgian
£260 $442 €380 Portrait of a Victorian lady with the head of a terrier (14x12cm-6x5in) s. panel. 18-Nov-3 Bonhams, Leeds #237
£300 $543 €438 Boxer dog as an 18th century gentleman (76x64cm-30x25in) s. 15-Apr-4 Gorringes, Worthing #656/R
£400 $724 €584 Old English sheepdog as a gentleman (76x64cm-30x25in) s. 15-Apr-4 Gorringes, Worthing #657/R
£460 $782 €672 Portrait of a gentleman, dressed in a suit, sitting at a desk with the head of a Great Dane (53x36cm-21x14in) s. 18-Nov-3 Bonhams, Leeds #236/R
£607 $1100 €886 Lady in red (58x52cm-23x20in) s. 30-Mar-4 Bonhams & Butterfields, San Francisco #144/R
£939 $1700 €1371 Red dress (107x86cm-42x34in) s. 30-Mar-4 Bonhams & Butterfields, San Francisco #139/R est:2500-3500
£994 $1800 €1451 Sunday best (105x82cm-41x32in) s. 30-Mar-4 Bonhams & Butterfields, San Francisco #140/R est:2500-3500
£1105 $2000 €1613 Maltese (66x56cm-26x22in) s. 30-Mar-4 Bonhams & Butterfields, San Francisco #141/R est:1500-2000
£1517 $2807 €2200 Portrait d'elegante a tete de chien (80x60cm-31x24in) s. 19-Jan-4 Horta, Bruxelles #232 est:1800-2200
£1933 $3500 €2822 Family portrait (74x62cm-29x24in) s. 30-Mar-4 Bonhams & Butterfields, San Francisco #142/R est:1500-2500
£1933 $3500 €2822 Bibliophile (81x65cm-32x26in) s. 30-Mar-4 Bonhams & Butterfields, San Francisco #143/R est:1020-1500

PONCET, Antoine (1928-) Swiss
Sculpture
£905 $1511 €1321 Libellailes (76cm-30in) s. i. green marble incl. base. 17-Nov-3 Waddingtons, Toronto #214/R est:1500-2500 (C.D 2000)
£2083 $3750 €3041 Aux ecoutes (81cm-32in) num.AP 4/6 polished bronze. 24-Apr-4 Du Mouchelle, Detroit #3245/R est:1000-2000
£2222 $3712 €3200 Tremblevague (69x61x15cm-27x24x6in) mono.num.1/6 base polished bronze prov.exhib.lit. 21-Oct-3 Artcurial Briest, Paris #406/R est:4000-5000
£3500 $5565 €5075 Vertveines (85cm-33in) init.num.3/6 polished bronze marble base. 11-Sep-3 Christie's, Kensington #176/R est:3000-4000

PONCET, Jean Baptiste (1827-1901) French
£1633 $2971 €2400 L'annonciation (22x24cm-9x9in) oil paper after Hipollyte Flandrin prov.lit. 8-Feb-4 Anaf, Lyon #11a/R

PONCHIN, Antoine (1872-1933) French
£2649 $4848 €4000 La Croisette a Cannes (60x73cm-24x29in) s. 9-Apr-4 Claude Aguttes, Neuilly #78/R est:3500-4000

PONCHIN, Jos Henri (1897-?) French
£8333 $14167 €12000 Oriental water carrier (130x97cm-51x38in) s. painted 1930 prov. 28-Oct-3 Il Ponte, Milan #281/R est:13000-15000

PONCHON, Antonin (1885-1965) French
£667 $1200 €1000 Quai de Saone et peniches (54x65cm-21x26in) s. 20-Apr-4 Chenu & Scrive, Lyon #143/R

POND, Dana (19/20th C) ?
£324 $550 €473 Portrait of a young man (76x64cm-30x25in) s. i.on stretcher. 18-Nov-3 Doyle, New York #28/R
£1628 $2800 €2377 The letter (81x102cm-32x40in) prov. 7-Dec-3 Hindman, Chicago #871/R est:500-700

POND, Elizabeth (1886-1955) American
£635 $1200 €927 House in country mountain landscape (25x36cm-10x14in) init. s.d.99 verso panel. 17-Feb-4 John Moran, Pasadena #186/R

POND, Harold W (1897-?) American
£412 $700 €602 Landscape with bridge (61x76cm-24x30in) s.d.1947. 22-Nov-3 Jackson's, Cedar Falls #85/R

PONDER, Richard (?) ?
£451 $718 €658 Road through the bush (74x48cm-29x19in) s. 1-May-3 Dunbar Sloane, Wellington #518 est:300-600 (NZ.D 1300)
£2030 $3451 €2964 Wild whisteria (90x59cm-35x23in) 26-Nov-3 Dunbar Sloane, Wellington #118/R est:3000-4000 (NZ.D 5400)

PONGA DEGLI ANCILLO, Lucia (1887-1966) Italian
£906 $1622 €1350 La Salute (45x50cm-18x20in) s. 25-May-4 Finarte Semenzato, Milan #97/R est:1500-1800
£1242 $2222 €1850 Saint Mark's Lagoon (45x50cm-18x20in) s. 25-May-4 Finarte Semenzato, Milan #96/R est:1700-1800

PONGA, Giuseppe (1856-1925) Italian
£576 $944 €800 Gallant scene in Venice (32x24cm-13x9in) s. board oval. 10-Jun-3 Pandolfini, Florence #69

PONGRATZ, Peter (1940-) German
£390 $651 €550 The great flood (60x90cm-24x35in) s.d.89 oil mixed media. 16-Oct-3 Dorotheum, Salzburg #775/R
£1049 $1783 €1500 Random walk (70x73cm-28x29in) s.d.1990 s.i.d.1990 verso. 28-Nov-3 Wiener Kunst Auktionen, Vienna #662/R est:1000-2000
£1645 $3026 €2500 Untitled (70x80cm-28x31in) s. 22-Jun-4 Wiener Kunst Auktionen, Vienna #424/R est:2500

PONOMARENKO, Mikhail (1958-) Russian
£531 $966 €780 Venise. s. 8-Feb-4 Lesieur & Le Bars, Le Havre #114
£646 $1176 €950 Soiree d'automne. s. 8-Feb-4 Lesieur & Le Bars, Le Havre #115/R

PONS, Jacques (1936-) French
£621 $1037 €900 Paysage mediterraneen (80x100cm-31x39in) s. 11-Nov-3 Lesieur & Le Bars, Le Havre #139

PONS, Louis (1927-) ?
Works on paper
£805 $1426 €1200 Allegorie (50x66cm-20x26in) s.d.1964 Indian ink. 28-Apr-4 Charbonneaux, Paris #212/R
£1268 $2193 €1800 Sainte-Nitouche (65x50cm-26x20in) s.i.d. juin 1999 collage panel. 15-Dec-3 Charbonneaux, Paris #228 est:800-1000

£1408 $2437 €2000 Mickey au Sahel (76x92cm-30x36in) s.i.d.1996 collage wood prov. 15-Dec-3 Charbonneaux, Paris #227/R est:1000-1200
£1549 $2680 €2200 Les filles de l'air (68x46cm-27x18in) s.i.d. sept 1995 verso collage panel. 15-Dec-3 Charbonneaux, Paris #229 est:800-1000
£12667 $23307 €19000 Impasse de l'oubli (185x123cm-73x48in) s.d.1988 i. verso collage panel prov.lit. 9-Jun-4 Artcurial Briest, Paris #358/R est:20000-25000

PONS-ARNAU, Francisco (1886-1955) Spanish
£300 $555 €438 Figures and horses in an Arab street (15x24cm-6x9in) s.d.1910 board. 9-Mar-4 Bonhams, Knightsbridge #99

PONSE, Joris (1723-1783) Dutch
£27000 $45900 €39420 Roses, peonies and other flowers with peaches on a stone ledge, landscape beyond (93x77cm-37x30in) s. panel. 29-Oct-3 Bonhams, New Bond Street #100/R est:7000-10000

PONSEN, Tunis (1891-1968) American
£2123 $3800 €3100 Provincetown landscape (81x91cm-32x36in) s. 21-Mar-4 Hindman, Chicago #832a/R est:2000-3000

PONSIOEN, Johannes Bernardus (1900-1969) Dutch
£1027 $1747 €1500 Still life with small bottle (24x20cm-9x8in) s. board. 5-Nov-3 Vendue Huis, Gravenhage #384 est:1500-2000
£1301 $2212 €1900 Still life with eggs and salt-sprinkler (26x33cm-10x13in) s. 5-Nov-3 Vendue Huis, Gravenhage #385/R est:2000-3000
£1958 $3329 €2800 Still life with jug and egg (35x45cm-14x18in) s. 24-Nov-3 Glerum, Amsterdam #91/R est:1200-1600

PONSON, Aime (1850-?) French
£1118 $1900 €1632 La Touque a Trouville (23x32cm-9x13in) s. s.i.verso oil paperboard. 20-Nov-3 Auctions by the Bay, Alameda #1011/R

PONSON, Luc Raphael (1835-1904) French
£604 $1124 €900 Chateau Gombert (18x26cm-7x10in) s. 3-Mar-4 Tajan, Paris #15
£2282 $4221 €3400 Cannes, villa de l'imperatrice de Russie (37x66cm-15x26in) s. i.verso. 14-Mar-4 Eric Pillon, Calais #80/R
£2639 $4407 €3800 Rocher au bout de la plage du Prado (38x62cm-15x24in) s. i.on stretcher. 25-Oct-3 Dianous, Marseille #428
£2847 $4755 €4100 Pecheur sur la Corniche (37x60cm-15x24in) s. 25-Oct-3 Dianous, Marseille #429
£4375 $6912 €6300 Bord de mer avec pecheurs a Sausset les Pins (42x55cm-17x22in) s. 25-Apr-3 Etude de Provence, Marseille #182 est:7500-8500
£5694 $9510 €8200 Brick dans le Bassin nord de Marseille (38x62cm-15x24in) s. i.on stretcher. 25-Oct-3 Dianous, Marseille #398

PONT VERGES, Pedro (20th C) Argentinian?
£559 $1000 €816 Growing sky (70x50cm-28x20in) acrylic. 11-May-4 Arroyo, Buenos Aires #75

PONTHUS-CINIER, Antoine (1812-1885) French
£500 $880 €730 Ruins by the lakeside (36x46cm-14x18in) s. i.verso. 20-May-4 Gardiner & Houlgate, Bath #509
£3147 $5350 €4500 Roman campagna (40x60cm-16x24in) s. 24-Nov-3 Dorotheum, Vienna #129/R est:4200-4800

PONTI, Pino (1905-1999) Italian
£680 $1218 €1000 Still life with guitar (50x60cm-20x24in) s.d.1948 prov. 16-Mar-4 Finarte Semenzato, Milan #217/R
£1014 $1784 €1500 Coffee pots (40x50cm-16x20in) s. 19-May-4 Il Ponte, Milan #1056 est:1600-1800
£1014 $1784 €1500 Cock and lamp (50x40cm-20x16in) s.d.1947. 19-May-4 Il Ponte, Milan #1062 est:1600-1800
£1958 $3329 €2800 Three sisters (47x37cm-19x15in) s.d.1931 board. 20-Nov-3 Finarte Semenzato, Milan #12/R est:2000-2200
£2098 $3566 €3000 Rural boys (30x33cm-12x13in) s.d.1944 board exhib.lit. 20-Nov-3 Finarte Semenzato, Milan #96/R est:1800-2200

PONTICELLI, Giovanni (fl.1855-1877) Italian
£1049 $1752 €1500 Cart (20x26cm-8x10in) s.d.1868. 26-Jun-3 Sant Agostino, Torino #133/R est:1500-1800

PONTING, Herbert G (1871-1935) American
Photographs
£1800 $2790 €2628 Ponies in the stable, Captain Oates (41x59cm-16x23in) i.num.48A gelatin silver print. 25-Sep-2 Christie's, London #331/R est:2000-4000
£2250 $4028 €3285 Capt Oates and ponies (30x39cm-12x15in) i. gelatin silver print prov. 13-May-4 Sotheby's, London #289/R est:1500-2000
£3000 $4650 €4380 Oates with the ponies on the Terra Nova (30x39cm-12x15in) gelatin silver print prov. 25-Sep-2 Christie's, London #329/R est:3000-5000
£3600 $6336 €5256 Terra Nova at the ice-foot, Cape Evans, 1911 (73x58cm-29x23in) toned green carbon print. 18-May-4 Bonhams, New Bond Street #41/R est:4000-6000
£5000 $7750 €7300 Terra Nova at the ice foot (74x58cm-29x23in) i.num.27 green toned carbon print. 25-Sep-2 Christie's, London #328/R est:2000-4000
£9500 $14724 €13870 Terra Nova in McMurdo Sound (58x74cm-23x29in) blue toned carbon print. 25-Sep-2 Christie's, London #159/R est:6000-8000

PONTORMO, Jacopo (1493-1558) Italian
Works on paper
£100000 $183000 €146000 Standing figure of a young boy, seen from behind, his face almost in profile (17x9cm-7x4in) blk chk htd white blue paper. 8-Jul-4 Sotheby's, London #30/R est:100000-140000

PONTORMO, Jacopo (attrib) (1493-1558) Italian
Works on paper
£27211 $48708 €40000 Etude d'homme nu, vu de trois-quarts (20x11cm-8x4in) pen brown ink brown wash traces sanguine prov. 17-Mar-4 Tajan, Paris #9/R est:15000-20000

PONTOY, Henri Jean (1888-1968) French
£403 $745 €600 Femme assise dans la rue Saint Le Lud (27x17cm-11x7in) s. i.verso canvas on cardboard. 15-Mar-4 Gros & Delettrez, Paris #28/R
£789 $1453 €1200 Marchande de fleurs (33x41cm-13x16in) s. 25-Jun-4 Millon & Associes, Paris #79
£1156 $2070 €1700 Jeune marocaine portant une corbeille de fruits (44x35cm-17x14in) s.d.36 oil paper. 21-Mar-4 Muizon & Le Coent, Paris #55
£1399 $2406 €2000 Au pied du vieil arbre (46x53cm-18x21in) s. isorel. 8-Dec-3 Tajan, Paris #314/R est:1000-1200
£1549 $2680 €2200 Village Africain (38x46cm-15x18in) s. cardboard. 10-Dec-3 Rossini, Paris #104/R
£1972 $3411 €2800 Cours d'eau Africain aux pirogues (65x81cm-26x32in) s. 10-Dec-3 Rossini, Paris #105
£2113 $3655 €3000 Sur la plage (24x33cm-9x13in) s. cardboard. 15-Dec-3 Gros & Delettrez, Paris #338/R est:2000-2500
£2113 $3655 €3000 Marche devant les remparts (24x33cm-9x13in) s. panel. 15-Dec-3 Gros & Delettrez, Paris #403/R est:2500-3000
£2183 $3777 €3100 Les remparts de Marakech et l'Atlas (21x26cm-8x10in) s. cardboard. 10-Dec-3 Rossini, Paris #103/R
£2465 $4264 €3500 Portrait de jeune Africaine (34x24cm-13x9in) s. panel. 10-Dec-3 Millon & Associes, Paris #110/R est:500-600
£2676 $4630 €3800 Panorama de Fes. Village de l'Atlas (26x34cm-10x13in) s. cardboard double-sided. 15-Dec-3 Gros & Delettrez, Paris #337/R est:2000-2500
£2766 $4619 €3900 Marrakech sur fond d'Atlas (20x27cm-8x11in) s. cardboard. 16-Jun-3 Gros & Delettrez, Paris #13/R est:1000-2000
£2817 $4873 €4000 Porteuse d'eau, Maroc (53x44cm-21x17in) s. panel double-sided. 15-Dec-3 Gros & Delettrez, Paris #76/R est:4000-5000
£2837 $4738 €4000 Rue au milieu des casbahs (41x33cm-16x13in) s. panel. 19-Oct-3 Rabourdin & Choppin de Janvry, Paris #117/R est:4000-5000
£3521 $6092 €5000 Cavaliers (54x65cm-21x26in) s. 15-Dec-3 Gros & Delettrez, Paris #325/R est:4000-5000
£4120 $6592 €5850 Les gargotiers (36x45cm-14x18in) s. 20-Sep-3 Compagnie Marocaine des Objets d'Art, Casablanca #162/R
£4225 $6803 €6000 Scene de plage (85x73cm-33x29in) s. i.verso. 22-Aug-3 Deauville, France #95/R est:6000-8000
£5106 $8528 €7200 Vue de Rabat Sale (38x46cm-15x18in) s. s.i.verso. 16-Jun-3 Gros & Delettrez, Paris #11/R est:1500-3000
£5282 $8451 €7500 Rue animee de souk (38x46cm-15x18in) s. panel. 20-Sep-3 Compagnie Marocaine des Objets d'Art, Casablanca #102/R
£5334 $9761 €8000 Souq Jedid a Fes (47x55cm-19x22in) s. i.verso. 3-Jun-4 Tajan, Paris #302/R est:5000-6000
£5634 $9014 €8000 Jeune fille aux bijoux (44x37cm-17x15in) s. 20-Sep-3 Compagnie Marocaine des Objets d'Art, Casablanca #77/R
£5634 $9014 €8000 Foret africaine (60x77cm-24x30in) s. 20-Sep-3 Compagnie Marocaine des Objets d'Art, Casablanca #42/R
£6338 $10965 €9000 Porteuses d'eau (45x55cm-18x22in) s. 15-Dec-3 Gros & Delettrez, Paris #326/R est:4000-5000
£6738 $11252 €9500 Fes (60x80cm-24x31in) s.d.1950 panel. 19-Oct-3 Rabourdin & Choppin de Janvry, Paris #118/R est:9000-12000
£9859 $15775 €14000 Ruelle animee (45x59cm-18x23in) s. 20-Sep-3 Compagnie Marocaine des Objets d'Art, Casablanca #103/R
£14085 $22535 €20000 Les lavandieres (60x100cm-24x39in) s. 20-Sep-3 Compagnie Marocaine des Objets d'Art, Casablanca #86/R
£14789 $23662 €21000 Kasbah (72x92cm-28x36in) s. 20-Sep-3 Compagnie Marocaine des Objets d'Art, Casablanca #104/R
£17606 $28169 €25000 Vue de Medina (65x85cm-26x33in) s. 20-Sep-3 Compagnie Marocaine des Objets d'Art, Casablanca #105/R
Works on paper
£355 $592 €500 Les flamboyants (44x50cm-17x20in) s. gouache. 16-Jun-3 Gros & Delettrez, Paris #17/R
£433 $797 €650 Village d'Algerie (15x24cm-6x9in) s.i.d.32 gouache. 14-Jun-4 Gros & Delettrez, Paris #259/R
£633 $1165 €950 Village d'Algerie (24x15cm-9x6in) s.i.d.1931 gouache. 14-Jun-4 Gros & Delettrez, Paris #258/R
£667 $1227 €1000 Village Oriental (30x24cm-12x9in) s.i.d.1931 gouache. 14-Jun-4 Gros & Delettrez, Paris #257/R
£709 $1184 €1000 La preparation du mil (36x45cm-14x18in) s. gouache. 16-Jun-3 Gros & Delettrez, Paris #18/R
£915 $1584 €1300 Portrait de jeune femme (44x36cm-17x14in) dr htd pastel. 15-Dec-3 Gros & Delettrez, Paris #334
£993 $1658 €1400 Village Africain sous les palmiers (42x58cm-17x23in) s. gouache. 16-Jun-3 Gros & Delettrez, Paris #15/R
£1277 $2132 €1800 Tete de femme (44x36cm-17x14in) pastel dr. 16-Jun-3 Gros & Delettrez, Paris #14 est:1000-2000
£1773 $2961 €2500 Le petit ane dans un village de montagne (44x37cm-17x15in) s. W/C gouache. 16-Jun-3 Gros & Delettrez, Paris #7/R est:1500-2300
£1773 $2961 €2500 Casbah (33x45cm-13x18in) s.i. W/C gouache. 19-Oct-3 Rabourdin & Choppin de Janvry, Paris #156/R est:2300-2600
£2128 $3553 €3000 Berger et chevres devant la Casbah d'Agdz (32x45cm-13x18in) s.i. W/C gouache. 16-Jun-3 Gros & Delettrez, Paris #3/R est:1500-2300
£2177 $3897 €3200 Paysage anime a l'entree d'une ville arabe (28x40cm-11x16in) s. gouache htd chl. 21-Mar-4 Muizon & Le Coent, Paris #54/R
£2270 $3790 €3200 Le marabout au bord de la mer (45x37cm-18x15in) W/C gouache. 16-Jun-3 Gros & Delettrez, Paris #10/R est:1500-2300
£2411 $4027 €3400 L'Atlas au printemps (31x43cm-12x17in) s. gouache. 16-Jun-3 Gros & Delettrez, Paris #6/R est:1500-2300
£2482 $4145 €3500 Campement devant les remparts de Tancita (29x42cm-11x17in) s.i. gouache. 16-Jun-3 Gros & Delettrez, Paris #5/R est:1500-2300
£2482 $4145 €3500 L'oued de Zagna (33x45cm-13x18in) s.i. gouache. 16-Jun-3 Gros & Delettrez, Paris #8/R est:1500-2300
£2533 $4661 €3800 Village de l'Atlas (30x40cm-12x16in) s. 14-Jun-4 Gros & Delettrez, Paris #34/R est:3800-4500
£2695 $4501 €3800 Village d'Amzoudz, Vallee de Ziz (40x56cm-16x22in) gouache. 16-Jun-3 Gros & Delettrez, Paris #4/R est:1500-2300
£2797 $4811 €4000 Jeune femme a l'oued (35x41cm-14x16in) s.d.1942 gouache. 8-Dec-3 Tajan, Paris #317/R est:4000-5000
£2837 $4738 €4000 Les porteuses d'eau dans la palmeraie (37x45cm-15x18in) gouache. 16-Jun-3 Gros & Delettrez, Paris #2/R est:1500-2300
£2908 $4856 €4100 Fes sous le soleil (36x46cm-14x18in) W/C gouache. 16-Jun-3 Gros & Delettrez, Paris #12/R est:1500-2300

£3262 $5448 €4600 Place du village ensoleille (38x46cm-15x18in) s. W/C gouache. 16-Jun-3 Gros & Delettrez, Paris #9/R est:1500-2300
£3521 $6092 €5000 Fes, le matin (40x53cm-16x21in) s. W/C gouache. 15-Dec-3 Gros & Delettrez, Paris #339/R est:3000-4000
£3617 $6040 €5100 A l'oued, le remplissage des jarres (45x60cm-18x24in) s. W/C gouache. 16-Jun-3 Gros & Delettrez, Paris #1/R est:2000-3000
£4472 $7155 €6350 Targa (37x44cm-15x17in) s. gouache. 20-Sep-3 Compagnie Marocaine des Objets d'Art, Casablanca #39/R
£4507 $7211 €6400 Kasbah dans la palmeraie (36x45cm-14x18in) s. gouache. 20-Sep-3 Compagnie Marocaine des Objets d'Art, Casablanca #75/R
£4542 $7268 €6450 Les remparts (42x58cm-17x23in) gouache. 20-Sep-3 Compagnie Marocaine des Objets d'Art, Casablanca #76/R
£4930 $7887 €7000 Le souk (55x59cm-22x23in) s. W/C. 20-Sep-3 Compagnie Marocaine des Objets d'Art, Casablanca #113/R
£6667 $12267 €10000 Les terrasses de Marrakech (46x61cm-18x24in) s. gouache chl. 14-Jun-4 Gros & Delettrez, Paris #52/R est:6000-8000

PONTY, Max (1904-1972) French
£7383 $13067 €11000 Dessinateurs (208x88cm-82x35in) s.d.45 masonite set of 4 prov. 27-Apr-4 Claude Aguttes, Neuilly #47/R est:12000-13000
£21477 $38013 €32000 Helice (240x210cm-94x83in) s. prov. 27-Apr-4 Claude Aguttes, Neuilly #48/R

PONZONE, Matteo (1586-1664) Italian
£7092 $11844 €10000 Udienza pontificia a un ambasciatore veneziano (80x234cm-31x92in) lit. 18-Jun-3 Christie's, Rome #448/R est:15000-20000

POOL, Kaye (20th C) American
£291 $500 €425 Indiana landscape (61x74cm-24x29in) s. exec.c.1950. 7-Dec-3 Treadway Gallery, Cincinnati #545/R

POOLE, Albert (1853-1934) American
Works on paper
£525 $850 €767 Architectural rendering of the EE Taylor Corp Shoe Factory, Brockton, Mass (84x150cm-33x59in) s. W/C gouache. 10-Aug-3 Skinner, Bolton #378a/R

POOLE, Eugene Alonzo (1841-1912) American
£2335 $4250 €3409 Sheep in wooded landscape (56x76cm-22x30in) s.d.94 prov. 15-Jun-4 John Moran, Pasadena #163 est:1500-2500

POOLE, George (?) British?
Works on paper
£325 $511 €471 On the boardwalk (77x58cm-30x23in) s. W/C. 26-Aug-3 Lawson Menzies, Sydney #244 (A.D 800)
£325 $511 €471 Shallow end (77x58cm-30x23in) s. W/C. 26-Aug-3 Lawson Menzies, Sydney #239 (A.D 800)

POOLE, Horatio Nelson (1884-1949) American
£285 $450 €416 House in a landscape (36x43cm-14x17in) s.verso board. 7-Sep-3 Treadway Gallery, Cincinnati #583/R
£1563 $2500 €2282 Dark Arroyos. s.d.1930. 20-Sep-3 Harvey Clar, Oakland #1302
£2500 $4250 €3650 Figures and horses in a coastal landscape (66x81cm-26x32in) s.d.48. 18-Nov-3 John Moran, Pasadena #92 est:4000-6000

POOLE, James (1804-1886) British
£450 $779 €657 View on the Yorkshire Moors with figure driving sheep down a track (41x56cm-16x22in) s. 11-Dec-3 Ewbank, Send #410/R
£700 $1309 €1022 Highland landscape with figure seated on a rock beside a pool (27x37cm-11x15in) s.i. 22-Jul-4 Tennants, Leyburn #824
£725 $1305 €1088 The church pool near Conway (66x91cm-26x36in) s.d.1850. 25-Apr-4 Goteborg Auktionsverk, Sweden #209/R (S.KR 10000)
£1050 $1817 €1533 Ashopton Derbyshire and Borrowdale, streams with figures fly fishing (41x53cm-16x21in) s. pair. 11-Dec-3 Ewbank, Send #409 est:1000-1500

POOLE, Paul Falconer (1807-1879) British
£400 $748 €584 At the well, young girl seated beside a well with an earthenware jug (24x20cm-9x8in) s.i.d.1850 prov. 22-Jul-4 Tennants, Leyburn #899
£550 $1029 €803 A little fun (15x20cm-6x8in) init.d.63 i.verso panel. 24-Feb-4 Bonhams, Knowle #104
£4300 $6837 €6278 Young women and girls setting out from a Highland Bothy (100x85cm-39x33in) s. 18-Mar-3 Anderson & Garland, Newcastle #550/R est:3000-5000

POOLE, Paul Falconer (attrib) (1807-1879) British
£403 $742 €588 Anxious moments (93x70cm-37x28in) bears sig. 14-Jun-4 Waddingtons, Toronto #132/R est:1500-2500 (C.D 1000)
£650 $1196 €949 Harvester by a stream (59x44cm-23x17in) 8-Jun-4 Bonhams, Knightsbridge #176/R

POOLEY, Geoffrey H (1908-) British
Works on paper
£500 $900 €730 Lock Leven and Morven mountains (34x50cm-13x20in) s.d.1973 pencil W/C. 21-Apr-4 Tennants, Leyburn #1037

POONS, Larry (1937-) American
£3147 $5350 €4500 Untitled, LP 12 A (222x81cm-87x32in) s.d.1976 verso. 18-Nov-3 Pierre Berge, Paris #22/R est:3000-4000
£5000 $9100 €7300 Broken Summer (300x98cm-118x39in) s.d.69 verso acrylic prov.exhib. 4-Feb-4 Sotheby's, Olympia #210/R est:2500-3500

POOR, Henry Varnum (1888-1970) American
£2762 $4750 €4033 High Tor and Haverstraw (41x51cm-16x20in) s. i.verso canvas on panel prov. 3-Dec-3 Doyle, New York #297/R est:4000-6000

POORE, Henry Rankin (1859-1940) American
£699 $1250 €1021 Cottage at Hamburg Cove, Lyme, Conn (25x33cm-10x13in) board. 8-Jan-4 James Julia, Fairfield #1080/R
£1189 $2200 €1736 Young kentucky hound - Radnor Hunt (20x25cm-8x10in) s. i. verso board exhib. 10-Feb-4 Doyle, New York #160/R est:1000-1500
£3571 $6500 €5214 Old White Horse of the dunes (61x88cm-24x35in) s. panel exhib. 29-Jun-4 Sotheby's, New York #223/R est:3000-5000

POORT, Ermine (1966-) Dutch
Works on paper
£382 $603 €550 Untitled (100x75cm-39x30in) s.d.2001 chk. 26-Apr-3 Auction Maastricht #84/R

POORTEN, Jacobus Johannes van (1841-1914) German
£374 $637 €546 Sunny wood with peasant woman (34x26cm-13x10in) s.d.96. 5-Nov-3 Dobiaschofsky, Bern #871/R (S.FR 850)
£658 $1211 €1000 Rhine landscape with a steam paddler (55x82cm-22x32in) s.d.1874. 25-Jun-4 Michael Zeller, Lindau #621/R
£1389 $2319 €2000 Forest clearing (87x140cm-34x55in) s. 24-Oct-3 Ketterer, Hamburg #95/R est:2400-2600
£1736 $2743 €2500 Woodland (85x140cm-33x55in) s. 6-Sep-3 Schopman, Hamburg #693/R est:2500

POORTENAAR, Jan (1886-1958) Dutch
£10764 $17976 €15715 Ais't Voorjaar is (150x150cm-59x59in) s. lit. 12-Oct-3 Sotheby's, Singapore #49/R est:15000-20000 (S.D 31000)
£13725 $24843 €20039 Stilleven met tijgerlelies (150x150cm-59x59in) s. lit. 4-Apr-4 Sotheby's, Singapore #45/R est:15000-20000 (S.D 42000)

POORTER, Willem de (1608-1648) Dutch
£8000 $14400 €11680 Interior with woman praying at a table, with books and other objects (34x30cm-13x12in) init. panel. 22-Apr-4 Sotheby's, London #51/R est:8000-12000
£19397 $35690 €28320 Mordechai with Bigthan and Theres (36x29cm-14x11in) panel prov.exhib.lit. 26-Mar-4 Koller, Zurich #3020/R est:30000-50000 (S.FR 45000)

POORTER, Willem de (attrib) (1608-1648) Dutch
£671 $1235 €1000 Le sacrifice d'Isaac (27x22cm-11x9in) panel. 24-Mar-4 Tajan, Paris #55

POORTVLIET, Rien (1932-1995) Dutch
£2857 $5200 €4200 Buzzard with its prey (60x75cm-24x30in) s. 3-Feb-4 Christie's, Amsterdam #248/R est:2000-3000
Works on paper
£2378 $3971 €3400 Deer in a woodland (38x29cm-15x11in) s. W/C. 30-Jun-3 Sotheby's, Amsterdam #375/R

POOSCH, Max von (1872-1960) Austrian
£450 $824 €657 Grazing the cattle (19x26cm-7x10in) s.d.18 panel. 8-Apr-4 Christie's, Kensington #76/R
£490 $832 €700 View of Mattsee (35x50cm-14x20in) s.d.36 board. 27-Nov-3 Dorotheum, Linz #457/R

POOT, Rik (1924-) Belgian
Sculpture
£1533 $2745 €2300 Figure (30x8cm-12x3in) s.d.67 polished bronze. 15-May-4 De Vuyst, Lokeren #256/R est:1500-2000

POOTER, Bernard de (1883-?) Belgian
£268 $491 €400 Nu dans un escalier (120x75cm-47x30in) s.d.1921. 8-Jul-4 Campo, Vlaamse Kaai #80
£671 $1228 €1000 La reunion de famille (75x105cm-30x41in) s.d.1921. 8-Jul-4 Campo, Vlaamse Kaai #81
£1477 $2702 €2200 Bohemienne (120x75cm-47x30in) s. 8-Jul-4 Campo, Vlaamse Kaai #86 est:350-450

POOTER, Frans de (1898-1987) Belgian
£333 $597 €500 Marine (50x65cm-20x26in) s.d.1956 panel. 16-May-4 MonsAntic, Maisieres #404
£364 $663 €550 La fermette du Trichon a Baulers (40x60cm-16x24in) s. panel. 15-Jun-4 Vanderkindere, Brussels #566
£596 $1085 €900 Paysage a Braine-le-Chateau (40x60cm-16x24in) s. panel. 15-Jun-4 Vanderkindere, Brussels #555
Works on paper
£403 $745 €600 View of Mediterranean Sea in Beaulieu (30x39cm-12x15in) s.d.1922 pastel. 13-Mar-4 De Vuyst, Lokeren #112

POOTOOGOOK (20th C) North American
Prints
£3378 $5743 €4932 Joyfully I see ten caribou (28x41cm-11x16in) num.45/50 stonecut. 3-Nov-3 Waddingtons, Toronto #278/R est:3000-5000 (C.D 7500)

POOTOOGOOK, Eegyvudluk (1931-) North American
Sculpture
£901 $1532 €1315 Bear/owl (20cm-8in) marbled green soapstone exec.c.1960. 3-Nov-3 Waddingtons, Toronto #119/R est:2000-3000 (C.D 2000)

POPE, Alexander (1849-1924) American

£690	$1250	€1007	Portrait of Roger Lewis Barstow jr (91x76cm-36x30in) s. prov. 16-Apr-4 James Julia, Fairfield #516/R est:1000-2000
£1117	$2000	€1631	Portrait of a dog (25x30cm-10x12in) s. 8-Jan-4 James Julia, Fairfield #450/R est:4000-8000
£3757	$6500	€5485	Pheasant in a forest interior (61x51cm-24x20in) s. prov. 10-Dec-3 Bonhams & Butterfields, San Francisco #6005/R est:3000-5000
£4469	$8000	€6525	Hanging woodcock with flowers (15x11cm-6x4in) s. 6-May-4 Shannon's, Milford #130/R est:6000-8000
£7821	$14000	€11419	Retrieved (66x56cm-26x22in) s.d.08. 16-May-4 CRN Auctions, Cambridge #2/R
£19553	$35000	€28547	English setter waiting for a walk (91x76cm-36x30in) s.d.11. 16-May-4 CRN Auctions, Cambridge #1/R
£81395	$140000	€118837	Lioness and her cubs (152x254cm-60x100in) s.d.1892. 5-Dec-3 Christie's, Rockefeller NY #100/R est:70000-90000

POPE, Gustav (19th C) British

Works on paper

£2174	$3891	€3174	Young woman in repose (22x27cm-9x11in) s.d.1891 prov. 15-May-4 Christie's, Sydney #50/R est:6000-8000 (A.D 5500)

POPE, Henry (1843-1908) British

£310	$561	€453	Landscape with a view of an old water mill with figures in the foreground (76x102cm-30x40in) s. 31-Mar-4 Brightwells, Leominster #972
£500	$850	€730	Rocky river landscape with figures fishing and a shepherd with sheep. s. i.verso. 6-Nov-3 Biddle & Webb, Birmingham #947

POPE, Perpetua (?) ?

£490	$926	€715	Kyrenia (60x90cm-24x35in) s. 19-Feb-4 Lyon & Turnbull, Edinburgh #1
£1400	$2604	€2044	Summer, Barra (46x56cm-18x22in) s. prov. 4-Mar-4 Christie's, Kensington #229/R est:400-600

POPE, Samuel (jnr) (fl.1881-1940) British

£1100	$1980	€1606	River landscape (67x52cm-26x20in) s.d.1912. 21-Jan-4 Sotheby's, Olympia #355/R est:1000-1500

POPELKA, Fojtech Hynek (1888-1961) ?

£532	$888	€750	Farmstead in early spring (37x53cm-15x21in) s. 14-Oct-3 Dorotheum, Vienna #110/R

POPET, Yves (1946-) French

£660	$1070	€964	Sans titre (56x56cm-22x22in) s.d.1994 tempera. 24-May-3 Burkhard, Luzern #108/R (S.FR 1400)

POPHAM, James (1884-?) British

Works on paper

£300	$510	€438	The Thames at Woolwich (33x43cm-13x17in) s. pastel. 25-Nov-3 Bonhams, Knightsbridge #48/R

POPHAM, W J (?) British

£620	$1066	€905	Caliph, three master in full sail (60x91cm-24x36in) s. 6-Dec-3 Shapes, Edinburgh #427/R

POPHAM, William J (?) British

£300	$552	€438	Tea Clipper (50x75cm-20x30in) s. 23-Mar-4 Anderson & Garland, Newcastle #409/R

POPLAVSKI, Ludwig Ludwigovitch (1852-1885) Russian

£7500	$13425	€10950	Mill (28x39cm-11x15in) 26-May-4 Sotheby's, London #34/R est:5000-7000

POPOFF, Andrei Andreievitch (1832-1896) Russian

£4514	$7358	€6500	Children playing in spring landscape (43x52cm-17x20in) s. 24-Sep-3 Neumeister, Munich #528/R est:2800

POPOVA, Liubov (1889-1924) Russian

Works on paper

£6780	$12000	€9899	Centrifuga (26x20cm-10x8in) pencil col crayon exec.c.1921 prov.exhib. 2-May-4 Bonhams & Butterfields, Los Angeles #3023/R est:15000-20000
£10667	$19520	€16000	Composition (40x30cm-16x12in) gouache board prov. 5-Jun-4 Lempertz, Koln #952/R est:15000-20000
£24000	$44160	€35040	Untitled (35x27cm-14x11in) d.1921-61 verso gouache brush India ink buff paper prov.exhib. 24-Jun-4 Christie's, London #367/R est:12000-15000

POPOVICI, Cristina (?) ?

£1099	$2033	€1605	Letter from Garcia Marquez (100x100cm-39x39in) s. oil acrylic. 9-Mar-4 Watson's, Christchurch #41 est:3500-4000 (NZ.D 3000)

POPOVSKI, Stefan (1870-1937) Polish

£764	$1207	€1100	Sunset (56x90cm-22x35in) s.d.1900. 5-Sep-3 Wendl, Rudolstadt #3565/R

POPP, Jon (1862-?) German

£567	$1043	€850	Halte au cafe (36x41cm-14x16in) s. cardboard. 14-Jun-4 Gros & Delettrez, Paris #225

POPPEL, Peter van (1945-) Dutch

£600	$1098	€900	Cart (18x24cm-7x9in) s.i.d.1970 verso panel. 7-Jun-4 Glerum, Amsterdam #333/R

Works on paper

£417	$679	€600	Floating document (15x10cm-6x4in) s.i.d.81 W/C gouache. 29-Sep-3 Sotheby's, Amsterdam #362/R

POPPEN, Johannes (1893-1944) German

£318	$490	€500	Lauenburg. s. 4-Sep-2 Schopman, Hamburg #164/R est:600

POPPI, Francesco Morandini (attrib) (1544-1597) Italian

£16000	$27680	€23360	Mary Magdalene (72x58cm-28x23in) panel. 9-Dec-3 Sotheby's, Olympia #373/R est:3000-5000

PORACCIA, Piero (1893-1965) Italian/French

£347	$580	€507	Pont de Sierre (24x31cm-9x12in) s.d.19 cardboard. 16-Nov-3 Koller, Geneva #1305 (S.FR 790)

PORAY, Stanislaus (1888-1948) American

£1455	$2750	€2124	Paval the silversmith (76x64cm-30x25in) s. i. verso. 17-Feb-4 John Moran, Pasadena #114a/R est:4000-6000

PORCELLI, Antonio (1800-1870) Italian

£2252	$4121	€3400	Itinerant musicians (23x30cm-9x12in) s.d.1826. 9-Apr-4 Bailly Pommery, Paris #37/R est:2000-3000

PORCELLIS, Jan (16/17th C) Dutch

£13333	$23867	€20000	Boats in choppy waters with distant Dutch three-master (46x74cm-18x29in) indis.sig. panel prov.lit. 17-May-4 Christie's, Amsterdam #99/R est:15000-25000

Works on paper

£24324	$42811	€36000	River landscape with boats and peasants along the bank (14x20cm-6x8in) init. black chk prov.lit. 19-May-4 Sotheby's, Amsterdam #66/R est:6000-8000

PORCELLIS, Jan I (attrib) (1584-1632) Dutch

£7534	$12808	€11000	Rowing boats and sailing vessels on a wide estuary (15x20cm-6x8in) bears i.verso black chk. 4-Nov-3 Sotheby's, Amsterdam #93/R est:7000-9000

PORDENONE, Giovanni Antonio (1483-1576) Italian

Works on paper

£25000	$45750	€36500	Neptune and a horse (16x18cm-6x7in) bears indis.i. pen brown ink wash htd white blue paper prov.lit. 8-Jul-4 Sotheby's, London #22/R est:18000-22000

PORDENONE, Giovanni Antonio (circle) (1483-1576) Italian

£11842	$21789	€18000	Venus disarming Cupid (110x84cm-43x33in) prov.lit. 24-Jun-4 Christie's, Paris #70/R est:6000-8000

POREAU, Oswald (1877-1955) Belgian

£270	$511	€400	Vase de pavots d'Islande (52x45cm-20x18in) s.d.1941 panel. 17-Feb-4 Vanderkindere, Brussels #439
£276	$497	€400	Saint-Hyppolyte, Doubs (38x46cm-15x18in) s.d.1948 s.i.verso panel. 20-Jan-4 Galerie Moderne, Brussels #162/R
£276	$497	€400	Citrons et figues (22x27cm-9x11in) s.d.1946 s.i.verso panel. 20-Jan-4 Galerie Moderne, Brussels #164/R
£310	$559	€450	Brume d'automne (16x22cm-6x9in) s.d.46 s.i.verso. 20-Jan-4 Galerie Moderne, Brussels #148/R
£310	$559	€450	Saint-Hippolyte, Doubs (38x46cm-15x18in) s.d.1948 s.i.verso panel. 20-Jan-4 Galerie Moderne, Brussels #170/R
£310	$559	€450	Le retour de la fermiere (19x17cm-7x7in) s.d.1936 s.i.verso panel. 20-Jan-4 Galerie Moderne, Brussels #208/R
£310	$559	€450	Port Bara, Morbihan (38x46cm-15x18in) s.d.1937 s.i.verso panel. 20-Jan-4 Galerie Moderne, Brussels #337/R
£331	$612	€480	Vase fleuri (50x60cm-20x24in) s.d.1941 panel. 16-Feb-4 Horta, Bruxelles #345
£345	$621	€500	Homards (50x70cm-20x28in) s.d.1947 s.i.verso. 20-Jan-4 Galerie Moderne, Brussels #167/R
£345	$621	€500	Le Moulin Clerieux (30x37cm-12x15in) s. i.d.1943 verso panel. 20-Jan-4 Galerie Moderne, Brussels #313/R
£347	$552	€500	Oeillets rouges (37x45cm-15x18in) s.d.1948 panel. 15-Sep-3 Horta, Bruxelles #327
£372	$654	€550	Oeillets roses (34x25cm-13x10in) s. s.i.verso panel. 18-May-4 Galerie Moderne, Brussels #261
£379	$683	€550	Raisins (27x35cm-11x14in) s.d.1944 s.i.verso panel. 20-Jan-4 Galerie Moderne, Brussels #328/R
£414	$745	€600	Carriole sur le chemin enneige (16x22cm-6x9in) s. panel. 20-Jan-4 Galerie Moderne, Brussels #139/R
£414	$745	€600	L'escaut a Orroir (13x19cm-5x7in) s. panel. 20-Jan-4 Galerie Moderne, Brussels #201/R
£414	$745	€600	Coin de cuisine, hiver (70x80cm-28x31in) s.d.1947 s.i.verso. 20-Jan-4 Galerie Moderne, Brussels #302/R
£436	$803	€650	Saint-Hippolyte dans le Doubs (40x45cm-16x18in) s.d.1948 panel. 23-Mar-4 Galerie Moderne, Brussels #177
£517	$931	€750	Zinnias (80x90cm-31x35in) s.d.1946. 20-Jan-4 Galerie Moderne, Brussels #334/R
£521	$870	€750	Fraises (33x45cm-13x18in) s.d.1938 panel. 21-Oct-3 Galerie Moderne, Brussels #353/R
£586	$1055	€850	La Corbeille d'Azalees (37x45cm-15x18in) s. i.verso panel. 20-Jan-4 Galerie Moderne, Brussels #137/R
£600	$1092	€900	Chickens and cows in a lane by barn and windmill (46x38cm-18x15in) s.d.1941. 20-Jun-4 Wilkinson, Doncaster #316
£621	$1117	€900	Saint Cado, Morbihan (60x50cm-24x20in) s.d.1937 i.verso. 20-Jan-4 Galerie Moderne, Brussels #294/R
£690	$1241	€1000	Roses (40x32cm-16x13in) s.d.1945 s.i.verso panel. 20-Jan-4 Galerie Moderne, Brussels #272/R
£1014	$1814	€1500	Maree montante au Diben dans le Finistere (88x120cm-35x47in) s.d.1947 s.i.d.verso. 10-May-4 Horta, Bruxelles #127 est:1800-2200

£1034 $1862 €1500 Nu de dos (65x45cm-26x18in) s.d.1924. 20-Jan-4 Galerie Moderne, Brussels #319/R est:500-700
£1034 $1862 €1500 Au bord de la Vesdre (33x40cm-13x16in) s.d.46 s.i.verso panel. 20-Jan-4 Galerie Moderne, Brussels #172/R est:450-650
£1103 $1986 €1600 Barques a Port-Louis, Morbihan, Cote de Loch-Malo en find d'apres midi (43x56cm-17x22in) s. s.i.verso panel. 20-Jan-4 Galerie Moderne, Brussels #190/R est:450-650
£1241 $2234 €1800 Crepes (46x39cm-18x15in) s.d.1944 s.i.verso panel. 20-Jan-4 Galerie Moderne, Brussels #180/R est:400-600
£1379 $2483 €2000 Brumes de mai, Nassogne (80x100cm-31x39in) s.d.1946. 20-Jan-4 Galerie Moderne, Brussels #275/R
Works on paper
£276 $510 €400 Les fugitifs (67x84cm-26x33in) s.d.1915 mixed media. 16-Feb-4 Horta, Bruxelles #344

PORET, Xavier de (1894-1975) Swiss
Works on paper
£1522 $2785 €2222 Chamois chasse (35x24cm-14x9in) s. chl gouache prov. 5-Jun-4 Galerie du Rhone, Sion #557/R est:4000-6000 (S.FR 3500)
£1594 $2614 €2200 Caniche royal (43x58cm-17x23in) studio st. crayon. 28-May-3 Coutau Begarie, Paris #337/R est:2200-2500
£1594 $2614 €2200 Etude de Bouledogue anglais (49x61cm-19x24in) studio st. crayon double-sided. 28-May-3 Coutau Begarie, Paris #338/R est:2200-2500
£1884 $3090 €2600 Ecureuil (25x32cm-10x13in) st.studio crayon. 28-May-3 Coutau Begarie, Paris #336/R est:1300-1500

PORGES, Clara (1879-?) Swiss
£705 $1198 €1029 Still life with violin, bow and music (53x62cm-21x24in) s. 5-Nov-3 Dobiaschofsky, Bern #873/R (S.FR 1600)
£1538 $2615 €2245 Silsersee (35x51cm-14x20in) s. 25-Nov-3 Germann, Zurich #103/R est:2000-3000 (S.FR 3400)
£2262 $3778 €3303 Silsersee (45x53cm-18x21in) s. board. 24-Jun-3 Germann, Zurich #154/R est:1500-2000 (S.FR 5000)
£5275 $8810 €7649 Fex valley chapel with Piz Tremoggia (80x94cm-31x37in) s. 23-Jun-3 Philippe Schuler, Zurich #3417 est:10000-15000 (S.FR 11500)
£10480 $19284 €15301 Cavloccio-See in Val Muretto (91x82cm-36x32in) s. 14-Jun-4 Philippe Schuler, Zurich #4232/R est:6000-8000 (S.FR 24000)
Works on paper
£517 $926 €755 Landscape with tree (37x50cm-15x20in) s. W/C. 12-May-4 Dobiaschofsky, Bern #880 (S.FR 1200)
£560 $1003 €818 Rocky coast in the summer (51x55cm-20x22in) s. W/C. 12-May-4 Dobiaschofsky, Bern #879/R (S.FR 1300)
£734 $1226 €1064 Mountain lake (56x57cm-22x22in) s. W/C. 23-Jun-3 Philippe Schuler, Zurich #3270/R (S.FR 1600)
£1145 $1947 €1672 Landscape with village (68x55cm-27x22in) s. W/C over pencil. 7-Nov-3 Dobiaschofsky, Bern #106/R est:3500 (S.FR 2600)
£1897 $3395 €2770 Mountain village (73x56cm-29x22in) s. w/C. 14-May-4 Dobiaschofsky, Bern #224/R est:4900 (S.FR 4400)
£2402 $4419 €3507 Lake landscape (44x56cm-17x22in) s. W/C. 8-Jun-4 Germann, Zurich #121/R est:4000-5000 (S.FR 5500)
£2941 $5000 €4294 Mountain lake (52x61cm-20x24in) s. W/C. 25-Nov-3 Germann, Zurich #96/R est:2500-3500 (S.FR 6500)
£3394 $5667 €4955 Church in mountains (56x77cm-22x30in) s. W/C. 24-Jun-3 Germann, Zurich #168 est:2000-3000 (S.FR 7500)

PORION, Charles (1814-?) French
£4500 $7740 €6570 Arab on horseback (128x92cm-50x36in) s.d.1890 prov. 4-Dec-3 Christie's, Kensington #228/R est:5000-7000

PORPORA, Paolo (1617-1673) Italian
£30556 $55000 €44612 Still life of a crab, shells and coral in a landscape (22x33cm-9x13in) 22-Jan-4 Sotheby's, New York #197/R est:30000-40000
£38000 $69540 €55480 Boletus, russulas and other mushrooms on a ledge (35x63cm-14x25in) 7-Jul-4 Christie's, London #79/R est:20000-30000

PORRE, Clement de (1874-1950) Belgian
£2533 $4535 €3800 Winter at the Law Palace of Gent (120x130cm-47x51in) s. 15-May-4 De Vuyst, Lokeren #102/R est:3800-4500

PORST, Wilhelm (attrib) (1829-1889) German
£1224 $2192 €1800 Shepherd with flock (29x36cm-11x14in) s.i.d.1859. 17-Mar-4 Neumeister, Munich #568/R est:1100

PORTACARRERO, René (20th C) ?
Works on paper
£2270 $4200 €3314 Figure (55x19cm-22x7in) s.d.56 gouache. 13-Jul-4 Christie's, Rockefeller NY #39/R est:3000-5000

PORTAELS, Jean François (1818-1895) Belgian
£400 $728 €584 Portrait of a North African beauty (46x38cm-18x15in) s. 17-Jun-4 Gorringes, Worthing #720/R
£524 $892 €750 Portrait du notaire Portaels-Janssens de Vilvoorde. s.d.1847. 1-Dec-3 Millon & Associes, Paris #97
£634 $1096 €900 White dog sitting in middle of flowers (50x40cm-20x16in) s.d.1884. 10-Dec-3 Hugo Ruef, Munich #2480/R
£878 $1660 €1300 Vue de Chypre (20x28cm-8x11in) s.d.1845 panel. 17-Feb-4 Vanderkindere, Brussels #109
£1275 $2257 €1900 Sorciere (85x116cm-33x46in) s. 30-Apr-4 Tajan, Paris #143 est:3000
£1554 $2937 €2300 Portrait d'une jeune paysanne Italienne (106x91cm-42x36in) s. 17-Feb-4 Vanderkindere, Brussels #187 est:1250-1750
£2333 $4293 €3500 Orientale au collier de perles (62x49cm-24x19in) s. 14-Jun-4 Gros & Delettrez, Paris #93/R est:4000-5000
£2449 $4384 €3600 Jeune femme a la couronne de fleurs (100x82cm-39x32in) s.d.1840. 16-Mar-4 Vanderkindere, Brussels #100 est:2000-3000
£3893 $7201 €5800 In the box (84x115cm-33x45in) s. 13-Mar-4 De Vuyst, Lokeren #413/R est:6000-8000
£6000 $10740 €9000 Au theatre a pesth (90x70cm-35x28in) s. i.verso exhib. 15-May-4 De Vuyst, Lokeren #421/R est:3000-4000
£8042 $13832 €11500 Jeune Orientale assoupie (72x91cm-28x36in) s.d.1847 canvas on panel oval. 8-Dec-3 Horta, Bruxelles #93 est:12000-18000
£9333 $16893 €14000 Triumph of Judith (34x55cm-13x22in) mono. panel. 3-Apr-4 Hans Stahl, Hamburg #69/R est:6000
£17442 $30000 €25465 Algerian flower seller (105x78cm-41x31in) s.i. 3-Dec-3 Doyle, New York #109/R est:20000-30000
Works on paper
£1111 $1767 €1600 Africain au couteau (56x43cm-22x17in) pastel. 9-Sep-3 Vanderkindere, Brussels #72

PORTAELS, Jean François (attrib) (1818-1895) Belgian
£795 $1446 €1200 Scenes antiques sur fond or (13x25cm-5x10in) panel three. 15-Jun-4 Vanderkindere, Brussels #568

PORTAIL, Jacques Andre (1695-1759) French
Works on paper
£4082 $7306 €6000 Un homme assis a une table, regardant vers le bas (17x14cm-7x6in) raphite red chk prov. 18-Mar-4 Christie's, Paris #254/R est:4000-6000
£29371 $50517 €42000 Jeune garcon assis tourne vers la gauche tenant un baton (29x18cm-11x7in) i. red blk chk brown grey wash prov. 2-Dec-3 Christie's, Paris #507/R est:6000-8000

PORTE, Eugene de la (20th C) French
£829 $1500 €1210 French salon interior (53x66cm-21x26in) s. 3-Apr-4 Nadeau, Windsor #67/R est:1000-2000

PORTEOUS, J (19/20th C) British?
£900 $1674 €1314 Red and white roses (43x36cm-17x14in) s.d.1915. 4-Mar-4 Mitchells, Cockermouth #762 est:1000-1500

PORTER, Arthur Bowmar (fl.1898-1934) British
£320 $544 €467 The Blue Pool, Guernsey (33x39cm-13x15in) s.indis.d. board. 27-Nov-3 Greenslade Hunt, Taunton #1019/R

PORTER, C E (1847-1923) American
£14205 $25000 €20739 Still life with white peonies in a crystal vase (46x41cm-18x16in) s. 1-Jan-4 Nadeau, Windsor #100/R est:10000-15000

PORTER, Charles E (1847-1923) American
£6250 $10000 €9125 Still life with cherries (25x41cm-10x16in) s. exhib. 20-Sep-3 Nadeau, Windsor #151/R
£7186 $12000 €10492 Roses in a vase (48x61cm-19x24in) s. prov. 23-Oct-3 Shannon's, Milford #25/R est:10000-15000
£8939 $16000 €13051 Fourteen apples (30x46cm-12x18in) s. prov. 6-May-4 Shannon's, Milford #34/R est:10000-15000
£11250 $18000 €16425 Still life of flowers (51x61cm-20x24in) s. exhib. 20-Sep-3 Nadeau, Windsor #150/R

PORTER, Eliot (1901-1990) American
Photographs
£1389 $2500 €2028 Untitled (19x24cm-7x9in) s. gelatin silver print prov. 23-Apr-4 Phillips, New York #206/R est:3000-5000

PORTER, Eric Horsbrugh (20th C) Irish?
£669 $1157 €950 Ascent (60x80cm-24x31in) s. board. 10-Dec-3 Bonhams & James Adam, Dublin #184/R

PORTER, Fairfield (1907-1975) American
£23952 $40000 €34970 Spruces (61x56cm-24x22in) s.d.1964 prov. 23-Oct-3 Shannon's, Milford #49/R est:40000-60000
£45676 $84500 €68514 Roses in bloom, Maine (61x71cm-24x28in) s.d.1961. 14-Jul-4 American Auctioneer #490132/R est:50000-80000
£68182 $120000 €99546 Edge in the afternoon (114x102cm-45x40in) s.d.1961 prov.exhib.lit. 18-May-4 Christie's, Rockefeller NY #132/R est:60000-80000
£69767 $120000 €101860 View over the baseball field (76x71cm-30x28in) s.d.1970 prov.exhib.lit. 3-Dec-3 Sotheby's, New York #77/R est:50000-70000
Works on paper
£462 $850 €675 Portrait of the artist's son (25x20cm-10x8in) s.d.1961 pen ink. 10-Jun-4 Swann Galleries, New York #196/R
£1413 $2600 €2063 Study for Broadway (15x13cm-6x5in) s. pen ink exec. c.1972. 10-Jun-4 Swann Galleries, New York #197/R est:1000-1500
£8378 $15500 €12567 Aline (56x56cm-22x22in) s.i.d.71 W/C. 14-Jul-4 American Auctioneer #490143/R est:25000-35000

PORTER, Frederick James (1883-1944) British
£300 $519 €438 Still life with pears and apples on a comport (33x41cm-13x16in) 9-Dec-3 Rosebery Fine Art, London #611/R

PORTER, James Amos (1905-1970) American
Works on paper
£2235 $4000 €3263 Haitian dancers (122x102cm-48x40in) s.i. mixed media oil canvas. 8-Jan-4 James Julia, Fairfield #460/R est:6000-10000

PORTER, Katherine (1941-) American
£250 $450 €365 Untitled (30x40cm-12x16in) s.d.1971 acrylic paper. 24-Apr-4 David Rago, Lambertville #534/R
£472 $850 €689 Untitled (18x24cm-7x9in) oil crayon paper. 24-Apr-4 David Rago, Lambertville #488/R

£667 $1200 €974 Dark X (79x101cm-31x40in) oil wax exhib. 24-Apr-4 David Rago, Lambertville #216/R est:2000-4000
£2270 $4200 €3314 Untitled (119x107cm-47x42in) s. prov. 13-Jul-4 Christie's, Rockefeller NY #64/R est:2000-3000
Works on paper
£222 $400 €324 Untitled (17x22cm-7x9in) s.d.1972 graphite acrylic. 24-Apr-4 David Rago, Lambertville #285/R
£250 $450 €365 Untitled (20x25cm-8x10in) graphite W/C gouache. 24-Apr-4 David Rago, Lambertville #101/R
£264 $475 €385 One thing after another, snow leopard (11x16cm-4x6in) i. ink gouache graph paper. 24-Apr-4 David Rago, Lambertville #235/R
£306 $550 €447 150 cumulus clouds no 2. s.i. pen ink gouache graph paper. 24-Apr-4 David Rago, Lambertville #56/R

PORTER, Liliana (1941-) Argentinian
Works on paper
£3022 $5500 €4412 Reconstruction with toy soldier (99x150cm-39x59in) s.d.1985 collage gouache prov. 29-Jun-4 Sotheby's, New York #567/R est:4000-5000

PORTER, Maud (19/20th C) British
£500 $895 €730 Portrait of a lady, seated in a black dress holding her dog (76x63cm-30x25in) s.d.1895. 27-May-4 Christie's, Kensington #96/R

PORTER, Paula (1884-?) Hungarian
£1449 $2623 €2116 Street in Munich (63x53cm-25x21in) s. oil on card. 16-Apr-4 Mu Terem Galeria, Budapest #186/R (H.F 550000)

PORTER, Rufus (1792-1884) American
Works on paper
£1173 $1900 €1713 Portrait of brown haired man in black jacket (10x10cm-4x4in) W/C pen. 1-Aug-3 North East Auctions, Portsmouth #601/R
£1235 $2000 €1803 Portrait of woman in black dress and embroidered cap (10x10cm-4x4in) W/C ink. 1-Aug-3 North East Auctions, Portsmouth #600/R
£2778 $4500 €4056 Portrait of man in blue and white striped waistcoat (13x10cm-5x4in) i. verso W/C pen prov. 1-Aug-3 North East Auctions, Portsmouth #602/R
£11111 $18000 €16222 Portraits of a family (13x10cm-5x4in) W/C pencil three prov. 1-Aug-3 North East Auctions, Portsmouth #603/R

PORTER, Tom (1948-) American
£297 $550 €434 In the kitchen (76x61cm-30x24in) s. board. 17-Jul-4 Susanin's, Chicago #5049/R
£378 $700 €552 Colombia gorge (81x102cm-32x40in) s. board. 17-Jul-4 Susanin's, Chicago #5050/R

PORTIELJE, Edward Antoon (1861-1949) Belgian
£743 $1308 €1100 Figures on beach at full moon (14x23cm-6x9in) s. panel. 24-May-4 Bernaerts, Antwerp #794
£2000 $3620 €3000 Couple dans un interieur Zelandais (24x17cm-9x7in) s. panel. 30-Mar-4 Campo & Campo, Antwerp #233/R est:3000-5000
£2133 $3861 €3200 Deux femmes Zelandaises prenant le the (22x27cm-9x11in) s. panel. 30-Mar-4 Campo & Campo, Antwerp #232/R est:3000-5000
£2400 $4320 €3600 Zeeland lace maker (22x27cm-9x11in) s. panel. 26-Apr-4 Bernaerts, Antwerp #36/R est:3000-3500
£6525 $10896 €9200 Proposal (40x32cm-16x13in) s. 20-Oct-3 Bernaerts, Antwerp #121/R est:8500-10000
£7914 $12978 €11000 Farewell scene (46x37cm-18x15in) s. panel. 4-Jun-3 Ketterer, Hamburg #82/R est:7000-7500
£8000 $13600 €11680 Welcome distraction (56x44cm-22x17in) s. panel. 19-Nov-3 Bonhams, New Bond Street #15/R est:8000-12000
£8621 $15862 €12587 Two girls at open window (47x38cm-19x15in) s. 26-Mar-4 Koller, Zurich #3114/R est:10000-15000 (S.FR 20000)
£9333 $16800 €14000 La poeme du jour (65x52cm-26x20in) s. 21-Apr-4 Christie's, Amsterdam #185/R est:10000-15000
£10072 $16518 €14000 Two young girls looking out of window (46x38cm-18x15in) s. 4-Jun-3 Ketterer, Hamburg #81/R est:9000-10000
£10795 $19000 €15761 Love letter (46x56cm-18x22in) s. 18-May-4 Bonhams & Butterfields, San Francisco #65/R est:6000-8000
£14667 $26400 €22000 Admiring the newborn (65x91cm-26x36in) s. 21-Apr-4 Christie's, Amsterdam #192/R est:22000-28000

PORTIELJE, Gerard (1856-1929) Belgian
£3356 $6007 €5000 Le garde (24x19cm-9x7in) s. panel. 25-May-4 Campo & Campo, Antwerp #230/R est:5000-7000
£4698 $8691 €7000 Brigadier (23x16cm-9x6in) s. panel. 13-Mar-4 De Vuyst, Lokeren #514/R est:4500-6000
£7333 $13273 €11000 Les mouvelles de la ville (15x20cm-6x8in) s. panel. 30-Mar-4 Campo & Campo, Antwerp #235/R est:4000-6000
£9333 $16893 €14000 Une partie interessante (25x31cm-10x12in) s. 30-Mar-4 Campo, Vlaamse Kaai #141/R est:12000-15000
£18440 $30794 €26000 Interior with farmer's wife and soldier (40x31cm-16x12in) s.d.1891 panel. 20-Oct-3 Bernaerts, Antwerp #118 est:20000-25000
Works on paper
£493 $853 €700 Schoolmaster (32x24cm-13x9in) s.i. pencil. 13-Dec-3 De Vuyst, Lokeren #261/R

PORTIELJE, Jon Frederik Pieter (1829-1908) Belgian/Dutch
£933 $1671 €1400 Portrait of a lady (57x48cm-22x19in) s.i. panel. 11-May-4 Vendu Notarishuis, Rotterdam #190/R
£1733 $3137 €2600 Figure de fille (29x22cm-11x9in) s.d.1899 verso panel. 30-Mar-4 Campo & Campo, Antwerp #238/R est:2000-3000
£2446 $4500 €3571 Feeding her pets (68x51cm-27x20in) s. i. verso. 27-Jun-4 Freeman, Philadelphia #22/R est:5000-8000
£5594 $9510 €8000 La belle otomane a la coiffe rouge (59x48cm-23x19in) s. panel. 18-Nov-3 Vanderkindere, Brussels #20/R est:5000-7500
£13103 $24241 €19000 Jeune fille au papillon (60x49cm-24x19in) s.i. panel. 19-Jan-4 Horta, Bruxelles #111/R est:20000-25000
£16000 $27520 €23360 Ophelia (182x124cm-72x49in) s.i. 3-Dec-3 Christie's, London #45/R est:18000-25000

PORTINARI, Candido (1903-1962) Brazilian
£18000 $32940 €27000 Cena de morro (46x54cm-18x21in) st.sig. cardboard painted c.1948 prov.lit. 7-Jun-4 Artcurial Briest, Paris #42/R est:50000-60000
£18182 $30909 €26000 Portrait of Amalia von Schwanenflugel (41x33cm-16x13in) s. painted c.1940. 25-Nov-3 Christie's, Amsterdam #183/R est:10000-15000
£22059 $37500 €32206 Pai e filho (27x21cm-11x8in) s.d.9.59 oil canvas on panel. 19-Nov-3 Sotheby's, New York #49/R est:25000-35000
£45055 $79747 €67583 Bahian woman (35x27cm-14x11in) s.d.1947. 27-Apr-4 Bolsa de Arte, Rio de Janeiro #68/R (B.R 246000)
Works on paper
£916 $1621 €1374 Head (22x17cm-9x7in) s.d.1947 graphite. 27-Apr-4 Bolsa de Arte, Rio de Janeiro #41/R (B.R 5000)
£12353 $21000 €18035 Noiva (73x46cm-29x18in) s.d.1940 sepia ink crayon prov. 19-Nov-3 Sotheby's, New York #90/R est:10000-15000

PORTO-ALEGRE, Manuel de Araujo (attrib) (1806-1879) Brazilian
Works on paper
£2747 $5000 €4011 River landscape with Indians (63x84cm-25x33in) gouache. 29-Jun-4 Sotheby's, New York #61/R est:6000-8000

PORTOCARRERO, René (1912-1986) Cuban
£3629 $6677 €5298 Carnival (80x99cm-31x39in) s.d.70. 14-Jun-4 Waddingtons, Toronto #199/R est:10000-15000 (C.D 9000)
£4706 $8000 €6871 Diablito (60x45cm-24x18in) s.d.63 prov. 18-Nov-3 Christie's, Rockefeller NY #124/R est:10000-15000
£7059 $12000 €10306 Flores - Flowers (61x46cm-24x18in) s.d.66 s.i.d.verso. 18-Nov-3 Christie's, Rockefeller NY #121/R est:15000-20000
£7059 $12000 €10306 Mujer de carnaval, Josephine Baker - Carnival woman (58x46cm-23x18in) s.i.d.66 prov. 18-Nov-3 Christie's, Rockefeller NY #151/R est:10000-15000
£19118 $32500 €27912 Catedral en rojo (72x53cm-28x21in) s.d.70 s.i.d.verso prov. 19-Nov-3 Sotheby's, New York #167/R est:12000-18000
Works on paper
£1481 $2665 €2162 Untitled (33x25cm-13x10in) s. mixed media card. 25-Apr-4 Subastas Odalys, Caracas #68 est:3000

PORTUGUESE SCHOOL, 18th C
Sculpture
£4200 $7140 €6132 Corpus Cristo (33cm-13in) painted ivory lit. 28-Oct-3 Sotheby's, London #41/R

PORTWAY, Douglas (1922-1993) South African
£1000 $1700 €1460 Figures in landscape (78x68cm-31x27in) s.d.53 s.i.d.verso board exhib. 26-Nov-3 Sotheby's, Olympia #163/R est:1000-1500
£1597 $2890 €2332 Trinity 1 (128x96cm-50x38in) s. i.verso. 30-Mar-4 Stephan Welz, Johannesburg #515/R est:10000-15000 (SA.R 19000)
£1800 $3186 €2628 London (111x111cm-44x44in) s.d.64 prov. 27-Apr-4 Bonhams, Knowle #140 est:200-300
£2642 $4730 €3857 Abstract composition (98x117cm-39x46in) s.d.66 prov. 31-May-4 Stephan Welz, Johannesburg #611/R est:12000-18000 (SA.R 32000)
Works on paper
£400 $708 €584 Ibiza (35x51cm-14x20in) gouache. 27-Apr-4 Bonhams, Knightsbridge #110/R
£500 $925 €730 Untitled (66x51cm-26x20in) s.d.1978 gouache. 11-Mar-4 Christie's, Kensington #363/R
£750 $1350 €1095 London no 12 (78x66cm-31x26in) gouache exhib. 20-Jan-4 Bonhams, Knightsbridge #171/R

PORWOLL, Hans (20th C) German?
£302 $535 €450 Hamburg-America Line freighter (50x60cm-20x24in) s. 28-Apr-4 Schopman, Hamburg #674/R
£570 $1010 €850 Harvesting by windmill (68x100cm-27x39in) s. 28-Apr-4 Schopman, Hamburg #638/R
£1141 $2019 €1700 Hamburg docks (68x100cm-27x39in) s. 28-Apr-4 Schopman, Hamburg #675/R est:1600

POSCHINGER, Hermann (1886-?) German
Works on paper
£280 $476 €400 Kochuttnigturm (44x58cm-17x23in) s.i. W/C paper on board. 19-Nov-3 Dorotheum, Klagenfurt #69

POSCHINGER, Richard von (1839-1915) German
£733 $1320 €1100 Cows by field hedge (20x32cm-8x13in) 26-Apr-4 Rieber, Stuttgart #1194/R
£2075 $3300 €3030 Cows and farmer in mountain lake landscape. s. 25-Feb-3 Bunch, West Chester #540/R
£2797 $4755 €4000 Cows by lake (38x106cm-15x42in) s.i. 24-Nov-3 Dorotheum, Vienna #176/R est:4000-5000
£8389 $15436 €12500 Starnberger See (65x134cm-26x53in) s. 24-Mar-4 Hugo Ruef, Munich #1072/R est:7000

POSCHINGER, Richard von (attrib) (1839-1915) German
£748 $1339 €1100 Countryside (24x34cm-9x13in) paper on board. 17-Mar-4 Neumeister, Munich #569/R

POSE, Eduard Wilhelm (1812-1878) German
£909 $1545 €1300 Extensive summer valley landscape (27x40cm-11x16in) mono. paper on panel. 20-Nov-3 Van Ham, Cologne #1804
£3733 $6869 €5600 Travellers on the path with an approaching storm (24x32cm-9x13in) mono.d.1836 i.verso. 12-Jun-4 Villa Grisebach, Berlin #102/R est:2500-3500
£15436 $27631 €23000 Olympus near Athens (68x87cm-27x34in) mono.d.1858. 27-May-4 Dorotheum, Vienna #1/R est:10000-12000

POSILLIPO SCHOOL (19th C) Italian
£5634 $9746 €8000 View of Amalfi coast (44x66cm-17x26in) bears sig paper on canvas. 10-Dec-3 Sotheby's, Milan #27/R est:8000-12000

POSKAS, Peter (1939-) American
£479 $800 €695 Neighbourhood (76x81cm-30x32in) 28-Jun-3 Susanin's, Chicago #5014
£1070 $1700 €1562 Uranus farm (86x127cm-34x50in) s. 14-Sep-3 Susanin's, Chicago #6017/R est:500-700

POSPOLITAKI, Yevgeni (1852-?) Russian
£1060 $1928 €1600 Jardin anime (34x51cm-13x20in) s. 15-Jun-4 Vanderkindere, Brussels #551 est:250-350

POSSART, Felix (1837-1928) German
£3500 $5600 €5075 Figures before an archway, Tangier (51x34cm-20x13in) s.i. 18-Sep-3 Christie's, Kensington #203/R est:3000-5000
£4027 $7208 €6000 On the terrasse in Tangiers (61x91cm-24x36in) s.d.1912. 27-May-4 Dorotheum, Vienna #114/R est:6500-7500
£4028 $6364 €5800 Terrace in Tangiers (60x90cm-24x35in) s.d.1912 lit. 19-Sep-3 Schloss Ahlden, Ahlden #1528/R est:5800
£4577 $7919 €6500 Musiciennes servant le pacha (62x42cm-24x17in) s. 15-Dec-3 Gros & Delettrez, Paris #476/R est:7500-9000

POSSENTI, Antonio (1933-) Italian
£430 $783 €650 Still life with shells (10x15cm-4x6in) s. board. 17-Jun-4 Galleria Pananti, Florence #401/R
£563 $1025 €850 Seascape with figure (18x13cm-7x5in) s. s.verso cardboard. 17-Jun-4 Galleria Pananti, Florence #91/R
£563 $1025 €850 Angler (15x19cm-6x7in) s. s.i.verso board. 17-Jun-4 Galleria Pananti, Florence #402/R
£563 $1025 €850 Painting (10x15cm-4x6in) s. s.verso board. 17-Jun-4 Galleria Pananti, Florence #405/R
£570 $1055 €850 Untitled (16x10cm-6x4in) s. board. 13-Mar-4 Meeting Art, Vercelli #168
£600 $1104 €900 Untitled (25x35cm-10x14in) s. cardboard. 12-Jun-4 Meeting Art, Vercelli #558/R
£667 $1227 €1000 Untitled (12x25cm-5x10in) s. s.verso board. 12-Jun-4 Meeting Art, Vercelli #348/R
£667 $1227 €1000 Untitled (11x25cm-4x10in) s. board. 12-Jun-4 Meeting Art, Vercelli #717/R
£738 $1366 €1100 Untitled (25x12cm-10x5in) s. s.verso board. 13-Mar-4 Meeting Art, Vercelli #461
£867 $1595 €1300 Untitled (30x20cm-12x8in) s. s.verso. 12-Jun-4 Meeting Art, Vercelli #240/R
£927 $1687 €1400 Night scene (40x30cm-16x12in) s. cardboard on canvas. 21-Jun-4 Pandolfini, Florence #484 est:1000-1200
£966 $1545 €1400 Italo Babbo's cousin (30x20cm-12x8in) s. s.i.verso panel. 13-Mar-3 Galleria Pace, Milan #108/R est:1600-2100
£966 $1612 €1400 For Aesopus (40x30cm-16x12in) s. board exhib. 17-Nov-3 Sant Agostino, Torino #102/R est:1600
£973 $1800 €1450 Palette (24x24cm-9x9in) s. s.i.verso. 13-Mar-4 Meeting Art, Vercelli #160
£986 $1637 €1400 Figure and animals (30x20cm-12x8in) s. s.verso acrylic on canvas on cardboard. 13-Jun-3 Farsetti, Prato #5/R
£993 $1808 €1500 Two in the woods (30x20cm-12x8in) s. s.i.verso cardboard on canvas. 17-Jun-4 Galleria Pananti, Florence #503/R est:1800-2000
£1000 $1810 €1500 In the countryside (30x20cm-12x8in) s. cardboard on canvas. 2-Apr-4 Farsetti, Prato #21/R est:1500-1800
£1000 $1840 €1500 Flower thief (30x20cm-12x8in) s. cardboard on canvas. 12-Jun-4 Meeting Art, Vercelli #664/R est:1500
£1034 $1728 €1500 Untitled (40x30cm-16x12in) s. s.verso canvas on cardboard. 14-Nov-3 Farsetti, Prato #490/R est:1400-1700
£1042 $1646 €1500 Painter and birds (100x70cm-39x28in) mixed media paper on canvas. 6-Sep-3 Meeting Art, Vercelli #467 est:1500
£1056 $1754 €1500 Untitled (20x30cm-8x12in) s. canvasboard. 14-Jun-3 Meeting Art, Vercelli #190/R est:1500
£1074 $1987 €1600 Pumpkin in the wood (30x20cm-12x8in) s. s.verso. 11-Mar-4 Galleria Pace, Milan #60/R est:1800-2300
£1123 $1842 €1550 Untitled (30x20cm-12x8in) s. s.verso. 29-May-3 Galleria Pace, Milan #37/R est:1500-1900
£1127 $1870 €1600 Room at night (30x20cm-12x8in) s.i.verso canvas on cardboard. 13-Jun-3 Farsetti, Prato #485/R
£1241 $1986 €1800 Italo Babbo's cousin (30x20cm-12x8in) s. s.i.verso panel. 13-Mar-3 Galleria Pace, Milan #58/R est:1600-2100
£1310 $2188 €1900 Pinocchio and two friends (30x20cm-12x8in) s. s.i.verso acrylic board. 14-Nov-3 Farsetti, Prato #203/R est:1900-2200
£1342 $2483 €2000 Three butterflies, two dogs and Vittorio Emanuele (40x30cm-16x12in) s. s.verso cardboard on canvas. 13-Mar-4 Meeting Art, Vercelli #496 est:1500
£1370 $2329 €2000 Untitled (30x40cm-12x16in) s. cardboard on canvas. 7-Nov-3 Galleria Rosenberg, Milan #63/R est:2000
£1523 $2772 €2300 Saint Lawrence's night (30x20cm-12x8in) s. 17-Jun-4 Galleria Pananti, Florence #474/R est:1800-2000
£1656 $3013 €2500 On the beach (39x49cm-15x19in) s. s.i.verso. 21-Jun-4 Pandolfini, Florence #365/R est:2600-2900
£1812 $3352 €2700 Room up North (40x30cm-16x12in) s. s.i.verso cardboard on canvas. 11-Mar-4 Galleria Pace, Milan #93/R est:3000-4000
£1879 $3477 €2800 Three sailors (30x40cm-12x16in) s. cardboard on canvas. 13-Mar-4 Meeting Art, Vercelli #457 est:2000
£2000 $3340 €2900 Sailors bathing (40x30cm-16x12in) s. i.verso canvas on cardboard. 14-Nov-3 Farsetti, Prato #97/R est:2800-3200
£2721 $4871 €4000 Puccini on Viareggio Beach (50x60cm-20x24in) s. cardboard on canvas prov. 16-Mar-4 Finarte Semenzato, Milan #290/R est:4000
£2778 $4389 €4000 Winter (80x80cm-31x31in) 6-Sep-3 Meeting Art, Vercelli #487a est:4000
£4333 $7973 €6500 Ships arriving (80x80cm-31x31in) s. acrylic. 11-Jun-4 Farsetti, Prato #582/R est:6500-7500
£4577 $7599 €6500 Two mates (60x100cm-24x39in) s. acrylic board lit. 13-Jun-3 Farsetti, Prato #576/R
£4828 $8062 €7000 The sea in a room (171x50cm-67x20in) s. s.i.verso board. 13-Nov-3 Finarte Semenzato, Rome #247/R est:6800-7500
Works on paper
£352 $585 €500 Untitled (35x25cm-14x10in) s. mixed media cardboard. 14-Jun-3 Meeting Art, Vercelli #206
£704 $1169 €1000 Howls and unicorn (35x25cm-14x10in) s. gouache acrylic cardboard. 13-Jun-3 Farsetti, Prato #251/R
£1060 $1928 €1600 Volcanoes and shells (40x30cm-16x12in) mixed media. 21-Jun-4 Pandolfini, Florence #472/R est:1500-1600

POSSIN, Rudolf (1861-1922) German
£415 $688 €602 Dutch girl (30x26cm-12x10in) s. panel. 16-Jun-3 Blomqvist, Lysaker #1177 (N.KR 4800)
£993 $1609 €1400 Dutch interior with men playing cards (100x80cm-39x31in) s. lit. 23-May-3 Karlheinz Kaupp, Staufen #1883

POSSNER, Hugo A (fl.1889-1933) American
£503 $900 €734 Setting up camp (40x50cm-16x20in) s. 14-May-4 Skinner, Boston #208/R

POSSOZ, Miley (20th C) ?
Works on paper
£240 $425 €350 Vielles maison a Horrfleur (25x36cm-10x14in) s. W/C. 2-May-4 William Jenack, New York #96
£307 $550 €448 Perroquet (25x23cm-10x9in) s. W/C. 11-Jan-4 William Jenack, New York #44
£509 $850 €743 Girl with fruit basket (38x30cm-15x12in) exec. c.1931. 25-Oct-3 Du Mouchelle, Detroit #3227/R

POST, C H (20th C) Belgian
£1457 $2652 €2200 Interieur anime (89x105cm-35x41in) s. 15-Jun-4 Vanderkindere, Brussels #140 est:1500-2500

POST, George (1906-1997) American
Works on paper
£469 $750 €685 Landscape with barn (46x61cm-18x24in) s.d.1938 W/C. 20-Sep-3 Sloans & Kenyon, Bethesda #629/R
£769 $1400 €1123 Boats at rest (43x58cm-17x23in) s. W/C. 15-Jun-4 John Moran, Pasadena #88c est:1500-2000
£782 $1400 €1142 San Francisco cityscape. s. W/C. 10-Jan-4 Harvey Clar, Oakland #1575
£833 $1500 €1216 Laundry day (36x43cm-14x17in) s. pencil W/C. 25-Apr-4 Bonhams & Butterfields, San Francisco #5547/R est:800-1200
£1347 $2250 €1967 View of Alcatraz from San Francisco (29x43cm-11x17in) s. W/C. 26-Oct-3 Bonhams & Butterfields, San Francisco #6542/R
£1984 $3750 €2897 Waterfront (43x64cm-17x25in) i. verso W/C prov. 17-Feb-4 John Moran, Pasadena #89/R est:2000-3000
£2335 $4250 €3409 Urban landscape, 4th Street Channel (38x43cm-15x17in) s. prov. 15-Jun-4 John Moran, Pasadena #132 est:1500-2000

POST, William Merritt (1856-1935) American
£398 $700 €581 After sunset (20x25cm-8x10in) s. canvas on board painted c.1900. 23-May-4 Treadway Gallery, Cincinnati #535/R
£813 $1300 €1187 Winter landscape with wagon tracks through snow (15x20cm-6x8in) s. panel. 22-Sep-3 O'Gallerie, Oregon #770/R est:700-900
£1688 $2700 €2464 Autumn landscape. s. 20-Sep-3 Nadeau, Windsor #58/R
£1931 $3456 €2819 Autumn landscape (76x102cm-30x40in) s. 4-May-4 Ritchie, Toronto #52/R est:6000-8000 (C.D 4750)
£2095 $3750 €3059 Stream in an autumn landscape (61x91cm-24x36in) s. prov. 6-May-4 Shannon's, Milford #251/R est:5000-7000
£2624 $4750 €3831 Stone bridge (61x76cm-24x30in) s. 16-Apr-4 James Julia, Fairfield #642/R est:6000-8000
£3892 $6500 €5682 Autumn landscape with stream (46x61cm-18x24in) s. prov. 23-Oct-3 Shannon's, Milford #204/R est:4000-6000
£3911 $7000 €5710 Autumn (76x104cm-30x41in) s. 6-May-4 Shannon's, Milford #19/R est:4000-6000
Works on paper
£364 $600 €528 Untitled, landscape with water, spring (33x41cm-13x16in) s. W/C. 7-Jul-3 Schrager Galleries, Milwaukee #1191
£531 $950 €775 Cloudy day, a river landscape (15x23cm-6x9in) s. W/C. 14-May-4 Skinner, Boston #83/R

POSTEL, Jules (1867-1955) Belgian
£282 $487 €400 Nu (45x60cm-18x24in) s. 9-Dec-3 Campo, Vlaamse Kaai #389
£293 $531 €440 Maison sous les arbres (45x60cm-18x24in) s. 30-Mar-4 Palais de Beaux Arts, Brussels #679
£507 $907 €750 L'estaminet du coin de la rue (45x60cm-18x24in) s. 10-May-4 Horta, Bruxelles #303
£570 $1055 €850 Pont a Bruges (80x90cm-31x35in) s. 15-Mar-4 Horta, Bruxelles #209
£738 $1366 €1100 L'etang (73x58cm-29x23in) s. 15-Mar-4 Horta, Bruxelles #208
£944 $1605 €1350 Pecheurs au bord de la Lys a Lathem-St-Martin (45x35cm-18x14in) s. 18-Nov-3 Vanderkindere, Brussels #199

POSTHUMA DE BOER, Ferdinand (1930-) Dutch
£671 $1242 €1000 L'adieu du jour (60x80cm-24x31in) s.d.93. 15-Mar-4 Sotheby's, Amsterdam #200/R est:1000-1500

POSTIGLIONE, Luca (1876-1936) Italian
£1007 $1852 €1500 Woman in interior (35x46cm-14x18in) s. 24-Mar-4 Il Ponte, Milan #598/R est:2500
£2113 $3507 €3000 Young girl with a candle (80x50cm-31x20in) s. 11-Jun-3 Christie's, Rome #95a/R est:2000-3000
£2200 $4004 €3212 Young beauty (37x31cm-15x12in) s. 16-Jun-4 Christie's, Kensington #115/R est:2000-3000

POSTIGLIONE, Raffaele (1818-1897) Italian
Works on paper
£1901 $3327 €2700 Hector and wife (52x37cm-20x15in) i. Chinese ink dr. 17-Dec-3 Finarte Semenzato, Milan #231/R est:2500-3000

POT, Hendrick Gerritsz (1585-1657) Dutch
£11000 $18700 €16060 Lute player (34x25cm-13x10in) init. panel. 31-Oct-3 Christie's, Kensington #29/R est:8000-12000

POTAMIANOS, Haralambos (1909-1958) Greek
£894 $1627 €1350 Buveur (35x27cm-14x11in) s. 19-Jun-4 Gerard, Besancon #101
£3000 $5370 €4380 Christ with crown of thorns (81x59cm-32x23in) s. 10-May-4 Sotheby's, Olympia #165/R est:3000-5000

POTEIRO, Antonio (1922-) Brazilian?
£1740 $3080 €2610 Insects and bugs (90x140cm-35x55in) s.d.2003 i.verso. 27-Apr-4 Bolsa de Arte, Rio de Janeiro #78/R (B.R 9500)
£3205 $5865 €4808 Caravan of camels (112x112cm-44x44in) s.d.2003. 6-Jul-4 Bolsa de Arte, Rio de Janeiro #142/R (B.R 17500)

POTERLET, Henry Louis Hippolyte (attrib) (1803-1835) French
£600 $1086 €900 Jeune femme au hanap (25x20cm-10x8in) exhib.lit. 30-Mar-4 Rossini, Paris #832/R
£667 $1207 €1000 Le tournoi (38x55cm-15x22in) oil paper on canvas after Rubens. 30-Mar-4 Rossini, Paris #830
Works on paper
£300 $543 €450 Ruelle (27x34cm-11x13in) graphite. 30-Mar-4 Rossini, Paris #834
£467 $845 €700 Quatre tetes d'hommes et deux tetes de femmes (11x19cm-4x7in) i. pen brown ink. 30-Mar-4 Rossini, Paris #836

POTERLET, Pierre Saint-Ange (attrib) (1804-1881) French
£867 $1569 €1300 Scene de cour (81x53cm-32x21in) 30-Mar-4 Rossini, Paris #833

POTEY, H (19th C) French
Works on paper
£288 $460 €400 Roses, peonies and pansies (33x25cm-13x10in) W/C gouache traces of blk crayon. 16-May-3 Tajan, Paris #171

POTGIETER, Adam (1899-1982) Dutch
£344 $550 €502 Floral still life. s. 20-Sep-3 Harvey Clar, Oakland #1370c

POTHAST, Bernard (1882-1966) Dutch/Belgian
£1277 $2132 €1800 Mere et ses enfants dans un interieur (50x60cm-20x24in) s. 17-Jun-3 Vanderkindere, Brussels #228 est:2000-2500
£2381 $4333 €3500 Parent's pride (31x43cm-12x17in) s. 3-Feb-4 Christie's, Amsterdam #252/R est:4000-6000
£3354 $5500 €4863 Woman mending with two young girls watching in an interior (25x30cm-10x12in) s. 4-Jun-3 Alderfer's, Hatfield #252/R est:3000-5000
£4435 $8161 €6475 Amusing the baby (29x35cm-11x14in) s. 9-Jun-4 Walker's, Ottawa #301/R est:12000-16000 (C.D 11000)
£7240 $12090 €10570 Young mother (56x45cm-22x18in) s. 17-Nov-3 Waddingtons, Toronto #168/R est:15000-20000 (C.D 16000)
£9000 $16380 €13140 Helping mother (50x60cm-20x24in) s. prov. 17-Jun-4 Christie's, London #12/R est:10000-15000
£9722 $16528 €14000 Blowing bubbles - a happy family (50x61cm-20x24in) s. 28-Oct-3 Christie's, Amsterdam #148/R est:12000-16000
£9827 $17000 €14347 Interior scene with mother and three children (71x91cm-28x36in) s. 10-Dec-3 Boos Gallery, Michigan #519/R est:20000-25000
£12500 $21250 €18000 New Baby (80x100cm-31x39in) s. 28-Oct-3 Christie's, Amsterdam #157/R est:20000-30000
£13000 $21710 €18980 Happy family (81x100cm-32x39in) s. 12-Nov-3 Sotheby's, Olympia #228/R est:5000-7000
£14800 $27232 €21608 Sewing lesson (51x61cm-20x24in) s. 25-Mar-4 Christie's, Kensington #169/R est:6000-8000

POTHAST, Willem Frederik Alfons (1877-1917) Dutch
£972 $1604 €1400 Peasant woman with cow in landscape (50x70cm-20x28in) s. 3-Jul-3 Dr Fritz Nagel, Stuttgart #510/R

POTIN, Jacques (1920-) French
£432 $800 €648 Le petit phare, Deauville. Mere et deux enfants (20x33cm-8x13in) s.i.verso one d.1965 two. 14-Jul-4 American Auctioneer #490119/R

POTRONAT, Lucien (1889-?) French
£360 $659 €540 Villa on the Cote d'Azur (46x54cm-18x21in) s.i.verso. 12-Jul-4 Mullucks Wells, Bishop's Stortford #408/R
£375 $600 €548 Houses overlooking a Mediterranean bay (46x56cm-18x22in) s. 19-Sep-3 Freeman, Philadelphia #155/R
£409 $650 €597 Cote d'Azur (45x55cm-18x22in) s. s.i.verso prov. 13-Sep-3 Weschler, Washington #683/R
£500 $945 €730 Villa on the Cote d'Azur (46x56cm-18x22in) s. 19-Feb-4 Christie's, Kensington #150/R
£600 $978 €870 Vieux Mas dans les Oliviers, Cote d'Azur (44x53cm-17x21in) s. 23-Sep-3 Bonhams, Leeds #139/R
£1000 $1700 €1460 Cottage on the Mediterranean coast (56x55cm-22x22in) s. pair. 6-Nov-3 Christie's, Kensington #845/R est:800-1200

POTSCH, Igo (1884-1939) Austrian
£355 $592 €500 Butcher's shop in Kahlenberg village (47x47cm-19x19in) i. verso panel. 16-Oct-3 Dorotheum, Salzburg #611/R
Works on paper
£1042 $1698 €1500 Friesach (68x74cm-27x29in) s. mixed media. 23-Sep-3 Wiener Kunst Auktionen, Vienna #54/R est:1500-2500

POTT, Laslett John (1837-1898) British
£340 $626 €496 Lady Jane Grey arriving at the tower (25x36cm-10x14in) s. 8-Jun-4 Gorringes, Lewes #2019
£5081 $7978 €7418 Proposal (103x78cm-41x31in) s. i.verso. 1-Sep-3 Shapiro, Sydney #339/R est:5000-7000 (A.D 12500)

POTT, Mellow Willems (?) American?
£500 $800 €730 Woman resting on forest path. s. panel. 20-Sep-3 Harvey Clar, Oakland #1226

POTTEAU, Philippe Jacques and ROUSSEAU, Louis (19/20th C) French
Photographs
£55000 $96800 €82500 Collection anthropologique du Museum d'histoire naturelle de Paris. albumen prints i.num. from 13 to 299 card 280. 21-May-4 Bloomsbury, London #39/R est:60000-80000

POTTEN, Christopher (?) British
£2500 $4650 €3650 Old curiosity shop (127x102cm-50x40in) i.d.1875 verso. 4-Mar-4 Christie's, Kensington #616 est:2500-3500

POTTER, Adolphe (1835-1911) Swiss
£1607 $2780 €2346 Evening landscape with figures gathering faggots (110x155cm-43x61in) s.d.1875 prov. 9-Dec-3 Rasmussen, Copenhagen #1668/R est:20000-25000 (D.KR 17000)
£5674 $9475 €8000 Italian landscape at sunset (69x120cm-27x47in) s.d.1877. 23-Jun-3 Finarte Semenzato, Rome #194/R

POTTER, Beatrix (1866-1943) British
Works on paper
£4500 $8235 €6570 Gentleman rabbit with letter (7x5cm-3x2in) pencil ink with autograph letter. 8-Jul-4 Sotheby's, London #350/R est:5000-7000
£30000 $51900 €43800 Rabbit stepping from his doorway into the snow with an umbrella (9x6cm-4x2in) s. pencil ink W/C oval exec.c.1892-93. 11-Dec-3 Sotheby's, London #240/R est:15000-20000

POTTER, Carter (1961-) American?
Sculpture
£1850 $3200 €2701 Film reel from vertigo (183x183cm-72x72in) init.i.d.1999 on stretcher section of film reel on wooden support. 10-Dec-3 Phillips, New York #672/R est:500-700

POTTER, Charles (1878-?) British
Works on paper
£380 $699 €555 Pass of Llanberis (58x88cm-23x35in) s.i. W/C. 23-Mar-4 Anderson & Garland, Newcastle #124

POTTER, George (?) Irish
£403 $721 €600 Studio interior (54x74cm-21x29in) s. board. 31-May-4 Hamilton Osborne King, Dublin #34
£592 $1089 €900 Female head study (51x32cm-20x13in) s. canvasboard. 22-Jun-4 De Veres Art Auctions, Dublin #131/R
£662 $1205 €1000 Dublin Bay, ferry departing (25x25cm-10x10in) s. 15-Jun-4 James Adam, Dublin #11/R
£1258 $2290 €1900 Dublin Bay from Dun Laoghaire (60x60cm-24x24in) s. 15-Jun-4 James Adam, Dublin #44/R est:2000-3000
£2431 $3816 €3500 Dublin Bay from Clarinda Park west (101x75cm-40x30in) s. exhib. 26-Aug-3 James Adam, Dublin #202/R est:3200-3500
£3311 $6026 €5000 Top of Corrig Avenue, late afternoon, Dun Laoghaire (120x100cm-47x39in) s. 15-Jun-4 James Adam, Dublin #20/R est:5000-6000

POTTER, Joan Alex (1945-) American
£2297 $4250 €3354 Still life with lemons. Still life with oranges (41x51cm-16x20in) s.d.75 pair. 15-Jul-4 Sotheby's, New York #68/R est:800-1200
£2778 $4500 €4028 Copper and grapes leaves (53x58cm-21x23in) 23-May-3 Altermann Galleries, Santa Fe #210

POTTER, Ken (1926-) American
Works on paper
£2513 $4750 €3669 Industrial/bridge (48x64cm-19x25in) s.d.1958 W/C exhib.prov. 17-Feb-4 John Moran, Pasadena #82/R est:3000-4000

POTTER, Mary (1900-1981) British
£900 $1584 €1314 Marsh pool (76x51cm-30x20in) prov.exhib. 18-May-4 Bonhams, Knightsbridge #175/R
£2600 $4134 €3796 Snow (51x31cm-20x12in) s.verso i.stretcher exhib. 10-Sep-3 Sotheby's, Olympia #292/R est:2500-3500
£5000 $8600 €7300 Sandcastles (15x21cm-6x8in) bears sig.i. panel prov.exhib. 2-Dec-3 Bonhams, New Bond Street #150/R est:1500-2000
£7500 $12750 €10950 By the sea (51x61cm-20x24in) prov. 26-Nov-3 Hamptons Fine Art, Godalming #229/R est:2500-4000
£15000 $26850 €21900 Winter window (64x51cm-25x20in) init. i.verso painted c.1950. 7-May-4 Mallams, Oxford #367/R est:3000-4000
Works on paper
£380 $692 €555 Dark painting (8x13cm-3x5in) chl W/C. 15-Jun-4 Bonhams, Knightsbridge #144

£450 $725 €653 Mosaic (18x13cm-7x5in) gouache on board. 15-Aug-3 Keys, Aylsham #647
£500 $805 €725 Twigs in a vase with a piano (23x18cm-9x7in) W/C. 15-Aug-3 Keys, Aylsham #648
£550 $1001 €803 Orange robe (34x25cm-13x10in) pencil W/C prov. 1-Jul-4 Christie's, Kensington #387/R

POTTER, P (17th C) Dutch
£1477 $2717 €2200 Fermiere et son troupeau (43x53cm-17x21in) s. panel. 23-Mar-4 Galerie Moderne, Brussels #211/R est:500-700

POTTER, Paulus (1625-1654) Dutch
£22000 $40260 €32120 Tethered bull covering cow (28x27cm-11x11in) s.d.1645 panel. 9-Jul-4 Christie's, Kensington #57/R est:10000-15000

POTTER, William J (1883-1964) American
£489 $900 €714 White house with picket fence (76x64cm-30x25in) s. 27-Mar-4 New Orleans Auction, New Orleans #599 est:600-900

POTTERS, Hermannsburg (20th C) Australian
Sculpture
£1961 $3510 €2863 Bush tucker dreaming mural (120x80cm-47x31in) terracotta matt glazed tiles 24 exec 1990 prov. 25-May-4 Lawson Menzies, Sydney #116/R est:4000-6000 (A.D 5000)

POTTHAST, Edward Henry (1857-1927) American
£3315 $6000 €4840 Western sunset (30x33cm-12x13in) s. 16-Apr-4 James Julia, Fairfield #598/R est:6000-8000
£3632 $6500 €5303 Laundry day (15x20cm-6x8in) s. board prov. 6-May-4 Shannon's, Milford #88/R est:5000-7000
£6286 $11000 €9178 Rocky cliffs (21x26cm-8x10in) s. canvas on board. 19-Dec-3 Sotheby's, New York #1095/R est:8000-12000
£8140 $14000 €11884 Landscape (30x40cm-12x16in) s. board. 3-Dec-3 Sotheby's, New York #11/R est:20000-30000
£8721 $15000 €12733 Moonlight campers (63x76cm-25x30in) s.i.on stretcher prov. 3-Dec-3 Sotheby's, New York #12/R est:20000-30000
£11299 $20000 €16497 Camp by Lake Louise (30x40cm-12x16in) s. canvas on board. 28-Apr-4 Christie's, Los Angeles #24/R est:25000-35000
£14773 $26000 €21569 Summer day (30x41cm-12x16in) s. s.i.verso board prov.exhib. 18-May-4 Christie's, Rockefeller NY #100/R est:30000-50000
£15988 $27500 €23342 Boating, Central park (30x40cm-12x16in) s. prov. 3-Dec-3 Doyle, New York #265/R est:30000-50000
£16456 $26000 €24026 Hunter and dog in an autumn landscape (61x76cm-24x30in) s. 7-Sep-3 Treadway Gallery, Cincinnati #659/R est:30000-50000
£16760 $30000 €24470 Picnic in the woods (61x76cm-24x30in) s. prov. 26-May-4 Doyle, New York #87a/R est:25000-35000
£20349 $35000 €29710 Harvest moon (30x41cm-12x16in) s. canvas on board prov. 4-Dec-3 Christie's, Rockefeller NY #73/R est:20000-30000
£23256 $40000 €33954 Down in the Grand Canyon (60x73cm-24x29in) s. i.on overlap prov. 3-Dec-3 Doyle, New York #253/R est:40000-60000
£56818 $100000 €82954 Child in surf (30x41cm-12x16in) s. panel prov. 19-May-4 Sotheby's, New York #1/R est:50000-75000
£85227 $150000 €124431 Beach scene (30x41cm-12x16in) s. panel prov. 18-May-4 Christie's, Rockefeller NY #99/R est:150000-250000
£93023 $160000 €135814 Girl playing with dog and playtime (22x30cm-9x12in) s. panel double-sided prov.exhib. 3-Dec-3 Sotheby's, New York #4/R est:100000-150000
£96591 $170000 €141023 In the surf (28x41cm-11x16in) s. panel prov. 19-May-4 Sotheby's, New York #2/R est:60000-80000
£98837 $170000 €144302 At the shore (30x41cm-12x16in) s. panel prov. 3-Dec-3 Sotheby's, New York #3/R est:125000-175000
Works on paper
£1657 $3000 €2419 Beach scene (13x15cm-5x6in) W/C. 16-Apr-4 Du Mouchelle, Detroit #2075/R est:3000-5000
£7065 $13000 €10315 Moonlight scene (71x51cm-28x20in) s. W/C crayon prov. 27-Jun-4 Freeman, Philadelphia #104/R est:6000-10000
£8939 $16000 €13051 Baby's day at the beach (36x29cm-14x11in) s. W/C graphite paperboard prov. 14-May-4 Skinner, Boston #336/R est:7000-9000

POTTHAST, Edward Henry (attrib) (1857-1927) American
£921 $1500 €1345 Bathers in the surf (20x30cm-8x12in) 28-Sep-3 Bonhams & Butterfields, Los Angeles #7017 est:1000-1500

POTTHOF, Hans (1911-2003) Swiss
£2358 $3821 €3443 Spain (41x60cm-16x24in) s. 24-May-3 Burkhard, Luzern #38/R est:5500-6500 (S.FR 5000)
£5172 $9259 €7551 In Provence (49x70cm-19x28in) s. i. stretcher. 14-May-4 Dobiaschofsky, Bern #207/R est:14000 (S.FR 12000)
Works on paper
£647 $1170 €945 Fishermen on shore (29x45cm-11x18in) s. chl. 31-Mar-4 Zurichsee Auktionen, Erlenbach #73/R (S.FR 1500)
£647 $1170 €945 Village (29x45cm-11x18in) s. chl. 31-Mar-4 Zurichsee Auktionen, Erlenbach #112/R (S.FR 1500)
£862 $1560 €1259 Zugerberg with Rigi (21x35cm-8x14in) s.i. W/C. 31-Mar-4 Zurichsee Auktionen, Erlenbach #110/R (S.FR 2000)
£1422 $2575 €2076 Waadtlander farmstead (42x28cm-17x11in) s. W/C. 31-Mar-4 Zurichsee Auktionen, Erlenbach #113/R est:3500-4500 (S.FR 3300)
£1509 $2731 €2203 By the Reuss (40x24cm-16x9in) s.d.86 W/C. 31-Mar-4 Zurichsee Auktionen, Erlenbach #106/R est:3500-4500 (S.FR 3500)
£1659 $2921 €2422 On the Reuss near Muhlau (35x60cm-14x24in) s.d.71 gouache prov. 22-May-4 Galerie Gloggner, Luzern #84/R est:2400-2600 (S.FR 3800)
£1724 $3086 €2517 Landscape near Rothenturm (28x43cm-11x17in) s.d.86 W/C bodycol. 14-May-4 Dobiaschofsky, Bern #210/R est:5500 (S.FR 4000)

POTTIER, Emile (?) Belgian?
£303 $557 €460 Penitence (54x42cm-21x17in) s.i. panel. 22-Jun-4 Palais de Beaux Arts, Brussels #299

POTTIER, Gaston (20th C) French
£282 $493 €400 Village de pecheurs en bord de mer (46x55cm-18x22in) s. 21-Dec-3 Thierry & Lannon, Brest #352
£333 $597 €500 Le pardon de Tronoen (45x55cm-18x22in) s. 16-May-4 Thierry & Lannon, Brest #356
£596 $1115 €900 Le port de Douarnenez, dechargement de poissons (60x90cm-24x35in) s.d.62. 24-Jul-4 Thierry & Lannon, Brest #209
£633 $1134 €950 Retour de peche a Douarnenez (59x91cm-23x36in) s. 16-May-4 Thierry & Lannon, Brest #357
£845 $1479 €1200 Port de Douarnenez (33x41cm-13x16in) s. 21-Dec-3 Thierry & Lannon, Brest #353

POTTNER, Emil (1872-?) German
£300 $519 €438 Barges moored on a canal side (54x60cm-21x24in) s. 9-Dec-3 Rosebery Fine Art, London #601/R
£1678 $2853 €2400 Poultry in yard (61x80cm-24x31in) s.d.1946. 20-Nov-3 Van Ham, Cologne #1986 est:400

POTTS, Ian (20th C) British
Works on paper
£900 $1674 €1314 Holborne Museum Park at Bath (100x80cm-39x31in) W/C. 8-Mar-4 Christie's, London #11

POTWOROWSKI, Peter (1898-1962) Polish
£1800 $3060 €2628 Blue House (64x76cm-25x30in) 18-Nov-3 Bonhams, Knightsbridge #171/R est:1000-1500
£2200 $3960 €3212 Blue House (64x76cm-25x30in) 20-Jan-4 Bonhams, Knightsbridge #240/R est:1000-1500
£4236 $7328 €6185 Park scene (39x53cm-15x21in) s.d.56. 14-Dec-3 Agra, Warsaw #76/R est:12000 (P.Z 28000)
Works on paper
£227 $406 €331 At the park (18x25cm-7x10in) W/C chk. 6-May-4 Agra, Warsaw #58/R (P.Z 1600)
£424 $767 €619 Still life (21x27cm-8x11in) W/C Indian ink. 4-Apr-4 Agra, Warsaw #51/R (P.Z 3000)
£803 $1332 €1172 Evening (25x20cm-10x8in) pastel pencil. 15-Jun-3 Agra, Warsaw #42/R (P.Z 5000)
£2188 $3653 €3194 Resting (19x25cm-7x10in) W/C. 19-Oct-3 Agra, Warsaw #30/R est:2000 (P.Z 14000)

POUGIALIS, Constantine (1894-?) American
£203 $350 €296 Untitled, architectural landscape (53x38cm-21x15in) tempera prov. 7-Dec-3 Hindman, Chicago #827/R
£472 $750 €689 Woman (51x38cm-20x15in) s. 14-Sep-3 Susanin's, Chicago #6077/R
Works on paper
£291 $500 €425 Fisherman's village (46x56cm-18x22in) s. W/C prov. 7-Dec-3 Hindman, Chicago #829/R

POUGNY, Jean (1894-1956) French
£276 $458 €400 Homme en habit (50x26cm-20x10in) s. 6-Oct-3 Blanchet, Paris #190
£276 $458 €400 Portrait homme (50x32cm-20x13in) s. 6-Oct-3 Blanchet, Paris #188
£310 $515 €450 Femme en robe a panier (49x32cm-19x13in) s. 6-Oct-3 Blanchet, Paris #168
£310 $515 €450 Homme en habit romantique (50x33cm-20x13in) s. 6-Oct-3 Blanchet, Paris #183
£345 $572 €500 Homme epoque Louis XIV (50x33cm-20x13in) s. 6-Oct-3 Blanchet, Paris #193
£345 $572 €500 Portrait de gentilhomme (49x32cm-19x13in) s. 6-Oct-3 Blanchet, Paris #169
£345 $572 €500 Femme en robe a panier (50x32cm-20x13in) s. 6-Oct-3 Blanchet, Paris #184
£379 $630 €550 Couple de paysans (50x29cm-20x11in) s. 6-Oct-3 Blanchet, Paris #176
£379 $630 €550 Homme en habit de mousquetaire (50x34cm-20x13in) s. 6-Oct-3 Blanchet, Paris #174
£379 $630 €550 Femme du Moyen Age (50x33cm-20x13in) s. 6-Oct-3 Blanchet, Paris #186
£414 $687 €600 Gentilhomme (45x33cm-18x13in) s. 6-Oct-3 Blanchet, Paris #171
£414 $687 €600 Femme en robe a panier (50x32cm-20x13in) s. 6-Oct-3 Blanchet, Paris #181
£414 $687 €600 Homme satyre a la hache (50x27cm-20x11in) s. 6-Oct-3 Blanchet, Paris #185
£448 $744 €650 Homme epoque Louis XIV (50x33cm-20x13in) s. 6-Oct-3 Blanchet, Paris #192
£448 $744 €650 Homme en habit Richelieu (50x33cm-20x13in) s. 6-Oct-3 Blanchet, Paris #182
£448 $744 €650 Homme de loi (50x28cm-20x11in) s. 6-Oct-3 Blanchet, Paris #180
£448 $744 €650 Couple debut XVIIeme (50x33cm-20x13in) s. 6-Oct-3 Blanchet, Paris #179
£483 $801 €700 Femme en bergeres (50x28cm-20x11in) s. 6-Oct-3 Blanchet, Paris #191
£483 $801 €700 Robe a panier (50x32cm-20x13in) s. 6-Oct-3 Blanchet, Paris #173
£517 $859 €750 Portrait de paysan (45x28cm-18x11in) s. 6-Oct-3 Blanchet, Paris #170
£517 $859 €750 Homme de cour (50x28cm-20x11in) s. 6-Oct-3 Blanchet, Paris #178
£517 $859 €750 Paysans du Moyen Age (50x33cm-20x13in) s. 6-Oct-3 Blanchet, Paris #177
£621 $1030 €900 Bergeres (50x32cm-20x13in) s. 6-Oct-3 Blanchet, Paris #187
£690 $1145 €1000 Robe a la francaise (50x35cm-20x14in) s. 6-Oct-3 Blanchet, Paris #172
£1585 $2741 €2250 Personnages dans le jardin (11x21cm-4x8in) s. prov.exhib.lit. 14-Dec-3 Versailles Encheres #149/R est:12000-15000

£1908 $3511 €2900 Arlequins (26x14cm-10x6in) studio st. canvas on wood prov. 28-Jun-4 Joron-Derem, Paris #160/R est:3500-4000
£2703 $5000 €3946 Charette - Le Fiacre (22x27cm-9x11in) s. corrugated cardboard on panel painted c.1945-46 prov.exhib. 12-Feb-4 Sotheby's, New York #41/R est:3000-5000
£2762 $4696 €3950 Nature morte, assiette et pipe (13x21cm-5x8in) i.verso painted c.1928-1929. 27-Nov-3 Calmels Cohen, Paris #45/R est:4000-5000
£3521 $5705 €5000 Suite no 7 (60x16cm-24x6in) canvas on panel painted c.1938 prov.exhib.lit. 5-Aug-3 Tajan, Paris #26/R est:5000-7000
£3974 $7232 €6000 Interieur aux cartes a jouer (27x35cm-11x14in) st.sig. paint paper on cardboard. 15-Jun-4 Rossini, Paris #130/R est:6000-9000
£6000 $11040 €9000 Scene de plage (16x30cm-6x12in) s. canvas on panel prov. 8-Jun-4 Artcurial Briest, Paris #153/R est:8000-12000
£6250 $10438 €9000 Nature morte, verre et poisson (27x41cm-11x16in) studio st. painted c.1928-1929 lit. 21-Oct-3 Artcurial Briest, Paris #292/R est:7000-9000
£6376 $11285 €9500 Gueridon blanc et bibelots (36x28cm-14x11in) s. board. 27-Apr-4 Artcurial Briest, Paris #207/R est:5000-7000
£7000 $12880 €10500 La lecon de piano (19x26cm-7x10in) s. canvas on panel prov.exhib.lit. 8-Jun-4 Artcurial Briest, Paris #154/R est:8000-12000
£8000 $13600 €11680 Petit Ane (23x33cm-9x13in) s. canvas on board prov.exhib.lit. 19-Nov-3 Sotheby's, London #201/R est:8000-12000
£8725 $16228 €13000 Nature morte, cartes et fruits (24x33cm-9x13in) s. lit. 2-Mar-4 Artcurial Briest, Paris #189 est:12000-15000
£9333 $17080 €14000 Le tramway (33x41cm-13x16in) s. 7-Jun-4 Artcurial Briest, Paris #23/R est:13000-16000
£16043 $30000 €23423 Scene de boulevard (45x56cm-18x22in) s. 25-Feb-4 Christie's, Rockefeller NY #41/R est:4000-6000
£50000 $89500 €73000 View through a window onto the port of St. Tropez (100x81cm-39x32in) s. i.verso. 26-May-4 Sotheby's, London #153/R est:50000-70000
£150000 $268500 €219000 Still life with hat and clock (50x76cm-20x30in) s. prov.lit. 26-May-4 Sotheby's, London #246/R est:100000-140000
Works on paper
£2148 $3973 €3200 Le golfe (26x38cm-10x15in) s.d.1924 gouache. 15-Mar-4 Blanchet, Paris #89/R est:3000-4000
£2684 $4993 €4000 Le billard (36x48cm-14x19in) s. gouache exec.c.1928. 2-Mar-4 Artcurial Briest, Paris #190/R est:4000-5000
£2817 $4873 €4000 Paysage parisien (36x45cm-14x18in) s. gouache. 9-Dec-3 Artcurial Briest, Paris #261/R est:5000-7000
£3020 $5346 €4500 Fenetre ouverte (56x41cm-22x16in) s. gouache exec c.1926-27. 27-Apr-4 Artcurial Briest, Paris #32/R est:3000-4000
£3819 $6378 €5500 Danseuses (59x45cm-23x18in) s. lead pencil drawing exec c.1926. 21-Oct-3 Artcurial Briest, Paris #295/R est:2000-3000
£4500 $7650 €6570 View of Tuileries, Paris (61x49cm-24x19in) s. gouache. 19-Nov-3 Sotheby's, London #194/R est:3000-5000
£6000 $11040 €9000 Maisons (29x21cm-11x8in) s. ink col. crayon exhib. 8-Jun-4 Artcurial Briest, Paris #103/R est:5000-7000
£7947 $14464 €12000 Fenetre (50x34cm-20x13in) st.sig. gouache. 15-Jun-4 Rossini, Paris #131/R est:1500-2000
£9500 $17480 €13870 Suprematisme (45x29cm-18x11in) s.d.1916 pen India ink pencil. 24-Jun-4 Christie's, London #373/R est:6000-9000

POUJOL, Amedee (20th C) French
£400 $728 €600 Abstraction lyrique (61x55cm-24x22in) s.i.d.3/4/03. 29-Jun-4 Gioffredo, Nice #38
£600 $1092 €900 Abstraction lyrique (169x61cm-67x24in) s.i.d.3/4/03. 29-Jun-4 Gioffredo, Nice #368

POULAKAS, Ioannis (1864-1942) Greek
Works on paper
£3000 $5250 €4380 Sailing boat (50x39cm-20x15in) s. pastel. 16-Dec-3 Bonhams, New Bond Street #7/R est:3000-5000

POULIN, Daryl (20th C) American
£317 $600 €463 Study of a cougar standing on outcropping of rock (61x91cm-24x36in) s. acrylic. 23-Feb-4 O'Gallerie, Oregon #754/R
£452 $800 €660 Cowboy choreography (76x102cm-30x40in) s.d.99 sold with a book. 3-May-4 O'Gallerie, Oregon #708/R
£688 $1300 €1004 Wild ones, two mounted cowboys (76x102cm-30x40in) s. 23-Feb-4 O'Gallerie, Oregon #132/R est:1000-1500

POULLEAU, Claude Rene Gabriel (1749-?) French
Works on paper
£890 $1513 €1300 Vue perspective de la nouvelle eglise Sainte-Genevieve (29x38cm-11x15in) i.d.1786 W/C pen ink. 6-Nov-3 Tajan, Paris #127 est:1200-1500

POULOS, Basilios (1941-) American
£617 $1000 €901 First silver (114x165cm-45x65in) s.i.d.1972 verso. 2-Aug-3 Neal Auction Company, New Orleans #388/R est:1500-2500

POULSEN, Georg (1911-) Danish
£271 $486 €396 Composition with flower (94x68cm-37x27in) s. s.i.verso. 10-May-4 Rasmussen, Vejle #627/R (D.KR 3000)
£275 $500 €402 Vessel on slipway (54x81cm-21x32in) s. 7-Feb-4 Rasmussen, Havnen #4211 (D.KR 3000)

POULSON, Ernest (19th C) British
£1477 $2717 €2200 English three masted bark, Ann Mitchell of Glasgow (60x90cm-24x35in) s.d.1850 lit. 26-Mar-4 Ketterer, Hamburg #26/R est:2500-3000

POULTON, James (19th C) British
£435 $800 €635 Larder (56x71cm-22x28in) s. 9-Jun-4 Doyle, New York #3063
£700 $1281 €1022 Still life with fruit (70x90cm-28x35in) 1-Feb-4 Lots Road Auctions, London #370
£2846 $4895 €4155 Still life of fruit on a bank (73x92cm-29x36in) 3-Dec-3 AB Stockholms Auktionsverk #2567/R est:40000-50000 (S.KR 37000)

POUMEYROL, Jean-Marie (1945-) French
£2600 $4732 €3900 Cave inondee (73x100cm-29x39in) s.d.1989. 4-Jul-4 Eric Pillon, Calais #162/R
£3099 $5361 €4400 Maison abandonnee sous la neige (100x73cm-39x29in) s.d.1990 panel. 14-Dec-3 Eric Pillon, Calais #226/R

POUND, Patrick (20th C) New Zealander
£515 $963 €752 Exhibition (121x180cm-48x71in) on linen. 24-Feb-4 Peter Webb, Auckland #49/R (NZ.D 1400)
Works on paper
£289 $535 €422 World famous books in outline (42x87cm-17x34in) mixed media collage on paper in box frame prov.exhib. 15-Mar-4 Sotheby's, Melbourne #137 (A.D 700)
£1405 $2599 €2051 Selling off the library (185x143cm-73x56in) collage executed 1996 prov.exhib. 15-Mar-4 Sotheby's, Melbourne #51/R est:2500-3500 (A.D 3400)

POUNDERS, Al (20th C) American
£546 $1000 €797 Umbrian landscape (94x124cm-37x49in) 10-Jul-4 Hindman, Chicago #416/R est:1000-1500
£599 $1000 €869 Passing storm, Polgeta (107x119cm-42x47in) s. i.d.1990 verso. 29-Jun-3 Butterfields, Los Angeles #7087/R est:400-600

POUPELET, Jane (1878-1932) French
Works on paper
£317 $548 €450 L'etable (23x31cm-9x12in) s. pen brown wash sanguine wash exec.c.1905-1910. 13-Dec-3 Martinot & Savignat, Pontoise #35/R
£2282 $4221 €3400 Taureau endormi (23x32cm-9x13in) s. ink wash dr. 14-Mar-4 St-Germain-en-Laye Encheres #138/R est:1000-1200

POURBUS, Frans (16/17th C) Flemish
£3067 $5551 €4600 Portrait of young woman wearing cap and stiff collar (36x28cm-14x11in) panel. 1-Apr-4 Van Ham, Cologne #1237/R est:4000

POURBUS, Frans (younger-attrib) (1570-1622) Flemish
£10959 $18630 €16000 Portrait of Marie d'Enghien de Kestergat, Lady d'Eyseringhem (69x59cm-27x23in) prov. 4-Nov-3 Sotheby's, Amsterdam #34/R est:15000-20000

POURBUS, Frans (younger-style) (1570-1622) Flemish
£6000 $10200 €8760 Portrait of a lady wearing black dress and white lace collar (92x76cm-36x30in) mono.d.1622. 30-Oct-3 Sotheby's, Olympia #92/R est:6000-8000
£7500 $12450 €10950 Portrait of a lady half-length in a black and white dress and white ruff (60x52cm-24x20in) 30-Sep-3 Sotheby's, London #40/R est:6000-8000

POURBUS, Peeter Jansz (1510-1584) Flemish
£13333 $24000 €19466 Portrait of a young man, said to be a member of the Overstolz de Efferen family of Cologne (42x28cm-17x11in) i.d.1560 panel prov. 23-Jan-4 Christie's, Rockefeller NY #31/R est:30000-50000
£52000 $89960 €75920 Portrait of a gentleman and his wife, both half length, wearing black (30x22cm-12x9in) panel pair. 11-Dec-3 Sotheby's, London #116/R est:8000-12000

POURTAU, Léon (1868-1898) French
£18000 $33120 €26280 St Tropez (60x50cm-24x20in) init.d.92 prov. 22-Jun-4 Sotheby's, London #130/R est:15000-20000

POUS, Jean (1875-1973) Spanish
Works on paper
£267 $491 €400 Crucifixion (32x25cm-13x10in) s. ball pen gouache lit. 9-Jun-4 Artcurial Briest, Paris #310/R

POUSETTE-DART, Richard (1916-1992) American
£13497 $22000 €19706 Writing space (58x76cm-23x30in) acrylic paper on board prov.exhib. 23-Sep-3 Christie's, Rockefeller NY #36/R est:7000-9000
£65868 $110000 €96167 By the pond (142x203cm-56x80in) s. painted 1961 prov.exhib. 12-Nov-3 Christie's, Rockefeller NY #322/R est:120000-180000
£94972 $170000 €138659 Two women (190x142cm-75x56in) s.d.62 verso prov. 12-May-4 Christie's, Rockefeller NY #132/R est:150000-200000
Works on paper
£8333 $15000 €12166 Untitled (22x30cm-9x12in) s.verso pencil titanium acrylic prov. 24-Apr-4 David Rago, Lambertville #135/R est:4000-6000
£11976 $20000 €17485 Village (57x76cm-22x30in) W/C prov. 13-Nov-3 Sotheby's, New York #261/R est:8000-12000

POUSSIN (circle) (?) French
£13986 $23776 €20000 Water from the rock (105x136cm-41x54in) painted c.1700. 28-Nov-3 Wendl, Rudolstadt #4141/R est:12000

POUSSIN, Nicolas (1594-1665) French
£500000 $865000 €730000 Holy Family with Saint John the Baptist (51x68cm-20x27in) prov.lit. 10-Dec-3 Christie's, London #66/R est:500000-700000

POUSSIN, Nicolas (after) (1594-1665) French
£5500 $10065 €8030 Finding of Moses (140x198cm-55x78in) prov. 9-Jul-4 Christie's, Kensington #194/R est:4000-6000
£6800 $12240 €9928 Moses striking the rock (105x137cm-41x54in) 23-Apr-4 Christie's, Kensington #169/R est:3000-5000

POUSSIN, Nicolas (circle) (1594-1665) French
£140000 $256200 €210000 Bacchanal (113x154cm-44x61in) prov. 1-Jun-4 Sotheby's, Milan #192/R est:30000-40000

POUSSIN, Nicolas (style) (1594-1665) French
£5467 $9785 €8200 Aurora and Cefalo (93x166cm-37x65in) 13-May-4 Babuino, Rome #68/R est:4000-6000

POUTOV, Alexandre (?) Russian?
Works on paper
£490 $832 €700 Les Dames papotent (32x44cm-13x17in) s. Indian ink. 27-Nov-3 Calmels Cohen, Paris #62/R

POVAROVA, Valentina (1954-) Russian
£268 $502 €400 Ice-skating (30x40cm-12x16in) s. 24-Feb-4 Durán, Madrid #734/R
£310 $518 €450 Ice-skating (39x30cm-15x12in) s. 17-Nov-3 Durán, Madrid #675/R
£355 $592 €500 Village covered in snow (40x30cm-16x12in) s. 20-Oct-3 Durán, Madrid #721/R

POVEDA Y JUAN, Vicente (1857-?) Spanish
Works on paper
£567 $1031 €850 Besa manos de dama (23x15cm-9x6in) s. W/C. 29-Jun-4 Segre, Madrid #70/R
£567 $1031 €850 Doncella with a cat (23x15cm-9x6in) s. W/C. 29-Jun-4 Segre, Madrid #71/R

POWDITCH, Peter (1942-) Australian
£492 $797 €718 Nude (86x60cm-34x24in) s.verso board. 30-Jul-3 Goodman, Sydney #70/R (A.D 1200)
£830 $1386 €1245 Bather (30x21cm-12x8in) s.d.69 i.verso oil acrylic board. 27-Oct-3 Goodman, Sydney #77/R (A.D 2000)
£916 $1667 €1337 Balcony I (106x137cm-42x54in) s.d.9/69 i.d.verso board prov. 16-Jun-4 Deutscher-Menzies, Melbourne #313/R est:3000-5000 (A.D 2400)
£1434 $2324 €2094 Sun-Day (151x136cm-59x54in) s.i.verso oil vinyl collage prov. 30-Jul-3 Goodman, Sydney #55/R est:3000-5000 (A.D 3500)
Works on paper
£248 $459 €362 Verandah 9 (190x134cm-75x53in) s.d.89-90 i.verso mixed media on board prov. 15-Mar-4 Sotheby's, Melbourne #78 (A.D 600)
£289 $535 €422 No.17 (85x28cm-33x11in) s.d.1996 i.verso mixed media on board prov.exhib. 15-Mar-4 Sotheby's, Melbourne #218 (A.D 700)

POWELL, Alfred (fl.1870-1901) British
Works on paper
£280 $515 €409 Cromer - a view from the outskirts of the town (27x37cm-11x15in) s. W/C. 23-Mar-4 Anderson & Garland, Newcastle #166/R
£340 $629 €496 View of Northbrook, Farnham, Surrey (33x50cm-13x20in) s. W/C pencil. 14-Jan-4 Lawrence, Crewkerne #1331

POWELL, Arthur J E (1864-1956) American
£988 $1600 €1433 River landscape in winter (30x41cm-12x16in) s. 8-Aug-3 Barridorf, Portland #325/R est:1200-1800

POWELL, C M (1775-1824) British
£2900 $4611 €4234 Dutch coastal scene with vessels in swell (27x37cm-11x15in) s.d.1824 panel. 10-Sep-3 Edgar Horn, Eastbourne #376/R est:4000-6000

POWELL, Charles Martin (1775-1824) British
£1600 $2864 €2336 Unloading the catch at the end of the day, with merchantmen at anchor (47x65cm-19x26in) s. panel. 26-May-4 Christie's, Kensington #609/R est:1500-2000
£2600 $4420 €3796 Frigate (45x61cm-18x24in) 19-Nov-3 Christie's, Kensington #466/R

POWELL, Charles Martin (attrib) (1775-1824) British
£1100 $1870 €1606 Blustery day off shore (46x64cm-18x25in) panel. 19-Nov-3 Christie's, Kensington #476/R

POWELL, John (fl.1769-1785) British
£449 $750 €656 Field of poppies (60x76cm-24x30in) s. i.verso. 19-Oct-3 Bonhams & Butterfields, Los Angeles #7058
Works on paper
£340 $578 €496 View of a country house (15x25cm-6x10in) s.d.1798 W/C. 25-Nov-3 Bonhams, Knightsbridge #74/R

POWELL, Joseph (1780-1834) British
Works on paper
£400 $688 €584 Crossing the ford (53x36cm-21x14in) s. pencil W/C. 3-Dec-3 Christie's, Kensington #140/R
£700 $1295 €1022 Landscape near Wareham Dorset (26x38cm-10x15in) s. W/C pencil. 14-Jan-4 Lawrence, Crewkerne #1330

POWELL, Joseph Rubens (fl.1835-1871) British
£1700 $3043 €2482 Girl with roses (74x53cm-29x21in) s. s.d.1854 verso. 26-May-4 AB Stockholms Auktionsverk #2399/R est:12000-15000 (S.KR 23000)

POWELL, Leonard Marlborough (fl.1883-1916) British
Works on paper
£310 $577 €453 Rolling hills (25x49cm-10x19in) s. i.verso W/C. 2-Mar-4 Bristol Auction Rooms #273/R

POWELL, Lucien Whiting (1846-1930) American
£350 $641 €511 The entrance to the Grand Canal (61x107cm-24x42in) s. 6-Jul-4 Hamptons Fine Art, Godalming #104
Works on paper
£495 $900 €723 The Citadel (51x69cm-20x27in) s. W/C prov. 7-Feb-4 Sloans & Kenyon, Bethesda #1252/R
£636 $1100 €929 Eagle Lake, Bar Harbour, Maine (36x53cm-14x21in) s. W/C. 13-Dec-3 Weschler, Washington #547
£1111 $2000 €1622 Middle Eastern street scene (60x48cm-24x19in) s. gouache prov. 24-Apr-4 Weschler, Washington #589/R est:1000-1500

POWELL, Moila (1895-1994) British
Works on paper
£1056 $1690 €1500 Howth harbour and lighthouse (33x44cm-13x17in) s. i.verso W/C prov. 16-Sep-3 Whyte's, Dublin #119/R est:1000-1500

POWELL, Sir Francis (1833-1914) British
Works on paper
£250 $463 €365 River scene with stone bridge (35x50cm-14x20in) s. W/C. 16-Jul-4 Charterhouse, Sherborne #614
£300 $501 €438 View of a lake and mountains with storm approaching, at Oban (53x29cm-21x11in) s.i. W/C. 7-Oct-3 Fellows & Sons, Birmingham #537/R
£920 $1454 €1334 Ailsa Craig (77x133cm-30x52in) s.d.1880 W/C exhib. 24-Jul-3 Dominic Winter, Swindon #59/R

POWELL, W (20th C) British?
Works on paper
£660 $1142 €964 Flying grouse (23x30cm-9x12in) s. sold with a companion. 9-Dec-3 Louis Taylor, Stoke on Trent #1210

POWELL, W E (19/20th C) British
Works on paper
£520 $900 €759 Study of a swooping bird of prey, the Montagu's Harrier (15x26cm-6x10in) s.d.26 W/C htd white. 10-Dec-3 Rupert Toovey, Partridge Green #99/R
£820 $1419 €1197 Study of a kingfisher perched on a tree trunk at edge of a river (22x10cm-9x4in) s. W/C gouache. 10-Dec-3 Rupert Toovey, Partridge Green #98/R

POWELL, William E (1878-1955) British
Works on paper
£250 $460 €365 Mallards landing by moonlight (22x28cm-9x11in) s. gouache. 10-Jun-4 Christie's, Kensington #277/R
£320 $573 €467 Pheasants in flight (35x25cm-14x10in) s. W/C. 25-May-4 Sworder & Son, Bishops Stortford #400/R
£346 $550 €505 Kiwis (25x20cm-10x8in) s. W/C. 23-Mar-3 Auctions by the Bay, Alameda #838/R
£409 $650 €597 Pelicans (20x25cm-8x10in) s. W/C. 23-Mar-3 Auctions by the Bay, Alameda #837/R
£447 $800 €653 Taking a stake in the country. Le soir (30x25cm-12x10in) s.i. W/C gouache over pencil two. 6-May-4 Doyle, New York #19/R
£479 $815 €700 Flying pheasants (42x52cm-17x20in) s. gouache prov. 5-Nov-3 Vendue Huis, Gravenhage #169/R
£726 $1300 €1060 Grouse drive. Over the top (28x38cm-11x15in) s. W/C gouache over pencil pair. 6-May-4 Doyle, New York #18/R est:2500-3500
£900 $1611 €1314 Statue in Kensington Gardens (34x24cm-13x9in) s.d.26 W/C. 25-May-4 Bonhams, Knightsbridge #81/R
£1000 $1820 €1460 Pelicans on a riverbank (18x23cm-7x9in) s. 5-Feb-4 Gorringes, Worthing #447/R est:1000-1500
£1000 $1820 €1460 Kiwis on a riverbank (23x18cm-9x7in) s. 5-Feb-4 Gorringes, Worthing #448/R est:1000-1500
£1100 $2057 €1606 Cock and hen pheasant amongst vegetation. Ducks in flight above marsh (22x28cm-9x11in) s. W/C gouache pair prov. 22-Jul-4 Tennants, Leyburn #687/R est:400-600

POWER, Harold Septimus (1878-1951) New Zealander
£389 $712 €584 In the park. board. 3-Jun-4 Joel, Victoria #165 (A.D 1000)
£785 $1452 €1146 Cattle drinking (29x49cm-11x19in) s. canvas on board. 10-Mar-4 Deutscher-Menzies, Melbourne #495/R est:2500-3500 (A.D 1900)
£810 $1304 €1183 Mitta valley (35x42cm-14x17in) s. canvas on board. 13-Oct-3 Joel, Victoria #372 est:1500-2000 (A.D 2000)
£813 $1455 €1187 Australian suburb (17x20cm-7x8in) s. 10-May-4 Joel, Victoria #304 est:2000-3000 (A.D 2000)
£2000 $3320 €2920 Harrowing, a team of two horses (21x36cm-8x14in) s. board. 2-Oct-3 Lane, Penzance #95/R est:2000-2500
£3390 $5763 €4949 Companions (82x57cm-32x22in) s. 24-Nov-3 Sotheby's, Melbourne #256/R est:8000-12000 (A.D 8000)
£3404 $5787 €4970 Shoeing the Horse (35x44cm-14x17in) s. canvas on board prov. 26-Nov-3 Deutscher-Menzies, Melbourne #173/R est:3000-5000 (A.D 8000)
£5106 $8681 €7455 The picnic (62x75cm-24x30in) s. 25-Nov-3 Christie's, Melbourne #205/R est:5000-7000 (A.D 12000)
£8000 $14720 €11680 Picnic (64x76cm-25x30in) s. 23-Mar-4 Bonhams, New Bond Street #116/R est:8000-12000
£8097 $13036 €11822 Debutante (123x98cm-48x39in) s. prov. 25-Aug-3 Sotheby's, Paddington #11/R est:15000-20000 (A.D 20000)
£19433 $31287 €28372 Coloured gown (100x72cm-39x28in) s. prov.exhib.lit. 25-Aug-3 Sotheby's, Paddington #3/R est:20000-30000 (A.D 48000)
Works on paper
£2034 $3458 €2970 Mending the plough (52x54cm-20x21in) s. W/C prov. 24-Nov-3 Sotheby's, Melbourne #197/R est:5000-7000 (A.D 4800)

POWER, James P (fl.1924-1938) British
£800 $1432 €1168 Cornish street (56x45cm-22x18in) s. 14-May-4 Christie's, Kensington #531/R

POWERS, Asahel (1813-1843) American
£2235 $4000 €3752 Folk portrait of a woman seated on a sofa wearing pearl necklace (66x58cm-26x23in) i.verso. 20-Mar-4 Pook & Pook, Downington #528 est:500-1000

POWERS, Hiram (1805-1873) American
Sculpture
£55233 $95000 €80640 Proserpine (51cm-20in) i. marble prov. 4-Dec-3 Christie's, Rockefeller NY #19/R
£58000 $106140 €84680 Proserpine (54cm-21in) s. white marble. 9-Jul-4 Sotheby's, London #103/R est:30000-50000
£59659 $105000 €87102 Proserpine (51cm-20in) s.i. marble exec c.1844-47 prov. 18-May-4 Christie's, Rockefeller NY #46/R est:60000-80000

POWERS, Marion (20th C) American
£344 $550 €502 Still life of grapes in a silver bowl with gourd shaped vessel (36x41cm-14x16in) s. 20-Sep-3 Jeffery Burchard, Florida #95/R

POWNALL, Leonard A (attrib) (fl.1897-1913) British
Works on paper
£480 $864 €701 Young woman in an interior with bread, pewter charges and coffee pot (23cm-9in circular) W/C prov. 20-Apr-4 Canterbury Auctions, UK #180
£680 $1224 €993 Wooden bridge over stream (25x36cm-10x14in) W/C prov. 20-Apr-4 Canterbury Auctions, UK #179

POY DALMAU, Emilio (1876-1933) Spanish
£533 $971 €800 Campesinos en taberna (22x29cm-9x11in) s. 29-Jun-4 Segre, Madrid #37/R
£604 $1081 €900 Donkeys (18x33cm-7x13in) s. board. 25-May-4 Durán, Madrid #680/R
£709 $1149 €1000 View of Segovia (59x24cm-23x9in) s. panel. 20-May-3 Ansorena, Madrid #27/R
£789 $1453 €1200 Procession (25x30cm-10x12in) s. board. 22-Jun-4 Durán, Madrid #110/R
£800 $1456 €1200 Virgin procession (24x28cm-9x11in) s. panel. 29-Jun-4 Segre, Madrid #36/R
£845 $1462 €1200 Crossing the bridge (40x30cm-16x12in) s. 15-Dec-3 Ansorena, Madrid #287/R
£987 $1816 €1500 Bull fight (25x30cm-10x12in) s. board. 22-Jun-4 Durán, Madrid #111/R est:1000
£1064 $1777 €1500 Young woman with fruit (38x56cm-15x22in) s. 20-Oct-3 Durán, Madrid #60/R
£1064 $1777 €1500 Spinners (50x66cm-20x26in) s. 20-Oct-3 Durán, Madrid #74/R
£1088 $1948 €1600 Bull fight (40x40cm-16x16in) s. 22-Mar-4 Durán, Madrid #124/R est:1300
£1200 $2220 €1752 Los rivales (101x90cm-40x35in) s.i.d.1922. 14-Jul-4 Sotheby's, Olympia #215/R est:1000-1500
£1510 $2673 €2250 Bullring, Chinchon (40x50cm-16x20in) s.d.33. 27-Apr-4 Durán, Madrid #85/R est:2000
£1510 $2673 €2250 Bull scene (40x54cm-16x21in) s. i.verso. 27-Apr-4 Durán, Madrid #84/R est:2000
£1630 $2674 €2250 Corrida de toros (40x40cm-16x16in) s. 27-May-3 Durán, Madrid #179/R est:2000
£1950 $3257 €2750 Fiesta de toros en Castilla (55x65cm-22x26in) s. i.verso. 23-Jun-3 Durán, Madrid #168/R est:2750

POYET, Bernard (1742-1824) French
Works on paper
£1189 $2045 €1700 Maison des filles du Duc de Chartres au couvent de Bellechasse a Paris (18x20cm-7x8in) s.i.d.1778 pen blk ink W/C htd white prov. 2-Dec-3 Christie's, Paris #515/R est:1500-2000

POYNTER, Sir Edward John (1836-1919) British
£850 $1343 €1233 Wooded landscape (10x18cm-4x7in) mono.d.1873 panel prov. 4-Sep-3 Christie's, Kensington #149/R
£1200 $2040 €1752 Orpheus with his lute (51x41cm-20x16in) mono.d.16. 20-Nov-3 Gorringes, Worthing #739/R est:1500-2000
£1897 $3396 €2770 Cave at Tintagel - Study for Cave of the Storm Nymphs (24x34cm-9x13in) mono.d.1900 prov. 15-May-4 Christie's, Sydney #151/R est:2000-3000 (A.D 4800)
£33000 $60720 €48180 Day dream (51x56cm-20x22in) mono. prov.exhib. 23-Mar-4 Bonhams, New Bond Street #74/R est:25000-35000
Works on paper
£2023 $3500 €2954 Revenge (30x22cm-12x9in) mono.d.1861 chl gouache. 11-Dec-3 Sotheby's, New York #66/R est:2500-3500
£5500 $9350 €8030 Design for the Guardian Fire and Life Assurance Company (61x40cm-24x16in) mono.i.d.1886 pencil W/C htd bodycol. 20-Nov-3 Christie's, London #150/R est:3000-5000
£13295 $23000 €19411 Water carriers of the Nile (32x24cm-13x9in) mono.d.1862 s.i.verso pencil gouache paper on board prov. 11-Dec-3 Sotheby's, New York #89/R est:10000-15000
£22000 $37400 €32120 Vestal, Portrait of Miss Violet Lindsay (46x29cm-18x11in) mono.d.1880 W/C prov.exhib. 27-Nov-3 Sotheby's, London #28/R est:10000-15000

POZZATI, Concetto (1935-) Italian
£528 $877 €750 Imagery (25x30cm-10x12in) s.d.01 verso acrylic enamel. 13-Jun-3 Farsetti, Prato #212
£600 $1086 €900 Untitled (25x35cm-10x14in) s.d.92. 2-Apr-4 Farsetti, Prato #232
£933 $1717 €1400 Little urban monument (30x30cm-12x12in) s.d.63 cardboard on canvas. 8-Jun-4 Finarte Semenzato, Milan #222/R est:1000-1200
£986 $1637 €1400 Impossible paesaggio quasi dal vero (25x30cm-10x12in) s.i.d.1995 verso oil acrylic. 14-Jun-3 Meeting Art, Vercelli #51/R
£1284 $2259 €1900 Oval guard (40x50cm-16x20in) s.i.d.1999 verso. 22-May-4 Galleria Pananti, Florence #376/R est:2000-3000
£1467 $2699 €2200 Impossible landscape (70x80cm-28x31in) s.d.90 verso acrylic enamel. 11-Jun-4 Farsetti, Prato #286/R est:2100-2400
£1477 $2643 €2200 What stage are we with flowers ? (50x60cm-20x24in) s.d.88 verso. 28-May-4 Farsetti, Prato #106/R est:1600-1900
£1538 $2615 €2200 Composition (65x75cm-26x30in) s.d.1972 verso. 20-Nov-3 Finarte Semenzato, Milan #18/R est:2200-2400
£1586 $2649 €2300 Guard (50x60cm-20x24in) s.d.199 acrylic enamel. 13-Nov-3 Galleria Pace, Milan #55/R est:4200
£1594 $2614 €2200 Orange guard (50x60cm-20x24in) s.i.d.1999 verso acrylic enamel. 29-May-3 Galleria Pace, Milan #67/R est:3100
£1667 $2983 €2500 Da e per Goya (65x75cm-26x30in) s.i.d.64 verso prov. 15-May-4 Van Ham, Cologne #853/R est:1500
£2609 $4278 €3600 One of Leger's leaves landed on my roof (100x120cm-39x47in) s.d.71 verso exhib.lit. 30-May-3 Farsetti, Prato #53
£2609 $4278 €3600 Three plus one (80x100cm-31x39in) s.i.d. 68 verso acrylic mirrors. 30-May-3 Farsetti, Prato #222/R
£2857 $5114 €4200 Still life (80x60cm-31x24in) s.d.73 verso oil mixed media. 16-Mar-4 Finarte Semenzato, Milan #375/R est:4200
£3067 $5643 €4600 Is the rose pink ? (100x120cm-39x47in) s.d.70 i.verso. 8-Jun-4 Finarte Semenzato, Milan #223/R est:1800-2000
Works on paper
£1081 $1903 €1600 Advertisement (24x35cm-9x14in) s.i.d.2003 mixed media card. 22-May-4 Galleria Pananti, Florence #347/R est:1800
£1141 $2111 €1700 Still life (57x76cm-22x30in) s.d.1987 mixed media card. 11-Mar-4 Galleria Pace, Milan #135/R est:1850-2400
£1389 $2194 €2000 Puppet show (40x50cm-16x20in) mixed media board exec.2003. 6-Sep-3 Meeting Art, Vercelli #321 est:1500
£1736 $2899 €2500 A che punto siamo con i fiori (102x152cm-40x60in) s.d.1988 W/C acrylic prov. 25-Oct-3 Cornette de St.Cyr, Paris #448 est:2500-3000
£1973 $3531 €2900 Untitled (80x100cm-31x39in) s.d.68 mixed media on canvas. 16-Mar-4 Finarte Semenzato, Milan #219/R est:1800

POZZATO, Paride (1899-1971) Italian
£532 $888 €750 Family in interior (21x39cm-8x15in) s.d.1923 i.verso board. 14-Oct-3 Finarte Semenzato, Milan #14/R
£734 $1263 €1050 Market square (18x24cm-7x9in) s. cardboard. 3-Dec-3 Stadion, Trieste #1056/R

POZZI, Donnino (1894-1946) Italian
£780 $1303 €1100 Still life with birds (46x46cm-18x18in) s. board. 17-Jun-3 Finarte Semenzato, Milan #362

POZZI, Francesco (1779-1844) Italian
Sculpture
£30000 $51000 €43800 Cyparissus (117cm-46in) s.d.1822 marble prov.exhib. 28-Oct-3 Sotheby's, London #86/R est:30000-50000

POZZI, Lucio (1936-) Italian
£556 $1000 €812 Double mirror level (11x8cm-4x3in) s.i.d.1989 canvas on wood two panels. 24-Apr-4 David Rago, Lambertville #151/R

POZZI, Stefano (1707-1768) Italian
Works on paper
£1224 $2192 €1800 Deux anges assis sur une corniche, regardant vers le bas (22x34cm-9x13in) black white chk. 18-Mar-4 Christie's, Paris #235/R est:700-1000

POZZO, Andrea (18th C) Spanish
£3315 $6000 €4840 Presentation of the Virgin at the temple (302x180cm-119x71in) prov. 3-Apr-4 Neal Auction Company, New Orleans #885/R est:10000-15000

POZZO, Andrea (attrib) (18th C) Spanish
£10067 $18523 €15000 Madonna appearing to St Ignatius of Loyola (215x169cm-85x67in) 24-Mar-4 Dorotheum, Vienna #50/R est:15000-20000

POZZO, Andrea (circle) (18th C) Spanish
£16197 $28345 €23000 Tribute (138x221cm-54x87in) 17-Dec-3 Christie's, Rome #499/R est:15000-20000

POZZO, Ugo (1900-1981) Italian
£387 $643 €550 Cavallino (24x27cm-9x11in) s. panel. 14-Jun-3 Meeting Art, Vercelli #406
£1611 $2980 €2400 Painting (61x50cm-24x20in) s. tempera card. 13-Mar-4 Meeting Art, Vercelli #368 est:1000

PRAAG, Arnold van (1926-) British
£350 $560 €511 Portrait of Lautrec (91x122cm-36x48in) s.i.verso board prov. 16-Sep-3 Bonhams, Knightsbridge #59

PRABHA, B (20th C) Indian
£4623 $8321 €6750 Fisherwoman (78x62cm-31x24in) s.d. 25-Apr-4 Christie's, Hong Kong #614/R est:45000-55000 (HK.D 65000)
£5435 $10000 €7935 Fisherwoman (76x66cm-30x26in) s.d.1977. 24-Mar-4 Sotheby's, New York #182/R est:4000-6000
£5978 $11000 €8728 Trees (96x86cm-38x34in) s.d.1960. 25-Mar-4 Christie's, Rockefeller NY #238/R est:6000-8000

PRACHENSKY, Markus (1932-) Austrian
£3147 $5350 €4500 Los Angeles-red (101x76cm-40x30in) cardboard. 1-Dec-3 Amberes, Antwerp #335
£8054 $14416 €12000 Red - violet - Jalisco - V (110x100cm-43x39in) s.i.d.1973 stretcher acrylic prov. 25-May-4 Dorotheum, Vienna #362/R est:13000-17000
£9396 $16631 €14000 Bali trumpet (131x165cm-52x65in) s.d. s.i.d. verso acrylic. 28-Apr-4 Wiener Kunst Auktionen, Vienna #297/R est:12000-22000
£9732 $17225 €14500 Untitled (102x130cm-40x51in) s.d. s.d. verso acrylic. 28-Apr-4 Wiener Kunst Auktionen, Vienna #273/R est:10000-18000

£10490	$17832	€15000	Puglia Marina-XIV-1978 (75x96cm-30x38in) s.d.78 s.i.d. verso acrylic canvas on panel prov. 26-Nov-3 Dorotheum, Vienna #80/R est:12000-15000
£10738	$19007	€16000	Untitled (130x165cm-51x65in) s.d. s.d. verso. 28-Apr-4 Wiener Kunst Auktionen, Vienna #304/R est:15000-25000
£12500	$21250	€18000	Maremma (130x165cm-51x65in) s.d.1985 exhib.lit. 28-Oct-3 Wiener Kunst Auktionen, Vienna #243/R est:18000-25000
£16783	$28531	€24000	Red on white Pulia II-1976 (150x120cm-59x47in) s.d.76 s.i.d. verso acrylic prov. 26-Nov-3 Dorotheum, Vienna #82/R est:16000-22000
£30201	$54060	€45000	Rouge sur gris - Aschaffenburg II (162x130cm-64x51in) s. s.d. verso s.i.d.1961 stretcher exhib. 25-May-4 Dorotheum, Vienna #257/R est:16000-22000
Works on paper			
£2222	$3622	€3200	Oliena (76x56cm-30x22in) s.d.91 s.i.d.91 verso ink. 23-Sep-3 Wiener Kunst Auktionen, Vienna #158/R est:2500-3500
£2517	$4280	€3600	Untitled (48x65cm-19x26in) s. Indian ink. 26-Nov-3 Dorotheum, Vienna #215/R est:4000-6000
£2550	$4514	€3800	Untitled (55x78cm-22x31in) s.d. mixed media. 28-Apr-4 Wiener Kunst Auktionen, Vienna #246/R est:3800-6000
£3147	$5350	€4500	Etruria (76x57cm-30x22in) s.d.1980 s.i.d.1980 gouache. 28-Nov-3 Wiener Kunst Auktionen, Vienna #613/R est:3800-5000
£5034	$8909	€7500	Etruria meridionale (75x56cm-30x22in) s.d. col Indian ink. 28-Apr-4 Wiener Kunst Auktionen, Vienna #295/R est:3500-6500
£5369	$9503	€8000	Rechberg (100x65cm-39x26in) s.d. mixed media board. 28-Apr-4 Wiener Kunst Auktionen, Vienna #240/R est:4500-8000

PRACHENSKY, Wilhelm Nikolaus (1898-1956) Austrian

£7383	$13067	€11000	Rattenberg (60x88cm-24x35in) s.d.1929 tempera board lit. 28-Apr-4 Wiener Kunst Auktionen, Vienna #81/R est:9000-16000
£9028	$15347	€13000	Autumn (25x25cm-10x10in) board lit. 28-Oct-3 Wiener Kunst Auktionen, Vienna #85/R est:10000-17000
£13889	$23611	€20000	Arlberg church (91x63cm-36x25in) s. board. 28-Oct-3 Wiener Kunst Auktionen, Vienna #87/R est:12000-25000
Works on paper			
£2517	$4280	€3600	Tyrolean landscape (20x28cm-8x11in) s.d.54 W/C. 26-Nov-3 Dorotheum, Vienna #185/R est:3200-4000
£3125	$5313	€4500	Durnstein (47x65cm-19x26in) s.i.d.29. Mai 1928 mixed media. 28-Oct-3 Wiener Kunst Auktionen, Vienna #86/R est:4500-9000

PRADA, Carlo (1884-1960) Italian

£671	$1201	€1000	Saint Martino (60x79cm-24x31in) s. board. 25-May-4 Finarte Semenzato, Milan #14/R
£1761	$2923	€2500	Riflessi sul lago (56x74cm-22x29in) s.d.1922 panel. 14-Jun-3 Meeting Art, Vercelli #150/R est:2500

PRADES, Alfred F de (fl.1844-1883) British

£1800	$3006	€2628	Huntsman adjusting saddle (44x59cm-17x23in) s.d.1885. 16-Oct-3 Lawrence, Crewkerne #705
£4261	$7500	€6221	Flat race between classic warriors (58x96cm-23x38in) 18-May-4 Sotheby's, New York #209/R est:5000-7000
Works on paper			
£500	$835	€730	Cavalry parade (34x44cm-13x17in) s. W/C. 14-Oct-3 Bonhams, Knightsbridge #192/R

PRADIER, Jean Jacques (1792-1852) French/Swiss

Sculpture			
£1000	$1810	€1500	Sapho (28cm-11in) i. Cast.Susse Fres. 1-Apr-4 Van Ham, Cologne #1138/R est:1000
£1192	$2181	€1800	Phryne (48cm-19in) s.i. silver black pat gilt base i.f.Susse. 6-Apr-4 Sotheby's, Olympia #119/R est:2000-3000
£1310	$2188	€1900	La toilette d'Atalante (25x14x19cm-10x6x7in) s.st.f.Susse brown pat bronze. 9-Jul-3 Peschetau-Badin Godeau & Leroy, Paris #12 est:2200-2500
£1400	$2548	€2100	Cleopatre (65cm-26in) bears sig. brown pat bronze incl marble base. 29-Jun-4 Gioffredo, Nice #81/R
£1620	$2900	€2365	Standing sappho (46cm-18in) s.d.1848 brown pat bronze pedestal. 20-Mar-4 Freeman, Philadelphia #894/R est:1500-2500
£1631	$2724	€2300	Sapho (45cm-18in) s.d.1848 red brown pat bronze. 12-Oct-3 St-Germain-en-Laye Encheres #50/R est:2200-2500
£1724	$2862	€2500	Buste de Joseph Balthazar (54cm-21in) s.d.1830 white marble prov. 2-Oct-3 Sotheby's, Paris #24/R
£1918	$3260	€2800	Atalante (23cm-9in) s.st.f.Susse pat bronze lit. 6-Nov-3 Sotheby's, Paris #144/R est:3000-5000
£2207	$3663	€3200	Medaillon (25x25cm-10x10in) s. i.verso bronze. 2-Oct-3 Sotheby's, Paris #25/R
£3077	$5292	€4400	Buste de Madame du Barry (75x73x52cm-30x29x20in) s. white marble. 8-Dec-3 Horta, Bruxelles #63 est:3000-4000
£3191	$5330	€4500	Sapho (45cm-18in) d.1848 pat bronze. 17-Jun-3 Christie's, Paris #108/R est:4000-6000
£3846	$6615	€5500	Seated woman. s. brown green pat bronze Cast f.Susse Fres. 2-Dec-3 Christie's, Paris #529/R est:1500-2500
£4483	$7441	€6500	Negresse aux calebasses (44cm-17in) s. brown pat bronze lit. 2-Oct-3 Sotheby's, Paris #30/R est:6000
£13000	$22100	€18980	Standing Sappho (45cm-18in) s.st.f.Paillard d.1848 pat bronze prov.lit. 28-Oct-3 Sotheby's, London #178/R

PRADIER, Raoul (1929-) French

£375	$683	€548	Abstract, lady, tress and cottage (64x81cm-25x32in) s.d.58. 4-Feb-4 John Nicholson, Haslemere #71

PRADILLA Y ORTIZ, Francisco (1848-1921) Spanish

£1418	$2369	€2000	Street in Granada (19x11cm-7x4in) s. board. 20-Oct-3 Durán, Madrid #72/R
£2931	$4895	€4250	Head of boy (37x30cm-15x12in) s. 17-Nov-3 Durán, Madrid #152/R est:3500
£3793	$6828	€5500	Landscape (19x28cm-7x11in) s.d.1869. 26-Jan-4 Ansorena, Madrid #194/R est:5500
£3901	$6514	€5500	Source (27x17cm-11x7in) board. 20-Oct-3 Durán, Madrid #175/R
£4138	$7448	€6000	Landscapes (21x12cm-8x5in) board pair. 26-Jan-4 Ansorena, Madrid #190/R est:5000
£4348	$8000	€6348	Naples Bay (22x40cm-9x16in) s.i. board. 22-Jun-4 Galeria y Remates, Montevideo #28/R est:7000-10000
£4698	$8409	€7000	Mass under heavenly skies (17x27cm-7x11in) s.i.d.1892 panel. 27-May-4 Dorotheum, Vienna #79/R est:4000-5000
£5556	$9056	€8000	Figure (46x33cm-18x13in) s. 23-Sep-3 Durán, Madrid #122/R est:5500
£6463	$10276	€9500	Jeanne la Folle (27x17cm-11x7in) s. panel. 23-Mar-3 Salle des ventes Pillet, Lyon la Foret #9 est:3000
£17000	$28900	€24820	Washerwomen (19x28cm-7x11in) s.d.73 panel. 18-Nov-3 Sotheby's, London #262/R
£19388	$30827	€28500	Souvenir of a Roman carnival (33x22cm-13x9in) s. i.d.1883 verso panel. 23-Mar-3 Salle des ventes Pillet, Lyon la Foret #8 est:5000
Works on paper			
£436	$772	€650	Abruzzo, Italy (23x15cm-9x6in) s. chl dr. 27-Apr-4 Durán, Madrid #681/R
£552	$993	€800	Praying (21x22cm-8x9in) s.d.1873 wash. 26-Jan-4 Durán, Madrid #29/R
£950	$1729	€1425	A moment of contemplation (34x18cm-13x7in) s. W/C gum arabic. 1-Jul-4 Christie's, Kensington #419/R
£1897	$3167	€2750	Italian woman with basket (30x21cm-12x8in) s. W/C. 17-Nov-3 Durán, Madrid #114/R est:2300
£2098	$3503	€3000	Street market in Zaragoza (32x22cm-13x9in) i.verso wash. 30-Jun-3 Ansorena, Madrid #434/R

PRADILLA, F (?) ?

Works on paper			
£900	$1503	€1314	Portrait of a lady standing by a chair in an interior (34x18cm-13x7in) s. W/C. 26-Jun-3 Greenslade Hunt, Taunton #484/R

PRADILLA, Francisco (1840-1921) Spanish

£461	$770	€650	Pueblo de la Sierra de la Demanda, Burgos (24x30cm-9x12in) s. panel. 23-Jun-3 Durán, Madrid #115/R

PRADILLA, Miguel (?) Spanish

£379	$633	€550	Pancorbo, Burgos (24x30cm-9x12in) s. board. 17-Nov-3 Durán, Madrid #46/R
£709	$1184	€1000	Procession in Villanueva del Camino (30x40cm-12x16in) s. 20-Oct-3 Durán, Madrid #44/R

PRAED, Michael J (1941-) British

£550	$1001	€803	Newlyn Harbour (61x76cm-24x30in) s. board. 15-Jun-4 David Lay, Penzance #239
£580	$1073	€847	Low water pools (28x46cm-11x18in) s. i.d.1975 verso. 10-Feb-4 David Lay, Penzance #269
Works on paper			
£250	$455	€365	Sails eclipse blue (56x36cm-22x14in) s. i.verso mixed media. 15-Jun-4 David Lay, Penzance #172

PRAGUE SCHOOL (16th C) Czechoslovakian

£9210	$16947	€14000	Crucifixion (54x45cm-21x18in) panel. 24-Jun-4 Tajan, Paris #9/R est:15000-20000
Works on paper			
£8904	$15137	€13000	Crouching male figure (28x19cm-11x7in) i.d.Juny 1596 pen brown grey ink. 4-Nov-3 Sotheby's, Amsterdam #1/R est:2500-3500

PRAGUE SCHOOL (17th C) Czechoslovakian

£7237	$13316	€11000	Allegory of Victory (71x49cm-28x19in) indis.sig. panel. 24-Jun-4 Tajan, Paris #8/R est:10000-15000
£19000	$32870	€27740	Belshazzar's Feast (87x165cm-34x65in) panel. 11-Dec-3 Sotheby's, London #121/R est:8000-12000

PRAMPOLINI, Enrico (1894-1956) Italian

£1933	$3557	€2900	Seven sins: gluttony (25x35cm-10x14in) i. tempera card painted 1955 exhib.lit. 12-Jun-4 Meeting Art, Vercelli #738/R est:2500
£2013	$3604	€3000	Study for wall decoration (23x37cm-9x15in) s. tempera board painted 1940 prov. 25-May-4 Sotheby's, Milan #9/R est:4000
£5072	$8319	€7000	Composition (21x24cm-8x9in) s. board prov. 27-May-3 Sotheby's, Milan #171/R est:7000-9000
£6250	$9875	€9000	Composition (21x24cm-8x9in) board painted 1953. 6-Sep-3 Meeting Art, Vercelli #579 est:8000
£14493	$23768	€20000	Composition (161x113cm-63x44in) s.d.51. 27-May-3 Sotheby's, Milan #272/R est:20000-30000
£19580	$33287	€28000	Sea captain II (64x50cm-25x20in) s. board painted 1947 lit. 29-Nov-3 Farsetti, Prato #543/R est:12000
£26573	$45175	€38000	Colourful architecture in Capri (41x33cm-16x13in) s. i.verso canvas on cardboard. 25-Nov-3 Sotheby's, Milan #175/R est:25000-30000
Works on paper			
£839	$1401	€1200	Standing figure (38x31cm-15x12in) s.d.1916 W/C pencil fabric on paper. 10-Oct-3 Winterberg, Heidelberg #1855/R
£1818	$3036	€2600	Dancer (29x24cm-11x9in) s. W/C pencil. 10-Oct-3 Winterberg, Heidelberg #1856/R est:1500

PRAMPOLINI, Hiero (1913-1973) Italian

£1361	$2435	€2000	Untitled (65x50cm-26x20in) s.d.57. 16-Mar-4 Finarte Semenzato, Milan #220/R est:500-600

PRANGENBERG, Norbert (1949-) British?

£667	$1193	€1000	Untitled (110x85cm-43x33in) s.i.d.1990-97 verso hessian. 15-May-4 Van Ham, Cologne #855
£667	$1193	€1000	Composition (110x90cm-43x35in) s.i.d.1992 verso. 15-May-4 Van Ham, Cologne #854/R

PRANTL, Karl (1923-) Austrian
Sculpture

£1608	$2734	€2300	Meditation stone (11x32x17cm-4x13x7in) marble prov. 27-Nov-3 Lempertz, Koln #361/R est:2500
£38194	$64931	€55000	Meditation stone (182x22x15cm-72x9x6in) amazonite. 28-Oct-3 Wiener Kunst Auktionen, Vienna #248/R est:55000-90000

PRASAD, Jaggu (1963-) Indian
Works on paper

£189	$350	€284	Peacocks on branches (51x38cm-20x15in) gouache W/C. 17-Jul-4 Skinner, Boston #693/R
£189	$350	€284	Family of peacocks (51x38cm-20x15in) gouache W/C. 17-Jul-4 Skinner, Boston #742/R

PRASCHL, Stefan (1910-1994) Austrian

£922	$1540	€1300	Tiger (40x65cm-16x26in) s. masonite. 14-Oct-3 Dorotheum, Vienna #159/R

Works on paper

£658	$1211	€1000	Venice (44x62cm-17x24in) s. mixed media. 22-Jun-4 Wiener Kunst Auktionen, Vienna #165/R
£658	$1211	€1000	Venice (42x59cm-17x23in) s. mixed media. 22-Jun-4 Wiener Kunst Auktionen, Vienna #169/R
£658	$1211	€1000	Landscape (50x65cm-20x26in) s. mixed media. 22-Jun-4 Wiener Kunst Auktionen, Vienna #170/R
£724	$1332	€1100	Landscape (44x62cm-17x24in) s. mixed media. 22-Jun-4 Wiener Kunst Auktionen, Vienna #162/R
£724	$1332	€1100	Landscape (44x62cm-17x24in) s. mixed media. 22-Jun-4 Wiener Kunst Auktionen, Vienna #164/R
£724	$1332	€1100	Venice (42x60cm-17x24in) s.d.1970 mixed media. 22-Jun-4 Wiener Kunst Auktionen, Vienna #166/R
£724	$1332	€1100	Landscape (44x62cm-17x24in) s. mixed media. 22-Jun-4 Wiener Kunst Auktionen, Vienna #171/R
£789	$1453	€1200	Venice (44x62cm-17x24in) s. mixed media. 22-Jun-4 Wiener Kunst Auktionen, Vienna #161/R
£789	$1453	€1200	Landscape (53x65cm-21x26in) s. mixed media. 22-Jun-4 Wiener Kunst Auktionen, Vienna #163/R
£789	$1453	€1200	Rome (41x56cm-16x22in) s. mixed media. 22-Jun-4 Wiener Kunst Auktionen, Vienna #157/R
£789	$1453	€1200	Landscape (44x62cm-17x24in) s. mixed media. 22-Jun-4 Wiener Kunst Auktionen, Vienna #160/R
£839	$1427	€1200	Landscape (51x70cm-20x28in) s. 28-Nov-3 Wiener Kunst Auktionen, Vienna #519/R
£909	$1545	€1300	Landscape with moon (55x70cm-22x28in) s.d.1975 mixed media. 28-Nov-3 Wiener Kunst Auktionen, Vienna #522/R
£979	$1664	€1400	Flowers (62x44cm-24x17in) s. mixed media. 28-Nov-3 Wiener Kunst Auktionen, Vienna #520/R
£979	$1664	€1400	Flowers (62x44cm-24x17in) s. 28-Nov-3 Wiener Kunst Auktionen, Vienna #521/R

PRASSINOS, Mario (1916-1985) Turkish

£1156	$2070	€1700	Composition (55x50cm-22x20in) s. oil paper painted c.1947. 19-Mar-4 Ribeyre & Baron, Paris #95 est:1200-1800
£1338	$2315	€1900	Sans titre (108x74cm-43x29in) s.d.28 aout 58 oil paper. 14-Dec-3 Versailles Encheres #77/R est:2000-2500
£1409	$2622	€2100	Bessy (41x32cm-16x13in) s. s.i.d.Nov 61 verso. 3-Mar-4 Artcurial Briest, Paris #511 est:1200-1500
£1554	$2782	€2300	Untitled (46x38cm-18x15in) s.i.d.74 verso. 4-May-4 Calmels Cohen, Paris #235/R est:1500-2000
£2676	$4630	€3800	Vue d'Eygaliere (73x92cm-29x36in) s.d. s.i.d.juin 62 verso. 14-Dec-3 Versailles Encheres #102/R est:4000-4500
£3400	$6086	€4964	Abstract composition (50x65cm-20x26in) s.d.Dec.55 card on canvas. 11-May-4 Bonhams, New Bond Street #104/R est:3000-4000
£5400	$9450	€7884	Untitled (66x50cm-26x20in) s.d.14 dec 55 card on canvas. 16-Dec-3 Bonhams, New Bond Street #137/R est:3000-4000
£5800	$10382	€8468	Trees in a landscape (80x121cm-31x48in) s.d.Dec 1983 paper on canvas. 10-May-4 Sotheby's, Olympia #77/R est:4000-6000

Works on paper

£833	$1500	€1250	Amour (35x25cm-14x10in) s.d.1945 graphite dr prov. 25-Apr-4 Versailles Encheres #17
£1049	$1804	€1500	Couple 7 (34x29cm-13x11in) bears studio st. ink exec.c.1946. 6-Dec-3 Renaud, Paris #267
£1088	$1948	€1600	Composition (55x50cm-22x20in) s.d.47 mixed media paper on canvas. 19-Mar-4 Ribeyre & Baron, Paris #98 est:1200-1800
£2000	$3580	€2920	Untitled (108x74cm-43x29in) s.d.26 Aout 58 ink. 10-May-4 Sotheby's, Olympia #78/R est:2000-3000
£3147	$5413	€4500	La femme instrumentale (30x24cm-12x9in) s. ink W/C exec.c.1935. 6-Dec-3 Renaud, Paris #265
£3200	$5728	€4672	Untitled (50x50cm-20x20in) s.d.62 gouache pastel pencil paper on canvas. 11-May-4 Bonhams, New Bond Street #110/R est:2500-3500

PRATELLA, A (19/20th C) Italian

£1750	$2870	€2555	Rural scene with figures (23x33cm-9x13in) s. board. 6-Jun-3 Biddle & Webb, Birmingham #196
£3179	$5785	€4800	Une place a Paris (45x90cm-18x35in) s. 18-Jun-4 Piasa, Paris #65/R est:1500-2000

PRATELLA, Ada (1901-1929) Italian

£1056	$1827	€1500	Green dress (45x40cm-18x16in) s. cardboard double-sided. 11-Dec-3 Christie's, Rome #95/R est:2000-3000

PRATELLA, Attilio (1856-1949) Italian

£1549	$2680	€2200	Lady on the sofa (50x36cm-20x14in) s. 11-Dec-3 Christie's, Rome #56
£1745	$3123	€2600	Landscape in Capri (28x31cm-11x12in) s. board. 25-May-4 Finarte Semenzato, Milan #114/R est:2500-3000
£3500	$6440	€5110	Carnevale (25x16cm-10x6in) s. panel. 25-Mar-4 Christie's, Kensington #140/R est:3000-5000
£4930	$8183	€7000	Boats and fishermen at Napoli (23x35cm-9x14in) s. panel. 11-Jun-3 Christie's, Rome #243/R est:6000-8000
£5500	$9460	€8030	Neapolitan fishermen (22x35cm-9x14in) s. panel. 4-Dec-3 Christie's, Kensington #57/R est:5000-7000
£5634	$9746	€8000	Choppy sea (18x49cm-7x19in) board. 11-Dec-3 Christie's, Rome #162/R est:7000-9000
£6000	$10860	€9000	Strolling in the countryside (22x35cm-9x14in) s. board. 30-Mar-4 Babuino, Rome #398/R est:5000
£6000	$10860	€9000	Fishermen near Capri (23x35cm-9x14in) s. board. 30-Mar-4 Babuino, Rome #399/R est:6000
£6333	$11653	€9500	Sailing boats (36x39cm-14x15in) s. tempera paper. 8-Jun-4 Sotheby's, Milan #4/R est:7000-10000
£7237	$13316	€11000	Fishermen in Naples Bay (22x37cm-9x15in) s. board. 23-Jun-4 Finarte Semenzato, Rome #57/R est:10000-12000
£10870	$17826	€15000	Public gardens in Naples (27x36cm-11x14in) s. board. 27-May-3 Finarte Semenzato, Milan #27/R est:12000-13000
£10962	$18964	€16005	Napolatean spring with the Vesuv in the background (22x35cm-9x14in) s. panel. 12-Dec-3 Kieselbach, Budapest #31/R (H.F 4200000)
£11765	$20000	€17177	Figures on a promenade with the Bay of Naples and Vesuvius beyond (23x41cm-9x16in) s. panel. 19-Nov-3 Bonhams & Butterfields, San Francisco #51/R
£14500	$23635	€21170	Neapolitan waterfront scene with numerous boats, fisherman and crowd (28x51cm-11x20in) s. 27-Sep-3 Rogers Jones, Clwyd #121/R
£15493	$26803	€22000	Fishermen (35x26cm-14x10in) s. 10-Dec-3 Sotheby's, Milan #16/R est:15000-25000
£16197	$28021	€23000	Mums at the park (22x35cm-9x14in) s. board. 9-Dec-3 Finarte Semenzato, Milan #68/R est:10000-12000
£17931	$29766	€26000	Fishermen in Naples Bay (30x45cm-12x18in) s. board. 1-Oct-3 Della Rocca, Turin #320/R est:26000-30000
£25352	$43859	€36000	Foria Street in Naples (40x60cm-16x24in) s. 10-Dec-3 Sotheby's, Milan #31/R est:20000-30000

Works on paper

£704	$1218	€1000	Around Naples (23x26cm-9x10in) s. mixed media. 11-Dec-3 Christie's, Rome #40/R
£1733	$3189	€2600	Figure in landscape (19x22cm-7x9in) s. W/C card. 10-Jun-4 Christie's, Rome #53/R est:1300-1800
£6250	$10625	€9000	Via Foria, Naples (27x45cm-11x18in) s. mixed media cardboard. 1-Nov-3 Meeting Art, Vercelli #106/R est:8000

PRATELLA, Attilio (attrib) (1856-1949) Italian

£704	$1218	€1000	View of Naples under the snow (17x17cm-7x7in) bears sig. panel. 11-Dec-3 Christie's, Rome #19/R
£733	$1313	€1100	Landscape (6x12cm-2x5in) s. board. 12-May-4 Stadion, Trieste #796

Works on paper

£2014	$3304	€2800	Seascape with fishermen (43x26cm-17x10in) gouache. 10-Jun-3 Pandolfini, Florence #155/R

PRATELLA, Fausto (1888-1964) Italian

£220	$400	€321	Gollo di Parrooli-Napoli (15x20cm-6x8in) s. s.i.d.19 3 verso wood panel. 7-Feb-4 Neal Auction Company, New Orleans #90
£749	$1273	€1094	Via Caracciolo di notte (19x30cm-7x12in) s. i. verso panel. 5-Nov-3 Dobiaschofsky, Bern #874/R (S.FR 1700)
£873	$1590	€1275	Fishing boats with Naples in the background (16x18cm-6x7in) s. panel. 16-Jun-4 Fischer, Luzern #2314/R (S.FR 2000)
£942	$1545	€1300	Seascape with boats (24x30cm-9x12in) s. board. 27-May-3 Il Ponte, Milan #906
£1159	$1901	€1600	Seascape with boats (24x30cm-9x12in) s. board. 27-May-3 Il Ponte, Milan #907
£1449	$2377	€2000	Sailing boats at harbour (18x24cm-7x9in) s. board. 27-May-3 Finarte Semenzato, Milan #12/R
£3235	$6016	€4723	Piccola marina, Naples (41x60cm-16x24in) s. exhib. 2-Mar-4 Rasmussen, Copenhagen #1419/R est:8000-10000 (D.KR 36000)

PRATELLA, Fausto (attrib) (1888-1964) Italian

£667	$1227	€1000	Boats and fishermen (30x40cm-12x16in) bears sig. 10-Jun-4 Christie's, Rome #46

PRATELLA, Ugo (?) Italian

£1223	$2006	€1700	View of Naples Bay (59x78cm-23x31in) 5-Jun-3 Adma, Formigine #797 est:1800-1900

PRATERE, Jules de (1879-1947) Belgian

£543	$923	€793	Three smoked herring on plate (50x60cm-20x24in) s. 19-Nov-3 Fischer, Luzern #2247/R (S.FR 1200)

PRATI, Giulio Cesare (1860-1918) Italian

£522	$955	€762	The conversation (40x49cm-16x19in) s.d.1885. 4-Jun-4 Zofingen, Switzerland #2505 (S.FR 1200)

PRATT, Christopher (1935-) Canadian

£6911	$12370	€10090	Portrait of a young woman (40x40cm-16x16in) s.d.1983 s.i.d.verso acrylic board prov.lit. 27-May-4 Heffel, Vancouver #77/R est:20000-25000 (C.D 17000)

Works on paper

£2000	$3660	€2920	Two hunters, my father and Tom Phippard hunting sea ducks (18x31cm-7x12in) s.d.1993 mixed media prov. 1-Jun-4 Hodgins, Calgary #108/R est:6000-8000 (C.D 5000)
£3049	$5457	€4452	Nude, girl sitting (36x36cm-14x14in) s.d.1980 i.verso pencil prov. 6-May-4 Heffel, Vancouver #114a/R est:8000-9000 (C.D 7500)

PRATT, Claude (1860-c.1935) British
Works on paper

£340	$609	€496	Study of a lady reading a letter by a cottage window (33x25cm-13x10in) s.d.1909 W/C pencil. 5-May-4 Goldings, Lincolnshire #506
£400	$688	€584	Portrait of an Edwardian gentleman (38x23cm-15x9in) s.d.1905 W/C. 4-Dec-3 Biddle & Webb, Birmingham #903

PRATT, Claude (attrib) (1860-c.1935) British
£280 $476 €409 Woman harvester resting (41x25cm-16x10in) s. board. 29-Oct-3 Bonhams, Chester #503

PRATT, Henry Lark (1805-1873) British
£30000 $53700 €43800 Extensive view of Derby, with figures and cattle in the foreground (70x93cm-28x37in) prov. 27-May-4 Christie's, Kensington #124/R est:10000-15000

PRATT, Jeffrey (?) British
£320 $563 €467 Slapton Sands (34x43cm-13x17in) s. 18-May-4 Woolley & Wallis, Salisbury #63/R
£740 $1302 €1080 Wash day, Kenya (35x45cm-14x18in) s. board. 18-May-4 Woolley & Wallis, Salisbury #129/R

PRATT, Jonathan (1835-1911) British
£360 $612 €526 Man by a doorway (31x25cm-12x10in) s. 18-Nov-3 Bonhams, Leeds #167/R

PRATT, Mary Frances (1935-) Canadian
£3659 $6549 €5342 Trout in a bowl (40x45cm-16x18in) s.d.1980 i.verso board prov. 6-May-4 Heffel, Vancouver #114/R est:10000-12000 (C.D 9000)
Prints
£1653 $2992 €2413 B.C delicious (33x53cm-13x21in) s.i.d.1994 num. wood block prov. 18-Apr-4 Levis, Calgary #315/R est:3000-3500 (C.D 4000)
£4065 $7276 €5935 Reflections of oranges (34x48cm-13x19in) s.i.d.96 num.67/75 aquatint. 31-May-4 Sotheby's, Toronto #158/R est:3000-4000 (C.D 10000)
Works on paper
£11179 $20010 €16321 Vase with silk flowers (86x112cm-34x44in) s.d.60 W/C pastel prov. 31-May-4 Sotheby's, Toronto #159/R est:30000-40000 (C.D 27500)

PRATT, William (1855-1936) British
£750 $1253 €1095 Potato field (29x39cm-11x15in) s.d.1928. 16-Oct-3 Bonhams, Edinburgh #224
£900 $1530 €1314 Gathering mussels (46x61cm-18x24in) s.d.1917. 10-Nov-3 Thomson Roddick & Medcalf, Edinburgh #243
£900 $1548 €1314 The way to the fold (48x74cm-19x29in) s.d.1910. 4-Dec-3 Mellors & Kirk, Nottingham #952
£5000 $9200 €7300 Home from the dunes (61x46cm-24x18in) s. prov. 23-Mar-4 Bonhams, New Bond Street #57/R est:5000-8000

PRAX, Valentine (1899-1981) French
£1200 $2076 €1752 Nature morte aux poissons et coquilles (42x60cm-17x24in) s. glass prov. 11-Dec-3 Christie's, Kensington #97/R est:800-1200
£1208 $2235 €1800 Les deux oiseaux (38x46cm-15x18in) s. 15-Mar-4 Blanchet, Paris #91/R est:1500-2000
£1879 $3495 €2800 Le livre et l'oiseau (50x65cm-20x26in) s. 2-Mar-4 Artcurial Briest, Paris #192 est:1800-2500
£2069 $3828 €3000 Pont de chemin de fer (67x100cm-26x39in) s. 19-Jan-4 Horta, Bruxelles #402 est:800-1200
£2292 $3827 €3300 Allegorie de la musique (65x81cm-26x32in) s. 21-Oct-3 Artcurial Briest, Paris #306/R est:3500-4000
£2414 $4345 €3500 Still life (60x73cm-24x29in) s.d.1925. 25-Jan-4 Chayette & Cheval, Paris #141/R est:3500-4000
£2448 $4088 €3500 Nature morte au panier (60x76cm-24x30in) s.d.1925. 30-Jun-3 Artcurial Briest, Paris #735/R est:3000-5000
£2533 $4636 €3800 Paysage mediterraneen avec maisons (65x81cm-26x32in) s. 7-Jun-4 Palais de Beaux Arts, Brussels #92/R est:4000-6000
£3020 $5618 €4500 L'enlevement d'Europe (85x105cm-33x41in) s. painted c.1950. 2-Mar-4 Artcurial Briest, Paris #193 est:5000-6000
£4225 $7014 €6000 La naissance de Venus (130x160cm-51x63in) s. painted c.1930 prov.exhib. 16-Jun-3 E & Eve, Paris #86/R
£4225 $7310 €6000 La peche (61x81cm-24x32in) s. 13-Dec-3 De Vuyst, Lokeren #574/R est:4800-5500
£5333 $9813 €8000 Jeune et la vieille sorcieres (130x97cm-51x38in) s. i.stretcher painted 1950 exhib. 8-Jun-4 Sotheby's, Amsterdam #68/R est:8000-12000
£6993 $12028 €10000 Untitled (81x115cm-32x45in) s.d.1925. 2-Dec-3 Calmels Cohen, Paris #47/R est:12000-15000
Works on paper
£1379 $2483 €2000 L'embarquement pour Cythere (52x72cm-20x28in) s. W/C gouache Indian ink. 25-Jan-4 Chayette & Cheval, Paris #147 est:2000-2500

PRE-RAPHAELITE GROUP (19th C) British
£5034 $9010 €7500 Madonn aof the Apple (68x52cm-27x20in) board. 26-May-4 Semenzato, Florence #222/R est:7000-8000

PREAULT, Auguste (1809-1879) French
Sculpture
£20000 $36400 €29200 Silence (41x41cm-16x16in) s. plaster round prov.lit. 17-Jun-4 Christie's, London #58/R est:20000-30000

PREAUX, Raymond (1916-) French
Works on paper
£315 $535 €450 Totem (33x6cm-13x2in) s. collage prov. 23-Nov-3 Cornette de St.Cyr, Paris #279
£420 $713 €600 Composition a l'oeil (38x9cm-15x4in) s. collage prov. 23-Nov-3 Cornette de St.Cyr, Paris #280
£1399 $2378 €2000 Composition constructiviste (14x8cm-6x3in) s. gouache prov. 23-Nov-3 Cornette de St.Cyr, Paris #281/R est:150-200

PREBLE, John (20th C) American
£703 $1300 €1055 Patio oranges (76x51cm-30x20in) s. canvasboard. 17-Jul-4 New Orleans Auction, New Orleans #884/R

PRECHTEL, Donald (1937-) American
£1397 $2500 €2040 Fort Clatsop (61x51cm-24x20in) 15-May-4 Altermann Galleries, Santa Fe #111/R

PRECHTL, Michael (1926-) German
£455 $773 €650 Master's dog (37x45cm-15x18in) s.i.d.1973. 20-Nov-3 Weidler, Nurnberg #7204/R
£769 $1308 €1100 Nurnberg Tarock garden (43x58cm-17x23in) s.i.d.73. 20-Nov-3 Weidler, Nurnberg #7203/R

PREDA, Ambrogio (1839-1906) Italian
£1534 $2500 €2240 Herdsman leading cattle in Alpine mountains (48x74cm-19x29in) s. 27-Sep-3 Thomaston Place, Thomaston #181

PREDA, Ambrogio (attrib) (1839-1906) Italian
£969 $1648 €1415 Lugano with Monte Bre (29x39cm-11x15in) i.d.1880 verso canvas on board. 5-Nov-3 Dobiaschofsky, Bern #876/R (S.FR 2200)

PREDECK, Ferdinand (1848-1909) German
£800 $1448 €1200 Paderborn (49x39cm-19x15in) mono. 1-Apr-4 Van Ham, Cologne #1606/R

PREDIGER, Hermann (1886-1970) German
Works on paper
£839 $1443 €1200 Two women bathing (45x55cm-18x22in) s. s.i.verso pastel exec. 1926. 6-Dec-3 Hans Stahl, Toestorf #21/R

PREECE, Patricia (1900-1971) British
£600 $1080 €876 Still life with basket of flowers (51x68cm-20x27in) prov. 20-Jan-4 Bonhams, Knightsbridge #250/R
£1000 $1820 €1460 Self-portrait (69x51cm-27x20in) 1-Jul-4 Christie's, Kensington #40/R est:1200-1800

PREEN, Hugo von (1854-?) Austrian
£664 $1129 €950 My property in Osternberg (40x50cm-16x20in) s. 27-Nov-3 Dorotheum, Linz #425/R

PREETORIUS, Willy (1882-?) German
£271 $434 €396 Romantic landscape (46x64cm-18x25in) s. s.i.d.1905 verso. 16-Sep-3 Philippe Schuler, Zurich #5469 (S.FR 600)

PREGARTBAUER, Louis (1899-1971) Austrian
Works on paper
£317 $555 €450 Weinor Tor (47x61cm-19x24in) s.d. pastel. 19-Dec-3 Dorotheum, Vienna #265/R
£461 $847 €700 Rainy Treben in front of Parliament (50x65cm-20x26in) s. pastel. 22-Jun-4 Wiener Kunst Auktionen, Vienna #228/R
£537 $993 €800 Venice (41x60cm-16x24in) s. pastel prov. 9-Mar-4 Dorotheum, Vienna #109/R
£537 $993 €800 Venice (44x56cm-17x22in) s. pastel prov. 9-Mar-4 Dorotheum, Vienna #110/R
£552 $1010 €800 Vienna (42x60cm-17x24in) s. pastel gouache prov. 27-Jan-4 Dorotheum, Vienna #131/R
£897 $1641 €1300 Venice (45x59cm-18x23in) s. pastel prov. 27-Jan-4 Dorotheum, Vienna #133/R
£1074 $1987 €1600 Salzburg (41x61cm-16x24in) s. pastel prov. 9-Mar-4 Dorotheum, Vienna #108/R est:1300-1800
£1103 $2019 €1600 Vienna (69x99cm-27x39in) s. pastel prov. 27-Jan-4 Dorotheum, Vienna #121/R est:1500-1800

PREGNO, Enzo (1898-1972) Italian
£305 $554 €460 Still life with watermelon (50x60cm-20x24in) s. s.verso. 17-Jun-4 Galleria Pananti, Florence #467/R
£331 $603 €500 Vase of flowers (35x25cm-14x10in) s. 17-Jun-4 Galleria Pananti, Florence #509/R
£662 $1205 €1000 Vase with yellow flower (70x50cm-28x20in) s. 17-Jun-4 Galleria Pananti, Florence #511/R
£935 $1534 €1300 Bottle with shell and sculpture (52x46cm-20x18in) s. prov. 10-Jun-3 Pandolfini, Florence #396/R est:1300-1400
£1258 $2290 €1900 Houses (56x48cm-22x19in) s. painted 1949 lit. 17-Jun-4 Galleria Pananti, Florence #592/R est:1800-2000

PREGO, Manuel (1915-1986) Spanish
£1370 $2329 €2000 Girl (37x27cm-15x11in) s. car. 4-Nov-3 Ansorena, Madrid #148/R est:1400
£1449 $2377 €2000 Mujer sentada meditando (55x45cm-22x18in) s. panel. 27-May-3 Durán, Madrid #689/R est:1000
£2305 $3849 €3250 Still life (55x78cm-22x31in) s. panel. 23-Jun-3 Durán, Madrid #155/R est:1500
Works on paper
£690 $1241 €1000 Female nude (29x19cm-11x7in) s.i. mixed media. 26-Jan-4 Ansorena, Madrid #312/R
£833 $1358 €1200 Old woman with dog (60x46cm-24x18in) s. mixed media. 23-Sep-3 Durán, Madrid #36/R

PREIFLER, Johann Justyn (18th C) ?
Works on paper
£329 $605 €500 Study of man (62x46cm-24x18in) s.d.1739 verso pencil htd lead. 22-Jun-4 Sotheby's, Milan #98

PREISLER, Jan (1872-1918) Czechoslovakian

£219 $373 €320 The final sleep (20x25cm-8x10in) 29-Nov-3 Dorotheum, Prague #58/R (C.KR 10000)
£7004 $11626 €10226 Bathing study (34x34cm-13x13in) 4-Oct-3 Dorotheum, Prague #18/R est:150000-280000 (C.KR 320000)
Works on paper
£3731 $6343 €5447 Study for temptation (20x23cm-8x9in) mono. pastel. 29-Nov-3 Dorotheum, Prague #122/R est:60000-90000 (C.KR 170000)

PREISS, F (1882-1943) German

Sculpture
£1200 $2004 €1752 Page boy (16cm-6in) s. pat bronze ivory. 13-Nov-3 Christie's, Kensington #322/R
£2081 $3330 €3038 Dancer with flowery dress (31cm-12in) s. bronze ivory. 19-Sep-3 Koller, Zurich #1294/R est:4000-6000 (S.FR 4600)
£15500 $25885 €22630 Dancing lady (37cm-15in) s. cold painted bronze ivory onyx base. 22-Oct-3 Wingetts, Wrexham #312/R est:2500-3500

PREISS, Ferdinand (1882-1943) German

£530 $964 €800 Market in Wurzburg (84x72cm-33x28in) s. 18-Jun-4 Bolland & Marotz, Bremen #825/R
Sculpture
£1119 $2058 €1700 Baguier - Femme a la souris (8cm-3in) s.ivory green onyx bowl. 25-Jun-4 Tajan, Paris #88/R est:1200-1500
£1150 $1817 €1679 Young girl offering a plate of fruit (10cm-4in) incised ivory green onyx base. 2-Sep-3 Woolley & Wallis, Salisbury #453/R est:600-800
£1184 $2179 €1800 Baguier - Femme au miroir (10cm-4in) s.ivory green onyx bowl. 25-Jun-4 Tajan, Paris #87/R est:1200-1500
£1200 $2148 €1752 Kneeling semi nude maiden, holding aloft a bowl of fruits (10cm-4in) s. ivory green onyx base exec.c.1920. 13-May-4 Bonhams, New Bond Street #204/R
£1500 $2655 €2190 Hoop girl (20cm-8in) s. painted bronze ivory marble base exec.c.1930. 27-Apr-4 Bonhams, Chester #95 est:1500-2500
£1600 $2864 €2336 Figure of a girl (21cm-8in) s. ivory gilt bronze onyx base exec.c.1920. 13-May-4 Bonhams, New Bond Street #202/R est:700-1000
£1700 $3179 €2482 Carmen (26cm-10in) s.st.f. gilt bronze ivory black marble pedestal exec.c.1930. 24-Feb-4 Sotheby's, Olympia #277/R est:1800-2500
£1800 $3222 €2628 Hoop girl (20cm-8in) s. ivory col painted bronze green onyx base exec.c.1930. 13-May-4 Bonhams, New Bond Street #209/R est:1500-2000
£2200 $3960 €3212 Art Deco Grecian with torch (28cm-11in) s. ivory bronze. 21-Apr-4 Lyon & Turnbull, Edinburgh #232/R est:2000-3000
£2300 $4117 €3358 Sonny boy (21cm-8in) s. ivory cold painted bronze onyx base exec.c.1930. 13-May-4 Bonhams, New Bond Street #208/R est:1500-2000
£3000 $5610 €4380 Young girl (17cm-7in) s. bronze ivory black marble pedestal exec.c.1930. 24-Feb-4 Sotheby's, Olympia #278/R est:1500-2500
£3200 $5728 €4672 Figure in a slinky top and hot pants standing on tip toe (17cm-7in) s. ivory onyx base exec.c.1925. 13-May-4 Bonhams, New Bond Street #205/R est:1500-2000
£3800 $6460 €5548 Aphrodite (22cm-9in) i. bronze ivory. 25-Nov-3 Sotheby's, Olympia #141/R est:2500-3500
£4000 $6800 €5840 Figure of a draped maiden (21cm-8in) i. bronze ivory. 25-Nov-3 Sotheby's, Olympia #138/R est:2500-3500
£4348 $8000 €6522 Cabaret girl (39cm-15in) i. carved ivory bronze lit. 27-Jun-4 Bonhams & Butterfields, Los Angeles #1252/R est:8000-12000
£5500 $9185 €8030 Bat dancer (24cm-9in) pat bronze ivory onyx base. 15-Oct-3 Christie's, Kensington #671/R
£5500 $10285 €8030 Tambourine dancer (36cm-14in) s. gilt bronze ivory marble plinth exec.c.1925. 24-Feb-4 Sotheby's, Olympia #275/R est:6000-7000
£6294 $10699 €9000 Champagne dancer (41cm-16in) i. enamelled pat.bronze ivory marble socle lit. 25-Nov-3 Dorotheum, Vienna #356/R est:6000-8000
£6522 $12000 €9783 Dancer (17cm-7in) i. carved ivory black slate onyx ivory. 27-Jun-4 Bonhams & Butterfields, Los Angeles #1249/R est:7000-10000
£6522 $12000 €9783 Lighter than air (35cm-14in) i. carved ivory bronze glass onyx prov.lit. 27-Jun-4 Bonhams & Butterfields, Los Angeles #1251/R est:8000-12000
£7400 $11766 €10804 Sunshade girl (23cm-9in) i. ivory. 9-Sep-3 Sotheby's, Olympia #367/R est:7500-8500
£7568 $14000 €11049 Tennis player (28cm-11in) s. cold painted bronze ivory exec.c.1925. 9-Mar-4 Christie's, Rockefeller NY #307/R est:10000-12000
£7800 $12402 €11388 Lighter than air (34cm-13in) i. ivory bronze base. 9-Sep-3 Sotheby's, Olympia #369/R est:8000-12000
£8152 $15000 €12228 Autumn dancer (26cm-10in) i. carved ivory gilt bronze onyx base prov.lit. 27-Jun-4 Bonhams & Butterfields, Los Angeles #1253/R est:15000-20000
£8152 $15000 €12228 Torch dancer (41cm-16in) i. carved ivory bronze slate onyx base lit. 27-Jun-4 Bonhams & Butterfields, Los Angeles #1257/R est:15000-20000
£8500 $15555 €12410 Archer (21cm-8in) i. bronze ivory. 3-Jun-4 Sotheby's, Olympia #268/R est:2500-3500
£8696 $16000 €13044 Sun worshipper (19cm-7in) i. carved ivory gilt bronze onyx base prov.lit. 27-Jun-4 Bonhams & Butterfields, Los Angeles #1255/R est:12000-18000
£8696 $16000 €13044 The stile (25cm-10in) st.f. PK i. carved ivory gilt bronze onyx base lit. 27-Jun-4 Bonhams & Butterfields, Los Angeles #1258/R est:12000-18000
£8800 $15752 €12848 Woman with mirror (31cm-12in) ivory pat bronze marble base exec.c.1925. 13-May-4 Bonhams, New Bond Street #206/R est:7000-10000
£9000 $15030 €13140 Spring awakening (36cm-14in) s. pat bronze ivory lit. 15-Oct-3 Christie's, Kensington #673/R
£9783 $18000 €14675 Invocation (36cm-14in) i. carved ivory bronze marble prov. 27-Jun-4 Bonhams & Butterfields, Los Angeles #1256/R est:20000-30000
£10811 $20000 €15784 Con brio (25cm-10in) cold pat. bronze green onyx base lit. 11-Mar-4 Sotheby's, New York #123/R est:10000-15000
£11500 $21505 €16790 Tennis player (27cm-11in) s. ivory bronze green onyx black marble base exec.c.1925. 24-Feb-4 Sotheby's, Olympia #276/R est:10000-12000
£12500 $23000 €18750 Bather with cap (25cm-10in) i. carved ivory bronze marble lit. 27-Jun-4 Bonhams & Butterfields, Los Angeles #1250/R est:25000-35000
£13500 $24165 €19710 Spring awakening (36cm-14in) s. ivory cold painted bronze marble base exec.c.1925. 13-May-4 Bonhams, New Bond Street #207/R est:12000-16000
£21000 $33390 €30660 Nude (29cm-11in) s. ivory. 9-Sep-3 Sotheby's, Olympia #368/R est:10000-12000

PREISS, Ferdinand (after) (1882-1943) German

Sculpture
£4121 $7500 €6182 Ecstasy (23cm-9in) i. ivory onyx marble plinth exec. c.1925. 16-Jun-4 Sotheby's, New York #241/R est:4000-6000
£4121 $7500 €6182 Thoughts (15cm-6in) ivory marble onyx base exec. c.1930. 16-Jun-4 Sotheby's, New York #256/R est:5000-7000
£4121 $7500 €6182 Thoughts (15cm-6in) i. ivory marble onyx base exec. c.1930. 16-Jun-4 Sotheby's, New York #257/R est:5000-7000
£4396 $8000 €6594 Figure of a tennis player (28cm-11in) i. bronze ivory exec. 1930. 16-Jun-4 Sotheby's, New York #266/R est:4000-6000
£5495 $10000 €8243 Salome dancing (30cm-12in) st.mono.i. bronze ivory onyx base exec. c.1925. 16-Jun-4 Sotheby's, New York #258/R est:5000-6000
£7143 $13000 €10715 Girl on a wall (33cm-13in) i. bronze ivory exec. c.1930. 16-Jun-4 Sotheby's, New York #238/R est:8000-10000
£7500 $13500 €10950 Torch dancer (42cm-17in) cold-painted bronze ivory lit. 22-Apr-4 Christie's, Kensington #535/R est:8000-12000
£8791 $16000 €13187 Ecstasy (30cm-12in) i. ivory onyx base exec. c.1930. 16-Jun-4 Sotheby's, New York #260/R est:10000-15000

PREISS, Ferdinand (attrib) (1882-1943) German

Sculpture
£7000 $10990 €10220 Figure of Bo Peep (43cm-17in) cold painted bronze green onyx base. 1-Sep-3 Bonhams, Chester #616/R est:800-1200

PREISSLER, Daniel (attrib) (1627-1665) German

Works on paper
£387 $700 €580 Maria with Infant Jesus on cloud (31x23cm-12x9in) wash pen ochre. 2-Apr-4 Winterberg, Heidelberg #218/R

PREISSLER, Johann Justin (1698-1771) German

Works on paper
£616 $1048 €900 Study for Saint John (58x34cm-23x13in) crayon. 6-Nov-3 Tajan, Paris #35/R

PREKAS, Paris (1926-1999) Greek

£15000 $26850 €21900 Vessels at port (97x97cm-38x38in) s. 10-May-4 Sotheby's, Olympia #106/R est:15000-20000

PRELL, Hermann (1854-1922) German

£694 $1160 €1000 Two Valkyries with rearing horse (90x79cm-35x31in) s.i.97 canvas o board. 22-Oct-3 Neumeister, Munich #741
£4261 $7500 €6221 Die wasserfrau (89x69cm-35x27in) s. canvasboard. 18-May-4 Bonhams & Butterfields, San Francisco #110/R est:3000-5000

PRELLER, Alexis (1911-1975) South African

£1200 $2124 €1752 Fish and egrets (20x24cm-8x9in) s.d.53 panel. 27-Apr-4 Bonhams, New Bond Street #103/R est:1000-1500
£1239 $2217 €1809 Figural composition (7x23cm-3x9in) s. board. 31-May-4 Stephan Welz, Johannesburg #353 est:2000-3000 (SA.R 15000)
£1849 $3346 €2700 Two birds (13x18cm-5x7in) s. panel. 30-Mar-4 Stephan Welz, Johannesburg #497/R est:15000-20000 (SA.R 22000)
£2414 $4031 €3524 Venetian pigeon (20x24cm-8x9in) s.d.56 panel prov. 20-Oct-3 Stephan Welz, Johannesburg #399/R est:12000-18000 (SA.R 28000)
£4129 $7391 €6028 Constellation (95x85cm-37x33in) s.d.66. 31-May-4 Stephan Welz, Johannesburg #619/R est:35000-45000 (SA.R 50000)
£12386 $22172 €18084 Malay sandals (49x59cm-19x23in) s.d.48 board. 31-May-4 Stephan Welz, Johannesburg #524/R est:80000-120000 (SA.R 150000)
£15517 $25914 €22655 Red blanket (80x67cm-31x26in) s.d.55 prov. 20-Oct-3 Stephan Welz, Johannesburg #315/R est:180000-220000 (SA.R 180000)
Sculpture
£6606 $11825 €9645 Gold King/Angel (92x107cm-36x42in) s.d.71 intaglio gold leaf on fibreglass exhib. 31-May-4 Stephan Welz, Johannesburg #576/R est:35000-50000 (SA.R 80000)
Works on paper
£372 $665 €543 Young woman (26x20cm-10x8in) s. brush ink. 31-May-4 Stephan Welz, Johannesburg #297 (SA.R 4500)
£1817 $3252 €2653 Female torso (33x21cm-13x8in) s.d.47 pencil. 31-May-4 Stephan Welz, Johannesburg #607 est:5000-8000 (SA.R 22000)

PRELLER, Friedrich Johann Christian Ernst (1804-1878) German

Works on paper
£3057 $5563 €4463 The children of the artist, Friedrich, Emil and Ernst (14x21cm-6x8in) i. pencil prov. 17-Jun-4 Kornfeld, Bern #51/R est:5000 (S.FR 7000)

PRELLER, Louis Friedrich (1838-1901) German

Works on paper
£336 $601 €500 Landscape with Romulus, augur and shepherds (38x58cm-15x23in) pencil htd white lit. 25-May-4 Karl & Faber, Munich #127/R

PRELOG, Drago J (1939-) Yugoslavian

£1600 $2880 €2400 Untitled (63x77cm-25x30in) s.d.1978 acrylic. 21-Apr-4 Dorotheum, Vienna #237/R est:1900-3000
Works on paper
£563 $986 €800 A hidden V (58x41cm-23x16in) collage ink col pencil acrylic. 19-Dec-3 Dorotheum, Vienna #379/R

PREM, Heimrad (1934-1978) German

£872 $1562 €1300 Untitled (35x37cm-14x15in) s.d. oil gouache. 25-May-4 Karl & Faber, Munich #437/R
£872 $1562 €1300 Untitled (47x68cm-19x27in) s.d.74 acrylic leather. 25-May-4 Karl & Faber, Munich #438/R
£1241 $2073 €1800 Untitled (48x76cm-19x30in) s.d.1974 acrylic leatherboard. 13-Nov-3 Neumeister, Munich #610/R est:800-900
£1327 $2123 €1924 Composition (28x33cm-11x13in) s.d.61 cardboard. 17-Sep-3 Kunsthallen, Copenhagen #43/R est:15000 (D.KR 14000)
£1678 $3003 €2500 Composition with brat (80x80cm-31x31in) 25-May-4 Karl & Faber, Munich #436/R est:5000
£2349 $4205 €3500 Trial (60x75cm-24x30in) s.d. 25-May-4 Karl & Faber, Munich #435/R est:4000

£4483 $7486 €6500 Study of woman. Children of our time (95x80cm-37x31in) s.d.1974 double-sided. 13-Nov-3 Neumeister, Munich #609/R est:2500-3000
Sculpture
£3611 $6031 €5200 Untitled - anti object (61x114x30cm-24x45x12in) s. canvas wood prov. 24-Oct-3 Ketterer, Hamburg #509/R est:6000-7000
Works on paper
£267 $477 €400 Untitled (27x30cm-11x12in) s. mixed media. 13-May-4 Neumeister, Munich #742/R
£906 $1541 €1323 Untitled (41x63cm-16x25in) s.d.65 gouache. 4-Nov-3 Bukowskis, Stockholm #280/R (S.KR 12000)
£948 $1744 €1384 Erotic figure composition (50x65cm-20x26in) s.d.66 pencil prov. 29-Mar-4 Rasmussen, Copenhagen #369/R (D.KR 10500)

PREMAZZI, Ludwig (1814-1891) Russian
Works on paper
£789 $1453 €1200 Residence d'ete (25x48cm-10x19in) s.d.1837 W/C. 28-Jun-4 Joron-Derem, Paris #123b
£2000 $3400 €2920 Crimean View (25x35cm-10x14in) s. W/C over pencil. 19-Nov-3 Sotheby's, London #12/R est:2500-3500

PREMONT, T du (?) French?
Sculpture
£1399 $2378 €2000 Femme noire au papillon (72cm-28in) st.f.Goldscheider num.1002 pat. terracotta. 18-Nov-3 Sotheby's, Paris #62/R est:2500-3000

PRENCIPE, Umberto (1879-?) Italian
£5634 $9352 €8000 Luci nell'orto (75x62cm-30x24in) s.d.903 i.verso. 11-Jun-3 Christie's, Rome #253/R est:8000-12000

PRENDERGAST, Maurice (1859-1924) American
£98837 $170000 €144302 Park scene (36x40cm-14x16in) s.i. panel painted c.1895-97 prov.lit. 3-Dec-3 Sotheby's, New York #5/R est:150000-250000
£142442 $245000 €207965 Late afternoon, moonlight at Marblehead (31x40cm-12x16in) init. painted c.1907-10 prov.lit. 3-Dec-3 Sotheby's, New York #34/R est:250000-350000
£988372 $1700000 €1443023 Promenade (48x107cm-19x42in) s. exhib.lit. 4-Dec-3 Christie's, Rockefeller NY #83/R est:500000-700000
Prints
£8982 $15000 €13114 School day (15x23cm-6x9in) mono. col monotype graphite executed c.1895-97. 11-Nov-3 Doyle, New York #360/R est:15000-25000
£28249 $50000 €41244 Lady Clark Matthews Owens (26x13cm-10x5in) col monotype print. 30-Apr-4 Sotheby's, New York #27/R est:60000-80000
Works on paper
£25568 $45000 €37329 Cherubs (39x48cm-15x19in) s. W/C paper on paper prov.lit. 18-May-4 Christie's, Rockefeller NY #85/R est:50000-70000
£42614 $75000 €62216 Street in Rouen (36x25cm-14x10in) s.i.d.1894 W/C pencil prov. 18-May-4 Christie's, Rockefeller NY #84/R est:30000-50000
£69767 $120000 €101860 Playtime at Salem Park, Massachusetts (35x50cm-14x20in) s. W/C pencil black chk executed c.1913-15 prov.exhib.lit. 3-Dec-3 Sotheby's, New York #47/R est:80000-120000
£289773 $510000 €423069 Band Concert, Luxembourg Gardens (41x20cm-16x8in) mono.d.1893 i.verso W/C pencil joined paper prov.lit. 19-May-4 Sotheby's, New York #21/R est:600000-800000
£1079546 $1900000 €1576137 Courtyard, West End library, Boston (36x51cm-14x20in) s. W/C pencil gouache exec c.1900-01 prov.lit. 18-May-4 Christie's, Rockefeller NY #75/R est:1200000-1800000

PRENDERGAST, Peter (1946-) British
£720 $1159 €1051 Tal-y-Bont (25x29cm-10x11in) s.d.1995 verso board. 19-Feb-3 Peter Wilson, Nantwich #57

PRENDONI, Attilio (1875-1942) Italian
Sculpture
£2534 $3953 €3700 Young ladies at bar. s. bronze marble wood base. 8-Apr-3 Il Ponte, Milan #562
£7000 $12110 €10220 Two fashionable ladies at the cafe (44x62x46cm-17x24x18in) s. brown pat bronze beige marble base lit. 12-Dec-3 Sotheby's, London #261/R est:5000-7000

PRENNSTEINER, Aurelia (1896-?) Austrian
£382 $623 €550 Parrots (60x47cm-24x19in) mono. panel. 23-Sep-3 Wiener Kunst Auktionen, Vienna #93/R

PRENTHEL, Hans (?) German?
£382 $623 €550 A quiet corner (82x65cm-32x26in) 29-Sep-3 Dr Fritz Nagel, Stuttgart #6930/R

PRENTICE, Levi Wells (1851-1935) American
£894 $1600 €1305 Portrait of artist's mother (36x25cm-14x10in) s. 7-May-4 Sloans & Kenyon, Bethesda #1213/R est:1500-1800
£2973 $5500 €4341 Towanda camp (25x46cm-10x18in) s. 11-Mar-4 Christie's, Rockefeller NY #9/R est:7000-9000
£3279 $6000 €4919 Lake Erie (28x46cm-11x18in) s.d.1886. 7-Jun-4 Everard, Savannah #476393/R est:8000-12000
£6977 $12000 €10186 Red currants (18x15cm-7x6in) s.d.1891. 7-Dec-3 Freeman, Philadelphia #118 est:12000-18000
£10778 $18000 €15736 View of the Adirondacks (66x112cm-26x44in) s.d.1873 prov. 23-Oct-3 Shannon's, Milford #77/R est:20000-30000
£12707 $23000 €18552 Basket of peaches (41x51cm-16x20in) s. prov. 31-Mar-4 Sotheby's, New York #82/R est:15000-25000
£13953 $24000 €20371 Basket of peaches (41x33cm-16x13in) s.d.1889 s.d.verso. 4-Dec-3 Christie's, Rockefeller NY #44/R est:30000-50000
£22727 $40000 €33181 Bushels of peaches (61x51cm-24x20in) s. prov. 18-May-4 Christie's, Rockefeller NY #6/R est:40000-60000
£26163 $45000 €38198 Apples (30x46cm-12x18in) s. prov. 4-Dec-3 Christie's, Rockefeller NY #1/R est:50000

PRENTZEL, Hans (1880-1956) German
£276 $461 €400 Besigheim (70x83cm-28x33in) s. 9-Jul-3 Hugo Ruef, Munich #176
£310 $518 €450 Kobolzell track (60x70cm-24x28in) s. panel. 9-Jul-3 Hugo Ruef, Munich #172
£310 $518 €450 Besigheim (58x76cm-23x30in) s. 9-Jul-3 Hugo Ruef, Munich #173
£379 $633 €550 Taubertal (71x83cm-28x33in) s. 9-Jul-3 Hugo Ruef, Munich #175
£567 $1020 €850 Old town, possibly Rothenburg o.d.T in summer (43x60cm-17x24in) s.d.1934 lit. 22-Apr-4 Allgauer, Kempten #3687/R
£849 $1494 €1240 Still life with vase of flowers (62x50cm-24x20in) s. 23-May-4 Agra, Warsaw #42/R (P.Z 6000)
£1793 $2994 €2600 Country garden (70x80cm-28x31in) s. i. verso. 9-Jul-3 Hugo Ruef, Munich #174/R est:600
£1875 $3131 €2738 In front of a house (72x60cm-28x24in) s.d.07. 19-Oct-3 Agra, Warsaw #35/R est:6000 (P.Z 12000)

PRENZEL, Robert (1866-1941) Australian
Sculpture
£3137 $5522 €4580 Blackbean watch stand (40cm-16in) carved wood prov. 19-May-4 Sotheby's, Melbourne #491/R est:10000-15000 (A.D 8000)
£6405 $11849 €9351 Drawing room easel (197cm-78in) s.d.1902 carved oak. 10-Mar-4 Deutscher-Menzies, Melbourne #378/R est:3000-5000 (A.D 15500)

PRESAS, Leopoldo (1915-) Argentinian
£1429 $2600 €2086 Thinking (25x17cm-10x7in) s. board. 5-Jul-4 Arroyo, Buenos Aires #82/R est:2000
£1648 $3000 €2406 Landscape (50x40cm-20x16in) s. 5-Jul-4 Arroyo, Buenos Aires #44/R est:3000
£1648 $3000 €2406 Figures (25x18cm-10x7in) s. board. 29-Jun-4 Arroyo, Buenos Aires #4/R est:3000
£2088 $3800 €3048 Figure (50x40cm-20x16in) s. board. 5-Jul-4 Arroyo, Buenos Aires #59/R est:3400
£2198 $4000 €3209 Dialogue (28x41cm-11x16in) s. cardboard. 5-Jul-4 Arroyo, Buenos Aires #7/R est:2500
£3022 $5500 €4412 Dusk in the fields (40x50cm-16x20in) s. 5-Jul-4 Arroyo, Buenos Aires #91/R est:4300
£3571 $6500 €5214 Vase of flowers in blue (80x60cm-31x24in) s. 29-Jun-4 Arroyo, Buenos Aires #106/R est:6500
£4645 $8500 €6782 Still life (60x80cm-24x31in) 1-Jun-4 Arroyo, Buenos Aires #58
£5307 $9500 €7748 Ophelia in the park (80x106cm-31x42in) 11-May-4 Arroyo, Buenos Aires #76
£5587 $10000 €8157 Figure in landscape (67x50cm-26x20in) s. 4-May-4 Arroyo, Buenos Aires #101/R est:5500
£7650 $14000 €11169 Figure (70x50cm-28x20in) 1-Jun-4 Arroyo, Buenos Aires #53
£7735 $14000 €11293 Still life in blue (60x80cm-24x31in) 30-Mar-4 Arroyo, Buenos Aires #101
£15470 $28000 €22586 Composition with nude (100x80cm-39x31in) 30-Mar-4 Arroyo, Buenos Aires #93
Works on paper
£824 $1500 €1203 Figure (48x37cm-19x15in) s. mixed media. 5-Jul-4 Arroyo, Buenos Aires #22/R est:1200
£3297 $6000 €4814 Still life (56x70cm-22x28in) s. pastel. 29-Jun-4 Arroyo, Buenos Aires #71/R est:4500

PRESCOTT, C Trevor (fl.1892-1897) British
£733 $1342 €1100 Lilies in a vase in an open room (100x75cm-39x30in) s. 7-Jun-4 Glerum, Amsterdam #35/R est:500-700

PRESCOTT, Claude (19/20th C) British?
£500 $900 €730 Portrait of C R W Nevinson (60x40cm-24x16in) s. board. 20-Jan-4 Bonhams, Knightsbridge #139/R

PRESCOTT, Frederick (20th C) American
Sculpture
£1500 $2685 €2190 Cowboys and Indians (185x185cm-73x73in) s.d.88 st. C1078 base welded steel kinetic sculpture. 22-Mar-4 Waddingtons, Toronto #615/R est:1000-1500 (C.D 3600)

PRESNAIL, Peter (20th C) American
£219 $400 €329 Still life 2 (79x58cm-31x23in) s.i. board. 31-Jul-4 Sloans & Kenyon, Bethesda #289

PRESSER, Josef (1907-1967) American
£449 $750 €656 Coming squall (30x41cm-12x16in) s. canvas on board. 20-Jun-3 Freeman, Philadelphia #200/R

PRESSLEY, Daniel (1918-1971) American
Sculpture
£4192 $7000 €6120 Old timey country doctor making a house call (28x74cm-11x29in) stained wood exhib. 15-Nov-3 Slotin Folk Art, Buford #184/R est:2000-4000

PRESSMANE, Joseph (1904-1967) French
£795 $1446 €1200 Tete d'une femme brune (27x22cm-11x9in) s. 16-Jun-4 Claude Boisgirard, Paris #135/R

£1049 $1783 €1500 Vue d'Ecouen (50x65cm-20x26in) s.d.1964 s.i.verso. 18-Nov-3 Pierre Berge, Paris #58/R est:1000-1500
£1457 $2652 €2200 Nu (55x38cm-22x15in) s. 16-Jun-4 Claude Boisgirard, Paris #136 est:900-1000
£1457 $2652 €2200 Le village boise (60x49cm-24x19in) s. 16-Jun-4 Claude Boisgirard, Paris #137/R est:800-1200

PRESSO, Ferdinando (19th C) Italian
£1867 $3398 €2800 View of Posillipo (43x66cm-17x26in) gouache. 30-Jun-4 Pierre Berge, Paris #69/R est:2800-3000

PREST, Trefor (1945-) Australian
Sculpture
£1545 $2425 €2256 Taffrail delights (152x65x42cm-60x26x17in) s.i.d.1989 wood copper tine steel. 27-Aug-3 Christie's, Sydney #578 est:800-1200 (A.D 3800)

PRESTEL, Johann Erdmann Gottlieb (younger) (1804-1885) German
£1667 $2983 €2500 Coach and horses (59x89cm-23x35in) s.d. prov. 14-May-4 Ketterer, Munich #105/R est:3000-4000

PRESTELE, Karl (1839-?) German
£778 $1369 €1136 Landscape, mountains beyond (42x63cm-17x25in) s. 23-May-4 Agra, Warsaw #44/R (P.Z 5500)

PRESTON, David (1948-) Australian
£4472 $8004 €6529 Near Taronga Park, a view of the harbour (180x360cm-71x142in) s.d.84 three panels painted with various other artists. 4-May-4 Sotheby's, Melbourne #268/R est:3000-5000 (A.D 11000)

PRESTON, Dorothy (1917-1993) American
£363 $650 €530 Love is the most universal formidable mysterious cosmic energies (97x132cm-38x52in) s. oil rice paper. 7-May-4 Sloans & Kenyon, Bethesda #1739/R

PRESTON, Harriet (20th C) American
£988 $1600 €1433 Monhegan hurricane (61x76cm-24x30in) s. prov. 8-Aug-3 Barridorf, Portland #323/R est:1500-2500

PRESTON, Jessie Goodwin (1880-?) American
Sculpture
£12973 $24000 €18941 Floriform candelabrum (52cm-20in) s. bronze exec.c.1900. 9-Mar-4 Christie's, Rockefeller NY #201/R est:4000-6000

PRESTON, Margaret Rose (1875-1963) Australian
£6383 $10851 €9319 Ti Tree (50x40cm-20x16in) s.d.56 canvasboard prov. 26-Nov-3 Deutscher-Menzies, Melbourne #57/R est:18000-24000 (A.D 15000)
£45455 $80455 €66364 Larkspur (51x44cm-20x17in) s.d.1929 prov.exhib.lit. 3-May-4 Christie's, Melbourne #67/R est:60000-80000 (A.D 110000)
Prints
£2024 $3259 €2955 Black swans, Wallis Lake, N S W (19x27cm-7x11in) s.i. woodblock print paper edn 14/50. 25-Aug-3 Sotheby's, Paddington #468/R est:5000-7000 (A.D 5000)
£2627 $4466 €3835 Flowers in a jug (28x20cm-11x8in) s. woodblock print prov. 24-Nov-3 Sotheby's, Melbourne #185/R est:6000-8000 (A.D 6200)
£3516 $6574 €5274 Mosman Bridge (25x19cm-10x7in) s. hand col woodcut. 20-Jul-4 Goodman, Sydney #23/R est:7000-10000 (A.D 9000)

PRESTON, Oliver (1963-) British
Works on paper
£400 $688 €584 Since we moved to the country our quality of life has doubled (63x48cm-25x19in) s.i. pencil black ink W/C. 3-Dec-3 Christie's, Kensington #343/R
£700 $1204 €1022 You don't think I invited you to Gstaad for the skiing (38x25cm-15x10in) s.i. pencil black ink W/C. 3-Dec-3 Christie's, Kensington #342/R

PRESTON, Rex N (?) British
£400 $652 €584 Ruined houses (30x39cm-12x15in) s.d.76. 25-Sep-3 Mellors & Kirk, Nottingham #763

PRESTOPINO, Gregorio (1907-) American
Works on paper
£373 $600 €545 Mexican abstract (61x48cm-24x19in) pastel prov. 20-Aug-3 James Julia, Fairfield #1471/R

PRETE, Juan del (1897-1987) Argentinian
£1923 $3500 €2808 Figure (33x25cm-13x10in) s.d.55 cardboard. 5-Jul-4 Arroyo, Buenos Aires #73/R est:2800
£2459 $4500 €3590 Figure (40x27cm-16x11in) cardboard. 1-Jun-4 Arroyo, Buenos Aires #80
£3077 $5600 €4492 Scene (35x49cm-14x19in) s.d.44 tempera paper. 29-Jun-4 Arroyo, Buenos Aires #59/R est:4000
£3297 $6000 €4814 Figures in town (44x23cm-17x9in) s. cardboard. 29-Jun-4 Arroyo, Buenos Aires #97/R est:5000
£5587 $10000 €8157 Figures (58x46cm-23x18in) s.d.81 board. 4-May-4 Arroyo, Buenos Aires #81/R est:6500
£8939 $16000 €13051 Untitled (48x42cm-19x17in) s.d.31. 4-May-4 Arroyo, Buenos Aires #55/R est:3800
£31868 $58000 €46527 Abstract (164x95cm-65x37in) s.d.58. 29-Jun-4 Arroyo, Buenos Aires #85/R est:40000

PRETI, Gregorio and Mattia (17th C) Italian
£45775 $73239 €65000 Card players with woman (121x171cm-48x67in) 21-Sep-3 Finarte, Venice #31/R est:60000-80000

PRETI, Mattia (1613-1699) Italian
£4255 $6894 €6000 Christ at the column (217x168cm-85x66in) 21-May-3 Babuino, Rome #43/R
£221477 $392013 €330000 Cimone and Pero (116x91cm-46x36in) 27-Apr-4 Porro, Milan #323/R est:250000
Works on paper
£333 $597 €500 Angel studies (19x17cm-7x7in) ochre. 13-May-4 Bassenge, Berlin #5263

PRETI, Mattia (attrib) (1613-1699) Italian
£2222 $4000 €3244 Saint interceding on behalf of plague sufferers (65x48cm-26x19in) 21-Jan-4 Doyle, New York #105/R est:3000-5000
£22000 $38060 €32120 Expulsion of Hagar and Ishmael (125x100cm-49x39in) 11-Dec-3 Sotheby's, London #192/R est:8000-12000

PRETRE, Jean Gabriel (fl.1800-1840) French
Works on paper
£690 $1152 €1000 Guepier a gorge bleue, promerops raye, et guepier a queue d'azur (16x9cm-6x4in) s. W/C brush col ink black crayon. 13-Nov-3 Binoche, Paris #27/R
£1931 $3225 €2800 Various animals (16x9cm-6x4in) s. W/C gouache black crayon 3 sheets 1 mount. 13-Nov-3 Binoche, Paris #33/R est:2500
£2345 $3916 €3400 Various animals. s. W/C gouache black crayon 3 sheets 1 mount. 13-Nov-3 Binoche, Paris #31/R est:2000

PRETRE, Jean Gabriel and TRAVIES, Edouard (19th C) French
Works on paper
£2069 $3455 €3000 Various animals. s. one d.1834 one d.1836 W/C gouache crayon 3 sheets 1 mount. 13-Nov-3 Binoche, Paris #30/R

PREUFS, Emillie (19th C) ?
£400 $756 €584 Female nude in her boudoir (53x36cm-21x14in) s.d.1894. 19-Feb-4 Christie's, Kensington #36

PREUSS, James (20th C) American?
£252 $400 €368 Bathing boys (91x61cm-36x24in) s.d.1966. 13-Sep-3 Auctions by the Bay, Alameda #468/R

PREUSS, Rudolf (1879-?) Austrian
Works on paper
£355 $592 €500 Landscape near Amras (21x30cm-8x12in) s.i.d.53 W/C. 16-Oct-3 Dorotheum, Salzburg #928/R
£496 $829 €700 Winter in Kuhtai (21x27cm-8x11in) s.i.d.27.12.24. 16-Oct-3 Dorotheum, Salzburg #909/R
£563 $1030 €850 Tins, Gschnitztaal (16x24cm-6x9in) s.i.d.26 W/C. 7-Apr-4 Dorotheum, Salzburg #20/R
£586 $973 €850 House on the Schneeberg (23x28cm-9x11in) s.i.d.1922 W/C. 30-Sep-3 Dorotheum, Vienna #339/R
£662 $1212 €1000 Fortress and harbour in Genua (34x49cm-13x19in) s.i.d.1932 W/C. 7-Apr-4 Dorotheum, Salzburg #199/R
£1034 $1717 €1500 Morning in Hintertux (32x24cm-13x9in) s.i.d.1928 W/C. 30-Sep-3 Dorotheum, Vienna #342/R est:1300-1500
£1060 $1939 €1600 Bergdorf Serfaus (32x49cm-13x19in) s.i.d.1833 W/C. 7-Apr-4 Dorotheum, Salzburg #201/R est:2400-3500

PREUSSER, Robert Ormerod (1919-1992) American
£1236 $2100 €1805 Line woven forms (37x58cm-15x23in) s.i.d.1947 verso board. 21-Nov-3 Skinner, Boston #599/R est:2000-3000

PREVERT, Jacques (1900-1977) French
Works on paper
£420 $722 €600 Grandes familles (23x18cm-9x7in) s.i.d.70 collage. 5-Dec-3 Maigret, Paris #6
£540 $885 €750 Le dromadaire. s.i. ink paper napkin. 6-Jun-3 David Kahn, Paris #53
£933 $1717 €1400 Untitled (42x27cm-17x11in) s. felt tip pen col crayon collage. 9-Jun-4 Piasa, Paris #203
£933 $1680 €1400 Untitled (19x14cm-7x6in) s.i. collage. 25-Apr-4 Versailles Encheres #188 est:1500-2000
£1133 $2085 €1700 Collage surrealiste (15x10cm-6x4in) s.i. collage. 9-Jun-4 Piasa, Paris #204/R est:1200-1500
£2098 $3608 €3000 Un personnage central feminin recouvert d'un masque etrange (30x21cm-12x8in) s. collage exec.c.1970. 6-Dec-3 Renaud, Paris #273
£2817 $4563 €4000 Composition (26x15cm-10x6in) s.i. collage. 11-Aug-3 Boscher, Cherbourg #769/R est:4000-6000
£2937 $5052 €4200 Un homme transperce de fleches parmi de nombreux personnages (32x22cm-13x9in) s. collage exec.c.1970. 6-Dec-3 Renaud, Paris #272/R
£3077 $5231 €4400 Scene mystique, la tentation (32x24cm-13x9in) s.i.d.69 collage. 24-Nov-3 Boscher, Cherbourg #801/R est:4000-6000
£3217 $5533 €4600 Une femme allongee pres d'un tronc d'arbre portant un masque curieux (50x32cm-20x13in) s.i.d.1957 collage. 6-Dec-3 Renaud, Paris #270/R
£4615 $7938 €6600 Le General Prevert (38x28cm-15x11in) s.i. collage. 6-Dec-3 Renaud, Paris #271/R
£4667 $8633 €7000 Belle cycliste (35x26cm-14x10in) collage exec.1955. 18-Jul-4 Sotheby's, Paris #291/R est:2000-3000

PREVERT, Jacques and VERDET, Andre (20th C) French
Works on paper
£500 $900 €750 Untitled (19x14cm-7x6in) s.i.d.1951 col crayon felt-tip pen. 25-Apr-4 Versailles Encheres #193

PREVIATI, Gaetano (1852-1920) Italian

£2254	$3741	€3200	Il sogno (9x23cm-4x9in) s. i.verso panel. 11-Jun-3 Christie's, Rome #132/R est:2300-2800
£10000	$18400	€15000	Iris (70x57cm-28x22in) s.i. 8-Jun-4 Sotheby's, Milan #106/R est:15000-20000

Works on paper

£940	$1729	€1400	Last (48x19cm-19x7in) s. W/C. 24-Mar-4 Il Ponte, Milan #634 est:1800
£17606	$29225	€25000	Madonna with angels (170x150cm-67x59in) s. chl canvas prov. 11-Jun-3 Christie's, Rome #283/R est:28000-35000

PREVIATI, Gaetano (attrib) (1852-1920) Italian

£520	$868	€759	Pierrot (25x18cm-10x7in) panel. 22-Oct-3 Cheffins, Cambridge #539/R

PREVOST, A and TRAVIES, Edouard (19th C) French

Works on paper

£1931	$3225	€2800	Various animals. s. one d.1834 one d.1835 W/C gouache crayon 3 sheets 1 mount. 13-Nov-3 Binoche, Paris #37/R est:3000

PREVOST-RITTER, Jean Henri Marie (1810-1898) Swiss

£556	$906	€800	Rocky lakeshore (27x46cm-11x18in) s.i. board. 24-Sep-3 Neumeister, Munich #530/R

PREVOT-VALERI, Andre (1890-1930) French

£282	$456	€400	Falaises a Landemer (25x33cm-10x13in) studio st. panel. 11-Aug-3 Boscher, Cherbourg #710
£524	$902	€750	Recolte (23x33cm-9x13in) s. i.verso panel. 7-Dec-3 Livinec, Gaudcheau & Jezequel, Rennes #59
£560	$1025	€818	Figures in a field gathering in the harvest with extensive landscape. s. 9-Jul-4 Moore Allen & Innocent, Cirencester #836
£839	$1427	€1200	Bergere et troupeau (50x61cm-20x24in) s. 28-Nov-3 Drouot Estimations, Paris #146
£1538	$2615	€2200	La pailleule, ramassage de varech (38x55cm-15x22in) s. 24-Nov-3 Boscher, Cherbourg #724/R est:1800-2000

PREVOT-VALERI, Auguste (1857-1930) French

£317	$529	€463	Shepherdess and flock in a river landscape (22x33cm-9x13in) s. 17-Nov-3 Waddingtons, Toronto #179/R (C.D 700)
£931	$1555	€1350	Berger et son troupeau de moutons (27x41cm-11x16in) s. 16-Nov-3 Muizon & Le Coent, Paris #52/R
£2759	$5103	€4000	Bergeres et meules de foin (59x81cm-23x32in) s. 16-Feb-4 Giraudeau, Tours #100

PREY, Juan de (1904-1962) Puerto Rican

£1176	$2000	€1717	Musicians (74x102cm-29x40in) s.d. 20-Nov-3 Auctions by the Bay, Alameda #1033/R

PREYER, Emilie (1849-1930) German

£17450	$31235	€26000	Still life of fruit (17x23cm-7x9in) s. 27-May-4 Dorotheum, Vienna #11/R est:30000-35000

Works on paper

£2483	$4146	€3600	Still life of fruit including grapes, walnuts, hazelnuts (21x29cm-8x11in) mono.d.18 7/12 84 pencil W/C. 15-Nov-3 Lempertz, Koln #1538/R est:4000

PREZIOSI, Amadeo (1816-1882) Italian

Works on paper

£486	$792	€700	Constantinople (21x38cm-8x15in) mono. ink. 23-Sep-3 Wiener Kunst Auktionen, Vienna #18/R
£600	$1104	€876	Veiled Turkish women (20x11cm-8x4in) s.d.1852 pencil W/C htd white pair. 23-Mar-4 Anderson & Garland, Newcastle #209
£1700	$3060	€2482	Turkish musician. Turkish infantryman (25x17cm-10x7in) s.d.1856 W/C pencil pair. 22-Apr-4 Lawrence, Crewkerne #770/R est:1200-1800
£3147	$5413	€4500	Constantinople (42x51cm-17x20in) s. W/C pen crayon oval. 8-Dec-3 Tajan, Paris #318/R est:3000-4000
£3200	$5344	€4672	Portrait of a Turkish man (43x31cm-17x12in) s. W/C over pencil htd bodycol. 14-Oct-3 Sotheby's, London #11/R est:2000-3000
£4000	$7320	€6000	La Corne d'Or a Constantinople (43x61cm-17x24in) s.d.1864 W/C pen crayon. 3-Jun-4 Tajan, Paris #304/R est:5000-7000
£5500	$10120	€8030	On the Golden Horn. On the Bosphorus before the Haiga Sophia (32x49cm-13x19in) s.d.1864 pencil W/C htd white pair. 25-Mar-4 Christie's, Kensington #58/R est:4000-6000
£14000	$23800	€20440	Les Gueux a Constantinople (26x34cm-10x13in) i.d.1876 W/C set of 80. 4-Nov-3 Bonhams, New Bond Street #81/R est:15000-20000
£136054	$243537	€200000	Vues de Malte, Italie, France, Bulgarie, Roumanie et Turquie. graphite brown wash W/C seventy-nine album prov. 18-Mar-4 Christie's, Paris #70/R est:70000-100000

PREZIOSI, Amadeo (attrib) (1816-1882) Italian

Works on paper

£310	$574	€450	Etude de derviche (21x16cm-8x6in) pencil W/C. 11-Feb-4 Beaussant & Lefèvre, Paris #203

PREZZI, Wilma Maria (1915-1964) American

£316	$500	€461	Arrangement of Oriental objects (86x71cm-34x28in) s. prov.exhib. 6-Apr-3 William Jenack, New York #223
£348	$550	€508	Wooden maitreya (91x76cm-36x30in) s. exhib. 6-Apr-3 William Jenack, New York #173
£815	$1500	€1223	Wooden maitreya (91x76cm-36x30in) s. 28-Mar-4 Carlsen Gallery, Greenville #371/R

PRIBYLOVSKI, Viktor (1919-1971) Russian

£380	$692	€555	Washing in the river (50x35cm-20x14in) board painted 1959. 20-Jun-4 Lots Road Auctions, London #362/R
£600	$1092	€876	By the pier (70x50cm-28x20in) s. board painted 1963. 20-Jun-4 Lots Road Auctions, London #372/R

PRICE, A J (20th C) Australian?

£3862	$6063	€5639	Prosperous farm (88x180cm-35x71in) oil metal. 27-Aug-3 Christie's, Sydney #539/R est:3000-5000 (A.D 9500)

PRICE, Alan (1926-2002) American

£964	$1600	€1407	Beached (30x61cm-12x24in) s.d.1968 masonite prov. 4-Oct-3 Neal Auction Company, New Orleans #1133/R est:1000-1500
£1325	$2200	€1935	Netting (36x58cm-14x23in) s.d.1968 masonite prov. 4-Oct-3 Neal Auction Company, New Orleans #1143/R est:1500-2500
£2561	$4250	€3739	On the porch (46x61cm-18x24in) s.d.1982 masonite prov. 4-Oct-3 Neal Auction Company, New Orleans #1132/R est:1500-2500

PRICE, Clayton Sumner (1874-1950) American

£6250	$11000	€9125	Indian woman milking. s. oil on paper prov. 22-May-4 Harvey Clar, Oakland #2438a

PRICE, Frank Corbyn (1862-?) British

Works on paper

£222	$384	€324	Towards the coming night (34x48cm-13x19in) s. i.verso W/C. 9-Dec-3 Pinneys, Montreal #78 (C.D 500)
£310	$533	€453	In the valley of the Arun (31x49cm-12x19in) s. W/C. 2-Dec-3 Sworder & Son, Bishops Stortford #476/R
£320	$586	€467	Earthworks with a horse, cart and figures, a farm beyond (18x27cm-7x11in) s. W/C. 6-Jul-4 Bearnes, Exeter #434/R

PRICE, George (1901-1995) American

Works on paper

£838	$1500	€1223	People asking direction at 1964 World's fair (51x43cm-20x17in) s. pen ink W/C. 15-May-4 Illustration House, New York #138/R est:1200-1800

PRICE, Glen (20th C) American

£369	$650	€539	Cosmic compulsion (43x43cm-17x17in) s. i.d.1949 verso board. 23-May-4 Treadway Gallery, Cincinnati #763/R

PRICE, James (fl.1842-1876) British

Works on paper

£800	$1432	€1168	Harvest time (52x76cm-20x30in) s. W/C. 26-May-4 Sotheby's, Olympia #53/R

PRICE, Janis (1933-) American

£667	$1200	€974	Autumn scene of valley view farm (91x117cm-36x46in) acrylic. 24-Apr-4 Slotin Folk Art, Buford #262/R est:400-600

PRICE, Ken (1935-) American

Sculpture

£8982	$15000	€13114	Untitled, pink rock (5x6x6cm-2x2x2in) painted ceramic two parts prov. 13-Nov-3 Sotheby's, New York #584/R est:12000-18000
£10778	$18000	€15736	Untitled (18x22x15cm-7x9x6in) painted ceramic prov.exhib. 13-Nov-3 Sotheby's, New York #585/R est:8000-12000

PRICE, Mary Elizabeth (1875-1960) American

£9827	$17000	€14347	Blue oval (36x28cm-14x11in) s. board. 10-Dec-3 Alderfer's, Hatfield #430/R est:4000-6000
£53073	$95000	€77487	Flower border I. s. board. 13-May-4 Dallas Auction Gallery, Dallas #281/R est:3500-6500

PRICE, Maureen Rose (?) British?

£280	$476	€409	La Garonne (31x36cm-12x14in) s. canvas on board. 4-Nov-3 Dreweatt Neate, Newbury #148/R

PRICE, Winchell Addison (1907-) Canadian

£181	$336	€264	August day (30x41cm-12x16in) s. i.verso canvasboard. 2-Mar-4 Ritchie, Toronto #116/R (C.D 450)
£500	$815	€730	Summer day (60x76cm-24x30in) s. board. 23-Sep-3 Ritchie, Toronto #106/R est:1000-1500 (C.D 1100)
£968	$1781	€1413	The lily pond (61x76cm-24x30in) s. s.i.d.1972 verso board. 9-Jun-4 Walker's, Ottawa #89/R est:2500-3000 (C.D 2400)

PRICERT, Raphael (20th C) ?

£279	$500	€407	Capri (38x48cm-15x19in) s. acrylic on board. 10-Jan-4 Susanin's, Chicago #5003/R

PRIDDEY, James (1916-1980) British

Works on paper

£300	$567	€438	Market hall and St. Martins, Bull Ring, Birmingham (53x37cm-21x15in) s. W/C. 17-Feb-4 Fellows & Sons, Birmingham #100/R

PRIEBE, Karl (1914-1976) American

£859	$1400	€1254	Dreaming of love (36x28cm-14x11in) s.d.1950 W/C gouache board. 24-Sep-3 Jackson's, Cedar Falls #774/R est:300-500

Works on paper
£216 $400 €315 Portrait of a girl (25x20cm-10x8in) s.d.1967 casein. 19-Jul-4 Schrager Galleries, Milwaukee #803/R
£251 $450 €366 Miss Lil Green (30x30cm-12x12in) s.d.1954 casein. 16-May-4 Wright, Chicago #212/R
£264 $475 €385 Shore Bird (5x13cm-2x5in) init.d.59 i.verso casein. 26-Jan-4 Schrager Galleries, Milwaukee #1444
£275 $460 €402 Owl on tree branch (36x25cm-14x10in) s.i. casein. 27-Oct-3 Schrager Galleries, Milwaukee #662/R
£279 $500 €407 Portrait (28x25cm-11x10in) s.d.1942 casein paperboard. 16-May-4 Wright, Chicago #207/R
£279 $500 €407 Still life (28x30cm-11x12in) s.d.1940 casein board. 16-May-4 Wright, Chicago #208/R
£389 $700 €568 Portrait of a girl (48x38cm-19x15in) s.d.67 casein. 26-Jan-4 Schrager Galleries, Milwaukee #1380
£419 $750 €612 St Julian with bird (48x64cm-19x25in) s.d.1976 casein prov.exhib. 16-May-4 Wright, Chicago #211/R
£500 $900 €730 Lady with artificial roses (28x23cm-11x9in) init.d.74 casein exhib. 26-Jan-4 Schrager Galleries, Milwaukee #1453
£2059 $3500 €3006 Untitled - woman and birds (61x28cm-24x11in) s.d.1944 gouache on board. 9-Nov-3 Wright, Chicago #193 est:1500-2000

PRIEBE, Rudolf (1889-1956) Polish
£692 $1279 €1010 Ships in a calm (70x100cm-28x39in) 14-Mar-4 Agra, Warsaw #28/R (P.Z 5000)
£707 $1245 €1032 Landscape (60x80cm-24x31in) s. 23-May-4 Agra, Warsaw #46/R (P.Z 5000)
£983 $1701 €1435 Ships drawn up on the shore (70x105cm-28x41in) s. painted c.1930. 14-Dec-3 Agra, Warsaw #5/R est:6000 (P.Z 6500)
£1097 $1712 €1602 Moored boats (60x60cm-24x24in) s. painted c.1930. 30-Mar-3 Agra, Warsaw #44/R est:5000 (P.Z 7000)

PRIECHENFRIED, Alois (1867-1953) German
£451 $736 €650 Bearded man filling pipe (12x9cm-5x4in) s. i. stretcher panel. 25-Sep-3 Dr Fritz Nagel, Stuttgart #1393/R
£486 $792 €700 Old man cleaning clock with feather (12x9cm-5x4in) s. i. stretcher panel. 25-Sep-3 Dr Fritz Nagel, Stuttgart #1392/R
£700 $1169 €1022 Zither concert (31x26cm-12x10in) s. 12-Nov-3 Sotheby's, Olympia #157/R
£839 $1443 €1200 Discord (53x38cm-21x15in) i.verso. 6-Dec-3 Dannenberg, Berlin #821/R
£2500 $4600 €3650 Jewellery box (39x31cm-15x12in) s. panel. 25-Mar-4 Christie's, Kensington #54/R est:3000-5000
£2535 $4208 €3600 Conversation in the kitchen (32x28cm-13x11in) s. 16-Jun-3 Dorotheum, Vienna #68/R est:3800-4000
£3829 $6586 €5590 Elderly Rabbi in his study (35x46cm-14x18in) s. panel. 8-Dec-3 Philippe Schuler, Zurich #3426/R est:10000-14000 (S.FR 8500)
£4469 $8000 €6525 Portrait of a Rabbi (38x29cm-15x11in) 18-Mar-4 Sotheby's, New York #265/R est:7000-9000
£6667 $12000 €9734 Le vieil erudit (34x45cm-13x18in) s. panel. 23-Apr-4 Sotheby's, New York #187/R est:12000-15000
£7263 $13000 €10604 Young boy at prayer (31x23cm-12x9in) s. 18-Mar-4 Sotheby's, New York #263/R est:8000-12000
£9444 $17000 €13788 Lecture de la Torah (41x52cm-16x20in) s. panel prov. 23-Apr-4 Sotheby's, New York #186/R est:20000-30000
£9452 $16352 €13800 A thoughtful rabbi wearing shawl seated at table (42x53cm-17x21in) s. panel prov. 9-Dec-3 Rasmussen, Copenhagen #1288/R est:80000-100000 (D.KR 100000)
£15294 $26000 €22329 Scholar in his study (41x52cm-16x20in) s. panel. 29-Oct-3 Christie's, Rockefeller NY #43/R est:15000-20000

PRIECHENFRIED, G Kalla (20th C) German
£3800 $6916 €5548 Moment's contemplation. Considering the letter (45x34cm-18x13in) s. panel pair. 16-Jun-4 Bonhams, New Bond Street #25/R est:2500-3500

PRIEST, Alfred (1810-1850) British
£320 $534 €467 Boats on a bend in the river (31x46cm-12x18in) 14-Oct-3 Bonhams, Ipswich #308
Prints
£450 $779 €657 Watermill in a landscape (64x76cm-25x30in) 10-Dec-3 Bonhams, Bury St Edmunds #560

PRIESTLEY, Edward (19th C) British
£667 $1200 €974 Shropshire farmstead (51x76cm-20x30in) s.i. 24-Jan-4 Skinner, Boston #190/R est:800-1200

PRIESTLEY, Glenn (20th C) Canadian
£1016 $1819 €1483 Winter night (120x181cm-47x71in) s.d.1986 board. 6-May-4 Heffel, Vancouver #115/R est:2000-3000 (C.D 2500)
£1607 $2764 €2346 Studio window (86x56cm-34x22in) s.d.85-86 board. 2-Dec-3 Joyner Waddington, Toronto #533 est:800-1200 (C.D 3600)

PRIESTLY, Anne (1948-) Australian
£244 $383 €356 Nuptial (122x92cm-48x36in) init.d.94 board prov. 27-Aug-3 Christie's, Sydney #700 (A.D 600)

PRIESTMAN, Bertram (1868-1951) British
£480 $797 €701 Two masted steam vessel in an estuary (6x9cm-2x4in) s.d.91 board. 2-Oct-3 Ewbank, Send #819
£540 $918 €788 Landscape with buildings (19x24cm-7x9in) init. canvasboard. 18-Nov-3 Bonhams, Leeds #271
£1200 $2148 €1752 Harbour scene (27x38cm-11x15in) s.d.03 panel. 16-Mar-4 Bonhams, Leeds #659/R est:1200-1500
£1301 $2328 €1899 Cattle at the water's edge (62x103cm-24x41in) s.d.09 prov. 4-May-4 Ritchie, Toronto #37/R est:4000-6000 (C.D 3200)
£2500 $4550 €3650 Herding cows along the tow path (71x91cm-28x36in) s. 1-Jul-4 Christie's, Kensington #68/R est:3000-5000
Works on paper
£300 $516 €438 Running up the estuary (16x24cm-6x9in) init.i.d.1897 verso pencil W/C. 3-Dec-3 Christie's, Kensington #233/R

PRIESTMAN, Bertram (attrib) (1868-1951) British
£260 $442 €380 Dales landscape (20x29cm-8x11in) 18-Nov-3 Bonhams, Leeds #269

PRIETO HURTADO, A (20th C) Spanish
£621 $1117 €900 Still life with grapes (33x55cm-13x22in) s.d.1901. 26-Jan-4 Ansorena, Madrid #386/R

PRIETO, César (1882-1976) Venezuelan
£272 $495 €408 Landscape (56x65cm-22x26in) s. 21-Jun-4 Subastas Odalys, Caracas #128
£1048 $1750 €1530 Landscape in a village (45x56cm-18x22in) s. 19-Oct-3 Subastas Odalys, Caracas #45/R

PRIETO, Franco (20th C) Spanish
£552 $861 €800 De la vida jitana - gypsy life (88x93cm-35x37in) s.d.1925. 1-Aug-2 Joel, Victoria #186 est:1000-1500 (A.D 1600)

PRIETO, Manuel Jimenez (1849-?) Spanish
£2414 $4345 €3500 Cheers! To victory! (26x18cm-10x7in) s. board. 26-Jan-4 Durán, Madrid #198/R est:2000

PRIEUR, Barthelemy (attrib) (1540-1611) French
Sculpture
£57895 $106526 €88000 Mere avec son enfant (24cm-9in) pat bronze sold with base lit. 23-Jun-4 Sotheby's, Paris #24/R est:60000-80000

PRIEUR, Etienne Romain Gabriel (1806-1879) French
£909 $1545 €1300 Paysage d'Ile de France (32x40cm-13x16in) s. cardboard. 27-Nov-3 Millon & Associes, Paris #138
£979 $1664 €1400 Vue de l'aqueduc d'Arcueil (32x45cm-13x18in) paper on canvas. 27-Nov-3 Millon & Associes, Paris #137/R

PRIEUR-BARDIN, François L (1870-1936) French
£1133 $2051 €1700 Vue d'Istanbul (12x32cm-5x13in) s.d.1904 panel. 1-Apr-4 Credit Municipal, Paris #73 est:400-500
£4000 $7360 €6000 Le Bosphore, la pointe du serail (24x40cm-9x16in) s.d.1900. 11-Jun-4 Claude Aguttes, Neuilly #170/R est:6000-8000
£6338 $11092 €9000 Barque au bord du Bosphore (27x40cm-11x16in) s. 16-Dec-3 Claude Aguttes, Neuilly #84/R est:12000-15000
£8000 $14720 €12000 Promenade sur le Bosphore (33x41cm-13x16in) s.d.1898. 11-Jun-4 Claude Aguttes, Neuilly #172/R est:12000-15000
£14085 $24366 €20000 Pont de Galata (69x85cm-27x33in) s.d.1904. 15-Dec-3 Gros & Delettrez, Paris #260/R est:20000-30000

PRIKING, Franz (1927-1979) French
£550 $1018 €803 Schale mit apfelen (50x65cm-20x26in) s. paper on paper. 14-Jul-4 Christie's, Kensington #1208/R
£828 $1382 €1200 Bouquet de fleurs (47x38cm-19x15in) s. 17-Nov-3 Charbonneaux, Paris #225
£915 $1584 €1300 Chalutier a maree basse (38x46cm-15x18in) s. prov. 13-Dec-3 Touati, Paris #154/R
£1007 $1802 €1500 Paysage (54x66cm-21x26in) s. 30-May-4 Eric Pillon, Calais #152/R
£1100 $1936 €1606 Still life against a blue background (61x46cm-24x18in) s. 18-May-4 Bonhams, Knightsbridge #72/R est:800-1200
£1224 $2192 €1800 Bouquet de coquelicots. s. 18-Mar-4 Peschetau-Badin Godeau & Leroy, Paris #83/R est:1500-2000
£1232 $2132 €1750 Le coq (50x65cm-20x26in) s. 13-Dec-3 Touati, Paris #153/R est:3000
£1469 $2453 €2100 Les barques (73x100cm-29x39in) s. 30-Jun-3 Artcurial Briest, Paris #757/R est:2000-3000
£1611 $2883 €2400 Nature morte (50x65cm-20x26in) s. 25-May-4 Chambelland & Giafferi, Paris #82/R est:4000-5000
£1678 $2970 €2500 Nature morte aux fleurs (50x65cm-20x26in) s. 27-Apr-4 Artcurial Briest, Paris #235/R est:2000-2500
£1972 $3451 €2800 Nature morte au verre (54x65cm-21x26in) s. 21-Dec-3 Thierry & Lannon, Brest #195/R est:3000-3500
£2083 $3479 €3000 Bouquet de fleurs (65x50cm-26x20in) s. 25-Oct-3 Dianous, Marseille #404
£2113 $3655 €3000 Venise (54x65cm-21x26in) s. s.i.verso. 13-Dec-3 Touati, Paris #152/R est:6000
£2207 $4039 €3200 Cheval esoterique (54x65cm-21x26in) s. 1-Feb-4 Feletin, Province #93
£2500 $4175 €3600 Nature morte au fleurs et calice (55x66cm-22x26in) s. 21-Oct-3 Artcurial Briest, Paris #365/R est:2500-3000
£2685 $4752 €4000 Nature morte (60x73cm-24x29in) s. 29-Apr-4 Claude Aguttes, Neuilly #233/R est:4000-5000
£3061 $4867 €4500 Vase of flowers (66x55cm-26x22in) s. 21-Mar-3 Bailly Pommery, Paris #128
Works on paper
£395 $726 €600 Bateaux a quai (30x47cm-12x19in) s. W/C ink. 28-Jun-4 Joron-Derem, Paris #240
£470 $874 €700 Tounesols au vase bleu (75x56cm-30x22in) s. mixed media. 3-Mar-4 Tajan, Paris #176
£507 $877 €720 Nature morte aux fruits (38x50cm-15x20in) s. W/C. 13-Dec-3 Martinot & Savignat, Pontoise #254
£552 $916 €800 Nature morte (32x50cm-13x20in) s. W/C. 30-Sep-3 Blanchet, Paris #318
£789 $1429 €1200 Paysage du Luberon (32x50cm-13x20in) s. W/C. 19-Apr-4 Boscher, Cherbourg #739

PRIM, Josep M (1907-1973) Spanish
£1056 $1827 €1500 Flowers and watering can (60x90cm-24x35in) s. 15-Dec-3 Ansorena, Madrid #22/R est:1500

PRIMITIVE SCHOOL, 19th C
£10000 $16600 €14600 Three pigs in a barn (46x68cm-18x27in) i. board. 1-Oct-3 Woolley & Wallis, Salisbury #322/R est:1200-1800

PRIN, R (20th C) French
£1118 $2024 €1700 Pacy sur Eure, peniches sur la Seine (64x90cm-25x35in) s. panel. 18-Apr-4 Rouillac, Vendome #162

PRIN, René (1905-1985) French
£282 $487 €400 Barque a Honfleur (22x34cm-9x13in) s. panel. 12-Dec-3 Piasa, Paris #163
£352 $609 €500 Pluie a Menton plage (46x61cm-18x24in) s. 12-Dec-3 Piasa, Paris #159
£423 $731 €600 Le Havre, le bateau vapeur (26x34cm-10x13in) s. panel. 12-Dec-3 Piasa, Paris #164

PRINA, Andre Julien (1886-1941) Italian
£395 $659 €577 Rade de Geneve (27x32cm-11x13in) mono. cardboard. 16-Nov-3 Koller, Geneva #1247 (S.FR 900)
£429 $686 €622 Young woman with flowers (27x20cm-11x8in) board. 15-May-3 Stuker, Bern #1447 (S.FR 900)

PRINA, Stephen (1954-) American
Works on paper
£586 $1037 €856 Exquisite corpse (92x154cm-36x61in) sepia wash off set lithograph diptych prov.lit. 27-Apr-4 AB Stockholms Auktionsverk #1126/R (S.KR 8000)

PRINCE ANDREW OF RUSSIA (20th C) Russian
Works on paper
£320 $563 €467 Still life with fruit on a ledge (25x23cm-10x9in) init.d.1949 gouache. 18-May-4 Woolley & Wallis, Salisbury #322/R

PRINCE OF WALES (c.1937-2002) Australian
£941 $1685 €1374 Body Marks (38x28cm-15x11in) acrylic board painted c.1994 prov. 25-May-4 Lawson Menzies, Sydney #8/R (A.D 2400)
£1098 $1965 €1603 Untitled (48x22cm-19x9in) painted 2001 prov. 25-May-4 Lawson Menzies, Sydney #299/R est:2500-3000 (A.D 2800)
Works on paper
£813 $1285 €1187 Body marks (58x55cm-23x22in) i.verso synthetic polymer paint linen prov. 28-Jul-3 Sotheby's, Paddington #507/R est:2000-4000 (A.D 2000)
£1829 $2890 €2670 Body marks (118x90cm-46x35in) i.verso synthetic polymer paint linen prov. 28-Jul-3 Sotheby's, Paddington #506/R est:2000-4000 (A.D 4500)
£3922 $7020 €5726 Wadjinginy Ceremonial body designs (92x34cm-36x13in) synthetic polymer paint linen diptych exec 2002 prov. 25-May-4 Lawson Menzies, Sydney #7/R est:10000-12000 (A.D 10000)
£12500 $23375 €18750 Body marks (180x122cm-71x48in) name.i.d.2000 verso synthetic polymer paint linen prov.exhib. 26-Jul-4 Sotheby's, Melbourne #115/R est:30000-50000 (A.D 32000)

PRINCE, Richard (1949-) Canadian
£5988 $10000 €8742 Untitled (53x56cm-21x22in) s.d.1999 acrylic col crayon pencil two sheets prov. 13-Nov-3 Sotheby's, New York #609/R est:8000-12000
£6145 $11000 €8972 Head drawing (51x47cm-20x19in) s.d.1997 acrylic ink conte crayon prov. 14-May-4 Phillips, New York #117/R est:5000-7000
£12291 $22000 €17945 Untitled (94x63cm-37x25in) s.d.1997 acrylic pencil silkscreen inks oilstick prov. 13-May-4 Sotheby's, New York #479/R est:4000-6000
£33520 $60000 €48939 I'm not Linda (147x241cm-58x95in) acrylic lacquer prov. 12-May-4 Christie's, Rockefeller NY #385/R est:20000-30000
£41899 $75000 €61173 Untitled, the way she looks in the morning (61x51cm-24x20in) s.d.1989 verso acrylic silkscreen ink prov. 12-May-4 Christie's, Rockefeller NY #375/R est:40000-60000
£42000 $77280 €61320 Seven or eleven (160x102cm-63x40in) s.i.d.1995 acrylic silkscreen two joined canvas prov. 24-Jun-4 Christie's, London #45/R est:40000-60000
£68000 $125120 €99280 What a kid I was (173x122cm-68x48in) s.i.d.1989 acrylic silkscreen ink on canvas prov.exhib. 24-Jun-4 Christie's, London #4/R est:50000-70000
£71856 $120000 €104910 Untitled (244x190cm-96x75in) s.d.1990 overlap acrylic silkscreen ink spray paint 2 parts prov. 13-Nov-3 Sotheby's, New York #460/R est:40000-60000
£83799 $150000 €122347 Two can keep a secret if two are dead (173x122cm-68x48in) s.i.d.1992 overlap acrylic silkscreen prov. 14-May-4 Phillips, New York #179/R est:40000-60000
£90000 $163800 €131400 It was driving me crazy (145x122cm-57x48in) s.i.d.1988 overlap acrylic silkscreen ink panel prov.exhib. 6-Feb-4 Sotheby's, London #107/R est:15000-20000
£122905 $220000 €179441 Couldn't read, couldn't write, couldn't swim (187x190cm-74x75in) s.i.d.1989 overlap acrylic acrylic silkscreen prov.exhib. 13-May-4 Sotheby's, New York #327/R est:150000-200000
£148045 $265000 €216146 The way she looks in the morning (218x120cm-86x47in) s.d.1988 overlap acrylic silkscreen canvas on panel prov.lit. 14-May-4 Phillips, New York #158/R est:80000-120000
£191617 $320000 €279761 Fireman and Drunk (244x190cm-96x75in) s.i.d.1989 verso acrylic silkscreen prov.exhib. 11-Nov-3 Christie's, Rockefeller NY #6/R est:120000-180000
£368715 $660000 €538324 My name (142x244cm-56x96in) s.d.1987 overlap acrylic silkscreen on canvas diptych prov.exhib. 13-May-4 Phillips, New York #12/R est:150000-200000
Photographs
£2331 $3800 €3403 Untitled (51x40cm-20x16in) s.d.1995 num.5/5 Ektacolor print prov. 23-Sep-3 Christie's, Rockefeller NY #176/R est:3000-5000
£2454 $4000 €3583 Untitled (51x40cm-20x16in) s.d.1995 num.5/5 Ektacolor print prov. 23-Sep-3 Christie's, Rockefeller NY #175/R est:3000-5000
£2577 $4200 €3762 Untitled (51x40cm-20x16in) s.d.1995 num.5/5 Ektacolor print prov. 23-Sep-3 Christie's, Rockefeller NY #170/R est:3000-5000
£2761 $4500 €4031 Untitled (51x40cm-20x16in) s.d.1995 num.5/5 Ektacolor print prov. 23-Sep-3 Christie's, Rockefeller NY #174/R est:3000-5000
£2800 $5068 €4088 Sissy Carrie (76x56cm-30x22in) polaroid executed 1986 prov. 1-Apr-4 Christie's, Kensington #338/R est:2000-3000
£2945 $4800 €4300 Untitled (51x40cm-20x16in) s.d.1995 num.5/5 Ektacolor print prov. 23-Sep-3 Christie's, Rockefeller NY #177/R est:3000-5000
£2989 $5500 €4364 Untitled, party series (51x41cm-20x16in) s.verso ektacolor print edition of 10 prov. 10-Jun-4 Phillips, New York #528/R est:3000-5000
£3114 $5200 €4546 Good revolution (52x42cm-20x17in) c-print engraved plaque mounted gold record prov. 14-Nov-3 Phillips, New York #290/R est:1500-2000
£4469 $8000 €6525 Monster truck (36x28cm-14x11in) s.d.1985-86 num.AP verso colour photograph prov. 13-May-4 Sotheby's, New York #336/R est:8000-12000
£11976 $20000 €17485 Untitled, Teddy, Elizabeth, Marlene and Astrid (220x122cm-87x48in) s.d.1987 num.1/2 verso ektacolor print prov. 13-Nov-3 Sotheby's, New York #490/R est:15000-20000
£15642 $28000 €22837 David Byrne (61x51cm-24x20in) s.i.d.1984 verso Ektacolor print edition of 2 prov. 14-May-4 Phillips, New York #157/R est:20000-30000
£16467 $27500 €24042 Untitled, Jeff Koons (61x51cm-24x20in) s.d.1984 num.1/2 c-print prov. 13-Nov-3 Sotheby's, New York #459/R est:30000-40000
£18000 $30060 €26280 Untitled, bangs, waves, palms (218x119cm-86x47in) ektacolor print edition of 2 prov. 22-Oct-3 Christie's, London #171/R est:12000-15000
£22346 $40000 €32625 Untitled (61x46cm-24x18in) s.d.1984 verso ektacolor print edition 1 of 2 prov. 12-May-4 Christie's, Rockefeller NY #379/R est:35000-45000
£22346 $40000 €32625 Untitled (61x46cm-24x18in) s.d.1984 verso ektacolor print edition 1 of 2 prov.lit. 12-May-4 Christie's, Rockefeller NY #380/R est:35000-45000
£23333 $42000 €34066 Cowboys and girlfriends (56x38cm-22x15in) s.d.1992 14 cibachrome prints prov. 23-Apr-4 Phillips, New York #43/R est:25000-35000
£26816 $48000 €39151 Untitled (61x46cm-24x18in) s.d.1984 verso ektacolor print edition 1 of 2 prov. 12-May-4 Christie's, Rockefeller NY #378/R est:35000-45000
£41899 $75000 €61173 Entertainment series, Russell (244x122cm-96x48in) ektacolor print prov.exhib. 12-May-4 Christie's, Rockefeller NY #374/R est:60000-80000
£42000 $77280 €61320 Man's hand with watch and cigarette, watch and piano, watch and pocket (41x58cm-16x23in) ektacolour photograph exec 1980 three parts prov. 24-Jun-4 Sotheby's, London #104/R est:12000-15000
£44000 $80080 €64240 Untitled, three hands with watches (41x58cm-16x23in) ektacolour photos edition 10 of 10 set of three prov.lit. 6-Feb-4 Sotheby's, London #106/R est:12000-15000
£46089 $82500 €67290 Kristy - from the Entertainer series (89x114cm-35x45in) ektacolour print exec 1982 edn 1/3 prov.exhib. 13-May-4 Sotheby's, New York #337/R est:70000-90000
£53892 $90000 €78682 Four women with hats (51x61cm-20x24in) each s.num.d.1980 verso ektacolor prints four prov.exhib. 12-Nov-3 Christie's, Rockefeller NY #522/R est:80000-120000
£55000 $100100 €80300 Untitled - Girlfriend (163x112cm-64x44in) ektacolour print executed 1993 prov.lit. 4-Feb-4 Christie's, London #6/R est:35000-45000
£60000 $110400 €87600 Untitled - 4 woman with their backs to the camera (51x61cm-20x24in) ektacolour photograph set of four. 23-Jun-4 Sotheby's, London #42/R est:50000-70000
£78212 $140000 €114190 Untitled, cowboy (71x102cm-28x40in) ektacolor print foamcore edition 2 of 2 prov.exhib.lit. 12-May-4 Christie's, Rockefeller NY #370/R est:120000-180000
£94972 $170000 €138659 Untitled, fashion (61x51cm-24x20in) s.d.1982 num.ap verso ektacolor print prov.lit. 12-May-4 Christie's, Rockefeller NY #373/R est:60000-80000
£125000 $227500 €182500 Untitled - Cowboy (110x72cm-43x28in) ektacolor print executed 1980-84 prov.lit. 4-Feb-4 Christie's, London #4/R est:90000-120000
£128492 $230000 €187598 Cowboy (174x103cm-69x41in) s.d.1999 num.3 verso ektacolor photograph prov. 13-May-4 Phillips, New York #19/R est:80000-120000
£139665 $250000 €203911 Untitled Cowboys (102x68cm-40x27in) ektacolour print from edn of 2 exec 1984 prov.exhib. 11-May-4 Christie's, Rockefeller NY #55/R est:180000-220000
£173653 $290000 €253533 Cowboy (233x532cm-92x209in) s.d.2000 digital print canvas prov. 12-Nov-3 Christie's, Rockefeller NY #524/R est:80000-120000
£197605 $330000 €288503 Spriritual America (61x51cm-24x20in) s.d.1983 num.10 ektacolor print prov.exhib.lit. 13-Nov-3 Phillips, New York #15/R est:200000-300000
£245509 $410000 €358443 Untitled - cowboy (250x144cm-98x57in) ektacolor print executed 1999 prov.exhib.lit. 13-Nov-3 Phillips, New York #12/R est:80000-120000
Works on paper
£2793 $5000 €4078 Peter Wilson (35x28cm-14x11in) s.d.2000 i.verso wax crayon felt tip pen ball point pen ink prov. 14-May-4 Phillips, New York #154/R est:7000-9000
£4469 $8000 €6525 Untitled Panama 1949 (90x67cm-35x26in) ink crayon pencil acrylic exec.1997 prov. 13-May-4 Sotheby's, New York #361/R est:8000-12000
£6145 $11000 €8972 Untitled Panama 1949 (90x67cm-35x26in) in, crayon pencil acrylic exec 1997 prov. 13-May-4 Sotheby's, New York #362/R est:8000-12000
£7263 $13000 €10604 Untitled (99x69cm-39x27in) s.i.d.12-2-89 graphite col pencil acrylic spray paint prov. 14-May-4 Phillips, New York #112/R est:6000-8000
£20000 $36400 €29200 Untitled, joke painting (60x46cm-24x18in) pencil silkscreen ink t-shirt on stretcher exec.c.1990 prov. 6-Feb-4 Sotheby's, London #108/R est:10000-15000
£21229 $38000 €30994 Untitled, what was the name of that tranquilizer (102x66cm-40x26in) s.d.85 verso graphite prov.exhib. 14-May-4 Phillips, New York #128/R est:15000-20000

PRINCE, Richard and SHERMAN, Cindy (20th C) Canadian/American
Photographs
£59880 $100000 €87425 Untitled - double portrait (51x61cm-20x24in) s.d.1980 num.8/10 col photograph in two parts prov.exhib.lit. 12-Nov-3 Sotheby's, New York #39/R est:100000-150000

PRINCESS CHARLOTTE BONAPARTE (1802-1838) French
Works on paper
£651 $1379 €1200 Route dans un paysage (10x14cm-4x6in) i.mount brown wash black pencil. 21-May-3 Daguerre, Paris #75/R

PRINCESS LUISE HOLLANDINE (1622-1709) German
£29000 $52200 €42340 Allegorical portrait of three ladies and a child as the finding of Erithonius (133x157cm-52x62in) 21-Apr-4 Christie's, London #34/R est:15000-20000

PRINCESS MARIA PILAR OF BAVARIA (1891-1987) German
£458 $819 €650 View of Barcelona (43x59cm-17x23in) s.d.72 lit. 8-Jan-4 Allgauer, Kempten #2339/R

PRINCESS MARIE (1865-1909) Danish/British
Works on paper
£331 $592 €483 Still life of dead bird and mushrooms (29x54cm-11x21in) s. W/C. 12-Jan-4 Rasmussen, Vejle #166/R (D.KR 3500)
£378 $677 €552 Still life of apples and fungi (27x51cm-11x20in) s. W/C. 12-Jan-4 Rasmussen, Vejle #163/R (D.KR 4000)

PRINCESS MATHILDE BONAPARTE (1820-1908) French
Works on paper
£2657 $4517 €3800 Portrait de femme en costume troubadour (54x43cm-21x17in) i. W/C gouache pierre noire. 1-Dec-3 Coutau Begarie, Paris #189/R est:4500-5000

PRINCESS OTTAVIA BORGHESE (1825-?) French?
£1399 $2336 €2000 Portrait of gentleman (39x32cm-15x13in) s.d.1825 after Frans van Mieris. 12-Oct-3 Salle des ventes Pillet, Lyon la Foret #4/R est:1500-2000

PRINET, René-Xavier (1861-1946) French
£3103 $5741 €4500 Villa Montebello, Cabourg (60x73cm-24x29in) s. 11-Feb-4 Beaussant & Lefèvre, Paris #150/R est:4000-5000
Works on paper
£276 $510 €400 Femme a son chevalet (65x50cm-26x20in) chl estompe. 11-Feb-4 Beaussant & Lefèvre, Paris #74/R
£276 $510 €400 Entrez (44x30cm-17x12in) init.studio st. chl estompe. 11-Feb-4 Beaussant & Lefèvre, Paris #94/R
£276 $510 €400 Voila t-il pas, chapitre IX (56x39cm-22x15in) init.studio st. chl estompe htd gouache. 11-Feb-4 Beaussant & Lefèvre, Paris #100/R
£276 $510 €400 C'est toi, Act 1 scene XII (29x44cm-11x17in) init.studio st. chl estompe. 11-Feb-4 Beaussant & Lefèvre, Paris #112/R
£276 $510 €400 Untitled (33x31cm-13x12in) chl estompe htd chk. 11-Feb-4 Beaussant & Lefèvre, Paris #149
£290 $536 €420 Modele nu en buste (62x47cm-24x19in) d.1882 studio st.verso chl estompe. 11-Feb-4 Beaussant & Lefèvre, Paris #64
£310 $574 €450 Femme assoupie (45x57cm-18x22in) studio st.verso sanguine double-sided. 11-Feb-4 Beaussant & Lefèvre, Paris #58
£310 $574 €450 Et la vue de cela, chapitre XXV (32x31cm-13x12in) init.studio st. chl estompe htd gouache. 11-Feb-4 Beaussant & Lefèvre, Paris #87/R
£310 $574 €450 C'est quelque chose de mieux que la beaute (33x48cm-13x19in) init.studio st. chl estompe. 11-Feb-4 Beaussant & Lefèvre, Paris #111/R
£310 $574 €450 Portrait de femme (49x31cm-19x12in) studio st.verso sanguine estompe. 11-Feb-4 Beaussant & Lefèvre, Paris #139
£345 $638 €500 Etude pour Le fauteuil d'osier (44x32cm-17x13in) studio st. black crayon cardboard. 11-Feb-4 Beaussant & Lefèvre, Paris #73/R
£345 $638 €500 Nu au fauteuil en osier (56x44cm-22x17in) studio st. chl marron crayon estompe. 11-Feb-4 Beaussant & Lefèvre, Paris #79
£345 $638 €500 Femme a la cheminee (59x44cm-23x17in) studio st. chl estompe. 11-Feb-4 Beaussant & Lefèvre, Paris #80/R
£345 $638 €500 On me conduisait a Tours chaque Samedi (33x48cm-13x19in) init.studio st. chl estompe. 11-Feb-4 Beaussant & Lefèvre, Paris #113/R
£379 $702 €550 Jeune femme au canape (31x48cm-12x19in) studio st. chl estompe. 11-Feb-4 Beaussant & Lefèvre, Paris #70/R
£379 $702 €550 Adieu Isabelle, Acte 1 scene III (33x31cm-13x12in) init.studio st. chl estompe htd gouache. 11-Feb-4 Beaussant & Lefèvre, Paris #93/R
£448 $829 €650 Etude pour Cours de dance (62x48cm-24x19in) studio st.verso gouache sanguine. 11-Feb-4 Beaussant & Lefèvre, Paris #53
£448 $829 €650 Nous vimes de loin deux messieurs descendre a la grille, chapitre XXI (33x48cm-13x19in) init.studio st. chl estompe. 11-Feb-4 Beaussant & Lefèvre, Paris #96/R
£483 $893 €700 Moi a votre place, chapitre XI (50x32cm-20x13in) init.studio st. chl estompe. 11-Feb-4 Beaussant & Lefèvre, Paris #95/R
£483 $893 €700 Voyons Jeanine pourquoi pleures-tu, Act 1 scene X (29x44cm-11x17in) init.studio st. chl estompe htd gouache. 11-Feb-4 Beaussant & Lefèvre, Paris #99
£517 $957 €750 Femme au rocking chair (45x58cm-18x23in) studio st. ink wash sanguine black crayon. 11-Feb-4 Beaussant & Lefèvre, Paris #68/R
£517 $957 €750 Maman colibri, projet de couverture (29x32cm-11x13in) s.studio st. W/C gouache. 11-Feb-4 Beaussant & Lefèvre, Paris #116/R
£552 $1021 €800 Sous la Coupole, reception d'Albert Besnard a l'Academie des Beaux-Arts (48x56cm-19x22in) studio st.verso chl estompe. 11-Feb-4 Beaussant & Lefèvre, Paris #63/R
£621 $1148 €900 Nu assis (61x46cm-24x18in) d.24 decembre 1881 studio st.verso chl estompe. 11-Feb-4 Beaussant & Lefèvre, Paris #55
£621 $1148 €900 Dans l'atelier (33x50cm-13x20in) studio st.verso gouache sanguine. 11-Feb-4 Beaussant & Lefèvre, Paris #136
£655 $1212 €950 Abritee derriere le rideau, chapitre II (32x25cm-13x10in) init.studio st. chl estompe htd white gouache. 11-Feb-4 Beaussant & Lefèvre, Paris #85/R
£690 $1276 €1000 Etude pour Villa d'Este, le jet d'eau (66x49cm-26x19in) studio st. chl estompe. 11-Feb-4 Beaussant & Lefèvre, Paris #71/R
£690 $1276 €1000 Nu de dos (57x45cm-22x18in) studio st. sanguine black crayon. 11-Feb-4 Beaussant & Lefèvre, Paris #77/R
£759 $1403 €1100 Il me regarda tout le temps d'une facon fort genante, chapitre VIII (39x48cm-15x19in) init.studio st. chl estompe. 11-Feb-4 Beaussant & Lefèvre, Paris #98/R
£828 $1531 €1200 Maree basse (49x65cm-19x26in) studio st. chl estompe. 11-Feb-4 Beaussant & Lefèvre, Paris #69/R
£828 $1531 €1200 Cabourg, transat devant les cabines (47x63cm-19x25in) studio st. chl estompe. 11-Feb-4 Beaussant & Lefèvre, Paris #78/R
£897 $1659 €1300 Femme assoupie (62x47cm-24x19in) studio st.verso col crayon estompe. 11-Feb-4 Beaussant & Lefèvre, Paris #54/R
£1379 $2552 €2000 Femme a sa lecture (62x48cm-24x19in) studio st.verso chl estompe. 11-Feb-4 Beaussant & Lefèvre, Paris #52/R est:500
£1379 $2552 €2000 Etude pour La bibliotheque (48x33cm-19x13in) studio st. chl estompe. 11-Feb-4 Beaussant & Lefèvre, Paris #82/R est:350
£1448 $2679 €2100 Etude pour Le gouter sur l'herbe (48x62cm-19x24in) studio st.verso chl estompe. 11-Feb-4 Beaussant & Lefèvre, Paris #84/R est:600
£1793 $3317 €2600 Cabourg, la promenade (48x63cm-19x25in) studio st. chl estompe. 11-Feb-4 Beaussant & Lefèvre, Paris #76/R est:700

PRINGELS, Léon (1901-1992) Belgian
£265 $482 €400 La lieutenance a Honfleur (65x100cm-26x39in) s.d.77 acrylic. 15-Jun-4 Vanderkindere, Brussels #565
£331 $603 €500 Vue d'Altea en Espagne (40x50cm-16x20in) s.d.74 panel. 15-Jun-4 Vanderkindere, Brussels #546
£397 $723 €600 Vue de l'Hotel de Ville de Bruxelles (60x50cm-24x20in) s.d.71. 15-Jun-4 Vanderkindere, Brussels #553
£430 $783 €650 Vase de fleurs (60x50cm-24x20in) s.d.73. 15-Jun-4 Vanderkindere, Brussels #174
£530 $964 €800 Fermette (22x27cm-9x11in) s. one d.74 one d.75 pair. 15-Jun-4 Vanderkindere, Brussels #564
£795 $1446 €1200 Coin d'Auderghem sous la neige. s.d.67. 15-Jun-4 Vanderkindere, Brussels #561
£1258 $2290 €1900 Nature morte au gibier (98x196cm-39x77in) s.d.66. 15-Jun-4 Vanderkindere, Brussels #563 est:600-800

PRINGLE, Mary (1880-1940) British
Works on paper
£580 $1015 €847 Portrait of an altar boy (74x48cm-29x19in) s.d.1906 W/C. 19-Dec-3 Mallams, Oxford #192/R

PRINNER, Anton (1902-1983) French
Works on paper
£541 $968 €800 Soleil levant (42x62cm-17x24in) s. crayon gouache. 4-May-4 Calmels Cohen, Paris #198
£574 $1028 €850 Soleil levant (42x62cm-17x24in) s. crayon gouache. 4-May-4 Calmels Cohen, Paris #199/R

PRINS, Benjamin (1860-1934) Dutch
£296 $545 €450 Still life with fruit and a jug (48x57cm-19x22in) 28-Jun-4 Dr Fritz Nagel, Stuttgart #7033/R
£559 $1000 €816 Notcutnal moonlit village landscape (86x102cm-34x40in) bears sig. 15-May-4 Jeffery Burchard, Florida #34

PRINS, Ferdinand de (1859-1908) Belgian
£268 $491 €400 Bergere dans un paysage (65x90cm-26x35in) s. 8-Jul-4 Campo, Vlaamse Kaai #87
£2148 $3801 €3200 Vachere et vaches dans un paysage (133x104cm-52x41in) s.d.1888. 27-Apr-4 Campo, Vlaamse Kaai #386 est:800-1200

PRINS, Pierre (1838-1913) French
£3800 $6992 €5548 Soleil couchant derriere les meules (50x61cm-20x24in) s. 24-Mar-4 Sotheby's, Olympia #77/R est:4000-5000
Works on paper
£400 $736 €600 Moisson (30x43cm-12x17in) s. chl estompe exec.c.1901 prov.lit. 14-Jun-4 Tajan, Paris #17/R
£400 $736 €600 Le chemin creux (42x31cm-17x12in) s. chl estompe prov.lit. 14-Jun-4 Tajan, Paris #18/R
£667 $1227 €1000 La maison et les cypres (36x39cm-14x15in) bears st.init. chl pastel exec.c.1903 prov.lit. 14-Jun-4 Tajan, Paris #16/R
£800 $1472 €1200 Le hameau dans les arbres (32x44cm-13x17in) s. pastel prov.lit. 14-Jun-4 Tajan, Paris #15/R
£1184 $2179 €1800 Paysage au travail (46x34cm-18x13in) s. pastel. 28-Jun-4 Joron-Derem, Paris #93/R est:2000-2200
£1223 $2006 €1700 Remorqueurs sur la Seine (22x33cm-9x13in) s. pastel. 6-Jun-3 Chochon-Barre & Allardi, Paris #84 est:600-700
£1667 $3067 €2500 La barque (30x53cm-12x21in) s. pastel prov. 14-Jun-4 Tajan, Paris #14 est:2500-3000
£1701 $3044 €2500 Paysage (43x52cm-17x20in) s. pastel. 19-Mar-4 Piasa, Paris #184/R est:3000
£2302 $3776 €3200 Pommier au bord du chemin en Seine et Oise (36x43cm-14x17in) s. pastel. 6-Jun-3 Chochon-Barre & Allardi, Paris #85/R est:2500-3000
£2374 $3894 €3300 La Seine au Pont Royal (50x70cm-20x28in) s. pastel. 6-Jun-3 Chochon-Barre & Allardi, Paris #86/R est:3500-3800
£4027 $7490 €6000 Environs de Saint-Evroult (36x43cm-14x17in) s. pastel exec c.1885 prov.exhib.lit. 3-Mar-4 Tajan, Paris #16/R est:3000-4000
£4027 $7490 €6000 Village au bord de la Seine (59x46cm-23x18in) s. pastel prov.exhib.lit. 3-Mar-4 Tajan, Paris #22/R est:4000-6000

PRINSEP, Valentine Cameron (1838-1904) British
£363 $650 €530 Portrait of Sir Frances Grant (28x20cm-11x8in) s. panel. 8-May-4 Susanin's, Chicago #6128/R
£398 $700 €581 Sir Francis Grant (41x33cm-16x13in) init. board. 28-May-4 Aspire, Cleveland #17/R
£30000 $55200 €43800 First awakening of Eve (114x135cm-45x53in) s.i. prov.exhib.lit. 11-Jun-4 Christie's, London #157/R est:40000-60000

PRINSEP, William (1794-1874) British
Works on paper
£1800 $2934 €2628 Hindu Collage in College Square, Calcutta (23x33cm-9x13in) pencil pen blk ink prov.exhib. 24-Sep-3 Christie's, London #33/R est:2000-3000

PRINSEP, William (attrib) (1794-1874) British
Works on paper
£2800 $4564 €4088 Fort William with the Esplande, Calcutta (23x36cm-9x14in) indis.sig. pencil W/C scratching out prov. 24-Sep-3 Christie's, London #34/R est:2000-3000

PRINZ, Christian August (1819-1867) Norwegian
£1126 $2027 €1644 Still life of fruit (32x41cm-13x16in) s.d.1853. 26-Jan-4 Lilla Bukowskis, Stockholm #487 est:20000-25000 (S.KR 15000)
£2402 $4299 €3507 Young herder (66x92cm-26x36in) s.d.1847. 22-Mar-4 Blomqvist, Oslo #326/R est:40000-60000 (N.KR 30000)

PRINZ, Karl Ludwig (1875-1944) Austrian
£905 $1620 €1321 White mosque in Skutari (39x51cm-15x20in) s.i.d.19.II.1916 i. verso canvas on board. 13-May-4 Stuker, Bern #287/R est:2500-3500 (S.FR 2100)
Works on paper
£517 $859 €750 Dolomites in evening light (19x29cm-7x11in) s. i. verso mixed media board. 30-Sep-3 Dorotheum, Vienna #361/R
£586 $973 €850 Mountain huts in winter (19x29cm-7x11in) s. mixed media board. 30-Sep-3 Dorotheum, Vienna #362/R
£621 $1030 €900 Otscher from Gosing (30x33cm-12x13in) W/C. 30-Sep-3 Dorotheum, Vienna #350/R

PRINZ, Otto (1906-1980) Austrian
Works on paper
£470 $841 €700 Untitled - woman and house (30x40cm-12x16in) s. bears d. pencil board prov. 25-May-4 Dorotheum, Vienna #320/R

PRIOLO, Paolo (1818-1892) Italian
Works on paper
£350 $644 €511 Flower seller (34x26cm-13x10in) s. pencil W/C. 25-Mar-4 Christie's, Kensington #233

PRIOR HAMBLEN SCHOOL, American
£3243 $6000 €4735 Portrait of a ship captain (72x59cm-28x23in) painted c.1850. 15-Jan-4 Sotheby's, New York #290/R est:6000-8000
£5556 $9000 €8112 Three young children (61x86cm-24x34in) framed oval. 1-Aug-3 North East Auctions, Portsmouth #844/R est:7000-10000
£5882 $10000 €8588 Portrait of a young child in red with flowers in one hand (33x28cm-13x11in) board prov. 31-Oct-3 North East Auctions, Portsmouth #1518 est:9000-12000
£10494 $17000 €15321 Girl in blue dress with bows and coral bead necklace and bracelets (36x25cm-14x10in) board prov. 1-Aug-3 North East Auctions, Portsmouth #837/R est:25000-35000

PRIOR HAMBLEN SCHOOL (19th C) American
£4265 $7975 €6227 Portrait of a young lady. 28-Feb-4 William A Smith, Plainfield #3/R
£9091 $16000 €13273 Portrait of a young boy wearing a patterned grey vest and black coat (69x53cm-27x21in) 18-May-4 Sotheby's, New York #105/R est:12000-18000

PRIOR, Manuel (1933-) Spanish
£331 $573 €470 Couple (116x114cm-46x45in) 15-Dec-3 Ansorena, Madrid #1000/R
£387 $670 €550 Book and bottle (65x81cm-26x32in) s.d.73 s.d.verso. 15-Dec-3 Ansorena, Madrid #1035/R
£789 $1453 €1200 Book and bottle (65x81cm-26x32in) s.d.73 s.i.verso. 22-Jun-4 Durán, Madrid #158/R

PRIOR, Margarita (1967-) Spanish
£403 $749 €600 Vase of flowers (100x81cm-39x32in) s. i.verso. 2-Mar-4 Ansorena, Madrid #898/R

PRIOR, Melton (1845-1910) British
Works on paper
£2600 $4602 €3796 Aftermath of the battle of Isandlwana. Death of General Colley at Majuba Hill (30x44cm-12x17in) s.d.May 21 1879 W/C two. 27-Apr-4 Bonhams, New Bond Street #96 est:300-500

PRIOR, William Matthew (1806-1873) American
£938 $1500 €1369 Half-length portrait of young woman wearing a blue dress (25x20cm-10x8in) s. 20-Sep-3 Pook & Pook, Downington #330/R est:2500-3500
£2315 $3750 €3380 Portrait of man with sideburns (38x28cm-15x11in) bears i.d. board. 1-Aug-3 North East Auctions, Portsmouth #841/R est:5000-7000
£2513 $4750 €3669 Portrait of brown eyed man (69x56cm-27x22in) i. verso. 22-Feb-4 Skinner, Boston #105/R est:3000-5000
£5027 $9500 €7339 Portrait of a boy (36x25cm-14x10in) board prov. 22-Feb-4 Skinner, Boston #74/R est:4000-6000
£5682 $10000 €8296 Portrait of a ship's captain and his wife (33x23cm-13x9in) i. panel pair. 22-May-4 Pook & Pook, Downington #726/R est:8000-12000
£8995 $17000 €13133 Portrait of a girl (36x25cm-14x10in) s. verso board prov. 22-Feb-4 Skinner, Boston #75/R est:4000-6000
£10811 $20000 €15784 Portrait of Susan Antoinette Murdock Raymond (88x65cm-35x26in) painted c.1850. 15-Jan-4 Sotheby's, New York #313/R est:20000-30000
£27778 $45000 €40556 Young girl in apricot dress holding bouquet and basket (81x61cm-32x24in) s.i. verso prov. 1-Aug-3 North East Auctions, Portsmouth #840/R est:40000-60000

PRIOR, William Matthew (attrib) (1806-1873) American
£531 $850 €775 Portrait of George Washington. Portrait of Martha Washington (58x48cm-23x19in) pair. 19-Sep-3 Freeman, Philadelphia #101/R
£2059 $3500 €3006 Portrait of Elizabeth Southwick (36x25cm-14x10in) i.verso cardboard. 1-Nov-3 Skinner, Boston #225/R est:3000-5000
£2469 $4000 €3580 Portraits of a young man and woman (38x28cm-15x11in) artist board pair. 10-Aug-3 Skinner, Bolton #64/R est:4000-6000
£2932 $4750 €4281 Portrait of young dark haired woman wearing lace trimmed black dress (36x25cm-14x10in) board prov. 1-Aug-3 North East Auctions, Portsmouth #848/R est:5000-7000
£37037 $60000 €54074 Family portraits (43x33cm-17x13in) board four prov. 1-Aug-3 North East Auctions, Portsmouth #884/R est:40000-60000

PRIOU, Louis (1845-?) French
£7059 $12000 €10306 Maternite Champetre (90x146cm-35x57in) s.d.82 exhib. 28-Oct-3 Sotheby's, New York #130/R est:15000-20000

PRITCHARD, G Thompson (1878-1962) American
£518 $850 €751 Autumn, Brentwood, Essex, England (64x76cm-25x30in) s. 4-Jun-3 Alderfer's, Hatfield #291/R
£915 $1500 €1327 Landscape with trees and house (61x76cm-24x30in) s. 4-Jun-3 Alderfer's, Hatfield #290/R est:1200-1500
£1005 $1900 €1467 River landscape (58x81cm-23x32in) bears i. stretcher. 17-Feb-4 John Moran, Pasadena #20b/R est:2000-3000
£1058 $2000 €1545 Winter wooded river landscape (61x74cm-24x29in) s. prov. 17-Feb-4 John Moran, Pasadena #162/R est:2500-3500
£1236 $2250 €1805 Coastal scene with crashing waves on rocks (61x76cm-24x30in) s. 15-Jun-4 John Moran, Pasadena #93b est:2000-3000
£1984 $3750 €2897 Boats in harbour (61x76cm-24x30in) bears sig. 17-Feb-4 John Moran, Pasadena #104/R est:1500-2500

PRITCHARD, Gwilym (1931-) British
£340 $578 €496 Tri Ty-Pentre Ycha (30x48cm-12x19in) tempera exhib. 27-Nov-3 Greenslade Hunt, Taunton #1041/R
£440 $801 €642 Landscape (60x120cm-24x47in) i.verso board. 21-Jun-4 Bonhams, Bath #366
£640 $1152 €934 North Wales coastalscape with cottage (33x43cm-13x17in) s. 24-Apr-4 Rogers Jones, Clwyd #149
Works on paper
£300 $546 €438 Hill and apple trees (12x19cm-5x7in) s. W/C. 15-Jun-4 Bonhams, Knightsbridge #72

PRITCHARD, J Ambrose (1858-1905) American
£1887 $3000 €2755 Marshes (51x76cm-20x30in) s. 12-Sep-3 Skinner, Boston #273/R est:2500-5500
£2514 $4500 €3670 Landscape with flowers (41x30cm-16x12in) s.d.92 prov. 6-May-4 Shannon's, Milford #231/R est:2500-3500

PRITCHETT, Edward (fl.1828-1864) British
£7000 $11690 €10220 View of the Grand Canal (33x57cm-13x22in) prov. 16-Oct-3 Lawrence, Crewkerne #731/R
£7000 $11900 €10220 St. Mark's Square, Venice (61x51cm-24x20in) s. 25-Nov-3 Christie's, London #160/R est:8000-12000
£9000 $15300 €13140 Royal naval collage, Greenwich, from the Thames, the royal observatory beyond (41x51cm-16x20in) 25-Nov-3 Christie's, London #155/R est:10000-15000
£11000 $18700 €16060 View of the Piazetta from the Dogana, Venice (48x65cm-19x26in) 25-Nov-3 Christie's, London #159/R est:12000-18000
£21000 $38640 €30660 Entrance to the Cannaregio, Venice. Rialto Bridge, Venice (25x35cm-10x14in) s. pair prov. 23-Mar-4 Bonhams, New Bond Street #42/R est:10000-15000
Works on paper
£2200 $4070 €3212 Embarking onto the gondola outside the church of Il Gesuati, Venice (24x34cm-9x13in) W/C. 9-Mar-4 Bonhams, New Bond Street #74/R est:1000-1500

PRITCHETT, Robert Taylor (1828-1907) British
Works on paper
£460 $782 €672 Jubilee celebration, Bombay. Poona (18x25cm-7x10in) mono.i.d.Feb 1887 W/C htd white pair. 4-Nov-3 Bonhams, New Bond Street #65/R

PRITTIE, Edwin John (20th C) British?
£251 $420 €366 Roman legion (64x89cm-25x35in) s. 14-Nov-3 Aspire, Cleveland #86

PRIVAT, Colette (1935-) French
£223 $400 €326 Bouquet multicolour (71x58cm-28x23in) s. i.verso. 8-Jan-4 Doyle, New York #36/R
£324 $550 €473 Le vase bleu (46x38cm-18x15in) s. 5-Nov-3 Doyle, New York #56/R
£521 $850 €761 Fruits (51x61cm-20x24in) s. i.verso. 17-Jul-3 Doyle, New York #41/R

PRIVAT, Gilbert Auguste (1892-1969) French
Sculpture
£1631 $2643 €2300 La science entouree d'ecoliers (110x120cm-43x47in) s. plaster relief lit. 24-May-3 Martinot & Savignat, Pontoise #85/R est:1800-2200

PRIVATO, Cosimo (1899-1971) Italian
£1189 $2045 €1700 Playing in the fields (39x52cm-15x20in) s. cardboard. 3-Dec-3 Stadion, Trieste #1054/R est:1200-1600
£66901 $115739 €95000 Women's life (43x105cm-17x41in) s. set of 10. 14-Dec-3 Finarte, Venice #4/R est:100000-140000

PROBST, Carl (1854-1924) Austrian
Works on paper
£483 $801 €700 Portrait of a Valkyrie (68x51cm-27x20in) s. pastel paper on canvas. 30-Sep-3 Dorotheum, Vienna #195/R

PROBST, Jakob (1880-1966) Swiss
Sculpture
£2423 $4119 €3538 Foal (92x92x39cm-36x36x15in) s.d.1951 green pat.bronze. 5-Nov-3 Dobiaschofsky, Bern #2462/R est:3000 (S.FR 5500)

PROBST, Thorwald (1886-1948) American
£688 $1300 €1004 Sierras landscape (41x51cm-16x20in) s. board prov. 17-Feb-4 John Moran, Pasadena #156/R

PROCACCINI, Andrea (1671-1734) Italian
£9929 $16582 €14000 Portrait of Francesca Gommi Maratta, wife of Carlo Maratta (90x73cm-35x29in) after Carlo Maratta prov. 18-Jun-3 Christie's, Rome #435/R est:15000-20000
£13000 $23400 €18980 Flight into Egypt (75x62cm-30x24in) prov. 21-Apr-4 Christie's, London #80/R est:10000-15000

PROCACCINI, Andrea (attrib) (1671-1734) Italian
£2384 $4339 €3600 Assunta (39x37cm-15x15in) 16-Jun-4 Christie's, Rome #293/R est:2500-3000

PROCACCINI, Camillo (1546-1629) Italian
Works on paper
£5000 $9000 €7300 Saint John the Baptist flanked by Saint Barbara and other saints (27x20cm-11x8in) i.d.1577 black chk pen brown ink wash. 22-Jan-4 Christie's, Rockefeller NY #25/R est:10000-15000

PROCACCINI, Camillo (circle) (1546-1629) Italian
£625 $1019 €900 Madonna (72x34cm-28x13in) 26-Sep-3 Bolland & Marotz, Bremen #478/R

PROCACCINI, Ercole (16/17th C) Italian
Works on paper
£301 $550 €439 Christ and Saint Peter (40x34cm-16x13in) i. pen col ink card stock. 29-Jan-4 Swann Galleries, New York #46/R

PROCACCINI, Giulio Cesare (1570-1625) Italian
£13333 $24000 €19466 Transfiguration (34x25cm-13x10in) copper prov. 23-Jan-4 Christie's, Rockefeller NY #197/R est:15000-20000
Works on paper
£1300 $2340 €1898 Figure studies (7x5cm-3x2in) pen brown ink pair. 20-Apr-4 Sotheby's, Olympia #1/R est:800-1200

PROCHAZKA, Antonin (1882-1945) Czechoslovakian
Works on paper
£1097 $1866 €1602 Riders (45x64cm-18x25in) mono. s.verso mixed media. 29-Nov-3 Dorotheum, Prague #140/R est:40000-60000 (C.KR 50000)

PROCHAZKA, Iaro (1886-1947) Czechoslovakian
£268 $498 €391 Merry stall holders in Paris (28x31cm-11x12in) s.i. canvas on board. 6-Mar-4 Dorotheum, Prague #56/R est:8000-12000 (C.KR 13000)
£412 $766 €602 Havelsky in Prague (50x65cm-20x26in) s. 6-Mar-4 Dorotheum, Prague #58/R est:20000-30000 (C.KR 20000)
£439 $746 €641 Prague corner (50x64cm-20x25in) s. cardboard. 29-Nov-3 Dorotheum, Prague #54/R est:15000-25000 (C.KR 20000)
£535 $996 €781 From Kampa (50x65cm-20x26in) s. 6-Mar-4 Dorotheum, Prague #68 est:18000-30000 (C.KR 26000)
£657 $1090 €959 Uhelny trh Square in Prague (48x64cm-19x25in) s. board. 4-Oct-3 Dorotheum, Prague #102/R est:30000-45000 (C.KR 30000)

PROCHAZKA, Josef (1909-) ?
£337 $594 €506 Landscape with pond (35x52cm-14x20in) s. cardboard. 22-May-4 Dorotheum, Prague #150 est:12000-18000 (C.KR 16000)
£525 $872 €767 At farm (50x66cm-20x26in) s. 4-Oct-3 Dorotheum, Prague #83 est:20000-30000 (C.KR 24000)

PROCKTOR, Patrick (1936-) British
£380 $684 €555 Tea in Athens (33x22cm-13x9in) s.i.d.6.8.63 oil on pastel. 20-Jan-4 Bonhams, Knightsbridge #43
£8000 $13280 €11680 Sacre Coeur par Rue Montalembert (136x92cm-54x36in) prov. 30-Sep-3 Sotheby's, London #20/R est:8500-12000
Works on paper
£250 $418 €365 Male nude (46x28cm-18x11in) s. pencil. 16-Oct-3 Christie's, Kensington #564
£300 $540 €438 Study of a torso and two heads (44x41cm-17x16in) s. pencil drawing. 20-Jan-4 Bonhams, Knightsbridge #33
£420 $701 €613 Lady Hillingdon (49x34cm-19x13in) s.i.d.91 pencil W/C pen black ink. 16-Oct-3 Christie's, Kensington #674/R
£420 $764 €613 Seated man in profile (29x23cm-11x9in) s. indis.i. d.72 W/C. 1-Jul-4 Christie's, Kensington #260
£550 $990 €803 Portrait of Prince Charles (38x36cm-15x14in) s.d.1969 W/C. 20-Jan-4 Bonhams, Knightsbridge #20/R
£570 $1032 €832 Down river from Battersea bridge (22x30cm-9x12in) s.d.76 W/C. 1-Apr-4 Olivers, Sudbury #73/R
£600 $1032 €876 Two nudes on a bed. Two nudes lying on the bed (39x29cm-15x11in) s.d.66 pencil pair. 3-Dec-3 Christie's, Kensington #641/R
£600 $1092 €876 Seated gentleman holding flowers (28x21cm-11x8in) s. i.d.72 W/C. 1-Jul-4 Christie's, Kensington #264/R
£650 $1183 €949 Six Harmonies Pagoda, Hangchow (46x61cm-18x24in) s. W/C prov. 1-Jul-4 Christie's, Kensington #315/R
£700 $1295 €1022 Six heads (91x127cm-36x50in) s.d.67 felt tip pen gouache. 11-Mar-4 Christie's, Kensington #201/R
£800 $1480 €1168 Still life delphiniums and candle (74x40cm-29x16in) s.d.69. 13-Feb-4 Sworder & Son, Bishops Stortford #78/R

PROCOPIO, Pino (1954-) Italian
£400 $736 €600 Inspiring muse (30x25cm-12x10in) s. 12-Jun-4 Meeting Art, Vercelli #942/R
£552 $921 €800 Ginevra's vegetable garden (30x40cm-12x16in) s. 13-Nov-3 Finarte Semenzato, Rome #270
£1000 $1840 €1500 Tropical paradise (50x50cm-20x20in) s. 12-Jun-4 Meeting Art, Vercelli #967/R est:1500

PROCTER, Burt (1901-1980) American
£1471 $2500 €2148 Outrigger (30x41cm-12x16in) s. i.verso masonite prov. 18-Nov-3 John Moran, Pasadena #137 est:1500-2000
£1587 $3000 €2317 Figures at water's edge - Polynesian beach scene (51x76cm-20x30in) s. masonite prov. 17-Feb-4 John Moran, Pasadena #145/R est:3000-4000
£1912 $3250 €2792 Pueblo scene (41x51cm-16x20in) s. masonite panel. 1-Nov-3 Santa Fe Art, Santa Fe #32/R est:4000-6000
£2647 $4500 €3865 Polynesian girl (76x51cm-30x20in) s. masonite prov. 18-Nov-3 John Moran, Pasadena #135 est:3000-4000
£2910 $5500 €4249 Figures in Polynesian scene (51x61cm-20x24in) s. masonite. 17-Feb-4 John Moran, Pasadena #65b/R est:3000-4000
£3261 $6000 €4761 Horses by a barn (46x91cm-18x36in) s. board. 8-Jun-4 Bonhams & Butterfields, San Francisco #4149/R est:3000-5000
£3529 $6000 €5152 Waters edge (51x76cm-20x30in) s. i.verso masonite prov. 18-Nov-3 John Moran, Pasadena #136 est:3000-4000

PROCTER, Dod (1892-1972) British
£1452 $2671 €2120 Kynance Cove (25x36cm-10x14in) i.verso board. 14-Jun-4 Waddingtons, Toronto #145/R est:3200-3600 (C.D 3600)
£7500 $13200 €10950 Jeanne's door (86x64cm-34x25in) s. s.i.verso board prov. 19-May-4 Sotheby's, Olympia #188/R est:3000-5000

PROCTER, Ernest (1886-1935) British
Works on paper
£350 $641 €511 Ambulance at Ancemont (23x23cm-9x9in) s.d.1917 pencil. 3-Jun-4 Lane, Penzance #54
£500 $935 €730 Thames scene with barges, houses on the embankment in the distance (19x28cm-7x11in) s.d.03 pencil W/C htd white. 22-Jul-4 Tennants, Leyburn #668

PROCTER, William (?) British?
£640 $1165 €934 Coastal scenes with figures and boats. pair. 3-Feb-4 Lawrences, Bletchingley #1706/R

PROCTOR, Adam E (1864-1913) British
£650 $1183 €949 Rest by the way, woman wearing a pink bonnet (45x29cm-18x11in) s. i.verso. 16-Jun-4 Rupert Toovey, Partridge Green #111/R
£1450 $2349 €2103 Sunlight and shadow (25x20cm-10x8in) init.d.1900 i.verso. 26-Jan-3 Desmond Judd, Cranbrook #802

PROCTOR, Albert (fl.1885-1904) British
Works on paper
£250 $460 €365 Feeding the ducks (28x74cm-11x29in) s. pencil W/C. 25-Mar-4 Christie's, Kensington #178
£380 $627 €555 Old Fort Jersey (20x33cm-8x13in) s. W/C. 3-Jul-3 Biddle & Webb, Birmingham #739
£440 $792 €642 In the Lleddr Valley North Wales (49x74cm-19x29in) s.i. W/C htd white exhib. 22-Apr-4 Mellors & Kirk, Nottingham #1006

PROCTOR, Alexander Phimister (1862-1950) American
Sculpture
£1374 $2500 €2006 Standing bear cub looking at a rabbit (10x8cm-4x3in) s.d.94 num.95 bronze. 15-Jun-4 John Moran, Pasadena #126a est:3000-4000
£2250 $3600 €3285 Bear cub and bunny (10cm-4in) s.d.94 st.f.Gorham bronze. 20-Sep-3 Jeffery Burchard, Florida #1/R
£2442 $4200 €3565 Spaniel and catch (20cm-8in) s.d.94 pat bronze. 2-Dec-3 Christie's, Rockefeller NY #72/R est:3000-5000

PROCTOR, Alexander Phimister (after) (1862-1950) American
Sculpture
£5429 $9500 €7926 Stalking panther (96x24cm-38x9in) init.s.verso green-brown pat bronze. 19-Dec-3 Sotheby's, New York #1093/R est:7000-9000

PROCTOR, Althea Mary (1879-1966) Australian
Works on paper
£313 $584 €470 Study of girl sleeping (28x29cm-11x11in) s. pencil crayon. 25-Jul-4 Lawson Menzies, Sydney #99/R (A.D 800)
£522 $872 €757 Fan (25x23cm-10x9in) s. pencil W/C. 30-Jun-3 Australian Art Auctions, Sydney #106 (A.D 1300)
£3484 $5504 €5087 The ballet (31x60cm-12x24in) s. W/C pencil gold prov.exhib. 2-Sep-3 Deutscher-Menzies, Melbourne #110/R est:9000-12000 (A.D 8500)
£4545 $8409 €6636 Picnic - the tame bird (24x48cm-9x19in) s. W/C fan shaped. 10-Mar-4 Deutscher-Menzies, Melbourne #102/R est:11000-14000 (A.D 11000)

PROCTOR, Robert Field (1879-1931) New Zealander
£326 $554 €476 Italian village scene (41x25cm-16x10in) s. canvasboard. 4-Nov-3 Peter Webb, Auckland #296/R (NZ.D 900)
£368 $688 €537 Old Mill Holland (43x47cm-17x19in) s. s.i.verso. 24-Feb-4 Peter Webb, Auckland #119/R (NZ.D 1000)
£874 $1591 €1276 Moroccan town scene (42x30cm-17x12in) s. canvasboard. 29-Jun-4 Peter Webb, Auckland #194/R est:1500-2000 (NZ.D 2500)
£1469 $2673 €2145 Moored boats, Auckland (32x51cm-13x20in) s. canvasboard. 29-Jun-4 Peter Webb, Auckland #160/R est:2500-3500 (NZ.D 4200)
£2256 $3835 €3294 Maori princess (50x65cm-20x26in) s. 26-Nov-3 Dunbar Sloane, Wellington #48/R est:7000-10000 (NZ.D 6000)

PROFILLET, Anne Marie (20th C) French
Sculpture
£2113 $3507 €3000 Le canard (21x23cm-8x9in) s. pat bronze Cast Susse. 13-Jun-3 Renaud, Paris #56/R est:1000

PROFIT, Carl (1963-) Austrian?
£423 $756 €600 Steam engine, DB 24009 (54x84cm-21x33in) s. i.verso board lit. 8-Jan-4 Allgauer, Kempten #2491/R

PROIETTI, Norberto (1927-) Italian
£4161 $7740 €6200 Trap (29x70cm-11x28in) s.d.1973 s.i.verso board. 4-Mar-4 Babuino, Rome #402 est:2500-3500
£4966 $9238 €7400 Monks flying (50x65cm-20x26in) s. board painted 1974 prov.lit. 4-Mar-4 Babuino, Rome #140 est:4000-5000

PROKOFIEV (19/20th C) Russian
£3243 $5805 €4800 Moonlight on the river (58x80cm-23x31in) s.d.1903. 8-May-4 Bukowskis, Helsinki #464/R est:1500-1700

PROKSCH, Peter (1935-) Austrian?
£845 $1479 €1200 Nymph and unicorn (16x11cm-6x4in) s.d.76 masonite. 19-Dec-3 Dorotheum, Vienna #269/R
£845 $1479 €1200 Fire and water (16x11cm-6x4in) s.d.76 masonite. 19-Dec-3 Dorotheum, Vienna #270/R
£3289 $6053 €5000 Lady and unicorn (30x30cm-12x12in) s.d.1999 oil egg-tempera panel. 22-Jun-4 Wiener Kunst Auktionen, Vienna #337/R est:3500

PRONK, Cornelis (1691-1759) Dutch
Works on paper
£405 $714 €600 Peat dredgers (21x16cm-8x6in) s.i. pen brown ink after Jan Luyken lit. 19-May-4 Sotheby's, Amsterdam #242/R
£578 $1035 €850 Rue animee dans un village (10x16cm-4x6in) s.verso W/C black pencil. 19-Mar-4 Piasa, Paris #107
£8784 $15459 €13000 View of the townhall, market-place and church of Vlaardingen (22x33cm-9x13in) pen brown black grey ink W/C black chk prov.exhib. 19-May-4 Sotheby's, Amsterdam #253/R est:3500-4500

PRONSATO, Domingo (1881-1971) Argentinian
£838 $1500 €1223 Church (34x47cm-13x19in) s. canvas on board. 4-May-4 Arroyo, Buenos Aires #26/R est:1200

PRONTCHENKO, Leonid (1956-) Russian
£267 $480 €400 Night (100x50cm-39x20in) s.d.2003. 26-Apr-4 Millon & Associes, Paris #229/R
£320 $576 €480 Theatre (145x100cm-57x39in) s.d.2001. 26-Apr-4 Millon & Associes, Paris #224/R
£400 $720 €600 Dolls' soul (100x130cm-39x51in) 26-Apr-4 Millon & Associes, Paris #225/R

PROOST, Alfons (1880-1957) Belgian
£362 $655 €550 L'etang devant la ferme (60x90cm-24x35in) s. panel. 19-Apr-4 Horta, Bruxelles #304
£1958 $3270 €2800 Enfants jouant sur le brise-lames a la mer du Nord (52x65cm-20x26in) mono. s.d.1950 verso. 13-Oct-3 Horta, Bruxelles #222/R est:3000-4000
£5282 $9137 €7500 Jardin de Plaisance (80x65cm-31x26in) s. i.verso. 13-Dec-3 De Vuyst, Lokeren #463/R est:4500-6000

PROOYEN, Albert Jurardus van (1834-1898) Dutch
£419 $725 €612 Woman on a burro crossing a stream with a goat and cows (18x28cm-7x11in) s. panel. 15-Dec-3 Winter Associates, Plainville #182/R
£769 $1308 €1100 After the hay harvest (15x30cm-6x12in) s. panel. 20-Nov-3 Van Ham, Cologne #1808
£1088 $1981 €1600 An engaging encounter (41x56cm-16x22in) s.d.31 Dec 1880 panel. 3-Feb-4 Christie's, Amsterdam #80/R est:1500-2000
£1329 $2259 €1900 Winter evening on Dutch canal (21x35cm-8x14in) s. panel. 20-Nov-3 Van Ham, Cologne #1807/R est:2000
£1389 $2194 €2000 Sailing activities in a river estuary (44x65cm-17x26in) s. 2-Sep-3 Christie's, Amsterdam #319/R est:2000-3000

PROPER, Ida Sedgwick (1876-1957) American
£2695 $4500 €3935 Paris park scenes (25x33cm-10x13in) board pair. 17-Oct-3 Du Mouchelle, Detroit #2001/R est:3000-3500

PROPHETER, Otto (1875-1927) German
£1124 $1865 €1641 Portrait of a lady (79x75cm-31x30in) s. painted c.1910. 15-Jun-3 Agra, Warsaw #32/R est:6000 (P.Z 7000)

PROSALENTIS, Emilios (1859-1926) Greek
£6000 $10200 €8760 Sailing in moonlit seas (27x41cm-11x16in) s. 18-Nov-3 Sotheby's, London #25/R est:6000-8000
£15000 $26850 €21900 On high seas (48x73cm-19x29in) s. 10-May-4 Sotheby's, Olympia #10/R est:12000-18000
Works on paper
£1500 $2685 €2190 Harbour view (14x32cm-6x13in) s.d.98 W/C prov. 11-May-4 Bonhams, New Bond Street #17/R est:1000-1500
£2200 $3850 €3212 Boats in the port of Cherbourg (22x35cm-9x14in) s.i.d.902 W/C. 16-Dec-3 Bonhams, New Bond Street #15/R est:1500-2000
£2700 $4725 €3942 View of the Parthenon (24x35cm-9x14in) s. W/C. 16-Dec-3 Bonhams, New Bond Street #25/R est:1500-2000
£3800 $6460 €5548 Sailboats (38x56cm-15x22in) s. W/C. 18-Nov-3 Sotheby's, London #123/R est:2000-3000
£4000 $7000 €5840 Caryatids. Propylaea (31x21cm-12x8in) s. W/C pair. 16-Dec-3 Bonhams, New Bond Street #11/R est:4000-6000

PROSALENTIS, Emilios (attrib) (1859-1926) Greek
£3000 $5160 €4380 Portrait of a gentleman, in a dark suit (70x56cm-28x22in) s.d.1872. 4-Dec-3 Christie's, Kensington #117/R est:3000-5000

PROSALENTIS, Spyros (19/20th C) Greek
Works on paper
£2200 $3938 €3212 Canal in Venice (28x16cm-11x6in) s. W/C. 11-May-4 Bonhams, New Bond Street #5/R est:1600-2000

PROSDOCINI, Alberto (1852-1925) Italian
Works on paper
£400 $688 €584 On the lagoon, Venice (33x34cm-13x13in) s. pencil W/C. 3-Dec-3 Christie's, Kensington #179/R
£407 $750 €594 Venetian scene with San Maria della Salute in the background (43x33cm-17x13in) s. W/C on board. 28-Mar-4 Bonhams & Butterfields, San Francisco #2717
£671 $1235 €1000 Venice, Lion column near San Marco (30x17cm-12x7in) s.cyrillic W/C. 26-Mar-4 Dorotheum, Vienna #193/R
£950 $1757 €1387 Venetian Canal scene (28x43cm-11x17in) s. W/C. 10-Mar-4 Sotheby's, Olympia #266/R est:600-800
£993 $1808 €1500 Fishing boats, Venice (41x67cm-16x26in) s. W/C. 16-Jun-4 Hugo Ruef, Munich #1173/R est:1200
£1351 $2108 €2000 Lagoon (22x34cm-9x13in) W/C. 30-Mar-3 Adma, Formigine #324 est:1300
£1486 $2319 €2200 Grand Canal (22x33cm-9x13in) W/C. 30-Mar-3 Adma, Formigine #319 est:1300
£1912 $3250 €2792 Venetian canal scene with figures in a gondola (47x66cm-19x26in) s.i. pencil W/C htd white on board. 19-Nov-3 Bonhams & Butterfields, San Francisco #54/R

PROSPER, Pierre Louis (?) Haitian
£567 $1014 €850 Hommage au CHE (80x60cm-31x24in) s. panel. 17-May-4 Rogeon, Paris #70

PROSSER, George Frederick (fl.1828-1868) British
Works on paper
£1500 $2490 €2190 Brocas, Eton (22x37cm-9x15in) s.i.d.1877 W/C. 1-Oct-3 Sotheby's, Olympia #69/R est:1500-2500

PROSSER, James Stanley (1887-1959) British
Works on paper
£250 $398 €365 Ballintoy harbour (23x33cm-9x13in) W/C drawing. 10-Sep-3 John Ross, Belfast #16/R
£250 $398 €365 Bathers and fishing boats (23x33cm-9x13in) W/C drawing. 10-Sep-3 John Ross, Belfast #84/R
£250 $398 €365 Red Bay (23x33cm-9x13in) s.d.25 W/C drawing. 10-Sep-3 John Ross, Belfast #97
£250 $398 €365 On the beach at Ballygally (23x33cm-9x13in) s.d.38 W/C drawing. 10-Sep-3 John Ross, Belfast #137/R
£250 $398 €365 Ballygally Castle (23x33cm-9x13in) s.d.29 W/C drawing. 10-Sep-3 John Ross, Belfast #151/R
£260 $413 €380 Canal barge (23x33cm-9x13in) W/C drawing. 10-Sep-3 John Ross, Belfast #63
£260 $447 €380 Still life (50x66cm-20x26in) s. W/C. 3-Dec-3 John Ross, Belfast #94
£280 $445 €409 Haystacks (23x33cm-9x13in) W/C drawing. 10-Sep-3 John Ross, Belfast #127/R
£280 $445 €409 Boathouse, Ballintoy (23x33cm-9x13in) s. W/C drawing. 10-Sep-3 John Ross, Belfast #184/R
£280 $445 €409 Prosser's house, Ballygally (23x33cm-9x13in) s.d.38 W/C drawing. 10-Sep-3 John Ross, Belfast #194/R
£300 $477 €438 Glens cottage (23x33cm-9x13in) s.d.24 W/C drawing. 10-Sep-3 John Ross, Belfast #5/R
£300 $477 €438 Old Mill (23x33cm-9x13in) W/C drawing. 10-Sep-3 John Ross, Belfast #85/R
£310 $493 €453 Collecting lobster pots (23x33cm-9x13in) W/C drawing. 10-Sep-3 John Ross, Belfast #175/R
£320 $509 €467 Driving sheep (23x33cm-9x13in) s.d.27 W/C drawing. 10-Sep-3 John Ross, Belfast #57/R
£320 $509 €467 Rest from chopping wood (23x33cm-9x13in) W/C drawing. 10-Sep-3 John Ross, Belfast #94/R
£350 $557 €511 White lady on the Antrim coast (23x33cm-9x13in) W/C drawing. 10-Sep-3 John Ross, Belfast #28/R
£350 $557 €511 Summer in the garden (33x23cm-13x9in) s.d.44 W/C drawing. 10-Sep-3 John Ross, Belfast #125/R
£380 $604 €555 Ballintoy (23x33cm-9x13in) W/C drawing. 10-Sep-3 John Ross, Belfast #88/R
£400 $636 €584 White Lady, Antrim coast (23x33cm-9x13in) s.d.48 W/C drawing. 10-Sep-3 John Ross, Belfast #106/R
£520 $827 €759 Feeding chickens, north Antrim (23x28cm-9x11in) s.d.31 W/C drawing. 10-Sep-3 John Ross, Belfast #1/R
£550 $875 €803 Bridge at Cushendun (23x33cm-9x13in) s.d.26 W/C drawing. 10-Sep-3 John Ross, Belfast #167/R

PROST, Felix (20th C) French
£333 $607 €500 Mediterranean harbour (24x44cm-9x17in) s.d.59 board. 1-Jul-4 Christie's, Amsterdam #442

PROST, Maurice (1894-1967) French
Sculpture
£2193 $4035 €3202 Panther at war with a snake (36x51cm-14x20in) s. dark brown pat bronze with black marble base. 23-Jun-4 Koller, Zurich #3037/R est:5000-7000 (S.FR 5000)
£3221 $5187 €4800 Panthere noire en marche (37cm-15in) s.i.d.1937 brown pat bronze st.f.Susse. 23-Feb-3 St Germain-en-Laye Encheres #118/R est:5000

PROTHEROE, Andrew (20th C) British
£5200 $8632 €7592 Bathers (158x158cm-62x62in) s.d.1992. 30-Sep-3 Sotheby's, London #428/R est:1000-1500

PROTHEROE, Thomas (fl.1904) British
£893 $1536 €1304 Harem musician at rest (61x51cm-24x20in) s.d.1881 i.verso on stretcher. 2-Dec-3 Ritchie, Toronto #48/R est:3000-4000 (C.D 2000)

PROUD, Alastair (1954-) British
£700 $1120 €1022 Young male cheetah resting (43x72cm-17x28in) s. board. 16-Sep-3 Rosebery Fine Art, London #520/R

PROUD, Geoffrey (1946-) Australian
£1405 $2599 €2051 Blue portrait (91x122cm-36x48in) s.d.81 enamel silver leaf board. 10-Mar-4 Deutscher-Menzies, Melbourne #480/R est:1500-2500 (A.D 3400)

£1557 $2523 €2273 Pretty girl (86x64cm-34x25in) s.d.87. 30-Jul-3 Goodman, Sydney #157/R est:1800-2500 (A.D 3800)
£2282 $3811 €3423 Untitled (181x151cm-71x59in) s.d.88. 27-Oct-3 Goodman, Sydney #101/R est:6000-8000 (A.D 5500)

PROUDFOOT, James (1908-) British
£300 $543 €438 Black hat (45x37cm-18x15in) s.d.40. 30-Mar-4 Sworder & Son, Bishops Stortford #537/R
£420 $714 €613 The dentist (120x90cm-47x35in) s.d.60 sold with artist's note book, dentist seal and photo. 30-Oct-3 Bracketts, Tunbridge Wells #1085/R

PROUT, John Skinner (1806-1876) British
Works on paper
£280 $448 €409 Continental townscape with cart and figures (30x20cm-12x8in) s. 16-Sep-3 Capes Dunn, Manchester #867/R
£340 $579 €496 Coastal seascape (15x21cm-6x8in) s. W/C ink. 26-Nov-3 Deutscher-Menzies, Melbourne #223/R (A.D 800)
£380 $631 €555 Old mill (28x36cm-11x14in) W/C. 2-Oct-3 Neales, Nottingham #679
£800 $1480 €1168 Woodcutters in an Austrialian Landscape (28x23cm-11x9in) W/C. 10-Mar-4 Sotheby's, Olympia #45/R
£894 $1601 €1305 Mountain landscape with figures (20x32cm-8x13in) s.d.1843 W/C gouache. 4-May-4 Sotheby's, Melbourne #148/R (A.D 2200)
£2893 $5351 €4224 Figures by a waterfall (31x11cm-12x4in) s. W/C executed c.1840 prov. 10-Mar-4 Deutscher-Menzies, Melbourne #166/R est:8000-10000 (A.D 7000)

PROUT, John Skinner (attrib) (1806-1876) British
Works on paper
£600 $978 €876 The Rows, Chester (23x32cm-9x13in) W/C. 23-Sep-3 Anderson & Garland, Newcastle #304

PROUT, Margaret Fisher (1875-1963) British
£397 $727 €600 Vase of flowers on a table (38x46cm-15x18in) s.d.1928 panel. 7-Apr-4 Piasa, Paris #153
£500 $810 €725 Ept at Giverny (49x61cm-19x24in) s. exhib. 30-Jul-3 Hamptons Fine Art, Godalming #284
£2100 $3696 €3066 Carousel (56x63cm-22x25in) s.d.1925. 19-May-4 Sotheby's, Olympia #200/R est:1200-1800
Works on paper
£260 $411 €377 Harnessed pair, two plough horses (22x35cm-9x14in) pastel. 2-Sep-3 Bonhams, Oxford #58

PROUT, Samuel (1783-1852) British
£260 $413 €380 Continental cathedral doorway (26x20cm-10x8in) init. 18-Mar-3 Anderson & Garland, Newcastle #378
Works on paper
£250 $463 €365 Figures in a street before a windmill in Holland (29x20cm-11x8in) W/C. 13-Jan-4 Bonhams, Oxford #278
£280 $442 €406 Plimstock church (31x43cm-12x17in) i. pencil wash dr. 24-Jul-3 Dominic Winter, Swindon #170/R
£280 $484 €409 Cathedral interior with figures at prayer (44x30cm-17x12in) s. W/C. 9-Dec-3 Bonhams, Oxford #34
£280 $484 €409 Figures in a cathedral interior (31x26cm-12x10in) s. W/C. 9-Dec-3 Bonhams, Oxford #72
£328 $600 €479 View of a church interior (19x25cm-7x10in) init. W/C. 29-Jan-4 Swann Galleries, New York #356/R
£350 $648 €511 Venice (18x30cm-7x12in) W/C htd bodycol. 10-Feb-4 David Lay, Penzance #138
£360 $569 €522 Old French buildings by a bridge, with figures (34x24cm-13x9in) init. pen wash dr bodycol. 24-Jul-3 Dominic Winter, Swindon #60/R
£360 $623 €526 Cathedral interior with figures before a tomb (35x25cm-14x10in) s. W/C. 9-Dec-3 Bonhams, Oxford #74
£360 $673 €526 Continental market, with figures amongst classical ruins (42x27cm-17x11in) s. W/C. 26-Feb-4 Bruton Knowles, Cheltenham #49
£420 $752 €613 Continental street scene (28x21cm-11x8in) s. W/C. 17-Mar-4 Bonhams, Chester #304
£450 $747 €657 Woman washing at a canal (24x17cm-9x7in) mono.i. W/C. 1-Oct-3 Sotheby's, Olympia #11/R
£560 $913 €818 Rhineland town with woman seated by a monument, castle in background (42x27cm-17x11in) s. W/C. 23-Sep-3 Anderson & Garland, Newcastle #272/R
£580 $969 €847 Figures on a town bridge (21x29cm-8x11in) s. W/C. 20-Oct-3 Bonhams, Bath #81
£600 $1092 €876 Continental town scene with washerwomen in the street (38x25cm-15x10in) s. W/C. 3-Feb-4 Gorringes, Bexhill #1068
£600 $1092 €876 Continental town scene with a group of figures (36x20cm-14x8in) s. W/C. 3-Feb-4 Gorringes, Bexhill #1069
£600 $1080 €876 Piazzetta, Venice (40x56cm-16x22in) W/C over pencil htd bodycol. 22-Apr-4 Lawrence, Crewkerne #744/R
£750 $1275 €1095 Entrance to the Continental cathedral (39x29cm-15x11in) W/C htd gum arabic. 4-Nov-3 Bonhams, New Bond Street #68/R
£750 $1350 €1095 Near Tavistock, Devon. Thatched cottages (17x24cm-7x9in) s. pencil W/C two prov. 21-Apr-4 Tennants, Leyburn #916
£800 $1336 €1168 Watching the gondolier, Venice (23x16cm-9x6in) pen black ink W/C. 16-Oct-3 Christie's, Kensington #68/R
£800 $1480 €1168 Caen, France (22x16cm-9x6in) W/C prov. 14-Jul-4 Sotheby's, Olympia #40/R
£1000 $1700 €1460 Figures before a thatched cottage, Devon (20x27cm-8x11in) pencil W/C prov. 20-Nov-3 Christie's, London #68/R est:700-1000
£1000 $1750 €1460 Continental town scene with figures (28x38cm-11x15in) W/C bodycol sold with another similar. 19-Dec-3 Mallams, Oxford #86/R est:1000-1500
£1100 $2035 €1606 Strasbourg, France (27x20cm-11x8in) s. W/C. 14-Jul-4 Sotheby's, Olympia #39/R est:1000-1500
£1310 $2411 €1913 Mayence Cathedral. Town street. The village fountain (42x29cm-17x11in) two s. W/C three prov. 9-Jun-4 Walker's, Ottawa #370/R est:2000-3000 (C.D 3250)
£1465 $2739 €2198 Rialto, Venice (42x50cm-17x20in) s. W/C prov. 20-Jul-4 Goodman, Sydney #92/R est:2000-3000 (A.D 3750)
£1500 $2550 €2190 Figures at the cathedral portal, Ulm. Street scene, Ulm (32x22cm-13x9in) W/C htd white pair. 4-Nov-3 Bonhams, New Bond Street #32/R est:1500-2000
£2000 $3200 €2920 Elizabeth Castle, Jersey (26x43cm-10x17in) W/C. 17-Sep-3 Bonhams, Brooks & Langlois, Jersey #106/R est:3000-4000
£2300 $4140 €3358 Grand Canal, Venice (25x36cm-10x14in) i. pencil bodycol prov. 21-Jan-4 Sotheby's, Olympia #145/R est:1000-1500
£3600 $6372 €5256 Busy Antwerp street scene with street vendors and Cathedral (76x58cm-30x23in) W/C prov. 27-Apr-4 Peter Francis, Wales #27/R est:3000-4000

PROUT, Samuel Gillespie (1822-1911) British
Works on paper
£380 $619 €555 St. Radigund's Abbey, Dover (23x34cm-9x13in) s.i. pencil W/C bodycol. 25-Sep-3 Mellors & Kirk, Nottingham #694
£550 $990 €803 Women washing clothes with St Ouen beyond, Rouen (31x22cm-12x9in) s. pen grey ink W/C over pencil bodycol. 21-Jan-4 Sotheby's, Olympia #165/R
£590 $1003 €850 Tavro, Cornwall, busy street scene (33x29cm-13x11in) W/C. 28-Oct-3 Mealy's, Castlecomer #133

PROUVE, V (1858-1943) French
£1678 $2853 €2400 Paysage du Midi (74x60cm-29x24in) d.1928. 30-Nov-3 Teitgen, Nancy #123

PROUVE, Victor (1858-1943) French
Works on paper
£263 $484 €400 Femme au bouquet de fleurs (50x65cm-20x26in) s. studio st. crayon exec 1936. 27-Jun-4 Teitgen, Nancy #91

PROVERBIO, Luciano (1936-) Italian
£448 $749 €650 Devil (35x50cm-14x20in) s.d.1972 paper. 17-Nov-3 Sant Agostino, Torino #113/R
£1156 $2070 €1700 Batman (72x100cm-28x39in) s. paper painted 1998. 22-Mar-4 Sant Agostino, Torino #489/R est:2000
£3034 $5068 €4400 Magician's shop (60x79cm-24x31in) s. s.d.1970 verso masonite. 17-Nov-3 Sant Agostino, Torino #270/R est:3000-4000
£3147 $5255 €4500 Secret room (70x100cm-28x39in) s. card painted 2001. 26-Jun-3 Sant Agostino, Torino #257/R est:4000-5000

PROVINO, Salvatore (1943-) Italian
£268 $497 €400 Pomegranate (22x33cm-9x13in) s. 13-Mar-4 Meeting Art, Vercelli #394
£333 $613 €500 Untitled (40x60cm-16x24in) s. paper on canvas. 12-Jun-4 Meeting Art, Vercelli #289/R
£336 $621 €500 Body (33x46cm-13x18in) s. 13-Mar-4 Meeting Art, Vercelli #22
£336 $621 €500 Colours of earth (60x40cm-24x16in) s. paper on canvas. 13-Mar-4 Meeting Art, Vercelli #109
£352 $585 €500 Ritmi di un corpo (40x50cm-16x20in) s. s.i.verso. 14-Jun-3 Meeting Art, Vercelli #342
£352 $585 €500 Magma (40x50cm-16x20in) s. s.i.verso. 14-Jun-3 Meeting Art, Vercelli #346
£367 $675 €550 Sea (40x60cm-16x24in) s. paper. 12-Jun-4 Meeting Art, Vercelli #404/R
£367 $675 €550 Winter landscape (40x60cm-16x24in) s. paper on canvas. 12-Jun-4 Meeting Art, Vercelli #689/R
£503 $931 €750 Birth (70x50cm-28x20in) s. s.verso lit. 13-Mar-4 Meeting Art, Vercelli #89
£503 $931 €750 Torn (70x50cm-28x20in) s. s.i.verso. 13-Mar-4 Meeting Art, Vercelli #360
£638 $1180 €950 Lights in the wood (40x50cm-16x20in) s. 13-Mar-4 Meeting Art, Vercelli #308
£671 $1242 €1000 Untitled (80x60cm-31x24in) s. s.verso. 13-Mar-4 Meeting Art, Vercelli #391
£1333 $2453 €2000 Landscape at speed (60x80cm-24x31in) s. painted 1998. 12-Jun-4 Meeting Art, Vercelli #466/R est:1000
£1678 $3003 €2500 Memory figure (80x60cm-31x24in) s.i.d.1991 verso lit. 30-May-4 Meeting Art, Vercelli #2 est:1000
£1761 $2923 €2500 Lettera al fuoco (80x140cm-31x55in) s. s.i.d.1999 verso. 14-Jun-3 Meeting Art, Vercelli #591/R est:2500
£2067 $3803 €3100 Expanding surface (100x100cm-39x39in) s. 12-Jun-4 Meeting Art, Vercelli #840/R est:2500

PROVIS, Alfred (19th C) British
£455 $773 €650 Sunday afternoon in peasant interior (17x25cm-7x10in) mono. panel. 22-Nov-3 Arnold, Frankfurt #611/R
£900 $1494 €1314 Interior of ruined mill near Chippenham (29x40cm-11x16in) s. s.i.stretcher. 1-Oct-3 Sotheby's, Olympia #118/R

PROWETT, James C (?-1946) British
£700 $1323 €1022 Footbridge to farmbuildings (24x31cm-9x12in) s. board. 19-Feb-4 Lyon & Turnbull, Edinburgh #149
£920 $1582 €1343 Brolic scene with figures beside a cottage (23x30cm-9x12in) s. panel. 6-Dec-3 Shapes, Edinburgh #419/R

PROWSE, Ruth (1883-1967) South African
£2312 $4139 €3376 Woodcarrier in a coastal landscape (29x44cm-11x17in) mono. 31-May-4 Stephan Welz, Johannesburg #547/R est:10000-15000 (SA.R 28000)
£3248 $5521 €4742 District six with Lion's Head in the distance (29x37cm-11x15in) mono.d.62 board. 4-Nov-3 Stephan Welz, Johannesburg #613/R est:12000-18000 (SA.R 38000)
£4483 $7486 €6545 Cape Town Street scene with hawker's cart (28x21cm-11x8in) mono. board. 20-Oct-3 Stephan Welz, Johannesburg #272/R est:12000-16000 (SA.R 52000)

PRUCHA, Gustav (1875-1952) Austrian
£986 $1706 €1400 Dutch flower market (70x100cm-28x39in) s. 10-Dec-3 Dorotheum, Vienna #196
£993 $1808 €1500 Group of people riding in a horse-drawn sleigh in a winter landscape (60x80cm-24x31in) s.d.44. 18-Jun-4 Bolland & Marotz, Bremen #727/R est:900
£1087 $2000 €1587 Tavern scene (61x74cm-24x29in) s. 26-Jun-4 Susanin's, Chicago #6064/R est:2000-4000
£1528 $2597 €2200 Flower market (55x68cm-22x27in) s. 28-Oct-3 Dorotheum, Vienna #2/R est:1800-2200

PRUDHON, Pierre Paul (1758-1823) French
Works on paper
£6197 $10721 €8800 Carte d'invitation figurant une allegorie de la musique (8x10cm-3x4in) blk white crayon blue paper prov.lit. 10-Dec-3 Piasa, Paris #62/R est:4000-5000
£13245 $24238 €20000 Etude de drape (25x26cm-10x10in) pierre noire htd white. 7-Apr-4 Doutrebente, Paris #22/R est:9000-12000
£14000 $25620 €20440 Modele (16x11cm-6x4in) chl chk blue paper prov.exhib.lit. 8-Jul-4 Sotheby's, London #147/R est:8000-12000
£21854 $39993 €33000 Etude de bras gauche (25x26cm-10x10in) pierre noire htd white. 7-Apr-4 Doutrebente, Paris #23/R est:7000-8000

PRUITT, A Kelly (1924-) American
£389 $650 €568 This is my land, Navajo Indian horseman (30x41cm-12x16in) 18-Oct-3 David Dike, Dallas #110/R

PRUNA, Pedro (1904-1977) Spanish
£1993 $3268 €2750 Solicitando perdon (34x27cm-13x11in) s. board. 27-May-3 Durán, Madrid #232/R est:2750
£1993 $3268 €2750 Escena dieciochesca (35x27cm-14x11in) s. board. 27-May-3 Durán, Madrid #233/R est:2750
£4577 $8011 €6500 Woman with boy (50x40cm-20x16in) s.d.1930 cardboard on board. 16-Dec-3 Segre, Madrid #110/R est:6000
£8859 $16478 €13200 Still life with bread and onion (73x92cm-29x36in) s.d.56. 2-Mar-4 Ansorena, Madrid #77/R est:13200
£13380 $23148 €19000 Woman in profile (92x73cm-36x29in) s. 15-Dec-3 Ansorena, Madrid #978/R est:19000
£13768 $22580 €19000 Feminine nude (54x73cm-21x29in) s. exhib. 27-May-3 Durán, Madrid #236/R est:15000
Works on paper
£552 $916 €800 Berthe (33x25cm-13x10in) s.i. gouache. 6-Oct-3 Blanchet, Paris #238
£552 $916 €800 Juge (32x25cm-13x10in) s.i. gouache. 6-Oct-3 Blanchet, Paris #242
£586 $973 €850 Chevalier (32x25cm-13x10in) s. gouache. 6-Oct-3 Blanchet, Paris #244
£592 $946 €840 Lady with veil (25x25cm-10x10in) s. W/C gouache board. 16-Sep-3 Segre, Madrid #284/R
£621 $1030 €900 Poete (32x25cm-13x10in) s.i. gouache. 6-Oct-3 Blanchet, Paris #239
£621 $1030 €900 Etude (32x25cm-13x10in) s. gouache. 6-Oct-3 Blanchet, Paris #246
£647 $1100 €945 Nude (30x20cm-12x8in) s.d.1928 ink W/C gouache. 9-Nov-3 Wright, Chicago #107 est:1500-2000
£690 $1145 €1000 Ulrich (32x25cm-13x10in) s.i. gouache. 6-Oct-3 Blanchet, Paris #240
£690 $1145 €1000 Chevalier (32x24cm-13x9in) s. gouache. 6-Oct-3 Blanchet, Paris #243/R
£690 $1145 €1000 Etude (32x25cm-13x10in) s. gouache. 6-Oct-3 Blanchet, Paris #245
£690 $1145 €1000 Roi (32x25cm-13x10in) s.i. gouache. 6-Oct-3 Blanchet, Paris #247
£690 $1145 €1000 Chevalier (32x25cm-13x10in) s.i. gouache. 6-Oct-3 Blanchet, Paris #248
£759 $1259 €1100 Roi des Ondins (32x25cm-13x10in) s.i. gouache. 6-Oct-3 Blanchet, Paris #241/R
£1316 $2382 €2000 Lady with veil (44x31cm-17x12in) s. mixed media. 14-Apr-4 Ansorena, Madrid #263/R est:2000
£1338 $2315 €1900 Saint George and the dragon (41x31cm-16x12in) s. W/C. 15-Dec-3 Ansorena, Madrid #157/R est:1900
£1796 $3000 €2622 Alice Roullier (65x49cm-26x19in) s.i.d.1926 pastel chl lit. 7-Oct-3 Sotheby's, New York #316 est:400-600

PRUNATI, Sante (attrib) (1652-1728) Italian
£1600 $2720 €2336 Triumph of Venus (46x84cm-18x33in) 29-Oct-3 Bonhams, New Bond Street #109/R est:1500-2000

PRUNELL, Carlos (1943-) South American
£256 $450 €374 Tiovivo (46x55cm-18x22in) s.d.99. 5-Jan-4 Galeria y Remates, Montevideo #124
£414 $650 €604 Musicians in a bar (54x65cm-21x26in) s. 1-Sep-3 Galeria y Remates, Montevideo #96
£529 $1000 €772 Wedding on the patio (97x130cm-38x51in) s. s.i.d.verso. 22-Feb-4 Galeria y Remates, Montevideo #19
£1364 $2400 €1991 Musicians by harbour (100x100cm-39x39in) s. 5-Jan-4 Galeria y Remates, Montevideo #120/R est:950-11000

PRUNES, Alex (1974-) Spanish
£403 $753 €600 Building by the sea (89x54cm-35x21in) s. 24-Feb-4 Durán, Madrid #45/R

PRUNIER, Gaston (1863-1927) French
£539 $900 €787 Street scene, le quatorze Juillet au Harve (33x23cm-13x9in) s. board. 11-Oct-3 Auctions by the Bay, Alameda #1615/R

PRUSHECK, Harvey Gregory (1887-?) American
£242 $450 €353 Flowers in a vase (51x41cm-20x16in) s. painted c.1930. 7-Mar-4 Treadway Gallery, Cincinnati #625/R

PRUSHECK, Harvey Gregory (attrib) (1887-?) American
£216 $400 €315 Still life (51x43cm-20x17in) s. panel. 13-Mar-4 DeFina, Austinburg #526/R

PRUSSIAN, Claire (20th C) American
Works on paper
£301 $550 €452 Prismacolor x II (132x102cm-52x40in) prismacolor gouache pencil. 10-Jul-4 Hindman, Chicago #421/R

PRUTSCHER, Otto (attrib) (1880-1949) Austrian
Sculpture
£2098 $3566 €3000 Door (203x63cm-80x25in) brass. 27-Nov-3 Wiener Kunst Auktionen, Vienna #31/R est:3000-6000

PRY, Charles (1915-) Belgian
£530 $964 €800 The rosary (75x51cm-30x20in) s. exhib. 21-Jun-4 Bernaerts, Antwerp #265

PRYDE, James (1869-1941) British
Works on paper
£1050 $1691 €1523 Les belles (15x16cm-6x6in) init. gouache. 21-Aug-3 Bonhams, Edinburgh #1039/R est:700-900

PRYN, Harald (1891-1968) Danish
£284 $455 €415 Stream in spring woods (65x90cm-26x35in) s. 22-Sep-3 Rasmussen, Vejle #356/R (D.KR 3000)
£340 $609 €496 Winter landscape with country road (70x97cm-28x38in) s.i.d.1927 prov. 12-Jan-4 Rasmussen, Vejle #120 (D.KR 3600)
£356 $647 €534 Winter landscape with houses at end of road (70x98cm-28x39in) s. 19-Jun-4 Rasmussen, Havnen #2069/R (D.KR 4000)
£356 $647 €534 Winter landscape from Dyrehaven near the Red Gate (68x100cm-27x39in) s. 19-Jun-4 Rasmussen, Havnen #2181/R (D.KR 4000)
£357 $608 €521 Winter landscape (65x93cm-26x37in) s. 29-Nov-3 Rasmussen, Havnen #2311 (D.KR 3800)
£360 $576 €526 Summer landscape with cattle and farmer (90x131cm-35x52in) s.d.1926. 22-Sep-3 Rasmussen, Vejle #240/R (D.KR 3800)
£415 $705 €606 Winter landscape with woodland road (70x100cm-28x39in) s. 10-Nov-3 Rasmussen, Vejle #331 (D.KR 4500)
£440 $713 €638 Winter's day in the woods (69x100cm-27x39in) s.i. 4-Aug-3 Rasmussen, Vejle #344/R (D.KR 4600)
£459 $739 €670 Winter's day in Kajerod (70x100cm-28x39in) s. 25-Aug-3 Lilla Bukowskis, Stockholm #968 (S.KR 6000)
£474 $758 €692 Winter landscape (70x100cm-28x39in) s.i. 22-Sep-3 Rasmussen, Vejle #371 (D.KR 5000)
£493 $887 €720 Winter landscape (56x74cm-22x29in) s. 24-Apr-4 Rasmussen, Havnen #2372/R (D.KR 5500)
£504 $917 €736 Winter landscape from Dyrehaven (50x70cm-20x28in) s.i. 7-Feb-4 Rasmussen, Havnen #2152 (D.KR 5500)
£543 $972 €793 Winter landscape with houses (69x99cm-27x39in) s. 10-May-4 Rasmussen, Vejle #202/R (D.KR 6000)
£556 $1000 €812 Wooded landscape Winter landscape (50x71cm-20x28in) s. two. 24-Apr-4 Rasmussen, Havnen #2228 (D.KR 6200)
£588 $1053 €858 Winter landscape with road and houses (70x100cm-28x39in) s. 10-May-4 Rasmussen, Vejle #203/R (D.KR 6500)
£706 $1199 €1031 Winter landscape (75x106cm-30x42in) s. 29-Nov-3 Rasmussen, Havnen #2312 (D.KR 7500)
£888 $1403 €1288 Road through wood, winter's day in sunshine (102x136cm-40x54in) s.i. 2-Sep-3 Rasmussen, Copenhagen #1932/R (D.KR 9500)
£986 $1774 €1440 Woodland road in winter (70x96cm-28x38in) s.i.d.1927. 24-Apr-4 Rasmussen, Havnen #2116/R (D.KR 11000)
£1000 $1590 €1450 Winter landscape (68x101cm-27x40in) s. indid i. 9-Sep-3 Bonhams, Knightsbridge #267/R est:1000-1500
£1613 $2903 €2355 Winter landscape near Hosterkob (103x136cm-41x54in) s.i. 24-Apr-4 Rasmussen, Havnen #2323/R est:5000 (D.KR 18000)
£1706 $2780 €2491 Winter landscape from Frederiksdal forest (70x100cm-28x39in) s. 28-Sep-3 Hindemae, Ullerslev #64/R est:15000-20000 (D.KR 18200)
£2747 $5000 €4011 Winter landscape from Hareskoven (102x134cm-40x53in) s.d.1949. 7-Feb-4 Rasmussen, Havnen #2173/R est:6000-8000 (D.KR 30000)

PSAIER, Pietro (1939-) American
£268 $502 €400 Melody (60x88cm-24x35in) s. 24-Feb-4 Durán, Madrid #1220
£750 $1388 €1095 Portrait of Gauguin (45x45cm-18x18in) s.d.69 prov. 11-Feb-4 Cheffins, Cambridge #463/R
Works on paper
£302 $565 €450 Maison Avenue de Warhol (88x60cm-35x24in) s.d.63 collage. 24-Feb-4 Durán, Madrid #1224/R
£319 $571 €475 Jimi Hendrix (113x113cm-44x44in) s. mixed media. 25-May-4 Durán, Madrid #1235/R
£336 $628 €500 Chanel n.5 (75x73cm-30x29in) s.d.81 mixed media. 24-Feb-4 Durán, Madrid #1172
£369 $690 €550 Study (89x54cm-35x21in) s. W/C collage ink. 24-Feb-4 Durán, Madrid #1223/R
£403 $721 €600 Chanel n. 5 (92x81cm-36x32in) s.d. mixed media on canvas. 25-May-4 Durán, Madrid #1231/R
£738 $1381 €1100 Marilyn (110x110cm-43x43in) mixed media on canvas. 24-Feb-4 Durán, Madrid #1173/R

PSAIER, Pietro and RAMOS, Mel (20th C) American
£550 $1018 €803 Chiquita, a naked girl in a banana (65x50cm-26x20in) init. acrylic silkscreen. 11-Feb-4 Cheffins, Cambridge #361/R

PSAIER, Pietro and WARHOL, Andy (20th C) American
Works on paper
£2700 $4995 €3942 Little Habana, Miami, Florida (90x152cm-35x60in) s.d.79 mixed media oil silkscreen prov. 11-Feb-4 Cheffins, Cambridge #359/R est:900-1000

PSEUDO FARDELLA (attrib) (17th C) Italian
£180000 $306000 €262800 Grapes, pears and apples on a forest floor. Peaches, apricots and figs on a forest floor (49x66cm-19x26in) pair. 29-Oct-3 Christie's, London #67/R est:15000-20000

PSEUDO GUARDI (18th C) Italian
£16667 $30000 €24334 Still life of flowers in a vase resting on a stone ledge with a plate of cherries (73x98cm-29x39in) canvas on board. 22-Jan-4 Sotheby's, New York #256/R est:30000-40000

PSEUDO HIEPES (fl.1650-1675) Spanish
£70000 $121100 €102200 Still life of a bowl of fruit, cheese honeycomb and rose on a dish with flowers in vase (78x115cm-31x45in) prov. 11-Dec-3 Sotheby's, London #29/R est:40000-60000

PSEUDO PIER FRANCESCO FIORENTINO (fl.c.1460-1500) Italian
£13187 $24000 €19253 Madonna and Child with the infant Saint John the Baptist and adoring Angels (58x32cm-23x13in) tempera on panel integral frame prov.lit. 17-Jun-4 Christie's, Rockefeller NY #34/R est:30000-40000

PSEUDO ROESTRAETEN (17th C) ?
£8904 $15137 €13000 Jug, teapot, watch and books on a draped table (63x78cm-25x31in) prov. 5-Nov-3 Christie's, Amsterdam #2/R est:3000-5000

PSEUDO SIMONS (attrib) (17th C) Flemish
£3200 $5760 €4672 Oyster, cherries, oranges and a glass of wine on a draped table (44x59cm-17x23in) bears sig. 21-Apr-4 Bonhams, New Bond Street #74/R est:3000-5000

PSYCHOPEDIS, Yiannis (1945-) Greek
Sculpture
£1800 $3222 €2628 Untitled (76x65x8cm-30x26x3in) s. mixed media cardboard. 11-May-4 Bonhams, New Bond Street #129/R est:1200-1800
Works on paper
£3000 $5370 €4380 Untitled (77x61cm-30x24in) s. mixed media collage board. 10-May-4 Sotheby's, Olympia #50/R est:3000-5000

PU JIAN (1901-1966) Chinese
Works on paper
£2134 $3841 €3116 Horse (104x61cm-41x24in) s.i. ink col hanging scroll. 25-Apr-4 Christie's, Hong Kong #143/R est:20000-30000 (HK.D 30000)

PU JIN (1879-1966) Chinese
Works on paper
£428 $728 €625 Horses (100x32cm-39x13in) s. ink hanging scroll. 18-Nov-3 Waddingtons, Toronto #1578/R est:900-1200 (C.D 950)

PU RU (1896-1963) Chinese
Works on paper
£927 $1547 €1353 Boating (12x60cm-5x24in) s.i. ink col scroll silk. 26-Oct-3 Christie's, Hong Kong #368/R est:25000-35000 (HK.D 12000)
£1931 $3224 €2819 Fish (56x28cm-22x11in) s.i.d.1958 ink col scroll. 26-Oct-3 Christie's, Hong Kong #369/R est:30000-50000 (HK.D 25000)
£1991 $3585 €2907 Listening to the stream (80x36cm-31x14in) s.d.1947 ink col hanging scroll. 25-Apr-4 Christie's, Hong Kong #3/R est:20000-25000 (HK.D 28000)
£3556 $6401 €5192 Fishing village (112x16cm-44x6in) s.i. ink col hanging scroll. 25-Apr-4 Christie's, Hong Kong #50/R est:20000-30000 (HK.D 50000)
£4623 $8321 €6750 Lady under a plantain (114x34cm-45x13in) i. ink col hanging scroll. 26-Apr-4 Sotheby's, Hong Kong #661/R est:50000-70000 (HK.D 65000)
£5405 $9027 €7891 Morning mushrooms (62x17cm-24x7in) s.i.d.1934 ink col hanging scroll. 27-Oct-3 Sotheby's, Hong Kong #278/R est:70000-90000 (HK.D 70000)
£5690 $10242 €8307 Scholars under a pine tree (92x34cm-36x13in) s.i. ink col. 26-Apr-4 Sotheby's, Hong Kong #664/R est:60000-80000 (HK.D 80000)
£7336 $12251 €10711 Wandering among endless peaks (7x107cm-3x42in) s.i. ink handscroll. 27-Oct-3 Sotheby's, Hong Kong #279/R est:60000-80000 (HK.D 95000)
£7824 $14083 €11423 Admiring the pine (12x519cm-5x204in) s.i. ink handscroll. 25-Apr-4 Christie's, Hong Kong #51/R est:80000-100000 (HK.D 110000)
£142248 $256046 €207682 Lofty landscape (48cm-19in) s.i. ink handscroll length 11.9 metres. 26-Apr-4 Sotheby's, Hong Kong #663/R est:2000000-3000000 (HK.D 2000000)

PU RU and ZHANG DAQIAN (20th C) Chinese
Works on paper
£21337 $38407 €31152 Lotus, couplet calligraphy (68x33cm-27x13in) s.i.d.1982 ink col scroll set of three. 25-Apr-4 Christie's, Hong Kong #114/R est:100000-120000 (HK.D 300000)

PUCCI, Osvalda (1944-) Italian
£340 $619 €500 Mars (50x50cm-20x20in) s.verso acrylic. 6-Feb-4 Galleria Rosenberg, Milan #140/R

PUCCI, Silvio (1892-1961) Italian
£563 $1025 €850 Landscape with farms (65x75cm-26x30in) s. 21-Jun-4 Pandolfini, Florence #194/R
£567 $1026 €850 Vase of flowers (56x47cm-22x19in) s. 2-Apr-4 Farsetti, Prato #412/R
£733 $1327 €1100 Basket with flowers (30x40cm-12x16in) s. 2-Apr-4 Farsetti, Prato #519/R
£867 $1569 €1300 Still life with eggs (40x50cm-16x20in) s. i.verso. 2-Apr-4 Farsetti, Prato #610/R
£1060 $1928 €1600 Women by farm (89x70cm-35x28in) s. 21-Jun-4 Pandolfini, Florence #213/R

PUCCIARELLI, Mario (1928-) Argentinian
Works on paper
£2616 $4500 €3819 Figure (146x114cm-57x45in) s. mixed media collage. 3-Dec-3 Naón & Cia, Buenos Aires #85/R est:4000-5000

PUCCINI, Biagio (attrib) (1675-1731) Italian
£2318 $4219 €3500 Crucifixion (60x49cm-24x19in) 16-Jun-4 Christie's, Rome #296/R est:3500-4500

PUCCINI, Mario (1869-1920) Italian
£2817 $4676 €4000 Ultimo raggio di sole nel bosco (31x41cm-12x16in) panel prov. 11-Jun-3 Christie's, Rome #251/R est:4000-6000
£16667 $30667 €25000 Fortress (33x21cm-13x8in) s. cardboard prov. 8-Jun-4 Sotheby's, Milan #96/R est:25000-35000
£20000 $36200 €30000 Wood (31x40cm-12x16in) s. cardboard lit. 2-Apr-4 Farsetti, Prato #564/R est:30000-35000
Works on paper
£2446 $4012 €3400 Quay (24x37cm-9x15in) s. pencil chl prov.lit. 10-Jun-3 Pandolfini, Florence #348/R est:3000-3200

PUCHI FONSECA, Manuel (20th C) Venezuelan
£2581 $4000 €3768 Last kiss (161x116cm-63x46in) s. painted 1911. 29-Sep-2 Subastas Odalys, Caracas #91/R

PUDLAT, Pudlo (1916-1992) North American
Works on paper
£3604 $6126 €5262 Man carrying reluctant wife (63x49cm-25x19in) sealskin stencil. 3-Nov-3 Waddingtons, Toronto #281/R est:3000-5000 (C.D 8000)

PUDLICH, Robert (1905-1962) German
£467 $835 €700 Wash table (42x32cm-17x13in) s. canvas on panel prov. 15-May-4 Van Ham, Cologne #857

PUECH, Denis (1854-1942) French
Sculpture
£1761 $3046 €2500 La sirene, Rome (60cm-24in) s. medaille pat bronze wood socle. 10-Dec-3 Rossini, Paris #41/R
£3289 $6053 €5000 Sirene (60cm-24in) st.f.Barbedienne pat bronze. 22-Jun-4 Palais de Beaux Arts, Brussels #630/R est:6000-10000
£3500 $6300 €5110 The siren (60cm-24in) s.i.d.1890 brown pat bronze st.f.F. Barbedienne. 21-Apr-4 Sotheby's, London #56/R est:3500-4500
£4722 $8028 €6800 La sirene (60x37x24cm-24x15x9in) brown pat bronze Cast F Barbedienne. 28-Oct-3 Rabourdin & Choppin de Janvry, Paris #67/R est:7000-7500
£7937 $15000 €11588 La sirene (97cm-38in) s.d.1890 white Carrara marble. 21-Feb-4 Brunk, Ashville #465/R est:3000-6000

PUECHEMAGRE, Frederic (19th C) French?
Works on paper
£352 $616 €500 Charrois sur les fortifications (31x48cm-12x19in) s. W/C. 19-Dec-3 Delvaux, Paris #4

PUENTE, Jose (?) Mexican?
£503 $891 €750 Bull scene (56x44cm-22x17in) s. 27-Apr-4 Durán, Madrid #601/R

PUENTE, Rogelio (1936-1996) Cuban
£973 $1800 €1460 Scion House, England (99x71cm-39x28in) s. 14-Jul-4 American Auctioneer #490347/R est:3000-5000

PUGA, Antonio (1602-1648) Spanish
£855 $1574 €1300 Still life with fried eggs and dead game (50x78cm-20x31in) 22-Jun-4 Durán, Madrid #590/R

PUGET, Pierre (1620-1694) French
Works on paper
£72222 $130000 €105444 Two umbrella pines in a hilly landscape (32x26cm-13x10in) i. pen black ink prov. 22-Jan-4 Christie's, Rockefeller NY #86/R est:30000-50000

PUGET, Pierre (attrib) (1620-1694) French
£855 $1574 €1300 Portarit de magistrat (75x60cm-30x24in) oval. 25-Jun-4 Rossini, Paris #37

PUGET, Pierre (studio) (1620-1694) French
Sculpture
£20000 $36800 €29200 Figure of a faun holding pan pipes (64cm-25in) brown pat bronze column base prov.lit. 10-Jun-4 Christie's, London #96/R est:30000-50000

PUGH, Clifton Ernest (1924-1990) Australian
£326 $593 €476 Swampland scene. board. 1-Jul-4 Joel, Victoria #324/R (A.D 850)
£373 $624 €560 Crustaceans (14x24cm-6x9in) s.d.61 newspaper. 27-Oct-3 Goodman, Sydney #68/R (A.D 900)
£1570 $2905 €2292 Portrait of John Rose, music djudicator (43x48cm-17x19in) s. exhib. 10-Mar-4 Deutscher-Menzies, Melbourne #518 est:1500-3000 (A.D 3800)
£1679 $3056 €2451 Dunes (71x78cm-28x31in) oil sand board prov.exhib. 16-Jun-4 Deutscher-Menzies, Melbourne #32/R est:4000-6000 (A.D 4400)
£2024 $3259 €2955 Rounding sheep (121x90cm-48x35in) s.d.68 board. 13-Oct-3 Joel, Victoria #412 est:5000-8000 (A.D 5000)

£2033 $3638 €2968 Mines road (71x91cm-28x36in) s. bears d.1955. 4-May-4 Sotheby's, Melbourne #258/R est:5000-7000 (A.D 5000)
£2553 $4340 €3727 Sad story (68x78cm-27x31in) s.d.55 board. 26-Nov-3 Deutscher-Menzies, Melbourne #116/R est:7000-9000 (A.D 6000)
£2979 $5064 €4349 Tree stumps and apostie birds (91x111cm-36x44in) s.d.86. 26-Nov-3 Deutscher-Menzies, Melbourne #117/R est:7000-9000 (A.D 7000)
£3072 $5222 €4485 After the bush fire (89x135cm-35x53in) s.d.Sept 62 composition board prov. 24-Nov-3 Sotheby's, Melbourne #105/R est:5000-8000 (A.D 7250)
£4025 $6843 €5877 Sheep drinking at a waterhole (90x120cm-35x47in) s.d.68 composition board. 24-Nov-3 Sotheby's, Melbourne #176/R est:6000-8000 (A.D 9500)
£4065 $6382 €5894 Government stump (91x121cm-36x48in) s.d.58 board prov.exhib. 27-Aug-3 Christie's, Sydney #587/R est:8000-12000 (A.D 10000)
£5372 $9132 €7843 Owl in bush landscape (90x120cm-35x47in) s. prov. 29-Oct-3 Lawson Menzies, Sydney #126/R est:15000-20000 (A.D 13000)
£6098 $9573 €8842 Crows in the bush (90x120cm-35x47in) s.d.73 board prov. 26-Aug-3 Christie's, Sydney #30/R est:15000-20000 (A.D 15000)
Works on paper
£298 $507 €435 Fallen Timber (54x73cm-21x29in) s.i.d.26-1-79 gouache. 26-Nov-3 Deutscher-Menzies, Melbourne #254/R (A.D 700)
£381 $648 €556 Landscape in Israel (54x74cm-21x29in) s.d.10.7.78 gouache prov. 24-Nov-3 Sotheby's, Melbourne #223 (A.D 900)
£405 $652 €591 Dry lake (56x75cm-22x30in) s. gouache. 13-Oct-3 Joel, Victoria #250 est:1000-1500 (A.D 1000)
£508 $864 €742 Landscape in Israel (55x74cm-22x29in) s.d.20.7.78 gouache prov. 24-Nov-3 Sotheby's, Melbourne #231 (A.D 1200)
£511 $868 €746 Mangroves (53x73cm-21x29in) s.d.15-6-82 gouache synthetic polymer paint. 26-Nov-3 Deutscher-Menzies, Melbourne #258/R (A.D 1200)
£1787 $3092 €2609 Tibooburra township (55x74cm-22x29in) s. gouache board. 10-Dec-3 Shapiro, Sydney #20/R est:4000-6000 (A.D 4200)
£4472 $8004 €6529 St Francis speaks to the birds (120x90cm-47x35in) sd.65 mixed media composition board. 4-May-4 Sotheby's, Melbourne #275/R est:5000-7000 (A.D 11000)

PUGH, David (1946-1994) Canadian
£203 $344 €296 Amethyst and Emerald Eve (61x76cm-24x30in) acrylic. 23-Nov-3 Levis, Calgary #538/R (C.D 450)
£407 $728 €594 Rundle nocturne (111x174cm-44x69in) s. 6-May-4 Heffel, Vancouver #116/R (C.D 1000)
£480 $878 €701 Pine tree (55x70cm-22x28in) s.i.d.1993. 1-Jun-4 Hodgins, Calgary #305/R (C.D 1200)
£520 $952 €759 Grassi Lakes (75x100cm-30x39in) s.i. 1-Jun-4 Hodgins, Calgary #24/R (C.D 1300)
£640 $1171 €934 Eagle cloud (90x75cm-35x30in) s.i. 1-Jun-4 Hodgins, Calgary #462/R (C.D 1600)
£920 $1684 €1343 The windmill (95x83cm-37x33in) s.i.d.1980 prov. 1-Jun-4 Hodgins, Calgary #433/R est:2000-2500 (C.D 2300)
£992 $1795 €1448 Northern sky (51x66cm-20x26in) s. i.d.1990 verso. 18-Apr-4 Levis, Calgary #96/R est:1500-2000 (C.D 2400)

PUGIN, Augustus Charles (attrib) (1769-1832) French
Works on paper
£500 $830 €730 Boston Stumps Lincs (23x18cm-9x7in) W/C. 3-Oct-3 Mallams, Oxford #114/R

PUGIN, Augustus Welby Northmore (1812-1852) British
Works on paper
£680 $1272 €1020 Brandenberg House (26x37cm-10x15in) s. pen ink W/C. 22-Jul-4 Dominic Winter, Swindon #85/R
£8000 $14560 €11680 Design for furniture for Chirk Castle (30x49cm-12x19in) s.i.d.1849 pencil set of three. 21-Jun-4 Christie's, London #503/R est:1500-3000

PUGLIA, Giuseppe (c.1600-1636) Italian
£4676 $7669 €6500 Saint John the Baptist (42x29cm-17x11in) prov.lit. 4-Jun-3 Sotheby's, Milan #93/R est:7000-10000

PUHONNY, Victor (1838-1909) Polish
£336 $617 €510 Black Forest landsape with peasant woman by farmstead (15x11cm-6x4in) s. bears d. panel. 24-Jun-4 Dr Fritz Nagel, Stuttgart #743/R
£533 $965 €800 By the stream (20x30cm-8x12in) mono.d.3.8.81 panel. 2-Apr-4 Winterberg, Heidelberg #509/R
£1042 $1771 €1500 Hunter in landscape (15x27cm-6x11in) s. panel. 28-Oct-3 Dorotheum, Vienna #148/R est:1800-2200

PUHRINGER, Hans (1875-1953) Austrian
£426 $711 €600 Portrait of young woman with red scarf (28x28cm-11x11in) s. 16-Oct-3 Dorotheum, Salzburg #597/R

PUIG BENLLOCH, Ramon (20th C) Spanish
£282 $524 €420 Figure (78x54cm-31x21in) s.d.74 board. 2-Mar-4 Ansorena, Madrid #885/R
£483 $869 €700 Harvesting (62x50cm-24x20in) s.d.75 board. 26-Jan-4 Durán, Madrid #603/R

PUIG Y SAURET, Domingo (1873-1951) South American
£299 $550 €437 River (75x55cm-30x22in) s. 22-Jun-4 Galeria y Remates, Montevideo #20

PUIG, Jean (20th C) Venezuelan?
£1291 $2195 €1885 Seascape (46x61cm-18x24in) s. 23-Nov-3 Subastas Odalys, Caracas #66 est:2000

PUIG, Luis (1894-1984) Spanish
£265 $482 €400 Woman in graden (61x39cm-24x15in) s. canvas on board. 19-Jun-4 Dannenberg, Berlin #546/R

PUIG, Vicente (?) ?
£483 $869 €700 Woman of the Thirties. s.d.35. 26-Jan-4 Ansorena, Madrid #265/R

PUIG-RODA, Gabriel (1865-1919) Spanish
Works on paper
£2852 $5049 €4250 Head of old Valencian man (54x45cm-21x18in) s.d.1912 W/C. 27-Apr-4 Durán, Madrid #689/R est:2500
£6154 $10277 €8800 Woman with guitar (49x35cm-19x14in) s.i. W/C. 30-Jun-3 Ansorena, Madrid #447/R est:9500

PUIGAUDEAU, Fernand du (1866-1930) French
£2000 $3580 €3000 Le port, vue nocturne (20x24cm-8x9in) i. 16-May-4 Thierry & Lannon, Brest #169/R est:3000-3500
£5000 $7950 €7250 Clair de lune sur la cote de Croisic (24x33cm-9x13in) s. 11-Sep-3 Christie's, Kensington #32/R est:4000-6000
£5986 $10475 €8500 Fenaison en Bretagne (25x31cm-10x12in) s. prov. 16-Dec-3 Claude Aguttes, Neuilly #9/R est:5000-8000
£7042 $12324 €10000 Rue du Bourg de Batz (38x29cm-15x11in) s. board. 21-Dec-3 Thierry & Lannon, Brest #194/R est:10000-12000
£7487 $14000 €10931 Promenade en barque de nuit a Briere (54x73cm-21x29in) s. 25-Feb-4 Christie's, Rockefeller NY #52/R est:10000-15000
£9000 $16560 €13140 Bords de Loire, Basse Indre (55x46cm-22x18in) s. prov. 22-Jun-4 Sotheby's, London #239/R est:8000-12000
£13333 $24533 €20000 Clair de lune (46x38cm-18x15in) s.d.1907. 8-Jun-4 Livinec, Gaudcheau & Jezequel, Rennes #92/R
£27000 $49140 €39420 Meules de foin et champ de coquelicots (46x61cm-18x24in) s. prov. 4-Feb-4 Sotheby's, London #202/R est:20000-30000
£28000 $50960 €40880 Retour de peche au croisic (48x80cm-19x31in) s.d.16 oil black crayon prov. 4-Feb-4 Sotheby's, London #228/R est:20000-25000
£30726 $55000 €44860 Vue de Grand Canal, Venise (76x113cm-30x44in) s. 5-May-4 Christie's, Rockefeller NY #270/R est:40000-60000
£39000 $70980 €56940 Table au bouquet jaune (56x61cm-22x24in) s. indis d. prov. 4-Feb-4 Sotheby's, London #201/R est:20000-30000

PUIGDENGOLAS BARELLA, Jose (1906-1987) Spanish
£2069 $3724 €3000 Vase of flowers (60x51cm-24x20in) s. 26-Jan-4 Durán, Madrid #115/R est:3000
£4895 $8175 €7000 Landscape in Cerdana (74x93cm-29x37in) s. s.i.d.1952 verso. 30-Jun-3 Ansorena, Madrid #443/R est:7000

PUIGVERT, Jean (20th C) French?
£280 $476 €400 Le pont (65x50cm-26x20in) s.d.1991. 27-Nov-3 Calmels Cohen, Paris #89/R

PUJIA, Antonio (1929-) Argentinian
Sculpture
£4098 $7500 €5983 Dancing couple (38cm-15in) bronze. 1-Jun-4 Arroyo, Buenos Aires #32
£4396 $8000 €6418 Boy (30cm-12in) s.d.70 bronze. 29-Jun-4 Arroyo, Buenos Aires #40/R est:7500
£10497 $19000 €15326 Portrait of Susana (64cm-25in) bronze. 30-Mar-4 Arroyo, Buenos Aires #65

PUJOL DE GUASTAVINO, Clement (1850-1905) French
£25000 $45000 €36500 In front of the palace (92x64cm-36x25in) s. 23-Apr-4 Sotheby's, New York #94/R est:50000-70000

PUJOL, Adrian (20th C) South American
£857 $1560 €1286 River Cunucunuma (114x128cm-45x50in) s. painted 1995. 21-Jun-4 Subastas Odalys, Caracas #92/R
£1146 $2085 €1719 Puerto Colombia (115x127cm-45x50in) s.verso acrylic painted 1998. 21-Jun-4 Subastas Odalys, Caracas #106/R

PUJOL, Joan (20th C) Spanish
£275 $500 €402 Still life of Chianti basket and stack of El Pais (28x20cm-11x8in) mono.d.1989 panel. 7-Feb-4 Sloans & Kenyon, Bethesda #877/R

PUJOS, Andre (1738-1788) French
Works on paper
£3252 $5821 €4748 The Marquis de Vilette and his wife (44x32cm-17x13in) s.d.1788 pencil pair exhib.prov. 25-May-4 Bukowskis, Stockholm #546/R est:25000-30000 (S.KR 44000)

PULACINI, Franco (1934-) Italian
Works on paper
£3521 $6162 €5000 Dance (48x84cm-19x33in) assemblage board exhib. 16-Dec-3 Finarte Semenzato, Milan #210/R est:3200

PULE, John (20th C) New Zealander?
£20979 $38182 €30629 High and low (200x358cm-79x141in) s.i.d.2001 diptych. 29-Jun-4 Peter Webb, Auckland #43/R est:45000-65000 (NZ.D 60000)

PULFER, Jack (?) British?
£450 $815 €657 Morning on the marshes (43x56cm-17x22in) s. 16-Apr-4 Keys, Aylsham #719

PULGA, Bruno (1922-) Italian
£532 $888 €750 Composition (90x79cm-35x31in) 12-Oct-3 St-Germain-en-Laye Encheres #193/R
£805 $1474 €1200 Composition (65x81cm-26x32in) prov. 7-Jul-4 Artcurial Briest, Paris #327 est:1500-2000

PULIGO, Domenico (style) (1492-1527) Italian
£7000 $12600 €10220 Mystic marriage of Saint Catherine (98x75cm-39x30in) panel. 20-Apr-4 Sotheby's, Olympia #201/R est:6000-9000

PULINCKX, Louis (1843-1910) Belgian
£480 $888 €701 Moment of calm on the river (45x66cm-18x26in) s. prov. 15-Jan-4 Christie's, Kensington #736/R
£480 $864 €701 Continental landscape with figures fishing from a small boat (46x81cm-18x32in) s. 21-Apr-4 Tennants, Leyburn #1150
£629 $1051 €900 Along the quai (30x40cm-12x16in) s. panel. 11-Oct-3 De Vuyst, Lokeren #296
£700 $1281 €1022 View of Antwerp (52x63cm-20x25in) s.d.74. 6-Apr-4 Bonhams, Knightsbridge #145/R
£733 $1320 €1100 Vast evening landscape with two women near the water (50x77cm-20x30in) s. 26-Apr-4 Bernaerts, Antwerp #114/R
£1600 $2512 €2320 Peaceful river landscape with fishermen sorting out their nets on a jetty (71x119cm-28x47in) s. 28-Aug-3 Christie's, Kensington #101/R est:800-1200

PULLER, John Anthony (fl.1821-1867) British
£400 $668 €584 Say please ! (33x26cm-13x10in) s. 12-Nov-3 Sotheby's, Olympia #25/R

PULLER, John Anthony (attrib) (fl.1821-1867) British
£1500 $2745 €2190 Rest by the wayside (44x54cm-17x21in) 6-Jul-4 Bearnes, Exeter #497/R est:800-1200

PULLICINO, Giorgio (attrib) (1779-1851) Maltese
£28000 $46760 €40880 View of Valetta from Marsamxett Harbour taken from Fort Manoel. View of Fort Manoel (59x130cm-23x51in) pair prov.lit. 14-Oct-3 Sotheby's, London #33/R est:30000-50000

PULLINEN, Laila (1933-) Finnish
Sculpture
£3514 $6289 €5200 Dolce (27cm-11in) s.d.79 bronze incl.socle. 8-May-4 Bukowskis, Helsinki #229/R est:4000-5000
£7000 $12530 €10500 A small step (50cm-20in) s.d.1990 num.3/3 polished pat.bronze. 15-May-4 Hagelstam, Helsinki #16/R est:8500
£13636 $23182 €19500 The Baltic Sea's daughter (80cm-31in) s.d.71 bronze. 29-Nov-3 Bukowskis, Helsinki #240/R est:8000-10000
Works on paper
£352 $563 €500 Nude (80x60cm-31x24in) s.d.1971 dr. 18-Sep-3 Hagelstam, Helsinki #995

PULMANN, Dora (1950-) Greek
£1600 $2864 €2336 Red II (160x140cm-63x55in) s.d.2003 acrylic chl linen exhib. 10-May-4 Sotheby's, Olympia #70/R est:1000-1500

PULVIRENTI, Rosario (1899-?) Italian
£1600 $2896 €2400 Portrait of Agnese Planeta (100x88cm-39x35in) s.d.1927. 30-Mar-4 Babuino, Rome #412/R est:2000-2500

PULZONE, Scipione (attrib) (1550-1598) Italian
£4507 $7887 €6400 Madonna praying (64x49cm-25x19in) i. slate. 17-Dec-3 Christie's, Rome #451/R est:4000-6000

PULZONE, Scipione (style) (1550-1598) Italian
£13158 $24211 €20000 Portrait de gentilhomme a mi-corps (99x70cm-39x28in) 24-Jun-4 Christie's, Paris #73/R est:15000-20000

PUMMIL, Robert (1936-) American
£2050 $3300 €2973 Riding shotgun (41x51cm-16x20in) 22-Aug-3 Altermann Galleries, Santa Fe #65
£2059 $3500 €3006 Palo duro riders (61x76cm-24x30in) 1-Nov-3 Altermann Galleries, Santa Fe #135

PUMPIN, Fritz (1901-1972) Swiss
£905 $1620 €1321 Village on hill (54x69cm-21x27in) s. 12-May-4 Dobiaschofsky, Bern #886/R est:1600 (S.FR 2100)
£1739 $3183 €2539 Early spring, Homburgerbach (54x73cm-21x29in) s.i.d.1950 verso. 4-Jun-4 Zofingen, Switzerland #2926/R est:4500 (S.FR 4000)

PUNCHATZ, Don (1936-) American
£2400 $4200 €3504 All the President's men (70x54cm-28x21in) each init. acrylic board diptych painted 1974 exhib.lit. 17-Dec-3 Christie's, Rockefeller NY #224/R est:3000-5000

PUNZ, Georg Albert (18th C) Austrian
£596 $1091 €900 Death of St Joseph with Mary and Jesus (35x24cm-14x9in) 7-Apr-4 Dorotheum, Salzburg #10/R

PUPINI, Biagio (attrib) (16th C) Italian
Works on paper
£2200 $3806 €3212 Madonna and Child with the infant Baptist (36x25cm-14x10in) black chk pen brown ink wash prov. 12-Dec-3 Christie's, Kensington #306 est:300-500

PUPUK, D P (1968-) Indonesian
£1215 $2030 €1774 Perempatan Tugu Yogya (79x69cm-31x27in) s.d.1997 s.i.d.verso. 12-Oct-3 Sotheby's, Singapore #188/R est:2500-3500 (S.D 3500)
£1376 $2202 €2009 Becak (74x88cm-29x35in) s.d.1999 s.i.d.2000 verso. 18-May-3 Sotheby's, Singapore #184/R est:3000-4000 (S.D 3840)
£2288 $4141 €3340 Sudut keraton yogya (95x145cm-37x57in) s.d.20 December 2003 s.i.d.verso. 4-Apr-4 Sotheby's, Singapore #181/R est:4000-6000 (S.D 7000)

PURCELL, Joseph (1927-) Canadian
£236 $368 €342 Nova Scotia harbour (46x61cm-18x24in) s. canvasboard. 26-Mar-3 Walker's, Ottawa #418/R (C.D 550)
£279 $435 €405 Summer day, Nova Scotia (71x96cm-28x38in) s. board. 26-Mar-3 Walker's, Ottawa #419/R (C.D 650)

PURDIE, Shirley (1948-) Australian
Works on paper
£781 $1461 €1172 Bow River country (140x100cm-55x39in) i.verso pigment exec. 2001 prov. 21-Jul-4 Shapiro, Sydney #26/R (A.D 2000)

PURIFICATO, Domenico (1915-1984) Italian
£2027 $3568 €3000 Women fighting (25x35cm-10x14in) painted 1941 exhib. 24-May-4 Christie's, Milan #219/R est:4000-6000
£2703 $4757 €4000 Portrait of the painter Anna Nascimbeni Tallone (59x45cm-23x18in) s. board painted 1944 prov.exhib. 24-May-4 Christie's, Milan #215/R est:5000-7000
£3636 $6182 €5200 Girl resting (60x80cm-24x31in) s. i.verso exhib. 24-Nov-3 Christie's, Milan #164/R est:4000-6000
£4667 $8587 €7000 Woman from Sperlonga (80x60cm-31x24in) s. 12-Jun-4 Meeting Art, Vercelli #389/R est:5000
Works on paper
£296 $518 €420 Peasant man (65x44cm-26x17in) s.d.63 Chinese ink card. 16-Dec-3 Finarte Semenzato, Milan #132/R
£467 $859 €700 Legnano battle (25x35cm-10x14in) s.i. Chinese ink W/C card. 10-Jun-4 Galleria Pace, Milan #32/R
£467 $859 €700 Legnano battle (25x35cm-10x14in) s.i. Chinese ink W/C card. 10-Jun-4 Galleria Pace, Milan #33/R
£1333 $2400 €2000 Peasants resting (35x50cm-14x20in) s. ink W/C. 22-Apr-4 Finarte Semenzato, Rome #131/R est:1800-2400

PURLA, Teresa (1961-) Australian
£364 $662 €531 Witchety Grub Dreaming (123x92cm-48x36in) acrylic. 1-Jul-4 Joel, Victoria #274/R (A.D 950)

PURO, Veikko (1884-1959) Finnish
£366 $586 €520 Harbour (49x42cm-19x17in) s.d.1919. 18-Sep-3 Hagelstam, Helsinki #910

PURRMANN, Hans (1880-1966) German
£5245 $8916 €7500 Girl's portrait (39x35cm-15x14in) s. i. stretcher prov. 26-Nov-3 Lempertz, Koln #925/R est:8000
£6000 $10980 €9000 Portrait of Regina (46x38cm-18x15in) s. panel double-sided prov. 5-Jun-4 Lempertz, Koln #956/R est:8000-10000
£11189 $19021 €16000 Educating Titian - after Tizian (28x45cm-11x18in) s. i. verso prov. 26-Nov-3 Lempertz, Koln #926/R est:18000-20000
£21127 $36549 €30000 Still life of flowers (74x62cm-29x24in) s. tempera. 13-Dec-3 Lempertz, Koln #178/R est:35000-40000
£34965 $59441 €50000 Bathers at Langenargen (54x66cm-21x26in) i. stretcher prov. 26-Nov-3 Dorotheum, Vienna #31/R est:45000-60000
£65000 $118300 €94900 Palmen am Hafen, Porto d'Ischia (65x73cm-26x29in) s. painted 1921 prov. 3-Feb-4 Christie's, London #187/R est:30000-40000
£68966 $115172 €100000 Porto d'Ischia (51x60cm-20x24in) s. painted c.1957 prov. 13-Nov-3 Neumeister, Munich #432/R est:50000-70000
£80000 $146400 €120000 Seascape near Lacco Ameno - Ischia (67x80cm-26x31in) s. prov.exhib. 5-Jun-4 Lempertz, Koln #958/R est:100000-120000
£90909 $154545 €130000 Porto d'Ischia (73x60cm-29x24in) s. prov. 28-Nov-3 Villa Grisebach, Berlin #72/R est:80000-100000
Works on paper
£556 $928 €800 Standing female nude (35x10cm-14x4in) pencil. 24-Oct-3 Ketterer, Hamburg #1034/R
£556 $928 €800 Standing female nude (37x28cm-15x11in) s. pencil. 24-Oct-3 Ketterer, Hamburg #1035/R
£600 $1098 €900 Rocky coast (39x58cm-15x23in) s. W/C pencil prov. 5-Jun-4 Lempertz, Koln #960/R
£933 $1708 €1400 Farmstead with trees (24x30cm-9x12in) i. W/C prov. 5-Jun-4 Lempertz, Koln #961/R
£1067 $1952 €1600 Waterside village (21x28cm-8x11in) W/C prov. 5-Jun-4 Lempertz, Koln #962/R est:500
£2133 $3904 €3200 Portrait of daughter, Regina (65x50cm-26x20in) s. gouache board prov. 5-Jun-4 Lempertz, Koln #959/R est:2500
£2517 $4280 €3600 Villa on Bellosguardo, Florence (48x67cm-19x26in) s. pencil W/C. 26-Nov-3 Lempertz, Koln #927/R est:4000

PURRMANN, Karl (1877-1966) German
£552 $921 €800 View of town, possibly Hall in Tyrol (68x55cm-27x22in) s.d.1926. 13-Nov-3 Neumeister, Munich #433/R
£633 $1140 €950 Alexander room in Wurzburg Castle (64x81cm-25x32in) s.d.1938. 26-Apr-4 Rieber, Stuttgart #921/R

PURSER, Sarah (1848-1943) British
£1678 $2853 €2400 Georgina, Lady Gore-Booth (23x15cm-9x6in) i. 25-Nov-3 Hamilton Osborne King, Dublin #277/R
£2448 $4161 €3500 Study of a young woman seated in an aesthetic interior. Study of a woman head (37x29cm-15x11in) panel double-sided. 25-Nov-3 Hamilton Osborne King, Dublin #117/R est:2000-3000
£2676 $4282 €3800 Kitchen garden near Paris. Landscapes, Les Ternes (15x22cm-6x9in) one i.verso panel pair prov.exhib.lit. 16-Sep-3 Whyte's, Dublin #83/R est:4000-6000
£3380 $5408 €4800 Head of a young boy (25x20cm-10x8in) i. canvas on board prov. 16-Sep-3 Whyte's, Dublin #86/R est:2000-3000
£7692 $13077 €11000 Portrait of Sir Henry Gore-Booth, seated on one of the Lissadell dining room chairs (122x88cm-48x35in) init.d.1884. 25-Nov-3 Hamilton Osborne King, Dublin #275/R est:5000-8000

£9790 $16643 €14000 Portrait of Georgina, Lady Gore-Booth (121x82cm-48x32in) lit. 25-Nov-3 Hamilton Osborne King, Dublin #276/R est:6000-10000
£139860 $237762 €200000 Double portrait of Constance and Eva Gore-Booth as young girls in a woodland (152x105cm-60x41in) lit. 25-Nov-3 Hamilton Osborne King, Dublin #278/R est:30000-50000

Works on paper
£550 $985 €803 Family pet (16x11cm-6x4in) pencil prov. 14-May-4 Christie's, London #30/R est:500-800
£550 $985 €803 Head of a lady (12x9cm-5x4in) pencil double-sided prov. 14-May-4 Christie's, London #31/R

PURSER, William (c.1790-c.1852) British
Works on paper
£1100 $1870 €1606 View on the Bosphorus (15x23cm-6x9in) s. pencil W/C scratching out. 20-Nov-3 Christie's, London #120/R est:1200-1800
£1100 $2002 €1606 View of the Acropolis and Athens with goatherd and goats in foreground (9x12cm-4x5in) s. W/C exec c.1815. 15-Jun-4 Bonhams, Oxford #37/R est:500-800

PURTSCHER, Alfons (1885-1962) Austrian
£250 $425 €365 Otto, hound in a landscape (41x51cm-16x20in) s.d.1926. 27-Nov-3 Christie's, Kensington #376/R
£638 $1167 €950 Brown horse with saddle in stable (41x51cm-16x20in) s.indis.d. lit. 8-Jul-4 Allgauer, Kempten #2198/R
Works on paper
£473 $832 €700 Three riders with dogs fox hunting (191x59cm-75x23in) s.d.1917. 21-May-4 Mehlis, Plauen #15169/R

PURUNTATAMERI, Stanislaus (1906-1987) Australian
Sculpture
£3711 $6939 €5567 Curlew (66cm-26in) earth pigments ironwood exec.c.1970 prov. 26-Jul-4 Sotheby's, Melbourne #53/R est:3000-5000 (A.D 9500)

PURVES-SMITH, Peter (1913-1949) Australian
£22128 $37617 €32307 Mother and child (60x44cm-24x17in) i.verso exhib.prov. 25-Nov-3 Christie's, Melbourne #6/R est:35000-40000 (A.D 52000)
Works on paper
£9924 $18061 €14489 Botanic Gardens (51x60cm-20x24in) s.d.1949 i.verso W/C gouache pen ink prov.exhib. 16-Jun-4 Deutscher-Menzies, Melbourne #59/R est:28000-35000 (A.D 26000)

PURVIS, Greeny Petyarre (1930-) Australian
Works on paper
£3137 $5616 €4580 Of my Country Aneltyeye (120x120cm-47x47in) synthetic polymer pant linen exec 2000 prov. 25-May-4 Lawson Menzies, Sydney #231/R est:8000-10000 (A.D 8000)

PURVIS, Louise (20th C) New Zealander
Works on paper
£526 $895 €768 Pukeko. mixed media. 26-Nov-3 Dunbar Sloane, Wellington #153/R est:1000-2000 (NZ.D 1400)

PURVIS, T G (fl.1900-1910) British
£1000 $1790 €1460 Four masted barque Springburn under full sail (58x89cm-23x35in) s.i. canvasboard. 26-May-4 Christie's, Kensington #641/R est:1000-1500

PURY, Edmond-Jean de (1845-1911) Swiss
£348 $637 €508 Fishing boats, Venice (33x50cm-13x20in) s. 4-Jun-4 Zofingen, Switzerland #2924 (S.FR 800)
£1293 $2315 €1888 Venice (112x60cm-44x24in) s.i. 13-May-4 Stuker, Bern #288/R est:4000-6000 (S.FR 3000)
£2609 $4774 €3809 Gitane (57x43cm-22x17in) s.d.1892 panel. 7-Jun-4 Christie's, Zurich #16/R est:3000-4000 (S.FR 6000)

PURYEAR, Martin (1941-) American
Sculpture
£156425 $280000 €228381 Untitled (155x209x112cm-61x82x44in) steel wire mesh tar Douglas fir exec 1990 prov.exhib. 11-May-4 Christie's, Rockefeller NY #45/R est:350000-450000
£299401 $500000 €437125 Amulet (160x157cm-63x62in) pine cypress executed 1985 prov.exhib. 12-Nov-3 Sotheby's, New York #3/R est:250000-350000
£311377 $520000 €454610 Untitled (198x89cm-78x35in) tar steel mesh pine Douglas fir executed 1987 prov.exhib. 12-Nov-3 Sotheby's, New York #8/R est:350000-450000

PURYGIN, Leonid (1951-1995) Russian
£5000 $8950 €7300 Erotic composition from the theory of relativity series (74x54cm-29x21in) s.i. board. 26-May-4 Sotheby's, London #321/R est:6000-8000

PUSA, Unto (1913-1973) Finnish
£1689 $3024 €2500 Irene apres de Goya (74x62cm-29x24in) s.d.68 exhib. 8-May-4 Bukowskis, Helsinki #235/R est:2500-3000
£2797 $4755 €4000 The sun (75x110cm-30x43in) s.d.61. 29-Nov-3 Bukowskis, Helsinki #310/R est:4000-6000
£14189 $25399 €21000 Shed II (130x97cm-51x38in) s.d.57 exhib. 8-May-4 Bukowskis, Helsinki #246/R est:5000-6000

PUSHMAN, Hovsep (1877-1966) American
£9945 $18000 €14520 An idol (43x33cm-17x13in) s. prov. 31-Mar-4 Sotheby's, New York #8/R est:12000-18000
£25000 $43000 €36500 When autumn comes (63x50cm-25x20in) s. panel prov. 3-Dec-3 Sotheby's, New York #58/R est:20000-30000
£27616 $47500 €40319 Peacock feather (86x63cm-34x25in) s. panel prov. 3-Dec-3 Sotheby's, New York #35/R est:20000-30000
£29070 $50000 €42442 Turkestan (63x58cm-25x23in) s. panel prov. 3-Dec-3 Sotheby's, New York #36/R est:40000-60000

PUSOLE, Pierluigi (1963-) Italian
£1216 $2141 €1800 I am (60x50cm-24x20in) painted 1998. 22-May-4 Galleria Pananti, Florence #349/R est:1800-2000
£1342 $2403 €2000 Untitled (50x99cm-20x39in) s. acrylic painted 1987 prov. 25-May-4 Sotheby's, Milan #218/R est:2000-3000
£1449 $2377 €2000 I am God (60x70cm-24x28in) init.verso acrylic board. 29-May-3 Galleria Pace, Milan #29 est:3300
£2365 $4162 €3500 TV. s.verso painted c.1989 prov. 24-May-4 Christie's, Milan #94 est:2000-3000
£2819 $5046 €4200 Untitled (50x210cm-20x83in) s. s.d.87 acrylic prov. 25-May-4 Sotheby's, Milan #217/R est:3000-4000
Works on paper
£667 $1227 €1000 Rai Four, vision (35x49cm-14x19in) s.i.d.1994 pencil pastel pen card. 12-Jun-4 Meeting Art, Vercelli #16a/R
£671 $1201 €1000 I am God (60x90cm-24x35in) mixed media exec.1996 prov. 25-May-4 Sotheby's, Milan #224/R
£2113 $3697 €3000 Rai Four Vision (60x80cm-24x31in) init.i.d.1994 mixed media on canvas prov. 16-Dec-3 Finarte Semenzato, Milan #237/R est:2800-3200

PUTALLAZ, Mizette (1932-) Swiss
£226 $391 €330 Colombes (17x12cm-7x5in) s. canvas on panel. 12-Dec-3 Galerie du Rhone, Sion #576 (S.FR 500)
£294 $509 €429 Allignement (11x34cm-4x13in) s. s.i.verso panel. 12-Dec-3 Galerie du Rhone, Sion #575 (S.FR 650)

PUTHUFF, Hanson Duvall (1875-1972) American
£1323 $2500 €1932 Landscape (30x41cm-12x16in) masonite prov. 17-Feb-4 John Moran, Pasadena #176/R est:2000-3000
£3439 $6500 €5021 Southern California landscape (33x38cm-13x15in) s. board prov. 17-Feb-4 John Moran, Pasadena #153/R est:4000-6000
£3804 $7000 €5554 Late afternoon light (45x53cm-18x21in) s. 8-Jun-4 Bonhams & Butterfields, San Francisco #4332/R est:4000-6000
£4913 $8500 €7173 Edge of the grove (30x40cm-12x16in) s. i.verso masonite prov. 10-Dec-3 Bonhams & Butterfields, San Francisco #6229/R est:3000-5000
£5495 $10000 €8023 November morning near the Salinas River (36x51cm-14x20in) s. 15-Jun-4 John Moran, Pasadena #38 est:12000-18000
£11765 $20000 €17177 Landscape, near La Canada (46x61cm-18x24in) s. i.verso. 18-Nov-3 John Moran, Pasadena #33 est:20000-30000
£24457 $45000 €35707 Mantle of mist (61x76cm-24x30in) s. i.verso. 8-Jun-4 Bonhams & Butterfields, San Francisco #4301/R est:30000-50000

PUTNAM, Arthur (1873-1930) American
Sculpture
£8824 $15000 €12883 Reclining lion (22x48cm-9x19in) i.num.29 brown pat. bronze. 29-Oct-3 Christie's, Los Angeles #70/R est:15000-25000

PUTSAGE, Marguerite (1868-1946) Belgian
£267 $477 €400 Dame assise (46x38cm-18x15in) s. 16-May-4 MonsAntic, Maisieres #458
£280 $501 €420 Interieur (40x32cm-16x13in) s. 16-May-4 MonsAntic, Maisieres #456

PUTTER, Pieter de (1600-1659) Dutch
£1300 $2210 €1898 Still life with a carp hanging from a piece od string (42x55cm-17x22in) prov. 30-Oct-3 Sotheby's, Olympia #65/R est:2000-3000
£1500 $2550 €2190 Still life with a pike and perch together with a stoneware jug and a fishing line on a table (37x51cm-15x20in) panel. 30-Oct-3 Sotheby's, Olympia #66/R est:1500-2000
£2500 $4575 €3650 Still life of sea bream, fishing basket and nest on a wooden table (38x53cm-15x21in) mono. panel. 6-Jul-4 Sotheby's, Olympia #552/R est:2500-3500

PUTTER, Pieter de (attrib) (1600-1659) Dutch
£2013 $3705 €3000 Still life with fish, dove, basket and fruit (64x76cm-25x30in) 26-Mar-4 Bolland & Marotz, Bremen #465/R est:3300

PUTTI, Giovanni (1771-1847) Italian
Sculpture
£7182 $13000 €10486 Group of the entombment (30x12cm-12x5in) terracotta. 16-Apr-4 Sotheby's, New York #28/R est:4000-6000

PUTTMAN, Donald (1926-) American
£882 $1500 €1288 Eagle dance (76x152cm-30x60in) s. masonite panel painted c.1970 prov. 1-Nov-3 Santa Fe Art, Santa Fe #29/R est:2000-4000

PUTZ, Leo (1869-1940) German
£1923 $3500 €2808 Seated figure (58x79cm-23x31in) s. 29-Jun-4 Sotheby's, New York #337/R est:5000-7000
£8392 $14434 €12000 Angra dos Reis with fishing boats (27x36cm-11x14in) s.i.d.1931 cardboard prov. 5-Dec-3 Ketterer, Munich #27/R est:12000-15000
£11312 $19231 €16516 Nude study (40x35cm-16x14in) s. lit. 19-Nov-3 Fischer, Luzern #1199/R est:25000-30000 (S.FR 25000)
£13333 $23867 €20000 Peonies (75x69cm-30x27in) s. i.d. stretcher. 13-May-4 Neumeister, Munich #473/R est:20000-25000
£13333 $23867 €20000 Two female nudes in wood (55x45cm-22x18in) prov. 14-May-4 Ketterer, Munich #126/R est:20000-30000
£14000 $25480 €21000 Peonies in a vase (76x69cm-30x27in) s.d.1937 lit. 3-Jul-4 Geble, Radolfzell #423/R est:20000

£17483	$30070	€25000	Two female nudes in the forest (55x45cm-22x18in) s. painted c.1920/25 prov. 5-Dec-3 Ketterer, Munich #28/R est:28000-35000
£25000	$46000	€38000	Study of a nude bathing (40x35cm-16x14in) s. lit. 22-Jun-4 Wiener Kunst Auktionen, Vienna #78/R est:35000
£27972	$47552	€40000	Evening sun, Adelheid (64x59cm-25x23in) s. prov. 28-Nov-3 Villa Grisebach, Berlin #16/R est:25000-40000
£29333	$52507	€44000	Quiet evening (60x65cm-24x26in) s. prov. 14-May-4 Ketterer, Munich #124/R est:30000-40000
£30201	$54060	€45000	Bathers (42x45cm-17x18in) i.verso lit. 27-May-4 Hassfurther, Vienna #65/R est:55000-65000
£33557	$59396	€50000	Girl with flowers (65x60cm-26x24in) s. prov.lit. 28-Apr-4 Wiener Kunst Auktionen, Vienna #93/R est:50000-80000
£68966	$115172	€100000	Late summer (70x85cm-28x33in) s.d.06 prov. 13-Nov-3 Neumeister, Munich #434/R est:80000-90000
£93750	$159375	€135000	Morning sun (98x83cm-39x33in) s. s.i.d.1911 verso prov.lit. 28-Oct-3 Wiener Kunst Auktionen, Vienna #62/R est:55000-100000
£111888	$190210	€160000	The sofa with Pauline (130x130cm-51x51in) s.d.08 lit. 25-Nov-3 Hassfurther, Vienna #64/R est:180000-200000

Works on paper

£413	$756	€603	Erotic fantasy (13x21cm-5x8in) mono. pencil. 4-Jun-4 Zofingen, Switzerland #2508 (S.FR 950)
£1379	$2303	€2000	Nude studie II, Model mara Aranaz (40x49cm-16x19in) chl col pastel board. 13-Nov-3 Neumeister, Munich #435/R est:1800-2000
£1722	$3134	€2600	Seated young girl (38x29cm-15x11in) s.d.1927 chk. 16-Jun-4 Hugo Ruef, Munich #1174 est:500

PUTZ, Leo (attrib) (1869-1940) German

Works on paper

£395	$726	€600	Nude study (26x20cm-10x8in) chl red ochre. 22-Jun-4 Wiener Kunst Auktionen, Vienna #146/R

PUTZHOFEN-HAMBUCHEN, Paul (19/20th C) German

£451	$745	€650	Niedeggen in the Eifel (70x90cm-28x35in) s. 3-Jul-3 Van Ham, Cologne #1411
£861	$1567	€1300	Castle ruins above the Rhine (70x90cm-28x35in) s. 18-Jun-4 Bolland & Marotz, Bremen #728/R
£933	$1699	€1400	Fishing boat on the Dutch coastline (47x66cm-19x26in) s. 1-Jul-4 Van Ham, Cologne #1564

PUVIS DE CHAVANNES, Pierre (1824-1898) French

£20423	$35331	€29000	L'Enfance de Sainte Genevieve, (137x303cm-54x119in) i. paper on canvas triptych. 10-Dec-3 Piasa, Paris #227/R est:30000-40000
£26761	$46296	€38000	Vue sur le chateau de Versailles et l'Orangerie (32x46cm-13x18in) s. exhib. 10-Dec-3 Piasa, Paris #161/R est:20000-30000
£100000	$182000	€146000	Fantaisie (47x31cm-19x12in) s. painted c.1886-1887 prov.exhib.lit. 17-Jun-4 Christie's, London #22/R est:60000-80000

Works on paper

£317	$548	€450	Etude de drape (36x23cm-14x9in) chl. 10-Dec-3 Piasa, Paris #180/R
£317	$548	€450	Femme a demie drapee debout (27x17cm-11x7in) blk crayon htd white blue chk blue paper. 10-Dec-3 Piasa, Paris #208
£387	$670	€550	Etude de composition (20x31cm-8x12in) blk crayon. 10-Dec-3 Piasa, Paris #198
£430	$800	€628	Old testament scene, Moses and the Jews in the wilderness (15x19cm-6x7in) pencil. 2-Mar-4 Swann Galleries, New York #529/R
£458	$792	€650	Mademoiselle de Sombreuil buvant un verre de sang pour sauver son pere (16x12cm-6x5in) blk crayon exhib. 10-Dec-3 Piasa, Paris #176
£493	$853	€700	Femme nue, le bras pose sur la cuisse (28x21cm-11x8in) blk crayon chl. 10-Dec-3 Piasa, Paris #165
£493	$853	€700	Male nude with arms raised (27x21cm-11x8in) blk crayon. 10-Dec-3 Piasa, Paris #185
£493	$853	€700	Personnage debout levant les bras (12x9cm-5x4in) blk crayon. 10-Dec-3 Piasa, Paris #224
£528	$914	€750	Petits anges decorant des vases et femme debout (44x33cm-17x13in) blk crayon tracing paper. 10-Dec-3 Piasa, Paris #215
£559	$934	€800	Etude pour pecheur (30x22cm-12x9in) studio st. chl chk. 30-Jun-3 Bailly Pommery, Paris #15
£563	$975	€800	Diverses etudes de compositions (30x19cm-12x7in) blk crayon. 10-Dec-3 Piasa, Paris #170
£599	$1036	€850	Tete de femme tournee vers la gauche (23x15cm-9x6in) blk crayon. 10-Dec-3 Piasa, Paris #206
£634	$1096	€900	Carton pour le decor du Pantheon (70x56cm-28x22in) chl. 10-Dec-3 Piasa, Paris #174
£634	$1096	€900	Femme nue allongee vue de face (31x24cm-12x9in) blk crayon beige paper. 10-Dec-3 Piasa, Paris #212
£634	$1096	€900	Homme nu courbe (30x23cm-12x9in) blk crayon beige paper. 10-Dec-3 Piasa, Paris #223
£634	$1096	€900	Etude de composition (30x14cm-12x6in) blk crayon. 10-Dec-3 Piasa, Paris #226
£704	$1218	€1000	Femme assise levant la main. Etude preparatoire pour Doux Pays (13x10cm-5x4in) blk crayon two. 10-Dec-3 Piasa, Paris #183/R
£704	$1218	€1000	Sainte Genevieve ravitaillant Paris. Retour de L'Enfant Prodigue - caricature (12x21cm-5x8in) one blk crayon second pen Indian ink two exhib.lit. 10-Dec-3 Piasa, Paris #217
£775	$1340	€1100	Differentes etudes pour Doux Pays et autres compositions (20x28cm-8x11in) blk crayon exhib. 10-Dec-3 Piasa, Paris #184
£775	$1340	€1100	Femme a mi-corps, penchee vers la droite. Personnage a l'antique vue de dos (28x19cm-11x7in) blk crayon second blk crayon white chk tracing paper two. 10-Dec-3 Piasa, Paris #193
£775	$1340	€1100	Femme assise, tete penchee vers la droite. Homme nu agenouille (30x23cm-12x9in) blk crayon two. 10-Dec-3 Piasa, Paris #202
£775	$1340	€1100	Etude pour La Pitie de Moscou. Pecheur debout dans une barque (16x10cm-6x4in) blk crayon chl two. 10-Dec-3 Piasa, Paris #222
£915	$1584	€1300	Femme adossee a un arbre et diverses etudes. Deux scenes de trois personnages (17x21cm-7x8in) blk crayon beige paper two. 10-Dec-3 Piasa, Paris #172
£915	$1584	€1300	Femme nue de dos, avec sa main ses cheveux (31x39cm-12x15in) blk crayon. 10-Dec-3 Piasa, Paris #188
£915	$1584	€1300	Le Berger. Deux etudes de nymphes pour le Bois sacre (22x23cm-9x9in) chl two. 10-Dec-3 Piasa, Paris #197/R
£986	$1706	€1400	Homme assis, accoude sur sa cuisse (31x24cm-12x9in) blk crayon. 10-Dec-3 Piasa, Paris #163
£986	$1706	€1400	Deux hommes debout discutant (29x16cm-11x6in) blk crayon beige paper. 10-Dec-3 Piasa, Paris #167
£986	$1706	€1400	Etude de drape (21x21cm-8x8in) blk crayon white chk pastel blue paper. 10-Dec-3 Piasa, Paris #179/R
£986	$1706	€1400	Femme assise de face (31x19cm-12x7in) blk crayon blue paper. 10-Dec-3 Piasa, Paris #181/R
£1056	$1827	€1500	Diverses etudes d'un homme nu (19x29cm-7x11in) blk crayon beige paper. 10-Dec-3 Piasa, Paris #178 est:600
£1056	$1827	€1500	Etude pour l'une des trois vertus theologales - La Charite (33x14cm-13x6in) blk crayon tracing paper sold with two other studies three exhib. 10-Dec-3 Piasa, Paris #220 est:1000
£1127	$1949	€1600	Femme nue debout vue de cote (43x24cm-17x9in) blk crayon. 10-Dec-3 Piasa, Paris #162/R est:1000
£1127	$1949	€1600	Tete de femme. Les bucherons (17x13cm-7x5in) one blk crayon second pen brown ink two exhib. 10-Dec-3 Piasa, Paris #214/R est:400
£1338	$2315	€1900	Paysage vu au travers d'arcades (19x37cm-7x15in) pastel. 10-Dec-3 Piasa, Paris #169/R est:1500
£1338	$2315	€1900	Tete de femme et le haut de sa robe. Homme oriental assis lisant (30x26cm-12x10in) blk crayon. 10-Dec-3 Piasa, Paris #199/R est:1200
£1338	$2315	€1900	Etude pour Doux pays (23x30cm-9x12in) chl. 10-Dec-3 Piasa, Paris #210 est:1200
£1408	$2437	€2000	Lanceurs de javelots en attente (35x23cm-14x9in) blk crayon beige paper. 10-Dec-3 Piasa, Paris #218 est:800
£1479	$2558	€2100	Scene de procession, etude pour le Revitaillement de Paris (24x22cm-9x9in) blk crayon. 10-Dec-3 Piasa, Paris #219 est:600
£1549	$2680	€2200	Femme assise (20x22cm-8x9in) sanguine. 10-Dec-3 Piasa, Paris #203/R est:1000
£1972	$3411	€2800	Le Christ au lien (48x28cm-19x11in) i. blk crayon tracing paper. 10-Dec-3 Piasa, Paris #177/R est:2000
£2098	$3608	€3000	Etudes (25x18cm-10x7in) dr three in one frame. 3-Dec-3 Tajan, Paris #21/R est:3500-4000
£2113	$3655	€3000	Personnages en bord de mer (22x30cm-9x12in) blk crayon pen. 10-Dec-3 Piasa, Paris #189/R est:1000
£2113	$3655	€3000	Homme debout, lancant un javelot (33x26cm-13x10in) blk crayon htd white chk blue paper. 10-Dec-3 Piasa, Paris #200 est:1500
£2183	$3777	€3100	Femme a demi nue portant des fleurs et un petit recipient (31x21cm-12x8in) blk crayon. 10-Dec-3 Piasa, Paris #164/R est:1000
£2254	$3899	€3200	Jeunes filles au bord de la mer (18x20cm-7x8in) chl sold with two others one chl one blk crayon three. 10-Dec-3 Piasa, Paris #213/R est:1500
£2394	$4142	€3400	Tete de femme au chapeau (20x13cm-8x5in) blk crayon with three other drawings four. 10-Dec-3 Piasa, Paris #194 est:1500
£2958	$5117	€4200	Femmes dans un paysage (24x30cm-9x12in) blk crayon exec c.1895. 10-Dec-3 Piasa, Paris #192/R est:2000
£2958	$5117	€4200	Etude de femme en priere (46x25cm-18x10in) chl white chk blue paper. 10-Dec-3 Piasa, Paris #216/R est:1500
£3169	$5482	€4500	Sainte Solange (48x20cm-19x8in) blk crayon tracing paper exhib. 10-Dec-3 Piasa, Paris #221/R est:1200
£3380	$5848	€4800	Etude de femme nue tenant un rameau (30x23cm-12x9in) blk crayon exhib. 10-Dec-3 Piasa, Paris #196/R est:2000
£3380	$5848	€4800	Homme nu assis vue de dos (30x22cm-12x9in) blk crayon beige paper. 10-Dec-3 Piasa, Paris #205/R est:2000
£3380	$5848	€4800	Femme regardant sa main (31x23cm-12x9in) blk crayon. 10-Dec-3 Piasa, Paris #207/R est:1500
£3662	$6335	€5200	Etude pour l'Hommage de Victor Hugo a la ville de Paris (26x50cm-10x20in) blk crayon tracing paper. 10-Dec-3 Piasa, Paris #171/R est:2000
£3662	$6335	€5200	Jeune homme nu, assis en croupe, tenant un baton (29x23cm-11x9in) blk crayon blue paper. 10-Dec-3 Piasa, Paris #225 est:1200
£3889	$7000	€5678	Woman walking to the right (56x27cm-22x11in) black chk prov. 22-Jan-4 Christie's, Rockefeller NY #149/R est:5000-7000
£4444	$8000	€6488	Man seen from behind (57x31cm-22x12in) black chk tracing paper laid down prov. 22-Jan-4 Christie's, Rockefeller NY #150/R est:6000-8000
£13028	$22539	€18500	Portrait of a man (33x23cm-13x9in) chl blue paper exhib. 10-Dec-3 Piasa, Paris #168/R est:6000
£13380	$23148	€19000	Toilette (26x21cm-10x8in) W/C gouache traces blk crayon exhib. 10-Dec-3 Piasa, Paris #187/R est:8000
£19014	$32894	€27000	Etude d'ensemble pour Doux pays (20x30cm-8x12in) W/C blk crayon exhib. 10-Dec-3 Piasa, Paris #209/R est:10000

PUY, Jean (1876-1960) French

£662	$1205	€1000	Olivier (23x35cm-9x14in) s. paper on cardboard. 19-Jun-4 St-Germain-en-Laye Encheres #172/R
£769	$1323	€1100	Recifs Bretons (32x45cm-13x18in) s.d.1939. 3-Dec-3 Tajan, Paris #341
£1972	$3411	€2800	Bouquet aux roses jaunes (51x68cm-20x27in) s. panel. 9-Dec-3 Artcurial Briest, Paris #226/R est:3000-4000
£2797	$4755	€4000	Bateaux a voile dans la rade (38x46cm-15x18in) painted c.1912 lit. 30-Nov-3 Anaf, Lyon #194 est:4000-5000
£3020	$5618	€4500	Nautre morte aux masques ou les trois tetes de platre. Nu dans l'atelier (75x94cm-30x37in) s. double-sided painted c.1902 prov.exhib.lit. 2-Mar-4 Artcurial Briest, Paris #137 est:3000-4000
£3401	$6190	€5000	Nature morte au raisin (33x41cm-13x16in) s.d.47 prov.exhib.lit. 8-Feb-4 Anaf, Lyon #253/R est:5000-6000
£3901	$6514	€5500	Baigneuse (73x50cm-29x20in) s. cardboard lit. 19-Oct-3 Anaf, Lyon #249/R est:6000-7000
£4000	$7360	€6000	La partance a Saint Malo (55x82cm-22x32in) s. i. stretcher prov. 11-Jun-4 Pierre Berge, Paris #238/R est:6000-7000
£5674	$9475	€8000	Nu couche de dos (54x79cm-21x31in) s.d.19 lit. 19-Oct-3 Anaf, Lyon #247/R est:7500-8000
£6028	$10067	€8500	Voiliers ancres au port (30x75cm-12x30in) s. cardboard on canvas painted c.1914 lit. 19-Oct-3 Anaf, Lyon #246 est:8500-9000
£6608	$11233	€9648	Belle ile (46x59cm-18x23in) s. i.d.1919 verso paper on board prov. 5-Nov-3 Dobiaschofsky, Bern #879/R est:17000 (S.FR 15000)
£9396	$16631	€14000	Bateaux dans le port de Saint-Tropez (50x61cm-20x24in) s. 27-Apr-4 Artcurial Briest, Paris #163/R est:10000-15000

Works on paper

£1049	$1752	€1500	Bateaux a Belle-Ile-en-Mer (13x21cm-5x8in) s. sanguine chl chl htd gouache. 29-Jun-3 Eric Pillon, Calais #107/R

PUY, Jean (attrib) (1876-1960) French

£1588	$2700	€2318	La femme aux fleurs (51x37cm-20x15in) s. 21-Nov-3 Skinner, Boston #403/R est:2000-4000

PUYBAREAU, Annie (1955-) French

£297	$550	€434	Les grenades (38x56cm-15x22in) s. 15-Jul-4 Doyle, New York #66/R

£598	$1100	€873	Deauville (51x66cm-20x26in) s. s.i.verso. 25-Mar-4 Doyle, New York #54/R est:1800-2200
£598	$1100	€873	Printemps a duclair (81x81cm-32x32in) s. s.i.verso. 23-Jun-4 Doyle, New York #5060/R est:2000-3000
£598	$1100	€873	Bouquet de roses (46x56cm-18x22in) s. 9-Jun-4 Doyle, New York #3064
£761	$1400	€1111	Voilier a Cabourg (38x56cm-15x22in) s. 9-Jun-4 Doyle, New York #3065
£894	$1600	€1305	Champ de phacelias (46x53cm-18x21in) s. i.verso. 8-Jan-4 Doyle, New York #38/R est:1000-1500
£1000	$1700	€1460	Le champs de dahlias (74x91cm-29x36in) s. 5-Nov-3 Doyle, New York #59/R est:1200-1800
£1687	$2750	€2463	Cabourg (51x61cm-20x24in) s. 24-Sep-3 Doyle, New York #70 est:2000-3000
£1890	$3250	€2759	Les jardins de boisguillaume (81x100cm-32x39in) s. i.verso. 3-Dec-3 Doyle, New York #162/R est:3000-5000

PUYENBROECK, Gregoor van (1906-1982) Belgian

£367	$664	€550	Vue de Montmartre (50x40cm-20x16in) s. 30-Mar-4 Campo & Campo, Antwerp #326/R

PUYENBROECK, Jan van (1887-1972) Belgian

£338	$605	€500	Still life of flowers (83x73cm-33x29in) 10-May-4 Amberes, Antwerp #341

PUYET, Jose (1922-) Spanish

£381	$700	€556	Mimi (61x51cm-24x20in) s.i.d.1967 verso. 25-Jun-4 Freeman, Philadelphia #243/R
£952	$1705	€1400	Young man from Florence (46x38cm-18x15in) s. s.i.verso. 22-Mar-4 Durán, Madrid #167/R
£1064	$1777	€1500	Galician woman (61x50cm-24x20in) s. 20-Oct-3 Durán, Madrid #76/R
£1361	$2435	€2000	Lucia (46x38cm-18x15in) s. 22-Mar-4 Durán, Madrid #154/R
£2586	$4319	€3750	Elegant night (79x63cm-31x25in) i.d.1968 verso. 17-Nov-3 Durán, Madrid #216/R est:1700
Works on paper			
£828	$1490	€1200	Head of man (31x23cm-12x9in) s. mixed media. 26-Jan-4 Ansorena, Madrid #75/R

PUYROCHE-WAGNER, Elise (1828-1895) German

£7000	$12040	€10220	Parakeet in a gilded cage under a canopy of summer flowers (112x89cm-44x35in) s. 4-Dec-3 Christie's, Kensington #101/R est:5000-8000

PUYTLINCK, Christoffel (1638-?) Dutch

£7692	$13231	€11000	Lievre, volaille, asperges et navets sur une tablette (110x90cm-43x35in) 3-Dec-3 Palais de Beaux Arts, Brussels #1272/R est:10000-12000

PUZZOVIO, Dalila (20th C) Argentinian?

Works on paper			
£503	$900	€734	Momentum series (35x50cm-14x20in) collage. 11-May-4 Arroyo, Buenos Aires #77
£549	$1000	€802	Momentum series (35x50cm-14x20in) s.d.99 pastel collage. 5-Jul-4 Arroyo, Buenos Aires #29/R

PWERLE, Angelina (1922-) Australian

£267	$484	€390	Untitled (94x152cm-37x60in) s.verso acrylic. 30-Mar-4 Lawson Menzies, Sydney #279 (A.D 650)
£2236	$3510	€3242	Bush plum dreaming (152x121cm-60x48in) i.d.9.9.99 verso synthetic polymer paint canvas prov. 26-Aug-3 Christie's, Sydney #237/R est:6000-8000 (A.D 5500)
Works on paper			
£1138	$1798	€1650	Untitled (122x91cm-48x36in) i.verso synthetic polymer paint linen prov. 28-Jul-3 Sotheby's, Paddington #367/R est:3000-5000 (A.D 2800)

PWERLE, Minnie (1922-) Australian

£1327	$2441	€1937	Aweyle Atnwengerrp (90x120cm-35x47in) acrylic linen. 29-Mar-4 Goodman, Sydney #175/R est:3500-5000 (A.D 3250)
£1429	$2629	€2086	Aweyle Atnwengerrp (90x120cm-35x47in) acrylic linen prov. 29-Mar-4 Goodman, Sydney #44/R est:3500-5000 (A.D 3500)
£1556	$2599	€2334	Awelye Atnwengerrp (120x90cm-47x35in) i.verso acrylic. 27-Oct-3 Goodman, Sydney #49/R est:3000-5000 (A.D 3750)
Works on paper			
£938	$1753	€1407	Awelye atnwengerrp (91x57cm-36x22in) i.verso synthetic polymer canvas exec. 2000 prov. 21-Jul-4 Shapiro, Sydney #116/R (A.D 2400)
£1882	$3369	€2748	Awelye Alwengerrp (90x121cm-35x48in) synthetic polymer paint linen exec 2002 prov. 25-May-4 Lawson Menzies, Sydney #31/R est:5000-7000 (A.D 4800)
£2109	$3945	€3164	Bush melon (180x92cm-71x36in) i. synthetic polymer canvas exec. 2002 prov. 21-Jul-4 Shapiro, Sydney #41/R est:6000-8000 (A.D 5400)
£2157	$3861	€3149	Awelye Alnwengerrp (120x90cm-47x35in) synthetic polymer paint canvas prov. 25-May-4 Lawson Menzies, Sydney #3/R est:5000-7000 (A.D 5500)
£2254	$3652	€3291	Awelye Atnwengerrp (90x120cm-35x47in) i.d.verso synthetic polymer canvas prov. 30-Jul-3 Goodman, Sydney #38/R est:5000-6000 (A.D 5500)
£5137	$9606	€7713	Bush melon (181x262cm-71x103in) i.verso synthetic polymer canvas exec. 2002 prov. 21-Jul-4 Shapiro, Sydney #113/R est:15000-20000 (A.D 13150)
£6667	$11933	€9734	Awelye Atnwengerrp (122x181cm-48x71in) synthetic polymer paint linen exec 2002 prov. 25-May-4 Lawson Menzies, Sydney #55/R est:10000-15000 (A.D 17000)

PYE, Patrick (1929-) Irish

£559	$951	€800	Fall and bystander (52x23cm-20x9in) s. i.verso tempera board exhib. 18-Nov-3 Whyte's, Dublin #68
£664	$1129	€950	Implements of The Passion (25x20cm-10x8in) s. s.i.d.1967 verso tempera panel exhib. 18-Nov-3 Whyte's, Dublin #8/R
£699	$1189	€1000	Agony in the garden (62x48cm-24x19in) s.d.1968 i.verso tempera panel exhib. 18-Nov-3 Whyte's, Dublin #142/R
£1000	$1790	€1460	My Arabia (34x60cm-13x24in) s.d.80/4 tempera board. 14-May-4 Christie's, Kensington #393/R est:800-1200

PYE, William (fl.1881-1908) British

£500	$795	€730	Lismore Castle, landscape with figure (38x77cm-15x30in) s. 11-Sep-3 Morphets, Harrogate #251

PYE, William (1938-) British

Sculpture			
£809	$1400	€1181	Three rings (119x91cm-47x36in) baked enamel aluminum chrome brass prov. 15-Dec-3 Hindman, Chicago #41/R est:2000-4000
£867	$1500	€1266	Untitled (58cm-23in) stainless steel prov. 15-Dec-3 Hindman, Chicago #40/R est:1500-2000

PYK, Madeleine (1934-) Swedish

£541	$973	€790	Elegant riders (46x37cm-18x15in) s.d.88. 26-Jan-4 Lilla Bukowskis, Stockholm #581 (S.KR 7200)
£550	$886	€803	Composition with figures and animals (67x50cm-26x20in) s. 25-Aug-3 Lilla Bukowskis, Stockholm #71 (S.KR 7200)
£638	$1149	€931	Road 13 (46x34cm-18x13in) s. 26-Jan-4 Lilla Bukowskis, Stockholm #591 (S.KR 8500)
£656	$1207	€984	Divers with dolphins (84x65cm-33x26in) s. 14-Jun-4 Lilla Bukowskis, Stockholm #19 (S.KR 9000)
£668	$1155	€975	View of Katarinahissen (62x50cm-24x20in) s.indis.d. 15-Dec-3 Lilla Bukowskis, Stockholm #42 (S.KR 8500)
£702	$1257	€1025	Swim straight up to heaven (95x64cm-37x25in) s. d.1971 verso. 28-May-4 Uppsala Auktionskammare, Uppsala #336/R (S.KR 9500)
£806	$1426	€1177	The French family (97x85cm-38x33in) s. 27-Apr-4 AB Stockholms Auktionsverk #659/R (S.KR 11000)
£1051	$1893	€1534	Self-portrait (57x35cm-22x14in) s. panel. 26-Apr-4 Bukowskis, Stockholm #218/R (S.KR 14500)
£1100	$1903	€1606	Beach (62x45cm-24x18in) s. 15-Dec-3 Lilla Bukowskis, Stockholm #813/R est:8000-10000 (S.KR 14000)
£1245	$2204	€1818	View of Maelaren, Stockholm (65x50cm-26x20in) s.d.1975. 27-Apr-4 AB Stockholms Auktionsverk #660/R est:6000-8000 (S.KR 17000)
£1312	$2414	€1968	Out walking (67x48cm-26x19in) s. 14-Jun-4 Lilla Bukowskis, Stockholm #716/R est:20000 (S.KR 18000)
£1378	$2480	€2012	The cat Josephine (67x47cm-26x19in) s. 26-Apr-4 Bukowskis, Stockholm #220/R est:15000-18000 (S.KR 19000)
£1392	$2464	€2032	Hand-sailing (46x38cm-18x15in) s,. 27-Apr-4 AB Stockholms Auktionsverk #790/R est:10000-12000 (S.KR 19000)
£1511	$2568	€2206	The last tram (77x94cm-30x37in) s. 5-Nov-3 AB Stockholms Auktionsverk #738/R est:20000-25000 (S.KR 20000)
£1511	$2568	€2206	The pub - with figures (99x91cm-39x36in) s.d.1975. 5-Nov-3 AB Stockholms Auktionsverk #818/R est:20000-25000 (S.KR 20000)
£1538	$2723	€2245	Summer holiday (46x34cm-18x13in) s/. 27-Apr-4 AB Stockholms Auktionsverk #872/R est:15000-18000 (S.KR 21000)
£1737	$2953	€2536	Walk along the beach (67x48cm-26x19in) s. 5-Nov-3 AB Stockholms Auktionsverk #740/R est:20000-25000 (S.KR 23000)
£1737	$2953	€2536	Mama (61x43cm-24x17in) s. 4-Nov-3 Bukowskis, Stockholm #301/R est:15000-18000 (S.KR 23000)
£1832	$3242	€2675	Head of a tiger (74x48cm-29x19in) s. 27-Apr-4 AB Stockholms Auktionsverk #789/R est:12000-15000 (S.KR 25000)
£2491	$4409	€3637	The tight-rope walker near Slussen (95x85cm-37x33in) s. 27-Apr-4 AB Stockholms Auktionsverk #795/R est:18000-20000 (S.KR 34000)
£2611	$4699	€3812	But first a Pommac (100x70cm-39x28in) s. 26-Apr-4 Bukowskis, Stockholm #219/R est:20000-25000 (S.KR 36000)
Works on paper			
£1435	$2440	€2095	In the stable (74x59cm-29x23in) s. mixed media canvas. 4-Nov-3 Bukowskis, Stockholm #309/R est:10000-12000 (S.KR 19000)
£1685	$2982	€2460	Tiger (91x63cm-36x25in) s.d.1987 mixed media. 27-Apr-4 AB Stockholms Auktionsverk #796/R est:10000-12000 (S.KR 23000)
£1964	$3338	€2867	In the studio (92x73cm-36x29in) s. mixed media. 4-Nov-3 Bukowskis, Stockholm #308/R est:15000-20000 (S.KR 26000)

PYKE, Guelda (1905-1994) Australian

£369	$583	€539	Shell Park orchard (56x80cm-22x31in) s. board. 2-Sep-3 Deutscher-Menzies, Melbourne #326/R (A.D 900)

PYLE, Aaron G (20th C) American?

£3352	$6000	€4894	Shucking corn (41x51cm-16x20in) s.i. i.verso painted c.1947. 16-Mar-4 Matthew's, Oregon #22/R est:2000-3000

PYLE, Howard (1853-1911) American

£18895	$32500	€27587	Beatrix and Esmond (79x53cm-31x21in) s. 7-Dec-3 Freeman, Philadelphia #158 est:30000-50000
£28409	$50000	€41477	Phoenician traders (61x41cm-24x16in) s. prov.exhib.lit. 19-May-4 Sotheby's, New York #180/R est:50000-75000
£35928	$60000	€52455	Slave auction in New York City square (41x30cm-16x12in) init. canvasboard en grisaille. 15-Nov-3 Illustration House, New York #117/R est:40000-60000
£79545	$140000	€116136	Cabin of the treasure seekers (61x41cm-24x16in) s.i. prov.exhib.lit. 19-May-4 Sotheby's, New York #179/R est:60000-80000
£352273	$620000	€514319	Captain Kett (79x51cm-31x20in) s. prov.lit. 19-May-4 Sotheby's, New York #176/R est:250000-350000
Works on paper			
£1255	$2272	€1832	American village scene (28x38cm-11x15in) s.d.1879 W/C ink paper on board prov. 1-Apr-4 Heffel, Vancouver #84/R est:3000-4000 (C.D 3000)

PYNACKER, Adam (attrib) (1622-1673) Dutch

£3819	$6226	€5500	Herders resting by waterfall and ruins (48x78cm-19x31in) 25-Sep-3 Dr Fritz Nagel, Stuttgart #1251/R est:6800
Works on paper			
£300	$519	€438	Tree on a hill (29x17cm-11x7in) i.mount brush grey ink wash prov. 12-Dec-3 Christie's, Kensington #518/R

PYNAS, Jan (attrib) (1583-1631) Dutch

£1333	$2413	€2000	Old Testament scene (61x82cm-24x32in) 2-Apr-4 Dr Fritz Nagel, Leipzig #3957/R est:2000

PYNE, Charles (1842-?) British
Works on paper
£300 $510 €438 Rabbits in a rural landscape (54x73cm-21x29in) s. W/C. 25-Nov-3 Bonhams, Knightsbridge #199/R

PYNE, Charles Claude (1802-1878) British
£461 $783 €673 Romantic scene with young woman knitting and two children in doorway (30x25cm-12x10in) s.d.78. 10-Nov-3 Rasmussen, Vejle #367/R (D.KR 5000)

PYNE, David (?) ?
£2000 $3180 €2920 Woman and children gathering sheathes of corn (51x76cm-20x30in) s. 30-Apr-3 Peter Wilson, Nantwich #68/R est:2000-2500

PYNE, Ganesh (1937-) Indian
£9239 $17000 €13489 White hand (39x35cm-15x14in) s.d. tempera lit. 24-Mar-4 Sotheby's, New York #203/R est:15000-20000
£9783 $18000 €14283 Swim (80x60cm-31x24in) tempera. 24-Mar-4 Sotheby's, New York #179/R est:12000-18000
£9957 $17923 €14537 Torch (54x50cm-21x20in) s.d. tempera. 25-Apr-4 Christie's, Hong Kong #616/R est:140000-160000 (HK.D 140000)
£16304 $30000 €23804 Skull (65x53cm-26x21in) s.d. board. 24-Mar-4 Sotheby's, New York #180/R est:30000-50000
Works on paper
£4076 $7500 €5951 Untitled (46x41cm-18x16in) s.d. mixed media paper on card. 25-Mar-4 Christie's, Rockefeller NY #235/R est:6000-8000
£4623 $8321 €6750 Baul singer (45x36cm-18x14in) s.d. mixed media. 25-Apr-4 Christie's, Hong Kong #617/R est:45000-65000 (HK.D 65000)

PYNE, George (1800-1884) British
Works on paper
£400 $680 €584 Christchurch, Oxford (15x20cm-6x8in) s.d.1859 W/C. 4-Nov-3 Dreweatt Neate, Newbury #45/R est:350-450
£650 $1203 €949 Merton College, Oxford (18x27cm-7x11in) W/C prov. 11-Feb-4 Cheffins, Cambridge #389/R
£900 $1467 €1314 Study of an art gallery (22x35cm-9x14in) i.d.1854 pencil W/C htd white. 24-Sep-3 Dreweatt Neate, Newbury #22/R
£1650 $3003 €2409 Five views of Christ Church, Oxford (7x11cm-3x4in) W/C five. 15-Jun-4 Bonhams, Oxford #65/R est:1500-2000
£2200 $4048 €3212 Views of Christ Church College, Oxford (18x26cm-7x10in) s. one d.1849 one d.1851 pencil W/C pair. 25-Mar-4 Christie's, Kensington #122/R est:2000-3000

PYNE, James Baker (1800-1870) British
£380 $635 €555 Italian lake scene (25x35cm-10x14in) s.d.1850 panel. 20-Oct-3 Bonhams, Bath #49
£380 $680 €555 Landscape with Roslin Castle (23x31cm-9x12in) s.verso panel. 10-May-4 Rasmussen, Vejle #2 (D.KR 4200)
£640 $1190 €934 Continental landscape (27x41cm-11x16in) s.d.1845. 2-Mar-4 Bamfords, Derby #455
£800 $1440 €1168 Fairy Glen, Betswy Coed (46x61cm-18x24in) bears sig.d.1846. 21-Jan-4 Sotheby's, Olympia #332/R
£1400 $2212 €2030 Fishermen landing a boat before a clifftop country house (36x61cm-14x24in) s.d.1837. 4-Sep-3 Christie's, Kensington #199/R est:1500-2500
£3779 $6500 €5517 View of the Bristol Channel (51x76cm-20x30in) s.indis.d. i. on stretcher. 6-Dec-3 Neal Auction Company, New Orleans #289/R est:7000-9000
£4400 $7040 €6380 Amalfi Bay of Naples (60x90cm-24x35in) s.d.1884. 17-Sep-3 James Thompson, Kirby Lonsdale #150/R
Works on paper
£280 $510 €409 The Ribblehead Viaduct, Yorkshire (17x25cm-7x10in) s.i. pencil W/C htd white scratching out. 1-Jul-4 Christie's, Kensington #76/R
£300 $537 €438 View over a Swiss lake (33x49cm-13x19in) s. W/C htd white. 25-May-4 Bonhams, Knightsbridge #4/R
£450 $752 €657 Figures on a bridge over a woodland stream (30x25cm-12x10in) pencil W/C prov. 16-Oct-3 Christie's, Kensington #178
£520 $931 €759 On the Bristol Road (23x35cm-9x14in) bear sig. W/C. 17-Mar-4 Bonhams, Chester #277
£620 $1054 €905 View of the Avon Gorge with cooks folly (21x31cm-8x12in) s.d.1841 W/C. 4-Nov-3 Bristol Auction Rooms #563

PYNE, James Baker (attrib) (1800-1870) British
£2700 $4995 €3942 Outside the Red Lion, nr Evesham (51x69cm-20x27in) 14-Jul-4 Sotheby's, Olympia #55/R est:3000-4000

PYNE, Robert Lorraine (19th C) American
£920 $1500 €1343 View of the Catskills (25x28cm-10x11in) s.d.1886 board. 28-Sep-3 Simpson's, Houston #233/R

PYNE, Thomas (1843-1935) British
Works on paper
£950 $1549 €1387 Quiet pastures (70x50cm-28x20in) s. W/C. 24-Sep-3 Dreweatt Neate, Newbury #75

PYNE, William Henry (attrib) (1769-1843) British
Works on paper
£620 $1110 €905 Figures unloading boats on the shore (65x97cm-26x38in) W/C over pencil htd board. 26-May-4 Sotheby's, Olympia #50/R

PYYKKO, Kimmo (1940-) Finnish
Sculpture
£1399 $2378 €2000 The warning bird (114cm-45in) s. wood. 29-Nov-3 Bukowskis, Helsinki #238/R est:2500-3000
£1399 $2378 €2000 Horizon (45x55cm-18x22in) s.d.99 steel wood. 29-Nov-3 Bukowskis, Helsinki #246/R est:1200-1500

QAJAR SCHOOL (19th C) Persian
Works on paper
£7500 $12525 €10950 Seated portrait (33x21cm-13x8in) i. gouache. 15-Oct-3 Sotheby's, London #35/R est:7000-9000

QAJAR, Nasir Al-Din Shah (19th C) Persian
Works on paper
£1800 $3186 €2628 Royal Garden (16x17cm-6x7in) i. col pencil. 27-Apr-4 Christie's, London #110/R est:2000-2500

QI BAISHI (1863-1957) Chinese
Works on paper
£315 $541 €450 Three crabs (51x34cm-20x13in) s. ink hanging scroll. 5-Dec-3 Lempertz, Koln #248
£1259 $2165 €1800 Chrysanthemums in a pot and two crabs on a plate (111x34cm-44x13in) s.i.d.1948 ink col hanging scroll. 5-Dec-3 Lempertz, Koln #245/R est:1300
£1351 $2378 €2000 Landscape (82x19cm-32x7in) s. seals Indian ink hanging scroll. 21-May-4 Dr Fritz Nagel, Stuttgart #1094/R est:1500
£1399 $2406 €2000 Five crabs (130x46cm-51x18in) s.i.d.1934 ink hanging scroll. 5-Dec-3 Lempertz, Koln #244/R est:1300
£1888 $3248 €2700 Peonies and two buzzing bees (100x34cm-39x13in) s. ink col hanging scroll. 5-Dec-3 Lempertz, Koln #246/R est:1500
£3800 $6346 €5548 Fruit sprays and foliage (63x37cm-25x15in) s.i. ink col. 14-Nov-3 Christie's, Kensington #269/R est:800-1200
£4247 $7093 €6201 Crabs (103x34cm-41x13in) s.d.1948 ink hanging scroll. 26-Oct-3 Christie's, Hong Kong #332/R est:60000-80000 (HK.D 55000)
£4600 $8234 €6716 Grapes (68x33cm-27x13in) s. col ink hanging scroll. 6-May-4 Sotheby's, London #108/R est:2500-3500
£4633 $7737 €6764 Various subjects (18x51cm-7x20in) i. ink col ink fan leaves 2 hanging scroll multiple artists. 26-Oct-3 Christie's, Hong Kong #201/R est:12000-15000 (HK.D 60000)
£5035 $8660 €7200 Two fishing rods with a shoal of small fish (133x35cm-52x14in) s.i. ink col hanging scroll. 5-Dec-3 Lempertz, Koln #247/R est:2300
£5405 $9027 €7891 Crabs (102x34cm-40x13in) s.i. ink hanging scroll lit. 26-Oct-3 Christie's, Hong Kong #257/R est:60000-80000 (HK.D 70000)
£6507 $11062 €9500 Fish and shrimps (112x34cm-44x13in) i.d.1944 seal. 7-Nov-3 Dr Fritz Nagel, Stuttgart #955/R est:3000
£7336 $12251 €10711 Shrimps (135x33cm-53x13in) s. ink hanging scroll. 26-Oct-3 Christie's, Hong Kong #333/R est:60000-80000 (HK.D 95000)
£7336 $12251 €10711 Shrimps (33x33cm-13x13in) s.i. ink. 27-Oct-3 Sotheby's, Hong Kong #303/R est:50000-70000 (HK.D 95000)
£7800 $13962 €11388 Shrimps (103x33cm-41x13in) s.d.Jiaxu 1946 ink hanging scroll. 6-May-4 Sotheby's, London #109/R est:3000-5000
£8235 $14000 €12023 Chrysanthemums and insect (333x99cm-131x39in) s. ink col hanging scroll prov. 4-Nov-3 Bonhams & Butterfields, San Francisco #3447/R est:3000-5000
£8494 $14185 €12401 Pumpkin and cicada (99x34cm-39x13in) s.i. ink col hanging scroll. 26-Oct-3 Christie's, Hong Kong #340/R est:60000-80000 (HK.D 110000)
£8494 $14185 €12401 Grapes and grasshopper (100x34cm-39x13in) s. ink col. 27-Oct-3 Sotheby's, Hong Kong #246/R est:80000-120000 (HK.D 110000)
£8535 $15363 €12461 Pumpkin (103x34cm-41x13in) s.i. ink col hanging scroll. 25-Apr-4 Christie's, Hong Kong #71/R est:100000-120000 (HK.D 120000)
£9246 $16643 €13499 Crabs and wine jar (135x33cm-53x13in) s.i. ink col hanging scroll. 25-Apr-4 Christie's, Hong Kong #68/R est:140000-180000 (HK.D 130000)
£9266 $15475 €13528 Cicada on a maple tree (30x36cm-12x14in) s. ink col. 27-Oct-3 Sotheby's, Hong Kong #241/R est:120000-150000 (HK.D 120000)
£9266 $15475 €13528 Grasshopper (30x36cm-12x14in) s. ink col. 27-Oct-3 Sotheby's, Hong Kong #242/R est:120000-150000 (HK.D 120000)
£9932 $16884 €14500 Mouse and grapes (89x46cm-35x18in) s.d.1939 seal Indian ink col hanging scroll. 7-Nov-3 Dr Fritz Nagel, Stuttgart #945/R est:5000
£9957 $17923 €14537 Wisteria (104x34cm-41x13in) s.i.d.1948 ink col hanging scroll. 25-Apr-4 Christie's, Hong Kong #67/R est:100000-120000 (HK.D 140000)
£9957 $17923 €14537 Grapes and squirrel (61x26cm-24x10in) s.d.1939 ink col. 26-Apr-4 Sotheby's, Hong Kong #609/R est:100000-150000 (HK.D 140000)
£10039 $16764 €14657 Chicks (102x34cm-40x13in) s.i. ink hanging scroll lit. 26-Oct-3 Christie's, Hong Kong #258/R est:80000-100000 (HK.D 130000)
£10669 $19203 €15577 Crabs (101x33cm-40x13in) s.i. hanging scroll. 25-Apr-4 Christie's, Hong Kong #20/R est:80000-100000 (HK.D 150000)
£10811 $18054 €15784 Wisteria and bees (102x34cm-40x13in) s.i. ink col hanging scroll lit. 26-Oct-3 Christie's, Hong Kong #259/R est:120000-150000 (HK.D 140000)
£10811 $18054 €15784 Rooster and chicks (101x34cm-40x13in) s.i. ink col hanging scroll. 26-Oct-3 Christie's, Hong Kong #334/R est:60000-80000 (HK.D 140000)
£10811 $19027 €16000 Autumn leaves, fruit and two wasps (32x22cm-13x9in) s. seal Indian ink col silk prov. 21-May-4 Dr Fritz Nagel, Stuttgart #1095/R est:1500
£10811 $19027 €16000 Crabs (137x34cm-54x13in) s.i. seal Indian ink hanging scroll. 21-May-4 Dr Fritz Nagel, Stuttgart #1193/R est:3000
£11380 $20484 €16615 Shrimps (34x34cm-13x13in) s.i. ink hanging scroll. 25-Apr-4 Christie's, Hong Kong #19/R est:15000-20000 (HK.D 160000)
£11583 $19344 €16911 Shrimps (101x33cm-40x13in) s.i. ink hanging scroll. 26-Oct-3 Christie's, Hong Kong #331/R est:45000-55000 (HK.D 150000)
£11583 $19344 €16911 Shrimps and fish (103x34cm-41x13in) s.i. ink hanging scroll. 26-Oct-3 Christie's, Hong Kong #335/R est:70000-90000 (HK.D 150000)
£12091 $21764 €17653 Amaranth and myna (131x33cm-52x13in) s. ink col. 26-Apr-4 Sotheby's, Hong Kong #606/R est:150000-200000 (HK.D 170000)
£12355 $20633 €18038 Shrimps (103x34cm-41x13in) s.i. ink hanging scroll lit. 26-Oct-3 Christie's, Hong Kong #256/R est:70000-90000 (HK.D 160000)
£12355 $20633 €18038 Eagle (90x42cm-35x17in) s. ink hanging scroll. 26-Oct-3 Christie's, Hong Kong #338/R est:70000-90000 (HK.D 160000)
£12355 $20633 €18038 Bridge (21x55cm-8x22in) s.i.d.1921 ink col fan. 27-Oct-3 Sotheby's, Hong Kong #240/R est:120000-180000 (HK.D 160000)
£14225 $25605 €20769 Chrysanthemum and wine (96x35cm-38x14in) s.i. ink col hanging scroll. 25-Apr-4 Christie's, Hong Kong #70/R est:150000-180000 (HK.D 200000)
£15000 $26850 €21900 Three doves (86x76cm-34x30in) s. col ink hanging scroll. 6-May-4 Sotheby's, London #107/R est:10000-15000
£15444 $25792 €22548 Chrysanthemum and crabs (105x34cm-41x13in) s.d. ink col. 27-Oct-3 Sotheby's, Hong Kong #245/R est:120000-150000 (HK.D 200000)
£16988 $28371 €24802 Peonies and peaches (101x34cm-40x13in) s.i. ink col hanging scroll. 26-Oct-3 Christie's, Hong Kong #202/R est:60000-80000 (HK.D 220000)
£18533 $30950 €27058 Chrysanthemum in a basket (139x34cm-55x13in) s. ink col hanging scroll. 27-Oct-3 Sotheby's, Hong Kong #244/R est:160000-200000 (HK.D 240000)
£19305 $32239 €28185 Rat by an oil lamp (68x34cm-27x13in) s.i. col ink. 27-Oct-3 Sotheby's, Hong Kong #304/R est:120000-150000 (HK.D 250000)

£19915	$35846	€29076	Loquat (81x34cm-32x13in) s.i. ink col. 26-Apr-4 Sotheby's, Hong Kong #610/R est:100000-150000 (HK.D 280000)
£21337	$38407	€31152	Morning glories (99x35cm-39x14in) s.i. ink col hanging scroll. 25-Apr-4 Christie's, Hong Kong #21/R est:70000-90000 (HK.D 300000)
£21337	$38407	€31152	Peaches (66x34cm-26x13in) s.i. ink col hanging scroll. 25-Apr-4 Christie's, Hong Kong #65/R est:80000-100000 (HK.D 300000)
£21622	$36108	€31568	Birds and bamboo (135x33cm-53x13in) s. ink col hanging scroll. 27-Oct-3 Sotheby's, Hong Kong #248/R est:200000-250000 (HK.D 280000)
£23000	$41170	€33580	Person crow on a melon (106x34cm-42x13in) s.d.1944 col in hanging scroll. 6-May-4 Sotheby's, London #106/R est:8000-12000
£24710	$41266	€36077	Chickens (67x34cm-26x13in) s.i. ink col hanging scroll prov. 27-Oct-3 Sotheby's, Hong Kong #302/R est:150000-200000 (HK.D 320000)
£24893	$44808	€36344	Blossoms (53x20cm-21x8in) s. ink col hanging scrolls pair. 26-Apr-4 Sotheby's, Hong Kong #550/R est:80000-120000 (HK.D 350000)
£25605	$46088	€37383	Rat and oil lamp (67x33cm-26x13in) s.i. ink col hanging scroll. 26-Apr-4 Sotheby's, Hong Kong #602/R est:150000-200000 (HK.D 360000)
£27027	$45135	€39459	Frogs, crabs, fish and prawns (33x33cm-13x13in) s.i.d.1936 ink set of four lit. 26-Oct-3 Christie's, Hong Kong #260/R est:200000-250000 (HK.D 350000)
£28450	$51209	€41537	Insects and water grass (73x40cm-29x16in) s.i. ink col hanging scroll. 25-Apr-4 Christie's, Hong Kong #69/R est:100000-150000 (HK.D 400000)
£32006	$57610	€46729	Begonia and sparrow (133x33cm-52x13in) s.i. ink col. 26-Apr-4 Sotheby's, Hong Kong #607/R est:180000-250000 (HK.D 450000)
£35562	$64011	€51921	Autumn feast (101x32cm-40x13in) s.i. ink col hanging scroll. 26-Apr-4 Sotheby's, Hong Kong #582/R est:250000-300000 (HK.D 500000)
£35562	$64011	€51921	Shrimps (70x35cm-28x14in) s.i.d.1948 ink col lit. 26-Apr-4 Sotheby's, Hong Kong #614/R est:120000-180000 (HK.D 500000)
£39118	$70413	€57112	Chrysanthemum and shrimps (93x36cm-37x14in) s.i. ink col scroll. 25-Apr-4 Christie's, Hong Kong #22/R est:180000-220000 (HK.D 550000)
£39118	$70413	€57112	Dragonflies (67x34cm-26x13in) s.i. ink col hanging scroll. 26-Apr-4 Sotheby's, Hong Kong #608/R est:250000-300000 (HK.D 550000)
£42471	$70927	€62008	Gourds and grasshopper (102x34cm-40x13in) s.i. ink col hanging scroll. 27-Oct-3 Sotheby's, Hong Kong #247/R est:300000-400000 (HK.D 550000)
£42674	$76814	€62304	Peaches (103x34cm-41x13in) s. i.d.1939 ink col. 26-Apr-4 Sotheby's, Hong Kong #599/R est:200000-250000 (HK.D 600000)
£46230	$83215	€67496	Amaranth (67x32cm-26x13in) s. ink col. 26-Apr-4 Sotheby's, Hong Kong #600/R est:150000-200000 (HK.D 650000)
£49787	$89616	€72689	Crabs and wine jar (66x33cm-26x13in) s.i. ink col scroll lit. 25-Apr-4 Christie's, Hong Kong #23/R est:120000-150000 (HK.D 700000)
£49787	$89616	€72689	Lotus pond (135x51cm-53x20in) s.i. ink col hanging scroll exhib.lit. 26-Apr-4 Sotheby's, Hong Kong #605/R est:250000-350000 (HK.D 700000)
£49787	$89616	€72689	Insects (24x32cm-9x13in) s. one i. ink col silk album four leaves prov. 26-Apr-4 Sotheby's, Hong Kong #611/R est:200000-250000 (HK.D 700000)
£53343	$96017	€77881	Wisteria and bees (180x48cm-71x19in) s.d.1930 ink col hanging scroll. 25-Apr-4 Christie's, Hong Kong #66/R est:250000-350000 (HK.D 750000)
£54054	$90270	€78919	Insects and flowers (45x25cm-18x10in) s.i. one d.1948 ink col set of four prov. 27-Oct-3 Sotheby's, Hong Kong #307/R est:450000-600000 (HK.D 700000)
£64011	$115220	€93456	Village treats (53x21cm-21x8in) s.i. ink hanging scroll four. 26-Apr-4 Sotheby's, Hong Kong #549/R est:150000-200000 (HK.D 900000)
£65637	$109614	€95830	Landscape of hibiscus town (96x44cm-38x17in) s.i. ink col scroll. 26-Oct-3 Christie's, Hong Kong #261/R est:500000-600000 (HK.D 850000)
£71042	$118641	€103721	Sailing along the willow bank (103x39cm-41x15in) s.i.d.1936 ink exhib. 27-Oct-3 Sotheby's, Hong Kong #345/R est:600000-800000 (HK.D 920000)
£216216	$361081	€315675	Flowers and insects (34x34cm-13x13in) s.i. ink col leaves 12 album. 26-Oct-3 Christie's, Hong Kong #337/R est:3000000-4000000 (HK.D 2800000)

QI BAISHI (attrib) (1863-1957) Chinese

£676	$1189	€1000	Painting with frogs (107x34cm-42x13in) 21-May-4 Dr Fritz Nagel, Stuttgart #1662
Works on paper			
£2432	$4281	€3600	Frogs (111x34cm-44x13in) s.i. seal Indian ink. 21-May-4 Dr Fritz Nagel, Stuttgart #1192/R est:1500
£2432	$4281	€3600	Scholar cleaning ears (110x34cm-43x13in) s. Indian ink col hanging scroll. 21-May-4 Dr Fritz Nagel, Stuttgart #1099/R est:1500

QI KUN (1894-1940) Chinese

Works on paper			
£2134	$3841	€3116	Autumn (62x33cm-24x13in) s.i. ink col. 26-Apr-4 Sotheby's, Hong Kong #673/R est:25000-30000 (HK.D 30000)
£7112	$12802	€10384	Landscapes (11x22cm-4x9in) s.i.d.1938 ink col album 12 leaves. 26-Apr-4 Sotheby's, Hong Kong #629/R est:35000-50000 (HK.D 100000)

QI LIANGKUN (1902-1956) Chinese

Works on paper			
£11380	$20484	€16615	Insects (12x18cm-5x7in) s. one d.1923 ink col album eight leaves prov.exhib.lit. 26-Apr-4 Sotheby's, Hong Kong #589/R est:160000-200000 (HK.D 160000)

QI YING (1790-1858) Chinese

Works on paper			
£7824	$14083	€11423	Calligraphy after the Two Wangs. s.i. ink handscrolls silk set of four. 25-Apr-4 Christie's, Hong Kong #444/R est:80000-100000 (HK.D 110000)

QIAN DU (1763-1844) Chinese

Works on paper			
£30000	$55200	€43800	Untitled (33x31cm-13x12in) s.i.d.1813 ink col silk album of ten. 9-Jun-4 Sotheby's, London #122/R est:10000-15000

QIAN GU (1508-c.1578) Chinese

Works on paper			
£4979	$8962	€7269	Reading under a pine tree (177x54cm-70x21in) s.d.1570 ink col hanging scroll. 25-Apr-4 Christie's, Hong Kong #357/R est:80000-100000 (HK.D 70000)

QIAN HUIAN (1833-1911) Chinese

Works on paper			
£1765	$3000	€2577	Figures drinking wine (257x86cm-101x34in) s.i.d.1902 ink col hanging scroll. 4-Nov-3 Bonhams & Butterfields, San Francisco #3448/R est:1500-2500

QIAN SHOUTIE (1896-1967) Chinese

Works on paper			
£541	$951	€800	Two walkers enjoying the valley view (68x45cm-27x18in) i.d.1962 seals Indian ink hanging scroll. 21-May-4 Dr Fritz Nagel, Stuttgart #1112/R

QIAN SONGYAN (1898-1985) Chinese

Works on paper			
£4800	$8832	€7008	Great view of the three gorges (87x48cm-34x19in) s. ink hanging scroll. 8-Jun-4 Bonhams, New Bond Street #53 est:1000-1500
£5792	$9672	€8456	Waterfall (121x66cm-48x26in) s. ink col hanging scroll. 26-Oct-3 Christie's, Hong Kong #291/R est:15000-20000 (HK.D 75000)
£8108	$14270	€12000	Mountains in evening light (58x41cm-23x16in) s.i.seals Indian ink col hanging scroll. 21-May-4 Dr Fritz Nagel, Stuttgart #1121/R est:600

QIN DA HU (1938-) Chinese

£240	$400	€350	Small ox horn (71x89cm-28x35in) s. 11-Oct-3 Nadeau, Windsor #24/R
£389	$650	€568	Year of the rooster (91x117cm-36x46in) s. 11-Oct-3 Nadeau, Windsor #13/R
£419	$700	€612	Year of the horse (61x81cm-24x32in) s. 11-Oct-3 Nadeau, Windsor #15/R
£449	$750	€656	Year of the dog (89x114cm-35x45in) s. 11-Oct-3 Nadeau, Windsor #14/R
£778	$1300	€1136	Last Emperor (114x89cm-45x35in) s. 11-Oct-3 Nadeau, Windsor #23/R
£838	$1400	€1223	Terracotta soldiers (86x114cm-34x45in) s. 11-Oct-3 Nadeau, Windsor #21/R

QIN LINGYUN (1914-) Chinese

Works on paper			
£274	$466	€400	Autumn mountains in white clouds (67x45cm-26x18in) s.d.1978 seal Indian ink col hanging scroll. 7-Nov-3 Dr Fritz Nagel, Stuttgart #967/R
£411	$699	€600	Landscape with field workers (65x42cm-26x17in) s.d.1978 seal Indian ink col hanging scroll. 7-Nov-3 Dr Fritz Nagel, Stuttgart #968/R

QING DYNASTY, Chinese

£60000	$100200	€87600	Ceremonial scenes (71x89cm-28x35in) on mirror glass pair. 12-Nov-3 Sotheby's, London #216/R est:40000-60000
Sculpture			
£24000	$40080	€35040	Untitled (17cm-7in) jade. 12-Nov-3 Sotheby's, London #207/R est:10000-15000
£617761	$1031660	€901931	Rocky landscape with sixteen Luohan and young acolyte (22x34cm-9x13in) jade prov. 26-Oct-3 Sotheby's, Hong Kong #32/R est:5000000-7000000 (HK.D 8000000)
Works on paper			
£7112	$12802	€10384	Still life of peonies in a wooden tub (177x83cm-70x33in) pigment silk. 25-Apr-4 Sotheby's, Hong Kong #89/R est:100000-150000 (HK.D 100000)
£125000	$208750	€182500	Military procession through landscape (39cm-15in) ink col on silk. 12-Nov-3 Sotheby's, London #197/R est:5000-7000

QING DYNASTY, 18th C Chinese

Sculpture			
£6178	$10317	€9020	Mountain (25cm-10in) white jade. 27-Oct-3 Christie's, Hong Kong #845/R est:100000-150000 (HK.D 80000)
£13900	$23212	€20294	Luohan group (21cm-8in) carved bamboo. 27-Oct-3 Christie's, Hong Kong #774/R est:100000-150000 (HK.D 180000)
Works on paper			
£92461	$166430	€134993	Imperial Buddhist votive painting (172x91cm-68x36in) ink gilt colours on silk. 26-Apr-4 Christie's, Hong Kong #999/R est:150000-200000 (HK.D 1300000)

QINNUAYUAK, Lucy (1915-1982) North American

Works on paper			
£1081	$1838	€1578	Three blue birds (56x80cm-22x31in) sealskin stencil. 3-Nov-3 Waddingtons, Toronto #289/R est:1500-2000 (C.D 2400)

QIU YING (attrib) (c.1510-1551) Chinese

Works on paper			
£4979	$8962	€7269	Heavenly abode (70x31cm-28x12in) s.i. ink col gold hanging scroll silk. 25-Apr-4 Christie's, Hong Kong #312/R est:60000-80000 (HK.D 70000)

QUADRONE, Giovanni Battista (1844-1898) Italian

£2837	$4738	€4000	Stream (24x26cm-9x10in) board prov. 20-Oct-3 Sant Agostino, Torino #279/R est:4500
£3169	$5482	€4500	Study of two men with hat (19x15cm-7x6in) s.i. board lit. 9-Dec-3 Finarte Semenzato, Milan #55/R est:4500-5000
£114094	$213356	€170000	Travelling in Sardinia (63x147cm-25x58in) s. prov.exhib.lit. 25-Feb-4 Porro, Milan #23/R est:170000-200000

QUADT, Jan (fl.1674-1696) Dutch

£2108	$3500	€3078	Rinaldo and Armida (46x56cm-18x22in) s. prov. 30-Sep-3 Christie's, Rockefeller NY #360/R est:2000-3000

QUAEDVLIEG, Carel Max Gerlach Anton (1823-1874) Dutch

£4500	$7740	€6570	Herding buffalo in the Roman campagna (28x54cm-11x21in) s. 4-Dec-3 Christie's, Kensington #40/R est:3000-5000
£5000	$9200	€7500	Buffalos (55x115cm-22x45in) s. 10-Jun-4 Christie's, Rome #143/R est:8000-10000

QUAGLIA, Carlo (1907-1970) Italian
£733 $1349 €1100 Garibaldi Street (25x35cm-10x14in) s. s.i.d.1968 verso board. 12-Jun-4 Meeting Art, Vercelli #373/R
£874 $1486 €1250 Villa Borghese (50x40cm-20x16in) s. canvas on cardboard. 18-Nov-3 Babuino, Rome #271/R
£1812 $2971 €2500 Houses by the beach, Celle (44x60cm-17x24in) s. cardboard prov.exhib. 27-May-3 Sotheby's, Milan #117/R est:2500-3000
£2708 $4279 €3900 Celle houses on the beach (44x60cm-17x24in) cardboard. 6-Sep-3 Meeting Art, Vercelli #465 est:3000

QUAGLINO, Massimo (1899-1982) Italian
£690 $1152 €1000 Houses in Castagnole (29x39cm-11x15in) s. board. 17-Nov-3 Sant Agostino, Torino #120/R
£1064 $1777 €1500 Big shell (35x45cm-14x18in) s. board. 20-Oct-3 Sant Agostino, Torino #172/R est:1500-2000
£1088 $1948 €1600 Elsa (50x70cm-20x28in) s. card. 22-Mar-4 Sant Agostino, Torino #533/R est:2000
£1119 $1869 €1600 Snow in Refrancore (37x45cm-15x18in) s. s.i.d.1978 verso board. 26-Jun-3 Sant Agostino, Torino #288/R est:1500-2000
£1329 $2219 €1900 The Po in Carignano (60x80cm-24x31in) s.s.i.verso lit. 26-Jun-3 Sant Agostino, Torino #287/R est:2500
£1818 $3036 €2600 Interior (70x50cm-28x20in) s. s.i.verso painted 1971 lit. 26-Jun-3 Sant Agostino, Torino #292/R est:2500
Works on paper
£461 $770 €650 Madonna del Portone Church, Asti (35x38cm-14x15in) s. W/C. 20-Oct-3 Sant Agostino, Torino #109/R
£709 $1184 €1000 Left down by emotion (74x73cm-29x29in) s. mixed media card. 20-Oct-3 Sant Agostino, Torino #149/R

QUAGLIO, Domenico (younger-attrib) (1787-1837) German
£6944 $11319 €10000 Schaiblingturm in Passau (37x29cm-15x11in) panel. 24-Sep-3 Neumeister, Munich #531/R est:3000

QUAGLIO, Franz (1844-1920) German
£903 $1472 €1300 Post coach stop (16x27cm-6x11in) s.d.1879 panel. 25-Sep-3 Dr Fritz Nagel, Stuttgart #1402/R
£1056 $1827 €1500 Hungarian vehicle on country road (21x27cm-8x11in) s.d.1898 panel. 10-Dec-3 Dorotheum, Vienna #152/R est:1600-2000
£1325 $2424 €2000 Peasant life (47x79cm-19x31in) s. 8-Apr-4 Dorotheum, Vienna #22/R est:2000-2300
£1333 $2427 €2000 Field camp (20x27cm-8x11in) s.d.1895 panel. 1-Jul-4 Van Ham, Cologne #1565/R est:2000
£1513 $2784 €2300 Stage-coach station with stage-coach and figures (21x27cm-8x11in) s.d.1893 panel. 25-Jun-4 Altus, Berlin #479/R est:2800
£2083 $3479 €3000 Horses with cart in front of Bavarian house (17x36cm-7x14in) s.d. panel. 24-Oct-3 Ketterer, Hamburg #97/R est:3500-4000
£2222 $3667 €3200 Bavarian post coach in Partenkirchen (24x32cm-9x13in) s. panel. 3-Jul-3 Van Ham, Cologne #1412/R est:2000
£2394 $4142 €3400 Soldiers resting and horses grazing in summer meadow (21x27cm-8x11in) s.d.1892 panel. 13-Dec-3 Lempertz, Koln #38/R est:3000

QUAGLIO, Gianni (1885-1960) Italian
£423 $739 €600 Hungaran gypsy girl (23x20cm-9x8in) init. s.i.verso cardboard on canvas. 17-Dec-3 Il Ponte, Milan #519

QUAGLIO, Lorenzo II (attrib) (1793-1869) German
Works on paper
£940 $1729 €1400 Pressing grapes outside village (32x46cm-13x18in) s.d.1850 W/C over pencil. 25-Mar-4 Dr Fritz Nagel, Stuttgart #506/R

QUAGLIO, Simon (1795-1878) German
Works on paper
£5895 $10729 €8607 Cloisters in an abbey (14x18cm-6x7in) mono. W/C prov.exhib. 17-Jun-4 Kornfeld, Bern #52/R est:7500 (S.FR 13500)

QUANCHI, Leo (?) ?
£313 $550 €457 Quiet pool (61x51cm-24x20in) s. painted c.1910. 23-May-4 Treadway Gallery, Cincinnati #551/R

QUANTE, Otto (1875-?) German
£333 $597 €500 Young woman in Schaumburg costume (56x45cm-22x18in) s. panel lit. 14-May-4 Schloss Ahlden, Ahlden #2860/R

QUARENGHI, Giacomo (1744-1817) Italian
Works on paper
£987 $1816 €1500 View with fountain, classical buildings and figures (14x11cm-6x4in) s. pen ink W/C. 22-Jun-4 Sotheby's, Milan #123/R est:1500-2000
£1119 $1902 €1600 Plan (37x29cm-15x11in) s. ink. 19-Nov-3 Finarte Semenzato, Milan #502/R est:1500-1800
£1184 $2179 €1800 Landscape with figures (11x16cm-4x6in) s. pen ink W/C. 22-Jun-4 Sotheby's, Milan #136/R est:2000-3000
£1579 $2905 €2400 Arc of Triumph (9x12cm-4x5in) s. pen ink W/C. 22-Jun-4 Sotheby's, Milan #122/R est:2500-3500

QUARTI, Ernesto Marchio (1907-1982) Italian
£922 $1540 €1300 Portrait of man (100x60cm-39x24in) s. 14-Oct-3 Finarte Semenzato, Milan #50/R
£993 $1658 €1400 Portrait of lady (110x68cm-43x27in) s. 14-Oct-3 Finarte Semenzato, Milan #49/R

QUARTLEY, Arthur (1839-1886) American
£1438 $2300 €2099 Summer evening, coast of Maine (25x18cm-10x7in) s.i.d.1879. 21-Sep-3 William Jenack, New York #36 est:1500-2500

QUARTO, Andrea (1959-) Italian
£268 $497 €400 Fantasy village (50x40cm-20x16in) s. 13-Mar-4 Meeting Art, Vercelli #208
£268 $497 €400 Enclosed garden (50x40cm-20x16in) s. i.verso lit. 13-Mar-4 Meeting Art, Vercelli #483
£333 $613 €500 Jerusalem (40x30cm-16x12in) s. i.verso. 12-Jun-4 Meeting Art, Vercelli #169/R
£400 $736 €600 Thunder reproaching the earth (50x70cm-20x28in) s. painted 2001 lit. 12-Jun-4 Meeting Art, Vercelli #563/R
£503 $931 €750 Mount Oreb (80x70cm-31x28in) s. painted 2001. 13-Mar-4 Meeting Art, Vercelli #318
£733 $1349 €1100 Oriental woman (90x90cm-35x35in) s. i.verso painted 2001 lit. 12-Jun-4 Meeting Art, Vercelli #969/R
£1074 $1987 €1600 Flower scent (120x140cm-47x55in) s. i.verso. 13-Mar-4 Meeting Art, Vercelli #362 est:1500
£1074 $1922 €1600 Green (130x110cm-51x43in) i.verso exhib.lit. 30-May-4 Meeting Art, Vercelli #63 est:1500

QUARTREMAIN, William Wells (fl.1906-1908) British
£1150 $1875 €1679 Brake in winter, the weir brake, Stratford-upon-Avon (37x53cm-15x21in) s.d.1925. 26-Sep-3 Bigwood, Stratford on Avon #409/R est:500-800
£1600 $2672 €2336 View of Holy Trinity church, Stratford upon Avon (25x37cm-10x15in) s. 27-Jun-3 Bigwood, Stratford on Avon #349/R est:1600-2000
Works on paper
£620 $1011 €905 Harvard house, view of the timbered buildings with the bookseller shop (28x18cm-11x7in) mono. W/C. 26-Sep-3 Bigwood, Stratford on Avon #414/R
£700 $1092 €1022 Hatton Rock, two figures in a rowing boat (24x37cm-9x15in) W/C. 28-Mar-3 Bigwood, Stratford on Avon #405/R
£950 $1549 €1387 Holy Trinity Church viewed from over the river with figures in boats (37x26cm-15x10in) s. W/C. 26-Sep-3 Bigwood, Stratford on Avon #420/R
£1100 $1925 €1606 Ford, Kenilworth, figure in a boat in the foreground (26x18cm-10x7in) s. W/C. 19-Dec-3 Bigwood, Stratford on Avon #356
£1400 $2184 €2044 Anne Hathaway's cottage with a mother and child walking on a path (16x24cm-6x9in) s. W/C. 28-Mar-3 Bigwood, Stratford on Avon #404 est:1500-1800
£1400 $2282 €2044 Shakespears Hotelm Chapel Street (21x34cm-8x13in) s.d.1910 W/C. 26-Sep-3 Bigwood, Stratford on Avon #413/R est:1500-2000
£1700 $3111 €2550 Bank buildings and Shakespeare Gallery Cafe, Stratford-on-Avon (23x36cm-9x14in) s.d.1924 W/C board. 12-Jul-4 Mullucks Wells, Bishop's Stortford #407/R est:300-500

QUAST, Jan Zacharias (1814-1891) Austrian
£872 $1605 €1300 Virgin under the cross (44x36cm-17x14in) s.d.1862. 24-Mar-4 Dorotheum, Vienna #440/R

QUAST, Pieter (1606-1647) Dutch
£3000 $5490 €4380 Elegant company in an interior (42x36cm-17x14in) bears sig panel. 7-Jul-4 Bonhams, New Bond Street #93/R est:3000-4000

QUATTROCIOCCHI, Domenico (1874-1941) Italian
£4225 $7014 €6000 Roma, Piazza Navonna con Sant'Agnese in Agone. Roma, Piazza Navona (28x21cm-11x8in) i.verso wood two. 11-Jun-3 Christie's, Rome #115/R est:5800-6500

QUAYLE, E Christian (fl.1894-1921) British
£600 $1002 €876 Milk maid in a Manx farmyard (46x64cm-18x25in) s. 20-Jun-3 Chrystals Auctions, Isle of Man #201
£1900 $3420 €2774 Harbour scene with figures on a quayside. Fishing boats beside wooden pier (21x35cm-8x14in) s. canvasboard pair. 21-Apr-4 Tennants, Leyburn #1100/R est:400-600
Works on paper
£400 $716 €584 Douglas Harbour (25x36cm-10x14in) s. W/C. 7-May-4 Chrystals Auctions, Isle of Man #304
£500 $860 €730 Gathering the lobster pots (30x48cm-12x19in) s. W/C. 5-Dec-3 Chrystals Auctions, Isle of Man #262
£500 $860 €730 Artists looking out over Injebreck (30x46cm-12x18in) W/C. 5-Dec-3 Chrystals Auctions, Isle of Man #262a
£540 $967 €788 Peel Castle (25x36cm-10x14in) s. W/C. 7-May-4 Chrystals Auctions, Isle of Man #306
£550 $985 €803 Douglas inner harbour (25x36cm-10x14in) s. W/C. 7-May-4 Chrystals Auctions, Isle of Man #305
£560 $1002 €818 Castle Rushen (25x36cm-10x14in) s. W/C. 7-May-4 Chrystals Auctions, Isle of Man #303
£600 $1002 €876 Farmer with two horses by a Manx Farm (46x64cm-18x25in) s. W/C. 20-Jun-3 Chrystals Auctions, Isle of Man #200/R
£800 $1432 €1168 Last tram up Prospect Hill (25x36cm-10x14in) s. W/C. 7-May-4 Chrystals Auctions, Isle of Man #307
£910 $1629 €1329 Manx Harbour scene (36x25cm-14x10in) s. W/C. 7-May-4 Chrystals Auctions, Isle of Man #309
£920 $1647 €1343 Fishing boats in Douglas Harbour (36x25cm-14x10in) s. W/C. 7-May-4 Chrystals Auctions, Isle of Man #308

QUAYTMAN, Harvey (1937-2002) American
£2973 $5500 €4341 Self-portrait with rust (62x62cm-24x24in) s.d.1986 i.stretcher acrylic rust prov. 12-Feb-4 Sotheby's, New York #305/R est:2500-3500
£5135 $9500 €7497 Perfect Beacon (117x117cm-46x46in) s.i.d.1988-9 overlap acrylic rust prov. 12-Feb-4 Sotheby's, New York #235/R est:1500-2000

QUEJIDO, Manuel (1946-) Spanish
£5782 $10350 €8500 I love Majorca (135x98cm-53x39in) s.i.d.89 verso acrylic. 22-Mar-4 Durán, Madrid #158/R est:4000
£7746 $13556 €11000 Mirror 13 (135x113cm-53x44in) s.i.d.1985 verso prov. 16-Dec-3 Segre, Madrid #175/R est:9000

QUELLIER, Andre (20th C) ?
£1435 $2440 €2095 Femme aux raisins (84x116cm-33x46in) s.d.71 panel. 5-Nov-3 AB Stockholms Auktionsverk #1100/R est:15000-18000 (S.KR 19000)

QUELLINUS, Artus (younger-attrib) (c.1625-1700) Flemish
Sculpture
£22000 $40260 €32120 Angel (137cm-54in) wood lit. 9-Jul-4 Sotheby's, London #99/R est:10000-15000

QUELLINUS, Erasmus (17th C) Flemish
£20134 $37450 €30000 David meeting Abigail (117x143cm-46x56in) s.d.1626. 2-Mar-4 Ansorena, Madrid #276/R est:30000
Works on paper
£21127 $36972 €30000 Un char de musiciens tire par quatre chevres, entoure de chanteurs (14x31cm-6x12in) pen brown ink col wash prov. 17-Dec-3 Christie's, Paris #23/R est:30000-50000

QUELLINUS, Erasmus II (style) (1607-1678) Flemish
£7534 $12808 €11000 Christ in the house of Martha and Mary (47x62cm-19x24in) copper prov. 4-Nov-3 Sotheby's, Amsterdam #8/R est:12000-18000

QUELLINUS, Erasmus II and VERBRUGGEN, Gaspar Pieter (17th C) Flemish
£13986 $23357 €20000 Relief of the Holy Family surrounded by garland (91x66cm-36x26in) prov. 30-Jun-3 Ansorena, Madrid #189/R est:20000

QUELLINUS, Jan Erasmus (1634-1715) Flemish
£28378 $49946 €42000 Thetis dips Achilles in a vase with water from the Styx (82x55cm-32x22in) s.d.1668 prov. 18-May-4 Sotheby's, Amsterdam #51/R est:25000-35000

QUELLINUS, Jan Erasmus (attrib) (1634-1715) Flemish
£17000 $31110 €24820 Volumnia with her sons before Coriolanus (230x211cm-91x83in) 8-Jul-4 Sotheby's, London #259/R est:10000-15000
Works on paper
£323 $518 €450 Saint Antoine surrounded with angels (30x22cm-12x9in) s. brown ink brn wash htd white gouche W/C. 16-May-3 Tajan, Paris #12

QUELVEE, François Albert (1884-1967) French
£379 $630 €550 Couple (73x54cm-29x21in) s. 1-Oct-3 Millon & Associes, Paris #55

QUENDEN, Phillipp A (1879-1937) ?
£240 $400 €350 Vicarage lawn, Yetminster (51x69cm-20x27in) s. 16-Nov-3 Simpson's, Houston #248
£399 $650 €583 Vicarage lawn Yetminster (51x69cm-20x27in) s. 28-Sep-3 Simpson's, Houston #383/R

QUENEAU, Raymond (1903-1976) French
Works on paper
£1133 $2085 €1700 Entree de port (19x27cm-7x11in) gouache. 9-Jun-4 Piasa, Paris #206/R est:1500-2000

QUENIOUX, Gustave Francois Raoul (1865-1949) French
Works on paper
£1342 $2483 €2000 La medina de Tunis. Le vendeur d'eau a Tunis (35x24cm-14x9in) s.i.d.1899 W/C pair. 15-Mar-4 Gros & Delettrez, Paris #116/R est:2000-2500

QUENTIN, Bernard (1923-) French
£436 $811 €650 Composition (39x97cm-15x38in) s. panel. 8-Mar-4 Rieunier, Paris #19/R
£451 $754 €650 Foule (60x50cm-24x20in) s. panel. 25-Oct-3 Cornette de St.Cyr, Paris #784/R
£503 $891 €750 Composition (48x92cm-19x36in) s. oil mixed media panel. 28-Apr-4 Charbonneaux, Paris #215
£671 $1188 €1000 Bataille (105x117cm-41x46in) s. panel. 28-Apr-4 Artcurial Briest, Paris #269/R
£1000 $1800 €1500 Untitled (141x206cm-56x81in) s. acrylic. 24-Apr-4 Cornette de St.Cyr, Paris #687/R est:2000
Sculpture
£1103 $2041 €1600 Ecriture (82x22cm-32x9in) s.num.1/8 black pat bronze lit. 13-Feb-4 Charbonneaux, Paris #132/R est:1600-1800
£1259 $2165 €1800 Sans titre (163x25cm-64x10in) mono.num.1/1 Corten steel. 3-Dec-3 Beaussant & Lefèvre, Paris #16/R est:800-1200
Works on paper
£270 $511 €400 Personnage (60x46cm-24x18in) s. felt pen. 21-Feb-4 Cornette de St.Cyr, Paris #376
£733 $1320 €1100 Encore (94x118cm-37x46in) s.d.1961 mixed media on carpet. 24-Apr-4 Cornette de St.Cyr, Paris #685

QUENTIN, Laurence (20th C) French
Works on paper
£280 $476 €400 Bongo Bong (110x120cm-43x47in) s. mixed media canvas. 29-Nov-3 Neret-Minet, Paris #160/R

QUERALT, Jaume (1949-) Spanish
£789 $1429 €1200 Shelves and toys (59x45cm-23x18in) 14-Apr-4 Ansorena, Madrid #258/R
Works on paper
£352 $616 €500 Bridge, Oporto (47x62cm-19x24in) s.d.1991 pastel. 16-Dec-3 Durán, Madrid #16/R
£426 $689 €600 Yorkshire (48x62cm-19x24in) s. pastel. 20-May-3 Ansorena, Madrid #424/R
£638 $1034 €900 Untitled (66x100cm-26x39in) s. gouache. 20-May-3 Ansorena, Madrid #996/R
£780 $1264 €1100 Munecas (75x110cm-30x43in) s.d.88 gouache. 20-May-3 Ansorena, Madrid #997/R
£1304 $2139 €1800 Composition (81x120cm-32x47in) s.d.1994 mixed media. 27-May-3 Durán, Madrid #122/R est:1800

QUERE, René (1932-) French
£355 $592 €500 Port de peche (27x24cm-11x9in) s. paper. 17-Jun-3 Galerie Moderne, Brussels #244
£596 $1115 €900 Marine a Audierne (45x60cm-18x24in) s. acrylic. 24-Jul-4 Thierry & Lannon, Brest #289
£880 $1540 €1250 Au bistrot - vue sur la mer (34x31cm-13x12in) s. panel. 21-Dec-3 Thierry & Lannon, Brest #411
Works on paper
£289 $479 €410 Pecheurs sur le quai (27x23cm-11x9in) s. gouache. 10-Jun-3 Adjug'art, Brest #88

QUERFURT, August (1696-1761) German
£313 $497 €450 Battle scene (19x34cm-7x13in) s. 11-Sep-3 Weidler, Nurnberg #322/R
£2649 $4821 €4000 Riding party setting out for the hunt (44x56cm-17x22in) copper prov. 16-Jun-4 Dorotheum, Vienna #167/R est:5000-7000
£4196 $7007 €6000 Scenes de cavalerie (43x58cm-17x23in) pair. 12-Oct-3 Salle des ventes Pillet, Lyon la Foret #36/R
£11111 $20000 €16222 Falconers in a landscape (22x31cm-9x12in) panel pair. 23-Jan-4 Christie's, Rockefeller NY #24/R est:20000-30000

QUERFURT, August (style) (1696-1761) German
£7154 $12305 €10445 Riders by camp (114x146cm-45x57in) 7-Dec-3 Uppsala Auktionskammare, Uppsala #41/R est:40000-50000 (S.KR 93000)

QUERNER, Curt (1904-1976) German
£382 $638 €550 Portrait of the musician Klaus Heintze (32x23cm-13x9in) i. verso masonite. 25-Oct-3 Dr Lehr, Berlin #409/R
£1250 $2088 €1800 Portrait of Regine Friedrich (60x50cm-24x20in) s.i. verso board. 25-Oct-3 Dr Lehr, Berlin #408/R est:900
Works on paper
£667 $1200 €1000 Reclining female nude (23x62cm-9x24in) s.d.14.10.69 s.i.d.7.1.68 verso W/C. 24-Apr-4 Dr Lehr, Berlin #389/R
£867 $1560 €1300 Seated female nude, arms above head (62x44cm-24x17in) s.d.17.9.67 i. verso W/C board. 24-Apr-4 Dr Lehr, Berlin #388/R
£1200 $2148 €1800 November (26x35cm-10x14in) mono.d.1.11.58 W/C. 15-May-4 Bassenge, Berlin #7107/R est:1200
£2400 $4320 €3600 Winter in Bornchen (44x58cm-17x23in) mono. W/C board double-sided. 24-Apr-4 Dr Lehr, Berlin #387/R est:3000

QUERVAIN, Daniel de (1937-) Swiss
Works on paper
£459 $766 €666 Young woman (69x49cm-27x19in) s.i.d. pencil chk W/C. 19-Jun-3 Kornfeld, Bern #887 est:1000 (S.FR 1000)

QUESADA, Jaime (1937-) Spanish
Works on paper
£347 $552 €500 Maternite (69x52cm-27x20in) s.d.61 W/C. 9-Sep-3 Palais de Beaux Arts, Brussels #262/R

QUESNE, Fernand le (1856-?) French
£8667 $15513 €13000 Girl in 18th Century costume (128x96cm-50x38in) s. 17-May-4 Finarte Semenzato, Rome #89/R est:15000-18000

QUESNET, Eugène (1816-1899) French
£993 $1659 €1400 Portrait de jeune femme en robe noire (97x74cm-38x29in) s.d.1844. 17-Oct-3 Tajan, Paris #133/R est:1000-1200

QUETGLAS, Matias (1946-) Spanish
£1926 $3389 €2850 White roses (18x43cm-7x17in) s. s.i.d.1989-93 verso board prov. 18-May-4 Segre, Madrid #258/R est:2850
Works on paper
£333 $607 €500 Nina de espaldas (31x23cm-12x9in) s.d.28-111-70 chl drawing. 29-Jun-4 Segre, Madrid #221/R
£490 $817 €700 Banista de espaldas (24x26cm-9x10in) s.d.oct.nov.1970 s.i.d.verso chl paper on masonite prov. 24-Jun-3 Segre, Madrid #194/R
£2632 $4842 €4000 Two painters, two models, two boys, two cats (30x62cm-12x24in) s.d.1989 mixed media board. 22-Jun-4 Durán, Madrid #144/R est:4000

QUIBEL, Raymond (?) ?
£455 $773 €650 Paysage fantastique (61x45cm-24x18in) s. oil paper on panel. 24-Nov-3 E & Eve, Paris #186
£567 $948 €800 Vue d'Amfreville a la mie voie (65x92cm-26x36in) s. 19-Oct-3 Imberdis, Pont Audemer #38

QUICK, Paul (20th C) German
£336 $571 €480 Capriccio Espagnol (170x125cm-67x49in) s.d.II 1993 acrylic paper. 29-Nov-3 Arnold, Frankfurt #430/R
£350 $594 €500 Composition in yellow (164x125cm-65x49in) s.d.1990 acrylic paper. 29-Nov-3 Arnold, Frankfurt #431/R
£385 $654 €550 Composition in green and black (147x250cm-58x98in) s.d.1998 acrylic paper. 29-Nov-3 Arnold, Frankfurt #432/R

QUICK, Richard (fl.1882-1889) British
£280 $468 €409 Portrait of Donna, a bloodhound (41x30cm-16x12in) i.d.6.80 s.d.June 1880 verso. 8-Oct-3 Christie's, Kensington #716
£300 $531 €438 Mare and foal (46x56cm-18x22in) s. 28-Apr-4 Halls, Shrewsbury #506/R

QUICK, Richard (attrib) (fl.1882-1889) British
£2200 $3740 €3212 Frigga a mastiff (51x41cm-20x16in) s.i.d.1887. 27-Nov-3 Christie's, Kensington #322/R est:1000-1500

QUIESSE, Claude (1938-) French
£1608 $2734 €2300 Chevauchee fantastique (130x196cm-51x77in) s.i.verso. 28-Nov-3 Blanchet, Paris #253 est:800-1000

QUIGLEY, Alan (?) British?
Works on paper
£350 $581 €511 St. George's market, Belfast (50x61cm-20x24in) s. wax crayon. 1-Oct-3 John Ross, Belfast #254
£350 $602 €511 Aran fishermen (66x50cm-26x20in) s. wax crayon. 3-Dec-3 John Ross, Belfast #228
£350 $641 €511 Horse dealers (66x50cm-26x20in) s. wax crayon. 2-Jun-4 John Ross, Belfast #102
£400 $744 €584 Collecting turf (50x66cm-20x26in) s. wax crayon. 3-Mar-4 John Ross, Belfast #235

QUIGLEY, Bill (20th C) American
£389 $700 €568 Untitled (50x24cm-20x9in) s.d.1985 verso acrylic liquitex. 24-Apr-4 David Rago, Lambertville #318/R

QUIGLEY, Edward B (1895-1986) American
£342 $550 €499 Sketch of wild horses grazing in a wooded landscape (30x41cm-12x16in) s. board. 20-Jan-3 O'Gallerie, Oregon #905
£1216 $2250 €1775 Wild horse raising dust in corral with cowboy cutting one out (30x41cm-12x16in) s. board. 19-Jan-4 O'Gallerie, Oregon #132/R est:2000-3000
£2459 $4500 €3590 Eight circus horse (46x61cm-18x24in) s. prov. 7-Jun-4 O'Gallerie, Oregon #130/R est:5000-7000
£4037 $6500 €5894 Small payment, three mounted cowboys (71x56cm-28x22in) s. 18-Aug-3 O'Gallerie, Oregon #806/R
£4037 $6500 €5894 Stormy (56x66cm-22x26in) s. 24-Feb-3 O'Gallerie, Oregon #839/R est:5000-6000

QUIGNON, Fernand Just (attrib) (1854-1941) French
£1831 $3277 €2600 Pont Louis-Philippe a Paris (26x34cm-10x13in) panel. 11-Jan-4 Rouillac, Vendome #384

QUILLIGAN, Ita (20th C) Irish
£526 $968 €800 Summer, West of Ireland (36x45cm-14x18in) init. canvasboard. 22-Jun-4 De Veres Art Auctions, Dublin #162

QUILLIVIC, Raymond (1942-) French
Works on paper
£364 $681 €550 Flotille sardiniere aux vieux port de Douarnenez (14x18cm-6x7in) s. gouache. 24-Jul-4 Thierry & Lannon, Brest #290
£366 $641 €520 Pardon de Ste Anne La Palud (17x36cm-7x14in) s. gouache. 21-Dec-3 Thierry & Lannon, Brest #414
£387 $678 €550 Concarneau, le port Peneroff (23x14cm-9x6in) s. gouache. 21-Dec-3 Thierry & Lannon, Brest #412
£400 $716 €600 Vent arriere dans le port (45x28cm-18x11in) s. gouache. 16-May-4 Thierry & Lannon, Brest #227b
£450 $842 €680 Armement pour la peche a la sardine devant les Plomarc'h (33x22cm-13x9in) s. gouache. 24-Jul-4 Thierry & Lannon, Brest #291/R

QUILLIVIC, René (1879-1969) French
£986 $1725 €1400 Poesie vesperale (50x65cm-20x26in) s. board. 21-Dec-3 Thierry & Lannon, Brest #197/R
£1056 $1849 €1500 Temps gris et pluvieux sur le sentier pres de la chaumiere (50x64cm-20x25in) s. board. 21-Dec-3 Thierry & Lannon, Brest #196 est:1400-1600

QUILTY, Joseph (20th C) Irish
£667 $1207 €1000 Gathering hay (46x59cm-18x23in) s. canvasboard. 30-Mar-4 De Veres Art Auctions, Dublin #109d/R

QUINAUX, Joseph (1822-1895) Belgian
£426 $711 €600 Woodland view with figure (26x32cm-10x13in) s. 20-Oct-3 Bernaerts, Antwerp #14/R
£839 $1427 €1200 Paysage avec cavalier, bucheron et chien (40x50cm-16x20in) s. panel. 18-Nov-3 Galerie Moderne, Brussels #669/R
£3000 $5520 €4380 Pastoral idyll (69x98cm-27x39in) s. 25-Mar-4 Christie's, Kensington #16/R est:2000-3000
Works on paper
£1757 $3145 €2600 Paysage de Savoie (77x128cm-30x50in) s. pastel. 5-May-4 Coutau Begarie, Paris #48j est:2000-3000

QUINCOCES, Alejandro (1951-) Spanish
£458 $801 €650 Pink land (35x35cm-14x14in) s. board exhib. 16-Dec-3 Durán, Madrid #673/R

QUINCY, Edmund (1903-1999) American
£346 $550 €505 American house (50x61cm-20x24in) s. exhib. 12-Sep-3 Skinner, Boston #431/R
£346 $550 €505 Lady in pink on a dock (60x50cm-24x20in) estate st.verso. 13-Sep-3 Weschler, Washington #785/R
£353 $650 €515 Woman in pink (61x51cm-24x20in) 25-Jun-4 Freeman, Philadelphia #182/R
£367 $675 €550 Trinita' dei Monti, Rome (74x60cm-29x24in) s. 8-Jun-4 Della Rocca, Turin #291/R
£915 $1500 €1327 Cambridge street scene (61x66cm-24x26in) s. 2-Jun-3 Grogan, Boston #695/R

QUINET, Mig (1908-2001) Belgian
£327 $584 €480 Nature morte aux oranges (38x54cm-15x21in) s. 17-Mar-4 Hotel des Ventes Mosan, Brussels #169
Works on paper
£563 $975 €800 Composition (55x50cm-22x20in) s.d.50 W/C gouache. 13-Dec-3 De Vuyst, Lokeren #264

QUINETTE, Jean Claude (20th C) French
Works on paper
£282 $456 €400 Barfleur (34x54cm-13x21in) s. W/C. 11-Aug-3 Boscher, Cherbourg #770

QUINN, Anthony (20th C) ?
Sculpture
£2235 $4000 €3263 Torso. s.i. white marble. 13-May-4 Dallas Auction Gallery, Dallas #277/R est:2000-4000
£3073 $5500 €4487 Scheherazade. s. marble onyx. 13-May-4 Dallas Auction Gallery, Dallas #262/R

QUINN, Brian (20th C) Irish
£282 $505 €420 Cattle by a stream, Pine Forest, Co Dublin (42x58cm-17x23in) s. 31-May-4 Hamilton Osborne King, Dublin #124/R
£336 $601 €500 Sandymount Green (27x50cm-11x20in) s.d.96. 31-May-4 Hamilton Osborne King, Dublin #21

QUINN, James Peter (1870-1951) Australian
£296 $531 €432 Head study of Doreen Eveline Webber (34x24cm-13x9in) s. prov. 15-May-4 Christie's, Sydney #496 (A.D 750)
£395 $708 €577 Doreen Eveline Webber (102x68cm-40x27in) s. prov. 15-May-4 Christie's, Sydney #475/R (A.D 1000)
£632 $1132 €923 Portrait of a young woman (75x49cm-30x19in) s. prov. 15-May-4 Christie's, Sydney #484/R (A.D 1600)

QUINN, Marc (1964-) British
Sculpture
£16760 $30000 €24470 Golden moreish morphology (110x90x100cm-43x35x39in) glass silver prov. 12-May-4 Christie's, Rockefeller NY #348/R est:30000-40000
£47486 $85000 €69330 Selma mustajbasic (89x56x145cm-35x22x57in) marble executed 2000. 13-May-4 Phillips, New York #60/R est:80000-120000

QUINN, William (20th C) American
£227 $400 €331 Image for orange and yellow (94x74cm-37x29in) s. i.verso. 22-May-4 Selkirks, St. Louis #632

QUINONES, Azalea (1953-) Venezuelan
£248 $405 €362 I am the sleepwalker (100x80cm-39x31in) s. painted 1990. 28-Sep-3 Subastas Odalys, Caracas #10
£479 $780 €699 Paquito and Carolina are their cats (70x60cm-28x24in) s. painted 1978. 20-Jul-3 Subastas Odalys, Caracas #130

QUINQUAND, Anna (1890-1984) French
Sculpture
£3028 $5239 €4300 Jeune africaine a la cruche (56cm-22in) s.st.f. Susse pat bronze exec. 1941 cire perdue. 12-Dec-3 Piasa, Paris #186/R est:2000-3000
£10204 $18265 €15000 Jeune africaine a la cruche (56cm-22in) s.d.1941 pat bronze Cast Susse. 21-Mar-4 St-Germain-en-Laye Encheres #39/R est:15000

QUINQUELA MARTIN, Benito (1890-1977) Argentinian
£24862 $45000 €36299 Boca (50x60cm-20x24in) cardboard. 30-Mar-4 Arroyo, Buenos Aires #71
£29834 $54000 €43558 Night scene (80x90cm-31x35in) board. 30-Mar-4 Arroyo, Buenos Aires #80
£109290 $200000 €159563 Sailing boats with lights on (162x142cm-64x56in) 1-Jun-4 Arroyo, Buenos Aires #78
Prints
£2376 $4300 €3469 Factory (50x65cm-20x26in) col eau forte. 30-Mar-4 Arroyo, Buenos Aires #1
Works on paper
£1484 $2700 €2167 Old town (23x21cm-9x8in) s.d.1966 pencil ink lit. 29-Jun-4 Arroyo, Buenos Aires #21/R est:1600

QUINSAC, Paul François (1858-?) French
£35294 $60000 €51529 In the studio (108x75cm-43x30in) s.d.1891 prov. 28-Oct-3 Sotheby's, New York #1/R est:100000-150000

QUINSAC, Paul François (attrib) (1858-?) French
£4000 $7360 €6000 Resting amongst ruins (75x108cm-30x43in) bears sig. 10-Jun-4 Christie's, Rome #94/R est:5000-7000

QUINTANA CASTILLO, Manuel (1928-) Venezuelan

£371	$675	€557	Untitled (29x23cm-11x9in) s.verso panel painted 1964. 21-Jun-4 Subastas Odalys, Caracas #61
£395	$660	€577	Untitled (50x40cm-20x16in) s. painted 1966. 13-Jul-3 Subastas Odalys, Caracas #91
£594	$920	€867	Untitled (40x30cm-16x12in) s. painted 1977. 3-Nov-2 Subastas Odalys, Caracas #73/R
£674	$1125	€984	Icon (56x46cm-22x18in) s. painted 1976. 19-Oct-3 Subastas Odalys, Caracas #104/R
Works on paper			
£270	$440	€394	Baldia II (41x41cm-16x16in) s. mixed media on canvas exec.1965. 28-Sep-3 Subastas Odalys, Caracas #39
£309	$575	€451	Small 1 (31x25cm-12x10in) s. mixed media panel exec.1990. 14-Mar-4 Subastas Odalys, Caracas #98
£544	$990	€816	Untitled (41x51cm-16x20in) s. mixed media on canvas exec.1958. 21-Jun-4 Subastas Odalys, Caracas #102
£703	$1125	€1026	Untitled (22x28cm-9x11in) W/C exec.1982. 21-Sep-3 Subastas Odalys, Caracas #79

QUINTANILLA, Luis (1893-1978) Spanish

£1042	$1719	€1500	Still life with oysters (60x50cm-24x20in) s. 2-Jul-3 Ansorena, Madrid #843/R
£1053	$1937	€1600	Boy and cat (61x50cm-24x20in) s. 22-Jun-4 Durán, Madrid #162/R est:1600

QUINTE, Lothar (1923-2000) German

£559	$951	€800	Composition - red on white (12x30cm-5x12in) i. verso tempera canvas on panel prov. 27-Nov-3 Lempertz, Koln #363
£625	$1044	€900	Untitled (63x97cm-25x38in) s.d. tempera. 24-Oct-3 Ketterer, Hamburg #511/R
£800	$1432	€1200	Horizontal stripes (69x95cm-27x37in) s.d. acrylic. 15-May-4 Bassenge, Berlin #7108/R
£1572	$2893	€2295	Untitled (120x69cm-47x27in) s.d.1977 verso. 8-Jun-4 Germann, Zurich #3/R est:2000-3000 (S.FR 3600)

QUINTERO, Daniel (1940-) Spanish

Works on paper			
£800	$1456	€1200	Hands (17x26cm-7x10in) s.d.1972 pencil. 29-Jun-4 Segre, Madrid #219/R
£1678	$2803	€2400	Sueno (62x48cm-24x19in) s. pencil drawing brown pencil. 24-Jun-3 Segre, Madrid #168/R est:2400
£2000	$3620	€3000	Boy and dog (63x40cm-25x16in) s.d.1973 pencil dr prov. 30-Mar-4 Segre, Madrid #248/R est:2500

QUINTIN, H J (19th C) British

£870	$1600	€1270	Prize bull in a farmyard (63x76cm-25x30in) s.d.1844. 27-Jun-4 Freeman, Philadelphia #53/R est:2000-3000
£8400	$13440	€12264	Three Hereford cows and calf beneath oak tree in landscape (66x81cm-26x32in) exhib. 17-Sep-3 Brightwells, Leominster #891/R est:8000-12000

QUINTON, Alfred Robert (1853-1934) British

Works on paper			
£350	$627	€511	The river Fowey, Cornwall (30x48cm-12x19in) s. W/C. 25-May-4 Bonhams, Knightsbridge #3/R
£613	$1000	€895	Devonshire cottage (18x28cm-7x11in) s. W/C. 17-Jul-3 Naón & Cia, Buenos Aires #16/R

QUINTON, Clement (1851-?) French

£526	$953	€800	Farmer and farmer's wife with horse and cart, Montigny (27x41cm-11x16in) s. 19-Apr-4 Glerum, Amsterdam #288/R
£625	$1131	€950	Cows watering (27x41cm-11x16in) s. 19-Apr-4 Glerum, Amsterdam #287/R
£724	$1310	€1100	Pause (49x65cm-19x26in) s. 19-Apr-4 Boscher, Cherbourg #831/R
£805	$1498	€1200	Retour des champs (50x65cm-20x26in) s. 3-Mar-4 Tajan, Paris #20/R est:1200-1500
£940	$1748	€1400	Labour (50x65cm-20x26in) s. 3-Mar-4 Tajan, Paris #21/R est:1500-2000
£1159	$1901	€1600	Les chevaux de labour (32x46cm-13x18in) s. exhib. 11-May-3 Osenat, Fontainebleau #198/R est:2000-2200

QUIROS, Antonio (1918-1984) Spanish

£5634	$9014	€8000	Head (77x28cm-30x11in) s. s.verso board. 16-Sep-3 Segre, Madrid #167a/R est:4500
£6333	$11527	€9500	Criada (60x73cm-24x29in) s. s.i. verso. 29-Jun-4 Segre, Madrid #131/R est:9500

QUIROS, Cesareo Bernaldo (1881-1968) Argentinian

£4412	$7500	€6442	Under the snow (22x30cm-9x12in) s. cardboard painted c.1933. 25-Nov-3 Galeria y Remates, Montevideo #176/R
£23352	$42500	€34094	In the fields (63x71cm-25x28in) s. board painted 1959 exhib.lit. 29-Jun-4 Arroyo, Buenos Aires #82/R est:35000
£24044	$44000	€35104	Army symbols (52x78cm-20x31in) cardboard. 1-Jun-4 Arroyo, Buenos Aires #67
£102210	$185000	€149227	Villa LInda, Florence (96x88cm-38x35in) 30-Mar-4 Arroyo, Buenos Aires #85

QUIRT, Walter (1902-1968) American

£2270	$4200	€3314	Give and take (91x102cm-36x40in) s. s.i.d.1951 verso prov. 13-Jul-4 Christie's, Rockefeller NY #117/R est:3000-5000

QUIRT, Walter (attrib) (1902-1968) American

Works on paper			
£1018	$1700	€1486	American social commentary, chained to a blackman (61x74cm-24x29in) s. gouache chl exec.c.1930. 19-Oct-3 William Jenack, New York #187 est:500-700

QUISTDORFF, V (1883-1953) Danish

£496	$928	€724	View from Copenhagen Harbour (40x47cm-16x19in) s.d.19 cardboard prov. 25-Feb-4 Kunsthallen, Copenhagen #515 (D.KR 5500)

QUISTDORFF, Victor (1883-1953) Danish

£284	$455	€415	Harbour scene with boats (34x46cm-13x18in) s.d.26. 22-Sep-3 Rasmussen, Vejle #318/R (D.KR 3000)
£378	$654	€552	Green painted steamer in Copenhagen Harbour (31x41cm-12x16in) s.d.1925. 9-Dec-3 Rasmussen, Copenhagen #1496/R (D.KR 4000)
£494	$919	€721	Sailing vessel and steamer at sea in a calm (17x23cm-7x9in) s.d.1951. 2-Mar-4 Rasmussen, Copenhagen #1448/R (D.KR 5500)
£769	$1323	€1100	Copenhagen (35x45cm-14x18in) s.d.1926 board. 4-Dec-3 Schopman, Hamburg #786/R
£860	$1548	€1256	Vessels off Copenhagen Harbour (28x40cm-11x16in) s. masonite. 24-Apr-4 Rasmussen, Havnen #2322 (D.KR 9600)
£903	$1426	€1300	Aarhus harbour (34x50cm-13x20in) s.d.1930. 6-Sep-3 Schopman, Hamburg #857/R

QUITTELIER, Henri (1884-1980) Belgian

£590	$986	€850	Etang (60x75cm-24x30in) s. 21-Oct-3 Galerie Moderne, Brussels #237/R

QUITTNER, Rudolf (1872-1910) Austrian

£347	$566	€500	Village (54x73cm-21x29in) s. 23-Sep-3 Wiener Kunst Auktionen, Vienna #133/R

QUITTON, Edovard (1842-1934) Belgian

£1667	$3000	€2500	Strange collection (15x19cm-6x7in) s.i.d.1879 panel. 21-Apr-4 Christie's, Amsterdam #201/R est:2500-3500

QUIVIERES, Augustin Marcotte de (1854-1907) French

£434	$786	€660	Paysage (72x60cm-28x24in) s. 18-Apr-4 Rouillac, Vendome #158
£625	$1131	€950	Bateaux en mer (92x60cm-36x24in) s. 18-Apr-4 Rouillac, Vendome #159
£1682	$2658	€2439	Sailing vessels off the French coast, evening (73x117cm-29x46in) s.d.1906 exhib. 2-Sep-3 Rasmussen, Copenhagen #1756/R est:12000 (D.KR 18000)

QUIZET, Alphonse (1885-1955) French

£298	$545	€450	Bord de canal (18x23cm-7x9in) s. board. 7-Apr-4 Piasa, Paris #101
£333	$610	€500	Garden meadow (60x73cm-24x29in) s. 5-Jun-4 Arnold, Frankfurt #698/R
£364	$667	€550	Peniches sur le canal (19x24cm-7x9in) s. isorel panel. 7-Apr-4 Piasa, Paris #100
£570	$1050	€850	Le Pre Saint-Gervais (30x39cm-12x15in) s. i.verso panel. 26-Mar-4 Neret-Minet, Paris #15/R
£699	$1203	€1000	Place de la Contrescarpe (34x24cm-13x9in) s. board prov. 2-Dec-3 Sotheby's, Amsterdam #198/R est:800-1200
£726	$1300	€1060	La route de Romainville (33x46cm-13x18in) s. i.verso masonite. 8-Jan-4 Doyle, New York #39/R
£769	$1308	€1100	Paris, les Hauts a Montmartre (66x74cm-26x29in) s. 27-Nov-3 Millon & Associes, Paris #220/R
£1033	$1901	€1550	Carrefour a Paris (55x46cm-22x18in) s. panel. 14-Jun-4 Tajan, Paris #63 est:1800-2000
£1074	$1997	€1600	Village avec la Grande Paroisse (38x46cm-15x18in) s. isorel. 3-Mar-4 Tajan, Paris #82 est:1200-1500
£1119	$1902	€1600	La gare de Menilmontant (61x73cm-24x29in) s. 27-Nov-3 Millon & Associes, Paris #212/R est:1200-1600
£1183	$2200	€1727	Montmartre under snowfall (46x38cm-18x15in) s. board. 3-Mar-4 Christie's, Rockefeller NY #61/R est:1500-2000
£1208	$2247	€1800	Rue de Montmartre (55x46cm-22x18in) s. isorel. 3-Mar-4 Tajan, Paris #79/R est:2000-3000
£1354	$2261	€1950	Maisons sous la neige (46x55cm-18x22in) s. isorel panel. 23-Oct-3 Credit Municipal, Paris #97 est:800-1000
£1538	$2615	€2200	Paris, la Porte des Lilas (66x81cm-26x32in) s. 27-Nov-3 Millon & Associes, Paris #207/R est:1000-1500
£1748	$2919	€2500	Maison (95x115cm-37x45in) s. 30-Jun-3 Artcurial Briest, Paris #750/R est:2500-3000
£1831	$3168	€2600	Le Pre Saint-Gervais (30x39cm-12x15in) s. i.verso panel. 10-Dec-3 Neret-Minet, Paris #54/R est:1200-1500
£1831	$3168	€2600	Le Pre Saint-Gervais (30x30cm-12x12in) s. i.verso panel. 10-Dec-3 Remi Ader, Paris #54/R est:1200-1500
£1987	$3636	€3000	Moulin a Montmartre (46x38cm-18x15in) s. isorel panel. 7-Apr-4 Piasa, Paris #103/R est:2000-3000
£3067	$5000	€4478	Maisons pres St Gervais (54x93cm-21x37in) s. 25-Sep-3 Christie's, Rockefeller NY #525/R est:6000-8000
£3147	$5255	€4500	Montmartre, scene de rue animee (45x37cm-18x15in) s. panel. 30-Jun-3 Artcurial Briest, Paris #749/R est:3000-4000
£4161	$7740	€6200	Rue de l'Abreuvoir (80x100cm-31x39in) s. panel. 3-Mar-4 Tajan, Paris #76/R est:6000-8000

QUMALUK, Levi (1919-) North American

Sculpture			
£1126	$1914	€1644	Hunter pulling a seal (15cm-6in) i. mottled dark soapstone. 3-Nov-3 Waddingtons, Toronto #651/R est:300-500 (C.D 2500)

QUOST, Ernest (1844-1931) French

£1467	$2640	€2200	Vase de fleurs (57x34cm-22x13in) 24-Apr-4 Hotel des Ventes de Vienne, Vienne #188
£2489	$4231	€3634	Vue de l'atelier Montmartre (111x130cm-44x51in) prov. 28-Nov-3 Zofingen, Switzerland #2662/R est:5500 (S.FR 5500)
£7000	$12600	€10500	Jardin fleuri (49x60cm-19x24in) 24-Apr-4 Hotel des Ventes de Vienne, Vienne #186
£9667	$17400	€14500	Panier de fruits (58x73cm-23x29in) 24-Apr-4 Hotel des Ventes de Vienne, Vienne #187

QUPPAPIK, Tikituk (1908-) North American
Sculpture
£901 $1532 €1315 Inuit woman (41cm-16in) marbled green soapstone. 3-Nov-3 Waddingtons, Toronto #93/R est:1000-1500 (C.D 2000)

RAACK-GEYER, Ruth Hildegard (1894-1975) German
Works on paper
£733 $1313 €1100 Geometric figure (74x49cm-29x19in) gouache on pencil prov. 14-May-4 Ketterer, Munich #412/R
£1333 $2387 €2000 Geometric composition (63x64cm-25x25in) gouache on pencil prov. 14-May-4 Ketterer, Munich #413/R est:1000-1500

RAADAL, Erik (1905-1941) Danish
£861 $1395 €1248 Landscape with country road (35x49cm-14x19in) init.d.35. 4-Aug-3 Rasmussen, Vejle #589/R (D.KR 9000)
Works on paper
£316 $591 €461 Self-portrait (21x20cm-8x8in) s.d.7 Juli 1943 pencil. 25-Feb-4 Kunsthallen, Copenhagen #191 (D.KR 3500)
£325 $608 €475 Figure composition (29x22cm-11x9in) study Indian ink pencil. 25-Feb-4 Kunsthallen, Copenhagen #192 (D.KR 3600)

RAADSIG, Peter (1806-1882) Danish
£280 $443 €406 Fisherman from Hornbaek (35x29cm-14x11in) init.d.1871. 2-Sep-3 Rasmussen, Copenhagen #1953/R (D.KR 3000)
£407 $729 €594 Danish summer landscape with farmers and hunters (33x47cm-13x19in) init.d.1868 s.verso prov. 10-May-4 Rasmussen, Vejle #109/R (D.KR 4500)
£642 $1149 €950 River landscape with forester and peasant woman (35x50cm-14x20in) s.d.1875 lit. 8-May-4 Schloss Ahlden, Ahlden #746/R
£945 $1635 €1380 From a Danish coast, summer (30x41cm-12x16in) init. 9-Dec-3 Rasmussen, Copenhagen #1477/R (D.KR 10000)
£4360 $6976 €6366 Summer's day in the fishing village with many figures (77x113cm-30x44in) s.d.1865. 22-Sep-3 Rasmussen, Vejle #238/R est:40000-60000 (D.KR 46000)

RAALTE, Marinus van (1872-1944) Dutch
£1342 $2483 €2000 Street scene (38x32cm-15x13in) s.verso board. 15-Mar-4 Sotheby's, Amsterdam #141/R est:800-1200

RAAPHORST, Cornelis (1875-1954) Dutch
£1986 $3316 €2800 Kittens playing (30x40cm-12x16in) s. 20-Oct-3 Glerum, Amsterdam #8/R est:3000-4000
£2000 $3580 €3000 Three young kittens on a cloth (23x29cm-9x11in) s. 11-May-4 Vendu Notarishuis, Rotterdam #39/R est:2000-2500
£4056 $6976 €5800 Kittens playing (51x69cm-20x27in) s. 8-Dec-3 Glerum, Amsterdam #54a/R est:3500-4500
£4195 $7216 €6000 Kittens at play (59x79cm-23x31in) s. 7-Dec-3 Sotheby's, Amsterdam #606/R
£4514 $7132 €6500 Fascinated felines (60x80cm-24x31in) s. 2-Sep-3 Christie's, Amsterdam #284/R est:6000-8000
£4706 $8000 €6871 Kittens at play (80x60cm-31x24in) s. 29-Oct-3 Christie's, Rockefeller NY #6/R est:15000-20000
£5592 $10289 €8500 Fascinated by fish (60x80cm-24x31in) s. 22-Jun-4 Christie's, Amsterdam #276/R est:6000-8000

RAATIKAINEN, Orvo (1914-2000) Finnish
£590 $986 €850 Winter landscape with river (52x74cm-20x29in) s. 23-Oct-3 Hagelstam, Helsinki #831
£805 $1482 €1200 Beach (85x55cm-33x22in) s.d.1972. 25-Mar-4 Hagelstam, Helsinki #816
£937 $1566 €1350 Boy fishing (70x50cm-28x20in) s.d.62. 26-Oct-3 Bukowskis, Helsinki #460/R
£1831 $2930 €2600 Boys fishing (70x55cm-28x22in) s.d.1970. 18-Sep-3 Hagelstam, Helsinki #798/R est:1200

RAAYMAKERS, Ronald (1949-) Dutch
£764 $1207 €1100 Spanish earthware (45x80cm-18x31in) s. 26-Apr-3 Auction Maastricht #85/R

RABA, Manuel (1928-1983) Spanish
Sculpture
£6081 $10703 €9000 Shape XXIX (120x105x35cm-47x41x14in) s.i.d.1973 verso wood exhib.lit. 18-May-4 Segre, Madrid #137/R est:9000
Works on paper
£423 $739 €600 Untitled (21x28cm-8x11in) s. gouache. 16-Dec-3 Segre, Madrid #216/R

RABARAMA (1969-) Italian
£1733 $3189 €2600 Transparency (66x42cm-26x17in) s.d.1997. 12-Jun-4 Meeting Art, Vercelli #834/R est:2000

RABAS, Vaclav (1885-1954) Czechoslovakian
£438 $727 €639 Forest interior (36x43cm-14x17in) s.d.33 board. 4-Oct-3 Dorotheum, Prague #92/R est:20000-30000 (C.KR 20000)
£1094 $1817 €1597 Still life with violin (71x94cm-28x37in) exhib. 4-Oct-3 Dorotheum, Prague #134/R est:50000-80000 (C.KR 50000)
£1687 $2970 €2531 Wild flowers (52x32cm-20x13in) s.d.43 s.i.verso. 22-May-4 Dorotheum, Prague #137/R est:70000-110000 (C.KR 80000)

RABASCALL, Joan (1935-) French
£315 $535 €450 Femme (16x24cm-6x9in) i.d.1965 verso oil photograph. 23-Nov-3 Cornette de St.Cyr, Paris #287
£315 $535 €450 Femme (16x24cm-6x9in) s.i.d.1966 verso oil report photographique prov. 23-Nov-3 Cornette de St.Cyr, Paris #288

RABE, Byron (20th C) Guatemalan?
Works on paper
£448 $770 €654 Ceremony (95x70cm-37x28in) mixed media exec.2002. 5-Dec-3 Arte Maya, Guatemala #74

RABE, Edmund Friedrich Theodor (attrib) (1815-1902) German
£625 $987 €900 Dragoon on horseback (27x22cm-11x9in) mono.verso board. 5-Sep-3 Wendl, Rudolstadt #3569/R

RABE, Otto (1841-?) German
£1049 $1752 €1500 Deer by woodland pond (128x104cm-50x41in) s. 28-Jun-3 Dannenberg, Berlin #752/R est:1200

RABERABA, Henoch (1914-1975) Australian
Works on paper
£255 $456 €372 Untitled (27x38cm-11x15in) s. W/C. 25-May-4 Lawson Menzies, Sydney #112/R (A.D 650)

RABERABA, Herbert (1916-1975) Australian
Works on paper
£275 $491 €402 Central Australian landscape (37x27cm-15x11in) s. W/C. 25-May-4 Lawson Menzies, Sydney #114/R (A.D 700)
£813 $1455 €1187 Ghost gums (35x51cm-14x20in) s. W/C. 10-May-4 Joel, Victoria #286/R est:800-1200 (A.D 2000)

RABES, Max (1868-1944) Austrian
£333 $543 €480 Still life with peppercorns (45x59cm-18x23in) s. i. verso. 25-Sep-3 Neumeister, Munich #2849
£769 $1308 €1100 The sad clown (92x78cm-36x31in) s. lit. 28-Nov-3 Schloss Ahlden, Ahlden #1577/R
£1181 $1972 €1700 Schloss Sanssouci in Potsdam (40x56cm-16x22in) s. lit. 25-Oct-3 Bergmann, Erlangen #960/R
£1200 $2040 €1800 Portrait of Russian soldier (56x44cm-22x17in) s.i. 25-Nov-3 Christie's, London #183/R est:1400-1600
£1200 $2040 €1800 Portrait of Russian soldier (56x44cm-22x17in) s.i. 25-Nov-3 Christie's, London #184/R est:1400-1600
£3147 $5255 €4500 Taormina (36x26cm-14x10in) i. 11-Oct-3 Dr Fritz Nagel, Leipzig #3914/R est:300
£3497 $5944 €5000 Cafe in old Cairo (32x40cm-13x16in) s.d.1891. 20-Nov-3 Van Ham, Cologne #1809/R est:5500
£6250 $10625 €9000 Telling a fairy tale (126x176cm-50x69in) s. s.i.stretcher. 28-Oct-3 Christie's, Amsterdam #190/R est:10000-15000

RABIER, Benjamin Armand (1869-1939) French
Works on paper
£294 $490 €420 Chat et araignee (24x19cm-9x7in) s. gouache. 6-Oct-3 Claude Aguttes, Neuilly #513/R
£315 $526 €450 Apparences (32x24cm-13x9in) s. Chinese ink. 6-Oct-3 Claude Aguttes, Neuilly #504/R
£315 $526 €450 Chocolat ou le chimpanze (32x23cm-13x9in) Chinese ink. 6-Oct-3 Claude Aguttes, Neuilly #519
£315 $526 €450 Aveugle et paralytique (33x23cm-13x9in) Chinese ink htd crayon. 6-Oct-3 Claude Aguttes, Neuilly #520b
£322 $537 €460 Zut ! On va encore dire que c'est moi (50x33cm-20x13in) Chinese ink dr. 6-Oct-3 Claude Aguttes, Neuilly #505/R
£329 $549 €470 Chocolat ou le chimpanze (32x23cm-13x9in) Chinese ink. 6-Oct-3 Claude Aguttes, Neuilly #517/R
£350 $584 €500 Force et Intelligence (32x24cm-13x9in) s. Chinese ink. 6-Oct-3 Claude Aguttes, Neuilly #499/R
£406 $677 €580 Natte de lili (32x24cm-13x9in) s. Chinese ink. 6-Oct-3 Claude Aguttes, Neuilly #509/R
£420 $701 €600 Sauterelle (27x19cm-11x7in) s. Chinese ink wash. 6-Oct-3 Claude Aguttes, Neuilly #520a
£490 $817 €700 Renard qui preche (33x23cm-13x9in) Chinese ink. 6-Oct-3 Claude Aguttes, Neuilly #515/R
£503 $841 €720 Elle s'appelle seulement la vache (27x18cm-11x7in) s.i. gouache. 6-Oct-3 Claude Aguttes, Neuilly #500/R
£559 $934 €800 Celebrite Parisienne (34x24cm-13x9in) i. Chinese ink htd crayon. 6-Oct-3 Claude Aguttes, Neuilly #512/R
£616 $1048 €900 Preparatifs (35x28cm-14x11in) s.i. pen ink W/C. 6-Nov-3 Tajan, Paris #241
£769 $1285 €1100 Sanglier, ecureuil et escargot (22x15cm-9x6in) s. W/C. 6-Oct-3 Claude Aguttes, Neuilly #514/R
£1399 $2336 €2000 Hercule galant (36x23cm-14x9in) s. Chinese ink. 6-Oct-3 Claude Aguttes, Neuilly #498/R est:250
£1888 $3153 €2700 Gedeon s'endormit et reva (32x25cm-13x10in) s. Chinese ink dr. 6-Oct-3 Claude Aguttes, Neuilly #510/R est:600

RABIN, Sam (1903-) British
£1000 $1820 €1460 Knockout (66x82cm-26x32in) s. board. 15-Jun-4 Bonhams, Knightsbridge #97/R est:1000-1500

RABINE, Oskar (1928-) Russian
£2516 $4000 €3673 Church through a window (69x89cm-27x35in) s.i.d.64 verso. 9-Sep-3 Arthur James, Florida #105
£3830 $6051 €5400 Sp. (96x146cm-38x57in) s.d.1989. 24-Jul-3 Claude Boisgirard, Paris #57/R
£5500 $9845 €8030 Self portrait (50x65cm-20x26in) painted c.1960. 26-May-4 Sotheby's, Olympia #468/R est:4000-6000
£5503 $10181 €8200 Marche Parisien avec deux chatons (116x81cm-46x32in) s.d.1988 oil collage. 15-Mar-4 Claude Boisgirard, Paris #98 est:6000-8000
£13000 $23270 €18980 Cross (90x110cm-35x43in) s.i.d.64 verso prov. 26-May-4 Sotheby's, London #312/R est:8000-12000

Works on paper			
£1258	$2290	€1900	La barricade (50x65cm-20x26in) s.d.1980 india ink W/C collage. 16-Jun-4 Claude Boisgirard, Paris #139/R est:800-1000
£5556	$10000	€8112	Self portrait (60x81cm-24x32in) s.d.1987 mixed media on canvas. 23-Apr-4 Sotheby's, New York #125/R est:10000-15000

RABINOWITCH, David (1943-) Canadian

£292	$487	€420	Sans titre (73x52cm-29x20in) mono.d.1971 acrylic. 25-Oct-3 Cornette de St.Cyr, Paris #449/R
£313	$522	€450	Sans titre (73x56cm-29x22in) mono. acrylic. 25-Oct-3 Cornette de St.Cyr, Paris #450
Sculpture			
£703	$1300	€1026	Sided mass (15x30x25cm-6x12x10in) steel exec 1968 prov.lit. 12-Feb-4 Sotheby's, New York #239/R est:2000-3000
£1528	$2551	€2200	Sculpture en six parties. prov. 25-Oct-3 Cornette de St.Cyr, Paris #454 est:10000-15000

RABIOGLIO, Domenico (1857-1903) Italian

£567	$948	€800	Landscape near Canavese (20x30cm-8x12in) s. board. 20-Oct-3 Sant Agostino, Torino #264/R
£638	$1066	€900	Along the river (16x21cm-6x8in) s. 20-Oct-3 Sant Agostino, Torino #263/R

RABUS, Carl (1898-1974) German

Works on paper			
£379	$633	€550	Fishing boats on the beach (49x63cm-19x25in) s.d.1949 W/C ink brush. 13-Nov-3 Neumeister, Munich #437/R

RABUZIN, Ivan (1919-) Yugoslavian

£1293	$2315	€1888	Landscape with three mountains (50x73cm-20x29in) s.d.1967 prov. 12-May-4 Dobiaschofsky, Bern #889/R est:6000 (S.FR 3000)
£1357	$2308	€1981	Landscape with three flowers (47x58cm-19x23in) s.d.1974. 19-Nov-3 Fischer, Luzern #1204/R est:2500-3000 (S.FR 3000)
£1800	$3276	€2628	Village called Big Flower (66x89cm-26x35in) mono.d.1960. 3-Feb-4 Gorringes, Bexhill #969/R est:2000-3000
£2000	$3580	€2920	Then village called big flower (68x91cm-27x36in) mono.d.1960. 26-May-4 Sotheby's, Olympia #359/R est:2000-3000

RABY, Edward (?) ?

£725	$1167	€1059	Still life (36x55cm-14x22in) s. 20-Aug-3 Dunbar Sloane, Auckland #96/R est:2000-3000 (NZ.D 2000)

RACH, Louis (1853-?) German

£367	$660	€550	Peasant kitchen with still life of vegetables (66x80cm-26x31in) s.i. 26-Apr-4 Rieber, Stuttgart #988/R

RACIM, Mohammed (1896-1975) Algerian

Works on paper			
£3467	$6379	€5200	Le roi Khosrow decouvre Chirin se baignant (18x13cm-7x5in) s.i. gouache htd gold exhib. 9-Jun-4 Oger, Dumont, Paris #89/R est:5000-6000

RACITI, Mario (1934-) Italian

£1000	$1840	€1500	Presence-absence (70x100cm-28x39in) s.i.verso painted 1972. 12-Jun-4 Meeting Art, Vercelli #728/R est:1000
£1667	$3067	€2500	Journey (50x70cm-20x28in) s.i.d.1968 verso oil mixed media. 8-Jun-4 Finarte Semenzato, Milan #465/R est:2500-3000

RACKHAM, Arthur (1867-1939) British

£12000	$21840	€17520	Song of the lark (36x52cm-14x20in) s. W/C. 1-Jul-4 Sotheby's, London #289/R est:12000-18000
Works on paper			
£580	$945	€841	Rural lane (24x18cm-9x7in) s.d.1889 W/C. 23-Sep-3 Bonhams, Knightsbridge #59/R
£580	$1003	€847	Two fantastical creatures dancing around a tree (11x12cm-4x5in) pencil ink. 11-Dec-3 Sotheby's, London #289/R
£2200	$3806	€3212	So the lazy girl went home, but she was quite covered with pitch (21x40cm-8x16in) s.d.1900 ink two sheets together prov. 11-Dec-3 Sotheby's, London #244/R est:1500-2000
£2400	$4152	€3504	See, saw, Margery Daw (21x27cm-8x11in) s. ink W/C. 11-Dec-3 Sotheby's, London #260a/R est:2500-3500
£2600	$4498	€3796	Before long the witch came by riding at a furious pace on a tom cat (16x17cm-6x7in) s.d.1900 ink W/C. 11-Dec-3 Sotheby's, London #243/R est:3000-4000
£3892	$6500	€5682	Standing executioner with axe wearing Ace of Clubs (10x10cm-4x4in) init. pen ink W/C gouache. 15-Nov-3 Illustration House, New York #77/R est:7000-9000
£4500	$7785	€6570	Young man presenting a bouquet to a girl standing in a drawing room (30x26cm-12x10in) s. ink W/C prov. 11-Dec-3 Sotheby's, London #293/R est:5000-7000
£5500	$9515	€8030	The son made a circle, and his father and he took their places within it (21x16cm-8x6in) s.d.1909 ink W/C. 11-Dec-3 Sotheby's, London #246/R est:6000-8000
£6111	$11000	€8922	The song of the lark (36x51cm-14x20in) s. i.verso W/C prov. 20-Jan-4 Arthur James, Florida #82
£8500	$14705	€12410	They were ruled by an old squaw spirit who hung up the new moons (36x26cm-14x10in) s.d.1904 ink W/C. 11-Dec-3 Sotheby's, London #248/R est:9000-12000
£8500	$14705	€12410	This healing and honeyed draught of mead deign to accept from me (25x18cm-10x7in) s.d.1910 ink W/C. 11-Dec-3 Sotheby's, London #270/R est:4000-6000
£8800	$16016	€12848	Crowned merman (29x19cm-11x7in) W/C pencil pen ink. 1-Jul-4 Sotheby's, London #285/R est:3000-5000
£9500	$16435	€13870	Two children in the basket of a balloon with a rook and other figures (30x24cm-12x9in) s.d.1896 ink W/C prov. 11-Dec-3 Sotheby's, London #242/R est:8000-12000
£10000	$17000	€14600	Companions (32x27cm-13x11in) s.d.05 pen ink W/C exhib. 4-Nov-3 Bonhams, New Bond Street #153/R est:3000-5000
£10000	$17300	€14600	Cesarino and the dragon (25x19cm-10x7in) s.d.1916 ink W/C prov. 11-Dec-3 Sotheby's, London #277/R est:8000-10000
£14000	$24220	€20440	Fairies disguising themselves as flowers (21x14cm-8x6in) s.d.06 ink W/C prov. 11-Dec-3 Sotheby's, London #250/R est:15000-20000
£14000	$24220	€20440	How Beaumains defeated the Red Knight (32x25cm-13x10in) s. ink W/C prov.exhib. 11-Dec-3 Sotheby's, London #279/R est:8000-12000
£14000	$24220	€20440	Peepshow (33x35cm-13x14in) ink W/C. 11-Dec-3 Sotheby's, London #304/R est:15000-20000
£15000	$27300	€21900	Rip van Winkle (18x26cm-7x10in) s.d.05 pen ink W/C. 1-Jul-4 Sotheby's, London #286/R est:15000-20000
£16000	$27680	€23360	When her Majesty wants to know the time (24x18cm-9x7in) s.d.06 ink W/C prov. 11-Dec-3 Sotheby's, London #252/R est:10000-15000
£17000	$29410	€24820	They harvested for Ahmed's princely hand in gardens of old (26x23cm-10x9in) s. ink W/C prov.exhib. 11-Dec-3 Sotheby's, London #292/R est:6000-8000
£19000	$34580	€27740	Alice and the Cheshire cat (25x18cm-10x7in) s.d.07 pen ink htd white. 1-Jul-4 Sotheby's, London #287/R est:10000-15000
£23000	$41860	€33580	Jack of Hearts (24x16cm-9x6in) s.d.1907 pen ink W/C pencil. 1-Jul-4 Sotheby's, London #288/R est:12000-18000
£26000	$44980	€37960	Mutually relieving one another they clambered up a narrow gully (25x18cm-10x7in) s.d.04 ink W/C prov. 11-Dec-3 Sotheby's, London #249/R est:15000-20000
£26000	$44980	€37960	Hey, up the chimney lass, hey after you (33x22cm-13x9in) s.d.07 ink W/C. 11-Dec-3 Sotheby's, London #258/R est:8000-10000
£30000	$51900	€43800	Sleeping Beauty (26x18cm-10x7in) s. ink W/C prov.exhib. 11-Dec-3 Sotheby's, London #278/R est:8000-10000
£35000	$60550	€51100	So up to the house top the coursers they flew (19x33cm-7x13in) s. ink W/C. 11-Dec-3 Sotheby's, London #299/R est:6000-8000
£42000	$72660	€61320	Come, now a roundel (27x18cm-11x7in) s.d.08 ink W/C. 11-Dec-3 Sotheby's, London #261/R est:15000-20000
£70000	$121100	€102200	Fairies are exquisite dancers (49x38cm-19x15in) s.d.06 ink W/C. 11-Dec-3 Sotheby's, London #251/R est:20000-25000

RACKHAM, W Leslie (1864-1944) British

£260	$478	€380	Ranworth (9x15cm-4x6in) s.i. 11-Jun-4 Keys, Aylsham #548
Works on paper			
£300	$501	€438	Ranworth (18x25cm-7x10in) s.i. W/C. 17-Oct-3 Keys, Aylsham #625

RACKLIFFE, Howard (1917-) American

£615	$1100	€898	Maine coast (76x38cm-30x15in) s. oil paperboard. 14-May-4 Skinner, Boston #271/R

RACKWITSZ, Pieter (1892-1968) Dutch

£403	$745	€600	Farm near wooded landscape (26x41cm-10x16in) s.d.2 Sep 13. 15-Mar-4 Sotheby's, Amsterdam #353a

RACLE, Paul (1932-) Swiss

£271	$462	€396	Composition (73x91cm-29x36in) s. 25-Nov-3 Germann, Zurich #875 (S.FR 600)
£271	$462	€396	Surreal composition (99x58cm-39x23in) s.d.1968 board. 25-Nov-3 Germann, Zurich #869 (S.FR 600)
£306	$562	€447	Composition (54x73cm-21x29in) s.d.1976. 8-Jun-4 Germann, Zurich #857 (S.FR 700)
£371	$683	€542	Compositio (68x50cm-27x20in) ns.d.1977. 8-Jun-4 Germann, Zurich #858 (S.FR 850)
£588	$1000	€858	Untitled (57x57cm-22x22in) s.d.1976 s.i. verso panel. 25-Nov-3 Germann, Zurich #870 (S.FR 1300)

RACOFF, Rotislaw (1904-) Russian

£486	$900	€710	Au bord de la Seine (33x25cm-13x10in) s.d.53 s.d.55 i. verso masonite two prov. 15-Jul-4 Sotheby's, New York #115/R
£500	$800	€730	City scene with bridge and lights (36x28cm-14x11in) s.d.53 masonite board. 20-Sep-3 Bunte, Elgin #1252
£625	$1000	€913	Docked boats with fishermen (36x28cm-14x11in) s.d.51 masonite board. 20-Sep-3 Bunte, Elgin #1251

RADA, Vlastimil (1895-1962) Czechoslovakian

Works on paper			
£288	$536	€420	Dialogue (24x18cm-9x7in) s. ink W/C. 6-Mar-4 Dorotheum, Prague #253 est:8000-12000 (C.KR 14000)
£746	$1269	€1089	Winter in a village (27x39cm-11x15in) s. ink W/C. 29-Nov-3 Dorotheum, Prague #163/R est:10000-15000 (C.KR 34000)

RADCLIFFE, W Radcliffe (fl.1881-1895) British

£268	$488	€391	Flock. d.1889. 1-Jul-4 Joel, Victoria #341/R (A.D 700)

RADDI, G (19th C) Italian

Sculpture			
£1400	$2506	€2100	Bon vivant (88cm-35in) s.i. pat wood. 16-May-4 Joron-Derem, Paris #182/R est:1500-2500

RADECKER, Antoon (1887-1960) Dutch

Sculpture			
£1304	$2139	€1800	Head (30cm-12in) i.d.24 green pat bronze. 27-May-3 Sotheby's, Amsterdam #371/R est:1800-2500

RADECKER, John (1885-1956) Dutch

Sculpture			
£30000	$55200	€45000	Monnik (30cm-12in) init.d.1924 brown pat. bronze one of six exhib.lit. 9-Jun-4 Christie's, Amsterdam #283/R est:45000-55000

RADECKER, Max (1914-) Dutch

Works on paper

£312 $509 €450 Mermaid (60x45cm-24x18in) s.d.56 gouache. 29-Sep-3 Sotheby's, Amsterdam #290

RADEMACHER, N G (1812-1885) Danish

£303 $485 €442 Viborggaard near Mariager Fjord (21x34cm-8x13in) s.d.1864. 22-Sep-3 Rasmussen, Vejle #402/R (D.KR 3200)

RADEMAKER, Abraham (1675-1735) Dutch

£6897 $11517 €10000 Rocky landscape (19x13cm-7x5in) tempera paper. 12-Nov-3 Sotheby's, Milan #102/R est:4000-6000

Works on paper

£340 $609 €500 Vue de seventer (12x19cm-5x7in) pen brown ink brown grey wash. 17-Mar-4 Tajan, Paris #20
£476 $852 €700 Vue d'Iselmonde (11x20cm-4x8in) s. pen brown ink brown wash. 17-Mar-4 Tajan, Paris #21
£514 $873 €750 Arcadian landscape with buildings, ruins and figures (17x23cm-7x9in) s. pen brown ink wash over black chk. 4-Nov-3 Sotheby's, Amsterdam #105/R
£642 $1130 €950 View of Mydrecht (16x28cm-6x11in) i.verso pen brown ink wash. 19-May-4 Sotheby's, Amsterdam #84/R
£1342 $2470 €2000 Depart en chaise a porteur d'une person de qualite (15x8cm-6x3in) s. gouache. 26-Mar-4 Pierre Berge, Paris #8 est:2500-3000

RADEMAKER, Abraham (attrib) (1675-1735) Dutch

Works on paper

£1250 $2300 €1900 River landscape with harbour (18x27cm-7x11in) pen gouache. 24-Jun-4 Dr Fritz Nagel, Stuttgart #505/R est:500

RADEN, Hermanus Willem van (1794-1846) Dutch

Works on paper

£629 $1051 €900 Flower still life (27x24cm-11x9in) s.indis.d. W/C sold with W/C by another hand. 30-Jun-3 Sotheby's, Amsterdam #43/R

RADERMACHER, Matthias (1804-1890) German

£1818 $3091 €2600 Portraits of Peter Theodor Sachse and his wife (59x48cm-23x19in) one s.d.1836 two. 22-Nov-3 Arnold, Frankfurt #613/R est:1600

RADERSCHEIDT, Anton (1892-1970) German

£455 $773 €650 Memorial in Dusseldorf (65x50cm-26x20in) s.d.54 oil tempera board. 26-Nov-3 Lempertz, Koln #938/R
£972 $1624 €1400 St Severin (55x48cm-22x19in) s.d. board. 24-Oct-3 Ketterer, Hamburg #512/R
£1000 $1790 €1500 Cornicella - Isola procida (56x39cm-22x15in) s.d. 15-May-4 Van Ham, Cologne #859/R est:2000
£4545 $7818 €6500 Figures (100x80cm-39x31in) board painted 1957. 4-Dec-3 Van Ham, Cologne #405/R est:6500
£10140 $17441 €14500 Portrait of a female (80x60cm-31x24in) mono.d.1930 exhib.lit. 4-Dec-3 Van Ham, Cologne #403/R est:14500

RADFORD, James (fl.1841-1859) British

£1116 $1920 €1629 Coastal scene, Boulogne (102x143cm-40x56in) s.i.verso on stretcher exhib. 2-Dec-3 Ritchie, Toronto #44/R est:6000-8000 (C.D 2500)

RADICE, Giovanni (?) Italian

£1014 $1664 €1400 Old houses (60x50cm-24x20in) s. 27-May-3 Il Ponte, Milan #880

RADICE, Mario (1900-1987) Italian

£667 $1227 €1000 Portrait of Marta Abba (42x38cm-17x15in) s. cardboard on canvas. 8-Jun-4 Finarte Semenzato, Milan #225/R est:500-600
£10738 $19221 €16000 Secret portrait 75 (66x66cm-26x26in) s. i.on stretcher prov.exhib. 25-May-4 Sotheby's, Milan #267/R est:15000-20000

Works on paper

£769 $1308 €1100 Reclining figure (10x28cm-4x11in) s. gouache. 20-Nov-3 Finarte Semenzato, Milan #175/R est:1000-1500
£1007 $1802 €1500 A.N.F.G. R.E.T.6 (17x14cm-7x6in) s. pencil felt-tip pen exec.1973 two prov. 25-May-4 Sotheby's, Milan #97/R est:1500
£2448 $4161 €3500 Composition RS (37x32cm-15x13in) s. mixed media card. 20-Nov-3 Finarte Semenzato, Milan #176/R est:3500-4000

RADIMSKY, Vaclav (1867-1946) Czechoslovakian

£1687 $2970 €2531 Landscape with a pond (40x50cm-16x20in) s. cardboard. 22-May-4 Dorotheum, Prague #90/R est:80000-120000 (C.KR 80000)
£2109 $3712 €3164 Landscape with a lake (50x61cm-20x24in) s. 22-May-4 Dorotheum, Prague #118/R est:100000-150000 (C.KR 100000)
£2883 $5362 €4209 Dead arm of the Elbe River (67x94cm-26x37in) s. board. 6-Mar-4 Dorotheum, Prague #66/R est:100000-150000 (C.KR 140000)
£3356 $6208 €5000 River landscape (66x95cm-26x37in) s. board on masonite. 9-Mar-4 Dorotheum, Vienna #7/R est:5500-7500
£3797 $6682 €5696 Cottage near water (66x80cm-26x31in) s. cardboard. 22-May-4 Dorotheum, Prague #82/R est:150000-250000 (C.KR 180000)
£4815 $7993 €7030 Bay (71x96cm-28x38in) s. board. 4-Oct-3 Dorotheum, Prague #29/R est:150000-220000 (C.KR 220000)
£5000 $8500 €7300 Extensive summer landscape with trees by a river with waterlilies in the foreground (65x93cm-26x37in) s. 19-Nov-3 Bonhams & Butterfields, San Francisco #86/R
£6471 $11000 €9448 River landscape in summer (74x100cm-29x39in) s. 19-Nov-3 Bonhams & Butterfields, San Francisco #87/R
£7059 $12000 €10306 River landscape in spring (81x100cm-32x39in) s. pair. 19-Nov-3 Bonhams & Butterfields, San Francisco #84/R
£7593 $13364 €11390 Summer landscape with a brook (60x81cm-24x32in) s.d.1904. 22-May-4 Dorotheum, Prague #56/R est:180000-300000 (C.KR 360000)
£7647 $13000 €11165 River landscape (74x100cm-29x39in) s. set of three. 19-Nov-3 Bonhams & Butterfields, San Francisco #85/R

RADITZ, Otto (20th C) ?

Works on paper

£524 $892 €750 Composition (29x22cm-11x9in) s.d.1928 collage gouache prov. 23-Nov-3 Cornette de St.Cyr, Paris #289/R

RADLER, Josef Karl (19/20th C) Austrian

Works on paper

£1342 $2403 €2000 Composition (30x20cm-12x8in) i. Indian ink W/C gouache prov. 25-May-4 Dorotheum, Vienna #268/R est:2200-3000
£1342 $2403 €2000 Composition (30x20cm-12x8in) i. Indian ink W/C gouache prov. 25-May-4 Dorotheum, Vienna #269/R est:2200-3000

RADZIWILL, Elise (1803-1833) Polish

Works on paper

£267 $480 €400 Salon of the Palais Radziwill (22x39cm-9x15in) W/C pencil. 24-Apr-4 Reiss & Sohn, Konigstein #5539

RADZIWILL, Franz (1895-1983) German

£10417 $16979 €15000 Still life (35x27cm-14x11in) s.d.1939 canvas on panel prov. 27-Sep-3 Dr Fritz Nagel, Stuttgart #9610/R est:22000
£13333 $24533 €20000 Interior cellar scene (40x46cm-16x18in) s. i.verso canvas on panel painted 1964 prov.exhib. 12-Jun-4 Villa Grisebach, Berlin #276/R est:15000-20000
£20000 $36800 €30000 Deserted houses (50x67cm-20x26in) s. i.verso canvas on panel painted 1963 prov.exhib. 12-Jun-4 Villa Grisebach, Berlin #277/R est:25000-35000
£33333 $61333 €50000 Kitchen in the old house in Dangast (79x84cm-31x33in) mono. double-sided prov.exhib. 11-Jun-4 Villa Grisebach, Berlin #42/R est:50000-60000
£40000 $73600 €60000 The landing of the glider (89x119cm-35x47in) s. i.verso canvas on panel prov.exhib. 11-Jun-4 Villa Grisebach, Berlin #47/R est:40000-60000

Works on paper

£313 $509 €450 Near Varel (11x20cm-4x8in) mono. pencil. 26-Sep-3 Bolland & Marotz, Bremen #364/R
£1259 $2140 €1800 Harbour (37x58cm-15x23in) s. pencil W/C bodycol. 29-Nov-3 Villa Grisebach, Berlin #657/R est:2200-2400
£2000 $3580 €3000 Portrait of bearded man (48x37cm-19x15in) mono. W/C on pencil. 15-May-4 Dr Sturies, Dusseldorf #153/R
£3597 $5899 €5000 Flying boat over Dangast harbour (20x37cm-8x15in) s.d. col chk pencil. 4-Jun-3 Ketterer, Hamburg #796/R est:6000-8000
£4000 $7360 €6000 Portrait of Otto Muller (51x40cm-20x16in) mono. W/C exhib. 1923 prov.exhib. 12-Jun-4 Villa Grisebach, Berlin #284/R est:7000-9000
£4861 $8118 €7000 Still life (35x26cm-14x10in) mono. W/C. 24-Oct-3 Ketterer, Hamburg #513/R est:7000-9000

RAE, Barbara (1943-) British

Works on paper

£340 $626 €496 Abstract buildings (20x20cm-8x8in) s. pencil mixed media. 29-Mar-4 Thomson Roddick & Medcalf, Edinburgh #262
£400 $668 €584 Fields at Pompaneira (33x37cm-13x15in) s. mixed media collage. 16-Oct-3 Bonhams, Edinburgh #66
£450 $851 €657 Evening, San Stefano (21x27cm-8x11in) s.i. W/C. 19-Feb-4 Lyon & Turnbull, Edinburgh #34
£550 $919 €803 Lammermoor - Gold field (28x33cm-11x13in) s. mixed media. 16-Oct-3 Lyon & Turnbull, Edinburgh #120
£600 $1104 €876 Summer isles (44x61cm-17x24in) s. mixed media. 10-Jun-4 Lyon & Turnbull, Edinburgh #48
£780 $1232 €1139 Noon cypresses, Tuscany (27x34cm-11x13in) s. mixed media collage exhib. 6-Sep-3 Shapes, Edinburgh #311
£2000 $3140 €2900 North Bridge, Edinburgh (57x82cm-22x32in) s. gouache. 27-Aug-3 Sotheby's, London #1163/R est:2000-3000
£2800 $5208 €4088 Istan road (80x107cm-31x42in) mixed media paper on board executed 1990 prov. 4-Mar-4 Christie's, Kensington #242/R est:3000-5000

RAE, Iso (fl.1880-1920) Australian

£345 $538 €500 Portrait of a lady (64x53cm-25x21in) s. 1-Aug-2 Joel, Victoria #302 est:1000-1500 (A.D 1000)

RAE, Jude (20th C) New Zealander?

£786 $1422 €1148 Blue china tea in fuser (55x60cm-22x24in) painted c.1996. 30-Mar-4 Peter Webb, Auckland #5/R est:2000-3000 (NZ.D 2200)

RAEBURN, Agnes (?-1955) British

£350 $662 €511 Old market cross, Alston (13x18cm-5x7in) s. panel. 19-Feb-4 Lyon & Turnbull, Edinburgh #59
£1300 $2379 €1898 Summer flowers (37x45cm-15x18in) s. panel. 8-Apr-4 Bonhams, Edinburgh #137 est:300-500

Works on paper

£250 $418 €365 View of cottages (28x36cm-11x14in) s. W/C. 10-Jul-3 Gorringes, Worthing #777

RAEBURN, Sir Henry (1756-1823) British

£640 $1100 €934 Portrait of a lady (76x61cm-30x24in) 7-Dec-3 Susanin's, Chicago #6015/R
£659 $1200 €962 Portrait of a gentleman (76x63cm-30x25in) prov. 29-Jun-4 Sotheby's, New York #50/R est:5000-7000
£5500 $10120 €8030 Portrait of Professor George Joseph Bell (74x61cm-29x24in) prov.exhib.lit. 26-Mar-4 Sotheby's, London #30/R est:6000-8000
£13000 $24310 €18980 Half length portrait of Mr Roberston (75x62cm-30x24in) prov.lit. 21-Jul-4 Lyon & Turnbull, Edinburgh #140/R est:3000-5000
£13966 $25000 €20390 Portrait of officer (76x63cm-30x25in) 27-May-4 Sotheby's, New York #212/R est:12000-18000

£18000 $33120 €26280 Portrait of right Hon, Robert Blair of Avontoun, seated in a black suit against a red curtain (90x70cm-35x28in) prov. 11-Jun-4 Christie's, London #23/R est:15000-20000
£36000 $65520 €52560 Portrait of Alexander Keith of Ravelston Midlothian (240x148cm-94x58in) prov.exhib.lit. 1-Jul-4 Sotheby's, London #125/R est:40000-60000
Works on paper
£3000 $5100 €4380 Portrait of James Paterson. Portrait of Mrs James Paterson (28x21cm-11x8in) pastel on vellum oval prov.exhib.lit. 27-Nov-3 Sotheby's, London #214/R est:6000-8000

RAEBURN, Sir Henry (attrib) (1756-1823) British
£542 $900 €791 Portrait of a gentleman, formerly identified as Henry MacKenzie (76x63cm-30x25in) 30-Sep-3 Christie's, Rockefeller NY #342/R
£1172 $2191 €1758 Portrait of Archibald Craufuird of Ardmilian. 20-Jul-4 Goodman, Sydney #87/R est:3000-5000 (A.D 3000)
£6145 $11000 €10318 Portrait of a gentleman (76x64cm-30x25in) 20-Mar-4 Pook & Pook, Downington #587/R est:3000-5000
Works on paper
£3846 $6423 €5500 Portrait de James et Madame James Peterson (31x24cm-12x9in) pastel oval pair prov.exhib.lit. 27-Jun-3 Millon & Associes, Paris #26/R est:3000-4000

RAEBURN, Sir Henry (circle) (1756-1823) British
£3352 $6000 €4894 Portrait of gentleman (92x71cm-36x28in) 27-May-4 Sotheby's, New York #268/R est:6000-8000
£7500 $13950 €10950 Double portrait of two boys in red suits, in a landscape (76x63cm-30x25in) 4-Mar-4 Christie's, Kensington #16/R est:5000-7000

RAEDECKER, Michael (1963-) American
£27607 $45000 €40306 Action (61x76cm-24x30in) s.d.1988 stretcher acrylic thread linen prov. 23-Sep-3 Christie's, Rockefeller NY #82/R est:15000-20000
£55000 $101200 €80300 Blind (91x274cm-36x108in) acrylic thread on canvas painted 1998 prov. 23-Jun-4 Sotheby's, London #37/R est:35000-45000
£55866 $100000 €81564 Outake (132x186cm-52x73in) s.i.d.1999 overlap acrylic thread prov.exhib. 13-May-4 Sotheby's, New York #313/R est:50000-70000

RAETZ, Markus (1941-) Swiss
Sculpture
£2262 $3778 €3303 Untitled (97x106x18cm-38x42x7in) s.d.1967 verso painted acrylic. 24-Jun-3 Germann, Zurich #19/R est:6000-9000 (S.FR 5000)
Works on paper
£2783 $4508 €4063 Mouth painting (16x21cm-6x8in) mono.i.d.9.VI.74/3 Indian ink brush two in one frame prov. 24-May-3 Burkhard, Luzern #62/R est:6000-8000 (S.FR 5900)
£5660 $9170 €8264 Going (62x90cm-24x35in) mono.d.77 pencil W/C lit.prov. 24-May-3 Burkhard, Luzern #64/R est:12000-16000 (S.FR 12000)

RAFAEL, Viktor (1900-1981) Hungarian
£3425 $6200 €5001 Sitting boy (80x70cm-31x28in) 16-Apr-4 Mu Terem Galeria, Budapest #185/R (H.F 1300000)

RAFFAEL, Joseph (1933-) American
£1000 $1700 €1460 Bright white lily (61x61cm-24x24in) oil on linen prov.exhib. 9-Nov-3 Bonhams & Butterfields, Los Angeles #4035/R

RAFFAELE, Frigerio (1875-?) ?
£233 $375 €340 Two monks cooking in an interior scene (28x36cm-11x14in) s. painted c.1915. 22-Feb-3 Bunte, Elgin #1266

RAFFAELLI, Jean François (1850-1924) French
£857 $1371 €1243 Seine shore in Paris (23x30cm-9x12in) s. panel. 15-May-3 Stuker, Bern #1449/R (S.FR 1800)
£950 $1587 €1387 On the beach (54x68cm-21x27in) bears sig. 21-Oct-3 Bonhams, Knightsbridge #35/R
£1200 $2148 €1800 Portrait du President Bartou (32x23cm-13x9in) cardboard. 16-May-4 Osenat, Fontainebleau #102/R est:1500-2000
£2747 $5000 €4011 Figure on a shaded path (26x33cm-10x13in) s. 29-Jun-4 Sotheby's, New York #95/R est:4000-6000
£3020 $5346 €4500 L'allee d'arbres en hiver (52x69cm-20x27in) s. panel. 27-Apr-4 Artcurial Briest, Paris #128/R est:5000-7000
£4444 $8000 €6488 Portrait of Louis de Bousses de Fourcaud (38x30cm-15x12in) s. board prov. 23-Apr-4 Sotheby's, New York #173/R est:3000-5000
£5500 $10120 €8030 Portrait de M Louis Amiable (33x26cm-13x10in) s. board painted 1883 prov.exhib. 24-Jun-4 Christie's, London #303/R est:5000-7000
£8000 $13760 €11680 La Place de la Bastille, Paris (55x43cm-22x17in) s. 3-Dec-3 Christie's, London #33/R est:10000-15000
£20833 $34792 €30000 Les oeillets (54x73cm-21x29in) s. prov.lit. 21-Oct-3 Sotheby's, Amsterdam #219/R est:30000-50000
£20833 $37500 €30416 Quai des Grands Augustins with Notre Dame beyond (65x87cm-26x34in) s. panel prov. 23-Apr-4 Sotheby's, New York #199/R est:20000-30000
£61111 $110000 €89222 Two workmen (50x68cm-20x27in) s. cardboard on panel prov. 23-Apr-4 Sotheby's, New York #30/R est:80000-120000
Works on paper
£320 $554 €467 Le bouteille du vin (19x16cm-7x6in) s. chl W/C. 11-Dec-3 Christie's, Kensington #21/R
£704 $1218 €1000 Poete mondain (13x22cm-5x9in) init. wash Chinese ink dr. 14-Dec-3 Eric Pillon, Calais #48/R
£1500 $2700 €2190 Les promenades d'un artist au mussee de Louvre (28x36cm-11x14in) s.i.d.Juillet 1908 ink W/C. 21-Jan-4 Sotheby's, Olympia #514/R est:1500-2000
£1781 $3028 €2600 Forcats (19x34cm-7x13in) s. crayon gouache. 6-Nov-3 Tajan, Paris #193/R
£3421 $6295 €5200 La ferme (27x41cm-11x16in) s. mixed media cardboard. 23-Jun-4 Maigret, Paris #23/R est:5000-6000
£4706 $8000 €6871 Le Verre d'Absinthe (65x81cm-26x32in) s. W/C pen lit. 28-Oct-3 Sotheby's, New York #11/R est:10000-12000

RAFFAELLI, Jean François (attrib) (1850-1924) French
£834 $1500 €1218 Along the Seine, Paris (25x33cm-10x13in) s. 24-Apr-4 Skinner, Boston #130 est:3000-5000

RAFFALT, Ignaz (1800-1857) Austrian
£1250 $2037 €1800 Farmstead in evening light (23x31cm-9x12in) s. panel. 24-Sep-3 Neumeister, Munich #532/R est:1800
£2133 $3819 €3200 Hunter with dog by river (27x34cm-11x13in) s. panel. 13-May-4 Dorotheum, Linz #447/R est:3000-3400
£3497 $5944 €5000 Gathering storm (30x37cm-12x15in) i. verso panel. 24-Nov-3 Dorotheum, Vienna #24/R est:3400-4000
£8333 $14333 €12166 Idyllic country farmhouse scene (48x63cm-19x25in) s.d.855. 8-Dec-3 Philippe Schuler, Zurich #3427/R est:3000-4000 (S.FR 18500)

RAFFALT, Johann Gualbert (attrib) (1836-1865) Austrian
£1745 $3263 €2600 Gypsies with campfire in the Pussta in the evening (45x72cm-18x28in) 24-Feb-4 Dorotheum, Vienna #131/R est:2600-3000

RAFFET, Auguste-Marie (1804-1860) French
Works on paper
£1000 $1810 €1500 Scene de campagne Napoleonienne (18x25cm-7x10in) pen brown ink black crayon brown wash prov.exhib. 30-Mar-4 Rossini, Paris #24/R est:1500-1800

RAFFIN, Andre (1927-) French
£552 $921 €800 Les mats (130x90cm-51x35in) s.d.1989. 17-Nov-3 Charbonneaux, Paris #226
£621 $1037 €900 Villerville (54x72cm-21x28in) s. 11-Nov-3 Lesieur & Le Bars, Le Havre #91
Works on paper
£310 $518 €450 Plage de Deauville (28x46cm-11x18in) s.d.73 W/C chl. 11-Nov-3 Lesieur & Le Bars, Le Havre #90

RAFFLER, Max (1902-1988) German
Works on paper
£282 $487 €400 Corn sowing in spring (30x39cm-12x15in) s. W/C. 10-Dec-3 Hugo Ruef, Munich #2561/R

RAFFORT, Étienne (1802-1885) French
Works on paper
£352 $609 €500 Paysage anime pres du moulin (21x29cm-8x11in) s. W/C. 14-Dec-3 Eric Pillon, Calais #2/R

RAFFRAY, Andre (1925-) French
Prints
£7333 $13567 €11000 Chez Arensberg (100x180cm-39x71in) print exec.2001 prov.exhib. 18-Jul-4 Sotheby's, Paris #274/R est:8000-12000

RAFFY LE PERSAN, Jean (1920-) French
£270 $484 €400 Le village (100x50cm-39x20in) s.d.1956. 5-May-4 Coutau Begarie, Paris #61
£298 $542 €450 Village sous la neige (16x63cm-6x25in) s. panel. 18-Jun-4 Piasa, Paris #164
£300 $549 €450 Symphonie en bleu (15x35cm-6x14in) bears sig.verso panel. 3-Jun-4 E & Eve, Paris #94
£385 $654 €550 Venise (16x22cm-6x9in) s. panel. 21-Nov-3 Coutau Begarie, Paris #42
£420 $713 €600 Scene champetre (60x82cm-24x32in) s. panel. 21-Nov-3 Coutau Begarie, Paris #43/R
£805 $1506 €1200 Paysage Griderwald. s. i.verso panel. 29-Feb-4 Versailles Encheres #161/R

RAFTOPOULOS, George (1972-) Australian?
£4472 $7020 €6484 Corfu 6 (120x180cm-47x71in) indis.sig. prov. 26-Aug-3 Christie's, Sydney #63/R est:8000-12000 (A.D 11000)

RAGALZI, Sergio (1951-) Italian
Works on paper
£528 $877 €750 Farfalla Notturna (72x102cm-28x40in) s.i.d.1991 verso mixed media board. 14-Jun-3 Meeting Art, Vercelli #57/R

RAGEE, Egevadluq (1920-1983) North American
Works on paper
£1446 $2603 €2169 Spirit in flight with dog (53x44cm-21x17in) stencil. 26-Apr-4 Waddingtons, Toronto #423/R est:1000-1500 (C.D 3500)

RAGGI, Pietro Paolo (c.1646-1724) Italian
Works on paper
£317 $555 €450 Clown (31x29cm-12x11in) pencil pen ink W/C. 17-Dec-3 Christie's, Rome #432

RAGGIO, Giuseppe (1823-1916) Italian
Works on paper
£5986 $10356 €8500 Horses watering (36x64cm-14x25in) s.d.73 W/C card. 11-Dec-3 Christie's, Rome #181/R est:8000-12000
£6338 $10965 €9000 Buffalos and keepers (36x64cm-14x25in) s.d.73 W/C card. 11-Dec-3 Christie's, Rome #180/R est:8000-12000

RAGIONE, Raffaele (1851-1925) Italian
£1761 $2923 €2500 Fountain (25x38cm-10x15in) s. 13-Jun-3 Farsetti, Prato #517/R

RAGN-JENSEN, Leif (1911-1993) Danish
£267 $485 €401 Coastal landscape with ducks (63x80cm-25x31in) s.d.1938. 19-Jun-4 Rasmussen, Havnen #2021/R (D.KR 3000)
£406 $689 €593 Partridge (30x45cm-12x18in) s.d.1973. 10-Nov-3 Rasmussen, Vejle #87 (D.KR 4400)

RAGON, Adolphe (?-1924) British
£260 $465 €380 Shipping in a harbour (36x25cm-14x10in) s. board. 11-May-4 Bonhams, Knightsbridge #184
£300 $549 €438 St. Andrews church, Gravesend (12x22cm-5x9in) s. s.d.1879 verso board. 6-Jul-4 Bonhams, Knightsbridge #41/R

RAGOT, Jules (19th C) French
£338 $595 €500 Vase garni de fleurs (40x30cm-16x12in) s. panel. 18-May-4 Galerie Moderne, Brussels #269
£464 $844 €700 Nature morte aux fruits (70x100cm-28x39in) s. 15-Jun-4 Vanderkindere, Brussels #164

RAHL, Carl (1812-1865) Austrian
£2189 $3633 €3196 Hercules and Omphale (61x49cm-24x19in) 4-Oct-3 Dorotheum, Prague #51/R est:100000-150000 (C.KR 100000)
£6711 $12013 €10000 Italian peasant family with fortune teller (100x138cm-39x54in) s.d.1841 i.verso exhib. 27-May-4 Dorotheum, Vienna #138/R est:12000-15000

RAHON, Alice (1916-1987) French
£612 $1096 €900 Constellation du paysage (11x36cm-4x14in) s.i.d.1957 verso panel. 21-Mar-4 Calmels Cohen, Paris #6/R
£744 $1369 €1086 Sparrows migrating (30x41cm-12x16in) s.d.1968 masonite prov. 25-Mar-4 Louis Morton, Mexico #70/R est:17000-19000 (M.P 15000)
£989 $1800 €1444 Bird and village (30x22cm-12x9in) s.d.58 board. 29-Jun-4 Sotheby's, New York #664/R est:2500-3500
Works on paper
£552 $950 €806 City without walls (41x51cm-16x20in) s.d.47 col pencil. 7-Dec-3 Freeman, Philadelphia #69

RAI, David (1952-) Austrian
Works on paper
£267 $491 €400 Seagull friend (28x28cm-11x11in) s.d.75 pencil. 9-Jun-4 Dorotheum, Salzburg #857/R

RAILTON, Ernest (19/20th C) British
Works on paper
£550 $968 €803 Whitby (23x41cm-9x16in) s.d.1909 W/C htd white. 20-May-4 Richardson & Smith, Whitby #656

RAIMONDI, Aldo (1902-1998) Italian
£2467 $4415 €3700 Hotel Savoy Palace, Gardone (100x70cm-39x28in) s.d.XII tempera card. 12-May-4 Stadion, Trieste #776/R est:1800-2200
Works on paper
£317 $548 €450 Vase of flowers (23x17cm-9x7in) s.i. W/C. 10-Dec-3 Sotheby's, Milan #128/R
£364 $607 €520 Cows in the stable (35x45cm-14x18in) s. W/C paper on cardboard. 10-Oct-3 Stadion, Trieste #671/R
£493 $853 €700 Head of old man (52x38cm-20x15in) s.d.1968 W/C. 9-Dec-3 Finarte Semenzato, Milan #75
£667 $1227 €1000 Santa Maria di Zara cathedral (72x51cm-28x20in) s.i.d.1962 W/C cardboard. 8-Jun-4 Sotheby's, Milan #81/R
£704 $1218 €1000 Goat and hen (35x50cm-14x20in) s. W/C. 10-Dec-3 Sotheby's, Milan #87/R
£800 $1472 €1200 Impero Street, Rome (45x55cm-18x22in) s.d.1956 W/C cardboard. 8-Jun-4 Sotheby's, Milan #82/R
£915 $1520 €1300 Tower Bridge, London. Porta Ticinese, Milan (36x50cm-14x20in) s. W/C two. 13-Jun-3 Farsetti, Prato #503
£915 $1584 €1300 Horses in the stable (35x50cm-14x20in) s. W/C. 10-Dec-3 Sotheby's, Milan #93/R
£1000 $1840 €1500 By the river (49x56cm-19x22in) s.i. W/C. 8-Jun-4 Sotheby's, Milan #83/R est:1500-2500
£1447 $2663 €2200 Scala Square (50x38cm-20x15in) s. W/C. 23-Jun-4 Finarte Semenzato, Rome #36/R est:2000-2500

RAIN, Charles (20th C) American
£3293 $5500 €4808 Columbine (30x20cm-12x8in) s.i.d.Jan verso masonite. 7-Oct-3 Sotheby's, New York #177 est:3000-4000

RAINBIRD, Victor Noble (1889-1936) British
£260 $413 €380 Breezy day - a yacht at sea (25x35cm-10x14in) s.i. 18-Mar-3 Anderson & Garland, Newcastle #236
£260 $413 €380 Stormy beach scene with a sailing ship grounded and figures in foreground (16x27cm-6x11in) s. 18-Mar-3 Anderson & Garland, Newcastle #245
£290 $461 €423 St Mary's Island (25x35cm-10x14in) s.i. 18-Mar-3 Anderson & Garland, Newcastle #248/R
£500 $795 €730 Fisher girls on a beach (18x25cm-7x10in) s. 18-Mar-3 Anderson & Garland, Newcastle #231/R
£570 $906 €832 Driven ashore (38x53cm-15x21in) s.i. 18-Mar-3 Anderson & Garland, Newcastle #234/R
Works on paper
£200 $328 €290 Durham (24x35cm-9x14in) s.i. W/C. 5-Jun-3 Heffel, Vancouver #23 (C.D 450)
£260 $478 €380 Call to Ulysses (33x25cm-13x10in) s.i.d.1930 W/C. 23-Mar-4 Anderson & Garland, Newcastle #231
£260 $473 €380 La Mere (25x19cm-10x7in) s.i. W/C. 29-Jun-4 Anderson & Garland, Newcastle #177
£260 $473 €380 Old Shields (28x19cm-11x7in) s.i. W/C. 29-Jun-4 Anderson & Garland, Newcastle #178
£290 $493 €423 Rural scene with bridge over the Tyne and figure on footpath (33x23cm-13x9in) s.i. W/C. 8-Nov-3 Jim Railton, Durham #1405/R
£300 $546 €438 Tynemouth - View of Friar's Haven (23x33cm-9x13in) s.i.d.1934 W/C. 29-Jun-4 Anderson & Garland, Newcastle #180
£310 $505 €453 L'automne, Normandy (32x23cm-13x9in) s.i.d.1932 W/C. 23-Sep-3 Anderson & Garland, Newcastle #205
£310 $505 €453 Tyne Harbour (24x37cm-9x15in) s.i.d.1932 W/C. 23-Sep-3 Anderson & Garland, Newcastle #210
£350 $571 €511 Fisher girl gazing over stormy seas (41x28cm-16x11in) s.d.1914 W/C. 26-Sep-3 Dee Atkinson & Harrison, Driffield #551/R
£360 $587 €526 Street scene in Rouen (35x24cm-14x9in) s.i. W/C. 23-Sep-3 Anderson & Garland, Newcastle #201
£560 $1014 €818 Daughter of the sea (42x27cm-17x11in) s.d.1914 i.verso W/C htd white. 30-Mar-4 David Duggleby, Scarborough #36/R
£600 $978 €876 Busy street scene in St Oven, Rouen. Busy street scene in Rouen (35x25cm-14x10in) s. W/C pair. 23-Sep-3 Anderson & Garland, Newcastle #200/R

RAINER, Arnulf (1929-) Austrian
£950 $1644 €1350 Untitled (13x8cm-5x3in) acrylic pencil pastel nylon photo. 9-Dec-3 Artcurial Briest, Paris #318/R est:1200-1300
£1133 $2029 €1700 Over painting (13x18cm-5x7in) s. oil chk board. 15-May-4 Van Ham, Cologne #867 est:400
£1667 $3067 €2500 Untitled (29x21cm-11x8in) s.d.70 oil crayon. 12-Jun-4 Villa Grisebach, Berlin #356/R est:2500-3500
£1818 $3091 €2600 Arbre (28x21cm-11x8in) paper. 1-Dec-3 Amberes, Antwerp #271/R
£3691 $6534 €5500 Composition (60x48cm-24x19in) mono.i. oil chk on photo. 28-Apr-4 Wiener Kunst Auktionen, Vienna #271/R est:4000-6000
£4000 $7360 €6000 Foot (50x40cm-20x16in) s.i. acrylic wax crayon asphalt photograph. 12-Jun-4 Villa Grisebach, Berlin #357/R est:6000-8000
£4545 $7818 €6500 Untitled (59x50cm-23x20in) s. black oil crayon over b/w photograph prov. 5-Dec-3 Ketterer, Munich #172/R est:6000-8000
£7500 $12525 €10950 Totenuberzeichnung (47x56cm-19x22in) init. acrylic black white photo exhib. 22-Oct-3 Christie's, London #101/R est:5000-7000
£8725 $15443 €13000 Treetop (63x48cm-25x19in) s.i.d. mixed media transparent paper. 28-Apr-4 Wiener Kunst Auktionen, Vienna #255/R est:7000-15000
£8725 $15617 €13000 Round corner (46x27cm-18x11in) s.i.d.60/64 verso. 25-May-4 Dorotheum, Vienna #79/R est:15000-20000
£9790 $16643 €14000 Composition (60x50cm-24x20in) s.i. oil chk on photo prov. 26-Nov-3 Dorotheum, Vienna #79/R est:10000-12000
£11888 $20210 €17000 Untitled (51x73cm-20x29in) mono. finger painting board on panel. 26-Nov-3 Dorotheum, Vienna #94/R est:16000-24000
£12676 $21930 €18000 Untitled (51x73cm-20x29in) s. board. 13-Dec-3 Lempertz, Koln #179/R est:4000
£14000 $25480 €20440 Tombe (70x50cm-28x20in) oil pastel canvas on board prov.exhib. 6-Feb-4 Sotheby's, London #197/R est:4000-6000
£14685 $25259 €21000 Untitled (121x80cm-48x31in) s. s.d.1987 verso oil over b/w photograph prov. 5-Dec-3 Ketterer, Munich #171/R est:30000-40000
£20000 $36400 €29200 Fete noire (50x70cm-20x28in) s. oil pastel canvas on board prov.exhib. 6-Feb-4 Sotheby's, London #198/R est:4000-6000
£34899 $61772 €52000 Cross (150x80cm-59x31in) s. panel prov. 28-Apr-4 Wiener Kunst Auktionen, Vienna #292/R est:40000-65000
£62937 $106993 €90000 Cross (186x101cm-73x40in) s.d.1979-81 verso panel prov. 28-Nov-3 Villa Grisebach, Berlin #86/R est:50000-70000
Prints
£2550 $4565 €3800 TRRR. Fly eater Feb 66 (92x64cm-36x25in) s. chk on offset lithograph. 25-May-4 Karl & Faber, Munich #502/R est:1000
£3221 $5766 €4800 Michelangelo chewing red flower (100x70cm-39x28in) s. offset lithograph. 25-May-4 Karl & Faber, Munich #503/R est:1200
£3289 $6053 €5000 The fly eater (91x65cm-36x26in) s.i.d. col pencil over lithograph. 22-Jun-4 Wiener Kunst Auktionen, Vienna #393/R est:5000
£3500 $6440 €5110 Haute coiffeur (50x35cm-20x14in) s.i.d.61 hand col etching. 24-Jun-4 Sotheby's, Olympia #572/R est:3500-4500
Works on paper
£849 $1375 €1240 Untitled (14x19cm-6x7in) s. mixed media on photo prov. 24-May-3 Burkhard, Luzern #68/R est:2000-3000 (S.FR 1800)
£1181 $1972 €1700 Sans titre (20x20cm-8x8in) s. s.i.verso graphite gouache etching. 25-Oct-3 Cornette de St.Cyr, Paris #285/R est:600-800
£1374 $2500 €2006 Van Gogh series (23x18cm-9x7in) chl over photograph executed 1987. 29-Jun-4 Sotheby's, New York #575/R est:2000-3000
£1678 $2803 €2400 Goya series (24x34cm-9x13in) s. mixed media prov. 29-Jun-3 Versailles Encheres #213/R
£1733 $3189 €2600 Der Heilige Gast (52x36cm-20x14in) s. col crayons on lithographic base. 8-Jun-4 Sotheby's, Amsterdam #271/R est:2000-3000
£2013 $3604 €3000 Censorship (24x20cm-9x8in) s. mixed media on photo. 25-May-4 Dorotheum, Vienna #77/R est:3000-4000
£2013 $3604 €3000 Censorship (23x18cm-9x7in) s. mixed media on photo. 25-May-4 Dorotheum, Vienna #78/R est:3000-4000
£2238 $3804 €3200 Marie Antoinette encyclopaedia and revolution (27x21cm-11x8in) s. mixed media over print. 28-Nov-3 Wiener Kunst Auktionen, Vienna #663/R est:3000-4500
£2448 $4210 €3500 Untitled (60x50cm-24x20in) s. gouache oil col wax crayon black and white photograph. 4-Dec-3 Van Ham, Cologne #411/R est:5000
£2685 $4752 €4000 Mescalin (21x28cm-8x11in) s.i.d. mixed media. 28-Apr-4 Wiener Kunst Auktionen, Vienna #228/R est:3000-5000
£3147 $5350 €4500 You are welcomed (42x29cm-17x11in) s.i.d.68 graphite ultraphan. 26-Nov-3 Dorotheum, Vienna #69/R est:5000-6500
£3169 $5483 €4500 Krote (60x50cm-24x20in) s.i. mixed media over photograph exec.1974 prov. 9-Dec-3 Artcurial Briest, Paris #489/R est:2500-3000
£3356 $5940 €5000 Untitled (43x60cm-17x24in) s.d. bears i. mixed media transparent. 28-Apr-4 Wiener Kunst Auktionen, Vienna #229/R est:5000-10000
£3662 $6335 €5200 Cathedral (60x50cm-24x20in) s.i. mixed media over photograph prov. 9-Dec-3 Artcurial Briest, Paris #490/R est:2500-3000
£4392 $7862 €6500 Serie face farces (46x59cm-18x23in) s. mixed media exec.1970-75. 4-May-4 Calmels Cohen, Paris #224/R est:4000-5000
£4412 $7500 €6442 Ohne titel (42x30cm-17x12in) s.i.d.1958-59 col crayon. 21-Nov-3 Swann Galleries, New York #156/R est:4000-6000
£5000 $9200 €7500 Ubermalung (48x61cm-19x24in) s. mixed media on blk white photograph. 9-Jun-4 Artcurial Briest, Paris #528/R est:7000-9000
£9396 $16819 €14000 Landscape (62x85cm-24x33in) s.i.d.62 oil chk graphite chk bodycol. 25-May-4 Dorotheum, Vienna #54/R est:22000-36000
£11268 $19493 €16000 Landscape (50x75cm-20x30in) s.i.d.64 mixed media board. 13-Dec-3 Lempertz, Koln #180/R est:3500

RAINERI, Carlo Antonio and Vittorio (18/19th C) Italian
Prints
£1884 $3090 €2600 Flamingoes. col engraving. 27-May-3 Il Ponte, Milan #1009/R est:1200-1500

RAINEY, Tristram (1910-) British
£320 $586 €467 Flowers (76x89cm-30x35in) exhib. 7-Apr-4 Woolley & Wallis, Salisbury #209/R

RAINEY, William (1852-1936) British
Works on paper
£620 $992 €905 Early morning Polperro, Cornish harbour study (23x38cm-9x15in) s. W/C. 8-Jan-3 Biddle & Webb, Birmingham #660

RAINS, Malcolm (1947-) Canadian
£772 $1383 €1127 Fruit from Taos (24x19cm-9x7in) s.d.1993 prov. 6-May-4 Heffel, Vancouver #117/R (C.D 1900)

RAITTILA, Tapani (1921-) Finnish
£764 $1276 €1100 Young maiden (21x18cm-8x7in) s.d.1975. 26-Oct-3 Bukowskis, Helsinki #461/R
£1119 $1902 €1600 View from Helsingfors (33x24cm-13x9in) s.d.86. 29-Nov-3 Bukowskis, Helsinki #42/R est:1300-1600

RAJ, G D Paul (20th C) ?
Works on paper
£276 $500 €403 Market scene with figures (61x74cm-24x29in) s. W/C. 18-Apr-4 Jeffery Burchard, Florida #250/R

RAJLICH, Thomas (1940-) Czechoslovakian
£458 $792 €650 Untitled (25x150cm-10x59in) s.d.1940 acrylic prov. 15-Dec-3 Charbonneaux, Paris #255
£2448 $4210 €3500 Untitled (80x80cm-31x31in) s.d.85 verso oil pencil prov. 2-Dec-3 Sotheby's, Amsterdam #347/R est:3000-5000
£5333 $9813 €8000 Untitled (25x25cm-10x10in) each s.d.74 stretcher acrylic four prov. 8-Jun-4 Sotheby's, Amsterdam #119/R est:6000-8000

RAKEL, Sigurd (1943-) German
£414 $691 €600 Female nude on chair (130x110cm-51x43in) s. i.d.1981 verso lit. 10-Jul-3 Allgauer, Kempten #2650/R
£483 $806 €700 Nude couple (130x140cm-51x55in) s. i.d.1982 verso. 10-Jul-3 Allgauer, Kempten #2651/R

RAKEMANN, Carl (1878-1965) American
£1635 $2600 €2387 Pierce Mill Dam, Rock Creek (76x91cm-30x36in) s. i.verso. 13-Sep-3 Weschler, Washington #726/R est:2000-3000

RAKES, Sarah (1955-) American
£240 $400 €350 Five cats, five bowls of milk (91x160cm-36x63in) acrylic. 15-Nov-3 Slotin Folk Art, Buford #436/R

RAKIA, David (1928-) American?
£1323 $2250 €1932 Workers paving a road in Tel Aviv (54x72cm-21x28in) s. i.d.1946 verso. 1-Dec-3 Ben-Ami, Tel Aviv #4297/R est:3000-4000

RAKOCZI, Basil (1908-1979) British
£1538 $2615 €2200 Fornalutx - from my terrace at Casa Monica (42x61cm-17x24in) s.d.1972 i.verso acrylic pencil paper. 18-Nov-3 Whyte's, Dublin #146/R est:1500-2000
£1972 $3155 €2800 Langoustines (72x91cm-28x36in) s.i.d.1961 s.verso prov. 16-Sep-3 Whyte's, Dublin #38/R est:3000-4000
£2000 $3580 €2920 Horseman (43x55cm-17x22in) s.d.61 oil paper prov. 14-May-4 Christie's, Kensington #444a est:1200-1800
£2819 $5046 €4200 Cubist still life with lemons and faces (56x68cm-22x27in) s. 26-May-4 James Adam, Dublin #132/R est:4500-6500
£3000 $5370 €4380 Three figures (49x63cm-19x25in) s.d.47 verso. 14-May-4 Christie's, Kensington #428/R est:3000-5000
£3000 $5370 €4380 Ville (38x63cm-15x25in) s. s.i.d.52 verso. 14-May-4 Christie's, Kensington #435/R est:3000-5000
£3092 $5689 €4700 Farmhouse in winter (54x74cm-21x29in) s. 22-Jun-4 De Veres Art Auctions, Dublin #18/R est:4000-6000
£3750 $6900 €5700 The Select Bar (39x46cm-15x18in) s. board. 22-Jun-4 De Veres Art Auctions, Dublin #13/R est:5000-7000
£3916 $6657 €5600 Tuna fishers (73x92cm-29x36in) s.i.d.75 s.d.verso. 25-Nov-3 De Veres Art Auctions, Dublin #82/R est:6000-9000
£4800 $8592 €7008 Three fishing boats (72x93cm-28x37in) s. s.d.1952 verso. 14-May-4 Christie's, Kensington #429/R est:4000-6000
£5500 $9185 €8030 Fille a l'oiseau exotique (125x45cm-49x18in) s. s.i.d.56 verso. 16-Oct-3 Christie's, Kensington #478/R est:4000-6000
Works on paper
£400 $716 €584 Zeus et Ganymede (25x41cm-10x16in) s. gouache. 14-May-4 Christie's, Kensington #433/R
£500 $895 €730 Garcons et coqs (11x64cm-4x25in) s. pen black ink. 14-May-4 Christie's, Kensington #432
£664 $1129 €950 The beach, Roquebrune, Provence (25x36cm-10x14in) s. i.d.1947 verso pen ink. 18-Nov-3 Whyte's, Dublin #69
£1000 $1790 €1460 La Tribu VI (48x60cm-19x24in) s. s.i.d.50 verso pencil W/C gouache. 14-May-4 Christie's, Kensington #440/R est:1000-1500
£1053 $1937 €1600 The lighthouse keeper (26x35cm-10x14in) s. mixed media. 22-Jun-4 De Veres Art Auctions, Dublin #185/R est:800-1200
£1200 $2172 €1800 Bateau (48x63cm-19x25in) s.i.d.1950 mixed media. 30-Mar-4 De Veres Art Auctions, Dublin #39/R est:600-900
£1268 $2028 €1800 Asleep in a fish (27x35cm-11x14in) s.d.1972 i.verso pen ink W/C col chk prov. 16-Sep-3 Whyte's, Dublin #8/R est:1000-1500
£1389 $2320 €2000 Nature morte (40x52cm-16x20in) s. gouache study verso oil on paper double-sided. 21-Oct-3 Artcurial Briest, Paris #232/R est:2000-3000
£1389 $2320 €2000 Costumes pour le ballet - Gypsy Taste (52x71cm-20x28in) s. s.i.d.1953 verso W/C gouache ink. 21-Oct-3 Artcurial Briest, Paris #233/R est:2000-2500

RAKOFF, Rastislaw (1904-1982) Russian
£334 $600 €500 La plage (33x26cm-13x10in) s.d.1958 panel. 26-Apr-4 Tajan, Paris #374
£533 $981 €800 Quai Montebello (35x27cm-14x11in) s.d.1955 panel. 9-Jun-4 Beaussant & Lefèvre, Paris #203/R
£839 $1443 €1200 La Seine (35x27cm-14x11in) s.d.51 panel. 3-Dec-3 Tajan, Paris #189

RAKOSI, Nandor (1832-1884) Hungarian
£2715 $4507 €3964 Shooting table (62x62cm-24x24in) s.d.1868 panel pair. 4-Oct-3 Kieselbach, Budapest #74/R (H.F 1000000)

RAKOWSKI, Mecislas de (1887-1947) Belgian
£490 $817 €700 Jour de marche (45x55cm-18x22in) s.d.1928. 13-Oct-3 Horta, Bruxelles #474

RALEIGH, Henry Patrick (1880-1944) American
Works on paper
£814 $1400 €1188 Six figures standing (43x61cm-17x24in) s.d.1932 brush ink W/C. 7-Dec-3 Hindman, Chicago #816/R est:1000-2000
£814 $1400 €1188 Nightclub scene (43x61cm-17x24in) s.d.1927 brush ink W/C. 7-Dec-3 Hindman, Chicago #817/R est:1000-2000
£988 $1700 €1442 Sabina and Carl sat silent (43x61cm-17x24in) s.d.1928 brush ink W/C. 7-Dec-3 Hindman, Chicago #815/R est:1000-2000

RALLI, Theodore Jacques (1852-1909) Greek
£35714 $59643 €51785 Evening prayers (81x65cm-32x26in) s.d.1876 prov. 17-Jun-3 Pinneys, Montreal #40 est:15000-20000 (C.D 80000)
£65000 $110500 €94900 Praying in a Greek church, Montparnasse (81x65cm-32x26in) s.d.1876 prov.exhib.lit. 18-Nov-3 Sotheby's, London #5/R est:65000-75000

RAM, Seeta (fl.1810-1822) Indian
Works on paper
£22000 $35860 €32120 Taj Mahal in morning light (41x61cm-16x24in) i. pencil W/C exhib.lit. 24-Sep-3 Christie's, London #119/R est:25000-35000

RAMA, Carol (1918-) Italian?
£4545 $7727 €6500 Untitled (69x49cm-27x19in) s.d.1964 oil mixed media. 25-Nov-3 Sotheby's, Milan #45/R est:5000-7000
Works on paper
£280 $467 €400 Untitled (27x27cm-11x11in) s.d.1991 mixed media. 26-Jun-3 Sant Agostino, Torino #207/R
£1088 $1948 €1600 Kiss (50x35cm-20x14in) i.d.1984 mixed media. 22-Mar-4 Sant Agostino, Torino #452/R est:2000
£1818 $3036 €2600 Untitled (51x66cm-20x26in) s.d.1978 verso collage mixed media exhib. 26-Jun-3 Sant Agostino, Torino #225/R est:1500-2000
£2098 $3503 €3000 Untitled (51x66cm-20x26in) s.d.1978 verso mixed media collage exhib. 26-Jun-3 Sant Agostino, Torino #226/R est:1500-2000
£2483 $4146 €3600 Untitled (104x75cm-41x30in) s.d.1966 mixed media. 17-Nov-3 Sant Agostino, Torino #306/R est:3500-4000
£3147 $5350 €4500 Untitled (62x48cm-24x19in) s.d.1968 Chinese ink W/C tempera mixed media. 25-Nov-3 Sotheby's, Milan #44/R est:3000-4000
£3810 $6819 €5600 Untitled (70x54cm-28x21in) s.d.1968 mixed media card. 22-Mar-4 Sant Agostino, Torino #552/R est:6000
£7500 $12525 €10950 Beker (32x45cm-13x18in) s.d.1966 mixed media. 20-Oct-3 Sotheby's, London #43/R est:7000-9000

RAMAH, Henri (1887-1947) Belgian
£461 $847 €700 Infante (71x56cm-28x22in) s.d.1919 exhib. 22-Jun-4 Palais de Beaux Arts, Brussels #301/R
£887 $1588 €1295 Women in field (46x55cm-18x22in) init. panel. 26-May-4 AB Stockholms Auktionsverk #2377/R (S.KR 12000)
£1162 $2010 €1650 Standing woman (67x50cm-26x20in) s. panel. 15-Dec-3 Bernaerts, Antwerp #253a est:1250-1500
£1351 $2554 €2000 Le marche aux bestiaux (51x67cm-20x26in) s. cardboard. 17-Feb-4 Vanderkindere, Brussels #10 est:1250-1750
£5921 $10895 €9000 Pecheurs (110x215cm-43x85in) s. 22-Jun-4 Palais de Beaux Arts, Brussels #302/R est:10000-15000
Works on paper
£304 $575 €450 Deux femmes atablees au jardin (25x19cm-10x7in) s. W/C. 17-Feb-4 Vanderkindere, Brussels #67
£507 $958 €750 Trois chats (21x15cm-8x6in) s. gouache. 17-Feb-4 Vanderkindere, Brussels #63
£1119 $1902 €1600 Paysage avec arbre et maison (50x74cm-20x29in) gouache exhib. 1-Dec-3 Palais de Beaux Arts, Brussels #110/R est:500-700
£3497 $5944 €5000 Au verger (68x52cm-27x20in) s. gouache. 1-Dec-3 Palais de Beaux Arts, Brussels #115/R est:4000-6000

RAMAH, Henri (attrib) (1887-1947) Belgian
£303 $557 €460 Cuisiniere de l'artiste (88x66cm-35x26in) 22-Jun-4 Palais de Beaux Arts, Brussels #300/R

RAMAUGE, Roberto (1890-1973) French/Argentinian
£604 $1069 €900 Landscape (23x34cm-9x13in) s. s.i.d.1969 verso cardboard. 27-Apr-4 Durán, Madrid #181/R
£2041 $3653 €3000 Landscape (52x64cm-20x25in) s. 22-Mar-4 Durán, Madrid #172/R est:2750

RAMBAUD, Antonin Marie (19/20th C) French
£271 $486 €396 Coastal landscape with figures (42x64cm-17x25in) s. 10-May-4 Rasmussen, Vejle #385/R (D.KR 3000)

RAMBELLI, Domenico (1886-1972) Italian
Sculpture
£20979 $35664 €30000 Woman singing (33cm-13in) bronze exec.1922 exhib.lit. 29-Nov-3 Farsetti, Prato #441/R est:25000-30000

RAMBERG, Johann Heinrich (1763-1840) German
Works on paper
£336 $561 €480 Angry (10x7cm-4x3in) s.i.d. htd white W/C over pencil. 10-Oct-3 Winterberg, Heidelberg #728
£811 $1451 €1200 Lovers discovered (43x54cm-17x21in) s.i.d.1799 W/C pen lit. 8-May-4 Schloss Ahlden, Ahlden #699/R

RAMBERG, Ulf (1935-) Swedish
Works on paper
£491 $835 €717 Art exhibition at Pelare (49x32cm-19x13in) s.verso mixed media collage. 4-Nov-3 Bukowskis, Stockholm #533/R (S.KR 6500)
£4714 $8484 €6882 Untitled (71x200cm-28x79in) W/C Indian ink 27 in one frame ex.1973-1989. 26-Apr-4 Bukowskis, Stockholm #488/R est:30000-40000 (S.KR 65000)

RAMBIE, Paul (1919-) ?
£336 $594 €500 Composition (38x55cm-15x22in) s.d.1969. 29-Apr-4 Claude Aguttes, Neuilly #115
£933 $1699 €1400 Deux personnages - Les yeux sont jaunes (54x73cm-21x29in) s. panel. 5-Jul-4 Le Mouel, Paris #86/R

RAMBO, Jules (20th C) Belgian
£1631 $2724 €2300 La robe rouge (70x60cm-28x24in) s.d.1926. 17-Jun-3 Vanderkindere, Brussels #26/R est:1500-2500

RAMBOUX, Johann Anton Alban (1790-1866) German
Works on paper
£3057 $5563 €4463 Roman family sitting in front of their house, with Saint Peters in background (15x15cm-6x6in) W/C. 17-Jun-4 Kornfeld, Bern #55/R est:5000 (S.FR 7000)

RAME, Jules Louis (1855-?) French
£3116 $5110 €4300 Moutons dans la bergerie (38x55cm-15x22in) s.d.1883. 11-May-3 Osenat, Fontainebleau #66/R est:3500-4000

RAMEAU, C (19th C) French?
£2657 $4438 €3800 Deux chiens gardant un tableau de chasse (110x137cm-43x54in) s. after Desportes. 13-Oct-3 Pierre Berge, Paris #24/R est:2500-3000

RAMEAU, Claude (1876-1955) French
£724 $1340 €1050 Bord de Loire (65x81cm-26x32in) s. 16-Feb-4 Giraudeau, Tours #101

RAMIREZ, Victoria (1942-) Spanish
£369 $661 €550 Still life in blue (50x73cm-20x29in) s. 25-May-4 Durán, Madrid #69/R

RAMIREZ-IBANEZ, Manuel (1856-1925) Spanish
£62500 $101875 €90000 Evening in Venice (80x111cm-31x44in) s.d.83. 23-Sep-3 Durán, Madrid #202/R est:70000

RAMIS, Sebastian (1947-) Spanish
Works on paper
£1655 $2979 €2400 Night (61x58cm-24x23in) s. mixed media. 26-Jan-4 Ansorena, Madrid #885/R est:2400

RAMMELL, George (20th C) Canadian
Sculpture
£2111 $3652 €3082 Ex-voto. d.1978 wood bronze. 9-Dec-3 Maynards, Vancouver #244 est:2500-3500 (C.D 4750)

RAMO, Joachim (1928-) Spanish
£922 $1540 €1300 Peinture 13 (89x116cm-35x46in) s.i.d.1966 verso. 23-Jun-3 Durán, Madrid #178/R

RAMOLO, Leonie (?) German?
£300 $540 €450 Big city street (67x98cm-26x39in) s. 22-Apr-4 Weidler, Nurnberg #6691

RAMON, Alfredo (1922-) Spanish
Works on paper
£268 $502 €400 Balconies in Madrid (35x26cm-14x10in) s. W/C. 24-Feb-4 Durán, Madrid #46/R

RAMONEDA, Francisco (1905-1977) Argentinian
£495 $900 €723 Landscape in Humahuaca (28x33cm-11x13in) s. cardboard. 5-Jul-4 Arroyo, Buenos Aires #19/R
£1397 $2500 €2040 Red shawl (65x60cm-26x24in) s.d.1934 board. 4-May-4 Arroyo, Buenos Aires #95/R est:1800

RAMOS ARTAL, Manuel (1855-1900) Spanish
£293 $489 €425 Study for boats (12x20cm-5x8in) s. board. 17-Nov-3 Durán, Madrid #155/R
£336 $601 €500 Landscape (15x25cm-6x10in) s. board. 25-May-4 Durán, Madrid #626/R
£521 $849 €750 Lake at dusk (16x30cm-6x12in) s.d.97 board. 23-Sep-3 Durán, Madrid #94/R
£521 $849 €750 Chapel by the river (15x25cm-6x10in) s.d.94 board. 23-Sep-3 Durán, Madrid #95/R
£552 $993 €800 Landscape (20x40cm-8x16in) s.d.1978 board. 26-Jan-4 Ansorena, Madrid #233a/R
£674 $1125 €950 Path in the shade (26x18cm-10x7in) s. board. 20-Oct-3 Durán, Madrid #206/R
£690 $1152 €1000 Match (26x18cm-10x7in) s. board. 17-Nov-3 Durán, Madrid #154/R
£709 $1184 €1000 Winter landscape (17x32cm-7x13in) s. board. 20-Oct-3 Durán, Madrid #205/R
£1389 $2264 €2000 Landscape (78x48cm-31x19in) s.d.98. 23-Sep-3 Durán, Madrid #51/R
£1611 $2996 €2400 Wood (34x53cm-13x21in) s. 2-Mar-4 Ansorena, Madrid #110/R est:2400

RAMOS, Domingo (1894-1967) Cuban
£4469 $8000 €6525 Landscape in Vinales (60x75cm-24x30in) s.d.1953 prov. 26-May-4 Sotheby's, New York #140/R est:10000-15000

RAMOS, Mel (1935-) American
£50898 $85000 €74311 Fantomah - Daughter of the Pharaohs (103x91cm-41x36in) prov.exhib.lit. 12-Nov-3 Christie's, Rockefeller NY #329/R est:80000-120000
£83832 $140000 €122395 Black Hawk (76x66cm-30x26in) s.d.1962 prov.lit. 12-Nov-3 Christie's, Rockefeller NY #328/R est:60000-80000
Works on paper
£8333 $13917 €12000 The rounder (91x49cm-36x19in) s.d. W/C. 24-Oct-3 Ketterer, Hamburg #514/R est:13000-15000
£83832 $140000 €122395 Princess (152x127cm-60x50in) s.i.d.1965 verso prov.lit. 13-Nov-3 Sotheby's, New York #216/R est:150000-200000

RAMOS, Roy dos (20th C) Venezuelan
Works on paper
£323 $500 €472 Fence (100x100cm-39x39in) s.verso mixed media on canvas exec.1999. 29-Sep-2 Subastas Odalys, Caracas #49

RAMOS, Tod (1956-) British
£1500 $2550 €2190 Tattentham Corner (38x51cm-15x20in) s. board. 19-Nov-3 Sotheby's, Olympia #140/R est:1000-1500

RAMPASO, Luciano (1934-) Italian
£324 $600 €473 Baccino, Venice (51x102cm-20x40in) s. 15-Jul-4 Doyle, New York #70/R
£435 $800 €635 Rialto bridge (38x56cm-15x22in) s. 9-Jun-4 Doyle, New York #3068
£491 $800 €717 La montee de Monmartre (76x61cm-30x24in) s. 24-Sep-3 Doyle, New York #75
£757 $1400 €1105 Rue de la paix (61x76cm-24x30in) s. 15-Jul-4 Doyle, New York #69/R est:1500-2500
£761 $1400 €1111 Maria de la sante (51x102cm-20x40in) s. s.i.stretcher. 25-Mar-4 Doyle, New York #56/R est:1800-2200

RAMPAZO, Luciano (1936-) French
£270 $500 €394 Gondala to St Marks (23x30cm-9x12in) s. 24-Jan-4 Jeffery Burchard, Florida #14/R

RAMPAZZINI, Roberto Alberto (1880-?) Italian
£738 $1307 €1100 Back home, Valtellina (35x50cm-14x20in) s. board. 1-May-4 Meeting Art, Vercelli #339

RAMPIN, Saverio (1930-) Italian
£224 $402 €330 Composition (50x60cm-20x24in) s. canvas on masonite. 16-Mar-4 Finarte Semenzato, Milan #221

RAMPL, Oswald (1911-) Austrian
£310 $568 €450 Summer landscape (100x144cm-39x57in) s. masonite. 27-Jan-4 Dorotheum, Vienna #142/R

RAMSAY, Allan (1713-1784) British
£3293 $5500 €4808 Portrait of a nobleman (76x61cm-30x24in) s. 19-Oct-3 Susanin's, Chicago #6021/R est:10000-20000
£14000 $23240 €20440 Portrait of Lord John Murray of Pitnacree, Perth, and Banner Cross Yorks (75x62cm-30x24in) s.i.d.1743 painted oval prov.exhib.lit. 30-Sep-3 Sotheby's, London #182/R est:15000-20000
£17000 $31280 €24820 Portrait of Sir John Hynde Cotton, 3rd B.T (123x97cm-48x38in) s.i. prov.exhib.lit. 26-Mar-4 Sotheby's, London #8/R est:15000-20000
£20000 $36800 €29200 Portrait of a naval officer, possibly Mr Sinclair (76x63cm-30x25in) s. painted oval prov.lit. 26-Mar-4 Sotheby's, London #17/R est:15000-20000
£21000 $36330 €30660 Portrait of Ruth Trevor in a red dress (75x62cm-30x24in) 11-Dec-3 Lyon & Turnbull, Edinburgh #30/R est:10000-15000
£38000 $69160 €55480 Portrait of Elizabeth Gunning, Duchess of Argyll (78x64cm-31x25in) s. prov.exhib.lit. 1-Jul-4 Sotheby's, London #126/R est:30000-50000

£40000 $68000 €58400 Portrait of Lady Jane Douglas as a shepherdess seated in a landscape (211x145cm-83x57in) s. painted c.1735 prov.exhib.lit. 25-Nov-3 Christie's, London #29/R est:50000-70000

RAMSAY, Allan (attrib) (1713-1784) British
£432 $800 €631 Portrait of a man, purportedly the Mayor of Norwich (61x48cm-24x19in) 15-Jul-4 Doyle, New York #71/R
£850 $1352 €1241 Portrait of the Reverend Patrick Bennet, minister of Polmont, Stirlingshire (72x59cm-28x23in) prov. 10-Sep-3 Cheffins, Cambridge #520/R
£1048 $1845 €1530 Portrait of artist's wife (73x55cm-29x22in) prov. 22-May-4 Galerie Gloggner, Luzern #86 est:1000-1200 (S.FR 2400)

RAMSAY, Allan (fl.1880-1920) British
£403 $742 €588 In Glenork near Blackmore (30x46cm-12x18in) s.indis d. s.i.d.1904 verso. 14-Jun-4 Waddingtons, Toronto #189/R est:1200-1800 (C.D 1000)
£1200 $2040 €1752 Mount Battock, Glenesk (51x76cm-20x30in) s.d.1901 s.i.d.verso. 30-Oct-3 Christie's, London #72a/R est:1500-2000

RAMSAY, Dennis (1925-) British
£251 $425 €366 Madonna and flowers (30x41cm-12x16in) s. tempera. 22-Nov-3 Jackson's, Cedar Falls #414/R
£806 $1500 €1177 By candlelight (43x62cm-17x24in) s.i. board prov. 5-Mar-4 Skinner, Boston #359/R est:1200-1800
£864 $1565 €1261 Still life with mandarins and walnuts (46x35cm-18x14in) s.d.MCMXCVII board. 31-Mar-4 Goodman, Sydney #395 (A.D 2100)
£1157 $2140 €1689 Interior with Australian flag (61x78cm-24x31in) s.d.MIXM canvas on board. 10-Mar-4 Deutscher-Menzies, Melbourne #468/R est:3000-4000 (A.D 2800)

RAMSAY, Hugh (1877-1906) Australian
Works on paper
£2459 $3885 €3590 Self portrait (50x37cm-20x15in) chl prov. 2-Sep-3 Deutscher-Menzies, Melbourne #206/R est:7000-9000 (A.D 6000)

RAMSAY, James (attrib) (1786-1854) British
£420 $769 €613 Portrait of gentleman wearing a dark coat and white stock (61x51cm-24x20in) 8-Jul-4 Duke & Son, Dorchester #280/R

RAMSDEN, Alma (20th C) American
£419 $700 €612 Turquoise jug (102x102cm-40x40in) 18-Oct-3 David Dike, Dallas #309/R

RAMSEY, Charles Frederick (1875-1951) American
Works on paper
£267 $425 €390 Woman reading (48x38cm-19x15in) s.d.1906 verso pastel sketch. 10-Sep-3 Alderfer's, Hatfield #390

RAMSEY, J (18/19th C) British
£13000 $23270 €18980 Flagship announcing her arrival with a salute at the fleet anchorage (71x128cm-28x50in) s.indis.d.1770. 26-May-4 Christie's, Kensington #571/R est:15000-20000

RAMSEY, Milne (1847-1915) American
£1766 $3250 €2578 Sailboats at sunset (20x31cm-8x12in) s.d. board. 27-Jun-4 Freeman, Philadelphia #107/R est:2000-3000
£1899 $3400 €3189 Sunset landscape (20x30cm-8x12in) s. board. 20-Mar-4 Pook & Pook, Downington #433/R est:800-1200
£1899 $3400 €3189 Landscape (15x25cm-6x10in) s. panel. 20-Mar-4 Pook & Pook, Downington #434/R est:500-1000
£2000 $3440 €2920 Visiting the Cardinal (25x20cm-10x8in) s. panel. 2-Dec-3 Bukowskis, Stockholm #294/R est:20000-25000 (S.KR 26000)
£2235 $4000 €3752 Coastal scene with ships in foreground (36x53cm-14x21in) s.d.8/08. 20-Mar-4 Pook & Pook, Downington #292/R est:1200-1800
£5988 $10000 €8742 Still life with lobster (69x58cm-27x23in) s.i.d.6.69 prov. 23-Oct-3 Shannon's, Milford #168/R est:8000-12000
£8380 $15000 €14070 Still life with ewer and fruit resting on a draped table (91x69cm-36x27in) s.d.2/72. 20-Mar-4 Pook & Pook, Downington #289/R est:15000-20000
Works on paper
£294 $500 €429 Sunset landscape (2x39cm-1x15in) s.d.12-04 W/C. 21-Nov-3 Skinner, Boston #455/R
£313 $500 €457 Coastal landscape (33x51cm-13x20in) s. i.verso W/C. 20-Sep-3 Pook & Pook, Downington #452/R
£688 $1100 €1004 Night-time landscape (30x48cm-12x19in) s.d.05 W/C. 20-Sep-3 Pook & Pook, Downington #451/R est:1200-1800

RAMUS, Aubrey (?) ?
Works on paper
£320 $534 €467 Fishing boat and other vessels off the harbour mouth (24x34cm-9x13in) s. W/C. 16-Oct-3 Lawrence, Crewkerne #659

RANALDI, Renato (1941-) Italian
Works on paper
£5068 $8919 €7500 Pirate painter (64x52cm-25x20in) s.i.d.2001 s.i.d.verso assemblage board. 22-May-4 Galleria Pananti, Florence #396/R est:7000-8000

RANC, Jean (circle) (1674-1735) French
£7800 $14040 €11388 Portrait of Donna Maria de Montaner y Canglada and her two sons (155x177cm-61x70in) i. 23-Apr-4 Christie's, Kensington #178/R est:4000-6000

RANCILLAC, Bernard (1931-) French
£1181 $1972 €1700 Composition (60x50cm-24x20in) s. oil paper on canvas. 25-Oct-3 Cornette de St.Cyr, Paris #788/R est:3000-4000
£1200 $2184 €1800 Dangers de la plage (34x26cm-13x10in) s.d.1965 decalcomania. 29-Jun-4 Cornette de St.Cyr, Paris #53/R est:2000-3000
£1818 $3036 €2600 Ellington Band (59x76cm-23x30in) s.i. acrylic paper on canvas. 11-Oct-3 Cornette de St.Cyr, Paris #99/R est:2000-2500
£1958 $3270 €2800 Wes (65x49cm-26x19in) s.i. acrylic paper on canvas. 11-Oct-3 Cornette de St.Cyr, Paris #104/R est:2000-2500
£4306 $7104 €6200 Dinah, d'apres photo W Claxton (150x150cm-59x59in) s.i.d.1997 verso acrylic. 2-Jul-3 Cornette de St.Cyr, Paris #132/R est:7000-8000
£5369 $9611 €8000 Diana (65x92cm-26x36in) s.i.d.87 verso prov. 27-May-4 Sotheby's, Paris #269/R est:5000-7000
£6000 $10920 €9000 Lighting (146x114cm-57x45in) s.i.d.1997 verso. 29-Jun-4 Cornette de St.Cyr, Paris #90/R est:10000-12000
£9333 $16987 €14000 Virginia, the light (131x197cm-52x78in) s.i.d.1986 verso. 29-Jun-4 Cornette de St.Cyr, Paris #91/R est:10000-12000
£15436 $28402 €23000 Strange Fruit (200x250cm-79x98in) s.i.d.1997 verso acrylic prov.lit. 29-Mar-4 Cornette de St.Cyr, Paris #122/R est:15000-20000
Sculpture
£6338 $10965 €9000 Handicap Venus international (201cm-79in) plaster prov.exhib. 9-Dec-3 Artcurial Briest, Paris #385/R est:10000-15000
Works on paper
£263 $484 €400 Untitled (47x33cm-19x13in) s.d.63 pastel. 27-Jun-4 Versailles Encheres #140
£270 $511 €400 Sans titre (48x34cm-19x13in) s.d.09/08/63 pastel. 21-Feb-4 Cornette de St.Cyr, Paris #386/R
£284 $536 €420 Sans titre (48x34cm-19x13in) s.i.d.15/08/63 pastel. 21-Feb-4 Cornette de St.Cyr, Paris #389
£326 $532 €470 Composition (43x31cm-17x12in) s. W/C. 18-Jul-3 Feletin, Province #195
£1806 $3016 €2600 Tina Turner et le batteur (58x75cm-23x30in) s. col wax crayon after photo prov. 21-Oct-3 Artcurial Briest, Paris #483/R est:3500-4000
£4196 $7007 €6000 Che guevara (151x117cm-59x46in) s. gouache ink screenprint. 11-Oct-3 Cornette de St.Cyr, Paris #101/R est:4000-6000

RANCILLAC, Jean Jules Paul (1934-) French
Sculpture
£1467 $2699 €2200 Un bon diable (41cm-16in) s.i.d.3/5/76 resin mixed media. 10-Jun-4 Camard, Paris #194/R est:2000-3000
£1867 $3435 €2800 Homme a la moustache (80cm-31in) s.d.78-80 resin mixed media. 10-Jun-4 Camard, Paris #193/R est:3000-4000

RANCOULET, Ernest (19th C) French
Sculpture
£894 $1600 €1305 Bust of a gentleman (74cm-29in) s. bronze. 11-Jan-4 William Jenack, New York #122 est:1000-1500
£1060 $1928 €1600 Repousseur de la Renaissance (6cm-2in) pat bronze. 15-Jun-4 Rossini, Paris #47/R est:1000-1400
£1133 $2029 €1700 Retour du marche (68cm-27in) s. pat bronze. 12-May-4 Brissoneau, France #274/R est:1200-1800
£1206 $2013 €1700 Paire de danseuses (21cm-8in) s. silver pat bronze socle. 15-Oct-3 Hotel des Ventes Mosan, Brussels #152 est:1500-2000
£1452 $2687 €2120 Figure of a young lady (47cm-19in) brown pat. bronze. 14-Mar-4 Agra, Warsaw #12/R (P.Z 10500)
£1529 $2600 €2232 A Trouville (55cm-22in) pat bronze. 25-Nov-3 Christie's, Rockefeller NY #442/R est:1500-2500
£1631 $2724 €2300 La porteuse de raisin (80cm-31in) s. brown pat bronze. 20-Jun-3 Drouot Estimations, Paris #204 est:2000-2500
£2482 $4145 €3500 La recompense (86cm-34in) i. bronze. 17-Oct-3 Berlinghof, Heidelberg #1182/R est:1600

RAND, Henry (1886-?) American
£2439 $4000 €3537 Autumn landscape (25x30cm-10x12in) s. board. 4-Jun-3 Alderfer's, Hatfield #386/R est:2500-3500

RAND, John Goffe (1801-1873) American
£4630 $7500 €6760 Portraits of Milford, New Hampshire couple (76x56cm-30x22in) i. verso panel pair lit. 1-Aug-3 North East Auctions, Portsmouth #833/R est:4000-6000

RANDALL, Maurice (fl.1899-1929) British
£400 $732 €584 Windsor Castle (25x33cm-10x13in) s.i.verso oil paper on board. 8-Jul-4 Duke & Son, Dorchester #235/R

RANDALL, Richard (?) British
Sculpture
£983 $1700 €1435 Boy (48cm-19in) bronze prov. 15-Dec-3 Hindman, Chicago #60/R est:1500-2000

RANDAVEL, Louis (1869-1947) French
Works on paper
£420 $701 €600 Orientale au panier de fruits (28x40cm-11x16in) s. W/C. 29-Jun-3 Eric Pillon, Calais #176/R

RANDERSON, Glenda (?) ?
£652 $1109 €952 Nikau palms (76x56cm-30x22in) s. oil stick. 4-Nov-3 Peter Webb, Auckland #29 est:2000-3000 (NZ.D 1800)

RANDOLPH, Lee F (1880-1956) American
£323 $600 €472 Along the coast (18x23cm-7x9in) s.i.verso canvas on board painted c.1910. 7-Mar-4 Treadway Gallery, Cincinnati #601/R
£538 $1000 €785 Hatywagon (20x25cm-8x10in) s.d.1909. 7-Mar-4 Treadway Gallery, Cincinnati #600/R est:600-800
£549 $900 €796 South coast of Brittany (20x15cm-8x6in) s.i.verso board painted c.1907. 7-Jun-3 Treadway Gallery, Cincinnati #1353

RANDS, Angus Bernard (1922-1985) British
£400 $748 €584 Winter landscape with a bridge in Arncliffe and hills beyond (46x71cm-18x28in) s. 22-Jul-4 Tennants, Leyburn #939
£550 $935 €803 View of Wharfedale, north Yorkshire (132x234cm-52x92in) s. 19-Nov-3 Tennants, Leyburn #1274

RANE, Bill (20th C) American
Works on paper
£222 $400 €324 Mother and child (67x96cm-26x38in) s. mixed media board. 25-Apr-4 Bonhams & Butterfields, San Francisco #5605/R

RANFT, Richard (1862-1931) Swiss
Works on paper
£789 $1453 €1200 L'elegante (46x36cm-18x14in) s. pastel. 28-Jun-4 Joron-Derem, Paris #161

RANFTL, Johann Matthias (1805-1854) Austrian
£1678 $3138 €2500 Man's portrait (63x49cm-25x19in) s.d.1829 one of pair. 24-Feb-4 Dorotheum, Vienna #31/R est:2500-3000
£2013 $3765 €3000 Woman's portrait (63x49cm-25x19in) s.d.1829 one of pair. 24-Feb-4 Dorotheum, Vienna #30/R est:2500-3000
£4861 $8264 €7000 Dozing in front of the fire (69x55cm-27x22in) s.d.1846 panel. 28-Oct-3 Wiener Kunst Auktionen, Vienna #13/R est:7000-20000
£5034 $9010 €7500 Girl in a red dress (42x34cm-17x13in) panel. 27-May-4 Dorotheum, Vienna #100/R est:5000-6000
£8531 $14503 €12200 Forest ranger (63x46cm-25x18in) s.d.1853 panel. 25-Nov-3 Hassfurther, Vienna #65/R est:9000-13000
Works on paper
£436 $803 €650 Young seated peasant (10x7cm-4x3in) i. verso W/C. 26-Mar-4 Dorotheum, Vienna #170/R
£570 $1050 €850 Dogs (22x28cm-9x11in) pencil. 26-Mar-4 Dorotheum, Vienna #117/R
£690 $1145 €1000 Peasant smoking pipe (35x28cm-14x11in) s.i.d.1852 W/C. 30-Sep-3 Dorotheum, Vienna #210/R
£1208 $2259 €1800 Dog (31x28cm-12x11in) mixed media. 24-Feb-4 Dorotheum, Vienna #2189 est:2000-2400

RANGER, Henry Ward (1858-1916) American
£745 $1200 €1080 End of summer (23x33cm-9x13in) s. 23-Aug-3 Harvey Clar, Oakland #1384
£1180 $1900 €1723 Landscape (30x36cm-12x14in) s. board sketch verso painted c.1910. 22-Feb-3 Bunte, Elgin #1275
£1902 $3500 €2777 Figure on a pathway near a stream (35x30cm-14x12in) s.d.1902 board. 27-Jun-4 Freeman, Philadelphia #97/R est:2000-3000
£1946 $3600 €2919 Landscape with stream (53x76cm-21x30in) s. 14-Jul-4 American Auctioneer #490208/R est:1000-1500
£2762 $4750 €4033 Stone wall (46x64cm-18x25in) s. board painted c.1900. 7-Dec-3 Treadway Gallery, Cincinnati #574/R est:5000-7000
£2793 $5000 €4078 On horseback in the surf (30x36cm-12x14in) s.indis.d. board prov. 6-May-4 Shannon's, Milford #247/R est:5000-7000
£3226 $6000 €4710 Near Mystic (71x91cm-28x36in) mono. 5-Mar-4 Skinner, Boston #454/R est:1000-1500

RANK BROADLEY, Ian (20th C) British?
Sculpture
£15000 $26850 €22500 Group of the wrestlers (197cm-78in) mono. brown pat. bronze. 25-May-4 Sotheby's, Billingshurst #388/R est:15000-25000

RANKEN, William Bruce Ellis (1881-1941) British
£320 $531 €467 A portrait of Agnes Ruth Finnie (95x69cm-37x27in) mono.d.1937 i.verso. 13-Jun-3 Jacobs & Hunt, Petersfield #227
£320 $509 €467 Portrait of a lady in pink dress (112x86cm-44x34in) s.d.1923 verso. 12-Sep-3 Gardiner & Houlgate, Bath #172/R
Works on paper
£217 $400 €317 Still life with figures and vases on a table (36x64cm-14x25in) s.d.1918 W/C pencil. 23-Mar-4 Arthur James, Florida #458/R
£4000 $6640 €5840 Head of a flower seller, Covent Garden (37x23cm-15x9in) blk chk W/C gouache. 30-Sep-3 Sotheby's, London #307/R est:1500-2000

RANKIN, Andrew Scott (1868-1942) British
Works on paper
£320 $589 €467 Stags in a highland landscape (28x44cm-11x17in) s. W/C. 10-Jun-4 Christie's, Kensington #229/R

RANKIN, David (1946-) Australian
£638 $1105 €931 Off the road (83x77cm-33x30in) s.i.d.9-75 verso oil mixed media. 10-Dec-3 Shapiro, Sydney #93 (A.D 1500)
£678 $1153 €990 Landscape III (75x80cm-30x31in) s.d.85 prov.exhib. 24-Nov-3 Sotheby's, Melbourne #101/R (A.D 1600)
£1017 $1729 €1485 Landscape II (75x105cm-30x41in) s.d.85 prov. 24-Nov-3 Sotheby's, Melbourne #145/R est:3000-5000 (A.D 2400)
£1149 $1953 €1678 Bitter Cherry (81x108cm-32x43in) s.i.d.1976 verso. 26-Nov-3 Deutscher-Menzies, Melbourne #159/R est:3500-5000 (A.D 2700)
£1626 $2911 €2374 Landscape - Red rust (171x102cm-67x40in) s.d.91 s.i.d.verso. 4-May-4 Sotheby's, Melbourne #161/R est:4000-6000 (A.D 4000)
£2479 $4587 €3619 Wanda sandhills (152x167cm-60x66in) s.d.84 s.i.d.verso. 10-Mar-4 Deutscher-Menzies, Melbourne #352/R est:7000-9000 (A.D 6000)
£3036 $4889 €4433 Ochre ridge (151x198cm-59x78in) s.d.92. 13-Oct-3 Joel, Victoria #445 est:5000-6000 (A.D 7500)
£3099 $5485 €4525 Menantic mantra (122x238cm-48x94in) s.d.95 i.verso prov. 3-May-4 Christie's, Melbourne #224/R est:6000-8000 (A.D 7500)
£3252 $5821 €4748 Inhaling the earth (182x121cm-72x48in) s.d.87 s.i.d.verso prov. 4-May-4 Sotheby's, Melbourne #116/R est:8000-12000 (A.D 8000)
£3306 $5851 €4827 Landscape (253x157cm-100x62in) s.d.84 board two panels. 3-May-4 Christie's, Melbourne #150/R est:8000-12000 (A.D 8000)
£4065 $6382 €5894 Ridge, Longshelf (168x130cm-66x51in) s.d.80 s.i.d.1980 stretcher prov.exhib.lit. 27-Aug-3 Christie's, Sydney #661/R est:5000-8000 (A.D 10000)
£5106 $8681 €7455 Jerusalem walls and windows (137x182cm-54x72in) s.d.92 s.i.d.92 verso. 25-Nov-3 Christie's, Melbourne #60/R est:10000-15000 (A.D 12000)
£8130 $12764 €11789 Ridge-mungo (136x212cm-54x83in) s.d.85 s.i.stretcher prov. 27-Aug-3 Christie's, Sydney #563/R est:5000-8000 (A.D 20000)
Works on paper
£2290 $4168 €3343 Red cottlesbridge (136x152cm-54x60in) s.d.91 s.i.d.verso synthetic polymer on canvas. 16-Jun-4 Deutscher-Menzies, Melbourne #231/R est:8000-12000 (A.D 6000)

RANKIN, George James (1864-1937) British
£580 $922 €847 Ptarmigan in winter plumage nesting on a ledge (51x71cm-20x28in) s. 18-Mar-3 Anderson & Garland, Newcastle #189/R
Works on paper
£260 $481 €380 Hedge sparrow and its nest (33x23cm-13x9in) s. W/C. 15-Jul-4 Mitchells, Cockermouth #554

RANKIN, Lucy E (20th C) American
£958 $1600 €1399 Roadrunner (76x61cm-30x24in) canvasboard. 18-Oct-3 David Dike, Dallas #253/R est:500-1000

RANN, Vollian Burr (1897-1956) American
£3374 $5500 €4926 Portrait of Frances Shea. Wharf (38x46cm-15x18in) s. double-sided exhib. 19-Jul-3 Outer Cape Auctions, Provincetown #31/R
Works on paper
£541 $1000 €790 Provincetown wharf (25x36cm-10x14in) s. gouache. 15-Feb-4 Outer Cape Auctions, Provincetown #79/R

RANSBEECK, Bert van (1957-) Belgian
Sculpture
£5600 $10024 €8400 Seer (101x61cm-40x24in) mono. arduin wood base. 15-May-4 De Vuyst, Lokeren #601/R est:4400-5000

RANSON, Paul (1864-1909) French
£2817 $4930 €4000 Paysage a la riviere et au grand arbre (61x50cm-24x20in) s. 21-Dec-3 Thierry & Lannon, Brest #198/R est:4000-6000
£7333 $13127 €11000 Paysage maritime a l'arbre double (73x60cm-29x24in) s. painted 1896. 16-May-4 Thierry & Lannon, Brest #170/R est:10000-12000
£7762 $13351 €11100 La tentation de Saint Antoine (48x76cm-19x30in) s. pastel exec.c.1900 prov.exhib.lit. 3-Dec-3 Beaussant & Lefèvre, Paris #73/R est:1500-1800
£13514 $24189 €20000 L'echo (73x52cm-29x20in) s. prov.exhib.lit. 7-May-4 Millon & Associes, Paris #87/R est:20000-30000
Works on paper
£28000 $51520 €42000 Falaises bleues (81x100cm-32x39in) s. s.i.d.1831 verso encaustic pel. 9-Jun-4 Tajan, Paris #7/R est:50000-60000

RANSONNETTE, Charles (1793-1877) French
Works on paper
£267 $483 €400 Clairiere (14x23cm-6x9in) s. W/C. 30-Mar-4 Rossini, Paris #1038

RANSVE, Bjorn (1944-) Norwegian
Works on paper
£258 $416 €377 Girl with flowers kneeling (58x44cm-23x17in) s. pastel. 25-Aug-3 Blomqvist, Lysaker #1220/R (N.KR 3000)

RANSY, Jacques (20th C) Belgian
£451 $709 €650 L'oiseau (25x43cm-10x17in) s.d.1961 panel. 26-Aug-3 Galerie Moderne, Brussels #316/R

RANSY, Jean (1910-1991) Belgian
£1333 $2427 €2000 Paysage fantastique a Tours et instruments a musique (60x80cm-24x31in) s. 4-Jul-4 MonsAntic, Maisieres #467 est:1800-2200

RANTANEN, Mari (1956-) Finnish
£600 $1074 €900 Pobeda (52x35cm-20x14in) s.d.1985 verso. 15-May-4 Hagelstam, Helsinki #229/R

RANTANEN, Silja (1955-) Finnish
£800 $1432 €1200 Blue and yellow (41x33cm-16x13in) s.d.1990 verso. 15-May-4 Hagelstam, Helsinki #228/R

RANTANEN, Ulla (1938-) Finnish
£1486 $2661 €2200 Mrs K (130x106cm-51x42in) s.d.71. 8-May-4 Bukowskis, Helsinki #257/R est:2500-3500
£4056 $6895 €5800 Nature's sign of the cross (81x81cm-32x32in) s.d.79. 29-Nov-3 Bukowskis, Helsinki #259/R est:4500-5000
Works on paper
£537 $999 €800 Meeting (69x93cm-27x37in) s.d.63 mixed media. 7-Mar-4 Bukowskis, Helsinki #426/R
£556 $928 €800 End of the meeting (69x96cm-27x38in) s.d.1968 mixed media. 26-Oct-3 Bukowskis, Helsinki #462/R

RANTTILA, Martti (1897-1964) Finnish
£403 $749 €600 Flute players (41x39cm-16x15in) s.d.23 exhib.prov. 7-Mar-4 Bukowskis, Helsinki #427/R

RANTZER, Philip (1956-) Israeli
Works on paper
£3911 $7000 €5710 Couple (81x111cm-32x44in) init.d.1995 wash ink dolls synthetic fur bulbs wire exhib. 18-Mar-4 Sotheby's, New York #76/R est:6000-8000

RANUCCI, Lucio (1924-) Italian
£404 $756 €590 Capo Miseno (59x79cm-23x31in) s.d.1990 s.i.d.verso. 24-Feb-4 Peter Webb, Auckland #178/R (NZ.D 1100)
£1812 $3352 €2700 Floral homage (76x38cm-30x15in) s.d.1970. 13-Mar-4 Meeting Art, Vercelli #177 est:1000

RANVIER-CHARTIER, Lucie (1867-1932) French
Works on paper
£493 $882 €700 Femme Orientale prenant le the (26x37cm-10x15in) s. W/C. 11-Jan-4 Rouillac, Vendome #79
£532 $888 €750 Bab el Khadra, Tunis (32x23cm-13x9in) s.i.d.1902 W/C. 19-Oct-3 Rabourdin & Choppin de Janvry, Paris #53/R

RANZMAYER, J (19th C) ?
£3356 $6007 €5000 Landscape with house in the evening sun (49x57cm-19x22in) s.indis.d. 27-May-4 Dorotheum, Vienna #141/R est:5500-6000

RANZONI, Daniele (1843-1889) Italian
Works on paper
£16000 $29440 €23360 Portrait of girl (39x29cm-15x11in) s. W/C. 8-Jun-4 Bonhams, New Bond Street #14/R est:5000-8000

RANZONI, Daniele (attrib) (1843-1889) Italian
Works on paper
£1000 $1790 €1500 Portrait of girl (35x24cm-14x9in) s. W/C. 12-May-4 Stadion, Trieste #710 est:200-300

RANZONI, Hans (elder) (1868-1956) Austrian
£694 $1132 €1000 River by evening sun (71x91cm-28x36in) s.d.908. 23-Sep-3 Wiener Kunst Auktionen, Vienna #114/R

RAO, Maximo (20th C) French?
£874 $1460 €1250 L'homme au turban rouge (110x130cm-43x51in) s.d.84 verso. 25-Jun-3 Digard, Paris #66/R

RAON, Jean (circle) (1630-1707) French
Sculpture
£9091 $15636 €13000 Head of a young girl (49cm-19in) marble red marble base exec c.1700. 2-Dec-3 Christie's, Paris #184/R est:15000-25000

RAOUL, Edouard (1886-?) Swiss?
£431 $772 €629 Elegant scene with elegant couple (46x37cm-18x15in) s. panel. 12-May-4 Dobiaschofsky, Bern #893 (S.FR 1000)

RAOUX, Jean (1677-1734) French
£32000 $58560 €46720 Four ages of man, la vieillesse (87x129cm-34x51in) s.d.1714 prov.lit. 7-Jul-4 Christie's, London #68/R est:15000-20000

RAOUX, Jean (attrib) (1677-1734) French
£6250 $10438 €9000 Les joueurs de cartes (64x77cm-25x30in) 23-Oct-3 Credit Municipal, Paris #28 est:8000-10000
Works on paper
£647 $1062 €900 Figure allegorique (30x19cm-12x7in) sanguine brown wash gouache. 6-Jun-3 Maigret, Paris #56

RAPACKI, Jozef (1871-1929) Polish
£3253 $5726 €4749 Wooded landscape (86x100cm-34x39in) s. 23-May-4 Agra, Warsaw #17/R (P.Z 23000)
Works on paper
£482 $799 €704 Italian landscape (37x21cm-15x8in) s. W/C. 15-Jun-3 Agra, Warsaw #44/R (P.Z 3000)

RAPETTI, Ottavio Giovanni (1849-?) Italian
£7447 $12436 €10500 Slaves (70x152cm-28x60in) s.d.1906. 17-Jun-3 Finarte Semenzato, Milan #524/R est:15000

RAPHAEL (after) (1483-1520) Italian
£6000 $10980 €8760 Madonna and Child (83x61cm-33x24in) 9-Jul-4 Christie's, Kensington #136/R est:4000-6000
£6338 $10965 €9000 Praying in the olive grove (25x32cm-10x13in) tempera board. 15-Dec-3 Ansorena, Madrid #111/R est:9000
£7102 $12500 €10369 Grand tour (147cm-58in circular) panel. 22-May-4 New Orleans Auction, New Orleans #559/R est:3500-5000
£7229 $12000 €10554 Madonna Della Sedia (140x114cm-55x45in) 4-Oct-3 Neal Auction Company, New Orleans #47/R est:7000-9000
£18600 $32178 €27156 Judgement of Paris (30x109cm-12x43in) panel prov. 9-Dec-3 Sotheby's, Olympia #375/R est:8000-10000
Works on paper
£5455 $9055 €7910 Cupid and Zeus (26x22cm-10x9in) i. pencil. 13-Jun-3 Zofingen, Switzerland #2312/R est:2500 (S.FR 12000)

RAPHAEL (circle) (1483-1520) Italian
£55000 $95150 €80300 Madonna and Child with a goldfinch (55x41cm-22x16in) panel prov.lit. 11-Dec-3 Sotheby's, London #12/R est:30000-50000

RAPHAEL (studio) (1483-1520) Italian
£13889 $25000 €20278 Holy Family with Saint John the Baptist (96x81cm-38x32in) panel. 22-Jan-4 Sotheby's, New York #224/R est:30000-50000

RAPHAEL (style) (1483-1520) Italian
£6040 $11114 €9000 Madonna (47cm-19in circular) panel. 25-Mar-4 Dr Fritz Nagel, Stuttgart #637/R est:10000
£6500 $11050 €9490 Madonna and Child with infant Saint John the Baptist (96x72cm-38x28in) 31-Oct-3 Christie's, Kensington #114/R est:2000-3000
£6593 $12000 €9626 Madonna (49x39cm-19x15in) panel. 17-Jun-4 Christie's, Rockefeller NY #35/R est:15000-20000
£20000 $34600 €29200 Vision of the True Cross (144x314cm-57x124in) 11-Dec-3 Sotheby's, London #129/R est:12000-15000

RAPHAEL (1483-1520) Italian
Works on paper
£155000 $283650 €226300 Head of a child. Study of a vessel, possibly an incense burner (11x9cm-4x4in) red chk over stylus pen brown ink double-sided. 8-Jul-4 Sotheby's, London #23/R est:50000-70000

RAPHAEL, Joseph (1869-1950) American
£2989 $5500 €4364 Self portrait. Study for self portrait (47x30cm-19x12in) board double-sided prov. 8-Jun-4 Bonhams & Butterfields, San Francisco #4265/R est:3000-5000
£4076 $7500 €5951 Study of roses. Portrait of the artist's daughter (31x25cm-12x10in) board double-sided prov. 8-Jun-4 Bonhams & Butterfields, San Francisco #4263/R est:7000-10000
£4118 $7000 €6012 Breton woman (43x38cm-17x15in) s. canvas on board prov. 18-Nov-3 John Moran, Pasadena #38 est:6000-8000
£5588 $9500 €8158 Art dealer, portrait of Nils Helgesen (48x38cm-19x15in) painted c.1910 sold with a photo. 18-Nov-3 John Moran, Pasadena #73 est:5000-7000
£9239 $17000 €13489 Daughters of the artist (40x32cm-16x13in) s.d.1913 prov. 8-Jun-4 Bonhams & Butterfields, San Francisco #4262/R est:8000-12000
£16304 $30000 €23804 Trees in Uccle (29x36cm-11x14in) s. prov. 8-Jun-4 Bonhams & Butterfields, San Francisco #4264/R est:10000-15000
£53977 $95000 €78806 Red Roofs (48x61cm-19x24in) s.i.d.1912. 19-May-4 Sotheby's, New York #20/R est:25000-35000
Works on paper
£417 $750 €609 Cannero, Riviera (41x57cm-16x22in) s.i. pencil W/C prov. 25-Apr-4 Bonhams & Butterfields, San Francisco #5515/R
£559 $950 €816 Near Uccle, Belgium (36x53cm-14x21in) s. Indian ink. 18-Nov-3 John Moran, Pasadena #133a
£1005 $1900 €1467 Portrait of woman in blue (38x30cm-15x12in) s.i. mixed media graphite W/C wash. 17-Feb-4 John Moran, Pasadena #138/R est:2000-3000
£1058 $2000 €1545 San Francisco Bay (28x51cm-11x20in) W/C prov. 17-Feb-4 John Moran, Pasadena #88/R est:3000-5000
£1324 $2250 €1933 Self portrait (46x36cm-18x14in) s. ink graphite. 18-Nov-3 John Moran, Pasadena #133 est:1000-2000
£3145 $5000 €4592 Landscape (23x33cm-9x13in) mono. W/C. 23-Mar-3 Auctions by the Bay, Alameda #862/R

RAPHAEL, Sarah (1960-2001) British
£900 $1638 €1314 Jose II (54x24cm-21x9in) canvas on board prov. 4-Feb-4 Sotheby's, Olympia #238/R
£1800 $3330 €2628 Portrait of Dan (36x19cm-14x7in) init. board prov. 11-Feb-4 Sotheby's, Olympia #271/R est:1500-2000
Works on paper
£1800 $3276 €2628 Pamyat 1 (116x148cm-46x58in) init.d.90 chl prov. 4-Feb-4 Sotheby's, Olympia #237/R est:2000-3000

RAPHAEL, William (1833-1914) Prussian/Canadian
£1429 $2386 €2072 Summer's day (39x28cm-15x11in) s. board. 17-Jun-3 Pinneys, Montreal #133 est:3200-3600 (C.D 3200)
£4054 $6892 €5919 Old pals (26x20cm-10x8in) s.d.1900 prov. 27-Nov-3 Heffel, Vancouver #109/R est:9000-12000 (C.D 9000)

RAPOTEC, Stanislaus (1913-1997) Australian
£1021 $1878 €1491 Untitled (91x122cm-36x48in) s.d.71 board. 29-Mar-4 Goodman, Sydney #54/R est:2000-3000 (A.D 2500)
£2236 $3510 €3242 Landscape after rain (137x122cm-54x48in) s.d.69 i.stretcher board prov. 27-Aug-3 Christie's, Sydney #647/R est:7000-12000 (A.D 5500)
£6911 $12370 €10090 Te Deum, Seville Cathedral (180x137cm-71x54in) s. composition board prov.exhib. 4-May-4 Sotheby's, Melbourne #279/R est:15000-20000 (A.D 17000)
£8051 $13686 €11754 Apollo II (183x137cm-72x54in) s.d.69 bears i.verso composition board prov. 24-Nov-3 Sotheby's, Melbourne #169/R est:5000-7000 (A.D 19000)
£8943 $14041 €12967 Untitled, hephaestus (183x137cm-72x54in) sd.70 board prov. 27-Aug-3 Christie's, Sydney #655/R est:10000-18000 (A.D 22000)
Works on paper
£611 $1111 €892 Tension X (67x97cm-26x38in) s.d.62 mixed media paper on board. 16-Jun-4 Deutscher-Menzies, Melbourne #362/R est:2500-4500 (A.D 1600)
£4959 $9174 €7240 Athene (183x137cm-72x54in) s.d.72 s.i.d.stretcher synthetic polymer on board prov. 10-Mar-4 Deutscher-Menzies, Melbourne #149/R est:15000-20000 (A.D 12000)

RAPOUS, Michele Antonio (1733-1819) Italian
£72917 $123958 €105000 Due nature morte con trionfo di fiori e frutta (128x116cm-50x46in) painted c.1770. 28-Oct-3 Della Rocca, Turin #157 est:90000-100000

RAPOUS, Michele Antonio (attrib) (1733-1819) Italian
£13333 $24400 €20000 Girl and hen. Girl and dog (101x102cm-40x40in) pair. 1-Jun-4 Sotheby's, Milan #171/R est:20000-30000

RAPP, Alex (1869-1927) Finnish
£282 $451 €400 Spring (43x51cm-17x20in) s. 18-Sep-3 Hagelstam, Helsinki #1013
£338 $605 €500 View from Vanda (30x48cm-12x19in) s.d.25/VII 27. 8-May-4 Bukowskis, Helsinki #102/R
£347 $580 €500 Winter's day (44x52cm-17x20in) s.d.26 exhib. 26-Oct-3 Bukowskis, Helsinki #464/R
£352 $563 €500 Landscape (50x55cm-20x22in) s.d.1908. 18-Sep-3 Hagelstam, Helsinki #989/R
£369 $679 €550 Spring landscape (41x33cm-16x13in) s.d.1904. 25-Mar-4 Hagelstam, Helsinki #892
£389 $649 €560 Kajsaniemi (62x50cm-24x20in) s.d.1912. 23-Oct-3 Hagelstam, Helsinki #804
£400 $716 €600 Rainbow (44x53cm-17x21in) s. 15-May-4 Hagelstam, Helsinki #136/R
£537 $999 €800 Streaming water (33x52cm-13x20in) s. 7-Mar-4 Bukowskis, Helsinki #428/R
£1533 $2745 €2300 Street scene, Tavastvagen, Helsingfors (17x40cm-7x16in) s. board. 15-May-4 Hagelstam, Helsinki #135/R est:1000

RAPP, Ginette (1928-1998) French?
£467 $835 €700 Afrique du Nord (38x42cm-15x17in) 16-May-4 Osenat, Fontainebleau #105/R

RAPP, Johann Rudolf (1827-1903) Swiss
£2172 $3692 €3171 Goat herder with goats, Urirotstock beyond (97x74cm-38x29in) s.i. 19-Nov-3 Fischer, Luzern #1244/R est:2500-3000 (S.FR 4800)

RAPPARD, Anton Gerhard Alexander van (1858-1892) Dutch
£3289 $6053 €5000 A man in his workshop (20x29cm-8x11in) s. panel. 22-Jun-4 Christie's, Amsterdam #166/R est:5000-7000
Works on paper
£664 $1110 €950 Flowers in a stoneware jug (50x33cm-20x13in) s.d.89 W/C. 30-Jun-3 Sotheby's, Amsterdam #169/R
£1389 $2319 €2000 Still life with a jug (33x39cm-13x15in) s.d.83 W/C prov. 21-Oct-3 Sotheby's, Amsterdam #139/R est:2000-3000

RAPPINI, Vittorio (1877-1939) Italian
Works on paper
£600 $1002 €876 Fruit seller. Leading the way (34x23cm-13x9in) s. W/C pair. 14-Oct-3 Bonhams, Knightsbridge #224/R
£600 $1104 €876 Musselman convent, Old Biska Tunis (36x26cm-14x10in) s. W/C. 8-Jun-4 Bonhams, Knightsbridge #18/R

RASCH, Heinrich (1840-1913) German
£604 $1111 €900 Field path from farmstead (29x12cm-11x5in) s. board. 24-Mar-4 Hugo Ruef, Munich #1076/R
£867 $1569 €1300 Dutch coast in summer (32x55cm-13x22in) s. 1-Apr-4 Van Ham, Cologne #1609/R
£867 $1577 €1300 Framers and cattle in the shade on the shores of Chiemsee (66x112cm-26x44in) s.d.1874. 1-Jul-4 Van Ham, Cologne #1566

RASCHEN, Henry (1854-1937) German/American
£879 $1600 €1283 Dutch interior (61x51cm-24x20in) s.d. prov. 19-Jun-4 Harvey Clar, Oakland #2404
£4520 $8000 €6599 Indian on horseback (25x30cm-10x12in) s. prov. 28-Apr-4 Christie's, Los Angeles #31/R est:3000-5000

RASENBERGER, Alfred (1885-1949) German
£318 $490 €500 Harvest landscape near Kamp-Lindfort (41x50cm-16x20in) s. 4-Sep-2 Schopman, Hamburg #103/R
£769 $1308 €1100 Lower Rhine city (34x46cm-13x18in) s. panel. 20-Nov-3 Van Ham, Cologne #1811/R
£1119 $1902 €1600 Winter on the ERft (61x81cm-24x32in) s.d.1919. 20-Nov-3 Van Ham, Cologne #1810/R est:1600

RASENBERGER, Gernot (1943-) German
£700 $1253 €1050 After the shoot (34x49cm-13x19in) s.i. 14-May-4 Schloss Ahlden, Ahlden #2896/R

RASENBERGER, Reinhold (20th C) Austrian
£667 $1207 €1000 Hilly summer landscape (40x51cm-16x20in) s. 1-Apr-4 Van Ham, Cologne #1610

RASETTI, Georges (19th C) French
£898 $1500 €1311 View of Plougastel (56x38cm-22x15in) s.d.1917 i.stretcher. 7-Oct-3 Sotheby's, New York #313 est:2000-3000

RASKIN, Joseph (1897-1981) American
£625 $1000 €913 Floral still life (76x51cm-30x20in) s. 21-Sep-3 Grogan, Boston #17/R

RASKIN, Saul (1878-1966) American
Works on paper
£852 $1500 €1244 Jacob and his family move to Egypt (22x28cm-9x11in) s.i. W/C. 1-Jan-4 Ben-Ami, Tel Aviv #4509/R est:2500-3500

RASMUSSEN, C (19th C) Scandinavian
£323 $548 €472 Coastal landscape from Greenland with icebergs, sailing vessel and hunters (41x48cm-16x19in) s. 10-Nov-3 Rasmussen, Vejle #324/R (D.KR 3500)

RASMUSSEN, Georg Anton (1842-1914) Norwegian
£447 $746 €630 Norwegian fjord with houses and fisherman in boat (17x27cm-7x11in) s.d.96 panel. 17-Oct-3 Behringer, Furth #1485/R
£559 $1029 €850 Crossing the fjord (18x28cm-7x11in) indis.s.d.96 panel. 22-Jun-4 Christie's, Amsterdam #210/R
£679 $1154 €991 Near Bergen (27x37cm-11x15in) s. bears d. board. 19-Nov-3 Fischer, Luzern #2251/R (S.FR 1500)
£1067 $1931 €1600 Fishing boat on lakeshore (26x38cm-10x15in) s. panel. 1-Apr-4 Van Ham, Cologne #1612
£1278 $2198 €1866 Fjord landscape from the west coast of Norway (27x39cm-11x15in) s.d.1872. 8-Dec-3 Blomqvist, Oslo #441/R est:20000-30000 (N.KR 15000)
£1467 $2655 €2200 Fjord in summer (35x53cm-14x21in) s.d.76. 1-Apr-4 Van Ham, Cologne #1613/R est:800
£1500 $2505 €2190 Sailing down the fjord (40x74cm-16x29in) s. s.verso. 12-Nov-3 Sotheby's, Olympia #209/R
£1745 $3246 €2600 Hauling in the nets on fjord in summer (42x64cm-17x25in) s.d.81. 6-Mar-4 Arnold, Frankfurt #825/R est:600
£1793 $2995 €2618 Mountain landscape on the west coast of Norway (50x70cm-20x28in) s.d.1864. 13-Oct-3 Blomqvist, Oslo #275/R est:25000-35000 (N.KR 21000)
£1897 $3490 €2770 Fjord (20x35cm-8x14in) s.d. 26-Mar-4 Koller, Zurich #3099/R est:3000-4000 (S.FR 4400)
£5691 $10415 €8309 On the fjord (65x98cm-26x39in) s.d.1877. 7-Jun-4 Blomqvist, Oslo #317/R est:70000-90000 (N.KR 70000)
£8333 $13750 €12000 Bavarian lake - cattle being loaded on ferry (105x157cm-41x62in) s.d.1885. 3-Jul-3 Van Ham, Cologne #1414/R est:1600

RASMUSSEN, Helge (20th C) Scandinavian
Works on paper
£284 $475 €415 Eagle in rough seas (53x74cm-21x29in) s. W/C gouache. 20-Jun-3 Freeman, Philadelphia #35/R

RASMUSSEN, I E C (1841-1893) Danish
£284 $508 €415 Seascape with vessels (34x26cm-13x10in) init. 12-Jan-4 Rasmussen, Vejle #17/R (D.KR 3000)
£806 $1306 €1177 Coastal landscape with sailing ship (29x51cm-11x20in) s.d.1871. 9-Aug-3 Hindemae, Ullerslev #32/R (D.KR 8500)
£854 $1383 €1247 Coastal landscape with woman mending nets (34x45cm-13x18in) init.d.66. 9-Aug-3 Hindemae, Ullerslev #31/R (D.KR 9000)
£895 $1638 €1307 Coastal landscape from the south of Fyn (26x40cm-10x16in) init. 9-Jun-4 Rasmussen, Copenhagen #1690/R (D.KR 10000)
£1262 $1993 €1830 Boats on the water, coast in background (12x24cm-5x9in) init. prov. 3-Sep-3 Museumsbygningen, Copenhagen #202 est:2000 (D.KR 13500)
£1267 $2268 €1850 Woman walking on woodland path. init. 10-May-4 Rasmussen, Vejle #58/R est:6000-8000 (D.KR 14000)
£1623 $3003 €2370 Coastal landscape with sailing vessels, snow-covered mountains in background (23x36cm-9x14in) panel. 15-Mar-4 Rasmussen, Vejle #181/R est:6000-8000 (D.KR 18000)
£1880 $3440 €2745 Eskimo couple watching the sunset over the fjord (34x51cm-13x20in) init.d.1870. 9-Jun-4 Rasmussen, Copenhagen #1771/R est:15000 (D.KR 21000)
£4476 $8192 €6535 Fishing boats in the breakers (78x136cm-31x54in) init.d.1887. 9-Jun-4 Rasmussen, Copenhagen #1818/R est:50000 (D.KR 50000)

RASMUSSEN, Jens Erik Carl (1841-1893) Danish
£4029 $7372 €5882 Fishermen in their boats off the Italian coast (61x100cm-24x39in) s.d.1878. 9-Jun-4 Rasmussen, Copenhagen #1447/R est:40000-50000 (D.KR 45000)
£4476 $8192 €6535 Young Eskimo in kayak off the coast (30x40cm-12x16in) init.d.1870. 9-Jun-4 Rasmussen, Copenhagen #1778/R est:50000-75000 (D.KR 50000)
£116801 $217251 €170529 Day in June on Godthaap fjord with Eskimos in boat on their summer journey (59x98cm-23x39in) s.d.1878 exhib. 2-Mar-4 Rasmussen, Copenhagen #1281/R est:200000-250000 (D.KR 1300000)

RASMUSSEN, N P (1847-1918) Danish
£419 $658 €612 Still life of pink roses (39x31cm-15x12in) mono.d.1916. 30-Aug-3 Rasmussen, Havnen #2185 (D.KR 4500)
£597 $1069 €872 Yellow and white flowers in vase (53x40cm-21x16in) init.d.22-23 april 1917. 10-May-4 Rasmussen, Vejle #466/R (D.KR 6600)
£627 $1129 €915 Winter landscape with hare (42x53cm-17x21in) init.d.1909. 24-Apr-4 Rasmussen, Havnen #2151/R (D.KR 7000)
£637 $1063 €930 Woodland with bird (40x60cm-16x24in) mono.d.15/12 94. 25-Oct-3 Rasmussen, Havnen #2221/R (D.KR 6800)

RASMUSSEN, Rasmus Carl (1847-1923) Danish
£724 $1296 €1057 Wooded landscape with mother and child on path (38x53cm-15x21in) mono.d.87. 10-May-4 Rasmussen, Vejle #85/R (D.KR 8000)

RASMUSSEN, Solve (19/20th C) Norwegian?
£518 $860 €751 Steamer and rowing boats on fjord (63x96cm-25x38in) s. 16-Jun-3 Blomqvist, Lysaker #1345 (N.KR 6000)

RASMUSSEN, Thorvald (1850-1919) Danish
£571 $971 €834 Historical Swedish battle scene (78x124cm-31x49in) s. 10-Nov-3 Rasmussen, Vejle #468/R (D.KR 6200)

RASSENFOSSE, Armand (1862-1934) Belgian
£1958 $3329 €2800 Nu accroupi (73x56cm-29x22in) s. panel. 27-Nov-3 Millon & Associes, Paris #180/R est:2500-3000

Works on paper
£467 $859 €700 Entree de chateau (31x22cm-12x9in) s.d.fevrier 1921 W/C. 14-Jun-4 Horta, Bruxelles #427
£470 $874 €700 Faunesse (19x9cm-7x4in) mono.i. graphite Indian ink. 2-Mar-4 Artcurial Briest, Paris #24
£470 $832 €700 Les menides (49x41cm-19x16in) s.d.1913 dr. 27-Apr-4 Campo & Campo, Antwerp #190
£816 $1461 €1200 Les filles de Milton, une tete ensanglantee ceinte de laurier (25x18cm-10x7in) s. col chk. 18-Mar-4 Christie's, Paris #313/R
£915 $1584 €1300 Femme au miroir (37x25cm-15x10in) s. graphite. 10-Dec-3 Hotel des Ventes Mosan, Brussels #161
£1074 $1976 €1600 Nu de dos (37x24cm-15x9in) s.d.1921 chl col crayon chk. 23-Mar-4 Galerie Moderne, Brussels #201/R est:700-1000
£1135 $1895 €1600 Nu au drape (38x30cm-15x12in) s.d.1925 dr. 14-Oct-3 Vanderkindere, Brussels #125
£1156 $2070 €1700 L'amour supreme, portrait d'une nonne (25x18cm-10x7in) s. col chk. 18-Mar-4 Christie's, Paris #312/R est:1500-2000
£3400 $5678 €4964 Elegant (33x15cm-13x6in) init. col chks pencil. 22-Oct-3 Sotheby's, Olympia #125/R est:1500-2000

RASTORFAR, Lorraine (20th C) New Zealander
£326 $554 €476 Blind (225x52cm-89x20in) s.d.1996 acrylic three hanging section. 4-Nov-3 Peter Webb, Auckland #137 (NZ.D 900)

RASTRUP, Lars (1862-1949) Danish
£537 $983 €784 Interior scene with two busy girls (59x49cm-23x19in) init.d.17. 9-Jun-4 Rasmussen, Copenhagen #2007/R (D.KR 6000)

RATEL, H (19th C) Italian?
£1216 $2141 €1800 View of Venice (40x32cm-16x13in) s.d.1866. 19-May-4 Il Ponte, Milan #528 est:600-700

RATHBONE, Harold (1858-?) British
Works on paper
£2000 $3260 €2920 Equinoctial sea Isle of Man (35x50cm-14x20in) s.d.1908 pastel. 25-Sep-3 Mellors & Kirk, Nottingham #733/R est:1200-1600

RATHBONE, John (1750-1807) British
£250 $448 €365 River with stone bridge and figures (24x31cm-9x12in) s. panel. 17-May-4 David Duggleby, Scarborough #681/R
Works on paper
£750 $1373 €1095 View of Rochester, Kent, with figures (28x42cm-11x17in) pen ink W/C prov. 28-Jan-4 Dreweatt Neate, Newbury #29/R

RATHBONE, John (attrib) (1750-1807) British
£529 $1000 €772 Woody landscape with cottage (22x32cm-9x13in) prov. 21-Feb-4 Weschler, Washington #256

RATHBONE, John (circle) (1750-1807) British
£7000 $12880 €10220 View of Coniston and Wetherlam, with cattle in the foreground (82x91cm-32x36in) 11-Jun-4 Christie's, London #43/R est:5000-8000

RATHJENS, William (1842-1882) British
£1071 $1843 €1564 Floral still life of chrysanthemums with a dish of fruit (56x51cm-22x20in) s. 2-Dec-3 Ritchie, Toronto #50/R est:3000-5000 (C.D 2400)

RATHMELL, Thomas (1912-1990) British
Works on paper
£250 $455 €365 Two nudes with outstretched hands (39x23cm-15x9in) s. W/C. 21-Jun-4 Bonhams, Bath #333

RATHSMAN, Siri (1895-1974) Swedish
£604 $1027 €882 Composition in red (72x90cm-28x35in) s.d.1949. 5-Nov-3 AB Stockholms Auktionsverk #741/R (S.KR 8000)
£642 $1091 €937 La jeune bete (37x55cm-15x22in) s.i.d.1942. 4-Nov-3 Bukowskis, Stockholm #228/R (S.KR 8500)
£1284 $2183 €1875 Studio interior with woman (84x65cm-33x26in) s.d.1925. 4-Nov-3 Bukowskis, Stockholm #116/R est:20000-25000 (S.KR 17000)

RATINCKX, Jos (1860-1937) Belgian
£1761 $3046 €2500 L'Alchemiste (27x37cm-11x15in) s. panel. 14-Dec-3 St-Germain-en-Laye Encheres #38/R est:2800-3000

RATNAVIRA, Gamini (20th C) Sri Lankan
Works on paper
£272 $500 €397 Leopard family (56x84cm-22x33in) s. mixed media. 13-Jun-4 Bonhams & Butterfields, Los Angeles #7027/R

RATTNER, Abraham (1895-1978) American
£2844 $4750 €4152 Autumn still life no 6 (53x65cm-21x26in) s. s.i.stretcher prov. 7-Oct-3 Sotheby's, New York #239 est:3000-5000
£3620 $6045 €5285 Evening landscape (89x115cm-35x45in) s. s.i.d.1953 stretcher prov. 17-Nov-3 Waddingtons, Toronto #21/R est:8000-12000 (C.D 8000)
Works on paper
£516 $950 €753 Figures and the sea (28x38cm-11x15in) s. W/C gouache board. 10-Jun-4 Swann Galleries, New York #198a/R

RATY, Albert (1889-1970) Belgian
£333 $597 €500 Portrait d'homme (46x38cm-18x15in) s.d.1931. 11-May-4 Vanderkindere, Brussels #609
£699 $1203 €1000 Personnages devant un calvaire (40x32cm-16x13in) s. panel. 5-Dec-3 Gros & Delettrez, Paris #66
£724 $1332 €1100 Paysage ardennais (24x33cm-9x13in) s. panel. 22-Jun-4 Palais de Beaux Arts, Brussels #304/R
£979 $1635 €1400 En Alsace, le vieux Pont Kaiserberg (33x41cm-13x16in) s. s.i.d.1937 verso board. 11-Oct-3 De Vuyst, Lokeren #302/R
£1597 $2540 €2300 View of village (50x60cm-20x24in) s. 9-Sep-3 Vanderkindere, Brussels #84
£2098 $3566 €3000 Village Ardennais (33x41cm-13x16in) s. panel. 1-Dec-3 Palais de Beaux Arts, Brussels #307/R est:3000-5000
£2465 $4264 €3500 Atelier de l'artiste, Alle sur Semois (50x60cm-20x24in) s. lit. 10-Dec-3 Hotel des Ventes Mosan, Brussels #256/R est:4000-5000
£3497 $5944 €5000 Sapiniere d'Ardennes (38x46cm-15x18in) s. 1-Dec-3 Palais de Beaux Arts, Brussels #305/R est:4000-6000
£3618 $6549 €5500 Village en Ardennes (50x60cm-20x24in) s. 19-Apr-4 Horta, Bruxelles #114/R est:6000-8000
£3667 $6710 €5500 Pecheurs sur la quai (54x65cm-21x26in) s. 7-Jun-4 Palais de Beaux Arts, Brussels #287/R est:5500-7500
£4167 $7458 €6250 Village sur la Semois, Bouillon (70x84cm-28x33in) s. 11-May-4 Vanderkindere, Brussels #220/R est:6250-8250
£5594 $9510 €8000 Paysage Ardennais (60x70cm-24x28in) s. prov. 1-Dec-3 Palais de Beaux Arts, Brussels #303/R est:8000-12000
£6738 $11252 €9500 Retour de chasse (70x80cm-28x31in) s. lit. 14-Oct-3 Vanderkindere, Brussels #40/R
Works on paper
£278 $442 €400 Nu allonge (23x31cm-9x12in) s. crayon ink dr. 9-Sep-3 Vanderkindere, Brussels #76
£528 $914 €750 Fermette en Ardennes (32x41cm-13x16in) s. wash. 9-Dec-3 Vanderkindere, Brussels #23

RAU, Adolf (1867-1908) German
£611 $966 €880 Early spring (79x105cm-31x41in) d. lit. 19-Sep-3 Schloss Ahlden, Ahlden #1607/R

RAU, Alexander (20th C) German
£1181 $1948 €1700 Young fisherwomen with baskets on Dutch beach (81x120cm-32x47in) s. 3-Jul-3 Van Ham, Cologne #1415/R est:1900

RAU, Emil (1858-1937) German
£2657 $4517 €3800 Happy home coming (71x54cm-28x21in) s. 20-Nov-3 Van Ham, Cologne #1812/R est:3000
£3843 $6879 €5611 A flirt (121x97cm-48x38in) s. 22-Mar-4 Blomqvist, Oslo #313/R est:40000-60000 (N.KR 48000)

RAU, Gustav A H (1880-1957) German
£625 $1044 €913 Dalias in a vase (50x50cm-20x20in) s.d.1935 acrylic gouache cardboard. 19-Oct-3 Agra, Warsaw #68/R (P.Z 4000)
£664 $1143 €950 Prehistoric grave under evening sky (100x74cm-39x29in) double-sided. 5-Dec-3 Bolland & Marotz, Bremen #394/R
£681 $1178 €994 Bouquet of lilac rhododendrons (50x50cm-20x20in) s. cardboard painted 1935. 14-Dec-3 Agra, Warsaw #69/R (P.Z 4500)

RAUBER, Wilhelm Carl (1849-1926) German
£1049 $1783 €1500 Before the battle (27x32cm-11x13in) mono. lit. 28-Nov-3 Schloss Ahlden, Ahlden #1457/R est:1800
£1333 $2387 €2000 Maiden reading a letter (48x38cm-19x15in) s.d.1874. 15-May-4 Hagelstam, Helsinki #44/R
£3667 $6600 €5500 Pause from the journey (75x126cm-30x50in) s.i.d.16 exhib. 21-Apr-4 Christie's, Amsterdam #21/R est:3000-5000

RAUCH, J (1868-1921) German
£1325 $2424 €2000 What does the future hold? (47x38cm-19x15in) s. 8-Apr-4 Dorotheum, Vienna #82 est:2000-2400

RAUCH, Johann Nepomuk (1804-1847) Austrian
£345 $576 €500 Two calves by tree trunk in landscape (25x32cm-10x13in) s.i.d.1830 lit. 10-Jul-3 Allgauer, Kempten #2652/R
£4895 $8322 €7000 Kloster Melk on the Donau (25x34cm-10x13in) s.d.27 copper. 24-Nov-3 Dorotheum, Vienna #28/R est:7000-9000

RAUCH, Neo (1960-) German
£3467 $6344 €5200 Untitled (42x32cm-17x13in) s.d.93 oil gouache pencil. 4-Jun-4 Lempertz, Koln #378/R est:2500
£16760 $30000 €24470 Ernte, harvest (147x98cm-58x39in) s.d.92 oil wash paper prov. 14-May-4 Phillips, New York #118/R est:35000-45000
£83832 $140000 €122395 Hafenstadt - seaport (130x205cm-51x81in) s.d.95 oil paper on canvas prov. 14-Nov-3 Phillips, New York #183/R est:40000-50000
£89385 $160000 €130502 Kamin (100x70cm-39x28in) s.d.00 prov. 12-May-4 Christie's, Rockefeller NY #322/R est:60000-80000

RAUDNITZ, Albert (1814-1899) German
£2210 $4000 €3227 Storytime (101x81cm-40x32in) s.i.d.87. 30-Mar-4 Christie's, Rockefeller NY #87/R est:5000-7000
£3911 $7000 €5710 Storytime. s. 13-May-4 Dallas Auction Gallery, Dallas #288/R est:5000-8000

RAUFFT, Franz Ludwig (1660-1719) Swiss
£805 $1482 €1200 Neptune and Amphitrite (75x66cm-30x26in) 25-Mar-4 Dr Fritz Nagel, Stuttgart #684/R

RAULIN, A (19th C) French
£6711 $12349 €10000 Vue de l'Acropole a Athenes (32x46cm-13x18in) s.d.1863. 24-Mar-4 Tajan, Paris #158/R est:7000-8000

RAUMANN, Joseph (1908-) Hungarian

£342	$582	€500	Le Havre (73x55cm-29x22in) s.d.1964. 9-Nov-3 Eric Pillon, Calais #232/R
£379	$633	€550	Canal Saint-Martin (46x55cm-18x22in) s. 11-Nov-3 Lesieur & Le Bars, Le Havre #92

RAUPP, Friedrich (1871-1949) German

£336	$624	€500	Coastal landscape, St Ives (52x93cm-20x37in) s. 7-Mar-4 Bukowskis, Helsinki #508/R
£704	$1218	€1000	Mending the nets (70x100cm-28x39in) s. 10-Dec-3 Christie's, Amsterdam #173

RAUPP, Karl (1837-1918) German

£1987	$3616	€3000	Two peasants in a rowing boat full of baskets (50x60cm-20x24in) s. 16-Jun-4 Hugo Ruef, Munich #1066/R est:2500
£8333	$13583	€12000	Gathering storm (117x90cm-46x35in) s.i.d.82. 24-Sep-3 Neumeister, Munich #534/R est:20000
£12500	$20625	€18000	Boat trip on the Chiemsee (81x156cm-32x61in) s.i. 2-Jul-3 Neumeister, Munich #746/R est:9000
£13974	$25432	€20402	Children feeding the ducklings (88x71cm-35x28in) s.i. lit. 16-Jun-4 Fischer, Luzern #1205/R est:12000-14000 (S.FR 32000)

RAUSCH, Leonhard (1813-1895) German

£1497	$2679	€2200	Watermill by stream (55x81cm-22x32in) s. 17-Mar-4 Neumeister, Munich #573/R est:2200
£2500	$4675	€3750	Landscape with figures about to cross ford (107x152cm-42x60in) s. 21-Jul-4 John Nicholson, Haslemere #198/R est:3000-5000

RAUSCHENBERG, Robert (1925-) American

£7784	$13000	€11365	Untitled (56x76cm-22x30in) s.i.d.82 solvent transfer pencil. 13-Nov-3 Sotheby's, New York #290/R est:12000-18000
£11976	$20000	€17485	Untitled (72x61cm-28x24in) s.d.87 oil paper. 7-Oct-3 Sotheby's, New York #411 est:10000-12000
£19000	$34580	€27740	Erosive hide (123x91cm-48x36in) s.d.89 acrylic aluminium prov. 6-Feb-4 Sotheby's, London #236/R est:8000-12000
£30726	$55000	€44860	Babel - Urban Bourbon Series (305x122cm-120x48in) acrylic enamel on aluminium exec 1988 prov.exhib. 13-May-4 Sotheby's, New York #240/R est:40000-50000
£72626	$130000	€106034	Boot (173x183cm-68x72in) s.i.d.79 verso solvent transfer fabric collage wood 3 parts prov. 13-May-4 Sotheby's, New York #220/R est:120000-180000
£1452514	$2600000	€2120670	Monk (35x30cm-14x12in) s.i.d.1955 oil printed paper collage on linen prov.exhib.lit. 11-May-4 Christie's, Rockefeller NY #18/R est:2000000-3000000

Prints

£1519	$2750	€2218	Avenue, from Tibetan Keys and Locks (183x46cm-72x18in) s.num.20/21 multiple wall relief photo-silkscreened decals. 19-Apr-4 Bonhams & Butterfields, San Francisco #303/R est:2000-3000
£1622	$3000	€2368	Test stone 3 (56x71cm-22x28in) s.d.1967 num.61/70 col lithograph. 12-Feb-4 Christie's, Rockefeller NY #186/R est:2500-3500
£1622	$3000	€2368	Ape, from Stoned Moon Series (93x63cm-37x25in) s.d.1970 num.P.P.II red lithograph. 12-Feb-4 Christie's, Rockefeller NY #187/R est:1200-1500
£1765	$3000	€2577	Sink (40x41cm-16x16in) s.i.d.1964 lithograph. 4-Nov-3 Christie's, Rockefeller NY #329/R est:2500-3500
£1765	$3000	€2577	Baby Bellini (76x57cm-30x22in) s.d.1993 etching aquatint. 4-Nov-3 Christie's, Rockefeller NY #334/R est:2000-3000
£1796	$3000	€2622	Speculations witness (174x80cm-69x31in) s.d.1996 num.46/55 col silkscreen. 21-Oct-3 Bonhams & Butterfields, San Francisco #1403/R
£1882	$3200	€2748	Mark (40x41cm-16x16in) s.i.d.1964 lithograph. 4-Nov-3 Christie's, Rockefeller NY #328/R est:3000-4000
£1923	$3500	€2808	Stuntman I (43x33cm-17x13in) color lithograph. 19-Jun-4 Du Mouchelle, Detroit #3188/R est:3000-5000
£2072	$3750	€3025	Waves (226x107cm-89x42in) s.d.1969 num.25/27 lithograph. 19-Apr-4 Bonhams & Butterfields, San Francisco #300/R est:2000-3000
£2119	$3750	€3094	Test stone 3 (59x79cm-23x31in) s.d.1967 num.32/71 lithograph. 30-Apr-4 Sotheby's, New York #438/R est:3000-4000
£2200	$4004	€3212	Carnegie Hall (150x102cm-59x40in) s.d.1990 num.40/60 col lithograph. 1-Jul-4 Sotheby's, London #433/R est:2500-3000
£2331	$3800	€3403	Front Roll (101x75cm-40x30in) s.d.1964 num.9/39 blk red lithograph on Rives BFK. 24-Sep-3 Christie's, Rockefeller NY #342/R est:3500-4500
£2353	$4000	€3435	Soviet-American Array VI (232x141cm-91x56in) s.d.88-90 etching aquatint. 4-Nov-3 Christie's, Rockefeller NY #333/R est:6000-8000
£2600	$4316	€3796	Samarkand stitches VII (125x112cm-49x44in) s.d.1988 col screenprint collage fabric edition of 62. 6-Oct-3 Sotheby's, London #300/R est:1500-2000
£2657	$4438	€3800	Hybrid (125x86cm-49x34in) s.d.70 num.41/52 col lithograph lit. 11-Oct-3 De Vuyst, Lokeren #303/R est:3800-4400
£3374	$5500	€4926	Signs (109x86cm-43x34in) s.d.1970 num.127/250 col screenprint wove paper. 24-Sep-3 Christie's, Rockefeller NY #346/R est:3000-4000
£3667	$6747	€5500	Hoarfrost editions - Scent (218x127cm-86x50in) num.19/30 transfere on tissue exec 1974 prov.exhib. 9-Jun-4 Artcurial Briest, Paris #489/R est:6000-8000
£4027	$7128	€6000	Hoarfrost editions - Sand (192x93cm-76x37in) s.d.1974 num.12/30 transfere on tissue. 28-Apr-4 Artcurial Briest, Paris #348/R est:6000-8000
£5000	$9150	€7500	Sling shots Lit No 8 - black state (215x143cm-85x56in) s.d. lithograph serigraph sailcloth neon reeds plastic. 4-Jun-4 Lempertz, Koln #381/R est:10000
£5085	$9000	€7424	Signs (90x68cm-35x27in) s.d.1970 num.233/250 col screenprint. 28-Apr-4 Christie's, Rockefeller NY #386/R est:4000-6000
£5650	$10000	€8249	Soviet American array VI (226x136cm-89x54in) s.d.88-90 num.20/59 intaglio print. 30-Apr-4 Sotheby's, New York #441/R est:5000-7000
£5667	$10427	€8500	Hoarfrost editions - Scrape (192x93cm-76x37in) s.num.26.32 transfere on tissue exec 1974 prov.exhib. 9-Jun-4 Artcurial Briest, Paris #490/R est:6000-8000
£6200	$11222	€9052	Ringer State (118x91cm-46x36in) offset lithograph screenprint transferred to collage paper bag. 1-Apr-4 Christie's, Kensington #281/R est:4000-6000
£9412	$16000	€13742	Stuntman I, II and III (58x45cm-23x18in) s. col lithograph set of 3. 31-Oct-3 Sotheby's, New York #724/R
£10000	$17000	€14600	Sky garden (226x106cm-89x42in) s.i.d.1969 lithograph col screenprint. 4-Nov-3 Christie's, Rockefeller NY #330/R est:15000-25000
£10615	$19000	€15498	Tampa drawing (165x101cm-65x40in) s.d.72 screenprint linen collage prov. 14-May-4 Phillips, New York #267/R est:20000-30000
£11765	$20000	€17177	Water stop (137x80cm-54x31in) s. col lithograph. 31-Oct-3 Sotheby's, New York #726/R
£251497	$420000	€367186	Chroma (152x315cm-60x124in) s.d.84 oil silkscreen transfer three attached canvases exhib. 12-Nov-3 Christie's, Rockefeller NY #383/R est:150000-200000

Sculpture

£1500	$2715	€2190	Box cars - bones and unions (86x67x8cm-34x26x3in) handmade paper bamboo fabric executed 1975 prov. 1-Apr-4 Christie's, Kensington #278/R est:2000-3000
£1737	$2953	€2536	Tampa clay (58x61x8cm-23x24x3in) s.i.d.72 burned clay collage in plexi box. 5-Nov-3 AB Stockholms Auktionsverk #965/R est:30000-40000 (S.KR 23000)
£1758	$3112	€2567	Tampa Clay (58x61x9cm-23x24x4in) s.d.72 burned clay collage in plexibox. 27-Apr-4 AB Stockholms Auktionsverk #1158/R est:30000-40000 (S.KR 24000)
£2941	$5000	€4294	Publicon-station V (46x151x20cm-18x59x8in) wood aluminium mirror silk. 31-Oct-3 Sotheby's, New York #729/R
£3390	$6000	€4949	Publicon station I (150x76x30cm-59x30x12in) wood construction. 30-Apr-4 Sotheby's, New York #440/R est:8000-12000
£3500	$6335	€5110	Quorum - bones and unions (163x114x11cm-64x45x4in) rag mud rope bamboo executed 1975 prov. 1-Apr-4 Christie's, Kensington #279/R est:1000-1500
£6769	$12319	€9883	Capitol - bones and unions (84x130cm-33x51in) bambus silk flag glass. 17-Jun-4 Kornfeld, Bern #708 est:12500 (S.FR 15500)
£10588	$18000	€15458	Publicon-station I (150x76x30cm-59x30x12in) wood plexiglas epoxy. 31-Oct-3 Sotheby's, New York #728/R
£16107	$29637	€24000	Spindle Top Rock (91cm-36in) s.d.1988 soldered painted metal. 29-Mar-4 Cornette de St.Cyr, Paris #56/R est:12000-15000
£64246	$115000	€93799	Traffic flower glut (127x192x20cm-50x76x8in) assembled metal parts exec 1987 prov.exhib. 13-May-4 Sotheby's, New York #243/R est:25000-35000
£137725	$230000	€201079	Braggard, shiner (242x237x47cm-95x93x19in) s.d.1988 acrylic metal rubber mirrored aluminum prov.exhib. 13-Nov-3 Sotheby's, New York #264/R est:100000-150000

Works on paper

£6500	$11765	€9490	Untitled (59x39cm-23x15in) s.d.79 paper collage solvent transfer on paper prov. 1-Apr-4 Christie's, Kensington #282/R est:7000-9000
£9097	$15192	€13100	Sans titre (32x24cm-13x9in) s. technique collage prov. 25-Oct-3 Cornette de St.Cyr, Paris #792/R est:15000-20000
£15569	$26000	€22731	Untitled (151x102cm-59x40in) s.d.79 solvent transfer paper collage prov. 12-Nov-3 Christie's, Rockefeller NY #369/R est:25000-35000
£20958	$35000	€30599	Hoarfrost (100x124cm-39x49in) silkscreen fabric prov. 13-Nov-3 Sotheby's, New York #250/R est:40000-60000
£25140	$45000	€36704	Rabbits (53x46cm-21x18in) s.d.86 phototransfer acrylic goldleaf board prov. 12-May-4 Christie's, Rockefeller NY #214/R est:25000-35000
£27000	$49140	€39420	Jade (155x59cm-61x23in) s.i.d.78 solvent transfer collage pencil prov. 6-Feb-4 Sotheby's, London #258/R est:25000-35000
£38000	$69160	€55480	Sunday (58x76cm-23x30in) init.d.68 i.verso correction fluid W/C ink stamps pencil. 5-Feb-4 Christie's, London #168/R est:7000-9000
£173184	$310000	€252849	For the living theatre (37x58cm-15x23in) s.i.d.1961 verso solvent transfer pencil W/C gouache prov.exhib. 13-May-4 Sotheby's, New York #141/R est:100000-150000

RAUSCHNABEL, William Fredrick (1883-1047) American

£1078	$1800	€1574	Farmer and horses ploughing a field at sunrise, marin (81x102cm-32x40in) s. 13-Jul-3 Butterfields, San Francisco #2037/R est:1000-1500

RAUSENBERGER, Eline (1944-) Belgian

£267	$480	€400	View on the Rialto bridge, Venice (61x50cm-24x20in) s.d.62 s. verso cardboard. 26-Apr-4 Bernaerts, Antwerp #580/R
£302	$553	€450	Le bar a striptease (40x40cm-16x16in) s.d.1969 eglomised. 8-Jul-4 Campo, Vlaamse Kaai #228

RAUTIAINEN, Hjalmar (20th C) Finnish

£381	$693	€560	Friends (37x46cm-15x18in) s.d.45. 8-Feb-4 Bukowskis, Helsinki #436/R

RAUTIO, Vaino (1894-1974) Finnish

£282	$451	€400	Reading (65x54cm-26x21in) s.d.1941. 21-Sep-3 Bukowskis, Helsinki #435/R

RAVA, Giovanni (1874-1944) Italian

£503	$891	€750	Spanish woman (58x48cm-23x19in) s.d.1927 canvas on cardboard. 1-May-4 Meeting Art, Vercelli #157
£1200	$2208	€1800	Mountainous landscape with peasant women (32x23cm-13x9in) s. cardboard. 8-Jun-4 Sotheby's, Milan #43/R est:1800-2500

RAVAGNAN, Carlo (19/20th C) Italian

Works on paper

£284	$460	€400	Piazza Unita, passeggiata (27x42cm-11x17in) s. W/C board. 22-May-3 Stadion, Trieste #201/R

RAVANAT, Theodore (1812-1863) French

Works on paper

£302	$562	€450	Chemin arbore, au fond un village (30x47cm-12x19in) mono. chl. 8-Mar-4 Rieunier, Paris #f
£416	$774	€620	Etude d'arbres (30x45cm-12x18in) mono. chl. 8-Mar-4 Rieunier, Paris #g

RAVANNE, Léon Gustave (1854-1904) French

£378	$650	€552	Honfleur, Le Havre (25x28cm-10x11in) s.d.1897. 6-Dec-3 Neal Auction Company, New Orleans #215
£1259	$2140	€1800	Bateaux de peche (35x28cm-14x11in) s. panel. 24-Nov-3 Boscher, Cherbourg #799/R est:1500-2000
£1408	$2282	€2000	Barques de peche a Grandchamp (27x35cm-11x14in) s.d.1899 panel. 11-Aug-3 Boscher, Cherbourg #788 est:1800-2000
£1690	$2924	€2400	L'arrivee des pecheurs (33x46cm-13x18in) s. 10-Dec-3 Millon & Associes, Paris #51/R est:2500-3000

RAVARY, Marcel (1940-) Canadian

£244	$423	€356	Jour d'hiver (51x61cm-20x24in) s.i.verso. 9-Dec-3 Pinneys, Montreal #178 (C.D 550)
£268	$447	€389	Les enfant dans le vieux Montreal (51x41cm-20x16in) s. 17-Jun-3 Pinneys, Montreal #150 (C.D 600)
£335	$569	€489	Soir d'hiver a Rosemont (40x51cm-16x20in) s. s.i.verso acrylic pov. 6-Nov-3 Heffel, Vancouver #96/R (C.D 750)
£511	$884	€746	Soir d'ete a Quebec (76x102cm-30x40in) s.i.verso. 9-Dec-3 Pinneys, Montreal #142 (C.D 1150)

RAVE, Christopher (1881-1933) German
£764 $1207 €1100 Bark on high seas (45x30cm-18x12in) s. 6-Sep-3 Schopman, Hamburg #858/R

RAVEEL, Roger (1921-) Belgian
£1867 $3341 €2800 Landscape with corn in the circle of Machelen (29x42cm-11x17in) s.d.80 acrylic pencil paper. 15-May-4 De Vuyst, Lokeren #263/R est:1700-2000
£3020 $5587 €4500 Hot-tempered pigeon in a chaotic circle (34x26cm-13x10in) s.d.1995 acrylic pen paper. 13-Mar-4 De Vuyst, Lokeren #510/R est:4400-5500
£3356 $6208 €5000 White emptiness of a hole (73x55cm-29x22in) s.d.82 acrylic pencil ink prov. 13-Mar-4 De Vuyst, Lokeren #576/R est:3000-4000
£7333 $13493 €11000 Man in front of mirror (74x54cm-29x21in) s.d.62 oil gouache pastel paper on board. 8-Jun-4 Sotheby's, Amsterdam #122/R est:4000-6000
£11268 $19493 €16000 Terrain a vendre (80x100cm-31x39in) s. 13-Dec-3 De Vuyst, Lokeren #580/R est:12000-14000
£22667 $41707 €34000 Vader plant een boompje in de witte ruimte van de aarde (111x141cm-44x56in) s.d.1985 prov.exhib. 9-Jun-4 Christie's, Amsterdam #331/R est:20000-25000
Works on paper
£1399 $2336 €2000 Composition (37x28cm-15x11in) s.d.1980-86 mixed media prov. 11-Oct-3 De Vuyst, Lokeren #308/R est:2200-3000
£1469 $2452 €2100 Landscape happening (20x26cm-8x10in) s.d.65 Indian ink. 11-Oct-3 De Vuyst, Lokeren #304/R est:2500-3000
£2609 $4278 €3600 Untitled (27x36cm-11x14in) s. pastel ink. 27-May-3 Sotheby's, Amsterdam #562/R est:3000-6000
£3200 $5728 €4800 Corn field (26x35cm-10x14in) s.d.1950 pencil prov. 15-May-4 De Vuyst, Lokeren #580/R est:4000-5000
£3333 $5967 €5000 Three white stakes in my garden with canes (26x34cm-10x13in) s. pencil prov.lit. 15-May-4 De Vuyst, Lokeren #487/R est:4500-5500

RAVEL, Daniel (1915-) French
£336 $594 €500 Sur des notes bleues et jaunes (54x65cm-21x26in) s. s.i.d. verso. 28-Apr-4 Artcurial Briest, Paris #489
£336 $594 €500 Composition (54x65cm-21x26in) s. painted c.1975. 28-Apr-4 Artcurial Briest, Paris #490

RAVEL, Edouard-John E (1847-1920) Swiss
Works on paper
£837 $1423 €1222 Mountain climber (34x24cm-13x9in) s.d.87 W/C. 7-Nov-3 Dobiaschofsky, Bern #26/R (S.FR 1900)
£1009 $1685 €1463 Vieux paysan (58x30cm-23x12in) s. i.verso crayon oil cardboard. 21-Jun-3 Galerie du Rhone, Sion #412 est:3000-4000 (S.FR 2200)

RAVEN, Samuel (1775-1847) British
£550 $1012 €803 Fox's lair (18x25cm-7x10in) panel prov. 10-Jun-4 Christie's, Kensington #48/R
£1050 $1848 €1533 Tabby cat. Spaniel (27x20cm-11x8in) s. panel pair. 18-May-4 Woolley & Wallis, Salisbury #100/R est:1200-1800
£3400 $6256 €4964 Pack of hounds. Hound bitch with her litter (18x23cm-7x9in) pair. 10-Jun-4 Christie's, Kensington #420/R est:2000-3000

RAVENSBERG, Ludwig Christian (1871-1958) Norwegian
Works on paper
£447 $823 €653 View towards the St.Louis Cathedral, Carthage (25x35cm-10x14in) s.i.d.20/5-21 pencil W/C exhib. 10-Jun-4 Grev Wedels Plass, Oslo #82/R (N.KR 5500)

RAVENSTEIN, Paul von (1854-1938) German
£704 $1127 €1000 Brisach landscape (50x72cm-20x28in) s. lit. 19-Sep-3 Karlheinz Kaupp, Staufen #2068/R
£1467 $2655 €2200 Stream (42x55cm-17x22in) s.d. 2-Apr-4 Winterberg, Heidelberg #1514/R est:1750

RAVENSWAAY, Huibert Antoine (1891-1972) Dutch
£268 $497 €400 View of a Dutch town in winter (40x60cm-16x24in) s. 15-Mar-4 Sotheby's, Amsterdam #289

RAVENSWAAY, J van (1789-1869) Dutch
£1773 $2801 €2500 Shepherd feeding sheep in barn (23x24cm-9x9in) i. panel. 22-Jul-3 Sigalas, Stuttgart #378/R est:2500

RAVENSWAAY, Jan van (1789-1869) Dutch
£4861 $7681 €7000 At rest in a barn (55x69cm-22x27in) s.d.1822 canvas on panel. 2-Sep-3 Christie's, Amsterdam #153/R est:3000-5000

RAVENSWAAY, Jan van (attrib) (1789-1869) Dutch
£1822 $2933 €2660 Resting flock (36x44cm-14x17in) s. 13-Oct-3 Joel, Victoria #241/R est:1000-1500 (A.D 4500)

RAVERAT, Gwendolen (1885-1957) British
Prints
£14000 $23380 €20440 Untitled. s.i. album of 77 woodcuts executed c.1916-21. 21-Oct-3 Sworder & Son, Bishops Stortford #268/R est:4000-6000

RAVESTEYN, Hubert van (1638-1691) Dutch
£1000 $1630 €1460 Peasants playing cards in an interior (33x24cm-13x9in) init. panel. 26-Sep-3 Christie's, Kensington #81/R est:1000-1500
£3378 $5946 €5000 Stable interior (42x32cm-17x13in) panel prov. 22-May-4 Lempertz, Koln #1118/R est:6000

RAVESTEYN, Jan Anthonisz van (1570-1657) Dutch
£20690 $34345 €30000 Portrait of elegant lady in wide lace collar (131x96cm-52x38in) lit. 1-Oct-3 Dorotheum, Vienna #273/R est:30000-50000
£23448 $38924 €34000 Portrait of young lady in large frill with pearl necklace (65x51cm-26x20in) i. 1-Oct-3 Dorotheum, Vienna #153/R est:15000-18000

RAVESTEYN, Jan Anthonisz van (attrib) (1570-1657) Dutch
£3333 $6000 €4866 Portrait of a lady with lace collar and cap (65x57cm-26x22in) panel. 21-Jan-4 Sotheby's, New York #70/R est:6000-8000

RAVET, Victor (1840-1895) Belgian
£660 $1049 €950 Homme assis dans un atelier (37x31cm-15x12in) s.d.1887 panel. 9-Sep-3 Palais de Beaux Arts, Brussels #267/R
£699 $1203 €1000 Having a drink (36x27cm-14x11in) s. panel. 7-Dec-3 Sotheby's, Amsterdam #581/R
£1099 $1836 €1550 La couturiere (26x36cm-10x14in) s.i.d.95 panel. 17-Jun-3 Vanderkindere, Brussels #107/R est:1000-1500
£1216 $2177 €1800 L'apprenti fumant la pipe (31x27cm-12x11in) s. 10-May-4 Horta, Bruxelles #130 est:1000-1500

RAVETTA, Enrico (1861-?) Italian
£582 $908 €850 Portrait of lady in white (95x112cm-37x44in) s.d.1904. 8-Apr-3 Il Ponte, Milan #514

RAVIER, Auguste François (1814-1895) French
£570 $1010 €850 Landscape in Fontainebleau (14x18cm-6x7in) init. cardboard oval. 1-May-4 Meeting Art, Vercelli #20
£733 $1335 €1100 Orage sur l'etang (20x26cm-8x10in) s. cardboard. 29-Jun-4 Chenu & Scrive, Lyon #157/R
£1170 $1849 €1650 Paysage au cours d'eau (21x34cm-8x13in) s. cardboard. 24-Jul-3 Adjug'art, Brest #337/R
£1192 $2170 €1800 Morestel (31x23cm-12x9in) 20-Jun-4 Versailles Encheres #38/R est:1800-2000
£1333 $2427 €2000 Crepuscule (23x31cm-9x12in) s. paper. 29-Jun-4 Chenu & Scrive, Lyon #152/R est:2000-2500
£1667 $3000 €2500 Paysage a l'etang (22x15cm-9x6in) s. cardboard. 20-Apr-4 Chenu & Scrive, Lyon #148/R est:2500-3000
£1773 $2961 €2500 Paysage au soleil couchant (34x26cm-13x10in) s. paper on canvas. 19-Jun-3 Millon & Associes, Paris #123/R est:2000-2200
£1867 $3416 €2800 Vue du Chateau de Saint-Hippolyte a Cremieux (24x33cm-9x13in) s. cardboard on canvas. 6-Jun-4 Osenat, Fontainebleau #36/R est:2000-2200
£2000 $3640 €3000 Chemin sous les remparts (34x50cm-13x20in) s. 29-Jun-4 Chenu & Scrive, Lyon #154/R est:3000-4000
£2000 $3600 €3000 Paysage vallonne (28x36cm-11x14in) canvas on panel. 20-Apr-4 Chenu & Scrive, Lyon #149/R est:3000-3500
£2535 $4208 €3600 Crepuscule a Morestel (25x33cm-10x13in) paper on canvas exhib. 10-Jun-3 Renaud, Paris #14/R est:4000-5000
£2933 $5368 €4400 Champrofond pres de Cremieux (27x36cm-11x14in) s. paper on cardboard. 6-Jun-4 Osenat, Fontainebleau #37/R est:5000-5500
£3867 $6999 €5800 Crepuscule (32x42cm-13x17in) st.sig. panel lit. 30-Mar-4 Rossini, Paris #308/R est:1500-2500
£5733 $10377 €8600 Lever de lune (32x2cm-13x1in) st.sig. lit. 30-Mar-4 Rossini, Paris #307/R est:2500-3500
Works on paper
£400 $720 €600 La terrasse de Morestel (34x25cm-13x10in) W/C wash crayon. 20-Apr-4 Chenu & Scrive, Lyon #146/R
£600 $1080 €900 Grottes de la Cervara, pres de Rome. Etude de paysage (27x42cm-11x17in) brown wash double-sided. 20-Apr-4 Chenu & Scrive, Lyon #17/R
£766 $1210 €1080 Etendue d'eau (20x27cm-8x11in) s. W/C. 24-Jul-3 Adjug'art, Brest #273/R
£861 $1567 €1300 Paysage au soleil couchant (21x29cm-8x11in) s. W/C htd gouache black crayon. 16-Jun-4 Piasa, Paris #220
£880 $1523 €1250 Coucher de soleil (29x20cm-11x8in) s. W/C. 12-Dec-3 Piasa, Paris #71
£927 $1687 €1400 Paysage (24x32cm-9x13in) W/C. 20-Jun-4 Versailles Encheres #39
£1000 $1820 €1500 Cremieu (17x20cm-7x8in) W/C. 29-Jun-4 Chenu & Scrive, Lyon #156/R est:1500-2000
£1409 $2622 €2100 Paysage (17x20cm-7x8in) s. W/C graphite prov. 2-Mar-4 Artcurial Briest, Paris #17/R est:1500-2000
£1733 $3155 €2600 Bord d'etang (23x32cm-9x13in) s. W/C. 29-Jun-4 Chenu & Scrive, Lyon #153/R est:2300-2500
£1892 $2951 €2800 Paysage au grand arbre (22x16cm-9x6in) s. W/C. 30-Mar-3 Versailles Encheres #16
£2324 $3858 €3300 Coucher de soleil (25x36cm-10x14in) s. W/C. 15-Jun-3 Peron, Melun #62
£2365 $3689 €3500 Etang (24x30cm-9x12in) s. W/C. 30-Mar-3 Versailles Encheres #15
£3243 $5059 €4800 Cremieu (18x36cm-7x14in) s. W/C. 30-Mar-3 Versailles Encheres #14
£4067 $7361 €6100 Paysage a l'etang autour de Cremieu (14x21cm-6x8in) s. W/C. 30-Mar-4 Rossini, Paris #309/R est:1800-2500

RAVILIOUS, Eric (1903-1942) British
Prints
£4000 $7360 €5840 Newhaven Harbour (51x76cm-20x30in) with sig. col lithograph. 28-Jun-4 Bonhams, New Bond Street #247/R est:1000-1500
Works on paper
£30000 $50100 €43800 Hull's mill (45x55cm-18x22in) s.i. W/C prov. 21-Oct-3 Sworder & Son, Bishops Stortford #282/R est:15000-20000

RAVN, Carsten Johan Nicolai (1854-1914) Danish
Works on paper
£280 $476 €400 Vue de parc (60x81cm-24x32in) pastel. 24-Nov-3 E & Eve, Paris #167

RAVN, Elise Sophie Andrea (1819-c.1890) Danish
£316 $591 €461 Self-portrait (51x39cm-20x15in) s.d.1856. 25-Feb-4 Museumsbygningen, Copenhagen #197/R (D.KR 3500)
£1078 $1854 €1574 Vase with flowers and bird's nest with eggs (31x23cm-12x9in) s. i.verso after van Huysum. 3-Dec-3 Museumsbygningen, Copenhagen #167/R (D.KR 11500)

£1218 $2096 €1778 Still life of pumpkin, flowers and fruit in Greek dish on marble ledge (51x65cm-20x26in) init. i.d.1842 verso. 3-Dec-3 Museumsbygningen, Copenhagen #166/R est:15000-20000 (D.KR 13000)
£1406 $2418 €2053 Red and white roses in Greek dish on marble ledge (34x44cm-13x17in) mono.d.1851. 3-Dec-3 Museumsbygningen, Copenhagen #164/R est:10000-15000 (D.KR 15000)
£2156 $3708 €3148 Red and white roses on bush (29x38cm-11x15in) init. mahogany. 3-Dec-3 Museumsbygningen, Copenhagen #161/R est:20000-25000 (D.KR 23000)

RAVN, Lars (1959-) Danish
£452 $810 €660 Woodland lake with two female nudes bathing (101x93cm-40x37in) s.d.1992. 10-May-4 Rasmussen, Vejle #707/R (D.KR 5000)
£498 $891 €727 Stevns 1989 - composition with eye, flowers and ear (71x61cm-28x24in) s.d.1989. 10-May-4 Rasmussen, Vejle #706/R (D.KR 5500)

RAWICZ, Jan (20th C) ?
£304 $492 €444 Town scene with figures in winter (35x50cm-14x20in) s,. 9-Aug-3 Hindemae, Ullerslev #47 (D.KR 3200)

RAWLINGS, Leo (1918-1990) British
Works on paper
£900 $1530 €1314 The 2/29th Australian infantry brigade fighting their way out of ambush (48x66cm-19x26in) s.d.1943 W/C prov. 4-Nov-3 Bonhams, New Bond Street #42/R

RAWLINS, Ethel Louise (fl.1900-1940) British
£340 $568 €496 Downland landscape (48x61cm-19x24in) s. exhib. 16-Oct-3 Mallams, Cheltenham #206/R

RAWLINSON, James (attrib) (1769-1848) British
£900 $1620 €1314 Portrait of a gentleman (74x60cm-29x24in) 21-Jan-4 Sotheby's, Olympia #45/R est:1000-1500

RAWORTH, William Henry (1820-1905) Australian
Works on paper
£329 $588 €480 Ship wreck (21x54cm-8x21in) s. W/C. 11-May-4 Watson's, Christchurch #15/R (NZ.D 950)
£405 $714 €600 Lac dans les montagnes (40x66cm-16x26in) s. W/C. 18-May-4 Galerie Moderne, Brussels #147/R
£541 $951 €800 Paysage avec chausseurs et riviere (30x63cm-12x25in) s. W/C pair. 18-May-4 Galerie Moderne, Brussels #222

RAWSON, Henry F (19th C) New Zealander
Works on paper
£559 $1018 €816 Inlet and mountans (36x63cm-14x25in) W/C prov. 29-Jun-4 Peter Webb, Auckland #94/R est:1500-2500 (NZ.D 1600)

RAY, Anatol Paul (fl.1850-1870) French
£1329 $2259 €1900 Landscape with people collecting wood (46x73cm-18x29in) s. lit. 28-Nov-3 Schloss Ahlden, Ahlden #1521/R est:2100

RAY, Gary (1952-) American
£189 $350 €276 California wildflowers (18x23cm-7x9in) s. board. 18-Jul-4 Bonhams & Butterfields, Los Angeles #7032/R
£235 $425 €343 Leo Carillo state park (20x25cm-8x10in) s. canvasboard. 18-Apr-4 Bonhams & Butterfields, Los Angeles #7007
£324 $600 €473 California landscape (23x30cm-9x12in) s. canvasboard. 18-Jan-4 Bonhams & Butterfields, Los Angeles #7005/R
£467 $850 €682 California coastal scene (20x25cm-8x10in) s. canvas on panel. 15-Jun-4 John Moran, Pasadena #151a
£635 $1200 €927 Santa Barbara coastal (28x36cm-11x14in) s. panel. 17-Feb-4 John Moran, Pasadena #158/R
£867 $1500 €1266 Malibu Creek State Park, last light (48x76cm-19x30in) s.d.03 i.verso masonite. 10-Dec-3 Bonhams & Butterfields, San Francisco #6340/R est:3000-5000
£1058 $2000 €1545 Eucalyptus flower field (41x51cm-16x20in) s.d.03. 17-Feb-4 John Moran, Pasadena #157/R est:1500-2500
£1156 $2000 €1688 Carpinteria Bluffs (46x61cm-18x24in) s.d.03 i.verso board. 10-Dec-3 Bonhams & Butterfields, San Francisco #6341/R est:3000-5000
£1223 $2250 €1786 Agoura Kannan Dume, summer (55x71cm-22x28in) s. i. stretcher. 8-Jun-4 Bonhams & Butterfields, San Francisco #4388/R est:3000-5000
£1511 $2750 €2206 Flower fields (51x61cm-20x24in) s.d.03 board. 15-Jun-4 John Moran, Pasadena #151 est:2000-3000

RAY, Richard Archibald (1884-1968) British
£720 $1310 €1051 Sailing trawlers in a harbour (60x91cm-24x36in) s.d.1946. 29-Jun-4 Anderson & Garland, Newcastle #376/R

RAY, Ruth (1919-1977) American
£686 $1200 €1002 The blue house (43x35cm-17x14in) s.d.1961. 19-Dec-3 Sotheby's, New York #1142/R

RAYA-SORKINE (1936-) French
£524 $965 €765 Voyage en famille (27x35cm-11x14in) s. i.verso. 14-Jun-4 Waddingtons, Toronto #267/R est:1000-1500 (C.D 1300)
£833 $1392 €1200 Francoise d'ou viens-tu (73x50cm-29x20in) s. s.i.d.mai 1964 verso. 21-Oct-3 Artcurial Briest, Paris #355
£2606 $4508 €3700 Promenade amoureuse (55x46cm-22x18in) s. s.i.verso. 10-Dec-3 Millon & Associes, Paris #117/R est:3500-4000
Works on paper
£331 $606 €500 Le violoniste (61x71cm-24x28in) s.d.60 W/C. 9-Apr-4 Claude Aguttes, Neuilly #92/R

RAYMOND, Lodovico (1825-1898) Italian
£17219 $31338 €26000 Sea wedding (114x180cm-45x71in) 21-Jun-4 Pandolfini, Florence #95/R est:18000-20000

RAYMOND, Marie (1908-1988) French
£521 $869 €750 L'arbre de vie (92x65cm-36x26in) s. s.i.d.1971 verso. 21-Oct-3 Artcurial Briest, Paris #674
£903 $1507 €1300 Composition (98x131cm-39x52in) s. 21-Oct-3 Artcurial Briest, Paris #675 est:600-800
£1119 $1902 €1600 Composition (81x99cm-32x39in) s. 18-Nov-3 Pierre Berge, Paris #33/R est:2000-3000
£1333 $2400 €2000 Composition (81x130cm-32x51in) s. 24-Apr-4 Cornette de St.Cyr, Paris #692/R est:3000
£3497 $5944 €5000 Composition (130x151cm-51x59in) s. 18-Nov-3 Pierre Berge, Paris #31/R est:6000-7000
£3497 $5944 €5000 Montagne (89x145cm-35x57in) s. i.verso exhib. 18-Nov-3 Pierre Berge, Paris #32/R est:3000-4000

RAYMOND, Maurice (20th C) ?
Works on paper
£452 $710 €660 Plain chant (56x71cm-22x28in) s.d.56 gouache. 26-Aug-3 Iegor de Saint Hippolyte, Montreal #134 (C.D 1000)

RAYMOND, Robert Maurice (20th C) French
£473 $846 €691 Landscape with houses (38x46cm-15x18in) s. 12-Jan-4 Rasmussen, Vejle #360/R (D.KR 5000)

RAYNAUD, Auguste (19th C) French
£5000 $8000 €7250 Awaiting his return (54x92cm-21x36in) s. 18-Sep-3 Christie's, Kensington #181/R est:4000-6000

RAYNAUD, Jean Pierre (1939-) French
£34000 $61880 €49640 Mur 814 (100x975cm-39x384in) enamel on metal plastic fibreglass thirteen panels prov.exhib.lit. 5-Feb-4 Christie's, London #155/R est:9000-12000
Prints
£3000 $5460 €4500 Grillage (78x63cm-31x25in) s.d.1974 verso serigraph iron lit. 29-Jun-4 Cornette de St.Cyr, Paris #57/R est:4500-5000
Sculpture
£1000 $1800 €1500 Blindage rouge (60x50x2cm-24x20x1in) s.i.d.1975 verso paint on metal. 25-Apr-4 Versailles Encheres #163 est:2000-2500
£2267 $4125 €3400 Archetype rouge (16x17x17cm-6x7x7in) st.sig. terracotta pot concrete exec.1968 lit. 29-Jun-4 Cornette de St.Cyr, Paris #58/R est:3000-4000
£10333 $18600 €15500 Souvenir de vacance (92x65x15cm-36x26x6in) s.i.d.1972 toy guns panel. 25-Apr-4 Versailles Encheres #167/R est:12000-15000
£10490 $17517 €15000 Carrelage and fleurs fanees (60x60cm-24x24in) s.d.1994 verso dried flowers collage plexiglas lit. 11-Oct-3 Cornette de St.Cyr, Paris #88/R est:10000-12000
£13158 $24211 €20000 Container et ceramique (91cm-36in) s.d.1985 painted metal ceramic lit. 27-Jun-4 Versailles Encheres #149/R est:20000-25000
£13287 $22588 €19000 Rosiers 5 plus 1 plus 1 plus 1 (92x160x20cm-36x63x8in) s. d.1972 verso wood silk panel prov.exhib. 19-Nov-3 Tajan, Paris #129/R est:20000-30000
£52000 $96200 €78000 Pot 815 (180x195cm-71x77in) num.4/8 polyester stone paint exec.1968 prov.exhib.lit. 18-Jul-4 Sotheby's, Paris #154/R est:50000-70000

RAYNAUD, Patrick (1946-) French
Sculpture
£2148 $3844 €3200 Valise d'Ingres: grande odalisque (164x75x47cm-65x30x19in) st.sig. case cibachrome neon lights exec.1990. 26-May-4 Christie's, Paris #116/R est:2000-3000

RAYNER, Gordon (20th C) Canadian
£2642 $4730 €3857 Passage (61x76cm-24x30in) s. i.d.Nov 65 verso acrylic prov. 31-May-4 Sotheby's, Toronto #27/R est:3000-5000 (C.D 6500)
Works on paper
£594 $1104 €867 Untitled (76x56cm-30x22in) s. mixed media masonite. 2-Mar-4 Ritchie, Toronto #167/R (C.D 1480)

RAYNER, Louise (1832-1924) British
Works on paper
£880 $1434 €1276 Meeting with the teacher (17x23cm-7x9in) s. W/C bodycol. 23-Sep-3 Bonhams, Knightsbridge #2/R
£3500 $5530 €5075 Figures by the Judgement Porch at Lincoln Cathedral (32x52cm-13x20in) s. W/C bodycol. 24-Jul-3 Lawrence, Crewkerne #839/R est:2000-2500
£4469 $8000 €6525 Bishop Lloyd's House, Watergate Street, Chester 1912 (37x24cm-15x9in) s. W/C htd gouache on card prov. 6-May-4 Doyle, New York #16/R est:15000-25000
£5000 $8500 €7300 Silver Street, Salisbury (22x17cm-9x7in) s. pencil W/C htd bodycol. 20-Nov-3 Christie's, London #96/R est:2500-3500
£6500 $11960 €9490 Break from divisions at Eton College (39x32cm-15x13in) s. pencil W/C bodycol. 25-Mar-4 Christie's, Kensington #126/R est:4000-6000
£7500 $12750 €10950 Rheims Cathedral, France (56x32cm-22x13in) s. pencil W/C htd bodycol. 20-Nov-3 Christie's, London #97/R est:3000-5000
£18000 $30600 €26280 Poultry Cross, Salisbury (39x58cm-15x23in) s. W/C htd bodycol. 4-Nov-3 Bonhams, New Bond Street #104/R est:10000-15000
£24000 $40800 €35040 Watergate Street, Chester (45x58cm-18x23in) s. pencil W/C htd bodycol prov. 20-Nov-3 Christie's, London #99/R est:12000-18000

RAYNER, Margaret (fl.1866-1895) British
Works on paper
£560 $930 €818 Interior of the Chapel at Haddon Hall, Derbyshire (51x40cm-20x16in) s. W/C bodycol. 1-Oct-3 Sotheby's, Olympia #46/R

RAYNER, Samuel (?-1874) British

Works on paper

£300	$501	€438	Wash day (33x51cm-13x20in) init.d.59 pencil W/C bodycol. 16-Oct-3 Christie's, Kensington #84/R
£800	$1464	€1168	Church interior (43x56cm-17x22in) W/C bodycol pair. 27-Jan-4 Bonhams, Knightsbridge #316/R

RAYO, Omar (1928-) Colombian

£594	$950	€867	Seiteis (43x43cm-17x17in) s. i.verso. 20-Sep-3 Sloans & Kenyon, Bethesda #1034/R
£2081	$3538	€3038	Guahibo (143x143cm-56x56in) s.i.d.1970 acrylic collage prov. 25-Nov-3 Germann, Zurich #31/R est:5000-7000 (S.FR 4600)

RAYSSE, Martial (1936-) French

£700	$1274	€1050	Projet (64x50cm-25x20in) cut paper. 29-Jun-4 Gioffredo, Nice #332
£20000	$37000	€30000	Pythagore dominant de sa stature immense la bonne ville de Nice (200x300cm-79x118in) oil collage painted 1983-84 prov.lit. 18-Jul-4 Sotheby's, Paris #261/R est:30000-40000
£73171	$120000	€106830	Sur 3 roses (32x21cm-13x8in) s.i.d.63 verso oil tempera silkscreen puffs rose board prov.exhib. 28-May-3 Sotheby's, Amsterdam #75/R est:60000-80000

Prints

£2113	$3655	€3000	Bel ete concentre. s.d.1967 num.45/80 screenprint simili velours. 9-Dec-3 Artcurial Briest, Paris #330a est:3500-4000
£36667	$67467	€55000	Premier essai pour portrait double (58x40cm-23x16in) s.i. serigraph mixed media canvas exec 1968 prov. 8-Jun-4 Artcurial Briest, Paris #228/R est:60000-80000

Works on paper

£470	$864	€700	Composition (24x35cm-9x14in) s.d.1957 verso. 24-Mar-4 Binoche, Paris #89
£909	$1564	€1300	Couronne aux palmiers (49x39cm-19x15in) pochoir pastel pair. 3-Dec-3 Beaussant & Lefèvre, Paris #14/R
£1081	$1902	€1600	Untitled (26x24cm-10x9in) pastel prov. 18-May-4 Tajan, Paris #87/R est:1500-1800
£1748	$3007	€2500	Sans titre (21x35cm-8x14in) s. gouache. 4-Dec-3 Piasa, Paris #70/R est:600-800
£2067	$3761	€3100	Bleu citron (33x50cm-13x20in) s. gouache exec.1955. 29-Jun-4 Cornette de St.Cyr, Paris #46/R est:3500-3800
£3147	$5255	€4500	Avion aux ailes jaunes (60x50cm-24x20in) collage exhib. 25-Jun-3 Digard, Paris #114/R est:4000-6000
£3311	$6257	€4900	Bel ete concentre, autoportrait (190x49cm-75x19in) s. felt pen screenprint collage sold with a book. 21-Feb-4 Cornette de St.Cyr, Paris #391/R est:4000-6000
£3399	$5778	€4963	France - the artist's wife (25x17cm-10x7in) s.d.62 mixed media collage. 5-Nov-3 AB Stockholms Auktionsverk #915/R est:25000-30000 (S.KR 45000)
£4667	$8587	€7000	Dame blanche (80x120cm-31x47in) s.i.d.1979 verso gouache panel prov.exhib. 9-Jun-4 Artcurial Briest, Paris #543/R est:8000-12000
£13195	$22035	€19000	Palmier (52x42cm-20x17in) i.verso mixed media collage panel prov.exhib.lit. 21-Oct-3 Artcurial Briest, Paris #486/R est:20000-25000
£26224	$45105	€37500	Propos de pomme et du reste (19x27cm-7x11in) s.i.d.63 verso mixed media object canvas prov. 4-Dec-3 Piasa, Paris #9/R est:12000-15000
£37762	$64951	€54000	Portrait d'Arman a l'epoque des allures d'objects (126x100cm-50x39in) s.i.d.63 verso photos acrylic screenprint object prov.exhib. 4-Dec-3 Piasa, Paris #24/R est:80000-100000

RAYWORTH, William Henry (19th C) British

Works on paper

£700	$1106	€1022	Lake Scenes (37x61cm-15x24in) both s.d.1884 W/C pair. 2-Sep-3 Gildings, Market Harborough #392

RAZA, Sayed Haider (1922-) Indian

£2402	$4371	€3507	Castillon VI (30x30cm-12x12in) s.d.67 i.verso masonite. 16-Jun-4 Fischer, Luzern #1159/R est:9000-12000 (S.FR 5500)
£3041	$5443	€4500	Polarite (30x30cm-12x12in) s.d.95 acrylic. 4-May-4 Calmels Cohen, Paris #229 est:1000-1500
£5163	$9500	€7538	Earth (49x36cm-19x14in) s.d.65 board. 25-Mar-4 Christie's, Rockefeller NY #206/R est:8000-12000
£5690	$10242	€8307	Germination (50x50cm-20x20in) s.d.03 i.verso acrylic. 25-Apr-4 Christie's, Hong Kong #607/R est:90000-110000 (HK.D 80000)
£9783	$18000	€14283	Untitled (25x25cm-10x10in) s.d.84 i.d.1984 verso acrylic four. 25-Mar-4 Christie's, Rockefeller NY #241/R est:7000-10000

RAZDA, B (19/20th C) Italian?

£2078	$3719	€3034	Interior with reclining female nude and youth (98x168cm-39x66in) s.i.d.1914. 22-Mar-4 Philippe Schuler, Zurich #6179 est:1400-1800 (S.FR 4800)

RAZE, Louis Laurent (1805-1873) British?

Works on paper

£1400	$2324	€2044	South west view of Canterbury Cathedral (18x25cm-7x10in) s.d.1838 W/C. 10-Jun-3 Canterbury Auctions, UK #126/R est:750-1000

RAZGOULINE, Victor (1948-) Russian

£800	$1440	€1200	Mer en Crimee (74x88cm-29x35in) s. 26-Apr-4 Millon & Associes, Paris #75/R

RAZUMOV, Konstantin (1974-) Russian

£250	$468	€375	Children playing with boat (24x33cm-9x13in) s. 21-Jul-4 John Nicholson, Haslemere #303/R
£250	$468	€375	My ballet shoes (22x27cm-9x11in) s. 21-Jul-4 John Nicholson, Haslemere #470
£275	$448	€402	At the drawing (33x24cm-13x9in) s. 28-Sep-3 John Nicholson, Haslemere #67/R
£275	$492	€402	Before the music lesson (27x19cm-11x7in) s. 5-May-4 John Nicholson, Haslemere #98
£278	$453	€400	In the park (50x40cm-20x16in) s. 16-Jul-3 Durán, Madrid #655/R
£284	$474	€400	Primary school (33x22cm-13x9in) s. 20-Oct-3 Durán, Madrid #722/R
£300	$489	€438	Near the window (35x24cm-14x9in) s. 28-Sep-3 John Nicholson, Haslemere #93/R
£300	$525	€438	Portrait of Marsha (35x27cm-14x11in) s. 17-Dec-3 John Nicholson, Haslemere #139
£300	$501	€438	In the bedroom (27x22cm-11x9in) s. 13-Jul-3 John Nicholson, Haslemere #6
£300	$501	€438	Girl in the red dress (35x24cm-14x9in) s. 13-Jul-3 John Nicholson, Haslemere #120/R
£300	$561	€450	Painter and model (35x24cm-14x9in) s. 21-Jul-4 John Nicholson, Haslemere #483
£302	$565	€450	Girl and kitten (27x35cm-11x14in) s. 24-Feb-4 Durán, Madrid #736/R
£325	$582	€475	Before sleeping (27x35cm-11x14in) s. 5-May-4 John Nicholson, Haslemere #87
£329	$605	€500	On the swing (46x33cm-18x13in) s. 22-Jun-4 Durán, Madrid #710/R
£350	$571	€511	Drawing Lesson (33x24cm-13x9in) s. 28-Sep-3 John Nicholson, Haslemere #2/R
£350	$585	€511	Before the dancing lesson (24x33cm-9x13in) s. 13-Jul-3 John Nicholson, Haslemere #3
£350	$627	€511	Etude of a girl with a book. 5-May-4 John Nicholson, Haslemere #32
£350	$627	€511	Girl with kitten (35x24cm-14x9in) s. 5-May-4 John Nicholson, Haslemere #74
£350	$627	€511	Rest in the hammock (24x35cm-9x14in) s. 5-May-4 John Nicholson, Haslemere #154
£350	$655	€525	Before bedtime (35x24cm-14x9in) s. 21-Jul-4 John Nicholson, Haslemere #456
£375	$671	€548	Favorite doll (33x24cm-13x9in) s. 5-May-4 John Nicholson, Haslemere #137
£375	$701	€563	Boudoir (35x24cm-14x9in) s. 21-Jul-4 John Nicholson, Haslemere #401/R
£400	$700	€584	Study of the girl-ballerina (27x22cm-11x9in) s. 17-Dec-3 John Nicholson, Haslemere #1/R
£400	$700	€584	Seated nude (33x23cm-13x9in) s. 17-Dec-3 John Nicholson, Haslemere #107/R
£400	$700	€584	Seated nude (43x30cm-17x12in) s. 17-Dec-3 John Nicholson, Haslemere #108
£400	$668	€584	Painter and his model (35x24cm-14x9in) s. 13-Jul-3 John Nicholson, Haslemere #5/R
£400	$716	€584	Model in the studio (33x19cm-13x7in) s. 5-May-4 John Nicholson, Haslemere #164/R
£442	$791	€650	Girl and kitten (41x33cm-16x13in) s. 22-Mar-4 Durán, Madrid #707/R
£450	$734	€657	Near the dressing table (46x38cm-18x15in) s. 28-Sep-3 John Nicholson, Haslemere #34
£450	$806	€657	Lesson in georaph (35x27cm-14x11in) s. 5-May-4 John Nicholson, Haslemere #46/R
£450	$806	€657	Etude of a girl ballet dancer (27x35cm-11x14in) s. 5-May-4 John Nicholson, Haslemere #99
£450	$842	€675	Ballet dancer (35x24cm-14x9in) s. 21-Jul-4 John Nicholson, Haslemere #402/R
£475	$774	€694	Portrait of the stranger (35x27cm-14x11in) s. 28-Sep-3 John Nicholson, Haslemere #46/R
£475	$831	€694	Morning (35x22cm-14x9in) s. 17-Dec-3 John Nicholson, Haslemere #41/R
£486	$792	€700	On the terrace (73x54cm-29x21in) s. 16-Jul-3 Durán, Madrid #654/R
£500	$895	€730	Le fantaisie (24x41cm-9x16in) s. 5-May-4 John Nicholson, Haslemere #3/R
£500	$815	€730	Model (27x22cm-11x9in) s. 28-Sep-3 John Nicholson, Haslemere #45/R
£500	$875	€730	Portrait of the girl in the garden among the white lilies (41x33cm-16x13in) s. 17-Dec-3 John Nicholson, Haslemere #39/R
£500	$895	€730	Little artist (27x41cm-11x16in) s. 5-May-4 John Nicholson, Haslemere #21/R
£500	$895	€730	Ballerina in points (36x27cm-14x11in) s. 5-May-4 John Nicholson, Haslemere #64
£500	$935	€750	First aid (46x38cm-18x15in) s. 21-Jul-4 John Nicholson, Haslemere #304
£500	$935	€750	Little ballerina in blue ribbon (37x27cm-15x11in) s. 21-Jul-4 John Nicholson, Haslemere #452/R
£500	$935	€750	Study of model (33x24cm-13x9in) s. 21-Jul-4 John Nicholson, Haslemere #454
£500	$935	€750	Portrait of little girl (33x24cm-13x9in) s. 21-Jul-4 John Nicholson, Haslemere #455/R
£525	$877	€767	Ballerina in the pink costume for the ballet (33x22cm-13x9in) s. 13-Jul-3 John Nicholson, Haslemere #121/R
£544	$974	€800	Applying make up at mirror (55x46cm-22x18in) s. 22-Mar-4 Durán, Madrid #708/R
£550	$897	€803	In the Nursery room (55x46cm-22x18in) s. 28-Sep-3 John Nicholson, Haslemere #92
£550	$897	€803	With a bird. s. 28-Sep-3 John Nicholson, Haslemere #145/R
£550	$919	€803	Morning make-up (41x27cm-16x11in) s. 13-Jul-3 John Nicholson, Haslemere #116/R
£550	$919	€803	Playing with a kitten (24x33cm-9x13in) s. 13-Jul-3 John Nicholson, Haslemere #122/R
£550	$985	€803	Before the performance (27x22cm-11x9in) s. 5-May-4 John Nicholson, Haslemere #1/R
£550	$985	€803	In the ballet class (33x41cm-13x16in) s. 5-May-4 John Nicholson, Haslemere #85
£550	$985	€803	Model dressing (35x27cm-14x11in) s. 5-May-4 John Nicholson, Haslemere #128/R
£550	$985	€803	My puppy (27x22cm-11x9in) s. 5-May-4 John Nicholson, Haslemere #239/R
£550	$985	€803	Girl in a red dress (35x24cm-14x9in) s. 5-May-4 John Nicholson, Haslemere #240/R
£600	$1050	€876	Model in the black dress (49x33cm-19x13in) s. 17-Dec-3 John Nicholson, Haslemere #40/R
£600	$1050	€876	Morning (46x33cm-18x13in) s. 17-Dec-3 John Nicholson, Haslemere #91/R
£600	$1050	€876	Before evening bathing (35x24cm-14x9in) s. 17-Dec-3 John Nicholson, Haslemere #102/R
£600	$1002	€876	Model and her canvas (35x24cm-14x9in) s. 13-Jul-3 John Nicholson, Haslemere #125/R

£600	$1074	€876	Before ballet lesson (33x24cm-13x9in) s. 5-May-4 John Nicholson, Haslemere #2/R
£600	$1122	€900	In the ballet studio (33x46cm-13x18in) s. 21-Jul-4 John Nicholson, Haslemere #302/R
£638	$1141	€950	Ballerinas (50x61cm-20x24in) s. 25-May-4 Durán, Madrid #728/R
£650	$1086	€949	After the dancing lessons (35x50cm-14x20in) s. 13-Jul-3 John Nicholson, Haslemere #2/R
£650	$1086	€949	Delicious honey (46x33cm-18x13in) s. 13-Jul-3 John Nicholson, Haslemere #73/R
£650	$1086	€949	A girl in the cafe (35x27cm-14x11in) s. 13-Jul-3 John Nicholson, Haslemere #76
£650	$1164	€949	At the opera (41x33cm-16x13in) s. 5-May-4 John Nicholson, Haslemere #118/R
£700	$1309	€1050	Dolly, be quiet (27x35cm-11x14in) s. 21-Jul-4 John Nicholson, Haslemere #301/R
£738	$1381	€1100	Garden (55x46cm-22x18in) s. 24-Feb-4 Durán, Madrid #735/R
£750	$1223	€1095	Near the window (50x40cm-20x16in) s. 28-Sep-3 John Nicholson, Haslemere #158
£775	$1294	€1132	Portrait of a lady in the black hat (41x33cm-16x13in) s. 13-Jul-3 John Nicholson, Haslemere #72/R
£800	$1336	€1168	Before bathing (65x50cm-26x20in) s. 13-Jul-3 John Nicholson, Haslemere #126/R
£800	$1496	€1200	Model in red stocking (41x24cm-16x9in) s. 21-Jul-4 John Nicholson, Haslemere #403/R
£870	$1426	€1200	Young girl at the piano (55x46cm-22x18in) s. 27-May-3 Durán, Madrid #779/R
£900	$1575	€1314	Packing up for the journey (33x24cm-13x9in) s. 17-Dec-3 John Nicholson, Haslemere #2/R
£900	$1575	€1314	Reflection (41x33cm-16x13in) s. 17-Dec-3 John Nicholson, Haslemere #137/R
£900	$1503	€1314	Portrait of a young lady in the hat of ostrich feathers (35x46cm-14x18in) s. 13-Jul-3 John Nicholson, Haslemere #74/R
£900	$1611	€1314	Reflections (55x33cm-22x13in) s. 5-May-4 John Nicholson, Haslemere #4/R
£900	$1683	€1350	Portrait in profile (35x24cm-14x9in) s. 21-Jul-4 John Nicholson, Haslemere #381/R
£1000	$1790	€1460	In the bedroom (50x35cm-20x14in) s. 5-May-4 John Nicholson, Haslemere #125/R
£1100	$1837	€1606	Bonjour (50x40cm-20x16in) s. 13-Jul-3 John Nicholson, Haslemere #117/R
£1100	$1969	€1606	Ballet dancer with a pink bow (35x27cm-14x11in) s. oval. 5-May-4 John Nicholson, Haslemere #126/R
£1200	$2004	€1752	Morning (51x36cm-20x14in) s. 18-Jun-3 John Nicholson, Haslemere #689 est:1500-2500
£1200	$1956	€1752	Morning (55x38cm-22x15in) s. 28-Sep-3 John Nicholson, Haslemere #1/R
£1200	$2148	€1752	On the balcony (50x40cm-20x16in) s. 5-May-4 John Nicholson, Haslemere #124/R
£1400	$2450	€2044	Nude (38x61cm-15x24in) s. 17-Dec-3 John Nicholson, Haslemere #64 est:1500-2000
£1400	$2618	€2100	Portrait of actress (41x33cm-16x13in) s. 21-Jul-4 John Nicholson, Haslemere #324 est:1600-2000
£1500	$2505	€2190	In the Baguteul Park (46x61cm-18x24in) s. 13-Jul-3 John Nicholson, Haslemere #119/R
£1500	$2685	€2190	Contemplation (41x27cm-16x11in) s. 5-May-4 John Nicholson, Haslemere #86/R
£1500	$2805	€2250	Morning in the boudoir (55x38cm-22x15in) s. 21-Jul-4 John Nicholson, Haslemere #354/R
£1600	$2672	€2336	In the cafe after the rain (50x61cm-20x24in) s. 13-Jul-3 John Nicholson, Haslemere #75/R
£1700	$3043	€2482	At the reception (55x38cm-22x15in) s. 5-May-4 John Nicholson, Haslemere #119/R
£1800	$3150	€2628	Young ballerina with kittens (46x61cm-18x24in) s. 17-Dec-3 John Nicholson, Haslemere #154/R est:2500-3500
£1800	$3366	€2700	Evening at the cafe (50x35cm-20x14in) s. 21-Jul-4 John Nicholson, Haslemere #395/R est:2000-3000
£1900	$3553	€2850	Portrait of Mashenka (22x27cm-9x11in) s. 21-Jul-4 John Nicholson, Haslemere #469 est:900-1000
£2000	$3500	€2920	Summer in the country (55x46cm-22x18in) s. 17-Dec-3 John Nicholson, Haslemere #38/R est:3000-4000
£2000	$3500	€2920	Rendevous (50x65cm-20x26in) s. 17-Dec-3 John Nicholson, Haslemere #94/R est:2500-3000
£2100	$3759	€3066	Expensive present (46x38cm-18x15in) s. 5-May-4 John Nicholson, Haslemere #123/R
£2200	$3850	€3212	In the Cafe (55x46cm-22x18in) s. 17-Dec-3 John Nicholson, Haslemere #90/R est:2000-2500
£2200	$3850	€3212	Girl with a Russian wolfhound (55x46cm-22x18in) s. 17-Dec-3 John Nicholson, Haslemere #157/R est:2000-2500
£2250	$4028	€3285	In the bar (55x46cm-22x18in) s. 5-May-4 John Nicholson, Haslemere #122/R
£2400	$4200	€3504	Cup of coffee (50x40cm-20x16in) s. 17-Dec-3 John Nicholson, Haslemere #136/R est:2800-3000
£2600	$4342	€3796	Sleeping beauty (50x73cm-20x29in) s. 13-Jul-3 John Nicholson, Haslemere #8/R
£2800	$4564	€4088	Waiting for a tea (61x50cm-24x20in) s. 28-Sep-3 John Nicholson, Haslemere #97/R
£3600	$6444	€5256	Reflections at dinner (50x40cm-20x16in) s. 5-May-4 John Nicholson, Haslemere #116/R
£4250	$7608	€6205	Evening light (38x46cm-15x18in) s. 5-May-4 John Nicholson, Haslemere #121/R
£5250	$9398	€7665	In the cafe (50x61cm-20x24in) s. 5-May-4 John Nicholson, Haslemere #120/R

RAZUMOVSKAYA, U V (1896-1987) Russian

£380	$700	€555	Sunset on the Kama River (25x32cm-10x13in) cardboard painted 1962. 27-Mar-4 Shishkin Gallery, Moscow #88/R
£1222	$2200	€1784	Moscow conversation (59x43cm-23x17in) 24-Apr-4 Shishkin Gallery, Moscow #33/R est:2000-3000

RE, Guglielmo da (1867-?) Italian

Works on paper

£1959	$3370	€2860	View of Asuncion (25x40cm-10x16in) s. W/C. 3-Dec-3 Naón & Cia, Buenos Aires #9/R est:3000-4000
£6512	$11200	€9508	Army (27x26cm-11x10in) s. W/C. 3-Dec-3 Naón & Cia, Buenos Aires #10/R est:500-1000

REA, Constance (19/20th C) British

£1400	$2590	€2044	Portrait of a beautiful lady in a landscape (63x52cm-25x20in) 9-Mar-4 Bonhams, Knightsbridge #347/R est:1500-2000
£2000	$3700	€2920	Slumber song (51x45cm-20x18in) 9-Mar-4 Bonhams, Knightsbridge #346/R est:2000-3000

READ, J Vine (?) British?

£480	$888	€701	Thoroughbred (48x58cm-19x23in) s. 11-Mar-4 John Ross, Belfast #809

READ, Thomas Buchanan (1822-1872) American

£1389	$2250	€2014	Portraits of George William Childs and his wife Hannah Bouvier. oval painted c.1850 pair. 26-Jul-3 Thomaston Place, Thomaston #138/R

REAL, Charles (1898-1979) French

£805	$1498	€1200	Maison rose (60x73cm-24x29in) s. 3-Mar-4 Tajan, Paris #49/R est:1200-1500

REALIER-DUMAS, Maurice (1860-1928) French

£1678	$3121	€2500	River boat on the Seine with village vie (27x35cm-11x14in) s.d.98 panel. 8-Mar-4 Bernaerts, Antwerp #613/R est:375-500

REAM, Carducius Plantagenet (1837-1917) American

£625	$1000	€913	Reclining lion (38x58cm-15x23in) s. painted c.1890. 20-Sep-3 Bunte, Elgin #1432
£698	$1200	€1019	Still life with grapes and peach (15x20cm-6x8in) s. 7-Dec-3 Hindman, Chicago #797/R
£719	$1200	€1050	Still life with fruit (15x18cm-6x7in) board. 17-Oct-3 Du Mouchelle, Detroit #20/R
£1163	$2000	€1698	Still life with raspberries (10x15cm-4x6in) s. 7-Dec-3 Hindman, Chicago #795/R est:1000-2000
£1511	$2750	€2206	Lion in pepose (37x57cm-15x22in) s. 29-Jun-4 Sotheby's, New York #195/R est:2000-4000
£2174	$4000	€3174	Apples (35x46cm-14x18in) s. 27-Jun-4 Freeman, Philadelphia #81/R est:4000-6000
£2333	$4200	€3406	Still life with apples (28x43cm-11x17in) s. 25-Jan-4 Hindman, Chicago #1022/R est:3000-5000
£3352	$6000	€4894	Still life with fruit and wine glass (10x14cm-4x6in) s. prov. 6-May-4 Shannon's, Milford #122/R est:6000-8000
£7186	$12000	€10492	Peaches by a basket (47x37cm-19x15in) s. board prov. 9-Oct-3 Christie's, Rockefeller NY #14/R est:12000-18000

REAM, Carducius Plantagenet (attrib) (1837-1917) American

£218	$375	€318	Still life with grapes and peach (20x23cm-8x9in) 7-Dec-3 Hindman, Chicago #794/R

REAM, Morston C (1840-1898) American

£10588	$18000	€15458	Still life of fruit and wine (30x41cm-12x16in) s. 30-Oct-3 Phillips, New York #28/R est:20000-25000

REAUGH, Charles Franklin (1860-1945) American

Works on paper

£1018	$1700	€1486	West Texas (10x18cm-4x7in) pastel. 18-Oct-3 David Dike, Dallas #76/R est:750-1500

REBAY, Hilla (1890-1967) American/French

Works on paper

£1235	$2100	€1803	Untitled (10x15cm-4x6in) s.verso W/C prov. 9-Nov-3 Wright, Chicago #268 est:600-800
£1706	$2900	€2491	Composition (28x43cm-11x17in) s. collage W/C prov. 9-Nov-3 Wright, Chicago #269 est:1000-1500

REBEYROLLE, Paul (1926-) French

£1727	$2832	€2400	Autoportrait (54x32cm-21x13in) s.d. i.verso panel. 3-Jun-3 Livinec, Gaudcheau & Jezequel, Rennes #103/R
£5804	$9693	€8300	Composition (60x120cm-24x47in) s.d.63. 25-Jun-3 Blanchet, Paris #141/R
£20134	$36040	€30000	Truite (90x116cm-35x46in) s.d.62 prov. 26-May-4 Christie's, Paris #102/R est:1500-2000
£21000	$38640	€30660	Paysage (120x120cm-47x47in) s.d.1962 prov. 24-Jun-4 Sotheby's, London #190/R est:8000-10000
£28477	$51828	€43000	La grenouille (60x118cm-24x46in) s.d.69 prov. 18-Jun-4 Piasa, Paris #234/R est:10000-12000
£52448	$87587	€75000	Les berets verts (308x249cm-121x98in) prov.exhib.lit. 11-Oct-3 Cornette de St.Cyr, Paris #131/R est:55000-65000

Works on paper

£1960	$3508	€2900	Arbre (27x32cm-11x13in) s. mixed media paper on canvas. 4-May-4 Calmels Cohen, Paris #210/R est:3000-3500
£4027	$7208	€6000	Collage (72x75cm-28x30in) s.d.63 mixed media prov. 26-May-4 Christie's, Paris #101/R est:1000-2000

REBOIRAS ROSALES, Arturo (1969-) Spanish

£426	$689	€600	Untitled (61x61cm-24x24in) s.d.98 verso panel. 20-May-3 Ansorena, Madrid #368/R

REBOLLEDO CORREA, Benito (1880-1964) Chilean

£1900	$3363	€2774	Cattle in a mountainous valley (71x101cm-28x40in) s.d.1920. 27-Apr-4 Bonhams, New Bond Street #136/R est:2000-3000
£2500	$4625	€3650	Girl on rocks (55x45cm-22x18in) s.d.1923. 14-Jul-4 Sotheby's, Olympia #265/R est:1500-2000

REBOUSSIN, Roger Andre Fernand (1881-1965) French
£1259 $2253 €1850 Babouins, Tchad (56x106cm-22x42in) s.i.d.1948. 21-Mar-4 St-Germain-en-Laye Encheres #96/R est:800
Works on paper
£476 $852 €700 Pileuse de mil (26x20cm-10x8in) studio st.i.d.1948 W/C. 21-Mar-4 St-Germain-en-Laye Encheres #62/R
£510 $913 €750 Femmes africaines (26x20cm-10x8in) studio st.i. W/C. 21-Mar-4 St-Germain-en-Laye Encheres #61/R

REBRY, Gaston (1933-) Canadian
£340 $622 €496 Un soir en Septembre (50x40cm-20x16in) s. prov. 1-Jun-4 Joyner Waddington, Toronto #478 (C.D 850)
£560 $1025 €818 Splendeur automnale (45x60cm-18x24in) s. 1-Jun-4 Joyner Waddington, Toronto #332/R (C.D 1400)
£600 $1098 €876 Apres midi en hiver (40x50cm-16x20in) s. prov. 1-Jun-4 Joyner Waddington, Toronto #430 (C.D 1500)
£653 $1110 €953 La roucher (41x51cm-16x20in) s. s.i.verso. 23-Nov-3 Levis, Calgary #118/R (C.D 1450)
£1036 $1761 €1513 Rouge d'automne (46x61cm-18x24in) s. s.i.verso. 23-Nov-3 Levis, Calgary #117/R est:1500-2000 (C.D 2300)
£1060 $1940 €1548 Parc National de la Maurice (45x60cm-18x24in) s.i.d.1990. 1-Jun-4 Hodgins, Calgary #265/R est:1500-2000 (C.D 2650)
£1126 $1914 €1644 Broken tree (76x61cm-30x24in) s. s.i.verso acrylic. 27-Nov-3 Heffel, Vancouver #186/R est:2000-3000 (C.D 2500)
£1200 $2196 €1752 L'Entree du Grand Lac Maurice-Que (45x60cm-18x24in) s. 1-Jun-4 Joyner Waddington, Toronto #260/R est:2000-2500 (C.D 3000)
£1786 $3071 €2608 Souches au bord du lac (75x60cm-30x24in) s. 2-Dec-3 Joyner Waddington, Toronto #270/R est:2000-2500 (C.D 4000)
£2036 $3400 €2973 On a cold day (75x100cm-30x39in) s.i. 17-Nov-3 Hodgins, Calgary #104/R est:3000-4000 (C.D 4500)

REBST, H (19th C) ?
Miniatures
£3500 $6055 €5110 Tsar Nicholas I in black coat (10x8cm-4x3in) s.d.1837 gilt-bronze frame. 9-Dec-3 Christie's, London #246/R est:1000-1500

REBULL TORROJA, Juan (1899-1981) Spanish
Works on paper
£486 $792 €700 Surrealist figure (21x24cm-8x9in) s.d.25 ink dr. 23-Sep-3 Durán, Madrid #619/R

RECALCATI, Antonio (1938-) Italian
£559 $951 €800 Untitled (25x40cm-10x16in) s.d.57 tempera ink paper on card two. 25-Nov-3 Sotheby's, Milan #64
£667 $1200 €1000 Woman (150x150cm-59x59in) painted 1962-72. 22-Apr-4 Finarte Semenzato, Rome #151/R
£769 $1285 €1100 The painter's questions (100x81cm-39x32in) mono.d.1999 acrylic. 29-Jun-3 Versailles Encheres #173/R
£839 $1552 €1250 Ambush (50x70cm-20x28in) s.i.d.1958 verso. 13-Mar-4 Meeting Art, Vercelli #500
£1111 $1756 €1600 More (100x80cm-39x31in) s. i.d.1967 verso acrylic. 27-Apr-3 Versailles Encheres #66
£1757 $3092 €2600 Print (99x80cm-39x31in) s.d.61 verso prov. 24-May-4 Christie's, Milan #109/R est:2500-3500
£2533 $4560 €3800 Underground (60x100cm-24x39in) s.d.63 verso exhib. 22-Apr-4 Finarte Semenzato, Rome #364/R est:3000-3500
£2817 $4930 €4000 Dread of war (170x140cm-67x55in) s.i.d.63 verso in 4 parts exhib. 16-Dec-3 Finarte Semenzato, Milan #360/R est:3800-4200
Works on paper
£1007 $1844 €1500 Figure ou empreinte (80x60cm-31x24in) s.d.1962/2 verso mixed media canvas prov.exhib. 7-Jul-4 Artcurial Briest, Paris #331 est:1500-2000

RECCO, Elena (17th C) Italian
£3333 $5567 €4800 Still life with fish and cat (48x61cm-19x24in) 22-Oct-3 Finarte Semenzato, Milan #29/R

RECCO, Giacomo (circle) (17th C) Italian
£20000 $36600 €29200 Figs in a basket, peaches a watermelon, scallops, fish and birds on a ledge in a landscape (110x145cm-43x57in) prov.lit. 7-Jul-4 Christie's, London #78/R est:20000-30000

RECCO, Giovan Battista (1630-1675) Italian
£14789 $25585 €21000 Nature morte aux poissons (54x69cm-21x27in) prov. 12-Dec-3 Renaud, Paris #131/R est:6000-8000

RECCO, Giuseppe (1634-1695) Italian
£67550 $122940 €102000 Flowers in a vase on column (131x91cm-52x36in) s.d. 16-Jun-4 Christie's, Rome #516/R est:80000-120000
£67550 $122940 €102000 Vase of flowers on column (13x91cm-5x36in) s.d.1670. 16-Jun-4 Christie's, Rome #515/R est:80000-120000
£68966 $115172 €100000 Still life with dish of sweets and mandolin (77x78cm-30x31in) s.d.1670. 15-Nov-3 Porro, Milan #236/R est:75000
£90000 $164700 €131400 Still lives with flowers (67x67cm-26x26in) octagonal pair. 8-Jul-4 Sotheby's, London #165/R est:25000-35000

RECCO, Giuseppe (attrib) (1634-1695) Italian
£8725 $16054 €13000 Still life with fish and crayfish (63x90cm-25x35in) one of pair. 24-Mar-4 Dorotheum, Vienna #224/R est:5000-7000
£10067 $18523 €15000 Still life with plucked turkey, fish and mushrooms (63x30cm-25x12in) one of pair. 24-Mar-4 Dorotheum, Vienna #225/R est:5000-7000

RECCO, Giuseppe (style) (1634-1695) Italian
£8462 $14554 €12355 Nature morte aux fruits et champignons (44x65cm-17x26in) indis.init. 3-Dec-3 AB Stockholms Auktionsverk #2716/R est:20000-25000 (S.KR 110000)

RECCO, Nicola Maria (18th C) Italian
£4577 $8011 €6500 Still life with fish (64x96cm-25x38in) s. 17-Dec-3 Finarte Semenzato, Milan #101/R est:5000-6000
£8453 $14793 €12000 Nature morte de poissons et de homard (65x107cm-26x42in) 18-Dec-3 Tajan, Paris #10/R est:12000-15000

RECCO, Nicola Maria (attrib) (18th C) Italian
£2217 $3969 €3237 Still life of fish (75x108cm-30x43in) 26-May-4 AB Stockholms Auktionsverk #2514/R est:35000-40000 (S.KR 30000)

RECHER, Peter Emil (1879-1948) German
£800 $1464 €1168 Venetian church, thought to be San Zaccaria (63x47cm-25x19in) s. board. 8-Apr-4 Christie's, Kensington #176/R

RECK, Hermine von (1833-1906) German
£552 $921 €800 Young man wearing red jacket (65x47cm-26x19in) s.d.1853. 9-Jul-3 Hugo Ruef, Munich #187

RECKELBUS, Louis (1864-1958) Belgian
Works on paper
£345 $638 €500 Maisonnette de pecheur a La Panne (37x26cm-15x10in) s. gouache. 13-Jan-4 Vanderkindere, Brussels #178

RECKNAGEL, John (19/20th C) German
Works on paper
£669 $1171 €950 Kerouhrien et l'arbre de Judee (55x38cm-22x15in) studio st. pastel. 21-Dec-3 Thierry & Lannon, Brest #264
£845 $1479 €1200 L'approche du bois a la Villa Combourg (48x30cm-19x12in) mono.d.1899 pastel. 21-Dec-3 Thierry & Lannon, Brest #98

RECKNAGEL, Otto (1845-1926) German
£1156 $2000 €1688 Portrait of a turkey on tree branch (150x99cm-59x39in) s. 10-Dec-3 Alderfer's, Hatfield #286/R est:2000-3000

RECKZIEGEL, Anton (1865-1936) Austrian
£385 $654 €550 Coastal landscape (54x114cm-21x45in) s. 27-Nov-3 Dorotheum, Linz #441/R

RECTOR, Bob (20th C) American
£240 $400 €350 Second Indy car, Dan Gurney (36x79cm-14x31in) s. 11-Oct-3 Nadeau, Windsor #177/R

REDDICLIFFE, Harold (20th C) American
£355 $650 €533 Poppies and irises (38x76cm-15x30in) 10-Jul-4 Hindman, Chicago #428/R

REDDINGTON, Charles (1929-) Australian
Works on paper
£901 $1424 €1315 The water carrier (49x73cm-19x29in) s.d.63 gouache chl. 2-Sep-3 Deutscher-Menzies, Melbourne #306/R est:500-700 (A.D 2200)

REDDY, Pakhal Tirumal (20th C) Indian
£1405 $2600 €2051 Reflections on a showcase (132x117cm-52x46in) s.d.1971 prov. 13-Jul-4 Christie's, Rockefeller NY #121/R est:800-1200

REDEIN, Alex (1912-1965) American
£270 $500 €394 Interior with figure (51x66cm-20x26in) s.d.80 oil collage paper prov. 13-Jul-4 Christie's, Rockefeller NY #120/R

REDEL, Eike (1951-) German
£400 $720 €600 Rhino with storks in the Savannah (40x50cm-16x20in) s. 22-Apr-4 Allgauer, Kempten #3693/R
£486 $768 €700 Tiger - trompe l'oeil. s. panel. 2-Sep-3 Christie's, Amsterdam #430/R
£2177 $3962 €3200 Tiger in lotusteich - tiger in lotus pond (60x100cm-24x39in) s. 3-Feb-4 Christie's, Amsterdam #606/R est:1000-1500

REDELIUS, Frank H (20th C) American
£881 $1400 €1286 Still life with venetian glass (61x51cm-24x20in) s.d.1963. 10-Sep-3 Sotheby's, New York #320 est:2000-3000
£881 $1400 €1286 Flowers in a vase (61x61cm-24x24in) s.d.1965 panel. 10-Sep-3 Sotheby's, New York #323 est:2000-3000

REDER, Bernard (1897-1963) Israeli
Sculpture
£773 $1400 €1129 Woman playing the cello (38cm-15in) s. bronze exec. 1950's. 1-Apr-4 Ben-Ami, Tel Aviv #4710/R est:2200-2800
£1359 $2500 €1984 Harp player (132x79x74cm-52x31x29in) s.i. brown pat. bronze exhib. 23-Jun-4 Doyle, New York #5089/R est:1000-1500

REDER, Christian (attrib) (1656-1729) German
£739 $1323 €1079 Pastoral landscape with cows, goats, dog and herders (26x39cm-10x15in) panel. 26-May-4 AB Stockholms Auktionsverk #2553/R (S.KR 10000)
£7500 $13425 €10950 Figures in an extensive Italianate landscape (48x65cm-19x26in) pair. 22-Mar-4 Bonhams & Brooks, Norfolk #210/R est:6000-8000

REDER, Heinrich Richard (1862-1942) German
£352 $630 €500 Moonrise over Lake Constance (14x22cm-6x9in) s.d.1926 board. 8-Jan-4 Allgauer, Kempten #2496/R

REDER, Heinrich von (1824-1909) German
£300 $537 €450 A warm rainy day in the Bayern Alps (76x22cm-30x9in) s. panel. 14-May-4 Behringer, Furth #1571/R

REDER-BROILI, Franz (1854-1918) German
£392 $666 €560 Amper in the evening (21x27cm-8x11in) s.i. i. verso board. 22-Nov-3 Arnold, Frankfurt #614
£559 $962 €800 Autumn landscape (23x30cm-9x12in) s. panel. 5-Dec-3 Michael Zeller, Lindau #767/R
£733 $1320 €1100 Meadows with birch trees (90x120cm-35x47in) s. 26-Apr-4 Rieber, Stuttgart #1325/R
£839 $1401 €1200 Stork in marsh landscape (23x30cm-9x12in) s. panel. 9-Oct-3 Michael Zeller, Lindau #735/R
£9790 $16643 €14000 Storm clouds gathering over Bavarian moorland with shepherd and flock (150x225cm-59x89in) s. 20-Nov-3 Dorotheum, Salzburg #175/R est:6000-7500

REDEWILL, Francis Hamilton (1879-1957) American
£256 $400 €374 California landscape (41x51cm-16x20in) s. board. 12-Apr-3 Auctions by the Bay, Alameda #259/R

REDFERN, June (20th C) ?
£380 $657 €555 The garden (30x40cm-12x16in) s.i.d.1994 verso. 11-Dec-3 Lyon & Turnbull, Edinburgh #81
£550 $875 €803 Evening light. The clearing (40x52cm-16x20in) s.d.1989/90 i.verso pair. 10-Sep-3 Sotheby's, Olympia #312/R

REDFIELD, Edward (1869-1965) American
£1117 $2000 €1631 Bucks County autumn, impressionist landscape (38x28cm-15x11in) s. board. 10-Jan-4 Pook & Pook, Downington #554/R
£1600 $2624 €2336 Snow bound cabin (43x33cm-17x13in) s. board. 6-Jun-3 Biddle & Webb, Birmingham #292
£4749 $8500 €6934 Winter solitude (38x30cm-15x12in) s.d.45 masonite. 8-Jan-4 James Julia, Fairfield #560/R est:8000-10000
£5163 $9500 €7538 Bend in the river (46x55cm-18x22in) s. i.indis.d. 27-Jun-4 Freeman, Philadelphia #183/R est:8000-12000
£8108 $15000 €11838 Monhegan winter (28x36cm-11x14in) s.d.1936 board. 13-Mar-4 Susanin's, Chicago #6042/R est:15000-20000
£29891 $55000 €43641 Bridge over a canal (58x81cm-23x32in) s.d.98. 27-Jun-4 Freeman, Philadelphia #209/R est:40000-60000
£71023 $125000 €103694 Brook and village in snow (63x86cm-25x34in) bears sig. d.95 prov. 18-May-4 Christie's, Rockefeller NY #77/R est:100000-150000
£156977 $270000 €229186 Canal in autumn (66x81cm-26x32in) s. prov.exhib. 3-Dec-3 Sotheby's, New York #24/R est:150000-250000
£282609 $520000 €412609 Briar patch (81x12cm-32x5in) s. prov.exhib.lit. 27-Jun-4 Freeman, Philadelphia #173/R est:400000-600000
£318182 $560000 €464546 Snow storm, Lambertville (82x102cm-32x40in) s. prov.lit. 18-May-4 Christie's, Rockefeller NY #105/R est:200000-300000
£363372 $625000 €530523 Old Mill, Washington's Crossing (81x102cm-32x40in) s. i.d.1937 stretcher verso prov.exhib. 7-Dec-3 Freeman, Philadelphia #187 est:300000-500000
Works on paper
£894 $1600 €1305 New England and connected farmhouse (28x38cm-11x15in) s. W/C. 8-Jan-4 James Julia, Fairfield #561/R est:1200-1500

REDGATE, A W (fl.1880-1906) British
£1250 $2150 €1825 Hemmington (28x43cm-11x17in) s. i.verso. 3-Dec-3 Andrew Hartley, Ilkley #1176 est:1000-1200

REDGATE, Arthur W (fl.1880-1906) British
£300 $555 €438 Pandy Mill, Bettws y Coed (34x44cm-13x17in) s.d.79 s.i.d.79 verso. 13-Jan-4 Bonhams, Oxford #272
£300 $567 €438 Milkmaid and child on a riverside track (61x91cm-24x36in) s. 19-Feb-4 Christie's, Kensington #215/R
£350 $630 €511 Backwater of the Trent (41x61cm-16x24in) s. s.i.verso. 22-Apr-4 Mellors & Kirk, Nottingham #1071
£360 $572 €526 Cattle in a misty glen (35x52cm-14x20in) s. 9-Sep-3 Bamfords, Derby #1134/R
£360 $648 €526 Horseman and shepherd with his flock (23x33cm-9x13in) s. board. 21-Apr-4 Cheffins, Cambridge #504/R
£420 $714 €613 The Trent, near Castle Donington (41x61cm-16x24in) s. s.i.verso. 25-Nov-3 Bonhams, Knowle #204
£480 $816 €701 Before the inn, a farmhand with horse and foal (52x66cm-20x26in) s. 25-Nov-3 Bonhams, Knowle #246
£520 $884 €759 Where the Soar meets the Trent (31x46cm-12x18in) s. 25-Nov-3 Bonhams, Knowle #208
£540 $1010 €788 Moored boats before a headland (51x73cm-20x29in) s. 24-Feb-4 Bonhams, Knowle #74
£600 $1116 €876 Cattle by a stream (61x91cm-24x36in) s. 4-Mar-4 Christie's, Kensington #509/R
£800 $1328 €1168 Trent at Weston (46x84cm-18x33in) s. s.i.verso. 2-Oct-3 Neales, Nottingham #750/R
£850 $1530 €1241 Outside the old house (40x65cm-16x26in) s. 22-Apr-4 Mellors & Kirk, Nottingham #1072/R
£923 $1588 €1348 View from Castle Donnington (40x66cm-16x26in) s. 3-Dec-3 AB Stockholms Auktionsverk #2614/R (S.KR 12000)
£1400 $2254 €2030 Vegetable seller with donkey and cart in Victorian rural hamlet (51x76cm-20x30in) s. exec.c.1880. 23-Feb-3 Desmond Judd, Cranbrook #1061
£1800 $2862 €2628 Hemington, three cattle in a meadow (49x74cm-19x29in) s.i. 9-Sep-3 Bamfords, Derby #1139/R
£1900 $3230 €2774 Summer meadow (61x91cm-24x36in) s. 25-Nov-3 Bonhams, Knowle #259/R est:2000-3000

REDGRAVE, Richard (1804-1888) British
Works on paper
£420 $773 €613 Holmsbury (18x38cm-7x15in) s.i.d.1876 verso pencil W/C. 25-Mar-4 Christie's, Kensington #120

REDIG, Laurent Herman (1822-1861) Dutch
£2462 $4234 €3595 Coastal landscape with figures skating in winter (33x43cm-13x17in) s. panel. 3-Dec-3 AB Stockholms Auktionsverk #2620/R est:20000-25000 (S.KR 32000)

REDILIUS, Frank H (20th C) American
£1074 $1750 €1568 Oriental trompe l'oeil (56x114cm-22x45in) s.d.58 masonite. 20-Jul-3 Jeffery Burchard, Florida #96

REDIN, Carl (1892-1944) American
£380 $700 €555 Desert scene with mountains in background (30x41cm-12x16in) s. board. 28-Mar-4 Bonhams & Butterfields, San Francisco #2735
£875 $1400 €1278 Landscape with adobe houses (28x33cm-11x13in) s. board. 19-Sep-3 Freeman, Philadelphia #98/R est:1500-2500
£941 $1600 €1374 Aspen grove (38x30cm-15x12in) s. canvas on panel prov. 1-Nov-3 Santa Fe Art, Santa Fe #241/R est:1000-2000

REDING, Leon (19th C) Belgian
£400 $740 €584 Portrait of a continental beauty (54x36cm-21x14in) indis.sig. 9-Mar-4 Bonhams, Knightsbridge #138/R
£6944 $11806 €10000 Passion for flowers (100x151cm-39x59in) s. 28-Oct-3 Christie's, Amsterdam #189/R est:8000-12000

REDLICH-VISZEG, Gustav von (20th C) Austrian
£1745 $3089 €2600 Apotheose: Crown Prince Rudolf welcoming mother (123x86cm-48x34in) s. 29-Apr-4 Dorotheum, Vienna #153/R est:5000-6000

REDMOND, Alec (20th C) American
£802 $1500 €1171 Policeman patrolling city at night, gun drawn (61x46cm-24x18in) s. painted c.1920. 26-Feb-4 Illustration House, New York #147 est:1800-2400

REDMOND, Granville (1871-1935) American
£2446 $4500 €3571 Landscape, Arroyo near Parkfield, California (21x26cm-8x10in) s.d.08 prov. 8-Jun-4 Bonhams & Butterfields, San Francisco #4229/R est:7000-9000
£2746 $4750 €4009 Cliffs by the sea (30x23cm-12x9in) s. canvas on board prov. 10-Dec-3 Bonhams & Butterfields, San Francisco #6203/R est:4000-6000
£5587 $10000 €8157 Fishing boat off the rocky coast of Catalina (18x25cm-7x10in) s. indis.i.verso board. 26-May-4 Doyle, New York #123/R est:6000-8000
£7609 $14000 €11109 Study of a seascape (21x27cm-8x11in) s. i.verso board painted 1918 prov. 8-Jun-4 Bonhams & Butterfields, San Francisco #4282/R est:8000-12000
£7937 $15000 €11588 California coast with poppies and lupine (23x30cm-9x12in) init. masonite. 17-Feb-4 John Moran, Pasadena #14/R est:1500-2000
£9524 $18000 €13905 River landscape - Twilight (20x30cm-8x12in) s. i.d.1914 verso board. 17-Feb-4 John Moran, Pasadena #71/R est:12000-18000
£13235 $22500 €19323 San Pedro Harbour (15x23cm-6x9in) s.d.1901 wood panel prov. 18-Nov-3 John Moran, Pasadena #12a est:10000-15000
£13736 $25000 €20055 Poppies and lupin in California landscape (13x18cm-5x7in) s. board prov. 15-Jun-4 John Moran, Pasadena #11 est:20000-30000
£17647 $30000 €25765 Coyote Point (30x46cm-12x18in) s. i.on stretcher. 29-Oct-3 Christie's, Los Angeles #62/R est:20000-30000
£21176 $36000 €30917 Sunset over Lake Merritt, Oakland (63x77cm-25x30in) s.d.1914 prov. 29-Oct-3 Christie's, Los Angeles #55/R est:30000-50000
£22487 $42500 €32831 Moonlit marshland (41x51cm-16x20in) s. 17-Feb-4 John Moran, Pasadena #47/R est:30000-50000
£25815 $47500 €37690 The sheep herder (61x76cm-24x30in) s.d.1912 prov. 8-Jun-4 Bonhams & Butterfields, San Francisco #4283/R est:60000-80000
£27473 $50000 €40111 Catalina Island (25x33cm-10x13in) s. s.d.1920 verso board prov. 15-Jun-4 John Moran, Pasadena #62 est:20000-30000
£43353 $75000 €63295 Resounding surf (56x76cm-22x30in) s. exhib. 10-Dec-3 Bonhams & Butterfields, San Francisco #6212/R est:50000-70000
£44304 $70000 €64684 California wildflowers (41x51cm-16x20in) s. 7-Sep-3 Treadway Gallery, Cincinnati #657/R est:80000-120000
£46243 $80000 €67515 Wildflowers in the marshes (51x76cm-20x30in) s.d.1912 prov.exhib. 10-Dec-3 Bonhams & Butterfields, San Francisco #6214/R est:100000-150000
£49133 $85000 €71734 Trees by a meadow stream (56x66cm-22x26in) s.d.09 prov. 10-Dec-3 Bonhams & Butterfields, San Francisco #6219/R est:60000-80000
£67797 $120000 €98984 Twilight (50x66cm-20x26in) s. prov. 28-Apr-4 Christie's, Los Angeles #47/R est:100000-150000

REDMOND, Thomas (attrib) (c.1745-1785) British
Miniatures
£1241 $2073 €1800 Lady (4cm-2in) oval. 12-Nov-3 Sotheby's, Milan #26/R est:900-1200

REDMORE, Edward King (1860-1941) British
£340 $629 €496 Shipping off a harbour (17x26cm-7x10in) s. board. 10-Feb-4 Bonhams, Knightsbridge #199/R
£340 $619 €496 Wreck by cliffs in a stormy sea (39x64cm-15x25in) s. 15-Jun-4 Bonhams, Oxford #112
£1200 $2040 €1752 Fishing boats off a coast line, with seabirds (41x66cm-16x26in) s. 19-Nov-3 Tennants, Leyburn #1033 est:800-1000

REDMORE, Henry (1820-1887) British
£1400 $2408 €2044 Shipping in heavy seas. Shipping at sunset (20x33cm-8x13in) s.d.1846 board pair. 2-Dec-3 Sotheby's, London #42/R est:1500-2500
£1500 $2685 €2190 Fishermen pulling in their nets (19x30cm-7x12in) s. indis.d. 26-May-4 Christie's, Kensington #692/R est:2000-3000
£1630 $2950 €2380 Ship caught in storm (24x42cm-9x17in) s.d.1871 board. 1-Apr-4 Ben-Ami, Tel Aviv #4754/R est:4000-6000
£1713 $3100 €2501 Ship on shore (24x42cm-9x17in) s.d.1871 board. 1-Apr-4 Ben-Ami, Tel Aviv #4755/R est:4000-6000
£2700 $4833 €3942 Figures on a life raft (24x44cm-9x17in) s.d. 17-May-4 David Duggleby, Scarborough #677/R est:2000-3000
£4800 $9072 €7008 Dutch barges lying offshore (22x30cm-9x12in) s. 17-Feb-4 Bonhams, New Bond Street #72/R est:1000-1500
£6738 $11252 €9500 Sailing ships and fishermen off coast (60x89cm-24x35in) s.d.1866. 17-Oct-3 Behringer, Furth #1649/R est:9000

£6831 $12500 €10247 Rescue of an English ship at sea (71x107cm-28x42in) s. 29-Jul-4 Eldred, East Dennis #290/R est:3000-5000
£7027 $13000 €10259 Royal Naval two-decker running along the coast at dusk (49x76cm-19x30in) s.d.1880 board. 10-Feb-4 Christie's, Rockefeller NY #235/R est:15000-20000
£7500 $12750 €10950 Naval two-decker (36x53cm-14x21in) s.d.1865 pair. 19-Nov-3 Christie's, Kensington #485/R
£8500 $14450 €12410 Sun setting over estuary (38x76cm-15x30in) s.d.1871. 19-Nov-3 Christie's, Kensington #486/R
£10500 $18795 €15330 Shipping off Flamborough Head (50x110cm-20x43in) s.d.1869. 17-May-4 David Duggleby, Scarborough #650/R est:10000-15000
£11000 $18700 €16060 Shipping on the Humber (31x46cm-12x18in) s,d,1860 pair. 19-Nov-3 Christie's, Kensington #483/R
£13000 $22100 €18980 Sailing boats unloading in an estuary (16x31cm-6x12in) s.d.1860 panel pair. 1-Dec-3 David Duggleby, Scarborough #347/R est:12000-16000
£15500 $27900 €22630 Figures in fishing boats off a rocky headland (61x102cm-24x40in) s.d.1881. 21-Apr-4 Tennants, Leyburn #1113/R est:10000-12000
£17000 $28900 €24820 The wreck buoy (61x102cm-24x40in) s.d.1877. 19-Nov-3 Tennants, Leyburn #1032/R est:10000-15000
£22000 $41580 €32120 The calm with figures on the shore. The storm with a ship in distress (40x76cm-16x30in) s.1886 pair. 23-Feb-4 David Duggleby, Scarborough #650/R est:15000-20000

REDMORE, Henry (attrib) (1820-1887) British
£580 $922 €841 Shipping scene (18x25cm-7x10in) panel. 9-Sep-3 David Duggleby, Scarborough #389
£900 $1530 €1314 Shipping on estuary at dusk (15x41cm-6x16in) board. 19-Nov-3 Christie's, Kensington #484/R

REDON, Georges (19/20th C) French
Prints
£2133 $3904 €3200 Theatre d'Ombres, la boite a musique (243x87cm-96x34in) s.d.98 col lithograph. 5-Jun-4 Gros & Delettrez, Paris #420/R est:2100-2400

REDON, Odilon (1840-1916) French
£3667 $6747 €5500 Maison hantee (45x32cm-18x13in) lithograph exec.1896. 10-Jun-4 Piasa, Paris #198/R
£13000 $23920 €18980 Les landes (18x23cm-7x9in) s. paper on board prov.exhib.lit. 23-Jun-4 Christie's, London #103/R est:10000-15000
£14000 $25760 €20440 Servante (23x18cm-9x7in) s. paper on card. 22-Jun-4 Sotheby's, London #139/R est:18000-25000
£35000 $58450 €51100 Portrait de femme (60x49cm-24x19in) s. board prov. 21-Oct-3 Sotheby's, London #35/R est:15000-20000
£158824 $270000 €231883 La chute d'Icare (66x47cm-26x19in) init. prov.lit. 4-Nov-3 Christie's, Rockefeller NY #28/R est:300000-400000
£279330 $500000 €407822 Vase de fleurs avec branches de pommier en fleurs (129x68cm-51x27in) s. painted c.1905 prov.exhib.lit. 4-May-4 Christie's, Rockefeller NY #11/R est:800000-1200000
£837989 $1500000 €1223464 Fleurs dans un vase vert (55x74cm-22x29in) s. painted 1910 prov.exhib.lit. 5-May-4 Sotheby's, New York #22/R est:1800000-2500000
Prints
£2000 $3440 €2920 Profil de lumiere (45x35cm-18x14in) lithograph. 2-Dec-3 Christie's, London #297/R est:3000-5000
£2118 $3600 €3092 Gnome (28x22cm-11x9in) lithograph edition of 25. 6-Nov-3 Swann Galleries, New York #404/R est:3000-5000
£2260 $4000 €3300 Plate III, from Planches d'Essai (24x22cm-9x9in) lithograph. 28-Apr-4 Christie's, Rockefeller NY #231/R est:5000-8000
£2471 $4200 €3608 Ari (32x25cm-13x10in) lithograph exec.1898. 4-Nov-3 Christie's, Rockefeller NY #197/R est:6000-10000
£3200 $5888 €4800 Vieux chevalier (30x23cm-12x9in) init. lithograph exec.1896. 10-Jun-4 Piasa, Paris #197
£8000 $14720 €12000 Beatrice (34x30cm-13x12in) col lithograph exec.1897. 10-Jun-4 Piasa, Paris #199
£20667 $38027 €31000 Homage to Goya (44x30cm-17x12in) lithograph album exec.1885. 10-Jun-4 Piasa, Paris #196/R
Works on paper
£1400 $2548 €2044 Chasseurs pres d'un etang (16x24cm-6x9in) s.d.1856 pencil prov.lit. 15-Jun-4 Bonhams, Knightsbridge #29/R est:800-1200
£4133 $7605 €6200 Tete de profil dans une courbe (25x20cm-10x8in) s. pen india ink chl prov.lit. 11-Jun-4 Claude Aguttes, Neuilly #194/R est:6000-8000
£5521 $9000 €8061 Centaure dans un paysage (25x19cm-10x7in) s. pencil prov.exhib. 25-Sep-3 Christie's, Rockefeller NY #507/R est:8000-12000
£6114 $11127 €8926 La fuite en Egypte - Mary with child on donkey (23x31cm-9x12in) mono. ink. 17-Jun-4 Kornfeld, Bern #710/R est:15000 (S.FR 14000)
£39301 $71528 €57379 Profil de femme, avec couronne de lauriers (41x23cm-16x9in) s. chl exec. c.1890. 18-Jun-4 Kornfeld, Bern #134/R est:70000 (S.FR 90000)
£88235 $150000 €128823 Trois vases de fleurs (72x53cm-28x21in) s. pastel paper on stretched paper exec c.1908-10 prov.lit. 6-Nov-3 Sotheby's, New York #205/R est:150000-200000
£142857 $255714 €210000 Ophelie (45x47cm-18x19in) s. pastel paper on canvas prov.lit. 17-Mar-4 Tajan, Paris #145/R est:200000-250000
£1899441 $3400000 €2773184 Vase au guerrier japonais (90x72cm-35x28in) s. pastel pencil paper on board exec.c.1905 prov.exhib.lit. 4-May-4 Christie's, Rockefeller NY #8/R est:2000000-3000000

REDONDELA, Agustin (1922-) Spanish
£3369 $5626 €4750 Village (21x26cm-8x10in) s. board. 20-Oct-3 Durán, Madrid #19/R
£3691 $6534 €5500 By the church (27x35cm-11x14in) s. s.i.d.2002 verso board. 27-Apr-4 Durán, Madrid #90/R est:5500
£3691 $6607 €5500 Houses in Brihuega (26x34cm-10x13in) s. i.d.03 board. 25-May-4 Durán, Madrid #147/R est:5500
£4225 $6761 €6000 Peasants (27x35cm-11x14in) s. s.i.d.2000 verso board prov. 16-Sep-3 Segre, Madrid #119/R est:6000
£4828 $8014 €7000 Houses in Brihuega (27x35cm-11x14in) s. s.i.d.2003 verso board. 1-Oct-3 Ansorena, Madrid #569/R est:6000
£5245 $8759 €7500 Paseo Maritmo (19x27cm-7x11in) s. panel. 24-Jun-3 Segre, Madrid #110/R est:3900
£5903 $9740 €8500 Door (27x35cm-11x14in) s. board. 2-Jul-3 Ansorena, Madrid #880/R
£5921 $10895 €9000 Old houses (46x55cm-18x22in) s.d.82 s.d.verso. 22-Jun-4 Durán, Madrid #172/R est:6000
£6207 $11172 €9000 Path in Budia (27x35cm-11x14in) s. board. 26-Jan-4 Durán, Madrid #162/R est:7000
£6944 $11458 €10000 Path (38x46cm-15x18in) i.verso. 2-Jul-3 Ansorena, Madrid #865/R
£7042 $12183 €10000 Village (44x36cm-17x14in) s. 10-Dec-3 Castellana, Madrid #195/R est:10000
£8966 $16138 €13000 Landscape (64x80cm-25x31in) s.d.1955 i.verso. 26-Jan-4 Ansorena, Madrid #199/R est:7000
£9028 $14354 €13000 Cereceda, Guadalajara (38x46cm-15x18in) s. 29-Apr-3 Durán, Madrid #156/R est:13000
£9211 $16947 €14000 Square in Sepulveda (54x65cm-21x26in) s. 22-Jun-4 Durán, Madrid #193/R est:12000
£13103 $24241 €19000 Village (63x80cm-25x31in) s. 14-Jan-4 Castellana, Madrid #243/R est:15000
Works on paper
£704 $1127 €1000 Village (16x24cm-6x9in) s.i. W/C. 16-Sep-3 Segre, Madrid #120/R
£828 $1490 €1200 Landscape in Vivero (16x24cm-6x9in) s. W/C. 26-Jan-4 Durán, Madrid #96/R
£1908 $3453 €2900 Church (48x33cm-19x13in) W/C. 14-Apr-4 Ansorena, Madrid #785/R est:2900

REDOUTE, Pierre Joseph (1759-1840) French
Works on paper
£2759 $4607 €4000 Etude de rose greffee (24x19cm-9x7in) s. W/C. 14-Nov-3 Drouot Estimations, Paris #48/R est:3000-4000
£7000 $12810 €10220 Bunch of pink roses with violas and other flowers (35x27cm-14x11in) s.d.1839 pencil W/C pair. 6-Jul-4 Christie's, London #149/R est:3000-5000
£8333 $15000 €12166 Asparagus horridus (47x34cm-19x13in) s. W/C pencil vellum prov. 22-Jan-4 Sotheby's, New York #115/R est:15000-20000
£8333 $15000 €12166 Sanseviera carnea (48x34cm-19x13in) s. W/C prov. 22-Jan-4 Sotheby's, New York #285/R est:20000-30000
£8333 $15000 €12166 Sisyrinchium collinum (48x34cm-19x13in) s. W/C prov. 22-Jan-4 Sotheby's, New York #287/R est:20000-30000
£13889 $25000 €20278 Arrowroot (47x34cm-19x13in) s. W/C pencil vellum prov. 22-Jan-4 Sotheby's, New York #113/R est:25000-35000
£13889 $25000 €20278 Anthericum milleflorum (47x34cm-19x13in) s. W/C pencil vellum prov. 22-Jan-4 Sotheby's, New York #116/R est:25000-35000
£19444 $35000 €28388 Belamcanda (48x34cm-19x13in) s. W/C prov. 22-Jan-4 Sotheby's, New York #284/R est:40000-60000
£19444 $35000 €28388 Gladiolus merianus (48x34cm-19x13in) s. W/C prov. 22-Jan-4 Sotheby's, New York #286/R est:40000-60000
£20134 $37449 €30000 Althaea (32x27cm-13x11in) s.d.1835 W/C. 8-Mar-4 Artcurial Briest, Paris #13/R est:10000
£22222 $40000 €32444 Inca lily (47x34cm-19x13in) s. W/C pencil vellum prov. 22-Jan-4 Sotheby's, New York #112/R est:50000-70000
£22222 $40000 €32444 Gladiolus laccatus (47x34cm-19x13in) s.acrylic W/C pencil vellum prov. 22-Jan-4 Sotheby's, New York #114/R est:40000-60000
£22535 $36056 €32000 Still life with roses and an anemone (33x24cm-13x9in) s.d.1832 W/C parchment. 22-Sep-3 Sotheby's, Amsterdam #81/R est:10000-15000

REDOUTE, Pierre Joseph (attrib) (1759-1840) French
Works on paper
£397 $723 €600 Bouquet de fleurs (34x29cm-13x11in) i.d.1839 W/C. 20-Jun-4 Versailles Encheres #64

REDPATH, Anne (1895-1965) British
£1700 $2669 €2465 Lane through the town (30x25cm-12x10in) s. panel. 27-Aug-3 Sotheby's, London #1235/R est:1000-1500
£5800 $10614 €8468 Doorway in St. Mark's Venice (75x62cm-30x24in) s. board prov. 8-Apr-4 Bonhams, Edinburgh #157/R est:7000-10000
£9800 $15778 €14210 Asters (29x33cm-11x13in) s. panel. 21-Aug-3 Bonhams, Edinburgh #1183/R est:3000-5000
£10000 $17200 €14600 In the ladies garden, Palacio de la Frontera (50x60cm-20x24in) s. board prov.exhib. 4-Dec-3 Bonhams, Edinburgh #12/R est:7000-10000
£11000 $17270 €15950 Yellow jug (61x61cm-24x24in) s. panel prov. 27-Aug-3 Sotheby's, London #1230/R est:8000-12000
£11500 $18515 €16675 Ponte Vecchio (40x31cm-16x12in) s. board. 21-Aug-3 Bonhams, Edinburgh #1056/R est:8000-12000
£12000 $21720 €17520 Freesias (51x61cm-20x24in) s. board prov.exhib. 19-Apr-4 Sotheby's, London #160/R est:12000-18000
£14000 $25340 €20440 Posy (22x18cm-9x7in) s. board prov. 19-Apr-4 Sotheby's, London #161/R est:4000-6000
£30000 $47100 €43500 Sitting room (91x91cm-36x36in) prov. 27-Aug-3 Sotheby's, London #1232/R est:30000-40000
£32000 $59520 €46720 White and yellow tulips in a blue and white jug (53x40cm-21x16in) s. panel. 4-Mar-4 Christie's, Kensington #195/R est:10000-15000
£42000 $71400 €61320 White tulips in a jug, on a low table with Penguin books (53x43cm-21x17in) s. board prov. 10-Nov-3 Thomson Roddick & Medcalf, Edinburgh #214 est:12000-18000
£50000 $85000 €73000 First flowers (56x46cm-22x18in) s. board exhib. 30-Oct-3 Christie's, London #197/R est:20000-30000
£55000 $86350 €79750 Lilies (61x51cm-24x20in) s. i.verso panel prov.exhib. 27-Aug-3 Sotheby's, London #1231/R est:25000-35000
Works on paper
£1600 $2512 €2320 Still life of flowers in a Venetian vase (38x28cm-15x11in) s. pen ink W/C. 27-Aug-3 Sotheby's, London #1236/R est:1000-1500
£2000 $3340 €2920 Daisies in the garden I (37x53cm-15x21in) s. W/C. 16-Oct-3 Bonhams, Edinburgh #49/R est:2000-3000
£3500 $6405 €5110 Strolling players (37x53cm-15x21in) s. pencil W/C prov. 8-Apr-4 Bonhams, Edinburgh #147/R est:4000-5000
£3600 $6120 €5256 Boats, Spain II (21x28cm-8x11in) W/C bodycol prov. 30-Oct-3 Christie's, London #200/R est:2000-3000
£4000 $7240 €5840 Still life with a coffee pot (34x44cm-13x17in) s. gouache over black chalk. 19-Apr-4 Sotheby's, London #158/R est:4000-6000
£4500 $8370 €6570 Borders landscape (42x44cm-17x17in) s. pencil W/C white chk. 4-Mar-4 Christie's, Kensington #193/R est:1000-1500
£4500 $8145 €6570 Red still life (28x37cm-11x15in) gouache prov. 19-Apr-4 Sotheby's, London #159/R est:4000-6000
£5800 $9338 €8410 Vase of flowers (55x56cm-22x22in) s. pencil W/C. 21-Aug-3 Bonhams, Edinburgh #1208/R est:3000-5000

£7500 $13875 €10950 Flowers by a pool (39x56cm-15x22in) s. W/C prov. 11-Feb-4 Sotheby's, Olympia #106/R est:5000-7000

REDPATH, Ophelia (20th C) British
£700 $1295 €1022 Wandering here and there (27x33cm-11x13in) s.d.2002 oil pastel gouache. 13-Feb-4 Sworder & Son, Bishops Stortford #93/R
£1800 $3330 €2628 Two low a mistress for so high a servant (75x55cm-30x22in) s.d.2002 oil pastel gouache. 13-Feb-4 Sworder & Son, Bishops Stortford #92/R
Works on paper
£840 $1554 €1226 Mother returning (57x41cm-22x16in) wax gouache. 13-Feb-4 Sworder & Son, Bishops Stortford #94/R

REDWOOD, Anna (20th C) British
£400 $704 €584 Red sail, Honfleur (25x29cm-10x11in) s. board. 18-May-4 Woolley & Wallis, Salisbury #31/R
£520 $915 €759 Daydream (39x19cm-15x7in) s. board. 18-May-4 Woolley & Wallis, Salisbury #38/R
£720 $1267 €1051 Summer afternoon painters (23x28cm-9x11in) s. board. 18-May-4 Woolley & Wallis, Salisbury #69/R
£840 $1478 €1226 Afternoon in the Tuileries (25x30cm-10x12in) s. board. 18-May-4 Woolley & Wallis, Salisbury #17/R
£1150 $2024 €1679 Boule (24x29cm-9x11in) s. board. 18-May-4 Woolley & Wallis, Salisbury #16/R est:200-300

REDWORTH, William Josiah (1873-1947) British
£1200 $2040 €1752 Launcelot, grey horse (43x43cm-17x17in) s.i.d.1904 verso. 27-Nov-3 Christie's, Kensington #111/R est:1500-2000

REE, Anita (1885-1933) German
Works on paper
£1583 $2596 €2200 Self portrait (26x19cm-10x7in) mono. pencil. 4-Jun-3 Ketterer, Hamburg #809/R est:1700-2000
£1748 $3007 €2500 Il Giovine Conte Pasquale Spine (22x17cm-9x7in) s.i. w/C. 2-Dec-3 Hauswedell & Nolte, Hamburg #556/R est:2500
£2238 $3849 €3200 Portrait of a Chinese woman (23x18cm-9x7in) W/C pencil. 2-Dec-3 Hauswedell & Nolte, Hamburg #555/R est:2000

REEB, David (1952-) Israeli
£824 $1400 €1203 Urban landscape (78x63cm-31x25in) s. cardboard on canvas. 1-Dec-3 Ben-Ami, Tel Aviv #4343/R est:2000-3000
£6145 $11000 €8972 Black and white studio contact (140x160cm-55x63in) s.d.1991 verso industrial paint exhib. 18-Mar-4 Sotheby's, New York #71/R est:12000-15000

REED, Marjorie (1915-1997) American
£1190 $2250 €1737 The Butterfield Stage rolls on (20x25cm-8x10in) s. i. verso canvasboard prov. 17-Feb-4 John Moran, Pasadena #184/R est:800-1200
£2060 $3750 €3008 Evening splendour (76x102cm-30x40in) s. i.verso prov. 15-Jun-4 John Moran, Pasadena #180b est:3000-5000
£2198 $4000 €3209 Stagecoach in a landscape (41x51cm-16x20in) s. i.verso canvasboard prov. 15-Jun-4 John Moran, Pasadena #180c est:2000-3000
£4121 $7500 €6017 The Butterfield Overland leaving Warners Station (76x102cm-30x40in) s. i.verso prov. 15-Jun-4 John Moran, Pasadena #180a est:4000-6000

REED, Peter Fishe (1817-1887) American
£535 $850 €781 Autumn forest landscape with creek (89x135cm-35x53in) s. 13-Sep-3 Weschler, Washington #730/R
£1734 $3000 €2532 Green Mountain forest (91x112cm-36x44in) s.d.1882 prov.exhib. 10-Dec-3 Bonhams & Butterfields, San Francisco #6003/R est:3000-5000

REED, William J (20th C) New Zealander
£484 $867 €707 Quiet afternoon (28x38cm-11x15in) s. board. 11-May-4 Watson's, Christchurch #8/R (NZ.D 1400)
£500 $905 €730 Jockey (37x39cm-15x15in) s. canvasboard. 4-Apr-4 International Art Centre, Auckland #309/R (NZ.D 1400)
£1598 $2716 €2333 Lakeside farm (45x58cm-18x23in) s. board prov. 27-Nov-3 International Art Centre, Auckland #92/R est:4000-6000 (NZ.D 4250)
£2249 $4026 €3284 Boy with boat (38x27cm-15x11in) s. painted c.1950. 12-May-4 Dunbar Sloane, Wellington #53/R est:2000-4000 (NZ.D 6500)
£2857 $5257 €4171 Red car in a southern landscape (45x60cm-18x24in) s. board prov. 25-Mar-4 International Art Centre, Auckland #21/R est:8000-12000 (NZ.D 8000)
£3008 $5113 €4392 Two women (45x34cm-18x13in) s. board. 27-Nov-3 International Art Centre, Auckland #66/R est:8000-12000 (NZ.D 8000)
£3261 $5283 €4728 Midnight wharf, Otago Harbour (60x90cm-24x35in) s. board prov. 31-Jul-3 International Art Centre, Auckland #15/R est:8000-12000 (NZ.D 9000)
Works on paper
£464 $840 €677 Oamaru breakwater (20x23cm-8x9in) s. mixed media. 4-Apr-4 International Art Centre, Auckland #311/R (NZ.D 1300)
£465 $799 €679 Man digging (44x30cm-17x12in) s. mixed media. 7-Dec-3 International Art Centre, Auckland #356/R (NZ.D 1250)
£595 $1023 €869 Naseby (27x30cm-11x12in) W/C. 7-Dec-3 International Art Centre, Auckland #360/R (NZ.D 1600)
£607 $1117 €886 Boats and sheds II (29x36cm-11x14in) s. mixed media prov. 25-Mar-4 International Art Centre, Auckland #25/R (NZ.D 1700)
£1128 $1917 €1647 Otago landscape (29x41cm-11x16in) s. W/C. 27-Nov-3 International Art Centre, Auckland #31/R est:3000-5000 (NZ.D 3000)

REEDER, Dixon (1912-1970) American
£449 $750 €656 Portrait (86x66cm-34x26in) 18-Oct-3 David Dike, Dallas #138/R
£1497 $2500 €2186 Green abstraction (76x46cm-30x18in) exhib. 18-Oct-3 David Dike, Dallas #157/R est:2500-5000
Works on paper
£240 $400 €350 Three graces (30x46cm-12x18in) mixed media. 18-Oct-3 David Dike, Dallas #135/R

REEDY, Leonard Howard (1899-1956) American
£1301 $2250 €1899 Hunting buffalo (63x77cm-25x30in) s. 10-Dec-3 Bonhams & Butterfields, San Francisco #6088/R est:3000-5000
Works on paper
£254 $425 €371 Snowbound (20x28cm-8x11in) s. W/C on board. 19-Oct-3 Jeffery Burchard, Florida #86
£269 $450 €393 Cowboy in a landscape (33x43cm-13x17in) s. W/C. 20-Jun-3 Freeman, Philadelphia #76/R
£284 $475 €415 Indians rounding up steers (33x43cm-13x17in) s. W/C. 20-Jun-3 Freeman, Philadelphia #67/R
£329 $550 €480 Cowtown Saturday night (23x30cm-9x12in) s. W/C. 19-Oct-3 Susanin's, Chicago #6087/R
£329 $550 €480 In the corral (20x28cm-8x11in) s. i.verso W/C on board. 19-Oct-3 Jeffery Burchard, Florida #86a
£329 $550 €480 Pursued by the sheriff (20x28cm-8x11in) s. i.verso W/C on board. 19-Oct-3 Jeffery Burchard, Florida #56b
£331 $600 €483 Riding scene (20x28cm-8x11in) W/C. 16-Apr-4 Du Mouchelle, Detroit #2086/R
£387 $700 €565 Cowboy on horseback (20x28cm-8x11in) W/C. 16-Apr-4 Du Mouchelle, Detroit #2088/R
£449 $750 €656 Cavalry (38x48cm-15x19in) s. W/C. 20-Jun-3 Freeman, Philadelphia #28/R
£457 $850 €667 Night rider (20x28cm-8x11in) s.i. W/C executed c.1935. 7-Mar-4 Treadway Gallery, Cincinnati #584/R
£497 $900 €726 Cowboy riding (18x28cm-7x11in) s. 16-Apr-4 Du Mouchelle, Detroit #2087/R
£525 $950 €767 Cowboy with a stagecoach beyond (20x28cm-8x11in) W/C. 16-Apr-4 Du Mouchelle, Detroit #2089/R
£719 $1200 €1050 Attack on the Union Pacific (23x30cm-9x12in) s. W/C. 19-Oct-3 Susanin's, Chicago #6086/R est:400-600
£723 $1150 €1056 Cowboy roping a mustang (20x25cm-8x10in) s. drawing. 13-Sep-3 Selkirks, St. Louis #55/R
£759 $1200 €1108 Night rider (20x28cm-8x11in) s.i. W/C. 7-Sep-3 Treadway Gallery, Cincinnati #586/R
£879 $1600 €1283 In the corral (20x28cm-8x11in) s. i.verso W/C prov. 15-Jun-4 John Moran, Pasadena #128a est:800-1200
£898 $1500 €1311 Indian encampment (38x48cm-15x19in) s. W/C. 20-Jun-3 Freeman, Philadelphia #6/R est:1000-1500
£1059 $1800 €1546 Indian party on horseback (8x11cm-3x4in) s. W/C. 18-Nov-3 John Moran, Pasadena #124a est:800-1500
£1738 $3250 €2537 Prairie fire. Wild ponies (23x30cm-9x12in) s. W/C pair. 24-Jul-4 Coeur d'Alene, Hayden #222/R est:2000-4000

REEKERS, Hendrik (1815-1854) Dutch
£9091 $16000 €13273 Still life with roses and other flowers in an oriental vase (32x24cm-13x9in) s. panel. 18-May-4 Bonhams & Butterfields, San Francisco #73/R est:12000-15000

REEKUM, Johannes Christoffel van (1877-1943) Dutch
Works on paper
£270 $476 €400 Three parrots on a perch (33x47cm-13x19in) s.d.32 W/C. 19-May-4 Sotheby's, Amsterdam #384/R

REES, Lloyd Frederick (1895-1988) Australian
£4255 $7234 €6212 Autumn morning (22x27cm-9x11in) s.i. verso canvas on board. 25-Nov-3 Christie's, Melbourne #104/R est:6000-8000 (A.D 10000)
£7724 $13825 €11277 At Coolangatta (24x26cm-9x10in) init. bears i.verso wood panel painted 1919 prov.lit. 4-May-4 Sotheby's, Melbourne #153/R est:15000-20000 (A.D 19000)
£13223 $24463 €19306 Coastal hills, New South Wales (41x59cm-16x23in) s.d.54 i.verso canvas on board prov.exhib. 10-Mar-4 Deutscher-Menzies, Melbourne #128/R est:25000-35000 (A.D 32000)
£13821 $24740 €20179 Paris Buildings (56x69cm-22x27in) s.d.61 i.verso canvas on composition board. 4-May-4 Sotheby's, Melbourne #59/R est:20000-30000 (A.D 34000)
£20325 $31911 €29471 Twilight in Tasmania (57x74cm-22x29in) s.d.76 canvas on board prov. 26-Aug-3 Christie's, Sydney #6/R est:40000-60000 (A.D 50000)
Works on paper
£1780 $3025 €2599 Italy (17x21cm-7x8in) s.d.1960 ink wash. 24-Nov-3 Sotheby's, Melbourne #99/R est:2000-4000 (A.D 4200)
£2429 $3911 €3546 Cathedral (28x19cm-11x7in) ink ink wash exec c.1920s. 25-Aug-3 Sotheby's, Paddington #395/R est:6000-8000 (A.D 6000)
£2653 $4882 €3873 Dreaming day on the Derwent (29x46cm-11x18in) s.d.83 W/C prov. 29-Mar-4 Goodman, Sydney #198/R est:4000-6000 (A.D 6500)
£2893 $5351 €4224 Tuscan landscape (33x39cm-13x15in) s.d.66 W/C chl pen ink. 10-Mar-4 Deutscher-Menzies, Melbourne #349/R est:7000-10000 (A.D 7000)
£2966 $5042 €4330 Sunlit landscape (35x55cm-14x22in) s.d.86 pastel. 24-Nov-3 Sotheby's, Melbourne #172/R est:7000-10000 (A.D 7000)
£4132 $7645 €6033 Tuscany II (34x44cm-13x17in) s. W/C chl pen ink prov. 10-Mar-4 Deutscher-Menzies, Melbourne #181/R est:12000-15000 (A.D 10000)
£5081 $7977 €7367 Standley chasm, ghost gums (38x50cm-15x20in) s.d.1976 crayon W/C prov. 26-Aug-3 Christie's, Sydney #205/R est:8000-10000 (A.D 12500)
£5894 $9254 €8546 Looking east, sundown (41x56cm-16x22in) s.d.78 W/C gouache ink prov.lit. 26-Aug-3 Christie's, Sydney #145/R est:12000-15000 (A.D 14500)
£6073 $9777 €8867 Tree on Sydney Harbour (19x24cm-7x9in) s.d.1933 pencil prov. 25-Aug-3 Sotheby's, Paddington #371/R est:10000-15000 (A.D 15000)
£14228 $25467 €20773 Villa Medici, Rome (32x46cm-13x18in) s.d.1931 ink exhib.lit. 4-May-4 Sotheby's, Melbourne #141/R est:25000-35000 (A.D 35000)

REES, Otto van (1884-1957) Dutch
£699 $1168 €1000 Portrait of Jos Croin (46x38cm-18x15in) s.l.d.39. 30-Jun-3 Sotheby's, Amsterdam #430/R
£2899 $4754 €4000 Untitled (39x18cm-15x7in) s.verso panel. 27-May-3 Sotheby's, Amsterdam #359/R est:2500-3500
£3623 $5942 €5000 Untitled (40x30cm-16x12in) s.d.30. 27-May-3 Sotheby's, Amsterdam #357/R est:5000-7000
£12587 $21650 €18000 Compositie (42x42cm-17x17in) s. s.i.verso canvas on board prov.exhib. 2-Dec-3 Sotheby's, Amsterdam #108/R est:10000-15000
£16000 $29440 €24000 Untitled (41x33cm-16x13in) s. painted 1916-1917 prov.exhib.lit. 9-Jun-4 Christie's, Amsterdam #233/R est:10000-15000
Works on paper
£470 $864 €700 Still life with a female torso (16x10cm-6x4in) mono. mixed media. 29-Mar-4 Glerum, Amsterdam #189

REESE, James (20th C) American
£1879 $3364 €2800 Three for money (68x49cm-27x19in) cardboard painted 1955. 27-May-4 Sotheby's, Paris #149/R est:1000-1500

REESE, Marx C E (1881-1960) Danish
£289 $534 €422 Seascape with man-of-war and steam ferry off Kronborg (42x46cm-17x18in) s. 15-Mar-4 Rasmussen, Vejle #67 (D.KR 3200)

REESE, Nancy (20th C) American
£294 $500 €429 Study of heads with foliage (201x165cm-79x65in) s.d.86 s.i.d.verso. 9-Nov-3 Bonhams & Butterfields, Los Angeles #4070/R
Works on paper
£647 $1100 €945 Master bouquet (175x201cm-69x79in) s.i.d.1987 verso mixed media on board. 9-Nov-3 Bonhams & Butterfields, Los Angeles #4071/R est:4000-6000

REEVE, Russell Sidney (1895-1970) British
£550 $1018 €803 Still life with tulips (61x51cm-24x20in) s.d.40 s.i.overlap. 11-Feb-4 Sotheby's, Olympia #91/R
£600 $1110 €876 Still life with dressing gown and slippers (81x65cm-32x26in) s. exhib. 11-Feb-4 Sotheby's, Olympia #90/R
£650 $1203 €949 Chelmondiston (46x61cm-18x24in) s.d.53 i.verso. 11-Feb-4 Sotheby's, Olympia #87/R
£650 $1203 €949 August flowers (40x51cm-16x20in) s.d.47 s.i.verso. 11-Feb-4 Sotheby's, Olympia #94/R
£700 $1295 €1022 Walberswick (30x40cm-12x16in) s.d.23. 11-Feb-4 Sotheby's, Olympia #86/R
£800 $1480 €1168 Blue and pink (61x51cm-24x20in) s. s.i.stretcher. 11-Feb-4 Sotheby's, Olympia #92/R
£900 $1665 €1314 Felixstowe to Ipswich coach (38x57cm-15x22in) sold with two W/C and pencil sketches by the same hand. 11-Feb-4 Sotheby's, Olympia #85/R est:400-600
£1100 $2035 €1606 Hendon Housing Estate (51x91cm-20x36in) s.d.1920. 11-Feb-4 Sotheby's, Olympia #83/R est:1000-1500
£1200 $2220 €1752 The old fish market and St Peter Mancroft Church, Norwich (51x40cm-20x16in) s.d.1914. 11-Feb-4 Sotheby's, Olympia #84/R est:1000-1500
£1200 $2220 €1752 Still life with daisies (40x51cm-16x20in) s.d.1926. 11-Feb-4 Sotheby's, Olympia #93/R est:500-700
£1200 $2112 €1752 Fenchurch Street Station (61x101cm-24x40in) s.i.d.1965 s.i.stretcher exhib. 19-May-4 Sotheby's, Olympia #202/R est:800-1200
£2400 $4440 €3504 Lucy and Russell (45x61cm-18x24in) s.d.1923. 11-Feb-4 Sotheby's, Olympia #88/R est:800-1200
Works on paper
£360 $666 €526 Sunday gathering (25x37cm-10x15in) black crayon. 11-Feb-4 Sotheby's, Olympia #1/R
£360 $652 €526 Young girl with rabbit (53x43cm-21x17in) s. red conte chk. 16-Apr-4 Keys, Aylsham #611
£420 $777 €613 Ducks (32x40cm-13x16in) s.d.52 W/C sold with another by the same hand. 11-Feb-4 Sotheby's, Olympia #31/R
£450 $832 €657 Quayside, Newcastle upon Tyne (30x41cm-12x16in) s.d.35 red crayon. 11-Feb-4 Sotheby's, Olympia #22/R
£450 $832 €657 Unloading timber (37x50cm-15x20in) W/C pencil. 11-Feb-4 Sotheby's, Olympia #36/R
£500 $925 €730 Kings Cross. Milk cans, Liverpool Street Station (24x34cm-9x13in) s.i. one d.1927 one d.1926 and 18/8/26 pen ink W/C pair. 11-Feb-4 Sotheby's, Olympia #10/R
£500 $925 €730 Ipswich (25x37cm-10x15in) s.i.d.33 W/C sold with another by the same hand. 11-Feb-4 Sotheby's, Olympia #41/R
£550 $1018 €803 Highland road, Norwich (23x30cm-9x12in) s.i.d.20/6/23 ink W/C sold with another by the same hand. 11-Feb-4 Sotheby's, Olympia #7/R
£550 $1018 €803 Portuguese cobblers at Monte Estoril (37x55cm-15x22in) s.i.d.47 black crayon. 11-Feb-4 Sotheby's, Olympia #45/R
£600 $1110 €876 The dog show (26x40cm-10x16in) black crayon. 11-Feb-4 Sotheby's, Olympia #16/R
£650 $1203 €949 Milking 1. Milking 2 (25x37cm-10x15in) one s. black crayon framed as a pair. 11-Feb-4 Sotheby's, Olympia #18/R
£650 $1203 €949 Pigs feeding (27x38cm-11x15in) s.d.36 W/C sold with another by the same hand. 11-Feb-4 Sotheby's, Olympia #29/R
£750 $1388 €1095 Van horse parade, Ipswich. The trainer (27x38cm-11x15in) one s.i.d.37 W/C one pencil W/C pair. 11-Feb-4 Sotheby's, Olympia #24/R
£800 $1480 €1168 Horse market, Norwich (24x35cm-9x14in) s.i. black crayon W/C. 11-Feb-4 Sotheby's, Olympia #26/R
£850 $1572 €1241 The vet visiting (25x43cm-10x17in) s. pencil col crayon sold with another by the same hand. 11-Feb-4 Sotheby's, Olympia #20/R est:600-800
£1100 $2035 €1606 Ploughing (27x40cm-11x16in) s. pencil W/C. 11-Feb-4 Sotheby's, Olympia #27/R est:500-700
£1300 $2405 €1898 Lion tamer (25x35cm-10x14in) s. W/C sold with four circus scenes by the same hand. 11-Feb-4 Sotheby's, Olympia #33/R est:600-800
£1300 $2405 €1898 Cadaques (24x34cm-9x13in) s.i.d.1928 pen ink W/C sold with another by the same hand. 11-Feb-4 Sotheby's, Olympia #51/R est:400-600

REEVES (?) ?
£3200 $5440 €4672 Stag hunt. Boar hunt (65x81cm-26x32in) s. pair. 19-Nov-3 Sotheby's, Olympia #39/R est:2000-3000

REEVES, Joseph Mason (jnr) (1898-1974) American
£1044 $1900 €1524 Landscapes. Seascape (23x33cm-9x13in) s. canvasboard five prov. 15-Jun-4 John Moran, Pasadena #196 est:1500-2000
£1236 $2250 €1805 Still lifes (25x20cm-10x8in) s. canvasboard five prov. 15-Jun-4 John Moran, Pasadena #197 est:1500-2000
£1374 $2500 €2006 Landscapes (20x25cm-8x10in) s. canvasboard five prov. 15-Jun-4 John Moran, Pasadena #195 est:1500-2000
£1471 $2500 €2148 Cowboy in ten gallon hat (16x13cm-6x5in) s. prov. 18-Nov-3 John Moran, Pasadena #116c est:2000-3000
£2060 $3750 €3008 American Indian. Boy in cowboy hat. Woman in bandanna. Farmer in hat. (30x28cm-12x11in) s. canvasboard four prov. 15-Jun-4 John Moran, Pasadena #193 est:1500-2000
£2335 $4250 €3409 Cityscapes. House in landscape (23x33cm-9x13in) s. canvasboard four prov. 15-Jun-4 John Moran, Pasadena #194 est:1500-2000

REEVES, Ruby Mary Olive (1904-1986) South African
Works on paper
£273 $470 €399 Greig fantasy (45x33cm-18x13in) s.d.1960 W/C. 3-Dec-3 Stephan Welz, Johannesburg #25 est:1200-1800 (SA.R 3000)

REEVES, Walter (fl.1882-1900) British
£700 $1204 €1022 Welsh cottage (40x60cm-16x24in) s. i.verso. 4-Dec-3 Mellors & Kirk, Nottingham #927/R
£1733 $3172 €2600 Chasse au canard. Chasse au faisan (38x55cm-15x22in) s. pair. 6-Jun-4 Osenat, Fontainebleau #253 est:3000-3500

REEVES, Wendy (?) British
£280 $468 €409 Mallard in flight over river at sunset (48x74cm-19x29in) s. 17-Oct-3 Keys, Aylsham #367

REFREGIER, Anton (1905-1979) American/Russian
£282 $450 €412 Summertime (122x41cm-48x16in) s.d.1967 masonite board. 20-Sep-3 Bunte, Elgin #385j
£329 $550 €480 Advertisement (66x48cm-26x19in) tempera board painted 1956. 17-Oct-3 Du Mouchelle, Detroit #2030/R
£938 $1500 €1369 Picking pears, Will the tree bear (79x117cm-31x46in) s.d.1964. 17-May-3 Bunte, Elgin #1313 est:300-500

REFSNES, Isak (1852-1928) Norwegian
£777 $1290 €1127 Stadthavet - seascape (50x76cm-20x30in) s. 16-Jun-3 Blomqvist, Lysaker #1346/R (N.KR 9000)
£976 $1785 €1425 Ship's portrait of sailing vessel (58x80cm-23x31in) s.d.1917. 7-Jun-4 Blomqvist, Oslo #245/R (N.KR 12000)
£1206 $2207 €1761 Sailing vessel by the coast (66x94cm-26x37in) s. panel. 2-Feb-4 Blomqvist, Lysaker #1233 est:18000-20000 (N.KR 15000)

REGAGNON, Andre Firmin (1902-) French
£374 $670 €550 Nature morte aux tournesols (62x50cm-24x20in) s. prov. 19-Mar-4 Oger, Dumont, Paris #20
£442 $791 €650 Le pont (46x55cm-18x22in) s. prov. 19-Mar-4 Oger, Dumont, Paris #19
£933 $1717 €1400 Scene de marche (145x88cm-57x35in) s. 9-Jun-4 Beaussant & Lefèvre, Paris #204/R

REGAMEY, Frederic (1849-1925) French
Works on paper
£374 $670 €550 Portrait de Lord Lytton (29x23cm-11x9in) s. black pencil pastel. 19-Mar-4 Piasa, Paris #134
£748 $1339 €1100 Salon de monsieur de La Rochefoucault, Duc de Doudeville (34x21cm-13x8in) i. black pencil pastel. 19-Mar-4 Piasa, Paris #137

REGELE, Rolf (1899-?) German
£464 $844 €700 View of the Dolomites (58x47cm-23x19in) s. card. 17-Jun-4 Finarte Semenzato, Milan #328

REGEMORTER, Ignatius Josephus van (1785-1873) Flemish
£1000 $1670 €1460 Drunken suitor (53x43cm-21x17in) s.d.1835 panel. 8-Oct-3 Christie's, Kensington #826/R est:1200-1800

REGEMORTER, Ignatius Josephus van (attrib) (1785-1873) Flemish
£345 $576 €500 Scene d'auberge (25x19cm-10x7in) panel. 17-Nov-3 Bernaerts, Antwerp #4

REGENBOOG, Jan Hendrik (1883-?) Dutch
£449 $750 €656 Morning in Holland. s. 18-Oct-3 Harvey Clar, Oakland #1206

REGGIANI, Filippo (1838-1905) Italian
£1079 $1770 €1500 Landscape (17x24cm-7x9in) 5-Jun-3 Adma, Formigine #646 est:1700-1800

REGGIANI, Mauro (1897-1980) Italian
£2759 $4607 €4000 Composition with spiral (55x38cm-22x15in) s. painted 1961. 14-Nov-3 Farsetti, Prato #276/R est:3200-3600
£2759 $4607 €4000 Composition 70 (44x42cm-17x17in) s. acrylic card painted 1972. 17-Nov-3 Sant Agostino, Torino #302/R est:3500-4500
£3356 $6208 €5000 Composition (46x44cm-18x17in) s. acrylic card painted 1972. 13-Mar-4 Meeting Art, Vercelli #404 est:5000
£4698 $8409 €7000 Composition (17x23cm-7x9in) s. s.verso board prov. 25-May-4 Sotheby's, Milan #137/R est:7000
£4730 $8324 €7000 Untitled (50x40cm-20x16in) s.d.1956 prov.lit. 24-May-4 Christie's, Milan #185/R est:5000-7000
£5282 $9243 €7500 Composition (31x40cm-12x16in) s.d.35 prov. 16-Dec-3 Porro, Milan #3/R est:10000-12000
£5435 $8913 €7500 Composition number 4 (116x89cm-46x35in) s.i.d.1954-8 verso lit. 30-May-3 Farsetti, Prato #84/R
£5862 $9790 €8500 Composition (30x40cm-12x16in) s. s.i.d.1955 verso. 14-Nov-3 Farsetti, Prato #277/R est:4200-5200
£6711 $12013 €10000 Composition 15 (81x65cm-32x26in) s.d.1970 verso exhib.lit. 28-May-4 Farsetti, Prato #352 est:6200-7200
£7667 $13800 €11500 Composition (43x59cm-17x23in) s. canvas on cardboard lit. 22-Apr-4 Finarte Semenzato, Rome #346/R est:11000-13000
£12752 $22826 €19000 Composition (55x38cm-22x15in) s. s.i.d.1935 verso exhib.lit. 25-May-4 Sotheby's, Milan #266/R est:15000-20000
£13287 $22587 €19000 Composition 4 (95x75cm-37x30in) s. prov.exhib.lit. 25-Nov-3 Sotheby's, Milan #169/R est:10000-15000
£15493 $25718 €22000 Composition in white and red number 3 (73x92cm-29x36in) s. s.i.verso lit. 13-Jun-3 Farsetti, Prato #345/R est:25000
£15862 $26490 €23000 Composition (66x57cm-26x22in) s.d.1952. 17-Nov-3 Sant Agostino, Torino #300/R est:23000-28000
£20979 $35664 €30000 Composition 38 (95x68cm-37x27in) s. prov. 24-Nov-3 Christie's, Milan #262/R est:30000-40000

REGGIANINI, Vittorio (1858-1939) Italian
£52941 $90000 €77294 Eavesdroppers (96x66cm-38x26in) s. 29-Oct-3 Christie's, Rockefeller NY #219/R est:100000-150000

REGGIOLI, Alessandro (1971-) Italian
Works on paper
£387 $643 €550 Aliante 3 (30x30cm-12x12in) s.i.verso mixed media collage panel. 14-Jun-3 Meeting Art, Vercelli #41/R
£423 $701 €600 Flight IV (30x30cm-12x12in) s.i.verso assemblage acrylic board on canvas. 13-Jun-3 Farsetti, Prato #2/R

REGILD, Carsten (1941-1992) Swedish
£566 $963 €826 Untitled (96x68cm-38x27in) s.d.87. 4-Nov-3 Bukowskis, Stockholm #646/R (S.KR 7500)
£1133 $1926 €1654 A tattooed lady - cut into pieces (146x206cm-57x81in) s.d.84. 4-Nov-3 Bukowskis, Stockholm #610/R est:12000-15000 (S.KR 15000)

REGINA, Guido la (1909-) Italian
£2027 $3568 €3000 Untitled (149x99cm-59x39in) s. painted 1954 exhib. 24-May-4 Christie's, Milan #107/R est:1500-2000

REGNAULT DE MAULMAIN, Émile (1836-1897) French
£2000 $3660 €3000 Cavalier dans la cour d'un palais (24x19cm-9x7in) s. 3-Jun-4 Tajan, Paris #265/R est:3000-4000
£14894 $24872 €21000 Caravane de marchands au Caire (64x53cm-25x21in) s.d.1881. 16-Jun-3 Gros & Delettrez, Paris #217/R est:12000-20000

REGNAULT, Baron Jean Baptiste (attrib) (1754-1829) French
£1300 $2119 €1898 Vestal Virgin (86x67cm-34x26in) 26-Sep-3 Christie's, Kensington #225/R est:1000-1500
Works on paper
£500 $865 €730 God creating the earth, the sun and the moon (17x13cm-7x5in) indis.sig. pen brown ink brown wash over black chk. 9-Dec-3 Bonhams, Knightsbridge #12/R

REGNAULT, Georges (1898-1979) French
£993 $1808 €1500 Machine de Marly (54x73cm-21x29in) s. s.i.d.1961 verso. 19-Jun-4 St-Germain-en-Laye Encheres #200/R est:600

REGNAULT, Henri (1843-1871) French
£2013 $3564 €3000 Odalisque (19x27cm-7x11in) mono. panel. 30-Apr-4 Tajan, Paris #145 est:3000-4000
£8553 $15737 €13000 Deux perroquets (72x50cm-28x20in) prov. 24-Jun-4 Christie's, Paris #141/R est:8000-12000
£13986 $24056 €20000 Rue a Tanger (54x33cm-21x13in) s. 8-Dec-3 Tajan, Paris #320/R est:15000-20000

REGNAULT, Sophie (1763-1825) French?
Works on paper
£2857 $5114 €4200 Portraits de Jean-Francois Heurtier et Marie-Victoire Heurtier (24cm-9in circular) s.d.1801 black white chk prov. 18-Mar-4 Christie's, Paris #262/R est:4000-6000

REGNIER, Auguste Jacques (attrib) (1787-1860) French
£600 $1086 €900 Paysage de Normandie (18x26cm-7x10in) oil paper on canvas. 30-Mar-4 Rossini, Paris #1040
£617 $1048 €901 Landscape with house by stream (39x55cm-15x22in) i.d.1816. 5-Nov-3 Dobiaschofsky, Bern #881/R (S.FR 1400)

REGNIER, Jean Desire (1801-?) Belgian
£435 $805 €653 Four terriers in an interior (53x69cm-21x27in) s. 14-Jul-4 American Auctioneer #490314/R

REGNIER, Nicolas (style) (1590-1667) Flemish
£25000 $39500 €36500 Penitent Magdalena (120x102cm-47x40in) 23-Jul-3 Hampton & Littlewood, Exeter #426/R est:1500-2000

REGNY, Alphee de (1799-1881) French
£4895 $8322 €7000 Paysage des environs de Naples (38x46cm-15x18in) s. 1-Dec-3 Millon & Associes, Paris #84/R est:3000-4000

REGO, Paula (1935-) Portuguese
£70000 $127400 €102200 Pregnant rabbit telling her parents (102x138cm-40x54in) acrylic prov.exhib. 6-Feb-4 Sotheby's, London #116/R est:25000-35000
Works on paper
£9500 $17480 €13870 Untitled (14x9cm-6x4in) s.verso gouache pen ink card prov. 24-Jun-4 Sotheby's, Olympia #412/R est:3000-4000
£100000 $184000 €146000 Sweeper (150x90cm-59x35in) pastel paper on aluminium executed 2002 exhib. 23-Jun-4 Sotheby's, London #2/R est:50000-70000

REGOS, Polykleitos (1903-1984) Greek
£3000 $5250 €4380 Episkopi, Ano Volos (40x39cm-16x15in) s.d.1935 panel exhib. 16-Dec-3 Bonhams, New Bond Street #108/R est:2200-3200
£5000 $8950 €7300 Thessaloniki (49x49cm-19x19in) s.d.1950 board. 10-May-4 Sotheby's, Olympia #8/R est:5000-7000
£6000 $10740 €8760 Meteora, the monasteries of St Trinity, Varlaam and Transfiguration (50x40cm-20x16in) s.d.1929 cardboard exhib. 11-May-4 Bonhams, New Bond Street #74/R est:2000-3000
£12000 $21000 €17520 Two friends (120x90cm-47x35in) s.d.1980 exhib. 16-Dec-3 Bonhams, New Bond Street #99/R est:7000-9000
£17000 $30430 €24820 Gregoriou Monastery, Mount Athos (100x75cm-39x30in) s.d.1979 oil egg tempera. 11-May-4 Bonhams, New Bond Street #79/R est:8000-12000

REGOYOS, Dario de (1857-1913) Spanish
£3667 $6747 €5500 In the bullring (13x16cm-5x6in) s. board. 10-Jun-4 Christie's, Rome #151/R est:1000-1500

REGTEREN ALTENA, Marie E van (1868-1958) Dutch
£556 $878 €800 Mixed bouquet in a ceramic jar (64x44cm-25x17in) init. 2-Sep-3 Christie's, Amsterdam #228
£625 $1150 €950 Flower still life (39x46cm-15x18in) s. 28-Jun-4 Sotheby's, Amsterdam #122/R
£1905 $3467 €2800 Blue tea-tin (29x54cm-11x21in) init. 3-Feb-4 Christie's, Amsterdam #159/R est:2500-3500

REGTEREN ALTENA, Martinus van (1866-1908) Dutch
£789 $1429 €1200 A young woman sitting at a table, knitting (43x33cm-17x13in) i. s.verso. 19-Apr-4 Glerum, Amsterdam #268/R

REHBERGER, Gustav (19/20th C) American
£3179 $5500 €4641 On top of the world (76x107cm-30x42in) s. 10-Dec-3 Bonhams & Butterfields, San Francisco #6054/R est:3000-5000

REHDER, Julius Christian (1861-?) German
£2813 $4697 €4107 Time for a rest (89x73cm-35x29in) s.d.89. 19-Oct-3 Agra, Warsaw #21/R est:8000 (P.Z 18000)

REHFISCH, Alison (1900-1975) Australian
£1245 $2079 €1868 Autumn landscape (34x41cm-13x16in) s. 27-Oct-3 Goodman, Sydney #206/R est:3000-5000 (A.D 3000)
£1901 $3517 €2775 Summer afternoon (50x61cm-20x24in) s. i.verso prov. 10-Mar-4 Deutscher-Menzies, Melbourne #321/R est:5500-7500 (A.D 4600)
£3719 $6880 €5430 Window piece (61x52cm-24x20in) s. i.verso board exhib. 10-Mar-4 Deutscher-Menzies, Melbourne #323/R est:9000-12000 (A.D 9000)

REHFOUS, Alfred (1860-1912) Swiss
Works on paper
£321 $536 €465 Discussion sur la place du village (40x24cm-16x9in) s. ink pierre noire. 21-Jun-3 Galerie du Rhone, Sion #413 (S.FR 700)

REHM, Helmut (1911-) Austrian
£603 $1007 €850 Hall in winter with Munz tower (36x48cm-14x19in) s. masonite. 16-Oct-3 Dorotheum, Salzburg #691/R

REHN, Frank Knox Morton (1848-1914) American
£447 $800 €653 Breaking waves under moonlight (20x25cm-8x10in) s. panel. 26-May-4 Doyle, New York #67/R
£898 $1500 €1311 Hollows and heights of the sea (76x127cm-30x50in) prov. 23-Oct-3 Shannon's, Milford #225/R est:3000-5000
£1033 $1900 €1508 Untitled - ocean at dawn (41x69cm-16x27in) s. 27-Jun-4 Hindman, Chicago #811/R est:1000-1500
£1136 $2000 €1659 Long Beach, New York (41x71cm-16x28in) s. painted 1893 prov. 23-May-4 Hindman, Chicago #154/R est:2000-3000
£1397 $2500 €2345 Landscape at sunset (36x51cm-14x20in) s. init.d.1906 verso. 20-Mar-4 Pook & Pook, Downington #568/R est:2000-3000
Works on paper
£690 $1250 €1007 Sailing off New England (33x46cm-13x18in) s. W/C. 16-Apr-4 James Julia, Fairfield #554/R est:1400-1800

REHNBERG, Hakan (1953-) Swedish
£2271 $4020 €3316 Blue II (77x85cm-30x33in) s.d.1987 verso oil wax steel panel diptych. 27-Apr-4 AB Stockholms Auktionsverk #1034/R est:25000-30000 (S.KR 31000)
£8686 $14766 €12682 Objection (150x100cm-59x39in) s.d.1990 panel four parts. 5-Nov-3 AB Stockholms Auktionsverk #1022/R est:80000-100000 (S.KR 115000)
Sculpture
£1245 $2204 €1818 Untitled (24cm-9in) init.num.2/6 partly painted iron. 27-Apr-4 AB Stockholms Auktionsverk #1035/R est:10000-12000 (S.KR 17000)
Works on paper
£471 $848 €688 Untitled (42x30cm-17x12in) s.d.1990 Indian ink. 26-Apr-4 Bukowskis, Stockholm #468/R (S.KR 6500)

REICH AN DER STOLPE, Siegfried (1912-) German
£769 $1308 €1100 Blue - gold (100x90cm-39x35in) s.d.1961 panel. 29-Nov-3 Arnold, Frankfurt #440/R

REICH, Adolf (1887-1963) Austrian
£474 $763 €692 Delivering the post (30x37cm-12x15in) s.d.1921. 25-Aug-3 Lilla Bukowskis, Stockholm #776 (S.KR 6200)
£1135 $1895 €1600 Consulting the fortune teller (45x37cm-18x15in) s.d.1929 panel. 14-Oct-3 Dorotheum, Vienna #48/R est:1400-2000
£1733 $3120 €2600 Putting on stockings (27x31cm-11x12in) s.d.1926 board. 21-Apr-4 Dorotheum, Vienna #40/R est:2000-3000

REICH-STAFFELSTEIN, A (1878-1942) German
£280 $439 €409 Town prospect with palace seen from water (54x80cm-21x31in) s. 30-Aug-3 Rasmussen, Havnen #2005 (D.KR 3000)

REICH-STAFFELSTEIN, Alexander (1878-1942) German
£361 $667 €527 Seascape with sailing vessel in fresh breeze (80x120cm-31x47in) s. 15-Mar-4 Rasmussen, Vejle #151/R (D.KR 4000)

EK, Jesse (1916-) American
$800 €628 Abstract composition (51x86cm-20x34in) s.d.1946 prov. 7-Mar-4 Treadway Gallery, Cincinnati #748/R

ICHEL, Hans (1892-1958) German
£6993 $12028 €10000 Fish (29x23cm-11x9in) s.i.d.1935 paper. 2-Dec-3 Hauswedell & Nolte, Hamburg #557/R est:6000
£16783 $28531 €24000 Moon over city (31x17cm-12x7in) mono.d.1934 board prov. 28-Nov-3 Villa Grisebach, Berlin #63/R est:10000-15000
Works on paper
£1711 $3147 €2600 Composition (16x10cm-6x4in) mono.d.1936 W/C lead pencil. 28-Jun-4 Joron-Derem, Paris #158/R est:2500-3000
£1987 $3616 €3000 Composition au poisson et a l'oiseau (22x28cm-9x11in) s.d.1936 W/C. 15-Jun-4 Blanchet, Paris #179/R est:3000-4000
£3662 $6335 €5200 Composition (17x28cm-7x11in) mono.d.1951 W/C ink prov.exhib. 9-Dec-3 Artcurial Briest, Paris #491/R est:3500-4000

REICHENBACH, Eugen (1840-1926) German
£420 $701 €600 Landscape with figures round campfire (45x84cm-18x33in) s.i. lit. 27-Jun-3 Auktionhaus Georg Rehm, Augsburg #8161/R
£764 $1245 €1100 Herders resting in sand quarry (45x84cm-18x33in) s.i.d.1897. 24-Sep-3 Neumeister, Munich #536/R

REICHERT, Carl (1836-1918) Austrian
£756 $1375 €1134 Dogs playing (21x26cm-8x10in) s. 19-Jun-4 Rasmussen, Havnen #2335/R (D.KR 8500)
£839 $1569 €1250 Portrait of St Bernard's dog (16x13cm-6x5in) s. panel. 24-Feb-4 Dorotheum, Vienna #293/R
£919 $1700 €1342 A stern warning - two pups (28x20cm-11x8in) s. panel. 10-Feb-4 Doyle, New York #146/R est:2000-3000
£973 $1800 €1421 The protector, a borzoi hound and puppy (28x20cm-11x8in) s. 10-Feb-4 Doyle, New York #145/R est:3000-5000
£1007 $1591 €1450 Disturbed siesta (21x26cm-8x10in) s.pseudonym J Hartung i. verso lit. 19-Sep-3 Schloss Ahlden, Ahlden #1601/R
£1243 $2250 €1815 English collie (15x13cm-6x5in) s. panel. 30-Mar-4 Bonhams & Butterfields, San Francisco #120/R est:2200-3300
£1329 $2259 €1900 Portrait of a dog (16x14cm-6x6in) s. panel. 20-Nov-3 Van Ham, Cologne #1814/R est:2000
£1389 $2361 €2000 Young dog (16x13cm-6x5in) s. panel. 28-Oct-3 Dorotheum, Vienna #219/R est:2000-2200
£1722 $3151 €2600 Friends (15x22cm-6x9in) s. panel. 8-Apr-4 Dorotheum, Vienna #216/R est:2600-3000
£1757 $3145 €2600 The puppies (35x27cm-14x11in) s. board. 8-May-4 Bukowskis, Helsinki #367/R est:1200-1400
£1892 $3500 €2762 Four dachshund puppies in a row (18x25cm-7x10in) s. panel. 10-Feb-4 Doyle, New York #145a/R est:1500-2500
£2667 $4853 €4000 Dachshund puppies (18x26cm-7x10in) s. with pseudonym panel. 1-Jul-4 Van Ham, Cologne #1568/R est:2600
£2797 $4755 €4000 Three dogs (25x18cm-10x7in) s. board. 24-Nov-3 Dorotheum, Vienna #196/R est:3500-4000
£4698 $8409 €7000 Hunting dog (34x29cm-13x11in) s.d.899 panel. 27-May-4 Dorotheum, Vienna #27/R est:2400-3000
£5000 $9000 €7500 Gordon setter (16x13cm-6x5in) s. panel prov. 21-Apr-4 Christie's, Amsterdam #19/R est:6000-8000
£5369 $9611 €8000 German short-haired dog family (15x23cm-6x9in) s. i.verso panel. 27-May-4 Dorotheum, Vienna #26/R est:4000-4500
£7718 $14201 €11500 Hunting dogs with booty (50x39cm-20x15in) si.d.08 panel. 27-Mar-4 L & B, Essen #184/R est:2000

REICHERT, Carl (attrib) (1836-1918) Austrian
£347 $573 €500 Kittens with bumblebee (22x17cm-9x7in) bears i. canvas on board. 3-Jul-3 Van Ham, Cologne #1416
£2649 $4821 €4000 Flora (78x62cm-31x24in) s.i.d.1867 verso after a painting by Titian. 16-Jun-4 Dorotheum, Vienna #283/R est:1500-2000

REICHLE, Paul (1900-1981) German
£2215 $3920 €3300 Composition with white area (70x90cm-28x35in) s.d. s.i.d. verso masonite. 30-Apr-4 Dr Fritz Nagel, Stuttgart #407/R est:800

REICHLEN, Eugene (1885-1971) Swiss
£407 $692 €594 Alpine huts (45x36cm-18x14in) s. 19-Nov-3 Fischer, Luzern #2252/R (S.FR 900)

REICHMANN, Georg Friedrich (1798-1853) German
£537 $988 €800 Portrait of young beauty (46x36cm-18x14in) s.d.1835. 27-Mar-4 L & B, Essen #185/R

REID, Archibald David (1844-1908) British
£268 $500 €402 Horses pulling a cart at the beach (20x30cm-8x12in) s. canvasboard. 25-Jul-4 Bonhams & Butterfields, San Francisco #6022/R
£3000 $5190 €4380 Bait gatherers (50x75cm-20x30in) s. 11-Dec-3 Lyon & Turnbull, Edinburgh #55/R est:2000-3000
Works on paper
£650 $1203 €949 Still life of hawthorn in an Oriental vase (34x24cm-13x9in) s. W/C. 14-Jul-4 Sotheby's, Olympia #124/R

REID, Flora MacDonald (fl.1880-1938) British
£300 $510 €438 An old woman (36x25cm-14x10in) s.i.verso. 30-Oct-3 Duke & Son, Dorchester #141
£320 $518 €464 Spoonful of soup (61x46cm-24x18in) s. d.1924 verso. 25-May-3 Desmond Judd, Cranbrook #1051
£750 $1245 €1095 Mother and child (41x26cm-16x10in) s.verso. 1-Oct-3 Woolley & Wallis, Salisbury #226/R
£1100 $2046 €1606 Springtime (69x46cm-27x18in) s.d.22 i.verso. 4-Mar-4 Christie's, Kensington #119/R est:700-1000
£2000 $3580 €2920 Youth and age, stroll with grandpa (26x36cm-10x14in) s. 26-May-4 Sotheby's, Olympia #199/R est:2000-3000
£4000 $7080 €5840 Rural landscape with two young girls picnicing (45x61cm-18x24in) s.d.1899. 27-Apr-4 Henry Adams, Chichester #703/R est:600-900

REID, George Agnew (1860-1947) Canadian
£864 $1408 €1261 Rapids (36x46cm-14x18in) s.d.1892 canvas on board. 23-Sep-3 Ritchie, Toronto #54/R est:1800-2000 (C.D 1900)
Works on paper
£402 $747 €587 Still life with daffodils (30x44cm-12x17in) s. pastel. 2-Mar-4 Ritchie, Toronto #68/R (C.D 1000)
£4065 $7276 €5935 Young boy in a field of daisies (35x26cm-14x10in) s. pastel paper on board prov. 31-May-4 Sotheby's, Toronto #2/R est:5000-7000 (C.D 10000)

REID, George Ogilvy (1851-1928) British
£290 $464 €423 Death of Robert Burns's father. s. 18-Sep-3 Bonhams, Edinburgh #312
£403 $742 €588 Quiet hour (26x18cm-10x7in) s. prov. 14-Jun-4 Waddingtons, Toronto #182/R est:800-1200 (C.D 1000)
£800 $1416 €1168 Evening on a highland stream (40x50cm-16x20in) s. 27-Apr-4 Bonhams, Knowle #75
£900 $1449 €1305 Best plan of attack (25x35cm-10x14in) s. 21-Aug-3 Bonhams, Edinburgh #1136
£1700 $2737 €2465 In time of war (29x39cm-11x15in) s. 21-Aug-3 Bonhams, Edinburgh #1190 est:1000-1500
£2000 $3220 €2900 Soldier's story (29x39cm-11x15in) s. 21-Aug-3 Bonhams, Edinburgh #1191 est:1000-1500
£2000 $3140 €2900 Encounter (26x37cm-10x15in) s. prov. 27-Aug-3 Sotheby's, London #930/R est:2000-3000

REID, Henry C (20th C) British
£250 $458 €365 Flowers in a clay vase (20x15cm-8x6in) mono.d.2004 verso acrylic on board. 2-Jun-4 John Ross, Belfast #75
£260 $426 €380 Soft day in the Mournes (25x35cm-10x14in) mono. d.2003 verso acrylic board. 4-Jun-3 John Ross, Belfast #223
£260 $447 €380 Storm clouds, Nephin Beg, County Mayo (20x20cm-8x8in) mono.d.2003 verso acrylic board. 3-Dec-3 John Ross, Belfast #205
£263 $484 €400 Bogland Nephin Beg, Mayo (20x26cm-8x10in) mono. 22-Jun-4 De Veres Art Auctions, Dublin #230/R
£263 $484 €400 Small harbour, evening light (11x5cm-4x2in) mono. board. 22-Jun-4 De Veres Art Auctions, Dublin #231
£280 $512 €409 Nephin Bog from Lought Conn (20x25cm-8x10in) mono.d.2003 verso acrylic on board. 2-Jun-4 John Ross, Belfast #128
£390 $671 €569 Blue flowers (25x20cm-10x8in) mono.d.2003 verso acrylic board. 3-Dec-3 John Ross, Belfast #260
£450 $837 €657 White flowers (25x20cm-10x8in) s.d.2003 verso acrylic on board. 3-Mar-4 John Ross, Belfast #104
Works on paper
£380 $707 €555 Quiet corner, Ardglass (43x30cm-17x12in) mono. mixed media. 3-Mar-4 John Ross, Belfast #6

REID, Isobelle Chestnut (1899-?) ?
£402 $683 €587 Seamstress (56x66cm-22x26in) board. 6-Nov-3 Heffel, Vancouver #97/R (C.D 900)
£444 $738 €648 Untitled, artist at her easel (64x53cm-25x21in) s. hard board. 5-Oct-3 Levis, Calgary #97/R (C.D 1000)

REID, Janet Kellogg (1894-?) American
£373 $600 €545 Gloucester scene (30x41cm-12x16in) s. canvasboard. 17-Aug-3 Jeffery Burchard, Florida #46

REID, John Robertson (1851-1926) British
£769 $1323 €1123 Music lesson (45x60cm-18x24in) s.d.1881. 3-Dec-3 AB Stockholms Auktionsverk #2621/R (S.KR 10000)
£807 $1300 €1178 Love sick poet (58x43cm-23x17in) s.d.1895. 22-Feb-3 Bunte, Elgin #1300
£1000 $1830 €1460 Portrait of a woman wearing a wide brimmed hat (41cm-16in circular) i. indis d.1912. 8-Jul-4 Duke & Son, Dorchester #283/R est:200-400
£2245 $4018 €3300 Girl in herb garden (66x50cm-26x20in) s. 17-Mar-4 Neumeister, Munich #575/R est:900
£3200 $5792 €4672 Blowing bubbles (51x76cm-20x30in) s.d.74. 19-Apr-4 Sotheby's, London #17/R est:3000-5000
£4500 $7470 €6570 Boys fishing in Looe Harbour (76x63cm-30x25in) s. indis.d. 1-Oct-3 Sotheby's, Olympia #153/R est:5000-7000
£6000 $9420 €8700 Montrose Harbour (107x145cm-42x57in) s.d.1904. 27-Aug-3 Sotheby's, London #1104/R est:5000-7000
Works on paper
£1100 $2035 €1606 Crabbing ground (25x35cm-10x14in) s. W/C. 14-Jul-4 Sotheby's, Olympia #113/R est:1200-1800

REID, John T (19th C) American
Works on paper
£402 $747 €587 Niagara Horseshoe Falls (46x76cm-18x30in) s. W/C paper on canvas. 2-Mar-4 Ritchie, Toronto #34/R (C.D 1000)

REID, Nano (1900-1981) Irish
£6711 $11879 €10000 Figure and waves (61x76cm-24x30in) s. board prov.exhib. 27-Apr-4 Whyte's, Dublin #85/R est:10000-12000
£9091 $15455 €13000 Where Oengus Og magnificently dwells (61x76cm-24x30in) s. i.verso board prov.exhib. 18-Nov-3 Whyte's, Dublin #59/R est:10000-12000
£10135 $19155 €15000 Old town walls (51x61cm-20x24in) s. oil masonite board prov.exhib.lit. 17-Feb-4 Whyte's, Dublin #17/R est:8000-10000
Works on paper
£503 $901 €750 Gloria Gloria (17x17cm-7x7in) mono.d.37 Indian ink W/C prov. 26-May-4 James Adam, Dublin #146/R
£900 $1611 €1314 Bull by a gate (25x39cm-10x15in) s. W/C prov.exhib. 14-May-4 Christie's, London #95/R

£1342 $2403 €2000 Knights at arms (39x50cm-15x20in) s. mixed media. 26-May-4 James Adam, Dublin #110/R est:2000-3000

REID, R Dow (20th C) American
Sculpture
£2139 $4000 €3209 Dolphins (13x20x10cm-5x8x4in) ivory soapstone prov. 24-Jul-4 Coeur d'Alene, Hayden #280/R est:1000-2000

REID, Robert (1862-1929) American
£19886 $35000 €29034 By the brook (84x92cm-33x36in) s. prov.exhib. 18-May-4 Christie's, Rockefeller NY #69/R est:25000-35000

REID, Robert Payton (1859-1945) British
£320 $509 €467 Thatched cottages (36x25cm-14x10in) s. board. 9-Sep-3 Gorringes, Lewes #2074
£400 $756 €584 Willow trees (28x34cm-11x13in) s. board. 19-Feb-4 Lyon & Turnbull, Edinburgh #43
£400 $756 €584 Oak tree in summer (28x34cm-11x13in) s. board. 19-Feb-4 Lyon & Turnbull, Edinburgh #136
£1800 $3222 €2628 Prt rabbits (50x76cm-20x30in) s.d.1882. 25-May-4 Sworder & Son, Bishops Stortford #337/R est:1500-2000
£2000 $3340 €2920 Fascinating story (96x122cm-38x48in) s. 12-Nov-3 Sotheby's, Olympia #107/R est:3000

REID, Stephen (1873-1948) British
£780 $1264 €1100 El coleccioista de porcelanas (47x37cm-19x15in) s.d.1914. 20-May-3 Segre, Madrid #60/R est:950
£5000 $9100 €7300 My love approaches (51x61cm-20x24in) s.d.29. 1-Jul-4 Sotheby's, London #318/R est:5000-7000

REID, William (jnr) (fl.1830-1840) Irish?
Works on paper
£280 $476 €400 View of the Giants Causeway, County Antrim (20x28cm-8x11in) i.verso W/C scratching out prov. 18-Nov-3 Whyte's, Dublin #190/R

REID, William Ronald (1920-1998) Canadian
Works on paper
£1470 $2309 €2132 Raven with broken beak (37x46cm-15x18in) s.d.1982 pencil dr. prov. 30-Aug-3 Heffel, Vancouver #26 est:3000-4000 (C.D 3250)

REID-HENRY, David M (1919-1977) British
Works on paper
£2600 $4758 €3796 Folio of studies of African animals, including lion, leopard and elephant (34x24cm-13x9in) some i.d. pencil. 28-Jul-4 Bonhams, Knightsbridge #51/R est:3000-4000
£5000 $9150 €7300 Folio of sketches of Birds of Prey, including Tiara, the artist's Crowned eagle (33x20cm-13x8in) some i.d. pencil. 28-Jul-4 Bonhams, Knightsbridge #50/R est:3000-4000

REIDY, Lilla (fl.1880s-1900) Australian
£732 $1310 €1069 Cottage garden (30x44cm-12x17in) s. board. 4-May-4 Sotheby's, Melbourne #132 (A.D 1800)
£1829 $3274 €2670 Alone (45x35cm-18x14in) canvas on board. 4-May-4 Sotheby's, Melbourne #325/R est:3000-5000 (A.D 4500)

REIFFEL, Charles (1862-1942) American
£3704 $7000 €5408 Sailing ship in moderate seas (43x48cm-17x19in) s. prov. 17-Feb-4 John Moran, Pasadena #113/R est:8000-10000
£14118 $24000 €20612 Maine Coast, Booth's Bay (54x65cm-21x26in) s. board. 29-Oct-3 Christie's, Los Angeles #48/R est:20000-30000
£37572 $65000 €54855 Summer (86x94cm-34x37in) s. i.verso exhib. 10-Dec-3 Bonhams & Butterfields, San Francisco #6241/R est:50000-70000
Works on paper
£1223 $2250 €1786 Colourful landscape (25x30cm-10x12in) s. mixed media prov. 8-Jun-4 Bonhams & Butterfields, San Francisco #4241/R est:3000-5000
£1599 $2750 €2335 Abstract mountain landscape. s. mixed media. 6-Dec-3 Harvey Clar, Oakland #1369
£2717 $5000 €3967 Lady with a bird (25x15cm-10x6in) s. W/C gouache. 8-Jun-4 Bonhams & Butterfields, San Francisco #4285/R est:5000-7000

REIFFENSTEIN, Carl Theodore (1820-1893) German
£3667 $6673 €5500 View of a little chapel at the edge of the forest (26x32cm-10x13in) mono.d.1843. 1-Jul-4 Van Ham, Cologne #1569/R est:1600
Works on paper
£545 $911 €780 Kuhlhornshof near Frankfurt am Main (9x13cm-4x5in) s.d.21 Oct 1868 W/C over pencil. 10-Oct-3 Winterberg, Heidelberg #732
£839 $1427 €1200 Aquaduct near Rome (22x28cm-9x11in) s.d.1853 W/C. 27-Nov-3 Bassenge, Berlin #5634/R

REIGNIER, Claude (1870-1954) French
£333 $600 €500 Soir d'orage sur l'etang (46x65cm-18x26in) s. 20-Apr-4 Chenu & Scrive, Lyon #150/R

REIGNIER, Jean Marie (1815-1886) French
Works on paper
£1224 $2192 €1800 Putti tenant un arc entoure de fruits et tenant un fleche entoure de fleurs (37x29cm-15x11in) s.d.1847 gouache trompe-l'oeil bas-relief pair. 18-Mar-4 Christie's, Paris #178/R est:2000-3000

REILLE, Karl (1886-1975) French
£1400 $2604 €2044 On the scent (27x22cm-11x9in) s. panel. 4-Mar-4 Christie's, London #435/R est:300-500
£1408 $2521 €2000 Saut de talus, Rallye de Cheverny et suiveurs (15x21cm-6x8in) 11-Jan-4 Rouillac, Vendome #209
£1479 $2647 €2100 Rappel des chiens, Rallye de Touraine (17x23cm-7x9in) 11-Jan-4 Rouillac, Vendome #205
£1479 $2647 €2100 Relais, valet de chiens assis, Rallye de Touraine (15x23cm-6x9in) 11-Jan-4 Rouillac, Vendome #206
£1479 $2647 €2100 Sonneurs pres de l'etang (15x20cm-6x8in) 11-Jan-4 Rouillac, Vendome #210
£1479 $2647 €2100 Traversee d'un harde, Euipage Normand (15x21cm-6x8in) 11-Jan-4 Rouillac, Vendome #211
£1549 $2773 €2200 Descente de chiens, Rallye de Touraine (15x21cm-6x8in) 11-Jan-4 Rouillac, Vendome #201
£1549 $2773 €2200 Veneurs, croisee d'allee, avec calvaire (16x21cm-6x8in) 11-Jan-4 Rouillac, Vendome #213
£1620 $2899 €2300 La bat lot (15x21cm-6x8in) 11-Jan-4 Rouillac, Vendome #203
£1818 $3091 €2600 Chasse a courre du Rallye Gaiement (22x27cm-9x11in) s. isorel. 20-Nov-3 Millon & Associes, Paris #120/R
£1831 $3277 €2600 Equipage et suiveurs (15x21cm-6x8in) 11-Jan-4 Rouillac, Vendome #214
£1972 $3530 €2800 Retraite Rallye de Touraine, passant devant Panchien, Baudry (15x21cm-6x8in) 11-Jan-4 Rouillac, Vendome #208
£2482 $4145 €3500 Le depart (19x27cm-7x11in) s. isorel panel. 12-Oct-3 St-Germain-en-Laye Encheres #44/R est:3000-3500
£2800 $5124 €4200 Rallye Touraine (32x45cm-13x18in) prov. 6-Jun-4 Rouillac, Vendome #52
£3028 $5420 €4300 Grand Piqueux du Rallye de Touraine (36x53cm-14x21in) exhib. 11-Jan-4 Rouillac, Vendome #202
£3624 $6705 €5400 Scenes de chasse a courre (16x22cm-6x9in) s. panel pair. 14-Mar-4 St-Germain-en-Laye Encheres #30/R est:6000
Works on paper
£725 $1188 €1000 La passage de la riviere (23x31cm-9x12in) s.i. W/C. 11-May-3 Osenat, Fontainebleau #144
£800 $1432 €1200 Scene de venerie (11x7cm-4x3in) d.30 mars 1935 W/C gouache. 12-May-4 Coutau Begarie, Paris #68/R
£800 $1432 €1200 Scene de venerie (7x13cm-3x5in) W/C gouache. 12-May-4 Coutau Begarie, Paris #208/R
£1259 $2165 €1800 Bat l'eau a Thezee, bord du Cher (21x29cm-8x11in) s.d.1900 W/C ink. 3-Dec-3 Coutau Begarie, Paris #212/R est:1800-2000
£1343 $2376 €2000 Sortie du paddock (31x47cm-12x19in) s.d.1923 W/C gouache. 27-Apr-4 Artcurial Briest, Paris #126 est:1200-1800
£1399 $2406 €2000 Equipage Champchevrier, cerf rentrant dans un etang (15x22cm-6x9in) s.d.1913 W/C. 8-Dec-3 Rossini, Paris #84/R est:1200-1500
£2053 $3757 €3100 Retour de chasse au sanglier (31x48cm-12x19in) s. gouache. 7-Apr-4 Piasa, Paris #54/R
£2113 $3782 €3000 Rendez-vous, le relais, Rallye de Touraine (21x27cm-8x11in) W/C gouache. 11-Jan-4 Rouillac, Vendome #207
£2754 $4516 €3800 Avant la course (24x32cm-9x13in) W/C gouache. 28-May-3 Coutau Begarie, Paris #190/R est:2000-2200
£2797 $4755 €4000 Le rendez-vous (31x44cm-12x17in) s. W/C gouache. 20-Nov-3 Millon & Associes, Paris #121/R
£2980 $4858 €4500 Hallali de cerf dans les rochers (32x43cm-13x17in) s. W/C gouache. 1-Feb-3 Dubee & Berron, Vernou en Sologne #113
£4225 $7310 €6000 Halte pendant la chasse a courre (39x44cm-15x17in) s. W/C gouache. 10-Dec-3 Piasa, Paris #153/R est:4000-4500

REILLY, Federico (1922-) Uruguayan
£529 $1000 €772 Coming back (50x61cm-20x24in) s. 22-Feb-4 Galeria y Remates, Montevideo #139/R
£2941 $5000 €4294 Resting (60x80cm-24x31in) s. 25-Nov-3 Galeria y Remates, Montevideo #112/R
£3412 $5800 €4982 Indian (65x54cm-26x21in) s. 25-Nov-3 Galeria y Remates, Montevideo #113/R

REILLY, Frank Joseph (1906-1967) American
£1117 $2000 €1631 Robe and sword (56x46cm-22x18in) s. 15-May-4 Illustration House, New York #29/R est:3000-4000

REIMANN, Friedrich (1896-1985) German
£280 $481 €400 Golden eagle against mountains (38x58cm-15x23in) s. board. 5-Dec-3 Michael Zeller, Lindau #769
£280 $481 €400 Hawk chasing duck across winter stream (38x58cm-15x23in) s. board. 5-Dec-3 Michael Zeller, Lindau #770/R
£280 $481 €400 Capercaillie (37x57cm-15x22in) s. board. 5-Dec-3 Michael Zeller, Lindau #771
£280 $481 €400 Swan flying over lake shore (38x58cm-15x23in) s. board. 5-Dec-3 Michael Zeller, Lindau #772
£379 $633 €550 Deer in clearing (254x343cm-100x135in) s. panel lit. 12-Jul-3 Bergmann, Erlangen #637/R

REIMERS, Heinrich (1824-1900) German
£1215 $1920 €1762 Ship's portrait of Laurits of Karrebeksminde (46x66cm-18x26in) s.d.1868. 2-Sep-3 Rasmussen, Copenhagen #1630/R est:8000 (D.KR 13000)

REIN, Johan Eimerich (1827-1891) Norwegian
£522 $903 €762 Coastal landscape near Hellesund (33x59cm-13x23in) s. 13-Dec-3 Blomqvist, Lysaker #1288/R (N.KR 6000)

REINA, Miela (1935-1972) Italian
£280 $481 €400 At the gate (31x21cm-12x8in) s.d.1962 tempera paper. 3-Dec-3 Stadion, Trieste #972

REINAGLE, Philip (1749-1833) British
£1648 $3000 €2406 Wild duck shooting (65x80cm-26x31in) 29-Jun-4 Sotheby's, New York #167/R est:6000-8000
£2793 $5000 €4078 Colonel Thornton's greyhounds (57x68cm-22x27in) prov. 27-May-4 Sotheby's, New York #201/R est:5000-7000

$80000 €63825 Meet in Dorsetshire with hunting portraits of Mr and Mrs Francis Fane (98x152cm-39x60in) prov.exhib.lit. 3-Jun-4 Christie's, Rockefeller NY #433/R est:80000-120000

REINAGLE, Philip (attrib) (1749-1833) British
£680 $1156 €993 Two spaniels on the moors (15x19cm-6x7in) panel. 19-Nov-3 Sotheby's, Olympia #19/R
£800 $1432 €1168 Farm yard (21x32cm-8x13in) with sig.i. oil paper on canvas sketch. 27-May-4 Christie's, Kensington #123/R est:600-800
£10383 $19000 €15159 Full cry (102x127cm-40x50in) with sig. prov. 3-Jun-4 Christie's, Rockefeller NY #874/R est:25000-40000

REINAGLE, Ramsay Richard (1775-1862) British
£500 $920 €730 Portrait of a lady seated, wearing a black dress (25x20cm-10x8in) s.d.1846. 8-Jun-4 Bonhams, Knightsbridge #139/R
£600 $1098 €876 Portrait of a seated gentleman (71x61cm-28x24in) s.d.1840. 7-Apr-4 Andrew Hartley, Ilkley #1100/R
£3000 $5490 €4380 Portrait of a young boy in a black coat (55x45cm-22x18in) init. oval. 7-Jul-4 Bonhams, New Bond Street #121/R est:3000-5000
Works on paper
£2400 $4440 €3504 View of Llangollen, Wales (28x44cm-11x17in) s. indis.d. W/C. 10-Mar-4 Sotheby's, Olympia #26/R est:2000-3000

REINAGLE, Ramsay Richard (attrib) (1775-1862) British
£800 $1488 €1168 Figures resting by a river in a Dutch landscape (41x51cm-16x20in) 4-Mar-4 Christie's, Kensington #420/R
£1259 $2140 €1800 Portrait of John Barnes of Finchley (90x69cm-35x27in) panel prov. 25-Nov-3 Hamilton Osborne King, Dublin #203/R

REINAGLE, Ramsay Richard (circle) (1775-1862) British
£5525 $10000 €8067 Toy spaniel (53x50cm-21x20in) 30-Mar-4 Bonhams & Butterfields, San Francisco #46/R est:4000-6000

REINCKE, Paul (1900-) Polish?
£1037 $1919 €1514 View of the sea (60x50cm-24x20in) 14-Mar-4 Agra, Warsaw #6/R (P.Z 7500)

REINDEL, Edna (1900-1990) American
£1258 $2000 €1837 Summer in Menemsha (26x31cm-10x12in) s.d.1937 board. 12-Sep-3 Skinner, Boston #425/R

REINER, Wenzel Lorenz (attrib) (1686-1743) Austrian
£9155 $15838 €13000 Busy Piazza Barberini in Rome (49x66cm-19x26in) 11-Dec-3 Dr Fritz Nagel, Stuttgart #499/R est:7000

REINHALT, Fritz (19/20th C) Austrian?
£694 $1181 €1000 Gmunden (39x56cm-15x22in) s. 28-Oct-3 Dorotheum, Vienna #260/R

REINHARD, John Maitland (1893-1959) American
£330 $600 €482 Flower fields in desert landscape (41x51cm-16x20in) s. prov. 15-Jun-4 John Moran, Pasadena #198

REINHARD, Josef (1749-1824) Swiss
£655 $1192 €956 Portrait of a gentleman (69x58cm-27x23in) s.d.1815 verso panel. 16-Jun-4 Fischer, Luzern #2319/R (S.FR 1500)
£786 $1431 €1148 Portrait of a couple (59x46cm-23x18in) panel. 16-Jun-4 Fischer, Luzern #1271/R (S.FR 1800)
£2183 $3974 €3187 Portrait of a man in uniform. Portrait of a woman in a red dress (73x59cm-29x23in) one s.d.1815 panel pair. 16-Jun-4 Fischer, Luzern #1264/R est:4000-6000 (S.FR 5000)

REINHARD, Raphael (attrib) (1820-1903) Swiss
£705 $1198 €1029 Portrait of Madame Paul Gabriel de Pourtales et ses filles (62x46cm-24x18in) i. stretcher. 5-Nov-3 Dobiaschofsky, Bern #883/R (S.FR 1600)

REINHARDT, Ad (1913-1967) American
£24000 $43680 €35040 Abstraction (51x41cm-20x16in) s.d.40 s.i.d.verso prov. 5-Feb-4 Christie's, London #166/R est:14000-18000
£35928 $60000 €52455 Abstract painting no 20 (127x51cm-50x20in) s.i.d.1956 overlap prov. 13-Nov-3 Sotheby's, New York #227/R est:60000-80000
£50000 $92000 €73000 Untitled (127x51cm-50x20in) painted 1950 prov. 24-Jun-4 Sotheby's, London #140/R est:50000-70000

REINHARDT, Carl August (1818-1877) German
£927 $1687 €1400 Sunset scene with a ship on the waters (75x105cm-30x41in) s.d.1871. 19-Jun-4 Quittenbaum, Hamburg #37

REINHARDT, Franz (1881-1946) German
£461 $770 €650 Rape of the Sabine women (60x68cm-24x27in) s.d.19. 16-Oct-3 Dorotheum, Salzburg #632/R

REINHARDT, Johann Jakob (1835-?) German
£839 $1427 €1200 View of Lake Starnberger (28x37cm-11x15in) mono. board. 28-Nov-3 Wendl, Rudolstadt #4152/R
£2113 $3655 €3000 River landscape with cows (65x91cm-26x36in) s.d.1859. 13-Dec-3 Lempertz, Koln #39/R est:3000

REINHARDT, Louis (?-1870) German
£406 $650 €593 Sheep resting in a meadow (51x64cm-20x25in) s. 19-Sep-3 Freeman, Philadelphia #158/R
£442 $791 €650 Sheep in the mountains (18x23cm-7x9in) panel. 18-Mar-4 Neumeister, Munich #2754/R
£972 $1585 €1400 Traunsee (44x81cm-17x32in) s. 26-Sep-3 Bolland & Marotz, Bremen #599/R est:1300

REINHARDT, Louis (attrib) (?-1870) German
£335 $600 €489 Landscape with trees (89x69cm-35x27in) with sig. 29-May-4 Brunk, Ashville #160/R

REINHARDT, Siegfried (1925-1984) American
£494 $850 €721 Bell ringer (28x43cm-11x17in) s.d.1953 masonite. 6-Dec-3 Selkirks, St. Louis #213/R
£500 $800 €730 Old man and young boy with bicycle (89x53cm-35x21in) s.d.1951 board. 21-Sep-3 William Jenack, New York #235
£1235 $2100 €1803 Boy drawing with chalk (64x33cm-25x13in) s.d.1951 masonite. 7-Nov-3 Selkirks, St. Louis #530/R est:400-600
£1844 $3300 €2692 Resurrection (122x46cm-48x18in) s.d.49 board. 11-Jan-4 William Jenack, New York #173 est:1000-1500

REINHARDT, Sophia (1775-1843) German
£1267 $2293 €1900 Portrait of young girl wearing white dress (108x83cm-43x33in) mono.d.1827 lit. 1-Apr-4 Frank Peege, Freiburg #1150/R est:1800

REINHARDT, Wilhelm (1815-1881) German
£1507 $2562 €2200 Deer in clearing (53x70cm-21x28in) s.d.1845. 5-Nov-3 Hugo Ruef, Munich #1091/R est:2200

REINHART, Benjamin Franklin (1829-1885) American
£3500 $5810 €5110 Kitty's pets (25x20cm-10x8in) mono.d.1866 s.i.verso panel. 1-Oct-3 Sotheby's, Olympia #129/R est:2000-3000

REINHART, Heinrich (1844-1929) Swiss
£633 $1077 €924 Portrait of boy with dog (84x64cm-33x25in) s.d.1878. 28-Nov-3 Zofingen, Switzerland #3131/R (S.FR 1400)

REINHART, Johann Christian (1761-1847) German
£50360 $82590 €70000 Paysage classique avec un berger et ses brebis (149x213cm-59x84in) s.d.1813. 6-Jun-3 Maigret, Paris #110/R est:70000-100000
Works on paper
£2098 $3566 €3000 Dead horse in street (41x51cm-16x20in) brush. 27-Nov-3 Bassenge, Berlin #5497 est:1200

REINHART, Johann Christian (attrib) (1761-1847) German
£6040 $11114 €9000 Classical landscape with two herdswomen and flock near ford (55x70cm-22x28in) mono. prov. 24-Mar-4 Dorotheum, Vienna #420/R est:6000-8000

REINHART, Lea (1877-1970) Austrian
£306 $556 €447 Still life (65x86cm-26x34in) s. 16-Jun-4 Fischer, Luzern #2320/R (S.FR 700)
£351 $650 €512 Chickens (20x23cm-8x9in) s. board. 13-Mar-4 Susanin's, Chicago #6202/R
£662 $1205 €1000 Richly covered table (21x27cm-8x11in) panel. 21-Jun-4 Dorotheum, Vienna #15

REINHART, Lorenz (18th C) Swiss
Works on paper
£281 $477 €410 Portraits of four women (16x24cm-6x9in) s.i.d.1. Janvier 1789 W/C. 19-Nov-3 Fischer, Luzern #2670 (S.FR 620)

REINHERZ, Conrad (1835-1892) German
£433 $789 €650 Young family with a rowing boat on Lake Chiem (24x42cm-9x17in) s. painted c.1880. 1-Jul-4 Weidler, Nurnberg #6519/R
£671 $1188 €1000 Bull and sheep under a tree (24x18cm-9x7in) s. panel lit. 30-Apr-4 Auktionhaus Georg Rehm, Augsburg #8086/R

REINHOLD, Bernhard (1824-1892) German
£1389 $2292 €2000 Self portrait painting in the Albanian mountains (29x38cm-11x15in) i. verso board. 2-Jul-3 Neumeister, Munich #747/R est:2000

REINHOLD, Franz (1816-1893) Austrian
£2254 $3741 €3200 Loading boat on Konigssee (88x126cm-35x50in) after Friedrich Gauermann. 16-Jun-3 Dorotheum, Vienna #198/R est:3000-3800

REINHOLD, Friedrich (younger) (1814-1881) Austrian
£694 $1181 €1000 Misurinasee, southern Tyrol (74x100cm-29x39in) s. 28-Oct-3 Dorotheum, Vienna #124
£6993 $11888 €10000 Traunsee with Schloss Orth (43x30cm-17x12in) s. i. veso. 24-Nov-3 Dorotheum, Vienna #165/R est:12000-15000

REINHOLD, Heinrich (1788-1825) Austrian
£7692 $13077 €11000 Shipwrecked (33x41cm-13x16in) s.d.1819 panel one of pair. 20-Nov-3 Dorotheum, Salzburg #111/R est:8000-10000
£22378 $38042 €32000 Walkers on high mountain plateau in Italy (33x42cm-13x17in) s.d.1819 one of pair. 20-Nov-3 Dorotheum, Salzburg #110/R est:8000-10000
Works on paper
£521 $849 €750 Hilly landscape near Olevano (27x38cm-11x15in) i. s. bears i. verso pencil studies verso. 26-Sep-3 Venator & Hansten, Koln #906
£1119 $1902 €1600 Woodland near Sorrento (42x28cm-17x11in) i.d.27.Juli 23 pencil. 21-Nov-3 Reiss & Sohn, Konigstein #286/R est:1000

£1133 $2040 €1700 Top of pine tree (29x22cm-11x9in) i.d.1820 oebcuk. 24-Apr-4 Reiss & Sohn, Konigstein #5545/R est:1000
£1678 $2803 €2400 Landscape in the Serpentara (16x20cm-6x8in) pencil. 10-Oct-3 Winterberg, Heidelberg #733/R est:1200
£1958 $3329 €2800 Mountain chapel near Sorrento (34x45cm-13x18in) pencil. 21-Nov-3 Reiss & Sohn, Konigstein #288/R est:800
£2657 $4517 €3800 Woodland near Sorrento (44x32cm-17x13in) Indian ink brush over pencil. 21-Nov-3 Reiss & Sohn, Konigstein #287/R est:800

REINICKE, Emil (1859-?) German
£2155 $3858 €3146 Naked woman by wood (67x51cm-26x20in) s. panel. 12-May-4 Dobiaschofsky, Bern #896/R est:6000 (S.FR 5000)

REINICKE, René (attrib) (1860-1926) German
Works on paper
£369 $654 €550 Elegant (34x23cm-13x9in) init.d.06 gouache. 30-Apr-4 Tajan, Paris #194

REINIGER, Otto (1863-1909) German
£300 $552 €450 Landscape with clouds (20x37cm-8x15in) 9-Jun-4 Dorotheum, Salzburg #545/R
£400 $720 €600 The Neckar (14x23cm-6x9in) mono. board. 26-Apr-4 Rieber, Stuttgart #1202/R
£946 $1693 €1400 Spring day in Swabia (59x49cm-23x19in) mono. 6-May-4 Michael Zeller, Lindau #832/R

REINIKE, Charles Henry (1906-1983) American
£5120 $8500 €7475 Louisiana cabin scene (76x91cm-30x36in) s. 4-Oct-3 Neal Auction Company, New Orleans #542/R est:5000-7000
Works on paper
£332 $550 €485 Fisherman and his dog (18x23cm-7x9in) s. W/C. 4-Oct-3 Neal Auction Company, New Orleans #1089
£332 $550 €485 In the doorway (18x23cm-7x9in) s. W/C. 4-Oct-3 Neal Auction Company, New Orleans #1090
£864 $1400 €1261 Italian ruins (69x46cm-27x18in) s. W/C. 2-Aug-3 Neal Auction Company, New Orleans #399/R est:1200-1800

REINKE, Walther (1897-1954) German
£347 $549 €500 Winter in Harburg mountains (50x60cm-20x24in) s.d.37 board. 6-Sep-3 Schopman, Hamburg #769/R

REINOHL-WERNER, Ella von (1885-1947) Austrian
£586 $1073 €850 Flowers (10x120cm-4x47in) s.d.17 prov. 27-Jan-4 Dorotheum, Vienna #16/R

REIP, Hugues (1964-) French
Works on paper
£694 $1146 €1000 Comme un chien (68x50cm-27x20in) s.d.28 mai 1991 mixed media canvas prov.exhib. 2-Jul-3 Cornette de St.Cyr, Paris #217/R

REIPKA, Jurgen (1936-) German
£537 $988 €800 Composition (78x59cm-31x23in) s.i.d. acrylic board. 26-Mar-4 Ketterer, Hamburg #1116/R

REISER, Carl (1877-1950) German
£2349 $4322 €3500 Flowers in jug and pot (80x100cm-31x39in) s.d.35 lit. 25-Mar-4 Karlheinz Kaupp, Staufen #2685 est:100
Works on paper
£345 $576 €500 Snow-covered mountain landscape (13x19cm-5x7in) s. i.d.41 verso gouache double-sided. 13-Nov-3 Neumeister, Munich #438/R

REISMAN, Ori (1924-1991) Israeli
£33520 $60000 €48939 Boulevard with cypress trees (147x114cm-58x45in) 18-Mar-4 Sotheby's, New York #57/R est:60000-80000

REISMAN, Philip (1904-1992) American
£2581 $4750 €3768 Busy day out on the sidewalk (35x61cm-14x24in) s.d.51 masonite. 8-Jun-4 Bonhams & Butterfields, San Francisco #4114/R est:3000-5000

REISS, Fritz (1857-1916) German
£1084 $1810 €1550 Rhine landscape (47x65cm-19x26in) s.d.1894. 27-Jun-3 Michael Zeller, Lindau #641/R est:1400

REISS, Fritz Winold (1886-1953) American/German
£706 $1250 €1031 Portrait of woman in blue Louis XVI costume and feathered headress (152x122cm-60x48in) silver enamel exec.c.1950. 1-May-4 Thomaston Place, Thomaston #818/R

REISS, Roland (1929-) American
Works on paper
£294 $500 €429 Adult fairy tales II (30x61cm-12x24in) s.i. mixed media on board. 9-Nov-3 Bonhams & Butterfields, Los Angeles #4072/R
£353 $600 €515 Infernal regions (74x33cm-29x13in) i. s.verso mixed media on board. 9-Nov-3 Bonhams & Butterfields, Los Angeles #4073/R

REISS, Wallace (20th C) German?
£376 $650 €549 The wanderers (48x84cm-19x33in) s.d.51 prov. 15-Dec-3 Hindman, Chicago #15/R

REISSNER, Martin Andreas (1798-1862) Russian
£1099 $2000 €1605 Devils Whirlpool on Cressem (89x76cm-35x30in) s.indis.d.1858 prov.exhib. 15-Jun-4 John Moran, Pasadena #168 est:3000-5000

REISZ, Hermann (1865-?) Austrian
£336 $601 €500 Village street with cows (26x40cm-10x16in) s. 27-May-4 Dorotheum, Graz #56/R
£470 $879 €700 Working horses (50x62cm-20x24in) s. panel. 24-Feb-4 Dorotheum, Vienna #86/R
£662 $1205 €1000 Hay day (24x41cm-9x16in) s. board. 21-Jun-4 Dorotheum, Vienna #326
£1111 $1889 €1600 Drinking in wine cellar (31x25cm-12x10in) s. bears d.18 panel. 28-Oct-3 Dorotheum, Vienna #217/R est:1800-2200

REITER, Johann Baptist (1813-1890) Austrian
£483 $801 €700 Portrait of man wearing black jacket with yellow lapels (12x8cm-5x3in) s.d.840 panel. 30-Sep-3 Dorotheum, Vienna #395/R
£2098 $3566 €3000 Portrait of a young lady with rose (23x18cm-9x7in) 27-Nov-3 Dorotheum, Linz #412/R est:3500-4500
£5245 $8916 €7500 Fortune-teller with newly married couple in a landscape (76x60cm-30x24in) s. canvas on canvas. 27-Nov-3 Dorotheum, Linz #411/R est:10000-14000
£15385 $26154 €22000 Girl looking at herself in mirror (55x43cm-22x17in) s.d.849. 24-Nov-3 Dorotheum, Vienna #64/R est:6000-8000

REITLINGER, Gerald Roberts (1900-1978) British
£600 $1110 €876 Provencale village (70x60cm-28x24in) 15-Jan-4 Christie's, Kensington #986/R

REKERS, Suzanne (1966-) Dutch
£694 $1097 €1000 Portrait of young man (100x100cm-39x39in) s.d.2002. 26-Apr-3 Auction Maastricht #87/R

REKINGER, Noel (1934-) Dutch
£245 $400 €358 Sailboats (48x58cm-19x23in) s. panel. 27-Sep-3 Charlton Hall, Columbia #508/R

REMBRANDT (1606-1669) Dutch
Prints
£1519 $2750 €2218 Pancake woman (11x8cm-4x3in) etching. 19-Apr-4 Bonhams & Butterfields, San Francisco #125/R est:1500-2000
£1667 $3000 €2434 Descent from the Cross (52x41cm-20x16in) etching engraving exec 1633. 22-Jan-4 Swann Galleries, New York #37 est:2000-3000
£1676 $3000 €2447 Abraham caressing Isaac (11x9cm-4x4in) etching. 6-May-4 Swann Galleries, New York #189a/R est:4000-6000
£1676 $3000 €2447 Flight into Egypt (10x5cm-4x2in) etching. 6-May-4 Swann Galleries, New York #219/R est:1500-2500
£1765 $3000 €2577 Christ driving the money changers from the temple (14x17cm-6x7in) etching drypoint. 6-Nov-3 Swann Galleries, New York #229/R est:2000-3000
£1765 $3000 €2577 Return of the Prodigal Son (16x14cm-6x6in) etching drypoint. 6-Nov-3 Swann Galleries, New York #239/R est:4000-6000
£1765 $3000 €2577 Presentation in the temple (22x29cm-9x11in) etching drypoint exec.c.1640. 6-Nov-3 Swann Galleries, New York #245/R est:4000-6000
£1776 $3268 €2700 Male nude (19x13cm-7x5in) eau forte. 22-Jun-4 Sotheby's, Milan #347/R est:1000-1500
£1788 $3200 €2610 Man wearing a high cap (10x9cm-4x4in) etching. 6-May-4 Swann Galleries, New York #166/R est:1500-2500
£1788 $3200 €2610 Christ driving the money changers from the temple (14x17cm-6x7in) etching drypoint. 6-May-4 Swann Galleries, New York #179/R est:2000-3000
£1788 $3200 €2610 Raising of Lazarus (15x11cm-6x4in) etching. 6-May-4 Swann Galleries, New York #206/R est:2000-3000
£1788 $3200 €2610 Clement de jonghe, printseller (21x16cm-8x6in) etching. 6-May-4 Swann Galleries, New York #215/R est:2500-3500
£1788 $3200 €2610 Christ at Emmaus (21x16cm-8x6in) etching. 6-May-4 Swann Galleries, New York #224/R est:2000-3000
£1788 $3200 €2610 Abraham Francen, Apothecary (16x21cm-6x8in) etching. 6-May-4 Swann Galleries, New York #233/R est:2000-3000
£1816 $3250 €2651 Raising of Lazarus (38x20cm-15x8in) etching. 14-May-4 Du Mouchelle, Detroit #2125/R est:1500-2000
£1882 $3200 €2748 Artist's mother (6x7cm-2x3in) etching exec.1628. 4-Nov-3 Christie's, Rockefeller NY #198/R est:2500-3500
£1882 $3200 €2748 Artist's mother with her hand on her chest (9x7cm-4x3in) etching. 6-Nov-3 Swann Galleries, New York #44/R est:2000-3000
£1899 $3400 €2773 Christ and woman of Samaria among ruins (12x10cm-5x4in) etching drypoint. 6-May-4 Swann Galleries, New York #176/R est:3500-5000
£1899 $3400 €2773 Three Oriental figures (14x11cm-6x4in) etching. 6-May-4 Swann Galleries, New York #197/R est:2000-3000
£1899 $3400 €2773 St. Jerome in a dark chamber (15x17cm-6x7in) etching. 6-May-4 Swann Galleries, New York #204/R est:1800-2200
£1899 $3400 €2773 Nude man seated and another standing with a woman and a baby (19x13cm-7x5in) etching. 6-May-4 Swann Galleries, New York #210/R est:1800-2200
£1899 $3400 €2773 Virgin and child with a cat and snake (9x15cm-4x6in) etching. 6-May-4 Swann Galleries, New York #220/R est:2000-3000
£1899 $3400 €2773 Christ seated disputing with the doctors (9x14cm-4x6in) etching. 6-May-4 Swann Galleries, New York #222/R est:1500-2500
£1899 $3400 €2773 Jan Lutma, goldsmith (20x15cm-8x6in) etching drypoint. 6-May-4 Swann Galleries, New York #228/R est:1500-2500
£1899 $3400 €2773 Abraham France, Apothecay (15x21cm-6x8in) etching. 6-May-4 Swann Galleries, New York #231/R est:1800-2200
£1899 $3400 €2773 Christ and the woman of Samaria (12x16cm-5x6in) etching drypoint. 6-May-4 Swann Galleries, New York #232/R est:2500-3500
£1931 $3225 €2800 Trois figures Orientales (14x11cm-5x4in) etching. 9-Jul-3 Tajan, Paris #46 est:1000-1200
£2000 $3400 €2920 Joseph and Potiphar's wife (9x12cm-4x5in) etching drypoint. 6-Nov-3 Swann Galleries, New York #228/R est:3500-5000
£2000 $3400 €2920 Woman bathing her feet at a brook (16x8cm-6x3in) etching. 6-Nov-3 Swann Galleries, New York #284/R est:4000-6000
£2000 $3440 €2920 Abraham and Isaac (16x13cm-6x5in) etching. 4-Dec-3 Sotheby's, London #116/R est:2000-2500
£2000 $3620 €3000 St Jerome praying (11x8cm-4x3in) etching. 2-Apr-4 Winterberg, Heidelberg #225 est:1150

£2000	$3640	€2920	Angel appearing to the shepherds (26x21cm-10x8in) etching drypoint engraving. 30-Jun-4 Christie's, London #58/R est:800-1200
£2011	$3600	€2936	Joseph and Potiphar's wife (10x10cm-4x4in) etching drypoint. 6-May-4 Swann Galleries, New York #59/R est:4000-6000
£2013	$3705	€3000	Abraham Francen (16x20cm-6x8in) etching. 26-Mar-4 Ketterer, Hamburg #156/R est:2500-3000
£2014	$3223	€2800	Abraham and Izaac (17x14cm-7x6in) engraving. 14-May-3 Finarte Semenzato, Milan #354/R est:1500-2500
£2059	$3500	€3006	Christ at Emmaus (21x16cm-8x6in) etching burin drypoint. 31-Oct-3 Sotheby's, New York #166/R
£2059	$3500	€3006	Man in arbour (7x6cm-3x2in) etching. 31-Oct-3 Sotheby's, New York #174/R
£2083	$3396	€3000	Woman at door talking to man with children (9x6cm-4x2in) etching. 25-Sep-3 Dr Fritz Nagel, Stuttgart #1166/R est:3900
£2098	$3608	€3000	Travelling musician (14x11cm-6x4in) etching. 5-Dec-3 Bolland & Marotz, Bremen #493/R est:3900
£2100	$3612	€3066	Abraham caressing Isaac (12x9cm-5x4in) etching executed c.1637. 2-Dec-3 Christie's, London #52 est:700-1000
£2100	$3612	€3066	Medea (23x18cm-9x7in) etching drypoint. 2-Dec-3 Christie's, London #62 est:1000-1500
£2118	$3600	€3092	Jan Uytenbogaert, the goldweigher (25x20cm-10x8in) etching drypoint. 6-Nov-3 Swann Galleries, New York #244/R est:3000-5000
£2123	$3800	€3100	Clement de Jonghe (20x18cm-8x7in) etching. 6-May-4 Swann Galleries, New York #81/R est:7000-10000
£2123	$3800	€3100	Jews in the Synagogue (7x13cm-3x5in) etching. 6-May-4 Swann Galleries, New York #212/R est:4000-6000
£2125	$3400	€3103	Self portrait drawing at a window (18x15cm-7x6in) etching. 20-Sep-3 Sloans & Kenyon, Bethesda #1006/R est:4000-6000
£2133	$3925	€3200	Goldsmith (8x6cm-3x2in) etching drypoing. 11-Jun-4 Hauswedell & Nolte, Hamburg #892/R est:1800
£2200	$4004	€3212	Jews in the Synagogue (7x13cm-3x5in) etching prov. 1-Jul-4 Sotheby's, London #84/R est:2000-2500
£2235	$3800	€3263	Strolling musicians (14x12cm-6x5in) etching exec.c.1635. 6-Nov-3 Swann Galleries, New York #235/R est:3000-5000
£2235	$3800	€3263	Abraham caressing Isaac (12x9cm-5x4in) etching exec.c.1637. 6-Nov-3 Swann Galleries, New York #240/R est:3000-5000
£2235	$3800	€3263	Jan Uytenbogaert, preacher of the Remonstrants (23x19cm-9x7in) etching drypoint. 6-Nov-3 Swann Galleries, New York #52/R est:5000-8000
£2235	$4000	€3263	Man at a desk wearing a cross and chain (13x10cm-5x4in) etching drypoint. 6-May-4 Swann Galleries, New York #72/R est:5000-8000
£2235	$4000	€3263	Christ at Emmaus (21x16cm-8x6in) etching. 6-May-4 Swann Galleries, New York #225/R est:3000-5000
£2267	$4103	€3400	Taking Christ down from the cross (53x41cm-21x16in) etching. 2-Apr-4 Winterberg, Heidelberg #224/R est:780
£2267	$4057	€3400	Peasant with hands behind back (6x5cm-2x2in) etching. 13-May-4 Bassenge, Berlin #5275/R est:2400
£2267	$4171	€3400	Christ and the Samaritan in ruins (12x10cm-5x4in) etching. 11-Jun-4 Hauswedell & Nolte, Hamburg #889/R est:3500
£2270	$4200	€3314	Bearded man, in an Oriental cap and robe, the artist's father (46x12cm-18x5in) etching. 12-Feb-4 Christie's, Rockefeller NY #400/R est:5000-7000
£2346	$4200	€3425	Angel departing from the family of Tobias (10x15cm-4x6in) etching drypoint. 6-May-4 Swann Galleries, New York #198/R est:2000-3000
£2346	$4200	€3425	Descent from the cross by torchlight (21x16cm-8x6in) etching. 6-May-4 Swann Galleries, New York #223/R est:1500-2500
£2346	$4200	€3425	Peter and John healing the dripple at the Gate of the Temple (18x22cm-7x9in) etching drypoint. 6-May-4 Swann Galleries, New York #232a/R est:4000-6000
£2349	$4322	€3500	St Hieronymus in room (15x17cm-6x7in) s.d. etching. 26-Mar-4 Ketterer, Hamburg #153/R est:2000-2200
£2353	$4000	€3435	Self portrait with Saskia (11x9cm-4x4in) etching. 6-Nov-3 Swann Galleries, New York #237/R est:2000-3000
£2353	$4000	€3435	Faust (21x16cm-8x6in) etching drypoint exec.c.1652. 6-Nov-3 Swann Galleries, New York #270/R est:3000-5000
£2353	$4000	€3435	Small lion hunt (15x12cm-6x5in) etching executed c.1629. 6-Nov-3 Swann Galleries, New York #36/R est:5000-8000
£2353	$4000	€3435	Angel departing from family of Tobias (10x16cm-4x6in) etching drypoint. 6-Nov-3 Swann Galleries, New York #67/R est:4000-6000
£2378	$4042	€3400	Self portrait (6x5cm-2x2in) etching. 27-Nov-3 Bassenge, Berlin #5303 est:3000
£2400	$4128	€3504	Artist drawing from the model (23x18cm-9x7in) etching exec.c.1639 prov. 4-Dec-3 Sotheby's, London #124/R est:2000-4000
£2414	$4031	€3500	Abraham caressant Isaac (12x9cm 4x3in) s.verso etching exec.c.1637. 9-Jul-3 Tajan, Paris #43 est:2500-3000
£2414	$4031	€3500	La presentation au temple (21x29cm-8x11in) etching drypoint exec.c.1639. 9-Jul-3 Tajan, Paris #45 est:1500-2000
£2416	$4446	€3600	Composition (11x6cm-4x2in) etching. 26-Mar-4 Venator & Hansten, Koln #1408 est:2100
£2458	$4400	€3589	Nude man seated on the ground with one leg extended (10x15cm-4x6in) etching. 6-May-4 Swann Galleries, New York #78/R est:3500-5000
£2458	$4400	€3589	Abraham caressing Isaac (11x9cm-4x4in) etching. 6-May-4 Swann Galleries, New York #189/R est:6000-9000
£2458	$4400	€3589	Peter and John healing the cripple at the gate of the temple (18x22cm-7x9in) etching drypoint. 6-May-4 Swann Galleries, New York #235/R est:2000-3000
£2471	$4200	€3608	Pancake woman (11x8cm-4x3in) etching drypoint. 6-Nov-3 Swann Galleries, New York #231/R est:2500-3500
£2471	$4200	€3608	Circumcision (9x6cm-4x2in) etching drypoint executed c.1630. 6-Nov-3 Swann Galleries, New York #37/R est:4000-6000
£2500	$4150	€3650	Christ and the woman of Samaria among ruins (12x10cm-5x4in) etching. 6-Oct-3 Sotheby's, London #43/R est:3000-4000
£2500	$4250	€3650	Self-portrait (13x11cm-5x4in) etching oval. 31-Oct-3 Sotheby's, New York #156/R
£2500	$4250	€3650	Death of the Virgin (41x31cm-16x12in) etching drypoint. 31-Oct-3 Sotheby's, New York #168
£2500	$4300	€3650	Young man in velvet (10x8cm-4x3in) etching. 4-Dec-3 Sotheby's, London #87/R est:3000-4000
£2500	$4550	€3650	Descent from the cross by torchlight (21x16cm-8x6in) etching drypoint. 30-Jun-4 Christie's, London #70/R est:2000-3000
£2500	$4550	€3650	Raising of Lazarus (36x25cm-14x10in) etching exec.c.1632 prov. 1-Jul-4 Sotheby's, London #91/R est:2000-3000
£2550	$4693	€3800	Christ banishing the traders from the temple (14x17cm-6x7in) etching. 26-Mar-4 Ketterer, Hamburg #150/R est:4000-4500
£2570	$4600	€3752	Samuel Menasseh Ben Israel (15x10cm-6x4in) etching. 6-May-4 Swann Galleries, New York #65/R est:6000-9000
£2588	$4400	€3778	Descent from the cross (53x41cm-21x16in) etching engraving. 6-Nov-3 Swann Galleries, New York #225/R est:1500-2500
£2588	$4400	€3778	Strolling musicians (14x12cm-6x5in) etching executed c.1635. 6-Nov-3 Swann Galleries, New York #58/R est:6000-9000
£2588	$4400	€3778	Faust (21x16cm-8x6in) etching drypoint executed 1652. 6-Nov-3 Swann Galleries, New York #76/R est:6000-9000
£2600	$4472	€3796	Negress lying down (8x16cm-3x6in) etching prov. 4-Dec-3 Sotheby's, London #97/R est:2000-3000
£2600	$4472	€3796	Raising of Lazarus (37x26cm-15x10in) etching drypoint executed c.1632. 2-Dec-3 Christie's, London #56 est:1000-1500
£2600	$4732	€3796	Crucifixion (10x7cm-4x3in) with sig. etching executed 1635. 30-Jun-4 Christie's, London #69/R est:1500-2500
£2600	$4732	€3796	Abraham and Isaac (16x13cm-6x5in) etching. 1-Jul-4 Sotheby's, London #86/R est:2000-3000
£2620	$4769	€3825	Return of the prodigal son. etching. 17-Jun-4 Kornfeld, Bern #97 est:7500 (S.FR 6000)
£2657	$4517	€3800	Abraham disowning Hagar and Ismael (12x9cm-5x4in) etching. 27-Nov-3 Bassenge, Berlin #5304/R est:2800
£2682	$4800	€3916	St. Jerome in a dark chamber (15x17cm-6x7in) etching. 6-May-4 Swann Galleries, New York #205/R est:2000-3000
£2682	$4800	€3916	Abraham and Isaac (16x13cm-6x5in) etching. 6-May-4 Swann Galleries, New York #208/R est:3000-5000
£2700	$4644	€3942	Woman bathing her feet at a brook (16x8cm-6x3in) etching drypoint. 2-Dec-3 Christie's, London #67 est:800-1200
£2706	$4600	€3951	Old woman sleeping (7x5cm-3x2in) etching executed c.1635-37. 6-Nov-3 Swann Galleries, New York #57/R est:3000-5000
£2765	$4700	€4037	Self portrait in a cap and scarf with the face dark (14x11cm-6x4in) etching. 6-Nov-3 Swann Galleries, New York #224/R est:3000-5000
£2778	$4528	€4000	Christ and the woman from Samaria (12x16cm-5x6in) etching. 25-Sep-3 Dr Fritz Nagel, Stuttgart #1167/R est:5000
£2797	$4755	€4000	Man's head (7x6cm-3x2in) etching. 27-Nov-3 Bassenge, Berlin #5327/R est:4500
£2800	$4648	€4088	Strolling musicians (14x12cm-6x5in) etching exec.c.1635. 6-Oct-3 Sotheby's, London #41/R est:1000-1500
£2833	$4618	€4080	In the Temple (21x29cm-8x11in) etching. 26-Sep-3 Venator & Hansten, Koln #683 est:4800
£2897	$4837	€4200	Vieil homme avec un chapeau de fourrure divise (15x14cm-5x5in) etching drypoint. 9-Jul-3 Tajan, Paris #49 est:3000
£2905	$5200	€4241	Perisan (10x8cm-4x3in) etching. 6-May-4 Swann Galleries, New York #53/R est:5000-8000
£2905	$5200	€4241	Peasant calling out (10x5cm-4x2in) etching. 6-May-4 Swann Galleries, New York #60/R est:6000-9000
£2905	$5200	€4241	Old man with beard, fur cap and velvet clock (15x13cm-6x5in) etching. 6-May-4 Swann Galleries, New York #168/R est:2000-3000
£2941	$5000	€4294	Raising of Lazarus (37x26cm-15x10in) etching engraving drypoint exec.c.1632. 6-Nov-3 Swann Galleries, New York #218/R est:3000-5000
£2941	$5000	€4294	Raising of Lazarus (37x26cm-15x10in) etching engraving drypoint exec.c.1632. 6-Nov-3 Swann Galleries, New York #222/R est:4000-6000
£2941	$5000	€4294	Head of Saskia and others (15x12cm-6x5in) etching. 6-Nov-3 Swann Galleries, New York #238/R est:2000-3000
£2941	$5000	€4294	Three Oriental figures (14x11cm-6x4in) etching drypoint. 6-Nov-3 Swann Galleries, New York #69/R est:6000-9000
£2941	$5000	€4294	Raising of Lazarus (15x11cm-6x4in) etching drypoint. 6-Nov-3 Swann Galleries, New York #72/R est:6000-9000
£2950	$4750	€4307	The Persian (10x8cm-4x3in) init.d.1632 etching. 20-Aug-3 James Julia, Fairfield #789/R est:5000-7000
£3000	$5160	€4380	Jan Uytenbogaert, the goldweigher (25x20cm-10x8in) etching. 4-Dec-3 Sotheby's, London #94/R est:4000-6000
£3000	$5160	€4380	Old man with beard, fur cap and velvet cloak (15x13cm-6x5in) etching exec.c.1632. 4-Dec-3 Sotheby's, London #120/R est:1500-2000
£3000	$5460	€4380	Death of the Virgin (41x31cm-16x12in) etching. 1-Jul-4 Sotheby's, London #85/R est:1200-1500
£3000	$5460	€4380	Descent from the cross by torchlight (21x16cm-8x6in) etching prov. 1-Jul-4 Sotheby's, London #87/R est:2000-3000
£3057	$5563	€4463	Man's head. etching. 17-Jun-4 Kornfeld, Bern #105/R est:10000 (S.FR 7000)
£3059	$5200	€4466	Angel appearing to the shepherds (26x21cm-10x8in) etching engraving drypoint. 6-Nov-3 Swann Galleries, New York #49/R est:3000-5000
£3106	$5000	€4535	Rembrandt with raised sabre (13x10cm-5x4in) s. etching. 20-Aug-3 James Julia, Fairfield #788/R est:5000-7000
£3176	$5400	€4637	Virgin and child in the clouds (17x10cm-7x4in) etching. 6-Nov-3 Swann Galleries, New York #68/R est:7000-10000
£3200	$5504	€4672	Raising of Lazarus (37x26cm-15x10in) etching exec.c.1632. 4-Dec-3 Sotheby's, London #113/R est:2000-3000
£3200	$5504	€4672	Bust of an old man with flowing beard (7x6cm-3x2in) etching exec.c.1630. 4-Dec-3 Sotheby's, London #117/R est:2000-2500
£3200	$5504	€4672	Three heads of women, one asleep (14x10cm-6x4in) etching. 4-Dec-3 Sotheby's, London #118/R est:1500-2000
£3200	$5504	€4672	Card player (9x8cm-4x3in) etching. 2-Dec-3 Christie's, London #65/R est:2000-3000
£3200	$5824	€4672	Flight into Egypt (9x6cm-4x2in) etching prov. 30-Jun-4 Christie's, London #61/R est:1500-2500
£3200	$5824	€4672	Circumcision in the stable (10x15cm-4x6in) etching prov. 1-Jul-4 Sotheby's, London #82/R est:3000-4000
£3217	$5469	€4600	Self portrait with Saskia (10x10cm-4x4in) etching. 27-Nov-3 Bassenge, Berlin #5302/R est:3500
£3235	$5500	€4723	Jan Uytenbogaert (22x18cm-9x7in) etching. 31-Oct-3 Sotheby's, New York #177
£3235	$5500	€4723	Raising of Lazarus (36x24cm-14x9in) etching engraving. 6-Nov-3 Swann Galleries, New York #45/R est:8000-12000
£3294	$5600	€4809	Death of the Virgin (41x31cm-16x12in) etching drypoint. 6-Nov-3 Swann Galleries, New York #242/R est:3500-5000
£3294	$5600	€4809	Abraham and Issac (16x13cm-6x5in) etching. 6-Nov-3 Swann Galleries, New York #258/R est:3000-5000
£3310	$5528	€4800	Les Juifs a la synagogue. etching drypoint. 9-Jul-3 Tajan, Paris #48 est:5000-6000
£3352	$6000	€4894	Hog (15x18cm-6x7in) etching drypoint. 20-Mar-4 Rachel Davis, Shaker Heights #442/R est:5000-8000
£3352	$6000	€4894	Polander leaning on a stick (8x5cm-3x2in) etching drypoint executed c.1632. 6-May-4 Swann Galleries, New York #54/R est:4000-6000
£3352	$6000	€4894	Ship of fortune (10x18cm-4x7in) etching. 6-May-4 Swann Galleries, New York #57 est:5000-8000
£3352	$6000	€4894	Return of the Prodigal Son (15x13cm-6x5in) etching. 6-May-4 Swann Galleries, New York #64/R est:6000-9000
£3357	$5706	€4800	Portrait de jeune garcon (9x8cm-4x3in) eau forte. 28-Nov-3 Tajan, Paris #59/R est:6000
£3449	$5759	€5000	L'ange quittant la famille de Tobie (10x15cm-4x6in) etching drypoint. 9-Jul-3 Tajan, Paris #44 est:5000-6000
£3529	$6000	€5152	Mordecai's triumph (18x21cm-7x8in) etching drypoint. 31-Oct-3 Sotheby's, New York #159/R
£3529	$6000	€5152	Circumcision (9x6cm-4x2in) etching drypoint exec.c.1630. 6-Nov-3 Swann Galleries, New York #213/R est:3000-5000
£3529	$6000	€5152	Persian (11x8cm-4x3in) etching. 6-Nov-3 Swann Galleries, New York #46/R est:7000-10000
£3529	$6000	€5152	Death of the Virgin (41x31cm-16x12in) etching drypoint. 6-Nov-3 Swann Galleries, New York #64/R est:7000-10000
£3529	$6000	€5152	Jan Uytenbogaert, the goldweigher (25x20cm-10x8in) etching drypoint. 6-Nov-3 Swann Galleries, New York #65/R est:4000-6000

£3557	$6545	€5300	The blind fiddler (8x5cm-3x2in) mono.d. etching. 26-Mar-4 Ketterer, Hamburg #154/R est:1800-2200
£3619	$6475	€5284	Good Samaritan (25x20cm-10x8in) etching. 20-Mar-4 Rachel Davis, Shaker Heights #441/R est:3000-5000
£3631	$6500	€5301	Woman bathing her feet at a brook (15x8cm-6x3in) etching. 6-May-4 Swann Galleries, New York #82/R est:7000-10000
£3631	$6500	€5301	Pancake woman (10x8cm-4x3in) etching drypoint. 6-May-4 Swann Galleries, New York #187/R est:4000-6000
£3631	$6500	€5301	Abraham and Isaac (16x13cm-6x5in) etching. 6-May-4 Swann Galleries, New York #209/R est:4000-6000
£3800	$6536	€5548	Flight into Egypt, night piece (13x11cm-5x4in) etching. 4-Dec-3 Sotheby's, London #95/R est:4000-6000
£3800	$6536	€5548	Triumph of Mordecai (17x21cm-7x8in) etching exec.c.1641. 4-Dec-3 Sotheby's, London #98/R est:4000-6000
£3800	$6916	€5548	Circumcision in the stable (10x15cm-4x6in) etching prov. 1-Jul-4 Sotheby's, London #73/R est:4000-6000
£3824	$6500	€5583	Beggars (16x13cm-6x5in) etching. 31-Oct-3 Sotheby's, New York #172/R
£3824	$6500	€5583	Christ preaching (15x21cm-6x8in) etching drypoint. 31-Oct-3 Sotheby's, New York #160/R
£3824	$6500	€5583	Persian (11x8cm-4x3in) etching. 6-Nov-3 Swann Galleries, New York #220/R est:7000-10000
£3824	$6500	€5583	Descent from the cross (53x41cm-21x16in) etching engraving. 6-Nov-3 Swann Galleries, New York #226/R est:4000-6000
£3824	$6500	€5583	Self portrait in a velvet cap with plume (13x10cm-5x4in) etching. 6-Nov-3 Swann Galleries, New York #241/R est:3000-5000
£3824	$6500	€5583	Return of the Prodigal Son (16x13cm-6x5in) etching. 6-Nov-3 Swann Galleries, New York #59/R est:6000-9000
£3911	$7000	€5710	Portrait of a boy (10x8cm-4x3in) etching. 6-May-4 Swann Galleries, New York #73/R est:10000-15000
£3911	$7000	€5710	Raising of Lazarus (37x26cm-15x10in) etching engraving drypoint. 6-May-4 Swann Galleries, New York #171/R est:4000-6000
£3911	$7000	€5710	Self portrait with Saskia (10x9cm-4x4in) etching. 6-May-4 Swann Galleries, New York #188/R est:4000-6000
£3911	$7000	€5710	An old man shading his eyes with his hands (14x11cm-6x4in) etching. 6-May-4 Swann Galleries, New York #191/R est:4000-6000
£3916	$6540	€5600	Angel disappearing before family of Tobias (10x15cm-4x6in) etching. 10-Oct-3 Winterberg, Heidelberg #373/R est:6800
£4000	$7280	€5840	Joseph telling his dreams (11x8cm-4x3in) etching. 1-Jul-4 Sotheby's, London #81/R est:2500-3500
£4000	$7280	€5840	Peasant family on the tramp. Beardless man in fur cloak and cap (11x9cm-4x4in) etching one exec.c.1652 pair prov. 1-Jul-4 Sotheby's, London #89/R est:2500-3000
£4118	$7000	€6012	Strolling musicians (14x11cm-6x4in) etching. 31-Oct-3 Sotheby's, New York #170
£4118	$7000	€6012	Return of the prodigal son (15x14cm-6x6in) etching. 31-Oct-3 Sotheby's, New York #167/R
£4190	$7500	€6117	Raising of Lazarus (38x25cm-15x10in) etching engraving drypoint executed c.1632. 6-May-4 Swann Galleries, New York #56/R est:5000-8000
£4190	$7500	€6117	Joseph telling his dreams (10x8cm-4x3in) etching. 6-May-4 Swann Galleries, New York #70/R est:4000-6000
£4190	$7500	€6117	Jan Cornelis Sylvius, preacher (28x18cm-11x7in) etching drypoint. 6-May-4 Swann Galleries, New York #76/R est:8000-12000
£4190	$7500	€6117	Joseph's coat brought to Jacob (11x8cm-4x3in) etching. 6-May-4 Swann Galleries, New York #173/R est:2000-3000
£4190	$7500	€6117	Presentation in the temple (21x29cm-8x11in) etching drypoint. 6-May-4 Swann Galleries, New York #196/R est:4000-6000
£4190	$7500	€6117	Return of the Prodigal son. Woman at a door hatch. Christ seated disputing with the doctor. etching three. 6-May-4 Swann Galleries, New York #236/R est:2500-3500
£4190	$7500	€6117	Jan Uytenbogaert. Christ seated disputing with the doctor. Christ at Emmaus. etching three. 6-May-4 Swann Galleries, New York #237/R est:3000-5000
£4196	$7133	€6000	Travelling musicians (14x11cm-6x4in) etching. 27-Nov-3 Bassenge, Berlin #5320/R est:7500
£4200	$7224	€6132	Peasant family on the tramp (11x9cm-4x4in) etching exec.c.1652 prov. 4-Dec-3 Sotheby's, London #122/R est:3500-4000
£4200	$7224	€6132	Self portrait in a cap and scarf with the face dark (13x10cm-5x4in) etching. 4-Dec-3 Sotheby's, London #125/R est:2000-3000
£4200	$7644	€6132	Blindness of Tobit (12x6cm-5x2in) etching. 30-Jun-4 Christie's, London #57/R est:1000-1500
£4297	$7864	€6274	The Descent from the Cross by torchlight (21x16cm-8x6in) etching drypoint. 9-Jun-4 Rasmussen, Copenhagen #2093/R est:25000-30000 (D.KR 48000)
£4333	$7757	€6500	Two male nudes (19x13cm-7x5in) etching. 13-May-4 Bassenge, Berlin #5277/R est:3500
£4367	$7948	€6376	Awakening of Lazarus. etching. 17-Jun-4 Kornfeld, Bern #95/R est:10000 (S.FR 10000)
£4412	$7500	€6442	Studies of the head of Saskia (15x12cm-6x5in) etching. 31-Oct-3 Sotheby's, New York #178
£4412	$7500	€6442	Pancake woman (10x8cm-4x3in) etching. 6-Nov-3 Swann Galleries, New York #54/R est:10000-15000
£4435	$7938	€6475	Medea - marriage of Jason and Creusa (24x18cm-9x7in) etching executed 1648 lit. 25-May-4 Bukowskis, Stockholm #559/R est:10000-15000 (S.KR 60000)
£4469	$8000	€6525	Self portrait drawing at a window (16x13cm-6x5in) etching drypoint. 6-May-4 Swann Galleries, New York #211/R est:3000-5000
£4500	$7740	€6570	Goldsmith (8x6cm-3x2in) etching. 4-Dec-3 Sotheby's, London #79/R est:5000-7000
£4500	$7740	€6570	Abraham caressing Isaac (12x9cm-5x4in) etching c.1637 prov. 2-Dec-3 Christie's, London #53/R est:5000-7000
£4500	$7740	€6570	Christ healing the sick (28x39cm-11x15in) etching drypoint executed c.1649 prov. 2-Dec-3 Christie's, London #57/R est:3000-5000
£4500	$7740	€6570	Descent from the Cross by torchlight (21x16cm-8x6in) etching drypoint. 2-Dec-3 Christie's, London #59/R est:5000-7000
£4500	$8190	€6570	Jan Cornelius Sylvius, preacher (17x14cm-7x6in) etching. 30-Jun-4 Christie's, London #78/R est:6000-8000
£4500	$8190	€6570	Return of the Prodigal Son (16x14cm-6x6in) etching prov. 1-Jul-4 Sotheby's, London #79/R est:2500-3500
£4667	$8447	€7000	Faust in study (20x16cm-8x6in) etching. 2-Apr-4 Winterberg, Heidelberg #229/R est:2200
£4667	$8587	€7000	Rembrandt's mother with hand on chest (10x7cm-4x3in) etching. 11-Jun-4 Hauswedell & Nolte, Hamburg #895/R est:5000
£4667	$8587	€7000	Rembrandt's mother (6x6cm-2x2in) etchign. 11-Jun-4 Hauswedell & Nolte, Hamburg #896/R est:5000
£4706	$8000	€6871	Nativity (16x17cm-6x7in) engraving. 31-Oct-3 Sotheby's, New York #179/R
£4749	$8500	€6934	Descent from the cross (53x41cm-21x16in) etching engraving. 6-May-4 Swann Galleries, New York #172/R est:3000-5000
£4800	$7968	€7008	Studies of the head of Saskia (15x12cm-6x5in) etching. 6-Oct-3 Sotheby's, London #44/R est:2000-2500
£4800	$8256	€7008	Old man shading his eyes with his hand (13x11cm-5x4in) etching exec.c.1639. 4-Dec-3 Sotheby's, London #123/R est:3000-4000
£5000	$8500	€7300	Jan Lutma (20x15cm-8x6in) etching drypoint burin. 31-Oct-3 Sotheby's, New York #176/R
£5000	$8500	€7300	Descent from the cross (52x41cm-20x16in) etching engraving. 6-Nov-3 Swann Galleries, New York #227/R est:5000-8000
£5000	$9100	€7300	Nude man seated and another standing, with a woman and a baby (20x13cm-8x5in) etching prov. 30-Jun-4 Christie's, London #75/R est:3000-5000
£5000	$9100	€7300	Self portrait with Saskia (10x9cm-4x4in) etching. 1-Jul-4 Sotheby's, London #70/R est:2000-3000
£5028	$9000	€7341	Virgin and child in the clouds (18x10cm-7x4in) etching drypoint. 6-May-4 Swann Galleries, New York #71/R est:8000-12000
£5028	$9000	€7341	Jan Antonides van der Linden, physician (18x10cm-7x4in) etching. 6-May-4 Swann Galleries, New York #83/R est:3000-5000
£5294	$9000	€7729	Bearded man in a velvet cap with jewel clasp (10x8cm-4x3in) etching. 6-Nov-3 Swann Galleries, New York #61/R est:12000-18000
£5307	$9500	€7748	Self portrait in a velvet cap with plume (13x10cm-5x4in) etching. 6-May-4 Swann Galleries, New York #192/R est:4000-6000
£5500	$10010	€8030	Jews in the Synagogue (7x13cm-3x5in) etching drypoint. 30-Jun-4 Christie's, London #72/R est:3000-5000
£5500	$10010	€8030	Landscape with a cottage and haybarn (13x32cm-5x13in) etching. 30-Jun-4 Christie's, London #76 est:3000-5000
£5587	$10000	€8157	Raising of Lazarus (37x26cm-15x10in) etching engraving drypoint. 6-May-4 Swann Galleries, New York #169/R est:4000-6000
£5594	$9510	€8000	Christ preaching - La petite tombe (15x20cm-6x8in) etching. 27-Nov-3 Bassenge, Berlin #5311/R est:9000
£5882	$10000	€8588	Christ before Pilate (55x44cm-22x17in) etching. 31-Oct-3 Sotheby's, New York #165/R
£6000	$10920	€8760	Joseph's coat brought to Jacob (11x8cm-4x3in) etching drypoint exec.c.1633. 1-Jul-4 Sotheby's, London #77/R est:6000-8000
£6114	$11127	€8926	Old man wearing fur hat. etching drypoint. 17-Jun-4 Kornfeld, Bern #102/R est:12500 (S.FR 14000)
£6145	$11000	€8972	Girl with a basket (8x8cm-3x3in) etching executed c.1642. 6-May-4 Swann Galleries, New York #74/R est:15000-20000
£6200	$10664	€9052	Beggars conversing (8x7cm-3x3in) mono.d.1630 etching lit. 3-Dec-3 Cheffins, Cambridge #538/R est:300-400
£6294	$10699	€9000	Proclamation to the shepherds (26x22cm-10x9in) etching. 27-Nov-3 Bassenge, Berlin #5307/R est:6000
£6500	$11180	€9490	Jews in a Synagogue (7x13cm-3x5in) etching drypoint prov. 2-Dec-3 Christie's, London #64/R est:4000-6000
£6500	$11830	€9490	Self portrait in a velvet cap with plume (13x10cm-5x4in) etching. 30-Jun-4 Christie's, London #52/R est:3000-5000
£6500	$11830	€9490	Naked woman seated on a mound (18x16cm-7x6in) etching prov. 30-Jun-4 Christie's, London #73/R est:4000-6000
£6550	$11921	€9563	Angel disappearing from family of Tobias. drypoint on etching. 17-Jun-4 Kornfeld, Bern #90/R est:17500 (S.FR 15000)
£6550	$11921	€9563	Flight to Egypt. drypoint on etching copperplate. 17-Jun-4 Kornfeld, Bern #93 est:20000 (S.FR 15000)
£6704	$12000	€9788	Three heads of women, one asleep (13x10cm-5x4in) etching. 6-May-4 Swann Galleries, New York #69/R est:8000-12000
£6711	$12349	€10000	Young girl carrying basket (8x6cm-3x2in) etching. 26-Mar-4 Venator & Hansten, Koln #1411/R est:8000
£6800	$11696	€9928	Adam and Eve (16x12cm-6x5in) etching. 4-Dec-3 Sotheby's, London #80/R est:4000-6000
£6800	$11696	€9928	Lieven Willemsz van Coppenol (26x26cm-10x10in) etching drypoint executed c.1658 prov. 2-Dec-3 Christie's, London #69/R est:3000-5000
£6987	$12716	€10201	Taking Jesus down from the cross (53x41cm-21x16in) i. etching drypoint lit. 16-Jun-4 Fischer, Luzern #2543/R est:3000-4000 (S.FR 16000)
£6993	$11888	€10000	Peter and John at the entrance of the Temple (18x22cm-7x9in) etching. 27-Nov-3 Bassenge, Berlin #5315/R est:7500
£7000	$12740	€10220	Shepherd and his family (10x7cm-4x3in) etching drypoint. 30-Jun-4 Christie's, London #74/R est:4000-6000
£7059	$12000	€10306	Hundred guilder (28x39cm-11x15in) etching drypoint burin. 31-Oct-3 Sotheby's, New York #164/R
£7519	$12782	€10978	Jan Lutma, Goldsmith (30x15cm-12x6in) with sig.i.d.1656 etching drypoint. 26-Nov-3 Dunbar Sloane, Wellington #54/R est:20000-30000 (NZ.D 20000)
£7647	$13000	€11165	Presentation in the temple (21x29cm-8x11in) etching drypoint executed c.1639. 6-Nov-3 Swann Galleries, New York #66/R est:18000-22000
£7821	$14000	€11419	Jan Uytenbogaert, the goldweigher (25x20cm-10x8in) etching drypoint. 6-May-4 Swann Galleries, New York #194/R est:3000-5000
£8000	$13760	€11680	Abraham's sacrifice (16x13cm-6x5in) etching prov. 4-Dec-3 Sotheby's, London #93/R est:6000-8000
£8000	$14560	€11680	Holy Family (10x7cm-4x3in) etching drypoint. 30-Jun-4 Christie's, London #63/R est:3000-5000
£8000	$14560	€11680	Pancake woman (11x8cm-4x3in) etching. 1-Jul-4 Sotheby's, London #78/R est:4000-6000
£8200	$14104	€11972	Pancake woman (11x8cm-4x3in) etching. 4-Dec-3 Sotheby's, London #115/R est:3000-4000
£8235	$14000	€12023	Hundred guilder (28x39cm-11x15in) etching drypoint burin. 31-Oct-3 Sotheby's, New York #163/R
£8500	$15470	€12410	Christ driving the money changers from the temple (14x17cm-6x7in) etching. 1-Jul-4 Sotheby's, London #74/R est:8000-12000
£8667	$15513	€13000	Self portrait wearing feathered beret (13x10cm-5x4in) etching. 13-May-4 Bassenge, Berlin #5269/R est:6000
£8824	$15000	€12883	Self-portrait (14x11cm-6x4in) etching. 31-Oct-3 Sotheby's, New York #154/R
£8824	$15000	€12883	Descent from the cross (53x41cm-21x16in) etching engraving. 6-Nov-3 Swann Galleries, New York #47/R est:10000-15000
£8939	$16000	€13051	Studies, heads of Saskia and others (13x10cm-5x4in) etching. 6-May-4 Swann Galleries, New York #66/R est:8000-12000
£9333	$16707	€14000	Old man with long beard (10x8cm-4x3in) etching. 13-May-4 Bassenge, Berlin #5281/R est:7500
£9412	$16000	€13742	Self portrait with a raised sabre (12x10cm-5x4in) etching. 6-Nov-3 Swann Galleries, New York #48/R est:8000-12000
£9412	$16000	€13742	Great Jewish bride (23x17cm-9x7in) etching drypoint. 6-Nov-3 Swann Galleries, New York #53/R est:20000-30000
£9500	$16340	€13870	Self portrait drawing at a window (16x13cm-6x5in) etching. 4-Dec-3 Sotheby's, London #88/R est:4000-6000
£10000	$17000	€14600	Self-portrait (10x9cm-4x4in) etching. 31-Oct-3 Sotheby's, New York #153/R
£10000	$18400	€15000	Rembrandt leaning (20x16cm-8x6in) etching drypoint. 11-Jun-4 Hauswedell & Nolte, Hamburg #884/R est:6000
£11000	$18920	€16060	Jan Six (25x19cm-10x7in) etching prov. 4-Dec-3 Sotheby's, London #90/R est:6000-9000
£11000	$20020	€16060	Christ preaching (15x21cm-6x8in) etching drypoint engraving. 30-Jun-4 Christie's, London #64/R est:5000-7000
£11790	$21459	€17213	Nude woman outdoors. etching. 17-Jun-4 Kornfeld, Bern #101/R est:20000 (S.FR 27000)

£11826	$21168	€17266	The Descent from the Cross by Torchlight (21x16cm-8x6in) etching drypoint exec.1654 lit. 25-May-4 Bukowskis, Stockholm #557/R est:150000-200000 (S.KR 160000)
£11858	$21225	€17313	Self-portrait leaning on a stone sill (20x16cm-8x6in) etching exec 1639 prov.lit. 15-May-4 Christie's, Sydney #405/R est:8000-12000 (A.D 30000)
£12000	$20640	€17520	Clement de Jonghe, printseller (21x16cm-8x6in) etching drypoint prov. 2-Dec-3 Christie's, London #68/R est:8000-12000
£12000	$22080	€18000	Christ in Emmaus (10x7cm-4x3in) etching drypoint. 11-Jun-4 Hauswedell & Nolte, Hamburg #890/R est:15000
£12291	$22000	€17945	Jews in the Synagogue (8x13cm-3x5in) etching drypoint. 6-May-4 Swann Galleries, New York #79/R est:25000-35000
£13000	$22360	€18980	Ephraim Bonus, Jewish physician (21x18cm-8x7in) etching. 4-Dec-3 Sotheby's, London #91/R est:15000-20000
£13408	$24000	€19576	Self portrait in velvet cap and plume (13x10cm-5x4in) etching. 6-May-4 Swann Galleries, New York #67/R est:20000-30000
£13500	$24570	€19710	Abraham caressing Isaac (12x9cm-5x4in) etching exec.c.1637 prov. 1-Jul-4 Sotheby's, London #80/R est:8000-12000
£13974	$25432	€20402	Epiphany. drypoint on etching. 17-Jun-4 Kornfeld, Bern #98/R est:25000 (S.FR 32000)
£14000	$25480	€20440	Great Jewish bride (22x17cm-9x7in) etching drypoint burin prov. 30-Jun-4 Christie's, London #79/R est:15000-20000
£15000	$25800	€21900	Self portrait with curly hair and white collar (6x5cm-2x2in) etching exec.c.1630 prov. 4-Dec-3 Sotheby's, London #86/R est:6000-8000
£15000	$27300	€21900	Self portrait leaning on a stone sill (20x16cm-8x6in) etching. 30-Jun-4 Christie's, London #53/R est:6000-8000
£15294	$26000	€22329	Star of kings, a night piece (9x14cm-4x6in) etching drypoint. 6-Nov-3 Swann Galleries, New York #75/R est:10000-15000
£15569	$26000	€22731	Great Jewish bride (23x18cm-9x7in) etching drypoint. 11-Nov-3 Doyle, New York #363/R est:10000-15000
£16000	$27520	€23360	Lieven Willemsz van Coppenol, writing master (26x19cm-10x7in) etching exec.c.1658 prov. 4-Dec-3 Sotheby's, London #89/R est:10000-15000
£16000	$28640	€24000	Lovers and death (11x8cm-4x3in) etching. 13-May-4 Bassenge, Berlin #5274 est:3000
£16000	$29120	€23360	Abraham caressing Isaac (12x9cm-5x4in) etching exec.c.1637 prov. 1-Jul-4 Sotheby's, London #75/R est:8000-12000
£16107	$29638	€24000	Christ preaching - la petite tombe (15x20cm-6x8in) etching. 26-Mar-4 Ketterer, Hamburg #50/R est:17000-20000
£17000	$29240	€24820	Jan Asselyn, painter (22x17cm-9x7in) etching exec.c.1647. 4-Dec-3 Sotheby's, London #92/R est:15000-20000
£17000	$30940	€24820	Jan Lutma, goldsmith (20x15cm-8x6in) etching prov. 1-Jul-4 Sotheby's, London #76/R est:12000-15000
£17450	$32107	€26000	Rembrandt with staring eyes (5x4cm-2x2in) etching. 26-Mar-4 Venator & Hansten, Koln #1410/R est:9000
£17467	$31790	€25502	Christ, appearing after the resurrection of the youth. etching. 17-Jun-4 Kornfeld, Bern #96/R est:40000 (S.FR 40000)
£17483	$29720	€25000	Landscape with artist (13x21cm-5x8in) etching drypoint. 27-Nov-3 Bassenge, Berlin #5325/R est:20000
£17877	$32000	€26100	Self portrait with plumed cap and lowered sabre (13x10cm-5x4in) etching. 6-May-4 Swann Galleries, New York #58/R est:15000-20000
£18000	$30960	€26280	Self portrait with Saskia (10x9cm-4x4in) etching prov. 4-Dec-3 Sotheby's, London #85/R est:18000-22000
£18341	$33380	€26778	Adam and Eve. etching. 17-Jun-4 Kornfeld, Bern #86/R est:25000 (S.FR 42000)
£19214	$34969	€28052	Blind Tobias. drypoint over etching. 17-Jun-4 Kornfeld, Bern #89/R est:60000 (S.FR 44000)
£20000	$36400	€29200	Christ healing the sick (28x39cm-11x15in) etching drypoint engraving. 30-Jun-4 Christie's, London #68/R est:10000-15000
£21229	$38000	€30994	Jan Six (25x20cm-10x8in) etching. 6-May-4 Swann Galleries, New York #77/R est:10000-15000
£24454	$44507	€35703	David praying. drypoint on etching. 17-Jun-4 Kornfeld, Bern #88/R est:50000 (S.FR 56000)
£24581	$44000	€35888	Self portrait with plumed cap (13x10cm-5x4in) etching. 6-May-4 Swann Galleries, New York #61/R est:25000-35000
£25698	$46000	€37519	Self portrait in a velvet cap (13x10cm-5x4in) etching. 6-May-4 Swann Galleries, New York #68/R est:25000-35000
£26471	$45000	€38648	Self-portrait (20x16cm-8x6in) etching. 31-Oct-3 Sotheby's, New York #155/R
£27948	$50865	€40804	Self portrait wearing round fur hat. etching. 17-Jun-4 Kornfeld, Bern #85/R est:17500 (S.FR 64000)
£29050	$52000	€42413	Landscape with three gabled cottages beside a road (25x64cm-10x25in) etching drypoint. 6-May-4 Swann Galleries, New York #80/R est:60000-90000
£30667	$54893	€46000	Christ healing the sick (28x39cm-11x15in) etching. 13-May-4 Bassenge, Berlin #5273/R est:24000
£32000	$55040	€46720	Faust (21x16cm-8x6in) etching exec.c.1652 prov. 4-Dec-3 Sotheby's, London #100/R est:40000-60000
£32402	$58000	€47307	Great Jewish bride (20x18cm-8x7in) etching drypoint. 6-May-4 Swann Galleries, New York #63/R est:20000-30000
£33333	$59667	€50000	Jan Cornelis Sylvius (28x19cm-11x7in) etching. 13-May-4 Bassenge, Berlin #5279/R est:20000
£34899	$64215	€52000	Christ healing the sick (28x40cm-11x16in) etching prov. 26-Mar-4 Ketterer, Hamburg #51/R est:22000-25000
£40000	$72800	€58400	Tetes, paysage et different sujets (46x31cm-18x12in) etching album of 32. 30-Jun-4 Christie's, London #81/R est:10000-15000
£55882	$95000	€81588	Recueil de quatre vingt cinq estampes originales. etching album. 6-Nov-3 Swann Galleries, New York #80/R est:80000-120000
£86765	$147500	€126677	Three trees (21x28cm-8x11in) Etching engraving drypoint. 6-Nov-3 Swann Galleries, New York #73/R est:60000-90000
£110000	$200200	€160600	Tetes, paysages et differents dujets (46x31cm-18x12in) etching album of 78. 30-Jun-4 Christie's, London #80/R est:30000-50000

REMBRANDT (after) (1606-1669) Dutch

£5500	$9900	€8030	Portrait of an elderly gentleman in Oriental dress (73x59cm-29x23in) 20-Apr-4 Sotheby's, Olympia #237/R est:2000-3000

REMBRANDT (circle) (1606-1669) Dutch

£6593	$12000	€9626	Portrait of a gentleman in a black costume (66x53cm-26x21in) i.d.1632 prov.exhib. 17-Jun-4 Christie's, Rockefeller NY #68/R est:12000-18000
£12778	$23000	€18656	Portrait of a bearded young man wearing a cap (23x17cm-9x7in) panel prov. 21-Jan-4 Sotheby's, New York #155/R est:10000-15000
£15000	$25500	€21900	Moses Trampling on Pharaoh's Crown (90x129cm-35x51in) panel prov. 29-Oct-3 Christie's, London #23/R est:7000-10000

REMBRANDT (school) (1606-1669) Dutch

£27000	$49410	€39420	Gideon visited by the Angel (126x95cm-50x37in) 7-Jul-4 Bonhams, New Bond Street #90/R est:2000-3000
£28000	$50400	€40880	Portrait of a bearded man wearing brown (40x31cm-16x12in) bears sig panel arched top. 20-Apr-4 Sotheby's, Olympia #238/R est:4000-6000
£60000	$103800	€87600	Portrait of a gentleman in a black hat and a lace falling collar (75x63cm-30x25in) panel prov.exhib.lit. 10-Dec-3 Christie's, London #37/R est:20000-30000

REMBRANDT (studio) (1606-1669) Dutch

£13699	$23288	€20000	St Peter repentant (64x50cm-25x20in) panel. 4-Nov-3 Sotheby's, Amsterdam #11/R est:20000-30000

REMBRANDT (style) (1606-1669) Dutch

£11667	$21000	€17034	Portrait of an old man (66x53cm-26x21in) prov.exhib. 22-Jan-4 Sotheby's, New York #264/R est:10000-15000

REMENICK, Seymour (1923-1999) American

£212	$400	€310	Fall landscape (20x30cm-8x12in) s. card. 22-Feb-4 Freeman, Philadelphia #54/R
£225	$425	€329	Dorchester, NJ (20x25cm-8x10in) panel prov. 22-Feb-4 Freeman, Philadelphia #38/R
£238	$450	€347	Trees (20x30cm-8x12in) s. 22-Feb-4 Freeman, Philadelphia #15/R
£238	$450	€347	Still life with fruit and knife (15x25cm-6x10in) s. canvas laid down. 22-Feb-4 Freeman, Philadelphia #23/R
£265	$500	€387	Ninth St merchant (36x30cm-14x12in) s. panel. 22-Feb-4 Freeman, Philadelphia #56/R
£284	$475	€415	Still life of fish (25x38cm-10x15in) s. panel. 20-Jun-3 Freeman, Philadelphia #113/R
£291	$550	€425	Still life with copper pitcher (20x28cm-8x11in) s. panel prov. 22-Feb-4 Freeman, Philadelphia #2/R
£291	$550	€425	Docked boats (20x41cm-8x16in) s. panel. 22-Feb-4 Freeman, Philadelphia #35/R
£299	$550	€437	Still life (20x28cm-8x11in) prov. 25-Jun-4 Freeman, Philadelphia #262/R
£317	$600	€463	Self portrait (30x23cm-12x9in) s. panel. 22-Feb-4 Freeman, Philadelphia #12/R
£317	$600	€463	Roof tops (15x23cm-6x9in) i.stretcher. 22-Feb-4 Freeman, Philadelphia #37/R
£317	$600	€463	Ninth Street market (30x28cm-12x11in) i.verso panel. 22-Feb-4 Freeman, Philadelphia #40/R
£344	$650	€502	Heart of storm Gloucester (216x25cm-85x10in) panel prov. 22-Feb-4 Freeman, Philadelphia #43/R
£370	$700	€540	Manayunk (20x41cm-8x16in) s. panel. 22-Feb-4 Freeman, Philadelphia #48/R
£423	$800	€618	Large tree by houses (18x25cm-7x10in) s. sold with a companion. 22-Feb-4 Freeman, Philadelphia #13/R
£450	$850	€657	Sunny day at Gloucester (20x25cm-8x10in) panel prov. 22-Feb-4 Freeman, Philadelphia #5/R
£450	$850	€657	Tree over a river (25x28cm-10x11in) s. oil paper. 22-Feb-4 Freeman, Philadelphia #14/R
£450	$850	€657	Still life with bread and cherries (20x30cm-8x12in) s. panel prov. 22-Feb-4 Freeman, Philadelphia #21/R
£476	$900	€695	Waterworks (15x20cm-6x8in) s. board. 22-Feb-4 Freeman, Philadelphia #16/R
£476	$900	€695	Inlet and shack (23x38cm-9x15in) panel. 22-Feb-4 Freeman, Philadelphia #36/R
£476	$900	€695	Dock, Gloucester (25x41cm-10x16in) s.i.d.May/August 1956 verso panel. 22-Feb-4 Freeman, Philadelphia #49/R
£476	$900	€695	Still life of bottle and bread (20x28cm-8x11in) s. panel. 22-Feb-4 Freeman, Philadelphia #58/R
£500	$800	€730	Holy family church, Mananyunk (66x102cm-26x40in) s. prov. 19-Sep-3 Freeman, Philadelphia #154/R
£503	$950	€734	Landscape, green (13x25cm-5x10in) canvas on panel sold with a companion prov. 22-Feb-4 Freeman, Philadelphia #44/R
£529	$1000	€772	Point Pleasant (28x38cm-11x15in) s. board prov. 22-Feb-4 Freeman, Philadelphia #3/R
£529	$1000	€772	The dock (30x46cm-12x18in) s. panel. 22-Feb-4 Freeman, Philadelphia #7/R
£543	$1000	€793	Abstract still life of musical instruments (91x127cm-36x50in) i.d.1947 stretcher verso. 27-Jun-4 Freeman, Philadelphia #141/R
£582	$1100	€850	Flowers in a blue vase (15x30cm-6x12in) s. panel. 22-Feb-4 Freeman, Philadelphia #8/R
£635	$1200	€927	St Michaels, Maryland (20x41cm-8x16in) panel prov. 22-Feb-4 Freeman, Philadelphia #50/R
£635	$1200	€927	Figure (38x30cm-15x12in) s. panel. 22-Feb-4 Freeman, Philadelphia #52/R
£688	$1300	€1004	Manayunk from across the Schuylkill (36x51cm-14x20in) s. panel. 22-Feb-4 Freeman, Philadelphia #1/R
£688	$1300	€1004	Vermont landscape (25x28cm-10x11in) i.d.1955 verso sold with a companion. 22-Feb-4 Freeman, Philadelphia #39/R
£741	$1400	€1082	Woodland (25x30cm-10x12in) s. 22-Feb-4 Freeman, Philadelphia #33/R
£794	$1500	€1159	Five green apples (25x33cm-10x13in) s. prov. 22-Feb-4 Freeman, Philadelphia #26/R est:300-500
£794	$1500	€1159	Gloucester dock (30x41cm-12x16in) s. panel prov. 22-Feb-4 Freeman, Philadelphia #42/R est:250-400
£899	$1700	€1313	Fairmount waterworks (33x28cm-13x11in) s. panel. 22-Feb-4 Freeman, Philadelphia #53/R est:300-500
£1005	$1900	€1467	Teapot (30x28cm-12x11in) i.stretcher. 22-Feb-4 Freeman, Philadelphia #47/R est:300-500
£1058	$2000	€1545	City scape (61x89cm-24x35in) prov. 22-Feb-4 Freeman, Philadelphia #46/R est:1000-1500
£1087	$2000	€1587	Manayunk (86x102cm-34x40in) s. prov. 27-Jun-4 Freeman, Philadelphia #135/R est:1500-2500
£1429	$2700	€2086	Bench, the green tea pot (122x86cm-48x34in) s.i.d.1947 verso. 22-Feb-4 Freeman, Philadelphia #19/R est:1500-2500
£1587	$3000	€2317	Table top still life (71x91cm-28x36in) s. painted c.1950. 22-Feb-4 Freeman, Philadelphia #41/R est:1500-2500
£1720	$3250	€2511	City scape (64x76cm-25x30in) s.i.verso. 22-Feb-4 Freeman, Philadelphia #6/R est:1000-1500
£2310	$4250	€3373	Abstract interior (119x74cm-47x29in) s. s.d.48 verso prov. 27-Jun-4 Freeman, Philadelphia #142/R est:1500-2500
£2616	$4500	€3819	Still life on chair (74x61cm-29x24in) i.stretcher prov. 7-Dec-3 Freeman, Philadelphia #229 est:500-800

Works on paper

£265	$500	€387	Tower (33x36cm-13x14in) s. W/C. 22-Feb-4 Freeman, Philadelphia #92/R
£423	$800	€618	Still life with covered vessel, bowl, apples and pears (13x23cm-5x9in) s. black ink wash. 22-Feb-4 Freeman, Philadelphia #68/R

REMENICK, Seymour (attrib) (1923-1999) American
£326 $600 €476 Still life (51x94cm-20x37in) prov. 25-Jun-4 Freeman, Philadelphia #251/R

REMFELDT, Per (20th C) Norwegian
£258 $416 €377 The mountain and the sea (94x76cm-37x30in) s. exhib. 25-Aug-3 Blomqvist, Lysaker #1224 (N.KR 3000)

REMFRY, David (1942-) British
£2300 $3634 €3335 Nude with irises (91x101cm-36x40in) i.verso. 3-Sep-3 Bonhams, Bury St Edmunds #402/R est:400-600
Works on paper
£300 $474 €435 Seated ballerina (101x68cm-40x27in) s.d.1991 W/C. 3-Sep-3 Bonhams, Bury St Edmunds #387
£360 $569 €522 Women before masks (68x102cm-27x40in) s.d.1989 i.verso.w. 3-Sep-3 Bonhams, Bury St Edmunds #388

REMIENS, A (20th C) ?
Sculpture
£1667 $3050 €2500 Faun's head (23cm-9in) mono. brown pat. bronze incl. grey marble base exec. 1920's. 7-Jun-4 Sotheby's, Amsterdam #126/R est:2500-3500

REMINGTON, Elizabeth H (1825-1917) American?
£5946 $11000 €8681 The two kings, corn, cotton (91x66cm-36x26in) s.i.d.1876 prov.exhib.lit. 11-Mar-4 Christie's, Rockefeller NY #15/R est:7000-9000

REMINGTON, Frederic (1861-1909) American
£34884 $60000 €50931 Then upon one knee uprising, Hiawatha aimed an arrow (71x51cm-28x20in) s.d.89 prov.lit. 3-Dec-3 Sotheby's, New York #146/R est:75000-100000
£34884 $60000 €50931 And her lovers, the rejected handsome men with paint and feathers (71x51cm-28x20in) s. en grisaille painted 1889 prov.lit. 3-Dec-3 Sotheby's, New York #147/R est:60000-80000
£46512 $80000 €67908 Cowboy fun in old Mexico (46x71cm-18x28in) s. panel painted c.1891 prov.lit. 3-Dec-3 Sotheby's, New York #138/R est:80000-120000
£73864 $130000 €107841 Pioneer (76x51cm-30x20in) s. i.verso painted c.1903 lit. 19-May-4 Sotheby's, New York #203/R est:125000-175000
Sculpture
£1111 $1744 €1600 Bronco Buster. bronze. 29-Aug-3 Deauville, France #217 est:1200-1500
£1955 $3500 €2854 Mountain man (71cm-28in) s. cast bronze black marble base exec.c.1920. 18-Mar-4 Richard Opfer, Timonium #243/R est:1500-2500
£13081 $22500 €19098 Sergeant (26cm-10in) i.num.28 brown pat. bronze prov.lit. 3-Dec-3 Sotheby's, New York #135/R est:20000-30000
£13953 $24000 €20371 Sergeant (25cm-10in) i. pat bronze. 4-Dec-3 Christie's, Rockefeller NY #71/R est:20000-30000
£19553 $35000 €28547 Bronco buster (56cm-22in) bronze. 14-May-4 Du Mouchelle, Detroit #2087/R est:40000-50000
£31977 $55000 €46686 Bronco buster (58cm-23in) i.num.114 dark brown pat. bronze prov.lit. 3-Dec-3 Sotheby's, New York #140/R est:60000-80000
£45349 $78000 €66210 Rattlesnake (56cm-22in) i. num.044 pat bronze lit. 4-Dec-3 Christie's, Rockefeller NY #70/R est:70000-90000
£48295 $85000 €70511 Bronco Buster (58cm-23in) i.base st.f.Roman Bronze Works green blk pat bronze prov.lit. 18-May-4 Christie's, Rockefeller NY #53/R est:70000-100000
£66860 $115000 €97616 Cheyenne (61cm-24in) i. brown pat. bronze prov.lit. 3-Dec-3 Sotheby's, New York #145/R est:80000-120000
£261628 $450000 €381977 Bronco buster (86cm-34in) i. num.11 pat bronze prov.lit. 4-Dec-3 Christie's, Rockefeller NY #69/R est:500000-700000
£581395 $1000000 €848837 Mountain man (71cm-28in) i.num.4 brown pat. bronze prov.lit. 3-Dec-3 Sotheby's, New York #139/R est:500000-700000
Works on paper
£9581 $16000 €13988 Trakehner, horse wrangler (44x34cm-17x13in) s.i. pen ink W/C gouache paper on board exhib.lit. 9-Oct-3 Christie's, Rockefeller NY #84/R est:15000-25000
£9626 $18000 €14054 Soldier with drawn sabre (33x23cm-13x9in) s. mixed media en grisaille prov.lit. 24-Jul-4 Coeur d'Alene, Hayden #245/R est:15000-25000
£21390 $40000 €31229 Squadron A - tent pegging (46x43cm-18x17in) s. gouache executed c.1896 lit. 24-Jul-4 Coeur d'Alene, Hayden #163/R est:20000-30000
£22727 $42500 €33181 Troop A, armory - picking up the handkerchief (48x53cm-19x21in) s. gouache lit. 24-Jul-4 Coeur d'Alene, Hayden #164/R est:20000-30000
£69519 $130000 €101498 Mexican haciendero (46x46cm-18x18in) s. W/C lit. 24-Jul-4 Coeur d'Alene, Hayden #162/R est:50000-75000
£133721 $230000 €195233 Pony war dance (53x58cm-21x23in) s. W/C gouache executed c.1890-91 prov.exhib.lit. 3-Dec-3 Sotheby's, New York #137/R est:150000-250000

REMINGTON, Frederic (attrib) (1861-1909) American
£2201 $3500 €3213 Indian family (56x76cm-22x30in) bears sig. in grisaille. 9-Mar-3 William Jenack, New York #377 est:1000-1500

REMINGTON, Mary (1910-) British
£360 $666 €526 Lustre bowl (25x33cm-10x13in) s. 9-Mar-4 Gorringes, Lewes #1980

REMOND, Jean (1872-1913) French
£4113 $7361 €6005 Landscape with house and garden (60x73cm-24x29in) s. 22-Mar-4 Philippe Schuler, Zurich #4455/R est:2000-2500 (S.FR 9500)

REMOND, Jean Charles Joseph (1795-1875) French
£1974 $3632 €3000 Ruines romaines pres de Palerme (25x35cm-10x14in) s. paper on canvas. 23-Jun-4 Sotheby's, Paris #58/R est:3000-4000
£2937 $5052 €4200 Church and ruins in a southern landscape (26x36cm-10x14in) s. 3-Dec-3 Neumeister, Munich #713/R est:2500
£4000 $7240 €6000 Stromboli, rivage aux falaises (19x32cm-7x13in) s.i.d.1842 oil paper on isorel. 30-Mar-4 Rossini, Paris #113/R est:2500-3500
£4255 $7106 €6000 Vue de l'Ile de Capri (32x46cm-13x18in) s.indis.d.18. 19-Oct-3 St-Germain-en-Laye Encheres #2/R est:6000-8000
£4500 $7200 €6525 Well earned rest (58x82cm-23x32in) s. 18-Sep-3 Christie's, Kensington #56/R est:5000-7000

REMOND, Jean Charles Joseph (attrib) (1795-1875) French
£3667 $6637 €5500 Etude de falaises (42x33cm-17x13in) cardboard. 30-Mar-4 Rossini, Paris #114 est:1200-1500
£4667 $8447 €7000 Torrent avec des rochers, les Gorges de la Cere, Cantal (27x38cm-11x15in) lit. 30-Mar-4 Rossini, Paris #115/R est:1800-2500

REMPS, Andrea Domenico (1620-1699) German
£6667 $12000 €9734 Trompe-l'oeil with partially covered painting of an Apostle, and other objects (73x65cm-29x26in) with sig.d.1767 prov.lit. 23-Jan-4 Christie's, Rockefeller NY #1/R est:10000-15000

REMSEY, Jeno (1885-1960) Hungarian
£1871 $3311 €2732 In a cafe in Paris (100x70cm-39x28in) s.d.965 board. 28-Apr-4 Kieselbach, Budapest #86/R (H.F 700000)

REMY, Ad (19/20th C) Italian
£760 $1398 €1110 Fishing in the Bay of Naples (38x30cm-15x12in) s. sold with companion two. 14-Jun-4 Bonhams, Bath #193

REMY, Eugene (?) French?
£1000 $1850 €1460 Cockerels and hens in a farmyard (18x27cm-7x11in) s. panel. 10-Feb-4 Bonhams, Knightsbridge #67/R est:800-1200

REMY, Jean (1893-?) French
£330 $600 €482 River Seine (23x36cm-9x14in) s. 7-Feb-4 Sloans & Kenyon, Bethesda #883/R

REN XUN (1835-1893) Chinese
Works on paper
£25483 $42556 €37205 Figure, landscape (27x30cm-11x12in) s.d.1879 ink col eight leaves album. 27-Oct-3 Sotheby's, Hong Kong #285/R est:180000-220000 (HK.D 330000)

REN YI (1840-1895) Chinese
Works on paper
£2134 $3841 €3116 Flower and bird (29cm-11in circular) s.i.d.1880. ink col silk fan leaf. 25-Apr-4 Christie's, Hong Kong #1/R est:15000-20000 (HK.D 30000)
£4623 $8321 €6750 Boating (18x53cm-7x21in) s.i.d.1883 ink col fan. 26-Apr-4 Sotheby's, Hong Kong #594/R est:50000-70000 (HK.D 65000)
£9246 $16643 €13499 Cock and hens (138x65cm-54x26in) s.i.d.1874 ink col hanging scroll. 25-Apr-4 Christie's, Hong Kong #76/R est:120000-150000 (HK.D 130000)
£23938 $39977 €34949 Symphony of nature. s.i.d.1874 ink col gold paper 10 leaves album. 27-Oct-3 Sotheby's, Hong Kong #318/R est:200000-300000 (HK.D 310000)
£25605 $46088 €37383 Monk and the horse (150x65cm-59x26in) s.i.d.1890 ink col hanging scroll. 26-Apr-4 Sotheby's, Hong Kong #572/R est:350000-450000 (HK.D 360000)
£81081 $135405 €118378 Portrait of Jiang Shinong at fifty (63x42cm-25x17in) s.i.d.1877 ink col. 27-Oct-3 Sotheby's, Hong Kong #316/R est:380000-500000 (HK.D 1050000)
£162162 $270811 €236757 Zhong kui (139x66cm-55x26in) s.d.1874 ink col hanging scroll. 27-Oct-3 Sotheby's, Hong Kong #284/R est:1300000-1800000 (HK.D 2100000)

REN ZHONG (1967-) Chinese
Works on paper
£11380 $20484 €16615 Scholars (57x32cm-22x13in) s.i. one d.2003 ink col scroll set of four. 25-Apr-4 Christie's, Hong Kong #140/R est:70000-90000 (HK.D 160000)

REN, Chuck (1941-1995) American
£3352 $6000 €4894 Winter scout (36x25cm-14x10in) acrylic board. 15-May-4 Altermann Galleries, Santa Fe #38/R

RENARD, Émile (1850-1930) French
£4362 $7721 €6500 Pres du puits (128x90cm-50x35in) s.d.1876. 27-Apr-4 Campo, Vlaamse Kaai #560/R est:4000-6000

RENARD, Fernand (1912-) French
£872 $1500 €1273 Still life with apricots (24x45cm-9x18in) s. prov. 2-Dec-3 Christie's, Rockefeller NY #108/R est:1500-2000

RENARD, P (20th C) French
Works on paper
£1342 $2470 €2000 Many figures on a snow covered Paris Boulevard (23x38cm-9x15in) s. W/C. 29-Mar-4 Glerum, Amsterdam #170 est:1400-1600
£1370 $2329 €2000 Paris street in the evening (43x61cm-17x24in) s. gouache. 5-Nov-3 Vendue Huis, Gravenhage #366/R est:2000-3000

RENARD, Paul (1871-1920) French
£599 $1000 €875 La Gare de l'Est a Paris (28x38cm-11x15in) s. board. 11-Oct-3 Auctions by the Bay, Alameda #1617/R
£851 $1421 €1200 Beach scene with elegant figures and children playing (20x40cm-8x16in) s. panel. 20-Oct-3 Glerum, Amsterdam #213/R

RENARD, Stephen J (1947-) British
£2100 $3612 €3066 Velsheda and Britannia raching off Cowes 1934 (37x50cm-15x20in) s.d.2002 i.on stretcher. 2-Dec-3 Sotheby's, London #132/R est:2000-3000
£8000 $13600 €11680 Westward (51x76cm-20x30in) s. s.i.d.2003 verso. 19-Nov-3 Christie's, Kensington #419/R
£11000 $18920 €16060 Candida and Britannia offshore 1933 (76x101cm-30x40in) s. i.on stretcher. 2-Dec-3 Sotheby's, London #130/R est:8000-12000

£14208 $26000 €20744 Satanita and White Heather, rigged as yawls, racing with Bynhild, I O Wight (106x155cm-42x61in) s. 29-Jul-4 Christie's, Rockefeller NY #312/R est:30000-50000
£15000 $26850 €21900 Britannia, Candida and Astra racing off the Royal Yacht Squadron Cowes (82x107cm-32x42in) s. 26-May-4 Christie's, Kensington #514/R est:12000-15000
£17486 $32000 €25530 Britannia, Lulworth and White Heather off Norris Castle, Cowes (38x51cm-15x20in) s. 29-Jul-4 Christie's, Rockefeller NY #304/R est:12000-18000
£35519 $65000 €51858 Yankee, Ranger and Endeavour II racing in the New York Club Cruise 1937 (106x152cm-42x60in) s. 29-Jul-4 Christie's, Rockefeller NY #313/R est:30000-50000

RENAUD VAN GINDERTAEL, Andree (20th C) French?
Works on paper
£276 $510 €400 Composition a fond rouge (15x24cm-6x9in) s.d.1960 collage tar. 13-Feb-4 Charbonneaux, Paris #66

RENAUD, Charles Jean (1891-?) French
£881 $1498 €1286 Hunting dog by pond (65x54cm-26x21in) s. 5-Nov-3 Dobiaschofsky, Bern #887/R (S.FR 2000)
£2155 $3858 €3146 Two hunting dogs on the scent (73x92cm-29x36in) s. 12-May-4 Dobiaschofsky, Bern #897/R est:7500 (S.FR 5000)

RENAUD, Paul Louis (19th C) French
Works on paper
£710 $1300 €1037 Figures admiring classical statues (50x64cm-20x25in) s.i.d.1825 pen ink W/C. 3-Jun-4 Christie's, Rockefeller NY #789/R est:400-600

RENAUD, Phil (1934-) American
Works on paper
£18286 $32000 €26698 Words of a Native Son (111x70cm-44x28in) s. printed paper newsprint collage board exec 1964 exhib.lit. 17-Dec-3 Christie's, Rockefeller NY #185/R est:1500-2000

RENAUDIN, Alfred (1866-1944) French
£1377 $2258 €1900 Paysage au pecheur (29x42cm-11x17in) s.d.96. 11-May-3 Osenat, Fontainebleau #225 est:2500-3000
£2198 $3935 €3209 Montmartre, Paris (55x73cm-22x29in) s.i.d.1916. 12-May-4 Dobiaschofsky, Bern #898/R est:5500 (S.FR 5100)
£2585 $4627 €3800 Blamont (48x71cm-19x28in) d.1924. 21-Mar-4 Teitgen, Nancy #76
£2789 $4993 €4100 La Meuse a Chalaines (49x72cm-19x28in) d.1920. 21-Mar-4 Teitgen, Nancy #77

RENAUDIN, Alfred (attrib) (1866-1944) French
£4930 $8183 €7000 Allvard (55x70cm-22x28in) painted 1927. 15-Jun-3 Teitgen, Nancy #94

RENAULT, A (19/20th C) ?
£3020 $5557 €4500 Still life with grapes in silver and parcelgilt tazza (46x37cm-18x15in) bears sig.d.1840 prov. 24-Mar-4 Dorotheum, Vienna #80/R est:5000-7000

RENAULT, Abel Pierre (1903-) French
£261 $425 €381 Landscape (47x63cm-19x25in) s. 28-Sep-3 Bonhams & Butterfields, Los Angeles #7052

RENAULT, Charles Edmond (1829-1905) French
£873 $1590 €1275 Grazing cows in a landscape with a village in the distance (38x56cm-15x22in) s.d.1887. 16-Jun-4 Fischer, Luzern #1134/R est:2000-2500 (S.FR 2000)

RENAULT, H (19th C) French
£6081 $11493 €9000 Le depart pour la chasse a cour (102x128cm-40x50in) s.d.1863. 17-Feb-4 Vanderkindere, Brussels #4/R est:3000-5000

RENAULT, Luigi P (1845-c.1910) Italian
Works on paper
£1049 $1783 €1500 The Severn entering Livorno harbour (41x56cm-16x22in) W/C exec.1852. 18-Nov-3 Cambi, Genoa #364/R est:1400-1600

RENAULT, Luigi P (attrib) (1845-c.1910) Italian
£2200 $3740 €3212 The brigantine Favourite under full sail (51x76cm-20x30in) 19-Nov-3 Christie's, Kensington #500/R est:2500-3000

RENAULT, Michele (fl.1830-1870) Continental
Works on paper
£671 $1235 €1000 The bark, Mary Jane (41x58cm-16x23in) s.i.d.1846 W/C over pencil. 26-Mar-4 Ketterer, Hamburg #29/R

RENBERG, Margareta (1941-) Swedish
£2175 $3916 €3176 Self-portrait with black skirt (120x90cm-47x35in) s. verso prov.exhib.lit. 26-Apr-4 Bukowskis, Stockholm #476/R est:35000-40000 (S.KR 30000)
£3481 $6265 €5082 The garden party (120x150cm-47x59in) s. d.00 verso prov.exhib.lit. 26-Apr-4 Bukowskis, Stockholm #475/R est:35000-40000 (S.KR 48000)

RENDON, Manuel (1894-1980) Ecuadorian/French
£5973 $10991 €8900 Trois personnages (81x60cm-32x24in) s. 29-Mar-4 Lombrail & Teucquam, Paris #118/R
£8939 $16000 €13051 Femme et enfant (46x38cm-18x15in) s. painted 1926 prov. 26-May-4 Sotheby's, New York #139/R est:20000-25000
£13767 $23404 €20100 Nu allonge (45x65cm-18x26in) s. prov. 9-Nov-3 Eric Pillon, Calais #168/R
£16760 $30000 €24470 Couple (130x89cm-51x35in) s. painted 1927 prov. 26-May-4 Sotheby's, New York #35/R est:30000-40000
£21333 $39253 €32000 Exploration (96x162cm-38x64in) s. painted c.1928. 10-Jun-4 Christie's, Paris #9/R est:40000-60000
£27933 $50000 €40782 Nu allonge (46x65cm-18x26in) s. prov. 26-May-4 Sotheby's, New York #34/R est:25000-30000
Works on paper
£1544 $2840 €2300 Trois personnages (35x25cm-14x10in) s. W/C. 29-Mar-4 Lombrail & Teucquam, Paris #119/R

RENE, Jean Jacques (1943-) French
£403 $745 €600 Les tuileries (24x33cm-9x13in) s. i.verso. 15-Mar-4 Blanchet, Paris #152/R
£1096 $1721 €1600 Ete a Deauville (54x73cm-21x29in) s. i.verso. 20-Apr-3 Deauville, France #155 est:1500-2000
£4266 $7252 €6100 Femme lisant sur la plage (46x55cm-18x22in) s. 28-Nov-3 Blanchet, Paris #166 est:2500-3000

RENEFER, Raymond (1879-1957) French
£345 $617 €504 Rue de village (61x50cm-24x20in) s. 12-May-4 Dobiaschofsky, Bern #899/R (S.FR 800)

RENER, Arthur Maria (1912-1991) Belgian
£333 $610 €500 Divinite (71x102cm-28x40in) s. panel. 7-Jun-4 Palais de Beaux Arts, Brussels #343

RENESON, Chet (20th C) American
Works on paper
£1117 $2000 €1631 Playing the fish (43x71cm-17x28in) s. W/C. 8-Jan-4 James Julia, Fairfield #432/R est:2000-4000

RENESSE, Constantin van (attrib) (1626-1680) Dutch
£7222 $13000 €10544 Rebecca and Eliezer at the well (92x71cm-36x28in) prov.lit. 22-Jan-4 Sotheby's, New York #5/R est:15000-20000

RENEVIER, Julien (1847-1907) Swiss
£3000 $5370 €4380 Still life of roses and mandolin (89x69cm-35x27in) s. 26-May-4 Sotheby's, Olympia #309/R est:2000-3000

RENGER-PATZSCH, Albert (1897-1966) German
£8333 $14167 €12000 Landscape near Hamborn (20x16cm-8x6in) gelatin silver. 30-Oct-3 Van Ham, Cologne #180/R est:1100
Photographs
£1667 $3000 €2434 Botanical study (17x12cm-7x5in) i.num.124 gelatin silver print. 23-Apr-4 Phillips, New York #259/R est:4000-6000
£2000 $3680 €3000 The Ruhr in winter (17x23cm-7x9in) i. verso bromide silver gelatin lit.exhib. 10-Jun-4 Villa Grisebach, Berlin #1256/R est:2000-2500
£2292 $3896 €3300 Iron hand in Essen (22x17cm-9x7in) gelatin silver. 30-Oct-3 Van Ham, Cologne #179/R est:1800
£2536 $4159 €3500 Schrebergarten landscape near Dusseldorf (16x23cm-6x9in) i. verso vintage bromide silver gelatin lit. 30-May-3 Villa Grisebach, Berlin #1321/R est:2800-3200
£2899 $4754 €4000 Brazilian melon tree (23x17cm-9x7in) i. verso vintage silver gelatin lit. 30-May-3 Villa Grisebach, Berlin #1319/R est:2800-3200
£3167 $5700 €4624 Botanical study (23x10cm-9x4in) i.num.89 verso gelatin silver print. 23-Apr-4 Phillips, New York #257/R est:4000-6000
£3472 $5903 €5000 Garden tulip (23x17cm-9x7in) i. gelatin silver lit. 31-Oct-3 Lempertz, Koln #281/R est:3000
£3497 $5944 €5000 Cranes in Herrenwyk factory (19x23cm-7x9in) silver gelatin lit.exhib. 27-Nov-3 Villa Grisebach, Berlin #1347/R est:4000-6000
£3600 $6336 €5400 Railway embankment, Central Station, Essen (22x16cm-9x6in) i.verso gelatin silver print printed c.1960. 21-May-4 Bloomsbury, London #247/R est:600-800
£3986 $6536 €5500 Echinocactus Huminingii (20x17cm-8x7in) i. verso vintage silver gelatin. 30-May-3 Villa Grisebach, Berlin #1318/R est:3000-4000
£4000 $7040 €6000 Oberhausenstrasse, Essen (22x16cm-9x6in) i.verso gelatin silver print printed c.1960 prov. 21-May-4 Bloomsbury, London #250 est:400-600
£4333 $7973 €6500 Erzgebirge, Riesa (17x20cm-7x8in) i. verso bromide silver gelatin. 10-Jun-4 Villa Grisebach, Berlin #1257/R est:2500-3000
£4348 $7130 €6000 Building in Essen Gelsenkirchen mining area (23x17cm-9x7in) i. verso vintage silver gelatin. 30-May-3 Villa Grisebach, Berlin #1320/R est:3000-4000
£7222 $13000 €10544 Landungsbrucken Hambug, Schiffsrumpf (27x37cm-11x15in) num.339 gelatin silver print. 23-Apr-4 Phillips, New York #8/R est:20000-30000

RENGETSU, Otagaki (1791-1875) Japanese
Works on paper
£950 $1587 €1387 White chrysanthemums (97x30cm-38x12in) s.i. ink col. 12-Nov-3 Christie's, London #22/R

RENGGLI, Eduard (1882-1939) Swiss
£294 $500 €429 Horse carts in old town (48x61cm-19x24in) s. 28-Nov-3 Zofingen, Switzerland #3132 (S.FR 650)

RENGGLI, Jean (19/20th C) Swiss
£294 $500 €429 French landscape (54x65cm-21x26in) s.i.d.1889. 28-Nov-3 Zofingen, Switzerland #3133 (S.FR 650)
£415 $755 €606 River landscape in autumn (52x69cm-20x27in) s. 16-Jun-4 Fischer, Luzern #2321/R (S.FR 950)
£1035 $1852 €1511 Children auction (46x60cm-18x24in) s.d.1879. 26-May-4 AB Stockholms Auktionsverk #2380/R (S.KR 14000)

RENGIFO, Cesar (1915-1980) Venezuelan
£351 $560 €512 Untitled (20x25cm-8x10in) s. cardboard. 16-Mar-3 Subastas Odalys, Caracas #32
£359 $575 €524 Untitled (23x18cm-9x7in) s. cardboard. 16-Mar-3 Subastas Odalys, Caracas #16

£5459 $9280 €7970 Rural scene (82x97cm-32x38in) s. painted 1963. 23-Nov-3 Subastas Odalys, Caracas #36/R est:12000
£6011 $10940 €9017 Landscape at dusk (82x97cm-32x38in) s. painted 1963. 21-Jun-4 Subastas Odalys, Caracas #24/R est:13000
Works on paper
£350 $560 €511 Untitled (15x12cm-6x5in) s. crayon. 21-Sep-3 Subastas Odalys, Caracas #42
£380 $600 €555 Untitled (47x29cm-19x11in) s. ink. 27-Apr-3 Subastas Odalys, Caracas #23
£735 $1250 €1073 Landscape (31x37cm-12x15in) s. ink exec.1982. 23-Nov-3 Subastas Odalys, Caracas #58/R
£1097 $1700 €1602 Figure (46x29cm-18x11in) s. mixed media. 3-Nov-2 Subastas Odalys, Caracas #21/R
£1416 $2605 €2124 Untitled (38x27cm-15x11in) s. mixed media exec.1975. 27-Jun-4 Subastas Odalys, Caracas #75

RENI, Guido (1575-1642) Italian
£20000 $36000 €29200 Chris crowned with thorns (61x50cm-24x20in) i.verso prov. 21-Apr-4 Christie's, London #78/R est:20000-30000
Works on paper
£9868 $18158 €15000 Madonna enthroned with angels, landscape beyond (26x17cm-10x7in) pen ink W/C prov.exhib. 22-Jun-4 Sotheby's, Milan #32/R est:15000-18000

RENI, Guido (after) (1575-1642) Italian
£6643 $11294 €9500 Portrait of a girl, wearing white headdress (61x47cm-24x19in) prov. 25-Nov-3 Hamilton Osborne King, Dublin #279/R

RENI, Guido (attrib) (1575-1642) Italian
Works on paper
£317 $507 €450 Seated Maria Magdalena (52x43cm-20x17in) i. verso chl lit. 19-Sep-3 Karlheinz Kaupp, Staufen #1896/R

RENI, Guido (circle) (1575-1642) Italian
£15232 $27874 €23000 Une sainte martyre (111x83cm-44x33in) oval. 7-Apr-4 Libert, Castor, Paris #8/R est:10000-12000

RENI, Guido (school) (1575-1642) Italian
£6667 $11933 €10000 Madonn ain adoration of the Child (72x95cm-28x37in) 17-May-4 Finarte Semenzato, Rome #94/R est:12000-14000

RENI, Guido (studio) (1575-1642) Italian
£47222 $85000 €68944 Saint Sebastian (79x62cm-31x24in) prov.lit. 23-Jan-4 Christie's, Rockefeller NY #45/R est:50000-70000
£88692 $158758 €129490 Apostle (66x50cm-26x20in) Russian mono. verso. 25-May-4 Bukowskis, Stockholm #428/R est:50000-60000 (S.KR 1200000)

RENI, Guido (style) (1575-1642) Italian
£4913 $8500 €7173 Portrait of a sybil (122x91cm-48x36in) 13-Dec-3 Sloans & Kenyon, Bethesda #800/R est:7000-9000
£6500 $11700 €9490 Saint John the Baptist (70x55cm-28x22in) prov. 20-Apr-4 Sotheby's, Olympia #323/R est:4000-6000
£6960 $12041 €10162 Charity (128x92cm-50x36in) 9-Dec-3 Sotheby's, Olympia #378/R est:2000-3000
£8054 $14819 €12000 Adam and Eve (80x105cm-31x41in) 29-Mar-4 Pandolfini, Florence #772 est:10000
£8392 $14014 €12000 Salomon designe comme successeur de David par Nathan (71x94cm-28x37in) 27-Jun-3 Millon & Associes, Paris #20/R est:7000-9000

RENICA, Giovanni (1808-1884) Italian
£9000 $16380 €13500 Wood (60x88cm-24x35in) s. 12-Jul-4 Il Ponte, Milan #517/R est:12000-13000
£12667 $23053 €19000 Mount Grigna on Lake Como (60x88cm-24x35in) s. 12-Jul-4 Il Ponte, Milan #507/R est:12000-13000
£20000 $36400 €30000 Mendrisio, Switzerland (66x90cm-26x35in) 12-Jul-4 Il Ponte, Milan #513 est:14000-15000

RENIE, Jean Émile (1835-1910) French
£1765 $3000 €2577 Peasant woman herding turkeys in a wooded setting (89x62cm-35x24in) s. panel. 19-Nov-3 Bonhams & Butterfields, San Francisco #99/R

RENISON, William (fl.1920`s) British
£260 $486 €380 Glen Finnan Peaks (28x35cm-11x14in) s. 25-Feb-4 Mallams, Oxford #173/R
£280 $493 €409 Lowestoft (30x24cm-12x9in) 20-May-4 Bonhams, Edinburgh #322

RENNER, Paul (1957-) Austrian
Works on paper
£382 $638 €550 Arsch-dreh-tritt (16x25cm-6x10in) s.i.d.1982-84 board. 24-Oct-3 Ketterer, Hamburg #1039/R

RENNER, Paul Friedrich August (1878-1956) German
£280 $502 €409 Lake shore in summer (48x70cm-19x28in) s. 12-May-4 Dobiaschofsky, Bern #3859 (S.FR 650)

RENNIE, George Melvin (1874-1953) British
£302 $556 €441 Morning, Loch Eck, Argyllshire (50x75cm-20x30in) s. s.i.verso. 9-Jun-4 Walker's, Ottawa #348/R (C.D 750)
£669 $1212 €977 High Corrie, Isle of Arran (40x61cm-16x24in) s. i.verso prov. 1-Apr-4 Heffel, Vancouver #85/R (C.D 1600)
£720 $1202 €1051 Loch Coruisk (70x91cm-28x36in) s. 23-Oct-3 Bonhams, Edinburgh #319
£950 $1748 €1387 Balmoral Castle from the Dee (25x36cm-10x14in) s. 10-Jun-4 Lyon & Turnbull, Edinburgh #127

RENNIE, John Barry (20th C) Canadian
Works on paper
£313 $538 €457 Hepatica in forest (49x37cm-19x15in) s.d.37 W/C. 2-Dec-3 Joyner Waddington, Toronto #378/R (C.D 700)

RENNO, Rosangela (1963-) Brazilian
£6667 $12267 €10000 Vicious circles. Candelaria (67x7cm-26x3in) acrylic film exec.1995 prov. 10-Jun-4 Christie's, Paris #96/R est:6500-8000

RENOIR, Pierre Auguste (1841-1919) French
£2888 $5314 €4216 Femme au - ladies with hat (24x21cm-9x8in) s. drypoint. 29-Mar-4 Rasmussen, Copenhagen #59/R est:10000-12000 (D.KR 32000)
£6044 $11000 €8824 Esquisse de paysage (8x10cm-3x4in) canvas on panel lit. 29-Jun-4 Sotheby's, New York #333/R est:12000-16000
£16000 $29120 €23360 Paysage (9x27cm-4x11in) st.sig. canvas on panel lit. 21-Jun-4 Bonhams, New Bond Street #1/R est:12000-15000
£16043 $30000 €23423 Paysage a Cagnes (6x14cm-2x6in) st.init. canvas on board prov.lit. 25-Feb-4 Christie's, Rockefeller NY #12/R est:14000-18000
£17401 $29581 €25405 Paysage aux environs d'Essoyes (32x41cm-13x16in) s. 5-Nov-3 Dobiaschofsky, Bern #889/R est:47000 (S.FR 39500)
£18000 $33120 €26280 Jeune fille (10x7cm-4x3in) s. prov.lit. 22-Jun-4 Sotheby's, London #220/R est:15000-20000
£18662 $32285 €26500 Le chemin ombrage (16x16cm-6x6in) mono. 10-Dec-3 Remi Ader, Paris #65/R est:30000-35000
£18662 $32285 €26500 Le chemin ombrage (16x16cm-6x6in) mono. lit. 10-Dec-3 Neret-Minet, Paris #65/R est:30000-35000
£20000 $36800 €29200 Nu allonge (11x18cm-4x7in) painted 1910-12 prov.exhib. 22-Jun-4 Sotheby's, London #219/R est:14000-18000
£38000 $60420 €55100 Femme nue assise (24x22cm-9x9in) 11-Sep-3 Christie's, Kensington #12/R est:25000-35000
£38000 $69160 €55480 Paysage de Cagnes (16x29cm-6x11in) st.sig. prov.lit. 3-Feb-4 Christie's, London #119/R est:30000-50000
£39106 $70000 €57095 Maison dans les arbres (19x26cm-7x10in) lit. 6-May-4 Doyle, New York #58/R est:60000-80000
£40000 $72800 €58400 Jeune femme debout (34x23cm-13x9in) s. painted 1895 prov.lit. 4-Feb-4 Sotheby's, London #214/R est:25000-35000
£43575 $78000 €63620 Fillettes (24x16cm-9x6in) s. painted c.1905-1907 prov.lit. 5-May-4 Christie's, Rockefeller NY #221/R est:60000-80000
£44118 $75000 €64412 La mer (17x27cm-7x11in) st.sig. painted 1895 prov.lit. 5-Nov-3 Christie's, Rockefeller NY #204/R est:40000-60000
£47486 $85000 €69330 Paysage (32x20cm-13x8in) indis.s. prov. 5-May-4 Christie's, Rockefeller NY #243/R est:100000-150000
£48035 $87424 €70131 Paysage a Cagnes-sur-Mer (18x27cm-7x11in) s. painted c.1910. 18-Jun-4 Kornfeld, Bern #135/R est:125000 (S.FR 110000)
£50279 $90000 €73407 Un de deux panneaux pour l'Oedipe - Oedipus Rex (96x36cm-38x14in) st.sig. painted c.1896 prov.exhib.lit. 6-May-4 Sotheby's, New York #237/R est:60000-80000
£53333 $95467 €80000 Baigneuse nue de dos (23x13cm-9x5in) prov.lit. 15-May-4 Van Ham, Cologne #868/R est:195000
£55866 $100000 €81564 Un de deux panneaux pour l'Oedipe - Jocasta (96x36cm-38x14in) st.sig. painted c.1895 prov.exhib.lit. 6-May-4 Sotheby's, New York #236/R est:60000-80000
£61453 $110000 €89721 Femme nue couchee (20x32cm-8x13in) st.sig. painted 1898 prov.lit. 6-May-4 Sotheby's, New York #234/R est:120000-180000
£79310 $131655 €115000 Nature morte aux roses (18x32cm-7x13in) s.lit. 2-Oct-3 Sotheby's, Paris #117/R est:100000
£80000 $147200 €116800 Paysage, Magagnosc (27x38cm-11x15in) s. prov. 22-Jun-4 Sotheby's, London #120/R est:60000-80000
£81560 $132128 €115000 Woman seated (28x19cm-11x7in) s. 20-May-3 Ansorena, Madrid #163/R est:115000
£85000 $154700 €124100 Esquisse de fleurs (25x28cm-10x11in) st.sig. painted c.1914 prov.lit. 3-Feb-4 Christie's, London #131/R est:80000-90000
£88235 $150000 €128823 Tete de femme (37x30cm-15x12in) s. prov.lit. 6-Nov-3 Sotheby's, New York #140/R est:150000-200000
£93103 $154552 €135000 Nature morte aux fruits (19x29cm-7x11in) s. lit. 2-Oct-3 Sotheby's, Paris #118/R est:120000
£94972 $170000 €138659 Tete de jeune femme (27x22cm-11x9in) st.sig. painted 1890 prov.lit. 5-May-4 Christie's, Rockefeller NY #219/R est:150000-200000
£110000 $202400 €160600 Barriere en foret (35x27cm-14x11in) s. painted c.1878 prov.lit. 22-Jun-4 Sotheby's, London #113/R est:120000-160000
£111765 $190000 €163177 Paysage (34x46cm-13x18in) s. painted 1915 prov.lit. 6-Nov-3 Sotheby's, New York #108/R est:200000-300000
£114525 $205000 €167207 Deux femmes dans un paysage (23x29cm-9x11in) s. prov. 6-May-4 Sotheby's, New York #220/R est:80000-120000
£115000 $209300 €167900 Jeune fille lisant (29x26cm-11x10in) s. painted 1904. 3-Feb-4 Christie's, London #113/R est:120000-180000
£117647 $200000 €171765 Tete de femme (35x41cm-14x16in) s. prov. 6-Nov-3 Sotheby's, New York #123/R est:200000-300000
£120000 $218400 €175200 La Poudrerie de La Rochelle (32x41cm-13x16in) s. prov. 3-Feb-4 Christie's, London #133/R est:120000-160000
£122905 $220000 €179441 Trees, autumn (45x66cm-18x26in) s. prov.lit. 5-May-4 Christie's, Rockefeller NY #236/R est:220000-280000
£147059 $250000 €214706 Buste de jeune fille (29x24cm-11x9in) s. painted 1913 prov. 6-Nov-3 Sotheby's, New York #133/R est:200000-300000
£156425 $280000 €228381 Bordighera, Italy (28x43cm-11x17in) st.sig. painted c.1888 prov.lit. 4-May-4 Christie's, Rockefeller NY #16/R est:300000-500000
£167598 $300000 €244693 Esquisse de Jugement de Paris (55x65cm-22x26in) st.sig. painted 1913 prov.lit. 5-May-4 Christie's, Rockefeller NY #240/R est:300000-400000
£170000 $312800 €248200 Bouquet de roses (35x38cm-14x15in) s. prov. 22-Jun-4 Sotheby's, London #112/R est:100000-150000
£178771 $320000 €261006 Maison de la poste a Cagnes (32x46cm-13x18in) s. painted 1907 prov.lit. 5-May-4 Christie's, Rockefeller NY #231/R est:180000-250000
£206704 $370000 €301788 Villa a Cagnes (30x43cm-12x17in) s. painted c.1910-12 prov.exhib. 6-May-4 Sotheby's, New York #223a/R est:400000-600000
£230000 $423200 €335800 Femme lisant (31x23cm-12x9in) st.sig. painted 1906 prov.exhib.lit. 22-Jun-4 Sotheby's, London #144/R est:120000-150000
£235294 $400000 €343529 Deux jeunes femmes dans un paysage (40x46cm-16x18in) st.sig. painted c.1916 prov.lit. 6-Nov-3 Sotheby's, New York #126/R est:400000-600000
£240000 $441600 €350400 Baigneuse nue assis au bord de la mer (81x65cm-32x26in) s. paper on canvas painted 1882 prov.lit. 22-Jun-4 Sotheby's, London #119/R est:250000-350000
£240000 $441600 €350400 Les nefliers (46x55cm-18x22in) s. prov.exhib. 23-Jun-4 Christie's, London #133/R est:250000-350000
£240223 $430000 €350726 Filette a la poupee (40x31cm-16x12in) st.sig. painted c.1897 prov.lit. 5-May-4 Christie's, Rockefeller NY #214/R est:350000-450000

£246667	$453867	€370000	Jeune fille a l'arbre (46x38cm-18x15in) s. 9-Jun-4 Le Roux & Morel, Paris #32/R est:270000-300000
£250000	$455000	€365000	Vue de prise des collettes, cagnes (28x46cm-11x18in) s. painted c.1910-11 prov.lit. 4-Feb-4 Sotheby's, London #208/R est:150000-200000
£270000	$496800	€394200	La ferme des Collettes, Cagnes (41x54cm-16x21in) s. painted 1910 prov.exhib. 23-Jun-4 Christie's, London #108/R est:250000-350000
£279330	$500000	€407822	Femme en rouge et blanc couchee dans l'herbe (33x41cm-13x16in) st.sig. painted 1918-19 prov.exhib. 4-May-4 Christie's, Rockefeller NY #7/R est:500000-700000
£307263	$550000	€448604	Portrait d'Andree penchee (41x35cm-16x14in) st.sig. painted c.1917 prov.lit. 5-May-4 Christie's, Rockefeller NY #227/R est:500000-700000
£341176	$580000	€498117	La baigneuse (41x32cm-16x13in) s. prov.lit. 4-Nov-3 Christie's, Rockefeller NY #24/R est:600000-900000
£430168	$770000	€628045	Mare aux oies (54x65cm-21x26in) s.d.98 prov.exhib.lit. 6-May-4 Sotheby's, New York #215/R est:400000-600000
£502793	$900000	€734078	Jeune femme a l'ombrelle (25x19cm-10x7in) mono. painted 1872 prov.lit. 6-May-4 Sotheby's, New York #125/R est:900000-1200000
£544118	$925000	€794412	Deux femmes avec des chapeaux a fleurs (56x52cm-22x20in) s. painted c.1915 prov.lit. 6-Nov-3 Sotheby's, New York #113/R est:400000-600000
£600000	$1092000	€876000	Belle cabaretiere (81x65cm-32x26in) s.d.1895 prov.exhib.lit. 21-Jun-4 Sotheby's, London #47/R est:600000-800000
£642458	$1150000	€937989	Liseuse (41x32cm-16x13in) s.d.77 prov.exhib.lit. 5-May-4 Sotheby's, New York #14/R est:1000000-1500000
£698324	$1250000	€1019553	Foret de Marly (65x55cm-26x22in) painted c.1895 prov.exhib. 5-May-4 Sotheby's, New York #11/R est:700000-900000
£705882	$1200000	€1030588	Gabrielle au Collier vert (56x48cm-22x19in) s. painted 1905 prov.lit. 5-Nov-3 Sotheby's, New York #13/R est:1250000-1750000
£823529	$1400000	€1202352	Les enfants au bord de la mer (56x46cm-22x18in) s. painted 1894 prov.exhib.lit. 4-Nov-3 Christie's, Rockefeller NY #13/R est:1200000-1600000
£2737430	$4900000	€3996648	Jeunes filles aux lilas (55x46cm-22x18in) s. painted c.1890 prov.exhib.lit. 6-May-4 Sotheby's, New York #123/R est:4000000-6000000
£3600000	$6552000	€5256000	Jeune femme se baignant (81x65cm-32x26in) s.d.88 prov.exhib.lit. 21-Jun-4 Sotheby's, London #8/R est:3500000-5000000

Prints

£1613	$3000	€2355	Claude Renoir, tourne a gauche (13x12cm-5x5in) lithograph. 2-Mar-4 Swann Galleries, New York #551/R est:2500-3500
£1765	$3000	€2577	Les laveuses (47x61cm-19x24in) lithograph exec.c.1912. 6-Nov-3 Swann Galleries, New York #420/R est:3000-5000
£1882	$3200	€2748	Le chapeau epingle (13x10cm-5x4in) st.sig. drypoint. 6-Nov-3 Swann Galleries, New York #415a/R est:3500-5000
£2000	$3680	€3000	Paul Cezanne (26x24cm-10x9in) lithograph exec.1902. 10-Jun-4 Piasa, Paris #204
£2059	$3500	€3006	Maternite (55x49cm-22x19in) lithograph. 4-Nov-3 Christie's, Rockefeller NY #201/R est:4000-6000
£2113	$3655	€3000	Etude pour une baigneuse (22x16cm-9x6in) drypoint vellum exec.c.1906. 11-Dec-3 Piasa, Paris #143
£2119	$3750	€3094	Maternite, grande planche (49x50cm-19x20in) lithograph. 30-Apr-4 Sotheby's, New York #219/R est:2000-3000
£2349	$4322	€3500	L'enfant au biscuit (32x26cm-13x10in) lithograph. 26-Mar-4 Ketterer, Hamburg #208/R est:3000-4000
£2349	$4322	€3500	Les laveuses (46x61cm-18x24in) lithograph. 26-Mar-4 Ketterer, Hamburg #209/R est:2500-3500
£2353	$4000	€3435	Les laveuses (47x60cm-19x24in) lithograph. 6-Nov-3 Swann Galleries, New York #421/R est:3000-5000
£2400	$4128	€3504	Maternite (59x75cm-23x30in) black grey lithograph edition of 200 exec.c.1912. 4-Dec-3 Sotheby's, London #215/R est:2000-3000
£2535	$4386	€3600	Baigneuse assise (22x14cm-9x6in) vernis mou vellum exec.c.1897. 11-Dec-3 Piasa, Paris #141
£2600	$4732	€3796	Une mere et deux enfants (34x45cm-13x18in) lithograph exec.c.1912. 1-Jul-4 Sotheby's, London #290 est:2500-3000
£2606	$4508	€3700	Odalisque (8x12cm-3x5in) lithograph exec.c.1904. 11-Dec-3 Piasa, Paris #148
£2657	$4571	€3800	Une mere et deux enfants (34x44cm-13x17in) lithograph. 2-Dec-3 Hauswedell & Nolte, Hamburg #562/R est:2000
£2775	$5079	€4052	Woman bathing, seated (22x13cm-9x5in) s. vernis mou etching. 9-Jun-4 Rasmussen, Copenhagen #2072/R est:20000 (D.KR 31000)
£2841	$5000	€4148	Maternite (53x48cm-21x19in) s. lithograph. 23-May-4 Hindman, Chicago #102/R est:5000-7000
£2973	$5500	€4341	Maternite (50x48cm-20x19in) black grey lithograph exec.c.1912. 12-Feb-4 Christie's, Rockefeller NY #401/R est:3500-4500
£3333	$6133	€5000	Chapeau epingle (16x10cm-6x4in) i. drypoint exec.1894. 10-Jun-4 Piasa, Paris #200
£3824	$6500	€5583	Maternite (51x49cm-20x19in) col lithograph exec.c.1912. 6-Nov-3 Swann Galleries, New York #419/R est:7000-10000
£4412	$7500	€6442	Enfants jouant a la balle (89x62cm-35x24in) lithograph. 31-Oct-3 Sotheby's, New York #450/R
£4483	$7487	€6500	La danse a la campagne (22x13cm-8x5in) s. i.verso varnish vellum exec.c.1890. 9-Jul-3 Tajan, Paris #337 est:4000-5000
£5085	$9000	€7424	Jeune femme en buste (63x49cm-25x19in) grey black lithograph executed c.1899. 30-Apr-4 Sotheby's, New York #218/R est:12000-16000
£5163	$9500	€7538	La danse a la campagne (22x13cm-9x5in) st.sig. soft ground etching exec.c.1890. 8-Jun-4 Auctions by the Bay, Alameda #1047/R
£5294	$9000	€7729	Danse a la campagne (33x25cm-13x10in) st.sig. etching. 4-Nov-3 Christie's, Rockefeller NY #199/R est:7000-10000
£5367	$9500	€7836	La danse a la campagne (22x13cm-9x5in) st.sig. soft-ground etching exec.c.1890. 28-Apr-4 Christie's, Rockefeller NY #232/R est:8000-12000
£5548	$9432	€8100	Enfant au biscuit. lithograph. 6-Nov-3 Piasa, Paris #144a/R
£5588	$9500	€8158	Danse a la campagne (22x14cm-9x6in) st.sig. etching. 31-Oct-3 Sotheby's, New York #449/R
£5588	$9500	€8158	L'enfant au biscuit, Jean Renoir (32x27cm-13x11in) col lithograph edition of 100. 6-Nov-3 Swann Galleries, New York #408/R est:12000-18000
£5658	$10411	€8600	La danse a la campagne (23x25cm-9x10in) vernis mou exec. c.1890. 25-Jun-4 Daguerre, Paris #45/R est:4000-4500
£5986	$10356	€8500	Le chapeau epingle (60x49cm-24x19in) black lithograph exec.c.1897 edition of 200. 11-Dec-3 Piasa, Paris #145/R
£6333	$11337	€9500	La danse a la campagne (22x14cm-9x6in) st.sig. vernis mou. 13-May-4 Bassenge, Berlin #5639/R est:4500
£6425	$11500	€9381	La danse a la campagne (22x14cm-9x6in) st.sig. soft ground etching. 6-May-4 Swann Galleries, New York #316/R est:7000-10000
£6690	$11574	€9500	La danse a la campagne (22x14cm-9x6in) vernis mou exec.c.1890. 11-Dec-3 Piasa, Paris #139/R
£7667	$14107	€11500	Chapeau epingle (60x49cm-24x19in) lithograph exec.1897. 10-Jun-4 Piasa, Paris #203/R
£8945	$14938	€12970	Jeune femme en buste - Mademoiselle Dieterle. lithograph. 19-Jun-3 Kornfeld, Bern #901/R est:20000 (S.FR 19500)
£36000	$65520	€52560	Le chapeau epingle (62x49cm-24x19in) col lithograph exec.c.1898. 1-Jul-4 Sotheby's, London #291/R est:28000-32000
£36620	$63352	€52000	Le chapeau epingle (60x49cm-24x19in) col lithograph edition of 200 exec.c.1898. 11-Dec-3 Piasa, Paris #146/R
£38000	$69160	€55480	Le chapeau epingle (61x50cm-24x20in) lithograph. 30-Jun-4 Christie's, London #318/R est:30000-50000
£39548	$70000	€57740	Le chapeau epingle (60x49cm-24x19in) s. col lithograph edition of 200 exec.c.1898. 28-Apr-4 Christie's, Rockefeller NY #233/R est:50000-80000
£40000	$72800	€58400	Enfants jouant a la balle (90x62cm-35x24in) col lithograph edition of 200. 1-Jul-4 Sotheby's, London #292/R est:42000-48000
£55000	$100100	€80300	Le chapeau epingle (90x62cm-35x24in) second sig. col lithograph edition of 200. 1-Jul-4 Sotheby's, London #293/R est:55000-65000

Sculpture

£5882	$11000	€8588	Tete de Coco (22x22cm-9x9in) st.sig. pat bronze Cast Valsuani prov.lit. 25-Feb-4 Christie's, Rockefeller NY #16/R est:5000-7000
£6906	$12500	€10083	Aline (24cm-9in) bronze. 30-Mar-4 Arroyo, Buenos Aires #40
£8500	$14705	€12410	Buste de la maternite, variante (23cm-9in) s.st.f.Susse green brown pat bronze conceived 1913 cast c.1940. 11-Dec-3 Christie's, Kensington #4/R est:8000-12000
£12941	$22000	€18894	Tete de Coco (27cm-11in) i.num.H.C.11/VI brown pat bronze st.f.C.Valsuani prov.lit. 6-Nov-3 Sotheby's, New York #127/R est:15000-20000

Works on paper

£8000	$14720	€12000	Portrait of a girl (29x23cm-11x9in) st.sig. blk chk prov.exhib. 8-Jun-4 Sotheby's, Amsterdam #60/R est:12000-15000
£8257	$13789	€11973	Vue du Port de Martigues (20x16cm-8x6in) W/C over pencil. 19-Jun-3 Kornfeld, Bern #900/R est:20000 (S.FR 18000)
£9000	$16380	€13140	Vue du port des Martigues (20x16cm-8x6in) W/C pencil exec.1888. 4-Feb-4 Sotheby's, London #404/R est:10000-15000
£18500	$30895	€27010	Bord de mer Mediterranean (13x24cm-5x9in) init. gouache W/C red ink. 21-Oct-3 Sotheby's, London #4/R est:12000-15000
£22000	$40480	€32120	Gabrielle (31x25cm-12x10in) s. sanguine buff paper prov. 24-Jun-4 Christie's, London #324/R est:15000-20000
£26028	$44247	€38000	Peches (16x30cm-6x12in) s. W/C over crayon prov. 6-Nov-3 Tajan, Paris #214/R
£38000	$69160	€55480	Cabanon et l'olivier (20x24cm-8x9in) with sig. W/C exec 1889-1895 prov.exhib. 5-Feb-4 Christie's, London #304/R est:28000-32000
£70175	$129123	€102456	Jeunes filles jouant a la balle (60x51cm-24x20in) pastel paper on board prov.exhib.lit. 23-Jun-4 Koller, Zurich #3023/R est:160000-240000 (S.FR 160000)
£82000	$150880	€119720	Femme nue assise (43x34cm-17x13in) s. sanguine prov. 24-Jun-4 Christie's, London #327/R est:50000-70000
£83916	$144336	€120000	Portrait of a lady (48x41cm-19x16in) s. pastel prov. 5-Dec-3 Ketterer, Munich #35/R est:120000-150000
£89385	$160000	€130502	Yole (32x48cm-13x19in) W/C prov.lit. 5-May-4 Sotheby's, New York #19/R est:70000-90000
£162011	$290000	€236536	Liseuse (59x46cm-23x18in) s.i. chl htd pastel paper on board prov.exhib. 4-May-4 Christie's, Rockefeller NY #6/R est:300000-400000
£260000	$473200	€379600	Femme nue se coiffant (61x47cm-24x19in) s. pastel prov.lit. 3-Feb-4 Sotheby's, London #35/R est:200000-300000
£312849	$560000	€456760	Danse (22x14cm-9x6in) init. pastel crayon exec.1883 prov.exhib.lit. 6-May-4 Sotheby's, New York #126/R est:200000-300000

RENOIR, Pierre Auguste and GUINO, Richard (19/20th C) French

Sculpture

£6587	$11000	€9617	La petite laveuse (27cm-11in) s.num.2/I brown pat bronze st.f.Valsuani lit. 7-Oct-3 Sotheby's, New York #256 est:10000-15000
£6800	$11356	€9928	Head of Venus (14cm-6in) i. bronze num.HCII/IV st.f.Valsuani cire perdue. 22-Oct-3 Sotheby's, Olympia #22/R est:7000-9000
£11765	$20000	€17177	Buste de Madame Renoir (58cm-23in) i. num.11/20 conceived c.1916-17 st.f.Valsuani lit. 6-Nov-3 Sotheby's, New York #106/R est:25000-35000
£15882	$27000	€23188	Buste de Madame Renoir (60cm-24in) st.sig. num.20/20 blk pat bronze st.f.Valsuani prov.lit. 5-Nov-3 Christie's, Rockefeller NY #232/R est:22000-28000

RENOM, Miguel (?) Spanish

£253	$470	€369	Big and small (45x60cm-18x24in) s. cardboard. 14-Mar-4 Subastas Odalys, Caracas #43/R
£452	$700	€660	Landscape (45x61cm-18x24in) s. cardboard. 3-Nov-2 Subastas Odalys, Caracas #86

RENOUARD, George A (1885-1954) American

£323	$600	€472	Bergen homestead, April 8th 1928 (20x25cm-8x10in) s. verso. 6-Mar-4 Page, Batavia #101
£376	$700	€549	Untitled (51x61cm-20x24in) canvasboard. 6-Mar-4 Page, Batavia #25
£447	$800	€653	Snowy road with houses (36x46cm-14x18in) s. 7-May-4 Sloans & Kenyon, Bethesda #1714/R
£511	$950	€746	Girl visiting grandpa. board. 6-Mar-4 Page, Batavia #90
£753	$1400	€1099	Seascape (61x76cm-24x30in) 6-Mar-4 Page, Batavia #127
£1359	$2500	€1984	The fishing fleet (50x61cm-20x24in) s. 8-Jun-4 Bonhams & Butterfields, San Francisco #4056/R est:3000-5000

RENOUARD, Paul Charles (1845-1924) French

Works on paper

£800	$1448	€1200	Danseuses (28x43cm-11x17in) mono. crayon. 3-Apr-4 Gerard, Besancon #8

RENOUART, Georges (19/20th C) French

£300	$546	€438	Parisian boulevard (50x70cm-20x28in) s.i. board. 16-Jun-4 Christie's, Kensington #75/R

RENOUF, Edda (1943-) ?

£352	$609	€500	Two inch rows (22x22cm-9x9in) s.i.d.1943 verso acrylic prov. 15-Dec-3 Charbonneaux, Paris #259

Works on paper

£254	$425	€371	Water sounds 1 (176x50cm-69x20in) chk. 19-Oct-3 Bonhams & Butterfields, Los Angeles #7082
£615	$1100	€898	Letter te (33x33cm-13x13in) s.i.d.1975 pencil pastel chk prov. 16-May-4 Wright, Chicago #386/R
£838	$1500	€1223	Letter S (33x33cm-13x13in) s.i.d.1975 pencil pastel chk prov. 16-May-4 Wright, Chicago #479/R est:1000-1500
£1117	$2000	€1631	Sound drawing (33x33cm-13x13in) s.i.d.1975 pencil pastel chk prov. 16-May-4 Wright, Chicago #478/R est:1000-1500

£1453 $2600 €2121 Incised lines and pastel (33x33cm-13x13in) s.i.d.1975 pencil pastel chk prov. 16-May-4 Wright, Chicago #475/R est:1000-1500

RENOUF, Émile (1845-1894) French
£805 $1498 €1200 Sous bois (82x66cm-32x26in) s. 7-Mar-4 Lesieur & Le Bars, Le Havre #119
£966 $1612 €1400 Plage du Havre (65x81cm-26x32in) s.d.1875. 11-Nov-3 Lesieur & Le Bars, Le Havre #93

RENOUX, Andre (1939-) French
£486 $792 €700 Vue du 19 rue Michel Ange (55x38cm-22x15in) s. i.d.1970 verso. 29-Sep-3 Charbonneaux, Paris #272

RENOUX, Charles (1795-1846) French
£3521 $6162 €5000 Personnages dans des ruines romaines (24x34cm-9x13in) s.d.1828. 17-Dec-3 Piasa, Paris #103/R est:4000-6000

RENOUX, Jules Ernest (1863-1932) French
£807 $1300 €1170 Chateau walkway (41x61cm-16x24in) s. 23-Aug-3 Harvey Clar, Oakland #1385
£1100 $1947 €1606 Place de L'Etoile entree de L'Avenue de Bois (27x35cm-11x14in) s.i.verso. 27-Apr-4 Bonhams, Knightsbridge #105/R est:400-600
£1330 $2381 €1942 Le Pont Royal (46x55cm-18x22in) s. 25-May-4 Bukowskis, Stockholm #375/R est:20000-25000 (S.KR 18000)
£1500 $2655 €2190 Avenue des Champs Elysees et Arc de Triomphe (38x46cm-15x18in) s. i.verso. 27-Apr-4 Bonhams, Knightsbridge #102/R est:600-800

RENQVIST, Torsten (1924-) Swedish
£806 $1426 €1177 Cretensisk island I (50x68cm-20x27in) init.d.62 panel exhib. 27-Apr-4 AB Stockholms Auktionsverk #918/R (S.KR 11000)
£1737 $2953 €2536 Composition (48x70cm-19x28in) init.d.52. 5-Nov-3 AB Stockholms Auktionsverk #725/R est:15000-18000 (S.KR 23000)
Sculpture
£1088 $1958 €1588 Scull of a pike (27cm-11in) init. bronze Cast Bergman exhib.lit. 26-Apr-4 Bukowskis, Stockholm #276/R est:10000-12000 (S.KR 15000)
£1160 $2088 €1694 Bird in flight (38cm-15in) init. bronze Cast Bergman. 26-Apr-4 Bukowskis, Stockholm #278/R est:2000-3000 (S.KR 16000)
£4396 $7780 €6418 Prayer (24x9x24cm-9x4x9in) init.d.68 carved wood lit. 27-Apr-4 AB Stockholms Auktionsverk #914/R est:40000-50000 (S.KR 60000)
Works on paper
£1832 $3242 €2675 Landscape with fragment (120x100cm-47x39in) init.d.60 collage mixed media canvas exhib. 27-Apr-4 AB Stockholms Auktionsverk #915/R est:25000-30000 (S.KR 25000)

RENSBURG, Eugène (1872-1956) Dutch
Works on paper
£685 $1164 €1000 Hague shopping street, Kingsday 1938 (52x35cm-20x14in) s.d.1938 W/C. 5-Nov-3 Vendue Huis, Gravenhage #199/R
£733 $1313 €1100 View of the market and town hall of Middelburg with many figures (58x78cm-23x31in) s.d.1926 W/C. 11-May-4 Vendu Notarishuis, Rotterdam #50/R

RENSHAW, Art (20th C) American
£1098 $1900 €1603 Hunters (23x40cm-9x16in) s. masonite prov.lit. 10-Dec-3 Bonhams & Butterfields, San Francisco #6125/R est:2500-3500

RENTERIA, Horacio (1912-1972) Mexican
£1392 $2547 €2032 View of Chimalistac (28x33cm-11x13in) s. masonite. 27-Jan-4 Louis Morton, Mexico #279/R est:32000-40000 (M.P 28000)
£3056 $5195 €4462 Girl with dog (67x54cm-26x21in) s. 30-Oct-3 Louis Morton, Mexico #54/R est:60000-70000 (M.P 58000)
£10615 $19000 €15498 Girl by church. Girl holding budgie (60x45cm-24x18in) pair. 26-May-4 Sotheby's, New York #70/R est:12000-18000

RENTINCK, Jan (1798-1846) Dutch
£1958 $3329 €2800 Still life with fish, vegetables, fishing nets and kitchen items (27x34cm-11x13in) s.d.1830 panel. 20-Nov-3 Van Ham, Cologne #1816/R est:1800

RENTZELL, August von (1810-1891) German
£372 $654 €550 Monk in monastery entrance (16x12cm-6x5in) s.d.1854 panel. 22-May-4 Lempertz, Koln #1589
£833 $1358 €1200 Woman with goats by water in mountains (25x37cm-10x15in) s.d.1850. 26-Sep-3 Bolland & Marotz, Bremen #600/R est:1400

RENUCCI, Renuccio (1880-1947) Italian
£704 $1232 €1000 Boat and anglers (27x36cm-11x14in) s. board. 17-Dec-3 Il Ponte, Milan #818
£986 $1706 €1400 Marsh (16x26cm-6x10in) board. 9-Dec-3 Pandolfini, Florence #272 est:1100-1200
£1014 $1664 €1400 Back from fishing. Sunset (30x40cm-12x16in) s.i.verso board pair. 27-May-3 Finarte Semenzato, Milan #157/R
£1133 $2085 €1700 Marsh (29x35cm-11x14in) s. board. 11-Jun-4 Farsetti, Prato #431/R est:1600-1900

RENVALL, Essi (1911-1979) Finnish
Works on paper
£282 $451 €400 Saying prayers (62x48cm-24x19in) s.d.59 mixed media. 21-Sep-3 Bukowskis, Helsinki #437/R

RENZI, Grace (1922-) American/French
£267 $485 €400 Idee du voyage I (90x116cm-35x46in) s. painted 1953. 5-Jul-4 Millon & Associes, Paris #288
£300 $546 €450 Songe marin (147x185cm-58x73in) painted 1956. 5-Jul-4 Millon & Associes, Paris #296
£300 $546 €450 De memoire (91x150cm-36x59in) painted 1953. 5-Jul-4 Millon & Associes, Paris #292
£300 $546 €450 Genie des jardins (92x123cm-36x48in) s. painted 1956. 5-Jul-4 Millon & Associes, Paris #290
£300 $546 €450 Coeur leger (90x107cm-35x42in) s. painted 1954. 5-Jul-4 Millon & Associes, Paris #287
£300 $546 €450 Intramuros (109x63cm-43x25in) s. painted 1956. 5-Jul-4 Millon & Associes, Paris #282/R
£400 $728 €600 Jardin persan (149x181cm-59x71in) s. painted 1956. 5-Jul-4 Millon & Associes, Paris #297
£667 $1213 €1000 Tropique (89x116cm-35x46in) s. painted 1954. 5-Jul-4 Millon & Associes, Paris #289
£733 $1335 €1100 Untitled (145x88cm-57x35in) panel painted 1956 triptych. 5-Jul-4 Millon & Associes, Paris #91/R

RENZONI, Louis (1952-) American?
Works on paper
£450 $811 €657 Composition with figures (76x56cm-30x22in) mixed media two. 26-Jan-4 Lilla Bukowskis, Stockholm #571 (S.KR 6000)

REOL, Marie Marguerite (1880-1963) French
£1338 $2342 €1900 Portrait de Louis Desire Lucas (55x46cm-22x18in) 21-Dec-3 Thierry & Lannon, Brest #202/R est:1200-1500
Works on paper
£563 $1053 €850 Portrait de Desire Lucas (55x46cm-22x18in) s. chl. 24-Jul-4 Thierry & Lannon, Brest #45

REPELIUS, Betsy (1848-1921) Dutch
£748 $1362 €1100 Valsch geblasen, amateur musicians (46x60cm-18x24in) s. 3-Feb-4 Christie's, Amsterdam #55 est:800-1200

REPETTO, Armando E (1893-1968) Argentinian
£714 $1300 €1042 Cupid's circle (14x20cm-6x8in) s. cardboard. 29-Jun-4 Arroyo, Buenos Aires #23/R
£1117 $2000 €1631 Landscape (23x34cm-9x13in) on palette. 11-May-4 Arroyo, Buenos Aires #82
£1374 $2500 €2006 Marsh (50x60cm-20x24in) s. 5-Jul-4 Arroyo, Buenos Aires #67/R est:2300
£2033 $3700 €2968 Composition (50x60cm-20x24in) s.d.59. 5-Jul-4 Arroyo, Buenos Aires #94/R est:1800
£3571 $6500 €5214 Dusk (22x33cm-9x13in) s.d.58 cardboard. 29-Jun-4 Arroyo, Buenos Aires #6/R est:2500
£5587 $10000 €8157 Castano Lucero (70x50cm-28x20in) s.i. s.i.d.1963 verso. 4-May-4 Arroyo, Buenos Aires #100/R est:2600

REPIN, Ilia (1844-1930) Russian
£8392 $14266 €12000 Portrait of lady (94x76cm-37x30in) s.d.1874. 29-Nov-3 Bukowskis, Helsinki #413/R est:12000-15000
£9000 $15300 €13500 Summer landscape (14x23cm-6x9in) i. board. 25-Nov-3 Christie's, London #173/R est:10000-12000
£22436 $35000 € Portrait of the painter Antti Faven (65x55cm-26x22in) s.cyrillic d.1922. 11-Apr-3 Christie's, Rockefeller NY #32/R est:30000-40000
£50000 $85000 €75000 Portrait of General Aleksei Nikolaevich Kuropatkin (26x22cm-10x9in) i. canvas on board exhib. 25-Nov-3 Christie's, London #160/R est:10000-15000
£70513 $110000 € Portrait of Fedor Gustavovich Terner (52x42cm-20x17in) s.cyrillic exhib.lit. 11-Apr-3 Christie's, Rockefeller NY #31/R est:60000-90000
£100000 $170000 €150000 Blind candura player (113x78cm-44x31in) s.d.1918 exhib. 25-Nov-3 Christie's, London #155/R est:35000-45000
Works on paper
£743 $1330 €1100 The glance (15x9cm-6x4in) s. pencil. 8-May-4 Bukowskis, Helsinki #456/R
£1351 $2419 €2000 Man with hat (17x10cm-7x4in) s. pencil. 8-May-4 Bukowskis, Helsinki #451/R est:2000-2500
£1600 $2720 €2400 Portrait of woman (16x12cm-6x5in) s. pencil. 25-Nov-3 Christie's, London #156/R est:2000-3000
£1689 $3024 €2500 Soldier (18x12cm-7x5in) s.d.1886 pencil. 8-May-4 Bukowskis, Helsinki #454/R est:1500-2000
£1690 $2924 €2400 Departure (17x25cm-7x10in) s. pencil. 13-Dec-3 Hagelstam, Helsinki #49/R est:2000
£1923 $3000 € Figures on the Nevskii Prospect in St Petersburg (29x40cm-11x16in) s.cyrillic i.verso chl exhib. 11-Apr-3 Christie's, Rockefeller NY #17/R est:3000-4500
£1944 $3208 €2800 Seated beggar (27x17cm-11x7in) s. brush over pencil. 2-Jul-3 Neumeister, Munich #483/R est:800
£2027 $3628 €3000 Salome (28x20cm-11x8in) s.d.1893 pencil. 8-May-4 Bukowskis, Helsinki #450/R est:3000-3500
£2162 $3870 €3200 The cossack (16x10cm-6x4in) s.d.1887 pencil. 8-May-4 Bukowskis, Helsinki #452/R est:1500-2000
£2162 $3870 €3200 Feodor Shaliapin (31x22cm-12x9in) s. pencil. 8-May-4 Bukowskis, Helsinki #455/R est:1200-1800
£3000 $4800 €4350 Reclining boy (35x26cm-14x10in) s. pen ink. 18-Sep-3 Christie's, Kensington #182/R est:1200-1800
£3673 $6576 €5400 Etude de bottine. Etude d'un ornament (18x10cm-7x4in) one i. graphite two one sheet. 17-Mar-4 Maigret, Paris #107/R est:600-800
£4000 $6800 €6000 Portrait of man, facing right (37x27cm-15x11in) i. pencil W/C. 25-Nov-3 Christie's, London #174/R est:4000-6000
£4353 $7400 €6355 Young woman sitting (23x18cm-9x7in) s.d.1892 W/C. 1-Dec-3 Ben-Ami, Tel Aviv #4360/R est:10000-13000
£5101 $9131 €7550 Mr Sasonov (30x22cm-12x9in) s. W/C pair. 8-May-4 Bukowskis, Helsinki #475/R est:3000-3500
£5282 $9137 €7500 Forest pond (23x32cm-9x13in) s.d.1878 W/C. 13-Dec-3 Hagelstam, Helsinki #48/R est:2000
£9000 $15300 €13140 Study of peasant boy and man. Study of two hands (23x20cm-9x8in) s.d.1871 pencil double-sided. 19-Nov-3 Sotheby's, London #32/R est:3000-5000

REPIN, Ilia (attrib) (1844-1930) Russian
£4582 $8203 €6690 The cossack (65x48cm-26x19in) bears sig. 26-May-4 AB Stockholms Auktionsverk #2444/R est:25000-30000 (S.KR 62000)

Works on paper
£423 $731 €600 Barge haulers on the Volga (28x38cm-11x15in) s. pencil. 13-Dec-3 Hagelstam, Helsinki #50/R
£1333 $2387 €2000 Man wearing blue coat (40x30cm-16x12in) s.d.1879 W/C. 15-May-4 Hagelstam, Helsinki #40/R est:2000

REPIN, Yuri Ilich (1877-1954) Russian
£1329 $2259 €1900 View over Helsinki (40x50cm-16x20in) s.d.1952. 29-Nov-3 Bukowskis, Helsinki #424/R est:2500-2800
£2703 $4838 €4000 Bridge over the Aura river (29x27cm-11x11in) s. canvas on board. 8-May-4 Bukowskis, Helsinki #461/R est:2000-2500

REPOUX, Claude Marie (1782-1868) French
£800 $1440 €1200 Paysage avec des moines (103x141cm-41x56in) d.1856. 25-Apr-4 Daniel Herry, Beaune #127

REPPEN, Jack (20th C) Canadian
Works on paper
£223 $384 €326 Untitled (27x45cm-11x18in) s.d.62 mixed media collage. 2-Dec-3 Joyner Waddington, Toronto #467 (C.D 500)
£280 $512 €409 View of Flin Flon (120x60cm-47x24in) s. inids.d. collage board. 1-Jun-4 Joyner Waddington, Toronto #222/R (C.D 700)

REPPEN, John Richard (1933-1964) Canadian
Works on paper
£261 $486 €381 Untitled (76x63cm-30x25in) s.d.63 mixed media board. 2-Mar-4 Ritchie, Toronto #184/R (C.D 650)

REPTON, Humphrey (1752-1818) British
Works on paper
£2600 $4654 €3796 North east view of Sall Church in Norfolk (12x18cm-5x7in) s.i.d.Dec 23 1779 monochrome wash. 22-Mar-4 Bonhams & Brooks, Norfolk #151/R est:1000-1500

REQUENA, Jose (20th C) Venezuelan
£245 $450 €368 Valley (30x40cm-12x16in) s. painted 1996. 27-Jun-4 Subastas Odalys, Caracas #21
£329 $560 €480 Camuri Grande (50x40cm-20x16in) s. painted 1976. 23-Nov-3 Subastas Odalys, Caracas #27/R
£771 $1310 €1126 Margarita (30x40cm-12x16in) s. painted 1975. 23-Nov-3 Subastas Odalys, Caracas #78
£882 $1500 €1288 Cuesta de Lara (60x74cm-24x29in) s. cardboard painted 1958. 23-Nov-3 Subastas Odalys, Caracas #5/R

REQUICHOT, Bernard (1929-1961) French
£2431 $3840 €3500 Traces graphiques (90x60cm-35x24in) masonite prov. 27-Apr-3 Versailles Encheres #122

RERBERG, Fedor Ivanovich (1865-1938) Russian
Works on paper
£278 $500 €406 Landscape (26x26cm-10x10in) mixed media. 24-Apr-4 Shishkin Gallery, Moscow #3/R

RESCALLI, Don Angelo (1884-c.1956) Italian
£1304 $2139 €1800 Autumn in Val Susa (33x23cm-13x9in) s. board. 27-May-3 Finarte Semenzato, Milan #9/R
£2536 $4159 €3500 Snowfall in Val Susa (42x33cm-17x13in) s. board. 27-May-3 Finarte Semenzato, Milan #21/R

RESCH, Joseph (1819-1901) German
£604 $1111 €900 Schloss Altenburg (35x52cm-14x20in) panel. 24-Mar-4 Hugo Ruef, Munich #1080/R

RESCHI, Pandolfo (1643-1699) Polish
£6500 $11700 €9490 Commander giving orders after a battle (47x67cm-19x26in) 22-Apr-4 Sotheby's, London #97/R est:5000-7000
£12752 $23846 €19000 Landscape with waterfall (104x143cm-41x56in) 29-Feb-4 Finarte, Venice #23/R est:16000-18000
£15172 $25338 €22000 Rocky landscape (73x61cm-29x24in) 12-Nov-3 Sotheby's, Milan #115/R est:20000-30000

RESCHI, Pandolfo (circle) (1643-1699) Polish
£3889 $7000 €5678 Travelers in an extensive landscape (89x115cm-35x45in) pair. 21-Jan-4 Sotheby's, New York #100/R est:6000-8000

RESCHIGNA, Gianlorenzo (1897-) Italian
£1127 $1949 €1600 Lake Maggiore (49x68cm-19x27in) s.i. board. 9-Dec-3 Pandolfini, Florence #261/R est:1000-1100

RESCHREITER, Rudolf (1868-?) German
£685 $1164 €1000 Dolomites - evening panorama (24x34cm-9x13in) s. tempera gouache lit. 8-Nov-3 Hans Stahl, Toestorf #16/R
Works on paper
£433 $780 €650 Farmstead in high mountains (39x28cm-15x11in) s. mixed media lit. 22-Apr-4 Allgauer, Kempten #3422/R

RESEN-STEENSTRUP, J (1868-1921) Danish
£469 $867 €685 Man with horse and cart, foal next to them (64x95cm-25x37in) mono. 15-Mar-4 Rasmussen, Vejle #468/R (D.KR 5200)

RESENDE, Julio (1917-) Portuguese
£10738 $19221 €16000 Figures (50x61cm-20x24in) s.d.1961 board. 31-May-4 Cabral Moncada Leiloes, Lisbon #88b/R est:16000-24000
Works on paper
£6711 $12013 €10000 Women (63x47cm-25x19in) s. mixed media. 31-May-4 Cabral Moncada Leiloes, Lisbon #88a/R est:6000-9000

RESHETNIKOV, Fyodor (1906-1989) Russian
£1229 $2200 €1794 The painter's wife, Lidia Brodskaya (70x49cm-28x19in) canvas on cardboard painted 1950's. 29-May-4 Shishkin Gallery, Moscow #36/R est:3000-4000

RESNICK, Milton (1917-2004) American
£1757 $3250 €2565 Untitled (38x43cm-15x17in) s.d.58 board prov. 10-Mar-4 Doyle, New York #66/R est:2500-3500
£1757 $3250 €2565 Untitled (66x51cm-26x20in) s.d.59 oil paper on board prov. 10-Mar-4 Doyle, New York #67/R est:2500-3500
£3631 $6500 €5301 Untitled (42x40cm-17x16in) s.d.56 ms. prov. 6-May-4 Doyle, New York #98/R est:2500-3500
£4469 $8000 €6525 Untitled (53x58cm-21x23in) s.d.58 s.d.verso prov. 6-May-4 Doyle, New York #94/R est:3000-5000
£6111 $11000 €8922 Straw 43 (40x30cm-16x12in) s.d.1982 verso corrguated board prov. 24-Apr-4 David Rago, Lambertville #160/R est:4000-6000
£8000 $14560 €11680 Untitled (87x56cm-34x22in) s.d.59 canvas on board prov. 4-Feb-4 Sotheby's, Olympia #191/R est:5000-7000
£24540 $40000 €35828 Untitled (264x179cm-104x70in) s.d.1959 verso prov. 23-Sep-3 Christie's, Rockefeller NY #22/R est:10000-15000
Works on paper
£2222 $4000 €3244 Untitled (24x18cm-9x7in) gouache. 24-Apr-4 David Rago, Lambertville #465/R est:800-1200

RESTELLI, Mario (1861-?) Italian
Sculpture
£1087 $1783 €1500 Pelican (28cm-11in) s. silver. 27-May-3 Il Ponte, Milan #365
£1087 $1783 €1500 Flamingo. s. silver. 27-May-3 Il Ponte, Milan #383
£1377 $2258 €1900 Monkey (40cm-16in) s. silver. 27-May-3 Il Ponte, Milan #375

RESTELLINI, Giampiero (1895-?) Italian
£278 $458 €400 Study for Saint Joseph (47x37cm-19x15in) s.d.1952 i.verso board. 1-Jul-3 Il Ponte, Milan #817
£362 $594 €500 Summer (30x24cm-12x9in) s.d.1960 i.verso board. 27-May-3 Il Ponte, Milan #885
£507 $832 €700 Light snowfall (30x25cm-12x10in) s.d.955 i.verso. 27-May-3 Il Ponte, Milan #870/R
£521 $859 €750 Arianna (29x23cm-11x9in) s.d.1955 i.verso board. 1-Jul-3 Il Ponte, Milan #780

RESTOUT, Jean (younger-attrib) (1692-1768) French
£1867 $3379 €2800 Vierge en buste (79x57cm-31x22in) 2-Apr-4 Rossini, Paris #29/R est:3000-4000
Works on paper
£2096 $3815 €3060 Tete de Christ (39x33cm-15x13in) chl prov. 16-Jun-4 Fischer, Luzern #2544 est:300-500 (S.FR 4800)

RETH, Alfred (1884-1966) French
£350 $594 €500 Portrait de femme (57x43cm-22x17in) s. oil paper prov. 23-Nov-3 Cornette de St.Cyr, Paris #304
£629 $1070 €900 Paysage aux chevaux (21x27cm-8x11in) s. cardboard on canvas prov. 23-Nov-3 Cornette de St.Cyr, Paris #303
£769 $1308 €1100 Paysage (39x33cm-15x13in) s.d.1961 prov. 23-Nov-3 Cornette de St.Cyr, Paris #293
£867 $1560 €1300 Carriole attelee dans une rue (55x46cm-22x18in) s. 26-Apr-4 Tajan, Paris #138 est:1500-2000
£946 $1788 €1400 Paysage cubiste (65x50cm-26x20in) s.d.1961 panel. 21-Feb-4 Cornette de St.Cyr, Paris #219/R
£1351 $2554 €2000 Baigneuse (33x46cm-13x18in) st.sig. panel. 21-Feb-4 Cornette de St.Cyr, Paris #218/R est:1800-2000
£1400 $2506 €2100 Paysage au marais (65x100cm-26x39in) s. 16-May-4 Feletin, Province #88
£1743 $2911 €2527 Abstract composition (100x74cm-39x29in) s.d.39 paper on board. 23-Jun-3 Philippe Schuler, Zurich #3570 est:3500-4000 (S.FR 3800)
£2215 $3964 €3300 Composition (60x50cm-24x20in) s.d.1960 oil collage. 30-May-4 Eric Pillon, Calais #271/R
£2308 $3923 €3300 Belle Isle, Morbihan (40x29cm-16x11in) s. panel collage prov. 23-Nov-3 Cornette de St.Cyr, Paris #292 est:300-400
£2349 $4370 €3500 Terrasse de cafe (38x32cm-15x13in) s. 3-Mar-4 Tajan, Paris #138/R est:2500-3000
£3846 $6538 €5500 Le palais, Belle Ile, Morbihan (62x51cm-24x20in) panel painted c.1914. 23-Nov-3 Cornette de St.Cyr, Paris #295 est:600-800
£5395 $9926 €8200 Portrait de Madame Renaud (100x81cm-39x32in) s. painted 1912. 24-Jun-4 Credit Municipal, Paris #59 est:8000-10000
£7042 $12183 €10000 Sans titre (123x245cm-48x96in) s. oil mixed media collage sand gravel panel. 14-Dec-3 Versailles Encheres #90/R est:8000-10000
£14355 $24834 €20958 Great lying nude (96x126cm-38x50in) painted c.1913. 12-Dec-3 Kieselbach, Budapest #201/R (H.F 5500000)
Works on paper
£310 $574 €450 Composition (28x22cm-11x9in) s.d.18 mars 1962 pencil. 13-Feb-4 Charbonneaux, Paris #70
£310 $574 €450 Composition (15x11cm-6x4in) init. pencil exec.c.1962. 13-Feb-4 Charbonneaux, Paris #71
£315 $535 €450 A Grandville (19x30cm-7x12in) s. graphite prov. 23-Nov-3 Cornette de St.Cyr, Paris #296/R
£315 $535 €450 Une jeune fille juive chez elle (31x20cm-12x8in) s. crayon chl prov. 23-Nov-3 Cornette de St.Cyr, Paris #307

£350	$594	€500	Abstraction (30x24cm-12x9in) s.d.1950 graphite prov. 23-Nov-3 Cornette de St.Cyr, Paris #298
£361	$603	€520	Sans titre (22x18cm-9x7in) s. gouache. 25-Oct-3 Cornette de St.Cyr, Paris #796
£385	$654	€550	Composition (30x19cm-12x7in) s.d.26 decembre 1926 graphite prov. 23-Nov-3 Cornette de St.Cyr, Paris #297
£417	$679	€600	Composition (31x23cm-12x9in) s.d.1950 ink crayon sand. 18-Jul-3 Charbonneaux, Paris #229
£626	$1120	€920	Composition geometrique (40x29cm-16x11in) s. graphite chl gouache ink collage exhib. 22-Mar-4 Digard, Paris #109/R
£1343	$2497	€2000	Untitled (61x50cm-24x20in) s.d.60 mixed media collage panel prov. 3-Mar-4 Tajan, Paris #140 est:1500-2000
£1408	$2437	€2000	Composition (32x42cm-13x17in) s. mixed media collage sand exec.c.1950 prov.exhib.lit. 14-Dec-3 Versailles Encheres #104/R est:2000-2500
£1667	$2783	€2400	Composition (120x243cm-47x96in) s.d.57 mixed media panel. 23-Oct-3 Credit Municipal, Paris #83 est:4000-5000
£1678	$3138	€2500	Sans titre (79x63cm-31x25in) s.d.1962 mixed media collage panel. 29-Feb-4 Versailles Encheres #184/R est:2000-3000
£1736	$2899	€2500	Harmonie de matieres (162x23cm-64x9in) s.d.1955 i.verso gouache sand panel wood particles. 25-Oct-3 Cornette de St.Cyr, Paris #797 est:800-1000
£1736	$2899	€2500	Composition (200x153cm-79x60in) s. mixed media panel. 23-Oct-3 Credit Municipal, Paris #82/R est:3000-3800
£1879	$3326	€2800	Composition (73x53cm-29x21in) s. W/C crayon. 28-Apr-4 Artcurial Briest, Paris #267 est:3000-4000
£2237	$4116	€3400	Composition (120x243cm-47x96in) s.d.57 mixed media panel. 24-Jun-4 Credit Municipal, Paris #58/R est:2000-3000
£2778	$4639	€4000	Composition (120x243cm-47x96in) s.d.57 mixed media panel. 23-Oct-3 Credit Municipal, Paris #80 est:6000-7500
£2797	$4755	€4000	Composition (40x31cm-16x12in) bears sig. mixed media paper on panel prov. 23-Nov-3 Cornette de St.Cyr, Paris #305/R est:300-400
£3067	$5643	€4600	Composition abstraite (60x45cm-24x18in) s.d.58 mixed media sand pigment paper on panel. 10-Jun-4 Camard, Paris #89/R est:2000-2500
£3194	$5335	€4600	Composition (243x120cm-96x47in) s.d.57 mixed media panel. 23-Oct-3 Credit Municipal, Paris #81/R est:6000-7500
£4500	$8280	€6570	Untitled (50x30cm-20x12in) s. plaster paint sand wood relief. 24-Jun-4 Sotheby's, Olympia #511/R est:4000-6000
£7832	$13315	€11200	Composition (100x100cm-39x39in) s.d.1964 mixed media panel prov. 23-Nov-3 Cornette de St.Cyr, Paris #294/R est:800-1000

RETH, Caspar von (1858-1913) German

£909	$1545	€1300	Three puppies playing (28x39cm-11x15in) s.d.1889 canvas on board. 20-Nov-3 Van Ham, Cologne #1815/R
£1562	$2656	€2250	Hunting dogs (38x48cm-15x19in) s.d.1891 one of pair. 28-Oct-3 Dorotheum, Vienna #12/R est:2400-2800
£1562	$2656	€2250	Hunting dogs (38x48cm-15x19in) s.d.1891 one of pair. 28-Oct-3 Dorotheum, Vienna #13/R est:2400-2800

RETHEL, Alfred (1816-1859) German

£1958	$3368	€2800	Taking leave of Dusseldorf (15x10cm-6x4in) mono.i. 5-Dec-3 Bolland & Marotz, Bremen #620/R est:1500

RETI, Istvan Stefan (1872-1945) Hungarian

£2610	$4515	€3811	Landscape in Nagybanya (55x68cm-22x27in) s.d.922. 12-Dec-3 Kieselbach, Budapest #14/R (H.F 1000000)

RETS, Jean (1910-1998) Belgian

£952	$1705	€1400	Ancien escalier menant a l'eglise Saint Jean (60x48cm-24x19in) s. i.verso. 17-Mar-4 Hotel des Ventes Mosan, Brussels #170
£1667	$3067	€2500	Untitled (50x70cm-20x28in) s.d.62. 8-Jun-4 Sotheby's, Amsterdam #251/R est:2500-3500
£2098	$3608	€3000	Composition circulaire (90x118cm-35x46in) s.d.62. 8-Dec-3 Horta, Bruxelles #44 est:1500-2000
£3380	$5848	€4800	Tamo (125x95cm-49x37in) s.d.64 s.i.d.1964 verso. 13-Dec-3 De Vuyst, Lokeren #576/R est:5000-6000
£4027	$7128	€6000	Crisna (120x120cm-47x47in) s.d.1967. 27-Apr-4 Campo, Vlaamse Kaai #562/R est:4800-5200
Works on paper			
£524	$876	€750	Composition (38x57cm-15x22in) s.d.69 gouache ink. 11-Oct-3 De Vuyst, Lokeren #315
£738	$1307	€1100	Composition (32x24cm-13x9in) s. gouache exec. 1967. 27-Apr-4 Campo, Vlaamse Kaai #561

RETT, Gustav (1889-1969) German

£274	$466	€400	High moorland with snow covered Allgau mountains (60x75cm-24x30in) panel lit. 6-Nov-3 Allgauer, Kempten #3551/R

RETTICH, Karl Lorenz (1841-1904) German

£2119	$3857	€3200	On the coast by Bordighera, Italy (39x60cm-15x24in) s.i. 18-Jun-4 Bolland & Marotz, Bremen #731/R est:2000

RETTIG, Heinrich (1859-1921) German

£271	$486	€396	Alpine landscape with lake (88x120cm-35x47in) s.d.1901. 10-May-4 Rasmussen, Vejle #174/R (D.KR 3000)

RETTIG, John (1860-1932) American

£938	$1500	€1369	Red interior (61x51cm-24x20in) s.i.d.1906. 19-Sep-3 Freeman, Philadelphia #77/R est:800-1200
£5814	$10000	€8488	Costume ball (66x91cm-26x36in) s.d.1915. 7-Dec-3 Treadway Gallery, Cincinnati #503/R est:10000-15000

RETTIG, Martin (20th C) American

£328	$600	€479	Roses (30x38cm-12x15in) s. board painted c.1940. 5-Jun-4 Treadway Gallery, Cincinnati #566/R

RETZLAFF, Ernst Carl Walter (1898-1976) German

£707	$1245	€1032	Mountainous landscape (70x100cm-28x39in) s. 23-May-4 Agra, Warsaw #45/R (P.Z 5000)

RETZSCH, Friedrich Moritz August (1779-1857) German

£313	$509	€450	Boy with lyre standing on swan (27x38cm-11x15in) i. verso panel. 25-Sep-3 Dr Fritz Nagel, Stuttgart #1303/R

REUMERT, Niels (1949-) Danish

£332	$531	€481	Monkey and mask (130x82cm-51x32in) s.d.84/85 verso. 17-Sep-3 Kunsthallen, Copenhagen #138 (D.KR 3500)
£473	$846	€691	Portrait - composition (66x54cm-26x21in) s.d.1988 verso. 12-Jan-4 Rasmussen, Vejle #603/R (D.KR 5000)
£1354	$2491	€1977	Drama (98x167cm-39x66in) s.d.89 verso prov. 29-Mar-4 Rasmussen, Copenhagen #428/R est:12000 (D.KR 15000)

REUS, Ankie de (1940-) Dutch

Works on paper			
£278	$439	€400	Untitled (52x42cm-20x17in) s.d.1999 gouache collage. 26-Apr-3 Auction Maastricht #89/R

REUSCH, Helga Ring (1865-1944) Norwegian

£813	$1455	€1187	Setting up the loom (25x21cm-10x8in) s. panel. 28-May-4 Uppsala Auktionskammare, Uppsala #159/R (S.KR 11000)
£1223	$2190	€1786	He is sorting his stamps (44x30cm-17x12in) s.d.1907 i.verso canvas on panel lit. 25-May-4 Grev Wedels Plass, Oslo #25/R est:15000-20000 (N.KR 15000)

REUSING, Fritz (1874-?) German

£433	$793	€650	Portrait of a man (152x77cm-60x30in) s.d.1927. 5-Jun-4 Arnold, Frankfurt #700
£733	$1335	€1100	Car driver (89x108cm-35x43in) s.d.1912. 30-Jun-4 Neumeister, Munich #651

REUTER, Einar (1881-?) Italian

£1189	$2021	€1700	Standing female nude holding fruit dish (101x50cm-40x20in) s. 20-Nov-3 Van Ham, Cologne #1818/R est:2500

REUTER, Elisabeth (1853-1903) German

£1043	$1732	€1523	View of the harbour (56x38cm-22x15in) s.d.97 canvas on plywood. 15-Jun-3 Agra, Warsaw #33/R est:5000 (P.Z 6500)

REUTER, Willem (attrib) (1642-1681) Flemish

£2416	$4446	€3600	Le repos des paysans devant une ferme et des ruines antiques (36x45cm-14x18in) 24-Mar-4 Tajan, Paris #74 est:2000-3000

REUTERDAHL, Henry (1871-1925) American/Swedish

Works on paper			
£307	$500	€448	Ship under the Aurora Borealis (20x25cm-8x10in) W/C gouache over pencil paper on board. 17-Jul-3 Doyle, New York #43/R

REUTERSWARD, Carl Fredrik (1934-) Swedish

£423	$719	€618	Spel Watteau (87x87cm-34x34in) s.d.1961-62 verso prov. 4-Nov-3 Bukowskis, Stockholm #291/R (S.KR 5600)
£906	$1541	€1323	Untitled (89x61cm-35x24in) s. tempera varnish paper on canvas. 5-Nov-3 AB Stockholms Auktionsverk #809/R (S.KR 12000)
£1662	$2825	€2427	Composition (116x154cm-46x61in) s. triptych. 4-Nov-3 Bukowskis, Stockholm #220/R est:25000-30000 (S.KR 22000)
Works on paper			
£1502	$2703	€2193	Abstract composition (201x139cm-79x55in) init. triptych W/C. 26-Jan-4 Lilla Bukowskis, Stockholm #633 est:25000-30000 (S.KR 20000)
£1538	$2723	€2245	De Kooning (90x65cm-35x26in) s. mixed media canvas. 27-Apr-4 AB Stockholms Auktionsverk #1129/R est:20000-25000 (S.KR 21000)

REUTERSWARD, Oscar (1915-2002) Swedish

£2393	$4307	€3494	Composition (93x73cm-37x29in) S. 26-Apr-4 Bukowskis, Stockholm #232/R est:12000-15000 (S.KR 33000)

REUTHER, Wolf (1917-) ?

£267	$477	€400	Rider/pianist (55x38cm-22x15in) sold with W/C. 13-May-4 Neumeister, Munich #750/R
£733	$1313	€1100	Horses (81x130cm-32x51in) s.d. verso. 13-May-4 Neumeister, Munich #749/R

REVEL, Gabriel (1642-1712) French

£11258	$20490	€17000	Saint Hubert (150x122cm-59x48in) mono. 20-Jun-4 Versailles Encheres #27/R est:15000-20000

REVENAUGH, Aurelius O (1840-1908) American

£1374	$2500	€2006	Portrait of a girl holding roses (92x67cm-36x26in) s. 29-Jun-4 Sotheby's, New York #201/R est:4000-6000

REVENGA SANCHO, Maria (1901-) Spanish

£1074	$1997	€1600	Seascape (47x53cm-19x21in) s. canvas on cardboard. 2-Mar-4 Ansorena, Madrid #206/R est:400

REVERON, Armando (1889-1954) Venezuelan

£86667	$159467	€130000	Self-portrait (93x63cm-37x25in) s.d.34 tempera oil paper on cardboard prov.exhib.lit. 10-Jun-4 Christie's, Paris #20/R est:80000-120000
Works on paper			
£4171	$7090	€6090	Figures (21x31cm-8x12in) s. chl. 23-Nov-3 Subastas Odalys, Caracas #153 est:6000

REVERON, Juanita (20th C) Venezuelan
Works on paper
£269 $450 €393 Self-portrait (48x40cm-19x16in) s. chl. 19-Oct-3 Subastas Odalys, Caracas #55

REVESZ, Andres (20th C) South American
£586 $920 €856 Coffee pot and onions (46x33cm-18x13in) painted 1969. 23-Nov-2 Subastas Odalys, Caracas #32
£593 $935 €866 Flowers (76x92cm-30x36in) painted 1955. 27-Apr-3 Subastas Odalys, Caracas #48

REVESZ, Imre (attrib) (1859-1945) Hungarian
£2282 $4085 €3400 Three girls on a garden bench (90x120cm-35x47in) s. 27-May-4 Dorotheum, Vienna #183/R est:4000-5000

REVILLA, Carlos (1940-) Peruvian
£1333 $2440 €2000 Vous qui avex fait des etudes dans les grandes universites (146x114cm-57x45in) s.d.70 verso. 7-Jun-4 Palais de Beaux Arts, Brussels #344/R est:2000-3000
£4698 $8315 €7000 Le divan d'arcier (130x200cm-51x79in) s.d.1972 verso exhib. 27-Apr-4 Campo, Vlaamse Kaai #562a/R est:5000-6000
Works on paper
£903 $1435 €1300 L'espace du dedans (114x146cm-45x57in) s.verso mixed media. 9-Sep-3 Palais de Beaux Arts, Brussels #264

REVILLE, H Whittaker (fl.1881-1903) British
£860 $1514 €1256 A Whitehorn cow in a stable (51x68cm-20x27in) s.d.1888. 18-May-4 Woolley & Wallis, Salisbury #155/R

REVOLD, Axel (1887-1962) Norwegian
£516 $831 €753 From Svolvaer (46x55cm-18x22in) s. exhib. 25-Aug-3 Blomqvist, Lysaker #1225 (N.KR 6000)
£1721 $3081 €2513 House by water (60x50cm-24x20in) init. 22-Mar-4 Blomqvist, Oslo #390/R est:15000-20000 (N.KR 21500)
£2135 $3565 €3117 Landscape (81x65cm-32x26in) s. 13-Oct-3 Blomqvist, Oslo #306/R est:20000-25000 (N.KR 25000)

REX, Oskar (1857-?) Austrian
£1200 $2184 €1800 Queen Marie Antoinette of France with guards (130x101cm-51x40in) s. canvas on panel. 30-Jun-4 Neumeister, Munich #652/R

REXACH, Juan (attrib) (c.1415-?) Spanish
£10870 $20000 €16305 Adoration of the Magi (91x91cm-36x36in) oil gilding cloth on panel prov.exhib. 8-Jun-4 Auctions by the Bay, Alameda #1028/R

REY SANTIAGO, Gabino (1928-) Spanish
£333 $540 €470 Marble mortar and pestle (66x81cm-26x32in) s. 20-May-3 Ansorena, Madrid #211/R

REY, Alphonse (1863-1938) French
Works on paper
£382 $603 €550 Les Saintes Maries de la mer. s.i. W/C. 25-Apr-3 Etude de Provence, Marseille #190

REY, Eduardo (20th C) South American
£239 $435 €359 Valley (40x80cm-16x31in) s. painted 2000. 21-Jun-4 Subastas Odalys, Caracas #36/R
£245 $445 €368 Roses (80x60cm-31x24in) s. painted 1997. 21-Jun-4 Subastas Odalys, Caracas #127
£253 $400 €369 Valley (40x78cm-16x31in) s. painted 2000. 1-Dec-2 Subastas Odalys, Caracas #103
£255 $470 €383 Roses (90x60cm-35x24in) s. painted 1997. 27-Jun-4 Subastas Odalys, Caracas #33
£411 $650 €600 Country club (76x122cm-30x48in) s. painted 2000. 1-Dec-2 Subastas Odalys, Caracas #104
£413 $690 €603 Country Club (76x122cm-30x48in) s. painted 2000. 19-Oct-3 Subastas Odalys, Caracas #126/R

REY, Paul Henri (1904-1981) French?
Sculpture
£1600 $2944 €2400 Totem la musique (110cm-43in) wood. 11-Jun-4 Piasa, Paris #20/R
£1600 $2944 €2400 Reve (240cm-94in) wood exhib. 11-Jun-4 Piasa, Paris #22/R

REY, Philippe (attrib) (18th C) French
£7042 $12324 €10000 Chantier naval (67x80cm-26x31in) pair. 17-Dec-3 Piasa, Paris #94/R est:8000-12000

REYCEND, Enrico (1855-1928) Italian
£4667 $8587 €7000 Spring harmonies (23x33cm-9x13in) s. cardboard. 14-Jun-4 Sant Agostino, Torino #304/R est:7000-9000
£5369 $9503 €8000 Seascape (24x32cm-9x13in) s. s.verso cardboard. 1-May-4 Meeting Art, Vercelli #253 est:8000
£7042 $12183 €10000 Landscape (43x47cm-17x19in) s. cardboard on canvas. 10-Dec-3 Sotheby's, Milan #64/R est:10000-15000
£9333 $17173 €14000 At the well (33x23cm-13x9in) board prov. 14-Jun-4 Sant Agostino, Torino #303/R est:14000-18000

REYES FERREIRA, Jesus (1882-1977) Mexican
Works on paper
£989 $1800 €1444 Rearing horse (74x48cm-29x19in) gouache gold paint. 29-Jun-4 Sotheby's, New York #667/R est:2500-3500
£4620 $8500 €6745 Child with her doll (74x48cm-29x19in) gouache. 10-Jun-4 Sotheby's, New York #263/R est:1500-2000

REYL, Frantisek (1910-) Czechoslovakian
£494 $919 €721 Girls at table (130x126cm-51x50in) s.d.31. 6-Mar-4 Dorotheum, Prague #118/R est:20000-30000 (C.KR 24000)

REYMANN, Joseph (19th C) French
£1200 $2208 €1752 Black rock at Boumerdes, Algeria (39x62cm-15x24in) s. 25-Mar-4 Christie's, Kensington #211/R est:1500-2000

REYMERSWAELE, Marinus van (attrib) (1493-1567) Dutch
£606 $1085 €885 Jesus with his followers (91x33cm-36x13in) panel prov. 22-Mar-4 Philippe Schuler, Zurich #6182 (S.FR 1400)
£10638 $17766 €15000 Cambiavalute (121x108cm-48x43in) i.verso. 18-Jun-3 Christie's, Rome #393 est:2000-3000

REYMERSWAELE, Marinus van (style) (1493-1567) Dutch
£8451 $14789 €12000 Collecteurs d'impots (92x73cm-36x29in) 17-Dec-3 Piasa, Paris #11/R est:3500-4500

REYMOND, Carlos (1884-1970) French
£400 $708 €584 Pink house (50x40cm-20x16in) init.d. 27-Apr-4 Bonhams, Knightsbridge #76/R
£845 $1479 €1200 Port de la Rochelle (38x46cm-15x18in) s. paper on canvas. 21-Dec-3 Thierry & Lannon, Brest #359
£2534 $4636 €3800 Marche au Maroc (58x79cm-23x31in) s. 3-Jun-4 Tajan, Paris #298/R est:3000-3500

REYNA, Antonio Maria de (1859-1937) Spanish
£872 $1597 €1300 Venice (25x15cm-10x6in) s. 12-Jul-4 Durán, Madrid #108/R
£872 $1597 €1300 Venice (19x14cm-7x6in) s. cardboard. 12-Jul-4 Durán, Madrid #137/R
£1200 $2148 €1800 Venice, La Misericordia (12x18cm-5x7in) s. cardboard on canvas. 12-May-4 Stadion, Trieste #769/R est:1200-1600
£2055 $3493 €3000 Venetian canal (31x17cm-12x7in) s.i. board. 4-Nov-3 Ansorena, Madrid #56/R est:2200
£4333 $7843 €6500 Patio (20x15cm-8x6in) s canvas on cardboard. 30-Mar-4 Segre, Madrid #103/R est:6500
£6579 $11908 €10000 Venice (20x35cm-8x14in) s. board. 14-Apr-4 Ansorena, Madrid #59/R est:10000
£8667 $15947 €13000 Venice, Rio San Polo (29x50cm-11x20in) s. 10-Jun-4 Christie's, Rome #104/R est:4000-6000
£11111 $21000 €16222 Grand Canal (35x75cm-14x30in) s. 22-Feb-4 Galeria y Remates, Montevideo #25/R est:7000-10000
£11184 $20579 €17000 View of La Salute. Palace in Venice (50x30cm-20x12in) one s. pair. 23-Jun-4 Finarte Semenzato, Rome #123/R est:15000-18000
£14000 $25760 €20440 On a Venetian backwater (74x34cm-29x13in) s.i. 23-Mar-4 Bonhams, New Bond Street #87/R est:10000-15000
£15845 $27729 €22500 Venetian canal (36x75cm-14x30in) s. 16-Dec-3 Durán, Madrid #210/R est:22500
£16304 $26739 €22500 Vista del Baccino de Venecia (34x70cm-13x28in) s. 27-May-3 Durán, Madrid #255/R est:22500
£16901 $29577 €24000 View of Venetian cana (34x74cm-13x29in) s.indis.d. 16-Dec-3 Segre, Madrid #86/R est:24000
£17361 $28299 €25000 Venetian canal (33x74cm-13x29in) s.i. 23-Sep-3 Durán, Madrid #182/R est:22500
£19366 $30986 €27500 View of church and canal in Venice (35x74cm-14x29in) s. 16-Sep-3 Segre, Madrid #92/R est:27500
£73826 $132148 €110000 Dusk in Venice (62x137cm-24x54in) s. 25-May-4 Durán, Madrid #219/R est:60000
Works on paper
£1447 $2620 €2200 View of Venice (32x20cm-13x8in) s. W/C. 14-Apr-4 Ansorena, Madrid #356/R est:1800

REYNA, Antonio Maria de (attrib) (1859-1937) Spanish
£326 $600 €476 Venezia (13x28cm-5x11in) bears sig.i. panel. 9-Jun-4 Doyle, New York #3023
£1056 $1827 €1500 Market in Naples (33x24cm-13x9in) canvas on cardboard. 11-Dec-3 Christie's, Rome #105a est:1500-2000

REYNARD, Grant (1887-1968) American
Works on paper
£301 $550 €439 Buildings in a mountain landscape (30x56cm-12x22in) s. W/C executed c.1950. 5-Jun-4 Treadway Gallery, Cincinnati #673/R

REYNAS, G (19/20th C) Spanish
£1940 $3472 €2832 Oriental carpet dealer (40x21cm-16x8in) s.i. 12-May-4 Dobiaschofsky, Bern #900/R est:1200 (S.FR 4500)

REYNDERS, Jan (1823-1889) Dutch
£2700 $4968 €3942 Dutch winter landscape with two ladies and a child in foreground (32x41cm-13x16in) s.d.1868 panel. 26-Mar-4 Bigwood, Stratford on Avon #305/R est:2000-3000

REYNE, Charles (?) French
£1477 $2732 €2200 Epagneul au bord de la mare (65x54cm-26x21in) s. 14-Mar-4 St-Germain-en-Laye Encheres #26/R est:2200-2500

REYNI, Ingalvur av (1920-) Icelandic
£993 $1827 €1450 Composition (35x40cm-14x16in) s.d.70. 29-Mar-4 Rasmussen, Copenhagen #254 (D.KR 11000)
£1173 $2159 €1713 Landscape near Torshavn, Justabour (50x70cm-20x28in) init. 29-Mar-4 Rasmussen, Copenhagen #263 est:4000 (D.KR 13000)
£2256 $4152 €3294 Girl (70x55cm-28x22in) s.d.70. 29-Mar-4 Rasmussen, Copenhagen #259/R est:10000 (D.KR 25000)
£2347 $4318 €3427 Village with mountains in background. s.d.81. 29-Mar-4 Rasmussen, Copenhagen #226/R est:12000 (D.KR 26000)
£2347 $4318 €3427 Coastal landscape, Torshavn (65x90cm-26x35in) s.d.72. 29-Mar-4 Rasmussen, Copenhagen #244/R est:15000-20000 (D.KR 26000)
£2708 $4982 €3954 Girl (130x100cm-51x39in) s.d.70. 29-Mar-4 Rasmussen, Copenhagen #258/R est:18000-20000 (D.KR 30000)
£2798 $5148 €4085 Composition (92x73cm-36x29in) S.D.99. 29-Mar-4 Rasmussen, Copenhagen #275/R est:12000-15000 (D.KR 31000)

REYNOLDS, Alan (1926-) British
£10000 $17200 €14600 Red winter leaf (26x34cm-10x13in) s.d.1954 board. 2-Dec-3 Bonhams, New Bond Street #152/R est:4000-6000
£10989 $20000 €16044 Structure - blue yellow black and white (53x60cm-21x24in) s. painted c.1964 board prov. 29-Jun-4 Sotheby's, New York #445/R est:4000-6000
Sculpture
£1500 $2730 €2190 Structures - Group II (93x140x1cm-37x55x0in) s.i.d.83 verso card wood base prov. 4-Feb-4 Sotheby's, Olympia #245/R est:800-1200
Works on paper
£1500 $2505 €2190 Abstract landscape (29x27cm-11x11in) s.d.59 W/C. 16-Oct-3 Christie's, Kensington #650/R est:1200-1800
£2300 $3979 €3358 Quiet landscape (51x61cm-20x24in) s.d.1957 W/C. 14-Dec-3 Desmond Judd, Cranbrook #1083
£3100 $5177 €4526 Hedgerow landscape (23x33cm-9x13in) d.1955 W/C. 16-Nov-3 Desmond Judd, Cranbrook #1024

REYNOLDS, Bernard (20th C) ?
Works on paper
£333 $600 €500 Maguire's field (63x50cm-25x20in) s. mixed media inspired by Patrick Kavanagh. 20-Apr-4 James Adam, Dublin #197/R
£400 $720 €600 Maguire (63x50cm-25x20in) s. mixed media inspired by Patrick Kavanagh. 20-Apr-4 James Adam, Dublin #196/R

REYNOLDS, Frederick George (1880-1932) Australian
£2069 $3228 €3000 Princess Bridge, Melbourne (86x147cm-34x58in) s.d.1915. 1-Aug-2 Joel, Victoria #263 est:6000-8000 (A.D 6000)

REYNOLDS, Frederick George (1828-1921) British
Works on paper
£732 $1310 €1069 Four double-sided landscapes (12x18cm-5x7in) mono. W/C double-sided four prov. 10-May-4 Joel, Victoria #419 est:1200-2000 (A.D 1800)

REYNOLDS, James (1926-) American
£2682 $4800 €3916 Hiding out (28x36cm-11x14in) board. 15-May-4 Altermann Galleries, Santa Fe #90/R
£10615 $19000 €15498 Give me a land where rains is rain (46x61cm-18x24in) board. 15-May-4 Altermann Galleries, Santa Fe #91/R

REYNOLDS, John (20th C) New Zealander
Works on paper
£1083 $1765 €1581 Abstract composition (50x129cm-20x51in) init.d.1986 pastel diptych. 23-Sep-3 Peter Webb, Auckland #114/R est:3000-5000 (NZ.D 3000)

REYNOLDS, Sir Joshua (1723-1792) British
£5587 $10000 €8157 Portrait of Sir Thomas Miller (77x63cm-30x25in) prov.lit. 27-May-4 Sotheby's, New York #271/R est:10000-15000
£7200 $12240 €10512 Portrait of Thomas Jaffray (74x62cm-29x24in) prov. 27-Nov-3 Sotheby's, London #143/R est:6000-8000
£10500 $19110 €15330 Portrait of Lionel Sackville, 1st Duke of Dorset (125x99cm-49x39in) 1-Jul-4 Sotheby's, London #120/R est:10000-15000
£12000 $20400 €17520 Portrait of a gentleman in a blue coat and a white stock (76x63cm-30x25in) prov. 29-Oct-3 Bonhams, New Bond Street #81/R est:2500-3500
£12667 $23180 €19000 Portrait de l'architecte Sir William Chambers (27x23cm-11x9in) cardboard. 3-Jun-4 E & Eve, Paris #34/R est:7000-8000
£15000 $25500 €21900 Portrait of John Lysaght, afterwards 2nd Lord Lisle (77x64cm-30x25in) init. prov.lit. 25-Nov-3 Christie's, London #31/R est:10000-15000
£15000 $27600 €21900 Portrait of Emma, countess of Mount Edgcumbe (62x52cm-24x20in) prov. 26-Mar-4 Sotheby's, London #25/R est:6000-8000
£16484 $30000 €24067 Portrait of King George III, full length seated in the Coronation Chair (239x148cm-94x58in) prov. 4-Feb-4 Christie's, Rockefeller NY #106/R est:10000-15000
£17000 $28900 €24820 Portrait of Mr Thomas wearing a red fur trimmed coat (74x61cm-29x24in) painted oval prov. 27-Nov-3 Sotheby's, London #163/R est:8000-12000
£17857 $32500 €26071 Portrait of George, Lord Vernon (77x63cm-30x25in) prov.exhib.lit. 29-Jun-4 Sotheby's, New York #57/R est:15000-20000
£30000 $54600 €43800 Portrait of John Simpson, of Bradley Hall, Northumberland (127x102cm-50x40in) prov.exhib.lit. 1-Jul-4 Sotheby's, London #121/R est:15000-20000
£44693 $80000 €65252 Portrait of Mrs Edmund Burke (76x62cm-30x24in) panel prov.lit. 27-May-4 Sotheby's, New York #240/R est:40000-60000
£65000 $110500 €94900 Portrait of the Hon Jane Sanford in a white and gold dress, in a landscape (102x127cm-40x50in) prov. 25-Nov-3 Christie's, London #33/R est:70000-100000
£66667 $120000 €97334 Portrait of Lord Robert Spencer (127x101cm-50x40in) prov.lit. 22-Jan-4 Sotheby's, New York #51/R est:150000-200000
£1150000 $1955000 €1679000 Portrait of Miss Hickey (73x60cm-29x24in) 27-Nov-3 Sotheby's, London #11/R est:500000-700000
£3000000 $5460000 €4380000 Portrait of Mrs Baldwin (141x110cm-56x43in) prov.exhib.lit. 1-Jul-4 Sotheby's, London #8/R est:3000000-4000000

REYNOLDS, Sir Joshua (after) (1723-1792) British
£14500 $26680 €21170 Portrait of Admiral Augustus Keppel in uniform (76x63cm-30x25in) prov.lit. 11-Jun-4 Christie's, London #22/R est:3000-5000

REYNOLDS, Sir Joshua (studio) (1723-1792) British
£5000 $8500 €7300 Young black (48x41cm-19x16in) prov.exhib.lit. 27-Nov-3 Sotheby's, London #154/R est:4000-6000
£5000 $8500 €7300 Portrait of Mary Robinson (74x61cm-29x24in) 27-Nov-3 Sotheby's, London #168/R est:5000-7000
£11000 $20240 €16060 Infant Jupiter (108x83cm-43x33in) prov.exhib.lit. 11-Jun-4 Christie's, London #25/R est:10000-20000

REYNOLDS, Sir Joshua (style) (1723-1792) British
£7500 $12525 €10950 Portrait of a lady, in a blue satin and lace dress (77x65cm-30x26in) 13-Nov-3 Christie's, Kensington #33/R est:3000-5000

REYNOLDS, Wellington Jarard (1869-?) American
£311 $500 €454 Sunset over tranquil waters (51x61cm-20x24in) 20-Aug-3 James Julia, Fairfield #1789/R
£1582 $2500 €2310 Sunrise over Lake Michigan (51x66cm-20x26in) s. board. 7-Sep-3 Treadway Gallery, Cincinnati #641/R est:2500-3500

REYNTJENS, Henrich Engelbert (1817-1900) Dutch
£250 $458 €365 Blind beggar (30x33cm-12x13in) s.d.1840. 7-Jul-4 Cheffins, Cambridge #23
£867 $1569 €1300 Discussion (42x35cm-17x14in) s.d.1840. 30-Mar-4 Campo & Campo, Antwerp #244/R
£1200 $2184 €1752 Doctor's visit (27x38cm-11x15in) panel. 5-Feb-4 Mellors & Kirk, Nottingham #552/R est:800-1200
£1733 $3120 €2600 Des pivoines (8x13cm-3x5in) s. s.i.verso panel. 20-Apr-4 Sotheby's, Amsterdam #26/R est:2500-3500
£5517 $9214 €8000 The drafting of the will through the notary public (36x59cm-14x23in) s. panel. 11-Nov-3 Vendu Notarishuis, Rotterdam #120/R est:5000-7000

REYNTJENS, Henrich Engelbert (attrib) (1817-1900) Dutch
£2238 $3804 €3200 La partie d'echecs dans un salon anime (31x40cm-12x16in) panel. 18-Nov-3 Vanderkindere, Brussels #32/R est:1500-2000

REYSSCHOOT, Peter Jan van (attrib) (1702-1772) Flemish
£750 $1200 €1095 Portrait of William Viscount Andover (76x64cm-30x25in) bears sig.d.1739 i.verso. 19-Sep-3 Freeman, Philadelphia #180/R est:1000-1500

REYZABAL ACEBRON, Jose Enrique (?) Spanish
£471 $772 €650 Casa de Campo, Madrid (74x91cm-29x36in) s. board. 27-May-3 Durán, Madrid #53/R

REZA, Muhammad (18th C) Asian
Works on paper
£1200 $2004 €1752 Partridge in landscape (10x7cm-4x3in) s.i. col dr. 15-Oct-3 Sotheby's, London #32/R est:1200-1800

REZEK, Ivo (1898-1979) Yugoslavian
Works on paper
£571 $970 €834 Female nude (29x37cm-11x15in) s.i.d.924 pencil. 29-Nov-3 Dorotheum, Prague #133/R est:8000-12000 (C.KR 26000)

REZIA, Felice A (fl.1866-1902) British
£250 $425 €365 Continental street scene (35x17cm-14x7in) s. board. 18-Nov-3 Bonhams, Leeds #162
£600 $1074 €876 Elegant figures on the beach. On the beach at low tide (20x40cm-8x16in) s. pair. 18-Mar-4 Christie's, Kensington #600/R
£1300 $2171 €1898 Italian lake scene. Town view (30x18cm-12x7in) s.d.1895 board pair. 7-Oct-3 Bonhams, Knightsbridge #159/R est:1000-1500

REZNICEK, Ferdinand von (1868-1909) German
£510 $939 €760 Couple sitting at table (41x28cm-16x11in) s. board. 27-Mar-4 Geble, Radolfzell #758/R
Works on paper
£336 $601 €500 Fine couple (28x21cm-11x8in) s. mixed media. 25-May-4 Karl & Faber, Munich #131
£761 $1400 €1111 Costumers leaving a ball (48x36cm-19x14in) s. i.verso ink gouache on board. 25-Mar-4 Doyle, New York #73/R est:800-1200

REZVANI, Serge (1928-) French
£1119 $1924 €1600 Untitled (59x73cm-23x29in) s.d.51 prov. 2-Dec-3 Calmels Cohen, Paris #92/R est:1500-1800

RHAYE, Yves (1936-1995) Belgian
£278 $464 €400 Composition (120x120cm-47x47in) s. 21-Oct-3 Campo, Vlaamse Kaai #532
£282 $487 €400 Composition (110x110cm-43x43in) s. 9-Dec-3 Campo, Vlaamse Kaai #392
£282 $487 €400 Composition (100x100cm-39x39in) s. 9-Dec-3 Campo, Vlaamse Kaai #395
£347 $580 €500 Composition (130x130cm-51x51in) s. 21-Oct-3 Campo, Vlaamse Kaai #531
£423 $731 €600 Composition (130x130cm-51x51in) s. 9-Dec-3 Campo, Vlaamse Kaai #393
£486 $812 €700 Composition (180x130cm-71x51in) s. 21-Oct-3 Campo, Vlaamse Kaai #528
£486 $812 €700 Fleurs d'os et de la mort (130x130cm-51x51in) 21-Oct-3 Campo, Vlaamse Kaai #530/R

RHEAD, Louis John (1857-1926) British/American
Prints
£2933 $5397 €4400 Swans (78x151cm-31x59in) col lithograph exec. 1896-97. 11-Jun-4 Villa Grisebach, Berlin #1505/R est:3000-4000

RHEAM, Henry Meynell (1859-1920) British
£1000 $1700 €1460 Schooner leaving Newlyn (53x69cm-21x27in) s. 21-Nov-3 Dee Atkinson & Harrison, Driffield #713/R est:500-800
Works on paper
£700 $1253 €1022 Portrait of a lady holding a bowl of violets (82x38cm-32x15in) mono.d.1901 pastel W/C. 16-Mar-4 Bonhams, Oxford #50/R
£1500 $2775 €2190 Mother and child (25x20cm-10x8in) s. W/C. 10-Feb-4 David Lay, Penzance #373/R est:600-800
£1850 $2997 €2701 Girl in pink (35x27cm-14x11in) init.d.1911. 27-Jan-3 Bristol Auction Rooms #527 est:2000-2500
£2000 $3640 €2920 Poppies (36x23cm-14x9in) s.d.1885 W/C. 15-Jun-4 David Lay, Penzance #680/R est:2000-2500
£2100 $3927 €3066 Interior scene with lady dressed in medieval costume with a greyhound (50x26cm-20x10in) mono.i. pencil W/C prov. 22-Jul-4 Tennants, Leyburn #704/R est:1000-1500
£2500 $4550 €3650 An old salt (33x25cm-13x10in) s.d.1917 W/C. 15-Jun-4 David Lay, Penzance #546 est:1000-1500

RHEAUME, Jeanne (1915-2000) Canadian
£1126 $1914 €1644 Yellow blooms (76x65cm-30x26in) s.d.1953 prov. 23-Nov-3 Levis, Calgary #315/R est:3000-3500 (C.D 2500)

RHEE, Seund Ja (1918-) Korean
£526 $968 €800 Composition (27x22cm-11x9in) s. painted 1962. 28-Jun-4 Joron-Derem, Paris #203/R
£1333 $2400 €2000 Nos vaisseaux (55x46cm-22x18in) s. s.i.d.1969 verso prov. 25-Apr-4 Versailles Encheres #37 est:2000-3000
£1678 $2970 €2500 Adolescence (65x47cm-26x19in) s.d.61 prov. 28-Apr-4 Artcurial Briest, Paris #281a/R est:2000-3000
Works on paper
£537 $950 €800 Composition (24x33cm-9x13in) s.d.60 gouache prov. 28-Apr-4 Artcurial Briest, Paris #281b

RHEIMS, Bettina (1952-) French?
Photographs
£2500 $4125 €3600 Nu (75x75cm-30x30in) s.d.25 avril 1 num.I/III cibachrome. 2-Jul-3 Cornette de St.Cyr, Paris #174/R est:4000-5000
£2797 $4755 €4000 Sans titre (80x80cm-31x31in) col photo aluminium prov. 25-Nov-3 Tajan, Paris #80/R est:4000-5000
£4667 $8587 €7000 7 Novembre, Paris (35x35cm-14x14in) s.i. verso col photo lit.exhib. 10-Jun-4 Villa Grisebach, Berlin #1258/R est:1500-2000

RHEIN, Fritz (1873-1948) German
£1333 $2400 €2000 In the kitchen garden (46x61cm-18x24in) s.d.19. 21-Apr-4 Christie's, Amsterdam #49/R est:3000-5000

RHEINEMANN, Albert Leopold (1833-?) German
£2185 $3977 €3300 North coast of Sicily (92x164cm-36x65in) mono.d.1900. 18-Jun-4 Bolland & Marotz, Bremen #734/R est:700

RHEINER, Louis (1863-1924) Swiss
£294 $500 €429 Portrait de son pere Edouard Rheiner (55x42cm 22x17in) i. stretcher. 28-Nov-3 Zofingen, Switzerland #3140 (S.FR 650)
£317 $538 €463 Self portrait (15x13cm-6x5in) s.i. verso board. 28-Nov-3 Zofingen, Switzerland #3141 (S.FR 700)
£430 $731 €628 Sous le petit Saleve pres Geneve (60x46cm-24x18in) s.i.d.90. 28-Nov-3 Zofingen, Switzerland #3135 (S.FR 950)
£724 $1231 €1057 Le pont (27x35cm-11x14in) s. 28-Nov-3 Zofingen, Switzerland #3139/R est:2000 (S.FR 1600)
Works on paper
£317 $538 €463 Bateaux pecheurs au port (24x31cm-9x12in) s.d.95 pastel. 28-Nov-3 Zofingen, Switzerland #3137/R (S.FR 700)
£543 $923 €793 Les sapins (63x49cm-25x19in) s. pastel. 28-Nov-3 Zofingen, Switzerland #3136 (S.FR 1200)

RHEINERT, Adolf (1880-1958) German
£586 $979 €850 Norwegian fjord landscape (203x330cm-80x130in) s. lit. 12-Jul-3 Bergmann, Erlangen #668/R
£622 $1151 €908 Landscape with the sea (27x35cm-11x14in) d.1915. 14-Mar-4 Agra, Warsaw #36/R (P.Z 4500)

RHEINERT, Gustave (20th C) ?
£1722 $3220 €2600 Retour de peche vers la greve (60x80cm-24x31in) s. isorel. 24-Jul-4 Thierry & Lannon, Brest #211/R est:2500-3000

RHEINSCHILD, Hazel (20th C) American
£1156 $2000 €1688 Landscape with poppies and lupin (46x61cm-18x24in) s. canvasboard. 10-Dec-3 Bonhams & Butterfields, San Francisco #6227/R est:2000-3000

RHIJNNEN, Johannes van (1859-1927) Dutch
£528 $914 €750 Farm yard with figures (80x100cm-31x39in) s. 15-Dec-3 Bernaerts, Antwerp #246/R

RHINE SCHOOL (17th C) German
Sculpture
£9333 $16707 €14000 Madonna and Child (81cm-32in) wood. 16-May-4 Joron-Derem, Paris #108/R est:10000-15000

RHO, Camillo (1872-1946) Italian
£374 $670 €550 Landscape (14x22cm-6x9in) s. board. 22-Mar-4 Sant Agostino, Torino #53/R
£671 $1188 €1000 Spring landscape (35x44cm-14x17in) s. board. 1-May-4 Meeting Art, Vercelli #46
£1135 $1895 €1600 Around Trana Convent (50x60cm-20x24in) s. 20-Oct-3 Sant Agostino, Torino #162/R est:2000

RHOADES, Jason (1965-) American
Sculpture
£1734 $3000 €2532 Potato gun (22x37x77cm-9x15x30in) pvc pipe metal clamps wire wire mesh electric lighter screwdriver. 10-Dec-3 Phillips, New York #560/R est:3000-5000

RHODES, John (1809-1842) British
Works on paper
£600 $1098 €876 Sheep in a field. Figures on horseback (31x41cm-12x16in) s.d.1837 W/C pair. 27-Jan-4 Bonhams, Knightsbridge #2/R
£650 $1190 €949 Face-off. Gathering blackberries (31x41cm-12x16in) s.d.1837 W/C pair. 27-Jan-4 Bonhams, Knightsbridge #3/R

RHODES, Joseph (1782-1854) British
£1800 $3006 €2628 Still life of fruit (76x64cm-30x25in) canvas on board. 26-Oct-3 Tayler & Fletcher, Cheltenham #6

RHODES, Joseph (attrib) (1782-1854) British
£900 $1620 €1314 Drovers resting on a mountainous landscape (64x82cm-25x32in) 21-Jan-4 Sotheby's, Olympia #91/R est:800-1200

RHODIN, Johan (attrib) (1755-?) Swedish?
£665 $1191 €971 Interior scene with woman tying her shoe (23x16cm-9x6in) 26-May-4 AB Stockholms Auktionsverk #2266/R (S.KR 9000)

RHOMBERG, Hanno (1820-1869) German
£1931 $3572 €2800 Wilhelmine Freifrau von Hohenhausen as child (48x38cm-19x15in) i. verso canvas on board prov. 14-Feb-4 Hans Stahl, Hamburg #182a/R est:900

RHYS, Oliver (fl.1876-1895) British
£400 $692 €584 Fisherman and boats on a pebble beach (31x46cm-12x18in) s. 10-Dec-3 Bonhams, Bury St Edmunds #552
£750 $1343 €1095 Young Spanish beauty seated on a stone step wearing a black mantilla (43x28cm-17x11in) s. 4-May-4 Gorringes, Bexhill #1307/R
£1350 $2120 €1958 Victorian female on rustic wooden bridge (61x41cm-24x16in) s.d.1883. 15-Dec-2 Desmond Judd, Cranbrook #814

RIAB, Boris (1898-1975) American/Russian
Works on paper
£302 $565 €450 Epagneul Breton rapportant un colvert (20x28cm-8x11in) W/C. 1-Mar-4 Coutau Begarie, Paris #119a/R

RIAL, Raul (20th C) Uruguayan
£478 $750 €698 Fruit bowl with pears and apples (48x36cm-19x14in) s. 1-Sep-3 Galeria y Remates, Montevideo #99

RIAN, Johannes (1891-1981) Norwegian
£412 $721 €602 Landscape from Heimdalen (38x46cm-15x18in) s.i.d.1956. 16-Dec-3 Grev Wedels Plass, Oslo #209/R (N.KR 4800)
£604 $1003 €876 Interior (40x32cm-16x13in) s. panel. 16-Jun-3 Blomqvist, Lysaker #1182/R (N.KR 7000)
£667 $1114 €974 Interior scene with woman (100x75cm-39x30in) s. 17-Nov-3 Blomqvist, Lysaker #1259/R (N.KR 8000)
£861 $1386 €1257 Landscape with evening sky (55x65cm-22x26in) s. 25-Aug-3 Blomqvist, Lysaker #1369 (N.KR 10000)
£1251 $2089 €1826 Landscape (66x75cm-26x30in) s. 17-Nov-3 Blomqvist, Lysaker #1260/R est:15000-20000 (N.KR 15000)
£1521 $2723 €2221 Village (33x41cm-13x16in) s. panel. 22-Mar-4 Blomqvist, Oslo #644/R est:15000-18000 (N.KR 19000)
£1870 $3422 €2730 Boy by fireplace (68x64cm-27x25in) s. 7-Jun-4 Blomqvist, Oslo #418/R est:18000-22000 (N.KR 23000)
£1922 $3440 €2806 Torremolinos (38x47cm-15x19in) s.i.d.1957 panel. 22-Mar-4 Blomqvist, Oslo #603/R est:20000-25000 (N.KR 24000)
£2520 $4612 €3679 Street in Ibiza (61x51cm-24x20in) s. s.i.d.1935 verso. 7-Jun-4 Blomqvist, Oslo #415/R est:25000-30000 (N.KR 31000)
£3670 $6570 €5358 Corner (90x81cm-35x32in) s.d.1968 i.stretcher. 25-May-4 Grev Wedels Plass, Oslo #97/R est:60000-80000 (N.KR 45000)
£4878 $8927 €7122 Interior scene with woman (100x74cm-39x29in) s.i.d.1931. 7-Jun-4 Blomqvist, Oslo #416/R est:30000-40000 (N.KR 60000)
£4894 $8760 €7145 Juan le Pine (59x50cm-23x20in) s.i.d.1949. 25-May-4 Grev Wedels Plass, Oslo #96/R est:70000-90000 (N.KR 60000)
£5604 $10032 €8182 Composition (80x100cm-31x39in) s.d.74. 22-Mar-4 Blomqvist, Oslo #634/R est:80000-100000 (N.KR 70000)
£6843 $11634 €9991 Composition (111x101cm-44x40in) s.d.65 exhib.lit. 19-Nov-3 Grev Wedels Plass, Oslo #99/R est:80000-100000 (N.KR 80000)
£14682 $26281 €21436 Nude female by telephone (66x56cm-26x22in) s. lit. 25-May-4 Grev Wedels Plass, Oslo #95/R est:200000-250000 (N.KR 180000)
Works on paper
£258 $416 €377 On the beach (35x41cm-14x16in) s. W/C. 25-Aug-3 Blomqvist, Lysaker #1226/R (N.KR 3000)
£327 $527 €477 Woman with head scarf (29x21cm-11x8in) s. gouache pencil. 25-Aug-3 Blomqvist, Lysaker #1229/R (N.KR 3800)

£344 $554 €502 Composition (27x30cm-11x12in) s. W/C. 25-Aug-3 Blomqvist, Lysaker #1228 (N.KR 4000)
£473 $762 €691 Woman and sailor with concertina (28x40cm-11x16in) s. Indian ink. 25-Aug-3 Blomqvist, Lysaker #1232 (N.KR 5500)
£602 $1006 €879 Bedouin women (26x21cm-10x8in) s. W/C exhib. 20-Oct-3 Blomqvist, Lysaker #1243/R (N.KR 7000)

RIANCHO GOMEZ DE MORA, Agustin (1841-1929) Spanish
Works on paper
£324 $567 €460 Woodcutters (25x36cm-10x14in) W/C prov. 16-Dec-3 Segre, Madrid #9/R

RIANGINA, S V (1891-1955) Russian
£444 $800 €648 Portrait of B Yakovlev (51x36cm-20x14in) oil on cardboard. 24-Apr-4 Shishkin Gallery, Moscow #7/R
£500 $900 €730 Worker innovator (40x28cm-16x11in) oil on plywood. 24-Apr-4 Shishkin Gallery, Moscow #8/R
Works on paper
£278 $500 €406 Joining the party (40x62cm-16x24in) gouache pencil sketch. 24-Apr-4 Shishkin Gallery, Moscow #10/R

RIARD, Fernand (1896-1959) Swiss
£366 $656 €534 Laupen castle and town in spring (60x72cm-24x28in) s.d.55 pavatex. 13-May-4 Stuker, Bern #771 (S.FR 850)

RIAZOLI (19th C) ?
£2400 $4296 €3504 Sailing ships on the Bosphorus, Istanbul beyond (49x65cm-19x26in) s. 18-Mar-4 Christie's, Kensington #643/R est:1000-1500

RIBA, Paul (1912-1977) American
£838 $1500 €1223 Chicadee and kinglet (56x84cm-22x33in) s. masonite. 19-Mar-4 Aspire, Cleveland #69 est:1000-1500
Works on paper
£1242 $1975 €1801 Pennsylvania countryside (56x66cm-22x26in) s. i.verso casien masonite exhib. 12-Sep-3 Aspire, Cleveland #107 est:800-1200

RIBA-ROVIRA, François (1913-) Spanish
£778 $1300 €1136 Still life arrangement on a table (46x61cm-18x24in) s. masonite. 29-Jun-3 William Jenack, New York #230

RIBAK, Louis (1902-1979) American
£335 $600 €489 Toreador and the bull (41x51cm-16x20in) s. board. 7-May-4 Sloans & Kenyon, Bethesda #1222/R
Works on paper
£214 $400 €312 Slate quarry (43x66cm-17x26in) s. s.i.verso gouache board. 29-Feb-4 Bonhams & Butterfields, San Francisco #4552

RIBARZ, Rudolf (1848-1904) Austrian
£10738 $19007 €16000 Southern village (43x64cm-17x25in) s.d.1879 panel. 28-Apr-4 Wiener Kunst Auktionen, Vienna #55/R est:15000-30000
£22222 $37778 €32000 Schloss Gondorf on the Moselle (78x152cm-31x60in) s.d.1892 lit. 28-Oct-3 Wiener Kunst Auktionen, Vienna #49/R est:20000-60000
Works on paper
£4828 $8014 €7000 Fraueninsel, Chiemsee (33x42cm-13x17in) s. mixed media board. 30-Sep-3 Dorotheum, Vienna #245/R est:5000-6000
£4895 $8322 €7000 Still life of flowers (77x56cm-30x22in) s. gouache. 28-Nov-3 Wiener Kunst Auktionen, Vienna #443/R est:6000-10000

RIBAS MONTENEGRO, Federico (1890-1952) Spanish
Works on paper
£329 $582 €490 Jumping the fence (26x28cm-10x11in) s. ink dr. 27-Apr-4 Durán, Madrid #632/R
£789 $1453 €1200 Woman of the Thirties (49x35cm-19x14in) s. pastel. 22-Jun-4 Durán, Madrid #614/R
£1172 $2110 €1700 Nudes (36x33cm-14x13in) s. chl dr. 26-Jan-4 Ansorena, Madrid #315/R est:1200

RIBAS RIUS, Ramon (1903-1983) American
£1056 $1827 €1500 Still life with melon (65x81cm-26x32in) s. 15-Dec-3 Ansorena, Madrid #21/R est:1500
£1208 $2247 €1800 Flowers (84x73cm-33x29in) s. 2-Mar-4 Ansorena, Madrid #3/R est:1800
Works on paper
£296 $536 €450 Market (15x17cm-6x7in) s.d.70 col dr. 14-Apr-4 Ansorena, Madrid #247

RIBAS Y OLIVER, Antonio (1845-1911) Spanish
£4762 $8524 €7000 Fishing harbour (8x12cm-3x5in) s. cardboard. 22-Mar-4 Durán, Madrid #182/R est:3750

RIBASCO (18th C) ?
Works on paper
£816 $1461 €1200 L'Adoration des Mages (21x30cm-8x12in) s.i.d.1704 pen brown ink. 18-Mar-4 Christie's, Paris #219/R

RIBAUPIERRE, François de (1886-1981) Swiss
£1293 $2315 €1888 La Couronne de Breonna vue de l'Alpe de Breonna (50x65cm-20x26in) mono. i. verso canvas on board. 14-May-4 Dobiaschofsky, Bern #99/R est:3800 (S.FR 3000)
£1422 $2546 €2076 Portrait of girl in Wallis costume (33x30cm-13x12in) mono. chl ochre. 13-May-4 Stuker, Bern #290/R est:3000-4000 (S.FR 3300)
£11468 $19151 €16629 Sortie de messe a Lannaz (70x109cm-28x43in) mono. cardboard prov.exhib.lit. 21-Jun-3 Galerie du Rhone, Sion #477/R est:30000-40000 (S.FR 25000)
£21739 $39783 €31739 Les fileuses (75x98cm-30x39in) mono. s.i.d.1943 verso tempera pavatex prov.exhib.lit. 5-Jun-4 Galerie du Rhone, Sion #558/R est:30000-40000 (S.FR 50000)
Works on paper
£226 $391 €330 Mazots valaisans (22x25cm-9x10in) init. pastel. 12-Dec-3 Galerie du Rhone, Sion #580 (S.FR 500)
£793 $1348 €1158 Portrait d'une petite valaisanne (20x20cm-8x8in) mono. ochre. 7-Nov-3 Dobiaschofsky, Bern #92/R (S.FR 1800)
£1322 $2247 €1930 Portrait d'une petite valaisanne (21x20cm-8x8in) mono. ochre. 7-Nov-3 Dobiaschofsky, Bern #90/R est:1900 (S.FR 3000)
£2802 $5015 €4091 Portrait d'une jeune valaisanne (29x29cm-11x11in) mono. pastel. 14-May-4 Dobiaschofsky, Bern #172/R est:8000 (S.FR 6500)
£5172 $9259 €7551 Deux fillettes d'Evolene (36x36cm-14x14in) mono.d. pastel exhib. 14-May-4 Dobiaschofsky, Bern #168/R est:14000 (S.FR 12000)

RIBCOWSKY, Dey de (1880-1936) American/Bulgarian
£407 $700 €594 Moonlight fishing (51x76cm-20x30in) s.d.1913. 7-Dec-3 Grogan, Boston #50/R
£436 $750 €637 Sunset over crashing waves (48x76cm-19x30in) s. 6-Dec-3 Selkirks, St. Louis #173
£437 $800 €638 Sunset seascape (51x76cm-20x30in) s. 5-Jun-4 Dan Ripley, Indianapolis #278
£659 $1200 €962 Monhegan Island, September 1, 1912 (76x102cm-30x40in) s.i.1912. 8-Feb-4 William Jenack, New York #11
£1105 $1900 €1613 On the Meramec (102x71cm-40x28in) s. 6-Dec-3 Selkirks, St. Louis #174/R est:1000-1500
£2941 $5000 €4294 Grand Canyon view from rim (30x24cm-12x9in) s. canvas on canvas prov. 18-Nov-3 John Moran, Pasadena #114 est:3000-5000
Works on paper
£582 $1100 €850 Wagon train in western landscape (51x76cm-20x30in) s. board prov. 17-Feb-4 John Moran, Pasadena #95/R

RIBEAUCOURT, Jules (1866-1932) French
£1056 $1827 €1500 Village (27x35cm-11x14in) s. panel. 13-Dec-3 Lempertz, Koln #349/R est:1200

RIBEIRO, Alceu (1919-) Uruguayan
£235 $400 €343 Still life with fruit bowl (52x36cm-20x14in) s. cardboard. 20-Nov-3 Galeria y Remates, Montevideo #43/R
£417 $750 €609 El Sena, Paris (51x61cm-20x24in) s. prov. 23-Jan-4 Freeman, Philadelphia #116/R
£556 $900 €806 Street scene (67x56cm-26x22in) s. 29-Jul-3 Galeria y Remates, Montevideo #80/R
£608 $1150 €888 Seascape (50x61cm-20x24in) s.d.verso prov. 22-Feb-4 Galeria y Remates, Montevideo #147/R
£679 $1250 €991 Composition (54x65cm-21x26in) s. prov. 22-Jun-4 Galeria y Remates, Montevideo #110/R
£739 $1300 €1079 Urban landscape (50x60cm-20x24in) s. 5-Jan-4 Galeria y Remates, Montevideo #58/R
£764 $1245 €1100 Landscape (35x64cm-14x25in) s. masonite. 16-Jul-3 Durán, Madrid #57/R
£909 $1600 €1327 Still life with pipe (38x48cm-15x19in) s. cardboard double-sided. 5-Jan-4 Galeria y Remates, Montevideo #59 est:1700-2000
£1078 $1800 €1574 Landscape (60x92cm-24x36in) s. s.i.verso. 7-Oct-3 Galeria y Remates, Montevideo #53/R
£1467 $2655 €2200 Still life with coffee mill (78x88cm-31x35in) s. wood. 30-Mar-4 Segre, Madrid #327/R est:1500
£2273 $4000 €3319 Composition K5 (46x40cm-18x16in) s.d.54 oil wooden collage panel. 5-Jan-4 Galeria y Remates, Montevideo #46/R est:4500-5500

RIBEIRO, Edgardo (1921-) Uruguayan
£235 $400 €343 Spanish village (49x60cm-19x24in) s. 20-Nov-3 Galeria y Remates, Montevideo #47/R
£265 $450 €387 Urban landscape (50x60cm-20x24in) s. cardboard. 20-Nov-3 Galeria y Remates, Montevideo #170/R
£347 $600 €507 Venetian canal (61x50cm-24x20in) s.d.65. 15-Dec-3 Galeria y Remates, Montevideo #122/R
£389 $650 €568 Ballerina (127x96cm-50x38in) s.d.58. 7-Oct-3 Galeria y Remates, Montevideo #97/R
£441 $750 €644 Street and cart (60x73cm-24x29in) s.d.70. 25-Nov-3 Galeria y Remates, Montevideo #72
£471 $800 €688 Harbour in Majorca (55x46cm-22x18in) s.d.72. 20-Nov-3 Galeria y Remates, Montevideo #172/R
£540 $950 €788 Fishermen beach (40x50cm-16x20in) s.d.63 cardboard. 5-Jan-4 Galeria y Remates, Montevideo #13
£540 $950 €788 Bilbao (73x61cm-29x24in) s.d.75. 5-Jan-4 Galeria y Remates, Montevideo #106/R
£739 $1300 €1079 Landscape (69x85cm-27x33in) s.d.45. 5-Jan-4 Galeria y Remates, Montevideo #57/R

RIBERA (?) Spanish
£18000 $32580 €27000 Academie d'homme (47x73cm-19x29in) 5-Apr-4 Deburaux, Boulogne #60b/R est:1800-2000

RIBERA (circle) (17th C) Spanish
£30405 $57466 €45000 Sainte (127x94cm-50x37in) 17-Feb-4 Vanderkindere, Brussels #115 est:2000-3000

RIBERA BERENGUER, Juan (1935-) Spanish
£436 $798 €650 Rocking chair (22x31cm-9x12in) s.d.65 verso board. 12-Jul-4 Durán, Madrid #74/R
£521 $885 €750 Bird at night (48x71cm-19x28in) s. s.i.d.1962 verso acrylic paper. 28-Oct-3 Segre, Madrid #201/R
£872 $1623 €1300 Madonna and Child (33x40cm-13x16in) s. s.verso board. 2-Mar-4 Ansorena, Madrid #249/R

Works on paper
£574 $1011 €850 Cat (48x71cm-19x28in) s.d.1961 gouache wash prov. 18-May-4 Segre, Madrid #256/R

RIBERA Y TALLER, Jose de (17th C) Spanish
£28188 $52430 €42000 Saint Peter's tears (96x76cm-38x30in) 2-Mar-4 Ansorena, Madrid #274/R est:36000

RIBERA, Francisco (1907-1990) Spanish
Works on paper
£690 $1152 €1000 Salamanca people (49x64cm-19x25in) s. dr gouache. 17-Nov-3 Durán, Madrid #61/R

RIBERA, Jusepe de (1588-1656) Spanish
£467 $849 €700 Old age (119x89cm-47x35in) painted with studio. 4-Jul-4 Finarte, Venice #8/R
£26667 $48800 €40000 Saint Bartholomew (178x137cm-70x54in) lit. 1-Jun-4 Sotheby's, Milan #116/R est:20000-30000
£68966 $114483 €100000 St Peter (81x66cm-32x26in) s.d.1644 prov. 1-Oct-3 Dorotheum, Vienna #267/R est:30000-50000
£277778 $500000 €405556 Saint Paul (76x63cm-30x25in) prov.exhib.lit. 23-Jan-4 Christie's, Rockefeller NY #85/R est:500000-700000
£460000 $795800 €671600 Saint Jerome (101x74cm-40x29in) 10-Dec-3 Christie's, London #57/R est:100000-150000

RIBERA, Jusepe de (attrib) (1588-1656) Spanish
£16667 $30500 €25000 Madonna and Child (105x98cm-41x39in) lit. 1-Jun-4 Sotheby's, Milan #153/R est:30000-40000

RIBERA, Jusepe de (studio) (1588-1656) Spanish
£19444 $35000 €28388 Saint Paul (120x97cm-47x38in) 22-Jan-4 Sotheby's, New York #187/R est:40000-60000
£30000 $51900 €43800 Lamentation (189x136cm-74x54in) prov.exhib. 10-Dec-3 Christie's, London #58/R est:30000-50000

RIBERA, Jusepe de (style) (1588-1656) Spanish
£6000 $10380 €8760 Saint Joseph and his flowering rod (66x80cm-26x31in) 12-Dec-3 Christie's, Kensington #213/R est:2000-3000

RIBERA, Pierre (1867-1932) French
£2000 $3600 €2920 Spanish beauty (65x49cm-26x19in) s. 21-Jan-4 Sotheby's, Olympia #511/R est:1000-1500
Works on paper
£612 $1096 €900 Jeune fille au miroir (59x45cm-23x18in) s. pastel. 19-Mar-4 Ribeyre & Baron, Paris #75/R

RIBERA, Roman (1848-1935) Spanish
£1620 $2835 €2300 Inn scene (71x88cm-28x35in) s. 16-Dec-3 Segre, Madrid #69/R est:2100

RIBERZANI, Daniel (1942-) American?
Works on paper
£209 $375 €305 Prairie (50x50cm-20x20in) s.verso mixed media. 21-Mar-4 Bonhams & Butterfields, Los Angeles #7135/R

RIBES COLL, Juan (1946-) Spanish
£319 $596 €475 Alarcon (32x68cm-13x27in) s. paper. 24-Feb-4 Durán, Madrid #47/R

RIBOT, Germain Theodore (1845-1893) French
£342 $582 €500 Vase de fleurs (40x32cm-16x13in) s. 5-Nov-3 Rabourdin & Choppin de Janvry, Paris #71
£1310 $2188 €1900 Le cuisinier (32x24cm-13x9in) panel. 12-Nov-3 Chassaing Rivet, Toulouse #216
£1484 $2700 €2167 Chefs tasting wine (23x33cm-9x13in) s. wood panel. 19-Jun-4 Jackson's, Cedar Falls #51/R est:1000-1500
£2534 $4308 €3700 Bouquet de fleurs dans une jardiniere en faience (60x73cm-24x29in) s. 5-Nov-3 Rabourdin & Choppin de Janvry, Paris #72/R est:4000-4500
£2754 $4516 €3800 Garcon de cuisine (33x25cm-13x10in) s. prov. 11-May-3 Osenat, Fontainebleau #182/R est:4000-4500
£3056 $5500 €4462 Nature morte au lapin (59x74cm-23x29in) s. 22-Apr-4 Christie's, Rockefeller NY #115/R est:10000-15000
£5114 $9000 €7466 Still life with apples, blue jug and silver topped mug (41x33cm-16x13in) s. prov. 18-May-4 Sotheby's, New York #41/R est:15000-20000
£14444 $26000 €21088 Peonies and poppies in a glass vase (61x50cm-24x20in) s. prov. 23-Apr-4 Sotheby's, New York #118/R est:25000-35000

RIBOT, Theodule (1823-1891) French
£600 $1074 €900 Still life with bottle, book and pot (20x14cm-8x6in) s. canvas on panel. 13-May-4 Bassenge, Berlin #5642
£709 $1149 €1000 Tete de fillette (24x18cm-9x7in) s. i.verso. 23-May-3 Sotheby's, Paris #17/R
£1987 $3616 €3000 Nature morte aux fleurs (26x21cm-10x8in) s. panel. 18-Jun-4 Piasa, Paris #61/R est:3000-4000
£2609 $4200 €3809 Reunion (20x23cm-8x9in) s. panel prov. 14-Jan-4 Christie's, Rockefeller NY #21/R est:3000-5000
£4161 $7740 €6200 Nature morte aux oignons et cruche (59x73cm-23x29in) s.d.1890. 3-Mar-4 Tajan, Paris #18/R est:3000-4000

RIBOT, Theodule (attrib) (1823-1891) French
£194 $350 €283 Money lender (33x23cm-13x9in) s.i. 24-Jan-4 Skinner, Boston #470

RIBOUX, Paul (?) ?
£304 $535 €450 Watermill (83x106cm-33x42in) s. 24-May-4 Bernaerts, Antwerp #624/R

RICARD, Louis Gustave (attrib) (1823-1873) French
£3235 $6016 €4723 Dark haired youth (38x31cm-15x12in) metal. 2-Mar-4 Rasmussen, Copenhagen #1490/R est:10000-12000 (D.KR 36000)

RICARD, René (1889-?) French
£533 $955 €800 Moisson a Kerichel, pres Concarneau (23x33cm-9x13in) s. panel. 16-May-4 Thierry & Lannon, Brest #366/R
£1408 $2437 €2000 Fenaisons (23x33cm-9x13in) s. panel. 14-Dec-3 Eric Pillon, Calais #39/R
Works on paper
£317 $526 €450 Port Sainte Claire a Annecy (63x48cm-25x19in) s.i. W/C. 10-Jun-3 Renaud, Paris #34
£352 $585 €500 Les vieilles prisons, Annecy (62x48cm-24x19in) s. W/C. 10-Jun-3 Renaud, Paris #33
£423 $701 €600 Le Thiou Annecy (63x79cm-25x31in) s. W/C. 10-Jun-3 Renaud, Paris #32

RICARD-CORDINGLEY, Georges (1873-1939) French
£336 $601 €500 Cote rocheuse (30x41cm-12x16in) s. 30-May-4 Eric Pillon, Calais #45/R
£567 $1026 €850 La Pointe du Raz par Brouillard (33x40cm-13x16in) peinture paper on canvas. 30-Mar-4 Rossini, Paris #1043
£733 $1327 €1100 Caboteur au soleil couchant (16x22cm-6x9in) st.sig. oil paper on canvas painted c.1900 lit. 30-Mar-4 Rossini, Paris #1045
£733 $1327 €1100 Ciel en Bretagne II (27x35cm-11x14in) peinture paper on canvas exhib. 30-Mar-4 Rossini, Paris #1048
£867 $1569 €1300 Ciel en Bretagne (27x35cm-11x14in) oil paper on canvas exhib. 30-Mar-4 Rossini, Paris #1044
£867 $1569 €1300 Falaises roses au bord de mer (27x35cm-11x14in) s.d.1909 oil paper on canvas. 30-Mar-4 Rossini, Paris #1046
£900 $1413 €1305 Fishing craft and other vessels in a Mediterranean harbour (36x46cm-14x18in) s. board. 28-Aug-3 Christie's, Kensington #203/R
£915 $1584 €1300 Mosquee (32x41cm-13x16in) s. 15-Dec-3 Gros & Delettrez, Paris #300
£933 $1689 €1400 Barque sur la plage (18x23cm-7x9in) mono. peinture paper. 30-Mar-4 Rossini, Paris #1047
£1092 $1987 €1594 Fishing boats leaving the harbour at sunset (59x65cm-23x26in) s. 16-Jun-4 Fischer, Luzern #2325/R est:1200-1500 (S.FR 2500)
£1092 $1987 €1594 Unloading the fishing boats in the morning (50x65cm-20x26in) s. 16-Jun-4 Fischer, Luzern #2326/R est:1200-1500 (S.FR 2500)
£1467 $2655 €2200 Rivage et cours d'eau avec barque (34x46cm-13x18in) indis.st. oil paper. 30-Mar-4 Rossini, Paris #1042 est:600-800
£1867 $3379 €2800 Voilier en mer (33x41cm-13x16in) s. peinture paper on canvas. 30-Mar-4 Rossini, Paris #1049/R est:600-800
£5000 $9050 €7500 Bateau echoue sur la greve (34x46cm-13x18in) s. oil paper. 30-Mar-4 Rossini, Paris #1041/R est:800-1200
Works on paper
£500 $905 €750 Etude d'Orientaux, Maroc (48x31cm-19x12in) W/C. 30-Mar-4 Rossini, Paris #1051

RICART, Enrique Cristobal (1893-1960) Spanish
£1538 $2569 €2200 Wine and grapes (47x63cm-19x25in) s.d.1926 oil ink cardboard. 30-Jun-3 Ansorena, Madrid #379/R est:1500

RICCHI, Pietro (attrib) (1605-1675) Italian
£3600 $6228 €5256 Hagar and the angel (82x71cm-32x28in) 9-Dec-3 Sotheby's, Olympia #390/R est:3000-5000

RICCHI, Pietro (circle) (1605-1675) Italian
£6056 $10599 €8600 Esther and Assuero (120x171cm-47x67in) 17-Dec-3 Christie's, Rome #390/R est:6000-8000
£7746 $13556 €11000 Peter denying (120x171cm-47x67in) 17-Dec-3 Christie's, Rome #388/R est:6000-8000

RICCI, Arturo (1854-1919) Italian
£5000 $9150 €7300 Proposal (41x53cm-16x21in) s. prov. 8-Jul-4 Duke & Son, Dorchester #258/R est:5000-10000
£52941 $90000 €77294 Courtiere (63x87cm-25x34in) s. 28-Oct-3 Sotheby's, New York #60a/R est:60000-80000

RICCI, Dante (1879-1957) Italian
Works on paper
£775 $1340 €1100 Rome seen from the Palatino (56x56cm-22x22in) s.d.920 W/C. 10-Dec-3 Finarte Semenzato, Rome #278/R

RICCI, Giuseppe (19/20th C) Italian
£845 $1462 €1200 Educated men (22x17cm-9x7in) i.verso oval pair. 9-Dec-3 Pandolfini, Florence #202/R

RICCI, Guido (1836-1897) Italian
£1151 $1888 €1600 View of village on the lake (80x97cm-31x38in) s. 10-Jun-3 Pandolfini, Florence #122 est:1400-1500

RICCI, Jerri (1916-1996) American?
Works on paper
£260 $450 €380 Reflections (41x58cm-16x23in) s. i.verso W/C. 15-Dec-3 Winter Associates, Plainville #47/R

RICCI, Marco (1676-1729) Italian

£28000	$47600	€40880	Capriccio of Roman ruins with soldiers beside the Statue of Marius (66x59cm-26x23in) i. 29-Oct-3 Christie's, London #98/R est:12000-18000
£250000	$457500	€365000	Wooded landscape with gentleman in a carriage on a road (81x112cm-32x44in) prov.exhib.lit. 7-Jul-4 Christie's, London #86/R est:250000-350000
Works on paper			
£3056	$5500	€4462	Capriccio with the pyramid of Caius Sestius (20x29cm-8x11in) pen brown ink wash prov. 22-Jan-4 Christie's, Rockefeller NY #63/R est:3000-5000
£12222	$22000	€17844	Landscape with shepherds by a river and bridge in the distance (32x46cm-13x18in) gouache. 21-Jan-4 Sotheby's, New York #81/R est:15000-20000
£83333	$150000	€121666	Capriccio with figures by tomb. Capriccio with figures at fountain (32x46cm-13x18in) gouache on kidskin pair prov.exhib.lit. 22-Jan-4 Sotheby's, New York #68/R est:100000-150000

RICCI, Marco (attrib) (1676-1729) Italian

£19718	$31746	€28000	Landscape with the Good Samaritan (74x98cm-29x39in) 8-May-3 Farsetti, Prato #578/R est:32000-36000
£21277	$35532	€30000	Landscape with figures (96x73cm-38x29in) 17-Jun-3 Finarte Semenzato, Milan #640/R est:35000-45000
Works on paper			
£1333	$2400	€1946	Estuary with ruins in the foreground (30x42cm-12x17in) bodycol. 22-Jan-4 Christie's, Rockefeller NY #213/R est:2000-3000

RICCI, Marco (circle) (1676-1729) Italian

£5031	$8000	€7345	Classical landscape with figures fleeing before a storm (99x93cm-39x37in) 13-Sep-3 Weschler, Washington #703/R est:7000-10000
£14000	$24220	€20440	Capriccio of a Mediterranean harbour with figures in classical ruins (60x99cm-24x39in) 12-Dec-3 Christie's, Kensington #279/R est:4000-6000
£17778	$32000	€25956	Architectural capriccio with classical ruins (91x116cm-36x46in) 23-Jan-4 Christie's, Rockefeller NY #71/R est:10000-15000
£72000	$131760	€105120	Travellers in a wagon on a track taking fright in a storm (99x92cm-39x36in) 7-Jul-4 Bonhams, New Bond Street #27/R est:7000-10000

RICCI, Marco (style) (1676-1729) Italian

£6040	$10812	€9000	Paysage de ville italienne avec ruines (94x152cm-37x60in) tempera. 25-May-4 Palais de Beaux Arts, Brussels #80/R est:7000-10000

RICCI, Marco and Sebastiano (circle) (17/18th C) Italian

£47222	$85000	€68944	Mountainous river landscape. Mountainous river landscape with a couple (142x274cm-56x108in) folding screens prov. 23-Jan-4 Christie's, Rockefeller NY #132/R est:40000-60000

RICCI, Pio (?-1919) Italian

Works on paper			
£1125	$1800	€1643	Suitor (23x18cm-9x7in) s. W/C. 20-Sep-3 New Orleans Auction, New Orleans #212/R

RICCI, Sebastiano (1659-1734) Italian

£63380	$101408	€90000	Amphitritis' triumph (64x78cm-25x31in) 21-Sep-3 Finarte, Venice #45/R est:110000

RICCI, Sebastiano (attrib) (1659-1734) Italian

Works on paper			
£300	$519	€438	Caricature of a scholar (10x9cm-4x4in) pen brown ink. 12-Dec-3 Christie's, Kensington #368/R

RICCI, Sebastiano (circle) (1659-1734) Italian

£14184	$23688	€20000	Susanna e i vecchioni (47x59cm-19x23in) 17-Jun-3 Finarte Semenzato, Milan #637/R est:12000-15000
£22000	$38060	€32120	Danae (84x234cm-33x92in) 12-Dec-3 Christie's, Kensington #261/R est:8000-12000

RICCIARDELLI, Gabriele (attrib) (fl.1745-1777) Italian

£61111	$110000	€89222	View of Castel dell'ovo from the Bay of Trentaremi, Naples. View of the Darsena, Naples (76x126cm-30x50in) pair. 22-Jan-4 Sotheby's, New York #174/R est:80000-120000

RICCIARDI, Caesar A (1892-1988) American

£202	$350	€295	Landscape with roadside house (30x41cm-12x16in) s. canvasboard. 10-Dec-3 Alderfer's, Hatfield #468
£204	$375	€298	Harbor scene (76x61cm-30x24in) s.d.69. 9-Jun-4 Alderfer's, Hatfield #505/R
£204	$375	€298	Still life (41x51cm-16x20in) s.d.59. 25-Jun-4 Freeman, Philadelphia #188/R
£217	$400	€317	Spring landscape with rowboat moored at river's edge (76x61cm-30x24in) s.d.70. 9-Jun-4 Alderfer's, Hatfield #506
£220	$350	€321	Landscape with farm building and outbuildings (61x76cm-24x30in) s.d.68. 10-Sep-3 Alderfer's, Hatfield #447
£231	$400	€337	Winter landscape with buildings and central evergreen tree (30x41cm-12x16in) s. canvasboard. 10-Dec-3 Alderfer's, Hatfield #469
£244	$400	€356	Floral still life (76x61cm-30x24in) s.d.70. 4-Jun-3 Alderfer's, Hatfield #364
£246	$425	€359	Lakeside landscape with road, picket fence and houses (30x41cm-12x16in) s. canvasboard. 10-Dec-3 Alderfer's, Hatfield #470
£255	$475	€372	Impressionist harbour scene with sailboats (41x30cm-16x12in) s. board. 3-Mar-4 Alderfer's, Hatfield #421
£274	$450	€400	Harbour scene (30x41cm-12x16in) s. canvasboard. 4-Jun-3 Alderfer's, Hatfield #365
£274	$475	€400	Harbour scene (41x30cm-16x12in) s. canvasboard. 10-Dec-3 Alderfer's, Hatfield #466
£335	$550	€489	Landscape with houses and trees (61x76cm-24x30in) s.d.69. 4-Jun-3 Alderfer's, Hatfield #360
£344	$550	€502	Mixed flowers in an urn (69x53cm-27x21in) s.d.1937 board. 19-Sep-3 Freeman, Philadelphia #91
£347	$600	€507	Autumnal forest landscape with view of distance hills (61x91cm-24x36in) s.d.55. 10-Dec-3 Alderfer's, Hatfield #465/R
£353	$650	€515	Autumn landscape with figure on road with distant mountains (61x91cm-24x36in) s.d.55. 9-Jun-4 Alderfer's, Hatfield #509
£377	$600	€550	Spring landscape with trees and hills (61x76cm-24x30in) s.d.72. 10-Sep-3 Alderfer's, Hatfield #305
£389	$650	€568	Boats in harbour (51x41cm-20x16in) s.verso board. 20-Jun-3 Freeman, Philadelphia #212/R
£396	$650	€578	Spring landscape with river and figures at washline (61x76cm-24x30in) s.d.70. 4-Jun-3 Alderfer's, Hatfield #362/R
£407	$750	€594	Impressionist winter landscape of steepled church (61x76cm-24x30in) s.d.52. 9-Jun-4 Alderfer's, Hatfield #503
£435	$800	€635	Portrait of red haired woman wearing a black dress and shawl (97x76cm-38x30in) s.d.1928. 9-Jun-4 Alderfer's, Hatfield #514/R
£440	$700	€642	Spring landscape (61x76cm-24x30in) s. 10-Sep-3 Alderfer's, Hatfield #448/R
£484	$900	€707	Landscape with lake and buildings, distant mountains (61x91cm-24x36in) s.d.1954. 3-Mar-4 Alderfer's, Hatfield #419/R est:800-1200
£489	$900	€714	Lagoon and fishing village (61x91cm-24x36in) s.d.65. 9-Jun-4 Alderfer's, Hatfield #504/R est:700-900
£503	$800	€734	Sailboats at anchor, all in shades of blue (61x76cm-24x30in) s. 10-Sep-3 Alderfer's, Hatfield #415/R
£535	$850	€781	Autumn landscape with figure on road, buildings and picket fence (61x91cm-24x36in) s.d.55. 10-Sep-3 Alderfer's, Hatfield #306
£597	$950	€872	Springtime landscape of river with moored boats and riverside buildings (61x91cm-24x36in) s.d.65. 10-Sep-3 Alderfer's, Hatfield #307/R
£818	$1300	€1194	Landscape with figures on road, trees and buildings, lake in the distance (61x76cm-24x30in) s.d.57. 10-Sep-3 Alderfer's, Hatfield #308/R
£1159	$1900	€1692	Winter landscape with house and bridge (61x76cm-24x30in) s.d.65. 4-Jun-3 Alderfer's, Hatfield #350/R est:800-1200

RICCIARDI, Oscar (1864-1935) Italian

£275	$500	€402	Canal in Venice (38x23cm-15x9in) s. 7-Feb-4 Auctions by the Bay, Alameda #1529/R
£725	$1188	€1000	Seascape with boat (15x20cm-6x8in) s. board. 27-May-3 Finarte Semenzato, Milan #128/R
£872	$1605	€1300	SS. Giovanni and Paolo's (39x22cm-15x9in) s. 24-Mar-4 Il Ponte, Milan #658/R
£1000	$1670	€1460	Italian figures on the shore. 21-Oct-3 Gorringes, Lewes #2092/R
£1067	$1963	€1600	Landscape (30x18cm-12x7in) s. board. 11-Jun-4 Farsetti, Prato #547/R est:1600-2000
£1111	$1889	€1600	Market after the rain (17x23cm-7x9in) s. board. 1-Nov-3 Meeting Art, Vercelli #74/R est:1000
£1200	$2196	€1752	Bustling Italian street (14x37cm-6x15in) s. panel. 8-Apr-4 Christie's, Kensington #164/R est:1000-1500
£1408	$2437	€2000	Amalfi coast (30x27cm-12x11in) s. 9-Dec-3 Finarte Semenzato, Milan #32/R
£1563	$2688	€2282	Awaiting the fishers' return (41x60cm-16x24in) s.i. 2-Dec-3 Ritchie, Toronto #112/R est:2500-4000 (C.D 3500)
£3200	$5824	€4672	Waiting for the catch, Naples (41x60cm-16x24in) s.i. 16-Jun-4 Christie's, Kensington #126/R est:2000-3000

RICCIO, Ernesto (1887-?) Argentinian

£2069	$3434	€3000	Majorca landscape (80x91cm-31x36in) s.d.1917. 30-Sep-3 Ansorena, Madrid #97/R est:3000

RICCIOLINI, Niccolo (1687-?) Italian

£6000	$10380	€8760	Saint John the Baptist announcing the coming of Christ (117x128cm-46x50in) 12-Dec-3 Christie's, Kensington #264/R est:5000-8000
Works on paper			
£546	$1000	€797	Virgin and Child with two male saints and angels (27x20cm-11x8in) i. pen brown ink wash. 29-Jan-4 Swann Galleries, New York #106/R

RICCITELLI, Domenico (1881-?) American/Italian

£217	$400	€317	Autumn scene (20x28cm-8x11in) s. i.verso canvas on board. 25-Jun-4 Freeman, Philadelphia #225/R

RICE, Anne Estelle (1879-1959) American

£1200	$2220	€1752	Village church (32x41cm-13x16in) card on canvas. 11-Feb-4 Sotheby's, Olympia #114/R est:1200-1800
£2000	$3140	€2900	Still life with jugs and glasses (33x40cm-13x16in) canvas collage. 27-Aug-3 Sotheby's, London #1167/R est:2000-3000
£2419	$4500	€3532	The moorings (33x41cm-13x16in) i. board prov.exhib. 5-Mar-4 Skinner, Boston #555/R est:4000-6000
£3500	$6265	€5110	The pink tablecloth (50x60cm-20x24in) s. board. 28-May-4 Lyon & Turnbull, Edinburgh #13/R est:1500-2000
£5000	$9050	€7300	River path, L'Oset Quimper (45x56cm-18x22in) s. prov.exhib. 19-Apr-4 Sotheby's, London #125/R est:5000-7000
Works on paper			
£1500	$2685	€2190	Antibes (37x28cm-15x11in) pencil W/C prov. 28-May-4 Lyon & Turnbull, Edinburgh #88 est:600-800

RICE, Gerret S (19th C) American

£323	$600	€472	Bust length portrait of William Henry Harrison (30x25cm-12x10in) board. 6-Mar-4 North East Auctions, Portsmouth #1034

RICE, Henry Webster (1853-1934) American

Works on paper			
£531	$950	€775	Kennebunkport workshop interior (38x33cm-15x13in) s.i.d.1892 W/C. 14-May-4 Skinner, Boston #192/R

RICE, Marion (20th C) American

£236	$425	€345	Figures beside lily pond (61x76cm-24x30in) s. 20-Apr-4 Arthur James, Florida #214/R

RICE, Noreen (20th C) British
£1100 $2013 €1606 Spring field (40x50cm-16x20in) s. 2-Jun-4 John Ross, Belfast #198 est:400-500
Works on paper
£3333 $6033 €5000 Friends of the forest (92x112cm-36x44in) s. pastel. 30-Mar-4 De Veres Art Auctions, Dublin #46/R est:3000-5000

RICE-PEREIRA, Irene (1907-1971) American
£1220 $2000 €1769 Spider web, foliate, crustacean and serpent forms (30x43cm-12x17in) s. prov. 31-May-3 Brunk, Ashville #30/R est:400-800
£1630 $3000 €2380 Abstract composition (107x81cm-42x32in) s. 10-Jun-4 Swann Galleries, New York #199/R est:3500-5000
£2059 $3500 €3006 Untitled (91x127cm-36x50in) s. 9-Nov-3 Wright, Chicago #235 est:3000-5000
£2439 $4000 €3537 Movement of light (112x102cm-44x40in) s. i.verso prov. 31-May-3 Brunk, Ashville #29/R est:1000-2000
£3354 $5500 €4863 Geometric composition (127x102cm-50x40in) s. prov. 31-May-3 Brunk, Ashville #111/R est:1500-2500
£3963 $6500 €5746 Composition (127x102cm-50x40in) s. prov. 31-May-3 Brunk, Ashville #521/R est:1500-2500
£4491 $7500 €6557 Reflection (32x29cm-13x11in) s.d.43 gold leaf oil glass tempera double-sided prov.exhib.lit. 11-Nov-3 Christie's, Rockefeller NY #160/R est:12000-18000
£5793 $9500 €8400 Light continuous (102x127cm-40x50in) s. i.verso prov. 31-May-3 Brunk, Ashville #446/R est:2000-4000
Works on paper
£823 $1300 €1202 Abstract (66x51cm-26x20in) s. collage mixed media prov. 7-Sep-3 Treadway Gallery, Cincinnati #703/R
£1176 $2000 €1717 Interaction of light (104x74cm-41x29in) s.i.d.1962 W/C chl. 9-Nov-3 Wright, Chicago #416 est:2000-3000
£4865 $9000 €7103 Transverse Parallels (84x82cm-33x32in) s. ink gouache pencil paper on board. 12-Feb-4 Sotheby's, New York #111/R est:3000-5000
£5488 $9000 €7958 Abstract composition with two knobs (41x30cm-16x12in) s.d.44 collage mixed media prov. 31-May-3 Brunk, Ashville #445/R est:500-1000

RICE-PEREIRA, Irene (attrib) (1907-1971) American
£1524 $2500 €2225 Geometric composition (112x102cm-44x40in) prov. 31-May-3 Brunk, Ashville #31/R est:1000-2000

RICH, Alfred William (1856-1921) British
Works on paper
£750 $1388 €1095 Cattle resting (27x39cm-11x15in) W/C bodycol sold with two others by same hand three. 10-Mar-4 Sotheby's, Olympia #145/R

RICH, Fran (20th C) American
Sculpture
£5163 $9500 €7538 Portrait of Katharine Hepburn (38cm-15in) i. terracotta. 10-Jun-4 Sotheby's, New York #556/R est:1000-1500
£5978 $11000 €8728 Portrait mask of Katharine Hepburn (23x25cm-9x10in) mono.d.65 greenish black pat. bronze. 10-Jun-4 Sotheby's, New York #555/R est:800-1200
£10326 $19000 €15076 Portrait of Katharine Hepburn (38x28cm-15x11in) greenish brown pat. bronze black marble base. 10-Jun-4 Sotheby's, New York #557/R est:1500-2000

RICH, John Hubbard (1876-1954) American
£1734 $3000 €2532 Portrait of a girl (61x43cm-24x17in) s. prov. 10-Dec-3 Bonhams & Butterfields, San Francisco #6279/R est:3000-5000
£1765 $3000 €2577 Young girl seated with doll (76x36cm-30x14in) s. 20-Nov-3 Auctions by the Bay, Alameda #1137
£2168 $3750 €3165 Still life with a Chinese figure and a geranium (61x51cm-24x20in) s. prov. 10-Dec-3 Bonhams & Butterfields, San Francisco #6271/R est:3000-5000
£2601 $4500 €3797 Still life with a bowl, fruit and a bottle (51x51cm-20x20in) s. prov. 10-Dec-3 Bonhams & Butterfields, San Francisco #6272/R est:3000-5000
£2746 $4750 €4009 Portrait of Maria (51x41cm-20x16in) s. prov. 10-Dec-3 Bonhams & Butterfields, San Francisco #6281/R est:4000-6000
£3235 $5500 €4723 Juan and Jose (28x33cm-11x13in) s. exhib. 18-Nov-3 John Moran, Pasadena #179 est:3000-5000

RICHARD, Alexandre Louis Marie Theodore (1782-1859) French
£7092 $11844 €10000 Vue d'un port dans le sud de la France (24x32cm-9x13in) mono. 19-Oct-3 St-Germain-en-Laye Encheres #1/R est:10000-12000

RICHARD, Durando Togo (1910-) ?
£264 $449 €385 Gypsy woman with guitar (64x50cm-25x20in) s. 5-Nov-3 Dobiaschofsky, Bern #891 (S.FR 600)
£372 $665 €550 Jeune lavandiere (65x90cm-26x35in) s. 10-May-4 Horta, Bruxelles #506
£600 $1134 €876 Strip poker (65x54cm-26x21in) s. 19-Feb-4 Christie's, Kensington #49/R

RICHARD, Herve (20th C) French
Works on paper
£321 $506 €500 Trois mats longeant la cote (32x23cm-13x9in) s. W/C. 12-Nov-2 Adjug'art, Brest #87/R

RICHARD, Leonard (1945-) Norwegian
£3740 $6844 €5460 Ray of sunshine (107x92cm-42x36in) s.d.1979 stretcher exhib.lit. 7-Jun-4 Blomqvist, Oslo #462/R est:40000-50000 (N.KR 46000)
£4390 $8034 €6409 Made-up picture of five summer landscapes (128x128cm-50x50in) init. painted c.2000-01 exhib.lit. 7-Jun-4 Blomqvist, Oslo #447/R est:50000-60000 (N.KR 54000)
£4404 $7882 €6430 Factory - summer night (80x206cm-31x81in) init.indis.d.92. 22-Mar-4 Blomqvist, Oslo #652/R est:65000-75000 (N.KR 55000)
£6016 $11010 €8783 Danish evening landscape (115x135cm-45x53in) init. s.d.1977 verso exhib. 7-Jun-4 Blomqvist, Oslo #466/R est:50000-60000 (N.KR 74000)

RICHARD, René (1895-1982) Canadian
£356 $615 €520 Goellette (28x38cm-11x15in) s. board. 9-Dec-3 Maynards, Vancouver #195 (C.D 800)
£680 $1170 €993 Summer landscape (31x37cm-12x15in) s. i.d.1956 verso board. 3-Dec-3 Cheffins, Cambridge #642
£800 $1464 €1168 Landscape (25x30cm-10x12in) s. board. 1-Jun-4 Joyner Waddington, Toronto #500 est:1000-1500 (C.D 2000)
£840 $1537 €1226 Paysage d'ete, Comte de Charlevoix (32x37cm-13x15in) s. board. 1-Jun-4 Joyner Waddington, Toronto #303/R est:800-1200 (C.D 2100)
£915 $1637 €1336 Barn, early spring (30x40cm-12x16in) s. i.verso board. 6-May-4 Heffel, Vancouver #119/R est:2000-3000 (C.D 2250)
£1111 $1922 €1622 Pres Baie St Paul (30x40cm-12x16in) s. i.verso board. 9-Dec-3 Pinneys, Montreal #148 est:2000-3000 (C.D 2500)
£1802 $3063 €2631 Farm houses by lakeshore (41x51cm-16x20in) s. masonite prov. 18-Nov-3 Sotheby's, Toronto #38/R est:2500-3000 (C.D 4000)
£6696 $11518 €9776 Journee ensoleillee (104x132cm-41x52in) s. board prov. 2-Dec-3 Joyner Waddington, Toronto #157/R est:8000-12000 (C.D 15000)
Works on paper
£670 $1152 €978 Campement et Canot (35x43cm-14x17in) s. ink prov. 2-Dec-3 Joyner Waddington, Toronto #314/R (C.D 1500)

RICHARDE, Ludvig (1862-1929) Swedish
£834 $1501 €1251 Seascape with man-war (85x52cm-33x20in) s.d.1898. 25-Apr-4 Goteborg Auktionsverk, Sweden #178/R (S.KR 11500)
£1216 $2177 €1800 At sea (23x39cm-9x15in) s.d.87. 8-May-4 Bukowskis, Helsinki #379/R est:1500-2000

RICHARDS, Ceri (1903-1971) British
£2700 $4833 €3942 La Cathedrale Engloutie (20x25cm-8x10in) s.d.62 prov. 28-May-4 Lyon & Turnbull, Edinburgh #75/R est:1500-2000
£3200 $5344 €4672 La Cathedrale Engloutie (30x36cm-12x14in) s.d.1961 prov. 21-Oct-3 Peter Francis, Wales #31/R est:3000-4000
£4200 $7392 €6132 Study for the rape of the Sabines (25x35cm-10x14in) s. i.stretcher. 19-May-4 Sotheby's, Olympia #257/R est:1500-2000
£4500 $7920 €6570 Cathedrale engloutie (61x30cm-24x12in) s.d.60 oil on canvas music score collage. 19-May-4 Sotheby's, Olympia #318/R est:3000-5000
Works on paper
£620 $1011 €905 Abstract study in gold, grey blue and white (16x23cm-6x9in) s.d.1963 W/C gouache bronze. 24-Sep-3 Dreweatt Neate, Newbury #19/R
£900 $1647 €1314 Based on a title from the 1st Book of Piano Preludes by Claude Debussy (23x18cm-9x7in) s.d.62 gouache. 28-Jul-4 Mallams, Oxford #260/R
£5900 $10738 €8614 Men working in a foundry (48x71cm-19x28in) s. indis d. W/C pen ink htd white. 21-Jun-4 Bonhams, Bath #322/R est:1500-2000
£6500 $11245 €9490 Sabine theme 3 (37x53cm-15x21in) s.d.1947 pen ink W/C. 11-Dec-3 Lyon & Turnbull, Edinburgh #111/R est:2000-3000
£15000 $27300 €21900 The bouquet (37x55cm-15x22in) s.d.51 W/C ink prov. 15-Jun-4 Bonhams, New Bond Street #115/R est:6000-8000

RICHARDS, Charles (1906-1992) American
£216 $350 €315 Chauvin (61x46cm-24x18in) s. prov. 2-Aug-3 Neal Auction Company, New Orleans #550
£261 $450 €381 Chauvin (58x43cm-23x17in) s. prov. 6-Dec-3 Neal Auction Company, New Orleans #1342
£1412 $2400 €2062 Ursuline Convent, French quarter by moonlight. s. canvasboard. 22-Nov-3 New Orleans Auction, New Orleans #1077/R est:1500-2500

RICHARDS, Frank (1863-1935) British
£420 $769 €613 Figures in a marshy landscape (18x36cm-7x14in) s. 7-Apr-4 Gardiner & Houlgate, Bath #45/R
Works on paper
£300 $546 €438 Sheep watering at the village pond (41x18cm-16x7in) s.d.93 pencil W/C. 1-Jul-4 Christie's, Kensington #133
£540 $1004 €788 Woman feeding geese on riverbank. River landscape (9x14cm-4x6in) s.i.d.1896 W/C bodycol pair. 2-Mar-4 Bearnes, Exeter #401

RICHARDS, Frederick Charles (1878-1932) British
£500 $795 €730 Lions of Westminster (23x33cm-9x13in) s. 9-Sep-3 Gorringes, Lewes #1843/R

RICHARDS, Frederick de Berg (1822-1903) American
£9302 $16000 €13581 On the beach, a city and pier in the distance (46x91cm-18x36in) s. indis.d.81. 7-Dec-3 Freeman, Philadelphia #159/R est:3000-5000
£10180 $17000 €14863 Distant sunset along the coast (46x91cm-18x36in) s.d.87. 23-Oct-3 Shannon's, Milford #120/R est:15000-25000
£10494 $17000 €15321 Scenic views of the Susquehanna river area (41x56cm-16x22in) s.i.d.verso pair. 3-Aug-3 North East Auctions, Portsmouth #1807/R est:10000-15000

RICHARDS, Frederick de Berg (attrib) (1822-1903) American
£967 $1750 €1412 Rugged western United States, mountains landscape with waterfall (74x61cm-29x24in) s. 3-Apr-4 Nadeau, Windsor #88/R est:2500-4000

RICHARDS, John Inigo (?-1810) British
Works on paper
£500 $915 €730 Figures outside a cottage (22x26cm-9x10in) init.d.1800 i.verso blk ink pencil W/C scratching out. 3-Jun-4 Christie's, London #114/R

RICHARDS, John Inigo (attrib) (?-1810) British
£1500 $2700 €2190 Italianate landscape (57x86cm-22x34in) 21-Jan-4 Sotheby's, Olympia #90/R est:1500-2000
Works on paper
£750 $1350 €1095 Group of landscapes (15x20cm-6x8in) gouache three. 21-Jan-4 Sotheby's, Olympia #87/R

RICHARDS, L (19th C) British
£1800 $3006 €2628 Near Dorking (40x61cm-16x24in) s. pair. 12-Nov-3 Sotheby's, Olympia #71/R est:800-1200

RICHARDS, Richard Peter (1840-1877) British
£320 $592 €467 On the Conway (46x76cm-18x30in) s. 9-Mar-4 Capes Dunn, Manchester #685
£3000 $4740 €4350 Cader Idris, North Wales (44x79cm-17x31in) s. 4-Sep-3 Christie's, Kensington #183/R est:3000-5000

RICHARDS, Theodore William (19th C) American
£1514 $2800 €2210 The 1885 America's Cup Race, Puritan vs Genesta (30x61cm-12x24in) s.d.1888 board prov. 10-Feb-4 Christie's, Rockefeller NY #202/R est:4000-6000

RICHARDS, Thomas (19/20th C) ?
£1923 $3500 €2808 Fox hunt (41x61cm-16x24in) s.d.1901 pair. 29-Jun-4 Sotheby's, New York #172/R est:4000-6000

RICHARDS, W (19th C) British
£2000 $3580 €3000 La lecon du pecheur Cotes de Cornouaille (30x61cm-12x24in) s. 16-May-4 Thierry & Lannon, Brest #171/R est:3000-4000
Works on paper
£1000 $1720 €1460 Britannia. Vigilant (34x25cm-13x10in) s. W/C pair. 2-Dec-3 Sotheby's, London #101/R est:1000-1500

RICHARDS, William (?) ?
£490 $817 €700 Moor landscape with figures (49x74cm-19x29in) s. 26-Jun-3 Weidler, Nurnberg #6512/R

RICHARDS, William Trost (1833-1905) American
£2395 $4000 €3497 Rocky coastline at sunset (19x36cm-7x14in) s.d.97 oil paper on board. 9-Oct-3 Christie's, Rockefeller NY #35/R est:4000-6000
£2793 $5000 €4078 Along a rocky coast (25x38cm-10x15in) i.verso canvas on board. 6-May-4 Shannon's, Milford #55/R est:6000-8000
£3824 $6500 €5583 Gentle surf (24x39cm-9x15in) s. canvasboard. 30-Oct-3 Phillips, New York #37/R est:4000-6000
£5882 $10000 €8588 Crashing surf (22x38cm-9x15in) s. canvasboard. 20-Nov-3 Auctions by the Bay, Alameda #1043/R
£5988 $10000 €8742 Crashing waves on a rocky coast (13x23cm-5x9in) s. s.d.1887 verso panel prov. 23-Oct-3 Shannon's, Milford #125/R est:9000-12000
£7186 $12000 €10492 On the New England coast (22x39cm-9x15in) s. board. 9-Oct-3 Christie's, Rockefeller NY #32/R est:5000-7000
£11491 $18500 €16777 At Newport (25x41cm-10x16in) s. i. verso board. 20-Aug-3 James Julia, Fairfield #1255/R est:30000-40000
£12857 $22500 €18771 Rocky promontory (23x39cm-9x15in) st.sig. board prov. 19-Dec-3 Sotheby's, New York #1077/R est:10000-15000
£15528 $25000 €22671 The beach at Cloverlly, Devonshire (43x74cm-17x29in) s. 20-Aug-3 James Julia, Fairfield #1256/R est:15000-20000
£23313 $38000 €34037 Summer afternoon (69x51cm-27x20in) s.d.94. 27-Sep-3 Charlton Hall, Columbia #500/R est:35000-45000
£26257 $47000 €38335 Rocky seascape (91x74cm-36x29in) s.d.03 canvas on board. 20-Mar-4 Sloans & Kenyon, Bethesda #1208/R est:20000-30000
£35928 $60000 €52455 Off the coast (61x76cm-24x30in) s.d.01 prov. 9-Oct-3 Christie's, Rockefeller NY #21/R est:20000-30000
£46512 $80000 €67908 Rocky surf off Rhode Island (46x89cm-18x35in) s.d.1898 prov. 3-Dec-3 Sotheby's, New York #119/R est:80000-120000
Works on paper
£237 $425 €346 Rocky landscape (15x25cm-6x10in) s. pencil. 8-May-4 Susanin's, Chicago #6073/R
£497 $900 €726 Rocky landscape (33x53cm-13x21in) pencil. 16-Apr-4 Du Mouchelle, Detroit #2125/R
£1173 $2100 €1713 Landscape (20x30cm-8x12in) s. W/C. 8-May-4 Susanin's, Chicago #6077/R est:600-800
£1497 $2500 €2186 Coastal scene (20x33cm-8x13in) s.d.1871 W/C. 23-Oct-3 Shannon's, Milford #239/R est:2500-3500
£1955 $3500 €2854 Sail in light (97x76cm-38x30in) s.d.93 W/C. 8-Jan-4 James Julia, Fairfield #709/R est:2000-4000
£2717 $5000 €3967 Crashing breakers (58x102cm-23x40in) s.d.1902 W/C paper on canvas. 27-Jun-4 Freeman, Philadelphia #76/R est:5000-8000
£3757 $6500 €5485 Moulin Hues Bay, Guernsey (23x41cm-9x16in) s. gouache. 13-Dec-3 Charlton Hall, Columbia #545/R est:2000-4000
£4491 $7500 €6557 Surf with sail boats in the distance (18x30cm-7x12in) s. W/C. 12-Jul-3 Auctions by the Bay, Alameda #416/R
£4839 $9000 €7065 Seascape depicting choppy ocean (23x33cm-9x13in) s. W/C. 3-Mar-4 Alderfer's, Hatfield #422/R est:6000-8000
£7182 $13000 €10486 Sea, rock and mist (62x88cm-24x35in) s.d.05 W/C board prov. 31-Mar-4 Sotheby's, New York #70/R est:12000-18000
£13953 $24000 €20371 Rocky coast (136x104cm-54x41in) s.d.90 W/C pencil prov. 4-Dec-3 Christie's, Rockefeller NY #28/R est:30000-50000

RICHARDSON, Alexander (fl.1843-1850) British
£3552 $6500 €5186 Study of sheep in a landscape (23x32cm-9x13in) panel sold with another by English Provincial School 19th C prov. 7-Apr-4 Sotheby's, New York #88/R est:6000-8000

RICHARDSON, Amy (?) British
£550 $1018 €803 Judith, a detail from Judith and Holofernes (57x50cm-22x20in) after Critofano Allori sold with other oil by same hand two. 14-Jul-4 Christie's, Kensington #806/R

RICHARDSON, Anne Worsham (20th C) American
Works on paper
£2312 $4000 €3376 Mallards (46x74cm-18x29in) s. gouache. 13-Dec-3 Charlton Hall, Columbia #546/R est:2500-3500

RICHARDSON, B (20th C) American
£484 $900 €707 Surrealist composition (18x15cm-7x6in) s.d.1951. 7-Mar-4 Treadway Gallery, Cincinnati #737/R

RICHARDSON, Charles (1829-1908) British
Works on paper
£380 $646 €555 Robin Hood's Bay, fishing boat off the coast (18x35cm-7x14in) s.i. W/C. 1-Dec-3 David Duggleby, Scarborough #240

RICHARDSON, Charles Douglas (1853-1932) British
Sculpture
£1352 $2137 €1974 Teh cloud (47cm-19in) s.i. pat.plaster. 2-Sep-3 Deutscher-Menzies, Melbourne #205/R est:5000-6000 (A.D 3300)

RICHARDSON, Constance Coleman (1905-) American
£392 $650 €568 Benedict farm (51x61cm-20x24in) 13-Jun-3 Du Mouchelle, Detroit #2379/R

RICHARDSON, Edith (1867-?) British
£480 $878 €701 Spring awakening (76x55cm-30x22in) s. 8-Apr-4 Christie's, Kensington #94/R

RICHARDSON, Edward (1810-1874) British
Works on paper
£1400 $2506 €2044 Carnarvon Castle (36x89cm-14x35in) s.d.1863 W/C. 17-Mar-4 Bonhams, Chester #216/R est:1200-1600
£1550 $2852 €2263 Mediterranean coastal scene (33x48cm-13x19in) s.d.1862 W/C. 26-Mar-4 Tring Auctions, Tring #351/R
£2000 $3600 €2920 Castle and town of Heidelberg on the Neckar (42x90cm-17x35in) W/C over pencil bodycol exhib. 21-Jan-4 Sotheby's, Olympia #199/R est:2000-3000

RICHARDSON, Francis Henry (1859-1934) American
£315 $500 €460 Cottages (30x41cm-12x16in) s. s.i.verso. 12-Sep-3 Skinner, Boston #266/R
Works on paper
£755 $1200 €1102 Isle of Shoals (31x64cm-12x25in) s.i.d.93 W/C gouache. 12-Sep-3 Skinner, Boston #271/R

RICHARDSON, Frederic Stuart (1855-1934) British
Works on paper
£250 $403 €363 Fishermen returning, York cliff (15x25cm-6x10in) W/C. 15-Aug-3 Keys, Aylsham #534
£560 $1014 €818 Thatched cottage (21x28cm-8x11in) s. W/C. 30-Mar-4 David Duggleby, Scarborough #55/R
£814 $1360 €1188 On the canal bridge, Holland (21x27cm-8x11in) s. s.i.verso W/C. 17-Nov-3 Waddingtons, Toronto #57/R est:600-800 (C.D 1800)

RICHARDSON, George (1808-1840) British
Works on paper
£600 $1002 €876 Dogana, Venice (25x38cm-10x15in) pencil W/C. 16-Oct-3 Christie's, Kensington #56/R

RICHARDSON, Gwyneth (20th C) New Zealander
Works on paper
£378 $684 €552 White lilies in a brass vase (49x62cm-19x24in) s. W/C. 30-Mar-4 Stephan Welz, Johannesburg #168 (SA.R 4500)

RICHARDSON, H Hughes (?) British
Works on paper
£420 $773 €613 Taormina, Sicily (32x19cm-13x7in) s.i. W/C. 23-Mar-4 Bonhams, Knightsbridge #181/R

RICHARDSON, H Linley (1878-1947) New Zealander
Works on paper
£364 $571 €528 Wellington City (38x62cm-15x24in) s. W/C. 27-Aug-3 Dunbar Sloane, Wellington #66 (NZ.D 1000)

RICHARDSON, John Isaac (1836-1913) British
Works on paper
£1200 $2244 €1752 Huntsman on horseback with foxhounds nearby (40x60cm-16x24in) s.d.1880 pencil W/C exhib. 22-Jul-4 Tennants, Leyburn #676 est:800-1000

RICHARDSON, Jonathan (snr) (1665-1745) British
£9444 $17000 €13788 Portrait of a gentleman, identified as the poet John Gray, seated with his dog in a landscape (112x100cm-44x39in) 23-Jan-4 Christie's, Rockefeller NY #171/R est:15000-20000

RICHARDSON, Louis H (1853-1923) American
£240 $400 €350 Landscape with trees (46x36cm-18x14in) s. board. 20-Jun-3 Freeman, Philadelphia #182/R

RICHARDSON, Mary Curtis (1848-1931) American
£291 $550 €425 Figure with a staff (25x18cm-10x7in) i.verso board. 22-Feb-4 Bonhams & Butterfields, Los Angeles #7019

RICHARDSON, Mary Neal (1859-1937) American
£307 $550 €448 Artist's camp, Camden, Maine (25x30cm-10x12in) s. 14-May-4 Skinner, Boston #157/R

RICHARDSON, R Esdaile (fl.1890s) British
Works on paper
£320 $576 €467 The arrival of the royal yacht Britannia in Portsmouth harbour, 1901 (56x81cm-22x32in) s. W/C. 25-Jan-4 Desmond Judd, Cranbrook #1075

RICHARDSON, Ray (1964-) British
£700 $1274 €1022 Soulpower (25x25cm-10x10in) s.i.d.1999 prov. 15-Jun-4 Bonhams, New Bond Street #128/R
£1000 $1820 €1460 It's the Stuntmonkey (25x30cm-10x12in) s.i.d.1994 prov. 15-Jun-4 Bonhams, New Bond Street #127/R est:1000-1500
£1600 $2960 €2336 Dropping a log (51x23cm-20x9in) s.i.d.1992. 11-Mar-4 Christie's, Kensington #332/R est:1000-1500

RICHARDSON, Robert (?) British
Works on paper
£580 $1038 €847 St Anne's Square, Manchester (37x50cm-15x20in) s. pastel. 17-Mar-4 Bonhams, Chester #256

RICHARDSON, Theodore J (1855-1914) American
Works on paper
£385 $700 €562 Seated native people by a log cabin (15x23cm-6x9in) s. W/C en grisaille prov. 15-Jun-4 John Moran, Pasadena #115a
£13369 $25000 €19519 Wrangell, Alaska (25x36cm-10x14in) s. W/C prov. 24-Jul-4 Coeur d'Alene, Hayden #185/R est:8000-12000

RICHARDSON, Thomas Miles (jnr) (1813-1890) British
£700 $1169 €1022 Skiddaw from Keswick. 21-Oct-3 Gorringes, Lewes #2080/R
Works on paper
£280 $504 €409 Scottish landscape with figure beside stone bridge with dog (22x32cm-9x13in) init. pencil W/C. 21-Apr-4 Tennants, Leyburn #930
£325 $582 €475 Quarry (22x34cm-9x13in) s.d.1834 prov. 10-May-4 Joel, Victoria #418 (A.D 800)
£360 $662 €526 View towards Conway Castle (39x62cm-15x24in) s. W/C. 23-Mar-4 Bonhams, Knightsbridge #72/R
£360 $655 €526 Dilston Castle, Northumberland (13x21cm-5x8in) s. W/C. 29-Jun-4 Anderson & Garland, Newcastle #234
£400 $668 €584 Castle of Baden (27x36cm-11x14in) s.i.d.1846 W/C bodycol. 14-Oct-3 Bonhams, Knightsbridge #39/R
£400 $736 €584 Figures on a coastal path, with boats in the bay beyond (24x35cm-9x14in) s.d.1879 pencil W/C. 25-Mar-4 Christie's, Kensington #264/R
£400 $716 €584 Continental mountainous lake scene (8x13cm-3x5in) s. W/C. 5-May-4 John Nicholson, Haslemere #431
£480 $773 €701 Figures beside an Italian lake (30x43cm-12x17in) s.d.1858 W/C. 15-Aug-3 Keys, Aylsham #501/R
£550 $1001 €803 Fisherwomen on a beach (14x22cm-6x9in) init.d.1839 W/C. 29-Jun-4 Anderson & Garland, Newcastle #235
£550 $1029 €825 River scene (20x30cm-8x12in) mono.d.1853 W/C. 21-Jul-4 John Nicholson, Haslemere #75
£600 $1020 €876 Travellers on a cart beside a river, a ruined castle beyond (15x23cm-6x9in) s.d.1876 pencil W/C sold with a pencil sketch prov. 4-Nov-3 Rowley Fine Art, Newmarket #367/R
£750 $1403 €1095 Travellers on a path on a hillside, the town of Trent beyond (27x44cm-11x17in) s.indis.d.1852 W/C prov. 24-Feb-4 Rowley Fine Art, Newmarket #413/R
£900 $1656 €1314 Figures in a woodland landscape (22x33cm-9x13in) s.d.1834 W/C. 23-Jun-4 Bonhams, Bury St Edmunds #307/R
£1000 $1700 €1460 Fishermen at sea (22x31cm-9x12in) s.d.1841 W/C htd white. 4-Nov-3 Bonhams, New Bond Street #82 est:600-900
£1000 $1700 €1460 Isola Bella, Lake Maggiore, Italy (22x33cm-9x13in) s.d.1861 W/C htd white prov. 4-Nov-3 Bonhams, New Bond Street #85/R est:1200-1800
£1000 $1820 €1460 Scottish river with an angler in the foreground (31x44cm-12x17in) s.d.1855 W/C. 29-Jun-4 Anderson & Garland, Newcastle #233/R est:1000-1800
£1150 $2024 €1679 Bringing down the game (14x38cm-6x15in) s.d.1856 W/C. 19-May-4 James Thompson, Kirby Lonsdale #102
£1300 $2210 €1898 Spital of Glenshee (36x87cm-14x34in) s.i. W/C over pencil htd bodycol. 27-Nov-3 Sotheby's, London #300/R est:1500-2000
£1300 $2392 €1898 Peasants on the coast before the Island of Ithaca (20x44cm-8x17in) s.d.1874 pencil W/C htd white. 25-Mar-4 Christie's, Kensington #105/R est:1000-1500
£1500 $2760 €2190 On the Italian lakes (13x22cm-5x9in) init.d.1858 W/C pair. 8-Jun-4 Bonhams, New Bond Street #61/R est:1500-2000
£2300 $3703 €3335 Peat moss, Ballachulish (18x46cm-7x18in) s.i.d.1848 W/C htd white prov. 21-Aug-3 Bonhams, Edinburgh #1117/R est:1800-2500
£2500 $4550 €3650 At Amalfi, Gulf of Salerno (65x75cm-26x30in) s.d.1853 prov. 1-Jul-4 Christie's, Kensington #353/R est:3000-5000
£3100 $5704 €4526 Isle of Nisida - looking towards the Bay of Naples from Solfatara (41x91cm-16x36in) s. W/C. 23-Mar-4 Anderson & Garland, Newcastle #314/R est:2500-4500
£3500 $5635 €5075 On the river Findhorn, nr Forres, Ross-shire (56x86cm-22x34in) indis sig. W/C htd white scratching out. 21-Aug-3 Bonhams, Edinburgh #1078/R est:1500-2500
£4000 $6800 €5840 Castel dell'Ovo, Naples with mount Vesuvius in the background (31x52cm-12x20in) s.d.1889 W/C. 4-Nov-3 Bonhams, New Bond Street #76/R est:1500-2000
£5500 $9350 €8030 Rhone Valley from the Forclass, Pass of the Tete Noire (66x100cm-26x39in) s.d.1876 pencil W/C gum arabic htd bodycol. 20-Nov-3 Christie's, London #110/R est:3000-5000
£6463 $11568 €9500 On the lake of Lugano (34x65cm-13x26in) s.d.1883 W/C gouache prov. 17-Mar-4 Maigret, Paris #17/R est:2000-3000
£7143 $12786 €10500 Glen Strae Lake Awe (34x64cm-13x25in) s.d.1881 W/C gouache. 17-Mar-4 Maigret, Paris #14/R est:2000-3000
£14286 $25571 €21000 Ben Nevis (34x63cm-13x25in) s.d.1880 W/C gouache. 17-Mar-4 Maigret, Paris #16/R est:2000-3000
£16327 $29224 €24000 Departing day, Ben Nevis (65x100cm-26x39in) s.d.1879 W/C gouache prov.exhib. 17-Mar-4 Maigret, Paris #15/R est:4000-6000

RICHARDSON, Thomas Miles (jnr-attrib) (1813-1890) British
Works on paper
£250 $415 €365 Figures in a Italian landscape (32x50cm-13x20in) W/C. 1-Oct-3 Woolley & Wallis, Salisbury #128/R
£720 $1224 €1051 Figures on a country road in a mountainous landscape (25x36cm-10x14in) indis i. pencil W/C htd white. 6-Nov-3 Christie's, Kensington #1024/R
£1000 $1850 €1460 Figures with a horse and cart on an upland country path (38x60cm-15x24in) W/C htd scratching out executed c.1880. 14-Jan-4 Lawrence, Crewkerne #1323/R est:1000-1500

RICHARDSON, Thomas Miles (snr) (1784-1848) British
£2700 $4833 €3942 Washing on the river (49x66cm-19x26in) s. 26-May-4 Sotheby's, Olympia #72/R est:3000-5000
Works on paper
£380 $684 €555 Dunstanborough Castle (25x36cm-10x14in) W/C pen ink over pencil htd bodycol. 22-Apr-4 Lawrence, Crewkerne #751
£580 $1038 €847 Vale of Callander (32x49cm-13x19in) s. W/C. 17-Mar-4 Bonhams, Chester #273
£580 $1044 €847 Side, Newcastle (24x16cm-9x6in) W/C pencil prov. 22-Apr-4 Lawrence, Crewkerne #750/R
£1700 $3128 €2482 Bonchurch, Isle of Wight (22x54cm-9x21in) s. pencil W/C. 25-Mar-4 Christie's, Kensington #255/R est:1000-1500
£1800 $3294 €2628 Askam, near Penrith (25x36cm-10x14in) i. pencil W/C htd white grey paper prov. 3-Jun-4 Christie's, London #110/R est:1000-1500
£2700 $4509 €3915 Mouth of the Tyne looking towards Tynemouth with figures (48x30cm-19x12in) mono.i.d.1835 pencil W/C. 11-Jul-3 Jim Railton, Durham #918/R est:2000-3000

RICHARDSON, Thomas Miles (snr-attrib) (1784-1848) British
Works on paper
£800 $1440 €1168 View of Derwentwater looking towards Skiddaw (20x33cm-8x13in) pencil W/C. 21-Apr-4 Tennants, Leyburn #928

RICHARDSON, Thomas Miles (19th C) British
Works on paper
£1200 $2076 €1752 Broad river valley with an angler conversing with a woman plus ruined castle (22x32cm-9x13in) W/C. 9-Dec-3 Anderson & Garland, Newcastle #200/R est:700-900

RICHARDSON, William (19th C) British
£420 $785 €630 Street scene, Yorkminster (76x64cm-30x25in) 22-Jul-4 Gorringes, Lewes #1771/R
Works on paper
£300 $501 €438 View of Salisbury Cathedral (30x43cm-12x17in) s.d.1887 pencil W/C. 16-Oct-3 Christie's, Kensington #62

RICHARDT, Ferdinand (1819-1895) Danish
£356 $647 €534 Landscape with Taarbaek Church (28x40cm-11x16in) s.d.1869. 19-Jun-4 Rasmussen, Havnen #2147/R (D.KR 4000)
£448 $819 €654 Sorterup Church near Slagelse (26x36cm-10x14in) s.d.1877. 9-Jun-4 Rasmussen, Copenhagen #1636/R (D.KR 5000)
£471 $800 €688 Landscape with riders (18x13cm-7x5in) s. canvas on panel prov. 1-Nov-3 Santa Fe Art, Santa Fe #122/R
£2457 $4251 €3587 Danish town by fjord, ladies walking in foreground (28x41cm-11x16in) s.d.1871. 9-Dec-3 Rasmussen, Copenhagen #1578/R est:15000-20000 (D.KR 26000)

RICHARDT, Ferdinand (attrib) (1819-1895) Danish
£947 $1752 €1383 View from Barritskov over Vejle Fjord (50x65cm-20x26in) 15-Mar-4 Rasmussen, Vejle #449/R (D.KR 10500)

RICHEBE, Horace (1871-1958) French
£872 $1605 €1300 Bord de mer (27x35cm-11x14in) s. panel. 29-Mar-4 Rieunier, Paris #55/R

RICHER, Paul M L Pierre (1849-1933) French
Sculpture
£1333 $2413 €2000 Le semeur (61cm-24in) s.i.d.1925 bronze. 30-Mar-4 Gioffredo, Nice #53/R

RICHERT, Charles Henry (1880-?) American
£698 $1200 €1019 Sargent Mountain, Maine (28x36cm-11x14in) s. 7-Dec-3 Grogan, Boston #62/R
Works on paper
£227 $400 €331 Landscape with birch trees in a field with distant mountains (36x25cm-14x10in) s. W/C. 3-Jan-4 Cobbs, Peterborough #220/R

RICHES, Charles M (19/20th C) British
£440 $801 €642 Farmyard scene with young child seated on a back of a calf (38x28cm-15x11in) s. 15-Jun-4 Canterbury Auctions, UK #92/R

RICHET, Léon (1847-1907) French
£280 $468 €409 Summer blooms (25x17cm-10x7in) s. panel. 8-Oct-3 Christie's, Kensington #957
£280 $476 €400 Vikings (55x46cm-22x18in) s. isorel exhib. 24-Nov-3 Boscher, Cherbourg #749
£300 $555 €438 Roses and daises in a vase on a table (46x39cm-18x15in) 14-Jul-4 Christie's, Kensington #1215

£315 $535 €450 Entree de ferme (55x46cm-22x18in) s. isorel exhib.lit. 24-Nov-3 Boscher, Cherbourg #752
£795 $1446 €1200 Chaumiere (27x37cm-11x15in) s.d.81 canvas on cardboard. 19-Jun-4 Binoche, Orleans #36
£800 $1336 €1168 Figure by a pond (29x42cm-11x17in) s. panel. 14-Oct-3 Bearnes, Exeter #386/R
£993 $1658 €1400 Paysenne au bord de l'eau pret d'un village (25x33cm-10x13in) s. prov. 20-Oct-3 Glerum, Amsterdam #104/R
£1000 $1600 €1460 Flowers in a vase (41x30cm-16x12in) s. 19-Sep-3 Freeman, Philadelphia #190/R est:1500-2000
£1210 $2226 €1767 Woman in a pastoral landscape (29x38cm-11x15in) s. panel. 14-Jun-4 Waddingtons, Toronto #286/R est:3000-5000 (C.D 3000)
£1342 $2483 €2000 Chemin du village (27x32cm-11x13in) s. cardboard. 14-Mar-4 St-Germain-en-Laye Encheres #83/R
£1536 $2750 €2243 Near Barbizon (39x48cm-15x19in) s. i.verso. 6-May-4 Doyle, New York #29/R est:3000-4000
£1577 $2539 €2350 La mare aux grands arbres (36x28cm-14x11in) s. 23-Feb-3 St-Germain-en-Laye Encheres #65/R est:1500-1800
£1818 $3091 €2600 Ferme Normande (42x67cm-17x26in) s.d.77. 24-Nov-3 Boscher, Cherbourg #739/R est:2000-3000
£1831 $3168 €2600 Wooded landscape near Barbizon (30x40cm-12x16in) s.d.75. 13-Dec-3 Lempertz, Koln #243/R est:3000
£1887 $3000 €2755 Flock (49x68cm-19x27in) s. 12-Sep-3 Skinner, Boston #243/R
£2101 $3446 €2900 Boisiere a Barbizon (25x35cm-10x14in) s. panel. 11-May-3 Osenat, Fontainebleau #113/R est:2500-2800
£2333 $4270 €3500 Paysanne pres du village (29x25cm-11x10in) s. paper on cardboard. 6-Jun-4 Osenat, Fontainebleau #119/R est:2800-3000
£2477 $4261 €3616 Landscape with a pond, wood collectors and village in distance (38x55cm-15x22in) s. 8-Dec-3 Philippe Schuler, Zurich #3428/R est:6000-8000 (S.FR 5500)
£2727 $4691 €3900 Summer park landscape with woman (50x65cm-20x26in) s. 5-Dec-3 Michael Zeller, Lindau #775/R est:1400
£2747 $5000 €4011 Wood gatherer (64x92cm-25x36in) s. 29-Jun-4 Sotheby's, New York #64/R est:10000-15000
£2899 $4754 €4000 Rochers a Fontainebleau (55x65cm-22x26in) s.d.91. 11-May-3 Osenat, Fontainebleau #117 est:4500-5000
£3116 $5110 €4300 La mare aux grands arbres (36x28cm-14x11in) s. 11-May-3 Osenat, Fontainebleau #115 est:4500-5000
£3147 $5413 €4500 Paysage a la clairiere (25x32cm-10x13in) s. panel. 7-Dec-3 Osenat, Fontainebleau #130 est:4500-5000
£3356 $5940 €5000 Lavandiere pres d'une chaumiere au bord d'une mare (33x41cm-13x16in) s. 27-Apr-4 Artcurial Briest, Paris #127/R est:4500-6000
£3497 $6014 €5000 Chemin en foret de Fontainebleau (41x59cm-16x23in) s. painted c.1870-75. 7-Dec-3 Osenat, Fontainebleau #128 est:5000-6000
£3662 $6408 €5200 Paysage anime aux environs de Fontainebleau (65x91cm-26x36in) s. 19-Dec-3 Delvaux, Paris #14/R est:5000-7000
£4474 $8232 €6800 Paysanne devant la mare a Fontainebleau (68x42cm-27x17in) s. 22-Jun-4 Calmels Cohen, Paris #41/R est:4000-6000
£4545 $7818 €6500 Chaumiere en bord de mer (31x41cm-12x16in) s. 7-Dec-3 Osenat, Fontainebleau #131 est:7000-7500
£5046 $8427 €7317 Landscape with old mill, small pond and chickens (73x59cm-29x23in) s.d.78. 23-Jun-3 Philippe Schuler, Zurich #3545/R est:6000-8000 (S.FR 11000)
£5245 $9021 €7500 Paysanne pres du village au bord de la riviere (51x66cm-20x26in) s. painted c.1870-1875. 7-Dec-3 Osenat, Fontainebleau #132 est:7000-8000
£5500 $9460 €8030 Return home (65x92cm-26x36in) s. 3-Dec-3 Christie's, London #24/R est:6000-9000
£6111 $11000 €8922 Ciel d'orage sur la campagne (52x66cm-20x26in) s. panel prov. 22-Apr-4 Christie's, Rockefeller NY #98/R est:10000-15000
£6790 $11000 €9846 Soleil couchant (63x90cm-25x35in) s. prov. 8-Aug-3 Barridorf, Portland #164/R est:15000-25000
£7609 $12478 €10500 Chaumiere a la mare (27x41cm-11x16in) s.d.76 prov. 11-May-3 Osenat, Fontainebleau #116/R est:7000-7500
£8099 $14011 €11500 Paysanne assise sur une brouette en foret (190x290cm-75x114in) s.d.1891. 12-Dec-3 Artus Associes, Paris #140
£14085 $23380 €20000 Grands arbres (162x130cm-64x51in) s. 15-Jun-3 Peron, Melun #136

RICHET, Léon (attrib) (1847-1907) French
£1275 $2346 €1900 Extensive wooded landscape with pond (23x33cm-9x13in) i. verso panel. 25-Mar-4 Dr Fritz Nagel, Stuttgart #751/R est:400

RICHEVILLAIN, Henri (19/20th C) ?
£1049 $1804 €1500 Villa blanche (47x73cm-19x29in) s. pair. 8-Dec-3 Tajan, Paris #309 est:1500-2000

RICHIER, Germaine (1904-1959) French
Sculpture
£2857 $4543 €4200 Femme-coq (12cm-5in) s. pat bronze el. 21-Mar-3 Bailly Pommery, Paris #143/R
£3473 $5800 €5071 Untitled - figure (26x9x8cm-10x4x3in) lead shells stone prov. 11-Nov-3 Christie's, Rockefeller NY #164/R est:7000-9000
£4803 $8742 €7012 Dancer (19cm-7in) bronze stone socle. 17-Jun-4 Kornfeld, Bern #712/R est:10000 (S.FR 11000)
£12000 $21840 €17520 La chinoise (25cm-10in) i. bronze st.f.A.Pastori prov.exhib. 4-Feb-4 Sotheby's, London #266/R est:10000-15000
£12676 $21930 €18000 Untitled (162x39x32cm-64x15x13in) col glass lead sold with base. 9-Dec-3 Artcurial Briest, Paris #413/R est:20000-25000
£13000 $23660 €18980 Guerrier No 2 (38x9x20cm-15x4x8in) s.num.3/6 bronze st.f.Valsuani prov.exhib.lit. 6-Feb-4 Sotheby's, London #176/R est:10000-15000
£25140 $45000 €36704 L'Aigle (65cm-26in) s. num.4/8 st.f.Valsuani brown pat bronze exec 1954 prov. 6-May-4 Sotheby's, New York #297/R est:40000-60000
£33567 $57064 €48000 Maquette du Christ d'Assy (45x32x8cm-18x13x3in) bronze edition 1/8. 25-Nov-3 Tajan, Paris #25b est:48000
£140000 $254800 €204400 Vierge Folle (137x38x28cm-54x15x11in) s.i. num.6/6 bronze Cast Susse Fondeur conceived 1946 prov.lit. 5-Feb-4 Sotheby's, London #35/R est:130000-150000
£153846 $261538 €220000 Le griffu (90x83x70cm-35x33x28in) s.num.H.C.2 bronze st.f.Susse exhib.lit. 25-Nov-3 Tajan, Paris #25/R est:150000-180000

RICHIR, Herman (1866-1942) Belgian
£345 $638 €500 Elegante a l'emeraude (116x95cm-46x37in) s.d.1921. 16-Feb-4 Horta, Bruxelles #320
£1528 $2429 €2200 Enfant prodigue (106x120cm-42x47in) s. 9-Sep-3 Vanderkindere, Brussels #36/R
£1736 $2760 €2500 Vase of flowers (100x75cm-39x30in) s. oval. 9-Sep-3 Vanderkindere, Brussels #14
£1888 $3210 €2700 La belle Espagnole (110x80cm-43x31in) s. exhib. 18-Nov-3 Vanderkindere, Brussels #109/R est:2500-4000
£10067 $18624 €15000 Still life (75x100cm-30x39in) s. 13-Mar-4 De Vuyst, Lokeren #444/R
Works on paper
£1379 $2483 €2000 La cueillette (60x50cm-24x20in) s.d.1927 W/C. 20-Jan-4 Galerie Moderne, Brussels #267/R est:1500-2000

RICHLY, Rudolf (1886-1975) Austrian
£467 $840 €700 Still life with fish, window and landscape (30x40cm-12x16in) s. 21-Apr-4 Dorotheum, Vienna #184

RICHMOND, Agnes M (1870-1964) American
£1529 $2600 €2232 Boatyard, Bearskin Neck (51x61cm-20x24in) s. 21-Nov-3 Skinner, Boston #564/R est:1200-1800
Works on paper
£1453 $2600 €2121 Horse with armored rider rears when confronted by woodland troll (51x36cm-20x14in) chl W/C gouache. 15-May-4 Illustration House, New York #80/R est:2500-3500

RICHMOND, Dorothy Kate (1861-1935) New Zealander
£13158 $22368 €19211 Maori woman with children (101x95cm-40x37in) init.d.1905 board prov.exhib. 26-Nov-3 Dunbar Sloane, Wellington #26/R est:35000-45000 (NZ.D 35000)
Works on paper
£583 $991 €851 Quiet inlet (24x28cm-9x11in) s.d.1931 W/C. 27-Nov-3 International Art Centre, Auckland #111/R (NZ.D 1550)
£616 $992 €899 Canterbury landscape with poplar trees (24x32cm-9x13in) init.d.1903 W/C. 12-Aug-3 Peter Webb, Auckland #74 (NZ.D 1700)
£727 $1142 €1054 Lake Taupo through trees (26x35cm-10x14in) s.d.1951 W/C. 27-Aug-3 Dunbar Sloane, Wellington #60/R (NZ.D 2000)
£779 $1394 €1137 Children on river bank (24x35cm-9x14in) s.d.1926 W/C. 12-May-4 Dunbar Sloane, Wellington #125/R est:2700-4700 (NZ.D 2250)
£1000 $1840 €1460 Dawson Falls, Taranaki, New Zealand (33x23cm-13x9in) s.d.1925 W/C. 25-Mar-4 International Art Centre, Auckland #106/R (NZ.D 2800)
£1321 $2392 €1929 Autumn bouquet (60x46cm-24x18in) i.verso W/C. 30-Mar-4 Peter Webb, Auckland #175/R est:3500-4500 (NZ.D 3700)
£2068 $3515 €3019 Rural scene (23x34cm-9x13in) s.d.1929 W/C. 27-Nov-3 International Art Centre, Auckland #127/R est:3000-5000 (NZ.D 5500)
£3000 $5010 €4380 Still life of roses in a vase (93x66cm-37x26in) s. W/C over pencil. 14-Oct-3 Sotheby's, London #182/R est:3000-5000

RICHMOND, George (1809-1896) British
£4200 $7140 €6132 Portrait of Octavius Wigram seated in a black suit holding a letter, in a library (128x182cm-50x72in) s.d.1861 prov.exhib.lit. 25-Nov-3 Christie's, London #47/R est:4000-6000
Works on paper
£250 $418 €365 Portrait of a gentleman, in evening dress (41x28cm-16x11in) s. pencil W/C. 8-Oct-3 Christie's, Kensington #1035/R
£300 $552 €438 Portrait of a young man (33x25cm-13x10in) i.verso W/C. 8-Jun-4 Gorringes, Lewes #1978
£700 $1281 €1022 Portrait of gentleman wearing the order of the garter (58x42cm-23x17in) s.d.1850 chl pastel. 9-Jul-4 Dreweatt Neate, Newbury #420/R
£1450 $2596 €2117 Portrait of William 8th Earl Waldegrave standing in naval uniform. Portrait of Sarah Waldegrave (31x26cm-12x10in) W/C bodycol over chk pair. 22-Mar-4 Bonhams & Brooks, Norfolk #144/R est:1200-1800

RICHMOND, James Crowe (1822-1898) Australian
Works on paper
£4511 $7669 €6586 Picnic near Ratanui (18x28cm-7x11in) init.d.1851 W/C. 26-Nov-3 Dunbar Sloane, Wellington #33/R est:15000-20000 (NZ.D 12000)

RICHMOND, Leonard (1889-1965) British
£320 $554 €467 At the farmhouse gate (49x60cm-19x24in) s. board. 9-Dec-3 Rosebery Fine Art, London #629/R
£360 $655 €526 Near Nancledra, Cornwall (50x60cm-20x24in) s. board. 21-Jun-4 Bonhams, Bath #455
£420 $664 €609 Landacre Bridge, Exmoor, West Somerset (49x59cm-19x23in) s.i.overlap. 24-Jul-3 Lawrence, Crewkerne #980/R
£420 $739 €613 Bungalows near San Francisco (46x60cm-18x24in) s. canvasboard. 18-May-4 Bonhams, Knightsbridge #182/R
£500 $935 €730 Lake Moraine, Canadian Rockies (19x14cm-7x6in) s. board. 24-Feb-4 Canterbury Auctions, UK #160/R
£590 $986 €850 The Bridge (51x60cm-20x24in) s. board. 24-Oct-3 Ketterer, Hamburg #517/R
£700 $1281 €1022 French street scene (37x48cm-15x19in) oil paper on canvas prov. 3-Jun-4 Lane, Penzance #125/R
£1900 $3515 €2774 Cornish harbour, possibly St Ives (40x50cm-16x20in) s. 16-Feb-4 Bonhams, Bath #50 est:300-500
£2700 $4995 €3942 St Ives, looking across to Porthmeor (50x60cm-20x24in) s. board. 16-Feb-4 Bonhams, Bath #49 est:400-600
Works on paper
£280 $521 €409 Figures strolling along avenue of trees (53x61cm-21x24in) s.d.1916 pastel. 2-Mar-4 Bearnes, Exeter #352/R
£356 $583 €516 Landscape of a village in southern France (39x53cm-15x21in) s. W/C board. 5-Jun-3 Heffel, Vancouver #76 (C.D 800)
£475 $793 €694 Untitled - view across a bridge. Untitled - town and figures (37x50cm-15x20in) s. pastel two. 17-Nov-3 Hodgins, Calgary #156/R est:600-800 (C.D 1050)

RICHMOND, Sir William Blake (1842-1921) British
Works on paper
£950 $1758 €1387 Study for the resurrection. Orpheus and Ulysses (25x45cm-10x18in) pastel. 14-Jul-4 Sotheby's, Olympia #95/R

£4615	$7661	€6738	Study of Perseus and Andromeda (76x61cm-30x24in) s.verso chl. 4-Oct-3 Kieselbach, Budapest #137/R (H.F 1700000)

RICHMOND, Thomas (snr) (1771-1837) British

Miniatures

£1100	$2024	€1606	Gentleman one wearing a blue. Gentleman wearing black coat (5cm-2in) double-sided gold frame plaited hair border. 24-Jun-4 Bonhams, New Bond Street #95/R est:800-1200
£1600	$2880	€2336	Self portrait as a young man (5cm-2in) ormolu mount oval prov.exhib.lit. 22-Apr-4 Bonhams, New Bond Street #46/R est:2000-3000

RICHTER, Abraham (attrib) (?-1642) German

£2621	$4377	€3800	Portraits of Burgermeister von Kronach and wife (99x78cm-39x31in) mono.d.1595 two. 9-Jul-3 Hugo Ruef, Munich #8/R est:2500

RICHTER, Albert (1845-1898) German

£1958	$3270	€2800	Mountains with stream (40x56cm-16x22in) s.d.1868. 10-Oct-3 Winterberg, Heidelberg #741/R est:3800
£2727	$4527	€3954	A camel caravan crossing the desert (18x46cm-7x18in) s.i. panel. 13-Jun-3 Zofingen, Switzerland #2374/R est:4800 (S.FR 6000)

RICHTER, Anton (attrib) (1781-1850) Austrian

£435	$800	€635	Portrait of Queen Louis of Prussia. Portrait of King Frederick William II (61x51cm-24x20in) indis i.d.1825 two. 23-Jun-4 Doyle, New York #5063/R

RICHTER, August (1801-1873) German

Works on paper

£349	$636	€510	Mountain landscape with riders (18x22cm-7x9in) brush sepia over pencil prov.exhib. 17-Jun-4 Kornfeld, Bern #60/R (S.FR 800)
£699	$1272	€1021	Onions and carrots (20x34cm-8x13in) wash sepia prov.exhib. 17-Jun-4 Kornfeld, Bern #64/R (S.FR 1600)
£961	$1748	€1403	Three fish, hanging with string (37x24cm-15x9in) W/C prov. 17-Jun-4 Kornfeld, Bern #63/R (S.FR 2200)
£1333	$2400	€1946	Interior with chair by a chest of drawers. Shepherd with his flock (18x22cm-7x9in) black chk brush col wash double-sided prov. 22-Jan-4 Christie's, Rockefeller NY #157/R est:1000-1500

RICHTER, Aurel (1870-1957) Hungarian

£462	$771	€660	Woman (64x48cm-25x19in) s. tempera W/C board. 10-Oct-3 Winterberg, Heidelberg #1872/R

RICHTER, Christian (1678-1732) Swedish

Miniatures

£1300	$2158	€1898	Oliver Cromwell (4cm-2in) init.d.1653 gilt metal frame rectangular after Samuel Cooper. 2-Oct-3 Sotheby's, Olympia #6/R est:800-1200
£8000	$14400	€11680	Carey, nee Fraser, Countess of Peterborough (8cm-3in) vellum gilt metal frame oval exhib.lit. 22-Apr-4 Bonhams, New Bond Street #11/R est:6000-8000

RICHTER, Christian (attrib) (1678-1732) Swedish

Miniatures

£2300	$4232	€3358	Lady in a pale green dress and red cloak, landscape beyond (15cm-6in) i. ormolu frame. 24-Jun-4 Bonhams, New Bond Street #45/R est:1000-1500

RICHTER, Daniel (1962-) German

£27933	$50000	€40782	Schluss mit fussball (169x131cm-67x52in) s.i.d.99 verso oil lacquer prov. 14-May-4 Phillips, New York #119/R est:30000-40000
£37989	$68000	€55464	Meisterin der puppen - mistress of puppets (269x230cm-106x91in) s.d.2002 oil lacquer prov.exhib.lit. 13-May-4 Phillips, New York #4/R est:60000-80000
£40667	$72793	€61000	Fuhlung, flirrung, fluchtung (172x215cm-68x85in) s.d.99. 12-May-4 Chochon-Barre & Allardi, Paris #48 est:1000-1500
£60000	$110400	€87600	Ein schoner traum von anarchie und gewalt (218x179cm-86x70in) s.i.d.99 verso prov. 24-Jun-4 Christie's, London #49/R est:35000-45000
£125749	$210000	€183594	Gedion (306x339cm-120x133in) s.i.d.2002 oil ink lacquer on canvas prov.exhib.lit. 13-Nov-3 Phillips, New York #57/R est:40000-60000

RICHTER, Edouard Frederic Wilhelm (1844-1913) French

£7181	$13285	€10700	Melancolie dans les jardins du harem (64x44cm-25x17in) s. 15-Mar-4 Gros & Delettrez, Paris #234/R est:15000-20000
£10667	$19520	€16000	Orientale a la rose (66x44cm-26x17in) s.i. 3-Jun-4 Tajan, Paris #272/R est:15000-20000

RICHTER, Gerhard (1932-) German

£1965	$3400	€2869	Kassel (42x59cm-17x23in) s.i. oil on offset print paper on board prov. 10-Dec-3 Phillips, New York #575/R est:2000-3000
£2797	$4755	€4000	Untitled - black, red, gold (21x7cm-8x3in) s.i.d.98 paper on board. 29-Nov-3 Villa Grisebach, Berlin #389/R est:3000-4000
£3667	$6747	€5500	Kassel (15x23cm-6x9in) s.d.1992 oil over print cardboard. 12-Jun-4 Villa Grisebach, Berlin #432/R est:3500-4500
£4121	$7500	€6017	Untitled - candle (89x89cm-35x35in) s.d.89 oil over col photograph. 29-Jun-4 Sotheby's, New York #579/R est:10000-15000
£5000	$8350	€7300	Untitled (10x14cm-4x6in) s.d.5 Dez. 1999 mount oil on colour photograph prov. 21-Oct-3 Sotheby's, London #366/R est:5000-7000
£5000	$9200	€7300	Vermalung (40x40cm-16x16in) s.d.71 verso paper prov.lit. 24-Jun-4 Sotheby's, London #280/R est:5000-7000
£5028	$9000	€7341	64 Variationen von Schwarz Rot Gold 414 (22x30cm-9x12in) s.verso acrylic masonite painted 1998 prov. 13-May-4 Sotheby's, New York #434/R est:8000-12000
£5594	$9510	€8000	Untitled (10x15cm-4x6in) s.d.8.2.92 verso oil on col photo. 27-Nov-3 Lempertz, Koln #369/R est:7000-8000
£5594	$9510	€8000	Souvenir (21x21cm-8x8in) 29-Nov-3 Villa Grisebach, Berlin #392/R est:8000-10000
£5800	$10034	€8468	Vermalung, braun (27x40cm-11x16in) s.d.92 verso lit. 11-Dec-3 Christie's, Kensington #271/R est:6000-8000
£5944	$10105	€8500	Composition - brown (27x40cm-11x16in) s.i.d.72 verso. 27-Nov-3 Lempertz, Koln #368/R est:7000
£7000	$11690	€10220	Black, red, gold (21x30cm-8x12in) both s.verso acrylic glass exec 1998 two prov. 21-Oct-3 Sotheby's, London #433/R est:8000-10000
£7500	$12525	€10950	Souvenir (21x21cm-8x8in) s. painted 1995 prov. 21-Oct-3 Sotheby's, London #442/R est:3000-4000
£7800	$13026	€11388	Souvenir (21x21cm-8x8in) s. painted 1995 prov. 21-Oct-3 Sotheby's, London #441/R est:3000-4000
£8392	$14266	€12000	Fingermalerei grau, peinture avec doigts gris (40x40cm-16x16in) oil paper prov. 25-Nov-3 Tajan, Paris #50/R est:10000-12000
£11000	$20020	€16060	Firenze (12x12cm-5x5in) s.d.2000 num.1/7 verso oil col photo prov.exhib.lit. 6-Feb-4 Sotheby's, London #135/R est:10000-15000
£11000	$20240	€16060	Miniatures (8x8cm-3x3in) s.d.1996 verso canvas on card prov.lit. 24-Jun-4 Sotheby's, London #283/R est:8000-10000
£12575	$21000	€18360	Blech 681-29 (20x27cm-8x11in) s.d.1988 prov.lit. 14-Nov-3 Phillips, New York #196/R est:15000-20000
£13000	$21710	€18980	Miniatures (23x23cm-9x9in) s.d.1996 canvas on card prov.lit. 21-Oct-3 Sotheby's, London #434/R est:8000-10000
£15000	$27300	€21900	Untitled (29x42cm-11x17in) s.d.1996 Fuji photographic paper prov. 5-Feb-4 Christie's, London #201/R est:15000-20000
£15000	$27600	€21900	Rot-Blau-Gelb (26x53cm-10x21in) s.d.73 verso prov.exhib.lit. 24-Jun-4 Sotheby's, London #276/R est:12000-15000
£16000	$28960	€23360	Rot blau gelb (26x53cm-10x21in) s.i.d.73 prov. 1-Apr-4 Christie's, Kensington #263/R est:15000-20000
£16000	$29440	€23360	Rot-Blau-Belf (26x53cm-10x21in) s.d.73 verso prov.exhib.lit. 24-Jun-4 Sotheby's, London #277/R est:12000-15000
£16760	$30000	€24470	Finger painting (60x78cm-24x31in) s.d.1972 oil paper prov. 14-May-4 Phillips, New York #258/R est:35000-45000
£20000	$33400	€29200	Grun-blau-rot (30x40cm-12x16in) s.d.93 verso prov.lit. 22-Oct-3 Christie's, London #99/R est:20000-30000
£20112	$36000	€29364	Fuji (29x37cm-11x15in) s.verso oil aluminum prov.lit. 14-May-4 Phillips, New York #261/R est:18000-25000
£26946	$45000	€39341	Grun-blau-rot (29x4cm-11x2in) s.d.93 verso prov.lit. 13-Nov-3 Sotheby's, New York #538/R est:30000-40000
£27933	$50000	€40782	Untitled (36x41cm-14x16in) s.d.92 i.verso prov. 13-May-4 Sotheby's, New York #423/R est:60000-80000
£27933	$50000	€40782	Graues Bild I (86x61cm-34x24in) s.d.Sept 1971 verso paper on panel prov. 13-May-4 Sotheby's, New York #440/R est:60000-80000
£28743	$48000	€41965	Untitled - house 6 Jan 90 (49x70cm-19x28in) s.d.6 Jan 90 oil on photograph prov. 14-Nov-3 Phillips, New York #197/R est:50000-70000
£29000	$53360	€42340	Grun-Blau-Rot (30x40cm-12x16in) s.d.93 verso prov.lit. 24-Jun-4 Sotheby's, London #281/R est:18000-25000
£30000	$55200	€43800	Grun blau rot (30x40cm-12x16in) s.d.93 prov.lit. 25-Jun-4 Christie's, London #215/R est:18000-22000
£30667	$56120	€46000	Park (63x81cm-25x32in) s.d.3. Mai 1990 oil on col photo. 4-Jun-4 Lempertz, Koln #386/R est:50000
£31138	$52000	€45461	Untitled (30x42cm-12x17in) s.d.17.Dec.1995 paper on board prov. 12-Nov-3 Christie's, Rockefeller NY #390/R est:40000-60000
£32000	$58240	€46720	Abstraktes Bild (29x37cm-11x15in) s.d.verso prov.lit. 5-Feb-4 Christie's, London #202/R est:30000-40000
£37333	$68320	€56000	Untitled (185cm-73in) s.i.d.1965 plastic prov.exhib. 4-Jun-4 Lempertz, Koln #385/R est:60000
£53333	$95467	€80000	Composition 773-3 (52x62cm-20x24in) s.i.d. verso. 15-May-4 Dr Sturies, Dusseldorf #156/R
£65000	$119600	€94900	Abstraktes bild (27x35cm-11x14in) s.d.1988 verso lit. 24-Jun-4 Sotheby's, London #284/R est:50000-70000
£70000	$128800	€102200	Abstrakates (71x61cm-28x24in) s.d.93 verso prov.exhib.lit. 25-Jun-4 Christie's, London #218/R est:70000-90000
£85000	$156400	€124100	Abstraktes bild (70x50cm-28x20in) s.d.1983 verso prov.lit. 25-Jun-4 Christie's, London #209/R est:70000-90000
£105000	$191100	€153300	Abstraktes (62x52cm-24x20in) s.d.1990 verso prov.lit. 5-Feb-4 Christie's, London #203/R est:70000-90000
£105000	$193200	€153300	Abstraktes bild (46x51cm-18x20in) s.d.92 prov.lit. 25-Jun-4 Christie's, London #210/R est:60000-80000
£145251	$260000	€212066	Abstraktes bild (82x112cm-32x44in) s.i.d.1990 prov.lit. 13-May-4 Phillips, New York #35/R est:250000-350000
£150838	$270000	€220223	Stadtbild M1 (85x90cm-33x35in) s.i.d.68 verso prov.exhib.lit. 11-May-4 Christie's, Rockefeller NY #3/R est:300000-400000
£155689	$260000	€227306	Abstraktes Bild (56x51cm-22x20in) s.d.1994 num.816-3 verso prov.lit. 12-Nov-3 Christie's, Rockefeller NY #389/R est:200000-300000
£155689	$260000	€227306	Abstraktes bild (61x51cm-24x20in) s. prov.lit. 13-Nov-3 Phillips, New York #19/R est:150000-200000
£170000	$309400	€248200	Abstraktes bild (95x100cm-37x39in) s.d.1991 verso board prov.exhib.lit. 5-Feb-4 Sotheby's, London #18/R est:200000-300000
£215569	$360000	€314731	Untitled, 618-4 (81x67cm-32x26in) s.d.1986 verso lit. 13-Nov-3 Sotheby's, New York #546a/R est:250000-350000
£220000	$404800	€321200	Grau - 338/1 (200x150cm-79x59in) s.d.1974 prov.lit. 24-Jun-4 Christie's, London #23/R est:200000-300000
£234637	$420000	€342570	Abstract painting 819-3 (61x71cm-24x28in) painted 1994 prov.exhib.lit. 13-May-4 Sotheby's, New York #424/R est:250000-350000
£273743	$490000	€399665	Abstraktes Bild - 756-2 (122x102cm-48x40in) s.d.1992 verso prov.exhib.lit. 12-May-4 Christie's, Rockefeller NY #197/R est:250000-350000
£320000	$572800	€480000	Abstract picture (112x102cm-44x40in) s.i.d. verso prov. 14-May-4 Ketterer, Munich #242/R est:250000-350000
£389222	$650000	€568264	Apples (92x67cm-36x26in) s.d.1988 prov.exhib.lit. 12-Nov-3 Sotheby's, New York #66/R est:600000-800000
£389222	$650000	€568264	Abstraktes Bild 721-1 (112x82cm-44x32in) s.d.1990 num.721-1 verso prov.lit. 12-Nov-3 Christie's, Rockefeller NY #387/R est:300000-400000
£449102	$750000	€655689	Abstraktes Bild (240x240cm-94x94in) s.d.1993 prov.lit. 11-Nov-3 Christie's, Rockefeller NY #56/R est:850000-1250000
£538922	$900000	€786826	Zehn Farben (135x120cm-53x47in) s.d.66 verso lacquer prov.lit. 11-Nov-3 Christie's, Rockefeller NY #9/R est:300000-400000
£670391	$1200000	€978771	Ausschnitt - Kreutz (200x200cm-79x79in) s.d.1971 verso prov.exhib.lit. 11-May-4 Christie's, Rockefeller NY #51/R est:800000-1200000
£726257	$1300000	€1060335	Girl in arm chair - Lilac (90x110cm-35x43in) s.d.1965 verso s.i.d.3.9.66 overlap prov.lit. 12-May-4 Sotheby's, New York #35/R est:1000000-1500000
£838323	$1400000	€1223952	Portrait Wunderlich (200x200cm-79x79in) s.d.67 verso prov.lit. 11-Nov-3 Christie's, Rockefeller NY #50/R est:1500000-2000000
£1005587	$1800000	€1468157	Wolken (200x300cm-79x118in) s.d.1970 verso prov.exhib.lit. 11-May-4 Christie's, Rockefeller NY #41/R est:2000000-3000000
£1117319	$2000000	€1631286	Bottle with apple (81x61cm-32x24in) s.d.1988 prov.lit. 12-May-4 Sotheby's, New York #30/R est:1200000-1800000
£1843576	$3300000	€2691621	4096 Farben (254x254cm-100x100in) s.i.d.1974 verso lacquer prov.exhib.lit. 11-May-4 Christie's, Rockefeller NY #34/R est:3000000-4000000
£2035928	$3400000	€2972455	Zwei kerzen - two candles (125x100cm-49x39in) s.d.1983 prov.exhib.lit. 12-Nov-3 Sotheby's, New York #43/R est:2500000-3500000

Photographs

£2533	$4535	€3800	Abstract photo (49x70cm-19x28in) s.i. gelatin silver. 15-May-4 Dr Sturies, Dusseldorf #160/R

£4348	$7130	€6000	Uran (100x70cm-39x28in) s.d. num.33/50 gelatin silver print. 27-May-3 Sotheby's, Amsterdam #621/R est:6000-8000
£10180	$17000	€14863	Onkel Rudi (87x50cm-34x20in) s.num.42/80 verso c-print prov.exhib. 13-Nov-3 Sotheby's, New York #422/R est:15000-20000
£10778	$18000	€15736	Ravine (75x56cm-30x22in) s.d.97 num.verso c-print plexiglas edition of 45 prov. 13-Nov-3 Sotheby's, New York #536/R est:18000-22000
£13000	$23660	€18980	Onkel Rudi (87x50cm-34x20in) s.num.17/80 verso cibachrome photo dibond prov.lit. 6-Feb-4 Sotheby's, London #129/R est:12000-15000
£16766	$28000	€24478	Untitled (53x37cm-21x15in) s.d.1996 num.45 cibachrome mounted on paperboard prov. 14-Nov-3 Phillips, New York #203/R est:10000-15000

Prints

£1622	$3000	€2368	Wolken (45x40cm-18x16in) s.d.1969 grey offset lithograph edition of 300. 12-Feb-4 Christie's, Rockefeller NY #193/R est:2000-3000
£1695	$3000	€2475	Mao (84x59cm-33x23in) s. lithograph edition of 500. 28-Apr-4 Christie's, Rockefeller NY #388/R est:4000-6000
£1765	$3000	€2577	Station (48x58cm-19x23in) s. offset print. 31-Oct-3 Sotheby's, New York #730/R
£1765	$3000	€2577	Auto (37x46cm-15x18in) s. offset lithograph. 31-Oct-3 Sotheby's, New York #732/R
£1963	$3200	€2866	Seestuck (90x70cm-35x28in) s.d.1991 offset col lithograph wove paper. 24-Sep-3 Christie's, Rockefeller NY #353/R est:900-1200
£2147	$3800	€3135	Abstraktes (50x70cm-20x28in) s.d.1989 num.40/50 photographic print. 28-Apr-4 Christie's, Rockefeller NY #391/R est:4000-6000
£2206	$3750	€3221	Wolken (45x40cm-18x16in) s. offset print. 31-Oct-3 Sotheby's, New York #731/R
£2260	$4000	€3300	9 von 180 farben (30x42cm-12x17in) s.d.1971 num.12/90 screenprint. 30-Apr-4 Sotheby's, New York #443/R est:2500-3500
£2353	$4000	€3435	Eis 2 (112x89cm-44x35in) s.d.2003 col screenprint. 4-Nov-3 Christie's, Rockefeller NY #336/R est:4000-6000
£2500	$4550	€3650	Mao (84x59cm-33x23in) s. violet-black collotype edition of 500. 1-Jul-4 Sotheby's, London #342/R est:3000-4000
£2595	$4800	€3789	Seestuck 2 (60x45cm-24x18in) s.d.1970 col offset lithograph edition of 100. 12-Feb-4 Christie's, Rockefeller NY #194/R est:2000-3000
£2667	$4773	€4000	Kassel (16x23cm-6x9in) s.i.d. varnish on offset. 15-May-4 Dr Sturies, Dusseldorf #161
£2761	$4500	€4031	Eis 2 (112x89cm-44x35in) s.d.2003 num.77/108 col screenprint on Somerset. 24-Sep-3 Christie's, Rockefeller NY #354/R est:4000-6000
£2796	$5200	€4082	Seestuck 2 (60x45cm-24x18in) s.d.1970 offset lithograph. 2-Mar-4 Swann Galleries, New York #566/R est:2500-3500
£3500	$5810	€5110	Mao (84x59cm-33x23in) s. violet-black collotype edition of 620. 6-Oct-3 Sotheby's, London #304/R est:3000-4000
£4500	$7740	€6570	Kerze (89x94cm-35x37in) s. col offset lithograph edition of 250. 4-Dec-3 Sotheby's, London #254/R est:2000-3000
£4667	$8587	€7000	Ice 2 (101x81cm-40x32in) s.d.2003 col serigraph one of 108. 12-Jun-4 Villa Grisebach, Berlin #429/R est:4000-6000
£4706	$8000	€6871	Kerze (89x94cm-35x37in) s. offset col lithograph. 4-Nov-3 Christie's, Rockefeller NY #335/R est:4000-6000
£5090	$8500	€7431	128 Fotos von einem bild (64x101cm-25x40in) s.d.98 num.60 portfolio of eight prints. 14-Nov-3 Phillips, New York #202/R est:8000-12000
£5500	$10010	€8030	Orchid, version 1 (30x37cm-12x15in) s.d.1998 num.2/25 verso col offset print prov. 1-Jul-4 Sotheby's, London #345/R est:6000-8000
£6704	$12000	€9788	Kerze, candle. s.d.26 Juni 2003 col offset lithograph edition of 250 prov.lit. 14-May-4 Phillips, New York #303/R est:20000-30000
£7500	$12900	€10950	Orchids (28x36cm-11x14in) s.d.98 col offset print. 4-Dec-3 Sotheby's, London #253/R est:8000-10000
£8667	$15513	€13000	Mao (84x59cm-33x23in) s.i.d. light print. 15-May-4 Dr Sturies, Dusseldorf #157/R
£10056	$18000	€14682	Orchid, version V (28x36cm-11x14in) s.d.31 oct 98 offset lithograph edition of 14 prov. 14-May-4 Phillips, New York #301/R est:20000-25000
£10734	$19000	€15672	Kerze (89x94cm-35x37in) s. col offset lithograph. 28-Apr-4 Christie's, Rockefeller NY #390/R est:18000-25000
£11976	$20000	€17485	Orchid (48x50cm-19x20in) s.d.21 Nov 98 offset lg. ink edition 1 of 24 prov. 13-Nov-3 Sotheby's, New York #537/R est:15000-20000
£26347	$44000	€38467	Kerze - candle (95x89cm-37x35in) offset lithograph black chk paperboard prov.exhib. 14-Nov-3 Phillips, New York #195/R est:28000-35000

Sculpture

£2457	$4250	€3587	Cross (19x19x1cm-7x7x0in) num.30/80 steel. 12-Dec-3 Sotheby's, New York #480/R est:1500-2000

Works on paper

£2797	$4755	€4000	Black red gold (21x7cm-8x3in) s.i.d.98 three part collage oil board. 27-Nov-3 Lempertz, Koln #370/R est:3500
£4790	$8000	€6993	Schwarz, rot, gold - black, red, gold (21x30cm-8x12in) s. synthetic resin on glass executed 1999 prov. 14-Nov-3 Phillips, New York #201/R est:8000-12000
£12291	$22000	€17945	Kerze (89x90cm-33x35in) s. blk crayon offset lithograph exec 1988 1 edn 250. 13-May-4 Sotheby's, New York #435/R est:18000-25000
£17000	$31280	€24820	Kerze (89x94cm-35x37in) s. black crayon on offset print prov.lit. 25-Jun-4 Christie's, London #269/R est:10000-15000
£26000	$47840	€37960	Woman in fitted kitchen (29x40cm-11x16in) s.d.65 pencil prov. 24-Jun-4 Sotheby's, London #219/R est:25000-35000
£67039	$120000	€97877	Dorf - village (72x102cm-28x40in) s.i.d.1987 v, graphite prov.exhib.lit. 13-May-4 Phillips, New York #31/R est:180000-250000

RICHTER, Giovanni (18th C) Italian

£30000	$51900	€43800	Doge's Palace, Venice, with the Doganna and the Molo, from the Giudecca (38x58cm-15x23in) prov. 10-Dec-3 Christie's, London #50/R est:20000-30000

RICHTER, Gottfried (1904-) German

£298	$542	€450	Steam locomotive with coaches in front of platform (18x24cm-7x9in) mono. board. 19-Jun-4 Bergmann, Erlangen #851
£694	$1160	€1000	City street (45x61cm-18x24in) mono. board. 25-Oct-3 Dr Lehr, Berlin #413/R
£694	$1160	€1000	Red townhall (46x61cm-18x24in) mono. i. verso panel. 25-Oct-3 Dr Lehr, Berlin #414/R
£694	$1160	€1000	Berlin (46x61cm-18x24in) mono. i. verso panel. 25-Oct-3 Dr Lehr, Berlin #415/R

RICHTER, Gustav Karl (attrib) (1823-1884) German

£1965	$3576	€2869	Portrait of Antoinette Marie Josephine Caroline Frieda (95x75cm-37x30in) oval prov. 16-Jun-4 Fischer, Luzern #1203/R est:4500-6000 (S.FR 4500)

RICHTER, Hans (1888-1975) German

£930	$1711	€1358	Composition (40x30cm-16x12in) mono.d.1962 s.d. verso canvas on panel prov. 8-Jun-4 Germann, Zurich #106/R (S.FR 2130)
£1351	$2378	€2000	Dymo sketch II (38x54cm-15x21in) init.d.68 s.i.d.on stretcher tempera pastel paper on canvas prov. 24-May-4 Christie's, Milan #75/R est:1200-1800
£2027	$3568	€3000	Composition (73x37cm-29x15in) s. s.verso painted c.1961 prov. 24-May-4 Christie's, Milan #95/R est:3000-4000

Works on paper

£486	$812	€700	Sketch for gap (37x28cm-15x11in) s. pencil. 24-Oct-3 Ketterer, Hamburg #1040/R
£533	$976	€800	Morning Spuk - hats (59x48cm-23x19in) s. felt collage transparent foil. 5-Jun-4 Lempertz, Koln #969/R
£2412	$4439	€3522	Metal collage (66x76cm-26x30in) s.d.74 copper aluminium plywood. 23-Jun-4 Koller, Zurich #3094/R est:5000-7000 (S.FR 5500)
£2517	$4505	€3700	Untitled (33x202cm-13x80in) s.d.64 mixed media paper on canvas prov. 16-Mar-4 Finarte Semenzato, Milan #40/R est:3500

RICHTER, Hans Theo (1902-1969) German

Works on paper

£333	$600	€500	Nude sitting on chair (42x33cm-17x13in) chk. 24-Apr-4 Dr Lehr, Berlin #397/R

RICHTER, Henry James (1772-1857) German

£2500	$4075	€3650	The tight shoe (61x74cm-24x29in) 23-Sep-3 John Nicholson, Haslemere #260/R est:4000-6000

RICHTER, Henry Leopold (1870-1960) American

£449	$750	€656	Late afternoon in winter, no 4 (51x61cm-20x24in) s. 26-Oct-3 Bonhams & Butterfields, San Francisco #6518a/R
£1765	$3000	€2577	Fruit vendor (24x20cm-9x8in) s. prov. 18-Nov-3 John Moran, Pasadena #108 est:3000-4000
£1912	$3250	€2792	Edge of the desert (24x30cm-9x12in) s.i.verso. 18-Nov-3 John Moran, Pasadena #123 est:3000-5000

RICHTER, Herbert Davis (1874-1955) British

£600	$1020	€876	Simple room (61x51cm-24x20in) s. s.i.verso. 6-Nov-3 Christie's, Kensington #930/R
£700	$1190	€1022	Cottage interior (41x51cm-16x20in) s. 26-Nov-3 Sotheby's, Olympia #47/R
£1200	$2004	€1752	Geraniums (61x51cm-24x20in) s. 16-Oct-3 Christie's, Kensington #376/R est:1500-2000
£1500	$2580	€2190	Bit of Devon country (64x76cm-25x30in) 3-Dec-3 Christie's, Kensington #534/R est:1500-2000
£1500	$2595	€2190	Room interior with still life (75x63cm-30x25in) s. init.d.1943 verso sold with copy of Art of H Davis Richter. 11-Dec-3 Lyon & Turnbull, Edinburgh #5/R est:1500-2000
£1958	$3329	€2800	Still life (58x104cm-23x41in) s.i. s.d.Nov 22 1922 verso. 25-Nov-3 De Veres Art Auctions, Dublin #159/R est:4000-6000

Works on paper

£250	$430	€365	Market square (49x39cm-19x15in) s. pastel. 3-Dec-3 Christie's, Kensington #467
£500	$915	€730	Discussion in a market place (30x36cm-12x14in) W/C bodycol. 27-Jan-4 Bonhams, Knightsbridge #350/R
£800	$1296	€1168	Spring time (77x65cm-30x26in) s.i. pastel prov.exhib. 30-Jul-3 Hamptons Fine Art, Godalming #89/R

RICHTER, Johan Anton (1665-1745) Swedish

£80556	$145000	€117612	View of San Giorgio Maggiore (57x95cm-22x37in) 22-Jan-4 Sotheby's, New York #66/R est:70000-90000
£86111	$155000	€125722	View of the Grand Canal (57x95cm-22x37in) 22-Jan-4 Sotheby's, New York #67/R est:70000-90000

RICHTER, Johan Anton (style) (1665-1745) Swedish

£6500	$11895	€9490	The Piazzetta, Venice looking towards the Libreria and the entrance to the Grand Canal (90x121cm-35x48in) prov. 9-Jul-4 Christie's, Kensington #196/R est:4000-6000

RICHTER, Karl (?) German

£270	$484	€400	Spring day on Dachauer Moos (70x100cm-28x39in) s. 6-May-4 Michael Zeller, Lindau #836

RICHTER, Leopold (1896-?) German

Works on paper

£269	$500	€393	Figures in a landscape (45x33cm-18x13in) init. mixed media. 5-Mar-4 Skinner, Boston #604/R

RICHTER, Ludwig Adrian (1803-1884) German

Works on paper

£267	$477	€400	Mother with children on her way to the field (9x14cm-4x6in) mono. pencil. 13-May-4 Bassenge, Berlin #5645
£480	$874	€701	Portrait of a young convalescent (20x14cm-8x6in) s. pencil. 16-Jun-4 Fischer, Luzern #2601/R (S.FR 1100)
£505	$843	€732	Mountainous wooded landscape with figures (10x16cm-4x6in) bister W/C. 23-Jun-3 Philippe Schuler, Zurich #3914 (S.FR 1100)
£570	$1050	€850	Blacksmiths (23x15cm-9x6in) d.27 Apr 58 Indian ink. 26-Mar-4 Dorotheum, Vienna #118/R
£900	$1557	€1314	View of Clausthal-Zellerfeld with figures by a pond (10x15cm-4x6in) i.verso black lead pen brown ink wash. 12-Dec-3 Christie's, Kensington #559/R
£1048	$1907	€1530	Two children with cat. Mother with child in henhouse (5x7cm-2x3in) pencil two prov.exhib. 17-Jun-4 Kornfeld, Bern #54/R (S.FR 2400)
£1556	$2800	€2272	Rocky landscape with waterfall, and mountains seen through clouds (40x30cm-16x12in) s.d.30 black lead pen black ink grey wash. 22-Jan-4 Christie's, Rockefeller NY #155/R est:3000-5000

£1778 $3200 €2596 Extensive mountain landscape with herdsmen making music (15x24cm-6x9in) black chk pen brown ink wash W/C prov. 22-Jan-4 Christie's, Rockefeller NY #156/R est:3000-5000
£2993 $5358 €4400 Is it her? (23x16cm-9x6in) s.i.d.1853 pen over pencil brown wash W/C htd white. 17-Mar-4 Neumeister, Munich #308/R est:1200

RICHTER, Ludwig Adrian (attrib) (1803-1884) German
£3500 $5600 €5110 Dejeuner sur l'herbe (54x65cm-21x26in) s. 18-Sep-3 Christie's, Kensington #19/R est:4000-5000

RICHTER, Max (1860-?) German
£280 $518 €409 Dock scene (48x67cm-19x26in) s.indis.d.1944. 16-Jul-4 Charterhouse, Sherborne #593

RICHTER, Otto (1867-?) German
Sculpture
£1325 $2411 €2000 Woman with dog (61cm-24in) s. green black pat.bronze. 19-Jun-4 Dannenberg, Berlin #192/R est:900

RICHTER, Wilhelm (1824-1892) Austrian
£744 $1235 €1086 Portrait of young man in uniform (24x19cm-9x7in) s.d.1855 board. 4-Oct-3 Dorotheum, Prague #14/R est:30000-45000 (C.KR 34000)
£861 $1567 €1300 Small fisherman in front of Italian coastal landscape (32x25cm-13x10in) s.i.indis.d. board on panel. 21-Jun-4 Dorotheum, Vienna #184/R

RICHTER, Willibald (19th C) Austrian
Works on paper
£596 $1091 €900 Interior of Stephansdom, Vienna (36x28cm-14x11in) s. gouache paper on panel. 7-Apr-4 Dorotheum, Salzburg #188/R

RICHTER, Wilmer Siegfried (1891-?) American
£1677 $2750 €2448 Quiet sight, Chester county farm (51x61cm-20x24in) s. board. 4-Jun-3 Alderfer's, Hatfield #380/R est:2500-3000

RICHTER-LUSSNITZ, Georg (1891-1938) German
£699 $1286 €1021 Easter Sunday (70x104cm-28x41in) s.d.20 s.i.d. verso canvas on board. 14-Jun-4 Philippe Schuler, Zurich #4342/R (S.FR 1600)

RICHTER-REICH, F M (1896-?) German
£280 $467 €400 Flower market, Amsterdam (60x80cm-24x31in) s. 30-Jun-3 Sotheby's, Amsterdam #407/R
£483 $801 €700 Flower market by Dutch canal (93x118cm-37x46in) s. 6-Oct-3 Bloss, Merzhausen #1226/R
£533 $965 €800 Flower market in Dutch city (70x50cm-28x20in) s. 1-Apr-4 Van Ham, Cologne #1620

RICHTERICH, Marco (1929-) Swiss
£386 $641 €560 Abstract composition (60x60cm-24x24in) i. verso. 13-Jun-3 Zofingen, Switzerland #2989 (S.FR 850)

RICHTERS, Marius (1878-1955) Dutch
£420 $701 €600 In the garden (48x39cm-19x15in) s.i. on stretcher. 30-Jun-3 Sotheby's, Amsterdam #267/R
£486 $792 €700 The Church of Terschelling (52x40cm-20x16in) s. 29-Sep-3 Sotheby's, Amsterdam #210
£500 $895 €750 Interior of St Lauren Church in Rotterdam (59x74cm-23x29in) s. 11-May-4 Vendu Notarishuis, Rotterdam #31
£533 $955 €800 Avenue of trees with Grindweg to Hillegersberg (69x98cm-27x39in) s.d.31. 11-May-4 Vendu Notarishuis, Rotterdam #41/R
£1067 $1909 €1600 Girl on a balcony with view of the Holland-Amerika liner (94x74cm-37x29in) s. 11-May-4 Vendu Notarishuis, Rotterdam #99/R est:1000-1500

RICKARD, Bruce (20th C) New Zealander
£3571 $6464 €5214 Foliage and Maori carving (152x152cm-60x60in) s.d.1994 enamel. 30-Mar-4 Peter Webb, Auckland #158/R est:10000-15000 (NZ.D 10000)

RICKENMANN, Ivan (1965-) Colombian
£500 $850 €730 Vestido de Brio puro Grandes, Bogota (150x120cm-59x47in) s.d.1999 acrylic. 30-Nov-3 Lots Road Auctions, London #343

RICKERBY, Arthur (1921-1972) American
Photographs
£1587 $3000 €2317 Admiral Nimitz signing instruments of surrender on USS Missouri (26x33cm-10x13in) silver print. 17-Feb-4 Swann Galleries, New York #66/R est:3500-4500

RICKEY, George (1907-2002) American
Sculpture
£4301 $8000 €6279 Untitled (27cm-11in) s.d.64 num.56/100 stainless steel wooden base. 5-Mar-4 Skinner, Boston #588/R est:3000-5000
£8392 $14434 €12000 Mobile M (41cm-16in) gilded steel. 3-Dec-3 Hauswedell & Nolte, Hamburg #955/R est:15000
£14970 $25000 €21856 Fleur de rocaille (37cm-15in) s.d.64 stainless steel bronze marble base prov. 13-Nov-3 Sotheby's, New York #104/R est:12000-16000
£22346 $40000 €32625 Three Parallelepipeds (63x25x25cm-25x10x10in) s.d.1985-87 num.3/3 base brushed aluminium wood prov. 12-May-4 Christie's, Rockefeller NY #205/R est:20000-30000
£23313 $38000 €34037 Untitled (81x10x20cm-32x4x8in) s.d.1977 num.1/3 stainless steel exhib. 23-Sep-3 Christie's, Rockefeller NY #37/R est:25000-35000
£25140 $45000 €36704 Eleven rotors with bronze (37x33x33cm-15x13x13in) s.d.69 base stainless steel bronze prov.exhib. 13-May-4 Sotheby's, New York #137/R est:20000-30000
£26816 $48000 €39151 Eight lines (159x140x15cm-63x55x6in) s.d.1963-87 base kinetic sculpture brushed aluminium prov. 12-May-4 Christie's, Rockefeller NY #210/R est:40000-60000
£33566 $57063 €48000 Lambda theme (234cm-92in) s.d.1987 steel prov. 27-Nov-3 Lempertz, Koln #377/R est:4000-5000
£36723 $65000 €53616 Untitled (147x38cm-58x15in) s.i.d.1972 stainless steel exhib. 2-May-4 Bonhams & Butterfields, Los Angeles #3040/R est:25000-35000
£75000 $138000 €109500 Two open rectangles excentric - Variation V (300cm-118in) stainless steel exec 1976 edn 2/3 prov.exhib. 24-Jun-4 Sotheby's, London #222/R est:60000-80000
£95808 $160000 €139880 Persephone-variation three (46x76x32cm-18x30x13in) s.d.66-68 stainless steel stone base prov.exhib. 13-Nov-3 Sotheby's, New York #105/R est:20000-25000
£107784 $180000 €157365 Six Random Lines Eccentric II (432x427cm-170x168in) s.d.1992-93 num.1/3 base kinetic sculpture stainless steel prov. 12-Nov-3 Christie's, Rockefeller NY #396/R est:180000-250000
£145251 $260000 €212066 One up, one down eccentric II (505cm-199in) stainless steel standing mobile exec 1977-90 prov.exhib. 13-May-4 Sotheby's, New York #179/R est:200000-300000
Works on paper
£15909 $28000 €23227 Sketch for Summer Kinetic Sculpture. sketch. 23-May-4 Hindman, Chicago #1108/R est:20000-25000

RICKMAN, Philip (1891-1982) British
Works on paper
£280 $468 €409 Snipe, wading amongst reed (28x40cm-11x16in) W/C htd bodycol. 14-Oct-3 Bonhams, Knightsbridge #41/R
£320 $586 €467 Throwing up from the Stoop, The Tay Estuary, Fotheringham (56x76cm-22x30in) W/C. 27-Jan-4 Gorringes, Lewes #1588
£340 $629 €496 Grouse over moorland (25x36cm-10x14in) s. gouache. 9-Mar-4 Gorringes, Lewes #2294
£450 $752 €657 Male pheasant (15x23cm-6x9in) s.d.1957 W/C. 17-Oct-3 Keys, Aylsham #525/R
£450 $824 €657 Crested Tits and a Firecrest (39x27cm-15x11in) s.d.1956 W/C htd white. 28-Jul-4 Bonhams, Knightsbridge #45/R
£480 $826 €701 Pheasants foraging in an autumnal landscape (25x37cm-10x15in) s. gouache. 3-Dec-3 Bonhams, Knightsbridge #19/R
£750 $1275 €1095 Woodcock in a winter landscape (40x56cm-16x22in) s.d.1965 W/C htd white. 27-Nov-3 Christie's, Kensington #232
£750 $1373 €1095 Blue tits (56x36cm-22x14in) s.d.1966 W/C. 28-Jul-4 Bonhams, Knightsbridge #46/R
£820 $1501 €1197 Cock pheasant dusting (16x23cm-6x9in) s.d.1957 W/C bodycol. 6-Jul-4 Bearnes, Exeter #452/R
£1300 $2405 €1898 Pair of partridges (58x40cm-23x16in) s.d.1962 W/C htd bodycol prov. 14-Jan-4 Lawrence, Crewkerne #1348/R est:1000-1500
£2200 $3740 €3212 Pheasants in the snow (54x75cm-21x30in) s.d.1959 gouache. 29-Oct-3 Bonhams, Chester #470/R est:1500-2000

RICO Y CEJUDO, Jose (1864-?) Spanish
£682 $1200 €996 Donkey tied up to a post, with a dog seated alongside (101x56cm-40x22in) s. 23-May-4 Bonhams & Butterfields, Los Angeles #7039/R

RICO Y ORTEGA, Martin (1833-1908) Spanish
£1342 $2403 €2000 Embarcadero (14x21cm-6x8in) s. board. 25-May-4 Durán, Madrid #188/R est:2000
£6000 $10200 €8760 Peasants (28x52cm-11x20in) s. 18-Nov-3 Sotheby's, London #258/R
£6711 $12550 €10000 Landscape with the Seine (81x82cm-32x32in) 24-Feb-4 Durán, Madrid #219/R est:10000
£6711 $12550 €10000 Landscape with the Seine (65x90cm-26x35in) 24-Feb-4 Durán, Madrid #220/R est:10000
£6800 $11560 €9928 Public Gardens, Venice (23x35cm-9x14in) s. prov. 19-Nov-3 Bonhams, New Bond Street #93/R est:5000-7000
£9259 $15000 €13426 Venice (25x34cm-10x13in) s. panel. 8-Aug-3 Barridorf, Portland #92/R est:15000-20000
£10738 $20081 €16000 Public gardens in Venice (24x36cm-9x14in) s. board. 24-Feb-4 Durán, Madrid #250/R est:15000
£11409 $20423 €17000 Venice (36x23cm-14x9in) s. board. 25-May-4 Durán, Madrid #201/R est:12000
£47222 $85000 €68944 Venetian canal scene (80x38cm-31x15in) s. prov. 22-Apr-4 Christie's, Rockefeller NY #218/R est:70000-90000
£65000 $110500 €94900 Santa Maria della Salute, Venice (124x84cm-49x33in) s. prov. 18-Nov-3 Sotheby's, London #261/R
Works on paper
£301 $503 €425 Landscape with houses (20x13cm-8x5in) s. dr. 20-Oct-3 Durán, Madrid #657/R
£1007 $1883 €1500 Kitten and sparrows (22x30cm-9x12in) s. W/C. 24-Feb-4 Durán, Madrid #189/R est:1500
£1310 $2359 €1900 Landscape in France (15x41cm-6x16in) s. W/C. 26-Jan-4 Ansorena, Madrid #301/R est:1800

RICOEUR, Nicolas (18th C) French
£15789 $29053 €24000 Vase de fleurs sur entablement de marbre (108x83cm-43x33in) 23-Jun-4 Sotheby's, Paris #27/R est:10000-15000

RICOIS, François Edme (1795-1881) French
£552 $922 €800 Femme au bouquet de fleurs (65x54cm-26x21in) s.d.1860. 17-Nov-3 Tajan, Paris #111
Works on paper
£5035 $8559 €7200 Le duc de Bordeaux et sa gouvernante la duchesse de Gontaut (19x27cm-7x11in) one bears sig. one d.1824 W/C pair. 1-Dec-3 Coutau Begarie, Paris #160/R est:2000-3000

RIDDEL, James (1858-1928) British
£600 $1032 €876 Wood cutters (48x66cm-19x26in) s. 6-Dec-3 Shapes, Edinburgh #415/R

RIDDELL, William Wallace (1877-1948) American
£353 $600 €515 Indian wells, California view (35x41cm-14x16in) s. canvasboard. 21-Nov-3 Skinner, Boston #330/R

RIDDER, Louis de (?) ?
£260 $413 €377 Rescue (67x105cm-26x41in) s. 9-Sep-3 Bonhams, Knightsbridge #132/R

RIDDLE, John (fl.1904-1934) British
£1000 $1670 €1460 Roses (59x49cm-23x19in) s.d.1944 exhib. 16-Oct-3 Lawrence, Crewkerne #754/R

RIDEOUT, P H (fl.1880-1900) British
£340 $568 €496 Coach and four (36x56cm-14x22in) s. 20-Jun-3 Chrystals Auctions, Isle of Man #267

RIDEOUT, Philip H (fl.1880-1912) British
£500 $925 €730 Stagecoach in a winter landscape and in a spring landscape (13x37cm-5x15in) s.indis.d. board pair. 13-Jan-4 Bonhams, Knightsbridge #229/R
£1400 $2576 €2044 Stage coach in a winter landscape. Stage coach in a summer landscape (20x27cm-8x11in) s.d.1890 pair board. 10-Jun-4 Christie's, Kensington #122/R est:1500-2000

RIDEOUT, Philip H (attrib) (fl.1880-1912) British
£650 $1216 €949 Coach and four in winter. Coach and four outside an inn with rider nearby (20x38cm-8x15in) panel pair. 22-Jul-4 Tennants, Leyburn #873

RIDER, Arthur G (1886-1975) American
£4403 $7000 €6428 Courtyard scene (51x41cm-20x16in) s. 14-Sep-3 Susanin's, Chicago #6062/R est:8000-12000
£4430 $7000 €6468 Through the archway, Capistrano (56x56cm-22x22in) s. 7-Sep-3 Treadway Gallery, Cincinnati #596/R est:5000-7000
£5291 $10000 €7725 Through the Archway, Capistrano (56x56cm-22x22in) s. prov. 17-Feb-4 John Moran, Pasadena #119/R est:4000-6000

RIDER, H Orne (1860-?) American
£645 $1200 €942 Gray day, farm buildings, Stow, Mass (40x60cm-16x24in) s. canvasboard. 5-Mar-4 Skinner, Boston #445/R

RIDGE, Hugh E (?) British
£250 $455 €365 Estuary (41x51cm-16x20in) s. 15-Jun-4 David Lay, Penzance #571
£380 $635 €555 St. Ives, dusk (41x51cm-16x20in) s. 14-Oct-3 David Lay, Penzance #102

RIDGEWELL, John (1937-) British
£500 $925 €730 Yorkshire coastal town (70x90cm-28x35in) s.d.66. 13-Feb-4 Sworder & Son, Bishops Stortford #69/R

RIDINGER, Johann Elias (1698-1767) German
£3279 $6000 €4787 Study of a lion (28x22cm-11x9in) init. oil paper. 29-Jan-4 Swann Galleries, New York #294/R est:8000-12000

RIDLEY, Matthew White (1837-1888) British
£2800 $4564 €4088 Two strings to the bow, small girls and boy on Black Middens Rocks, North Shields (69x105cm-27x41in) exhib. 23-Sep-3 Anderson & Garland, Newcastle #364/R est:3000-5000

RIDOLA, Matteo (1888-1974) Italian
£590 $1003 €850 Composition with silver, lemons and china (80x100cm-31x39in) s. board. 1-Nov-3 Meeting Art, Vercelli #382

RIDOLFI, Claudio (attrib) (1570-1644) Italian
£2817 $4930 €4000 Moses found. King committing suicide (22x34cm-9x13in) en grisaille pair. 17-Dec-3 Christie's, Rome #454/R est:4000-6000
Works on paper
£1633 $2922 €2400 La Vierge a l'Enfant avec St Jerome et une sainte (15x26cm-6x10in) i. black chk pen brown ink wash htd white prov. 18-Mar-4 Christie's, Paris #80/R est:800-1200

RIDOLFO, Michele di (circle) (1795-1854) Italian
£11702 $18957 €16500 Portrait of young man with medallion (58x47cm-23x19in) board. 21-May-3 Babuino, Rome #5/R est:5000-7000

RIEBES, Moritz (1804-1883) German
£5517 $9214 €8000 Still life of fruit with mountain background (79x65cm-31x26in) s.d.1867. 15-Nov-3 Lempertz, Koln #1682/R est:6500

RIECKE, George (1848-1924) ?
£291 $530 €440 Two cows grazing in a meadow (25x35cm-10x14in) s. 18-Jun-4 Bolland & Marotz, Bremen #737
£435 $700 €635 Approaching storm (36x30cm-14x12in) s. 20-Aug-3 James Julia, Fairfield #1628/R
£449 $750 €656 Territorial dispute (15x20cm-6x8in) s. 18-Jun-3 Doyle, New York #65/R
£865 $1600 €1298 Rural landscape with sheep (58x74cm-23x29in) s. painted c.1888. 14-Jul-4 Dallas Auction Gallery, Dallas #250/R est:1500-2500

RIEDEL, August (1799-1883) German
£699 $1203 €1000 Accostage en bord de riviere (10x17cm-4x7in) s. panel. 7-Dec-3 Osenat, Fontainebleau #194
£5594 $9510 €8000 Neapolitan fisherman's family sitting on the beach (111x138cm-44x54in) mono. i.verso lit. 28-Nov-3 Schloss Ahlden, Ahlden #1405/R est:8500
£6667 $12067 €10000 Neapolitan fishing family on seashore (110x140cm-43x55in) mono. 1-Apr-4 Van Ham, Cologne #1620a/R est:6800

RIEDEL, August (attrib) (1799-1883) German
£3147 $5255 €4500 Young woman from the Campagna in church holding baby (95x79cm-37x31in) 9-Oct-3 Michael Zeller, Lindau #737/R est:4500

RIEDEL, Wilhelm (1832-1876) German
£863 $1416 €1200 Study of rock. Landscape (25x41cm-10x16in) card two. 10-Jun-3 Pandolfini, Florence #75
£1467 $2655 €2200 Extensive mountain landscape (92x142cm-36x56in) s.d.1859. 1-Apr-4 Van Ham, Cologne #1621/R est:3000

RIEDER, C (19th C) ?
£1545 $2580 €2256 German landscapes (26x21cm-10x8in) s. three. 25-Oct-3 Rasmussen, Havnen #2084/R est:5000 (D.KR 16500)

RIEDER, J (19th C) German
Sculpture
£1429 $2557 €2100 African fighter (32cm-13in) s. dark pat.bronze lit. 20-Mar-4 Bergmann, Erlangen #1212 est:750-2100

RIEDER, Marcel (1852-1942) French
£1042 $1646 €1500 Child's supper (130x89cm-51x35in) s. 2-Sep-3 Christie's, Amsterdam #190/R est:1500-2000

RIEDL, Alois (1935-) Austrian
Works on paper
£400 $736 €600 Sofa, striped (41x43cm-16x17in) mono.d.72 mixed media. 9-Jun-4 Dorotheum, Salzburg #717/R

RIEDLIN, Adolf (1892-1969) German
£403 $741 €600 Portrait of the pianist Margit Vogel (100x45cm-39x18in) s.d.1938 lit. 25-Mar-4 Karlheinz Kaupp, Staufen #2690/R

RIEFENSTAHL, Leni (1902-) German
Photographs
£1778 $3200 €2596 Sports Olympic games (23x28cm-9x11in) gelatin silver print prov.lit. 23-Apr-4 Phillips, New York #228/R est:2500-3500
£2000 $3680 €3000 Pathenon pillars (28x23cm-11x9in) i. verso bromide silver gelatin lit.exhib. 10-Jun-4 Villa Grisebach, Berlin #1259/R est:3000-4000
£3147 $5350 €4500 High jump, Berlin Olympics (18x28cm-7x11in) i. verso silver gelatin lit.exhib. 27-Nov-3 Villa Grisebach, Berlin #1353/R est:3000-3500

RIEGEN, Nicolaas (1827-1889) Dutch
£1678 $3087 €2500 Sailing ships off Dutch coast (27x36cm-11x14in) s. 25-Mar-4 Dr Fritz Nagel, Stuttgart #750/R est:1400
£2222 $3511 €3200 Two master in choppy waters by a coast (23x36cm-9x14in) s. panel. 2-Sep-3 Christie's, Amsterdam #306/R est:3500-4500
£3221 $5766 €4800 Bateaux de peche sur une mer houleuse (44x66cm-17x26in) s. 25-May-4 Palais de Beaux Arts, Brussels #562/R est:5000-7000
£4000 $7200 €6000 Shipping on choppy waters by a coast (44x67cm-17x26in) s. 21-Apr-4 Christie's, Amsterdam #5/R est:2500-3500
£4167 $7083 €6000 Sailing barge entering a waterway (31x46cm-12x18in) s. panel. 28-Oct-3 Christie's, Amsterdam #11/R est:6000-8000
£4861 $8264 €7000 Shipping on a choppy sea (65x99cm-26x39in) s.d.1871. 28-Oct-3 Christie's, Amsterdam #74/R est:6000-8000
£4861 $8118 €7000 Fishing boats off a jetty (51x81cm-20x32in) s. 21-Oct-3 Sotheby's, Amsterdam #1/R est:4000-6000

RIEGEN, Nicolaas (attrib) (1827-1889) Dutch
£1319 $2150 €1900 River landscape (20x30cm-8x12in) panel. 29-Sep-3 Sotheby's, Amsterdam #66
£2023 $3500 €2954 Harbour scene (38x53cm-15x21in) 12-Dec-3 Du Mouchelle, Detroit #2180/R est:200-400

RIEGER, Albert (1834-1905) Austrian
£704 $1127 €1000 Stream in mountains with goats grazing (53x42cm-21x17in) s. panel. 18-Sep-3 Rieber, Stuttgart #1018
£1100 $1837 €1606 Woodland camp (72x99cm-28x39in) s.d.1870. 12-Nov-3 Sotheby's, Olympia #182/R
£1391 $2531 €2100 Landscape near Lake Como (56x95cm-22x37in) s. i.verso. 18-Jun-4 Bolland & Marotz, Bremen #739/R est:2700
£1408 $2437 €2000 View of Wettersteinebirge and Rosenlauigletscher (73x100cm-29x39in) s.d.1870. 10-Dec-3 Dorotheum, Vienna #119/R est:4000-4800
£1667 $2750 €2400 Mill by mountain stream (100x74cm-39x29in) s. 2-Jul-3 Neumeister, Munich #751/R est:1800
£20979 $35664 €30000 Athenian ruins (198x132cm-78x52in) s. 24-Nov-3 Dorotheum, Vienna #14/R est:15000-20000

RIEGER, August (1886-1941) Austrian
£3497 $5944 €5000 Still life of flowers (68x55cm-27x22in) s. panel. 28-Nov-3 Wiener Kunst Auktionen, Vienna #486/R est:5000-10000

RIEMERSCHMID, Richard (1868-1957) German
£1020 $1827 €1500 Farmstead in wood (32x41cm-13x16in) mono. 20-Mar-4 Bergmann, Erlangen #1113 est:1500

RIEMERSCHMID, Rudolf (1873-1953) German
£694 $1132 €1000 Lower alpine landscape with lake in autumn (80x240cm-31x94in) mono. 25-Sep-3 Neumeister, Munich #2858/R

RIEPER, August (1865-1940) German
£486 $768 €700 Devil in hell dancing with lots of naked women (38x64cm-15x25in) s. i.verso. 5-Sep-3 Wendl, Rudolstadt #3580/R
£743 $1330 €1100 Archivist (81x61cm-32x24in) s. panel. 8-May-4 Dawo, Saarbrucken #128/R

RIERA FERRARI, Joan (?) Spanish
Works on paper
£704 $1218 €1000 Bust (51x70cm-20x28in) s. mixed media. 15-Dec-3 Ansorena, Madrid #1020/R

RIERA Y ARAGO, Jose M (1954-) Spanish
Sculpture
£1824 $3211 €2700 Mosquito (200x38x11cm-79x15x4in) s.d.1986 iron fabric prov.exhib. 18-May-4 Segre, Madrid #245/R est:2700

RIERA, Albert (20th C) French
£671 $1201 €1000 Place des Abesses (73x92cm-29x36in) s. i.d.25/12/26 verso. 25-May-4 Chambelland & Giafferi, Paris #80/R

RIERA, Javier (1964-) Spanish
£310 $496 €440 Untitled (41x33cm-16x13in) s.verso painted c.1995. 16-Sep-3 Segre, Madrid #174/R
£322 $537 €460 Untitled (41x33cm-16x13in) s.verso. 24-Jun-3 Segre, Madrid #159/R
£2333 $4223 €3500 Untitled (250x200cm-98x79in) s.verso oil mixed media painted 1997 exhib.lit. 30-Mar-4 Segre, Madrid #173/R est:3500

RIES, Henry (1917-) German
Photographs
£2000 $3680 €3000 Downtown Manhattan (34x26cm-13x10in) s.i. verso silver gelatin. 10-Jun-4 Villa Grisebach, Berlin #1261/R est:1500-2000

RIES, Ignacio de (1612-1661) Spanish
£160000 $289600 €240000 Saint Rufina (92x60cm-36x24in) prov.lit. 30-Mar-4 Segre, Madrid #46/R est:18000

RIESCH, Cesare (1906-) Italian
£423 $731 €600 Ladies on the beach (30x49cm-12x19in) s. board. 9-Dec-3 Pandolfini, Florence #269

RIESENBERG, Sidney (1885-?) American
£4192 $7000 €6120 Stagecoach fleeing marauding Indians (102x79cm-40x31in) s. painted c.1930. 15-Nov-3 Illustration House, New York #14/R est:6000-9000

RIESENER, Léon (1808-1878) French
£333 $603 €500 Hercule et le sanglier d'Ermyanthe (26x48cm-10x19in) exhib. 30-Mar-4 Rossini, Paris #258/R
£1027 $1603 €1500 Venus' birth (80x62cm-31x24in) s. 8-Apr-3 Il Ponte, Milan #620
£1600 $2896 €2400 Le tigre (46x61cm-18x24in) lit. 30-Mar-4 Rossini, Paris #259/R est:1200-1800
£2667 $4827 €4000 Une des filles de l'artiste, Louise, le benedicite (50x35cm-20x14in) oil paper on canvas exhib.lit. 30-Mar-4 Rossini, Paris #255/R est:2000-3000
£10000 $18100 €15000 Nature morte aux potirons (83x103cm-33x41in) s.indis.d.1838. 30-Mar-4 Rossini, Paris #257/R est:3000-5000

RIESENER, Léon (attrib) (1808-1878) French
£2333 $4223 €3500 Portrait presume d'une des filles de l'artiste, Louise (64x53cm-25x21in) oval. 30-Mar-4 Rossini, Paris #254/R est:3000-5000

RIESS, Paul (1857-1933) German
£340 $619 €500 Shady peasant garden in Mecklenburg (56x86cm-22x34in) s. i. verso. 4-Feb-4 Neumeister, Munich #747/R
£849 $1494 €1240 Landscape with trees (57x86cm-22x34in) s. 23-May-4 Agra, Warsaw #40/R (P.Z 6000)

RIESTRA, Adolfo (1944-1989) Mexican
Sculpture
£2143 $3750 €3129 Jarra blanca con boyos (54cm-21in) i.d.88 verso num.1/20 painted bronze one of 20. 19-Dec-3 Sotheby's, New York #1196/R est:6000-8000

RIETER, Julius (1830-1897) Swiss
£1207 $2160 €1762 Mountain stream (29x23cm-11x9in) s. 13-May-4 Stuker, Bern #291/R est:2800-3500 (S.FR 2800)
£1524 $2438 €2210 Wellhorn and Wetterhorn (72x95cm-28x37in) s. 15-May-3 Stuker, Bern #1456 est:4000-5000 (S.FR 3200)

RIETMANN, Ludwig (19th C) Swiss
£747 $1269 €1091 Kloster Pfaffers (28x36cm-11x14in) i.d.1866 stretcher. 28-Nov-3 Zofingen, Switzerland #2482/R est:2000 (S.FR 1650)

RIETSCHEL, Ernest Friedrich August (1804-1861) German
Works on paper
£633 $1134 €950 Portrait of the sculptor Bertel Thorvaldsen (25x21cm-10x8in) s.i.d. pencil. 13-May-4 Bassenge, Berlin #5647

RIETSCHEL, Otto (1822-1887) German
£2723 $4711 €3976 The toy dealers (131x99cm-52x39in) s.d.1870 lit. 14-Dec-3 Agra, Warsaw #4/R est:18000 (P.Z 18000)

RIETTI, Arturo (1863-1942) Italian
£599 $1036 €850 Hotel on the Pyrenees (27x39cm-11x15in) s. i.verso cardboard. 10-Dec-3 Sotheby's, Milan #11/R
£604 $1111 €900 Japanese figures (65x50cm-26x20in) s.d.1940. 24-Mar-4 Il Ponte, Milan #489/R
£604 $1111 €900 Portrait of bearded man (80x60cm-31x24in) s. 24-Mar-4 Il Ponte, Milan #530/R
£1087 $1783 €1500 Woman from Trieste (53x44cm-21x17in) s.d.1913 cardboard. 27-May-3 Il Ponte, Milan #931
£1275 $2283 €1900 Self-portrait (80x60cm-31x24in) s. 25-May-4 Finarte Semenzato, Milan #63/R est:1800-2000
£1400 $2506 €2100 Novice (48x36cm-19x14in) s. tempera mixed media board. 12-May-4 Stadion, Trieste #781/R est:1500-2000
£2340 $3909 €3300 Still life (39x50cm-15x20in) s. board. 14-Oct-3 Finarte Semenzato, Milan #56/R
£2667 $4773 €4000 Trieste (52x45cm-20x18in) s. cardboard. 12-May-4 Stadion, Trieste #672/R est:2500-3500
Works on paper
£406 $698 €580 Portrait of girl (38x35cm-15x14in) s.d.26 pastel cardboard. 3-Dec-3 Stadion, Trieste #1031/R
£604 $1111 €900 Portrait of man with moustaches (61x46cm-24x18in) mixed media. 24-Mar-4 Il Ponte, Milan #676/R
£2517 $4204 €3600 Portrait of Gabriele d'Annunzio (48x38cm-19x15in) s. pastel cardboard. 10-Oct-3 Stadion, Trieste #551/R est:1800-2500

RIEU, Gilles (20th C) French
£699 $1203 €1000 Composition (100x100cm-39x39in) i.d.2001 oil acrylic. 8-Dec-3 Christie's, Paris #80/R

RIFKA, Judy (20th C) ?
£541 $1000 €790 Still life V (104x74cm-41x29in) s. acrylic oil paper painted 1986 prov. 15-Jul-4 Sotheby's, New York #103

RIGALT Y FARRIOLS, Luis (1814-1894) Spanish
Works on paper
£387 $620 €550 Wooded landscape (25x31cm-10x12in) s.d.1871 pencil dr. 16-Sep-3 Segre, Madrid #2/R
£493 $789 €700 Landscape in sarria (13x19cm-5x7in) s.d.1875 pencil dr. 16-Sep-3 Segre, Madrid #3/R

RIGAUD, F (20th C) ?
Sculpture
£1042 $1740 €1500 Dancer (40x67x23cm-16x26x9in) i. verso pat.metal ebonite onyx marble. 25-Oct-3 Auktionhaus Herr, Cologne #318/R
£1500 $2685 €2190 Figure (52cm-20in) s. gilt cold painted bronze alabaster. 13-May-4 Christie's, Kensington #212/R est:2300-3000

RIGAUD, Hyacinthe (attrib) (1659-1743) French
£2411 $3906 €3400 Portrait of Count Douglas (100x80cm-39x31in) i. lit. 23-May-3 Karlheinz Kaupp, Staufen #1675/R est:2500
£3642 $6666 €5500 Portrait de Francoise d'Aubigne, Marquise de Maintenon (73x59cm-29x23in) 7-Apr-4 Libert, Castor, Paris #33/R est:3000-4000
£5405 $9514 €8000 Portrait of young man (39x28cm-15x11in) s. 18-May-4 Sotheby's, Milan #475/R est:2000-4000
£6111 $11000 €8922 Studies of spaniels and whippets, study of a white headdress (26x35cm-10x14in) panel. 22-Jan-4 Sotheby's, New York #216/R est:12000-15000
£10877 $19579 €16316 Portrait of Armand du Plessis de Vignerod - Duke of Richelieu (89x72cm-35x28in) 25-Apr-4 Goteborg Auktionsverk, Sweden #229/R est:200000 (S.KR 150000)

RIGAUD, Hyacinthe (studio) (1659-1743) French
£3056 $5500 €4462 Portrait of a gentleman, believed to be an officer of the parliament (81x65cm-32x26in) i. 23-Jan-4 Christie's, Rockefeller NY #110/R est:3000-5000
£19231 $35000 €28077 Portrait of Louis de France, Duc de Bourgogne in armour, battlefield beyond (137x100cm-54x39in) 17-Jun-4 Christie's, Rockefeller NY #27/R est:15000-20000

RIGAUD, Hyacinthe (style) (1659-1743) French
£5500 $9130 €8030 Portrait of a Knight of the Royal and Military order of St Louis (131x97cm-52x38in) prov. 30-Sep-3 Sotheby's, London #6/R est:6000-8000

RIGAUD, Jean (1912-1999) French
£788 $1339 €1150 Moulin a Noirmoutier (38x55cm-15x22in) s. 9-Nov-3 Eric Pillon, Calais #229/R
£800 $1448 €1200 Ile d'Yeu, Port de Joinville, temps gris (19x27cm-7x11in) s. s.i.d.1970 verso prov. 2-Apr-4 Rossini, Paris #68
£1700 $3128 €2550 Saint Pierre, le semaphore et le phare (60x81cm-24x32in) s. i.d.1964 verso. 13-Jun-4 Lombrail & Teucquam, Paris #110/R
£1867 $3435 €2800 Camaret (50x61cm-20x24in) s.i.d.1951 panel. 11-Jun-4 Pierre Berge, Paris #234/R est:3000-3500
£1921 $3591 €2900 Grand Pavois, le Belem (27x35cm-11x14in) s. 24-Jul-4 Thierry & Lannon, Brest #212/R est:1500-2000
£2200 $4070 €3300 Le Sagres a quai (33x46cm-13x18in) s.d.1978. 14-Jul-4 Livinec, Gaudcheau & Jezequel, Rennes #125/R

RIGAUD, John Francis (1742-1810) British
£300 $537 €438 Death of Prince Stephen (229x152cm-90x60in) 7-May-4 Mallams, Oxford #413

RIGAUD, Pierre Gaston (1874-?) French
£748 $1190 €1100 Venise (61x46cm-24x18in) s.d.1914 prov. 23-Mar-3 St-Germain-en-Laye Encheres #61
£816 $1298 €1200 Chez l'artiste (73x60cm-29x24in) s. prov. 23-Mar-3 St-Germain-en-Laye Encheres #60
£1020 $1622 €1500 Port de Bordeaux (48x65cm-19x26in) s.i.d.1906 verso prov. 23-Mar-3 St-Germain-en-Laye Encheres #59/R
£1047 $1800 €1529 Contis, Lames (46x61cm-18x24in) s.d.1922. 7-Dec-3 Hindman, Chicago #804/R est:2000-4000
£1224 $2192 €1800 Soir d'or, Corse (54x46cm-21x18in) s.d.1931 s.i.verso panel. 21-Mar-4 St-Germain-en-Laye Encheres #3/R est:1800-2000
£1395 $2400 €2037 Wooded river bank (53x74cm-21x29in) s.d.1906. 6-Dec-3 Neal Auction Company, New Orleans #162/R est:3000-5000
£1514 $2800 €2210 Contis - landes (38x56cm-15x22in) s.d.1904. 17-Jan-4 New Orleans Auction, New Orleans #503/R est:3000-5000

RIGAUX, Albert (1950-) Belgian
£503 $931 €750 Les enfants au cerceau (41x51cm-16x20in) s. 15-Mar-4 Horta, Bruxelles #260

RIGAUX, Albert (snr) (?) Belgian
£267 $480 €400 Animated beach view (36x65cm-14x26in) s. 26-Apr-4 Bernaerts, Antwerp #979/R

RIGAUX, Jack (20th C) Canadian
£3400 $6222 €4964 Foothills near Millarville (135x244cm-53x96in) s.d.1987-89. 1-Jun-4 Hodgins, Calgary #176/R est:4000-6000 (C.D 8500)

RIGAUX, Louis (1887-1954) Belgian
£282 $487 €400 Boutique (50x60cm-20x24in) s. 9-Dec-3 Vanderkindere, Brussels #82
£387 $670 €550 Nature morte au necessaire de la denteliere (80x70cm-31x28in) s. 9-Dec-3 Vanderkindere, Brussels #104
£387 $670 €550 Vase de fleurs (54x45cm-21x18in) s. 9-Dec-3 Vanderkindere, Brussels #41
£387 $670 €550 Paysage enneige (45x50cm-18x20in) s. 9-Dec-3 Vanderkindere, Brussels #83
£420 $713 €600 Overyssche, petit etang du chateau (37x46cm-15x18in) s.d.1922 panel. 1-Dec-3 Palais de Beaux Arts, Brussels #103
£552 $1021 €800 Vache au pre (59x70cm-23x28in) s. 13-Jan-4 Vanderkindere, Brussels #172
£586 $1084 €850 Paysage au Ruisseau (73x56cm-29x22in) s. 13-Jan-4 Vanderkindere, Brussels #176
£634 $1096 €900 Vue d'Overijse (60x49cm-24x19in) s. 9-Dec-3 Vanderkindere, Brussels #98
£1479 $2558 €2100 Vue d'Overijse au crepuscule (100x80cm-39x31in) s. 9-Dec-3 Vanderkindere, Brussels #15 est:1000-1500

RIGBY, Adrian C (1962-) British
Works on paper
£300 $510 €438 Boobies (30x23cm-12x9in) s. W/C. 30-Oct-3 Chrystals Auctions, Isle of Man #221
£310 $527 €453 Redstart in landscape (30x23cm-12x9in) s. W/C. 30-Oct-3 Chrystals Auctions, Isle of Man #217
£320 $531 €467 Ringed plover (40x52cm-16x20in) s. W/C prov. 1-Oct-3 Woolley & Wallis, Salisbury #122/R
£400 $680 €584 Stoat (30x48cm-12x19in) s. W/C. 30-Oct-3 Chrystals Auctions, Isle of Man #219
£500 $850 €730 Stag. Fawn (30x23cm-12x9in) s. W/C pair. 30-Oct-3 Chrystals Auctions, Isle of Man #220
£950 $1615 €1387 Ptarmigans (46x71cm-18x28in) s. gouache. 19-Nov-3 Sotheby's, Olympia #84/R

RIGBY, Cuthbert (1850-1935) British
Works on paper
£660 $1142 €964 Figures watching ferry (20x38cm-8x15in) s.d.1896. 9-Dec-3 Louis Taylor, Stoke on Trent #1206

RIGET, Karl Age (1933-2001) Danish
£338 $615 €507 Casino composition (80x80cm-31x31in) s.d.76. 19-Jun-4 Rasmussen, Havnen #4245/R (D.KR 3800)
£362 $648 €529 Geometric composition (96x71cm-38x28in) 10-May-4 Rasmussen, Vejle #511/R (D.KR 4000)
£3787 $7006 €5529 Composition (170x170cm-67x67in) s.d.81. 15-Mar-4 Rasmussen, Vejle #551/R est:50000 (D.KR 42000)

RIGG, Ernest Higgins (1868-1947) British
£400 $636 €580 Lake scene with reeds (30x40cm-12x16in) s. board. 9-Sep-3 David Duggleby, Scarborough #343
£440 $770 €642 Thresher in a cornfield (23x33cm-9x13in) s. panel. 19-Dec-3 Mallams, Oxford #250/R
£520 $827 €754 Still life of flowers in blue and white mug (34x24cm-13x9in) s. canvas on board. 9-Sep-3 David Duggleby, Scarborough #303/R
£559 $934 €800 Young woman writing (45x41cm-18x16in) s. 28-Jun-3 Bolland & Marotz, Bremen #725/R
£580 $969 €847 Sheep on the Moors (28x38cm-11x15in) s. board. 10-Oct-3 Richardson & Smith, Whitby #107/R
£800 $1272 €1160 Letter (46x41cm-18x16in) s. 9-Sep-3 David Duggleby, Scarborough #304n
£820 $1394 €1197 Feeding the ducks (31x39cm-12x15in) s. canvasboard. 18-Nov-3 Bonhams, Leeds #256/R
£950 $1758 €1387 Geese on a river bank (30x40cm-12x16in) s. board. 16-Feb-4 Bonhams, Bath #62
£960 $1632 €1402 Roadside chat (49x67cm-19x26in) s. 18-Nov-3 Bonhams, Leeds #257/R
£1200 $2244 €1752 Extensive landscape with a farmer feeding sheep from a horse drawn cart (32x40cm-13x16in) s. canvasboard. 22-Jul-4 Tennants, Leyburn #933/R est:600-800
£2000 $3320 €2920 Still life of roses (40x33cm-16x13in) s. 1-Oct-3 Sotheby's, Olympia #60/R est:800-1200
£3000 $5370 €4380 Gathering kindling (49x59cm-19x23in) s. 26-May-4 Sotheby's, Olympia #196/R est:3000-5000
£3400 $6086 €4964 Sunlit landscape with children playing on a riverbank in the foreground (50x67cm-20x26in) s. 11-May-4 Bonhams, Knightsbridge #267/R est:2000-3000
£4000 $7320 €5840 Portrait of the artist's daughter at the piano (76x61cm-30x24in) s. 7-Apr-4 Andrew Hartley, Ilkley #1157/R est:4000-5000
£4200 $7602 €6132 Snow covered landscape, near Mickleby, Whitby (70x90cm-28x35in) s. 30-Mar-4 David Duggleby, Scarborough #231/R est:4000-6000
£5300 $8427 €7685 Fisherman's farewell in Arguments yard (57x50cm-22x20in) s.d.96. 9-Sep-3 David Duggleby, Scarborough #340/R est:5000-7000

RIGG, Jack (1927-) British
£350 $634 €511 Scarborough Harbour (33x43cm-13x17in) s. board. 15-Apr-4 Richardson & Smith, Whitby #89
£360 $652 €526 Off Scarborough (38x48cm-15x19in) s. 15-Apr-4 Richardson & Smith, Whitby #92
£380 $646 €555 Whiby from Sandseed (38x74cm-15x29in) s.d.1987. 21-Nov-3 Dee Atkinson & Harrison, Driffield #706/R
£400 $680 €584 Low water, Bridlington (23x33cm-9x13in) s.d.1995 s.verso. 21-Nov-3 Dee Atkinson & Harrison, Driffield #714/R
£600 $978 €876 Fishing boat BCK 28 (41x58cm-16x23in) s. board. 26-Sep-3 Dee Atkinson & Harrison, Driffield #530/R
£750 $1223 €1095 Fishing boat KY261 (48x76cm-19x30in) s. board. 26-Sep-3 Dee Atkinson & Harrison, Driffield #529/R
£1100 $2079 €1606 Winter's day, Maldon Essex (45x65cm-18x26in) s.d.1988 board prov. 23-Feb-4 David Duggleby, Scarborough #642/R est:1200-1500

RIGGS, Robert (1896-1970) American
£231 $400 €337 Gun shop (30x23cm-12x9in) s. tempera board. 13-Dec-3 Weschler, Washington #608
£331 $600 €483 Newt on white background (23x28cm-9x11in) board. 16-Apr-4 American Auctioneer #329/R
£663 $1200 €968 Burma Road (36x25cm-14x10in) board. 16-Apr-4 American Auctioneer #327/R
£1163 $2000 €1698 Coronation scene (28x30cm-11x12in) i. board. 3-Dec-3 Doyle, New York #311/R est:3000-5000
£15193 $27500 €22182 Slave market, Charlestone, SC (64x53cm-25x21in) board. 16-Apr-4 American Auctioneer #331/R est:30000-60000
Prints
£2706 $4600 €3951 Dust storm (36x36cm-14x14in) s. lithograph exec.c.1941. 6-Nov-3 Swann Galleries, New York #709/R est:4000-6000
Works on paper
£442 $800 €645 Strut (38x28cm-15x11in) ink. 16-Apr-4 American Auctioneer #330/R
£2210 $4000 €3227 Winner (53x69cm-21x27in) W/C. 16-Apr-4 American Auctioneer #328/R est:4000-5000

RIGHETTI, F (1738-1819) Italian
Sculpture
£173333 $318933 €260000 Bustes de bacchanales (76x13cm-30x5in) s.d.1788 b. marble copper. 11-Jun-4 Maigret, Paris #203/R est:15000-20000

RIGHETTI, Francesco (1738-1819) Italian
Sculpture
£21477 $39517 €32000 Tete de Jupiter. Tete de Junon (47cm-19in) s.d.1788 bronze pair. 26-Mar-4 Daguerre, Paris #136/R est:25000-30000

RIGHETTI, Francesco (after) (1738-1819) Italian
Sculpture
£11189 $18685 €16000 Paetus et Arria et le Pasquino (62cm-24in) s.i.d.1790 green pat bronze alabaster marble socle pair. 24-Jun-3 Christie's, Paris #415/R est:15000-20000

RIGHETTI, Giovanni Battista (18/19th C) Italian
Sculpture
£1988 $3200 €2902 Portrait of Titian (60cm-24in) s. carved pine relief. 14-Jan-4 Christie's, Rockefeller NY #274/R est:4000-6000

RIGHETTI, Luigi (19th C) British?
Works on paper
£800 $1440 €1168 Design for a candelabrum (48x30cm-19x12in) pen black ink W/C. 20-Apr-4 Sotheby's, Olympia #201/R

RIGHI, Frederico (1908-1986) Italian
£400 $716 €600 Cathedral interior (49x59cm-19x23in) s. double-sided. 12-May-4 Stadion, Trieste #784/R

RIGHINI, Sigismund (1870-1937) German
£2183 $3908 €3187 Allmend, Zurich (19x26cm-7x10in) prov. 26-May-4 Sotheby's, Zurich #142/R est:6500-7500 (S.FR 5000)
£2466 $4020 €3600 Folkestone, on the beach (18x24cm-7x9in) mono.i.d.1910 verso exhib. 29-Sep-3 Christie's, Zurich #45/R est:3000-5000 (S.FR 5500)
£2752 $4596 €3990 Female nude (97x48cm-38x19in) mono.d.1901 lit. 23-Jun-3 Philippe Schuler, Zurich #3418/R est:7000-9000 (S.FR 6000)
Works on paper
£226 $385 €330 Coastal landscape (16x31cm-6x12in) col pen. 18-Nov-3 Hans Widmer, St Gallen #1171 (S.FR 500)
£1031 $1681 €1505 Self portrait (20x14cm-8x6in) d.4.6.33 col pen transparent paper prov.lit. 29-Sep-3 Christie's, Zurich #54/R est:2500-3500 (S.FR 2300)

RIGO, Martin (1949-) Spanish
£544 $990 €800 Ruins (73x92cm-29x36in) s. 3-Feb-4 Segre, Madrid #191/R

RIGOLOT, Albert (1862-1932) French
£647 $1157 €945 Evening coastline (33x46cm-13x18in) s. 12-May-4 Dobiaschofsky, Bern #902/R est:2400 (S.FR 1500)
£940 $1748 €1400 Paysage d'automne a l'etang (23x34cm-9x13in) s. panel. 3-Mar-4 Ferri, Paris #149 est:1200-1300
£1078 $1929 €1574 Evening lakeshore (50x73cm-20x29in) s. 12-May-4 Dobiaschofsky, Bern #903/R est:4800 (S.FR 2500)
£1678 $2970 €2500 Pont sur la riviere en automne (46x55cm-18x22in) s. 30-Apr-4 Tajan, Paris #155/R est:3500
£2600 $4316 €3796 River landscape (50x73cm-20x29in) s. 1-Oct-3 Sotheby's, Olympia #282/R est:1500-2000
£2667 $4880 €4000 Marais (38x55cm-15x22in) s. 6-Jun-4 Osenat, Fontainebleau #70/R est:5000-5500
£2933 $5368 €4400 Etang entoure d'arbres (55x73cm-22x29in) s. 6-Jun-4 Anaf, Lyon #187/R est:3000-4000
£3500 $6475 €5110 River bank in summer (54x74cm-21x29in) s. 10-Mar-4 Sotheby's, Olympia #247/R est:2000-3000
£5319 $8883 €7500 Equinoxe d'automne (105x172cm-41x68in) s. exhib. 19-Jun-3 Millon & Associes, Paris #135/R est:6000-10000
Works on paper
£1135 $1895 €1600 Bords de riviere sous la neige (64x100cm-25x39in) s. pastel. 19-Jun-3 Millon & Associes, Paris #136/R est:1500-1800
£1477 $2746 €2200 Sous-bois enneige (65x92cm-26x36in) s. pastel. 3-Mar-4 Ferri, Paris #148 est:2000-2500
£2667 $4907 €4000 Automne (91x66cm-36x26in) s. pastel. 9-Jun-4 Beaussant & Lefèvre, Paris #205/R est:1000-1200
£2754 $4516 €3800 Les boisieres, sous-bois enneige (60x92cm-24x36in) s. pastel. 11-May-3 Osenat, Fontainebleau #15/R est:3500-4000
£3061 $5480 €4500 Gardeuse d'oies au bord d'un etang (65x92cm-26x36in) s. prov. 19-Mar-4 Millon & Associes, Paris #74/R est:3000-4000

RIGOLOT, Albert (attrib) (1862-1932) French
£4070 $7000 €5942 L'Etang borde d'arbres (51x91cm-20x36in) 6-Dec-3 Neal Auction Company, New Orleans #164/R est:7000-8000

RIGOT, Georges (20th C) ?
Sculpture
£1750 $3132 €2555 Pyjama girl (33cm-13in) cold painted bronze ivory onyx marble base. 22-Mar-4 Waddingtons, Toronto #756/R est:2000-3000 (C.D 4200)

RIIHIKOSKI, Olli Pekka (20th C) Finnish
£417 $696 €600 The plains are calling (15x20cm-6x8in) s.d.1984. 23-Oct-3 Hagelstam, Helsinki #899

RIIS, Bendik (1911-1988) Norwegian
£343 $601 €501 Portrait of Arne Isaksen (46x38cm-18x15in) indis.sig.i.d.18. panel prov. 16-Dec-3 Grev Wedels Plass, Oslo #211/R (N.KR 4000)
£599 $1018 €875 Landscape with brook covered in hoare frost (32x49cm-13x19in) s. i.verso. 19-Nov-3 Grev Wedels Plass, Oslo #84/R (N.KR 7000)
£1281 $2293 €1870 Landscape with waterfall. Landscape with trees (31x37cm-12x15in) s. one panel two. 22-Mar-4 Blomqvist, Oslo #406/R est:20000-25000 (N.KR 16000)
Works on paper
£634 $1167 €926 Portrait of Thora Marie Riis (53x47cm-21x19in) s. pastel. 29-Mar-4 Blomqvist, Lysaker #1246/R (N.KR 8000)

RIJKELIJKHUYSEN, Hermanus Jan Hendrik (1813-1883) Dutch
£263 $476 €400 Lake landscape with mountain in the background (17x24cm-7x9in) s. panel. 19-Apr-4 Glerum, Amsterdam #54
£660 $1076 €950 Winter landscape (31x40cm-12x16in) s. panel. 29-Sep-3 Sotheby's, Amsterdam #45/R

RIKET, Léon (1876-1938) Belgian
£267 $483 €400 Bordure de riviere (116x106cm-46x42in) s. 30-Mar-4 Campo, Vlaamse Kaai #147/R
£360 $666 €526 Figures on a stone bridge (50x60cm-20x24in) s. 10-Feb-4 Bonhams, Knightsbridge #283/R
£408 $731 €600 Vue d'une ferme (30x41cm-12x16in) panel. 22-Mar-4 Amberes, Antwerp #233
£563 $975 €800 Vachere et son troupeau dans le sous-bois (50x70cm-20x28in) s. 9-Dec-3 Vanderkindere, Brussels #38
£563 $986 €800 Voilier le long de l'Escaut (50x70cm-20x28in) s. 16-Dec-3 Galerie Moderne, Brussels #764/R
£625 $1044 €900 Nature morte (50x64cm-20x25in) s. 21-Oct-3 Campo, Vlaamse Kaai #1054
£743 $1308 €1100 Castle at Deurne (70x100cm-28x39in) s. 24-May-4 Bernaerts, Antwerp #636/R

RIKKERS, Willem (1812-1873) Dutch
£451 $713 €650 Sunset landscape with exotic plants (42x53cm-17x21in) mono.d.1869. 5-Sep-3 Wendl, Rudolstadt #3582/R

RILEY, Bridget (1931-1984) British
£95000 $172900 €138700 Songbird (107x93cm-42x37in) s.d.82 s.i.d.1982 verso linen prov. 6-Feb-4 Sotheby's, London #119/R est:40000-60000
£98000 $179340 €143080 Echo (129x43cm-51x17in) s.d.62 i.d.verso board prov. 4-Jun-4 Christie's, London #112/R est:30000-50000
£105000 $192150 €153300 Bright day (169x145cm-67x57in) s.i.d.1981 oil on linen prov.exhib. 4-Jun-4 Christie's, London #113/R est:60000-80000
£122905 $220000 €179441 Rill (228x96cm-90x38in) s.d.76 s.i.d.1976 verso linen prov.exhib. 12-May-4 Christie's, Rockefeller NY #318/R est:150000-200000
Prints
£2542 $4500 €3711 Elapse. s.i. col screenprint. 30-Apr-4 Sotheby's, New York #445/R est:3000-4000
£2825 $5000 €4125 Untitled (48x96cm-19x38in) incised sig.d.1965 num.62/75 screenprint on plexiglas. 30-Apr-4 Sotheby's, New York #444/R est:4000-6000
£3107 $5500 €4536 Elapse (103x64cm-41x25in) s.i.d.1982 col screenprint edition of 260. 28-Apr-4 Christie's, Rockefeller NY #393/R est:4000-6000
£3200 $5856 €4672 Fete (53x76cm-21x30in) s.i.d.1989 num.4/10 col screenprint. 3-Jun-4 Christie's, Kensington #474/R est:1500-2000
£3500 $6405 €5110 Coloured greys (57x57cm-22x22in) s.i.num.6/125 col screenprint. 3-Jun-4 Christie's, Kensington #472/R est:2500-3000
£3593 $6000 €5246 Fragment 5 (64x81cm-25x32in) s.d.1965 num.36/75 screenprint on plexiglass. 11-Nov-3 Doyle, New York #371/R est:1500-2000
£3593 $6000 €5246 Fragment 6 (76x74cm-30x29in) s.d.1965 num.35/75 screenprint on plexiglas. 11-Nov-3 Doyle, New York #372/R est:2000-3000
£3892 $6500 €5682 Fragment 1 (66x84cm-26x33in) s.d.1965 num.37/75 screenprint on plexiglas. 11-Nov-3 Doyle, New York #369/R est:2500-3500
£3892 $6500 €5682 Fragment 7 (51x99cm-20x39in) s.d.1965 num.32/75 screenprint on plexiglas. 11-Nov-3 Doyle, New York #373/R est:3000-4000
£4237 $7500 €6186 Fragment no 5 (55x99cm-22x39in) s.d.1965 num.15/75 verso black white screenprint plexiglas. 28-Apr-4 Christie's, Rockefeller NY #392/R est:4000-6000
£4491 $7500 €6557 Fragment 3 (64x81cm-25x32in) s.d.1965 num.16/75 screenprint n plexiglass. 11-Nov-3 Doyle, New York #370/R est:3000-4000
£5000 $9200 €7300 Untitled (75x34cm-30x13in) s.d.1964 num.9/50 silkscreen. 29-Mar-4 Bonhams, New Bond Street #242/R est:2000-3000
£6500 $10790 €9490 Untitled (69x65cm-27x26in) s.d.1965 verso silkscreen on plexiglas edition of 75. 6-Oct-3 Sotheby's, London #137/R est:4000-6000
£8982 $15000 €13114 Nineteen greys (76x76cm-30x30in) s.i.d.1968 screenprints set of four. 11-Nov-3 Doyle, New York #374/R est:4000-6000
£11000 $20240 €16060 Nineteen greys A-D (76x76cm-30x30in) s.i. silkscreen prints set of four. 29-Mar-4 Bonhams, New Bond Street #24/R est:10000-15000
Works on paper
£5000 $9100 €7300 July 23 bassacs (21x28cm-8x11in) s.i.d.95 gouache pencil prov. 6-Feb-4 Sotheby's, London #120/R est:4000-6000
£6500 $11050 €9490 Woman at tea table (48x74cm-19x29in) s. col crayon pastel prov. 21-Nov-3 Christie's, London #25/R est:3000-5000
£6643 $11427 €9500 Composition (50x30cm-20x12in) s.d. gouache on pencil. 3-Dec-3 Hauswedell & Nolte, Hamburg #956/R est:1500
£8000 $14720 €11680 Untitled (64x39cm-25x15in) s. gouache pencil exec 1969 prov.lit. 24-Jun-4 Sotheby's, London #146/R est:8000-12000
£9000 $16380 €13140 Analysis (43x45cm-17x18in) s.i.d.1981 gouache graph paper prov. 4-Feb-4 Sotheby's, Olympia #25/R est:3000-4000
£9053 $16387 €13217 R 1405 - red, blue and green disk (51x67cm-20x26in) s.i.d.75 synthetic polymer pencil on paper exhib. 30-Mar-4 Lawson Menzies, Sydney #267/R est:10000-15000 (A.D 22000)
£9500 $17290 €13870 Serpentine Study 12 Group A (39x38cm-15x15in) s.i.d.99 gouache prov. 4-Feb-4 Sotheby's, Olympia #82/R est:3000-5000
£12085 $20544 €17644 Study 26/11/85 (56x52cm-22x20in) s.d.85 gouache prov. 5-Nov-3 AB Stockholms Auktionsverk #918/R est:50000-70000 (S.KR 160000)
£21694 $40134 €31673 Orpheus study 8 (97x61cm-38x24in) s.i.d.77 gouache prov. 10-Mar-4 Deutscher-Menzies, Melbourne #85/R est:20000-30000 (A.D 52500)
£24000 $40080 €35040 Study for Deny (25x68cm-10x27in) s.i.d.66 gouache. 16-Oct-3 Christie's, Kensington #701/R est:4000-6000
£391061 $700000 €570949 Serif (162x162cm-64x64in) s. i.d.1964 verso emulsion on hardboard prov.exhib.lit. 13-May-4 Phillips, New York #43/R est:500000-700000

RILEY, Harold (1934-) British
£4100 $7503 €5986 Young street urchin carrying a basket (74x43cm-29x17in) s.d.62 board. 6-Apr-4 Capes Dunn, Manchester #845/R
Works on paper
£270 $494 €394 Profile portrait of a lady (31x24cm-12x9in) s.d.68 chk. 6-Jul-4 Peter Wilson, Nantwich #107/R
£320 $550 €467 Eviction (32x20cm-13x8in) s.d.63 chl. 3-Dec-3 Christie's, Kensington #647/R
£340 $622 €496 Shoulder length portrait of a young girl (45x28cm-18x11in) s.d.69 col chk. 6-Jul-4 Peter Wilson, Nantwich #112/R
£380 $695 €555 Portrait study of a lady facing left (33x15cm-13x6in) s.d.1962 pencil htd white buff paper. 6-Apr-4 Capes Dunn, Manchester #807/R
£380 $695 €555 Street scene with figures walking dog in foreground, buildings beyond (26x25cm-10x10in) s.d.68 chk. 6-Jul-4 Peter Wilson, Nantwich #108/R
£410 $750 €599 Study of figure seated in a barbers shop (37x25cm-15x10in) s.d.69 chl. 6-Jul-4 Peter Wilson, Nantwich #110/R
£620 $1135 €905 Industrial landscape with figures in foreground, canal and factories beyond (34x25cm-13x10in) s.d.69 chk. 6-Jul-4 Peter Wilson, Nantwich #111/R
£700 $1281 €1022 Steps entrance with building in background (28x18cm-11x7in) s. pastel. 6-Apr-4 Capes Dunn, Manchester #822/R
£720 $1289 €1051 At the Cinema (21x29cm-8x11in) s.d.62 pastel. 17-Mar-4 Bonhams, Chester #266
£900 $1647 €1314 Seedley Cinema (18x18cm-7x7in) s.d.79 pastel drawing. 6-Apr-4 Capes Dunn, Manchester #835/R
£950 $1739 €1387 Country Cinema Broughton Salford (25x20cm-10x8in) s.d.74 pastel drawing. 6-Apr-4 Capes Dunn, Manchester #836/R
£1100 $2013 €1606 Gas works at sunset (23x25cm-9x10in) s.d.1974 pastel drawing. 6-Apr-4 Capes Dunn, Manchester #834/R

RILEY, John (1646-1691) British
£1500 $2745 €2190 Portrait of Mr Marriott of Alscot Park (74x62cm-29x24in) lit. 8-Jul-4 Sotheby's, London #220/R est:2000-3000
£3147 $5413 €4500 Portrait of lady in landscape (127x102cm-50x40in) 2-Dec-3 Sotheby's, Milan #83/R est:5000-7000
£4000 $6320 €5800 Portrait of Sir John Streynsham Master (76x63cm-30x25in) prov. 4-Sep-3 Christie's, Kensington #13/R est:4000-6000
£5500 $9350 €8030 Portrait of Ann Lee , wearing a brown dress, with her dog on lap (124x100cm-49x39in) i. 27-Nov-3 Sotheby's, London #120/R est:6000-8000
£12000 $21840 €17520 Portraits of Thomas Brotherton and his wife Margaret (125x99cm-49x39in) i. pair. 1-Jul-4 Sotheby's, London #113/R est:12000-18000

RILEY, John (attrib) (1646-1691) British
£920 $1720 €1380 Portrait of George Holman Esqr (75x62cm-30x24in) i. 26-Jul-4 Bonhams, Bath #49/R
£2500 $4500 €3650 Portrait of John Dobson (76x64cm-30x25in) oval. 21-Jan-4 Sotheby's, Olympia #10/R est:1200-1800
£3500 $5810 €5110 Portrait of a gentleman, half length, wearing brown robes and white jabot (74x61cm-29x24in) painted oval. 30-Sep-3 Sotheby's, London #58/R est:4000-6000

RILEY, Kenneth (1919-) American
£3464 $6200 €5057 Mesa verde (30x41cm-12x16in) board. 15-May-4 Altermann Galleries, Santa Fe #141/R
£10615 $19000 €15498 Geronimo dust and sun (38x25cm-15x10in) board. 15-May-4 Altermann Galleries, Santa Fe #55/R
£12849 $23000 €18760 Tentavie agreement (46x51cm-18x20in) 15-May-4 Altermann Galleries, Santa Fe #56/R

RILEY, Mimo (20th C) American
£419 $700 €612 Pear (74x104cm-29x41in) init.d.98 oil on paper. 15-Nov-3 Sloans & Kenyon, Bethesda #112/R

RILEY, Thomas (fl.1878-1892) British
£1300 $2418 €1898 Trysting place (32x24cm-13x9in) s. 4-Mar-4 Christie's, Kensington #585/R est:800-1200

RILEY, William Edward (1852-1937) British
Works on paper
£181 $334 €264 Dinant (37x25cm-15x10in) s. W/C. 14-Jun-4 Waddingtons, Toronto #54/R (C.D 450)

RIMBAKT, Louis (20th C) American
£543 $1000 €793 Tugboats in harbour (38x56cm-15x22in) s. paper. 10-Jun-4 Swann Galleries, New York #199a/R

RIMBERT, René (1896-1991) French
£10140 $17441 €14500 Vue de l'eglise (65x46cm-26x18in) s. mono.i.d.1953 verso prov.exhib.lit. 3-Dec-3 Tajan, Paris #287/R est:15000-20000

RIMBOECK, Max (1890-?) German
£1314 $2431 €1918 Young woman seated (80x68cm-31x27in) 14-Mar-4 Agra, Warsaw #3/R (P.Z 9500)

RIMINALDI, Orazio (1586-1631) Italian
£439597 $778087 €655000 Holy and unholy LOve (155x115cm-61x45in) prov.exhib.lit. 2-May-4 Finarte, Venice #92/R

RIMINGTON, Alexander Wallace (c.1854-1918) British
Works on paper
£500 $860 €730 Moonlight procession over a bridge, Venice (48x74cm-19x29in) s.d.08 pencil W/C. 3-Dec-3 Christie's, Kensington #192/R

RIMMER, Itzu (1948-) Israeli
£492 $900 €718 Ayalon Valley (74x98cm-29x39in) s. s.i.d.2004 verso. 1-Jun-4 Ben-Ami, Tel Aviv #4891/R est:1100-1500
£537 $950 €784 Lachish (74x98cm-29x39in) s. s.i.d.verso. 1-May-4 Ben-Ami, Tel Aviv #4831/R est:1200-1400
£588 $1100 €858 Kfar Silver Junction (76x102cm-30x40in) s. s.i.d.verso. 1-Mar-4 Ben-Ami, Tel Aviv #4714/R

RIMOLDI, Pietro Adamo (1869-?) Italian
£467 $845 €700 Vase of flowers (59x40cm-23x16in) s. board. 31-Mar-4 Finarte Semenzato, Milan #557

RIMPATTA DA BOLOGNA, Antonio (16th C) Italian
£18792 $34577 €28000 Madonna and Child (49x39cm-19x15in) tempera gold panel. 24-Mar-4 Dorotheum, Vienna #57/R est:30000-36000

RINALDI, Claudio (19th C) Italian
£764 $1420 €1115 Man with chianti bottle (45x34cm-18x13in) s.i. 2-Mar-4 Rasmussen, Copenhagen #1561/R (D.KR 8500)
£6000 $10320 €8760 Grandmother's favourites (81x61cm-32x24in) s.d.1886. 4-Dec-3 Christie's, Kensington #52/R est:6000-8000

RINALDO, Antonio (19th C) Italian
£1329 $2219 €1900 Winter, family scene (34x22cm-13x9in) s. board exhib.lit. 24-Jun-3 Finarte Semenzato, Rome #143/R

RINALDO, Karen (20th C) American
£1271 $2250 €1856 Harbour at Camden, Maine (22x28cm-9x11in) s.i.d.81. 2-May-4 Bonhams & Butterfields, San Francisco #1091/R est:500-750
Works on paper
£198 $350 €289 Brewster herring run (28x22cm-11x9in) pencil W/C. 2-May-4 Bonhams & Butterfields, San Francisco #1141/R
£226 $400 €330 Curragh, docked at Hyannis Port (28x21cm-11x8in) s. pencil W/C. 2-May-4 Bonhams & Butterfields, San Francisco #1095/R

RINCKLAKE, Johann Christoph (1764-1813) German
£3716 $6652 €5500 Sporting dog lying down (16x21cm-6x8in) prov. 5-May-4 Sotheby's, Amsterdam #296/R est:400-600

RINDERSPACHER, Ernst (1879-1949) Swiss
Works on paper
£353 $600 €515 Mountain lake in evening (19x24cm-7x9in) s. col glass. 28-Nov-3 Zofingen, Switzerland #3146 (S.FR 780)
£353 $600 €515 Mountain wood at night (20x24cm-8x9in) s. col glass. 28-Nov-3 Zofingen, Switzerland #3147 (S.FR 780)

RINDIN, V F (20th C) Russian
Works on paper
£2000 $3580 €2920 Set design for Don Quixote (36x51cm-14x20in) s.d.1946 gouache. 26-May-4 Sotheby's, London #209/R est:3000-5000

RINDISBACHER, Peter (1806-1834) Swiss
Works on paper
£109375 $175000 €159688 Western winter landscape with Indian, buffalo and dogs (20x38cm-8x15in) s. W/C pen. 20-Sep-3 Pook & Pook, Downington #340/R est:50000-80000
£112500 $180000 €164250 Western landscape of a buffalo hunt (20x38cm-8x15in) s. W/C pen. 20-Sep-3 Pook & Pook, Downington #341/R est:50000-80000

RING, Alice Blair (1869-1947) American
£745 $1200 €1080 European landscape of figures on a cobble stone bridge (51x41cm-20x16in) s. 17-Aug-3 Jeffery Burchard, Florida #53

RING, Hermann Tom (1521-1595) German
£23333 $41767 €35000 Portrait of a gentleman, with gold chain and pendant (67x46cm-26x18in) mono.i.d.15om51 panel prov.exhib.lit. 17-May-4 Christie's, Amsterdam #66/R est:20000-30000

RING, Laurits Andersen (1854-1933) Danish
£1348 $2507 €1968 Evening at Vedbaek Strand, with approaching storm (64x47cm-25x19in) s.d.93 prov. 2-Mar-4 Rasmussen, Copenhagen #1388/R est:15000-20000 (D.KR 15000)
£1432 $2621 €2091 Coastal landscape in winter (18x30cm-7x12in) 7-Jun-4 Museumsbygningen, Copenhagen #159/R est:6000-8000 (D.KR 16000)
£1448 $2592 €2114 Autumn landscape with harvesting (20x33cm-8x13in) s. 10-May-4 Rasmussen, Vejle #96/R est:15000-20000 (D.KR 16000)
£1567 $2664 €2288 A foggy morning - post boat from Thuro to Svendborg (29x39cm-11x15in) s. 10-Nov-3 Rasmussen, Vejle #268/R est:8000-12000 (D.KR 17000)
£1890 $3270 €2759 Country road near Mogenstrup (30x45cm-12x18in) s.d.1889. 9-Dec-3 Rasmussen, Copenhagen #1549/R est:15000 (D.KR 20000)
£2836 $4905 €4141 Old thatched house with woman in afternoon sunshine (30x39cm-12x15in) s.d.1910. 9-Dec-3 Rasmussen, Copenhagen #1281/R est:30000-40000 (D.KR 30000)
£4043 $7520 €5903 Marshy landscape near Baldersbronde town (29x39cm-11x15in) s.d.1911. 2-Mar-4 Rasmussen, Copenhagen #1249/R est:25000-30000 (D.KR 45000)
£4476 $8192 €6535 Visiting grandfather (42x48cm-17x19in) s.d.93 exhib.prov. 9-Jun-4 Rasmussen, Copenhagen #1491/R est:30000-50000 (D.KR 50000)
£4480 $8065 €6541 The bridge to Enoe. s. 24-Apr-4 Rasmussen, Havnen #2223/R est:7000-10000 (D.KR 50000)
£6739 $12534 €9839 View across Roskilde Fjord, rooftops in foreground (40x61cm-16x24in) s. exhib.prov. 2-Mar-4 Rasmussen, Copenhagen #1250/R est:30000-40000 (D.KR 75000)
£7188 $13369 €10494 Winter's day with farm house by country road, possibly Baldersbronde (33x41cm-13x16in) s.d.1908. 2-Mar-4 Rasmussen, Copenhagen #1210/R est:40000-50000 (D.KR 80000)
£25067 $45873 €36598 Autumn landscape with harvesters and corn (73x100cm-29x39in) s.d.30/8 92 exhib. 9-Jun-4 Rasmussen, Copenhagen #1474/R est:250000-350000 (D.KR 280000)

RING, Laurits Andersen (attrib) (1854-1933) Danish
£561 $886 €813 Bjergsted near Roskilde (19x24cm-7x9in) s. prov. 3-Sep-3 Museumsbygningen, Copenhagen #196 (D.KR 6000)

RING, Ole (1902-1972) Danish
£474 $758 €692 Harbour scene with buildings (26x30cm-10x12in) s. 22-Sep-3 Rasmussen, Vejle #407/R (D.KR 5000)
£504 $917 €736 Thatched house in village (25x34cm-10x13in) s. 7-Feb-4 Rasmussen, Havnen #2071/R (D.KR 5500)
£537 $983 €784 Country road in autumn with trees (25x36cm-10x14in) s.d.1931. 7-Jun-4 Museumsbygningen, Copenhagen #160/R (D.KR 6000)
£662 $1184 €967 Country road by poplars (25x34cm-10x13in) s. 12-Jan-4 Rasmussen, Vejle #128/R (D.KR 7000)
£797 $1299 €1164 From the bridge in Koge (20x24cm-8x9in) s.d.31. 27-Sep-3 Rasmussen, Havnen #2268/R (D.KR 8500)
£797 $1299 €1164 Street scene from Kirkestraede, Koge (35x49cm-14x19in) s.d.1939. 27-Sep-3 Rasmussen, Havnen #2269/R (D.KR 8500)
£806 $1452 €1177 Winter's day with mill in background (40x35cm-16x14in) s. 24-Apr-4 Rasmussen, Havnen #2352/R (D.KR 9000)
£1343 $2457 €1961 Grey day in the village (42x73cm-17x29in) s.d.48. 9-Jun-4 Rasmussen, Copenhagen #1673/R est:15000 (D.KR 15000)
£1432 $2621 €2091 From Frederiksholm Canal (45x62cm-18x24in) s. 9-Jun-4 Rasmussen, Copenhagen #1611/R est:25000-35000 (D.KR 16000)
£1522 $2785 €2222 Winter's day in St.Magleby (38x47cm-15x19in) s. 9-Jun-4 Rasmussen, Copenhagen #1757/R est:20000 (D.KR 17000)
£1611 $2949 €2352 Winter's day in the village of Hoje Taastrup (41x56cm-16x22in) s. prov. 9-Jun-4 Rasmussen, Copenhagen #1756/R est:25000-30000 (D.KR 18000)
£1724 $2707 €2517 Autumn day by village pond (67x100cm-26x39in) s.d.1945. 30-Aug-3 Rasmussen, Havnen #2114/R est:20000-30000 (D.KR 18500)
£1791 $3277 €2615 By the village pond, Ammendrup (70x100cm-28x39in) s.d.1942. 9-Jun-4 Rasmussen, Copenhagen #1687/R est:30000 (D.KR 20000)
£1846 $3175 €2695 By the bakery (67x91cm-26x36in) s. 3-Dec-3 AB Stockholms Auktionsverk #2598/R est:30000-35000 (S.KR 24000)
£2865 $5243 €4183 Spring day from Christianshavn canal (45x60cm-18x24in) s. 9-Jun-4 Rasmussen, Copenhagen #1610/R est:30000-40000 (D.KR 32000)
£3271 $5168 €4743 Sailing vessels, Frederiksholm's Canal (85x120cm-33x47in) s. 2-Sep-3 Rasmussen, Copenhagen #1524/R est:40000-50000 (D.KR 35000)
£13429 $24575 €19606 Summer's day at Nyhavn, Copenhagen (45x66cm-18x26in) s.d.1948. 9-Jun-4 Rasmussen, Copenhagen #1454/R est:150000-200000 (D.KR 150000)
£14500 $26390 €21170 The first thaw (72x101cm-28x40in) s. 15-Jun-4 Sotheby's, London #348/R est:12000-18000

RING, Pieter de (1615-1660) Dutch
£9790 $16839 €14000 Still life with lobster and fruit (106x97cm-42x38in) bears sig. lit. 3-Dec-3 Neumeister, Munich #496/R est:6000

RINGDAHL, Johan Julius (1813-1882) Swedish
Works on paper
£347 $622 €507 Children playing with soap bubbles (14x19cm-6x7in) s.d.1846 pencil prov.exhib.lit. 26-May-4 AB Stockholms Auktionsverk #2332/R (S.KR 4700)

RINGEISEN, Josef (fl.1905) German
£805 $1498 €1200 Reclining nude nymphs at the seaside (69x118cm-27x46in) s. 5-Mar-4 Wendl, Rudolstadt #3837/R

RINGEL, Franz (1940-) Austrian
Works on paper
£403 $745 €600 Untitled (21x15cm-8x6in) s.d.99 mixed media. 9-Mar-4 Dorotheum, Vienna #245
£436 $807 €650 Untitled (21x15cm-8x6in) s.d.99 mixed media. 9-Mar-4 Dorotheum, Vienna #246
£759 $1388 €1100 Head (48x36cm-19x14in) s.d.96 pencil oil chk. 27-Jan-4 Dorotheum, Vienna #256/R
£1974 $3632 €3000 Self portrait (100x70cm-39x28in) s.d.1986 mixed media lit. 22-Jun-4 Wiener Kunst Auktionen, Vienna #355/R est:2500-3500
£2797 $4755 €4000 Untitled (56x75cm-22x30in) s.d.1973 mixed media. 28-Nov-3 Wiener Kunst Auktionen, Vienna #632/R est:4000-7000
£3147 $5350 €4500 Untitled (76x55cm-30x22in) s.d.73 pencil oil chk scratched. 26-Nov-3 Dorotheum, Vienna #269/R est:3400-4500
£3147 $5350 €4500 Untitled (61x73cm-24x29in) s.d.1968 mixed media col crayon. 28-Nov-3 Wiener Kunst Auktionen, Vienna #642/R est:5000-8000
£3356 $5940 €5000 Composition (110x77cm-43x30in) s.i.d. mixed media. 28-Apr-4 Wiener Kunst Auktionen, Vienna #250/R est:5000-7000

RINGER, Oton (20th C) Argentinian
£604 $1100 €882 Resting (40x50cm-16x20in) s.d.79 board. 5-Jul-4 Arroyo, Buenos Aires #6/R

RINGGLI, Gotthard (1575-1635) Swiss
Works on paper
£8108 $14270 €12000 Ezekiel in the valley of the Dry Bones (20cm-8in circular) s.indis.i.d.1600 pen col ink col wash prov.exhib.lit. 19-May-4 Sotheby's, Amsterdam #5/R est:15000-20000

RINGNESS, Charles (1923-) Canadian
Works on paper
£723 $1345 €1056 Popcorn (97x124cm-38x49in) mixed media encaustic prov. 4-Mar-4 Heffel, Vancouver #37/R (C.D 1800)

RINGS, Percy (1901-1994) German
Works on paper
£303 $507 €440 Composition (59x46cm-23x18in) s.d.85 W/C gouache lit. 10-Jul-3 Allgauer, Kempten #2342/R

RINK, Paulus Philippus (1861-1903) Dutch
£556 $906 €800 Children playing with a doll (50x65cm-20x26in) s. 29-Sep-3 Sotheby's, Amsterdam #177/R

RINONE, Francesco (1901-1982) Italian
£671 $1188 €1000 Still life (65x65cm-26x26in) s.d.1933 board. 1-May-4 Meeting Art, Vercelli #166

RINTEL, Theo van (1936-) Belgian
£336 $614 €500 La veranda (70x80cm-28x31in) s. 8-Jul-4 Campo, Vlaamse Kaai #279
£403 $713 €600 Vue de jardin impressioniste (60x70cm-24x28in) s. 27-Apr-4 Campo & Campo, Antwerp #258

RINZI, Ernest (1836-1909) British
Miniatures
£1800 $3006 €2628 Lady Randolph Churchill (8cm-3in) s. gold mount. 7-Oct-3 Bonhams, New Bond Street #125/R est:400-600

RIO BRANCO, Miguel (1946-) Brazilian?
Photographs
£5634 $9747 €8000 Eyes (120x120cm-47x47in) s. num.1/3 cibachrome on aluminium exec.2000 prov. 9-Dec-3 Artcurial Briest, Paris #455/R est:8000-10000
£17333 $31893 €26000 Blue tango 20 (46x56cm-18x22in) cibachrome exec.1984 prov.lit. 10-Jun-4 Christie's, Paris #95/R est:8000-12000
Works on paper
£389 $700 €568 Untitled (41x51cm-16x20in) s.d.68 mixed media canvas. 24-Apr-4 Weschler, Washington #584/R

RIO, Gustavo del (1959-) ?
Works on paper
£524 $902 €750 Surreal scene (108x82cm-43x32in) s. W/C. 8-Dec-3 Bloss, Merzhausen #815/R

RIOPELLE, Jean-Paul (1923-2002) Canadian
£4000 $6680 €5840 Assaut (44x55cm-17x22in) s. paper on canvas painted 1960 prov.lit. 21-Oct-3 Sotheby's, London #396/R est:4000-6000
£4698 $8738 €7000 Untitled (89x61cm-35x24in) acrylic collage paper on canvas painted 1989 prov.exhib.lit. 3-Mar-4 Tajan, Paris #238/R est:8000-10000
£6479 $11208 €9200 Arche (59x79cm-23x31in) s. oil paper prov.exhib. 14-Dec-3 Versailles Encheres #124/R est:12000-15000
£6993 $11678 €10000 Composition (14x24cm-6x9in) painted c.1960. 11-Oct-3 Cornette de St.Cyr, Paris #60/R est:10000-12000
£8000 $13360 €11680 Tempo (24x19cm-9x7in) executed 1958 prov. 22-Oct-3 Bonhams, New Bond Street #86/R est:6000-8000
£10163 $18191 €14838 Des le Matin (33x22cm-13x9in) s.i.d.1967 verso prov. 31-May-4 Sotheby's, Toronto #14/R est:25000-35000 (C.D 25000)
£12162 $21406 €18000 Arches (59x78cm-23x31in) s. paper on canvas prov.exhib. 18-May-4 Tajan, Paris #43/R est:22000-25000
£12195 $21829 €17805 Antheor (24x14cm-9x6in) s.i.d.1961 prov. 31-May-4 Sotheby's, Toronto #13/R est:20000-30000 (C.D 30000)
£13043 $21391 €18000 Iceberg 31 (60x73cm-24x29in) painted 1977. 27-May-3 Sotheby's, Milan #192/R est:15000-20000
£16667 $30667 €25000 Untitled (29x58cm-11x23in) s. verso triptych prov.exhib. 8-Jun-4 Artcurial Briest, Paris #273/R est:18000-23000
£18000 $32760 €26280 Untitled (100x81cm-39x32in) s.d.62. 6-Feb-4 Sotheby's, London #183/R est:14000-18000
£23026 $42368 €35000 Avalanche (80x63cm-31x25in) s.i.d.1966 verso. 27-Jun-4 Versailles Encheres #96/R est:40000-50000
£24390 $43659 €35609 Vol des chutes (73x92cm-29x36in) s. painted c.1959 prov.lit. 27-May-4 Heffel, Vancouver #48/R est:40000-50000 (C.D 60000)
£25176 $42798 €36000 Sans titre (56x56cm-22x22in) s. prov.lit. 25-Nov-3 Tajan, Paris #9/R est:28000-32000
£26000 $47320 €37960 Untitled (50x65cm-20x26in) s.d.1959. 6-Feb-4 Sotheby's, London #164/R est:20000-30000
£27027 $47568 €40000 Ravenna (51x61cm-20x24in) s. s.i.verso painted 1954 prov. 24-May-4 Christie's, Milan #311/R est:40000-60000
£29000 $48430 €42340 Provence (38x55cm-15x22in) s. s.i.verso executed 1956 prov. 22-Oct-3 Bonhams, New Bond Street #85/R est:15000-20000
£29279 $49775 €42747 Reflets (100x81cm-39x32in) s. prov. 18-Nov-3 Sotheby's, Toronto #79/R est:70000-90000 (C.D 65000)
£30070 $51119 €43000 Plein cabas d'enfants (65x81cm-26x32in) s.d.62. 29-Nov-3 Farsetti, Prato #481/R est:35000-45000
£32895 $60526 €50000 Tourbillon (100x100cm-39x39in) s.d.1963 i.verso prov.exhib.lit. 27-Jun-4 Versailles Encheres #91/R est:55000-60000
£33000 $60720 €48180 Untitled (65x81cm-26x32in) s. exec c.1960 prov. 24-Jun-4 Sotheby's, London #174/R est:30000-40000
£33784 $57432 €49325 Composition 2 (128x162cm-50x64in) s. 18-Nov-3 Sotheby's, Toronto #28/R est:300000-500000 (C.D 75000)
£33784 $57432 €49325 Engloutis (73x60cm-29x24in) s.d.59 prov. 18-Nov-3 Sotheby's, Toronto #116/R est:80000-100000 (C.D 75000)
£34722 $54861 €50000 Composition (54x81cm-21x32in) s.d.1964 prov. 27-Apr-3 Versailles Encheres #31
£36000 $65880 €52560 Composition (70x75cm-28x30in) s. prov.lit. 1-Jun-4 Joyner Waddington, Toronto #55/R est:100000-150000 (C.D 90000)
£38889 $64167 €56000 Composition rouge et noire (40x80cm-16x31in) s.d.1953 prov.lit. 2-Jul-3 Cornette de St.Cyr, Paris #29/R est:60000-80000
£42254 $70141 €60000 La chute du mersier (81x65cm-32x26in) s. painted 1974. 14-Jun-3 Meeting Art, Vercelli #370/R
£42838 $74967 €60830 Tristesse blanche (73x100cm-29x39in) s. painted c.1957. 16-Dec-3 Porro, Milan #32/R est:80000-90000
£54054 $91892 €78919 E' Terre (88x116cm-35x46in) s. s.i.d.1949 verso prov.exhib.lit. 27-Nov-3 Heffel, Vancouver #56/R est:70000-90000 (C.D 120000)
£58036 $99821 €84733 Jour de fetes (80x98cm-31x39in) s.d.1958 exhib. 2-Dec-3 Joyner Waddington, Toronto #73/R est:60000-70000 (C.D 130000)
£60000 $110400 €87600 Sans titre (81x100cm-32x39in) s. s.stretcher prov. 25-Jun-4 Christie's, London #107/R est:35000-45000
£70000 $128800 €102200 La proue (73x92cm-29x36in) s. s.i.stretcher prov.exhib.lit. 25-Jun-4 Christie's, London #108/R est:50000-70000
£89820 $150000 €131137 Untitled (85x125cm-33x49in) s.d.1953 i.stretcher. 13-Nov-3 Sotheby's, New York #175/R est:100000-150000
£100000 $182000 €146000 Untitled (100x81cm-39x32in) s.d.53 prov.exhib.lit. 5-Feb-4 Sotheby's, London #12/R est:120000-150000
£100671 $180201 €150000 Ete indien (89x16cm-35x6in) s. painted c.1958 prov.exhib. 26-May-4 Christie's, Paris #77/R est:50000-70000
£201117 $360000 €293631 Echo d'horizon (96x129cm-38x51in) s.d.54 s.i.stretcher prov. 13-May-4 Sotheby's, New York #108/R est:150000-200000
£363129 $650000 €530168 Untitled (124x224cm-49x88in) s. s.d.50 verso prov. 12-May-4 Sotheby's, New York #27/R est:400000-600000
Works on paper
£2455 $4223 €3584 Pastel No 3 (51x70cm-20x28in) s.d.65 pastel. 2-Dec-3 Joyner Waddington, Toronto #144/R est:5000-7000 (C.D 5500)
£5067 $9323 €7600 Composition (75x57cm-30x22in) s.d.63 gouache. 11-Jun-4 Pierre Berge, Paris #76 est:10000-12000
£5405 $9189 €7891 Untitled (60x90cm-24x35in) s.i. pastel prov. 18-Nov-3 Sotheby's, Toronto #143/R est:5000-7000 (C.D 12000)

RIOPELLE, Jean-Paul (attrib) (1923-2002) Canadian
£4453 $7170 €6501 Abstract (60x65cm-24x26in) 13-Oct-3 Joel, Victoria #385/R est:5000-8000 (A.D 11000)

RIORDON, Eric (1906-1948) Canadian
£446 $746 €647 Last rays, Laurentians (20x25cm-8x10in) s.i.verso board prov. 17-Jun-3 Pinneys, Montreal #94 est:1000-1500 (C.D 1000)
£893 $1536 €1304 Last Rays, Laurentians (19x25cm-7x10in) s. board prov. 2-Dec-3 Joyner Waddington, Toronto #419 est:1000-1500 (C.D 2000)
£1600 $2928 €2336 Yoho Valley (45x65cm-18x26in) s.i. 1-Jun-4 Hodgins, Calgary #130/R est:2500-3500 (C.D 4000)
£1786 $3071 €2608 Sugaring time (30x40cm-12x16in) s. canvasboard prov. 2-Dec-3 Joyner Waddington, Toronto #43/R est:2000-3000 (C.D 4000)
£1786 $3071 €2608 Winter wonderland (47x65cm-19x26in) s. prov. 2-Dec-3 Joyner Waddington, Toronto #170/R est:3000-3500 (C.D 4000)
Works on paper
£380 $695 €555 Winter stream (27x36cm-11x14in) s.d.1930 pastel. 1-Jun-4 Hodgins, Calgary #375/R (C.D 950)

RIOS, Ricardo de los (attrib) (1846-1929) Spanish
£1879 $3326 €2800 Dans l'atelier (104x63cm-41x25in) bears sig.indis.d. 30-Apr-4 Tajan, Paris #127/R est:3000-4000

RIOU, Edouard (1833-1900) French
£789 $1453 €1200 Elegantes sur la jetee a Trouville (34x24cm-13x9in) s.d.90. 25-Jun-4 Millon & Associes, Paris #38/R

RIOULT, Louis Edouard (1790-1855) French
£3356 $6174 €5000 Two naked girls (54x46cm-21x18in) s.d.1829. 25-Mar-4 Dr Fritz Nagel, Stuttgart #766/R est:2800
Works on paper
£493 $853 €700 Paquebot dans le port d'Alger (47x62cm-19x24in) s. W/C gouache. 15-Dec-3 Gros & Delettrez, Paris #472

RIP, Willem C (1856-1922) Dutch
£759 $1403 €1100 River landscape with farmstead (39x55cm-15x22in) s. 13-Feb-4 Auktionhaus Georg Rehm, Augsburg #8115/R
£769 $1284 €1100 Spaarndam Bridge (24x33cm-9x13in) s. s.i.verso. 30-Jun-3 Sotheby's, Amsterdam #193/R
£1769 $3219 €2600 Omstreken van Loosduinen, fisherman in the dunes (31x47cm-12x19in) s. s.i.verso panel. 3-Feb-4 Christie's, Amsterdam #392 est:1200-1600
£1842 $3389 €2800 Windmills near Dordrecht (44x55cm-17x22in) s. s.indis.i.verso. 22-Jun-4 Christie's, Amsterdam #175/R est:3000-5000
£2361 $4014 €3400 Dutch landscape at sunset (31x49cm-12x19in) s. i. verso. 28-Oct-3 Dorotheum, Vienna #113/R est:3500-4000
£2639 $4169 €3800 Zomermorgen in Bergschenhoek (42x50cm-17x20in) s. s.i.verso. 2-Sep-3 Christie's, Amsterdam #293/R est:800-1200
£4422 $8048 €6500 Opkomende bui bji middelaar (76x53cm-30x21in) s.d.1913 s.i.d.verso. 3-Feb-4 Christie's, Amsterdam #364/R est:3000-5000
Works on paper
£442 $805 €650 Fishermen in the dunes (19x27cm-7x11in) s.d.85 W/C htd white. 3-Feb-4 Christie's, Amsterdam #385
£658 $1211 €1000 Extensive Polderlandscape with men in a boat (31x57cm-12x22in) s. W/C htd white. 28-Jun-4 Sotheby's, Amsterdam #30/R

RIPALDA, Fernando (1937-) Spanish
£336 $628 €500 Harbour (36x102cm-14x40in) s.d.65 board. 24-Feb-4 Durán, Madrid #667/R

RIPAMONTE, Carlos Pablo (1874-1968) Argentinian
£659 $1200 €962 Landscape (25x31cm-10x12in) s. 5-Jul-4 Arroyo, Buenos Aires #72/R
£824 $1450 €1203 Mowing (38x49cm-15x19in) s. 5-Jan-4 Galeria y Remates, Montevideo #94/R
£824 $1500 €1203 Orchids (56x48cm-22x19in) s. 5-Jul-4 Arroyo, Buenos Aires #84/R est:1500
£1044 $1900 €1524 Clarity (25x30cm-10x12in) s. 29-Jun-4 Arroyo, Buenos Aires #8/R est:1500
£1657 $3000 €2419 Peasant (41x32cm-16x13in) board. 30-Mar-4 Arroyo, Buenos Aires #14
£1749 $3200 €2554 Peasant (24x14cm-9x6in) cardboard. 1-Jun-4 Arroyo, Buenos Aires #8
£2597 $4700 €3792 Killing (41x32cm-16x13in) cardboard. 30-Mar-4 Arroyo, Buenos Aires #8
£2692 $4900 €3930 Peasant man (60x50cm-24x20in) s. 29-Jun-4 Arroyo, Buenos Aires #27 est:4000
£3825 $7000 €5585 Sealing (37x45cm-15x18in) cardboard. 1-Jun-4 Arroyo, Buenos Aires #55
Works on paper
£1117 $2000 €1631 Dream landscapes (45x54cm-18x21in) pencil dr pair. 11-May-4 Arroyo, Buenos Aires #83

RIPARI, Virgilio (1843-1902) Italian
£266 $425 €388 Venetian view (51x41cm-20x16in) s. 19-Sep-3 Freeman, Philadelphia #129/R
£449 $750 €656 Venetian view (41x51cm-16x20in) s. 20-Jun-3 Freeman, Philadelphia #97/R
£1074 $2008 €1600 Venice (51x40cm-20x16in) s. 24-Feb-4 Dorotheum, Vienna #38/R est:2000-2200
£1748 $2920 €2500 Gondolas in the Lagoon (51x76cm-20x30in) s. 24-Jun-3 Finarte Semenzato, Rome #137/R
£4564 $8397 €6800 Peasant women (34x53cm-13x21in) s. 24-Mar-4 Il Ponte, Milan #507/R est:1000

RIPIJINGIMPI, Paddy Henry (attrib) (c.1925-1999) Australian
Sculpture
£1220 $1927 €1781 Bima (87cm-34in) earth pigments ironwood exec.c.1972 prov.lit. 28-Jul-3 Sotheby's, Paddington #263 est:2000-3000 (A.D 3000)

RIPLEY, Aiden Lassell (1896-1969) American
Works on paper
£323 $600 €472 A summer's day (23x17cm-9x7in) s. i.verso W/C prov. 5-Mar-4 Skinner, Boston #438/R
£530 $900 €774 Snow scene (22x29cm-9x11in) W/C. 21-Nov-3 Skinner, Boston #496/R est:800-1200
£882 $1500 €1288 Leopard with prey outside a cave with huge cobweb (79x61cm-31x24in) s.d.1921 pencil. 28-Nov-3 Thomaston Place, Thomaston #814
£1529 $2600 €2232 Chicken coop, Lexington, Massachusetts (51x73cm-20x29in) s. W/C. 21-Nov-3 Skinner, Boston #474/R est:1800-2200
£2235 $4000 €3263 Making canvas (38x48cm-15x19in) s. W/C. 8-Jan-4 James Julia, Fairfield #38/R est:2500-5000
£2285 $4250 €3336 Farm view, Lexington, Massachussetts (37x53cm-15x21in) i. W/C. 5-Mar-4 Skinner, Boston #485/R est:4000-6000
£4491 $7500 €6557 Evening train (56x76cm-22x30in) s. W/C board. 9-Oct-3 Christie's, Rockefeller NY #87/R est:5000-7000
£9626 $18000 €14054 Ruffed grouse (30x46cm-12x18in) s. W/C. 24-Jul-4 Coeur d'Alene, Hayden #220/R est:10000-20000
£12353 $21000 €18035 Early snow, hunting scene (44x60cm-17x24in) s.d.1937 W/C prov. 21-Nov-3 Skinner, Boston #341/R est:15000-25000

RIPOLLES, Juan (1932-) Spanish
£590 $1003 €850 Beauties (38x55cm-15x22in) s.d.1970. 28-Oct-3 Segre, Madrid #272/R
£699 $1168 €1000 Untitled (46x54cm-18x21in) s.d.1985 paper on panel prov. 24-Jun-3 Segre, Madrid #243/R
£1127 $1972 €1600 Lady with dog (46x27cm-18x11in) s.d.1970. 16-Dec-3 Segre, Madrid #192/R est:500

RIPPEL, Morris (b.1930) American
Works on paper
£3235 $5500 €4723 Road to Mora (33x56cm-13x22in) s.d.76 W/C prov. 1-Nov-3 Santa Fe Art, Santa Fe #13/R est:10000-12000

RIPPINGILLE, Edward Villiers (1798-1859) British
£650 $1086 €949 Fireside tale (43x36cm-17x14in) panel. 13-Nov-3 Christie's, Kensington #313/R

RIPPL-RONAI, Jozsef (1861-1927) Hungarian
£8511 $14213 €12000 Dans un champ (20x25cm-8x10in) s.d.1901 cardboard. 19-Jun-3 Millon & Associes, Paris #129/R
£25030 $45305 €36544 Tourbillon (50x74cm-20x29in) s. oil on card. 16-Apr-4 Mu Terem Galeria, Budapest #140/R (H.F 9500000)
£73080 $126429 €106697 Man in a hat - Portrait of Count Somssich (49x69cm-19x27in) s. cardboard. 12-Dec-3 Kieselbach, Budapest #64/R (H.F 28000000)
Works on paper
£814 $1352 €1188 One of the eminent figures of Vienna (18x17cm-7x7in) s.d.1913 dec 4 pencil. 4-Oct-3 Kieselbach, Budapest #58/R (H.F 300000)
£855 $1514 €1248 Female nude (33x28cm-13x11in) s.d.1899 walnut ink. 28-Apr-4 Kieselbach, Budapest #10/R (H.F 320000)
£940 $1626 €1372 Dr Geza Molnar and Pal Szinyei Merse in the Lantos Restaurant (20x16cm-8x6in) s. green chl. 12-Dec-3 Kieselbach, Budapest #7/R (H.F 360000)
£1958 $3329 €2800 Sta Lucia (29x40cm-11x16in) s.i. pastel. 26-Nov-3 Dorotheum, Vienna #25/R est:3000-5000
£6787 $11266 €9909 Main street of Kapos being paved (42x53cm-17x21in) s. pastel. 4-Oct-3 Kieselbach, Budapest #145/R (H.F 2500000)
£8352 $14449 €12194 Portrait of Lajos Kossuth (31x23cm-12x9in) s. pastel. 12-Dec-3 Kieselbach, Budapest #92/R (H.F 3200000)
£9620 $17027 €14045 Portrait of Odon Rippl-Ronai, the painter's brother (32x25cm-13x10in) pastel cardboard. 28-Apr-4 Kieselbach, Budapest #119/R (H.F 3600000)
£12587 $21399 €18000 Figures in garden (32x41cm-13x16in) s. pastel chl board prov. 26-Nov-3 Dorotheum, Vienna #28/R est:20000-22000
£16965 $29350 €24769 Winter evening (40x57cm-16x22in) s. pastel. 12-Dec-3 Kieselbach, Budapest #125/R (H.F 6500000)
£25030 $45305 €36544 Zorka in white blouse (52x42cm-20x17in) s. pastel. 16-Apr-4 Mu Terem Galeria, Budapest #173/R (H.F 9500000)
£37411 $66218 €54620 Lady in white gloves with white fur collar (52x41cm-20x16in) s. pastel. 28-Apr-4 Kieselbach, Budapest #51/R (H.F 14000000)
£46152 $76612 €67382 Zorka resting (53x42cm-21x17in) s. pastel. 4-Oct-3 Kieselbach, Budapest #77/R (H.F 17000000)

RIPPLINGER, Henry (1939-) Canadian
£600 $1098 €876 Old barn (60x105cm-24x41in) s.d.1979 board. 1-Jun-4 Hodgins, Calgary #325/R (C.D 1500)

RIQUER E INGLADA, Alejandro de (1856-1920) Spanish
Works on paper
£828 $1490 €1200 Modernist woman (30x22cm-12x9in) s.d.1897 W/C. 26-Jan-4 Ansorena, Madrid #304/R

RISAN, John A (1934-) Norwegian
£275 $460 €402 Composition (32x42cm-13x17in) S. 20-Oct-3 Blomqvist, Lysaker #1248 (N.KR 3200)

RISBERG, Roger (1956-) Swedish?
£5136 $8731 €7499 Inauguration - Happy Christmas (170x144cm-67x57in) mono.d.89 acrylic three. 4-Nov-3 Bukowskis, Stockholm #634/R est:50000-60000 (S.KR 68000)

RISHELL, Robert (1917-1976) American
£4620 $8500 €6745 Thunderheads over Monument Valley (101x76cm-40x30in) s. 8-Jun-4 Bonhams & Butterfields, San Francisco #4141/R est:6000-8000

RISHER, Anna Priscilla (1875-1946) American
£359 $600 €524 California coast (32x39cm-13x15in) s. board. 19-Oct-3 Bonhams & Butterfields, Los Angeles #7003

RISI POGLIANI, Cornelia (1877-1946) Italian
£315 $526 €450 Varese Lake (43x53cm-17x21in) s. 10-Oct-3 Stadion, Trieste #526/R
£385 $662 €550 Grey day on Lake Como (45x52cm-18x20in) s. painted c.1910. 3-Dec-3 Stadion, Trieste #1029/R

RISLEY, Tom (1947-) Australian
Works on paper
£972 $1564 €1419 Book (97x107cm-38x42in) s.d.Feb 1997 verso mixed media construction prov. 25-Aug-3 Sotheby's, Paddington #301/R (A.D 2400)
£2024 $3259 €2955 Three vessels (180x201cm-71x79in) s.d.Jan '91 verso mixed media canvasboard prov.exhib. 25-Aug-3 Sotheby's, Paddington #428/R est:5000-8000 (A.D 5000)

RISPOLI, Franco (1921-) Italian
£382 $649 €550 Portrait of lady (60x50cm-24x20in) s. 1-Nov-3 Meeting Art, Vercelli #392

RISS, Thomas (1871-1959) Austrian
£800 $1472 €1200 Lake Garda landscape (48x70cm-19x28in) s.i. board. 9-Jun-4 Dorotheum, Salzburg #551/R
Works on paper
£1192 $2181 €1800 Portrait of Ludwig Meister (42x31cm-17x12in) s.i.d.28.9.16 W/C mixed media board. 7-Apr-4 Dorotheum, Salzburg #177/R est:2000-2400

RISSANEN, Juho (1873-1950) Finnish
£2394 $4142 €3400 Making twigs for the sauna (41x51cm-16x20in) s.d.1916 board. 13-Dec-3 Hagelstam, Helsinki #143/R est:1500
£2817 $4873 €4000 House in landscape (68x56cm-27x22in) s.d.1920. 13-Dec-3 Hagelstam, Helsinki #144/R est:4000
£6081 $10885 €9000 Gathering shells on the beach (88x95cm-35x37in) s.d.1926. 8-May-4 Bukowskis, Helsinki #159/R est:5000-8000
Works on paper
£333 $613 €500 The meeting (63x47cm-25x19in) s.d.1927 W/C. 9-Jun-4 Bukowskis, Helsinki #527/R
£556 $928 €800 Girl (81x57cm-32x22in) s.d.1913 chl. 23-Oct-3 Hagelstam, Helsinki #989
£667 $1193 €1000 Old man from Savolax (38x24cm-15x9in) s. W/C. 15-May-4 Hagelstam, Helsinki #134/R
£2797 $4755 €4000 The Holy Child (57x92cm-22x36in) s.d.1939 mixed media triptych. 29-Nov-3 Bukowskis, Helsinki #165/R est:4000-6000

RISSO, Vittorio (1901-1949) Italian
£436 $772 €650 Flowers (59x53cm-23x21in) s. board. 1-May-4 Meeting Art, Vercelli #303

RIST, Pipilotti (1962-) German
Photographs
£3784 $7000 €5525 We step to your table (120x160cm-47x63in) s.i.d.99 num.3/5 verso video still C-print on glass prov.lit. 12-Feb-4 Sotheby's, New York #356/R est:4000-6000
Sculpture
£2703 $5000 €3946 Closet circuit. toilet camera other objects exec 2000 prov. 12-Feb-4 Sotheby's, New York #357/R est:8000-12000
£15569 $26000 €22731 Hallo, guten tag! kassmund (40x30x5cm-16x12x2in) s. num.10 verso videotape recorder LCD colour television prov. 14-Nov-3 Phillips, New York #184/R est:15000-20000

RISUENO, Joaquin (1957-) Spanish
£1149 $2022 €1700 Untitled (81x116cm-32x46in) s.d.1987 verso exhib.lit. 18-May-4 Segre, Madrid #125/R est:1500
£3333 $6033 €5000 Dusk in the porch (162x114cm-64x45in) s.d.1985 verso exhib.lit. 30-Mar-4 Segre, Madrid #244/R est:600

RITA (20th C) Austrian
Works on paper
£268 $481 €400 Composition (29x19cm-11x7in) s. col pen W/C. 25-May-4 Dorotheum, Vienna #326/R
£268 $481 €400 Going out clothes (41x29cm-16x11in) s.d.1971 Indian ink W/C. 25-May-4 Dorotheum, Vienna #327/R
£302 $541 €450 Head (36x28cm-14x11in) s. chk W/C. 25-May-4 Dorotheum, Vienna #325/R

RITCHIE, John (fl.1841-1875) British
£14118 $24000 €20612 Sale of the Captains goods, an auction in the grounds of a country house (51x76cm-20x30in) mono. prov. 28-Oct-3 Sotheby's, New York #70/R est:30000-40000
£42000 $77280 €61320 Extracting a thorn (41x51cm-16x20in) s. prov. 26-Mar-4 Sotheby's, London #61/R est:25000-35000

RITCHIE, Maxine (1949-) Australian?
£1293 $2017 €1875 Eclipse (63x84cm-25x33in) s. acrylic canvas on board. 1-Aug-2 Joel, Victoria #183 est:3000-5000 (A.D 3750)
£4472 $7020 €6484 Blue water iris (66x94cm-26x37in) s.i.d.2000 acrylic canvas on board. 26-Aug-3 Christie's, Sydney #274/R est:8000-12000 (A.D 11000)
Works on paper
£3688 $5828 €5384 Mango's - aura series I (66x49cm-26x19in) s. s.i.d.Oct 2001 verso synthetic polymer canvas on board. 2-Sep-3 Deutscher-Menzies, Melbourne #276/R est:4500-5500 (A.D 9000)

RITMAN, Lieke (20th C) ?
Works on paper
£300 $546 €438 Marazion. s.d.73 mixed media with tree lidded boxes. 15-Jun-4 David Lay, Penzance #531

RITMAN, Louis (1889-1963) American/Russian
£284 $500 €415 Portrait of a man (41x33cm-16x13in) 23-May-4 Hindman, Chicago #169/R
£523 $900 €764 Portrait of a girl (53x41cm-21x16in) 7-Dec-3 Hindman, Chicago #790/R
£2035 $3500 €2971 Village (55x65cm-22x26in) s. prov. 3-Dec-3 Doyle, New York #239/R est:5000-7000
£2616 $4500 €3819 Village church (37x45cm-15x18in) panel prov. 3-Dec-3 Doyle, New York #240/R est:3000-5000
£5233 $9000 €7640 Red dress (62x77cm-24x30in) bears sig prov. 3-Dec-3 Doyle, New York #238/R est:8000-12000
£6977 $12000 €10186 Park bench (76x91cm-30x36in) s. prov. 4-Dec-3 Christie's, Rockefeller NY #90/R

RITSCHEL, William (1864-1949) American
£9412 $16000 €13742 Brittany boats (56x71cm-22x28in) s. canvas on canvas. 18-Nov-3 John Moran, Pasadena #59 est:7000-9000
£10582 $20000 €15450 Sailboat in stormy seas (53x64cm-21x25in) s.d.96 prov. 17-Feb-4 John Moran, Pasadena #172/R est:10000-15000

RITSCHL, Otto (1885-1976) German
£1111 $1856 €1600 Composition (34x24cm-13x9in) mono. i. verso masonite prov. 24-Oct-3 Ketterer, Hamburg #521/R est:2000-3000
£1467 $2625 €2200 Composition 43/8 (33x29cm-13x11in) s. 15-May-4 Van Ham, Cologne #880/R est:1200
£2098 $3608 €3000 Composition 66/35 (100x80cm-39x31in) s.d. s.i.d. verso prov. 5-Dec-3 Ketterer, Munich #335/R est:5000-7000
£2416 $4277 €3600 Composition 57/18 (130x97cm-51x38in) s.d. s.i. verso prov. 30-Apr-4 Dr Fritz Nagel, Stuttgart #933/R est:3900
£2667 $4907 €4000 Composition 46/14 (52x40cm-20x16in) s.d. s.i. verso panel. 11-Jun-4 Hauswedell & Nolte, Hamburg #1501/R est:4000
£4514 $7538 €6500 Composition 69/60 (130x97cm-51x38in) s.d. i. verso prov. 24-Oct-3 Ketterer, Hamburg #522/R est:6500-7500
£4800 $8784 €7200 Composition 58/23 (97x130cm-38x51in) s.d.58 s.i.d.1958/23 verso prov. 4-Jun-4 Lempertz, Koln #388/R est:5000
£5000 $8950 €7500 Old monk (131x98cm-52x39in) s.d. s.i.d. verso oil dispersion. 15-May-4 Dr Sturies, Dusseldorf #164/R
Works on paper
£533 $981 €800 Composition (50x32cm-20x13in) s.d.51 W/C pen ink over pencil. 12-Jun-4 Villa Grisebach, Berlin #826/R
£933 $1717 €1400 Abstract half figure (25x33cm-10x13in) s. W/C pen ink. 12-Jun-4 Villa Grisebach, Berlin #823/R est:1000-1200

RITSEMA, Coba (1876-1961) Dutch
£493 $893 €750 Portrait of Isaac Israels (30x20cm-12x8in) s. panel. 19-Apr-4 Glerum, Amsterdam #270/R
£1528 $2414 €2200 Stilleven met weitas (82x109cm-32x43in) s. lit. 2-Sep-3 Christie's, Amsterdam #224/R est:1500-2000
£1701 $3095 €2500 Bloemstuk, pink flowers in a vase (68x81cm-27x32in) init. 3-Feb-4 Christie's, Amsterdam #169/R est:2500-3500
£1944 $3072 €2800 Still life with soup terrine and flowers (72x91cm-28x36in) s. 2-Sep-3 Christie's, Amsterdam #219/R est:2500-3500
£5555 $9055 €8000 Portrait of the mother of the artist (85x63cm-33x25in) s.verso prov.exhib. 29-Sep-3 Sotheby's, Amsterdam #98/R

RITSEMA, Jacob Coenraad (1869-1943) Dutch
£395 $726 €600 View of S Graveland in springtime (61x77cm-24x30in) s. canvas on board. 28-Jun-4 Sotheby's, Amsterdam #61/R

RITTASE, William M (1894-1968) American?
Photographs
£2260 $4000 €3300 Streamliner, reading R.R (20x24cm-8x9in) gelatin silver print executed c.1930. 27-Apr-4 Christie's, Rockefeller NY #267/R est:5000-7000

RITTENBERG, Henry R (1879-1969) American
£2500 $4000 €3650 Still life with fruit and nude statue (76x91cm-30x36in) prov. 20-Sep-3 Pook & Pook, Downington #360/R est:5000-7000

RITTER, Anne Gregory (1868-1929) American
£235 $400 €343 Floral still life (41x30cm-16x12in) s. board. 22-Nov-3 Jackson's, Cedar Falls #89/R

RITTER, Eduard (attrib) (1808-1853) Austrian
£1325 $2411 €2000 Exciting reading (29x22cm-11x9in) i.verso panel. 21-Jun-4 Dorotheum, Vienna #177 est:2200-2400

RITTER, Eduard (1820-1892) German
£16667 $30000 €24334 Interior of a living room (40x50cm-16x20in) s.d.1846. 22-Jan-4 Sotheby's, New York #275/R est:8000-12000

RITTER, Louis (19th C) ?
£9140 $17000 €13344 Beaulieu, Seine (37x76cm-15x30in) s.i.d.1886. 5-Mar-4 Skinner, Boston #499/R est:1000-1500

RITTER, Paul (elder) (1829-1907) German
£629 $1000 €918 Old millhouse (91x74cm-36x29in) s. 13-Sep-3 Weschler, Washington #689/R
£2486 $4500 €3630 Along the river (76x117cm-30x46in) s. 31-Mar-4 Sotheby's, New York #94/R est:4000-6000
Works on paper
£909 $1518 €1300 St Sebald (23x32cm-9x13in) s. gouache. 26-Jun-3 Weidler, Nurnberg #7009/R

RITTER, Wilhelm Georg (1850-1926) German
£486 $768 €700 Peasant at ford with horses (30x52cm-12x20in) s.d.76 lit. 19-Sep-3 Schloss Ahlden, Ahlden #1507/R

RITTIG, Peter (1789-1840) German
Works on paper
£839 $1427 €1200 Portrait of Rudolf Schadow (18x13cm-7x5in) pencil. 21-Nov-3 Reiss & Sohn, Konigstein #294/R est:1500

RITTINGER, Marian (17th C) Austrian
Sculpture
£4138 $6869 €6000 Bust of God the Father (55cm-22in) wood. 30-Sep-3 Dorotheum, Vienna #175/R est:6500-7500

RITTMEYER, Emil (1820-1904) Swiss
£1121 $2006 €1637 Interlaken with Jungfrau (37x50cm-15x20in) mono.d.1883. 13-May-4 Stuker, Bern #292/R est:2500-3000 (S.FR 2600)

RITTS, Herb (1952-2003) American
Photographs
£2000 $3400 €2920 Mel Gibson, Hollywood (51x41cm-20x16in) s.i.d.1985 num.16/25 verso toned silver print lit. 19-Nov-3 Sotheby's, Olympia #225/R est:1000-1500
£2096 $3500 €3060 Paul, torso, Los Angeles (48x37cm-19x15in) s.i.d.1990 num.5/25 verso toned gelatin silver print lit. 20-Oct-3 Christie's, Rockefeller NY #160/R est:2000-3000
£2147 $3800 €3135 Female torso, detail, Hollywood (48x37cm-19x15in) s.d.1989 num.5/25 gelatin silver print lit. 27-Apr-4 Christie's, Rockefeller NY #179/R est:3000-4000
£2200 $3740 €3212 Dizzy Gillespie, Paris (47x38cm-19x15in) s.i.d.1989 num.14/25 gelatin silver print. 18-Nov-3 Christie's, Kensington #147/R est:2000-3000
£2210 $4000 €3227 Fred with tires II (25x25cm-10x10in) s.i.d.1984 num.11/25 verso gelatin silver print. 19-Apr-4 Daniel Cooney, Brooklyn #469064/R
£2518 $4029 €3500 Jack Nicholson III (32x25cm-13x10in) s. num.7/25 verso silver gelatin print exec.1988. 19-May-3 Sotheby's, Milan #106/R est:4000
£3143 $5500 €4589 Madonna (46x41cm-18x16in) i.d.1985 dye transfer print exec 1985. 17-Dec-3 Christie's, Rockefeller NY #269/R est:4000-6000
£3672 $6500 €5361 Cindy Crawford, Costa Careyes, 1998 (35x48cm-14x19in) s.d.1998 num.9/25 gelatin silver print. 27-Apr-4 Christie's, Rockefeller NY #180/R est:3000-5000
£3672 $6500 €5361 Carrie in the sand, Paradise Cove, 1988 (56x49cm-22x19in) s.i.d.1988 num.AP/2 verso platinum print. 27-Apr-4 Christie's, Rockefeller NY #181/R est:4000-6000

RITTUN, Thorstein (1929-) Norwegian
£241 $441 €352 Coastal landscape (50x61cm-20x24in) s. 2-Feb-4 Blomqvist, Lysaker #1240 (N.KR 3000)
£324 $518 €470 Windfall with birds (60x66cm-24x26in) s. 22-Sep-3 Blomqvist, Lysaker #1243 (N.KR 3800)
£448 $720 €654 Walking on the shore (110x90cm-43x35in) s. 25-Aug-3 Blomqvist, Lysaker #1235/R (N.KR 5200)
£473 $790 €691 Three women (90x27cm-35x11in) s. 20-Oct-3 Blomqvist, Lysaker #1250/R (N.KR 5500)
£520 $957 €780 In the poultry yard (65x53cm-26x21in) s. 14-Jun-4 Blomqvist, Lysaker #1311/R (N.KR 6400)
£584 $975 €853 Two woman (99x79cm-39x31in) s. 17-Nov-3 Blomqvist, Lysaker #1263/R (N.KR 7000)
£643 $1177 €939 Two women (99x79cm-39x31in) s. 2-Feb-4 Blomqvist, Lysaker #1239 (N.KR 8000)

RITZ, Lorenz Justin (1796-1870) Swiss
£2661 $4443 €3858 Paire de portraits des epoux de Sepibus (66x53cm-26x21in) one s.d.verso pair prov. 21-Jun-3 Galerie du Rhone, Sion #458/R est:6000-8000 (S.FR 5800)

RITZ, Raphael (1829-1894) Swiss
£4310 $7716 €6293 Chamois (31x41cm-12x16in) s.d.28.X.79. 14-May-4 Dobiaschofsky, Bern #39/R est:9500 (S.FR 10000)
£8190 $14659 €11957 Mass by the lake (35x50cm-14x20in) canvas on board. 17-May-4 Beurret, Zurich #15/R est:3000-4000 (S.FR 19000)

RITZ, Raphael (attrib) (1829-1894) Swiss
£873 $1590 €1275 Old stone fountain (22x32cm-9x13in) i. canvas on cardboard. 16-Jun-4 Fischer, Luzern #2328/R (S.FR 2000)

RITZBERGER, Albert (1853-1915) German
£6000 $10920 €8760 A pensive moment (87x65cm-34x26in) s.d.12/7/1891. 15-Jun-4 Sotheby's, London #50a/R est:5000-7000

RITZENHOFEN, Hubert (1879-1961) Dutch
£400 $728 €600 On the Dutch coast (60x80cm-24x31in) s. 1-Jul-4 Van Ham, Cologne #1574
£420 $713 €600 Fishing boats at sea on moonlit night (91x96cm-36x38in) s. 22-Nov-3 Arnold, Frankfurt #618/R
£694 $1132 €1000 Amsterdam flower market (70x100cm-28x39in) s. 26-Sep-3 Bolland & Marotz, Bremen #678/R

RITZEROW, Antonie (1877-?) German
£524 $892 €750 White horses (81x71cm-32x28in) s. 28-Nov-3 Wendl, Rudolstadt #4156/R

RITZOW, Charlotte (1971-) German
Works on paper
£333 $613 €500 Give and take (60x80cm-24x31in) s. mixed media on canvas exec.2004. 12-Jun-4 Meeting Art, Vercelli #452/R
£352 $585 €500 Il Bacio 1 (40x30cm-16x12in) s. s.artist st.verso mixed media canvas exec 1996. 14-Jun-3 Meeting Art, Vercelli #426
£633 $1165 €950 Instinct (100x100cm-39x39in) s. mixed media on canvas exec.2002. 12-Jun-4 Meeting Art, Vercelli #908/R

RIVA, Egidio (1866-1946) Italian
£382 $649 €550 Lake landscape (29x45cm-11x18in) s. s.verso board. 1-Nov-3 Meeting Art, Vercelli #354
£403 $713 €600 Venice (18x24cm-7x9in) s. cardboard. 1-May-4 Meeting Art, Vercelli #309
£671 $1201 €1000 Naviglio in Milan (24x30cm-9x12in) s. board. 25-May-4 Finarte Semenzato, Milan #149/R
£1342 $2403 €2000 San Lorenzo columns under the snow, Milan (24x30cm-9x12in) s. board. 25-May-4 Finarte Semenzato, Milan #148/R est:500-600

RIVA, Giacomo (19th C) Italian
Works on paper
£1776 $3268 €2700 Gallant scene. Peasant in interior (48x33cm-19x13in) s. W/C two. 23-Jun-4 Finarte Semenzato, Rome #24/R est:3000-3200

RIVA, Giovanni (1890-1973) Italian
£649 $1162 €948 Peasants with ox working the fields (38x70cm-15x28in) s. 22-Mar-4 Philippe Schuler, Zurich #4426/R (S.FR 1500)

RIVA, Giuseppe (19th C) Italian
Works on paper
£750 $1275 €1095 Young couple seated in a village square. Young girls in a kitchen (48x33cm-19x13in) s. pencil W/C pair. 6-Nov-3 Christie's, Kensington #989/R

RIVA, Ugo (1951-) Italian
Sculpture
£1853 $3318 €2705 Female nude on throne (208x56x60cm-82x22x24in) mono.i.d. 12-May-4 Dobiaschofsky, Bern #2544/R est:2600 (S.FR 4300)

RIVALTA, Augusto (1838-1925) Italian
Sculpture
£1135 $1895 €1600 Faune and nymph (48x22x24cm-19x9x9in) s. bronze. 20-Oct-3 Sant Agostino, Torino #67/R est:2000

RIVAROLI, Giuseppe (1885-1943) Italian
£839 $1443 €1200 On the Piave (62x90cm-24x35in) s. canvas on board. 3-Dec-3 Stadion, Trieste #1139/R
£942 $1545 €1300 Female nude with children (24x31cm-9x12in) s.i.d.1921 board. 27-May-3 Finarte Semenzato, Milan #51/R est:1300-1600
£1206 $2013 €1700 Rural celebrations (39x51cm-15x20in) s. board. 14-Oct-3 Finarte Semenzato, Milan #4
£1268 $2104 €1800 Scena con carrozza e cavalieri (50x65cm-20x26in) s.d.1918. 11-Jun-3 Christie's, Rome #95/R est:2000-2500
Works on paper
£500 $895 €750 Music (44x31cm-17x12in) s. W/C. 12-May-4 Stadion, Trieste #651/R

RIVAS GARCIA, Ramen (1930-) Spanish
£872 $1623 €1300 Beach in Combarro (38x46cm-15x18in) s. s.verso board. 2-Mar-4 Ansorena, Madrid #129/R

RIVAS, Antonio (19th C) Italian
£1467 $2655 €2200 Odalisk with flower (12x17cm-5x7in) s. board. 30-Mar-4 Segre, Madrid #73/R
£1467 $2655 €2200 Odalisk (12x17cm-5x7in) s. board. 30-Mar-4 Segre, Madrid #74/R
£2600 $4732 €3796 Blowing bubbles by the river (38x62cm-15x24in) s.i. 16-Jun-4 Christie's, Kensington #102/R est:2000-3000
£4500 $7515 €6570 Harem (29x47cm-11x19in) s.i.d.89 panel. 14-Oct-3 Sotheby's, London #46/R est:5000-7000
£5500 $10010 €8030 Dance for the Sultan (34x57cm-13x22in) s.i. panel. 16-Jun-4 Bonhams, New Bond Street #85/R est:6000-8000
£6000 $11040 €9000 Le concert au harem (60x40cm-24x16in) s. 14-Jun-4 Gros & Delettrez, Paris #127/R est:9000-12000

RIVAS, Lucio (20th C) ?
£391 $625 €571 Untitled (73x61cm-29x24in) 16-Mar-3 Subastas Odalys, Caracas #42
£1131 $1810 €1651 Baby playing with sand (100x75cm-39x30in) s. painted 1974. 21-Sep-3 Subastas Odalys, Caracas #71/R

RIVERA, Diego (1886-1957) Mexican
£2882 $5245 €4208 Mother with child in her arms (49x40cm-19x16in) s.d.28 tempera paper board. 20-Jun-4 Agra, Warsaw #41/R (P.Z 20000)
£235294 $400000 €343529 Nina con muneca - Child with doll (77x61cm-30x24in) s.d.1954 prov.exhib.lit. 18-Nov-3 Christie's, Rockefeller NY #37/R est:400000-500000
£264706 $450000 €386471 Paisaje de toledo (61x51cm-24x20in) s.d.1913 prov.exhib.lit. 19-Nov-3 Sotheby's, New York #5/R est:500000-700000
Works on paper
£1070 $2000 €1562 Portrait. s. 25-Feb-4 Dallas Auction Gallery, Dallas #105b/R
£1341 $2400 €1958 Paisaje montanoso (15x28cm-6x11in) s. W/C. 8-May-4 Susanin's, Chicago #6069/R est:1800-2800
£1796 $3250 €2622 Untitled (20x15cm-8x6in) conte crayon. 16-Apr-4 Du Mouchelle, Detroit #2037/R est:1000-1800
£2429 $4250 €3546 Estudio de Campesinos (39x27cm-15x11in) s.d.39 chl prov. 19-Dec-3 Sotheby's, New York #1161/R est:6000-8000
£2825 $5000 €4125 Cabeza de Perfil con Rebozo (42x28cm-17x11in) s. pencil prov. 2-May-4 Bonhams & Butterfields, Los Angeles #3104/R est:8000-12000
£3235 $5500 €4723 Houses in a green field (17x20cm-7x8in) s.d.28 W/C pencil prov. 9-Nov-3 Bonhams & Butterfields, Los Angeles #4122/R est:5000-7000
£4000 $7000 €5840 Nina cargando cubetas (43x30cm-17x12in) s.d.46 ink. 19-Dec-3 Sotheby's, New York #1165/R est:10000-15000
£4118 $7000 €6012 Estudio para mujer desnuda - Study for female nude (46x31cm-18x12in) s. ink exec. c.1919. 18-Nov-3 Christie's, Rockefeller NY #86/R est:8000-10000
£4144 $7500 €6050 Nino con sombrero (36x25cm-14x10in) pencil. 16-Apr-4 Du Mouchelle, Detroit #2072/R est:8000-10000
£5269 $8957 €7693 Study for mural painting at the university (53x83cm-21x33in) s. pencil. 30-Oct-3 Louis Morton, Mexico #69/R est:115000-120000 (M.P 100000)
£6471 $11000 €9448 Illustration for Ilya ehrenburg's (19x14cm-7x6in) s. ink rice paper executed 1916 prov.lit. 19-Nov-3 Sotheby's, New York #97/R est:12000-18000

£6704	$12000	€9788	Untitled (28x39cm-11x15in) s.d.1939 chl prov. 26-May-4 Sotheby's, New York #92/R est:12000-18000
£9040	$16000	€13198	Cabeza de hombre (46x30cm-18x12in) s. chl pastel prov. 2-May-4 Bonhams & Butterfields, Los Angeles #3106/R est:15000-20000
£9412	$16000	€13742	Mercado - Marketplace (22x29cm-9x11in) s. ink exec.1930 prov. 18-Nov-3 Christie's, Rockefeller NY #129/R est:20000-25000
£11173	$20000	€16313	Two peasants (19x28cm-7x11in) s. ink W/C. 26-May-4 Sotheby's, New York #94/R est:18000-22000
£13333	$24533	€20000	Pont d'Arcueil (37x53cm-15x21in) s.d.18 W/C crayon prov.exhib. 10-Jun-4 Christie's, Paris #3/R est:32000-48000
£14118	$24000	€20612	Picapedrero - Masonworker (40x30cm-16x12in) s.d.1944 W/C prov. 18-Nov-3 Christie's, Rockefeller NY #105/R est:25000-35000
£18824	$32000	€27483	Hombre con petatas - Man carrying bedding (38x27cm-15x11in) s.d.1941 W/C ink prov. 18-Nov-3 Christie's, Rockefeller NY #117/R est:30000-40000
£22353	$38000	€32635	Pareja de indios - Indian couple (38x27cm-15x11in) s.d.41 W/C ink prov. 18-Nov-3 Christie's, Rockefeller NY #116/R est:30000-40000
£23529	$40000	€34352	Danzante (39x28cm-15x11in) s. W/C executed c.1948 prov. 19-Nov-3 Sotheby's, New York #4/R est:40000-50000
£27933	$50000	€40782	Palmera Farm (48x62cm-19x24in) s. W/C crayon exec.c.1935. 26-May-4 Sotheby's, New York #2/R est:30000-40000
£28235	$48000	€41223	Vendedoras en el mercado - Vendors at the marketplace (27x38cm-11x15in) s. W/C ink painted 1935 prov.lit. 18-Nov-3 Christie's, Rockefeller NY #26/R est:35000-45000
£30726	$55000	€44860	Carrier (38x28cm-15x11in) s. ink W/C prov. 26-May-4 Sotheby's, New York #3/R est:40000-50000
£32353	$55000	€47235	Tehuanas en el mercado (27x38cm-11x15in) s. W/C ink painted 1935 prov.lit. 18-Nov-3 Christie's, Rockefeller NY #27/R est:35000-45000

RIVERA, Elias J (1937-) American

£1471	$2500	€2148	Oaxaca Market IV (30x23cm-12x9in) s. painted c.1990 prov. 1-Nov-3 Santa Fe Art, Santa Fe #46/R est:4000-6000

RIVERA, Jose de (1904-) American

£3235	$5500	€4723	Untitled (33x33cm-13x13in) board. 9-Nov-3 Wright, Chicago #231 est:2000-3000
£3911	$7000	€5710	Untitled (33x33cm-13x13in) board double-sided prov.exhib. 16-May-4 Wright, Chicago #241/R est:5000-7000

RIVERA, Manuel (1927-1995) Spanish

£1993	$3268	€2750	Composition (43x31cm-17x12in) s.d.69 blk painting paper prov. 27-May-3 Durán, Madrid #150/R est:2500
£9000	$14310	€13050	Espejo dorado (100x81cm-39x32in) s. s.i.d.1965 oil board steel construction prov. 11-Sep-3 Christie's, Kensington #180/R est:8000-12000
£9500	$15105	€13775	Espejo sin tiempo no.1 (101x81cm-40x32in) s. s.i.d.1965 verso oil board steel construction prov. 11-Sep-3 Christie's, Kensington #186/R est:8000-12000
£12000	$21840	€17520	Espejo Sumergido (81x100cm-32x39in) s.i.d.1965 verso oil metal wire mesh panel prov.exhib. 5-Feb-4 Christie's, London #111/R est:8000-12000
£15000	$25050	€21900	Azul (100x81cm-39x32in) s. s.i.d.1966 verso metal paint wood prov. 22-Oct-3 Christie's, London #7/R est:8000-12000
£15000	$25050	€21900	Espejo purpura (100x81cm-39x32in) s. s.i.d.1965 verso metal paint wood prov. 22-Oct-3 Christie's, London #8/R est:8000-12000
£25000	$45500	€36500	Metamorfosis Heraldica (162x114cm-64x45in) s. s.i.d.1960 verso oil metal wire mesh panel prov.exhib. 5-Feb-4 Christie's, London #112/R est:15000-20000
Sculpture			
£13333	$24533	€20000	Metamorfosis (46x69cm-18x27in) s.i.d.59 ironwire wirenetting steel frame exec.1959 unique. 9-Jun-4 Christie's, Amsterdam #290/R est:1500-2000
£20000	$36800	€29200	Espejo del Rio (162x114cm-64x45in) s. metal paint on wood executed 1965 prov.exhib. 25-Jun-4 Christie's, London #165/R est:15000-20000
£24000	$44160	€35040	Espejo para la infanta Margarita (162x114cm-64x45in) s. s.i.d.1965 verso metal paint on wood pencil. 25-Jun-4 Christie's, London #166/R est:15000-20000
Works on paper			
£1145	$1947	€1672	Abstract composition (44x43cm-17x17in) s.d.69 mixed media prov. 5-Nov-3 Dobiaschofsky, Bern #893/R est:2700 (S.FR 2600)
£1145	$1947	€1672	Abstract composition (62x46cm-24x18in) s.d.69 mixed media prov. 5-Nov-3 Dobiaschofsky, Bern #894/R est:2800 (S.FR 2600)
£1974	$3632	€3000	Study (44x47cm-17x19in) s.d.1976 dr gouache. 22-Jun-4 Durán, Madrid #124/R est:3000
£3261	$5348	€4500	La Forja (72x51cm-28x20in) s.d.68 mixed media prov. 27-May-3 Durán, Madrid #163/R est:4500
£15493	$26803	€22000	Cortina del Alba (130x89cm-51x35in) s. s.i.d.1965 verso mixed media panel. 9-Dec-3 Artcurial Briest, Paris #410/R est:10000-12000

RIVERA, Oscar Garcia (1915-1971) Cuban

£815	$1500	€1190	Ring o'roses (42x65cm-17x26in) s. board. 27-Jun-4 Freeman, Philadelphia #153/R est:3000-5000

RIVERS, Elizabeth (1903-1964) British

Works on paper			
£479	$838	€680	Figures in a rural village landscape (27x41cm-11x16in) s. W/C. 16-Dec-3 James Adam, Dublin #205/R

RIVERS, Larry (1923-2002) American

£5946	$11000	€8681	Evolution of a flower (37x42cm-15x17in) s. oil pencil paper collage exec 1963 prov. 12-Feb-4 Sotheby's, New York #94/R est:3000-5000
£7784	$13000	€11365	King of clubs (25x20cm-10x8in) s.d.61 verso prov. 13-Nov-3 Sotheby's, New York #203/R est:12000-15000
£8791	$16000	€12835	Berdie with red face (122x113cm-48x44in) s.d.58 verso prov. 29-Jun-4 Sotheby's, New York #454/R est:15000-20000
£14000	$25900	€21000	Seated Webster (130x97cm-51x38in) s.d.89 canvas on panel prov.exhib. 18-Jul-4 Sotheby's, Paris #240/R est:15000-20000
£14835	$27000	€21659	Still life (58x68cm-23x27in) s.d.54 exhib. 29-Jun-4 Sotheby's, New York #429/R est:15000-20000
£16216	$30000	€23675	Untitled (75x84cm-30x33in) s.d.59 canvas on masonite prov. 12-Feb-4 Sotheby's, New York #88/R est:15000-20000
£44693	$80000	€65252	Cousin (152x132cm-60x52in) s.i.d.60 verso prov. 12-May-4 Christie's, Rockefeller NY #156/R est:40000-60000
Prints			
£2500	$4250	€3650	Blue collar holiday (120x96cm-47x38in) s. col lithograph. 31-Oct-3 Sotheby's, New York #734/R
Sculpture			
£20000	$37000	€30000	Cropped bed (123x150x160cm-48x59x63in) mixed media oil fabric exec.1967 prov.exhib. 18-Jul-4 Sotheby's, Paris #225/R est:30000-40000
£33520	$60000	€48939	Dutch Masters Silver (246x178x36cm-97x70x14in) wall relief acrylic oil chl fibreboard collage canvas prov.exhib. 12-May-4 Christie's, Rockefeller NY #150/R est:100000-150000
Works on paper			
£811	$1500	€1184	Study of a man reclining (33x42cm-13x17in) pencil. 13-Jul-4 Christie's, Rockefeller NY #6/R est:1000-1500
£1357	$2308	€1981	Untitled (39x34cm-15x13in) s.d.1953 pencil prov. 25-Nov-3 Germann, Zurich #88/R est:4000-7000 (S.FR 3000)
£1730	$3200	€2526	Untitled (45x39cm-18x15in) s.i.d.1954 gouache paper on board prov. 13-Jul-4 Christie's, Rockefeller NY #9/R est:1000-1500
£3235	$5500	€4723	Parts of face. s.d.1967 W/C pencil crayon collage. 9-Nov-3 Wright, Chicago #456 est:3000-4000
£6000	$10920	€8760	Faith, virtuous living (88x99cm-35x39in) s. s.i.d.1984 verso pencil chl pastel prov. 30-Jun-4 Christie's, Kensington #163/R est:5000-7000
£14970	$25000	€21856	Dancing with a dancer (74x58cm-29x23in) s.d.86 pencil col pencil crayon paper on wood prov. 13-Nov-3 Sotheby's, New York #289/R est:15000-20000

RIVERS, Laura (?) British?

Works on paper			
£260	$442	€380	Spring (36x26cm-14x10in) s.i. W/C. 29-Oct-3 Bonhams, Chester #410

RIVERS, Leopold (1852-1905) British

£480	$802	€701	Figures and a carriage on a country road (46x71cm-18x28in) s.d.1896. 12-Nov-3 Halls, Shrewsbury #330/R
£1350	$2471	€1971	Shepherd returning home (91x74cm-36x29in) s. 8-Apr-4 Christie's, Kensington #112/R est:1000-1500
£1567	$2804	€2350	Paysage de Barbizon (40x66cm-16x26in) s. 16-May-4 Feletin, Province #104
Works on paper			
£320	$554	€467	Children on a bridge with church and cottages by a lock at sunset (37x45cm-15x18in) s. W/C. 9-Dec-3 Bonhams, Oxford #53
£450	$797	€675	Young girl feeding chickens outside a cottage (14x19cm-6x7in) s. W/C. 27-Apr-4 Holloways, Banbury #198/R
£520	$967	€759	Great Sheffords, Berks - shepherd penning sheep (38x54cm-15x21in) s. W/C. 2-Mar-4 Bearnes, Exeter #340/R
£1300	$2171	€1898	Last bright gleam of parting day (58x98cm-23x39in) s. W/C. 8-Oct-3 Rupert Toovey, Partridge Green #110/R est:1200-1800

RIVERS, Richard Godfrey (1859-1925) Australian

£810	$1304	€1183	Mount Wellington in the mist (22x28cm-9x11in) s. board. 13-Oct-3 Joel, Victoria #361 est:1000-1500 (A.D 2000)
£810	$1304	€1183	Tasmania (22x28cm-9x11in) s. board. 13-Oct-3 Joel, Victoria #362 est:1000-1500 (A.D 2000)

RIVERS, Watkin (19th C) American?

£615	$1100	€898	Moonlit river. Sunset in the mountains (23x38cm-9x15in) s. two. 8-Jan-4 Doyle, New York #41/R

RIVIER, Louis (1885-1963) Swiss

Works on paper			
£633	$1096	€924	Guerison des paralytiques (18x23cm-7x9in) mono. col crayon exhib. 12-Dec-3 Galerie du Rhone, Sion #583 (S.FR 1400)
£699	$1286	€1021	Madonna with child (34x26cm-13x10in) s.d.1948 col pen paper on panel. 8-Jun-4 Germann, Zurich #861 (S.FR 1600)
£1176	$2035	€1717	Ronde des enfants (49x111cm-19x44in) s.verso gouache cardboard. 12-Dec-3 Galerie du Rhone, Sion #581 est:1000-1500 (S.FR 2600)

RIVIERE, Adriaan de la (1857-1941) Dutch

£278	$453	€400	Market scene (39x29cm-15x11in) s. 29-Sep-3 Sotheby's, Amsterdam #153/R
£280	$481	€400	Still life with bread and fruit (50x70cm-20x28in) s. 7-Dec-3 Sotheby's, Amsterdam #657/R
£300	$546	€450	Monnik in the studio (36x47cm-14x19in) s. 30-Jun-4 Vendue Huis, Gravenhage #152
£612	$1114	€900	At work in the street (40x27cm-16x11in) s. panel. 3-Feb-4 Christie's, Amsterdam #194
£658	$1191	€1000	Still life with stone bottle and Nieuwe Rotterdammer (64x41cm-25x16in) s. canvas on panel. 19-Apr-4 Glerum, Amsterdam #182
£748	$1362	€1100	Cuisine de campagne (29x39cm-11x15in) 9-Feb-4 Amberes, Antwerp #274
£816	$1486	€1200	L'adjudication (29x39cm-11x15in) 9-Feb-4 Amberes, Antwerp #273
£897	$1497	€1300	Many people at the market (29x39cm-11x15in) s. 11-Nov-3 Vendu Notarishuis, Rotterdam #163/R
£2055	$3493	€3000	Figures in a street (41x26cm-16x10in) s. panel exhib. 5-Nov-3 Vendue Huis, Gravenhage #358/R est:4000-6000

RIVIERE, Briton (1840-1920) British

£38000	$69920	€55480	Sympathy (76x63cm-30x25in) 11-Jun-4 Christie's, London #112/R est:30000-50000

RIVIERE, Denis (20th C) ?

£671	$1188	€1000	Ciel (97x130cm-38x51in) s. verso painted 2003. 28-Apr-4 Artcurial Briest, Paris #475/R
Works on paper			
£470	$832	€700	Valeureux combattants de Babylone (130x162cm-51x64in) mixed media canvas exec c.1992. 28-Apr-4 Artcurial Briest, Paris #476

RIVIERE, Henri (1864-1951) French

£933 $1708 €1400 Paysage de riviere (20x40cm-8x16in) mono.d.1942 W/C. 3-Jun-4 E & Eve, Paris #289

Prints

£2333 $4177 €3500 Le lendemain de tempete baie de Launay, Loguivy (22x34cm-9x13in) col woodcut one of ten exec. 1914. 16-May-4 Thierry & Lannon, Brest #11 est:3500-4000
£2517 $4280 €3600 Enterrement (34x24cm-13x9in) col engraving. 28-Nov-3 Tajan, Paris #384 est:2200
£2797 $4755 €4000 Cheval et village (22x34cm-9x13in) col engraving. 28-Nov-3 Tajan, Paris #382/R est:2500
£3147 $5350 €4500 Vague (34x52cm-13x20in) col engraving. 28-Nov-3 Tajan, Paris #383/R est:3000
£5855 $10598 €8900 Pardon de Sainte-Anne la Palud (34x114cm-13x45in) mono. col engraving exhib.lit. 17-Apr-4 Livinec, Gaudcheau & Jezequel, Rennes #100/R
£5855 $10598 €8900 Pardon a Sainte Anne la Palud. engraving. 17-Apr-4 Bretagne Encheres, St Malo #100 est:9000-10000

Works on paper

£403 $753 €600 Place de Paris animee (26x21cm-10x8in) s. ink wash W/C. 29-Feb-4 Osenat, Fontainebleau #225
£733 $1313 €1100 La petite aiguille, paysage aux oliviers (26x41cm-10x16in) s. W/C. 16-May-4 Thierry & Lannon, Brest #276
£833 $1525 €1250 Saint-Nizier (25x40cm-10x16in) mono.i.d.1912 W/C. 3-Jun-4 E & Eve, Paris #286
£1067 $1952 €1600 Morgat (25x40cm-10x16in) mono.i.d.1914 W/C. 3-Jun-4 E & Eve, Paris #287 est:1200-1500
£1342 $2470 €2000 Paysage (24x39cm-9x15in) st.sig. W/C. 28-Mar-4 Anaf, Lyon #226 est:1000-1200
£1400 $2562 €2100 Morgat (25x40cm-10x16in) mono.i.d.1915 W/C. 3-Jun-4 E & Eve, Paris #285 est:1200-1500
£2533 $4636 €3800 Belle-Ile en mer (20x40cm-8x16in) mono.i.d.1910 W/C. 3-Jun-4 E & Eve, Paris #288 est:1500-2000
£3867 $7076 €5800 Loguivy (40x25cm-16x10in) mono.i.d.1909 W/C. 3-Jun-4 E & Eve, Paris #290/R est:1500-2000
£4930 $8627 €7000 L'enterrement aux parapluies (33x24cm-13x9in) studio st. wash. 21-Dec-3 Thierry & Lannon, Brest #120/R est:1200-1500

RIVIERE, Henri (attrib) (1864-1951) French

£1141 $2019 €1700 Omnibus (27x22cm-11x9in) mono.d.1915. 29-Apr-4 Claude Aguttes, Neuilly #60/R est:700-800

RIVIERE, Henry Parsons (1811-1888) British

Works on paper

£800 $1384 €1168 At the spring (32x23cm-13x9in) s.d.1859 W/C. 11-Dec-3 Lyon & Turnbull, Edinburgh #104/R
£2400 $4080 €3504 River Tiber and the castel Sant Angelo, Rome (27x46cm-11x18in) s.d.1879 W/C htd white. 4-Nov-3 Bonhams, New Bond Street #77/R est:1000-1500

RIVIERE, Hugh Goldwin (1869-1956) British

£600 $1110 €876 Lord Southwark in his robes (117x90cm-46x35in) s.d.1911. 16-Feb-4 Bonhams, Bath #32
£3400 $5678 €4964 Portrait of Rosalind Monica Wagner (125x100cm-49x39in) s.d.1931. 21-Oct-3 Bonhams, Knightsbridge #183/R est:3000-5000

RIVIERE, Joseph (1912-) French

Sculpture

£4667 $8353 €7000 Femme accroupie (63cm-25in) s. num.II/IV pat bronze. 17-May-4 Sotheby's, Paris #77/R est:8000-10000

RIVIERE, Theodore (1857-1912) French

Sculpture

£6667 $12267 €10000 L'elephant fureur de Baal (24cm-9in) s.d.92 pat bronze. 11-Jun-4 Claude Aguttes, Neuilly #94/R est:8000-10000

RIVOIRE, François (1842-1919) French

Works on paper

£450 $810 €657 Still life of poppies (33x23cm-13x9in) s. W/C. 20-Apr-4 Clarke Gammon, Guildford #31
£6000 $10920 €8760 Basket of roses and hydrangeas on a mossy bank (65x88cm-26x35in) s. W/C bodycol. 16-Jun-4 Christie's, Kensington #57/R est:2000-3000

RIX, Julian (1850-1903) American

£1006 $1800 €1469 Where the brook falls (36x43cm-14x17in) s. 26-May-4 Doyle, New York #118/R est:3000-5000
£1566 $2600 €2286 Southern landscape with Flatboat (66x97cm-26x38in) s. 4-Oct-3 Neal Auction Company, New Orleans #360/R est:3000-5000
£1757 $3250 €2565 The brook in the forest (145x122cm-57x48in) 13-Feb-4 Du Mouchelle, Detroit #2109/R est:3000-4000
£2206 $3750 €3221 Country road (41x61cm-16x24in) 29-Nov-3 Carlsen Gallery, Greenville #116/R
£2910 $5500 €4249 Moonrise over clear lake (53x71cm-21x28in) s. i. verso prov. 17-Feb-4 John Moran, Pasadena #168/R est:4000-6000
£3468 $6000 €5063 Morning Mist (46x66cm-18x26in) s. prov. 10-Dec-3 Bonhams & Butterfields, San Francisco #6143/R est:4000-6000
£3889 $7000 €5678 New England summertime landscape (56x77cm-22x30in) s.d.97. 24-Apr-4 Weschler, Washington #608/R est:1000-1500

RIZEK, Emil (1901-1985) Austrian

£1290 $2065 €1883 View of Vienna (50x66cm-20x26in) s. 18-May-3 Sotheby's, Singapore #36/R est:3000-4000 (S.D 3600)
£1505 $2409 €2197 Santtentrager in Singapore (45x40cm-18x16in) s. tempera lit. 18-May-3 Sotheby's, Singapore #47/R est:2000-3000 (S.D 4200)
£1993 $3089 €2910 Fetching water (61x43cm-24x17in) s. tempera paper. 6-Oct-2 Sotheby's, Singapore #22/R est:1800-2500 (S.D 5500)
£3226 $5161 €4710 Entrance of a temple (60x47cm-24x19in) s. 18-May-3 Sotheby's, Singapore #20/R est:8000-12000 (S.D 9000)
£5797 $8986 €8464 Market in Norden (75x101cm-30x40in) 6-Oct-2 Sotheby's, Singapore #53/R est:10000-12000 (S.D 16000)

Sculpture

£1227 $2037 €1779 Allegory of Autumn (36cm-14in) s. bronze alabaster Cast.Schumacher. 13-Jun-3 Zofingen, Switzerland #2280/R est:2500 (S.FR 2700)

RIZO, Mauricio (20th C) Latin American

£184 $305 €267 Nocturno 2 (102x82cm-40x32in) d.1998. 12-Jun-3 Louis Morton, Mexico #211 est:950-1100 (M.P 3200)
£207 $343 €300 Una calle de Jinotegana (89x114cm-35x45in) d.1996. 12-Jun-3 Louis Morton, Mexico #202 est:1100-1300 (M.P 3600)

RIZZARDA, C (?) Italian?

Sculpture

£2797 $4755 €4000 Flamingo (200cm-79in) s. wrought iron marble base. 19-Nov-3 Cambi, Genoa #299/R est:3000-3500

RIZZETTI, Carlo (1969-) Italian

Works on paper

£986 $1637 €1400 San Daniele (80x70cm-31x28in) s.d.2000 verso col plastic collage. 14-Jun-3 Meeting Art, Vercelli #59/R

RIZZI, Antonio (1869-1940) Italian

£310 $518 €450 View of Venice (20x30cm-8x12in) s. board. 17-Nov-3 Durán, Madrid #627
£328 $547 €475 Venice (20x30cm-8x12in) s. board. 17-Nov-3 Durán, Madrid #630/R

RIZZI, Emilio (1881-1952) Italian

£1974 $3632 €3000 Portrait of gentleman. Portrait of lady (132x82cm-52x32in) s.d.1907 pair prov. 22-Jun-4 Babuino, Rome #587/R est:2000-3000

RIZZI, Marco Antonio (attrib) (1648-1723) Italian

£23333 $41767 €35000 Still lives of fruit with grapes and pumpkin (92x131cm-36x52in) pair. 17-May-4 Finarte Semenzato, Rome #114/R est:40000-42000

RIZZO, Pippo (1897-1964) Italian

£4730 $8324 €7000 Marching (62x48cm-24x19in) s. te/. card painted c.1926 exhib. 24-May-4 Christie's, Milan #284/R est:6400-6800

RIZZOLI, Giuseppe (1785-1868) Italian

Sculpture

£2759 $4579 €4000 St Jerome (59x25cm-23x10in) terracotta. 30-Sep-3 Dorotheum, Vienna #170/R est:7000-9000

ROACH, John Charles (20th C) American

£414 $750 €604 Slag train moving down Furnace Row (48x53cm-19x21in) s.i. masonite. 3-Apr-4 David Rago, Lambertville #109/R

ROASIO, Maurizio (1946-) Italian

£2721 $4871 €4000 Two skies (50x40cm-20x16in) s.d.1984 exhib.lit. 22-Mar-4 Sant Agostino, Torino #483/R est:4200

Works on paper

£1724 $2879 €2500 RB3 (35x50cm-14x20in) collage exec.2002 exhib.lit. 17-Nov-3 Sant Agostino, Torino #153/R est:3200
£3034 $5068 €4400 Roz Bras (74x75cm-29x30in) mixed media board exec.2002 exhib.lit. 17-Nov-3 Sant Agostino, Torino #141/R est:4500-5500

ROASIO, Pino (1924-) Italian

£300 $552 €450 Interior (57x44cm-22x17in) s.d.1942 board. 8-Jun-4 Della Rocca, Turin #348/R

ROBATHIN, Max (1882-?) Austrian

£400 $720 €600 Extensive landscape with wayside shrine (66x85cm-26x33in) s. canvas on panel. 22-Apr-4 Dorotheum, Graz #25/R
£528 $877 €750 Mountain landscape (38x47cm-15x19in) s. 12-Jun-3 Dorotheum, Graz #48/R
£669 $1111 €950 Mountain landscape with wayside cross (39x54cm-15x21in) s. canvas on panel. 12-Jun-3 Dorotheum, Graz #49/R
£1181 $1924 €1700 Mountain landscape (78x100cm-31x39in) s. panel. 25-Sep-3 Dorotheum, Graz #20 est:750

ROBB, Samuel A (attrib) (1851-?) American

Sculpture

£7821 $14000 €11419 Cigar store Indian (185cm-73in) painted wood base prov. 8-Jan-4 James Julia, Fairfield #550/R est:15000-25000

ROBB, William George (1872-1940) British

£260 $491 €380 Fete champetre (24x29cm-9x11in) s. board. 19-Feb-4 Lyon & Turnbull, Edinburgh #48
£260 $491 €380 Moonlit scene with shepherd and flock (25x30cm-10x12in) s. board. 19-Feb-4 Lyon & Turnbull, Edinburgh #41
£2200 $3806 €3212 Frisking light in Frolick (50x60cm-20x24in) s. i.verso. 10-Dec-3 Rupert Toovey, Partridge Green #208/R est:600-1000

ROBBE, Henri (1807-1899) Belgian

£676	$1189	€1000	Roses (16x20cm-6x8in) s. panel. 18-May-4 Galerie Moderne, Brussels #166/R
£1074	$1922	€1600	Nature morte aux fleurs (50x38cm-20x15in) s. 25-May-4 Campo & Campo, Antwerp #238/R est:1200-1500
£1987	$3616	€3000	Nature morte aux fleurs (44x51cm-17x20in) s. 16-Jun-4 Hotel des Ventes Mosan, Brussels #171/R est:1400-1800
£3600	$6588	€5400	Coin de jardin avec bouquet de roses et hortensias (92x75cm-36x30in) s. 7-Jun-4 Palais de Beaux Arts, Brussels #288/R est:5250-7500

ROBBE, Henri (attrib) (1807-1899) Belgian

£733	$1320	€1100	Still life with fruit (44x50cm-17x20in) 26-Apr-4 Bernaerts, Antwerp #246/R

ROBBE, Louis (1806-1887) Belgian

£336	$621	€500	The guardsman (26x21cm-10x8in) mono. canvas on panel. 13-Mar-4 De Vuyst, Lokeren #279
£483	$893	€700	Chevre couchee (31x49cm-12x19in) mono.d.76. 13-Jan-4 Vanderkindere, Brussels #469
£621	$1148	€900	Berger dans un paysage avec troncs d'arbres (27x40cm-11x16in) s. 19-Jan-4 Horta, Bruxelles #389
£629	$1083	€900	Vue du marais (32x42cm-13x17in) s. i.verso. 8-Dec-3 Horta, Bruxelles #459
£878	$1572	€1300	Berger et son troupeau dans un paysage (34x50cm-13x20in) s.d.22/8 64. 10-May-4 Horta, Bruxelles #95
£909	$1518	€1300	Landscape with grazing cows (30x44cm-12x17in) s. 11-Oct-3 De Vuyst, Lokeren #316
£1111	$1856	€1600	Trois moutons (41x60cm-16x24in) mono. 21-Oct-3 Galerie Moderne, Brussels #242/R
£1268	$2193	€1800	Vaches au paturage (35x54cm-14x21in) s. 9-Dec-3 Campo, Vlaamse Kaai #398 est:800-900
£1824	$3266	€2700	Troupeau de moutons et ane dans un paysage (34x50cm-13x20in) s. 10-May-4 Horta, Bruxelles #94 est:2500-3000
£2013	$3725	€3000	Troupeau dans un paysage anime (34x55cm-13x22in) s. 15-Mar-4 Horta, Bruxelles #68 est:2500-3500
£4667	$8400	€7000	Young shepherdess (41x60cm-16x24in) s. panel. 21-Apr-4 Christie's, Amsterdam #200/R est:7000-9000

ROBBE, Louis (attrib) (1806-1887) Belgian

£1119	$1924	€1600	Vaches et moutons dans un paysage (34x54cm-13x21in) bears sig. 2-Dec-3 Campo & Campo, Antwerp #310 est:1400-1800

ROBBE, Manuel (1872-1936) French

£8511	$13787	€12000	Le 14 juillet, fete foraine et manege (73x59cm-29x23in) s.d.1899. 23-May-3 Sotheby's, Paris #47/R est:4000-6000

ROBBES, Aristide (19/20th C) French

£1007	$1652	€1400	Le marche de Rennes (46x32cm-18x13in) s. 3-Jun-3 Livinec, Gaudcheau & Jezequel, Rennes #68/R

ROBBIA, Giovanni della (fl.1510-1520) Italian

£62069	$103655	€90000	Uomo illustre (93cm-37in circular) majolica glazed relief lit.prov. 15-Nov-3 Lempertz, Koln #1202/R est:120000

ROBBIA, Luca della (studio) (15th C) Italian

Sculpture

£16742	$26787	€24443	Madonna with child (55cm-22in) painted col stucco prov. 19-Sep-3 Koller, Zurich #1033/R est:30000-50000 (S.FR 37000)

ROBBIA, della (studio) (15/16th C) Italian

Sculpture

£8500	$15555	€12410	Madonna and Child (67cm-26in) glazed terracotta relief prov. 9-Jul-4 Sotheby's, London #53/R est:10000-15000

ROBBINS, Bruce (20th C) American

£1093	$2000	€1596	Linkage (71x229cm-28x90in) d.1983 oil oil slick graphite varnish paper on wood. 10-Apr-4 Cobbs, Peterborough #94/R

ROBELLAZ, Emile (1844-1882) Swiss

£474	$849	€692	Officer and old man at table (31x29cm-12x11in) mono. paper on board. 12-May-4 Dobiaschofsky, Bern #905/R (S.FR 1100)

ROBERT, Albert (19th C) ?

£570	$1021	€850	Moine (22x18cm-9x7in) s.d.1859 cardboard. 25-May-4 Campo & Campo, Antwerp #239

ROBERT, Frere (1907-1997) French

Works on paper

£11074	$19823	€16500	Personnages pour un cantique (192x245cm-76x96in) s.d.1966 num.479 tapestry lit. 27-May-4 Tajan, Paris #175/R est:8000-10000

ROBERT, Henry (1881-1961) French

£261	$477	€381	Roses de Noel (46x38cm-18x15in) s.i.d.1942 verso. 4-Jun-4 Zofingen, Switzerland #2931 (S.FR 600)
£1571	$2514	€2278	Freiburg (55x46cm-22x18in) s.d.41. 15-May-3 Stuker, Bern #1460/R est:1500-2000 (S.FR 3300)
£1982	$3370	€2894	Lac de Gruyeres pres du Bry (54x65cm-21x26in) s. 7-Nov-3 Dobiaschofsky, Bern #79/R est:7000 (S.FR 4500)

ROBERT, Hubert (1733-1808) French

£1544	$2887	€2300	Fountain with figures (62x47cm-24x19in) 26-Feb-4 Cambi, Genoa #303/R est:1500-2000
£3974	$7272	€6000	Couple de promeneurs et un enfant devant une statue dans un parc (31x39cm-12x15in) paper on canvas. 7-Apr-4 Libert, Castor, Paris #41/R est:5000-7000
£7667	$13877	€11500	Le dessinateur (39x50cm-15x20in) s. panel prov. 2-Apr-4 Rossini, Paris #30/R est:12000-15000
£10490	$18042	€15000	Vue des jardins de la Villa Mattei (35x53cm-14x21in) i. red chk prov. 2-Dec-3 Christie's, Paris #512/R est:20000-30000
£16197	$28345	€23000	Dessinateur devant les cascatelles, Tivoli (36x28cm-14x11in) 17-Dec-3 Piasa, Paris #85/R est:15000-20000
£16667	$30000	€24334	Figures by waterfall in a wooded landscape (58x46cm-23x18in) 22-Jan-4 Sotheby's, New York #247/R est:30000-40000
£19000	$34770	€27740	Capriccio (76x99cm-30x39in) 8-Jul-4 Sotheby's, London #179/R est:20000-30000
£19553	$35000	€28547	Pastoral scene (99x136cm-39x54in) 27-May-4 Sotheby's, New York #43/R est:40000-60000
£32895	$60526	€50000	Projet pour l'amenagement de la Place de la Concorde (60x72cm-24x28in) s.d.1808 prov.exhib.lit. 23-Jun-4 Sotheby's, Paris #37/R est:60000-80000
£40001	$72802	€60000	Famille dans une grotte (36x45cm-14x18in) s.d.1794 panel prov. 30-Jun-4 Pierre Berge, Paris #53/R est:40000-60000
£50000	$90000	€73000	Ruined gallery with shepherd by a fountain. Fountain surrounded by an arcade with peasants (37x27cm-15x11in) indis sig. panel pair. 21-Apr-4 Christie's, London #66/R est:40000-60000
£65000	$112450	€94900	Rome, view of the Piazza della Rotonda with the pantheon and figures (54x72cm-21x28in) s.i.d.1776. 11-Dec-3 Sotheby's, London #34/R est:30000-50000
£80000	$138400	€116800	Sack of two pyramids (53x64cm-21x25in) 10-Dec-3 Christie's, London #68/R est:80000-120000
£98684	$181579	€150000	Paysage de cascade avec bergers (208x168cm-82x66in) s.d.1789. 25-Jun-4 Piasa, Paris #50/R est:150000-200000
£150000	$259500	€219000	La passerelle sur la cascade (154x142cm-61x56in) 10-Dec-3 Christie's, London #76/R est:150000-250000
£160000	$276800	€233600	La fontaine a la vestale (155x145cm-61x57in) s. 10-Dec-3 Christie's, London #77/R est:100000-150000
£258503	$462721	€380000	Architecture colossale de fantaisie (131x97cm-52x38in) s. lit. 19-Mar-4 Beaussant & Lefèvre, Paris #72/R est:120000-150000

Works on paper

£680	$1217	€1000	Personnages dans des ruines. Personnages dans un jardin (9x6cm-4x2in) sanguine two prov. 17-Mar-4 Tajan, Paris #69
£979	$1635	€1400	Vue de la villa et de l'escalier de Caprarola (18x23cm-7x9in) pierre noire prov. 26-Jun-3 Artcurial Briest, Paris #507 est:1500-1800
£1049	$1752	€1500	Paniers et selle dans un grange (23x18cm-9x7in) pierre noire prov. 26-Jun-3 Artcurial Briest, Paris #506 est:1500-1800
£1156	$2070	€1700	Le temple de Vesta a Tivoli (36x45cm-14x18in) red chk. 18-Mar-4 Christie's, Paris #264/R est:600-800
£1600	$2928	€2336	Woman filling a water jar at a fountain (20x21cm-8x8in) red chk pen ink wash. 6-Jul-4 Christie's, London #146/R est:1000-1500
£1700	$2941	€2482	Washerwomen in a stream by a rustic cottage (18x23cm-7x9in) black chk prov. 12-Dec-3 Christie's, Kensington #458/R est:2000-3000
£2400	$4152	€3504	Church of San Rocco at Cori (18x23cm-7x9in) i. black chk prov. 12-Dec-3 Christie's, Kensington #457/R est:2000-3000
£3147	$5255	€4500	La statue (34x26cm-13x10in) s.d.25 avril 1771 sanguine prov. 26-Jun-3 Artcurial Briest, Paris #503 est:4500-5000
£8333	$15000	€12166	Temple of the Sybil at Tivoli (32x44cm-13x17in) pen ink W/C over black chk prov.lit. 21-Jan-4 Sotheby's, New York #113/R est:15000-20000
£11268	$19493	€16000	Peristyle d'un palais romain anime des personnages (29x36cm-11x14in) i.d.1776 sanguine. 10-Dec-3 Piasa, Paris #42/R est:18000
£48592	$84063	€69000	Chapiteau du temple d'Apollon, perche sur un echafaudage (33x46cm-13x18in) d.1762 sanguine prov. 10-Dec-3 Piasa, Paris #49/R est:30000-40000

ROBERT, Hubert (attrib) (1733-1808) French

£2587	$4630	€3777	Classic landscape with temple ruins and figures (67x47cm-26x19in) painted c.1760. 26-May-4 AB Stockholms Auktionsverk #2548/R est:35000-40000 (S.KR 35000)
£3133	$5671	€4700	Group of women in ruins of Roman temple (42x58cm-17x23in) gouache oval. 1-Apr-4 Van Ham, Cologne #1240/R est:3800
£12222	$22000	€17844	L'arbre brise (59x79cm-23x31in) prov. 22-Jan-4 Sotheby's, New York #242/R est:25000-35000

Works on paper

£417	$679	€600	Landscape with wooden bridge and wayside stone altar (32x42cm-13x17in) ochre htd white. 26-Sep-3 Bolland & Marotz, Bremen #457/R
£979	$1850	€1429	Partially nude female bather by a column in a landscape (76x56cm-30x22in) chk W/C additions by another hand. 23-Feb-4 Winter Associates, Plainville #134/R est:2000-2500
£5769	$9923	€8423	Fantasy landscape with Roman statues and ruins. one s.i.indis.d.1767 Indian ink wash pair. 3-Dec-3 AB Stockholms Auktionsverk #2656/R est:75000-100000 (S.KR 75000)

ROBERT, Hubert (school) (1733-1808) French

£16000	$28640	€24000	Landscape with Tivoli waterfall. Capriccio with Titus arch (66x48cm-26x19in) pair. 17-May-4 Finarte Semenzato, Rome #107/R est:25000-30000

ROBERT, Hubert (studio) (1733-1808) French

£5800	$10614	€8468	Extensive landscape with children playing on a see-saw before a ruined temple (228x315cm-90x124in) 6-Jul-4 Bonhams, Knightsbridge #265a/R est:5000-7000
£14000	$25620	€20440	Le jet d'eau (193x85cm-76x33in) prov.exhib. 7-Jul-4 Christie's, London #67/R est:15000-20000

ROBERT, Leopold-Louis (1794-1835) French

£397	$723	€600	Une paysanne italienne (16x10cm-6x4in) paper. 21-Jun-4 Tajan, Paris #138
£1238	$1981	€1795	Boy's portrait (35x27cm-14x11in) s.d.1831. 15-May-3 Stuker, Bern #1462/R est:2000-2500 (S.FR 2600)
£9211	$15382	€13448	L'Ara-Coeli, couvent a Rome (45x35cm-18x14in) s.indis.d.182 i.verso. 16-Nov-3 Koller, Geneva #1227/R est:9000-12000 (S.FR 21000)
£11207	$20060	€16362	Palm reader with young woman at well (61x49cm-24x19in) s.d.1820. 17-May-4 Beurret, Zurich #5/R est:18000-25000 (S.FR 26000)

Works on paper

£348	$637	€508	Homme de profil (28x20cm-11x8in) s.d.1833 crayon. 5-Jun-4 Galerie du Rhone, Sion #212 (S.FR 800)

£400 $732 €584 Musicians before a shrine of the Virgin (22x28cm-9x11in) s.i. black chk. 7-Jul-4 Bonhams, Knightsbridge #87/R
£430 $783 €650 Jeunesse et vieillesse (19x21cm-7x8in) s. graphite. 16-Jun-4 Hotel des Ventes Mosan, Brussels #182
£2643 $4493 €3859 Le brigand amoureux (22x29cm-9x11in) s.d.1832 W/C. 7-Nov-3 Dobiaschofsky, Bern #64/R est:2000 (S.FR 6000)

ROBERT, Leopold-Louis (attrib) (1794-1835) French
£749 $1273 €1094 La Rancon (21x27cm-8x11in) mono. i. stretcher paper on canvas. 7-Nov-3 Dobiaschofsky, Bern #32/R (S.FR 1700)
£1233 $2097 €1800 Italian brigands resting (84x70cm-33x28in) mono. 5-Nov-3 Dobiaschofsky, Bern #898/R est:3200 (S.FR 2800)

ROBERT, Louis (19th C) French
£563 $986 €800 Portrait de la fille de l'artiste, Madame Emile von Marcke de Lummen (59x48cm-23x19in) oval. 17-Dec-3 Delorme & Bocage, Paris #36

ROBERT, Louis Remy (1811-1882) French
Photographs
£2600 $4576 €3796 Grange a Sevres (27x37cm-11x15in) waxed paper negative. 19-May-4 Christie's, London #24/R est:2000-3000
£3800 $6688 €5548 Parc du Chateau de Versailles (34x26cm-13x10in) waxed paper negative. 19-May-4 Christie's, London #26/R est:3000-4000

ROBERT, Maurice (1909-) Swiss
£370 $676 €540 Interieur (73x60cm-29x24in) s.d.1932. 4-Jun-4 Zofingen, Switzerland #2932 (S.FR 850)

ROBERT, Nicolas (1614-1685) French
Works on paper
£1034 $1728 €1500 Sporophile bouvernon (39x29cm-15x11in) W/C gouache black crayon brush col ink vellum or possibly studio. 13-Nov-3 Binoche, Paris #14/R est:1500
£1241 $2073 €1800 Chardonneret elegant albinos partiel (38x27cm-15x11in) W/C gouache black crayon brush col ink vellum or possibly studio. 13-Nov-3 Binoche, Paris #6/R est:2000-3000
£1241 $2073 €1800 Chardonneret melanique (39x29cm-15x11in) W/C gouache black crayon brush col ink vellum or possibly studio. 13-Nov-3 Binoche, Paris #16/R est:1500
£1379 $2303 €2000 Toki de Schlegel (32x29cm-13x11in) W/C gouache black crayon brush col ink vellum or possibly studio. 13-Nov-3 Binoche, Paris #12/R est:2000
£1379 $2303 €2000 Gobe-mouche a collier (36x28cm-14x11in) W/C gouache black crayon brush col ink vellum or possibly studio. 13-Nov-3 Binoche, Paris #15/R est:1500
£1379 $2303 €2000 Sporophile a col fauve (34x29cm-13x11in) W/C gouache black crayon brush col ink vellum or possibly studio. 13-Nov-3 Binoche, Paris #21/R est:2000-3000
£1655 $2764 €2400 Merle (36x28cm-14x11in) W/C gouache black crayon brush col ink vellum or possibly studio. 13-Nov-3 Binoche, Paris #19/R est:2000-3000
£1793 $2994 €2600 Grive musicienne albinos (36x29cm-14x11in) W/C gouache black crayon brush col ink vellum or possibly studio. 13-Nov-3 Binoche, Paris #5/R est:3000-4000
£1793 $2994 €2600 Gorge bleue a miroir male en plumage d'eclipse (39x31cm-15x12in) W/C gouache black crayon brush col ink vellum or possibly studio. 13-Nov-3 Binoche, Paris #13/R est:2000-3000
£2000 $3340 €2900 Capucin de Nevermann (35x29cm-14x11in) W/C gouache black crayon brush col ink vellum or possibly studio. 13-Nov-3 Binoche, Paris #4/R est:2000-3000
£2069 $3455 €3000 Jeune goeland brun (36x29cm-14x11in) W/C gouache black crayon brush col ink vellum or possibly studio. 13-Nov-3 Binoche, Paris #18/R est:3000-4000
£2069 $3455 €3000 Moineau melanure (36x28cm-14x11in) W/C gouache black crayon brush col ink vellum or possibly studio. 13-Nov-3 Binoche, Paris #20/R est:3000-4000
£2414 $4031 €3500 Bruant zizi male, et bruant (38x28cm-15x11in) W/C gouache black crayon brush col ink vellum or possibly studio. 13-Nov-3 Binoche, Paris #23/R est:4000-5000
£2759 $4607 €4000 Sporophile gris-de-plomb (40x31cm-16x12in) W/C gouache black crayon brush col ink vellum or possibly studio. 13-Nov-3 Binoche, Paris #17/R est:3000-4000
£3586 $5989 €5200 Tangara (36x30cm-14x12in) W/C gouache black crayon brush col ink vellum or possibly studio. 13-Nov-3 Binoche, Paris #22/R est:3000-4000
£4483 $7486 €6500 Grive litorne albinos partiel (38x30cm-15x12in) W/C gouache black crayon brush col ink vellum or possibly studio. 13-Nov-3 Binoche, Paris #2/R est:3000-4000
£4828 $8062 €7000 Tadorne de Belon albinos partiel (34x26cm-13x10in) W/C gouache black crayon brush col ink vellum or possibly studio. 13-Nov-3 Binoche, Paris #3/R est:3000-4000
£5862 $9790 €8500 Urubu a tete rouge (37x25cm-15x10in) W/C gouache black crayon brush col ink vellum or possibly studio. 13-Nov-3 Binoche, Paris #1/R est:3000-4000
£8276 $13821 €12000 Penelope siffleuse (32x27cm-13x11in) W/C gouache black crayon brush col ink vellum or possibly studio. 13-Nov-3 Binoche, Paris #24/R est:4000

ROBERT, Nicolas (attrib) (1614-1685) French
Works on paper
£3537 $6332 €5200 Branche de fleurs (37x27cm-15x11in) gouache vellum. 17-Mar-4 Tajan, Paris #37/R est:2000-3000

ROBERT, Paul (?) ?
Works on paper
£400 $736 €600 Rue animee, Tunis (41x32cm-16x13in) s. gouache. 14-Jun-4 Gros & Delettrez, Paris #60/R

ROBERT, Paul Andre Felix (1901-1977) Swiss
£431 $772 €629 Hunting still life (65x54cm-26x21in) s. 12-May-4 Dobiaschofsky, Bern #908/R (S.FR 1000)

ROBERT, Philippe (1881-1930) Swiss
£705 $1198 €1029 Greek island (19x39cm-7x15in) s.d.1920 canvas on board. 7-Nov-3 Dobiaschofsky, Bern #78/R (S.FR 1600)
£705 $1198 €1029 Portrait of Helene Ulrich Ledermann (50x45cm-20x18in) s.d.1918 i. verso. 5-Nov-3 Dobiaschofsky, Bern #902/R (S.FR 1600)

ROBERT, Theophile (1879-1954) Swiss
£4333 $7930 €6500 Nu endormi dans un paysage (45x78cm-18x31in) s.d.28. 6-Jun-4 Anaf, Lyon #489/R est:5000-6000
£20175 $37123 €29456 Nude between two servants (118x135cm-46x53in) s.d.1927. 23-Jun-4 Koller, Zurich #3071/R est:12000-18000 (S.FR 46000)
Works on paper
£1121 $2006 €1637 Herding family (56x39cm-22x15in) mono. gouache. 14-May-4 Dobiaschofsky, Bern #175/R est:2800 (S.FR 2600)

ROBERTI, Domenico (circle) (1642-1707) Italian
£12000 $20400 €17520 Capriccio of Roman ruins (142x110cm-56x43in) 31-Oct-3 Christie's, Kensington #158/R est:10000-12000

ROBERTO, Luigi (1845-1910) Italian
£313 $500 €457 SS Mulgrave (51x76cm-20x30in) s.i. 21-Sep-3 Grogan, Boston #93/R
Works on paper
£280 $510 €409 S.S. Frenville of London in a gale in the Bay of Biscay (43x61cm-17x24in) s. gouache. 17-Jun-4 Clevedon Sale Rooms #1016/R
£500 $850 €730 S.S. Trekieve (43x62cm-17x24in) s.i.d.1888 bodycol. 19-Nov-3 Christie's, Kensington #360/R
£811 $1500 €1184 USS Congress lying at her mooring off Naples (43x63cm-17x25in) s.i.d.1886 bodycol. 10-Feb-4 Christie's, Rockefeller NY #146/R est:2000-3000
£962 $1550 €1405 Ship portrait of the USS Congress (43x64cm-17x25in) s. prov. gouache. 20-Aug-3 James Julia, Fairfield #941/R est:1000-1500
£1100 $1870 €1606 Schooner (43x64cm-17x25in) s.i.d.1885 bodycol pair. 19-Nov-3 Christie's, Kensington #354/R
£1300 $2210 €1898 Steam yacht (37x58cm-15x23in) s. bodycol pair. 19-Nov-3 Christie's, Kensington #362/R
£1400 $2380 €2044 Topsail schooner (41x58cm-16x23in) s.i. bodycol pair. 19-Nov-3 Christie's, Kensington #352/R
£1632 $2725 €2350 Yacht (33x58cm-13x23in) s.d.1888 gouache. 26-Oct-3 Lesieur & Le Bars, Le Havre #182

ROBERTO, Luigi (attrib) (fl.1870-1900) Italian
Works on paper
£650 $1105 €949 Brigantine Prairie Flower of Jersey entering the Bay of Naples (44x65cm-17x26in) i.d.1871 bodycol. 19-Nov-3 Christie's, Kensington #350/R

ROBERTS, Arthur Henry (1819-1900) French
£1049 $1783 €1500 Hunter with two children (67x53cm-26x21in) s.d.1863 panel. 24-Nov-3 Dorotheum, Vienna #47/R est:3000-3500

ROBERTS, Arthur Spencer (1920-) British
£700 $1281 €1022 Rhino in the bush, Mount Kilimanjaro beyond (91x121cm-36x48in) s. 28-Jul-4 Bonhams, Knightsbridge #160/R
Works on paper
£300 $549 €438 Tiger cubs with a butterfly (53x76cm-21x30in) s.i. pencil. 28-Jul-4 Bonhams, Knightsbridge #158/R
£360 $659 €526 Seal Point Siamese cats chasing a bee (68x52cm-27x20in) s.i. pastel W/C. 28-Jul-4 Bonhams, Knightsbridge #159/R
£600 $1098 €876 King of the Jungle (53x73cm-21x29in) s. pastel. 28-Jul-4 Bonhams, Knightsbridge #157/R

ROBERTS, Benjamin (fl.1847-1872) British
£940 $1485 €1363 Still life of summer fruit by a wicker basket (39x52cm-15x20in) exhib. 24-Jul-3 Lawrence, Crewkerne #939/R

ROBERTS, Cyril (1871-1949) British
Works on paper
£300 $477 €438 Portrait of a standing lady (115x75cm-45x30in) s.d.1924 pastel. 13-Sep-3 Windibank, Dorking #151

ROBERTS, David (1796-1864) British
£17000 $31280 €24820 Approach to the forum (46x91cm-18x36in) s.d.1860 i.verso prov.exhib.lit. 11-Jun-4 Christie's, London #147/R est:10000-15000
£18500 $34040 €27010 View of the church of Santa Maria Della Salute, on the Grand Canal (31x52cm-12x20in) i. oil paper on canvas. 26-Mar-4 Sotheby's, London #81/R est:18000-24000
£68000 $125120 €99280 Interview with the Viceroy of Egypt at his palace in Alexandria (35x51cm-14x20in) s.i.verso panel lit. 26-Mar-4 Sotheby's, London #50/R est:10000-15000
Prints
£2900 $5423 €4350 The destruction of Jerusalem by the Romans under the command of Titus (69x107cm-27x42in) lithograph. 22-Jul-4 Dominic Winter, Swindon #258 est:400-600
Works on paper
£1057 $1797 €1543 Venice (27x40cm-11x16in) s.d.1854 w/C. 5-Nov-3 Dobiaschofsky, Bern #904/R est:4500 (S.FR 2400)
£1300 $2171 €1898 Street scene, Madrid (25x16cm-10x6in) i. W/C over pencil. 14-Oct-3 Sotheby's, London #110/R est:1500-2000
£1300 $2366 €1898 The Church of St Pierre, Caen (36x25cm-14x10in) i. pencil W/C htd white scratching out prov.exhib. 1-Jul-4 Christie's, Kensington #374/R est:1200-1800
£1800 $3312 €2628 Fleet Street at temple bar with the church of St. Dunstans-In-The-West (23x19cm-9x7in) i. pencil W/C htd white. 26-Mar-4 Sotheby's, London #118/R est:2000-3000
£2000 $3340 €2920 Roman capriccio (15x23cm-6x9in) s.d.1830 W/C. 12-Nov-3 Halls, Shrewsbury #285/R est:2000-3000
£2162 $4000 €3157 Temple ruins (36x43cm-14x17in) W/C. 13-Feb-4 Du Mouchelle, Detroit #2249/R est:1600-1800
£3000 $5100 €4380 Street in Cairo, Egypt (34x20cm-13x8in) s.d.1841 pencil W/C htd bodycol prov. 20-Nov-3 Christie's, London #122/R est:2500-3500
£5000 $8500 €7300 Rock of Moses, Wady-el-Leja, Mount Horeb (35x25cm-14x10in) i. W/C over pencil htd bodycol. 27-Nov-3 Sotheby's, London #303/R est:7000-10000
£5800 $10556 €8468 Figures worshipping in the Mosque of Cordova (34x25cm-13x10in) s.d.1833 pencil W/C bodycol. 1-Jul-4 Christie's, Kensington #373/R est:2000-3000

£12000 $20400 €17520 St. Sophia, Constantinople, from the Bosphoros (20x29cm-8x11in) s.d.1824 pencil pen W/C grum arabic bodycol scratching out prov. 20-Nov-3 Christie's, London #71/R est:15000-25000
£14000 $23800 €20440 Medinet Habou, Thebes, Egypt (32x49cm-13x19in) s.i.d.1838 pencil W/C htd white exhib. 20-Nov-3 Christie's, London #125/R est:15000-20000
£14000 $25620 €20440 Hypaethral temple, Philae, Egypt (35x24cm-14x9in) s.id.1838 pencil W/C htd bodycol. 3-Jun-4 Christie's, London #102/R est:15000-20000

ROBERTS, Douglas (1919-1976) Australian
£573 $1042 €837 Peak in Horricks Pass, South Australia (47x62cm-19x24in) s.d.47 exhib. 16-Jun-4 Deutscher-Menzies, Melbourne #335/R est:2000-3000 (A.D 1500)

ROBERTS, E (19th C) British
Works on paper
£500 $930 €730 Sailing clipper Loch Torridon, Glasgow (41x64cm-16x25in) s.i. gouache. 3-Mar-4 Brightwells, Leominster #954/R

ROBERTS, Edwin (1840-1917) British
£500 $880 €730 Sweet melody (46x36cm-18x14in) s. 19-May-4 Christie's, Kensington #593
£1552 $2778 €2266 Monkey up a pole (61x51cm-24x20in) s. i. verso. 13-May-4 Stuker, Bern #294/R est:5000-7000 (S.FR 3600)
£1744 $3000 €2546 In the kitchen. mono. 7-Dec-3 Hindman, Chicago #728/R est:3000-5000
£1900 $3002 €2755 Young puppet maker (61x51cm-24x20in) s.d.1880. 4-Sep-3 Christie's, Kensington #281 est:1000-1500
£2700 $5049 €3942 Unmasked (61x51cm-24x20in) s. i.verso. 24-Feb-4 Bonhams, Knowle #56/R est:1000-1500
£6500 $11050 €9490 Stolen lock (91x71cm-36x28in) s. 19-Nov-3 Bonhams, New Bond Street #53/R est:4000-6000
£8000 $13600 €11680 To market to buy a fat pig (51x86cm-20x34in) s. s.i.verso. 19-Nov-3 Bonhams, New Bond Street #54/R est:5000-7000

ROBERTS, Gary Lynn (1953-) American
£2941 $5000 €4294 Taming the nueces strip (61x76cm-24x30in) 1-Nov-3 Altermann Galleries, Santa Fe #10
£3352 $6000 €4894 Loner (76x61cm-30x24in) 15-May-4 Altermann Galleries, Santa Fe #24/R
£4118 $7000 €6012 Strange sign (76x102cm-30x40in) 1-Nov-3 Altermann Galleries, Santa Fe #11

ROBERTS, Glenda (20th C) New Zealander
£567 $1004 €828 Field of summer flowers (118x135cm-46x53in) s. acrylic. 28-Apr-4 Dunbar Sloane, Auckland #76/R (NZ.D 1600)
£855 $1471 €1248 Overgrown path (150x150cm-59x59in) s. 3-Dec-3 Dunbar Sloane, Auckland #69/R (NZ.D 2300)
Works on paper
£278 $442 €406 Parade at Napier (59x68cm-23x27in) s. gouache. 1-May-3 Dunbar Sloane, Wellington #69/R (NZ.D 800)
£526 $895 €768 Lindis Pass, central Otago. s. gouache. 26-Nov-3 Dunbar Sloane, Wellington #117/R est:1200-1500 (NZ.D 1400)

ROBERTS, H Larpent (?-1890) British
£600 $1062 €876 Home of the robin (28x25cm-11x10in) init. board arched top. 28-Apr-4 Halls, Shrewsbury #511/R

ROBERTS, Henry Benjamin (1831-1915) British
£480 $883 €701 Feeding chickens (33x24cm-13x9in) s.d.1863. 8-Jun-4 Bonhams, Knightsbridge #205/R
Works on paper
£1400 $2506 €2044 Flower of the flock (64x51cm-25x20in) s.d.76 W/C gouache. 26-May-4 Sotheby's, Olympia #171/R est:1500-2500

ROBERTS, Hilda (1901-1982) British
£6643 $11294 €9500 Born into Quaker family (69x89cm-27x35in) s. 25-Nov-3 De Veres Art Auctions, Dublin #83/R est:8000-12000
Works on paper
£629 $1070 €900 Aran fishermen (23x29cm-9x11in) s. gouache. 25-Nov-3 De Veres Art Auctions, Dublin #84/R
£769 $1308 €1100 Aran donkey (23x31cm-9x12in) s. gouache. 25-Nov-3 De Veres Art Auctions, Dublin #85/R est:1200-1600
£979 $1664 €1400 Aran woman (38x28cm-15x11in) s. chl. 25-Nov-3 De Veres Art Auctions, Dublin #86/R est:900-1200

ROBERTS, Holly (1951-) American
£363 $650 €530 Two dogs fighting. s.i. oil on silver print. 13-May-4 Dallas Auction Gallery, Dallas #234/R
£2095 $3750 €3059 Horse running. s. oil silver print triptych. 13-May-4 Dallas Auction Gallery, Dallas #335/R est:6000-8000

ROBERTS, James (fl.1858-1876) British
£400 $640 €584 Highland cattle near loch at sunset (60x101cm-24x40in) s.d.1874. 17-Sep-3 Bonhams, Brooks & Langlois, Jersey #58/R

ROBERTS, Joseph L (attrib) (fl.1850-1870) American
£1075 $2000 €1570 Still life with apples and grapes (28x38cm-11x15in) indis.s. 3-Mar-4 Christie's, Rockefeller NY #7/R est:3000-5000

ROBERTS, Julie (1963-) American
£5215 $8500 €7614 Operating table, yellow 1 (91x91cm-36x36in) s.i.d.1995 verso oil acrylic prov. 23-Sep-3 Christie's, Rockefeller NY #74/R est:8000-12000

ROBERTS, Lancelot (?-1950) British
£3200 $5440 €4672 Children warming themselves beside a fire (56x69cm-22x27in) 30-Oct-3 Duke & Son, Dorchester #238/R est:1000-2000
Works on paper
£340 $588 €496 Young shipwright (61x43cm-24x17in) s. pastel. 11-Dec-3 Neales, Nottingham #547/R

ROBERTS, Paul (20th C) ?
£1800 $3312 €2628 Fickle heart (121x182cm-48x72in) s.d.77. 24-Jun-4 Sotheby's, Olympia #480/R est:2000-3000

ROBERTS, Priscilla (1916-) American
£1374 $2500 €2006 Dawn (35x46cm-14x18in) s. s.i.verso masonite. 29-Jun-4 Sotheby's, New York #324/R est:2000-3000

ROBERTS, Spencer (?) British
£450 $806 €657 Cattle watering, early morning (53x76cm-21x30in) s. 27-May-4 Christie's, Kensington #238/R
£1400 $2380 €2044 Hunting in the snow (91x122cm-36x48in) s. 27-Nov-3 Christie's, Kensington #44/R est:1500-2000

ROBERTS, Thomas (1748-1778) Irish
£135000 $241650 €197100 View of the weir in Lucan House Demesne, Co Dublin (61x102cm-24x40in) prov.lit. 14-May-4 Christie's, London #22/R est:70000-100000
£320000 $572800 €467200 Extensive lakeside landscape with ruined castle. Wooded river landscape (48x67cm-19x26in) pair prov.lit. 14-May-4 Christie's, London #108/R est:150000-250000

ROBERTS, Thomas Keith (1909-1998) Canadian
£240 $384 €350 East wind, Mt Louis, Gaspe (41x56cm-16x22in) s. board. 16-Sep-3 Maynards, Vancouver #356 (C.D 525)
£339 $532 €492 Perce Rock (15x30cm-6x12in) s.verso. 30-Aug-3 Heffel, Vancouver #27 (C.D 750)
£362 $654 €529 Late October in the beech woods (27x35cm-11x14in) s. hard board prov. 18-Apr-4 Levis, Calgary #100/R (C.D 875)
£365 $584 €533 Sugar time (20x25cm-8x10in) s. board. 16-Sep-3 Maynards, Vancouver #351 (C.D 800)
£750 $1275 €1095 Birch trees on lake shore (20x25cm-8x10in) s. board. 26-Nov-3 Sotheby's, Olympia #128/R
£832 $1390 €1215 September morning, Grandes Piles (30x41cm-12x16in) s. masonite. 12-Jul-3 Auctions by the Bay, Alameda #391/R
£900 $1647 €1314 View of St Margaret's Bay (40x55cm-16x22in) s. s.i.verso board prov. 3-Jun-4 Heffel, Vancouver #49/R est:2000-3000 (C.D 2250)
£960 $1757 €1402 Maple Bush (35x50cm-14x20in) s. board prov. 1-Jun-4 Joyner Waddington, Toronto #347/R est:2000-2500 (C.D 2400)
£978 $1692 €1428 Sous bois en automne (50x66cm-20x26in) s. isorel. 15-Dec-3 Iegor de Saint Hippolyte, Montreal #42b (C.D 2200)
£1116 $1897 €1629 Harbour bake shop in winter (51x66cm-20x26in) s. board prov. 6-Nov-3 Heffel, Vancouver #98/R est:3000-4000 (C.D 2500)
£1161 $1996 €1695 Spring Foliage - Trent Valley (60x75cm-24x30in) s. canvasboard. 2-Dec-3 Joyner Waddington, Toronto #511 est:2500-3500 (C.D 2600)
£1600 $2928 €2336 Spring landscape (40x50cm-16x20in) s. prov. 1-Jun-4 Joyner Waddington, Toronto #319/R est:2000-2500 (C.D 4000)
£1689 $2872 €2466 Glen Williams (61x76cm-24x30in) s. i.verso board. 27-Nov-3 Heffel, Vancouver #145/R est:1800-2200 (C.D 3750)

ROBERTS, Thomas Sautelle (attrib) (1760-1826) British
£6579 $12105 €10000 County Wicklow landscape with Sugarloaf beyond (52x74cm-20x29in) 22-Jun-4 Mealy's, Castlecomer #795/R est:8000-15000

ROBERTS, Thomas William (1856-1931) Australian
£3252 $5106 €4715 Approaching storm, north coast Tasmania (11x20cm-4x8in) s.d.29 board prov. 26-Aug-3 Christie's, Sydney #337/R est:8000-12000 (A.D 8000)
£6198 $10971 €9049 Snodland ferry (9x29cm-4x11in) i.d.30 Aug 05 panel prov.lit. 3-May-4 Christie's, Melbourne #113/R est:15000-20000 (A.D 15000)
£7054 $11780 €10581 Summer landscape (19x25cm-7x10in) painted c.1887-88. 27-Oct-3 Goodman, Sydney #134/R est:17000-20000 (A.D 17000)
£16529 $30579 €24132 Portrait of the artist's son Caleb (91x61cm-36x24in) canvas on board painted c.1905 prov.exhib. 10-Mar-4 Deutscher-Menzies, Melbourne #63/R est:30000-40000 (A.D 40000)

ROBERTS, Will (1910-2000) British
£600 $1020 €876 Still life with red rose (31x25cm-12x10in) init. s.d.1980 verso. 18-Nov-3 Sotheby's, Olympia #68/R
£850 $1386 €1241 Penclawdd cockle woman with horse and cart (28x38cm-11x15in) init. board. 27-Sep-3 Rogers Jones, Clwyd #100
£850 $1445 €1241 Farmer (25x20cm-10x8in) s.i.d.1984 verso board. 18-Nov-3 Sotheby's, Olympia #60/R
£900 $1530 €1314 Man in red (21x26cm-8x10in) init. board. 18-Nov-3 Sotheby's, Olympia #63/R
£900 $1530 €1314 Tynywaun (41x52cm-16x20in) init. s.i.d.1980 verso. 18-Nov-3 Sotheby's, Olympia #62/R
£950 $1615 €1387 Reading the paper (31x26cm-12x10in) board. 18-Nov-3 Sotheby's, Olympia #67/R
£1000 $1820 €1460 Cefn Seison Fach (50x60cm-20x24in) s. i.d.1964 verso board. 21-Jun-4 Bonhams, Bath #323 est:500-700
£1500 $2550 €2190 Market cafe (40x51cm-16x20in) init. s.i.d.81 verso. 18-Nov-3 Sotheby's, Olympia #61/R est:1200-1800
£3400 $6222 €5100 Man with a spade (58x76cm-23x30in) i.d.1962 verso board. 28-Jul-4 Mallams, Oxford #351/R est:400-600

ROBERTS, William (1895-1980) British
£1500 $2745 €2190 Portrait of a lady (51x41cm-20x16in) s. 27-Jan-4 Gorringes, Lewes #1520/R est:1500-2000
£1750 $3185 €2555 View of a Welsh Town. 3-Feb-4 Lawrences, Bletchingley #1702/R
£10000 $17200 €14600 Judgement of Paris (43x33cm-17x13in) s. prov.exhib. 3-Dec-3 Sotheby's, London #4/R est:10000-15000

Works on paper
£900 $1413 €1305 Boxing match (13x17cm-5x7in) s.d.71 pencil squared for transfer prov. 28-Aug-3 Christie's, Kensington #500/R
£1500 $2640 €2190 Flying Dutchman (21x16cm-8x6in) i. pen ink executed c.1915 exhib. 19-May-4 Sotheby's, Olympia #90/R est:1500-2000
£2000 $3180 €2920 Old man carrying wood (54x36cm-21x14in) pencil W/C prov. 10-Sep-3 Sotheby's, Olympia #150/R est:2000-3000
£5200 $9464 €7592 Loading a howitzer (17x12cm-7x5in) s. pen ink pencil. 15-Jun-4 Bonhams, New Bond Street #22/R est:3000-4000
£7800 $14430 €11388 Window dressing (49x34cm-19x13in) s. pencil W/C exec c.1957 exhib. 10-Mar-4 Sotheby's, Olympia #123/R est:7000-10000

ROBERTS, William Goodridge (1904-1974) Canadian
£1120 $2050 €1635 Knowlton, Quebec (40x50cm-16x20in) s. board prov. 1-Jun-4 Joyner Waddington, Toronto #278/R est:3000-4000 (C.D 2800)
£1280 $2342 €1869 Road, late autumn (50x60cm-20x24in) s. board prov. 1-Jun-4 Joyner Waddington, Toronto #304/R est:4000-5000 (C.D 3200)
£1305 $2428 €1905 Buttercups and daisies (23x18cm-9x7in) s. masonite prov. 2-Mar-4 Ritchie, Toronto #69/R est:1000-1500 (C.D 3250)
£1520 $2782 €2219 Portrait of the artist's wife (40x30cm-16x12in) s. board prov. 1-Jun-4 Joyner Waddington, Toronto #284/R est:2500-3000 (C.D 3800)
£1840 $3367 €2686 Landscape St Jovite (50x60cm-20x24in) s. panel lit. 1-Jun-4 Joyner Waddington, Toronto #152/R est:5000-7000 (C.D 4600)
£2036 $3197 €2973 Yamaska (51x61cm-20x24in) s. canvas on board. 26-Aug-3 Iegor de Saint Hippolyte, Montreal #136 (C.D 4500)
£2139 $3637 €3123 Still life with fruit, books and flowers (30x41cm-12x16in) s. board. 21-Nov-3 Walker's, Ottawa #52/R est:5000-7000 (C.D 4750)
£2200 $4026 €3212 Blue water, Mediterranean (62x90cm-24x35in) s. prov. 1-Jun-4 Joyner Waddington, Toronto #206/R est:5000-7000 (C.D 5500)
£2232 $3839 €3259 Pine Grove, Agay (59x71cm-23x28in) s. painted 1954 prov. 2-Dec-3 Joyner Waddington, Toronto #166/R est:5000-7000 (C.D 5000)
£2236 $4002 €3265 Trees, laurentians (40x50cm-16x20in) s. i.verso board prov. 27-May-4 Heffel, Vancouver #163/R est:5000-7000 (C.D 5500)
£2252 $3829 €3288 Still life with fruit, books and bottles (9x18cm-4x7in) s. board. 21-Nov-3 Walker's, Ottawa #47/R est:2500-3500 (C.D 5000)
£2703 $4595 €3946 Gouffre River (61x91cm-24x36in) s. masonite prov. 18-Nov-3 Sotheby's, Toronto #185/R est:7000-9000 (C.D 6000)
£2846 $5093 €4155 Trees and river (46x60cm-18x24in) s. masonite prov. 31-May-4 Sotheby's, Toronto #107/R est:8000-10000 (C.D 7000)
£3000 $5490 €4380 Still life (30x40cm-12x16in) s. board. 1-Jun-4 Joyner Waddington, Toronto #194/R est:6000-8000 (C.D 7500)
£3427 $6306 €5003 Still life with purple and yellow cloths (81x81cm-32x32in) s. i.verso board prov. 9-Jun-4 Walker's, Ottawa #147/R est:9000-12000 (C.D 8500)
£3571 $6143 €5214 Sunlit shoreline (50x60cm-20x24in) s. board prov. 2-Dec-3 Joyner Waddington, Toronto #21/R est:6000-8000 (C.D 8000)
£3604 $6126 €5262 Paysage au bord de l'eau (65x91cm-26x36in) s. prov. 18-Nov-3 Sotheby's, Toronto #184/R est:10000-12000 (C.D 8000)
£3604 $6126 €5262 Wild flowers (41x25cm-16x10in) s. s.i.d.1952 verso board. 27-Nov-3 Heffel, Vancouver #132/R est:9000-12000 (C.D 8000)
£3829 $6509 €5590 Laurentian landscape (63x81cm-25x32in) s. i.verso board painted c.1955 prov.lit. 27-Nov-3 Heffel, Vancouver #182/R est:6000-8000 (C.D 8500)
£4556 $7471 €6652 Still life with lemons (51x41cm-20x16in) s. prov. 28-May-3 Maynards, Vancouver #24/R est:8000-10000 (C.D 10250)
£4878 $8732 €7122 Autumn, Laurentians (61x91cm-24x36in) s.i.d.1949 masonite prov. 31-May-4 Sotheby's, Toronto #58/R est:9000-12000 (C.D 12000)
£5405 $9189 €7891 Lake Massawippi (81x111cm-32x44in) s. masonite prov. 18-Nov-3 Sotheby's, Toronto #139/R est:12000-15000 (C.D 12000)
£6911 $12370 €10090 Flowers on a chair (72x54cm-28x21in) s. board painted 1940 prov.lit. 27-May-4 Heffel, Vancouver #109/R est:18000-22000 (C.D 17000)
£7317 $13098 €10683 Laurentian hillside (79x122cm-31x48in) s. masonite prov.exhib. 31-May-4 Sotheby's, Toronto #106/R est:18000-22000 (C.D 18000)
£10400 $19032 €15184 Interior of the artist's home (112x80cm-44x31in) s. board lit. 1-Jun-4 Joyner Waddington, Toronto #27/R est:25000-30000 (C.D 26000)
Works on paper
£260 $475 €380 Man and woman seated on a couch (26x20cm-10x8in) s. pencil. 1-Jun-4 Joyner Waddington, Toronto #519 (C.D 650)
£691 $1237 €1009 Georgian Bay (26x36cm-10x14in) i.verso W/C prov.exhib. 27-May-4 Heffel, Vancouver #166/R (C.D 1700)
£714 $1229 €1042 Market Scene, Ottawa (21x30cm-8x12in) s. W/C. 2-Dec-3 Joyner Waddington, Toronto #256/R (C.D 1600)
£1280 $2342 €1869 Lake Oxford Landscape (51x70cm-20x28in) s. W/C prov. 1-Jun-4 Joyner Waddington, Toronto #4/R est:4000-6000 (C.D 3200)

ROBERTSHAW, Des (20th C) Australian
£426 $787 €622 Figure in red (76x65cm-30x26in) s. board. 13-Jul-4 Watson's, Christchurch #13/R (NZ.D 1200)

ROBERTSON, Andrew (1777-1845) British
Miniatures
£1700 $3060 €2482 Young lady wearing a white dress and ruby brooch (8cm-3in) mono.d.1812 gold frame oval exhib. 22-Apr-4 Bonhams, New Bond Street #142/R est:1500-2500
£2400 $4008 €3504 Maria Travers (8cm-3in) gilt metal mount on green plush base painted c.1810. 12-Nov-3 Halls, Shrewsbury #112/R est:600-800

ROBERTSON, Arthur (?-1911) British
£4600 $7314 €6670 Song (75x52cm-30x20in) s.d.1889. 9-Sep-3 Bonhams, Knightsbridge #225a/R est:1500-2000

ROBERTSON, Beatrice Hagarty (1879-?) Canadian
£221 $411 €323 Roses in white jug (41x30cm-16x12in) s. panel. 2-Mar-4 Ritchie, Toronto #73/R (C.D 550)
£227 $370 €331 On the beach (16x23cm-6x9in) board prov. 23-Sep-3 Ritchie, Toronto #105/R (C.D 500)
£387 $630 €565 Woman with parasol (16x21cm-6x8in) board prov. 23-Sep-3 Ritchie, Toronto #104/R (C.D 850)
£991 $1775 €1447 Petunias (41x51cm-16x20in) s. panel. 8-Jan-4 James Julia, Fairfield #977a/R est:600-800

ROBERTSON, Charles (1760-1821) Irish
Miniatures
£1300 $2210 €1898 Field officer of Irish Volunteers (7cm-3in) gold frame oval. 18-Nov-3 Bonhams, New Bond Street #85/R est:1000-1500
£1900 $3420 €2774 Sarah Anne, Countess of Westmorland (6cm-2in) gilt mount rec. papier mache frame oval prov.exhib. 22-Apr-4 Bonhams, New Bond Street #76/R est:1000-1500

ROBERTSON, Charles (1844-1891) British
Works on paper
£1100 $1727 €1595 Fishing vessels in the Grand Harbour, Valetta (18x26cm-7x10in) mono. pencil W/C sold with W/C by another hand. 28-Aug-3 Christie's, Kensington #398/R est:500-700
£2400 $4248 €3504 Past repair (25x18cm-10x7in) s. W/C. 27-Apr-4 Bonhams, New Bond Street #66/R est:2000-3000

ROBERTSON, David T (1879-1952) British
£580 $922 €847 Horses and workers in a potato field (21x30cm-8x12in) s. 18-Mar-3 Anderson & Garland, Newcastle #366
£660 $1049 €964 Haycart in a field (14x55cm-6x22in) s. 18-Mar-3 Anderson & Garland, Newcastle #365/R
Works on paper
£500 $920 €730 Cattle grazing by a river in a summer meadow (49x70cm-19x28in) s. W/C. 23-Mar-4 Anderson & Garland, Newcastle #305
£800 $1448 €1168 Haycart in river landscape (51x69cm-20x27in) s. W/C. 15-Apr-4 Richardson & Smith, Whitby #96/R
£900 $1656 €1314 Two horses lead to stabling in a snow storm (51x74cm-20x29in) s. W/C. 23-Mar-4 Anderson & Garland, Newcastle #306
£2000 $3620 €2920 Haystacking (33x48cm-13x19in) s. W/C. 15-Apr-4 Richardson & Smith, Whitby #98/R est:600-1000

ROBERTSON, George Edward (1864-?) British
£380 $711 €555 Portrait of Gertrude Smedley nee Edwards, wearing green dress (34x27cm-13x11in) s.d.85. 22-Jul-4 Tennants, Leyburn #800
£1400 $2590 €2044 Discussing the catch (76x56cm-30x22in) s. 10-Mar-4 Sotheby's, Olympia #219/R est:800-1200
£1800 $3330 €2628 St Ives Harbour (55x44cm-22x17in) s. 10-Mar-4 Sotheby's, Olympia #220/R est:800-1200
£2198 $4000 €3209 Unannounced visitor (69x51cm-27x20in) s. 7-Feb-4 Neal Auction Company, New Orleans #420/R est:6000-9000
£4000 $7400 €5840 Bouquet (56x76cm-22x30in) s. 10-Mar-4 Sotheby's, Olympia #210/R est:1500-2000

ROBERTSON, Glenn (20th C) American
£261 $475 €381 Elephant (28x44cm-11x17in) s.d.74 board. 7-Feb-4 Sloans & Kenyon, Bethesda #889/R

ROBERTSON, Henry Robert (1839-1921) British
Works on paper
£280 $504 €409 Country church (13x20cm-5x8in) mono.d.1920 pen brown ink W/C over pencil. 21-Jan-4 Sotheby's, Olympia #245/R
£600 $1074 €876 HMS Victory lying at her permanent mooring in Portsmouth harbour (18x16cm-7x6in) pencil W/C. 26-May-4 Christie's, Kensington #411/R

ROBERTSON, James (1813-1888) ?
Photographs
£1958 $3270 €2800 Batterie devant Sebastopol apres la prise (18x25cm-7x10in) salt print exec.1855. 10-Oct-3 Tajan, Paris #68/R est:2000-2500

ROBERTSON, James (attrib) (1813-1888) ?
Photographs
£2937 $4905 €4200 Seller, Constantinoples (19x15cm-7x6in) salt print exec.c.1860. 10-Oct-3 Tajan, Paris #69/R est:2800-3000
£3636 $6073 €5200 Portrait d'homme dans le cimetiere de Scutari (19x14cm-7x6in) salt print exec.c.1860 lit. 10-Oct-3 Tajan, Paris #70/R est:2800-3000

ROBERTSON, James Downie (1931-) British
£400 $736 €584 Landscape (40x40cm-16x16in) s. board. 10-Jun-4 Lyon & Turnbull, Edinburgh #83
Works on paper
£600 $954 €876 Croft (76x101cm-30x40in) s.d.66 gouache board. 10-Sep-3 Sotheby's, Olympia #222/R

ROBERTSON, Royal (1936-) American
£500 $900 €730 Satyr. oil maker ink on paper. 24-Apr-4 Slotin Folk Art, Buford #533/R
£833 $1500 €1216 Times of Evil doers (56x71cm-22x28in) paint on poster. 24-Apr-4 Slotin Folk Art, Buford #537/R est:300-500
Works on paper
£556 $1000 €812 Visionary drawing no.8 (79x64cm-31x25in) glitter ink on postcard. 24-Apr-4 Slotin Folk Art, Buford #534/R est:300-500

ROBERTSON, Sarah Margaret (1891-1948) Canadian
Works on paper
£636 $1037 €929 Lilies on the pond (28x40cm-11x16in) s. W/C prov. 23-Sep-3 Ritchie, Toronto #147/R est:1000-1500 (C.D 1400)
£1120 $2050 €1635 Holly hocks (27x37cm-11x15in) s. W/C painted 1935 prov. 1-Jun-4 Joyner Waddington, Toronto #227/R est:3000-5000 (C.D 2800)

ROBERTSON, Scott (20th C) American
£464 $850 €696 South of Whitehall (107x188cm-42x74in) 10-Jul-4 Hindman, Chicago #440/R est:500-700

ROBERTSON, Struan (fl.1903-1938) British
Works on paper
£1500 $2355 €2175 Feeding the chickens (24x34cm-9x13in) s. pastel prov. 27-Aug-3 Sotheby's, London #1093/R est:1500-2000

ROBERTSON, Suze (1856-1922) Dutch
£952 $1524 €1380 Old woman in village street (69x42cm-27x17in) s. 15-May-3 Stuker, Bern #1073/R est:1500-2000 (S.FR 2000)
£1316 $2382 €2000 A woman bleaching on the lawn in front of white houses (45x56cm-18x22in) s. panel. 19-Apr-4 Glerum, Amsterdam #273/R est:1500-2000
£1748 $2919 €2500 The artist's studio (40x155cm-16x61in) 30-Jun-3 Sotheby's, Amsterdam #227/R
£1875 $3131 €2700 Koffievrouwtje (42x26cm-17x10in) s. panel prov. 21-Oct-3 Sotheby's, Amsterdam #122/R est:3000-5000
£2639 $4486 €3800 Poort te Harderwijk (55x45cm-22x18in) s. panel. 28-Oct-3 Christie's, Amsterdam #176/R est:3000-5000

ROBERTSON, T (19th C) ?
£6800 $11968 €9928 Herdsman and Aberdeen Angus bull and cows against the Strichan hills (80x120cm-31x47in) s.d.1859. 18-May-4 Woolley & Wallis, Salisbury #223/R est:2000-3000

ROBERTSON, Tom (1850-1947) British
£320 $598 €480 Palace of the Kaid of Armsmiz, from the river (25x33cm-10x13in) s. wood panel. 22-Jul-4 Gorringes, Lewes #1882
£380 $711 €570 Old cottages, Oudon (25x30cm-10x12in) s. board. 22-Jul-4 Gorringes, Lewes #1886/R
£420 $785 €630 Near Haddon Hall, Derbyshire (23x28cm-9x11in) s. wood panel. 22-Jul-4 Gorringes, Lewes #1881
£500 $835 €730 Off Concale, Brittany (19x24cm-7x9in) s. board. 20-Oct-3 Bonhams, Bath #134
£550 $1029 €825 Gorse on cliff tops (18x23cm-7x9in) s. board. 22-Jul-4 Gorringes, Lewes #1880
£650 $1216 €975 Street in the Medina, Mogador and Street in Mogador (36x25cm-14x10in) s. board pair. 22-Jul-4 Gorringes, Lewes #1885
£950 $1777 €1425 On the beach, Valery sur Somme (25x30cm-10x12in) s. 22-Jul-4 Gorringes, Lewes #1879
£1000 $1670 €1460 On the Loire at Loudon (19x24cm-7x9in) s. board sold with a companion. 20-Oct-3 Bonhams, Bath #133 est:400-600
£1000 $1790 €1460 Portobello (44x61cm-17x24in) s. 28-May-4 Lyon & Turnbull, Edinburgh #2/R est:1000-1500
£1000 $1870 €1500 Breton stream (28x36cm-10x14in) s. wood panel. 22-Jul-4 Gorringes, Lewes #1883/R est:400-600
£1100 $2057 €1650 Syrian coaster (20x25cm-8x10in) s. board. 22-Jul-4 Gorringes, Lewes #1884 est:250-350
£1400 $2618 €2100 Fishing boats on a calm sea (71x91cm-28x36in) s. 22-Jul-4 Gorringes, Lewes #1878/R est:1000-1500
£2100 $3759 €3066 On the Loire (20x25cm-8x10in) s. board. 28-May-4 Lyon & Turnbull, Edinburgh #65/R est:800-1200

ROBERTSON, Victor John (fl.1892-1909) British
£769 $1285 €1123 Farmer and horse crossing a bridge (67x97cm-26x38in) s. 17-Nov-3 Waddingtons, Toronto #100/R (C.D 1700)
£1800 $2844 €2610 Cottage garden (69x46cm-27x18in) s. 4-Sep-3 Christie's, Kensington #269/R est:1200-1800

ROBERTSON, Walford Graham (1867-1948) British
£1333 $2400 €2000 Young girl (122x60cm-48x24in) s.d.1914. 26-Apr-4 Rieber, Stuttgart #1219/R est:2400
Works on paper
£320 $592 €467 Young buds sleep in the root's white core (13x17cm-5x7in) init. pen ink. 9-Mar-4 Bonhams, Knightsbridge #89/R

ROBERTSON, Walter (attrib) (?-1801) British
Miniatures
£2000 $3600 €2920 Officer of Royal Artillery (7cm-3in) gold frame oval exhib.lit. 22-Apr-4 Bonhams, New Bond Street #120/R est:1000-1500

ROBERTSON-SWANN, Ron (1941-) Australian
Works on paper
£909 $1682 €1327 Long Island Sound (88x179cm-35x70in) s.d.1972 i.verso synthetic polymer. 15-Mar-4 Sotheby's, Melbourne #130 est:1200-1800 (A.D 2200)

ROBERTY, Andre Felix (1887-1963) French
£500 $885 €730 Nue a sa toilette (65x54cm-26x21in) s. board. 29-Apr-4 Christie's, Kensington #292/R

ROBIE, Jean Baptiste (1821-1910) Belgian
£594 $1010 €850 Vase de fleurs, coupe de fruits et calices sur une table (16x14cm-6x6in) s.i.verso. 1-Dec-3 Palais de Beaux Arts, Brussels #304/R
£1562 $2750 €2281 Still life with flowers and casket on a ledge (16x14cm-6x6in) s.i.verso panel. 18-May-4 Bonhams & Butterfields, San Francisco #70/R est:3000-5000
£1901 $3289 €2700 Vase de fleurs (32x25cm-13x10in) s. panel. 14-Dec-3 Eric Pillon, Calais #8/R
£3288 $5589 €4800 Composition avec peches et raisins (58x94cm-23x37in) s. 10-Nov-3 Horta, Bruxelles #111
£4196 $7133 €6000 Nature morte aux raisins et a la verseuse en etain (90x73cm-35x29in) s.d.1851. 18-Nov-3 Vanderkindere, Brussels #39/R est:6000-8000
£13408 $24000 €19576 Bouquet de roses (28x20cm-11x8in) s. panel prov. 6-May-4 Shannon's, Milford #118/R est:12000-18000
£15294 $26000 €22329 Still life of roses (42x53cm-17x21in) panel. 29-Oct-3 Christie's, Rockefeller NY #154/R est:40000-60000
£15493 $27113 €22000 Bouquet d'orchidees dans un vase sur un entablement (81x61cm-32x24in) s. 16-Dec-3 Artcurial Briest, Paris #249/R est:12000-15000

ROBIER, Wagner (19/20th C) French
£5000 $8500 €7300 View of Athens (54x92cm-21x36in) s. 18-Nov-3 Sotheby's, London #68/R est:5000-7000

ROBILLIARD, Marianne H W (fl.1908-1920) British
£1500 $2805 €2250 Passing storm (122x91cm-48x36in) sold with two related photos. 22-Jul-4 Gorringes, Lewes #1954/R est:1500-2000

ROBIN, Georges (19/20th C) French
£699 $1189 €1000 Le Seine niortoise pres de Niort (55x66cm-22x26in) s. 18-Nov-3 Galerie Moderne, Brussels #892
£2803 $4400 €4092 Farm on the lake (64x91cm-25x36in) s. 1-Sep-3 William A Smith, Plainfield #15/R
£3328 $5225 €4859 Port village with boats (66x81cm-26x32in) s. 1-Sep-3 William A Smith, Plainfield #6/R
£5430 $8525 €7928 River through French country village (53x64cm-21x25in) s. 1-Sep-3 William A Smith, Plainfield #3/R

ROBIN, Louis (1845-?) French
£2500 $4175 €3650 Visitor (46x61cm-18x24in) s. 11-Nov-3 Bonhams, Knightsbridge #101/R est:2500-3500

ROBINET, Gustave Paul (elder) (1845-1932) French
£905 $1538 €1321 Winter lake landscape (27x37cm-11x15in) s. 19-Nov-3 Fischer, Luzern #1266/R (S.FR 2000)
£1638 $2932 €2391 Young woman above Vierwaldstattersee (51x70cm-20x28in) s. 12-May-4 Dobiaschofsky, Bern #910/R est:5000 (S.FR 3800)

ROBINS, Evelyn R (19th C) British
£1300 $2327 €1898 Elopement (45x73cm-18x29in) s.d.1886. 11-May-4 Bonhams, Knightsbridge #68/R est:700-900

ROBINS, Sylvia (20th C) New Zealander?
£453 $729 €661 Gathering Toheroas (37x59cm-15x23in) s. board. 12-Aug-3 Peter Webb, Auckland #220 (NZ.D 1250)

ROBINS, Thomas Sewell (1814-1880) British
Works on paper
£280 $440 €406 Fishing vessel returning home (18x34cm-7x13in) init.d.74 pencil W/C bodycol. 28-Aug-3 Christie's, Kensington #456/R
£280 $524 €420 Shipping in harbour (15x25cm-6x10in) init. W/C. 22-Jul-4 Gorringes, Lewes #1738
£1800 $3060 €2628 Fishing smack in high seas (31x49cm-12x19in) s. pencil W/C htd bodycol scratching out prov. 20-Nov-3 Christie's, London #91/R est:2000-3000
£3800 $6460 €5548 Fishing boats in choppy seas off the coast (33x50cm-13x20in) s. W/C over pencil htd bodycol prov. 27-Nov-3 Sotheby's, London #265/R est:3000-5000

ROBINSON, Albert Henry (1881-1956) Canadian
£3862 $6913 €5639 Harbour, St Malo (21x26cm-8x10in) s. i.verso panel exhib. 27-May-4 Heffel, Vancouver #102/R est:10000-12000 (C.D 9500)

ROBINSON, Annie (1961-) Irish
£369 $661 €550 Evening stars sing out (25x35cm-10x14in) s. 31-May-4 Hamilton Osborne King, Dublin #10

ROBINSON, Bird (20th C) American
£187 $350 €273 View of Little Compton (30x36cm-12x14in) init. acrylic prov. 29-Feb-4 Bonhams & Butterfields, San Francisco #4593

ROBINSON, Boardman (1876-1952) American
£495 $900 €723 Figures in an interior (51x36cm-20x14in) cardboard. 15-Jun-4 John Moran, Pasadena #189
£4813 $7750 €7027 Ten Pound Island, Gloucester Harbour (51x61cm-20x24in) s. 20-Aug-3 James Julia, Fairfield #1301/R est:3500-4500

ROBINSON, Chas Dorman (1847-1933) American
£924 $1700 €1349 Breaking surf (50x66cm-20x26in) s.d.1908 prov. 8-Jun-4 Bonhams & Butterfields, San Francisco #4209/R est:3000-5000
£938 $1500 €1369 Fishing on the Bay. s. 20-Sep-3 Harvey Clar, Oakland #1277
£1852 $3500 €2704 Monterey coastal at sunset (51x66cm-20x26in) s. prov. 17-Feb-4 John Moran, Pasadena #150/R est:3000-4000
£3743 $7000 €5465 Butte cliff at sunset (51x76cm-20x30in) s.d.1909 canvas on board prov. 24-Jul-4 Coeur d'Alene, Hayden #252/R est:5000-10000
£4891 $9000 €7141 Spring morning in the Santa Inez mountains, Santa Barbara, California (61x86cm-24x34in) s.i.d.1919 prov. 8-Jun-4 Bonhams & Butterfields, San Francisco #4189/R est:8000-12000
£4913 $8500 €7173 Blooming hillside with a river in the distance (41x61cm-16x24in) s. prov. 10-Dec-3 Bonhams & Butterfields, San Francisco #6188/R est:6000-8000
£10983 $19000 €16035 Fog storm on the Bay (61x91cm-24x36in) s.i. prov. 10-Dec-3 Bonhams & Butterfields, San Francisco #6176/R est:15000-20000
Works on paper
£4913 $8500 €7173 Lake Louise (51x66cm-20x26in) s. prov. 10-Dec-3 Bonhams & Butterfields, San Francisco #6187/R est:8000-12000

ROBINSON, Dorothy Napangardi (1956-) Australian
Works on paper
£3333 $5967 €4866 Karntakurlangu Jukurrpa (91x91cm-36x36in) synthetic polymer linen exec 2000 prov. 25-May-4 Lawson Menzies, Sydney #18/R est:10000-12000 (A.D 8500)
£10156 $18992 €15234 Mina Mina Tjukurrpa (155x120cm-61x47in) s.i.verso synthetic polymer linen exec. 2002 prov. 21-Jul-4 Shapiro, Sydney #36/R est:25000-35000 (A.D 26000)

£11064 $19140 €16153 Mina Mina (122x182cm-48x72in) i.verso synthetic polymer paint linen prov. 10-Dec-3 Shapiro, Sydney #156/R est:30000-50000 (A.D 26000)
£14844 $27758 €22266 Karntakurlangu Jukurrpa (123x152cm-48x60in) i.verso synthetic polymer linen exec. 2001 prov.exhib. 21-Jul-4 Shapiro, Sydney #58/R est:35000-50000 (A.D 38000)
£14902 $26675 €21757 Salt on Mina Mina (173x121cm-68x48in) synthetic polymer paint linen exec 2000 prov. 25-May-4 Lawson Menzies, Sydney #33/R est:30000-40000 (A.D 38000)
£20851 $36072 €30442 Salt crystals on Mina Mina (137x213cm-54x84in) i.verso synthetic polymer paint linen prov. 10-Dec-3 Shapiro, Sydney #190/R est:45000-60000 (A.D 49000)
£30851 $53372 €45042 Women's dreaming (183x122cm-72x48in) synthetic polymer paint prov.exhib. 10-Dec-3 Shapiro, Sydney #153/R est:50000-70000 (A.D 72500)

ROBINSON, E John (1922-) American
£223 $400 €326 Spring twilight. s. 18-Mar-4 Skinner, Bolton #590/R

ROBINSON, Frank E (?) ?
Works on paper
£262 $482 €383 Palace pier, Brighton Pavilion (51x91cm-20x36in) s.i. W/C. 14-Jun-4 Waddingtons, Toronto #76/R est:800-1200 (C.D 650)

ROBINSON, George Crosland (1858-1930) British
£378 $684 €552 Seascape near Rooi Els (39x59cm-15x23in) s. 30-Mar-4 Stephan Welz, Johannesburg #437/R est:5000-8000 (SA.R 4500)
£420 $761 €613 Washerwomen in an autumn landscape (49x59cm-19x23in) s. 30-Mar-4 Stephan Welz, Johannesburg #475/R est:6000-8000 (SA.R 5000)
£431 $720 €629 Welgelegen Farm, Faure Station (29x39cm-11x15in) s. i.verso. 20-Oct-3 Stephan Welz, Johannesburg #507 est:2500-3500 (SA.R 5000)

ROBINSON, Gladys Lloyd (20th C) American
£482 $900 €704 Coconut trees at Los Tules (35x80cm-14x31in) init. prov. 29-Feb-4 Bonhams & Butterfields, San Francisco #4558

ROBINSON, Hal (1875-1933) American
£447 $800 €653 River landscape (36x30cm-14x12in) s. 8-Jan-4 James Julia, Fairfield #959/R
£670 $1200 €978 Connecticut landscape (25x20cm-10x8in) s. 7-May-4 Sloans & Kenyon, Bethesda #1710/R
£692 $1100 €1010 Sunset through the trees (34x34cm-13x13in) 12-Sep-3 Skinner, Boston #405/R
£765 $1300 €1117 Forest interior (30x46cm-12x18in) s. 5-Nov-3 Doyle, New York #63/R est:1000-1500
£1237 $2300 €1806 Searchlight across the water (41x51cm-16x20in) s. painted c.1915. 7-Mar-4 Treadway Gallery, Cincinnati #582/R est:1500-2000
£1290 $2400 €1883 Hudson River palisades (23x18cm-9x7in) s. canvas on board. 3-Mar-4 Christie's, Rockefeller NY #36/R est:1000-1500
£1343 $2457 €1961 Spring landscape (63x76cm-25x30in) s. 9-Jun-4 Rasmussen, Copenhagen #1711/R est:15000 (D.KR 15000)
£2395 $4000 €3497 Winter road along the Hudson (76x102cm-30x40in) s. 23-Oct-3 Shannon's, Milford #218/R est:4000-6000

ROBINSON, John N (1912-1994) American
£1341 $2400 €1958 Christmas door (61x51cm-24x20in) init. s.d.1958 verso canvasboard. 7-May-4 Sloans & Kenyon, Bethesda #1632/R est:1500-2000
£5307 $9500 €7748 Reclining woman (48x61cm-19x24in) s.d.1952 verso prov. 7-May-4 Sloans & Kenyon, Bethesda #1630/R est:5000-7000
£5587 $10000 €8157 Breakfast at the Robinson's (61x76cm-24x30in) init. acrylic canvasboard. 7-May-4 Sloans & Kenyon, Bethesda #1634/R est:4000-6000

ROBINSON, Markey (1918-1999) Irish
£423 $739 €600 Middle Eastern landscape with figures (17x23cm-7x9in) s. 16-Dec-3 James Adam, Dublin #206/R
£479 $838 €680 Middle Eastern landscape with figure (16x23cm-6x9in) s. 16-Dec-3 James Adam, Dublin #207/R
£521 $912 €740 Galway hookers (8x19cm-3x7in) board. 16-Dec-3 James Adam, Dublin #4/R
£547 $989 €820 Coastal scene with figures (16x28cm-6x11in) s. gouache board. 30-Mar-4 De Veres Art Auctions, Dublin #187
£577 $1011 €820 Figure outside cottages in a landscape (11x14cm-4x6in) board. 16-Dec-3 James Adam, Dublin #24/R
£775 $1356 €1100 Coastal fishing village with figures (12x18cm-5x7in) s. board. 16-Dec-3 James Adam, Dublin #185/R
£900 $1431 €1305 Two women wending their way home (18x25cm-7x10in) s. i.verso board. 11-Sep-3 Morphets, Harrogate #269/R
£1074 $1922 €1600 Waiting on the shore. Boats coming in (10x29cm-4x11in) both s. board pair. 31-May-4 Hamilton Osborne King, Dublin #103/R est:600-1000
£1329 $2259 €1900 Collecting the turf (23x38cm-9x15in) s. board. 18-Nov-3 Whyte's, Dublin #216/R est:2000-3000
£1400 $2324 €2044 Cottages, Connemara (22x45cm-9x18in) s. board. 1-Oct-3 John Ross, Belfast #256 est:500-600
£1400 $2534 €2100 Clown (50x31cm-20x12in) s. board. 31-Mar-4 James Adam, Dublin #132/R est:1500-1800
£1700 $3111 €2482 Figures by the roadside, Donegal (12x5cm-5x2in) s. board. 2-Jun-4 John Ross, Belfast #172 est:1200-1500
£2027 $3831 €3000 Storyteller (23x23cm-9x9in) s. board. 17-Feb-4 Whyte's, Dublin #9/R est:1500-2000
£2282 $4039 €3400 Road to the village (33x51cm-13x20in) s. board. 27-Apr-4 Whyte's, Dublin #254/R est:2000-3000
£2797 $4755 €4000 Four figures (76x102cm-30x40in) board prov. 18-Nov-3 Whyte's, Dublin #65/R est:4000-6000
£3000 $4920 €4380 Figures on path (61x106cm-24x42in) s. board. 4-Jun-3 John Ross, Belfast #123 est:5000
£3000 $5370 €4380 Yachts off the coast (51x75cm-20x30in) s. board. 14-May-4 Christie's, Kensington #417/R est:3000-5000
£3221 $5702 €4800 Regatta (46x48cm-18x19in) s. panel. 27-Apr-4 Whyte's, Dublin #184/R est:3000-5000
£3800 $6878 €5700 Whole new world of meaning (57x90cm-22x35in) s. board. 31-Mar-4 James Adam, Dublin #35/R est:6000-9000
£3800 $7068 €5548 Watching the boats, Galway (61x116cm-24x46in) s. board. 3-Mar-4 John Ross, Belfast #66 est:3500-4000
£3800 $7068 €5548 Village by the Mournes (61x122cm-24x48in) s. board. 3-Mar-4 John Ross, Belfast #126 est:4000-5000
£3851 $7279 €5700 Village by the shore (46x71cm-18x28in) s. board. 17-Feb-4 Whyte's, Dublin #228/R est:4000-6000
£3916 $6657 €5600 Coastal village with shawlies (51x70cm-20x28in) s. panel. 18-Nov-3 Whyte's, Dublin #214/R est:6000-8000
£4027 $7128 €6000 Shawlies on a road (51x76cm-20x30in) s. board. 27-Apr-4 Whyte's, Dublin #79/R est:4000-6000
£4527 $8556 €6700 Dock scene (41x76cm-16x30in) s. board. 17-Feb-4 Whyte's, Dublin #7/R est:4000-5000
£5282 $8451 €7500 Galway window (91x61cm-36x24in) s. board. 16-Sep-3 Whyte's, Dublin #131/R est:6000-8000
£6000 $10320 €8760 Stars of the morning (35x96cm-14x38in) s.d.1961 verso. 3-Dec-3 John Ross, Belfast #191 est:5000-6000
£6622 $12515 €9800 Avenue (61x81cm-24x32in) s. board prov. 17-Feb-4 Whyte's, Dublin #223/R est:6000-8000
£11189 $19021 €16000 Flower market, Place de la Madeleine, Paris (51x61cm-20x24in) s. board. 18-Nov-3 Whyte's, Dublin #34/R est:10000-12000
£13380 $21408 €19000 Figures in a street, Paris (42x52cm-17x20in) s. board. 16-Sep-3 Whyte's, Dublin #65/R est:10000-12000
£13423 $23758 €20000 Fishing village (47x57cm-19x22in) s. board prov.lit. 27-Apr-4 Whyte's, Dublin #68/R est:12000-15000
£15000 $26850 €21900 MacGillycuddy's Reeks, Co Kerry (73x98cm-29x39in) s. board prov. 13-May-4 Sotheby's, London #104/R est:15000-20000
Sculpture
£1892 $3576 €2800 Woman in a garden (112x18cm-44x7in) wood carving. 17-Feb-4 Whyte's, Dublin #214/R est:1200-1500
Works on paper
£280 $465 €409 Boats and landscape (15x22cm-6x9in) s. mixed media. 1-Oct-3 John Ross, Belfast #9
£280 $465 €409 Seascape, West of Ireland (12x25cm-5x10in) s. mixed media. 1-Oct-3 John Ross, Belfast #53
£280 $521 €409 Palm trees (10x15cm-4x6in) s. mixed media. 3-Mar-4 John Ross, Belfast #234
£282 $505 €420 Sailing boat off the coast (12x20cm-5x8in) s. W/C. 31-May-4 Hamilton Osborne King, Dublin #208
£300 $498 €438 North Africa (9x33cm-4x13in) s. mixed media. 1-Oct-3 John Ross, Belfast #41
£320 $525 €467 Fishing boat (12x20cm-5x8in) s. mixed media. 4-Jun-3 John Ross, Belfast #38
£350 $581 €511 Trees near the Mournes (12x20cm-5x8in) s. pen ink W/C wash. 1-Oct-3 John Ross, Belfast #79
£350 $651 €511 Cottage and trees (17x30cm-7x12in) s. mixed media. 3-Mar-4 John Ross, Belfast #180
£403 $721 €600 Coastal Scene (13x24cm-5x9in) s. gouache. 31-May-4 Hamilton Osborne King, Dublin #171
£450 $747 €657 Out the window (25x33cm-10x13in) s. mixed media. 1-Oct-3 John Ross, Belfast #73
£497 $904 €750 Fisherman (21x25cm-8x10in) s. gouache board. 15-Jun-4 James Adam, Dublin #195/R
£500 $830 €730 Tall ships in the harbour (17x33cm-7x13in) s. mixed media. 1-Oct-3 John Ross, Belfast #77
£500 $830 €730 Clown (40x33cm-16x13in) s. mixed media. 1-Oct-3 John Ross, Belfast #145
£530 $964 €800 Figures in the desert (19x48cm-7x19in) s. gouache board two panels. 15-Jun-4 James Adam, Dublin #197/R
£550 $913 €803 Fishing boats in the harbour (22x22cm-9x9in) mono. mixed media. 1-Oct-3 John Ross, Belfast #198
£550 $990 €803 Sailing boats with blue mountain beyond (16x32cm-6x13in) s. gouache board. 20-Jan-4 Bonhams, Knightsbridge #277/R
£550 $985 €820 Lake landscape (33x50cm-13x20in) s. gouache. 31-May-4 Hamilton Osborne King, Dublin #65/R
£550 $985 €820 Figure by the shore (30x19cm-12x7in) s. gouache. 31-May-4 Hamilton Osborne King, Dublin #70/R
£580 $963 €847 Boats, Cork (20x56cm-8x22in) s. mixed media. 1-Oct-3 John Ross, Belfast #114
£592 $1089 €900 Watching the boats (20x30cm-8x12in) s. gouache. 22-Jun-4 De Veres Art Auctions, Dublin #239/R
£596 $1085 €900 Coastal landscape. s. gouache. 15-Jun-4 James Adam, Dublin #161/R
£600 $1116 €876 Moroccan landscape (10x40cm-4x16in) s. mixed media. 3-Mar-4 John Ross, Belfast #205
£625 $1150 €950 Edge of a village (16x28cm-6x11in) s. gouache prov. 22-Jun-4 De Veres Art Auctions, Dublin #256
£671 $1201 €1000 Study of a soldier (25x13cm-10x5in) s. gouache. 31-May-4 Hamilton Osborne King, Dublin #87/R
£700 $1281 €1022 Walking home (33x56cm-13x22in) s. mixed media. 2-Jun-4 John Ross, Belfast #33
£750 $1373 €1095 Watching the boat, Donegal (20x30cm-8x12in) s. mixed media. 2-Jun-4 John Ross, Belfast #162
£850 $1462 €1241 Clown (35x20cm-14x8in) s. mixed media. 3-Dec-3 John Ross, Belfast #26
£900 $1548 €1314 Clown with accordion (78x15cm-31x6in) s. mixed media. 3-Dec-3 John Ross, Belfast #117a
£900 $1548 €1314 The clown and Pierrot (56x40cm-22x16in) s. mixed media. 3-Dec-3 John Ross, Belfast #142b
£921 $1695 €1400 Village view (60x31cm-24x12in) s. gouache prov. 22-Jun-4 De Veres Art Auctions, Dublin #127/R
£921 $1695 €1400 At the circus (30x46cm-12x18in) s. gouache prov. 22-Jun-4 De Veres Art Auctions, Dublin #259
£950 $1701 €1387 Returning home (32x51cm-13x20in) s. gouache board. 14-May-4 Christie's, Kensington #418/R
£1000 $1830 €1460 Watching the boats (33x50cm-13x20in) s. mixed media. 2-Jun-4 John Ross, Belfast #242 est:750-850
£1100 $1892 €1606 Boats off the Galway coast (17x38cm-7x15in) s. mixed media. 3-Dec-3 John Ross, Belfast #32 est:800-1000
£1100 $1892 €1606 The clown with the doves (56x38cm-22x15in) s. mixed media. 3-Dec-3 John Ross, Belfast #142a est:900-1200
£1184 $2179 €1800 Celtic images (51x21cm-20x8in) s. gouache board. 22-Jun-4 De Veres Art Auctions, Dublin #186/R est:2000-3000
£1250 $2300 €1900 Houses in Morocco (41x51cm-16x20in) s. gouache board. 22-Jun-4 De Veres Art Auctions, Dublin #169/R est:2000-3000
£1342 $2403 €2000 Sailing boats on the shore (20x32cm-8x13in) gouache. 31-May-4 Hamilton Osborne King, Dublin #102/R est:800-1200
£1447 $2663 €2200 Clown (34x28cm-13x11in) s. gouache board. 22-Jun-4 De Veres Art Auctions, Dublin #172a est:1400-1800
£1549 $2479 €2200 Still life with melon and vase (52x33cm-20x13in) s. gouache board prov. 16-Sep-3 Whyte's, Dublin #221/R est:2000-2500

£1711 $3147 €2600 Two figures at a sea shore village (22x69cm-9x27in) s. gouache prov. 22-Jun-4 De Veres Art Auctions, Dublin #2/R est:2000-3000
£1733 $3137 €2600 Interior (49x32cm-19x13in) s. gouache. 30-Mar-4 De Veres Art Auctions, Dublin #1/R est:2500-3500
£1806 $2943 €2600 Mountain village (51x66cm-20x26in) gouache. 23-Sep-3 De Veres Art Auctions, Dublin #146 est:1500-2000
£1842 $3389 €2800 Cottages and lone figure (49x78cm-19x31in) s. gouache. 22-Jun-4 De Veres Art Auctions, Dublin #168/R est:3000-4000
£2013 $3564 €3000 Romantic Garbo (51x33cm-20x13in) s. i.verso gouache board prov. 27-Apr-4 Whyte's, Dublin #256/R est:2000-3000
£2098 $3566 €3000 Continental street scene (58x46cm-23x18in) s. gouache board. 18-Nov-3 Whyte's, Dublin #135/R est:3000-4000
£2148 $3801 €3200 Nude with basket of fruit (51x32cm-20x13in) s. gouache board. 27-Apr-4 Whyte's, Dublin #186/R est:2000-3000
£2148 $3844 €3200 Returning home (31x49cm-12x19in) gouache. 31-May-4 Hamilton Osborne King, Dublin #142/R est:2000-3000
£2254 $3606 €3200 Village with green roofed towers (30x50cm-12x20in) s. gouache board. 16-Sep-3 Whyte's, Dublin #222/R est:2500-3500
£2416 $4277 €3600 Shawlies, sailboats and seagulls (43x53cm-17x21in) s. gouache board. 27-Apr-4 Whyte's, Dublin #81/R est:2500-3500
£2500 $4650 €3650 Paris (48x58cm-19x23in) s. mixed media. 3-Mar-4 John Ross, Belfast #100 est:2000-3000
£2550 $4514 €3800 Street scene, Mediterranean town (33x51cm-13x20in) s. gouache board. 27-Apr-4 Whyte's, Dublin #248/R est:2500-3500
£2703 $5108 €4000 Tabletop still life (48x32cm-19x13in) s. gouache board. 17-Feb-4 Whyte's, Dublin #196/R est:2500-3500
£2703 $5108 €4000 Village with boats (30x46cm-12x18in) s. gouache on board. 17-Feb-4 Whyte's, Dublin #229/R est:4000-5000
£2819 $4989 €4200 Views on the Seine, Paris (17x24cm-7x9in) gouache board pair prov. 27-Apr-4 Whyte's, Dublin #8/R est:4000-6000
£2953 $5227 €4400 Watching sailboats from the shore (36x51cm-14x20in) s. gouache board. 27-Apr-4 Whyte's, Dublin #257/R est:2000-3000
£3067 $5551 €4600 Dancers (50x40cm-20x16in) s. gouache prov. 31-Mar-4 James Adam, Dublin #129/R est:3000-5000
£3200 $5312 €4672 Fishing village, West of Ireland (19x30cm-7x12in) s. mixed media. 1-Oct-3 John Ross, Belfast #58 est:1600-2000
£3600 $6588 €5256 Galway family (58x73cm-23x29in) s. mixed media. 2-Jun-4 John Ross, Belfast #68 est:3500-4000
£3851 $7279 €5700 Cottages and church from harvest field (33x51cm-13x20in) s. gouache on board. 17-Feb-4 Whyte's, Dublin #230/R est:3000-4000
£4196 $7133 €6000 Five men in hats (51x76cm-20x30in) s. gouache board. 18-Nov-3 Whyte's, Dublin #215/R est:6000-8000
£4225 $6761 €6000 Shawlies and rowing boats at village edge (50x74cm-20x29in) s. gouache board. 16-Sep-3 Whyte's, Dublin #130/R est:3000-4000
£5235 $9266 €7800 Homecoming (36x50cm-14x20in) s. gouache board. 27-Apr-4 Whyte's, Dublin #249/R est:2000-3000
£5467 $9895 €8200 Coastal landscape (51x99cm-20x39in) s. gouache board. 30-Mar-4 De Veres Art Auctions, Dublin #170/R est:5000-7000
£9028 $14715 €13000 Early spring, Ireland (43x71cm-17x28in) s. gouache board. 24-Sep-3 James Adam, Dublin #84/R est:3000-4000

ROBINSON, Matthias (fl.1856-1885) British
£420 $664 €609 Caught in the act (37x30cm-15x12in) init.d.66. 4-Sep-3 Christie's, Kensington #267/R

ROBINSON, Peter (1966-) New Zealander
£1071 $1939 €1564 Why pay less (20x29cm-8x11in) i. oil stick printed workshop catalogue. 30-Mar-4 Peter Webb, Auckland #14/R est:3000-4000 (NZ.D 3000)
£2068 $3515 €3019 Say mouldy' like in cheese (86x111cm-34x44in) acrylic. 26-Nov-3 Dunbar Sloane, Wellington #10/R est:4500-6500 (NZ.D 5500)
£2168 $3945 €3165 Weiss (50x40cm-20x16in) s.i.d.17.12.76 verso acrylic. 29-Jun-4 Peter Webb, Auckland #17/R est:5000-8000 (NZ.D 6200)
£3610 $5884 €5271 Composition with two aeroplanes (37x87cm-15x34in) paper triptych. 23-Sep-3 Peter Webb, Auckland #2/R est:5000-7000 (NZ.D 10000)
£5903 $9385 €8618 Whytes limited, trusted dealers for more than 150 years (103x146cm-41x57in) s.verso exhib. 1-May-3 Dunbar Sloane, Wellington #20/R est:12000-18000 (NZ.D 17000)

ROBINSON, Phyllis Hollands (20th C) American
£1534 $2500 €2240 London fog (61x91cm-24x36in) s. 28-Sep-3 Simpson's, Houston #229/R

ROBINSON, Ray Manderville (?) American?
£269 $500 €393 Bluebird. acrylic on board. 6-Mar-4 Page, Batavia #132
£269 $500 €393 Chipmunk standing tall. acrylic on board. 6-Mar-4 Page, Batavia #133

ROBINSON, Theodore (1852-1896) American
£2329 $3750 €3400 Portrait of a bull (13x15cm-5x6in) 20-Aug-3 James Julia, Fairfield #1002/R est:2000-3000
£56818 $100000 €82954 Grain field (41x51cm-16x20in) s. painted 1894 prov.exhib.lit. 19-May-4 Sotheby's, New York #34/R est:80000-120000
£406977 $700000 €594186 Washing day (46x56cm-18x22in) s. painted 1895 prov.exhib.lit. 3-Dec-3 Sotheby's, New York #22/R est:700000-900000
Works on paper
£16471 $28000 €24048 Red haired lady in an orchard (19x24cm-7x9in) s.d.1884 W/C over pencil prov.exhib.lit. 30-Oct-3 Phillips, New York #65/R est:30000-50000

ROBINSON, Thomas (?-1810) British
£1059 $1800 €1546 Orchard at Cajacet, Rhode Island landscape (50x76cm-20x30in) 21-Nov-3 Skinner, Boston #254/R est:1000-1200

ROBINSON, Thomas Harris (1835-1888) American
£2174 $4000 €3174 Horse pasture (51x76cm-20x30in) s. 27-Jun-4 Freeman, Philadelphia #106/R est:2000-3000

ROBINSON, William (19th C) British
£4043 $6872 €5903 Poppies (51x41cm-20x16in) s. painted c.1975. 26-Nov-3 Deutscher-Menzies, Melbourne #36/R est:14000-18000 (A.D 9500)
Works on paper
£540 $999 €788 Cheshire watermill (51x72cm-20x28in) s.d.1892 W/C. 14-Jul-4 Bonhams, Chester #336
£13115 $20721 €19148 The Twin Falls (54x74cm-21x29in) s.i.d.2000 pastel prov.exhib. 2-Sep-3 Deutscher-Menzies, Melbourne #83/R est:28000-34000 (A.D 32000)

ROBINSON, William Francis (1936-) Australian
£14463 $25599 €21116 Gums in the afternoon light (37x42cm-15x17in) s.d.92 prov. 3-May-4 Christie's, Melbourne #13/R est:35000-45000 (A.D 35000)
£16116 $28525 €23529 Flying fox landscape (56x66cm-22x26in) s. i.d.1989 verso prov. 3-May-4 Christie's, Melbourne #69/R est:40000-60000 (A.D 39000)
£45455 $84091 €66364 Canungra evening landscape (136x187cm-54x74in) s. prov. 15-Mar-4 Sotheby's, Melbourne #37/R est:120000-180000 (A.D 110000)
£45455 $80455 €66364 Farmyard construction (86x118cm-34x46in) s. lit. 3-May-4 Christie's, Melbourne #45/R est:120000-180000 (A.D 110000)
£61983 $114669 €90495 Botan Creek, rainforest 1989 (147x193cm-58x76in) s. prov.exhib. 10-Mar-4 Deutscher-Menzies, Melbourne #40/R est:170000-220000 (A.D 150000)
£63830 $108511 €93192 Birkdale farm with Jacaranda (91x118cm-36x46in) s. painted c.1983 prov. 25-Nov-3 Christie's, Melbourne #34a/R est:150000-200000 (A.D 150000)
£84746 $144068 €123729 Canyon Gorge from Springrook (138x183cm-54x72in) s.d.98 bears i.verso exhib. 24-Nov-3 Sotheby's, Melbourne #24/R est:200000-300000 (A.D 200000)
Prints
£1908 $3473 €2786 Blue pools (62x79cm-24x31in) s.i.d.2000 lithograph. 16-Jun-4 Deutscher-Menzies, Melbourne #440/R est:3500-4500 (A.D 5000)
Works on paper
£3244 $5905 €4736 Lattice verandah and striped tablecloth (40x54cm-16x21in) s. pastel. 16-Jun-4 Deutscher-Menzies, Melbourne #216/R est:7500-10000 (A.D 8500)
£3926 $6674 €5732 Pug on cane chair (62x46cm-24x18in) s. pastel executed c.1976. 29-Oct-3 Lawson Menzies, Sydney #25/R est:10000-15000 (A.D 9500)
£4472 $7020 €6484 Studies for the four seasons (73x54cm-29x21in) one s. W/C pencil pair. 26-Aug-3 Christie's, Sydney #263 est:5000-7000 (A.D 11000)
£5488 $9823 €8012 Morning, sun and mist (25x35cm-10x14in) s.d.98 i.verso pastel W/C pencil prov.exhib. 4-May-4 Sotheby's, Melbourne #172/R est:14000-18000 (A.D 13500)
£6489 $11809 €9474 Study for creation landscape (69x77cm-27x30in) s. pastel prov. 16-Jun-4 Deutscher-Menzies, Melbourne #67/R est:20000-30000 (A.D 17000)
£7724 $12126 €11200 Landscape (54x75cm-21x30in) s. pastel prov. 26-Aug-3 Christie's, Sydney #32/R est:20000-25000 (A.D 19000)

ROBINSON, William Heath (1872-1944) British
Works on paper
£700 $1211 €1022 Exceeding odious and hateful to thieves and robbers (55x38cm-22x15in) s. ink prov.exhib. 11-Dec-3 Sotheby's, London #307
£1200 $2160 €1752 Figures in a procession (23x26cm-9x10in) s. ink. 21-Apr-4 Tennants, Leyburn #1004 est:600-800
£1900 $3268 €2774 Noble U boat Commander sharing his rations with a famished hake (34x27cm-13x11in) s.i. pencil black ink lit. 3-Dec-3 Christie's, Kensington #264/R est:2000-3000
£2200 $3806 €3212 Jousting knight on horseback (26x16cm-10x6in) init. ink W/C prov.exhib. 11-Dec-3 Sotheby's, London #310/R est:2000-3000
£3000 $5190 €4380 Hans Andersen's Fairy Tales (34x25cm-13x10in) ink prov.exhib. 11-Dec-3 Sotheby's, London #308/R est:1500-2000
£3500 $6020 €5110 The check (38x28cm-15x11in) s.i. pencil black ink grey wash. 3-Dec-3 Christie's, Kensington #265/R est:700-900
£4000 $7200 €5840 Waterlow Park, Highgate (32x40cm-13x16in) s. i.verso pen ink W/C prov. 21-Apr-4 Tennants, Leyburn #1003/R est:1200-1500
£5500 $9515 €8030 The Devil he blew upon his nails, and the little devils ran (35x25cm-14x10in) s. ink W/C prov.exhib. 11-Dec-3 Sotheby's, London #311/R est:4000-6000

ROBINSON, William S (1861-1945) American
£3632 $6500 €5303 Biloxi, Mississippi (30x41cm-12x16in) s. i.d.1935 verso board. 6-May-4 Shannon's, Milford #179/R est:3000-5000

ROBINSON, William S (attrib) (1861-1945) American
£694 $1200 €1013 Barn near old Lyme, Connecticut (20x25cm-8x10in) board. 13-Dec-3 Charlton Hall, Columbia #525/R est:600-800

ROBINSON, William T (1852-?) American
£414 $750 €604 Sword fight (15x15cm-6x6in) s. panel. 16-Apr-4 James Julia, Fairfield #960/R
£647 $1100 €945 Chicken coop (35x43cm-14x17in) s. 21-Nov-3 Skinner, Boston #276/R est:500-700
£692 $1100 €1010 Winter marshes (27x44cm-11x17in) s. board. 12-Sep-3 Skinner, Boston #459/R

ROBITAILLE, Gilles (1954-) Canadian
£360 $659 €526 Quand la peche est terminee (60x90cm-24x35in) s.i. acrylic. 1-Jun-4 Hodgins, Calgary #79/R (C.D 900)

ROBJENT, Richard (1937-) British
Works on paper
£380 $654 €555 Brace of partridge (18x23cm-7x9in) s.d.1985 W/C pair. 3-Dec-3 Bonhams, Knightsbridge #27/R
£450 $774 €657 Grouse by a stream (30x40cm-12x16in) s. gouache. 3-Dec-3 Bonhams, Knightsbridge #20/R

ROBLES, Julian (1933-) American
£7821 $14000 €11419 Taming macaws of the Anasazi parrot clan AD1300 (107x142cm-42x56in) 15-May-4 Altermann Galleries, Santa Fe #134/R

ROBLIN, Richard (1940-) Canadian
£402 $747 €587 From the pink house series (170x137cm-67x54in) i.d.10/83 verso acrylic prov. 2-Mar-4 Ritchie, Toronto #198/R (C.D 1000)

ROBOZ, Zsuzsi (20th C) British/Hungarian

Works on paper			
£1300	$2171	€1898	Model (78x58cm-31x23in) s. pastel. 21-Oct-3 Bonhams, Knightsbridge #63b/R est:400-600

ROBSON, George Fennel (1788-1833) British

Works on paper			
£500	$920	€730	Richmond Castle (23x33cm-9x13in) s. W/C. 23-Mar-4 Anderson & Garland, Newcastle #288/R
£720	$1296	€1051	Pass of Aberglasyln, north Wales (18x26cm-7x10in) W/C over pencil. 21-Jan-4 Sotheby's, Olympia #108/R
£850	$1462	€1241	Cows grazing in a water meadow (43x63cm-17x25in) d.1823 pencil W/C. 3-Dec-3 Christie's, Kensington #117/R
£1400	$2562	€2044	LLangollen (24x36cm-9x14in) W/C. 7-Apr-4 Woolley & Wallis, Salisbury #130/R est:800-1200
£1800	$3312	€2628	Goats on a rocky outcrop above a highland glen (40x60cm-16x24in) W/C over pencil scratching out. 26-Mar-4 Sotheby's, London #127/R est:2000-3000
£2200	$3784	€3212	Estuary scene with drovers, cattle and stormy sky (66x91cm-26x36in) 3-Dec-3 Neal & Fletcher, Woodbridge #330/R est:800-1200
£2500	$4500	€3650	Harlech Castle with girl approaching doorway and sheep grazing nearby (48x70cm-19x28in) pencil W/C. 21-Apr-4 Tennants, Leyburn #915/R est:2500-3000

ROBUS, Hugo (1885-1964) American

Sculpture			
£1706	$2900	€2491	Spectator no.3. s.num.3/9 bronze. 9-Nov-3 Wright, Chicago #150 est:3000-4000

ROCA DELPECH COSTA, Santiago (20th C) Spanish

£671	$1248	€1000	Stage door (61x50cm-24x20in) s.d.76 s.i.d.1976 verso. 2-Mar-4 Ansorena, Madrid #880/R

ROCA SASTRE, Jose (1928-1997) Spanish

Works on paper			
£379	$683	€550	Landscape (31x46cm-12x18in) s.d.80 pastel. 26-Jan-4 Durán, Madrid #97/R

ROCA Y MARSAL, Pedro (?) Spanish

£423	$731	€600	View of Granada. canvas on cardboard. 15-Dec-3 Ansorena, Madrid #267/R

ROCA, Junn (1948-) American

£1471	$2500	€2148	Landscape (46x61cm-18x24in) s. masonite. 18-Nov-3 John Moran, Pasadena #145a est:1500-2500

ROCCA, Ketty la (1938-1976) Italian

Works on paper			
£4966	$8890	€7400	Disc thrower resting (25x58cm-10x23in) s.d.74 assemblage dr. 28-May-4 Farsetti, Prato #277/R est:3600-4000

ROCCA, Luigi (1952-) American

£2060	$3750	€3008	American diner pantry (100x99cm-39x39in) s. acrylic painted c.1995. 29-Jun-4 Sotheby's, New York #629/R est:2500-3500
£3022	$5500	€4412	Albert Kaufman auto repair truck (150x198cm-59x78in) s. acrylic painted c.1995. 29-Jun-4 Sotheby's, New York #628/R est:2500-3500

ROCCA, Michele (1670-1751) Italian

£6711	$12550	€10000	Annunciation (48x37cm-19x15in) exhib.lit. 29-Feb-4 Finarte, Venice #17/R est:10000-12000

ROCCA, Michele (attrib) (1670-1751) Italian

£4800	$8160	€7008	Massacre of the Innocents (48x80cm-19x31in) 31-Oct-3 Christie's, Kensington #129/R est:4000-6000
£6500	$11245	€9490	Offering of Abigail (116x87cm-46x34in) 10-Dec-3 Bonhams, New Bond Street #40/R est:5000-7000
£11333	$20287	€17000	Galateatriumphing (77x92cm-30x36in) 17-May-4 Finarte Semenzato, Rome #74/R est:12000-14000

ROCCATAGLIATA, Niccolo (attrib) (16/17th C) Italian

Sculpture			
£1528	$2429	€2200	Putto (19cm-7in) brown pat bronze. 9-Sep-3 Vanderkindere, Brussels #166/R
£2500	$3975	€3600	Putto (19cm-7in) brown pat bronze. 9-Sep-3 Vanderkindere, Brussels #164/R
£15541	$27351	€23000	Putti playing music (19cm-7in) gilt bronze marble base. 18-May-4 Sotheby's, Milan #432/R est:10000-15000

ROCCATI, Luigi (1906-1967) Italian

£567	$948	€800	Erbe Square, Verona (23x49cm-9x19in) s.d.1956 cardboard. 20-Oct-3 Sant Agostino, Torino #134/R
£567	$948	€800	Lamberti Tower, Verona (49x23cm-19x9in) s.d.1956 cardboard. 20-Oct-3 Sant Agostino, Torino #142/R
£709	$1184	€1000	Flowers (70x50cm-28x20in) s. board. 20-Oct-3 Sant Agostino, Torino #116/R
£748	$1339	€1100	From the window (63x49cm-25x19in) s.d.1946 tempera paper. 22-Mar-4 Sant Agostino, Torino #374/R
£828	$1382	€1200	Hill in Chieri (48x66cm-19x26in) s.d.1960 board. 17-Nov-3 Sant Agostino, Torino #122/R
£884	$1583	€1300	Morning in Ranello (30x60cm-12x24in) s. s.i.d.1960 verso. 22-Mar-4 Sant Agostino, Torino #352/R
£897	$1497	€1300	Still life (41x41cm-16x16in) s. card. 17-Nov-3 Sant Agostino, Torino #125/R
£966	$1612	€1400	Figure (67x47cm-26x19in) s. cardboard. 17-Nov-3 Sant Agostino, Torino #90/R
£1517	$2534	€2200	Square in Chieri (49x67cm-19x26in) s. board. 17-Nov-3 Sant Agostino, Torino #123/R est:1200-1600
Works on paper			
£426	$711	€600	Vase of flowers (58x38cm-23x15in) s. mixed media card. 20-Oct-3 Sant Agostino, Torino #115/R
£567	$948	€800	Landscape (46x67cm-18x26in) s. mixed media. 20-Oct-3 Sant Agostino, Torino #126/R

ROCCHI, Fortunato (1822-1909) Italian

£592	$1089	€900	Landscape (28x53cm-11x21in) s. board. 23-Jun-4 Finarte Semenzato, Rome #64/R

ROCCHI, Francesco de (1902-1978) Italian

£2754	$4516	€3800	Portrait of girl (51x34cm-20x13in) s. exhib. 27-May-3 Sotheby's, Milan #62/R est:3000
£3067	$5643	€4600	Sunset on Baveno Lake (50x59cm-20x23in) s.d.46 board. 8-Jun-4 Finarte Semenzato, Milan #454/R est:3000-3500
£4493	$7368	€6200	Venice (46x55cm-18x22in) s.d.46 prov. 27-May-3 Sotheby's, Milan #63/R est:4000
£5797	$9507	€8000	Sunset at the seaside (73x60cm-29x24in) s.d.36 board prov.exhib. 27-May-3 Sotheby's, Milan #183/R est:5000-7000
£6944	$10972	€10000	Sunset at the seaside (73x60cm-29x24in) board painted 1936. 6-Sep-3 Meeting Art, Vercelli #744 est:10000

ROCHART, Simon Jacques (1788-1872) French

Miniatures			
£4500	$8055	€6570	Arthur Wellesley, Duke of Wellington, wearing a red coat (9cm-4in) s.d.1815 gilt metal frame rec. 25-May-4 Christie's, London #189/R est:4000-6000
Works on paper			
£550	$1001	€803	Portrait of a girl in a white dress (31x23cm-12x9in) s.d.1840 W/C arched top. 1-Jul-4 Mellors & Kirk, Nottingham #694/R

ROCHAT, Alexandre (1895-1981) Swiss

£388	$694	€566	Village street (59x73cm-23x29in) s. i. stretcher. 12-May-4 Dobiaschofsky, Bern #911/R (S.FR 900)

ROCHE RABELL, Arnaldo (1955-) Puerto Rican

£22346	$40000	€32625	Flower lovers (150x210cm-59x83in) s.d.1989 prov. 26-May-4 Sotheby's, New York #129/R est:25000-30000

ROCHE, Alexander (1861-1921) British

£450	$828	€657	Summer (34x44cm-13x17in) s. board. 10-Jun-4 Lyon & Turnbull, Edinburgh #125
£780	$1435	€1139	An east neuk harbour (30x41cm-12x16in) s. 25-Mar-4 Bonhams, Edinburgh #380
£800	$1464	€1168	Greyhound Inn (26x33cm-10x13in) s. panel. 6-Jul-4 Bearnes, Exeter #515/R
£900	$1665	€1314	Wet day, St Monans (41x51cm-16x20in) s. 10-Mar-4 Sotheby's, Olympia #221/R est:1000-2000
£1000	$1790	€1460	The artist's studio (60x50cm-24x20in) s. 28-May-4 Lyon & Turnbull, Edinburgh #67/R est:1000-1500
£2000	$3620	€2920	Poplars in Jersey (27x36cm-11x14in) s. panel prov. 19-Apr-4 Sotheby's, London #48/R est:3000-4000

ROCHE, Alexis Louis (1891-1961) Swiss

£308	$524	€450	Voilier (38x46cm-15x18in) s.d.58 panel exhib. 5-Nov-3 Dobiaschofsky, Bern #905/R (S.FR 700)

ROCHE, Marcel (1890-1959) French

£483	$893	€700	Still life with apples and pears (32x54cm-13x21in) s. board. 14-Feb-4 Hans Stahl, Hamburg #80/R
£775	$1340	€1100	Fenetre fleurie sur le port (60x73cm-24x29in) s. 14-Dec-3 Eric Pillon, Calais #174/R
£1138	$1889	€1650	Bathers (28x36cm-11x14in) s. cardboard. 1-Oct-3 Millon & Associes, Paris #148/R

ROCHE, Walter (19th C) British

£400	$732	€584	Wooded river landscape (58x43cm-23x17in) s. 6-Jul-4 Bonhams, Knightsbridge #47/R
Sculpture			
£3200	$5536	€4672	Polo player (32cm-13in) s.d.1882 brown pat bronze. 12-Dec-3 Bracketts, Tunbridge Wells #727/R est:1800-2200

ROCHEGROSSE, Georges (1859-1938) French

£751	$1344	€1096	Salome (17x12cm-7x5in) wood panel prov. 15-May-4 Christie's, Sydney #390/R (A.D 1900)
£810	$1401	€1150	Gorges de Franchard (12x30cm-5x12in) s. panel. 13-Dec-3 Martinot & Savignat, Pontoise #229
£4225	$7310	€6000	Jeux d'enfant (17x27cm-7x11in) s. panel. 12-Dec-3 Artus Associes, Paris #152

ROCHELT AMANN, Juan Jose (1881-1953) Spanish

£2993	$5238	€4250	View of Toledo (54x68cm-21x27in) s. s.i.d.1942 verso. 16-Dec-3 Durán, Madrid #159/R est:4000
Works on paper			
£451	$736	€650	Arrabales de Bilbao (32x49cm-13x19in) s. pastel. 16-Jul-3 Durán, Madrid #59/R

ROCHER, Alexandre (1729-?) French
Works on paper
£1127 $1972 €1600 Pastoral scene (31x41cm-12x16in) s.d.1798 fo. card on panel. 17-Dec-3 Piasa, Paris #63 est:800-1000

ROCHER, Charles (1890-1962) French
£347 $641 €520 Cale dans un port Breton (55x46cm-22x18in) s.d.1925. 14-Jul-4 Livinec, Gaudcheau & Jezequel, Rennes #245

ROCHER, Ernest (1871-1938) French
£336 $617 €500 Vase garni de fleurs (65x50cm-26x20in) s. 23-Mar-4 Galerie Moderne, Brussels #162
£369 $679 €550 Nature morte aux cerises (30x40cm-12x16in) d.35 canvas on board. 23-Mar-4 Galerie Moderne, Brussels #231
£694 $1132 €1000 Still life. s. 23-Sep-3 Galerie Moderne, Brussels #709
£759 $1403 €1100 Meule (30x49cm-12x19in) studio st.verso canvas on panel. 16-Feb-4 Horta, Bruxelles #115

ROCHER, Maurice (1918-) French
£987 $1816 €1500 Marechale (65x50cm-26x20in) s. s.d.1979 verso prov. 27-Jun-4 Versailles Encheres #127/R est:1500-1800
£1974 $3632 €3000 Carmen 3 (130x97cm-51x38in) s. s.d.1984 verso prov.lit. 27-Jun-4 Versailles Encheres #126/R est:3000-4000

ROCHI, Alonso (1898-?) Spanish
£516 $857 €748 Jardin en la ciudad (98x110cm-39x43in) s.d.1956. 12-Jun-3 Louis Morton, Mexico #133/R est:2000-3000 (M.P 9000)

ROCHUSSEN, Charles (1814-1894) Dutch
£676 $1189 €1000 Biblical scene (60x74cm-24x29in) mono. 18-May-4 Galerie Moderne, Brussels #146
£1701 $3095 €2500 La terasse, elegant company on a terrace (20x26cm-8x10in) s.d.52 panel prov.lit. 3-Feb-4 Christie's, Amsterdam #125/R est:2000-3000
£2639 $4407 €3800 Falconry attended by Jacoba van Beijeren (27x37cm-11x15in) init.d.79 i.verso panel lit. 21-Oct-3 Sotheby's, Amsterdam #30/R est:4000-6000
£4000 $7200 €6000 Military exercise (31x48cm-12x19in) init.d.63 panel. 20-Apr-4 Sotheby's, Amsterdam #47/R est:4000-6000
£10000 $18000 €15000 Visit at the fair in Utrecht (92x170cm-36x67in) init.d.62 exhib.lit. 20-Apr-4 Sotheby's, Amsterdam #176/R est:25000-35000
Works on paper
£403 $741 €600 Royal troupe in flower garden (17x29cm-7x11in) mono. W/C. 29-Mar-4 Glerum, Amsterdam #125
£805 $1490 €1200 Military camp at Milligen (14x20cm-6x8in) init. W/C. 15-Mar-4 Sotheby's, Amsterdam #102/R est:1200-1600

ROCHUSSEN, Charles (attrib) (1814-1894) Dutch
£667 $1193 €1000 Soldiers in battle (35x53cm-14x21in) 11-May-4 Vendu Notarishuis, Rotterdam #56/R

ROCHUSSEN, Henri (1812-1889) Dutch
Works on paper
£403 $745 €600 Interior scene (34x28cm-13x11in) s. W/C. 15-Mar-4 Sotheby's, Amsterdam #71/R

ROCK, Geoffrey (1923-2000) Canadian
£290 $519 €423 The remaining leaves. s.i.verso board. 22-Mar-4 Mullucks Wells, Bishop's Stortford #494/R
£442 $822 €645 Sunday morning (61x50cm-24x20in) s. s.i.d.1981 verso board prov. 4-Mar-4 Heffel, Vancouver #38/R (C.D 1100)
£450 $765 €657 Still life, vase of flowers on a ledge (43x33cm-17x13in) s. board. 5-Nov-3 John Nicholson, Haslemere #545
£489 $812 €714 Untitled, wild flowers (60x50cm-24x20in) s. hard board prov. 5-Oct-3 Levis, Calgary #99/R (C.D 1100)
£1104 $2054 €1612 The open window (77x61cm-30x24in) s. s.d.1967 verso masonite prov. 4-Mar-4 Heffel, Vancouver #39/R est:2000-3000 (C.D 2750)

ROCKBURNE, Dorothea (1934-) Canadian
Works on paper
£824 $1500 €1203 Drawing which makes itself (76x101cm-30x40in) s. pencil. 29-Jun-4 Sotheby's, New York #474/R est:2000-3000
£1892 $3500 €2762 Curve (75x56cm-30x22in) s.i.d.91 pastel chl pencil. 12-Feb-4 Sotheby's, New York #156/R est:2500-3500

ROCKENSCHAUB, Gerwald (1952-) Austrian
£1099 $2000 €1605 Untitled (45x40cm-18x16in) init.d.85 verso oil metallic paint. 29-Jun-4 Sotheby's, New York #585/R est:3000-4000

ROCKLINE, Vera (1896-1934) American
£1879 $3326 €2800 Jeune femme endormie (54x74cm-21x29in) s. 29-Apr-4 Claude Aguttes, Neuilly #65 est:1500-1800
£14000 $25060 €20440 Reclining nude (54x73cm-21x29in) s. 26-May-4 Sotheby's, London #121/R est:7000-9000

ROCKMAN, Alexis (1962-) American
£1892 $3500 €2762 Insect politics (122x81cm-48x32in) s.i.d.1989 prov. 13-Jul-4 Christie's, Rockefeller NY #70/R est:2000-3000

ROCKMORE, Noel (1928-1995) American
£369 $650 €539 Portrait of Frank Bilodeaux (122x91cm-48x36in) s. acrylic painted c.1980. 23-May-4 Treadway Gallery, Cincinnati #655/R
£495 $900 €723 Stephanie Dinkins (102x76cm-40x30in) s.d.66 prov. 7-Feb-4 Neal Auction Company, New Orleans #503/R
£649 $1200 €948 Little girl on a small town street (38x53cm-15x21in) s.i.d.1964 panel. 17-Jan-4 New Orleans Auction, New Orleans #746/R est:1000-1500
£706 $1200 €1031 Female nude (61x41cm-24x16in) s.d.69 masonite prov. 22-Nov-3 New Orleans Auction, New Orleans #1247 est:1500-2500
£919 $1700 €1342 Portrait of Jim Robinson (25x20cm-10x8in) s. oil goldleaf masonite. 17-Jul-4 New Orleans Auction, New Orleans #879/R est:1000-1500
£919 $1700 €1342 Gunfire, Percy Humphrey and Frank Demond (56x71cm-22x28in) s.d.79. 17-Jul-4 New Orleans Auction, New Orleans #880/R est:800-1200
£1145 $1900 €1672 Dizzy Gillespie (30x30cm-12x12in) s.i.d.62. 4-Oct-3 Neal Auction Company, New Orleans #597/R est:3000-5000
£1163 $2000 €1698 Stovall son (33x18cm-13x7in) s.i.d.69 masonite prov. 6-Dec-3 Neal Auction Company, New Orleans #605 est:1000-1500
£1202 $2200 €1755 Self portrait with life support (76x122cm-30x48in) s.d.84 i.verso. 5-Jun-4 Neal Auction Company, New Orleans #427/R est:3500-5000
£1381 $2500 €2016 Voodoo ceremony (99x145cm-39x57in) s.d.1983 i.verso. 3-Apr-4 Neal Auction Company, New Orleans #543/R est:3000-5000
£1625 $2600 €2373 Woman of Cairo (61x61cm-24x24in) s.d.90 i.verso. 20-Sep-3 New Orleans Auction, New Orleans #899/R
£1807 $3000 €2638 Bill Russell and Pretty Baby (102x76cm-40x30in) s.i.d.66 prov. 4-Oct-3 Neal Auction Company, New Orleans #599/R est:3000-5000
£3243 $6000 €4735 All Saints Day (102x127cm-40x50in) s.i. 17-Jul-4 New Orleans Auction, New Orleans #877/R est:1800-2500

ROCKSTUHL, Alois Gustav (1798-1877) Russian
Miniatures
£4200 $7266 €6132 Young lady (7cm-3in) s. gold mount oval. 9-Dec-3 Christie's, London #261/R est:2000-3000
£6000 $10380 €8760 Paul I, Tsar of Russia. Tsarina Maria Feodorovna (11cm-4in) i.d.1872 gilt-metal frame oval pair. 9-Dec-3 Christie's, London #250/R est:3000-4000

ROCKWELL, Augustus (1822-1882) American
£629 $1000 €918 Still life with trout (46x91cm-18x36in) 12-Sep-3 Skinner, Boston #259/R

ROCKWELL, Cleveland (1837-1907) American
£1056 $1700 €1542 Ohio winter (28x43cm-11x17in) s. board prov. 24-Feb-3 O'Gallerie, Oregon #825/R est:3000-5000
£2581 $4750 €3768 Mount Rainier from the Puyallup River Indian Trail (30x45cm-12x18in) s. i.verso painted 1886. 8-Jun-4 Bonhams & Butterfields, San Francisco #4119/R est:3000-5000

ROCKWELL, Norman (1894-1978) American
£11976 $20000 €17485 Head studies of a girl, Peggy Best sketch class (88x82cm-35x32in) s. lit. 9-Oct-3 Christie's, Rockefeller NY #100/R est:8000-12000
£17045 $30000 €24886 Hot mill (58x51cm-23x20in) init. canvas on masonite prov.lit. 19-May-4 Sotheby's, New York #184/R est:20000-30000
£34884 $60000 €50931 Look, mom--no cavities! (28x28cm-11x11in) s. painted c.1957 prov.lit. 3-Dec-3 Sotheby's, New York #156/R est:25000-35000
Works on paper
£2471 $4250 €3608 St Nicholas (10x8cm-4x3in) s.d.1918 gouache. 7-Dec-3 Treadway Gallery, Cincinnati #593/R est:2000-3000
£3488 $6000 €5092 St Nicholas (10x8cm-4x3in) s.d.1918 gouache. 7-Dec-3 Treadway Gallery, Cincinnati #594/R est:2000-3000
£3704 $6000 €5371 Gift (16x13cm-6x5in) mono.i. dr. prov.lit. 8-Aug-3 Barridorf, Portland #273/R est:6000-9000
£8000 $14000 €11680 Study for a family tree (20x35cm-8x14in) s.i. verso chl paper on board three prov. 19-Dec-3 Sotheby's, New York #1151a/R est:3000-5000
£8649 $16000 €12628 Seasons (37x25cm-15x10in) init. pencil prov. 11-Mar-4 Christie's, Rockefeller NY #86/R est:12000-18000
£9659 $17000 €14102 Washington Bicentennial (20x20cm-8x8in) s. pencil exec c.1970s prov.lit. 19-May-4 Sotheby's, New York #183/R est:8000-12000
£19886 $35000 €29034 Spirit of 76 (36x28cm-14x11in) s. pencil exec 1975 prov.lit. 19-May-4 Sotheby's, New York #182/R est:15000-25000

ROCQUE, Georges la (19th C) French
Works on paper
£267 $477 €400 Le rapport (10x15cm-4x6in) W/C wash ink. 12-May-4 Coutau Begarie, Paris #93/R

RODA, Leonardo (1868-1933) Italian
£662 $1205 €1000 Seascape with fishermen (30x47cm-12x19in) s. board. 17-Jun-4 Finarte Semenzato, Milan #281/R est:1000-1500
£1633 $2922 €2400 Pasture (32x48cm-13x19in) s. board. 22-Mar-4 Sant Agostino, Torino #250/R est:2500
£1633 $2922 €2400 Alpine pasture (32x48cm-13x19in) s. board. 22-Mar-4 Sant Agostino, Torino #252/R est:2500
£1748 $2920 €2500 Mount Cervino (32x48cm-13x19in) s.d.1911 board. 26-Jun-3 Sant Agostino, Torino #69/R est:3000
£1806 $3069 €2600 Trees in bloom (32x48cm-13x19in) s.d.1920. 1-Nov-3 Meeting Art, Vercelli #95/R est:2000
£1806 $3069 €2600 Pasture (32x48cm-13x19in) s.d.1920 board lit. 1-Nov-3 Meeting Art, Vercelli #327/R est:2000
£1844 $3079 €2600 Mount Cervino (63x47cm-25x19in) s. cardboard. 20-Oct-3 Sant Agostino, Torino #86/R est:2200
£1944 $3306 €2800 Mountainous landscape (33x18cm-13x7in) s.d.919 cardboard. 29-Oct-3 Il Ponte, Milan #513
£2533 $4661 €3800 Mount Cervino (31x46cm-12x18in) s. board. 14-Jun-4 Sant Agostino, Torino #203/R est:1500-2000
£2667 $4907 €4000 Blooming rhododendrons in the muntains (50x85cm-20x33in) s. 14-Jun-4 Sant Agostino, Torino #290/R est:2200-2800
£2837 $4738 €4000 Mount Cervino (62x80cm-24x31in) s. 20-Oct-3 Sant Agostino, Torino #99/R est:2400
£2953 $5227 €4400 Seascape (48x64cm-19x25in) s. cardboard. 1-May-4 Meeting Art, Vercelli #114 est:4000
£3000 $5520 €4500 Rhododendrons (50x85cm-20x33in) s. 14-Jun-4 Sant Agostino, Torino #202/R est:2800

£3356	$5940	€5000	Mount Blanc, Courmayeur (70x100cm-28x39in) s. lit. 1-May-4 Meeting Art, Vercelli #458 est:5000
£4167	$7083	€6000	Mountain lake (60x80cm-24x31in) s. 1-Nov-3 Meeting Art, Vercelli #213/R est:5000
£4514	$7674	€6500	Last snow (63x78cm-25x31in) s.d.1926. 1-Nov-3 Meeting Art, Vercelli #440/R est:5000
£5172	$8586	€7500	Cottages and poppies (80x102cm-31x40in) s. 1-Oct-3 Della Rocca, Turin #58a
£6000	$11040	€9000	Peak (60x130cm-24x51in) s. 14-Jun-4 Sant Agostino, Torino #289/R est:3500-4500
£6159	$10101	€8500	Mountainous landscape of with Mount Cervino (140x100cm-55x39in) s. 27-May-3 Finarte Semenzato, Milan #1/R est:6000-7000
£6944	$11806	€10000	Mount Blanc (70x101cm-28x40in) s. 1-Nov-3 Meeting Art, Vercelli #233/R est:10000
£7333	$13493	€11000	Pasture in the mountains (119x169cm-47x67in) s. 8-Jun-4 Sotheby's, Milan #57/R est:3000-5000
£8054	$14255	€12000	Sledge (100x140cm-39x55in) s.d.1920. 1-May-4 Meeting Art, Vercelli #255 est:10000

RODAKOWSKI, Henryk (1823-1894) Polish

£1441	$2622	€2104	Landscape with river and hills (29x34cm-11x13in) painted c.1878-1889. 20-Jun-4 Agra, Warsaw #42/R (P.Z 10000)

RODCHENKO, Alexander (1891-1956) Russian

Photographs

£1587	$3000	€2317	Factory kitchen, caldron, 1931 (23x30cm-9x12in) gelatin silver print. 17-Feb-4 Christie's, Rockefeller NY #344/R est:7000-9000
£1587	$3000	€2317	Ball bearing plant, female worker at a workbench, 1932 (29x20cm-11x8in) gelatin silver print. 17-Feb-4 Christie's, Rockefeller NY #350/R est:10000-15000
£1693	$3200	€2472	Botanical Garden, tropical leaves floating on water, 1929 (15x22cm-6x9in) gelatin silver print. 17-Feb-4 Christie's, Rockefeller NY #319/R est:6000-8000
£1693	$3200	€2472	Children's village in Sokolniki Park, 1932 (18x24cm-7x9in) gelatin silver print. 17-Feb-4 Christie's, Rockefeller NY #329/R est:7000-9000
£1852	$3500	€2704	Firemen being dispatched, 1932 (17x29cm-7x11in) gelatin silver print. 17-Feb-4 Christie's, Rockefeller NY #295/R est:8000-10000
£1852	$3500	€2704	Portrait, 1931 (24x17cm-9x7in) gelatin silver print. 17-Feb-4 Christie's, Rockefeller NY #310/R est:10000-15000
£1852	$3500	€2704	Monkeys, 1932 (19x29cm-7x11in) gelatin silver print. 17-Feb-4 Christie's, Rockefeller NY #323/R est:8000-10000
£1852	$3500	€2704	Factory canteen, dinner, 1931 (19x30cm-7x12in) gelatin silver print. 17-Feb-4 Christie's, Rockefeller NY #349/R est:7000-9000
£1957	$3209	€2700	Moges (17x23cm-7x9in) i. verso vintage silver gelatin lit. 30-May-3 Villa Grisebach, Berlin #1332/R est:2500-3500
£2116	$4000	€3089	Bears, 1932 (30x24cm-12x9in) gelatin silver print. 17-Feb-4 Christie's, Rockefeller NY #325/R est:8000-10000
£2116	$4000	€3089	Petrovskii Park, new buildings, Dynamo Stadium District, 1932 (29x20cm-11x8in) gelatin silver print. 17-Feb-4 Christie's, Rockefeller NY #309/R est:8000-10000
£2222	$4200	€3244	Boulevard, Alley, 1932 (29x23cm-11x9in) gelatin silver print. 17-Feb-4 Christie's, Rockefeller NY #317/R est:8000-10000
£2222	$4200	€3244	Transportation of goods, 1932 (24x29cm-9x11in) gelatin silver print. 17-Feb-4 Christie's, Rockefeller NY #337/R est:5000-7000
£2381	$4500	€3476	Dynamo stadium, tennis. 1932 (23x29cm-9x11in) gelatin silver print. 17-Feb-4 Christie's, Rockefeller NY #300/R est:20000-30000
£2381	$4500	€3476	Zoo, pelicans and giraffes (41x29cm-16x11in) gelatin silver print diptych. 17-Feb-4 Christie's, Rockefeller NY #322/R est:18000-22000
£2381	$4500	€3476	Factory kitchen, at the caldron, 1931 (24x30cm-9x12in) gelatin silver print. 17-Feb-4 Christie's, Rockefeller NY #345/R est:6000-8000
£2381	$4500	€3476	Rusakov club auditorium, 1929 (29x19cm-11x7in) gelatin silver print. 17-Feb-4 Christie's, Rockefeller NY #355/R est:10000-15000
£2646	$5000	€3863	Arbat, bus station, 1932 (23x29cm-9x11in) gelatin silver print. 17-Feb-4 Christie's, Rockefeller NY #312/R est:10000-15000
£2646	$5000	€3863	Portrait of a boy, 1932 (29x23cm-11x9in) gelatin silver print. 17-Feb-4 Christie's, Rockefeller NY #326/R est:7000-9000
£2646	$5000	€3863	Interior of an apartment in the Ginsburg building on Novinskii Boulevard, 1932 (23x30cm-9x12in) gelatin silver print. 17-Feb-4 Christie's, Rockefeller NY #331/R est:8000-10000
£2646	$5000	€3863	Milk union, bottling milk, 1929 (27x23cm-11x9in) gelatin silver print. 17-Feb-4 Christie's, Rockefeller NY #348/R est:5000-7000
£2910	$5500	€4249	By the banner, pioneer camp named after the third definitive, 1930 (29x22cm-11x9in) gelatin silver print. 17-Feb-4 Christie's, Rockefeller NY #298/R est:15000-20000
£2910	$5500	€4249	Watering streets, 1929 (24x29cm-9x11in) gelatin silver print. 17-Feb-4 Christie's, Rockefeller NY #333/R est:7000-9000
£3175	$6000	€4636	Street paving, constructing pavement on the Leningrad Highway, 1929 (24x18cm-9x7in) gelatin silver print. 17-Feb-4 Christie's, Rockefeller NY #332/R est:12000-18000
£3439	$6500	€5021	Demonstration near Miasnitskaia Gate (230x23cm-91x9in) gelatin silver print. 17-Feb-4 Christie's, Rockefeller NY #291/R est:20000-30000
£3439	$6500	€5021	Moges, Moscow electric station, 1929 (18x29cm-7x11in) gelatin silver print. 17-Feb-4 Christie's, Rockefeller NY #336/R est:25000-35000
£3704	$7000	€5408	Draftsmen, 1932 (29x24cm-11x9in) gelatin silver print. 17-Feb-4 Christie's, Rockefeller NY #314/R est:10000-15000
£3968	$7500	€5793	Mayday demonstration on Miasnitskaia Street (29x20cm-11x8in) gelatin silver print. 17-Feb-4 Christie's, Rockefeller NY #290/R est:30000-40000
£3968	$7500	€5793	Dynamo stadium, sports parade, 1932 (24x29cm-9x11in) gelatin silver print. 17-Feb-4 Christie's, Rockefeller NY #304/R est:25000-35000
£3968	$7500	€5793	Dynamo Water Stadium on the Moscoe River, boats and dock, 1932 (24x29cm-9x11in) gelatin silver print. 17-Feb-4 Christie's, Rockefeller NY #306/R est:15000-20000
£3968	$7500	€5793	Ginsburg building on Novinskii Boulevard (24x29cm-9x11in) gelatin silver print. 17-Feb-4 Christie's, Rockefeller NY #315/R est:20000-30000
£4233	$8000	€6180	Orchestra, 1932 (23x30cm-9x12in) gelatin silver print. 17-Feb-4 Christie's, Rockefeller NY #299/R est:10000-15000
£4233	$8000	€6180	Dynamo stadium, grandstand, 1932 (29x22cm-11x9in) gelatin silver print. 17-Feb-4 Christie's, Rockefeller NY #303/R est:25000-35000
£4762	$9000	€6953	Central Park of culture and leisure, Alley, 1932 (23x29cm-9x11in) gelatin silver print. 17-Feb-4 Christie's, Rockefeller NY #318/R est:15000-20000
£4762	$9000	€6953	Man with a cap, 1932 (17x23cm-7x9in) gelatin silver print collage. 17-Feb-4 Christie's, Rockefeller NY #342/R est:18000-22000
£5291	$10000	€7725	Winter, Teatralnaia Square, 1931 (22x30cm-9x12in) gelatin silver print. 17-Feb-4 Christie's, Rockefeller NY #293/R est:18000-22000
£5291	$10000	€7725	On the boulevard, 1932 (48x30cm-19x12in) gelatin silver print diptych. 17-Feb-4 Christie's, Rockefeller NY #343/R est:12000-18000
£5820	$11000	€8497	Reading hall of the Lenin Library, 1932 (30x24cm-12x9in) gelatin silver print. 17-Feb-4 Christie's, Rockefeller NY #357/R est:20000-30000
£6878	$13000	€10042	Viewing firemen on Red Square, 1932 (24x29cm-9x11in) gelatin silver print. 17-Feb-4 Christie's, Rockefeller NY #294/R est:25000-35000
£6878	$13000	€10042	Pushkin Square, 1932 (30x24cm-12x9in) gelatin silver print. 17-Feb-4 Christie's, Rockefeller NY #334/R est:20000-30000
£7407	$14000	€10814	Column of dynamo sport society members, 1932 (24x29cm-9x11in) gelatin silver print. 17-Feb-4 Christie's, Rockefeller NY #302/R est:20000-30000
£7407	$14000	€10814	Dynamo Water Stadium, diving, 1932 (29x23cm-11x9in) gelatin silver print. 17-Feb-4 Christie's, Rockefeller NY #305/R est:25000-35000
£7937	$15000	€11588	Sports parade on Red Square, 1930 (23x30cm-9x12in) gelatin silver print. 17-Feb-4 Christie's, Rockefeller NY #292/R est:20000-30000
£7937	$15000	€11588	Column of Dynamo sport society members moving towards Red Square, 1932 (24x30cm-9x12in) gelatin silver print. 17-Feb-4 Christie's, Rockefeller NY #301/R est:25000-35000
£8466	$16000	€12360	Planetarium building, projector made by Zeiss, 1932 (43x29cm-17x11in) gelatin silver print. 17-Feb-4 Christie's, Rockefeller NY #338/R est:50000-70000
£8466	$16000	€12360	Arbat, street traffic, 1932 (23x30cm-9x12in) gelatin silver print. 17-Feb-4 Christie's, Rockefeller NY #352/R est:10000-15000
£8466	$16000	€12360	Student campus in Lefortovom new buildings (42x29cm-17x11in) gelatin silver print. 17-Feb-4 Christie's, Rockefeller NY #353/R est:50000-70000
£8466	$16000	€12360	Holiday illumination, May 1 1932, Bolshoi Theater at night (42x29cm-17x11in) gelatin silver print. 17-Feb-4 Christie's, Rockefeller NY #359/R est:60000-80000
£10053	$19000	€14677	Izvestiia building, Editorial headquarters of the Izvestiia newspaper, 1932 (24x30cm-9x12in) gelatin silver print. 17-Feb-4 Christie's, Rockefeller NY #313/R est:15000-20000
£10582	$20000	€15450	Radio listener, 1929 (24x29cm-9x11in) gelatin silver print. 17-Feb-4 Christie's, Rockefeller NY #330/R est:18000-22000
£12698	$24000	€18539	Pushkin Square, Mayday Illumination, Tverskaia, 1932 (42x29cm-17x11in) gelatin silver print. 17-Feb-4 Christie's, Rockefeller NY #360/R est:70000-90000
£13228	$25000	€19313	Morning exerise. lefortovo student campus, 1932 (15x23cm-6x9in) gelatin silver print two. 17-Feb-4 Christie's, Rockefeller NY #296/R est:60000-80000
£15569	$26000	€22731	Mother (25x19cm-10x7in) s.i. gelatin silver print exec.1924 prov.lit. 17-Oct-3 Phillips, New York #11/R est:20000-30000
£15873	$30000	€23175	Metro, Mayady illumination, 1932 (25x29cm-10x11in) gelatin silver print. 17-Feb-4 Christie's, Rockefeller NY #358/R est:30000-40000
£16766	$28000	€24478	Pine trees in Puschkino (21x15cm-8x6in) i.verso gelatin silver print exec. 1927 prov.lit. 17-Oct-3 Phillips, New York #12/R est:8000-12000

Works on paper

£10490	$18042	€15000	Composition (15x11cm-6x4in) W/C pen Indian ink prov.exhib. 5-Dec-3 Ketterer, Munich #99/R est:15000-18000
£50667	$92720	€76000	Untitled - abstract composition (33x20cm-13x8in) s.cyrillic d.1918 W/C gouache Indian ink on pencil prov. 5-Jun-4 Lempertz, Koln #970/R est:50000-70000

RODDE, Karl Gustav (1830-1906) German

£590	$962	€850	Italian country road in evening (72x94cm-28x37in) s. 26-Sep-3 Bolland & Marotz, Bremen #602/R
£872	$1605	€1300	Shepherd in extensive Westphalian landscape (77x114cm-30x45in) s.d.1856. 26-Mar-4 Bolland & Marotz, Bremen #580/R
£1172	$1957	€1711	Summer landscape (23x18cm-9x7in) s.d.29 cardboard. 19-Oct-3 Agra, Warsaw #47/R est:5000 (P.Z 7500)
£1563	$2609	€2282	Wintry landscape with sunset (23x18cm-9x7in) s. cardboard. 19-Oct-3 Agra, Warsaw #38/R est:5000 (P.Z 10000)
£1733	$3155	€2600	Travellers on a country road in an extensive landscape (100x125cm-39x49in) s. 1-Jul-4 Van Ham, Cologne #1575/R est:1400

RODDE, Michel (1913-) French

£304	$575	€450	Paysage (50x100cm-20x39in) s. 21-Feb-4 Cornette de St.Cyr, Paris #220
£353	$600	€515	Coastal scene (53x46cm-21x18in) s. prov. 22-Nov-3 Jackson's, Cedar Falls #396/R

RODE, Edmund (1876-1965) German

£4362	$7809	€6500	Children holding pots of flowers (40x32cm-16x13in) s. 27-May-4 Dorotheum, Vienna #25/R est:6500-7500
£7383	$13215	€11000	Children playing (56x69cm-22x27in) s. 27-May-4 Dorotheum, Vienna #187/R est:9000-12000

RODE, Godfred (1862-1937) Danish

£379	$607	€553	Cattle by stones (75x125cm-30x49in) init.d.1918 exhib. 22-Sep-3 Rasmussen, Vejle #305 (D.KR 4000)

RODECK, Karl (1841-1909) Dutch

£462	$794	€660	River, boot and town under full moon (52x41cm-20x16in) s. 6-Dec-3 Hans Stahl, Toestorf #88/R
£633	$1146	€950	Moonlit scene with house on shore and fishing boats (47x65cm-19x26in) s. 3-Apr-4 Hans Stahl, Hamburg #73/R

RODENBERG, Carla (1941-) Dutch

£274	$466	€400	Portrait of a young man (120x90cm-47x35in) s.d.79. 5-Nov-3 Vendue Huis, Gravenhage #512/R

RODER, Endre (1933-) British/Hungarian

£650	$1196	€949	Younger sister (90x90cm-35x35in) s. oil on plywood. 29-Mar-4 Bonhams, Bath #50/R

RODER, Paul (1897-1958) German?

£590	$986	€850	Hallig (61x81cm-24x32in) s.i.d. 24-Oct-3 Ketterer, Hamburg #219/R

RODGER, George (1908-1995) British

Photographs

£5000	$9000	€7300	Victorious Nubian wrestler (25x18cm-10x7in) i. gelatin silver print. 24-Apr-4 Phillips, New York #13/R est:4000-6000

RODGERS, Emma (20th C) British

Sculpture

£3200	$5952	€4672	Bull (40x45x20cm-16x18x8in) bronze. 8-Mar-4 Christie's, London #10

RODGERS, Patsy Dan (20th C) Irish

£642	$1213	€950	Tory Lighthouse (47x47cm-19x19in) s.i. board. 17-Feb-4 Whyte's, Dublin #112
£1149	$2171	€1700	Gale force nine, Tory Island (46x60cm-18x24in) s. i. board. 17-Feb-4 Whyte's, Dublin #111/R est:1500-2000

RODHE, Lennart (1916-) Swedish

£549	$973	€802	Composition (20x26cm-8x10in) mono.d.79-01-26. 27-Apr-4 AB Stockholms Auktionsverk #676/R (S.KR 7500)
£2644	$4494	€3860	Landscape (39x47cm-15x19in) mono.d.45 panel prov. 5-Nov-3 AB Stockholms Auktionsverk #777/R est:40000-50000 (S.KR 35000)
£4230	$7190	€6176	DN (30x49cm-12x19in) mono. sketch. 4-Nov-3 Bukowskis, Stockholm #237a/R est:40000-50000 (S.KR 56000)
£5495	$9725	€8023	The orchard (98x80cm-39x31in) mono. tempera collage panel painted c.1956 prov.lit. 27-Apr-4 AB Stockholms Auktionsverk #757/R est:50000-60000 (S.KR 75000)

Works on paper

£415	$706	€606	The orchard (11x27cm-4x11in) mono.d.1955 gouache. 5-Nov-3 AB Stockholms Auktionsverk #783/R (S.KR 5500)
£566	$963	€826	Composition (50x40cm-20x16in) mono. gouache. 5-Nov-3 AB Stockholms Auktionsverk #785/R (S.KR 7500)
£2115	$3595	€3088	Movement (10x15cm-4x6in) mono. W/C. 4-Nov-3 Bukowskis, Stockholm #231/R est:5000-6000 (S.KR 28000)

RODIN, A (1840-1917) French

Sculpture

£4500	$8055	€6570	Le lion qui pleure. s.i.d.1881 i.verso green pat bronze lit. 21-Mar-4 Desmond Judd, Cranbrook #652

RODIN, Auguste (1840-1917) French

Sculpture

£1007	$1862	€1500	Saint Jean Baptiste (10cm-4in) s. pat bronze. 14-Mar-4 Eric Pillon, Calais #44/R
£1399	$2406	€2000	Le penseur (36cm-14in) s.num.477 black brown green pat bronze marble base. 6-Dec-3 Dannenberg, Berlin #254/R est:2000
£2151	$4000	€3140	Reverend Pere Julien Eymard (15x11x11cm-6x4x4in) bronze st.f.Alexis Rudier. 2-Mar-4 Swann Galleries, New York #578/R est:5000-8000
£2395	$4000	€3497	Petite tete de femme (6cm-2in) s. bronze edition 8 of 10 prov. 7-Oct-3 Sotheby's, New York #253 est:3000-5000
£2667	$4773	€4000	Buste de Suzon (46cm-18in) s. dark pat bronze red marble socle. 11-May-4 Vanderkindere, Brussels #484/R est:5000-7500
£3497	$5839	€5000	Buste de Suzon (25cm-10in) s. medaille pat bronze. 13-Oct-3 Horta, Bruxelles #118/R est:6200-8700
£4342	$7859	€6600	Buste de Suzon (24cm-9in) s. medaille pat bronze sold with marble socle. 19-Apr-4 Horta, Bruxelles #125/R est:4000-6000
£4500	$8280	€6570	Buste de Jacques de Wissant, esquisse pour la tete (11cm-4in) i. dark green pat bronze st.f.Georges Rudier prov. 24-Mar-4 Sotheby's, Olympia #25/R est:3000-5000
£4895	$8322	€7000	La resurrection d'Adonis (22x38x18cm-9x15x7in) s. plaster exhib.lit. 18-Nov-3 Pierre Berge, Paris #96/R est:8000-10000
£5294	$9000	€7729	Henri Becque (15cm-6in) i. blk pat bronze Cast Alexis Rudier prov.lit. 6-Nov-3 Sotheby's, New York #102/R est:6000-8000
£6471	$11000	€9448	Suzon (27cm-11in) i. brown pat bronze Cast Bruxelles lit. 6-Nov-3 Sotheby's, New York #101/R est:10000-15000
£6471	$11000	€9448	Fille pleurante (20cm-8in) i. blk pat bronze conceived 1885 Cast Alexis Rudier prov.lit. 6-Nov-3 Sotheby's, New York #107/R est:6000-8000
£6993	$11888	€10000	Petite tete de damnee (9cm-4in) s. pat bronze Cast Rudier prov. 21-Nov-3 Lombrail & Teucquam, Paris #58/R est:1500-2000
£7000	$12740	€10220	Suzon (39cm-15in) i. bronze prov. 4-Feb-4 Sotheby's, London #221/R est:8000-12000
£7059	$12000	€10306	Pleureuse (20cm-8in) raised sig.i. brown pat bronze Cast A.Rudier prov.lit. 6-Nov-3 Sotheby's, New York #128/R est:6000-8000
£7186	$12000	€10492	Eternelle idole, femme seule (17cm-7in) s.num.6 bronze edition of 12 st.f.Georges Rudier prov. 7-Oct-3 Sotheby's, New York #251 est:6000-8000
£7821	$14000	€11419	Mouvement de danse C (26cm-10in) s.d.1956 num.11 brown green pat bronze conceived c.1911 prov.lit. 5-May-4 Christie's, Rockefeller NY #262/R est:15000-20000
£8000	$14560	€11680	Petite main gauche (5cm-2in) s. dark brown pat bronze exec. c.1890-1900 prov. 3-Feb-4 Christie's, London #105/R est:8000-12000
£8021	$15000	€11711	Suzon (40cm-16in) s.st.f.Cie des Bronzes pat bronze lit. 25-Feb-4 Christie's, Rockefeller NY #24/R est:18000-25000
£8939	$16000	€13051	Buste de Balzac, etude type C (16cm-6in) s. i.f.A Rudier blk pat bronze conceived c.1893 prov.lit. 5-May-4 Christie's, Rockefeller NY #267/R est:20000-30000
£9231	$15877	€13477	Buste d'homme de l'Eternel Printemps (73cm-29in) s. dark green pat.bronze incl. black stone socle. 3-Dec-3 AB Stockholms Auktionsverk #2642/R est:60000-70000 (S.KR 120000)
£9333	$17173	€14000	Suzon (44cm-17in) s. golden pat bronze incl. marble base. 14-Jun-4 Horta, Bruxelles #163/R est:8000-12000
£10280	$17476	€14700	Visage de femme (20cm-8in) terracotta prov.lit. 21-Nov-3 Lombrail & Teucquam, Paris #57/R est:5000-6000
£11765	$22000	€17177	Tete de garcon qui rit (13cm-5in) s.st.f.Rudier pat bronze prov.lit. 25-Feb-4 Christie's, Rockefeller NY #38/R est:6000-8000
£12000	$22080	€17520	Torse de jeune femme (22cm-9in) s.i. num.6 brown pat bronze exec. 1962 st.f. Rudier prov.lit. 23-Jun-4 Christie's, London #106/R est:12000-18000
£12353	$21000	€18035	Polypheme (24cm-9in) i. blk pat bronze conceived 1888 Cast Alexis Rudier prov.lit. 6-Nov-3 Sotheby's, New York #105/R est:15000-20000
£13408	$24000	€19576	Camille Claudel au bonnet (27cm-11in) s.d.1967 i.f.Georges Rudier verso blk green pat bronze prov.lit. 5-May-4 Christie's, Rockefeller NY #206/R est:30000-40000
£13408	$24000	€19576	Tete de pleureuse de la Porte de l'Enfer (21cm-8in) terracotta exec c.1880-1885 prov. 5-May-4 Christie's, Rockefeller NY #245/R est:25000-35000
£14118	$24000	€20612	Buste feminin ou A la ville (30cm-12in) s.i. terracotta prov.lit. 5-Nov-3 Christie's, Rockefeller NY #233/R est:25000-35000
£15642	$28000	€22837	Mouvement de danse E (37cm-15in) s.d.1956 num.6 green brown pat bronze conceived c.1911 prov.lit. 5-May-4 Christie's, Rockefeller NY #261/R est:20000-30000
£16000	$29120	€23360	Buste de Suzon (33cm-13in) s. Sevres biscuit sold with base exec. 1873 prov.lit. 3-Feb-4 Christie's, London #126/R est:10000-15000
£17836	$32818	€26753	Balzac nu (76x41x29cm-30x16x11in) i. plaster exec. 1892 prov.lit. 8-Jun-4 Artcurial Briest, Paris #133/R est:30000-40000
£22000	$40040	€32120	Deux mains superposees (8cm-3in) s. dark brown pat bronze exec. c.1890-1900 prov.lit. 3-Feb-4 Christie's, London #104/R est:20000-30000
£22346	$40000	€32625	Eustache de Saint-Pierre (47cm-19in) s. i.f.A.Rudier green blk pat bronze conceived 1884-95 prov.lit. 5-May-4 Christie's, Rockefeller NY #269/R est:50000-70000
£22346	$40000	€32625	Grande baigneuse accroupie avec bras (32cm-13in) st.sig.i.d.1969 num.N.7 f.G Rudier conceived 1886 prov.exhib.lit. 6-May-4 Sotheby's, New York #205/R est:50000-70000
£24161	$43248	€36000	Tete de Balzac (19cm-7in) s. pat bronze prov.lit. 26-May-4 Christie's, Paris #20/R est:22000-30000
£29330	$52500	€42822	Buste de Victor Hugo (57cm-22in) i. painted plaster conceived 1883 prov.lit. 6-May-4 Sotheby's, New York #225/R est:30000-40000
£31724	$57103	€46000	L'eternal printemps (25x30x20cm-10x12x8in) s.num.19 brown pat bronze st.f.F. Barbedienne lit. 26-Jan-4 Gros & Delettrez, Paris #40/R est:20000-25000
£32353	$55000	€47235	Adam au pilier (42cm-17in) s.d.1967 num.2 blk green pat bronze Cast Rudier prov.lit. 5-Nov-3 Christie's, Rockefeller NY #227/R est:35000-45000
£32353	$55000	€47235	Saint Jean Baptiste prechant (79cm-31in) raised sig.i.d.1962 green brown pat bronze Cast G.Rudier lit. 6-Nov-3 Sotheby's, New York #119/R est:60000-80000
£34916	$62500	€50977	Metamorphoses d'Ovid (41cm-16in) i. i.f.G Rudier dark brown pat bronze conceived c.1885 prov.lit. 6-May-4 Sotheby's, New York #223/R est:50000-70000
£35294	$60000	€51529	Eve au pilier (42cm-17in) s.d.1967 num.2 brown green pat bronze Cast Rudier prov.lit. 5-Nov-3 Christie's, Rockefeller NY #226/R est:35000-45000
£36000	$65520	€52560	L'eternel printemps (40cm-16in) bronze i.f.F Bardedienne conceived 1884 lit. 4-Feb-4 Sotheby's, London #215/R est:30000-40000
£37500	$62625	€54000	Saint-Jean Baptiste prechant (50cm-20in) s. brown pat. bronze exec. c.1898-1908 st.f.Thiebaut prov. lit. 21-Oct-3 Christie's, Paris #73/R est:35000-45000
£38000	$69920	€55480	Grande main de Pierre et Jacues de Wiessant (34cm-13in) i. bronze st.f.Georges Rudier conceived c.1887-89 lit. 22-Jun-4 Sotheby's, London #232/R est:20000-30000
£47486	$85000	€69330	L'eternal Printemps, second etat, 4eme reduction (25cm-10in) s. gold pat bronze f.Barbedienne conceived 1884 lit. 5-May-4 Christie's, Rockefeller NY #239/R est:90000-120000
£48000	$88320	€70080	Le baiser (39cm-15in) s.st.f. Barbedienne black pat bronze conceived c.1885-86 lit. 23-Jun-4 Christie's, London #107/R est:55000-75000
£49655	$82428	€72000	Eternel printemps (24cm-9in) s.i. bronze prov.lit. 2-Oct-3 Sotheby's, Paris #135/R est:40000
£51049	$86783	€73000	Pierre de Wiessant (45x17x17cm-18x7x7in) s. pat bronze Cast Rudier lit. 21-Nov-3 Lombrail & Teucquam, Paris #52/R est:25000-30000
£53073	$95000	€77487	Pierre de Wiessant (45cm-18in) s. i.f.A rudier brown pat bronze conceived 1895 prov.lit. 5-May-4 Christie's, Rockefeller NY #247/R est:90000-120000
£55882	$95000	€81588	Suzon (41cm-16in) s.i. white marble incl base prov.lit. 5-Nov-3 Christie's, Rockefeller NY #213/R est:60000-80000
£61453	$110000	€89721	Frere et soeur (38cm-15in) s. i.f.A Rudier brown pat bronze conceived c.1890-91 prov.lit. 5-May-4 Christie's, Rockefeller NY #229/R est:100000-150000
£61765	$105000	€90177	Balzac nu (75cm-30in) i.d.1965 brown green pat bronze Cast G.Rudier prov.lit. 6-Nov-3 Sotheby's, New York #122/R est:120000-180000
£62937	$106993	€90000	Andrieu d'Andres (45x17x17cm-18x7x7in) s. pat bronze Cast Rudier lit. 21-Nov-3 Lombrail & Teucquam, Paris #53/R est:25000-30000
£64336	$109371	€92000	Faunesse (54x29x20cm-21x11x8in) s. pat bronze Cast Rudier lit. 21-Nov-3 Lombrail & Teucquam, Paris #51/R est:40000-50000
£65000	$118300	€94900	L'eternel printemps (38cm-15in) s.st.f.Barbedienne brown green pat bronze exec. c.1898-1918 prov. 3-Feb-4 Christie's, London #106/R est:40000-60000
£66207	$122483	€96000	Le baiser (40cm-16in) s. dark pat bronze Cast Barbedienne. 16-Feb-4 Horta, Bruxelles #122/R est:25000-35000
£67133	$115469	€96000	L'eternel printemps (40cm-16in) s.i.num.58307 pat bronze st.f.F. Barbedienne prov.exhib.lit. 3-Dec-3 Beaussant & Lefèvre, Paris #81/R est:80000-100000
£72626	$130000	€106034	Andrieu d'Andres (43cm-17in) s. i.f.A Rudier brown pat bronze conceived 1895 prov.lit. 5-May-4 Christie's, Rockefeller NY #246/R est:90000-120000
£83799	$150000	€122347	Baiser, troisieme reduction (39cm-15in) s. i.f.Barbedienne brn pat bronze conceived c.1885 prov.exhib.lit. 5-May-4 Christie's, Rockefeller NY #208/R est:120000-160000
£83799	$150000	€122347	Faunesse agenouille (53cm-21in) s. i.f.A.Rudier blk green pat bronze conceived 1884 prov.lit. 5-May-4 Christie's, Rockefeller NY #248/R est:150000-200000
£83799	$150000	€122347	Baiser (39cm-15in) i. i.f.Barbedienne brown pat bronze conceived 1886 prov.lit. 6-May-4 Sotheby's, New York #211/R est:100000-150000
£92105	$169474	€140000	Le penseur (37cm-15in) s.st.f. Rudier pat bronze prov.lit. 23-Jun-4 Maigret, Paris #42/R est:110000-130000
£97765	$175000	€142737	Jeune mere a la grotte (38cm-15in) s. brown pat bronze conceived 1885 prov.exhib.lit. 5-May-4 Christie's, Rockefeller NY #205/R est:120000-180000
£98667	$176613	€148000	L'eternel printemps (51cm-20in) s.i. green pat bronze st.f. Barbedienne exec. 1884 prov. 16-May-4 Thierry & Lannon, Brest #20/R est:80000-100000
£102941	$175000	€150294	L'age d'Airain (41cm-16in) s.i. brown green pat bronze Cast G Rudier prov.lit. 5-Nov-3 Christie's, Rockefeller NY #163/R est:100000-150000
£111765	$190000	€163177	Le baiser (44cm-17in) s.i. brown pat bronze Cast Barbedienne lit. 5-Nov-3 Christie's, Rockefeller NY #225/R est:120000-160000
£147059	$250000	€214706	L'eternal printemps (66cm-26in) st. brown pat bronze conceived 1884 st.f.Barbedienne prov.lit. 6-Nov-3 Sotheby's, New York #137/R est:180000-250000
£170000	$312800	€248200	Eternel printemps (65cm-26in) st.f.Barbedienne brown pat bronze prov.lit. 22-Jun-4 Christie's, London #5/R est:140000-180000
£197279	$353129	€290000	Ugolin et ses enfants (41x61x41cm-16x24x16in) s. brown pat bronze st.f.Gonon exec c.1881-82 prov.lit. 19-Mar-4 Millon & Associes, Paris #54/R est:100000-150000
£230769	$392308	€330000	Eve (75x24x29cm-30x9x11in) s. pat bronze Cast Rudier lit. 21-Nov-3 Lombrail & Teucquam, Paris #50/R est:120000-150000
£251397	$450000	€367040	Iris, messagere des dieux (94cm-37in) s.st.f.Rudier pat bronze exec.1890-91 prov.lit. 6-May-4 Sotheby's, New York #132/R est:500000-700000
£270000	$491400	€394200	Tete de Saint-Jean Baptiste sur un plateau (20x35cm-8x14in) s. marble exec. c.1892-1893 prov.exhib.lit. 3-Feb-4 Christie's, London #111/R est:100000-150000
£323529	$550000	€472352	Iris, messagere des dieux (95cm-37in) i. green pat. bronze st.f.Georges Rudier cast 1963 prov.lit. 5-Nov-3 Sotheby's, New York #12/R est:500000-700000
£500000	$915000	€730000	Penseur (71cm-28in) s.st.f.Rudier green pat bronze prov.lit. 2-Feb-4 Christie's, London #11/R est:400000-600000
£550000	$1001000	€803000	Cariatide tombee portant une sphere (47cm-19in) s. marble prov.lit. 21-Jun-4 Sotheby's, London #3/R est:600000-800000

Works on paper

£1978	$3600	€2888	Dancing nude (46x30cm-18x12in) graphite wash prov. 8-Feb-4 William Jenack, New York #120 est:3600
£2246	$3750	€3279	Nu etendu (25x32cm-10x13in) s. pencil wash prov. 7-Oct-3 Sotheby's, New York #252 est:4000-6000

£2371 $4244 €3462 Les danseuses (21x30cm-8x12in) s. W/C over pencil prov. 12-May-4 Dobiaschofsky, Bern #913/R est:2500 (S.FR 5500)
£3061 $5480 €4500 Femme nue allongee (30x44cm-12x17in) s. black pencil W/C. 19-Mar-4 Piasa, Paris #191/R est:4500-5000
£3500 $5845 €5110 Nu - la fortune (32x25cm-13x10in) s.i. pencil black crayon prov. 21-Oct-3 Sotheby's, London #101/R est:4000-6000
£4570 $8500 €6672 Etude de femme nue (18x25cm-7x10in) init. W/C pencil. 2-Mar-4 Swann Galleries, New York #579 est:4000-6000
£5000 $7950 €7250 Etude pour un genie aile (31x20cm-12x8in) s. pencil executed c.1890. 11-Sep-3 Christie's, Kensington #7/R est:5000-7000
£5369 $9611 €8000 Etude de figures (37x24cm-15x9in) ink crayon prov.exhib. 26-May-4 Christie's, Paris #21/R est:8000-12000
£8531 $14503 €12200 Femme debout s'habillant (50x32cm-20x13in) s.i. crayon dr htd W/C. 21-Nov-3 Lombrail & Teucquam, Paris #59/R est:6000-8000
£8667 $15947 €13000 Loie Fuller (32x24cm-13x9in) studio st. W/C. 9-Jun-4 Tajan, Paris #11/R est:8000-10000
£10000 $18400 €15000 Hors du bain (32x25cm-13x10in) s.i. W/C pencil. 10-Jun-4 Hauswedell & Nolte, Hamburg #602/R est:6000
£12057 $19532 €17000 Modele assis et modele a la chemise. i.visiting card one W/C one W/C gouache two in one frame. 21-May-3 Daguerre, Paris #33/R est:9000-10000

RODIN, Auguste (attrib) (1840-1917) French
Works on paper
£474 $849 €692 Female nude (28x17cm-11x7in) mono. W/C on pencil. 13-May-4 Stuker, Bern #296/R (S.FR 1100)
£1250 $2088 €1800 Standing female nude (32x24cm-13x9in) s. W/C over pencil lit. 25-Oct-3 Bergmann, Erlangen #1554/R est:1800

RODIONOV, Nikolai Mikhailovich (1896-?) Russian
£391 $728 €571 Ram (70x56cm-28x22in) s.d. 6-Mar-4 Dorotheum, Prague #128 est:10000-15000 (C.KR 19000)

RODIUS, Charles (1802-1860) Australian
Works on paper
£7660 $13021 €11184 King Jack Waterman (18x12cm-7x5in) s.i.d.1834 crayon chl W/C. 26-Nov-3 Deutscher-Menzies, Melbourne #121/R est:8000-12000 (A.D 18000)

RODLING, N (20th C) Scandinavian
Sculpture
£2143 $3837 €3129 Mermaid (78cm-31in) s. green pat.bronze Cast Otto Meyers. 26-May-4 AB Stockholms Auktionsverk #2230/R est:10000-12000 (S.KR 29000)

RODMAN, Hazel (20th C) American
£351 $650 €512 Passing parade. init. canvasboard exhib. 13-Mar-4 DeFina, Austinburg #871/R

RODMELL, Harry Hudson (1896-1984) British
Works on paper
£300 $552 €438 Trawler coming into harbour (30x43cm-12x17in) s. W/C exhib. 14-Jun-4 Bonhams, Bath #186

RODOCANACHI, Paolo (1891-1955) Italian?
£541 $951 €800 Chinese boat (38x50cm-15x20in) s.i.verso board. 19-May-4 Il Ponte, Milan #1040

RODON, Francisco (1934-) Puerto Rican
£105333 $193813 €158000 Borges (306x142cm-120x56in) painted c.1975 prov.exhib. 10-Jun-4 Christie's, Paris #68/R est:160000-200000

RODRIGO, Eugenio Oliva (1857-1925) Spanish
£2482 $4145 €3500 Botigeros de Granada (27x17cm-11x7in) s. panel. 23-Jun-3 Durán, Madrid #80/R est:350

RODRIGO, Vicente Pascual (1955-) Spanish
£780 $1264 €1100 Composition ochre (41x33cm-16x13in) s.d.1990 mixed media canvas panel. 20-May-3 Ansorena, Madrid #294/R

RODRIGUE, George (1944-) American
£1130 $2000 €1650 Sunday boat ride (51x61cm-20x24in) s. 2-May-4 Bonhams & Butterfields, Los Angeles #3078/R est:3000-5000
£2907 $5000 €4244 Louisiana Bayou (20x28cm-8x11in) s. s.d.1969 verso. 6-Dec-3 Neal Auction Company, New Orleans #561/R est:6000-10000
£3253 $5400 €4749 Cabin on the Bayou (28x36cm-11x14in) s.verso. 4-Oct-3 Neal Auction Company, New Orleans #515/R est:2500-3500
£5588 $9500 €8158 Hot nights (41x51cm-16x20in) s.i.d.1991 verso. 9-Nov-3 Bonhams & Butterfields, Los Angeles #4039/R
£6757 $12500 €9865 Mt Carmel's sacred heart (76x102cm-30x40in) s. painted 1976. 17-Jul-4 New Orleans Auction, New Orleans #881/R est:12000-18000
£8529 $14500 €12452 Bayou landscape with village (76x102cm-30x40in) s.d.1991 verso. 22-Nov-3 New Orleans Auction, New Orleans #1271/R est:12000-18000

RODRIGUEZ BAIXERAS, Rafael (1947-1989) Spanish
£845 $1479 €1200 Modern veil (40x100cm-16x39in) s. s.i.d.1987 verso prov. 16-Dec-3 Segre, Madrid #184/R

RODRIGUEZ BONOME, Santiango (1901-?) Spanish
Sculpture
£811 $1500 €1184 Femme elegante (66cm-26in) s. pat bronze exec. 1927. 17-Jul-4 New Orleans Auction, New Orleans #896/R est:1800-2500
£3819 $6493 €5500 Buste de jeune Africain (47x13x13cm-19x5x5in) black pat bronze Cast Barbedienne. 28-Oct-3 Rabourdin & Choppin de Janvry, Paris #24/R est:6200-6500

RODRIGUEZ BRONCHU, Salvador (1912-) Spanish
£395 $714 €600 Pool (22x27cm-9x11in) s. board. 14-Apr-4 Ansorena, Madrid #219/R
£845 $1479 €1200 Carriages (25x38cm-10x15in) s. s.i.verso board. 16-Dec-3 Durán, Madrid #76/R
£884 $1583 €1300 Cuenca (67x80cm-26x31in) s. s.i.verso. 22-Mar-4 Durán, Madrid #566/R
£915 $1602 €1300 Arabs (26x39cm-10x15in) s. s.i.verso board. 16-Dec-3 Durán, Madrid #75/R
£1007 $1883 €1500 Beach (22x32cm-9x13in) s. s.i.verso board. 24-Feb-4 Durán, Madrid #181/R est:1400

RODRIGUEZ CASTELAO, Alfonso (1886-1950) Spanish
Works on paper
£563 $975 €800 Figures (30x21cm-12x8in) s. ink pencil. 15-Dec-3 Ansorena, Madrid #196/R
£833 $1358 €1200 Emigrants (19x19cm-7x7in) s. ink dr. 23-Sep-3 Durán, Madrid #136/R
£5172 $9310 €7500 Woman thinking (43x48cm-17x19in) s.d.1941. 26-Jan-4 Durán, Madrid #163/R est:7500

RODRIGUEZ DE TOLEDO, Francisco (17/18th C) Spanish
£1678 $3121 €2500 Ordination of Saint Ildefonso (178x113cm-70x44in) s.d.1718. 2-Mar-4 Ansorena, Madrid #262/R est:2500

RODRIGUEZ LOZANO, Manuel (1896-1974) Mexican
£933 $1699 €1400 Crucifixion (51x32cm-20x13in) s. panel. 29-Jun-4 Segre, Madrid #41/R

RODRIGUEZ SAN CLEMENT, Francisco (1861-1956) Spanish
£1418 $2369 €2000 Bailora (45x37cm-18x15in) s. 23-Jun-3 Durán, Madrid #143/R est:1800

RODRIGUEZ SANCHEZ CLEMENT, Francisco (1893-1968) Spanish
£1135 $1895 €1600 Flamenco dancer (63x53cm-25x21in) s. 20-Oct-3 Durán, Madrid #138/R
£2500 $4400 €3700 Flamenco dance (76x60cm-30x24in) s. 18-May-4 Segre, Madrid #97/R est:2500
£2585 $4705 €3800 Sleeping beauty (46x65cm-18x26in) s. prov. 3-Feb-4 Segre, Madrid #360/R est:3000
£4138 $7655 €6000 Untitled (80x100cm-31x39in) s.d.1932. 14-Jan-4 Castellana, Madrid #185/R est:3500

RODRIGUEZ, Alfred C (1862-1890) American
£543 $1000 €815 Windmill on the coast (45x56cm-18x22in) s. board. 8-Jun-4 Auctions by the Bay, Alameda #1078/R

RODRIGUEZ, Alirio (1934-) Venezuelan
£645 $1000 €942 By the abyss (60x50cm-24x20in) s. painted 1970. 3-Nov-2 Subastas Odalys, Caracas #102/R
£2017 $3180 €2945 Before 117 (100x90cm-39x35in) s. painted 1990. 27-Apr-3 Subastas Odalys, Caracas #52/R
£13247 $24375 €19871 New mankind (190x180cm-75x71in) s. acrylic painted 1985. 27-Jun-4 Subastas Odalys, Caracas #72/R est:24000
Works on paper
£283 $520 €425 Untitled (25x34cm-10x13in) s. crayon exec.1977. 27-Jun-4 Subastas Odalys, Caracas #103

RODRIGUEZ, Arturo (1956-) Cuban
£1429 $2500 €2086 Small portrait (46x36cm-18x14in) s.d.1987 verso. 19-Dec-3 Sotheby's, New York #1213/R est:3500-4500

RODRIGUEZ, Guillermo Ciro (20th C) Uruguayan?
£1136 $2000 €1659 Punta del Este (42x59cm-17x23in) s. painted c.1935. 5-Jan-4 Galeria y Remates, Montevideo #84/R est:2500-3500

RODRIGUEZ, Joaquin (19th C) Spanish
£1096 $1863 €1600 Smokers. Surgery (44x56cm-17x22in) s.d.1850 s.verso pair. 4-Nov-3 Ansorena, Madrid #74/R est:1500

RODRIGUEZ, Jose Miguel (1931-) Spanish
£442 $805 €650 Nearly always they come in the evenings and sometimes they seem to smile at you (60x73cm-24x29in) s.d.1981 s.i.d.verso prov. 3-Feb-4 Segre, Madrid #331/R

RODRIGUEZ, Mariano (1912-1990) Cuban
£1736 $3194 €2535 Cock (62x48cm-24x19in) s.d.1985 paper. 25-Mar-4 Louis Morton, Mexico #56/R est:40000-45000 (M.P 35000)
£4469 $8000 €6525 Farms in landscape with cocks fighting (63x47cm-25x19in) s.d.86 acrylic tempera paper prov. 26-May-4 Sotheby's, New York #157/R est:10000-15000
£7692 $14000 €11230 Two figures (119x96cm-47x38in) s.d.61. 29-Jun-4 Sotheby's, New York #656/R est:10000-15000
£18824 $32000 €27483 Malabaristas (86x119cm-34x47in) s.d.55 prov.exhib.lit. 18-Nov-3 Christie's, Rockefeller NY #47/R est:35000-40000
Works on paper
£9497 $17000 €13866 Woman (51x56cm-20x22in) s.d.42 ink W/C prov. 26-May-4 Sotheby's, New York #141/R est:18000-22000

RODRIGUEZ, Rabbions (?) ?
£359 $600 €524 Portrait of a Samoyed dog (49x60cm-19x24in) s. 19-Oct-3 Bonhams & Butterfields, Los Angeles #7049

RODRIGUEZ, Ruben (1955-) ?
Works on paper
£315 $525 €450 Women (100x80cm-39x31in) s. mixed media. 30-Jun-3 Sotheby's, Amsterdam #486

RODWAY, Florence (1881-1971) Australian
Works on paper
£3719 $6583 €5430 Romanian blouse (102x48cm-40x19in) s.d.1912 pastel prov.exhib. 3-May-4 Christie's, Melbourne #54/R est:10000-15000 (A.D 9000)

ROE, Basil (19th C) British
£420 $769 €613 Landscape at sunset with cottage and figures on a track (40x61cm-16x24in) s. 27-Jan-4 Holloways, Banbury #353

ROE, Clarence (1850-1909) British
£260 $434 €380 Lakeland landscape (50x76cm-20x30in) s. 7-Oct-3 Bonhams, Knightsbridge #187
£300 $501 €438 Waterfall near Ingleton (48x38cm-19x15in) s. 8-Oct-3 Andrew Hartley, Ilkley #1165
£300 $510 €438 View on the east coast, possibly looking towards Whitby (20x30cm-8x12in) panel. 19-Nov-3 Tennants, Leyburn #1047
£500 $920 €730 Stag in a midnight winter landscape (33x50cm-13x20in) s. board. 10-Jun-4 Christie's, Kensington #228/R
£600 $1086 €876 Eagles Rock, near Oban on the west coast of Scotland (61x92cm-24x36in) s.d.1860-61. 31-Mar-4 Bonhams, Knightsbridge #22/R
£1300 $2418 €1898 Stag and hinds in a highland landscape (56x91cm-22x36in) s. 4-Mar-4 Christie's, Kensington #31/R est:1500-2000
£1700 $2669 €2465 In the highlands. On alert (51x76cm-20x30in) s. pair. 27-Aug-3 Sotheby's, London #1002/R est:1500-2000
£1800 $3276 €2628 Scottish highland scene with long horn cattle (61x91cm-24x36in) s. 4-Feb-4 John Nicholson, Haslemere #122/R est:2000-3000
£2400 $4080 €3504 Stags watering by a moonlit loch (76x127cm-30x50in) s. 27-Nov-3 Christie's, Kensington #199/R est:3000-5000
£2500 $4250 €3650 Stags in a highland landscape (49x74cm-19x29in) s. 27-Nov-3 Christie's, Kensington #196/R est:3000-5000

ROE, Clarence (attrib) (1850-1909) British
£1700 $2890 €2482 Horse and rider with sheep in a highland landscape (76x127cm-30x50in) bears sig. 27-Nov-3 Greenslade Hunt, Taunton #1012/R est:1500-2500

ROE, Fred (1864-1947) British
£469 $877 €704 Exchange (60x90cm-24x35in) s. 21-Jul-4 Goodman, Sydney #157 (A.D 1200)
Works on paper
£300 $549 €438 Boulogne fisherfolk - four character studies (40x36cm-16x14in) s.i. W/C htd bodycol. 6-Jul-4 Bearnes, Exeter #419
£320 $576 €467 March of the City of London regiments past the Mansion House (69x51cm-27x20in) s.i.d.1919 sketch. 22-Apr-4 Charles Ross, Woburn #240
£950 $1758 €1387 Two gentlemen in 17th century costume seated in an interior, one at an easel (58x74cm-23x29in) i. W/C bodycol. 11-Mar-4 Duke & Son, Dorchester #41/R

ROE, Frederick Rushing (?) ?
£452 $800 €660 Gypsy camp (17x19cm-7x7in) s. board. 2-May-4 Bonhams & Butterfields, San Francisco #1168/R

ROE, Robert Ernest (fl.1860-1880) British
£260 $471 €380 Steam and sailing vessels in a choppy sea (34x50cm-13x20in) s. 30-Mar-4 David Duggleby, Scarborough #230/R
£1957 $3327 €2857 Wreck of the Scarborough with the Grand Hotel in the Foreground (51x91cm-20x36in) s.d.83. 26-Nov-3 Deutscher-Menzies, Melbourne #296d/R est:4000-6000 (A.D 4600)
£4100 $7339 €5986 Wreck in the South Bay Scarborough with lifeboat (50x90cm-20x35in) s.d.82. 17-May-4 David Duggleby, Scarborough #690/R est:3000-5000

ROE, Robert Henry (1822-1905) British
£650 $1196 €949 Morning. Night (30x25cm-12x10in) s. pair. 8-Jun-4 Bonhams, Knightsbridge #177/R

ROED, Holger Peter (1846-1874) Danish
£894 $1600 €1305 Viking with a harp (46x36cm-18x14in) init. i.verso. 21-Mar-4 Hindman, Chicago #777/R est:2000-3000

ROED, Jorgen (1808-1888) Danish
£517 $880 €755 Portrait of the young Mr Puggaard (76x55cm-30x22in) s.d.1874. 29-Nov-3 Rasmussen, Havnen #2300 (D.KR 5500)
£1121 $1772 €1625 Susanne Kobke nee Ryder (16x14cm-6x6in) painted c.1838. 2-Sep-3 Rasmussen, Copenhagen #1929/R est:6000 (D.KR 12000)
£1229 $2126 €1794 Seated Neapolitan boy (22x19cm-9x7in) s. 9-Dec-3 Rasmussen, Copenhagen #1332/R est:6000-8000 (D.KR 13000)

ROEDE, Jan (1914-) Dutch
£2533 $4636 €3800 Un couple (55x46cm-22x18in) s.d.67 canvas on board. 7-Jun-4 Glerum, Amsterdam #268/R est:4000-5000
£3217 $5533 €4600 Twee personen op rood (46x61cm-18x24in) s.d.68 prov. 2-Dec-3 Sotheby's, Amsterdam #272/R est:5500-7500
£3467 $6379 €5200 Children and cat (45x55cm-18x22in) s.d.46 prov. 9-Jun-4 Christie's, Amsterdam #152/R est:4500-6000
£4333 $7973 €6500 Mother with children and bicycle (46x55cm-18x22in) s.d.62 prov. 8-Jun-4 Sotheby's, Amsterdam #278/R est:5000-7000
£6000 $11040 €9000 Aparte werkelijkheid II (120x140cm-47x55in) s.d.78/95 s.i.stretcher lit. 9-Jun-4 Christie's, Amsterdam #379/R est:4000-6000

ROEDEL, Auguste (1859-1900) French
Works on paper
£227 $400 €331 Young lady on a swing (48x41cm-19x16in) s. W/C gouache. 23-May-4 Hindman, Chicago #103/R

ROEDER, Emy (1890-1971) German
Sculpture
£4366 $7554 €6200 Tripoli II (51cm-20in) mono. red pat.bronze exhib. 13-Dec-3 Lempertz, Koln #350/R est:1000
Works on paper
£350 $594 €500 Calf licking back leg (21x13cm-8x5in) mono.d.47 chk over pencil ochre prov. 26-Nov-3 Lempertz, Koln #944/R
£420 $713 €600 Two resting goats (36x36cm-14x14in) s. chk. 26-Nov-3 Lempertz, Koln #945/R
£528 $914 €750 Kneeling figure - evening nude Paris (40x30cm-16x12in) mono.i.d.62 chk. 13-Dec-3 Lempertz, Koln #351/R

ROEDER, Max (1866-1947) German
£385 $654 €550 Italian mountain landscape with fortress (28x38cm-11x15in) s. panel. 20-Nov-3 Van Ham, Cologne #1820
£387 $624 €550 Italian coast (77x110cm-30x43in) s. 22-Aug-3 Altus, Berlin #598/R
£1736 $2865 €2500 Acropolis, Athens (123x93cm-48x37in) s.d.37. 3-Jul-3 Van Ham, Cologne #1424/R est:3000
£1867 $3397 €2800 Italian coastal landscape (65x88cm-26x35in) s.d.23. 1-Jul-4 Van Ham, Cologne #1576/R est:1500
£4698 $8785 €7000 Acropolis, Athens (122x93cm-48x37in) s.d.37. 24-Feb-4 Dorotheum, Vienna #7/R est:5000-6000

ROEDER, Max (attrib) (1866-1947) German
£1007 $1872 €1500 Villa on the south coast (77x100cm-30x39in) i. 5-Mar-4 Wendl, Rudolstadt #3839/R est:420

ROEDERSTEIN, Ottilie Wilhelmine (1859-1937) Swiss
£862 $1543 €1259 Still life with flowers in dark vase (55x46cm-22x18in) mono. 12-May-4 Dobiaschofsky, Bern #914/R est:2500 (S.FR 2000)

ROEDIG, Moritz (1844-1918) German
£638 $1173 €950 Woman in costume (115x90cm-45x35in) s.d.1868. 27-Mar-4 Dannenberg, Berlin #617/R

ROEDYAT (1930-) Indonesian
£2174 $3370 €3174 Self portrait (57x41cm-22x16in) s.d.65 sold with W/C by MA'ARUF, MULJADI three. 6-Oct-2 Sotheby's, Singapore #125/R est:6000-9000 (S.D 6000)

ROEGGE, Wilhelm (snr) (1829-1908) German
£855 $1548 €1300 Important news (35x42cm-14x17in) s. panel. 19-Apr-4 Glerum, Amsterdam #295/R
£972 $1585 €1400 Men meeting in Dutch interior (37x44cm-15x17in) s. 25-Sep-3 Neumeister, Munich #2861/R
£3892 $6500 €5682 Interior scene with figures (66x107cm-26x42in) 17-Oct-3 Du Mouchelle, Detroit #2115/R est:6000-8000

ROEKENS, Paulette van (1896-?) American
£2616 $4500 €3819 Across the Sound (38x51cm-15x20in) i.stretcher prov. 7-Dec-3 Freeman, Philadelphia #191 est:2000-3000
£5435 $10000 €7935 Little girl in pink (51x41cm-20x16in) s. 27-Jun-4 Freeman, Philadelphia #191/R est:2000-3000
£12579 $20000 €18365 Tents and Balloons (30x36cm-12x14in) s. s.d.1974 verso. 10-Sep-3 Alderfer's, Hatfield #372/R est:10000-15000
£17442 $30000 €25465 Entering new hope (63x76cm-25x30in) s.d.25. 3-Dec-3 Sotheby's, New York #25/R est:20000-30000

ROELAND, Jannes (1935-) Dutch
£5000 $9200 €7500 Compositie met twee hamers I (100x90cm-39x35in) s.d.1977 verso prov.exhib. 8-Jun-4 Sotheby's, Amsterdam #125/R est:6000-8000

ROELANDSE, Johannes Cornelius (1888-?) Dutch
£349 $601 €500 Amsterdam zoo (40x60cm-16x24in) s. s.i.verso. 7-Dec-3 Sotheby's, Amsterdam #709

ROELOFS, Albert (1877-1920) Dutch
£27778 $47222 €40000 Immersed in contemplation (48x39cm-19x15in) s. panel. 28-Oct-3 Christie's, Amsterdam #168/R est:15000-20000

ROELOFS, Willem (1822-1897) Dutch
£987 $1786 €1500 Cows in a meadow, forest in the background (13x21cm-5x8in) s. canvas on panel. 19-Apr-4 Glerum, Amsterdam #110/R est:1500-2000
£1250 $2037 €1800 Cow in a field (22x30cm-9x12in) mono.d.82 canvas on panel. 29-Sep-3 Sotheby's, Amsterdam #71/R
£1733 $3120 €2600 Bords du gein pres d'abcoude (14x25cm-6x10in) s. s.i.verso oil paper on panel. 20-Apr-4 Sotheby's, Amsterdam #144/R est:2000-3000
£2721 $4952 €4000 Boerenwooning onder boomen, Noorden (34x28cm-13x11in) s.i.d.1880 canvas on panel prov. 3-Feb-4 Christie's, Amsterdam #137/R est:4000-6000
£2958 $5117 €4200 Landscape with cows by water (30x44cm-12x17in) s. panel prov. 13-Dec-3 Lempertz, Koln #244/R est:2000
£4027 $7208 €6000 A la lisiere du bois (49x69cm-19x27in) s. 25-May-4 Campo & Campo, Antwerp #240/R est:7000-9000
£6579 $11908 €10000 Landscape near Leidschendam (28x43cm-11x17in) s.i. 19-Apr-4 Glerum, Amsterdam #105/R est:3000-5000
£6944 $11597 €10000 Country road along a waterway near the Hague (44x27cm-17x11in) s.i. canvas on panel. 21-Oct-3 Sotheby's, Amsterdam #155/R est:10000-15000
£8000 $14400 €12000 Cowherd and his cattle at sunset (44x69cm-17x27in) s. 20-Apr-4 Sotheby's, Amsterdam #228/R est:12000-16000

£9028 $15347 €13000 Etang a Noorden printemps (28x45cm-11x18in) s. i.verso canvas on panel. 28-Oct-3 Christie's, Amsterdam #116/R est:6000-8000
£9028 $15076 €13000 Summer landscape with a tea house on the river Vecht (52x65cm-20x26in) s.d.1862. 21-Oct-3 Sotheby's, Amsterdam #169/R est:7000-9000
£10526 $19053 €16000 Grazing cows and ducks in a polder landscape (48x74cm-19x29in) s. 19-Apr-4 Glerum, Amsterdam #107/R est:12000-16000
£11806 $19715 €17000 Horseman along a waterway (29x53cm-11x21in) s. panel. 21-Oct-3 Sotheby's, Amsterdam #171/R est:10000-15000
£20000 $36000 €30000 Figures on a country road along a waterway, windmill in the distance (47x73cm-19x29in) s. 20-Apr-4 Sotheby's, Amsterdam #219/R est:20000-30000
£41667 $70833 €60000 Populous crowd enjoying a day on the ice with Rotterdam in the distance (55x73cm-22x29in) s.i.d.1867 prov.exhib.lit. 28-Oct-3 Christie's, Amsterdam #135/R est:60000-80000
£55556 $92778 €80000 Watering cows in a summer landscape (50x87cm-20x34in) s. 21-Oct-3 Sotheby's, Amsterdam #249/R est:80000-120000

Works on paper
£559 $1029 €850 Figures in a landscape (32x42cm-13x17in) s. W/C. 28-Jun-4 Sotheby's, Amsterdam #46/R
£909 $1600 €1327 Polder landscape with windmills (20x33cm-8x13in) s. W/C. 22-May-4 New Orleans Auction, New Orleans #122 est:700-1000
£1014 $1784 €1500 Landscape with trees (17x26cm-7x10in) init.i.d.Aug 1884 prov.lit. 19-May-4 Sotheby's, Amsterdam #343/R est:400-600
£1027 $1747 €1500 Village farm (24x33cm-9x13in) s.d.1844 wash. 5-Nov-3 Vendue Huis, Gravenhage #102/R est:500-700
£1027 $1747 €1500 Landscape with horse and wagon (20x43cm-8x17in) s. W/C prov. 5-Nov-3 Vendue Huis, Gravenhage #103/R est:2500-3000
£2800 $5040 €4200 Summer landscape with grazing cows (25x42cm-10x17in) s. W/C. 20-Apr-4 Sotheby's, Amsterdam #101/R est:3000-5000

ROELOFS, Willem Elisa (1874-1940) Dutch
£616 $1048 €900 Still life with flowers and pumpkin (79x59cm-31x23in) s. 5-Nov-3 Vendue Huis, Gravenhage #311/R
£987 $1816 €1500 Still life with eggs (19x29cm-7x11in) s. plywood. 22-Jun-4 Christie's, Amsterdam #271/R est:500-700

ROEMER, Georg (1868-1922) German
Sculpture
£1333 $2387 €2000 Head of Doryphoros (67cm-26in) pat bronze copper ivory brass with dark brown base lit. 14-May-4 Von Zezschwitz, Munich #56/R est:1600

ROEMERS, Gerhard Cohn (1900-1965) German
£374 $637 €546 Paris et le Pont St Michel (33x46cm-13x18in) s. i. stretcher. 5-Nov-3 Dobiaschofsky, Bern #3686 (S.FR 850)

ROERICH, Nikolai Konstantinovitch (1874-1947) American/Russian
£25150 $42000 €36719 Fairy tale (56x84cm-22x33in) i.verso tempera exhib.lit. 21-Oct-3 Christie's, Rockefeller NY #96 est:40000-60000
£26946 $45000 €39341 Creation (56x84cm-22x33in) i.verso tempera exhib.lit. 21-Oct-3 Christie's, Rockefeller NY #97 est:30000-50000
£38462 $60000 € Ocean series, Strength (50x79cm-20x31in) mono. tempera board painted 1922 prov.exhib.lit. 11-Apr-3 Christie's, Rockefeller NY #47/R est:40000-60000
£60897 $95000 € Ocean series, Reverie (55x83cm-22x33in) tempera painted 1922 prov.exhib.lit. 11-Apr-3 Christie's, Rockefeller NY #45/R est:60000-90000
£61111 $110000 €89222 Sacred grove, Snegourotchka - snow maiden (59x79cm-23x31in) painted 1917 prov.exhib. 23-Apr-4 Sotheby's, New York #101/R est:60000-80000

Works on paper
£1007 $1862 €1500 Heroica (16x22cm-6x9in) init. i.verso W/C. 14-Mar-4 Eric Pillon, Calais #174/R
£3205 $5000 € Himalayan landscape (30x45cm-12x18in) i.verso gouache ink cardboard prov. 11-Apr-3 Christie's, Rockefeller NY #48/R est:5000-7000
£4192 $7000 €6120 Costume design of a shipbuilder for Peer Gynt (25x16cm-10x6in) s.i. pencil tempera exhib.lit. 21-Oct-3 Christie's, Rockefeller NY #99 est:8000-10000
£4192 $7000 €6120 Shadow of the teacher (16x25cm-6x10in) init. chl chk W/C. 7-Oct-3 Sotheby's, New York #266 est:5000-7000
£11538 $18000 € Study for the painting Maitreya (30x45cm-12x18in) mono. i.verso gouache W/C cardboard prov.lit. 11-Apr-3 Christie's, Rockefeller NY #49/R est:6000-8000

ROERICH, Nikolai Konstantinovitch (attrib) (1874-1947) American/Russian
£27703 $49588 €41000 Vision dans les montagnes en Indes (58x70cm-23x28in) mono. canvas on cardboard. 5-May-4 Coutau Begarie, Paris #54/R est:5000-8000

ROESEN, Severin (fl.1848-1872) American/German
£19886 $35000 €29034 Still life with fruit (36x46cm-14x18in) s. panel prov. 19-May-4 Sotheby's, New York #74/R est:40000-60000
£46512 $80000 €67908 Abundance of fruit (63x76cm-25x30in) s. prov. 4-Dec-3 Christie's, Rockefeller NY #22/R
£68182 $120000 €99546 Flowers in a landscape (48x58cm-19x23in) s. round prov. 19-May-4 Sotheby's, New York #73/R est:125000-175000
£136364 $240000 €199091 Vase of flowers in footed glass bowl with bird's nest (102x76cm-40x30in) s.d.1852 canvas on panel prov.exhib.lit. 18-May-4 Christie's, Rockefeller NY #7/R est:150000-250000
£795455 $1400000 €1161364 Still life with flowers and fruit in a landscape (91x127cm-36x50in) s. prov. 19-May-4 Sotheby's, New York #51/R est:300000-500000

ROESSINGH, Henry de Buys (1899-1955) German
£367 $664 €550 Bruyere (50x67cm-20x26in) 30-Mar-4 Campo, Vlaamse Kaai #148

ROESSINGH, Louis Albert (1873-1951) Dutch/Belgian
£839 $1443 €1200 Bouleaux dans un paysage de bruyere (70x97cm-28x38in) s.d.1904. 8-Dec-3 Horta, Bruxelles #224
£4545 $7818 €6500 Little girl in a landscape (50x80cm-20x31in) s. 7-Dec-3 Sotheby's, Amsterdam #617/R
£6040 $10691 €9000 Berger et son troupeau dans la bruyere (110x130cm-43x51in) s.d.1902. 27-Apr-4 Campo, Vlaamse Kaai #568/R est:2500-3000
£6249 $10187 €9000 Shepherd with his flock (58x118cm-23x46in) s. 29-Sep-3 Sotheby's, Amsterdam #76/R

Works on paper
£455 $782 €650 Vues des dunes (57x78cm-22x31in) s. mixed media. 8-Dec-3 Horta, Bruxelles #225

ROESSLER, Georg (1861-1925) German
£625 $1031 €900 Woman wearing hat. Man wearing hat (23x18cm-9x7in) s.i. panel pair. 3-Jul-3 Neumeister, Munich #2898/R
£750 $1343 €1095 Frau in Tracht. Mann in Tracht (23x17cm-9x7in) s. panel pair. 20-Mar-4 Lacy Scott, Bury St.Edmunds #463/R
£1016 $1696 €1483 Woman with tall bonnet (23x18cm-9x7in) s. painted c.1890. 19-Oct-3 Agra, Warsaw #53/R (P.Z 6500)

ROESSLER, Walter (19/20th C) Russian
£278 $506 €420 Portrait d'un paysan bavarois (15x11cm-6x4in) s.indis.i. panel. 16-Jun-4 Hotel des Ventes Mosan, Brussels #155
£310 $574 €450 Peasant with hat (16x11cm-6x4in) s.i. panel. 12-Feb-4 Weidler, Nurnberg #302/R
£464 $848 €700 Pipe smoker (18x14cm-7x6in) s. panel. 8-Apr-4 Dorotheum, Vienna #74/R

ROESTENBURG, Martinus Wouterus (1909-1966) Dutch
Works on paper
£602 $1023 €879 Window in RC church, Little Waihi (25x11cm-10x4in) s. mixed media. 27-Nov-3 International Art Centre, Auckland #143/R (NZ.D 1600)

ROESTRATEN, Pieter Gerritsz van (1630-1700) Dutch
£950 $1739 €1387 Still life with silver bowl, candlestick, grapes and peaches on marble ledge (75x62cm-30x24in) 6-Jul-4 Peter Wilson, Nantwich #19/R

ROESTRATEN, Pieter Gerritsz van (style) (1630-1700) Dutch
£8500 $15300 €12410 Vanitas still life with skull (60x71cm-24x28in) 20-Apr-4 Sotheby's, Olympia #295/R est:1500-2000

ROFFIAEN, Jean François (1820-1898) Belgian
£594 $1022 €850 Vue de Campine (28x42cm-11x17in) s. 8-Dec-3 Horta, Bruxelles #21
£667 $1067 €967 Pilatus in morning mist (42x56cm-17x22in) s.d.1850 panel. 15-May-3 Stuker, Bern #1464/R (S.FR 1400)
£1100 $1749 €1606 Figure on a path in a river landscape (25x39cm-10x15in) s.d.1840 panel prov. 9-Sep-3 Bonhams, Knightsbridge #226/R est:1000-1500
£1655 $3062 €2400 Paysage anime (30x35cm-12x14in) s.d.1840 panel. 16-Feb-4 Horta, Bruxelles #91 est:1200-1500
£2069 $3455 €3000 Mountain landscape with lake (46x61cm-18x24in) s. 15-Nov-3 Lempertz, Koln #1684/R est:3500
£2711 $4500 €3958 Mount Rosa (49x88cm-19x35in) s.d.1869 prov.exhib.lit. 30-Sep-3 Christie's, Rockefeller NY #447/R est:4000-6000
£2817 $4873 €4000 Le Matterhorn, canton de Bern (34x53cm-13x21in) s. 9-Dec-3 Campo, Vlaamse Kaai #399/R est:4000-5000
£3217 $5372 €4600 Vianden au bord de l'Our au grand duche du Luxembourg (49x42cm-19x17in) s. 13-Oct-3 Horta, Bruxelles #193/R est:3000-4000

ROFFIGNAC, Martial de (1845-1904) French
Sculpture
£1405 $2600 €2051 Two dogs in landscape (28x48cm-11x19in) s. brown pat.bronze. 10-Feb-4 Doyle, New York #222/R

ROGAK, Helen (20th C) Canadian
£680 $1244 €993 Irises (75x120cm-30x47in) s.i. 1-Jun-4 Hodgins, Calgary #156/R (C.D 1700)

ROGAN, J H (19th C) ?
£724 $1296 €1057 Italian street scene with figures (79x64cm-31x25in) s. 10-May-4 Rasmussen, Vejle #503/R (D.KR 8000)

ROGER, Augustin (19th C) French
£639 $1054 €920 L'enterrement au village (27x35cm-11x14in) bears sig.d.1822 exhib. 1-Jul-3 Lemoine & Ferrando, Paris #45

ROGER, Guillaume (1867-1943) French
£1059 $1800 €1546 Harbor scene with windmill (38x56cm-15x22in) s.i.d.1915. 22-Nov-3 New Orleans Auction, New Orleans #675/R est:1200-1800

Works on paper
£479 $800 €699 Breton girl on the shore (51x74cm-20x29in) s. pastel paper on canvas. 25-Oct-3 Rachel Davis, Shaker Heights #456/R

ROGER, Suzanne (1898-1986) French
£1987 $3636 €3000 Les masques (65x81cm-26x32in) s. 7-Apr-4 Piasa, Paris #209/R est:3000-4000
£2431 $4059 €3500 Massacre (130x162cm-51x64in) s. prov. 21-Oct-3 Artcurial Briest, Paris #237/R est:3000-4000

ROGERS, Barbara (20th C) American
Works on paper
£222 $400 €324 Tropical debris (76x52cm-30x20in) s.d.1989 mixed media. 25-Apr-4 Bonhams & Butterfields, San Francisco #5628/R

ROGERS, Charles Albert (1848-1918) American
£2446 $4500 €3669 Public kitchen, old Chinatown (38x57cm-15x22in) s.d.1916. 8-Jun-4 Bonhams & Butterfields, San Francisco #4205/R est:3000-5000

ROGERS, Frank Whiting (1854-?) American
£7568 $14000 €11049 Portrait of a dog named Lassie (74x91cm-29x36in) s.d.1877 exhib. 10-Feb-4 Doyle, New York #261/R est:6000-8000

ROGERS, Howard (1932-) American
£234 $425 €342 Two greyhounds in a country landscape (30x24cm-12x9in) s. 7-Feb-4 Sloans & Kenyon, Bethesda #291/R
£3911 $7000 €5710 Deborah in red (41x61cm-16x24in) 15-May-4 Altermann Galleries, Santa Fe #155/R
£10695 $20000 €15615 Shouldn't be far now (76x102cm-30x40in) s. prov. 24-Jul-4 Coeur d'Alene, Hayden #239/R est:15000-25000
Sculpture
£1135 $2100 €1657 Reclining female nude in a wave pedestal (46cm-18in) s.d.1990 num.16/35 pat bronze onyx walnut base. 24-Jan-4 Jeffery Burchard, Florida #88/R est:2000-3000

ROGERS, Hubert (1898-1982) American?
£2206 $3750 €3221 Old Faithful (127x89cm-50x35in) s.d.26 prov. 1-Nov-3 Santa Fe Art, Santa Fe #160/R est:3000-5000

ROGERS, John (1829-1904) American
Works on paper
£272 $500 €397 Industrial landscape with freight ship with tugboat with cranes alongside (51x74cm-20x29in) s. W/C. 9-Jun-4 Alderfer's, Hatfield #427
£299 $550 €437 Industrial landscape with cargo ship (53x74cm-21x29in) s. W/C. 9-Jun-4 Alderfer's, Hatfield #428/R
£353 $650 €515 Industrial landscape with factory silos, pipes and power lines (51x71cm-20x28in) s. W/C. 9-Jun-4 Alderfer's, Hatfield #426/R

ROGERS, Juanita (1934-) American
£306 $550 €447 Army men and snakes (23x30cm-9x12in) tempera construction on paper. 24-Apr-4 Slotin Folk Art, Buford #526/R
£306 $550 €447 Blue windmill (51x66cm-20x26in) oil on paper prov. 24-Apr-4 Slotin Folk Art, Buford #527/R
£333 $600 €486 Woman next to tree stump (23x28cm-9x11in) oil on paper prov. 24-Apr-4 Slotin Folk Art, Buford #528/R

ROGERS, Margaret Esther (1872-1961) American
£469 $750 €685 Tabletops, Davenport, CA (208x262cm-82x103in) s. 18-May-3 Auctions by the Bay, Alameda #1137/R

ROGERS, Mary J (19th C) American
£778 $1300 €1136 New England pastoral scene (56x68cm-22x27in) s. 16-Nov-3 Bonhams & Butterfields, Los Angeles #7009/R est:1000-1500

ROGERS, Nathaniel (1788-1844) American
Miniatures
£1955 $3500 €2854 US Infantry Officer (8x5cm-3x2in) gilded frame oval exec.c.1812-13 prov. 18-Mar-4 Richard Opfer, Timonium #277/R

ROGERS, Otto Donald (1935-) Canadian
£1520 $2782 €2219 Klee memory (120x117cm-47x46in) painted 1986. 1-Jun-4 Joyner Waddington, Toronto #132/R est:2500-3500 (C.D 3800)
Works on paper
£488 $873 €712 Paper 77 number 1 (55x68cm-22x27in) s.d.1977 i.verso W/C. 6-May-4 Heffel, Vancouver #123/R (C.D 1200)

ROGERS, Philip Hutchins (1794-1853) British
£2000 $3340 €2920 View of Plymouth Water, Devon (34x57cm-13x22in) s.d.1817. 7-Oct-3 Bonhams, Knightsbridge #343/R est:2000-3000

ROGERS, W (?) British
£2134 $3820 €3116 Listening to the fish story. Brining in the catch (27x22cm-11x9in) s. two prov. 4-May-4 Ritchie, Toronto #18/R est:1500-2000 (C.D 5250)

ROGERS, Wendell (20th C) American
£276 $500 €403 Beach dunes (51x61cm-20x24in) s. 2-Apr-4 Eldred, East Dennis #46/R

ROGET, John Lewis (1828-1908) British
Works on paper
£350 $595 €511 Bec du Nez, Sark (17x24cm-7x9in) i.verso W/C. 25-Nov-3 Martel Maides, Guernsey #182
£867 $1569 €1300 Cashel (13x17cm-5x7in) i.d.30 May 1896 wash prov. 30-Mar-4 De Veres Art Auctions, Dublin #126/R

ROGGE, Emy (1866-?) German
£476 $818 €680 Evening at the moor ditch (72x54cm-28x21in) s. 5-Dec-3 Bolland & Marotz, Bremen #408/R
£795 $1446 €1200 Girls at the seaside (38x47cm-15x19in) s. board. 18-Jun-4 Bolland & Marotz, Bremen #379/R

ROGHMAN, Geertruyt (17th C) Dutch
Works on paper
£608 $1070 €900 Young woman spinning (14x15cm-6x6in) i. verso chk. 22-May-4 Lempertz, Koln #1346/R

ROGIERS, Arthur (attrib) (19th C) ?
£805 $1426 €1200 Pianiste dans l'atelier (24x38cm-9x15in) bears sig.d.1908. 30-Apr-4 Tajan, Paris #126

ROGISTER, Marie Louise von (1899-1991) German
£1000 $1790 €1500 No 7.8 (50x73cm-20x29in) s.d.58 s.i. stretcher. 15-May-4 Van Ham, Cologne #884/R est:1600

ROGNER, Heinrich Nicolaus (1813-?) German
£599 $1036 €850 Portrait of Eduard Ranninger (26x21cm-10x8in) s.d.1837 metal. 10-Dec-3 Hugo Ruef, Munich #2484/R

ROGNONI, Angelo (1896-1957) Italian
Works on paper
£671 $1201 €1000 Lady and dog. Woman at table (35x24cm-14x9in) s.i. W/C Chinese ink exec.1918 two prov. 25-May-4 Sotheby's, Milan #14/R

ROGNONI, Franco (1913-1999) Italian
£411 $699 €600 Nude (13x18cm-5x7in) s. 7-Nov-3 Galleria Rosenberg, Milan #148/R
£690 $1103 €1000 Venice at night (20x20cm-8x8in) s. s.verso. 13-Mar-3 Galleria Pace, Milan #27/R
£811 $1427 €1200 Whisper (41x33cm-16x13in) s. s.i.d.93 verso paper on canvas. 24-May-4 Christie's, Milan #48/R
£833 $1533 €1250 Figures at night (18x30cm-7x12in) s. card. 12-Jun-4 Meeting Art, Vercelli #224
£986 $1637 €1400 Figura nella notte (33x41cm-13x16in) s. tempera paper. 14-Jun-3 Meeting Art, Vercelli #188/R
£1197 $1987 €1700 Ercole e onfale (48x35cm-19x14in) s.i.d.1961 paper on canvas. 14-Jun-3 Meeting Art, Vercelli #469/R est:1500
£1408 $2465 €2000 Landscape (54x45cm-21x18in) s. tempera paper on canvas. 17-Dec-3 Il Ponte, Milan #1198 est:1200-1400
£1867 $3435 €2800 Lady in pink (38x47cm-15x19in) s. s.i.d.1974 verso. 12-Jun-4 Meeting Art, Vercelli #737/R est:2000
Works on paper
£268 $497 €400 Venice (29x21cm-11x8in) s.d.1990 mixed media. 13-Mar-4 Meeting Art, Vercelli #219
£282 $468 €400 Figura (29x19cm-11x7in) s. pastel. 14-Jun-3 Meeting Art, Vercelli #219
£290 $484 €420 Woman holding flower (17x14cm-7x6in) s.d.1975 W/C. 13-Nov-3 Galleria Pace, Milan #24/R
£435 $713 €600 Shakespeare's storm (49x36cm-19x14in) s.i.d.1957 mixed media paper on canvas. 29-May-3 Galleria Pace, Milan #9/R
£470 $869 €700 Don Quixote (28x17cm-11x7in) s. mixed media. 11-Mar-4 Galleria Pace, Milan #22/R
£533 $981 €800 Figure (33x24cm-13x9in) Chinese ink W/C paper on canvas sold with pastel by Ennio Finzi. 10-Jun-4 Galleria Pace, Milan #29/R
£567 $1043 €850 Woman (30x20cm-12x8in) s. mixed media paper on canvas. 12-Jun-4 Meeting Art, Vercelli #663/R
£897 $1434 €1300 Venice (17x53cm-7x21in) s. mixed media card. 13-Mar-3 Galleria Pace, Milan #147/R est:1500-2000
£1172 $1876 €1700 Town at night (33x41cm-13x16in) s. mixed media paper on canvas. 13-Mar-3 Galleria Pace, Milan #117/R est:2000-3000
£1172 $1876 €1700 Mandolin (20x30cm-8x12in) s. mixed media canvas prov. 13-Mar-3 Galleria Pace, Milan #131/R

ROGOVIN, Milton (1909-) American
Photographs
£2333 $4200 €3406 Untitled (21x19cm-8x7in) s.i. i.d.verso gelatin silver print prov. 23-Apr-4 Phillips, New York #117/R est:3000-5000

ROGOWAY, Alfred (1905-1990) American
£432 $800 €631 Dancing couple (38x33cm-15x13in) s. acrylic on board. 17-Jan-4 Susanin's, Chicago #117/R

ROH, Franz (1890-1965) German
Photographs
£4167 $7500 €6084 Apparition (22x15cm-9x6in) s.num. i.verso gelatin silver print. 22-Apr-4 Phillips, New York #38/R est:8000-12000
Works on paper
£420 $713 €600 Le poete (16x15cm-6x6in) studio st.verso collage engraving exec.c.1925 prov. 23-Nov-3 Cornette de St.Cyr, Paris #311

ROHDE, Fredrik (1816-1886) Danish
£500 $785 €725 Bringing home the harvest (28x32cm-11x13in) init.d.1852. 28-Aug-3 Christie's, Kensington #92
£537 $983 €784 Figures on frozen canal (28x37cm-11x15in) s.d.1869. 9-Jun-4 Rasmussen, Copenhagen #1596/R (D.KR 6000)
£539 $1003 €787 Winter landscape with couple walking (26x34cm-10x13in) mono. 2-Mar-4 Rasmussen, Copenhagen #1649/R (D.KR 6000)
£595 $1066 €869 Figures on country road (24x29cm-9x11in) s.d.1865. 12-Jan-4 Rasmussen, Vejle #377/R (D.KR 6300)
£1121 $1772 €1625 View across frozen sea (22x30cm-9x12in) mono.d.1850 panel. 2-Sep-3 Rasmussen, Copenhagen #1990/R est:15000 (D.KR 12000)
£1701 $2943 €2483 Winter landscape with bare trees by coast, storm approaching (20x23cm-8x9in) mono.d.1849 panel. 9-Dec-3 Rasmussen, Copenhagen #1552/R est:6000 (D.KR 18000)
£3412 $5460 €4982 Landscape with Roskilde Cathedral (60x84cm-24x33in) mono.d.1842. 22-Sep-3 Rasmussen, Vejle #428/R est:40000 (D.KR 36000)

ROHDE, Herman (19th C) American
£647 $1100 €945 Middle eastern market view (40x61cm-16x24in) s. 21-Nov-3 Skinner, Boston #319/R est:500-600

ROHDE, Johan (1856-1935) Danish

£269	$484	€393	Spanish mountain village (44x52cm-17x20in) s.d.1916. 24-Apr-4 Rasmussen, Havnen #2105/R (D.KR 3000)
£269	$484	€393	The meadow at Ribe, winter (69x80cm-27x31in) s.d.1922. 24-Apr-4 Rasmussen, Havnen #2108/R (D.KR 3000)
£289	$540	€422	In the heather at Fanoe (33x41cm-13x16in) s.d.1917 cardboard. 25-Feb-4 Museumsbygningen, Copenhagen #153 (D.KR 3200)
£303	$485	€439	Beached fishing boats, Terrasina (28x43cm-11x17in) s.d.02 cardboard. 17-Sep-3 Kunsthallen, Copenhagen #467 (D.KR 3200)
£356	$647	€534	Landscape with farm (53x65cm-21x26in) s. 19-Jun-4 Rasmussen, Havnen #2049/R (D.KR 4000)
£406	$759	€593	Landscape from Spottrup in Salling (46x59cm-18x23in) init.d.1890. 25-Feb-4 Museumsbygningen, Copenhagen #171/R (D.KR 4500)
£588	$1053	€858	Girl from Fano wearing national costume (36x30cm-14x12in) init.i.d.1911. 10-May-4 Rasmussen, Vejle #317/R (D.KR 6500)
£716	$1311	€1045	View from Randers, evening (88x106cm-35x42in) s. 9-Jun-4 Rasmussen, Copenhagen #1608/R (D.KR 8000)
£2076	$3882	€3031	View of Christianshavn (84x103cm-33x41in) s.d.1919. 25-Feb-4 Kunsthallen, Copenhagen #288/R est:18000 (D.KR 23000)

ROHDE, Karl (1806-1873) German

£379	$633	€550	Girl's portrait (64x51cm-25x20in) s. lit. 12-Jul-3 Bergmann, Erlangen #626/R

ROHDE, Werner (20th C) German

£265	$482	€400	Country landscape with stream (65x80cm-26x31in) s. i.verso board. 18-Jun-4 Bolland & Marotz, Bremen #381/R

ROHL, Karl Peter (1890-1975) German

Works on paper

£1867	$3341	€2800	Music score (24x31cm-9x12in) s.d. Indian ink prov. 14-May-4 Ketterer, Munich #416/R est:3000-4000

ROHLFS, Christian (1849-1938) German

£2133	$3904	€3200	Head (35x38cm-14x15in) mono. s.i. verso tempera. 5-Jun-4 Lempertz, Koln #977/R est:4000
£3356	$6007	€5000	Tulips (48x38cm-19x15in) mono.d. tempera chk. 25-May-4 Karl & Faber, Munich #507/R est:9000-10000
£3430	$6310	€5008	Der sitzende Mann - Man seated (17x13cm-7x5in) s. paper prov. 29-Mar-4 Rasmussen, Copenhagen #142/R est:15000 (D.KR 38000)
£4514	$7538	€6500	Anenomes (34x51cm-13x20in) mono.d. i. verso tempera board. 25-Oct-3 Dr Lehr, Berlin #429/R est:7000
£8667	$15947	€13000	Tree (61x51cm-24x20in) mono.d.21 tempera paper on cardboard prov. 12-Jun-4 Villa Grisebach, Berlin #225/R est:9000-12000
£10067	$18523	€15000	Yellow and white composition. mono.d.32 tempera paper. 26-Mar-4 Karrenbauer, Konstanz #1766/R est:10000
£10667	$19093	€16000	Wall in Weimar graveyard (61x49cm-24x19in) s.d.92 lit. 15-May-4 Van Ham, Cologne #885/R est:18000
£11468	$19151	€16629	Red flowers in vase. mono.d.23 oil chk over Indian ink. 19-Jun-3 Kornfeld, Bern #903/R est:12500 (S.FR 25000)
£14000	$25760	€21000	Blue pine tree (56x75cm-22x30in) mono.d.20 tempera paper prov.lit. 12-Jun-4 Villa Grisebach, Berlin #275/R est:14000-18000
£17483	$29720	€25000	Baltic - Misdroy beach (51x70cm-20x28in) mono.d.25 water tempera board. 26-Nov-3 Lempertz, Koln #949/R est:20000-22000
£17483	$30070	€25000	Vase with bunch of roses and trophy (51x69cm-20x27in) mono.d.1924 oil tempera chk prov. 5-Dec-3 Ketterer, Munich #86/R est:25000-30000
£18667	$34347	€28000	Daisies (60x48cm-24x19in) mono.d.31 s.i.verso tempera prov. 12-Jun-4 Villa Grisebach, Berlin #274/R est:28000-32000
£18881	$32098	€27000	Woman gathering wood (94x73cm-37x29in) mono. bears d.1888. 26-Nov-3 Lempertz, Koln #946/R est:14000-16000
£32000	$58240	€46720	Zwei Figuren (67x45cm-26x18in) painted 1930 prov.lit. 3-Feb-4 Christie's, London #216/R est:25000-35000
£38667	$71147	€58000	Carnations and roses (76x100cm-30x39in) mono.d.25 s.i. stretcher tempera prov.exhib. 11-Jun-4 Villa Grisebach, Berlin #1575/R est:40000-60000
£40000	$73600	€60000	Crook (100x60cm-39x24in) mono.d.18 s.i.verso exhib.lit. 11-Jun-4 Villa Grisebach, Berlin #34/R est:60000-80000
£59441	$101049	€85000	In the Sauerland - young forest (61x80cm-24x31in) mono. i. stretcher prov.exhib.lit. 28-Nov-3 Villa Grisebach, Berlin #45/R est:40000-60000

Prints

£2081	$3476	€3038	The smoker (32x19cm-13x7in) s.i. col linocut. 27-Jun-3 Falk & Falk, Zurich #877/R est:4000 (S.FR 4600)
£2400	$4296	€3600	The smoker (32x20cm-13x8in) mono. W/C on linocut. 15-May-4 Dr Sturies, Dusseldorf #167/R
£2533	$4661	€3800	Two dancers (29x31cm-11x12in) s. woodcut. 10-Jun-4 Hauswedell & Nolte, Hamburg #603/R est:4500
£2620	$4769	€3825	Peasant. s. woodcut. 17-Jun-4 Kornfeld, Bern #718/R est:7500 (S.FR 6000)
£3057	$5563	€4463	Dancer - Egyptian. s. linocut. 17-Jun-4 Kornfeld, Bern #716/R est:7500 (S.FR 7000)

Works on paper

£245	$416	€350	Figure studies (16x12cm-6x5in) d.IV 98 chk board. 29-Nov-3 Villa Grisebach, Berlin #659/R
£267	$477	€400	Shore path in Ascona (19x14cm-7x6in) col pen. 15-May-4 Bassenge, Berlin #7115
£490	$832	€700	Two kneeling nudes (14x17cm-6x7in) mono. chl board. 29-Nov-3 Villa Grisebach, Berlin #660/R
£556	$928	€800	Expulsion of Hagar (23x18cm-9x7in) Indian ink pencil wash. 24-Oct-3 Ketterer, Hamburg #526/R
£800	$1432	€1200	Blossom (35x25cm-14x10in) col chk. 15-May-4 Bassenge, Berlin #7114/R
£1200	$2148	€1800	Pre-alpine landscape (57x75cm-22x30in) mono. chl. 15-May-4 Bassenge, Berlin #7113/R est:3000
£1879	$3458	€2800	Dancer (35x24cm-14x9in) mono.d. Indian ink w/c chk. 26-Mar-4 Ketterer, Hamburg #612/R est:3200-5000
£2431	$4059	€3500	Dancer (35x24cm-14x9in) mono.d. Indian ink W/C chk. 24-Oct-3 Ketterer, Hamburg #528/R est:4000-6000
£2569	$4291	€3700	Standing female nude (65x50cm-26x20in) mono. chl prov. 24-Oct-3 Ketterer, Hamburg #527/R est:3800-4000
£3497	$5944	€5000	Petunia (17x24cm-7x9in) i.d.1932 verso chk water tempera. 26-Nov-3 Lempertz, Koln #951/R est:5500
£4000	$7360	€6000	Portrait of Annelise (72x51cm-28x20in) mono.d.25 i.verso water-tempera. 11-Jun-4 Villa Grisebach, Berlin #1546/R est:9000-12000
£4196	$7133	€6000	Landscape near Weimar (23x29cm-9x11in) mono. pastel paper on board. 29-Nov-3 Villa Grisebach, Berlin #116/R est:6000-8000
£4484	$7489	€6547	Yellow house with red roof (53x44cm-21x17in) mono. pastel chk tempera. 24-Oct-3 Hans Widmer, St Gallen #17/R est:10000-18000 (S.FR 10000)
£4861	$8118	€7000	Guinea fowl (30x49cm-12x19in) mono. W/C prov. 24-Oct-3 Ketterer, Hamburg #524/R est:7000-9000
£6667	$12200	€10000	Men in black suits followed by young woman (18x18cm-7x7in) mono. W/C bodycol. 5-Jun-4 Lempertz, Koln #971/R est:10000
£7000	$12740	€10220	Weiblicher halbakt - Female half nude (50x55cm-20x22in) init. gouache exec.c.1918 prov. 4-Feb-4 Sotheby's, London #549/R est:7000-9000
£7343	$12629	€10500	Cabbage and endives I (52x69cm-20x27in) mono.d.1923 i.verso water-tempera prov. 5-Dec-3 Ketterer, Munich #77/R est:9000-12000
£8000	$14720	€12000	Red flowers (44x29cm-17x11in) mono. red chk tempera exec. c.1930-35. 12-Jun-4 Villa Grisebach, Berlin #309/R est:10000-15000
£13380	$23148	€19000	Red poppies in vase (49x67cm-19x26in) mono.d.19 W/C tempera. 13-Dec-3 Lempertz, Koln #181/R est:15000-18000
£15385	$26154	€22000	Ghiridone in the snow (58x79cm-23x31in) mono.d.37 W/C pencil exhib. 26-Nov-3 Lempertz, Koln #954/R est:25000
£17483	$29720	€25000	Two women talking (48x35cm-19x14in) mono. bears d.22 water tempera double-sided prov. 28-Nov-3 Villa Grisebach, Berlin #54/R est:18000-24000
£30769	$52308	€44000	Snowy mountain and lake (58x79cm-23x31in) mono.d.35 i. verso water tempera prov. 26-Nov-3 Lempertz, Koln #953/R est:45000
£40000	$73600	€60000	Poppy in a glass vase (67x48cm-26x19in) mono.d.19 water tempera paper on cardboard. 11-Jun-4 Villa Grisebach, Berlin #33/R est:60000-80000

ROHLING, Carl (1849-1922) German

£1399	$2336	€2000	Lucky meeting with the queen (77x57cm-30x22in) s. i. verso. 9-Oct-3 Michael Zeller, Lindau #739/R est:1800

ROHLING, Ernst August (1845-1887) German

£458	$792	€650	Gallant couple in Renaissance costume (84x63cm-33x25in) s.d.1875. 12-Dec-3 Berlinghof, Heidelberg #1124/R

ROHNER, Georges (1913-2000) French

£385	$728	€570	Tomate (30x30cm-12x12in) s. 21-Feb-4 Cornette de St.Cyr, Paris #397
£403	$749	€600	La Vallee du Lot (26x45cm-10x18in) s. isorel. 3-Mar-4 Ferri, Paris #347
£403	$749	€600	Village du Lot (16x22cm-6x9in) s. isorel. 3-Mar-4 Ferri, Paris #349
£563	$975	€800	Roses blanches et vase gris (24x18cm-9x7in) s.d.1954. 10-Dec-3 Ferri, Paris #86/R
£625	$1044	€900	Deux boules (24x41cm-9x16in) s. 21-Oct-3 Christie's, Paris #186/R
£638	$1186	€950	La Vallee du Lot (26x45cm-10x18in) s. 3-Mar-4 Ferri, Paris #348
£764	$1276	€1100	Paysage aux peupliers (24x33cm-9x13in) s. 21-Oct-3 Christie's, Paris #182/R
£1064	$1777	€1500	Nature morte a la pipe et a la boite (50x50cm-20x20in) s. 19-Jun-3 Millon & Associes, Paris #260 est:1500-2000
£1111	$1856	€1600	Paysage du Midi (44x140cm-17x55in) s. 21-Oct-3 Christie's, Paris #181/R est:1000-1500
£1250	$2088	€1800	Buste de femme (24x41cm-9x16in) s. 21-Oct-3 Christie's, Paris #184/R est:800-1200
£1611	$2996	€2400	Jeux de societe (46x65cm-18x26in) s. 3-Mar-4 Tajan, Paris #184 est:2500-3000
£3472	$5799	€5000	Le violon (73x116cm-29x46in) s. lit. 21-Oct-3 Christie's, Paris #190/R est:1800-2000
£4167	$6958	€6000	Le vin a la maison (55x46cm-22x18in) s. 21-Oct-3 Christie's, Paris #189/R est:3000-5000
£5208	$8698	€7500	Nu II - Micheline (114x146cm-45x57in) s. prov.exhib.lit. 21-Oct-3 Christie's, Paris #188/R est:8000-10000
£5903	$9858	€8500	Les poires (54x81cm-21x32in) s.d.52 exhib.lit. 21-Oct-3 Christie's, Paris #185/R est:2500-3000
£9375	$15656	€13500	La partie de cartes (73x92cm-29x36in) s. 21-Oct-3 Christie's, Paris #187/R est:2000-3000
£10417	$17396	€15000	Fruits et legumes (100x50cm-39x20in) four exhib. lit. 21-Oct-3 Christie's, Paris #183/R est:7000-9000

Works on paper

£313	$522	€450	La pomme (29x24cm-11x9in) s.i. W/C ink pencil prov. 21-Oct-3 Christie's, Paris #107/R
£382	$638	€550	Le Pont des Arts, Paris (14x21cm-6x8in) s. W/C gouache. 21-Oct-3 Christie's, Paris #106/R
£451	$754	€650	Tomates et poire (38x57cm-15x22in) s. W/C gouache pencil. 21-Oct-3 Christie's, Paris #108/R
£590	$986	€850	Le vin a la maison (66x51cm-26x20in) s.i. pencil study prov. 21-Oct-3 Christie's, Paris #103/R
£590	$986	€850	La mer (57x38cm-22x15in) s. W/C pencil. 21-Oct-3 Christie's, Paris #105/R
£625	$1044	€900	Les oranges (33x50cm-13x20in) s.i. W/C pencil. 21-Oct-3 Christie's, Paris #102/R
£764	$1276	€1100	La bibliotheque (28x38cm-11x15in) s. pencil. 21-Oct-3 Christie's, Paris #110/R
£903	$1508	€1300	Nature morte aux livres et a la pipe (34x43cm-13x17in) s. W/C pencil gouache. 21-Oct-3 Christie's, Paris #109/R
£972	$1624	€1400	Le Pont Neuf, Paris (38x56cm-15x22in) s. W/C pencil. 21-Oct-3 Christie's, Paris #99/R
£972	$1624	€1400	Nature morte aux pommes et au vase de pensees (38x57cm-15x22in) s.i. W/C pencil prov. 21-Oct-3 Christie's, Paris #101/R

ROHNER, Hans (1898-1972) Swiss

£588	$1000	€858	Mountain village in summer (33x46cm-13x18in) s. hessian. 28-Nov-3 Zofingen, Switzerland #3149/R (S.FR 1300)
£814	$1385	€1188	Landscape in Bayern (52x58cm-20x23in) s. s.i.d.1926 verso canvas on board. 22-Nov-3 Burkhard, Luzern #71/R (S.FR 1800)
£2489	$4231	€3634	Portrait of a girl (68x51cm-27x20in) oil tempera board. 22-Nov-3 Burkhard, Luzern #70/R est:2200-2600 (S.FR 5500)

ROHRHIRSCH, Karl (1875-1954) German

£300	$555	€438	Haymaking (13x17cm-5x7in) s.i. board. 13-Jan-4 Bonhams, Knightsbridge #19a

ROHRICHT, Wolf (1886-1953) German
£537 $988 €800 Lake in winter mountain landscape (80x100cm-31x39in) s. 24-Mar-4 Hugo Ruef, Munich #1254
£1164 $1979 €1700 Schliersee (80x64cm-31x25in) s. panel. 5-Nov-3 Hugo Ruef, Munich #1257/R est:700
Works on paper
£347 $580 €500 Sketch for stage set (34x25cm-13x10in) mono. W/C Indian ink. 24-Oct-3 Ketterer, Hamburg #1047/R

ROI, Pietro (attrib) (1820-1896) Italian
£972 $1526 €1400 Woman and child by lake in evening (40x53cm-16x21in) bears mono. 30-Aug-3 Hans Stahl, Toestorf #53/R

ROIDOT, Henri (1877-1960) Belgian
£278 $442 €400 Chemin de campagne (38x60cm-15x24in) s. 15-Sep-3 Horta, Bruxelles #238
£451 $718 €650 Saules sous le soleil (40x50cm-16x20in) s. 15-Sep-3 Horta, Bruxelles #237
£655 $1212 €950 La mare aux canards a Linkebeek (26x33cm-10x13in) s. cardboard. 16-Feb-4 Horta, Bruxelles #321
£867 $1551 €1300 In the field (20x32cm-8x13in) s. board. 15-May-4 De Vuyst, Lokeren #280/R
£1064 $1777 €1500 Shepherd with his flock under apple blossom trees (50x60cm-20x24in) s. 20-Oct-3 Glerum, Amsterdam #212/R est:1500-2000
£1088 $1948 €1600 Etang a Linkebeek (40x49cm-16x19in) s. panel. 16-Mar-4 Vanderkindere, Brussels #231 est:800-1200
£1111 $1811 €1600 Landscape (80x100cm-31x39in) s. 29-Sep-3 Sotheby's, Amsterdam #225
£6711 $12416 €10000 Retour des champs a Linkebeek (141x192cm-56x76in) s. lit. 13-Mar-4 De Vuyst, Lokeren #440/R est:10000-12000

ROIG GUTIERREZ, Francisco (1882-1958) Spanish
£604 $1081 €900 Seascape (41x54cm-16x21in) s. 25-May-4 Durán, Madrid #686/R

ROIG Y SOLER, Juan (1852-1909) Spanish
£9420 $15449 €13000 Village street (53x43cm-21x17in) s. 27-May-3 Durán, Madrid #237/R est:11000

ROIG, Jose (19/20th C) Spanish
£1117 $2000 €1631 Traful lake (57x76cm-22x30in) 11-May-4 Arroyo, Buenos Aires #84
£3144 $5250 €4590 Tarde tranquila, Mina Clavero (61x71cm-24x28in) s. 16-Nov-3 Simpson's, Houston #195/R

ROILOS, Georgios (1867-1928) Greek
£900 $1575 €1314 Coastal landscape with pine trees (20x35cm-8x14in) s. board. 16-Dec-3 Bonhams, New Bond Street #57/R
£2800 $4900 €4088 Portrait of a gentleman (66x60cm-26x24in) s. 16-Dec-3 Bonhams, New Bond Street #26/R est:1500-2000
£15000 $26850 €21900 Farmhouse (80x110cm-31x43in) s. prov. 11-May-4 Bonhams, New Bond Street #22/R est:8000-12000
Works on paper
£1400 $2506 €2044 Evzon (41x35cm-16x14in) s. W/C. 10-May-4 Sotheby's, Olympia #140/R est:1200-1800

ROJAS, Carlos (1933-) Colombian
£968 $1500 €1413 Untitled (80x80cm-31x31in) s.verso painted 1974. 29-Sep-2 Subastas Odalys, Caracas #83

ROJAS, Edwin (20th C) South American
£2105 $3874 €3200 The sisters-in-law (64x79cm-25x31in) s. 22-Jun-4 De Veres Art Auctions, Dublin #121/R est:3000-4000

ROJAS, Elmar (1938-) Guatemalan
£574 $952 €832 Mis universo (83x71cm-33x28in) s.d.1976. 12-Jun-3 Louis Morton, Mexico #116/R est:14000-18000 (M.P 10000)
£688 $1143 €998 Angel brujo (105x76cm-41x30in) s.d.1976. 12-Jun-3 Louis Morton, Mexico #119/R est:17000-20000 (M.P 12000)
£3571 $6500 €5214 Sin titulo (109x109cm-43x43in) s.d.82 prov. 29-Jun-4 Sotheby's, New York #671/R est:4000-6000

ROJAS, Ignacio (19/20th C) Italian
£490 $817 €700 Woman in profile (17x12cm-7x5in) s. board. 24-Jun-3 Finarte Semenzato, Rome #139/R

ROJE, Arsen (20th C) Yugoslavian
£2386 $4200 €3484 Name of Love (112x178cm-44x70in) s.i.d.1986 verso prov. 23-May-4 Hindman, Chicago #1006/R est:2000-3000

ROJKA, Fritz (1878-1939) Austrian
£608 $1070 €900 Beach (12x19cm-5x7in) s. board. 22-May-4 Lempertz, Koln #1592

ROJO, Octavio (1951-) Uruguayan?
£269 $450 €393 Interior scene (44x61cm-17x24in) s. cardboard prov. 7-Oct-3 Galeria y Remates, Montevideo #86

ROKA, Charles Antonio (1912-1999) Norwegian/Hungarian
£511 $818 €741 Woman with jug of wine (80x65cm-31x26in) s. 22-Sep-3 Blomqvist, Lysaker #1247/R (N.KR 6000)
£872 $1605 €1273 Girl with hair band (81x65cm-32x26in) s. 29-Mar-4 Blomqvist, Lysaker #1250/R (N.KR 11000)
£912 $1678 €1332 Beautiful woman (80x65cm-31x26in) s. 29-Mar-4 Blomqvist, Lysaker #1248/R (N.KR 11500)
£1150 $2116 €1679 Female nude (60x80cm-24x31in) s. panel. 29-Mar-4 Blomqvist, Lysaker #1249/R est:10000-12000 (N.KR 14500)
£1166 $2133 €1702 Gypsy girl (80x60cm-31x24in) s. 2-Feb-4 Blomqvist, Lysaker #1245/R est:6000-8000 (N.KR 14500)
£3913 $6770 €5713 Dancer resting (80x65cm-31x26in) s. exhib. 13-Dec-3 Blomqvist, Lysaker #1294 est:25000-30000 (N.KR 45000)

ROLAND, Henry (1920-) Belgian
£426 $711 €600 La super diva (100x80cm-39x31in) s. s.i.verso. 15-Oct-3 Hotel des Ventes Mosan, Brussels #262

ROLAND, Philippe Laurent (1746-1816) French
Sculpture
£36000 $62280 €52560 Rosemarie Charlotte and Camille Rousseau (61cm-24in) s. terracotta pair lit. 11-Dec-3 Christie's, London #108/R est:40000-60000

ROLANDO, Charles (1844-1893) Australian
£1224 $2253 €1787 Cattle grazing (51x91cm-20x36in) s. 29-Mar-4 Goodman, Sydney #195/R est:3000-4000 (A.D 3000)
£3602 $6123 €5259 Cattle by a stream in a pastoral landscape (88x138cm-35x54in) s. prov. 24-Nov-3 Sotheby's, Melbourne #257/R est:3000-5000 (A.D 8500)
£3664 $6669 €5349 In the buffalo Ranges, Victoria (61x105cm-24x41in) s.d.1892. 16-Jun-4 Deutscher-Menzies, Melbourne #169/R est:12000-15000 (A.D 9600)
£3817 $6947 €5573 Cattle fording a river (77x140cm-30x55in) s. 16-Jun-4 Deutscher-Menzies, Melbourne #168/R est:12000-15000 (A.D 10000)

ROLARD, François Laurent (1842-1912) French
Sculpture
£1329 $2259 €1900 Farewell (76cm-30in) i. bronze. 20-Nov-3 Van Ham, Cologne #1256/R est:1900
£1457 $2666 €2200 Semi nude figure of a girl (117cm-46in) s. bronze. 6-Apr-4 Sotheby's, Olympia #188/R est:1000-1500
£3169 $5482 €4500 Chef arabe (48cm-19in) s.d.1874 pat bronze lit. 15-Dec-3 Gros & Delettrez, Paris #175/R est:4000-6000

ROLDAN, Juan (1940-) Spanish
£855 $1574 €1300 Landscape (81x81cm-32x32in) s. 22-Jun-4 Durán, Madrid #657/R

ROLET, Christian (1945-) Belgian
£306 $486 €440 La coiffure (31x42cm-12x17in) s.d.75. 9-Sep-3 Palais de Beaux Arts, Brussels #268

ROLF, F (19/20th C) ?
£1690 $2806 €2400 Venice (37x59cm-15x23in) s. 16-Jun-3 Dorotheum, Vienna #157/R est:1800-2400

ROLFE, Alexander F (fl.1839-1873) British
£7784 $13000 €11365 Thames from Richmond Hill (81x137cm-32x54in) d.1862. 7-Oct-3 Sotheby's, New York #107 est:7000-9000

ROLFE, H L (19th C) British
£1500 $2655 €2190 Speckled trout (33x23cm-13x9in) board. 28-Apr-4 Hales, Bovey Tracey #458

ROLFE, Henry Leonidas (fl.1847-1881) British
£1800 $3222 €2628 Prize catch (46x76cm-18x30in) s.d.1862. 11-May-4 Bonhams, Knightsbridge #252/R est:1500-2000
£2600 $4420 €3796 Day's catch (32x39cm-13x15in) s.d.1868. 27-Nov-3 Christie's, Kensington #250/R est:1000-1500

ROLFSEN, Alf (1895-1979) Norwegian
£429 $751 €626 Woman seated with her hands on her head (62x60cm-24x24in) s.i.d.55. 16-Dec-3 Grev Wedels Plass, Oslo #214/R (N.KR 5000)

ROLING, Gerard Victor Alphons (1904-1981) Dutch
Works on paper
£467 $854 €700 Horses at the lake (51x76cm-20x30in) s.d.63 Indian ink. 7-Jun-4 Glerum, Amsterdam #199/R

ROLL, Alain (1897-1978) French
£319 $533 €450 Lovers on riverbank (22x27cm-9x11in) s. i. verso. 16-Oct-3 Dorotheum, Salzburg #657/R

ROLLA, Adolfo Giuseppe (1899-1967) Italian
£486 $826 €700 Small river (36x47cm-14x19in) s. s.i.verso board. 1-Nov-3 Meeting Art, Vercelli #368
£517 $859 €750 Snow (15x22cm-6x9in) s. board. 1-Oct-3 Della Rocca, Turin #22/R
£694 $1181 €1000 Mohajerine, Damasco (50x65cm-20x26in) s.i.d.1937 i.d.verso. 1-Nov-3 Meeting Art, Vercelli #85/R
£1656 $3013 €2500 Dawn on the Angiolino, Gemignano, Italy (36x47cm-14x19in) s. s.d.1946 verso board exhib. 21-Jun-4 Pandolfini, Florence #211/R est:2600-2800
£1667 $2833 €2400 Eighteenth century bridge in Agnona (80x90cm-31x35in) s. i.verso. 1-Nov-3 Meeting Art, Vercelli #325/R est:2000

ROLLAN, Jordi (1940-) Spanish
£383 $620 €540 Untitled (65x54cm-26x21in) s.d.91. 20-May-3 Ansorena, Madrid #382/R

ROLLAND, Antoni Vidal (1889-1970) Spanish
£276 $500 €420 On the beach (46x38cm-18x15in) s.d.1965. 14-Apr-4 Ansorena, Madrid #249/R

ROLLAND, Henri (1897-1941) French
£430 $731 €628 Women in park (40x49cm-16x19in) i. panel. 19-Nov-3 Fischer, Luzern #2258/R (S.FR 950)

ROLLE, August H O (1875-1941) American
£1285 $2300 €1876 Sunset (13x15cm-5x6in) board. 7-May-4 Sloans & Kenyon, Bethesda #1691/R est:500-700

ROLLETT, Herbert (1872-1932) British
£270 $500 €394 Wooded landscape scene, possibly Weelsby Woods near Grimsby (21x26cm-8x10in) s. 10-Feb-4 Dickinson, Davy & Markham, Brigg #847
£1257 $2250 €1835 Over the fields to the village. s. 10-Jan-4 Harvey Clar, Oakland #1579

ROLLI (20th C) ?
£1458 $2435 €2100 Italian woman selling fruit (68x41cm-27x16in) s. 26-Oct-3 Bukowskis, Helsinki #581/R est:400

ROLLIN, Claude (1950-) Canadian
£207 $374 €302 Petite Riviere, St. Francois, Charlevoix, Quebec (41x51cm-16x20in) s. s.i.verso. 18-Apr-4 Levis, Calgary #540/R (C.D 500)

ROLLINS, Nana Bickford (20th C) American
Works on paper
£230 $425 €336 Winter village scene with figures, horse drawn sleighs and church (33x43cm-13x17in) s. gouache. 24-Jan-4 Jeffery Burchard, Florida #30a/R

ROLLINS, Tim and K O S (20th C) American
Works on paper
£351 $650 €512 Untitled (18x13cm-7x5in) indis.s. ink gouache printed paper. 13-Jul-4 Christie's, Rockefeller NY #147/R

ROLLINS, Warren E (1861-1962) American
£529 $900 €772 Portrait of an Indian brave (9x7cm-4x3in) s. canvas on canvas prov. 18-Nov-3 John Moran, Pasadena #119b
£1070 $2000 €1562 Pueblo woman in a doorway (51x25cm-20x10in) s. prov. 29-Feb-4 Bonhams & Butterfields, San Francisco #4536 est:2500-3500
£1099 $2000 €1605 The Mesa (46x76cm-18x30in) s. i.verso. 15-Jun-4 John Moran, Pasadena #110 est:2000-3000
£1176 $2000 €1717 Southwest adobe cabin (9x9cm-4x4in) s. canvasboard prov. 18-Nov-3 John Moran, Pasadena #112 est:1500-2000
£1198 $2000 €1749 New Mexico landscape with buildings (28x38cm-11x15in) s. 19-Oct-3 Jeffery Burchard, Florida #55
£1497 $2500 €2186 Santa Fe, New Mexico (28x38cm-11x15in) s.i.verso. 19-Oct-3 Jeffery Burchard, Florida #55a
£1618 $2750 €2362 Indian figure with black ware pottery vessel (33x23cm-13x9in) s. board prov. 18-Nov-3 John Moran, Pasadena #159 est:1500-2000
£2353 $4000 €3435 Figures in southwest landscape (36x20cm-14x8in) s. prov. 18-Nov-3 John Moran, Pasadena #158 est:1500-2000
£2717 $5000 €3967 Santa Fe, New Mexico (27x38cm-11x15in) s. i.verso prov. 8-Jun-4 Bonhams & Butterfields, San Francisco #4133/R est:3000-5000
£13235 $22500 €19323 Meditation (61x91cm-24x36in) s.d.1910 prov.lit. 1-Nov-3 Santa Fe Art, Santa Fe #56/R est:20000-25000
Works on paper
£647 $1100 €945 The mission (38x30cm-15x12in) s.i. conte crayon graphite prov. 1-Nov-3 Santa Fe Art, Santa Fe #12/R
£932 $1500 €1351 Desert landscape (13x18cm-5x7in) pastel paper on board. 22-Aug-3 Altermann Galleries, Santa Fe #150
£3209 $6000 €4685 Santa Fe landscape (30x41cm-12x16in) s. mixed media prov. 24-Jul-4 Coeur d'Alene, Hayden #161/R est:3000-5000

ROLLMAN, Charlotte (20th C) American
Works on paper
£301 $550 €452 Ox bow (74x104cm-29x41in) W/C. 10-Jul-4 Hindman, Chicago #445/R

ROLLMANN, Julius (1827-1865) German
£8108 $14270 €12000 Venice (63x57cm-25x22in) s.d.1865. 22-May-4 Lempertz, Koln #1593/R est:12000

ROLLOF, Ulf (1961-) Swedish
£906 $1541 €1323 Untitled (80x97cm-31x38in) s. pigment beeswax canvas on panel. 4-Nov-3 Bukowskis, Stockholm #593/R (S.KR 12000)
Works on paper
£798 $1436 €1165 Untitled (123x60cm-48x24in) s.d.99 W/C triptych. 26-Apr-4 Bukowskis, Stockholm #494/R (S.KR 11000)
£831 $1412 €1213 Untitled (41x180cm-16x71in) s.d.99 W/C triptych. 4-Nov-3 Bukowskis, Stockholm #631/R (S.KR 11000)

ROLOFF, Paul (1877-1951) German
£1127 $1949 €1600 View of Aschauer valley (60x70cm-24x28in) s. 10-Dec-3 Hugo Ruef, Munich #2485/R est:600

ROLPH, Joseph Thomas (1831-1916) Canadian
Works on paper
£311 $516 €454 Untitled, rowing among the Toronto Islands (26x37cm-10x15in) s.d.1902 W/C. 5-Oct-3 Levis, Calgary #291/R (C.D 700)
£342 $635 €499 High park (89x40cm-35x16in) s.d.1878 W/C. 2-Mar-4 Ritchie, Toronto #58/R (C.D 850)

ROLSHOVEN, Julius (1858-1930) American
Works on paper
£331 $600 €483 View of the arcade in the Boboli gardens (46x61cm-18x24in) s.i. pastel. 16-Apr-4 James Julia, Fairfield #1005/R

ROLT, Vivian (1874-1933) British
£720 $1310 €1051 Harvesters in a landscape (25x76cm-10x30in) s. 5-Feb-4 Gorringes, Worthing #428
Works on paper
£340 $547 €493 Figures on a heathland path with windmill in distance (36x51cm-14x20in) s.d.1912 W/C. 15-Aug-3 Keys, Aylsham #502/R

ROLYAT, Victor (19/20th C) British
£280 $468 €409 Lakeland landscape (30x42cm-12x17in) s. 11-Nov-3 Bonhams, Knightsbridge #38/R
£659 $1100 €962 Sheep grazing beside a lake (51x76cm-20x30in) s. 18-Jun-3 Doyle, New York #67/R

ROMADIN, N M (1903-1987) Russian
£556 $1000 €812 Sketch for the painting Twelve (50x42cm-20x17in) oil on cardboard. 24-Apr-4 Shishkin Gallery, Moscow #42/R est:2000-2500
£1111 $2000 €1622 Spring at Vladimir region (21x70cm-8x28in) oil on cardboard. 24-Apr-4 Shishkin Gallery, Moscow #41/R est:3000-4000
£1944 $3500 €2838 Sketch of a model (39x55cm-15x22in) oil on cardboard. 24-Apr-4 Shishkin Gallery, Moscow #40/R est:2000-2500
£2446 $4500 €3571 Nude (63x141cm-25x56in) plywood painted 1976. 27-Mar-4 Shishkin Gallery, Moscow #72/R est:10000-12000
£3913 $7200 €5713 Ladozhsky lake (61x85cm-24x33in) paper on cardboard painted 1959. 27-Mar-4 Shishkin Gallery, Moscow #73/R est:6000-8000

ROMAGNOLI, Giovanni (1893-1976) Italian
£2878 $4719 €4000 Still life (46x36cm-18x14in) board. 5-Jun-3 Adma, Formigine #419 est:3600-3800

ROMAGNONI, Bepi (1930-1964) Italian
Works on paper
£379 $633 €550 Untitled (50x70cm-20x28in) s. Chinese ink gouache lit. 13-Nov-3 Galleria Pace, Milan #7/R
£379 $633 €550 Man with cigar (70x50cm-28x20in) s.d.1956 Chinese ink. 13-Nov-3 Galleria Pace, Milan #57/R
£533 $981 €800 Composition (50x70cm-20x28in) s.d.1958 mixed media. 10-Jun-4 Galleria Pace, Milan #5/R

ROMAIN, Hippolyte (20th C) French
Works on paper
£336 $628 €500 Bistrot Rue de Seine (41x54cm-16x21in) s.i.d.2000 gouache. 29-Feb-4 Versailles Encheres #307

ROMAKO, Anton (1832-1889) Austrian
£20000 $34000 €29200 Portrait of the Countess Maria Magda Kuefstein (79x64cm-31x25in) s. prov. 18-Nov-3 Sotheby's, London #314/R
Works on paper
£671 $1235 €1000 Bather (31x20cm-12x8in) s. pencil. 26-Mar-4 Dorotheum, Vienna #138/R
£1141 $2099 €1700 Bacchantal scene (31x20cm-12x8in) s. pencil one of pair. 26-Mar-4 Dorotheum, Vienna #136/R est:1200-1600
£2207 $3663 €3200 Woman wearing turban receiving gifts (26x19cm-10x7in) s. W/C paper on board. 30-Sep-3 Dorotheum, Vienna #243/R est:3000-3500

ROMAN SCHOOL (16th C) Italian
Works on paper
£10000 $18300 €14600 Historiated initial with the Adoration of the Shepherds (26x26cm-10x10in) init.d.1516 gouache vellum on board on wood round prov.exhib. 8-Jul-4 Sotheby's, London #1/R est:10000-15000
£11268 $19718 €16000 Apollon et Marsias (20x15cm-8x6in) pen brown ink wash prov. 17-Dec-3 Christie's, Paris #1/R est:8000-12000

ROMAN SCHOOL (17th C) Italian
£4605 $8474 €7000 Still life of fruit with peaches and pumpkin (72x59cm-28x23in) 22-Jun-4 Finarte Semenzato, Rome #300/R est:6000-8000
£5592 $10289 €8500 Nature morte aux fruits et a la pasteque (48x38cm-19x15in) 25-Jun-4 Doutrebente, Paris #5/R est:2000-3000
£5705 $10497 €8500 Rebecca and Eliezer at the well (97x117cm-38x46in) 29-Mar-4 Pandolfini, Florence #741 est:8000
£5986 $9637 €8500 Natura morta con uva e fiori (84x118cm-33x46in) 8-May-3 Farsetti, Prato #43 est:11000-13000
£6475 $10619 €9000 Man with dead game (98x68cm-39x27in) 4-Jun-3 Sotheby's, Milan #123/R est:10000-15000
£7000 $12600 €10220 Still life of melon, grapes, apples and figs (76x64cm-30x25in) i.verso prov. 22-Apr-4 Sotheby's, London #105/R est:6000-8000
£7000 $12810 €10220 Portrait of a gentleman in a brown jacket (8x6cm-3x2in) copper oval. 7-Jul-4 Christie's, London #92/R est:7000-10000

£7500	$13500	€10950	Still life of melon, peaches and pears (60x74cm-24x29in) 22-Apr-4 Sotheby's, London #108/R est:6000-8000
£8553	$15737	€13000	Madonna in prayer (77x61cm-30x24in) 24-Jun-4 Dr Fritz Nagel, Stuttgart #635/R est:11500
£8803	$15405	€12500	Rinaldo and Armida (72x87cm-28x34in) prov. 17-Dec-3 Christie's, Rome #418/R est:15000-20000
£8889	$16000	€12978	Still life of peaches and plums in a glass bowl, and other fruits on a ledge (48x64cm-19x25in) 21-Jan-4 Sotheby's, New York #130/R est:10000-15000
£9500	$17385	€13870	Contest between Apollo and Pan (74x92cm-29x36in) 8-Jul-4 Sotheby's, London #316/R est:8000-12000
£9732	$17906	€14500	Moses found in the river (89x117cm-35x46in) 29-Mar-4 Pandolfini, Florence #740/R est:8000
£11333	$20513	€17000	Still life of flowers with figs and apples. Still life of flowers with grapes and pears (40x49cm-16x19in) pair. 30-Mar-4 Babuino, Rome #46/R est:5000-7000
£12324	$21320	€17500	Nature morte aux fleurs. Nature morte aux fruits (59x75cm-23x30in) pair. 10-Dec-3 Remi Ader, Paris #74/R est:12000-15000
£12324	$21320	€17500	Nature morte aux fleurs. Nature morte aux fruits (59x75cm-23x30in) two. 10-Dec-3 Neret-Minet, Paris #74/R est:12000-15000
£15000	$25950	€21900	Portrait of a gentleman, full length wearing black pointing to a map of Africa (179x117cm-70x46in) prov. 11-Dec-3 Sotheby's, London #191/R est:12000-18000
£15827	$25957	€22000	Paradise Lost (114x156cm-45x61in) 4-Jun-3 Sotheby's, Milan #64/R est:10000-15000
£16500	$29700	€24090	David learning of the death of Saul (206x290cm-81x114in) i.verso prov. 22-Apr-4 Sotheby's, London #65/R est:15000-20000
£16783	$28867	€24000	Derision of Christ (90x65cm-35x26in) 2-Dec-3 Sotheby's, Milan #77/R est:7000-10000
£17000	$31110	€24820	Man dashing children against rocks (80x105cm-31x41in) i. oval. 8-Jul-4 Sotheby's, London #317/R est:10000-15000
£17222	$31000	€25144	Portrait of man (7x5cm-3x2in) i. copper oval. 22-Jan-4 Sotheby's, New York #14/R est:15000-20000
£17730	$29610	€25000	San Pietro (73x96cm-29x38in) 18-Jun-3 Christie's, Rome #439/R est:7000-10000
£32000	$55360	€46720	Still life of figs and apricots in a basket with various fruits on a ledge (69x95cm-27x37in) painted c.1630. 11-Dec-3 Sotheby's, London #31/R est:30000-40000
£32000	$55360	€46720	Still life of fruits and flowers in a glass vase, with a scarlet macaw (81x105cm-32x41in) mono. 11-Dec-3 Sotheby's, London #32/R est:20000-30000
£36620	$64085	€52000	Anthony and Cleopatra (244x173cm-96x68in) 17-Dec-3 Christie's, Rome #510/R est:40000-60000
£113333	$207400	€170000	View of Villa Medici (122x171cm-48x67in) s.i.d.1651. 1-Jun-4 Sotheby's, Milan #195/R est:50000-80000
Works on paper			
£7237	$13316	€11000	Visit (28x21cm-11x8in) pen ink W/C over pencil prov. 22-Jun-4 Sotheby's, Milan #16/R est:3000-4000

ROMAN SCHOOL (17th/18th C) Italian

Sculpture			
£135135	$237838	€200000	Female busts (127x43x26cm-50x17x10in) marble sold with base set of 4. 18-May-4 Sotheby's, Milan #481/R est:200000-300000

ROMAN SCHOOL (18th C) Italian

£4474	$8232	€6800	Holy Family (112x91cm-44x36in) 22-Jun-4 Babuino, Rome #35/R est:4000-5000
£4667	$8353	€7000	Annunciation (132x92cm-52x36in) 12-May-4 Finarte Semenzato, Milan #72/R est:8000-12000
£5479	$9315	€8000	Magdalene (67x88cm-26x35in) 9-Nov-3 Finarte, Venice #131/R est:9000-11000
£5517	$9214	€8000	Ulysses and Circe (15x21cm-6x8in) tempera paper on board. 12-Nov-3 Sotheby's, Milan #106/R est:6000-8000
£5517	$9214	€8000	River landscape (30x35cm-12x14in) tempera paper. 12-Nov-3 Sotheby's, Milan #155/R est:8000-12000
£5556	$9167	€8000	Five putti with flower garland (117x157cm-46x62in) 3-Jul-3 Dr Fritz Nagel, Stuttgart #450/R est:2400
£6000	$10740	€9000	View of the Coliseum (60x87cm-24x34in) 17-May-4 Finarte Semenzato, Rome #69/R est:10000-12000
£6993	$12028	€10000	Portrait of doctor (75x63cm-30x25in) 2-Dec-3 Sotheby's, Milan #123/R est:7000-10000
£9155	$14739	€13000	Apollo e Marsia (205x135cm-81x53in) 8-May-3 Farsetti, Prato #705/R est:13500-14500
£9500	$15770	€13870	River God (61x76cm-24x30in) 30-Sep-3 Sotheby's, London #32/R est:6000-8000
£9859	$17254	€14000	View of the Pantheon (57x122cm-22x48in) 19-Dec-3 Pierre Berge, Paris #74/R est:15000-20000
£10000	$18300	€14600	Finding of Moses (33x28cm-13x11in) 8-Jul-4 Sotheby's, London #318/R est:5000-7000
£10811	$19027	€16000	River landscapes (21x29cm-8x11in) tempera paper pair. 18-May-4 Sotheby's, Milan #508/R est:12000-18000
£11111	$20000	€16222	Study of a female figure (63x47cm-25x19in) 22-Jan-4 Sotheby's, New York #212/R est:20000-30000
£14000	$24220	€20440	Venus appearing to Aeneas, urging him to escape from burning Troy (97x137cm-38x54in) 11-Dec-3 Sotheby's, London #25/R est:10000-20000
£16667	$30500	€25000	Annunciation (116x159cm-46x63in) 1-Jun-4 Sotheby's, Milan #31/R est:8000-12000
£20000	$36000	€29200	Interior of San Paolo fuori le mura, Rome, with monks and elegant figures (102x127cm-40x50in) 21-Apr-4 Christie's, London #76/R est:20000-30000
£20690	$34552	€30000	Views of Rome (23x34cm-9x13in) i. tempera vellum pair. 12-Nov-3 Sotheby's, Milan #167/R est:20000-30000
£37086	$67497	€56000	Head of an apostle (63x48cm-25x19in) painted c.1700 prov. 16-Jun-4 Dorotheum, Vienna #5/R est:3500-4500
£38000	$65740	€55480	Juno, Mercury and Argus. The Flaying of Marsyas (98x136cm-39x54in) pair. 11-Dec-3 Sotheby's, London #24/R est:30000-40000
£65000	$112450	€94900	Judgement of Midas after the contest between Apollo and Pan (98x136cm-39x54in) 11-Dec-3 Sotheby's, London #23/R est:25000-35000
Sculpture			
£6419	$11297	€9500	Goat (13cm-5in) bronze. 18-May-4 Sotheby's, Milan #114/R est:2000-4000
£14667	$26253	€22000	Putti playing (80x65x40cm-31x26x16in) white marble. 17-May-4 Finarte Semenzato, Rome #177/R est:15000-18000
Works on paper			
£3611	$6500	€5272	View of the arch of Constantine with the Colioseum beyond, Rome (21x38cm-8x15in) gouache. 22-Jan-4 Sotheby's, New York #176/R est:8000-12000

ROMAN SCHOOL (19th C) Italian

£5405	$9514	€8000	Rome, Vesta's Temple (22x15cm-9x6in) 18-May-4 Sotheby's, Milan #533/R est:4000-6000
£8108	$14270	€12000	Rome, Pilotta Street (37x52cm-15x20in) 18-May-4 Sotheby's, Milan #534/R est:7000-10000
Sculpture			
£4605	$8474	€7000	Galata dying (30x58x29cm-12x23x11in) pat bronze. 22-Jun-4 Finarte Semenzato, Rome #114/R est:7000-8000
£4698	$8315	€7000	Tireur d'epine (33cm-13in) pat bronze Cast Nelli sold with base. 29-Apr-4 Sotheby's, Paris #108/R est:1500-2000
£7092	$11844	€10000	Young man (73x42x25cm-29x17x10in) white marble. 23-Jun-3 Finarte Semenzato, Rome #111/R
£10638	$17766	€15000	Roman emperor (56x52x23cm-22x20x9in) marble. 23-Jun-3 Finarte Semenzato, Rome #112/R

ROMAN, Dominique (1824-1911) French?

Photographs			
£3497	$5840	€5000	Arles, Hotel de Ville (33x43cm-13x17in) photograph in 2 parts exec.c.1855 prov.exhib. 10-Oct-3 Tajan, Paris #147/R est:4500-5000
£4196	$7007	€6000	Arles, les Alyscamps (37x52cm-15x20in) photograph exec.c.1855 prov.exhib. 10-Oct-3 Tajan, Paris #146/R est:7000-8000
£4895	$8175	€7000	Arles, Saint-Trophime (48x38cm-19x15in) photograph exec.c.1855 prov.exhib. 10-Oct-3 Tajan, Paris #148/R est:8000-10000
£5595	$9343	€8000	Arles, theatre romain (39x53cm-15x21in) photograph prov. 10-Oct-3 Tajan, Paris #149/R est:8000-10000
£5944	$9927	€8500	Arles, Place de la Republique (49x38cm-19x15in) photograph prov. 10-Oct-3 Tajan, Paris #145/R est:10000-12000

ROMAN, Max Wilhelm (1849-1910) German

£268	$494	€400	Venice (45x41cm-18x16in) s. i. verso board lit. 25-Mar-4 Karlheinz Kaupp, Staufen #2695/R
£428	$787	€650	Southern landscape with a monk (17x27cm-7x11in) 28-Jun-4 Dr Fritz Nagel, Stuttgart #7145/R
£1333	$2400	€2000	Italian washerwomen (55x26cm-22x10in) s. 26-Apr-4 Rieber, Stuttgart #1205/R est:2300

ROMANELLI, A (19th C) Italian

Sculpture			
£8735	$14500	€12753	Dionysus (183x86x71cm-72x34x28in) i. bears d.1868 green pat bronze. 4-Oct-3 Neal Auction Company, New Orleans #955/R est:2500-3500

ROMANELLI, Fratelli (19/20th C) Italian

Sculpture			
£8434	$14000	€12314	Kneeling Venus (84x53x43cm-33x21x17in) s.base white marble octagonal plinth beaded rim. 4-Oct-3 Neal Auction Company, New Orleans #151/R est:12000-15000

ROMANELLI, Giovanni Francesco (1610-1662) Italian

£390000	$674700	€569400	Flight of Aeneas and his family from the sack of Troy (157x213cm-62x84in) prov.lit. 10-Dec-3 Christie's, London #87/R est:100000-150000
Works on paper			
£1056	$1900	€1542	Herm below a satyr and a putto supporting the portrait of a cardinal (28x16cm-11x6in) black chk. 22-Jan-4 Christie's, Rockefeller NY #48/R est:2000-3000
£1778	$3200	€2596	Two putti decorating an incense burner with garlands (22x21cm-9x8in) red black chk. 22-Jan-4 Christie's, Rockefeller NY #47/R est:2000-3000
£2200	$3960	€3212	Design for a fan representing the rape of the Sabines (24x48cm-9x19in) i.mount gouache W/C black chk prov.lit. 20-Apr-4 Sotheby's, Olympia #124/R est:2000-3000

ROMANELLI, Giovanni Francesco (style) (1610-1662) Italian

£20385	$35062	€29762	Mythological figure scene with Hercules and Omphale. 2-Dec-3 Bukowskis, Stockholm #348/R est:150000-175000 (S.KR 265000)

ROMANELLI, Pasquale (1812-1887) Italian

Sculpture			
£1676	$3000	€2447	Bust of a gypsy girl (58cm-23in) s. white marble. 20-Mar-4 Freeman, Philadelphia #888/R est:1000-1500
£4067	$6750	€5938	Rebecca (48x33x20cm-19x13x8in) s.base i.headband white marble blk marble socle. 4-Oct-3 Neal Auction Company, New Orleans #195/R est:2000-3000
£7059	$12000	€10306	Nymph and Cupid (111cm-44in) s. marble onyx base. 28-Oct-3 Christie's, Rockefeller NY #99/R
£13529	$23000	€19752	Venus and Cupid (205cm-81in) s. marble. 28-Oct-3 Christie's, Rockefeller NY #183/R
£21111	$38000	€30822	Figure of Ruth Gleaning (114cm-45in) s. white marble. 23-Apr-4 Christie's, Rockefeller NY #175/R est:20000-30000
£29412	$50000	€42942	Ruth gleaning (115cm-45in) s. marble. 28-Oct-3 Christie's, Rockefeller NY #131/R

ROMANELLI, Raffaelo (1856-1928) Italian

Sculpture			
£10843	$18000	€15831	Rebecca (216x53x41cm-85x21x16in) s.base i. carrara marble inc green marble pedestal. 4-Oct-3 Neal Auction Company, New Orleans #314/R est:1800-22000
£11446	$19000	€16711	Rebecca Jacob at the Well (191x61x43cm-75x24x17in) s.verso marble inc rocaille plinth green marble pedestal. 4-Oct-3 Neal Auction Company, New Orleans #392/R est:18000-25000
£11765	$20000	€17177	Jacob and Rachel (96cm-38in) s. marble. 28-Oct-3 Christie's, Rockefeller NY #140/R

ROMANENKO, Valery Yakovlevich (1948-) Russian

£543	$907	€793	Night window (102x77cm-40x30in) s.d.1994 s.i.d.verso lit. 17-Nov-3 Waddingtons, Toronto #291/R (C.D 1200)

ROMANI, Giuseppe (16/17th C) Italian
£8966 $14883 €13000 Saturn and Cronus (101x84cm-40x33in) prov. 1-Oct-3 Dorotheum, Vienna #15/R est:8000-12000

ROMANI, Juana (1869-1924) Italian
£1532 $2634 €2237 Female nude from behind (73x60cm-29x24in) s.i.d.12-8-02 panel. 8-Dec-3 Philippe Schuler, Zurich #3455 est:2500-3000 (S.FR 3400)
£4146 $6800 €6012 Judith hiding preparing to behead Holofernes (99x71cm-39x28in) s. panel prov. 31-May-3 Brunk, Ashville #55/R est:10000-20000

ROMANI, Mario (19/20th C) Italian
£4032 $7500 €5887 A grand salon (66x92cm-26x36in) s. 5-Mar-4 Skinner, Boston #222/R est:800-1200

ROMANIDIS, Konstantin (1884-1972) Greek
£1200 $2040 €1752 Along the shore (25x33cm-10x13in) s. panel. 18-Nov-3 Sotheby's, London #92/R est:1200-1800
£2800 $5012 €4088 Sailing in choppy seas (32x47cm-13x19in) s. panel. 11-May-4 Bonhams, New Bond Street #4/R est:3000-5000
£3500 $5950 €5110 Stream in Kifissia (63x87cm-25x34in) s. 18-Nov-3 Sotheby's, London #131/R est:4000-6000
£5000 $8950 €7300 Monastery in Daphni (37x50cm-15x20in) s. panel. 11-May-4 Bonhams, New Bond Street #49/R est:3000-5000
£11000 $18700 €16060 Sailing along the coast (61x100cm-24x39in) s. 18-Nov-3 Sotheby's, London #94/R est:8000-12000

ROMANINO, Girolamo (circle) (1484-1562) Italian
£7047 $12967 €10500 Le Christ portant sa croix (75x59cm-30x23in) painted c.1600. 24-Mar-4 Tajan, Paris #11/R est:3000-4000

ROMANO, Elio (1906-1996) Italian
Works on paper
£460 $750 €672 Natura morta (38x56cm-15x22in) s. 28-Sep-3 Simpson's, Houston #248/R

ROMANO, Ettore (attrib) (19th C) Italian
Works on paper
£1467 $2699 €2200 View of Naples (38x56cm-15x22in) gouache card. 10-Jun-4 Christie's, Rome #35/R est:2300-2500
£1467 $2699 €2200 Palazzo Donn'Anna, Naples (38x56cm-15x22in) gouache card. 10-Jun-4 Christie's, Rome #36/R est:2300-2500

ROMANO, G (?) Italian
£2649 $4821 €4000 Large seascape (100x150cm-39x59in) s. 21-Jun-4 Dorotheum, Vienna #67/R est:4500-5000

ROMANO, Giulio (1499-1546) Italian
Works on paper
£4762 $8524 €7000 Janus (20x9cm-8x4in) i. pen brown ink. 19-Mar-4 Piasa, Paris #8/R est:7000-8000

ROMANO, Giulio (attrib) (1499-1546) Italian
Works on paper
£500 $860 €730 Putti with triumph carriage. Indian ink. 7-Dec-3 Uppsala Auktionskammare, Uppsala #81/R (S.KR 6500)
£7222 $13000 €10544 Christ holding the cross (35x18cm-14x7in) black chk pen brown ink prov. 22-Jan-4 Christie's, Rockefeller NY #13/R est:10000-15000

ROMANO, Umberto (1905-1984) American
£218 $350 €318 Man (41x30cm-16x12in) s. s.i.d.1948-1961 verso masonite board. 22-Feb-3 Bunte, Elgin #1191
£256 $450 €374 Untitled flowers (76x64cm-30x25in) s. board. 3-Jan-4 Outer Cape Auctions, Provincetown #72/R
£647 $1100 €945 Portrait of the artist's wife (107x138cm-42x54in) s.d.1939. 21-Nov-3 Skinner, Boston #430/R est:1000-1500

ROMANTIC SCHOOL (19th C) Dutch
£7042 $11338 €10000 The letter (127x95cm-50x37in) 8-May-3 Farsetti, Prato #353/R est:12000-14000
£21477 $38443 €32000 Elegante a l'eventail. Elegante a la corbeille. Bergere. Elegante au chapeau (130x93cm-51x37in) oval four. 25-May-4 Palais de Beaux Arts, Brussels #560/R est:7000-10000

ROMANY, Adele (1769-1846) French
£2500 $3950 €3600 Mother and child (23x20cm-9x8in) mono. lit. oval. 19-Sep-3 Schloss Ahlden, Ahlden #1470/R est:3600

ROMBAUX, Egide (1865-1942) Belgian
Sculpture
£1189 $1985 €1700 Eglantine (55cm-22in) s.st.f.H. Luppens green pat bronze. 13-Oct-3 Horta, Bruxelles #188 est:1800-2200
£2759 $4966 €4000 Les trois Graces (42cm-17in) s. pat bronze. 20-Jan-4 Galerie Moderne, Brussels #1524/R est:1000-1500

ROMBERG DE VAUCORBEIL, Maurice (1862-1943) French
Works on paper
£1084 $1864 €1550 Vielles rues a Tanger (38x62cm-15x24in) s. W/C paper on canvas. 5-Dec-3 Chochon-Barre & Allardi, Paris #144/R est:1200-1500

ROMBOUTS, Adriaen (17th C) Dutch?
£3221 $5766 €4800 Joyeuse compagnie dans un interieur de cuisine (36x46cm-14x18in) 25-May-4 Palais de Beaux Arts, Brussels #540/R est:5500-7000

ROMBOUTS, Theodor (school) (1597-1637) Flemish
£18667 $33413 €28000 Card players (152x223cm-60x88in) prov. 17-May-4 Finarte Semenzato, Rome #109/R est:30000-35000

ROMEDA, Bruno (20th C) ?
Sculpture
£1334 $2454 €2000 Untitled (74x71x11cm-29x28x4in) s.d.84 wood painted plaster prov. 9-Jun-4 Artcurial Briest, Paris #539/R est:1200-1500

ROMER, Max (20th C) Portuguese?
£906 $1622 €1350 Funchal, Madeira (22x30cm-9x12in) s.d.1957 tempera. 31-May-4 Cabral Moncada Leiloes, Lisbon #92/R
£1074 $1922 €1600 Saint John Fortress, Madeira (22x30cm-9x12in) s. tempera. 31-May-4 Cabral Moncada Leiloes, Lisbon #90/R est:800-1200

ROMERO DE TORRES, Julio (1879-1930) Spanish
£19718 $34507 €28000 Portrait of woman (35x33cm-14x13in) s. i.verso. 16-Dec-3 Segre, Madrid #94/R est:15000

ROMERO OROZCO, Honorio (1867-c.1920) Spanish
£543 $891 €750 Male nude (34x49cm-13x19in) s.d. 87 a 88. 27-May-3 Durán, Madrid #682/R

ROMERO RESSENDI, Baldomero (1922-1977) Spanish
£1275 $2257 €1900 Mask (60x50cm-24x20in) s.d.1967 s.i.verso. 27-Apr-4 Durán, Madrid #67/R est:900
£1931 $3476 €2800 Scarecrows (40x31cm-16x12in) s.indis.d. board. 26-Jan-4 Ansorena, Madrid #257/R est:1200
£2207 $3972 €3200 Table dance (43x36cm-17x14in) s.d.1967 board. 26-Jan-4 Ansorena, Madrid #908/R est:1000
£2482 $4145 €3500 Gypsy with parrot (55x31cm-22x12in) s. panel painted 1956. 23-Jun-3 Durán, Madrid #195/R est:3000

ROMERO Y LOPEZ, Jose Maria (c.1815-1880) Spanish
£4027 $7128 €6000 Magdalen (177x128cm-70x50in) s.d.1847. 27-Apr-4 Durán, Madrid #208/R est:4500

ROMERO, Angelo (19th C) Spanish
£1087 $1783 €1500 Marisquera (40x27cm-16x11in) s. 27-May-3 Durán, Madrid #174/R est:500

ROMERO, Betsabee (1963-) Mexican
Sculpture
£9333 $17173 €14000 Ornate caps (33x33cm-13x13in) tyres Talvera ceramic set of 3 exec.2003 prov. 10-Jun-4 Christie's, Paris #99/R est:12000-16000
£19553 $35000 €28547 Llantas (79x79cm-31x31in) carved rubber tyres set of 5 exec.2001 prov. 26-May-4 Sotheby's, New York #174/R est:12000-18000

ROMERO, Carlos Orozco (1898-1984) Mexican
£2260 $4000 €3300 Desert landscape (46x61cm-18x24in) s.d.1944 prov. 2-May-4 Bonhams & Butterfields, Los Angeles #3099/R est:10000-15000
£4802 $8500 €7011 Three women in a landscape (80x63cm-31x25in) s. 2-May-4 Bonhams & Butterfields, Los Angeles #3098/R est:8000-12000

ROMERO, Nelson (1951-) South American
Works on paper
£294 $500 €429 Violin player drinking (75x54cm-30x21in) s.d.1989 pencil. 25-Nov-3 Galeria y Remates, Montevideo #3/R
£324 $550 €473 Interior with model (75x55cm-30x22in) s.d.1989 pencil. 25-Nov-3 Galeria y Remates, Montevideo #5
£382 $650 €558 Peasants having lunch (75x54cm-30x21in) s.d.1989 pencil. 25-Nov-3 Galeria y Remates, Montevideo #4/R
£647 $1100 €945 Self-portrait (56x38cm-22x15in) s.d.1989 ink. 25-Nov-3 Galeria y Remates, Montevideo #106/R

ROMEYN, Willem (1624-1694) Dutch
£2333 $4177 €3500 Italianate mountainous landscape with cattle and sheep (30x37cm-12x15in) bears another sig. panel prov. 17-May-4 Christie's, Amsterdam #34/R est:4000-6000
£3000 $5490 €4380 Cow, sheep and goats before a farmstead in an Italianate landscape (35x43cm-14x17in) panel painted oval. 7-Jul-4 Bonhams, New Bond Street #37/R est:2000-3000

ROMEYN, Willem (attrib) (1624-1694) Dutch
£1800 $3240 €2628 Shepherd family at rest by a tree (38x51cm-15x20in) 23-Apr-4 Christie's, Kensington #30/R est:2000-3000

ROMIJN, Gust (1922-) Dutch
£646 $1176 €950 Spaansch dorp - Almunecar (50x60cm-20x24in) init.d.55 prov. 3-Feb-4 Christie's, Amsterdam #539

ROMILLY, George T (fl.1852-1875) British

£3000 $5520 €4380 Saying grace (56x63cm-22x25in) s. prov.exhib. 11-Jun-4 Christie's, London #179/R est:3000-5000

ROMITI, Gino (1881-1967) Italian

£533 $955 €800 Little seascape (22x29cm-9x11in) s. board. 12-May-4 Stadion, Trieste #795
£867 $1569 €1300 Seascape (10x15cm-4x6in) s.d. board. 2-Apr-4 Farsetti, Prato #436
£979 $1635 €1400 Rural path with figures (30x39cm-12x15in) s. board. 26-Jun-3 Sant Agostino, Torino #83/R
£979 $1635 €1400 Road with figures (30x39cm-12x15in) s. board. 26-Jun-3 Sant Agostino, Torino #84/R
£1049 $1752 €1500 Seascape (30x40cm-12x16in) s. board. 26-Jun-3 Sant Agostino, Torino #85/R
£1295 $2124 €1800 Night at sea (27x34cm-11x13in) s.d.XIII board. 10-Jun-3 Pandolfini, Florence #206 est:700-900
£1325 $2411 €2000 Field with haystacks and chickens (30x40cm-12x16in) s. masonite prov. 21-Jun-4 Pandolfini, Florence #189/R est:2200-2400
£1367 $2242 €1900 Children (23x30cm-9x12in) board. 5-Jun-3 Adma, Formigine #782 est:600-800
£1409 $2523 €2100 Painter's room (26x20cm-10x8in) s. 25-May-4 Finarte Semenzato, Milan #50/R est:1200-1500
£1933 $3499 €2900 Path (18x24cm-7x9in) s. board. 2-Apr-4 Farsetti, Prato #475/R est:2900-3200
£2535 $4386 €3600 Landscape (68x48cm-27x19in) s.d. 9-Dec-3 Pandolfini, Florence #365/R est:2600-2800
£2667 $4907 €4000 Landscape with olive trees. Tamerici (19x25cm-7x10in) s. panel pair prov. 10-Jun-4 Christie's, Rome #178/R est:1600-1800
£3546 $5922 €5000 Landscape with traveller. Path in the park (7x13cm-3x5in) s. cardboard pair. 14-Oct-3 Finarte Semenzato, Milan #139/R est:4500

ROMITI, Sergio (1928-) Italian

£664 $1129 €950 Untitled (25x35cm-10x14in) s. tempera paper on canvas. 20-Nov-3 Finarte Semenzato, Milan #122
£1761 $2923 €2500 Red and green butchery (60x50cm-24x20in) s. acrylic. 11-Jun-3 Finarte Semenzato, Milan #555/R
£2000 $3680 €3000 Untitled (35x49cm-14x19in) s. paper painted 1953. 14-Jun-4 Sant Agostino, Torino #382/R est:3000-3500
£2292 $3621 €3300 Red and green butchery (50x60cm-20x24in) 6-Sep-3 Meeting Art, Vercelli #572 est:3000
£4895 $8322 €7000 Table (50x65cm-20x26in) s. s.verso prov. 20-Nov-3 Finarte Semenzato, Milan #224/R est:7000-8000
£4930 $8183 €7000 Horizontal still life (50x65cm-20x26in) s. painted 1954. 11-Jun-3 Finarte Semenzato, Milan #653/R
£6081 $10703 €9000 Still life (55x75cm-22x30in) s.d.55 exhib. 24-May-4 Christie's, Milan #97/R est:3000-4000
£6993 $11888 €10000 Grey composition (45x60cm-18x24in) s.d.1960 exhib.lit. 28-Nov-3 Farsetti, Prato #277/R est:10000-12000

ROMM, Nina (20th C) South African

Works on paper
£345 $576 €504 Lady with a cat (75x55cm-30x22in) mixed media. 20-Oct-3 Stephan Welz, Johannesburg #656 est:2000-3000 (SA.R 4000)

ROMMLER, Lui (?) German

£872 $1632 €1300 Tavern (90x87cm-35x34in) s. panel. 28-Feb-4 Quittenbaum, Hamburg #98/R

ROMNEY, George (1734-1802) British

£11111 $20000 €16222 Portrait of William Augustus, 3rd Earl of De La Warr (136x107cm-54x42in) prov.lit. 23-Jan-4 Christie's, Rockefeller NY #135/R est:8000-12000
£16000 $27200 €23360 Portrait of a lady, said to be Miss Emily Bertie (33x31cm-13x12in) prov. 27-Nov-3 Sotheby's, London #153/R est:8000-12000
£17000 $28900 €24820 Portrait of Lady Herries in a grey dress and white collar with wide brimmed hat (76x63cm-30x25in) lit. 25-Nov-3 Christie's, London #40/R est:7000-10000
£18000 $33120 €26280 Self portrait, in a red coat (61x49cm-24x19in) prov.lit. 11-Jun-4 Christie's, London #27/R est:20000-30000
£36000 $66240 €52560 Portrait of Mr Morley, in a red coat (76x63cm-30x25in) prov.exhib.lit. 11-Jun-4 Christie's, London #28/R est:25000-35000
£47511 $79344 €69366 Judith Irving (76x63cm-30x25in) painted c.1783 prov.exhib.lit. 17-Nov-3 Waddingtons, Toronto #133/R est:30000-40000 (C.D 105000)
£82000 $150880 €119720 Portrait of Miss Andrewes in yellow dress (76x63cm-30x25in) prov. 9-Jun-4 Christie's, London #10/R est:50000-70000
£82000 $150880 €119720 Portrait of lady, in white dress and pink shawl (95x74cm-37x29in) prov.lit. 9-Jun-4 Christie's, London #11/R est:40000-60000
£110000 $187000 €160600 Portrait of Francis Lind, seated before a music stand on a pink chair (127x102cm-50x40in) prov.lit. 26-Nov-3 Christie's, London #6/R est:100000-150000
£175000 $318500 €255500 Portrait of Elizabeth Chafyn-Grove (127x101cm-50x40in) prov.exhib.lit. 1-Jul-4 Sotheby's, London #10/R est:80000-120000
£360000 $612000 €525600 Portrait of Mrs Anne Carwardine and her eldest son, Thomas (75x62cm-30x24in) prov.exhib.lit. 27-Nov-3 Sotheby's, London #9/R est:200000-300000
Works on paper
£750 $1253 €1095 Study of Lady Hamilton. Horse (11x18cm-4x7in) pen ink double-sided prov. 22-Oct-3 Cheffins, Cambridge #442/R
£1500 $2775 €2190 Mother and child (15x10cm-6x4in) ink dr. prov. 10-Feb-4 David Lay, Penzance #392/R est:600-700
£1800 $3312 €2628 Study of John Howard, prison reformer, visiting a Lazaetto (14x23cm-6x9in) pencil. 26-Mar-4 Sotheby's, London #94/R est:2000-3000
£6338 $11092 €9000 Mythological scene (34x49cm-13x19in) crayon wash. 19-Dec-3 Pierre Berge, Paris #23/R est:2000-2500

ROMNEY, George (attrib) (1734-1802) British

£3030 $5000 €4394 Youth in white wig (46x38cm-18x15in) s.d.1800 canvas on composition board. 7-Jul-3 Schrager Galleries, Milwaukee #1525

ROMO, Jose Luis (1953-) Mexican?

£1714 $3000 €2502 Coliflor con insectos (74x101cm-29x40in) s. s.i.d.1994 verso prov. 19-Dec-3 Sotheby's, New York #1215/R est:4000-6000

ROMULO, Teodulo (1943-) Mexican

£686 $1200 €1002 Cowboy (65x50cm-26x20in) s.d.1977 oil gold leaf paper. 19-Dec-3 Sotheby's, New York #1226/R
Sculpture
£518 $896 €756 Homage to happiness (52x30x29cm-20x12x11in) s.d.1997 bronze. 9-Dec-3 Louis Morton, Mexico #108/R est:12000-14000 (M.P 10000)

RON, Lior (1971-) Israeli

£869 $1477 €1269 Wanna get naked and start a revolution? (120x45cm-47x18in) s. acrylic. 4-Nov-3 Bukowskis, Stockholm #653/R (S.KR 11500)

RONALD, David (20th C) British?

£260 $481 €380 Coastal view, with wild flowers in the foreground (17x23cm-7x9in) s. panel. 10-Feb-4 Bonhams, Knightsbridge #118/R

RONALD, William S (1926-1998) Canadian

£181 $334 €264 Abstract composition (20x25cm-8x10in) s. 9-Jun-4 Walker's, Ottawa #163/R (C.D 450)
£290 $485 €421 Sans titre (41x30cm-16x12in) s. acrylic. 17-Jun-3 Pinneys, Montreal #151 (C.D 650)
£444 $769 €648 Untitled (41x41cm-16x16in) s.d.89 acrylic. 9-Dec-3 Pinneys, Montreal #158 (C.D 1000)
£1626 $2911 €2374 Debussy (122x107cm-48x42in) s.d.90 i.verso acrylic prov. 31-May-4 Sotheby's, Toronto #97/R est:4000-6000 (C.D 4000)
£2703 $4595 €3946 Squeeze me pink (122x244cm-48x96in) s.i.d.69 verso prov. 18-Nov-3 Sotheby's, Toronto #107/R est:7000-10000 (C.D 6000)
Works on paper
£241 $448 €352 Composition (33x48cm-13x19in) s.d.51 ink gouache. 2-Mar-4 Ritchie, Toronto #176/R (C.D 600)
£562 $1046 €821 Untitled (55x76cm-22x30in) s.d.92 W/C. 2-Mar-4 Ritchie, Toronto #175/R (C.D 1400)

RONALDSON, Thomas Martine (1881-1942) British

£4500 $7650 €6570 Portrait of a lady (126x94cm-50x37in) s. 30-Oct-3 Christie's, London #183/R est:1500-2500

RONAY, Stephen (1900-?) American

£357 $650 €521 The poet (33x41cm-13x16in) s.i. 8-Feb-4 William Jenack, New York #91

RONCALLI, Cristoforo (1552-1626) Italian

£8621 $14397 €12500 Flight to Egypt (27x20cm-11x8in) copper. 15-Nov-3 Porro, Milan #212/R est:10000
Works on paper
£308 $529 €440 Putti in clouds (12x18cm-5x7in) init.i.verso brown ink. 5-Dec-3 Bolland & Marotz, Bremen #467
£1200 $2160 €1752 Jesuit Saint kneeling in front of a crucifix (23x15cm-9x6in) bears i. red chk prov. 20-Apr-4 Sotheby's, Olympia #11/R est:1400-1800
£1400 $2422 €2044 Martyr saint standing at an altar looking heavenwards (30x20cm-12x8in) i.verso red chk. 12-Dec-3 Christie's, Kensington #333/R est:1500-2000

RONCI, L (?) ?

Works on paper
£2345 $3916 €3400 Vues de Rome (53x36cm-21x14in) s. W/C pair. 17-Nov-3 Tajan, Paris #10/R est:1500-2000

RONDA, Omar (1947-) Italian

Photographs
£5000 $9200 €7500 Frozen (50x50cm-20x20in) s.i.verso photograph resin flag exec.2002. 8-Jun-4 Finarte Semenzato, Milan #312/R est:5000-5500
£5000 $9200 €7500 American frozen (50x50cm-20x20in) s.i.d.2004 verso photograph plastic flag. 8-Jun-4 Finarte Semenzato, Milan #311/R est:5500-6500
Works on paper
£1081 $1903 €1600 Frozen (80x60cm-31x24in) s. plastic light exec.1992. 22-May-4 Galleria Pananti, Florence #384/R est:1500-3000
£2465 $4092 €3500 Frozen (62x62cm-24x24in) s.d.1996 s.i.d.verso plastic mixed media wood. 14-Jun-3 Meeting Art, Vercelli #43/R est:500
£3378 $5946 €5000 American frozen (70x70cm-28x28in) s.i.d.2003 verso plastic. 24-May-4 Christie's, Milan #190/R est:6000-7000
£4698 $8691 €7000 American flag, frozen (70x70cm-28x28in) s.d.2003 verso plastic. 13-Mar-4 Meeting Art, Vercelli #397 est:5000

RONDANI, Francesco (attrib) (1490-1550) Italian

Works on paper
£1974 $3632 €3000 Putti (31x21cm-12x8in) sanguine. 22-Jun-4 Sotheby's, Milan #26/R est:2500-3500

RONDAS, Willi (1907-1975) British/Belgian

£400 $680 €584 Marazion, from the sea (60x70cm-24x28in) s.verso canvasboard. 29-Oct-3 Hampton & Littlewood, Exeter #540/R

RONDE, Philippe (1815-1883) German

Works on paper
£1127 $1870 €1600 Eglise de San Diego et rue de Parian a Aguas Calientes, Mexique (16x22cm-6x9in) s. W/C. 15-Jun-3 Muizon & Le Coent, Paris #8

RONDEL, Frederick (1826-1892) American

£323	$600	€472	Seascape with rocky shoreline (20x30cm-8x12in) s. 3-Mar-4 Alderfer's, Hatfield #309
£1304	$2100	€1904	Landscape with stream (36x51cm-14x20in) 24-Aug-3 William Jenack, New York #30 est:200-300
£8125	$13000	€11863	Landscape with figures crossing a river, towing a hay cart (46x76cm-18x30in) s.indis.d. 20-Sep-3 Jeffery Burchard, Florida #43/R

RONDEL, Henri (1857-1919) French

£1648	$3000	€2406	Portrait of a young beauty (74x60cm-29x24in) s. prov. 29-Jun-4 Sotheby's, New York #83/R est:3000-5000
£1900	$3515	€2774	Young beauty (61x50cm-24x20in) s. 15-Jan-4 Christie's, Kensington #749/R est:1500-2000

RONDINONE, Ugo (1963-) French

£39106	$70000	€57095	No.253-fuenfzehnterdezemberzweitausendundeins (150x400cm-59x157in) s. acrylic on polyester. 13-May-4 Phillips, New York #6/R est:30000-40000
£41899	$75000	€61173	Sechsundzwanzigsterfebruarzweitausendundull no 175 (270cm-106in circular) acrylic prov. 12-May-4 Christie's, Rockefeller NY #320/R est:70000-90000
£44693	$80000	€65252	Sechsundzwanzigstermaizweitausendundnull no 200 (270cm-106in circular) acrylic prov. 14-May-4 Phillips, New York #107/R est:40000-60000
£50898	$85000	€74311	No 174 zweiundzwanzigsterfebruar zweitausendundnull (270cm-106in circular) acrylic prov. 13-Nov-3 Sotheby's, New York #443/R est:60000-80000
£53892	$90000	€78682	No.70 (274x500cm-108x197in) acrylic painted 1996 prov.exhib.lit. 13-Nov-3 Phillips, New York #3/R est:40000-60000
£58683	$98000	€85677	Funfzehnteroktoberneunzehn hundertachtundneunzig no.114 (220cm-87in circular) acrylic painted 1999 prov.exhib. 14-Nov-3 Phillips, New York #107/R est:40000-60000

Photographs

£23952	$40000	€34970	Dreizehntermaerzneunzehnhun dertachtundneunzig (254x228cm-100x90in) black white photo fifteen lit. 13-Nov-3 Sotheby's, New York #444/R est:40000-60000

Works on paper

£17935	$33000	€26185	Zweiterjunineunzehnhundertneunundneunzig (200x300cm-79x118in) Indian ink prov. 10-Jun-4 Phillips, New York #407/R est:25000-35000
£32402	$58000	€47307	Dreiundzwanzigsterdezemberzweitausend (200x300cm-79x118in) s.d.2000 verso Indian ink prov. 14-May-4 Phillips, New York #191/R est:25000-35000

RONEK, Jaroslav (1892-?) Czechoslovakian

£669	$1198	€950	Two steam engines (50x59cm-20x23in) s. board lit. 8-Jan-4 Allgauer, Kempten #2499/R
£738	$1351	€1100	Two steam locomotives (35x50cm-14x20in) s. canvas on board lit. 8-Jul-4 Allgauer, Kempten #2205/R

RONEY, Harold (1899-1986) American

£299	$500	€437	Fall landscape (20x25cm-8x10in) canvasboard. 18-Oct-3 David Dike, Dallas #318/R

RONG DAKUAI (20th C) Chinese

Works on paper

£541	$951	€800	Boats on river bend in spring (64x73cm-25x29in) i. seal hanging scroll. 21-May-4 Dr Fritz Nagel, Stuttgart #1215/R

RONGET, Elisabeth (20th C) French

£403	$745	€600	Vase de fleurs cubiste (50x40cm-20x16in) s. cardboard. 15-Mar-4 Claude Boisgirard, Paris #100
£1381	$2500	€2016	Odalesque (86x127cm-34x50in) s. prov. 30-Mar-4 Sotheby's, New York #362/R est:4000-5000

RONIG, Ludwig Ernst (1885-1960) German

£1000	$1790	€1500	Flowers (49x43cm-19x17in) s. panel. 15-May-4 Van Ham, Cologne #887/R est:1800

RONINI, A (19th C) ?

£1761	$3046	€2500	View of the Grand Canal going towards La Salute (69x102cm-27x40in) s. 14-Dec-3 Finarte, Venice #30/R est:800-1000

RONMY, Guillaume Frederic (1786-1854) French

£1733	$3137	€2600	Vue du tombeau des Horaces et des Curiaces a Albano (16x22cm-6x9in) s. i.d.1812 verso panel. 2-Apr-4 Rossini, Paris #32/R est:3000-4000
£3793	$7017	€5500	Marchand chargeant le charroi (91x55cm-36x22in) s. 16-Feb-4 Horta, Bruxelles #107 est:6500-8500

RONNBERG, Hanna (1862-1946) Finnish

£1757	$3145	€2600	Winter's day (27x47cm-11x19in) s.d.1895. 8-May-4 Bukowskis, Helsinki #162/R est:2500-3000
£2465	$3944	€3500	View towards the sea (65x53cm-26x21in) s.d.1924. 18-Sep-3 Hagelstam, Helsinki #921/R est:4000
£3056	$5103	€4400	Landscape, Rago (42x60cm-17x24in) s.d.1905. 23-Oct-3 Hagelstam, Helsinki #898/R est:3000
£4054	$7257	€6000	The artist's villa at Brando (55x46cm-22x18in) s.d.1934. 8-May-4 Bukowskis, Helsinki #48/R est:4000-4500

RONNER, Henriette (1821-1909) Dutch

£1056	$1701	€1500	Mother's joy - bitch with puppies (13x16cm-5x6in) s. panel. 22-Aug-3 Altus, Berlin #528/R est:2300
£1250	$2300	€1900	Taking a nap (29x28cm-11x11in) mono. paper on cardboard. 22-Jun-4 Christie's, Amsterdam #33/R est:1200-1600
£1399	$2336	€2000	Good friends (28x37cm-11x15in) s. panel. 30-Jun-3 Sotheby's, Amsterdam #220/R
£1667	$2717	€2400	Dogs playing on a sunny afternoon (32x47cm-13x19in) s. 29-Sep-3 Sotheby's, Amsterdam #73/R
£3128	$5600	€4567	Reading lesson (15x23cm-6x9in) s. panel. 8-Jan-4 James Julia, Fairfield #1061/R est:1500-2000
£3618	$6549	€5500	Kittens playing on a stool, a mother cat in a basket (27x36cm-11x14in) s. paper on panel. 19-Apr-4 Glerum, Amsterdam #26/R est:6000-8000
£3741	$6810	€5500	In the basket (34x47cm-13x19in) s. oil paper on panel. 3-Feb-4 Christie's, Amsterdam #120/R est:5000-7000
£3793	$7017	€5500	Attelage de chiens (61x50cm-24x20in) s. 19-Jan-4 Horta, Bruxelles #115/R est:6000-8000
£3846	$6423	€5500	Dog and magpie (39x32cm-15x13in) s. panel. 11-Oct-3 De Vuyst, Lokeren #319/R est:5000-6000
£4333	$7800	€6500	Furry friend (27x31cm-11x12in) s. oil paper on panel. 21-Apr-4 Christie's, Amsterdam #10/R est:4000-6000
£4483	$7486	€6545	Three kittens (23x30cm-9x12in) s. panel. 20-Oct-3 Stephan Welz, Johannesburg #204/R est:50000-70000 (SA.R 52000)
£4600	$8418	€6716	Guardians of the hamper (59x88cm-23x35in) s. 8-Jul-4 Lawrence, Crewkerne #1619/R est:3000-5000
£5263	$9526	€8000	Two kittens on a red cushion (28x24cm-11x9in) s. paper on panel. 19-Apr-4 Glerum, Amsterdam #20/R est:3000-3500
£7000	$12950	€10220	Chat (26x21cm-10x8in) s. panel exhib. 14-Jul-4 Sotheby's, Olympia #233/R est:7000-9000
£8000	$14400	€12000	Intruder in the pantry (65x43cm-26x17in) s. panel prov. 21-Apr-4 Christie's, Amsterdam #206/R est:12000-16000
£8333	$14167	€12000	Angora brun (37x52cm-15x20in) s.d.1905 panel. 28-Oct-3 Christie's, Amsterdam #233/R est:15000-20000
£8621	$15862	€12587	Cat and dog playing (103x79cm-41x31in) s. 26-Mar-4 Koller, Zurich #3111/R est:28000-38000 (S.FR 20000)
£10667	$19200	€16000	Utter contentment (24x32cm-9x13in) s.d.1891 panel prov. 21-Apr-4 Christie's, Amsterdam #209/R est:8000-12000
£12500	$20875	€18000	Study of cats (32x35cm-13x14in) s.d.97 panel. 21-Oct-3 Sotheby's, Amsterdam #175/R est:10000-15000
£13333	$24000	€20000	Study, kittens on a table (28x37cm-11x15in) s. oil paper on panel prov. 21-Apr-4 Christie's, Amsterdam #227/R est:15000-20000
£16667	$28333	€24000	Three of a kind (27x36cm-11x14in) s.d.1903 panel. 28-Oct-3 Christie's, Amsterdam #214/R est:15000-20000
£17500	$31850	€25550	Three little kittens (27x36cm-11x14in) s. panel lit. 15-Jun-4 Sotheby's, London #213/R est:7000-10000
£17568	$31446	€26000	Quatre chiens chassant le lievre (75x110cm-30x43in) s. 10-May-4 Horta, Bruxelles #217/R est:30000-40000
£20000	$34000	€29200	Tabby on red settee (32x39cm-13x15in) s. panel. 18-Nov-3 Sotheby's, London #350/R
£20833	$34792	€30000	Kittens playing with a fan (21x27cm-8x11in) s. panel. 21-Oct-3 Sotheby's, Amsterdam #210/R est:30000-40000
£30000	$51600	€43800	Two resting cats (35x45cm-14x18in) s.d.93 panel. 3-Dec-3 Christie's, London #17/R est:10000-15000
£48611	$81181	€70000	Three kittens playing by a stove (33x44cm-13x17in) s. panel prov.exhib. 21-Oct-3 Sotheby's, Amsterdam #192/R est:50000-70000
£50000	$90000	€75000	Tea time (24x32cm-9x13in) s.d.1905 panel. 20-Apr-4 Sotheby's, Amsterdam #207/R est:50000-70000

Works on paper

£284	$474	€400	Chatons. s.d.96 ink. 17-Jun-3 Galerie Moderne, Brussels #165/R
£603	$1007	€850	Chien et pigeons. mono. W/C. 17-Jun-3 Galerie Moderne, Brussels #275/R
£603	$1007	€850	Chien attaquant un canard. mono. W/C. 17-Jun-3 Galerie Moderne, Brussels #276/R
£603	$1007	€850	Chat surprenant un chien. s. W/C. 17-Jun-3 Galerie Moderne, Brussels #277/R
£603	$1007	€850	Chien surpris par un oiseau. mono. W/C. 17-Jun-3 Galerie Moderne, Brussels #278/R
£674	$1125	€950	Chien et chat. mono. W/C. 17-Jun-3 Galerie Moderne, Brussels #274/R
£1088	$1948	€1600	Chat endormi sur l'appui de fenetre (17x22cm-7x9in) W/C. 22-Mar-4 Amberes, Antwerp #234
£5245	$8916	€7500	In the supply cupboard (46x31cm-18x12in) s. W/C. 20-Nov-3 Van Ham, Cologne #1824/R est:6800
£6122	$11143	€9000	Asleep in the artist's studio (53x77cm-21x30in) s. panel oil on canvas prov. 3-Feb-4 Christie's, Amsterdam #87/R est:4000-6000

RONNER, Henriette (attrib) (1821-1909) Dutch

£1300	$2119	€1898	Family of cats in a basket with a kitten on cushion in foreground (30x39cm-12x15in) panel. 28-Sep-3 Wilkinson, Doncaster #277/R

RONNQUIST, Lotten (1864-1912) Swedish

£923	$1588	€1348	Lake landscape (38x59cm-15x23in) s.d.90. 7-Dec-3 Uppsala Auktionskammare, Uppsala #192/R (S.KR 12000)
£1577	$2838	€2302	Winter landscape with trees (65x50cm-26x20in) 26-Jan-4 Lilla Bukowskis, Stockholm #150/R est:12000-15000 (S.KR 21000)
£1923	$3308	€2808	Winter view of Harnosand (64x49cm-25x19in) 2-Dec-3 Bukowskis, Stockholm #179d/R est:20000-25000 (S.KR 25000)
£3104	$5557	€4532	On the way home (149x120cm-59x47in) s.d.90. 26-May-4 AB Stockholms Auktionsverk #2270/R est:40000-50000 (S.KR 42000)

RONOVSKY, Frantisek (1929-) Czechoslovakian

£438	$727	€639	Landscape with Buchlov Castle (51x120cm-20x47in) s. 4-Oct-3 Dorotheum, Prague #89/R est:20000-30000 (C.KR 20000)

RONTINI, Ferruccio (1893-1964) Italian

£533	$981	€800	Fire in the fields (22x20cm-9x8in) s. cardboard. 10-Jun-4 Christie's, Rome #166/R
£596	$1085	€900	Mother and child (20x11cm-8x4in) s. board. 21-Jun-4 Pandolfini, Florence #184/R
£638	$1066	€900	The Botena in Vicchio (24x43cm-9x17in) s.d.42 board. 14-Oct-3 Finarte Semenzato, Milan #17
£733	$1327	€1100	Landscape (36x51cm-14x20in) s. cardboard on canvas. 2-Apr-4 Farsetti, Prato #494/R
£845	$1462	€1200	Angler (34x50cm-13x20in) s. board. 9-Dec-3 Pandolfini, Florence #264/R est:1200-1400
£863	$1416	€1200	Big house in Vicchio (34x60cm-13x24in) s.d.XVII i.verso board. 10-Jun-3 Pandolfini, Florence #214/R
£933	$1689	€1400	Shepherdesses (30x40cm-12x16in) s. 2-Apr-4 Farsetti, Prato #518/R
£1130	$2000	€1650	Untitled, landscape with farmers and oxen (50x70cm-20x28in) s. panel. 2-May-4 Bonhams & Butterfields, Los Angeles #3000/R est:3000-5000
£1408	$2437	€2000	Farms covered insnow (50x100cm-20x39in) s. 9-Dec-3 Pandolfini, Florence #235 est:2500-3000
£1467	$2655	€2200	Winter landscape (35x50cm-14x20in) s. cardboard on canvas. 2-Apr-4 Farsetti, Prato #449/R est:1100-1400

£1942 $3186 €2700 Landscape with labourers (70x100cm-28x39in) s.d.37 prov. 10-Jun-3 Pandolfini, Florence #278/R est:2700-2900
£2000 $3580 €3000 Spring (70x100cm-28x39in) s. s.i.verso. 13-May-4 Babuino, Rome #567/R est:2000-3000

RONZELLI, Giuseppe (attrib) (1663-1729) Italian
£6376 $11732 €9500 Travellers in wooded landscape (74cm-29in circular) tondo prov. 24-Mar-4 Dorotheum, Vienna #346/R est:11000-15000
£35000 $60550 €51100 Extensive river landscape with travelers on a track. Extensive river landscape with figures track (139x195cm-55x77in) pair. 10-Dec-3 Bonhams, New Bond Street #17/R est:35000-45000

RONZONI, Pietro (1780-1862) Italian
£738 $1321 €1100 Landscape (22x32cm-9x13in) s. cardboard. 25-May-4 Finarte Semenzato, Milan #139/R

RONZONI, Pietro (attrib) (1780-1862) Italian
£2908 $4856 €4100 Landscape with ruins (18x17cm-7x7in) copper. 14-Oct-3 Finarte Semenzato, Milan #66/R est:4000

ROOBJEE, Pjeroo (1945-) Belgian
£1477 $2613 €2200 Figure (200x150cm-79x59in) s.d.1988. 27-Apr-4 Campo & Campo, Antwerp #196/R est:2500-3000

ROOD, Henry (jnr) (1902-) American
£411 $650 €600 Panoramic view of valley with river and mountains (20x25cm-8x10in) s. canvasboard. 6-Sep-3 Brunk, Ashville #299

ROOD, Jan (1710-1770) Dutch
Works on paper
£520 $899 €759 Seascape with many sailing boats (26x35cm-10x14in) s.d.1770 pen pencil wash grisaille. 9-Dec-3 Rasmussen, Copenhagen #1751/R (D.KR 5500)

ROODENBURG, Hendrikus Elias (1895-1983) Dutch
£385 $643 €550 Flower still life (51x41cm-20x16in) s.d.1929 board. 30-Jun-3 Sotheby's, Amsterdam #264/R

ROOKE, Thomas Matthew (1842-1942) British
£650 $1151 €949 Evian, Normandy (61x51cm-24x20in) s. 28-Apr-4 Halls, Shrewsbury #490/R
Works on paper
£350 $648 €511 Spire of Senles cathedral from market place (58x23cm-23x9in) s.i.d.1900 W/C. 14-Jan-4 Brightwells, Leominster #896/R
£800 $1464 €1168 Cottage on headland near Hasting, early morning (9x25cm-4x10in) id.1868 pencil W/C prov.exhib. 3-Jun-4 Christie's, London #27/R
£1500 $2745 €2190 Fairlight, Sussex (20x23cm-8x9in) i.d.1868 pencil W/C htd touches bodycol prov.exhib. 3-Jun-4 Christie's, London #26/R est:2000-3000

ROOKE, Thomas Matthew (attrib) (1842-1942) British
Works on paper
£1500 $2700 €2190 Cottages near Lucas, Redcoats Green. Derelict stables at Lucas (32x47cm-13x19in) pencil W/C. 21-Apr-4 Tennants, Leyburn #1044 est:1000-1500

ROOKER, Michael Angelo (1743-1801) British
Works on paper
£500 $900 €730 Old farmhouse amongst trees with figure standing beside nearby gate (19x29cm-7x11in) pencil grey sepia wash. 21-Apr-4 Tennants, Leyburn #921
£1000 $1850 €1460 Fonell Hall, Yorkshire (21x31cm-8x12in) s. W/C prov. 9-Mar-4 Bonhams, New Bond Street #32/R est:1000-1500

ROONEY, J P (1947-) British
£380 $623 €555 Awaiting the catch (40x50cm-16x20in) s. board. 4-Jun-3 John Ross, Belfast #181
£380 $654 €555 Galway village (12x122cm-5x48in) s. board. 3-Dec-3 John Ross, Belfast #80
£400 $688 €584 Waiting for the catch (50x61cm-20x24in) s. board. 3-Dec-3 John Ross, Belfast #192
£400 $732 €584 Waiting for the catch, Donegal (40x50cm-16x20in) s. board. 2-Jun-4 John Ross, Belfast #50
£450 $747 €657 Unloading the boats (40x51cm-16x20in) s. board. 1-Oct-3 John Ross, Belfast #121
£450 $774 €657 Irish shawlies in the village (38x76cm-15x30in) s. board. 3-Dec-3 John Ross, Belfast #120
£480 $787 €701 Mending the cart (40x50cm-16x20in) s. board. 4-Jun-3 John Ross, Belfast #65
£480 $826 €701 Galway village (12x122cm-5x48in) s. board. 3-Dec-3 John Ross, Belfast #143
£520 $863 €759 Donegal fishing village (15x122cm-6x48in) s. board. 1-Oct-3 John Ross, Belfast #80
£520 $952 €759 Fishing village, West of Ireland (15x122cm-6x48in) s. board. 2-Jun-4 John Ross, Belfast #81
£520 $952 €759 Village, West of Ireland (20x91cm-8x36in) s. board. 2-Jun-4 John Ross, Belfast #137
£580 $1061 €847 Unloading the catch, Clifden, Connemara (40x50cm-16x20in) s. board. 2-Jun-4 John Ross, Belfast #83

ROONEY, Mick (1944-) British
£1800 $3168 €2628 At the hairdressers (53x43cm-21x17in) s.d.90 board prov. 19-May-4 Sotheby's, Olympia #297/R est:2000-3000
£2800 $4928 €4088 Reading the signs (51x46cm-20x18in) painted 1990. 19-May-4 Sotheby's, Olympia #295/R est:3000-4000
Works on paper
£360 $659 €526 Balancing act (38x31cm-15x12in) init.d.77 gouache. 7-Jul-4 Cheffins, Cambridge #78/R

ROONEY, Robert (1937-) Australian
£2846 $4467 €4127 Variations slippery seal 4 (107x107cm-42x42in) s.i.d.4.1967 verso acrylic. 27-Aug-3 Christie's, Sydney #523/R est:5000-8000 (A.D 7000)
£4878 $7659 €7073 After colonial cubism (122x198cm-48x78in) s.i.d.1993 verso acrylic. 27-Aug-3 Christie's, Sydney #597/R est:7000-10000 (A.D 12000)
£6405 $11849 €9351 Silly symphony 2 (125x244cm-49x96in) s.d.1988 i.verso synthetic polymer prov. 15-Mar-4 Sotheby's, Melbourne #31/R est:10000-15000 (A.D 15500)

ROOPE, Len (1917-) British
Works on paper
£400 $664 €584 Veteran's club house, Workington (25x30cm-10x12in) s.d.1972 W/C. 2-Oct-3 Mitchells, Cockermouth #785/R
£400 $716 €584 Vale of Lorton (25x36cm-10x14in) s.d.1987 W/C. 13-May-4 Mitchells, Cockermouth #1020
£440 $730 €642 Edinburgh (18x28cm-7x11in) s. W/C. 2-Oct-3 Mitchells, Cockermouth #787
£500 $830 €730 Allonby evening (23x30cm-9x12in) s. W/C. 2-Oct-3 Mitchells, Cockermouth #784/R

ROORE, Jacques Ignatius de (1686-1747) Flemish
£662 $1205 €1000 Scene d'idolatrie (58x50cm-23x20in) 21-Jun-4 Tajan, Paris #76

ROOS, Adriaan (1919-) Dutch
Works on paper
£667 $1220 €1000 Abstract composition (200x172cm-79x68in) s.d.70/71 mixed media. 7-Jun-4 Glerum, Amsterdam #215/R

ROOS, Cajetan (1690-1770) Italian
£1223 $2225 €1786 Italian landscape with cattle and a herdsman (38x47cm-15x19in) panel. 16-Jun-4 Fischer, Luzern #1176/R est:3000-4000 (S.FR 2800)
£1844 $3079 €2600 Landscape scene (74x97cm-29x38in) 18-Jun-3 Christie's, Rome #321 est:2500-3000

ROOS, Cajetan (attrib) (1690-1770) Italian
£3356 $6174 €5000 Herders and flock in Roman Campagna (35x61cm-14x24in) prov. 24-Mar-4 Dorotheum, Vienna #276/R est:5000-6000
£3497 $5944 €5000 Wild boar hunt in southern landscape with ruins. Goats in Italian landscape (65x87cm-26x34in) panel two. 20-Nov-3 Van Ham, Cologne #1405/R est:6000
£3741 $6697 €5500 River landscape with herders and cattle (97x136cm-38x54in) 17-Mar-4 Neumeister, Munich #373/R est:3200

ROOS, Cajetan (circle) (1690-1770) Italian
£5369 $9611 €8000 Voyageurs, bergers et troupeau dans un paysage vallonne (108x135cm-43x53in) 25-May-4 Palais de Beaux Arts, Brussels #68/R

ROOS, Cornelis François (1802-1874) Dutch
£273 $500 €399 Autumn landscape with blue sky breaking through the clouds (30x55cm-12x22in) s. 10-Jul-4 Auctions by the Bay, Alameda #408/R

ROOS, Erik (20th C) Swiss?
Works on paper
£544 $990 €800 Verschuiving (12x39cm-5x15in) s.i.d.1975 crayon on three sheets sold with another by same hand. 3-Feb-4 Christie's, Amsterdam #557

ROOS, Jacob (1682-?) Italian
£2887 $5053 €4100 Paysan et troupeau (102x126cm-40x50in) 17-Dec-3 Piasa, Paris #36/R est:4000-6000
£3401 $6190 €5000 Italianate landscape with a herdsman and his cattle (81x104cm-32x41in) prov. 3-Feb-4 Christie's, Amsterdam #13/R est:5000-7000

ROOS, Johann Heinrich (1631-1685) German
£6333 $11337 €9500 Young shepherd with sheep, goats and cows in the meadow in the dunes (38x47cm-15x19in) s. 17-May-4 Glerum, Amsterdam #22/R est:10000-15000
Works on paper
£406 $677 €580 Herder holding stick (23x17cm-9x7in) wash chk. 10-Oct-3 Winterberg, Heidelberg #380

ROOS, Johann Heinrich (attrib) (1631-1685) German
£579 $950 €840 Landscape with sheep and goats on a mountain side (38x56cm-15x22in) prov. 31-May-3 Brunk, Ashville #344/R
£5556 $9167 €8000 Traveller and herdsman in mountainous Italian landscape (196x118cm-77x46in) 3-Jul-3 Van Ham, Cologne #1010/R est:6000
£7241 $12093 €10500 Shepherds returning home with flock (225x170cm-89x67in) 9-Jul-3 Hugo Ruef, Munich #16/R est:4500
Works on paper
£604 $1111 €900 Paysan et troupeau (22x31cm-9x12in) pierre noire wash. 24-Mar-4 Claude Boisgirard, Paris #12/R

ROOS, Johann Melchior (1659-1731) German
£2385 $4102 €3482 Shepherd with sheep (81x99cm-32x39in) 3-Dec-3 AB Stockholms Auktionsverk #2681/R est:20000-25000 (S.KR 31000)
£3385 $5822 €4942 Pastoral landscape (60x72cm-24x28in) 3-Dec-3 AB Stockholms Auktionsverk #2733/R est:20000-25000 (S.KR 44000)

ROOS, Nicholas Oswald (1940-) South African
£776 $1296 €1133 Namibian landscape in red and yellow (65x100cm-26x39in) s.d.80 i.verso canvas on board. 20-Oct-3 Stephan Welz, Johannesburg #410/R est:8000-12000 (SA.R 9000)
£905 $1512 €1321 Namibian landscape with full moon (121x121cm-48x48in) s.d.86 acrylic canvas on board. 20-Oct-3 Stephan Welz, Johannesburg #413/R est:10000-15000 (SA.R 10500)

ROOS, Nina (1956-) Finnish
£5287 $8988 €7719 Untitled (128x120cm-50x47in) acrylic on plexiglass prov. 5-Nov-3 AB Stockholms Auktionsverk #1027/R est:40000-50000 (S.KR 70000)
Works on paper
£580 $1044 €847 Senta IV (125x125cm-49x49in) mixed media zinc. 26-Apr-4 Bukowskis, Stockholm #505/R (S.KR 8000)

ROOS, Philipp Peter (1657-1706) German
£634 $1096 €900 Bergers dans un paysage (51x65cm-20x26in) 15-Dec-3 Bailly Pommery, Paris #54/R
£805 $1498 €1200 Shepherds with their herds (69x88cm-27x35in) i.verso. 5-Mar-4 Wendl, Rudolstadt #3842/R
£1656 $3013 €2500 Shepherdess resting with her flock (82x130cm-32x51in) 16-Jun-4 Hugo Ruef, Munich #871/R est:1800
£2254 $3944 €3200 Goat in landscape (74x98cm-29x39in) 17-Dec-3 Christie's, Rome #337/R est:3000-4000
£2817 $4930 €4000 Shepherd (73x97cm-29x38in) 17-Dec-3 Christie's, Rome #339/R est:4000-6000
£2837 $4738 €4000 Bull with herds (96x136cm-38x54in) 17-Jun-3 Finarte Semenzato, Milan #420/R
£9091 $15455 €13000 Herder with animals in Italian mountain landscape with ruins (180x356cm-71x140in) 20-Nov-3 Dorotheum, Salzburg #67/R est:20000-30000
£11189 $19021 €16000 Herder with animals in Italian mountain landscape (180x356cm-71x140in) 20-Nov-3 Dorotheum, Salzburg #66/R est:20000-30000
£13793 $24828 €20000 Goats (97x135cm-38x53in) 26-Jan-4 Ansorena, Madrid #51/R est:20000
£13793 $24828 €20000 Shepherd with goats (97x135cm-38x53in) 26-Jan-4 Ansorena, Madrid #53/R est:20000
£20000 $36600 €29200 Shepherds surrounded by his flock within a landscape (123x168cm-48x66in) pair lit. 7-Jul-4 Christie's, London #77/R est:20000-30000
£21918 $37260 €32000 Landscape with shepherd and herd (95x132cm-37x52in) 4-Nov-3 Ansorena, Madrid #103/R est:18000
£33566 $57734 €48000 Bergers et troupeaux (146x225cm-57x89in) pair. 8-Dec-3 Claude Aguttes, Neuilly #23/R est:30000-35000
£80000 $145600 €120000 Rural scenes (196x292cm-77x115in) pair lit. 5-Jul-4 Marc Kohn, Paris #51/R est:120000-150000

ROOS, Philipp Peter (attrib) (1657-1706) German
£909 $1600 €1327 Sheep and shepherd (34x48cm-13x19in) 19-May-4 Doyle, New York #6059/R est:2000-3000
£993 $1808 €1500 Shepherd with his flock and goat in the Roman campagna (47x66cm-19x26in) 16-Jun-4 Dorotheum, Vienna #261/R est:2000-3000
£993 $1808 €1500 Shepherd and his flock (43x72cm-17x28in) 16-Jun-4 Dorotheum, Vienna #262/R est:1500-2000
£1325 $2411 €2000 Landscape with a flock of sheep (76x101cm-30x40in) 16-Jun-4 Dorotheum, Vienna #292/R est:1000-1500
£3326 $5953 €4856 Pastoral landscape (39x45cm-15x18in) 26-May-4 AB Stockholms Auktionsverk #2559/R est:30000-35000 (S.KR 45000)
£3974 $7232 €6000 Old Testament scene (94x122cm-37x48in) 18-Jun-4 Bolland & Marotz, Bremen #528/R est:4200
£4200 $7560 €6132 Scenes with drovers, shepherds, cattle and flock (49x63cm-19x25in) pair. 23-Apr-4 Christie's, Kensington #139/R est:4000-6000
£4386 $7325 €6404 Pastoral (121x178cm-48x70in) prov. 15-Nov-3 Galerie Gloggner, Luzern #95/R est:12000-14000 (S.FR 10000)
£4698 $8644 €7000 Cattle and horse resting in rocky landscape (95x130cm-37x51in) 24-Mar-4 Hugo Ruef, Munich #883/R est:1500
£4718 $7549 €6700 Italian landscape with cattle (74x97cm-29x38in) lit. 19-Sep-3 Karlheinz Kaupp, Staufen #1893/R est:1000

ROOS, Theodor (1638-1698) German
£2128 $3553 €3000 Allegorie du commerce (89x100cm-35x39in) s.indis.d.170. 17-Oct-3 Tajan, Paris #61/R est:4000-5000
£32414 $54131 €47000 Sword of Damacles (56x66cm-22x26in) s.d.1672 prov.lit. 15-Nov-3 Lempertz, Koln #1129/R est:40000-50000

ROOSEN, Maria (1957-) Dutch
Works on paper
£507 $832 €700 Couple (56x76cm-22x30in) s.i. W/C prov. 27-May-3 Sotheby's, Amsterdam #577/R

ROOSENBOOM, Albert (1845-1875) Belgian
£1413 $2600 €2063 Blowing bubbles (24x19cm-9x7in) s. 27-Jun-4 Freeman, Philadelphia #29/R est:3000-5000
£1500 $2685 €2190 Grazed elbow. Song bird (24x19cm-9x7in) s. pair. 26-May-4 Sotheby's, Olympia #281/R est:1000-1500

ROOSENBOOM, E (19th C) Belgian?
£3916 $6540 €5600 Patineurs au bord de la chaumiere (61x77cm-24x30in) s. 13-Oct-3 Horta, Bruxelles #155/R est:7000-9000

ROOSENBOOM, Margaretha (1843-1896) Dutch
£3077 $5231 €4400 Autumn still life with grapes, peaches and dead songbird (40x33cm-16x13in) s.d.1859 panel. 20-Nov-3 Van Ham, Cologne #1825/R est:2500
£6667 $12000 €10000 Still life with roses and grapes (33x46cm-13x18in) s. panel. 20-Apr-4 Sotheby's, Amsterdam #165/R est:20000-30000
£23000 $38180 €33580 Still life of roses and strawberries (31x42cm-12x17in) s. panel. 1-Oct-3 Sotheby's, Olympia #246/R est:5000-7000
Works on paper
£4527 $8103 €6700 Still life of roses (67x49cm-26x19in) s. W/C. 8-May-4 Bukowskis, Helsinki #400/R est:6000-8000
£20833 $35417 €30000 Swag of tulips (74x50cm-29x20in) s. W/C htd white. 28-Oct-3 Christie's, Amsterdam #234/R est:20000-30000

ROOSENBOOM, Margaretha (attrib) (1843-1896) Dutch
£809 $1400 €1181 Still life of flowers and vegetables (23x18cm-9x7in) s. board. 13-Dec-3 Weschler, Washington #502

ROOSENBOOM, Nicolaas Johannes (1805-1880) Dutch
£1468 $2700 €2143 Dutch canal scene, winter (50x65cm-20x26in) s. 27-Jun-4 Freeman, Philadelphia #17/R est:3000-5000
£3077 $5292 €4400 Peasant with white horse on the beach next to fishing boats (44x58cm-17x23in) s. panel. 3-Dec-3 Neumeister, Munich #719/R est:4000
£3552 $6500 €5186 Landscape with fields, trees and windmills (46x33cm-18x13in) s. i.verso board. 10-Apr-4 Cobbs, Peterborough #124a/R
£4500 $7740 €6570 Dutch winter landscape (19x25cm-7x10in) s. panel. 4-Dec-3 Christie's, Kensington #184/R est:5000-7000
£7383 $13215 €11000 Skaters in front of windmill (54x69cm-21x27in) s. 27-May-4 Dorotheum, Vienna #18/R est:10000-12000
£16216 $29027 €24000 Plaisir d'hiver (46x61cm-18x24in) panel. 10-May-4 Amberes, Antwerp #302/R

ROOSKENS, Anton (1906-1976) Dutch
£355 $592 €500 Le dragon (44x70cm-17x28in) paper. 17-Jun-3 Galerie Moderne, Brussels #196
£528 $950 €771 Abstract (23x30cm-9x12in) s.d.66 acrylic ink paper. 23-Jan-4 Freeman, Philadelphia #85/R
£1678 $2887 €2400 Untitled (20x25cm-8x10in) s.d.72 panel. 2-Dec-3 Sotheby's, Amsterdam #295/R est:3000-4000
£2989 $5500 €4364 Composition black (29x35cm-11x14in) s.d.51 i.d. verso paper on canvas prov. 27-Jun-4 Freeman, Philadelphia #67/R est:1500-2500
£5594 $9510 €8000 Figure (100x80cm-39x31in) sd.72 prov. 25-Nov-3 Christie's, Amsterdam #270/R est:7000-9000
£5634 $9408 €8226 Imaginary mask (109x64cm-43x25in) s.d.59. 7-Oct-3 Rasmussen, Copenhagen #42/R est:70000 (D.KR 60000)
£9302 $16000 €13581 Indiaanse motieven (76x64cm-30x25in) init.d.48 prov.exhib. 7-Dec-3 Freeman, Philadelphia #82 est:25000-40000
£10667 $19627 €16000 Het gesprek 2 (98x130cm-39x51in) s.d.75 i.verso prov.exhib.lit. 9-Jun-4 Christie's, Amsterdam #319/R est:15000-20000
£16279 $28000 €23767 South Sea Motif (56x69cm-22x27in) s.d.51 prov.exhib. 7-Dec-3 Freeman, Philadelphia #83 est:20000-30000
£18116 $29710 €25000 Untitled (93x73cm-37x29in) s. 27-May-3 Sotheby's, Amsterdam #401/R est:25000-35000
£23333 $42933 €35000 Composite met Zonnen (73x90cm-29x35in) s. s.i.1950 verso exhib. 8-Jun-4 Sotheby's, Amsterdam #83/R est:30000-40000
Works on paper
£373 $679 €560 Figure composition (30x20cm-12x8in) s. crayon. 19-Jun-4 Rasmussen, Havnen #4279 (D.KR 4200)
£578 $1052 €850 Nocturne 62 (24x32cm-9x13in) s.d.58 i.verso wax crayon ink gouache. 3-Feb-4 Christie's, Amsterdam #609
£1267 $2318 €1900 Figure in a boat (23x26cm-9x10in) s.d.67 col chk. 7-Jun-4 Glerum, Amsterdam #421/R est:1400-1600
£1600 $2928 €2400 Scene with bird (64x50cm-25x20in) s.d.71 gouache. 7-Jun-4 Glerum, Amsterdam #361/R est:2500-3000
£1628 $2800 €2377 Playing child (36x46cm-14x18in) init.d.50 gouache prov. 7-Dec-3 Freeman, Philadelphia #84 est:1500-2500
£1630 $3000 €2380 Cobra (37x29cm-15x11in) init.d.48 gouache crayon prov. 27-Jun-4 Freeman, Philadelphia #66/R est:1500-2500
£1867 $3435 €2800 Untitled (24x31cm-9x12in) s.d.66 wax crayon gouache. 9-Jun-4 Christie's, Amsterdam #151/R est:2000-3000
£1896 $3033 €2749 Fantasy animal (50x60cm-20x24in) s.d.75 gouache. 17-Sep-3 Kunsthallen, Copenhagen #2/R est:25000 (D.KR 20000)
£2000 $3680 €3000 Savanne II, Nairobi (37x48cm-15x19in) s.i.d.1954 pastel gouache W/C exhib. 9-Jun-4 Christie's, Amsterdam #149/R est:3000-5000
£2035 $3500 €2971 Spooks (30x23cm-12x9in) init.d.49 gouache pencil prov. 7-Dec-3 Freeman, Philadelphia #85 est:1500-2500
£4000 $7360 €6000 Figure (35x28cm-14x11in) init.d.49 gouache blk chk prov. 9-Jun-4 Christie's, Amsterdam #125/R est:4000-6000

ROOSVAAL-KALLSTENIUS, Gerda (1864-1939) Swedish
£1478 $2646 €2158 Interior scene with mother and child (36x29cm-14x11in) init. panel. 26-May-4 AB Stockholms Auktionsverk #2200/R est:20000-25000 (S.KR 20000)
£2217 $3969 €3237 Old man by flowering meadow (61x45cm-24x18in) s.i.d.94 canvas on panel. 28-May-4 Uppsala Auktionskammare, Uppsala #179/R est:30000-40000 (S.KR 30000)

ROOTH, W H (?) ?
£1500 $2685 €2190 Horse watering in a landscape (35x20cm-14x8in) s. pair. 22-Mar-4 Bonhams & Brooks, Norfolk #241/R est:500-800

ROOTIUS, Jan Albertsz (attrib) (1624-1666) Dutch
£3571 $6500 €5214 Portrait of a young lady, bust-length, in a black dress with a fan in her hand (72x59cm-28x23in) panel prov. 4-Feb-4 Christie's, Rockefeller NY #71/R est:5000-7000

ROOVER, Carlo de (1900-1986) Belgian
£556 $928 €800 Still life with coffee pot (84x87cm-33x34in) s. panel. 21-Oct-3 Campo & Campo, Antwerp #97

ROPAR, Dennis (1971-) Australian
Works on paper
£744 $1376 €1086 Homage XII 2003 (150x150cm-59x59in) s. synthetic polymer. 10-Mar-4 Deutscher-Menzies, Melbourne #366/R est:1800-2400 (A.D 1800)

ROPE, George Thomas (1846-1929) British
£480 $859 €701 Wooded landscape (19x23cm-7x9in) s. panel. 22-Mar-4 Bonhams & Brooks, Norfolk #368/R

ROPELE, Walter (1934-) Swiss

£1092 $1987 €1594 A small celebration (60x80cm-24x31in) s. acrylic painted 2002. 16-Jun-4 Fischer, Luzern #1342/R est:2500-3000 (S.FR 2500)
£1310 $2384 €1913 In the shade in the garden (100x100cm-39x39in) s.d.03 acrylic. 16-Jun-4 Fischer, Luzern #1344/R est:2500-3500 (S.FR 3000)
£1528 $2782 €2231 Garden view (100x100cm-39x39in) s.d.03 acrylic. 16-Jun-4 Fischer, Luzern #1343/R est:2500-3500 (S.FR 3500)

ROPER, Geoffrey (1942-) British

£250 $460 €365 Venice canal (20x26cm-8x10in) board. 29-Mar-4 Thomson Roddick & Medcalf, Edinburgh #251
£300 $567 €438 Granton fleet (47x105cm-19x41in) mono.d.75 board. 19-Feb-4 Lyon & Turnbull, Edinburgh #146
£800 $1472 €1168 Saturday crowd, umbrellas march (92x120cm-36x47in) s.i.verso. 29-Mar-4 Thomson Roddick & Medcalf, Edinburgh #249

ROPS, Felicien (1833-1898) Belgian

£2113 $3655 €3000 Cour de chateau (16x25cm-6x10in) wood exhib. 9-Dec-3 Campo, Vlaamse Kaai #401 est:900-1100
£2667 $4907 €4000 Paysage (27x35cm-11x14in) canvas on panel prov.lit. 10-Jun-4 Camard, Paris #13/R est:4000-5000

Prints

£2095 $3749 €3100 L'incantation (42x27cm-17x11in) s.num.18/200 engraving. 7-May-4 Millon & Associes, Paris #34 est:1500-2000
£2365 $4233 €3500 Satan semant l'ivraie (30x21cm-12x8in) st. engraving. 7-May-4 Millon & Associes, Paris #23/R est:1500-2000
£2649 $4821 €4000 L'incantation (42x27cm-17x11in) s. num.39/50 engraving. 16-Jun-4 Hotel des Ventes Mosan, Brussels #318 est:2500-3000
£2770 $4959 €4100 L'agonie (26x36cm-10x14in) i. engraving. 7-May-4 Millon & Associes, Paris #14/R est:1500-2000
£3221 $5960 €4800 La tentation de Saint Antoine (43x27cm-17x11in) s. col etching edition 4/50. 15-Mar-4 Horta, Bruxelles #202 est:2000-3000
£4392 $7861 €6500 Ca mord au bal masque (45x29cm-18x11in) engraving. 7-May-4 Millon & Associes, Paris #33/R est:800-1000

Works on paper

£680 $1218 €1000 Vieille femme des iles Loffoden, Norvege (22x19cm-9x7in) s. ink. 16-Mar-4 Vanderkindere, Brussels #160
£938 $1500 €1369 Offertoire (15x21cm-6x8in) s. col pen ink. 18-Sep-3 Swann Galleries, New York #567/R est:1000-1500
£1000 $1790 €1500 Rimes de joie (28x18cm-11x7in) pencil. 15-May-4 De Vuyst, Lokeren #282 est:600-1000
£1769 $3166 €2600 Eventail fait pour Melle G Blanc (17x47cm-7x19in) pen Indian ink tracing paper. 19-Mar-4 Millon & Associes, Paris #24/R est:2000-3000
£2041 $3653 €3000 Homme a la pipe (19x14cm-7x6in) crayon prov. 19-Mar-4 Millon & Associes, Paris #25/R est:3000-4000
£6122 $10959 €9000 Theodora (20x13cm-8x5in) mono. blk crayon sanguine. 19-Mar-4 Millon & Associes, Paris #29/R est:10000-15000
£6803 $12177 €10000 Sataniques (11x17cm-4x7in) crayon W/C. 19-Mar-4 Millon & Associes, Paris #26/R est:8000-12000
£6803 $12177 €10000 Abus confiance (17x12cm-7x5in) s. chl sanguine scratching out. 19-Mar-4 Millon & Associes, Paris #31/R est:10000-15000
£7551 $13516 €11100 Printemps - Satyriasis (18x27cm-7x11in) s.i. col crayon sanguine. 19-Mar-4 Millon & Associes, Paris #32/R est:10000-15000
£8707 $15586 €12800 Clownerie intime (12x9cm-5x4in) i. Indian ink red crayon. 19-Mar-4 Millon & Associes, Paris #28/R est:8000-12000
£8844 $15830 €13000 Voyage au pays des vieux dieux (18x16cm-7x6in) crayon Indian ink W/C. 19-Mar-4 Millon & Associes, Paris #33/R est:14000-18000
£9252 $16561 €13600 Exercices de devotion de Mr Henri Roch (26x19cm-10x7in) s. col crayon Indian ink. 19-Mar-4 Millon & Associes, Paris #34/R est:14000-18000
£10000 $18200 €14600 Chemin de la Cour d'Assises (24x17cm-9x7in) init. gouache W/C pencil card prov.exhib.lit. 5-Feb-4 Christie's, London #327/R est:12000-18000
£17450 $32457 €26000 La balancoire a cythere, neuvieme dizain (26x18cm-10x7in) mono. gouache W/C htd black crayon paper on cardboard. 2-Mar-4 Artcurial Briest, Paris #14/R est:6000-8000
£20135 $35639 €30000 Tentation (30x20cm-12x8in) s. col dr prov. 30-Apr-4 Tajan, Paris #147/R est:35000-40000
£24000 $43680 €35040 Demangeaison (21x18cm-8x7in) mono. pastel blk chk pencil card prov.exhib.lit. 5-Feb-4 Christie's, London #326/R est:18000-24000

ROQUE, Jean Jacques (1880-1926) French

£1745 $3211 €2600 Barque et pecheurs au port (60x80cm-24x31in) s. 29-Mar-4 Rieunier, Paris #51/R est:3000-4000

ROQUEPLAN, Camille (1803-1855) French

£1408 $2282 €2000 Young woman sitting (32x24cm-13x9in) s.verso. 11-Aug-3 Boscher, Cherbourg #785/R est:3000-4000
£2133 $3861 €3200 La dame blanche (46x38cm-18x15in) exhib.lit. 30-Mar-4 Rossini, Paris #241/R est:3000-5000
£2333 $4247 €3500 Cattle drinking from a river (32x24cm-13x9in) indis.mono. lit. 1-Jul-4 Van Ham, Cologne #1581/R est:2000
£2467 $4465 €3700 Vue du Val-Fleury et de l'aqueduc (41x33cm-16x13in) exhib. 30-Mar-4 Rossini, Paris #242/R est:2500-4000
£3500 $6440 €5110 Suitor (57x47cm-22x19in) s.d.1839. 23-Mar-4 Bonhams, New Bond Street #108/R est:4000-6000
£5467 $9895 €8200 L'idylle des cerises (153x122cm-60x48in) painted c.1835 exhib.lit. 30-Mar-4 Rossini, Paris #243/R est:8000-15000

Works on paper

£2465 $4264 €3500 Charrette sur un pont au soleil couchant (32x47cm-13x19in) s. W/C gouache. 10-Dec-3 Piasa, Paris #74/R est:3000

ROQUEPLAN, Camille (attrib) (1803-1855) French

£362 $605 €529 Shipping off the coast (45x66cm-18x26in) s. 17-Nov-3 Waddingtons, Toronto #184/R (C.D 800)

RORBYE, Martinus (1803-1848) Danish

£348 $633 €508 Portrait of young southern boy (26x22cm-10x9in) init. 7-Feb-4 Rasmussen, Havnen #2315 (D.KR 3800)
£2336 $3785 €3295 Grapes harvest (55x46cm-22x18in) 21-May-3 Babuino, Rome #211/R est:2000-2500
£5991 $10184 €8747 Young Italian man looking at landscape from a villa (47x38cm-19x15in) with sig. panel. 10-Nov-3 Rasmussen, Vejle #2/R est:75000-100000 (D.KR 65000)
£6714 $12287 €9802 Portrait of Frederikke Eleonora Cathrine Rorbye (31x23cm-12x9in) s.d.1848 prov. 9-Jun-4 Rasmussen, Copenhagen #1578/R est:40000 (D.KR 75000)
£12534 $22936 €18300 A Greek tailor (24x32cm-9x13in) i. painted c.1846-48. 9-Jun-4 Rasmussen, Copenhagen #1436/R est:150000 (D.KR 140000)

Works on paper

£662 $1145 €967 A shoemaker (21x27cm-8x11in) i.d.1835 pencil. 9-Dec-3 Rasmussen, Copenhagen #1734/R (D.KR 7000)
£806 $1474 €1177 From the bazaar in Athens (27x42cm-11x17in) i. pencil col pencil lit. 7-Jun-4 Museumsbygningen, Copenhagen #7/R (D.KR 9000)
£1121 $1772 €1625 Italian woman standing (28x22cm-11x9in) s. W/C pencil. 2-Sep-3 Rasmussen, Copenhagen #2013/R est:15000-25000 (D.KR 12000)
£1611 $2949 €2352 Figures by Borsrampen (22x15cm-9x6in) s.d.1848 Indian ink wash prov. 9-Jun-4 Rasmussen, Copenhagen #2056/R est:20000-30000 (D.KR 18000)

RORUP, Ellen Krause (1905-1990) Danish

£487 $838 €711 Autumn landscape with reaper and binder (65x77cm-26x30in) init. 3-Dec-3 Museumsbygningen, Copenhagen #110 (D.KR 5200)

RORUP, Viggo (1903-1971) Danish

£451 $844 €658 Mountain landscape, summer, Greece (60x73cm-24x29in) s.d.59 exhib. 25-Feb-4 Kunsthallen, Copenhagen #190/R (D.KR 5000)

ROSA, B (19/20th C) French

Sculpture

£1931 $3225 €2800 Bull (18cm-7in) pat.bronze Cast.Peyrol. 9-Jul-3 Hugo Ruef, Munich #1837 est:300

ROSA, Buddy di (20th C) ?

Sculpture

£1216 $2299 €1800 Mister cactus (108cm-43in) s.num.1/8 paint resin. 21-Feb-4 Cornette de St.Cyr, Paris #282/R est:2500-3000
£1736 $2899 €2500 Mister cactus (108cm-43in) s. resin edition of 8. 25-Oct-3 Cornette de St.Cyr, Paris #662/R est:2500-3000
£2778 $4583 €4000 Le petit ange (105x80x90cm-41x31x35in) s.num.7/8 paint resin lit. 2-Jul-3 Cornette de St.Cyr, Paris #161/R est:2500-3000
£2778 $4583 €4000 Mister cactus (105cm-41in) s.num.6/8 resin. 2-Jul-3 Cornette de St.Cyr, Paris #162/R est:3000-4000

ROSA, Ercole (1846-1893) Italian

Sculpture

£9000 $15570 €13140 The broken lamp (89cm-35in) white marble socle lit. 12-Dec-3 Sotheby's, London #252/R est:10000-15000

ROSA, Fabian de la (1869-1937) Philippino

£13900 $23212 €20294 Un recuerdo de la Villa Borghese - Rembembrance of the Villa Borghese (43x56cm-17x22in) s.i.d.1909 prov. 26-Oct-3 Christie's, Hong Kong #29/R est:180000-250000 (HK.D 180000)
£60215 $96344 €87914 Laundry women (61x76cm-24x30in) s.d.March 1922. 18-May-3 Sotheby's, Singapore #69/R est:150000-250000 (S.D 168000)

ROSA, G (19th C) ?

£1711 $3147 €2600 Idyllic landscape with animals and herders (50x59cm-20x23in) s.i. 24-Jun-4 Dr Fritz Nagel, Stuttgart #749/R est:1400

ROSA, Herve di (1959-) French

£733 $1349 €1100 L'incroyable Mr Jaune (50x50cm-20x20in) acrylic board triptych painted 1981 prov. 9-Jun-4 Artcurial Briest, Paris #518
£934 $1680 €1400 Professeur X (244x103cm-96x41in) s.d.1983 verso acrylic exhib. 26-Apr-4 Tajan, Paris #248/R est:1300-1500
£1197 $2095 €1700 Docker (55x46cm-22x18in) s.i. acrylic. 18-Dec-3 Cornette de St.Cyr, Paris #150/R est:1500-2000
£1879 $3439 €2800 Composition (179x103cm-70x41in) s.d.90 acrylic. 7-Jul-4 Artcurial Briest, Paris #248 est:3000-4000
£1913 $3386 €2850 Autoportrait dans la jungle (117x103cm-46x41in) s.d.1982 acrylic. 29-Apr-4 Claude Aguttes, Neuilly #154 est:1000-1200
£1974 $3632 €3000 Chasse (102x153cm-40x60in) s.d.1990-91 acrylic paper on canvas prov. 27-Jun-4 Versailles Encheres #180/R est:2500-3000
£2667 $4907 €4000 Centaure contre minotaure (150x130cm-59x51in) s.d.1991 exhib. 14-Jun-4 Tajan, Paris #238/R est:4000-5000

ROSA, L (19th C) ?

£3356 $6007 €5000 On Burano Island (31x42cm-12x17in) s.d.1881. 27-May-4 Dorotheum, Vienna #89/R est:3200-3800

ROSA, Leonardo (?) ?

Works on paper

£305 $500 €445 Nr 1372 (38x34cm-15x13in) s.i.d.1991 gouache ink black chk on paper prov. 28-May-3 Sotheby's, Amsterdam #161/R

ROSA, Martin la (1972-) Argentinian

£13966 $25000 €20390 Summer (140x150cm-55x59in) s. s.i.d.2002 verso prov. 26-May-4 Sotheby's, New York #145/R est:12000-18000

ROSA, Pacecco di (1600-1654) Italian

£5755 $9439 €8000 Angels (76x63cm-30x25in) pair. 4-Jun-3 Sotheby's, Milan #119/R est:6000-8000

ROSA, Pacecco di (attrib) (1600-1654) Italian

£2958 $5176 €4200 Magdalen (167x126cm-66x50in) 17-Dec-3 Christie's, Rome #381a est:1500-2000

ROSA, Raffaele de (1940-) Italian

£300 $552 €450 Horse (50x70cm-20x28in) s. 11-Jun-4 Farsetti, Prato #499/R
£369 $683 €550 Castor (40x30cm-16x12in) s. i.verso. 13-Mar-4 Meeting Art, Vercelli #468
£400 $736 €600 Mythology (35x60cm-14x24in) s. s.verso. 12-Jun-4 Meeting Art, Vercelli #652
£400 $736 €600 Acastus, Pelia's son (30x35cm-12x14in) s. 12-Jun-4 Meeting Art, Vercelli #939/R
£1000 $1840 €1500 Pegasus (80x80cm-31x31in) s. 12-Jun-4 Meeting Art, Vercelli #383/R est:1500

ROSA, Richard di (1963-) French

Sculpture
£1042 $1646 €1500 Percutioniste (82x60x40cm-32x24x16in) s.d.1994 painted wood metal exhib. 27-Apr-3 Versailles Encheres #129
£1215 $1920 €1750 Cactus (105cm-41in) s. num.4/8 resin. 27-Apr-3 Versailles Encheres #130

ROSA, Salvator (1615-1673) Italian

£4934 $9079 €7500 Biblical scene (56x50cm-22x20in) board. 22-Jun-4 Durán, Madrid #201/R est:7500
£35000 $64050 €51100 Wooded landscape with herders and cattle resting (72x134cm-28x53in) mono. 7-Jul-4 Sotheby's, London #49/R est:30000-40000
£113475 $189504 €160000 Ritrovamento di Mose (200x122cm-79x48in) prov.lit. 18-Jun-3 Christie's, Rome #418/R est:100000-150000
Works on paper
£1020 $1827 €1500 Une homme etendu sur le sol (8x13cm-3x5in) i. black chk prov. 18-Mar-4 Christie's, Paris #65/R est:1500-2000
£1053 $1937 €1600 Man between two trees in landscape (10x14cm-4x6in) pen ink W/C. 22-Jun-4 Sotheby's, Milan #42/R est:1200-1500
£1400 $2562 €2044 Two figures by a tree near a river (13x19cm-5x7in) pen ink. 6-Jul-4 Christie's, London #59/R est:1500-2000
£1556 $2800 €2272 Horseman falling over the brow of a hill, his arms outstretched (27x19cm-11x7in) indis.i. pen brown ink wash. 22-Jan-4 Christie's, Rockefeller NY #53/R est:1500-2000
£2000 $3660 €2920 Young man in a plumed hat, two studies of heads and another of a nude (18x23cm-7x9in) i. pen ink. 6-Jul-4 Christie's, London #58/R est:2000-4000
£5000 $9150 €7300 Portrait of a bearded man (17x13cm-7x5in) bears attrib pen brown ink wash. 8-Jul-4 Sotheby's, London #54/R est:5000-7000
£10556 $19000 €15412 Allegory of a young artist (29x43cm-11x17in) i. red chk pen brown ink grey wash. 22-Jan-4 Christie's, Rockefeller NY #42/R est:2000-3000
£232394 $406690 €330000 Une allegorie de la peinture en guenilles assise dans l'atelier de l'artiste (22x30cm-9x12in) i. black chk pen brown ink wash prov. 17-Dec-3 Christie's, Paris #15/R est:100000-150000

ROSA, Salvator (after) (1615-1673) Italian

£5500 $9900 €8030 Mediterranean harbour at sunset with figures on a quay (101x172cm-40x68in) 23-Apr-4 Christie's, Kensington #186/R est:3000-5000
£7800 $14274 €11388 Jacob's ladder (62x74cm-24x29in) prov. 9-Jul-4 Christie's, Kensington #193/R est:3000-5000
£9722 $15361 €14000 Rocky Italianate landscape with horsemen by a bridge (100x125cm-39x49in) 2-Sep-3 Christie's, Amsterdam #63/R est:5000-7000

ROSA, Salvator (attrib) (1615-1673) Italian

£5846 $10055 €8535 Landscape with Jacob's Story in The Old Testament (109x92cm-43x36in) 2-Dec-3 Bukowskis, Stockholm #354/R est:80000-100000 (S.KR 76000)

ROSA, Salvator (circle) (1615-1673) Italian

£8725 $16054 €13000 Rocky arch with figures (57x81cm-22x32in) 24-Mar-4 Dorotheum, Vienna #347/R est:3000-5000

ROSA, Salvator (style) (1615-1673) Italian

£5036 $8259 €7000 Seascape with travellers (74x99cm-29x39in) 4-Jun-3 Sotheby's, Milan #51/R est:4000-6000
£10345 $17276 €15000 Tobias and the angel (28x42cm-11x17in) tempera paper on board prov. 12-Nov-3 Sotheby's, Milan #107/R est:12000-16000

ROSAI, Ottone (1895-1957) Italian

£4895 $8322 €7000 Men at table (50x65cm-20x26in) s. prov. 24-Nov-3 Christie's, Milan #16/R est:10000-15000
£5245 $8916 €7500 Five men at table (18x36cm-7x14in) s. board painted 1956. 29-Nov-3 Farsetti, Prato #433/R est:6000-7000
£5333 $9653 €8000 Still life with pears (18x25cm-7x10in) s.d.45 cardboard. 2-Apr-4 Farsetti, Prato #522/R est:8000-11000
£5405 $9514 €8000 Interior with figures (18x36cm-7x14in) s. board. 22-May-4 Galleria Pananti, Florence #468/R est:8000-10000
£5594 $9510 €8000 Men from Montedomi (20x15cm-8x6in) s.d.46 cardboard on canvas prov. 26-Nov-3 Pandolfini, Florence #24 est:8000-8200
£6667 $12267 €10000 Mad man (69x49cm-27x19in) s.d.46 cardboard prov. 8-Jun-4 Finarte Semenzato, Milan #369/R est:10000-12000
£6667 $12267 €10000 Three men (45x59cm-18x23in) painted 1957 prov. 8-Jun-4 Finarte Semenzato, Milan #368/R est:10000-12000
£7931 $13245 €11500 Conversation (33x41cm-13x16in) s. painted c.1956. 14-Nov-3 Farsetti, Prato #499/R est:11500-12500
£8054 $14416 €12000 Countryside (31x65cm-12x26in) s.d.44 s.verso cardboard exhib. 25-May-4 Sotheby's, Milan #117/R est:15000
£8621 $14397 €12500 Woman with parcel (60x45cm-24x18in) s.s id.1952 verso prov.exhib.lit. 13-Nov-3 Finarte Semenzato, Rome #314/R est:10000-12000
£9790 $16643 €14000 Landscape with trees and house (36x50cm-14x20in) s.d.45 cardboard. 29-Nov-3 Farsetti, Prato #425/R est:10000-15000
£10067 $18020 €15000 San Leonardo Street (27x41cm-11x16in) s.d.47 s.verso. 25-May-4 Sotheby's, Milan #127/R est:20000
£10667 $19307 €16000 Santo Spirito, Florence (65x50cm-26x20in) s. painted 1954 lit. 2-Apr-4 Farsetti, Prato #626/R est:15000-18000
£10870 $17826 €15000 House along the Arno (65x50cm-26x20in) s. prov. 27-May-3 Sotheby's, Milan #189/R est:15000-20000
£10870 $17826 €15000 Men at table (40x50cm-16x20in) s. prov. 27-May-3 Sotheby's, Milan #236/R est:15000-25000
£11034 $17655 €16000 Wood (33x26cm-13x10in) s. panel painted 1932. 13-Mar-3 Galleria Pace, Milan #142/R est:23000-28000
£11921 $21695 €18000 Circle (70x85cm-28x33in) s. painted 1946 lit. 17-Jun-4 Galleria Pananti, Florence #624/R est:2000-25000
£12000 $22080 €18000 Still life with apples (40x50cm-16x20in) s.d.47 board. 11-Jun-4 Farsetti, Prato #568/R est:18000-22000
£12667 $22800 €19000 Snooker (57x70cm-22x28in) s.d.43 exhib. 22-Apr-4 Finarte Semenzato, Rome #321/R est:20000-22000
£12667 $23307 €19000 Landscape (50x70cm-20x28in) s. painted 1956 prov.exhib.lit. 8-Jun-4 Finarte Semenzato, Milan #435/R est:13000-15000
£12752 $22826 €19000 Cortona (70x51cm-28x20in) s. d.1954 verso prov. 25-May-4 Sotheby's, Milan #131/R est:20000
£13245 $24106 €20000 Street in Florence (60x45cm-24x18in) s. board. 17-Jun-4 Galleria Pananti, Florence #627/R est:20000-25000
£13605 $24354 €20000 Street in Florence (60x45cm-24x18in) s. painted 1956 prov. 16-Mar-4 Finarte Semenzato, Milan #456/R est:20000
£13986 $23776 €20000 House on the Arno (65x50cm-26x20in) s. painted 1956. 29-Nov-3 Farsetti, Prato #503/R est:20000-25000
£14000 $25760 €21000 Landscape (65x50cm-26x20in) s. painted 1955. 11-Jun-4 Farsetti, Prato #585/R est:20000-24000
£14667 $26987 €22000 Little church (70x50cm-28x20in) s. painted 1956. 8-Jun-4 Finarte Semenzato, Milan #370/R est:15000-18000
£15385 $26154 €22000 Road to Ripoli (70x50cm-28x20in) s. painted 1956 exhib.lit. 29-Nov-3 Farsetti, Prato #502/R est:20000-25000
£16667 $27333 €23000 Marina (40x50cm-16x20in) s.d.41. 31-May-3 Farsetti, Prato #700/R est:20000-25000
£16783 $28531 €24000 San Leonardo Street (70x50cm-28x20in) s. masonite. 29-Nov-3 Farsetti, Prato #429/R est:22000-28000
£19580 $33287 €28000 San Leonardo Street (49x40cm-19x16in) s.d.43 cardboard on canvas. 25-Nov-3 Sotheby's, Milan #194/R est:18000-22000
£23776 $40420 €34000 Road triumph (80x60cm-31x24in) s. painted 1952 exhib. 24-Nov-3 Christie's, Milan #167/R est:15000-20000
£26667 $49067 €40000 Street in Florence (105x70cm-41x28in) s. cardboard painted 1956 exhib. 8-Jun-4 Finarte Semenzato, Milan #436/R est:40000-42000
£29530 $52859 €44000 Landscape (100x73cm-39x29in) s. painted c.1950. 29-May-4 Farsetti, Prato #444/R est:40000-50000
Works on paper
£347 $549 €500 Peasants (14x10cm-6x4in) pencil dr. 6-Sep-3 Meeting Art, Vercelli #408
£467 $845 €700 Portrait (19x14cm-7x6in) s.d.1940 ink dr. 2-Apr-4 Farsetti, Prato #2/R
£467 $845 €700 Portrait of young man (20x15cm-8x6in) s.d.1927 pencil dr. 2-Apr-4 Farsetti, Prato #203/R
£600 $1086 €900 Portrait (21x16cm-8x6in) s.d.942 ink dr double-sided. 2-Apr-4 Farsetti, Prato #29/R
£633 $1146 €950 Portrait (17x14cm-7x6in) s.d.1939 ink dr. 2-Apr-4 Farsetti, Prato #28/R
£845 $1462 €1200 Portrait (23x18cm-9x7in) ink. 9-Dec-3 Pandolfini, Florence #310
£1042 $1646 €1500 Santa Maria's Church (40x51cm-16x20in) chl dr. 6-Sep-3 Meeting Art, Vercelli #655 est:1500
£1538 $2569 €2200 Snookers (17x11cm-7x4in) s.d.1927 pencil lit. 26-Jun-3 Sant Agostino, Torino #140/R est:1800
£1622 $2854 €2400 Street with walls (30x23cm-12x9in) s.d.1929 Chinese ink. 22-May-4 Galleria Pananti, Florence #425/R est:2000-2200
£3357 $5706 €4800 Rural road (51x40cm-20x16in) s.d. pencil. 24-Nov-3 Christie's, Milan #120/R est:2500-3500

ROSAIRE, Arthur Dominique (1879-1922) Canadian

£447 $800 €653 Untitled (15x19cm-6x7in) s. panel prov. 6-May-4 Heffel, Vancouver #124/R (C.D 1100)
£541 $919 €790 Landscape with figures (11x15cm-4x6in) studio st. board prov.lit. 21-Nov-3 Walker's, Ottawa #58/R (C.D 1200)
£670 $1152 €978 Scene nautique (40x50cm-16x20in) s. board. 2-Dec-3 Joyner Waddington, Toronto #188/R (C.D 1500)
£1000 $1830 €1460 Birch Forest (29x39cm-11x15in) s.d.1902 board. 1-Jun-4 Joyner Waddington, Toronto #262/R est:2500-3000 (C.D 2500)
£1048 $1929 €1530 Near the entrance to the Montreal River (28x39cm-11x15in) s.d.1902 i.verso panel. 9-Jun-4 Walker's, Ottawa #141/R est:2000-2500 (C.D 2600)

ROSALBIN DE BUNCEY, Marie Abraham (attrib) (19th C) French

£407 $692 €594 Venus and Adonis (32x46cm-13x18in) i. 19-Nov-3 Fischer, Luzern #2259/R (S.FR 900)

ROSALES, Eduardo (1836-1873) Spanish

£940 $1663 €1400 Cathedral entrance (35x27cm-14x11in) s. canvas on cardboard. 27-Apr-4 Durán, Madrid #132/R
£1736 $2760 €2500 Muerte de Carlos V (35x47cm-14x19in) s.d.1869. 29-Apr-3 Durán, Madrid #119/R est:2250

ROSANO, A (19/20th C) ?

Works on paper
£7042 $12183 €10000 Marchand de tapis (52x36cm-20x14in) s. W/C. 15-Dec-3 Gros & Delettrez, Paris #477/R est:12000-15000

ROSARIO, Antonio del (20th C) Venezuelan?

£298 $490 €435 Oranges (85x138cm-33x54in) s. painted 2002. 1-Jun-3 Subastas Odalys, Caracas #70

ROSAS, Mel (1950-) American

Works on paper
£383 $700 €559 Angst (74x104cm-29x41in) W/C. 10-Jul-4 Hindman, Chicago #446/R

ROSATI, Giulio (1858-1917) Italian
£2700 $4590 €3942 Contemplation (32x19cm-13x7in) s.d.96 panel. 19-Nov-3 Bonhams, New Bond Street #82/R est:3000-5000
£7639 $12604 €11000 Cardinal's salon (47x69cm-19x27in) s. 3-Jul-3 Van Ham, Cologne #1428/R est:3000
Works on paper
£1769 $3166 €2600 Gard de Harem observant des colombes folatres dans la fontaine du patio (36x23cm-14x9in) s. W/C gouache. 17-Mar-4 Tajan, Paris #110/R est:1000-1200
£2592 $4175 €3784 Welcomed visitor (38x56cm-15x22in) s. W/C. 20-Aug-3 James Julia, Fairfield #795/R est:8000-10000
£4000 $6880 €5840 Caravan in desert at dusk (38x54cm-15x21in) s. W/C. 2-Dec-3 Bukowskis, Stockholm #278/R est:40000-45000 (S.KR 52000)
£4444 $8000 €6488 Men on horseback (54x36cm-21x14in) s. W/C. 21-Jan-4 Sotheby's, New York #173/R est:5000-7000
£4444 $8000 €6488 Merchant (51x33cm-20x13in) s. W/C. 21-Jan-4 Sotheby's, New York #174/R est:5000-7000
£12766 $21319 €18000 Le cheval du Pacha (35x52cm-14x20in) s. W/C. 16-Jun-3 Gros & Delettrez, Paris #58/R est:15000-18000

ROSATI, James (20th C) ?
Sculpture
£3514 $6500 €5130 Box Delphi III (122x54x44cm-48x21x17in) mono. green pat bronze Cast 1960/61 edn 1/3 prov.exhib. 12-Feb-4 Sotheby's, New York #189/R est:1500-2000

ROSATIS, Waldemar (1898-1964) German
£556 $928 €800 Interior of Petri church in Lubeck (51x44cm-20x17in) s. 24-Oct-3 Ketterer, Hamburg #101/R

ROSCH, Carl (1884-?) German
£321 $536 €465 Cows in meadow (20x26cm-8x10in) mono. oil study board. 23-Jun-3 Philippe Schuler, Zurich #3419 (S.FR 700)
£588 $1000 €858 Small landscape (27x35cm-11x14in) mono.d.51. 18-Nov-3 Hans Widmer, St Gallen #1173 (S.FR 1300)
Works on paper
£295 $490 €428 Early spring landscape (28x38cm-11x15in) mono.d.26 W/C. 13-Jun-3 Zofingen, Switzerland #2990 (S.FR 650)
£298 $498 €432 Houses in village (15x18cm-6x7in) mono.d. chl. 23-Jun-3 Philippe Schuler, Zurich #3274 (S.FR 650)
£362 $615 €529 Four people working in the fields (17x21cm-7x8in) mono.d.1943 pastel. 25-Nov-3 Germann, Zurich #977 (S.FR 800)
£390 $651 €566 Women wearing headscarves (22x30cm-9x12in) mono.d. W/C over chl. 23-Jun-3 Philippe Schuler, Zurich #3272 (S.FR 850)
£407 $692 €594 Diessenhofen (20x25cm-8x10in) mono. col chk. 18-Nov-3 Hans Widmer, St Gallen #1174 (S.FR 900)

ROSCIO, Domenico (1832-1880) Italian
£22069 $36855 €32000 Rome, the Pincio with band (37x46cm-15x18in) s.d.1863 cardboard. 12-Nov-3 Sotheby's, Milan #178/R est:25000-35000

ROSCOE, Ada (19th C) New Zealander
Works on paper
£376 $639 €549 First boarding house, Kinloch, Lake Wakatipu (46x38cm-18x15in) s.i.verso W/C. 26-Nov-3 Dunbar Sloane, Wellington #110/R est:1000-2000 (NZ.D 1000)

ROSCOE, S G Williams (1852-c.1922) British
Works on paper
£380 $680 €555 River landscape with cottages, figures and boats (33x51cm-13x20in) s. W/C. 7-May-4 Christopher Matthews, Yorkshire #320
£560 $885 €812 On the Stover Canal, Newton, Devon (34x50cm-13x20in) s. W/C. 24-Jul-3 Dominic Winter, Swindon #62/R
£2000 $3400 €2920 Two figures resting by a lock (32x48cm-13x19in) s. W/C. 4-Nov-3 Bonhams, New Bond Street #99/R est:1500-2000

ROSE, A (?) ?
£450 $811 €657 Fishing barques by Catania (40x31cm-16x12in) s. 26-Jan-4 Lilla Bukowskis, Stockholm #110 (S.KR 6000)
£993 $1818 €1500 Fishermen returning home (50x82cm-20x32in) s. 8-Apr-4 Dorotheum, Vienna #211/R est:1800-2000
£1192 $2170 €1800 Idyllic landscape with farm houses (73x100cm-29x39in) s.d.79. 21-Jun-4 Dorotheum, Vienna #235/R est:1800-2000

ROSE, Alison Helen (1900-?) British
£500 $925 €730 Cuchulainn and the Grey of Macha (61x61cm-24x24in) s. board. 9-Mar-4 Gorringes, Lewes #2261

ROSE, Charles Arthur (?) American
£676 $1150 €987 Interior scene with lady seated at a spinet (64x76cm-25x30in) s. 8-Nov-3 Van Blarcom, South Natick #8/R

ROSE, David (1936-) Australian
£366 $574 €531 Bateau Bay, morning VIII (136x136cm-54x54in) s.i.d.1974 prov. 27-Aug-3 Christie's, Sydney #646 (A.D 900)

ROSE, Felix Leonce (19th C) French
£250 $403 €365 Coastal view with fisher folk by and in their boats (13x18cm-5x7in) s. 15-Aug-3 Keys, Aylsham #754

ROSE, Gerard de (1918-1987) British
£450 $707 €653 White cottage (51x36cm-20x14in) i.verso board. 28-Aug-3 Christie's, Kensington #332

ROSE, Guy (1867-1925) American
£225989 $400000 €329944 In the high Canadian Rockies (70x74cm-28x29in) painted c.1914-1920 prov.exhib.lit. 28-Apr-4 Christie's, Los Angeles #36/R est:300000-500000
£480226 $850000 €701130 The model (61x50cm-24x20in) s. prov.exhib.lit. 28-Apr-4 Christie's, Los Angeles #9/R est:600000-800000
Works on paper
£16304 $30000 €23804 Figures on a balcony in moonlight (38x25cm-15x10in) s. mixed media prov. 8-Jun-4 Bonhams & Butterfields, San Francisco #4222/R est:30000-50000

ROSE, H Randolph (fl.1880-1907) British
£500 $915 €730 Village ferry (64x101cm-25x40in) 8-Jul-4 Lawrence, Crewkerne #1642/R

ROSE, Herman (1909-) American
£440 $800 €642 Grazing cows (30x46cm-12x18in) s. 20-Jun-4 Charlton Hall, Columbia #565/R

ROSE, Iver (1899-1972) American
£206 $350 €301 Portrait of a cellist (41x61cm-16x24in) s. board. 21-Nov-3 Eldred, East Dennis #697/R
£462 $850 €675 Three patriarchs (25x20cm-10x8in) s. board. 26-Jun-4 Susanin's, Chicago #6008/R
£3804 $7000 €5554 Quarry workers (43x46cm-17x18in) s. paper. 10-Jun-4 Swann Galleries, New York #202/R est:4000-6000

ROSE, Jean-Baptiste de la (elder) (1612-1687) French
Works on paper
£816 $1461 €1200 Projet de boiserie (16x28cm-6x11in) i. pen black ink wash. 19-Mar-4 Piasa, Paris #28

ROSE, Joe (?) ?
Works on paper
£960 $1700 €1402 Chairperson (56x41cm-22x16in) s.indis.d. s.d.verso mixed media. 2-May-4 Bonhams & Butterfields, Los Angeles #3015/R est:1500-2000

ROSE, Julius (1828-1911) German
£486 $768 €700 Mountain pasture on summer's day (21x31cm-8x12in) s. 6-Sep-3 Arnold, Frankfurt #645/R
£1014 $1693 €1450 Boat in high seas (59x41cm-23x16in) s. 10-Oct-3 Stadion, Trieste #70/R
£1538 $2646 €2200 Extensive landscape (72x106cm-28x42in) s. 3-Dec-3 Stadion, Trieste #998/R est:2500-3500
£3020 $5648 €4500 Alpine landscape (79x120cm-31x47in) s.i.d.1890. 24-Feb-4 Durán, Madrid #226/R est:1300

ROSE, Knut (1936-2002) Norwegian
£714 $1313 €1042 Still life (44x60cm-17x24in) s.verso painted c.1958 lit. 29-Mar-4 Blomqvist, Lysaker #1251/R (N.KR 9000)
£952 $1751 €1390 Roof tops, possibly Arcueil (46x55cm-18x22in) s.d.1962 verso lit. 29-Mar-4 Blomqvist, Lysaker #1252/R est:15000-18000 (N.KR 12000)
£2082 $3726 €3040 Figures in a blue room (31x44cm-12x17in) s. acrylic paper lit. 22-Mar-4 Blomqvist, Oslo #620/R est:18000-22000 (N.KR 26000)
£2402 $4299 €3507 Street scene, Oslo (97x93cm-38x37in) s.d.61 verso exhib.lit. 22-Mar-4 Blomqvist, Oslo #650/R est:22000-24000 (N.KR 30000)
Works on paper
£516 $831 €753 Composition, Svanoy (24x26cm-9x10in) s. W/C. 25-Aug-3 Blomqvist, Lysaker #1240/R (N.KR 6000)

ROSE, Lily (19th C) British
£680 $1217 €993 Merry tale (61x51cm-24x20in) 27-May-4 Christie's, Kensington #281

ROSE, Manuel (1872-1961) Uruguayan
£432 $700 €626 Piriapolis (37x45cm-15x18in) s. fibre-board. 29-Jul-3 Galeria y Remates, Montevideo #133/R
£688 $1300 €1004 Nude (43x29cm-17x11in) s. on palette. 22-Feb-4 Galeria y Remates, Montevideo #6/R
£1176 $2000 €1717 Toreador (38x31cm-15x12in) s. 25-Nov-3 Galeria y Remates, Montevideo #51/R
£1481 $2400 €2147 Crowded beach (37x46cm-15x18in) s.d.1940 board. 29-Jul-3 Galeria y Remates, Montevideo #132/R est:1200-1600
£2857 $5400 €4171 Nude (93x65cm-37x26in) s. 22-Feb-4 Galeria y Remates, Montevideo #53/R est:6000
£7353 $12500 €10735 Woman (61x54cm-24x21in) 25-Nov-3 Galeria y Remates, Montevideo #159/R
£8529 $14500 €12452 Trees (73x73cm-29x29in) s.d.1917 cardboard. 25-Nov-3 Galeria y Remates, Montevideo #142/R
£12059 $20500 €17606 Women (60x55cm-24x22in) lit. 25-Nov-3 Galeria y Remates, Montevideo #158/R
£15294 $26000 €22329 Dance (74x92cm-29x36in) s.d.1950. 25-Nov-3 Galeria y Remates, Montevideo #141/R
£24118 $41000 €35212 Garden in bloom (130x130cm-51x51in) prov.lit. 25-Nov-3 Galeria y Remates, Montevideo #38/R
£26136 $46000 €38159 My garden (95x83cm-37x33in) s.d.42 prov. 5-Jan-4 Galeria y Remates, Montevideo #71/R est:48000-55000
Works on paper
£412 $700 €602 Woman in profile with hat (29x21cm-11x8in) s. pencil. 25-Nov-3 Galeria y Remates, Montevideo #17

ROSE, N (?) ?
£865 $1600 €1298 Mountainous river landscape (107x155cm-42x61in) s. 18-Jul-4 Bonhams & Butterfields, Los Angeles #7010/R est:1500-2500

ROSE, Robert Traill (1863-1942) British
Works on paper
£265 $482 €400 Saint Gervasio's Church (27x38cm-11x15in) s. W/C. 21-Jun-4 Pandolfini, Florence #34/R

ROSE, William (1929-1997) Australian
£426 $723 €622 Untitled (132x88cm-52x35in) s.d.80 acrylic board prov. 25-Nov-3 Christie's, Melbourne #272 (A.D 1000)

ROSE, William S (1810-1873) British
£250 $430 €365 Corn stooks, Ben Lomond beyond (39x59cm-15x23in) s.d.1890. 6-Dec-3 Shapes, Edinburgh #413

ROSE-INNES, Alexander (1915-1996) South African
£1724 $2879 €2517 Negligee, a young woman at a mirror (40x30cm-16x12in) s. 20-Oct-3 Stephan Welz, Johannesburg #260/R est:8000-12000 (SA.R 20000)
£2353 $4259 €3435 Outside the artist's home with Wynberg Church beyond (39x49cm-15x19in) s. canvasboard. 30-Mar-4 Stephan Welz, Johannesburg #506/R est:9000-12000 (SA.R 28000)
£3193 $5780 €4662 Ming pot (49x39cm-19x15in) s.i.verso. 30-Mar-4 Stephan Welz, Johannesburg #525/R est:10000-15000 (SA.R 38000)
£3361 $6084 €4907 Two women in a kitchen (49x39cm-19x15in) s. 30-Mar-4 Stephan Welz, Johannesburg #484/R est:9000-12000 (SA.R 40000)
£3529 $6388 €5152 Still life with fruit, flowers and ginger jar (48x58cm-19x23in) s. canvas on board. 30-Mar-4 Stephan Welz, Johannesburg #530/R est:12000-16000 (SA.R 42000)
£4129 $7391 €6028 Three women around a table in an interior (52x64cm-20x25in) s. canvas on board. 31-May-4 Stephan Welz, Johannesburg #601/R est:30000-40000 (SA.R 50000)
£7845 $14042 €11454 Repairing the boat, Arniston (60x86cm-24x34in) s.i.verso. 31-May-4 Stephan Welz, Johannesburg #551/R est:30000-40000 (SA.R 95000)
Works on paper
£299 $509 €437 Cottages in a mountainous landscape (37x55cm-15x22in) s. chl W/C. 4-Nov-3 Stephan Welz, Johannesburg #674 est:3000-5000 (SA.R 3500)
£431 $720 €629 Fishermen's cottages (35x53cm-14x21in) s. W/C. 20-Oct-3 Stephan Welz, Johannesburg #813 est:2000-3000 (SA.R 5000)
£908 $1626 €1326 Seated woman (42x29cm-17x11in) s. pastel. 31-May-4 Stephan Welz, Johannesburg #564 (SA.R 11000)

ROSELAND, Harry (1868-1950) American
£595 $1100 €869 Portrait of a woman with a blue ribbon, possibly the artist's wife (36x28cm-14x11in) s. board. 15-Jul-4 Doyle, New York #72/R est:1500-2500
£2174 $4000 €3174 Floral still life (76x64cm-30x25in) s.d.98. 26-Jun-4 Susanin's, Chicago #6071/R est:4000-6000
£2174 $4000 €3174 Reading the cards (45x61cm-18x24in) s.d.31 prov. 8-Jun-4 Bonhams & Butterfields, San Francisco #4010/R est:5000-7000
£2890 $5000 €4219 What are the cards telling me (57x72cm-22x28in) s. 10-Dec-3 Bonhams & Butterfields, San Francisco #6023/R est:7000-10000
£3198 $5500 €4669 Genre scene of a little black girl eating a bowl of soup (33x28cm-13x11in) s. board. 6-Dec-3 South Bay, Long Island #108/R
£3763 $7000 €5494 Budding genius (30x50cm-12x20in) s. 5-Mar-4 Skinner, Boston #271/R est:5000-7000
£4265 $7250 €6227 Reading her cards (31x41cm-12x16in) 21-Nov-3 Skinner, Boston #296/R est:8000-12000

ROSELAND, Harry (attrib) (1868-1950) American
Works on paper
£492 $900 €718 Boy with an instrument (46x36cm-18x14in) bears sig W/C. 5-Jun-4 Treadway Gallery, Cincinnati #578/R

ROSELDE, Eduardo (19th C) Spanish
£699 $1168 €1000 Spot in Granada (19x25cm-7x10in) s. board. 30-Jun-3 Ansorena, Madrid #235/R

ROSELL, Alexander (1859-1922) British
£282 $450 €412 Interior scene with man and woman (25x33cm-10x13in) s. painted c.1900. 20-Sep-3 Bunte, Elgin #1416
£375 $600 €548 Interior scene with figures (25x33cm-10x13in) s. 20-Sep-3 Bunte, Elgin #1415
£480 $830 €701 Found, a mother and two children searching for a pet cat (54x74cm-21x29in) s. 9-Dec-3 Anderson & Garland, Newcastle #484/R
£650 $1105 €949 Interior scene with Dutch girl feeding a young child in a cradle (25x33cm-10x13in) s. prov. 19-Nov-3 Tennants, Leyburn #1230
£707 $1223 €1032 A little help (25x33cm-10x13in) s. 15-Dec-3 Lilla Bukowskis, Stockholm #402 (S.KR 9000)
£739 $1323 €1079 Love at first sight (56x76cm-22x30in) s. 28-May-4 Uppsala Auktionskammare, Uppsala #97/R (S.KR 10000)
£1000 $1830 €1460 This way. Old friends (24x31cm-9x12in) both s. one i. stretcher pair. 8-Jul-4 Lawrence, Crewkerne #1647/R est:1000-1500
£1486 $2750 €2170 Trusted friend (76x64cm-30x25in) init.d.1909. 10-Feb-4 Doyle, New York #251/R est:5000-7000
£1700 $2941 €2482 Carol Singers in a winter landscape by a window (56x43cm-22x17in) s.d.1890. 11-Dec-3 Mitchells, Cockermouth #909/R est:1000-1500
£2800 $4648 €4088 New clogs. Mending the spinning wheel (24x31cm-9x12in) both s. pair. 1-Oct-3 Sotheby's, Olympia #131/R est:800-1200
£3400 $6222 €4964 Sailor's return (49x60cm-19x24in) s. 3-Jun-4 Lane, Penzance #75/R est:4000-5000

ROSELLI, Carlo (1939-) Italian
£333 $613 €500 Courtship (30x30cm-12x12in) s. painted 2002. 12-Jun-4 Meeting Art, Vercelli #210/R
£352 $585 €500 La Folla (45x25cm-18x10in) s. painted 2002. 14-Jun-3 Meeting Art, Vercelli #608
£470 $869 €700 Strolling in Rome (30x30cm-12x12in) s. 13-Mar-4 Meeting Art, Vercelli #159
£500 $920 €750 Rooftops in Rome (25x50cm-10x20in) acrylic lit. 12-Jun-4 Meeting Art, Vercelli #231/R
£503 $931 €750 Strolling in Via del Corso (30x30cm-12x12in) s. 13-Mar-4 Meeting Art, Vercelli #187
£667 $1227 €1000 Strolling in Via del Corso (60x40cm-24x16in) s. acrylic lit. 12-Jun-4 Meeting Art, Vercelli #593
£671 $1201 €1000 Paper room (30x60cm-12x24in) s. s.verso lit. 30-May-4 Meeting Art, Vercelli #70
£1000 $1840 €1500 Snooker game (50x80cm-20x31in) s. lit. 12-Jun-4 Meeting Art, Vercelli #986/R est:1500

ROSELLO, Joaquin Luque (1866-1932) Spanish
£9868 $17862 €15000 Solemnisation of a marriage (67x122cm-26x48in) s.d.1897. 19-Apr-4 Glerum, Amsterdam #294/R est:15000-20000

ROSELLO, Jose Maria (20th C) Spanish
£417 $688 €600 Bull fight (60x73cm-24x29in) s. s.i.d.verso. 2-Jul-3 Ansorena, Madrid #839/R

ROSEN, Friedrich Carl (1897-1952) German
£282 $504 €400 Alpine winter landscape (55x69cm-22x27in) s. board lit. 8-Jan-4 Allgauer, Kempten #2500/R

ROSEN, Jan (1854-1936) Polish
£1404 $2514 €2050 At the race course (16x24cm-6x9in) s.d.1881 panel. 26-May-4 AB Stockholms Auktionsverk #2425/R est:15000-18000 (S.KR 19000)
£10938 $18266 €15969 Cavalrymen by a well (37x51cm-15x20in) s.d.1890. 19-Oct-3 Agra, Warsaw #3/R est:60000 (P.Z 70000)

ROSENBAUM, Richard (19th C) American
Works on paper
£220 $400 €321 Approaching horse and carriage (51x33cm-20x13in) s. W/C. 7-Feb-4 Neal Auction Company, New Orleans #116

ROSENBERG, Christian (1816-1883) Danish
£293 $533 €428 Hroar and Helge fleeing from their father's murderer (27x28cm-11x11in) s. 7-Feb-4 Rasmussen, Havnen #2033/R (D.KR 3200)

ROSENBERG, Edward (1858-1934) Swedish
£956 $1539 €1396 Winter landscape (59x95cm-23x37in) s. 25-Aug-3 Lilla Bukowskis, Stockholm #863 (S.KR 12500)
£1400 $2548 €2044 Tranquil river landscape (64x101cm-25x40in) s.d.89. 16-Jun-4 Christie's, Kensington #192/R est:1500-2000

ROSENBERG, Fritz (1883-?) Austrian
Sculpture
£1517 $2534 €2200 Nude dancer draped in transparent cloth (50cm-20in) pat.bronze stone socle. 9-Jul-3 Hugo Ruef, Munich #1839/R est:1800

ROSENBERG, Gustaf Valdemar (1891-1919) Finnish
£556 $928 €800 Beach huts, Borgaa (38x50cm-15x20in) s. 23-Oct-3 Hagelstam, Helsinki #930
£3020 $5557 €4500 La Dame Melancolique (71x56cm-28x22in) s.verso. 25-Mar-4 Hagelstam, Helsinki #924 est:3000

ROSENBERG, Paul (1881-1959) ?
£615 $1100 €898 Portrait of a young man. i. 13-May-4 Dallas Auction Gallery, Dallas #174/R est:500-800

ROSENBERG, Samuel (1896-1972) American
£195 $350 €285 Mother and child (67x57cm-26x22in) s. board. 21-Mar-4 Bonhams & Butterfields, Los Angeles #7324/R

ROSENBORG, Ralph (1913-) American
£270 $500 €394 Ocean scene (25x38cm-10x15in) s.d.1954 oil handmade linen. 17-Jul-4 Outer Cape Auctions, Provincetown #134/R
£447 $800 €653 Monhegan Island seascape (36x48cm-14x19in) s.d.1959 board prov. 16-May-4 Wright, Chicago #406/R

ROSENGRAVE, Harry (1899-1985) Australian
£246 $388 €359 The forest (61x91cm-24x36in) s.d.74 board. 2-Sep-3 Deutscher-Menzies, Melbourne #362/R (A.D 600)
£325 $582 €475 Flat pattern still life, George Bell School homework (26x34cm-10x13in) s.d.55 board. 10-May-4 Joel, Victoria #219 (A.D 800)
£573 $1042 €837 Underground mutton man (91x106cm-36x42in) s.d.1967 s.verso board. 16-Jun-4 Deutscher-Menzies, Melbourne #570/R est:1800-2500 (A.D 1500)

ROSENGREN, Gustav (1893-1963) Swedish
£769 $1323 €1123 Street scene, Drottninggatan, Uppsala in winter (63x49cm-25x19in) s. panel. 7-Dec-3 Uppsala Auktionskammare, Uppsala #213/R (S.KR 10000)

ROSENHAUER, Theodor (1901-1996) German
£10490 $17832 €15000 Little railway in winter - Dresden (76x100cm-30x39in) s. 29-Nov-3 Villa Grisebach, Berlin #371/R est:15000-20000
Works on paper
£1667 $2983 €2500 Fishing boats (44x59cm-17x23in) s.d. W/C. 14-May-4 Ketterer, Munich #70/R est:2500-3000

ROSENHOF, Franz Rosel von (1626-1700) Austrian
£7000 $11900 €10220 Wooded landscape with two stags and a deer in a clearing (52x58cm-20x23in) s.i.d.1675. 31-Oct-3 Christie's, Kensington #72/R est:7000-10000

ROSENKRANTZ, Anna (19/20th C) Danish
£898 $1671 €1311 Cosy corner of a nice lounge (23x21cm-9x8in) s.d.1905. 2-Mar-4 Rasmussen, Copenhagen #1642/R (D.KR 10000)

ROSENKRANTZ, Arild (1870-1964) Danish
£271 $500 €396 The future (33x44cm-13x17in) init.d.61. 15-Mar-4 Rasmussen, Vejle #603 (D.KR 3000)
Works on paper
£307 $567 €448 Evening (43x54cm-17x21in) s. pastel. 15-Mar-4 Rasmussen, Vejle #616 (D.KR 3400)
£336 $527 €491 Religious scene with figures (31x49cm-12x19in) s. pastel. 30-Aug-3 Rasmussen, Havnen #2262 (D.KR 3600)

ROSENQUIST, James (1933-) American
£28188 $51865 €42000 Sieve (75x187cm-30x74in) s.d.1974 acrylic collage paper on canvas. 29-Mar-4 Cornette de St.Cyr, Paris #51/R est:25000-35000
£30726 $55000 €44860 Hot lake (122x284cm-48x112in) s.i.d.1975 verso prov. 12-May-4 Christie's, Rockefeller NY #160/R est:40000-60000
£39106 $70000 €57095 Horizon pendulum (91x229cm-36x90in) acrylic collage exec 1975 prov. 13-May-4 Sotheby's, New York #244/R est:45000-65000
£67039 $120000 €97877 Glare - Speed of light (198x183cm-78x72in) s.i.d.2001 verso s. overlap canvas on panel prov.exhib. 12-May-4 Christie's, Rockefeller NY #200/R est:70000-90000
£223464 $400000 €326257 Brighter than the sun (145x229cm-57x90in) s.i.d.1961 verso prov.exhib.lit. 12-May-4 Sotheby's, New York #33/R est:600000-800000
£251397 $450000 €367040 Air hammer (198x164cm-78x65in) s.i.d.1962 verso oil fenestrated canvas prov.exhib.lit. 12-May-4 Sotheby's, New York #41/R est:500000-600000
Prints
£1765 $3000 €2577 Skull snap (151cm-59in circular) s. col lithograph pressed paper pulp. 31-Oct-3 Sotheby's, New York #740/R
£2353 $4000 €3435 Where the water goes (261x147cm-103x58in) s. col lithograph pressed paper pulp. 31-Oct-3 Sotheby's, New York #736/R
£2401 $4250 €3505 Stars and stripes at the speed of light (107x73cm-42x29in) s.i.d.2000 lithograph. 30-Apr-4 Sotheby's, New York #453/R est:3000-5000
£2703 $5000 €3946 Industrial cottage (49x112cm-19x44in) s.i.d.1978-80 num.57/100 col lithograph. 12-Feb-4 Sotheby's, New York #150/R est:2500-3500
£2941 $5000 €4294 Sunset on the time zone (202x147cm-80x58in) s. col lithograph pressed paper pulp. 31-Oct-3 Sotheby's, New York #739/R
£3824 $6500 €5583 Sun sets on the time zone (202x147cm-80x58in) s.i.d.1989 pressed pulp paper lithograph collage. 4-Nov-3 Christie's, Rockefeller NY #340/R est:5000-7000
£4412 $7500 €6442 Sky hole (263x149cm-104x59in) s.i.d.1989 pressed pulp paper lithograph collage. 4-Nov-3 Christie's, Rockefeller NY #341/R est:9000-12000
£4706 $8000 €6871 Space dust (169x267cm-67x105in) s. col lithograph pressed paper pulp. 31-Oct-3 Sotheby's, New York #741/R
£5367 $9500 €7836 Expo 67 mural firepole (85x47cm-33x19in) s.d.1976 num.40/41 lithograph. 30-Apr-4 Sotheby's, New York #446/R est:7000-9000
£8475 $15000 €12374 Time door time d'or (248x305cm-98x120in) s.i.d.1989 col lithograph. 30-Apr-4 Sotheby's, New York #449/R est:8000-12000
£8475 $15000 €12374 Space dust (168x266cm-66x105in) s.i.d.1989 lithograph. 30-Apr-4 Sotheby's, New York #450/R est:8000-12000
£8824 $15000 €12883 Bird of Paradise (246x215cm-97x85in) s. col lithograph pressed paper pulp. 31-Oct-3 Sotheby's, New York #735/R
£8824 $15000 €12883 F-111 (93x178cm-37x70in) s.i.d.1974 lithograph col screenprint set of 4. 4-Nov-3 Christie's, Rockefeller NY #339/R est:10000-15000
£10000 $17000 €14600 House of fire (138x304cm-54x120in) s. col lithograph pressed paper pulp. 31-Oct-3 Sotheby's, New York #742/R
£14124 $25000 €20621 Bird of paradise approaches the hot water planet (246x215cm-97x85in) s.i.d.1989 col lithograph diptych. 30-Apr-4 Sotheby's, New York #448/R est:15000-20000
Works on paper
£1730 $3200 €2526 Skull snap (150cm-59in circular) s.i.d.1989 num.6/38 col pressed paper pulp lithograph. 12-Feb-4 Christie's, Rockefeller NY #200/R est:2000-3000
£5765 $10319 €8417 Untitled composition (55x111cm-22x44in) s.d.1977 W/C ink paper collage pastel prov. 28-May-4 Uppsala Auktionskammare, Uppsala #357/R est:80000-100000 (S.KR 78000)

ROSENSTAND, Emil (1852-1932) German
Works on paper
£391 $652 €571 Flirting in the park (49x32cm-19x13in) s.d.08 W/C gouache. 19-Oct-3 Agra, Warsaw #70/R (P.Z 2500)

ROSENSTAND, Vilhelm (1838-1915) Danish
£311 $566 €467 Study for the well known painting - Tordenskjold in Marstrand, 1866 (46x26cm-18x10in) mono. 19-Jun-4 Rasmussen, Havnen #2324/R (D.KR 3500)
£415 $767 €606 Italian woman in national costume anno 1880 (28x22cm-11x9in) mono.d.80. 15-Mar-4 Rasmussen, Vejle #409/R (D.KR 4600)

ROSENSTEIN, Erna (1913-) Polish?
£282 $511 €423 Pochody (24x31cm-9x12in) s.d.1975 oil canvas on panel. 4-Apr-4 Agra, Warsaw #66/R (P.Z 2000)

ROSENSTOCK, Isidore (1880-1956) French
£700 $1253 €1022 Still life of flowers in vase (55cm-22in circular) s. W/C. 26-May-4 Sotheby's, Olympia #312/R
Works on paper
£187 $350 €281 Bouquet of roses (73x53cm-29x21in) s. pencil W/C. 25-Jul-4 Bonhams & Butterfields, San Francisco #6073/R
£263 $484 €400 Port anime (37x52cm-15x20in) s. W/C. 25-Jun-4 Daguerre, Paris #173
£270 $500 €394 Still life with roses (46x33cm-18x13in) s. W/C prov. 15-Jul-4 Sotheby's, New York #41
£280 $445 €409 Pond in country house garden (36x53cm-14x21in) s. W/C. 9-Sep-3 Gorringes, Lewes #2054
£319 $533 €450 Roses dans un vase en porcelaine (44x41cm-17x16in) s. W/C. 19-Oct-3 Peron, Melun #316

ROSENTHAL, Albert (1863-1939) American
£791 $1400 €1155 Portrait of General Anthony Wayne (76x64cm-30x25in) i.d.1905 verso after Charles Wilson Peale. 27-Apr-4 Doyle, New York #25
£2703 $5000 €3946 My studio (76x63cm-30x25in) s.i.d.1913 prov. 11-Mar-4 Christie's, Rockefeller NY #25/R est:8000-12000
£5525 $10000 €8067 Mrs Bryan H Owsley (127x89cm-50x35in) s.d.1910 prov.exhib. 31-Mar-4 Sotheby's, New York #59/R est:8000-12000

ROSENTHAL, August (1820-?) German
£521 $859 €750 Chapel in morning mist (51x56cm-20x22in) 7-Jul-3 Dr Fritz Nagel, Stuttgart #7084

ROSENTHAL, Clement (1956-) French
£9097 $15010 €13100 Sans titre (160x160cm-63x63in) s.d.verso. 2-Jul-3 Cornette de St.Cyr, Paris #212/R est:6000-8000

ROSENTHAL, Doris (20th C) American
£234 $391 €342 Young girls in the market (41x51cm-16x20in) s. 17-Jun-3 Maynards, Vancouver #322 (C.D 525)
£1571 $2750 €2294 La ciudad - the city (69x61cm-27x24in) s. s.i.verso prov. 19-Dec-3 Sotheby's, New York #1228/R est:2000-4000

ROSENTHAL, Fritz (1870-1939) Swedish
£503 $936 €750 Winter landscape (67x91cm-26x36in) s.d.33. 7-Mar-4 Bukowskis, Helsinki #509/R

ROSENTHAL, Harry (20th C) ?
Sculpture
£5594 $9510 €8000 La musique (125cm-49in) num.3/3 green pat bronze Cast Ri de Andreize. 20-Nov-3 Claude Aguttes, Neuilly #187/R est:9000-10000

ROSENTHAL, Toby Edward (1849-1917) American
£17333 $31200 €26000 His Madonna (115x85cm-45x33in) s.i.d.1916 prov. 21-Apr-4 Christie's, Amsterdam #168/R est:10000-15000

ROSENTHAL, Tony (1914-) American
Sculpture
£1647 $2800 €2405 One who runs (61x36cm-24x14in) s.d.1953 bronze prov. 9-Nov-3 Wright, Chicago #292 est:3000-4000
£4076 $7500 €5951 Ghost of a hero (241x20x20cm-95x8x8in) s.d.1957 red brass exhib. 28-Mar-4 Wright, Chicago #600/R est:7000-9000

ROSENTHALIS, Moshe (1922-) Israeli
£227 $400 €331 Ships at sea (17x25cm-7x10in) s. cardboard. 1-Jan-4 Ben-Ami, Tel Aviv #4358/R
£254 $425 €371 At the easel (25x18cm-10x7in) s. 20-Jun-3 Freeman, Philadelphia #192/R
£346 $550 €505 Still life with flowers (23x18cm-9x7in) s. panel. 5-May-3 O'Gallerie, Oregon #794/R
£588 $1000 €858 Portrait of a woman (81x65cm-32x26in) s.d.1988. 1-Dec-3 Ben-Ami, Tel Aviv #4320/R
£994 $1800 €1451 Jerusalem in blue (46x54cm-18x21in) s. painted 1961. 1-Apr-4 Ben-Ami, Tel Aviv #4768/R est:2200-3000
£994 $1800 €1451 The model in the studio (55x44cm-22x17in) s. painted 1970's. 1-Apr-4 Ben-Ami, Tel Aviv #4769/R est:2200-3000

ROSETSU, Nagasawa (1754-1799) Japanese
£274 $466 €400 Woman in Tang era costume (79x29cm-31x11in) s. silk hanging scroll. 8-Nov-3 Dr Fritz Nagel, Stuttgart #1775/R est:800

ROSETSU, Nagasawa (attrib) (1754-1799) Japanese
Works on paper
£1096 $1863 €1600 Smoked fish with two rats (121x49cm-48x19in) s. Indian ink col hanging scroll. 8-Nov-3 Dr Fritz Nagel, Stuttgart #1778/R est:1400

ROSETTI, Domenico (1650-1736) Italian
£422 $700 €616 History of Alexander the Great (64x104cm-25x41in) 4-Oct-3 Neal Auction Company, New Orleans #249

ROSEWE, Fritz (1940-) German
£946 $1693 €1400 Someone is singing (100x100cm-39x39in) s.i. painted 2002. 7-May-4 Paul Kieffer, Pforzhiem #8011
£946 $1693 €1400 Sad occasion (100x100cm-39x39in) s.i. painted 1995. 7-May-4 Paul Kieffer, Pforzhiem #8012

ROSHARDT, Walter (1897-1966) Swiss
Works on paper
£786 $1446 €1148 Mau - woman's portrait (19x12cm-7x5in) s. W/C. 14-Jun-4 Philippe Schuler, Zurich #4158/R (S.FR 1800)

ROSI, Alessandro (1627-1707) Italian
Sculpture
£17000 $29410 €24820 Dancing nymph with roses (214cm-84in) s. white marble column base lit. 12-Dec-3 Sotheby's, London #243/R est:15000-20000

ROSIER (?) ?
£50704 $87718 €72000 Attaque de l'etat-major de l'Empereur par les Cosaques au depart de Moscou (137x164cm-54x65in) s.d.1827. 10-Dec-3 Remi Ader, Paris #76/R est:15000-18000
£50704 $87718 €72000 Attaque de l'etat-major de l'Empereur par les Cosaques (137x164cm-54x65in) s.d.1827. 10-Dec-3 Neret-Minet, Paris #76/R est:15000-18000

ROSIER, Amedee (1831-1898) French
£1000 $1800 €1500 Sunset over the Lagoon, Venice (18x23cm-7x9in) s. panel. 26-Apr-4 Rieber, Stuttgart #971/R est:2500
£1633 $2922 €2400 Voilier au crepuscule (19x35cm-7x14in) s. panel. 21-Mar-4 St-Germain-en-Laye Encheres #2/R est:2500-3000
£1781 $3027 €2600 Venise, pecheurs dans la lagune (26x37cm-10x15in) s. panel. 9-Nov-3 Eric Pillon, Calais #21/R
£2465 $4264 €3500 Saint Mark's (36x58cm-14x23in) i.verso board. 14-Dec-3 Finarte, Venice #42/R est:2800-3500
£3448 $6310 €5000 L'entree du port (28x45cm-11x18in) peinture panel. 1-Feb-4 Robin & Fattori, Granville #12
£3916 $6736 €5600 Port au clair de lune (31x46cm-12x18in) s. panel. 8-Dec-3 Cornette de St.Cyr, Paris #68/R est:4500-5000
£8500 $15470 €12410 Les murs anciens de Constantinople (25x41cm-10x16in) s. panel. 15-Jun-4 Sotheby's, London #141/R est:6000-8000
Works on paper
£550 $880 €798 Vue de Venise (15x21cm-6x8in) s. pen ink W/C gouache. 18-Sep-3 Christie's, Kensington #80/R
£634 $1096 €900 Venise (25x22cm-10x9in) s. W/C. 15-Dec-3 Bailly Pommery, Paris #78/R
£680 $1218 €1000 Venise au crepuscule (16x27cm-6x11in) s. W/C. 19-Mar-4 Ribeyre & Baron, Paris #63/R

ROSIERSE, Johannes (1818-1901) Dutch
£2083 $3542 €3000 Family by candle light (50x39cm-20x15in) s. panel. 28-Oct-3 Dorotheum, Vienna #118/R est:3000-3500
£2762 $5000 €4033 Lesson from grandmother (55x72cm-22x28in) s. panel prov. 30-Mar-4 Christie's, Rockefeller NY #85/R est:6000-8000

ROSIGNANO, Livio (1924-) Italian
£867 $1551 €1300 Green landscape (49x59cm-19x23in) s.d.54 board double-sided. 12-May-4 Stadion, Trieste #826/R est:700-1000

ROSLER, Charles (attrib) (19/20th C) ?
Works on paper
£260 $432 €380 Madonna and Child (45x30cm-18x12in) W/C. 1-Oct-3 Woolley & Wallis, Salisbury #121/R

ROSLER, Martha (1943-) American?
Photographs
£19461 $32500 €28413 Bringing the war home, house beautiful (51x61cm-20x24in) s.d.1967-72/1990 num.2/10 verso col photo 10 parts prov. 13-Nov-3 Sotheby's, New York #405/R est:12000-18000

ROSLIN, Alexander (1718-1793) Swedish
£13077 $22492 €19092 Count d'Arlingcourt Jnr (57x42cm-22x17in) painted c.1780 prov. 2-Dec-3 Bukowskis, Stockholm #304/R est:80000-100000 (S.KR 170000)
£42000 $75600 €61320 Portrait of a gentleman in a velvet jacket with green medal ribbon (73x59cm-29x23in) oval. 21-Apr-4 Christie's, London #62/R est:7000-10000

ROSOMAN, Leonard (1913-) British
£1000 $1850 €1460 Bombed buildings (48x67cm-19x26in) s. prov. 10-Mar-4 Cheffins, Cambridge #49/R est:400-500
£9000 $16380 €13140 Pianist (122x152cm-48x60in) s. prov. 4-Feb-4 Sotheby's, Olympia #95/R est:6000-8000
Works on paper
£225 $425 €329 Fire on hillside, Lake Toba (49x60cm-19x24in) s. gouache. 22-Feb-4 Bonhams & Butterfields, Los Angeles #7074
£378 $700 €552 Flowers of Grace (46x48cm-18x19in) s. gouache panel. 10-Mar-4 Doyle, New York #44/R

ROSS, Alice E (fl.1886-1937) British
£1650 $3053 €2409 At the seaside (39x49cm-15x19in) 14-Jul-4 Bonhams, Chester #465/R est:1000-1400

ROSS, Alvin (1920-1975) American
£318 $550 €464 Still life with cabinet (61x51cm-24x20in) s. board. 13-Dec-3 Weschler, Washington #615

ROSS, Christian Meyer (1843-1904) Norwegian
£1959 $3370 €2860 Young man with pipe (52x34cm-20x13in) s. lit. 8-Dec-3 Blomqvist, Oslo #476/R est:30000-40000 (N.KR 23000)
Works on paper
£371 $631 €542 Boy's portrait (24x20cm-9x8in) s. pastel oval. 28-Nov-3 Zofingen, Switzerland #2483 (S.FR 820)

ROSS, Darby Jampitjinpa (c.1910-) Australian
Works on paper
£3125 $5844 €4688 Yankirri jukurrpa, emu drawing (51x61cm-20x24in) bears name.d.1986 verso synthetic polymer paint canvasboard prov. 26-Jul-4 Sotheby's, Melbourne #413/R est:8000-12000 (A.D 8000)
£3320 $6209 €4980 Warlukurlangu jukurrpa, fire country dreaming (196x76cm-77x30in) bears name.verso synthetic polymer paint linen prov. 26-Jul-4 Sotheby's, Melbourne #416/R est:12000-18000 (A.D 8500)

ROSS, Frederick J (1927-) Canadian
£2439 $4366 €3561 Rocking horse (122x91cm-48x36in) s. tempera on masonite. 31-May-4 Sotheby's, Toronto #105/R est:3000-5000 (C.D 6000)
Works on paper
£491 $845 €717 Large study for black hat (72x50cm-28x20in) s. ink chk prov.lit. 2-Dec-3 Joyner Waddington, Toronto #95/R (C.D 1100)

ROSS, James (18/19th C) British
£6000 $10200 €8760 Death of the stag (74x101cm-29x40in) 19-Nov-3 Tennants, Leyburn #1006/R est:6000-7000
Works on paper
£326 $600 €476 Winter landscape, barn and snowy fields (43x56cm-17x22in) s. W/C. 9-Jun-4 Alderfer's, Hatfield #549

ROSS, Robert Henry Alison (1898-1940) British
£300 $558 €438 Portrait of Professor Frederick Niecks (76x63cm-30x25in) i. 4-Mar-4 Christie's, Kensington #19/R

ROSS, Robert Thorburn (1816-1876) British
£800 $1360 €1168 Still life of trout (30x40cm-12x16in) s.d.1851. 19-Nov-3 Sotheby's, Olympia #36/R

ROSS, Sir William Charles (1794-1860) British
Miniatures
£1500 $2580 €2190 Lady Fores, in a white dress (9cm-4in) s.i.d.1844 fitted red leather case. 2-Dec-3 Christie's, Kensington #81/R est:600-800
Works on paper
£900 $1530 €1314 Portrait of a young lady, traditionally identified as Lady Caroline Lennox (19x15cm-7x6in) i. col pencil W/C htd white. 20-Nov-3 Christie's, London #22/R

ROSSBACH, Max (1871-?) German
Works on paper
£340 $619 €500 Tour Saint Jacques, Paris (30x32cm-12x13in) s. pastel. 3-Feb-4 Sigalas, Stuttgart #518/R

ROSSBERG, Sara (1952-C) American
Works on paper
£432 $800 €631 Head of a woman (51x41cm-20x16in) init. d.1989 W/C. 15-Jul-4 Sotheby's, New York #107

ROSSE, Susan Penelope (1652-1700) British
Miniatures
£3000 $5100 €4380 Vicountess (2cm-1in) oval. 18-Nov-3 Bonhams, New Bond Street #16/R est:3000-5000

ROSSEAU, Percival (1859-1937) American
£4942 $8500 €7215 Griffon retrieving a mallard (57x39cm-22x15in) s.d.1914 panel. 5-Dec-3 Christie's, Rockefeller NY #90/R est:6000-8000
£39244 $67500 €57296 Madter's son (66x81cm-26x32in) s.d.1913 i.verso prov. 3-Dec-3 Sotheby's, New York #133/R est:30000-50000

ROSSEELS, Jacques (1828-1912) Flemish
£590 $939 €850 Landscape with cowherd (21x30cm-8x12in) s. 15-Sep-3 Bernaerts, Antwerp #69/R

ROSSELLI, Matteo (1578-1650) Italian
£5028 $9000 €7341 Adoration of the shepherds (115x99cm-45x39in) 27-May-4 Sotheby's, New York #92a/R est:12000-16000
£15000 $27450 €21900 Saint Cecilia (118x100cm-46x39in) prov. 8-Jul-4 Sotheby's, London #307/R est:8000-12000
£16667 $30500 €25000 Holy Family (33x27cm-13x11in) board. 1-Jun-4 Sotheby's, Milan #147/R est:25000-40000
£26667 $48000 €38934 Portrait of Ferdinando II de Medici (186x104cm-73x41in) prov. 23-Jan-4 Christie's, Rockefeller NY #57/R est:30000-40000

ROSSELLI, Matteo (attrib) (1578-1650) Italian
£4577 $7370 €6500 Sacred family (13x13cm-5x5in) copper round. 8-May-3 Farsetti, Prato #543/R est:7000-8000
Works on paper
£1300 $2249 €1898 Seated woman drawing on a board laid on her lap (27x22cm-11x9in) i.verso red chk. 12-Dec-3 Christie's, Kensington #326 est:500-700

ROSSELLO, Jose Maria (1950-) Spanish
£268 $502 €400 My version of Orfeu Mirall (65x54cm-26x21in) s.d.2003 s.i.d.verso. 24-Feb-4 Durán, Madrid #1170/R

ROSSELLO, Mario (1927-) Italian
£400 $736 €600 Space (100x80cm-39x31in) s.i.d.69 verso prov.exhib.lit. 8-Jun-4 Finarte Semenzato, Milan #231/R
£629 $1070 €900 Eaters (100x80cm-39x31in) s. s.i.d.63 verso prov. 25-Nov-3 Sotheby's, Milan #62

ROSSER, Albert (?) British
£520 $816 €759 Head of Ullswater, from near Glenridding (25x35cm-10x14in) s. i.verso. 10-Dec-2 Bamfords, Derby #707/R
Works on paper
£270 $467 €394 Ennerdale lake and the Anglers Hotel (18x25cm-7x10in) s. W/C. 11-Dec-3 Mitchells, Cockermouth #923/R

£300 $537 €438 Rydal water (25x36cm-10x14in) s. W/C. 13-May-4 Mitchells, Cockermouth #1017/R
£340 $632 €496 Langdale Pikes from Elterwater (23x33cm-9x13in) s. W/C. 4-Mar-4 Mitchells, Cockermouth #754
£360 $670 €526 Derwentwater and Catbells (25x33cm-10x13in) s. W/C. 4-Mar-4 Mitchells, Cockermouth #755/R
£400 $664 €584 Thirlmere lake and Raven Crag (25x36cm-10x14in) s. W/C. 2-Oct-3 Mitchells, Cockermouth #782/R
£420 $781 €613 Crummock Water and Buttermere (25x36cm-10x14in) s. W/C. 4-Mar-4 Mitchells, Cockermouth #756
£480 $859 €701 Applethwaite, foot of Skiddaw (25x36cm-10x14in) s. W/C. 13-May-4 Mitchells, Cockermouth #1006/R
£520 $832 €759 River Derwent at Grange in Borrowdale (25x33cm-10x13in) s. 15-May-3 Mitchells, Cockermouth #1033
£520 $832 €759 Crummock and Buttermere lakes from the slopes of Melbreak (25x36cm-10x14in) s. 15-May-3 Mitchells, Cockermouth #1034/R

ROSSER, Barbara (?) American?
£475 $850 €694 Farm scene (51x61cm-20x24in) masonite. 16-May-4 Wright, Chicago #154/R
£475 $850 €694 Boatyard (51x61cm-20x24in) s. board. 16-May-4 Wright, Chicago #165/R

ROSSERT, Paul (1851-1918) French
£4333 $7800 €6500 Day at the beach (20x33cm-8x13in) s. panel. 20-Apr-4 Sotheby's, Amsterdam #40a/R est:5000-7000

ROSSET, Joseph (c.1703-1786) French
Sculpture
£3618 $6658 €5500 Voltaire. Rousseau (24cm-9in) one s. alabaster lit. pair. 23-Jun-4 Sotheby's, Paris #104/R est:6000-8000

ROSSET-GRANGER, Paul Edouard (1853-?) French
£480 $802 €701 Le sommeil de bebe (45x38cm-18x15in) s. board. 7-Oct-3 Bonhams, Knightsbridge #115
£2217 $3969 €3237 Beauty on a tiger skin (69x41cm-27x16in) s.i.d.1889. 28-May-4 Uppsala Auktionskammare, Uppsala #127/R est:15000-20000 (S.KR 30000)

ROSSETTI, Dante Gabriel (1828-1882) British
Works on paper
£40000 $72800 €58400 Portrait of Mrs Georgina Fernandez (53x38cm-21x15in) mono.d.1874 pastel green paper prov.lit. 1-Jul-4 Sotheby's, London #275/R est:40000-60000
£60000 $110400 €87600 Portrait of Christina Rossetti (43x36cm-17x14in) i.d.1877 pastel prov.exhib.lit. 9-Jun-4 Christie's, London #33/R est:60000-80000
£92486 $160000 €135030 Belcolore (40cm-16in circular) mono.d.1868 mixed media paper on panel prov.exhib.lit. 11-Dec-3 Sotheby's, New York #34/R est:180000-220000
£100000 $182000 €146000 Study of Marie Spartali for Dante's dream (37x30cm-15x12in) mono.d.1870 col chk. 1-Jul-4 Sotheby's, London #22/R est:80000-120000
£110000 $202400 €160600 Study of Alexa Wilding (53x38cm-21x15in) mono.d.1873 pastel prov.exhib.lit. 9-Jun-4 Christie's, London #20a/R est:80000-120000
£1300000 $2392000 €1898000 Pandora (94x66cm-37x26in) mono.d.1869 pastel prov.exhib.lit. 9-Jun-4 Christie's, London #20/R est:800000-1200000

ROSSETTI, Dante Gabriel (after) (1828-1882) British
£25692 $45988 €37510 Beata Beatrix (69x49cm-27x19in) mono. prov.exhib. 15-May-4 Christie's, Sydney #115/R est:40000-50000 (A.D 65000)

ROSSI (?) ?
£823 $1472 €1202 Coast in evening (98x168cm-39x66in) 22-Mar-4 Philippe Schuler, Zurich #6181 (S.FR 1900)
Sculpture
£16352 $26000 €23874 White marble figural statue (198cm-78in) marble incl. pedestal. 13-Sep-3 Selkirks, St. Louis #395/R est:13000-16000

ROSSI, A (?) ?
£1200 $2184 €1752 Portrait of a young girl walking in the sand dunes (60x45cm-24x18in) s.d.1919 canvas on board. 17-Jun-4 Clevedon Sale Rooms #1071/R

ROSSI, Alberto (1858-1936) Italian
£709 $1184 €1000 Peasant and donkey (43x28cm-17x11in) s. cardboard on canvas. 20-Oct-3 Sant Agostino, Torino #82/R
£2449 $4384 €3600 Dispatch rider (25x20cm-10x8in) s. board. 22-Mar-4 Sant Agostino, Torino #235/R est:2600
£2486 $4500 €3630 Harem bath (44x29cm-17x11in) s.d.1899 board. 30-Mar-4 Christie's, Rockefeller NY #74/R est:5000-7000
£4610 $7699 €6500 Papyrus in Ghiach, Cairo (80x119cm-31x47in) s.i.d.1901. 20-Oct-3 Sant Agostino, Torino #298/R est:8000
Works on paper
£2667 $4880 €4000 Egyptienne au bandeau orange (78x50cm-31x20in) s. pastel. 3-Jun-4 Tajan, Paris #330/R est:4000-6000
£3334 $6101 €5000 Egyptienne a la jarre (70x49cm-28x19in) s. pastel cardboard. 3-Jun-4 Tajan, Paris #331/R est:5000-7000

ROSSI, Alberto Maria (1879-1965) Argentinian
£5191 $9500 €7579 Stable and clown (50x60cm-20x24in) cardboard on canvas. 1-Jun-4 Arroyo, Buenos Aires #19
£6145 $11000 €8972 Anatole France Street, Lanus (62x76cm-24x30in) s. board. 4-May-4 Arroyo, Buenos Aires #89/R est:8000

ROSSI, Alexander M (fl.1870-1905) British
£2200 $3564 €3212 Urchin boy seated studying a photograph (54x44cm-21x17in) s. 27-Jan-3 Bristol Auction Rooms #549 est:1000-1500
Works on paper
£1800 $3276 €2628 Loyal companions (56x77cm-22x30in) s. pencil W/C htd white. 1-Jul-4 Christie's, Kensington #187/R est:2000-3000
£12000 $21480 €17520 Which shall I have? (79x65cm-31x26in) i. W/C exhib. 26-May-4 Sotheby's, Olympia #184/R est:12000-18000

ROSSI, Angelo (attrib) (1670-1752) Italian
Works on paper
£1200 $2076 €1752 Caricature of a prelate and his servant (10x5cm-4x2in) pen brown ink prov. 12-Dec-3 Christie's, Kensington #371/R est:700-1000

ROSSI, Angelo de (1671-1715) Italian
Sculpture
£18000 $32940 €26280 Farnese Hercules (34cm-13in) s. bronze wooden base lit. 9-Jul-4 Sotheby's, London #93/R est:8000-12000

ROSSI, Antonio (1700-1753) Italian
£1860 $3200 €2716 Bath (44x29cm-17x11in) s.d.1899 board. 2-Dec-3 Christie's, Rockefeller NY #47/R est:5000-7000

ROSSI, Carlo (1921-) British
£680 $1136 €993 Hill town, Tuscany (50x75cm-20x30in) s.d.1961 board. 16-Oct-3 Bonhams, Edinburgh #13

ROSSI, Dino (1904-) Italian
Works on paper
£362 $615 €529 Hotel Euler, Basel (35x49cm-14x19in) s.d.1947 mixed media board. 19-Nov-3 Fischer, Luzern #2261/R (S.FR 800)

ROSSI, Egisto (19th C) Italian
Works on paper
£320 $554 €467 Mother and her child (14x17cm-6x7in) black chk htd white prov. 12-Dec-3 Christie's, Kensington #415/R

ROSSI, G (?) Italian
Sculpture
£1193 $2051 €1742 Head of woman (70cm-28in) s.d.1873 white marble. 8-Dec-3 Blomqvist, Oslo #50 est:6000 (N.KR 14000)

ROSSI, Gino (1884-1947) Italian
£8042 $13671 €11500 Holy Family (20x20cm-8x8in) tempera paper on canvas exhib. 29-Nov-3 Farsetti, Prato #416/R est:10000-15000
£60403 $108121 €90000 Landscape (29x35cm-11x14in) s. cardboard on canvas painted c.1920. 29-May-4 Farsetti, Prato #505/R est:90000-120000
Works on paper
£2685 $4805 €4000 Two figures (24x33cm-9x13in) W/C exhib.lit. 29-May-4 Farsetti, Prato #406/R est:4000-5000

ROSSI, Giovan Battista (style) (fl.1749-1782) Italian
£34667 $62053 €52000 Scenes with putti. en grisaille set of 4. 17-May-4 Finarte Semenzato, Rome #490/R est:60000-65000

ROSSI, Ilario (1911-1994) Italian
£270 $422 €400 Still life (24x34cm-9x13in) 30-Mar-3 Adma, Formigine #626

ROSSI, Lucius (attrib) (1846-1913) French
£707 $1300 €1032 Woman in black (36x25cm-14x10in) s. panel. 9-Jun-4 Doyle, New York #3071

ROSSI, Luigi (1853-1923) Swiss
£1081 $2043 €1600 Face of woman (47x36cm-19x14in) s. 20-Feb-4 Stadion, Trieste #159/R est:1500-2000
£4525 $7240 €6607 Peasant woman resting (35x26cm-14x10in) s. panel. 16-Sep-3 Philippe Schuler, Zurich #3251/R est:4000-5000 (S.FR 10000)
£8597 $13756 €12552 Peasant sharpening scythe (60x45cm-24x18in) s. 16-Sep-3 Philippe Schuler, Zurich #3250/R est:8000-10000 (S.FR 19000)
£18261 $33417 €26661 Venticello (83x55cm-33x22in) s. prov.lit. 7-Jun-4 Christie's, Zurich #22/R est:30000-50000 (S.FR 42000)
Works on paper
£591 $981 €857 Piazza San Marco a la sera (24x17cm-9x7in) s. pastel. 13-Jun-3 Zofingen, Switzerland #2995/R (S.FR 1300)

ROSSI, Mariano (1731-1807) Italian
£2081 $3828 €3100 Allegory of Art (35x39cm-14x15in) 24-Mar-4 Finarte Semenzato, Rome #93/R est:3500

ROSSI, Nicholas (18/19th C) ?
Miniatures
£1329 $2259 €1900 Portrait de Marie-Anne Bertheir de Wagram (13x11cm-5x4in) s. i.verso gilt bronze frame oval. 26-Nov-3 Daguerre, Paris #170/R est:800-1000

ROSSI, Pasquale de (attrib) (1641-1725) Italian
£4930 $8528 €7000 Lacemaker (40x51cm-16x20in) 11-Dec-3 Dr Fritz Nagel, Stuttgart #487/R est:9800

ROSSI, Pietro de (c.1761-1831) Italian
Miniatures
£3800 $6840 €5548 Young lady, her hair upswept (4cm-2in circular) s.i.d.1809 enamel gilt metal frame exhib. 22-Apr-4 Bonhams, New Bond Street #43/R est:2000-3000
£7000 $12110 €10220 Ivan Petrovich Arkarov, Governor of Moscow (6x5cm-2x2in) gilt-metal mount octagonal. 9-Dec-3 Christie's, London #262/R est:2000-3000

ROSSI, Remo (1909-1982) Swiss
Sculpture
£1747 $3179 €2551 Female head (44cm-17in) s.i.d.1935. 16-Jun-4 Fischer, Luzern #1591/R est:3000-4000 (S.FR 4000)
£1894 $3220 €2765 Acrobats (101cm-40in) dark brown pat.bronze. 7-Nov-3 Dobiaschofsky, Bern #130/R est:5000 (S.FR 4300)
£2172 $3475 €3171 Female nude (48cm-19in) s.d.1953 gold pat.bronze. 16-Sep-3 Philippe Schuler, Zurich #3179/R est:4000-6000 (S.FR 4800)

ROSSI, Vanni (1894-1973) Italian
£3901 $6514 €5500 Hollow (72x52cm-28x20in) s. board. 14-Oct-3 Finarte Semenzato, Milan #137/R

ROSSI-SCOTTI, Lemmo Comte de (1848-1926) Italian
£1382 $2542 €2100 On the way to Rieti (20x37cm-8x15in) s.d.1877 i.verso. 23-Jun-4 Finarte Semenzato, Rome #81/R est:2500-3000

ROSSINI, Francesco (1904-) South American
£222 $420 €324 Monte Conero, Ancona (40x60cm-16x24in) s. 22-Feb-4 Galeria y Remates, Montevideo #33

ROSSINI, Romano (1886-1951) Italian
£3467 $6205 €5200 From my window (54x44cm-21x17in) s.d.1934 board. 12-May-4 Stadion, Trieste #671/R est:3500-4500

ROSSITER, Charles (1827-?) British
£950 $1615 €1387 Very industrious (25x20cm-10x8in) i.overlap. 19-Nov-3 Bonhams, New Bond Street #49/R

ROSSLER, Alfred (1906-1982) German
Works on paper
£1389 $2319 €2000 Giudecca (49x61cm-19x24in) s.i. W/C. 24-Oct-3 Ketterer, Hamburg #530/R est:2500-3000

ROSSLER, Ludwig Christian Friedrich Wilhelm (1842-1910) German
£333 $610 €500 Old city on a river (24x30cm-9x12in) s. d.1906 verso panel. 5-Jun-4 Arnold, Frankfurt #703/R
£2292 $3735 €3300 Peasants outside tavern (85x125cm-33x49in) s.d.74. 24-Sep-3 Neumeister, Munich #538/R est:1800

ROSSMANN, Max (1888-?) German
£347 $549 €500 Sunday artist (21x43cm-8x17in) mono. i. verso lit. 19-Sep-3 Schloss Ahlden, Ahlden #1590/R

ROSSO, Jose D (1898-1958) Argentinian
£559 $1000 €816 Streets (34x47cm-13x19in) cardboard. 11-May-4 Arroyo, Buenos Aires #85

ROSSO, Mino (1904-1963) Italian
Sculpture
£7483 $13395 €11000 Portrait oF Sironi (32x24x10cm-13x9x4in) s.d.1938 verso wood lit. 22-Mar-4 Sant Agostino, Torino #501/R est:8000

ROSSUM DU CHATTEL, Fredericus Jacobus van (1856-1917) Dutch
£11333 $20400 €17000 View of the Kleine Haven in Dordrecht (80x115cm-31x45in) s. 20-Apr-4 Sotheby's, Amsterdam #235/R est:10000-15000
Works on paper
£580 $969 €847 By the canalside (40x28cm-16x11in) s. W/C. 16-Oct-3 Lyon & Turnbull, Edinburgh #93
£789 $1453 €1200 Setting out on a quiet morning (35x51cm-14x20in) s. W/C pastel. 22-Jun-4 Christie's, Amsterdam #201/R
£987 $1786 €1500 Snowy landscape in the area around The Hague with a country house (60x36cm-24x14in) s. W/C. 19-Apr-4 Glerum, Amsterdam #117/R est:1500-2000
£2000 $3600 €3000 Fisherman in his boat on a canal (40x28cm-16x11in) s. W/C. 20-Apr-4 Sotheby's, Amsterdam #150/R est:2000-3000

ROSSUM DU CHATTEL, Fredericus Jacobus van (attrib) (1856-1917) Dutch
£320 $573 €480 Winter landscape (33x22cm-13x9in) panel lit. 14-May-4 Schloss Ahlden, Ahlden #2785/R

ROSSUM, Jacobus Willem van (1881-1963) Dutch
£470 $874 €700 Girl reading with Beret (24x36cm-9x14in) s. 4-Mar-4 Auction Maastricht #1122/R

ROSSYN, D (19th C) Russian?
£4000 $6800 €5840 Portrait of Tsar Alexander II (88x68cm-35x27in) s.d.1890. 19-Nov-3 Sotheby's, London #18/R est:4000-6000

ROST, Richard (19/20th C) German?
£490 $817 €700 Summer morning in the Allgau (90x100cm-35x39in) s. 9-Oct-3 Michael Zeller, Lindau #741/R

ROSTEL, Agathe (fl.1871-1893) German
£31000 $56420 €45260 Christmas morning (95x124cm-37x49in) s. lit. 15-Jun-4 Sotheby's, London #42/R est:25000-35000

ROSTRUP-BOYESEN, P (1882-1952) Danish
£280 $443 €406 Still life of vase with flowers and other objects (28x33cm-11x13in) mono. 3-Sep-3 Museumsbygningen, Copenhagen #135 (D.KR 3000)
£474 $758 €687 Summer's day at the entrance to H.Orsted's Park (72x78cm-28x31in) mono. 17-Sep-3 Kunsthallen, Copenhagen #263/R (D.KR 5000)

ROSTRUP-BOYESEN, Peter (1882-1952) Danish
£541 $1001 €790 Mother and daughter chatting on the sofa (36x47cm-14x19in) mono. 15-Mar-4 Rasmussen, Vejle #599/R (D.KR 6000)

ROSZAK, Theodore (1907-1981) American
£15909 $28000 €23227 Abstraction with faces and skyscrapers (31x26cm-12x10in) s. masonite painted c.1934 prov. 18-May-4 Christie's, Rockefeller NY #127/R est:15000-25000

ROTA, Giovanni (fl.1860-1900) Italian
£2699 $4750 €3941 Young beauty (61x51cm-24x20in) s. 18-May-4 Bonhams & Butterfields, San Francisco #58/R est:3000-5000

ROTA, Giuseppe (1777-1821) Italian
£1923 $3500 €2808 Beauty in a plumed Hat (36x25cm-14x10in) s. panel. 7-Feb-4 Neal Auction Company, New Orleans #559/R est:4000-6000

ROTARI, Pietro (1707-1762) Italian
£4600 $8234 €6716 Portrait of a Russian lady (49x39cm-19x15in) 26-May-4 Sotheby's, Olympia #360/R est:3000-5000
£24000 $43200 €35040 Thetis dipping Achilles in the styx (211x161cm-83x63in) 21-Apr-4 Christie's, London #100/R est:10000-15000
£29655 $49524 €43000 Head of young woman (48x36cm-19x14in) prov.exhib.lit. 15-Nov-3 Porro, Milan #227/R est:32000
£40268 $75302 €60000 Angelica and Medoro. Mercurius and Bacchus (151x121cm-59x48in) pair. 25-Feb-4 Porro, Milan #58/R est:60000
Works on paper
£43103 $79310 €62930 Portrait of a princess (46x35cm-18x14in) pastel prov. 26-Mar-4 Koller, Zurich #501/R est:16000-24000 (S.FR 100000)

ROTARI, Pietro (attrib) (1707-1762) Italian
Works on paper
£6200 $10726 €9052 Portrait of a girl holding a carnival mask (39x31cm-15x12in) pastel. 12-Dec-3 Christie's, Kensington #395/R est:3000-5000

ROTARI, Pietro (circle) (1707-1762) Italian
£5755 $9439 €8000 Portrait of girl (44x36cm-17x14in) 4-Jun-3 Sotheby's, Milan #143/R est:7000-10000

ROTELLA, Mimmo (1918-) Italian
£2172 $3692 €3171 South American (18x21cm-7x8in) s. collage canvas exec. 1955. 22-Nov-3 Burkhard, Luzern #189/R est:4000-5000 (S.FR 4800)
£4476 $7474 €6400 Il bulbo giallo (50x37cm-20x15in) oil collage metal prov. 11-Oct-3 Cornette de St.Cyr, Paris #82/R est:6000-8000
£4476 $7608 €6400 Lady of the Hill (104x67cm-41x26in) s.d.90 acrylic collage. 26-Nov-3 Pandolfini, Florence #133 est:6500-6700
£4545 $7727 €6500 Fenicia (55x42cm-22x17in) s. i.d.1990 verso overpainted newsprint on canvas prov. 26-Nov-3 Dorotheum, Vienna #107/R est:6500-7000
£5705 $10211 €8500 Pope (94x196cm-37x77in) s.d.63 prov. 25-May-4 Sotheby's, Milan #208/R est:7000-9000
£6338 $11092 €9000 Servants (116x81cm-46x32in) s. s.i.d.1968-74 verso paint. 17-Dec-3 Il Ponte, Milan #1112/R est:8000-9000
£7383 $13215 €11000 Coats of arm (40x150cm-16x59in) exec.1963 in 6 parts prov.exhib. 25-May-4 Sotheby's, Milan #209/R est:3000-5000
£8389 $15017 €12500 Pope (90x120cm-35x47in) triptych exec.1963 prov.exhib. 25-May-4 Sotheby's, Milan #210/R est:5000-7000
£13333 $24667 €20000 Saint Sebastian (300x150cm-118x59in) paint decollage exec.1988 prov.exhib. 18-Jul-4 Sotheby's, Paris #262/R est:15000-20000
£20290 $33275 €28000 Stroll (173x103cm-68x41in) s.d.60 i.d.verso exhib.lit. 27-May-3 Sotheby's, Milan #297/R est:20000-30000
Sculpture
£2657 $4517 €3800 Untitled (118x22cm-46x9in) s.d.75 plexiglas poster. 25-Nov-3 Sotheby's, Milan #60/R est:3000-4000
Works on paper
£395 $726 €600 La magnifica preda (100x70cm-39x28in) s.i. decollage. 22-Jun-4 Wiener Kunst Auktionen, Vienna #379/R
£395 $726 €600 La vita, Il mito (104x69cm-41x27in) s.i. decollage. 22-Jun-4 Wiener Kunst Auktionen, Vienna #380/R
£604 $1111 €900 Provocation 1 (33x26cm-13x10in) s.d.1971 rubbing impression sheet prov. 24-Mar-4 Joron-Derem, Paris #156/R
£688 $1129 €950 Untitled (105x78cm-41x31in) s.i. decollage board. 27-May-3 Sotheby's, Milan #120
£764 $1276 €1100 Erotella - Madame Claude (41x29cm-16x11in) s. mixed media canvas. 21-Oct-3 Artcurial Briest, Paris #551
£769 $1308 €1123 Decollage (25x30cm-10x12in) collage. 22-Nov-3 Burkhard, Luzern #118/R (S.FR 1700)
£800 $1472 €1200 Erotelliques (86x185cm-34x73in) s.i. mixed media plexiglass. 11-Jun-4 Pierre Berge, Paris #54
£940 $1729 €1400 Provocation III (40x63cm-16x25in) s.d.1973 rubbing out impression sheet prov. 24-Mar-4 Joron-Derem, Paris #158
£972 $1624 €1400 Erotella (41x30cm-16x12in) s. mixed media canvas. 21-Oct-3 Artcurial Briest, Paris #552 est:300-500

£1074	$1976	€1600	Provocation II (41x58cm-16x23in) s.d.1972 subbing out impression sheet prov. 24-Mar-4 Joron-Derem, Paris #157 est:1800-2000
£1140	$2098	€1664	Decollage (30x25cm-12x10in) s.verso paper-collage prov. 23-Jun-4 Koller, Zurich #3293 est:1400-2000 (S.FR 2600)
£1325	$2411	€2000	Mec-Art (24x17cm-9x7in) s.i.d.1966 mec art. 17-Jun-4 Galleria Pananti, Florence #539/R est:400-500
£1351	$2378	€2000	Untitled (130x179cm-51x70in) s.i. decollage cardboard. 24-May-4 Christie's, Milan #4/R est:2000-3000
£1690	$2958	€2400	Nude (50x37cm-20x15in) s.d.1973 decollage. 16-Dec-3 Finarte Semenzato, Milan #3131/R est:1800-2200
£1745	$3088	€2600	Sur le mur (30x40cm-12x16in) s.d.87 s.i.d.verso decoupage canvas. 28-Apr-4 Artcurial Briest, Paris #375/R est:1500-2000
£2215	$3964	€3300	Discov (50x40cm-20x16in) s. s.verso collage acrylic. 28-May-4 Farsetti, Prato #141/R est:2600-2900
£2333	$4293	€3500	Mec-Art (54x81cm-21x32in) s.d.63-65 mixed media on canvas. 11-Jun-4 Farsetti, Prato #219/R est:2600-2900
£2552	$4261	€3700	Untitled (58x30cm-23x12in) s. mixed media paper on canvas. 13-Nov-3 Finarte Semenzato, Rome #414/R est:3500-4500
£2754	$4516	€3800	Untitled (20x24cm-8x9in) s.d.59 decollage on canvas. 27-May-3 Sotheby's, Milan #121 est:2000-3000
£2797	$4755	€4000	Untitled (15x12cm-6x5in) s.d.58 decollage prov. 25-Nov-3 Sotheby's, Milan #67 est:1000-1500
£2817	$4676	€4000	Orizzonti perduti (35x49cm-14x19in) s.d.1990 s.i.d.verso decoupage. 14-Jun-3 Meeting Art, Vercelli #107/R est:4000
£2817	$4676	€4000	Frutta (30x30cm-12x12in) s.d.1998 decoupage paper on canvas. 14-Jun-3 Meeting Art, Vercelli #322/R
£3043	$4991	€4200	R.R.T. (32x27cm-13x11in) s. s.i.d.1957 verso decollage on canvas. 27-May-3 Sotheby's, Milan #211/R est:3000-4000
£3659	$6000	€5342	Demi regard (35x40cm-14x16in) s.d.60 paper collage on canvas prov.exhib. 28-May-3 Sotheby's, Amsterdam #76/R est:5000-7000
£3662	$6408	€5200	Untitled (16x11cm-6x4in) s.d.56 decollage pair prov. 16-Dec-3 Porro, Milan #45/R est:3000-5000
£4762	$8667	€7000	Milan (50x70cm-20x28in) s. decollage on canvas exec.1990. 6-Feb-4 Galleria Rosenberg, Milan #101/R est:7000
£4803	$8838	€7012	Cocktail (135x91cm-53x36in) s.d.1963 s.i.d. verso mec art mixed media canvas prov. 8-Jun-4 Germann, Zurich #81/R est:8000-12000 (S.FR 11000)
£5862	$9790	€8500	Catium (54x74cm-21x29in) s.d.1992 decollage paint on canvas exhib. lit. 14-Nov-3 Farsetti, Prato #338/R est:8500-9500
£6207	$10366	€9000	Untitled (27x36cm-11x14in) s. s.i.verso decollage. 14-Nov-3 Farsetti, Prato #278/R est:2200-2400
£6552	$10941	€9500	On the road (74x54cm-29x21in) s.d.93 decollage paint on canvas exhib.lit. 14-Nov-3 Farsetti, Prato #127/R est:9000-11000
£6711	$12013	€10000	Voyeurisme (74x50cm-29x20in) s. s.i.d.1988 verso decollage acrylic exhib.lit. 28-May-4 Farsetti, Prato #98/R est:10000-12000
£7042	$11690	€10000	Voyeurisme (74x50cm-29x20in) s. i.d.1988 verso decollage acrylic on canvas. 13-Jun-3 Farsetti, Prato #382/R
£7246	$11884	€10000	The Nile treasures (74x54cm-29x21in) s. i.d.1978 verso decollage acrylic on canvas. 30-May-3 Farsetti, Prato #344/R
£8000	$14720	€12000	Untitled (42x43cm-17x17in) s. decollage prov.lit. 14-Jun-4 Porro, Milan #45/R est:6000-8000
£9060	$16671	€13500	Guerra (56x35cm-22x14in) s.d.1962 collage of posters canvas exec 1962 lit. 29-Mar-4 Cornette de St.Cyr, Paris #63/R est:7000-8000
£9507	$16637	€13500	Reve rouge et jaune (55x46cm-22x18in) s.d.1957 s.i.d.verso torn paper on canvas. 18-Dec-3 Cornette de St.Cyr, Paris #106/R est:6000-8000
£10204	$18571	€15000	Legend from far away (99x74cm-39x29in) s. decollage on canvas exec.1996 lit. 6-Feb-4 Galleria Rosenberg, Milan #157/R est:15000
£12587	$21399	€18000	Untitled (70x58cm-28x23in) s.i.d.62 verso decollage on canvas. 25-Nov-3 Sotheby's, Milan #250/R est:20000-25000
£13000	$23530	€18980	Omaggio fontana (48x43cm-19x17in) s.d.60 s.i.d.verso torn poster acrylic on canvas prov. 1-Apr-4 Christie's, Kensington #238/R est:6000-8000
£13986	$23776	€20000	Today at the cinema (126x101cm-50x40in) s. s.i.verso decollage on canvas exec.1970. 25-Nov-3 Sotheby's, Milan #255/R est:22000-25000
£16901	$28056	€24000	Half past nine pm (54x87cm-21x34in) s. s.i.verso decollage on canvas. 11-Jun-3 Finarte Semenzato, Milan #656/R
£21739	$35652	€30000	Bike 175 (70x85cm-28x33in) s.i.d.60 verso decollage on canvas lit. 27-May-3 Sotheby's, Milan #293/R est:20000-30000
£27972	$47552	€40000	Beer (134x91cm-53x36in) decollage exec.1962 exhib.lit. 24-Nov-3 Christie's, Milan #330/R est:40000-60000
£36667	$67833	€55000	Untitled (267x262cm-105x103in) s.d.59 decollage on canvas prov.exhib. 18-Jul-4 Sotheby's, Paris #254/R est:30000-40000
£40000	$66800	€58400	Eroi in allegria (155x94cm-61x37in) s. s.i.d.1962 verso torn poster canvas prov.exhib.lit. 21-Oct-3 Christie's, London #48/R est:40000-60000
£47297	$83243	€70000	Cinecitta', Rome (181x136cm-71x54in) s. s.i.d.1963 verso decollage on canvas prov.exhib.lit. 24-May-4 Christie's, Milan #334/R est:65000-90000
£50000	$83500	€73000	Cook it in a broth (134x90cm-53x35in) s. s.i.d.1963 verso decollage on canvas prov.exhib.lit. 20-Oct-3 Sotheby's, London #27/R est:40000
£450000	$751500	€657000	With a smile (154x132cm-61x52in) s.d.62 s.i.d.verso decollage on canvas prov.exhib.lit. 20-Oct-3 Sotheby's, London #41/R est:40000

ROTEN-CALPINI, Berthe (1873-1962) Swiss

£431	$772	€629	Valais mountain landscape (53x41cm-21x16in) s. 12-May-4 Dobiaschofsky, Bern #918/R (S.FR 1000)
£1586	$2696	€2316	Summer landscape in Wallis (64x82cm-25x32in) s. 5-Nov-3 Dobiaschofsky, Bern #910/R est:1500 (S.FR 3600)

ROTENBERG, Harold (1905-) American

£280	$500	€409	Gloucester (25x30cm-10x12in) s. s.i.d.1939 verso canvasboard. 14-May-4 Skinner, Boston #236/R

ROTH, Andreas (20th C) Swiss

£226	$400	€330	Lake Louise, Colorado (56x71cm-22x28in) s.d.1947. 1-May-4 Harvey Clar, Oakland #1246
£313	$500	€457	Floral still life (64x43cm-25x17in) s.d.1937. 20-Sep-3 Sloans & Kenyon, Bethesda #633/R
£374	$637	€546	Rigi (62x110cm-24x43in) s.d.1923 i. verso. 5-Nov-3 Dobiaschofsky, Bern #911/R (S.FR 850)
£500	$800	€730	Mountain landscape with a reflective lake (130x170cm-51x67in) s.d.1940. 18-May-3 Auctions by the Bay, Alameda #1115/R

ROTH, Arnold (1929-) American

Works on paper			
£267	$500	€390	Santa and reindeer overstay their welcome (20x23cm-8x9in) s. pen ink W/C en grisaille. 26-Feb-4 Illustration House, New York #149
£2286	$4000	€3338	History of sex (51x38cm-20x15in) W/C ink four pasted on ills board exec 1973 exhib. 17-Dec-3 Christie's, Rockefeller NY #222/R est:4000-6000

ROTH, August (1864-1952) Austrian

£1408	$2338	€2000	In farmstead (70x88cm-28x35in) s.d.98. 16-Jun-3 Dorotheum, Vienna #26/R est:2000-2500

ROTH, Dieter (1930-1998) German

£2238	$3804	€3200	Three against one (16x24cm-6x9in) s.i.d.77 board prov. 27-Nov-3 Lempertz, Koln #388/R est:3000
£3467	$6344	€5200	Small island picture (35x30cm-14x12in) food kitchen waste plaster acrylic panel. 4-Jun-4 Lempertz, Koln #394/R est:4500
£5245	$8916	€7500	Eagle (81x116cm-32x46in) s.d.1984-85 acrylic Indian ink feltpen collage board foil. 27-Nov-3 Lempertz, Koln #387/R est:9000
Prints			
£2067	$3782	€3100	Graphic with cocoa (71x101cm-28x40in) i. col silkscreen cocoa board. 4-Jun-4 Lempertz, Koln #397/R est:2500
Sculpture			
£1500	$2745	€2250	Untitled (38x25x6cm-15x10x2in) cloth paper. 4-Jun-4 Lempertz, Koln #392/R est:3000
£2400	$4320	€3600	Motorbiker (12x17x11cm-5x7x4in) s.i. tin. 24-Apr-4 Reiss & Sohn, Konigstein #5835/R est:2000
£3147	$5350	€4500	Hare (18x19x9cm-7x7x4in) straw rabbit droppings lit. 27-Nov-3 Lempertz, Koln #395/R est:5000
£5000	$8500	€7300	Entenjagd (55x65x64cm-22x26x25in) wooden case plastic chocolate. 4-Nov-3 Christie's, Rockefeller NY #342/R est:6000-8000
£15642	$28000	€22837	Untitled (50x70x4cm-20x28x2in) s.d.85 Polaroid photos acrylic gouache assemblage board prov. 14-May-4 Phillips, New York #271/R est:20000-25000
Works on paper			
£267	$491	€400	Musical (36x23cm-14x9in) pencil. 11-Jun-4 Hauswedell & Nolte, Hamburg #1505/R
£367	$675	€550	H-e-ard melodies (20x24cm-8x9in) i. verso Indian ink gouache. 11-Jun-4 Hauswedell & Nolte, Hamburg #1509/R
£699	$1286	€1021	The rose (23x33cm-9x13in) s.i.d.1978 pencil. 8-Jun-4 Germann, Zurich #864/R (S.FR 1600)
£961	$1768	€1403	Flowers (37x25cm-15x10in) s.i.d.1997 mixed media on col laser copy. 8-Jun-4 Germann, Zurich #863 (S.FR 2200)
£1818	$3091	€2600	Stain (32x24cm-13x9in) s.i.d.83 mixed media. 26-Nov-3 Dorotheum, Vienna #284/R est:2600-2800
£1818	$3091	€2600	Number thirteen (34x24cm-13x9in) s.i.d.1983 mixed media. 26-Nov-3 Dorotheum, Vienna #293/R est:2600-2800
£2333	$4177	€3500	Small sunset (43x31cm-17x12in) mono.d.70 mixed media. 15-May-4 Van Ham, Cologne #889/R est:3800
£2448	$4161	€3500	World course (37x47cm-15x19in) i. verso crushed wrapped chocolate figures board. 27-Nov-3 Lempertz, Koln #391/R est:3800
£2517	$4280	€3600	Two bulbs (34x43cm-13x17in) crushed light bulbs glue. 27-Nov-3 Lempertz, Koln #397/R est:2800
£2667	$4880	€4000	Flower speak (21x30cm-8x12in) s.i.d.75 feltpen graphite. 4-Jun-4 Lempertz, Koln #395/R est:3000
£2733	$5002	€4100	Middle sunset (69x50cm-27x20in) s.d.70 sausage slice plastic bag. 4-Jun-4 Lempertz, Koln #398/R est:4200
£3333	$6100	€5000	Self portrait as potato (30x40cm-12x16in) s.i.d.Juni 73 graphite board prov. 4-Jun-4 Lempertz, Koln #391/R est:4800
£4615	$7846	€6600	Small island picture (35x30cm-14x12in) material kitchen waste plaster acrylic panel. 27-Nov-3 Lempertz, Koln #385/R est:5000
£10333	$18910	€15500	Bastel-novelle (26x37cm-10x15in) s.i. paper collage acrylic glue ink col pen pencil lit. 4-Jun-4 Lempertz, Koln #393/R est:12000-15000

ROTH, Dieter and RAINER, Arnulf (20th C) German/Austrian

£1000	$1830	€1500	Composition (20x30cm-8x12in) s.i. oil col oil chk pencil board. 4-Jun-4 Lempertz, Koln #411/R est:2000
Works on paper			
£1748	$2972	€2500	Untitled - flat refuse (21x29cm-8x11in) s. s.d.78 verso paper collage graphite col pen. 27-Nov-3 Lempertz, Koln #398/R est:2500-3000

ROTH, Dieter and WEWERKA, Stefan (20th C) German

Works on paper			
£294	$491	€429	Untitled (25x25cm-10x10in) mono.d.1967 pencil felt pen prov. 24-Jun-3 Germann, Zurich #1031 (S.FR 650)

ROTH, Eleanor (1902-1974) American

Works on paper			
£359	$600	€524	Still life (30x43cm-12x17in) s. W/C. 16-Nov-3 Simpson's, Houston #103a/R

ROTH, Ernest David (1879-1964) American

Works on paper			
£326	$600	€476	Cityscape (30x25cm-12x10in) pencil two sheets. 10-Jun-4 Swann Galleries, New York #203/R

ROTH, George (jnr-attrib) (fl.1768-1777) British

£880	$1575	€1285	Portrait of Reverend Thomas Webster of Chedgrave. Portrait of his wife in a black bonnet (16x13cm-6x5in) i.d.1784 verso oval pair. 22-Mar-4 Bonhams & Brooks, Norfolk #277/R

ROTH, George Andries (1809-1887) Dutch

£1118	$2024	€1700	Summer landscape with woman on a country path (26x18cm-10x7in) s. panel. 19-Apr-4 Glerum, Amsterdam #48/R est:1500-1700

ROTH, Judith (20th C) American

£437	$800	€656	Dancer at rest II (122x175cm-48x69in) 10-Jul-4 Hindman, Chicago #450/R

ROTH, Peter (1830-1866) German
£733 $1327 €1100 Portrait of young, dark haired woman. Portrait of young man (67x53cm-26x21in) one s.d.1864 one s. 1-Apr-4 Van Ham, Cologne #1623

ROTH, Philipp (1841-1921) German
£284 $474 €400 Water source in trees. s. i.d.1864 verso. 17-Oct-3 Behringer, Furth #1538/R
£290 $484 €420 Farmstead in Nederlinger Moos (14x14cm-6x6in) s. panel. 9-Jul-3 Hugo Ruef, Munich #190
£490 $832 €700 Cattle in summer pasture (16x22cm-6x9in) mono.d.873 canvas on board. 20-Nov-3 Van Ham, Cologne #1823
£541 $968 €800 Autumn landscape (20x24cm-8x9in) s.d.95 board on board. 6-May-4 Michael Zeller, Lindau #838
£775 $1340 €1100 Muhlthal wood near Munich (47x62cm-19x24in) s.i. 11-Dec-3 Dr Fritz Nagel, Stuttgart #542/R
£972 $1585 €1400 Clouds over lake landscape (22x33cm-9x13in) s.i. panel. 25-Sep-3 Dr Fritz Nagel, Stuttgart #1404/R
£1007 $1852 €1500 Two fishermen in punt (36x63cm-14x25in) s. lit. 26-Mar-4 Karrenbauer, Konstanz #1767/R est:1400
£1156 $2070 €1700 Cows by water (15x20cm-6x8in) s. 17-Mar-4 Neumeister, Munich #580/R est:1600
£1467 $2669 €2200 Extensive landscape with stream and figure (37x60cm-15x24in) s. board. 30-Jun-4 Neumeister, Munich #653/R
£1611 $2996 €2400 Landscape with a farmhouse (34x44cm-13x17in) s. board. 5-Mar-4 Wendl, Rudolstadt #3840/R est:1200
£2349 $4322 €3500 Summer landscape with sheep (50x75cm-20x30in) s. 24-Mar-4 Hugo Ruef, Munich #1084/R est:2000
£2797 $4811 €4000 Near the Dachau (22x32cm-9x13in) s. i.verso paper on cardboard prov. 5-Dec-3 Ketterer, Munich #20/R est:2000-3000
£2993 $5358 €4400 Cows by water (58x80cm-23x31in) s. 17-Mar-4 Neumeister, Munich #579/R est:3800
Works on paper
£252 $400 €368 Landscape with country lane (28x37cm-11x15in) s.d.1905 W/C. 13-Sep-3 Weschler, Washington #687/R
£1400 $2534 €2100 Farmstead on Dachaurer Moos (38x54cm-15x21in) s. bears i. gouache pencil. 2-Apr-4 Winterberg, Heidelberg #525/R est:980

ROTH, Richard (20th C) American
£667 $1200 €1000 Fishing on the Bodensee (60x91cm-24x36in) s. 21-Apr-4 Dorotheum, Vienna #44/R

ROTH, Willi (1908-1952) Swiss
Works on paper
£271 $462 €396 Winter street (18x25cm-7x10in) s.d.44 col pen. 18-Nov-3 Hans Widmer, St Gallen #1175 (S.FR 600)

ROTHAUG, Alexander (1870-1946) Austrian
£1200 $2160 €1800 Woodland nymph (64x47cm-25x19in) s. 21-Apr-4 Dorotheum, Vienna #34/R est:1900-2600
£1333 $2387 €2000 Sunny pre-alpine landscape with cows (24x20cm-9x8in) s. i. verso. 13-May-4 Dorotheum, Linz #441 est:3000-3400
£2291 $4101 €3345 Romischer lanthaus auf Eriner (62x93cm-24x37in) s. exhib. 25-May-4 Bukowskis, Stockholm #343/R est:15000-20000 (S.KR 31000)
£2797 $4755 €4000 Mediaeval scene (190x250cm-75x98in) 28-Nov-3 Wiener Kunst Auktionen, Vienna #528/R est:5000-10000
Works on paper
£345 $572 €500 At the spring (17x13cm-7x5in) s. W/C board. 30-Sep-3 Dorotheum, Vienna #367/R

ROTHAUG, Leopold (1868-1959) Austrian
£405 $689 €591 The eagle's nest (42x58cm-17x23in) s. 21-Nov-3 Walker's, Ottawa #214/R (C.D 900)

ROTHBORT, Lawrence (1920-1963) American
£1243 $2200 €1815 Landscape (66x86cm-26x34in) board. 2-May-4 Grogan, Boston #74/R

ROTHBORT, Samuel (1882-1971) American
£424 $750 €619 Rothbort family portrait (157x122cm-62x48in) estate st.verso masonite. 2-May-4 William Jenack, New York #112
£568 $1000 €829 Family portrait (122x117cm-48x46in) s. masonite. 23-May-4 William Jenack, New York #236 est:1500-2000
£1469 $2600 €2145 Wedding portrait (107x122cm-42x48in) s. masonite. 2-May-4 William Jenack, New York #87
£1816 $3250 €2651 Artist at work, Fifth Avenue bus stop (53x53cm-21x21in) s. i.verso canvas on board painted c.1930-40 prov. 26-May-4 Doyle, New York #146/R est:5000-7000
£2235 $4000 €3263 Geroge Washington Bridge and the little red lighthouse (51x61cm-20x24in) s. canvas on board. 26-May-4 Doyle, New York #147/R est:4000-6000
£3073 $5500 €4487 Beach at Coney Island (36x51cm-14x20in) s. masonite. 6-May-4 Shannon's, Milford #243/R est:3000-5000
£4190 $7500 €6117 Summer day at Coney island (51x61cm-20x24in) s. canvas on board. 6-May-4 Shannon's, Milford #209/R est:4000-6000
£4360 $7500 €6366 Skaters in Prospect Park, Brooklyn (62x75cm-24x30in) prov. 3-Dec-3 Doyle, New York #267/R est:5000-7000
£4942 $8500 €7215 New York street scene (62x75cm-24x30in) s. prov. 3-Dec-3 Doyle, New York #268/R est:6000-8000

ROTHE, Gatja Helgart (1935-) ?
£333 $600 €500 Untitled (100x70cm-39x28in) 26-Apr-4 Rieber, Stuttgart #1127/R
£1467 $2640 €2200 Figure frieze (200x65cm-79x26in) 26-Apr-4 Rieber, Stuttgart #1126/R est:1980

ROTHENBERG, Susan (1945-) American
£25140 $45000 €36704 Reflections (112x102cm-44x40in) s.i.d.1981 verso prov.exhib. 13-May-4 Sotheby's, New York #466/R est:30000-40000
£95808 $160000 €139880 Untitled (67x91cm-26x36in) s.d.1976 verso acrylic pencil prov. 13-Nov-3 Sotheby's, New York #251a/R est:50000-70000
£538922 $900000 €786826 Layering (169x210cm-67x83in) s.i.d.1974-76 acrylic tempera prov.exhib.lit. 12-Nov-3 Sotheby's, New York #25/R est:600000-800000
Prints
£2206 $3750 €3221 Boneman (76x51cm-30x20in) s. mezzotint. 31-Oct-3 Sotheby's, New York #745/R
£3107 $5500 €4536 Stumblebum (218x107cm-86x42in) s.d.1985-6 num.27/40 col lithograph. 28-Apr-4 Christie's, Rockefeller NY #397/R est:6000-8000
Sculpture
£1216 $2250 €1775 Fish (27cm-11in) init. num.11/14 cast pewter Cast 1990. 12-Feb-4 Sotheby's, New York #230/R est:3500-4500
Works on paper
£5587 $10000 €8157 Untitled (58x46cm-23x18in) chl pastel exec 1988 prov. 13-May-4 Sotheby's, New York #467/R est:7000-9000

ROTHENSTEIN, Michael (1908-1994) British
Works on paper
£850 $1352 €1233 Azalea in the window (55x69cm-22x27in) s.d.1989 W/C. 9-Sep-3 Sworder & Son, Bishops Stortford #429/R

ROTHENSTEIN, Sir William (1872-1945) British
£2793 $5000 €4078 Rabbi with torah (76x69cm-30x27in) exhib. 18-Mar-4 Sotheby's, New York #286/R est:7000-9000
Works on paper
£276 $516 €403 Houses by a canal (21x39cm-8x15in) s. col pencil W/C. 24-Feb-4 Peter Webb, Auckland #177/R (NZ.D 750)
£350 $637 €511 Country lane (21x30cm-8x12in) pencil pastel prov. 1-Jul-4 Christie's, Kensington #50
£380 $646 €555 Effet de sirene (37x24cm-15x9in) i. chl lit. 26-Nov-3 Sotheby's, Olympia #4/R
£4144 $7500 €6050 Portrait of Sir Francis Darwin (36x25cm-14x10in) s.d.1915 pencil htd col sold with 14 dr. 30-Mar-4 Christie's, Rockefeller NY #126/R est:200-300

ROTHKO, Mark (1903-1970) American
£389222 $650000 €568264 Untitled (102x65cm-40x26in) acrylic paper on canvas painted 1968 prov.exhib. 12-Nov-3 Sotheby's, New York #56/R est:700000-900000
£680000 $1237600 €992800 Untitled green or blue (101x64cm-40x25in) acrylic oil paper on canvas painted 1968 prov.exhib. 5-Feb-4 Sotheby's, London #17/R est:300000-400000
£820000 $1508800 €1197200 Untitled (147x103cm-58x41in) tempera paper on canvas painted 1969 prov. 24-Jun-4 Christie's, London #15/R est:450000-650000
£3832336 $6400000 €5595211 Untitled (175x162cm-69x64in) s.num.A-12 d.1963 prov.lit. 11-Nov-3 Christie's, Rockefeller NY #28/R est:4000000-6000000
£4469274 $8000000 €6525140 No 15 (237x221cm-93x87in) s.d.1958 i.verso prov.lit. 11-May-4 Christie's, Rockefeller NY #21/R est:8000000-12000000
£4730539 $7900000 €6906587 No.8 - white stripe (207x232cm-81x91in) s. i.d.1958 verso. 12-Nov-3 Sotheby's, New York #14/R est:8000000-10000000
Works on paper
£14371 $24000 €20982 Untitled (43x28cm-17x11in) s. gouache executed c.1945 prov. 14-Nov-3 Phillips, New York #147/R est:25000-35000

ROTHLISBERGER, William (1862-1943) Swiss
£281 $477 €410 Marais de Cornaux et la Cote (35x50cm-14x20in) mono.d.14.IX.18 exhib. 19-Nov-3 Fischer, Luzern #2257/R (S.FR 620)
£298 $498 €432 Les roseaux (56x90cm-22x35in) s.d. exhib. 21-Jun-3 Galerie du Rhone, Sion #417/R (S.FR 650)

ROTHLISBERGER, Willy (1914-1977) Swiss
£226 $385 €330 House with garden (69x86cm-27x34in) jute on masonite. 1-Dec-3 Koller, Zurich #6542/R (S.FR 500)

ROTHMAN, Lenke (1929-) Swedish
£259 $463 €378 Towards evil eye (115x73cm-45x29in) s.d.1967. 28-May-4 Uppsala Auktionskammare, Uppsala #354 (S.KR 3500)

ROTHSCHILD, Henri (1931-1992) Danish?
£361 $664 €527 Coastal landscape (89x116cm-35x46in) s.d.76 masonite. 29-Mar-4 Rasmussen, Copenhagen #553 (D.KR 4000)

ROTHSTEIN, Anna Fell (1890-?) American
£205 $380 €299 Harbour scene with piers and houses against a mountainous background (69x104cm-27x41in) s. board. 16-Jan-4 Aspire, Cleveland #47/R

ROTHSTEIN, Theresa (?) American?
£266 $425 €388 Cool Blue Mountains. s. 20-Sep-3 Harvey Clar, Oakland #1289

ROTHSTEN, Carl Abraham (1826-1877) Swedish
£480 $860 €701 Ulriksdals Palace (38x50cm-15x20in) mono.d.73. 28-May-4 Uppsala Auktionskammare, Uppsala #135/R (S.KR 6500)
£628 $1125 €917 Landscape from Sodertelje (27x37cm-11x15in) s.verso. 26-May-4 AB Stockholms Auktionsverk #2218/R (S.KR 8500)
£739 $1323 €1079 View of Kalmar town in winter (26x39cm-10x15in) init. 26-May-4 AB Stockholms Auktionsverk #2171/R (S.KR 10000)
£769 $1308 €1100 Shepherds on cliff by waterside (44x59cm-17x23in) init. 29-Nov-3 Bukowskis, Helsinki #369/R
£961 $1720 €1403 Pastoral landscape with waterway (41x50cm-16x20in) init.d.1856. 26-May-4 AB Stockholms Auktionsverk #2313/R (S.KR 13000)
£1109 $1984 €1619 Gripsholms Palace from the south, summer (24x27cm-9x11in) init. 26-May-4 AB Stockholms Auktionsverk #2274/R est:15000-18000 (S.KR 15000)
£1130 $2079 €1695 Landscape with cattle (38x47cm-15x19in) s. one d.1869 pair. 14-Jun-4 Lilla Bukowskis, Stockholm #256/R est:15000-18000 (S.KR 15500)

£1154 $1985 €1685 The waterfall at Alvkarleby - moonlight (49x70cm-19x28in) s. 3-Dec-3 AB Stockholms Auktionsverk #2521/R est:15000-18000 (S.KR 15000)
£2365 $4234 €3453 View of Stockholm (40x58cm-16x23in) mono.d.1875. 28-May-4 Uppsala Auktionskammare, Uppsala #132/R est:18000-20000 (S.KR 32000)
£2385 $4102 €3482 From Stockholm's river with the old town in background (42x72cm-17x28in) s.d.1861 copper oval prov. 2-Dec-3 Bukowskis, Stockholm #321a/R est:40000-45000 (S.KR 31000)
£3843 $6880 €5611 View of Stockholm from Saltsjoen (72x85cm-28x33in) mono.d.1858. 25-May-4 Bukowskis, Stockholm #416/R est:25000-30000 (S.KR 52000)

ROTHSTEN, Carl Abraham (attrib) (1826-1877) Swedish
£923 $1588 €1348 View over Askersund (39x58cm-15x23in) 3-Dec-3 AB Stockholms Auktionsverk #2508/R (S.KR 12000)
£1923 $3308 €2808 Entrance to Stockholm (38x57cm-15x22in) 3-Dec-3 AB Stockholms Auktionsverk #2506/R est:30000-40000 (S.KR 25000)

ROTIG, Georges Frederic (1873-1961) French
£897 $1497 €1300 Chevreuils (33x41cm-13x16in) s.d.44. 11-Nov-3 Lesieur & Le Bars, Le Havre #94
£2994 $5000 €4371 Moose in the woods (74x53cm-29x21in) s.i.d. 20-Jun-3 Freeman, Philadelphia #260/R est:1500-2500
£3793 $6334 €5500 Famille de lions (81x100cm-32x39in) s.d.35 exhib. 17-Nov-3 Tajan, Paris #182/R est:3000-4000
£4967 $9089 €7500 Le harde de sangliers dans la neige (54x65cm-21x26in) s.d.1925. 9-Apr-4 Claude Aguttes, Neuilly #71/R est:4000-6000
Works on paper
£625 $981 €900 Combat de cerfs (20x14cm-8x6in) s. gouache double-sided. 29-Aug-3 Deauville, France #141
£680 $1082 €1000 Etudes de gibier (43x33cm-17x13in) s. pastel. 23-Mar-3 Salle des ventes Pillet, Lyon la Foret #10
£775 $1340 €1100 Cerf et sa harde (31x23cm-12x9in) s.d.03 gouache. 12-Dec-3 Libert, Castor, Paris #25/R
£884 $1583 €1300 Wild boar on lakeshore (24x30cm-9x12in) s.d.02. 17-Mar-4 Neumeister, Munich #311/R
£1076 $1690 €1550 Couple de chevreuils (14x14cm-6x6in) s.i. gouache. 29-Aug-3 Deauville, France #140/R
£1449 $2377 €2000 Compagnie de sangliers au repos dans la neige (23x31cm-9x12in) gouache. 28-May-3 Coutau Begarie, Paris #171/R est:1100-1300
£2603 $4425 €3800 Troupeau de bouquetins dans la montagne (45x64cm-18x25in) s.d.1910 W/C gouache. 9-Nov-3 Eric Pillon, Calais #49/R

ROTINI, Valerio (1911-) Italian
£403 $713 €600 Countryside in Piedmonte (60x75cm-24x30in) s. 1-May-4 Meeting Art, Vercelli #373

ROTKY, Carl (1891-1977) Austrian
£567 $1031 €850 Landscape (82x68cm-32x27in) s. fibreboard. 1-Jul-4 Neumeister, Munich #2789
Works on paper
£300 $540 €450 Hilly landscape in the Steier (20x29cm-8x11in) s. w/C. 22-Apr-4 Dorotheum, Graz #125
£367 $660 €550 Hilly landscape in southern Steier (22x29cm-9x11in) s. W/C. 22-Apr-4 Dorotheum, Graz #123/R
£420 $722 €600 Poppies (45x63cm-18x25in) s. W/C. 4-Dec-3 Dorotheum, Graz #78/R
£528 $877 €750 Farmstead in winter (32x23cm-13x9in) mono. pencil W/C. 12-Jun-3 Dorotheum, Graz #117/R
£660 $1075 €950 Hilly landscape (35x40cm-14x16in) s. W/C. 25-Sep-3 Dorotheum, Graz #35/R

ROTTENHAMMER, Hans (attrib) (16/17th C) German
£6338 $10141 €9000 Resurrection of Lazarus (27x38cm 11x15in) copper prov. 19-Sep-3 Karlheinz Kaupp, Staufen #1894/R est:2500

ROTTENHAMMER, Hans (style) (16/17th C) German
£15000 $27450 €21900 Annunciation to the Virgin (62x41cm-24x16in) copper. 8-Jul-4 Sotheby's, London #250/R est:15000-20000

ROTTENHAMMER, Johann (1564-1625) German
Works on paper
£8333 $15000 €12166 Adoration of the Magi (19x16cm-7x6in) pen ink grey wash over black chk prov. 21-Jan-4 Sotheby's, New York #21/R est:15000-20000

ROTTENHAMMER, Johann (attrib) (1564-1625) German
£2735 $4895 €3993 The Holy Family with infant St John and angels (24x18cm-9x7in) copper. 26-May-4 AB Stockholms Auktionsverk #2499/R est:30000-40000 (S.KR 37000)

ROTTENHAMMER, Johann (circle) (1564-1625) German
£8333 $15000 €12166 Dancing amoretti dressed as the Gods (17x20cm-7x8in) copper. 23-Jan-4 Christie's, Rockefeller NY #164/R est:18000-22000

ROTTER, Paul (1806-1894) German
£1075 $2000 €1570 Expansive landscape with luminous skies (25x35cm-10x14in) s. 5-Mar-4 Skinner, Boston #275/R est:3000-5000

ROTTERDAM SCHOOL (17th C) Dutch
£7500 $13725 €10950 Italianate landscape with hunters and drovers beside a copse (126x111cm-50x44in) bears sig. 6-Jul-4 Sotheby's, Olympia #464/R est:6000-8000

ROTTERDAM, Verena (1965-) Austrian
£524 $892 €750 Mozart (100x85cm-39x33in) s.d.2003 s.i.d.verso acrylic photograph. 27-Nov-3 Dorotheum, Linz #540/R

ROTTERUD, Bjarne (1928-) Norwegian
£652 $1128 €952 Autumn dream (100x100cm-39x39in) s. 13-Dec-3 Blomqvist, Lysaker #1299 (N.KR 7500)

ROTTMANN, Carl (1798-1850) German
£2254 $3741 €3200 Fidenaie am Tiber in the Romagna (12x23cm-5x9in) i. verso paper. 16-Jun-3 Dorotheum, Vienna #96/R est:1800-2400
£7333 $13347 €11000 Obersee with Watzmann (58x78cm-23x31in) s. 30-Jun-4 Neumeister, Munich #655/R est:10000
Works on paper
£4755 $7941 €6800 Gulf of Genova (17x34cm-7x13in) W/C over pencil. 10-Oct-3 Winterberg, Heidelberg #749/R est:1200
£13986 $23357 €20000 Naxos (51x75cm-20x30in) W/C pencil. 10-Oct-3 Winterberg, Heidelberg #748/R est:4800

ROTTMANN, Vazlav (19/20th C) ?
£1323 $2289 €1932 Young lady wearing white evening dress and roses in white hat (130x85cm-51x33in) s.d.1907. 9-Dec-3 Rasmussen, Copenhagen #1675/R est:15000 (D.KR 14000)

ROTTMAYR, Johann Michael (1654-1730) Austrian
£1208 $2223 €1800 St Ignatius von Loyola (97x78cm-38x31in) s. 24-Mar-4 Hugo Ruef, Munich #881/R est:600
£33557 $61745 €50000 Allegory of astronomy and liberal arts (273cm-107in circular) tondo lit. 24-Mar-4 Dorotheum, Vienna #233/R est:70000-90000

ROUAN, François (1943-) French
£37763 $64197 €54000 Bababianco (200x170cm-79x67in) s.i.d.1986 verso prov. 25-Nov-3 Tajan, Paris #63/R est:60000-65000
Works on paper
£845 $1462 €1200 Untitled (30x56cm-12x22in) s.d.1965 gouache collage. 9-Dec-3 Artcurial Briest, Paris #576a est:800-1200
£1333 $2426 €2000 1988 (148x80cm-58x31in) s.d.1988 wax painting. 30-Jun-4 Calmels Cohen, Paris #79b est:30000-40000
£5634 $9746 €8000 Figures tremblees (93x70cm-37x28in) s.i.d.1984 gouache prov. 14-Dec-3 Versailles Encheres #200/R est:10000-12000

ROUARGUE, Adolphe (1810-1870) French
Works on paper
£470 $864 €700 Wenzel bridge, Prague (11x17cm-4x7in) s. wash pen. 26-Mar-4 Dorotheum, Vienna #103/R

ROUART, Henri-Stanislas (1833-1912) French
£450 $765 €657 Figure by a gate of a country house (61x51cm-24x20in) s. 25-Nov-3 Bonhams, Knowle #209
£8333 $15083 €12500 Lecture au jardin (50x61cm-20x24in) s. 1-Apr-4 Credit Municipal, Paris #52/R est:1500-2000

ROUAULT, Andre Thomas (?-1949) French
Works on paper
£537 $993 €800 Jeune femme assise (41x36cm-16x14in) s.d.1928 W/C. 15-Mar-4 Gros & Delettrez, Paris #177/R

ROUAULT, Georges (1871-1958) French
£13974 $25432 €20402 Trois juges (13x22cm-5x9in) s.d.1906 oil W/C. 18-Jun-4 Kornfeld, Bern #137/R est:20000 (S.FR 32000)
£15493 $25099 €22000 Deux silhouettes et voilier sous le soleil (16x23cm-6x9in) i.verso cardboard on canvas prov. 5-Aug-3 Tajan, Paris #30/R est:22000-28000
£26667 $48000 €40000 Christ en majeste (49x30cm-19x12in) s. cardboard. 24-Apr-4 Cornette de St.Cyr, Paris #401/R est:6000-8000
£30612 $54796 €45000 Paysage biblique - Stella Vespertina (22x28cm-9x11in) s.i. prov.lit. 19-Mar-4 Millon & Associes, Paris #88/R est:40000-60000
£32000 $58240 €46720 Rencontre a la porte doree (41x29cm-16x11in) init. prov.lit. 4-Feb-4 Sotheby's, London #327/R est:35000-45000
£44219 $79151 €65000 Paysage biblique, Christ et pecheurs (46x57cm-18x22in) studio st. paper on canvas prov. 21-Mar-4 Calmels Cohen, Paris #173/R est:100000-150000
£50000 $92000 €73000 Christ et Disciples (39x30cm-15x12in) s. painted 1943-4 prov.lit. 22-Jun-4 Sotheby's, London #275/R est:50000-70000
£50279 $90000 €73407 Bouquet II (56x46cm-22x18in) s. oil paper on canvas painted 1929-1939. 5-May-4 Christie's, Rockefeller NY #255/R est:100000-150000
£62000 $114080 €90520 Paysage Biblique (30x42cm-12x17in) studio st. verso paper on canvas painted c.1950-3 prov. 22-Jun-4 Sotheby's, London #260/R est:60000-80000
£90000 $163800 €131400 Carmencita II (48x30cm-19x12in) s. card on panel painted 1947 exhib. 3-Feb-4 Christie's, London #260/R est:90000-120000
£91176 $155000 €133117 Pierrot (44x29cm-17x11in) s. paper on canvas painted 1937 prov.lit. 5-Nov-3 Christie's, Rockefeller NY #291/R est:180000-250000
£246667 $451400 €370000 Pierrot (90x65cm-35x26in) s. s.i.verso painted c.1937-38 prov.exhib.lit. 7-Jun-4 Artcurial Briest, Paris #37/R est:400000-600000
Prints
£1676 $3000 €2447 Trister Os (31x20cm-12x8in) color aquatint. 6-May-4 Swann Galleries, New York #569/R est:4000-6000
£1788 $3200 €2610 La dame a la huppe (31x21cm-12x8in) color aquatint. 6-May-4 Swann Galleries, New York #573/R est:3000-5000
£2119 $3750 €3094 Nu de profil (31x21cm-12x8in) col aquatint. 30-Apr-4 Sotheby's, New York #222/R est:4000-6000
£2155 $3858 €3146 Christ on the cross (65x49cm-26x19in) s.i.d.1936 col aquatint. 12-May-4 Dobiaschofsky, Bern #1980/R est:10000 (S.FR 5000)
£2246 $3750 €3279 Automne (43x56cm-17x22in) s.i.d.1933 lithograph. 11-Nov-3 Doyle, New York #376/R est:4000-6000
£2349 $4346 €3500 Le Christ en croix (77x57cm-30x22in) s.i. col etching aquatint edition of 175. 15-Mar-4 Blanchet, Paris #34/R est:4000-6000
£2353 $4000 €3435 Automne (44x59cm-17x23in) s. lithograph. 31-Oct-3 Sotheby's, New York #459/R
£2353 $4000 €3435 Nu de profil (31x20cm-12x8in) col aquatint edition of 250. 6-Nov-3 Swann Galleries, New York #715/R est:6000-9000

£2500	$4000	€3650	Judas (32x22cm-13x9in) col aquatint edition of 270. 18-Sep-3 Swann Galleries, New York #576/R est:2000-3000
£4067	$7320	€6100	Christ en croix (65x50cm-26x20in) s. num.42/175 col aquatint. 24-Apr-4 Cornette de St.Cyr, Paris #253/R est:3000
£4749	$8500	€6934	La baire de trepasses (62x45cm-24x18in) s.num.46/175 color aquatint. 6-May-4 Swann Galleries, New York #574/R est:4000-6000
£7919	$14651	€11800	Automne (50x66cm-20x26in) s.i. col etching aquatint edition of 175. 15-Mar-4 Blanchet, Paris #33/R est:6000-8000
£8042	$13671	€11500	Automne (50x65cm-20x26in) s. col aquatint. 28-Nov-3 Tajan, Paris #402 est:12000-15000
£11765	$20000	€17177	Cirque (44x34cm-17x13in) col aquatint set of 8. 31-Oct-3 Sotheby's, New York #455/R
£14118	$24000	€20612	Automne (51x67cm-20x26in) col aquatint. 6-Nov-3 Swann Galleries, New York #716/R est:25000-35000

Sculpture

£6000	$10020	€8760	Juge et condamnes (16cm-6in) s.i.d.1908 base painted glazed ceramic vase exec 1908. 22-Oct-3 Sotheby's, Olympia #90/R est:6000-8000

Works on paper

£2797	$4755	€4000	Conference faite chez le pere ubu par un habitant de la planete Mars (15x24cm-6x9in) i. Indian ink wash prov.lit. 23-Nov-3 Cornette de St.Cyr, Paris #312/R est:300-400
£5200	$9568	€7800	Modele (25x21cm-10x8in) s.i.d.1927 Indian ink wash. 9-Jun-4 Le Roux & Morel, Paris #73/R est:8000-10000
£7000	$11690	€10220	Nu au miroir I (29x31cm-11x12in) gouache W/C executed 1907 lit. 21-Oct-3 Sotheby's, London #120/R est:8000-12000
£14000	$25760	€20440	Paysage anime (54x64cm-21x25in) s.d.1905 W/C brush ink pastel lit. 24-Mar-4 Sotheby's, Olympia #10/R est:8000-12000
£18882	$32476	€27000	Fleurs decoratives I (41x28cm-16x11in) s. gouache paper on canvas lit. 3-Dec-3 Tajan, Paris #20/R est:20000-30000
£19553	$35000	€28547	Madame Baigniers et son fils (22x17cm-9x7in) s.d.1906 W/C pencil prov.exhib.lit. 6-May-4 Sotheby's, New York #203/R est:30000-40000
£21812	$40352	€32500	Passion (41x31cm-16x12in) mixed media panel. 14-Mar-4 Eric Pillon, Calais #206/R
£22346	$40000	€32625	Soliques du clown (58x43cm-23x17in) s.d.1930 W/C pastel brush India ink paper on board prov.lit. 5-May-4 Christie's, Rockefeller NY #115/R est:35000-45000
£24832	$44450	€37000	Ballerines (35x24cm-14x9in) mixed media. 30-May-4 Eric Pillon, Calais #232/R
£45000	$82800	€65700	Pierrot (52x51cm-20x20in) W/C gouache pastel brushink prov.exhib.lit. 22-Jun-4 Sotheby's, London #453/R est:50000-70000

ROUAULT, Georges Dominique (1904-) French

Works on paper

£286	$511	€420	Les quais (29x41cm-11x16in) s. W/C. 22-Mar-4 Digard, Paris #103
£286	$511	€420	Vue de Tuileries (29x41cm-11x16in) s. W/C. 22-Mar-4 Digard, Paris #104/R
£313	$560	€460	Vue sur la fontaine (29x41cm-11x16in) s. W/C. 22-Mar-4 Digard, Paris #105
£354	$633	€520	Vue de Notre Dame de Paris (29x41cm-11x16in) s. W/C. 22-Mar-4 Digard, Paris #102/R
£807	$1300	€1178	Apres la lessive des mariniers - a Paris street scene (23x30cm-9x12in) s. W/C gouache. 24-Feb-3 O'Gallerie, Oregon #813/R

ROUBAL, Franz (1884-1967) Austrian

£467	$849	€700	Haymaking (33x46cm-13x18in) s.d.1945 board. 1-Jul-4 Van Ham, Cologne #1583
£559	$962	€800	View to Grimming (31x40cm-12x16in) s.d.1945 board. 4-Dec-3 Dorotheum, Graz #33/R
£704	$1169	€1000	Forest clearing (39x26cm-15x10in) s.d.25 board. 12-Jun-3 Dorotheum, Graz #51/R
£833	$1358	€1200	Summer landscape with Grimming (40x52cm-16x20in) s.mono.d.1957 board. 25-Sep-3 Dorotheum, Graz #26/R
£1049	$1804	€1500	Farmer with horses and plough in front of Grimming (73x92cm-29x36in) s.d.1958. 4-Dec-3 Dorotheum, Graz #34/R est:1100
£1056	$1754	€1500	Deer (24x29cm-9x11in) s.d.29 board. 12-Jun-3 Dorotheum, Graz #52/R
£1538	$2646	€2200	Grimming with grazing cows (81x140cm-32x55in) s.d.1942. 4-Dec-3 Dorotheum, Graz #35/R est:2200

Works on paper

£315	$541	€450	Wild horses from Solutre (32x46cm-13x18in) s.d.1955 chl. 4-Dec-3 Dorotheum, Graz #183/R
£317	$526	€450	Animal study (44x31cm-17x12in) s. pencil. 12-Jun-3 Dorotheum, Graz #181/R
£336	$601	€500	Battle scene (29x43cm-11x17in) s. gouache. 27-May-4 Dorotheum, Graz #205/R

ROUBAUD, Franz (1856-1928) Russian

£948	$1697	€1384	Peasant with ox plough (13x18cm-5x7in) s.d.93 panel. 12-May-4 Dobiaschofsky, Bern #920/R est:1500 (S.FR 2200)
£959	$1630	€1400	Head of Tscherkessen rider (34x23cm-13x9in) s. board. 5-Nov-3 Hugo Ruef, Munich #1094
£1806	$2979	€2600	Czech rider (18x13cm-7x5in) s.d.93 panel. 2-Jul-3 Neumeister, Munich #753/R est:1800
£3000	$5100	€4500	Study of rocky riverbed (30x39cm-12x15in) s.i.d.05 board. 25-Nov-3 Christie's, London #208/R est:1500-2000
£3082	$5240	€4500	Freedom, the will of the people (70x105cm-28x41in) s. 5-Nov-3 Hugo Ruef, Munich #1095/R est:1500
£3200	$5440	€4800	Study of mountainous landscape (31x49cm-12x19in) prov. 25-Nov-3 Christie's, London #209/R est:1500-2000
£4800	$8160	€7008	Charging warrior (41x24cm-16x9in) s. 19-Nov-3 Sotheby's, London #64/R est:3000-4000
£4800	$8592	€7008	Lone Cossack horseman (18x13cm-7x5in) s.d.93 board. 26-May-4 Sotheby's, Olympia #366/R est:2000-3000
£6000	$10920	€9000	Tscherkessen rider (36x27cm-14x11in) s. panel. 30-Jun-4 Neumeister, Munich #663/R est:6000
£6000	$10920	€9000	Guards in evening (53x40cm-21x16in) s. 30-Jun-4 Neumeister, Munich #664 est:6000
£6667	$12133	€10000	Sabre waving rider (101x71cm-40x28in) s. 30-Jun-4 Neumeister, Munich #661/R est:8000
£7483	$13395	€11000	Market scene (40x51cm-16x20in) s. 17-Mar-4 Neumeister, Munich #589/R est:5000
£11972	$20711	€17000	Tscherkessen rider in Caucasus (27x21cm-11x8in) s.d.1884 panel. 13-Dec-3 Lempertz, Koln #41/R est:2000
£12000	$21840	€18000	Tscherkessen rider in Caucasus (62x39cm-24x15in) s. 30-Jun-4 Neumeister, Munich #659/R est:16000
£13826	$25439	€20600	Young Tscherkessen riders (62x41cm-24x16in) s. lit. 25-Mar-4 Karlheinz Kaupp, Staufen #2699/R est:6500
£14000	$23800	€20440	Caucasian warriors crossing the river (59x83cm-23x33in) s. 19-Nov-3 Sotheby's, London #63/R est:12000-18000
£16000	$29120	€24000	Rider on falcon hunt in Caucasus (62x39cm-24x15in) s. 30-Jun-4 Neumeister, Munich #657/R est:19000
£16779	$30872	€25000	Tscherkessen rider stealing girl (62x40cm-24x16in) s. 24-Mar-4 Hugo Ruef, Munich #1095/R est:9800
£17013	$29433	€24839	Cossack riding fast down a mountain slope (60x45cm-24x18in) s. 9-Dec-3 Rasmussen, Copenhagen #1528/R est:20000 (D.KR 180000)
£17450	$32107	€26000	Caucasian highland rider in sunlight (62x49cm-24x19in) s. i. verso. 24-Mar-4 Hugo Ruef, Munich #1094/R est:9800
£17687	$31660	€26000	Tscherkess horseman with guitar (43x32cm-17x13in) s. panel. 17-Mar-4 Neumeister, Munich #587/R est:8000
£20408	$36531	€30000	Man on horseback stealing woman (62x39cm-24x15in) s. 17-Mar-4 Neumeister, Munich #585/R est:20000
£25333	$46107	€38000	Tscherkessen riders crossing river (54x72cm-21x28in) s. 30-Jun-4 Neumeister, Munich #658/R est:16000
£26000	$47320	€39000	Tscherkessen riders with wagons crossing river (63x94cm-25x37in) s. 30-Jun-4 Neumeister, Munich #660/R est:14000
£26573	$45706	€38000	Horse rider with rifle at the ready (62x39cm-24x15in) i. 3-Dec-3 Neumeister, Munich #722/R est:4000
£27155	$49151	€39646	Oriental scene with riders and figures outside Mosque (80x125cm-31x49in) s. 31-Mar-4 Zurichsee Auktionen, Erlenbach #9/R est:18000-24000 (S.FR 63000)
£27972	$48112	€40000	Horse riders breaking away from a battle (71x84cm-28x33in) s. 3-Dec-3 Neumeister, Munich #721/R est:10000
£29530	$54336	€44000	Tscherkessen riders (70x101cm-28x40in) s. 27-Mar-4 Geble, Radolfzell #760/R est:3500
£32653	$58449	€48000	Tscherkess horsemen crossing river (70x100cm-28x39in) s. 17-Mar-4 Neumeister, Munich #588/R est:8000
£33473	$60586	€48871	A skirmish in the Caucasus (49x76cm-19x30in) s.i.d.1893 prov. 1-Apr-4 Heffel, Vancouver #88/R est:18000-22000 (C.D 80000)
£35000	$59500	€52500	Horsemen at river (94x63cm-37x25in) s. 25-Nov-3 Christie's, London #187/R est:20000-30000
£35374	$63320	€52000	Attack (96x141cm-38x56in) s. 17-Mar-4 Neumeister, Munich #586/R est:10000
£43333	$78867	€65000	Cavalry battle in the Caucasus (85x150cm-33x59in) s. 30-Jun-4 Neumeister, Munich #656/R est:28000
£55944	$96224	€80000	Battle between horse riders (85x150cm-33x59in) s. 3-Dec-3 Neumeister, Munich #720/R est:12000
£57823	$103503	€85000	Tscherkessen horsemen starting attack (80x125cm-31x49in) s. 17-Mar-4 Neumeister, Munich #584/R est:20000
£80000	$136000	€116800	Fighting Cossacks (108x178cm-43x70in) s. 19-Nov-3 Sotheby's, London #65/R est:30000-40000

Works on paper

£15000	$25500	€22500	Study for the Borodino Panorama (81x162cm-32x64in) st.sig. chk htd white prov. 25-Nov-3 Christie's, London #188/R est:15000-20000

ROUBAUD, Jean Baptiste (1871-?) French

£386	$707	€560	Les rochers rouges, Le Treyas, corniche d'or (33x41cm-13x16in) s.d.1927 panel exhib. 31-Jan-4 Neret-Minet, Paris #153/R

ROUBAUD, Noele (1890-?) French

£300	$543	€450	Jeune etudiant (53x44cm-21x17in) s. 31-Mar-4 Sotheby's, Paris #151/R

ROUBILLE, Auguste (1872-1955) French

£461	$770	€650	La danseuse (80x60cm-31x24in) s. 17-Jun-3 Vanderkindere, Brussels #134
£1429	$2557	€2100	Jeune femme a sa fenetre (21x15cm-8x6in) s.i. panel. 19-Mar-4 Ribeyre & Baron, Paris #70 est:300-500

Works on paper

£909	$1545	€1300	Elegante au caniche en corsage (36x22cm-14x9in) mono. Chinese ink gouache. 18-Nov-3 Sotheby's, Paris #20/R est:2000-3000

ROUBOS, Leon (1959-) Australian

£511	$868	€746	Pedestrian crossing (43x68cm-17x27in) s.d.1990 acrylic board prov. 25-Nov-3 Christie's, Melbourne #170/R (A.D 1200)
£596	$1013	€870	Pedestrian and traffic line (89x110cm-35x43in) s. enamel board. 25-Nov-3 Christie's, Melbourne #292/R (A.D 1400)
£661	$1170	€965	Traffic Island (44x58cm-17x23in) s. enamel board. 3-May-4 Christie's, Melbourne #269/R est:1000-1500 (A.D 1600)

ROUBTZOFF, Alexandre (1884-1949) French?

£667	$1213	€1000	Pont d'Avignon (20x38cm-8x15in) s.d.1937 canvas on cardboard. 4-Jul-4 Eric Pillon, Calais #150/R
£780	$1303	€1100	Porte Saint-Denis (29x20cm-11x8in) s.i.d.1925 canvas on cardboard. 19-Oct-3 Rabourdin & Choppin de Janvry, Paris #113/R
£1560	$2606	€2200	P. de Vimines (44x27cm-17x11in) s.d.1936 canvas on cardboard. 19-Oct-3 Rabourdin & Choppin de Janvry, Paris #112/R est:2300-2600
£1600	$2832	€2336	Sunbather (28x44cm-11x17in) s.i.d.25 Juillet 1935 canvas on board. 27-Apr-4 Bonhams, Knightsbridge #5/R est:1500-2000
£2254	$3899	€3200	Jardin a Soukra (17x27cm-7x11in) s.d.1917 panel exhib. 15-Dec-3 Gros & Delettrez, Paris #157/R est:3000-4500
£2958	$5117	€4200	Tunis (17x27cm-7x11in) s.i.d.1919. 15-Dec-3 Gros & Delettrez, Paris #317/R est:2000-3000
£3169	$5482	€4500	Fete a Tunis (19x29cm-7x11in) s.i.d.1914 canvas on cardboard. 15-Dec-3 Gros & Delettrez, Paris #315/R est:4500-6000
£3191	$5330	€4500	Vue de La Marsa (35x46cm-14x18in) s.i.d.1916 canvas on cardboard. 16-Jun-3 Gros & Delettrez, Paris #184/R est:2000-2500
£3334	$6101	€5000	Rue a Nabeul (17x27cm-7x11in) s.i.d.1919. 3-Jun-4 Tajan, Paris #329/R est:2500-3000
£3688	$6159	€5200	Puit de Metameur (19x28cm-7x11in) s.i. canvas on panel. 16-Jun-3 Gros & Delettrez, Paris #183/R est:4500-6000
£7000	$12810	€10500	Minaret a Sidi-Bou-Said (25x36cm-10x14in) s.i.d.1948. 3-Jun-4 Tajan, Paris #305/R est:5000-6000
£7042	$12183	€10000	Amandiers en fleurs (29x37cm-11x15in) s.d.1918. 15-Dec-3 Gros & Delettrez, Paris #313/R est:10000-12000

Works on paper

£400	$732	€600	Dome de la Mosquee El-Hawa a Tunis (11x19cm-4x7in) mono.i.d.1949 chl. 3-Jun-4 Tajan, Paris #325/R
£667	$1220	€1000	Salammbo (11x19cm-4x7in) mono.i.d.1941 chl htd W/C. 3-Jun-4 Tajan, Paris #310/R
£667	$1220	€1000	Le Mausolee de Sidi-Bou-Haj, a El-Kef (10x19cm-4x7in) mono.i.d.1948 chl htd W/C. 3-Jun-4 Tajan, Paris #312/R
£667	$1220	€1000	Une place a Zaghouan (10x14cm-4x6in) mono.i.d.1931 chl htd W/C. 3-Jun-4 Tajan, Paris #313/R
£867	$1586	€1300	Jardin fleuri a Sidi-Bou-Said (11x19cm-4x7in) mono.i.d.1941 pen. W/C. 3-Jun-4 Tajan, Paris #307/R est:1200-1500
£1000	$1830	€1500	Mausolee a Tunis. Mausolee de Sidi Ali Azouz a Tunis (11x19cm-4x7in) mono.i.d.1941 one chl one pen two. 3-Jun-4 Tajan, Paris #318/R est:1600-2000
£1000	$1830	€1500	Vue de Oum-Jdour. La Mosquee de Beit Allah a Hergla (19x11cm-7x4in) mono.i. one d.1945 one d.1949 chl two. 3-Jun-4 Tajan, Paris #319/R est:1600-2000
£1067	$1952	€1600	Minaret a Tunis. La Mosquee El-Hawa a Tunis (20x11cm-8x4in) mono.i.d.1949 chl two. 3-Jun-4 Tajan, Paris #317/R est:1600-2000
£1067	$1952	€1600	Mausolee a Gammarth. Paysage a Sidi-Bou-Said (10x14cm-4x6in) mono.i. one d.1930 one d.1931 chl two. 3-Jun-4 Tajan, Paris #321/R est:1600-2000
£1067	$1952	€1600	Mosquee a Zaghouan. Cafe a Tunis (10x14cm-4x6in) mono.i.d.1931 chl two. 3-Jun-4 Tajan, Paris #322/R est:1600-2000
£1134	$2074	€1700	Les terrasses de Sidi-Bou-Said. L'attente a la gare CFA de Constantine (11x19cm-4x7in) mono.i. one d.1941 one d.1938 chl two. 3-Jun-4 Tajan, Paris #323/R est:1600-2000

ROUBY, A (1849-?) French

£1100	$2079	€1606	Elegant company boarding a gondola, Doge's Palace beyond (33x56cm-13x22in) s. 19-Feb-4 Christie's, Kensington #174/R est:1000-1500

ROUBY, Alfred (1849-1909) French

£733	$1357	€1100	Bouquet de fleurs (73x54cm-29x21in) s. 14-Jul-4 Livinec, Gaudcheau & Jezequel, Rennes #235/R
£800	$1336	€1168	Flowers overflowing from a basket by a vase on a draped table (60x93cm-24x37in) s. 8-Oct-3 Christie's, Kensington #965/R
£845	$1403	€1200	Bouquet de fleurs (61x46cm-24x18in) s. 15-Jun-3 Peron, Melun #243
£1678	$2853	€2400	Vase de fleurs (61x46cm-24x18in) s. 24-Nov-3 Boscher, Cherbourg #735/R est:2000-2500

ROUCH, Blanche L (20th C) American

£321	$500	€469	California landscape (61x76cm-24x30in) s. masonite. 12-Apr-3 Auctions by the Bay, Alameda #250/R

ROUGELET, Benedict (1834-1894) French

Sculpture

£11111	$20000	€16222	Group of three putti (68cm-27in) s. white marble. 23-Apr-4 Christie's, Rockefeller NY #141/R est:20000-30000

ROUGEMONT, Guy de (1935-) French

£3919	$6897	€5800	Triptyque quadrille (100x195cm-39x77in) s.i.d.1978 verso triptych prov.exhib. 18-May-4 Tajan, Paris #100/R est:6000-7000

Sculpture

£1722	$3134	€2600	Colonne multicolore (236x9x9cm-93x4x4in) PVC wooden base. 15-Jun-4 Camard, Paris #99/R est:3000-3200
£12000	$21840	€18000	Cloud table (39x200x90cm-15x79x35in) mirror finish stainless steel exec.c.1969 lit. 30-Jun-4 Christie's, Kensington #136/R est:6000-9000
£24503	$44596	€37000	Nuage (45x138x110cm-18x54x43in) metal exec.c.1970 exhib.lit. 15-Jun-4 Camard, Paris #102/R est:45000-55000

ROUGEMONT, Philippe de (1891-1965) Swedish

£588	$1053	€858	Portrait of female nude (77x64cm-30x25in) s. 10-May-4 Rasmussen, Vejle #399/R (D.KR 6500)

ROUGET, Alfred (19/20th C) French

£839	$1401	€1200	Desert scene (33x41cm-13x16in) s. i.verso. 30-Jun-3 Ansorena, Madrid #428/R

ROUGET, Georges (attrib) (1784-1869) French

£2585	$4627	€3800	Portrait de jeune garcon (55x46cm-22x18in) 19-Mar-4 Beaussant & Lefèvre, Paris #78/R est:2000-2200

ROUGHSEY, Dick (1924-1985) Australian

£992	$1835	€1448	Wood gathering, Mornington (40x50cm-16x20in) s.d.73 i.verso. 10-Mar-4 Deutscher-Menzies, Melbourne #577/R est:2500-3500 (A.D 2400)
£1074	$1988	€1568	Woman collecting firewood (30x40cm-12x16in) s.d.82 board prov. 10-Mar-4 Deutscher-Menzies, Melbourne #299/R est:1000-2000 (A.D 2600)
£1311	$2125	€1914	Dingo dance (40x51cm-16x20in) s.d.79 acrylic board. 30-Jul-3 Goodman, Sydney #123/R est:1000-1500 (A.D 3200)
£1953	$3652	€2930	Untitled (75x91cm-30x36in) s.d.1978 prov. 26-Jul-4 Sotheby's, Melbourne #516/R est:5000-7000 (A.D 5000)

Works on paper

£1234	$2135	€1802	Gossiping, Mornington Island (36x46cm-14x18in) i.d.1972 verso synthetic polymer paint board prov. 10-Dec-3 Shapiro, Sydney #133 est:3500-5000 (A.D 2900)
£1445	$2703	€2168	Untitled (22x29cm-9x11in) s. synthetic polymer masonite exec. c. 1970 prov. 21-Jul-4 Shapiro, Sydney #134/R est:3000-5000 (A.D 3700)
£3725	$6669	€5439	Mambil and Debil (58x165cm-23x65in) natural earth pigments bark exec 1969 prov. 25-May-4 Lawson Menzies, Sydney #254/R est:8000-10000 (A.D 9500)

ROUILLARD, Françoise (1796-1833) French

Miniatures

£1014	$1784	€1500	Portrait of young woman wearing fur collar (8x6cm-3x2in) i. gouache ivory lit. oval. 21-May-4 Lempertz, Koln #582/R est:800

ROUILLARD, Jean Sebastien (1789-1852) French

£3357	$5773	€4800	Portrait de Napoleon sur le champ de bataille (66x34cm-26x13in) s. 2-Dec-3 Sotheby's, Paris #74/R est:3000-4000

ROUKHIN, Evgeny (1943-1976) Russian

£5556	$10000	€8112	Pliers (69x65cm-27x26in) s. 23-Apr-4 Sotheby's, New York #128/R est:10000-15000

ROULAND, Orlando (1871-1945) American

£22013	$35000	€32139	When night comes on (96x91cm-38x36in) s. 12-Sep-3 Skinner, Boston #481/R est:18000

ROULET, Henry (1915-) Swiss

£545	$905	€790	Interieur/Petite intimite (24x19cm-9x7in) s.i.d.1968. 13-Jun-3 Zofingen, Switzerland #2999 (S.FR 1200)
£1207	$2160	€1762	Le journal (27x35cm-11x14in) s. i.d.1963 stretcher. 14-May-4 Dobiaschofsky, Bern #166/R est:1900 (S.FR 2800)
£1333	$2133	€1933	Les joueurs (46x55cm-18x22in) s. i.d.1966 verso. 15-May-3 Stuker, Bern #1471/R est:1500-2000 (S.FR 2800)
£1584	$2692	€2313	L'oiseleur (35x27cm-14x11in) s.i. verso. 28-Nov-3 Zofingen, Switzerland #3155 est:3500 (S.FR 3500)
£1855	$3154	€2708	Cirque (46x55cm-18x22in) s.i. verso. 28-Nov-3 Zofingen, Switzerland #3154/R est:4800 (S.FR 4100)
£1864	$3094	€2703	Venice (38x61cm-15x24in) i.d.1970 verso. 13-Jun-3 Zofingen, Switzerland #2998/R (S.FR 4100)

ROULIN, François Desire (1796-1874) French

Works on paper

£55000	$89650	€80300	Various scenes. W/C 13 grey wash pen ink 2 fifteen. 25-Sep-3 Christie's, London #437/R est:60000-80000

ROULIN, Louis François Marie (19th C) French

£3333	$6033	€5000	Portrait de Barye, sculpteur et peintre (35x27cm-14x11in) s.i.d.1835 lit. 30-Mar-4 Rossini, Paris #240 est:600-1000

ROULLAND, Jean (1931-) French

Sculpture

£1074	$1987	€1600	Tete (19cm-7in) pat bronze. 14-Mar-4 Eric Pillon, Calais #232/R

ROULLET, Gaston (1847-1925) French

£603	$977	€850	Vue de Venise (27x36cm-11x14in) s. painted c.1890-1900. 24-May-3 Martinot & Savignat, Pontoise #7
£813	$1455	€1187	Port du Brus (26x35cm-10x14in) s. panel. 26-May-4 AB Stockholms Auktionsverk #2391/R (S.KR 11000)
£1049	$1804	€1500	Gondoles a Venise (33x45cm-13x18in) s.i. 7-Dec-3 Osenat, Fontainebleau #182 est:2200-2500
£1060	$1928	€1600	La Venus service entre Trieste et Venise (26x37cm-10x15in) s.i. 16-Jun-4 Renaud, Paris #39 est:350-400
£1500	$2385	€2175	Barges on a Dutch canal (38x54cm-15x21in) s.i. prov. 9-Sep-3 Bonhams, Knightsbridge #228/R est:1000-1500
£1800	$3312	€2628	French landscape (28x48cm-11x19in) s.i. 25-Mar-4 Christie's, Kensington #5/R est:1200-1500
£1837	$3288	€2700	Village du Tonkin (16x46cm-6x18in) s.i.d.1886 panel. 21-Mar-4 St-Germain-en-Laye Encheres #132/R est:2000-2500
£2138	$3506	€2950	Venise, barque de pecheurs a quai (45x70cm-18x28in) s.d. 11-May-3 Osenat, Fontainebleau #162/R est:3500-4000
£3667	$6710	€5500	Dechargement des poissons (55x70cm-22x28in) s.i. 6-Jun-4 Osenat, Fontainebleau #183/R est:6000-6500
£3871	$6194	€5652	Le port de Hang-Hoa au Tonkin (32x55cm-13x22in) s.d.29 Dec 1885. 18-May-3 Sotheby's, Singapore #122/R est:4000-6000 (S.D 10800)
£6233	$9786	€9100	Arrivage des bois de Norvege (100x71cm-39x28in) s.i.d.1876. 20-Apr-3 Deauville, France #96/R est:7000-9000

Works on paper

£264	$473	€385	Lake Harrison (27x38cm-11x15in) s.i. W/C exec. c.1890 prov. 27-May-4 Heffel, Vancouver #62 (C.D 650)
£461	$770	€650	Kairouan (26x37cm-10x15in) s.i. chl. 23-Jun-3 Ribeyre & Baron, Paris #23

ROUNTREE, Harry (1878-1950) British

Works on paper

£840	$1554	€1226	Rabbit audience. Little girl with a goblin by a tree (33x23cm-13x9in) s.i. W/C pencil two sold with two books. 14-Jan-4 Lawrence, Crewkerne #1345 est:300-400
£1437	$2400	€2098	Lovebirds (33x23cm-13x9in) s. W/C exec.c.1910. 15-Nov-3 Illustration House, New York #82/R est:1200-1800

ROUQUET, Jean Andre (1701-1758) French

Miniatures

£1500	$2550	€2190	Young gentleman (3cm-1in) enamel gilt frame oval. 18-Nov-3 Bonhams, New Bond Street #39/R
£3200	$5728	€4672	Young lady in pink embroidered dress (5cm-2in) enamel gilt metal frame prov. 25-May-4 Christie's, London #4/R est:2000-3000

ROURA, Lluis (1943-) Spanish

£915	$1584	€1300	Landscape (35x35cm-14x14in) s.d.1985. 15-Dec-3 Ansorena, Madrid #1011/R

ROUS, Martin (jnr) (1962-) Dutch

£903	$1426	€1300	Untitled (90x120cm-35x47in) s.d.2002 verso. 26-Apr-3 Auction Maastricht #91/R

ROUSE, Lionel (20th C) British?

£1000 $1840 €1460 Bentley versus Mercedes at Le Mans 1930 (92x61cm-36x24in) s. acrylic board. 25-Jun-4 Bonhams, New Bond Street #287 est:1000-1500
£1300 $2392 €1898 Mercedes W 125 versus Maserati (91x61cm-36x24in) s. acrylic. 25-Jun-4 Bonhams, New Bond Street #288 est:1000-1500

ROUSE, Robert William Arthur (fl.1883-1927) British

Works on paper
£270 $435 €392 Winters afternoon, Church Lane, Surrey (23x30cm-9x12in) s. W/C. 15-Aug-3 Keys, Aylsham #476

ROUSSE, Charles (fl.1870-1890) British

Works on paper
£250 $443 €365 Cheapside (38x28cm-15x11in) s. W/C. 28-Apr-4 Halls, Shrewsbury #450/R

ROUSSE, Frank (fl.1897-1915) British

£460 $731 €672 Fishermen loading cobbles on a Yorkshire beach (30x45cm-12x18in) s. 18-Mar-3 Anderson & Garland, Newcastle #288
£740 $1258 €1080 Beached fishing vessels possibly Bridlington (21x46cm-8x18in) s. board. 1-Dec-3 David Duggleby, Scarborough #322/R
Works on paper
£280 $504 €409 Whitby Sands from Upgang (26x36cm-10x14in) s.i. pencil W/C. 21-Apr-4 Tennants, Leyburn #953
£310 $493 €450 Whitby quayside with paddle steamer (38x25cm-15x10in) s. W/C. 9-Sep-3 David Duggleby, Scarborough #157
£310 $561 €453 Moorland stream (32x52cm-13x20in) s. W/C. 30-Mar-4 David Duggleby, Scarborough #48/R
£339 $566 €495 Fisherfolk on the beach (21x36cm-8x14in) s. W/C. 17-Nov-3 Waddingtons, Toronto #62/R (C.D 750)
£340 $541 €493 Henrietta Street and Tate Hill Sands (24x35cm-9x14in) s.d.92 W/C. 9-Sep-3 David Duggleby, Scarborough #114
£340 $615 €496 Harbour with the abbey in the background (26x36cm-10x14in) s. W/C. 30-Mar-4 David Duggleby, Scarborough #27/R
£350 $557 €508 Fishing boats by the quayside Whitby (36x26cm-14x10in) s.d.98 W/C. 9-Sep-3 David Duggleby, Scarborough #159
£360 $601 €526 Whitby harbour (23x33cm-9x13in) s. W/C. 8-Oct-3 Andrew Hartley, Ilkley #1083
£380 $604 €551 Moored rowing boats on the River Esk. s.d.97 W/C. 9-Sep-3 David Duggleby, Scarborough #9/R
£400 $636 €580 Fishergirl on the shore (26x36cm-10x14in) s. W/C. 9-Sep-3 David Duggleby, Scarborough #127
£410 $652 €595 Dockend Whitby (36x26cm-14x10in) s.d.98 W/C. 9-Sep-3 David Duggleby, Scarborough #158/R
£420 $714 €613 Fishing folk on a beach with ships beyond (21x14cm-8x6in) s. gouache. 30-Oct-3 Bracketts, Tunbridge Wells #1011/R
£500 $795 €725 Mending nets on the shoreline (30x46cm-12x18in) s. W/C. 9-Sep-3 David Duggleby, Scarborough #83/R
£500 $905 €730 Near the Marine Hotel, Whitby (25x15cm-10x6in) s. W/C. 15-Apr-4 Richardson & Smith, Whitby #123/R
£500 $900 €730 Tate Hill Pier, Whitby (26x37cm-10x15in) s. pencil W/C. 21-Apr-4 Tennants, Leyburn #952
£550 $990 €803 The harbour from town station, Whitby (26x36cm-10x14in) s.i. pencil W/C. 21-Apr-4 Tennants, Leyburn #954
£600 $1086 €876 Whitby harbour (31x21cm-12x8in) s. W/C. 30-Mar-4 David Duggleby, Scarborough #16/R
£620 $1147 €905 Cobles in a Yorkshire harbour (20x38cm-8x15in) s. W/C. 13-Feb-4 Keys, Aylsham #465
£650 $1190 €949 Off Whitby (29x40cm-11x16in) s. W/C htd white. 27-Jan-4 Bonhams, Knightsbridge #221/R
£750 $1358 €1095 River estuary view with fisherman by their boats (38x51cm-15x20in) s. W/C. 16-Apr-4 Keys, Aylsham #501/R
£750 $1365 €1095 Unloading the day's catch (17x27cm-7x11in) s. W/C bodycol pair. 1-Jul-4 Christie's, Kensington #308/R
£800 $1336 €1168 Upper Harbour, Whitby (20x30cm-8x12in) s. W/C. 10-Oct-3 Richardson & Smith, Whitby #113/R
£800 $1360 €1168 Figures, horse and cart on a beach, Whitby. Unloading the catch (24x47cm-9x19in) s. pencil W/C pair. 19-Nov-3 Tennants, Leyburn #856
£820 $1484 €1197 Whitby harbour (34x50cm-13x20in) s. W/C. 30-Mar-4 David Duggleby, Scarborough #216/R
£860 $1367 €1247 Fishing boats in Whitby Harbour with abbey beyond (40x60cm-16x24in) s. W/C. 9-Sep-3 David Duggleby, Scarborough #53/R
£900 $1548 €1314 Sorting the catch on Whitby Sands (28x43cm-11x17in) s. W/C. 4-Dec-3 Richardson & Smith, Whitby #418/R
£900 $1629 €1314 Robin Hoods Bay from the cliff top (20x28cm-8x11in) s. W/C. 30-Mar-4 David Duggleby, Scarborough #37/R
£1000 $1670 €1460 Busy day in Whitby Harbour (25x43cm-10x17in) s. W/C. 10-Oct-3 Richardson & Smith, Whitby #98/R est:1000-1500
£1150 $1829 €1668 Fishing boats on the mud banks Whitby Harbour (37x27cm-15x11in) s. W/C. 9-Sep-3 David Duggleby, Scarborough #70 est:1200-1500
£1400 $2226 €2030 Fishing boats in Whitby Harbour (49x29cm-19x11in) s.d.96 W/C. 9-Sep-3 David Duggleby, Scarborough #212/R est:1500-2000
£1500 $2715 €2190 Misty morning in Whitby (25x46cm-10x18in) s. W/C. 15-Apr-4 Richardson & Smith, Whitby #141/R est:1200-1800

ROUSSE, Frank (attrib) (fl.1897-1915) British

Works on paper
£280 $482 €409 Coastal scene with a village nestled in the foreground (20x28cm-8x11in) s. W/C. 5-Dec-3 ELR Auctions, Sheffield #659

ROUSSEAU, Adrien (19th C) French

£2657 $4571 €3800 Paysage au grands arbres (54x65cm-21x26in) s. 7-Dec-3 Osenat, Fontainebleau #243 est:2800-3200

ROUSSEAU, Albert (1908-1982) Canadian

£402 $671 €583 Scene a Quebec (27x21cm-11x8in) s. board. 17-Jun-3 Pinneys, Montreal #171 (C.D 900)
£402 $691 €587 Village Scene (25x40cm-10x16in) s. board. 2-Dec-3 Joyner Waddington, Toronto #532 (C.D 900)
£489 $846 €714 La petite mansarde (20x25cm-8x10in) s. isorel painted c.1960. 15-Dec-3 Iegor de Saint Hippolyte, Montreal #43 (C.D 1100)
£1208 $2211 €1764 Coin, rue Richelieu Quebec (31x61cm-12x24in) s. i.verso. 27-Jan-4 Iegor de Saint Hippolyte, Montreal #29 (C.D 2900)
£1250 $2288 €1825 Charlevoix (46x61cm-18x24in) s. i.verso. 27-Jan-4 Iegor de Saint Hippolyte, Montreal #28 (C.D 3000)
£1250 $2288 €1825 Baie St Paul (61x91cm-24x36in) s. i.verso. 27-Jan-4 Iegor de Saint Hippolyte, Montreal #30 (C.D 3000)
£3665 $5754 €5351 Untitled (91x122cm-36x48in) s. i.verso. 26-Aug-3 Iegor de Saint Hippolyte, Montreal #137 (C.D 8100)

ROUSSEAU, Camille (?) French?

£355 $643 €540 At the park (20x25cm-8x10in) s. board. 14-Apr-4 Ansorena, Madrid #14/R

ROUSSEAU, Charles (1862-1916) Belgian

£2289 $3800 €3342 Stag Hunt (64x91cm-25x36in) s. 4-Oct-3 Neal Auction Company, New Orleans #147/R est:4000-6000

ROUSSEAU, E (19th C) French

Sculpture
£1690 $2924 €2400 Drunk. s. brown pat bronze ivory. 15-Dec-3 Bernaerts, Antwerp #323/R est:2500-2750

ROUSSEAU, Helen (1896-1992) American

£815 $1500 €1190 Saualito Beach (76x102cm-30x40in) s. acrylic board. 27-Jun-4 Bonhams & Butterfields, San Francisco #3835/R est:1900-2750

ROUSSEAU, Henri Emilien (1875-1933) French

£586 $979 €850 Paysage de Provence (23x32cm-9x13in) s.d.28 mars 1933 verso panel. 12-Nov-3 Chassaing Rivet, Toulouse #214
£1745 $3246 €2600 Le Pacha Marocain (15x11cm-6x4in) s. i.verso panel. 2-Mar-4 Artcurial Briest, Paris #114/R est:3000-4000
£2113 $3655 €3000 Assemblee ecclesiastique sous les grandes orgues de la basilique (65x54cm-26x21in) s.d.24. 12-Dec-3 Libert, Castor, Paris #66/R est:2000-3000
£2844 $4750 €4124 Cavalier au manteau rouge (33x24cm-13x9in) s. init.verso panel. 21-Jun-3 Galerie du Rhone, Sion #494/R est:3500-4500 (S.FR 6200)
£4000 $7320 €6000 Caid a cheval. Cavalier au cheval alezan (15x12cm-6x5in) s. cardboard pair. 3-Jun-4 Tajan, Paris #275/R est:6000-8000
£4000 $7320 €6000 Caid a cheval. Porte-drapeau a cheval (20x16cm-8x6in) s. pair. 3-Jun-4 Tajan, Paris #335/R est:6000-8000
£6200 $11284 €9052 Desert meeting (54x74cm-21x29in) s. 16-Jun-4 Bonhams, New Bond Street #90/R est:5000-7000
£9603 $17477 €14500 Cavaliers arabes a la mare (50x65cm-20x26in) s. 18-Jun-4 Piasa, Paris #14/R est:8000-10000
£10000 $16700 €14600 Un convoi dans le sud oranais (61x81cm-24x32in) s.d.24 prov. 14-Oct-3 Sotheby's, London #94/R est:10000-15000
£10347 $18522 €15107 Siegneure Marocain (65x54cm-26x21in) s.d.25. 25-May-4 Bukowskis, Stockholm #376/R est:40000-50000 (S.KR 140000)
£20980 $36085 €30000 Cavaliers au point d'eau (54x73cm-21x29in) s. 8-Dec-3 Tajan, Paris #323/R est:15000-17000
£21277 $35532 €30000 Cavalier de fantasia (73x60cm-29x24in) s. 19-Jun-3 Millon & Associes, Paris #142/R est:15000-20000
£33775 $61808 €51000 Caid et sa suite (65x92cm-26x36in) s.d.1924. 7-Apr-4 Doutrebente, Paris #54/R est:18000-22000
Works on paper
£1000 $1830 €1500 Vieille porte a Sidi-Bou Medine (34x28cm-13x11in) s.i. W/C htd white. 3-Jun-4 Tajan, Paris #336/R est:1000-1500

ROUSSEAU, Henri Julien Felix (1844-1910) French

£9497 $17000 €13866 Marine landscape, the cliff. s.i. panel. 13-May-4 Dallas Auction Gallery, Dallas #310/R est:30000-50000
£17195 $28715 €25105 Le douanier (21x19cm-8x7in) s. panel lit. 24-Jun-3 Germann, Zurich #48/R est:30000-50000 (S.FR 38000)

ROUSSEAU, Jacques de (1600-1638) Dutch

£48951 $84196 €70000 Head of an old man (65x49cm-26x19in) prov.lit. 2-Dec-3 Christie's, Paris #716/R est:10000-15000

ROUSSEAU, Léon (1829-1881) French

Works on paper
£1206 $1953 €1700 Bouquet de lilas (99x80cm-39x31in) pastel. 21-May-3 Daguerre, Paris #24 est:1200-1500

ROUSSEAU, Philippe (1816-1887) French

£2715 $4969 €4100 Voliere de perroquets. Voliere de pigeons (33x24cm-13x9in) mono. panel pair. 7-Apr-4 Libert, Castor, Paris #54/R est:5000-7000
£7351 $13452 €11100 Le repas de chiots (97x130cm-38x51in) s.d.1864. 9-Apr-4 Claude Aguttes, Neuilly #39/R est:10000-12000

ROUSSEAU, Philippe (attrib) (1816-1887) French

£704 $1232 €1000 Nature morte aux pommes, poires et noix (22x27cm-9x11in) 16-Dec-3 Claude Aguttes, Neuilly #112/R

ROUSSEAU, Theodore (1812-1867) French

£393 $715 €574 Last rays of sunshine (14x23cm-6x9in) mono. panel. 16-Jun-4 Fischer, Luzern #2329/R (S.FR 900)
£800 $1440 €1200 Sunset or sunrise (16x28cm-6x11in) mono. panel. 26-Apr-4 Rieber, Stuttgart #1005
£1389 $2500 €2028 Landscape with trees (20x15cm-8x6in) mono. panel. 26-Apr-4 Winter Associates, Plainville #100/R est:3200-3800
£1983 $3549 €2895 Allee de chataigners (6x10cm-2x4in) i.d.1867 i. verso verso panel. 12-May-4 Dobiaschofsky, Bern #921/R est:4500 (S.FR 4600)

£2000 $3660 €2920 Bords de Riviere with a steam train (30x61cm-12x24in) d.1865 panel prov. 8-Jul-4 Duke & Son, Dorchester #228/R est:2000-4000
£2907 $5000 €4244 Landscape at sunset, stormy skies (23x28cm-9x11in) s. panel. 6-Dec-3 Selkirks, St. Louis #649/R est:4000-5000
£3167 $5795 €4750 Sentier en foret (26x45cm-10x18in) peinture a l'essence. 6-Jun-4 Osenat, Fontainebleau #160/R est:7000-8000
£3333 $6033 €5000 Interieur de foret a l'automne (27x24cm-11x9in) s. oil paper on canvas exhib.lit. 30-Mar-4 Rossini, Paris #215/R est:5000-8000
£3636 $6255 €5200 Paturage au bord de l'eau, soleil couchant (32x52cm-13x20in) s. panel painted c.1840 prov.lit. 5-Dec-3 Gros & Delettrez, Paris #52 est:4500-7000
£3867 $7000 €5646 Mountains landscape (64x79cm-25x31in) 16-Apr-4 Du Mouchelle, Detroit #2121/R est:8000-12000
£4348 $7130 €6000 Le petit ruisseau en foret (50x32cm-20x13in) oil paper on canvas painted c.1828-1829. 11-May-3 Osenat, Fontainebleau #133/R est:6500-7000
£4800 $8640 €7008 Sunset (11x21cm-4x8in) panel. 21-Jan-4 Sotheby's, Olympia #400/R est:3000-5000
£5082 $9250 €7623 Landscape with stormy sky (25x18cm-10x7in) s. 16-Jun-4 Wolf's, New York #486702/R est:8000-12000
£5864 $9500 €8503 Lisiere de foret, soleil couchant (15x22cm-6x9in) s. oil paper on panel. 8-Aug-3 Barridorf, Portland #40/R est:5000-7000
£7333 $13273 €11000 Chemin a ornieres dans la lande de Barbizon (24x32cm-9x13in) mono. panel lit. 30-Mar-4 Rossini, Paris #218/R est:4000-7000
£10000 $18400 €15000 Paysage d'Auvergne (20x32cm-8x13in) init. paper painted 1830 lit. 9-Jun-4 Beaussant & Lefèvre, Paris #207/R est:12000
£13333 $24400 €20000 Effet de contre-jour (20x25cm-8x10in) s. panel. 6-Jun-4 Osenat, Fontainebleau #166/R est:20000-22000
£14444 $26000 €21088 Versant de la vallee de Saint-Vincent, Auvergne (23x30cm-9x12in) init. oil paper prov.exhib.lit. 22-Apr-4 Christie's, Rockefeller NY #86/R est:30000-40000
£19333 $34993 €29000 La Salveve et l'Arve pres de Geneve (17x41cm-7x16in) st.mono. panel painted c.1834 exhib.lit. 30-Mar-4 Rossini, Paris #212/R est:8000-12000
£19444 $35000 €28388 Marine (23x34cm-9x13in) oil paper on canvas prov.lit. 23-Apr-4 Sotheby's, New York #1/R est:30000-40000
£22222 $40000 €32444 Porteuse de fagots (42x65cm-17x26in) s. panel painted c.1836-40 prov.lit. 22-Apr-4 Christie's, Rockefeller NY #89/R est:50000-70000
£25333 $45853 €38000 La mare aux fees en foret de Fontainebleau (24x33cm-9x13in) s. peinture paper on canvas exhib.lit. 30-Mar-4 Rossini, Paris #214/R est:6000-10000
£269444 $485000 €393388 Soleil couchant sur les sables du Jean-de-Paris (90x117cm-35x46in) s. prov.lit. 23-Apr-4 Sotheby's, New York #8/R est:300000-400000

Works on paper
£267 $483 €400 Clairiere en foret (20x28cm-8x11in) st.sig. graphite. 3-Apr-4 Gerard, Besancon #9
£533 $965 €800 Pres du Falgoux Rochers a Pic, Cantal (16x25cm-6x10in) st.mono. black crayon. 30-Mar-4 Rossini, Paris #217
£599 $1071 €850 Promenade animee dans la campagne (20x13cm-8x5in) ink pen. 11-Jan-4 Rouillac, Vendome #82
£900 $1665 €1314 Paysage Rocheux (9x15cm-4x6in) studio st. crayon prov. 10-Mar-4 Sotheby's, Olympia #234/R est:1000-1500
£1200 $1920 €1740 Une cathedrale ruinee (19x30cm-7x12in) st.init. pencil prov. 18-Sep-3 Christie's, Kensington #1/R est:800-1200
£1259 $2165 €1800 Le grand chene pres de la mare (13x15cm-5x6in) black pen. 7-Dec-3 Osenat, Fontainebleau #25 est:2000-2500
£1370 $2329 €2000 Vue de Place de la Concorde (8x14cm-3x6in) studio st.i. pen ink crayon double-sided. 6-Nov-3 Tajan, Paris #203/R
£1400 $2562 €2100 Paysage aux arbres (8x15cm-3x6in) mono. ink. 6-Jun-4 Osenat, Fontainebleau #159 est:2000-2200
£1505 $2800 €2197 Gardien de moutons. Landscape (11x29cm-4x11in) black chk double-sided. 2-Mar-4 Swann Galleries, New York #602/R est:3000-5000
£1773 $2961 €2500 Les arbres a Saint Cloud (40x27cm-16x11in) studio st.i. black crayon. 19-Jun-3 Millon & Associes, Paris #3/R est:2500-3000
£2804 $4430 €4066 Hilly landscape with trees, man in boat on lake in foreground (28x44cm-11x17in) st.init. chl pastel. 3-Sep-3 Museumsbygningen, Copenhagen #250/R est:8000-10000 (D.KR 30000)
£3889 $7000 €5678 Extensive landscape with large tree (21x30cm-8x12in) black lead pen brown ink prov.lit. 22-Jan-4 Christie's, Rockefeller NY #139/R est:4000-6000
£5800 $10034 €8468 Les bords de l'etang (17x21cm-7x8in) s. pastel prov. 11-Dec-3 Lyon & Turnbull, Edinburgh #50/R est:1500-2000
£8000 $14480 €12000 Arbres et rochers, paysage en foret de Fontainebleau (43x62cm-17x24in) st.mono. pastel chl panel exhib. 30-Mar-4 Rossini, Paris #216/R est:12000-20000
£22059 $37500 €32206 Allee sous bois (28x42cm-11x17in) st.init. W/C gouache panel prov.lit. 28-Oct-3 Sotheby's, New York #96/R est:10000-15000

ROUSSEAU, Theodore (attrib) (1812-1867) French
£1233 $2097 €1800 Evening landscape (13x24cm-5x9in) mono. panel. 5-Nov-3 Dobiaschofsky, Bern #914/R est:2500 (S.FR 2800)
£12222 $22000 €17844 Paysage forestier (42x65cm-17x26in) s. 22-Apr-4 Christie's, Rockefeller NY #114/R est:15000-20000

ROUSSEAU, Victor (1865-1954) Belgian
Sculpture
£1000 $1830 €1500 L'ecolier (52cm-20in) s.i. pat bronze. 6-Jun-4 Anaf, Lyon #308/R est:300-400
£1200 $2196 €1800 Femme allongee aux jambes repliees (26x27x15cm-10x11x6in) s.d.1939 terracotta. 7-Jun-4 Palais de Beaux Arts, Brussels #292/R est:1000-1500
£1333 $2400 €2000 Two nude women (30cm-12in) s. terracotta. 26-Apr-4 Bernaerts, Antwerp #188/R est:1500-1750
£1565 $2801 €2300 Homme debout tenant une guirlande, l'offrande (30x19x11cm-12x7x4in) s. brown pat bronze bears st.f.Petermann Buxelles. 18-Mar-4 Peschetau-Badin Godeau & Leroy, Paris #63 est:2000-2500
£2667 $4880 €4000 Priere a l'Aurore, couple agenouille (86x70x50cm-34x28x20in) plaster exec. 1942-43. 7-Jun-4 Palais de Beaux Arts, Brussels #290/R est:4000-5000
£2800 $5152 €4200 Dance (36x10x23cm-14x4x9in) s. bronze. 8-Jun-4 Sotheby's, Milan #159/R est:3000-6000
£4196 $7133 €6000 Nu assis (36x38x19cm-14x15x7in) s. st.f.FONrie Nle des Bronzes pat bronze red marble. 1-Dec-3 Palais de Beaux Arts, Brussels #309/R est:5500-7500
£4545 $7591 €6500 Homme nu drape (48cm-19in) s.st.f.Pettermann a Saint Gilles black pat bronze marble socle. 13-Oct-3 Horta, Bruxelles #185/R est:4000-6000
£5556 $8833 €8000 Couple enlace surmontant un coupe (30x31x21cm-12x12x8in) pat bronze marble base Cast J Petermann. 9-Sep-3 Palais de Beaux Arts, Brussels #358/R est:2500-3500
£6733 $12187 €10100 Intimite (59x40x16cm-23x16x6in) s.st.f.Petermann pat bronze. 1-Apr-4 Millon & Associes, Paris #9/R est:10000-15000

ROUSSEAU-DECELLE, René (1881-1964) French
£268 $494 €400 Young girl reading in blooming garden (35x27cm-14x11in) s. panel. 27-Mar-4 Dannenberg, Berlin #619/R

ROUSSEFF, W Vladimir (1890-?) American/Bulgarian
£929 $1700 €1356 Still life (46x61cm-18x24in) s. 5-Jun-4 Treadway Gallery, Cincinnati #688/R est:2000-3000
£1913 $3500 €2793 Picnic, Fish Creek (81x91cm-32x36in) s.d.1933. 5-Jun-4 Treadway Gallery, Cincinnati #686/R est:3000-5000

ROUSSEL, Charles-Emanuel-Joseph (1861-1936) French
£699 $1168 €1000 Soleil couchant sur le village (10x14cm-4x6in) s. panel. 29-Jun-3 Eric Pillon, Calais #39/R
£4085 $7066 €5800 Couple de pecheurs sur la plage (89x116cm-35x46in) s.d.1883. 14-Dec-3 Eric Pillon, Calais #9/R

ROUSSEL, K X (1867-1944) French
£5882 $10000 €8588 Dancing faun and nymph (102x72cm-40x28in) s. board. 1-Dec-3 Koller, Zurich #6558 est:4000-7000 (S.FR 13000)

ROUSSEL, Ker Xavier (1867-1944) French
Works on paper
£245 $391 €340 Buste of female nude (23x30cm-9x12in) sanguine htd white chk blue paper. 16-May-3 Tajan, Paris #217
£280 $496 €409 Paysage avec maison (12x18cm-5x7in) s. pencil. 27-Apr-4 Bonhams, Knightsbridge #130/R
£436 $811 €650 Amour dans les branchages (19x10cm-7x4in) s. lead pencil drawing. 3-Mar-4 Tajan, Paris #42/R
£448 $807 €650 Silene en bleu (16x11cm-6x4in) mono. i.verso pastel. 26-Jan-4 Gros & Delettrez, Paris #20
£1972 $3411 €2800 Paysage (22x34cm-9x13in) s. pastel. 12-Dec-3 Renaud, Paris #106/R est:1500-2000
£3793 $6334 €5500 Bacchanale dans un paysage (55x73cm-22x29in) s. pastel paper on panel. 16-Nov-3 Muizon & Le Coent, Paris #42/R
£9500 $15865 €13870 Infant's bedroom (15x11cm-6x4in) pen ink prov. 22-Oct-3 Sotheby's, Olympia #3/R est:1500-2000

ROUSSEL, Pierre (1927-1995) French
£1049 $1752 €1500 Petit chemin (60x73cm-24x29in) s. 29-Jun-3 Eric Pillon, Calais #228/R
£1049 $1752 €1500 Chemin dans le verger (81x65cm-32x26in) s. 29-Jun-3 Eric Pillon, Calais #223/R
£2168 $3620 €3100 Brodeuse (100x81cm-39x32in) s. 29-Jun-3 Eric Pillon, Calais #222/R
Works on paper
£1536 $2750 €2243 Yvonne dans l'atelier du theatre (79x54cm-31x21in) s. gouache chl pastel pencil card exhib. 6-May-4 Sotheby's, New York #455/R est:3000-5000

ROUSSEL, Theodore (1847-1926) British
Works on paper
£550 $935 €803 Tents and figures, St Leonards-on-Sea (23x34cm-9x13in) init.indis.d.92 i.verso pencil W/C prov. 19-Nov-3 Tennants, Leyburn #862

ROUSSIL, Robert (1925-) Canadian
Sculpture
£2679 $4607 €3911 Dindonnet (62cm-24in) s.i.XX d.61 bronze. 2-Dec-3 Joyner Waddington, Toronto #359/R est:1200-1500 (C.D 6000)

ROUSSOFF, Alexandre Nicolaievitch (1844-1928) Russian
£1591 $2800 €2323 Cathedral (48x33cm-19x13in) s.d.1901. 23-May-4 Hindman, Chicago #52/R est:1200-1800
Works on paper
£539 $1003 €787 Canal scene (46x32cm-18x13in) s. W/C. 2-Mar-4 Rasmussen, Copenhagen #1320/R (D.KR 6000)

ROUSSOFF, Alexandre Nicolaievitch (attrib) (1844-1928) Russian
£1200 $1884 €1740 Bustling Italianate market place (44x29cm-17x11in) indis sig. 28-Aug-3 Christie's, Kensington #240/R est:400-600

ROUVEYRE, Andre (1879-1962) French
Works on paper
£367 $675 €550 Portrait de Robert Montesquiou (9x12cm-4x5in) pen crayon. 9-Jun-4 Piasa, Paris #213
£467 $859 €700 Portrait de Jacqueline Apollinaire (27x20cm-11x8in) s.i. pen exec. c.1938. 9-Jun-4 Piasa, Paris #216

ROUVIER, Pierre (c.1742-?) French
Miniatures
£2800 $5040 €4088 Lady in a blue-grey dress and gauze shawl (6cm-2in circular) i.verso gold frame exhib.lit. 22-Apr-4 Bonhams, New Bond Street #85/R est:1500-2500

ROUVIERE, Daniel (20th C) French
£395 $714 €600 Nature morte aux livres et au faisan (60x73cm-24x29in) s. 19-Apr-4 Boscher, Cherbourg #882

ROUX, Antoine (younger) (1799-1872) French
Works on paper
£1400 $2380 €2044 Beatrice of Dundee in Smyrna Bay (43x58cm-17x23in) i.d.1832 pen ink W/C. 19-Nov-3 Christie's, Kensington #355/R est:1800-2200

ROUX, Antoine de (1901-1986) French
£276 $505 €400 Meuble vert, crayon rouge, crayon noir (81x65cm-32x26in) s. 2-Feb-4 Millon & Associes, Paris #37
£280 $510 €420 Balade a velo (73x60cm-29x24in) s. 5-Jul-4 Millon & Associes, Paris #141
£300 $546 €450 Enfant dessinant (81x65cm-32x26in) 5-Jul-4 Millon & Associes, Paris #149
£310 $568 €450 Le garcon nu (92x73cm-36x29in) s. i.d.1925 verso. 2-Feb-4 Millon & Associes, Paris #19
£310 $568 €450 Statuette Afircaine et chaise noire (81x65cm-32x26in) s.d.1939. 2-Feb-4 Millon & Associes, Paris #38
£310 $568 €450 Composition aux volutes blanches rouges (89x116cm-35x46in) s. 2-Feb-4 Millon & Associes, Paris #94/R
£320 $582 €480 Jeune fille a la poupee (81x65cm-32x26in) 5-Jul-4 Millon & Associes, Paris #151
£345 $631 €500 Nature morte au crayon rouge (73x54cm-29x21in) s. s.i.verso. 2-Feb-4 Millon & Associes, Paris #32
£345 $631 €500 La feuille jaune sur la table (73x92cm-29x36in) s. 2-Feb-4 Millon & Associes, Paris #39
£379 $694 €550 Portrait presume de Soutine (46x38cm-18x15in) 2-Feb-4 Millon & Associes, Paris #3
£379 $694 €550 Fillette a la poupee (73x60cm-29x24in) s. 2-Feb-4 Millon & Associes, Paris #33
£379 $694 €550 L'alerte (162x130cm-64x51in) s.d.1944. 2-Feb-4 Millon & Associes, Paris #52
£414 $757 €600 Portrait presume de Sborowski (81x65cm-32x26in) s. 2-Feb-4 Millon & Associes, Paris #14
£414 $757 €600 Nature morte au papier froisse (116x89cm-46x35in) s. 2-Feb-4 Millon & Associes, Paris #45/R
£448 $820 €650 Le petit garcon ecrivant (116x89cm-46x35in) 2-Feb-4 Millon & Associes, Paris #46
£483 $883 €700 Conversation a velo (55x46cm-22x18in) s. 2-Feb-4 Millon & Associes, Paris #30
£517 $947 €750 Nature morte au pain et au tomates, Ecuyere (50x73cm-20x29in) s. double-sided. 2-Feb-4 Millon & Associes, Paris #31
£552 $1010 €800 Nature morte aux des (60x73cm-24x29in) s. s.i.d.1930 verso. 2-Feb-4 Millon & Associes, Paris #11
£552 $1010 €800 Baton et masque (81x100cm-32x39in) s. 2-Feb-4 Millon & Associes, Paris #22
£552 $1010 €800 Portrait de Jean Daste (81x65cm-32x26in) i.verso. 2-Feb-4 Millon & Associes, Paris #15
£552 $1010 €800 Mere et enfant. 2-Feb-4 Millon & Associes, Paris #50
£600 $1092 €900 Noix (73x60cm-29x24in) s. 5-Jul-4 Millon & Associes, Paris #140
£621 $1136 €900 Nature morte aux des (60x73cm-24x29in) s. s.i.verso. 2-Feb-4 Millon & Associes, Paris #7/R
£621 $1136 €900 L'homme a la fenetre ouverte (89x116cm-35x46in) s. 2-Feb-4 Millon & Associes, Paris #47
£690 $1262 €1000 Nature morte au marteau et a la tenaille (73x60cm-29x24in) s. 2-Feb-4 Millon & Associes, Paris #10
£690 $1262 €1000 La garniture de cheminee (100x81cm-39x32in) s. s.d.1930 verso. 2-Feb-4 Millon & Associes, Paris #12
£690 $1262 €1000 Nature morte a l'antique avec photos (100x81cm-39x32in) 2-Feb-4 Millon & Associes, Paris #21
£690 $1262 €1000 La table aux papiers (90x90cm-35x35in) s. s.d.1931 verso. 2-Feb-4 Millon & Associes, Paris #18
£690 $1262 €1000 Nature morte aux photos et aux gants (124x77cm-49x30in) s. s.d.1931. 2-Feb-4 Millon & Associes, Paris #24
£690 $1262 €1000 Nu allonge (97x130cm-38x51in) 2-Feb-4 Millon & Associes, Paris #25
£690 $1262 €1000 Queue de billard et haut de forme (130x97cm-51x38in) s.i.verso. 2-Feb-4 Millon & Associes, Paris #26
£759 $1388 €1100 Deux jeunes filles, deux velos (81x65cm-32x26in) 2-Feb-4 Millon & Associes, Paris #35/R
£793 $1451 €1150 Nature morte au buvard (60x73cm-24x29in) s. 2-Feb-4 Millon & Associes, Paris #9
£862 $1578 €1250 Conversation a bicyclette (92x73cm-36x29in) s. 2-Feb-4 Millon & Associes, Paris #40
£897 $1641 €1300 Nature morte aux citrons et aux huitres (46x38cm-18x15in) 2-Feb-4 Millon & Associes, Paris #6
£897 $1641 €1300 Les deux clowns (162x130cm-64x51in) s. 2-Feb-4 Millon & Associes, Paris #29
£1034 $1893 €1500 Sport (60x73cm-24x29in) s. s.i.verso. 2-Feb-4 Millon & Associes, Paris #8
£1034 $1893 €1500 Le violon (65x92cm-26x36in) s. s.i.d.1930 verso. 2-Feb-4 Millon & Associes, Paris #17/R
£1034 $1893 €1500 Le mannequin (100x81cm-39x32in) s. s.d.1930 verso. 2-Feb-4 Millon & Associes, Paris #20
£1207 $2209 €1750 Le metro (162x130cm-64x51in) s. 2-Feb-4 Millon & Associes, Paris #53
£1241 $2272 €1800 Le trictrac (81x60cm-32x24in) s. s.i.d.1931 verso. 2-Feb-4 Millon & Associes, Paris #13
£1379 $2524 €2000 Filles a velo et voiture (97x130cm-38x51in) 2-Feb-4 Millon & Associes, Paris #49
£1414 $2587 €2050 La liseuse, trois personnages attables (54x81cm-21x32in) s. i.d.1930 verso double-sided. 2-Feb-4 Millon & Associes, Paris #23
£1414 $2587 €2050 Couple a table dans l'atelier (162x130cm-64x51in) s. 2-Feb-4 Millon & Associes, Paris #28/R
£2069 $3786 €3000 Fleurs et chaise rouge (81x65cm-32x26in) mono. 2-Feb-4 Millon & Associes, Paris #36/R
£2828 $5174 €4100 La table de travail (162x130cm-64x51in) s.d.1930 s.i.d.1931 1932 verso. 2-Feb-4 Millon & Associes, Paris #27/R

ROUX, Carl (1826-1894) German
£280 $504 €420 Mountain landscape (33x48cm-13x19in) 26-Apr-4 Rieber, Stuttgart #1223/R
£872 $1597 €1300 Coming home from haymaking (29x38cm-11x15in) s.d.1880 lit. 8-Jul-4 Allgauer, Kempten #2206/R

ROUX, Constant (1865-1929) French
Sculpture
£1200 $2004 €1752 Achilles child (35cm-14in) s. pat bronze. 15-Oct-3 Christie's, Kensington #650/R
£1900 $3553 €2774 Bust of a Phyrigian (44x38cm-17x15in) s.st.f.Susse bronze green marble plinth. 24-Feb-4 Sotheby's, Olympia #263/R est:2000-3000
£2312 $4000 €3376 Gladiator (67x41x39cm-26x16x15in) with sig. bronze st.f.Susse. 11-Dec-3 Sotheby's, New York #40/R est:4000-6000

ROUX, Constantin le (?-1909) French
£1538 $2569 €2200 Still life of grapes and peaches (46x55cm-18x22in) s. 30-Jun-3 Ansorena, Madrid #368/R est:2200

ROUX, François Geoffroy (1811-1882) French
Works on paper
£2700 $4833 €3942 Francois-Georges reefed down in heavy seas (41x58cm-16x23in) s.i.d.1872 brown ink W/C scratching out. 26-May-4 Christie's, Kensington #388/R est:2000-3000

ROUX, Frederic (1805-1874) French
Works on paper
£2300 $3680 €3358 British paddle steamer St Winifred cruising off Marseilles (44x58cm-17x23in) s.i.d.1824 pen ink W/C htd white. 16-Sep-3 Bonhams, New Bond Street #20/R est:1500-2500
£2500 $4475 €3650 Frigate at anchor in a bay undergoing an extensive refit (20x32cm-8x13in) s.d.1834 pencil blk ink W/C. 26-May-4 Christie's, Kensington #386/R est:2000-3000
£2703 $5000 €3946 Forty-four gun French frigate under reduced sail in the Mediterranean (59x82cm-23x32in) s.d.1832 pencil grey ink W/C board prov. 10-Feb-4 Christie's, Rockefeller NY #145/R est:6000-8000

ROUX, Gaston Louis (1904-1988) French
£367 $656 €550 Le bateau a voiles (33x46cm-13x18in) s.d.28. 15-May-4 Van Ham, Cologne #892

ROUX, Georges (?-1929) French
£1126 $2049 €1700 Les roses de Trianon (40x61cm-16x24in) s. 15-Jun-4 Vanderkindere, Brussels #168/R est:1500-2000

ROUX, Guillermo (1929-) Argentinian
£93443 $171000 €136427 Ball (114x145cm-45x57in) tempera paper. 1-Jun-4 Arroyo, Buenos Aires #65

ROUX, Joseph Ange Antoine (1765-1835) French
Works on paper
£850 $1522 €1241 H M S Trusty of 50 guns (18x23cm-7x9in) 26-May-4 Christie's, Kensington #387/R
£2800 $5012 €4088 French brig riding the swell at the entrance to the port of Cette (21x29cm-8x11in) s.i. pencil blk ink W/C. 26-May-4 Christie's, Kensington #390/R est:3000-5000
£2800 $5012 €4088 French corvette of 22 guns in the Mediterranean (22x29cm-9x11in) s.i. pencil blk ink W/C. 26-May-4 Christie's, Kensington #391/R est:3000-5000
£4828 $8834 €7000 Combat de la corvette Le Decius contre la fregate Anglaise Lapwing (47x65cm-19x26in) s.i.d.1807 W/C. 31-Jan-4 Neret-Minet, Paris #167/R est:7000-8000
£5000 $9100 €7500 Le brick St Jean Baptiste pris par un coup de vent aux Iles d'Hieres (43x58cm-17x23in) s.i.d.1820 W/C. 3-Jul-4 Neret-Minet, Paris #180/R est:7000-8000
£5400 $9828 €8100 Le brick arme l'Amelie, babord amure devant le fort St Jean (42x58cm-17x23in) s.d.1824 W/C. 3-Jul-4 Neret-Minet, Paris #179/R est:8000-9000
£5862 $9790 €8500 Trois mats en rade de Toulon (42x58cm-17x23in) s.d.1811 W/C. 11-Jul-3 Rabourdin & Choppin de Janvry, Paris #18/R est:5800-6800

ROUX, Louis (1817-1903) French
Works on paper
£909 $1518 €1300 Goelette (51x72cm-20x28in) s. W/C gouache. 27-Jun-3 Doutrebente, Paris #45
£1645 $3026 €2500 Les trois mats Svisda Mimubelli (50x71cm-20x28in) s.d.1877 W/C. 24-Jun-4 Claude Boisgirard, Paris #18/R est:3500-4000

ROUX, Morris C E (jnr) (fl.1960s) American
£452 $800 €660 Foggy view of Portland Head Lighthouse (61x91cm-24x36in) painted c.1960. 1-May-4 Thomaston Place, Thomaston #360/R

ROUX, Oswald (1880-1960) Austrian
£483 $883 €700 Horses outside the circus (29x45cm-11x18in) i. panel. 27-Jan-4 Dorotheum, Vienna #140/R
£2083 $3396 €3000 Winter in Lower Alps (59x70cm-23x28in) s. 23-Sep-3 Wiener Kunst Auktionen, Vienna #120/R est:700-1200

ROUX, Vincent (?) French
£872 $1500 €1273 Arlequin (57x44cm-22x17in) init. 2-Dec-3 Christie's, Rockefeller NY #112/R est:1000-1500

ROUX-CHAMPION, Joseph Victor (1871-1953) French
Works on paper
£352 $616 €500 Maison pres de la cote (25x35cm-10x14in) s. W/C. 21-Dec-3 Thierry & Lannon, Brest #72
£458 $801 €650 Barques sur la berge (24x31cm-9x12in) s. W/C. 21-Dec-3 Thierry & Lannon, Brest #242

ROVERE, Giovanni Battista della (1561-c.1630) Italian

Works on paper

£395	$726	€600	Esther and Assuero (18x15cm-7x6in) pen ink W/C double-sided prov. 22-Jun-4 Sotheby's, Milan #33
£1225	$2192	€1800	Resurrection du Christ (14x15cm-6x6in) pen brown ink brown wash htd white gouache. 17-Mar-4 Tajan, Paris #7/R est:2000
£1849	$3144	€2700	Altar (34x24cm-13x9in) pen ink wash. 6-Nov-3 Tajan, Paris #3
£1900	$3477	€2774	Madonna and Child appearing to five Saints (26x20cm-10x8in) pen ink corner cut prov. 6-Jul-4 Christie's, London #23/R est:1200-1600
£3889	$7000	€5678	Marriage of the Virgin (26x20cm-10x8in) i.verso black chk pen brown ink wash. 22-Jan-4 Christie's, Rockefeller NY #30/R est:4000-6000

ROVERO, Giovanni (1885-1971) Italian

£612	$1096	€900	Ski competition in Bardonecchia (24x33cm-9x13in) s. cardboard lit. 22-Mar-4 Sant Agostino, Torino #538/R
£1818	$3036	€2600	Children on the beach (32x43cm-13x17in) s. 26-Jun-3 Sant Agostino, Torino #62/R est:1200

ROVERS, Jos (1893-1976) Dutch

£1974	$3632	€3000	Reclining female nude (99x148cm-39x58in) s. paper. 28-Jun-4 Sotheby's, Amsterdam #230/R est:3000-4000

Works on paper

£308	$524	€450	The three graces (51x61cm-20x24in) s. W/C. 5-Nov-3 Vendue Huis, Gravenhage #312

ROVINSKY, Serge (20th C) ?

£3468	$6000	€5063	Figure panel (248x148cm-98x58in) mono. lacquered wood prov. 11-Dec-3 Sotheby's, New York #61/R est:8000-12000

ROVNER, Michal (1957-) Israeli

Photographs

£2514	$4600	€3670	Overhang no.5 (71x71cm-28x28in) c-print five panel. 5-Jun-4 Susanin's, Chicago #5095/R est:3000-5000
£3955	$7000	€5774	One person against nature II (77x125cm-30x49in) num.3/7 color coupler print prov.lit. 27-Apr-4 Christie's, Rockefeller NY #366/R est:7000-9000
£4098	$7500	€5983	Overhanging no.4 (94x94cm-37x37in) c-print triptych. 5-Jun-4 Susanin's, Chicago #5096/R est:4000-6000
£4237	$7500	€6186	One person against nature I (78x72cm-31x28in) s.i.d.1992 num.6/7 color coupler print. 27-Apr-4 Christie's, Rockefeller NY #367/R est:6000-8000
£4396	$8000	€6418	Outside no.2 (101x76cm-40x30in) s. col coupler print. 29-Jun-4 Sotheby's, New York #630/R est:8000-12000
£4469	$8000	€6525	Co-existence II D3 (56x75cm-22x30in) cibachrome print exec 2000 edn 2/3 prov. 13-May-4 Sotheby's, New York #338/R est:8000-10000
£5307	$9500	€7748	Outside no 13 (101x76cm-40x30in) col coupler print edition 10 of 10. 18-Mar-4 Sotheby's, New York #83/R est:8000-12000
£5367	$9500	€7836	Red Mountain, 1997 (116x116cm-46x46in) s.i.d.1997 verso color coupler print prov. 27-Apr-4 Christie's, Rockefeller NY #369/R est:7000-9000
£6215	$11000	€9074	Merging P no.1, 1997 (108x105cm-43x41in) s.i.d.1997 num.6/7 verso color coupler print prov.lit. 27-Apr-4 Christie's, Rockefeller NY #368/R est:6000-8000

Prints

£8939	$16000	€13051	Mutual interest no 1 (122x236cm-48x93in) chromogenic col print Fujiflex exhib. 18-Mar-4 Sotheby's, New York #84/R est:15000-20000

ROWAN, Marian Ellis (1848-1922) Australian

Works on paper

£255	$457	€372	Penstemon digitalis (54x38cm-21x15in) gouache olive green paper. 28-May-4 Lawson Menzies, Sydney #2143 (A.D 650)
£275	$491	€402	Yellow oleander (50x35cm-20x14in) s. gouache light green paper. 28-May-4 Lawson Menzies, Sydney #2132 (A.D 700)
£314	$562	€458	Clematis (54x38cm-21x15in) s. gouache green paper. 28-May-4 Lawson Menzies, Sydney #2133 (A.D 800)
£314	$562	€458	Morning Glory (54x38cm-21x15in) s. gouache. 28-May-4 Lawson Menzies, Sydney #2153 (A.D 800)
£791	$1415	€1187	Flowering gum and moth (52x37cm-20x15in) s. W/C gouache. 17-May-4 Sotheby's, Melbourne #580 (A.D 2000)
£813	$1455	€1187	Flowers and berries (54x65cm-21x26in) s. W/C htd white. 10-May-4 Joel, Victoria #387/R est:2000-3000 (A.D 2000)
£826	$1529	€1206	Flowers (53x37cm-21x15in) s. gouache. 10-Mar-4 Deutscher-Menzies, Melbourne #533/R est:1500-2300 (A.D 2000)
£894	$1601	€1305	Rock orchids (53x36cm-21x14in) s.d.1894 W/C gouache card. 4-May-4 Sotheby's, Melbourne #130/R (A.D 2200)
£909	$1682	€1327	Mushroom and toadstools (26x36cm-10x14in) s. gouache W/C. 10-Mar-4 Deutscher-Menzies, Melbourne #282/R est:1500-2000 (A.D 2200)

ROWBOTHAM, Charles (1856-1921) British

£400	$636	€584	Italian lake scene with female figures and boats in the foreground (12x18cm-5x7in) s. 18-Mar-3 Anderson & Garland, Newcastle #355
£1600	$2544	€2336	Monte Carlo (44x27cm-17x11in) s. 18-Mar-3 Anderson & Garland, Newcastle #356/R est:700-1100
£1800	$2862	€2628	Bay of Naples. Bay of Spezzia (15x22cm-6x9in) s.d.1907 pair. 18-Mar-3 Anderson & Garland, Newcastle #357/R est:900-1300

Works on paper

£280	$476	€409	On the Arun, at Loxwood, Sussex (16x30cm-6x12in) s. i.mount pencil W/C. 19-Nov-3 Tennants, Leyburn #987a
£320	$534	€467	Figure resting on a coastal path, with boats sailing in the bay (16x30cm-6x12in) s. pencil W/C. 8-Oct-3 Christie's, Kensington #1096
£380	$692	€555	Figures beside an Italian lake (18x46cm-7x18in) s.d.1880 W/C. 5-Feb-4 Gorringes, Worthing #459
£400	$728	€584	Lake Lugano (27x18cm-11x7in) s. W/C. 15-Jun-4 Rosebery Fine Art, London #457/R
£450	$810	€657	Beilstein on the Mosel (13x19cm-5x7in) s. W/C. 21-Jan-4 Sotheby's, Olympia #204/R
£560	$1019	€818	Brando, Corsica. s. W/C bodycol. 3-Feb-4 Sworder & Son, Bishops Stortford #248/R
£650	$1105	€949	Two women seated beside a barge on a lake with a town and mountains beyond (13x18cm-5x7in) s. W/C bodycol. 30-Oct-3 Duke & Son, Dorchester #71/R
£850	$1556	€1241	Bay of Naples. Lake Constance (12x23cm-5x9in) s. W/C pair. 28-Jan-4 Hampton & Littlewood, Exeter #381/R
£850	$1573	€1241	Near Amalfi (20x48cm-8x19in) s. W/C. 9-Mar-4 Gorringes, Lewes #2023
£850	$1522	€1241	Distant view of Messina Harbour and Mount Etna (20x51cm-8x20in) s.d.1895 W/C htd white. 7-May-4 Mallams, Oxford #203/R
£880	$1390	€1285	At Varenna, lake Como (22x50cm-9x20in) s. W/C bodycol. 23-Jul-3 Hampton & Littlewood, Exeter #417/R
£900	$1638	€1314	Harbour scene with children in the foreground (15x30cm-6x12in) s. W/C. 16-Jun-4 Andrew Hartley, Ilkley #1004
£1000	$1800	€1460	Italian views (12x19cm-5x7in) s. W/C three. 21-Jan-4 Sotheby's, Olympia #203/R est:1000-1500
£1100	$1837	€1606	Bay of Naples, with children picnicking on the banks (22x49cm-9x19in) s. W/C. 22-Oct-3 Cheffins, Cambridge #472/R est:800-1000
£1180	$2148	€1723	Day of Sorrento. At Vevey, Switzerland (21x17cm-8x7in) s.d.1908 W/C pair. 29-Jun-4 Anderson & Garland, Newcastle #252 est:500-800
£1200	$2208	€1752	Amalfi. Cannes (11x14cm-4x6in) s.i.d.1884 W/C bodycol pair. 23-Mar-4 Bonhams, Knightsbridge #160/R est:1200-1800
£1200	$2184	€1752	Mothers with their children. Idle gossip on the edge of Italian lake (15x27cm-6x11in) s. W/C bodycol pair prov. 1-Jul-4 Christie's, Kensington #395/R est:800-1200
£1300	$2041	€1885	Quayside market, Italy. Coastal road, Southern Italy (19x15cm-7x6in) s.d.1900 pencil W/C pair. 28-Aug-3 Christie's, Kensington #403/R est:800-1200
£1300	$2210	€1898	Thun and the Bernese Alps (13x18cm-5x7in) s.d.1908 W/C bodycol. 30-Oct-3 Duke & Son, Dorchester #70/R est:600-1200
£1350	$2336	€1971	Italian coastal views with figures conversing and gathering flowers (23x29cm-9x11in) s. W/C pair. 9-Dec-3 Anderson & Garland, Newcastle #339 est:500-800
£1500	$2505	€2190	Views over the Italian lakes (45x27cm-18x11in) s. W/C htd bodycol pair. 14-Oct-3 Bonhams, Knightsbridge #160/R est:1200-1800
£1500	$2760	€2190	Figures on a hillside overlooking the Bay of Naples (19x47cm-7x19in) s.d.1894 W/C. 23-Mar-4 Anderson & Garland, Newcastle #313/R est:480-620
£1800	$3006	€2628	View across lake Maggiore, Italy. View beside lake Lugano (20x49cm-8x19in) s. W/C pair. 22-Oct-3 Cheffins, Cambridge #473 est:1500-2000
£1900	$3496	€2774	Figures and boats on the shore of an Italian lake (19x47cm-7x19in) s. W/C. 23-Mar-4 Anderson & Garland, Newcastle #312/R est:480-620
£2800	$4648	€4088	Italian lake scene with town and figures. River scene with boats (20x49cm-8x19in) s.d.1886 W/C htd bodycol pair. 1-Oct-3 George Kidner, Lymington #160/R est:1500-2000

ROWBOTHAM, Charles (attrib) (1856-1921) British

Works on paper

£950	$1672	€1387	Italian lake scene (32x45cm-13x18in) W/C. 18-May-4 Woolley & Wallis, Salisbury #287/R

ROWBOTHAM, Claude (1864-1949) British

Works on paper

£520	$962	€759	Temple Island, near Henley (19x48cm-7x19in) s.d.1901 W/C. 17-Jul-4 Bonhams, Knightsbridge #184/R
£750	$1373	€1095	Views across the Italian lakes (10x17cm-4x7in) s.d.1890 W/C bodycol set of three. 27-Jan-4 Bonhams, Knightsbridge #370/R

ROWBOTHAM, Thomas Charles Leeson (1823-1875) British

£750	$1373	€1095	Figures in a cart in a mountainous landscape (18x46cm-7x18in) s.d.1862. 7-Apr-4 Gardiner & Houlgate, Bath #103/R

Works on paper

£260	$478	€380	Crossing the bridge (17x42cm-7x17in) s.d.1860 W/C. 23-Mar-4 Bonhams, Knightsbridge #249
£290	$467	€423	Lake Como (19x46cm-7x18in) s.d.1871 W/C. 12-Aug-3 Peter Webb, Auckland #46/R (NZ.D 800)
£300	$510	€438	Windmill near Peckham (12x16cm-5x6in) init.d.1845 prov. 4-Nov-3 Rowley Fine Art, Newmarket #370
£350	$644	€511	Cattle watering before a ruined castle (23x33cm-9x13in) s.d.1854 pencil W/C. 25-Mar-4 Christie's, Kensington #43
£400	$736	€584	View of a Mediterranean town (17x41cm-7x16in) s.d.1879 W/C. 23-Mar-4 Bonhams, Knightsbridge #30/R
£450	$832	€657	Highlanders on a mountain pass (22x34cm-9x13in) s.d.1866 W/C. 10-Mar-4 Sotheby's, Olympia #137/R
£451	$736	€650	Fortress on the Rhine (21x31cm-8x12in) s. W/C. 26-Sep-3 Venator & Hansten, Koln #918/R
£490	$832	€700	Old fortress on the Rhine (21x30cm-8x12in) mono. W/C board. 20-Nov-3 Van Ham, Cologne #1827
£700	$1253	€1022	Figures crossing an Alpine ravine (33x23cm-13x9in) s.d.1856 W/C. 17-Mar-4 Bonhams, Chester #287
£1150	$2059	€1679	Eel bucks on the Thames (24x37cm-9x15in) s.d.1872 W/C. 17-Mar-4 Bonhams, Chester #286 est:800-1200
£3000	$5550	€4380	Rouen from St Catherine's Hill, France (70x108cm-28x43in) s.d.1849 W/C exhib. 9-Mar-4 Bonhams, New Bond Street #49/R est:4000-6000

ROWBOTHAM, Thomas Charles Leeson (attrib) (1823-1875) British

Works on paper

£259	$463	€378	Scottish landscape with lake (24x35cm-9x14in) W/C htd white. 13-May-4 Stuker, Bern #9196 (S.FR 600)

ROWBOTHAM, Thomas Leeson (snr) (1783-1853) British

Works on paper

£300	$489	€438	Italian coastal view with figures on a terrace in the foreground (52x72cm-20x28in) s. W/C. 23-Sep-3 Anderson & Garland, Newcastle #282/R

ROWDEN, Thomas (1842-1926) British

£480	$864	€701	Exmoor ponies (40x61cm-16x24in) s. 20-Apr-4 Bonhams, Leeds #330

Works on paper

£246	$423	€359	Cattle resting near cliff's edge (20x39cm-8x15in) s. W/C. 2-Dec-3 Ritchie, Toronto #31/R (C.D 550)
£300	$546	€438	Cattle and sheep by a river (20x38cm-8x15in) s. W/C. 15-Jun-4 David Lay, Penzance #554

£340 $622 €496 Sheep grazing beside a tor (28x36cm-11x14in) s. W/C bodycol. 8-Jul-4 Duke & Son, Dorchester #42
£380 $597 €555 Cattle on the Devon coast (16x36cm-6x14in) s. W/C. 16-Apr-3 Bamfords, Derby #597/R
£410 $644 €599 Moorland ponies and sheep grazing (17x48cm-7x19in) s. W/C. 16-Apr-3 Bamfords, Derby #598/R
£440 $801 €642 River Ockment and Belstone Tor - with cattle watering (20x35cm-8x14in) s. W/C. 21-Jun-4 Bonhams, Bath #396/R
£480 $869 €701 Dartmoor ponies in a landscape (18x33cm-7x13in) s. W/C htd white. 2-Apr-4 Moore Allen & Innocent, Cirencester #750/R
£500 $835 €730 Dartmoor ponies (18x48cm-7x19in) W/C. 15-Oct-3 Brightwells, Leominster #876
£500 $860 €730 Extensive moor landscape with cattle grazing and watering in foreground (43x69cm-17x27in) s. W/C. 5-Dec-3 Keys, Aylsham #444/R
£500 $900 €730 Highland cattle by stream (18x46cm-7x18in) s. W/C htd white. 23-Jan-4 British Auctioneer #505/R
£540 $902 €788 Ponies and sheep (23x48cm-9x19in) s. W/C. 17-Oct-3 Keys, Aylsham #494
£600 $1002 €876 Cattle in highland landscape (22x37cm-9x15in) s.d.96 W/C two. 14-Oct-3 Bonhams, Knightsbridge #75/R
£600 $1002 €876 Devonshire cornfield (49x75cm-19x30in) s.d.1886 W/C. 14-Oct-3 Bearnes, Exeter #317/R
£620 $1122 €905 On Dartmoor, Dartmoor ponies in a moorland landscape (18x48cm-7x19in) s.d.1898 i.verso W/C. 16-Apr-4 Honiton Galleries, Honiton #630/R
£700 $1295 €1022 Corpach, near Ben Nevis, Argyleshire. Dart near Postbridge, Dartmoor, Devon (20x37cm-8x15in) s. W/C htd bodycol prov. 14-Jan-4 Lawrence, Crewkerne #1333/R est:500-800
£750 $1403 €1095 Coastal scene with cattle grazing. Dartmoor ponies beside a stream (23x47cm-9x19in) s. pencil W/C pair. 22-Jul-4 Tennants, Leyburn #743
£1000 $1760 €1460 Brampfords Pike, Devon (29x52cm-11x20in) s.d.1900 W/C. 19-May-4 Dreweatt Neate, Newbury #102/R est:600-800

ROWE, E A (1863-1922) British
Works on paper
£1500 $2730 €2190 Rumwood Court, Maidstone (25x36cm-10x14in) s. W/C. 16-Jun-4 Brightwells, Leominster #859/R est:200-300

ROWE, E Arthur (1863-1922) British
Works on paper
£520 $962 €759 Evening in the garden of the Villa Carlotta (18x13cm-7x5in) s. i.verso W/C. 10-Feb-4 David Lay, Penzance #89
£520 $957 €759 View from the villa Vrandini (17x25cm-7x10in) s. W/C. 23-Mar-4 Rosebery Fine Art, London #985

ROWE, George (1796-1864) British
Works on paper
£6870 $12504 €10030 End of the rainbow, golden square, Bendigo (31x57cm-12x22in) s. W/C prov. 16-Jun-4 Deutscher-Menzies, Melbourne #118/R est:20000-25000 (A.D 18000)

ROWE, Hooper (20th C) British
Works on paper
£360 $572 €526 BP Ethyl, controls horsepower (67x95cm-26x37in) s. gouache collage. 10-Sep-3 Sotheby's, Olympia #64/R

ROWE, Nellie Mae (1900-1982) American
£4167 $7500 €6084 Black poodle, groomed for kissing (58x74cm-23x29in) prov. 24-Apr-4 Slotin Folk Art, Buford #317/R est:5000-8000
Works on paper
£250 $450 €365 Seated child (28x23cm-11x9in) s.verso col pencil ink. 24-Apr-4 Slotin Folk Art, Buford #319/R
£539 $900 €787 Woman in a plant (46x30cm-18x12in) col pencil. 15-Nov-3 Slotin Folk Art, Buford #139/R
£539 $900 €787 Woman with bird (28x20cm-11x8in) mixed media. 15-Nov-3 Slotin Folk Art, Buford #141/R
£1317 $2200 €1923 Woman with dog (46x23cm-18x9in) mixed media paperboard. 15-Nov-3 Slotin Folk Art, Buford #137/R est:1000-1500
£4000 $7200 €5840 Yellow girl with green pig (38x51cm-15x20in) crayon executed c.1981. 24-Apr-4 Slotin Folk Art, Buford #318/R est:4000-6000
£6287 $10500 €9179 Purple dog (53x61cm-21x24in) crayon prov. 15-Nov-3 Slotin Folk Art, Buford #138/R est:5000-8000

ROWELL, John Thomas (1894-1973) Australian
£335 $609 €489 Queensland beach scene. board. 5-Feb-4 Joel, Victoria #130 (A.D 800)
£780 $1443 €1139 Summer morning, Mornington, Australia (43x58cm-17x23in) s. 11-Mar-4 Duke & Son, Dorchester #155/R
£1012 $1630 €1478 At Mornington (19x29cm-7x11in) s. board painted c.1935. 13-Oct-3 Joel, Victoria #269/R est:1500-2000 (A.D 2500)

ROWELL, Kenneth (1920-) Australian
Works on paper
£372 $632 €558 Costume designs (41x29cm-16x11in) W/C pencil. 28-Oct-3 Goodman, Sydney #298/R (A.D 900)
£661 $1223 €965 Dark domain (113x126cm-44x50in) s. synthetic polymer prov. 15-Mar-4 Sotheby's, Melbourne #212 est:700-900 (A.D 1600)
£826 $1529 €1206 Prospecting (113x126cm-44x50in) s. synthetic polymer prov. 15-Mar-4 Sotheby's, Melbourne #213 est:700-900 (A.D 2000)

ROWLANDSON, George Derville (1861-1928) British
£260 $481 €380 Over the Pass (30x22cm-12x9in) s. card. 18-Jul-4 Lots Road Auctions, London #344/R
£1500 $2700 €2190 Flower garden at Snelston Hall (49x45cm-19x18in) s. prov. 22-Apr-4 Mellors & Kirk, Nottingham #1146/R est:1500-2000
£2557 $4500 €3733 Surprised (61x86cm-24x34in) s.d.1910. 18-May-4 Bonhams & Butterfields, San Francisco #165/R est:4000-6000
£2793 $5000 €4078 Gentleman taking a fence (51x76cm-20x30in) s. prov. 27-May-4 Sotheby's, New York #290/R est:8000-12000
£2793 $5000 €4078 Pytchley hunt (51x76cm-20x30in) s. 27-May-4 Sotheby's, New York #289/R est:8000-12000
£4100 $6396 €5986 Unwelcome intruders (43x53cm-17x21in) s. painted c.1890. 20-Oct-2 Desmond Judd, Cranbrook #855
£7558 $13000 €11035 Old old story. Admiration and courtship (61x46cm-24x18in) s. one i. pair prov. 5-Dec-3 Christie's, Rockefeller NY #59/R est:10000-15000
Works on paper
£380 $612 €551 Refusing at the brook (25x36cm-10x14in) s. W/C. 13-Aug-3 Andrew Hartley, Ilkley #729/R
£2000 $3580 €3000 Riders jumping (25x36cm-10x14in) s. W/C set of 4. 13-May-4 Babuino, Rome #228/R est:800-1200
£2933 $5251 €4400 Riders jumping (25x36cm-10x14in) s. W/C set of 6. 13-May-4 Babuino, Rome #227/R est:1500-2000
£4000 $6800 €5840 Sporting scenes (11x15cm-4x6in) init.i. pen ink W/C set of twelve. 27-Nov-3 Christie's, Kensington #200/R est:4000-6000

ROWLANDSON, Thomas (1756-1827) British
Works on paper
£250 $450 €365 Gentleman bowing to a couple (12x14cm-5x6in) pen brown ink W/C over pencil. 21-Jan-4 Sotheby's, Olympia #109/R
£299 $500 €437 Figures along the beach (15x23cm-6x9in) s. ink wash. 16-Nov-3 William Jenack, New York #314
£360 $583 €522 Triumph of Galatea (14x19cm-6x7in) pen ink W/C. 30-Jul-3 Hamptons Fine Art, Godalming #133
£500 $900 €730 Seated man, rocking on his chair (15x12cm-6x5in) pen grey ink. 20-Apr-4 Sotheby's, Olympia #203/R
£500 $910 €730 Studies of male heads (22x17cm-9x7in) pencil brown ink prov. 1-Jul-4 Christie's, Kensington #42
£550 $1001 €803 The new arrival (10x17cm-4x7in) pencil brown ink prov. 1-Jul-4 Christie's, Kensington #40/R
£599 $1000 €875 English village scene (33x48cm-13x19in) s. W/C. 16-Nov-3 Simpson's, Houston #160
£600 $1098 €876 Devonshire landscape with ox team in the foreground (18x46cm-7x18in) i. pencil pen ink W/C. 7-Apr-4 Gardiner & Houlgate, Bath #125/R
£600 $1092 €876 Winter frolics (13x20cm-5x8in) W/C brown ink. 1-Jul-4 Christie's, Kensington #35/R
£600 $1092 €876 The three graces (18x14cm-7x6in) pencil brown ink W/C prov. 1-Jul-4 Christie's, Kensington #39/R
£650 $1190 €949 Reclining female nude (11x20cm-4x8in) s. pen ink. 27-Jan-4 Bonhams, Knightsbridge #20/R
£650 $1196 €949 Sailors clinging to a mast (28x22cm-11x9in) pen ink W/C. 23-Mar-4 Bonhams, Knightsbridge #179/R
£650 $1196 €949 Infantry officer with his soldier servant (15x11cm-6x4in) i.verso pencil W/C prov. 25-Mar-4 Christie's, Kensington #6/R
£720 $1318 €1051 Figures preparing for embarkation (10x18cm-4x7in) pencil pen ink W/C. 7-Apr-4 Gardiner & Houlgate, Bath #158/R
£800 $1288 €1160 Reclining female nude (13x20cm-5x8in) s. pen ink wash. 15-Aug-3 Keys, Aylsham #543/R
£800 $1456 €1168 Attacking the night watchman (19x15cm-7x6in) black ink W/C prov. 1-Jul-4 Christie's, Kensington #37/R
£800 $1456 €1168 A picnic at the roadside (23x23cm-9x9in) s. pencil brown ink W/C prov. 1-Jul-4 Christie's, Kensington #45
£820 $1476 €1197 Figures laughing (13x17cm-5x7in) pen brown ink W/C over pencil. 21-Jan-4 Sotheby's, Olympia #107/R
£900 $1647 €1314 Corfe Castle, Dorsetshire (13x20cm-5x8in) i. W/C pen ink. 8-Jul-4 Duke & Son, Dorchester #98/R
£1000 $1720 €1460 Manorbeer Castle, Pembroke (13x22cm-5x9in) s.d.1820 pencil grey ink W/C. 3-Dec-3 Christie's, Kensington #15/R est:1200-1800
£1100 $2002 €1606 Perpetual laughter (22x18cm-9x7in) i.verso pencil brown ink prov. 1-Jul-4 Christie's, Kensington #41/R est:700-1000
£1100 $2002 €1606 A town bred bratt (17x14cm-7x6in) s.i.d.1802 pencil brown ink W/C prov. 1-Jul-4 Christie's, Kensington #43/R est:1000-1500
£1150 $2070 €1679 Figure watering his cart horses in a stream (21x30cm-8x12in) pen brown ink W/C over pencil. 21-Jan-4 Sotheby's, Olympia #113/R est:1000-1500
£1300 $2210 €1898 Alchemy of Love (12x14cm-5x6in) pencil pen grey ink W/C. 20-Nov-3 Christie's, London #33/R est:1000-1500
£1300 $2366 €1898 The massacre (15x23cm-6x9in) brown ink W/C prov. 1-Jul-4 Christie's, Kensington #36/R est:1000-1500
£1400 $2562 €2044 How to pass a carriage (9x15cm-4x6in) with sig. i. pencil grey ink W/C prov. 3-Jun-4 Christie's, London #83/R est:700-1000
£1400 $2548 €2044 Captain Barclay's Rally Match - the start (15x24cm-6x9in) pen brown ink W/C over pencil. 1-Jul-4 Sotheby's, London #191/R est:1500-2000
£1400 $2548 €2044 Harvesters merrymaking (24x37cm-9x15in) s. pencil brown ink W/C. 1-Jul-4 Christie's, Kensington #34/R est:800-1200
£1420 $2500 €2073 Beggar makers (14x23cm-6x9in) s.i. pen ink W/C prov. 18-May-4 Sotheby's, New York #123/R est:2500-3500
£1450 $2306 €2117 Game of billiards (24x27cm-9x11in) s. indis.i. pen grey ink colour wash. 18-Mar-3 Anderson & Garland, Newcastle #387/R est:1500-2500
£1500 $2805 €2190 Doctor Syntax in a Court of Justice (12x19cm-5x7in) pen ink W/C. 24-Feb-4 Rowley Fine Art, Newmarket #417/R est:1000-1500
£1500 $2686 €2250 Refreshments for ladies (28x22cm-11x9in) s. pen ink W/C pencil exec.c.1790. 27-May-4 Bloomsbury, London #105/R est:1500-2000
£1500 $2686 €2250 Irate visitor, caricature of a gentleman (26x21cm-10x8in) s. pen ink W/C pencil exec.c.1790. 27-May-4 Bloomsbury, London #107/R est:1500-2000
£1600 $2928 €2336 Tumbling huntsmen (13x20cm-5x8in) pencil grey ink W/C prov. 3-Jun-4 Christie's, London #84/R est:800-1200
£1639 $3000 €2393 Soldiers sword fighting on horseback with battle in background (17x25cm-7x10in) W/C pair. 10-Jul-4 Auctions by the Bay, Alameda #430/R
£1700 $3111 €2482 Dr Syntax at a country inn (14x23cm-6x9in) pencil red ink W/C prov. 3-Jun-4 Christie's, London #89/R est:2000-3000
£1700 $3043 €2482 Picture of Misery (28x20cm-11x8in) pen ink W/C. 26-May-4 Mallams, Oxford #306/R est:700-900
£1800 $2862 €2628 Gallant Soldier (17x13cm-7x5in) pen brown ink colour wash. 18-Mar-3 Anderson & Garland, Newcastle #388 est:1000-1800
£1800 $3366 €2628 Doctor Syntax being pursued (12x21cm-5x8in) pen ink W/C. 24-Feb-4 Rowley Fine Art, Newmarket #418/R est:800-1200
£1800 $3294 €2628 Mother and child (13x20cm-5x8in) pencil grey ink grey pink wash prov. 3-Jun-4 Christie's, London #82/R est:2000-3000
£1800 $3294 €2628 Dr Syntax on a blustery day (13x20cm-5x8in) with sig. pencil brown ink W/C prov. 3-Jun-4 Christie's, London #90/R est:1200-1800
£1800 $3276 €2628 Travelling players (27x21cm-11x8in) pen brown grey ink W/C over pencil. 1-Jul-4 Sotheby's, London #184/R est:2000-3000
£1800 $3276 €2628 Study in life drawing (14x23cm-6x9in) i. pen brown ink W/C over pencil. 1-Jul-4 Sotheby's, London #192/R est:1500-2000

£1800	$3276	€2628	Nymphs bathing (18x25cm-7x10in) pen brown ink W/C over pencil. 1-Jul-4 Sotheby's, London #193/R est:2000-3000
£1900	$3230	€2774	In the garden at Ham House (21x29cm-8x11in) with sig.d.1808 pencil pen ink W/C. 20-Nov-3 Christie's, London #16/R est:2000-3000
£2000	$3700	€2920	Ploughing in a river landscape (20x53cm-8x21in) pen ink W/C. 9-Mar-4 Bonhams, New Bond Street #24/R est:2000-3000
£2200	$4070	€3212	The duel (13x23cm-5x9in) s. pen ink W/C. 9-Mar-4 Bonhams, New Bond Street #25/R est:1500-2000
£2200	$4048	€3212	Farrier's yard (15x24cm-6x9in) pen ink W/C over pencil. 26-Mar-4 Sotheby's, London #99/R est:1500-2000
£2200	$4026	€3212	Doctor's visit (16x12cm-6x5in) with sig. i. pencil red ink W/C prov. 3-Jun-4 Christie's, London #87/R est:1000-1500
£2200	$4026	€3212	High street in a country town (14x22cm-6x9in) pencil grey ink W/C prov. 3-Jun-4 Christie's, London #91/R est:1500-2000
£2200	$3938	€3212	Playing in parts (10x17cm-4x7in) pen ink W/C. 26-May-4 Sotheby's, Olympia #42/R est:1200-1800
£2400	$4392	€3504	View of cottage and barnyard (22x38cm-9x15in) with sig. i.verso pencil pen ink W/C. 3-Jun-4 Christie's, London #95/R est:2000-3000
£2400	$4392	€3504	Crab hunting for prawns (27x21cm-11x8in) i. grey ink W/C prov. 3-Jun-4 Christie's, London #98/R est:1500-2000
£3000	$5490	€4380	Ladies of easy virtue mounting a wagon outside an inn (15x24cm-6x9in) pencil grey red ink W/C prov. 3-Jun-4 Christie's, London #86/R est:3000-5000
£3000	$5490	€4380	Prize fighters (29x23cm-11x9in) with i.d.1806 pencil red brown ink W/C prov.lit. 3-Jun-4 Christie's, London #88/R est:1500-2000
£3500	$6405	€5110	Britannia's support or the conspirators defeated (21x28cm-8x11in) i. pencil grey brown ink grey wash prov.lit. 3-Jun-4 Christie's, London #93/R est:2000-3000
£3500	$6370	€5110	Kiss in the kitchen (27x21cm-11x8in) pen brown ink W/C over pencil. 1-Jul-4 Sotheby's, London #185/R est:3000-4000
£3600	$6120	€5256	Barber's shop (18x26cm-7x10in) pen ink W/C over pencil. 27-Nov-3 Sotheby's, London #244/R est:2000-3000
£3600	$6120	€5256	Brown Willy Rocks, Bodmin Moor (29x47cm-11x19in) i. pen ink W/C over pencil. 27-Nov-3 Sotheby's, London #250/R est:2000-3000
£3600	$6588	€5256	Barracks, an officer being dressed (13x20cm-5x8in) i. pencil brown ink W/C prov. 3-Jun-4 Christie's, London #81/R est:4000-6000
£3800	$6954	€5548	Portrait of Doctor Guise (29x23cm-11x9in) i. grey red ink W/C prov. 3-Jun-4 Christie's, London #97/R est:1500-2000
£4000	$6800	€5840	Travellers landing on the coast of Holland (25x41cm-10x16in) s. pen ink W/C over pencil. 27-Nov-3 Sotheby's, London #263/R est:4000-6000
£4500	$8235	€6570	River ferry on the Thames (14x23cm-6x9in) pencil grey ink W/C prov. 3-Jun-4 Christie's, London #85/R est:3000-5000
£4500	$8235	€6570	Quarterly Duns of Clamorous Tax-gatherers (31x24cm-12x9in) i.d.1805 pencil brown ink W/C. 3-Jun-4 Christie's, London #96/R est:2000-3000
£4500	$8190	€6570	Fall in beer (37x23cm-15x9in) pen brown ink W/C over pencil prov lit. 1-Jul-4 Sotheby's, London #186/R est:5000-7000
£4500	$8190	€6570	Elegant company on Blackfriars Bridge (14x23cm-6x9in) pen grey in, W/C over pencil. 1-Jul-4 Sotheby's, London #190/R est:3000-4000
£6200	$11284	€9052	Doctor's consultation (28x22cm-11x9in) pen brown ink W/C over pencil. 1-Jul-4 Sotheby's, London #183/R est:3000-5000
£7000	$12740	€10220	View on the Thames with numerous ships and figures on the wharf (27x43cm-11x17in) s. pen brown ink W/C over pencil. 1-Jul-4 Sotheby's, London #188/R est:7000-9000
£8800	$16016	€12848	Strong waters at Bath (24x38cm-9x15in) pen brown grey ink W/C over pencil. 1-Jul-4 Sotheby's, London #189/R est:5000-7000
£9500	$17385	€13870	Parson and the milkmaids (18x22cm-7x9in) pencil blk ink W/C prov. 3-Jun-4 Christie's, London #94/R est:4000-6000
£13000	$23920	€18980	Tuileries gardens, Paris (21x29cm-8x11in) pen ink W/C over pencil. 26-Mar-4 Sotheby's, London #100/R est:6000-8000
£17000	$30940	€24820	Furniture auction (19x25cm-7x10in) pen brown ink grey wash over pencil prov. 1-Jul-4 Sotheby's, London #187/R est:18000-24000

ROWLANDSON, Thomas (attrib) (1756-1827) British

Works on paper

£280	$468	€409	Man and woman embracing with a horse beside them (21x18cm-8x7in) pencil prov. 22-Oct-3 Cheffins, Cambridge #444
£340	$568	€496	Evening, before the night (12x18cm-5x7in) W/C prov. 22-Oct-3 Cheffins, Cambridge #447
£464	$850	€677	Grotesque man eating pork (25x21cm-10x8in) init. W/C. 29-Jan-4 Swann Galleries, New York #353/R

ROWNTREE, Harry (19/20th C) British

Works on paper

£350	$595	€511	Head of a Pekinese (20x15cm-8x6in) s. pencil bodycol. 27-Nov-3 Christie's, Kensington #396/R

ROWNTREE, Kenneth (1915-1997) British

£320	$582	€467	Boules at Acomb (50x45cm-20x18in) i.d.1988 verso board. 15-Jun-4 Bonhams, Leeds #87
£620	$1141	€905	Butterfly in a landscape (38x50cm-15x20in) s. acrylic board sold with another by same hand two. 14-Jun-4 Bonhams, Bath #79
£1000	$1830	€1460	View of a stately home (33x43cm-13x17in) s. 28-Jul-4 Mallams, Oxford #425/R est:700-900
£1800	$3294	€2628	College barge on the Isis (38x48cm-15x19in) s. 28-Jul-4 Mallams, Oxford #424/R est:600-800

Works on paper

£2800	$4452	€4088	Designs for the county guides (76x53cm-30x21in) two s. four board four card set of eight in four pieces. 10-Sep-3 Sotheby's, Olympia #85/R est:400-600

ROWORTH, Edward (1880-1964) British

£256	$436	€374	Extensive landscape, western Cape (39x57cm-15x22in) s. board. 4-Nov-3 Stephan Welz, Johannesburg #305 est:2000-3000 (SA.R 3000)
£259	$432	€378	After the storm (50x75cm-20x30in) s. 20-Oct-3 Stephan Welz, Johannesburg #796 est:3000-5000 (SA.R 3000)
£319	$578	€466	Evening on the River, Parys (24x34cm-9x13in) board. 30-Mar-4 Stephan Welz, Johannesburg #191 est:1800-2200 (SA.R 3800)
£345	$576	€504	Approaching storm (60x90cm-24x35in) s. 20-Oct-3 Stephan Welz, Johannesburg #783 est:4000-6000 (SA.R 4000)
£347	$621	€507	River Valley, Knysna (48x72cm-19x28in) s. canvas on board. 31-May-4 Stephan Welz, Johannesburg #123 (SA.R 4200)
£388	$648	€566	Groot Drakenstein mountains from the Berg River (50x60cm-20x24in) s.i.verso board. 20-Oct-3 Stephan Welz, Johannesburg #808 est:2000-4000 (SA.R 4500)
£413	$739	€603	River Sonderend at Stormsvlei (49x75cm-19x30in) s.d.1952 i.verso board. 31-May-4 Stephan Welz, Johannesburg #128 (SA.R 5000)
£454	$813	€663	Mountainous landscape (49x59cm-19x23in) s. board. 31-May-4 Stephan Welz, Johannesburg #206 (SA.R 5500)
£470	$799	€686	Old nectar, Stellenbosch (49x60cm-19x24in) s. board. 4-Nov-3 Stephan Welz, Johannesburg #680 est:4000-6000 (SA.R 5500)
£550	$919	€803	Sun gleams, Reit Vlei, Cape Flats, South Africa (60x71cm-24x28in) s. i.verso board. 7-Oct-3 Bonhams, Knightsbridge #216/R
£700	$1239	€1022	Springtime, Stellenbosch (51x61cm-20x24in) s. 27-Apr-4 Bonhams, New Bond Street #102/R

Works on paper

£253	$465	€369	View across grasslands with stream (40x75cm-16x30in) W/C. 8-Jun-4 Dales, Durban #8 (SA.R 3000)

ROY, Dolf van (1858-1943) Belgian

£369	$687	€550	Haystacks and chickens (40x50cm-16x20in) s. 8-Mar-4 Bernaerts, Antwerp #747/R
£400	$720	€600	Still life with roses and books (51x70cm-20x28in) s. 26-Apr-4 Bernaerts, Antwerp #406/R
£403	$749	€600	Seated lady (32x42cm-13x17in) s. panel. 8-Mar-4 Bernaerts, Antwerp #103/R
£467	$840	€700	Still life with books (39x65cm-15x26in) s. 26-Apr-4 Bernaerts, Antwerp #255/R
£743	$1330	€1100	Composition au collier de perles et aux roses (55x69cm-22x27in) s. 10-May-4 Horta, Bruxelles #467
£743	$1308	€1100	The letter (57x43cm-22x17in) s. panel. 24-May-4 Bernaerts, Antwerp #381/R
£1241	$2297	€1800	Composition aux fleurs et aux chinoiseries (60x90cm-24x35in) s. 16-Feb-4 Horta, Bruxelles #154/R est:2200-3000
£1800	$3330	€2628	Standing nude (65x49cm-26x19in) s. panel. 14-Jul-4 Sotheby's, Olympia #267/R est:2000-3000

ROY, Dolf van (attrib) (1858-1943) Belgian

£387	$678	€550	Portrait de femme (92x70cm-36x28in) 16-Dec-3 Galerie Moderne, Brussels #637

ROY, G B (19th C) French

£1159	$1901	€1600	Choir boys singing (87x69cm-34x27in) s. 27-May-3 Finarte Semenzato, Milan #122/R est:1400-1600

ROY, Jamini (1887-1972) Indian

£1000	$1670	€1460	Cat holding a kitten (40x39cm-16x15in) s. tempera sold with book. 17-Oct-3 Christie's, Kensington #517/R est:1000-1500
£1902	$3500	€2777	Untitled (27x38cm-11x15in) s. tempera card. 24-Mar-4 Sotheby's, New York #158/R est:4000-6000
£3804	$7000	€5554	Untitled (60x70cm-24x28in) tempera paper. 24-Mar-4 Sotheby's, New York #159/R est:4000-6000
£4348	$8000	€6348	Krishna and Balaram with cattle (53x174cm-21x69in) tempera cloth board prov. 24-Mar-4 Sotheby's, New York #157/R est:8000-12000
£5163	$9500	€7538	Untitled (54x79cm-21x31in) tempera. 24-Mar-4 Sotheby's, New York #156/R est:10000-15000

Works on paper

£755	$1200	€1102	Elephants. Figures in a cart (36x47cm-14x19in) s. gouache pair. 13-Sep-3 Weschler, Washington #711/R
£838	$1400	€1223	Krishna and figure (43x33cm-17x13in) s. gouache card. 20-Jun-3 Freeman, Philadelphia #23/R
£1063	$1700	€1552	Man riding an elephant (10x15cm-4x6in) s. gouache. 20-Sep-3 Jeffery Burchard, Florida #8/R
£1132	$1800	€1653	Lord Shiva. Nandi with llama (44x25cm-17x10in) s. gouache pair. 13-Sep-3 Weschler, Washington #710/R est:1000-1500
£1200	$2208	€1752	Seated male figure holding an implement (34x18cm-13x7in) s. gouache. 23-Mar-4 Rosebery Fine Art, London #761/R est:400-600
£1300	$2392	€1898	Portrait of of three women (39x28cm-15x11in) s. gouache. 23-Mar-4 Rosebery Fine Art, London #762/R est:600-800
£1676	$3000	€2447	Animal studies (32x38cm-13x15in) s. W/C two. 10-May-4 Bonhams & Butterfields, San Francisco #4158/R est:2500-4000
£2276	$4097	€3323	Mother and child (41x27cm-16x11in) s. gouache on card. 25-Apr-4 Christie's, Hong Kong #593/R est:20000-28000 (HK.D 32000)
£2374	$4250	€3466	Ruler on horseback (48x53cm-19x21in) s. W/C. 10-May-4 Bonhams & Butterfields, San Francisco #4156/R est:2500-4000
£3352	$6000	€4894	Man on a leopard (54x54cm-21x21in) s. W/C. 10-May-4 Bonhams & Butterfields, San Francisco #4155/R est:4000-6000
£3631	$6500	€5301	Mahadeva and Ganesh (58x41cm-23x16in) W/C. 10-May-4 Bonhams & Butterfields, San Francisco #4154/R est:4000-6000
£5307	$9500	€7748	Mother and child (74x39cm-29x15in) s. W/C. 10-May-4 Bonhams & Butterfields, San Francisco #4157/R est:6000-8000

ROY, Jean Baptiste de (1759-1839) Belgian

£2128	$3553	€3000	Vaches au paturages (91x133cm-36x52in) s.d.1796. 17-Oct-3 Renaud, Paris #32/R est:4000-6000

ROY, Jean le (1894-1918) French

Works on paper

£267	$491	€400	Autoportrait (10x27cm-4x11in) s. ink col crayon. 9-Jun-4 Piasa, Paris #132

ROY, Joseph le (1812-1860) Belgian

Works on paper

£634	$1096	€900	Soldats espagnols revenant de la maraude (29x38cm-11x15in) s.d.1836. 9-Dec-3 Vanderkindere, Brussels #458

ROY, Louis George Eleonor (1862-1907) French

£403	$713	€600	Au bord de l'etang (27x35cm-11x14in) s.d.1905 cardboard. 28-Apr-4 Charbonneaux, Paris #219

Works on paper

£1325	$2424	€2000	L'aurore (12x39cm-5x15in) s.d.97 W/C gouache fan shaped lit. 7-Apr-4 Doutrebente, Paris #60/R est:2000-2200

ROY, Marius (1833-?) French
£313 $500 €457 Camp fire. s. panel. 20-Sep-3 Nadeau, Windsor #77/R
£3022 $5500 €4412 Mess (33x45cm-13x18in) s. panel. 29-Jun-4 Sotheby's, New York #98/R est:5000-7000

ROY, Pierre (1880-1950) Italian
£7601 $12618 €11097 Pot au feu (73x60cm-29x24in) s. 4-Oct-3 Kieselbach, Budapest #107/R (H.F 2800000)
£9649 $17754 €14088 Nature morte avec moules (21x26cm-8x10in) s. prov.exhib. 23-Jun-4 Koller, Zurich #3150/R est:12000-18000 (S.FR 22000)
£22000 $40260 €32120 La fortune au repos (55x33cm-22x13in) s. painted c.1933 prov.exhib. 2-Feb-4 Christie's, London #92/R est:20000-25000
£42781 $80000 €62460 Interior (92x65cm-36x26in) s. painted c.1937 exhib. 25-Feb-4 Christie's, Rockefeller NY #11/R est:18000-24000

ROY-AUDY, Jean Baptiste (1778-c.1848) Canadian
£7143 $11929 €10357 Lieutenant Colonel Maximilien Globensky (70x59cm-28x23in) canvas on board prov. 17-Jun-3 Pinneys, Montreal #131 est:8000-12000 (C.D 16000)

ROYBET, Ferdinand (1840-1920) French
£452 $756 €660 An important message (40x33cm-16x13in) s. 17-Nov-3 Waddingtons, Toronto #189/R (C.D 1000)
£1300 $2405 €1898 In the studio (28x23cm-11x9in) s. board. 10-Mar-4 Sotheby's, Olympia #305/R est:1000-1500
£1500 $2505 €2190 Guard (61x44cm-24x17in) s. panel. 7-Oct-3 Bonhams, Knightsbridge #164/R est:800-1200
£1513 $2784 €2300 Almee et cacatoes (22x32cm-9x13in) s. panel. 22-Jun-4 Ribeyre & Baron, Paris #45 est:3000-4000
£1800 $3294 €2628 La jeune fille au chapeau rose (30x23cm-12x9in) s. panel prov. 8-Apr-4 Christie's, Kensington #45/R est:1500-2000
£2953 $5286 €4400 Le gentilhomme (41x27cm-16x11in) s. panel. 25-May-4 Chambelland & Giafferi, Paris #62/R est:5000-6000
£3867 $7000 €5646 Young cavalier (100x80cm-39x31in) s. 30-Mar-4 Christie's, Rockefeller NY #81/R est:4000-6000
£4000 $6640 €5840 Portrait of a cavalier (100x80cm-39x31in) s. panel. 1-Oct-3 Sotheby's, Olympia #252/R est:3000-5000
£6463 $11568 €9500 Mousquetaire a la collerette blanche (60x44cm-24x17in) s. panel. 19-Mar-4 Oger, Dumont, Paris #21/R est:3000-4000
£8725 $15617 €13000 Portrait de Juana Romani (130x69cm-51x27in) s.d.1891 panel. 25-May-4 Chambelland & Giafferi, Paris #64/R est:12000-15000
£9929 $16582 €14000 Jeune orientale au perroquet (55x45cm-22x18in) s. panel prov. 16-Jun-3 Gros & Delettrez, Paris #472/R est:15000-18000
£16000 $27520 €23360 Odalisque (72x170cm-28x67in) s. prov. 3-Dec-3 Christie's, London #100/R est:20000-30000
£47059 $80000 €68706 Troubadours (113x146cm-44x57in) s.d.1887 panel. 28-Oct-3 Sotheby's, New York #60/R est:100000-150000
Works on paper
£887 $1436 €1250 Saint Jean Baptiste (44x38cm-17x15in) chl htd white prov. 23-May-3 Sotheby's, Paris #14/R est:500-700

ROYEN, Willem van (1672-1742) Dutch
Works on paper
£5743 $10108 €8500 Two silver pheasants and a black crowned night heron in a landscape (30x44cm-12x17in) s.d.1735 i.verso W/C gouache black chk prov.exhib. 19-May-4 Sotheby's, Amsterdam #201/R est:4500-5500

ROYER, Henri (1869-1938) French
£2069 $3724 €3000 Les vieux pecheurs, Bretagne (81x65cm-32x26in) s. 26-Jan-4 Gros & Delettrez, Paris #35/R est:3000-4000
£3497 $5839 €5000 Modele (81x54cm-32x21in) s.d.1890. 7-Oct-3 Livinec, Gaudcheau & Jezequel, Rennes #100/R

ROYER, Lionel-Noel (1852-1926) French
£7000 $11690 €10220 Girl with puppet (149x71cm-59x28in) mono.d.1889 prov.lit. 12-Nov-3 Sotheby's, Olympia #213/R est:7000-9000
£9220 $15397 €13000 Elegante contemplant la mer (37x24cm-15x9in) s. panel. 17-Jun-3 Christie's, Paris #68/R est:6000-8000

ROYERE, Jean (1902-1981) French
Sculpture
£17114 $30292 €25500 Mille-pattes (162cm-64in) polished metal lit. 27-Apr-4 Claude Aguttes, Neuilly #204/R est:8000-9000

ROYLE, Herbert (1870-1958) British
£335 $600 €489 River pastoral (28x36cm-11x14in) s. painted c.1900. 16-Mar-4 Matthew's, Oregon #53/R
£620 $1159 €905 Ben Liathach and Loch Clare, Glen Torridon, Wester Ross' (11x15cm-4x6in) s.i.verso board. 25-Feb-4 Mallams, Oxford #152
£900 $1638 €1314 Harbour (40x60cm-16x24in) s. board. 1-Jul-4 Christie's, Kensington #89/R
£1000 $1830 €1460 Ben Liathack, Loch Torridon (28x38cm-11x15in) s. i.verso board. 7-Apr-4 Andrew Hartley, Ilkley #1156/R est:1000-1500
£1800 $3060 €2628 Approach to Barden Tower (29x39cm-11x15in) s. board. 18-Nov-3 Bonhams, Leeds #274/R est:1800-2200
£1800 $3330 €2628 Hebridean croft, a crofter making his way down to the shoreline (30x54cm-12x21in) s. board. 11-Mar-4 Morphets, Harrogate #274/R est:1800-2200
£2500 $4625 €3650 Figure with horse and cart by a bridge (43x33cm-17x13in) s. board. 15-Jul-4 Richardson & Smith, Whitby #455
£2800 $5180 €4088 Farmyard scene (48x58cm-19x23in) s. board. 12-Feb-4 Andrew Hartley, Ilkley #872/R est:4000-5000
£3000 $5550 €4380 On the Nevern, Pembrokeshire (38x58cm-15x23in) s. 12-Feb-4 Andrew Hartley, Ilkley #881/R est:3000-4000
£3100 $5270 €4526 Canal landscape on a breezy day (49x59cm-19x23in) s. 18-Nov-3 Bonhams, Leeds #273/R est:1800-2500
£3200 $5344 €4672 Scottish coastal scene (28x38cm-11x15in) s. board. 8-Oct-3 Andrew Hartley, Ilkley #1157/R est:3500-5500
£3200 $5344 €4672 Scottish loch from over the haunted glen of Mary Rose (48x58cm-19x23in) s. 8-Oct-3 Andrew Hartley, Ilkley #1159/R est:3500-5500
£3200 $5504 €4672 Village street scene (36x43cm-14x17in) s. oval. 3-Dec-3 Andrew Hartley, Ilkley #1231 est:3000-4000
£3200 $5632 €4672 Nessfield in Wharfedale (46x38cm-18x15in) s. 19-May-4 James Thompson, Kirby Lonsdale #150
£4000 $6880 €5840 Boats on loch (28x41cm-11x16in) s. i.verso. 3-Dec-3 Andrew Hartley, Ilkley #1247 est:3000-5000
£4600 $7912 €6716 Old Alligin Pier Loch Torridon (43x58cm-17x23in) s. 3-Dec-3 Andrew Hartley, Ilkley #1225/R est:3000-5000
£4600 $8418 €6716 Burnsall, in Wharfedale (30x41cm-12x16in) s. board. 7-Apr-4 Andrew Hartley, Ilkley #1144/R est:3000-4000
£4600 $8142 €6716 Springtime at Nessfield (43x53cm-17x21in) s. 29-Apr-4 Gorringes, Lewes #2306 est:1500-2000
£4800 $8736 €7008 Scottish lake scene with sailboats (58x89cm-23x35in) s. board prov. 16-Jun-4 Andrew Hartley, Ilkley #1129/R est:6000-8000
£5000 $9000 €7300 The Arches, Bolton Abbey, Wharfedale (51x61cm-20x24in) s. 21-Apr-4 Tennants, Leyburn #1267/R est:5000-7000
£6000 $10920 €8760 Winter in Wharfedale (30x40cm-12x16in) s. board. 15-Jun-4 Bonhams, Leeds #161/R est:6000-8000
£6800 $11696 €9928 Beamsley Beacon (51x61cm-20x24in) s. board. 3-Dec-3 Andrew Hartley, Ilkley #1232 est:5000-7000
£7000 $12600 €10220 Figures picking bluebells in a wood near Nessfield, Wharfedale (76x63cm-30x25in) s. prov. 21-Apr-4 Tennants, Leyburn #1268/R est:7000-9000
£7200 $13176 €10512 Manor Farm, Nesfield (38x48cm-15x19in) s. 7-Apr-4 Andrew Hartley, Ilkley #1150/R est:3000-5000
£7250 $12108 €10585 Cattle resting near the wharfe, Nesfield, Ilkeley (48x74cm-19x29in) s. 8-Oct-3 Andrew Hartley, Ilkley #1155/R est:7000-10000
£7750 $14338 €11315 Cattle watering at Bolton Abbey (28x38cm-11x15in) s. board prov. 12-Feb-4 Andrew Hartley, Ilkley #889/R est:5000-6000
£8000 $14080 €11680 Winter sunlit village scene (20x22cm-8x9in) s. board. 19-May-4 James Thompson, Kirby Lonsdale #50
£8500 $15470 €12410 Tree felling at Denton Hall woods (69x89cm-27x35in) s. 16-Jun-4 Andrew Hartley, Ilkley #1139/R est:5000-7000
£11000 $20020 €16060 Bluebell wood, near Bolton Abbey (58x47cm-23x19in) s. prov. 15-Jun-4 Bonhams, Leeds #159/R est:7000-9000
£24000 $40800 €35040 Entrance to Canada docks (68x103cm-27x41in) s. 18-Nov-3 Bonhams, Leeds #276/R est:15000-20000
Works on paper
£600 $954 €870 Manor Houses Nessfield (33x23cm-13x9in) s. W/C. 9-Sep-3 David Duggleby, Scarborough #120/R

ROYLE, Stanley (1888-1961) British
£470 $879 €686 Priory gatehouse, Worksop (51x61cm-20x24in) s. board. 24-Feb-4 Bonhams, Knowle #136
£800 $1360 €1168 On Ringinlow moors (25x35cm-10x14in) s. 18-Nov-3 Bonhams, Leeds #152
£5600 $8848 €8120 Down by the stream (48x61cm-19x24in) s.d.1917. 4-Sep-3 Christie's, Kensington #142/R est:5000-7000
£5600 $10024 €8176 River landscape with buildings in winter (29x39cm-11x15in) s.d.1928 board. 16-Mar-4 Bonhams, Leeds #572/R est:900-1200
£8000 $14320 €11680 Village scene in the snow (29x39cm-11x15in) s.d.1927 board. 16-Mar-4 Bonhams, Leeds #571/R est:1000-1500
Works on paper
£336 $555 €487 Fishing village of Prospect, NS (25x34cm-10x13in) i.d.1933 verso pencil dr. 3-Jul-3 Heffel, Vancouver #31/R (C.D 750)
£480 $888 €701 River landscape with buildings (12x16cm-5x6in) col chks. 10-Mar-4 Sotheby's, Olympia #96/R
£1400 $2478 €2044 Head of an Indian girl (22x22cm-9x9in) s.d.1948 pencil pastel canvasboard. 27-Apr-4 Bonhams, Knowle #142 est:150-200
£2000 $3400 €2920 Shepherdess (34x48cm-13x19in) s.d.1922 i.verso pencil W/C. 19-Nov-3 Tennants, Leyburn #945/R est:1800-2200
£2600 $4420 €3796 Gathering blackberries (35x50cm-14x20in) s.d.22 i.mount pencil W/C. 19-Nov-3 Tennants, Leyburn #946/R est:1500-1800

ROYLE, Stanley (attrib) (1888-1961) British
£360 $612 €526 Seascape, depicting harbour walls, possibly of Mousehole (39x49cm-15x19in) panel. 6-Nov-3 Ambrose, Loughton #25/R

ROYO, Jose (19/20th C) Spanish
£1480 $2724 €2250 Woman with hat (63x53cm-25x21in) s. 22-Jun-4 Durán, Madrid #584/R est:1500

ROYO, Neus Martin (1968-) Spanish
£369 $690 €550 Seashore (46x46cm-18x18in) s.d.2002 s.i.d.verso. 24-Feb-4 Durán, Madrid #34/R

ROYON, Louis (1882-1968) Belgian
£400 $716 €600 Marine (50x80cm-20x31in) s. panel. 11-May-4 Vanderkindere, Brussels #43

ROZANOVA, Olga (1886-1918) Russian
Prints
£30000 $54600 €43800 War, Voina. 9 wooducts 1 collage 5 text pages complete set lit. 1-Jul-4 Sotheby's, London #182/R est:35000-40000
Works on paper
£4079 $6934 €5955 Mars' fight with Scorpion - from The universal war (21x30cm-8x12in) collage exhib. 4-Nov-3 Bukowskis, Stockholm #268/R est:70000-80000 (S.KR 54000)

ROZEN, Jerome George (1895-1987) American
£598 $1100 €873 Chicago waterfront scene (76x51cm-30x20in) s. 25-Jun-4 Freeman, Philadelphia #289/R

ROZENBERG, Helene (1908-1975) ?
£399 $686 €570 L'arbre de vie (46x38cm-18x15in) s.d. 3-Dec-3 Tajan, Paris #234

£441 $758 €630 Le jardin enchante (55x46cm-22x18in) s. exhib. 3-Dec-3 Tajan, Paris #235

ROZIER, Dominique Hubert (1840-1901) French
£1854 $3375 €2800 Panier de roses (60x74cm-24x29in) s. 18-Jun-4 Piasa, Paris #64/R est:1500-2000
£2222 $4000 €3244 Floral still life with urn, tazza and string of pearls (74x61cm-29x24in) s. 26-Jan-4 Schrager Galleries, Milwaukee #1316

ROZIER, Jules (1821-1882) French
£282 $487 €400 Bords de riviere (24x41cm-9x16in) s.d.82 panel. 10-Dec-3 Maigret, Paris #73
£316 $581 €480 Les bords de l'Oise au soleil couchant (18x33cm-7x13in) s. 25-Jun-4 Daguerre, Paris #135
£912 $1724 €1350 La mare aux canards (27x41cm-11x16in) s. cardboard. 17-Feb-4 Vanderkindere, Brussels #111
£1397 $2500 €2040 Sunset over river with barge and figures (23x41cm-9x16in) s.d.1882 panel. 7-May-4 Sloans & Kenyon, Bethesda #1666/R est:2000-2500
£1449 $2377 €2000 Bergere et ses moutons au bord de la riviere (27x41cm-11x16in) s.d.1863 panel. 11-May-3 Osenat, Fontainebleau #213 est:2200-2500
£1457 $2666 €2200 Paysage a la mare (23x35cm-9x14in) s. panel. 9-Apr-4 Claude Aguttes, Neuilly #4/R est:750-900
£1611 $2980 €2400 Bateaux sur la Seine (33x46cm-13x18in) s. 14-Mar-4 Eric Pillon, Calais #36/R
£7895 $14527 €12000 Granville, barque et pecheurs sur la greve (21x33cm-8x13in) s.i.d.1878 panel. 22-Jun-4 Calmels Cohen, Paris #48/R est:4000-5000

ROZWADOWSKI, Zygmunt (1870-1950) Polish
£1284 $2132 €1875 Girl picking flowers in a field (45x33cm-18x13in) s. painted c.1900. 15-Jun-3 Agra, Warsaw #30/R est:8000 (P.Z 8000)

RU XIAO FAN (1954-) Chinese
£333 $607 €500 Fruit (70x80cm-28x31in) s.d.91 verso exhib. 29-Jun-4 Chenu & Scrive, Lyon #163/R

RUANO LLOPIS, Carlo (1879-1950) Spanish
£604 $1081 €900 Joselito (40x30cm-16x12in) s. board. 25-May-4 Durán, Madrid #150/R
£638 $1141 €950 Cock (40x30cm-16x12in) s. 25-May-4 Durán, Madrid #651/R
£704 $1218 €1000 Bull scene (157x110cm-62x43in) s. 10-Dec-3 Castellana, Madrid #190/R

RUANO LLOPIS, Lluis (20th C) Venezuelan?
£323 $500 €472 Untitled (41x51cm-16x20in) s. 3-Nov-2 Subastas Odalys, Caracas #80
£361 $560 €527 Untitled (45x36cm-18x14in) s. 3-Nov-2 Subastas Odalys, Caracas #17

RUANO, Jorge (1952-) South American
£441 $750 €644 Studio (74x60cm-29x24in) s. 20-Nov-3 Galeria y Remates, Montevideo #89/R
£441 $750 €644 Beach (51x61cm-20x24in) s.d.91. 25-Nov-3 Galeria y Remates, Montevideo #1/R

RUBBIANI, Felice (1677-1752) Italian
£23490 $43926 €35000 Vases with flowers (90x39cm-35x15in) pair. 25-Feb-4 Porro, Milan #30/R est:33000

RUBBO, Anthony Dattilo (1870-1955) Australian
£246 $388 €359 Gypsy girl (49x36cm-19x14in) s. 2-Sep-3 Deutscher-Menzies, Melbourne #344/R (A.D 600)
£447 $801 €653 Snake Gully (39x49cm-15x19in) s. board. 10-May-4 Joel, Victoria #321 (A.D 1100)
£744 $1376 €1086 Track through the clearing (39x29cm-15x11in) s. i.verso board prov. 10-Mar-4 Deutscher-Menzies, Melbourne #496/R est:2000-4000 (A.D 1800)
£870 $1557 €1270 On the lake (52x72cm-20x28in) s. 15-May-4 Christie's, Sydney #495/R est:2000-3000 (A.D 2200)
£2236 $4002 €3265 Shelly beach, Manly (19x24cm-7x9in) s. wood panel. 4-May-4 Sotheby's, Melbourne #135 est:3000-5000 (A.D 5500)

RUBELLI, Egidio de (19th C) Italian
£2000 $3640 €3000 Lake Como at moonlight (60x100cm-24x39in) s. 12-Jul-4 Il Ponte, Milan #485 est:3200-3400

RUBEN, Franz Leo (1842-1920) German
£470 $879 €700 Spring on Lake Garda (35x76cm-14x30in) s. board. 24-Feb-4 Dorotheum, Vienna #11/R
£1154 $1985 €1685 Girl selling fruit in the market (45x33cm-18x13in) s. panel. 3-Dec-3 AB Stockholms Auktionsverk #2608/R est:15000-20000 (S.KR 15000)
£1650 $2953 €2409 Little onion seller (46x34cm-18x13in) s. panel. 26-May-4 Sotheby's, Olympia #318/R est:1500-2000
£5903 $10035 €8500 Early morning on the laguna, Venice (49x79cm-19x31in) s.i.d.1891. 28-Oct-3 Christie's, Amsterdam #30/R est:2000-3000

RUBENS (after) (1577-1640) Flemish
£2349 $4064 €3430 Susan and the Old (96x72cm-38x28in) 12-Dec-3 Kieselbach, Budapest #124/R (H.F 900000)
£5422 $9000 €7916 Birth of Louis XIII at Fontainebleau (175x145cm-69x57in) 4-Oct-3 Neal Auction Company, New Orleans #886/R est:8000-12000
£6757 $11892 €10000 Allegory of war and Peace (71x89cm-28x35in) copper prov. 18-May-4 Sotheby's, Amsterdam #50/R est:10000-15000
£7000 $12110 €10220 Holy Family under an apple trees with saints and the infant Baptist (88x123cm-35x48in) panel. 12-Dec-3 Christie's, Kensington #19/R est:6000-8000
£8000 $14640 €11680 Portrait of Isabella of Bourbon (66x48cm-26x19in) lit. 8-Jul-4 Sotheby's, London #213/R est:3000-5000
£10800 $18684 €15768 Virgin and Child with Saint George, Mary Magdalene, Jerome and Augustine (265x193cm-104x76in) prov. 9-Dec-3 Sotheby's, Olympia #316/R est:4000-6000
Miniatures
£12000 $21480 €17520 Allegory showing the effects of War (42cm-17in) s.d.1813 i.verso enamel rec. 27-May-4 Sotheby's, London #62/R est:15000-20000

RUBENS (attrib) (1577-1640) Flemish
£444 $800 €648 Conversion of Saint Paul (59x81cm-23x32in) panel prov.lit. 21-Jan-4 Sotheby's, New York #162/R

RUBENS (circle) (1577-1640) Flemish
£5298 $9642 €8000 Head of the Infant Baptist (42x33cm-17x13in) panel. 16-Jun-4 Dorotheum, Vienna #423/R est:5000-7000
£8333 $15000 €12166 Saint Felix of Cantalice (105x72cm-41x28in) panel prov. 22-Jan-4 Sotheby's, New York #281/R est:20000-30000
£10490 $18042 €15000 Portrait of a man (58x46cm-23x18in) prov.lit. 2-Dec-3 Christie's, Paris #140/R est:5000-7000
£17021 $28426 €24000 Baby Jesus and young Saint John in a landscape scene (120x173cm-47x68in) 18-Jun-3 Christie's, Rome #458/R est:8000-12000

RUBENS (studio) (1577-1640) Flemish
£9333 $16707 €14000 Saint Francis receiving the Stigmata (49x37cm-19x15in) panel exhib.lit. 17-May-4 Christie's, Amsterdam #80/R est:5000-7000
£33557 $61745 €50000 Marriage of St Catherine (64x49cm-25x19in) panel prov. 24-Mar-4 Dorotheum, Vienna #102/R est:15000-20000
£93960 $172886 €140000 Defeat of Sanherib, King of Assyria at the gates of Jerusalem (97x122cm-38x48in) panel prov. 24-Mar-4 Dorotheum, Vienna #198/R est:35000-50000

RUBENS (style) (1577-1640) Flemish
£9091 $15636 €13000 Portrait of a woman (65x53cm-26x21in) oval prov. 2-Dec-3 Christie's, Paris #141/R est:6000-8000
£10738 $19758 €16000 Lions in grotto (124x203cm-49x80in) 17th/18th C prov. 24-Mar-4 Dorotheum, Vienna #120/R est:12000-16000

RUBENS, Sir Peter Paul (1577-1640) Flemish
£5240 $9537 €7650 Worshipping the Holy Child (152x122cm-60x48in) 16-Jun-4 Fischer, Luzern #1017/R est:12000-18000 (S.FR 12000)
£10480 $19074 €15301 The wild boar hunt (137x165cm-54x65in) 16-Jun-4 Fischer, Luzern #1018/R est:12000-15000 (S.FR 24000)
£18621 $31097 €27000 Le Christ chez Marthe et Marie (150x250cm-59x98in) 17-Nov-3 Bernaerts, Antwerp #149/R est:30000-40000
£141844 $229787 €200000 Posible retrato del dominico P Buzzara (67x52cm-26x20in) prov. panel. 20-May-3 Ansorena, Madrid #98/R est:200000
£2200000 $4026000 €3212000 Night scene with old lady holding basket and candle (79x64cm-31x25in) panel prov.exhib.lit. 7-Jul-4 Sotheby's, London #30/R est:2000000-3000000
Works on paper
£10500 $19215 €15330 Head of a man after the antique (34x22cm-13x9in) bears i. blk white chk exhib.lit. 8-Jul-4 Sotheby's, London #76/R est:6000-8000
£180995 $289593 €264253 Adoration of the Magi (48x65cm-19x26in) panel prov.exhib.lit. 19-Sep-3 Koller, Zurich #3009/R (S.FR 400000)

RUBENS, Sir Peter Paul and SNYDERS, Frans (after) (17th C) Flemish
£11189 $19245 €16000 Un couple dans une cuisine avec du gibier (95x157cm-37x62in) 2-Dec-3 Christie's, Paris #409/R est:10000-15000

RUBENSTEIN, Lewis (20th C) American
Works on paper
£272 $500 €397 American milling company (30x20cm-12x8in) s.i.d.1937 W/C pencil gouache. 10-Jun-4 Swann Galleries, New York #204/R

RUBERT, Gino (1969-) ?
£1429 $2600 €2100 Untitled (76x86cm-30x34in) s.i.d.1996 verso oil collage photograph prov. 3-Feb-4 Segre, Madrid #376a/R est:2100

RUBERTO, Ferdinando (19th C) Italian
£814 $1385 €1188 Baja. Veduta dell'Isola di Nisita (34x49cm-13x19in) i. gouache pair. 28-Nov-3 Zofingen, Switzerland #2484/R est:1500 (S.FR 1800)

RUBEZAK, Jan (20th C) ?
£2766 $5118 €4038 Landscape with house (55x70cm-22x28in) 14-Mar-4 Agra, Warsaw #48/R (P.Z 20000)

RUBIN, Reuven (1893-1974) Israeli
£10241 $17000 €14952 Pansies (31x26cm-12x10in) s.i. 2-Oct-3 Christie's, Tel Aviv #48/R est:12000-16000
£11446 $19000 €16711 Small Bouquet (31x26cm-12x10in) s.i. 2-Oct-3 Christie's, Tel Aviv #49/R est:12000-16000
£13235 $22500 €19323 Harvest of Olives (38x47cm-15x19in) s. prov. 6-Nov-3 Sotheby's, New York #324/R est:25000-35000
£18033 $33000 €26328 On the road to Jerusalem (38x46cm-15x18in) s. i.d.1971 stretcher. 1-Jun-4 Ben-Ami, Tel Aviv #4908/R est:28000-35000
£23529 $40000 €34352 The old olive trees (54x73cm-21x29in) s. s.i.d.1960 stretcher. 1-Dec-3 Ben-Ami, Tel Aviv #4317/R est:48000-60000
£24064 $45000 €35133 Horse trainer (91x58cm-36x23in) s. prov. 25-Feb-4 Christie's, Rockefeller NY #89/R est:35000-45000
£24096 $40000 €35180 At the Well (50x66cm-20x26in) s. i.stretcher prov. 2-Oct-3 Christie's, Tel Aviv #70/R est:25000-35000
£32000 $57280 €46720 Misty morning in Galilee (54x73cm-21x29in) s. s.i.d.1958 stretcher. 11-May-4 Sotheby's, Olympia #603/R est:15000-20000
£32353 $55000 €47235 Flute player (78x54cm-31x21in) s. s.i.stretcher painted 1947 prov.exhib. 6-Nov-3 Sotheby's, New York #351/R est:40000-60000
£33520 $60000 €48939 Road to Rosh Pina (62x75cm-24x30in) s. s.i.d.1951 stretcher. 18-Mar-4 Sotheby's, New York #5/R est:50000-70000
£38235 $65000 €55823 Rider in the Negev (60x81cm-24x32in) s. s.i.d.1965 verso prov. 6-Nov-3 Sotheby's, New York #352/R est:40000-50000

£39106 $70000 €57095 Simhat Torah (81x65cm-32x26in) s. painted c.1947-53 prov. 18-Mar-4 Sotheby's, New York #15/R est:70000-90000
£39106 $70000 €57095 Vase of flowers (93x74cm-37x29in) s. painted c.1960 prov. 18-Mar-4 Sotheby's, New York #16/R est:70000-90000
£78212 $140000 €114190 Fire Chariot (146x97cm-57x38in) s. s.i.d.1965 stretcher prov.exhib. 5-May-4 Christie's, Rockefeller NY #348/R est:140000-180000
£145251 $260000 €212066 Ramparts of Zion (78x96cm-31x38in) s. painted c.1924 prov. 18-Mar-4 Sotheby's, New York #17/R est:200000-300000
Works on paper
£241 $434 €350 Untitled (48x39cm-19x15in) s. W/C. 21-Jan-4 Tajan, Paris #135
£550 $985 €803 Camel (20x15cm-8x6in) s.i. pen brown ink chk. 11-May-4 Sotheby's, Olympia #606/R
£800 $1432 €1168 Couple (25x18cm-10x7in) s.d.1971 biro pencil. 11-May-4 Sotheby's, Olympia #551/R
£1374 $2500 €2006 Threshing wheat in the biblical way (50x56cm-20x22in) s.i.d.1936 ink wash prov. 29-Jun-4 Sotheby's, New York #411/R est:1500-2000
£1872 $3500 €2733 Fisherman's family (37x44cm-15x17in) s.i.d.1971 W/C over pen brush ink prov. 25-Feb-4 Christie's, Rockefeller NY #94/R est:4000-5000
£2941 $5500 €4294 Portrait of family (49x65cm-19x26in) s.i. W/C pen ink exec.1968 prov. 25-Feb-4 Christie's, Rockefeller NY #93/R est:5000-7000
£3373 $5600 €4925 Horses (61x104cm-24x41in) s. s.i.d.1961 verso W/C pen Indian ink board. 2-Oct-3 Christie's, Tel Aviv #8/R est:4000-6000
£3494 $5800 €5101 Rest on the flight (50x64cm-20x25in) s. init.d.1961 verso W/C pen Indian ink. 2-Oct-3 Christie's, Tel Aviv #76/R est:7000-9000
£4190 $7500 €6117 Backgammon players (50x66cm-20x26in) s. ink. 18-Mar-4 Sotheby's, New York #8/R est:4000-6000
£4294 $7000 €6269 Portrait of a family (65x48cm-26x19in) s.d.1970 pen brush black ink gouache prov. 25-Sep-3 Christie's, Rockefeller NY #640/R est:7000-9000
£4400 $7348 €6424 Le retour (79x58cm-31x23in) s. W/C brush pen ink gouache prov. 22-Oct-3 Sotheby's, Olympia #186/R est:2500-3800
£4749 $8500 €6934 Two Rabbis holding torah (36x41cm-14x16in) W/C. 18-Mar-4 Sotheby's, New York #285/R est:7000-9000
£5028 $9000 €7341 Road to Galilee (38x57cm-15x22in) s. W/C prov. 14-May-4 Skinner, Boston #311/R est:10000-15000
£6145 $11000 €8972 Arabian horses (77x105cm-30x41in) s. s.i.d.1955 verso red brush col ink. 18-Mar-4 Sotheby's, New York #7/R est:6000-8000

RUBIN, Victor (1950-) Australian
£268 $484 €391 Notre Dame, Paris (55x75cm-22x30in) s.d.Feb 1998 oil paper. 31-Mar-4 Goodman, Sydney #398 (A.D 650)
£366 $575 €531 White House 1976 (102x82cm-40x32in) 26-Aug-3 Lawson Menzies, Sydney #395 est:500-700 (A.D 900)
£847 $1441 €1237 Sunflowers and grapefruit (121x91cm-48x36in) s. d.4.1.2002 verso. 24-Nov-3 Sotheby's, Melbourne #136/R est:3000-5000 (A.D 2000)
£972 $1564 €1419 Luna Park VII (92x122cm-36x48in) s. board. 13-Oct-3 Joel, Victoria #389 est:2000-2500 (A.D 2400)
£1053 $1695 €1537 Luna Park - and the Mr Whippie van in the dark blue and sparkle of the night (90x121cm-35x48in) s. s.i.d.2002 verso composition board. 25-Aug-3 Sotheby's, Paddington #298/R est:3000-5000 (A.D 2600)

RUBIN, Yadid (1938-) Israeli
£7821 $14000 €11419 Trees (100x200cm-39x79in) s.d.2001 verso exhib. 18-Mar-4 Sotheby's, New York #65/R est:7000-9000

RUBINO, Edoardo (1871-1954) Italian
Sculpture
£1724 $2862 €2500 Dancer (58cm-23in) s. bronze. 1-Oct-3 Della Rocca, Turin #259/R
£2394 $4142 €3400 Face of woman (42cm-17in) s. bronze. 9-Dec-3 Pandolfini, Florence #294/R est:1200-1500
£5534 $9905 €8080 Head of Medusa (40x40cm-16x16in) init. bronze prov. 15-May-4 Christie's, Sydney #285/R est:10000-15000 (A.D 14000)

RUBIO, Rosa Maria (1961-) ?
£544 $990 €800 Untitled (70x50cm-28x20in) oil sand polymer paper on cardboard exhib.lit. 3-Feb-4 Segre, Madrid #316/R

RUBOVICS, Markus (1867-1947) Hungarian
£448 $749 €650 Sheep in autumn landscape (20x27cm-8x11in) s. panel lit. 10-Jul-3 Allgauer, Kempten #2660/R
£524 $876 €750 Landscape with lake (60x80cm-24x31in) 10-Oct-3 Stadion, Trieste #124/R
£632 $1145 €923 Winter landscape (21x26cm-8x10in) s. oil on wood. 16-Apr-4 Mu Terem Galeria, Budapest #171/R (H.F 240000)
£1357 $2253 €1981 Sails on lake Balaton (100x150cm-39x59in) s. 4-Oct-3 Kieselbach, Budapest #160/R (H.F 500000)

RUCKER, Robert (1932-2000) American
£3142 $5750 €4587 French quarter antique store (41x51cm-16x20in) s. 5-Jun-4 Neal Auction Company, New Orleans #395/R est:3000-5000
Works on paper
£464 $850 €677 French quarter corner (20x15cm-8x6in) s. W/C. 5-Jun-4 Neal Auction Company, New Orleans #394

RUCKERT, Erich A (1920-) German
£336 $617 €500 Woman with flowers and vase in hand (53x75cm-21x30in) s.d.89 tempera wash. 27-Mar-4 Geble, Radolfzell #800/R

RUCKERT, Otto (1887-?) German
£2400 $4296 €3600 Putto on Unicorn (140x107cm-55x42in) s.d. panel. 13-May-4 Neumeister, Munich #476/R est:3000-3500

RUCKERT, Wilhelm (19/20th C) German
£940 $1748 €1400 Cats in artist's studio (53x74cm-21x29in) s. panel. 6-Mar-4 Arnold, Frankfurt #830/R

RUCKERT, Wilhelm (attrib) (19/20th C) German
£872 $1623 €1300 Students outside tavern with Rhine beyond (99x154cm-39x61in) 6-Mar-4 Arnold, Frankfurt #831/R

RUCKRIEM, Ulrich (1938-) German
Works on paper
£533 $976 €800 Double drawing (29x42cm-11x17in) s. verso pencil prov. 4-Jun-4 Lempertz, Koln #415/R
£667 $1220 €1000 Untitled (42x30cm-17x12in) graphite on three pieces of paper. 4-Jun-4 Lempertz, Koln #416/R

RUCKTESCHELL, Walter von (1882-1941) German
£753 $1175 €1100 Indian woman (70x56cm-28x22in) s.d.1914. 10-Apr-3 Weidler, Nurnberg #4400/R

RUCOLE, Pierre (?) ?
£1056 $1827 €1500 Oasis in the desert with figures (40x111cm-16x44in) s. 9-Dec-3 Finarte Semenzato, Milan #124/R est:1500-1700

RUDA, Edwin (1922-) American
Works on paper
£264 $475 €385 Untitled, study for shaped paintings (17x22cm-7x9in) s.d.1966 col pencil graph paper. 24-Apr-4 David Rago, Lambertville #377/R

RUDAKOV, Konstantin Ivanovich (1891-1949) Russian
Works on paper
£336 $624 €500 Prostitute smoking with man before mirror (29x21cm-11x8in) pastel W/C bodycol Indian ink pencil. 6-Mar-4 Arnold, Frankfurt #833/R
£470 $874 €700 Prostitute meeting client (30x21cm-12x8in) pastel W/C bodycol Indian ink. 6-Mar-4 Arnold, Frankfurt #832/R

RUDBERG, Gustav (1915-1994) Swedish
£493 $888 €740 Coastal landscape with sailing boat in bay (51x60cm-20x24in) s. 25-Apr-4 Goteborg Auktionsverk, Sweden #357/R (S.KR 6800)
£944 $1605 €1378 Hazy landscape, Hven (66x74cm-26x29in) s. 5-Nov-3 AB Stockholms Auktionsverk #875/R (S.KR 12500)
£1015 $1827 €1482 Coastal landscape off Hven. Seascape with vessel (52x80cm-20x31in) s. canvas on panel double-sided. 26-Apr-4 Bukowskis, Stockholm #192/R (S.KR 14000)
£1099 $1945 €1605 Landscape view from Hven (68x83cm-27x33in) init. double-sided. 27-Apr-4 AB Stockholms Auktionsverk #830/R est:18000-20000 (S.KR 15000)
£1147 $1846 €1675 Bay at Hven. Study of Mona Lisa (81x81cm-32x32in) s. double-sided. 25-Aug-3 Lilla Bukowskis, Stockholm #829 est:20000-22000 (S.KR 15000)
£1197 $2154 €1748 Landscape from Kyrkbacken, Hven (60x87cm-24x34in) s. 26-Apr-4 Bukowskis, Stockholm #197/R est:20000-25000 (S.KR 16500)
£1223 $1969 €1786 Landscape from Prastavangen, Hven (48x68cm-19x27in) s. 25-Aug-3 Lilla Bukowskis, Stockholm #781 est:8000-10000 (S.KR 16000)
£1360 $2311 €1986 Clouds over Husviken, Hven (70x70cm-28x28in) s. d.86 verso. 5-Nov-3 AB Stockholms Auktionsverk #873/R est:12000-15000 (S.KR 18000)
£1538 $2723 €2245 Fishing village, Hven (76x84cm-30x33in) s. 27-Apr-4 AB Stockholms Auktionsverk #762/R est:25000-30000 (S.KR 21000)
£1662 $2825 €2427 Early morning, Hven (63x97cm-25x38in) s. 4-Nov-3 Bukowskis, Stockholm #211/R est:25000-30000 (S.KR 22000)
£1668 $3002 €2435 Harbour with boats (42x79cm-17x31in) s. 26-Apr-4 Bukowskis, Stockholm #199/R est:20000-25000 (S.KR 23000)
£1846 $3175 €2695 Vessel at anchor, Hven (52x81cm-20x32in) s. d.68 verso. 7-Dec-3 Uppsala Auktionskammare, Uppsala #276/R est:18000-20000 (S.KR 24000)
£1920 $3130 €2803 Fairway church hill (69x76cm-27x30in) 29-Sep-3 Lilla Bukowskis, Stockholm #499 est:18000-20000 (S.KR 25000)
£1978 $3501 €2888 Coastal landscape with bay, Hven (62x73cm-24x29in) s. 27-Apr-4 AB Stockholms Auktionsverk #763/R est:22000-25000 (S.KR 27000)
£2039 $3467 €2977 Landscape from Hven on a day in March (55x90cm-22x35in) s. 5-Nov-3 AB Stockholms Auktionsverk #874/R est:15000-20000 (S.KR 27000)
£2175 $3916 €3176 Bright day, Kyrkbacken, Hven (51x67cm-20x26in) s. d.66 verso. 26-Apr-4 Bukowskis, Stockholm #198/R est:15000-18000 (S.KR 30000)
£2417 $4109 €3529 Vessel at anchor, Sundet. Portrait sketch (94x75cm-37x30in) s. double-sided. 4-Nov-3 Bukowskis, Stockholm #212/R est:20000-25000 (S.KR 32000)
£3172 $5393 €4631 The southern slopes at Hven (37x60cm-15x24in) s. 4-Nov-3 Bukowskis, Stockholm #210/R est:20000-25000 (S.KR 42000)
£3223 $5705 €4706 Light morning, Hven (78x81cm-31x32in) s/. 27-Apr-4 AB Stockholms Auktionsverk #875/R est:20000-25000 (S.KR 44000)
£6420 $10914 €9373 Calm day in Oresund (95x80cm-37x31in) s. 4-Nov-3 Bukowskis, Stockholm #216/R est:70000-80000 (S.KR 85000)

RUDDER, Isidore de (1855-1943) Belgian
Sculpture
£2553 $4264 €3600 Bust of a young woman with snake and flower garland (57cm-22in) s. brown pat bronze col marble socle Cast H.Luppens and Co. 20-Oct-3 Bernaerts, Antwerp #35 est:1250-1500

RUDE, François (1784-1855) French
Sculpture
£1517 $2534 €2200 Petit pecheur (20x21cm-8x8in) st.f.Susse pat bronze exhib. 11-Nov-3 Lesieur & Le Bars, Le Havre #125
£1946 $3134 €2900 Le pecheur Napolitain (36cm-14in) brown pat bronze. 23-Feb-3 St-Germain-en-Laye Encheres #23/R est:3000
£4200 $7686 €6132 Tete de Gaulois (65cm-26in) s. pat bronze. 9-Jul-4 Sotheby's, London #140/R est:3000-5000
£14000 $23800 €20440 Hebe et l'aigle de Jupiter (77cm-30in) s.st.f.Thiebaut pat bronze lit. 28-Oct-3 Sotheby's, London #183/R

RUDE, Olaf (1886-1957) Danish
£350 $584 €500 Self portrait in blue shird with yellow specks (50x39cm-20x15in) mono. 28-Jun-3 Bolland & Marotz, Bremen #883
£948 $1744 €1384 Portrait of the artist Axel Simonsen (110x90cm-43x35in) s.d.44 prov.exhib.lit. 29-Mar-4 Rasmussen, Copenhagen #517/R (D.KR 10500)
£993 $1827 €1450 View from the artist's studio with the painter Karling's house (60x73cm-24x29in) s.d.30 prov. 29-Mar-4 Rasmussen, Copenhagen #483/R (D.KR 11000)
£1129 $1919 €1648 Red roof tops, Nykobing F (41x58cm-16x23in) s. exhib. 26-Nov-3 Kunsthallen, Copenhagen #311/R est:8000 (D.KR 12000)
£1156 $2103 €1734 The artist's own home, Bornholm (54x65cm-21x26in) s. 19-Jun-4 Rasmussen, Havnen #4199/R est:15000 (D.KR 13000)
£1264 $2325 €1845 Gentleman wearing renaissance clothes (130x90cm-51x35in) s.d.1919. 29-Mar-4 Rasmussen, Copenhagen #224/R est:12000-15000 (D.KR 14000)
£1309 $2408 €1911 Landscape with trees (54x65cm-21x26in) s. 29-Mar-4 Rasmussen, Copenhagen #565/R est:12000-15000 (D.KR 14500)
£1354 $2491 €1977 View of the sea from a house (53x65cm-21x26in) s. 29-Mar-4 Rasmussen, Copenhagen #193/R est:10000-12000 (D.KR 15000)
£1398 $2195 €2041 Sowed fields (81x117cm-32x46in) s.d.32 exhib.prov. 30-Aug-3 Rasmussen, Havnen #4358/R est:15000-20000 (D.KR 15000)
£1408 $2352 €2056 Landscape with houses (54x65cm-21x26in) s.d.31. 7-Oct-3 Rasmussen, Copenhagen #377/R est:15000-18000 (D.KR 15000)
£1423 $2306 €2078 Summer's day in the country (89x110cm-35x43in) s. 9-Aug-3 Hindemae, Ullerslev #1086/R est:3000 (D.KR 15000)
£1534 $2823 €2240 Landscape with figures, farms in background (60x92cm-24x36in) s.indis.d. 29-Mar-4 Rasmussen, Copenhagen #569/R est:18000-22000 (D.KR 17000)
£1534 $2869 €2240 Adam and Eve (40x36cm-16x14in) painted c.1925 prov. 25-Feb-4 Kunsthallen, Copenhagen #232/R est:20000 (D.KR 17000)
£1784 $2979 €2605 Coastal landscape with boat (47x66cm-19x26in) s.d.34 prov. 7-Oct-3 Rasmussen, Copenhagen #302/R est:15000 (D.KR 19000)
£2347 $4388 €3427 Landscape with red house, Svaneke (72x191cm-28x75in) s.d.37. 25-Feb-4 Kunsthallen, Copenhagen #237/R est:30000 (D.KR 26000)
£2581 $4387 €3768 Pykkekullekaer - landscape with pine trees by water (73x92cm-29x36in) s.d.29 exhib.lit. 10-Nov-3 Rasmussen, Vejle #632/R est:30000-40000 (D.KR 28000)
£3592 $6429 €5244 Grey day, Marienlyst Ostersobad, winter 1909 (82x111cm-32x44in) s. exhib. 12-Jan-4 Rasmussen, Vejle #559/R est:30000-40000 (D.KR 38000)
£3944 $6586 €5758 Still life of objects on table (80x100cm-31x39in) s.d.38 exhib.prov. 7-Oct-3 Rasmussen, Copenhagen #130/R est:40000-50000 (D.KR 42000)
£5415 $9964 €7906 Nude model in front of still life with cloth and jug (147x100cm-58x39in) s.d.22 prov.exhib.lit. 29-Mar-4 Rasmussen, Copenhagen #187/R est:75000-100000 (D.KR 60000)
£11965 $21537 €17469 Woman with tea cup (84x63cm-33x25in) s.d.1917. 26-Apr-4 Bukowskis, Stockholm #256/R est:160000-180000 (S.KR 165000)
£14218 $22749 €20616 Cubist cow (72x87cm-28x34in) painted c.1913. 17-Sep-3 Kunsthallen, Copenhagen #64/R est:150000 (D.KR 150000)
£36101 $66426 €52707 Lady with glass - cubist figure composition (87x71cm-34x28in) s.d.19 prov. 29-Mar-4 Rasmussen, Copenhagen #2/R est:150000-200000 (D.KR 400000)
Works on paper
£284 $455 €412 Bastemosen in Almindingen, Bornholm (38x49cm-15x19in) s.d.23.8.36 W/C exhib. 17-Sep-3 Kunsthallen, Copenhagen #267 (D.KR 3000)
£341 $613 €498 Landscape (27x36cm-11x14in) pencil W/C. 24-Apr-4 Rasmussen, Havnen #4024 (D.KR 3800)

RUDEL, Jean Aristide (1884-1959) French
£6667 $12267 €10000 Les mouettes (146x195cm-57x77in) s. i.verso prov. 14-Jun-4 Tajan, Paris #81/R est:10000-12000

RUDELL, Carl (1852-1920) German
Works on paper
£345 $576 €500 Snowy Gothic church (36x27cm-14x11in) s. W/C. 15-Nov-3 Lempertz, Koln #1548
£367 $667 €550 Old church building in Rhens-am-Rhein (48x32cm-19x13in) s.d.1910 i.verso W/C. 1-Jul-4 Van Ham, Cologne #1584
£405 $714 €600 Eiffel landscape with farmstead (33x24cm-13x9in) s.d.32 W/C. 22-May-4 Lempertz, Koln #1449
£541 $951 €800 Town in Frank region - possibly Rothenburg ob der Tauber (33x24cm-13x9in) s.d.97. 22-May-4 Lempertz, Koln #1450
£608 $1070 €900 In Rothenburg ob der Tauber (33x24cm-13x9in) s.d.97. 22-May-4 Lempertz, Koln #1451
£828 $1382 €1200 Lower Rhine landscape with trees along stream (31x44cm-12x17in) s. W/C. 15-Nov-3 Lempertz, Koln #1549 est:1500

RUDGE, Bradford (1805-1885) British
Works on paper
£350 $595 €511 Figures at the entrance to a cave, an extesive landscape beyond (23x32cm-9x13in) s.d.61 pencil W/C bodycol. 6-Nov-3 Christie's, Kensington #999/R

RUDGES, John (attrib) (19th C) British?
£310 $555 €453 Mother and daughter with a goat in mountain landscape (29x24cm-11x9in) indis.s.d.1853 board. 11-May-4 Dreweatt Neate, Newbury #473

RUDIN, Nelly (1928-) Swiss
£1719 $2923 €2510 NO 3809 (80x80cm-31x31in) s.d.1993 verso acrylic canvas on board. 22-Nov-3 Burkhard, Luzern #177/R est:3500-4500 (S.FR 3800)
£1834 $3375 €2678 Untitled (60x60cm-24x24in) s.i.d. verso prov. 8-Jun-4 Germann, Zurich #48 est:2000-3000 (S.FR 4200)

RUDISUHLI, Eduard (1875-1938) Swiss
£313 $494 €450 Evening landscape with stream (40x52cm-16x20in) s. board. 5-Sep-3 Wendl, Rudolstadt #3588/R
£345 $617 €504 Fortress on coast at night (17x22cm-7x9in) s. board. 13-May-4 Stuker, Bern #301 (S.FR 800)
£474 $849 €692 Fortress on coast at night (17x22cm-7x9in) s. board. 13-May-4 Stuker, Bern #302 (S.FR 1100)
£609 $1114 €889 Extensive landscape with cornfield (53x80cm-21x31in) s. cardboard. 4-Jun-4 Zofingen, Switzerland #2940 (S.FR 1400)
£611 $1113 €892 Autumn woodland scene (29x36cm-11x14in) s. canvas on cardboard. 16-Jun-4 Fischer, Luzern #2231/R (S.FR 1400)
£727 $1207 €1054 Moonlit landscape (50x77cm-20x30in) board. 13-Jun-3 Zofingen, Switzerland #3003/R est:2000 (S.FR 1600)
£882 $1500 €1288 Autumnal wood (52x78cm-20x31in) s. board. 19-Nov-3 Fischer, Luzern #1281/R (S.FR 1950)

RUDISUHLI, Hermann (1864-1944) Swiss
£302 $556 €450 Trees by stream (21x28cm-8x11in) s. panel. 24-Mar-4 Hugo Ruef, Munich #1097
£340 $609 €500 Rocky stream (33x44cm-13x17in) s. board. 18-Mar-4 Neumeister, Munich #2761
£370 $614 €540 Mediterranean study of a temple entrance set into a cliff face (48x71cm-19x28in) s. board. 2-Oct-3 Biddle & Webb, Birmingham #620
£377 $640 €550 Autumn landscape (52x74cm-20x29in) s. board. 5-Nov-3 Hugo Ruef, Munich #1097
£417 $679 €600 Shepherd with flock on lakeshore (49x70cm-19x28in) s.i. board. 24-Sep-3 Neumeister, Munich #541/R
£417 $679 €600 Autumn landscape with classical temple (33x41cm-13x16in) s. 24-Sep-3 Neumeister, Munich #542
£423 $731 €600 Interior of the forest (60x45cm-24x18in) s. cardboard. 10-Dec-3 Hugo Ruef, Munich #2489/R
£548 $932 €800 Autumn landscape (57x75cm-22x30in) s. 5-Nov-3 Hugo Ruef, Munich #1096/R
£738 $1358 €1100 Spring (51x43cm-20x17in) mono. i. verso board lit. 25-Mar-4 Karlheinz Kaupp, Staufen #2701/R
£1300 $2366 €1950 Autumn wood (52x70cm-20x28in) s.i.d.1903 board. 30-Jun-4 Neumeister, Munich #665/R

RUDISUHLI, Hermann (attrib) (1864-1944) Swiss
£543 $923 €793 Holy grove (64x94cm-25x37in) 19-Nov-3 Fischer, Luzern #2262/R (S.FR 1200)

RUDISUHLI, Jakob Lorenz (1835-1918) Swiss
£1560 $2605 €2262 Autumn meadow (73x100cm-29x39in) s. s.i. verso. 23-Jun-3 Philippe Schuler, Zurich #3421/R est:2500-3000 (S.FR 3400)
£1629 $2769 €2378 Lake in the morning (91x111cm-36x44in) s.i. 28-Nov-3 Zofingen, Switzerland #3157/R est:800 (S.FR 3600)

RUDISUHLI, Jakob Lorenz (attrib) (1835-1918) Swiss
£524 $954 €765 Caritas Romana (156x191cm-61x75in) after an Old Master. 16-Jun-4 Fischer, Luzern #2234/R (S.FR 1200)

RUDNAY, Gyula (1878-1957) Hungarian
£626 $1084 €914 Man in front of red background (49x35cm-19x14in) s. canvas on cardboard. 12-Dec-3 Kieselbach, Budapest #140/R (H.F 240000)
£814 $1352 €1188 Feast (42x53cm-17x21in) s. 4-Oct-3 Kieselbach, Budapest #191/R (H.F 300000)
£962 $1703 €1405 Carousers (54x45cm-21x18in) s. 28-Apr-4 Kieselbach, Budapest #82/R (H.F 360000)
£1336 $2365 €1951 Horse coach (38x52cm-15x20in) s.d.917. 28-Apr-4 Kieselbach, Budapest #147/R (H.F 500000)
£1436 $2483 €2097 Riders (46x54cm-18x21in) s.d.916. 12-Dec-3 Kieselbach, Budapest #123/R (H.F 550000)
Works on paper
£395 $715 €577 Wain with hussars (20x29cm-8x11in) s. W/C. 16-Apr-4 Mu Terem Galeria, Budapest #92/R (H.F 150000)

RUDOLPH, Wilhelm (1889-?) German
£300 $546 €450 Flowering shrub with white blossom (43x65cm-17x26in) s. fibreboard. 1-Jul-4 Neumeister, Munich #2790
£496 $829 €700 Park landscape with stream and stone bridge (51x63cm-20x25in) bears sig. lit. 16-Oct-3 Dorotheum, Salzburg #626/R
£2292 $3827 €3300 Still life with jug and apple (38x50cm-15x20in) s. i. stretcher double-sided. 25-Oct-3 Dr Lehr, Berlin #431/R est:2500

RUDOWICZ, Teresa (1928-1994) Polish
£678 $1227 €1017 Abstract (50x65cm-20x26in) s.d.1958 paper on canvas. 4-Apr-4 Agra, Warsaw #31/R (P.Z 4800)
Works on paper
£565 $1023 €848 Untitled (46x34cm-18x13in) s.d.1959 collage paper board on canvas. 4-Apr-4 Agra, Warsaw #27/R (P.Z 4000)
£921 $1648 €1382 Untitled (50x44cm-20x17in) collage Chinese ink wash exec.1959. 6-May-4 Agra, Warsaw #24/R (P.Z 6500)
£1059 $1917 €1589 Untitled (50x43cm-20x17in) s.d.1958 collage oil canvas. 4-Apr-4 Agra, Warsaw #46/R (P.Z 7500)

RUDT, August von (19/20th C) German
£280 $467 €400 Extensive river landscape (34x48cm-13x19in) s. 27-Jun-3 Auktionhaus Georg Rehm, Augsburg #8172/R

RUE, Louis-Felix de la (1731-1765) French
Works on paper
£288 $472 €400 Le triomphe de Neptune (23x37cm-9x15in) pen brown ink grey wash. 6-Jun-3 Maigret, Paris #55
£369 $661 €550 Dragon slaying (15x24cm-6x9in) s. pen W/C wash. 25-May-4 Karl & Faber, Munich #40/R
£476 $852 €700 Offrande au dieu Bacchus (25x41cm-10x16in) pen black ink brown wash. 17-Mar-4 Tajan, Paris #55
£1184 $2179 €1800 Scene de bacchanale avec des faunes enlevant une femme (37x52cm-15x20in) pen ink wash. 25-Jun-4 Rossini, Paris #15/R est:2000-3000

RUE, Philibert Benoit de la (1718-1780) French
Works on paper
£329 $605 €500 Soldat en pied dans un paysage (26x19cm-10x7in) s.d.1760 graphite india ink grey wash. 23-Jun-4 Millon & Associes, Paris #32

RUEDA, Gerardo (1926-) Spanish
£1733 $3137 €2600 Abstract (22x49cm-9x19in) s.d.1957 acrylic paper. 30-Mar-4 Segre, Madrid #323/R est:1500
£2028 $3387 €2900 Espacial Gris (72x65cm-28x26in) s.d.1991 oil collage board. 24-Jun-3 Segre, Madrid #126/R est:2700
£10638 $17234 €15000 Composition (61x65cm-24x26in) s. painted c.1953-54. 20-May-3 Ansorena, Madrid #325/R est:12000
Works on paper
£667 $1207 €1000 Souvenir (35x35cm-14x14in) s.d.1989 collage exhib.lit. 30-Mar-4 Segre, Madrid #192/R
£811 $1427 €1200 Collage (15x15cm-6x6in) s.d.1980 collage prov. 18-May-4 Segre, Madrid #205/R
£1081 $1903 €1600 Tricolor (40x30cm-16x12in) s.d.1984 num.25/25 collage. 18-May-4 Segre, Madrid #278/R est:1500
£1329 $2219 €1900 Collage (35x31cm-14x12in) s.d.1985 collage paper on panel prov. 24-Jun-3 Segre, Madrid #124/R est:1300

RUEGG, Ernst Georg (1883-1948) Swiss
£271 $434 €396 Reinsfelden (15x20cm-6x8in) s. paper. 16-Sep-3 Philippe Schuler, Zurich #5634 (S.FR 600)
£769 $1231 €1123 Seated figure in rocky landscape (41x50cm-16x20in) s.d.1923. 16-Sep-3 Philippe Schuler, Zurich #3252/R est:1500-2000 (S.FR 1700)

RUELAS, Julio (1870-1907) Mexican
Works on paper
£459 $767 €666 Magna Voluptas (15x23cm-6x9in) s.d.1901 Indian ink card. 24-Jun-3 Louis Morton, Mexico #148/R (M.P 8000)

RUETER, Georg (1875-1966) Dutch
£264 $430 €380 Portrait of a little girl (42x35cm-17x14in) s. 29-Sep-3 Sotheby's, Amsterdam #162/R
£839 $1401 €1200 Red versus blue background (34x32cm-13x13in) s. 30-Jun-3 Sotheby's, Amsterdam #114/R
£1361 $2476 €2000 Pink carnation in a white vase (38x46cm-15x18in) s. 3-Feb-4 Christie's, Amsterdam #177/R est:1500-2000

RUF, Donald Louis (1906-1981) American
£233 $400 €340 County fair (51x61cm-20x24in) s. painted c.1940. 7-Dec-3 Treadway Gallery, Cincinnati #611/R
£464 $850 €677 Cowboy (41x51cm-16x20in) s. painted c.1940. 5-Jun-4 Treadway Gallery, Cincinnati #605/R

RUFF, Thomas (1958-) German
£16760 $30000 €24470 Nudes eli02, NUD088 (102x129cm-40x51in) s.i.d.2001 num.1/5 verso chromogenic col print prov.lit. 12-May-4 Christie's, Rockefeller NY #437/R est:30000-40000
£33520 $60000 €48939 22H 33M/minus 55 degrees (258x185cm-102x73in) s.i.d.1992 verso verso c-print Diasec face prov.exhib. 14-May-4 Phillips, New York #184/R est:40000-60000
Photographs
£1300 $2392 €1898 Nudes FN 06 (33x22cm-13x9in) s.d.2001/03 num.025/100 verso chromogenice col print lit. 24-Jun-4 Sotheby's, Olympia #618/R est:1000-1500
£2000 $3620 €2920 Haus Nr. 1l (31x54cm-12x21in) s.num.23/30 c-print executed 1987 prov.lit. 1-Apr-4 Christie's, Kensington #331/R est:2000-3000
£10056 $18000 €14682 H E K 03 (203x160cm-80x63in) s.i.d.2000 verso c-print Diasec face prov.lit. 14-May-4 Phillips, New York #185/R est:20000-30000
£11173 $20000 €16313 Nudes - FT 26 (136x106cm-54x42in) s.i.d.2002 num.4/5 verso laserchrome print on Diasec face prov. 13-May-4 Sotheby's, New York #322/R est:20000-30000
£13333 $24000 €19466 H.T.B 09, 2000 (95x140cm-37x55in) s.i.d.verso num.5/5 chromogenic colour print on diasec prov. 23-Apr-4 Phillips, New York #7/R est:30000-40000
£13333 $24000 €19466 MN23, 1999 (160x112cm-63x44in) s.d.1999 verso chromogenic colour print prov.lit. 23-Apr-4 Phillips, New York #148/R est:25000-35000
£13408 $24000 €19576 H T B 01 (185x236cm-73x93in) s.d.1999 verso c-print Diasec face prov.lit. 14-May-4 Phillips, New York #186/R est:30000-40000
£14000 $25760 €20440 Nacht 6 II (189x190cm-74x75in) s.d.1992 chromagenic col print prov.lit. 25-Jun-4 Christie's, London #220/R est:14000-16000
£14525 $26000 €21207 Portrait - Ch Jendreiko (206x160cm-81x63in) s.d.1994 num.1/4 verso cibachrome print prov.lit. 13-May-4 Sotheby's, New York #334/R est:2000-30000
£14970 $25000 €21856 Nuds, MN 23 (155x107cm-61x42in) s.d.1999 num.3/5 verso c-print prov. 13-Nov-3 Sotheby's, New York #524/R est:30000-40000
£15000 $27600 €21900 H.T.B 07 (130x178cm-51x70in) s.d.1990 c-print prov.lit. 25-Jun-4 Christie's, London #221/R est:15000-20000
£15000 $27600 €21900 W.H.S 02 (130x170cm-51x67in) s.i.d.02 c-print prov.lit. 25-Jun-4 Christie's, London #222/R est:15000-20000
£16000 $29440 €23360 Nudes C 01 (114x80cm-45x31in) s.d.1999 num.3/5 laserchrome diasec print prov.lit. 24-Jun-4 Sotheby's, London #315/R est:15000-20000
£16760 $30000 €24470 Portrait - N Hackert (206x160cm-81x63in) s.d.1998 num.3/4 verso cibachrome print prov.lit. 13-May-4 Sotheby's, New York #335/R est:20000-30000
£16760 $30000 €24470 Nudes inn06, NUD063 (154x122cm-61x48in) s.d.2000 num.2/5 verso chromogenic col print prov.lit. 12-May-4 Christie's, Rockefeller NY #436/R est:30000-40000
£16766 $28000 €24478 Nudes dyk 09 (122x155cm-48x61in) s. num.1/5 d.2000 verso chromogenic colour print prov.lit. 12-Nov-3 Christie's, Rockefeller NY #582/R est:15000-20000
£18000 $33120 €26280 Nudes NI 20 (90x135cm-35x53in) s.d.2000 num..4/5 verso laserchrome diasec print prov.lit. 24-Jun-4 Sotheby's, London #316/R est:18000-25000
£19444 $35000 €28388 Nudes GF10 (176x112cm-69x44in) s.d.2000 num.1/5 chromogenic colour print mounted on diasec face. 23-Apr-4 Phillips, New York #29/R est:30000-40000
£19553 $35000 €28547 Substrat 18 II (216x183cm-85x72in) s.i.d.2003 verso col coupler print edition 1 of 3 prov. 12-May-4 Christie's, Rockefeller NY #435/R est:40000-60000
£19553 $35000 €28547 Portrait, P Stadbaumer, POR 086 (210x165cm-83x65in) s.d.1990 num.1/4 verso chromogenic col print prov.exhib.lit. 12-May-4 Christie's, Rockefeller NY #438/R est:25000-35000
£22000 $40040 €32120 Nacht 19 III (190x190cm-75x75in) s.i.d.1995 num.2/2 verso C-print on diasec prov.exhib.lit. 5-Feb-4 Sotheby's, London #45/R est:20000-30000
£24000 $43680 €35040 Nudes wh 13 (153x110cm-60x43in) s.i.d.2001 num.2/5 chromagenic colour print prov.lit. 5-Feb-4 Christie's, London #234/R est:15000-20000
£25449 $42500 €37156 Haus no 11 (170x269cm-67x106in) s.d.1987 num.1/4 verso c-print prov. 13-Nov-3 Sotheby's, New York #503/R est:25000-35000
£26347 $44000 €38467 Nudes (145x110cm-57x43in) s.d.2000 num.5 verso c-print mounted diasec prov.lit. 13-Nov-3 Phillips, New York #53/R est:40000-60000
£27933 $50000 €40782 Substrat 8 II (164x305cm-65x120in) s.i.d.2002 verso col coupler print edition of 3 prov. 12-May-4 Christie's, Rockefeller NY #434/R est:60000-80000
£27933 $50000 €40782 Substrat 5 III (165x305cm-65x120in) s.d.2002 num.5/III inkjet on paper with diasec face prov. 13-May-4 Phillips, New York #13/R est:40000-60000
£29330 $52500 €42822 Stern 20H 54M - 55 1990 (252x180cm-99x71in) s.d.1992 num.1/2 verso Cibachrome print prov. 13-May-4 Sotheby's, New York #318/R est:60000-80000
£29940 $50000 €43712 Nudes ama O1 (148x130cm-58x51in) s. num.1/5 d.2000 verso chromogenic colour print prov.lit. 12-Nov-3 Christie's, Rockefeller NY #581/R est:30000-40000
£30556 $55000 €44612 Sub ol (240x187cm-94x74in) s.i. d.2001 verso inkjet print mounted on diasec face prov.lit. 23-Apr-4 Phillips, New York #61/R est:40000-60000
£36313 $65000 €53017 Nudes Ru 05 (150x109cm-59x43in) s.d.2000 verso num.5 c-print mounted with diasec face prov.lit. 13-May-4 Phillips, New York #61/R est:40000-60000
£41899 $75000 €61173 Substrat 71 (160x301cm-63x119in) s.d.2002 num.2/3 verso Cibachrome print prov. 13-May-4 Sotheby's, New York #316/R est:65000-85000
£42000 $70140 €61320 17h 16m/-45 (285x186cm-112x73in) s.i.d.1990 num.1/2 verso col coupler print prov.lit. 22-Oct-3 Christie's, London #172/R est:25000-35000
£43114 $72000 €62946 17H 38M, -30 (258x185cm-102x73in) s.i. num.2 verso c-print diasec in wooden frame prov.exhib.lit. 14-Nov-3 Phillips, New York #186/R est:50000-70000
Prints
£1700 $3128 €2482 18H 12M/-40o (67x45cm-26x18in) s.num.16/40 verso granolithograph lit. 24-Jun-4 Sotheby's, Olympia #444/R est:1000-1500
£3784 $7000 €5525 Stars (67x44cm-26x17in) grano-lithographs suite of 8 exec 1990. 12-Feb-4 Sotheby's, New York #364/R est:5000-7000
£6000 $10920 €8760 20H 54M/55 (100x70cm-39x28in) s.d.1991 num.8/20 verso col coupler print prov.lit. 4-Feb-4 Sotheby's, Olympia #70/R est:3000-4000
Sculpture
£7000 $12670 €10220 3D Schwarzwald. two plinths with wooden box two c-prints. 1-Apr-4 Christie's, Kensington #333/R est:8000-12000

RUFFALO, Carlos Roberto (?) Uruguayan
£283 $490 €413 Beach (20x32cm-8x13in) s. 15-Dec-3 Galeria y Remates, Montevideo #127/R

RUFFO, Jacobus (attrib) (18th C) Italian
£2473 $4500 €3611 Flowers in an urn with fruit, a villa beyond (62x88cm-24x35in) s.d.1766 verso. 4-Feb-4 Christie's, Rockefeller NY #78/R est:4000-6000

RUFS, F (20th C) ?
£3692 $6351 €5390 Woman with pearl necklace (69x56cm-27x22in) init. 2-Dec-3 Bukowskis, Stockholm #295/R est:20000-25000 (S.KR 48000)

RUGENDAS, Georg Philipp (attrib) (17/18th C) German
£1918 $3260 €2800 Cavalry battle (29x38cm-11x15in) canvas on panel two. 5-Nov-3 Hugo Ruef, Munich #860 est:1800
£5895 $10847 €8607 Battle scenes (31x61cm-12x24in) pair. 14-Jun-4 Philippe Schuler, Zurich #4325/R est:8000-10000 (S.FR 13500)
Works on paper
£271 $506 €396 Men on horseback in soldier camp (13x19cm-5x7in) i. pen wash. 25-Feb-4 Museumsbygningen, Copenhagen #124 (D.KR 3000)

RUGENDAS, Georg Philipp I (1666-1742) German
£1056 $1827 €1500 Cavalry battle (32x46cm-13x18in) canvas on panel. 11-Dec-3 Dr Fritz Nagel, Stuttgart #476/R est:2200
£1656 $2700 €2418 Messager (72x92cm-28x36in) canvas on board. 17-Jul-3 Naón & Cia, Buenos Aires #64/R
Works on paper
£946 $1693 €1400 Cavalry battles (19x24cm-7x9in) Indian ink brush wash two. 4-May-4 Hartung & Hartung, Munich #4072/R

RUGENDAS, Georg Philipp I (attrib) (1666-1742) German
£2685 $4966 €4000 Cavalry battles (16x25cm-6x10in) one mono. panel pair. 15-Mar-4 Sotheby's, Amsterdam #41/R est:2500-3500
£4362 $8027 €6500 Battle scene (37x49cm-15x19in) lit. 29-Mar-4 Pandolfini, Florence #693/R est:5000

RUGENDAS, Georg Philipp I (studio) (1666-1742) German
£6207 $11483 €9000 Cavalry battle in Arcadian landscape (96x130cm-38x51in) 14-Feb-4 Hans Stahl, Hamburg #181/R est:3000

RUGENDAS, Johann Georg Lorenz I (c.1730-1799) German
Works on paper
£329 $605 €500 Horse team pulling a cow on a sledge (28x42cm-11x17in) s.d.1751 pen pencil. 25-Jun-4 Michael Zeller, Lindau #779/R

RUGENDAS, Johann Moritz (1802-1858) German
£17969 $33423 €26235 Landscape with oxcart in Valparaiso, Chile (33x41cm-13x16in) 2-Mar-4 Rasmussen, Copenhagen #1290/R est:200000 (D.KR 200000)
£22059 $37500 €32206 Jinete chileno (23x30cm-9x12in) s.d.1853 prov. 19-Nov-3 Sotheby's, New York #43/R est:40000-60000
£44118 $75000 €64412 Matrimonio indigena - Native wedding (33x41cm-13x16in) painted c.1850. 18-Nov-3 Christie's, Rockefeller NY #85/R est:60000-80000
£175000 $285250 €255500 Santiago de Chile from the hill of Santa Lucia looking to the west (58x91cm-23x36in) s.d.1841. 25-Sep-3 Christie's, London #433/R est:60000-80000
Works on paper
£12821 $23462 €19232 Rancher on horseback (25x30cm-10x12in) s. W/C. 6-Jul-4 Bolsa de Arte, Rio de Janeiro #38/R (B.R 70000)
£26471 $45000 €38648 Landscapes and sketches (31x21cm-12x8in) s.i. graphite album executed 1819-1853. 19-Nov-3 Sotheby's, New York #42/R est:50000-60000

RUGENDAS, Johann Moritz (attrib) (1802-1858) German
£11724 $19579 €17000 Cacique de la tribu Indienne Pequen (45x38cm-18x15in) bears indis.init. 17-Nov-3 Tajan, Paris #16/R est:10000-12000

RUGGERI, Piero (1930-) Italian
£379 $633 €550 Samurai (14x17cm-6x7in) s. s.i.verso tempera board. 17-Nov-3 Sant Agostino, Torino #157/R
£483 $806 €700 Black and yellow diagonal (20x14cm-8x6in) s. s.i.verso board. 17-Nov-3 Sant Agostino, Torino #167/R
£559 $934 €800 Composition (66x48cm-26x19in) s. tempera paper painted 1995. 26-Jun-3 Sant Agostino, Torino #229/R
£828 $1382 €1200 Red and black figure (30x24cm-12x9in) s. s.i.verso painted 1972. 17-Nov-3 Sant Agostino, Torino #159/R
£966 $1612 €1400 Figure (80x60cm-31x24in) s. s.verso. 17-Nov-3 Sant Agostino, Torino #156/R
£1000 $1840 €1500 Untitled (24x30cm-9x12in) s.d.1987 verso. 12-Jun-4 Meeting Art, Vercelli #353/R est:1000
£1056 $1754 €1500 Napoleone (80x70cm-31x28in) s. s.i.d.1972 verso panel. 14-Jun-3 Meeting Art, Vercelli #61/R est:1500
£1088 $1948 €1600 Figures (60x50cm-24x20in) s. 22-Mar-4 Sant Agostino, Torino #486/R est:2000
£1361 $2435 €2000 Napoleon (100x100cm-39x39in) s.i.verso. 22-Mar-4 Sant Agostino, Torino #485/R est:2500
£1379 $2303 €2000 Composition (50x40cm-20x16in) s.i.d.1973 verso. 17-Nov-3 Sant Agostino, Torino #139/R est:1600
£1467 $2699 €2200 Figure (80x60cm-31x24in) s. s.verso. 14-Jun-4 Sant Agostino, Torino #390/R est:1500-2000
£1600 $2944 €2400 Curves in grey (50x40cm-20x16in) s.i.d.1994 verso. 12-Jun-4 Meeting Art, Vercelli #506/R est:2000
£1733 $3189 €2600 Composition (50x40cm-20x16in) s. s.i.verso. 14-Jun-4 Sant Agostino, Torino #387/R est:1200-1600
£1867 $3435 €2800 Untitled (60x50cm-24x20in) s. 14-Jun-4 Sant Agostino, Torino #388/R est:1200-1600
£3467 $6379 €5200 Red head (60x50cm-24x20in) s. s.i.d.1961 verso. 12-Jun-4 Meeting Art, Vercelli #111/R est:4000
Works on paper
£345 $576 €500 Untitled (48x33cm-19x13in) s. W/C. 17-Nov-3 Sant Agostino, Torino #158/R
£483 $806 €700 Landscape (70x49cm-28x19in) s.d.1977 pastel. 17-Nov-3 Sant Agostino, Torino #42/R
£483 $806 €700 Landscape (65x50cm-26x20in) s.d.1975. 17-Nov-3 Sant Agostino, Torino #164/R
£816 $1461 €1200 Untitled (65x46cm-26x18in) s.d.1961 mixed media. 22-Mar-4 Sant Agostino, Torino #340/R

RUGGIERO, Amedeo (?) Italian
£493 $853 €700 Portrait of man (20x16cm-8x6in) 9-Dec-3 Pandolfini, Florence #212/R

RUGGIERO, Pasquale (1851-1916) Italian
£3020 $5618 €4500 Serendade dans la Baie de Naples (38x48cm-15x19in) s.i.d.1887. 2-Mar-4 Artcurial Briest, Paris #113/R est:4000-5000
£6000 $10800 €8760 The dance (39x74cm-15x29in) s.i.d.88 s.i.verso. 21-Jan-4 Sotheby's, Olympia #460/R est:6000-8000

RUHLIN, Reinhard (20th C) Swiss?
Works on paper
£352 $599 €514 Life and death (100x69cm-39x27in) s.d.71 pencil col pen. 5-Nov-3 Dobiaschofsky, Bern #1858 (S.FR 800)

RUHM, Gerhard (1930-) Austrian
Works on paper
£423 $739 €600 Untitled (24x18cm-9x7in) s.d.1970 collage. 19-Dec-3 Dorotheum, Vienna #278/R
£559 $951 €800 Mother as her child (39x29cm-15x11in) s.i.d.92 pencil. 26-Nov-3 Dorotheum, Vienna #337/R

RUHTENBERG, Cornelis (1923-) American/Latvian
£346 $550 €505 Portrait of two women. Portrait of two sitting women (33x50cm-13x20in) s.d.47 one masonite one board pair. 13-Sep-3 Weschler, Washington #787/R

RUIFROK, Wilhelmus (20th C) New Zealander
£326 $518 €476 See what you are and are not (52x38cm-20x15in) s.i. board. 9-Sep-3 Watson's, Christchurch #29 (NZ.D 900)

RUIN, Ingrid (1881-1956) Finnish
£486 $812 €700 Woman (96x64cm-38x25in) s.d.1921. 23-Oct-3 Hagelstam, Helsinki #1012
£660 $1102 €950 On the shore (48x35cm-19x14in) i.verso. 23-Oct-3 Hagelstam, Helsinki #867
£2077 $3572 €3032 Country girl in light of open fire (47x38cm-19x15in) s.d.1916. 3-Dec-3 AB Stockholms Auktionsverk #2324/R est:15000-18000 (S.KR 27000)

RUINART DE BRINANT, Jules (1838-1898) French
£1300 $2366 €1898 Unloading on a French quay (23x34cm-9x13in) s.d.1830 panel. 16-Jun-4 Christie's, Kensington #40/R est:1000-1500

RUISINGER, E (?) ?
Sculpture
£4200 $6678 €6132 Nude (40cm-16in) i. silvered ivory onyx plinth exec.c.1930. 9-Sep-3 Sotheby's, Olympia #371/R est:1800-2500

RUITER DE WITT, Maria de (1947-) Dutch
£3441 $5505 €5024 Two beautiful nudes (80x100cm-31x39in) s. 18-May-3 Sotheby's, Singapore #17/R est:8000-12000 (S.D 9600)
£3623 $5616 €5290 Masterclass (170x120cm-67x47in) s. 6-Oct-2 Sotheby's, Singapore #32/R est:10000-15000 (S.D 10000)
Works on paper
£2703 $4865 €3946 Girl by the Puri Lukisan (80x100cm-31x39in) s. pastel. 25-Apr-4 Christie's, Hong Kong #514/R est:32000-48000 (HK.D 38000)

RUIZ BALERDI, Rafael (1934-1992) Spanish
Works on paper
£986 $1577 €1400 Untitled (99x70cm-39x28in) s.d.1965 W/C card. 16-Sep-3 Segre, Madrid #139/R

RUIZ LUNA, Justo (1865-1926) Spanish
£3356 $6275 €5000 Guard (69x46cm-27x18in) s. 24-Feb-4 Durán, Madrid #234/R est:5000

RUIZ OCAMPO, Hernando (1911-1978) ?
£4167 $6958 €6084 Untitled (84x63cm-33x25in) s.d.77 canvas on board. 12-Oct-3 Sotheby's, Singapore #56/R est:12000-18000 (S.D 12000)
£4902 $8873 €7157 Untitled (101x76cm-40x30in) s.d.77. 4-Apr-4 Sotheby's, Singapore #95/R est:15000-20000 (S.D 15000)
£6522 $10109 €9522 In the beginning (71x55cm-28x22in) s.d.61 canvas on board. 6-Oct-2 Sotheby's, Singapore #66/R est:13000-18000 (S.D 18000)
£10870 $16848 €15870 Revelation (73x113cm-29x44in) s.d.61. 6-Oct-2 Sotheby's, Singapore #86/R est:16000-22000 (S.D 30000)

RUIZ PULIDO, Cristobal (1881-1962) Spanish
£621 $1117 €900 Portrait of lady (91x68cm-36x27in) s.i.d.35. 26-Jan-4 Ansorena, Madrid #80/R
£664 $1109 €950 Model in the study (60x45cm-24x18in) s. canvas on cardboard. 30-Jun-3 Ansorena, Madrid #304/R
£664 $1109 €950 Portrait of woman (51x41cm-20x16in) s.d.1952. 30-Jun-3 Ansorena, Madrid #325/R

RUIZ REY, Jose Antonio (1695-1767) Spanish
£12587 $21399 €18000 Caprice de la cote Mediterraneenne (24x52cm-9x20in) s. copper. 1-Dec-3 Millon & Associes, Paris #21/R est:20000-30000

RUIZ SANCHEZ MORALES, Manuel (1853-1922) Spanish
Works on paper
£423 $731 €600 Urban view (10x16cm-4x6in) s. W/C. 15-Dec-3 Ansorena, Madrid #151/R
£604 $1069 €900 Water carrier (38x22cm-15x9in) s. W/C. 27-Apr-4 Durán, Madrid #150/R
£1389 $2264 €2000 Prenderia Street (48x28cm-19x11in) s. W/C. 23-Sep-3 Durán, Madrid #113/R est:2000

RUIZ, Antonio (1897-1964) Mexican
£52941 $90000 €77294 Autorretrato (86x60cm-34x24in) painted 1914 prov.exhib.lit. 19-Nov-3 Sotheby's, New York #47/R est:80000-100000

RUIZ, Benigino Y (1880-1929) American
£2381 $4500 €3476 Barbizon style atmospheric landscape (13x20cm-5x8in) s. panel. 17-Feb-4 John Moran, Pasadena #187/R est:1000-2000

RUIZ, Christiane (20th C) Spanish?
£1678 $2970 €2500 Au-dela du reve (89x116cm-35x46in) s. 29-Apr-4 Claude Aguttes, Neuilly #261 est:2500-2700

RUIZ, Franz (18/19th C) French?
£629 $1051 €900 Portrait de femme au collier de perles (90x72cm-35x28in) d.1803. 12-Oct-3 Teitgen, Nancy #103

RUIZ, Juan (18th C) Spanish
£88889 $160000 €129778 Naples, view from the Bay taken from Posillipo looking towards Mount Vesuvius (48x166cm-19x65in) prov.lit. 22-Jan-4 Sotheby's, New York #69/R est:150000-200000

RUIZ, M (?) ?
£994 $1690 €1451 Apples (50x70cm-20x28in) s. 23-Nov-3 Subastas Odalys, Caracas #129/R est:2000

RUIZ-PIPO, Manolo (1929-1998) Spanish
£204 $474 €400 Les arbres sous la pluie (37x28cm-15x11in) s.d.1958 cardboard. 19-Oct-3 Charbonneaux, Paris #127
£478 $875 €698 Nu debout (41x27cm-16x11in) s. s.d.1969 verso prov. 5-Jun-4 Galerie du Rhone, Sion #390 (S.FR 1100)
£1135 $1895 €1600 Nature morte a la cafetiere (32x41cm-13x16in) s.d.56 oil paper on canvas. 19-Oct-3 Charbonneaux, Paris #129/R est:1100-1200
£1206 $2013 €1700 Nature morte a la carafe (32x41cm-13x16in) s.d.56 oil paper on canvas. 19-Oct-3 Charbonneaux, Paris #128/R est:1200-1500
£1544 $2856 €2300 Village du Midi (37x52cm-15x20in) s. paper on canvas. 14-Mar-4 St-Germain-en-Laye Encheres #140/R est:2500
£2148 $3844 €3200 Jeune femme a la marmite (41x33cm-16x13in) s. isorel. 25-May-4 Chambelland & Giafferi, Paris #84/R est:2000-2500
£2174 $3978 €3174 Nu a la serviette (92x65cm-36x26in) s. 5-Jun-4 Galerie du Rhone, Sion #389/R est:2500-3500 (S.FR 5000)
£2270 $3790 €3200 Nu se coiffant (73x54cm-29x21in) s.i.d.1960 verso. 12-Oct-3 St-Germain-en-Laye Encheres #151/R est:3000-3500
£2391 $4376 €3491 Maternite (80x50cm-31x20in) s. s.d.1971 verso. 5-Jun-4 Galerie du Rhone, Sion #391/R est:2000-3000 (S.FR 5500)
£2482 $4145 €3500 Femme aux seins nus (50x35cm-20x14in) s.d.1975 verso. 12-Oct-3 St-Germain-en-Laye Encheres #161 est:3500-4000
£2550 $4718 €3800 Jeune fille a la pomme (35x46cm-14x18in) s. s.verso. 14-Mar-4 St-Germain-en-Laye Encheres #139/R est:4000

£2550 $4718 €3800 Mere allaitant (115x89cm-45x35in) s. s.i.verso. 14-Mar-4 St-Germain-en-Laye Encheres #142/R est:4000
£3972 $6633 €5600 Diotima (146x89cm-57x35in) s.i.d.1982 verso lit. 12-Oct-3 St-Germain-en-Laye Encheres #158/R est:6000-7000
£4085 $7066 €5800 Drunk Pulcinella (81x65cm-32x26in) s. i.verso painted 1970. 14-Dec-3 Eric Pillon, Calais #234/R
£4255 $7106 €6000 Violaine et Renault Hilleret (130x97cm-51x38in) s.i.d.1969 verso. 12-Oct-3 St-Germain-en-Laye Encheres #162/R est:3000-4000
Works on paper
£355 $592 €500 La famille (28x20cm-11x8in) s. pen. 12-Oct-3 St-Germain-en-Laye Encheres #134
£426 $711 €600 Scene de tauromachie (31x48cm-12x19in) s. gouache. 19-Oct-3 Charbonneaux, Paris #124
£496 $829 €700 Les passants sous la pluie (31x48cm-12x19in) s. gouache. 19-Oct-3 Charbonneaux, Paris #125
£496 $829 €700 Couple (26x18cm-10x7in) s. gouache lit. 12-Oct-3 St-Germain-en-Laye Encheres #119/R
£592 $1089 €900 Brodeuse (23x21cm-9x8in) s. wax crayon. 24-Jun-4 Credit Municipal, Paris #29
£603 $1007 €850 Torero (31x22cm-12x9in) s. gouache W/C. 12-Oct-3 St-Germain-en-Laye Encheres #165
£709 $1184 €1000 Femme a l'orange (37x47cm-15x19in) s.d.1956 gouache. 19-Oct-3 Charbonneaux, Paris #126/R
£922 $1540 €1300 Promenade en ane (35x45cm-14x18in) s. gouache. 12-Oct-3 St-Germain-en-Laye Encheres #125/R
£993 $1658 €1400 Le Pont Neuf a Paris (31x48cm-12x19in) s. gouache lit. 12-Oct-3 St-Germain-en-Laye Encheres #123/R
£1206 $2013 €1700 La corrida (32x48cm-13x19in) s.d.1965 black ink wash lit. 12-Oct-3 St-Germain-en-Laye Encheres #136 est:1500-2000
£1325 $2411 €2000 Bathers (32x48cm-13x19in) s. gouache. 19-Jun-4 St-Germain-en-Laye Encheres #161/R est:2000
£1447 $2663 €2200 Etrangere (63x49cm-25x19in) s. wax crayon. 24-Jun-4 Credit Municipal, Paris #30/R est:1200-1500
£1915 $3198 €2700 Corrida a Barcelone (36x47cm-14x19in) s.i.d.1956 gouache. 12-Oct-3 St-Germain-en-Laye Encheres #164/R est:2500-3000
£2199 $3672 €3100 Scene de tauromachie (30x48cm-12x19in) s.d.1965 gouache lit. 12-Oct-3 St-Germain-en-Laye Encheres #153/R est:3500-4000
£2270 $3790 €3200 Torero blesse (50x64cm-20x25in) s.d.1955 W/C gouache. 12-Oct-3 St-Germain-en-Laye Encheres #149/R est:3000-3500
£2624 $4382 €3700 Deux taureaux dans le pre (50x65cm-20x26in) gouache W/C paper on canvas lit. 12-Oct-3 St-Germain-en-Laye Encheres #150/R est:3000

RUL, Henri (1862-1942) Belgian
£347 $580 €500 Petit chemin (33x41cm-13x16in) s. 21-Oct-3 Campo & Campo, Antwerp #265/R
£369 $687 €550 Landscape with path by stream (36x25cm-14x10in) s. 8-Mar-4 Bernaerts, Antwerp #78/R
£537 $961 €800 Ramasseuse de bois mort (40x60cm-16x24in) s.d.1888. 25-May-4 Campo & Campo, Antwerp #249
£800 $1440 €1200 Houses in Knokke (33x49cm-13x19in) s. 26-Apr-4 Bernaerts, Antwerp #119/R

RULE, Gallagher (20th C) American
Sculpture
£1000 $1700 €1460 Will Rogers (41cm-16in) bronze. 1-Nov-3 Altermann Galleries, Santa Fe #109
£1706 $2900 €2491 John Wayne (38cm-15in) bronze. 1-Nov-3 Altermann Galleries, Santa Fe #110

RULLENS, Jules (1858-1936) Belgian
£667 $1193 €1000 The artist at work (37x57cm-15x22in) s. 15-May-4 De Vuyst, Lokeren #289

RUMELYAN, Vahan (20th C) Armenian
£1408 $2352 €2056 Composition (175x210cm-69x83in) s.d.89. 7-Oct-3 Rasmussen, Copenhagen #117/R est:15000 (D.KR 15000)

RUMM, August (1888-?) ?
£2797 $4671 €4000 Portrait of young woman with dark hair (110x106cm-43x42in) s.d.1928. 9-Oct-3 Michael Zeller, Lindau #742/R est:2100

RUMMELSPACHER, Joseph (1852-1921) German
£297 $532 €440 Heathland on Sylt (66x96cm-26x38in) s. i. verso. 8-May-4 Hans Stahl, Toestorf #84/R

RUMOHR, Knut (1916-2002) Norwegian
£413 $690 €603 Composition (22x28cm-9x11in) s. tempera. 20-Oct-3 Blomqvist, Lysaker #1262 (N.KR 4800)
£602 $1006 €879 Composition (38x50cm-15x20in) s. tempera. 20-Oct-3 Blomqvist, Lysaker #1261 (N.KR 7000)
£1033 $1663 €1508 Landscape IX (78x60cm-31x24in) s. tempera. 25-Aug-3 Blomqvist, Lysaker #1242/R (N.KR 12000)
£1121 $2006 €1637 Composition (100x80cm-39x31in) s.d.66 tempera. 22-Mar-4 Blomqvist, Oslo #633/R est:18000-22000 (N.KR 14000)
£1201 $2150 €1753 Blue and red composition (58x71cm-23x28in) s.d.58 tempera. 22-Mar-4 Blomqvist, Oslo #662/R est:18000-22000 (N.KR 15000)
£1281 $2293 €1870 Composition (86x70cm-34x28in) s.d.67 tempera. 22-Mar-4 Blomqvist, Oslo #628/R est:18000-22000 (N.KR 16000)
£3042 $5446 €4441 Blue composition (68x60cm-27x24in) s.d.58 tempera. 22-Mar-4 Blomqvist, Oslo #609/R est:30000-35000 (N.KR 38000)
£3407 $5860 €4974 Thawing (125x100cm-49x39in) s.d.96 tempera. 8-Dec-3 Blomqvist, Oslo #553/R est:30000-35000 (N.KR 40000)
£4089 $7032 €5970 Blue landscape (110x170cm-43x67in) s.d.90 tempera. 8-Dec-3 Blomqvist, Oslo #552/R est:50000-70000 (N.KR 48000)
Works on paper
£1009 $1685 €1473 Winter landscape (67x68cm-26x27in) s. gouache. 17-Nov-3 Blomqvist, Lysaker #1272/R est:10000-12000 (N.KR 12100)

RUMOROSO, Enrique (19th C) ?
£1596 $2665 €2250 Fruit (36x26cm-14x10in) s. board. 20-Oct-3 Durán, Madrid #165/R

RUMP, Charles Frederick (?) British
£360 $619 €526 A wherry approaching St Benets Abbey on the Norfolk Broads (38x58cm-15x23in) s.d.1904. 5-Dec-3 Keys, Aylsham #270

RUMPF, Philipp (1821-1896) German
£1333 $2387 €2000 Lady walking in the park reading (18x24cm-7x9in) mono.d.77. 14-May-4 Behringer, Furth #1602/R est:2000

RUMPLER, Franz (1848-1922) Austrian
£464 $848 €700 Landscape (11x16cm-4x6in) s. panel. 8-Apr-4 Dorotheum, Vienna #234/R
£1389 $2361 €2000 Woman in red by roses (37x27cm-15x11in) canvas on panel. 28-Oct-3 Dorotheum, Vienna #162/R est:2000-2300
£5369 $9611 €8000 A model by a rose covered window (72x41cm-28x16in) s.d.1905 panel. 27-May-4 Dorotheum, Vienna #95/R est:9000-12000

RUNACRES, Frank (1904-1974) British
£360 $601 €526 Passing over Richmond bridge (51x76cm-20x30in) s. board. 7-Oct-3 Bonhams, Knightsbridge #69/R

RUNCI, Edward (1920-1985) American
£1879 $3364 €2800 Heat wave (71x56cm-28x22in) s. painted c.1950. 27-May-4 Sotheby's, Paris #126/R est:800-1200
£2349 $4205 €3500 The declaration (71x56cm-28x22in) s. painted 1947 lit. 27-May-4 Sotheby's, Paris #124/R est:1000-1500
£2416 $4325 €3600 Cutout (76x61cm-30x24in) s. lit. 27-May-4 Sotheby's, Paris #127/R est:1500-2000
£2550 $4565 €3800 The escape (74x58cm-29x23in) s. lit. 27-May-4 Sotheby's, Paris #125/R est:1000-1500
£3020 $5406 €4500 Look out behind (76x61cm-30x24in) s. painted c.1954. 27-May-4 Sotheby's, Paris #123/R est:1000-1500

RUNCIMAN, Alexander (attrib) (1736-1785) British
£450 $752 €657 Figures in an Italianate landscape (21x28cm-8x11in) panel. 13-Nov-3 Christie's, Kensington #68/R

RUNDALIZEV, Mikhail Viktorovich (1871-1935) Russian
£3548 $6529 €5180 River landscape, autumn (77x102cm-30x40in) s.d.1927. 14-Jun-4 Waddingtons, Toronto #352/R est:3000-4000 (C.D 8800)

RUNDLE, John (20th C) New Zealander
£346 $619 €505 Darran Range, Fjiorland (58x119cm-23x47in) s.d.80 board. 12-May-4 Dunbar Sloane, Wellington #495/R (NZ.D 1000)

RUNDSPADEN, Karl (1882-1967) German
£252 $413 €350 Hamburg harbour (44x65cm-17x26in) s.d. 4-Jun-3 Ketterer, Hamburg #14/R

RUNGALDIER, Ignaz (1799-1876) Austrian
Works on paper
£552 $916 €800 Portrait of woman wearing white dress sitting in armchair (20x17cm-8x7in) s. W/C. 30-Sep-3 Dorotheum, Vienna #400/R

RUNGE, Julius Friedrich Ludwig (1843-1922) German
£276 $461 €400 Kiel (40x50cm-16x20in) panel. 9-Jul-3 Hugo Ruef, Munich #194
£342 $582 €500 Rocky coast with tower and gathering storm (41x55cm-16x22in) s. 6-Nov-3 Allgauer, Kempten #3560/R
£709 $1269 €1035 Seascape with herring fishermen (42x80cm-17x31in) s. 12-Jan-4 Rasmussen, Vejle #44/R (D.KR 7500)

RUNGIUS, Carl (1869-1959) American/German
£10160 $19000 €14834 Ram head (23x28cm-9x11in) s.i. canvas on board prov. 24-Jul-4 Coeur d'Alene, Hayden #57/R est:10000-15000
£10695 $20000 €15615 Deer head (23x28cm-9x11in) s.i. canvas on board prov. 24-Jul-4 Coeur d'Alene, Hayden #56/R est:10000-15000
£12032 $22500 €17567 Mountain goat head (23x28cm-9x11in) s.i. canvas on board prov. 24-Jul-4 Coeur d'Alene, Hayden #58/R est:10000-15000
£13369 $25000 €19519 Draft horse (36x46cm-14x18in) s. 24-Jul-4 Coeur d'Alene, Hayden #55/R est:10000-20000
£14706 $27500 €21471 Caribou head (23x28cm-9x11in) s.i. canvas on board prov. 24-Jul-4 Coeur d'Alene, Hayden #78/R est:10000-15000
£18717 $35000 €27327 Pack horse (36x38cm-14x15in) s. canvas on board prov. 24-Jul-4 Coeur d'Alene, Hayden #54/R est:10000-20000
£24709 $42500 €36075 Call of the elk (41x61cm-16x24in) s. painted c.1900-05. 3-Dec-3 Sotheby's, New York #143/R est:40000-60000
£29412 $55000 €42942 Antelope (36x41cm-14x16in) s.d.1898 canvas on board prov. 24-Jul-4 Coeur d'Alene, Hayden #79/R est:10000-20000
£32086 $60000 €46846 Saddle pony (51x46cm-20x18in) s.i.d.1950 canvas on board prov. 24-Jul-4 Coeur d'Alene, Hayden #53/R est:15000-25000
£46512 $80000 €67908 Moose in the woods (61x81cm-24x32in) s.i. prov. 3-Dec-3 Sotheby's, New York #142/R est:80000-120000
£62500 $110000 €91250 Call of the wild (81x117cm-32x46in) s. 3-Jan-4 Cobbs, Peterborough #84/R
£74866 $140000 €109304 Two mountains sheep (64x76cm-25x30in) s. prov. 24-Jul-4 Coeur d'Alene, Hayden #52/R est:150000-200000
Prints
£1600 $2928 €2336 Among the crags (19x27cm-7x11in) s. etching drypoint exec.1935 prov. 1-Jun-4 Hodgins, Calgary #372/R est:3000-4000 (C.D 4000)
£1600 $2928 €2336 The wanderer (19x27cm-7x11in) s. etching drypoint exec. 1935 prov. 1-Jun-4 Hodgins, Calgary #373/R est:3500-4500 (C.D 4000)

£1728	$2800	€2506	Answer from the barren (16x22cm-6x9in) s. etching. 8-Aug-3 Barridorf, Portland #269/R est:1200-1800
£2036	$3400	€2973	Above Timberline (20x27cm-8x11in) s. drypoint etching. 17-Nov-3 Hodgins, Calgary #89/R est:3000-4000 (C.D 4500)
£2160	$3500	€3132	Goats (20x27cm-8x11in) s. etching. 8-Aug-3 Barridorf, Portland #267/R est:1200-1800
£2273	$4250	€3319	Old bull (28x23cm-11x9in) s.i. etching prov.lit. 24-Jul-4 Coeur d'Alene, Hayden #217/R est:3000-5000
£2406	$4500	€3513	Above timberline (20x28cm-8x11in) s. etching prov.lit. 24-Jul-4 Coeur d'Alene, Hayden #4/R est:3000-5000
£2406	$4500	€3513	An old fighter (15x20cm-6x8in) s.i. etching prov.lit. 24-Jul-4 Coeur d'Alene, Hayden #216/R est:3000-5000
£2674	$5000	€3904	Challenge (15x20cm-6x8in) s.i. etching prov.lit. 24-Jul-4 Coeur d'Alene, Hayden #5/R est:3000-5000
£2674	$5000	€3904	Morning mist (15x20cm-6x8in) s.i. etching prov.lit. 24-Jul-4 Coeur d'Alene, Hayden #6/R est:3000-5000
£2941	$5500	€4294	Ivan (20x28cm-8x11in) s.i. etching prov.lit. 24-Jul-4 Coeur d'Alene, Hayden #3/R est:3000-5000
£3209	$6000	€4685	Coming to the call (20x28cm-8x11in) s.i. etching prov.lit. 24-Jul-4 Coeur d'Alene, Hayden #2/R est:3000-5000
£4278	$8000	€6246	White flag (20x28cm-8x11in) s.i. etching prov.lit. 24-Jul-4 Coeur d'Alene, Hayden #7/R est:3000-5000
£4813	$9000	€7027	Mule deer (20x28cm-8x11in) s.i. etching prov.lit. 24-Jul-4 Coeur d'Alene, Hayden #1/R est:3000-5000
£4813	$9000	€7027	Challenged (20x28cm-8x11in) s.i. etching prov.lit. 24-Jul-4 Coeur d'Alene, Hayden #8/R est:3000-5000
Works on paper			
£4813	$9000	€7027	Ram's head (28x23cm-11x9in) s.i. pencil prov. 24-Jul-4 Coeur d'Alene, Hayden #218/R est:4000-6000
£10056	$18000	€14682	Moose, mist, lake (38x56cm-15x22in) s.i. gouache en grisaille. 16-Mar-4 Matthew's, Oregon #65/R est:14000-18000

RUNQUIST, Arthur (1891-1971) American

£344	$650	€502	Two figures on a rock (46x61cm-18x24in) s. 23-Feb-4 O'Gallerie, Oregon #475/R

RUNZE, W (1887-1972) German

£1198	$2000	€1749	Three men over the table (61x81cm-24x32in) 19-Oct-3 Susanin's, Chicago #6054/R est:800-1200

RUNZE, Wilhelm (1887-1972) German

£800	$1464	€1200	Female nude in the drawing-room (40x54cm-16x21in) s. 5-Jun-4 Arnold, Frankfurt #705/R

RUOFF, Fritz (1906-) German

Sculpture			
£1333	$2387	€2000	Black on blue (86x3x69cm-34x1x27in) s. s.i.d. verso relief wood frame board oil prov. 14-May-4 Ketterer, Munich #283/R est:2000-3000
Works on paper			
£278	$453	€400	Untitled (16x16cm-6x6in) s. W/C Indian ink. 27-Sep-3 Dr Fritz Nagel, Stuttgart #9332/R

RUOKOKOSKI, Jalmari (1886-1936) Finnish

£352	$563	€500	Still life of fish (27x37cm-11x15in) s. 21-Sep-3 Bukowskis, Helsinki #442/R
£400	$716	€600	Still life of flowers and pears (35x33cm-14x13in) s.d.1917 canvas on board. 15-May-4 Hagelstam, Helsinki #143/R
£436	$803	€650	Still life (36x54cm-14x21in) s.d.1916. 25-Mar-4 Hagelstam, Helsinki #1073
£490	$911	€730	Mother and children (41x36cm-16x14in) s.d.1915. 7-Mar-4 Bukowskis, Helsinki #436/R
£634	$1014	€900	The dark haired (53x47cm-21x19in) s.d.1914. 21-Sep-3 Bukowskis, Helsinki #447/R
£694	$1160	€1000	Portrait of lady (64x56cm-25x22in) s.d.1914. 26-Oct-3 Bukowskis, Helsinki #479/R
£937	$1566	€1350	Flowers (35x44cm-14x17in) s.d.1924. 26-Oct-3 Bukowskis, Helsinki #477/R
£1014	$1814	€1500	Winter landscape from Hyvinge (56x60cm-22x24in) s.d.1916. 8-May-4 Bukowskis, Helsinki #55/R est:1500-1800
£1014	$1814	€1500	Winter landscape, Lapland (47x65cm-19x26in) s. 8-May-4 Bukowskis, Helsinki #202/R est:1500-1800
£1042	$1740	€1500	Landscape from Lapland (42x52cm-17x20in) s.d.1909. 26-Oct-3 Bukowskis, Helsinki #478/R est:1400
£1127	$1949	€1600	Still life of roses (50x55cm-20x22in) s.d.1919. 13-Dec-3 Hagelstam, Helsinki #145/R est:2000
£1208	$2223	€1800	Lady wearing hat (63x53cm-25x21in) s.d.1935. 25-Mar-4 Hagelstam, Helsinki #900 est:2000
£1250	$2088	€1800	Yellow marigolds in blue vase (36x46cm-14x18in) s.d.1929 lit. 26-Oct-3 Bukowskis, Helsinki #476/R est:1200
£1477	$2717	€2200	Girl (56x48cm-22x19in) s.d.1924. 25-Mar-4 Hagelstam, Helsinki #991 est:500
£1875	$3131	€2700	Still life of fish (83x85cm-33x33in) s.d.1926. 26-Oct-3 Bukowskis, Helsinki #475/R est:1600
£2867	$4874	€4100	The chauffeur (65x62cm-26x24in) s.d.1914 lit. 29-Nov-3 Bukowskis, Helsinki #23/R est:3000-4000
Works on paper			
£267	$491	€400	Flowers (34x36cm-13x14in) s.d.1927 W/C. 9-Jun-4 Bukowskis, Helsinki #536/R

RUOPPOLO, Gian Battista (1629-1693) Italian

£28000	$48440	€40880	Turnips in a basket with cauliflower, cardoon, apples and a copper pot on a ledge (62x75cm-24x30in) 10-Dec-3 Christie's, London #90/R est:15000-20000
£61074	$114208	€91000	Still life of fruit with grapes, watermelon and figs (71x105cm-28x41in) 25-Feb-4 Porro, Milan #28/R est:80000
£70345	$117476	€102000	Still life with grapes, peaches and apples (60x74cm-24x29in) 15-Nov-3 Porro, Milan #235/R est:62000

RUOPPOLO, Gian Battista (attrib) (1629-1693) Italian

£6579	$12105	€10000	Still life with oranges and orange blossom (30x41cm-12x16in) 24-Jun-4 Dr Fritz Nagel, Stuttgart #634/R est:15000
£15493	$26803	€22000	Still life with two cabbages and celery (50x67cm-20x26in) 11-Dec-3 Dr Fritz Nagel, Stuttgart #423/R est:25000

RUOPPOLO, Gian Battista (circle) (1629-1693) Italian

£5862	$9790	€8500	Still life with fruit, plate, lizards (80x100cm-31x39in) 9-Jul-3 Hugo Ruef, Munich #14/R est:8000

RUOPPOLO, Giuseppe (attrib) (1639-1710) Italian

£33113	$60265	€50000	Still lives with fruit and vegetables (76x95cm-30x37in) octagonal pair. 16-Jun-4 Christie's, Rome #477/R est:30000-40000

RUOPPOLO, Giuseppe (circle) (1639-1710) Italian

£9000	$15570	€13140	Mushrooms, pomegranates and other fruits on a stone ledge (42x59cm-17x23in) 10-Dec-3 Bonhams, New Bond Street #60/R est:6000-8000

RUOPPOLO, Giuseppe (style) (1639-1710) Italian

£11000	$20130	€16060	Still life of fruit in landscape (71x88cm-28x35in) prov. 8-Jul-4 Sotheby's, London #324/R est:10000-15000

RUOT (1939-) ?

£1719	$2923	€2510	Concert (80x80cm-31x31in) s. 25-Nov-3 Germann, Zurich #107/R est:4000-6000 (S.FR 3800)

RUPE, Dan (20th C) American

£216	$400	€315	Bay windows (66x56cm-26x22in) s. 15-Feb-4 Outer Cape Auctions, Provincetown #40/R

RUPERTI, Madya (1903-1981) Swiss/Russian

Works on paper			
£345	$631	€500	Untitled (45x42cm-18x17in) s.d.60 gouache. 27-Jan-4 Dorotheum, Vienna #185/R
£455	$755	€660	Untitled (17x24cm-7x9in) mono.d.62 material collage board. 13-Jun-3 Zofingen, Switzerland #3002 (S.FR 1000)

RUPP, Walter (1902-) German

Sculpture			
£955	$1585	€1385	Seated female nude (38x36cm-15x14in) s.d.1945 dark pat.bronze num.8/12 Cast.C.Valsuani. 13-Jun-3 Zofingen, Switzerland #2243/R est:2500 (S.FR 2100)

RUPPE, Michael (1863-?) Austrian

£267	$491	€400	Walker with view of village (48x64cm-19x25in) s. 9-Jun-4 Dorotheum, Salzburg #535/R
£839	$1427	€1200	Salzberg with Untersberg in evening light (68x97cm-27x38in) s. board. 20-Nov-3 Dorotheum, Salzburg #215/R

RUPPERSBERG, Allen (1944-) American

Works on paper			
£2500	$4550	€3650	Art for Mammoth adventures (203x305cm-80x120in) collage four parts exec 1995 prov. 4-Feb-4 Sotheby's, Olympia #59/R est:3000-4000

RUPPERSTAHL, E M (20th C) Austrian?

£2837	$4738	€4000	Where to (170x63cm-67x25in) s.i.d.02 jute. 14-Oct-3 Dorotheum, Vienna #315/R est:1200-1500

RUPPERT, Otto von (1841-?) German

£3315	$6000	€4840	Nomads resting by the river with pyramids beyond (49x39cm-19x15in) s.i. 30-Mar-4 Christie's, Rockefeller NY #75/R est:7000-9000

RUPPRECHT, Otto (1846-1893) German

£1399	$2378	€2000	Summer idyll on farmstead (40x50cm-16x20in) s.i. 22-Nov-3 Arnold, Frankfurt #625/R est:1600

RUPPRECHT, Wilhelm (19th C) German

£543	$1000	€793	European country village (69x99cm-27x39in) s. 26-Jun-4 Susanin's, Chicago #6050/R est:1000-2000

RURIYA, John (20th C) Australian

Works on paper			
£488	$771	€712	Cabbage palms (79x37cm-31x15in) earth pigments eucalyptus bark exec.c.1962 prov. 28-Jul-3 Sotheby's, Paddington #449 (A.D 1200)

RUSCHA, Edward (1937-) American

£6000	$11040	€8760	Fleetwood (30x23cm-12x9in) s.d.2001 i. verso acrylic card prov. 24-Jun-4 Sotheby's, London #248/R est:6000-8000
£26946	$45000	€39341	South to Sunset (41x51cm-16x20in) s.i.d.1999 acrylic prov. 12-Nov-3 Christie's, Rockefeller NY #391/R est:50000-70000
£27933	$50000	€40782	N No (51x61cm-20x24in) s.d.1993 verso acrylic linen prov.exhib. 13-May-4 Sotheby's, New York #249/R est:50000-70000
£30726	$55000	€44860	Light (44x87cm-17x34in) sprayed enamel acrylic paper collage board exec 89-90 prov. 12-May-4 Christie's, Rockefeller NY #173/R est:35000-45000
£56886	$95000	€83054	Pole (153x102cm-60x40in) s.d.86 acrylic paper prov. 13-Nov-3 Sotheby's, New York #283/R est:50000-70000
£67039	$120000	€97877	Brave men (152x102cm-60x40in) s.d.86 acrylic paper prov. 12-May-4 Christie's, Rockefeller NY #174/R est:120000-180000
£67039	$120000	€97877	Major and the Minor (157x229cm-62x90in) s.d.1982 verso prov. 12-May-4 Christie's, Rockefeller NY #198/R est:180000-220000

£67039 $120000 €97877 Exhibition of sleepers (102x152cm-40x60in) s.d.1985 acrylic pigment prov. 13-May-4 Sotheby's, New York #226/R est:70000-90000
£83799 $150000 €122347 Polyester Hearts (97x97cm-38x38in) s.i.d.1990 stretcher acrylic prov. 12-May-4 Christie's, Rockefeller NY #196/R est:180000-250000
£89820 $150000 €131137 Table (129x168cm-51x66in) s.d.1996 verso s.i.d.1996 stretcher acrylic prov.exhib. 13-Nov-3 Sotheby's, New York #279/R est:150000-200000
£107784 $180000 €157365 Toy, Plans, Parts, Wheels (56x203cm-22x80in) s.i.d.1982 verso prov. 12-Nov-3 Christie's, Rockefeller NY #382/R est:200000-250000
£134078 $240000 €195754 Joshua (203x117cm-80x46in) s.d.1987 verso s.i.d.stretcher acrylic prov.exhib.lit. 13-May-4 Sotheby's, New York #227/R est:200000-300000
£142458 $255000 €207989 Kay eye doubles (56x203cm-22x80in) s.i.d.1979overlap prov.exhib. 13-May-4 Phillips, New York #29/R est:250000-350000
£195531 $350000 €285475 Boulangerie (25x35cm-10x14in) s.d.1961 paper prov.exhib.lit. 11-May-4 Christie's, Rockefeller NY #10/R est:200000-300000
£260000 $473200 €379600 Amphetamine, pencil (51x61cm-20x24in) s.i.d.1969 on stretcher prov. 4-Feb-4 Christie's, London #40/R est:140000-200000
£287425 $480000 €419641 Truth (136x153cm-54x60in) s.d.1973 verso prov.exhib. 12-Nov-3 Sotheby's, New York #53/R est:450000-650000
£307263 $550000 €448604 News (244x183cm-96x72in) s.d.1990 verso s.i.d.stretcher acrylic prov.exhib. 11-May-4 Christie's, Rockefeller NY #4/R est:400000-600000
£307263 $550000 €448604 Uncertain trail (119x305cm-47x120in) s.i.d.1986 stretcher acrylic prov.exhib. 11-May-4 Christie's, Rockefeller NY #33/R est:400000-600000
£407186 $680000 €594492 Name (150x370cm-59x146in) acrylic painted 1987 prov.exhib. 11-Nov-3 Christie's, Rockefeller NY #54/R est:400000-600000
£838323 $1400000 €1223952 Mind - Red (152x140cm-60x55in) s.d.1968 verso prov.exhib.lit. 11-Nov-3 Christie's, Rockefeller NY #43/R est:1200000-1800000
£1017964 $1700000 €1486227 Not only securing the last letter but damaging it as well, boss (150x140cm-59x55in) s.i.d.1964 on stretcher prov.exhib.lit. 12-Nov-3 Sotheby's, New York #10/R est:1800000-2200000
£1787710 $3200000 €2610057 Damage (183x170cm-72x67in) painted 1964 prov.exhib.lit. 11-May-4 Christie's, Rockefeller NY #48/R est:1800000-2500000

Photographs
£6587 $11000 €9617 Surrealism soaped and scrubbed (27x27cm-11x11in) with sig.d.2/11 chromogenic print. 21-Oct-3 Swann Galleries, New York #300/R est:10000-15000
£11976 $20000 €17485 Sunset strip, greenblatts no 14 (50x76cm-20x30in) s.d.1976-1995 num.14/25 verso black white photo prov. 13-Nov-3 Sotheby's, New York #280/R est:10000-15000
£27933 $50000 €40782 Gasoline stations (49x58cm-19x23in) st.i. num.10/25 ten gelatin silver prints on board prov.lit. 12-May-4 Christie's, Rockefeller NY #142/R est:60000-80000
£33520 $60000 €48939 Nine swimming pools (41x41cm-16x16in) s.num.6/30 d.1968-1997 nine colour coupler prints prov.exhib.lit. 12-May-4 Christie's, Rockefeller NY #141/R est:60000-80000
£37989 $68000 €55464 Parking lots (39x39cm-15x15in) init.num.35 verso gelatin silver prints 30 album prov.exhib.lit. 14-May-4 Phillips, New York #243/R est:50000-70000

Prints
£1946 $3250 €2841 Lisp (51x71cm-20x28in) s.d.1970 num.6/90 col lithograph. 21-Oct-3 Bonhams & Butterfields, San Francisco #1411/R
£2545 $4250 €3716 Now (153x102cm-60x40in) s.d.1990 num.51/60 col lithograph. 21-Oct-3 Bonhams & Butterfields, San Francisco #1413/R
£2684 $4750 €3919 Sea of desire (44x65cm-17x26in) s.d.1984 num.9/25 lithograph. 30-Apr-4 Sotheby's, New York #455/R est:3000-5000
£2945 $4800 €4300 Rooster (112x77cm-44x30in) s.d.1988 num.18/50 etching col aquatint on Somerset. 24-Sep-3 Christie's, Rockefeller NY #369/R est:3000-5000
£3352 $6000 €4894 Big dipper over desert (61x91cm-24x36in) s.d.1982 num.8/48 aquatint. 16-May-4 Wright, Chicago #323/R est:1000-1500
£4237 $7500 €6186 1984 (35x45cm-14x18in) s.i.d.1967 hand col lithograph. 30-Apr-4 Sotheby's, New York #457/R est:4000-5000
£4908 $8000 €7166 Ship (114x86cm-45x34in) s.d.86 num.26/30 brown lithograph on Arches. 24-Sep-3 Christie's, Rockefeller NY #368/R est:4000-6000
£7910 $14000 €11549 Cheese mold standard with olive (50x94cm-20x37in) s.d.1969 num.123/150 col screenprint. 30-Apr-4 Sotheby's, New York #458/R est:8000-12000
£10588 $18000 €15458 Clock (103x86cm-41x34in) s. mixografia. 31-Oct-3 Sotheby's, New York #747/R
£14118 $24000 €20612 Double standard (65x103cm-26x41in) s. col screenprint exec.1969. 4-Nov-3 Christie's, Rockefeller NY #343/R est:30000-40000

Sculpture
£5587 $10000 €8157 Me (20x13x3cm-8x5x1in) s.d.2001 inside acrylic on 1930 clothbound edn of book. 13-May-4 Sotheby's, New York #252/R est:8000-12000

Works on paper
£694 $1160 €1000 Blankenese houses (30x40cm-12x16in) s. W/C over pencil. 24-Oct-3 Ketterer, Hamburg #532/R
£1389 $2319 €2000 Venetian canal (62x48cm-24x19in) s. W/C. 24-Oct-3 Ketterer, Hamburg #531/R est:2500-3000
£19632 $32000 €28663 Gray black skinny sex (29x74cm-11x29in) s.i.d.1979 verso pastel prov. 23-Sep-3 Christie's, Rockefeller NY #93/R est:15000-20000
£27933 $50000 €40782 Polynesian sickness (53x74cm-21x29in) s.i.d.1984 dry pigment prov. 13-May-4 Sotheby's, New York #232/R est:50000-70000
£36313 $65000 €53017 Jelly (35x34cm-14x13in) s.i.d.1964 prov. 13-May-4 Sotheby's, New York #150/R est:50000-70000
£37126 $62000 €54204 Styrene (58x73cm-23x29in) s.d.1974 verso gunpowder pastel prov. 12-Nov-3 Christie's, Rockefeller NY #337/R est:65000-85000
£38000 $69160 €55480 Fats (29x74cm-11x29in) init.d.1972 gun powder pastel pencil prov. 5-Feb-4 Christie's, London #183/R est:30000-40000
£40223 $72000 €58726 Room (29x74cm-11x29in) s.d.1972 gunpowder prov. 12-May-4 Christie's, Rockefeller NY #163/R est:40000-60000
£47486 $85000 €69330 Vanish (29x74cm-11x29in) s.d.1972 gunpowder pastel prov. 13-May-4 Sotheby's, New York #151/R est:40000-60000
£75000 $136500 €109500 These are brave days (101x152cm-40x60in) s.d.1989 dry pigment gouache prov.exhib. 5-Feb-4 Christie's, London #180/R est:50000-70000

RUSCHE, Helmut (1952-) Austrian
£867 $1560 €1300 Clown with glass heart (64x96cm-25x38in) s.d.78 masonite. 21-Apr-4 Dorotheum, Vienna #234/R

RUSCHI, Francesco (17th C) Italian
£14444 $26000 €21088 Venus mourning the Death of Adonis (148x120cm-58x47in) 23-Jan-4 Christie's, Rockefeller NY #46/R est:12000-18000
£30872 $55262 €46000 Venus mourning Adonis (123x170cm-48x67in) prov.lit. 26-May-4 Porro, Milan #41/R est:75000-90000

RUSHBURY, Julia (1930-) British
£600 $1056 €876 Wintry town scene (62x48cm-24x19in) s. i. verso board. 18-May-4 Fellows & Sons, Birmingham #95/R

RUSHBURY, Sir Henry (1889-1968) British
Works on paper
£350 $602 €511 The Louvre (23x36cm-9x14in) pen ink wash. 5-Dec-3 Keys, Aylsham #427
£375 $638 €548 Montmartre House (33x23cm-13x9in) s.d.1925 W/C prov. 5-Nov-3 John Nicholson, Haslemere #571
£500 $860 €730 Custom House, Weymouth (28x41cm-11x16in) s. W/C. 2-Dec-3 Gorringes, Lewes #2444
£500 $895 €730 Study of an Italian fountain (45x31cm-18x12in) s. W/C. 25-May-4 Bonhams, Knightsbridge #18/R
£600 $1032 €876 Antwerp (29x43cm-11x17in) s.i.d.1933 pencil brown ink W/C. 3-Dec-3 Christie's, Kensington #219/R
£700 $1204 €1022 Schiavoni, evening, Venice (28x41cm-11x16in) s.i. i.verso pencil brown ink W/C. 3-Dec-3 Christie's, Kensington #222/R
£780 $1342 €1139 Durham (26x42cm-10x17in) s.i.d.1933 pencil black ink W/C sold with another by K.Steel. 3-Dec-3 Christie's, Kensington #218/R
£850 $1462 €1241 Rome (28x42cm-11x17in) s.i. pencil brown ink W/C. 3-Dec-3 Christie's, Kensington #223/R

RUSHENT, Kathleen (20th C) Canadian
£407 $680 €594 Untitled - railroad crossing (90x120cm-35x47in) s. 17-Nov-3 Hodgins, Calgary #319/R (C.D 900)

RUSHTON, George Robert (1869-1947) British
Works on paper
£380 $688 €555 Suffolk landscape with Orford Castle in the distance (23x33cm-9x13in) s. W/C. 16-Apr-4 Keys, Aylsham #483

RUSINOL, Santiago (1861-1931) Spanish
£120000 $204000 €175200 View along the river Jucar, Cuenca (100x130cm-39x51in) s. exhib.lit. 18-Nov-3 Sotheby's, London #230/R

RUSKIEWICZ, Franciszek (1819-1883) Polish
£2837 $4596 €4000 River landscape with figures (55x69cm-22x27in) s. lit. 23-May-3 Karlheinz Kaupp, Staufen #1908 est:400

RUSKIN, John (1819-1900) British
Works on paper
£629 $1000 €918 Study of Venetian columns. Sketches of a woman (15x22cm-6x9in) s.i.d.11th October 1845 ink pencil double-sided. 13-Sep-3 Weschler, Washington #668/R
£800 $1464 €1168 Eton College (8x10cm-3x4in) s.verso W/C pencil prov. 8-Jul-4 Duke & Son, Dorchester #128/R
£1300 $2210 €1898 Italian gothic spire (17x11cm-7x4in) s. grey wash pencil htd white prov. 27-Nov-3 Sotheby's, London #305/R est:1500-2000
£1800 $3060 €2628 View in the Alps (12x15cm-5x6in) pen ink W/C over pencil htd white. 27-Nov-3 Sotheby's, London #304/R est:2000-3000
£2400 $4080 €3504 Interior of No.90 The High Street, Oxford (26x17cm-10x7in) pencil htd white exhib.lit. 27-Nov-3 Sotheby's, London #306/R est:2000-3000
£2600 $4420 €3796 View of Edinburgh (18x23cm-7x9in) s.i.d.1837 d.1879 pencil corners cut. 30-Oct-3 Christie's, London #15/R est:1800-2500
£2800 $5152 €4088 Houses at Neuchatel, Switzerland (12x17cm-5x7in) s.i. W/C over pencil htd white. 26-Mar-4 Sotheby's, London #125/R est:3000-5000
£4730 $8750 €7095 View of Venice (13x15cm-5x6in) W/C prov. 14-Jul-4 American Auctioneer #490255/R est:6000-8000
£13000 $22100 €18980 View of Geneva, Switzerland (16x23cm-6x9in) init.i.d.1854 pencil pen ink W/C htd white scratching out prov. 20-Nov-3 Christie's, London #132/R est:10000-15000
£60000 $109800 €87600 Oxalis and heather (18x27cm-7x11in) with i. pencil W/C htd bodycol scratching out prov.exhib.lit. 3-Jun-4 Christie's, London #155/R est:10000-15000
£240000 $408000 €350400 Bellinzona, Switzerland, looking north towards the St. Gotthard pass (52x35cm-20x14in) pencil W/C bodycol prov.lit. 20-Nov-3 Christie's, London #49/R est:60000-80000

RUSKIN, John (attrib) (1819-1900) British
Works on paper
£2703 $5000 €4055 Mountains and clouds (23x15cm-9x6in) W/C prov. 14-Jul-4 American Auctioneer #490254/R est:3000-5000

RUSLI (1922-) Indonesian
£1720 $2753 €2511 Boats (50x59cm-20x23in) s.d.21-7-84. 18-May-3 Sotheby's, Singapore #173/R est:4000-6000 (S.D 4800)
£1853 $3095 €2705 Boats by the beach (60x75cm-24x30in) mono.d.21-8-77. 26-Oct-3 Christie's, Hong Kong #68/R est:22000-32000 (HK.D 24000)
£2451 $4436 €3578 Odalan (65x50cm-26x20in) s.d.1969. 3-Apr-4 Glerum, Singapore #12/R est:4000-5000 (S.D 7500)
£3922 $7098 €5726 Wanita dan Gedang Hijau, Upacara (90x117cm-35x46in) s.d.1966 i.verso prov. 3-Apr-4 Glerum, Singapore #29/R est:8000-11000 (S.D 12000)
£17391 $26957 €25391 Temple (100x130cm-39x51in) s.d.1964. 6-Oct-2 Sotheby's, Singapore #131/R est:15000-20000 (S.D 48000)

RUSS, Franz (elder) (1817-1892) Austrian
£958 $1600 €1399 Christ Child and lamb (46x37cm-18x15in) s. 16-Nov-3 Bonhams & Butterfields, Los Angeles #7031/R est:2000-3000

RUSS, Robert (1847-1922) Austrian
£8333 $14167 €12000 Limone on Lake Garda (31x40cm-12x16in) s. panel. 28-Oct-3 Wiener Kunst Auktionen, Vienna #48/R est:12000-25000
£12227 $22253 €17851 Coastal landscape near Sorrent (31x45cm-12x18in) s. 16-Jun-4 Fischer, Luzern #1233/R est:5000-7000 (S.FR 28000)
£17450 $31235 €26000 Conversation in an overgrown garden (24x32cm-9x13in) s. board. 27-May-4 Dorotheum, Vienna #174/R est:20000-23000

£33557 $59396 €50000 Courtyard in Stein an der Donau (115x90cm-45x35in) s. 28-Apr-4 Wiener Kunst Auktionen, Vienna #60/R est:70000-140000

Works on paper

£1879 $3458 €2800 Park landscape (23x15cm-9x6in) s. W/C bodycol. 26-Mar-4 Dorotheum, Vienna #224/R est:1400-1600

RUSSEL, Theodore (1614-1689) British

£3529 $6000 €5152 Portrait of lady, said to be the Duchess of Orleans (40x32cm-16x13in) panel. 25-Nov-3 Christie's, Rockefeller NY #493/R est:4000-6000

RUSSELL, Andrew J (1830-1902) American

Photographs

£2754 $4600 €4021 Executives of the Union Pacific and well wishers (23x31cm-9x12in) albumen print. 21-Oct-3 Swann Galleries, New York #23/R est:7000-8000

RUSSELL, Charles M (1864-1926) American

£31977 $55000 €46686 Cowboy riding his horse uphill (30x41cm-12x16in) s. W/C traces pencil prov. 7-Dec-3 Freeman, Philadelphia #124 est:40000-60000
£197861 $370000 €288877 Wild meat for wild men (51x91cm-20x36in) s.d.1890 prov.exhib.lit. 24-Jul-4 Coeur d'Alene, Hayden #173/R est:250000-350000

Sculpture

£1677 $2700 €2432 Awkward situation (10x18cm-4x7in) bronze edition of 12. 22-Aug-3 Altermann Galleries, Santa Fe #215
£1860 $3200 €2716 Medecine man (18cm-7in) i. pat bronze. 2-Dec-3 Christie's, Rockefeller NY #76/R est:3000-5000
£2793 $5000 €4078 Mountain goat (15cm-6in) bronze. 15-May-4 Altermann Galleries, Santa Fe #75/R
£3073 $5500 €4487 Buffalo (13cm-5in) bronze. 15-May-4 Altermann Galleries, Santa Fe #74/R
£3106 $5000 €4504 Red bird (30x36x20cm-12x14x8in) num.6/13 bronze. 22-Aug-3 Altermann Galleries, Santa Fe #85
£64171 $120000 €93690 Bronc twister (46x33x23cm-18x13x9in) bronze executed c.1929-34 prov.exhib.lit. 24-Jul-4 Coeur d'Alene, Hayden #34/R est:75000-150000
£80214 $150000 €117112 Bluffers (18cm-7in) s. bronze prov.lit. 24-Jul-4 Coeur d'Alene, Hayden #168/R est:60000-90000

Works on paper

£4011 $7500 €5856 Kyle Lowry on Colonel (13x13cm-5x5in) s. pencil prov. 24-Jul-4 Coeur d'Alene, Hayden #254/R est:5000-10000
£14706 $27500 €21471 It was a perilous moment and an unfortunate hour (28x25cm-11x10in) s. mixed media lit. 24-Jul-4 Coeur d'Alene, Hayden #203/R est:15000-25000
£18717 $35000 €27327 Young scout (43x33cm-17x13in) s. pen ink prov.lit. 24-Jul-4 Coeur d'Alene, Hayden #35/R est:20000-30000
£32353 $55000 €47235 Deer hunting (22x40cm-9x16in) init. W/C gouache prov. 21-Nov-3 Skinner, Boston #337/R est:75000-125000
£36932 $65000 €53921 Indian with his Winchester (46x46cm-18x18in) s. W/C prov. 19-May-4 Sotheby's, New York #202/R est:60000-80000
£48295 $85000 €70511 Cowboy on the range (36x51cm-14x20in) s. W/C prov. 19-May-4 Sotheby's, New York #201/R est:80000-120000
£58824 $110000 €85883 Friend thed, letter (28x20cm-11x8in) s. W/C pen ink two prov.lit. 24-Jul-4 Coeur d'Alene, Hayden #104/R est:125000-175000
£67901 $110000 €98456 Chase (38x65cm-15x26in) s.d.1900 ink pencil dr. prov. 8-Aug-3 Barridorf, Portland #259/R est:60000-90000
£294118 $550000 €429412 Navajo lookout, surveying the plains (38x53cm-15x21in) s. W/C prov. 24-Jul-4 Coeur d'Alene, Hayden #76/R est:400000-600000

RUSSELL, Clarissa (1809-1854) American

Miniatures

£11111 $18000 €16222 Timothy Francis Waters with King Charles spaniel (13x10cm-5x4in) i. verso ivory lit. 1-Aug-3 North East Auctions, Portsmouth #343/R est:12000-18000
£24691 $40000 €36049 Seated young children on colourful floor cloth (13x10cm-5x4in) ivory pair framed together. 1-Aug-3 North East Auctions, Portsmouth #345/R

RUSSELL, Clarissa (attrib) (1809-1854) American

Works on paper

£882 $1500 €1288 Portrait of a young child in a yellow dress (20x15cm-8x6in) W/C. 21-Nov-3 Eldred, East Dennis #836/R est:3000-5000

RUSSELL, Deborah (1951-) Australian

£289 $535 €422 Elephant (76x66cm-30x26in) init. s.i.verso prov. 15-Mar-4 Sotheby's, Melbourne #104 (A.D 700)
£372 $688 €543 TCH, TCH, TCH, TCH (45x55cm-18x22in) indis sig. s.i.d.1989 verso linen on canvas prov. 15-Mar-4 Sotheby's, Melbourne #66 est:1000-2000 (A.D 900)
£372 $688 €543 Ballpark (45x55cm-18x22in) init. s.i.d.1989verso oil on linen prov. 15-Mar-4 Sotheby's, Melbourne #136 est:1000-2000 (A.D 900)
£372 $688 €543 Bottom of the garden (45x55cm-18x22in) init. s.i.d.1989 verso linen on canvas. 15-Mar-4 Sotheby's, Melbourne #139 est:1000-2000 (A.D 900)
£393 $726 €574 Walk (45x55cm-18x22in) s.d.1989 i.verso oil on linen prov. 15-Mar-4 Sotheby's, Melbourne #135 est:1000-2000 (A.D 950)
£413 $764 €603 Haystack (45x55cm-18x22in) init. s.i.d.1989 verso linen on canvas prov. 15-Mar-4 Sotheby's, Melbourne #140 est:1000-2000 (A.D 1000)
£413 $731 €603 Untitled (22x30cm-9x12in) s.d.94 verso board prov. 3-May-4 Christie's, Melbourne #257/R (A.D 1000)

RUSSELL, Edward J (1835-1906) American

Works on paper

£452 $800 €660 Naval battle (48x81cm-19x32in) s.i.d.1906 W/C board. 27-Apr-4 Doyle, New York #26

RUSSELL, George (1867-1935) Irish

£1831 $2930 €2600 Two girls by a lake at night (41x61cm-16x24in) 16-Sep-3 Whyte's, Dublin #107/R est:3000-4000
£2000 $3580 €2920 Youth with dreams to dream (53x81cm-21x32in) mono. prov.exhib. 14-May-4 Christie's, Kensington #366/R est:2000-3000
£2349 $4158 €3500 Guardian of the village (41x51cm-16x20in) s. 27-Apr-4 Whyte's, Dublin #52/R est:4000-6000
£4400 $8008 €6424 Evening, two girls on a county Donegal hillside (41x53cm-16x21in) mono. 15-Jun-4 David Lay, Penzance #513/R est:2000-3000
£5369 $9503 €8000 Dawning of the New Republic (36x51cm-14x20in) s. i.verso prov. 27-Apr-4 Whyte's, Dublin #111/R est:8000-10000
£5634 $9014 €8000 Two ladies on the Strand (41x53cm-16x21in) mono. 16-Sep-3 Whyte's, Dublin #105/R est:8000-10000
£5800 $10382 €8468 On the beach (41x53cm-16x21in) init. 14-May-4 Christie's, London #202/R est:5000-8000
£6500 $11830 €9490 Country Donegal farm boy and his companion walking on a headland (41x53cm-16x21in) mono. 15-Jun-4 David Lay, Penzance #523/R est:4000-6000
£8054 $14416 €12000 Nocturne (52x80cm-20x31in) mono. 31-May-4 Hamilton Osborne King, Dublin #155/R est:10000-15000
£9000 $16290 €13500 Three children playing in the sand dunes (41x54cm-16x21in) mono. prov. 30-Mar-4 De Veres Art Auctions, Dublin #58a/R est:10000-15000
£11268 $19493 €16000 Women and children paddling (43x56cm-17x22in) mono. 10-Dec-3 Bonhams & James Adam, Dublin #61/R est:10000-15000
£12752 $22570 €19000 Woman by a rock pool (41x53cm-16x21in) s. 27-Apr-4 Whyte's, Dublin #26/R est:8000-10000
£14865 $28095 €22000 Two girls by the shore (51x66cm-20x26in) mono. 17-Feb-4 Whyte's, Dublin #51/R est:12000-15000
£18310 $31676 €26000 Women and children paddling (40x61cm-16x24in) mono. 10-Dec-3 Bonhams & James Adam, Dublin #62/R est:10000-15000

RUSSELL, George Horne (1861-1933) Canadian

£264 $473 €385 St Andrews, New Brunswick (24x30cm-9x12in) s. board prov. 6-May-4 Heffel, Vancouver #125/R (C.D 650)
£364 $593 €531 St. Andrews by the sea, N.B, Canada (24x30cm-9x12in) s. i.verso panel prov. 23-Sep-3 Ritchie, Toronto #67/R (C.D 800)
£960 $1757 €1402 Portrait of a man with a pipe (41x35cm-16x14in) s. 1-Jun-4 Joyner Waddington, Toronto #344/R est:3000-5000 (C.D 2400)
£960 $1757 €1402 Riverside home by moonlight (50x65cm-20x26in) s. 1-Jun-4 Joyner Waddington, Toronto #383/R est:1500-2000 (C.D 2400)
£1429 $2300 €2086 Duck pond (36x51cm-14x20in) s. prov. 20-Aug-3 James Julia, Fairfield #751/R est:2000-4000
£1584 $2550 €2313 Summer sailing days at St Andrews (46x66cm-18x26in) s. prov. 20-Aug-3 James Julia, Fairfield #750/R est:2000-4000
£2140 $3638 €3124 Herder and sheep (86x108cm-34x43in) s. prov. 18-Nov-3 Sotheby's, Toronto #99/R est:4000-6000 (C.D 4750)
£5600 $10248 €8176 Mill Point - Montreal Harbour (60x81cm-24x32in) s. 1-Jun-4 Joyner Waddington, Toronto #116/R est:10000-15000 (C.D 14000)

Works on paper

£250 $408 €365 Cottage (22x29cm-9x11in) s. W/C prov. 23-Sep-3 Ritchie, Toronto #84/R (C.D 550)
£318 $519 €464 Summer scene (20x26cm-8x10in) s. W/C prov. 23-Sep-3 Ritchie, Toronto #82/R (C.D 700)

RUSSELL, Gyrth (1892-1970) Canadian

£350 $637 €511 Dinas Powis woods (41x58cm-16x23in) s.i.d.1963 board. 15-Jun-4 David Lay, Penzance #119
£550 $1001 €803 Penarth Pier with either the Waverley of the Balmoral (23x35cm-9x14in) 21-Jun-4 Bonhams, Bath #347
£750 $1365 €1095 Demonstration sketch - ship with tugs (44x74cm-17x29in) s. board. 21-Jun-4 Bonhams, Bath #345/R
£900 $1665 €1314 Fisherman's harbour, King's Lynn (47x54cm-19x21in) s. 11-Feb-4 Sotheby's, Olympia #154/R est:800-1200
£1400 $2618 €2100 Mevagissy harbour (37x53cm-15x21in) s. board. 21-Jul-4 Anthemion, Cardiff #616/R est:300-500
£2000 $3440 €2920 Harbour scene (47x57cm-19x22in) s. canvasboard. 2-Dec-3 Bonhams, New Bond Street #3/R est:2000-3000
£3200 $5440 €4672 Colourful corner (53x76cm-21x30in) s. 26-Nov-3 Sotheby's, Olympia #51/R est:2500-3500

Works on paper

£280 $512 €409 Yorkshire Cobbles (30x41cm-12x16in) s. W/C. 27-Jan-4 Gorringes, Lewes #1727
£280 $524 €420 Customs House, Kings Lynn (23x36cm-9x14in) s. 20-Jul-4 Peter Francis, Wales #68

RUSSELL, James (fl.1878-1887) British

Works on paper

£368 $600 €537 Largs (13x18cm-5x7in) s. W/C. 28-Sep-3 Simpson's, Houston #181/R

RUSSELL, John (1745-1806) British

£244 $450 €356 Portrait of F Kimble, actor (74x61cm-29x24in) i. 9-Jun-4 Alderfer's, Hatfield #323
£3200 $5440 €4672 Portrait of a gentleman, identified as George Bruere, Governor of Bermuda (93x71cm-37x28in) prov. 25-Nov-3 Christie's, London #35/R est:3000-5000

Works on paper

£450 $828 €657 Portrait of a gentleman, in a blue jacket (59x44cm-23x17in) pastel oval. 25-Mar-4 Christie's, Kensington #9/R
£500 $910 €750 Portrait of John Johnson (39x33cm-15x13in) pastel prov. 15-Jun-4 Rosebery Fine Art, London #579
£620 $1110 €905 Portrait of Charles Dawkins as a boy, with a sleeping dog (66x51cm-26x20in) pastel. 22-Mar-4 Bonhams & Brooks, Norfolk #186/R
£2000 $3640 €2920 Portrait of a Turk (59x48cm-23x19in) pastel. 1-Jul-4 Sotheby's, London #132/R est:2000-3000
£3400 $6018 €4964 Portraits of Miss Paterson and Mr Hardcastle (60x45cm-24x18in) one s.d.1785 pastel oval pair. 27-Apr-4 Henry Adams, Chichester #646/R est:2000-3000
£6500 $12025 €9750 Portrait of of a young lady with a bonnet (61x45cm-24x18in) s.d.1801 pastel. 14-Jul-4 Sotheby's, Olympia #36/R est:3000-5000

RUSSELL, John (attrib) (1745-1806) British

£1000 $1840 €1500 Portraits of young boys wearing lace collars (33x28cm-13x11in) oval pair prov. 24-Jun-4 Ewbank, Send #533/R est:800-1200

RUSSELL, John (fl.1869-1918) British

£452 $756 €660 Mallards protecting their young from a pike (68x127cm-27x50in) s. 17-Nov-3 Waddingtons, Toronto #104/R (C.D 1000)

£650 $1034 €949 Still life of brown and rainbow trout (38x77cm-15x30in) s. 9-Sep-3 Bonhams, Knightsbridge #150/R
£3100 $5549 €4526 Still life of fish and creel (37x75cm-15x30in) one s. two. 17-May-4 David Duggleby, Scarborough #685/R est:1000-1500

RUSSELL, John Bucknell (1819-1893) British
£1000 $1860 €1460 Kitchen window (91x71cm-36x28in) s. 4-Mar-4 Christie's, Kensington #125/R est:1200-1800
£5814 $10000 €8488 Salmon and trout on a river bank (46x91cm-18x36in) s. 5-Dec-3 Christie's, Rockefeller NY #96/R est:10000-15000

RUSSELL, John Peter (1859-1930) Australian
£30364 $48887 €44331 Needles, Belle-Ile, Brittany (50x61cm-20x24in) s.indis.d.188 i.verso painted c.1886-87 exhib.lit. 25-Aug-3 Sotheby's, Paddington #8/R est:80000-120000 (A.D 75000)
£64050 $113368 €93513 La Mer a La Spezia (60x72cm-24x28in) s.i. painted c.1896 prov.exhib.lit. 3-May-4 Christie's, Melbourne #55/R est:200000-300000 (A.D 155000)
£113821 $178699 €165040 Belle-Ile, le Pere Polyte, Polyte pecheur (65x81cm-26x32in) s. prov.exhib.lit. 26-Aug-3 Christie's, Sydney #100/R est:350000-400000 (A.D 280000)
Works on paper
£270 $500 €394 Ocean view from a rocky shoreline (25x51cm-10x20in) s. W/C. 19-Jan-4 O'Gallerie, Oregon #39/R
£4959 $9174 €7240 Lavagna. Village scene (18x24cm-7x9in) s.i.d.12 W/C double-sided. 10-Mar-4 Deutscher-Menzies, Melbourne #197/R est:8000-12000 (A.D 12000)

RUSSELL, John Wentworth (1879-1959) Canadian
Works on paper
£383 $705 €559 Gardens at St Cloud, Paris (39x31cm-15x12in) s.i.d.51 W/C. 9-Jun-4 Walker's, Ottawa #119/R (C.D 950)
£968 $1781 €1413 Reclining nude, Paris (30x47cm-12x19in) s.i. W/C. 9-Jun-4 Walker's, Ottawa #118/R est:2500-3000 (C.D 2400)

RUSSELL, Kathleen (1940-) British
£560 $986 €818 Beach scene with figures and sun umbrellas (104x142cm-41x56in) acrylic board. 18-May-4 Woolley & Wallis, Salisbury #65/R

RUSSELL, Lady William (19th C) British
£1700 $2720 €2482 Interior of Lady Russell's drawing room at Carlsbad (28x30cm-11x12in) i.d.1844-45 verso lit. 16-Sep-3 Gorringes, Bexhill #1694/R est:200-300

RUSSELL, Moses B (attrib) (1810-1884) American
Miniatures
£1913 $3500 €2793 Two little girls with a kitten (10x8cm-4x3in) W/C gouache on ivory. 6-Jun-4 Skinner, Boston #7/R est:700-900

RUSSELL, Sir Walter Westley (1867-1949) British
Works on paper
£320 $589 €467 Lane (22x35cm-9x14in) s.d.1935 W/C. 29-Mar-4 Bonhams, Bath #34/R

RUSSELL, William George (1860-?) American
Works on paper
£279 $450 €407 Run aground (18x28cm-7x11in) s. W/C. 20-Aug-3 James Julia, Fairfield #1100/R

RUSSIAN SCHOOL, 18th C
£5921 $10895 €9000 Portrait presume de Catharine II de Russie (65x49cm-26x19in) 25-Jun-4 Daguerre, Paris #113/R est:8000-10000
Sculpture
£7500 $13425 €10950 Hunter with his borzois, equestrian group (42cm-17in) bronze st.f.Wierffel. 26-May-4 Sotheby's, London #463/R est:4000-6000

RUSSIAN SCHOOL, 19th C
£3846 $6538 €5500 Legend of Elias (145x77cm-57x30in) d.1827 oil tempera panel. 20-Nov-3 Van Ham, Cologne #1832/R est:6000
£5000 $8950 €7300 Boat on the shore (49x68cm-19x27in) s. 26-May-4 Sotheby's, London #49/R est:5000-7000
£5282 $9244 €7500 La source (50x50cm-20x20in) indis.sig.d.1846. 18-Dec-3 Tajan, Paris #144/R est:3000-4000
£5667 $10427 €8500 La halte au campement (41x65cm-16x26in) indis.sig.d.1881. 14-Jun-4 Gros & Delettrez, Paris #230/R est:4000-6000
£5847 $10758 €8537 Old peasant (102x76cm-40x30in) bears sig prov. 14-Jun-4 Waddingtons, Toronto #353/R est:15000-20000 (C.D 14500)
£6000 $10740 €8760 Bear hunt (69x105cm-27x41in) indis sig. 26-May-4 Sotheby's, London #77/R est:6000-8000
£6000 $10740 €8760 Military scene (19x33cm-7x13in) oil paper on board. 26-May-4 Sotheby's, Olympia #365/R est:2000-3000
£6093 $11150 €9200 Voilier en pleine mer (121x162cm-48x64in) s.d.1880. 9-Apr-4 Claude Aguttes, Neuilly #135/R est:6000-8000
£6711 $12550 €10000 Gold transport (68x107cm-27x42in) i. 24-Feb-4 Dorotheum, Vienna #123/R est:3000-4000
£7500 $13425 €10950 Black Sea coast (71x115cm-28x45in) s. 26-May-4 Sotheby's, London #54/R est:5000-7000
£7761 $13891 €11331 Lady dressed in deep red (50x38cm-20x15in) panel. 25-May-4 Bukowskis, Stockholm #386/R est:25000-30000 (S.KR 105000)
£8026 $14768 €12200 Paysans russes dans une carriole (27x37cm-11x15in) panel. 25-Jun-4 Piasa, Paris #138/R est:2000-2500
£10000 $17900 €14600 Trompe l'oeil (38x52cm-15x20in) 26-May-4 Sotheby's, London #17/R est:8000-12000
£11000 $19690 €16060 Peasant interior (40x57cm-16x22in) 26-May-4 Sotheby's, London #15/R est:5000-7000
£12000 $21840 €18000 Birch wood in summer (86x140cm-34x55in) s.d.1863. 1-Jul-4 Van Ham, Cologne #1588/R est:1200
£14000 $23800 €20440 Portrait of Emperor Paul I (83x65cm-33x26in) 19-Nov-3 Sotheby's, London #21/R est:8000-10000
£15000 $25500 €21900 Portrait of Anna Efremovna Orenovina in Caucasian costume (68x54cm-27x21in) i.verso painted 1827. 19-Nov-3 Sotheby's, London #1/R est:5000-7000
£16000 $29440 €24000 Vue d'Odessa (44x53cm-17x21in) bears sig. 14-Jun-4 Tajan, Paris #11/R est:3000-5000
£28000 $50120 €40880 Portrait of Catherine the Great (82x67cm-32x26in) 26-May-4 Sotheby's, London #476/R est:12000-18000
Sculpture
£5000 $8650 €7300 Alexander I of Russia (36cm-14in) dark brown pat. bronze. 11-Dec-3 Christie's, London #134/R est:2000-3000
£64430 $117906 €96000 Untitled (153cm-60in) gilt bronze pair. 6-Jul-4 Marc Kohn, Paris #40/R
£90559 $153951 €129500 Egyptian statues (235x45cm-93x18in) bronze pair. 24-Nov-3 Marc Kohn, Paris #89/R
Miniatures
£6500 $11245 €9490 Grand Duke Constantine Pavlovich (10cm-4in) gilt-bronze frame oval. 9-Dec-3 Christie's, London #249/R est:1500-2500
£7500 $13425 €10950 Nobleman and his wife, standing in a landscape (19cm-7in) gilt metal frame rec. 27-May-4 Sotheby's, London #64/R est:3000-5000
Works on paper
£60000 $107400 €87600 Topographical views of St. Petersburg (58x89cm-23x35in) gouache set of five. 26-May-4 Sotheby's, London #12/R est:20000-25000

RUSSIAN SCHOOL, 19th/20th C
£5819 $10649 €8496 The punishment (65x85cm-26x33in) indis.sig. painted c.1900. 9-Jun-4 Rasmussen, Copenhagen #1617/R est:12000 (D.KR 65000)

RUSSIAN SCHOOL, 20th C
£5298 $9642 €8000 Still life with red fruit (49x69cm-19x27in) s.d.1921. 19-Jun-4 St-Germain-en-Laye Encheres #192/R est:800
£5333 $9600 €8000 Landscape with farmstead (62x80cm-24x31in) mono.cyrillic. 21-Apr-4 Dorotheum, Vienna #24/R est:8000-12000
£6058 $9511 €8845 Interior scene with two young girls sewing (44x59cm-17x23in) indis.sig.d.1931. 30-Aug-3 Rasmussen, Havnen #2234 est:10000 (D.KR 65000)

RUSSMAN, Felix (1888-1962) American
£814 $1400 €1188 Autumn moon (76x91cm-30x36in) s. i.verso painted c.1920. 7-Dec-3 Treadway Gallery, Cincinnati #522/R
£872 $1500 €1273 Cloudy sky (51x61cm-20x24in) s. canvas laid down painted c.1920. 7-Dec-3 Treadway Gallery, Cincinnati #520/R est:1500-2000

RUSSO, Germano (1935-) Italian
£203 $350 €296 Lunch in the park garden (76x99cm-30x39in) s. with fingerprint d.1973 masonite. 7-Dec-3 Hindman, Chicago #779/R

RUSSO, Mario (1925-2000) Italian
£268 $499 €400 Bather (60x40cm-24x16in) s. s.i.verso. 4-Mar-4 Babuino, Rome #381
£700 $1190 €1022 Clown (97x69cm-38x27in) s.d.61 panel. 5-Nov-3 John Nicholson, Haslemere #554/R

RUSSOLO, Luigi (1885-1947) Italian
£1325 $2411 €2000 Composition in blue (66x81cm-26x32in) s. canvas on board. 19-Jun-4 Dannenberg, Berlin #610/R est:2000
£3716 $6541 €5500 Woman, tree and cloud (64x84cm-25x33in) s.d.1944 s.i.d.verso board prov. 24-May-4 Christie's, Milan #212/R est:6500-8500

RUSSOV, A (19/20th C) ?
£622 $1132 €933 Still life of lobster, wine, cherries and flowers on table (91x119cm-36x47in) s.d.08. 19-Jun-4 Rasmussen, Havnen #2235/R (D.KR 7000)

RUST, Don (1932-) American
£223 $400 €326 Spotted owl family (91x91cm-36x36in) s. sold with the plate. 15-May-4 Jeffery Burchard, Florida #111
£251 $450 €366 Barred owl family (91x91cm-36x36in) s.d.1993. 15-May-4 Jeffery Burchard, Florida #112
£671 $1201 €1000 Private lesson (75x60cm-30x24in) s. 27-May-4 Sotheby's, Paris #129/R

RUST, Johan Adolph (1828-1915) Dutch
£461 $770 €650 Moored carrier boat (38x52cm-15x20in) panel. 20-Oct-3 Glerum, Amsterdam #25/R
£2000 $3600 €3000 Fisherfolk on a riverbank by a town (16x23cm-6x9in) s. panel. 20-Apr-4 Sotheby's, Amsterdam #7/R est:3000-5000
£2381 $4333 €3500 Entering a harbour in a stiff breeze (22x30cm-9x12in) s. indis d.1845 panel. 3-Feb-4 Christie's, Amsterdam #64/R est:3000-5000
£4514 $7674 €6500 Barrelmakers on the busy Elandsgracht, Amsterdam (55x74cm-22x29in) s. 28-Oct-3 Christie's, Amsterdam #21/R est:7000-9000

RUST, Oscar (20th C) American
£291 $500 €425 O-Bal-Gal-Lala, Sioux Chief, 101 years old (28x23cm-11x9in) s. painted c.1895. 7-Dec-3 Treadway Gallery, Cincinnati #585/R

RUSTI, Olav (1850-1920) Norwegian
£559 $878 €816 Monastery passage with Franciscan monks and doves (41x33cm-16x13in) s.d.78. 30-Aug-3 Rasmussen, Havnen #2156/R (D.KR 6000)

RUSTIGE, Heinrich Franz Gaudenz von (1810-1900) German
£2113 $3380 €3000 Drinker (43x55cm-17x22in) s. 18-Sep-3 Rieber, Stuttgart #1024/R est:4800

RUSTIN, Jean (1928-) French

£1067 $1920 €1600 Femme sur un lit (35x27cm-14x11in) s.i.d.1985 verso. 20-Apr-4 Chenu & Scrive, Lyon #152/R est:1500-2000
£2533 $4560 €3800 Untitled (41x33cm-16x13in) s.d.1983 prov. 25-Apr-4 Versailles Encheres #151 est:3500-4500
£2632 $4842 €4000 Etude de tete (27x35cm-11x14in) s.d.1973 s.i.d.verso prov. 27-Jun-4 Versailles Encheres #128/R est:3000-4000
£10855 $19974 €16500 Amies (162x130cm-64x51in) s.d.1973 s.i.d. verso. 28-Jun-4 Joron-Derem, Paris #189/R est:14000-17000
Works on paper
£700 $1288 €1050 Homme nu sur le carrelage (30x24cm-12x9in) s.d.82 col crayon. 10-Jun-4 Camard, Paris #202
£861 $1567 €1300 Homme. s.d.83 black crayon col crayon. 16-Jun-4 Renaud, Paris #61/R

RUSZCZYC, Ferdynand (1870-1936) Polish

£2247 $3730 €3281 Zarosla (13x17cm-5x7in) s. 15-Jun-3 Agra, Warsaw #18/R est:9000 (P.Z 14000)
£10972 $17116 €16019 Landscape study (41x46cm-16x18in) s.d.00 cardboard. 30-Mar-3 Agra, Warsaw #6/R est:50000 (P.Z 70000)

RUSZKOWSKI, Zdzislaw (1907-1990) Polish

£700 $1120 €1022 Still life with a comport of fruit, bowl of fruit and grapes (40x54cm-16x21in) s. 16-Sep-3 Rosebery Fine Art, London #540/R
£1600 $2752 €2336 Portrait of Doris Pamela Hodin (61x51cm-24x20in) indis.sig. 3-Dec-3 Christie's, Kensington #669/R est:1000-1500
£6500 $12025 €9490 Landscape from Iceland (76x51cm-30x20in) s. lit. 11-Mar-4 Christie's, Kensington #93/R est:800-1200
Works on paper
£250 $455 €365 Landscape at sunset (32x49cm-13x19in) s. pastel W/C. 1-Jul-4 Christie's, Kensington #207
£260 $424 €377 Boats in Kyrenia harbour (21x33cm-8x13in) s. pencil W/C. 23-Sep-3 Bonhams, Leeds #87
£420 $756 €613 Portrait of Pamela and Annabelle Hodin (53x75cm-21x30in) W/C prov. 20-Apr-4 Rosebery Fine Art, London #609
£650 $1086 €949 Boats in a bay (33x49cm-13x19in) s. W/C. 16-Oct-3 Christie's, Kensington #440

RUTER, Heinrich (1877-?) German?

£833 $1325 €1200 La caravane franchissant la porte de la ville (60x60cm-24x24in) s. 15-Sep-3 Horta, Bruxelles #45

RUTGERS, Abraham (17th C) Dutch

Works on paper
£23333 $42000 €34066 View of Gouda seen from the South East (19x32cm-7x13in) i.verso black chk brown ink col wash prov.exhib. 22-Jan-4 Christie's, Rockefeller NY #117/R est:20000-30000

RUTH, Jan de (1922-) American

£235 $400 €343 Standing nude female with pink drapery (127x81cm-50x32in) s. 7-Nov-3 Selkirks, St. Louis #441

RUTHART, Karl Andreas (attrib) (1630-1703) German

£11086 $19845 €16186 Hunting scene with dogs and bears fighting (147x224cm-58x88in) bears sig. 26-May-4 AB Stockholms Auktionsverk #2537/R est:150000-200000 (S.KR 150000)

RUTHART, Karl Andreas (circle) (1630-1703) German

£5500 $9515 €8030 Wooded landscape with stags and hinds by a stream (89x137cm-35x54in) 10-Dec-3 Bonhams, New Bond Street #121/R est:5000-7000

RUTHERFORD, Harry (1903-) British

£550 $1007 €803 Technical College Hyde - View from Harry Rutherford's backgarden (53x64cm-21x25in) s. 6-Apr-4 Capes Dunn, Manchester #841/R
£600 $1002 €876 Back garden (59x90cm-23x35in) s. panel. 16-Oct-3 Lawrence, Crewkerne #752

RUTHERSTON, Albert (1881-1953) British

Works on paper
£480 $888 €701 Study of a seated lady (24x26cm-9x10in) s.d.1910 s.i.d.verso chl. 11-Mar-4 Christie's, Kensington #5
£800 $1376 €1168 Grasse (51x48cm-20x19in) s.d.1910 pencil W/C pen brown ink. 3-Dec-3 Christie's, Kensington #468/R

RUTHLING, Ford (1933-) American

£237 $425 €346 Flowers (183cm-72in circular) s.i. 13-May-4 Dallas Auction Gallery, Dallas #180b/R

RUTHS, Amelie (1871-1956) German

£351 $639 €530 Still life with statuettes (63x91cm-25x36in) s.d.1926. 19-Jun-4 Quittenbaum, Hamburg #41

RUTHS, Valentin (1825-1905) German

£433 $780 €650 Landscape (34x53cm-13x21in) s. paper on masonite. 24-Apr-4 Reiss & Sohn, Konigstein #5374/R
£887 $1480 €1250 Sunny wood in early autumn (34x51cm-13x20in) panel. 21-Jun-3 Hans Stahl, Hamburg #109/R

RUTHVEN, Jerry (1947-) American

£233 $400 €340 Landscape (43x58cm-17x23in) s. 7-Dec-3 Susanin's, Chicago #6063/R
£435 $700 €631 Willow creek (23x30cm-9x12in) 22-Aug-3 Altermann Galleries, Santa Fe #164

RUTIMANN, Bruno R (20th C) ?

£1629 $2769 €2378 Untitled (125x140cm-49x55in) mono. acrylic. 25-Nov-3 Germann, Zurich #882 est:4000-5000 (S.FR 3600)

RUTLAND, T (19th C) British

£1000 $1640 €1460 Blind fiddler (56x79cm-22x31in) s.d.1843 after David Wilkie. 27-May-3 John Taylors, Louth #594

RUTTEN, Johannes (1809-1884) Dutch

£308 $524 €450 Little house by the water (10x8cm-4x3in) mono. panel. 5-Nov-3 Vendue Huis, Gravenhage #54a

RUTTKAY, Gyorgy (1898-1975) Hungarian

£1697 $2935 €2478 Trip (80x61cm-31x24in) s. 12-Dec-3 Kieselbach, Budapest #17/R (H.F 650000)
Works on paper
£434 $721 €634 Composition with horse (30x20cm-12x8in) s. mixed media board. 4-Oct-3 Kieselbach, Budapest #80/R (H.F 160000)

RUTZ, A (20th C) German

£362 $648 €529 Pair of lions on the shore (63x75cm-25x30in) s.d.1921. 10-May-4 Rasmussen, Vejle #248/R (D.KR 4000)

RUYSCH, Aletta van (1860-1930) Dutch

£395 $726 €600 A kitchen still life (19x24cm-7x9in) s. 22-Jun-4 Christie's, Amsterdam #171/R

RUYSCH, Rachel (circle) (1664-1750) Dutch

£6000 $10980 €8760 Still life of flowers (63x53cm-25x21in) 9-Jul-4 Christie's, Kensington #64/R est:3000-5000

RUYSCH, Rachel (style) (1664-1750) Dutch

£10270 $19000 €14994 Still life of flowers in a glass vase resting on a ledge (46x46cm-18x18in) 17-Jan-4 Sotheby's, New York #1127/R est:5000-7000

RUYSDAEL, Jacob Salomonsz van (1630-1681) Dutch

£54054 $95135 €80000 Wooded landscape with a shepherd watering his herd in a wallow (84x115cm-33x45in) mono.d.1656 panel prov. 18-May-4 Sotheby's, Amsterdam #21/R est:30000-50000

RUYSDAEL, Jacob van (1628-1682) Dutch

£400 $720 €600 River landscape (54x70cm-21x28in) panel. 26-Apr-4 Rieber, Stuttgart #1091/R
£1733 $3120 €2600 Woodview with horsemen (71x57cm-28x22in) s. panel. 26-Apr-4 Bernaerts, Antwerp #58/R est:1500-2000
£17195 $27511 €25105 Extensive landscape with figures (48x58cm-19x23in) bears sig. lit. 19-Sep-3 Koller, Zurich #3012/R est:25000-35000 (S.FR 38000)
Prints
£5594 $9510 €8000 Hillside huts (19x28cm-7x11in) etching. 27-Nov-3 Bassenge, Berlin #5338a est:600
Works on paper
£10000 $18300 €14600 Landscape with a farmhouse by a river (9x14cm-4x6in) black chk brush ink wash prov. 6-Jul-4 Christie's, London #174/R est:4000-6000

RUYSDAEL, Jacob van (attrib) (1628-1682) Dutch

£4514 $7358 €6500 Low tide (36x47cm-14x19in) s. i. verso. 26-Sep-3 Bolland & Marotz, Bremen #481/R est:9000
£7718 $14201 €11500 River landscape with hunters (68x88cm-27x35in) mono. 25-Mar-4 Dr Fritz Nagel, Stuttgart #620/R est:4000

RUYSDAEL, Jacob van (style) (1628-1682) Dutch

£5500 $9515 €8030 Mountainous landscape with Roman tower by a stream (84x67cm-33x26in) bears sig.d.1670 panel. 12-Dec-3 Christie's, Kensington #78/R est:6000-8000

RUYSDAEL, Salomon van (1600-1670) Dutch

£6993 $11678 €10000 Battle scene (54x63cm-21x25in) s.d.1658. 30-Jun-3 Bailly Pommery, Paris #45/R
£24324 $42811 €36000 Still life with a cockerel, two lapwings, duck and other birds on a stone ledge (56x45cm-22x18in) s.d.1660 panel prov.exhib.lit. 18-May-4 Sotheby's, Amsterdam #91/R est:40000-60000
£32895 $60527 €50000 Fihermen in wooded landscape (39cm-15in circular) mono.d.1635 panel prov.lit. 24-Jun-4 Tajan, Paris #26/R est:30000-40000
£55000 $100650 €80300 Sandy landscape with travellers (61x85cm-24x33in) s.d.1642 panel. 8-Jul-4 Sotheby's, London #127/R est:60000-80000
£680000 $1244400 €992800 Wooded river landscape with figures on a bank awaiting the ferry (52x83cm-20x33in) s.d.1651 panel prov. 7-Jul-4 Christie's, London #56/R est:700000-1000000

RUYSDAEL, Salomon van (circle) (1600-1670) Dutch

£12500 $21250 €18250 Winter landscape with figures skating on a frozen waterway (40x61cm-16x24in) panel. 31-Oct-3 Christie's, Kensington #31/R est:6000-8000

RUYSDAEL, Salomon van (studio) (1600-1670) Dutch

£3311 $6026 €5000 Wooded river landscape with farmhouses and ferry (41x61cm-16x24in) panel. 16-Jun-4 Dorotheum, Vienna #105/R est:6000-10000

RUYTEN, Jan Michael (1813-1881) Belgian
£2817 $4873 €4000 River Scheldt in Amsterdam (20x24cm-8x9in) s.d.1852 panel. 13-Dec-3 De Vuyst, Lokeren #413/R est:4000-6000
£3194 $5207 €4600 Belgian street scene (28x37cm-11x15in) s.d.45 panel. 24-Sep-3 Neumeister, Munich #544/R est:3000
£4861 $8118 €7000 Daily activities on the beach (76x102cm-30x40in) s.i. 21-Oct-3 Sotheby's, Amsterdam #4/R est:5000-7000
£6376 $11732 €9500 Fishing boats and busy harbour town (71x98cm-28x39in) s. lit. 25-Mar-4 Karlheinz Kaupp, Staufen #2702/R est:2500
£13194 $22431 €19000 Bustling city life around the Vleeeshal, Antwerp (100x80cm-39x31in) s. indis.i.d.70. 28-Oct-3 Christie's, Amsterdam #13/R est:12000-16000

RUYTER, Jan de (18th C) Dutch
Works on paper
£600 $1038 €876 Road in a village with two peasants. Cottage with herdsmen and cattle (10x20cm-4x8in) i. pen grey ink wash pair prov. 12-Dec-3 Christie's, Kensington #539/R

RUYTER, Lisa (1968-) German?
£9333 $17173 €14000 Wild West (183x122cm-72x48in) s.i.d.1999 verso acrylic prov. 8-Jun-4 Artcurial Briest, Paris #289/R est:18000-22000
£10778 $18000 €15736 Black room (122x152cm-48x60in) s.d.2002 on overlap acrylic prov. 14-Nov-3 Phillips, New York #103/R est:10000-15000
£11976 $20000 €17485 Scenic route (213x152cm-84x60in) s.i.d.2000 acrylic prov. 14-Nov-3 Phillips, New York #214/R est:18000-25000
£16766 $28000 €24478 Bridge on the River Kwai (183x122cm-72x48in) s.i.d.1999 acrylic prov. 12-Nov-3 Christie's, Rockefeller NY #504/R est:12000-18000

RUYTINX, Alfred (1871-?) Belgian
£333 $597 €500 Barques echouees sur la plage (28x52cm-11x20in) s. canvas on panel. 11-May-4 Vanderkindere, Brussels #141
£385 $654 €550 Nature morte aux fruits (54x65cm-21x26in) s. 18-Nov-3 Galerie Moderne, Brussels #657/R
£800 $1448 €1200 Nature morte aux raisins et melon (64x54cm-25x21in) s. 30-Mar-4 Campo & Campo, Antwerp #252/R
£828 $1531 €1200 Composition aux roses et raisins (57x42cm-22x17in) s. panel. 19-Jan-4 Horta, Bruxelles #480

RUZICKA, Dr Drahomir Josef (1870-1960) American
Photographs
£3000 $5370 €4500 Pennsylvania Station in New York (35x27cm-14x11in) s.i.d. verso silver bromide lit. 14-May-4 Van Ham, Cologne #210/R est:3800
£3955 $7000 €5774 Penn Station studies (34x27cm-13x11in) s.i. one d.1924 one d.1939 i.num.verso warm-toned photo pair. 28-Apr-4 Sotheby's, New York #114/R est:5000-7000

RUZICKA, Othmar (1877-1962) Austrian
£414 $757 €600 Travelling with a mule (60x80cm-24x31in) s. jute. 27-Jan-4 Dorotheum, Vienna #98/R

RUZICKA-LAUTENSCHLAGER, Hans (1862-1933) Austrian
£426 $681 €618 Vienna 1928 (42x52cm-17x20in) s. 22-Sep-3 Blomqvist, Lysaker #1250 (N.KR 5000)

RUZICSKAY, Gyorgy (1896-?) Russian?
Works on paper
£285 $450 €416 Venice, San Marco (28x36cm-11x14in) s. pastel. 6-Apr-3 William Jenack, New York #295

RYABUSHKIN, Andrei Petrovich (1861-1904) Russian
Works on paper
£1000 $1700 €1460 Two Muzhiks startled by a racing troika (31x48cm-12x19in) s.d.1886 chl htd gouache. 19-Nov-3 Sotheby's, London #70/R est:1000-1500
£1399 $2378 €2000 Handing out alms (27x47cm-11x19in) s. pen pencil. 29-Nov-3 Bukowskis, Helsinki #415/R est:2000-3000
£1900 $3401 €2774 Portraits of dogs (29x35cm-11x14in) s.d.1934 W/C two different sizes. 26-May-4 Sotheby's, Olympia #487/R est:800-1200

RYAN, Adrian (1920-1998) British
£750 $1253 €1095 Fruit on a plate (28x46cm-11x18in) s. 21-Oct-3 Bonhams, Knightsbridge #89/R
£820 $1443 €1197 Mousehole Harbour (46x60cm-18x24in) 18-May-4 Bonhams, Knightsbridge #129/R
£980 $1725 €1431 Cattle by hill farm, Wales (50x60cm-20x24in) s. s.i.d.53 verso. 18-May-4 Bonhams, Knightsbridge #126/R

RYAN, Anne (1889-1954) American
Works on paper
£3333 $6133 €5000 Untitled No 595 (12x9cm-5x4in) cloth paper collage paper on panel. 11-Jun-4 Hauswedell & Nolte, Hamburg #1515/R est:4000
£4190 $7500 €6117 Untitled No 236 (20x16cm-8x6in) s. paper thread silver foil fabric collage exec c.1950 prov. 13-May-4 Sotheby's, New York #106/R est:4000-6000
£6145 $11000 €8972 Untitled No 10 (18x13cm-7x5in) printed paper sand paper fabric collage on Howell paper prov. 13-May-4 Sotheby's, New York #105/R est:4000-6000

RYAN, John (?) ?
Works on paper
£386 $710 €575 Bloomsday (38x70cm-15x28in) s.i. W/C. 23-Mar-4 Mealy's, Castlecomer #1115/R

RYAN, Nina (1947-) Australian
£248 $459 €362 First flight (130x150cm-51x59in) s.d.1991 i.verso. 15-Mar-4 Sotheby's, Melbourne #106 (A.D 600)

RYAN, Thomas (1929-) Irish
£979 $1664 €1400 Bantry Bay (30x71cm-12x28in) s. i.d.September 1964 verso prov. 18-Nov-3 Whyte's, Dublin #162/R
£1329 $2259 €1900 Pink rose on a white envelope (21x24cm-8x9in) s.i. canvasboard. 25-Nov-3 De Veres Art Auctions, Dublin #49/R est:900-1200
£1399 $2378 €2000 Roses and invitation (23x18cm-9x7in) s. canvas on board. 18-Nov-3 Whyte's, Dublin #229/R est:1800-2200
£1486 $2809 €2200 Edge of wood, morning, County Meath, 1978 (44x34cm-17x13in) s. canvasboard. 17-Feb-4 Whyte's, Dublin #117/R est:2000-3000
£1800 $3222 €2628 CualacBan (51x61cm-20x24in) s.d.1968 s.i.d.July 1968 verso. 14-May-4 Christie's, Kensington #380/R est:1500-2000
£1972 $3155 €2800 Silver cup with roses (19x24cm-7x9in) s. canvas on board. 16-Sep-3 Whyte's, Dublin #180/R est:1800-2200
£2027 $3831 €3000 Still life with apples (37x47cm-15x19in) s. board. 17-Feb-4 Whyte's, Dublin #115/R est:3000-4000
£2111 $3800 €3082 Pier at Erelough, Roundstone (30x51cm-12x20in) s. i.d.1970 verso board. 24-Apr-4 Weschler, Washington #553/R est:4000-6000
£2400 $4296 €3504 Irish press (25x20cm-10x8in) s. s.i.d.2003 verso board exhib. 14-May-4 Christie's, Kensington #391/R est:2000-3000
£2685 $4752 €4000 Back field with Johnny (36x46cm-14x18in) s. i.d.August 1971 verso canvasboard. 27-Apr-4 Whyte's, Dublin #234/R est:2000-3000
£2953 $5227 €4400 Spring on the Broadmeadow (51x51cm-20x20in) s. 27-Apr-4 Whyte's, Dublin #212/R est:3000-4000
£4000 $7160 €5840 Eavan by the pool (41x51cm-16x20in) s. s.i.d.02 verso board exhib. 14-May-4 Christie's, Kensington #390/R est:4000-6000
Works on paper
£524 $892 €750 Claddagh Duff (25x34cm-10x13in) s.i.d.31 August 1976 verso W/C over pencil. 18-Nov-3 Whyte's, Dublin #30/R
£537 $961 €800 Street scene in Bergen (18x25cm-7x10in) s. W/C. 31-May-4 Hamilton Osborne King, Dublin #128/R
£1111 $1811 €1600 The Art Critic (17x14cm-7x6in) s.d.1983 pen ink W/C prov. 24-Sep-3 James Adam, Dublin #141/R est:1000-1500
£1146 $1868 €1650 Aran boy on a pier above a currach (19x39cm-7x15in) s.i.d.19 august 1972 chl pastel. 24-Sep-3 James Adam, Dublin #59a/R est:1000-1500

RYAN, Tom (1922-) American
£1070 $2000 €1562 Sundown farm (30x41cm-12x16in) s. canvasboard prov. 24-Jul-4 Coeur d'Alene, Hayden #264/R est:1500-2500
£20588 $35000 €30058 Texas dust (56x38cm-22x15in) board. 1-Nov-3 Altermann Galleries, Santa Fe #143
Works on paper
£1341 $2400 €1958 Two horses (20x30cm-8x12in) pastel. 15-May-4 Altermann Galleries, Santa Fe #122/R

RYBACK, Issachar (1897-1935) Russian
£852 $1500 €1244 Portrait of a woman (25x23cm-10x9in) s. 23-May-4 Treadway Gallery, Cincinnati #698/R est:3000-5000
£9677 $18000 €14128 Peasants with goat (28x38cm-11x15in) s.d.1918 oil on paper. 7-Mar-4 Treadway Gallery, Cincinnati #692/R est:6000-8000
£9677 $18000 €14128 Milking the cow (28x38cm-11x15in) s.d.1918 oil on paper. 7-Mar-4 Treadway Gallery, Cincinnati #691/R est:6000-8000
Works on paper
£17877 $32000 €26100 Cubist Composition (32x24cm-13x9in) s.i.d.1918 gouache W/C prov. 5-May-4 Christie's, Rockefeller NY #116/R est:15000-20000

RYBOT, Major N V L (1874-1961) British?
£300 $543 €438 Mont Mado Quarry and Mill, Jersey (67x49cm-26x19in) i.verso. 1-Apr-4 Martel Maides, Guernsey #235/R

RYCHTER-MAY, Anna (?-1955) British
Works on paper
£320 $589 €467 An old Jew in Jerusalem and his grandson (28x19cm-11x7in) s.i. i.verso W/C. 23-Jun-4 Bonhams, Bury St Edmunds #331
£800 $1472 €1168 Walls of Jerusalem at the Jana Gate (23x29cm-9x11in) s.i. i.verso W/C. 23-Jun-4 Bonhams, Bury St Edmunds #335
£880 $1619 €1285 Walls of Jerusalem with the Golden Gate (22x34cm-9x13in) s.i. i.verso W/C. 23-Jun-4 Bonhams, Bury St Edmunds #332/R

RYCKAERT, David (attrib) (16/17th C) Flemish
£2365 $4234 €3453 Jupiter and Mercury visiting Philemont and Baucis (54x80cm-21x31in) panel. 28-May-4 Uppsala Auktionskammare, Uppsala #22/R est:40000-50000 (S.KR 32000)

RYCKAERT, David III (1612-1661) Flemish
£2685 $4805 €4000 L'amateur (35x28cm-14x11in) panel. 25-May-4 Palais de Beaux Arts, Brussels #81/R est:5000-6000
£2685 $4993 €4000 Still life in inn (41x52cm-16x20in) s. board. 2-Mar-4 Ansorena, Madrid #295/R est:4000
£4483 $7441 €6500 Inn interior with figures and still life (41x52cm-16x20in) mono. board. 30-Sep-3 Ansorena, Madrid #29/R est:6000
£4698 $8644 €7000 Reunion de buveurs dans un auberge (59x81cm-23x32in) panel. 26-Mar-4 Piasa, Paris #8/R est:7000-8000
£4800 $8304 €7008 Barn interior with a still life of kitchen utensils and an owl (34x47cm-13x19in) panel prov. 9-Dec-3 Sotheby's, Olympia #350/R est:4000-6000
£9685 $16658 €14140 Inn with drinking and smoking peasants (40x57cm-16x22in) s.d.1638 panel. 8-Dec-3 Philippe Schuler, Zurich #3430/R est:25000-30000 (S.FR 21500)

RYCKAERT, David III (attrib) (1612-1661) Flemish
£1086 $1846 €1586 The fish handler (65x55cm-26x22in) mono. 1-Dec-3 Koller, Zurich #6403 est:1500-2500 (S.FR 2400)
£1268 $2218 €1800 La tentation de Saint Antoine (31x41cm-12x16in) panel. 19-Dec-3 Delvaux, Paris #93/R est:2000-3000
£2308 $3969 €3370 Man with beer mug and chalk pipe (57x43cm-22x17in) panel. 2-Dec-3 Bukowskis, Stockholm #365/R est:15000-18000 (S.KR 30000)
£3667 $6563 €5500 Peasants drinking and playing cards in an inn (40x58cm-16x23in) 17-May-4 Christie's, Amsterdam #37/R est:4000-6000

RYCKAERT, Marten (1587-1631) Flemish
£6993 $12028 €10000 Paysage bucolique anime de bergers et de gentilshommes (21x28cm-8x11in) copper. 3-Dec-3 Palais de Beaux Arts, Brussels #672/R est:10000-12000
£10791 $17698 €15000 Cascade dans un paysage rocheux anime de bergers et de chevres (21x392cm-8x154in) mono.d.1629 panel. 6-Jun-3 Drouot Estimations, Paris #38/R est:15000-20000
£15000 $27000 €21900 Wooded river landscape with goatherds resting with their goats and dogs by a waterfall (23x28cm-9x11in) init.d.1626 panel octagonal. 21-Apr-4 Christie's, London #23/R est:15000-25000

RYCKAERT, Marten (attrib) (1587-1631) Flemish
£1400 $2562 €2100 Christ sur le lac de Tiberiade (19x7cm-7x3in) panel. 6-Jun-4 Rouillac, Vendome #12

RYCKHALS, Frans (1600-1647) Dutch
£5263 $9684 €8000 Stable interior (11x15cm-4x6in) s. panel. 24-Jun-4 Christie's, Paris #46/R est:2000-3000
Works on paper
£4452 $7568 €6500 Study of trees (18x15cm-7x6in) black chk prov.lit. 4-Nov-3 Sotheby's, Amsterdam #34/R est:2500-3500

RYCKHALS, Frans (attrib) (1600-1647) Dutch
£3873 $6779 €5500 Le cochon ecorche (50x64cm-20x25in) bears mono.d.1641 panel. 18-Dec-3 Tajan, Paris #95/R est:4000-5000

RYDBERG, Gustaf (1835-1933) Swedish
£449 $750 €656 Landscape with pond (12x23cm-5x9in) s.d.1884. 7-Oct-3 Sotheby's, New York #117
£692 $1191 €1010 Study of cliffs on the Riviera (38x62cm-15x24in) init.d.02 lit. 3-Dec-3 AB Stockholms Auktionsverk #2477/R (S.KR 9000)
£887 $1588 €1295 Young boy (25x12cm-10x5in) mono. d.1865 verso sold with palette and brushes. 28-May-4 Uppsala Auktionskammare, Uppsala #195/R (S.KR 12000)
£1099 $2000 €1605 Fisherman's hut (45x62cm-18x24in) s.d.1871. 29-Jun-4 Sotheby's, New York #137/R est:4000-6000
£1330 $2381 €1942 Summer landscape with farm, Skaane (32x47cm-13x19in) s.d.1923. 26-May-4 AB Stockholms Auktionsverk #2181/R est:15000-20000 (S.KR 18000)
£1796 $3000 €2622 Rocky hill (43x64cm-17x25in) s.d.1835. 7-Oct-3 Sotheby's, New York #112 est:4000-6000
£1846 $3175 €2695 Coastal landscape with farm, Skaane (44x72cm-17x28in) s.d.1920. 3-Dec-3 AB Stockholms Auktionsverk #2475/R est:25000-30000 (S.KR 24000)
£1848 $3307 €2698 Stone wall and large trees, St.Olov (44x71cm-17x28in) mono.i.d.1904 prov.exhib.lit. 28-May-4 Uppsala Auktionskammare, Uppsala #193/R est:20000-25000 (S.KR 25000)
£2308 $3969 €3370 Summer landscape with farm, Skaane (50x75cm-20x30in) s.d.1904. 3-Dec-3 AB Stockholms Auktionsverk #2423/R est:30000-40000 (S.KR 30000)
£2365 $4234 €3453 Landscape from Visby, Skaane (47x65cm-19x26in) s.d.1923 prov.lit. 28-May-4 Uppsala Auktionskammare, Uppsala #194/R est:15000-18000 (S.KR 32000)
£2395 $4000 €3497 Cattle at pasture (45x65cm-18x26in) s.d.1869. 7-Oct-3 Sotheby's, New York #111 est:6000-8000
£3843 $6880 €5611 Landscape from Ringsjoen (57x86cm-22x34in) s. 28-May-4 Uppsala Auktionskammare, Uppsala #192/R est:25000-30000 (S.KR 52000)

RYDBERG, Gustaf (attrib) (1835-1933) Swedish
£1078 $1800 €1574 Working on the field (43x70cm-17x28in) s.d.1889. 7-Oct-3 Sotheby's, New York #116 est:2000-4000

RYDE, Alison (20th C) New Zealander
Works on paper
£484 $867 €707 Sun glows on the old garden wall (74x51cm-29x20in) s.d.91 W/C. 11-May-4 Watson's, Christchurch #183/R (NZ.D 1400)
£692 $1239 €1010 Summer Terrace, Italy (54x54cm-21x21in) s. W/C. 11-May-4 Watson's, Christchurch #147/R (NZ.D 2000)

RYDENG, Leif (1913-1975) Danish
£280 $439 €409 Coastal landscape from Vroj with ducks (60x74cm-24x29in) s. 30-Aug-3 Rasmussen, Havnen #4061/R (D.KR 3000)
£369 $627 €539 Cormorants on cliffs (60x70cm-24x28in) mono. i.d.65 verso. 10-Nov-3 Rasmussen, Vejle #706/R (D.KR 4000)
£722 $1329 €1054 Breakers - frightened birds by the sea (154x121cm-61x48in) init.d.35. 29-Mar-4 Rasmussen, Copenhagen #485/R (D.KR 8000)

RYDER, Albert Pinkham (1847-1917) American
£53977 $95000 €78806 At the ford (30x29cm-12x11in) panel prov.exhib. 18-May-4 Christie's, Rockefeller NY #63/R est:40000-60000

RYDER, Chauncey F (1868-1949) American
£1257 $2250 €1835 Through stacks of hay (36x25cm-14x10in) s. panel. 26-May-4 Doyle, New York #53/R est:1500-2500
£1381 $2500 €2016 European park with building (20x25cm-8x10in) s. board. 16-Apr-4 James Julia, Fairfield #663/R est:2000-4000
£1899 $3000 €2754 Wooded landscape (30x41cm-12x16in) s. 27-Jul-3 Simpson's, Houston #350
£2174 $4000 €3174 Impressionist landscape of field and stream in foreground (30x41cm-12x16in) s. 9-Jun-4 Alderfer's, Hatfield #429 est:1000-1500
£3797 $6000 €5544 Misty morning (41x51cm-16x20in) s. 7-Sep-3 Treadway Gallery, Cincinnati #593/R est:3000-5000
£5090 $8500 €7431 Village in the valley (63x76cm-25x30in) s. canvas over panel prov. 9-Oct-3 Christie's, Rockefeller NY #53/R est:8000-12000
£8108 $15000 €11838 Sand Hill (82x112cm-32x44in) s. prov.exhib. 11-Mar-4 Christie's, Rockefeller NY #54/R est:8000-12000
Works on paper
£355 $650 €533 Hilly landscape (25x33cm-10x13in) W/C. 9-Jul-4 Du Mouchelle, Detroit #2015/R

RYDER, Henry Orne (1860-1907) American
£1304 $2100 €1904 Summer stroll (46x33cm-18x13in) s. 20-Aug-3 James Julia, Fairfield #1691/R est:1500-2500

RYDER, Jack van (1898-1968) American
£1872 $3500 €2733 Devil's kitchen (46x46cm-18x18in) s.d.1925 canvas on board prov. 24-Jul-4 Coeur d'Alene, Hayden #275/R est:1500-2500
£2406 $4500 €3513 Walpi, New Mexico (46x51cm-18x20in) s.d.1926 canvas on board prov. 24-Jul-4 Coeur d'Alene, Hayden #274/R est:2000-4000

RYDER, Platt Powell (1821-1896) American
£566 $900 €826 Fountain (23x16cm-9x6in) i.verso board. 13-Sep-3 Weschler, Washington #727/R

RYDER, Sophie (1963-) British
Sculpture
£1400 $2464 €2044 Boxing hares (34x30cm-13x12in) s. wire wheel base. 18-May-4 Woolley & Wallis, Salisbury #355/R est:800-1200
£4000 $7040 €5840 Lady hare and horse (44x54cm-17x21in) s. num.8/12. 18-May-4 Woolley & Wallis, Salisbury #354/R est:6000-8000
£6000 $10560 €8760 Maquette for minotaur and hare (35x25cm-14x10in) s.d.94 num.10/12 bronze. 18-May-4 Woolley & Wallis, Salisbury #371/R est:6000-8000
Works on paper
£660 $1208 €964 What makes me smile, study of a lady hare in foetal position. s.d.04 chl. 9-Jul-4 Moore Allen & Innocent, Cirencester #975/R
£1300 $2288 €1898 Hare's head with dancing ladies (99x119cm-39x47in) s.d.95 collage. 18-May-4 Woolley & Wallis, Salisbury #42/R est:1500-2500
£1900 $3344 €2774 Minotaur sniffing a sunflower (61x48cm-24x19in) s. collage. 18-May-4 Woolley & Wallis, Salisbury #44/R est:1000-1500
£2900 $5104 €4234 Minotaur head (119x119cm-47x47in) s.d.97 wire collage. 18-May-4 Woolley & Wallis, Salisbury #43/R est:2500-3500
£3600 $6336 €5256 Hare head (110x195cm-43x77in) s.d.95 wire dr. 18-May-4 Woolley & Wallis, Salisbury #46/R est:2500-3500
£4200 $7686 €6132 Running hare. Pack of dogs (81x57cm-32x22in) s.d.88 collage two prov. 4-Jun-4 Christie's, London #153/R est:2000-3000
£4300 $7568 €6278 Lady hare with dog (139x86cm-55x34in) s.d.96 chk. 18-May-4 Woolley & Wallis, Salisbury #45/R est:2500-3500

RYDER, Susan (1944-) British
£380 $684 €555 Woman at her dressing table (30x38cm-12x15in) init. board. 20-Jan-4 Bonhams, Knightsbridge #121/R
£500 $835 €730 Study (91x76cm-36x30in) s. 8-Oct-3 Christie's, Kensington #923/R
£1000 $1850 €1460 Bedroom chair (60x60cm-24x24in) s.i.stretcher. 11-Mar-4 Christie's, Kensington #310/R est:1000-1500
£1550 $2728 €2263 A London drawing room (38x54cm-15x21in) s. 18-May-4 Woolley & Wallis, Salisbury #33/R est:400-600
£2200 $4004 €3212 Brantome (51x70cm-20x28in) s. 1-Jul-4 Christie's, Kensington #112/R est:1000-1500

RYERSON, Luther L (19th C) American
£284 $475 €415 Hudson river landscape (20x36cm-8x14in) s. 29-Jun-3 William Jenack, New York #314

RYERSON, Margery Austen (1886-?) American
£939 $1700 €1371 Urban landscape with figures, cars and houses (30x38cm-12x15in) s. board. 2-Apr-4 Eldred, East Dennis #880/R est:500-1000
Works on paper
£320 $550 €467 Columbus Circle, 1933 (25x32cm-10x13in) W/C chl prov.exhib. 3-Dec-3 Doyle, New York #260/R

RYKALA, Jacek (20th C) Polish
£994 $1650 €1451 Whispers (122x123cm-48x48in) oil collage painted 1993. 2-Oct-3 Agra, Warsaw #11/R est:3000 (P.Z 6500)

RYLAARSDAM, Jan (1911-) Dutch
£438 $700 €639 Street scene with figures (61x51cm-24x20in) s. 17-May-3 Bunte, Elgin #1293
£1316 $2421 €2000 Ships in a harbour (53x70cm-21x28in) s. board. 22-Jun-4 Christie's, Amsterdam #468/R est:2000-3000
£1633 $2971 €2400 Loosdrechtse plassen (60x80cm-24x31in) s. 3-Feb-4 Christie's, Amsterdam #356/R est:700-900
£2100 $3297 €3045 Off the place Rocheouart, Paris (61x51cm-24x20in) s. 28-Aug-3 Christie's, Kensington #228/R est:400-600
£2500 $4600 €3800 Flower girls (70x50cm-28x20in) s. 22-Jun-4 Christie's, Amsterdam #539/R est:2000-3000
£4276 $7868 €6500 Cafe scene (60x50cm-24x20in) s. 22-Jun-4 Christie's, Amsterdam #536/R est:4000-6000
Works on paper
£559 $934 €800 Rue St Denis, Paris (25x18cm-10x7in) s.i. W/C htd white. 30-Jun-3 Sotheby's, Amsterdam #351/R
£660 $1042 €950 Kolkje, Amsterdam, The Netherlands (33x36cm-13x14in) s.i. W/C pencil pen ink. 2-Sep-3 Christie's, Amsterdam #379

RYLAND, Henry (1856-1924) British
Works on paper
£450 $765 €657 Classical maiden dancing on a terrace (38x54cm-15x21in) s. W/C. 29-Oct-3 Bonhams, Chester #385
£500 $910 €730 An allegory of freedom (35x41cm-14x16in) s. pencil W/C. 1-Jul-4 Christie's, Kensington #148/R

RYLANDER, H C (1939-) Danish
£542 $1013 €791 Separated from the dreams (97x52cm-38x20in) init. 25-Feb-4 Kunsthallen, Copenhagen #170/R (D.KR 6000)

RYLANDER, Hans Chr (1939-) Danish
£664 $1062 €963 Shadow and compass (250x97cm-98x38in) s.d.1994-95 verso. 17-Sep-3 Kunsthallen, Copenhagen #100/R (D.KR 7000)

RYLOV, Arkadij (1870-1939) Russian
£2733 $5029 €4100 Paysage de campagne (33x47cm-13x19in) s.d.1925 cardboard. 9-Jun-4 Oger, Dumont, Paris #80/R est:1500-2000

RYMAN, Robert (1930-) American
£11173 $20000 €16313 Part 9 (38x38cm-15x15in) s.d.93 s.i.d.verso oil cardboard screws tape prov. 12-May-4 Christie's, Rockefeller NY #411/R est:25000-35000
£269461 $450000 €393413 Region I (81x76cm-32x30in) s. i.d.78 oil elvacite linen on canvas four fasteners bolts prov. 12-Nov-3 Sotheby's, New York #6/R est:300000-400000
Prints
£1963 $3200 €2866 Untitled, from On the Bowery (65x65cm-26x26in) s.i.d.1969 col screenprint heavy wove paper. 24-Sep-3 Christie's, Rockefeller NY #371/R est:1200-1800
Works on paper
£11173 $20000 €16313 Eagle turquoise 6H 2 (31x31cm-12x12in) s.d.66 pencil on Chemex coffee filter paper prov.exhib. 13-May-4 Sotheby's, New York #170/R est:25000-35000
£25150 $42000 €36719 Untitled (35x35cm-14x14in) s.d.74 epoxy on plastivellum on card prov.exhib.lit. 12-Nov-3 Christie's, Rockefeller NY #599/R est:20000-30000

RYN, Nico van (1887-1962) Dutch
£382 $623 €550 Portrait. Flower still life (29x23cm-11x9in) board double-sided. 29-Sep-3 Sotheby's, Amsterdam #160/R
£382 $623 €550 A crucifix (59x48cm-23x19in) board. 29-Sep-3 Sotheby's, Amsterdam #161

RYOTT, James Russell (attrib) (fl.1810-1860) British
£1220 $1915 €1781 Hounds of the Newcastle Hunt in 1806 (53x68cm-21x27in) i.verso. 26-Aug-3 Christie's, Sydney #375/R est:2500-4500 (A.D 3000)

RYSBRACK, Jean Michel (1693-1770) Flemish
Works on paper
£8200 $13940 €11972 Designs for the monument to Earl Stanhope in Westminster Abbey (38x26cm-15x10in) pen ink htd white bodycol two. 27-Nov-3 Sotheby's, London #237/R est:3000-5000

RYSBRACK, Pieter (1655-1729) Flemish
£19231 $33077 €28077 Landscape with hunting still life (83x113cm-33x44in) 2-Dec-3 Bukowskis, Stockholm #372/R est:175000-200000 (S.KR 250000)

RYSBRACK, Pieter (attrib) (1655-1729) Flemish
£2956 $5292 €4316 Hunting still life of birds (63x46cm-25x18in) pair. 26-May-4 AB Stockholms Auktionsverk #2562/R est:30000-40000 (S.KR 40000)
£3000 $5100 €4380 Arcadian landscape with figures making a sacrifice before an altar. Figures borne upon a cloud (66x83cm-26x33in) pair. 29-Oct-3 Bonhams, New Bond Street #92/R est:3000-4000
£3692 $6351 €5390 Hunting still lives with birds (63x47cm-25x19in) pair. 3-Dec-3 AB Stockholms Auktionsverk #2689/R est:25000-30000 (S.KR 48000)

RYSER, Fritz (1910-1990) Swiss
£261 $477 €381 Autumnal still life with grapes and apples (32x43cm-13x17in) s.d.1981 board. 4-Jun-4 Zofingen, Switzerland #2942 (S.FR 600)
£276 $469 €403 Basle old town (46x38cm-18x15in) s. i. verso board. 28-Nov-3 Zofingen, Switzerland #3158 (S.FR 610)
£330 $562 €482 Bernese Oberland landscape (35x50cm-14x20in) s.d.49 panel. 5-Nov-3 Dobiaschofsky, Bern #920 (S.FR 750)
£388 $694 €566 Meadow flowers in glass (50x40cm-20x16in) s. 12-May-4 Dobiaschofsky, Bern #926/R (S.FR 900)
£455 $755 €660 Still life with quince (50x70cm-20x28in) s.d.1946 i. verso masonite. 13-Jun-3 Zofingen, Switzerland #3005/R (S.FR 1000)
£474 $849 €692 Still life with quince (38x55cm-15x22in) s.d.87. 12-May-4 Dobiaschofsky, Bern #925/R (S.FR 1100)

RYSSELBERGHE, Theo van (1862-1926) Belgian
£1733 $3189 €2600 Two children (46x30cm-18x12in) studio st. blk chk. 8-Jun-4 Sotheby's, Amsterdam #181/R est:3000-4000
£2133 $3925 €3200 Pink roses over a fence (43x47cm-17x19in) st.sig. cardboard. 9-Jun-4 Christie's, Amsterdam #87/R est:4000-6000
£2837 $4738 €4000 Paysage rural anime (30x23cm-12x9in) s.d.80 panel. 15-Oct-3 Hotel des Ventes Mosan, Brussels #112/R est:6000-8000
£3000 $5400 €4500 Allegorie de Sybille, hommage a Pinturicchio (22x41cm-9x16in) panel lit. 26-Apr-4 Tajan, Paris #97/R est:4600-5000
£3169 $5482 €4500 Nature morte aux muguets (32x37cm-13x15in) s. lit. 13-Dec-3 De Vuyst, Lokeren #439/R est:8000-10000
£4722 $7886 €6800 Enfants pres de la ferme (30x59cm-12x23in) s. panel lit. 21-Oct-3 Campo & Campo, Antwerp #336/R est:8000-10000
£5072 $8319 €7000 Moroccan boy (73x58cm-29x23in) mono. 27-May-3 Sotheby's, Amsterdam #491/R est:3000-4000
£6690 $11574 €9500 Woman with white hat (46x38cm-18x15in) mono.d.24 lit. 13-Dec-3 De Vuyst, Lokeren #456/R est:10000-12500
£15642 $28000 €22837 Dahlias (50x42cm-20x17in) mono.i.d.12 prov. 5-May-4 Christie's, Rockefeller NY #242/R est:30000-40000
£19000 $34960 €27740 Nu debout (100x65cm-39x26in) mono.d.19 prov.exhib.lit. 22-Jun-4 Sotheby's, London #246/R est:15000-20000
£26163 $45000 €38198 Flowering trees, Southern France (50x61cm-20x24in) mono.d.26 prov.exhib. 3-Dec-3 Doyle, New York #121/R est:20000-30000
£36000 $60120 €52560 La baie se St. Clair (73x91cm-29x36in) mono.d.1923. 22-Oct-3 Bonhams, New Bond Street #20/R est:35000-45000
£36000 $60120 €52560 Deux baigneuses sous les pins au bord de la mer (116x89cm-46x35in) mono.d.1925. 22-Oct-3 Bonhams, New Bond Street #24/R est:40000-60000
£54667 $97853 €82000 La Madrague, jardin avec villa et fontaine (65x81cm-26x32in) mono.d.1924 lit. 15-May-4 De Vuyst, Lokeren #457/R
£175000 $322000 €255500 Point du Rossignol I (46x56cm-18x22in) mono.d.1904 prov.lit. 22-Jun-4 Sotheby's, London #133/R est:80000-120000
Works on paper
£600 $1074 €900 Autoportrait, la tete vers la gauche (21x20cm-8x8in) studio st. d.1920 pencil lit. 15-May-4 De Vuyst, Lokeren #369
£2000 $3340 €2920 Portrait de mme van Rysselberghe (31x23cm-12x9in) st.studio d.5 Fev 07 chl prov.exhib. 22-Oct-3 Bonhams, New Bond Street #8/R est:2000-3000
£2345 $4338 €3400 Cueillette (9x16cm-4x6in) s.d.87. 19-Jan-4 Horta, Bruxelles #228/R est:3500-5000
£2667 $4773 €4000 Berberes (30x38cm-12x15in) mono. black chk prov.lit. 15-May-4 De Vuyst, Lokeren #368/R est:2200-3000
£4134 $7606 €6200 Cinq baigneuses (66x74cm-26x29in) sanguine prov.exhib.lit. 8-Jun-4 Artcurial Briest, Paris #124/R est:7000-8000
£6000 $11040 €8760 Mademoiselle Nele van de Velde (53x40cm-21x16in) mono.d.1903 chl prov. 22-Jun-4 Sotheby's, London #418/R est:5000-7000

RYSSELBERGHE, Theo van (attrib) (1862-1926) Belgian
£1210 $2226 €1767 Baigneuse en bord de mer (30x34cm-12x13in) canvasboard prov. 14-Jun-4 Waddingtons, Toronto #39/R est:1500-2500 (C.D 3000)

RYSWYCK, Edward van (1871-1936) Belgian
£1133 $2029 €1700 Nature morte aux mandarines et au tambourin (61x80cm-24x31in) s. 11-May-4 Vanderkindere, Brussels #96 est:1700-2000
£1200 $2160 €1800 Still life with flowers, lobster and samovar (128x93cm-50x37in) s. 26-Apr-4 Bernaerts, Antwerp #245/R est:2000-3000

RYSWYCK, T van (?) Belgian?
Sculpture
£1088 $1981 €1600 Chien couche. green pat bronze Cast Batardy. 9-Feb-4 Amberes, Antwerp #619
£3077 $5231 €4400 Deux dromadaires (52x68cm-20x27in) brown pat plaster socle. 1-Dec-3 Amberes, Antwerp #577

RYTTER, Poul (20th C) Danish?
£367 $656 €550 Village street (39x50cm-15x20in) s.i.d. 15-May-4 Van Ham, Cologne #893/R

RYUKOSAI, Jihei (fl.1770-1809) Japanese
Prints
£4000 $7360 €5840 Onoe Shinshichi I as Oboshi Yuranosuke (31x14cm-12x6in) print exec. 1792. 8-Jun-4 Sotheby's, London #342/R est:1000-1500

RYUSAI (19th C) Japanese
Sculpture
£2027 $3568 €3000 Dancing geisha with fans (35cm-14in) s. bronze. 22-May-4 Dr Fritz Nagel, Stuttgart #2258/R est:3200

RYUUN (19th C) Japanese
Sculpture
£2800 $4676 €4060 Monkey trainer (23x31cm-9x12in) s. ivory. 18-Jun-3 Christie's, London #149/R est:1800-2000

SAABYE, Eveline (19th C) Danish
£1806 $3015 €2600 Spring flowers (25x34cm-10x13in) mono.d. 24-Oct-3 Ketterer, Hamburg #102/R est:2800-3200

SAABYE, Svend (1913-) Danish
£300 $489 €438 Landscape from Svendborg Sund (75x125cm-30x49in) s. 27-Sep-3 Rasmussen, Havnen #4117 (D.KR 3200)
£318 $532 €464 Landscape (69x88cm-27x35in) s. 25-Oct-3 Rasmussen, Havnen #4001 (D.KR 3400)
£326 $583 €476 Green landscape from Langeso (110x136cm-43x54in) s.d.1941-42. 10-May-4 Rasmussen, Vejle #699/R (D.KR 3600)
£469 $806 €685 Landscape with cattle and river (105x136cm-41x54in) s. 3-Dec-3 Museumsbygningen, Copenhagen #111 (D.KR 5000)
£538 $968 €785 Girl (100x80cm-39x31in) s.i.d.1940 verso. 24-Apr-4 Rasmussen, Havnen #4051/R (D.KR 6000)
£724 $1296 €1057 Summer landscape with trees (66x96cm-26x38in) s. 10-May-4 Rasmussen, Vejle #700/R (D.KR 8000)
£2254 $4170 €3291 Bear claws (180x85cm-71x33in) s.i.stretcher. 15-Mar-4 Rasmussen, Vejle #550/R est:25000-30000 (D.KR 25000)

SAAF, Erik (1856-1934) Swedish
£2098 $3566 €3000 Coastal landscape (58x92cm-23x36in) s.d.85. 29-Nov-3 Bukowskis, Helsinki #377/R est:2500-3000

SAAL, Georg (1818-1870) German
£1689 $2973 €2500 Norwegian fjord (38x54cm-15x21in) s.d.1853. 22-May-4 Lempertz, Koln #1597/R est:2600
£3603 $6449 €5260 Landscape from Finnmark (60x98cm-24x39in) s.d.1852 exhib. 22-Mar-4 Blomqvist, Oslo #315/R est:55000-65000 (N.KR 45000)

SAARINEN, Yrjo (1899-1958) Finnish
£1056 $1827 €1500 Portrait of woman (46x38cm-18x15in) s.d.1948 lit. 13-Dec-3 Hagelstam, Helsinki #151/R est:2000
£1608 $2734 €2300 Riku Sarkola (65x54cm-26x21in) s.d.1946 lit. 29-Nov-3 Bukowskis, Helsinki #170/R est:2300-2600

£1748 $2972 €2500 Houses in landscape (50x65cm-20x26in) s.d.1940. 29-Nov-3 Bukowskis, Helsinki #32/R est:2500-2800
Works on paper
£431 $719 €620 The inn in Kuopio (22x28cm-9x11in) s.i.d.28 W/C. 26-Oct-3 Bukowskis, Helsinki #481/R
£729 $1218 €1050 Woman sewing (31x24cm-12x9in) s.d.32 W/C. 26-Oct-3 Bukowskis, Helsinki #483/R
£946 $1693 €1400 Winter landscape from Paattene (32x48cm-13x19in) s.d.1942 W/C. 8-May-4 Bukowskis, Helsinki #104/R
£1373 $2197 €1950 The silk stockings (29x35cm-11x14in) s.d.30 W/C exhib. 21-Sep-3 Bukowskis, Helsinki #455/R est:600

SAAVEDRA, Santos (1903-1997) Spanish
£461 $747 €650 Toro saliendo de chiqueros (40x50cm-16x20in) s. 20-May-3 Ansorena, Madrid #23/R

SABATELLI, Luigi (attrib) (1772-1850) Italian
Works on paper
£503 $926 €750 Scene from the 'DEluge' (54x44cm-21x17in) ink dr. 29-Mar-4 Pandolfini, Florence #571/R

SABATER, Daniel (1888-1951) Spanish
£301 $503 €425 Woman with hat (45x36cm-18x14in) s. cardboard. 20-Oct-3 Durán, Madrid #150/R
£333 $613 €500 L'Espagnole (35x26cm-14x10in) s. s.i.d.1947 verso panel. 9-Jun-4 Beaussant & Lefèvre, Paris #212
£467 $859 €700 Les vagabonds (33x40cm-13x16in) s. s.d.1949 verso panel. 9-Jun-4 Beaussant & Lefèvre, Paris #209/R
£559 $962 €800 La Esmeralda (41x33cm-16x13in) s.i. s.i.d.1949 verso panel. 3-Dec-3 Beaussant & Lefèvre, Paris #74
£933 $1717 €1400 L'oiseleur (46x55cm-18x22in) s.i. s.i.d.1951 verso. 9-Jun-4 Beaussant & Lefèvre, Paris #211
£1232 $2020 €1700 Joven desconsolada (80x64cm-31x25in) s. 27-May-3 Durán, Madrid #96/R est:1200
£2211 $3957 €3250 Love of Saint Teresa of Avila (100x81cm-39x32in) s. i.verso. 22-Mar-4 Durán, Madrid #212/R est:1600
£2759 $4966 €4000 A little kiss and nothing else (98x78cm-39x31in) s.i. s.i.d.1935 verso. 26-Jan-4 Ansorena, Madrid #230/R est:4000
£2778 $4528 €4000 Love of Saint Teresa of Avila (100x81cm-39x32in) s. 23-Sep-3 Durán, Madrid #213/R est:1600

SABATIER, Anne Marie (1947-) French
£582 $1042 €850 Place des Abbesses (65x92cm-26x36in) s.i.d.80. 12-May-4 Dobiaschofsky, Bern #927/R (S.FR 1350)

SABATIER, Louis Anet (19th C) French
£12847 $21455 €18500 Sur le pont du paquebot (65x41cm-26x16in) s. lit. 22-Oct-3 Ribeyre & Baron, Paris #16/R est:12000-18000

SABATTIER, Louis (19th C) French
Works on paper
£521 $849 €750 Procession in French village (36x54cm-14x21in) s. W/C htd white. 24-Sep-3 Neumeister, Munich #292

SABBAGH, Georges (1887-1951) French
£528 $914 €750 Portrait d'Egyptienne (33x23cm-13x9in) s.d.1933 panel. 10-Dec-3 Millon & Associes, Paris #96/R

SABBATINI, Lorenzo (c.1530-1577) Italian
Works on paper
£1439 $2302 €2000 Study of angel (30x19cm-12x7in) pen ink W/C. 14-May-3 Finarte Semenzato, Milan #487/R est:500-800

SABBATINI, Lorenzo (attrib) (c.1530-1577) Italian
£3241 $5413 €4700 Deposition (30x22cm-12x9in) copper. 15-Nov-3 Porro, Milan #211/R

SABBIDES, Simeon (1859-1927) Greek
£11000 $18700 €16060 Portrait of man (44x34cm-17x13in) 18-Nov-3 Sotheby's, London #87/R est:6000-8000

SABLET, François Jean (1745-1819) French/Swiss
£2174 $3978 €3174 Portrait of a gentleman (23x20cm-9x8in) s. prov. 7-Jun-4 Christie's, Zurich #3/R est:6000-8000 (S.FR 5000)

SABLET, François Jean (attrib) (1745-1819) French/Swiss
£704 $1232 €1000 Bergere et troupeau (16x22cm-6x9in) indis.sig. panel. 17-Dec-3 Piasa, Paris #77
£1343 $2470 €2000 Portrait d'une jeune officier (24x20cm-9x8in) panel. 24-Mar-4 Tajan, Paris #150 est:2000-3000

SABLET, Jacques Henri (attrib) (1749-1803) Swiss
£1310 $2384 €1913 Seated woman with a spinning wheel, accompanied by a dog (24x19cm-9x7in) panel. 16-Jun-4 Fischer, Luzern #1273/R est:3000-4000 (S.FR 3000)

SABON, Laurent (1852-?) Swiss
£344 $575 €502 Figures by river (46x34cm-18x13in) s. panel. 20-Oct-3 Blomqvist, Lysaker #1269 (N.KR 4000)

SABOURAUD, Émile (1900-1996) French
£556 $906 €800 Nu dans la foret (71x46cm-28x18in) s. 18-Jul-3 Feletin, Province #127
£655 $1088 €950 Saint Cyprien, les arbres secs (54x65cm-21x26in) s.verso. 5-Oct-3 Lombrail & Teucquam, Paris #317
£805 $1498 €1200 Le port de Dieppe (54x73cm-21x29in) s.d.1961. 3-Mar-4 Ferri, Paris #323
£1418 $2369 €2000 Homme accoude (66x47cm-26x19in) s. 16-Jun-3 Gros & Delettrez, Paris #191/R est:2000-3000
£1905 $3029 €2800 Nature morte a la cafetiere jaune (81x54cm-32x21in) s. 23-Mar-3 St-Germain-en-Laye Encheres #67/R

SABY, Bernard (1925-1975) French
Works on paper
£340 $609 €500 Untitled (49x64cm-19x25in) s. crayons prov. 21-Mar-4 Calmels Cohen, Paris #143/R

SACAILLAN, Edouard (1957-) Greek
£7000 $12530 €10220 Untitled (150x150cm-59x59in) s.d.96-98 paper on canvas. 10-May-4 Sotheby's, Olympia #82/R est:4000-6000

SACCAGGI, Cesare (1868-1934) Italian
£2479 $4016 €3495 Portrait of young woman (65x54cm-26x21in) board. 21-May-3 Babuino, Rome #209/R est:2000
Works on paper
£312 $521 €440 Woman and dog (21x10cm-8x4in) s. mixed media. 20-Oct-3 Sant Agostino, Torino #322/R

SACCARO, John (1913-1981) American
£4545 $8000 €6636 Untitled (124x99cm-49x39in) s.d.1956. 23-May-4 Treadway Gallery, Cincinnati #757/R est:2500-4500
Works on paper
£435 $700 €635 Sunday morning stroller (55x75cm-22x30in) s.d.39 W/C exhib. 17-Aug-3 Bonhams & Butterfields, San Francisco #5811
£565 $1000 €825 Cantatas (39x39cm-15x15in) init. s.i.d.1951 verso mixed media board. 2-May-4 Bonhams & Butterfields, Los Angeles #3042/R

SACCHETTI, Enrico (1874-1960) Italian
£374 $670 €550 Around Monza (32x43cm-13x17in) s. board. 22-Mar-4 Sant Agostino, Torino #156/R

SACCHI, Andrea (1599-1661) Italian
£150000 $274500 €219000 Daedalus and Icarus (136x98cm-54x39in) prov.lit. 7-Jul-4 Christie's, London #100/R est:200000-300000

SACCHI, Andrea (circle) (1599-1661) Italian
£11111 $20000 €16222 Three ages of man (86x108cm-34x43in) 22-Jan-4 Sotheby's, New York #259/R est:25000-35000

SACCO OITANA, Alessandro (1862-1932) Italian
£417 $708 €600 Hens (46x82cm-18x32in) s.d.1891. 1-Nov-3 Meeting Art, Vercelli #48

SACCOMANDI, Sergio (1946-) Italian
Works on paper
£280 $467 €400 Snowfall (49x39cm-19x15in) s. mixed media card exhib. 26-Jun-3 Sant Agostino, Torino #234/R
£280 $467 €400 San Francesco al Campo (49x39cm-19x15in) s. mixed media card exhib. 26-Jun-3 Sant Agostino, Torino #233/R

SACCOMANI, Giuseppe (19/20th C) Italian?
Works on paper
£420 $722 €600 Raging horse (50x70cm-20x28in) s. mixed media. 3-Dec-3 Stadion, Trieste #960/R
£455 $782 €650 Cock fight (50x60cm-20x24in) s. mixed media. 3-Dec-3 Stadion, Trieste #956

SACHAROFF, Olga (1889-1969) Russian
£1267 $2267 €1900 Bouquet (22x18cm-9x7in) panel. 17-May-4 Chayette & Cheval, Paris #187 est:1300-1500
Works on paper
£4362 $7721 €6500 Women with Spanish shawls (33x43cm-13x17in) s. W/C. 27-Apr-4 Durán, Madrid #73/R est:6000

SACHAROFF, Olga (attrib) (1889-1969) Russian
£521 $849 €750 Winter landscape (46x64cm-18x25in) s.d.1912. 16-Jul-3 Durán, Madrid #540/R

SACHERI, Giuseppe (1863-1950) Italian
£694 $1181 €1000 Back from pasture (40x44cm-16x17in) s. paper on canvas. 1-Nov-3 Meeting Art, Vercelli #270
£922 $1540 €1300 October in the Netherlands (22x27cm-9x11in) s. paper. 20-Oct-3 Sant Agostino, Torino #270/R
£1348 $2250 €1900 White mill (31x39cm-12x15in) s. s.i.verso card. 20-Oct-3 Sant Agostino, Torino #269/R est:2200
£1544 $2732 €2300 White mill (31x39cm-12x15in) s. s.i.verso cardboard. 1-May-4 Meeting Art, Vercelli #228 est:2000
£2721 $4871 €4000 Harbour (22x35cm-9x14in) s.d.1896. 22-Mar-4 Sant Agostino, Torino #245/R est:2200

SACHS, Michael (1837-1893) German
£608 $1070 €900 German lake with mountains (30x41cm-12x16in) s. 19-May-4 Dorotheum, Klagenfurt #21/R
£608 $1070 €900 German lake landscape with mountains (30x42cm-12x17in) s. 19-May-4 Dorotheum, Klagenfurt #22/R

SACHS, Tom (1966-) American
Sculpture
£1268 $2218 €1800 One dollar (27x22x5cm-11x9x2in) dollar bills coins adhesive tape directory exec 1996. 18-Dec-3 Cornette de St.Cyr, Paris #183/R est:1800-2000
£10056 $18000 €14682 Miffy (24x11x11cm-9x4x4in) s.d.2002 num. of 25 acrylic Bondo cast bronze prov. 14-May-4 Phillips, New York #341/R est:5000-7000
Works on paper
£1359 $2500 €1984 Untitled, come out with your hands up you French fuck (28x22cm-11x9in) s.d.1997 verso pen ink felt tipped pen prov. 10-Jun-4 Phillips, New York #486/R est:2500-3000

SACHSE AND COMPANY (fl.c.1849-1870) American
Prints
£3191 $5330 €4500 Panoramic view of Washington City (51x85cm-20x33in) lithograph. 23-Jun-3 Durán, Madrid #713/R est:100

SACKS, Walter Thomas (1901-?) American
Works on paper
£279 $500 €407 Rustic foot bridge (51x61cm-20x24in) s. i.verso gouache. 21-Mar-4 Jeffery Burchard, Florida #58/R

SACKSICK, Gilles (1942-) French
£533 $955 €800 Bouquet de lilas (65x23cm-26x9in) s.d.2002 verso canvas on panel. 12-May-4 Brissoneau, France #102

SACRE, Émile (1844-1882) Belgian
£338 $595 €500 Portrait of a woman (32x21cm-13x8in) s. panel. 24-May-4 Bernaerts, Antwerp #371/R

SADAHIDE, Hashimoto (1807-1873) Japanese
Prints
£1536 $2750 €2243 Hizen nagasski maruyama kakuchu no kukei. s. print. 10-May-4 Bonhams & Butterfields, San Francisco #4107/R est:2500-4000

SADALI, Ahmad (1924-1987) Indonesian
£260 $435 €380 Bintang Merah (35x45cm-14x18in) s. s.i.d.23/6 76 verso. 12-Oct-3 Sotheby's, Singapore #177/R (S.D 750)
£1993 $3089 €2910 Moulded by the weather, fashioned by the wind (100x110cm-39x43in) s.d.68 s.i.d.1968 verso. 6-Oct-2 Sotheby's, Singapore #163/R est:5000-7000 (S.D 5500)
£5435 $8424 €7935 Abstract (73x59cm-29x23in) s.d.71 oil acrylic. 6-Oct-2 Sotheby's, Singapore #165/R est:8000-10000 (S.D 15000)
£7742 $12387 €11303 Green pyramid (80x80cm-31x31in) s.d.84. 18-May-3 Sotheby's, Singapore #180/R est:18000-25000 (S.D 21600)

SADANANDAN, V M (20th C) Indian
£260 $447 €380 Weeping women (75x120cm-30x47in) s. board. 3-Dec-3 Cheffins, Cambridge #653/R

SADEE, Philippe (1837-1904) Dutch
£5000 $9000 €7500 Market scene in Frankfurt (35x50cm-14x20in) init.d.17 Sept 91 panel. 20-Apr-4 Sotheby's, Amsterdam #114/R est:8000-12000
£8500 $15470 €12410 Looking out to sea (55x68cm-22x27in) s.d.1886. 16-Jun-4 Bonhams, New Bond Street #14/R est:8000-12000
£26590 $46000 €38821 Welcoming the boats (74x99cm-29x39in) s.d.96. 13-Dec-3 Sloans & Kenyon, Bethesda #803/R est:12000-18000
£63333 $114000 €95000 Return of the fishing fleet, Katwijk (74x101cm-29x40in) s.d.1896. 20-Apr-4 Sotheby's, Amsterdam #199/R est:70000-100000
Works on paper
£272 $495 €400 At the spinning wheel (54x34cm-21x13in) s. chl black chk prov. 3-Feb-4 Christie's, Amsterdam #144

SADEE, Philippe (attrib) (1837-1904) Dutch
£1806 $2979 €2600 Fishing boats off coast with approaching storm (69x103cm-27x41in) bears sig. 3-Jul-3 Van Ham, Cologne #1436/R est:2400

SADELER, Egidius II (1570-1629) Flemish
Prints
£2123 $3800 €3100 Bartholomacus Spranger and his wife Christina Muller (30x43cm-12x17in) engraving. 6-May-4 Swann Galleries, New York #42/R est:3000-5000

SADELLIER, Victor (19th C) ?
£300 $555 €438 Consequences of vice (30x41cm-12x16in) s. 15-Jan-4 Christie's, Kensington #812/R

SADKOWSKI, Alex (1934-) Swiss
£262 $482 €383 Lovers in car (52x38cm-20x15in) s.d. board. 14-Jun-4 Philippe Schuler, Zurich #5747 (S.FR 600)
£271 $462 €396 Titineleda with admirer (70x50cm-28x20in) s.d.1971/1972 oil resin lit. 25-Nov-3 Germann, Zurich #884 (S.FR 600)
£452 $769 €660 Two women (60x55cm-24x22in) s. 18-Nov-3 Hans Widmer, St Gallen #1177 (S.FR 1000)
£647 $1170 €945 Flowers (29x17cm-11x7in) s.d.71 panel. 31-Mar-4 Zurichsee Auktionen, Erlenbach #69/R est:1500-2000 (S.FR 1500)
£786 $1446 €1148 The pianist (42x37cm-17x15in) s.d.1975/1977 lit. 8-Jun-4 Germann, Zurich #93/R (S.FR 1800)
£1509 $2731 €2203 Poetess (48x44cm-19x17in) s.d.84 acrylic pavatex. 31-Mar-4 Zurichsee Auktionen, Erlenbach #166/R est:2500-3500 (S.FR 3500)
£1834 $3375 €2678 Woman with scar (128x87cm-50x34in) s.d.1972/73 lit. 8-Jun-4 Germann, Zurich #91/R est:4000-6000 (S.FR 4200)
Works on paper
£328 $603 €479 Table with flower (54x43cm-21x17in) s.d.1962 gouache board. 8-Jun-4 Germann, Zurich #869 (S.FR 750)
£776 $1404 €1133 Star woman (69x49cm-27x19in) s.d.21.4.87 Indian ink. 31-Mar-4 Zurichsee Auktionen, Erlenbach #142/R (S.FR 1800)

SADLER, Walter Dendy (1854-1923) British
£300 $555 €438 Haddon Hall (50x75cm-20x30in) s.i.d.85. 16-Feb-4 Bonhams, Bath #187
£500 $895 €730 Huntsman with clay pipe, outside a country inn (51x43cm-20x17in) mono. 5-May-4 Goldings, Lincolnshire #528
£720 $1310 €1051 Ferry, with a figure holding an umbrella waiting at a river side. indis.s.d. 3-Feb-4 Lawrences, Bletchingley #1566
£728 $1326 €1100 General scene (20x27cm-8x11in) s. panel. 19-Jun-4 Bergmann, Erlangen #778
£1605 $2825 €2343 Strings to his bow (61x46cm-24x18in) s. 28-May-4 Aspire, Cleveland #20/R est:800-1200
£4800 $7968 €7008 Westphalian peasant girl feeding chickens (84x60cm-33x24in) s.d.1874 exhib. 1-Oct-3 Sotheby's, Olympia #84/R est:3000-5000
£50000 $90000 €73000 Old and crusted (85x120cm-33x47in) s. prov.exhib. 21-Apr-4 Cheffins, Cambridge #488/R est:30000-50000

SADLER, William (18/19th C) British
£729 $1189 €1050 Figures travelling on a path (9x27cm-4x11in) board prov. 24-Sep-3 James Adam, Dublin #27/R est:800-1200

SADLER, William (attrib) (18/19th C) British
£694 $1181 €1000 Darige at Powerscourt. Bridge at Baline (18x24cm-7x9in) pair. 28-Oct-3 Mealy's, Castlecomer #493
£811 $1427 €1200 Eruption of Vesuvius (19x26cm-7x10in) board. 22-May-4 Lempertz, Koln #1598/R

SADLER, William (jnr) (1782-1839) British
£2819 $4989 €4200 Distant view of Powerscourt waterfall, C Wicklow, with horseman (28x43cm-11x17in) panel painted c.1830. 27-Apr-4 Whyte's, Dublin #130/R est:3000-5000
£3733 $6757 €5600 Entrance to Dublin port with shipping (21x26cm-8x10in) panel. 31-Mar-4 James Adam, Dublin #3/R est:3000-5000
£5200 $8840 €7592 Capriccio river landscape with a classical town in the distance at sunset (60x92cm-24x36in) panel. 29-Oct-3 Bonhams, New Bond Street #119/R est:2500-3000

SADOVNIKOV, Vasili Semenovich (1800-1879) Russian
Works on paper
£15000 $26850 €21900 View of the Moscow Kremlin (23x35cm-9x14in) W/C htd gouache over panel. 26-May-4 Sotheby's, London #10/R est:6000-8000
£15000 $26850 €21900 Russian street vendor types (14x11cm-6x4in) W/C ink group of eight. 26-May-4 Sotheby's, London #11/R est:8000-12000

SADUN, Piero (1919-1974) Italian
£1333 $2453 €2000 Transparence 2 (115x105cm-45x41in) s.verso exhib. 8-Jun-4 Finarte Semenzato, Milan #234 est:1000-1500
£1604 $3000 €2342 Identity (96x114cm-38x45in) s. painted 1957 prov. 25-Feb-4 Christie's, Rockefeller NY #111/R est:3000-5000
£1818 $3091 €2600 Composition in grey (80x100cm-31x39in) s.i. prov. 24-Nov-3 Christie's, Milan #259 est:2500-3000

SAEDELEER, Elisabeth de (1902-1972) Belgian
£338 $595 €500 Winter landscape with figures (85x95cm-33x37in) s. 18-May-4 Galerie Moderne, Brussels #142/R
£385 $642 €550 L'ete (26x37cm-10x15in) s. 13-Oct-3 Horta, Bruxelles #436

SAEDELEER, Valerius de (1867-1941) Belgian
£5594 $9510 €8000 Moulins au lever du soleil (49x78cm-19x31in) s. 1-Dec-3 Palais de Beaux Arts, Brussels #46/R est:5000-7000

SAEGHER, Rodolphe de (1871-1941) Belgian
£966 $1786 €1400 Coucher de soleil sur les toits rouges (38x46cm-15x18in) s. 19-Jan-4 Horta, Bruxelles #27
Works on paper
£559 $1012 €850 Enfants au bord de mer (25x31cm-10x12in) s. chl. 19-Apr-4 Horta, Bruxelles #30

SAELE, Hans (1945-) Norwegian
£361 $631 €527 From Faerder Lighthouse (73x100cm-29x39in) s. i.stretcher. 16-Dec-3 Grev Wedels Plass, Oslo #226/R (N.KR 4200)
£2129 $3407 €3087 Mother and daughter at Goksjo (81x100cm-32x39in) s. 22-Sep-3 Blomqvist, Lysaker #1295/R est:15000-20000 (N.KR 25000)

SAENE, Maurice van (1919-2000) Belgian
£3521 $6092 €5000 Seascape (80x100cm-31x39in) s. 13-Dec-3 De Vuyst, Lokeren #582/R est:5000-6000
Works on paper
£433 $776 €650 Nude sitting (96x68cm-38x27in) s. black chk. 15-May-4 De Vuyst, Lokeren #371

SAENGER, Lucie von (1902-) Russian
£1208 $2223 €1800 Still life of flowers (100x120cm-39x47in) s. 24-Mar-4 Hugo Ruef, Munich #1100 est:1800

SAENREDAM, Jan Pietersz (1565-1607) Dutch
Prints
£2238 $3804 €3200 Adoration of the shepherds (44x36cm-17x14in) copperplate after Karel van Mander 3 plates. 27-Nov-3 Bassenge, Berlin #5351 est:1800
£4133 $7399 €6200 Sine Bacchus et Ceres friget Venus (27x20cm-11x8in) copperplate after Abraham Bloemaert. 13-May-4 Bassenge, Berlin #5295/R est:2800
£4800 $8592 €7200 Allegory of good and angry humanity (52x37cm-20x15in) copperplate after Cornelis Ketel. 13-May-4 Bassenge, Berlin #5298/R est:4000

SAENREDAM, Pieter Jansz (1597-1665) Dutch
£916667 $1650000 €1338334 Haarlem, interior of the Nieuwe Kerk (30x31cm-12x12in) s.d.1658 panel. 22-Jan-4 Sotheby's, New York #90/R est:600000-800000

SAENZ DE TEJADA, Carlos (1897-1958) Spanish
Works on paper
£594 $993 €850 Clowns (44x32cm-17x13in) W/C. 30-Jun-3 Ansorena, Madrid #12/R

SAENZ Y SAENZ, Pedro (1867-1927) Spanish
£1918 $3260 €2800 Vestalin (129x80cm-51x31in) s. 5-Nov-3 Hugo Ruef, Munich #1101/R est:1500

SAENZ, Monica and VALDES, Mariana (20th C) South American
£1005 $1900 €1467 Landscape with tree and lizard (228x185cm-90x73in) s. acrylic. 22-Feb-4 Galeria y Remates, Montevideo #138/R est:2000-3000

SAETTI, Bruno (1902-1984) Italian
£867 $1551 €1300 Portrait of man (36x25cm-14x10in) s. 12-May-4 Stadion, Trieste #824
£933 $1689 €1400 Sunny landscape (38x53cm-15x21in) s. s.verso tempera paper. 2-Apr-4 Farsetti, Prato #5/R
£1067 $1963 €1600 Vase of flowers (40x27cm-16x11in) s. tempera paper on card. 8-Jun-4 Finarte Semenzato, Milan #235/R est:1200-1600
£1769 $3166 €2600 Siena (18x23cm-7x9in) s.d.1940 board prov. 16-Mar-4 Finarte Semenzato, Milan #301/R est:2500
£1905 $3410 €2800 Siena (18x23cm-7x9in) s.d.1940 boardprov. 16-Mar-4 Finarte Semenzato, Milan #300/R est:2500
£2177 $3897 €3200 Canal in Venice (18x29cm-7x11in) s. cardboard painted 1940 prov. 16-Mar-4 Finarte Semenzato, Milan #302/R est:2800
£2448 $4087 €3500 Still life (40x50cm-16x20in) s. tempera paper on canvas prov.lit. 26-Jun-3 Sant Agostino, Torino #198/R est:3000-3500
£2690 $4303 €3900 Composition (31x37cm-12x15in) s. tempera paper on canvas painted 1963. 13-Mar-3 Galleria Pace, Milan #64/R est:4500-6000
£3000 $5370 €4500 Caorle (37x50cm-15x20in) s.d.1957 tempera mixed media cardboard. 12-May-4 Stadion, Trieste #706/R est:2500-3500
£3357 $5706 €4800 Still life of fruit (24x37cm-9x15in) s. canvas on masonite painted c.1965. 24-Nov-3 Christie's, Milan #64/R est:3000-4000
£3623 $5942 €5000 Composition (50x70cm-20x28in) s. tempera paper on canvas. 29-May-3 Galleria Pace, Milan #126/R est:7500
£4362 $7809 €6500 Sunny landscape (35x50cm-14x20in) s. s.i.d.80 verso fresco canvas on board. 29-May-4 Farsetti, Prato #471/R est:3000-4000
£6522 $10696 €9000 Paesaggio col sole (50x60cm-20x24in) s. fresco. 31-May-3 Farsetti, Prato #748/R est:9000-11000
£8503 $15221 €12500 Still life with white bottle (41x60cm-16x24in) s.d.1944 prov. 16-Mar-4 Finarte Semenzato, Milan #303/R est:12000
£14094 $25228 €21000 Ants' ferry (95x130cm-37x51in) s. s.i.d.1975 verso fresco lit. 29-May-4 Farsetti, Prato #476/R est:15000-18000
Works on paper
£621 $1037 €900 Maternity (67x48cm-26x19in) s.i.d.1967 Chinese ink. 13-Nov-3 Galleria Pace, Milan #35/R
£652 $1070 €900 Reclining female nude (48x68cm-19x27in) s.d.1983 Chinese ink. 29-May-3 Galleria Pace, Milan #55
£748 $1339 €1100 Beat girl (75x55cm-30x22in) s.d.1967 Chinese ink W/C prov. 16-Mar-4 Finarte Semenzato, Milan #231/R
£1517 $2534 €2200 Sunny landscape (45x55cm-18x22in) s. mixed media paper on canvas. 14-Nov-3 Farsetti, Prato #218/R est:200-2500

SAEYS, Jakob Ferdinand (circle) (1658-1725) Flemish
£5862 $9731 €8500 Baroque palace architecture with figures and swans (135x95cm-53x37in) 1-Oct-3 Dorotheum, Vienna #130/R est:4500-6000

SAEZ, Luis (1925-) Spanish
£1549 $2479 €2200 Abstraction (67x56cm-26x22in) s. painted c.1960. 16-Sep-3 Segre, Madrid #173/R est:1000
£3472 $5903 €5000 Painting 3 (100x85cm-39x33in) s. s.i.d.1960 verso exhib. 28-Oct-3 Segre, Madrid #203/R est:1800

SAFFORD, Charles (20th C) American
£472 $850 €689 Abstract (76x61cm-30x24in) s. 25-Apr-4 Bonhams & Butterfields, San Francisco #5608/R

SAFRAN, Bernard (20th C) American
£442 $800 €645 River (36x48cm-14x19in) board. 16-Apr-4 American Auctioneer #348/R

SAFTLEVEN, Cornelis (1607-1681) Dutch
£1150 $2105 €1679 Barn interior with goats and lady milking (30x38cm-12x15in) panel. 9-Jul-4 Christie's, Kensington #22/R
£5068 $8919 €7500 Farmstead with pigs, chicken a peasant feeding pigs (37x50cm-15x20in) indis sig. panel. 18-May-4 Sotheby's, Amsterdam #102/R est:6000-8000
£6897 $11448 €10000 Dune landscape with ruins, shepherd and flock (40x52cm-16x20in) s.d.1639 panel. 1-Oct-3 Dorotheum, Vienna #202/R est:10000-15000
£13077 $22492 €19092 Interior scene with figures (50x75cm-20x30in) s.indis.d.1637 panel prov. 3-Dec-3 AB Stockholms Auktionsverk #2667/R est:50000-60000 (S.KR 170000)
£22000 $40260 €32120 Huntsman feeding dogs under porch (39x56cm-15x22in) panel prov.lit. 8-Jul-4 Sotheby's, London #126/R est:18000-25000
£27972 $47552 €40000 Fairytale interior (85x106cm-33x42in) s. lit.prov. 20-Nov-3 Van Ham, Cologne #1409/R est:12000
Works on paper
£1700 $3111 €2482 Sleeping dog (8x12cm-3x5in) black chk wash pen ink framing lines. 6-Jul-4 Christie's, London #181/R est:700-1000
£1781 $3027 €2600 Saint Francis receiving the Stigmata (25x18cm-10x7in) mono.d.1633 black chk prov.lit. 4-Nov-3 Sotheby's, Amsterdam #63/R est:2000-3000

SAFTLEVEN, Herman (1609-1685) Dutch
£9000 $16200 €13140 Extensive river landscape with a monastery on a cliff (43x58cm-17x23in) mono.d.1672 panel. 21-Apr-4 Christie's, London #42/R est:7000-10000
£12676 $20282 €18000 Romantic landscape (49x72cm-19x28in) s.d.1634 panel lit. 19-Sep-3 Karlheinz Kaupp, Staufen #1897/R est:4500
£33000 $57090 €48180 Rhenish river landscape with figures unloading barges and sailboats (23x32cm-9x13in) mono.d.1664 s.i.d.verso oak panel. 11-Dec-3 Sotheby's, London #69/R est:20000-30000
Works on paper
£600 $1104 €900 View from Vogelschau over river valley (14x18cm-6x7in) chk brush. 11-Jun-4 Hauswedell & Nolte, Hamburg #903/R
£2055 $3493 €3000 Figures by the city wall of Utrecht with the Bijhouwertoren to the right (28x22cm-11x9in) black chk pen ink wash. 5-Nov-3 Christie's, Amsterdam #127/R est:3000-5000
£5556 $10000 €8112 Sheet of studies of peasants, riders and wagons (29x20cm-11x8in) black chk brown wash. 21-Jan-4 Sotheby's, New York #68/R est:10000-15000
£5822 $9897 €8500 Male peasant leaning, with hat and stick (8x5cm-3x2in) mono. black chk col wash playing card lit. 4-Nov-3 Sotheby's, Amsterdam #68/R est:6000-8000
£7534 $12808 €11000 Peasant woman walking, carrying goods in a basket and sling (8x5cm-3x2in) mono. black chk col wash playing card lit. 4-Nov-3 Sotheby's, Amsterdam #69/R est:6000-8000

SAGARZAZU, Javier (1946-) Spanish?
Works on paper
£748 $1362 €1100 Still life of fruit and doll (38x58cm-15x23in) s.d.1978 W/C. 3-Feb-4 Segre, Madrid #132/R

SAGE, Henry James (1868-1953) British
£400 $720 €584 Figures and a cart on a parkland track (30x41cm-12x16in) s. 20-Apr-4 Clarke Gammon, Guildford #95
Works on paper
£260 $450 €380 Cottages at St. Catherine's (25x18cm-10x7in) s. W/C. 9-Dec-3 Clarke Gammon, Guildford #79
£300 $519 €438 St. Martha's Guildford (20x36cm-8x14in) s. W/C. 9-Dec-3 Clarke Gammon, Guildford #82
£400 $692 €584 Peep showing St. Catherine's Spring, Guilford (23x15cm-9x6in) s. W/C. 9-Dec-3 Clarke Gammon, Guildford #74
£600 $1038 €876 Peep at the bottom of Quarry Street showing St. Mary's Church (23x15cm-9x6in) s. W/C. 9-Dec-3 Clarke Gammon, Guildford #75
£600 $1080 €876 Off Buryfields Street, Guildford (18x28cm-7x11in) s. W/C. 20-Apr-4 Clarke Gammon, Guildford #85/R
£750 $1193 €1095 North Street looking south (25x18cm-10x7in) s. W/C. 24-Feb-4 Clarke Gammon, Guildford #50/R
£850 $1471 €1241 Surrey Lane near Guildford, with rustic bridge over the Tillingbourne River (23x36cm-9x14in) s. W/C. 9-Dec-3 Clarke Gammon, Guildford #77
£850 $1471 €1241 Castle arch, Guildford (25x23cm-10x9in) s. W/C. 9-Dec-3 Clarke Gammon, Guildford #81
£1100 $1903 €1606 Shalford Church and war memorial (18x28cm-7x11in) s. W/C. 9-Dec-3 Clarke Gammon, Guildford #80 est:200-300
£4200 $7266 €6132 Quarry Street from the High Street showing St. Mary's church (23x33cm-9x13in) s. W/C. 9-Dec-3 Clarke Gammon, Guildford #83/R est:400-600

SAGE, Kay (1898-1963) American
£7955 $14000 €11614 Les Rouleaux (65x50cm-26x20in) init. painted 1937 prov. 18-May-4 Christie's, Rockefeller NY #126/R est:20000-30000

SAGER-NELSON, Olof (1868-1896) Swedish
£11086 $19845 €16186 Summer landscape with girl (33x40cm-13x16in) s.d.89 lit. 26-May-4 AB Stockholms Auktionsverk #2350/R est:125000-150000 (S.KR 150000)

SAGERY, Chr (19th C) French
£380 $615 €555 Wash day by the river (47x38cm-19x15in) s. 9-Aug-3 Hindemae, Ullerslev #110/R (D.KR 4000)

SAGES, Jenny (1933-) Australian
£1951 $3493 €2848 Bungle bungles (151x244cm-59x96in) s.d.87 i.verso. 4-May-4 Sotheby's, Melbourne #313/R est:4000-6000 (A.D 4800)

SAGEWKA, Ernst (1883-1959) German
£909 $1545 €1300 Evening sun in the Senne (80x95cm-31x37in) s.d. mono.i.d. verso prov. 21-Nov-3 Reiss & Sohn, Konigstein #515/R est:2000

SAGITO, Ivan (1957-) Oriental
£10458 $18928 €15269 From where am i (100x127cm-39x50in) s.d.85. 4-Apr-4 Sotheby's, Singapore #179/R est:25000-35000 (S.D 32000)
£17361 $28993 €25347 Topeng and Gadis (109x138cm-43x54in) s.d.1995. 12-Oct-3 Sotheby's, Singapore #181/R est:35000-55000 (S.D 50000)

SAGRESTANI, Giovanni Camillo (1660-1731) Italian
£9396 $17289 €14000 Finding of Moses (91x75cm-36x30in) 24-Mar-4 Dorotheum, Vienna #84/R est:14000-20000

SAGUIL, Nena (1914-1998) Asian
£15972 $26674 €23319 Newsboy (71x55cm-28x22in) s.d.49 canvas on board. 12-Oct-3 Sotheby's, Singapore #60/R est:18000-28000 (S.D 46000)
£22464 $34819 €32797 Nudes (60x76cm-24x30in) s.d.51 tempera board. 6-Oct-2 Sotheby's, Singapore #87/R est:7000-9000 (S.D 62000)

SAHLSTEN, Anna (1859-1931) Finnish
£845 $1352 €1200 Union street, Helsinki (21x20cm-8x8in) s. 18-Sep-3 Hagelstam, Helsinki #1045

SAHRAOUI, Schems Eddine (1948-) Tunisian
£355 $592 €500 Le minaret (24x19cm-9x7in) s.i. 19-Oct-3 Peron, Melun #340
£385 $662 €550 Vue de marche. 2-Dec-3 Claude Aguttes, Neuilly #65

SAILA, Pauta (1916-) North American
Sculpture
£1157 $2083 €1689 Bird (33cm-13in) s. marbled green soapstone. 26-Apr-4 Waddingtons, Toronto #269/R est:3000-4000 (C.D 2800)
£1802 $3063 €2631 Winged walrus with tusks (56cm-22in) s. marbled green soapstone exec.c.1970. 3-Nov-3 Waddingtons, Toronto #329/R est:3000-5000 (C.D 4000)
£2252 $3829 €3288 Dancing polar bear (41cm-16in) marbled white stone. 3-Nov-3 Waddingtons, Toronto #102/R est:6000-9000 (C.D 5000)
£5405 $9189 €7891 Polar bear standing with head raised (48cm-19in) mottled green soapstone. 3-Nov-3 Waddingtons, Toronto #325/R est:12000-16000 (C.D 12000)
£6757 $11486 €9865 Dancing polar bear with it's mouth open (43cm-17in) marbled green soapstone. 3-Nov-3 Waddingtons, Toronto #115/R est:12000-16000 (C.D 15000)

SAILA, Pitaloosie (1942-) North American
Works on paper
£586 $995 €856 Inuit woman and birds (63x48cm-25x19in) s. ink exec.c.1969. 3-Nov-3 Waddingtons, Toronto #215/R (C.D 1300)

SAIN, Edouard Alexandre (1830-1910) French
£800 $1456 €1200 Female nude in the woods (55x38cm-22x15in) s.d.1897 s.verso. 12-Jul-4 Il Ponte, Milan #994
£905 $1620 €1321 Children playing on beach near Biarritz (42x55cm-17x22in) s.i.d.1861 panel. 12-May-4 Dobiaschofsky, Bern #929/R est:2500 (S.FR 2100)
£2381 $4262 €3500 Maid looking at reflection in shop window (32x27cm-13x11in) s.d.58 panel. 17-Mar-4 Neumeister, Munich #590/R est:3500
£3947 $7263 €6000 Vue de Capri. Vue de Pompei (21x32cm-8x13in) s.i. canvas on cardboard pair. 24-Jun-4 Christie's, Paris #145/R est:6000-8000

SAIN, Paul Jean Marie (1853-1908) French
£280 $467 €400 Sous les bouleaux (40x27cm-16x11in) s. canvas on panel. 13-Oct-3 Horta, Bruxelles #412
£533 $955 €800 Plage animee (22x33cm-9x13in) s. panel. 16-May-4 Thierry & Lannon, Brest #172
£640 $1171 €960 Allee du moulin (25x35cm-10x14in) s. panel. 6-Jun-4 Osenat, Fontainebleau #281/R
£800 $1472 €1200 La route Saint-Antoine a Bastia, Corse (22x33cm-9x13in) s. panel. 14-Jun-4 Tajan, Paris #86
Works on paper
£400 $640 €580 Preparing spices for market (62x47cm-24x19in) s. pen ink. 18-Sep-3 Christie's, Kensington #207/R

SAINT CLAIR, Norman (1863-1912) American
Works on paper
£588 $1100 €882 Rocky cove (21x49cm-8x19in) s. W/C. 25-Jul-4 Bonhams & Butterfields, San Francisco #6082/R
£1236 $2250 €1805 Summer landscape (36x23cm-14x9in) s. W/C. 15-Jun-4 John Moran, Pasadena #90 est:900-1400
£1236 $2250 €1805 Landscape (30x28cm-12x11in) s. W/C prov. 15-Jun-4 John Moran, Pasadena #90a est:1000-1500
£1648 $3000 €2406 California landscape (30x48cm-12x19in) s. W/C. 15-Jun-4 John Moran, Pasadena #84 est:2500-3500

ST JOHN, Edwin (19th C) British
Works on paper
£226 $378 €330 Figures on the hillside off the Bay of Naples (48x31cm-19x12in) s. W/C. 17-Nov-3 Waddingtons, Toronto #61/R (C.D 500)
£500 $835 €730 On Lake Como (25x51cm-10x20in) s. W/C. 20-Jun-3 Chrystals Auctions, Isle of Man #214/R
£580 $916 €847 Italian river scene with angler seated on wall (43x64cm-17x25in) s.d.1887 W/C. 7-Sep-3 Desmond Judd, Cranbrook #744
£580 $916 €847 Continental river scene, cathedral beyond (43x64cm-17x25in) s.d.1887 W/C. 7-Sep-3 Desmond Judd, Cranbrook #745
£650 $1086 €949 On the Adriatic. On the Rhine (15x23cm-6x9in) s. W/C pair. 14-Oct-3 Bonhams, Knightsbridge #211/R

ST JOHN, Terry (1934-) American
£1765 $3000 €2577 Oakland estuary (60x75cm-24x30in) s. i.d.1988 verso prov. 9-Nov-3 Bonhams & Butterfields, Los Angeles #4046/R

ST JOHN-JONES, Herbert (fl.1905-1923) British
£350 $557 €511 On the edge of the moor (36x56cm-14x22in) s.d.1923 verso. 12-Sep-3 Halls, Shrewsbury #835
£650 $1047 €943 Coaching scene with figures and horses outside a village inn (10x36cm-4x14in) s.d.1898. 15-Aug-3 Keys, Aylsham #752
£750 $1328 €1095 Rose of Walaby 19th winner of the shorthorn dairy prize (36x49cm-14x19in) s.i. 28-Apr-4 Peter Wilson, Nantwich #61
£820 $1517 €1197 Warble and sailor - North Stafford Hunt (45x61cm-18x24in) s.i. 14-Jul-4 Bonhams, Chester #499
£1200 $2040 €1752 On the edge of the moor (35x55cm-14x22in) s. i.d.1923 verso. 26-Nov-3 Peter Wilson, Nantwich #106/R est:500-600
£1400 $2646 €2044 Orphan Bowden Choice (29x41cm-11x16in) s.i.d.1917. 18-Feb-4 Peter Wilson, Nantwich #41
£1800 $3276 €2628 Chorlton Clinker, study of a shire in a landscape (71x91cm-28x36in) s.d.1916 i.verso. 29-Jun-4 Beeston Castle Salerooms, Tarporley #410/R est:800-1200
£1900 $3515 €2774 The Christmas mail, Stafford and Chester coach passing the Crown Inn (25x51cm-10x20in) s.d.1917 i.verso. 9-Mar-4 Capes Dunn, Manchester #675/R
£2100 $3360 €3066 Portrait of three Great Danes, Highfiels Viking, Bess and Schomberg (99x69cm-39x27in) s.d.1903. 16-Sep-3 Louis Taylor, Stoke on Trent #1040
£2500 $4550 €3650 Chorlton fear none (71x91cm-28x36in) s.d.1934 i.verso mill board. 29-Jun-4 Beeston Castle Salerooms, Tarporley #411/R est:800-1200
Works on paper
£450 $851 €657 North Stafford, Forger and Foreman, pair of hounds (21x31cm-8x12in) s.i.indis.d. W/C. 18-Feb-4 Peter Wilson, Nantwich #65

ST JONES, Herbert (19th C) British
£1300 $2067 €1898 Short horn bull, Ronald (41x51cm-16x20in) s.d. 30-Apr-3 Peter Wilson, Nantwich #66 est:250-300
£1700 $2703 €2482 Short horn bull (41x51cm-16x20in) s. i.verso. 30-Apr-3 Peter Wilson, Nantwich #67/R est:300-500

SAINT, Daniel (1778-1847) French
Miniatures
£1818 $3091 €2600 Portrait de Napoleon Bonaparte (12x9cm-5x4in) s. i.verso wooden frame oval prov. 26-Nov-3 Daguerre, Paris #168/R est:2000-3000
£3400 $6120 €4964 Colette de Reiset, Barone de Beurnonville (8cm-3in) s. ormolu mount oval exhib. 22-Apr-4 Bonhams, New Bond Street #148/R est:2000-3000

SAINT, Louise Anne (1865-?) French
Works on paper
£362 $666 €550 Portrait d'homme fumant (45x37cm-18x15in) W/C gouache cardboard. 25-Jun-4 Daguerre, Paris #146
£362 $666 €550 Portrait d'homme (41x31cm-16x12in) W/C gouache cardboard. 25-Jun-4 Daguerre, Paris #147

SAINT-ANDRE, Simon Renard de (1614-1677) French
£3800 $6802 €5700 Vanitas (25x21cm-10x8in) exhib.lit. 17-May-4 Finarte Semenzato, Rome #51/R est:6000-8000

SAINT-AUBIN, Augustin de (1736-1807) French
Works on paper
£282 $487 €400 Bacchante (17x11cm-7x4in) crayon stumping out. 10-Dec-3 Piasa, Paris #64
£400 $692 €584 Portrait of a man carrying a tricorn hat (10cm-4in circular) col chk col wash prov.lit. 12-Dec-3 Christie's, Kensington #442
£1778 $3200 €2596 Bare breasted woman leaning over a pedestal, a woman in the background (18x13cm-7x5in) black chk graphite. 22-Jan-4 Christie's, Rockefeller NY #101/R est:4000-6000
£2303 $4237 €3500 Portrait presume du graveur Nicolas Cochin (12cm-5in circular) s.d.1769 graphite prov. 23-Jun-4 Sotheby's, Paris #21/R est:4000-6000

SAINT-AUBIN, Augustin de (attrib) (1736-1807) French
Works on paper
£408 $649 €600 Portrait de femme (10x7cm-4x3in) crayon oval. 23-Mar-3 St-Germain-en-Laye Encheres #8

SAINT-AUBIN, Gabriel de (1724-1780) French
£180272 $322687 €265000 Le triomphe de Pompee dans Rome a l'imitation de Paul Emile (21x39cm-8x15in) W/C gouache pen black ink pencil lit. 19-Mar-4 Piasa, Paris #58/R est:80000
Prints
£1765 $3000 €2577 La mort de Germanicus (21x16cm-8x6in) etching. 6-Nov-3 Swann Galleries, New York #91/R est:4000-6000
£2089 $3551 €3050 Mort de Germanicus. eau forte. 6-Nov-3 Piasa, Paris #34
Works on paper
£1656 $3013 €2500 Trajan dechire ses vetements pour servir a bander les plaies des blesses (20x15cm-8x6in) pen ink wash black crayon. 16-Jun-4 Piasa, Paris #104/R est:4000
£1722 $3134 €2600 Accius Naevius, augure, assure Tarquin l'Ancien que sa pensee lui est connue (20x15cm-8x6in) mono.i. pen ink wash htd white gouache. 16-Jun-4 Piasa, Paris #86/R est:4000
£1854 $3375 €2800 Camille se rend maitre de Veies que les Romains assiegeaient depuis dix ans (21x15cm-8x6in) pen ink wash. 16-Jun-4 Piasa, Paris #94/R est:4000
£1987 $3616 €3000 L'imprudence du Consul Minucius reparee par Cincinnatus (20x15cm-8x6in) i. pen ink wash. 16-Jun-4 Piasa, Paris #92/R est:4000
£1987 $3616 €3000 La mort de Melius qui avait forme une conspiration (20x15cm-8x6in) pen ink wash htd white gouache. 16-Jun-4 Piasa, Paris #93/R est:4000
£2318 $4219 €3500 Auguste s'occupe des embellissements de Rome (20x15cm-8x6in) black ink stump pen. 16-Jun-4 Piasa, Paris #100/R est:3000
£2517 $4580 €3800 Clio, la Muse de l'histoire accoudee sur le portrait du medaillon de Monsieur Philippe (22x16cm-9x6in) i.d.1766 black crayon oval. 16-Jun-4 Piasa, Paris #77/R est:4000
£2649 $4821 €4000 Ancus Martius envoie des Feciales declarer la guerre aux Latins (20x14cm-8x6in) i. black crayon stump pen ink wash htd white. 16-Jun-4 Piasa, Paris #84/R est:4000

£2781 $5062 €4200 La defense du pont de Rome par Horatius Cocles et deux autres guerriers intrepides (20x14cm-8x6in) i. pen ink wash htd white gouache. 16-Jun-4 Piasa, Paris #88/R est:6000
£2781 $5062 €4200 Coriolan se retire chez les Volsques (20x15cm-8x6in) i. pen ink wash htd white gouache. 16-Jun-4 Piasa, Paris #90/R est:6000
£2980 $5424 €4500 Pompe funebre et apotheose de Cesar (20x16cm-8x6in) black crayon pen ink sanguine. 16-Jun-4 Piasa, Paris #99/R est:3000
£3974 $7232 €6000 L'apotheose de Romulus (20x14cm-8x6in) i. black crayon stump pen ink htd white velin. 16-Jun-4 Piasa, Paris #80/R est:4000
£4636 $8437 €7000 Barbarie de Caligula (20x15cm-8x6in) black crayon stump pen ink wash. 16-Jun-4 Piasa, Paris #102/R est:6000
£4967 $9040 €7500 Le traite des Romains avec les Gaulois rompu par Camille (20x15cm-8x6in) pen ink wash. 16-Jun-4 Piasa, Paris #95/R est:6000
£4967 $9040 €7500 Regulus condamne aux plus affreux supplices (20x15cm-8x6in) pen ink wash htd white gouache. 16-Jun-4 Piasa, Paris #97/R est:5000
£6291 $11450 €9500 La victoire de Tarquin l'Ancien sur les Sabins et les Etrusques par l'incendie du pont de bateaux (20x14cm-8x6in) i. pen ink wash htd white gouache. 16-Jun-4 Piasa, Paris #85/R est:6000
£7947 $14464 €12000 La victoire d'Hannibal sur les Romains a la journee de Cannes (20x15cm-8x6in) pen ink black crayon wash sepia sanguine. 16-Jun-4 Piasa, Paris #98/R est:10000
£8079 $14705 €12200 La couronne et le sceptre offerts a Numa (20x14cm-8x6in) i. black crayon stump ink htd white. 16-Jun-4 Piasa, Paris #81/R est:4000
£8940 $16272 €13500 La mort de Lucrece (20x14cm-8x6in) i. pen ink wash htd white. 16-Jun-4 Piasa, Paris #87/R est:8000
£10596 $19285 €16000 La mort de Germanicus (20x15cm-8x6in) black crayon stump pen ink htd sanguine white gouache. 16-Jun-4 Piasa, Paris #101/R est:6000
£14238 $25914 €21500 La destruction d'Albe sous les ordres d'Horace (20x14cm-8x6in) mono.i. pen india ink wash htd sanguine black crayon. 16-Jun-4 Piasa, Paris #83/R est:6000
£29932 $53578 €44000 La statue de Louis XV, vue dans l'encadrement (17x11cm-7x4in) black pencil pen col ink grey wash lit. 19-Mar-4 Piasa, Paris #57/R est:12000
£105442 $188742 €155000 La bataille d'Ecnome gagnee sur mer par les Romains (21x40cm-8x16in) W/C gouache pen col ink black pencil lit. 19-Mar-4 Piasa, Paris #56/R est:60000

SAINT-AUBYN, Catherine (1760-1836) British?
Works on paper
£380 $619 €555 Bearded man (15x14cm-6x6in) s.verso red chk. 24-Sep-3 Peter Wilson, Nantwich #82

SAINT-CHARLES, Joseph (1868-1945) Canadian
£356 $615 €520 View of a village along the Richelieu River (21x26cm-8x10in) s. board. 9-Dec-3 Pinneys, Montreal #129 (C.D 800)

SAINT-DELIS, Henri de (1878-1949) French
£503 $936 €750 Nature morte au pichet (31x44cm-12x17in) s. panel. 7-Mar-4 Lesieur & Le Bars, Le Havre #124
£1946 $3620 €2900 Le jardin de l'Hotel de ville (22x27cm-9x11in) s. 7-Mar-4 Lesieur & Le Bars, Le Havre #121/R
£2654 $4750 €3875 Into the woods (38x46cm-15x18in) s. 6-May-4 Doyle, New York #69/R est:6000-8000
£3125 $5219 €4500 Sortie du port (28x32cm-11x13in) s. canvas board. 21-Oct-3 Artcurial Briest, Paris #185/R est:4000-5000
£4333 $7887 €6500 Honfleur, sortie du port (27x35cm-11x14in) s. panel. 4-Jul-4 Eric Pillon, Calais #131/R
£5369 $9987 €8000 Le Havre, l'avant port (73x92cm-29x36in) st.sig. 7-Mar-4 Lesieur & Le Bars, Le Havre #120
£29371 $49049 €42000 La plage (73x92cm-29x36in) s. exhib. 30-Jun-3 Artcurial Briest, Paris #728/R est:30000-35000
£35694 $58182 €51400 Le Vevey en Suisse, paysage anime (73x93cm-29x37in) s. 21-Jul-3 Lesieur & Le Bars, Le Havre #60
Works on paper
£423 $685 €600 L'attelage (21x30cm-8x12in) s. W/C. 11-Aug-3 Boscher, Cherbourg #881
£1141 $2122 €1700 Village Normand (24x31cm-9x12in) s. W/C. 7-Mar-4 Lesieur & Le Bars, Le Havre #123
£1172 $1958 €1700 Paysage suisse (12x17cm-5x7in) s. W/C. 11-Nov-3 Lesieur & Le Bars, Le Havre #96
£1172 $1958 €1700 Paysage de montagne (12x17cm-5x7in) s. W/C. 11-Nov-3 Lesieur & Le Bars, Le Havre #98
£1517 $2534 €2200 Charrette a l'ane (22x30cm-9x12in) s. W/C. 11-Nov-3 Lesieur & Le Bars, Le Havre #100
£1586 $2649 €2300 Bateau a aube (11x17cm-4x7in) s. W/C. 11-Nov-3 Lesieur & Le Bars, Le Havre #97
£1931 $3225 €2800 Quai a Honfleur (23x30cm-9x12in) s. W/C. 11-Nov-3 Lesieur & Le Bars, Le Havre #99
£2207 $3686 €3200 Quatorze juillet (21x27cm-8x11in) s. W/C. 11-Nov-3 Lesieur & Le Bars, Le Havre #95
£2958 $4910 €4200 Defile du 14 juillet sur le port (30x47cm-12x19in) s. W/C. 11-Jun-3 Delorme & Bocage, Paris #36/R est:1200-1500
£3200 $5888 €4800 Honfleur, l'entree du port (31x48cm-12x19in) s. W/C. 8-Jun-4 Artcurial Briest, Paris #122/R est:5000-6000

SAINT-DELIS, René de (1877-1958) French
£347 $566 €500 Paysage (32x46cm-13x18in) s. panel. 21-Jul-3 Lesieur & Le Bars, Le Havre #76
£793 $1324 €1150 Nature morte au samovar (50x61cm-20x24in) s. 11-Nov-3 Lesieur & Le Bars, Le Havre #101

SAINT-EDME, A de (19th C) French?
£1862 $3110 €2700 Peintre dans le vallon de Brainvail (127x82cm-50x32in) s.d.1883. 17-Nov-3 Tajan, Paris #138/R est:3000-4000

SAINT-EVRE, Gillot (1791-1858) French
£1958 $3329 €2800 Don Quichotte a l'auberge (50x61cm-20x24in) s.d.1823. 1-Dec-3 Millon & Associes, Paris #92/R est:1200-1500

SAINT-EXUPERY, Antoine de (20th C) French
Works on paper
£1333 $2453 €2000 Femme assise (27x15cm-11x6in) crayon stump. 9-Jun-4 Piasa, Paris #222/R est:2000-2500

SAINT-FLEURANT, Louisianne (1924-) Haitian
£300 $537 €450 La robe bayadere (60x60cm-24x24in) s. 17-May-4 Rogeon, Paris #151

SAINT-GAUDENS, Augustus (1848-1907) American
Sculpture
£14371 $24000 €20982 Mildred and William Dean Howells (22x34cm-9x13in) i. brown pat bronze prov.lit. 9-Oct-3 Christie's, Rockefeller NY #6/R est:10000-15000
£36000 $62280 €52560 Head of Victory (32cm-13in) s.i. green brown pat bronze marble base lit. 12-Dec-3 Sotheby's, London #230/R est:8000-12000
£75581 $130000 €110348 Amor caritas (102cm-40in) i.d.MDCCCXC pat bronze prov.lit. 4-Dec-3 Christie's, Rockefeller NY #34/R est:100000-150000

SAINT-GAUDENS, Augustus (after) (1848-1907) American
Sculpture
£113636 $200000 €165909 Figure of Diana (279cm-110in) gilded bronze Cast Roman Bronze Works prov.lit. 21-May-4 North East Auctions, Portsmouth #470/R est:15000-25000

SAINT-GERMIER, Joseph (1860-1925) French
£414 $745 €600 Street in Biskra (26x15cm-10x6in) s.i.d.1891 board. 26-Jan-4 Ansorena, Madrid #158/R

SAINT-HILAIRE (19th C) French
£2333 $4293 €3500 Rivages du Bosphore (24x40cm-9x16in) pair. 14-Jun-4 Gros & Delettrez, Paris #491/R est:2800-3500

SAINT-HILAIRE, Julien B L (20th C) French
£724 $1332 €1100 Matelot attable devant un pastis (92x71cm-36x28in) s.d.1932. 22-Jun-4 Chassaing Rivet, Toulouse #346

SAINT-HILAIRE, Micheline (1947-) Canadian
£214 $364 €312 Nocturne (91x76cm-36x30in) s. prov. 23-Nov-3 Levis, Calgary #567/R (C.D 475)

SAINT-IGNY, Jean de (attrib) (c.1600-c.1649) French
Works on paper
£291 $500 €425 Costume studies (39x28cm-15x11in) chk. 2-Dec-3 Christie's, Rockefeller NY #150/R

SAINT-JEAN, Paul (1842-1875) French
£15436 $28403 €23000 La belle Andalouse (99x80cm-39x31in) s. 28-Mar-4 Anaf, Lyon #243/R est:20000-25000

SAINT-JEAN, Simon (1808-1860) French
£12587 $21650 €18000 Fruits sur une terrasse avec un bas-relief representant Silene (83x117cm-33x46in) s.d.1843 prov.exhib.lit. 2-Dec-3 Christie's, Paris #359/R est:8000-12000

SAINT-LAURENT, Yves (1936-) French
Works on paper
£267 $491 €400 Croquis de robe (30x11cm-12x4in) crayon. 11-Jun-4 Pierre Berge, Paris #168
£333 $613 €500 Croquis de robe (30x11cm-12x4in) crayon. 11-Jun-4 Pierre Berge, Paris #169
£1133 $2085 €1700 Six croquis (48x63cm-19x25in) s.i. crayon. 11-Jun-4 Pierre Berge, Paris #167 est:400-600

SAINT-MARCEAUX, René (1845-1915) French
Sculpture
£872 $1544 €1300 Arlequin (69cm-27in) s.i. pat bronze exec.1879 lit. 30-Apr-4 Tajan, Paris #63/R est:1800
£1800 $3276 €2700 Arlequin (86cm-34in) s.st.f.Colas pat bronze. 30-Jun-4 Delvaux, Paris #63/R est:2200-2300
£2759 $5103 €4000 Arlequin (68cm-27in) s.d.1879 brown pat bronze Cast Barbedienne. 19-Jan-4 Horta, Bruxelles #104 est:4000-6000
£7500 $12750 €10800 Arlequin Salon de 1880 (102x38x37cm-40x15x15in) brown pat bronze Cast Barbedienne. 28-Oct-3 Rabourdin & Choppin de Janvry, Paris #72/R est:9200-10000

SAINT-MARCEL, Edme de (1819-1890) French
Works on paper
£389 $700 €568 Doe (11x17cm-4x7in) mono. conte crayon pencil prov. 21-Jan-4 Doyle, New York #11

SAINT-MICHEL, Joseph de (fl.1756-1776) French
Works on paper
£411 $699 €600 Portrait presume de la Comtesse de Perrochel (40x31cm-16x12in) s.d.1779 pastel. 6-Nov-3 Tajan, Paris #130

SAINT-NON, L'Abbe de (1727-1791) French
Works on paper
£480 $860 €701 Hercules and Cocus (16x21cm-6x8in) s.d.1788 Indian ink wash. 25-May-4 Bukowskis, Stockholm #547/R (S.KR 6500)

SAINT-OURS, Jean-Pierre (1752-1809) Swiss
£2045 $3395 €2965 Portrait d'une jeune femme (60x49cm-24x19in) s.d.1806. 13-Jun-3 Zofingen, Switzerland #2378/R est:1200 (S.FR 4500)

SAINT-PHALLE, Niki de (1930-2002) French
£10738 $19758 €16000 Woman's portrait (92x73cm-36x29in) s. prov. 26-Mar-4 Ketterer, Hamburg #624/R est:12000-15000
£18919 $33298 €28000 Black widow spider (45x43cm-18x17in) s. i.d.1963 verso paint mixed media on wood prov.exhib. 18-May-4 Tajan, Paris #73/R est:30000-35000
Sculpture
£1067 $1963 €1600 Do you like my brain (15x16cm-6x6in) hand painted ceramic tile prov. 8-Jun-4 Sotheby's, Amsterdam #293/R est:2000-3000
£2000 $3680 €3000 Prototype of the powder box (9x12cm-4x5in) painted ceramic box prov. 8-Jun-4 Sotheby's, Amsterdam #290/R est:3000-4000
£2667 $4907 €4000 Motherhood (18x15cm-7x6in) s. hand painted ceramic tile. 8-Jun-4 Sotheby's, Amsterdam #292/R est:2500-3500
£2770 $5236 €4100 Obelisque (18cm-7in) s.num.1/10 paint resin. 21-Feb-4 Cornette de St.Cyr, Paris #280 est:4500-5000
£3000 $5520 €4500 L'arbre de vie (70cm-28in) painted goldpainted resin silkscreen on steel iron base edn of 75. 8-Jun-4 Sotheby's, Amsterdam #294/R est:3500-4500
£3125 $5219 €4500 L'arbre de vie (68cm-27in) s.num.38/75 metal resin paint. 25-Oct-3 Cornette de St.Cyr, Paris #304/R est:4000-5000
£3221 $5766 €4800 Obelisque aux coeurs (28cm-11in) num.3/10 painted resin. 26-May-4 Christie's, Paris #109/R est:2500-3500
£3728 $6860 €5443 Nana oiseau (20cm-8in) s.verso num.6/99 resin plaster col laquer. 23-Jun-4 Koller, Zurich #3294/R est:3000-5000 (S.FR 8500)
£3728 $6860 €5443 Petite Nana oiseau (13cm-5in) s.verso num.27/99 resin plaster col matt lacquer. 23-Jun-4 Koller, Zurich #3295/R est:2800-3500 (S.FR 8500)
£3776 $6420 €5400 Nana (26cm-10in) s. synthetic. 29-Nov-3 Villa Grisebach, Berlin #329/R est:4500-6000
£4000 $7360 €5840 Petit obelisque au serpent (28x12x12cm-11x5x5in) st.sig. num.5/10 painted polyester exec 1987 prov. 24-Jun-4 Sotheby's, London #258/R est:4000-8000
£4027 $7208 €6000 Obelisque aux fleurs (31cm-12in) num.3/4EA painted resine.c.1987. 26-May-4 Christie's, Paris #111/R est:2500-3500
£4167 $6792 €6000 Nana (27cm-11in) st.sig. verso i. col polyester. 27-Sep-3 Dr Fritz Nagel, Stuttgart #9628/R est:6500
£4200 $7728 €6132 Nana boule (8cm-3in) s. painted plaster felt tip pen. 24-Jun-4 Sotheby's, Olympia #491/R est:4000-5000
£4698 $8409 €7000 Obelisque au serpent (30cm-12in) num.4/4EA painted resin. 26-May-4 Christie's, Paris #110/R est:2500-3500
£4895 $8322 €7000 Untitled - La baigneuse ou Nana de Berlin (26cm-10in) s.i. col stoneware. 27-Nov-3 Lempertz, Koln #4089/R est:7000
£5245 $8916 €7500 Untitled - Nana pregnant (14cm-6in) s. col plaster. 27-Nov-3 Lempertz, Koln #409/R est:10000
£5442 $9741 €8000 Nana-Boule (13x10x10cm-5x4x4in) s.d.1970 painted resin. 16-Mar-4 Finarte Semenzato, Milan #386/R est:6000-7000
£5656 $9615 €8258 Nana soleil (34x19x20cm-13x7x8in) s.d.2001 resin vase. 25-Nov-3 Germann, Zurich #123/R est:15000-20000 (S.FR 12500)
£6044 $11000 €8824 Monkeys. s.num.6/10 painted plaster two pieces. 29-Jun-4 Sotheby's, New York #601/R est:10000-15000
£6294 $10699 €9000 Fountain (44x49x13cm-17x19x5in) s. num.7/15 painted ceramic. 28-Nov-3 Farsetti, Prato #316/R est:7500-8500
£8252 $13780 €11800 Vache-vase (54x63x118cm-21x25x46in) s.num. paint resin edition of 50. 11-Oct-3 Cornette de St.Cyr, Paris #32/R est:10000-12000
£8741 $14598 €12500 La Californienne (34cm-13in) s.num.8/150 paint resin. 11-Oct-3 Cornette de St.Cyr, Paris #87/R est:10000-12000
£8873 $14375 €12600 Nana Fontaine (49x49cm-19x19in) s.d.1991 num.39/150 resin. 5-Aug-3 Tajan, Paris #71/R est:15000-18000
£9500 $17290 €13870 Nana (20cm-8in) s. painted resin exec 1968. 4-Feb-4 Sotheby's, Olympia #158/R est:4000-6000
£9500 $17290 €13870 Nana (36x41x28cm-14x16x11in) oil acrylic mirrored glass plaster prov. 5-Feb-4 Christie's, London #154/R est:8000-12000
£9790 $16643 €14000 Sphynx (25x44x31cm-10x17x12in) s. num.7/10 painted ceramic. 28-Nov-3 Farsetti, Prato #317/R est:12500-14500
£10333 $19117 €15500 Tete de femme (30cm-12in) s.d.1970 painted resin prov. 18-Jul-4 Sotheby's, Paris #256/R est:8000-12000
£10574 $17976 €15438 Le Dragon (34cm-13in) s.d.1976 polychrome painted hard plastic exhib.prov. 5-Nov-3 AB Stockholms Auktionsverk #961/R est:40000-50000 (S.KR 140000)
£10839 $18101 €15500 Petit temoin (30cm-12in) s.i. paint resin exec.c.1970 prov. 11-Oct-3 Cornette de St.Cyr, Paris #86/R est:12000-15000
£11354 $20664 €16577 Sphinx, l'imperatrice (30x39x25cm-12x15x10in) synthetic material W/C col pencil exec. 1979-1983. 18-Jun-4 Kornfeld, Bern #138/R est:25000 (S.FR 26000)
£11500 $19205 €16790 Nana (21x18x10cm-8x7x4in) s.d.1968 underside painted polyester prov.exhib. 21-Oct-3 Sotheby's, London #344/R est:8000-12000
£11500 $21160 €16790 Taureau (40x63x28cm-16x25x11in) st.sig. num.37/50 painted polyester exec 1990 prov.lit. 24-Jun-4 Sotheby's, London #159/R est:9000-12000
£12752 $22571 €19000 Nana Mode (38x18x18cm-15x7x7in) s. num.EA IV/V under base resin polyester paint prov. 28-Apr-4 Artcurial Briest, Paris #353/R est:18000-22000
£20979 $36084 €30000 L'ange luminaire (96x53x29cm-38x21x11in) i. num.32/50 col polyester glazed clay triangular metal base prov. 5-Dec-3 Ketterer, Munich #189/R est:20000-30000
£22000 $40480 €33000 Obelisque aux coeurs rouges (145x47x47cm-57x19x19in) s. num.EA 1/11 polyester col varnish polyurethane prov.exhib. 8-Jun-4 Artcurial Briest, Paris #234/R est:35000-45000
£26000 $47320 €37960 Ange luminaire (98cm-39in) sig. num.2/5 painted polyester exec 1995 prov. 5-Feb-4 Christie's, London #159/R est:20000-30000
£26000 $47840 €37960 Birdman (42cm-17in) painted plaster executed c.1972 prov. 25-Jun-4 Christie's, London #126/R est:20000-30000
£30000 $55200 €43800 King (150cm-59in) double sided mirror coloured glass mosaic metal prov.exhib. 24-Jun-4 Sotheby's, London #162/R est:35000-45000
£30000 $55200 €43800 Fil du discours (125x48x34cm-49x19x13in) s. num.IV/IV painted polyester lightbulbs bronze base prov. 24-Jun-4 Sotheby's, London #263/R est:35000-45000
£38000 $68780 €55480 Adam et Eve (55x10x15cm-22x4x6in) painted papier mache oxidised iron executed 1976-77 prov. 1-Apr-4 Christie's, Kensington #219/R est:25000-35000
£40000 $73600 €58400 Nana (69cm-27in) painted fiberglass on iron base executed c.1972 prov. 25-Jun-4 Christie's, London #127/R est:25000-35000
£50000 $92000 €73000 Grand fauteuil au serpent - table stool and urn. st.sig. num.18/20 painted polyester three parts. 24-Jun-4 Sotheby's, London #256/R est:35000-45000
£57927 $95000 €84573 Le petit cheval (32cm-13in) plastic toys fabric cotton thread exec.1963 prov.exhib. 28-May-3 Sotheby's, Amsterdam #78/R est:60000-80000
£191617 $320000 €279761 Lune (300x121x103cm-118x48x41in) glass tile mirror tile painted polyester exec 1987 prov.lit. 12-Nov-3 Christie's, Rockefeller NY #397/R est:180000-250000
£240000 $444000 €360000 Vie en rose (272x230x64cm-107x91x25in) painted polyester exec.1968 prov.exhib.lit. 18-Jul-4 Sotheby's, Paris #163/R est:200000-300000
Works on paper
£811 $1395 €1184 Vanitas (56x73cm-22x29in) s. mixed media serigraph lithograph metal foil collage. 2-Dec-3 Koller, Zurich #3381/R est:1300-2000 (S.FR 1800)

SAINT-PHALLE, Niki de and TINGUELY, Jean (20th C) French/Swiss
Sculpture
£9146 $15000 €13353 Nana dansant (45cm-18in) num.114/150 painted bronze motor metal base prov.exhib. 28-May-3 Sotheby's, Amsterdam #104/R est:15000-20000
£253333 $468667 €380000 Monde (430x185x160cm-169x73x63in) painted polyester iron engine exec.1989 prov.exhib.lit. 18-Jul-4 Sotheby's, Paris #155/R est:250000-300000
Works on paper
£1268 $2193 €1800 Hommage aux Sandberg (67x63cm-26x25in) s.i. crayon on napkin prov. 9-Dec-3 Artcurial Briest, Paris #520/R est:1200-1500

SAINT-PIERRE, Gaston Casimir (1833-1916) French
£30000 $55200 €45000 Jeune fille en costume ottoman (130x77cm-51x30in) s. canvas on panel. 14-Jun-4 Gros & Delettrez, Paris #111/R est:45000-60000

SAINT-QUENTIN, Jacques Philippe Jos de (1783-?) French
Works on paper
£574 $1011 €850 Two putti amongst clouds, holding torches (31x23cm-12x9in) s.d.1761 black white chk. 19-May-4 Sotheby's, Amsterdam #161/R

SAINT-SAENS, Marc (c.1903-) French
Works on paper
£263 $484 €400 Personnage (49x50cm-19x20in) s. ink. 22-Jun-4 Chassaing Rivet, Toulouse #370

SAINT-VIANCE, Thierry (20th C) French
£2047 $3623 €3050 L'adolescent (130x97cm-51x38in) mono. acrylic paper on canvas. 29-Apr-4 Claude Aguttes, Neuilly #224/R est:3100-3150

SAINTCLAIR, Murielle (20th C) French?
Works on paper
£1972 $3194 €2800 Sans titre (100x70cm-39x28in) s.d.1982 mixed media. 5-Aug-3 Tajan, Paris #77/R est:3000-4000

SAINTHILL, Loudon (1919-1969) Australian
Works on paper
£600 $1110 €876 Paul Schofield as Richard II (46x31cm-18x12in) s. gouache chk pen ink prov. 11-Feb-4 Cheffins, Cambridge #404/R
£1527 $2779 €2229 Strange creatures of Shemakhan, bridal procession, act III (45x71cm-18x28in) s.i. W/C gouache prov.exhib. 16-Jun-4 Deutscher-Menzies, Melbourne #40/R est:4000-6000 (A.D 4000)

SAINTIN, Henri (1846-1899) French
£596 $1085 €900 Le port de Rouen (12x21cm-5x8in) s.i.d.1874 panel. 20-Jun-4 Salle des ventes Pillet, Lyon la Foret #35/R
£4079 $7506 €6200 La cigogne. Le heron. La grue. Le flamand rose (128x49cm-50x19in) s.d.1883. 22-Jun-4 Calmels Cohen, Paris #49/R est:6000-8000

SAINTIN, Jules Émile (1829-1894) French
£1447 $2663 €2200 Italienne (54x49cm-21x19in) s. 24-Jun-4 Credit Municipal, Paris #35 est:1500-2000
£1467 $2655 €2200 L'Italienne (54x49cm-21x19in) s. 1-Apr-4 Credit Municipal, Paris #28 est:3000-4000

SAINZ DE MORALES, Gumersindo (1900-1976) Spanish
£235 $400 €343 Flamenco dancers (61x91cm-24x36in) s. 5-Nov-3 Doyle, New York #65/R
£510 $913 €750 Maternity (99x80cm-39x31in) s. 22-Mar-4 Durán, Madrid #114/R
£2083 $3396 €3000 Little gypsies (100x73cm-39x29in) s.d.50. 23-Sep-3 Durán, Madrid #58/R

SAINZ Y SAINZ, Casimiro (1853-1898) Spanish
£2378 $3971 €3400 Paisaje con rio y casa (26x38cm-10x15in) s. 24-Jun-3 Segre, Madrid #80/R est:2900
£2958 $5176 €4200 Landscape (14x23cm-6x9in) s. board. 16-Dec-3 Segre, Madrid #80/R est:1400
£18116 $29710 €25000 Chulas santanderinas (36x25cm-14x10in) one s.d.77 panel pair lit. 27-May-3 Durán, Madrid #243/R est:6000

SAITO, Kikuo (20th C) Japanese
£377 $600 €550 Oliver cross (117x203cm-46x80in) acrylic. 14-Sep-3 Susanin's, Chicago #6035/R
£578 $1000 €844 Untitled (46x508cm-18x200in) acrylic prov. 15-Dec-3 Hindman, Chicago #112/R
£751 $1300 €1096 Untitled (51x483cm-20x190in) acrylic prov. 15-Dec-3 Hindman, Chicago #113/R est:2000-4000
£1757 $3250 €2565 Rusty Slip (125x206cm-49x81in) s.d.1980 i.verso. 12-Feb-4 Sotheby's, New York #268/R est:1500-2500

SAITO, Kiyoshi (1907-) Japanese
Prints
£2095 $3750 €3059 Autumn (84x54cm-33x21in) print. 10-May-4 Bonhams & Butterfields, San Francisco #4115/R est:2000-3000
£2235 $4000 €3263 Steady gaze (84x55cm-33x22in) s.d.1957 num.33/100 print. 10-May-4 Bonhams & Butterfields, San Francisco #4118/R est:2000-3000

SAITO, Seiji (1933-) American/Japanese
Sculpture
£2514 $4500 €3670 Dancer. s.i. bronze. 13-May-4 Dallas Auction Gallery, Dallas #251/R est:1800-2200

SAITO, Yoshishige (1904-) Japanese
£5435 $10000 €7935 Untitled (31x25cm-12x10in) s.d.65 oil on wood. 23-Mar-4 Christie's, Rockefeller NY #132/R est:8000-10000

SAIVE, Jean Baptiste de (1540-1624) Flemish
£3500 $6300 €5110 Annunciation (85x55cm-33x22in) s. panel. 21-Apr-4 Bonhams, New Bond Street #4/R est:4000-6000
£136986 $232877 €200000 Market scene (141x222cm-56x87in) 4-Nov-3 Ansorena, Madrid #99/R

SAKAI, Kazuya (1927-2001) Argentinian
£2235 $4000 €3263 Painting (70x100cm-28x39in) 4-May-4 Arroyo, Buenos Aires #78/R est:3800
£2235 $4000 €3263 Painting (59x108cm-23x43in) 4-May-4 Arroyo, Buenos Aires #79/R est:3800
£2326 $4000 €3396 Pintura no.53 (149x114cm-59x45in) s.i.d.1960 verso oil acrylic. 3-Dec-3 Doyle, New York #91/R est:800-1200
£3577 $5830 €5222 Yin (114x146cm-45x57in) s.d.61. 17-Jul-3 Naón & Cia, Buenos Aires #25/R
£13736 $25000 €20055 Untitled (53x39cm-21x15in) s.d.60 ink dr. 29-Jun-4 Arroyo, Buenos Aires #75/R est:2000
Works on paper
£1229 $2200 €1794 Graphics (31x44cm-12x17in) ink. 11-May-4 Arroyo, Buenos Aires #86
£1955 $3500 €2854 Untitled (60x50cm-24x20in) s.d.64 mixed media. 4-May-4 Arroyo, Buenos Aires #47/R est:3000
£3077 $5600 €4492 Untitled (33x64cm-13x25in) s.d.61 ink pair. 5-Jul-4 Arroyo, Buenos Aires #90/R est:1800
£3978 $7200 €5808 Abstraction I. Abstraction II (63x49cm-25x19in) mixed media pair. 30-Mar-4 Arroyo, Buenos Aires #79

SAKU, Kojun (19th C) Japanese
Sculpture
£6849 $11644 €10000 Shakudo dragon (26cm-10in) s. gold silver. 8-Nov-3 Dr Fritz Nagel, Stuttgart #1768/R est:9000

SALA Y FRANCES, Emilio (1850-1910) Spanish
£2013 $3725 €3000 Priere dans le desert (33x43cm-13x17in) s. i.verso lit. 15-Mar-4 Gros & Delettrez, Paris #143/R est:3000-3500
£2013 $3745 €3000 Woman with headscarf (32x23cm-13x9in) 2-Mar-4 Ansorena, Madrid #39/R est:3000
£2414 $4345 €3500 Flowers in landscape (33x22cm-13x9in) s. 26-Jan-4 Ansorena, Madrid #389/R est:3500

SALA, Anri (1974-) Albanian
Photographs
£3334 $6134 €5000 Casa Zoo III (110x165cm-43x65in) col photo on aluminium exec 2001 prov.exhib.lit. 8-Jun-4 Artcurial Briest, Paris #293/R est:5000-6000

SALA, Eliseo (1813-1879) Italian
£764 $1299 €1100 Portrait of Elisa Dozzio Guerrini (73x60cm-29x24in) s. i.verso. 29-Oct-3 Il Ponte, Milan #528
£1111 $1889 €1600 Portrait of gentleman with moustaches (61x49cm-24x19in) s.d.1873. 29-Oct-3 Il Ponte, Milan #525 est:1600-1800
£3889 $6611 €5600 Portrait of man with cigar (98x81cm-39x32in) oval. 29-Oct-3 Il Ponte, Milan #566/R est:2200-2500
£6111 $10389 €8800 Portrait of lady with fan (98x81cm-39x32in) s.d.1835 oval. 29-Oct-3 Il Ponte, Milan #565/R est:2200-2500
Works on paper
£738 $1307 €1100 Lady (24x21cm-9x8in) s.d.1854 mixed media card. 1-May-4 Meeting Art, Vercelli #374

SALA, Eugène de (1899-1987) Danish
£343 $631 €501 Still life of yellow flowers (63x50cm-25x20in) s. panel. 29-Mar-4 Rasmussen, Copenhagen #497 (D.KR 3800)
£361 $675 €527 Composition (60x50cm-24x20in) s. panel. 25-Feb-4 Kunsthallen, Copenhagen #290 (D.KR 4000)
£431 $698 €625 Still life of yellow potted plant (56x47cm-22x19in) s. panel. 4-Aug-3 Rasmussen, Vejle #605/R (D.KR 4500)
£451 $830 €658 Eglise Saint-Pierre et Sacre Coeur (45x65cm-18x26in) s. board. 29-Mar-4 Rasmussen, Copenhagen #505/R (D.KR 5000)
£451 $830 €658 Still life of bottles and glass (73x49cm-29x19in) s. plywood. 29-Mar-4 Rasmussen, Copenhagen #520/R (D.KR 5000)
£458 $833 €669 Self-portrait in black (140x100cm-55x39in) s.d.1924 panel. 7-Feb-4 Rasmussen, Havnen #4144/R (D.KR 5000)
£467 $738 €677 Reclining nude female (59x89cm-23x35in) s. 3-Sep-3 Museumsbygningen, Copenhagen #3 (D.KR 5000)
£583 $1073 €875 Still life (39x34cm-15x13in) s. panel. 14-Jun-4 Lilla Bukowskis, Stockholm #294/R (S.KR 8000)
£986 $1646 €1440 Cabaret du Lapin Agile Concert (75x85cm-30x33in) s. artist's board. 7-Oct-3 Rasmussen, Copenhagen #360/R (D.KR 10500)
£1173 $2159 €1713 Notre dame de lesbes, functionel composition (180x220cm-71x87in) s. 29-Mar-4 Rasmussen, Copenhagen #459/R est:15000-20000 (D.KR 13000)
£1595 $2872 €2329 Untitled (49x41cm-19x16in) s. exhib. 26-Apr-4 Bukowskis, Stockholm #261a/R est:15000-20000 (S.KR 22000)
£2916 $4958 €4257 Nature morte (122x91cm-48x36in) s. panel painted c.1926. 26-Nov-3 Kunsthallen, Copenhagen #312/R est:25000 (D.KR 31000)

SALA, Jean (1895-?) Spanish
£1400 $2324 €2044 La coquette (63x41cm-25x16in) s. panel. 1-Oct-3 Sotheby's, Olympia #221/R est:1500-2000

SALA, Juan (1867-1918) Spanish
£2144 $3365 €3130 Interior scene with woman flirting with man in garden (62x50cm-24x20in) s.i. 30-Aug-3 Rasmussen, Havnen #2028/R est:15000-20000 (D.KR 23000)
Works on paper
£474 $758 €692 Mother and child (90cm-35in circular) s. pastel. 22-Sep-3 Rasmussen, Vejle #30/R (D.KR 5000)
£1793 $2994 €2600 Portrait de jeune femme (130x99cm-51x39in) s.i.d.1909 pastel oval. 16-Nov-3 Muizon & Le Coent, Paris #57

SALA, Paolo (1859-1929) Italian
£941 $1600 €1374 Forest interior (61x41cm-24x16in) indis sig.d. 5-Nov-3 Doyle, New York #66/R est:1000-1500
£1164 $1816 €1700 Fox (35x24cm-14x9in) s.i. board. 8-Apr-3 Il Ponte, Milan #552
£3800 $6992 €5548 Wooded path (48x72cm-19x28in) s. board. 23-Mar-4 Bonhams, New Bond Street #84/R est:4000-6000
£7047 $12966 €10500 Lake landscape (12x24cm-5x9in) i. board. 24-Mar-4 Il Ponte, Milan #639/R est:1500
Works on paper
£667 $1213 €1000 Autumnal landscape with shepherd (40x58cm-16x23in) s. W/C. 12-Jul-4 Il Ponte, Milan #476/R
£692 $1100 €1010 Evening in Venice (36x53cm-14x21in) s. W/C laid down. 4-May-3 William Jenack, New York #291
£855 $1574 €1300 Strolling along the Thames (18x23cm-7x9in) s. W/C. 23-Jun-4 Finarte Semenzato, Rome #39/R
£1389 $2361 €2000 Views of Como Lake (22x36cm-9x14in) s. W/C pair. 28-Oct-3 Il Ponte, Milan #285/R
£1611 $2964 €2400 Views of Lake Como (22x36cm-9x14in) s. W/C pair. 24-Mar-4 Il Ponte, Milan #624/R est:2200
£2000 $3320 €2920 Piazza San Marco, Venice (49x32cm-19x13in) s.i. W/C. 1-Oct-3 Sotheby's, Olympia #268/R est:2000-3000
£2013 $3564 €3000 Ploughing (45x60cm-18x24in) s. W/C paper on cardboard. 1-May-4 Meeting Art, Vercelli #342 est:3000
£2083 $3750 €3041 Walk in the woods (132x75cm-52x30in) s. W/C. 21-Jan-4 Sotheby's, New York #175/R est:2000-3000
£2416 $4518 €3600 Spinners (20x24cm-8x9in) s. W/C lit. 25-Feb-4 Porro, Milan #14/R est:3000
£2819 $5046 €4200 View of Lake Maggiore (21x31cm-8x12in) s. W/C cardboard. 25-May-4 Finarte Semenzato, Milan #2/R est:1000-1400
£5500 $10065 €8030 Grand Canal with Santa Maria della Salute, Venice. Doge's Palace , and the Molo (36x53cm-14x21in) s.i. pencil W/C htd white two. 6-Jul-4 Christie's, London #88/R est:3000-5000

SALA, Paolo (attrib) (1859-1929) Italian
Works on paper
£533 $981 €800 Strolling along the lake (38x49cm-15x19in) bears sig. W/C card. 10-Jun-4 Christie's, Rome #100

SALABET, Jean (20th C) French
£339 $600 €495 Paris street scene (28x36cm-11x14in) s. 2-May-4 William Jenack, New York #74
£348 $650 €508 View of the Place Vendome, Paris (26x36cm-10x14in) s.i. 29-Feb-4 Bonhams & Butterfields, San Francisco #4517
£350 $601 €500 Parisien flower market (27x35cm-11x14in) s.i. 4-Dec-3 Neumeister, Munich #2838
£535 $850 €781 L'Arc de Triomphe in Paris (28x36cm-11x14in) s. 10-Sep-3 Alderfer's, Hatfield #350
£649 $1200 €948 Place de la Madeleine. The flower vendor (28x36cm-11x14in) s. pair. 17-Jul-4 New Orleans Auction, New Orleans #425/R
£652 $1200 €952 Rue Royale, Paris (28x36cm-11x14in) s.i. 28-Mar-4 Bonhams & Butterfields, San Francisco #2723 est:800-1200
£652 $1200 €952 Rue de la Madelaine, Paris (28x36cm-11x14in) s.i. 28-Mar-4 Bonhams & Butterfields, San Francisco #2724 est:800-1200
£1198 $2000 €1749 View of the Champs-Elysees (46x55cm-18x22in) s. 26-Oct-3 Bonhams & Butterfields, San Francisco #6474/R
£1278 $2250 €1866 View of Notre Dame, Paris (46x55cm-18x22in) s. 23-May-4 Bonhams & Butterfields, Los Angeles #7054/R
£1591 $2943 €2323 Street scene (27x35cm-11x14in) 14-Mar-4 Agra, Warsaw #52/R (P.Z 11500)
£2194 $3423 €3203 Autumn evening in Sekwana (27x35cm-11x14in) s. 30-Mar-3 Agra, Warsaw #24/R est:6000 (P.Z 14000)
£2557 $4500 €3733 Paris in the spring (46x55cm-18x22in) s. 23-May-4 Bonhams & Butterfields, Los Angeles #7053/R
Works on paper
£671 $1242 €1000 Elegantes et passantes, Place de la Concorde (29x39cm-11x15in) s. W/C gouache. 14-Mar-4 St-Germain-en-Laye Encheres #177/R

SALAS, Rafael (1830-1906) Ecuadorian
£3911 $7000 €5710 Simon Bolivar (82x62cm-32x24in) s. prov. 26-May-4 Sotheby's, New York #80/R est:10000-15000

SALAS, Tito (1888-1974) Venezuelan
£781 $1250 €1140 Study (80x97cm-31x38in) s.verso. 21-Sep-3 Subastas Odalys, Caracas #113/R
£4412 $7500 €6442 Nude (81x54cm-32x21in) s. 23-Nov-3 Subastas Odalys, Caracas #112/R
£4790 $8000 €6993 Christ (86x68cm-34x27in) s. 13-Jul-3 Subastas Odalys, Caracas #17/R est:20000
£11686 $20100 €17062 Untitled (56x66cm-22x26in) s. masonite. 7-Dec-3 Subastas Odalys, Caracas #78 est:22000
Works on paper
£368 $625 €537 Untitled (19x24cm-7x9in) s crayon. 23-Nov-3 Subastas Odalys, Caracas #118
£453 $780 €661 Maternity (40x27cm-16x11in) s. graphite. 7-Dec-3 Subastas Odalys, Caracas #69/R

£624 $1060 €911 Untitled (24x41cm-9x16in) s. chl. 23-Nov-3 Subastas Odalys, Caracas #98
£710 $1100 €1037 Untitled (49x57cm-19x22in) s. graphite exec.1941. 3-Nov-2 Subastas Odalys, Caracas #76/R
£1522 $2435 €2222 Untitled (54x74cm-21x29in) s. mixed media. 21-Sep-3 Subastas Odalys, Caracas #109/R

SALATHE, Friedrich (1793-1860) French
Works on paper
£873 $1590 €1275 Panorama from a train of Zugersee, Rigi and Pilatus (33x44cm-13x17in) pen ink pencil wash prov. 17-Jun-4 Kornfeld, Bern #65/R (S.FR 2000)
£1572 $2861 €2295 Palace of Count Divito in Gravedona on Lake Maggiore (24x34cm-9x13in) s.i.d.1814 gouache grey groundwork prov. 17-Jun-4 Kornfeld, Bern #66/R est:3000 (S.FR 3600)
£2707 $4928 €3952 Italian landscape (22x31cm-9x12in) W/C prov. 17-Jun-4 Kornfeld, Bern #67/R est:3000 (S.FR 6200)

SALAZAR, Abel (1889-1946) Portuguese
£671 $1201 €1000 Washing clothes (49cm-19in) s. on wooden knife. 31-May-4 Cabral Moncada Leiloes, Lisbon #80/R

SALAZAR, Alfredo (?) Spanish
£671 $1255 €1000 Cuenca (40x100cm-16x39in) s.d.99 s.i.d.verso. 24-Feb-4 Durán, Madrid #48/R

SALAZAR, Braulio (1917-) Spanish
£431 $720 €629 Lagoon with washerwomen (50x60cm-20x24in) s. painted 1993. 13-Jul-3 Subastas Odalys, Caracas #26
£494 $780 €721 Woman with wheat (120x100cm-47x39in) s. 27-Apr-3 Subastas Odalys, Caracas #7
£553 $940 €807 Figure (34x24cm-13x9in) s. painted 1967. 23-Nov-3 Subastas Odalys, Caracas #49/R

SALAZZA, Simone (1863-1930) Italian
£1769 $3166 €2600 Landscape in Piemonte (40x65cm-16x26in) s. cardboard. 22-Mar-4 Sant Agostino, Torino #184/R est:2500-3500
£2069 $3434 €3000 Ayas Valley (65x40cm-26x16in) init. i.verso cardboard. 1-Oct-3 Della Rocca, Turin #222/R est:3500

SALCEDO, Doris (1958-) Colombian
Sculpture
£18000 $32220 €27000 Atrabiliaros (80x200cm-31x79in) multiple exhib. 12-May-4 Chochon-Barre & Allardi, Paris #112 est:1000-1500

SALCI, Gabriele (18th C) Italian
£20144 $33036 €28000 Still life with musical instruments, flowers, fruit and vegetables (131x100cm-52x39in) 4-Jun-3 Sotheby's, Milan #18/R est:15000-20000

SALCI, Gabriele (attrib) (18th C) Italian
£1056 $1849 €1500 Birds and dead game (73x98cm-29x39in) 17-Dec-3 Christie's, Rome #307 est:2000-3000

SALDANA, Mateo (?) Latin American
£1054 $1791 €1539 Landscape with haystacks (38x48cm-15x19in) s. 29-Oct-3 Louis Morton, Mexico #38/R est:22000-25000 (M.P 20000)

SALDANHA, Ione (1921-) Brazilian
£8791 $15560 €13187 Untitled (78x61cm-31x24in) s. 27-Apr-4 Bolsa de Arte, Rio de Janeiro #102/R (B.R 48000)
Sculpture
£3297 $5835 €4946 Bamboo (175cm-69in) s. bamboo acrylic ink. 27-Apr-4 Bolsa de Arte, Rio de Janeiro #107/R (B.R 18000)

SALEH, Raden (c.1814-1880) Javanese
£30797 $47736 €44964 Braving the storm (41x58cm-16x23in) s.d.1840. 6-Oct-2 Sotheby's, Singapore #60/R est:25000-35000 (S.D 85000)

SALEH, Raden (attrib) (c.1814-1880) Javanese
Works on paper
£3793 $6334 €5500 La chasse au cerf dans l'Ile de Java (24x39cm-9x15in) W/C. 16-Nov-3 Muizon & Le Coent, Paris #31/R

SALEMME, Attilio (1911-1955) American
Works on paper
£538 $1000 €785 Time of inspection (20x30cm-8x12in) s. W/C ink executed c.1950. 7-Mar-4 Treadway Gallery, Cincinnati #694/R est:2000-3000

SALENTIN, Hubert (1822-1910) German
£15862 $26490 €23000 Girl on donkey with dog (112x78cm-44x31in) s.d.1898 prov.lit. 15-Nov-3 Lempertz, Koln #1688/R est:20000-25000

SALES ROVIRALTA, Francesco (1904-1977) Spanish
£364 $667 €550 Composition (100x65cm-39x26in) s.d.60 s.i.d.verso. 7-Apr-4 Piasa, Paris #237
£464 $848 €700 Village (54x73cm-21x29in) s.d.65. 7-Apr-4 Piasa, Paris #233
£596 $1091 €900 Composition (73x92cm-29x36in) s.d.69 s.i.d.verso. 7-Apr-4 Piasa, Paris #241
£704 $1127 €1000 Still life of flowers (55x38cm-22x15in) s. s.verso. 16-Sep-3 Segre, Madrid #114/R
£915 $1465 €1300 Chess board (73x54cm-29x21in) sd.1974 s.i.d.verso. 16-Sep-3 Segre, Madrid #113/R
£960 $1757 €1450 Toreador (81x54cm-32x21in) s.d.67. 7-Apr-4 Piasa, Paris #235
Works on paper
£317 $548 €450 Arbre en hiver (61x47cm-24x19in) s.d.53 gouache. 12-Dec-3 Piasa, Paris #212
£397 $727 €600 Nature morte au pichet et a la poire (50x64cm-20x25in) s. bears studio st.verso mixed media. 7-Apr-4 Piasa, Paris #234
£775 $1340 €1100 Nature morte a la guitare (73x54cm-29x21in) s.d.60 gouache. 12-Dec-3 Piasa, Paris #210/R

SALES, Carl von (1791-1870) Austrian
£1129 $2077 €1648 Portrait of a lady in Empire period dress (66x53cm-26x21in) s.d.1814. 14-Jun-4 Waddingtons, Toronto #305/R est:4000-6000 (C.D 2800)
£1698 $2700 €2479 Portraits (70x56cm-28x22in) s.d.1817 pair. 12-Sep-3 Skinner, Boston #213/R

SALGADO COSME, Demetrio (1915-) Spanish
£552 $921 €800 Woman in red seated (81x65cm-32x26in) s. 17-Nov-3 Durán, Madrid #51/R
£753 $1281 €1100 Seated woman in interior (81x65cm-32x26in) s. 4-Nov-3 Ansorena, Madrid #441/R

SALGADO, Sebastiao (1944-) ?
Photographs
£1519 $2750 €2218 Serra Pelada, Brazil (29x44cm-11x17in) s.i.d.1986 verso gelatin silver print prov. 19-Apr-4 Bonhams & Butterfields, San Francisco #476/R est:2000-3000
£1977 $3500 €2886 Goldminers, Sierra Palada, Brazil (35x24cm-14x9in) s.i.d.1986 verso gelatin silver print. 27-Apr-4 Christie's, Rockefeller NY #335/R est:3500-4500
£2222 $3778 €3200 Tehad (29x43cm-11x17in) s.i.d. verso gelatin silver. 31-Oct-3 Lempertz, Koln #299/R est:3000
£2515 $4200 €3672 Goldminers, Sierra Palada, Brazil (30x45cm-12x18in) s.d.1986/1991 verso gelatin silver print prov. 20-Oct-3 Christie's, Rockefeller NY #51/R est:2500-3500
£2542 $4500 €3711 Goldminers, Sierra Palada, Brazil (29x44cm-11x17in) s.i.d.1986 gelatin silver print. 27-Apr-4 Christie's, Rockefeller NY #336/R est:5000-7000
£2874 $4800 €4196 Goldminers, Sierra Palada, Brazil (54x35cm-21x14in) s.i.d.1986/1991 verso gelatin silver print prov. 20-Oct-3 Christie's, Rockefeller NY #50/R est:3000-5000
£3390 $6000 €4949 Selected Serra Pelada images (43x29cm-17x11in) s.i.d.1986 photo. 28-Apr-4 Sotheby's, New York #238/R est:6000-8000
£3593 $6000 €5246 Campo de Korem, Ethiopia. Ecuador (30x43cm-12x17in) one s.i.d.verso one s. i.verso photo exec.1984 and 1982 two prov. 17-Oct-3 Sotheby's, New York #171/R est:1500-2500
£4237 $7500 €6186 Goldminers, Sierra Palada, Brazil (44x29cm-17x11in) s.i.d.1986 verso gelatin silver print. 27-Apr-4 Christie's, Rockefeller NY #334/R est:5000-7000

SALGE, Michel (1932-) Swiss?
£679 $1154 €991 Le pretendant (50x50cm-20x20in) s. 19-Nov-3 Fischer, Luzern #2267/R (S.FR 1500)

SALICATH, Ornulf (1888-1962) Norwegian
£391 $677 €571 Woman by water (75x61cm-30x24in) canvas on panel. 13-Dec-3 Blomqvist, Lysaker #1300/R (N.KR 4500)
£826 $1429 €1206 Couple on jetty (59x51cm-23x20in) s. 13-Dec-3 Blomqvist, Lysaker #1301/R (N.KR 9500)
£1278 $2198 €1866 Woman resting (73x83cm-29x33in) s,. 8-Dec-3 Blomqvist, Oslo #480/R est:20000-25000 (N.KR 15000)

SALIERES, Nicolas (?) French
£1348 $2250 €1900 Jeune femme a la mandoline (81x62cm-32x24in) s. 21-Jun-3 Peron, Melun #72

SALIETTI, Alberto (1892-1961) Italian
£1181 $1865 €1700 Magi (45x35cm-18x14in) tempera card. 6-Sep-3 Meeting Art, Vercelli #423 est:1500
£3077 $5231 €4400 Roman peasant woman (66x50cm-26x20in) s. board. 20-Nov-3 Finarte Semenzato, Milan #98/R est:3500-4000
Works on paper
£805 $1490 €1200 Still life (36x30cm-14x12in) s.d.1953 Chinese ink W/C. 13-Mar-4 Meeting Art, Vercelli #478

SALIGER, Ivo (1894-1975) Austrian
£667 $1200 €1000 Madonna with Infant Jesus (103x82cm-41x32in) s. masonite. 21-Apr-4 Dorotheum, Vienna #125/R

SALIMBENI, Ventura (1568-1613) Italian
£2302 $3776 €3200 Saint Catherine of Siena and Mary Magdalene (44x30cm-17x12in) 4-Jun-3 Sotheby's, Milan #26/R est:3000-4000
£18000 $32940 €26280 Saints Mary Magdalene and Catherine (73x58cm-29x23in) s.i. exhib.lit. 8-Jul-4 Sotheby's, London #204/R est:20000-30000
Works on paper
£604 $1111 €900 Christ with sleeping youths in Garden of Gethsemane (29x21cm-11x8in) i. wash pen htd white prov. 26-Mar-4 Dorotheum, Vienna #55/R

SALIMBENI, Ventura (circle) (1568-1613) Italian
£5500 $9900 €8030 Holy Family with Saint Catherine of Siena and the infant Saint John the Baptist (74x55cm-29x22in) 20-Apr-4 Sotheby's, Olympia #203/R est:3000-4000

SALINAS Y TERUEL, Augustin (1862-1915) Spanish
£582 $990 €850 Yg. woman with shawl (19x14cm-7x6in) s. board oval. 4-Nov-3 Ansorena, Madrid #302/R

£1408	$2437	€2000	Seascape in Anzio (14x24cm-6x9in) board. 11-Dec-3 Christie's, Rome #122/R est:1000-1500
£6250	$11313	€9500	Landscape in Paestum, Italy (80x177cm-31x70in) s.i. 14-Apr-4 Ansorena, Madrid #161/R est:8500
£7895	$14526	€12000	Fruit market (37x65cm-15x26in) s. 22-Jun-4 Durán, Madrid #196/R est:12000
Works on paper			
£1184	$2179	€1800	Italian woman playing the lyre (55x31cm-22x12in) s. W/C. 22-Jun-4 Durán, Madrid #168/R est:1800

SALINAS, Manuel (1940-) Spanish

£9091	$15182	€13000	Untitled (215x200cm-85x79in) s.d.1982 verso prov. 24-Jun-3 Segre, Madrid #136/R est:5500

SALINAS, Pablo (1871-1946) Spanish

£1733	$3137	€2600	Cardinal and lady (18x24cm-7x9in) s.i. board lit. 30-Mar-4 Babuino, Rome #380/R est:1500-2000
£2465	$4092	€3500	Napoli a Mergellini (13x24cm-5x9in) s.d.94 panel. 11-Jun-3 Christie's, Rome #196/R est:4000-6000
£3211	$5362	€4656	Elegante sur le sofa (24x18cm-9x7in) s. 21-Jun-3 Galerie du Rhone, Sion #90/R est:3000-4000 (S.FR 7000)
£6338	$10521	€9000	Concertino a palazzo (31x48cm-12x19in) s. panel. 11-Jun-3 Christie's, Rome #265/R est:10000-15000
£6376	$11859	€9500	Card game (24x40cm-9x16in) s. board. 2-Mar-4 Ansorena, Madrid #81/R est:9500
£6667	$11933	€10000	Lady in interior (23x13cm-9x5in) s.i. board. 13-May-4 Babuino, Rome #342/R est:2500-3000
£7609	$12478	€10500	Game of chess (24x35cm-9x14in) s. board. 27-May-3 Finarte Semenzato, Milan #93/R est:12000-13000
£11111	$20000	€16222	Semi nude in an interior (24x18cm-9x7in) s.i. panel. 22-Apr-4 Christie's, Rockefeller NY #247/R est:15000-20000
£11888	$20448	€17000	Le gouter du Cardinal (26x32cm-10x13in) s.i. panel. 5-Dec-3 Gros & Delettrez, Paris #58/R est:15000-20000
£15556	$28000	€22712	Musical interlude (26x41cm-10x16in) s.i. prov. 22-Apr-4 Christie's, Rockefeller NY #231/R est:30000-50000
£18456	$32668	€27500	Tea time (23x41cm-9x16in) s. 27-Apr-4 Durán, Madrid #186/R est:27000
£20833	$37500	€30416	Familia de su Excelencia (35x51cm-14x20in) s.i. prov. 23-Apr-4 Sotheby's, New York #120/R est:20000-30000
£21812	$38607	€32500	Combing her hair (33x40cm-13x16in) s. 27-Apr-4 Durán, Madrid #185/R est:30000
£22222	$40000	€32444	Evening with the Cardinal (13x22cm-5x9in) one s. panel pair prov. 23-Apr-4 Sotheby's, New York #122/R est:15000-20000
£27586	$49655	€40000	Tea time (24x32cm-9x13in) s. board. 26-Jan-4 Durán, Madrid #216/R est:25000
£30000	$54600	€43800	Presentation of the portrait (40x66cm-16x26in) s.i. 17-Jun-4 Christie's, London #94/R est:35000-45000
£30797	$50507	€42500	La Cabrera (65x119cm-26x47in) s. 27-May-3 Durán, Madrid #262/R est:35000
£38889	$70000	€56778	Valuation of jewels (39x66cm-15x26in) s. prov. 23-Apr-4 Sotheby's, New York #121/R est:30000-50000
£39855	$65362	€55000	Jolgorio (39x67cm-15x26in) s. exhib. 27-May-3 Durán, Madrid #263/R est:35000
£62500	$101875	€90000	Bacia de Oro, Spain (39x66cm-15x26in) s. 23-Sep-3 Durán, Madrid #201/R est:70000

SALINAS, Porfirio (1910-1972) American

£2198	$4000	€3209	Western landscape (41x51cm-16x20in) s.d.1961. 29-Jun-4 Sotheby's, New York #260/R est:3000-5000
£2793	$5000	€4078	Summer landscape (51x41cm-20x16in) 15-May-4 Altermann Galleries, Santa Fe #172/R
£3067	$5000	€4478	Texas hill country (30x41cm-12x16in) s. 28-Sep-3 Simpson's, Houston #290/R
£4469	$8000	€6525	Autumn Hill country (61x76cm-24x30in) 15-May-4 Altermann Galleries, Santa Fe #173/R
£5090	$8500	€7431	Texas stream with horse (51x61cm-20x24in) 18-Oct-3 David Dike, Dallas #231/R est:9000-12000
£5294	$9000	€7729	Autumn landscape (61x76cm-24x30in) 1-Nov-3 Altermann Galleries, Santa Fe #192
£5780	$10000	€8439	Landscape with Texas bluebells (46x76cm-18x30in) s. 10-Dec-3 Boos Gallery, Michigan #522/R est:12000-15000
£6704	$12000	€9788	Texas landscape (64x76cm-25x30in) 15-May-4 Altermann Galleries, Santa Fe #171/R
£11377	$19000	€16610	Dusty trail (64x76cm-25x30in) 18-Oct-3 David Dike, Dallas #212/R est:10000-15000

SALINGRE, Gustav (1878-?) German

£2098	$3503	€3000	Inn (88x110cm-35x43in) s. 30-Jun-3 Ansorena, Madrid #204/R est:3000

SALINI, Lino (1889-1944) German

£333	$610	€500	Street cafe, Monus (56x48cm-22x19in) s.d.1929 board. 5-Jun-4 Arnold, Frankfurt #707/R

SALINI, Tommaso (1575-1625) Italian

£26056	$45599	€37000	Bacchus (100x74cm-39x29in) 17-Dec-3 Christie's, Rome #478/R est:30000-40000

SALIOLA, Antonio (1939-) Italian

£1399	$2378	€2000	Park tales (70x60cm-28x24in) s.d.1986 s.i.d.verso. 26-Nov-3 Pandolfini, Florence #88/R est:2000-3000

SALIS CAMINO, Jose (1863-1926) Spanish

£473	$832	€700	Landscape with path. Landscape with houses (16x23cm-6x9in) mono.i.d.1920 cardboard double-sided. 18-May-4 Segre, Madrid #29/R

SALIS-SOGLIO, Carl Albert von (1886-1941) Swiss

£305	$506	€442	Cowherds in the mountains (60x74cm-24x29in) mono. 13-Jun-3 Zofingen, Switzerland #3006 (S.FR 670)
£1538	$2615	€2200	Trees in a mountain landscape (69x79cm-27x31in) s. lit. 28-Nov-3 Schloss Ahlden, Ahlden #1600/R est:1400

SALISBURY, Alda West (1879-1933) American

£1006	$1800	€1469	Flowers in a vase (64x76cm-25x30in) s. prov. 6-May-4 Shannon's, Milford #170/R est:2500-3500

SALISBURY, Frank O (1874-1962) British

£420	$773	€613	Bishop of Bath and Wells (48x36cm-19x14in) s.i.d.1937 canvasboard. 14-Jun-4 Bonhams, Bath #197
£3889	$7000	€5678	Coronation of George VI and Queen Elizabeth in Westminster Abbey (56x96cm-22x38in) s.i. 24-Apr-4 Weschler, Washington #546/R est:2000-3000

SALKIN, Fernand (1862-?) French

£1056	$1827	€1500	Personnage dans une ruelle (41x33cm-16x13in) s. panel. 15-Dec-3 Gros & Delettrez, Paris #50/R est:1000-1500

SALLE, Andre Augustin (1891-?) French

Sculpture			
£1383	$2240	€1950	Elephant et petit singe (13x31cm-5x12in) s.st.f.Meroni-Radice brown pat bronze exec.c.1920/1930. 24-May-3 Martinot & Savignat, Pontoise #113/R est:2000-2200

SALLE, David (1952-) American

£7821	$14000	€11419	Untitled (38x51cm-15x20in) s.i.d.2000-01 verso diptych prov. 14-May-4 Phillips, New York #314/R est:18000-25000
£10000	$16700	€14600	Hotel Dixie (152x122cm-60x48in) s.i.d.1992 verso acrylic silkscreen ink prov.exhib.lit. 21-Oct-3 Sotheby's, London #443/R est:10000-15000
£20958	$35000	€30599	Untitled, summer 1997 (76x56cm-30x22in) s.i.d.97 acrylic wash paper. 13-Nov-3 Sotheby's, New York #593/R est:8000-12000
£22346	$40000	€32625	Man is like a tree (183x244cm-72x96in) s. stretcher two parts prov. 13-May-4 Sotheby's, New York #451/R est:45000-65000
£25449	$42500	€37156	Smells burns is vacant (168x234cm-66x92in) oil acrylic prov.exhib.lit. 13-Nov-3 Sotheby's, New York #589/R est:30000-40000
£30726	$55000	€44860	Untitled (260x229cm-102x90in) acrylic diptych prov. 13-May-4 Phillips, New York #25/R est:70000-90000
£33520	$60000	€48939	We back them up (102x147cm-40x58in) s.i.d.1979 overlap acrylic chl prov. 13-May-4 Sotheby's, New York #456/R est:25000-35000
£33520	$60000	€48939	Pitcher (115x154cm-45x61in) acrylic ceramic pitcher wood prov. 12-May-4 Christie's, Rockefeller NY #471/R est:35000-45000
£43333	$80167	€65000	Flagrant eyeball (132x268cm-52x106in) acrylic chl oil painted 1987 prov. 18-Jul-4 Sotheby's, Paris #229/R est:60000-80000
Works on paper			
£2100	$3864	€3066	Untitled (76x105cm-30x41in) s.d.82 brush ink. 24-Jun-4 Sotheby's, Olympia #594/R est:2000-3000

SALLEMBIER, Henri (1753-1820) French

Works on paper			
£680	$1217	€1000	Jeune homme dans un paysage de Ruines (9x16cm-4x6in) s. sanguine. 17-Mar-4 Tajan, Paris #88

SALLES, Pierre Alexandre (attrib) (1867-1915) French

£400	$736	€600	Joueur de violon (17x24cm-7x9in) s. paper on panel. 9-Jun-4 Oger, Dumont, Paris #75

SALLES-WAGNER, Adelaide (1825-1890) German

£340	$569	€480	La dame a l'eventail (46x38cm-18x15in) s. 15-Oct-3 Hotel des Ventes Mosan, Brussels #129
Works on paper			
£238	$426	€350	Tete de femme se reposant (18x26cm-7x10in) black crayon stumping out. 17-Mar-4 Tajan, Paris #149

SALLI, Aares (1914-) Finnish

£403	$741	€600	Winter landscape (40x50cm-16x20in) s.d.1981. 25-Mar-4 Hagelstam, Helsinki #866

SALLINEN, Tyko (1879-1955) Finnish

£352	$563	€500	Outhouses (27x38cm-11x15in) s.d.1926. 18-Sep-3 Hagelstam, Helsinki #792/R
£544	$990	€800	Red cottage (46x55cm-18x22in) s.d.44. 8-Feb-4 Bukowskis, Helsinki #444/R
£1149	$2056	€1700	House on cliff by sea (46x56cm-18x22in) s.d.1931 exhib. 8-May-4 Bukowskis, Helsinki #173/R est:2000-2500
£1197	$1915	€1700	Landscape from Kytalja (35x46cm-14x18in) s.d.20. 21-Sep-3 Bukowskis, Helsinki #459/R est:2000
£1689	$3024	€2500	The red croft (50x60cm-20x24in) s.d.22. 8-May-4 Bukowskis, Helsinki #156/R est:2500-2800
£2098	$3566	€3000	Still life of vegetables and fish (46x57cm-18x22in) s.d.1916. 29-Nov-3 Bukowskis, Helsinki #105/R est:4000-5000
£2254	$3899	€3200	Beached boat (26x36cm-10x14in) s. canvas on board painted c.1907-08. 13-Dec-3 Hagelstam, Helsinki #150/R est:2000
£2378	$4042	€3400	Summer's day in the country (33x46cm-13x18in) s.d.39. 29-Nov-3 Bukowskis, Helsinki #89/R est:3000-3500
£2797	$4755	€4000	Two girls in the sauna (100x81cm-39x32in) s.d.45. 29-Nov-3 Bukowskis, Helsinki #173/R est:3500-5000
£3378	$6047	€5000	The evacuees (100x81cm-39x32in) s.d.40. 8-May-4 Bukowskis, Helsinki #160/R est:6000-9000
£4507	$7797	€6400	View from Berghall, Helsinki (46x51cm-18x20in) s.d.1917 prov. 13-Dec-3 Hagelstam, Helsinki #149/R est:4000
Works on paper			
£383	$704	€570	Tytarsaari (31x42cm-12x17in) s.d.1939 W/C. 25-Mar-4 Hagelstam, Helsinki #887
£403	$749	€600	Old croft (26x39cm-10x15in) s.d.28 W/C prov. 7-Mar-4 Bukowskis, Helsinki #437/R

£437	$731	€630	Old barn (30x42cm-12x17in) s.d.43 W/C. 26-Oct-3 Bukowskis, Helsinki #488/R
£458	$732	€650	Landscape with village (29x24cm-11x9in) s.d.21 W/C. 21-Sep-3 Bukowskis, Helsinki #457/R
£600	$1074	€900	Village (31x42cm-12x17in) s.d.1929. 15-May-4 Hagelstam, Helsinki #142/R

SALMI, Max (1931-1995) Finnish

£387	$620	€550	Maahinen (39x58cm-15x23in) s.d.1967. 18-Sep-3 Hagelstam, Helsinki #818/R
£403	$741	€600	Beach (40x40cm-16x16in) s.d.1968. 25-Mar-4 Hagelstam, Helsinki #1008
£542	$905	€780	Composition (49x40cm-19x16in) s.d.1959. 23-Oct-3 Hagelstam, Helsinki #1023
£671	$1235	€1000	Road to beach (40x60cm-16x24in) s.d.1960. 25-Mar-4 Hagelstam, Helsinki #1007
£676	$1209	€1000	Kharon (30x48cm-12x19in) s.d.66 board. 8-May-4 Bukowskis, Helsinki #278/R
£811	$1451	€1200	Dream (40x40cm-16x16in) s.d.66 board. 8-May-4 Bukowskis, Helsinki #275/R
£933	$1671	€1400	Morning (70x50cm-28x20in) s.d.1973 board. 15-May-4 Hagelstam, Helsinki #210/R
£1014	$1814	€1500	Mirror (44x50cm-17x20in) s.d.69 board. 8-May-4 Bukowskis, Helsinki #233/R est:1500-1800
£1049	$1783	€1500	Composition (49x69cm-19x27in) s.d.70 board. 29-Nov-3 Bukowskis, Helsinki #269/R est:1300-1600
£1074	$1976	€1600	Cage bird (72x55cm-28x22in) s.d.1972. 25-Mar-4 Hagelstam, Helsinki #912 est:800
£1189	$2021	€1700	Blue dream (69x100cm-27x39in) s.indis.d.6. 29-Nov-3 Bukowskis, Helsinki #257/R est:1700-2000
£1329	$2259	€1900	Ceremony master (50x50cm-20x20in) s.d.83 board. 29-Nov-3 Bukowskis, Helsinki #291/R est:1600-2000
£1469	$2497	€2100	On the beach (40x40cm-16x16in) s.d.66 board. 29-Nov-3 Bukowskis, Helsinki #276/R est:1000-1200
£1538	$2615	€2200	Play (50x50cm-20x20in) s.d.74 board. 29-Nov-3 Bukowskis, Helsinki #280/R est:1500-1800
£2168	$3685	€3100	Fossil (64x50cm-25x20in) s.d.70 board. 29-Nov-3 Bukowskis, Helsinki #253/R est:1200-1500

SALMON, Balliol J (1868-1953) British

Works on paper

£430	$744	€628	Entrance Hall, Drury Lane (36x66cm-14x26in) s.i.d.1907 pencil htd white. 9-Dec-3 Bristol Auction Rooms #398

SALMON, John (?) British

Works on paper

£400	$668	€584	Dutch fishing boats (23x54cm-9x21in) s.d.1865 W/C pencil bodycol. 16-Oct-3 Lawrence, Crewkerne #645

SALMON, John Cuthbert (1844-1917) British

£350	$581	€511	Figure in wooded landscape clearing (69x91cm-27x36in) 2-Oct-3 Biddle & Webb, Birmingham #899

Works on paper

£300	$549	€438	Llanberris Pass, North Wales (35x25cm-14x10in) s. W/C. 7-Apr-4 Dreweatt Neate, Newbury #56
£550	$935	€803	Salvaging the derelict (45x70cm-18x28in) s.d.1874 W/C. 25-Nov-3 Bonhams, Knightsbridge #44/R
£660	$1049	€957	View of Whitby (36x53cm-14x21in) s. W/C. 9-Sep-3 David Duggleby, Scarborough #123a
£750	$1275	€1095	View of Louth, Lincolnshire showing St. James Church (21x32cm-8x13in) W/C htd bodycol. 4-Nov-3 Bonhams, New Bond Street #127/R
£1200	$2040	€1752	Ships off Bridlington, Yorkshire (34x52cm-13x20in) s.d.1874 W/C. 25-Nov-3 Bonhams, Knightsbridge #192/R est:800-1200

SALMON, John Francis (1808-1886) British

£500	$835	€730	Bridlington, Yorkshire, landing a cutter. 21-Oct-3 Gorringes, Lewes #2045/R

SALMON, Robert (1775-1844) American

£700	$1190	€1022	Afternoon on the lake (19x23cm-7x9in) panel. 19-Nov-3 Christie's, Kensington #458/R
£4348	$7000	€6348	Fishing party beaching a boat (30x41cm-12x16in) s. verso panel prov. 20-Aug-3 James Julia, Fairfield #715/R est:15000-20000
£8108	$15000	€11838	English and American merchantmen in the Clyde (20x25cm-8x10in) board. 10-Feb-4 Christie's, Rockefeller NY #169/R est:12000-15000
£14706	$25000	€21471	Loch Lomond (20x25cm-8x10in) init.d.1841 verso board prov. 21-Nov-3 Skinner, Boston #209/R est:7000-9000
£26000	$44200	€37960	Armed merchant vessel passing the custom house at Greenock, on the Clyde (49x76cm-19x30in) 27-Nov-3 Sotheby's, London #104/R est:30000-40000
£36932	$65000	€53921	English Cutter (42x62cm-17x24in) s.i.d.1832 verso panel prov.lit. 18-May-4 Christie's, Rockefeller NY #19/R est:50000-70000
£55556	$90000	€80556	Harbour, Liverpool (31x41cm-12x16in) i.verso panel prov. 8-Aug-3 Barridorf, Portland #76/R est:40000-60000

SALMON, Theodore Frederic (1811-1876) French

£2681	$4397	€3700	L'agrenage a la ferme. s.d.1854 panel exhib. 11-May-3 Osenat, Fontainebleau #56/R est:3200-3500

SALMSON, Fred (1941-) Swedish?

£604	$1027	€882	Untitled (102x123cm-40x48in) init.d.84. 4-Nov-3 Bukowskis, Stockholm #617/R (S.KR 8000)

SALMSON, Hugo (1844-1894) Swedish

£1692	$2911	€2470	Boy playing flute for girls in summer meadow (47x36cm-19x14in) s. 3-Dec-3 AB Stockholms Auktionsverk #2269/R est:20000-25000 (S.KR 22000)
£5543	$9922	€8093	Girl wearing red dress (100x73cm-39x29in) s. 25-May-4 Bukowskis, Stockholm #21/R est:80000-100000 (S.KR 75000)

SALMSON, Jean Jules (1823-1902) French

Sculpture

£2500	$4500	€3650	Figures of Reynolds and Hogarth (56x57cm-22x22in) s. brown pat bronze pair lit. 21-Apr-4 Sotheby's, London #63/R est:3000-5000

SALOKIVI, Santeri (1886-1940) Finnish

£556	$928	€800	Venice (21x13cm-8x5in) s. 23-Oct-3 Hagelstam, Helsinki #929
£1477	$2717	€2200	View of Rome (31x40cm-12x16in) s.i.d.1914. 25-Mar-4 Hagelstam, Helsinki #946 est:2000
£1600	$2864	€2400	Suomen Joutsen (44x37cm-17x15in) 15-May-4 Hagelstam, Helsinki #166/R est:1800
£1711	$3149	€2550	Harbour (30x37cm-12x15in) s. 25-Mar-4 Hagelstam, Helsinki #952 est:2000
£2703	$4838	€4000	Resting on the beach (32x40cm-13x16in) exhib. 8-May-4 Bukowskis, Helsinki #154/R est:3500-4000
£2727	$4636	€3900	Farm in morning sunshine (64x89cm-25x35in) s.d.39. 29-Nov-3 Bukowskis, Helsinki #218/R est:4500-5000
£2797	$4755	€4000	Red croft (45x54cm-18x21in) s.d.30. 29-Nov-3 Bukowskis, Helsinki #117/R est:4000-4500
£2797	$4755	€4000	Cattle in water (45x56cm-18x22in) s.d.31. 29-Nov-3 Bukowskis, Helsinki #143/R est:5000-6000
£2905	$5201	€4300	On the beach (15x16cm-6x6in) s. board. 8-May-4 Bukowskis, Helsinki #172/R est:2000-2400
£3497	$5944	€5000	The return home (40x48cm-16x19in) s.d.36. 29-Nov-3 Bukowskis, Helsinki #76/R est:3500-3800
£4595	$8224	€6800	On the beach (46x38cm-18x15in) s.d.28. 8-May-4 Bukowskis, Helsinki #63/R est:3500-4500
£5070	$8772	€7200	Boast by the shore of Aura river (31x41cm-12x16in) s.d.1918 board. 13-Dec-3 Hagelstam, Helsinki #148/R est:6000
£5874	$9986	€8400	Boats on the beach (38x46cm-15x18in) s.i.d.1936. 29-Nov-3 Bukowskis, Helsinki #114/R est:6000-7000
£7343	$12483	€10500	Summer's day on the beach (21x31cm-8x12in) s.d.33 board. 29-Nov-3 Bukowskis, Helsinki #53/R est:5000-6000
£7432	$13304	€11000	Resting in the shadow (38x45cm-15x18in) s.d.24. 8-May-4 Bukowskis, Helsinki #33/R est:5000-6000
£10140	$17238	€14500	View from Getabergen, Aaland (47x56cm-19x22in) s.i.d.32. 29-Nov-3 Bukowskis, Helsinki #161/R est:5000-6000

SALOMAN (18th C) Swedish?

£1478	$2646	€2158	The Holy Family with St John (39x32cm-15x13in) s.d.1795 copper. 28-May-4 Uppsala Auktionskammare, Uppsala #63/R est:25000-30000 (S.KR 20000)

SALOME (1954-) German

£347	$566	€500	Untitled (30x40cm-12x16in) s.d.2000 acrylic. 26-Sep-3 Bolland & Marotz, Bremen #804/R
£1067	$1909	€1600	In the wave (26x35cm-10x14in) s.d. 13-May-4 Neumeister, Munich #759/R est:1000-1500
£1765	$3000	€2577	In hellem light (152x122cm-60x48in) s.i.d.88 s.i.d.verso acrylic. 9-Nov-3 Bonhams & Butterfields, Los Angeles #4038/R
£3493	$6428	€5100	Peter the model (200x200cm-79x79in) s.i.d.1982 prov. 8-Jun-4 Germann, Zurich #5/R est:10000-15000 (S.FR 8000)
£4333	$7930	€6500	Autumn swimmers (140x160cm-55x63in) s.d.88 s.i.d.88 verso acrylic. 4-Jun-4 Lempertz, Koln #419/R est:7000
£4333	$7930	€6500	Carneval swimmers II (183x183cm-72x72in) s.d.95 s.i.d.95 verso acrylic. 4-Jun-4 Lempertz, Koln #420/R est:7000-9000
£4895	$8322	€7000	Shower VII (200x140cm-79x55in) s.i.d.87 acrylic. 29-Nov-3 Villa Grisebach, Berlin #381/R est:7000-9000
£5245	$8916	€7500	Swimmer (50x90cm-20x35in) s.d.92 s.i.d. verso resin canvas five part. 27-Nov-3 Lempertz, Koln #412/R est:6000-7000
£6294	$10699	€9000	Waterlilies (160x200cm-63x79in) s.d.94 s.i.d.94 verso acrylic. 29-Nov-3 Villa Grisebach, Berlin #383/R est:7000-9000
£28169	$48732	€40000	Ultramarine (100x101cm-39x40in) i. s.d.89 verso acrylic. 13-Dec-3 Lempertz, Koln #182/R est:2000

Works on paper

£533	$981	€800	Water lilies (26x20cm-10x8in) s.i.d.92 W/C over pencil waterboard. 12-Jun-4 Villa Grisebach, Berlin #830/R
£833	$1525	€1250	Untitled - male nude (91x60cm-36x24in) s.d.83 col chk. 4-Jun-4 Lempertz, Koln #421/R

SALOMON, G (?) ?

£638	$1173	€950	In the harem (47x24cm-19x9in) s. 25-Mar-4 Hagelstam, Helsinki #817

SALOMON, Jacques (20th C) ?

£1100	$1837	€1606	Waiting in the wings (179x75cm-70x30in) s. sold with two sketches in one frame. 8-Oct-3 Christie's, Kensington #654/R est:600-800

SALOMON, Solomon (1869-1937) American

£898	$1500	€1311	Venice (51x61cm-20x24in) board. 18-Oct-3 David Dike, Dallas #277/R est:2000-4000

SALOMONSEN, Pauline (19th C) Danish?

£1682	$2658	€2439	Flowers in basket on tree trunk in woodland (56x47cm-22x19in) 2-Sep-3 Rasmussen, Copenhagen #1735/R est:20000-25000 (D.KR 18000)

SALONEN, Lauri (20th C) Finnish

£285	$475	€410	Coastal landscape (58x92cm-23x36in) s.d.1925. 26-Oct-3 Bukowskis, Helsinki #490/R

SALONEN, Wille (20th C) Finnish

£313	$570	€460	Archipelago (65x95cm-26x37in) s. 8-Feb-4 Bukowskis, Helsinki #447/R
£423	$786	€630	Summer landscape (48x73cm-19x29in) s. 7-Mar-4 Bukowskis, Helsinki #439/R

£493 $789 €700 Knocked down tree (69x109cm-27x43in) s. 21-Sep-3 Bukowskis, Helsinki #463/R

SALOSMAA, Aarno (1941-) Finnish
£503 $926 €750 Cushion. s.d.1974. 25-Mar-4 Hagelstam, Helsinki #916

SALSBURY, Robert (fl.1883-1890) British
£335 $600 €489 On the Colne at West Drayton (51x61cm-20x24in) s.d.1890. 21-Mar-4 Jeffery Burchard, Florida #20a/R

SALT, J (19th C) British
£1538 $2646 €2200 Venetian scene (35x62cm-14x24in) s. 3-Dec-3 Stadion, Trieste #315/R est:1500-2000

SALT, James (19th C) British
£720 $1159 €1051 Misty Venetian backwater with figures in boat on the canal (69x48cm-27x19in) s. 12-Aug-3 Canterbury Auctions, UK #170/R
£800 $1480 €1168 Venetian view (46x82cm-18x32in) s. 14-Jul-4 Sotheby's, Olympia #111/R
£1500 $2550 €2190 Venetian capriccios of figures and gondolas on canals (36x62cm-14x24in) s. pair. 26-Nov-3 Hamptons Fine Art, Godalming #185 est:1500-1800
£4200 $7392 €6132 Venetian views. pair. 19-May-4 John Bellman, Billingshurst #1811/R est:400-600
£13000 $24180 €18980 Venetian cappriccio. Venetian backwater (46x81cm-18x32in) s. pair. 4-Mar-4 Christie's, Kensington #563/R est:5000-8000

SALT, John (1937-) British
£3297 $6000 €4814 Arresting vehicle with decomposing seats (134x200cm-53x79in) s.overlap painted 1972 prov. 29-Jun-4 Sotheby's, New York #488/R est:10000-15000
Works on paper
£2819 $5046 €4200 Untitled (29x43cm-11x17in) s.d.90 W/C prov.lit. 27-May-4 Sotheby's, Paris #250/R est:1000-1500

SALTER, John William (19th C) British
Works on paper
£480 $768 €701 London Bridge, Torbay (34x50cm-13x20in) s.d.1877 W/C. 18-Sep-3 Bearnes, Exeter #447

SALTFLEET, Frank (c.1860-1937) British
Works on paper
£400 $668 €584 Going in with the tide (33x48cm-13x19in) s.i. W/C. 17-Oct-3 Keys, Aylsham #505
£1350 $2214 €1971 Summer Breeze, fishing fleet at sea with gulls and distant steamer (48x69cm-19x27in) s. W/C bodycol htd white. 29-May-3 Neales, Nottingham #716/R est:1200-1800

SALTI, Giulio (1899-1984) Italian
£331 $553 €480 Portrait of young woman (43x34cm-17x13in) s. cardboard. 14-Nov-3 Farsetti, Prato #412/R
£1067 $1931 €1600 Still life with roses and violin (44x60cm-17x24in) s. board. 2-Apr-4 Farsetti, Prato #406/R est:1600-2000

SALTO, Axel (1889-1961) Danish
£4693 $8635 €6852 The crazy Turk (69x105cm-27x41in) s. painted c.1938 prov.lit. 29-Mar-4 Rasmussen, Copenhagen #128/R est:30000 (D.KR 52000)
Works on paper
£301 $512 €439 Three jugs (29x42cm-11x17in) s.d.27/2 Indian ink. 26-Nov-3 Kunsthallen, Copenhagen #316/R (D.KR 3200)
£583 $992 €851 Three large vases (42x53cm-17x21in) s.d.21/8 54 Indian ink. 26-Nov-3 Kunsthallen, Copenhagen #319/R (D.KR 6200)

SALTOFT, Edvard Anders (1883-1939) Danish
Works on paper
£280 $439 €409 Harbour scene (41x65cm-16x26in) s. pastel. 30-Aug-3 Rasmussen, Havnen #2019/R (D.KR 3000)
£298 $468 €435 The Russian Army marching forward (72x99cm-28x39in) s. pastel. 30-Aug-3 Rasmussen, Havnen #2222 (D.KR 3200)
£851 $1472 €1242 Army on the march in snow storm (69x91cm-27x36in) indis.sig. pastel. 9-Dec-3 Rasmussen, Copenhagen #1756/R (D.KR 9000)

SALTZMANN, Carl (1847-1923) German
£875 $1609 €1313 Winter at sea (70x60cm-28x24in) s. 14-Jun-4 Lilla Bukowskis, Stockholm #620 (S.KR 12000)
£1111 $1811 €1600 Steamer in storm (60x91cm-24x36in) s.d.1915 board. 26-Sep-3 Bolland & Marotz, Bremen #604/R est:1500
£1549 $2680 €2200 SM Yacht Hohenzollern auf hoher See (38x60cm-15x24in) s.d.1902. 10-Dec-3 Christie's, Amsterdam #182/R est:2000-3000
£1818 $3091 €2600 Evening on Lake Garda (78x129cm-31x51in) s.d.77. 20-Nov-3 Van Ham, Cologne #1836/R est:2400

SALTZMANN, Henri Gustave (1811-1872) Swiss
£588 $941 €858 Landscape in Roman Campagna (14x31cm-6x12in) s. panel. 16-Sep-3 Philippe Schuler, Zurich #3253 (S.FR 1300)

SALUCCI, Alessandro (attrib) (17th C) Italian
£1733 $3189 €2600 Scene de port mediterraneen avec Antoine et Cleopatre (63x79cm-25x31in) 11-Jun-4 Maigret, Paris #42/R est:3000-4000

SALUSTRI, Piero (1957-) Italian
£621 $1037 €900 Still life (40x70cm-16x28in) s.d.LXXXV. 13-Nov-3 Finarte Semenzato, Rome #237/R

SALVADO, Jacinto (1892-1983) Spanish
£1974 $3632 €3000 Composition (130x89cm-51x35in) s.d.59 s.d.verso. 22-Jun-4 Durán, Madrid #143/R est:3000
£2138 $3934 €3250 Abstract (89x131cm-35x52in) s.d.1958 s.d.verso. 22-Jun-4 Durán, Madrid #142/R est:3000

SALVADOR Y DE SOLA, Yago Cesar (1890-?) Spanish
£669 $1157 €950 Christ of the Blood (115x82cm-45x32in) i.d.1914 verso. 15-Dec-3 Ansorena, Madrid #86/R

SALVADORI, Aldo (1905-2002) Italian
£331 $603 €500 Figure at cafe (25x30cm-10x12in) s.d.1999 chl. 17-Jun-4 Galleria Pananti, Florence #448/R
£676 $1189 €1000 Portrait of young woman (45x30cm-18x12in) s. tempera paper. 22-May-4 Galleria Pananti, Florence #424/R
£1259 $2102 €1800 Flowers and figure (19x13cm-7x5in) s. oil pastel. 26-Jun-3 Sant Agostino, Torino #186/R est:1200
£1538 $2569 €2200 Reading (14x18cm-6x7in) s. 26-Jun-3 Sant Agostino, Torino #241/R est:1400
£1831 $3168 €2600 Basket with flowers (33x40cm-13x16in) s.d.985 s.i.d.verso. 9-Dec-3 Pandolfini, Florence #148/R est:2000-3000
£2113 $3697 €3000 Portrait of woman (50x30cm-20x12in) s. 16-Dec-3 Finarte Semenzato, Milan #320/R est:1300-1700
£2817 $4676 €4000 Bust of woman (40x60cm-16x24in) s. 11-Jun-3 Finarte Semenzato, Milan #705/R
£3287 $5587 €4700 Young woman in nightdress (73x45cm-29x18in) s. s.d.1971 verso. 20-Nov-3 Finarte Semenzato, Milan #97/R est:4500-4800
£7042 $11690 €10000 Young woman (99x64cm-39x25in) s. painted 1970. 11-Jun-3 Finarte Semenzato, Milan #718/R est:6500
Works on paper
£276 $461 €400 Figure (33x24cm-13x9in) s.d.1976 pastel. 17-Nov-3 Sant Agostino, Torino #85/R
£276 $461 €400 Figure (32x25cm-13x10in) s.i.d.1979 pencil pastel. 17-Nov-3 Sant Agostino, Torino #170/R
£385 $642 €550 Girl with hat (39x31cm-15x12in) s.i. pencil. 26-Jun-3 Sant Agostino, Torino #156/R
£387 $643 €550 Nude (34x25cm-13x10in) s.d.57 pencil dr. 13-Jun-3 Farsetti, Prato #287
£464 $844 €700 Reclining figure (20x30cm-8x12in) s. pastel. 17-Jun-4 Galleria Pananti, Florence #449/R
£467 $845 €700 Girl (29x20cm-11x8in) s. Chinese ink water. 2-Apr-4 Farsetti, Prato #96
£690 $1152 €1000 Flowers and figure (11x14cm-4x6in) s. pastel. 17-Nov-3 Sant Agostino, Torino #79/R
£800 $1472 €1200 Seated girl (19x22cm-7x9in) s. W/C pastel. 8-Jun-4 Finarte Semenzato, Milan #236/R

SALVADORI, Nino (1918-) Italian
£347 $590 €500 Neapolitan boys (50x70cm-20x28in) s. 1-Nov-3 Meeting Art, Vercelli #287

SALVARANI, Arcangelo (1882-1953) Italian
Works on paper
£600 $1098 €900 Cows at pasture (36x26cm-14x10in) W/C. 4-Jun-4 Tuttarte, Modena #285

SALVATI, O (19/20th C) Italian
£280 $518 €409 Portrait of a seated male reading a newspaper (60x44cm-24x17in) s. 9-Mar-4 Bonhams, Knowle #306

SALVATORE, Mario (20th C) Italian
£563 $901 €800 Old peasant woman in the kitchen (100x70cm-39x28in) s. 19-Sep-3 Finarte, Venice #473/R

SALVATORE, Victor (1885-1965) American
£367 $660 €550 Marine with fishing boats (40x70cm-16x28in) s.d.1904. 26-Apr-4 Bernaerts, Antwerp #105/R

SALVETTI, Antonio (1854-1931) Italian
£282 $487 €400 Sunset in the countryside (24x34cm-9x13in) s.d.1917. 9-Dec-3 Pandolfini, Florence #97
£881 $1523 €1250 Street with tree (40x50cm-16x20in) s.d. card. 9-Dec-3 Pandolfini, Florence #208/R
£2416 $4446 €3600 Fisherman (45x29cm-18x11in) s.i.d.1888 board. 24-Mar-4 Il Ponte, Milan #656/R est:700

SALVIATI (16th C) Italian
£311 $500 €451 View of Capri (71x99cm-28x39in) s. 17-Aug-3 Jeffery Burchard, Florida #75b

SALVIATI, Francesco (1510-1563) Italian
Works on paper
£1800 $3240 €2700 Battle scene (21x29cm-8x11in) pen brush sepia ink. 21-Apr-4 Finarte Semenzato, Milan #537/R est:1600-1900
£5442 $9741 €8000 Un bras droit ecorche, avec des etudes des os et articulations (19x21cm-7x8in) red chk prov. 18-Mar-4 Christie's, Paris #51/R est:8000-12000
£19444 $35000 €28388 Hercules and the Nemean lion (24x18cm-9x7in) red chl prov. 22-Jan-4 Christie's, Rockefeller NY #22/R est:35000-45000

SALVIATI, Giovanni (1881-1950) Italian

£1056	$1827	€1500	Sailing boats (14x23cm-6x9in) s. cardboard. 10-Dec-3 Sotheby's, Milan #13 est:1500-2000
Works on paper			
£338	$608	€493	Venetian canal scene (58x40cm-23x16in) s. W/C. 26-Jan-4 Lilla Bukowskis, Stockholm #37 (S.KR 4500)

SALVINI, Innocente (1889-?) Italian

£1486	$2616	€2200	Landscape (48x58cm-19x23in) s. painted 1969. 19-May-4 Il Ponte, Milan #1055 est:2200-2500
£2817	$4676	€4000	La guardiana (100x70cm-39x28in) 11-Jun-3 Christie's, Rome #89/R est:1000-1500

SALVINO, Andrea (1969-) Italian

£1408	$2465	€2000	Meeting and discussion (40x62cm-16x24in) s.d.1995 verso. 16-Dec-3 Finarte Semenzato, Milan #208/R est:2000-2200
£1549	$2711	€2200	Untitled (70x60cm-28x24in) s.i.d.1999 verso. 16-Dec-3 Finarte Semenzato, Milan #235/R est:2000-2400

SALVO (1947-) Italian

£2029	$3328	€2800	Untitled (14x9cm-6x4in) card prov. 27-May-3 Sotheby's, Milan #122 est:1200-1500
£2083	$3292	€3000	Little train (25x20cm-10x8in) cardboard on canvas. 6-Sep-3 Meeting Art, Vercelli #429 est:3000
£2098	$3566	€3000	Road (35x25cm-14x10in) s.i.d.86 prov. 24-Nov-3 Christie's, Milan #112/R est:2000-3000
£3056	$4828	€4400	Flowers (30x23cm-12x9in) board oval. 6-Sep-3 Meeting Art, Vercelli #425 est:4000
£3147	$5350	€4500	Alessandria (30x40cm-12x16in) s.d.1993 verso exhib. 24-Nov-3 Christie's, Milan #295/R est:5000-7000
£3521	$6162	€5000	Alberobello (36x46cm-14x18in) s.verso board. 16-Dec-3 Finarte Semenzato, Milan #307/R est:4800-5200
£4054	$7135	€6000	Alberobello (32x24cm-13x9in) s.i.verso board prov. 24-May-4 Christie's, Milan #170/R est:6000-9000
£4138	$6621	€6000	Milan (45x30cm-18x12in) s.i.verso. 13-Mar-3 Galleria Pace, Milan #81/R est:7200-9300
£4196	$7133	€6000	Thirteen oranges (45x35cm-18x14in) s.i.d.82 prov. 24-Nov-3 Christie's, Milan #190/R est:6000-8000
£4861	$7681	€7000	Valley (40x60cm-16x24in) 6-Sep-3 Meeting Art, Vercelli #361 est:6000
£6040	$10812	€9000	Street lamp and minaret (60x70cm-24x28in) s.d.90 verso prov. 25-May-4 Sotheby's, Milan #221/R est:9000-12000
£6294	$10699	€9000	Ruins (71x58cm-28x23in) s.d.90 oval prov. 25-Nov-3 Sotheby's, Milan #254/R est:8000-10000
£6333	$11463	€9500	One evening (70x50cm-28x20in) s.i. 2-Apr-4 Farsetti, Prato #356/R est:1100-1400
£7047	$12614	€10500	Night landscape (80x60cm-31x24in) s.verso. 28-May-4 Farsetti, Prato #211/R est:9000-11000
£8054	$14899	€12000	Palace Hotel, Bustan (70x70cm-28x28in) s.i.verso. 13-Mar-4 Meeting Art, Vercelli #278 est:10000
£8054	$14416	€12000	Ottomana (80x100cm-31x39in) s. i.d.91 verso. 25-May-4 Sotheby's, Milan #320/R est:12000-15000
£9722	$15361	€14000	Winter (90x70cm-35x28in) 6-Sep-3 Meeting Art, Vercelli #745 est:12000
£18116	$29710	€25000	Night, street, lamp-post (192x110cm-76x43in) s.i.d.81 on stretcher. 27-May-3 Sotheby's, Milan #301/R est:25000-30000
£20408	$36531	€30000	Church in the woods (100x120cm-39x47in) painted 1979 prov. 16-Mar-4 Finarte Semenzato, Milan #464/R est:40000
Sculpture			
£1812	$2971	€2500	Turtle and eagle (45x65x2cm-18x26x1in) s.d.72 num.15/50 marble prov. 27-May-3 Sotheby's, Milan #123/R est:2500-3000
£1812	$2971	€2500	Weasel and file (45x65x2cm-18x26x1in) s.d.72 num.21/50 marble prov. 27-May-3 Sotheby's, Milan #124/R est:2500-3000
Works on paper			
£733	$1349	€1100	Landscape (40x30cm-16x12in) s.d.1986 felt-tip pen card. 10-Jun-4 Galleria Pace, Milan #66/R
£759	$1267	€1100	Rural landscape (23x17cm-9x7in) pastel. 17-Nov-3 Sant Agostino, Torino #148/R
£972	$1536	€1400	Alberobello (22x16cm-9x6in) mixed media card on canvas. 6-Sep-3 Meeting Art, Vercelli #529
£1088	$1948	€1600	Spring (29x21cm-11x8in) s.i. pastel. 16-Mar-4 Finarte Semenzato, Milan #234/R est:900
£2113	$3507	€3000	Landscape (98x68cm-39x27in) s.d.1994 verso pastel tempera cardboard. 14-Jun-3 Meeting Art, Vercelli #634/R est:3000
£3500	$5845	€5110	Senza titolo, tricolore (30x38cm-12x15in) s.d.1971 verso col pastel chk card prov.lit. 21-Oct-3 Christie's, London #69/R est:3500-5000

SALZMANN, Alexander von (1870-?) Russian

Works on paper			
£1126	$2049	€1700	Figures on square covered in snow (39x14cm-15x6in) s.i. gouache. 15-Jun-4 Rossini, Paris #66 est:400-600

SALZMANN, Auguste (1824-1872) French

£4000	$7160	€6000	Jerusalem (23x33cm-9x13in) photograph. 14-May-4 Piasa, Paris #46/R est:3000-4000
£5467	$9785	€8200	Jerusalem (33x23cm-13x9in) photograph. 14-May-4 Piasa, Paris #32/R est:5000-6000
£6000	$10740	€9000	Jerusalem (23x33cm-9x13in) photograph. 14-May-4 Piasa, Paris #58/R est:2000-3000
Photographs			
£1944	$3500	€2838	Jerusalem vallee de Josaphant (23x32cm-9x13in) salt print lit. 22-Apr-4 Phillips, New York #160/R est:5000-7000
£2000	$3580	€3000	Jerusalem (23x33cm-9x13in) photograph. 14-May-4 Piasa, Paris #41/R est:2000-3000
£2133	$3819	€3200	Jerusalem (33x23cm-13x9in) photograph. 14-May-4 Piasa, Paris #4/R est:2000-3000
£2133	$3819	€3200	Jerusalem (23x32cm-9x13in) photograph. 14-May-4 Piasa, Paris #5/R est:2000-3000
£2667	$4773	€4000	Jerusalem (23x33cm-9x13in) photograph. 14-May-4 Piasa, Paris #33/R est:3000-4000
£2800	$5012	€4200	Jerusalem (32x23cm-13x9in) photograph. 14-May-4 Piasa, Paris #10/R est:2000-3000
£3000	$5370	€4500	Jerusalem (24x34cm-9x13in) photograph. 14-May-4 Piasa, Paris #38/R est:3000-4000
£3000	$5370	€4500	Jerusalem (33x23cm-13x9in) photograph. 14-May-4 Piasa, Paris #53/R est:3000-4000
£3467	$6205	€5200	Jerusalem (24x33cm-9x13in) photograph. 14-May-4 Piasa, Paris #2/R est:4000-6000
£3667	$6563	€5500	Jerusalem (23x33cm-9x13in) photograph. 14-May-4 Piasa, Paris #18/R est:3000-4000
£3667	$6563	€5500	Jerusalem (33x24cm-13x9in) photograph. 14-May-4 Piasa, Paris #22/R est:4000-5000
£3667	$6563	€5500	Jerusalem (23x33cm-9x13in) photograph. 14-May-4 Piasa, Paris #24/R est:4000-5000
£3867	$6921	€5800	Jerusalem (24x34cm-9x13in) photograph. 14-May-4 Piasa, Paris #69/R est:2000-3000
£4000	$7160	€6000	Jerusalem (23x33cm-9x13in) photograph. 14-May-4 Piasa, Paris #57/R est:15000-20000
£4133	$7399	€6200	Jerusalem (23x33cm-9x13in) photograph. 14-May-4 Piasa, Paris #88/R est:2000-3000
£4533	$8115	€6800	Jerusalem (33x23cm-13x9in) photograph. 14-May-4 Piasa, Paris #31/R est:2000-3000
£5000	$8950	€7500	Jerusalem (23x33cm-9x13in) photograph pair. 14-May-4 Piasa, Paris #13/R
£5200	$9308	€7800	Jerusalem (23x32cm-9x13in) photograph. 14-May-4 Piasa, Paris #72/R est:6000-8000
£5200	$9308	€7800	Jerusalem (33x23cm-13x9in) photograph. 14-May-4 Piasa, Paris #93/R est:3000-4000
£5333	$9547	€8000	Jerusalem (32x23cm-13x9in) photograph. 14-May-4 Piasa, Paris #9/R est:3000-4000
£5333	$9547	€8000	Jerusalem (23x31cm-9x12in) photograph. 14-May-4 Piasa, Paris #29/R est:2000-3000
£5467	$9785	€8200	Jerusalem (24x33cm-9x13in) photograph. 14-May-4 Piasa, Paris #21/R est:4000-5000
£5667	$10143	€8500	Jerusalem (23x32cm-9x13in) photograph. 14-May-4 Piasa, Paris #26/R est:2000-3000
£5667	$10143	€8500	Jerusalem (32x23cm-13x9in) photograph. 14-May-4 Piasa, Paris #62/R est:3000-4000
£6000	$10740	€9000	Jerusalem (22x33cm-9x13in) photograph. 14-May-4 Piasa, Paris #19/R est:3000-4000
£6133	$10979	€9200	Jerusalem (22x32cm-9x13in) photograph. 14-May-4 Piasa, Paris #14/R est:4000-6000
£6533	$11695	€9800	Jerusalem (23x34cm-9x13in) photograph. 14-May-4 Piasa, Paris #39/R est:3000-4000
£6800	$12172	€10200	Jerusalem (23x32cm-9x13in) photograph. 14-May-4 Piasa, Paris #30/R est:2000-3000
£7000	$12530	€10500	Jerusalem (33x23cm-13x9in) photograph. 14-May-4 Piasa, Paris #92/R est:4000-6000
£7333	$13127	€11000	Jerusalem (33x23cm-13x9in) photograph. 14-May-4 Piasa, Paris #94/R est:3000-4000
£7667	$13723	€11500	Jerusalem (23x33cm-9x13in) photograph pair. 14-May-4 Piasa, Paris #8/R
£7667	$13723	€11500	Jerusalem (23x33cm-9x13in) photograph. 14-May-4 Piasa, Paris #25/R est:2000-3000
£8000	$14320	€12000	Jerusalem (23x33cm-9x13in) photograph. 14-May-4 Piasa, Paris #17/R est:4000-6000
£8000	$14320	€12000	Jerusalem (33x23cm-13x9in) photograph pair. 14-May-4 Piasa, Paris #95/R est:2000-3000
£8133	$14559	€12200	Jerusalem (33x24cm-13x9in) photograph. 14-May-4 Piasa, Paris #91/R est:5000-6000
£8333	$14917	€12500	Jerusalem (33x24cm-13x9in) photograph. 14-May-4 Piasa, Paris #51/R est:3000-4000
£8667	$15513	€13000	Jerusalem (33x23cm-13x9in) photograph. 14-May-4 Piasa, Paris #78/R est:5000-6000
£9333	$16707	€14000	Jerusalem (23x33cm-9x13in) photograph. 14-May-4 Piasa, Paris #76/R est:3000-4000
£10000	$17900	€15000	Jerusalem (23x33cm-9x13in) photograph. 14-May-4 Piasa, Paris #48/R est:3000-4000
£11000	$19690	€16500	Jerusalem (23x32cm-9x13in) photograph. 14-May-4 Piasa, Paris #36/R est:5000-6000
£11667	$20883	€17500	Jerusalem (33x23cm-13x9in) photograph. 14-May-4 Piasa, Paris #6/R est:4000-6000
£12667	$22673	€19000	Jerusalem (23x32cm-9x13in) photograph. 14-May-4 Piasa, Paris #42/R est:4000-5000
£13667	$24463	€20500	Jerusalem (23x32cm-9x13in) photograph. 14-May-4 Piasa, Paris #37/R est:5000-6000
£14667	$26253	€22000	Jerusalem (33x23cm-13x9in) photograph. 14-May-4 Piasa, Paris #40/R est:6000-8000
£20000	$35800	€30000	Jerusalem (23x32cm-9x13in) photograph. 14-May-4 Piasa, Paris #96/R est:5000-6000

SALZMANN, Gottfried (1943-) Austrian

Works on paper			
£451	$754	€650	Landscape (40x58cm-16x23in) s. W/C. 24-Oct-3 Ketterer, Hamburg #1059/R
£915	$1602	€1300	Hamburg (21x14cm-8x6in) s. W/C. 19-Dec-3 Dorotheum, Vienna #311/R
£1974	$3632	€3000	New York (60x45cm-24x18in) s. W/C. 22-Jun-4 Wiener Kunst Auktionen, Vienna #332/R est:3000

SAMACCHINI, Orazio (1532-1577) Italian

£51034	$85228	€74000	Holy Family (67x58cm-26x23in) board. 15-Nov-3 Porro, Milan #249/R est:75000

SAMAIN, Eugène (1935-) Belgian

£333	$610	€500	Composition de figures (69x99cm-27x39in) s. 7-Jun-4 Palais de Beaux Arts, Brussels #383

SAMANIEGO Y JARAMILLO, Manuel (1767-1824) Ecuadorian

£1333	$2427	€2000	El Buen Pastor (46x37cm-18x15in) exhib. 29-Jun-4 Segre, Madrid #47/R est:2000
£23529	$40000	€34352	El Espanol (38x46cm-15x18in) s. prov.lit. 19-Nov-3 Sotheby's, New York #2/R est:40000-60000

SAMANT, Mohan B (1926-) Indian
£629 $1000 €918 Abstract figural group (96x86cm-38x34in) 13-Sep-3 Weschler, Washington #708/R
Works on paper
£252 $400 €368 Untitled (44x32cm-17x13in) s.d.53 mixed media board prov. 13-Sep-3 Weschler, Washington #709/R

SAMARAS, Lucas (1936-) American/Greek
£5000 $8950 €7300 Still life of flowers (61x45cm-24x18in) canvas on board painted c.1958-59. 10-May-4 Sotheby's, Olympia #44/R est:3000-5000
£18000 $32580 €26280 Untitled no.5 (76x63cm-30x25in) acrylic canvas on board painted 1973 prov. 1-Apr-4 Christie's, Kensington #239/R est:3000-5000
Photographs
£1796 $3000 €2622 Photo-transformation (8x8cm-3x3in) d.1974 verso SX-70 Polaroid print prov. 17-Oct-3 Sotheby's, New York #280/R est:4000-6000
Sculpture
£10000 $16700 €14600 Book 8 (29x31x18cm-11x12x7in) found objects nail cloth exec.c.1962 prov. 22-Oct-3 Christie's, London #75/R est:8000-12000
Works on paper
£1000 $1700 €1460 Large drawing (35x42cm-14x17in) ink W/C pen over pencil prov.exhib. 18-Nov-3 Sotheby's, London #56/R
£5676 $10500 €8287 Large Drawing 27 (42x35cm-17x14in) init.i.d.9/66 verso pencil ink prov. 12-Feb-4 Sotheby's, New York #177/R est:4000-6000
£9581 $16000 €13988 Reconstruction no 112 (230x243cm-91x96in) sewn fabric stretched over canvas exec 1980 prov. 12-Nov-3 Christie's, Rockefeller NY #394/R est:12000-18000
£9730 $18000 €14206 Large drawing 18 (42x35cm-17x14in) ink crayon exec 1966 prov.exhib. 12-Feb-4 Sotheby's, New York #175/R est:4000-6000

SAMAYA, Omar Ben (19th C) Algerian
Works on paper
£500 $915 €750 L'arbre aux preceptes religieux (48x31cm-19x12in) s. gouache htd. 3-Jun-4 Tajan, Paris #93

SAMBA, Cheri (1956-) Zairean
£1467 $2684 €2200 Lutte contre les moustiques (90x109cm-35x43in) s. 7-Jun-4 Palais de Beaux Arts, Brussels #191/R est:2000-3000
£1678 $3003 €2500 Amour transfere (94x88cm-37x35in) s.i.d.1981 prov.exhib. 26-May-4 Christie's, Paris #108/R est:3000-5000
£1730 $3200 €2526 Conference Nationale (66x82cm-26x32in) s.d.91 s.i.d. verso acrylic prov.exhib. 13-Jul-4 Christie's, Rockefeller NY #41/R est:1500-2000

SAMBERGER, Leo (1861-1949) German
£1027 $1747 €1500 Portrait of Graf Arcos (104x72cm-41x28in) s. 5-Nov-3 Hugo Ruef, Munich #1103/R est:1500

SAMBO, Edgardo Cappelletti (1882-1966) Italian
£281 $512 €425 Boy (61x50cm-24x20in) s. board. 18-Jun-4 Stadion, Trieste #114/R
£439 $830 €650 Interior (40x32cm-16x13in) s. board. 20-Feb-4 Stadion, Trieste #222/R
£1200 $2148 €1800 Portraitof girl (85x65cm-33x26in) s. 12-May-4 Stadion, Trieste #636/R est:1400-1800

SAMBORSKI, Stefan (1898-1974) Polish
£1328 $2218 €1939 Portrait of a woman (27x21cm-11x8in) tempera oil paper. 19-Oct-3 Agra, Warsaw #42/R est:2000 (P.Z 8500)
Works on paper
£1204 $1998 €1758 Cactus (35x17cm-14x7in) W/C. 15-Jun-3 Agra, Warsaw #31/R est:2000 (P.Z 7500)

SAMI TORNE, Miguel (1937-) Spanish
Works on paper
£284 $460 €400 Arcos (70x55cm-28x22in) s.d.89 mixed media paper on panel. 20-May-3 Ansorena, Madrid #369/R

SAMIOS, Paulos (1948-) ?
£4200 $7140 €6132 Smokers (195x130cm-77x51in) s.d.86 prov. 18-Nov-3 Sotheby's, London #99/R est:4000-6000
£4800 $8160 €7008 Smokers (129x194cm-51x76in) s. s.d.84 verso prov. 18-Nov-3 Sotheby's, London #98/R est:4000-6000

SAMMONS, Carl (1888-1968) American
£587 $1050 €857 Evening primroses, Palm Spring (15x20cm-6x8in) s. i.verso canvasboard. 21-Mar-4 Jeffery Burchard, Florida #80/R
£604 $1100 €882 Nocturnal landscape (15x20cm-6x8in) s. canvasboard prov. 15-Jun-4 John Moran, Pasadena #166
£615 $1100 €898 Desert gold, Palm Springs (15x20cm-6x8in) s. i.d.1944 verso canvasboard. 21-Mar-4 Jeffery Burchard, Florida #80a/R
£629 $1050 €918 Desert gold, Palm Springs (15x20cm-6x8in) s. i.d.1941 verso canvasboard. 19-Oct-3 Jeffery Burchard, Florida #91a
£659 $1100 €962 California poppies, Carmel, California (15x20cm-6x8in) s. s.i.verso canvasboard. 19-Oct-3 Jeffery Burchard, Florida #91
£659 $1200 €962 Desert wild flowers (20x25cm-8x10in) s. i.verso canvasboard prov. 15-Jun-4 John Moran, Pasadena #2a
£714 $1300 €1042 Flower field (20x25cm-8x10in) s. canvasboard prov. 15-Jun-4 John Moran, Pasadena #2
£719 $1200 €1050 Point Lobos (15x20cm-6x8in) s. i.verso canvasboard. 19-Oct-3 Jeffery Burchard, Florida #91b
£765 $1300 €1117 Desert wild flowers (15x20cm-6x8in) s. canvas on canvas. 18-Nov-3 John Moran, Pasadena #55a
£808 $1350 €1180 Mountains with sage blossoms (30x41cm-12x16in) s. canvasboard. 19-Oct-3 Jeffery Burchard, Florida #90b
£808 $1350 €1180 Desert gold Palm Springs (30x41cm-12x16in) s. i.verso cb/. 19-Oct-3 Jeffery Burchard, Florida #90c
£898 $1500 €1311 Cypress trees, Carmel by the sea. s. canvasboard. 15-Nov-3 Harvey Clar, Oakland #1228
£1301 $2250 €1899 Palm Springs (30x41cm-12x16in) s. canvasboard. 10-Dec-3 Bonhams & Butterfields, San Francisco #6328/R est:3000-5000
£1377 $2300 €2010 Western landscape with sage blossoms and snow capped mountains in the distance (51x66cm-20x26in) s. painted c.1945. 19-Oct-3 Jeffery Burchard, Florida #90a
£1405 $2600 €2051 Flowers and showers, Palm Springs (36x46cm-14x18in) s. s.i.verso board. 24-Jan-4 Jeffery Burchard, Florida #86/R est:3000-5000
£1630 $3000 €2380 Desert in bloom (50x66cm-20x26in) s. 8-Jun-4 Bonhams & Butterfields, San Francisco #4352/R est:3000-5000
£1879 $3250 €2743 Verbenas and sand dunes (51x66cm-20x26in) s. i.d.1948 verso prov. 10-Dec-3 Bonhams & Butterfields, San Francisco #6327/R est:3000-5000
£1882 $3200 €2748 Desert wild flowers, Palm Spring (30x41cm-12x16in) s. i.verso canvasboard. 29-Oct-3 Christie's, Los Angeles #10/R est:3000-5000
£1912 $3250 €2792 Virginia lake (30x41cm-12x16in) s. canvasboard prov. 18-Nov-3 John Moran, Pasadena #139 est:1500-2500
£1984 $3750 €2897 Santa Barbara Mission/flower fields (30x41cm-12x16in) s. canvasboard prov. 17-Feb-4 John Moran, Pasadena #142/R est:2500-3500
£2096 $3500 €3060 Humboldt county hills. California (61x76cm-24x30in) s. s.i.d.1944 verso. 19-Oct-3 Jeffery Burchard, Florida #90
£2168 $3750 €3165 17 Mile Drive, Carmel by the Sea. Wild Flowers, Palm Springs, California (30x41cm-12x16in) s. i.verso canvasboard pair prov. 10-Dec-3 Bonhams & Butterfields, San Francisco #6193/R est:3000-5000
£2168 $3750 €3165 June lake, High Sierra (30x41cm-12x16in) s. canvasboard prov. 10-Dec-3 Bonhams & Butterfields, San Francisco #6310/R est:3000-5000
£2206 $3750 €3221 River landscape (30x41cm-12x16in) s. canvasboard prov. 18-Nov-3 John Moran, Pasadena #138 est:1500-2500
£2941 $5000 €4294 Desert springtime (61x76cm-24x30in) s. i.d.1944 verso. 18-Nov-3 John Moran, Pasadena #55 est:5000-7500
£4348 $8000 €6348 Cypress Tree, 17 Mile Drive, Carmel, California (50x66cm-20x26in) s. 8-Jun-4 Bonhams & Butterfields, San Francisco #4345/R est:4000-6000
Works on paper
£1058 $2000 €1545 Mountain landscape (33x48cm-13x19in) s.d.1918 pastel prov. 17-Feb-4 John Moran, Pasadena #122/R est:1500-2500
£1190 $2250 €1737 Mountain landscape - Mattole River (36x56cm-14x22in) s. pastel. 17-Feb-4 John Moran, Pasadena #121/R est:1500-2500
£3968 $7500 €5793 Western scene of figures, barn rider (33x66cm-13x26in) s.d.1941 W/C gouache prov. 17-Feb-4 John Moran, Pasadena #123/R est:5000-7000

SAMMONS, Katharine (20th C) American
£274 $450 €397 Winter landscape (30x61cm-12x24in) s. painted c.1940. 7-Jun-3 Treadway Gallery, Cincinnati #1395

SAMOCK, Arpad (20th C) ?
£461 $847 €700 Southern coastal landscape with fishing boats (70x100cm-28x39in) s. 25-Jun-4 Michael Zeller, Lindau #597/R

SAMORE, Sam (20th C) ?
Photographs
£2000 $3580 €3000 Allegorie de la beaute (80x220cm-31x87in) d.96 photo. 12-May-4 Chochon-Barre & Allardi, Paris #47/R est:1000-1500
£2275 $3800 €3322 Untitled, Manet (115x211cm-45x83in) gelatin silver print executed 1995 prov. 14-Nov-3 Phillips, New York #229/R est:3000-4000
£3293 $5500 €4808 Untitled - allegories of beauty (86x138cm-34x54in) gelatin silver print executed 1995 prov. 14-Nov-3 Phillips, New York #227/R est:3000-4000

SAMPLE, Paul (1896-1974) American
£4469 $8000 €6525 Young fisherman (20x14cm-8x6in) s. canvas on board prov.exhib. 6-May-4 Shannon's, Milford #127/R est:8000-12000
£5978 $11000 €8728 Town near hills (30x43cm-12x17in) s. board prov. 8-Jun-4 Bonhams & Butterfields, San Francisco #4101/R est:10000-15000
£10497 $19000 €15326 October meadows (66x96cm-26x38in) s. prov. 31-Mar-4 Sotheby's, New York #24/R est:10000-15000
Works on paper
£323 $550 €472 Laborers (34x27cm-13x11in) s.d.43 W/C graphite. 21-Nov-3 Skinner, Boston #585/R
£414 $750 €604 Procession at St Francis in Assisi (23x33cm-9x13in) W/C. 16-Apr-4 American Auctioneer #349/R
£694 $1200 €1013 Beach still life (23x34cm-9x13in) s. W/C prov. 13-Dec-3 Weschler, Washington #557
£1381 $2500 €2016 Fred Metcalf with flute (56x43cm-22x17in) W/C. 16-Apr-4 American Auctioneer #350/R
£1941 $3300 €2834 Dry docks (25x35cm-10x14in) s. W/C. 21-Nov-3 Skinner, Boston #569/R est:3500-5500
£2353 $4400 €3435 Fishing scene (18x28cm-7x11in) s. W/C prov. 28-Feb-4 William A Smith, Plainfield #58/R
£2358 $3750 €3443 Hillside farm (28x37cm-11x15in) s. W/C. 12-Sep-3 Skinner, Boston #458/R est:900
£2419 $4500 €3532 Central Park in winter (37x41cm-15x16in) s. pencil W/C. 3-Mar-4 Christie's, Rockefeller NY #29/R est:3000-5000
£11210 $17600 €16367 Winter landscape (30x58cm-12x23in) s. W/C. 1-Sep-3 William A Smith, Plainfield #1/R

SAMPSON, Alden (1853-?) American
£389 $650 €568 Landscape with lake (41x51cm-16x20in) s. 20-Jun-3 Freeman, Philadelphia #180/R
£1599 $2750 €2335 Cliffs along the Maine coast (41x51cm-16x20in) s. 7-Dec-3 Grogan, Boston #47/R

SAMPSON, James Henry (fl.1869-1879) British
£320 $509 €464 Wreck off the headland with abbey in background (42x57cm-17x22in) s. 9-Sep-3 David Duggleby, Scarborough #366
£660 $1043 €957 Evening (65x105cm-26x41in) s.d.1874 s.i.stretcher. 24-Jul-3 Lawrence, Crewkerne #946/R

SAMPSON, John (20th C) British
£1500 $2775 €2190 HMS Repulse (70x149cm-28x59in) s.d.1917. 14-Jul-4 Sotheby's, Olympia #134/R est:1000-1500

SAMPSON, Joseph Ernest (1887-1946) Canadian
£727 $1185 €1061 Fall leaves, Canoe Lake (30x23cm-12x9in) s. i.verso panel. 23-Sep-3 Ritchie, Toronto #81/R (C.D 1600)
£1227 $2111 €1791 Canoe Lake (22x30cm-9x12in) s. panel exhib. 2-Dec-3 Joyner Waddington, Toronto #273/R est:800-1200 (C.D 2750)
£2455 $4223 €3584 Boudoir (92x120cm-36x47in) s.d.1913 board. 2-Dec-3 Joyner Waddington, Toronto #320/R est:2000-3000 (C.D 5500)

SAMUEL, Charles (1862-?) Belgian
Sculpture
£10596 $19285 €16000 Bust of Nele (34cm-13in) ivory wood prov. 15-Jun-4 Christie's, Amsterdam #355/R est:20000-30000

SAMUELSEN, Arne (1950-) Norwegian
£584 $975 €853 Symmetric landscape (70x100cm-28x39in) s. 17-Nov-3 Blomqvist, Lysaker #1291/R (N.KR 7000)

SAMUELSON, Bruce (1946-) American
£235 $425 €343 Abstract figure (201x152cm-79x60in) s.d.78 verso. 2-Apr-4 Freeman, Philadelphia #193
£235 $425 €343 Crucified form (193x157cm-76x62in) s.d.78. 2-Apr-4 Freeman, Philadelphia #194
£240 $400 €350 Torso (246x124cm-97x49in) s.i.d.74 verso exhib. 20-Jun-3 Freeman, Philadelphia #205/R
£313 $500 €457 Female nude (168x102cm-66x40in) s.d.1978. 19-Sep-3 Freeman, Philadelphia #166/R
£329 $550 €480 Figure study (119x135cm-47x53in) s.verso prov. 20-Jun-3 Freeman, Philadelphia #172/R
£375 $600 €548 Figurative abstract (152x122cm-60x48in) s.d.79 verso. 19-Sep-3 Freeman, Philadelphia #197/R
£389 $650 €568 Nude figure (168x122cm-66x48in) s.d.78 verso. 20-Jun-3 Freeman, Philadelphia #157/R
£444 $800 €648 Abstract figure (147x117cm-58x46in) s.d.1983 verso. 23-Jan-4 Freeman, Philadelphia #224/R
£594 $950 €867 Nude abstract (168x122cm-66x48in) s.d.1982 verso. 19-Sep-3 Freeman, Philadelphia #126/R

SAMUELSON, Ulrik (1935-) Swedish
£2039 $3467 €2977 The red room (31x21cm-12x8in) s.d.1965 verso oil varnish wood. 5-Nov-3 AB Stockholms Auktionsverk #938/R est:12000-15000 (S.KR 27000)
£4103 $7262 €5990 Picture III (31x20cm-12x8in) s.d.1965 verso oil varnish wood. 27-Apr-4 AB Stockholms Auktionsverk #1105/R est:20000-25000 (S.KR 56000)
£5495 $9725 €8023 Absolutely still (120x120cm-47x47in) init. s.d.1993 verso prov.lit. 27-Apr-4 AB Stockholms Auktionsverk #924/R est:50000-60000 (S.KR 75000)
Sculpture
£5136 $8731 €7499 Necromancy object (195x201x680cm-77x79x268in) init. s.verso wall object exhib.lit. 5-Nov-3 AB Stockholms Auktionsverk #939/R est:60000-80000 (S.KR 68000)

SAN JOSE, Francisco (1919-1981) Spanish
£268 $491 €400 Portrait of Joaquin Benitez Lumbreras (100x81cm-39x32in) s.i.d.1974 s.i.d.verso. 12-Jul-4 Durán, Madrid #133/R
£496 $804 €700 Castillo de Pior (22x27cm-9x11in) s.d.1980 s.i.d.verso. 20-May-3 Segre, Madrid #127/R
£1159 $1901 €1600 La procesion del Cristo (54x65cm-21x26in) s.d.1979 s.i.d.verso. 27-May-3 Durán, Madrid #111/R est:1500
£1310 $2188 €1900 Pipe smoker (46x38cm-18x15in) s. exhib. 17-Nov-3 Durán, Madrid #121/R est:1900
£1333 $2413 €2000 Common houses in Caracas (54x81cm-21x32in) s. 30-Mar-4 Segre, Madrid #262/R est:2000
£1479 $2366 €2100 Rural road and shed (38x53cm-15x21in) s.d.1945 s.i.d.versoboard. 16-Sep-3 Segre, Madrid #123a/R
£1724 $3103 €2500 View of Caracas (41x52cm-16x20in) s. canvas on board. 26-Jan-4 Durán, Madrid #117/R est:1200
£2069 $3455 €3000 Street in Alarcon (46x56cm-18x22in) s.d.74. 11-Nov-3 Castellana, Madrid #76/R est:3000
£2586 $4655 €3750 Palm trees in Moriche (66x92cm-26x36in) s.d.1967 s.i.d.verso. 26-Jan-4 Durán, Madrid #116/R est:2000
£7586 $13655 €11000 Houses in Caracas (54x81cm-21x32in) s. i.verso. 26-Jan-4 Ansorena, Madrid #898/R est:11000
Works on paper
£283 $516 €425 Fisherman (33x52cm-13x20in) s. W/C. 29-Jun-4 Segre, Madrid #107/R
£299 $518 €425 Fishing (33x52cm-13x20in) s. W/C. 15-Dec-3 Ansorena, Madrid #171/R
£307 $555 €460 Chatting in the bar (33x22cm-13x9in) s. ink dr prov. 30-Mar-4 Segre, Madrid #130/R
£308 $514 €440 Mujeres (34x47cm-13x19in) s. Indian ink. 24-Jun-3 Segre, Madrid #197/R
£317 $555 €450 Landscape with houses (21x27cm-8x11in) s.d.1942 W/C double-sided. 16-Dec-3 Durán, Madrid #51
£833 $1417 €1200 Village (33x41cm-13x16in) s.d.1969 W/C. 28-Oct-3 Segre, Madrid #177/R

SAN-YU (1901-1966) Chinese
£291607 $524893 €425746 White and pink chrysanthemum in a navy background (68x98cm-27x39in) s.d.1932 prov.lit. 25-Apr-4 Christie's, Hong Kong #706/R est:2000000-3000000 (HK.D 4100000)
Works on paper
£2000 $3600 €3000 Etude de nu feminin (56x37cm-22x15in) s. ink. 26-Apr-4 Tajan, Paris #85/R est:3000-3200
£8535 $15363 €12461 Lady in sketch (25x39cm-10x15in) s. W/C ink. 25-Apr-4 Christie's, Hong Kong #752/R est:35000-45000 (HK.D 120000)

SANBORN, Percy A (1849-1929) American
£5294 $9000 €7729 Ships portrait of the WM H Conner. i. 28-Nov-3 Thomaston Place, Thomaston #750
£7937 $15000 €11588 Portrait of the clipper 'Great Republic' (66x102cm-26x40in) s.i. 22-Feb-4 Skinner, Boston #131/R est:15000-20000
£12733 $20500 €18590 Ship portrait of the Charlotte W White (51x86cm-20x34in) s. 20-Aug-3 James Julia, Fairfield #542/R est:15000-25000
£13043 $21000 €19043 Portrait of the ship Great Republic (69x117cm-27x46in) s.i. prov. 20-Aug-3 James Julia, Fairfield #541/R est:20000-25000

SANCHA, Francisco (1874-1937) Spanish
£2014 $3424 €2900 Children in cart drawn by donkey (84x110cm-33x43in) s.d.1910. 28-Oct-3 Segre, Madrid #101/R est:2900

SANCHEZ (?) Spanish
£391 $700 €571 Two fisherwomen on the shore with their catch (61x71cm-24x28in) s. 20-Mar-4 Selkirks, St. Louis #524

SANCHEZ CARRALERO, Jose (1942-) Spanish
£1361 $2476 €2000 Landscape (60x81cm-24x32in) s. 3-Feb-4 Segre, Madrid #125/R est:1800

SANCHEZ COELLO, Alonso (circle) (c.1531-1588) Spanish
£9000 $16470 €13140 Portrait of a lady in a grey slashed dress and black wrap (57x43cm-22x17in) prov. 7-Jul-4 Bonhams, New Bond Street #33/R est:4000-6000
£12759 $23348 €18500 Portrait de Donnapolissena Unganada (216x111cm-85x44in) 31-Jan-4 Osenat, Fontainebleau #612

SANCHEZ LAREO, Miguel (1969-) Spanish
£414 $745 €600 Vase of flowers (72x92cm-28x36in) s.d.2001. 26-Jan-4 Durán, Madrid #588/R
£496 $829 €700 Rural landscape (73x92cm-29x36in) s.d.2001. 23-Jun-3 Durán, Madrid #641/R
Works on paper
£312 $506 €440 Playa de Muxia (70x100cm-28x39in) s.d.2002 W/C. 20-May-3 Ansorena, Madrid #977/R

SANCHEZ NAVARRO, Vicente (?) Spanish
£276 $497 €400 Beach (16x24cm-6x9in) s. board. 26-Jan-4 Durán, Madrid #569/R
£310 $559 €450 Bull scene (19x24cm-7x9in) s.d.86 board. 26-Jan-4 Durán, Madrid #570/R
£426 $711 €600 Toros en el pueblo (33x41cm-13x16in) s.i. 23-Jun-3 Durán, Madrid #111/R

SANCHEZ SACRISTAN, Jose Vicente (20th C) Spanish
£685 $1164 €1000 View of Madrid (117x90cm-46x35in) s. 4-Nov-3 Ansorena, Madrid #890/R

SANCHEZ SOLA, Eduardo (1869-1949) Spanish
£8966 $14972 €13000 Joke (95x122cm-37x48in) 17-Nov-3 Durán, Madrid #212/R est:12000

SANCHEZ SOLA, Emilio (c.1874-c.1925) Spanish
£6000 $11040 €8760 Playtime (79x120cm-31x47in) bears sig. 23-Mar-4 Bonhams, New Bond Street #92/R est:6000-9000

SANCHEZ, Emilio (1921-) Cuban
£1342 $2456 €2000 El Ventanal (184x92cm-72x36in) mono. painted 1973 prov. 7-Jul-4 Artcurial Briest, Paris #336/R est:2000-3000

SANCHEZ, Ideal (20th C) Argentinian
£1209 $2200 €1765 Visitors (120x80cm-47x31in) s. s.i.d.1969 verso. 5-Jul-4 Arroyo, Buenos Aires #64/R est:1400
£1374 $2500 €2006 Morning (47x55cm-19x22in) exhib.lit. 29-Jun-4 Arroyo, Buenos Aires #72/R est:2500

SANCHEZ, Mario (20th C) American
Sculpture
£6111 $11000 €8922 Old Island days, cookoo doing the choo choo (43x86cm-17x34in) painted wood relief. 24-Apr-4 Slotin Folk Art, Buford #316/R est:3000-5000

SANCHEZ, Pepi (1932-) Spanish
£451 $736 €650 Aceiteras (41x33cm-16x13in) s.d.61 panel. 16-Jul-3 Durán, Madrid #108/R
£528 $924 €750 Oil containers (33x41cm-13x16in) s.d.61 board. 16-Dec-3 Durán, Madrid #72/R
£603 $1007 €850 Nina con lazo verde (41x33cm-16x13in) s.d.65 panel. 23-Jun-3 Durán, Madrid #114
£621 $1037 €900 Girl in red (41x33cm-16x13in) s. board. 17-Nov-3 Durán, Madrid #89/R
£764 $1245 €1100 Girl with rose (41x33cm-16x13in) s. board. 23-Sep-3 Durán, Madrid #114/R

SANCHEZ, Perea (18/19th C) Spanish
£738 $1358 €1100 Still life with eggs (46x60cm-18x24in) s. 24-Mar-4 Hugo Ruef, Munich #1255/R

SANCHEZ, Tomas (1948-) Cuban

£10000 $18400 €15000 Untitled (56x76cm-22x30in) s.d.91 acrylic paper on canvas prov. 10-Jun-4 Christie's, Paris #55/R est:16000-20000
£20588 $35000 €30058 Recorriendo orillas (41x51cm-16x20in) s.d.1993 s.i.d.verso acrylic masonite prov. 18-Nov-3 Christie's, Rockefeller NY #57/R est:25000-35000
£24000 $44160 €36000 Silence whilst in contemplation (61x45cm-24x18in) s.d.03 acrylic. 10-Jun-4 Christie's, Paris #56/R est:24000-32000
£44693 $80000 €65252 Worshipping a tree (51x61cm-20x24in) s.d.03 s.i.d.2003 verso acrylic. 26-May-4 Sotheby's, New York #144/R est:30000-45000
£60000 $110400 €90000 Meditating by canal (76x101cm-30x40in) s.d.95 acrylicprov. 10-Jun-4 Christie's, Paris #57/R est:55000-75000
£64706 $110000 €94471 Oidor de aguas (76x101cm-30x40in) s.d.1996 s.i.d.verso acrylic prov. 18-Nov-3 Christie's, Rockefeller NY #58/R est:70000-90000
Works on paper
£7042 $12324 €10000 View of the other bank (35x55cm-14x22in) s.i.d.1986 W/C prov. 16-Dec-3 Segre, Madrid #274/R est:10000
£14118 $24000 €20612 Pescador de charco (41x51cm-16x20in) s.d.82 s.i.d.verso gouache. 19-Nov-3 Sotheby's, New York #173/R est:30000-35000

SANCHEZ, Trino (1968-) Venezuelan

£2353 $4000 €3435 Tren en el sotano - Train in the basement (120x150cm-47x59in) s. s.i.verso painted c.2000 prov. 18-Nov-3 Christie's, Rockefeller NY #171/R est:10000-15000
£5475 $8925 €7994 Landscape in yellow (98x119cm-39x47in) s. acrylic. 20-Jul-3 Subastas Odalys, Caracas #106

SANCHEZ-PERRIER, Emilio (1855-1907) Spanish

£6000 $10920 €8760 Birch trees on the riverbank (41x33cm-16x13in) s. panel. 16-Jun-4 Christie's, Kensington #145/R est:2000-3000
£18824 $32000 €27483 River landscape in Pontoise (27x35cm-11x14in) s.i. panel prov.exhib. 29-Oct-3 Christie's, Rockefeller NY #196/R est:15000-20000
£19928 $32681 €27500 Afueras de Venecia (35x54cm-14x21in) s.d.85 exhib. 27-May-3 Durán, Madrid #302b/R est:20000
Works on paper
£296 $518 €420 View of the marshes in Guadalquivir (24x36cm-9x14in) s.i. chl dr. 16-Dec-3 Segre, Madrid #11/R

SANCHIS YAGO, Rafael (1891-1974) Spanish

Works on paper
£658 $1211 €1000 Young woman (45x30cm-18x12in) s.d.1919 col dr. 22-Jun-4 Durán, Madrid #582/R

SANCHO, Jose (1925-) Spanish

£567 $919 €800 Still life with pomegrantes (27x41cm-11x16in) s. 20-May-3 Ansorena, Madrid #71/R
£828 $1490 €1200 Still life with mushrooms (39x47cm-15x19in) s. 26-Jan-4 Ansorena, Madrid #387/R
£1702 $2757 €2400 Still life with violin (61x85cm-24x33in) s. 20-May-3 Ansorena, Madrid #64/R est:1800

SANCHO, Miguel (1957-) Spanish?

Works on paper
£369 $687 €550 Untitled (60x60cm-24x24in) s.verso mixed media canvas. 3-Mar-4 Ferri, Paris #39

SANCTIS, Giuseppe de (1858-1924) Italian

£2958 $5117 €4200 Red hat (60x45cm-24x18in) s. 11-Dec-3 Christie's, Rome #140/R est:3000-5000

SAND, George (1804-1876) French

Works on paper
£667 $1227 €1000 Paysage de fantaisie avec pecheur, lac et montagnes bleues (7x10cm-3x4in) W/C prov. 9-Jun-4 Piasa, Paris #230/R
£719 $1200 €1050 Rocky landscape (15x25cm-6x10in) i.verso W/C. 16-Nov-3 William Jenack, New York #53
£1100 $2024 €1650 Paysage de montagne avec bergerie (14x19cm-6x7in) W/C exhib. 9-Jun-4 Piasa, Paris #227/R est:1500-2000
£1333 $2453 €2000 Ruine gothique (9x7cm-4x3in) wash htd pen exhib. 9-Jun-4 Piasa, Paris #226/R est:1500-2000
£1533 $2821 €2300 Chemin escarpe avec chapelle, ermite et calvaire (13x17cm-5x7in) s. crayon exhib. 9-Jun-4 Piasa, Paris #225/R est:1500-2000
£1667 $3067 €2500 Paysage mineral a la falaise (7x6cm-3x2in) W/C prov. 9-Jun-4 Piasa, Paris #232/R est:2500-3000
£1733 $3189 €2600 Grande falaise dans la mer (8x11cm-3x4in) W/C prov. 9-Jun-4 Piasa, Paris #231/R est:2500-3000
£2200 $4048 €3300 Arbre mort au bord d'une mare (9x13cm-4x5in) W/C prov. 9-Jun-4 Piasa, Paris #233/R est:2000-2500
£14789 $25880 €21000 Diverses vues du Berry. W/C ten album. 19-Dec-3 Gros & Delettrez, Paris #137/R est:20000-25000

SAND, Lennart (1946-) Swedish

£517 $926 €755 Snow-covered landscape with bear (60x87cm-24x34in) s.d.00. 28-May-4 Uppsala Auktionskammare, Uppsala #247 (S.KR 7000)
£665 $1191 €971 Sea birds by waterway (138x138cm-54x54in) s.d.85. 28-May-4 Uppsala Auktionskammare, Uppsala #256/R (S.KR 9000)

SAND, Maurice (1823-1889) French

Works on paper
£671 $1242 €1000 Passage du guet (32x43cm-13x17in) s. W/C gouache. 14-Mar-4 Eric Pillon, Calais #3/R

SAND, Vebjorn (1966-) Norwegian

£792 $1275 €1156 Landscape from Hvaler (40x70cm-16x28in) s. 25-Aug-3 Blomqvist, Lysaker #1267/R (N.KR 9200)

SANDALINAS, Joan (1903-1991) Spanish

£483 $801 €700 Inspired by Picasso (20x16cm-8x6in) s.i. board double-sided. 1-Oct-3 Ansorena, Madrid #546/R
Works on paper
£310 $515 €450 Composition (16x24cm-6x9in) s.i.d.1979 verso W/C. 1-Oct-3 Ansorena, Madrid #389/R
£345 $572 €500 Man with guitar and fan (10x10cm-4x4in) s. W/C. 1-Oct-3 Ansorena, Madrid #355/R
£517 $859 €750 Family (39x26cm-15x10in) s. W/C. 1-Oct-3 Ansorena, Madrid #548/R
£1224 $2229 €1800 Figure (29x21cm-11x8in) s.d.1926 W/C. 3-Feb-4 Segre, Madrid #351/R est:1500

SANDBACK, Fred (1943-) American

Works on paper
£2378 $4042 €3400 Drawing (20x28cm-8x11in) s.d.67 verso pencil prov. 26-Nov-3 Dorotheum, Vienna #222/R est:3500-4000

SANDBERG, Armid (1876-1927) Finnish

£292 $487 €420 Landscape from Sordavala (31x43cm-12x17in) s. 23-Oct-3 Hagelstam, Helsinki #807/R

SANDBERG, Hjalmar (1847-1888) Swedish

£329 $616 €480 Landscape with waterway and punt (20x23cm-8x9in) s.d.82 panel. 29-Feb-4 Uppsala Auktionskammare, Uppsala #66 (S.KR 4500)

SANDBERG, Johan Gustaf (1782-1854) Swedish

£994 $1600 €1451 Self-portrait (28x24cm-11x9in) s. 25-Aug-3 Lilla Bukowskis, Stockholm #170 (S.KR 13000)

SANDBERG, Ragnar (1902-1972) Swedish

£793 $1348 €1158 Boy wearing orange jumper (63x56cm-25x22in) init.d.31. 5-Nov-3 AB Stockholms Auktionsverk #736/R (S.KR 10500)
£982 $1699 €1434 Model study (79x50cm-31x20in) s. 15-Dec-3 Lilla Bukowskis, Stockholm #644 (S.KR 12500)
£1473 $2504 €2151 View II (23x14cm-9x6in) init.d.50. 5-Nov-3 AB Stockholms Auktionsverk #683/R est:20000-25000 (S.KR 19500)
£1523 $2741 €2224 Bathers (24x32cm-9x13in) init.d.37 cardboard. 26-Apr-4 Bukowskis, Stockholm #43/R est:30000-35000 (S.KR 21000)
£2418 $4279 €3530 Elsa (29x36cm-11x14in) init.d.47 exhib.prov. 27-Apr-4 AB Stockholms Auktionsverk #876/R est:40000-50000 (S.KR 33000)
£2564 $4538 €3743 Bathers (22x27cm-9x11in) init.d.32 cardboard. 27-Apr-4 AB Stockholms Auktionsverk #682/R est:35000-40000 (S.KR 35000)
£2568 $4366 €3749 Figures and boat by jetty (28x35cm-11x14in) init.d.35 paper on panel. 5-Nov-3 AB Stockholms Auktionsverk #894/R est:20000-25000 (S.KR 34000)
£2568 $4366 €3749 Summer landscape, Paarp (27x45cm-11x18in) init.d.45. 4-Nov-3 Bukowskis, Stockholm #185/R est:40000-45000 (S.KR 34000)
£2946 $5008 €4301 The small boom, Gothenburg (22x31cm-9x12in) init. panel. 4-Nov-3 Bukowskis, Stockholm #179/R est:50000-60000 (S.KR 39000)
£3097 $5264 €4522 In the rowing boat (25x32cm-10x13in) indis.init. paper. 5-Nov-3 AB Stockholms Auktionsverk #682/R est:35000-40000 (S.KR 41000)
£3516 $6224 €5133 Femore jetty, Stenungsund (55x64cm-22x25in) panel prov.lit. 27-Apr-4 AB Stockholms Auktionsverk #736/R est:60000-80000 (S.KR 48000)
£4154 $7062 €6065 Chatting on the park bench (27x35cm-11x14in) init.d.69 panel. 5-Nov-3 AB Stockholms Auktionsverk #756/R est:40000-50000 (S.KR 55000)
£5589 $9502 €8160 Boat at anchor on quay (24x41cm-9x16in) init.d.38. 4-Nov-3 Bukowskis, Stockholm #16/R est:60000-80000 (S.KR 74000)
£5801 $10442 €8469 Landscape from Halland (36x45cm-14x18in) init.d.33. 26-Apr-4 Bukowskis, Stockholm #135/R est:100000-125000 (S.KR 80000)
£5891 $10015 €8601 Coastal landscape, Dragsmark (29x36cm-11x14in) init. d.32 verso. 4-Nov-3 Bukowskis, Stockholm #107/R est:50000-60000 (S.KR 78000)
£6420 $10914 €9373 Still life of apples (34x43cm-13x17in) s. 5-Nov-3 AB Stockholms Auktionsverk #662/R est:60000-80000 (S.KR 85000)
£7326 $12967 €10696 Still life of figure (27x47cm-11x19in) init. 27-Apr-4 AB Stockholms Auktionsverk #650/R est:125000-150000 (S.KR 100000)
£8308 $14124 €12130 The sailing trip (29x40cm-11x16in) init.d.35 panel. 4-Nov-3 Bukowskis, Stockholm #184/R est:100000-125000 (S.KR 110000)
£8702 $15664 €12705 The blue tram car (28x48cm-11x19in) init. 26-Apr-4 Bukowskis, Stockholm #32/R est:120000-140000 (S.KR 120000)
£8702 $15664 €12705 The tram station, La Bommen (24x36cm-9x14in) init.d.38 canvas on panel. 26-Apr-4 Bukowskis, Stockholm #144/R est:120000-140000 (S.KR 120000)
£9063 $15408 €13232 Nature morte with teapot (32x48cm-13x19in) init.d.44. 5-Nov-3 AB Stockholms Auktionsverk #652/R est:100000-125000 (S.KR 120000)
£9441 $16050 €13784 Man and seagulls (66x60cm-26x24in) 4-Nov-3 Bukowskis, Stockholm #109/R est:60000-80000 (S.KR 125000)
£10196 $17334 €14886 Summer, canal-lock (62x71cm-24x28in) init. 4-Nov-3 Bukowskis, Stockholm #198/R est:175000-200000 (S.KR 135000)
£10574 $17976 €15438 The rowing trip (35x40cm-14x16in) init.d.36 panel. 4-Nov-3 Bukowskis, Stockholm #27/R est:125000-150000 (S.KR 140000)
£14728 $25038 €21503 La plage les Sablettes (25x58cm-10x23in) init.d.37. 4-Nov-3 Bukowskis, Stockholm #57/R est:150000-175000 (S.KR 195000)
£15861 $26964 €23157 Football players (69x77cm-27x30in) init. exhib.lit. 5-Nov-3 AB Stockholms Auktionsverk #684/R est:250000-300000 (S.KR 210000)
£18882 $32100 €27568 The bakery (37x45cm-15x18in) init.d.39. 5-Nov-3 AB Stockholms Auktionsverk #634/R est:125000-150000 (S.KR 250000)
£19260 $32742 €28120 Football players (41x60cm-16x24in) init.d.37. 4-Nov-3 Bukowskis, Stockholm #19/R est:200000-250000 (S.KR 255000)
£23443 $41495 €34227 The Sandberg family, Stenungsund (65x80cm-26x31in) init.d.31 i.verso prov. 27-Apr-4 AB Stockholms Auktionsverk #734/R est:200000-225000 (S.KR 320000)
£32967 $58352 €48132 Bathers (65x100cm-26x39in) init. painted c.1971 exhib.lit. 27-Apr-4 AB Stockholms Auktionsverk #684/R est:300000-350000 (S.KR 450000)
Works on paper
£272 $462 €397 Bathers (11x18cm-4x7in) init.d.67 Indian ink. 4-Nov-3 Bukowskis, Stockholm #24/R (S.KR 3600)
£363 $616 €530 On the beach (10x10cm-4x4in) init.d.3.6.64 Indian ink. 4-Nov-3 Bukowskis, Stockholm #25/R (S.KR 4800)
£729 $1341 €1094 Tree of women (27x35cm-11x14in) init.d.1940 crayon. 14-Jun-4 Lilla Bukowskis, Stockholm #178 (S.KR 10000)

£755	$1284	€1102	Beach huts and boats (28x35cm-11x14in) init. chl. 4-Nov-3 Bukowskis, Stockholm #26/R (S.KR 10000)
£1088	$1958	€1588	Sunglasses and bathing costumes (26x34cm-10x13in) s.init.d.3.7.41 crayon. 26-Apr-4 Bukowskis, Stockholm #133/R est:20000-25000 (S.KR 15000)
£1172	$2075	€1711	The croquette players VI (26x34cm-10x13in) init.d.41 crayon. 27-Apr-4 AB Stockholms Auktionsverk #681/R est:15000-20000 (S.KR 16000)
£1208	$2054	€1764	Self-portrait (24x19cm-9x7in) s.d.31 Indian ink. 4-Nov-3 Bukowskis, Stockholm #181/R est:18000-20000 (S.KR 16000)
£2175	$3916	€3176	In the avenue (31x27cm-12x11in) init.d.36 mixed media. 26-Apr-4 Bukowskis, Stockholm #141a/R est:30000-35000 (S.KR 30000)

SANDBY, Paul (1730-1809) British

Works on paper

£410	$767	€615	Figures by a ruined abbey (17x23cm-7x9in) s. pen ink grey wash. 26-Jul-4 Bonhams, Bath #7/R
£545	$927	€780	Cattle, sheep and drover in a rugged wooded landscape (28x43cm-11x17in) W/C. 18-Nov-3 Mealy's, Castlecomer #1268/R
£550	$1012	€803	View of a castle (9x12cm-4x5in) W/C pencil. 22-Jun-4 Bonhams, Knightsbridge #159/R
£700	$1204	€1022	Rural landscape (30x44cm-12x17in) i.d.1799 pencil W/C. 3-Dec-3 Christie's, Kensington #7/R
£700	$1295	€1022	Charlotte and Anna Sandby (12x11cm-5x4in) pen ink wash prov. 14-Jul-4 Sotheby's, Olympia #33/R
£900	$1530	€1314	Young lady with two beaux (10x13cm-4x5in) pencil brown wash prov. 4-Nov-3 Bonhams, New Bond Street #43/R
£1100	$1837	€1606	Shepherd driving his flock before a Scottish castle (11x18cm-4x7in) pencil pen ink W/C prov. 16-Oct-3 Christie's, Kensington #25/R est:600-800
£2300	$3841	€3358	Long Meg from the gate. Lond Meg and her daughters. View of Windermere (30x51cm-12x20in) i. W/C three. 8-Oct-3 Andrew Hartley, Ilkley #1031/R est:2400-2800
£3800	$6992	€5548	Llangollen, Denbighshire (37x47cm-15x19in) s.i. W/C bodycol. 26-Mar-4 Sotheby's, London #108/R est:2500-3500
£4000	$6800	€5840	Brook End Farm, near Easton Lodge, Essex (20x28cm-8x11in) i.verso W/C bodycol pair prov. 4-Nov-3 Bonhams, New Bond Street #33/R est:6000-9000
£4000	$6800	€5840	View of the Powder Magazine in Hyde Park (19x25cm-7x10in) i.d.1797 pencil W/C exhib. 20-Nov-3 Christie's, London #15/R est:2000-3000
£5500	$10120	€8030	Onion seller (18x12cm-7x5in) W/C over pencil prov. 26-Mar-4 Sotheby's, London #92/R est:3000-5000
£20000	$36400	€29200	View of Windsor Castle and part of the town from the Spital Hill (27x59cm-11x23in) i. pen grey ink W/C over pencil laid paper prov. 1-Jul-4 Sotheby's, London #174/R est:20000-30000

SANDBY, Paul (attrib) (1730-1809) British

Works on paper

£750	$1373	€1095	Italianate landscape (21x27cm-8x11in) W/C prov. 28-Jan-4 Dreweatt Neate, Newbury #20/R
£982	$1807	€1434	Country lane (36x54cm-14x21in) W/C. 25-Mar-4 International Art Centre, Auckland #167/R (NZ.D 2750)

SANDECKI, Albert Edward (1935-) American

Works on paper

£430	$800	€628	Gables (56x69cm-22x27in) s. pencil W/C prov.exhib. 3-Mar-4 Christie's, Rockefeller NY #50/R

SANDER, August (1876-1964) German

Photographs

£2083	$3542	€3000	Family of Professor Seuffert (16x23cm-6x9in) prov. gelatin silver board. 30-Oct-3 Van Ham, Cologne #195/R est:2200
£2095	$3749	€3100	Young men (28x20cm-11x8in) s.d. verso silver gelatin lit. 8-May-4 Lempertz, Koln #248/R est:1800
£2095	$3749	€3100	St Andreas (20x17cm-8x7in) i. verso silver gelatin lit. 8-May-4 Lempertz, Koln #249/R est:2000
£2986	$5076	€4300	Bricklayer (27x22cm-11x9in) gelatin silver. 30-Oct-3 Van Ham, Cologne #197/R est:4800
£3611	$6139	€5200	Westerwald peasant family (28x22cm-11x9in) gelatin silver. 31-Oct-3 Lempertz, Koln #301/R est:2500
£3819	$6493	€5500	Master butcher and family (28x21cm-11x8in) gelatin silver. 30-Oct-3 Van Ham, Cologne #190/R est:3000
£10000	$18000	€14600	Portrait of Richard Strauss (15x11cm-6x4in) s. gelatin silver print prov.lit. 23-Apr-4 Phillips, New York #10/R est:25000-35000
£15569	$26000	€22731	Portrait of Otto Dix (23x17cm-9x7in) s.d.1924 gelatin silver print vellum prov.lit. 17-Oct-3 Phillips, New York #88/R est:25000-35000

SANDER, Ludwig (1906-1975) American

£378	$700	€567	Sky I (33x36cm-13x14in) s. masonite prov. 14-Jul-4 American Auctioneer #490402/R
£833	$1500	€1216	Untitled (10x10cm-4x4in) s.d.1963 verso. 24-Apr-4 David Rago, Lambertville #463/R est:400-800
£1317	$2200	€1923	Pawnee XIV (51x56cm-20x22in) s.verso. 25-Oct-3 David Rago, Lambertville #379 est:800-1200
£1436	$2600	€2097	Sioux II (56x51cm-22x20in) 3-Apr-4 David Rago, Lambertville #234/R est:900-1400
£1796	$3250	€2622	Untitled (56x102cm-22x40in) s.verso. 3-Apr-4 David Rago, Lambertville #236/R est:900-1400
£1934	$3500	€2824	Chippewa V (51x56cm-20x22in) s.verso. 3-Apr-4 David Rago, Lambertville #233/R est:900-1400
£1946	$3250	€2841	Rappanhanock IV (56x102cm-22x40in) s.verso. 25-Oct-3 David Rago, Lambertville #378 est:800-1200
£2210	$4000	€3227	Untitled (56x102cm-22x40in) s.verso. 3-Apr-4 David Rago, Lambertville #235/R est:900-1400
£2246	$3750	€3279	Georgic XI (56x102cm-22x40in) s.verso. 25-Oct-3 David Rago, Lambertville #377 est:800-1200
£3293	$5500	€4808	Genessee VII (56x102cm-22x40in) s.verso. 25-Oct-3 David Rago, Lambertville #376 est:800-1200

Works on paper

£608	$1100	€888	Untitled (66x51cm-26x20in) s. chl. 3-Apr-4 David Rago, Lambertville #230/R est:800-1200
£718	$1300	€1048	Abstractions (36x36cm-14x14in) s. one d.1970 chl pair. 3-Apr-4 David Rago, Lambertville #232/R est:900-1400

SANDERS, Christopher (1905-1991) British

£850	$1590	€1275	Tulips (43x43cm-17x17in) s. 26-Jul-4 Bonhams, Bath #41/R
£3537	$5800	€5129	Sunlight, shade and irises (81x81cm-32x32in) s. prov. 31-May-3 Brunk, Ashville #337/R est:3000-6000

SANDERS, David (1936-) American

£1353	$2300	€1975	Away from the herd (61x91cm-24x36in) 1-Nov-3 Altermann Galleries, Santa Fe #137

Works on paper

£2235	$4000	€3263	Commanche Chief - Chief Quanah Parker (58x43cm-23x17in) pastel. 15-May-4 Altermann Galleries, Santa Fe #10/R

SANDERS, Edmond (?-c.1961) Belgian

£845	$1462	€1200	Still life with flowers (100x85cm-39x33in) s. 13-Dec-3 De Vuyst, Lokeren #276

SANDERS, Henry (1918-1992) German

Works on paper

£320	$576	€467	Siena (48x64cm-19x25in) s.i. gouache. 20-Jan-4 Bonhams, Knightsbridge #237/R

SANDERS, Phillip (20th C) British

£420	$773	€613	Friend or foe (25x33cm-10x13in) s. board. 10-Jun-4 Christie's, Kensington #426/R
£450	$828	€657	Hounds at a stable door (33x25cm-13x10in) s. board. 10-Jun-4 Christie's, Kensington #428/R
£500	$850	€730	Hunting day (41x30cm-16x12in) s. 27-Nov-3 Christie's, Kensington #381/R
£500	$920	€730	Going home, East Kent hunt (56x38cm-22x15in) s. 10-Jun-4 Christie's, Kensington #196/R
£600	$1104	€876	Hunting on Romney Marsh (41x51cm-16x20in) s. 10-Jun-4 Christie's, Kensington #198/R
£1000	$1700	€1460	Heavy horse class, Ludlow, Shropshire (75x119cm-30x47in) s. 27-Nov-3 Christie's, Kensington #153/R est:1000-1500

SANDERSON, Archibald (fl.1928-1939) British

Works on paper

£260	$481	€380	On a Pembrokeshire Farm (28x35cm-11x14in) s.i. W/C over pencil. 13-Feb-4 Sworder & Son, Bishops Stortford #5/R

SANDERSON, Charles Wesley (1838-1905) American

Works on paper

£409	$650	€597	Near Argenteuil, France (72x51cm-28x20in) s.d.90 W/C. 12-Sep-3 Skinner, Boston #248/R

SANDERSON, Robert (fl.1858-1908) British

£438	$700	€639	Figures n path over bridge (30x46cm-12x18in) s. indis d. 20-Sep-3 Sloans & Kenyon, Bethesda #140/R
£1242	$2000	€1813	An awkward nurse (20x15cm-8x6in) 20-Aug-3 James Julia, Fairfield #986/R est:2000-3000

SANDERSON-WELLS, John (1872-1955) British

£300	$549	€438	Cattle watering in a meadow (44x60cm-17x24in) s. 6-Apr-4 Bonhams, Chester #949
£780	$1295	€1139	The plan (20x26cm-8x10in) s. board. 1-Oct-3 Sotheby's, Olympia #146/R
£2400	$4080	€3504	Huntsman on horseback with foxhounds in the foreground (22x30cm-9x12in) s. panel. 19-Nov-3 Tennants, Leyburn #1190a/R est:1800-2500
£2500	$4525	€3650	Cottage rose (20x25cm-8x10in) s.i. panel. 2-Apr-4 Moore Allen & Innocent, Cirencester #409/R est:2500-3500
£3000	$4980	€4380	Coaching party the Sun Inn (34x49cm-13x19in) s. 1-Oct-3 Woolley & Wallis, Salisbury #193/R est:3000-4000
£4200	$7854	€6132	Hunting scene with huntsmen on horseback and hounds setting out (17x25cm-7x10in) s. panel. 22-Jul-4 Tennants, Leyburn #869/R est:2500-3000
£5814	$10000	€8488	Full cry. Over the fence (41x61cm-16x24in) s. pair. 5-Dec-3 Christie's, Rockefeller NY #116/R est:12000-18000
£6200	$11408	€9052	A good send off. Twas a very quiet wedding (39x60cm-15x24in) s. pair prov. 29-Mar-4 Thomson Roddick & Medcalf, Edinburgh #215 est:4000-6000
£8500	$14450	€12410	Black Magic at Muckinger Wood (74x89cm-29x35in) s. 27-Nov-3 Christie's, Kensington #123/R est:4000-6000

Works on paper

£260	$432	€380	Mounted cavalry officer (41x53cm-16x21in) s. W/C. 3-Oct-3 Mallams, Oxford #130/R
£300	$552	€438	Cattle watering by a stream (22x34cm-9x13in) s. W/C. 23-Mar-4 Bonhams, Knightsbridge #229
£850	$1556	€1275	Pack (39x35cm-15x14in) s. W/C. 27-Jul-4 Henry Adams, Chichester #385
£2000	$3260	€2920	Milkmaid and her dog crossing a meadow in morning sunlight (51x71cm-20x28in) s. W/C. 23-Sep-3 Anderson & Garland, Newcastle #284/R est:1500-2500

SANDHAM, Charles Alfred (1865-1949) Canadian

£432	$721	€631	Untitled - three hunters on snowshoe (31x50cm-12x20in) s.d.1937 board. 17-Nov-3 Hodgins, Calgary #304/R est:500-700 (C.D 955)

SANDHAM, Henry (1842-1910) Canadian

Works on paper

£968	$1781	€1413	After Vespers, Quebec (48x34cm-19x13in) s.i. W/C. 9-Jun-4 Walker's, Ottawa #116/R est:3000-4000 (C.D 2400)

£4911 $8446 €7170 Fishing Camp (70x50cm-28x20in) s. W/C. 2-Dec-3 Joyner Waddington, Toronto #161/R est:3000-4000 (C.D 11000)

SANDIFER, Rosie (1946-) American
Sculpture
£5588 $9500 €8158 Aquarian (213x56x71cm-84x22x28in) s.num.4/9 bronze fountain st.f. prov. 1-Nov-3 Santa Fe Art, Santa Fe #189/R est:15000-20000

SANDOR, Moricz (1885-1924) Hungarian
£992 $1716 €1448 Walk (45x54cm-18x21in) s. 12-Dec-3 Kieselbach, Budapest #206/R (H.F 380000)

SANDORFI, Istvan (1948-) French
£18310 $31676 €26000 Safi (162x97cm-64x38in) s.i.d.1999 verso prov. 14-Dec-3 Rabourdin & Choppin de Janvry, Paris #65/R est:27000-50000

SANDOVAL, A (19/20th C) Spanish
£1087 $1783 €1500 Alrededores de Gijon (60x100cm-24x39in) s.i.d.1919. 27-May-3 Durán, Madrid #119/R est:1500

SANDOZ, Adolf Karol (1845-?) Polish
£2448 $4210 €3500 Promenade dans les jardins de la Mosquee (45x58cm-18x23in) s.d.86. 8-Dec-3 Tajan, Paris #308/R est:2500-3000

SANDOZ, Edouard-Marcel (1881-1971) Swiss
Sculpture
£941 $1600 €1374 Lapin modele 4 (5cm-2in) s. dark brown pat. st.f.Susse. 22-Nov-3 Jackson's, Cedar Falls #385/R est:500-750
£1224 $1947 €1800 Jeune Arabe (9cm-4in) s.num.6 gilt brown pat bronze st.f.Susse sold with base lit. 20-Mar-3 Cornette de St.Cyr, Paris #150 est:1500-1800
£1259 $2140 €1800 Lapin bijou (5x6x4cm-2x2x2in) s. pat bronze Cast Susse lit. 25-Nov-3 Millon & Associes, Paris #33/R est:2500-3000
£1267 $2331 €1900 Lapin une oreille dressee (6cm-2in) s. brown pat. bronze st.f. Susse lit. 10-Jun-4 Camard, Paris #30/R est:1000-1200
£1275 $2257 €1900 Acrobat (29cm-11in) s. bronze alabaster socle. 27-Apr-4 Durán, Madrid #293/R est:900
£1275 $2283 €1900 Lapin oreille dressee (6cm-2in) s. num.12 pat bronze Cast Susse. 30-May-4 Eric Pillon, Calais #111/R
£1277 $2068 €1800 Le cochon d'Inde (4x8cm-2x3in) s.st.f.Susse green brown pat bronze lit. 24-May-3 Martinot & Savignat, Pontoise #105/R est:2300-2500
£1300 $2210 €1898 Bird seated on a bell shaped flower base (21cm-8in) s.i. bronze bell st.f. 25-Nov-3 Bonhams, Knowle #418/R est:400-600
£1399 $2378 €2000 Lapin bijou (5x6x4cm-2x2x2in) s. pat bronze Cast Susse lit. 25-Nov-3 Millon & Associes, Paris #30/R est:2500-3000
£1399 $2378 €2000 Lapin (7x8x3cm-3x3x1in) s.st.f.Susse pat bronze. 25-Nov-3 Millon & Associes, Paris #32/R est:2000-2500
£1674 $2846 €2444 Lapin (8cm-3in) s. pat.bronze Cast.Susse Fres lit. 7-Nov-3 Dobiaschofsky, Bern #185/R est:3800 (S.FR 3800)
£1678 $2970 €2500 Hibou (11x3x3cm-4x1x1in) s. pat bronze Cast Susse. 27-Apr-4 Claude Aguttes, Neuilly #111/R est:1500-1800
£1879 $3364 €2800 Lapin modele 6 (7cm-3in) s. pat bronze. 30-May-4 Eric Pillon, Calais #109/R
£2013 $3564 €3000 Basset (7x6x3cm-3x2x1in) s.i. pat bronze lit. 27-Apr-4 Claude Aguttes, Neuilly #110/R est:1500-1800
£2133 $3925 €3200 Fennec assis (13cm-5in) s. num.9 green brown pat bronze cire perdue st.f. Susse lit. 10-Jun-4 Camard, Paris #28/R est:2500-3000
£2133 $3925 €3200 Fennec couche (7cm-3in) s. brown pat. bronze cire perdue st.f. Susse lit. 10-Jun-4 Camard, Paris #29/R est:2500-3000
£2245 $3569 €3300 Lapin (9cm-4in) s.st.f.F. Barbedienne brown pat bronze sold with base exhib.lit. 20-Mar-3 Cornette de St.Cyr, Paris #152 est:1000-1500
£2400 $4368 €3600 Chien de mer (16x15cm-6x6in) s.st.f. Valsuani brown pat. bronze cire perdue lit. 29-Jun-4 Millon & Associes, Paris #25/R est:3000-4000
£2797 $4755 €4000 Figure of a monkey (18cm-7in) s. wood circular base. 18-Nov-3 Christie's, Amsterdam #331/R est:1200-1500
£2819 $5243 €4200 Crapaud a l'arret (5x11cm-2x4in) s. pierre noire lit. 4-Mar-4 Tajan, Paris #13/R est:6000-7000
£2819 $5215 €4200 Fennec couche. s.st.f.Susse pat bronze. 14-Mar-4 St-Germain-en-Laye Encheres #125/R est:1000-1200
£2867 $4931 €4100 Oiseau bleu (21cm-8in) s.st.f.Susse bronze bell. 3-Dec-3 Coutau Begarie, Paris #234/R est:2000-2500
£2937 $4993 €4200 Chien danois (14cm-6in) s. pat bronze lit. 25-Nov-3 Millon & Associes, Paris #29/R est:5000-6000
£3007 $5112 €4300 Porte-veine (8cm-3in) s.num.C472 brown pat bronze lit. 20-Nov-3 Camard, Paris #218/R est:2000-2300
£3154 $5646 €4700 Lapin lechant la patte (9cm-4in) s. pat bronze Cast Susse. 30-May-4 Eric Pillon, Calais #106/R
£3356 $6007 €5000 Macrurius dresse (13cm-5in) s. pat bronze Cast Valsuani. 30-May-4 Eric Pillon, Calais #46/R
£3800 $6954 €5548 Running goose (8x20cm-3x8in) s. bronze. 3-Jun-4 Sotheby's, Olympia #265/R est:800-1200
£4200 $7014 €6132 Lapin couche (9cm-4in) s. pat bronze. 15-Oct-3 Christie's, Kensington #656/R
£5600 $9520 €8176 Seated fennec (29cm-11in) s.i. bronze st.f.Susse cire perdue. 25-Nov-3 Sotheby's, Olympia #127/R est:2000-3000
£5867 $10795 €8800 Singe (18x10x10cm-7x4x4in) s. silver lit. 11-Jun-4 Piasa, Paris #29/R est:8000-10000
£5944 $10105 €8500 Danseuse nue (5x4cm-2x2in) s. pat bronze Cast Valsuani marble base. 25-Nov-3 Millon & Associes, Paris #23/R est:8000-10000
£6000 $10980 €8760 Poisson (24x33cm-9x13in) s. pink quartz prov. 5-Jun-4 Galerie du Rhone, Sion #559/R est:1000-15000 (S.FR 13800)
£6800 $12444 €9928 Seated fennec (28cm-11in) s.i. bronze. 3-Jun-4 Sotheby's, Olympia #264/R est:3000-5000
£8163 $14613 €12000 Fennec (29cm-11in) s.st.f.Susse pat bronze lit. 17-Mar-4 Tajan, Paris #18/R est:4000-5000
£10000 $18200 €15000 Singes (28x70x21cm-11x28x8in) s. wood lit. 29-Jun-4 Millon & Associes, Paris #22/R est:15000-20000
£17483 $29720 €25000 Crapaud (16x22x13cm-6x9x5in) s. amethyst lit. 24-Nov-3 Tajan, Paris #44/R est:28000-30000

SANDQVIST, Rolf (1919-) Finnish
£455 $773 €650 Labyrinth (55x81cm-22x32in) s.d.87. 29-Nov-3 Bukowskis, Helsinki #258/R

SANDROCK, Leonhard (1867-1945) German
£1933 $3461 €2900 Harbour fishermen - Hamburg (49x66cm-19x26in) s. lit. 14-May-4 Schloss Ahlden, Ahlden #2906/R est:2500
£2448 $4210 €3500 View of St Katharein, the canal and the church (76x72cm-30x28in) s. 6-Dec-3 Quittenbaum, Hamburg #104/R est:1000

SANDROCK, Leonhard (attrib) (1867-1945) German
£692 $1191 €990 Small harbour with town in the distance (24x31cm-9x12in) i.verso board. 6-Dec-3 Hans Stahl, Toestorf #80/R

SANDRUCCI, Giovanni (1828-1897) Italian
£3107 $5500 €4536 Peasant woman with basket of grapes and other fruit (94x66cm-37x26in) s.i. 2-May-4 Bonhams & Butterfields, San Francisco #1026/R est:3000-5000

SANDS, Frederick (?) ?
Works on paper
£1000 $1700 €1460 Seaweed gathering at St Ouens Jersey (35x51cm-14x20in) s. W/C exhib. 25-Nov-3 Martel Maides, Guernsey #201/R est:700-900
£1200 $1920 €1752 Beaurieres, near Digne (40x61cm-16x24in) s. W/C. 17-Sep-3 Bonhams, Brooks & Langlois, Jersey #108/R est:1200-1500
£1200 $1920 €1752 La Rocca Tower, St Quen's Bay (40x61cm-16x24in) s. W/C. 17-Sep-3 Bonhams, Brooks & Langlois, Jersey #109/R est:1200-1500
£1200 $1920 €1752 La Pulente (40x60cm-16x24in) s. W/C. 17-Sep-3 Bonhams, Brooks & Langlois, Jersey #111/R est:1200-1500
£1200 $1920 €1752 East Coast scene (40x60cm-16x24in) s. W/C. 17-Sep-3 Bonhams, Brooks & Langlois, Jersey #114/R est:1200-1500
£1300 $2080 €1898 Seymour Tower (40x60cm-16x24in) s. W/C. 17-Sep-3 Bonhams, Brooks & Langlois, Jersey #112/R est:1200-1500

SANDS, Henry H (fl.1886-1906) British
£495 $900 €723 Two girls outside country village (33x43cm-13x17in) s.d.1885. 7-Feb-4 Sloans & Kenyon, Bethesda #1257/R
Works on paper
£500 $920 €730 Plough team (30x46cm-12x18in) s.d.1892 pencil W/C. 25-Mar-4 Christie's, Kensington #168/R

SANDY, Bertram (20th C) British
Works on paper
£800 $1472 €1168 Captain Ball on the warpath. Shot down in flames (35x25cm-14x10in) s. pencil W/C. 25-Mar-4 Christie's, Kensington #263/R

SANDYS, Emma (attrib) (1834-1877) British
Works on paper
£1250 $2263 €1825 Portrait of young woman in pre-Raphaelite manner (48x36cm-19x14in) s. pencil crayon. 31-Mar-4 Brightwells, Leominster #980 est:500-700

SANDYS, Frederick (1832-1904) British
Works on paper
£26000 $44200 €37960 Cassandra (32x35cm-13x14in) init.i. col chks prov.exhib.lit. 20-Nov-3 Christie's, London #139/R est:30000-50000

SANDYS-LUMSDAINE, Leesa (1936-) British
£250 $458 €365 Roberto with Braulio Baeza up (26x23cm-10x9in) s. board prov. 7-Apr-4 Woolley & Wallis, Salisbury #271/R
£280 $512 €409 Brigadier Gerard with Joe Mercer up (28x32cm-11x13in) s.i.d.71 board prov. 7-Apr-4 Woolley & Wallis, Salisbury #270/R
£380 $695 €555 Nijinsky with Lester Piggot up (24x27cm-9x11in) board prov. 7-Apr-4 Woolley & Wallis, Salisbury #272/R

SANDZEN, Birger (1871-1954) American/Swedish
£3179 $5500 €4641 Summer Meadow (50x36cm-20x14in) init.d.92 i.verso prov.exhib. 10-Dec-3 Bonhams & Butterfields, San Francisco #6069/R est:4000-6000
£14535 $25000 €21221 At river's edge (51x61cm-20x24in) panel prov. 3-Dec-3 Sotheby's, New York #155/R est:20000-30000
£16949 $30000 €24746 Early fall, Estes Park, Colorado (25x20cm-10x8in) s. s.i.d.1926 verso board. 28-Apr-4 Christie's, Los Angeles #51/R est:10000-15000
£17647 $30000 €25765 Farm on the hill, landscape (46x56cm-18x22in) s.i.stretcher prov. 18-Nov-3 John Moran, Pasadena #40a est:30000-50000
£19118 $32500 €27912 Twilight in the mountains, Estes Park, Colorado (14x18cm-6x7in) s. i.verso board. 18-Nov-3 John Moran, Pasadena #117b est:15000-25000
£21676 $37500 €31647 Kansas Creek (41x51cm-16x20in) s. masonite prov. 10-Dec-3 Bonhams & Butterfields, San Francisco #6046/R est:25000-35000
£28532 $52500 €41657 Fruit in an Indian bowl (45x61cm-18x24in) s. 8-Jun-4 Bonhams & Butterfields, San Francisco #4129/R est:40000-60000
£28902 $50000 €42197 Glimpse of Long's peak, Estes Park, Colorado (56x71cm-22x28in) s.i.verso masonite prov.exhib. 10-Dec-3 Bonhams & Butterfields, San Francisco #6109/R est:30000-50000
£31792 $55000 €46416 Trees by a river with clouds in the distance (51x61cm-20x24in) s. prov. 10-Dec-3 Bonhams & Butterfields, San Francisco #6045/R est:20000-25000
£31977 $55000 €46686 Landscape (61x86cm-24x34in) s.d.1919 prov. 3-Dec-3 Sotheby's, New York #154/R est:40000-60000
£37206 $63250 €54321 Autumn, Smoky Hill river, Kansas (51x61cm-20x24in) s. s.i.d.1944 verso canvas on panel prov.lit. 1-Nov-3 Santa Fe Art, Santa Fe #196/R est:40000-50000
£50000 $85000 €73000 At the timberline, landscape (61x91cm-24x36in) s.d.1923 prov.exhib. 18-Nov-3 John Moran, Pasadena #40 est:80000-120000
Works on paper
£3468 $6000 €5063 Rocky Coast, Rockport, Massachusetts (22x30cm-9x12in) exec 1948 pencil W/C prov.exhib. 10-Dec-3 Bonhams & Butterfields, San Francisco #6070/R est:5000-7000

£3672 $6500 €5361 High peaks (25x35cm-10x14in) s.d.1932 W/C. 28-Apr-4 Christie's, Los Angeles #49/R est:3000-5000

SANE, Jean François (1732-1779) French
£2800 $5040 €4088 Interior with a soldier greeting his wife and child (25x38cm-10x15in) s. panel sold with 6 other paintings by various hands. 20-Apr-4 Sotheby's, Olympia #367/R est:1500-2000

SANEJOUAND, Jean Michel (1934-) French
£1760 $3046 €2500 Calligraphies d'humeur (50x100cm-20x39in) s.i.d.1974 verso acrylic prov. 9-Dec-3 Artcurial Briest, Paris #576/R est:1200-1500

SANESI, Nicola (1818-1889) Italian
£504 $826 €700 Declaration (25x20cm-10x8in) s.i.verso cardboard. 10-Jun-3 Pandolfini, Florence #59/R

SANFILIPPO, Antonio (1923-1980) Italian
£1517 $2534 €2200 Composition (15x20cm-6x8in) s. s.d.1957 verso oil hydropaint board. 14-Nov-3 Farsetti, Prato #293/R est:550-650
Works on paper
£1678 $2853 €2400 Untitled (70x100cm-28x39in) s. mixed media prov. 26-Nov-3 Pandolfini, Florence #67/R est:2600-2800
£1818 $3091 €2600 Untitled (100x70cm-39x28in) s.d.62 mixed media prov. 26-Nov-3 Pandolfini, Florence #66/R est:2600-2800
£5862 $9790 €8500 Untitled (54x65cm-21x26in) s. hydropaint on canvas exec.1956. 14-Nov-3 Farsetti, Prato #302/R est:8500

SANG, Frederick Jacques (19th C) French
£420 $777 €613 Limehouse dock (23x15cm-9x6in) s. s.i.verso board. 9-Mar-4 Bonhams, Knightsbridge #219/R
£455 $773 €650 Les quais a Jersey (32x46cm-13x18in) s.i.d.1876 canvas on panel. 24-Nov-3 Boscher, Cherbourg #884
£620 $1035 €905 Limehouse Reach, low tide. Misty day, ship moored near Greenwich (17x25cm-7x10in) s. i.verso board pair. 7-Oct-3 Bonhams, Knightsbridge #80/R
£1020 $1857 €1500 Vue du Trocadero et la Seine (32x46cm-13x18in) s.i.d.1878 prov. 3-Feb-4 Christie's, Amsterdam #242 est:1500-2000

SANGALLO, Antonio (younger) (1483-1546) Italian
Works on paper
£2800 $4844 €4088 Elevation and ground plan of the tomb of Pietro de'Medici (43x27cm-17x11in) i. black chk pen brown ink wash prov. 12-Dec-3 Christie's, Kensington #305/R est:2000-3000

SANGBERG, Monica (20th C) ?
£3529 $6000 €5152 Children with dog in spring meadow (110x150cm-43x59in) s.d.1977. 28-Nov-3 Zofingen, Switzerland #2671/R est:6500 (S.FR 7800)

SANGSTER, Hendrick Alexander (1825-1901) Dutch
£428 $774 €650 Portrait of a lady sitting in a silk dress (98x76cm-39x30in) s.d.1862. 19-Apr-4 Glerum, Amsterdam #30/R

SANI, Alessandro (19/20th C) Italian
£325 $581 €475 Seated man with pipe (15x10cm-6x4in) bears sig. 22-Mar-4 Philippe Schuler, Zurich #6184 (S.FR 750)
£667 $1200 €974 Dinner served (18x23cm-7x9in) s. panel. 20-Jan-4 Arthur James, Florida #641
£722 $1300 €1054 Dinner guest (18x25cm-7x10in) s. panel. 20-Jan-4 Arthur James, Florida #640
£2155 $3858 €3146 Chess game (45x58cm-18x23in) s. 12-May-4 Dobiaschofsky, Bern #931/R est:7000 (S.FR 5000)
£17000 $30940 €24820 Grandfather's gift (89x71cm-35x28in) s. 17-Jun-4 Christie's, London #84/R est:20000-30000

SANI, Giuseppe (1869-1943) Italian
£642 $1001 €950 View of square in Ferrara (70x49cm-28x19in) 30-Mar-3 Adma, Formigine #614

SANNUY, Juan (1850-1908) South American?
Works on paper
£1630 $3000 €2380 Military uniforms (31x14cm-12x6in) s.d.1860 W/C pair. 22-Jun-4 Galeria y Remates, Montevideo #60/R est:1700-2500

SANO di PIETRO (1406-1481) Italian
£25694 $43681 €37000 Virgin (38x36cm-15x14in) tempera board lit. 29-Oct-3 Il Ponte, Milan #745/R est:40000
£69784 $114446 €97000 Vierge a l'enfant entouree de quatre saints, et deux anges (56x43cm-22x17in) tempera gold panel. 6-Jun-3 Drouot Estimations, Paris #43/R est:30000-35000
£120000 $219600 €175200 Lady Perna being cured on approaching Saint Bernardino's body (24x41cm-9x16in) tempera panel gold ground prov.exhib.lit. 7-Jul-4 Sotheby's, London #37/R est:120000-180000

SANOJA, Julio (20th C) Venezuelan?
Sculpture
£928 $1550 €1355 Figure (45x42x19cm-18x17x7in) s. bronze. 19-Oct-3 Subastas Odalys, Caracas #92/R est:3000

SANON, Roosvelt (1952-) Haitian
£267 $477 €400 Chemin dans la foret (51x77cm-20x30in) s. 17-May-4 Rogeon, Paris #224

SANQUIRICO, Alessandro (1777-1849) Italian
£2483 $4569 €3700 Remembrances (24x35cm-9x14in) 24-Mar-4 Il Ponte, Milan #664 est:500-600
Works on paper
£903 $1535 €1300 La Scala, Milan (7x8cm-3x3in) s.i.d.1831 W/C. 29-Oct-3 Il Ponte, Milan #571

SANQUIRICO, Pio (1847-1900) Italian
£1762 $2996 €2573 Children fishing for apple (49x79cm-19x31in) s. 5-Nov-3 Dobiaschofsky, Bern #924/R est:3800 (S.FR 4000)
£4362 $7809 €6500 Children fishing for an apple (49x79cm-19x31in) s. 27-May-4 Dorotheum, Vienna #201/R est:6500-7000

SANQUIRICO, Pio (attrib) (1847-1900) Italian
£352 $599 €514 Portrait of a youth (45x30cm-18x12in) 5-Nov-3 Dobiaschofsky, Bern #926/R (S.FR 800)
£352 $599 €514 Portrait of a girl (45x30cm-18x12in) 5-Nov-3 Dobiaschofsky, Bern #925/R (S.FR 800)

SANRAKU, Kano (style) (1559-1635) Japanese
Works on paper
£10000 $16700 €14600 Horses and Zen monks. Tiger and Lohans. Peony and Zen monks (114x46cm-45x18in) ink set of 3. 12-Nov-3 Christie's, London #8/R est:700-900

SANS CORBELLA, Tomas (1869-1911) Spanish
£552 $916 €800 Landscape with trees (87x68cm-34x27in) s. 1-Oct-3 Ansorena, Madrid #720/R

SANSALVADORE, Piero (1892-1955) Italian
£360 $634 €526 Polperro Harbour, Cornwall (44x35cm-17x14in) s.d.1947 i. verso board. 18-May-4 Fellows & Sons, Birmingham #3/R
£400 $668 €584 Brixham Harbour, Devon (44x34cm-17x13in) i.d.1943 board. 7-Oct-3 Fellows & Sons, Birmingham #386/R

SANSOM, Gareth Laurence (1939-) Australian
£992 $1567 €1448 Cosmic cows (80x100cm-31x39in) s.i.d.1979 verso oil enamel collage board. 2-Sep-3 Deutscher-Menzies, Melbourne #329/R est:1000-1500 (A.D 2420)

SANT, George (attrib) (fl.1856-1877) British
£600 $1002 €876 Poignant farewell (51x91cm-20x36in) 8-Oct-3 Christie's, Kensington #747/R

SANT, James (1820-1916) British
£549 $900 €802 Messenger (33x25cm-13x10in) s. 1-Jun-3 William Jenack, New York #228
£1200 $2064 €1752 Portrait of two girls (23cm-9in circular) bears sig. indis.i. d.September 23 1848 board. 4-Dec-3 Mellors & Kirk, Nottingham #890/R est:1200-1500
£4206 $6645 €6099 Double portrait of Alexander Gould Barrett and his sister as children (158x97cm-62x38in) i.verso exhib. 3-Sep-3 Museumsbygningen, Copenhagen #223/R est:40000-60000 (D.KR 45000)
£9000 $15300 €13140 Portrait of a girl, reading a book (76x63cm-30x25in) 25-Nov-3 Christie's, London #187/R est:8000-12000

SANT, James (attrib) (1820-1916) British
£1500 $2505 €2190 Portrait of a young lady said to be Geraldine Fuller (60x50cm-24x20in) oval. 14-Oct-3 Bearnes, Exeter #367/R est:1500-2500
£2900 $5481 €4234 For those in peril on the sea, mother and daughter sitting by an open window (42x57cm-17x22in) 17-Feb-4 Fellows & Sons, Birmingham #27/R

SANT, Julia (19/20th C) British?
£260 $455 €380 Still life of spring flowers and fruit (69x56cm-27x22in) s. 17-Dec-3 Bonhams, Leeds #760

SANTA BARBARA (19th C) Portuguese
Miniatures
£1000 $1730 €1460 Pedro V, King of Portugal in blue coat with gold embroidered collar (4cm-2in) s.d.1851 silver-gilt mount oval. 9-Dec-3 Christie's, London #221/R est:1000-1500

SANTA MARIA, Andres de (1860-1945) Colombian
£10588 $18000 €15458 Christ walking on the waters (41x52cm-16x20in) panel. 19-Nov-3 Sotheby's, New York #85/R est:10000-15000

SANTA MARIA, Marceliano (1866-1952) Spanish
£5705 $10097 €8500 Landscape in Burgos (56x60cm-22x24in) s. 27-Apr-4 Durán, Madrid #135/R est:7000
£13793 $24828 €20000 View of Pradoluengo (64x55cm-25x22in) s. 26-Jan-4 Ansorena, Madrid #208/R est:18000

SANTAFEDE, Fabrizio (1559-c.1634) Italian
£42254 $73944 €60000 Christ captured (235x183cm-93x72in) prov. 17-Dec-3 Christie's, Rome #503/R est:100000-120000

SANTAMARIA, Fidel (?) South American?
£303 $545 €442 Day on the coast (46x56cm-18x22in) s. cardboard. 25-Apr-4 Subastas Odalys, Caracas #70/R

£406 $730 €593 Cheeky (59x49cm-23x19in) s. 25-Apr-4 Subastas Odalys, Caracas #69/R
£464 $835 €677 Fishermen (59x49cm-23x19in) s. canvas on masonite. 25-Apr-4 Subastas Odalys, Caracas #20

SANTASUSAGNA, Ernest (1900-1964) Spanish
£652 $1070 €900 Young women with fan (102x82cm-40x32in) s. 27-May-3 Durán, Madrid #48/R
£915 $1584 €1300 Maternity (50x40cm-20x16in) s. 15-Dec-3 Ansorena, Madrid #364/R

SANTERRE, Jean Baptiste (1651-1717) French
£50658 $93211 €77000 Jeune femme au billet doux (91x73cm-36x29in) 23-Jun-4 Sotheby's, Paris #11/R est:30000-40000

SANTERRE, Jean Baptiste (attrib) (1651-1717) French
£2958 $5117 €4200 Portrait de musicienne (91x72cm-36x28in) 10-Dec-3 Beaussant & Lefèvre, Paris #25/R est:4000-5000
£3007 $5112 €4300 L'enfant au jeu de cartes (59x73cm-23x29in) bears sig.d.1709. 1-Dec-3 Millon & Associes, Paris #12/R est:4000-6000
Works on paper
£1409 $2593 €2100 Tete de femme (28x22cm-11x9in) col crayon. 24-Mar-4 Claude Boisgirard, Paris #32/R est:1500

SANTERRE, Jean Baptiste (studio) (1651-1717) French
£3846 $7000 €5615 Portrait of a lady said to Marie Adelaide de Savoie, Duchesse de Bourgogne (92x73cm-36x29in) 4-Feb-4 Christie's, Rockefeller NY #100/R est:8000-12000
£5629 $10245 €8500 Jeune fille au billet doux - Mademoiselle Desmares (90x67cm-35x26in) 15-Jun-4 Artcurial Briest, Paris #217/R est:6000-7000

SANTHO, Milos (19th C) Hungarian
£1517 $2534 €2200 In the art shop (59x49cm-23x19in) s. 9-Jul-3 Hugo Ruef, Munich #196/R est:2000

SANTI, Giuseppe (?-1825) Italian
Works on paper
£3309 $5295 €4600 Muzio Scevola in font of Porsenna (21x32cm-8x13in) i.verso pen W/C. 14-May-3 Finarte Semenzato, Milan #505/R est:1700-2700
£3741 $5986 €5200 Allegory of Painting and Sculpture (21x32cm-8x13in) i.verso pen W/C. 14-May-3 Finarte Semenzato, Milan #504/R est:1700-2200

SANTI, Sebastiano (1789-1865) Italian
£5503 $9741 €8200 Portrait of the artist's daughter (109x54cm-43x21in) s. 2-May-4 Finarte, Venice #1/R est:8000-10000

SANTIAGO, Carlos de (1875-1951) South American
£441 $750 €644 Landscape with fields (44x52cm-17x20in) s. 25-Nov-3 Galeria y Remates, Montevideo #13/R
£471 $800 €688 Landscape with lake (44x52cm-17x20in) s. 25-Nov-3 Galeria y Remates, Montevideo #14
£1647 $2800 €2405 Naples Bay (60x50cm-24x20in) s. 25-Nov-3 Galeria y Remates, Montevideo #137/R
£2353 $4000 €3435 Lake (88x98cm-35x39in) s. 25-Nov-3 Galeria y Remates, Montevideo #135/R
£3529 $6000 €5152 Landscape with church (80x90cm-31x35in) s. 25-Nov-3 Galeria y Remates, Montevideo #136/R

SANTINI, A (?) ?
£1336 $2392 €1951 Family in kitchen (61x83cm-24x33in) s. 12-May-4 Dobiaschofsky, Bern #932/R est:3000 (S.FR 3100)

SANTOMASO, Giuseppe (1907-1990) Italian
£2365 $4162 €3500 Untitled (42x34cm-17x13in) s.d.46 tempera paper on cardboard. 24-May-4 Christie's, Milan #73/R est:3500-5000
£2838 $4995 €4200 Composition with boat (50x64cm-20x25in) s. cardboard painted c.1955. 19-May-4 Il Ponte, Milan #1084 est:5000-6000
£8392 $14434 €12000 Un'angolo ad ovest (72x60cm-28x24in) s.d. 3-Dec-3 Hauswedell & Nolte, Hamburg #972/R est:16000
£8667 $15513 €13000 Untitled (26x33cm-10x13in) s.d. oil tempera paper on canvas exhib. 14-May-4 Ketterer, Munich #255/R est:12000-15000
£10067 $18020 €15000 Untitled (51x68cm-20x27in) s.d.1975 oil collage. 30-May-4 Meeting Art, Vercelli #54 est:15000
£16779 $30034 €25000 Grey and blue space (140x110cm-55x43in) sd.73. 25-May-4 Sotheby's, Milan #143/R est:30000
£20290 $33275 €28000 Grey space (146x114cm-57x45in) s.d.82 s.i.d.verso oil mixed media prov.exhib.lit. 27-May-3 Sotheby's, Milan #271/R est:30000-40000
£23000 $38410 €33580 Spazio blu e segno bianco (37x72cm-15x28in) s.i.d.72 verso i.d.1972 stretcher sand acrylic prov.lit. 22-Oct-3 Christie's, London #50/R est:25000-35000
£30000 $50100 €43800 Memento (130x162cm-51x64in) s.d.64 oil sand prov.exhib.lit. 21-Oct-3 Christie's, London #24/R est:30000-50000
£30435 $49913 €42000 Tension (70x112cm-28x44in) s.d.53 exhib.lit. 27-May-3 Sotheby's, Milan #277/R est:45000-55000
£30986 $51437 €44000 Sense of time (80x80cm-31x31in) s.d.61 exhib.lit. 11-Jun-3 Finarte Semenzato, Milan #657/R est:38000
£33557 $60067 €50000 Untitled (128x75cm-50x30in) s.d.55. 25-May-4 Sotheby's, Milan #269/R est:60000-80000
£45455 $80000 €66364 Pietra antica (122x114cm-48x45in) s.d.1959. 22-May-4 Selkirks, St. Louis #802/R est:18000-24000
£50336 $90101 €75000 Grey wall (100x100cm-39x39in) s.d.65 s.d.65 verso prov.exhib.lit. 25-May-4 Sotheby's, Milan #280/R est:30000-40000
£76923 $130769 €110000 Night song 2 (162x130cm-64x51in) s.d.60 exhib.lit. 24-Nov-3 Christie's, Milan #335/R est:60000-90000
£77703 $136757 €115000 Night song 3 (162x130cm-64x51in) s.d.60 i.verso prov.exhib.lit. 24-May-4 Christie's, Milan #343/R est:12000-150000
£118243 $208108 €175000 Tale (116x146cm-46x57in) s.d.61 exhib.lit. 24-May-4 Christie's, Milan #331/R est:60000-90000
Works on paper
£979 $1684 €1400 Composition (37x31cm-15x12in) s.d. W/C collage. 3-Dec-3 Hauswedell & Nolte, Hamburg #974/R
£1399 $2378 €2000 Untitled (34x26cm-13x10in) s.d.73 W/C collage. 20-Nov-3 Finarte Semenzato, Milan #109/R est:2000-2500
£1493 $2538 €2180 Untitled (19x13cm-7x5in) s.d.73 W/C ink. 22-Nov-3 Burkhard, Luzern #143/R est:3400-3800 (S.FR 3300)
£1747 $3214 €2551 Senza titolo (41x32cm-16x13in) s.d.1976 mixed media collage prov. 8-Jun-4 Germann, Zurich #111/R est:6000-8000 (S.FR 4000)
£2412 $4439 €3522 Composition (32x25cm-13x10in) s.d.1983 chl washed pastel collage prov. 23-Jun-4 Koller, Zurich #3140/R est:5500-7000 (S.FR 5500)
£2797 $4811 €4000 Senza titolo (43x33cm-17x13in) s.d. mixed media collage. 3-Dec-3 Hauswedell & Nolte, Hamburg #973/R est:5000
£3333 $6033 €5000 Composition (57x63cm-22x25in) s. mixed media. 2-Apr-4 Farsetti, Prato #307/R est:5000-6000
£6338 $10521 €9000 Untitled (74x56cm-29x22in) s.d.1984 mixed media collage paper on canvas. 14-Jun-3 Meeting Art, Vercelli #599/R est:9000
£6993 $11888 €10000 Stamps 8 (75x57cm-30x22in) s. s.i.verso collage mixed media card on canvas. 24-Nov-3 Christie's, Milan #136/R est:10000-13000
£7047 $13108 €10500 Composition (47x68cm-19x27in) s.d.61 W/C ink prov. 3-Mar-4 Artcurial Briest, Paris #513/R est:2000-3000
£8392 $14266 €12000 Untitled (47x67cm-19x26in) s.d.61 mixed media. 25-Nov-3 Sotheby's, Milan #46/R est:8000-10000
£10811 $19027 €16000 Untitled (69x47cm-27x19in) s.d.55 mixed media paper on board prov. 24-May-4 Christie's, Milan #156/R est:15000-20000
£16779 $30034 €25000 Untitled (110x140cm-43x55in) s.d.73 verso s.d.on stretcher mixed media on canvas prov.lit. 25-May-4 Sotheby's, Milan #303/R est:25000-30000

SANTORO, Francesco Raffaello (1844-1927) Italian
£1048 $1929 €1530 Tyrolean street scene (20x44cm-8x17in) s.d.1876 panel. 14-Jun-4 Waddingtons, Toronto #329/R est:1500-2500 (C.D 2600)
£2958 $4910 €4200 Le fonti del Clitumno (95x150cm-37x59in) s. 11-Jun-3 Christie's, Rome #82/R est:1300-1800
Works on paper
£580 $1003 €847 Servant girl seated knitting in a cowshed (52x70cm-20x28in) s.i. W/C. 9-Dec-3 Rosebery Fine Art, London #652/R

SANTORO, Rubens (1859-1942) Italian
£2606 $4508 €3700 Portrait of man (79x64cm-31x25in) s.d.1935. 10-Dec-3 Finarte Semenzato, Rome #288/R est:4000-6000
£4225 $7310 €6000 On the door (55x50cm-22x20in) s. prov. 11-Dec-3 Christie's, Rome #174/R est:7000-9000
£4396 $8000 €6418 Balcony in Venice (19x10cm-7x4in) s.i. panel. 29-Jun-4 Sotheby's, New York #105/R est:5000-7000
£5267 $9533 €7900 View of village (60x37cm-24x15in) prov.lit. 30-Mar-4 Babuino, Rome #286/R est:3000
£29167 $52500 €42584 Along the canal (49x37cm-19x15in) s. 23-Apr-4 Sotheby's, New York #102/R est:25000-35000
£30000 $49800 €43800 Palazzo Contarini, Venice (50x37cm-20x15in) s. 1-Oct-3 Sotheby's, Olympia #262/R est:15000-25000
£30000 $49800 €43800 Canale san Barnaba, Venice (50x37cm-20x15in) s. 1-Oct-3 Sotheby's, Olympia #263/R est:15000-25000
£44444 $80000 €64888 On the Mediterranean coast (38x64cm-15x25in) s.d.87 prov. 23-Apr-4 Sotheby's, New York #80/R est:30000-40000
£47059 $80000 €68706 Church of San Trovaso, a Venetian backwater (41x32cm-16x13in) s. panel prov. 29-Oct-3 Christie's, Rockefeller NY #246/R est:60000-80000

SANTOS VIANA, Raul (1946-) Spanish
£347 $590 €500 Segovia (73x54cm-29x21in) s.d.1973 s.i.verso. 28-Oct-3 Segre, Madrid #356/R

SANTOS, Abilio dos (1926-) Portuguese
£470 $841 €700 View of town with figures (19x13cm-7x5in) s.d.1952 paper. 31-May-4 Cabral Moncada Leiloes, Lisbon #224/R

SANTOS, Angeles (1912-) Spanish
£2138 $3848 €3100 Landscape (32x45cm-13x18in) s. 26-Jan-4 Ansorena, Madrid #172/R est:1500
£3793 $6828 €5500 Coastal view (50x73cm-20x29in) s. 26-Jan-4 Ansorena, Madrid #183/R est:3000

SANTOS, Fermin (1909-1997) Spanish
£337 $563 €475 D Luis, D Angel y Fermin Santos pasando por la calle de la Redondilla, Madrid (42x33cm-17x13in) s. s.i.d.1953 verso. 23-Jun-3 Durán, Madrid #112
£337 $563 €475 El Rastro, Madrid antiguo romantico y novelesco (33x41cm-13x16in) s. i.verso. 23-Jun-3 Durán, Madrid #113/R
£399 $654 €550 Gran Via y Capitol, Madrid (41x33cm-16x13in) s. s.i.verso. 27-May-3 Durán, Madrid #11/R
£399 $654 €550 Church of San Andres and Los Mancebos street, ancient Madrid (41x33cm-16x13in) s. s.i.verso. 27-May-3 Durán, Madrid #10/R
£461 $770 €650 Arco de Cuchilleros (65x50cm-26x20in) s. s.i.verso. 23-Jun-3 Durán, Madrid #110/R
£496 $829 €700 Saturno (81x60cm-32x24in) s. 23-Jun-3 Durán, Madrid #104/R
£552 $993 €800 Cascorro Square (54x64cm-21x25in) s. i.verso. 26-Jan-4 Ansorena, Madrid #155/R
£567 $919 €800 Landscape of the Casa de Campo de Madrid (60x73cm-24x29in) s. i.verso. 20-May-3 Ansorena, Madrid #24/R
£1064 $1777 €1500 Carlos Arniches Street, Madrid (100x85cm-39x33in) s. 20-Oct-3 Durán, Madrid #161/R

SANTOS, Fernando dos (1892-1965) Portuguese
£1074 $1922 €1600 Houses by Sintra wood (29x37cm-11x15in) s.d.1957 panel. 31-May-4 Cabral Moncada Leiloes, Lisbon #94/R est:1500-2250

SANTRY, Daniel (1858-1915) American
£615 $1100 €898 Mt Lafayette from Sugar Hill, NH (20x36cm-8x14in) s. s.i.verso canvasboard. 8-Jan-4 James Julia, Fairfield #927/R

SANTRY, Terence John (1910-1990) Australian
£264 $415 €383 Circus lady (52x38cm-20x15in) canvas on board. 26-Aug-3 Lawson Menzies, Sydney #155 (A.D 650)
£288 $522 €420 Fortune and misfortune (40x46cm-16x18in) s. board. 31-Mar-4 Goodman, Sydney #515 (A.D 700)
£325 $511 €471 Cargo ship in Sydney Harbour (68x91cm-27x36in) canvas on board. 26-Aug-3 Lawson Menzies, Sydney #185 (A.D 800)
£325 $511 €471 Sydney Harbour, Luna Park (61x91cm-24x36in) canvas on board. 26-Aug-3 Lawson Menzies, Sydney #186 (A.D 800)
£366 $575 €531 Boy playing cricket (60x39cm-24x15in) s. board. 26-Aug-3 Lawson Menzies, Sydney #173 est:500-700 (A.D 900)
£569 $893 €825 Farm (61x91cm-24x36in) s. canvas on board. 26-Aug-3 Lawson Menzies, Sydney #190 est:1500-2000 (A.D 1400)
£569 $893 €825 Street scene (71x92cm-28x36in) s. canvas on board. 26-Aug-3 Lawson Menzies, Sydney #194 est:1500-3000 (A.D 1400)
£573 $1042 €837 Gossips (27x23cm-11x9in) s. oil pen ink board. 16-Jun-4 Deutscher-Menzies, Melbourne #569/R est:1800-2500 (A.D 1500)
£1362 $2315 €1989 Carcoar, New South Wales (54x91cm-21x36in) s. canvas on composition board. 26-Nov-3 Deutscher-Menzies, Melbourne #243/R est:3500-4500 (A.D 3200)
Works on paper
£331 $562 €497 Greyhounds (50x72cm-20x28in) s. W/C. 28-Oct-3 Goodman, Sydney #343/R (A.D 800)

SANTVOORT, Pieter Dircksz van (attrib) (1604-1653) Dutch
Works on paper
£811 $1427 €1200 Wooded mountain landscape with distant castle (23x32cm-9x13in) d.1623 i.verso black chk brown wash prov. 19-May-4 Sotheby's, Amsterdam #15/R

SANUTO, Giulio (fl.1540-1588) Italian
Prints
£6294 $10699 €9000 L'enfant monstrueux (24x18cm-9x7in) engraving. 27-Nov-3 Bassenge, Berlin #5182/R est:6000

SANVISENS, Ramon (1917-1987) Spanish
£880 $1523 €1250 Landscape (21x32cm-8x13in) s. board. 10-Dec-3 Castellana, Madrid #1/R

SANVITALE, Lucretia (17th C) Italian
£2378 $4042 €3400 Mother of God with child and two angels holding crown above head (39x32cm-15x13in) s. verso copper. 20-Nov-3 Dorotheum, Salzburg #58/R est:5200-6000

SANZ CORBELLO, Tomas (20th C) Spanish
£524 $876 €750 Landscape (87x68cm-34x27in) s. 30-Jun-3 Ansorena, Madrid #254/R

SANZ MAGALLON, Jose Luis (1926-2000) Spanish
£263 $476 €400 Sea (35x73cm-14x29in) s. 14-Apr-4 Ansorena, Madrid #17/R
£284 $474 €400 Desnudo de espaldas (65x50cm-26x20in) s. 23-Jun-3 Durán, Madrid #706/R
£395 $714 €600 Breakfast (46x65cm-18x26in) s. 14-Apr-4 Ansorena, Madrid #194/R
£395 $714 €600 Arosa River (40x80cm-16x31in) s. 14-Apr-4 Ansorena, Madrid #206/R
£399 $654 €550 Barcos, reflejos (24x33cm-9x13in) s. s.i.verso masonite. 27-May-3 Durán, Madrid #724/R
£414 $745 €600 Girl (50x25cm-20x10in) s. 26-Jan-4 Durán, Madrid #90/R
£423 $739 €600 Bilbao harbour (45x68cm-18x27in) s. cardboard. 16-Dec-3 Durán, Madrid #36/R
£507 $832 €700 Ciudad (52x77cm-20x30in) s.d.69. 27-May-3 Durán, Madrid #1295/R
£552 $916 €800 The Seine (37x46cm-15x18in) s.d.1979 board. 1-Oct-3 Ansorena, Madrid #728/R

SANZ, Demetrio (20th C) Spanish
Works on paper
£336 $601 €500 Bulls (50x70cm-20x28in) s. chl dr. 25-May-4 Durán, Madrid #623/R
£369 $661 €550 Three bulls (35x50cm-14x20in) s. chl dr. 25-May-4 Durán, Madrid #65/R
£369 $661 €550 Bulls (35x50cm-14x20in) s. chl dr. 25-May-4 Durán, Madrid #64/R
£369 $661 €550 Bulls (50x70cm-20x28in) s. chl dr. 25-May-4 Durán, Madrid #625/R
£537 $950 €800 Four horses (50x70cm-20x28in) s. chl dr. 27-Apr-4 Durán, Madrid #692/R
£738 $1321 €1100 Head of horses (50x70cm-20x28in) s. chl dr. 25-May-4 Durán, Madrid #63/R

SANZ, Eduardo (1928-) Spanish
£2069 $3434 €3000 Painting 21 (99x149cm-39x59in) s. i.verso oil fabric. 1-Oct-3 Ansorena, Madrid #565/R est:3000
£2639 $4354 €3800 Sea (50x50cm-20x20in) s. s.i.d.1995 verso. 2-Jul-3 Ansorena, Madrid #915/R

SAOZI (1940-) French
£442 $791 €650 Au bord du vertige blanc et noir (91x72cm-36x28in) s. prov. 21-Mar-4 Calmels Cohen, Paris #144/R

SAPONARO, Salvatore (1886-?) Italian
Sculpture
£1589 $2893 €2400 Salome (47cm-19in) pat bronze. 18-Jun-4 Stadion, Trieste #512/R est:600-800

SAPORETTI, Edgardo (1865-1909) Italian
£2000 $3620 €3000 Gate and flowers (17x13cm-7x5in) s.d.90 board. 2-Apr-4 Farsetti, Prato #543/R est:2200-2500

SAPORITI, Rinaldo (1840-1913) Italian
£507 $832 €700 Beached boats (50x70cm-20x28in) s. cardboard. 27-May-3 Finarte Semenzato, Milan #105/R
£2254 $3899 €3200 Landscape with peasants and cows (71x100cm-28x39in) s. 9-Dec-3 Finarte Semenzato, Milan #96/R est:3000-3500

SAPP, Allen (1929-) Canadian
£424 $729 €619 Having a smoke (11x16cm-4x6in) s. acrylic canvas on board prov. 2-Dec-3 Joyner Waddington, Toronto #427 (C.D 950)
£447 $800 €653 We'll be done soon (25x30cm-10x12in) s. i.verso. 6-May-4 Heffel, Vancouver #128/R (C.D 1100)
£541 $919 €790 Nice night for some hockey (30x25cm-12x10in) s. i.verso acrylic. 27-Nov-3 Heffel, Vancouver #75/R (C.D 1200)
£558 $1010 €815 Man chopping wood for the house (30x41cm-12x16in) s. i.d.2003 verso acrylic prov. 18-Apr-4 Levis, Calgary #105/R est:1500-2000 (C.D 1350)
£560 $1025 €818 Getting hay in the field at Red Pheasant (30x40cm-12x16in) s.i. acrylic. 1-Jun-4 Hodgins, Calgary #32/R (C.D 1400)
£610 $1091 €891 Taking wood to town (40x50cm-16x20in) s. i.d.1972 verso acrylic prov. 6-May-4 Heffel, Vancouver #126/R (C.D 1500)
£620 $1122 €905 Going to catch fish (41x51cm-16x20in) s. i.d.1996 verso acrylic prov. 18-Apr-4 Levis, Calgary #104/R est:2000-2500 (C.D 1500)
£625 $1063 €913 My grandfather Albert Soonia's place (41x51cm-16x20in) s. acrylic prov. 6-Nov-3 Heffel, Vancouver #102/R est:1200-1500 (C.D 1400)
£698 $1187 €1019 Working in the bush (41x51cm-16x20in) s. acrylic prov. 23-Nov-3 Levis, Calgary #119/R (C.D 1550)
£720 $1318 €1051 Indian drums (45x60cm-18x24in) s. acrylic prov. 1-Jun-4 Joyner Waddington, Toronto #273/R est:2000-2500 (C.D 1800)
£766 $1302 €1118 Cutting trees down (50x40cm-20x16in) s. i.verso acrylic. 27-Nov-3 Heffel, Vancouver #148/R est:1000-1200 (C.D 1700)
£933 $1531 €1362 Going into the house (41x51cm-16x20in) s.d.1987 acrylic. 28-May-3 Maynards, Vancouver #11 est:2200-2400 (C.D 2100)
£1040 $1903 €1518 Just about finished for today (40x50cm-16x20in) s. acrylic painted 1980 prov. 1-Jun-4 Joyner Waddington, Toronto #171/R est:2000-2500 (C.D 2600)
£1040 $1903 €1518 Time for a break (45x60cm-18x24in) s. acrylic. 1-Jun-4 Hodgins, Calgary #296/R est:2250-2750 (C.D 2600)
£1198 $2169 €1749 Untitled - rider in snow (41x51cm-16x20in) s. acrylic prov. 18-Apr-4 Levis, Calgary #103/R est:2000-2500 (C.D 2900)
£1220 $2183 €1781 Has half a load of wood (45x61cm-18x24in) s. i.d.1974 verso acrylic prov. 27-May-4 Heffel, Vancouver #21/R est:2000-2500 (C.D 3000)
£1240 $2244 €1810 Busy cutting wood (61x91cm-24x36in) s. acrylic prov. 18-Apr-4 Levis, Calgary #102/R est:3500-4000 (C.D 3000)
£1760 $3221 €2570 Two men stooking (45x60cm-18x24in) s. acrylic. 1-Jun-4 Joyner Waddington, Toronto #121/R est:2000-2500 (C.D 4400)
£2703 $4595 €3946 Some kids didn't have skates (76x121cm-30x48in) s. i.d.1976 verso acrylic prov. 27-Nov-3 Heffel, Vancouver #77/R est:3500-4500 (C.D 6000)

SAPPER, Richard (1891-1964) German
£403 $713 €600 Girls bathing (40x35cm-16x14in) s.d. i. stretcher. 30-Apr-4 Dr Fritz Nagel, Stuttgart #428/R

SAPUNOV, Nikolai Nikolaievich (1880-1912) Russian
£7586 $12669 €11000 Bouquet de fleurs (33x25cm-13x10in) s.d.1909 panel. 17-Nov-3 Claude Boisgirard, Paris #84/R est:2000-2500

SARA, Carlo (1844-1905) Italian
£694 $1200 €1013 Floral still life (53x107cm-21x42in) s. 10-Dec-3 Boos Gallery, Michigan #536/R est:800-1200

SARASIN, Regnault (1886-1943) Swiss
£490 $842 €700 Glaciers (53x65cm-21x26in) s. 3-Dec-3 Stadion, Trieste #1049/R

SARAZIN, Jacques (studio) (c.1592-1660) French
Sculpture
£12000 $20760 €17520 Lamentation, the Virgin with Christ, St John and Mary Magdalen (54x66cm-21x26in) terracotta exec.c.1640 prov.lit. 12-Dec-3 Sotheby's, London #216/R est:12000-18000

SARAZIN, Jean Philippe (attrib) (?-c.1795) French
£4079 $7505 €6200 Bergers et troupeaux pres de riviere (32x40cm-13x16in) panel pair. 25-Jun-4 Piasa, Paris #110/R est:7000-9000

SARDI, Jean (1947-) French
£1034 $1728 €1500 Still life of flowers (73x89cm-29x35in) s. 13-Nov-3 Neumeister, Munich #445/R est:1200-1400

SARESTONIEMI, Reidar (1925-1981) Finnish
£633 $1165 €950 The guard (45x57cm-18x22in) s.d.49 prov. 9-Jun-4 Bukowskis, Helsinki #560/R
£2550 $4693 €3800 Laplanders (60x50cm-24x20in) s. 25-Mar-4 Hagelstam, Helsinki #963 est:1000
£4196 $7133 €6000 Autumn has arrived (67x75cm-26x30in) s.d.58 exhib. 29-Nov-3 Bukowskis, Helsinki #306/R est:6000-8000
£10473 $18747 €15500 Panorama landscape from Lapland (81x116cm-32x46in) s.d.63. 8-May-4 Bukowskis, Helsinki #314/R est:12000-16000
£11888 $20210 €17000 Hazy morning (80x100cm-31x39in) s.d.72. 29-Nov-3 Bukowskis, Helsinki #264/R est:17000-22000
£14667 $26253 €22000 EEG from the living sea (115x115cm-45x45in) s.d.1973. 15-May-4 Hagelstam, Helsinki #215/R est:20000

£20979 $35664 €30000 You can't get away from this blue stuff (150x150cm-59x59in) s.d.73. 29-Nov-3 Bukowskis, Helsinki #254/R est:30000-40000

SARET, Alan (1944-) American
Sculpture
£7568 $14000 €11049 Nest of Comets (107x71x48cm-42x28x19in) Wire. 12-Feb-4 Sotheby's, New York #308/R est:1500-2500
Works on paper
£419 $700 €612 Four went entering (101x67cm-40x26in) col pencil. 19-Oct-3 Bonhams & Butterfields, Los Angeles #7087
£889 $1600 €1298 Untitled (11x22cm-4x9in) one s.d.1967 verso col pencil graphite one ink W/C. 24-Apr-4 David Rago, Lambertville #527/R est:200-400
£1333 $2400 €1946 Untitled (8x11cm-3x4in) one exec.1982 col pencil three. 24-Apr-4 David Rago, Lambertville #110/R est:400-800
£4444 $8000 €6488 Eight drawings (9x12cm-4x5in) four s.d.1983 col pencil eight. 24-Apr-4 David Rago, Lambertville #417/R est:600-1200

SARFATI, Alfred (20th C) ?
Works on paper
£284 $474 €400 Sidi Bou Said (38x25cm-15x10in) s. W/C. 19-Oct-3 Rabourdin & Choppin de Janvry, Paris #40

SARG, Mary (1911-) American
£761 $1400 €1111 Beached sailboat with huts in background (46x61cm-18x24in) s.d.33. 9-Jun-4 Alderfer's, Hatfield #515 est:400-600

SARGEANT, Bruce (20th C) British?
£750 $1245 €1095 Portrait of John Dugdale (51x40cm-20x16in) s. painted 1996 sold with figure study in oil two. 30-Sep-3 Sotheby's, London #382/R

SARGEANT, Geneve Rixford (1868-?) American
£1098 $1900 €1603 Judy - girl with braids (81x61cm-32x24in) s. prov.exhib. 10-Dec-3 Bonhams & Butterfields, San Francisco #6277/R est:2000-3000

SARGENT, Frederick (?-1899) British
£700 $1190 €1022 Roman maidens in a palace interior (34x26cm-13x10in) s.d.1897 panel. 25-Nov-3 Bonhams, Knowle #197/R

SARGENT, J S (1856-1925) American/British
Works on paper
£650 $1125 €949 Study for the winds (43x36cm-17x14in) chl prov. 10-Dec-3 Edgar Horn, Eastbourne #270/R

SARGENT, John Singer (1856-1925) British/American
£92486 $160000 €135030 Portrait of Cicely Horner (61x41cm-24x16in) s.d.1910 canvas laid down prov.lit. 10-Dec-3 Bonhams & Butterfields, San Francisco #6016/R est:300000-500000
£2840909 $5000000 €4147727 Venetian Loggia (71x81cm-28x32in) s. prov.exhib.lit. 19-May-4 Sotheby's, New York #18/R est:3000000-4000000
£4460228 $7850000 €6511933 Robert Louis Stevenson and his wife (51x61cm-20x24in) s.d.1885 prov.exhib.lit. 19-May-4 Sotheby's, New York #12/R est:5000000-7000000
Works on paper
£524 $965 €765 Portrait of Melisande (11x9cm-4x4in) s.i.verso pencil card prov. 9-Jun-4 Walker's, Ottawa #342/R (C.D 1300)
£3867 $7000 €5646 Studies for Astarte's veil (25x36cm-10x14in) pencil double-sided prov. 31-Mar-4 Sotheby's, New York #37/R est:8000-12000
£15385 $28000 €22462 Figures studies (47x61cm-19x24in) pencil chl paper on board pair. 29-Jun-4 Sotheby's, New York #208/R est:3000-5000
£19000 $32300 €27740 Portrait of Mrs Godfrey William Paget Mellor - Norah Alston (61x48cm-24x19in) s.d.1912 chl prov.lit. 20-Nov-3 Christie's, London #181/R est:4000-6000
£19886 $35000 €29034 Portrait of Laurence - Peter - Alexander Harrison esq (36x25cm-14x10in) pencil exec c.1900 prov.exhib.lit. 19-May-4 Sotheby's, New York #8/R est:20000-30000
£42614 $75000 €62216 Portrait of Mrs Reginald Grenville Eves (61x48cm-24x19in) s.d.1912 chl prov.lit. 19-May-4 Sotheby's, New York #9/R est:30000-50000
£81395 $140000 €118837 Boats in Venice (36x50cm-14x20in) s. W/C prov.exhib. 4-Dec-3 Christie's, Rockefeller NY #38/R est:120000-180000
£159091 $280000 €232273 Drying sails (36x51cm-14x20in) s.i. W/C paper on board exec c.1909 prov.exhib. 19-May-4 Sotheby's, New York #43/R est:200000-300000
£1363636 $2400000 €1990909 Madame Roger-Jourdain (30x56cm-12x22in) s. W/C pencil exec c.1883-85 prov.exhib.lit. 19-May-4 Sotheby's, New York #7/R est:1000000-1500000

SARGENT, Louis August (1881-1965) British
£400 $692 €584 Evening light, figures on a beach, St Ives (28x38cm-11x15in) s. board. 11-Dec-3 Lane, Penzance #141

SARGENT, Margarett W (1892-1978) American
Works on paper
£280 $500 €409 Taxi stand, Cuba (11x16cm-4x6in) s. W/C graphite. 14-May-4 Skinner, Boston #183/R
£615 $1100 €898 Blue socks (48x32cm-19x13in) s.d.1931 graphite W/C gouache. 14-May-4 Skinner, Boston #370/R

SARGENT, Paul Turner (1880-1946) American
£253 $400 €369 California landscape (30x18cm-12x7in) s. board. 7-Sep-3 Treadway Gallery, Cincinnati #585/R
£262 $450 €383 Early winter, Illinois (25x33cm-10x13in) painted c.1918. 7-Dec-3 Treadway Gallery, Cincinnati #554/R
£301 $475 €439 Haystacks (18x25cm-7x10in) canvas on board. 7-Sep-3 Treadway Gallery, Cincinnati #651/R
£305 $500 €442 California coast (14x17cm-6x7in) board painted c.1925 prov. 7-Jun-3 Treadway Gallery, Cincinnati #1470
£323 $600 €472 Summer clouds (15x20cm-6x8in) canvas on board painted c.1927. 7-Mar-4 Treadway Gallery, Cincinnati #591/R
£348 $550 €508 Turbulent skies (18x25cm-7x10in) canvas on board. 7-Sep-3 Treadway Gallery, Cincinnati #629/R
£396 $650 €574 Wildflowers (10x13cm-4x5in) painted c.1915 prov. 7-Jun-3 Treadway Gallery, Cincinnati #1422
£396 $650 €574 River landscape (10x13cm-4x5in) painted c.1915 prov. 7-Jun-3 Treadway Gallery, Cincinnati #1424
£396 $650 €574 River island (12x16cm-5x6in) s. board painted c.1918. 7-Jun-3 Treadway Gallery, Cincinnati #1447
£430 $800 €628 Midwestern landscape (25x36cm-10x14in) canvas on board painted c.1927. 7-Mar-4 Treadway Gallery, Cincinnati #589/R
£696 $1100 €1016 Seated woman in a California landscape (61x51cm-24x20in) 7-Sep-3 Treadway Gallery, Cincinnati #620/R
£759 $1200 €1108 Autumn stream (51x41cm-20x16in) s.d.1930 canvas on board. 7-Sep-3 Treadway Gallery, Cincinnati #663/R
£814 $1400 €1188 Working the soil (46x61cm-18x24in) s.d.1918. 7-Dec-3 Treadway Gallery, Cincinnati #631/R
£829 $1500 €1210 Mountain scene (51x61cm-20x24in) s. 3-Apr-4 Charlton Hall, Columbia #555/R est:1200-1800
£968 $1800 €1413 Sunlit path in autumn (46x36cm-18x14in) painted c.1920. 7-Mar-4 Treadway Gallery, Cincinnati #558/R est:1000-1500
£1280 $2100 €1856 Farmyard with chickens (14x17cm-6x7in) s. board painted c.1920. 7-Jun-3 Treadway Gallery, Cincinnati #1448 est:2000-3000

SARIAN, Martiros (1880-1972) Armenian
£2759 $4607 €4000 Tundra landscape with oxen (50x40cm-20x16in) s.d.1959. 13-Nov-3 Neumeister, Munich #447/R est:800-1000
£4138 $6910 €6000 Donkey rider in front of mountain scene (49x60cm-19x24in) s.d.1957. 13-Nov-3 Neumeister, Munich #446/R est:1000-1200
Works on paper
£1429 $2300 €2086 Courtyard (41x58cm-16x23in) s. gouache. 24-Aug-3 William Jenack, New York #130 est:800-1200

SARKA, Charles Nicolas (1879-1960) American
Works on paper
£227 $400 €331 Where the surf thunders, Tahiti (25x36cm-10x14in) s. W/C prov. 3-Jan-4 Collins, Maine #48/R

SARKISIAN, Paul (1928-) American
Works on paper
£1977 $3500 €2886 Five envelopes with landscape (71x91cm-28x36in) s.d.1976 s.d.verso mixed media exhib. 2-May-4 Bonhams & Butterfields, Los Angeles #3089/R est:5000-7000

SARKISIAN, Sarkis (1909-1977) American
£1018 $1700 €1486 The collaborators (48x36cm-19x14in) tempera or casein board. 17-Oct-3 Du Mouchelle, Detroit #2211/R est:200-400
£1622 $3000 €2368 Wine and lobster (76x91cm-30x36in) 13-Feb-4 Du Mouchelle, Detroit #2003/R est:2000-4000
£2312 $4000 €3376 Dying clown (102x152cm-40x60in) 12-Dec-3 Du Mouchelle, Detroit #2124/R est:6000-7000

SARLI, Domingo (1904-1989) South American
£847 $1600 €1237 Horses watering (89x112cm-35x44in) prov. 22-Feb-4 Galeria y Remates, Montevideo #72/R est:3000

SARMENTO, Juliao (1948-) Portuguese
£7000 $12880 €10220 Plateau (73x59cm-29x23in) s.i.d.1992 oil chl sand resin on canvas prov. 25-Jun-4 Christie's, London #256/R est:7000-9000
£7200 $13104 €10512 Trafaria (151x224cm-59x88in) acrylic spraypaint paper on board prov. 6-Feb-4 Sotheby's, London #241/R est:7000-9000
£42000 $76440 €61320 Emma 4 (189x220cm-74x87in) s.i.d.1990/91 verso acrylic graphite sand prov.exhib. 5-Feb-4 Christie's, London #223/R est:15000-20000
£50279 $90000 €73407 Suffering, despair and ascent (287x690cm-113x272in) s.i.d.1997 verso 3 parts prov. 13-May-4 Sotheby's, New York #349/R est:40000-60000
Works on paper
£5135 $9500 €7497 Muscatel and Quicksilver (70x100cm-28x39in) s.i.d.1997 verso mixed media canvas prov.exhib. 12-Feb-4 Sotheby's, New York #321/R est:6000-8000
£7027 $13000 €10259 Lies and sweets (53x66cm-21x26in) s.i.d.1997 verso mixed media canvas prov.exhib. 12-Feb-4 Sotheby's, New York #334/R est:6000-8000
£22973 $42500 €33541 Hand up to shield her eyes (190x220cm-75x87in) s.i.d.1993/94 verso mixed media canvas prov. 12-Feb-4 Sotheby's, New York #320/R est:18000-25000

SARNARI, Franco (1933-) Italian
£470 $874 €700 Tree (60x50cm-24x20in) s.d.1971 verso. 4-Mar-4 Babuino, Rome #60
£1245 $2116 €1780 Light (49x38cm-19x15in) s.i.verso pair. 18-Nov-3 Babuino, Rome #25/R est:1000-1500
£1993 $3388 €2850 Perspective (70x122cm-28x48in) s.i.verso. 18-Nov-3 Babuino, Rome #30/R est:1000-1500
Works on paper
£580 $987 €830 Fragments (32x30cm-13x12in) s.i. pastel. 18-Nov-3 Babuino, Rome #96

SARNOFF, Arthur (1912-2000) American
£2484 $4000 €3627 Grand panorama (61x91cm-24x36in) s. s.i. verso. 20-Aug-3 James Julia, Fairfield #1423/R est:4500-5500
Works on paper
£241 $450 €352 Happy family in field of daisies (53x36cm-21x14in) s. gouache col exec.c.1940. 26-Feb-4 Illustration House, New York #152
£838 $1400 €1223 The clay goddess (36x51cm-14x20in) s. gouache red black. 15-Nov-3 Illustration House, New York #138/R

SAROYAN, William (1908-1981) American
Works on paper
£321 $600 €469 Fresno (53x84cm-21x33in) s.i.d.March 16 1970 W/C prov.exhib. 29-Feb-4 Bonhams & Butterfields, San Francisco #4597
£399 $650 €583 April 4, 1967 (58x86cm-23x34in) s. W/C. 28-Sep-3 Bonhams & Butterfields, Los Angeles #7074

SARRAILLON, Benjamin (1900-1989) ?
£3147 $5413 €4500 Women at the fountain (72x100cm-28x39in) s. 8-Dec-3 Tajan, Paris #321/R est:4500-5500

SARRAZIN, Jean Baptiste (18th C) French
Works on paper
£1020 $1827 €1500 Village de pecheurs au bord d'un fleuve (15x23cm-6x9in) mono. W/C gouache prov. 17-Mar-4 Tajan, Paris #74/R est:1500

SARRI, Sergio (1938-) Italian
£387 $643 €550 Piano d'analisi (80x80cm-31x31in) s. s.i.d.1972. 14-Jun-3 Meeting Art, Vercelli #581
£800 $1472 €1200 Peculiar tools (99x79cm-39x31in) s.i.d.1973 verso acrylic exhib. 8-Jun-4 Finarte Semenzato, Milan #240/R est:1000-1200
£1087 $2011 €1620 Lulu (116x89cm-46x35in) s.i.d.1984 verso acrylic. 13-Mar-4 Meeting Art, Vercelli #57 est:500

SARRO, Adelio (1950-) Brazilian
£436 $772 €650 Man squatting (61x41cm-24x16in) s.d. 30-Apr-4 Dr Fritz Nagel, Stuttgart #430/R

SARSONY, Robert (1938-) American
£250 $400 €365 Dr Pepper (30x41cm-12x16in) s. masonite board painted c.1971. 20-Sep-3 Bunte, Elgin #294

SARTELLE, Herbert (1885-1955) American
£283 $450 €413 Desert landscape in bloom (41x51cm-16x20in) s. 5-May-3 O'Gallerie, Oregon #866/R
£472 $750 €689 Mountain landscape with stream (61x76cm-24x30in) s. 5-May-3 O'Gallerie, Oregon #840/R
£769 $1400 €1123 California mountain glow (61x76cm-24x30in) s. 19-Jun-4 Jackson's, Cedar Falls #3/R est:1000-1500
£943 $1500 €1377 Desert landscape with distant purple mountains (64x76cm-25x30in) s. 10-Sep-3 Alderfer's, Hatfield #373 est:400-600

SARTO, Andrea del (1487-1530) Italian
£194444 $350000 €283888 Madonna and Child with Infant Saint John in landscape (98x78cm-39x31in) panel prov.lit. 22-Jan-4 Sotheby's, New York #46/R est:400000-600000

SARTO, Andrea del (after) (1487-1530) Italian
£56818 $100000 €82954 Porta Pinti Madonna (193x124cm-76x49in) panel prov.lit. 19-May-4 Doyle, New York #6131/R est:70000-90000

SARTO, Andrea del (attrib) (1487-1530) Italian
Works on paper
£1189 $2021 €1700 Monk (42x26cm-17x10in) bears sig. ochre. 21-Nov-3 Reiss & Sohn, Konigstein #127 est:800

SARTO, Andrea del (circle) (1487-1530) Italian
£13333 $24000 €19466 Holy Family with saint Elizabeth and the infant Saint John the Baptist (88x69cm-35x27in) panel prov. 23-Jan-4 Christie's, Rockefeller NY #202/R est:20000-30000

SARTO, Andrea del (style) (1487-1530) Italian
£6154 $10585 €8985 Anna and Mary with infants Jesus and St John (118x95cm-46x37in) panel. 7-Dec-3 Uppsala Auktionskammare, Uppsala #46/R est:20000-25000 (S.KR 80000)
£10417 $17708 €15000 Holy Family (115x97cm-45x38in) board lit. 29-Oct-3 Il Ponte, Milan #747/R est:22000
£12000 $20760 €17520 Parable of the vineyard, calling the workers. Payment of workers (57x97cm-22x38in) en grisaille panel pair. 9-Dec-3 Sotheby's, Olympia #367/R est:6000-8000

SARTORE, Hugo (1935-) Uruguayan
£572 $940 €835 Nude (70x50cm-28x20in) s. 1-Jun-3 Subastas Odalys, Caracas #42
£1899 $3000 €2773 Composition (96x103cm-38x41in) s. 1-Dec-2 Subastas Odalys, Caracas #39/R
Sculpture
£1297 $2400 €1894 Construction (87x34x8cm-34x13x3in) s. s.i. verso painted wood construction exhib. 13-Jul-4 Christie's, Rockefeller NY #35/R est:3000-5000

SARTORELLI, Francesco (1856-1939) Italian
£320 $550 €467 Bridge over an Alp's stream (30x41cm-12x16in) s. 7-Dec-3 Grogan, Boston #20/R
£563 $975 €800 Courtyard in Tremezzo (20x25cm-8x10in) s. cardboard. 10-Dec-3 Sotheby's, Milan #56
£1448 $2462 €2114 Peasant woman sitting in landscape, lake beyond (42x81cm-17x32in) s. 19-Nov-3 Fischer, Luzern #1101/R est:2200-2500 (S.FR 3200)
£1544 $2763 €2300 Lake landscape (50x89cm-20x35in) s. 25-May-4 Finarte Semenzato, Milan #86/R est:1800-2000
£4348 $7130 €6000 Sunset on the rice field (74x150cm-29x59in) s. 27-May-3 Il Ponte, Milan #942

SARTORIO, Filippo (1903-1970) Italian
£333 $613 €500 Elfrida (45x35cm-18x14in) s.i.verso painted 1960. 12-Jun-4 Meeting Art, Vercelli #545/R

SARTORIO, Giulio Aristide (1861-1932) Italian
£10417 $17708 €15000 Saladin's tomb (60x75cm-24x30in) s.i.d.MCMXIX cardboard on canvas prov. 28-Oct-3 Il Ponte, Milan #284/R
£17606 $30458 €25000 Fregene beach (79x57cm-31x22in) s.d.MCMXXVII canvas on board prov. 10-Dec-3 Sotheby's, Milan #124/R est:25000-35000
£22535 $38986 €32000 Fishermen in Ardea (37x58cm-15x23in) s.i.d.MCMX prov. 11-Dec-3 Christie's, Rome #192/R est:13000-18000
Works on paper
£3521 $6092 €5000 June, coming rain (17x58cm-7x23in) s.d.1892 pastel card. 11-Dec-3 Christie's, Rome #193/R est:5000-7000
£4196 $7007 €6000 Ploughing (21x65cm-8x26in) s.d.1899 pastel card. 24-Jun-3 Finarte Semenzato, Rome #64/R est:4200
£5800 $9976 €8468 Coastal inlet, Italy (27x60cm-11x24in) s.i. pencil pastel. 4-Dec-3 Christie's, Kensington #35/R est:2000-3000

SARTORIS, Alberto (1901-?) American
£237 $425 €346 La citta Ritrovata (81x69cm-32x27in) s.i. oil varnish. 13-May-4 Dallas Auction Gallery, Dallas #386/R
£670 $1200 €978 Untitled (99x147cm-39x58in) s. 13-May-4 Dallas Auction Gallery, Dallas #412/R est:400-800

SARTORIUS, Francis (elder) (1734-1804) British
£3873 $6701 €5500 Bay hunter and groom in a landscape (46x56cm-18x22in) s.d.1772. 10-Dec-3 Christie's, Amsterdam #871/R est:3000-5000
£15000 $27600 €21900 Four racehorses outside the rubbing down (73x118cm-29x46in) s. 26-Mar-4 Sotheby's, London #38/R est:15000-20000
£19718 $34113 €28000 Laburnum, with jockey up (63x76cm-25x30in) s.i.d.1782. 10-Dec-3 Christie's, Amsterdam #872/R est:4000-6000
£21000 $36960 €30660 Chaise match run on Newmarket Heath on Wednesday 29 August 1750 (51x77cm-20x30in) i. 21-May-4 Christie's, London #82/R est:12000-18000

SARTORIUS, Francis (younger) (1777-?) British
£940 $1758 €1410 Shipwrecks off rocky coasts (29x44cm-11x17in) panel pair. 20-Jul-4 Dreweatt Neate, Newbury #204/R

SARTORIUS, J N (1759-1828) British
£4375 $7437 €6300 Study of a chestnut horse in a landscape (60x76cm-24x30in) bears sig d.1804. 28-Oct-3 Mealy's, Castlecomer #230

SARTORIUS, John Francis (c.1775-1831) British
£11000 $19360 €16060 Dead snipe hanging from a nail (34x30cm-13x12in) s. canvas on panel prov. 21-May-4 Christie's, London #32/R est:2500-3500

SARTORIUS, John Nott (1759-1828) British
£2320 $4200 €3387 Over the fence (35x44cm-14x17in) s.d.1811 prov. 30-Mar-4 Christie's, Rockefeller NY #41/R est:3000-5000
£2500 $4250 €3650 Gentleman on a chestnut hunter (37x46cm-15x18in) 27-Nov-3 Christie's, Kensington #53/R est:3000-4000
£2600 $4758 €3796 Coursing (36x47cm-14x19in) s.d.1812. 28-Jul-4 Bonhams, Knightsbridge #151/R est:3000-4000
£3800 $6308 €5548 Chestnut hunter in a landscape (34x43cm-13x17in) s.d.1799. 1-Oct-3 Woolley & Wallis, Salisbury #307/R est:3000-5000
£4400 $7304 €6424 Whipper in with a horse and hounds (34x43cm-13x17in) s/. 1-Oct-3 Woolley & Wallis, Salisbury #306/R est:4000-6000
£6011 $11000 €8776 Lost scent (51x62cm-20x24in) s. indis d. prov. 3-Jun-4 Christie's, Rockefeller NY #432/R est:15000-20000
£6500 $11830 €9490 Full cry. The kill (34x43cm-13x17in) pair. 1-Jul-4 Sotheby's, London #163/R
£10000 $17600 €14600 Full cry. The kill (42x53cm-17x21in) both s.d.1819 prov. pair. 21-May-4 Christie's, London #50/R est:8000-12000
£19000 $32300 €27740 Racehorse held by a groom beside a building (62x74cm-24x29in) s.d.1772 prov. 19-Nov-3 Tennants, Leyburn #1211/R est:4000-5000
£49180 $90000 €71803 Run with Mr James Drake Brockham's hounds at Beachborough Kent. Hunting scenes (51x62cm-20x24in) s.d.1792 set of six prov. 3-Jun-4 Christie's, Rockefeller NY #437/R est:80000-120000

SARTORIUS, John Nott (after) (1759-1828) British
Sculpture
£4545 $8000 €6636 Neck and neck (22cm-9in) brown pat. bronze. 18-May-4 Sotheby's, New York #199/R est:2000-3000

SARTORIUS, William (18th C) British
£880 $1628 €1285 Still life with fruit in basket (41x46cm-16x18in) 12-Feb-4 Andrew Hartley, Ilkley #814

SARTORIUS, William (attrib) (18th C) British
£1600 $2976 €2336 Peaches and plum on a silver dish. Peaches, grapes, red and whitecurrants and apple on a ledge (30x36cm-12x14in) pair. 4-Mar-4 Christie's, Kensington #657/R est:1500-2000
£1800 $3114 €2628 Still life of grapes, peaches and currants on a marble ledge (30x35cm-12x14in) sold with a companion. 11-Dec-3 Lyon & Turnbull, Edinburgh #28/R est:2000-3000
£6500 $11895 €9490 Wooded landscape with a dead swan, pheasants, hare and other birds, view of a country house (142x166cm-56x65in) 7-Jul-4 Bonhams, New Bond Street #102/R est:7000-10000

SARVIG, Edvard (1894-1968) Danish
£311 $567 €454 Woman by the sea (101x120cm-40x47in) 7-Feb-4 Rasmussen, Havnen #2215 (D.KR 3400)

SASPORTAS, Yehudit (1969-) Israeli
£5587 $10000 €8157 Fan (163x277cm-64x109in) acrylic MDF prov.exhib. 18-Mar-4 Sotheby's, New York #86/R est:10000-15000

SASS, Johannes (1897-1972) German
£1333 $2453 €2000 At the beach (105x85cm-41x33in) s.i.d.1953 verso tempera. 12-Jun-4 Villa Grisebach, Berlin #318/R est:2500-3500

SASSE, Jorg (1962-) American?
Photographs
£4000 $6680 €5840 9619, 1999 (146x220cm-57x87in) s.i.d.1999 num.3/4 verso c-print plexiglas prov. 22-Oct-3 Christie's, London #154/R est:4000-6000
£4800 $8016 €7008 5671, 1996 (103x180cm-41x71in) s.i.d.1996 num.1/6 c-print plexiglas prov. 22-Oct-3 Christie's, London #167/R est:4000-6000

SASSENBROUCK, Achille van (1886-1979) Belgian
£403 $745 €600 Paysage enneige (38x45cm-15x18in) s. panel. 15-Mar-4 Horta, Bruxelles #462
£420 $722 €600 Le faucheur sur fond de paysage (61x37cm-24x15in) s. panel. 8-Dec-3 Horta, Bruxelles #255
£500 $900 €750 Farmhouse in the snow (74x74cm-29x29in) s. panel. 26-Apr-4 Bernaerts, Antwerp #433/R
£671 $1242 €1000 Self portrait in army uniform (43x33cm-17x13in) s. 13-Mar-4 De Vuyst, Lokeren #367
£775 $1340 €1100 Sunny winter day (80x90cm-31x35in) s. 13-Dec-3 De Vuyst, Lokeren #366
£1067 $1909 €1600 Fishing boats in the harbour (80x90cm-31x35in) s. lit. 15-May-4 De Vuyst, Lokeren #373/R est:1500-2200
£1268 $2193 €1800 Mountain pool (80x90cm-31x35in) s. 13-Dec-3 De Vuyst, Lokeren #365/R est:2000-2200
Works on paper
£604 $1117 €900 Children (76x102cm-30x40in) s.d.1923 pastel. 13-Mar-4 De Vuyst, Lokeren #365

SASSI, Pietro (1834-1905) Italian
£667 $1193 €1000 View over Roman Forum to the Colosseum (14x22cm-6x9in) i.d. verso panel. 13-May-4 Bassenge, Berlin #5651/R

SASSNICK, Bruno (19/20th C) German?
£300 $501 €438 Portrait of a lady, in Oriental dress (74x50cm-29x20in) s.d.1906-08. 8-Oct-3 Christie's, Kensington #700/R

SASSOFERRATO (1609-1685) Italian
£10000 $18000 €14600 Head of the Madonna (43x34cm-17x13in) i. 21-Jan-4 Sotheby's, New York #57/R est:15000-20000
£15000 $27450 €21900 Virgin in prayer (40x34cm-16x13in) lit. 8-Jul-4 Sotheby's, London #214/R est:6000-8000
£15086 $27759 €22026 Madonna and Child (50x37cm-20x15in) prov.lit. 26-Mar-4 Koller, Zurich #3056/R est:20000-30000 (S.FR 35000)
£20000 $36600 €29200 Madonna and Child (74x62cm-29x24in) 8-Jul-4 Sotheby's, London #313/R est:12000-15000
£26027 $44247 €38000 Virgin praying (47x36cm-19x14in) 4-Nov-3 Ansorena, Madrid #42/R est:30000
£30000 $51900 €43800 Virgin annunciate surrounded by a garland of flowers (75x60cm-30x24in) 10-Dec-3 Christie's, London #85/R est:20000-30000

SASSOFERRATO (after) (1609-1685) Italian
£5556 $9056 €8000 Mary with child (80x70cm-31x28in) 24-Sep-3 Neumeister, Munich #363/R est:9000

SASSOFERRATO (studio) (1609-1685) Italian
£8500 $15300 €12410 Madonna and Child (49x38cm-19x15in) prov. 20-Apr-4 Sotheby's, Olympia #329/R est:5000-7000

SASSU, Aligi (1912-2000) Italian
£1867 $3360 €2800 Bay (12x20cm-5x8in) s. s.i.d.1972 verso board. 22-Apr-4 Finarte Semenzato, Rome #300/R est:2400-3500
£2000 $3580 €3000 Novice. Spanish landscape (11x22cm-4x9in) one oil acrylic cardboard one W/C two. 12-May-4 Stadion, Trieste #701/R est:3000-4000
£3873 $6430 €5500 Appearing (50x36cm-20x14in) s. tempera paper on canvas. 11-Jun-3 Finarte Semenzato, Milan #715/R
£7383 $13215 €11000 Yellow sky (17x29cm-7x11in) s. s.i.d.1968 verso prov.exhib. 25-May-4 Sotheby's, Milan #48/R est:7000
£10067 $18020 €15000 Little horses (33x49cm-13x19in) s. s.i.d.1942 verso cardboard. 30-May-4 Meeting Art, Vercelli #89 est:15000
£11565 $20701 €17000 Vase of flowers on pink coffee table (65x55cm-26x22in) s. cardboard on canvas. 16-Mar-4 Finarte Semenzato, Milan #333/R est:22000
£13333 $24533 €20000 Lioness downing a horse (50x69cm-20x27in) s. painted 1958. 8-Jun-4 Finarte Semenzato, Milan #348/R est:20000-22000
£15942 $26145 €22000 Worker (49x35cm-19x14in) s. paper on canvas exhib.lit. 27-May-3 Sotheby's, Milan #216/R est:15000-20000
£19310 $30897 €28000 River crossing (50x60cm-20x24in) s. s.i.d.1957 verso prov. 13-Mar-3 Galleria Pace, Milan #127/R est:40000-50000
Sculpture
£1000 $1840 €1500 Horses in love (40x33x23cm-16x13x9in) pat bronze. 12-Jun-4 Meeting Art, Vercelli #235/R est:1000
£1000 $1840 €1500 Venus (55x14x26cm-22x6x10in) s.i. num.57/150 pat bronze. 12-Jun-4 Meeting Art, Vercelli #378/R est:1000
Works on paper
£240 $374 €350 Donkey head. Chinese ink dr. 8-Apr-3 Il Ponte, Milan #1002
£500 $920 €750 Landscape in La Vittoria (25x33cm-10x13in) s. W/C exec.1997. 12-Jun-4 Meeting Art, Vercelli #297/R
£594 $993 €850 Bored (35x49cm-14x19in) s. s.i.d.1961 verso pencil. 26-Jun-3 Sant Agostino, Torino #162/R
£621 $1037 €900 Portrait (35x25cm-14x10in) s. ink. 13-Nov-3 Finarte Semenzato, Rome #147
£699 $1189 €1000 Meeting (22x28cm-9x11in) s. felt-tip pen. 20-Nov-3 Finarte Semenzato, Milan #49/R
£933 $1717 €1400 Warrior resting (32x22cm-13x9in) s. W/C. 12-Jun-4 Meeting Art, Vercelli #665/R
£993 $1808 €1500 Horses (12x17cm-5x7in) s. mixed media. 17-Jun-4 Galleria Pananti, Florence #95/R est:1500-1800
£1014 $1784 €1500 Girl with green eyes (24x33cm-9x13in) pastel. 19-May-4 Il Ponte, Milan #1093 est:1800-2000
£1342 $2483 €2000 Landscape in Lombardy (34x63cm-13x25in) W/C card. 13-Mar-4 Meeting Art, Vercelli #517 est:2000
£1400 $2576 €2100 Untitled (35x35cm-14x14in) s. W/C. 12-Jun-4 Meeting Art, Vercelli #611/R est:2000
£1408 $2338 €2000 Mujeres en un alanido de color (15x21cm-6x8in) s.d.1996 col ink cardboard. 14-Jun-3 Meeting Art, Vercelli #685/R est:2000
£1467 $2699 €2200 Old Milan (41x71cm-16x28in) W/C lead. 12-Jun-4 Meeting Art, Vercelli #255/R est:2000
£1701 $3044 €2500 Lady with hat (51x41cm-20x16in) s. mixed media paper on canvas. 22-Mar-4 Sant Agostino, Torino #494/R est:3500
£1931 $3090 €2800 Two figures at the bar (44x33cm-17x13in) s. mixed media. 13-Mar-3 Galleria Pace, Milan #73/R est:3000-4000
£2657 $4517 €3800 Bull scene (50x71cm-20x28in) s. s.i.d.1966 verso pastel chl. 25-Nov-3 Sotheby's, Milan #32/R est:2000-3000
£2667 $4800 €4000 Old riders (34x48cm-13x19in) s. ink paper on canvas exec.1973. 22-Apr-4 Finarte Semenzato, Rome #93/R est:4000-4500
£3448 $5759 €5000 Woman at mirror (100x70cm-39x28in) s. col ink cardboard. 17-Nov-3 Sant Agostino, Torino #279/R est:5000-7000
£6711 $12416 €10000 Dictator Aguirre (50x65cm-20x26in) s. s.i.d.1984 verso mixed media paper on canvas lit. 13-Mar-4 Meeting Art, Vercelli #559 est:10000

SASSY, Attila (1880-?) Hungarian
£1879 $3326 €2800 Luxure (111x82cm-44x32in) s.d.1912. 27-Apr-4 Artcurial Briest, Paris #140 est:2000-2500

SATO, Key (1906-1978) Japanese
£1476 $2746 €2200 Paysage d'homme (81x100cm-32x39in) s.d.72 s.i.d.72 verso. 3-Mar-4 Artcurial Briest, Paris #514 est:400-600
Works on paper
£789 $1453 €1200 Composition (28x35cm-11x14in) s.d.1972 mixed media. 27-Jun-4 Versailles Encheres #8

SATO, Peter (1945-1994) American
Works on paper
£800 $1400 €1168 Untitled (112x77cm-44x30in) pastel exec c.1992. 17-Dec-3 Christie's, Rockefeller NY #277/R
£914 $1600 €1334 Untitled (112x77cm-44x30in) s. pastel exec c.1992. 17-Dec-3 Christie's, Rockefeller NY #278/R est:1000-1500

SATO, Takezo (1891-1972) Japanese
Works on paper
£550 $935 €803 Devon shore (33x43cm-13x17in) s. W/C. 4-Nov-3 Bonhams, New Bond Street #12/R

SATORU, Abe (20th C) American?
Sculpture
£2391 $4400 €3491 Proud Tree (56cm-22in) s.d.63 base patinated metal. 12-Jun-4 Susanin's, Chicago #5101

SATRIANO DE CONDA (19/20th C) ?
Works on paper
£490 $817 €700 Les remparts de Mcoum au Maroc (36x54cm-14x21in) s.d.1915 W/C. 25-Jun-3 Maigret, Paris #36

SATRUSTEGUI, Rafael (1960-) Spanish
£510 $929 €750 Double black (146x114cm-57x45in) s. s.i.d.86 verso acrylic prov. 3-Feb-4 Segre, Madrid #326/R

SATTLER, Hermann (1892-1945) German
£313 $516 €450 Cows watering (36x50cm-14x20in) s. board. 3-Jul-3 Van Ham, Cologne #1437
£387 $670 €550 Farmer with two horses (70x90cm-28x35in) s. 10-Dec-3 Hugo Ruef, Munich #2490
£775 $1387 €1100 Horse and chariot racing (70x90cm 28x35in) s. i.verso board lit. 8-Jan-4 Allgauer, Kempten #2503/R

SATTLER, Hubert (1817-1904) Austrian
£521 $885 €750 Abbazia (14x18cm-6x7in) s.pseudonym J Stauffer panel. 28-Oct-3 Dorotheum, Vienna #181/R
£662 $1205 €1000 View of the Reinfall (20x27cm-8x11in) s. panel. 21-Jun-4 Dorotheum, Vienna #41/R
£986 $1706 €1400 View of the Jungfrau from Interlaken and the Untersee (20x27cm-8x11in) mono. panel. 10-Dec-3 Dorotheum, Vienna #2/R
£986 $1706 €1400 View of Zurich (11x16cm-4x6in) mono. board. 10-Dec-3 Dorotheum, Vienna #247/R
£1049 $1783 €1500 Swiss mountain valley (42x53cm-17x21in) mono. 20-Nov-3 Dorotheum, Salzburg #117/R est:2200-3000
£1800 $3330 €2628 Midday peace (41x32cm-16x13in) s. 15-Jan-4 Christie's, Kensington #836/R est:1000-1500

SATTLER, Hubert (attrib) (1817-1904) Austrian
£511 $900 €746 Grand tour painting of visitors at a tomb in a cathedral (79x64cm-31x25in) s. 21-May-4 North East Auctions, Portsmouth #899/R

£35000 $59500 €51100 Bathing in the Bosphorus (74x100cm-29x39in) i. 18-Nov-3 Sotheby's, London #307/R

SATTLER, Josef Ignaz (1725-1767) Austrian
Works on paper
£442 $791 €650 Joseph reconnu par ses freres (70x50cm-28x20in) s.i.d.1750 verso col chk pen brown ink four joined sheets. 18-Mar-4 Christie's, Paris #331/R

SAUBER, Robert (1868-1936) British
£270 $451 €394 Fete-Champetre (30x40cm-12x16in) s. panel. 20-Oct-3 Bonhams, Bath #69
£700 $1309 €1022 Study of a pretty girl wearing a blue floral dress (60x73cm-24x29in) s. 22-Jul-4 Tennants, Leyburn #895

SAUDEK, Jan (1935-) Czechoslovakian
Photographs
£1977 $3500 €2886 Marie no 142 (27x23cm-11x9in) s. photo 1972/printed later prov.lit. 27-Apr-4 Sotheby's, New York #35/R est:1000-2000

SAUER, Walter (1889-1972) Belgian
£5594 $9622 €8000 Scene de fete (84x66cm-33x26in) s.d.1927 panel. 2-Dec-3 Sotheby's, Amsterdam #74/R est:8000-12000
Works on paper
£350 $594 €500 La dentelliere. mono. crayon. 18-Nov-3 Galerie Moderne, Brussels #785/R
£367 $664 €550 Portrait de femme (22x17cm-9x7in) mono.d.1917 mixed media. 30-Mar-4 Campo, Vlaamse Kaai #151
£759 $1403 €1100 Jeune femme partiellement denudee (41x27cm-16x11in) s.d.1918 crayon drawing. 19-Jan-4 Horta, Bruxelles #65/R
£1034 $1914 €1500 Jeune femme nue s'etirant (31x25cm-12x10in) mono.d.1917 drawing. 19-Jan-4 Horta, Bruxelles #67 est:1200-1500
£2098 $3566 €3000 Mathilde enceinte (60x42cm-24x17in) mono.d.5 septembre 1919 dr. 1-Dec-3 Palais de Beaux Arts, Brussels #114/R est:3000-5000
£2207 $4083 €3200 Meditation (41x32cm-16x13in) s.d.1920 crayon drawing. 19-Jan-4 Horta, Bruxelles #66 est:1500-2000
£3200 $5728 €4800 Femme aux mains jointes (37cm-15in circular) s.d.1919 pastel black chk lit. 15-May-4 De Vuyst, Lokeren #444/R est:2500-3000

SAUERBIER, Kathleen (1903-1991) Australian
Works on paper
£725 $1320 €1059 Market, Montreuil-sur-mer (35x52cm-14x20in) s.i.d.1926 pastel. 16-Jun-4 Deutscher-Menzies, Melbourne #99/R est:2000-3000 (A.D 1900)

SAUERLAND, Philipp (1677-1762) German
£35714 $65000 €52142 Still life of shells and butterflies (31x38cm-12x15in) prov.exhib.lit. 17-Jun-4 Christie's, Rockefeller NY #22/R est:25000-35000

SAUERWEIN, Frank P (1871-1910) American
£1590 $2750 €2321 Nightfall at the Capistrano Mission (51x76cm-20x30in) s. board prov. 10-Dec-3 Bonhams & Butterfields, San Francisco #6314/R est:3000-5000
£14706 $27500 €21471 Indian teepee (15x23cm-6x9in) s.d.1904 board prov.exhib.lit. 24-Jul-4 Coeur d'Alene, Hayden #49/R est:5000-10000
Works on paper
£2059 $3500 €3006 Indian village (15x23cm-6x9in) s.d.1902 W/C prov. 1-Nov-3 Santa Fe Art, Santa Fe #170/R est:6000-8000

SAUGY, Louis (1863-?) French
Works on paper
£2802 $5015 €4091 In the Alps (21x27cm-8x11in) s. silhouette. 14-May-4 Dobiaschofsky, Bern #50/R est:6000 (S.FR 6500)

SAUL, F (19th C) ?
Sculpture
£8649 $16000 €12628 Nude woman (94cm-37in) carrara marble. 13-Feb-4 Du Mouchelle, Detroit #2107/R est:4000-6000

SAUL, Peter (1934-) American
Works on paper
£11043 $18000 €16123 Untitled (68x68cm-27x27in) s.d.64 crayon ink prov. 23-Sep-3 Christie's, Rockefeller NY #52/R est:8000-12000

SAULNIER, Odette (1928-) French
Works on paper
£278 $439 €400 Eline Vere (30x21cm-12x8in) s.d.2002 assemblage. 26-Apr-3 Auction Maastricht #93/R

SAUMAREZ, Marion (1885-1978) British
£480 $888 €701 Le beau Camille (90x70cm-35x28in) init. prov. 11-Feb-4 Cheffins, Cambridge #454/R
£1200 $2220 €1752 Portrait of Marie with violets in her hair (63x52cm-25x20in) prov. 11-Feb-4 Cheffins, Cambridge #448/R est:300-500
£1700 $3145 €2482 The old monk (63x52cm-25x20in) prov. 11-Feb-4 Cheffins, Cambridge #450/R est:200-300
£3000 $5550 €4380 Portrait of Ellen Griffiths, Madame Breakwell (90x71cm-35x28in) prov. 11-Feb-4 Cheffins, Cambridge #451/R est:800-1200
£3600 $6660 €5256 The Arab robe (63x42cm-25x17in) prov.exhib. 11-Feb-4 Cheffins, Cambridge #449/R est:800-1200
£5200 $9620 €7592 Madame Breakwell, seated at a window (180x112cm-71x44in) prov. 11-Feb-4 Cheffins, Cambridge #453/R est:2500-3500

SAUNDERS, Charles L (?-1915) British
£879 $1600 €1283 Punters on a river by a cottage (61x97cm-24x38in) s. 7-Feb-4 Sloans & Kenyon, Bethesda #1270/R est:1500-2500

SAUNDERS, Joseph I (fl.1772-1811) British
Miniatures
£1900 $3496 €2774 Harriet Abrams, wearing a white dress (7cm-3in) mono. gold frame seed pearl plaited hair border prov. 24-Jun-4 Bonhams, New Bond Street #104/R est:800-1200

SAUNDERS, Norman (1906-1988) American
£2994 $5000 €4371 Young woman figure skater has caught a chill (71x56cm-28x22in) s. painted c.1936-37. 15-Nov-3 Illustration House, New York #104/R est:5000-8000

SAUNDERS, Raymond (1934-) American
Works on paper
£240 $400 €350 Untitled (74x59cm-29x23in) W/C. 19-Oct-3 Bonhams & Butterfields, Los Angeles #7086
£300 $500 €438 RS-86-24 (74x58cm-29x23in) W/C. 19-Oct-3 Bonhams & Butterfields, Los Angeles #7085

SAUNIER, Noel (1847-1890) French
£2895 $5239 €4400 Cortege des lions en cage (55x82cm-22x32in) s. 19-Apr-4 Boscher, Cherbourg #833/R

SAURA, Antonio (1930-1998) Spanish
£1655 $2748 €2400 Untitled (77x55cm-30x22in) s.d.62 prov. 1-Oct-3 Ansorena, Madrid #392/R est:2400
£3020 $5346 €4500 Figure (33x24cm-13x9in) s.d.57 paper. 27-Apr-4 Durán, Madrid #75/R est:4500
£4167 $6875 €6000 Dog and face (26x24cm-10x9in) paper. 2-Jul-3 Ansorena, Madrid #863e/R
£8451 $14789 €12000 Crucifixion (41x31cm-16x12in) s.d.1993 acrylic paper prov. 16-Dec-3 Segre, Madrid #130/R est:4000
£9396 $16819 €14000 Autodafe (31x48cm-12x19in) s.d.86 oil collage mixed media board prov.exhib. 25-May-4 Dorotheum, Vienna #104/R est:14000-20000
£18092 $33289 €27500 Tete (48x36cm-19x14in) s. board exhib. 22-Jun-4 Durán, Madrid #192/R est:21000
£21127 $36549 €30000 Sp. (60x73cm-24x29in) s.d.58. 15-Dec-3 Ansorena, Madrid #980/R est:30000
£21277 $35532 €30000 Fifteen faces (130x97cm-51x38in) s.d.75 paint collage on panel prov.exhib. 20-Oct-3 Durán, Madrid #227/R est:30000
£24490 $43838 €36000 Sangre del Nacar (60x73cm-24x29in) s.d.1953 verso prov.1953. 21-Mar-4 Calmels Cohen, Paris #62/R est:20000-25000
£33103 $54952 €48000 Composition (60x73cm-24x29in) s.d.58. 1-Oct-3 Ansorena, Madrid #577/R est:48000
£34000 $61540 €49640 Retrato (53x74cm-21x29in) s.d.1960 prov. 1-Apr-4 Christie's, Kensington #241/R est:12000-18000
£36232 $59420 €50000 Portrait numbered 73 (59x73cm-23x29in) s. s.d.59 verso. 27-May-3 Durán, Madrid #2393/R est:36000
£40560 $68953 €58000 Portrait imaginaire de Philippe II (130x97cm-51x38in) prov. 25-Nov-3 Tajan, Paris #40/R est:60000-70000
£70000 $127400 €102200 Lesa (130x61cm-51x24in) s.d.56 s.i.d.verso prov.exhib. 4-Feb-4 Christie's, London #28/R est:55000-75000
£80000 $145600 €116800 Crucifixion X (130x162cm-51x64in) s.d.60 s.i.d.1960 stretcher prov.exhib.lit. 5-Feb-4 Sotheby's, London #40/R est:80000-120000
£85000 $156400 €124100 Hisha (162x128cm-64x50in) s.d.58 prov. 24-Jun-4 Christie's, London #35/R est:80000-120000
£140000 $257600 €204400 Catorce retratos (71x301cm-28x119in) one s. oil on fourteen canvases prov. 25-Jun-4 Christie's, London #169/R est:90000-120000
Works on paper
£2098 $3503 €3000 Roses (41x30cm-16x12in) s.d.1958 Indian ink page de garde. 11-Oct-3 Cornette de St.Cyr, Paris #68/R est:3000-4000
£2536 $4159 €3500 Untitled (48x37cm-19x15in) s.d.75 ink. 27-May-3 Sotheby's, Amsterdam #426/R est:3000-4000
£2553 $4136 €3600 Untitled (20x26cm-8x10in) s.d.77 mixed media. 20-May-3 Ansorena, Madrid #329/R est:3600
£3472 $5729 €5000 Figure (22x17cm-9x7in) ink. 2-Jul-3 Ansorena, Madrid #863d/R
£3497 $5839 €5000 1-no 7 (70x50cm-28x20in) s.d.5.7.58 Indian ink torn paper. 11-Oct-3 Cornette de St.Cyr, Paris #67/R est:5000-6000
£4667 $8587 €7000 Untitled (38x28cm-15x11in) s.d.79 gouache ink card. 8-Jun-4 Sotheby's, Amsterdam #299/R est:2500-3500
£4828 $8062 €7000 Compositions (49x16cm-19x6in) s.d.57 ink dr set of 4. 17-Nov-3 Durán, Madrid #177/R est:7000
£5000 $9200 €7500 Untitled (39x28cm-15x11in) s.d.79 gouache ink pencil card. 8-Jun-4 Sotheby's, Amsterdam #300/R est:2500-3500
£6338 $11092 €9000 Images (26x26cm-10x10in) s.d.75 ink dr set of 4. 16-Dec-3 Durán, Madrid #170/R est:7500
£7383 $13215 €11000 Frame (70x49cm-28x19in) s.d.65 ink prov. 26-May-4 Christie's, Paris #99/R est:7000-9000
£9722 $16042 €14000 Faces (20x42cm-8x17in) s.i.d.86 verso mixed media. 2-Jul-3 Ansorena, Madrid #863c/R est:14000
£19504 $32571 €27500 Composition (61x89cm-24x35in) s.d.62 mixed media collage. 20-Oct-3 Durán, Madrid #118/R
£41611 $77396 €62000 Untitled (112x163cm-44x64in) s.d.90 mixed media paper on canvas lit. 2-Mar-4 Ansorena, Madrid #855/R est:62000

SAURFELT, Leonard (1840-?) French
£1585 $2900 €2378 Figures in a landscape (56x79cm-22x31in) s.d.1892. 7-Jun-4 Everard, Savannah #476915/R est:1000-1500
£3103 $5183 €4500 Les lavandieres. Marche a Rouen (41x31cm-16x12in) s. panel pair. 16-Nov-3 Muizon & Le Coent, Paris #35/R

SAUSSY, Hattie (attrib) (1890-1978) American
£588 $1000 €858 Quiet waters (30x41cm-12x16in) init.i. canvasboard. 22-Nov-3 Jackson's, Cedar Falls #100/R est:500-750

SAUTHIER, Claude (1929-) Swiss
£776 $1389 €1133 Winter landscape (63x90cm-25x35in) s. panel. 14-May-4 Dobiaschofsky, Bern #101/R est:3500 (S.FR 1800)

SAUTIN, René (1881-1968) French
£699 $1168 €1000 Bord de Seine (33x41cm-13x16in) s.d.1925 cardboard on panel. 29-Jun-3 St-Germain-en-Laye Encheres #11/R
£1034 $1728 €1500 Chaumiere (46x55cm-18x22in) s. cardboard lit. 11-Nov-3 Lesieur & Le Bars, Le Havre #102
£1138 $1900 €1650 Risle a Montfort (38x55cm-15x22in) s. cardboard lit. 11-Nov-3 Lesieur & Le Bars, Le Havre #103
£2282 $4244 €3400 Le barrage de pont Audemer (54x73cm-21x29in) s.d.1930 cardboard. 7-Mar-4 Lesieur & Le Bars, Le Havre #127

SAUTS, Dirck (17th C) Dutch
£18000 $31140 €26280 Still life of crabs, oysters, apricots, a roemer and a pipe upon a stone ledge (23x32cm-9x13in) 168. 11-Dec-3 Sotheby's, London #167/R est:20000-30000

SAUTS, Dirck (attrib) (17th C) Dutch
£2113 $3697 €3000 Nature morte au plat d'huitres et verre de vine sur un entablement (51x47cm-20x19in) 18-Dec-3 Tajan, Paris #84 est:3000-4000

SAUTTER, Walter (1911-1991) Swiss
£270 $465 €394 The island of Chios (51x72cm-20x28in) mono.d.1977 acrylic paper. 8-Dec-3 Philippe Schuler, Zurich #3224 (S.FR 600)
£360 $620 €526 Snow melting (60x73cm-24x29in) mono.d.1973. 8-Dec-3 Philippe Schuler, Zurich #3356 (S.FR 800)

SAUVAGE, A S (?) French?
£1007 $1883 €1500 Nature morte aux canards (90x60cm-35x24in) 1-Mar-4 Coutau Begarie, Paris #167/R est:1000-1200

SAUVAGE, Philippe François (19th C) French
£1200 $2004 €1752 Playmates at the kitchen window (33x22cm-13x9in) s. panel. 8-Oct-3 Christie's, Kensington #822/R est:1500-2000

SAUVAGE, Pierre Paul (circle) (18/19th C) French
£8099 $14011 €11500 Le Massacre des Innocents (104x142cm-41x56in) painted c.1800. 12-Dec-3 Artus Associes, Paris #143

SAUVAGE, Pieter Joseph (1744-1818) Flemish
Miniatures
£4500 $8055 €6570 Jugate profiles of king Louis XVI, Queen Marie Antoinette and the Dauphin (7cm-3in circular) s. en grisaille. 25-May-4 Christie's, London #94/R est:2000-3000
Works on paper
£1241 $2272 €1800 Bacchanale 1. Bacchanale 2 (22x21cm-9x8in) wash pair. 1-Feb-4 Feletin, Province #120

SAUVAGE, Pieter Joseph (attrib) (1744-1818) Flemish
Miniatures
£1400 $2548 €2100 Jeune garcon (5cm-2in circular) en grisaille lit. 30-Jun-4 Pierre Berge, Paris #109/R est:1800-2000

SAUVAGE, Pieter Joseph (circle) (1744-1818) Flemish
£4645 $8500 €6782 Trompe l'oeil with putti and garlands surrounding a bas-relief (79x140cm-31x55in) 3-Jun-4 Christie's, Rockefeller NY #1170/R est:2000-3000

SAUVAGE, Serge (20th C) French
£578 $1035 €850 Marche Oriental (35x46cm-14x18in) s. 16-Mar-4 Vanderkindere, Brussels #41
£646 $1157 €950 Ostende, la petite plage (45x55cm-18x22in) s. cardboard. 16-Mar-4 Vanderkindere, Brussels #67
£662 $1205 €1000 Boulevard parisien anime (47x40cm-19x16in) s. cardboard. 15-Jun-4 Vanderkindere, Brussels #103
£680 $1218 €1000 La rue Nollet a Paris (40x50cm-16x20in) s. 16-Mar-4 Vanderkindere, Brussels #99
£850 $1522 €1250 La Porte Saint-Denis a Paris (45x68cm-18x27in) s. panel. 16-Mar-4 Vanderkindere, Brussels #91
£918 $1644 €1350 Marche a St-Eustache (60x81cm-24x32in) s. panel. 16-Mar-4 Vanderkindere, Brussels #87
£1497 $2679 €2200 Ostende, la petite plage (45x55cm-18x22in) s. cardboard. 16-Mar-4 Vanderkindere, Brussels #82 est:700-900

SAUVAGEAU, Louis (1822-?) French
Sculpture
£2667 $4800 €3894 Femme et amour - le feu (81cm-32in) s. bronze. 25-Apr-4 Hindman, Chicago #1575/R est:6000-8000
£3108 $5470 €4600 Femme et Amour (80cm-31in) s. pat bronze. 18-May-4 Galerie Moderne, Brussels #1517/R est:3500-4500

SAUVAIGE, Marcel Louis (?-1927) French
£397 $743 €600 Angelus breton (27x40cm-11x16in) s. board. 24-Jul-4 Thierry & Lannon, Brest #405

SAUVEE, Simon (20th C) French
£189 $350 €276 Still life pipe, cup, apple and a pitcher (23x18cm-9x7in) s.d.1953. 12-Mar-4 Jackson's, Cedar Falls #1012/R

SAUVIGNIER, Frederic (1873-1949) French
£375 $600 €548 Stars over the Alps (46x61cm-18x24in) s. 20-Sep-3 Sloans & Kenyon, Bethesda #145/R

SAUZAY, Adrien Jacques (1841-1928) French
£1207 $2016 €1750 Le village (33x62cm-13x24in) s. panel. 17-Nov-3 Tajan, Paris #155/R est:2000-3000
£1208 $2235 €1800 Bord de riviere (35x61cm-14x24in) s. 14-Mar-4 Eric Pillon, Calais #39/R
£1212 $2170 €1770 River landscape with washerwoman (32x61cm-13x24in) s. panel. 22-Mar-4 Philippe Schuler, Zurich #4429/R est:3500-4000 (S.FR 2800)
£2500 $4075 €3600 Paysage avec pecheur (33x62cm-13x24in) s.d.1876 panel. 26-Sep-3 Rabourdin & Choppin de Janvry, Paris #54/R est:1800-2000
£4000 $6640 €5840 On the Seine (46x62cm-18x24in) s. prov. 1-Oct-3 George Kidner, Lymington #185/R est:3000-4000

SAVAGE, Anne (1896-1971) Canadian
£2054 $3532 €2999 Fall landscape (22x30cm-9x12in) s. panel prov. 2-Dec-3 Joyner Waddington, Toronto #3/R est:3000-4000 (C.D 4600)
£2477 $4212 €3616 Young girls in a fishing village (29x34cm-11x13in) s. panel prov.lit. 27-Nov-3 Heffel, Vancouver #32/R est:6000-8000 (C.D 5500)
£2477 $4212 €3616 Road to Lake Wonish (30x36cm-12x14in) s. i.verso panel lit. 21-Nov-3 Walker's, Ottawa #57/R est:6000-8000 (C.D 5500)
£3604 $6126 €5262 La paysanne (30x35cm-12x14in) s. panel. 27-Nov-3 Heffel, Vancouver #143/R est:3000-4000 (C.D 8000)
£4800 $8784 €7008 Foliage (60x45cm-24x18in) s. 1-Jun-4 Joyner Waddington, Toronto #70/R est:12000-15000 (C.D 12000)
£4878 $8732 €7122 Laurentian landscape (30x35cm-12x14in) s. panel painted c.1930 double-sided prov.lit. 27-May-4 Heffel, Vancouver #120/R est:6000-8000 (C.D 12000)
£11111 $18222 €16222 Orchard near Lake Wonish (53x91cm-21x36in) s. board painted c.1938. 28-May-3 Maynards, Vancouver #100/R est:20000-24000 (C.D 25000)

SAVAGE, Augusta Christine (1900-1962) American
Sculpture
£9497 $17000 €13866 Head of a young black man (46cm-18in) s. bronzed plaster cast. 7-May-4 Sloans & Kenyon, Bethesda #1629/R est:4000-6000
£15934 $29000 €23264 Gamin (23cm-9in) i.verso polychromed plaster exec.c.1930. 19-Jun-4 Jackson's, Cedar Falls #14/R est:13000-17000

SAVAGE, Cedric (1901-1969) New Zealander
£275 $508 €402 Landscape (33x43cm-13x17in) s. board. 9-Mar-4 Watson's, Christchurch #105 (NZ.D 750)
£297 $512 €434 South Coast farm, Australia (28x38cm-11x15in) s.d.1930 board. 7-Dec-3 International Art Centre, Auckland #296/R (NZ.D 800)
£346 $619 €505 Kapiti Coast (34x50cm-13x20in) s. board painted c.1960 prov. 12-May-4 Dunbar Sloane, Wellington #192/R est:800-1500 (NZ.D 1000)
£350 $637 €511 Landscape, poplar tree (37x47cm-15x19in) s. i.verso board. 17-Jun-4 Clevedon Sale Rooms #1014
£435 $704 €631 Landscape with bridge (29x37cm-11x15in) s. board. 31-Jul-3 International Art Centre, Auckland #183/R est:1200-1600 (NZ.D 1200)
£484 $867 €707 Haystack (33x41cm-13x16in) s. board. 12-May-4 Dunbar Sloane, Wellington #228 est:500-1000 (NZ.D 1400)
£486 $773 €710 Spanish kitchen with Cedric at table (48x45cm-19x18in) s. canvas on board. 1-May-3 Dunbar Sloane, Wellington #62/R est:1000-2000 (NZ.D 1400)
£554 $991 €809 Landscape with river (51x70cm-20x28in) s. board. 12-May-4 Dunbar Sloane, Wellington #227 est:1000-2000 (NZ.D 1600)
£625 $1150 €913 Quiet lane (44x59cm-17x23in) s. board. 25-Mar-4 International Art Centre, Auckland #139/R (NZ.D 1750)
£937 $1491 €1368 Morning light, Old Silges (64x79cm-25x31in) s. canvas on board. 1-May-3 Dunbar Sloane, Wellington #84/R est:2000-3000 (NZ.D 2700)
£1128 $1917 €1647 Greek landscape (50x57cm-20x22in) s. board. 26-Nov-3 Dunbar Sloane, Wellington #79/R est:3000-4500 (NZ.D 3000)
£1128 $1917 €1647 Boats on the dry (54x68cm-21x27in) s. board. 26-Nov-3 Dunbar Sloane, Wellington #80/R est:3000-4500 (NZ.D 3000)
£1465 $2711 €2139 Boats in the dry (54x69cm-21x27in) s. board. 9-Mar-4 Watson's, Christchurch #10 est:5000-7500 (NZ.D 4000)
£1964 $3614 €2867 Spring time in Spain (54x64cm-21x25in) s. board. 25-Mar-4 International Art Centre, Auckland #80 est:3500-5500 (NZ.D 5500)
£2109 $3311 €3058 Fishing boats at Mediterranean port (50x68cm-20x27in) s. 27-Aug-3 Dunbar Sloane, Wellington #54/R est:5000-6000 (NZ.D 5800)
£2257 $3589 €3295 Fisherman of Aegina, Greece (50x69cm-20x27in) s. board. 1-May-3 Dunbar Sloane, Wellington #36/R est:6000-9000 (NZ.D 6500)
Works on paper
£346 $619 €505 Autumn (36x56cm-14x22in) s. W/C. 12-May-4 Dunbar Sloane, Wellington #191 est:1000-2000 (NZ.D 1000)
£1053 $1789 €1537 Yellow awning (51x63cm-20x25in) s. W/C prov. 26-Nov-3 Dunbar Sloane, Wellington #78/R est:3000-5000 (NZ.D 2800)
£1128 $1917 €1647 Country lane, Toledo (50x64cm-20x25in) s. W/C. 27-Nov-3 International Art Centre, Auckland #94/R est:3000-5000 (NZ.D 3000)

SAVAGE, Eugene (1883-1978) American
£2473 $4500 €3611 Figure in tropical landscape (28x38cm-11x15in) s.d.53 i.verso canvasboard prov. 15-Jun-4 John Moran, Pasadena #183 est:2000-3000
£10000 $17000 €14600 Bathers (74x71cm-29x28in) exhib. 30-Oct-3 Phillips, New York #77/R est:20000-30000

SAVANDER, Marjaana (20th C) Finnish
£465 $744 €660 Silk hen (60x40cm-24x16in) s. 18-Sep-3 Hagelstam, Helsinki #907/R
£1189 $2021 €1700 The house jug (71x47cm-28x19in) s.d.1991. 29-Nov-3 Bukowskis, Helsinki #250/R est:1000-1500

SAVARY, Robert (1920-) French
£1301 $2212 €1900 Printemps a Grasse (146x114cm-57x45in) s. painted 1969. 9-Nov-3 Eric Pillon, Calais #202/R

SAVELLI, Angelo (1911-1995) Italian
£611 $1100 €892 Untitled (22x27cm-9x11in) s.i.d.1974 verso acrylic cut canvas. 24-Apr-4 David Rago, Lambertville #548/R

£889	$1600	€1298	Ashent num 9 series (24x24cm-9x9in) s.i.d.1978/79 verso acrylic string collage. 24-Apr-4 David Rago, Lambertville #325/R est:100-200
£1000	$1800	€1460	Paradise VI (12x10cm-5x4in) s.i.d.1969 verso acrylic rope wood. 24-Apr-4 David Rago, Lambertville #200/R est:100

SAVERY, Jacob I (c.1545-1602) Dutch

Prints

£3000	$5370	€4500	Deer hunt (20x30cm-8x12in) etching copperplate. 13-May-4 Bassenge, Berlin #5301 est:3000
£3533	$6325	€5300	Deer hunt by water, chapel and tower (19x29cm-7x11in) etching copperplate. 13-May-4 Bassenge, Berlin #5302/R est:3000

SAVERY, Roeland (1576-1639) Dutch

£31868	$58000	€46527	Wooded landscape with cow, birds and other animals by a lake (63x92cm-25x36in) indis s.d. panel prov. 17-Jun-4 Christie's, Rockefeller NY #13/R est:60000-80000
£130000	$224900	€189800	Stag, deers, heron and other animals in a forest (76x109cm-30x43in) s. prov.exhib.lit. 10-Dec-3 Christie's, London #40/R est:120000-160000
£433333	$788667	€650000	Animals coming out ot the Ark (56x105cm-22x41in) s.d.1619 panel prov.lit. 29-Jun-4 Sotheby's, Paris #32/R est:800000-1200000

SAVERY, Roeland (attrib) (1576-1639) Dutch

£1800	$2934	€2628	Juno and attendants receiving the adoration of the birds (61x73cm-24x29in) 23-Sep-3 Anderson & Garland, Newcastle #423/R est:2000-3500

SAVERYS, Albert (1886-1964) Belgian

£2800	$5152	€4200	Still life with summer bouquet in a pink vase (50x40cm-20x16in) s. board. 9-Jun-4 Christie's, Amsterdam #82/R est:4000-6000
£3169	$5070	€4500	Still life with roses in a vase (59x50cm-23x20in) s. board. 22-Sep-3 Sotheby's, Amsterdam #311/R est:3000-5000
£3333	$6133	€5000	Still life with pink roses in a glass vase (60x49cm-24x19in) s. board. 9-Jun-4 Christie's, Amsterdam #80/R est:5000-7000
£3819	$6378	€5500	Sas van Astene (40x50cm-16x20in) s. panel. 21-Oct-3 Campo & Campo, Antwerp #267/R est:4000-6000
£4167	$6958	€6000	Bateaux au port (110x100cm-43x39in) s. 21-Oct-3 Campo & Campo, Antwerp #268/R est:6500-7500
£4545	$7818	€6500	Flower path (76x63cm-30x25in) painted c.1913-14. 2-Dec-3 Sotheby's, Amsterdam #55/R est:7000-9000
£4667	$8540	€7000	Soleil couchant sur la Lys (95x110cm-37x43in) s. prov. 7-Jun-4 Palais de Beaux Arts, Brussels #295/R est:7000-8500
£5655	$10462	€8200	Pont avec train sur la Lys (60x80cm-24x31in) s. 13-Jan-4 Vanderkindere, Brussels #27/R est:6250-8750
£6294	$10510	€9000	Jour de marche (45x60cm-18x24in) s. 13-Oct-3 Horta, Bruxelles #147/R est:7500-9500
£6944	$11597	€10000	La traversee de la Lys (55x82cm-22x32in) s. 21-Oct-3 Campo, Vlaamse Kaai #551/R est:10500-12000
£7639	$12757	€11000	Hiver sur la Lys (76x101cm-30x40in) s. 21-Oct-3 Campo, Vlaamse Kaai #550 est:12000-15000
£9155	$14648	€13000	Flower still lifes (60x50cm-24x20in) s. board pair. 22-Sep-3 Sotheby's, Amsterdam #310/R est:8000-12000
£11189	$19245	€16000	Landscape (80x100cm-31x39in) s. panel. 2-Dec-3 Sotheby's, Amsterdam #50/R est:15000-20000
£53333	$98133	€80000	Stille Avonden (151x125cm-59x49in) s.d.15 prov.exhib.lit. 8-Jun-4 Sotheby's, Amsterdam #40/R est:40000-60000

SAVERYS, Albert (attrib) (1886-1964) Belgian

£3618	$6658	€5500	Busy Flemish village street in winter (80x100cm-31x39in) s. 24-Jun-4 Dr Fritz Nagel, Stuttgart #750/R est:4000

SAVERYS, Jan (1924-) Belgian

Works on paper

£1141	$2042	€1700	Abstract composition (58x49cm-23x19in) s.d. chl chks. 25-May-4 Karl & Faber, Munich #519/R est:1200

SAVIAKJUK, Elisapie Taqaq (1914-) North American

Sculpture

£785	$1413	€1178	Inuit hunter carrying a polar bear (25cm-10in) s. grey soapstone. 26-Apr-4 Waddingtons, Toronto #134/R est:500-700 (C.D 1900)

SAVIGNAC, Camille de (19th C) French

£357	$571	€518	Girl with crab (96x66cm-38x26in) s. 15-May-3 Stuker, Bern #1140 (S.FR 750)

SAVIGNY (?) French

£2381	$3786	€3500	Un steamer de la CGT (90x54cm-35x21in) s. 21-Mar-3 Neret-Minet, Paris #717 est:2500-3000
£9220	$15397	€13000	Caique sur le Bosphore (68x92cm-27x36in) s. canvas on panel. 16-Jun-3 Gros & Delettrez, Paris #103/R est:9000-12000

SAVIGNY, Henri (1895-1944) French?

£1844	$3079	€2600	Le Grand Canal a Venise (48x65cm-19x26in) s. 19-Oct-3 Anaf, Lyon #272/R est:2500-2800

SAVILLE, Jenny (1970-) British

£180000	$331200	€262800	Knead (137x157cm-54x62in) s.d.1995-96 verso prov.exhib.lit. 24-Jun-4 Christie's, London #27/R est:180000-220000

SAVIN, Maurice (1894-1973) French

£280	$481	€400	La route en hiver (47x38cm-19x15in) s. 5-Dec-3 Maigret, Paris #112/R
£470	$864	€700	Still life (46x55cm-18x22in) s. 24-Mar-4 Joron-Derem, Paris #166
£493	$853	€700	Nature morte a la table et au pichet (64x53cm-25x21in) s. 10-Dec-3 Ferri, Paris #88/R
£759	$1259	€1100	Les meules (54x73cm-21x29in) s. 30-Sep-3 Blanchet, Paris #328/R
£1040	$1800	€1518	Deux femmes (58x71cm-23x28in) s.d.1964 prov. 9-Dec-3 Arthur James, Florida #108
£1057	$1797	€1543	Bedroom interior (32x44cm-13x17in) s. board. 5-Nov-3 Dobiaschofsky, Bern #930/R est:2600 (S.FR 2400)
£1145	$1947	€1672	Venus (92x73cm-36x29in) s. i. verso lit. 5-Nov-3 Dobiaschofsky, Bern #929/R est:5000 (S.FR 2600)
£1409	$2593	€2100	Les moissons (53x72cm-21x28in) s.d.1966 prov. 26-Mar-4 Neret-Minet, Paris #16/R est:2000
£5034	$9010	€7500	Venus (92x73cm-36x29in) s. i.. 30-May-4 Eric Pillon, Calais #119/R

SAVINI, Alfonso (1836-1908) Italian

£1150	$1840	€1679	Classical female holding a yarn winder in an interior (46x33cm-18x13in) s.d.1874. 16-Sep-3 Capes Dunn, Manchester #772

SAVINIO, Alberto (1891-1952) Italian

£14685	$24965	€21000	Portrait of woman (31x22cm-12x9in) s. tempera paper on canvas painted 1950. 29-Nov-3 Farsetti, Prato #539/R est:10000
£30769	$52308	€44000	Untitled (169x84cm-67x33in) oil tempera masonite painted 1949 lit. 29-Nov-3 Farsetti, Prato #538/R est:25000
£53691	$96107	€80000	Untitled (32x26cm-13x10in) s. tempera cardboard painted 1948-50. 29-May-4 Farsetti, Prato #432/R est:70000-85000
£209790	$356643	€300000	Ulysses and Polifemus (50x65cm-20x26in) s. tempera painted 1932 exhib.lit. 29-Nov-3 Farsetti, Prato #516/R est:300000-350000
£419580	$713287	€600000	Town of promises (97x146cm-38x57in) s.d.1928 prov.exhib.lit. 24-Nov-3 Christie's, Milan #329/R est:680000-900000

SAVIO, John (1902-1938) Norwegian

£2146	$3755	€3133	Man and woman on sleigh pulled by reindeer (24x33cm-9x13in) s. panel. 16-Dec-3 Grev Wedels Plass, Oslo #215/R est:15000-20000 (N.KR 25000)

Works on paper

£328	$545	€476	Female nude (25x11cm-10x4in) s. W/C exhib. 16-Jun-3 Blomqvist, Lysaker #1207/R (N.KR 3800)

SAVITSKY, Georgy (20th C) Russian

Works on paper

£629	$1070	€900	Meeting at the masquerade (23x25cm-9x10in) s.d.1917 mixed media. 29-Nov-3 Bukowskis, Helsinki #420/R

SAVITSKY, Jack (1910-1991) American

£278	$500	€406	Crucified miner (66x48cm-26x19in) board prov. 24-Apr-4 Slotin Folk Art, Buford #356/R
£359	$600	€524	Still life with boot (38x43cm-15x17in) board prov. 15-Nov-3 Slotin Folk Art, Buford #201/R
£419	$700	€612	Kennedy and son (10x25cm-4x10in) board prov. 15-Nov-3 Slotin Folk Art, Buford #198/R
£472	$850	€689	Coal miner boot still life (71x41cm-28x16in) board prov. 24-Apr-4 Slotin Folk Art, Buford #360/R
£667	$1200	€974	Adam and Eve (23x30cm-9x12in) board prov. 24-Apr-4 Slotin Folk Art, Buford #361/R est:1000-3000
£833	$1500	€1216	Reading railroad train (25x66cm-10x26in) board prov. 24-Apr-4 Slotin Folk Art, Buford #359/R est:2000-4000
£889	$1600	€1298	Peaceable Kingdom (23x48cm-9x19in) board prov. 24-Apr-4 Slotin Folk Art, Buford #357/R est:2000-4000
£944	$1700	€1378	Coal miner Jack (51x41cm-20x16in) canvasboard prov. 24-Apr-4 Slotin Folk Art, Buford #358/R est:1000-3000
£1677	$2800	€2448	Noah's ark (33x61cm-13x24in) board prov. 15-Nov-3 Slotin Folk Art, Buford #197/R est:2000-4000
£1946	$3250	€2841	Adam and Eve in the garden (46x66cm-18x26in) board prov. 15-Nov-3 Slotin Folk Art, Buford #200/R est:2000-4000
£1976	$3300	€2885	Mauch Chunk, PA 1892 (53x61cm-21x24in) board prov. 15-Nov-3 Slotin Folk Art, Buford #199/R est:1000-3000

Works on paper

£250	$450	€365	Farm couple, 1975 (76x61cm-30x24in) ink. 24-Apr-4 Slotin Folk Art, Buford #624/R
£269	$450	€393	Girl and lambs (46x38cm-18x15in) col pencil prov. 15-Nov-3 Slotin Folk Art, Buford #415/R
£278	$500	€406	Still life (36x43cm-14x17in) col pencil. 24-Apr-4 Slotin Folk Art, Buford #503/R
£329	$550	€480	Indian woman with baby (61x46cm-24x18in) ink graphite prov. 15-Nov-3 Slotin Folk Art, Buford #413/R
£333	$600	€486	Adam and Eve (76x61cm-30x24in) ink prov. 24-Apr-4 Slotin Folk Art, Buford #623/R
£359	$600	€524	Nude and devil (46x61cm-18x24in) ink graphite prov. 15-Nov-3 Slotin Folk Art, Buford #412/R
£359	$600	€524	Coal miner with breaker boy (61x46cm-24x18in) ink graphite prov. 15-Nov-3 Slotin Folk Art, Buford #414/R
£599	$1000	€875	Reading RR passing through mining town (46x61cm-18x24in) ink prov. 15-Nov-3 Slotin Folk Art, Buford #417/R

SAVITSKY, Konstantin Apollonovich (1844-1905) Russian

£40000	$68000	€60000	Portrait of street musician (107x80cm-42x31in) s.d.1868. 25-Nov-3 Christie's, London #137/R est:40000-60000

SAVOLDO, Giovanni Girolamo (1480-1548) Italian

£485916	$840634	€690000	Saint Dominique. Saint Veneranda. Saint Anthony. Saint Vincent (150x98cm-59x39in) prov.lit. in 4 parts. 14-Dec-3 Finarte, Venice #155/R

SAVONA, Virio da (1901-1995) Italian

£500	$920	€750	Landscape (50x60cm-20x24in) s.d.1961. 12-Jun-4 Meeting Art, Vercelli #936/R

SAVONANZI, Emilio (attrib) (1580-1660) Italian
£3620 $6154 €5285 Saint praying (87x115cm-34x45in) 19-Nov-3 Fischer, Luzern #1045/R est:8000-12000 (S.FR 8000)

SAVORY, Eva (fl.1920-1937) British
£420 $777 €613 Figures on a shoreline with a fort beyond (61x76cm-24x30in) s.d.1925 exhib. 14-Jul-4 Christie's, Kensington #1124/R

SAVRY, H (1823-1907) Dutch
£2313 $4140 €3400 Vaches dans la prairie (49x78cm-19x31in) panel. 22-Mar-4 Amberes, Antwerp #236

SAVRY, Hendrick (1823-1907) Dutch
£1844 $3079 €2600 Small livestock in the meadow (23x28cm-9x11in) s. panel. 20-Oct-3 Glerum, Amsterdam #32 est:2000-3000
£5674 $9475 €8000 Pastoral scene with shepherd, shepherdess and cattle (60x72cm-24x28in) s. 20-Oct-3 Bernaerts, Antwerp #482/R est:8000-10000

SAVRY, Hendrick (attrib) (1823-1907) Dutch
£1399 $2406 €2000 Cows in a meadow (65x100cm-26x39in) indis.s. 7-Dec-3 Sotheby's, Amsterdam #580a

SAVVAS, Nike (1964-) Australian
Works on paper
£410 $647 €599 Fly away (83x121cm-33x48in) s.i.d.1999 synthetic polymer prov. 2-Sep-3 Deutscher-Menzies, Melbourne #180/R (A.D 1000)

SAWCZUK, Bill (?) American
£7487 $14000 €11231 Signs of the season (102x122cm-40x48in) s. 24-Jul-4 Coeur d'Alene, Hayden #206/R est:10000-15000

SAWERT, Karl (attrib) (1888-?) German
£1200 $2172 €1800 Stormy day on Sylt (47x68cm-19x27in) s. i. verso. 3-Apr-4 Badum, Bamberg #18/R est:1800

SAWFORD-DYE, Ernest (1873-1965) Canadian
Works on paper
£242 $445 €353 Lambing time (24x34cm-9x13in) s. i.verso W/C. 9-Jun-4 Walker's, Ottawa #124/R (C.D 600)

SAWKA, Jan (1946-) Polish?
Works on paper
£636 $1150 €954 Abstract composition (75x54cm-30x21in) s.d.1977 Indian ink pen paper board. 4-Apr-4 Agra, Warsaw #71/R (P.Z 4500)

SAWREY, Hugh (1923-1999) Australian
£749 $1378 €1094 Old Dolly, the sulky mare (51x61cm-20x24in) s. 28-Jun-4 Australian Art Auctions, Sydney #81 (A.D 2000)
£1121 $1748 €1625 Tilbooroo horses (23x29cm-9x11in) s. board. 1-Aug-2 Joel, Victoria #306 est:1800-2500 (A.D 3250)
£1374 $2501 €2006 Pram (19x25cm-7x10in) s. s.i.verso board. 16-Jun-4 Deutscher-Menzies, Melbourne #513/R est:2500-4000 (A.D 3600)
£1570 $2905 €2292 Beef tea, she neaver nagged (35x30cm-14x12in) s. s.i.verso board. 10-Mar-4 Deutscher-Menzies, Melbourne #298/R est:4000-6000 (A.D 3800)
£1592 $2929 €2324 Street, Redfern (51x61cm-20x24in) s. 28-Jun-4 Australian Art Auctions, Sydney #121 (A.D 4250)
£1685 $3101 €2460 Wedding of the painted doll (31x41cm-12x16in) s. 28-Jun-4 Australian Art Auctions, Sydney #96 (A.D 4500)
£1908 $3186 €2767 The Yarners, Diamantina Lake Station (30x35cm-12x14in) s. board. 30-Jun-3 Australian Art Auctions, Sydney #75 (A.D 4750)
£2008 $3353 €2912 Quinn's farm (30x35cm-12x14in) s. board. 30-Jun-3 Australian Art Auctions, Sydney #134 (A.D 5000)
£2054 $3224 €2999 Morning mist over the western tiers - Midland Tasmania (70x90cm-28x35in) s. 24-Nov-2 Goodman, Sydney #29/R est:4500-6500 (A.D 5750)
£2099 $3821 €3065 Wool rollers, binde-bango shed (30x35cm-12x14in) s. s.i.verso. 16-Jun-4 Deutscher-Menzies, Melbourne #297/R est:3000-4000 (A.D 5500)
£2099 $3821 €3065 Home from town (30x35cm-12x14in) s. s.i.verso board prov. 16-Jun-4 Deutscher-Menzies, Melbourne #515/R est:3500-5500 (A.D 5500)
£2236 $4002 €3265 Through the homestead gates (29x38cm-11x15in) s. i.verso board. 10-May-4 Joel, Victoria #291 est:2500-3000 (A.D 5500)
£2273 $3864 €3319 Never never men (30x40cm-12x16in) s. s.i.verso. 29-Oct-3 Lawson Menzies, Sydney #119/R est:5000-7000 (A.D 5500)
£2996 $5542 €4374 Thunderbolt robbing the coach (31x41cm-12x16in) s. s.i.verso. 10-Mar-4 Deutscher-Menzies, Melbourne #491/R est:3000-4000 (A.D 7250)
£2996 $5513 €4374 Stage coach, Cobb and Co (44x61cm-17x24in) s. board. 28-Jun-4 Australian Art Auctions, Sydney #95 (A.D 8000)
£3049 $5457 €4452 Ah Sam's horse (50x60cm-20x24in) s. s.i.verso prov. 4-May-4 Sotheby's, Melbourne #229/R est:4500-6500 (A.D 7500)
£3320 $5544 €4980 The shearers picnic (50x60cm-20x24in) s. acrylic. 27-Oct-3 Goodman, Sydney #164/R est:8000-12000 (A.D 8000)
£3367 $6196 €4916 Bewildered Padre, Country Padre series (47x58cm-19x23in) s. i.verso board. 29-Mar-4 Goodman, Sydney #212/R est:7000-10000 (A.D 8250)
£3435 $6252 €5015 Stockmen by a waterhole, Western Queensland (30x41cm-12x16in) s. s.i.d. 16-Jun-4 Deutscher-Menzies, Melbourne #301/R est:7000-10000 (A.D 9000)
£3435 $6252 €5015 Mouth organ player (50x60cm-20x24in) s. s.i.stretcher. 16-Jun-4 Deutscher-Menzies, Melbourne #304/R est:7500-10000 (A.D 9000)
£3729 $6339 €5444 Along the moonie (75x100cm-30x39in) s. i.verso prov. 24-Nov-3 Sotheby's, Melbourne #139/R est:8000-12000 (A.D 8800)
£3933 $7236 €5742 Country race meeting (50x61cm-20x24in) s. 28-Jun-4 Australian Art Auctions, Sydney #110 (A.D 10500)
£4307 $7925 €6288 Filling the water canteen, Saxby waterhole (76x101cm-30x40in) s. board. 28-Jun-4 Australian Art Auctions, Sydney #136 (A.D 11500)
£4580 $8336 €6687 Clandestine meeting, Queensland (61x51cm-24x20in) s. s.i.verso. 16-Jun-4 Deutscher-Menzies, Melbourne #300/R est:9000-12000 (A.D 12000)
£4962 $9031 €7245 Smoko in the shearing shed, Cuttaburra (51x61cm-20x24in) s. s.i.verso board prov. 16-Jun-4 Deutscher-Menzies, Melbourne #296/R est:7000-10000 (A.D 13000)
£5081 $9096 €7418 Bagging the chestnut colt (73x98cm-29x39in) s. i.verso composition board prov. 4-May-4 Sotheby's, Melbourne #260/R est:12000-18000 (A.D 12500)
£5466 $8800 €7980 Farm House, Quinn's Farm series, Meringandan, Darling Downs, Queensland (74x98cm-29x39in) s. i.verso. 25-Aug-3 Sotheby's, Paddington #361 est:8000-12000 (A.D 13500)
£5932 $10085 €8661 Bush breed, Western Queensland (75x101cm-30x40in) s. s.i.verso prov. 24-Nov-3 Sotheby's, Melbourne #146/R est:6000-8000 (A.D 14000)
£6568 $11165 €9589 Rod Heieman's packhorses, Bramwell Station, Cape York Penninsula (75x100cm-30x39in) s. i.verso prov. 24-Nov-3 Sotheby's, Melbourne #108/R est:8000-12000 (A.D 15500)
£6612 $12231 €9654 Territory blokes (50x60cm-20x24in) s. i.verso prov. 10-Mar-4 Deutscher-Menzies, Melbourne #310/R est:8000-12000 (A.D 16000)
£7851 $13347 €11462 Cockatoo (74x98cm-29x39in) s. s.i.verso board. 29-Oct-3 Lawson Menzies, Sydney #44/R est:18000-25000 (A.D 19000)
£7851 $13347 €11462 When Smithy rung the shed (74x100cm-29x39in) s. i.verso. 29-Oct-3 Lawson Menzies, Sydney #45/R est:20000-25000 (A.D 19000)
£10744 $19876 €15686 Moriaty's shout (75x100cm-30x39in) s. s.i.stretcher. 10-Mar-4 Deutscher-Menzies, Melbourne #308/R est:17000-20000 (A.D 26000)
£10744 $19876 €15686 When quigley won the Boulia cup (76x102cm-30x40in) s. s.i.d.verso prov. 10-Mar-4 Deutscher-Menzies, Melbourne #309/R est:16000-24000 (A.D 26000)

SAWYER, Helen (1900-1999) American
£265 $475 €387 Tropical landscape with figures picnicking under trees (41x51cm-16x20in) s. i.verso. 29-May-4 Brunk, Ashville #446/R
£580 $1050 €847 Untitled ladies (56x46cm-22x18in) s. board. 3-Apr-4 Outer Cape Auctions, Provincetown #65/R
£730 $1350 €1066 Autumn dunes, Truro (51x61cm-20x24in) s. 17-Jul-4 Outer Cape Auctions, Provincetown #62/R
£1061 $1900 €1549 In autumn (30x41cm-12x16in) s. 16-May-4 CRN Auctions, Cambridge #32/R
Works on paper
£245 $400 €358 Untitled landscape (23x33cm-9x13in) s. W/C. 19-Jul-3 Outer Cape Auctions, Provincetown #97/R

SAWYIER, Paul (1865-1917) American
Works on paper
£1183 $2200 €1727 Mountain Stream (11x17cm-4x7in) s.d.15 pencil W/C. 3-Mar-4 Christie's, Rockefeller NY #26/R est:2000-3000
£9945 $18000 €14520 Abandoned sheer, Kentucky River (36x48cm-14x19in) s. W/C. 3-Apr-4 Neal Auction Company, New Orleans #427/R est:12000-18000

SAX, Theodore Jozef (1782-1846) Dutch
£7778 $14000 €11356 Still life of lilacs and other flowers in a glass vase, bird's nest resting on a marble ledge (41x34cm-16x13in) s. panel prov.exhib. 22-Jan-4 Sotheby's, New York #238/R est:15000-20000

SAXELIN, Oskar (1862-1949) Finnish
£278 $464 €400 Still life of flowers (27x46cm-11x18in) s. 23-Oct-3 Hagelstam, Helsinki #810/R
£625 $1044 €900 Coastal landscape (18x25cm-7x10in) s. 23-Oct-3 Hagelstam, Helsinki #806/R

SAY, Frederick Richard (c.1827-1860) British
£750 $1380 €1095 Portrait of a gentleman thought to be Abel Smith ESQ. MP (75x61cm-30x24in) 8-Jun-4 Bonhams, Knightsbridge #180/R

SAY, Frederick Richard (attrib) (c.1827-1860) British
£400 $716 €584 Portrait of Sir Edward Celebrooke (92x71cm-36x28in) i.verso. 27-May-4 Christie's, Kensington #95/R

SAYAGO, Adolfo (1963-) Uruguayan
£240 $400 €350 Seascape (58x58cm-23x23in) s.d.81. 7-Oct-3 Galeria y Remates, Montevideo #82
£353 $600 €515 Boats (60x60cm-24x24in) s. 20-Nov-3 Galeria y Remates, Montevideo #165/R

SAYER, John (20th C) American
Works on paper
£437 $800 €656 Tulips (53x48cm-21x19in) pastel. 10-Jul-4 Hindman, Chicago #462/R

SAYER, Raymond (19th C) American
Works on paper
£377 $600 €550 Urban street and green with figures (33x48cm-13x19in) s.d.1897 W/C. 10-Sep-3 Alderfer's, Hatfield #271/R

SAYERS, Reuben (1815-1888) British
£1200 $2220 €1752 Portrait of a young girl holding a rabbit (91x71cm-36x28in) oval. 10-Feb-4 Bonhams, Knightsbridge #164/R est:1000-1800

SAYRE, Fred Grayson (1879-1938) American
£1648 $3000 €2406 Pool in a mountain eucalyptus landscape (76x91cm-30x36in) s. 15-Jun-4 John Moran, Pasadena #58b est:4000-6000
£2793 $5000 €4190 Desert landscape (51x61cm-20x24in) s. 16-May-4 Abell, Los Angeles #417/R

SBISA, Carlo (1889-1964) Italian
£3497 $6014 €5000 Landscape near te Isonzo (60x72cm-24x28in) s.d.1928. 3-Dec-3 Stadion, Trieste #1097/R est:3000-4000

SCACCABAROZZI, Antonio (1936-) Italian
£1220 $2000 €1781 Quadrati, 5, come prestesto (60x60cm-24x24in) s.i.d.1971 white painted perforated canvas prov. 28-May-3 Sotheby's, Amsterdam #106/R est:1000-1500
Sculpture
£1341 $2200 €1958 Varoazione sul quadrato number 5 (60x60cm-24x24in) s.i.d.77 verso white board prov. 28-May-3 Sotheby's, Amsterdam #115/R est:1000-1500

SCACCIATI, Andrea (1642-1704) Italian
£9200 $15916 €13432 Flowers in an urn on a marble ledge (66x53cm-26x21in) prov. 12-Dec-3 Christie's, Kensington #271/R est:7000-10000

SCACCIATI, Andrea (attrib) (1642-1704) Italian
£4667 $8540 €7000 Still life with vase of flowers (83x66cm-33x26in) 1-Jun-4 Sotheby's, Milan #174/R est:7000-10000
£5800 $10614 €8468 Carnation, narcissism cornflowers and other flowers in a bronze urn on a ledge (73x68cm-29x27in) 7-Jul-4 Bonhams, New Bond Street #123/R est:3000-5000

SCADDON, Robert (fl.1743-1774) British
£3000 $5400 €4380 Portrait of a gentleman (45x35cm-18x14in) s.d.1747. 21-Jan-4 Sotheby's, Olympia #7/R est:1000-1500

SCAGLIA, Cesare (1866-1944) Italian
£521 $885 €750 Valsesiana (60x45cm-24x18in) s. lit. 1-Nov-3 Meeting Art, Vercelli #57

SCAGLIA, Girolamo (attrib) (fl.1657-1686) Italian
£18121 $33342 €27000 Young woman spinning (115x178cm-45x70in) 27-Mar-4 Farsetti, Prato #340/R est:30000

SCAGLIA, Michele (1859-1918) Italian
£369 $653 €550 Landscape with dog (40x24cm-16x9in) s.indis.d. board. 1-May-4 Meeting Art, Vercelli #300
£503 $891 €750 Countryside in Piedmonte (23x34cm-9x13in) init. board. 1-May-4 Meeting Art, Vercelli #224
£733 $1349 €1100 Still life (35x45cm-14x18in) s. board. 14-Jun-4 Sant Agostino, Torino #205/R
£1241 $2061 €1800 Hand reading (72x103cm-28x41in) s. 1-Oct-3 Della Rocca, Turin #16/R est:2000-2500
£2482 $4145 €3500 Card game at the inn (34x52cm-13x20in) board. 20-Oct-3 Sant Agostino, Torino #273/R est:3500-4500

SCAGLIONE, Giuseppe Oreste (1887-?) Italian
£272 $487 €400 Vase of flowers (70x50cm-28x20in) s. cardboard. 22-Mar-4 Sant Agostino, Torino #20/R

SCAGLIONE, Raffaele (1945-) Italian
Works on paper
£600 $1104 €900 Praying in the fields (50x70cm-20x28in) s. s.i.verso pastel on vellum exec.2004. 10-Jun-4 Galleria Pace, Milan #49/R
£685 $1164 €1000 Untitled (50x70cm-20x28in) s.verso pastel. 7-Nov-3 Galleria Rosenberg, Milan #98/R

SCAILLIET, Émile Philippe (1846-1911) French
Sculpture
£3100 $5642 €4526 Naked figure of Paris holding half the golden apple (34cm-13in) s.d.1874 ivory bronze red marble stand. 29-Jun-4 Sotheby's, Olympia #415/R est:2000-3000

SCAIOLA, Giuseppe (1951-) Italian
£333 $613 €500 He does not play the horn, hedoes not play the drum (50x40cm-20x16in) s.i.d.1984 acrylic. 12-Jun-4 Meeting Art, Vercelli #16

SCALATELLI, Gino (20th C) Italian
Works on paper
£1232 $2020 €1700 View of the Thames with boats (70x100cm-28x39in) s.i. W/C. 27-May-3 Il Ponte, Milan #928 est:1400-1500

SCALBERT, Jules (1851-?) French
£703 $1300 €1026 Interior scene with female nude (64x53cm-25x21in) s. 24-Jan-4 Jeffery Burchard, Florida #56a/R
£10000 $18000 €14600 Crown of roses (130x97cm-51x38in) s. 22-Apr-4 Christie's, Rockefeller NY #137/R est:20000-30000
Works on paper
£365 $653 €540 Elegante mirant son buste (76x45cm-30x18in) s.i.d.1900 pastel. 10-May-4 Horta, Bruxelles #507

SCALBERT, Jules (attrib) (1851-?) French
£6419 $11490 €9500 Toilette (80x46cm-31x18in) 10-May-4 Amberes, Antwerp #304a/R

SCALDAFERRI, Sante (20th C) El Salvadorian
£376 $700 €549 Retirantes, Bahia (59x49cm-23x19in) s.d.1989 i.d.verso panel prov. 5-Mar-4 Skinner, Boston #595/R
£806 $1500 €1177 Remembiando os Velhos Tempos, Bahia (99x99cm-39x39in) s.d.1986 s.i.d.verso panel prov. 5-Mar-4 Skinner, Boston #600/R est:1000-1500

SCALELLA, Jules (1895-?) American
£1372 $2250 €2003 Impressionist landscape with canal and house (46x51cm-18x20in) s.d.1925. 4-Jun-3 Alderfer's, Hatfield #382/R est:2000-3000

SCALUTELLI, Gino (?) Italian
Works on paper
£500 $895 €750 Fishing in the lagoon (24x31cm-9x12in) s. W/C. 12-May-4 Stadion, Trieste #726/R

SCANAVINO, Emilio (1922-1986) Italian
£306 $548 €450 Plot (35x28cm-14x11in) s.d.65 s.i.d.verso paint on terracotta. 16-Mar-4 Finarte Semenzato, Milan #235
£347 $566 €500 Rite (30x43cm-12x17in) tempera cardboard painted 1952. 24-Sep-3 Cambi, Genoa #1192
£909 $1545 €1300 Untitled (30x31cm-12x12in) acrylic paper painted 1960. 19-Nov-3 Cambi, Genoa #432
£1389 $2194 €2000 Untitled (49x69cm-19x27in) mixed media card. 6-Sep-3 Meeting Art, Vercelli #288 est:2000
£1399 $2378 €2000 Untitled (35x50cm-14x20in) s. acrylic chl. 20-Nov-3 Finarte Semenzato, Milan #26/R est:2200-2400
£1733 $3120 €2600 Plots (68x12cm-27x5in) s. tempera card. 22-Apr-4 Finarte Semenzato, Rome #215/R est:2200-2500
£1901 $3327 €2700 Plot (51x35cm-20x14in) s. card. 16-Dec-3 Finarte Semenzato, Milan #335/R est:1300-1700
£2245 $3816 €3210 From above (30x30cm-12x12in) s.i.verso painted 1974 prov. 18-Nov-3 Babuino, Rome #516/R est:1000-1500
£2276 $3641 €3300 Untitled (49x52cm-19x20in) s. acrylic board. 13-Mar-3 Galleria Pace, Milan #68/R est:3600-4600
£2324 $3858 €3300 Untitled (60x47cm-24x19in) s. acrylic cardboard prov. 11-Jun-3 Finarte Semenzato, Milan #579/R est:2800
£2448 $4161 €3500 Study (46x38cm-18x15in) s. s.d.1962 verso. 24-Nov-3 Christie's, Milan #217/R est:3000-4000
£2826 $4635 €3900 Untitled (68x96cm-27x38in) s. acrylic cardboard. 29-May-3 Galleria Pace, Milan #54/R est:6000
£3194 $5431 €4600 Image A (37x51cm-15x20in) s.d.1961 cardboard prov.lit. 28-Oct-3 Il Ponte, Milan #244/R
£4196 $7133 €6000 Ladder (100x81cm-39x32in) s.verso canvas on board lit. 20-Nov-3 Finarte Semenzato, Milan #231/R est:6000-7000
£5634 $9352 €8000 Shapes in evolution (40x50cm-16x20in) s.d.57 prov.exhib.lit. 11-Jun-3 Finarte Semenzato, Milan #659/R
£6338 $10521 €9000 Triangolo Spezzato (100x100cm-39x39in) s.verso painted 1968. 14-Jun-3 Meeting Art, Vercelli #558/R est:9000
£6667 $12267 €10000 Impossible to be a geometrical form (100x100cm-39x39in) s. painted 1971. 8-Jun-4 Finarte Semenzato, Milan #362/R est:12000-15000
£7047 $12614 €10500 First composition (65x81cm-26x32in) s.d.59 s.i.d.verso exhib.lit. 25-May-4 Sotheby's, Milan #83/R est:7000
£8108 $14270 €12000 White image (90x115cm-35x45in) s.d.1957 s.i.d.verso. 24-May-4 Christie's, Milan #235/R est:6000-8000
£8333 $13667 €11500 Sindone (116x90cm-46x35in) s.d.1957 s.i.d.verso prov.lit. 27-May-3 Sotheby's, Milan #126/R est:6000-8000
£9091 $15455 €13000 Circle (100x100cm-39x39in) s. s.i.verso. 24-Nov-3 Christie's, Milan #213/R est:10000-15000
£9091 $15455 €13000 Icon (100x100cm-39x39in) s. board lit. 20-Nov-3 Finarte Semenzato, Milan #193/R est:8500-9000
£9155 $15197 €13000 Sesso morto (73x102cm-29x40in) s.d.1961 panel. 14-Jun-3 Meeting Art, Vercelli #592/R est:10000
£11111 $17556 €16000 Endless alphabet (81x100cm-32x39in) painted 1982. 6-Sep-3 Meeting Art, Vercelli #608 est:15000
£12667 $23307 €19000 Endless alphabet (146x112cm-57x44in) s. s.i.verso painted 1981 lit. 12-Jun-4 Meeting Art, Vercelli #870/R est:15000
£14094 $25228 €21000 Curved image (100x100cm-39x39in) s.i.d.1968 verso lit. 30-May-4 Meeting Art, Vercelli #56 est:15000
£14765 $27315 €22000 I built a white triangle (150x150cm-59x59in) s.d.1966 lit. 13-Mar-4 Meeting Art, Vercelli #410 est:20000
Works on paper
£336 $621 €500 Untitled (25x17cm-10x7in) s.d.1962 pencil pastel. 13-Mar-4 Meeting Art, Vercelli #314
£503 $931 €750 Untitled (20x28cm-8x11in) s.d.1957 Chinese ink. 13-Mar-4 Meeting Art, Vercelli #299
£528 $877 €750 Esplosione (27x19cm-11x7in) s.d.1955 Indian ink. 14-Jun-3 Meeting Art, Vercelli #56/R
£775 $1286 €1100 Untitled (23x31cm-9x12in) s.d.1954 mixed media paper on board. 13-Jun-3 Farsetti, Prato #168/R
£933 $1717 €1400 Untitled (34x24cm-13x9in) s.d.58 pencil. 8-Jun-4 Finarte Semenzato, Milan #246/R est:1500-2000
£1379 $2303 €2000 Composition (34x48cm-13x19in) s.d.60 mixed media paper on canvas. 14-Nov-3 Farsetti, Prato #284/R est:1600-1900
£1497 $2679 €2200 Untitled (25x35cm-10x14in) s. mixed media. 22-Mar-4 Sant Agostino, Torino #434/R
£1517 $2428 €2200 Untitled (16x35cm-6x14in) s.d.1966 1967 mixed media three. 13-Mar-3 Galleria Pace, Milan #94/R est:1700-2200
£1600 $2944 €2400 Study (34x45cm-13x18in) s. mixed media cardboard exec.1964. 12-Jun-4 Meeting Art, Vercelli #491/R est:2000
£4333 $7800 €6500 Untitled (45x54cm-18x21in) s.d.1958 mixed media on canvas. 22-Apr-4 Finarte Semenzato, Rome #216/R est:3500-4000
£4800 $8832 €7200 Composition (98x69cm-39x27in) s. mixed media board prov. 14-Jun-4 Porro, Milan #37/R est:6500-8000

SCANDINAVIAN SCHOOL, 18th C
£9396 $17289 €14000 The Penitent Magdalene (106x83cm-42x33in) 25-Mar-4 Hagelstam, Helsinki #1047 est:1800

SCANGA, Italo (1932-) American
Sculpture
£2825 $5000 €4125 Untitled (86x63cm-34x25in) s.d.1976 wood paint. 2-May-4 Bonhams & Butterfields, Los Angeles #3051/R est:3000-5000

SCANLAN, Robert Richard (c.1801-1876) Irish
Works on paper
£980 $1695 €1431 Portrait of James Meyer Esquire and his two favourite spaniels. i.verso W/C. 14-Dec-3 Desmond Judd, Cranbrook #1104
£980 $1695 €1431 Louisa Joana, Anne Sophia and Eliza Meyer, daughters of Christian Paul Meyer. i.verso W/C. 14-Dec-3 Desmond Judd, Cranbrook #1105

£1333 $2413 €2000 Musicians, playing a fiddle, a flute, a guitar and a box organ (22x16cm-9x6in) s. three d.1833 W/C set of four. 31-Mar-4 James Adam, Dublin #31/R

SCAPATICCI, Giulio (1933-) Italian

£267 $491 €400 Landscape from the window (40x50cm-16x20in) s.d.1969. 12-Jun-4 Meeting Art, Vercelli #192

SCARAMUZZA, Francesco (1803-1896) Italian

Works on paper

£900 $1557 €1314 Cupid and Psyche (43x54cm-17x21in) col chk. 12-Dec-3 Christie's, Kensington #411

SCARAVAGLIONE, Concetta Maria (1900-1975) American

Sculpture

£1676 $3000 €2447 Woman (53x18cm-21x7in) s.verso walnut. 16-May-4 Wright, Chicago #130/R est:2000-3000

SCARBOROUGH, Frederick W (fl.1896-1939) British

Works on paper

£300 $537 €438 Fishing haven (33x51cm-13x20in) s.i. W/C. 25-May-4 Gildings, Market Harborough #410
£380 $635 €555 Approaching the harbour wall (25x33cm-10x13in) s. W/C bodycol. 14-Oct-3 David Lay, Penzance #348/R
£586 $995 €856 Low tide, Fifeshire (25x34cm-10x13in) s.i. W/C. 21-Nov-3 Walker's, Ottawa #250/R (C.D 1300)
£620 $1128 €930 Gunter-rigged sailing vessels moored off a coastal harbour (33x51cm-13x20in) s.i. W/C. 20-Jun-4 Wilkinson, Doncaster #300
£650 $1164 €949 London Bridge (24x16cm-9x6in) s.i. W/C bodycol. 26-May-4 Christie's, Kensington #451/R
£1000 $1810 €1460 Shipping in a harbour (18x47cm-7x19in) s. W/C. 2-Apr-4 Bracketts, Tunbridge Wells #414/R est:700-1000
£1050 $1901 €1533 Low tie, Pittenweem, Fifeshire (24x33cm-9x13in) s. W/C. 30-Mar-4 Sworder & Son, Bishops Stortford #585/R est:1000-1200
£1200 $1908 €1752 Sailing boats in the Thames estuary (24x49cm-9x19in) s. W/C. 10-Sep-3 Cheffins, Cambridge #447
£1448 $2418 €2114 Low tide, Largo, Fife (23x33cm-9x13in) s.i. W/C. 17-Nov-3 Waddingtons, Toronto #72/R est:1500-2000 (C.D 3200)
£1900 $3174 €2774 Shipping on the Thames near London Bridge (24x34cm-9x13in) s. W/C. 17-Nov-3 Waddingtons, Toronto #73/R est:1500-2500 (C.D 4200)
£1900 $3458 €2774 Pool of London (24x34cm-9x13in) s.i. W/C htd white. 1-Jul-4 Mellors & Kirk, Nottingham #721/R est:1200-1600
£2841 $5000 €4148 Greenwich Reach, London (25x36cm-10x14in) s.i. pencil W/C htd white. 18-May-4 Bonhams & Butterfields, San Francisco #184/R est:2000-3000
£3000 $5100 €4380 Whiby harbour. Early morning, Lowestoft (33x16cm-13x6in) s. W/C pair. 29-Oct-3 Bonhams, Chester #393/R est:1500-2500
£3000 $5100 €4380 Off LImehouse (52x34cm-20x13in) s.i. pencil W/C. 19-Nov-3 Christie's, Kensington #383/R
£4500 $7785 €6570 Blackwall Reach, London (17x52cm-7x20in) s.i. W/C. 11-Dec-3 Lyon & Turnbull, Edinburgh #84/R est:2000-3000

SCARBROUGH, Frank William (fl.1896-1939) British

Works on paper

£340 $568 €496 Vessels on the Thames, St Paul's beyond (18x30cm-7x12in) s. W/C. 10-Oct-3 Richardson & Smith, Whitby #83
£750 $1253 €1095 Fishing boats off Lynn, Norfolk (24x33cm-9x13in) s. W/C. 9-Jul-3 Peter Wilson, Nantwich #79
£800 $1336 €1168 Fishing boats, Yarmouth (23x33cm-9x13in) s. W/C. 9-Jul-3 Peter Wilson, Nantwich #80
£1100 $1936 €1606 London Bridge, London (30x61cm-12x24in) W/C. 22-May-4 British Auctioneer #735 est:800-900
£1500 $2640 €2190 Tower Bridge, London (30x61cm-12x24in) W/C. 22-May-4 British Auctioneer #736 est:800 900
£1800 $3294 €2628 Eventide, Lynn. Unloading (39x20cm-15x8in) both s. W/C pair. 6-Jul-4 Bearnes, Exeter #412/R est:600-800
£2050 $3588 €2993 Arrival of boats, Whitby (15x23cm-6x9in) s.i.d.13 April 1912 W/C. 16-Dec-3 Capes Dunn, Manchester #740
£3200 $5120 €4672 Sunset on the Thames London (23x33cm-9x13in) s.i. W/C htd white. 16-Sep-3 Bonhams, New Bond Street #38/R est:2000-3000
£6000 $9600 €8760 London Bridge. Early morning, Blackwall Reach, London (24x34cm-9x13in) s.i. W/C htd white pair. 16-Sep-3 Bonhams, New Bond Street #47/R est:5000-8000

SCARCELLINO, Ippolito (1551-1620) Italian

£8333 $13917 €12000 Madonna and Child with Saint John (60x57cm-24x22in) 22-Oct-3 Finarte Semenzato, Milan #58/R est:12000-15000
£10072 $16518 €14000 Christ appearing to the Madonna (80x35cm-31x14in) prov. 4-Jun-3 Sotheby's, Milan #69/R est:6000-8000
£15000 $25950 €21900 Conversion of Saint Paul (40x56cm-16x22in) panel prov. 11-Dec-3 Sotheby's, London #179/R est:8000-12000
£16547 $27137 €23000 Adoration of the Shepherds (80x35cm-31x14in) prov. 4-Jun-3 Sotheby's, Milan #70/R est:6000-8000
£16547 $27137 €23000 Wedding of the Virgin (80x35cm-31x14in) prov. 4-Jun-3 Sotheby's, Milan #68/R est:6000-8000
£19444 $35000 €28388 Fidelity, Abundance, Fame and Vanity (35x147cm-14x58in) 22-Jan-4 Sotheby's, New York #20/R est:20000-30000
£21583 $35396 €30000 Saint Joseph and the Angel (80x35cm-31x14in) prov. 4-Jun-3 Sotheby's, Milan #71/R est:6000-8000
£23000 $41400 €33580 Resurrection of Christ (22x19cm-9x7in) i. silvered copper. 22-Apr-4 Sotheby's, London #61/R est:8000-12000

Works on paper

£884 $1583 €1300 Etude d'homme nu (38x13cm-15x5in) black pencil white chk. 19-Mar-4 Piasa, Paris #17

SCARCELLINO, Ippolito (attrib) (1551-1620) Italian

£2667 $4880 €4000 Madonna enthroned wth Saint Dominique, Saint Francis and Saint George (66x35cm-26x14in) 1-Jun-4 Sotheby's, Milan #11/R est:4000-6000

SCARCELLINO, Ippolito (circle) (1551-1620) Italian

£6500 $11245 €9490 Holy Family (26x20cm-10x8in) panel. 12-Dec-3 Christie's, Kensington #182/R est:7000-10000

SCARFE, Gerald (1936-) British

Works on paper

£480 $802 €701 Caricature studies (53x47cm-21x19in) s. ink htd white. 14-Oct-3 Bonhams, New Bond Street #249

SCARI, A (?) ?

£724 $1209 €1057 Countryman with his dogs and horses in a field (26x39cm-10x15in) s. 17-Nov-3 Waddingtons, Toronto #303/R (C.D 1600)

SCARLETT, Rolph (1889-1984) American

£1173 $2100 €1713 Untitled (23x23cm-9x9in) s. 16-May-4 Wright, Chicago #244/R est:900-1200

Works on paper

£233 $400 €340 Untitled, abstraction (28x23cm-11x9in) estate st.verso gouache board painted c.1940. 7-Dec-3 Treadway Gallery, Cincinnati #706/R
£407 $728 €594 Composition (28x21cm-11x8in) init. mixed media. 4-May-4 Ritchie, Toronto #57/R est:1000-1500 (C.D 1000)
£435 $800 €635 Modernist composition (33x41cm-13x16in) s. mixed media. 10-Jun-4 Swann Galleries, New York #205/R
£436 $750 €637 Untitled, abstraction (18x23cm-7x9in) estate st.verso gouache board painted c.1940. 7-Dec-3 Treadway Gallery, Cincinnati #707/R
£447 $800 €653 Untitled (10x13cm-4x5in) gouache pencil. 16-May-4 Wright, Chicago #249/R
£818 $1300 €1194 Geometric abstract (23x28cm-9x11in) s. W/C gouache. 4-May-3 William Jenack, New York #168
£1374 $2500 €2006 Abstract (38x28cm-15x11in) s. W/C gouache. 8-Feb-4 William Jenack, New York #237 est:2500
£1647 $2800 €2405 Untitled (38x28cm-15x11in) s. gouache on board. 9-Nov-3 Wright, Chicago #236 est:800-1200
£1706 $2900 €2491 Untitled (20x20cm-8x8in) i.verso gouache. 9-Nov-3 Wright, Chicago #234 est:2000-3000

SCARPA, Gino (1924-) Italian

Works on paper

£348 $602 €508 The happy dancer at St.Zani Polo (100x64cm-39x25in) s. W/C Indian ink. 13-Dec-3 Blomqvist, Lysaker #1334/R (N.KR 4000)

SCARPITTA, Salvatore (1919-) American

£6522 $10696 €9000 Composition (100x71cm-39x28in) s.d.56 tempera paper on canvas. 30-May-3 Farsetti, Prato #300/R

SCARVELLI, Spyridon (1868-1942) Greek

Works on paper

£528 $914 €750 Felouques aux bords du Nil (36x22cm-14x9in) s. W/C. 15-Dec-3 Gros & Delettrez, Paris #454
£750 $1373 €1095 Graves (37x22cm-15x9in) s. W/C. 7-Jul-4 Cheffins, Cambridge #5
£800 $1416 €1168 Pyramids at Giza (23x34cm-9x13in) s.i. W/C. 27-Apr-4 Bonhams, New Bond Street #61/R
£1000 $1670 €1460 Three Egyptian views (17x29cm-7x11in) s. W/C gouache three. 14-Oct-3 Sotheby's, London #78/R est:1000-2000
£1000 $1790 €1460 Street in Cairo (31x18cm-12x7in) s. W/C. 11-May-4 Bonhams, New Bond Street #16/R est:1000-1500
£1400 $2338 €2044 Dhows on the Nile, Egypt (25x43cm-10x17in) s. W/C over pencil htd bodycol. 14-Oct-3 Sotheby's, London #86/R est:1200-1800
£1700 $3043 €2482 Cairo, Eygpt. Tomb of the califs (38x24cm-15x9in) s.i.verso W/C. 26-May-4 Sotheby's, Olympia #303/R est:600-800
£1800 $3150 €2628 View of the Nile (37x23cm-15x9in) s. W/C prov. 16-Dec-3 Bonhams, New Bond Street #21/R est:1000-1500
£1800 $3276 €2628 Temple ruins at dusk. Arabs spinning before a mosque (25x40cm-10x16in) s. pencil W/C two. 1-Jul-4 Christie's, Kensington #337/R est:2000-3000
£2000 $3400 €2920 Pontikonissi, Corfu (27x44cm-11x17in) s. W/C over pencil. 18-Nov-3 Sotheby's, London #127/R est:1500-2000
£2100 $3675 €3066 Figures in a street in Cairo (36x25cm-14x10in) s. W/C. 16-Dec-3 Bonhams, New Bond Street #20/R est:1000-1500
£2200 $3674 €3212 Figures on a street, North Africa (17x37cm-7x15in) two s. W/C over pencil set three. 14-Oct-3 Sotheby's, London #79/R est:1500-2000

SCATIZZI, Sergio (1918-) Italian

£265 $482 €400 Flowers (35x17cm-14x7in) s.i.verso board. 21-Jun-4 Pandolfini, Florence #368
£265 $482 €400 Roses (31x23cm-12x9in) s. s.i.verso board. 21-Jun-4 Pandolfini, Florence #369
£272 $487 €400 Vase of flowers (15x11cm-6x4in) s. prov. 16-Mar-4 Finarte Semenzato, Milan #236
£300 $543 €450 Landscape (49x34cm-19x13in) s. card on cardboard. 2-Apr-4 Farsetti, Prato #417
£317 $549 €450 Volterra (30x40cm-12x16in) s.i.d.56 s.verso paper. 9-Dec-3 Pandolfini, Florence #89
£317 $549 €450 Sea and the moon (20x15cm-8x6in) s. s.i.verso board. 9-Dec-3 Pandolfini, Florence #137
£331 $603 €500 Landscape (48x33cm-19x13in) s. cardboard. 21-Jun-4 Pandolfini, Florence #463
£352 $609 €500 Vase of flowers (38x30cm-15x12in) s. cardboard. 9-Dec-3 Pandolfini, Florence #124
£387 $670 €550 Sea (14x23cm-6x9in) s. s.i.verso board. 9-Dec-3 Pandolfini, Florence #91
£396 $649 €550 Summer landscape (50x35cm-20x14in) s. s.i.verso cardboard. 10-Jun-3 Pandolfini, Florence #410
£423 $731 €600 Flowers (44x21cm-17x8in) s. s.i.verso board. 9-Dec-3 Pandolfini, Florence #111/R
£458 $792 €650 Around Volterra (35x25cm-14x10in) s. s.i.d.1996 verso board. 9-Dec-3 Pandolfini, Florence #59
£458 $792 €650 Beach in Donoratico. Flowers (10x32cm-4x13in) s. s.i.verso two. 9-Dec-3 Pandolfini, Florence #112

£458 $792 €650 Santa Maria del Fiore, Florence (26x16cm-10x6in) s.i.d.1956 verso board. 9-Dec-3 Pandolfini, Florence #115/R
£464 $844 €700 Flowers (50x40cm-20x16in) s. s.i.verso. 21-Jun-4 Pandolfini, Florence #346/R
£504 $826 €700 Rose (30x24cm-12x9in) s. s.i.verso board. 10-Jun-3 Pandolfini, Florence #397/R
£530 $964 €800 Flowers (47x37cm-19x15in) s. painted 1984 board. 17-Jun-4 Galleria Pananti, Florence #606/R
£563 $975 €800 Rose (18x27cm-7x11in) s. s.i.verso cardboard. 9-Dec-3 Pandolfini, Florence #110/R
£563 $975 €800 Vase of flowers (37x29cm-15x11in) s. card. 9-Dec-3 Pandolfini, Florence #133/R
£599 $1036 €850 Castiglioncello (12x34cm-5x13in) s. s.i.verso masonite. 9-Dec-3 Pandolfini, Florence #121/R
£600 $1104 €900 Summer landscape in Valdarno (54x80cm-21x31in) s.d.1984 board. 12-Jun-4 Meeting Art, Vercelli #945/R
£652 $1070 €900 Landscape (60x40cm-24x16in) s. masonite. 29-May-3 Galleria Pace, Milan #41
£728 $1326 €1100 Landscapes (45x57cm-18x22in) s. s.i.verso one on board one on cardboard pair. 21-Jun-4 Pandolfini, Florence #383
£775 $1340 €1100 Beach in Maremma (31x23cm-12x9in) s. s.i.verso board. 9-Dec-3 Pandolfini, Florence #130/R
£795 $1446 €1200 Roses (71x50cm-28x20in) s.d.1955 cardboard. 17-Jun-4 Galleria Pananti, Florence #555/R
£897 $1434 €1300 Venice (40x60cm-16x24in) s. s.i.verso panel prov. 13-Mar-3 Galleria Pace, Milan #140/R est:1350-1850
£915 $1584 €1300 Vase of flowers with brooms (50x35cm-20x14in) s. card. 9-Dec-3 Pandolfini, Florence #134/R est:180-220
£986 $1706 €1400 View of Florence (36x48cm-14x19in) s. tempera mixed media paper on canvas. 9-Dec-3 Pandolfini, Florence #117/R est:300-400
£1014 $1784 €1500 Landscape 41 (50x70cm-20x28in) board lit. 22-May-4 Galleria Pananti, Florence #433/R est:1500-2000
£1167 $2147 €1750 Flowers (40x50cm-16x20in) s. 11-Jun-4 Farsetti, Prato #279 est:1100-1400
£1351 $2378 €2000 Lagoon (51x72cm-20x28in) s. cardboard. 22-May-4 Galleria Pananti, Florence #427/R est:2200-2500
£1467 $2699 €2200 Valdarno, Tuscany (50x60cm-20x24in) painted 1964 prov.exhib. 8-Jun-4 Finarte Semenzato, Milan #249/R est:300-500
Works on paper
£282 $487 €400 Seascape (37x49cm-15x19in) s. W/C chl. 9-Dec-3 Pandolfini, Florence #414/R

SCATTOLA, Ferruccio (1873-1950) Italian
£347 $590 €500 Horses (23x34cm-9x13in) s. cardboard. 1-Nov-3 Meeting Art, Vercelli #264
£420 $722 €600 Landscape (22x35cm-9x14in) s. board. 3-Dec-3 Stadion, Trieste #1092
£1000 $1840 €1500 Venice (23x34cm-9x13in) s. board. 8-Jun-4 Della Rocca, Turin #278/R est:1300-1700
£2000 $3680 €3000 Procession (25x20cm-10x8in) s. board. 8-Jun-4 Sotheby's, Milan #26/R est:3000-5000
£3521 $6092 €5000 Figures on the beach (64x85cm-25x33in) s. 10-Dec-3 Sotheby's, Milan #68/R est:5000-7000
Works on paper
£350 $584 €500 La Spezia Bay (25x34cm-10x13in) s. mixed media cardboard. 24-Jun-3 Finarte Semenzato, Rome #129/R

SCAUFLAIRE, Edgar (1893-1960) Belgian
£476 $852 €700 Nature morte (37x23cm-15x9in) s. panel. 17-Mar-4 Hotel des Ventes Mosan, Brussels #128
£709 $1184 €1000 Scene campagnarde (51x66cm-20x26in) s.d.1942 cardboard. 15-Oct-3 Hotel des Ventes Mosan, Brussels #208
£851 $1421 €1200 Arlequin sur fond fleuri (47x31cm-19x12in) s.i.d.1941 verso eglomise. 15-Oct-3 Hotel des Ventes Mosan, Brussels #210
£986 $1706 €1400 La ferme (75x100cm-30x39in) s.d.34 i.verso. 10-Dec-3 Hotel des Ventes Mosan, Brussels #216
£1206 $2013 €1700 Le marin (53x39cm-21x15in) s. d.1935 verso panel. 15-Oct-3 Hotel des Ventes Mosan, Brussels #200 est:1200-1500
£1972 $3411 €2800 Le fetiche (99x75cm-39x30in) s.d.1959 oil paper. 10-Dec-3 Hotel des Ventes Mosan, Brussels #197 est:3000-4000
£2238 $3804 €3200 Vue panoramique d'une ville avec arlequin (51x65cm-20x26in) s.d.36 cardboard. 1-Dec-3 Palais de Beaux Arts, Brussels #119/R est:3200-4000
Works on paper
£319 $508 €460 La tentation de Saint Antoine (31x48cm-12x19in) s.d.1928 pencil. 9-Sep-3 Palais de Beaux Arts, Brussels #270
£915 $1584 €1300 Femme au vase (49x31cm-19x12in) s.d.1928 pastel. 10-Dec-3 Hotel des Ventes Mosan, Brussels #166

SCAVULLO, Francesco (1921-2004) American?
Photographs
£2260 $4000 €3300 Antonia, Hong Kong (45x33cm-18x13in) s.d.1962 num.8/15 gelatin silver print. 27-Apr-4 Christie's, Rockefeller NY #322/R est:3000-5000

SCHAAN, Paul (19/20th C) French
£1974 $3632 €3000 Un su sucre (46x37cm-18x15in) s. panel. 28-Jun-4 Joron-Derem, Paris #256/R est:3000-4000
£4722 $8500 €6894 Portrait of Napoleon Bonaparte in his library (56x41cm-22x16in) s.d.1914 panel. 24-Apr-4 Weschler, Washington #557/R est:6000-8000

SCHAAP, Egbert Rubertus Derk (1862-1939) Dutch
£867 $1569 €1300 Amsterdam (110x136cm-43x54in) s. 1-Apr-4 Van Ham, Cologne #1629

SCHAAP, Hendrik (1878-1955) Dutch
£342 $582 €500 Rotterdam street (30x22cm-12x9in) s. board. 5-Nov-3 Vendue Huis, Gravenhage #200
£420 $701 €600 Street scene (80x60cm-31x24in) s. 30-Jun-3 Sotheby's, Amsterdam #352
£667 $1213 €1000 Marche aux fleurs a Rotterdam (45x60cm-18x24in) s. 4-Jul-4 MonsAntic, Maisieres #476
£867 $1551 €1300 Harbour scene with workers on the quay (49x69cm-19x27in) s. 11-May-4 Vendu Notarishuis, Rotterdam #46/R
£1164 $1979 €1700 City view of Rotterdam near Het Steiger (68x48cm-27x19in) s.d.56. 5-Nov-3 Vendue Huis, Gravenhage #201/R est:1200-1600

SCHAAP, Henri (1778-1850) Dutch
£590 $933 €850 De Nieuwe Amsterdam in open water (50x79cm-20x31in) s. 2-Sep-3 Christie's, Amsterdam #304

SCHAAR, Pierre (1872-?) Belgian
Sculpture
£1267 $2267 €1900 Tete de chien (43cm-17in) s. white marble. 11-May-4 Vanderkindere, Brussels #480 est:400-600

SCHAAR, Sipke van der (1879-1961) Dutch
£625 $987 €900 Houses at an oasis (96x142cm-38x56in) s. 2-Sep-3 Christie's, Amsterdam #262

SCHACHAR, Gil (1965-) Israeli
Sculpture
£2514 $4500 €3670 Untitled (35x24x26cm-14x9x10in) wax pigment epoxy paint exhib. 18-Mar-4 Sotheby's, New York #90/R est:5000-7000

SCHACHNER, Therese (1890-c.1930) Austrian
£333 $600 €500 Roses (51x35cm-20x14in) s. tempera board. 21-Apr-4 Dorotheum, Vienna #36/R
£667 $1227 €1000 St Gilgen with view towards Abersee (46x60cm-18x24in) s. board. 9-Jun-4 Dorotheum, Salzburg #546/R
Works on paper
£436 $803 €650 Wood on Plankenberg (34x27cm-13x11in) s.i. W/C. 26-Mar-4 Dorotheum, Vienna #347

SCHACHT, Karen (attrib) (1900-1987) German
£1294 $2199 €1850 Fishing hut (27x36cm-11x14in) i.d.1929 verso cardboard. 28-Nov-3 Wendl, Rudolstadt #4166/R est:250

SCHACHT, Rudolf (1900-1974) German
£278 $458 €400 Shepherds with flock (67x50cm-26x20in) s. panel. 3-Jul-3 Neumeister, Munich #2905
£538 $915 €770 Horses in meadow (35x44cm-14x17in) s. board. 20-Nov-3 Weidler, Nurnberg #7172
£552 $1021 €800 Peasant ploughing (40x50cm-16x20in) s. lit. 13-Feb-4 Auktionhaus Georg Rehm, Augsburg #8120/R
£1111 $1756 €1600 Midnight mail (70x80cm-28x31in) s. 2-Sep-3 Christie's, Amsterdam #180/R est:1500-2000
£1399 $2378 €2000 Horse and cart beneath medieval stone arch (71x61cm-28x24in) s.d.1919. 20-Nov-3 Weidler, Nurnberg #7001/R est:1350

SCHACHT, Wilhelm (1872-?) German
£451 $736 €650 A new order (62x49cm-24x19in) s. i. stretcher. 26-Sep-3 Bolland & Marotz, Bremen #605/R
£816 $1461 €1200 Postman in Rothenburg ob der Tauber (61x48cm-24x19in) s. lit. 20-Mar-4 Bergmann, Erlangen #1130
£816 $1461 €1200 Rothenburg ob der Tauber (61x50cm-24x20in) s. lit. 20-Mar-4 Bergmann, Erlangen #1131
£1097 $1712 €1602 Ducks in orchard (60x80cm-24x31in) s. painted c.1900. 30-Mar-3 Agra, Warsaw #45/R est:5000 (P.Z 7000)

SCHAD, Christian (1894-1982) German
£37415 $66973 €55000 Portrait de femme de profil (23x15cm-9x6in) s.d.35. 19-Mar-4 Millon & Associes, Paris #118/R est:20000-30000
Works on paper
£833 $1392 €1200 Civita vecchia (18x13cm-7x5in) s.d. Indian ink brush W/C over pencil board. 25-Oct-3 Dr Lehr, Berlin #444/R
£1469 $2497 €2100 Reclining female nude (29x43cm-11x17in) s.d.27 graphite. 26-Nov-3 Lempertz, Koln #963/R est:2000
£4196 $7133 €6000 Parisian house - Father Cafard (27x18cm-11x7in) i. verso pencil prov.exhib. 26-Nov-3 Lempertz, Koln #965/R est:7000
£5594 $9510 €8000 Farewell (27x18cm-11x7in) s. i.d.29 verso Indian ink prov.exhib.lit. 26-Nov-3 Lempertz, Koln #964/R est:8000-9000

SCHAD, Robert (1953-) German
Sculpture
£1007 $1782 €1500 Untitled (90x130cm-35x51in) iron material. 30-Apr-4 Dr Fritz Nagel, Stuttgart #958/R est:2500

SCHAD-ROSSA, Paul (1862-1916) German
£2384 $4339 €3600 Twilight (104x14cm-41x6in) s.d.1908. 19-Jun-4 Quittenbaum, Hamburg #42/R est:3700

SCHADE, Johann (18th C) German
Works on paper
£500 $830 €725 Jean Calas saying farewell to family (55x63cm-22x25in) s.i. W/C. 13-Jun-3 Zofingen, Switzerland #2379/R (S.FR 1100)

SCHADE, Karl Martin (1862-1954) Austrian
£567 $948 €800 Early summer on the Miesa near Tachau (65x80cm-26x31in) s. 14-Oct-3 Dorotheum, Vienna #86/R

SCHADL, Janos (1892-1944) Hungarian
£1283 $2270 €1873 Still life with cyclamen (60x48cm-24x19in) s. board. 28-Apr-4 Kieselbach, Budapest #47/R (H.F 480000)
£2371 $4292 €3462 Walking at the lake (86x100cm-34x39in) s. 16-Apr-4 Mu Terem Galeria, Budapest #133/R (H.F 900000)

SCHADOW, Gottfried (attrib) (1764-1850) German
Works on paper
£1364 $2277 €1950 Seated Eve with apple and snake (23x18cm-9x7in) pencil. 28-Jun-3 Dannenberg, Berlin #768/R

SCHADOW, Wilhelm von (1788-1862) German
£1409 $2593 €2100 Mourning of Christ (40x32cm-16x13in) board. 26-Mar-4 Bolland & Marotz, Bremen #582/R est:2300
Works on paper
£7692 $13077 €11000 Mignon (20x15cm-8x6in) s. W/C htd gold. 27-Nov-3 Bassenge, Berlin #5642/R est:2800

SCHAEFELS, Hendrik Frans (1827-1904) Belgian
£1479 $2558 €2100 Baiser (53x43cm-21x17in) s.d.1879 panel. 9-Dec-3 Vanderkindere, Brussels #29 est:2000-3000
£1796 $3000 €2622 Returning to mother (56x45cm-22x18in) s.d.1866 panel. 7-Oct-3 Sotheby's, New York #152 est:3000-5000
£2721 $4952 €4000 Oud Antwerpen (82x118cm-32x46in) 9-Feb-4 Amberes, Antwerp #283

SCHAEFER, Carl Fellman (1903-1995) Canadian
£6250 $10750 €9125 Bright sun (50x60cm-20x24in) s.d.36 prov.exhib. 2-Dec-3 Joyner Waddington, Toronto #108/R est:12000-15000 (C.D 14000)
Works on paper
£356 $583 €520 Autumn waterfall (23x28cm-9x11in) W/C executed c.1952. 28-May-3 Maynards, Vancouver #40 (C.D 800)
£541 $919 €790 Mill at New Dundee, Waterloo County (28x38cm-11x15in) s.d.1955 i.d.1955 verso W/C prov. 23-Nov-3 Levis, Calgary #120/R (C.D 1200)
£720 $1318 €1051 Mill at New Dundee (27x36cm-11x14in) s.d.25.7.55 W/C. 1-Jun-4 Joyner Waddington, Toronto #10/R est:1800-2000 (C.D 1800)
£732 $1310 €1069 Spring at Raven Lake (27x38cm-11x15in) s.d.1972 W/C. 27-May-4 Heffel, Vancouver #118/R est:2000-2500 (C.D 1800)
£800 $1464 €1168 Hillside near Raven Lake (27x36cm-11x14in) s.d.12.10.58 W/C prov. 1-Jun-4 Joyner Waddington, Toronto #219/R est:2000-2500 (C.D 2000)
£880 $1610 €1285 Houses on a hill (17x17cm-7x7in) s.d.29 ink prov. 1-Jun-4 Joyner Waddington, Toronto #120/R est:2500-3000 (C.D 2200)
£982 $1689 €1434 Boatyard, Kingston (27x37cm-11x15in) s.d.29.7.52 W/C. 2-Dec-3 Joyner Waddington, Toronto #179/R est:2000-3000 (C.D 2200)
£1116 $1920 €1629 Clearing at Carnarvon, Haliburton (27x37cm-11x15in) s.d.19.5.59. 2-Dec-3 Joyner Waddington, Toronto #224/R est:2500-3000 (C.D 2500)

SCHAEFER, Harry (1891-1944) American
£223 $400 €326 Beach dunes, likely Oregon (30x41cm-12x16in) masonite prov. 16-Mar-4 Matthew's, Oregon #76/R

SCHAEFER, Jurgen (1941-) German
£604 $1111 €900 Life (49x38cm-19x15in) s.d. acrylic panel. 26-Mar-4 Ketterer, Hamburg #628/R

SCHAEFFER, Henri (1900-1975) French
£440 $800 €642 Paris, Le Moulin Rouge (41x51cm-16x20in) s. 7-Feb-4 Auctions by the Bay, Alameda #1533/R
£782 $1400 €1142 Winter street scene in Paris (21x18cm-8x7in) 9-Jan-4 Du Mouchelle, Detroit #2268/R
£838 $1475 €1223 Paris street scene (46x56cm-18x22in) s. 23-May-4 Hindman, Chicago #64/R est:1500-2500
£1000 $1840 €1500 La Madeleine (46x55cm-18x22in) s. 14-Jun-4 Tajan, Paris #72 est:1500-2000

SCHAEFFER, Mead (1898-1980) American
£11976 $20000 €17485 Colonial troops with Indian guides (64x86cm-25x34in) s.d.1921. 15-Nov-3 Illustration House, New York #113/R est:12000-18000
£16760 $30000 €24470 Three musketeers (81x66cm-32x26in) 15-May-4 Illustration House, New York #22/R est:15000-25000

SCHAEFLEIN, Wilfrid (20th C) German
Works on paper
£382 $638 €550 Berlin street (27x33cm-11x13in) s.i.d. W/C Indian ink over pencil on board. 25-Oct-3 Dr Lehr, Berlin #445/R

SCHAEP, Henri Adolphe (1826-1870) Dutch
£3819 $6035 €5500 Ships in stormy seas (72x105cm-28x41in) s. lit. 19-Sep-3 Schloss Ahlden, Ahlden #1570/R est:2400
£5000 $9200 €7300 Elegant figures seated by a fountain, a harbour beyond (52x75cm-20x30in) s.d.1852 panel. 23-Mar-4 Bonhams, New Bond Street #3/R est:5000-7000
£10417 $17396 €15000 Shipping in choppy seas (67x88cm-26x35in) s.d.50. 21-Oct-3 Sotheby's, Amsterdam #193/R est:15000-20000

SCHAEPHERDERS, Jaak (1890-1964) Belgian
£408 $731 €600 Still life of flowers (76x69cm-30x27in) s. 18-Mar-4 Neumeister, Munich #2766

SCHAETTE, Carl (1884-1951) German
£933 $1680 €1400 Marsh landscape with windmills (70x90cm-28x35in) s. 21-Apr-4 Dorotheum, Vienna #41/R
£938 $1566 €1369 Lowland scene with mountains in the background (81x100cm-32x39in) s. painted c.1930. 19-Oct-3 Agra, Warsaw #56/R est:6000 (P.Z 6000)

SCHAFER, Frederick Ferdinand (1839-1927) American
£276 $500 €403 Yosemite valley (30x25cm-12x10in) s. board. 16-Apr-4 James Julia, Fairfield #737/R
£435 $700 €631 Tropical sunset (30x25cm-12x10in) s. 24-Aug-3 Bonhams & Butterfields, Los Angeles #7065
£455 $800 €664 Sierra Creek (25x20cm-10x8in) s. board. 23-May-4 Bonhams & Butterfields, San Francisco #6600/R
£522 $950 €762 On the Columbia (25x46cm-10x18in) s.i. 19-Jun-4 Harvey Clar, Oakland #2402
£629 $1000 €918 Yosemite mountains landscape with waterfall (56x91cm-22x36in) s. 13-Sep-3 Auctions by the Bay, Alameda #423/R
£765 $1400 €1117 Extensive northwest mountain landscape (91x61cm-36x24in) 10-Apr-4 Auctions by the Bay, Alameda #1560/R
£934 $1700 €1364 California mountain landscape (30x46cm-12x18in) s. 15-Jun-4 John Moran, Pasadena #148 est:1000-1500
£952 $1800 €1390 Horse and rider in panoramic river landscape - Mt Shasta in distance (18x25cm-7x10in) s. board. 17-Feb-4 John Moran, Pasadena #10a/R est:2000-3000
£1190 $2250 €1737 Wooded river landscape (25x30cm-10x12in) s. prov. 17-Feb-4 John Moran, Pasadena #167/R est:1500-2000
£1494 $2750 €2181 Sunset at Lake Tahoe (76x74cm-30x29in) s. i. stretcher. 8-Jun-4 Bonhams & Butterfields, San Francisco #4179/R est:3000-5000
£1494 $2750 €2181 Twilight with Mt Shasta in the distance (68x55cm-27x22in) s. prov. 8-Jun-4 Bonhams & Butterfields, San Francisco #4259/R est:3000-5000
£1589 $2750 €2320 Morning on Silver Lake (61x41cm-24x16in) s.d.85 i.verso prov. 10-Dec-3 Bonhams & Butterfields, San Francisco #6140/R est:3000-5000
£2011 $3700 €2936 Evening on Donner Lake (50x91cm-20x36in) s. prov. 8-Jun-4 Bonhams & Butterfields, San Francisco #4178/R est:5000-7000
£2312 $4000 €3376 Bridal Veil Falls, Yosemite Valley (43x41cm-17x16in) s. i.verso prov. 10-Dec-3 Bonhams & Butterfields, San Francisco #6153/R est:6000-8000
£2446 $4500 €3571 Three Brothers, Merced River. Bridal Veil Falls (76x50cm-30x20in) s. pair. 8-Jun-4 Bonhams & Butterfields, San Francisco #4181/R est:6000-8000
£3261 $6000 €4761 Sunset on the Three Sisters, Oregon (76x127cm-30x50in) s. i.verso. 8-Jun-4 Bonhams & Butterfields, San Francisco #4180/R est:6000-8000
£4046 $7000 €5907 Bear Lake in the Wasatch Mountains, Utah (76x127cm-30x50in) s.i.verso prov. 10-Dec-3 Bonhams & Butterfields, San Francisco #6149/R est:6000-8000
£4751 $7934 €6936 Mt. Hood from the Dalles, Oregon (75x126cm-30x50in) s.i. 17-Nov-3 Hodgins, Calgary #91/R est:8000-10000 (C.D 10500)

SCHAFER, H (19th C) British/French
£1000 $1600 €1460 Street scene (41x30cm-16x12in) s. 17-May-3 Bunte, Elgin #1227 est:1200-1800

SCHAFER, Heinrich Hermann (1815-1884) German
£690 $1276 €1000 Les abords de la cathedrale de Strasbourg animes (26x21cm-10x8in) s. cardboard. 13-Jan-4 Vanderkindere, Brussels #55
£1399 $2378 €2000 Ruelle animee au pied de la cathedrale (40x31cm-16x12in) s.d.1874. 18-Nov-3 Vanderkindere, Brussels #44 est:2000-3000

SCHAFER, Heinrich Hermann (attrib) (1815-1884) German
£1133 $2029 €1700 Ruelle animee au pied de la Cathedrale dAnvers (41x30cm-16x12in) mono.d.1887 i.verso. 11-May-4 Vanderkindere, Brussels #123 est:1700-2000

SCHAFER, Henry Thomas (1854-1915) British
£311 $538 €454 City square (30x25cm-12x10in) s. canvas on board. 9-Dec-3 Maynards, Vancouver #147 (C.D 700)
£380 $631 €555 Ulm, Bavaria (38x28cm-15x11in) mono.d.1887 i.verso. 3-Oct-3 Mallams, Oxford #262/R
£500 $860 €730 Ulm, Bavaria (38x28cm-15x11in) mono.d.1887. 5-Dec-3 Keys, Aylsham #709
£533 $923 €778 Normandy (41x30cm-16x12in) init.d.1887. 9-Dec-3 Maynards, Vancouver #146a est:800-1000 (C.D 1200)
£550 $864 €798 Nuremberg, Bavaria (30x22cm-12x9in) s.i.verso. 28-Aug-3 Christie's, Kensington #220/R
£620 $1122 €905 Continental market place (29x24cm-11x9in) s. panel. 30-Mar-4 David Duggleby, Scarborough #148/R
£680 $1251 €993 Nurenberg, Germany (29x26cm-11x10in) mono. i.verso. 29-Mar-4 Bonhams, Bath #110/R
£700 $1253 €1022 Cologne, Germany. Utrecht, Holland (40x29cm-16x11in) both init.d.1882 s.i.verso pair. 17-Mar-4 Bonhams, Chester #329
£850 $1343 €1233 Rouen, Normandy. St. Wulfran's Abbeville, Normandy (30x41cm-12x16in) mono.d.1888 s.i.verso pair. 4-Sep-3 Christie's, Kensington #203/R
£906 $1458 €1323 Strasbourg, Alsree. St Pierre, Caen, Normandy (39x29cm-15x11in) s.d.1875 s.i.verso pair. 12-Aug-3 Peter Webb, Auckland #169/R (NZ.D 2500)
£1450 $2422 €2117 Figures before continental buildings (48x38cm-19x15in) one s. pair. 17-Oct-3 Keys, Aylsham #757 est:400-600
£1531 $2740 €2250 Cathedral interior (46x35cm-18x14in) s. 22-Mar-4 Durán, Madrid #209/R est:250
£1600 $2960 €2336 Fecamp, Normandy. Rouen (39x29cm-15x11in) one s.d.71 one mono.d.1883 pair. 13-Jan-4 Bonhams, Knightsbridge #259/R est:1500-2000
£1800 $3330 €2628 St Ouen, Rouen, Normandy. Fecamp, Normandy (45x35cm-18x14in) s. pair. 13-Jan-4 Bonhams, Knightsbridge #91/R est:2000-3000
£1800 $3348 €2628 Morlaix, Brittany. Hildesheim, Germany (41x30cm-16x12in) mono.d.1885 i.verso pair. 4-Mar-4 Christie's, Kensington #571/R est:1500-2000
£2000 $3720 €2920 Strasbourg, Alsace. St. Pierre, Caen, Normandy (41x30cm-16x12in) s.d.75 i.verso pair. 4-Mar-4 Christie's, Kensington #569/R est:2000-3000
£6800 $11560 €9928 Peacock fan (48x79cm-19x31in) s.d.1879. 19-Nov-3 Bonhams, New Bond Street #66/R est:4000-6000
Works on paper
£280 $501 €409 Freiburg, morning scene (24x19cm-9x7in) s.i. W/C htd white. 25-May-4 Bonhams, Knightsbridge #51/R
£299 $550 €437 Evreux, Normandy (61x43cm-24x17in) s.i. W/C. 13-Jun-4 Bonhams & Butterfields, Los Angeles #7007/R
£310 $567 €453 Abbeville, Normandy (25x20cm-10x8in) s.i. W/C. 27-Jan-4 Bristol Auction Rooms #591/R
£364 $600 €531 Louviers, Normandi (43x33cm-17x13in) s.i. W/C. 7-Jul-3 Schrager Galleries, Milwaukee #1271
£378 $700 €552 Freiburg, Baden, market scene with canal and church in background (46x33cm-18x13in) s. W/C gouache. 16-Feb-4 Quinn's, Falls Church #325/R
£405 $750 €591 Iglesia de San Miguel, Jerez, Spain (46x33cm-18x13in) s.i. W/C gouache. 16-Feb-4 Quinn's, Falls Church #324/R

£420 $773 €613 Place de la Croix de St Pierre, Rouen, Normandy (46x34cm-18x13in) s.i. W/C. 10-Jun-4 Morphets, Harrogate #531/R
£450 $837 €657 St Ouen Rouen, Normandy (46x33cm-18x13in) s.i. 5-Mar-4 Dee Atkinson & Harrison, Driffield #688
£850 $1547 €1241 Chapel of the High Altar, Toledo, Spain (63x46cm-25x18in) s.i. pencil black ink W/C. 1-Jul-4 Christie's, Kensington #368/R
£1100 $2035 €1606 Milan Cathedral, Italy. Burgos Cathedral, Spain (45x34cm-18x13in) s.i. W/C pair. 9-Mar-4 Bonhams, Knightsbridge #32/R est:1200-1800
£1156 $2070 €1700 San Miguel Church, Jerez de la Frontera (47x35cm-19x14in) s. W/C. 22-Mar-4 Durán, Madrid #208/R est:750

SCHAFER, Henry Thomas (attrib) (1854-1915) British
Works on paper
£400 $720 €584 Figures by a church in a continental town (35x31cm-14x12in) i. W/C over pencil bodycol two joined sheets. 21-Jan-4 Sotheby's, Olympia #135/R

SCHAFER, Karl (1888-1956) German
£1533 $2791 €2300 View of Vilshofen on the banks of the Donau (50x60cm-20x24in) s. board lit. 3-Jul-4 Badum, Bamberg #16/R est:2600

SCHAFER, Maria (1854-?) German
£1389 $2194 €2000 Pilgrims on Jacob's road (97x127cm-38x50in) s. 5-Sep-3 Wendl, Rudolstadt #3593/R est:1600

SCHAFFER, Adalbert (1815-1871) Hungarian
£4110 $6986 €6000 Still life of flowers and fruit (60x70cm-24x28in) s.d.57 board. 5-Nov-3 Hugo Ruef, Munich #1109/R est:1200

SCHAFFER, Henri (19th C) ?
£650 $1034 €949 Continental street scene (29x24cm-11x9in) s.d.1875. 9-Sep-3 Rowley Fine Art, Newmarket #443/R

SCHAFFNER, Franz (1876-?) German
£278 $439 €400 Finkenwerder Ewer, Cuxhaven harbour (42x98cm-17x39in) s. 6-Sep-3 Schopman, Hamburg #861/R

SCHAFFNER, Marcel (1931-) Swiss
£1357 $2308 €1981 Composition (53x43cm-21x17in) s. painted 1953. 22-Nov-3 Burkhard, Luzern #22/R est:3000-4000 (S.FR 3000)

SCHAFFRAN, Emerich (1883-1962) Austrian
£1379 $2524 €2000 The Rax (116x200cm-46x79in) s. prov. 27-Jan-4 Dorotheum, Vienna #14/R est:2000-2800

SCHAFFRATH, Hans (20th C) ?
£1361 $2435 €2000 Baie de Rio (68x96cm-27x38in) s. 21-Mar-4 St-Germain-en-Laye Encheres #8/R est:1500-2000

SCHAGEN, Gerbrand Frederik van (1880-1968) Dutch
£275 $500 €402 Farmer at work in his kitchen garden (41x61cm-16x24in) s. 19-Jun-4 Harvey Clar, Oakland #2172
£349 $583 €500 Moored boats near a draw-bridge (14x27cm-6x11in) s. panel. 30-Jun-3 Sotheby's, Amsterdam #165
£367 $656 €550 Feeding the hens (31x40cm-12x16in) s.d.32 i.d. verso lit. 14-May-4 Schloss Ahlden, Ahlden #2912/R
£510 $929 €750 Na du bui, village of Vollenhove after the rain (40x50cm-16x20in) s.d.41 i.stretcher. 3-Feb-4 Christie's, Amsterdam #361
£660 $1042 €950 Checking rhe eel trap (41x70cm-16x28in) s.d.1941. 2-Sep-3 Christie's, Amsterdam #245
£6250 $11313 €9500 Sailing boats for hire at the Loosdrechtse Lake (68x98cm-27x39in) s.d.1934. 19-Apr-4 Glerum, Amsterdam #179/R est:3000-5000

SCHAKEWITS, Josef (1848-1913) Belgian
£556 $906 €800 Retour des pecheurs (26x42cm-10x17in) s. 23-Sep-3 Galerie Moderne, Brussels #768/R
£1958 $3329 €2800 Le retour des pecheurs (89x142cm-35x56in) s. i.d.1904 verso. 1-Dec-3 Palais de Beaux Arts, Brussels #120/R est:2500-3500

SCHALCH, Johann Jacob (1723-1789) Swiss
£2586 $4629 €3776 Summer landscape with cows (38x45cm-15x18in) s.d.1770 panel. 14-May-4 Dobiaschofsky, Bern #45/R est:6500 (S.FR 6000)

SCHALCKEN, Godfried (1643-1706) Dutch
£3082 $5240 €4500 Portrait of a gentleman, in front of a stone balustrade with curtain (28x21cm-11x8in) s. panel exhib.lit. 4-Nov-3 Sotheby's, Amsterdam #94/R est:4000-6000
£4225 $7310 €6000 Portrait of a woman on a balcony (42x34cm-17x13in) s. copper prov. 11-Dec-3 Dr Fritz Nagel, Stuttgart #463/R est:9000
£8145 $13032 €11892 Still life with peaches, grapes and melons with butterfly (40x35cm-16x14in) s. panel prov.lit. 19-Sep-3 Koller, Zurich #3061/R est:20000-30000 (S.FR 18000)
£15000 $27000 €21900 Portrait of a gentleman in a brocaded red jacket and black cape. Portrait of lady in a brown velvet (74x63cm-29x25in) s. oval pair. 21-Apr-4 Christie's, London #32/R est:15000-20000
£55000 $99000 €80300 Portrait of a young man (32x26cm-13x10in) s. canvas on panel prov. 22-Apr-4 Sotheby's, London #48/R est:20000-30000
£208333 $375000 €304166 Woman weaving garland (27x20cm-11x8in) s. panel prov.lit. 22-Jan-4 Sotheby's, New York #25/R est:200000-300000
£266667 $480000 €389334 Lovers (76x63cm-30x25in) prov.exhib.lit. 21-Jan-4 Doyle, New York #85/R est:80000-120000

SCHALCKEN, Godfried (attrib) (1643-1706) Dutch
£500 $910 €750 Young boy with a farmer (23x18cm-9x7in) panel. 1-Jul-4 Van Ham, Cologne #1161
£3724 $6219 €5400 Young woman holding burning candle (36x29cm-14x11in) i. panel prov. 15-Nov-3 Lempertz, Koln #1137/R est:4000

SCHALCKEN, Godfried (circle) (1643-1706) Dutch
£2853 $5250 €4165 Woman reading a letter by candlelight (38x28cm-15x11in) 26-Jun-4 Sloans & Kenyon, Bethesda #1075/R est:5000-7000

SCHALCKEN, Godfried (style) (1643-1706) Dutch
£24000 $41520 €35040 Saint Francis in meditation (82x68cm-32x27in) prov.lit. 9-Dec-3 Sotheby's, Olympia #419/R est:5000-7000

SCHALIN, Greta (1897-1993) Finnish
£676 $1209 €1000 Still life of lilacs (40x50cm-16x20in) s.d.1981. 8-May-4 Bukowskis, Helsinki #157/R
£739 $1183 €1050 Still life of flowers (46x55cm-18x22in) s.d.87. 21-Sep-3 Bukowskis, Helsinki #465/R
£980 $1754 €1450 Still life of flowers (50x40cm-20x16in) s.d.45 board. 8-May-4 Bukowskis, Helsinki #73/R
£1014 $1814 €1500 Summer flowers (26x23cm-10x9in) s.d.73 canvas on board. 8-May-4 Bukowskis, Helsinki #165/R est:800-1000
£1538 $2615 €2200 Midsummer roses (55x46cm-22x18in) s.d.1975. 29-Nov-3 Bukowskis, Helsinki #50/R est:1700-2000
£2238 $3804 €3200 Red tulips (40x31cm-16x12in) s.d.38 board. 29-Nov-3 Bukowskis, Helsinki #74/R est:1400-1600

SCHALL, Jean Frederic (1752-1825) French
£1429 $2600 €2086 Young woman with a dove (32x24cm-13x9in) prov.exhib. 4-Feb-4 Christie's, Rockefeller NY #18/R est:5000-7000
£1667 $3000 €2434 Couple kissing (33x30cm-13x12in) panel prov. 23-Jan-4 Christie's, Rockefeller NY #118/R est:5000-7000
£2747 $5000 €4011 Seated young woman by her dressing table (27x23cm-11x9in) panel prov. 4-Feb-4 Christie's, Rockefeller NY #101/R est:3000-5000
£6667 $12000 €9734 Dancing lady in a landscape (28x19cm-11x7in) panel. 23-Jan-4 Christie's, Rockefeller NY #205/R est:15000-20000
£9790 $16839 €14000 Ladies running in the fields (23x19cm-9x7in) panel pair. 2-Dec-3 Christie's, Paris #103/R est:6000-8000

SCHALL, Jean Frederic (attrib) (1752-1825) French
£526 $968 €800 Jeune elegante dans le parc (37x30cm-15x12in) 25-Jun-4 Piasa, Paris #124
£2267 $4125 €3400 Portrait of a girl (42x36cm-17x14in) 1-Jul-4 Van Ham, Cologne #1596/R est:3200

SCHALL, Lothar (20th C) ?
£868 $1415 €1250 Composition in red, green and blue (113x15cm-44x6in) canvas on panel exhib. 27-Sep-3 Dr Fritz Nagel, Stuttgart #9627/R

SCHALLER, Mark (1962-) Australian
£382 $695 €558 Still life (64x53cm-25x21in) 16-Jun-4 Deutscher-Menzies, Melbourne #581/R est:1200-1800 (A.D 1000)
£420 $764 €613 Flowers (91x40cm-36x16in) s. i.d.1998 verso. 16-Jun-4 Deutscher-Menzies, Melbourne #580/R est:1500-2500 (A.D 1100)
£649 $1180 €948 Excavators (121x110cm-48x43in) 5-Feb-4 Joel, Victoria #119 (A.D 1550)
£810 $1304 €1183 Pot belly stove (183x135cm-72x53in) s.d.99 s.i.d.2000. 13-Oct-3 Joel, Victoria #390 est:2000-3000 (A.D 2000)
£1527 $2779 €2229 Lygon Street (137x183cm-54x72in) s.i.d.2003 verso oilstick. 16-Jun-4 Deutscher-Menzies, Melbourne #50/R est:5000-7000 (A.D 4000)
£1545 $2765 €2256 Untitled (152x107cm-60x42in) prov. 4-May-4 Sotheby's, Melbourne #117 est:3000-5000 (A.D 3800)
£1756 $3195 €2564 Standing nude (182x137cm-72x54in) s.d.00 s.i.d.verso prov. 16-Jun-4 Deutscher-Menzies, Melbourne #38/R est:5000-7000 (A.D 4600)
£1908 $3473 €2786 Still life - purple and green 2000 (183x121cm-72x48in) s.d.00 s.i.d.verso prov. 16-Jun-4 Deutscher-Menzies, Melbourne #39/R est:5000-7000 (A.D 5000)
Works on paper
£2273 $4205 €3319 Figures in the street (175x220cm-69x87in) s.d.88 mixed media on board prov. 15-Mar-4 Sotheby's, Melbourne #5 est:6000-8000 (A.D 5500)

SCHALLER, Mark (attrib) (1962-) Australian
£502 $914 €733 Untitled. painted c.1980. 5-Feb-4 Joel, Victoria #163 (A.D 1200)

SCHALLER, Stephan (attrib) (fl.1757-1778) Hungarian
£8966 $14883 €13000 Assumption of the Virgin (172x106cm-68x42in) prov. 1-Oct-3 Dorotheum, Vienna #242/R est:10000-15000

SCHAMPHELEER, Edmond de (1824-1899) Belgian
£514 $950 €750 In the Clearing (30x48cm-12x19in) s. i.verso panel. 15-Jul-4 Doyle, New York #26/R

SCHANKER, Louis (1903-1981) American
£297 $475 €434 Untitled (48x74cm-19x29in) s.d.1972 acrylic collage. 20-Sep-3 Bunte, Elgin #385m
Works on paper
£588 $1000 €858 Untitled (48x74cm-19x29in) s.d.1972 collage acrylic on board. 9-Nov-3 Wright, Chicago #306 est:1000-1500
£1286 $2250 €1878 Football (35x42cm-14x17in) s.d.38 col crayon black ink pencil prov. 19-Dec-3 Sotheby's, New York #1019/R est:1200-1800

SCHANTZ, Philip von (1928-1998) Swedish
£2027 $3649 €2959 Summer shadow with red facade (100x70cm-39x28in) s.d.86. 26-Jan-4 Lilla Bukowskis, Stockholm #463 est:12000-15000 (S.KR 27000)
£2341 $3980 €3418 Pitchfork (55x46cm-22x18in) init.d.77. 5-Nov-3 AB Stockholms Auktionsverk #1059/R est:25000-30000 (S.KR 31000)
£3927 $6677 €5733 Trunks of silver birch (46x55cm-18x22in) init.d.78. 5-Nov-3 AB Stockholms Auktionsverk #1067/R est:30000-40000 (S.KR 52000)

£4641 $8354 €6776 Still life of glass and eggs (32x34cm-13x13in) init.d.72-74. 26-Apr-4 Bukowskis, Stockholm #231/R est:25000-30000 (S.KR 64000)
Works on paper
£1774 $3175 €2590 Scoop with potatoes (41x54cm-16x21in) s. W/C. 28-May-4 Uppsala Auktionskammare, Uppsala #326/R est:20000-25000 (S.KR 24000)
£4230 $7190 €6176 Plums (39x37cm-15x15in) init.d.97 mixed media. 5-Nov-3 AB Stockholms Auktionsverk #1065/R est:50000-60000 (S.KR 56000)

SCHANZ, Heinz (1927-) German
£590 $962 €850 Untitled (62x55cm-24x22in) s.d.1969 tempera. 27-Sep-3 Dr Fritz Nagel, Stuttgart #9341/R
£694 $1132 €1000 Head (82x63cm-32x25in) s.d.1962 i. verso tempera. 27-Sep-3 Dr Fritz Nagel, Stuttgart #9342/R

SCHAPER, Friedrich (1869-1956) German
£549 $1000 €802 Wooded road (43x61cm-17x24in) s.d.30. 7-Feb-4 Neal Auction Company, New Orleans #974
£662 $1205 €1000 Forest hut in the woods (37x46cm-15x18in) indis.i. verso stretcher. 19-Jun-4 Hans Stahl, Hamburg #152
£940 $1729 €1400 Windmill near Dose (70x60cm-28x24in) s.d. i. verso. 26-Mar-4 Ketterer, Hamburg #211/R
£1074 $1976 €1600 Farmstead in Meldorf (39x52cm-15x20in) s. 26-Mar-4 Ketterer, Hamburg #271/R est:750
£1103 $2041 €1600 Hamburg (39x30cm-15x12in) s. board. 14-Feb-4 Hans Stahl, Hamburg #167/R est:1700
£1141 $2099 €1700 Sulze near Celle (40x50cm-16x20in) s. 26-Mar-4 Ketterer, Hamburg #272/R est:750
£1523 $2772 €2300 Farmer's wife with white goats in the field (17x27cm-7x11in) s. panel. 19-Jun-4 Hans Stahl, Hamburg #153/R est:1800
£1722 $3134 €2600 Village pond in Langenhorn near Hamburg (31x40cm-12x16in) s.d.45 i.verso cardboard. 19-Jun-4 Hans Stahl, Hamburg #154/R est:2700
£1818 $3036 €2600 Farmerswife with cows (40x50cm-16x20in) s.d.20 double-sided. 11-Oct-3 Hans Stahl, Hamburg #121/R est:2200

SCHAPERKOTTER, Gerardus Johannes (1914-) Dutch
£972 $1536 €1400 At the beach (52x72cm-20x28in) indis sig.d.63. 2-Sep-3 Christie's, Amsterdam #480/R est:700-900

SCHARER, Hans (1927-1997) Swiss
£755 $1223 €1102 Female acrobat (50x37cm-20x15in) s.d.71 tempera W/C Indian ink study verso. 24-May-3 Burkhard, Luzern #14/R (S.FR 1600)
£896 $1452 €1308 Nude on red sofa (37x52cm-15x20in) s.d.71 tempera W/C Indian ink. 24-May-3 Burkhard, Luzern #15/R (S.FR 1900)
£1048 $1928 €1530 Mister X (65x45cm-26x18in) s.d.1988 paper prov. 8-Jun-4 Germann, Zurich #872 (S.FR 2400)
£1132 $1834 €1653 Italia (70x50cm-28x20in) s.d.82 paper exhib. 24-May-3 Burkhard, Luzern #16/R est:2800-3200 (S.FR 2400)
£1226 $1987 €1790 Untitled (92x74cm-36x29in) s.d.58 s.d. verso. 24-May-3 Burkhard, Luzern #17/R est:2000-3000 (S.FR 2600)
£1604 $2598 €2342 Untitled (95x116cm-37x46in) s. s.d.1960 verso oil mortar. 24-May-3 Burkhard, Luzern #18/R est:3000-4000 (S.FR 3400)
£1887 $3057 €2755 Untitled (65x54cm-26x21in) s.d.90. 24-May-3 Burkhard, Luzern #179/R est:4000-5000 (S.FR 4000)
Sculpture
£1900 $3174 €2774 Two small madonnas (70x61x5cm-28x24x2in) s.d.1972 oil mortar stone glass string pavatex prov.exhib. 24-Jun-3 Germann, Zurich #123 est:5000-10000 (S.FR 4200)
Works on paper
£631 $1085 €921 Sans (42x29cm-17x11in) s.d.1987 W/C. 8-Dec-3 Philippe Schuler, Zurich #3225/R (S.FR 1400)
£769 $1285 €1123 Untitled (60x87cm-24x34in) s.d.1983 mixed media. 24-Jun-3 Germann, Zurich #122/R (S.FR 1700)
£873 $1537 €1275 Untitled (50x35cm-20x14in) s.d.76 W/C on Indian ink prov. 22-May-4 Galerie Gloggner, Luzern #91/R est:1800-2200 (S.FR 2000)

SCHARF, George (1788-1860) German
£800 $1472 €1168 Original dog meat shop (16x19cm-6x7in) 11-Jun-4 Keys, Aylsham #657/R

SCHARF, Kenny (1958-) American
£1497 $2500 €2186 Composition with faces (41x27cm-16x11in) s.d.84-5 verso canvasboard prov. 7-Oct-3 Sotheby's, New York #406 est:5000-7000
£3988 $6500 €5822 Tangello purpletempelo (122x152cm-48x60in) s.i.d.85 verso acrylic oil prov. 23-Sep-3 Christie's, Rockefeller NY #188/R est:7000-9000
£6587 $11000 €9617 Horizon (213x151cm-84x59in) s.i.d.85 verso acrylic oil spray enamel prov. 12-Nov-3 Christie's, Rockefeller NY #624/R est:10000-15000
£8939 $16000 €13051 Intense relationships (41x30cm-16x12in) s.d.Italy 87 acrylic canvas on board prov. 13-May-4 Sotheby's, New York #478/R est:5000-7000
£14970 $25000 €21856 Admire an admiral (161x160cm-63x63in) s.i.d.88 verso oil acrylic gem stone prov. 13-Nov-3 Sotheby's, New York #608/R est:8000-10000
£18994 $34000 €27731 Green waves (147x223cm-58x88in) s.i.d.83 verso oil spray paint shaped canvas prov. 13-May-4 Sotheby's, New York #476/R est:12000-18000
Works on paper
£719 $1200 €1050 Composition with happy face (60x47cm-24x19in) s.d.1985 verso gouache prov. 7-Oct-3 Sotheby's, New York #408
£1347 $2250 €1967 Lick tickles (66x96cm-26x38in) s.i.d.1/1/84 i.verso gouache prov. 7-Oct-3 Sotheby's, New York #405 est:2500-3500

SCHARFF, Erwin (1887-1955) German
Sculpture
£4196 $7217 €6000 Bather (44x16x18cm-17x6x7in) s.d.1914 bronze lit. 4-Dec-3 Van Ham, Cologne #454/R est:3000

SCHARFF, William (1886-1959) Danish
£452 $768 €660 Study for The moorlady brewing (85x74cm-33x29in) s.d.1928 panel. 29-Nov-3 Rasmussen, Havnen #4018/R (D.KR 4800)
£496 $913 €724 Study for The moor-lady brewing (82x71cm-32x28in) s.d.1926 cardboard prov. 29-Mar-4 Rasmussen, Copenhagen #455 (D.KR 5500)
£542 $1013 €791 The artist's grandmother by pots on table (75x100cm-30x39in) s.d.1937. 25-Feb-4 Museumsbygningen, Copenhagen #72/R (D.KR 6000)
£542 $856 €786 Two workers - composition in blue (125x100cm-49x39in) s. study exhib. 3-Sep-3 Museumsbygningen, Copenhagen #123 (D.KR 5800)
£567 $1015 €828 Portrait of young girl (65x60cm-26x24in) s. 12-Jan-4 Rasmussen, Vejle #481/R (D.KR 6000)
£627 $1129 €915 Figures at table (115x148cm-45x58in) s. 24-Apr-4 Rasmussen, Havnen #4234/R (D.KR 7000)
£677 $1245 €988 Portrait of seated boy (100x80cm-39x31in) s.d.1924. 29-Mar-4 Rasmussen, Copenhagen #38/R (D.KR 7500)
£709 $1269 €1035 Reclining female nude (72x120cm-28x47in) s. 12-Jan-4 Rasmussen, Vejle #482/R (D.KR 7500)
£722 $1329 €1054 Study of female nude (111x65cm-44x26in) s. 29-Mar-4 Rasmussen, Copenhagen #467/R (D.KR 8000)
£2166 $4051 €3162 The artist's sister Johanne sewing. Cubist composition (99x81cm-39x32in) double-sided exhib.prov. 25-Feb-4 Museumsbygningen, Copenhagen #77/R est:10000-15000 (D.KR 24000)
£3430 $6310 €5008 Seated female model - possibly the artist's wife (125x81cm-49x32in) init.d.17 lit. 29-Mar-4 Rasmussen, Copenhagen #28/R est:20000-25000 (D.KR 38000)
£13146 $21953 €19193 Poultry among ill weeds that grow apace - cubist composition (135x84cm-53x33in) s.d.1917 paper on canvas lit. 7-Oct-3 Rasmussen, Copenhagen #131/R est:80000-100000 (D.KR 140000)
Works on paper
£281 $458 €410 Mountain landscape (39x49cm-15x19in) s.i.d.1939 W/C. 27-Sep-3 Rasmussen, Havnen #4167 (D.KR 3000)
£329 $560 €480 Landscape (72x97cm-28x38in) s.d.1927 W/C. 29-Nov-3 Rasmussen, Havnen #4395 (D.KR 3500)
£366 $667 €534 Landscape composition (44x58cm-17x23in) s.indis.i.d.1944 col pencil prov. 7-Feb-4 Rasmussen, Havnen #4139 (D.KR 4000)

SCHARL, Josef (1896-1954) German
£431 $772 €629 Two wos (35x53cm-14x21in) s.d.1919 board. 12-May-4 Dobiaschofsky, Bern #934/R (S.FR 1000)
£1141 $2042 €1700 Tiger lilies in red vase (27x29cm-11x11in) s.d. tempera. 25-May-4 Karl & Faber, Munich #523/R est:1800
£1409 $2523 €2100 Thunderstorm at Cape Cod (35x49cm-14x19in) s.i.d.1954 tempera. 25-May-4 Karl & Faber, Munich #524/R est:4000
£1818 $3091 €2600 Still life with fruit (29x38cm-11x15in) s.d.1945 tempera prov. 26-Nov-3 Lempertz, Koln #967/R est:2200
Works on paper
£323 $600 €472 Ohne titel (31x24cm-12x9in) s.d.1930 pen ink. 2-Mar-4 Swann Galleries, New York #611/R

SCHATTANEK, Karl (1884-1967) Austrian
£426 $711 €600 Tyrol (23x23cm-9x9in) s.mono.d.22 i. verso board. 16-Oct-3 Dorotheum, Salzburg #650/R

SCHATZ, Arnold (1929-1999) German
£280 $476 €400 Pheasant by birch hedge in winter (50x60cm-20x24in) s. 22-Nov-3 Arnold, Frankfurt #629/R
£521 $859 €750 Fox in the snow (70x101cm-28x40in) s. 3-Jul-3 Neumeister, Munich #2906/R
£567 $1037 €850 Flying ducks over autumn moor (60x90cm-24x35in) s. 5-Jun-4 Arnold, Frankfurt #708/R
£867 $1551 €1300 Wild boar (70x99cm-28x39in) s. 14-May-4 Schloss Ahlden, Ahlden #2894/R

SCHATZ, Bezalel (1912-1978) Israeli
£341 $600 €498 Landscape of the casino building in Tel Aviv (24x25cm-9x10in) s. canvas on board prov. 1-Jan-4 Ben-Ami, Tel Aviv #4254/R
£621 $1100 €907 Portrait of Jew in Jerusalem (32x23cm-13x9in) board painted c.1930 prov. 1-May-4 Ben-Ami, Tel Aviv #4806/R est:1400-1800
£1271 $2250 €1856 Jerusalem and the dome of the rock (66x81cm-26x32in) s. painted c.1950 prov. 1-May-4 Ben-Ami, Tel Aviv #4815/R est:3000-4000
£1393 $2550 €2034 Figure (100x35cm-39x14in) s.d.1952 s.d.verso board. 1-Jun-4 Ben-Ami, Tel Aviv #4899/R est:2000-3000
£1412 $2400 €2062 Landscape of Jerusalem and the Tower of David (71x57cm-28x22in) canvas on board painted c.1930 prov. 1-Dec-3 Ben-Ami, Tel Aviv #4256/R est:3000-4000
£1978 $3600 €2967 Masks (82x97cm-32x38in) s.d.1947. 1-Jul-4 Ben-Ami, Tel Aviv #4948/R est:4000-6000
£2623 $4800 €3830 Street in Jerusalem (81x65cm-32x26in) s. 1-Jun-4 Ben-Ami, Tel Aviv #4870/R est:4000-6000

SCHATZ, Boris (1867-1932) Russian
£1676 $3000 €2447 Evil thoughts (23x21cm-9x8in) i. panel. 18-Mar-4 Sotheby's, New York #221/R est:6000-8000
Sculpture
£4915 $8700 €7176 Sofer Stam (52x54cm-20x21in) s.i. hand painted plaster relief prov. 1-May-4 Ben-Ami, Tel Aviv #4805/R est:7000-10000

SCHATZ, Louise (1912-) Israeli
Works on paper
£237 $420 €346 Abstract composition (35x45cm-14x18in) s. W/C prov. 1-May-4 Ben-Ami, Tel Aviv #4809/R
£254 $450 €371 Abstract composition (35x30cm-14x12in) s. W/C prov. 1-May-4 Ben-Ami, Tel Aviv #4808/R
£264 $450 €385 Autumn dance (38x54cm-15x21in) s.i.d.1962 W/C prov. 1-Dec-3 Ben-Ami, Tel Aviv #4248/R
£355 $650 €518 Iris (36x25cm-14x10in) s.d.1989 W/C. 1-Jun-4 Ben-Ami, Tel Aviv #4898/R

SCHATZ, Manfred (1925-) German
£1224 $2192 €1800 Deer in field (40x55cm-16x22in) 18-Mar-4 Neumeister, Munich #2767 est:300

£1399 $2378 €2000 Wild ducks over moorland (60x80cm-24x31in) s. 20-Nov-3 Van Ham, Cologne #1840/R est:1800
£1538 $2615 €2200 Pheasants in forest clearing (60x80cm-24x31in) s. 20-Nov-3 Van Ham, Cologne #1841/R est:2500
£1633 $2922 €2400 Wild boar in winter wood (60x80cm-24x31in) s. 18-Mar-4 Neumeister, Munich #2768/R est:350
£1678 $3087 €2500 Wild boar in snowy winter landscape (70x109cm-28x43in) s. lit. 25-Mar-4 Karlheinz Kaupp, Staufen #2705/R est:1000
£2098 $3608 €3000 Pheasants in winter wood (62x80cm-24x31in) s. 4-Dec-3 Schopman, Hamburg #699/R est:2800
£2324 $3718 €3300 Two stags in morning light (110x160cm-43x63in) s. lit. 19-Sep-3 Karlheinz Kaupp, Staufen #2020/R est:500
£2569 $4060 €3700 Ducks flying over reeds (60x78cm-24x31in) s. 6-Sep-3 Schopman, Hamburg #821/R est:3200

SCHATZ, Otto Rudolf (1901-1961) Austrian
£987 $1816 €1500 Landscape with houses (15x20cm-6x8in) mono. panel. 22-Jun-4 Wiener Kunst Auktionen, Vienna #74/R est:1500
£2069 $3786 €3000 Landscape (25x20cm-10x8in) mono. panel. 27-Jan-4 Dorotheum, Vienna #38/R est:2400-3400
£4828 $8062 €7000 Studio scene in new York (55x65cm-22x26in) s. 13-Nov-3 Neumeister, Munich #451/R est:3500-3800
£5517 $10097 €8000 Paris (32x44cm-13x17in) mono. paper on board. 27-Jan-4 Dorotheum, Vienna #94/R est:3000-4000
Works on paper
£336 $601 €500 Fascination (19x21cm-7x8in) W/C. 27-May-4 Hassfurther, Vienna #70
£570 $1021 €850 Flagellantism (19x24cm-7x9in) black chk gouache. 27-May-4 Hassfurther, Vienna #69
£638 $1066 €900 Figures round table (23x43cm-9x17in) gouache. 14-Oct-3 Dorotheum, Vienna #140/R
£738 $1321 €1100 Flying carpet (20x24cm-8x9in) mixed media. 27-May-4 Hassfurther, Vienna #71
£805 $1490 €1200 Three graces (17x11cm-7x4in) chk col pen W/C. 9-Mar-4 Dorotheum, Vienna #101/R
£1733 $3120 €2600 Caller. Doppelganger. Evening. s.mono.i.d.1920 mixed media three. 21-Apr-4 Dorotheum, Vienna #58/R est:2000-2600
£3087 $5526 €4600 Back view of female nude (41x34cm-16x13in) mono.d.22 black chk oil gouache. 27-May-4 Hassfurther, Vienna #68/R est:2500-3500

SCHATZ, Zahara (1916-1999) Israeli
Sculpture
£1500 $2550 €2190 Abstract (115x340x40cm-45x134x16in) brass prov. 1-Dec-3 Ben-Ami, Tel Aviv #4261/R est:2000-3000

SCHAUENBERG, Walter (1884-1943) Swiss
£591 $981 €857 Heiternplatz, Zofingen in summer (72x87cm-28x34in) s.d.1925. 13-Jun-3 Zofingen, Switzerland #3008 (S.FR 1300)

SCHAUER, Otto (1923-1985) German
£1049 $1804 €1500 Nature morte (65x54cm-26x21in) s. s.d.1963 verso. 2-Dec-3 Calmels Cohen, Paris #96/R est:1500-1800

SCHAUMAN, Sigrid (1877-1979) Finnish
£1831 $3168 €2600 Landscape, Tolo (41x33cm-16x13in) canvas on board. 13-Dec-3 Hagelstam, Helsinki #172/R est:3000
£4056 $6895 €5800 View from a park (46x38cm-18x15in) s. 29-Nov-3 Bukowskis, Helsinki #181/R est:4000-5000
£4133 $7399 €6200 Landscape from Tolo (41x33cm-16x13in) board prov. 15-May-4 Hagelstam, Helsinki #162/R est:5000
£4730 $8466 €7000 View from Brunnsparken (27x32cm-11x13in) s.d.45 board exhib. 8-May-4 Bukowskis, Helsinki #163/R est:5000-6000
Works on paper
£318 $569 €464 Girl in profile (49x38cm-19x15in) s. chl prov. 28-May-4 Uppsala Auktionskammare, Uppsala #200 (S.KR 4300)

SCHAUMANN, Peter (20th C) German
£282 $524 €420 View of Regensburg across the Donau (60x50cm-24x20in) s. i.verso. 5-Mar-4 Wendl, Rudolstadt #3849/R

SCHAUMBURG, Jules (1839-1886) Belgian
£2486 $4600 €3729 Sailing ships in port (58x74cm-23x29in) s.d.1862. 14-Jul-4 American Auctioneer #490209/R est:1500-2500
£16000 $29600 €23360 Shipping off Calcultta (78x116cm-31x46in) s.d.1869. 14-Jul-4 Sotheby's, Olympia #170/R est:12000-18000
Works on paper
£4600 $8142 €6716 Shipping in the Hoogly River, Calcutta (46x66cm-18x26in) s. one d.1874 W/C pair. 27-Apr-4 Bonhams, New Bond Street #44/R est:4000-6000

SCHAUSS, Ferdinand (1832-1916) German
£5491 $9500 €8017 Paix apres la tempete (109x195cm-43x77in) indis sig. prov. 11-Dec-3 Sotheby's, New York #150/R est:12000-18000

SCHAUSS, Martin (attrib) (1867-1927) German
Sculpture
£1034 $1655 €1500 Beauty and pain (53cm-21in) s. bronze marble base Cast Noach. 12-Mar-3 Auction Maastricht #641/R est:1500-2000
£1275 $2372 €1900 Female nude (37cm-15in) s. bronze marble base st.f.Noach. 4-Mar-4 Auction Maastricht #158/R est:1500-2000

SCHAUTA, Friedrich (1822-1895) Austrian
£2378 $4042 €3400 Pheasants by pond (124x175cm-49x69in) s. 24-Nov-3 Dorotheum, Vienna #173/R est:3200-3800

SCHAYENBURG, Pieter van (attrib) (17th C) Dutch
£1528 $2521 €2200 Still life with fish in basket (96x75cm-38x30in) 3-Jul-3 Van Ham, Cologne #1011/R est:2500

SCHEBEK, Ferdinand (1875-1949) Austrian
£759 $1267 €1100 Bearded Rabbi (17x12cm-7x5in) s. panel. 15-Nov-3 Lempertz, Koln #1690/R
£1325 $2411 €2000 Ducks by the water (55x66cm-22x26in) s.i. 21-Jun-4 Dorotheum, Vienna #165/R est:2000-2500
£1342 $2510 €2000 Birds in reeds (55x66cm-22x26in) s.i. 24-Feb-4 Dorotheum, Vienna #99/R est:2000-2200

SCHEDRIN, Sylvester Feodosievich (attrib) (1791-1830) Russian
£8000 $13600 €11680 Italian Coastal scene (16x25cm-6x10in) bears sig.d.1828 canvas on board. 19-Nov-3 Sotheby's, London #7/R est:3000-5000

SCHEDRIN, Sylvester Feodosievich (circle) (1791-1830) Russian
£18056 $32500 €26362 Italianate landscape (35x50cm-14x20in) 23-Apr-4 Sotheby's, New York #28/R est:12000-18000

SCHEEL, Ernst (1861-?) German
Photographs
£1958 $3329 €2800 Stairway with lift in Hamburg factory (22x16cm-9x6in) i. verso silver gelatin lit.exhib. 27-Nov-3 Villa Grisebach, Berlin #1379/R est:2800-3200
£2657 $4517 €3800 Spiral staircase in factory, Hamburg (22x16cm-9x6in) i. verso silver gelatin lit.exhib. 27-Nov-3 Villa Grisebach, Berlin #1378/R est:2800-3200
£3261 $5348 €4500 Interior of CHF Muller factory in Hamburg (17x22cm-7x9in) i.verso vintage silver gelatin lit. 30-May-3 Villa Grisebach, Berlin #1342/R est:2500-3000

SCHEEMAECKERS, Peeter II (1691-1781) Flemish
Sculpture
£12500 $22000 €18250 William Shakespeare, after the monument at Poet's Corner (33x19cm-13x7in) ivory ebony base. 21-May-4 Bracketts, Tunbridge Wells #186/R est:700-1000

SCHEERBOOM, Andries (1832-1891) Dutch
£855 $1574 €1300 Portrait of Caspar Leonard van Gyen. Portrait of Mrs C E van Gyen-Klussener (22x19cm-9x7in) one s.d.1858 one s.d.1859 panel pair. 22-Jun-4 Christie's, Amsterdam #6/R
£1850 $3367 €2701 Dutch town view with figures conversing (27x36cm-11x14in) s.d.63 panel prov. 16-Jun-4 Bonhams, New Bond Street #3/R est:1500-2000

SCHEERES, Hendricus Johannes (1829-1864) Dutch
£233 $400 €340 Domestic scene with Dutch girl (23x18cm-9x7in) s.d.1858 mono.verso panel. 7-Dec-3 Treadway Gallery, Cincinnati #489/R
£479 $800 €695 Blacksmith (18x15cm-7x6in) s.d.58 board. 29-Jun-3 Butterfields, Los Angeles #7029/R
£750 $1275 €1095 Polishing armour at the blacksmith's forge (23x18cm-9x7in) s.d.50 panel. 6-Nov-3 Christie's, Kensington #816/R
£1000 $1720 €1460 Important letter (55x45cm-22x18in) s. 4-Dec-3 Christie's, Kensington #169/R est:1500-2000
£1127 $1972 €1600 Young woman holding glass (20x15cm-8x6in) s.d.53 panel. 19-Dec-3 Pierre Berge, Paris #35/R est:1400-1800

SCHEFFEL, Johan Hendrik (attrib) (1690-1781) Swedish
£2615 $4498 €3818 Portrait of Johan Gabriel Sack (77x57cm-30x22in) 3-Dec-3 AB Stockholms Auktionsverk #2332/R est:15000-18000 (S.KR 34000)

SCHEFFER, Ary (1795-1858) French
£1867 $3416 €2800 Portrait presume de Monsieur Chaloux Brillan (41x31cm-16x12in) i.verso. 6-Jun-4 Rouillac, Vendome #4
£2763 $5084 €4200 Portrait de la Comtesse Walther (119x88cm-47x35in) s.d.1842 oval. 25-Jun-4 Piasa, Paris #122 est:4000-6000
£3087 $5681 €4600 La bataille de Tolbiac (49x56cm-19x22in) oil pencil. 26-Mar-4 Neret-Minet, Paris #24/R est:2000-3000
£8800 $14696 €12848 Portrait of lady (119x74cm-47x29in) s.d.1841. 12-Nov-3 Sotheby's, Olympia #146/R est:5000-7000
£40000 $68800 €58400 Paolo and Francesca (33x46cm-13x18in) s. panel. 3-Dec-3 Christie's, London #23/R est:40000-60000

SCHEFFER, Henri (1798-1862) French
£921 $1695 €1400 A comporting presence (22x19cm-9x7in) s.d.1833 panel. 22-Jun-4 Christie's, Amsterdam #20/R

SCHEFFLER, Felix Anton (1701-1760) German
Works on paper
£559 $951 €800 St Dominicus (41x23cm-16x9in) chk htd white. 27-Nov-3 Bassenge, Berlin #5505

SCHEGGI, C (19th C) Italian
Sculpture
£2617 $4633 €3900 Femme a la serpe (74cm-29in) s. marble. 27-Apr-4 Campo, Vlaamse Kaai #21/R est:4500-6500

SCHEGGI, Paolo (1940-1971) Italian
Sculpture
£10490 $17832 €15000 Intersurface (100x80x5cm-39x31x2in) s.d.1967 acrylic. 28-Nov-3 Farsetti, Prato #246/R est:15000-18000

SCHEIBE, Richard (1879-1964) German

Sculpture

£2400	$4416	€3600	Seated monkey (11x8x9cm-4x3x4in) bronze. 10-Jun-4 Hauswedell & Nolte, Hamburg #617/R est:2500
£3067	$5643	€4600	Female head (9x7x7cm-4x3x3in) bronze. 10-Jun-4 Hauswedell & Nolte, Hamburg #616/R est:3000
£3200	$5888	€4800	Standing monkey (20x9x7cm-8x4x3in) bronze. 10-Jun-4 Hauswedell & Nolte, Hamburg #618/R est:2500

SCHEIBER, Hugo (1873-1950) Hungarian

£1034	$1728	€1500	Le cocher (43x60cm-17x24in) s.d. oil gouache cardboard. 17-Nov-3 Claude Boisgirard, Paris #85/R est:1000-1500
£1336	$2365	€1951	Shadowy path (51x42cm-20x17in) s. tempera paper. 28-Apr-4 Kieselbach, Budapest #167/R (H.F 500000)
£1581	$2861	€2308	Couple smoking cigarette (54x45cm-21x18in) s. tempera on paper. 16-Apr-4 Mu Terem Galeria, Budapest #76/R (H.F 600000)
£2004	$3547	€2926	Woman in a hat (62x43cm-24x17in) s.d.1940 tempera paper. 28-Apr-4 Kieselbach, Budapest #59/R (H.F 750000)
£2371	$4292	€3462	Dancer with guitar (66x49cm-26x19in) s. tempera. 16-Apr-4 Mu Terem Galeria, Budapest #71/R (H.F 900000)
£2937	$4993	€4200	Figures (38x33cm-15x13in) s.d.1932 board. 20-Nov-3 Finarte Semenzato, Milan #120/R est:4000-4500
£3125	$5500	€4563	Horse and carriage (38x46cm-15x18in) s.d.1930. 1-Jan-4 Ben-Ami, Tel Aviv #4403/R est:6000-8000
£3207	$5676	€4682	Waterside (80x63cm-31x25in) s. 28-Apr-4 Kieselbach, Budapest #43/R (H.F 1200000)
£4176	$7225	€6097	Portrait with Red-Yellow background (66x49cm-26x19in) s. cardboard painted c.1920. 12-Dec-3 Kieselbach, Budapest #77/R (H.F 1600000)
£4479	$8107	€6539	Sailing boats (64x47cm-25x19in) s. tempera pastel on paper. 16-Apr-4 Mu Terem Galeria, Budapest #176/R (H.F 1700000)
£8144	$13520	€11890	Self portrait (55x45cm-22x18in) oil paper. 4-Oct-3 Kieselbach, Budapest #134/R (H.F 3000000)
£13287	$22853	€19000	Woman (98x78cm-39x31in) s. oil on card painted c.1920 prov. 2-Dec-3 Sotheby's, Amsterdam #105/R est:6000-9000
£13574	$22533	€19818	Street carnival (56x72cm-22x28in) s. 4-Oct-3 Kieselbach, Budapest #81/R (H.F 5000000)

Works on paper

£641	$1135	€936	Man with a pipe (54x44cm-21x17in) s. mixed media. 28-Apr-4 Kieselbach, Budapest #184/R (H.F 240000)
£783	$1355	€1143	Tramp (58x46cm-23x18in) s. mixed media. 12-Dec-3 Kieselbach, Budapest #152/R (H.F 300000)
£811	$1451	€1200	Nue (69x48cm-27x19in) s. mixed media. 10-May-4 Horta, Bruxelles #335
£869	$1477	€1269	Blue eye and black heart (31x39cm-12x15in) s. mixed media. 4-Nov-3 Bukowskis, Stockholm #269/R (S.KR 11500)
£950	$1577	€1387	Park (34x41cm-13x16in) s. mixed media. 4-Oct-3 Kieselbach, Budapest #26/R (H.F 350000)
£992	$1716	€1448	Green-Blue dressed girls (59x43cm-23x17in) s. mixed media. 12-Dec-3 Kieselbach, Budapest #25/R (H.F 380000)
£1067	$1963	€1600	Kneeling female nude (74x55cm-29x22in) s. pastel chl. 12-Jun-4 Karlheinz Kaupp, Staufen #1178 est:250
£1305	$2258	€1905	Nude in landscape (48x69cm-19x27in) s. mixed media. 12-Dec-3 Kieselbach, Budapest #162/R (H.F 500000)
£1317	$2384	€1923	Lady wearing glasses (27x39cm-11x15in) s. coal on paper. 16-Apr-4 Mu Terem Galeria, Budapest #77/R (H.F 500000)
£1336	$2365	€1951	Blonde vampire (66x49cm-26x19in) s. mixed media. 28-Apr-4 Kieselbach, Budapest #185/R (H.F 500000)
£1357	$2253	€1981	Avenue of poplars (61x43cm-24x17in) s. mixed media. 4-Oct-3 Kieselbach, Budapest #156/R (H.F 500000)
£1397	$2500	€2040	Portrait of a woman holding a flower (57x49cm-22x19in) s. pastel. 18-Mar-4 Sotheby's, New York #118/R est:3000-4000
£1470	$2601	€2146	Tramp (63x46cm-25x18in) s. mixed media. 28-Apr-4 Kieselbach, Budapest #14/R (H.F 550000)
£1566	$2709	€2286	Dance (66x48cm-26x19in) s. mixed media. 12-Dec-3 Kieselbach, Budapest #83/R (H.F 600000)
£1566	$2709	€2286	Nude in the studio (67x47cm-26x19in) s. mixed media. 12-Dec-3 Kieselbach, Budapest #208/R (H.F 600000)
£1629	$2704	€2378	Dancer (48x33cm-19x13in) s. mixed media. 4-Oct-3 Kieselbach, Budapest #27/R (H.F 600000)
£1629	$2704	€2378	Lakeside landscape (50x42cm-20x17in) s. mixed media. 4-Oct-3 Kieselbach, Budapest #75/R (H.F 600000)
£1629	$2704	€2378	Man with a cigarette (70x49cm-28x19in) s. mixed media. 4-Oct-3 Kieselbach, Budapest #86/R (H.F 600000)
£1697	$2935	€2478	Town in winter (51x40cm-20x16in) s. mixed media. 12-Dec-3 Kieselbach, Budapest #128/R (H.F 650000)
£1697	$2935	€2478	Woman in hat with pearl necklace (39x42cm-15x17in) s. mixed media. 12-Dec-3 Kieselbach, Budapest #202/R (H.F 650000)
£1713	$3100	€2501	Twilight street (69x49cm-27x19in) s. pastel. 16-Apr-4 Mu Terem Galeria, Budapest #181/R (H.F 650000)
£1737	$3074	€2536	Blonde and red (69x49cm-27x19in) s. mixed media. 28-Apr-4 Kieselbach, Budapest #88/R (H.F 650000)
£1765	$2929	€2577	Portrait of a man (60x43cm-24x17in) s. pastel. 4-Oct-3 Kieselbach, Budapest #188/R (H.F 650000)
£2088	$3612	€3048	Rambler Knight (58x43cm-23x17in) s. mixed media. 12-Dec-3 Kieselbach, Budapest #76/R (H.F 800000)
£2393	$4307	€3494	Society lady with cigarette (67x47cm-26x19in) s. pastel. 26-Apr-4 Bukowskis, Stockholm #242/R est:25000-30000 (S.KR 33000)
£2443	$4056	€3567	In a bar (66x51cm-26x20in) s. mixed media. 4-Oct-3 Kieselbach, Budapest #190/R (H.F 900000)
£3067	$5581	€4600	Figural composition (56x41cm-22x16in) s. mixed media lit. 3-Jul-4 Badum, Bamberg #75/R est:4600
£3207	$5676	€4682	Woman dressed in red in a night-club (69x49cm-27x19in) s. mixed media. 28-Apr-4 Kieselbach, Budapest #168/R (H.F 1200000)
£4344	$7211	€6342	Vamp (60x44cm-24x17in) s. mixed media. 4-Oct-3 Kieselbach, Budapest #8 (H.F 1600000)
£4437	$7676	€6478	Vamp in a hat (62x48cm-24x19in) mixed media. 12-Dec-3 Kieselbach, Budapest #18/R (H.F 1700000)

SCHEIBITZ, Thomas (1968-) German

£29940	$50000	€43712	Haus (150x270cm-59x106in) s.i.d.98 prov.exhib. 12-Nov-3 Christie's, Rockefeller NY #506/R est:10000-15000
£37989	$68000	€55464	Untitled no 372 (145x250cm-57x98in) s.d.2003 overlap i.stretcher oil linen prov. 14-May-4 Phillips, New York #120/R est:40000-60000
£49162	$88000	€71777	Untitled, num 128 (150x270cm-59x106in) s.d.1997 verso acrylic prov. 12-May-4 Christie's, Rockefeller NY #321/R est:35000-55000

SCHEIBL, Hubert (1951-) Austrian

£769	$1308	€1100	Untitled (88x31cm-35x12in) s.d.1986 verso board. 19-Nov-3 Dorotheum, Klagenfurt #28
£1399	$2378	€2000	W CU (80x50cm-31x20in) s.i.d.1993/4. 28-Nov-3 Wiener Kunst Auktionen, Vienna #685/R est:3000-5000

SCHEID, Lore (1889-1946) German

£493	$789	€700	St Gilgen (66x53cm-26x21in) s. lit. 19-Sep-3 Karlheinz Kaupp, Staufen #1979

SCHEIDL, Franz Anton von (1731-1801) Austrian

£563	$986	€800	Between generating and decaying, the white death (70x60cm-28x24in) s. i.d.1992 verso. 19-Dec-3 Dorotheum, Vienna #414/R

SCHEIDL, Roman (1949-) Austrian

£603	$1007	€850	Two small objects (50x40cm-20x16in) s. s.i.d.1990 verso. 14-Oct-3 Dorotheum, Vienna #298/R

Works on paper

£345	$631	€500	Untitled (50x64cm-20x25in) s.d.93 brush Indian ink. 27-Jan-4 Dorotheum, Vienna #257/R

SCHEINHAMMER, Otto (1897-1982) German

£342	$606	€510	Southern harbour landscape (65x76cm-26x30in) s. 30-Apr-4 Dr Fritz Nagel, Stuttgart #432/R
£403	$741	€600	Mittenwald in winter (65x75cm-26x30in) s. 24-Mar-4 Hugo Ruef, Munich #1109/R
£483	$893	€700	Chiemsee with Fraueninsel (60x78cm-24x31in) s. lit. 13-Feb-4 Auktionhaus Georg Rehm, Augsburg #8122
£1288	$2279	€1880	Boats on the Nile (75x65cm-30x26in) s. 12-Jun-4 Falk & Falk, Zurich #1037/R est:2800 (S.FR 3000)

SCHEIRING, Leopold (1884-?) Austrian

Works on paper

£397	$727	€600	Hohensalzburg (16x25cm-6x10in) s.i. W/C. 7-Apr-4 Dorotheum, Salzburg #195/R

SCHEITS, Matthias (1640-1700) German

Works on paper

£733	$1313	€1100	Paul and Magician of Elymas (25x20cm-10x8in) mono.i. pen wash. 13-May-4 Bassenge, Berlin #5304/R
£800	$1472	€1200	Parable (24x19cm-9x7in) mono. pen wash. 11-Jun-4 Hauswedell & Nolte, Hamburg #905/R

SCHELCK, Maurice (1906-1978) Belgian

£625	$1044	€900	Fleurs (50x40cm-20x16in) s. panel. 21-Oct-3 Campo, Vlaamse Kaai #554
£667	$1193	€1000	Summer landscape (40x50cm-16x20in) s. panel. 15-May-4 De Vuyst, Lokeren #292/R
£1074	$1901	€1600	Nature morte aux fleurs (87x70cm-34x28in) s. 27-Apr-4 Campo & Campo, Antwerp #201/R est:3000-5000
£1389	$2319	€2000	Paysage d'hiver (60x80cm-24x31in) s. panel. 21-Oct-3 Campo, Vlaamse Kaai #553/R est:1500-1800
£1549	$2680	€2200	La Lys en hiver (80x100cm-31x39in) s. panel. 9-Dec-3 Campo, Vlaamse Kaai #431/R est:2300-2800

SCHELFHOUT, Andreas (1787-1870) Dutch

£1242	$2000	€1813	Winter skating (23x36cm-9x14in) s. panel. 20-Aug-3 James Julia, Fairfield #702/R est:6000-8000
£1497	$2679	€2200	Enjoying the ice (18x27cm-7x11in) panel. 17-Mar-4 Neumeister, Munich #592/R est:2800
£3333	$6000	€5000	Two figures in a summer landscape (34x40cm-13x16in) s. panel. 20-Apr-4 Sotheby's, Amsterdam #25/R est:6000-8000
£4706	$8000	€6871	Winter landscape with cottages and boats by a frozen river, figures skating beyond (22x27cm-9x11in) s. panel. 19-Nov-3 Bonhams & Butterfields, San Francisco #61/R
£7483	$13619	€11000	Best friends, dog portrait (32x27cm-13x11in) s.d.47 panel. 3-Feb-4 Christie's, Amsterdam #54/R est:4000-6000
£9500	$16340	€13870	Winter skaters on the lake (22x28cm-9x11in) s.i. panel. 3-Dec-3 Christie's, London #1/R est:7000-10000
£13333	$24000	€20000	Travelers in an extensive landscape (11x18cm-4x7in) s.d.46 panel. 20-Apr-4 Sotheby's, Amsterdam #181/R est:25000-35000
£13333	$24000	€20000	Peasants in a cornfield (22x30cm-9x12in) s. board lit. 20-Apr-4 Sotheby's, Amsterdam #189/R est:20000-30000
£17361	$28993	€25000	Figurers in a winter landscape (15x19cm-6x7in) s. panel prov. 21-Oct-3 Sotheby's, Amsterdam #176/R est:18000-25000
£19000	$34960	€27740	Figures and cattle beside a lake in a wooded landscape (53x71cm-21x28in) indis.sig.d.1818 panel. 23-Mar-4 Bonhams, New Bond Street #10/R est:10000-15000
£19444	$33056	€28000	Panoramic summer landscape with travellers resting in the dunes (13x18cm-5x7in) s. panel. 28-Oct-3 Christie's, Amsterdam #213/R est:14000-18000
£20833	$35417	€30000	Skaters on the ice with a koek en zopie in the distance (9x11cm-4x4in) s. panel. 28-Oct-3 Christie's, Amsterdam #209/R est:15000-20000
£21127	$36549	€30000	Wooded landscape with farmsteads (41x53cm-16x21in) s.d.1843 panel. 13-Dec-3 Lempertz, Koln #247/R est:8000
£23000	$41860	€33580	View of Dordrecht (13x17cm-5x7in) s.d.45 panel prov. 15-Jun-4 Sotheby's, London #152/R est:10000-15000
£25333	$45600	€38000	Skaters on a frozen waterway (18x26cm-7x10in) s.d.51 panel prov.lit. 20-Apr-4 Sotheby's, Amsterdam #161/R est:30000-40000
£29167	$48708	€42000	Winter landscape with figures on frozen river (17x24cm-7x9in) s. panel. 21-Oct-3 Sotheby's, Amsterdam #183/R est:40000-60000
£56667	$102000	€85000	Figures with a horse sledge on the ice, town in the distance (27x32cm-11x13in) s.d.49 panel prov.lit. 20-Apr-4 Sotheby's, Amsterdam #186/R est:60000-80000
£70000	$126000	€105000	Summer landscape with a ferry (37x51cm-15x20in) s.d.57 panel. 20-Apr-4 Sotheby's, Amsterdam #193/R est:50000-70000

£72917 $123958 €105000 Sunlit winter landscape with a huntsman conversing with villagers on the ice (64x81cm-25x32in) s.d.1834. 28-Oct-3 Christie's, Amsterdam #223/R est:50000-70000
£72917 $123958 €105000 Skaters on the ice by windmills, a koek and zopie in the distance (40x51cm-16x20in) s. panel prov. 28-Oct-3 Christie's, Amsterdam #239/R est:120000-180000
£120000 $216000 €180000 Skaters on a frozen river near a koek en zopie (26x38cm-10x15in) s.d.57 panel prov.exhib.lit. 20-Apr-4 Sotheby's, Amsterdam #169/R est:180000-220000
£180000 $324000 €270000 Shepherdess with a flock and travellers in a summer landscape (111x146cm-44x57in) s.d.1849 prov.lit. 21-Apr-4 Christie's, Amsterdam #215/R est:300000-500000
Works on paper
£329 $595 €500 Fisherman with dog sitting towards the quay (20x17cm-8x7in) s.verso sepia. 19-Apr-4 Glerum, Amsterdam #97/R
£442 $805 €650 River landscape with cattle on a path (17x27cm-7x11in) s. pen ink wash. 3-Feb-4 Christie's, Amsterdam #90/R
£612 $1096 €900 Paysage anime (21x24cm-8x9in) s. W/C wash. 19-Mar-4 Oger, Dumont, Paris #39
£658 $1211 €1000 Paysage (15x21cm-6x8in) s. brown pen W/C. 23-Jun-4 Millon & Associes, Paris #47
£800 $1432 €1200 Hilly landscape with birch trees (23x31cm-9x12in) mono.i. W/C over pen. 13-May-4 Bassenge, Berlin #5654
£828 $1382 €1200 Landscape with six horses pulling loaded cart (24x33cm-9x13in) s. verso W/C. 15-Nov-3 Lempertz, Koln #1551 est:1200
£979 $1664 €1400 The Rhine at Bingen (26x33cm-10x13in) mono.i. brush over pencil. 27-Nov-3 Bassenge, Berlin #5643/R
£1500 $2550 €2190 Figures outside a farmstead (29x33cm-11x13in) s. pen ink W/C exec.c.1812-1815. 19-Nov-3 Bonhams, New Bond Street #2/R est:1000-1500
£1818 $3036 €2600 Travellers on a road (27x32cm-11x13in) s.d.26 ink. 30-Jun-3 Sotheby's, Amsterdam #141
£2162 $3805 €3200 Studies of boats (14x39cm-6x15in) init.i.d.14 January 30 W/C black chk two joined sheets prov.lit. 19-May-4 Sotheby's, Amsterdam #342/R est:1500-2000
£5556 $9444 €8000 Wooded winter landscape with figures by a cottage (18x26cm-7x10in) s. pencil blk ink W/C htd white prov. 28-Oct-3 Christie's, Amsterdam #99/R est:7000-9000

SCHELFHOUT, Andreas (attrib) (1787-1870) Dutch
£3497 $5944 €5000 River landscape with ice skaters (32x42cm-13x17in) i. panel prov. 28-Nov-3 Wiener Kunst Auktionen, Vienna #431/R est:5000-15000

SCHELL, Francis H (1834-1909) American
Works on paper
£900 $1700 €1314 Portrait of 1893 America's Cup contenders 'Vigilant' and 'Valkyrie' (36x58cm-14x23in) s.i. W/C. 22-Feb-4 Skinner, Boston #365/R est:800-1200

SCHELL, Sherill (1877-1964) American
Photographs
£6667 $12000 €9734 Chrysler building, New York City (41x26cm-16x10in) s. gelatin silver print. 22-Apr-4 Phillips, New York #60/R est:12000-18000

SCHELLENBERG, Johann Ulrich (1709-1795) Swiss
£762 $1273 €1113 Lucern, lake and Rigiberg (30x40cm-12x16in) i. verso panel. 24-Oct-3 Hans Widmer, St Gallen #132/R est:1400-2800 (S.FR 1700)

SCHELLER, Emil (1880-1942) ?
£261 $477 €381 Young bather sitting at the water's edge (90x55cm-35x22in) s. 4-Jun-4 Zofingen, Switzerland #2946 (S.FR 600)

SCHELLER, Hans Walter (1896-1964) Swiss
£295 $490 €428 Sunny day on Untersee lakeshore (60x83cm-24x33in) s.i. verso. 13-Jun-3 Zofingen, Switzerland #3009 (S.FR 650)

SCHELLER, Rudolf (1889-1984) German
£400 $720 €600 Peasant family with cows and sheep drinking (70x91cm-28x36in) s. tempera lit. 22-Apr-4 Allgauer, Kempten #3713/R
Works on paper
£420 $701 €600 Man from Allgau (45x29cm-18x11in) s. ochre chk. 27-Jun-3 Michael Zeller, Lindau #653/R

SCHELLING, George Luther (1938-) American
£396 $650 €578 Mesozoic, depicting shark (122x91cm-48x36in) s. 4-Jun-3 Alderfer's, Hatfield #307

SCHELOUMOFF, Athanasei (1912-1976) Russian
£448 $749 €650 Troika on wolf hunt in winter landscape (69x102cm-27x40in) s. panel lit. 12-Jul-3 Bergmann, Erlangen #645/R
£1823 $3300 €2662 Welcomed visitors (43x58cm-17x23in) s. 16-Apr-4 James Julia, Fairfield #661/R est:800-1200
£1854 $3375 €2800 Trojka pursued by wolves (50x70cm-20x28in) s. 21-Jun-4 Dorotheum, Vienna #160/R est:2000-2300

SCHELOUMOV, Athanas (1892-1983) Russian
£671 $1228 €1000 Horse in the paddock (60x100cm-24x39in) s. lit. 8-Jul-4 Allgauer, Kempten #2211/R
£1000 $1800 €1500 Troika fleeing from wolves (50x70cm-20x28in) s. lit. 22-Apr-4 Allgauer, Kempten #3714/R est:300
£15000 $25500 €21900 Cossacks in retreat (40x60cm-16x24in) s. 19-Nov-3 Sotheby's, London #55/R est:6000-8000

SCHELS, Walter (1936-) German
Photographs
£2754 $4516 €3800 Joseph Beuys (110x73cm-43x29in) s. s.i.d. verso silver gelatin. 30-May-3 Villa Grisebach, Berlin #1348/R est:3800-4200

SCHELTEMA, J H (1861-1938) Dutch
£2043 $3472 €2983 Sheep at a creek (40x61cm-16x24in) s. 26-Nov-3 Deutscher-Menzies, Melbourne #174/R est:5000-7000 (A.D 4800)
£2893 $5351 €4224 Cattle resting (51x76cm-20x30in) s. painted c.1920 prov. 10-Mar-4 Deutscher-Menzies, Melbourne #286/R est:8000-10000 (A.D 7000)
£4580 $8336 €6687 Watering the horses (46x76cm-18x30in) s. 16-Jun-4 Deutscher-Menzies, Melbourne #172/R est:14000-18000 (A.D 12000)
£5957 $10128 €8697 Bullock team (71x102cm-28x40in) s. 26-Nov-3 Deutscher-Menzies, Melbourne #131/R est:12000-18000 (A.D 14000)

SCHELTEMA, Jan Hendrik (1861-1938) Dutch
£1103 $1721 €1599 After milking (24x54cm-9x21in) s. canvas on board. 1-Aug-2 Joel, Victoria #148 est:2000-3000 (A.D 3200)
£1463 $2620 €2136 Cattle in the yard (44x75cm-17x30in) s. 4-May-4 Sotheby's, Melbourne #101/R est:3000-5000 (A.D 3600)
£1626 $2911 €2374 Landscape on the Western plains (39x62cm-15x24in) s. canvas on board. 10-May-4 Joel, Victoria #267 est:6000-10000 (A.D 4000)
£1653 $2926 €2413 Midday rest (40x61cm-16x24in) s. 3-May-4 Christie's, Melbourne #288/R est:2500-3500 (A.D 4000)
£2024 $3259 €2955 Visitors (62x55cm-24x22in) s. bears i.verso canvas on board prov. 25-Aug-3 Sotheby's, Paddington #476/R est:5000-7000 (A.D 5000)
£4656 $7496 €6798 At the end of the day (42x74cm-17x29in) s. 13-Oct-3 Joel, Victoria #346/R est:8500-12500 (A.D 11500)
£5285 $9459 €7716 Drover (60x103cm-24x41in) s. 10-May-4 Joel, Victoria #336/R est:12000-15000 (A.D 13000)
£7115 $12735 €10388 On the Buffalo River, Victoria (80x130cm-31x51in) s. prov. 15-May-4 Christie's, Sydney #4/R est:15000-25000 (A.D 18000)
£8264 $14628 €12065 Hunter's reward (49x75cm-19x30in) s. prov. 3-May-4 Christie's, Melbourne #101/R est:12000-16000 (A.D 20000)

SCHELTEMA, Jan Hendrik (attrib) (1861-1938) Dutch
£2869 $4533 €4189 Cows grazing near Romsey (61x91cm-24x36in) prov. 2-Sep-3 Deutscher-Menzies, Melbourne #294/R est:4000-6000 (A.D 7000)

SCHENAU, Johann Eleazar (attrib) (1737-1806) German
£8609 $15669 €13000 Jeune garcon jouant avec chat pres de sa mere (41x32cm-16x13in) 15-Jun-4 Claude Aguttes, Neuilly #60/R est:10000-12000

SCHENCK, August Friedrich Albrecht (1828-1901) Danish
£940 $1729 €1400 Troupeau de moutons et corbeaux (21x16cm-8x6in) s. panel. 29-Mar-4 Rieunier, Paris #20/R

SCHENDEL, Mira (1919-1988) Brazilian
£4118 $7000 €6012 Sem titulo - Untitled (45x23cm-18x9in) s.d.65 oil monotype prov.exhib. 18-Nov-3 Christie's, Rockefeller NY #188/R est:4000-6000
Works on paper
£2235 $3800 €3263 Sem titulo - Untitled (25x35cm-10x14in) ink exec.1964 prov. 18-Nov-3 Christie's, Rockefeller NY #189/R est:3000-4000
£3824 $6500 €5583 Sem titulo - Untitled (47x23cm-19x9in) chl oilstick exec.1964 three prov. 18-Nov-3 Christie's, Rockefeller NY #186/R est:6000-8000
£5000 $8500 €7300 Sem titulo - Untitled (31x44cm-12x17in) s.d.63 one i. ink ink wash chl. two prov. 18-Nov-3 Christie's, Rockefeller NY #15/R est:4000-5000
£5588 $9500 €8158 Sem titulo - Untitled (20x20cm-8x8in) pencil letter set plexiglass exec. c.1970 prov. 18-Nov-3 Christie's, Rockefeller NY #20/R est:10000-15000
£6333 $11653 €9500 Untitled (87x105cm-34x41in) chl exec. 1965. 10-Jun-4 Christie's, Paris #90/R est:8000-10000
£7333 $13493 €11000 Untitled (85x115cm-33x45in) chl exec.1965. 10-Jun-4 Christie's, Paris #91/R est:8000-10000

SCHENDEL, Petrus van (1806-1870) Belgian
£3210 $5200 €4655 Studying by candlelight (48x37cm-19x15in) s.d.1858. 8-Aug-3 Barridorf, Portland #97/R est:4000-6000
£3333 $5667 €4800 Haybarge on a moonlit river (19x27cm-7x11in) s. panel. 28-Oct-3 Christie's, Amsterdam #9/R est:5000-7000
£15278 $25972 €22000 Tranquil moment (56x45cm-22x18in) s. panel. 28-Oct-3 Christie's, Amsterdam #46/R est:8000-12000
£16667 $30000 €25000 Accusation (74x61cm-29x24in) s. panel. 20-Apr-4 Sotheby's, Amsterdam #184/R est:25000-35000
£88050 $140000 €128553 Market at night (71x58cm-28x23in) s. board. 12-Sep-3 Skinner, Boston #229/R est:50000
£100694 $171181 €145000 Girl selling vegetables at the night-market with the Dam Palace in the distance (65x50cm-26x20in) s. panel prov. 28-Oct-3 Christie's, Amsterdam #243/R est:80000-120000

SCHENDEL, van (?) ?
£1050 $1932 €1533 Man reading a newspaper by candle-light with a pipe and a glass of wine (39x31cm-15x12in) panel. 23-Mar-4 Anderson & Garland, Newcastle #346/R est:400-700

SCHENK, Claus (1946-) German
£329 $582 €490 Broken times (80x120cm-31x47in) s. lit. 30-Apr-4 Auktionhaus Georg Rehm, Augsburg #7654

SCHENK, Karl (1905-1973) Swiss
£617 $1048 €901 Boys bathing (39x49cm-15x19in) s. 7-Nov-3 Dobiaschofsky, Bern #143/R (S.FR 1400)
£1121 $2006 €1637 Boy on rocking horse (55x46cm-22x18in) s. panel. 14-May-4 Dobiaschofsky, Bern #145/R est:4800 (S.FR 2600)
£1552 $2778 €2266 Young shepherdess (77x115cm-30x45in) s. i. verso panel. 14-May-4 Dobiaschofsky, Bern #146/R est:5000 (S.FR 3600)

SCHENKEL, Hermann (1948-) German
Works on paper
£268 $475 €400 Franzi (80x100cm-31x39in) s.d. mixed media tempera col chk. 30-Apr-4 Dr Fritz Nagel, Stuttgart #433/R

SCHENKEL, Jan Jacob (1829-1900) Dutch
£1447 $2620 €2200 Church interior with figures (52x40cm-20x16in) s. panel. 19-Apr-4 Glerum, Amsterdam #34/R est:2000-3000

SCHENKER, Albert (1899-1973) Swiss
£226 $385 €330 Cornfield (57x70cm-22x28in) mono.d.1941 i. verso tempera board. 18-Nov-3 Hans Widmer, St Gallen #1181 (S.FR 500)

SCHENKER, Jacques Matthias (1854-1927) German
£403 $749 €600 Oeschinensee near Kindersteg, Kanton Bern (65x101cm-26x40in) s. i.d.1899 verso. 6-Mar-4 Arnold, Frankfurt #840/R
£435 $800 €635 Mountains with lake (23x36cm-9x14in) panel. 11-Jun-4 Du Mouchelle, Detroit #2026/R
£705 $1198 €1029 Small riverside town (76x57cm-30x22in) s. 5-Nov-3 Dobiaschofsky, Bern #933/R (S.FR 1600)
£995 $1692 €1453 Dartmouth beach (15x22cm-6x9in) s.d.80 panel. 19-Nov-3 Fischer, Luzern #1293/R (S.FR 2200)
£1667 $2833 €2400 Sunny winter landscape (61x85cm-24x33in) s. 28-Oct-3 Dorotheum, Vienna #184/R est:2600-3200

SCHENNIS, Hans Friedrich (1852-1918) German
£403 $741 €600 Storm over sea (38x55cm-15x22in) s. lit. 25-Mar-4 Karlheinz Kaupp, Staufen #2706/R
£839 $1427 €1200 Narrow streets in southern city (33x25cm-13x10in) bears mono. canvas on board. 20-Nov-3 Van Ham, Cologne #1846

SCHENONE PUIG, Dolcey (1896-1952) Uruguayan?
£3118 $5300 €4552 Big house (99x86cm-39x34in) s. 25-Nov-3 Galeria y Remates, Montevideo #46/R

SCHEPELERN, Frederik Anton (1796-1883) Danish
£359 $668 €524 Pirate and his bride in a cave (44x36cm-17x14in) prov. 2-Mar-4 Rasmussen, Copenhagen #1528/R (D.KR 4000)
£584 $1086 €853 Niels Ebbesen challenging Count Gert (60x76cm-24x30in) painted c.1830 exhib.prov. 2-Mar-4 Rasmussen, Copenhagen #1477/R (D.KR 6500)

SCHER, Julia (1954-) American?
Prints
£2156 $3600 €3148 Red securityland warnings (30x25cm-12x10in) screenprint on glass executed 1995 prov. 14-Nov-3 Phillips, New York #315/R est:4000-6000

SCHERBRING, Carl (1859-1899) German
£2254 $3741 €3200 Spring idyll (59x73cm-23x29in) s.d.97. 16-Jun-3 Dorotheum, Vienna #124/R est:4500-5000

SCHERER, Elisabeth (1931-) German
£329 $605 €500 View of Lindau harbour with the Austrian Alps in the distance (31x40cm-12x16in) s. tempera board. 25-Jun-4 Michael Zeller, Lindau #614/R

SCHERER, Hermann (1893-1927) Swiss
£95652 $175043 €139652 Stormy landscape (120x140cm-47x55in) s. prov.exhib.lit. 7-Jun-4 Christie's, Zurich #92/R est:180000-250000 (S.FR 220000)
£117391 $214826 €171391 The conversation (144x115cm-57x45in) prov.exhib.lit. 7-Jun-4 Christie's, Zurich #93/R est:100000-150000 (S.FR 270000)
Sculpture
£165217 $302348 €241217 Boy and girl (145x68x28cm-57x27x11in) poplar wood prov.exhib.lit. 7-Jun-4 Christie's, Zurich #98/R est:400000-600000 (S.FR 380000)
Works on paper
£1217 $2228 €1777 Breggiaschlucht (58x44cm-23x17in) chk. 7-Jun-4 Christie's, Zurich #89/R est:3000-5000 (S.FR 2800)
£1719 $2923 €2510 Female nude (47x32cm-19x13in) chl exec. 1924-26 prov. 22-Nov-3 Burkhard, Luzern #80/R est:4000-5000 (S.FR 3800)
£1957 $3580 €2857 Study for Totenklage (48x32cm-19x13in) black chk ink double-sided prov.lit. 7-Jun-4 Christie's, Zurich #91/R est:5000-7000 (S.FR 4500)
£3982 $6769 €5814 Dancer (47x32cm-19x13in) col chk exec. 1925-26 prov. 22-Nov-3 Burkhard, Luzern #81/R est:10000-12000 (S.FR 8800)
£5505 $9193 €7982 Bathers by river (55x43cm-22x17in) s. gouache prov. 23-Jun-3 Philippe Schuler, Zurich #3284/R est:12000-16000 (S.FR 12000)

SCHERER, Jan Baptist (1869-1910) German
Works on paper
£662 $1205 €1000 Girl on a park bench (100x72cm-39x28in) s.d.1907 pastel lit. 19-Jun-4 Bergmann, Erlangen #830

SCHERFIG, Hans (1905-1979) Danish
£451 $844 €658 Still life of bottles (51x43cm-20x17in) s. 25-Feb-4 Kunsthallen, Copenhagen #280/R (D.KR 5000)
£722 $1350 €1054 Still life of green bottle and brown bowl (51x43cm-20x17in) s. 25-Feb-4 Kunsthallen, Copenhagen #297/R (D.KR 8000)
£1715 $3155 €2504 Elephant with young (34x47cm-13x19in) s. plywood. 29-Mar-4 Rasmussen, Copenhagen #479/R est:25000 (D.KR 19000)
£4739 $7583 €6872 Jungle picture (57x69cm-22x27in) cardboard. 17-Sep-3 Kunsthallen, Copenhagen #281/R est:50000 (D.KR 50000)
£4964 $9134 €7247 Jungle picture with rhino, monkey and birds (40x75cm-16x30in) s. masonite. 29-Mar-4 Rasmussen, Copenhagen #220/R est:30000-40000 (D.KR 55000)

SCHERFT, Johan (1970-) Dutch
£972 $1536 €1400 Still life with crisps (45x50cm-18x20in) s.d.2003. 26-Apr-3 Auction Maastricht #146/R

SCHERMAN, Tony (1950-) Canadian
Works on paper
£1465 $2593 €2139 Blue umbrella (152x152cm-60x60in) s.d.1976 verso mixed media canvas. 27-Apr-4 AB Stockholms Auktionsverk #1179/R est:18000-20000 (S.KR 20000)
£1689 $2872 €2466 Study for Death of Echo (59x31cm-23x12in) s.i.d.1994 encaustic prov. 27-Nov-3 Heffel, Vancouver #119/R est:2500-3500 (C.D 3750)
£1802 $3063 €2631 Still life (61x61cm-24x24in) s.i.d.82 verso encaustic canvas prov. 18-Nov-3 Sotheby's, Toronto #18/R est:4000-6000 (C.D 4000)
£2642 $4730 €3857 Lena's daughter. Cupid (65x51cm-26x20in) s.d.86 and 95 pair. 31-May-4 Sotheby's, Toronto #160/R est:4000-6000 (C.D 6500)
£3988 $6500 €5822 Venus (183x122cm-72x48in) s.i.d.81 overlap prov. 23-Sep-3 Christie's, Rockefeller NY #187/R est:3000-5000
£4279 $7275 €6247 Four birds (122x91cm-48x36in) s.i.verso encaustic canvas prov. 18-Nov-3 Sotheby's, Toronto #19/R est:10000-15000 (C.D 9500)
£4800 $8784 €7008 Otherside of Tuscany II (150x180cm-59x71in) encaustic prov. 1-Jun-4 Joyner Waddington, Toronto #147/R est:15000-18000 (C.D 12000)
£8108 $13784 €11838 The death of echo (121x106cm-48x42in) s.i.d.1993-1994 verso encaustic canvas prov.lit. 27-Nov-3 Heffel, Vancouver #117/R est:20000-25000 (C.D 18000)

SCHERMER, Cornelis (1824-1915) Dutch
£671 $1242 €1000 Preparing for a ride (16x20cm-6x8in) s. panel. 15-Mar-4 Sotheby's, Amsterdam #62/R est:1000-1500
£2667 $4800 €4000 Ploughing farmer (52x70cm-20x28in) s. 20-Apr-4 Sotheby's, Amsterdam #156/R est:3500-5500
£3741 $5949 €5500 Attelage et cavaliers en habits de chasse a courre (24x35cm-9x14in) s. panel. 23-Mar-3 Mercier & Cie, Lille #215/R est:4500-5500

SCHERPEREEL, Koen (1961-1997) Belgian
Works on paper
£633 $1134 €950 The friend (70x100cm-28x39in) s.d.88 pastel. 15-May-4 De Vuyst, Lokeren #295

SCHERRES, Alfred (1864-1924) German
£451 $745 €650 Rivershore, Danzig (22x50cm-9x20in) s.i. i. verso panel. 2-Jul-3 Neumeister, Munich #758

SCHERREWITZ, Johan (1868-1951) Dutch
£1250 $1975 €1800 Woodcutter at work (32x48cm-13x19in) s. 2-Sep-3 Christie's, Amsterdam #277/R est:2000-3000
£1500 $2505 €2190 Day's end (28x42cm-11x17in) s. 12-Nov-3 Sotheby's, Olympia #181/R est:1500-2000
£1700 $3179 €2550 Milking time. Cows going to the stable (26x31cm-10x12in) s. panel pair. 26-Jul-4 Bonhams, Bath #77/R est:1500-2000
£2000 $3600 €3000 Returning home (35x54cm-14x21in) s. 20-Apr-4 Sotheby's, Amsterdam #149/R est:3000-5000
£2800 $5040 €4200 At the stable (50x60cm-20x24in) s. 20-Apr-4 Sotheby's, Amsterdam #155/R est:2000-3000
£4028 $6726 €5800 Shepherd and his flock in a wooded landscape (66x51cm-26x20in) s. 21-Oct-3 Sotheby's, Amsterdam #125/R est:3000-5000
£4167 $6958 €6000 Returning home (35x26cm-14x10in) s. panel. 21-Oct-3 Sotheby's, Amsterdam #102/R est:4000-6000
£4861 $8118 €7000 Cows returning from pasture (77x107cm-30x42in) s. prov. 21-Oct-3 Sotheby's, Amsterdam #131/R est:6000-8000
£8145 $13602 €11892 Bomschuit on Scheveningen Beach (62x54cm-24x21in) s. 17-Nov-3 Waddingtons, Toronto #167/R est:15000-20000 (C.D 18000)

SCHETKY, John Christian (1778-1874) British
£1111 $1922 €1622 Fresh breeze off the Dutch coast (41x61cm-16x24in) panel prov. 9-Dec-3 Maynards, Vancouver #162 est:4000-4500 (C.D 2500)
£1222 $2200 €1784 Portrait of H.M.S. Talbout in action at the battle of Navarino (61x86cm-24x34in) i.on stretcher. 24-Jan-4 Skinner, Boston #570 est:400-600
£4121 $7500 €6017 Squall off the Dutch coast (25x36cm-10x14in) i. panel prov. 17-Jun-4 Christie's, Rockefeller NY #59/R est:4000-6000
Works on paper
£350 $581 €511 Mouth of Portsmouth Harbour, Oct 31st. 1834 (19x33cm-7x13in) s.i.verso W/C. 1-Oct-3 Woolley & Wallis, Salisbury #95/R

SCHEUCHZER, Wilhelm (1803-1866) Swiss
£1812 $3244 €2700 Villa Pliniana on Lake Como (19x22cm-7x9in) s.d.1825 board. 25-May-4 Finarte Semenzato, Milan #138/R est:2000-2800

SCHEUERER, Julius (1859-1913) German
£451 $754 €650 Ducks by water (13x16cm-5x6in) i. board. 22-Oct-3 Neumeister, Munich #756/R
£570 $1050 €850 Poultry yard (14x18cm-6x7in) s. panel. 27-Mar-4 Dannenberg, Berlin #620/R
£769 $1238 €1123 In the summer fields (24x31cm-9x12in) s. board. 13-Oct-3 Joel, Victoria #262 est:800-1200 (A.D 1900)
£930 $1600 €1358 Rooster and hens in a grass field (18x13cm-7x5in) s. panel. 6-Dec-3 Neal Auction Company, New Orleans #108 est:1000-2000
£1484 $2700 €2167 Rooster and chickens in a field (23x36cm-9x14in) s. panel. 7-Feb-4 Neal Auction Company, New Orleans #257/R est:2500-3500
£1724 $2879 €2500 Ducks and hens by pond (20x30cm-8x12in) s. panel. 9-Jul-3 Hugo Ruef, Munich #206/R est:2500
£2431 $4010 €3500 Poultry by pond (15x41cm-6x16in) s. panel. 3-Jul-3 Van Ham, Cologne #1439/R est:3800
£3472 $5903 €5000 Huhnerhof (10x13cm-4x5in) s. panel. 28-Oct-3 Christie's, Amsterdam #68/R est:5000-7000

SCHEUERER, Julius (attrib) (1859-1913) German
£1497 $2679 €2200 Poultry (20x25cm-8x10in) panel lit. 20-Mar-4 Bergmann, Erlangen #1091 est:2200

SCHEUERER, Otto (1862-1934) German
£299 $536 €440 Deer in forest clearing (50x70cm-20x28in) s.i. 18-Mar-4 Neumeister, Munich #2770/R
£367 $664 €550 Pheasants in wood (30x40cm-12x16in) s.i. board. 2-Apr-4 Winterberg, Heidelberg #534

£436 $803 €650 Ducks by pond (18x24cm-7x9in) s.i. board. 27-Mar-4 L & B, Essen #190/R
£567 $896 €800 Doves on roof (22x35cm-9x14in) s. board. 22-Jul-3 Sigalas, Stuttgart #380/R
£1259 $2140 €1800 Poultry yard (16x21cm-6x8in) s. board two. 20-Nov-3 Van Ham, Cologne #1847/R est:2500
£1325 $2411 €2000 Poultry at the railway station (50x70cm-20x28in) s. canvas on panel. 19-Jun-4 Bergmann, Erlangen #808
£1528 $2521 €2200 Poultry outside barn (26x37cm-10x15in) i. board. 2-Jul-3 Neumeister, Munich #760/R est:2000

SCHEUREN, Caspar Johann Nepomuk (1810-1887) German
£433 $784 €650 Rider outside small village church in snowy winter landscape (17x24cm-7x9in) s.d.1858 W/C pencil. 1-Apr-4 Van Ham, Cologne #1631
£780 $1264 €1100 Monastery (20x29cm-8x11in) s. prov.lit. 23-May-3 Karlheinz Kaupp, Staufen #1983/R
Works on paper
£486 $792 €700 Old village on lower Rhine (11x23cm-4x9in) bears i.d.18.11.68 pen transparent paper. 26-Sep-3 Venator & Hansten, Koln #923
£625 $1019 €900 Traditional house on the Mosel (26x20cm-10x8in) s. pen transparent paper. 26-Sep-3 Venator & Hansten, Koln #922
£1747 $3179 €2551 Salzburg fortress (14x24cm-6x9in) W/C over pen bistre dr prov.exhib. 17-Jun-4 Kornfeld, Bern #68/R est:5000 (S.FR 4000)
£2431 $4010 €3500 Koblenz (26x35cm-10x14in) s. W/C. 3-Jul-3 Van Ham, Cologne #1441/R est:3200

SCHEURER, Wilhelm (1861-1933) German
£800 $1408 €1168 Duck pond (18x24cm-7x9in) indis sig. panel. 19-May-4 Christie's, Kensington #643/R

SCHGOER, Julius (1847-1885) German
£3147 $5350 €4500 Deer hunt (99x180cm-39x71in) s. 24-Nov-3 Dorotheum, Vienna #51/R est:4000-6000

SCHIANCHI, Federico (1858-1919) Italian
Works on paper
£987 $1816 €1500 Figures and ruins on big road (18x57cm-7x22in) s. W/C. 22-Jun-4 Babuino, Rome #440/R est:500-700
£1100 $1760 €1606 The Tiber, Rome. Figures by a fountain, Rome in the distance (25x36cm-10x14in) s. W/C pair. 16-Sep-3 Gorringes, Bexhill #1657/R est:600-800
£1119 $1869 €1600 The Appia (34x53cm-13x21in) s. W/C. 24-Jun-3 Finarte Semenzato, Rome #17/R
£1333 $2453 €2000 View of the Coliseum (35x54cm-14x21in) s. W/C card. 10-Jun-4 Christie's, Rome #86/R est:2200-2500
£1351 $2108 €2000 Naples Bay (35x54cm-14x21in) W/C. 30-Mar-3 Adma, Formigine #1061 est:2000

SCHIAVO, Paolo (attrib) (1397-1478) Italian
£60403 $108121 €90000 Gaio's life (39x162cm-15x64in) tempera gold board. 27-May-4 Semenzato, Florence #192/R est:80000-100000

SCHIAVONE, Andrea (1522-1563) Italian
Prints
£2657 $4517 €3800 Apostle (21x11cm-8x4in) etching. 27-Nov-3 Bassenge, Berlin #5271/R est:6000

SCHIAVONE, Andrea (attrib) (1522-1563) Italian
Works on paper
£1111 $2000 €1622 Biblical scene (15x20cm-6x8in) pen ink wash prov. 21-Jan-4 Doyle, New York #45 est:1500-2500

SCHIAVONE, Giorgio di Tomaso (attrib) (c.1436-1504) Italian
£45000 $77850 €65700 Madonna and Child with Angels (68x40cm-27x16in) gold ground panel prov.exhib.lit. 10-Dec-3 Christie's, London #106/R est:30000-40000

SCHIAVONI, Felice (attrib) (1803-1881) Italian
£2174 $3565 €3000 Portrait of seated lady with fan (118x90cm-46x35in) 27-May-3 Finarte Semenzato, Milan #91/R est:4000-5000

SCHIAVONI, Natale (1777-1858) Italian
£1338 $2315 €1900 Girl holding flower (62x49cm-24x19in) 9-Dec-3 Pandolfini, Florence #199/R est:1200-1300
£1418 $2369 €2000 Nymphs bathing (23x30cm-9x12in) s. cardboard. 14-Oct-3 Finarte Semenzato, Milan #97/R
£3873 $6701 €5500 Holy Family resting on the flight (51x61cm-20x24in) s. 11-Dec-3 Dr Fritz Nagel, Stuttgart #490/R est:8000

SCHIBIG, Philippe (1940-) Swiss
Works on paper
£566 $917 €826 Untitled (32x26cm-13x10in) s.d.67 pencil biro. 24-May-3 Burkhard, Luzern #178/R (S.FR 1200)
£814 $1385 €1188 Untitled (35x27cm-14x11in) s.d.74 pen. 22-Nov-3 Burkhard, Luzern #226/R (S.FR 1800)
£905 $1538 €1321 The removable island (36x25cm-14x10in) s.d.75 pen. 22-Nov-3 Burkhard, Luzern #223/R (S.FR 2000)
£1176 $2000 €1717 Termite city (39x30cm-15x12in) s.d.80 mixed media collage. 22-Nov-3 Burkhard, Luzern #221/R est:2500-3500 (S.FR 2600)

SCHICK, Henri (1870-1946) French
Works on paper
£270 $484 €400 Au tennis, projet de feuille d'eventail (23x39cm-9x15in) s.d. W/C. 7-May-4 Millon & Associes, Paris #57
£405 $726 €600 Au restaurant, projet de feuille d'eventail (24x41cm-9x16in) s.i.d.06 black crayon col crayon gouache. 7-May-4 Millon & Associes, Paris #56
£608 $1089 €900 Jeune fille aux fleurs (48x23cm-19x9in) s. W/C. 7-May-4 Millon & Associes, Paris #59

SCHICK, Rudolf (1840-1887) German
Works on paper
£301 $511 €430 Lago di Tartaro (16x28cm-6x11in) i.d. pencil. 21-Nov-3 Reiss & Sohn, Konigstein #302/R

SCHICKHARDT, Karl (1866-1933) German
£347 $566 €500 River landscape in autumn (38x50cm-15x20in) s. board. 27-Sep-3 Dr Fritz Nagel, Stuttgart #9345/R

SCHICKLING, Erich (1924-) German?
Works on paper
£423 $756 €600 Bouquet of flowers in a glass vase (72x50cm-28x20in) s.d.72 W/C gouache lit. 8-Jan-4 Allgauer, Kempten #2149/R

SCHIDER, Fritz (1846-1907) Austrian
£4545 $7818 €6500 House visit, doctor feeling the pulse of a lady in her living room (58x78cm-23x31in) s.i. panel. 3-Dec-3 Neumeister, Munich #730/R est:6500

SCHIDONE, Bartolomeo (1578-1615) Italian
£236913 $443027 €353000 Saint JOhn the Baptist in the desert (136x92cm-54x36in) prov.exhib.lit. 25-Feb-4 Porro, Milan #75/R est:330000

SCHIDONE, Bartolomeo (circle) (1578-1615) Italian
£7394 $12940 €10500 Saint Sebastian (137x92cm-54x36in) 17-Dec-3 Christie's, Rome #455/R est:8000-12000

SCHIEDGES, Peter Paulus (1812-1876) Dutch
£658 $1211 €1000 A three-master in distress near a coast (23x31cm-9x12in) s. panel. 22-Jun-4 Christie's, Amsterdam #3/R
£1007 $1802 €1500 La rentree d'un voilier charge de marchandises (39x52cm-15x20in) s.d.1864 wood. 25-May-4 Campo & Campo, Antwerp #258 est:3000-3500
£1074 $1922 €1600 Bateau a vapeur et voilier dans la tempete (39x52cm-15x20in) indis.sig. wood. 25-May-4 Campo & Campo, Antwerp #257 est:3000-3500
£1781 $3027 €2600 Ship by the harbour mouth (23x33cm-9x13in) s. panel. 5-Nov-3 Vendue Huis, Gravenhage #33/R est:3000-4000
£2013 $3604 €3000 Naufrage (45x60cm-18x24in) s. 25-May-4 Campo & Campo, Antwerp #259/R est:4000-6000
£2105 $3811 €3200 Sailing ship on calm water (36x45cm-14x18in) s.d.63 panel. 19-Apr-4 Glerum, Amsterdam #8/R est:1200-1500
£3311 $6026 €5000 Dutch coastal landscape with sailing boat (72x100cm-28x39in) s.d.1860. 18-Jun-4 Bolland & Marotz, Bremen #749/R est:7400
£3819 $6493 €5500 Shipping off the coast of the Molukken (36x48cm-14x19in) s.d.1853 panel. 28-Oct-3 Christie's, Amsterdam #16/R est:6000-8000
£4166 $6791 €6000 Shepherd with his flock (80x120cm-31x47in) s. 29-Sep-3 Sotheby's, Amsterdam #79/R
£4218 $7550 €6200 Fisherman in rowing boat (111x154cm-44x61in) 17-Mar-4 De Zwann, Amsterdam #4566/R est:3000-4000
£4276 $7740 €6500 Polder landscape with a fisherman on the water and a mill in the background (96x120cm-38x47in) s. 19-Apr-4 Glerum, Amsterdam #193/R est:3000-4000
£4800 $8880 €7008 Barges off the coast (24x22cm-9x9in) s.d.01 board. 10-Mar-4 Sotheby's, Olympia #239/R est:3000-5000

SCHIEDGES, Peter Paulus (younger) (1860-1922) Dutch
Works on paper
£369 $616 €520 Polder landscape with pigs by a ditch (35x53cm-14x21in) s. gouache prov. 20-Oct-3 Glerum, Amsterdam #127/R

SCHIEFER, Johannes (20th C) American
£252 $400 €368 Urban landscape with figures on cobblestone street (51x41cm-20x16in) s. 10-Sep-3 Alderfer's, Hatfield #335/R
£314 $500 €458 La Seine, Paris (51x61cm-20x24in) s. 10-Sep-3 Alderfer's, Hatfield #336
£314 $500 €458 Teporlian Mexico (64x76cm-25x30in) s. 10-Sep-3 Alderfer's, Hatfield #338
£324 $550 €473 Route de Cezanne (71x61cm-28x24in) s. i.on stretcher. 5-Nov-3 Doyle, New York #68/R
£1006 $1600 €1469 La Seine, Paris (51x61cm-20x24in) s. 10-Sep-3 Alderfer's, Hatfield #337/R est:500-600

SCHIELE, Egon (1890-1918) Austrian
£24306 $41319 €35000 Landscape (20x21cm-8x8in) i. verso paper on board prov.lit. 28-Oct-3 Wiener Kunst Auktionen, Vienna #65/R est:35000-70000
Prints
£6497 $11500 €9486 Kauernde (48x32cm-19x13in) st.sig.d.1914 num.5/100 green drypoint. 28-Apr-4 Christie's, Rockefeller NY #237/R est:12000-16000
£7345 $13000 €10724 Kauernde (47x31cm-19x12in) dark green drypoint. 30-Apr-4 Sotheby's, New York #223/R est:10000-15000
£8235 $14000 €12023 Secession 49 (68x53cm-27x21in) col lithograph exec.1918. 4-Nov-3 Christie's, Rockefeller NY #205/R est:18000-20000
£8667 $15947 €13000 Male nude - self portrait (42x21cm-17x8in) s.d.1912 pen brush lithograph. 10-Jun-4 Hauswedell & Nolte, Hamburg #620/R est:8000
£23529 $40000 €34352 Girl (40x54cm-16x21in) lithograph exec.1918. 4-Nov-3 Christie's, Rockefeller NY #206/R est:18000-22000
Works on paper
£1074 $1976 €1600 Nude girl (20x27cm-8x11in) i.d.1911 pencil. 26-Mar-4 Auktionhaus Georg Rehm, Augsburg #8157/R est:1000
£5034 $9010 €7500 Portrait of man wearing glasses and with moustache (53x38cm-21x15in) s.d.Mai 07 chk prov. 25-May-4 Dorotheum, Vienna #2/R est:8000-16000

£5245	$8916	€7500	Portrait of a man (46x32cm-18x13in) s.d.11.1.07 ochre prov. 26-Nov-3 Dorotheum, Vienna #2/R est:8000-13000
£12676	$22183	€18000	Loving couple (48x32cm-19x13in) s.d.1912 pencil prov. 19-Dec-3 Dorotheum, Vienna #10/R est:13000-18000
£22346	$40000	€32625	Standing nude woman masturbating (45x29cm-18x11in) s.d.1913 pencil prov.exhib.lit. 6-May-4 Sotheby's, New York #315/R est:40000-60000
£22819	$40846	€34000	Portrait of Dr Hugo Koller (47x30cm-19x12in) chk prov. 25-May-4 Dorotheum, Vienna #20/R est:34000-45000
£32000	$58240	€46720	Man and woman embracing (44x28cm-17x11in) s.d.1918 chl prov.lit. 4-Feb-4 Sotheby's, London #427/R est:40000-60000
£32123	$57500	€46900	Standing nude (45x29cm-18x11in) crayon exec 1918 prov.exhib.lit. 6-May-4 Sotheby's, New York #312/R est:50000-70000
£36364	$62545	€52000	Poldi (13x18cm-5x7in) s.i.d.1914 black chk prov. 5-Dec-3 Ketterer, Munich #45/R est:35000-45000
£40503	$72500	€59134	Seated female nude (45x29cm-18x11in) s.d.1913 pencil prov.exhib.lit. 6-May-4 Sotheby's, New York #318/R est:60000-80000
£47486	$85000	€69330	Lesbisches Paar (29x46cm-11x18in) s.d.1917 crayon prov.lit. 6-May-4 Sotheby's, New York #316/R est:80000-120000
£48000	$88320	€70080	Sitzendes Madchen, ihren Mund bedeckend (45x28cm-18x11in) s.d.1914 pencil prov.exhib.lit. 24-Jun-4 Christie's, London #389/R est:60000-80000
£77181	$136611	€115000	Nude girl (45x29cm-18x11in) s.d.1918 chl lit.prov. 28-Apr-4 Wiener Kunst Auktionen, Vienna #106/R est:90000-150000
£83832	$140000	€122395	Kneeling nude girl (45x29cm-18x11in) s.d.1918 black crayon paper on board. 11-Nov-3 Christie's, Rockefeller NY #165/R est:40000-60000
£85000	$154700	€124100	Portrait of Frau Dr. Horak. Standing figure (44x31cm-17x12in) init.i. g. W/C chl pencil double-sided executed 1910 prov.lit. 3-Feb-4 Sotheby's, London #5/R est:80000-120000
£88235	$150000	€128823	Schuhanziehende Frau (48x32cm-19x13in) s.d.1912 W/C pencil prov.exhib.lit. 5-Nov-3 Christie's, Rockefeller NY #131/R est:140000-180000
£125000	$212500	€180000	Female torso (47x36cm-19x14in) s.d.1913 pencil W/C prov.lit. 28-Oct-3 Wiener Kunst Auktionen, Vienna #64/R est:180000-320000
£150000	$273000	€219000	Baby (44x31cm-17x12in) init.d.10 W/C crayon htd white prov.exhib.lit. 21-Jun-4 Sotheby's, London #32/R est:200000-300000
£150000	$273000	€219000	Crouching female nude (30x47cm-12x19in) s.d.1914 gouache W/C crayon prov.exhib.lit. 21-Jun-4 Sotheby's, London #34/R est:300000-400000
£160000	$291200	€233600	Stehendes Madchen mit durchsichtigem Kleid - Standing girl with transparent dress (45x31cm-18x12in) init.d.10 W/C chl pencil. 4-Feb-4 Sotheby's, London #475/R est:80000-120000
£234637	$420000	€342570	Semi-nude girl holding her breast, facing right (45x31cm-18x12in) s.d.1910 gouache chl prov.exhib.lit. 6-May-4 Sotheby's, New York #103/R est:300000-400000
£250000	$455000	€365000	Houses and pine trees (45x33cm-18x13in) gouache crayon pencil exec.1915 prov.exhib.lit. 21-Jun-4 Sotheby's, London #31/R est:250000-350000
£302013	$540604	€450000	Boy wearing green socks (48x31cm-19x12in) s.d.1911 pencil W/C gouache prov. 25-May-4 Dorotheum, Vienna #18/R est:130000-200000
£348993	$617718	€520000	Self portrait with outstretched arms (32x48cm-13x19in) W/C pencil prov.lit. 28-Apr-4 Wiener Kunst Auktionen, Vienna #105/R est:300000-600000
£380000	$691600	€554800	Seated man (45x31cm-18x12in) init.d.10 gouache W/C crayon prov.exhib.lit. 21-Jun-4 Sotheby's, London #27/R est:300000-400000
£468532	$796504	€670000	Two women (55x36cm-22x14in) mono.d.1911 W/C gouache over pencil prov. 26-Nov-3 Lempertz, Koln #968/R est:300000-350000
£620000	$1128400	€905200	Portrait of Arnold Schonberg with left arm raised (46x29cm-18x11in) s.d.1917 gouache W/C crayon prov.exhib.lit. 21-Jun-4 Sotheby's, London #29/R est:250000-350000
£650000	$1183000	€949000	Seated male nude (44x31cm-17x12in) init.d.10 W/C chl pencil prov.exhib.lit. 21-Jun-4 Sotheby's, London #21/R est:350000-450000
£650000	$1183000	€949000	Russian prisoner of war (45x31cm-18x12in) s.d.1915 gouache W/C crayon prov.exhib.lit. 21-Jun-4 Sotheby's, London #33/R est:250000-350000
£680000	$1237600	€992800	Seated nude with purple stockings (43x29cm-17x11in) init.d.10 gouache W/C crayon prov.exhib.lit. 21-Jun-4 Sotheby's, London #24/R est:350000-450000
£700000	$1274000	€1022000	Seated female nude with tilted head (45x31cm-18x12in) init.d.10 gouache W/C crayon prov.exhib.lit. 21-Jun-4 Sotheby's, London #30/R est:300000-400000
£720000	$1310400	€1051200	Self-portrait with folded hands (47x31cm-19x12in) s.d.1913 gouache pencil prov.exhib.lit. 21-Jun-4 Sotheby's, London #22/R est:500000-700000
£950000	$1729000	€1387000	Movement (48x35cm-19x14in) s.d.1913 gouache W/C crayon prov.exhib.lit. 21-Jun-4 Sotheby's, London #28/R est:600000-800000
£1200000	$2184000	€1752000	Reclining woman in yellow dress (31x49cm-12x19in) s. gouache W/C pencil exec.1914 prov.exhib.lit. 21-Jun-4 Sotheby's, London #26/R est:600000-800000
£1350000	$2457000	€1971000	Girl with green pinafore (45x22cm-18x9in) init.d.10 g. W/C black crayon prov.exhib.lit. 3-Feb-4 Sotheby's, London #3/R est:500000-700000
£1700000	$3094000	€2482000	Lovers (48x32cm-19x13in) s.d.1913 gouache W/C pencil prov.exhib.lit. 21-Jun-4 Sotheby's, London #23/R est:1200000-1800000

SCHIELE, H (?) ?

£349	$642	€510	Still life of flowers (85x100cm-33x39in) s. oval. 29-Mar-4 Blomqvist, Lysaker #1299 (N.KR 4400)

SCHIELL, W (19th C) German

Works on paper

£2200	$3520	€3212	Unter den Linden, Berlin (30x45cm-12x18in) s. pencil W/C. 18-Sep-3 Christie's, Kensington #59/R est:800-1200

SCHIER, Franz (1852-1922) German

£2000	$3640	€3000	Japanese woman (40x26cm-16x10in) leather. 30-Jun-4 Neumeister, Munich #668/R est:2000

SCHIERHOLZ, Caroline (1831-?) German

£307	$561	€460	Ledy, a sitting dog (51x48cm-20x19in) s.d.1858 i.d.verso. 5-Jun-4 Arnold, Frankfurt #711/R
£600	$1098	€900	Nette, a resting cat (36x52cm-14x20in) s.d.1858 i.d.verso. 5-Jun-4 Arnold, Frankfurt #710/R

SCHIERL, Josef (fl.1835-1845) German

£3147	$5413	€4500	Sleeping girl. Girl crying over a letter (41x34cm-16x13in) i.d.1845 verso pair. 3-Dec-3 Neumeister, Munich #731/R est:4500

SCHIERTZ, August Ferdinand (1804-1878) German

£556	$917	€800	Sunrise (35x47cm-14x19in) s. lit. 5-Jul-3 Geble, Radolfzell #481/R

SCHIERTZ, Franz Wilhelm (1813-1887) German

£3237	$5309	€4500	Fjord beach in Norway (79x118cm-31x46in) mono.d. 4-Jun-3 Ketterer, Hamburg #97/R est:4500-5500

SCHIESS, Adrian (1959-) Swiss

Works on paper

£317	$538	€463	Untitled (10x14cm-4x6in) s.d.1985 verso W/C varnish paper on board. 25-Nov-3 Germann, Zurich #888 (S.FR 700)

SCHIESS, Ernst Traugott (1872-1919) Swiss

£264	$449	€385	Sicily (40x24cm-16x9in) i. verso board. 5-Nov-3 Dobiaschofsky, Bern #3697 (S.FR 600)
£362	$615	€529	Three pink roses (32x46cm-13x18in) s. bears d. board. 19-Nov-3 Fischer, Luzern #2274/R (S.FR 800)
£432	$717	€626	Streetscene I - Tunis (35x48cm-14x19in) board prov. 13-Jun-3 Zofingen, Switzerland #3013 (S.FR 950)
£432	$717	€626	Tunis (39x52cm-15x20in) board prov. 13-Jun-3 Zofingen, Switzerland #3014 (S.FR 950)
£437	$803	€638	Worker (29x42cm-11x17in) board. 14-Jun-4 Philippe Schuler, Zurich #4233 (S.FR 1000)
£485	$824	€708	North African street (30x42cm-12x17in) s.d.17 board. 5-Nov-3 Dobiaschofsky, Bern #937/R (S.FR 1100)
£543	$995	€793	Two female nudes in an interior scene. Bather (38x55cm-15x22in) s. cardboard double-sided. 4-Jun-4 Zofingen, Switzerland #2947 (S.FR 1250)

SCHIESS, Hans Rudolf (1904-1978) Swiss

£6522	$11935	€9522	Spring morning (120x150cm-47x59in) mono.d.28 prov.exhib. 7-Jun-4 Christie's, Zurich #103/R est:8000-12000 (S.FR 15000)

SCHIESS, Tobias (1925-) Swiss

£560	$1003	€818	Deucalion et Pyrrha (97x146cm-38x57in) s.d.62 i. verso. 12-May-4 Dobiaschofsky, Bern #936/R (S.FR 1300)

SCHIESTL, Heinz (1864-1940) German

£537	$983	€800	Lute player with scroll (41x27cm-16x11in) mono. board lit. 8-Jul-4 Allgauer, Kempten #2212/R
£537	$983	€800	Violin player with scroll (41x28cm-16x11in) mono.i. board. 8-Jul-4 Allgauer, Kempten #2213/R

SCHIESTL-ARDING, Albert (20th C) ?

£694	$1132	€1000	Still life with dahlias and apples (65x52cm-26x20in) prov. 26-Sep-3 Bolland & Marotz, Bremen #369/R
£839	$1443	€1200	Bunch of colourful tulips (68x57cm-27x22in) mono.d.33 panel. 5-Dec-3 Bolland & Marotz, Bremen #414/R
£1049	$1804	€1500	Self portrait (81x64cm-32x25in) s.d.1920 canvas on board. 5-Dec-3 Bolland & Marotz, Bremen #412/R est:1600
£1049	$1804	€1500	Still life with flower bowl (75x100cm-30x39in) mono. panel. 5-Dec-3 Bolland & Marotz, Bremen #413/R est:1500
£1074	$2008	€1600	Snowy garden in Worpswede (71x54cm-28x21in) mono.d.35 board. 28-Feb-4 Bolland & Marotz, Bremen #285/R est:1300
£1806	$2943	€2600	Blooming garden in Worpswede (73x64cm-29x25in) mono.d.35 board double-sided. 26-Sep-3 Bolland & Marotz, Bremen #367/R est:2000

SCHIFANO, Mario (1934-1998) Italian

£733	$1349	€1100	Untitled (20x30cm-8x12in) s. enamel painted 1997. 12-Jun-4 Meeting Art, Vercelli #372/R
£769	$1285	€1123	Acerbo (40x40cm-16x16in) s. verso prov. 24-Jun-3 Germann, Zurich #115 (S.FR 1700)
£1000	$1800	€1500	Fish (100x70cm-39x28in) s. enamel paper exhib. 22-Apr-4 Finarte Semenzato, Rome #142/R est:1200-1500
£1056	$1754	€1500	Untitled (30x20cm-12x8in) s.verso enamel. 14-Jun-3 Meeting Art, Vercelli #85/R est:1500
£1342	$2497	€2000	Chip (20x30cm-8x12in) s.i. verso enamel painted 1997. 4-Mar-4 Babuino, Rome #124 est:1000-1500
£1389	$2194	€2000	Untitled (98x69cm-39x27in) mixed media paper on canvas. 6-Sep-3 Meeting Art, Vercelli #297 est:2000
£1538	$2615	€2200	Untitled (30x40cm-12x16in) s. plastic enamel prov. 25-Nov-3 Sotheby's, Milan #54/R est:1500-2000
£1589	$2893	€2400	The making of Rio de Janeiro (38x48cm-15x19in) s.i.verso enamel acrylic painted 1996. 17-Jun-4 Galleria Pananti, Florence #48/R est:2500-3000
£1667	$3067	€2500	Bike (70x100cm-28x39in) s. enamel collage paper. 8-Jun-4 Finarte Semenzato, Milan #411/R est:2500-3000
£1701	$3044	€2500	Landscape (66x66cm-26x26in) s. enamel collage paper painted 1991. 16-Mar-4 Finarte Semenzato, Milan #470/R est:3000
£2077	$3531	€2970	Skull (50x50cm-20x20in) s.verso painted 1989. 18-Nov-3 Babuino, Rome #240/R est:2000-3000
£2133	$3861	€3200	Television (50x70cm-20x28in) s.verso enamel plexiglas. 2-Apr-4 Farsetti, Prato #50/R est:3000-4000
£2174	$3565	€3000	Untitled. Untitled. Sailing boat (24x18cm-9x7in) s.verso enamel painted 1988 three. 27-May-3 Sotheby's, Milan #129 est:1500-2000
£2378	$4042	€3400	Paesaggio (150x150cm-59x59in) s. verso acrylic. 27-Nov-3 Lempertz, Koln #4176/R est:3500
£2657	$4517	€3800	Flowers (60x40cm-24x16in) enamel. 18-Nov-3 Babuino, Rome #313/R est:1800-2200
£2667	$4907	€4000	Untitled (50x70cm-20x28in) s. enamel painted 1978 prov. 8-Jun-4 Finarte Semenzato, Milan #341/R est:4000-5000
£2685	$4993	€4000	Night (80x60cm-31x24in) s.i.d.1996 verso enamel. 4-Mar-4 Babuino, Rome #431 est:3000-4000
£2721	$4871	€4000	Your fishtank is made of ten parts (100x70cm-39x28in) s.i. enamel collage. 16-Mar-4 Finarte Semenzato, Milan #359/R est:4500
£2746	$4806	€3900	Television (50x70cm-20x28in) s.verso enamel. 16-Dec-3 Finarte Semenzato, Milan #312/R est:3800-4200
£2819	$5046	€4200	Untitled (47x65cm-19x26in) s.verso enamel. 25-May-4 Sotheby's, Milan #205/R est:4000-6000
£2909	$4945	€4160	Page (35x50cm-14x20in) s.i.verso enamel prov. 18-Nov-3 Babuino, Rome #287/R est:2500-3500
£2937	$4993	€4200	Cavallo (100x120cm-39x47in) s. verso acrylic. 27-Nov-3 Lempertz, Koln #417/R est:3000
£2973	$5232	€4400	Untitled (60x60cm-24x24in) s.verso enamel acrylic painted 1989. 22-May-4 Galleria Pananti, Florence #493/R est:1500-1700

£2993	$5358	€4400	Untitled (50x70cm-20x28in) s. enamel prov. 16-Mar-4 Finarte Semenzato, Milan #336/R est:3200
£3061	$5480	€4500	Untitled (61x81cm-24x32in) s.indis.d. 16-Mar-4 Finarte Semenzato, Milan #471/R est:4200
£3197	$5723	€4700	Fragment (30x20cm-12x8in) s.i.verso enamel set of 4 painted 1997. 16-Mar-4 Finarte Semenzato, Milan #349/R est:5000
£3329	$5659	€4760	Going up (60x60cm-24x24in) s. oil pigment painted 1989. 18-Nov-3 Babuino, Rome #403/R est:2500-3000
£3333	$5967	€5000	Anaemic landscape (60x100cm-24x39in) s. exhib. 17-May-4 Chayette & Cheval, Paris #222/R est:5000-7000
£3448	$5759	€5000	Aquatic (63x82cm-25x32in) s.verso enamel acrylic. 13-Nov-3 Finarte Semenzato, Rome #252/R est:3800-4500
£3490	$6491	€5200	Anaemic landscape (70x100cm-28x39in) s. enamel. 4-Mar-4 Babuino, Rome #138 est:3000-4000
£3497	$5944	€5000	Untitled (142x90cm-56x35in) s. s.verso enamel. 24-Nov-3 Christie's, Milan #85/R est:4000-6000
£3667	$6747	€5500	Untitled (70x100cm-28x39in) s. enamel. 8-Jun-4 Finarte Semenzato, Milan #412/R est:4500-5000
£3667	$6747	€5500	Untitled (100x100cm-39x39in) s. lit. 12-Jun-4 Meeting Art, Vercelli #509/R est:5000
£3716	$6541	€5500	Homage to De Chirico (80x90cm-31x35in) s.verso. 22-May-4 Galleria Pananti, Florence #496/R est:5000-6000
£3784	$6659	€5600	Untitled (50x50cm-20x20in) s.verso enamel acrylic painted 1989. 22-May-4 Galleria Pananti, Florence #492/R est:1500-1700
£4000	$7200	€6000	Futurism in colour (80x100cm-31x39in) s. enamel. 22-Apr-4 Finarte Semenzato, Rome #323/R est:3500-4000
£4000	$7200	€6000	Flowers (80x40cm-31x16in) masonite painted 1956. 22-Apr-4 Finarte Semenzato, Rome #354/R est:3800-4200
£4027	$7208	€6000	Untitled (80x110cm-31x43in) s.verso enamel canvas on plexiglas. 25-May-4 Sotheby's, Milan #206/R est:6000-8000
£4067	$7483	€6100	Untitled (135x107cm-53x42in) s. enamel. 12-Jun-4 Meeting Art, Vercelli #124/R est:2500
£4130	$6774	€5700	Lonely spirits (89x59cm-35x23in) s.i. enamel. 30-May-3 Farsetti, Prato #260/R
£4196	$7133	€6000	Untitled (79x95cm-31x37in) s. enamel. 28-Nov-3 Farsetti, Prato #33/R est:3200-4200
£4225	$7014	€6000	Untitled (68x95cm-27x37in) s. enamel painted 1973-1978. 14-Jun-3 Meeting Art, Vercelli #106/R est:5000
£4225	$7014	€6000	Boccioni (50x70cm-20x28in) enamel emulsion exhib. 11-Jun-3 Finarte Semenzato, Milan #550/R
£4333	$7800	€6500	Anemic landscape (60x100cm-24x39in) s. acrylic prov. 22-Apr-4 Finarte Semenzato, Rome #177/R est:4000-5000
£4333	$7973	€6500	Palm tree (100x70cm-39x28in) s. enamel. 12-Jun-4 Meeting Art, Vercelli #868/R est:5000
£4483	$7486	€6500	Farm (64x84cm-25x33in) s.i.verso enamel. 14-Nov-3 Farsetti, Prato #134/R est:5500-6500
£4483	$7486	€6500	Walls (40x60cm-16x24in) s. enamel. 13-Nov-3 Finarte Semenzato, Rome #424/R est:4800-5500
£4483	$7486	€6500	Landscape (30x46cm-12x18in) s.d.1956 verso enamel canvas on board. 13-Nov-3 Finarte Semenzato, Rome #423/R est:3800-4500
£4503	$8196	€6800	Untitled (120x120cm-47x47in) s. enamel painted 1979. 17-Jun-4 Galleria Pananti, Florence #620/R est:8000-10000
£4730	$8324	€7000	Untitled (30x100cm-12x39in) s.verso enamel acrylic painted 1994. 22-May-4 Galleria Pananti, Florence #467/R est:6000-8000
£4828	$8062	€7000	Landscape with clouds (91x97cm-36x38in) s. enamel painted 1979 lit. 14-Nov-3 Farsetti, Prato #332/R est:7000-8000
£4930	$8183	€7000	Untitled (105x115cm-41x45in) s. enamel. 14-Jun-3 Meeting Art, Vercelli #357/R est:7000
£5072	$8319	€7000	Mates (76x51cm-30x20in) s. enamel pencil collage paper on plexiglass prov.lit. 27-May-3 Sotheby's, Milan #210/R est:8000-10000
£5333	$9600	€8000	Anemic landscape (100x70cm-39x28in) s.verso enamel. 22-Apr-4 Finarte Semenzato, Rome #274/R est:8000-10000
£5405	$9514	€8000	Muse (150x199cm-59x78in) s.verso painted 1996. 22-May-4 Galleria Pananti, Florence #497/R est:7000-9000
£5479	$9315	€8000	Odd canes (80x100cm-31x39in) s.verso enamel acrylic. 7-Nov-3 Galleria Rosenberg, Milan #80/R est:8000
£5594	$9510	€8000	Untitled (50x70cm-20x28in) s.verso enamel prov. 25-Nov-3 Sotheby's, Milan #65/R
£5594	$9510	€8000	Horse (100x100cm-39x39in) s.i. enamel. 26-Nov-3 Pandolfini, Florence #153/R est:8000-9000
£6122	$10959	€9000	Landscape (70x100cm-28x39in) s. painted 1979-80. 16-Mar-4 Finarte Semenzato, Milan #346/R est:10000
£6294	$10699	€9000	Untitled (70x99cm-28x39in) s.d.1961 enamel paper on canvas. 20-Nov-3 Finarte Semenzato, Milan #117/R est:8000-8500
£6338	$10521	€9000	Coca Cola (82x56cm-32x22in) s. enamel. 13-Jun-3 Farsetti, Prato #379/R
£6711	$12416	€10000	Facades (100x200cm-39x79in) s.verso enamel painted 1990 lit. 13-Mar-4 Meeting Art, Vercelli #395 est:10000
£6711	$12013	€10000	Facade (100x200cm-39x79in) s.verso enamel painted 1990 lit. 30-May-4 Meeting Art, Vercelli #53 est:10000
£6757	$11892	€10000	Facade (99x199cm-39x78in) s. enamel prov.exhib. 24-May-4 Christie's, Milan #180/R est:6000-8000
£7343	$12483	€10500	Untitled (107x107cm-42x42in) s. enamel. 24-Nov-3 Christie's, Milan #89/R est:4000-6000
£7971	$13072	€11000	Untitled (70x50cm-28x20in) s. s.d.64 verso enamel chl. 27-May-3 Sotheby's, Milan #209e/R est:13000-18000
£8392	$14266	€12000	Untitled (162x130cm-64x51in) s.verso enamel. 26-Nov-3 Pandolfini, Florence #157/R est:11500-12500
£9790	$16643	€14000	Palm tree (128x104cm-50x41in) s. enamel prov. 25-Nov-3 Sotheby's, Milan #55/R est:8000-10000
£9790	$16643	€14000	Portrait in landscape (100x70cm-39x28in) s. enamel pencil paper on canvas. 25-Nov-3 Sotheby's, Milan #251/R est:20000-30000
£11232	$18420	€15500	Anemic landscape (50x100cm-20x39in) s.d.65 verso enamel prov. 27-May-3 Sotheby's, Milan #296/R est:15000-20000
£11486	$20216	€17000	Colour trip in the dark (190x150cm-75x59in) s.i.d.1984 verso enamel acrylic. 22-May-4 Galleria Pananti, Florence #506/R est:10000-12000
£12000	$21600	€18000	Space (80x80cm-31x31in) s. enamel painted 1967 exhib.lit. 22-Apr-4 Finarte Semenzato, Rome #344/R est:16000-18000
£12081	$21624	€18000	Anemic landscape (50x100cm-20x39in) s.i. s.d.65 verso prov. 25-May-4 Sotheby's, Milan #313/R est:20000
£12838	$22595	€19000	Wheat field (150x200cm-59x79in) s.verso enamel acrylic. 22-May-4 Galleria Pananti, Florence #504/R est:7000-8000
£13333	$24000	€20000	Koh (200x200cm-79x79in) enamel tin on board. 22-Apr-4 Finarte Semenzato, Rome #278/R est:20000-22000
£13986	$23776	€20000	At the seaside (200x200cm-79x79in) s.i.verso enamel painted 1979 exhib.lit. 20-Nov-3 Finarte Semenzato, Milan #116/R est:20000-22000
£18792	$33638	€28000	All the stars (130x100cm-51x39in) s.d.67 verso enamel plexiglas prov. 25-May-4 Sotheby's, Milan #296/R est:20000-30000
£18841	$30899	€26000	True love (80x80cm-31x31in) s. enamel pencil prov. 27-May-3 Sotheby's, Milan #292/R est:23000-28000
£20270	$35676	€30000	View (138x240cm-54x94in) s.i. enamel. 24-May-4 Christie's, Milan #308/R est:30000-40000
£27027	$47568	€40000	Totem maze from Freud's point of view (224x330cm-88x130in) i. acrylic enamel painted 1970 exhib. 24-May-4 Christie's, Milan #333/R est:40000-60000
£52174	$85565	€72000	Untitled (127x251cm-50x99in) s.d.64 verso enamel pastel collage paper on canvas prov.exhib. 27-May-3 Sotheby's, Milan #294/R est:60000-80000
Photographs			
£14000	$23380	€20440	Ora esatta (115x144cm-45x57in) s.d.70 verso gelatin silver print canvas prov.exhib.lit. 21-Oct-3 Christie's, London #50/R est:14000-18000
Prints			
£2000	$3680	€3000	Untitled (100x70cm-39x28in) s. serigraph. 11-Jun-4 Farsetti, Prato #72/R est:3000-3500
£7297	$11384	€10800	Four seasons (70x100cm-28x39in) serigraph. 30-Mar-3 Adma, Formigine #1200 est:10000
Sculpture			
£3490	$6247	€5200	Palm tree (220cm-87in) s.i. aluminium exec.1980. 25-May-4 Sotheby's, Milan #195/R est:2500-3000
Works on paper			
£778	$1400	€1136	Cezanne in una fotografia. Untitled (39x27cm-15x11in) s.d.1982 one W/C acrylic mylar one paint mylar pair. 24-Apr-4 David Rago, Lambertville #389/R
£800	$1472	€1200	Untitled (100x70cm-39x28in) s. mixed media. 12-Jun-4 Meeting Art, Vercelli #416/R
£800	$1472	€1200	Untitled (100x70cm-39x28in) s. mixed media. 12-Jun-4 Meeting Art, Vercelli #829/R
£1034	$1728	€1500	Untitled (55x40cm-22x16in) s. collage two. 13-Nov-3 Finarte Semenzato, Rome #175 est:1600-1800
£1049	$1783	€1500	Untitled (100x70cm-39x28in) mixed media exec.1979-80. 19-Nov-3 Cambi, Genoa #456/R est:1400-1600
£1049	$1783	€1500	Untitled (32x32cm-13x13in) s.d.93 assemblage enamel on canvas prov. 25-Nov-3 Sotheby's, Milan #57/R est:1500-2000
£1208	$2054	€1764	Senza titolo (61x81cm-24x32in) s.d.84 mixed media canvas. 5-Nov-3 AB Stockholms Auktionsverk #1008/R est:8000-10000 (S.KR 16000)
£1241	$2073	€1800	Landscape. View (55x40cm-22x16in) s.i. mixed media collage two. 13-Nov-3 Finarte Semenzato, Rome #174 est:1600-1800
£1622	$2854	€2400	View (100x70cm-39x28in) s.i. mixed media card prov. 24-May-4 Christie's, Milan #238/R est:2200-2800
£1629	$2769	€2378	Composition (80x109cm-31x43in) s. verso mixed media prov. 25-Nov-3 Germann, Zurich #889 est:1500-2000 (S.FR 3600)
£1737	$2953	€2536	Senza titolo (91x71cm-36x28in) s.d.84 verso mixed media. 5-Nov-3 AB Stockholms Auktionsverk #917/R est:12000-15000 (S.KR 23000)
£2000	$3680	€3000	Untitled (70x100cm-28x39in) s. mixed media collage exec.1974. 8-Jun-4 Finarte Semenzato, Milan #250/R est:2000-3000
£2448	$4161	€3500	Untitled (70x100cm-28x39in) s. ink enamel. 24-Nov-3 Christie's, Milan #26/R est:2400-2800
£2448	$4161	€3500	Italian landscape (70x100cm-28x39in) s. mixed media. 24-Nov-3 Christie's, Milan #31/R est:3000-3500
£2826	$4635	€3900	Untitled (48x38cm-19x15in) s. enamel paper on cardboard. 30-May-3 Farsetti, Prato #31/R
£3333	$6133	€5000	Apollinaire (79x49cm-31x19in) s.i.verso collage enamel on canvas prov.exhib.lit. 14-Jun-4 Porro, Milan #49/R est:6500-8000
£3514	$6184	€5200	Untitled (100x75cm-39x30in) s. pencil enamel on canvas exec.1975. 24-May-4 Christie's, Milan #85/R est:3500-5000
£3667	$6600	€5500	Detail (50x70cm-20x28in) s. mixed media paper on canvas prov. 22-Apr-4 Finarte Semenzato, Rome #272/R est:4000-5000
£4054	$6324	€6000	Abstract (70x100cm-28x39in) mixed media pair. 30-Mar-3 Adma, Formigine #1195a est:7000
£4730	$8324	€7000	All stars (100x70cm-39x28in) s. enamel paint paper on masonite prov.lit. 24-May-4 Christie's, Milan #150/R est:8500-10500
£4895	$8322	€7000	Dry throat (111x81cm-44x32in) s.i.verso sand enamel on canvas exec.1988. 20-Nov-3 Finarte Semenzato, Milan #142/R est:8000-10000
£5333	$9813	€8000	Coca-Cola (100x95cm-39x37in) s. enamel. 8-Jun-4 Finarte Semenzato, Milan #340/R est:5000-6000
£5944	$10105	€8500	Mates (51x77cm-20x30in) collage enamel exec.1968 prov.lit. 24-Nov-3 Christie's, Milan #172/R est:5500-6000

SCHIFF, M (20th C) ?

£1000	$1830	€1500	Sewing at the open window (30x36cm-12x14in) s.d.1908 panel. 5-Jun-4 Arnold, Frankfurt #712/R est:300

SCHIFFERLE, Claudia (1955-) Swiss

£1357	$2267	€1981	Untitled (97x44cm-38x17in) s.d.1982 verso varnish tin. 24-Jun-3 Germann, Zurich #34/R est:3000-3500 (S.FR 3000)
Works on paper			
£262	$482	€383	Untitled (21x27cm-8x11in) s.d.1985 verso chl. 8-Jun-4 Germann, Zurich #873 (S.FR 600)
£611	$1125	€892	Untitled (47x64cm-19x25in) s.d.1982 verso gouache. 8-Jun-4 Germann, Zurich #874 (S.FR 1400)
£769	$1308	€1123	Untitled (70x100cm-28x39in) gouache. 25-Nov-3 Germann, Zurich #136/R est:2000-2500 (S.FR 1700)
£1041	$1769	€1520	Beggar with tourist (41x58cm-16x23in) s.i.d.1984 verso gouache. 22-Nov-3 Burkhard, Luzern #214/R (S.FR 2300)

SCHIKANEDER, Jacob (1855-1924) Czechoslovakian

£15000	$27300	€21900	Interior (91x77cm-36x30in) s. prov. 15-Jun-4 Sotheby's, London #81/R est:5000-7000

SCHILCHER, Friedrich (1811-1881) Austrian

£347	$566	€500	Country beauty (27x22cm-11x9in) s. 23-Sep-3 Wiener Kunst Auktionen, Vienna #44/R
£647	$1157	€945	Portrait of young shepherdess (49x42cm-19x17in) s.d.1853. 12-May-4 Dobiaschofsky, Bern #937/R est:2400 (S.FR 1500)

SCHILCHER, Hans (1879-?) German

£405	$632	€600	Beer garden (20x50cm-8x20in) s. i. verso canvas on board. 28-Mar-3 Altus, Berlin #534

SCHILCHER, Hermann (1935-) German
Sculpture
£1091 $1811 €1582 Woman playing flute (42cm-17in) mono.d.1980 bronze. 13-Jun-3 Zofingen, Switzerland #2283/R est:1200 (S.FR 2400)

SCHILDER, Andrei Nikolaevich (1861-1919) Russian
£5556 $10000 €8112 Town view, winter (56x68cm-22x27in) s. 23-Apr-4 Sotheby's, New York #24/R est:10000-15000
£11538 $19615 €16500 Reflections - River landscape (58x100cm-23x39in) s.d.1891. 29-Nov-3 Bukowskis, Helsinki #428/R est:3000-4000
£16667 $30000 €24334 Summer (49x65cm-19x26in) s. 23-Apr-4 Sotheby's, New York #7/R est:10000-15000
£20000 $35800 €29200 Trees in summer (32x46cm-13x18in) s.d.29 July 1915 board. 26-May-4 Sotheby's, London #35/R est:4000-6000

SCHILFFARTH, Doris (20th C) German
Works on paper
£268 $475 €400 At the end of the performance (35x23cm-14x9in) s. mixed media. 30-Apr-4 Auktionhaus Georg Rehm, Augsburg #7601/R

SCHILKING, Heinrich (1815-1895) German
Works on paper
£313 $516 €450 Magdeburg (17x54cm-7x21in) s.d.1852 W/C. 3-Jul-3 Van Ham, Cologne #1442

SCHILL, Emil (1870-1958) Swiss
£306 $562 €447 View of Arvigrat (24x32cm-9x13in) s. panel. 14-Jun-4 Philippe Schuler, Zurich #5748 (S.FR 700)
£917 $1687 €1339 Landscape with shepherd boy playing fiddle (58x100cm-23x39in) s.d. 14-Jun-4 Philippe Schuler, Zurich #4234/R (S.FR 2100)
£1810 $3241 €2643 Autumn landscape with trees in Switzerland (75x93cm-30x37in) s.d.1943. 14-May-4 Dobiaschofsky, Bern #218/R est:3500 (S.FR 4200)
£2500 $4150 €3625 Nut tree (76x94cm-30x37in) s.i.d.1912 verso. 13-Jun-3 Zofingen, Switzerland #3016/R est:2500 (S.FR 5500)
Works on paper
£1584 $2692 €2313 Kilchzimmer near Langenbruck (52x60cm-20x24in) s.i.d.1908. 28-Nov-3 Zofingen, Switzerland #3162 est:1500 (S.FR 3500)

SCHILLE, Alice (1969-1955) American
Works on paper
£2011 $3600 €2936 Summer on Gloucester Beach (30x38cm-12x15in) s. W/C. 16-May-4 CRN Auctions, Cambridge #23a/R

SCHILLER, Frits (1886-1971) Dutch
Works on paper
£467 $849 €700 Beach and boulevard (45x53cm-18x21in) s.d.63 W/C. 1-Jul-4 Christie's, Amsterdam #446

SCHILLING, Bertha (?) ?
£979 $1664 €1400 Landscape (80x90cm-31x35in) s. 28-Nov-3 Wendl, Rudolstadt #4168/R
£1267 $2305 €1900 Summer's day on the banks of the Wumme (70x79cm-28x31in) s. panel. 1-Jul-4 Van Ham, Cologne #1597/R est:1900

SCHILLING, Frede (1928-) Danish
£905 $1620 €1321 Shapes in interior II - composition in colour (120x150cm-47x59in) s.d.85. 10-May-4 Rasmussen, Vejle #739/R (D.KR 10000)
£1176 $2106 €1717 Shapes in interior III - composition in colour (120x150cm-47x59in) s.d.85. 10-May-4 Rasmussen, Vejle #721/R est:7000-10000 (D.KR 13000)
£1267 $2268 €1850 Shapes in exterior III - composition in colour (120x150cm-47x59in) s.d.85. 10-May-4 Rasmussen, Vejle #720/R est:7000-10000 (D.KR 14000)
£1357 $2430 €1981 Shapes in exterior I - composition in colour (120x150cm-47x59in) s.d.85. 10-May-4 Rasmussen, Vejle #722/R est:7000-10000 (D.KR 15000)
£1357 $2430 €1981 Shapes in interior I - composition in colour (120x150cm-47x59in) s.d.85. 10-May-4 Rasmussen, Vejle #740/R est:7000-10000 (D.KR 15000)
£1357 $2430 €1981 Shapes in exterior II - composition in colour (120x150cm-47x59in) s.d.85. 10-May-4 Rasmussen, Vejle #741/R est:7000-10000 (D.KR 15000)

SCHILT, Martinus (1867-1921) Dutch
£1974 $3632 €3000 A breakfast still life (50x40cm-20x16in) s. 22-Jun-4 Christie's, Amsterdam #170/R est:2500-3500

SCHIMMEL, Wilhelm (1817-1890) American/German
Sculpture
£2353 $4000 €3435 Squirrel holding a nut (15cm-6in) carved painted wood. 31-Oct-3 North East Auctions, Portsmouth #1633
£3488 $6000 €5092 Rooster (8x5cm-3x2in) polychrome prov. 6-Dec-3 Pook & Pook, Downington #174/R est:1500-2000
£4192 $7000 €6120 Spreadwing eagle (28x42cm-11x17in) carved wood. 11-Nov-3 Christie's, Rockefeller NY #231/R est:7000-10000

SCHINDLER, Albert (1805-1861) Austrian
£6500 $11180 €9490 Peek-a-boo (34x28cm-13x11in) panel. 4-Dec-3 Christie's, Kensington #142/R est:7000-10000

SCHINDLER, Carl (1821-1842) Austrian
Works on paper
£1342 $2470 €2000 Military funeral (10x14cm-4x6in) W/C paper on board. 26-Mar-4 Dorotheum, Vienna #188/R est:3000-3500

SCHINDLER, Emil Jakob (1842-1892) Austrian
£1800 $3258 €2700 Autumn wood (63x52cm-25x20in) s. 1-Apr-4 Van Ham, Cologne #1632/R est:2600
£2762 $5000 €4033 Boats at dock along the riverbank (33x46cm-13x18in) prov. 30-Mar-4 Christie's, Rockefeller NY #54/R est:6000-8000
£12500 $21250 €18000 Dutch landscape (33x46cm-13x18in) lit. 28-Oct-3 Wiener Kunst Auktionen, Vienna #38/R est:18000-35000
£13889 $23611 €20000 Ragusa (54x48cm-21x19in) lit.prov. 28-Oct-3 Wiener Kunst Auktionen, Vienna #39/R est:18000-50000
£16779 $29698 €25000 Probably Salzburg (23x41cm-9x16in) s. panel prov. 28-Apr-4 Wiener Kunst Auktionen, Vienna #47/R est:25000-50000

SCHINDLER, Emil Jakob (attrib) (1842-1892) Austrian
£1748 $2972 €2500 Landscape near Salzburg (40x30cm-16x12in) bears i. board. 24-Nov-3 Dorotheum, Vienna #180/R est:5000-7000

SCHINKEL, Karl Friedrich (1781-1841) German
Prints
£11888 $20210 €17000 Gothic church behind trees (48x34cm-19x13in) pen lithograph htd white. 27-Nov-3 Bassenge, Berlin #5645/R est:18000
Works on paper
£556 $928 €800 Italian coastal landscape (7x20cm-3x8in) i. pencil. 24-Oct-3 Ketterer, Hamburg #226/R

SCHINKEL, Karl Friedrich (attrib) (1781-1841) German
£403 $741 €600 Sketch for dome (31x29cm-12x11in) Indian ink brush over pencil. 26-Mar-4 Bolland & Marotz, Bremen #426/R

SCHINNAGL, Maximilian Joseph (attrib) (1697-1762) German
£3067 $5581 €4600 Mountain landscape (33x46cm-13x18in) panel one of pair. 30-Jun-4 Neumeister, Munich #482/R est:3500
£3667 $6673 €5500 Mountain landscape (33x46cm-13x18in) panel one of pair. 30-Jun-4 Neumeister, Munich #481/R est:3500

SCHINZEL, Reinhart (1879-1954) Austrian
£490 $832 €700 Furnitz with Dobratsch (14x16cm-6x6in) s. s.i. verso board. 19-Nov-3 Dorotheum, Klagenfurt #32
£769 $1308 €1100 Landscape (22x32cm-9x13in) s. board. 19-Nov-3 Dorotheum, Klagenfurt #31

SCHIODTE, Harald (1852-1924) Danish
£397 $734 €580 Interior scene with gentleman (56x47cm-22x19in) s.d.1880. 15-Mar-4 Rasmussen, Vejle #423/R (D.KR 4400)
£675 $1100 €986 Interior scene with figures and dog (50x59cm-20x23in) s. 27-Sep-3 Rasmussen, Havnen #2129 (D.KR 7200)

SCHIOLER, Inge (1908-1971) Swedish
£1099 $1945 €1605 The plant on the window ledge (38x46cm-15x18in) s. panel. 27-Apr-4 AB Stockholms Auktionsverk #711/R est:25000-30000 (S.KR 15000)
£1160 $2088 €1694 Willow twigs in vase (38x46cm-15x18in) s. panel. 26-Apr-4 Bukowskis, Stockholm #47/R est:20000-25000 (S.KR 16000)
£1832 $3242 €2675 Lady dressed in blue (73x65cm-29x26in) painted c.1930 prov. 27-Apr-4 AB Stockholms Auktionsverk #706/R est:30000-40000 (S.KR 25000)
£2175 $3916 €3176 Sandy beach at Koster (22x24cm-9x9in) s. 26-Apr-4 Bukowskis, Stockholm #147/R est:25000-30000 (S.KR 30000)
£2308 $3969 €3370 Landscape from Koster (27x33cm-11x13in) s.d.1958. 7-Dec-3 Uppsala Auktionskammare, Uppsala #277/R est:18000-20000 (S.KR 30000)
£2683 $4830 €3917 Landscape, Koster (30x42cm-12x17in) s.d.1960. 26-Apr-4 Bukowskis, Stockholm #46/R est:40000-50000 (S.KR 37000)
£2784 $4927 €4065 Girl with brown hair (81x65cm-32x26in) with sig. painted c.1932/33 exhib.prov. 27-Apr-4 AB Stockholms Auktionsverk #701/R est:30000-40000 (S.KR 38000)
£3263 $5874 €4764 Still life (62x50cm-24x20in) s. panel. 26-Apr-4 Bukowskis, Stockholm #31/R est:50000-70000 (S.KR 45000)
£4396 $7780 €6418 Leafy forest in May, Southern Koster (50x55cm-20x22in) s.d.1961. 27-Apr-4 AB Stockholms Auktionsverk #704/R est:60000-80000 (S.KR 60000)
£4532 $7704 €6617 Coastal landscape with bay, Koster (37x41cm-15x16in) s.d.1961. 5-Nov-3 AB Stockholms Auktionsverk #651/R est:60000-80000 (S.KR 60000)
£4714 $8484 €6882 Woodland glade (50x61cm-20x24in) s. 26-Apr-4 Bukowskis, Stockholm #136/R est:60000-80000 (S.KR 65000)
£6647 $11299 €9705 Landscape, Morholmsroset (74x82cm-29x32in) s. exhib. 4-Nov-3 Bukowskis, Stockholm #105/R est:100000-125000 (S.KR 88000)
£7252 $13053 €10588 Silver birches by edge of sea (55x50cm-22x20in) s.d.1966. 26-Apr-4 Bukowskis, Stockholm #41/R est:100000-125000 (S.KR 100000)
£7326 $12967 €10696 Coastal landscape with bay, Koster (72x82cm-28x32in) s. exhib. 27-Apr-4 AB Stockholms Auktionsverk #705/R est:125000-150000 (S.KR 100000)
£9063 $15408 €13232 The barn in summer, Southern Koster (73x81cm-29x32in) s.d.1963. 5-Nov-3 AB Stockholms Auktionsverk #664/R est:150000-175000 (S.KR 120000)
£9524 $16857 €13905 Unloading the ship, Stockholm (47x55cm-19x22in) s. painted c.1932 exhib.lit. 27-Apr-4 AB Stockholms Auktionsverk #708/R est:150000-200000 (S.KR 130000)
£9819 $16692 €14336 Beach on a windy day (66x73cm-26x29in) s.d.1969. 5-Nov-3 AB Stockholms Auktionsverk #758/R est:125000-150000 (S.KR 130000)
£12088 $21396 €17648 Coastal landscape, Koster (38x46cm-15x18in) s. panel. 27-Apr-4 AB Stockholms Auktionsverk #703/R est:80000-100000 (S.KR 165000)
£12690 $22843 €18527 September ocean (59x73cm-23x29in) s. d.1955 verso. 26-Apr-4 Bukowskis, Stockholm #36/R est:175000-200000 (S.KR 175000)
£12821 $22692 €18719 Girl wearing blue (81x65cm-32x26in) st.sig. panel painted c.1932/33 prov.exhib.lit. 27-Apr-4 AB Stockholms Auktionsverk #702/R est:30000-40000 (S.KR 175000)
£13919 $24637 €20322 Late summer landscape, Tjur Island (65x79cm-26x31in) s. painted c.1932 exhib.lit. 27-Apr-4 AB Stockholms Auktionsverk #714/R est:160000-180000 (S.KR 190000)
£14141 $25453 €20646 Aspen forest by meadow, Koster (81x73cm-32x29in) s.d.1966. 26-Apr-4 Bukowskis, Stockholm #35/R est:150000-175000 (S.KR 195000)
£14350 $24396 €20951 Flowers in the bay, Koster (58x68cm-23x27in) s.d.56. 4-Nov-3 Bukowskis, Stockholm #113/R est:125000-150000 (S.KR 190000)
£14503 $26106 €21174 Beach on a windy day (66x73cm-26x29in) s. painted 1969. 26-Apr-4 Bukowskis, Stockholm #137/R est:175000-200000 (S.KR 200000)

£17372	$29532	€25363	House near bay, Koster (74x82cm-29x32in) s. 5-Nov-3 AB Stockholms Auktionsverk #841/R est:150000-175000 (S.KR 230000)
£21148	$35952	€30876	Fishing hut and boat, Koster (66x73cm-26x29in) s.d.1966. 4-Nov-3 Bukowskis, Stockholm #95a/R est:300000-350000 (S.KR 280000)
Works on paper			
£500	$860	€730	Landscape (19x23cm-7x9in) mono. pastel exhib. 7-Dec-3 Uppsala Auktionskammare, Uppsala #228 (S.KR 6500)
£668	$1155	€975	Landscape (46x38cm-18x15in) s. pastel. 15-Dec-3 Lilla Bukowskis, Stockholm #953 (S.KR 8500)
£870	$1566	€1305	Landscape with mountain, Koster (48x62cm-19x24in) s.d.1961 pastel lit. 25-Apr-4 Goteborg Auktionsverk, Sweden #349/R (S.KR 12000)
£870	$1566	€1305	Green trees and red fence (46x39cm-18x15in) s. pastel lit. 25-Apr-4 Goteborg Auktionsverk, Sweden #381/R (S.KR 12000)
£1088	$1958	€1588	Tree in autumn (27x35cm-11x14in) s.d.1957 W/C prov. 26-Apr-4 Bukowskis, Stockholm #42/R est:15000-18000 (S.KR 15000)
£1133	$1926	€1654	White flowers (43x36cm-17x14in) s. gouache. 4-Nov-3 Bukowskis, Stockholm #17/R est:18000-20000 (S.KR 15000)
£1171	$1990	€1710	Dark trees (46x61cm-18x24in) s. pastel exhib.prov. 4-Nov-3 Bukowskis, Stockholm #114/R est:18000-20000 (S.KR 15500)
£1172	$2075	€1711	Still life of flowers (44x36cm-17x14in) s. gouache. 27-Apr-4 AB Stockholms Auktionsverk #707/R est:20000-25000 (S.KR 16000)
£1538	$2723	€2245	Self-portrait (44x37cm-17x15in) s. gouache. 27-Apr-4 AB Stockholms Auktionsverk #709/R est:12000-15000 (S.KR 21000)
£1626	$2911	€2374	Begonia in a pot (45x37cm-18x15in) s. gouache exhib.prov. 28-May-4 Uppsala Auktionskammare, Uppsala #289/R est:12000-15000 (S.KR 22000)
£1978	$3501	€2888	Still life of flowers (45x38cm-18x15in) s. mixed media panel. 27-Apr-4 AB Stockholms Auktionsverk #710/R est:15000-18000 (S.KR 27000)
£2039	$3467	€2977	Roses (42x36cm-17x14in) s. W/C. 4-Nov-3 Bukowskis, Stockholm #102/R est:20000-25000 (S.KR 27000)
£2115	$3595	€3088	View through window (33x25cm-13x10in) s.d.1957 W/C. 5-Nov-3 AB Stockholms Auktionsverk #733/R est:6000-8000 (S.KR 28000)
£2341	$3980	€3418	Flowers and willow (40x32cm-16x13in) s. pastel. 4-Nov-3 Bukowskis, Stockholm #101/R est:30000-35000 (S.KR 31000)

SCHIOTT, August (1823-1895) Danish

£332	$564	€485	Boys bathing near Aalsgaarde, North Sjaelland (33x43cm-13x17in) mono. 10-Nov-3 Rasmussen, Vejle #145/R (D.KR 3600)
£473	$846	€691	Coastal landscape with beached boats (24x32cm-9x13in) init. 12-Jan-4 Rasmussen, Vejle #7/R (D.KR 5000)
£1172	$2169	€1711	Portrait of Ida comtesse Marie Bille Brahe (69x55cm-27x22in) s.d.1854 oval prov. 15-Mar-4 Rasmussen, Vejle #399/R est:8000-10000 (D.KR 13000)
£1280	$2047	€1869	View of Cairo (38x62cm-15x24in) exhib. 22-Sep-3 Rasmussen, Vejle #165/R est:6000-8000 (D.KR 13500)
£1323	$2289	€1932	The artist's fiancee Miss Oline Mathilde Lund (41x32cm-16x13in) s.d.1847. 9-Dec-3 Rasmussen, Copenhagen #1337/R est:6000-8000 (D.KR 14000)
£1987	$3616	€3000	Academie de jeune homme debout (93x56cm-37x22in) 15-Jun-4 Artcurial Briest, Paris #239/R est:3000-4000
£7162	$13107	€10457	Young girl talking to fisherman mending his nets (70x98cm-28x39in) s. prov. 9-Jun-4 Rasmussen, Copenhagen #1505/R est:100000-150000 (D.KR 80000)

SCHIOTTZ-JENSEN, N F (1855-1941) Danish

£358	$655	€523	Stream through landscape (40x48cm-16x19in) s. 9-Jun-4 Rasmussen, Copenhagen #1961/R (D.KR 4000)
£373	$585	€545	Wooded landscape with figures carrying faggots (59x51cm-23x20in) s.d.1926. 30-Aug-3 Rasmussen, Havnen #2190 (D.KR 4000)
£539	$1003	€787	Norwegian fjord landscape (36x49cm-14x19in) s.i.d.1890. 2-Mar-4 Rasmussen, Copenhagen #1214/R (D.KR 6000)
£541	$1001	€790	View from Capri with woman and girl on road (76x52cm-30x20in) s.i.d.1900. 15-Mar-4 Rasmussen, Vejle #352/R (D.KR 6000)
£640	$1087	€934	From an Italian loggia with two women and child (52x43cm-20x17in) s. 29-Nov-3 Rasmussen, Havnen #2000/R (D.KR 6800)
£652	$1024	€952	Italian scene with woman and children on steps (52x41cm-20x16in) s. 30-Aug-3 Rasmussen, Havnen #2173/R (D.KR 7000)
£851	$1523	€1242	Coastal landscape with fishermen by beached boat (37x60cm-15x24in) s.i.d.1910. 12-Jan-4 Rasmussen, Vejle #3/R (D.KR 9000)
£985	$1802	€1438	Man on country road with dog pulling cart (142x123cm-56x48in) init.d.1887 exhib. 9-Jun-4 Rasmussen, Copenhagen #1728/R (D.KR 11000)
£1276	$2284	€1863	Women fetching water at well in Ravello (42x61cm-17x24in) s.d.1925. 12-Jan-4 Rasmussen, Vejle #386/R est:12000-15000 (D.KR 13500)
£1323	$2369	€1932	Italian mountain landscape with family on path (53x78cm-21x31in) s.i.d.1921 exhib. 12-Jan-4 Rasmussen, Vejle #387/R est:12000-15000 (D.KR 14000)
£1432	$2621	€2091	Sunny fishing village, Capri (47x71cm-19x28in) s.i.d.1892. 9-Jun-4 Rasmussen, Copenhagen #1796/R est:15000 (D.KR 16000)
£1682	$2658	€2439	Young man resting in a hammock (42x58cm-17x23in) s.d.1885. 2-Sep-3 Rasmussen, Copenhagen #1685/R est:8000-10000 (D.KR 18000)

SCHIOTTZ-JENSEN, Niels F (1855-1941) Danish

£487	$794	€711	Southern landscape with young woman (34x22cm-13x9in) s. 28-Sep-3 Hindemae, Ullerslev #19/R (D.KR 5200)
£3936	$6416	€5747	Italian girl with basket waiting for her friend (37x28cm-15x11in) s.init. 28-Sep-3 Hindemae, Ullerslev #18/R est:40000-50000 (D.KR 42000)
£4924	$9011	€7189	Figures in a garden, sunshine (57x50cm-22x20in) s.d.1884 exhib.prov. 9-Jun-4 Rasmussen, Copenhagen #1492/R est:60000-80000 (D.KR 55000)
£6272	$11290	€9157	Italian scene with women by well (64x51cm-25x20in) s. 24-Apr-4 Rasmussen, Havnen #2350/R est:7000-10000 (D.KR 70000)
£6667	$12000	€9734	An afternoon's rest (41x56cm-16x22in) s.d.1885. 22-Apr-4 Christie's, Rockefeller NY #1/R est:12000-18000
£31000	$56420	€45260	Lady reading (62x45cm-24x18in) s.d.1894 exhib. 15-Jun-4 Sotheby's, London #324/R est:15000-20000

SCHIPPER, Marinus (1897-?) Dutch

£966	$1612	€1400	Still life with bronze head (49x37cm-19x15in) s.d.1928 canvas on canvas. 13-Nov-3 Neumeister, Munich #452/R

SCHIPPERS, Joseph (1868-1950) Belgian

£872	$1562	€1300	La mer (57x82cm-22x32in) s. 25-May-4 Campo & Campo, Antwerp #260/R
£1486	$2616	€2200	Cat's head (27x25cm-11x10in) s. panel. 24-May-4 Bernaerts, Antwerp #694 est:2000-3000
£1757	$3145	€2600	Reading (15x18cm-6x7in) panel. 10-May-4 Amberes, Antwerp #305/R
£2394	$4142	€3400	Rough sea (111x200cm-44x79in) s. 13-Dec-3 De Vuyst, Lokeren #569/R est:4500-6000
£2400	$4296	€3600	Le vieux politique (27x21cm-11x8in) s.d.1900 panel. 11-May-4 Vanderkindere, Brussels #98 est:1200-1800
£2500	$4175	€3600	Singe (18x17cm-7x7in) s. panel. 21-Oct-3 Campo, Vlaamse Kaai #554a/R est:1000-1500
£7047	$12614	€10500	Juge prevenue et gendarme (39x30cm-15x12in) s.d.1943. 25-May-4 Campo & Campo, Antwerp #261/R est:10000-15000
£8054	$14899	€12000	The sick (55x41cm-22x16in) s.d.1933 s.i.d.1933 verso. 13-Mar-4 De Vuyst, Lokeren #475/R est:10000-12000
£12587	$21650	€18000	Deux petits singes (38x46cm-15x18in) s.d.1907 panel. 2-Dec-3 Campo & Campo, Antwerp #322/R est:10000-15000
£19333	$34993	€29000	Le banquier (50x60cm-20x24in) s.d.1926. 30-Mar-4 Campo, Vlaamse Kaai #154/R est:12000-15000
£19718	$34113	€28000	Chemist (55x70cm-22x28in) s. s.i.d.1943. 13-Dec-3 De Vuyst, Lokeren #486/R est:18000-21000
Works on paper			
£1000	$1810	€1500	Suzanne au bain (31x23cm-12x9in) s. pastel. 30-Mar-4 Campo & Campo, Antwerp #259/R est:1750-2250

SCHIPPERUS, Pieter Adrianus (1840-1929) Dutch

£750	$1253	€1095	Man on a track before a farm (22x28cm-9x11in) s. panel. 7-Oct-3 Bonhams, Knightsbridge #147/R
£1645	$2977	€2500	Farmer's wife near cows in a meadow in front of a mill (64x90cm-25x35in) bears sig. 19-Apr-4 Glerum, Amsterdam #203/R est:4000-6000
£1645	$2977	€2500	Farmer near cows in a meadow with a man and a boat in the foreground (65x91cm-26x36in) bears sig. 19-Apr-4 Glerum, Amsterdam #204/R est:4000-6000
£4000	$7160	€5840	Canal scene with masted boats and figures on a quayside (46x61cm-18x24in) s. 7-May-4 Christopher Matthews, Yorkshire #308 est:1000-1500
Works on paper			
£428	$774	€650	Rozenburg, Limburg (23x14cm-9x6in) s.i. W/C. 19-Apr-4 Glerum, Amsterdam #69
£461	$834	€700	Horse and cart on a country path beside a river, Limburg (23x33cm-9x13in) s.d.1918 W/C htd white. 19-Apr-4 Glerum, Amsterdam #49/R
£724	$1310	€1100	Entrance gate to the Haagse Bosch (48x33cm-19x13in) s. W/C. 19-Apr-4 Glerum, Amsterdam #47/R
£753	$1281	€1100	Grand Canal, Venice. Sospire bridge, Venice (23x34cm-9x13in) s. W/C pair. 5-Nov-3 Vendue Huis, Gravenhage #182
£1538	$2569	€2200	Winter in the forest (46x82cm-18x32in) s. gouache W/C prov. 11-Oct-3 De Vuyst, Lokeren #325/R est:2000-2400
£2303	$4237	€3500	Summer landscape with windmill. The hay harvest (22x32cm-9x13in) both s. W/C pair. 28-Jun-4 Sotheby's, Amsterdam #53/R est:3000-5000

SCHIRM, Carl Cowen (1852-1928) German

£268	$494	€400	Rock shore of Halensee (23x32cm-9x13in) mono.d.XXVII Aug 09 board on panel. 26-Mar-4 Bolland & Marotz, Bremen #584/R
£470	$864	€700	Halensee (37x51cm-15x20in) s. 26-Mar-4 Bolland & Marotz, Bremen #583/R
£2031	$3392	€2965	Autumn landscape (70x95cm-28x37in) s. painted c.1900. 19-Oct-3 Agra, Warsaw #31/R est:10000 (P.Z 13000)

SCHIRMER, Johann Wilhelm (1807-1863) German

£1477	$2717	€2200	Sunny woodland (58x71cm-23x28in) s. board lit. 25-Mar-4 Karlheinz Kaupp, Staufen #2710/R est:250
£7483	$13395	€11000	Extensive river valley in the mountains (44x57cm-17x22in) mono. 17-Mar-4 Neumeister, Munich #594/R est:9000
£9310	$15548	€13500	Alpine landscape with wild river (41x59cm-16x23in) mono. 15-Nov-3 Lempertz, Koln #1692/R est:8000
Works on paper			
£439	$786	€650	River landscape with farmers and a castle on the hill (30x43cm-12x17in) s. pen col chk. 7-May-4 Paul Kieffer, Pforzhiem #8051
£733	$1313	€1100	River landscape with gathering storm (23x40cm-9x16in) brush wash on pen. 13-May-4 Bassenge, Berlin #5656/R
£1342	$2470	€2000	Campagna study (32x46cm-13x18in) W/C over pen prov. 26-Mar-4 Ketterer, Hamburg #212/R est:1200-1400
£3846	$6538	€5500	Autumn river landscape (31x44cm-12x17in) s. WC. 20-Nov-3 Van Ham, Cologne #1848/R est:5500

SCHIRMER, Johann Wilhelm (attrib) (1807-1863) German

£897	$1659	€1300	Mountain lake with village and snowy peaks (25x20cm-10x8in) canvas on board. 14-Feb-4 Hans Stahl, Hamburg #86/R
Works on paper			
£267	$483	€400	Shepherd with flock in hilly landscape with trees (17x27cm-7x11in) i. verso pencil. 2-Apr-4 Winterberg, Heidelberg #535

SCHIRREN, Ferdinand (1872-1944) Belgian

£14765	$27315	€22000	Nude sitting in interior (115x90cm-45x35in) s.d.1925. 13-Mar-4 De Vuyst, Lokeren #551/R est:20000-24000
Works on paper			
£1250	$2037	€1800	Nature morte aux pommes rouges. s. W/C. 23-Sep-3 Galerie Moderne, Brussels #804/R
£1667	$2783	€2400	Cloud (30x37cm-12x15in) s.d.1920 W/C. 21-Oct-3 Campo, Vlaamse Kaai #557/R est:2500-2800
£1944	$3247	€2800	Villa dans le sud (52x88cm-20x35in) s. W/C. 21-Oct-3 Campo, Vlaamse Kaai #556 est:2500-3500
£2778	$4639	€4000	Paysage (68x74cm-27x29in) s. W/C exhib. 21-Oct-3 Campo, Vlaamse Kaai #555/R est:4000-4500

SCHIRRMACHER, Fritz (1893-1948) German

£1800	$3222	€2700	Girl with Christmas tree (66x66cm-26x26in) s. prov. 14-May-4 Ketterer, Munich #74/R est:900-1200

SCHIVERT, Victor (1863-?) Rumanian

£1192	$2170	€1800	Small figure (93x77cm-37x30in) s. 19-Jun-4 Bergmann, Erlangen #831
£1379	$2303	€2000	The last trip - executioner with nude woman (141x111cm-56x44in) s. lit. 10-Jul-3 Allgauer, Kempten #2669/R est:1800

SCHIWETZ, Edward M (1898-1984) American
Works on paper
£1108 $1850 €1618 Kilgore up town (28x43cm-11x17in) pastel. 18-Oct-3 David Dike, Dallas #239/R est:2000-4000

SCHIWETZ, Edward M (attrib) (1898-1984) American
£2147 $3500 €3135 Houston ship channel (61x91cm-24x36in) 28-Sep-3 Simpson's, Houston #295/R

SCHJERFBECK, Helene (1862-1946) Finnish
£15385 $26154 €22000 Portrait of young man (25x32cm-10x13in) s. board painted c.1890 lit. 29-Nov-3 Bukowskis, Helsinki #177/R est:20000-25000
£46154 $79385 €67385 English peasant woman - autumn rose (115x91cm-45x36in) s. painted 1887-1888 prov.exhib.lit. 3-Dec-3 AB Stockholms Auktionsverk #2572/R est:600000-800000 (S.KR 600000)
£60000 $109200 €87600 A view of a yard in Tammisaari (42x36cm-17x14in) init. exec.1919-20 exhib.lit. 15-Jun-4 Sotheby's, London #319/R est:60000-80000
£66667 $119333 €100000 Common hepaticas in chip basket (25x30cm-10x12in) s. 15-May-4 Hagelstam, Helsinki #107/R est:100000
£280000 $509600 €408800 Shadow on the wall (45x38cm-18x15in) init. canvas on panel painted 1883 prov.exhib.lit. 3-Feb-4 Christie's, London #140/R est:300000-400000
£339161 $576573 €485000 Lady wearing purple (65x44cm-26x17in) s. painted c.1920. 29-Nov-3 Bukowskis, Helsinki #174/R est:400000-500000
Prints
£2692 $4631 €3930 The story book (52x62cm-20x24in) mono. lithograph hand col. pastel prov.lit. 3-Dec-3 AB Stockholms Auktionsverk #2635/R est:40000-50000 (S.KR 35000)
£2956 $5292 €4316 The convalescent (36x55cm-14x22in) s.num.25/30 col lithograph exec.c.1938-39. 25-May-4 Bukowskis, Stockholm #276/R est:50000-60000 (S.KR 40000)
£3077 $5292 €4492 The convalescent (49x67cm-19x26in) mono.num.9/70 lithograph in five colours lit. 3-Dec-3 AB Stockholms Auktionsverk #2634/R est:50000-60000 (S.KR 40000)
£3077 $5292 €4492 In front of the open fire (63x48cm-25x19in) mono. lithograph hand col pastel lit. 3-Dec-3 AB Stockholms Auktionsverk #2636/R est:40000-50000 (S.KR 40000)
£3252 $5821 €4748 The satin shoes. mono. lithograph in four colours prov.lit. 26-May-4 AB Stockholms Auktionsverk #2611/R est:30000-40000 (S.KR 44000)
£3333 $5967 €5000 The satin shoes (53x65cm-21x26in) lithograph in two colours prov. 15-May-4 Hagelstam, Helsinki #109/R est:2000
£3497 $5944 €5000 Costume picture (55x43cm-22x17in) s. lithograph. 29-Nov-3 Bukowskis, Helsinki #179/R est:3500-4000
£3695 $6615 €5395 The satin shoe (37x42cm-15x17in) s.num.22/50 col lithograph. 25-May-4 Bukowskis, Stockholm #275/R est:50000-60000 (S.KR 50000)
Works on paper
£946 $1693 €1400 Rafaello (19x30cm-7x12in) pencil. 8-May-4 Bukowskis, Helsinki #197/R
£986 $1577 €1400 Street musician (20x13cm-8x5in) dr. 21-Sep-3 Bukowskis, Helsinki #466/R
£2400 $4296 €3600 The artist's mother (20x14cm-8x6in) s. pencil. 15-May-4 Hagelstam, Helsinki #108/R est:4000
£5405 $9676 €8000 Girl (20x12cm-8x5in) s. mixed media. 8-May-4 Bukowskis, Helsinki #181/R est:8000-10000
£15521 $27783 €22661 Portrait of girl with hat (44x33cm-17x13in) s. pastel exec.c.1885-86. 25-May-4 Bukowskis, Stockholm #340/R est:200000-225000 (S.KR 210000)
£45000 $81900 €65700 The reading girl (27x21cm-11x8in) init. chl gouache exec. c.1910 prov. 3-Feb-4 Christie's, London #142/R est:50000-70000

SCHJERVEN, Sissel (20th C) Norwegian
£293 $539 €440 Bowl of fruit in front of window (66x54cm-26x21in) s. 14-Jun-4 Blomqvist, Lysaker #1348 (N.KR 3600)
£302 $502 €438 Still life of flowers (100x81cm-39x32in) s. 16-Jun-3 Blomqvist, Lysaker #1212 (N.KR 3500)

SCHJOLBERG, Guido (?) ?
£366 $673 €549 Studio interior (90x70cm-35x28in) s. 14-Jun-4 Blomqvist, Lysaker #1349 (N.KR 4500)

SCHJOTH, Claus (1852-?) Norwegian
£334 $557 €488 In a calm (19x36cm-7x14in) s. panel. 17-Nov-3 Blomqvist, Lysaker #1296 (N.KR 4000)

SCHLABITZ, Adolf (1854-1943) German
£604 $1123 €900 Tyrolean hunter (59x51cm-23x20in) s.d.1915. 5-Mar-4 Wendl, Rudolstadt #3850/R
£1528 $2521 €2200 Summer morning in Brizlegg/Tirol (78x145cm-31x57in) s.d.1887 canvas on board. 3-Jul-3 Van Ham, Cologne #1445/R est:2200

SCHLACHTER, Jakobus (attrib) (18th C) Austrian
£11842 $21790 €18000 Hunting scene (65x82cm-26x32in) i. 24-Jun-4 Tajan, Paris #29/R est:20000-30000

SCHLAGETER, Karl (1894-1990) Swiss
£283 $517 €413 Woman with fish (40x30cm-16x12in) s.d.1959 cardboard. 4-Jun-4 Zofingen, Switzerland #2949 (S.FR 650)
£396 $674 €578 Mother and child (41x31cm-16x12in) s.d.25 panel. 5-Nov-3 Dobiaschofsky, Bern #939/R (S.FR 900)
£459 $766 €666 Washerwomen (86x65cm-34x26in) s.d.1957 canvas on masonite. 23-Jun-3 Philippe Schuler, Zurich #3422 (S.FR 1000)
£600 $1104 €900 Swiss mountain lake (47x65cm-19x26in) s.d.23. 9-Jun-4 Dorotheum, Salzburg #608/R

SCHLANDERER, Josef (18th C) Austrian
£651 $1106 €950 Portrait of nobleman (91x70cm-36x28in) s.d.1799. 5-Nov-3 Hugo Ruef, Munich #1114/R

SCHLATTER, Ernst Emil (1883-1954) Swiss
£673 $1123 €983 Amboss from Roslenalp (61x78cm-24x31in) s.d.32 s.i. verso. 24-Oct-3 Hans Widmer, St Gallen #9/R est:1600-3200 (S.FR 1500)

SCHLEGEL, Frits (19th C) ?
£1254 $2258 €1831 Portrait of Italian woman by well (68x46cm-27x18in) s.d.1905. 24-Apr-4 Rasmussen, Havnen #2179/R est:7000-10000 (D.KR 14000)

SCHLEGEL, Julius (1830-1880) German
£1689 $3024 €2500 Italian landscapes (26x32cm-10x13in) s.d.51 s.d.1851 i. verso two lit. 8-May-4 Schloss Ahlden, Ahlden #787/R est:2800

SCHLEGEL, Karl (20th C) ?
£2905 $5373 €4241 Kitchen interior scene with woman cooking (132x159cm-52x63in) 14-Mar-4 Agra, Warsaw #61/R (P.Z 21000)

SCHLEGELL, William von (20th C) ?
£255 $475 €372 Still life with fruit before a window (41x51cm-16x20in) board. 5-Mar-4 Skinner, Boston #425/R

SCHLEICH, August (1814-1865) German
£633 $1077 €924 Hare (17x22cm-7x9in) mono. i. verso panel. 28-Nov-3 Zofingen, Switzerland #2486/R (S.FR 1400)

SCHLEICH, Eduard (19th C) German
£1109 $1984 €1619 Alpine landscape (43x35cm-17x14in) bears sig. 26-May-4 AB Stockholms Auktionsverk #2456/R est:15000-18000 (S.KR 15000)

SCHLEICH, Eduard (elder) (1812-1874) German
£1067 $1941 €1600 Landscape with mountains in the distance (16x36cm-6x14in) s. board. 1-Jul-4 Van Ham, Cologne #1601 est:900
£1156 $2070 €1700 Extensive landscape (33x66cm-13x26in) s. lit. 20-Mar-4 Bergmann, Erlangen #1104 est:1500-1700
£1293 $2314 €1900 Coastal landscape (14x40cm-6x16in) s. panel. 17-Mar-4 Neumeister, Munich #596/R est:1500
£2416 $4446 €3600 High mountain landscape (41x32cm-16x13in) s. lit. 26-Mar-4 Auktionhaus Georg Rehm, Augsburg #8158/R est:3800
£2517 $4330 €3600 Ship near the coast in moonlight (31x63cm-12x25in) s. canvas on canvas prov. 5-Dec-3 Ketterer, Munich #6/R est:4000-6000
£3467 $6344 €5200 Herd by the sea (36x31cm-14x12in) s. paper on canvas. 6-Jun-4 Osenat, Fontainebleau #32/R est:5000-6000
£4225 $7310 €6000 Isar landscape (19x30cm-7x12in) 10-Dec-3 Hugo Ruef, Munich #2499/R est:1200
£4667 $8493 €7000 Starnberger See (37x87cm-15x34in) s. panel. 30-Jun-4 Neumeister, Munich #670/R est:6000
£6597 $10885 €9500 Cows watering in pond (27x47cm-11x19in) s. panel. 2-Jul-3 Neumeister, Munich #764/R est:4800

SCHLEICH, Eduard (younger) (1853-1893) German
£1507 $2562 €2200 Landscape with stream (28x42cm-11x17in) s. 5-Nov-3 Hugo Ruef, Munich #1115/R est:2000
£2113 $3655 €3000 Riverside village with peasants returning home (30x45cm-12x18in) s. 13-Dec-3 Lempertz, Koln #42/R est:2000
£2632 $4842 €4000 Pre-alpine landscape beneath cloudy skies (30x63cm-12x25in) s. 24-Jun-4 Dr Fritz Nagel, Stuttgart #755/R est:4500

SCHLEICH, Robert (1845-1934) German
£611 $1076 €892 Country scene (6x4cm-2x2in) s. panel prov. 22-May-4 Galerie Gloggner, Luzern #95/R (S.FR 1400)
£845 $1462 €1200 Sledge (8x14cm-3x6in) s. panel. 13-Dec-3 Lempertz, Koln #250/R
£1507 $2562 €2200 Boat carrying two horses (20x28cm-8x11in) s. panel. 5-Nov-3 Hugo Ruef, Munich #1113/R est:2000
£1645 $3026 €2500 Haymaking (11x13cm-4x5in) s. panel. 25-Jun-4 Michael Zeller, Lindau #535/R est:1000
£1867 $3397 €2800 Enjoying the ice by Dutch city (7x19cm-3x7in) s.d.1898 panel. 30-Jun-4 Neumeister, Munich #672/R est:1800
£2200 $4004 €3300 Shepherd with flock and peasant woman (8x9cm-3x4in) s. panel. 30-Jun-4 Neumeister, Munich #671/R est:2000
£2657 $4571 €3800 Haying with approaching storm clouds overhead (18x15cm-7x6in) s. panel. 3-Dec-3 Neumeister, Munich #732/R est:3000

SCHLEICHER, Carl (19th C) Austrian
£1736 $2830 €2500 Game of cards (16x21cm-6x8in) s. panel. 26-Sep-3 Bolland & Marotz, Bremen #607/R est:2300
£2800 $4676 €4088 Religious dispute (25x32cm-10x13in) s. panel. 12-Nov-3 Sotheby's, Olympia #192/R est:2000-3000

SCHLEIME, Cornelia (1953-) ?
£8333 $15333 €12500 Girl with a dog (145x120cm-57x47in) s.d.97 verso acrylic asphalt lacquer. 12-Jun-4 Villa Grisebach, Berlin #444/R est:5000-7000
£11189 $19021 €16000 Untitled (160x200cm-63x79in) s.d.96-98 verso acrylic asphalt varnish shellac prov. 29-Nov-3 Villa Grisebach, Berlin #387/R est:14000-18000
Works on paper
£600 $1098 €900 Untitled - self portrait (51x73cm-20x29in) mono.d.86 gouache. 4-Jun-4 Lempertz, Koln #427/R
£1467 $2684 €2200 Averdatsche (60x80cm-24x31in) s.d.92 col Indian ink canvas lit. 4-Jun-4 Lempertz, Koln #426/R est:2500

SCHLEISNER, C A (1810-1882) Danish
£354 $574 €513 Fisherman in doorway smoking pipe (29x22cm-11x9in) init. 4-Aug-3 Rasmussen, Vejle #479 (D.KR 3700)
£473 $818 €691 Old man playing clarinet (29x22cm-11x9in) s. 9-Dec-3 Rasmussen, Copenhagen #1413/R (D.KR 5000)
£806 $1474 €1177 Kitchen interior with two children looking at a lobster (23x29cm-9x11in) s. 9-Jun-4 Rasmussen, Copenhagen #1736/R (D.KR 9000)
£895 $1638 €1307 Children taking shelter by boat on beach (41x53cm-16x21in) s.d.1854. 9-Jun-4 Rasmussen, Copenhagen #1802/R (D.KR 10000)

£898 $1553 €1311 Small boy going to be washed (29x22cm-11x9in) s. 9-Dec-3 Rasmussen, Copenhagen #1415/R (D.KR 9500)

SCHLEISNER, Christian Andreas (1810-1882) Danish
£1600 $2864 €2400 Children collecting wood (40x51cm-16x20in) s. lit. 14-May-4 Schloss Ahlden, Ahlden #2869/R est:1900
£2032 $3638 €2967 Old fisherman holding basket looking out to sea (94x76cm-37x30in) s.d.1863. 12-Jan-4 Rasmussen, Vejle #354/R est:20000-30000 (D.KR 21500)

SCHLEMMER, Oskar (1888-1943) German
£48951 $83217 €70000 Woman holding up her hand, small painting II (26x16cm-10x6in) s.i.d.1932 verso pencil nettle on board prov.exhib.lit. 28-Nov-3 Villa Grisebach, Berlin #662/R est:70000-90000
£116000 $213440 €174000 Red group, small painting IV (25x20cm-10x8in) s.i.d.1932 verso oil over pencil canvas on cardboard prov.exhib. 11-Jun-4 Villa Grisebach, Berlin #50/R est:90000-110000
£180000 $327600 €262800 Against one another (50x70cm-20x28in) s.i.d.1928 verso oil caparol spray paint linen on board prov.exhi. 21-Jun-4 Sotheby's, London #43/R est:200000-300000
Sculpture
£20000 $36800 €30000 Relief H (65x27cm-26x11in) aluminium exhib. 10-Jun-4 Hauswedell & Nolte, Hamburg #621/R est:45000
Works on paper
£2254 $3606 €3200 Figure in uniform with nude (11x8cm-4x3in) pen envelope. 19-Sep-3 Sigalas, Stuttgart #347/R est:3500
£14685 $24965 €21000 Three figures - diagonal and vertical (15x11cm-6x4in) i.d.636 col crayons pencil prov. 28-Nov-3 Villa Grisebach, Berlin #64/R est:10000-15000
£20000 $36800 €30000 Interior scene (14x21cm-6x8in) col gold silver pencil exec. c.1940 prov.exhib. 12-Jun-4 Villa Grisebach, Berlin #262/R est:18000-24000

SCHLEPPEGRELL, Walter (1891-?) German
£1325 $2411 €2000 Industry (85x68cm-33x27in) s.d.26. 18-Jun-4 Bolland & Marotz, Bremen #953/R est:2000

SCHLESINGER, Felix (1833-1910) German
£12500 $20375 €18000 Girl and boy in stable (36x40cm-14x16in) s. panel. 24-Sep-3 Neumeister, Munich #547/R est:20000
£13514 $23784 €20000 Two children playing with rabbits (28x37cm-11x15in) s. prov. 22-May-4 Lempertz, Koln #1601/R est:25000
Works on paper
£423 $756 €600 Children playing with rabbits in the woods (16x20cm-6x8in) s. pencil W/C lit. 8-Jan-4 Allgauer, Kempten #2150/R

SCHLESINGER, Felix (attrib) (1833-1910) German
£2066 $3740 €3016 Untitled - new bunny (17x27cm-7x11in) s. panel prov. 18-Apr-4 Levis, Calgary #213/R est:7000-9000 (C.D 5000)

SCHLESINGER, Henri-Guillaume (1814-1893) French
£5422 $9000 €7916 Two Sisters (155x117cm-61x46in) s. 4-Oct-3 Neal Auction Company, New Orleans #185 est:7500-10000
£9412 $16000 €13742 Afternoon stroll (81x65cm-32x26in) s.d.1872. 29-Oct-3 Christie's, Rockefeller NY #136/R est:18000-25000
£48000 $86400 €70080 Ce n'est pas moi (81x102cm-32x40in) s.d.1872 exhib. 21-Jan-4 Sotheby's, Olympia #442/R est:8000-12000

SCHLESINGER, Johann (1768-1848) German
£1667 $2617 €2400 Zentmeier children (35x28cm-14x11in) s.d.1825 i. verso three. 30-Aug-3 Hans Stahl, Toestorf #17/R est:1500

SCHLESINGER, Karl (1825-1893) Swiss
£2484 $4000 €3627 Family group in a hilly landscape praying before a meal (64x84cm-25x33in) s.d.1853 canvas on board. 17-Aug-3 Jeffery Burchard, Florida #80
£4000 $7280 €5840 Homeward bound (77x112cm-30x44in) s. i.d.1860. 16-Jun-4 Christie's, Kensington #19/R est:4000-6000

SCHLICHTEN, Jan Philipp van (attrib) (1681-1745) Dutch
£10067 $18523 €15000 Three Bavarian Palatine Princesses making music (41x52cm-16x20in) lit.prov. 24-Mar-4 Dorotheum, Vienna #239/R est:15000-18000

SCHLICHTER, Rudolf (1890-1955) German
Works on paper
£503 $841 €720 Miesing near Bayrischzell (36x47cm-14x19in) s. i. verso W/C over pencil. 10-Oct-3 Winterberg, Heidelberg #1947
£1053 $1937 €1600 White lilies (57x45cm-22x18in) s.d.1937 verso W/C ink pencil lit. 26-Jun-4 Karrenbauer, Konstanz #1760/R est:750
£1389 $2319 €2000 Composition (62x50cm-24x20in) s.d. i. verso W/C board. 25-Oct-3 Dr Lehr, Berlin #450/R est:3000
£1712 $2911 €2500 Drowning figure sees beauty (75x55cm-30x22in) s.i. WC. 8-Nov-3 Geble, Radolfzell #841/R est:2500
£8333 $13917 €12000 Indian and General (50x64cm-20x25in) s. W/C Indian ink brush figure study verso. 25-Oct-3 Dr Lehr, Berlin #447/R est:12000

SCHLICHTING CARLSEN, Carl (1852-1903) Danish
£271 $486 €396 Coastal landscape with rising sun (23x37cm-9x15in) s.d.1900 exhib. 10-May-4 Rasmussen, Vejle #178/R (D.KR 3000)
£373 $679 €560 Summer's day in the back garden (41x63cm-16x25in) s.d.89. 19-Jun-4 Rasmussen, Havnen #2048/R (D.KR 4200)
£403 $726 €588 Boy bringing cattle across bridge (34x52cm-13x20in) s.d.97. 24-Apr-4 Rasmussen, Havnen #2343/R (D.KR 4500)
£431 $698 €625 Wooded landscape with deer (42x88cm-17x35in) s.d.85. 4-Aug-3 Rasmussen, Vejle #337/R (D.KR 4500)
£562 $917 €821 Hanging out the washing (20x29cm-8x11in) s.d.83 panel. 27-Sep-3 Rasmussen, Havnen #2105 (D.KR 6000)

SCHLICHTING, Waldemar (1896-1970) German
£280 $439 €409 Breakers against the coast (61x81cm-24x32in) s. 30-Aug-3 Rasmussen, Havnen #2194/R (D.KR 3000)
£347 $549 €500 Dune beach in afternoon light (60x80cm-24x31in) s. 6-Sep-3 Arnold, Frankfurt #655/R
£1314 $2431 €1918 Ship in fishing village (55x80cm-22x31in) 14-Mar-4 Agra, Warsaw #31/R (P.Z 9500)

SCHLICHTKRULL, J C (1866-1945) Danish
£314 $565 €458 Couple of dogs in their basket (19x29cm-7x11in) mono. canvas on panel. 24-Apr-4 Rasmussen, Havnen #2185 (D.KR 3500)

SCHLIECKER, August Eduard (1833-1911) German
£1467 $2655 €2200 Wooded lake with fishing boats by moonlight (31x47cm-12x19in) s. canvas on panel. 3-Apr-4 Hans Stahl, Hamburg #78/R est:2300

SCHLIMARSKI, Heinrich Hans (1859-1913) Austrian
£1457 $2652 €2200 Young girl (32x23cm-13x9in) s. panel. 21-Jun-4 Dorotheum, Vienna #254/R est:2000-2300
£2308 $3969 €3370 Cleopatra (87x67cm-34x26in) s. 3-Dec-3 AB Stockholms Auktionsverk #2550/R est:15000-20000 (S.KR 30000)

SCHLOBACH, Willy (1865-1951) Belgian
£700 $1274 €1022 Fleurs en souvenir a l'aimable Madame Mohzien (42x37cm-17x15in) mono. s.i.verso board. 16-Jun-4 Christie's, Kensington #50/R
£921 $1695 €1400 Lake Constance landscape with church tower (80x110cm-31x43in) s.d.1947 panel. 25-Jun-4 Michael Zeller, Lindau #504/R
£1119 $1902 €1600 Paysage au crepuscule (25x38cm-10x15in) s.d.83 panel. 1-Dec-3 Palais de Beaux Arts, Brussels #124/R est:1200-1800

SCHLODERER, Otto (19/20th C) ?
£550 $995 €803 German short haired pointer on the scent (20x26cm-8x10in) s.i.d.1910 board. 31-Mar-4 Bonhams, Knightsbridge #25/R

SCHLOESSER, Carl (1832-1914) German
£1300 $2327 €1898 Tasting the soup (51x36cm-20x14in) s. 26-May-4 Sotheby's, Olympia #279/R est:1500-2000
£1793 $2995 €2600 En visite (60x83cm-24x33in) s.d.1867. 17-Nov-3 Tajan, Paris #126 est:2500-3000
£2083 $3542 €3000 Political discussion (65x57cm-26x22in) s.d.1879. 28-Oct-3 Christie's, Amsterdam #85/R est:3000-5000
£2907 $5000 €4244 Playing the piano (61x45cm-24x18in) s.d.1880 prov. 2-Dec-3 Christie's, Rockefeller NY #53/R est:6000-8000
£5500 $9185 €8030 Singing lesson (36x50cm-14x20in) s.d.1862. 12-Nov-3 Sotheby's, Olympia #195/R est:4000-6000

SCHLOESSER, Maud (fl.1895-1914) British
£300 $501 €438 Summer landscape (22x45cm-9x18in) s. 12-Nov-3 Sotheby's, Olympia #80/R

SCHLOGL, Josef von (1851-1913) Austrian
£350 $601 €500 Benedict wall on Walchensee (46x27cm-18x11in) s.d.1914 panel. 8-Dec-3 Bloss, Merzhausen #818/R
£1361 $2435 €2000 View from Benediktenwand of Walchensee (45x26cm-18x10in) s.d.1914 i. verso panel lit. 20-Mar-4 Bergmann, Erlangen #1081 est:1300-2000
£1408 $2437 €2000 The three pinnacles of Monte Pirano (41x59cm-16x23in) s.d.1911. 10-Dec-3 Dorotheum, Vienna #241/R est:2000-2500
£2098 $3566 €3000 Schloss Tyrol with view of Meran (49x38cm-19x15in) s.d. 21-Nov-3 Reiss & Sohn, Konigstein #27/R est:1200
£3311 $6060 €5000 Glacier in Tyrol (32x43cm-13x17in) s.d.1903 panel. 8-Apr-4 Dorotheum, Vienna #236/R est:5000-6000

SCHLOSS, Ruth (1922-) Israeli
£601 $1100 €877 Figures and donkeys (38x61cm-15x24in) s. 1-Jun-4 Ben-Ami, Tel Aviv #4890/R est:1200-1600
Works on paper
£335 $570 €489 Figures in the Maabara (48x68cm-19x27in) s. ink W/C gouache exec. 1950's. 1-Dec-3 Ben-Ami, Tel Aviv #4346/R

SCHLOSSER, Adolf (1939-) Austrian
Sculpture
£1351 $2378 €2000 Untitled - Pine grove in Bustarviejo (32x29x10cm-13x11x4in) s.d.1997 verso lead copper photograph collage prov. 18-May-4 Segre, Madrid #135/R est:1800

SCHLOSSER, Gerard (1931-) French
£3472 $5729 €5000 Avec blossom dearie (50x50cm-20x20in) s.i.d.1993 verso acrylic. 2-Jul-3 Cornette de St.Cyr, Paris #135/R est:4500-5000
£4333 $7973 €6500 Je n'irai pas demain (100x100cm-39x39in) s.i.d.Mai 74 verso acrylic. 10-Jun-4 Camard, Paris #190/R est:5000-6000
£4406 $7357 €6300 Je ne comprends pas (80x80cm-31x31in) s.i.d.1992 verso acrylic. 11-Oct-3 Cornette de St.Cyr, Paris #102/R est:5000-6000
£5369 $9611 €8000 J'ai envie de moules (113x146cm-44x57in) s.i.d.1965 verso acrylic prov.lit. 27-May-4 Sotheby's, Paris #273/R est:8000-12000
£5369 $9611 €8000 Tu dors (97x130cm-38x51in) s.i.d.1965 verso acrylic prov.lit. 27-May-4 Sotheby's, Paris #276/R est:8000-12000
£5944 $10105 €8500 Je n'ai jamais autant ri (150x150cm-59x59in) s.i.d.1978 verso acrylic prov. 25-Nov-3 Tajan, Paris #57/R est:6000-8000
£6294 $10510 €9000 Il est psychiatre (130x130cm-51x51in) s.i.d.1996 verso acrylic. 11-Oct-3 Cornette de St.Cyr, Paris #103/R est:7000-8000
£6867 $12497 €10300 C'est en face (80x80cm-31x31in) s.i.d.1997 verso. 5-Jul-4 Le Mouel, Paris #64/R est:6500-8000
£7383 $13215 €11000 Pousse-toi un peu (96x129cm-38x51in) s.i.d.1965 verso acrylic prov.lit. 27-May-4 Sotheby's, Paris #272/R est:10000-15000

£7692 $12846 €11000 Par moments (150x150cm-59x59in) s.i.d.1997-1998 verso acrylic. 11-Oct-3 Cornette de St.Cyr, Paris #97/R est:12000-15000
£8053 $14818 €12000 Je ne sais pais, je ne la vois plus (150x150cm-59x59in) s.i.d.1976 verso acrylic sanded canvas lit. 29-Mar-4 Cornette de St.Cyr, Paris #115/R est:10000-12000
£8054 $14416 €12000 C'est la meme (150x150cm-59x59in) s.i.d.1990 verso acrylic prov.lit. 27-May-4 Sotheby's, Paris #279/R est:12000-15000
£8725 $15617 €13000 Le bas (129x193cm-51x76in) s.i.d.66 verso prov.lit. 27-May-4 Sotheby's, Paris #267/R est:15000-20000
£9722 $16042 €14000 Un peau plus tard (120x120cm-47x47in) s.i.d.2000 verso acrylic. 2-Jul-3 Cornette de St.Cyr, Paris #136/R est:10000-15000
£10403 $19141 €15500 Cathedrale (85x60cm-33x24in) s.i.d.1966 verso acrylic sanded canvas lit. 29-Mar-4 Cornette de St.Cyr, Paris #77/R est:10000-12000
£10417 $17188 €15000 Ils ne sont pas marrants au bureau (100x100cm-39x39in) s.i.d.1975 verso acrylic. 2-Jul-3 Cornette de St.Cyr, Paris #133/R est:15000-18000
£13287 $22189 €19000 Au deuxieme acte (200x200cm-79x79in) s.i.d.1997 verso acrylic. 11-Oct-3 Cornette de St.Cyr, Paris #100/R est:15000-18000
£13889 $23194 €20000 Qu'est-ce que tu deviens (140x144cm-55x57in) s.id.1967 verso acrylic prov. 21-Oct-3 Artcurial Briest, Paris #559/R est:20000-25000
£14765 $27167 €22000 Ca fait trente ans (270x340cm-106x134in) s.i.d.1998 verso acrylic sanded canvas. 29-Mar-4 Cornette de St.Cyr, Paris #116/R est:20000-30000
£15625 $25781 €22500 Tu viens (130x161cm-51x63in) s.i.d.1966 verso acrylic prov.lit. 2-Jul-3 Cornette de St.Cyr, Paris #123/R est:25000-30000
£16779 $30034 €25000 Tu envoies les papiers a la securite sociale (163x130cm-64x51in) s.i.d.72 verso lit. 27-May-4 Sotheby's, Paris #268/R est:18000-25000
£24832 $45691 €37000 Tu sais que Josette va se Marier (200x200cm-79x79in) s.i.d.1970 verso acrylic sanded canvas lit. 29-Mar-4 Cornette de St.Cyr, Paris #80/R est:25000-30000
Works on paper
£342 $629 €520 Untitled (14x12cm-6x5in) s.d.68 mixed media after Cezanne. 24-Jun-4 Credit Municipal, Paris #24
£493 $853 €700 Untitled (19x19cm-7x7in) s.d.1969 gouache. 9-Dec-3 Arcurial Briest, Paris #542a/R
£1074 $1922 €1600 Untitled (12x25cm-5x10in) s.d.67 col crayon ink diptych prov. 27-May-4 Sotheby's, Paris #270/R est:800-1200

SCHLOTTER, Eberhard (1921-) German?
Works on paper
£336 $594 €500 Still life with fruit (26x30cm-10x12in) mono.d. W/C. 30-Apr-4 Dr Fritz Nagel, Stuttgart #435a/R
£503 $891 €750 Still life with aubergines AND NETS (45x120cm-18x47in) mono. mixed media oil sand. 30-Apr-4 Dr Fritz Nagel, Stuttgart #437/R
£1034 $1728 €1500 The big shadow (69x44cm-27x17in) mono.i.d.1954 mixed media. 13-Nov-3 Neumeister, Munich #624/R est:1200-1400
£1477 $2613 €2200 Southern town landscape in midday heat (71x86cm-28x34in) mono. s. verso mixed media oil sand. 30-Apr-4 Dr Fritz Nagel, Stuttgart #436/R est:1500

SCHLUMBERGER, Guillemette (1966-) French?
£1748 $2972 €2500 Apres l'effort 2000 (55x46cm-22x18in) s. oil tempera. 27-Nov-3 Calmels Cohen, Paris #90/R est:1000-1200

SCHLUTER, August (1858-1928) German
£537 $988 €800 Fishermen on Caniogli beach, Italy (71x100cm-28x39in) s.d.26 i. verso. 26-Mar-4 Bolland & Marotz, Bremen #586/R

SCHMAEDEL, Max von (1856-?) German
£3609 $6750 €5269 Lady with bird (117x58cm-46x23in) s. 29-Feb-4 Grogan, Boston #7/R

SCHMALIX, Hubert (1952-) Austrian
£979 $1664 €1400 Head (58x46cm-23x18in) s.d.1980 i. verso acrylic board. 26-Nov-3 Dorotheum, Vienna #310/R
£3356 $5940 €5000 Tenerife (79x55cm-31x22in) s.i.d. verso panel. 28-Apr-4 Wiener Kunst Auktionen, Vienna #312/R est:5000-10000
£4167 $7083 €6000 Untitled (120x120cm-47x47in) s.d.Mai 83 verso. 28-Oct-3 Wiener Kunst Auktionen, Vienna #280/R est:6000-9000
£7383 $13067 €11000 Hector Berlioz (200x200cm-79x79in) s.d. stretcher prov.exhib. 28-Apr-4 Wiener Kunst Auktionen, Vienna #289/R est:11000-20000
Sculpture
£3147 $5350 €4500 Jesus Christus (65cm-26in) pat bronze. 28-Nov-3 Wiener Kunst Auktionen, Vienna #674/R est:4500-9000
Works on paper
£345 $631 €500 Untitled (41x59cm-16x23in) mono. W/C gouache. 27-Jan-4 Dorotheum, Vienna #227/R
£524 $892 €750 Head and cross (63x48cm-25x19in) s.d.83 gouache. 26-Nov-3 Dorotheum, Vienna #307/R
£704 $1232 €1000 Untitled (64x88cm-25x35in) s.indis.d. verso gouache. 19-Dec-3 Dorotheum, Vienna #359/R
£1074 $1922 €1600 Untitled (75x56cm-30x22in) s.d.02 mixed media. 25-May-4 Dorotheum, Vienna #120/R est:1800-2500
£2148 $3844 €3200 Untitled (75x56cm-30x22in) s.d.02 mixed media. 25-May-4 Dorotheum, Vienna #121/R est:1800-2500
£2448 $4161 €3500 Untitled (102x82cm-40x32in) s.d.1983 gouache. 28-Nov-3 Wiener Kunst Auktionen, Vienna #677/R est:3500-6000

SCHMALZ, Herbert Gustave (1856-1935) British
£1374 $2500 €2006 Portrait of Robert Browning and Elizabeth Barrett (84x104cm-33x41in) s.i. 8-Feb-4 William Jenack, New York #240 est:2500
£12000 $21480 €17520 Quite corner of the garden (112x86cm-44x34in) s. 27-May-4 Christie's, Kensington #292/R est:4000-6000

SCHMALZIGAUG, Jules (1882-1917) Belgian
Works on paper
£1972 $3411 €2800 View of beach in Schevening (30x39cm-12x15in) s. pastel prov. 13-Dec-3 De Vuyst, Lokeren #557/R est:2800-3500

SCHMAUK, Carl (1868-1947) German
£692 $1279 €1010 Peasants on woodland path (60x58cm-24x23in) 14-Mar-4 Agra, Warsaw #4/R (P.Z 5000)

SCHMELCHER, Herbert (20th C) German
£303 $557 €460 Landscape (40x50cm-16x20in) s.d.84. 25-Jun-4 Michael Zeller, Lindau #666

SCHMELTZ, Bruno (1943-) French
£428 $774 €650 La Place de la Concorde (50x150cm-20x59in) s. 18-Apr-4 Rouillac, Vendome #170
£461 $834 €700 Paris, Pyramide V (80x40cm-31x16in) s.d.1990. 18-Apr-4 Rouillac, Vendome #168
£592 $1072 €900 La defense II (65x81cm-26x32in) s.d.1989. 18-Apr-4 Rouillac, Vendome #167
£1250 $2263 €1900 Deux hommes et une femme (175x114cm-69x45in) s.d.1985. 18-Apr-4 Rouillac, Vendome #169
£2721 $4871 €4000 Dali (80x120cm-31x47in) 19-Mar-4 Millon & Associes, Paris #215b est:800-1000

SCHMID, David Alois (1791-1861) Swiss
Works on paper
£1310 $2384 €1913 House belonging to Niklaus von der Flue (11x14cm-4x6in) s. exec. c.1833 W/C pencil. 16-Jun-4 Fischer, Luzern #2904/R est:1500-1800 (S.FR 3000)

SCHMID, David Alois (attrib) (1791-1861) Swiss
Works on paper
£181 $308 €264 Girl in Swiss national costume (38x57cm-15x22in) i. W/C over pencil. 28-Nov-3 Falk & Falk, Zurich #356 (S.FR 400)
£345 $617 €504 Swiss costumes (17x52cm-7x20in) W/C over pencil. 12-May-4 Dobiaschofsky, Bern #1328/R (S.FR 800)

SCHMID, Henri (1924-) Swiss
£437 $803 €638 Female nude (69x56cm-27x22in) s.d. 14-Jun-4 Philippe Schuler, Zurich #4235 (S.FR 1000)
£586 $1007 €856 Interior scene with anemones (81x45cm-32x18in) 8-Dec-3 Philippe Schuler, Zurich #3358 (S.FR 1300)
£780 $1302 €1131 River landscape in evening (81x100cm-32x39in) s. 23-Jun-3 Philippe Schuler, Zurich #3423/R (S.FR 1700)
£873 $1607 €1275 Still life of flowers (100x115cm-39x45in) s.d.1969. 8-Jun-4 Germann, Zurich #877 (S.FR 2000)
£995 $1662 €1453 Shore (77x81cm-30x32in) s.d.1970. 24-Jun-3 Germann, Zurich #155/R (S.FR 2200)
£1357 $2267 €1981 The circus has arrived (73x115cm-29x45in) s.d.1970. 24-Jun-3 Germann, Zurich #156 est:3000-4000 (S.FR 3000)

SCHMID, Konrad (1899-1958) Swiss
£550 $919 €798 Theatre foyer (81x66cm-32x26in) s. 23-Jun-3 Philippe Schuler, Zurich #8465 (S.FR 1200)

SCHMID, Kurt (1917-1985) German
£805 $1490 €1200 Millstattersee (61x91cm-24x36in) masonite. 9-Mar-4 Dorotheum, Vienna #119

SCHMID, Mathias (1835-1923) Austrian
£2300 $4186 €3358 Town house, Foldkirch (61x34cm-24x13in) s.i. 16-Jun-4 Christie's, Kensington #185/R est:1500-2000
£5034 $9262 €7500 Boy and girl in high mountain pasture (25x32cm-10x13in) s.i.d.1889. 24-Mar-4 Hugo Ruef, Munich #1114/R est:800
£12414 $20731 €18000 Alpine conference (92x83cm-36x33in) s. i. verso. 9-Jul-3 Hugo Ruef, Munich #208/R est:1200

SCHMID, Mathias (attrib) (1835-1923) Austrian
£328 $547 €479 Figure in a doorway (61x34cm-24x13in) s.i.d.1872. 20-Oct-3 Stephan Welz, Johannesburg #439 est:1000-1500 (SA.R 3800)

SCHMID, Richard (1934-) American
£2118 $3600 €3092 Manhattan Street scene near Penn Station (30x51cm-12x20in) with sig.i. masonite painted c.1964. 22-Nov-3 Jackson's, Cedar Falls #82/R est:3500-4500
£2941 $5000 €4294 Nude (38x28cm-15x11in) s. i.d.1963 verso masonite. 22-Nov-3 Jackson's, Cedar Falls #81/R est:5000-7500
£4469 $8000 €6525 Spring morning in Gaylordsville (18x24cm-7x9in) s. s.i.d.1964 linen prov. 6-May-4 Shannon's, Milford #99/R est:10000-15000
£5587 $10000 €8157 Manhattan street near Penn Station (30x51cm-12x20in) board. 15-May-4 Altermann Galleries, Santa Fe #152/R
£14118 $24000 €20612 Michelle (61x91cm-24x36in) 1-Nov-3 Altermann Galleries, Santa Fe #194
Works on paper
£2353 $4000 €3435 Figure of a girl (61x46cm-24x18in) chl. 1-Nov-3 Altermann Galleries, Santa Fe #195

SCHMID, Wilhelm (1892-1971) Swiss
£346 $620 €505 Still life with white pot (13x10cm-5x4in) s. panel. 22-Mar-4 Philippe Schuler, Zurich #6045 (S.FR 800)
£362 $615 €529 Still life of fruit (16x22cm-6x9in) prov. 28-Nov-3 Zofingen, Switzerland #3168 (S.FR 800)
£381 $682 €556 La masque (22x15cm-9x6in) s. i. verso panel. 22-Mar-4 Philippe Schuler, Zurich #6044 (S.FR 880)
£917 $1532 €1330 Sated figure (59x49cm-23x19in) s. board on masonite. 23-Jun-3 Philippe Schuler, Zurich #3424 (S.FR 2000)
£4414 $7593 €6444 Southern landscape with small town (54x65cm-21x26in) s. 8-Dec-3 Philippe Schuler, Zurich #3359 est:2500-3500 (S.FR 9800)
Works on paper
£339 $577 €495 Mountain village (29x39cm-11x15in) s. gouache. 28-Nov-3 Zofingen, Switzerland #3164 (S.FR 750)

SCHMIDT, Albert (1883-1970) Swiss
£214 $400 €312 Bridge bathed in sun (25x33cm-10x13in) bears sig. board. 25-Feb-4 Doyle, New York #64/R
£1293 $2315 €1888 Winter in the mountains (48x5cm-19x2in) s. panel. 14-May-4 Dobiaschofsky, Bern #152/R est:3600 (S.FR 3000)
£1674 $2846 €2444 Three standing female nudes (65x54cm-26x21in) s. 7-Nov-3 Dobiaschofsky, Bern #133/R est:4800 (S.FR 3800)

SCHMIDT, Alexander (1842-1903) Danish
£777 $1244 €1134 Danish landscape with view of fjord, boy and girl in foreground (42x52cm-17x20in) s.d.75. 22-Sep-3 Rasmussen, Vejle #335/R (D.KR 8200)

SCHMIDT, Alfred (1867-?) German
£278 $453 €400 Chiemsee with Fraueninsel (26x41cm-10x16in) s. board. 27-Sep-3 Dr Fritz Nagel, Stuttgart #9346/R

SCHMIDT, Allan (1923-1989) Danish
£379 $697 €553 Composition (98x57cm-39x22in) init. init.d.60 verso. 29-Mar-4 Rasmussen, Copenhagen #359 (D.KR 4200)
£406 $747 €593 I variation - red and yellow composition (73x62cm-29x24in) init. s.d.1962 verso prov. 29-Mar-4 Rasmussen, Copenhagen #361/R (D.KR 4500)

SCHMIDT, Alwin (1900-) American?
Works on paper
£535 $1000 €781 Street scene with ice wagon (43x43cm-17x17in) s. W/C. 26-Feb-4 Illustration House, New York #154

SCHMIDT, Bernhard (1820-1870) Swiss
£1528 $2414 €2200 View of the village of Hohen Demzin, Mecklenburg Vopommern, Germany (40x64cm-16x25in) s. 2-Sep-3 Christie's, Amsterdam #176/R est:1200-1600

SCHMIDT, Carl (1885-1969) American
£1524 $2500 €2210 Covered wagon (16x20cm-6x8in) s. canvasboard painted c.1930. 7-Jun-3 Treadway Gallery, Cincinnati #1469 est:1500-2000

SCHMIDT, Christian (1835-?) German
£2545 $4250 €3716 Still life with beer (41x44cm-16x17in) s. canvas on panel prov. 7-Oct-3 Sotheby's, New York #69/R est:4000-6000

SCHMIDT, Eduard (1806-1862) German
£2907 $5000 €4244 Coastal city (69x96cm-27x38in) s. 3-Dec-3 Doyle, New York #106/R est:10000-15000

SCHMIDT, F (?) ?
£1167 $2123 €1750 Landscape with a view of the village and the train (35x50cm-14x20in) s.d.1849. 1-Jul-4 Weidler, Nurnberg #321/R
£2155 $3858 €3146 City with river (60x67cm-24x26in) s.d.1850. 12-May-4 Dobiaschofsky, Bern #940/R est:4900 (S.FR 5000)

SCHMIDT, Franz (19/20th C) ?
Works on paper
£280 $467 €400 Pegnitz (17x23cm-7x9in) s. 26-Jun-3 Weidler, Nurnberg #7038
£350 $584 €500 Sinwell tower (22x16cm-9x6in) s. 26-Jun-3 Weidler, Nurnberg #7017/R

SCHMIDT, Frederic Albert (1846-1916) German
£563 $907 €800 Stormy evening - Italian landscape (80x60cm-31x24in) s. 22-Aug-3 Altus, Berlin #550/R
£1622 $2903 €2400 View of Cap von Noli between olive trees (80x100cm-31x39in) s. i. verso. 6-May-4 Michael Zeller, Lindau #858/R est:1800

SCHMIDT, Friedrich Georg (fl.1857-1881) German
Works on paper
£50000 $77500 €73000 Skizzen aus dem Osten (10x32cm-4x13in) W/C album. 26-Sep-2 Christie's, London #92/R est:60000-80000

SCHMIDT, Georg Adam (1791-1844) Dutch
£5000 $8950 €7500 Farm interior (70x93cm-28x37in) s. panel prov. 17-May-4 Glerum, Amsterdam #25/R est:4000-6000

SCHMIDT, George (1944-) American
£964 $1600 €1407 Closer walk with Pete (51x51cm-20x20in) s. painted c.1970 prov. 4-Oct-3 Neal Auction Company, New Orleans #1150/R est:2500-3500

SCHMIDT, Hamborg (20th C) American
£2038 $3750 €3057 Steamship in ice field (46x61cm-18x24in) painted 1888. 28-Mar-4 Carlsen Gallery, Greenville #369/R

SCHMIDT, Hans (1877-?) German
£405 $726 €600 Two pheasants (30x50cm-12x20in) s. panel lit. 8-May-4 Sebok, Bamberg #1767/R
£524 $876 €750 Two carthorses drinking from trough (58x41cm-23x16in) s. 28-Jun-3 Dannenberg, Berlin #773/R

SCHMIDT, Harold von (1893-1982) American
£1294 $2200 €1889 Celebration, West Townsend (71x81cm-28x32in) 1-Nov-3 Altermann Galleries, Santa Fe #49
£1453 $2600 €2121 Man and gorilla confronting each other (89x71cm-35x28in) s. 15-May-4 Illustration House, New York #36/R est:3000-6000

SCHMIDT, Izaak (1740-1818) Dutch
Works on paper
£800 $1432 €1200 River landscape with herdsman and cattle (16x22cm-6x9in) s. W/C. 13-May-4 Bassenge, Berlin #5477/R

SCHMIDT, Jay (1929-) American
£1242 $2000 €1801 Always problems (61x91cm-24x36in) board. 22-Aug-3 Altermann Galleries, Santa Fe #98

SCHMIDT, Johann Martin (1718-1801) German
£9396 $16631 €14000 St Magdalen, Joseph and Infant Jesus (40x33cm-16x13in) copper. 28-Apr-4 Wiener Kunst Auktionen, Vienna #2/R est:7000-12000
£13986 $23776 €20000 Pieta (42x30cm-17x12in) zinc. 20-Nov-3 Dorotheum, Salzburg #17/R est:22000-30000

SCHMIDT, Johann Martin (attrib) (1718-1801) German
£1192 $2170 €1800 Virgin Immaculate with an angel and the Holy Spirit in front of a glove (40x32cm-16x13in) prov. 16-Jun-4 Dorotheum, Vienna #425/R est:900-1200

SCHMIDT, Karl (1890-1962) American
£1875 $3000 €2738 California landscape, the poppies. s.d.1916 board. 20-Sep-3 Harvey Clar, Oakland #1542
£6936 $12000 €10127 Dramatic California sunset (22x45cm-9x18in) s.d.1928 board triptych prov. 10-Dec-3 Bonhams & Butterfields, San Francisco #6191/R est:4000-6000
Works on paper
£500 $850 €730 Eucalyptus landscape (23x30cm-9x12in) s. gouache prov. 18-Nov-3 John Moran, Pasadena #4
£1445 $2500 €2110 Orange rocks and crashing waves. Seascape (23x30cm-9x12in) s. W/C gouache pair prov. 10-Dec-3 Bonhams & Butterfields, San Francisco #6306/R est:3000-5000

SCHMIDT, Kurt (1901-) German
£439 $773 €650 Worthersee (100x100cm-39x39in) mono.d.65 panel. 19-May-4 Dorotheum, Klagenfurt #23/R
£524 $892 €750 Worthersee with Schrotenturm and Mittagskogel (80x100cm-31x39in) mono.d.64 panel. 19-Nov-3 Dorotheum, Klagenfurt #30
£903 $1508 €1300 Glass picture (28x38cm-11x15in) s.d. verso tempera glass on panel. 25-Oct-3 Dr Lehr, Berlin #453/R
Works on paper
£1200 $2148 €1800 Geometric composition (19x16cm-7x6in) s.d. gouache over pencil board prov. 14-May-4 Ketterer, Munich #423/R est:2000-2200

SCHMIDT, Lucien Louis J B (1825-1891) French
£867 $1595 €1300 Trophees (70x59cm-28x23in) s.d.1875 pair. 9-Jun-4 Beaussant & Lefèvre, Paris #213/R

SCHMIDT, Ludwig (1816-1906) German
£464 $844 €700 Country landscape with farmers in foreground, lake and mountains (28x37cm-11x15in) s. 17-Jun-4 Frank Peege, Freiburg #1080/R

SCHMIDT, Mary Jane (20th C) American
£261 $425 €381 Night hawk (163x117cm-64x46in) s. acrylic diptych. 19-Jul-3 Susanin's, Chicago #5013

SCHMIDT, Max (1818-1901) German
£2083 $3396 €3000 Italian mountain landscape with cow herder (70x94cm-28x37in) s. 26-Sep-3 Bolland & Marotz, Bremen #610/R est:3000
£2113 $3655 €3000 Looking out over the Ostsee (84x116cm-33x46in) s. 10-Dec-3 Christie's, Amsterdam #680/R est:3000-5000

SCHMIDT, Oskar (1825-1871) German
£1041 $1697 €1500 The alchemist (17x12cm-7x5in) s. panel. 29-Sep-3 Sotheby's, Amsterdam #26/R

SCHMIDT, Paul (1912-) Swiss
£280 $502 €409 Untitled (71x57cm-28x22in) s.d.1968. 12-May-4 Dobiaschofsky, Bern #943/R (S.FR 650)

SCHMIDT, Reinhold (1861-?) German
£833 $1317 €1200 Showing off the hunting bounty (109x221cm-43x87in) s.d.1914. 5-Sep-3 Wendl, Rudolstadt #3605/R

SCHMIDT, Rosa (1888-?) Italian
£280 $467 €400 Roses in green jug (41x34cm-16x13in) s. board. 28-Jun-3 Bolland & Marotz, Bremen #796/R
£280 $467 €400 Wild roses in green vase (44x33cm-17x13in) canvas on board. 28-Jun-3 Bolland & Marotz, Bremen #797/R

SCHMIDT, Rudolf (1873-1963) Austrian
Works on paper
£336 $617 €500 Freyng (14x15cm-6x6in) s.i. W/C. 26-Mar-4 Dorotheum, Vienna #247
£403 $741 €600 Flower market (13x16cm-5x6in) s. W/C. 26-Mar-4 Dorotheum, Vienna #248
£470 $864 €700 Market in square (12x16cm-5x6in) s. W/C. 26-Mar-4 Dorotheum, Vienna #281/R

£470 $864 €700 Albertinarampe and Philippshof (13x17cm-5x7in) s. W/C. 26-Mar-4 Dorotheum, Vienna #269/R
£621 $1030 €900 Karlsplatz (12x14cm-5x6in) s. W/C. 30-Sep-3 Dorotheum, Vienna #304/R
£900 $1620 €1314 Stuttgart, figures on a pavement with buildings nearby (11x16cm-4x6in) s. i.verso pencil W/C. 21-Apr-4 Tennants, Leyburn #960/R

SCHMIDT, Theodor (1855-?) German
£2128 $3447 €3000 The new dress (17x13cm-7x5in) s.d.1887 panel lit. 23-May-3 Karlheinz Kaupp, Staufen #1768/R est:1500

SCHMIDT, Tim (20th C) American?
£824 $1400 €1203 Watering hole (36x46cm-14x18in) s. canvas on masonite panel prov. 1-Nov-3 Santa Fe Art, Santa Fe #18/R est:2000-3000

SCHMIDT-CASSEL, Gustav (1867-?) German
Sculpture
£1074 $1976 €1600 Woman with flower (48cm-19in) s.d.09. 24-Mar-4 Hugo Ruef, Munich #1656/R est:450

SCHMIDT-HAMBURG, Robert (1885-1963) German
£400 $716 €600 The Bremen (48x36cm-19x14in) s.i. tempera lit. 14-May-4 Schloss Ahlden, Ahlden #2932/R
£940 $1729 €1400 The bark, Gorch Fock in full sail (26x33cm-10x13in) s.i. tempera board prov. 26-Mar-4 Ketterer, Hamburg #42/R
£1074 $1976 €1600 Seydlitz in the North Sea (29x40cm-11x16in) s. tempera board prov. 26-Mar-4 Ketterer, Hamburg #43/R est:1400-1600
£1736 $2899 €2500 Fully rigged sailing ship off coast (68x98cm-27x39in) s.i. 24-Oct-3 Ketterer, Hamburg #34/R est:3000-3500
£2098 $3608 €3000 Steamship Rio Brava in the sunlight on the open sea (71x100cm-28x39in) s. lit. 6-Dec-3 Hans Stahl, Toestorf #142 est:3300
Works on paper
£347 $549 €500 Karl Christian - ship's portrait (27x38cm-11x15in) s. gouache. 6-Sep-3 Schopman, Hamburg #864/R

SCHMIDT-HOFER, Otto (19/20th C) German
Sculpture
£1563 $2609 €2282 Panther (30x82cm-12x32in) s. pat bronze exec.c.1920. 19-Oct-3 Agra, Warsaw #37/R est:10000 (P.Z 10000)

SCHMIDT-KESTNER, Erich (1877-?) German
Sculpture
£3500 $6300 €5110 Amazon with a horse (32cm-13in) s.st.f.Aktien Gesellschaft brown pat bronze sold with socle. 21-Apr-4 Sotheby's, London #152/R est:3500-4500

SCHMIDT-KIRSTEIN, Helmut (1909-1985) German
£738 $1358 €1100 Composition (74x43cm-29x17in) s.d.56 s.d.1949 stretcher hessian. 26-Mar-4 Ketterer, Hamburg #633/R

SCHMIDT-NIECHCIOL, Arnold (1893-1960) German
Works on paper
£333 $597 €500 Woman's portrait (49x33cm-19x13in) mono.d. W/C. 15-May-4 Dr Sturies, Dusseldorf #190/R

SCHMIDT-ROTTLUFF, Karl (1884-1976) German
£27972 $47552 €40000 Nude (39x25cm-15x10in) s.d.1909 woodcut prov. 28-Nov-3 Villa Grisebach, Berlin #19/R est:12000-15000
£56667 $104267 €85000 Landscape with poplar (77x123cm-30x48in) s. s.i.verso masonite prov.exhib. 11-Jun-4 Villa Grisebach, Berlin #58/R est:90000-120000
£111888 $190210 €160000 Winter landsape in Erzgerbirge (76x112cm-30x44in) s.i. prov.exhib. 28-Nov-3 Villa Grisebach, Berlin #75/R est:160000-200000
£720000 $1317600 €1051200 Leuchtturm an der Ostsee (77x90cm-30x35in) s.d.1913 prov.exhib.lit. 2-Feb-4 Christie's, London #29/R est:450000-650000
Prints
£360 $590 €500 Four fishermen at tavern table (39x49cm-15x19in) woodcut. 3-Jun-3 Sigalas, Stuttgart #520/R
£2000 $3660 €3000 Russian houses (40x50cm-16x20in) s.i. woodcut. 5-Jun-4 Lempertz, Koln #986/R est:2500
£2215 $4075 €3300 Christ amongst the women (40x50cm-16x20in) s.i. woodcut. 26-Mar-4 Ketterer, Hamburg #635/R est:3000-3500
£2400 $4392 €3600 St Francis (60x49cm-24x19in) s.i. woodcut. 5-Jun-4 Lempertz, Koln #987/R est:3000
£2400 $4392 €3600 Little prophetess (118x12cm-46x5in) woodcut. 5-Jun-4 Lempertz, Koln #989/R est:3200
£2800 $5152 €4200 Sisters (40x49cm-16x19in) s. woodcut exec. 1914. 11-Jun-4 Villa Grisebach, Berlin #1537/R est:5000-7000
£3334 $5967 €5000 Emmaus (29x36cm-11x14in) s.i.d. woodcut. 14-May-4 Ketterer, Munich #133/R est:4500-5500
£3352 $6000 €4894 Frauenkopf (17x24cm-7x9in) s.d.1916 woodcut. 6-May-4 Swann Galleries, New York #575/R est:8000-12000
£3472 $5799 €5000 Life story (49x60cm-19x24in) s.i. woodcut. 24-Oct-3 Ketterer, Hamburg #535/R est:5000-6000
£3672 $6500 €5361 Katzen (40x50cm-16x20in) woodcut laid on board. 28-Apr-4 Christie's, Rockefeller NY #238/R est:4000-6000
£3846 $6423 €5500 Youth (50x40cm-20x16in) s. woodcut. 10-Oct-3 Winterberg, Heidelberg #1956/R est:2800
£4333 $7973 €6500 Sunshine (39x49cm-15x19in) s.i. woodcut exec. 1914. 11-Jun-4 Villa Grisebach, Berlin #1538/R est:4000-6000
£4545 $7727 €6500 Sisters (40x50cm-16x20in) s. woodcut. 26-Nov-3 Lempertz, Koln #974/R est:7000-9000
£4895 $8322 €7000 Prophet (50x39cm-20x15in) s. woodcut. 29-Nov-3 Villa Grisebach, Berlin #162/R est:7000-9000
£5000 $9200 €7500 Girl leaning back on hands (23x31cm-9x12in) s.d.1911 woodcut. 10-Jun-4 Hauswedell & Nolte, Hamburg #629/R est:10000
£5022 $9140 €7332 Mourners on the beach. s.i. woodcut. 17-Jun-4 Kornfeld, Bern #736/R est:12500 (S.FR 11500)
£5315 $9141 €7600 Dunes with houses and boats (29x34cm-11x13in) s. col woodcut. 2-Dec-3 Hauswedell & Nolte, Hamburg #611/R est:10000
£5459 $9934 €7970 Memel. s.i. woodcut. 17-Jun-4 Kornfeld, Bern #737/R est:15000 (S.FR 12500)
£5594 $9510 €8000 Moses (44x27cm-17x11in) s. woodcut. 29-Nov-3 Villa Grisebach, Berlin #188/R est:8000-10000
£6000 $11040 €9000 Crouching girl (29x20cm-11x8in) s. lithograph. 10-Jun-4 Hauswedell & Nolte, Hamburg #626/R est:10000
£6294 $10699 €9000 Female prophet (50x40cm-20x16in) s. woodcut. 26-Nov-3 Lempertz, Koln #975/R est:6000-8000
£6667 $12267 €10000 Mourning on the beach (39x50cm-15x20in) s. woodcut. 10-Jun-4 Hauswedell & Nolte, Hamburg #634/R est:10000
£7667 $14107 €11500 Nudes (30x40cm-12x16in) s.d.1912 woodcut. 10-Jun-4 Hauswedell & Nolte, Hamburg #630/R est:14000
£9667 $17787 €14500 Girl (34x40cm-13x16in) s.i.d.1911 lithograph. 10-Jun-4 Hauswedell & Nolte, Hamburg #625/R est:18000
£9790 $16643 €14000 Melancholy (50x39cm-20x15in) s.i. woodcut. 26-Nov-3 Lempertz, Koln #973/R est:14000
£10667 $19627 €16000 Girl with a tambourine (29x20cm-11x8in) s.d.71 woodcut. 12-Jun-4 Villa Grisebach, Berlin #201/R est:16000-18000
£11189 $19021 €16000 Kneeling figure (50x39cm-20x15in) s. woodcut. 26-Nov-3 Lempertz, Koln #971/R est:8000-10000
£12587 $21399 €18000 Dusk (39x50cm-15x20in) s. woodcut prov. 28-Nov-3 Villa Grisebach, Berlin #25/R est:18000-24000
£13333 $24533 €20000 Two nudes (39x50cm-15x20in) s.d.1914 woodcut. 10-Jun-4 Hauswedell & Nolte, Hamburg #633/R est:15000
£34965 $59441 €50000 Couple near forest (29x39cm-11x15in) s.d.1909 woodcut prov. 28-Nov-3 Villa Grisebach, Berlin #18/R est:15000-20000
Works on paper
£2133 $3819 €3200 Still life with flowers in vase and bottle (40x54cm-16x21in) s.i.d. Indian ink brush. 13-May-4 Neumeister, Munich #484/R est:3500-4000
£2454 $4000 €3583 Blumenstrauss (66x50cm-26x20in) s. gouache brush Indian ink gray wash chk col wax crayon exhib. 25-Sep-3 Christie's, Rockefeller NY #617/R est:6000-8000
£2837 $4738 €4000 Cloudy skies over Leba See (26x40cm-10x16in) s. col chk over Indian ink brush. 17-Oct-3 Behringer, Furth #1983/R est:5000
£4667 $8587 €7000 Reeds at the water's edge (27x39cm-11x15in) s. ink col chk exec. c.1940 prov. 12-Jun-4 Villa Grisebach, Berlin #303/R est:7000-9000
£6667 $12000 €10000 Buddleia (70x50cm-28x20in) i. W/C Indian ink brush board. 24-Apr-4 Dr Lehr, Berlin #422/R est:15000
£8297 $15100 €12114 Coastline near Jershoft (10x15cm-4x6in) mono. W/C Indian ink. 17-Jun-4 Kornfeld, Bern #735/R est:12500 (S.FR 19000)
£8734 $15895 €12752 Two crouching female nudes (33x41cm-13x16in) s.d.1912 chk. 17-Jun-4 Kornfeld, Bern #734/R est:22500 (S.FR 20000)
£10490 $17832 €15000 Landscape with blue house (39x54cm-15x21in) s. Indian ink brush W/C. 29-Nov-3 Villa Grisebach, Berlin #225/R est:18000-24000
£13333 $24533 €20000 Sunlit woodland scene (49x45cm-19x18in) s. s.i.verso W/C ink exec. after 1945. 12-Jun-4 Villa Grisebach, Berlin #207/R est:14000-18000
£14685 $24965 €21000 Still life of flowers (54x40cm-21x16in) s.i. col chk Indian ink brush prov. 29-Nov-3 Villa Grisebach, Berlin #242/R est:12000-15000
£15385 $26462 €22000 Trees in garden (50x70cm-20x28in) s. W/C. 2-Dec-3 Hauswedell & Nolte, Hamburg #603/R est:28000
£17333 $31893 €26000 Still life with bottles and jugs (68x49cm-27x19in) s. ink W/C exec. c.1940-50 prov. 12-Jun-4 Villa Grisebach, Berlin #220/R est:25000-35000
£18182 $31273 €26000 Garden gate (70x52cm-28x20in) s. i.verso W/C black Indian ink prov. 5-Dec-3 Ketterer, Munich #88/R est:25000-30000
£19000 $34960 €27740 Still life of flowers (50x70cm-20x28in) s. W/C exec.1961 prov. 22-Jun-4 Sotheby's, London #504/R est:7000-9000
£20000 $36400 €29200 Strasse mit schuppen und baumen - Street with sheds and trees (42x34cm-17x13in) s.d.1918 i.verso gouache W/C over pencil prov. 4-Feb-4 Sotheby's, London #542/R est:20000-30000
£20000 $36800 €30000 Lakeside reeds (50x68cm-20x27in) s.i. W/C ink exec. 1934 prov. 12-Jun-4 Villa Grisebach, Berlin #307/R est:30000-40000
£21333 $39253 €32000 Cypressesin Brissago (50x68cm-20x27in) s. i.verso W/C gouache India ink brush prov. 11-Jun-4 Villa Grisebach, Berlin #52/R est:30000-40000
£24476 $41608 €35000 Farmhouse in moonlight (51x70cm-20x28in) s.i. W/C prov.exhib.lit. 28-Nov-3 Villa Grisebach, Berlin #43/R est:40000-50000
£33333 $61333 €50000 Water lilies I (51x69cm-20x27in) s. i.verso W/C India ink brush prov. 11-Jun-4 Villa Grisebach, Berlin #53/R est:50000-60000
£34965 $60140 €50000 Landscape with two trees and farmsteads (46x66cm-18x26in) s.d.1911 s.d. verso W/C carpenter's pencil. 2-Dec-3 Hauswedell & Nolte, Hamburg #601/R est:50000
£39161 $67357 €56000 Water lilies II (48x64cm-19x25in) s. i.verso W/C exec.1946. 4-Dec-3 Van Ham, Cologne #455/R est:60000
£47486 $85000 €69330 Landscape with seated figure (50x69cm-20x27in) s. W/C prov.exhib. 6-May-4 Sotheby's, New York #323/R est:50000-70000

SCHMIDT-UPHOFF, Hans Erich (1911-2002) German?
£333 $600 €500 Still life on table with wine (82x62cm-32x24in) board. 24-Apr-4 Dr Lehr, Berlin #423/R
£382 $638 €550 Pott - portrait of a clown (35x25cm-14x10in) s.i.d.23.12.49 board. 25-Oct-3 Dr Lehr, Berlin #465/R

SCHMIDT-WEHRLIN, Emile (19/20th C) ?
£1200 $2184 €1800 View of Antibes (55x46cm-22x18in) s.i. 4-Jul-4 Eric Pillon, Calais #152/R

SCHMIDTMANN, Hermann (1869-1936) German
£514 $873 €750 Fishing on Adriatic coast (45x65cm-18x26in) s. 8-Nov-3 Hans Stahl, Toestorf #38/R
£1176 $1834 €1717 Picking herbs in the fields (60x80cm-24x31in) s. 30-Mar-3 Agra, Warsaw #42/R est:7000 (P.Z 7500)

SCHMIECHEN, Hermann (1855-?) German
£1667 $2833 €2400 Greek coast in the evening (91x130cm-36x51in) s. i. verso. 28-Oct-3 Dorotheum, Vienna #222/R est:2800-3400

SCHMIEGELOW, Pedro Ernst Johann (1863-1943) German
£280 $476 €400 Entrance to a park (34x49cm-13x19in) s. tempera oil mixed media board. 28-Nov-3 Wendl, Rudolstadt #4176/R
£633 $1140 €950 Farmstead in the Rhon (43x64cm-17x25in) s. 26-Apr-4 Rieber, Stuttgart #837/R

£903	$1472	€1300	Sunset on the Nile at Assuan (44x69cm-17x27in) s.d.1914 canvas on board. 26-Sep-3 Bolland & Marotz, Bremen #611/R est:850

SCHMITERLOW, Bertram (1920-2002) Swedish

£8308	$14124	€12130	Figure scene (100x110cm-39x43in) s. lit. 5-Nov-3 AB Stockholms Auktionsverk #876/R est:50000-60000 (S.KR 110000)
£13187	$23341	€19253	The eye (62x77cm-24x30in) s.i. painted 1995 exhib.lit. 27-Apr-4 AB Stockholms Auktionsverk #803/R est:60000-80000 (S.KR 180000)

SCHMITT, David (18th C) ?

£3500	$5950	€5110	Elegant riders resting beside a fountain. Riders taking refreshments (42x51cm-17x20in) s. panel pair. 29-Oct-3 Bonhams, New Bond Street #93/R est:3000-5000

SCHMITT, L (19th C) German

£1096	$1863	€1600	Berchtesgaden (28x40cm-11x16in) s.d.1873. 5-Nov-3 Hugo Ruef, Munich #1120/R est:1500

SCHMITT, Nathanael (1847-1918) German

£420	$701	€600	Clouds over water (31x28cm-12x11in) s. panel. 10-Oct-3 Winterberg, Heidelberg #763/R
£650	$1086	€949	Prayer of thanks (35x28cm-14x11in) s. 8-Oct-3 Christie's, Kensington #702/R

SCHMITT, Robert (1924-1990) Austrian

£5369	$9503	€8000	Seated nude in chair (100x80cm-39x31in) mono.d. exhib.lit. 28-Apr-4 Wiener Kunst Auktionen, Vienna #218/R est:8000-10000

SCHMITZ, Anton (1855-?) German

£1467	$2669	€2200	Stag roaring (33x44cm-13x17in) s.i.d.02 canvas on masonite. 30-Jun-4 Neumeister, Munich #673/R

SCHMITZ, C T (?) ?

£1050	$1649	€1523	Fisherfolk at a fjord village (92x128cm-36x50in) s. 28-Aug-3 Christie's, Kensington #209/R est:1500-2000

SCHMITZ, Carl Ludwig (19th C) German

£567	$1037	€850	Mountain lake with farm buildings and small boat with hay (62x93cm-24x37in) s. canvas on canvas. 5-Jun-4 Arnold, Frankfurt #714/R

SCHMITZ, Georg (1851-?) German

£833	$1358	€1200	Fishing hut on the Bille (63x88cm-25x35in) s. i. stretcher. 26-Sep-3 Bolland & Marotz, Bremen #612/R est:1100
£1156	$2000	€1688	Hamburg Harbour, winter (23x36cm-9x14in) s.i.d.1893 prov. 11-Dec-3 Sotheby's, New York #230/R est:3000-5000

SCHMITZ, L (19th C) ?

£1208	$2259	€1800	Riverside town (47x73cm-19x29in) s. 24-Feb-4 Dorotheum, Vienna #47/R est:1800-2000

SCHMITZ, Philipp (1824-1887) German

£625	$1000	€913	Interior with children and pets (69x56cm-27x22in) s. 21-Sep-3 William Jenack, New York #16

SCHMITZBERGER, Josef (1851-?) German

£2238	$3849	€3200	Woodland clearing with fox and roebuck (88x70cm-35x28in) 4-Dec-3 Dorotheum, Graz #37/R est:1500
£4000	$7280	€5840	Young puppies and a fawn (58x76cm-23x30in) s. 4-Feb-4 John Nicholson, Haslemere #157/R est:4000-6000
£4333	$7843	€6500	Two deer on snowy morning in the mountains (131x109cm-52x43in) s. 1-Apr-4 Van Ham, Cologne #1635/R est:3500

SCHMOGNER, Walter (1943-) Austrian

£2961	$5447	€4500	Moment (100x70cm-39x28in) mono.d. s.i.d.1990 verso acrylic. 22-Jun-4 Wiener Kunst Auktionen, Vienna #437/R est:4500

SCHMUCKER, Hannes (20th C) German?

£336	$594	€500	Still life with bottles and lemon (36x50cm-14x20in) mono.d.50 panel. 28-Apr-4 Schopman, Hamburg #578/R

SCHMURR, Wilhelm (1878-1959) German

£567	$1014	€850	Hayricks in summer (45x53cm-18x21in) s. panel. 15-May-4 Van Ham, Cologne #908/R
Works on paper			
£690	$1276	€1000	Two women (41x37cm-16x15in) s. W/C bodycol. 14-Feb-4 Hans Stahl, Hamburg #89/R

SCHMUTZER, Ferdinand (1833-1915) Austrian

£1342	$2510	€2000	Woman from Wachau (38x27cm-15x11in) s.d.18.III.1905 panel. 24-Feb-4 Dorotheum, Vienna #257/R est:2200-2600

SCHMUTZLER, Leopold (1864-1941) German

£493	$853	€700	Gypsy girl with her guitar (100x74cm-39x29in) s. cardboard. 10-Dec-3 Christie's, Amsterdam #661/R
£667	$1200	€1000	Woman's portrait (66x50cm-26x20in) s. 26-Apr-4 Rieber, Stuttgart #1237/R
£949	$1700	€1386	Boy and a girl (76x52cm-30x20in) s. 21-Mar-4 Bonhams & Butterfields, Los Angeles #7345/R est:1500-2500
£1020	$1827	€1500	Young woman laughing (71x51cm-28x20in) s. board. 17-Mar-4 Neumeister, Munich #597/R est:3000
£1250	$1987	€1800	Young woman with red shawl (66x49cm-26x19in) s. 11-Sep-3 Weidler, Nurnberg #324/R est:1100
£2500	$4550	€3650	Bathers at a woodland pool (66x86cm-26x34in) s. 16-Jun-4 Christie's, Kensington #234/R est:3000-4000
£2500	$4550	€3650	Divine reflection (115x93cm-45x37in) s. 16-Jun-4 Christie's, Kensington #238/R est:3500-4500

SCHMUTZLER, Leopold (attrib) (1864-1941) German

£1389	$2319	€2000	Female nude (70x49cm-28x19in) lit. 25-Oct-3 Bergmann, Erlangen #975/R

SCHNAAR, Heinrich Wilhelm (1820-1914) German

£267	$488	€400	Farm on edge of village (27x36cm-11x14in) s. 5-Jun-4 Arnold, Frankfurt #715

SCHNABEL, Julian (1951-) American

£22156	$37000	€32348	Bingo (181x115cm-71x45in) oil on tarpaulin painted 1990 prov. 14-Nov-3 Phillips, New York #163/R est:25000-35000
£28261	$52000	€41261	Leda and the swan (300x213cm-118x84in) oil fabric collage tarpaulin prov. 10-Jun-4 Phillips, New York #418/R est:50000-70000
£33520	$60000	€48939	Turba philosophorum (305x366cm-120x144in) oil gesso tarpaulin prov. 12-May-4 Christie's, Rockefeller NY #472/R est:40000-60000
£44693	$80000	€65252	La Voz de Antonio Molina (209x240cm-82x94in) i. prov.exhib. 12-May-4 Christie's, Rockefeller NY #473/R est:80000-120000
£44910	$75000	€65569	Untitled (244x183cm-96x72in) oil modelling paste velvet prov. 13-Nov-3 Sotheby's, New York #590/R est:70000-90000
£50279	$90000	€73407	Tower of Babel, for AA (183x303cm-72x119in) s.i.d.1976-1978 verso oil wood modeling paste prov.lit. 12-May-4 Christie's, Rockefeller NY #470/R est:80000-120000
£65333	$118253	€98000	Monjas de calle. i. s.i.d.1993 verso prov.exhib.lit. 30-Mar-4 Segre, Madrid #159/R est:93000
£89820	$150000	€131137	Untitled - Albondigas (244x305cm-96x120in) oil modeling paste suede on dropcloth painted 1992 prov.exhib. 12-Nov-3 Sotheby's, New York #69/R est:150000-200000
£110000	$183700	€160600	Holy Night (305x274cm-120x108in) oil modelling paste on velvet exec 1984 prov. 21-Oct-3 Sotheby's, London #372/R est:70000-90000
Prints			
£1977	$3500	€2886	Boy from Naples (181x125cm-71x49in) s. num.24/35 etching. 30-Apr-4 Sotheby's, New York #461/R est:3000-4000
£2794	$4750	€4079	Piston (122x91cm-48x36in) s. aquatint. 31-Oct-3 Sotheby's, New York #754/R
£2794	$4750	€4079	Brenda (152x91cm-60x36in) s. aquatint. 31-Oct-3 Sotheby's, New York #751/R
£2941	$5000	€4294	Harp (183x122cm-72x48in) s. aquatint. 31-Oct-3 Sotheby's, New York #752/R
£3129	$5601	€4600	Flowers in autumn (101x75cm-40x30in) s. serigraph resin exec.1999. 16-Mar-4 Finarte Semenzato, Milan #391/R est:3500-4000
£3235	$5500	€4723	Landscape (123x91cm-48x36in) s. aquatint. 31-Oct-3 Sotheby's, New York #753/R
£3333	$5967	€5000	Victor Hugo demo (114x101cm-45x40in) s.d. col silkscreen resin board. 15-May-4 Van Ham, Cologne #909/R est:5000
Sculpture			
£53333	$98667	€80000	Lady Macbeth (346x122x122cm-136x48x48in) s.d.90 num.1/4 bronze prov.exhib. 18-Jul-4 Sotheby's, Paris #157/R est:60000-80000
£60000	$111000	€90000	Galileo's table (280x285x105cm-110x112x41in) s.d.89 num.2/4 bronze prov.exhib. 18-Jul-4 Sotheby's, Paris #158/R est:70000-90000
Works on paper			
£6500	$11830	€9490	Study for Voltaire (95x126cm-37x50in) s.i.d.1981 brush ink gouache. 4-Feb-4 Sotheby's, Olympia #222/R est:2000-3000
£11976	$20000	€17485	Untitled (124x96cm-49x38in) s.d.81 brush ink wash pencil prov. 13-Nov-3 Sotheby's, New York #601/R est:3000-5000
£22148	$40752	€33000	Composition (211x176cm-83x69in) mono.d.1989 mixed media. 24-Mar-4 Binoche, Paris #92/R est:35000-50000
£73333	$135667	€110000	Self-portrait in white T-shirt (152x119cm-60x47in) s.verso collage plates wood prov. 18-Jul-4 Sotheby's, Paris #232/R est:100000-120000

SCHNACKENBERG, Roy (1934-) American

£437	$800	€638	Untitled (91x122cm-36x48in) 10-Jul-4 Hindman, Chicago #464/R
£3714	$6500	€5422	Horse Sense (54x122cm-21x48in) masonite painted 1967 exhib. 17-Dec-3 Christie's, Rockefeller NY #159/R est:1500-2000

SCHNACKENBERG, Walter (1880-1961) German

£23353	$39000	€34095	Untitled (201x250cm-79x98in) painted 1990 prov. 14-Nov-3 Phillips, New York #159/R est:30000-40000

SCHNAKENBERG, Henry (1892-1970) American

£457	$750	€667	Landscape with grove of trees and distant mountains (41x51cm-16x20in) s. prov. 31-May-3 Brunk, Ashville #32/R

SCHNARS-ALQUIST, Hugo (1855-1939) German

£3356	$6174	€5000	Steamer and other ships off Sta. Cruz, Tenerife (30x44cm-12x17in) s.i. 26-Mar-4 Ketterer, Hamburg #45/R est:5500-6500
£10490	$17517	€15000	Elb panorama with ships (114x182cm-45x72in) s.d.1922 prov. 11-Oct-3 Hans Stahl, Hamburg #165/R est:19000

SCHNEE, Hermann (1840-1926) German

£671	$1235	€1000	Ruins of Salzburg near Kissingen (75x98cm-30x39in) s.i. i. stretcher. 26-Mar-4 Bolland & Marotz, Bremen #589/R
£909	$1564	€1300	Charcoal-kiln in Harz (80x62cm-31x24in) s. 5-Dec-3 Bolland & Marotz, Bremen #626/R
£1337	$2500	€1952	German river scene with ferry crossing Medieval town (74x112cm-29x44in) s.d.82. 28-Feb-4 Thomaston Place, Thomaston #60/R

SCHNEIDAU, Christian von (1893-1976) American

£248	$400	€362	Sunset glow over Catalina Island (36x46cm-14x18in) s. s.i.verso board. 24-Feb-3 O'Gallerie, Oregon #880/R

SCHNEIDEN, Christian von (?) ?

£329	$550	€480	Portrait of a lady (92x72cm-36x28in) 16-Nov-3 Bonhams & Butterfields, Los Angeles #7008/R

SCHNEIDER, Carlos (1889-1932) Swiss

£317	$538	€463	St Francis of Assissi and four of his brothers (29x21cm-11x8in) tempera. 18-Nov-3 Hans Widmer, St Gallen #1190 (S.FR 700)
£2867	$5131	€4300	Winter landscape (140x100cm-55x39in) s. prov. 14-May-4 Ketterer, Munich #73/R est:2000-3000
£3667	$6563	€5500	Seated girl nude (140x100cm-55x39in) s. prov. 14-May-4 Ketterer, Munich #72/R est:2000-3000
Works on paper			
£294	$500	€429	Southern landscape with palm trees (30x23cm-12x9in) W/C over pencil. 18-Nov-3 Hans Widmer, St Gallen #1192 (S.FR 650)
£362	$615	€529	Ill man sitting on bed supported by woman (22x28cm-9x11in) W/C on chl double-sided. 18-Nov-3 Hans Widmer, St Gallen #1189/R (S.FR 800)
£367	$623	€536	Fruit harvest (23x22cm-9x9in) chl. 18-Nov-3 Hans Widmer, St Gallen #1187 (S.FR 810)
£679	$1154	€991	Young woman asleep on sofa (25x23cm-10x9in) W/C on pencil. 18-Nov-3 Hans Widmer, St Gallen #1188 est:500-1500 (S.FR 1500)
£679	$1154	€991	Trees in Bundner winter landscape (25x36cm-10x14in) s. d.15. Ocktober 1914 verso. 18-Nov-3 Hans Widmer, St Gallen #1194 est:900-2000 (S.FR 1500)

SCHNEIDER, Christian (1917-) French

£296	$512	€420	Port Bail, Cotentin (54x65cm-21x26in) s. d.1982 verso. 13-Dec-3 Martinot & Savignat, Pontoise #182

SCHNEIDER, Gerard (1896-1986) Swiss

£764	$1245	€1100	Sans titre (27x37cm-11x15in) s. i.verso acrylic. 29-Sep-3 Charbonneaux, Paris #279
£764	$1276	€1100	Composition (36x51cm-14x20in) s.d.76 acrylic paper. 21-Oct-3 Artcurial Briest, Paris #677
£921	$1695	€1400	Composition (12x18cm-5x7in) s. acrylic paper prov. 27-Jun-4 Versailles Encheres #9
£995	$1692	€1453	Composition (27x37cm-11x15in) s.d.1978 oil gouache prov. 25-Nov-3 Germann, Zurich #21/R est:2000-3000 (S.FR 2200)
£1719	$2923	€2510	Composition (72x52cm-28x20in) s.d.1983 prov. 25-Nov-3 Germann, Zurich #19/R est:4000-5000 (S.FR 3800)
£2000	$3620	€3000	Composition (46x55cm-18x22in) s. acrylic. 1-Apr-4 Credit Municipal, Paris #30 est:1800-2000
£2303	$4237	€3500	Composition (46x55cm-18x22in) s. acrylic. 24-Jun-4 Credit Municipal, Paris #54/R
£2550	$4693	€3800	Composition (55x46cm-22x18in) s.d.1971 acrylic. 24-Mar-4 Joron-Derem, Paris #133/R est:4000-5000
£2587	$4321	€3700	Composition (32x50cm-13x20in) s.d.1978 acrylic paper on canvas. 29-Jun-3 Versailles Encheres #30/R
£2685	$4940	€4000	Composition (54x75cm-21x30in) s.d.1982 acrylic paper on canvas. 24-Mar-4 Joron-Derem, Paris #139/R est:3800-4500
£3077	$5231	€4492	Composition (46x54cm-18x21in) s. acrylic prov. 22-Nov-3 Burkhard, Luzern #117/R est:5000-7000 (S.FR 6800)
£3125	$4938	€4500	Composition 98L (60x73cm-24x29in) s.d.1977 acrylic prov. 27-Apr-3 Versailles Encheres #50
£3200	$5888	€4800	Composition (75x107cm-30x42in) s.d.78 acrylic paper on canvas prov. 9-Jun-4 Artcurial Briest, Paris #461/R est:5000-6000
£3378	$5946	€5000	Composition M45 (46x38cm-18x15in) s. painted 1978. 22-May-4 Galleria Pananti, Florence #478/R est:6000-7000
£3600	$6480	€5400	Composition 98J (46x55cm-18x22in) s. s.i.d.1971 verso acrylic. 25-Apr-4 Versailles Encheres #72 est:5000-6000
£3691	$6866	€5500	Composition (149x146cm-59x57in) s.d.1984 acrylic. 3-Mar-4 Tajan, Paris #235/R est:6000-7000
£3819	$6035	€5500	Composition 30L (65x81cm-26x32in) s.d.1975 acrylic prov. 27-Apr-3 Versailles Encheres #43
£3919	$6897	€5800	Untitled (74x106cm-29x42in) s.d.1975 acrylic paper on canvas on panel prov. 18-May-4 Tajan, Paris #68/R est:6000-8000
£4722	$7461	€6800	Composition 471 (60x73cm-24x29in) s.d.1969 iv. acrylic prov. 27-Apr-3 Versailles Encheres #49
£5211	$8651	€7400	51K (81x100cm-32x39in) s.d.1974 i.verso. 11-Jun-3 Finarte Semenzato, Milan #592/R
£6623	$12053	€10000	Untitled (65x81cm-26x32in) i.verso. 18-Jun-4 Piasa, Paris #37/R est:10000-15000
£6897	$12759	€10000	Composition (96x130cm-38x51in) s.d.1970. 13-Feb-4 Charbonneaux, Paris #86/R est:8000-12000
£7639	$12069	€11000	SG9 (65x80cm-26x31in) 6-Sep-3 Meeting Art, Vercelli #605 est:10000
£7746	$12859	€11000	JG 3 (81x100cm-32x39in) s. i.verso. 14-Jun-3 Meeting Art, Vercelli #118/R est:10000
£8451	$14620	€12000	Composition abstraite (151x203cm-59x80in) s.d.79 acrylic. 12-Dec-3 Piasa, Paris #49/R est:12000-15000
£10417	$17188	€15000	Sans titre (89x116cm-35x46in) s.d.1952 prov. 2-Jul-3 Cornette de St.Cyr, Paris #35/R est:15000-20000
£11189	$18685	€16000	Composition 99L (89x116cm-35x46in) s.d.1977 acrylic. 29-Jun-3 Versailles Encheres #74/R
£17450	$31235	€26000	81M (150x200cm-59x79in) s.d.1979 i.verso. 30-May-4 Meeting Art, Vercelli #52 est:15000
£20333	$36600	€30500	Composition 59G (130x97cm-51x38in) s.d.65 i.verso prov. 25-Apr-4 Versailles Encheres #92 est:30000-35000
£24000	$43200	€36000	Opus 42B (86x116cm-34x46in) s.d.53 prov.exhib. 25-Apr-4 Versailles Encheres #84 est:30000-35000
£27273	$45545	€39000	Composition C59 (130x97cm-51x38in) s.d.1957 prov. 29-Jun-3 Versailles Encheres #70/R
£33803	$58479	€48000	Opus 95D (130x162cm-51x64in) s.d.5.60 i.verso prov.lit. 14-Dec-3 Versailles Encheres #120/R est:40000-50000
Works on paper			
£302	$561	€450	Untitled (14x17cm-6x7in) s.d.1982 gouache wash. 3-Mar-4 Tajan, Paris #2356
£805	$1442	€1200	Composition (21x29cm-8x11in) s.d.80 ink wash pastel. 26-May-4 Christie's, Paris #81/R
£839	$1427	€1200	Untitled (27x21cm-11x8in) s.d.20.54 Indian ink gouache. 27-Nov-3 Lempertz, Koln #421/R
£1042	$1646	€1500	Untitled (23x30cm-9x12in) mixed media paper on canvas. 6-Sep-3 Meeting Art, Vercelli #310 est:1500
£1049	$1783	€1500	Untitled (22x18cm-9x7in) s.d.9 51 gouache. 27-Nov-3 Lempertz, Koln #420/R est:1800
£1207	$2160	€1762	Untitled (52x75cm-20x30in) s.d.11-62 gouache paper on canvas. 12-May-4 Dobiaschofsky, Bern #944 est:3900 (S.FR 2800)
£1223	$2250	€1786	Composition (36x50cm-14x20in) s.d.1972 gouache prov. 8-Jun-4 Germann, Zurich #22/R est:3000-5000 (S.FR 2800)
£1382	$2542	€2100	Composition (36x53cm-14x21in) s.d.1974 gouache. 24-Jun-4 Credit Municipal, Paris #53/R
£1754	$3228	€2561	Composition (48x63cm-19x25in) s. gouache col varnish. 23-Jun-4 Koller, Zurich #3136/R est:3000-5000 (S.FR 4000)
£3618	$6658	€5500	Composition (52x75cm-20x30in) s.d.1962 gouache paper on canvas exhib. 27-Jun-4 Versailles Encheres #67/R est:4500-5000
£3667	$6600	€5500	Composition (52x74cm-20x29in) s.d.61 gouache W/C. 25-Apr-4 Versailles Encheres #71 est:4000-5000
£7383	$13658	€11000	Untitled (149x105cm-59x41in) s. mixed media cardboard. 13-Mar-4 Meeting Art, Vercelli #409 est:10000

SCHNEIDER, Gregor (1969-) German

Photographs			
£2027	$3628	€3000	Puff (80x88cm-31x35in) s.i.d.98 col photo from video. 8-May-4 Lempertz, Koln #257/R est:3000
Sculpture			
£8500	$15640	€12410	Grabstein totes haus, Rheydt (78x47x33cm-31x19x13in) s.i.d.2000 painted plaster prov. 25-Jun-4 Christie's, London #236/R est:8000-12000

SCHNEIDER, Herbert (1924-1984) German

£2535	$4386	€3600	Country happiness (60x50cm-24x20in) s. s.i.d.1975 verso acrylic oil. 13-Dec-3 Lempertz, Koln #352/R est:900
Works on paper			
£564	$1009	€840	That was summer (41x51cm-16x20in) s. W/C. 25-May-4 Karl & Faber, Munich #532

SCHNEIDER, Hermann (1847-1918) German

£461	$770	€650	Landscape (62x84cm-24x33in) s. 20-Oct-3 Durán, Madrid #612/R

SCHNEIDER, Johan Ludvig (attrib) (1809-1870) Danish

£1689	$3024	€2500	Summer lake landscape (70x98cm-28x39in) 6-May-4 Michael Zeller, Lindau #861/R est:2500

SCHNEIDER, Otto Henry (1865-1950) American

£565	$1000	€825	Two figures on a wooded path (20x16cm-8x6in) s. 2-May-4 Bonhams & Butterfields, San Francisco #1167/R
£586	$950	€856	Late afternoon low tide Sunset Cliffs California (33x41cm-13x16in) s. board. 31-Jul-3 Eldred, East Dennis #877/R

SCHNEIDER, Susan Hayward (1876-?) American

£251	$425	€366	Fruit still life (36x41cm-14x16in) s.d.1918. 22-Nov-3 Jackson's, Cedar Falls #102/R

SCHNEIDER, Walter (1903-) Swiss

£717	$1198	€1047	Self portrait with pipe, brush and palette (80x60cm-31x24in) s.d.1950. 24-Oct-3 Hans Widmer, St Gallen #90/R est:1400-3000 (S.FR 1600)

SCHNEIDER, William G (1863-1915) American

Works on paper			
£412	$750	€618	Portrait of a woman in a green kimono (43x20cm-17x8in) s.i.d.94 W/C. 16-Jun-4 Wolf's, New York #486787/R

SCHNEIDER-SEENUSS, Leo (1868-?) German

£336	$617	€500	Young woman with fish in basket (97x77cm-38x30in) s. 24-Mar-4 Hugo Ruef, Munich #1257

SCHNEIDERFRANKEN, Joseph (1876-1943) German

£814	$1385	€1188	Inferno (62x52cm-24x20in) s.i. verso. 28-Nov-3 Zofingen, Switzerland #2673/R est:3000 (S.FR 1800)

SCHNEIDERS, Toni (1920-) German

Photographs			
£1958	$3329	€2800	Lichtenfels railway station (23x30cm-9x12in) s.i.d. silver gelatin. 27-Nov-3 Villa Grisebach, Berlin #1386/R est:1500-2000

SCHNEIDT, Max (1858-1937) German

£1067	$1931	€1600	Goose maid in summer meadow behind farmstead (32x23cm-13x9in) s.d.89 panel. 1-Apr-4 Van Ham, Cologne #1636/R est:1600

SCHNELL, Elfriede (1897-1930) Polish

£430	$783	€650	At the cobbler's (80x94cm-31x37in) mono. 16-Jun-4 Hugo Ruef, Munich #1088/R

SCHNELLE, William G (1897-?) American

£326	$600	€476	Summer morning, Rensselaerville, New York (41x51cm-16x20in) s. 23-Jun-4 Doyle, New York #5067/R
£2695	$4500	€3935	Young woman (51x41cm-20x16in) s. indis.d. prov. 23-Oct-3 Shannon's, Milford #259/R est:4000-6000

SCHNETZ, Jean Victor (1787-1870) French

£4333	$7973	€6500	Portrait de Monsieur Destouches (74x61cm-29x24in) s.i.d.1818. 11-Jun-4 Maigret, Paris #80/R est:2500-3500

Works on paper

£775 $1340 €1100 Un pere enlacant son fils (21x16cm-8x6in) s.d.1826 pen brown ink brown wash traces blk crayon. 10-Dec-3 Piasa, Paris #85

SCHNETZINGER, Karl (?) ?

£230 $375 €336 Untitled no.47 (105x109cm-41x43in) 28-Sep-3 Bonhams & Butterfields, Los Angeles #7058

Works on paper

£404 $650 €590 Untitled (127x110cm-50x43in) s.d.87. 24-Aug-3 Bonhams & Butterfields, Los Angeles #7049

SCHNETZLER, Johann Ulrich (1704-1763) Swiss

£1965 $3576 €2869 The arrival of Bacchus at Adriadne's (64x80cm-25x31in) s.d.1754. 16-Jun-4 Fischer, Luzern #1269/R est:5000-7000 (S.FR 4500)

SCHNEUER, David (1905-1988) Polish

£824 $1400 €1203 The brothel (34x25cm-13x10in) s. oil htd pencil cardboard painted late 1970's. 1-Dec-3 Ben-Ami, Tel Aviv #4326/R est:1500-2000

SCHNITZER, Theodor (1866-1939) German

£382 $623 €550 Near Langenargen (42x43cm-17x17in) s.d. 27-Sep-3 Dr Fritz Nagel, Stuttgart #9349/R

SCHNITZLER, Michael (1782-1861) German

£424 $699 €610 Dead birds (19x15cm-7x6in) s. panel. 2-Jul-3 Neumeister, Munich #768/R

SCHNOBB, Jean Guy (1946-) Canadian

£498 $831 €727 Cascades (60x90cm-24x35in) s.i. 17-Nov-3 Hodgins, Calgary #177/R est:900-1200 (C.D 1100)

SCHNOOR, Alvina (19th C) American

£497 $800 €726 Rocky Mountains (53x79cm-21x31in) 15-Aug-3 Du Mouchelle, Detroit #55/R

SCHNORR VON CAROLSFELD, Hans (1764-1841) German

Works on paper

£3026 $5568 €4600 Mercury and Diana with dogs in the woods (74x54cm-29x21in) mixed media ink pen grisaille. 26-Jun-4 C & K, Leipzig #769/R est:500

SCHNORR VON CAROLSFELD, Julius (1794-1872) German

£2252 $4098 €3400 Three figures from the Nibelungen (43x53cm-17x21in) lit. 19-Jun-4 Dannenberg, Berlin #615/R est:2000

Works on paper

£719 $1151 €1000 Biblical scene (24x18cm-9x7in) init. pencil W/C. 14-May-3 Finarte Semenzato, Milan #517/R

£3108 $5470 €4600 Wakening of the widow's son (21x26cm-8x10in) mono.d.Dec./1825 i. verso prov.lit. 22-May-4 Lempertz, Koln #1460/R est:4000

£4000 $7360 €6000 Julius Macabeer conquering the enemy and cleaning out the temple (21x26cm-8x10in) i. pen over pencil. 11-Jun-4 Hauswedell & Nolte, Hamburg #1067/R est:8000

SCHNYDER, Albert (1898-1989) German

£733 $1312 €1070 Groupe de chevaux (41x56cm-16x22in) tempera. 14-May-4 Dobiaschofsky, Bern #115/R est:2500 (S.FR 1700)

£862 $1543 €1259 Getting dressed (59x42cm-23x17in) s.i.d.1956 W/C on chl squared paper. 13-May-4 Stuker, Bern #307/R est:2000-3000 (S.FR 2000)

£2609 $4774 €3809 Child at the table (77x67cm-30x26in) prov.exhib. 7-Jun-4 Christie's, Zurich #125/R est:7000-9000 (S.FR 6000)

£2915 $4751 €4256 The reapers (58x77cm-23x30in) s.d.1943 verso. 29-Sep-3 Christie's, Zurich #91/R est:5000-6000 (S.FR 6500)

£3664 $6558 €5349 La Scheulte a Vicques (65x81cm-26x32in) 14-May-4 Dobiaschofsky, Bern #113/R est:12000 (S.FR 8500)

£4977 $8462 €7266 Paysage a Ocourt (65x80cm-26x31in) s.i.d.1951 stretcher. 25-Nov-3 Germann, Zurich #73/R est:12000-16000 (S.FR 11000)

£5727 $9736 €8361 Le hameau (59x146cm-23x57in) 7-Nov-3 Dobiaschofsky, Bern #16/R est:20000 (S.FR 13000)

£6897 $12345 €10070 En Ajoie (73x92cm-29x36in) 14-May-4 Dobiaschofsky, Bern #107/R est:12000 (S.FR 16000)

£8190 $14659 €11957 Paysage en ete (73x147cm-29x58in) 14-May-4 Dobiaschofsky, Bern #98/R est:22000 (S.FR 19000)

SCHOBEL, Georg (1860-1941) German

£350 $550 €508 Mutual admiration (48x39cm-19x15in) s.i. board. 28-Aug-3 Christie's, Kensington #72/R

£609 $993 €889 Palace interior (67x58cm-26x23in) s. 27-Sep-3 Rasmussen, Havnen #2157 (D.KR 6500)

SCHOBELT, Paul (1838-1893) German

£1119 $1869 €1600 Portrait of Pawel Tretjakow (99x78cm-39x31in) s. 28-Jun-3 Bolland & Marotz, Bremen #732/R est:1800

SCHOBER, Peter Jakob (1897-1983) German

£1007 $1782 €1500 Still life with flowers and pipe (80x65cm-31x26in) s.d. prov. 30-Apr-4 Dr Fritz Nagel, Stuttgart #936/R est:1500

£1127 $1803 €1600 Fishing boats in Venice harbour (50x60cm-20x24in) s.d.1924 board. 18-Sep-3 Rieber, Stuttgart #1080/R est:2500

£1611 $2851 €2400 Southern landscape with buildings and figures (64x76cm-25x30in) s.d. 30-Apr-4 Dr Fritz Nagel, Stuttgart #935/R est:1400

£1879 $3326 €2800 Still life with flowers (81x65cm-32x26in) s.d. 30-Apr-4 Dr Fritz Nagel, Stuttgart #934/R est:2400

SCHOCK, Maya (20th C) American

£417 $750 €609 Journey within no 28 (152x127cm-60x50in) s.indis.d.July 1972 verso acrylic collage. 23-Jan-4 Freeman, Philadelphia #202/R

SCHODL, Max (1834-1921) Austrian

£1056 $1827 €1500 Still life with ornaments (32x34cm-13x13in) s.d.1911 panel. 10-Dec-3 Dorotheum, Vienna #202/R est:1500-1600

£1389 $2361 €2000 Oriental still life (24x20cm-9x8in) s.d.1886 panel. 28-Oct-3 Dorotheum, Vienna #197/R est:200-2400

SCHODLBERGER, Johann Nepomuk (1779-1853) Austrian

£2308 $3923 €3300 Evening prayer in the mountains (35x42cm-14x17in) s.d.1826. 24-Nov-3 Dorotheum, Vienna #8/R est:3800-4500

Works on paper

£541 $951 €800 Rhenish river landscape (24x38cm-9x15in) init. pen brown ink col wash black chk prov.exhib. 19-May-4 Sotheby's, Amsterdam #309/R

£594 $1022 €850 Country house (20x27cm-8x11in) W/C. 3-Dec-3 Neumeister, Munich #426/R

SCHOEFF, Johannes (1608-1666) Dutch

£3333 $5967 €5000 Extensive wooded landscape with herdsman resting his cattle (58x69cm-23x27in) panel prov.lit. 17-May-4 Christie's, Amsterdam #31/R est:4000-6000

£30000 $51900 €43800 River landscape with peasants netting fish from boats (59x80cm-23x31in) s.d.1647 prov.lit. 11-Dec-3 Sotheby's, London #66/R est:20000-30000

Works on paper

£1370 $2329 €2000 Extensive landscape with church and trees (18x31cm-7x12in) bears i. pen brown ink blue wash. 4-Nov-3 Sotheby's, Amsterdam #28/R est:3000-4000

SCHOEFFT, August Theodor (1809-1888) Hungarian

£2817 $4873 €4000 Le Duc Saint Simeon (76x66cm-30x26in) s. 12-Dec-3 Piasa, Paris #89 est:3000-4000

SCHOEN, Klaus (1931-) German

£378 $642 €552 Geometrical rhythms (120x110cm-47x43in) s.d.79 verso. 5-Nov-3 AB Stockholms Auktionsverk #950/R (S.KR 5000)

SCHOENBECK, Albert (19th C) German

£433 $776 €650 Winter landscape near Potsdam (33x46cm-13x18in) lit. 14-May-4 Schloss Ahlden, Ahlden #2855/R

SCHOENHOLTZ, Michael (1937-) German

Sculpture

£1042 $1740 €1500 Flame and ash (35x43x40cm-14x17x16in) mono.d. marble granite socle prov.exhib. 24-Oct-3 Ketterer, Hamburg #537/R est:1500-1700

£1174 $2079 €1750 Year of the Woman (109x39x40cm-43x15x16in) mono.i.d. bronze Cast.Bildgiesserei Kraas prov.exhib. 30-Apr-4 Dr Fritz Nagel, Stuttgart #959/R est:3500

SCHOEVAERDTS, Mathys (c.1665-1723) Flemish

£1241 $2073 €1800 Fish market (32x44cm-13x17in) 15-Nov-3 Lempertz, Koln #1139/R est:2000

£2113 $3655 €3000 Landscape with figures (18x20cm-7x8in) copper. 15-Dec-3 Ansorena, Madrid #302/R est:3000

£2384 $4339 €3600 Une reunion de paysans devant des ruines antiques dans un paysage (33x41cm-13x16in) 21-Jun-4 Tajan, Paris #77 est:4000-6000

£7383 $13584 €11000 View across Flemish town with figures (42x60cm-17x24in) 24-Mar-4 Dorotheum, Vienna #389/R est:8000-12000

£13000 $23400 €18980 Coastal landscape with merchants and peasants. Coastal landscape with fishermen loading the catch (13x18cm-5x7in) s. panel pair. 21-Apr-4 Christie's, London #5/R est:12000-18000

£20000 $36600 €29200 River landscape with figures (43x60cm-17x24in) 9-Jul-4 Christie's, Kensington #31/R est:12000

£28571 $45429 €42000 Le retour du marche (31x44cm-12x17in) panel. 23-Mar-3 Mercier & Cie, Lille #163/R est:48000-50000

SCHOEVAERDTS, Mathys (attrib) (c.1665-1723) Flemish

£19580 $33678 €28000 Village street. Peasants departing for the market (24x34cm-9x13in) prov. 2-Dec-3 Christie's, Paris #715/R est:12000-18000

SCHOEVAERDTS, Mathys (circle) (c.1665-1723) Flemish

£9000 $15300 €13140 Village landscape with elegant company in ferries crossing a river (61x92cm-24x36in) prov. 31-Oct-3 Christie's, Kensington #50/R est:6000-8000

SCHOFF, Otto (1888-1938) German

Works on paper

£278 $464 €400 Sultry dreams (24x32cm-9x13in) W/C chk pencil. 25-Oct-3 Dr Lehr, Berlin #466/R

£333 $557 €480 Reclining girl (32x25cm-13x10in) s. W/C over Indian ink board. 25-Oct-3 Dr Lehr, Berlin #467/R

SCHOFFER, Nicolas (1912-) French

Sculpture

£10333 $19013 €15500 Tour lumiere de la defense (93x21x21cm-37x8x8in) aluminium exec 1967 prov.lit. 9-Jun-4 Artcurial Briest, Paris #494/R est:10000-15000

SCHOFIELD, David (?) British?

£500 $930 €730 Birdwatching (65x58cm-26x23in) s. board. 6-Mar-4 Shapes, Edinburgh #441/R

SCHOFIELD, John William (1865-1944) British

£250	$408	€363	Portrait of a fashionable lady (38x32cm-15x13in) s. 23-Sep-3 Bonhams, Leeds #121
£633	$1000	€924	Portrait of a young Edward, Prince of Wales (79x64cm-31x25in) s. 6-Sep-3 Brunk, Ashville #190
£4800	$8928	€7008	Portrait of a girl, seated on a chair wearing blue dress, holding a doll (63x76cm-25x30in) s.d.1896. 4-Mar-4 Christie's, Kensington #392/R est:4000-6000
Works on paper			
£950	$1587	€1387	Moonlit farmstead with farmer and sheep (54x74cm-21x29in) s.d.1923 W/C. 9-Jul-3 Peter Wilson, Nantwich #71

SCHOFIELD, John William (attrib) (1865-1944) British

£1500	$2685	€2190	Portrait of a boy, seated in a blue coat and breeches, a Jack Russell by his side (96x71cm-38x28in) 27-May-4 Christie's, Kensington #102/R est:1200-1800

SCHOFIELD, Kershaw (1872-1941) British

£280	$448	€406	Farmhouse with geese (51x75cm-20x30in) s.d.1904. 16-Sep-3 Bonhams, Knightsbridge #247
£360	$619	€526	River meadow with cattle (46x58cm-18x23in) s. board. 3-Dec-3 Andrew Hartley, Ilkley #1239
£360	$666	€526	Gathering faggots (43x53cm-17x21in) s. 15-Jul-4 Richardson & Smith, Whitby #426
£400	$748	€584	Sheep grazing in a water meadow trees nearby (46x55cm-18x22in) s. board. 22-Jul-4 Tennants, Leyburn #944
£420	$659	€609	Faggot gatherer on a stormy day (46x58cm-18x23in) s. 28-Aug-3 Christie's, Kensington #144
£420	$785	€613	Shepherdess seated under trees with sheep grazing in pasture nearby (34x44cm-13x17in) s. board. 22-Jul-4 Tennants, Leyburn #942
£500	$935	€730	Winter landscape with trees beside a stream (19x25cm-7x10in) s. board. 22-Jul-4 Tennants, Leyburn #940
£500	$935	€730	Figures and sheep in a sunlit meadow (46x60cm-18x24in) s. panel prov. 22-Jul-4 Tennants, Leyburn #943
£700	$1288	€1022	Impressionist river landscape (18x23cm-7x9in) s. 11-Jun-4 Keys, Aylsham #655/R
£2700	$5049	€3942	Girl seated beneath trees in a wooded landscape, sheep grazing nearby (71x91cm-28x36in) s. 22-Jul-4 Tennants, Leyburn #945/R est:3000-4000

SCHOFIELD, Walter Elmer (1867-1944) American

£3727	$6000	€5441	House in landscape (38x41cm-15x16in) s. panel. 20-Aug-3 James Julia, Fairfield #13330/R est:8000-10000
£3779	$6500	€5517	Waves breaking on rocks (46x53cm-18x21in) s. board prov. 7-Dec-3 Freeman, Philadelphia #210 est:4000-6000
£5435	$10000	€7935	Breakers on the shore (53x68cm-21x27in) s.d.03 prov. 27-Jun-4 Freeman, Philadelphia #184/R est:10000-15000
£6250	$11000	€9125	Old bridge, landscape (25x30cm-10x12in) i. 21-May-4 Pook & Pook, Downington #319/R est:5000-7000
£8824	$15000	€12883	After the storm (66x76cm-26x30in) s. i.verso prov. 29-Oct-3 Christie's, Los Angeles #54/R est:15000-25000
£11047	$19000	€16129	Docks, Penzance (53x69cm-21x27in) s. painted c.1902 prov.exhib. 7-Dec-3 Freeman, Philadelphia #198 est:15000-25000
£12500	$23000	€18250	Coast - St Ives (68x53cm-27x21in) partial sig. i. stretcher verso prov. 27-Jun-4 Freeman, Philadelphia #204/R est:10000-15000
£12791	$22000	€18675	King's Garden, Godolphin Manor (74x91cm-29x36in) painted 1940 prov.exhib. 7-Dec-3 Freeman, Philadelphia #199 est:25000-40000
£13043	$24000	€19043	Evening clouds at St Ives Bay (53x68cm-21x27in) s. i. verso prov. 27-Jun-4 Freeman, Philadelphia #212/R est:10000-15000
£20930	$36000	€30558	Polperro (76x91cm-30x36in) s. i.d.1912 verso prov. 7-Dec-3 Freeman, Philadelphia #197 est:20000-30000
£24457	$45000	€35707	Canal, Bruges (71x91cm-28x36in) s. prov. 27-Jun-4 Freeman, Philadelphia #172/R est:20000-30000
£27174	$50000	€39674	Cottages by a turn in the road (66x76cm-26x30in) s. indis.d. prov. 27-Jun-4 Freeman, Philadelphia #178/R est:25000-40000
£29891	$55000	€43641	Sunlit houses (50x61cm-20x24in) s. s.d.1921 verso exhib. 27-Jun-4 Freeman, Philadelphia #186/R est:15000-25000
£31977	$55000	€46686	Sunlit cottages by a river (51x61cm-20x24in) s. 7-Dec-3 Freeman, Philadelphia #214 est:25000-40000
£40698	$70000	€59419	Montmartre (94x119cm-37x47in) painted c.1896 prov.exhib.lit. 7-Dec-3 Freeman, Philadelphia #195 est:20000-30000
£43478	$80000	€63478	Spring landscape (76x91cm-30x36in) s. prov. 27-Jun-4 Freeman, Philadelphia #199/R est:25000-40000
£104651	$180000	€152790	River in winter (102x122cm-40x48in) s. prov. 7-Dec-3 Freeman, Philadelphia #196 est:100000-200000

SCHOLANDER, Fredrik (1816-1881) Swedish

Works on paper			
£417	$658	€600	After church (43x34cm-17x13in) s.d.1871 W/C lit. 19-Sep-3 Schloss Ahlden, Ahlden #1644/R
£1075	$1753	€1570	Venetian scene (60x49cm-24x19in) s. W/C. 29-Sep-3 Lilla Bukowskis, Stockholm #662 (S.KR 14000)

SCHOLDER, Fritz (1937-) American

£5587	$10000	€8157	Near the Opera. s.i. 13-May-4 Dallas Auction Gallery, Dallas #311/R est:8000-12000

SCHOLDERER, Otto (1834-1902) German

£2083	$3396	€3000	Woman's portrait (72x62cm-28x24in) mono.d.1866. 25-Sep-3 Dr Fritz Nagel, Stuttgart #1413/R est:4000
£2267	$4103	€3400	Young woman (72x62cm-28x24in) s.d. 2-Apr-4 Winterberg, Heidelberg #541/R est:3200
£6250	$10188	€9000	Self portrait (60x50cm-24x20in) s. 25-Sep-3 Dr Fritz Nagel, Stuttgart #1414/R est:10000

SCHOLDERER, Otto (attrib) (1834-1902) German

£2098	$3566	€3000	Returning home from the harvest (44x61cm-17x24in) sketch. 22-Nov-3 Arnold, Frankfurt #633/R est:6000

SCHOLLE, Charles F (1891-1987) American

£406	$650	€593	Boxing match (155x231cm-61x91in) s. 18-May-3 Auctions by the Bay, Alameda #1073/R

SCHOLLHORN, Hans (1892-1981) Swiss

£452	$769	€660	Villeneuve harbour on Lake Geneva (40x32cm-16x13in) mono. s.i.d.1947 verso board. 18-Nov-3 Hans Widmer, St Gallen #1196 (S.FR 1000)
£905	$1448	€1321	Marseilles, Place Gelu (33x41cm-13x16in) s.d.1927 i. verso. 16-Sep-3 Philippe Schuler, Zurich #3254 est:1200-1500 (S.FR 2000)
Works on paper			
£411	$736	€600	Circus horse (19x16cm-7x6in) mono. W/C. 22-Mar-4 Philippe Schuler, Zurich #4210 (S.FR 950)

SCHOLLHORN, Hermann (1883-1977) Swiss

£458	$732	€650	Still life of fruit with jug under window (43x57cm-17x22in) s.d.1941 board. 18-Sep-3 Rieber, Stuttgart #1349

SCHOLTE, Rob (1958-) Dutch

£1733	$3189	€2600	Mondriaan revisited, composition gris et rouge (130x130cm-51x51in) s.i.d.1998 verso prov. 9-Jun-4 Christie's, Amsterdam #363/R est:1500-3500

SCHOLTEN, Hendrik Jacobus (1824-1907) Dutch

£604	$1081	€900	Les amoureux (37x42cm-15x17in) s.d.1865 verso panel. 25-May-4 Campo & Campo, Antwerp #262
£2550	$4718	€3800	Mother by the cradle (38x30cm-15x12in) s. panel. 13-Mar-4 De Vuyst, Lokeren #287/R est:4000-5000
Works on paper			
£442	$800	€645	Playing with the baby (25x29cm-10x11in) s. W/C. 18-Apr-4 Bonhams & Butterfields, Los Angeles #7051

SCHOLTEN, Peter von (1784-1854) Danish

Works on paper			
£514	$812	€745	Nyholm from Langelinie (19x32cm-7x13in) s.d.April 1834 W/C prov. 3-Sep-3 Museumsbygningen, Copenhagen #201/R (D.KR 5500)

SCHOLTZ, Heinz (1925-) German

£733	$1313	€1100	Frankfurt am Main (43x53cm-17x21in) s. copperplate lit. 14-May-4 Schloss Ahlden, Ahlden #2870/R

SCHOLTZ, Julius (1825-1893) German

£4000	$7280	€6000	Shepherd boy sleeping in a mountainous landscape (26x31cm-10x12in) s.d.1874 board. 1-Jul-4 Van Ham, Cologne #1605/R est:6000

SCHOLZ, Georg (1890-1945) German

£300000	$510000	€438000	Von Kommenden Dingen (75x97cm-30x38in) s.d.1922 s.d.verso board prov.exhib.lit. 5-Nov-3 Sotheby's, New York #38/R est:200000-300000

SCHOLZ, Max (1855-?) German

£2662	$4365	€3700	Thinnebach (50x64cm-20x25in) mono. masonite. 4-Jun-3 Ketterer, Hamburg #849/R est:3800-4400

SCHOLZ, Paul (1859-1940) Austrian

£347	$566	€500	Church in Weissenkirchen, Wachau (56x46cm-22x18in) s. i. verso. 25-Sep-3 Dorotheum, Graz #24
£486	$792	€700	Bruges landscape (42x54cm-17x21in) s. canvas on board. 25-Sep-3 Dorotheum, Graz #21/R
£537	$961	€800	Courtyard in Weisskirchen in Wachau. s. canvas on board. 27-May-4 Dorotheum, Graz #58/R
£625	$1019	€900	Still life of fruit and vegetables (141x138cm-56x54in) s. 25-Sep-3 Dorotheum, Graz #25
£704	$1169	€1000	Street in Gmund, Karnten (43x49cm-17x19in) s. i. verso canvas on board. 12-Jun-3 Dorotheum, Graz #60/R

SCHOLZ, Werner (1898-1982) German

£4676	$7669	€6500	Five finger peaks (76x67cm-30x26in) mono. masonite prov.exhib. 4-Jun-3 Ketterer, Hamburg #848/R est:8000-10000
£5667	$10427	€8500	Poppies (52x70cm-20x28in) s.d.44 board. 11-Jun-4 Villa Grisebach, Berlin #1571/R est:4000-6000
£12667	$23307	€19000	In the park. Dead child (74x74cm-29x29in) one mono.d.27 one mono.d.30 cardboard double-sided prov.exhib.lit. 11-Jun-4 Villa Grisebach, Berlin #1565/R est:10000-15000
£40000	$73600	€60000	Les affliges (74x74cm-29x29in) mono.d.30 i.verso cardboard prov.exhib.lit. 11-Jun-4 Villa Grisebach, Berlin #1566/R est:15000-20000
Works on paper			
£400	$716	€600	Butterfly (49x63cm-19x25in) mono. pastel chk. 15-May-4 Van Ham, Cologne #912/R
£400	$716	€600	Dark butterfly (47x63cm-19x25in) d.1953 pastel paper on board. 13-May-4 Neumeister, Munich #764/R
£455	$782	€650	Humming birds (48x62cm-19x24in) mono.i. pastel paper on board. 4-Dec-3 Van Ham, Cologne #459/R
£594	$1022	€850	Butterfly (48x62cm-19x24in) mono. pastel col crayon. 4-Dec-3 Van Ham, Cologne #458

SCHOMMER, François (1850-1935) French

£1042	$1740	€1500	Nu aux bas rouges (49x30cm-19x12in) s. 21-Oct-3 Artcurial Briest, Paris #157 est:1400-1800

SCHON, Arthur (1887-1940) Belgian

£1812	$2971	€2500	Cabaret (60x51cm-24x20in) s. s.i.d.1928 verso. 27-May-3 Sotheby's, Amsterdam #508/R est:3000-4000

SCHON, Frantisek (1882-?) Czechoslovakian
£268 $498 €391 Oasis Tozen in Tunis (47x68cm-19x27in) s. board. 6-Mar-4 Dorotheum, Prague #48/R est:8000-15000 (C.KR 13000)

SCHON, Friedrich Wilhelm (1810-1868) German
£4196 $7133 €6000 Girl praying (35x29cm-14x11in) mono. panel. 20-Nov-3 Van Ham, Cologne #1853/R est:7000

SCHON, Karl (1868-?) German
£470 $864 €700 Paddle steamer Cobra off Helgoland (35x91cm-14x36in) s. 26-Mar-4 Ketterer, Hamburg #46/R

SCHON, Otto (1893-) German
£667 $1213 €1000 Child playing (67x53cm-26x21in) s.d.1927. 1-Jul-4 Weidler, Nurnberg #6565/R

SCHONBAUER, Henry (1894-?) Hungarian
Sculpture
£1792 $3100 €2616 Reclining male (34x62x19cm-13x24x7in) with sig. cold painted terracotta. 11-Dec-3 Sotheby's, New York #158/R est:1500-2000

SCHONBERGER, Alfred Karl Julius Otto von (1845-?) German
£267 $488 €400 Mountain valley with farm in summertime (46x54cm-18x21in) s.d.1883. 5-Jun-4 Arnold, Frankfurt #717/R
£500 $915 €750 Late afternoon in Kronberg (54x82cm-21x32in) s. 5-Jun-4 Arnold, Frankfurt #716/R
£738 $1373 €1100 Kronberg (14x18cm-6x7in) s. panel. 6-Mar-4 Arnold, Frankfurt #845/R

SCHONBERGER, Armand (1885-1974) Hungarian
£353 $586 €515 Blond girl (49x34cm-19x13in) s. oil paper. 4-Oct-3 Kieselbach, Budapest #189/R (H.F 130000)
£1249 $2073 €1824 Nudes (67x48cm-26x19in) s. tempera paper. 4-Oct-3 Kieselbach, Budapest #194/R (H.F 460000)
£2539 $4493 €3707 Three ladies (55x46cm-22x18in) s. cardboard. 28-Apr-4 Kieselbach, Budapest #125/R (H.F 950000)
£3654 $6321 €5335 Lovers (38x33cm-15x13in) s. cardboard. 12-Dec-3 Kieselbach, Budapest #10/R (H.F 1400000)
£3952 $7153 €5770 In the harbour (45x59cm-18x23in) s. canvas on card. 16-Apr-4 Mu Terem Galeria, Budapest #23/R (H.F 1500000)
£4008 $7095 €5852 Still life of flower with an open book (61x45cm-24x18in) s.d.1929. 28-Apr-4 Kieselbach, Budapest #66/R (H.F 1500000)
£4959 $8579 €7240 Town - Houses in Buda (60x60cm-24x24in) s. 12-Dec-3 Kieselbach, Budapest #52/R (H.F 1900000)
£6850 $12399 €10001 Obuda (65x50cm-26x20in) s. oil on card. 16-Apr-4 Mu Terem Galeria, Budapest #135/R (H.F 2600000)
£17369 $30744 €25359 Company by table (45x43cm-18x17in) s. oil paper painted 1920's. 28-Apr-4 Kieselbach, Budapest #60/R (H.F 6500000)
£17369 $30744 €25359 Port (70x70cm-28x28in) s. cardboard. 28-Apr-4 Kieselbach, Budapest #169/R (H.F 6500000)
Works on paper
£1277 $2132 €1800 Untitled (49x34cm-19x13in) s. chk. 14-Oct-3 Dorotheum, Vienna #93/R est:800-1200
£1958 $3386 €2859 Still life (69x48cm-27x19in) s. mixed media. 12-Dec-3 Kieselbach, Budapest #121/R (H.F 750000)
£2108 $3815 €3078 Friends (70x49cm-28x19in) s. pastel tempera. 16-Apr-4 Mu Terem Galeria, Budapest #167/R (H.F 800000)
£2240 $4054 €3270 Swarming in the coffee house (51x35cm-20x14in) s. pastel. 16-Apr-4 Mu Terem Galeria, Budapest #70/R (H.F 850000)
£11758 $20811 €17167 Grinder (56x80cm-22x31in) W/C oil. 28-Apr-4 Kieselbach, Budapest #102/R (H.F 4400000)
£17126 $30998 €25004 Musicians (56x79cm-22x31in) s. mixed media. 16-Apr-4 Mu Terem Galeria, Budapest #78/R (H.F 6500000)

SCHONBERGER, Martin (attrib) (1864-?) Swiss
£347 $573 €500 Gosausee in evening (15x26cm-6x10in) mono. panel. 3-Jul-3 Neumeister, Munich #2910

SCHONBRUNNER, Ignaz (1835-1921) Austrian
£500 $920 €750 Still life with tea service and plant (60x80cm-24x31in) s.d.1937. 11-Jun-4 Wendl, Rudolstadt #4267/R

SCHONCHEN, Leopold (1855-1935) German
£544 $990 €800 Waves breaking on shore (32x45cm-13x18in) s. board. 3-Feb-4 Sigalas, Stuttgart #521/R
£986 $1765 €1400 Mending the nets, on the shore of a lake with sailing boat (45x64cm-18x25in) s. lit. 8-Jan-4 Allgauer, Kempten #2509/R

SCHONEBECK, Eugen (1936-) German
Works on paper
£4667 $8540 €7000 Untitled (29x20cm-11x8in) mono.d.63 Indian ink double-sided lit. 4-Jun-4 Lempertz, Koln #429/R est:2500
£5333 $9760 €8000 Untitled (29x20cm-11x8in) mono.d.62 i. verso Indian ink. 4-Jun-4 Lempertz, Koln #430/R est:3800

SCHONER, Georg Friedrich Adolph (1774-1841) German
£10345 $19034 €15104 Portrait of Heinrich Pestalozzi (71x57cm-28x22in) s.i. verso oval. 26-Mar-4 Koller, Zurich #3083/R est:20000-30000 (S.FR 24000)

SCHONFELD, Johann Heinrich (1609-1682) German
£6164 $10479 €9000 The Infant Christ as Salvator Mundi (42x67cm-17x26in) s. 9-Nov-3 Finarte, Venice #51/R est:8000-11000

SCHONGAUER, Ludwig (1440-1492) German
£22000 $38060 €32120 Arrest of Christ. The Entombment (36x20cm-14x8in) panel two wings of altarpiece. 10-Dec-3 Christie's, London #41/R est:20000-30000

SCHONGAUER, Martin (1445-1491) German
Prints
£1705 $3000 €2489 Man of Sorrows. engraving prov. 23-May-4 Hindman, Chicago #12/R est:4000-6000
£2096 $3500 €3060 Christ carrying the cross (28x43cm-11x17in) engraving exec.c.1480 prov. 21-Oct-3 Bonhams & Butterfields, San Francisco #1147/R
£2216 $3900 €3235 Christ before Annas (10x15cm-4x6in) engraving. 28-May-4 Aspire, Cleveland #90/R est:6000-8000
£2346 $4200 €3425 Christ crowned with thorns (15x10cm-6x4in) engraving executed c.1480. 6-May-4 Swann Galleries, New York #4/R est:3000-5000
£3147 $5350 €4500 Madonna on crescent moon (17x11cm-7x4in) copperplate. 27-Nov-3 Bassenge, Berlin #5358 est:2500
£5000 $9200 €7500 Carrying the cross (27x43cm-11x17in) copperplate. 11-Jun-4 Hauswedell & Nolte, Hamburg #908/R est:8000
£6040 $11114 €9000 St John the Baptist (15x10cm-6x4in) mono. copperplate prov. 26-Mar-4 Ketterer, Hamburg #54/R est:5000-6000
£6145 $11000 €8972 Christ before Pilate (15x13cm-6x5in) engraving executed c.1480. 6-May-4 Swann Galleries, New York #5/R est:6000-9000
£12081 $22228 €18000 Christ on the cross (16x11cm-6x4in) mono. copperplate. 26-Mar-4 Ketterer, Hamburg #52/R est:4000-5000
£13408 $24000 €19576 Christ appearing to Mary Magdalene (15x15cm-6x6in) engraving executed c.1480-90. 6-May-4 Swann Galleries, New York #7/R est:10000-15000
£13986 $23776 €20000 Capture of Christ (17x12cm-7x5in) copperplate. 27-Nov-3 Bassenge, Berlin #5357 est:24000
£28859 $53101 €43000 St Anthony tempted by demons (31x23cm-12x9in) mono. copperplate prov. 26-Mar-4 Ketterer, Hamburg #53/R est:13000-15000

SCHONGAUER, Martin (style) (1445-1491) German
£19000 $34770 €27740 Christ, Man of Sorrows, Virgin and Saint John (45x33cm-18x13in) panel prov. 8-Jul-4 Sotheby's, London #244/R est:15000-20000

SCHONIAN, Alfred (1856-1936) German
£350 $601 €500 Girl with geese by water (16x24cm-6x9in) s. panel. 5-Dec-3 Michael Zeller, Lindau #785/R
£430 $731 €628 Poultry (12x25cm-5x10in) s. panel. 28-Nov-3 Zofingen, Switzerland #2676/R (S.FR 950)
£430 $731 €628 Poultry (12x25cm-5x10in) s. panel. 28-Nov-3 Zofingen, Switzerland #2677/R (S.FR 950)
£521 $849 €750 Poultry yard (14x18cm-6x7in) s. panel. 26-Sep-3 Bolland & Marotz, Bremen #613/R
£800 $1440 €1200 Avenue in park (120x90cm-47x35in) s.d.1901. 26-Apr-4 Rieber, Stuttgart #875/R
£805 $1482 €1200 Sussex hen with chicks (13x18cm-5x7in) s. panel. 24-Mar-4 Hugo Ruef, Munich #1117
£1132 $1992 €1653 Hens in courtyard (20x27cm-8x11in) s. board. 23-May-4 Agra, Warsaw #28/R (P.Z 8000)

SCHONICHE, Gottfried (1740-c.1816) German/Dutch
Works on paper
£594 $1022 €850 Portrait of a man. Portrait of a woman (64x49cm-25x19in) i.d.1893 verso pastel pair. 3-Dec-3 Neumeister, Munich #427/R

SCHONLEBER, Elisabeth (1877-?) German
£433 $667 €680 Asters in vase (38x44cm-15x17in) i. verso. 4-Sep-2 Schopman, Hamburg #108/R

SCHONLEBER, Gustav (1851-1917) German
£1086 $1738 €1586 Shore landscape near Besigheim (26x41cm-10x16in) s.d.1886 i. verso board. 16-Sep-3 Philippe Schuler, Zurich #3353/R est:2500-3000 (S.FR 2400)
£2817 $4873 €4000 Nervi (28x34cm-11x13in) s.d.86 i. verso board. 13-Dec-3 Lempertz, Koln #43/R est:3000
£3067 $5581 €4600 View towards Rothenburg in the evening light (42x54cm-17x21in) s.d.1906 board prov.exhib.lit. 1-Jul-4 Van Ham, Cologne #1604/R est:2500
Works on paper
£417 $679 €600 Fishing off Dutch coast (27x22cm-11x9in) s.d.1887 W/C. 19-Jul-3 Berlinghof, Heidelberg #264

SCHONPFLUG, Fritz (1873-1951) Austrian
Works on paper
£329 $605 €500 Fiaker (20x28cm-8x11in) s. W/C. 22-Jun-4 Wiener Kunst Auktionen, Vienna #195/R
£559 $951 €800 Caricature of the Military (29x32cm-11x13in) s. W/C. 27-Nov-3 Dorotheum, Linz #612/R

SCHOOCK, Hendrik (1630-1707) Dutch
£52273 $92000 €76319 Still life of tulips, roses, blackberries and other flowers in a glass vase on a ledge (54x43cm-21x17in) s.i. panel prov. 18-May-4 Bonhams & Butterfields, San Francisco #22/R est:25000-35000

SCHOOFS, Rudolf (1932-) German
Works on paper
£486 $812 €700 Bones (50x80cm-20x31in) s.d. pencil pastel chk. 24-Oct-3 Ketterer, Hamburg #1078/R

SCHOON, Theo (1915-1985) New Zealander
Works on paper
£558 $959 €815 Untitled (49x73cm-19x29in) pencil. 7-Dec-3 International Art Centre, Auckland #200/R (NZ.D 1500)

SCHOONBROOD, Henri (1898-1972) Dutch
£336 $624 €500 Lost son (110x80cm-43x31in) s.d.1944. 4-Mar-4 Auction Maastricht #1107/R
£537 $999 €800 Girl with book (50x60cm-20x24in) s.d.1944. 4-Mar-4 Auction Maastricht #1108/R

SCHOONHOVEN VAN BEURDEN, Alexander Franciscus van (1883-1963) Dutch
£625 $987 €900 Village in the distance (30x40cm-12x16in) s. 2-Sep-3 Christie's, Amsterdam #401

SCHOONHOVEN, Jan J (1914-1994) Dutch
£5000 $9200 €7500 Geheel (64x49cm-25x19in) init.d.58 s.i.d. verso board prov. 8-Jun-4 Sotheby's, Amsterdam #108/R est:5000-7000
£6333 $11653 €9500 Motel (60x40cm-24x16in) init.d.56 s.i.d. verso oil card on board prov. 8-Jun-4 Sotheby's, Amsterdam #96/R est:4000-6000
£12195 $20000 €17805 Golfkarton (29x20cm-11x8in) s.d.1964 verso white paint corregated cardboard on wood prov.exhi. 28-May-3 Sotheby's, Amsterdam #66/R est:12000-15000
£13986 $23776 €20000 R69-11 (30x30cm-12x12in) s.i.d.1969 verso white painted cardboard relief prov. 25-Nov-3 Christie's, Amsterdam #316/R est:20000-30000
£27972 $47552 €40000 Sterren-gerekt-3 (63x43cm-25x17in) s.i.d.1968 verso white painted cardboard relief. 25-Nov-3 Christie's, Amsterdam #314/R est:40000-60000
Sculpture
£2899 $4754 €4000 Machien (74x48cm-29x19in) s.d.57 s.i.d.1957 verso paint. 27-May-3 Sotheby's, Amsterdam #442/R est:5000-7000
£10976 $18000 €16025 Untitled (15x10cm-6x4in) s.d.1964 verso white paint paper-mache on wood prov.exhib. 28-May-3 Sotheby's, Amsterdam #25/R est:12000-15000
£13415 $22000 €19586 Untitled (15x10cm-6x4in) s.d.1964 verso white paint paper-mache on wood prov.exhib. 28-May-3 Sotheby's, Amsterdam #26/R est:12000-15000
£17073 $28000 €24927 Untitled (15x10cm-6x4in) s.d.1964 verso white paint paper-mache on wood prov.exhib. 28-May-3 Sotheby's, Amsterdam #24/R est:12000-15000
£25333 $46613 €38000 R 72-31 (43x43cm-17x17in) s.i.d.1972 verso relief prov. 9-Jun-4 Christie's, Amsterdam #335/R est:30000-50000
£36232 $59420 €50000 R72-73-M-13 (126x86cm-50x34in) s.i.d.1973 verso white paint paper-mache prov. 27-May-3 Sotheby's, Amsterdam #438/R est:60000-80000
£36232 $59420 €50000 R72-73-M2 (126x86cm-50x34in) s.i.d.1973 verso white paint paper-mache prov. 27-May-3 Sotheby's, Amsterdam #443/R est:60000-90000
£52448 $90210 €75000 Quadraten (126x102cm-50x40in).i.d.1969 v. white painted papermache on wood p. 2-Dec-3 Sotheby's, Amsterdam #164/R est:50000-70000
£73333 $134933 €110000 Series of nine white reliefs (15x10cm-6x4in) s.i.d.1964 verso white painted paper-mache wood nine prov.exhib. 8-Jun-4 Sotheby's, Amsterdam #98/R est:135000-150000
Works on paper
£1119 $1924 €1600 T90-16 (44x29cm-17x11in) s.i.d.1990 s.i.d.verso Indian ink ball point pen. 2-Dec-3 Sotheby's, Amsterdam #175/R est:1600-1800
£1304 $2139 €1800 T82-78 (50x33cm-20x13in) s.i.d.1982 ink. 27-May-3 Sotheby's, Amsterdam #445/R est:1800-2200
£1833 $3373 €2750 T80-47 (48x29cm-19x11in) s.i.d.1980 ink. 8-Jun-4 Sotheby's, Amsterdam #116/R est:2000-3000
£1867 $3435 €2800 T80-59 (48x29cm-19x11in) s.i.d.1980 ink. 8-Jun-4 Sotheby's, Amsterdam #117/R est:2000-3000
£1888 $3248 €2700 T81-25 (44x29cm-17x11in) s.i.d.1981 s.i.d.verso Indian ink. 2-Dec-3 Sotheby's, Amsterdam #174/R est:1800-2200
£2133 $3925 €3200 T62-108 (50x37cm-20x15in) s.i.d.1962 verso ink prov. 8-Jun-4 Sotheby's, Amsterdam #106/R est:2000-3000
£2133 $3925 €3200 T62-114 (50x37cm-20x15in) s.i.d.1962 verso ink prov. 8-Jun-4 Sotheby's, Amsterdam #107/R est:2000-3000
£2333 $4293 €3500 T62-101 (50x37cm-20x15in) s.i.d.1962 verso ink prov. 8-Jun-4 Sotheby's, Amsterdam #111/R est:2000-3000
£7692 $13231 €11000 Peinture zero - 3 (60x40cm-24x16in) s.i.d.1968 verso whirewash ink on panel prov. 2-Dec-3 Sotheby's, Amsterdam #173/R est:3500-4000
£8000 $14720 €12000 T 62-25 T 62-81 T 62-45 T 62-24 (50x32cm-20x13in) each s.i. verso ink four prov. 8-Jun-4 Sotheby's, Amsterdam #101/R est:8000-12000
£31469 $53497 €45000 R 72 - 73 - M - 11 (126x86cm-50x34in) s. verso col papiermache panel prov.exhib. 27-Nov-3 Lempertz, Koln #423/R est:45000-50000

SCHOOP, Max Ulrich (1903-1990) German
Sculpture
£1659 $3053 €2422 Otter (62cm-24in) s.d. brown gold pat.bronze. 14-Jun-4 Philippe Schuler, Zurich #4178/R est:5000-7000 (S.FR 3800)

SCHOOTEN, Floris van (1590-1657) Dutch
£22148 $41416 €33000 Still life of fruit with bread (40x56cm-16x22in) board. 25-Feb-4 Porro, Milan #60/R est:32000
£30000 $51900 €43800 Still life of cheese and various foods and objects on a table draped with cloth (39x55cm-15x22in) oak panel prov. 11-Dec-3 Sotheby's, London #60/R est:30000-40000
£92000 $164680 €138000 Pewter plates with oysters, fish, tobacco and other objects on a table (36x49cm-14x19in) mono.i. panel prov.exhib.lit. 17-May-4 Christie's, Amsterdam #81/R est:120000-160000

SCHOOTEN, Floris van (attrib) (1590-1657) Dutch
£4355 $7273 €6358 Market scene with two women and the fruits of the autumn (51x82cm-20x32in) panel. 13-Oct-3 Blomqvist, Oslo #266/R est:30000-40000 (N.KR 51000)

SCHOPF, Gustav Georg (1899-1986) German
£373 $597 €530 Steamroller, tram, cyclists (35x35cm-14x14in) board. 18-Sep-3 Rieber, Stuttgart #1034/R
£493 $789 €700 Racers (108x79cm-43x31in) board. 18-Sep-3 Rieber, Stuttgart #1030
£600 $1080 €900 Spring in the village (70x100cm-28x39in) board. 26-Apr-4 Rieber, Stuttgart #1078/R

SCHOPFER, Franziska (1763-1836) German
Works on paper
£5782 $10350 €8500 Princess Alexandra Amalie and Prince Adalbert Wilhelm (15x12cm-6x5in) s.d.1830 W/C htd white. 17-Mar-4 Neumeister, Munich #390/R est:7000

SCHOPIN, F H (19th C) French
£5173 $8638 €7500 La belle Egyptienne (154x130cm-61x51in) bears sig.d.1866. 17-Nov-3 Tajan, Paris #22/R est:8000-10000

SCHOPIN, Frederic Henri (attrib) (1804-1880) French
Prints
£20000 $33400 €29000 Le bucher de Sardanapale (60x91cm-24x36in) i.verso lit. 17-Nov-3 Tajan, Paris #83/R est:30000-40000

SCHOPPE, Julius (elder) (1795-1868) German
£2766 $4481 €3900 Portrait of A Schadow, aged 17 (52x41cm-20x16in) s.i.d.1814 lit. 23-May-3 Karlheinz Kaupp, Staufen #1752/R est:400

SCHOR, Johann Paul (attrib) (1615-1674) Austrian
£13245 $24106 €20000 Agar and the angel (125x173cm-49x68in) prov. 16-Jun-4 Christie's, Rome #440/R est:20000-30000

SCHORER, Hans Friedrich (17th C) German
Works on paper
£543 $891 €750 Venus with Bacchus and Ceres (25x20cm-10x8in) mono. pen wash. 30-May-3 Bassenge, Berlin #7775

SCHORK, Hans (1849-?) Austrian
Sculpture
£1189 $2045 €1700 La semeuse (84cm-33in) s. bronze. 2-Dec-3 Campo & Campo, Antwerp #324/R est:1800-2000

SCHORSTEIN, Lucien de (19/20th C) French
£841 $1329 €1219 Place de La Concorde et l'Orangerie (67x51cm-26x20in) s. 2-Sep-3 Rasmussen, Copenhagen #1664/R (D.KR 9000)

SCHOTEL, Anthonie Pieter (1890-1958) Dutch
£629 $1082 €900 Fisherman near the coast of Bretagne (41x50cm-16x20in) s. board. 7-Dec-3 Sotheby's, Amsterdam #697/R
£1250 $1975 €1800 Shipping on the Merwede with Dordrecht beyond (61x81cm-24x32in) s. 2-Sep-3 Christie's, Amsterdam #340/R est:1500-2000
£1842 $3334 €2800 Spakenburg Harbour (40x40cm-16x16in) s. i.verso canvas on panel. 19-Apr-4 Glerum, Amsterdam #170/R est:1400-1600
£1944 $3072 €2800 View of the Parkhaven seen from St. Job, Rotterdam (45x56cm-18x22in) s.d.21. 2-Sep-3 Christie's, Amsterdam #290/R est:4000-6000
£2517 $4204 €3600 Fishing boat with sail, Volendam (50x50cm-20x20in) s. i.verso prov. 30-Jun-3 Sotheby's, Amsterdam #207/R
£2585 $4705 €3800 Couple in a cafe (40x29cm-16x11in) s.i. panel. 3-Feb-4 Christie's, Amsterdam #297/R est:2000-3000
£3158 $5811 €4800 Canal with moored boats (40x50cm-16x20in) s. 28-Jun-4 Sotheby's, Amsterdam #180/R est:1000-1500
£3472 $5903 €5000 Early morning - a barge on the river Vecht (80x100cm-31x39in) s. 28-Oct-3 Christie's, Amsterdam #153/R est:6000-8000
£9211 $16947 €14000 A view of the Leidseplein, Amsterdam (60x70cm-24x28in) s. i. on stretcher lit. 22-Jun-4 Christie's, Amsterdam #313/R est:10000-15000
Works on paper
£417 $658 €600 Women conversing on a bridge, Bruges (54x45cm-21x18in) s.d.24 bodycol gouache. 2-Sep-3 Christie's, Amsterdam #287

SCHOTEL, J C (1787-1838) Dutch
Works on paper
£822 $1397 €1200 Ship-building yard (31x43cm-12x17in) s.d.1816 sepia. 5-Nov-3 Vendue Huis, Gravenhage #29

SCHOTEL, Jan Christianus (1787-1838) Dutch
£791 $1298 €1100 Sailing ship and boat off Dutch coast (36x50cm-14x20in) Indian ink brush pen pencil prov. 4-Jun-3 Ketterer, Hamburg #18/R
£15385 $26462 €22000 Marine landscape (39x51cm-15x20in) s. panel. 2-Dec-3 Christie's, Paris #221/R est:12000-18000
£19868 $36358 €30000 Boats in the storm (71x93cm-28x37in) s. 9-Apr-4 Bailly Pommery, Paris #36/R est:20000-30000

SCHOTEL, Jan Christianus (attrib) (1787-1838) Dutch
£850 $1521 €1241 Canal landscape (14x19cm-6x7in) panel prov. 25-May-4 Bukowskis, Stockholm #527a/R (S.KR 11500)
Works on paper
£800 $1432 €1168 Barges in close quarters at the mouth of the estuary (22x30cm-9x12in) brown ink grey wash. 26-May-4 Christie's, Kensington #377/R
£1074 $1976 €1600 Sailing ship and boat off Dutch coast (36x50cm-14x20in) Indian ink brush on pen pencil. 26-Mar-4 Ketterer, Hamburg #47/R est:1000-1200

SCHOTEL, Petrus Jan (1808-1865) Dutch
£3819 $6493 €5500 Busy shipping by a jetty (32x46cm-13x18in) s. panel. 28-Oct-3 Christie's, Amsterdam #78/R est:3000-5000
£10000 $18000 €15000 Sailing vessels on the Zuiderzee (46x62cm-18x24in) s. panel prov. 20-Apr-4 Sotheby's, Amsterdam #191/R est:10000-15000

Works on paper

£2432 $4281 €3600 Fishing boats in harbour (33x44cm-13x17in) i. verso pen wash prov. 22-May-4 Lempertz, Koln #1461/R est:2700

SCHOTH, Albert (?) ?

£251 $450 €366 Unloading the catch onto the shore (23x30cm-9x12in) s. card on board. 16-Mar-4 Bonhams & Butterfields, San Francisco #6139/R

SCHOTH, Anton (1859-1906) Austrian

£382 $603 €550 View across a river of a town with a church (24x45cm-9x18in) s. 5-Sep-3 Wendl, Rudolstadt #3611/R

£521 $823 €750 Fishermen in their boats (24x45cm-9x18in) s. 5-Sep-3 Wendl, Rudolstadt #3612/R

SCHOTT, Walter (1861-1938) German

Sculpture

£2200 $3740 €3212 Woman playing with ball (35cm-14in) s. pat bronze. 28-Oct-3 Sotheby's, London #101/R

SCHOTZ, Benno (1891-1984) British

Sculpture

£2000 $3220 €2900 Woman with towel (39cm-15in) mono. bronze exhib. 21-Aug-3 Bonhams, Edinburgh #900/R est:1500-2000

£2500 $4025 €3625 Unde undressing (42cm-17in) mono.d.1929 bronze on onyx plinth. 21-Aug-3 Bonhams, Edinburgh #899/R est:1000-1500

SCHOU, Henning (19th C) ?

£1469 $2497 €2100 Voiliers au large d'un port au Danemark (68x107cm-27x42in) mono. painted c.1900. 18-Nov-3 Vanderkindere, Brussels #87 est:2000-3000

SCHOU, Karl (1870-1938) Danish

£361 $667 €527 Interior scene with woman by window (49x40cm-19x16in) init. 15-Mar-4 Rasmussen, Vejle #410/R (D.KR 4000)

£374 $591 €542 Interior scene with man watching two marble sculptures, evening (42x46cm-17x18in) init. 2-Sep-3 Rasmussen, Copenhagen #1969/R (D.KR 4000)

SCHOU, L A (1838-1867) Danish

£449 $751 €656 Charity - old man by church collection box (69x46cm-27x18in) s. 25-Oct-3 Rasmussen, Havnen #2017 (D.KR 4800)

SCHOU, Ludvig Abelin (1838-1867) Danish

£4402 $7131 €6383 Portrait of nude woman seen from the side, seated on stone in wood (68x50cm-27x20in) 4-Aug-3 Rasmussen, Vejle #82/R est:60000-80000 (D.KR 46000)

SCHOU, P A (1844-1914) Danish

£449 $836 €656 The widow (83x63cm-33x25in) mono. exhib.prov. 2-Mar-4 Rasmussen, Copenhagen #1543/R (D.KR 5000)

£538 $968 €785 Sitting room interior (70x93cm-28x37in) mono. 24-Apr-4 Rasmussen, Havnen #2082 (D.KR 6000)

SCHOUBOE, Henrik (1876-1949) Danish

£340 $609 €496 Bathing nymph (123x115cm-48x45in) mono. 12-Jan-4 Rasmussen, Vejle #523/R (D.KR 3600)

£397 $711 €580 Birgitte in the garden, female nude (61x56cm-24x22in) mono. 12-Jan-4 Rasmussen, Vejle #527/R (D.KR 4200)

£510 $914 €745 Garden scene with lady seated wearing light dress (90x80cm-35x31in) mono. 12-Jan-4 Rasmussen, Vejle #525/R (D.KR 5400)

£1418 $2538 €2070 Landscape with female nude (115x104cm-45x41in) mono. exhib. 12-Jan-4 Rasmussen, Vejle #524/R est:6000-8000 (D.KR 15000)

SCHOUBOE, Pablo (1874-1941) Danish

£3000 $4890 €4380 Bay of Rio de Janeiro from the road to Petropolis (62x85cm-24x33in) s. 24-Sep-3 Christie's, London #126/R est:700-1000

SCHOUKAIEFF, Vassili Ivanowitch (1887-?) Russian?

£5704 $9868 €8100 Seated couple under pine trees by the sea (61x50cm-24x20in) s.d.1928. 14-Dec-3 Eric Pillon, Calais #116/R

SCHOUMAN, Aert (1710-1792) Dutch

£5667 $10143 €8500 Portrait of a family, said to be Yoan van Wageningen and children (58x50cm-23x20in) s.d.1749 i.verso panel. 17-May-4 Christie's, Amsterdam #103/R est:6000-8000

Works on paper

£1111 $2000 €1622 Exotic birds on a tree (37x26cm-15x10in) i.verso black chk W/C. 22-Jan-4 Christie's, Rockefeller NY #188/R est:2000-3000

£1351 $2378 €2000 Egyptian goat (15x20cm-6x8in) i.verso W/C black chk exhib. 19-May-4 Sotheby's, Amsterdam #207/R est:2400-2800

£1486 $2616 €2200 Newborn chick (13x18cm-5x7in) bears i. pen black ink W/C black chk. 19-May-4 Sotheby's, Amsterdam #220/R est:3000-4000

£1556 $2800 €2272 Sparrowhawk on a branch (37x26cm-15x10in) i.d.1775 verso black chk W/C. 22-Jan-4 Christie's, Rockefeller NY #178/R est:2000-4000

£1667 $3000 €2434 Brace of pheasants, cock and hen (36x26cm-14x10in) i.d.1761 verso black chk W/C. 22-Jan-4 Christie's, Rockefeller NY #171/R est:3000-4000

£1667 $3000 €2434 Two long-tailed tits and a bunting (36x26cm-14x10in) init.i.d.1770 black chk W/C. 22-Jan-4 Christie's, Rockefeller NY #173/R est:3000-5000

£1667 $3000 €2434 Guineafowl (37x25cm-15x10in) i.d.1762 black chk W/C. 22-Jan-4 Christie's, Rockefeller NY #179/R est:3000-4000

£1667 $3000 €2434 Sleeping dog. Anteater. Resting cow (20x15cm-8x6in) s.i.d.1765 verso black chk W/C three in one mount. 22-Jan-4 Christie's, Rockefeller NY #190/R est:4000-6000

£1667 $3000 €2434 Black crownbird (27x37cm-11x15in) i.d.1768 i.verso black chk W/C. 22-Jan-4 Christie's, Rockefeller NY #196/R est:2000-3000

£1778 $3200 €2596 Skimmer and dove on the sea shore (26x38cm-10x15in) s. i.verso black chk W/C. 22-Jan-4 Christie's, Rockefeller NY #195/R est:3000-5000

£2041 $3653 €3000 Un jeune homme couronnant de fleurs une musicienne dans un parc (29x20cm-11x8in) d.1778 graphite W/C. 18-Mar-4 Christie's, Paris #196/R est:2000-3000

£2111 $3800 €3082 Purple heron on a sand bank (38x25cm-15x10in) i.d.1755 verso black chk W/C. 22-Jan-4 Christie's, Rockefeller NY #187/R est:3000-5000

£2333 $4200 €3406 Bird of Paradise and a parakeet (40x26cm-16x10in) i.d.1783 verso black chk W/C. 22-Jan-4 Christie's, Rockefeller NY #174/R est:3000-5000

£2333 $4200 €3406 Two turtle doves on a tree (37x26cm-15x10in) i.verso black chk W/C. 22-Jan-4 Christie's, Rockefeller NY #182/R est:3000-4000

£2667 $4800 €3894 West Indian goose by a pond (36x26cm-14x10in) i.d.1765 verso black chk W/C. 22-Jan-4 Christie's, Rockefeller NY #185/R est:3000-5000

£2759 $4579 €4000 Chardon dans un paysage (41x27cm-16x11in) s. graphite W/C. 30-Sep-3 Christie's, Paris #15/R est:4000-6000

£2778 $5000 €4056 Merganser standing on rocks with another behind (33x26cm-13x10in) i.d.1756 mount black chk W/C. 22-Jan-4 Christie's, Rockefeller NY #180/R est:3000-5000

£2838 $4995 €4200 View on the river Lek near Ameide (11x18cm-4x7in) init.i.d.1752 verso W/C black chk exhib. 19-May-4 Sotheby's, Amsterdam #219/R est:3500-4500

£3082 $5240 €4500 Duck (36x27cm-14x11in) W/C gouache. 4-Nov-3 Sotheby's, Amsterdam #143/R est:5000-7000

£3333 $6000 €4866 Jay with outstretched wings and a wren on a tree beside an estuary (34x25cm-13x10in) s.i.d.1778 mount black chk W/C. 22-Jan-4 Christie's, Rockefeller NY #184/R est:5000-7000

£3611 $6500 €5272 Kestrel perching on a branch, a windmill beyond (38x25cm-15x10in) s.i.d.1752 black chk W/C. 22-Jan-4 Christie's, Rockefeller NY #176/R est:5000-7000

£3611 $6500 €5272 Egyptian goose on the shore (36x25cm-14x10in) i.d.1756 verso black chk W/C. 22-Jan-4 Christie's, Rockefeller NY #186/R est:3000-5000

£3889 $7000 €5678 Two merlins perching on a tree (42x26cm-17x10in) i.mount black chk W/C. 22-Jan-4 Christie's, Rockefeller NY #177/R est:4000-6000

£3889 $7000 €5678 Monkey seated on a rock looking at a civet (26x38cm-10x15in) s.d.1764 i.verso black chk W/C. 22-Jan-4 Christie's, Rockefeller NY #193/R est:4000-6000

£4392 $7730 €6500 Silver pheasants, the cock with an Indian pitta, and the hen (19x29cm-7x11in) s. pen col ink W/C black chk pair prov.exhib.lit. 19-May-4 Sotheby's, Amsterdam #212/R est:8500-10000

£4392 $7730 €6500 Cockerel, hen, chicks, guinea fowl and dog by ruined column (26x22cm-10x9in) s.i.d.1758 W/C gouache prov.exhib.lit. 19-May-4 Sotheby's, Amsterdam #221/R est:5500-6500

£4722 $8500 €6894 Sun bittern displaying (37x26cm-15x10in) i.d.1760 mount black chk W/C. 22-Jan-4 Christie's, Rockefeller NY #181/R est:4000-6000

£4722 $8500 €6894 Crownbird at the foot of a tree, a terrace in the background (28x40cm-11x16in) indis.i.verso black chk W/C. 22-Jan-4 Christie's, Rockefeller NY #194/R est:4000-6000

£5068 $8919 €7500 Dutch river landscape with spoonbill, stork, goose, and other birds (25x20cm-10x8in) W/C black chk exhib.lit. 19-May-4 Sotheby's, Amsterdam #204/R est:9000-12000

£5068 $8919 €7500 Guinea pig, with a hummingbird on a branch above (36x25cm-14x10in) s.d.1760 i.verso W/C exhib.lit. 19-May-4 Sotheby's, Amsterdam #208/R est:9000-12000

£5278 $9500 €7706 Bird of Paradise in an exotic landscape (43x28cm-17x11in) i.d.1776 verso black chk W/C. 22-Jan-4 Christie's, Rockefeller NY #170/R est:6000-8000

£6111 $11000 €8922 Two green parakeet and a Brazilian robin perching on a tree (32x22cm-13x9in) i.d.1796 verso black chk W/C. 22-Jan-4 Christie's, Rockefeller NY #172/R est:3000-5000

£9459 $16649 €14000 Peacock (34x24cm-13x9in) W/C gouache black chk exhib.lit. 19-May-4 Sotheby's, Amsterdam #224/R est:6000-8000

£12778 $23000 €18656 Golden pheasant standing on a log with a female pheasant and her chicks (25x37cm-10x15in) s. i.d.1761 verso black chk W/C. 22-Jan-4 Christie's, Rockefeller NY #192/R est:4000-6000

£13514 $23784 €20000 Jan Snellen with his mother, Margaretha van T Wedde, and his first wife (43x34cm-17x13in) s.d.1746 W/C gouache prov.exhib.lit. 19-May-4 Sotheby's, Amsterdam #217/R est:25000-35000

£17568 $30919 €26000 View of Dordrecht from the south-west, with cattle and milkmaid (17x26cm-7x10in) s.i.d.1739 i.verso W/C gouache prov.exhib.lit. 19-May-4 Sotheby's, Amsterdam #206/R est:7000-9000

£21622 $38054 €32000 Bergamot plant (43x28cm-17x11in) s.d.1753 W/C prov.exhib.lit. 19-May-4 Sotheby's, Amsterdam #209/R est:25000-35000

SCHOUMAN, Aert (attrib) (1710-1792) Dutch

£2824 $4800 €4123 Assembly of pheasants in a landscape (69x51cm-27x20in) prov. 22-Nov-3 Jackson's, Cedar Falls #1/R est:3000-5000

£2824 $4800 €4123 Pheasants in a landscape (69x51cm-27x20in) prov. 22-Nov-3 Jackson's, Cedar Falls #2/R est:3000-5000

Works on paper

£2703 $4757 €4000 Black winged stilt (48x32cm-19x13in) i.verso W/C gouache black chk prov. 19-May-4 Sotheby's, Amsterdam #226/R est:2800-3500

£5000 $9000 €7300 Whydah bird and a continga (38x25cm-15x10in) black chk W/C. 22-Jan-4 Christie's, Rockefeller NY #183/R est:3000-5000

SCHOUMAN, Aert (studio) (1710-1792) Dutch

£82237 $151316 €125000 Birds in a park (197x162cm-78x64in) pair. 25-Jun-4 Piasa, Paris #30/R est:25000-30000

SCHOUMAN, Izaak (1801-1878) Dutch

Works on paper

£514 $873 €750 Shipping in heavy sea, breakwater to the right (25x32cm-10x13in) s. black chk pen ink W/C framing lines prov. 5-Nov-3 Christie's, Amsterdam #134/R

SCHOUMAN, Martinus (1770-1848) Dutch

£2778 $4389 €4000 Stiff breeze (70x92cm-28x36in) s. 2-Sep-3 Christie's, Amsterdam #308/R est:4000-6000

£4422 $8048 €6500 Threemaster Louisa Prinses der Nederlanden in full sail (72x94cm-28x37in) s. 3-Feb-4 Christie's, Amsterdam #65/R est:4000-6000

£20541 $38000 €29990 English flagship, Venerable, engaging the Dutch flagship, Vrijheid (81x118cm-32x46in) prov. 10-Feb-4 Christie's, Rockefeller NY #159/R est:25000-35000

SCHOUMAN, Martinus (attrib) (1770-1848) Dutch

Works on paper

£1149	$2022	€1700	Extensive river landscape with sailing vessels and figures (20x33cm-8x13in) W/C. 19-May-4 Sotheby's, Amsterdam #274/R est:1000-1500

SCHOUTEN, Bart Leroy (20th C) Belgian

£484	$890	€707	On the terrace (36x58cm-14x23in) s. canvas on panel. 14-Jun-4 Waddingtons, Toronto #225/R est:1200-1400 (C.D 1200)
£679	$1133	€991	At the carnival (50x59cm-20x23in) s. 17-Nov-3 Waddingtons, Toronto #29/R (C.D 1500)

SCHOUTEN, Henry (1864-1927) Belgian

£265	$482	€400	Vase de fleurs (45x30cm-18x12in) s. 15-Jun-4 Vanderkindere, Brussels #51
£274	$466	€400	Le retour a l'ecurie (60x45cm-24x18in) s. 4-Nov-3 Servarts Themis, Bruxelles #622
£278	$442	€400	Vaches s'abreuvant (73x51cm-29x20in) s. 15-Sep-3 Horta, Bruxelles #302
£280	$481	€400	Nature morte aux raisins (31x40cm-12x16in) s. 2-Dec-3 Campo & Campo, Antwerp #325
£313	$522	€450	Panier aux lilas (40x80cm-16x31in) s. 21-Oct-3 Galerie Moderne, Brussels #335/R
£350	$584	€500	Vaches au paturage (80x60cm-31x24in) s. 7-Oct-3 Palais de Beaux Arts, Brussels #581
£390	$651	€550	Cows in the meadow (36x56cm-14x22in) s. panel. 20-Oct-3 Bernaerts, Antwerp #483/R
£400	$728	€600	Fermiere et ses chevres (44x60cm-17x24in) s. 4-Jul-4 MonsAntic, Maisieres #480
£490	$832	€700	Poules et coq (40x30cm-16x12in) s. 18-Nov-3 Galerie Moderne, Brussels #679/R
£490	$842	€700	Cows standing in a pond (62x91cm-24x36in) s. 3-Dec-3 Neumeister, Munich #734/R
£521	$828	€750	Vaches et poules au pre (80x120cm-31x47in) s. 9-Sep-3 Vanderkindere, Brussels #62
£528	$914	€750	Fermiere et ses vaches au pre (32x40cm-13x16in) s. 9-Dec-3 Vanderkindere, Brussels #121
£537	$999	€800	Goats in pasture (48x57cm-19x22in) s. 8-Mar-4 Bernaerts, Antwerp #755/R
£563	$975	€800	Landscape with cows (80x60cm-31x24in) s. 13-Dec-3 De Vuyst, Lokeren #280
£567	$1020	€850	Cows and ducks at the waters edge (54x67cm-21x26in) s. 26-Apr-4 Bernaerts, Antwerp #131/R
£599	$1036	€850	Coq et poules (33x39cm-13x15in) s. 9-Dec-3 Vanderkindere, Brussels #117
£600	$1074	€900	Vacher et son troupeau (90x60cm-35x24in) s. 11-May-4 Vanderkindere, Brussels #47
£720	$1318	€1051	Highland cattle (80x60cm-31x24in) s. panel. 1-Jun-4 Hodgins, Calgary #299/R (C.D 1800)
£795	$1446	€1200	Poules et coqs (40x60cm-16x24in) s. 15-Jun-4 Galerie Moderne, Brussels #331/R
£804	$1367	€1150	Vaches au pre (71x100cm-28x39in) s. 18-Nov-3 Vanderkindere, Brussels #209
£855	$1574	€1300	Sheep on a sandy track (61x45cm-24x18in) s. 22-Jun-4 Christie's, Amsterdam #135/R
£872	$1605	€1300	Les chevaux (60x90cm-24x35in) s. 23-Mar-4 Galerie Moderne, Brussels #350/R
£909	$1518	€1300	Deux brabancons tirant une herse (80x118cm-31x46in) s. 13-Oct-3 Horta, Bruxelles #247
£909	$1518	€1300	Combat de coqs (60x76cm-24x30in) s. 13-Oct-3 Horta, Bruxelles #248
£909	$1518	€1300	Retour a la bergerie (80x100cm-31x39in) s. 13-Oct-3 Horta, Bruxelles #249
£978	$1800	€1428	Shepherds (74x100cm-29x39in) s. 22-Jun-4 Galeria y Remates, Montevideo #38/R est:2000-3000
£979	$1664	€1400	Jeune berger et moutons rentrant a la bergerie (60x90cm-24x35in) s. 1-Dec-3 Palais de Beaux Arts, Brussels #311/R
£987	$1786	€1500	Chiens de chasse et chasseur dans les dunes (80x60cm-31x24in) s. 19-Apr-4 Horta, Bruxelles #440 est:750-800
£993	$1808	€1500	Riviere avec vaches et fermier (86x86cm-34x34in) s. panel. 16-Jun-4 Hotel des Ventes Mosan, Brussels #173 est:1800-2000
£1020	$1857	€1500	Donkeys in a meadow (40x54cm-16x21in) s. 3-Feb-4 Christie's, Amsterdam #283 est:1500-2000
£1067	$1941	€1600	Rentree a l'ecurie (81x60cm-32x24in) s. 4-Jul-4 MonsAntic, Maisieres #479 est:1000-1500
£1074	$1976	€1600	Debourrage des chevaux (80x100cm-31x39in) s. 28-Mar-4 MonsAntic, Maisieres #428 est:1800-2200
£1127	$2017	€1600	Cattle out at pasture (81x100cm-32x39in) s. lit. 8-Jan-4 Allgauer, Kempten #2511/R est:900
£1133	$2040	€1700	Les chevaux (42x60cm-17x24in) s. 20-Apr-4 Galerie Moderne, Brussels #240/R est:1000-1500
£1224	$2229	€1800	Ploughing the land (41x71cm-16x28in) s. 3-Feb-4 Christie's, Amsterdam #261/R est:2000-3000
£1250	$1962	€1800	Berger et ses moutons (100x80cm-39x31in) s. 26-Aug-3 Galerie Moderne, Brussels #227/R est:1000-1500
£1259	$2140	€1800	Les anes au pre (64x44cm-25x17in) s. 18-Nov-3 Vanderkindere, Brussels #154 est:1400-1800
£1267	$2293	€1900	Poules et chevres a la ferme (38x55cm-15x22in) s. panel. 30-Mar-4 Campo & Campo, Antwerp #261/R est:1600-1800
£1333	$2400	€2000	Plowing farmer with horses and dog near a river (120x80cm-47x31in) s. 26-Apr-4 Bernaerts, Antwerp #126/R est:2000-2500
£1370	$2329	€2000	Hunter with dogs in the dunes (42x73cm-17x29in) s. 5-Nov-3 Vendue Huis, Gravenhage #232/R est:1500-2000
£1400	$2506	€2100	Chevres, vaches et moutons (40x60cm-16x24in) s. set of three. 11-May-4 Vanderkindere, Brussels #237 est:1800-2400
£1408	$2437	€2000	Canards et Dindons (65x50cm-26x20in) s. pair. 9-Dec-3 Vanderkindere, Brussels #6 est:1000-1500
£1447	$2620	€2200	Corbeille aux roses et cerises (55x65cm-22x26in) s. with alias Jos Klaas. 19-Apr-4 Horta, Bruxelles #441 est:650-850
£1477	$2732	€2200	Trois chiens devant un nid (60x90cm-24x35in) s. 15-Mar-4 Horta, Bruxelles #24 est:1000-1500
£1500	$2505	€2190	Cart horses on a coastal road (45x69cm-18x27in) s. 7-Oct-3 Bonhams, Knightsbridge #353/R est:1500-2000
£1514	$2528	€2195	Cows grazing by pond (82x100cm-32x39in) s. 23-Jun-3 Philippe Schuler, Zurich #3547 est:2000-2500 (S.FR 3300)
£1600	$2912	€2400	Horse and two foals in open flat countryside (60x80cm-24x31in) s. 20-Jun-4 Wilkinson, Doncaster #319 est:2500-3500
£1655	$3062	€2400	Vaches et canards (60x90cm-24x35in) s. 16-Feb-4 Horta, Bruxelles #28 est:1000-1500
£1667	$2650	€2400	Vaches au paturage (80x120cm-31x47in) s. 9-Sep-3 Palais de Beaux Arts, Brussels #271/R est:2000-3000
£1678	$2803	€2400	Jetees de fleurs sur un entablement (61x90cm-24x35in) bears another sig. 13-Oct-3 Horta, Bruxelles #246 est:1800-2200
£1711	$3147	€2600	Chevaux et pigeons dans l'ecurie (98x90cm-39x35in) s. 22-Jun-4 Palais de Beaux Arts, Brussels #308/R est:4000-5000
£1793	$3228	€2600	Berger et son troupeau (60x90cm-24x35in) s. 20-Jan-4 Galerie Moderne, Brussels #210/R est:1000-1500
£2254	$3899	€3200	Chevaux sauvages (100x150cm-39x59in) s. 9-Dec-3 Campo, Vlaamse Kaai #432/R est:2300-2600
£4000	$7360	€5840	Setters on the scent (102x81cm-40x32in) s. 10-Jun-4 Christie's, Kensington #399/R est:4000-6000
£6200	$10540	€9052	Turkey. Cockerel (99x81cm-39x32in) s. pair. 19-Nov-3 Bonhams, New Bond Street #6/R est:4000-6000

SCHOUTEN, Henry (attrib) (1864-1927) Belgian

£333	$600	€500	Les vaches (54x65cm-21x26in) 20-Apr-4 Galerie Moderne, Brussels #397

SCHOUTEN, Paul (1860-1922) Belgian

£284	$474	€400	Berger et son troupeau (75x100cm-30x39in) s. 17-Jun-3 Galerie Moderne, Brussels #352
£604	$1081	€900	Poules et poussins (27x36cm-11x14in) s. panel. 25-May-4 Campo & Campo, Antwerp #264
£839	$1443	€1200	Cheval avec deux poulins (60x80cm-24x31in) s. 2-Dec-3 Campo & Campo, Antwerp #326

SCHOUW, Adrianus van der (1873-1946) Dutch

Works on paper

£674	$1125	€950	View of entrance to Rotterdam harbour (37x51cm-15x20in) s. W/C. 20-Oct-3 Glerum, Amsterdam #120/R

SCHOVELIN, Axel Thorsen (1827-1893) Danish

£280	$443	€406	Damages on tree trunk (28x38cm-11x15in) s. 2-Sep-3 Rasmussen, Copenhagen #1941 (D.KR 3000)
£373	$585	€545	Autumn landscape near Ordrup (39x62cm-15x24in) s.i.d.1854. 30-Aug-3 Rasmussen, Havnen #2252/R (D.KR 4000)
£587	$922	€857	Woodland lake with oak trees (43x62cm-17x24in) s. 30-Aug-3 Rasmussen, Havnen #2291 (D.KR 6300)
£588	$940	€858	Ermitage with woodland lake (26x38cm-10x15in) s. 22-Sep-3 Rasmussen, Vejle #338/R (D.KR 6200)
£671	$1229	€980	View towards Frederiksborgh Palace with boat on water (37x46cm-15x18in) s. 9-Jun-4 Rasmussen, Copenhagen #1840/R (D.KR 7500)
£1402	$2215	€2033	Coastal landscape with thatched farmhouse, North Sjaelland (68x94cm-27x37in) s. 2-Sep-3 Rasmussen, Copenhagen #1613/R est:15000 (D.KR 15000)
£1448	$2592	€2114	Landscape from Gudebaek (58x92cm-23x36in) s. 10-May-4 Rasmussen, Vejle #88/R est:3000-4000 (D.KR 16000)
£2238	$4096	€3267	Early spring landscape with greenery (61x92cm-24x36in) s. exhib. 9-Jun-4 Rasmussen, Copenhagen #1679/R est:25000-35000 (D.KR 25000)
£2617	$4135	€3795	Stags by large trees in Dyrehagen (116x135cm-46x53in) s. 2-Sep-3 Rasmussen, Copenhagen #1550/R est:30000 (D.KR 28000)
£13233	$22892	€19320	From the village Kragholm at Faareveile Manor, Langeland (71x95cm-28x37in) s.verso. 9-Dec-3 Rasmussen, Copenhagen #1561/R est:8000 (D.KR 140000)

SCHOW, May (1913-1993) American

Works on paper

£299	$500	€437	Portrait of a woman (48x30cm-19x12in) W/C. 18-Oct-3 David Dike, Dallas #329/R
£539	$900	€787	Sunday afternoon gathering (36x53cm-14x21in) W/C. 18-Oct-3 David Dike, Dallas #330/R

SCHOYEN, Erik (1871-1957) Norwegian

£482	$883	€704	Pilot and vessel (44x70cm-17x28in) s. 2-Feb-4 Blomqvist, Lysaker #1271 (N.KR 6000)
£732	$1346	€1098	Two master in fresh breeze (64x49cm-25x19in) s. 14-Jun-4 Blomqvist, Lysaker #1352/R (N.KR 9000)

SCHOYEN, Harald (19/20th C) Norwegian

£775	$1293	€1132	Birches by water (68x93cm-27x37in) s. 20-Oct-3 Blomqvist, Lysaker #1287/R (N.KR 9000)

SCHOYERER, Josef (1844-1923) German

£362	$615	€529	Mountain lake (22x30cm-9x12in) s. panel. 19-Nov-3 Fischer, Luzern #2278/R (S.FR 800)
£367	$660	€550	Mountain landscape with stream (60x87cm-24x34in) s. 21-Apr-4 Neumeister, Munich #2717/R
£420	$713	€600	Autumn landscape (14x20cm-6x8in) s. panel. 20-Nov-3 Van Ham, Cologne #1855
£1267	$2280	€1900	Mountain village with peasants and cattle (77x109cm-30x43in) s.i. 21-Apr-4 Neumeister, Munich #2716/R est:1000
£1521	$2815	€2221	River landscape (18x21cm-7x8in) 14-Mar-4 Agra, Warsaw #37/R (P.Z 11000)
£2500	$4550	€3650	Alpine farming town (78x110cm-31x43in) s. 16-Jun-4 Christie's, Kensington #201/R est:2500-3500

SCHRADER, Karl Heinz (1925-) German

£333	$527	€480	Swedish ship in English Channel (30x60cm-12x24in) s.i. i. verso board. 19-Sep-3 Schloss Ahlden, Ahlden #1571/R

SCHRADER-VELGEN, Carl Hans (1876-1945) German

£1007	$1852	€1500	Avenue in Haimhausen in August (77x94cm-30x37in) s. i.d.1922 verso double-sided lit. 25-Mar-4 Karlheinz Kaupp, Staufen #2716/R est:600
£2308	$3923	€3300	Still life of flowers including gladioli, dahlias (70x58cm-28x23in) s. 20-Nov-3 Van Ham, Cologne #1856/R est:5000

£2550 $4693 €3800 Three female nudes by water (74x89cm-29x35in) s. lit. 25-Mar-4 Karlheinz Kaupp, Staufen #2717/R est:600

SCHRAEGLE, Gustav Peter Franz (1867-1925) German

£315 $535 €450 Runkel an der Lahn (69x47cm-27x19in) s.d.1915. 22-Nov-3 Arnold, Frankfurt #635
£387 $708 €580 Summer landscape (30x45cm-12x18in) s.d.1911. 5-Jun-4 Arnold, Frankfurt #720
£500 $915 €750 Reclining female nude (57x81cm-22x32in) s.d.1912. 5-Jun-4 Arnold, Frankfurt #718/R

SCHRAG, Karl (1912-1995) American/German

£1351 $2500 €1972 Sunflowers, last glow (127x91cm-50x36in) s. 10-Mar-4 Doyle, New York #71/R est:3000-5000
Works on paper
£652 $1200 €952 Palm trees, grey and yellow sky I (30x41cm-12x16in) s. W/C crayon prov. 25-Jun-4 Freeman, Philadelphia #79/R
£688 $1100 €1004 Midsummer (73x58cm-29x23in) s. brush black ink. 18-Sep-3 Swann Galleries, New York #589/R

SCHRAM, Alois Hans (1864-1919) Austrian

£417 $679 €600 Autumn mood in Deutsch Altenburg (34x39cm-13x15in) panel. 23-Sep-3 Wiener Kunst Auktionen, Vienna #61/R
£1290 $2194 €1883 At the county hall - figures waiting, among them a bride and groom (75x100cm-30x39in) 10-Nov-3 Rasmussen, Vejle #408/R est:15000-20000 (D.KR 14000)
£2700 $4995 €3942 Portrait of a lady (80x60cm-31x24in) s.d.1906. 14-Jul-4 Sotheby's, Olympia #269/R est:800-1200
£2964 $5306 €4327 Faun and Nymph (46x49cm-18x19in) s.d.1897 prov. 15-May-4 Christie's, Sydney #123/R est:6000-8000 (A.D 7500)
£5245 $8916 €7500 Chatting under blossom tree (57x77cm-22x30in) s.d.1899 paenl. 24-Nov-3 Dorotheum, Vienna #17/R est:6000-8000
£8000 $14560 €11680 Counting the bounty (74x108cm-29x43in) s.d.1886 prov. 15-Jun-4 Sotheby's, London #124/R est:8000-12000

SCHRAM, Wouter Jorinus (1895-1987) Dutch

£2222 $3622 €3200 Female nude (101x80cm-40x31in) s. 29-Sep-3 Sotheby's, Amsterdam #320
£2431 $3840 €3500 Still life with a glass of milk, bread, fruit and a knife on a table (66x60cm-26x24in) s. 2-Sep-3 Christie's, Amsterdam #439/R est:2000-3000

SCHRAMM-HECKMANN, Liselotte (20th C) German

£490 $832 €700 View of Rhena in the snow (41x60cm-16x24in) mono.d.1943 i.d.verso board lit. 28-Nov-3 Schloss Ahlden, Ahlden #1533/R
£733 $1313 €1100 Flowers (43x38cm-17x15in) i.d.19 48 i. verso panel. 15-May-4 Van Ham, Cologne #913/R

SCHRAMM-ZITTAU, Rudolf (1874-1950) German

£397 $723 €600 Deer in a mountainous landscape (60x80cm-24x31in) s. 16-Jun-4 Hugo Ruef, Munich #1090
£903 $1426 €1300 Winter woodland with deer (60x103cm-24x41in) s. 6-Sep-3 Arnold, Frankfurt #656/R
£1342 $2470 €2000 Ehrwald in Tyrol with Zugspitze (70x100cm-28x39in) s.d.45. 24-Mar-4 Hugo Ruef, Munich #1118/R est:1300
£1542 $2621 €2251 Fox in winter (34x59cm-13x23in) s. canvas on panel. 5-Nov-3 Dobiaschofsky, Bern #942/R est:4500 (S.FR 3500)
£1854 $3375 €2800 Hens in a garden (50x70cm-20x28in) s. cardboard. 16-Jun-4 Hugo Ruef, Munich #1091/R est:900
£1958 $3368 €2800 Ducks swimming in a pond (35x60cm-14x24in) s. 3-Dec-3 Neumeister, Munich #736/R est:2500

SCHRANZ, Anton (1769-1839) Austrian

Works on paper
£3000 $5490 €4500 Sujets grecs (25x18cm-10x7in) s. W/C crayon ten. 3-Jun-4 Tajan, Paris #334/R est:2000-3000

SCHRANZ, Giuseppe (1803-?) Maltese

£11000 $19690 €16060 Grand Harbour, Valetta, Malta with fisherfolk in the foreground (41x64cm-16x25in) 5-May-4 John Nicholson, Haslemere #530/R est:5000-7000

SCHRANZ, John (attrib) (1794-1882) Maltese

Works on paper
£1400 $2282 €2044 Grand Harbour, Valetta (21x30cm-8x12in) W/C exec.c.1845. 24-Sep-3 Christie's, London #205/R est:1000-1500
£2600 $4238 €3796 HMS Hibernia 120 guns off Fort St Angelo Malta (37x53cm-15x21in) W/C pencil exec.c.1830. 24-Sep-3 Christie's, London #203/R est:2000-3000
£2600 $4238 €3796 Sliema harbour, Malta (36x49cm-14x19in) W/C. 24-Sep-3 Christie's, London #204/R est:2000-3000

SCHRANZ, Joseph (attrib) (1803-1847) German

£7000 $11900 €10220 View of Corfu (53x81cm-21x32in) 18-Nov-3 Sotheby's, London #3/R est:7000-9000
Works on paper
£450 $774 €657 Temple of Olympian Zeus, Athens (15x25cm-6x10in) pencil W/C. 3-Dec-3 Christie's, Kensington #33/R

SCHRAUDOLPH, Robert (1887-1978) German

£280 $467 €400 Castle ruins in Pinzgau (64x81cm-25x32in) s. i. verso. 9-Oct-3 Michael Zeller, Lindau #752/R

SCHRECKENGOST, Victor (1906-) American

Works on paper
£413 $740 €603 Bovine (30x36cm-12x14in) s. W/C ink executed c.1962. 19-Mar-4 Aspire, Cleveland #68

SCHREIBER, Charles Baptiste (1845-1903) French

£426 $711 €600 La caravane dans le desert (29x45cm-11x18in) s. panel. 17-Jun-3 Vanderkindere, Brussels #25
£1608 $2734 €2300 Rose cavalier (32x41cm-13x16in) s. 20-Nov-3 Van Ham, Cologne #1857/R est:1800

SCHREIBER, Conrad Peter (1816-1894) German

£658 $1211 €1000 View of the Landeck Castle in Tirol (59x47cm-23x19in) s. tempera board. 26-Jun-4 C & K, Leipzig #772/R
Works on paper
£600 $1092 €900 Southern landscapes with water fall and stone bridge (60x48cm-24x19in) s. one d.1868 gouache two. 30-Jun-4 Neumeister, Munich #427a
£680 $1218 €1000 Southern sea coast (46x57cm-18x22in) s.d.1867 and 1868 gouache two. 17-Mar-4 Neumeister, Munich #313/R

SCHREIBER, George Lawrence (1862-1940) American

£359 $600 €524 Impressionist landscape (61x76cm-24x30in) s. 16-Nov-3 Bonhams & Butterfields, Los Angeles #7015/R
£389 $650 €568 Portrait of a lady (61x46cm-24x18in) s. 16-Nov-3 Bonhams & Butterfields, Los Angeles #7014/R

SCHREIBER, Georges (1904-1977) American

£1117 $2000 €1631 Ein Liberium (76x66cm-30x26in) s.i. on stretcher. 16-May-4 Wright, Chicago #170/R est:3000-5000
£1765 $3000 €2577 Rustic wedding (89x104cm-35x41in) s.d.1935. 9-Nov-3 Wright, Chicago #182 est:3000-5000
Sculpture
£1118 $1900 €1632 Ostrich egg (25x15cm-10x6in) painted ostrich egg prov. 9-Nov-3 Wright, Chicago #146 est:2000-3000
Works on paper
£414 $750 €604 Oregan farms (53x76cm-21x30in) W/C. 16-Apr-4 American Auctioneer #361/R

SCHREIBER, Gustav Adolf (1889-1958) German

£694 $1132 €1000 Nice coast (82x110cm-32x43in) s.d.1956. 26-Sep-3 Bolland & Marotz, Bremen #371/R

SCHREINER, Friedrich Wilhelm (1836-?) German

£1538 $2615 €2200 Country house in summer landscape with river (79x131cm-31x52in) s. 20-Nov-3 Van Ham, Cologne #1858/R est:1400

SCHREINER, Hans (1930-) German

£313 $509 €450 Composition in brown and blue (29x40cm-11x16in) s.d.1957 masonite. 27-Sep-3 Dr Fritz Nagel, Stuttgart #9351/R
£382 $623 €550 Composition in brown (21x30cm-8x12in) s.d.1963. 27-Sep-3 Dr Fritz Nagel, Stuttgart #9353/R

SCHREITTER VON SCHWARZENFELD, Adolf (1854-1923) Austrian

£634 $1135 €900 Interior inn scene with girl, two hunters and a fox (55x68cm-22x27in) s. i.verso lit. 8-Jan-4 Allgauer, Kempten #2512/R
£775 $1239 €1100 Peasant boy with cattle during time of thirty year war (32x65cm-13x26in) s.d.1906. 18-Sep-3 Rieber, Stuttgart #770/R

SCHRETER, Zygmunt (c.1896-1977) French

£417 $696 €600 Portrait de femme (55x46cm-22x18in) studio st. 21-Oct-3 Artcurial Briest, Paris #298
£417 $696 €600 Jeune homme au pull-over (55x33cm-22x13in) studio st. 21-Oct-3 Artcurial Briest, Paris #299
£451 $754 €650 Jeune femme au verre (48x36cm-19x14in) studio st.verso board. 21-Oct-3 Artcurial Briest, Paris #300
£451 $754 €650 Paysage (46x61cm-18x24in) studio st. isorel panel. 21-Oct-3 Artcurial Briest, Paris #303
£470 $860 €700 Paysage au canal (33x40cm-13x16in) s. 7-Jul-4 Artcurial Briest, Paris #112
£486 $812 €700 Paysage aux terres rouges (60x92cm-24x36in) studio st. 21-Oct-3 Artcurial Briest, Paris #296
£486 $812 €700 Jeune femme assise (55x46cm-22x18in) studio st. 21-Oct-3 Artcurial Briest, Paris #297
£486 $812 €700 L'enfant bleu (41x33cm-16x13in) studio st.verso. 21-Oct-3 Artcurial Briest, Paris #301
£486 $812 €700 Scene de Theatre (33x31cm-13x12in) studio st.verso board. 21-Oct-3 Artcurial Briest, Paris #302
£1074 $1987 €1600 Autoportrait (46x38cm-18x15in) s. 15-Mar-4 Claude Boisgirard, Paris #101 est:1600-1800
£1391 $2531 €2100 Atelier d'artiste (65x54cm-26x21in) s. 16-Jun-4 Claude Boisgirard, Paris #143/R est:2200-2500
£1678 $3104 €2500 Fleurs sur une chaise (61x38cm-24x15in) s. 15-Mar-4 Claude Boisgirard, Paris #102/R est:2500-3000

SCHREUDER VAN DE COOLWIJK, Jan W H (1868-1962) Dutch

£514 $873 €750 Landscape with nudes sitting (18x25cm-7x10in) s. panel. 5-Nov-3 Vendue Huis, Gravenhage #204
£10204 $18571 €15000 Before the mirror. Reading (36x25cm-14x10in) one s. one s.d.18 pair exhib. 3-Feb-4 Christie's, Amsterdam #203/R est:6000-8000

SCHREUER, Wilhelm (1866-1933) German

£600 $1098 €900 Farmer departing in front of farm (37x58cm-15x23in) mono. board. 5-Jun-4 Arnold, Frankfurt #721/R
£692 $1191 €990 Two merry drinkers in the inn (44x35cm-17x14in) mono. cardboard. 6-Dec-3 Hans Stahl, Toestorf #27/R
£759 $1403 €1100 Three people in bar (54x38cm-21x15in) mono. board. 14-Feb-4 Hans Stahl, Hamburg #90/R

£1042 $1698 €1500 Scene in salon (46x65cm-18x26in) mono. 25-Sep-3 Dr Fritz Nagel, Stuttgart #1420/R est:1700
£11268 $19493 €16000 In the coffee house (38x50cm-15x20in) s. 13-Dec-3 Lempertz, Koln #44/R est:2000
Works on paper
£2000 $3620 €3000 Verspers (50x60cm-20x24in) mono. mixed media. 1-Apr-4 Van Ham, Cologne #1638/R est:3000
£3846 $6538 €5500 Ballroom (76x98cm-30x39in) mono. mixed media. 20-Nov-3 Van Ham, Cologne #1862a/R est:7000

SCHREYER, Adolf (1828-1899) German
£397 $723 €600 Horses and sleigh (31x43cm-12x17in) s. panel. 16-Jun-4 Hugo Ruef, Munich #1092
£1289 $2100 €1882 Wallachian water carrier (15x20cm-6x8in) s. prov. 19-Jul-3 Skinner, Boston #30 est:2500-3500
£2533 $4661 €3800 Arab at the oasis (51x41cm-20x16in) s. 11-Jun-4 Wendl, Rudolstadt #4270/R est:1900
£3448 $6172 €5034 Bedouins on horseback (72x109cm-28x43in) 12-May-4 Dobiaschofsky, Bern #945/R est:9000 (S.FR 8000)
£4196 $7133 €6000 Homeward bound (23x32cm-9x13in) s. panel lit. 28-Nov-3 Schloss Ahlden, Ahlden #1535/R est:9000
£5921 $10895 €9000 Chevaux emballes dans la neige (39x62cm-15x24in) s. panel. 25-Jun-4 Millon & Associes, Paris #42/R est:8000-12000
£6593 $12000 €9626 Horses and horsemen with carriage (43x104cm-17x41in) s. 7-Feb-4 Sloans & Kenyon, Bethesda #1283/R est:13000-15000
£14118 $24000 €20612 Messenger (58x94cm-23x37in) s. 29-Oct-3 Christie's, Rockefeller NY #50/R est:30000-50000
£15333 $27907 €23000 Arabs on horseback near Oasis (96x55cm-38x22in) s. 30-Jun-4 Neumeister, Munich #676/R est:35000
£22222 $40000 €32444 Retreat (111x175cm-44x69in) s.d.1863 prov. 22-Apr-4 Christie's, Rockefeller NY #211/R est:40000-60000
£27778 $50000 €40556 Scout's report (71x101cm-28x40in) s. 22-Apr-4 Christie's, Rockefeller NY #210/R est:30000-50000
£29932 $53578 €44000 Arabs on horseback in landscape (87x118cm-34x46in) s. 17-Mar-4 Neumeister, Munich #598/R est:38000
Works on paper
£738 $1358 €1100 Oriental horseman leading horse on foot (16x19cm-6x7in) i. pencil. 25-Mar-4 Dr Fritz Nagel, Stuttgart #509/R

SCHREYER, Franz (1858-?) German
£562 $938 €821 Herbsttag am Moorbach (82x108cm-32x43in) s. 25-Oct-3 Rasmussen, Havnen #2134/R (D.KR 6000)

SCHREYER, Lothar (1886-1966) German
Works on paper
£567 $1015 €850 Constructive composition (29x17cm-11x7in) mono.i.d.21 i. verso W/C pencil prov. 14-May-4 Ketterer, Munich #424/R
£690 $1241 €1000 Composition. s. gouache. 20-Jan-4 Galerie Moderne, Brussels #222

SCHREYVOGEL, Charles (1861-1912) American
£1087 $1750 €1587 Western ranch view (13x20cm-5x8in) s. board. 20-Aug-3 James Julia, Fairfield #1461/R est:4000-6000
Sculpture
£3416 $5500 €4953 Last drop (30x46x13cm-12x18x5in) bronze. 22-Aug-3 Altermann Galleries, Santa Fe #81
£29070 $50000 €42442 Last drop (30x48cm-12x19in) i. dark brown pat. bronze prov.lit. 3-Dec-3 Sotheby's, New York #144/R est:50000-70000

SCHREYVOGEL, Charles (attrib) (1861-1912) American
Works on paper
£749 $1250 €1094 Portrait of an Indian (41x15cm-16x6in) chl. 18-Oct-3 David Dike, Dallas #25/R

SCHRIECK, Otto Marseus van (1619-1678) Dutch
£12000 $21960 €17520 Forest floor still life with snake, two butterflies and a lizard (60x48cm-24x19in) 7-Jul-4 Bonhams, New Bond Street #135/R est:15000-20000
£19444 $35000 €28388 Still life of a thistle and other flowers surrounded by moths and other insects (58x45cm-23x18in) s. 22-Jan-4 Sotheby's, New York #225/R est:20000-30000

SCHRIECK, Otto Marseus van (attrib) (1619-1678) Dutch
£11745 $21611 €17500 Serpents, papillons et lezards dans un paysage de sous-bois (60x49cm-24x19in) 29-Mar-4 Rieunier, Paris #12/R est:5000-7000

SCHRIJNDER, Joseph Alphons (1894-1968) Dutch
£246 $410 €357 Ducks approaching (80x60cm-31x24in) s. 17-Jun-3 Pinneys, Montreal #70a (C.D 550)
£347 $565 €500 Moor sheep (50x60cm-20x24in) s. 29-Sep-3 Sotheby's, Amsterdam #283
£525 $902 €750 Birds in a landscape (40x50cm-16x20in) s. 7-Dec-3 Sotheby's, Amsterdam #649
£696 $1247 €1025 Rape-seed field with farm on the horizon (50x60cm-20x24in) 17-Mar-4 De Zwann, Amsterdam #4596/R
£909 $1518 €1300 Brown duck with drake (60x50cm-24x20in) s.i. on stretcher. 30-Jun-3 Sotheby's, Amsterdam #239
£1119 $1869 €1600 Duck flying over Texel (70x60cm-28x24in) s. 30-Jun-3 Sotheby's, Amsterdam #433
Works on paper
£559 $934 €800 Game drivers pole jumping in a polder landscape (46x34cm-18x13in) s. W/C. 30-Jun-3 Sotheby's, Amsterdam #434/R

SCHRIKKEL, Louis (1902-1995) Dutch
£1259 $2165 €1800 Fancy party (50x39cm-20x15in) s.d.1936. 7-Dec-3 Sotheby's, Amsterdam #760
£2088 $3612 €3048 Musicians (66x43cm-26x17in) s.d.27 panel. 12-Dec-3 Kieselbach, Budapest #20/R (H.F 800000)
Works on paper
£855 $1574 €1300 Farmers at work (23x14cm-9x6in) s. gouache. 22-Jun-4 Christie's, Amsterdam #572/R

SCHRIMPF, Georg (1889-1938) German
£130000 $236600 €189800 Figuren vor Landschaft (66x86cm-26x34in) painted 1924 prov.lit. 3-Feb-4 Christie's, London #209/R est:50000-70000
Works on paper
£1538 $2615 €2200 Bathers. s.d.1924 W/C over pencil. 29-Nov-3 Villa Grisebach, Berlin #668/R est:1500-2000

SCHRODER, Albert Friedrich (1854-1939) German
£1630 $3000 €2380 Reading lesson (43x56cm-17x22in) s.i. panel prov. 27-Jun-4 Freeman, Philadelphia #37/R est:3000-5000
£2402 $4227 €3507 A glass of wine (70x83cm-28x33in) s.i. prov. 22-May-4 Galerie Gloggner, Luzern #98 est:2800-3500 (S.FR 5500)

SCHRODER, Joseph (?) ?
£300 $549 €438 Adventurous proposal (51x61cm-20x24in) 27-Jan-4 Gorringes, Lewes #1630

SCHRODER, Poul (1894-1957) Danish
£366 $667 €534 Woman seated by table with vase of flowers (73x55cm-29x22in) s. 7-Feb-4 Rasmussen, Havnen #4076/R (D.KR 4000)
£369 $627 €539 Small still life (45x58cm-18x23in) s. exhib. 10-Nov-3 Rasmussen, Vejle #676/R (D.KR 4000)
£523 $963 €764 Summer landscape with houses in background (54x65cm-21x26in) s.verso prov. 29-Mar-4 Rasmussen, Copenhagen #557/R (D.KR 5800)
£1083 $1993 €1581 Portrait of seated woman (102x75cm-40x30in) s. 29-Mar-4 Rasmussen, Copenhagen #441/R est:18000-20000 (D.KR 12000)
£1354 $2491 €1977 Still life of chair and view to garden (98x72cm-39x28in) s. prov. 29-Mar-4 Rasmussen, Copenhagen #440/R est:15000-18000 (D.KR 15000)

SCHRODER, Sierk (1903-2002) Dutch
£274 $466 €400 Nude from behind with cloth (60x40cm-24x16in) s. 5-Nov-3 Vendue Huis, Gravenhage #474
£6993 $12028 €10000 La toilette (70x50cm-28x20in) s.d.22. 2-Dec-3 Sotheby's, Amsterdam #22/R est:7000-10000
Works on paper
£270 $476 €400 Seated female nude (39x31cm-15x12in) s.d.74 brown chk. 19-May-4 Sotheby's, Amsterdam #371/R
£342 $582 €500 Model in brown dress (45x30cm-18x12in) s. pencil. 5-Nov-3 Vendue Huis, Gravenhage #472
£476 $818 €680 Nude standing (60x36cm-24x14in) s.d.80 brown chk. 8-Dec-3 Glerum, Amsterdam #400/R
£559 $962 €800 Woman in white kimono (45x26cm-18x10in) s.d.70 pencil htd white. 8-Dec-3 Glerum, Amsterdam #351/R
£559 $962 €800 Study of motion (35x52cm-14x20in) s.d.73 pencil. 8-Dec-3 Glerum, Amsterdam #387/R
£625 $987 €900 Seated woman (66x46cm-26x18in) s.d.80 W/C pastel pencil. 2-Sep-3 Christie's, Amsterdam #392
£664 $1143 €950 Nude sitting (60x40cm-24x16in) s.d.70 brown chk. 8-Dec-3 Glerum, Amsterdam #323/R
£664 $1143 €950 Landscape (38x58cm-15x23in) s.d.79 W/C. 8-Dec-3 Glerum, Amsterdam #381/R
£909 $1564 €1300 Woman sitting (65x45cm-26x18in) s.d.1980 W/C. 8-Dec-3 Glerum, Amsterdam #376/R
£1042 $1646 €1500 Branch of apple blossom (46x31cm-18x12in) s.d.82 W/C. 2-Sep-3 Christie's, Amsterdam #391 est:1200-1600
£2083 $3292 €3000 Seated nude (47x32cm-19x13in) s.d.79 W/C pastel. 2-Sep-3 Christie's, Amsterdam #389/R est:1500-2000
£2378 $4090 €3400 Studio with reclining half nude (55x65cm-22x26in) s.d.69 brown chk pencil. 8-Dec-3 Glerum, Amsterdam #327/R est:3000-5000
£2667 $4907 €4000 A seated nude (58x44cm-23x17in) s.d.74 W/C blk chk. 9-Jun-4 Christie's, Amsterdam #114/R est:3500-4500
£2800 $5152 €4200 Seated nude (51x41cm-20x16in) s.d.79 W/C blk chk. 9-Jun-4 Christie's, Amsterdam #118/R est:2500-3500
£5245 $8916 €7500 Lady in a blue kimono (49x36cm-19x14in) s.d.86 W/C. 25-Nov-3 Christie's, Amsterdam #2/R est:2500-3500

SCHRODER, T (19th C) German
£878 $1370 €1300 Moonlit landscape with boats on Werbellin lake. s.i.d.1877. 28-Mar-3 Altus, Berlin #612/R

SCHRODER, Walter G (fl.1885-1932) British
£900 $1593 €1314 Granary (45x55cm-18x22in) board exhib. 27-Apr-4 Bonhams, Knightsbridge #207/R

SCHRODER-SONNENSTERN, F (1892-1982) German
Works on paper
£6333 $11653 €9500 Der betende lowe, oder die geschandete kraft (65x94cm-26x37in) s.i.d.1952 col crayon wax pastel board prov.lit. 9-Jun-4 Artcurial Briest, Paris #376/R est:10000-12000
£8451 $14620 €12000 Modern Eve (73x51cm-29x20in) s.i.d.1963 s.d.verso col crayon exhib. 9-Dec-3 Artcurial Briest, Paris #474/R est:8000-12000

SCHRODER-SONNENSTERN, Friedrich (1892-1982) German
Works on paper
£467 $859 €700 The magic mill (68x47cm-27x19in) s.i.d.1959 pencil col pencil gold-colour board. 12-Jun-4 Villa Grisebach, Berlin #832/R
£699 $1189 €1000 Hearts in snow (49x71cm-19x28in) s.i.d.1960 pencil col crayon gold silver board. 29-Nov-3 Villa Grisebach, Berlin #895/R est:800-1000

£764 $1276 €1100 Fantasy picture (51x73cm-20x29in) s.mono.i.d. s.mono.d. verso col pen board. 25-Oct-3 Dr Lehr, Berlin #468/R
£909 $1545 €1300 F S Sonnenstern's figure (49x71cm-19x28in) i.d.1960 pencil col pen board. 29-Nov-3 Villa Grisebach, Berlin #896/R est:800-1000
£909 $1545 €1300 State fool's ship (49x71cm-19x28in) s.i.d.1963 pencil col crayon board. 29-Nov-3 Villa Grisebach, Berlin #898/R est:800-1000
£979 $1664 €1400 Composition with animal and figure (49x71cm-19x28in) s.i.d.1961 pencil col pen board. 29-Nov-3 Villa Grisebach, Berlin #897/R est:800-1000
£995 $1692 €1453 Moon king (71x48cm-28x19in) s.i.d.1960 col pen. 25-Nov-3 Germann, Zurich #115/R est:1800-2300 (S.FR 2200)
£1595 $2872 €2329 Die Mondmoralische Schopfung (50x71cm-20x28in) s.d.1968 wax crayon lit. 26-Apr-4 Bukowskis, Stockholm #241/R est:6000-8000 (S.KR 22000)
£1600 $2864 €2400 Atom bomb (50x72cm-20x28in) s.d.1957 col chk board prov. 15-May-4 Van Ham, Cologne #916/R est:1000
£2000 $3600 €3000 Composition (72x50cm-28x20in) s.mono.i.d. col chk board. 24-Apr-4 Dr Lehr, Berlin #427/R est:2000
£2098 $3566 €3000 Protector of the moon (70x50cm-28x20in) s.i.d.1960 i.d. verso col chk paper on board. 29-Nov-3 Villa Grisebach, Berlin #334/R est:3000-4000
£2333 $4177 €3500 Comic dramatic tragedy of passion (51x73cm-20x29in) s.i.d.1957 col pen board prov. 15-May-4 Van Ham, Cologne #917/R est:1000
£2333 $4293 €3500 The donkey beater (68x47cm-27x19in) s.i.d.1962 pencil col pencil board. 12-Jun-4 Villa Grisebach, Berlin #833/R est:800-1000
£3334 $6134 €5000 Der Lebensnarrenlault (57x86cm-22x34in) s.i.d.1956 col crayons wax pastel board prov. 9-Jun-4 Artcurial Briest, Paris #382/R est:6000-8000
£6333 $11653 €9500 Di Pariser Teenagerkonigin (86x55cm-34x22in) s.i.d.1962 col crayons wax pastel board prov. 9-Jun-4 Artcurial Briest, Paris #377/R est:10000-12000

SCHRODL, Anton (1823-1906) Austrian
£403 $721 €600 Huts by mountain stream (58x50cm-23x20in) d.1883. 27-May-4 Dorotheum, Graz #59/R
£704 $1261 €1000 Evening mountain landscape with walkers resting (22x27cm-9x11in) s. board lit. 8-Jan-4 Allgauer, Kempten #2513/R
£1389 $2264 €2000 Mountain hut in Ferleiten (27x42cm-11x17in) s. canvas on board prov. 24-Sep-3 Neumeister, Munich #551/R est:1800
£1399 $2378 €2000 High mountain pasture (25x41cm-10x16in) s. board. 24-Nov-3 Dorotheum, Vienna #177/R est:3000-4000
£1457 $2666 €2200 Ram in barn (37x54cm-15x21in) s. 8-Apr-4 Dorotheum, Vienna #239/R est:2000-2500
£2797 $4671 €4000 Chamonix valley with Mont Blanc (43x58cm-17x23in) s. i. verso lit. 27-Jun-3 Auktionhaus Georg Rehm, Augsburg #8187/R est:5000

SCHRODL, Anton (attrib) (1823-1906) Austrian
£1208 $2223 €1800 Rams in stable (65x103cm-26x41in) 25-Mar-4 Dr Fritz Nagel, Stuttgart #760/R est:2400

SCHRODL, Norbert (1842-1912) Austrian
£750 $1373 €1095 Portrait of a lady in a white silk dress (74x60cm-29x24in) s.d.1866 oval. 8-Apr-4 Christie's, Kensington #39
£833 $1417 €1200 Vegetation with reeds (27x45cm-11x18in) i.d.75 i. verso canvas on board. 28-Oct-3 Dorotheum, Vienna #140/R

SCHRODTER, Adolf (1805-1875) German
Works on paper
£524 $954 €765 Country fair (13x38cm-5x15in) pen wash htd white prov. 16-Jun-4 Fischer, Luzern #2610/R (S.FR 1200)
£655 $1192 €956 Country fair (13x45cm-5x18in) pen wash htd white prov. 16-Jun-4 Fischer, Luzern #2609/R (S.FR 1500)
£786 $1431 €1148 Country fair (13x52cm-5x20in) pen wash htd white prov. 16-Jun-4 Fischer, Luzern #2608/R (S.FR 1800)

SCHROEDER, Georg Engelhardt (1684-1750) Swedish
£11923 $20508 €17408 Portrait of King Fredrik I (194x142cm-76x56in) 2-Dec-3 Bukowskis, Stockholm #303/R est:100000-150000 (S.KR 155000)

SCHROEDER, Georg Engelhardt (attrib) (1684-1750) Swedish
£1032 $1662 €1507 Count Joachim von Duben (78x64cm-31x25in) i.verso. 25-Aug-3 Lilla Bukowskis, Stockholm #924 (S.KR 13500)

SCHROERS, Hans (1903-1969) German?
£278 $464 €400 Village idyll (34x39cm-13x15in) s. canvas on board. 24-Oct-3 Ketterer, Hamburg #1080/R

SCHROETER, Richard (1873-?) German
£1067 $1931 €1600 Sailing boats at anchor in harbour (55x70cm-22x28in) s.d.1920. 1-Apr-4 Van Ham, Cologne #1643 est:900

SCHROFER, Willem (1898-1968) Dutch
£2098 $3608 €3000 Composition with rectangles (65x85cm-26x33in) 2-Dec-3 Sotheby's, Amsterdam #115/R est:4000-6000

SCHROFFENEGGER, Ernst Matthias (1905-1994) Austrian
£284 $474 €400 Obermieming in Tyrol (48x63cm-19x25in) s. tempera. 16-Oct-3 Dorotheum, Salzburg #859/R

SCHROM, Ernst (1902-1969) Austrian
Works on paper
£300 $540 €450 Kahlenberg village (28x38cm-11x15in) s.mono.d.18.IX.63 w/C. 21-Apr-4 Dorotheum, Vienna #198/R
£621 $1136 €900 Schloss Laxenburg (33x45cm-13x18in) s. W/C gouache. 27-Jan-4 Dorotheum, Vienna #126/R
£634 $1109 €900 Hohe Warte, Vienna XIX (30x37cm-12x15in) s.i.d.1961 W/C. 19-Dec-3 Dorotheum, Vienna #190/R

SCHROTER, Annette (1956-) German
£903 $1472 €1300 The burden III (150x120cm-59x47in) mono.d.1990 i. stretcher cotton. 27-Sep-3 Dr Fritz Nagel, Stuttgart #9629/R

SCHROTTER, Alfred von (1856-1935) Austrian
£738 $1321 €1100 White Lipizzaner horses grazing (40x56cm-16x22in) s.d.1914. 27-May-4 Dorotheum, Graz #60/R

SCHROTZBERG, Franz (1811-1889) Austrian
£676 $1209 €1000 Banus Jelaciz, Croatian leader (29x20cm-11x8in) s.d. verso. 6-May-4 Michael Zeller, Lindau #868/R

SCHRYVER, Louis Marie de (1862-1942) French
£6145 $11000 €8972 On the Boulevard (33x46cm-13x18in) s.d.1927 prov. 6-May-4 Shannon's, Milford #24/R est:8000-12000
£10000 $17000 €14600 Flower seller near the Arc de Triomphe (22x16cm-9x6in) s.d.1897 panel. 28-Oct-3 Sotheby's, New York #162/R est:15000-20000
£29412 $50000 €42942 Flower seller (57x43cm-22x17in) s.d.1898. 19-Nov-3 Bonhams & Butterfields, San Francisco #117/R

SCHUBERG, Clara (1862-?) German
£320 $550 €467 Peonies (56x46cm-22x18in) s. 7-Dec-3 Hindman, Chicago #796/R

SCHUBERT, Carl (1795-1855) Austrian
Works on paper
£350 $584 €500 Church doorway (27x20cm-11x8in) W/C. 9-Oct-3 Michael Zeller, Lindau #755/R
£350 $584 €500 Tyrolean farmsteads (20x26cm-8x10in) W/C. 9-Oct-3 Michael Zeller, Lindau #757

SCHUBERT, Heinrich Carl (1827-1897) Austrian
£596 $1085 €900 Hunter in a mountain landscape (76x60cm-30x24in) s. panel. 16-Jun-4 Hugo Ruef, Munich #1093/R
Works on paper
£604 $1111 €900 Donau landscape (24x30cm-9x12in) s. W/C. 26-Mar-4 Dorotheum, Vienna #214/R

SCHUBERT, Rod (?) ?
Works on paper
£900 $1611 €1314 Devil's Peak, South Australia (122x183cm-48x72in) s.d.88 mixed media. 28-May-4 Lyon & Turnbull, Edinburgh #71/R

SCHUBERT-SOLDERN, Viktor (1834-1912) Czechoslovakian
£986 $1637 €1400 Last meeting (40x31cm-16x12in) s. panel. 16-Jun-3 Dorotheum, Vienna #147

SCHUBRING, Sanna (1913-) German
£833 $1317 €1200 Still life with apple basket and cup (54x81cm-21x32in) s. 6-Sep-3 Schopman, Hamburg #773/R

SCHUCH, H (19th C) ?
£1389 $2264 €2000 Father and daughter in serious discussion (80x94cm-31x37in) s.d.1875. 24-Sep-3 Neumeister, Munich #552/R est:3000

SCHUCH, Werner Wilhelm Gustav (1843-1918) German
£5021 $9088 €7331 Cossack horsemen (50x71cm-20x28in) s.i. prov. 1-Apr-4 Heffel, Vancouver #92/R est:3000-5000 (C.D 12000)

SCHUELER, Jon R (1916-1992) American
£313 $550 €457 Summer sea remembered (76x91cm-30x36in) s.i.verso painted c.1973. 23-May-4 Treadway Gallery, Cincinnati #759/R

SCHUFFENECKER, Claude Émile (1851-1934) French
£900 $1611 €1350 Le village (15x13cm-6x5in) cardboard. 16-May-4 Thierry & Lannon, Brest #368
£4184 $6988 €5900 Falaises d'etretat (38x46cm-15x18in) st.mono. painted c.1892 lit. 19-Jun-3 Millon & Associes, Paris #213/R est:6000-7000
£6376 $11860 €9500 Vallee enneigee (38x46cm-15x18in) mono. 3-Mar-4 Tajan, Paris #34/R est:6000-8000
£9375 $15656 €13500 Route animee en hiver (46x55cm-18x22in) s.d.87. 21-Oct-3 Fraysse & Associes, Paris #19/R
£16667 $27834 €24000 Portrait d'homme (46x55cm-18x22in) i. board painted c.1895. 21-Oct-3 Artcurial Briest, Paris #193/R est:25000-35000
£20588 $35000 €30058 Au bord du lac (54x65cm-21x26in) prov. 6-Nov-3 Sotheby's, New York #154/R est:40000-50000
£22346 $40000 €32625 Route sous la neige (46x55cm-18x22in) s.d.87 prov.exhib.lit. 6-May-4 Sotheby's, New York #242/R est:18000-25000
£28170 $49297 €40000 Femme dans la lande bretonne (54x65cm-21x26in) mono.d.90 prov. 18-Dec-3 Tajan, Paris #12/R est:40000-60000
Works on paper
£282 $493 €400 Mere et enfant (15x11cm-6x4in) studio st. 21-Dec-3 Thierry & Lannon, Brest #453
£458 $801 €650 Les falaises (10x16cm-4x6in) studio st. pastel. 21-Dec-3 Thierry & Lannon, Brest #266
£739 $1300 €1079 Young French girl (61x51cm-24x20in) pastel. 28-May-4 Aspire, Cleveland #120/R est:1500-2000
£845 $1479 €1200 Paysage (11x14cm-4x6in) studio st. pastel. 21-Dec-3 Thierry & Lannon, Brest #265
£867 $1551 €1300 La ramasseuse de Varech (7x32cm-3x13in) pastel. 16-May-4 Thierry & Lannon, Brest #96
£894 $1672 €1350 Personnage sur le chemin (16x10cm-6x4in) pastel. 24-Jul-4 Thierry & Lannon, Brest #110

£1000	$1790	€1500	Paysage de neige (31x9cm-12x4in) pastel. 16-May-4 Thierry & Lannon, Brest #93/R est:1500-2000
£1049	$1804	€1500	Falaise a Yport (48x32cm-19x13in) st.sig. pastel. 8-Dec-3 Christie's, Paris #65/R est:700-900
£1667	$2983	€2500	Falaises d'Etretat (31x40cm-12x16in) pastel. 16-May-4 Thierry & Lannon, Brest #95/R est:2500-3000
£2042	$3574	€2900	Les peupliers en Bretagne (26x47cm-10x19in) s. pastel. 21-Dec-3 Thierry & Lannon, Brest #100/R est:3000-3200
£2378	$4090	€3400	Route de campagne en Bretagne (12x15cm-5x6in) st.sig. pastel. 5-Dec-3 Chochon-Barre & Allardi, Paris #147/R est:3500-4000

SCHUFRIED, Dominik (1810-?) Austrian

£2797	$4755	€4000	Rest in the wood (63x80cm-25x31in) one of pair. 24-Nov-3 Dorotheum, Vienna #26/R est:4000-5000

SCHUHKNECHT, Adolf (1889-?) German

£1383	$2559	€2019	Ship in a breeze (80x120cm-31x47in) 14-Mar-4 Agra, Warsaw #56/R (P.Z 10000)

SCHUHMACHER, Wim (1894-1986) Dutch

£2933	$5397	€4400	Jan Wiegers en een model, Schets (55x41cm-22x16in) s.i. prov.lit. 8-Jun-4 Sotheby's, Amsterdam #225/R est:4000-6000
£6993	$11888	€10000	Flowers (70x61cm-28x24in) s. s.i.verso painted c.1916-1917. 25-Nov-3 Christie's, Amsterdam #184/R est:10000-20000
£8392	$14434	€12000	Veld met hooimijt (31x46cm-12x18in) s. painted 1914 lit. 2-Dec-3 Sotheby's, Amsterdam #103/R est:12000-15000
Works on paper			
£1333	$2440	€2000	Landscape with meadow and trees (53x74cm-21x29in) s.d.1918 prov.lit. 7-Jun-4 Glerum, Amsterdam #122/R est:2000-3000
£6993	$11888	€10000	Portrait of a man from Senegal (100x81cm-39x32in) s. blk chk exec 1929 prov.exhib.lit. 25-Nov-3 Christie's, Amsterdam #177/R est:3000-5000

SCHUIL, Han (1958-) ?

Works on paper			
£467	$859	€700	Untitled (56x76cm-22x30in) s.d.93 W/C prov.lit. 9-Jun-4 Christie's, Amsterdam #366/R

SCHULDT, Fritiof (1891-1978) Swedish

£1133	$1926	€1654	Still life of jugs, flowers and brushes (73x93cm-29x37in) s.d.46 prov. 4-Nov-3 Bukowskis, Stockholm #152/R est:15000-20000 (S.KR 15000)
£5946	$10703	€8681	View from the terrace of the villa by the sea, Smedsudden (44x32cm-17x13in) s.d.20 exhib.prov. 26-Apr-4 Bukowskis, Stockholm #181/R est:20000-25000 (S.KR 82000)

SCHULER, Paul (19/20th C) ?

£690	$1152	€1000	Green valley with mountain village before snowy mountains (100x141cm-39x56in) s. 10-Jul-3 Allgauer, Kempten #2673/R

SCHULMAN, David (1881-1966) Dutch

£638	$1066	€900	Landscape with farmers (21x32cm-8x13in) s. cardboard. 20-Oct-3 Glerum, Amsterdam #180 est:1000-1500
£658	$1211	€1000	Moored sailing vessels in a harbour (32x48cm-13x19in) plywood. 22-Jun-4 Christie's, Amsterdam #190/R
£921	$1695	€1400	Farmhouse (26x36cm-10x14in) s. canvas on panel. 28-Jun-4 Sotheby's, Amsterdam #143/R
£1020	$1857	€1500	Conversing on the quay (30x40cm-12x16in) s. 3-Feb-4 Christie's, Amsterdam #347/R est:1000-1500
£1250	$2037	€1800	Farmer van Bakker on the path in Blaricum (56x86cm-22x34in) s.i.verso. 29-Sep-3 Sotheby's, Amsterdam #190/R
£1399	$2406	€2000	View of Edam in winter (24x30cm-9x12in) s. i.verso panel. 7-Dec-3 Sotheby's, Amsterdam #715/R
£1497	$2724	€2200	View of Oude Schans with the Sint Antoniesluis, Amsterdam (32x43cm-13x17in) s. 3-Feb-4 Christie's, Amsterdam #321/R est:1200-1600
£1711	$3147	€2600	Winterochtend, Laren (100x60cm-39x24in) s. i. stretcher. 28-Jun-4 Sotheby's, Amsterdam #128/R est:2000-3000
£1769	$3219	€2600	Winter in Blaricum at dusk (35x37cm-14x15in) s. 3-Feb-4 Christie's, Amsterdam #357/R est:1000-1500
£2177	$3962	€3200	Boederji Blaricum winter, farmhouses in the snow, Blaricum (61x92cm-24x36in) s. s.i.stretcher. 3-Feb-4 Christie's, Amsterdam #354/R est:3000-5000
£2339	$4303	€3415	Winter near Laren (56x84cm-22x33in) s. prov. 14-Jun-4 Waddingtons, Toronto #249/R est:3000-5000 (C.D 5800)
£2857	$5200	€4200	Bulbfields near bentveld (47x75cm-19x30in) s. s.i.on stretcher. 3-Feb-4 Christie's, Amsterdam #315/R est:3500-4500
£3087	$5711	€4600	View of the Prins Hendrikkade, Amsterdam (51x71cm-20x28in) s. 15-Mar-4 Sotheby's, Amsterdam #133/R est:2000-2500
£3472	$5486	€5000	Tegen avond Blaricum (60x80cm-24x31in) s. s.i. on stretcher. 2-Sep-3 Christie's, Amsterdam #298/R est:2500-3500
£4276	$7868	€6500	View of Laren in winter (60x80cm-24x31in) s. 28-Jun-4 Sotheby's, Amsterdam #126/R est:2500-3500

SCHULMAN, Lion (1851-1943) Dutch

£839	$1401	€1200	Travellers in a summer landscape (25x42cm-10x17in) s. panel. 30-Jun-3 Sotheby's, Amsterdam #184/R
£1215	$1955	€1774	Path in the forest (75x62cm-30x24in) s. 13-Oct-3 Joel, Victoria #427 est:1000-1500 (A.D 3000)
£2600	$4784	€3796	Figures chatting on a tree lined path (76x63cm-30x25in) s.i. 23-Mar-4 Bonhams, New Bond Street #15/R est:2500-3500

SCHULTEN, Arnold (1809-1874) German

£1042	$1719	€1500	Swiss mountain lake in summer (21x32cm-8x13in) s.d.1861. 3-Jul-3 Van Ham, Cologne #1453/R est:1800

SCHULTEN, Curtius (1893-?) ?

£420	$722	€600	Dancers on the promenade (48x62cm-19x24in) s.d.1928. 4-Dec-3 Van Ham, Cologne #462/R
£455	$773	€650	Still life of flowers with tulips, poppies (83x70cm-33x28in) s.d.1936. 20-Nov-3 Van Ham, Cologne #1863

SCHULTHEISS, Karl (attrib) (1852-1944) German

£445	$757	€650	Woman (47x40cm-19x16in) 5-Nov-3 Hugo Ruef, Munich #1131

SCHULTHEISS, Natalie (1865-1952) Austrian

£479	$815	€700	Still life with lobster (20x30cm-8x12in) s. board. 5-Nov-3 Hugo Ruef, Munich #1133
£890	$1514	€1300	Still life with cherries (53x39cm-21x15in) s. 5-Nov-3 Hugo Ruef, Munich #1135
£1745	$3123	€2600	Still life with cherries (54x39cm-21x15in) s. 27-May-4 Dorotheum, Vienna #235/R est:2800-3200

SCHULTHESS, Jorg (1941-) Swiss

£485	$824	€708	Tree for Rosch haschana (90x100cm-35x39in) s.d.1968 i. verso lit. 5-Nov-3 Dobiaschofsky, Bern #943/R (S.FR 1100)

SCHULTZ, Alexander (1901-1981) Norwegian

£365	$632	€533	Landscape (43x50cm-17x20in) s. panel. 13-Dec-3 Blomqvist, Lysaker #1336/R (N.KR 4200)
£688	$1150	€1004	Norwegian landscape (55x74cm-22x29in) s. 20-Oct-3 Blomqvist, Lysaker #1285/R (N.KR 8000)
£852	$1465	€1244	Landscape with house (50x65cm-20x26in) s.d.75. 8-Dec-3 Blomqvist, Oslo #517/R (N.KR 10000)
£852	$1465	€1244	Winter landscape with skiers (51x61cm-20x24in) s. 8-Dec-3 Blomqvist, Oslo #533/R (N.KR 10000)
£937	$1612	€1368	Winter landscape with house (51x61cm-20x24in) s. 8-Dec-3 Blomqvist, Oslo #540/R (N.KR 11000)
£979	$1752	€1429	Landscape with houses (50x61cm-20x24in) s.d.71. 25-May-4 Grev Wedels Plass, Oslo #90/R (N.KR 12000)
£1361	$2436	€1987	House in landscape (50x62cm-20x24in) s. 22-Mar-4 Blomqvist, Oslo #601/R est:12000-15000 (N.KR 17000)
Works on paper			
£354	$647	€517	House in landscape (39x54cm-15x21in) s. W/C. 2-Feb-4 Blomqvist, Lysaker #1270 (N.KR 4400)

SCHULTZ, George F (1869-?) American

£294	$500	€429	Rocky cove - Monhegan Island (61x81cm-24x32in) s. 22-Nov-3 Jackson's, Cedar Falls #83/R
Works on paper			
£323	$600	€472	Sailing vessel off the coast (51x69cm-20x27in) s. W/C executed c.1910. 7-Mar-4 Treadway Gallery, Cincinnati #512/R
£601	$950	€877	Figure near a cottage (51x71cm-20x28in) s. W/C board. 7-Sep-3 Treadway Gallery, Cincinnati #570/R

SCHULTZ, Herman Theodore (1816-1862) German

£406	$650	€593	Portrait of an elegant lady (69x51cm-27x20in) s. board. 19-Sep-3 Freeman, Philadelphia #185/R

SCHULTZ, William (20th C) American

£389	$650	€568	Planetary abstraction (61x51cm-24x20in) d.4.24.48 s.verso board. 15-Nov-3 Sloans & Kenyon, Bethesda #95/R

SCHULTZBERG, Anshelm (1862-1945) Swedish

£407	$728	€594	Wooded landscape (33x25cm-13x10in) s.d.1896 panel. 28-May-4 Uppsala Auktionskammare, Uppsala #221 (S.KR 5500)
£976	$1757	€1425	Outhouse buildings near Ulvshyttan, Dalarne (60x80cm-24x31in) s.d.1938. 26-Jan-4 Lilla Bukowskis, Stockholm #296 (S.KR 13000)
£1160	$2088	€1740	Landscape from Gasenberg's huts in Grangarde (50x73cm-20x29in) s.d.1934. 25-Apr-4 Goteborg Auktionsverk, Sweden #175/R est:20000 (S.KR 16000)
£1276	$2347	€1914	Winter landscape with red barn (89x114cm-35x45in) s. 14-Jun-4 Lilla Bukowskis, Stockholm #335 est:15000-18000 (S.KR 17500)
£1330	$2381	€1942	Summer landscape with boy fishing. s.d.83. 25-May-4 Bukowskis, Stockholm #218/R est:20000-25000 (S.KR 18000)
£1453	$2514	€2121	Winter in Djurgarden (55x73cm-22x29in) s.d.1931. 15-Dec-3 Lilla Bukowskis, Stockholm #876 est:12000-15000 (S.KR 18500)
£1462	$2514	€2135	Winter landscape in sunshine (60x80cm-24x31in) s.d.1938. 7-Dec-3 Uppsala Auktionskammare, Uppsala #139/R est:18000-20000 (S.KR 19000)
£1538	$2646	€2245	Winter landscape from Svinkullarne in Varmland (73x110cm-29x43in) s.i.d.1941. 2-Dec-3 Bukowskis, Stockholm #179a/R est:20000-25000 (S.KR 20000)
£1692	$2911	€2470	Winter landscape with brook and barn (84x110cm-33x43in) s/. 2-Dec-3 Bukowskis, Stockholm #109/R est:20000-25000 (S.KR 22000)
£2143	$3837	€3129	Harbour in Venice (61x80cm-24x31in) s.d.24/11 1926. 25-May-4 Bukowskis, Stockholm #36/R est:25000-30000 (S.KR 29000)
£2217	$3969	€3237	Winter landscape with sunset over Wasebyn, Elfdalen (79x115cm-31x45in) s. 26-May-4 AB Stockholms Auktionsverk #2116/R est:40000-50000 (S.KR 30000)
£2217	$3969	€3237	Day in January - landscape from Filipstad (81x111cm-32x44in) s.d.1923. 25-May-4 Bukowskis, Stockholm #147/R est:20000-25000 (S.KR 30000)
£2217	$3969	€3237	Winter landscape from Varmland (81x117cm-32x46in) s. 25-May-4 Bukowskis, Stockholm #193/R est:30000-35000 (S.KR 30000)
£2278	$3941	€3326	Winter landscape in afternoon sunshine (90x70cm-35x28in) s. 15-Dec-3 Lilla Bukowskis, Stockholm #362/R est:20000-25000 (S.KR 29000)
£2327	$4189	€3397	Fruit tree in blossom (101x118cm-40x46in) s.i.d.1913. 26-Jan-4 Lilla Bukowskis, Stockholm #360 est:20000-25000 (S.KR 31000)
£2956	$5292	€4316	Cabins in snowy landscape, Alvdalen, Dalarne (68x105cm-27x41in) s. 26-May-4 AB Stockholms Auktionsverk #2236/R est:50000-60000 (S.KR 40000)
£3308	$5689	€4830	Outhouses covered in snow, Alvdalen, Dalarna (69x106cm-27x42in) s. 2-Dec-3 Bukowskis, Stockholm #108/R est:20000-25000 (S.KR 43000)
£3400	$6086	€4964	Day in February - landscape from Filipstad (117x139cm-46x55in) s.d.1917. 25-May-4 Bukowskis, Stockholm #146/R est:35000-40000 (S.KR 46000)
£3846	$6615	€5615	Barns in Grez, France (38x55cm-15x22in) s.d.89 canvas on panel exhib.prov. 2-Dec-3 Bukowskis, Stockholm #165a/R est:15000-20000 (S.KR 50000)
£4462	$7674	€6515	Midwinter - landscape from Bjursastrakten (80x116cm-31x46in) s. 3-Dec-3 AB Stockholms Auktionsverk #2473/R est:40000-50000 (S.KR 58000)
£4615	$7938	€6738	Trees in autumn sunshine (41x29cm-16x11in) s.i.d.1889 prov.exhib.lit. 2-Dec-3 Bukowskis, Stockholm #164/R est:60000-80000 (S.KR 60000)

Works on paper
£1109 $1984 €1619 Landscape view - winter scene from Djurgarden, Stockholm (32x40cm-13x16in) s.d.1924 i.verso gouache. 26-May-4 AB Stockholms Auktionsverk #2104/R est:15000-18000 (S.KR 15000)

SCHULTZE, Bernard (1915-) German
£1000 $1790 €1500 Tree of life (19x14cm-7x6in) s. panel on board. 15-May-4 Van Ham, Cologne #918/R est:2800
£2000 $3580 €3000 Djith (85x60cm-33x24in) s.i.d. verso oil relief. 15-May-4 Bassenge, Berlin #7129/R est:4000
£5000 $9150 €7500 Tabuskri (120x50cm-47x20in) s.d.1960 s.i.d. verso. 4-Jun-4 Lempertz, Koln #434/R est:10000
£6250 $10438 €9000 White flow (79x60cm-31x24in) s.d. s.i.d. verso prov. 24-Oct-3 Ketterer, Hamburg #538/R est:9000-12000
£6643 $11294 €9500 Composition (100x120cm-39x47in) s.d.88 s.i.d. verso. 27-Nov-3 Lempertz, Koln #432/R est:10000
£8042 $13671 €11500 Raging Roland (95x95cm-37x37in) s.d.82 s.i.d. verso. 27-Nov-3 Lempertz, Koln #430/R est:13000
£11189 $19245 €16000 With blue (120x100cm-47x39in) s.d. s.i.d. verso oil sand varnish prov. 5-Dec-3 Ketterer, Munich #308/R est:10000-15000
£13986 $23776 €20000 Dance of the grimaces around atom fear (200x260cm-79x102in) s.d.86/87 s.i.d. verso. 27-Nov-3 Lempertz, Koln #431/R est:18000-20000
£22667 $41707 €34000 Wailing wall (135x101cm-53x40in) s. s.i.d.1953 verso masonite prov.exhib.lit. 11-Jun-4 Villa Grisebach, Berlin #79/R est:25000-30000
Sculpture
£2639 $4407 €3800 Fylsett (105x81x28cm-41x32x11in) s.i.d. verso relief oil textiles string plastic canvas. 25-Oct-3 Dr Lehr, Berlin #469/R est:5000
Works on paper
£400 $732 €600 Unknown points in time (39x31cm-15x12in) s.i.d.12/55 W/C Indian ink. 4-Jun-4 Lempertz, Koln #437/R
£490 $842 €700 Composition (45x64cm-18x25in) s.d.12.56 ink. 4-Dec-3 Van Ham, Cologne #465/R
£537 $961 €800 A long story (64x47cm-25x19in) s.i.d.83 mixed media pen Indian ink W/C col pen prov. 25-May-4 Dorotheum, Vienna #393/R
£594 $1022 €850 It might be a birth (52x38cm-20x15in) s.d.98 W/C. 4-Dec-3 Van Ham, Cologne #466/R
£600 $1104 €900 Composition (46x61cm-18x24in) s.d.11/9/58 i. verso col chks. 11-Jun-4 Hauswedell & Nolte, Hamburg #1526/R
£625 $1044 €900 Animal contour (56x37cm-22x15in) s.i.d. col pen. 24-Oct-3 Ketterer, Hamburg #539/R
£664 $1143 €950 3/1/55 (64x49cm-25x19in) s.i.d. mixed media. 3-Dec-3 Hauswedell & Nolte, Hamburg #984/R
£667 $1220 €1000 Islands (48x62cm-19x24in) s.i.d.71 W/C col pen paper on board prov. 4-Jun-4 Lempertz, Koln #438/R
£1208 $2162 €1800 Untitled (43x59cm-17x23in) s.i.d.1959. 25-May-4 Dorotheum, Vienna #247/R est:1800-2200
£1241 $2073 €1800 Colour composition (45x62cm-18x24in) s.d.11.7.57 mixed media. 14-Nov-3 Altus, Berlin #655/R est:2200
£1268 $2193 €1800 Kneeling Vincenzo-Migof (70x45cm-28x18in) s.i.d.69 i. verso col pen. 13-Dec-3 Lempertz, Koln #184/R est:1500
£1448 $2419 €2100 Migof-Spalt (148x48cm-58x19in) s.i.d.1975 pencil board. 13-Nov-3 Neumeister, Munich #626/R est:2000-2500
£2098 $3608 €3000 4/48/58 (102x73cm-40x29in) s.i.d. col pen. 3-Dec-3 Hauswedell & Nolte, Hamburg #986/R est:3000
£2308 $3969 €3300 Composition (47x73cm-19x29in) mono. mixed media exec. c.1955. 4-Dec-3 Van Ham, Cologne #464/R est:5000
£4667 $8540 €7000 Untitled (80x60cm-31x24in) s.i.d.61 s.i. verso Indian ink oil paper collage on canvas. 4-Jun-4 Lempertz, Koln #435/R est:7000

SCHULTZE, Carl (1856-1935) German
£764 $1276 €1100 Romantic winter landscape (48x69cm-19x27in) s. lit. 25-Oct-3 Bergmann, Erlangen #932/R

SCHULTZE, Max (1845-1926) German
£900 $1431 €1305 Happy monk (62x49cm-24x19in) s.i. 9-Sep-3 Bonhams, Knightsbridge #89/R

SCHULTZE, Robert (1828-1919) German
£1056 $1827 €1500 Alpine glory, Alps in summer at Lauterbrunnen, Switzerland (37x49cm-15x19in) s. panel exhib. 10-Dec-3 Christie's, Amsterdam #671/R est:1500-2000
£1611 $3012 €2400 Norwegian coast (70x111cm-28x44in) s. i. verso. 24-Feb-4 Dorotheum, Vienna #12/R est:2000-2300

SCHULZ, Adrien (1851-1931) French
£385 $662 €562 Landscape with cattle grazing (39x64cm-15x25in) s.d.1895. 7-Dec-3 Uppsala Auktionskammare, Uppsala #104 (S.KR 5000)
£464 $848 €700 Bord de mare anime en automne (22x27cm-9x11in) s. panel. 7-Apr-4 Piasa, Paris #58
£940 $1729 €1400 Chemin de la Grande Vallee Fontainebleau (33x41cm-13x16in) s. i. verso board. 25-Mar-4 Dr Fritz Nagel, Stuttgart #759/R
£1267 $2280 €1900 Wood near Fontainebleau (50x65cm-20x26in) s. 26-Apr-4 Rieber, Stuttgart #1166/R est:2500
£2055 $3226 €3000 Troupeau de moutons pres du village (41x46cm-16x18in) s. 20-Apr-3 Deauville, France #58 est:3800-4300

SCHULZ, Bruno (1893-1942) Polish
Works on paper
£3906 $6523 €5703 Untitled (14x14cm-6x6in) pencil exec.c.1930. 19-Oct-3 Agra, Warsaw #18/R est:5000 (P.Z 25000)

SCHULZ, Charles M (1922-2000) American
Works on paper
£4192 $7000 €6120 Charlie Brown is reluctant to hand in his homework (13x48cm-5x19in) s.i. pen ink. 15-Nov-3 Illustration House, New York #64/R est:4000-6000

SCHULZ, Friedrich (1823-1875) German
£2635 $4717 €3900 Prince Friedrich Carl of Prussia at the Battle of Sedan (73x59cm-29x23in) s. lit. 8-May-4 Schloss Ahlden, Ahlden #692/R est:3800

SCHULZ, Fritz W (1884-1962) German
£278 $439 €400 Three master (70x100cm-28x39in) s. 6-Sep-3 Arnold, Frankfurt #657/R

SCHULZ, Julius Carl (19th C) German
£2937 $5052 €4200 High mountain landscape in winter (91x73cm-36x29in) s. 5-Dec-3 Michael Zeller, Lindau #788/R est:3800

SCHULZ, Karl Friedrich (1796-1866) German
Works on paper
£360 $659 €526 Figures in a winter landscape (26x34cm-10x13in) s.d.1837 W/C. 27-Jan-4 Bonhams, Knightsbridge #34/R

SCHULZ, Leopold (attrib) (1804-1873) Austrian
£3692 $6351 €5390 Portrait of girl and boy (150x115cm-59x45in) 2-Dec-3 Bukowskis, Stockholm #434/R est:50000-60000 (S.KR 48000)

SCHULZ, Oscar (fl.1878-1896) German
£1020 $1827 €1500 Two girls behind hut (46x36cm-18x14in) s.i.d.78. 17-Mar-4 Neumeister, Munich #600/R est:1500

SCHULZ, Walter (1895-1918) American
Works on paper
£280 $467 €400 Cuxhaven (22x30cm-9x12in) s.d.1945 i. verso pencil. 11-Oct-3 Hans Stahl, Hamburg #167

SCHULZ, Wilhelm (1865-1952) German
£246 $425 €359 Still life with red poppies with daisies in a green vase (46x28cm-18x11in) s. board. 10-Dec-3 Alderfer's, Hatfield #311

SCHULZ-MATAN, Walter (1889-?) German
£1200 $2148 €1800 House with wind pump (62x51cm-24x20in) s.d.28 lit. 14-May-4 Schloss Ahlden, Ahlden #2936/R est:1800
£3497 $6014 €5000 Houses in front of a snowy landscape (60x81cm-24x32in) s.d.1929 verso. 5-Dec-3 Ketterer, Munich #92/R est:5000-7000

SCHULZ-STRADTMANN, Otto (1892-1960) German
£345 $576 €500 English Garden (50x60cm-20x24in) s. 9-Jul-3 Hugo Ruef, Munich #214
£483 $806 €700 English Garden (60x80cm-24x31in) s. 9-Jul-3 Hugo Ruef, Munich #211
£520 $899 €759 Interior from Maria church, Lubeck (103x82cm-41x32in) s.d.1922. 9-Dec-3 Rasmussen, Copenhagen #1661/R (D.KR 5500)
£552 $921 €800 Village in late autumn (50x58cm-20x23in) s. board. 9-Jul-3 Hugo Ruef, Munich #212
£552 $921 €800 Blutenburg (50x60cm-20x24in) s. 9-Jul-3 Hugo Ruef, Munich #213/R
£621 $1037 €900 Pipping with St Wolfgang Church (60x70cm-24x28in) s. 9-Jul-3 Hugo Ruef, Munich #210/R
£822 $1282 €1200 Isar valley (50x35cm-20x14in) s. panel. 10-Apr-3 Weidler, Nurnberg #310/R

SCHULZE, Andreas (1955-) German
£5667 $10370 €8500 Untitled (200x400cm-79x157in) s.d.1982 verso acrylic cotton exhib. 4-Jun-4 Lempertz, Koln #440/R est:10000

SCHULZE, Emil (1863-?) German
£852 $1500 €1244 Pensive male figure on rocky shore (114x94cm-45x37in) s.d.1909. 22-May-4 New Orleans Auction, New Orleans #139/R est:1200-1800

SCHULZE, Horst (?) ?
£300 $549 €450 Summer landscape (100x100cm-39x39in) s.d.1915. 5-Jun-4 Arnold, Frankfurt #722/R

SCHULZE, Kurt (1877-) German
£559 $951 €800 The Frauenkirche in Dresden (97x75cm-38x30in) s.i. lit. 28-Nov-3 Schloss Ahlden, Ahlden #1544/R

SCHUMACHER, Daniel (fl.1754-1786) American
Works on paper
£2250 $3600 €3285 Seven flowers surrounding a central script (20x33cm-8x13in) s. W/C ink. 20-Sep-3 Pook & Pook, Downington #456/R est:3500-4500

SCHUMACHER, Emil (1912-1999) German
£2489 $4156 €3634 Untitled (26x51cm-10x20in) s.d.1974 s.d. verso enamel terracotta prov. 24-Jun-3 Germann, Zurich #106/R est:6000-8000 (S.FR 5500)
£9333 $16707 €14000 Composition G (50x70cm-20x28in) s.d. oil varnish. 15-May-4 Dr Sturies, Dusseldorf #195/R
£13333 $23867 €20000 Abstract in white and red (70x50cm-28x20in) s.d. 15-May-4 Bassenge, Berlin #7131/R est:30000
£13986 $23776 €20000 Composition (98x65cm-39x26in) s.d.57. 29-Nov-3 Bassenge, Berlin #6978/R est:30000
£18000 $33120 €27000 G 33-73 (79x55cm-31x22in) s.d.73 oil tempera paper collage cardboard prov. 11-Jun-4 Villa Grisebach, Berlin #78/R est:30000-40000
£24000 $44160 €36000 Pilo (80x60cm-31x24in) s.d. s.d. stretcher oil sand. 11-Jun-4 Hauswedell & Nolte, Hamburg #1529/R est:30000

£26667 $47733 €40000 Hen house (61x48cm-24x19in) s.d.48 panel exhib. 15-May-4 Van Ham, Cologne #921/R est:48000
£33333 $61000 €50000 Untitled (70x58cm-28x23in) s.d.70 acrylic sisal prov. 4-Jun-4 Lempertz, Koln #445/R est:70000-80000
£62937 $108252 €90000 Lamatan (140x96cm-55x38in) s.d. i.d. verso oil sand prov. 5-Dec-3 Ketterer, Munich #344/R est:120000-150000
£115385 $196154 €165000 Soman (100x80cm-39x31in) s.d.62 i. stretcher oil sand prov.exhib.lit. 27-Nov-3 Lempertz, Koln #433/R est:120000-140000
Prints
£2013 $3705 €3000 Self portrait (32x25cm-13x10in) s.d. linocut. 26-Mar-4 Ketterer, Hamburg #642/R est:1800-2400
Sculpture
£3394 $5769 €4955 Untitled (431x32x4cm-170x13x2in) s.d.1974 enamel terracotta prov. 25-Nov-3 Germann, Zurich #117/R est:6000-8000 (S.FR 7500)
Works on paper
£2098 $3608 €3000 Composition (28x35cm-11x14in) s.d. Indian ink brush. 3-Dec-3 Hauswedell & Nolte, Hamburg #990/R est:3000
£5000 $9150 €7500 Untitled (29x23cm-11x9in) s.d.81 goauche packing paper. 4-Jun-4 Lempertz, Koln #446/R est:5000
£5369 $9503 €8000 Untitled (48x65cm-19x26in) s.i.d. goauche col chk double-sided. 30-Apr-4 Dr Fritz Nagel, Stuttgart #961/R est:12000
£16000 $29280 €24000 Untitled (54x65cm-21x26in) s.d.84 gouache oil chk packing paper prov.exhib. 4-Jun-4 Lempertz, Koln #447/R est:18000-20000
£26432 $44934 €38591 Abstract composition (100x81cm-39x32in) bears sig.d.60 i. stretcher mixed media oil sand canvas. 5-Nov-3 Dobiaschofsky, Bern #944/R est:60000 (S.FR 60000)
£28169 $48732 €40000 GC 11 (53x70cm-21x28in) s.d.90 mixed media. 13-Dec-3 Lempertz, Koln #185/R est:12000

SCHUMACHER, Ernst (1905-1963) German
£537 $950 €800 White houses (50x66cm-20x26in) s.d.50. 28-Apr-4 Schopman, Hamburg #580/R
£591 $1045 €880 Villa in Pineta/Rome (50x65cm-20x26in) s. board. 28-Apr-4 Schopman, Hamburg #579/R
£2098 $3566 €3000 Thouars - first version (70x100cm-28x39in) s.d.48. 29-Nov-3 Villa Grisebach, Berlin #261/R est:3500-4500
£2098 $3566 €3000 Fishing houses (55x75cm-22x30in) s.d.51 prov. double-sided. 29-Nov-3 Villa Grisebach, Berlin #262/R est:3000-4000
£2098 $3566 €3000 Green house (50x65cm-20x26in) s. panel. 29-Nov-3 Villa Grisebach, Berlin #264/R est:3000-4000

SCHUMACHER, Harald (1836-1912) Danish
£284 $455 €415 Southern landscape with woman and child by pergola (37x50cm-15x20in) init. 22-Sep-3 Rasmussen, Vejle #168/R (D.KR 3000)
£358 $655 €523 From Nuremberg with Henkerstieg in background (51x40cm-20x16in) init. 9-Jun-4 Rasmussen, Copenhagen #1906/R (D.KR 4000)
£451 $834 €658 Almind hills by Hald Lake (82x112cm-32x44in) s.d.71 exhib.prov. 15-Mar-4 Rasmussen, Vejle #482 (D.KR 5000)
£455 $728 €664 Almind Hills near Hald Lake (81x111cm-32x44in) s.d.71. 22-Sep-3 Rasmussen, Vejle #326/R (D.KR 4800)
£895 $1638 €1307 Loggia , Capri (48x60cm-19x24in) init. 9-Jun-4 Rasmussen, Copenhagen #1912/R (D.KR 10000)
£898 $1671 €1311 Ellekilde north of Kronborg (48x82cm-19x32in) s. 2-Mar-4 Rasmussen, Copenhagen #1347/R (D.KR 10000)

SCHUMACHER, Hugo (1939-) Swiss
Works on paper
£294 $500 €429 Fish head (24x30cm-9x12in) col pen. 28-Nov-3 Zofingen, Switzerland #3170 (S.FR 650)
£294 $500 €429 Larches (24x30cm-9x12in) col pen. 28-Nov-3 Zofingen, Switzerland #3171 (S.FR 650)

SCHUMACHER, Mathias (20th C) German
£6081 $10703 €9000 The Last Judgement (94x80cm-37x31in) s.d. canvas on panel prov. 22-May-4 Lempertz, Koln #1132/R est:6000

SCHUMANN, Carl Franz (1767-1827) German
Works on paper
£940 $1729 €1400 Napoleon on battlefield at Esslingen (32x41cm-13x16in) i. verso pen Indian ink brush. 26-Mar-4 Venator & Hansten, Koln #1646/R

SCHUMANN, Christian (1970-) American
£4749 $8500 €6934 Untitled, pocket/white (183x152cm-72x60in) s.d.1993 overlap acrylic col pencil graphite ink collage prov. 14-May-4 Phillips, New York #331/R est:10000-15000
£5988 $10000 €8742 Things are going to get worse (152x102cm-60x40in) s.d.1995 overlap acrylic paper collage prov. 13-Nov-3 Sotheby's, New York #610/R est:10000-15000
£8939 $16000 €13051 Flatbush (183x152cm-72x60in) s.i.d.April 1999 overlap acrylic gouache pen ink collage prov. 14-May-4 Phillips, New York #102/R est:20000-30000
£9497 $17000 €13866 Useless (166x183cm-65x72in) s.i.d.1999 overlap acrylic mixed media collage prov.exhib. 13-May-4 Sotheby's, New York #474/R est:15000-20000
£20958 $35000 €30599 Untitled (164x296cm-65x117in) acrylic gouache graphite paper collage painted 1992 prov. 14-Nov-3 Phillips, New York #113/R est:20000-30000

SCHUMANN, Henriette (1911-2002) French
£364 $667 €550 Nature morte aux citrons et au moulin a cafe (81x60cm-32x24in) init.d.2-66. 7-Apr-4 Piasa, Paris #230

SCHUMM, Tim (20th C) Canadian
£269 $489 €393 Phipps Point (51x61cm-20x24in) s.d.1992 acrylic. 5-Feb-4 Heffel, Vancouver #058/R (C.D 650)

SCHUNBACH, Franz (1898-1975) Hungarian
£1844 $3079 €2600 Ferry across the Inn at Angath (46x56cm-18x22in) s.d.1970. 16-Oct-3 Dorotheum, Salzburg #654/R est:2000-3000

SCHUNEMANN, L (fl.1666-1667) British?
£1500 $2700 €2190 Portrait of Sir Peter Wedderburn of Gosford (124x100cm-49x39in) i. 21-Jan-4 Sotheby's, Olympia #70/R est:2000-3000
£2500 $4500 €3650 Portrait of a nobleman, probably George, 4th Earl of Linlithgow. i. 21-Jan-4 Sotheby's, Olympia #74/R est:3000-4000
£2600 $4680 €3796 Portrait of Lady Margaret Hamilton (120x96cm-47x38in) i. 21-Jan-4 Sotheby's, Olympia #69/R est:2000-3000
£4800 $8640 €7008 Portrait of an officer, probably John Leslie, 1st Duke of Rothes (122x98cm-48x39in) 21-Jan-4 Sotheby's, Olympia #75/R est:3000-4000

SCHUPPEN, Jacob van (attrib) (1670-1751) Dutch
£1560 $2605 €2200 Un peintre a son chevalet (43x32cm-17x13in) 17-Oct-3 Tajan, Paris #68/R est:2000-3000

SCHURCH, Erwin (1939-) Swiss
£439 $732 €641 Fastnacht in Lucern (60x85cm-24x33in) s. prov. 15-Nov-3 Galerie Gloggner, Luzern #97 (S.FR 1000)

SCHURCH, Johann Robert (1895-1941) Swiss
£550 $919 €798 Portrait of Gregor Rabinovitch (46x37cm-18x15in) s. 23-Jun-3 Philippe Schuler, Zurich #3426 (S.FR 1200)
£591 $981 €857 Woman's portrait (56x46cm-22x18in) s. s.i.d.19 verso. 13-Jun-3 Zofingen, Switzerland #3021 (S.FR 1300)
£1009 $1685 €1463 Self portrait (35x24cm-14x9in) s.d.1918. 23-Jun-3 Philippe Schuler, Zurich #3425/R (S.FR 2200)
£1293 $2315 €1888 Lago Maggiore (61x92cm-24x36in) s. i. stretcher. 14-May-4 Dobiaschofsky, Bern #160/R est:3600 (S.FR 3000)
£4977 $8611 €7266 Two woman (54x41cm-21x16in) s. board. 9-Dec-3 Sotheby's, Zurich #65/R est:2500-3500 (S.FR 11000)
Works on paper
£385 $654 €562 Lady in an armchair (21x24cm-8x9in) s. W/C. 1-Dec-3 Koller, Zurich #6514 (S.FR 850)
£661 $1123 €965 In the studio (21x16cm-8x6in) s. Indian ink brush wash. 5-Nov-3 Dobiaschofsky, Bern #1880/R (S.FR 1500)
£721 $1240 €1053 Readers (20x26cm-8x10in) s.d.1926 W/C ink. 8-Dec-3 Philippe Schuler, Zurich #3227 (S.FR 1600)
£849 $1375 €1240 The artist Max Hunziker (32x24cm-13x9in) s.i.d.1925. 24-May-3 Burkhard, Luzern #39/R (S.FR 1800)
£1041 $1769 €1520 Female nude (47x31cm-19x12in) s.d.1940 W/C on Indian ink. 25-Nov-3 Germann, Zurich #895 est:3000-4000 (S.FR 2300)

SCHURCH, Paul (1886-1939) Swiss
£317 $538 €463 Old village street (37x58cm-15x23in) s. 28-Nov-3 Zofingen, Switzerland #3172 (S.FR 700)
£341 $566 €494 Last rays of sunshine - farmstead in Trimbach near Olten (55x63cm-22x25in) s.d.1916. 13-Jun-3 Zofingen, Switzerland #3022 (S.FR 750)
£1000 $1830 €1460 San Bernardino (40x60cm-16x24in) s.i. 4-Jun-4 Zofingen, Switzerland #2953 (S.FR 2300)

SCHURIG, Felix (1852-1907) German
£1042 $1646 €1500 Woman studying book (65x48cm-26x19in) s.d.83. 6-Sep-3 Schopman, Hamburg #700/R est:2000

SCHURJIN, Raul (1907-1983) Argentinian
£894 $1600 €1305 Costeritas (60x30cm-24x12in) board. 11-May-4 Arroyo, Buenos Aires #89

SCHURMANN, Killian (1962-) Irish
Sculpture
£1216 $2299 €1800 Cormorant (36x41cm-14x16in) s.d.1998 num.2 glass thermocollage two. 17-Feb-4 Whyte's, Dublin #218/R est:1800-2200

SCHURR, Claude (1920-) French
£323 $550 €472 Harbour scene (53x46cm-21x18in) s. 22-Nov-3 Jackson's, Cedar Falls #395/R
£412 $700 €602 Audierne (38x25cm-15x10in) s. prov. 22-Nov-3 Jackson's, Cedar Falls #410/R
£430 $805 €650 Au loin Penmarc (38x46cm-15x18in) s. 25-Jul-4 Feletin, Province #55
£738 $1366 €1100 Lumiere blanche a Cannes (50x61cm-20x24in) s. 14-Mar-4 Feletin, Province #78
£874 $1503 €1250 Les filets verts St Guenole (54x65cm-21x26in) s. 7-Dec-3 Feletin, Province #93
£2941 $5500 €4294 Port de Nice (100x81cm-39x32in) s. prov. 25-Feb-4 Christie's, Rockefeller NY #110/R est:3000-4000

SCHURTENBERGER, Ernst (1931-) Swiss
£307 $513 €448 Untitled (59x70cm-23x28in) mono.d.70 i. stretcher prov. 15-Nov-3 Galerie Gloggner, Luzern #99 (S.FR 700)
£448 $726 €654 Landscape (27x35cm-11x14in) mono.d.1979 s.i.d. verso. 24-May-3 Burkhard, Luzern #8/R (S.FR 950)

SCHUSSLER, Karl (1941-) Austrian
Works on paper
£385 $654 €550 Man with crocodile (69x49cm-27x19in) s.d.93 mixed media. 19-Nov-3 Dorotheum, Klagenfurt #73

SCHUSTER, Donna (1883-1953) American
£1301 $2250 €1899 Barn out back (41x51cm-16x20in) board. 10-Dec-3 Bonhams & Butterfields, San Francisco #6237/R est:3000-5000
£6593 $12000 €9626 Golden hills, California (30x41cm-12x16in) s. i.verso board prov. 15-Jun-4 John Moran, Pasadena #41 est:6000-9000

Works on paper
£1176 $2000 €1717 Harbour (36x51cm-14x20in) s. W/C prov.exhib. 18-Nov-3 John Moran, Pasadena #90b est:2500-3500
£2941 $5000 €4294 Mending nets, probably Terminal Island, Wilmington, CA (38x53cm-15x21in) s. W/C prov.exhib. 18-Nov-3 John Moran, Pasadena #85 est:4000-6000

SCHUSTER, Josef (1812-1890) Austrian
£1189 $2021 €1700 Still life with fruit and bird (19x26cm-7x10in) s. panel exhib.lit. 28-Nov-3 Schloss Ahlden, Ahlden #1401/R est:2200
£2752 $4596 €3990 Still life with white grapes and tankard (42x34cm-17x13in) s.d.848 panel. 23-Jun-3 Philippe Schuler, Zurich #3548/R est:4000-5000 (S.FR 6000)
£2752 $4596 €3990 Still life with flowers and ivy (42x34cm-17x13in) s.d.848 panel. 23-Jun-3 Philippe Schuler, Zurich #3549/R est:4000-5000 (S.FR 6000)

SCHUSTER, Joseph (1873-1945) Austrian
£629 $1083 €900 Still life with fruit bowl (55x44cm-22x17in) s.d.1943 board. 3-Dec-3 Neumeister, Munich #738/R

SCHUSTER, Karl Maria (1871-1953) Austrian
£1909 $3169 €2768 Capri (80x60cm-31x24in) s.i.d.1906. 13-Jun-3 Zofingen, Switzerland #2529/R est:3500 (S.FR 4200)

SCHUSTER, Ludwig (1820-1873) Austrian
£563 $975 €800 Mountain landscape with hut (30x37cm-12x15in) 10-Dec-3 Dorotheum, Vienna #145/R
£1379 $2303 €2000 Mountain landscapes with huts and figures (30x37cm-12x15in) s.d.849 lit. two. 10-Jul-3 Allgauer, Kempten #2675/R est:2000

SCHUSTER-WOLDAN, Raffael (1870-1951) German
£664 $1143 €950 Woman under pergola (46x51cm-18x20in) i. s.i.d.1901 verso board. 5-Dec-3 Bolland & Marotz, Bremen #628/R

SCHUT, Cornelis (17th C) Flemish
£1528 $2490 €2200 Descente du Saint-Esprit (52x38cm-20x15in) 23-Sep-3 Galerie Moderne, Brussels #867/R

SCHUT, Cornelis (attrib) (17th C) Flemish
£1705 $3000 €2489 Assumption of the Virgin (98x116cm-39x46in) 19-May-4 Doyle, New York #6072/R est:5000-7000
Works on paper
£685 $1164 €1000 Assumption of the Virgin (38x30cm-15x12in) pen brown ink grey wash over black chk. 4-Nov-3 Sotheby's, Amsterdam #41/R

SCHUT, Cornelis (circle) (17th C) Flemish
£6538 $11246 €9545 Mars and Venus (68x128cm-27x50in) painted c.1680. 3-Dec-3 AB Stockholms Auktionsverk #2677/R est:70000-80000 (S.KR 85000)

SCHUT, Cornelis (elder) (1597-1655) Flemish
£110000 $201300 €160600 Susanna and the elders (119x107cm-47x42in) prov.lit. 7-Jul-4 Sotheby's, London #24/R est:30000-50000

SCHUT, Cornelis (elder-attrib) (1597-1655) Flemish
£1241 $2073 €1800 La mort de Saint Laurent (356x230cm-140x91in) 17-Nov-3 Bernaerts, Antwerp #311 est:1250-1500

SCHUT, Cornelis III (1629-1685) Dutch
Works on paper
£685 $1164 €1000 Vision of St Francis (37x26cm-15x10in) pen brown ink black chk. 4-Nov-3 Sotheby's, Amsterdam #42/R

SCHUTT, Gustav (1890-1968) Austrian
£6040 $10691 €9000 From Varignano d'Arco (100x97cm-39x38in) s.d.1922 i. verso. 28-Apr-4 Wiener Kunst Auktionen, Vienna #85/R est:5600-8000

SCHUTTE, Thomas (1954-) German
£7485 $12500 €10928 Untitled (131x110cm-52x43in) s.d.1983 oil gouache graphite prov. 14-Nov-3 Phillips, New York #262/R est:10000-15000
£8000 $14480 €11680 Watermelon (140x109cm-55x43in) s.d.1986 acrylic on paper executed 1986 prov. 1-Apr-4 Christie's, Kensington #243/R est:6000-8000
Sculpture
£10056 $18000 €14682 Urns (80x35x35cm-31x14x14in) painted ceramic vessel 2 parts exec 1999 prov. 13-May-4 Sotheby's, New York #344/R est:18000-25000
Works on paper
£1733 $3189 €2600 Blue blood nose (50x65cm-20x26in) s.i. ink exec 1989 prov. 9-Jun-4 Artcurial Briest, Paris #549/R est:2500-3000
£3067 $5612 €4600 Untitled (28x28cm-11x11in) s.d.96 Indian ink W/C pencil. 4-Jun-4 Lempertz, Koln #432/R est:2500
£20958 $35000 €30599 Big heads (100x70cm-39x28in) each s. graphite ink yellow paper diptych exec 1992 prov. 12-Nov-3 Christie's, Rockefeller NY #505/R est:10000-15000

SCHUTTER, Theodor Cornelis (fl.c.1760) Dutch
Works on paper
£1351 $2378 €2000 Views of Castle Hardenbroek, and view of a farm with roofed haystacks (19x27cm-7x11in) one i.verso pen col ink wash three prov.lit. 19-May-4 Sotheby's, Amsterdam #247/R est:500-700
£1892 $3330 €2800 View of T Huijs Oud-Woulven (19x28cm-7x11in) i.mount pen grey ink wash prov.lit. 19-May-4 Sotheby's, Amsterdam #251/R est:1200-1800

SCHUTZ, Christian Georg (18/19th C) German
£4930 $8528 €7000 River landscape (16x22cm-6x9in) s.d.1786 panel. 13-Dec-3 Lempertz, Koln #45/R est:6000

SCHUTZ, Christian Georg (attrib) (18/19th C) German
£1986 $3377 €2900 Romantic river landscape (32x41cm-13x16in) bears sig. 8-Nov-3 Hans Stahl, Toestorf #110/R est:1700
£2013 $3705 €3000 Wooded river landscape with figures (40x51cm-16x20in) 24-Mar-4 Dorotheum, Vienna #324/R est:2000-2500
£2685 $4940 €4000 Mountainous river landscape with figures (26x40cm-10x16in) s. panel. 24-Mar-4 Dorotheum, Vienna #260/R est:5000-7000

SCHUTZ, Christian Georg I (1718-1791) German
£1250 $1975 €1800 Extensive Rhenish landscape with travelers in the foreground (26x31cm-10x12in) bears sig panel. 2-Sep-3 Christie's, Amsterdam #95/R est:2000-3000
£2703 $4649 €3946 Mountain landscape with waterfall, figures and animals (33x42cm-13x17in) s.d.1764 panel. 8-Dec-3 Philippe Schuler, Zurich #3432/R est:6000-8000 (S.FR 6000)
£5245 $8759 €7500 Rhine landscape (42x51cm-17x20in) s. 28-Jun-3 Bolland & Marotz, Bremen #605/R est:8200

SCHUTZ, Christian Georg I (attrib) (1718-1791) German
£1788 $3254 €2700 River landscape with ruins and resting walkers (98x123cm-39x48in) 18-Jun-4 Bolland & Marotz, Bremen #535/R est:2400

SCHUTZ, Christian Georg II (1758-1823) German
£4545 $7591 €6500 Feldberg, Taunus at sunset (32x40cm-13x16in) 28-Jun-3 Bolland & Marotz, Bremen #607/R est:6500

SCHUTZ, Christian Georg II (attrib) (1758-1823) German
£2252 $4098 €3400 Cavaliers dans un paysageabstrait Paysan et troupeau (23x33cm-9x13in) panel pair. 15-Jun-4 Claude Aguttes, Neuilly #40 est:2500-3000
£2632 $4842 €4000 Rhine landscape with ruins (22x30cm-9x12in) pair. 24-Jun-4 Dr Fritz Nagel, Stuttgart #669/R est:3800
Works on paper
£594 $1010 €850 Rhine landscape (16x28cm-6x11in) gouache. 27-Nov-3 Bassenge, Berlin #5647

SCHUTZ, Erich (?) Austrian
£471 $800 €688 Only for you, my friend. Harem scene (36x33cm-14x13in) s. black ink W/C over pencil on card two. 5-Nov-3 Doyle, New York #69/R

SCHUTZ, Franz (attrib) (1751-1781) German
£1467 $2655 €2200 Extensive river valley in summer (37x51cm-15x20in) 1-Apr-4 Van Ham, Cologne #1244 est:2200

SCHUTZ, J (19/20th C) ?
£340 $619 €500 Alpine idylle (62x82cm-24x32in) s.d.1930. 3-Feb-4 Christie's, Amsterdam #236

SCHUTZ, Jan Frederik (1817-1888) Dutch
£8500 $13600 €12410 Dutch small craft and a brig drying their sails in a calm (70x105cm-28x41in) s.d.78. 16-Sep-3 Bonhams, New Bond Street #64/R est:3000-5000

SCHUTZ, Johann Georg (1755-1813) German
£4698 $8644 €7000 Rhine landscape (24x32cm-9x13in) panel. 24-Mar-4 Dorotheum, Vienna #268/R

SCHUTZ, Johann Georg (attrib) (1755-1813) German
Works on paper
£1875 $2963 €2700 Rescue after shipwreck (18x21cm-7x8in) 6-Sep-3 Schopman, Hamburg #866/R est:2700

SCHUTZ, Johannes (20th C) Swiss
£545 $905 €790 Mountain lake in summer (62x82cm-24x32in) s.d.1935. 13-Jun-3 Zofingen, Switzerland #2530/R (S.FR 1200)

SCHUTZ, Willem Joannes (1854-1933) Dutch
£658 $1191 €1000 Ships in the harbour mouth (17x26cm-7x10in) s. panel. 19-Apr-4 Glerum, Amsterdam #4/R

SCHUTZE, Wilhelm (1840-1898) German
£530 $964 €800 Still life with lobster, oysters and lemons (64x84cm-25x33in) s. board oval. 18-Jun-4 Bolland & Marotz, Bremen #752/R
£1644 $2795 €2400 Still life of flowers in vase (48x59cm-19x23in) s. board lit. 6-Nov-3 Allgauer, Kempten #3577/R est:1400

SCHUTZMANN, Pia (1940-) Italian
£941 $1599 €1374 Composition (100x75cm-39x30in) s.d.1990 verso. 26-Nov-3 Kunsthallen, Copenhagen #137/R (D.KR 10000)

SCHUYFF, Peter (1958-) Dutch
£299 $500 €437 Rose bowl (25x20cm-10x8in) acrylic prov. 7-Oct-3 Sotheby's, New York #414
£2793 $5000 €4078 Untitled (241x240cm-95x94in) s.i.d.1986 verso acrylic prov. 14-May-4 Phillips, New York #357/R est:3000-5000

SCHUYLER, Remington (1887-1953) American
£1846 $3250 €2695 Fond memories (102x68cm-40x27in) s. 23-May-4 Bonhams & Butterfields, Los Angeles #7057/R

SCHUZ, Friedrich (1874-1954) German
£331 $603 €500 Young girl resting in the sunshine (30x41cm-12x16in) s. board. 18-Jun-4 Bolland & Marotz, Bremen #753/R
£972 $1536 €1400 Genua harbour (61x50cm-24x20in) s. panel lit. 19-Sep-3 Schloss Ahlden, Ahlden #1616/R

SCHUZ, Theodor (1830-1900) German
£1761 $2817 €2500 Children playing near Haigerloch (11x17cm-4x7in) bears mono.sig. i. verso board. 19-Sep-3 Sigalas, Stuttgart #424/R est:3500

SCHWABE, Carlos (1866-1926) Swiss
£1079 $1770 €1500 Metje en Suisse (28x35cm-11x14in) s.i. panel. 6-Jun-3 Chochon-Barre & Allardi, Paris #90/R est:2500-3000
£13636 $23182 €19500 Le jugement de Paris (168x295cm-66x116in) s.d.1924 lit. 27-Nov-3 Millon & Associes, Paris #164/R est:15000-18000
Works on paper
£833 $1500 €1216 La deliverance (30x23cm-12x9in) s. ink W/C on board exhib. 21-Jan-4 Sotheby's, New York #257/R est:1500-2500
£944 $1700 €1378 Allegorical composition (43x29cm-17x11in) mono.d.2.91 ink wash exhib. 21-Jan-4 Sotheby's, New York #256/R est:1800-2500
£3667 $6747 €5500 Le faune (31x48cm-12x19in) s.d.1923 pastel sanguine chl col crayon. 11-Jun-4 Claude Aguttes, Neuilly #110/R est:5000-7000

SCHWABE, Henry August (1843-1916) American/German
£4037 $6500 €5894 Woman with fan, 1911 (107x56cm-42x22in) s. 20-Aug-3 James Julia, Fairfield #1226/R est:5000-10000

SCHWABEN, Hans W (19th C) ?
Works on paper
£950 $1767 €1387 Largo Harbour at low water (35x46cm-14x18in) s. i.verso W/C bodycol. 4-Mar-4 Christie's, Kensington #165/R

SCHWACHA, George (1908-) American
£353 $650 €515 Landscape with rolling hills (46x61cm-18x24in) s. masonite. 9-Jun-4 Alderfer's, Hatfield #520/R

SCHWAGER, Richard (1822-1880) German
Miniatures
£5208 $8854 €7500 Kaiser Franz Joseph and Kaiserin Elisabeth. s.d.1856 ivory. 28-Oct-3 Wiener Kunst Auktionen, Vienna #24/R est:3000-10000
Works on paper
£658 $1211 €1000 Portrait of a young girl (12x9cm-5x4in) s.d.1856 W/C ivory oval. 22-Jun-4 Wiener Kunst Auktionen, Vienna #18/R

SCHWALB, Marie (19/20th C) German?
£629 $1070 €900 Still life with copper pot and strawberries (51x61cm-20x24in) s. lit. 28-Nov-3 Schloss Ahlden, Ahlden #1439/R

SCHWALBE, Ole (1929-1990) Danish
£751 $1254 €1096 Study - Sign - Concrete composition (55x55cm-22x22in) s.d.59-60 verso. 7-Oct-3 Rasmussen, Copenhagen #166/R (D.KR 8000)
£766 $1240 €1111 Black light (92x73cm-36x29in) s.d.66 verso. 4-Aug-3 Rasmussen, Vejle #540/R (D.KR 8000)
£903 $1661 €1318 Surreal composition (45x35cm-18x14in) s.d.1949 plywood prov. 29-Mar-4 Rasmussen, Copenhagen #316/R (D.KR 10000)
£939 $1568 €1371 Venezia II (73x66cm-29x26in) s.d.1963 verso. 7-Oct-3 Rasmussen, Copenhagen #167/R (D.KR 10000)
£1041 $1863 €1520 Roman evenings - geometric still life (92x73cm-36x29in) s.d.1965-66 verso. 10-May-4 Rasmussen, Vejle #510/R est:12000-15000 (D.KR 11500)
£1422 $2275 €2062 Study - Mabillon (33x65cm-13x26in) s.d.59 verso. 17-Sep-3 Kunsthallen, Copenhagen #19/R est:20000 (D.KR 15000)

SCHWANTHALER, Johann Georg (1740-1810) Austrian
Sculpture
£10667 $19413 €16000 Deer with cross appearing before St Hubert (24x40x16cm-9x16x6in) wood lit. 30-Jun-4 Neumeister, Munich #294/R est:7500

SCHWAR, Wilhelm (1860-1943) German
£3642 $6629 €5500 Cat family with butterfly in idyllic garden scene (41x51cm-16x20in) s. lit. 19-Jun-4 Bergmann, Erlangen #806 est:5500
£6711 $12349 €10000 The big friend (25x33cm-10x13in) s.d.1904. 26-Mar-4 Bolland & Marotz, Bremen #591/R est:3800

SCHWARTZ, Adolf (1869-1926) Austrian
£662 $1212 €1000 Banjaluka (47x35cm-19x14in) s. canvas on board. 8-Apr-4 Dorotheum, Vienna #114/R

SCHWARTZ, Andrew T (1867-1942) American
£403 $750 €588 Autumn landscape with rolling hills dotted with boulders (41x51cm-16x20in) canvasboard. 3-Mar-4 Alderfer's, Hatfield #374
£645 $1200 €942 Gathering flowers (41x51cm-16x20in) s. painted c.1920. 7-Mar-4 Treadway Gallery, Cincinnati #568/R est:2000-3000
£939 $1700 €1371 Autumn splendor (41x51cm-16x20in) s. 16-Apr-4 James Julia, Fairfield #757/R est:1700-2000

SCHWARTZ, Bucky (1932-) Israeli
Sculpture
£1506 $2500 €2199 Broken circle (49cm-19in) brushed aluminium exec 1970 pro. 2-Oct-3 Christie's, Tel Aviv #105/R est:2700-4400

SCHWARTZ, Davis F (1879-1969) American
£261 $475 €381 Sonoran Desert (30x41cm-12x16in) s. canvasboard. 19-Jun-4 Harvey Clar, Oakland #2197/R
Works on paper
£529 $1000 €772 Carmel mission (41x51cm-16x20in) s.i. W/C. 21-Feb-4 Jeffery Burchard, Florida #95a/R

SCHWARTZ, Esther (19/20th C) French
£1597 $2603 €2300 Bain des putti (49x63cm-19x25in) s. pair. 26-Sep-3 Millon & Associes, Paris #66 est:900

SCHWARTZ, Lester (20th C) American
£1202 $2200 €1755 Balinese mother (109x81cm-43x32in) s. 31-Jan-4 South Bay, Long Island #212
£1639 $3000 €2393 Young chorus girl (102x132cm-40x52in) 31-Jan-4 South Bay, Long Island #212a

SCHWARTZ, Mommie (1876-1942) Dutch
£4000 $7360 €6000 Farmyard. Still life with fruits on a table (42x56cm-17x22in) s. plywood double-sided. 9-Jun-4 Christie's, Amsterdam #196/R est:6000-8000
Works on paper
£294 $499 €420 Arti et Amicitiae (80x60cm-31x24in) s. mixed media. 24-Nov-3 Glerum, Amsterdam #603/R
£594 $1010 €850 Art evening with dancing, Gertrud Leistikow (114x81cm-45x32in) s. gouache. 24-Nov-3 Glerum, Amsterdam #604/R
£1678 $2853 €2400 Broadway, a Hat of Distinction (48x32cm-19x13in) init. gouache collage. 24-Nov-3 Glerum, Amsterdam #605/R

SCHWARTZ, Stephan (1851-1924) Austrian
Sculpture
£1189 $2045 €1700 Male nude (35cm-14in) i. brown pat.bronze. 5-Dec-3 Dorotheum, Vienna #203/R est:700-1000

SCHWARTZ, William S (1896-1977) American
£703 $1300 €1026 Pansies (28x23cm-11x9in) s. 13-Mar-4 Susanin's, Chicago #6045/R
£1657 $3000 €2419 On the beach (51x38cm-20x15in) board. 16-Apr-4 American Auctioneer #362/R est:3000-4500
£4144 $7500 €6050 Symphonic forms num 64 (76x102cm-30x40in) s. s.i.stretcher. 18-Apr-4 Jeffery Burchard, Florida #82/R
£8380 $15000 €12235 West side dwellings, Chicago (28x39cm-11x15in) s. s.i.verso prov. 6-May-4 Shannon's, Milford #134/R est:12000-18000
£8383 $14000 €12239 Gas plant (76x91cm-30x36in) s. s.i.d.1941 verso. 9-Oct-3 Christie's, Rockefeller NY #88/R est:6000-8000
£8721 $15000 €12733 Village (89x94cm-35x37in) s. s.i.d.1927 verso. 7-Dec-3 Treadway Gallery, Cincinnati #692/R est:18000-22000
Works on paper
£366 $600 €531 Still life (51x41cm-20x16in) s. W/C paperboard exec.c.1930. 7-Jun-3 Treadway Gallery, Cincinnati #1506
£652 $1200 €952 Cubist draped figure (25x15cm-10x6in) s.d.1926 pencil prov. 25-Jun-4 Freeman, Philadelphia #63/R
£1420 $2500 €2073 Old man by the sea (53x43cm-21x17in) s. W/C exec.c.1940. 23-May-4 Treadway Gallery, Cincinnati #739/R est:2500-3000
£1706 $2900 €2491 Over Fifty and abandoned (56x76cm-22x30in) s. W/C gouache executed c.1930 prov. 9-Nov-3 Wright, Chicago #224 est:3000-4000
£3529 $6000 €5152 Galena, Illinois (43x61cm-17x24in) s. W/C gouache executed c.1930. 9-Nov-3 Wright, Chicago #225 est:4000-5000
£4118 $7000 €6012 Company town (48x64cm-19x25in) s. W/C gouache executed c.1930. 9-Nov-3 Wright, Chicago #227 est:4000-5000
£4324 $8000 €6313 On the veranda (48x63cm-19x25in) s. i.verso W/C gouache exhib. 11-Mar-4 Christie's, Rockefeller NY #94/R est:6000-8000

SCHWARTZENBERG, Simon (1895-?) Rumanian
£489 $842 €700 Couple devant les maisons (46x55cm-18x22in) s.d.1959. 3-Dec-3 Tajan, Paris #195

SCHWARTZKOPF, Earl (1888-?) American
£543 $1000 €793 Coastal town (61x74cm-24x29in) s.d.45 masonite prov. 28-Mar-4 Bonhams & Butterfields, San Francisco #2734 est:2000-3000

SCHWARZ, Alfred (1867-1951) German
£2215 $4075 €3300 Portrait of Debutant (33x26cm-13x10in) s.d.1896 panel lit. 25-Mar-4 Karlheinz Kaupp, Staufen #2724/R est:350

SCHWARZ, August (19/20th C) American
£2553 $4264 €3600 La montagne, die spannotee (73x92cm-29x36in) s.d.03. 19-Oct-3 St-Germain-en-Laye Encheres #21/R est:1200-1800

SCHWARZ, Christoph (attrib) (1545-1592) German
£2632 $4842 €4000 St John the Baptist preaching (98x87cm-39x34in) panel. 24-Jun-4 Dr Fritz Nagel, Stuttgart #657/R est:8000

SCHWARZ, Feri (1869-1923) Russian

Works on paper			
£789	$1453	€1200	Landstrasse-Hauptstrasse (22x27cm-9x11in) s.i. W/C. 22-Jun-4 Wiener Kunst Auktionen, Vienna #186/R

SCHWARZ, Hans (1922-2003) Austrian

£900	$1701	€1314	Cafe tables in the sun (101x122cm-40x48in) W/C. 17-Feb-4 Bonhams, Knightsbridge #162
Works on paper			
£260	$491	€380	Country House (56x76cm-22x30in) W/C. 17-Feb-4 Bonhams, Knightsbridge #95
£260	$491	€380	Portrait of France (76x56cm-30x22in) W/C. 17-Feb-4 Bonhams, Knightsbridge #36
£260	$491	€380	Reclining nude (64x48cm-25x19in) W/C. 17-Feb-4 Bonhams, Knightsbridge #38
£260	$491	€380	Shepherd with his flock (56x76cm-22x30in) W/C. 17-Feb-4 Bonhams, Knightsbridge #53
£260	$491	€380	Wooded landscape (56x76cm-22x30in) W/C. 17-Feb-4 Bonhams, Knightsbridge #93
£260	$491	€380	Barges in Deptford (56x76cm-22x30in) W/C. 17-Feb-4 Bonhams, Knightsbridge #96
£260	$491	€380	Workmen (56x76cm-22x30in) W/C. 17-Feb-4 Bonhams, Knightsbridge #107
£260	$491	€380	Village in France (56x76cm-22x30in) W/C. 17-Feb-4 Bonhams, Knightsbridge #127
£260	$491	€380	Still life with coffee pot and kettle (56x76cm-22x30in) W/C. 17-Feb-4 Bonhams, Knightsbridge #128
£260	$491	€380	By the Thames (76x56cm-30x22in) W/C. 17-Feb-4 Bonhams, Knightsbridge #151
£260	$491	€380	Canada Geese (56x76cm-22x30in) W/C. 17-Feb-4 Bonhams, Knightsbridge #158
£280	$529	€409	Geese by the pond (56x76cm-22x30in) W/C. 17-Feb-4 Bonhams, Knightsbridge #15
£280	$529	€409	Feeding the pigeons (56x76cm-22x30in) W/C. 17-Feb-4 Bonhams, Knightsbridge #23
£280	$529	€409	Summer's afternoon (56x76cm-22x30in) W/C. 17-Feb-4 Bonhams, Knightsbridge #54
£280	$529	€409	Buildings by a river (56x76cm-22x30in) W/C. 17-Feb-4 Bonhams, Knightsbridge #97
£280	$529	€409	Village Street (56x76cm-22x30in) W/C. 17-Feb-4 Bonhams, Knightsbridge #147
£280	$529	€409	Garden, Storgursey (56x76cm-22x30in) W/C. 17-Feb-4 Bonhams, Knightsbridge #148
£280	$529	€409	Monkton Farm, Somerset (56x76cm-22x30in) W/C. 17-Feb-4 Bonhams, Knightsbridge #159
£280	$529	€409	Portrait of a woman (61x46cm-24x18in) W/C. 17-Feb-4 Bonhams, Knightsbridge #176
£300	$567	€438	Yachts, Marseillan (56x76cm-22x30in) W/C. 17-Feb-4 Bonhams, Knightsbridge #5
£300	$567	€438	Man with horse (76x56cm-30x22in) W/C. 17-Feb-4 Bonhams, Knightsbridge #37
£300	$567	€438	Landscape with sheep and horses (56x76cm-22x30in) W/C. 17-Feb-4 Bonhams, Knightsbridge #46
£300	$567	€438	Bird pond, Greenwich Park (42x29cm-17x11in) W/C. 17-Feb-4 Bonhams, Knightsbridge #90
£300	$567	€438	Bottles and jars (45x76cm-18x30in) W/C. 17-Feb-4 Bonhams, Knightsbridge #125
£300	$567	€438	Landscape with yellow fields (56x76cm-22x30in) W/C. 17-Feb-4 Bonhams, Knightsbridge #134
£300	$567	€438	Lena in Kilve, Low tide (56x76cm-22x30in) W/C. 17-Feb-4 Bonhams, Knightsbridge #140
£300	$567	€438	Woman reading (51x49cm-20x19in) W/C. 17-Feb-4 Bonhams, Knightsbridge #118
£320	$605	€467	Canary Wharf (56x76cm-22x30in) W/C. 17-Feb-4 Bonhams, Knightsbridge #20
£320	$605	€467	Plant on a sewing table (76x56cm-30x22in) W/C. 17-Feb-4 Bonhams, Knightsbridge #87
£320	$605	€467	Riverside, Greenwich (56x76cm-22x30in) W/C. 17-Feb-4 Bonhams, Knightsbridge #91
£320	$605	€467	Portrait of Lord Thorneycroft (72x49cm-28x19in) W/C. 17-Feb-4 Bonhams, Knightsbridge #117
£320	$605	€467	View of the village (76x56cm-30x22in) W/C. 17-Feb-4 Bonhams, Knightsbridge #150
£340	$643	€496	Two Cows (30x40cm-12x16in) W/C. 17-Feb-4 Bonhams, Knightsbridge #24
£340	$643	€496	Landscape with a stream (56x76cm-22x30in) W/C. 17-Feb-4 Bonhams, Knightsbridge #50
£340	$643	€496	Self portrait with cactus. W/C. 17-Feb-4 Bonhams, Knightsbridge #59
£340	$643	€496	Blue and purple flowers in a vase (76x56cm-30x22in) W/C. 17-Feb-4 Bonhams, Knightsbridge #120
£340	$643	€496	Orange Landscape (56x76cm-22x30in) W/C. 17-Feb-4 Bonhams, Knightsbridge #130
£340	$643	€496	Barges in Greenwich (56x76cm-22x30in) W/C. 17-Feb-4 Bonhams, Knightsbridge #135
£360	$680	€526	Autumn in Somerset (35x48cm-14x19in) W/C. 17-Feb-4 Bonhams, Knightsbridge #11
£360	$680	€526	Farm in Somerset (54x74cm-21x29in) W/C. 17-Feb-4 Bonhams, Knightsbridge #17
£360	$680	€526	Tourists at Greenwich Pier (76x96cm-30x38in) W/C. 17-Feb-4 Bonhams, Knightsbridge #30
£360	$680	€526	Orchestra (122x92cm-48x36in) W/C. 17-Feb-4 Bonhams, Knightsbridge #42
£360	$680	€526	Trees under a blue sky (56x76cm-22x30in) W/C. 17-Feb-4 Bonhams, Knightsbridge #51
£360	$680	€526	Continental landscape with cypress trees (56x76cm-22x30in) W/C. 17-Feb-4 Bonhams, Knightsbridge #74
£360	$680	€526	Sheep grazing (56x76cm-22x30in) W/C. 17-Feb-4 Bonhams, Knightsbridge #77
£360	$680	€526	Pot plant (54x69cm-21x27in) W/C. 17-Feb-4 Bonhams, Knightsbridge #83
£360	$680	€526	Jardin Public, Marseillan (53x75cm-21x30in) W/C. 17-Feb-4 Bonhams, Knightsbridge #103
£360	$680	€526	Autumnal trees (56x76cm-22x30in) W/C. 17-Feb-4 Bonhams, Knightsbridge #112
£360	$680	€526	Landscape with cows (56x76cm-22x30in) W/C. 17-Feb-4 Bonhams, Knightsbridge #133
£360	$680	€526	Boxing Match (56x76cm-22x30in) W/C. 17-Feb-4 Bonhams, Knightsbridge #152
£360	$680	€526	Greenwich Park (54x70cm-21x28in) W/C. 17-Feb-4 Bonhams, Knightsbridge #144
£360	$680	€526	Green Fence (56x76cm-22x30in) W/C. 17-Feb-4 Bonhams, Knightsbridge #145
£380	$718	€555	Sun terrace (65x76cm-26x30in) W/C. 17-Feb-4 Bonhams, Knightsbridge #3
£380	$718	€555	Man on a beach (56x76cm-22x30in) W/C. 17-Feb-4 Bonhams, Knightsbridge #6
£380	$718	€555	Street in Collioure (40x20cm-16x8in) W/C. 17-Feb-4 Bonhams, Knightsbridge #89
£380	$718	€555	Whitstable (56x76cm-22x30in) W/C. 17-Feb-4 Bonhams, Knightsbridge #94
£380	$718	€555	Minehead, Somerset (56x76cm-22x30in) W/C. 17-Feb-4 Bonhams, Knightsbridge #113
£380	$718	€555	Cows in a landscape (86x54cm-34x21in) W/C. 17-Feb-4 Bonhams, Knightsbridge #138
£380	$718	€555	Coastal view (56x76cm-22x30in) W/C. 17-Feb-4 Bonhams, Knightsbridge #163
£380	$718	€555	Bridge over the river (76x56cm-30x22in) W/C. 17-Feb-4 Bonhams, Knightsbridge #153
£400	$756	€584	Sunday in the park (56x76cm-22x30in) W/C. 17-Feb-4 Bonhams, Knightsbridge #4
£400	$756	€584	Families on the beach (30x52cm-12x20in) W/C. 17-Feb-4 Bonhams, Knightsbridge #28
£400	$756	€584	Spanish hotel and self portrait (102x100cm-40x39in) W/C. 17-Feb-4 Bonhams, Knightsbridge #62
£400	$756	€584	View from the hill (56x76cm-22x30in) W/C. 17-Feb-4 Bonhams, Knightsbridge #101
£400	$756	€584	Landscape near Morella (56x76cm-22x30in) W/C. 17-Feb-4 Bonhams, Knightsbridge #109
£420	$794	€613	Boats in the harbour (56x76cm-22x30in) W/C. 17-Feb-4 Bonhams, Knightsbridge #76
£420	$794	€613	Jugglers (56x76cm-22x30in) W/C. 17-Feb-4 Bonhams, Knightsbridge #129
£420	$794	€613	Portrait of a seated gentleman (90x34cm-35x13in) W/C. 17-Feb-4 Bonhams, Knightsbridge #137
£420	$794	€613	Gates to Greenwich Park (56x76cm-22x30in) W/C. 17-Feb-4 Bonhams, Knightsbridge #155
£440	$832	€642	Sunday stroll (56x76cm-22x30in) W/C. 17-Feb-4 Bonhams, Knightsbridge #16
£440	$832	€642	Cafe in the jardin des plantes (60x90cm-24x35in) W/C. 17-Feb-4 Bonhams, Knightsbridge #48
£440	$832	€642	Street at night (76x56cm-30x22in) W/C. 17-Feb-4 Bonhams, Knightsbridge #123
£450	$851	€657	Country stream (75x55cm-30x22in) W/C. 17-Feb-4 Bonhams, Knightsbridge #71
£480	$907	€701	Lena reading (56x76cm-22x30in) W/C. 17-Feb-4 Bonhams, Knightsbridge #22
£480	$907	€701	Tourists in Greenwich (38x64cm-15x25in) W/C. 17-Feb-4 Bonhams, Knightsbridge #79
£480	$907	€701	Queen Mother's birthday parade (55x76cm-22x30in) W/C. 17-Feb-4 Bonhams, Knightsbridge #126
£480	$907	€701	Pigeons (75x108cm-30x43in) W/C. 17-Feb-4 Bonhams, Knightsbridge #142
£500	$945	€730	On the beach, with black dog (56x76cm-22x30in) W/C. 17-Feb-4 Bonhams, Knightsbridge #1
£500	$945	€730	Sheep in the Quantocks (60x75cm-24x30in) W/C. 17-Feb-4 Bonhams, Knightsbridge #21
£500	$945	€730	Four jugs and a mug (54x75cm-21x30in) W/C. 17-Feb-4 Bonhams, Knightsbridge #84
£500	$945	€730	Lac du verdon (50x65cm-20x26in) W/C. 17-Feb-4 Bonhams, Knightsbridge #108
£500	$945	€730	Westminster View of the Houses of Parliament (53x62cm-21x24in) W/C. 17-Feb-4 Bonhams, Knightsbridge #143
£500	$945	€730	Church (76x91cm-30x36in) W/C. 17-Feb-4 Bonhams, Knightsbridge #146
£520	$983	€759	Children fishing at Camargue (46x61cm-18x24in) W/C. 17-Feb-4 Bonhams, Knightsbridge #31
£520	$983	€759	Portrait of a Nigerian man (77x101cm-30x40in) W/C. 17-Feb-4 Bonhams, Knightsbridge #39
£520	$983	€759	Julian and Stephen (122x92cm-48x36in) W/C. 17-Feb-4 Bonhams, Knightsbridge #44
£520	$983	€759	Autumnal landscape (56x76cm-22x30in) W/C. 17-Feb-4 Bonhams, Knightsbridge #49
£520	$983	€759	Nelson's Column with the National Gallery beyond (60x46cm-24x18in) W/C. 17-Feb-4 Bonhams, Knightsbridge #86
£520	$983	€759	Plum tree (56x76cm-22x30in) W/C. 17-Feb-4 Bonhams, Knightsbridge #156
£550	$1040	€803	Gran du Roi (56x76cm-22x30in) W/C. 17-Feb-4 Bonhams, Knightsbridge #2
£550	$1040	€803	Dolwen Garden (54x73cm-21x29in) W/C. 17-Feb-4 Bonhams, Knightsbridge #18
£550	$1040	€803	Self portrait in a deckchair (120x102cm-47x40in) W/C. 17-Feb-4 Bonhams, Knightsbridge #25
£550	$1040	€803	Jim Murphy in the garden (128x96cm-50x38in) W/C. 17-Feb-4 Bonhams, Knightsbridge #34
£550	$1040	€803	Simon, Pinky and Mirror (94x126cm-37x50in) W/C. 17-Feb-4 Bonhams, Knightsbridge #72
£550	$1040	€803	Portrait of Robert Carrier (122x84cm-48x33in) W/C. 17-Feb-4 Bonhams, Knightsbridge #116
£550	$1040	€803	Whitstable (59x84cm-23x33in) W/C. 17-Feb-4 Bonhams, Knightsbridge #165
£550	$1040	€803	Boxing Ring (45x60cm-18x24in) W/C. 17-Feb-4 Bonhams, Knightsbridge #173
£580	$1096	€847	View of Greenwich (86x121cm-34x48in) W/C. 17-Feb-4 Bonhams, Knightsbridge #81
£600	$1134	€876	Crowded beach (82x105cm-32x41in) W/C. 17-Feb-4 Bonhams, Knightsbridge #9
£600	$1134	€876	Martin Lawrence singing (122x95cm-48x37in) W/C. 17-Feb-4 Bonhams, Knightsbridge #66
£620	$1172	€905	St James's Park (72x92cm-28x36in) W/C. 17-Feb-4 Bonhams, Knightsbridge #14
£650	$1229	€949	Mending nets, Le Gran du Roi (56x76cm-22x30in) W/C. 17-Feb-4 Bonhams, Knightsbridge #19
£650	$1229	€949	Portrait of France (120x110cm-47x43in) W/C. 17-Feb-4 Bonhams, Knightsbridge #121

£650 $1229 €949 Rangers House, Greenwich Park (56x76cm-22x30in) W/C. 17-Feb-4 Bonhams, Knightsbridge #174
£650 $1229 €949 Julian and France at the Greenwich Observatory (120x154cm-47x61in) W/C. 17-Feb-4 Bonhams, Knightsbridge #180
£680 $1285 €993 Landscape with stormy skies (56x76cm-22x30in) W/C. 17-Feb-4 Bonhams, Knightsbridge #131
£700 $1323 €1022 By the Pool (75x120cm-30x47in) W/C. 17-Feb-4 Bonhams, Knightsbridge #55
£720 $1361 €1051 Spring in Fairfield (54x73cm-21x29in) W/C. 17-Feb-4 Bonhams, Knightsbridge #12
£720 $1361 €1051 Putney, Embankment (135x84cm-53x33in) W/C. 17-Feb-4 Bonhams, Knightsbridge #136
£750 $1418 €1095 Flock grazing (56x76cm-22x30in) W/C. 17-Feb-4 Bonhams, Knightsbridge #13
£750 $1418 €1095 Grinning (80x110cm-31x43in) W/C. 17-Feb-4 Bonhams, Knightsbridge #56
£820 $1550 €1197 Gael Cassidy playing the flute (122x80cm-48x31in) W/C. 17-Feb-4 Bonhams, Knightsbridge #45
£850 $1607 €1241 Windy Day (120x120cm-47x47in) W/C. 17-Feb-4 Bonhams, Knightsbridge #40
£850 $1607 €1241 Low tide, Kilve (69x104cm-27x41in) W/C. 17-Feb-4 Bonhams, Knightsbridge #105
£850 $1607 €1241 Lena reading in the sun (120x122cm-47x48in) W/C. 17-Feb-4 Bonhams, Knightsbridge #122
£950 $1796 €1387 Bathers 1 (96x120cm-38x47in) W/C. 17-Feb-4 Bonhams, Knightsbridge #7
£950 $1796 €1387 Four men in a bar (122x122cm-48x48in) W/C. 17-Feb-4 Bonhams, Knightsbridge #26
£1000 $1890 €1460 Flower garden (56x76cm-22x30in) W/C. 17-Feb-4 Bonhams, Knightsbridge #75 est:300-500
£1050 $1985 €1533 Cliffs in Kilve (74x120cm-29x47in) W/C. 17-Feb-4 Bonhams, Knightsbridge #141 est:600-800
£1100 $2079 €1606 Portobello Road Market (120x94cm-47x37in) W/C. 17-Feb-4 Bonhams, Knightsbridge #27 est:600-800
£1300 $2457 €1898 Portrait of Monseigneur Bruce Kent (122x90cm-48x35in) W/C. 17-Feb-4 Bonhams, Knightsbridge #115 est:600-800
£1300 $2457 €1898 Sheep farmer (122x120cm-48x47in) W/C. 17-Feb-4 Bonhams, Knightsbridge #161 est:700-900
£1600 $3024 €2336 Bathing huts (68x88cm-27x35in) W/C. 17-Feb-4 Bonhams, Knightsbridge #8 est:600-800
£3600 $6804 €5256 Boys on a beach (122x138cm-48x54in) W/C. 17-Feb-4 Bonhams, Knightsbridge #181 est:800-1000

SCHWARZ, Heinz (1920-) Swiss
Sculpture
£1938 $3295 €2829 Female nude (72cm-28in) s. light pat.bronze marble socle. 7-Nov-3 Dobiaschofsky, Bern #131/R est:3500 (S.FR 4400)

SCHWARZ, Rudolf (1878-?) German
£541 $1001 €790 Mountain landscape with river and Burg Rheinstein (71x81cm-28x32in) s. 15-Mar-4 Rasmussen, Vejle #109/R (D.KR 6000)

SCHWARZ-WALDEGG, Fritz (1889-?) Austrian
£432 $717 €626 Violinist (75x50cm-30x20in) s.d.1911 board. 13-Jun-3 Zofingen, Switzerland #2531 (S.FR 950)

SCHWARZENBACH, Armin (1914-2000) Swiss
£485 $824 €708 Autumn alpine landscape with mountain stream (64x58cm-25x23in) s.d.50. 5-Nov-3 Dobiaschofsky, Bern #947/R (S.FR 1100)
Works on paper
£308 $524 €450 Summer meadow (68x47cm-27x19in) s. col chk. 5-Nov-3 Dobiaschofsky, Bern #946/R (S.FR 700)

SCHWARZENBACH, Hans (1911-1983) Swiss
Works on paper
£264 $449 €385 Mountain stream (45x31cm-18x12in) s. gouache exhib. 5-Nov-3 Dobiaschofsky, Bern #948/R (S.FR 600)

SCHWARZER, Ludwig (1912-) Austrian
£800 $1440 €1200 Flowers (68x58cm-27x23in) board. 21-Apr-4 Dorotheum, Vienna #221/R
£2098 $3566 €3000 Private theatre box (36x50cm-14x20in) s. panel. 27-Nov-3 Dorotheum, Linz #538/R est:4000-5000
Works on paper
£633 $1140 €950 Reclining Venus (18x25cm-7x10in) s. Indian ink W/C. 21-Apr-4 Dorotheum, Vienna #167/R

SCHWARZMAIER, Hanns (1914-) Italian
£503 $926 €750 Flowers (50x60cm-20x24in) s.d. acrylic. 26-Mar-4 Ketterer, Hamburg #1150/R

SCHWARZSCHILD, Alfred (1874-?) German
£3356 $6007 €5000 Children playing (73x153cm-29x60in) s.i.d.1902. 27-May-4 Dorotheum, Vienna #55/R est:5000-6000

SCHWATSCHKE, John (1943-) Irish
£268 $481 €400 Storm on the river, Waterford (40x50cm-16x20in) s.i. verso. 31-May-4 Hamilton Osborne King, Dublin #25/R
£500 $820 €730 Ploughing march (61x76cm-24x30in) mono. d.2003 verso. 4-Jun-3 John Ross, Belfast #95
£503 $926 €750 Heat wave, Dublin (81x102cm-32x40in) s.i. 23-Mar-4 Mealy's, Castlecomer #1112/R
£750 $1343 €1095 Summer outing (61x76cm-24x30in) mono.d.2003 s.i.verso. 14-May-4 Christie's, Kensington #395/R
£805 $1426 €1200 Closing down the north wharf, Waterford (46x53cm-18x21in) mono. s.i.verso panel. 27-Apr-4 Whyte's, Dublin #247/R
£933 $1689 €1400 Puck fiar (75x92cm-30x36in) mono.i. 30-Mar-4 De Veres Art Auctions, Dublin #174
£972 $1585 €1400 Musical chairs (51x51cm-20x20in) mono. s.i.verso. 23-Sep-3 De Veres Art Auctions, Dublin #201/R
£1000 $1800 €1500 Sensation (50x40cm-20x16in) s.d.2003 s.i.verso. 20-Apr-4 James Adam, Dublin #73/R est:1000-1500
£1049 $1783 €1500 A doctor calls again (91x76cm-36x30in) mono.d.1999 s.i.verso exhib. 18-Nov-3 Whyte's, Dublin #219/R est:2000-3000
£1074 $1976 €1600 Audition (51x61cm-20x24in) s.i. 23-Mar-4 Mealy's, Castlecomer #1138/R est:700-1100
£1757 $3320 €2600 Lyric in the afternoon (61x51cm-24x20in) mono.i. s.d.2003 verso. 17-Feb-4 Whyte's, Dublin #245/R est:1500-1800
£1972 $3155 €2800 Party at Kate Kearney's (61x76cm-24x30in) mono.d.1999 i.verso. 16-Sep-3 Whyte's, Dublin #219/R est:2000-3000

SCHWEDLER, Robert (19th C) German
£1879 $3458 €2800 Officer taking leave of his family (103x90cm-41x35in) s.d.1864 i. verso. 25-Mar-4 Dr Fritz Nagel, Stuttgart #765/R est:1800

SCHWEGLER, Xaver (1832-1902) Swiss
£1086 $1846 €1586 Interior with dead birds on chair (32x26cm-13x10in) s. 19-Nov-3 Fischer, Luzern #1261/R (S.FR 2400)
£1086 $1846 €1586 Ennetburgen (34x50cm-13x20in) mono.d.Sept 51 paper on canvas. 19-Nov-3 Fischer, Luzern #1263/R est:3000-4000 (S.FR 2400)

SCHWEICKART, Lothar Ignaz (attrib) (1702-1779) German
£2215 $4075 €3300 Portrait of Bishop Franz Christoph von Hutten (94x75cm-37x30in) 25-Mar-4 Dr Fritz Nagel, Stuttgart #667/R est:600

SCHWEICKHARDT, Hendrik Willem (1746-1797) German
£1000 $1870 €1500 Winter landscape with figures on the ice (33x41cm-13x16in) s. wood panel. 22-Jul-4 Gorringes, Lewes #1943/R est:1200-1800
£2800 $4844 €4088 Three putti holding garlands of flowers beside classical column (78x108cm-31x43in) shaped top. 10-Dec-3 Bonhams, New Bond Street #96/R est:3000-4000
£5369 $9879 €8000 Farmhouses and village near frozen river with ice skaters (35x48cm-14x19in) panel. 24-Mar-4 Dorotheum, Vienna #266/R est:8000-12000
£9500 $17385 €13870 Winter landscape with peasants skating (72x99cm-28x39in) s. 9-Jul-4 Christie's, Kensington #133/R est:7000-10000
£10959 $18630 €16000 Canal landscape with peasant family by their cottage, and piles of peat (45x65cm-18x26in) s.d.1785 prov.lit. 4-Nov-3 Sotheby's, Amsterdam #102/R est:15000-20000
£41000 $74620 €59860 Dutch winter scene with skaters (28x37cm-11x15in) s.d.1783 panel prov. 5-Feb-4 Mellors & Kirk, Nottingham #587/R est:10000-14000
Works on paper
£313 $522 €450 Shepherd and travelling musician (19x15cm-7x6in) wash Indian ink sold with another. 24-Oct-3 Ketterer, Hamburg #231/R

SCHWEIG, Suzanne (1918-) American
£872 $1500 €1273 Dunes (122x163cm-48x64in) s. mono.d.1970 verso. 7-Dec-3 Treadway Gallery, Cincinnati #643/R est:2000-4000

SCHWEINFURTH, Ernst (1818-1877) German
£6597 $10753 €9500 Beached sailing boat with Neapolitan fishermen dancing (78x112cm-31x44in) s.i.d.1859. 25-Sep-3 Dr Fritz Nagel, Stuttgart #1421/R est:14000

SCHWEINITZ, Rudolf (1839-1896) German
Sculpture
£3800 $6840 €5548 Nude listening to a gnome (80cm-31in) s.d.1893 white marble lit. 21-Apr-4 Sotheby's, London #48/R est:4000-6000

SCHWEITZER, Adolf Gustav (1847-1914) German
£267 $480 €400 Steamboat in fjord landscape (28x33cm-11x13in) s.d.1887 board on panel. 26-Apr-4 Rieber, Stuttgart #1310/R
£2657 $4517 €3800 Woman gathering wood in snowy winter wood (74x124cm-29x49in) s.d.1899. 20-Nov-3 Van Ham, Cologne #1865/R est:4400

SCHWEITZER, Reinhold (1876-1940) German
£1103 $2019 €1600 Oriental rider (95x72cm-37x28in) s. 27-Jan-4 Dorotheum, Vienna #10/R est:1200-1400

SCHWEIZER, Albert (1886-1948) Swiss
£455 $755 €660 River landscape in Basel area (50x68cm-20x27in) s. panel. 13-Jun-3 Zofingen, Switzerland #3023 (S.FR 1000)
£478 $875 €698 Summer river landscape (50x65cm-20x26in) s. 4-Jun-4 Zofingen, Switzerland #2957 (S.FR 1100)
£588 $1000 €858 Bridge near Kloster Schonthal (50x65cm-20x26in) s. 28-Nov-3 Zofingen, Switzerland #3173 (S.FR 1300)
£591 $981 €857 Laupersdorf - old village street (40x50cm-16x20in) s.i. verso. 13-Jun-3 Zofingen, Switzerland #3024 (S.FR 1300)

SCHWEIZER, Ernst (1874-1929) Swiss
£407 $652 €594 Still life with jug and fruit (51x69cm-20x27in) s. board. 16-Sep-3 Philippe Schuler, Zurich #5635 (S.FR 900)

SCHWEMER, C (19th C) German
£2400 $4296 €3504 Adoration of the shepherds (134x101cm-53x40in) i.verso. 22-Mar-4 Bonhams & Brooks, Norfolk #294/R est:1000-1500

SCHWENDY, Albert (1820-1902) German
£3147 $5350 €4500 City (47x39cm-19x15in) mono.d.1847. 29-Nov-3 Villa Grisebach, Berlin #101/R est:3000-5000

SCHWENINGER, Carl (elder) (1818-1887) Austrian
£1127 $1870 €1600 Early afternoon in the country (44x93cm-17x37in) bears sig.d.881. 12-Jun-3 Dorotheum, Graz #64/R
£2000 $3320 €2920 Moment to herself (82x58cm-32x23in) s.i. 1-Oct-3 Sotheby's, Olympia #212/R est:2000-3000

SCHWENINGER, Carl (younger) (1854-1903) Austrian
£1221 $2100 €1783 Flowers from an admirer (43x30cm-17x12in) s.i. panel. 7-Dec-3 Freeman, Philadelphia #22 est:3000-5000
£2013 $3705 €3000 Young couple with baby on terrace (80x60cm-31x24in) s.i. 27-Mar-4 Dannenberg, Berlin #623/R est:1200
Works on paper
£280 $476 €400 Mandolin player (24x17cm-9x7in) s. wash ink. 27-Nov-3 Dorotheum, Linz #599/R

SCHWENKER, Johanna Maria (20th C) German
£972 $1624 €1400 Bregenz harbour (49x61cm-19x24in) i. stretcher. 25-Oct-3 Dr Lehr, Berlin #473/R

SCHWERDTFEGER, Max (1881-?) German
£397 $723 €600 Fetish (68x51cm-27x20in) mono.d.1925 i.verso. 19-Jun-4 Quittenbaum, Hamburg #96/R

SCHWERIN, Amelie von (1819-1897) Swedish
£2956 $5292 €4316 Cattle watering (129x191cm-51x75in) s.i. 26-May-4 AB Stockholms Auktionsverk #2269/R est:35000-40000 (S.KR 40000)

SCHWERTBERGER, Dieter (1942-) Austrian
£3691 $6829 €5500 Composition (58x82cm-23x32in) mono. i. verso masonite. 9-Mar-4 Dorotheum, Vienna #160/R est:2200-2800

SCHWESIG, Karl (1898-1955) German
£4000 $7320 €6000 War harbour Toulon (80x65cm-31x26in) s. i. stretcher canvas on panel prov.exhib. 5-Jun-4 Lempertz, Koln #995/R est:6000
£7692 $13077 €11000 Workers' tavern (93x94cm-37x37in) s.d.1922 exhib. 26-Nov-3 Lempertz, Koln #977/R est:6000
Works on paper
£417 $696 €600 Flieger, the cellist (52x41cm-20x16in) s.i.d. W/C board. 24-Oct-3 Ketterer, Hamburg #1085/R

SCHWICHTENBERG, Martel (1896-1945) German
£2667 $4773 €4000 Cacti (59x49cm-23x19in) s.d. 13-May-4 Neumeister, Munich #491/R est:1200-1400
£6667 $12000 €10000 Untitled (70x50cm-28x20in) mono. board double-sided. 24-Apr-4 Dr Lehr, Berlin #430/R est:7500
Works on paper
£660 $1102 €950 Man between two women (30x23cm-12x9in) s.d. pencil board. 25-Oct-3 Dr Lehr, Berlin #474/R

SCHWICKER, A (?) ?
£993 $1808 €1500 Still life with birds and fruit (50x70cm-20x28in) s.i. i.verso. 21-Jun-4 Pandolfini, Florence #125/R est:1600-1800

SCHWIERING, Heinrich (1860-?) German
£360 $644 €540 Schaumberg peasant woman (51x36cm-20x14in) s. board lit. 14-May-4 Schloss Ahlden, Ahlden #2862/R

SCHWIERING, O Conrad (1930-) American
£5587 $10000 €8157 Autumn gold (61x74cm-24x29in) 14-May-4 Du Mouchelle, Detroit #2005/R est:4000-5000

SCHWIMMER, Max (1895-1960) German
£1867 $3341 €2800 Studio in Leipzig (55x46cm-22x18in) s. 14-May-4 Ketterer, Munich #77/R est:2000-2500
£6333 $11337 €9500 Mountain landscape with pine trees and hayricks (49x59cm-19x23in) s.d. 14-May-4 Ketterer, Munich #78/R est:2500-3500
Works on paper
£267 $480 €400 Baltic harbour (11x16cm-4x6in) s. W/C on pencil board. 24-Apr-4 Dr Lehr, Berlin #438/R
£267 $480 €400 Untitled - in pissoir (31x22cm-12x9in) s. Indian ink brush. 24-Apr-4 Dr Lehr, Berlin #439/R
£360 $648 €540 Untitled - female nude on red cloth (22x19cm-9x7in) W/C on pencil board double-sided. 24-Apr-4 Dr Lehr, Berlin #437/R
£433 $780 €650 Untitled - The Three Graces (14x18cm-6x7in) mono. w/C on pencil board. 24-Apr-4 Dr Lehr, Berlin #436/R

SCHWIND, Moritz von (1804-1871) Austrian
£330 $525 €482 Cottage kitchen interior (25x30cm-10x12in) s. 9-Sep-3 Gorringes, Lewes #2034
£6040 $11054 €9000 Portrait of the music conductor Franz Lachner (58x52cm-23x20in) s.d.1849. 9-Jul-4 Dawo, Saarbrucken #14/R est:4500
Works on paper
£483 $806 €700 Artist's studio (36x18cm-14x7in) i. pencil prov. 15-Nov-3 Lempertz, Koln #1556
£503 $926 €750 Figure studies (35x22cm-14x9in) i. pen pencil double-sided. 26-Mar-4 Dorotheum, Vienna #91/R
£537 $988 €800 Death of Ilbrand (16x21cm-6x8in) mono.i.pencil lit. 25-Mar-4 Karlheinz Kaupp, Staufen #2727/R
£795 $1454 €1200 History of Graf Eberstein (22x134cm-9x53in) W/C. 7-Apr-4 Dorotheum, Salzburg #183/R
£7222 $13000 €10544 Four nymphs tying Pan to a tree (21x36cm-8x14in) s.d.i85i black chk pen brown grey ink W/C. 22-Jan-4 Christie's, Rockefeller NY #152/R est:6000-8000

SCHWINGE, Friedrich Wilhelm (1852-1913) German
£308 $524 €450 Northern German landscape (42x58cm-17x23in) s.d.1904 board. 8-Nov-3 Hans Stahl, Toestorf #91/R
£432 $708 €600 Poppy field by city (54x74cm-21x29in) s.d. tempera paper on board. 4-Jun-3 Ketterer, Hamburg #98/R
£594 $1022 €850 Stream through fields (28x38cm-11x15in) s. i. verso board. 4-Dec-3 Schopman, Hamburg #749/R
£903 $1508 €1300 Deer in forest clearing (70x50cm-28x20in) s. bears d. 24-Oct-3 Ketterer, Hamburg #104/R
Works on paper
£302 $535 €450 Old Hamburg (36x25cm-14x10in) s.d.86 W/C. 28-Apr-4 Schopman, Hamburg #649/R
£331 $603 €500 Country scene (55x77cm-22x30in) s.d.1903 i.verso gouache ink board. 19-Jun-4 Quittenbaum, Hamburg #47/R

SCHWITTERS, Kurt (1887-1948) German
£2133 $3925 €3200 Portrait of a man in a bow tie smoking a pipe (52x41cm-20x16in) masonite painted 1940 exhib. 12-Jun-4 Villa Grisebach, Berlin #290/R est:2500-3500
£3200 $5888 €4672 Portrait of Mr Gaskell (54x44cm-21x17in) init.d.45 i.verso board prov.lit. 24-Mar-4 Sotheby's, Olympia #63/R est:1200-1800
£19000 $34960 €27740 Untitled (14x12cm-6x5in) s.d.1947 oil collage board on artist mount prov. 24-Jun-4 Christie's, London #397/R est:18000-25000
£23529 $40000 €34352 C67 Alte Hohle (39x33cm-15x13in) init.d.46 i.mount oil over wood and plaster on panel prov. 5-Nov-3 Christie's, Rockefeller NY #308/R est:50000-70000
Works on paper
£4800 $8016 €7008 Untitled - Tra act (14x11cm-6x4in) init.d.47 collage paper on mount exhib. 21-Oct-3 Sotheby's, London #44/R est:4000-6000
£4895 $8322 €7000 Reminders (7x11cm-3x4in) mono.d.1919 collage on postcard pieces. 29-Nov-3 Arnold, Frankfurt #485/R est:8000
£10500 $19320 €15330 Untitled (13x10cm-5x4in) s.d.1931 collage prov.lit. 22-Jun-4 Sotheby's, London #474/R est:8000-10000
£12353 $21000 €18035 Elfenben, Gratt, Grout (20x16cm-8x6in) s.mount i.verso collage paper on cart exec c.1937-38 prov.exhib. 6-Nov-3 Sotheby's, New York #213/R est:20000-30000
£13000 $23920 €18980 29/4 - Merzzeichnung (15x11cm-6x4in) s.d.29/4 collage paper laid down prov.lit. 24-Jun-4 Christie's, London #396/R est:4000-6000
£13761 $22982 €19953 Composition (25x16cm-10x6in) collage board. 19-Jun-3 Kornfeld, Bern #932/R est:20000 (S.FR 30000)
£14000 $25760 €20440 I 20 - i-Zeichnung (22x15cm-9x6in) s.i.d.20 mount prov.lit. 24-Jun-4 Christie's, London #395/R est:8000-12000
£17964 $30000 €26227 Mirage (29x23cm-11x9in) init.d.46 gouache paper collage paper on board prov. 11-Nov-3 Christie's, Rockefeller NY #168/R est:30000-40000
£22059 $37500 €32206 Orsgrunnsdan (36x27cm-14x11in) i.d.1937/38 verso collage paper on card prov.exhib. 6-Nov-3 Sotheby's, New York #215/R est:20000-30000
£29940 $50000 €43712 Mz 386 Hopf (27x24cm-11x9in) s.d.1922 i.verso paper collage prov.exhib.lit. 11-Nov-3 Christie's, Rockefeller NY #167/R est:35000-45000
£32000 $58240 €46720 Mz 30 21 (30x25cm-12x10in) s.i.d. collage paper on artist mount prov.exhib.lit. 5-Feb-4 Christie's, London #369/R est:18000-24000
£32000 $58240 €46720 Untitled (25x21cm-10x8in) s. collage paper on artist mount exec c.1936-1937 prov.exhib.lit. 5-Feb-4 Christie's, London #374/R est:12000-18000
£39106 $70000 €57095 Z 57 Abstraction (14x19cm-6x7in) i.on mount chl exec.1918 prov.exhib.lit. 6-May-4 Sotheby's, New York #109/R est:50000-70000
£40000 $72800 €58400 With hand (31x23cm-12x9in) s. collage paper on artist mount exec 1923 prov.exhib.lit. 5-Feb-4 Christie's, London #370/R est:15000-20000
£52000 $95680 €75920 Mz 182 (9x8cm-4x3in) init.d.21 collage prov.exhib.lit. 24-Jun-4 Christie's, London #394/R est:15000-20000
£52402 $95371 €76507 Asinet 9 (26x20cm-10x8in) s.d.1923 collage paper paint prov.exhib. 18-Jun-4 Kornfeld, Bern #140/R est:100000 (S.FR 120000)
£82969 $151004 €121135 Collage (16x13cm-6x5in) mono.i.d.21 collage paper material oil prov.exhib. 18-Jun-4 Kornfeld, Bern #139/R est:100000 (S.FR 190000)

SCHWIZGEBEL, Christian (20th C) Swiss
Works on paper
£529 $899 €772 Animals in wood (17x28cm-7x11in) s. d.Dezember 1958 verso silhouette. 5-Nov-3 Dobiaschofsky, Bern #1882 (S.FR 1200)
£617 $1048 €901 Peasant girl (19x31cm-7x12in) s. d.August 1958 verso silhouette. 5-Nov-3 Dobiaschofsky, Bern #1881 (S.FR 1400)
£661 $1123 €965 Animals in the countryside (19x30cm-7x12in) s. silhouette. 5-Nov-3 Dobiaschofsky, Bern #1883/R (S.FR 1500)

SCHWOB, Susanne Madeleine (1888-1967) Swiss
£273 $453 €396 Brighton on Sea (48x36cm-19x14in) s.d.1924 i. verso. 13-Jun-3 Zofingen, Switzerland #3026 (S.FR 600)
£283 $517 €413 Fleurs (44x67cm-17x26in) s.d.1918. 4-Jun-4 Zofingen, Switzerland #2958 (S.FR 650)

SCHYL, Jules (1893-1977) Swedish
£461 $751 €673 Landscape from Skaane (60x73cm-24x29in) s. 29-Sep-3 Lilla Bukowskis, Stockholm #635 (S.KR 6000)
£688 $1108 €1004 Spanish musicians (41x31cm-16x12in) s. 25-Aug-3 Lilla Bukowskis, Stockholm #773 (S.KR 9000)
£765 $1231 €1117 Composition (83x56cm-33x22in) s. sold with book. 25-Aug-3 Lilla Bukowskis, Stockholm #659 (S.KR 10000)
£906 $1541 €1323 Expectation (85x66cm-33x26in) s.d.45. 5-Nov-3 AB Stockholms Auktionsverk #660/R (S.KR 12000)
£906 $1541 €1323 Harbour scene with still life, Marstrand (69x58cm-27x23in) s. i.d.1946 verso. 5-Nov-3 AB Stockholms Auktionsverk #661/R (S.KR 12000)
£1026 $1815 €1498 View across southern town (51x64cm-20x25in) s. 27-Apr-4 AB Stockholms Auktionsverk #726/R est:12000-15000 (S.KR 14000)
£1171 $1990 €1710 Landscape with trees (49x41cm-19x16in) s. i.d.1920 stretcher. 4-Nov-3 Bukowskis, Stockholm #4/R est:8000-10000 (S.KR 15500)
£1337 $2273 €1952 At the cafe (50x39cm-20x15in) s. d.1930 verso panel. 5-Nov-3 AB Stockholms Auktionsverk #905/R est:20000-25000 (S.KR 17700)
£1473 $2504 €2151 Cubist model (54x67cm-21x26in) s. 4-Nov-3 Bukowskis, Stockholm #168/R est:15000-20000 (S.KR 19500)
£2344 $4149 €3422 San Salute (81x58cm-32x23in) s. d.1954 verso. 27-Apr-4 AB Stockholms Auktionsverk #669/R est:20000-25000 (S.KR 32000)

SCIALOJA, Toti (1914-1998) Italian

£800	$1440	€1200	Untitled (56x28cm-22x11in) s. tempera card painted 1993. 22-Apr-4 Finarte Semenzato, Rome #94
£1379	$2303	€2000	Untitled (44x81cm-17x32in) s.d.81 tempera collage cardboard. 13-Nov-3 Finarte Semenzato, Rome #186/R est:2000-2500
£2759	$4607	€4000	Still life with three objects (38x46cm-15x18in) s.verso painted 1949. 13-Nov-3 Finarte Semenzato, Rome #334/R est:4000-5000
£3521	$5845	€5000	Untitled (115x60cm-45x24in) s.d.1989 verso vinyl canvas. 14-Jun-3 Meeting Art, Vercelli #359/R est:5000
£5944	$10105	€8500	Red one (175x234cm-69x92in) s.i.d.1972 verso acrylic prov. 24-Nov-3 Christie's, Milan #171/R est:5000-7000
£10333	$19013	€15500	Still life (50x73cm-20x29in) s.d.1949 prov.exhib.lit.. 14-Jun-4 Porro, Milan #38/R est:12000-14000
Works on paper			
£1351	$2378	€2000	Composition (50x35cm-20x14in) mixed media glue card exec.1990. 19-May-4 Il Ponte, Milan #1100 est:2200-2400
£1678	$2853	€2400	Untitled (100x70cm-39x28in) s.d.1989 verso mixed media paper on canvas. 20-Nov-3 Finarte Semenzato, Milan #4/R est:2000-2500
£2448	$4161	€3500	Untitled (33x50cm-13x20in) s.d.59 collage mixed media cardboard. 24-Nov-3 Christie's, Milan #33/R est:1500-2000

SCIASCIA, Filippo (1972-) Italian

£333	$613	€500	Untitled (130x100cm-51x39in) s.d.1997 enamel. 12-Jun-4 Meeting Art, Vercelli #432/R

SCILTIAN, Gregorio (1900-1985) Russian

£1884	$3090	€2600	Composition (38x28cm-15x11in) s. i.verso board. 29-May-3 Galleria Pace, Milan #46/R est:3500
£4133	$7605	€6200	Hanging cloth (40x30cm-16x12in) s.d.CDLXVII. 8-Jun-4 Finarte Semenzato, Milan #366/R est:6000-8000
£4930	$8627	€7000	Basket with cherries, strawberries and lemons (45x60cm-18x24in) s. board. 17-Dec-3 Il Ponte, Milan #1085/R est:8000-9000
£6944	$11806	€10000	Composition with shell, monocular in seascape (70x55cm-28x22in) s. board. 28-Oct-3 Il Ponte, Milan #279/R
£7821	$14000	€11419	Corsican landscape (61x50cm-24x20in) s.d.27 prov. 6-May-4 Doyle, New York #123/R est:2000-3000
£9459	$16649	€14000	Self-portrait (45x35cm-18x14in) s. prov.exhib.lit. 24-May-4 Christie's, Milan #175/R est:15000-20000
£18116	$29710	€25000	Journey on mysterious island (110x165cm-43x65in) s. board prov.exhib.lit. 27-May-3 Sotheby's, Milan #247/R est:25000-30000

SCIPIONE (1904-1933) Italian

Works on paper			
£2333	$4293	€3500	Apocalypse (45x60cm-18x24in) pencil prov.exhib.lit. 8-Jun-4 Finarte Semenzato, Milan #254/R est:2000-2500
£4698	$8409	€7000	Nudes in Ponte Sant'Angelo (18x22cm-7x9in) s. ink W/C paper on cardboard. 29-May-4 Farsetti, Prato #422/R est:5000-6000

SCIUTI, Giuseppi (1834-1911) Italian

£2500	$4600	€3800	Bust of ancient Roman (93x59cm-37x23in) s. 23-Jun-4 Finarte Semenzato, Rome #107/R est:2000-2500
£12000	$20400	€17520	Tribute to Caesar (74x135cm-29x53in) s.i. 19-Nov-3 Bonhams, New Bond Street #98/R est:12000-18000

SCIVER, Pearl Aiman van (1896-1966) American

£867	$1500	€1266	Floral still life (127x102cm-50x40in) s. 10-Dec-3 Alderfer's, Hatfield #438/R est:1800-2200
£1932	$3400	€2821	Kennebunkport, townscape (76x64cm-30x25in) s.i. 21-May-4 Pook & Pook, Downington #320/R est:1500-2000

SCKELL, Fritz (1885-?) German

£1135	$2066	€1657	Malayasian bathing scene (78x142cm-31x56in) s. 16-Jun-4 Fischer, Luzern #1251/R est:2200-2600 (S.FR 2600)

SCKELL, Louis (1869-1950) German

£493	$882	€700	Deer in a forest clearing with mountains in background (80x100cm-31x39in) s. i. lit. 8-Jan-4 Allgauer, Kempten #2519/R
£1042	$1719	€1500	Mountain farmstead by stream (55x68cm-22x27in) s. 2-Jul-3 Neumeister, Munich #773/R est:1800

SCKELL, Ludwig (1833-1912) German

£1027	$1747	€1500	Inn valley (20x27cm-8x11in) s. panel. 5-Nov-3 Hugo Ruef, Munich #1112/R est:1500
£1053	$1937	€1600	At the sawmill (65x85cm-26x33in) s. 22-Jun-4 Christie's, Amsterdam #79/R est:2000-3000
£1096	$1863	€1600	Lime kiln in the mountains (51x62cm-20x24in) s.d.1874. 5-Nov-3 Hugo Ruef, Munich #1111/R est:900
£1127	$1949	€1600	View of the Zugspitze (40x50cm-16x20in) s. panel. 10-Dec-3 Hugo Ruef, Munich #2492/R est:1200
£1486	$2661	€2200	Farmstead with cattle herder by mountain stream (85x65cm-33x26in) s. lit. 8-May-4 Dawo, Saarbrucken #36/R est:2000
£1667	$2783	€2400	High mountain landscape (85x64cm-33x25in) s. 24-Oct-3 Ketterer, Hamburg #105/R est:2500-3000
£2349	$4205	€3500	Landscape with house by pond (21x45cm-8x18in) s. 25-May-4 Karl & Faber, Munich #135/R est:4000
£2518	$4129	€3500	Pre-alpine landscape (43x90cm-17x35in) s.i.d. 4-Jun-3 Ketterer, Hamburg #99/R est:7000-9000
£3020	$5557	€4500	Bavarian river landscape (28x49cm-11x19in) mono. 25-Mar-4 Dr Fritz Nagel, Stuttgart #758/R est:4800
Works on paper			
£743	$1308	€1100	Schloss Schonbusch Park near Aschaffenburg (25x24cm-10x9in) i. pencil. 22-May-4 Lempertz, Koln #1462/R

SCLIAR, Carlos (attrib) (1920-) Brazilian

£1392	$2464	€2088	Yellow and red flowers (56x37cm-22x15in) s.i.d.1988 vinyl collage canvas on panel. 27-Apr-4 Bolsa de Arte, Rio de Janeiro #35/R (B.R 7600)
£1648	$2918	€2472	Still life with a lantern, bottle and fruit (75x55cm-30x22in) s.i.d.20 Jan 1972 verso vinyl canvas on panel. 27-Apr-4 Bolsa de Arte, Rio de Janeiro #33/R (B.R 9000)

SCOGNAMIGLIO, Cavaliero Antonio (19th C) Italian

£450	$806	€657	Desert landscape with mother and children in foreground (63x51cm-25x20in) s.i. 11-May-4 Bonhams, Knightsbridge #172/R

SCOGNAMIGLIO, Edwardo (19th C) Italian

£351	$650	€512	The barnyard meal (28x41cm-11x16in) s. 16-Jan-4 Aspire, Cleveland #56/R

SCOGNAMIGLIO, Giovanni (18th C) Italian

£350	$648	€511	Figures at an Italianate market (30x21cm-12x8in) s. 15-Jan-4 Christie's, Kensington #971
£2200	$3520	€3190	Fishing in the shadow of Vesuvius (72x102cm-28x40in) s. 18-Sep-3 Christie's, Kensington #102/R est:2500-3500

SCOGNAMIGLIO, Giuseppe (19th C) Italian

£1167	$2112	€1750	Applying make up (37x22cm-15x9in) s. 30-Mar-4 Babuino, Rome #404 est:400-600

SCOGNAMIGLIO, Roberto (1883-1965) Italian

£467	$835	€700	Alley with trees (30x27cm-12x11in) s. cardboard. 13-May-4 Babuino, Rome #536
£563	$975	€800	Rome, Piazza del Popolo (35x45cm-14x18in) s.d.1924 cardboard. 11-Dec-3 Christie's, Rome #92
£733	$1327	€1100	Market square in Naples (30x21cm-12x8in) s. 30-Mar-4 Babuino, Rome #407

SCOMPARINI, Eugenio (1845-1913) Italian

£3378	$6385	€5000	Venice (50x62cm-20x24in) s.d.1868. 20-Feb-4 Stadion, Trieste #630/R est:4000

SCOPPA, A (?) ?

£2254	$3899	€3200	View with boats and fishermen (70x100cm-28x39in) s. board. 11-Dec-3 Christie's, Rome #32/R est:2300-2800

SCOPPA, Giuseppe (19th C) Italian

Works on paper			
£3400	$5678	€4964	Carriages and figures on the Via della Riviera di Chiaia, Naples (46x86cm-18x34in) s.i. bodycol. 8-Oct-3 Christie's, Kensington #1097/R est:800-1200

SCOPPETTA, Pietro (1863-1920) Italian

£2482	$4145	€3500	Parasol (16x10cm-6x4in) s. board. 20-Oct-3 Sant Agostino, Torino #282/R est:4500
£3200	$5888	€4800	Landscape with figures (26x38cm-10x15in) s. canvas on cardboard. 10-Jun-4 Christie's, Rome #192/R est:4500-6000
£4082	$7306	€6000	Paris (9x14cm-4x6in) s.i. card. 22-Mar-4 Sant Agostino, Torino #234/R est:8000
£4225	$7014	€6000	Signora seduta, in interno (45x34cm-18x13in) s. 11-Jun-3 Christie's, Rome #225/R est:6500-8000
£4577	$7599	€6500	Alla toilette (40x28cm-16x11in) s. canvas on board prov.lit. 11-Jun-3 Christie's, Rome #224/R est:6500-8000
£6338	$10521	€9000	Capri, sea with fishermen (16x26cm-6x10in) s. panel prov.exhib.lit. 11-Jun-3 Christie's, Rome #237/R est:9000-10000
£6690	$11574	€9500	Girl with flowers (49x27cm-19x11in) s. 10-Dec-3 Finarte Semenzato, Rome #249/R est:10000-11000
£6711	$11879	€10000	P. (25x32cm-10x13in) s.i. cardboard. 1-May-4 Meeting Art, Vercelli #116 est:7000
£7000	$12040	€10220	L'Arc de Triomphe. Promenade a Champs Elysees, Paris (13x18cm-5x7in) s. one i. board pair. 4-Dec-3 Christie's, Kensington #27/R est:6000-8000
£7092	$11844	€10000	Seascape with fishermen in Capri (17x28cm-7x11in) s. board. 20-Oct-3 Sant Agostino, Torino #275/R est:7000
£7200	$12384	€10512	Dans le parc. Promenade dans le parc, Paris (12x18cm-5x7in) s.i. board pair. 4-Dec-3 Christie's, Kensington #30/R est:6000-8000
Works on paper			
£350	$601	€500	St Peters Cathedral in Rome (25x19cm-10x7in) s. W/C. 4-Dec-3 Dorotheum, Graz #80/R
£704	$1218	€1000	Chez Maxim (22x16cm-9x6in) s. W/C. 10-Dec-3 Finarte Semenzato, Rome #162/R
£915	$1584	€1300	Figure at window (13x18cm-5x7in) s. W/C. 10-Dec-3 Sotheby's, Milan #127/R

SCORDIA, Antonio (1918-) Central American

£1333	$2400	€2000	Beach (38x60cm-15x24in) s.d.57 s.i.d.verso. 22-Apr-4 Finarte Semenzato, Rome #289/R est:1800-2400

SCOREL, Jan van (style) (1495-1562) Dutch

£20000	$36600	€29200	Resting during the Flight into Egypt (88x69cm-35x27in) panel prov. 8-Jul-4 Sotheby's, London #243/R est:12000-18000

SCORIEL, Jean Baptiste (1883-1956) Belgian

£284	$508	€420	Vallee ensoleillee (50x60cm-20x24in) s.d. 10-May-4 Horta, Bruxelles #466/R
£315	$536	€460	Vent sur le hameau (60x70cm-24x28in) s.d.1941. 4-Nov-3 Servarts Themis, Bruxelles #624
£400	$724	€600	Vent sur le hameau (60x70cm-24x28in) s.d.1941. 30-Mar-4 Palais de Beaux Arts, Brussels #692
£594	$1010	€850	Barques a Tamines (80x110cm-31x43in) s. 18-Nov-3 Galerie Moderne, Brussels #857/R

SCORTESCO, Paul (1895-?) French

£599	$1036	€850	Peniche (47x56cm-19x22in) s. exhib. 10-Dec-3 Millon & Associes, Paris #113/R

SCORZA, Sinibaldo (attrib) (1589-1631) Italian
£4500 $8100 €6570 The creation (149x182cm-59x72in) 23-Apr-4 Christie's, Kensington #212/R est:6000-8000

SCORZELLI, Eugenio (1890-1958) Italian
£403 $713 €600 Figure in landscape (8x15cm-3x6in) s. board. 1-May-4 Meeting Art, Vercelli #337
£524 $876 €750 Procida (19x22cm-7x9in) s. cardboard. 24-Jun-3 Finarte Semenzato, Rome #101
£772 $1366 €1150 Back from fishing (12x18cm-5x7in) s. board. 1-May-4 Meeting Art, Vercelli #431
£966 $1603 €1400 Hunting scene (12x18cm-5x7in) s. board. 1-Oct-3 Della Rocca, Turin #251/R
£1812 $3207 €2700 Horses ploughing (25x45cm-10x18in) s. cardboard on canvas. 1-May-4 Meeting Art, Vercelli #247 est:2500

SCORZELLI, Eugenio (attrib) (1890-1958) Italian
£1399 $2406 €2000 London street (25x36cm-10x14in) s. panel. 4-Dec-3 Neumeister, Munich #2849/R est:700

SCORZINI, Alessandro (1858-1933) Italian
£1689 $2635 €2500 Houses (26x28cm-10x11in) board. 30-Mar-3 Adma, Formigine #342 est:2500-3000

SCOTT, Adam Sherriff (1887-1980) Canadian
£676 $1149 €987 Between friends (70x96cm-28x38in) s. 21-Nov-3 Walker's, Ottawa #72/R (C.D 1500)
£826 $1496 €1206 Untitled - woman in blue (117x91cm-46x36in) prov. 18-Apr-4 Levis, Calgary #108/R est:1200-1500 (C.D 2000)
£1116 $1864 €1618 Eskimo encampment (61x76cm-24x30in) s. i.verso. 17-Jun-3 Pinneys, Montreal #136 est:3000-4000 (C.D 2500)
£1333 $2440 €1946 Eskimo fishing through the ice (61x92cm-24x36in) s. i.verso. 27-Jan-4 Iegor de Saint Hippolyte, Montreal #32 (C.D 3200)
£1786 $3071 €2608 Eskimo encampment, Baffin Island (60x75cm-24x30in) s. 2-Dec-3 Joyner Waddington, Toronto #296/R est:4000-5000 (C.D 4000)
£2252 $3829 €3288 Portrait of a young woman (61x51cm-24x20in) s. prov. 18-Nov-3 Sotheby's, Toronto #48/R est:5000-7000 (C.D 5000)
£11200 $20496 €16352 Old time sugaring (75x95cm-30x37in) s. board. 1-Jun-4 Joyner Waddington, Toronto #28/R est:15000-20000 (C.D 28000)

SCOTT, Alexander (?-c.1932) British
£300 $540 €438 Landscape in India, with palm trees, a valley and mountains (56x82cm-22x32in) s.d.96. 21-Apr-4 Tennants, Leyburn #1153
£3356 $6275 €5000 Dalaughiri in Tibit (150x180cm-59x71in) s. 24-Feb-4 Dorotheum, Vienna #82/R est:6500-7500

SCOTT, Angus (?) British
£700 $1120 €1022 Pied Piper (112x58cm-44x23in) s. 16-Sep-3 Gorringes, Bexhill #1618/R

SCOTT, Campbell (19/20th C) British
£475 $850 €694 Highland loch landscape (61x91cm-24x36in) 14-May-4 Du Mouchelle, Detroit #2004/R
£652 $1200 €952 Loch Vernacher, Scotland (61x91cm-24x36in) s. i. stretcher. 26-Jun-4 Sloans & Kenyon, Bethesda #1058/R

SCOTT, Charles Hepburn (fl.1907-1924) British
£897 $1480 €1301 Sea, sky, sand and seaweed (66x91cm-26x36in) s. prov. 3-Jul-3 Heffel, Vancouver #34/R est:3000-4000 (C.D 2000)

SCOTT, Clyde Eugene (1884-1959) American
£949 $1500 €1386 Desert plateau (61x76cm-24x30in) s. 7-Sep-3 Treadway Gallery, Cincinnati #668/R est:2000-3000

SCOTT, D (20th C) British
£1600 $2864 €2336 Washing day (68x61cm-27x24in) s.d.1931 canvas on board. 14-May-4 Christie's, Kensington #316/R est:600-800

SCOTT, David (1806-1849) British
£2500 $4250 €3650 Family of cheetahs (101x101cm-40x40in) s. acrylic board. 19-Nov-3 Bracketts, Tunbridge Wells #52/R est:3500-4500

SCOTT, Derek (20th C) British
£260 $486 €390 Tug with clipper under tow (66x81cm-26x32in) s. 20-Jul-4 Peter Francis, Wales #5
£260 $486 €390 Wreck of the barque Admiral Prinz Adalbert, Mumbles Head 1883 (53x81cm-21x32in) s.d.93. 20-Jul-4 Peter Francis, Wales #29/R
£400 $748 €600 Royal National Lifeboat, Pentland, on station at Mumbles (56x81cm-22x32in) s.d.94. 20-Jul-4 Peter Francis, Wales #3
£1000 $1870 €1500 Brave attempt, wreck of the barque Admiral Prinz Adalbert (56x81cm-22x32in) s.d.93. 20-Jul-4 Peter Francis, Wales #4 est:100-200

SCOTT, Dudley (19th C) British
£320 $598 €467 Harvesting scene (55x72cm-22x28in) s. canvas on board. 24-Feb-4 Bonhams, Knowle #64

SCOTT, Frank Edwin (1862-1929) American
£1333 $2453 €2000 Street in Paris (81x64cm-32x25in) s. 8-Jun-4 Sotheby's, Milan #86/R est:2000-4000

SCOTT, George (?) ?
Works on paper
£634 $1096 €900 Un avion survolant Monte-Carlo (41x63cm-16x25in) s.i.d.1920 grey wash htd white gouache blk crayon beige paper. 10-Dec-3 Piasa, Paris #155
£1725 $2985 €2450 Meeting aerien vu du ciel (41x63cm-16x25in) s.d.1920 grey wash htd white gouache blk crayon beige paper. 10-Dec-3 Piasa, Paris #156/R est:1000-1500

SCOTT, Georges Bertin (1873-1942) French
Works on paper
£839 $1443 €1200 Cavalier arabe chargeant (23x29cm-9x11in) s.d.1940 W/C. 8-Dec-3 Tajan, Paris #310/R

SCOTT, Geraldine Armstrong (1900-) American
£615 $1100 €898 Portrait of a Native American man (35x28cm-14x11in) s. board prov. 14-May-4 Skinner, Boston #212/R
£1319 $2400 €1926 Indiana landscape (74x99cm-29x39in) s.d.1927 i.verso. 1-Jul-4 Dan Ripley, Indianapolis #148

SCOTT, Harold Winfield (1899-1977) American
£2374 $4250 €3466 Advancing cavalry soldiers (81x56cm-32x22in) s. prov. 15-May-4 Illustration House, New York #16/R est:3000-4500
£2395 $4000 €3497 Stagecoach hold-up (64x46cm-25x18in) s. sold with magazine cover copy. 15-Nov-3 Illustration House, New York #17/R est:3000-4500

SCOTT, Henry (1911-1966) British
£4372 $8000 €6383 Young America clear off the Horn (35x51cm-14x20in) s. prov. 29-Jul-4 Christie's, Rockefeller NY #305/R est:10000-15000
£4645 $8500 €6782 Clipper ship City of Adelaide (35x51cm-14x20in) s. 29-Jul-4 Christie's, Rockefeller NY #301/R est:6000-8000
£7104 $13000 €10372 Clipper ship Loch Etive (35x51cm-14x20in) s. 29-Jul-4 Christie's, Rockefeller NY #300/R est:6000-8000
£8197 $15000 €11968 American clipper Glory of the Seas (66x100cm-26x39in) s.d.67. 29-Jul-4 Christie's, Rockefeller NY #308/R est:15000-20000
£8197 $15000 €11968 Storm weather tea clipper Spindrift (71x107cm-28x42in) s. prov. 29-Jul-4 Christie's, Rockefeller NY #307/R est:15000-20000
£8649 $16000 €12628 Homeward run, tea clipper, Crest of the Wave running up the Channel (71x107cm-28x42in) s. 10-Feb-4 Christie's, Rockefeller NY #252/R est:15000-20000

SCOTT, Hugh B (19/20th C) British
£275 $500 €402 Scottish landscape with sheep (42x63cm-17x25in) s/. 7-Feb-4 Rasmussen, Havnen #2157 (D.KR 3000)

SCOTT, Ian (1945-) New Zealander
£297 $512 €434 Lattice 26 (42x42cm-17x17in) acrylic paper. 7-Dec-3 International Art Centre, Auckland #269/R (NZ.D 800)
£533 $997 €778 Lattice (70x54cm-28x21in) acrylic paper. 24-Feb-4 Peter Webb, Auckland #28/R (NZ.D 1450)
£725 $1167 €1059 Drawing no.11 2235/37 (50x50cm-20x20in) s. i.d.81 verso acrylic on paper. 20-Aug-3 Dunbar Sloane, Auckland #72/R est:2000-3000 (NZ.D 2000)
£1049 $1909 €1532 Lattice (80x80cm-31x31in) s.d.July 1976 verso. 29-Jun-4 Peter Webb, Auckland #182/R est:3000-4000 (NZ.D 3000)
£1250 $2300 €1825 Lattice no 28 (101x102cm-40x40in) s.d.1977 verso. 25-Mar-4 International Art Centre, Auckland #8/R est:3500-5500 (NZ.D 3500)
£1377 $2341 €2010 Anawhata stream and beach (89x120cm-35x47in) s.i.d.1996 s.d.verso board. 4-Nov-3 Peter Webb, Auckland #200/R est:2000-3000 (NZ.D 3800)
£1389 $2208 €2028 Jet black (101x76cm-40x30in) s. i.d.1984 verso acrylic. 1-May-3 Dunbar Sloane, Wellington #60/R est:1000-3000 (NZ.D 4000)
£1469 $2673 €2145 Lattice no.84 (114x114cm-45x45in) i. s.d.1982 verso acrylic. 29-Jun-4 Peter Webb, Auckland #9/R est:5000-7000 (NZ.D 4200)
£1642 $2840 €2397 Lattice, small no 210 (60x60cm-24x24in) s.i.d.1981 verso. 9-Dec-3 Peter Webb, Auckland #16/R est:3500-4500 (NZ.D 4400)
£1773 $3138 €2589 Small lattice no 230 (76x76cm-30x30in) s.verso. 28-Apr-4 Dunbar Sloane, Auckland #23/R est:5000-8000 (NZ.D 5000)
£1902 $3082 €2758 Lattice no.79 (180x180cm-71x71in) s.d.1982 verso acrylic prov. 31-Jul-3 International Art Centre, Auckland #30/R est:3000-6000 (NZ.D 5250)
£2015 $3486 €2942 Small lattice no 29 (81x81cm-32x32in) s.i.d.1979 verso. 9-Dec-3 Peter Webb, Auckland #9/R est:3500-5000 (NZ.D 5400)
£2098 $3818 €3063 Small lattice no. 132 (91x91cm-36x36in) i. s.i.verso acrylic. 29-Jun-4 Peter Webb, Auckland #8/R est:4000-6000 (NZ.D 6000)

SCOTT, James (?) British
£700 $1302 €1022 La Sardana, debajp de los pinos (50x76cm-20x30in) s.d.97 board. 3-Mar-4 John Ross, Belfast #186

SCOTT, James Fraser (1877-1932) Australian
£347 $552 €507 Portrait of a gentleman (60x49cm-24x19in) s. 1-May-3 Dunbar Sloane, Wellington #92 est:1000-1800 (NZ.D 1000)
£602 $1023 €879 Under the trees, park scene Paris (44x29cm-17x11in) s.i.verso. 26-Nov-3 Dunbar Sloane, Wellington #104 est:2000-3000 (NZ.D 1600)
£694 $1104 €1013 Weaver (60x49cm-24x19in) s. 1-May-3 Dunbar Sloane, Wellington #52/R est:1500-2500 (NZ.D 2000)

SCOTT, James R (fl.1854-1871) British
£580 $1079 €847 Towards the custom house, Venice (61x91cm-24x36in) s.d.99 board. 3-Mar-4 John Ross, Belfast #237

SCOTT, Johan (1953-) Swedish
£492 $801 €718 Untitled (150x132cm-59x52in) s.d.1990. 29-Sep-3 Lilla Bukowskis, Stockholm #835 (S.KR 6400)
£1026 $1815 €1498 Untitled (70x100cm-28x39in) s.d.89 oil acrylic plastic prov. 27-Apr-4 AB Stockholms Auktionsverk #977/R (S.KR 14000)
£1586 $2696 €2316 Untitled (73x63cm-29x25in) s.d.2001 verso prov.exhib.lit. 4-Nov-3 Bukowskis, Stockholm #603/R est:8000-10000 (S.KR 21000)

SCOTT, John (1907-1987) American
£1123 $2100 €1640 Band of gauchos with leader on horseback (76x53cm-30x21in) s. painted c.1930. 26-Feb-4 Illustration House, New York #156 est:2500-4000

Works on paper
£559 $900 €811 Dove hunt (33x48cm-13x19in) gouache. 22-Aug-3 Altermann Galleries, Santa Fe #225
£608 $1100 €888 Nautical scene (51x33cm-20x13in) s. gouache sold with illustration by Robert Addison. 3-Apr-4 Susanin's, Chicago #5045/R
£1099 $2000 €1605 The raiders (46x64cm-18x25in) s. gouache board. 7-Feb-4 Dan Ripley, Indianapolis #20

SCOTT, John (1849-1919) British
£760 $1292 €1110 Summer evening (25x35cm-10x14in) s. canvasboard exhib. 25-Nov-3 Bonhams, Knowle #233
£1202 $2200 €1755 Working the banner (86x46cm-34x18in) s.i.d.1879. 5-Jun-4 Neal Auction Company, New Orleans #294/R est:2500-4000
£4743 $8490 €6925 Joan of Arc (106x171cm-42x67in) s.d.1883 prov. 15-May-4 Christie's, Sydney #202/R est:20000-30000 (A.D 12000)
Works on paper
£800 $1360 €1168 Lady reading a book in an interior (25x34cm-10x13in) s. W/C over pencil. 1-Dec-3 Bonhams, Bath #73/R
£1100 $1969 €1606 Loves young dream. His first brush (37x53cm-15x21in) s. i.verso W/C pair. 17-Mar-4 Bonhams, Chester #307 est:1200-1800

SCOTT, John (1802-1885) British
£1639 $3000 €2393 Harbour scene, possibly Liverpool (36x46cm-14x18in) s. 5-Jun-4 Neal Auction Company, New Orleans #126/R est:3000-5000
£1900 $3591 €2774 Shipping off Tynemouth (25x46cm-10x18in) s.d.1865. 17-Feb-4 Bonhams, New Bond Street #27/R est:1000-1500

SCOTT, John (20th C) New Zealander
Works on paper
£625 $1150 €913 Sonnet series (57x75cm-22x30in) s.d.1985 mixed media. 25-Mar-4 International Art Centre, Auckland #23/R (NZ.D 1750)

SCOTT, John W A (1815-1907) American
£2374 $4250 €3466 Fisherman at dusk (46x76cm-18x30in) s.d.72. 6-May-4 Shannon's, Milford #228/R est:3000-5000
£2443 $4300 €3567 Landscape of a haying scene with men loading one wagon drawn by oxen (43x28cm-17x11in) init. 3-Jan-4 Cobbs, Peterborough #14/R
£4192 $7000 €6120 New England Farm - probably the White Mountains (56x91cm-22x36in) init. 23-Oct-3 Shannon's, Milford #110/R est:7000-9000

SCOTT, Julian (1846-1901) American
£5000 $8000 €7300 Portrait of an artist (155x117cm-61x46in) s.d.1887. 18-May-3 Auctions by the Bay, Alameda #1038/R

SCOTT, Lorenzo (1934-) American
£236 $425 €345 Scene from Shakespearean play (81x97cm-32x38in) 24-Apr-4 Slotin Folk Art, Buford #466/R
£419 $700 €612 Subway with devils (56x102cm-22x40in) 15-Nov-3 Slotin Folk Art, Buford #298/R
£444 $800 €648 Three children jumping rope (71x102cm-28x40in) 24-Apr-4 Slotin Folk Art, Buford #464/R
£500 $900 €730 Adam and Eve in the garden (102x71cm-40x28in) 24-Apr-4 Slotin Folk Art, Buford #463/R
£659 $1100 €962 Child visited by angels (135x91cm-53x36in) 15-Nov-3 Slotin Folk Art, Buford #296/R
£778 $1300 €1136 Adam and Eve (132x79cm-52x31in) s. canvas on board. 15-Nov-3 Slotin Folk Art, Buford #295/R
£898 $1500 €1311 Children courting (86x102cm-34x40in) 15-Nov-3 Slotin Folk Art, Buford #297/R est:1000-2000

SCOTT, Mabel (20th C) American
£559 $1000 €816 New York rooftops (102x76cm-40x30in) s. 16-May-4 Wright, Chicago #156/R

SCOTT, Marweha (19/20th C) ?
£394 $642 €575 Landscape with stream (33x51cm-13x20in) s. painted c.1900. 24-Sep-3 Louis Morton, Mexico #84/R est:8000-10000 (M.P 7000)

SCOTT, Michael (20th C) American?
£380 $608 €555 Still life with terracotta jug and pears (90x60cm-35x24in) s. 19-May-3 Bruton Knowles, Cheltenham #203/R

SCOTT, Patrick (1921-) Irish
£3421 $6295 €5200 Flowers in a bog (61x76cm-24x30in) s.d.62 verso. 22-Jun-4 De Veres Art Auctions, Dublin #138/R est:7000-9000
£6667 $12067 €10000 Device on the sun (122x102cm-48x40in) s. prov. 31-Mar-4 James Adam, Dublin #126/R est:7000-10000
£10135 $19155 €15000 Gold painting 8/93 (86x86cm-34x34in) s.i.verso gold leaf tempera exhib. 17-Feb-4 Whyte's, Dublin #30/R est:15000-20000
£10738 $19007 €16000 Pyre II (61x61cm-24x24in) s.i.verso tempera prov.exhib. 27-Apr-4 Whyte's, Dublin #86/R est:10000-12000
Works on paper
£940 $1663 €1400 Drawing series E (64x48cm-25x19in) s.d.1978 Indian ink prov. 27-Apr-4 Whyte's, Dublin #88/R
£1733 $3137 €2600 Glowing (69x64cm-27x25in) s.d.61 mixed media prov. 30-Mar-4 De Veres Art Auctions, Dublin #43/R est:3000-5000

SCOTT, Robert Austin (1941-) Canadian
£1205 $2241 €1759 Zosia (45x274cm-18x108in) s.i.d.1984 verso acrylic prov.exhib. 4-Mar-4 Heffel, Vancouver #40/R est:3000-4000 (C.D 3000)

SCOTT, Robert Bagge (fl.1886-1896) British
£380 $612 €551 On the dunes at dawn, Ratwijk (20x28cm-8x11in) s. 15-Aug-3 Keys, Aylsham #725

SCOTT, Roger (20th C) American
£246 $425 €359 Summer lake landscape (61x76cm-24x30in) s. 13-Dec-3 Charlton Hall, Columbia #575/R

SCOTT, Samuel (style) (1703-1772) British
£5000 $7900 €7250 Old Westminster Bridge (60x109cm-24x43in) lit. 4-Sep-3 Christie's, Kensington #84/R est:4000-6000
£5000 $8350 €7300 Pagoda bridge at Hampton Court (66x96cm-26x38in) 13-Nov-3 Christie's, Kensington #237/R est:3000-5000
£11000 $17380 €15950 York buildings waterworks looking towards Westminster (56x91cm-22x36in) prov. 4-Sep-3 Christie's, Kensington #90/R est:4000-6000

SCOTT, Sandy (1943-) American
Sculpture
£2890 $5000 €4219 Bald Eagle Off Cannery Point (114cm-45in) s.i.d.1993 green pat bronze incl base prov. 10-Dec-3 Bonhams & Butterfields, San Francisco #6134/R est:6000-8000

SCOTT, Septimus Edwin (1879-c.1952) British
£260 $421 €380 The plough team homeward bound (25x34cm-10x13in) s. board. 27-Jan-3 Bristol Auction Rooms #478
£780 $1295 €1139 Rider and two horses on a bridge (25x34cm-10x13in) s. board. 1-Oct-3 Woolley & Wallis, Salisbury #196/R

SCOTT, Sir Peter (1909-1989) British
£1000 $1830 €1460 Greylags on the Marshes (36x44cm-14x17in) s.d.1942. 7-Apr-4 Woolley & Wallis, Salisbury #265/R est:1000-1200
£1400 $2576 €2044 Night attack (64x76cm-25x30in) s.d.1943. 8-Jun-4 Gorringes, Lewes #2152/R est:1000-1500
£2000 $3340 €2920 Barnacle geese, widgeons, and pintails (51x76cm-20x30in) s.d.1948 prov. 18-Jun-3 John Nicholson, Haslemere #665/R est:3000-5000
£2200 $3740 €3212 Mallards over a marsh (38x46cm-15x18in) s.d.1945. 27-Nov-3 Christie's, Kensington #234/R
£3000 $4740 €4350 Pink feet flighting to a wheat field in the Fen country (19x39cm-7x15in) s.d.1933 i.verso. 24-Jul-3 Lawrence, Crewkerne #973/R est:400-600
£3800 $6460 €5548 Mallards gliding in. GEESE FEEDING (38x46cm-15x18in) s.d.1945 double-sided. 27-Nov-3 Christie's, Kensington #238/R est:2000-3000
£6500 $11050 €9490 Pink feet in the Severn estuary (71x91cm-28x36in) s.d.1961 prov. 26-Nov-3 Sotheby's, Olympia #69/R est:3000-5000
£6800 $12444 €9928 North Wind - Bewick swans (70x90cm-28x35in) s.d.1957 prov. 8-Jul-4 Lawrence, Crewkerne #1667/R est:5000-8000
£9000 $16560 €13140 Snow geese (76x112cm-30x44in) s.d.1939. 10-Jun-4 Christie's, Kensington #260a/R est:10000-15000
Works on paper
£400 $740 €584 Geese (15x23cm-6x9in) s.d.1929 W/C htd bodycol. 14-Feb-4 Hogben, Folkstone #137
£500 $935 €730 Study of geese in flight (26x38cm-10x15in) pencil W/C htd white. 22-Jul-4 Tennants, Leyburn #686
£850 $1462 €1241 Wild geese in flight (30x36cm-12x14in) s. W/C. 3-Dec-3 Cheffins, Cambridge #582/R

SCOTT, Tom (1854-1927) British
Works on paper
£400 $732 €584 Stormy day at St. Mary's Loch (16x24cm-6x9in) s.d.1916 W/C. 8-Apr-4 Bonhams, Edinburgh #151
£680 $1136 €993 Landscape at Abernyte (28x43cm-11x17in) s. W/C. 8-Oct-3 Andrew Hartley, Ilkley #1012/R
£1120 $2061 €1635 Returning home (15x20cm-6x8in) s. W/C. 12-Jun-4 Dickins, Middle Claydon #53
£1400 $2408 €2044 Yarrow valley, near Selkirk (17x24cm-7x9in) init.d.85 W/C. 4-Dec-3 Bonhams, Edinburgh #66/R est:800-1000
£1400 $2562 €2044 Fishing the Tweed (24x37cm-9x15in) init.d.1913 W/C. 8-Apr-4 Bonhams, Edinburgh #187/R est:1500-2000
£1400 $2576 €2044 Horses at rivers edge by the village bridge (23x36cm-9x14in) s. W/C. 12-Jun-4 Dickins, Middle Claydon #52
£1504 $2556 €2196 Newark Castle (25x36cm-10x14in) s.d.1903 W/C. 27-Nov-3 International Art Centre, Auckland #189/R est:1500-2500 (NZ.D 4000)
£2200 $4026 €3212 Two boys shrimping at low tide (20x33cm-8x13in) s.d.98 W/C. 28-Jul-4 Mallams, Oxford #254/R est:1000-1500
£3300 $6039 €4818 Border keep (42x31cm-17x12in) s.i.d.90 W/C lit. 8-Apr-4 Bonhams, Edinburgh #188/R est:2500-4000
£3500 $6405 €5110 On the road above Selkirk (25x34cm-10x13in) s.d.1919 W/C. 8-Apr-4 Bonhams, Edinburgh #186/R est:1500-2000
£3500 $6335 €5110 Wick Harbour (25x41cm-10x16in) s.i. W/C. 16-Apr-4 Keys, Aylsham #522/R est:2500-3000
£3600 $6516 €5256 Spring day (27x37cm-11x15in) s.i.d.96 W/C. 19-Apr-4 Sotheby's, London #94/R est:1500-2000
£11000 $18920 €16060 Border Widow's lament (64x79cm-25x31in) s.d.1901 W/C scratching out. 4-Dec-3 Bonhams, Edinburgh #65/R est:6000-8000

SCOTT, Tony (1950-) Australian
£289 $535 €422 Temple series green (141x38cm-56x15in) s.d.1990 i. oil gold leaf canvasboard on board. 15-Mar-4 Sotheby's, Melbourne #35 (A.D 700)

SCOTT, Walt (1894-1970) American
Works on paper
£251 $450 €366 Person on a cliff with rotted tree root in stormy weather (33x38cm-13x15in) W/C gouache. 15-May-4 Jeffery Burchard, Florida #186
£335 $600 €489 Person in a forest (46x66cm-18x26in) s. gouache. 15-May-4 Jeffery Burchard, Florida #185

SCOTT, William (1913-1989) British
£19000 $32300 €27740 Pear and plate (46x46cm-18x18in) s.d.79 verso prov. 21-Nov-3 Christie's, London #19/R est:15000-20000

£32000 $58240 €46720 Still life 1 (32x36cm-13x14in) s. i.d.1935 verso board prov. 15-Jun-4 Bonhams, New Bond Street #61/R est:20000-30000
£38000 $64600 €55480 Two related no.1 (61x61cm-24x24in) s.d.73 verso prov.exhib. 21-Nov-3 Christie's, London #21/R est:20000-30000
£51748 $87972 €74000 Frying pan and eggs (81x65cm-32x26in) s. painted 1952 prov.exhib. 18-Nov-3 Whyte's, Dublin #74/R est:80000-100000
£56000 $101920 €81760 Soldier and girl sleeping (41x51cm-16x20in) s.d.42 prov.exhib.lit. 15-Jun-4 Bonhams, New Bond Street #60/R est:40000-60000
£82000 $150060 €119720 Orchre still life II (122x122cm-48x48in) s.i. prov.exhib. 4-Jun-4 Christie's, London #126/R est:40000-60000
£100000 $183000 €146000 Harbour, Port Manech (51x61cm-20x24in) s.d.39 prov.exhib.lit. 4-Jun-4 Christie's, London #127/R est:60000-100000
£165000 $280500 €240900 Bowl and frying basket (51x61cm-20x24in) i.on stretcher painted 1950 prov. 21-Nov-3 Christie's, London #63/R est:60000-80000

Prints

£2098 $3566 €3000 Pot and three pears (41x61cm-16x24in) s. lithograph. 25-Nov-3 De Veres Art Auctions, Dublin #25/R est:800-1200
£2100 $3570 €3066 Composition (50x65cm-20x26in) s.d.1982 col lithograph. 30-Oct-3 Christie's, Kensington #155/R est:1500-2000
£2900 $5336 €4234 Black pan, beige cup on brown (58x76cm-23x30in) s.d.1970 num.83/100 screenprint. 28-Jun-4 Bonhams, New Bond Street #262/R est:2500-3500
£3400 $6222 €4964 Still life (67x88cm-26x35in) s.d.1973 num.80/250 col lithograph. 3-Jun-4 Christie's, Kensington #482/R est:2000-3000
£3467 $6275 €5200 Composition from thirty-five artists (50x66cm-20x26in) s.d.82 col lithograph edition of 50. 30-Mar-4 De Veres Art Auctions, Dublin #100/R est:4000-6000
£3600 $6624 €5256 Still life (59x88cm-23x35in) s.d.1970 num.87/100 lithograph. 29-Mar-4 Bonhams, New Bond Street #252/R est:2500-3500
£3947 $7263 €6000 Still life (67x88cm-26x35in) s.d.1973 col lithograph. 22-Jun-4 De Veres Art Auctions, Dublin #67/R est:5000-7000

Works on paper

£750 $1343 €1095 Still life (15x17cm-6x7in) pencil prov. 14-May-4 Christie's, Kensington #473a/R
£3000 $5100 €4380 Form with ochre (21x25cm-8x10in) pastel executed 1971 exhib. 21-Nov-3 Christie's, London #20/R est:2000-3000
£4200 $7686 €6132 Avon suite no.5 (28x38cm-11x15in) s.d.76 pencil black white crayon wash prov.exhib. 4-Jun-4 Christie's, London #125/R est:4000-6000
£7133 $12126 €10200 Still life of bowls and pan (21x26cm-8x10in) s.d.74 gouache prov. 25-Nov-3 De Veres Art Auctions, Dublin #87/R est:9000-12000
£8000 $13360 €11680 Blue field (27x37cm-11x15in) s. W/C bodycol. 16-Oct-3 Christie's, Kensington #705/R est:8000-12000
£10000 $18200 €14600 Shelter (14x20cm-6x8in) pen ink gouache wash prov. 15-Jun-4 Bonhams, New Bond Street #63/R est:2000-3000
£10490 $17832 €15000 Orange arm (28x38cm-11x15in) s. gouache prov. 25-Nov-3 De Veres Art Auctions, Dublin #194/R est:15000-20000
£16000 $28640 €23360 Composition (28x39cm-11x15in) gouache prov.lit. 13-May-4 Sotheby's, London #74/R est:12000-18000
£21500 $39345 €31390 Three forms (55x76cm-22x30in) s. chl executed 1958 prov. 4-Jun-4 Christie's, London #124/R est:10000-15000
£24000 $43920 €35040 Composition (56x75cm-22x30in) s.d.61 collage chl gouache white chk prov. 4-Jun-4 Christie's, London #117/R est:15000-20000
£28322 $48147 €40500 Still life (68x84cm-27x33in) mixed media prov. 25-Nov-3 De Veres Art Auctions, Dublin #77/R est:25000-35000
£62000 $113460 €90520 Sewing machine (52x68cm-20x27in) s. W/C bodycol thinned oil executed 1942 prov. 4-Jun-4 Christie's, London #123/R est:40000-60000

SCOTT, William Bell (1811-1890) British

£30000 $55200 €43800 Eve of the DEluge (74x115cm-29x45in) s.d.1865 prov.exhib.lit. 9-Jun-4 Christie's, London #22/R est:30000-50000

Works on paper

£2767 $4953 €4040 Study of a young woman's head (35x25cm-14x10in) pencil prov. 15-May-4 Christie's, Sydney #499/R est:6000-8000 (A.D 7000)

SCOTT, William Bell (attrib) (1811-1890) British

£360 $637 €526 Pause for refreshment (20x25cm-8x10in) board. 28-Apr-4 Halls, Shrewsbury #521/R

SCOTT, William Edouard (1884-1964) American

£745 $1200 €1088 Interior scene (23x36cm-9x14in) board on wood panel. 22-Feb-3 Bunte, Elgin #1290

SCOTT, William Henry Stothard (1783-1850) British

Works on paper

£270 $486 €394 Figures beside a cottage. s.d.1845 W/C. 22-Jan-4 Rendalls, Ashburton #1920

SCOTTISH SCHOOL (19th C)

£8800 $14168 €12760 Portrait of James Campbell of Jura (100x126cm-39x50in) 21-Aug-3 Bonhams, Edinburgh #1125/R est:6000-8000

Sculpture

£7800 $12558 €11310 Scottish piper (165x92cm-65x36in) polychrome painted. 21-Aug-3 Bonhams, Edinburgh #917/R est:3000-5000

SCOUEZEC, Maurice le (1881-1940) French

£1007 $1883 €1500 Descente de croix (63x80cm-25x31in) paper. 24-Feb-4 Thierry & Lannon, Brest #320/R
£1467 $2625 €2200 Le peintre clerge (70x60cm-28x24in) s. paper. 16-May-4 Thierry & Lannon, Brest #154/R est:3500-4000
£3873 $6778 €5500 Paysage vallonne au toit rouge (50x74cm-20x29in) s.d. 31 aout 21 board. 21-Dec-3 Thierry & Lannon, Brest #177/R est:5000-6000
£16197 $28345 €23000 Lavandieres a Landivisiau (144x199cm-57x78in) paper on canvas. 21-Dec-3 Thierry & Lannon, Brest #176/R est:7000-8000

Works on paper

£667 $1193 €1000 Femmes africaines et l'enfant (28x21cm-11x8in) W/C chl. 16-May-4 Thierry & Lannon, Brest #61/R
£667 $1193 €1000 Le parc (25x43cm-10x17in) W/C. 16-May-4 Thierry & Lannon, Brest #63/R
£1338 $2342 €1900 Scene de marche, environs de Montparnasse (33x25cm-13x10in) s.d.21 W/C. 21-Dec-3 Thierry & Lannon, Brest #62 est:1200-1500
£1620 $2835 €2300 Le cirque (42x63cm-17x25in) s. 21-Dec-3 Thierry & Lannon, Brest #63 est:2500-3000
£2333 $4177 €3500 Jour de Pardon a Plouescat (50x65cm-20x26in) s.i.d.1929 W/C. 16-May-4 Thierry & Lannon, Brest #62/R est:3000-4000

SCOUGALL, David (attrib) (17th C) British

£900 $1620 €1314 Portrait of Mr Gibson of Durie (122x98cm-48x39in) i. 21-Jan-4 Sotheby's, Olympia #79/R est:1000-2000
£3000 $5400 €4380 Portrait of Miss Suzanne Menzies (71x59cm-28x23in) i. painted oval. 21-Jan-4 Sotheby's, Olympia #80/R est:2000-3000
£3200 $5760 €4672 Portrait of Lady Christian Lindsay (122x100cm-48x39in) i. 21-Jan-4 Sotheby's, Olympia #81/R est:2000-3000

SCOULER, James (1740-1812) British

Miniatures

£1400 $2576 €2044 Abraham Hume, wearing a white dress with wide pink waistband (4cm-2in) gold frame. 24-Jun-4 Bonhams, New Bond Street #49/R est:800-1200
£3200 $5728 €4672 Young gentleman in a red coat. Young lady in a blue dress (3cm-1in) s.d.1774 pair silver bracelet clasp frame with seed pears rubys. 25-May-4 Christie's, London #71/R est:1500-2500

SCOULLER, Glen (1950-) British

£2300 $4232 €3358 Boats and red markers, Hastings (56x50cm-22x20in) s. 29-Mar-4 Thomson Roddick & Medcalf, Edinburgh #192 est:2000-2500

Works on paper

£260 $434 €380 Farmyard (19x24cm-7x9in) s. pencil W/C. 16-Oct-3 Lyon & Turnbull, Edinburgh #15
£720 $1318 €1051 Pink and yellow buildings, S Jeannet (53x70cm-21x28in) s. W/C. 8-Apr-4 Bonhams, Edinburgh #33/R
£720 $1318 €1051 Balcony, La Gaude (51x70cm-20x28in) s. W/C. 8-Apr-4 Bonhams, Edinburgh #34
£800 $1464 €1168 Beached boats at St. Laurent de Var (53x72cm-21x28in) s. W/C. 8-Apr-4 Bonhams, Edinburgh #17
£820 $1501 €1197 Old French houses (50x72cm-20x28in) s. W/C. 8-Apr-4 Bonhams, Edinburgh #18
£1100 $2024 €1606 Owl and sunflower (52x70cm-20x28in) s. W/C. 29-Mar-4 Thomson Roddick & Medcalf, Edinburgh #191 est:1000-1200

SCOUPREMAN, Pierre (1873-1960) Belgian

£521 $828 €750 Marche aux fleurs au Parvis de Saint Gilles (60x70cm-24x28in) s.d.1935. 15-Sep-3 Horta, Bruxelles #374

SCRIVER, Robert Macfie (1914-1999) American

Sculpture

£1059 $1800 €1546 Symbol of the pros (30cm-12in) bronze. 1-Nov-3 Altermann Galleries, Santa Fe #22
£3743 $7000 €5465 Old timers. Cowboy on a horse (33x30x15cm-13x12x6in) bronze pair prov. 24-Jul-4 Coeur d'Alene, Hayden #106/R est:4000-8000
£6952 $13000 €10150 Reride. Buffalo hunter (51x51x18cm-20x20x7in) bronze pair prov. 24-Jul-4 Coeur d'Alene, Hayden #256/R est:4000-8000

SCRIVO (1942-) Belgian?

£5903 $9858 €8500 Life's different roads number 140179 (60x60cm-24x24in) s. d.1979 verso panel. 21-Oct-3 Campo & Campo, Antwerp #270/R est:5000-6000

SCROPPO, Filippo (1910-1993) Italian

£699 $1168 €1000 Cosmic (60x80cm-24x31in) s.i.d.1974 verso. 26-Jun-3 Sant Agostino, Torino #223/R
£1259 $2102 €1800 Composition (70x55cm-28x22in) s. 26-Jun-3 Sant Agostino, Torino #211/R est:2000
£2069 $3455 €3000 Rythms (118x85cm-46x33in) s. s.i.d.1959 verso masonite exhib.lit. 17-Nov-3 Sant Agostino, Torino #309/R est:3000-4000
£3357 $5706 €4800 Contacts (110x60cm-43x24in) s. s.i.d.1955 verso tempera board prov.exhib.lit. 26-Nov-3 Pandolfini, Florence #43/R est:4200-4500
£3793 $6334 €5500 Urban spaces (100x100cm-39x39in) s.verso painted1951 exhib.lit. 17-Nov-3 Sant Agostino, Torino #305/R est:3500-4500

SCUFFI, Marcello (1948-) Italian

£517 $864 €750 Night scene (50x35cm-20x14in) s. s.i.d.87 verso. 14-Nov-3 Farsetti, Prato #75/R
£528 $877 €750 Il Bagno abbandonato (50x35cm-20x14in) s. s.i.d.1996 verso. 14-Jun-3 Meeting Art, Vercelli #447/R
£733 $1327 €1100 Old trains (70x50cm-28x20in) s. painted 2000. 2-Apr-4 Farsetti, Prato #507/R
£933 $1717 €1400 Remembering a sea, but which one ? (50x40cm-20x16in) s. painted 1998. 12-Jun-4 Meeting Art, Vercelli #529/R
£1103 $1843 €1600 Circus (40x80cm-16x31in) s. i.verso. 14-Nov-3 Farsetti, Prato #436/R est:1600-2000
£1267 $2331 €1900 Circus (70x70cm-28x28in) s. s.i.verso. 12-Jun-4 Meeting Art, Vercelli #612/R est:1500

Works on paper

£317 $526 €450 Pescaia (35x50cm-14x20in) s.i.d.2001 W/C cardboard. 14-Jun-3 Meeting Art, Vercelli #601

SCULL, Elsie (20th C) American

£497 $800 €726 Fisherman's cottages, Monhegan Island, Maine (41x51cm-16x20in) s.d. 20-Aug-3 James Julia, Fairfield #1670/R

SCULLY, Sean (1946-) American/Irish

£13000 $21710 €18980 Place (76x56cm-30x22in) s.i.d.5.15.94 oil paper prov. 22-Oct-3 Christie's, London #86/R est:4000-6000
£19000 $34390 €27740 Triangular diptych - cream (121x121cm-48x48in) s.i.d.1974 prov. 1-Apr-4 Christie's, Kensington #32/R est:6000-8000

£27000	$48870	€39420	Small mirror (51x41cm-20x16in) s.i.d.1998 verso canvas on board prov. 1-Apr-4 Christie's, Kensington #325/R est:25000-35000
£27933	$50000	€40782	Rosa (51x50cm-20x20in) s.i.d.85 verso linen prov. 13-May-4 Sotheby's, New York #462/R est:30000-40000
£55000	$100100	€80300	Beach (165x92cm-65x36in) s.i.d.1983 verso three joined canvases prov. 5-Feb-4 Christie's, London #191/R est:40000-60000
£77844	$130000	€113652	Stranger (244x315cm-96x124in) s.i.d.1987 verso three attached canvases prov. 12-Nov-3 Christie's, Rockefeller NY #628/R est:80000-120000
£125000	$230000	€182500	Dead sea (244x183cm-96x72in) painted 1989 prov.exhib.lit. 23-Jun-4 Sotheby's, London #35/R est:80000-120000
Prints			
£1519	$2750	€2218	Union no 2 (38x45cm-15x18in) s.i.d.1985 col etching aquatint. 19-Apr-4 Bonhams & Butterfields, San Francisco #308/R est:1800-2500
£2517	$4280	€3600	Barcelona diptych no.4 (65x50cm-26x20in) s.i.d.96 etching. 25-Nov-3 De Veres Art Auctions, Dublin #88/R est:3500-4500
£2587	$4399	€3700	Raval no.1 (56x76cm-22x30in) s.i.d.96 etching. 25-Nov-3 De Veres Art Auctions, Dublin #89/R est:3500-4500
£2700	$4887	€3942	Standing 2 (119x90cm-47x35in) s.i.d.86 num.19/35 woodcut. 1-Apr-4 Christie's, Kensington #323/R est:1000-1500
£3092	$5689	€4700	Standing 2 (119x91cm-47x36in) s.i.d.1986 col woodcut one of 35 prov. 22-Jun-4 De Veres Art Auctions, Dublin #67b/R est:5000-7000
£7000	$11690	€10220	Enter 6 (45x34cm-18x13in) s.i.num.37/40 complete suite of six lithograph. 22-Oct-3 Bonhams, New Bond Street #103/R est:4000-6000
Works on paper			
£304	$550	€444	Untitled (20x15cm-8x6in) s.d.1996 W/C. 19-Apr-4 Daniel Cooney, Brooklyn #469126/R
£11500	$20815	€16790	Untitled (57x75cm-22x30in) s.d.8.31.89 pastel chl prov. 1-Apr-4 Christie's, Kensington #324/R est:5000-7000
£14595	$27000	€21309	Untitled (57x76cm-22x30in) s.d.3 7 83 pastel. 12-Feb-4 Sotheby's, New York #261/R est:15000-20000
£21000	$35070	€30660	2.25.97 (57x75cm-22x30in) s.i.d.2.25.97 W/C prov. 22-Oct-3 Christie's, London #85/R est:5000-7000

SCULTHORPE, Peter (1948-) American

Works on paper			
£2310	$4250	€3373	Farm hand (69x48cm-27x19in) s. W/C. 11-Jun-4 David Rago, Lambertville #259/R est:3000-5000

SCURI, Enrico (1806-1884) Italian

£4255	$7106	€6000	Portrait of Rembrandt (62x51cm-24x20in) painted c.1821-23 lit. 20-Oct-3 Sant Agostino, Torino #324/R est:5000-7000

SDRUSCIA, Achille (?-1993) Italian

£414	$691	€600	Roman landscape (50x60cm-20x24in) s. s.i.d.1963 verso. 13-Nov-3 Finarte Semenzato, Rome #291

SEABROOKE, Elliott (1886-1950) British

£500	$910	€730	Boating lake, Arundel (62x98cm-24x39in) s. 15-Jun-4 Bonhams, Knightsbridge #15/R
£600	$960	€870	Summer landscape (51x61cm-20x24in) s.d.1943 double-sided. 16-Sep-3 Bonhams, Knightsbridge #13/R
Works on paper			
£280	$512	€409	Barges, Amsterdam (27x32cm-11x13in) pastel. 28-Jan-4 Dreweatt Neate, Newbury #40/R

SEABY, Allen William (1867-1953) British

Works on paper			
£260	$478	€380	Fulmer petrels, nesting time, Farnes (40x58cm-16x23in) s. gouache linen. 10-Jun-4 Lyon & Turnbull, Edinburgh #6
£1100	$2057	€1606	Woodcock nesting amongst bracken. Bird amongst reeds (28x39cm-11x15in) s. pencil W/C htd white pair. 22-Jul-4 Tennants, Leyburn #682 est:500-600

SEAGO, E (1910-1974) British

£400	$668	€584	Figures on a road leading to a village (30x43cm-12x17in) s. 8-Oct-3 Andrew Hartley, Ilkley #1131

SEAGO, Edward (1910-1974) British

£1100	$2013	€1606	Portrait of a boy (49x38cm-19x15in) s.d. 6-Jun-4 Lots Road Auctions, London #336 est:600-900
£1200	$2004	€1752	Cattle watering (18x23cm-7x9in) 21-Oct-3 Gorringes, Lewes #2191/R
£1700	$3111	€2482	Lost - two huntsmen on the Downs (49x37cm-19x15in) s.d.39 card. 28-Jan-4 Henry Adams, Chichester #291/R est:1500-2000
£2500	$4300	€3650	Landscape near Ludham (29x45cm-11x18in) s. board prov. 2-Dec-3 Bonhams, New Bond Street #38/R est:3000-4000
£2600	$4576	€3796	Ammunition dispersed on the road near Borghi (22x30cm-9x12in) board prov. 19-May-4 Sotheby's, Olympia #148/R est:3000-5000
£2600	$4576	€3796	Icebergs at Base W off the Grahamland coast (49x64cm-19x25in) s. canvas on board prov.exhib.lit. 18-May-4 Woolley & Wallis, Salisbury #23/R est:1500-2500
£3500	$6475	€5110	St. Benet's Abbey, Norfolk (21x27cm-8x11in) s. board prov. 11-Mar-4 Christie's, Kensington #89/R est:1500-2000
£3800	$6688	€5548	Trees and cattle (39x29cm-15x11in) s. board prov. 19-May-4 Sotheby's, Olympia #117/R est:4000-6000
£3894	$6152	€5685	Foothills of the Atlas, Morocco (51x76cm-20x30in) s. i. verso board. 2-Sep-3 Deutscher-Menzies, Melbourne #448/R est:8000-12000 (A.D 9500)
£4000	$6800	€5840	October afternoon (28x40cm-11x16in) s. board prov. 26-Nov-3 Sotheby's, Olympia #81/R est:3000-5000
£4500	$7650	€6570	Street corner in Duclair (30x40cm-12x16in) s. board prov. 26-Nov-3 Sotheby's, Olympia #77/R est:4000-6000
£4500	$7650	€6570	Wells cathedral (21x26cm-8x10in) init. canvas on board prov. 26-Nov-3 Sotheby's, Olympia #80/R est:2500-3500
£4500	$7920	€6570	Bybrook (46x61cm-18x24in) s.d.37 prov. 21-May-4 Christie's, London #68/R est:5000-8000
£4839	$8903	€7065	Otalaya, Portugal (46x61cm-18x24in) s. i.stretcher. 14-Jun-4 Waddingtons, Toronto #162/R est:8000-12000 (C.D 12000)
£5495	$10000	€8023	Canal in Venice (50x75cm-20x30in) s. board. 29-Jun-4 Sotheby's, New York #330/R est:10000-15000
£5500	$9350	€8030	Cottages by the marsh (49x75cm-19x30in) s. board. 26-Nov-3 Sotheby's, Olympia #75/R est:6000-8000
£5800	$9222	€8468	Summer morning on east coast estuary (26x35cm-10x14in) s. i.verso board. 10-Sep-3 Sotheby's, Olympia #214/R est:1200-1800
£6193	$11086	€9042	Frozen dyke (39x59cm-15x23in) s. i.verso board prov. 31-May-4 Stephan Welz, Johannesburg #451/R est:50000-70000 (SA.R 75000)
£6200	$10912	€9052	In the covered wool market, Istanbul (40x30cm-16x12in) s. board. 19-May-4 Sotheby's, Olympia #107/R est:3000-5000
£6452	$11871	€9420	Petit Andeley (30x41cm-12x16in) s. i.verso board. 14-Jun-4 Waddingtons, Toronto #161/R est:10000-15000 (C.D 16000)
£6500	$11895	€9490	Barges under sail (27x36cm-11x14in) s. board prov. 4-Jun-4 Christie's, London #26/R est:5000-7000
£6606	$11825	€9645	November morning, Ludham, Norfolk (54x90cm-21x35in) s. i.verso board exhib. 31-May-4 Stephan Welz, Johannesburg #452/R est:50000-70000 (SA.R 80000)
£7000	$11900	€10220	Road to Estoril (25x41cm-10x16in) s. board prov. 21-Nov-3 Christie's, London #28/R est:5000-8000
£7000	$11900	€10220	Ericeira, Portugal (51x66cm-20x26in) s. prov. 21-Nov-3 Christie's, London #132/R est:6000-8000
£7000	$11900	€10220	Morning sunlight, Ponza (51x66cm-20x26in) s. board prov. 21-Nov-3 Christie's, London #137/R est:7000-10000
£7407	$12000	€10740	Morning sunlight, Ponza, Italy (51x66cm-20x26in) s. board exhib. 8-Aug-3 Barridorf, Portland #120/R est:18000-22000
£8000	$13600	€11680	Nieuwe Kerk, Delft (66x51cm-26x20in) s. prov. 21-Nov-3 Christie's, London #131/R est:7000-10000
£8000	$14640	€11680	Piazza del Duomo, Como (22x27cm-9x11in) init.d.50 panel prov. 4-Jun-4 Christie's, London #30/R est:4000-6000
£8000	$14720	€11680	Barges on the North Holland Canal (46x61cm-18x24in) s. 8-Jun-4 Gorringes, Lewes #2080/R est:8000-12000
£8200	$14432	€11972	Blasted oak (51x76cm-20x30in) s. board. 19-May-4 Sotheby's, Olympia #120/R est:7000-10000
£8500	$14450	€12410	Small boat pontoon, Porto Cervo (35x51cm-14x20in) s. board prov. 21-Nov-3 Christie's, London #29/R est:7000-10000
£8500	$15555	€12410	Reach of the lower Thames (28x41cm-11x16in) s. board prov. 4-Jun-4 Christie's, London #3/R est:6000-8000
£8600	$14792	€12556	Midsummer, San Antonio (51x76cm-20x30in) s. board prov. 3-Dec-3 Christie's, Kensington #475/R est:10000-15000
£9274	$17065	€13540	The Seine near Fontainebleau (40x61cm-16x24in) s. i.verso masonite. 14-Jun-4 Waddingtons, Toronto #160b/R est:15000-20000 (C.D 23000)
£9500	$16340	€13870	Lisbon, Cais das Colunas (46x61cm-18x24in) s. board prov.lit. 3-Dec-3 Sotheby's, London #17/R est:9000-12000
£9500	$16340	€13870	Corner House, Venice (67x51cm-26x20in) s. s.i.d.1961 verso board prov.exhib. 3-Dec-3 Sotheby's, London #41/R est:8000-12000
£9500	$17385	€13870	Ruins of Babingley church, King's Lynn, Norfolk (30x41cm-12x16in) s. panel prov. 4-Jun-4 Christie's, London #27/R est:6000-8000
£9800	$17248	€14308	Winner of the barge race (30x40cm-12x16in) s. board. 19-May-4 Sotheby's, Olympia #149/R est:6000-8000
£10000	$17000	€14600	Norfolk by road (63x76cm-25x30in) s. prov. 21-Nov-3 Christie's, London #133/R est:10000-15000
£10000	$17000	€14600	Old tide mill, Deben at Woodbridge (35x51cm-14x20in) s. board prov. 21-Nov-3 Christie's, London #136/R est:5000-8000
£11290	$20774	€16483	Pont Alexandre III, Paris (46x61cm-18x24in) s. i.verso board. 14-Jun-4 Waddingtons, Toronto #159/R est:20000-25000 (C.D 28000)
£11290	$20774	€16483	Wet sands, Waxham (40x61cm-16x24in) s. i.verso masonite. 14-Jun-4 Waddingtons, Toronto #160a/R est:15000-20000 (C.D 28000)
£11500	$20930	€16790	Marsh Gate (51x76cm-20x30in) s. board. 1-Jul-4 Christie's, Kensington #91/R est:8000-12000
£12000	$20640	€17520	Norfolk river (30x40cm-12x16in) s. i.verso board. 3-Dec-3 Sotheby's, London #18/R est:6000-8000
£12000	$20640	€17520	Breeze in the harbour, Hong Kong (51x76cm-20x30in) s.i.verso board prov.exhib. 3-Dec-3 Sotheby's, London #61/R est:12000-18000
£12000	$21120	€17520	Stall in the Champs Elysees (51x61cm-20x24in) s. i.verso board prov. 19-May-4 Sotheby's, Olympia #118/R est:12000-18000
£12000	$21960	€17520	Canal scene, Choggia (51x76cm-20x30in) s. board. 4-Jun-4 Christie's, London #29/R est:15000-20000
£12195	$20000	€17683	Thames Barges at low water, Pinmill (41x61cm-16x24in) s. i.verso masonite prov. 31-May-3 Brunk, Ashville #545/R est:10000-20000
£12500	$23000	€18250	Wet day Dordrecht (63x76cm-25x30in) s. i.stretcher. 14-Jun-4 Waddingtons, Toronto #160/R est:20000-25000 (C.D 31000)
£13000	$22100	€18980	Oxford Street from Marble Arch, 2nd June 1953 (51x66cm-20x26in) s. prov. 21-Nov-3 Christie's, London #130/R est:15000-25000
£13000	$23790	€18980	Norfolk by-road (50x65cm-20x26in) s. board. 2-Jun-4 Sotheby's, London #36/R est:10000-15000
£13122	$21914	€19158	The Thames at Henley (27x40cm-11x16in) s. i. verso masonite. 17-Nov-3 Waddingtons, Toronto #129/R est:8000-10000 (C.D 29000)
£13500	$23220	€19710	Thames barges on the Hard-Pin mill (41x61cm-16x24in) s. board prov. 2-Dec-3 Bonhams, New Bond Street #37/R est:6000-8000
£13649	$23476	€19928	Little Palazzo, Venice (50x65cm-20x26in) s.i.verso prov. 3-Dec-3 Stephan Welz, Johannesburg #8/R est:60000-90000 (SA.R 150000)
£15000	$25800	€21900	Cloud Shadow, Suffolk (51x76cm-20x30in) s. i.verso board prov. 3-Dec-3 Sotheby's, London #62/R est:12000-18000
£15000	$26850	€21900	Buckingham Palace (45x61cm-18x24in) s. 16-Mar-4 Bonhams, New Bond Street #60/R est:15000-20000
£15000	$27450	€21900	Bourdzi Fortress, Nauplion (66x91cm-26x36in) s. board prov. 2-Jun-4 Sotheby's, London #33/R est:15000-20000
£16000	$27200	€23360	Spritsail barges racing in the Harwich estuary (51x76cm-20x30in) s. board prov. 21-Nov-3 Christie's, London #134/R est:10000-15000
£20000	$36600	€29200	Stranded boat (66x91cm-26x36in) s.d.51 prov. 2-Jun-4 Sotheby's, London #37/R est:20000-30000
£20000	$36600	€29200	February (63x76cm-25x30in) s. prov. 4-Jun-4 Christie's, London #25/R est:20000-30000
£20000	$36600	€29200	Little Palazzo, Venice (51x66cm-20x26in) s. board prov.exhib. 4-Jun-4 Christie's, London #28/R est:20000-30000
£22748	$39126	€33212	Junks at Sauchi Wan, Hong Kong (65x90cm-26x35in) s.i.verso board prov. 3-Dec-3 Stephan Welz, Johannesburg #9/R est:100000-140000 (SA.R 250000)
£32000	$54400	€46720	Norfolk Broads (71x102cm-28x40in) s. prov. 21-Nov-3 Christie's, London #27/R est:20000-30000
£42000	$71400	€61320	Blythburgh, Suffolk (71x102cm-28x40in) s. prov.lit. 21-Nov-3 Christie's, London #26/R est:25000-35000
£45000	$82350	€65700	Circus encampment (63x76cm-25x30in) s.d.31 panel. 4-Jun-4 Christie's, London #132/R est:10000-15000
£48000	$81600	€70080	Morning sunlight, Honfleur (71x102cm-28x40in) s. prov. 21-Nov-3 Christie's, London #129/R est:25000-35000
£280000	$492800	€408800	Derby Day (56x76cm-22x30in) s.d.36 panel. 21-May-4 Christie's, London #5/R est:20000-30000
Works on paper			
£350	$634	€511	Illustration from rabbit skin cap (28x20cm-11x8in) s. pencil. 16-Apr-4 Keys, Aylsham #856
£400	$736	€584	Rabbit skin cap (5x7cm-2x3in) s. pencil dr. 11-Jun-4 Keys, Aylsham #555

£550	$913	€803	Headland (36x49cm-14x19in) s. W/C. 2-Oct-3 Locke & England, Leamington Spa #174/R
£720	$1246	€1051	Beached fishing boats on the Norfolk coast. W/C. 9-Dec-3 Lawrences, Bletchingley #1833
£1100	$1991	€1606	Runswick Bay (36x51cm-14x20in) s. W/C. 15-Apr-4 Richardson & Smith, Whitby #95/R est:500-800
£2600	$4810	€3796	Early morning on the Grand Canal, Venice (24x31cm-9x12in) s. W/C prov. 11-Mar-4 Christie's, Kensington #92/R est:1000-1500
£2742	$5045	€4003	Norfolk farm (27x37cm-11x15in) s. 14-Jun-4 Waddingtons, Toronto #98/R est:6000-8000 (C.D 6800)
£2800	$4760	€4088	Old fort on the Italian coast (28x38cm-11x15in) s. W/C. 26-Nov-3 Sotheby's, Olympia #108/R est:2500-3500
£2800	$5236	€4200	Flooded marsh (27x37cm-11x15in) s. W/C. 26-Jul-4 Bonhams, Bath #28/R est:800-1200
£3800	$6536	€5548	Cattle by the Hundred Dyke, Thurne (26x37cm-10x15in) s. W/C prov. 2-Dec-3 Bonhams, New Bond Street #35/R est:2500-3000
£5000	$9150	€7300	Beach scene near Fuengirola (27x37cm-11x15in) s. W/C. 3-Jun-4 Christie's, London #195/R est:5000-7000
£5200	$8944	€7592	The small holding, Norfolk (33x48cm-13x19in) s. W/C prov. 5-Dec-3 Keys, Aylsham #576/R est:3000-5000
£6800	$11968	€9928	Grey day, Honfleur (37x56cm-15x22in) s. W/C. 19-May-4 Sotheby's, Olympia #93/R est:3000-5000

SEALY, Allen Culpeper (1850-1927) British

£1000	$1700	€1460	Trainer on his pony (49x59cm-19x23in) s.d.1899 board. 27-Nov-3 Christie's, Kensington #120 est:1000-1500
£3243	$6000	€4735	King of the Mountains - Saint Bernard (71x91cm-28x36in) s.d.1884 prov. 10-Feb-4 Doyle, New York #166/R est:6000-8000

SEALY, Douglas (1937-) Australian

£262	$482	€383	Drover's daughter. s. board. 25-Jun-4 Lawson Menzies, Sydney #2275 (A.D 700)
£357	$561	€521	Old farm at Richmond (49x59cm-19x23in) s. masonite board. 24-Nov-2 Goodman, Sydney #86/R est:500-700 (A.D 1000)

SEARLE, Ronald (1920-) British

Works on paper

£420	$764	€613	Pere Ubu (45x29cm-18x11in) s.i.d.1965 black ink wash col pencil. 1-Jul-4 Christie's, Kensington #570
£500	$910	€730	The hand of authority (33x18cm-13x7in) s.d.1993 pencil black ink lit. 1-Jul-4 Christie's, Kensington #563/R
£500	$910	€730	Evolution (37x48cm-15x19in) s.i.d.2001 pencil black ink lit. 1-Jul-4 Christie's, Kensington #557/R
£600	$1032	€876	Cover design for Punch, The Grand National and Boat Race Issue (34x28cm-13x11in) init.i. black ink collage. 3-Dec-3 Christie's, Kensington #315/R
£700	$1274	€1022	Superwoman (47x40cm-19x16in) s.i. pencil black ink lit. 1-Jul-4 Christie's, Kensington #564/R
£700	$1274	€1022	Starting your own business (43x29cm-17x11in) s.i.d.1981 pencil black ink W/C. 1-Jul-4 Christie's, Kensington #566/R
£700	$1274	€1022	Spectators for the largest single cheese ever produced (46x34cm-18x13in) s.d.1964. 1-Jul-4 Christie's, Kensington #567/R
£700	$1274	€1022	Le Rond Pointe, Champs Elysee (25x19cm-10x7in) s.i.d.May 8 pencil brown ink. 1-Jul-4 Christie's, Kensington #571
£800	$1456	€1168	Tower of London (36x23cm-14x9in) s.i.d.1965 black ink wash lit. 1-Jul-4 Christie's, Kensington #559/R
£800	$1456	€1168	Fabric tie removed (30x23cm-12x9in) s. pencil black ink W/C lit. 1-Jul-4 Christie's, Kensington #565/R
£850	$1547	€1241	Extremities rubbed (32x25cm-13x10in) s.i. pencil black ink W/C lit. 1-Jul-4 Christie's, Kensington #562/R
£950	$1634	€1387	Dinner with the family (38x38cm-15x15in) s.i. pencil brown ink lit. 3-Dec-3 Christie's, Kensington #333/R
£1000	$1720	€1460	Clandestine marriage, Lord Ogleby (43x30cm-17x12in) s.i.d.1994 pencil black ink. 3-Dec-3 Christie's, Kensington #319/R est:600-800
£1000	$1720	€1460	Crazy Gang at the Victoria Palace, in clown jewels (39x41cm-15x16in) s.i.d.1959 black ink lit. 3-Dec-3 Christie's, Kensington #320/R est:700-900
£1000	$1720	€1460	Christmas Carol, Scrooge and the ghost of Christmas present (36x28cm-14x11in) s.i.d.1961 black ink W/C lit. 3-Dec-3 Christie's, Kensington #322/R est:500-700
£1000	$1820	€1460	The Gods are angry (38x48cm-15x19in) s. pencil black ink lit. 1-Jul-4 Christie's, Kensington #555/R est:800-1200
£1100	$1892	€1606	He only does it to start us all off (37x24cm-15x9in) s.i. black ink lit. 3-Dec-3 Christie's, Kensington #318/R est:400-600
£1100	$1892	€1606	Christmas Carol, Scrooge and Bob Cratchit (27x33cm-11x13in) s.i.d.1961 pencil black ink W/C lit. 3-Dec-3 Christie's, Kensington #321/R est:400-600
£1100	$1892	€1606	Lorelei (38x26cm-15x10in) s.i. pencil black ink bodycol. 3-Dec-3 Christie's, Kensington #323/R est:400-600
£1100	$1892	€1606	Imaginary portraits, Brendan Behan (44x34cm-17x13in) s.i.d.May 22/4 July 1962 brown ink brown wash lit. 3-Dec-3 Christie's, Kensington #324/R est:300-500
£1100	$1892	€1606	Emlyn Williams as Charles Dickens (35x22cm-14x9in) s.i.d.1952 pencil black ink. 3-Dec-3 Christie's, Kensington #326/R est:300-500
£1100	$1892	€1606	Title page to Shell Holiday guide to London (32x42cm-13x17in) s.i.d.1965 brown ink wash lit. 3-Dec-3 Christie's, Kensington #330/R est:600-800
£1100	$1892	€1606	Horse and rider (40x43cm-16x17in) s.d.22.10.1961 black ink W/C. 3-Dec-3 Christie's, Kensington #332/R est:600-800
£1200	$2064	€1752	Dream sequence (45x35cm-18x14in) s.i.d.88 pencil black ink W/C. 3-Dec-3 Christie's, Kensington #331/R est:800-1200
£1200	$2184	€1752	Oscar Wilde meets John Gay (39x23cm-15x9in) s.d.1992 pencil black ink lit. 1-Jul-4 Christie's, Kensington #550/R est:500-700
£1200	$2184	€1752	Jean Cocteau (39x24cm-15x9in) s.i.d.1955 pencil black ink lit. 1-Jul-4 Christie's, Kensington #552/R est:700-900
£1400	$2408	€2044	Now, or never (30x35cm-12x14in) s.i. pencil black ink col crayon. 3-Dec-3 Christie's, Kensington #334/R est:500-700
£1500	$2580	€2190	Whizz for Atomms, Peason and Molesworth (24x36cm-9x14in) s.i.d.1956 brown ink lit. 3-Dec-3 Christie's, Kensington #311/R est:700-900
£1500	$2580	€2190	Souls in torment, mirror, mirror, on the wall (25x34cm-10x13in) init.d.1953 pencil brown ink lit. 3-Dec-3 Christie's, Kensington #325/R est:500-700
£1500	$2580	€2190	Shell guide to London, museum visits (34x27cm-13x11in) s.i.d.1965 pencil black ink lit. 3-Dec-3 Christie's, Kensington #327/R est:500-700
£1500	$2580	€2190	Exploring London, the Mint (36x25cm-14x10in) s.i.d.1965 black ink W/C collage lit. 3-Dec-3 Christie's, Kensington #328/R est:500-700
£1600	$2912	€2336	Oliver asks for more (25x29cm-10x11in) s.i.d.1965 pencil black ink lit. 1-Jul-4 Christie's, Kensington #560/R est:500-700
£1600	$2912	€2336	A Christmas Carol (34x25cm-13x10in) s.i.d.1961 black ink wash lit. 1-Jul-4 Christie's, Kensington #561/R est:500-700
£1600	$2912	€2336	Children's cooking classes at the Ritz (42x39cm-17x15in) s.i. pencil black ink lit. 1-Jul-4 Christie's, Kensington #556/R est:1000-1500
£1800	$3276	€2628	At the vets (38x42cm-15x17in) s.i. pencil black ink. 1-Jul-4 Christie's, Kensington #558/R est:800-1200
£1900	$3268	€2774	Piccadilly (34x26cm-13x10in) s.i.d.1965 pencil black ink W/C lit. 3-Dec-3 Christie's, Kensington #329/R est:500-700
£1900	$3458	€2774	Molesworth: Produktivity in skool (35x26cm-14x10in) s.i.d.1956 pencil black ink lit. 1-Jul-4 Christie's, Kensington #554/R est:800-1200
£2000	$3440	€2920	Molesworth, Grate Latin lies, the customs of the Gauls were honourable (21x36cm-8x14in) s.i.d.1954 pencil black ink lit. 3-Dec-3 Christie's, Kensington #316/R est:600-800
£2200	$3784	€3212	OK crime pictures corrupt me (24x18cm-9x7in) s.i.d.1953 brown ink lit. 3-Dec-3 Christie's, Kensington #312/R est:600-800
£2200	$4004	€3212	Winston Churchill on the way out (25x16cm-10x6in) s.i.d.1954 black ink wash lit. 1-Jul-4 Christie's, Kensington #549/R est:800-1200
£2200	$4004	€3212	Crackers (27x23cm-11x9in) s.i. black ink W/C. 1-Jul-4 Christie's, Kensington #568/R est:800-1200
£2300	$4186	€3358	Winston Churchill speaking at the Guildhall, Cambridge (21x16cm-8x6in) s.i.d.1939 pencil lit. 1-Jul-4 Christie's, Kensington #551/R est:600-800
£2600	$4472	€3796	Quiet day at the office (42x49cm-17x19in) s.i. pencil black ink. 3-Dec-3 Christie's, Kensington #337/R est:700-900
£2600	$4472	€3796	Jacket cover design for Shell Holiday Guide to London (30x49cm-12x19in) s.i.d.1965 pencil black ink crayon W/C lit. 3-Dec-3 Christie's, Kensington #339/R est:800-1200
£2600	$4732	€3796	Molesworth: Great escape routes (34x25cm-13x10in) s.i.d.1953 pencil black ink lit. 1-Jul-4 Christie's, Kensington #553/R est:700-900
£2900	$4930	€4234	Studies of Japanese guards (17x22cm-7x9in) s.i.d.August 1945 pen ink sold with letters. 4-Nov-3 Bonhams, New Bond Street #40/R est:3000-5000
£3800	$6536	€5548	Frontispiece nicely mounted (31x23cm-12x9in) s. black ink W/C lit. 3-Dec-3 Christie's, Kensington #336/R est:500-700
£4200	$7224	€6132	Dented at head (31x23cm-12x9in) s. pencil black ink W/C lit. 3-Dec-3 Christie's, Kensington #335/R est:600-800

SEARS, Philip Shelton (1867-1953) American

Sculpture

£2825	$5000	€4125	Figure of a youth (36cm-14in) s. brown pat bronze Cast T.F.McGann and Sons. 2-May-4 Bonhams & Butterfields, San Francisco #1517/R est:1500-2000

SEARS, Taber (1870-1950) American

Works on paper

£279	$500	€407	North Water Street, cottage (30x38cm-12x15in) s. W/C. 8-Jan-4 James Julia, Fairfield #1033/R

SEARY, E Leone (19/20th C) American?

£882	$1650	€1288	Profile of a horse, Merry Lark. s. 28-Feb-4 William A Smith, Plainfield #62/R

SEATH, Ethel (20th C) Canadian

Works on paper

£2477	$4212	€3616	Landscape with houses (33x43cm-13x17in) s. W/C prov. 27-Nov-3 Heffel, Vancouver #199/R est:3000-4000 (C.D 5500)

SEAWEED, Willie (20th C) American

Sculpture

£13587	$25000	€20381	Kwakiutl hamatsa crooked-beak mask (71cm-28in) cedar bark. 14-Jun-4 Bonhams & Butterfields, San Francisco #1130/R est:800-1200

SEBASTIAN (?) ?

Sculpture

£1036	$1792	€1513	Untitled (42x15x11cm-17x6x4in) s.d.1997 painted metal. 9-Dec-3 Louis Morton, Mexico #117/R est:26000 (M.P 20000)

SEBEN, Henri van (1825-1913) Belgian

£824	$1400	€1203	Mother and children walking through a wheat field (28x20cm-11x8in) s. panel. 31-Oct-3 North East Auctions, Portsmouth #1212 est:1000-2000
£1408	$2437	€2000	Cour de ferme animee (32x40cm-13x16in) s.d.1855 mahogany panel. 9-Dec-3 Vanderkindere, Brussels #11/R est:2000-3000
£1769	$3219	€2600	Figures and animals in a small street, Arnemuiden (123x90cm-48x35in) s. s.i.verso. 3-Feb-4 Christie's, Amsterdam #390 est:2000-3000
£1888	$3210	€2700	Les petits voleurs chez la marchande de fruits et legumes (61x91cm-24x36in) s.d.1852. 18-Nov-3 Vanderkindere, Brussels #45 est:1250-1750

SEBES, Pieter Willem (1830-1906) Dutch

£1224	$2229	€1800	Pretty dress (82x65cm-32x26in) indis sig. s.d.1874 verso. 3-Feb-4 Christie's, Amsterdam #69/R est:2000-3000
£2699	$4750	€3941	Les devoirs (83x66cm-33x26in) s. 18-May-4 Bonhams & Butterfields, San Francisco #77/R est:4000-6000

SEBIDI, Mmakgabo Mapula Helen (1943-) South African

Works on paper

£1239	$2217	€1809	Running away from the truth (157x75cm-62x30in) s.d.1999 pastel collage. 31-May-4 Stephan Welz, Johannesburg #591/R est:15000-25000 (SA.R 15000)

SEBILLE, Albert (1874-1953) French

£347	$641	€520	Bateau en cale seche (46x38cm-18x15in) 14-Jul-4 Livinec, Gaudcheau & Jezequel, Rennes #122b/R
£1701	$2704	€2500	Ile de France, un paquebot (60x48cm-24x19in) 21-Mar-3 Neret-Minet, Paris #653 est:3500-4500
£2431	$4059	€3500	Escadre royale (135x250cm-53x98in) s. 26-Oct-3 Lesieur & Le Bars, Le Havre #99

Works on paper

£288	$460	€400	Vaisseau turc (51x67cm-20x26in) s. gouache W/C. 18-May-3 Claude Boisgirard, Paris #156

£324 $518 €450 Trois-mats arme sur une mer formee (51x66cm-20x26in) s. gouache W/C. 18-May-3 Claude Boisgirard, Paris #155

SEBILLEAU, Paul (?-1907) French
£559 $951 €800 Paysage de foret (75x54cm-30x21in) s. 28-Nov-3 Blanchet, Paris #71

SEBIRE, Gaston (1920-2001) French
£227 $400 €331 Still life of anemones (36x53cm-14x21in) s. 21-May-4 North East Auctions, Portsmouth #1330/R
£253 $400 €369 Verre aux petites marguerites - still life with vase of flowers (25x18cm-10x7in) s.verso i.on stretcher. 6-Sep-3 Brunk, Ashville #295
£435 $800 €635 Matin en Espagne (28x46cm-11x18in) 11-Jun-4 Du Mouchelle, Detroit #2086/R
£441 $750 €644 Seaside (25x36cm-10x14in) s. prov. 22-Nov-3 Jackson's, Cedar Falls #393/R
£529 $900 €772 Parasol rouge (20x28cm-8x11in) s. s.verso prov. 5-Nov-3 Doyle, New York #70/R
£915 $1584 €1300 Bouquet fond bleu (92x65cm-36x26in) s. 10-Dec-3 Rossini, Paris #110/R
£933 $1689 €1400 Marine pres de Honfleur (38x55cm-15x22in) s. 1-Apr-4 Credit Municipal, Paris #63
£1056 $1711 €1500 Vue de bord de mer (54x65cm-21x26in) s. 11-Aug-3 Boscher, Cherbourg #775 est:1500-1800
£1229 $2200 €1794 Femme fiant. s.i. 13-May-4 Dallas Auction Gallery, Dallas #320/R est:2000-4000
£1397 $2500 €2040 Bouquet jaune et violet (145x94cm-57x37in) s. 20-Mar-4 Selkirks, St. Louis #534/R est:2000-2500
£1564 $2800 €2283 Still life with flowers (130x86cm-51x34in) s. 8-May-4 Susanin's, Chicago #6104/R est:1500-2000
£1600 $2960 €2400 Chalutiers en peche (50x65cm-20x26in) s. paper on canvas. 14-Jul-4 Livinec, Gaudcheau & Jezequel, Rennes #141
£1676 $3000 €2447 La plage a Cabourg (81x99cm-32x39in) s. i.verso. 8-Jan-4 Doyle, New York #42/R est:1500-2500
£1901 $3289 €2700 Ciel gris sur la plage (46x65cm-18x26in) s. 13-Dec-3 Touati, Paris #163/R est:800
£2847 $4641 €4100 Paysage pres de Collioure (96x130cm-38x51in) s. 26-Sep-3 Rabourdin & Choppin de Janvry, Paris #46/R est:3500-4000
£3200 $5888 €4672 Menton, Le Matin (73x92cm-29x36in) s.i. 24-Mar-4 Sotheby's, Olympia #86/R est:1500-2000

SEBOROVSKI, Carole (20th C) American?
Works on paper
£350 $571 €511 Diagonal brackets (56x76cm-22x30in) charcoal and graphite exec.1987 prov. 23-Sep-3 John Nicholson, Haslemere #171
£450 $734 €657 Drawn and held to the edge (51x51cm-20x20in) charcoal exec.1987 prov. 23-Sep-3 John Nicholson, Haslemere #172
£588 $1000 €858 Untitled (86x61cm-34x24in) chl. 21-Nov-3 Swann Galleries, New York #194/R est:1000-1500
£824 $1400 €1203 Triptych (81x30cm-32x12in) mixed media. 21-Nov-3 Swann Galleries, New York #195/R est:1000-1500

SEBOY, Ole Johnson (18/19th C) Danish
£1631 $2920 €2381 Galease near Bergen Harbour (37x55cm-15x22in) s.i.d.1823. 25-May-4 Grev Wedels Plass, Oslo #32/R est:30000 (N.KR 20000)
Works on paper
£816 $1460 €1191 The schooner Courieren (33x44cm-13x17in) s.i.d.1824 gouache. 25-May-4 Grev Wedels Plass, Oslo #31/R (N.KR 10000)
£1020 $1825 €1489 Ship's portrait of De aten Sodsken Nyested (33x48cm-13x19in) s.i.d.1827 gouache. 25-May-4 Grev Wedels Plass, Oslo #30/R (N.KR 12500)

SEBREE, Charles (1912-) American
£1220 $2000 €1769 Woman in a white turban (15x10cm-6x4in) foamboard painted c.1960. 7-Jun-3 Treadway Gallery, Cincinnati #1505 est:2000-3000

SEBREGTS, Lode (1906-2002) Belgian
£379 $702 €550 Diane (125x100cm-49x39in) s.d.47. 19-Jan-4 Horta, Bruxelles #280
£634 $1096 €900 Au bar (85x65cm-33x26in) s. 9-Dec-3 Campo, Vlaamse Kaai #433
Works on paper
£382 $607 €550 Jeune femme nue de face (94x63cm-37x25in) s.d.95 sold with biography of the artist. 15-Sep-3 Horta, Bruxelles #277

SEBRON, Hippolyte Victor Valentin (1801-1879) French
£10174 $17500 €14854 Bateaux a Vapeur Geants - Study for giant steamboats (41x48cm-16x19in) prov. 6-Dec-3 Neal Auction Company, New Orleans #517/R est:5000-7000
Works on paper
£408 $731 €600 Interieur d'eglise (30x24cm-12x9in) s. gouache. 19-Mar-4 Ribeyre & Baron, Paris #52/R

SECCOMBE, Colonel F S (fl.1876-1885) British
Works on paper
£300 $558 €438 Moonlight cavalry charge at Kassassin (46x83cm-18x33in) s. W/C bodycol. 2-Mar-4 Bearnes, Exeter #392/R

SECHAUD, Paul (1906-1982) Swiss
£452 $783 €660 Bouquet de mimosas (73x60cm-29x24in) s. 12-Dec-3 Galerie du Rhone, Sion #588/R (S.FR 1000)
£459 $766 €666 Nature morte aux roses jaunes (73x60cm-29x24in) s. 21-Jun-3 Galerie du Rhone, Sion #420/R (S.FR 1000)
£917 $1532 €1330 Bouquet de mimosas et bleuets (73x60cm-29x24in) s. 21-Jun-3 Galerie du Rhone, Sion #419/R est:1000-1500 (S.FR 2000)
£1299 $2325 €1897 Still life with pink carnations (73x60cm-29x24in) s. 22-Mar-4 Philippe Schuler, Zurich #4360 est:1200-1600 (S.FR 3000)

SECHE, Josef (1880-1978) German
£268 $494 €400 Portrait of fisherman from Breitbrunn an Ammersee (75x54cm-30x21in) s. board. 24-Mar-4 Hugo Ruef, Munich #1103
£621 $1148 €900 Dancers on stairway (83x61cm-33x24in) s.d.1942 lit. 12-Feb-4 Weidler, Nurnberg #4502/R

SECKEL, Josef (1881-1945) Dutch
£486 $792 €700 Still life with apples in a basket (37x45cm-15x18in) s. 29-Sep-3 Sotheby's, Amsterdam #229/R

SEDDON, Beatrice (?) ?
Works on paper
£399 $678 €583 Woman with umbrella (40x34cm-16x13in) s.d.1924 W/C. 4-Nov-3 Peter Webb, Auckland #65/R est:1200-1800 (NZ.D 1100)

SEDELNIKOV, Nikolia (1905-) American?
Photographs
£2395 $4000 €3497 Lynching in front of the U.S Capitol (19x13cm-7x5in) init. hand painted silver print. 21-Oct-3 Swann Galleries, New York #176/R est:5000-7500

SEDGLEY, Peter (1930-) British
£669 $1157 €950 Study on white filed yellow blue yellow orange (47x47cm-19x19in) s.i.d.73 verso acrylic board. 13-Dec-3 Lempertz, Koln #355/R
£704 $1218 €1000 Study in blue and yellow (51x51cm-20x20in) s.i.d.73 verso acrylic board. 13-Dec-3 Lempertz, Koln #354/R
£900 $1638 €1314 Abstract (61x61cm-24x24in) acrylic. 30-Jun-4 Christie's, Kensington #45/R
£1100 $1936 €1606 Study in blue and yellow (50x50cm-20x20in) s.i.d.73 acrylic on card. 19-May-4 Sotheby's, Olympia #323/R est:1200-1800
£1100 $1936 €1606 Study on white field yellow blue, yellow and rouge (43x43cm-17x17in) s.i. i.d.73 verso acrylic on card. 19-May-4 Sotheby's, Olympia #324/R est:1000-1500

SEDGWICK, J (19th C) British
Works on paper
£1400 $2548 €2100 Jerusalem from the Mount of Olives (48x70cm-19x28in) s.i.d.47 pencil W/C scratching out gum arabic. 1-Jul-4 Christie's, Kensington #61/R est:600-1000

SEDLACEK, Franz (1891-1944) German
£22819 $40846 €34000 Flowers, butterfiles and beetle (40x30cm-16x12in) i. verso panel prov. 25-May-4 Dorotheum, Vienna #41/R est:10000-14000
Works on paper
£2400 $4320 €3600 Hallstatter glacier (29x23cm-11x9in) mono.i.d.1938 pencil. 21-Apr-4 Dorotheum, Vienna #57/R est:2200-3600

SEDLACEK, Robert (1881-1957) Austrian
£490 $832 €700 Pergola near Capri (67x98cm-26x39in) s. 27-Nov-3 Dorotheum, Linz #518/R

SEDLACEK, Stephan (1868-1936) Czechoslovakian
£600 $1092 €876 Courting couple (67x52cm-26x20in) s. 15-Jun-4 Bonhams, Leeds #108
£622 $1076 €908 Unwelcome visitor (53x41cm-21x16in) s. board. 9-Dec-3 Pinneys, Montreal #63 (C.D 1400)
£728 $1326 €1100 Interior scene with gentlemen and ladies (54x68cm-21x27in) s. 18-Jun-4 Bolland & Marotz, Bremen #755/R
£1189 $2021 €1700 Requesting a dance (70x106cm-28x42in) s. 28-Nov-3 Schloss Ahlden, Ahlden #1449/R est:1800
£2647 $4578 €3865 The slight spring - young girl in landscape (80x60cm-31x24in) s. 9-Dec-3 Rasmussen, Copenhagen #1571/R est:10000-15000 (D.KR 28000)

SEDLACEK, Vojtech (1892-1973) Czechoslovakian
£337 $594 €506 Summer landscape with two trees (36x55cm-14x22in) s.d.46 tempera paper. 22-May-4 Dorotheum, Prague #246/R est:12000-18000 (C.KR 16000)
£700 $1163 €1022 Pathway to suburb (20x29cm-8x11in) s.d.38 panel. 4-Oct-3 Dorotheum, Prague #80/R est:20000-30000 (C.KR 32000)
Works on paper
£633 $1114 €950 Autumn in Vochoz near Limberk (48x55cm-19x22in) s.d.42 gouache exhib. 22-May-4 Dorotheum, Prague #250/R est:15000-27000 (C.KR 30000)

SEDLAK, Gunter Silva (1941-) Austrian
Works on paper
£800 $1472 €1200 Negrilia (150x100cm-59x39in) s.i.d.1988 verso mixed media. 9-Jun-4 Dorotheum, Salzburg #694/R

SEDOV, Aleksander (1928-) Russian
£278 $453 €400 Beauties (39x67cm-15x26in) painted 1948. 24-Sep-3 Cambi, Genoa #1395

SEDOV, Grigori Semenovich (attrib) (1836-1884) Russian
Works on paper
£1479 $2558 €2100 Portrait of Catherine the Great (43x34cm-17x13in) pastel. 13-Dec-3 Hagelstam, Helsinki #46/R est:2500

SEDRAC, Serge (1878-1974) French
£250 $403 €365 Snow covered river landscape (46x61cm-18x24in) s. 12-Aug-3 Bonhams, Ipswich #229

£380 $673 €555 Winter scene (46x61cm-18x24in) s. 27-Apr-4 Bonhams, Knightsbridge #229/R
£2013 $3725 €3000 Steppe russe au soleil couchant (50x100cm-20x39in) s. panel. 14-Mar-4 Eric Pillon, Calais #175/R

SEEBACH, Clara von (19th C) French
£867 $1569 €1300 Still life of flowers (31x50cm-12x20in) s.d.1894 lit. 1-Apr-4 Frank Peege, Freiburg #1136/R

SEEBERGER, Gustav (1812-1888) German
£1342 $2470 €2000 Woman praying in cloister (44x38cm-17x15in) s.d.1880. 26-Mar-4 Auktionhaus Georg Rehm, Augsburg #8163/R est:2600
£2098 $3566 €3000 Cloister (46x54cm-18x21in) s.d.1844. 20-Nov-3 Van Ham, Cologne #1867/R est:2800

SEEFISCH, Hermann Ludwig (1816-1879) German
£2778 $4389 €4000 Vierwaldstadter See (55x68cm-22x27in) s.d.1845 lit. 19-Sep-3 Schloss Ahlden, Ahlden #1515/R est:3800

SEEGER, Hermann (1857-1920) German
£1014 $1814 €1500 Summer's day by the sea (40x30cm-16x12in) s. panel lit. 8-May-4 Schloss Ahlden, Ahlden #803/R est:1200
£1284 $2298 €1900 Rest (30x40cm-12x16in) s. bears d. lit. 8-May-4 Schloss Ahlden, Ahlden #805/R est:1200
£1761 $3046 €2500 Looking out to sea at Fano Island, Denmark (33x44cm-13x17in) s. i.d.1913 verso canvas on cardboard. 10-Dec-3 Christie's, Amsterdam #679/R est:3000-5000
£1818 $3091 €2600 Tete a tete (18x23cm-7x9in) s. panel. 20-Nov-3 Van Ham, Cologne #1867a/R est:2000
£3108 $5470 €4600 Young Goethe and Friederike Brion in Pfarr Garden, Sesenheim (81x59cm-32x23in) s.d.1898 exhib.prov.lit. 22-May-4 Lempertz, Koln #1606/R est:2000

SEEKATZ, Johann Conrad (attrib) (1719-1768) German
£378 $700 €552 Breakfast on the road (20x15cm-8x6in) board. 13-Mar-4 Susanin's, Chicago #6082/R
£3667 $6637 €5500 Christ on the road to Emmaus (22x29cm-9x11in) panel. 1-Apr-4 Van Ham, Cologne #1245/R est:7000
£5369 $9879 €8000 Young birdcatchers. Young fishermen (41x27cm-16x11in) panel prov. two. 24-Mar-4 Dorotheum, Vienna #414/R est:2500-3500

SEEL, Adolf (1829-1907) German
£872 $1605 €1300 Village sexton (47x36cm-19x14in) s. 24-Mar-4 Hugo Ruef, Munich #1104/R

SEELOS, Gottfried (1829-1900) Austrian
Works on paper
£280 $476 €400 Konigssee near Berchtesgaden with St Bartholoma and Watzmann (26x40cm-10x16in) s.d.1865 pencil chk wash board. 27-Nov-3 Bassenge, Berlin #5649
£1342 $2470 €2000 Zenoburg near Meran (32x42cm-13x17in) s.i.d.1850 pencil W/C. 26-Mar-4 Dorotheum, Vienna #239/R est:800-1000
£1944 $3169 €2800 Three pinnacles (53x42cm-21x17in) W/C. 23-Sep-3 Wiener Kunst Auktionen, Vienna #32/R est:500-1000

SEEMAN, Enoch (17/18th C) German/Polish
£7000 $11900 €10220 Portrait of Mary Rand, seated in an oyster satin dress with blue ribbons, in an interior (127x102cm-50x40in) i. prov. 25-Nov-3 Christie's, London #17/R est:8000-12000
£7500 $12750 €10950 Portrait of Thomas Plumer Byde and his bother, John Byde (126x101cm-50x40in) 27-Nov-3 Sotheby's, London #134/R est:8000-12000

SEEMAN, Enoch (attrib) (17/18th C) German/Polish
£2198 $4000 €3209 Portrait of a lady, said to be Miss Sophia Edgecombe, three-quarter-length (128x101cm-50x40in) 4-Feb-4 Christie's, Rockefeller NY #107/R est:5000-7000

SEEREY-LESTER, John (1945-) British
£480 $878 €701 Victorian street scene with figures in foreground, industrial city beyond (49x39cm-19x15in) 6-Jul-4 Peter Wilson, Nantwich #14/R
£600 $1038 €876 Black panther resting on a tree (60x49cm-24x19in) s. 9-Dec-3 Anderson & Garland, Newcastle #416
£720 $1224 €1051 Emperor penguins (53x43cm-21x17in) s.d.82. 30-Oct-3 Chrystals Auctions, Isle of Man #233
£800 $1360 €1168 Wolf and cubs (58x91cm-23x36in) s.d.82. 30-Oct-3 Chrystals Auctions, Isle of Man #290
£900 $1530 €1314 Polar bears (43x53cm-17x21in) s.d.82. 30-Oct-3 Chrystals Auctions, Isle of Man #234
£950 $1615 €1387 Moose (48x74cm-19x29in) s.d.1982. 30-Oct-3 Chrystals Auctions, Isle of Man #267
£1000 $1700 €1460 Mountain lion and cub (69x91cm-27x36in) s.d.82. 30-Oct-3 Chrystals Auctions, Isle of Man #275 est:1000-2000
£1000 $1700 €1460 Grizzly and cubs (71x91cm-28x36in) s.d.82. 30-Oct-3 Chrystals Auctions, Isle of Man #276 est:1000-2000
£1000 $1700 €1460 North American buffalo (61x91cm-24x36in) s. 30-Oct-3 Chrystals Auctions, Isle of Man #288 est:1500-2500
£1050 $1785 €1533 Zebra watering. s.d.1982. 30-Oct-3 Chrystals Auctions, Isle of Man #286 est:1000-2000
£1100 $1870 €1606 Water buffalo (61x74cm-24x29in) s.d.83. 30-Oct-3 Chrystals Auctions, Isle of Man #292 est:800-1200
£1200 $2040 €1752 Mountain cat (51x76cm-20x30in) s.d.82. 30-Oct-3 Chrystals Auctions, Isle of Man #294 est:1200-2200
£1200 $2040 €1752 Hippo and young (61x76cm-24x30in) s.d.83. 30-Oct-3 Chrystals Auctions, Isle of Man #300 est:1000-2000
£1500 $2550 €2190 Leopards and cubs (76x102cm-30x40in) s.d.82. 30-Oct-3 Chrystals Auctions, Isle of Man #296 est:1500-2500
£1600 $2720 €2336 Elephants watering (58x74cm-23x29in) s.d.82. 30-Oct-3 Chrystals Auctions, Isle of Man #302 est:1000-2000
£1700 $2890 €2482 Cheetah and cubs (69x89cm-27x35in) s.d.82. 30-Oct-3 Chrystals Auctions, Isle of Man #298 est:1000-2000
£3235 $5500 €4723 Southern belles - white doves (76x41cm-30x16in) acrylic on masonite. 1-Nov-3 Altermann Galleries, Santa Fe #170
Works on paper
£500 $850 €730 Hyena dozing (41x53cm-16x21in) s.d.80 pastel. 30-Oct-3 Chrystals Auctions, Isle of Man #263
£500 $850 €730 Hippopotamus (38x53cm-15x21in) s.d.79 pastel. 30-Oct-3 Chrystals Auctions, Isle of Man #264
£560 $952 €818 Ostriches and brood (36x53cm-14x21in) s.d.78 pastel. 30-Oct-3 Chrystals Auctions, Isle of Man #262
£700 $1190 €1022 Mountain lion (38x53cm-15x21in) s.d.79 pastel. 30-Oct-3 Chrystals Auctions, Isle of Man #265

SEERY, John (1941-) American
£243 $450 €355 Untitled (65x76cm-26x30in) acrylic collage paper painted 1971 prov. 13-Jul-4 Christie's, Rockefeller NY #45/R

SEEVAGEN, Lucien (1887-1959) French
£263 $484 €400 Paysage de Provence (27x65cm-11x26in) s. 22-Jun-4 Chassaing Rivet, Toulouse #380
£296 $545 €450 Village en Bretagne (19x46cm-7x18in) s. panel. 22-Jun-4 Chassaing Rivet, Toulouse #376
£383 $700 €559 View of Florence. s.d.1930. 10-Apr-4 Auctions by the Bay, Alameda #1518/R
£828 $1548 €1250 Le port de Dourarnenez, vue du Ris (33x41cm-13x16in) s. canvas on board. 24-Jul-4 Thierry & Lannon, Brest #246/R
£1000 $1790 €1500 Discussion devant les chaumieres pres de Brehat (37x92cm-15x36in) s. 16-May-4 Thierry & Lannon, Brest #369/R est:1000-1200

SEFFER-GUERRA, Alessandro (1832-1905) Italian
£16438 $27945 €24000 Campitello Square with band playing music (46x70cm-18x28in) s.i.d.1866. 9-Nov-3 Finarte, Venice #6/R est:20000-25000
£22260 $37842 €32500 King Vittorio Emanuele II in Belluno (56x81cm-22x32in) s. 9-Nov-3 Finarte, Venice #7/R est:30000-35000

SEGAL, Arthur (1875-1944) Rumanian
£3631 $6500 €5301 Narcissen (49x29cm-19x11in) s.d.1908 prov. 18-Mar-4 Sotheby's, New York #119/R est:5000-7000
£10490 $17832 €15000 Still life with bottles (40x50cm-16x20in) s.d.1942 panel. 29-Nov-3 Villa Grisebach, Berlin #210/R est:9000-12000

SEGAL, George (1924-2000) American
Sculpture
£1387 $2400 €2025 Hand over breast (35x25x18cm-14x10x7in) cast relief one of 75 prov. 10-Dec-3 Phillips, New York #474/R est:2000-3000
£1946 $3308 €2841 Nude torso (84x33x9cm-33x13x4in) s.d.1975 num.18/20 relief papermache. 22-Nov-3 Burkhard, Luzern #191/R est:4000-6000 (S.FR 4300)
£2139 $3700 €3123 Girl on chair (91x61x28cm-36x24x11in) Polychrome plaster wood one of 150 prov. 10-Dec-3 Phillips, New York #418/R est:4000-6000
£4595 $8500 €6709 Sleeping girl, hand on face (43x63cm-17x25in) s.i.d.1970 plaster over gauze. 12-Feb-4 Sotheby's, New York #101/R est:4000-6000
£4908 $8000 €7166 Figure VIII (51x95x23cm-20x37x9in) s.d.70 num.AP1 white plaster. 24-Sep-3 Christie's, Rockefeller NY #375/R est:5000-7000
£13497 $22000 €19706 Neysa (135x76x30cm-53x30x12in) acrylic plaster wood metal relief prov.exhib. 23-Sep-3 Christie's, Rockefeller NY #91/R est:25000-35000
£20958 $35000 €30599 Untitled, nude with necklace (71x31x16cm-28x12x6in) cast plaster exec.c.1985 prov. 13-Nov-3 Sotheby's, New York #286/R est:15000-20000
£26946 $45000 €39341 Bas-Relief III - Girl with arm on a chair (86x64x18cm-34x25x7in) wall relief plaster wood exec 1971 prov.exhib. 12-Nov-3 Christie's, Rockefeller NY #395/R est:30000-40000
£56886 $95000 €83054 Portrait - Vera List (132x69x102cm-52x27x40in) plaster metal executed 1965 prov.exhib.lit. 12-Nov-3 Sotheby's, New York #11/R est:100000-150000
£100000 $185000 €150000 Man looking through the window (244x94x71cm-96x37x28in) s.d.85 num.1/1 pat bronze prov.exhib. 18-Jul-4 Sotheby's, Paris #159/R est:150000-200000
£195531 $350000 €285475 The Artist in his loft (229x175x152cm-90x69x60in) plaster wood glass porcelain metal exec 1969 prov.exhib.lit. 12-May-4 Sotheby's, New York #44/R est:350000-450000
Works on paper
£1200 $2148 €1800 Still life with female nude (44x30cm-17x12in) s. pastel paper on board. 15-May-4 Van Ham, Cologne #929 est:700
£1667 $3050 €2500 Untitled (45x30cm-18x12in) s.d.64 pastel prov. 4-Jun-4 Lempertz, Koln #453/R est:3000
£2095 $3750 €3059 Untitled - nude dressing gown (46x30cm-18x12in) s.d.65 pastel. 6-May-4 Doyle, New York #96/R est:2000-3000
£2471 $4250 €3608 Untitled - woman bathing (46x30cm-18x12in) s.d.64 pastel prov. 3-Dec-3 Doyle, New York #82/R est:3500-5000
£10429 $17000 €15226 Untitled (46x30cm-18x12in) s.d.62 pastel five prov.exhib. 23-Sep-3 Christie's, Rockefeller NY #92/R est:5000-7000

SEGAL, Simon (1898-1969) French
£276 $497 €400 Phare (60x73cm-24x29in) s. 25-Jan-4 Chayette & Cheval, Paris #158
£280 $467 €400 Poissons (38x55cm-15x22in) s. 25-Jun-3 Blanchet, Paris #58
£345 $621 €500 Female head (54x72cm-21x28in) s. 25-Jan-4 Chayette & Cheval, Paris #159
£345 $621 €500 Female head (54x72cm-21x28in) s. 25-Jan-4 Chayette & Cheval, Paris #160
£537 $961 €800 Portrait de jeune femme aux cheveux courts (73x54cm-29x21in) s. 30-May-4 Eric Pillon, Calais #127/R
£671 $1201 €1000 Cote rocheuse (60x73cm-24x29in) s. 30-May-4 Eric Pillon, Calais #122/R
£1294 $2160 €1850 Femme espagnole (73x54cm-29x21in) s. prov.exhib.lit. 25-Jun-3 Blanchet, Paris #60/R
£2448 $4087 €3500 Gisele (100x65cm-39x26in) s. painted 1948 prov.exhib. 25-Jun-3 Blanchet, Paris #59/R
Works on paper
£385 $642 €550 Paturage (42x56cm-17x22in) s. pastel. 25-Jun-3 Blanchet, Paris #46

SEGALL, Julius (1860-1925) American/German
£389 $700 €568 Forest fire, Peshtigo, Wisconsin (51x76cm-20x30in) s. 26-Jan-4 Schrager Galleries, Milwaukee #1381

SEGANTINI, Giovanni (1858-1899) Italian
£5634 $9746 €8000 Still life with watermelon (24x35cm-9x14in) painted c.1879-81. 10-Dec-3 Sotheby's, Milan #79/R est:5000-7000
£21719 $37575 €31710 Ritratto Maschile (48x43cm-19x17in) mono.i. painted 1880-1882 prov.lit. 9-Dec-3 Sotheby's, Zurich #31/R est:30000-40000 (S.FR 48000)
£26906 $43857 €39283 Landscape at dusk (80x100cm-31x39in) mono. prov.exhib.lit. 29-Sep-3 Christie's, Zurich #16/R est:70000-90000 (S.FR 60000)
Works on paper
£9155 $15197 €13000 Ragazzo che munge nella stalla (39x28cm-15x11in) chl. 11-Jun-3 Christie's, Rome #280/R est:15000-20000
£12556 $20466 €18332 Landscape with two sheep (17x20cm-7x8in) mono.d.1885 i. verso chl prov.lit. 29-Sep-3 Christie's, Zurich #17/R est:25000-35000 (S.FR 28000)
£20000 $36800 €30000 Middayon the Alps (37x22cm-15x9in) init.i.d.1892 pastel lit. 8-Jun-4 Sotheby's, Milan #92/R est:30000-50000

SEGANTINI, Gottardo (1882-1974) Italian
£1357 $2308 €1981 Still life with carnations and eggs in basket (38x45cm-15x18in) s.d.1957 pavatex. 18-Nov-3 Hans Widmer, St Gallen #1201/R est:3000-6500 (S.FR 3000)
£1940 $3472 €2832 Chalet en Engadine (30x40cm-12x16in) s.d.1906. 13-May-4 Pierre Berge, Paris #36/R est:12000-15000 (S.FR 4500)
£5677 $10162 €8288 Zollikon, summer landscape (60x50cm-24x20in) s.i.d.1918. 26-May-4 Sotheby's, Zurich #140/R est:14000-18000 (S.FR 13000)
£9649 $17754 €14088 Evening time at Silvaplaner Lake (50x70cm-20x28in) s.d. i.verso panel. 23-Jun-4 Koller, Zurich #3066/R est:12000-18000 (S.FR 22000)
£13575 $23484 €19820 Majorca in winter (60x55cm-24x22in) s.i.d.1917. 9-Dec-3 Sotheby's, Zurich #97/R est:30000-40000 (S.FR 30000)
£15217 $27848 €22217 White church, Maloya (89x61cm-35x24in) d.1914 s.i.verso. 4-Jun-4 Zofingen, Switzerland #2959/R est:35000 (S.FR 35000)
£30702 $56491 €44825 Church of St Moritz (81x91cm-32x36in) s.d.1945 panel prov. 23-Jun-4 Koller, Zurich #3060/R est:70000-90000 (S.FR 70000)
£30986 $51437 €44000 Landscape of Engadina (105x120cm-41x47in) s.verso lit. 11-Jun-3 Christie's, Rome #282/R est:33000-38000

SEGAR, William (attrib) (16/17th C) British
£9000 $14940 €13140 Portrait of a lady half length, with embroidered dress, white ruff holding a fan (75x60cm-30x24in) 30-Sep-3 Sotheby's, London #45/R est:10000-15000

SEGARRA CHIAS, Pablo (1945-) Spanish
£671 $1255 €1000 Gypsy (29x24cm-11x9in) s. board. 24-Feb-4 Durán, Madrid #16/R

SEGELCKE, Severin (1867-1940) Norwegian
£325 $598 €475 Village street scene (76x103cm-30x41in) s. 10-Jun-4 Grev Wedels Plass, Oslo #218/R (N.KR 4000)

SEGER, Ernst (1868-1939) German
Sculpture
£1042 $1656 €1500 Dancing girl (17x36x24cm-7x14x9in) i. pat.bronze onyx socle. 15-Sep-3 Dorotheum, Vienna #181/R est:1000-1300
£1109 $1984 €1619 Female nude with drapery (51cm-20in) s. marble. 28-May-4 Uppsala Auktionskammare, Uppsala #406/R est:3000-4000 (S.KR 15000)
£1119 $1924 €1600 Dancer (45cm-18in) i. brown pat.bronze. 4-Dec-3 Schopman, Hamburg #426/R est:1200
£1538 $2646 €2200 Young woman (21cm-8in) i. alabaster ivory marble socle. 4-Dec-3 Schopman, Hamburg #427/R est:340

SEGERSTRAHLE, Lennart (1892-1975) Finnish
£493 $789 €700 Beached boat (35x52cm-14x20in) s. 21-Sep-3 Bukowskis, Helsinki #467/R
£660 $1102 €950 Swans in flight (22x35cm-9x14in) s. 26-Oct-3 Bukowskis, Helsinki #495/R
£699 $1189 €1000 On the lap (44x34cm-17x13in) s.d.1968 board. 29-Nov-3 Bukowskis, Helsinki #152/R
£1399 $2378 €2000 Reconciliation (103x78cm-41x31in) s.d.1970. 29-Nov-3 Bukowskis, Helsinki #201/R est:2500-3000
£2027 $3628 €3000 Crows (67x98cm-26x39in) s.d.1913. 8-May-4 Bukowskis, Helsinki #188/R est:3000-3500
£2027 $3628 €3000 Mother and baby (105x75cm-41x30in) s.d.1956. 8-May-4 Bukowskis, Helsinki #207/R est:3000-3500
£2400 $4296 €3600 Autumn landscape from Padasjoki (41x60cm-16x24in) s.d.1919. 15-May-4 Hagelstam, Helsinki #159/R est:3500
£3067 $5489 €4600 Magpie (38x40cm-15x16in) s.d.1919. 15-May-4 Hagelstam, Helsinki #158/R est:2500
£13129 $23895 €19300 Swans in flight (68x97cm-27x38in) s.d.1912. 8-Feb-4 Bukowskis, Helsinki #449/R est:2200
£18243 $32655 €27000 Seagulls by the nest (61x80cm-24x31in) s.d.1921. 8-May-4 Bukowskis, Helsinki #107/R est:6000-8000
Works on paper
£278 $464 €400 Fisherman (47x55cm-19x22in) s.d.1938 W/C. 26-Oct-3 Bukowskis, Helsinki #493/R
£420 $713 €600 The seal hunters making camp (39x52cm-15x20in) s.d.1938 W/C. 29-Nov-3 Bukowskis, Helsinki #213/R

SEGHERS, Daniel and SCHUT, Cornelis (17th C) Flemish
£48951 $84196 €70000 Madonna and child in a garland of flowers (66x54cm-26x21in) panel prov. 2-Dec-3 Christie's, Paris #502/R est:30000-40000

SEGHERS, Gerard (1591-1651) Flemish
£4930 $8528 €7000 Ascension of Christ (31x23cm-12x9in) copper. 11-Dec-3 Dr Fritz Nagel, Stuttgart #468/R est:12000
£26316 $48422 €40000 Noli me tangere (44x32cm-17x13in) s.verso panel en grisaille prov. 24-Jun-4 Tajan, Paris #10/R est:15000-20000

SEGHERS, Lode (1906-2002) Belgian
Works on paper
£1000 $1840 €1500 Nude (96x68cm-38x27in) s.i.d.27 blk chk col crayon gouache pencil lit. 9-Jun-4 Christie's, Amsterdam #94/R est:1500-2000

SEGOFFIN, Victor (1867-1925) French
Sculpture
£2055 $3493 €3000 La joueuse de cumbales (59cm-23in) s.d.1905 brown pat bronze Cast Susse. 5-Nov-3 Rabourdin & Choppin de Janvry, Paris #96/R est:3500-4000
£2759 $4579 €4000 Nu debout (54cm-21in) s.d.1899 brown pat bronze. 2-Oct-3 Sotheby's, Paris #39/R

SEGRELLES, Eustaquio (1936-) Spanish
£517 $931 €750 Houses (38x55cm-15x22in) s. 26-Jan-4 Durán, Madrid #666/R
£933 $1689 €1400 Olive trees (99x50cm-39x20in) s. 30-Mar-4 Segre, Madrid #93/R
£940 $1748 €1400 Fishermen (38x55cm-15x22in) s. s.d.86 verso. 2-Mar-4 Ansorena, Madrid #32/R
£1910 $3113 €2750 Sol de Levante, Valencia (50x65cm-20x26in) s. s.i.d.2003 verso. 16-Jul-3 Durán, Madrid #129/R est:2750
£2083 $3396 €3000 Playa de La Malvarrosa, Valencia (50x65cm-20x26in) s. s.i.d.2003 verso. 16-Jul-3 Durán, Madrid #131/R est:2750
£2434 $4406 €3700 Figures on the beach (40x80cm-16x31in) s. 14-Apr-4 Ansorena, Madrid #52/R est:3500
£3546 $5922 €5000 Regreso de los pescadores (61x76cm-24x30in) s. s.i.d.2000 verso. 23-Jun-3 Durán, Madrid #237/R est:4500
£6579 $12105 €10000 Beach in Valencia (80x170cm-31x67in) s.i. s.i.verso. 22-Jun-4 Durán, Madrid #198/R est:10000

SEGRELLES, Jose (1885-1969) Spanish
£16107 $29960 €24000 Woman with jugs (88x65cm-35x26in) s. 2-Mar-4 Ansorena, Madrid #52/R est:24000
Works on paper
£345 $621 €500 Old oriental man (26x20cm-10x8in) W/C. 26-Jan-4 Ansorena, Madrid #295/R
£1172 $2110 €1700 Theatre scene (24x21cm-9x8in) s. wash. 26-Jan-4 Durán, Madrid #104/R est:1600
£1399 $2336 €2000 Great Council Meeting (43x32cm-17x13in) s. W/C. 30-Jun-3 Ansorena, Madrid #26/R

SEGUI PALOU, Bertolome (1887-1976) Spanish
Works on paper
£377 $640 €550 Landscape with bridge (23x33cm-9x13in) s. W/C. 4-Nov-3 Ansorena, Madrid #159/R
£638 $1034 €900 Landscape of Majorca (23x30cm-9x12in) s. W/C. 20-May-3 Ansorena, Madrid #962/R

SEGUI, Antonio (1934-) Argentinian
£667 $1226 €1000 Still life with bottle (64x56cm-25x22in) s.d.12.12.92 verso oil collage paper on canvas prov. 9-Jun-4 Artcurial Briest, Paris #445/R
£1143 $2000 €1669 One-eyed man (46x38cm-18x15in) s.d.80. 19-Dec-3 Sotheby's, New York #1223/R est:2500-3500
£1286 $2250 €1878 Man with glasses (52x46cm-20x18in) s.d.80 verso. 19-Dec-3 Sotheby's, New York #1218/R est:2500-3500
£1800 $3258 €2628 Personnage (81x65cm-32x26in) s.d.72 acrylic. 1-Apr-4 Christie's, Kensington #251/R est:1500-2000
£3423 $6298 €5100 Dans la ville (100x100cm-39x39in) s.d.1985 acrylic. 29-Mar-4 Cornette de St.Cyr, Paris #99/R est:4000-6000
£4056 $6773 €5800 Casita de fin de semana (33x41cm-13x16in) s.d.1978 s.i.d.2/3/78 verso prov. 11-Oct-3 Cornette de St.Cyr, Paris #19/R est:3000-4000
£4706 $8000 €6871 Caja grande, Carlota (82x108cm-32x43in) s. board prov. 18-Nov-3 Christie's, Rockefeller NY #181/R est:10000-15000
£5495 $10000 €8023 Pueblito nervioso (73x92cm-29x36in) s.d.84 prov. 29-Jun-4 Sotheby's, New York #684/R est:8000-10000
£5667 $10200 €8500 Travaux des champs (50x150cm-20x59in) s. 25-Apr-4 Versailles Encheres #149 est:7000-8000
£6250 $10438 €9000 La tour Eiffel (200x200cm-79x79in) s.d.1981 oil paper on canvas. 25-Oct-3 Cornette de St.Cyr, Paris #808/R est:6000-8000
£9091 $15182 €13000 Distancia de la Mirada no 1 (150x150cm-59x59in) s.d.1974 s.i.d.3/4/1974 verso prov. 11-Oct-3 Cornette de St.Cyr, Paris #18/R est:10000-15000
Sculpture
£1389 $2194 €2000 Traveller (15cm-6in) num.3/24 green pat bronze. 27-Apr-3 Versailles Encheres #128
£1389 $2194 €2000 Compradito (16cm-6in) num.5/24 green pat bronze. 27-Apr-3 Versailles Encheres #127
£1528 $2551 €2200 El viajero (152x142cm-60x56in) num.13/24 base bronze. 21-Oct-3 Artcurial Briest, Paris #577/R est:2000-2500
£1608 $2686 €2300 Traveller (15cm-6in) s. num.6/24 silver bronze base. 29-Jun-3 Versailles Encheres #230/R
£1667 $2783 €2400 Compradito (16x7cm-6x3in) num.13/24 base bronze. 21-Oct-3 Artcurial Briest, Paris #578/R est:2000-2500
£2098 $3503 €3000 Compradito (16cm-6in) s. num.3/24 silver bronze base. 29-Jun-3 Versailles Encheres #231/R
Works on paper
£390 $651 €550 Composition aux deux personnages (21x15cm-8x6in) s. mixed media. 20-Jun-3 Drouot Estimations, Paris #213
£672 $1236 €1000 Greve (28x21cm-11x8in) s.d.1994 ink drawing. 29-Mar-4 Cornette de St.Cyr, Paris #118/R
£780 $1303 €1100 Composition au personnage (36x52cm-14x20in) s.d.1988 mixed media cardboard oval. 20-Jun-3 Drouot Estimations, Paris #208
£780 $1303 €1100 Composition aux trois personnages (19x47cm-7x19in) s.d.1984 mixed media. 20-Jun-3 Drouot Estimations, Paris #212
£851 $1421 €1200 Composition au personnage (52x25cm-20x10in) s. mixed media cardboard. 20-Jun-3 Drouot Estimations, Paris #206
£887 $1480 €1250 Composition au personnage (35x52cm-14x20in) s.d.1987 mixed media cardboard oval. 20-Jun-3 Drouot Estimations, Paris #207/R

£1042 $1719 €1500 Deux personnages (51x64cm-20x25in) s. pastel. 2-Jul-3 Cornette de St.Cyr, Paris #147/R est:1500-2000
£1429 $2500 €2086 Man (63x73cm-25x29in) s.d.1974 mixed media canvas. 19-Dec-3 Sotheby's, New York #1220/R est:3500-4500
£1857 $3250 €2711 Man with dog (57x73cm-22x29in) mixed media. 19-Dec-3 Sotheby's, New York #1206/R est:3500-4500
£2081 $3828 €3100 Cabecita para Jugar (38x46cm-15x18in) s.i.verso mixed media newspaper on canvas. 24-Mar-4 Joron-Derem, Paris #154 est:3800-4200
£19337 $35000 €28232 Positive-negative (73x92cm-29x36in) mixed media on canvas. 30-Mar-4 Arroyo, Buenos Aires #69

SEGUI, Jorge (1945-) Argentinian
£276 $475 €403 Night game (91x76cm-36x30in) s. painted 1981. 7-Dec-3 Subastas Odalys, Caracas #80/R
Sculpture
£6553 $11140 €9567 Little vampire (72x55x48cm-28x22x19in) s.verso bronze exec.1992. 23-Nov-3 Subastas Odalys, Caracas #115/R

SEGUIER, J (?) ?
£2200 $3982 €3212 Studies of mushrooms. Studies of plants (28x20cm-11x8in) mono. board set of four. 30-Mar-4 Sworder & Son, Bishops Stortford #532/R est:300-400

SEGUIN, Adrien (1926-) French
£423 $756 €600 Bateaux au port (24x33cm-9x13in) s. cardboard. 11-Jan-4 Rouillac, Vendome #393

SEGUIN, Armand (1869-1903) French
£577 $912 €900 Bretonnes au bord de la falaise (65x50cm-26x20in) s.d.1891 exhib. 12-Nov-2 Adjug'art, Brest #96/R
Prints
£4161 $7365 €6200 Femme aux figues. col eau forte exec.1899. 29-Apr-4 Piasa, Paris #304/R est:2500-3000

SEGUIN, Oliver (20th C) Mexican
Works on paper
£614 $1100 €896 Los Nuevos Liegando I (161x239cm-63x94in) mixed media. 21-Mar-4 Bonhams & Butterfields, Los Angeles #7137/R est:150-200
£1061 $1900 €1549 Juillet (198x200cm-78x79in) mixed media. 21-Mar-4 Bonhams & Butterfields, Los Angeles #7138/R est:150-200

SEGUIN-BERTAULT, Paul (1869-1964) French
£903 $1507 €1300 Au theatre (18x24cm-7x9in) s. panel. 21-Oct-3 Artcurial Briest, Paris #158 est:800-1000

SEGURA IGLESIAS, Agustin (1900-1988) Spanish
£537 $950 €800 Old woman with statue of the Infant (70x58cm-28x23in) s.d.46. 27-Apr-4 Durán, Madrid #166/R
£759 $1366 €1100 Portrait of young woman (65x54cm-26x21in) s. 26-Jan-4 Ansorena, Madrid #79/R
£986 $1577 €1400 Portrait of HRH Princess Marie Christine of Belgium (77x55cm-30x22in) s. 22-Sep-3 Sotheby's, Amsterdam #157/R est:800-1200
£1127 $1803 €1600 Portrait of HRH Princess Marie Christine of Belgium, age 14 (70x55cm-28x22in) s.d.65. 22-Sep-3 Sotheby's, Amsterdam #156/R est:800-1200

SEHRING, A (20th C) American/Russian
£943 $1500 €1377 Young boy fishing at side of pond among wildflowers and trees (61x51cm-24x20in) s. 10-Sep-3 Alderfer's, Hatfield #293/R est:1000-1500

SEIBELS, Carl (1844-1877) German
£3958 $6254 €5700 Cows grazing by pond (62x94cm-24x37in) s. lit. 19-Sep-3 Schloss Ahlden, Ahlden #1587/R est:6500

SEIBEZZI, Fioravante (1906-1975) Italian
£533 $965 €800 Venice (40x50cm-16x20in) s. 2-Apr-4 Farsetti, Prato #302/R
£1000 $1840 €1500 Spring landscape (61x50cm-24x20in) s. panel. 10-Jun-4 Christie's, Rome #116 est:700-1000

SEIBOLD, Christian (attrib) (1697-1768) German
£54545 $93818 €78000 Portrait d'enfant en armure (55x41cm-22x16in) 8-Dec-3 Claude Aguttes, Neuilly #25/R est:4500

SEIDEL, A (1820-1904) German
£1399 $2406 €2000 Harvest by pre alpine lake (54x75cm-21x30in) s. 4-Dec-3 Neumeister, Munich #2851/R est:300

SEIDEL, August (1820-1904) German
£612 $1096 €900 Mountain landscape with travellers (17x25cm-7x10in) s. canvas on panel. 17-Mar-4 Neumeister, Munich #604/R
£680 $1218 €1000 Mountain landscape with ruined walls (18x29cm-7x11in) mono. paper on board. 17-Mar-4 Neumeister, Munich #605/R
£816 $1461 €1200 Cows by water (26x44cm-10x17in) mono. 17-Mar-4 Neumeister, Munich #602/R
£833 $1358 €1200 Capri coast with Faraglioni in evening (59x78cm-23x31in) s. 26-Sep-3 Bolland & Marotz, Bremen #615/R est:1300
£855 $1574 €1300 Evening river landscape (28x45cm-11x18in) s.d.98. 24-Jun-4 Dr Fritz Nagel, Stuttgart #753/R
£1111 $1811 €1600 Italian coast (51x70cm-20x28in) s. canvas on masonite. 24-Sep-3 Neumeister, Munich #556/R est:1800
£1184 $2179 €1800 Southern landscape with lake (28x45cm-11x18in) s. 24-Jun-4 Dr Fritz Nagel, Stuttgart #754/R est:700
£1197 $2071 €1700 Castle grounds on a lake (35x42cm-14x17in) mono. paper on canvas. 10-Dec-3 Hugo Ruef, Munich #2491/R est:1200
£1250 $1987 €1800 At the blacksmith's (45x66cm-18x26in) mono. 11-Sep-3 Weidler, Nurnberg #6505/R est:1000
£1389 $2292 €2000 Campagna landscape with Sedia del Diavolo (19x40cm-7x16in) canvas on board. 2-Jul-3 Neumeister, Munich #771/R est:1200
£1875 $3094 €2700 Rocky summit (24x42cm-9x17in) mono. 2-Jul-3 Neumeister, Munich #770/R est:3000
£2653 $4749 €3900 Southern mountain landscape (13x31cm-5x12in) mono. board. 17-Mar-4 Neumeister, Munich #603/R est:1000
£2667 $4853 €4000 Herder with cows returning home (33x39cm-13x15in) s. panel. 30-Jun-4 Neumeister, Munich #680/R est:4000

SEIDEL, Brian (1928-) Australian
£531 $977 €775 Rugged Range, East Kimberley (101x121cm-40x48in) s.d.90 s.i.d.1990 verso. 29-Mar-4 Goodman, Sydney #205/R (A.D 1300)
£1488 $2752 €2172 Sorrento I (106x112cm-42x44in) s.d.1987. 10-Mar-4 Deutscher-Menzies, Melbourne #325/R est:4000-6000 (A.D 3600)
£3404 $5787 €4970 Summer figure interior (147x152cm-58x60in) s.d.66 s.i.d.1966 verso lit. 25-Nov-3 Christie's, Melbourne #96/R est:9000-12000 (A.D 8000)

SEIDEL, Emory P (1881-?) American
Sculpture
£9730 $18000 €14206 Untitled, two figures with birds (51cm-20in) s. bronze exec.c.1926. 9-Mar-4 Christie's, Rockefeller NY #405/R est:4000-6000

SEIDENBEUTEL, Efraim (1903-1945) Polish
£3458 $6397 €5049 Still life with cup on a drapped table (70x49cm-28x19in) 14-Mar-4 Agra, Warsaw #68/R (P.Z 25000)

SEIDENSTUCKER, Friedrich (1882-1966) German
Photographs
£1733 $3189 €2600 Untitled (13x18cm-5x7in) silver gelatin. 10-Jun-4 Villa Grisebach, Berlin #1280/R est:600-800

SEIDL, Ernst (19/20th C) German
£675 $1100 €986 Portrait of a woman (33x23cm-13x9in) s. panel. 17-Jul-3 Doyle, New York #46/R

SEIDLER, Louise (1786-1866) German
Works on paper
£347 $549 €500 Portrait of a young woman (32x21cm-13x8in) i.verso chk htd white card. 5-Sep-3 Wendl, Rudolstadt #3145/R

SEIFERT, Alfred (1850-1901) Czechoslovakian
£543 $923 €793 Woman's head before autumnal foliage (42x31cm-17x12in) s. panel. 19-Nov-3 Fischer, Luzern #2294/R (S.FR 1200)
£3800 $6840 €5548 Portrait of a girl (33x23cm-13x9in) s. panel. 21-Jan-4 Sotheby's, Olympia #414/R est:1000-1500
£9091 $15455 €13000 May time (125x88cm-49x35in) s. 24-Nov-3 Dorotheum, Vienna #15/R est:5000-6000

SEIFERT, Victor Heinrich (1870-1953) German
Sculpture
£1013 $1580 €1600 Girl drinking from bowl (63x70cm-25x28in) s. dark brown pat.bronze. 18-Oct-2 Von Zezschwitz, Munich #16/R est:1500
£1225 $2229 €1789 School girl (60cm-24in) s. pat bronze exec 1920. 20-Jun-4 Agra, Warsaw #43/R (P.Z 8500)
£1611 $2949 €2352 Standing youth (66cm-26in) s. pat.bronze incl.grey marble socle. 2-Jun-4 Rasmussen, Copenhagen #1305/R est:20000 (D.KR 18000)
£1818 $3091 €2600 The school girl (56cm-22in) s. pat bronze stone base incl. 28-Nov-3 Schloss Ahlden, Ahlden #515/R est:2800
£1879 $3495 €2800 Nymph (85cm-33in) s. bronze. 6-Mar-4 Arnold, Frankfurt #364/R est:600
£2028 $3488 €2900 Standing female nude drinking from a bowl (64cm-25in) i.verso pat bronze st.f.Gladenbeck und Sohn. 5-Dec-3 Bolland & Marotz, Bremen #1111/R est:1600
£2038 $3179 €2975 On the way to school (65cm-26in) s. pat bronze exec.c.1920. 30-Mar-3 Agra, Warsaw #25/R est:13000 (P.Z 13000)
£2133 $3904 €3200 Story time (53cm-21in) i. brown pat. bronze incl. base. 7-Jun-4 Sotheby's, Amsterdam #10/R est:1500-2000
£2649 $4821 €4000 Female nude with raised arms (62cm-24in) s. bronze incl. stone base. 16-Jun-4 Hugo Ruef, Munich #1765/R est:600
£2665 $4157 €3891 Nude female (70cm-28in) s. pat bronze exec.c.1910. 30-Mar-3 Agra, Warsaw #22/R est:16000 (P.Z 17000)

SEIFFERT, Carl Friedrich (1809-1891) German
£1748 $2920 €2500 Reichenbach (50x42cm-20x17in) s. i. verso. 9-Oct-3 Michael Zeller, Lindau #763/R est:2500

SEIGNAC, Guillaume (1870-1924) French
£2372 $4245 €3463 Bather (25x21cm-10x8in) s. wood panel prov. 15-May-4 Christie's, Sydney #361/R est:4000-6000 (A.D 6000)
£11176 $19000 €16317 Diana, the huntress (56x46cm-22x18in) s. 29-Oct-3 Christie's, Rockefeller NY #128/R est:15000-20000
£26000 $47320 €37960 L'odalisque aux colombes (46x55cm-18x22in) s. prov. 15-Jun-4 Sotheby's, London #113/R est:20000-30000
£43210 $70000 €62655 Nymphe (145x83cm-57x33in) s. 8-Aug-3 Barridorf, Portland #87/R est:70000-90000
£43210 $70000 €62655 Love's target (147x98cm-58x39in) s. prov.lit. 8-Aug-3 Barridorf, Portland #166/R est:50000-75000
£64706 $110000 €94471 Venus and Cupid (142x89cm-56x35in) s. 28-Oct-3 Sotheby's, New York #37/R est:100000-150000

SEIGNAC, Paul (1826-1904) French
£2335 $4250 €3409 New pet (32x24cm-13x9in) s. panel. 29-Jun-4 Sotheby's, New York #66/R est:4000-6000

£3480 $6020 €5081 Woman and children in front of a church statue (54x45cm-21x18in) s. panel painted c.1860. 14-Dec-3 Agra, Warsaw #3/R est:18000 (P.Z 23000)
£6000 $10920 €8760 Mother's little helper (36x27cm-14x11in) s. 16-Jun-4 Christie's, Kensington #158/R est:6000-8000
£6338 $10965 €9000 Girls (36x27cm-14x11in) s. board. 9-Dec-3 Finarte Semenzato, Milan #1/R est:9000-10000

SEIGNEURGENS, Ernest Louis Augustin (1820-1904) French
£800 $1480 €1200 Homme assis au chien (25x19cm-10x7in) s. panel. 14-Jul-4 Livinec, Gaudcheau & Jezequel, Rennes #165

SEIGNOL (20th C) French
£1304 $2139 €1800 Piqueux et griffons vendeens (145x98cm-57x39in) 28-May-3 Coutau Begarie, Paris #155/R est:1800-2000

SEIGNOL, Claudius (20th C) French
£588 $1000 €858 Three cats at the dog's feeding bowl (46x65cm-18x26in) s. 1-Dec-3 Koller, Zurich #6518/R est:1500-2500 (S.FR 1300)
£733 $1320 €1100 Le depart pour la chasse (67x90cm-26x35in) s. 20-Apr-4 Chenu & Scrive, Lyon #154/R

SEIJO Y RUBIO, Jose (1881-1970) Spanish
£503 $891 €750 Night time (50x40cm-20x16in) s. 27-Apr-4 Durán, Madrid #610/R
£1064 $1777 €1500 Rural landscape (36x59cm-14x23in) s. 23-Jun-3 Durán, Madrid #167/R est:1500

SEIKI, Yokoyama (1793-1865) Japanese
Works on paper
£420 $722 €600 Two crows in a tree in a landscape with stream (41x51cm-16x20in) s. ink col silk hanging scroll. 5-Dec-3 Lempertz, Koln #770/R

SEILER, Carl Wilhelm Anton (1846-1921) German
£789 $1429 €1200 A pipe smoking town crier, sitting on his drum (22x17cm-9x7in) s.d.1875 panel prov. 19-Apr-4 Glerum, Amsterdam #90/R
£1034 $1728 €1500 Two elegant men in salon (25x32cm-10x13in) s.d.1908 panel. 9-Jul-3 Hugo Ruef, Munich #197/R est:1500
£1042 $1719 €1500 Two men eating midday meal (16x13cm-6x5in) s.d.1900 panel. 3-Jul-3 Van Ham, Cologne #1458/R est:1700
£1486 $2750 €2170 Discussion (23x33cm-9x13in) s.d.1919 panel. 15-Jul-4 Sotheby's, New York #29/R est:2500-3500
£5200 $9308 €7592 Consultation (23x17cm-9x7in) s.d.1884 panel. 26-May-4 Sotheby's, Olympia #278/R est:2000-3000
Works on paper
£273 $495 €410 Self portrait (39x29cm-15x11in) Indian ink. 2-Apr-4 Winterberg, Heidelberg #546

SEILER, Carl Wilhelm Anton (attrib) (1846-1921) German
£442 $791 €650 Man reading newspaper (23x14cm-9x6in) board. 18-Mar-4 Neumeister, Munich #2777/R

SEILER, Hans (1907-1986) Swiss
£633 $1140 €950 Composition (45x55cm-18x22in) s.d.1951 prov. 24-Apr-4 Cornette de St.Cyr, Paris #712
£667 $1200 €1000 Pont Levis (38x55cm-15x22in) s. s.i.verso. 24-Apr-4 Cornette de St.Cyr, Paris #714/R
£867 $1560 €1300 Battage (38x54cm-15x21in) s. 24-Apr-4 Cornette de St.Cyr, Paris #716/R
£867 $1560 €1300 Vue sur la Marne (23x32cm-9x13in) s.d.1947 s.i.verso cardboard. 24-Apr-4 Cornette de St.Cyr, Paris #715
£987 $1816 €1500 Untitled (46x55cm-18x22in) s.d.1951 prov. 27-Jun-4 Versailles Encheres #47/R est:1500-2000
£1049 $1752 €1500 Untitled (27x41cm-11x16in) s. prov. 29-Jun-3 Versailles Encheres #27/R
Works on paper
£280 $504 €420 Composition (22x28cm-9x11in) s.d.1956 gouache. 24-Apr-4 Cornette de St.Cyr, Paris #713
£359 $595 €520 Port de Douarnenez (23x24cm-9x9in) s.d.1965 gouache prov. 30-Sep-3 Blanchet, Paris #331/R
£880 $1523 €1250 Port de Douarnenez (23x24cm-9x9in) s.d.1965 gouache prov.exhib. 14-Dec-3 Versailles Encheres #21/R

SEINSHEIM, August Karl de (1789-1869) German
Works on paper
£7042 $12183 €10000 Madonna on throne with 14 auxiliary saints (61x39cm-24x15in) mono.d.1820 mixed media panel. 13-Dec-3 Lempertz, Koln #46/R est:6000

SEISHI, Saku (19th C) Japanese
Sculpture
£2230 $3924 €3300 Archer (46cm-18in) s. verso gilt bronze. 22-May-4 Dr Fritz Nagel, Stuttgart #2261/R est:3600

SEITER, Daniel (1649-1705) Italian
£9333 $16893 €14000 Lucretia (97x71cm-38x28in) prov. 30-Mar-4 Babuino, Rome #50/R est:8000-12000
Works on paper
£4225 $7394 €6000 Diane et Endymion (26x19cm-10x7in) i.verso pen brown ink grey wash prov. 17-Dec-3 Christie's, Paris #32/R est:3000-5000

SEITER, Pietro (1687-?) Italian
£8451 $14620 €12000 Trompe l'oeil with flowers (42x50cm-17x20in) s.d.1731. 9-Dec-3 Pandolfini, Florence #38/R est:7000-10000

SEITHER, Anna Barber (fl.1903-1915) American
£302 $550 €441 Italian street scene (28x23cm-11x9in) s.i.d.1903. 7-Feb-4 Sloans & Kenyon, Bethesda #1286/R

SEITZ, Johann (1887-1967) Polish
Works on paper
£700 $1239 €1022 Coastal views of Dubrovnik (22x35cm-9x14in) s.i.d.1933 bodycol two. 27-Apr-4 Bonhams, New Bond Street #52/R

SEITZ, Anton (1829-1900) German
£2586 $4759 €3776 Girl reading (34x24cm-13x9in) s. panel. 26-Mar-4 Koller, Zurich #3093/R est:7000-12000 (S.FR 6000)
£2586 $4629 €3776 Girl minding baby in crib (20x16cm-8x6in) s. panel. 17-May-4 Beurret, Zurich #17/R est:3000-4000 (S.FR 6000)
£9524 $17048 €14000 Four children round fire in ruins (38x28cm-15x11in) s. panel. 17-Mar-4 Neumeister, Munich #608/R est:5000

SEITZ, Carl (1824-?) German
£374 $670 €550 Wood snipe in landscape (14x19cm-6x7in) s.d.54 board. 20-Mar-4 Bergmann, Erlangen #1094

SEITZ, Georg (attrib) (1810-1870) German
£1987 $3616 €3000 Large still life of fruit with roses (74x100cm-29x39in) 21-Jun-4 Dorotheum, Vienna #80/R est:2400-3000

SEITZ, Gustav (1906-1969) German
Sculpture
£1049 $1804 €1500 Danae (9x22x11cm-4x9x4in) bronze. 3-Dec-3 Hauswedell & Nolte, Hamburg #994/R est:1500
£2083 $3396 €3000 Seated girl (22cm-9in) s. verso dark pat.bronze. 27-Sep-3 Dr Fritz Nagel, Stuttgart #9623/R est:3800
£11333 $20853 €17000 Sappho's head (32cm-13in) black pat bronze stone base exec. 1965 st.f. Schmake. 12-Jun-4 Villa Grisebach, Berlin #343/R est:7000-9000
£11538 $19615 €16500 Kneeling negro woman (54cm-21in) s. brown pat.bronze Cast.Barth Berlin. 29-Nov-3 Villa Grisebach, Berlin #268/R est:9000-12000

SEITZ, Otto (1846-1912) German
£1049 $1804 €1500 Love letter (38x24cm-15x9in) s. panel. 5-Dec-3 Bolland & Marotz, Bremen #629/R est:1600

SEITZ, Rudolf von (1842-1910) German
£1867 $3341 €2800 Still life with landscape (85x151cm-33x59in) i. stretcher lit. 14-May-4 Schloss Ahlden, Ahlden #2798/R est:2200

SEIWERT, Franz Wilhelm (1894-1933) German
Prints
£10000 $18400 €15000 Created beings (30x25cm-12x10in) s. woodcut album of 7 one of 10 exec.1917/19. 12-Jun-4 Villa Grisebach, Berlin #238/R est:5500-7500
Sculpture
£7000 $12810 €10500 Woman's head (26cm-10in) glazed clay exhib. 5-Jun-4 Lempertz, Koln #999/R est:10000-11000
Works on paper
£1007 $1852 €1500 Plan for stained glass window in Cafe Namur in Luxembourg (30x20cm-12x8in) col pen. 26-Mar-4 Ketterer, Hamburg #648/R est:1500-1700

SEKAER, Peter (1901-1950) American/Danish
Photographs
£1958 $3329 €2800 Farm boy (17x20cm-7x8in) i. verso silver gelatin. 27-Nov-3 Villa Grisebach, Berlin #1392/R est:2800-3200

SEKOTO, Gerard (1913-1993) South African
£4577 $7370 €6500 Femme en rouge (30x17cm-12x7in) canvas on panel. 22-Aug-3 Deauville, France #121 est:3000-4000
£8621 $14397 €12587 Donkey cart (20x24cm-8x9in) s. canvas on board. 20-Oct-3 Stephan Welz, Johannesburg #293/R est:25000-35000 (SA.R 100000)
Works on paper
£1197 $2034 €1748 White houses, Eastwood, Pretoria (30x47cm-12x19in) s. i.verso gouache. 4-Nov-3 Stephan Welz, Johannesburg #675/R est:9000-12000 (SA.R 14000)
£1624 $2761 €2371 Young woman running (55x37cm-22x15in) s.d.72 W/C gouache. 4-Nov-3 Stephan Welz, Johannesburg #646/R est:12000-15000 (SA.R 19000)
£2393 $4068 €3494 Figures on a township street (37x55cm-15x22in) s.d.72 W/C gouache. 4-Nov-3 Stephan Welz, Johannesburg #668/R est:14000-18000 (SA.R 28000)
£2465 $3968 €3500 Market day (60x44cm-24x17in) s. pastel. 22-Aug-3 Deauville, France #132 est:1800-2500
£2477 $4434 €3616 Dancing women (38x55cm-15x22in) s.d.71 gouache. 31-May-4 Stephan Welz, Johannesburg #588/R est:15000-20000 (SA.R 30000)
£2735 $4650 €3993 Mother and child on a busy street (55x37cm-22x15in) s.d.72 W/C gouache. 4-Nov-3 Stephan Welz, Johannesburg #669 est:14000-18000 (SA.R 32000)
£4741 $7918 €6922 Three men walking (31x25cm-12x10in) s. W/C. 20-Oct-3 Stephan Welz, Johannesburg #292/R est:25000-35000 (SA.R 55000)

SEKRET, Valery (1950-) Russian
£250 $408 €365 Autumn in Paris (36x55cm-14x22in) s. 28-Sep-3 John Nicholson, Haslemere #106
£250 $438 €365 Sunny day (27x41cm-11x16in) s. 17-Dec-3 John Nicholson, Haslemere #67/R
£275 $481 €402 At the seaside of Azov (27x46cm-11x18in) s. 17-Dec-3 John Nicholson, Haslemere #168/R

£275 $514 €413 Children playing on the beach (27x46cm-11x18in) s. 21-Jul-4 John Nicholson, Haslemere #343
£299 $499 €430 Soleil couchant sur la Seine (40x50cm-16x20in) s. 26-Oct-3 Feletin, Province #150/R
£300 $489 €438 Evening ebb on the sea (41x33cm-16x13in) s. 28-Sep-3 John Nicholson, Haslemere #22/R
£300 $525 €438 First snow (55x46cm-22x18in) s. 17-Dec-3 John Nicholson, Haslemere #3/R
£300 $525 €438 Holidays by the sea (24x35cm-9x14in) s. 17-Dec-3 John Nicholson, Haslemere #87
£302 $541 €450 Holiday at the seaside (27x35cm-11x14in) s. canvas on cardboard. 25-May-4 Durán, Madrid #733/R
£308 $505 €425 Junto al Mar Negro (24x33cm-9x13in) s.verso. 27-May-3 Durán, Madrid #785/R
£319 $571 €475 Morning on the Seine (46x38cm-18x15in) s. 25-May-4 Durán, Madrid #732/R
£325 $582 €475 First lights (38x46cm-15x18in) s. 5-May-4 John Nicholson, Haslemere #111
£336 $594 €500 Normandy beach (38x61cm-15x24in) s. 27-Apr-4 Durán, Madrid #727/R
£350 $655 €525 Landscape in Crimea (30x60cm-12x24in) s. 21-Jul-4 John Nicholson, Haslemere #345
£350 $613 €511 Children at Gursuf (24x49cm-9x19in) s. cardboard. 17-Dec-3 John Nicholson, Haslemere #128/R
£350 $585 €511 Beach in Cabourg (30x60cm-12x24in) s. 13-Jul-3 John Nicholson, Haslemere #67/R
£350 $627 €511 On Monparnas (35x50cm-14x20in) s. 5-May-4 John Nicholson, Haslemere #36
£389 $634 €560 View of the Seine (50x65cm-20x26in) s. 23-Sep-3 Durán, Madrid #668/R
£400 $700 €584 Beach in Trouville (33x55cm-13x22in) s. 17-Dec-3 John Nicholson, Haslemere #48/R
£400 $668 €584 Beach in Normandy (27x46cm-11x18in) s. 13-Jul-3 John Nicholson, Haslemere #70/R
£400 $748 €600 Beginning of the evening (30x60cm-12x24in) s. 21-Jul-4 John Nicholson, Haslemere #461
£414 $691 €600 Paris at night (38x55cm-15x22in) s. 17-Nov-3 Durán, Madrid #680/R
£435 $713 €600 Paris at night (46x38cm-18x15in) s. 27-May-3 Durán, Madrid #784/R
£436 $781 €650 Sunny day, Notre-Dame (50x61cm-20x24in) s. 25-May-4 Durán, Madrid #731/R
£436 $781 €650 Night on Italian avenue (50x61cm-20x24in) s. 25-May-4 Durán, Madrid #734/R
£450 $788 €657 In the poppy field (50x40cm-20x16in) s. 17-Dec-3 John Nicholson, Haslemere #33/R
£451 $736 €650 Dusk lights (46x61cm-18x24in) s. 23-Sep-3 Durán, Madrid #667/R
£500 $815 €720 Beach in Normandy (38x55cm-15x22in) s. 23-Sep-3 Durán, Madrid #670/R
£500 $875 €730 Still life with white chrysanthemums (50x61cm-20x24in) s. 17-Dec-3 John Nicholson, Haslemere #69/R
£550 $963 €803 Parisian Club (38x55cm-15x22in) s. 17-Dec-3 John Nicholson, Haslemere #32/R
£550 $919 €803 Beach in Trouville (27x46cm-11x18in) s. 13-Jul-3 John Nicholson, Haslemere #66/R
£556 $906 €800 Grand Boulevard (54x65cm-21x26in) s. 23-Sep-3 Durán, Madrid #669/R
£600 $1122 €900 Beach in Cabourg (30x60cm-12x24in) s. 21-Jul-4 John Nicholson, Haslemere #414/R
£616 $1010 €850 Noche en los grandes bulevares (46x61cm-18x24in) s. 27-May-3 Durán, Madrid #783/R

SEKULA, Sonja (1918-1963) American/Swiss
Works on paper
£281 $477 €410 Sketch for text by Rilke (21x15cm-8x6in) mono.d.VIII.55 pen. 18-Nov-3 Hans Widmer, St Gallen #1202 (S.FR 620)
£317 $529 €463 Together (49x37cm-19x15in) s.i.d.1957 pencil gouache. 24-Jun-3 Germann, Zurich #1045 (S.FR 700)

SEKULIC, Sava (20th C) ?
Works on paper
£1533 $2821 €2300 Untitled (34x32cm-13x13in) gouache prov.exhib. 9-Jun-4 Artcurial Briest, Paris #391 est:2500-3000
£1600 $2944 €2400 Wooden man (47x30cm-19x12in) d.1986 gouache lead pencil isorel prov.exhib.lit. 9-Jun-4 Artcurial Briest, Paris #390/R est:2500-3000

SELBY, Prideaux John (1788-1867) British
£460 $823 €672 Vulture, Carrion crow and magpie with dead hare (72x104cm-28x41in) i. panel. 18-Mar-4 Neales, Nottingham #784

SELBY, William (1933-) British
£380 $692 €555 Exhibition (24x29cm-9x11in) s. board. 15-Jun-4 Bonhams, Leeds #52

SELDEN, Roger (1945-) American
£278 $464 €400 Grigio contrepunti neon (180x160cm-71x63in) s.d.1988 verso acrylic neon prov. 25-Oct-3 Cornette de St.Cyr, Paris #456
Works on paper
£352 $616 €500 Composition (66x48cm-26x19in) s.d.1976 mixed media card. 16-Dec-3 Finarte Semenzato, Milan #284/R
£1399 $2378 €2000 Composition (100x50cm-39x20in) s.d.1982 verso mixed media on canvas. 20-Nov-3 Finarte Semenzato, Milan #5/R est:2000-2500

SELDENER, Henrika (1800-1883) Swedish
£1892 $3386 €2800 Hunting (79x100cm-31x39in) s.d.1834. 8-May-4 Bukowskis, Helsinki #382/R est:3000-4000

SELFE, Madeline (20th C) British
£343 $615 €501 West Somerset foxhounds, Chapel Leigh Farm (66x91cm-26x36in) s.s. 19-Mar-4 Aspire, Cleveland #41

SELIGER, Charles (1926-) American
£581 $1000 €848 River at night. Bird (19x23cm-7x9in) s.d.60 one s.d.5.55 one oil and one W/C. 3-Dec-3 Doyle, New York #50/R est:1000-1500

SELIGMAN, Edgar (19/20th C) British
£480 $816 €701 Market Day. s.d.03. 30-Nov-3 Lots Road Auctions, London #361

SELIGMANN, Georg (1866-1924) Danish
£281 $458 €410 Summer landscape with woodland path (38x46cm-15x18in) init. 27-Sep-3 Rasmussen, Havnen #2281 (D.KR 3000)
£448 $819 €654 Workload being distributed among the men at the yard (75x85cm-30x33in) s. 9-Jun-4 Rasmussen, Copenhagen #1671/R (D.KR 5000)

SELIGMANN, Kurt (1900-1962) American/Swiss
Works on paper
£1141 $2099 €1700 Personage lyrique (48x38cm-19x15in) ink. 24-Mar-4 Joron-Derem, Paris #105 est:2500-3000
£7333 $13346 €11000 Inconcerned, Ulysses listens to the Siren's song (64x98cm-25x39in) s.i.d.1943 lead pencil W/C. 30-Jun-4 Calmels Cohen, Paris #68/R est:12000-15000

SELINGER, Jean Paul (1850-1909) American
£395 $700 €577 Massachusetts coastal scene with lighthouse (33x20cm-13x8in) s. panel. 2-May-4 Grogan, Boston #73/R

SELKAINAHO, Reino (1914-1979) Finnish
£286 $520 €420 Fishermen at sea (27x36cm-11x14in) s.d.69. 8-Feb-4 Bukowskis, Helsinki #450/R

SELL, Christian (elder) (1831-1883) German
£429 $700 €626 Cavalry skirmish during Franco-Prussian war (15x20cm-6x8in) s. panel. 24-Sep-3 Doyle, New York #99
£699 $1203 €1000 Two soldiers with horses (33x45cm-13x18in) s. 5-Dec-3 Michael Zeller, Lindau #792/R
£764 $1299 €1100 Soldiers resting (18x24cm-7x9in) s. panel. 28-Oct-3 Dorotheum, Vienna #115
£803 $1332 €1172 Troops on patrol (32x45cm-13x18in) s.d.1867. 15-Jun-3 Agra, Warsaw #41/R (P.Z 5000)
£805 $1498 €1200 Help arrives (17x24cm-7x9in) s. panel. 6-Mar-4 Arnold, Frankfurt #850/R
£1000 $1790 €1500 Italian cavalry on the march (27x44cm-11x17in) s. panel. 13-May-4 Bassenge, Berlin #5661/R est:1200
£1149 $2056 €1700 Prussian cavalry (28x27cm-11x11in) s. 6-May-4 Michael Zeller, Lindau #880/R est:1200
£1259 $2165 €1800 Prussian soldier on horseback (24x26cm-9x10in) s. 5-Dec-3 Michael Zeller, Lindau #793/R est:1200
£1342 $2470 €2000 The signal to attack (12x16cm-5x6in) s.d.1875 panel. 25-Mar-4 Dr Fritz Nagel, Stuttgart #763/R est:1200
£1342 $2470 €2000 Scene from Franco-Prussian war (14x18cm-6x7in) s.d.1880 panel. 25-Mar-4 Dr Fritz Nagel, Stuttgart #764/R est:1200

SELL, Christian (younger) (1854-1925) German
£313 $561 €470 Five Prussian soldiers in a skirmish in a winter landscape (14x18cm-6x7in) s. panel. 14-May-4 Behringer, Furth #1521/R
£333 $607 €500 Rider with two soldiers in a winter landscape (13x18cm-5x7in) s. panel. 1-Jul-4 Van Ham, Cologne #1615
£333 $607 €500 Prussian soldier with two captives (12x15cm-5x6in) s. panel. 1-Jul-4 Van Ham, Cologne #1616
£367 $656 €550 Three French cavalrymen fleeing from pursuing Prussian soldiers (13x18cm-5x7in) s. panel. 14-May-4 Behringer, Furth #1522/R
£414 $766 €600 Winter scene from Franco-Prussian war 1870/71 (11x16cm-4x6in) s. panel. 14-Feb-4 Hans Stahl, Hamburg #92/R
£667 $1213 €1000 Portrait of a dapple-grey horse (60x80cm-24x31in) s. 1-Jul-4 Van Ham, Cologne #1617
£800 $1432 €1200 Guarding the prisoners (12x16cm-5x6in) s. panel lit. 14-May-4 Schloss Ahlden, Ahlden #2807/R
£1111 $1756 €1600 Horseback fight (18x24cm-7x9in) s. panel. 19-Sep-3 Schloss Ahlden, Ahlden #1547/R est:1400

SELLAIO, Arcangelo Jacopo del (1478-1531) Italian
£190000 $347700 €277400 Annunciation (131x79cm-52x31in) tempera panel pair prov.exhib.lit. 7-Jul-4 Sotheby's, London #40/R est:80000-120000

SELLAIO, Jacopo del (1441-1493) Italian
£160000 $276800 €233600 Madonna and Child, the youthful Saint John the Baptist and an angel in a landscape beyond (92cm-36in circular) tempera panel prov.exhib. 10-Dec-3 Christie's, London #79/R est:100000-150000

SELLAIO, Jacopo del (circle) (1441-1493) Italian
£16000 $27200 €23360 Madonna and Child with young Saint John the Baptist (88x55cm-35x22in) i. gold ground panel arched top. 29-Oct-3 Christie's, London #80/R est:10000-15000

SELLAR, Charles A (1856-1926) British
£4000 $7240 €5840 Kitchen garden (61x46cm-24x18in) s. 19-Apr-4 Sotheby's, London #14/R est:4000-6000

SELLENATI, J (?) Italian
£5369 $9611 €8000 Market scene, possible in Vienna (32x46cm-13x18in) s. panel. 27-May-4 Dorotheum, Vienna #124/R est:6000-7000

SELLENY, Josef (1824-1875) Austrian
£3147 $5350 €4500 Woodland path to Bad Schalders near Brixen, southern Tyrol (53x40cm-21x16in) s.d.871 panel. 24-Nov-3 Dorotheum, Vienna #122/R est:3400-4200
Works on paper
£435 $800 €635 View looking towards the shore temple at Mahabalipuram (30x43cm-12x17in) i.verso pen ink wash gouache prov. 25-Mar-4 Doyle, New York #59/R

SELLITTO, Carlo (1581-1614) Italian
£105634 $184859 €150000 Christ washing the Apostles' feet (233x182cm-92x72in) prov.lit. 17-Dec-3 Christie's, Rome #502/R est:150000-200000

SELLMAYR, Ludwig (1834-1901) German
£969 $1648 €1415 Cattle grazing in wood (32x43cm-13x17in) s.i.d.1881 panel. 5-Nov-3 Dobiaschofsky, Bern #962/R (S.FR 2200)

SELMAN, Jan Collins (20th C) American
£227 $400 €331 View to the sea, Newcomb Hollow (53x69cm-21x27in) s. paper painted c.1996. 3-Jan-4 Outer Cape Auctions, Provincetown #90/R

SELMY, Eugène (1874-?) French
£1748 $3007 €2500 Marrakech (55x46cm-22x18in) s.i. 5-Dec-3 Maigret, Paris #87/R est:1800-2000
£2098 $3608 €3000 Two women on a roof (73x93cm-29x37in) s. 5-Dec-3 Maigret, Paris #92/R est:1800-2000

SELMYHR, Conrad (1877-1944) Norwegian
£259 $430 €376 Breakers by the coast (60x79cm-24x31in) s. 16-Jun-3 Blomqvist, Lysaker #1348/R (N.KR 3000)
£334 $557 €488 Coastal landscape (45x59cm-18x23in) s. 17-Nov-3 Blomqvist, Lysaker #1298/R (N.KR 4000)
£370 $677 €540 Cheese farm in Jotunheimen (66x106cm-26x42in) s. 2-Feb-4 Blomqvist, Lysaker #1272 (N.KR 4600)
£1259 $2140 €1800 Marine (62x100cm-24x39in) s. 18-Nov-3 Vanderkindere, Brussels #245 est:750-1250

SELOUS, Henry Courtney (1811-1890) British
£694 $1104 €1000 Cows in alpine meadow (54x80cm-21x31in) s. 13-Sep-3 Quittenbaum, Hamburg #27/R

SELTZER, Olaf C (1877-1957) American
£14205 $25000 €20739 Bronc on a frosty morn (25x64cm-10x25in) s.d.99 panel. 19-May-4 Sotheby's, New York #210/R est:20000-30000
£14706 $27500 €21471 King of the forest (30x23cm-12x9in) s. board. 24-Jul-4 Coeur d'Alene, Hayden #100/R est:15000-25000
£29412 $55000 €42942 Swiftcurrent Lake (84x122cm-33x48in) s. 24-Jul-4 Coeur d'Alene, Hayden #209/R est:40000-60000
Works on paper
£2941 $5500 €4294 Prairie wolf (18x18cm-7x7in) s. W/C prov. 24-Jul-4 Coeur d'Alene, Hayden #139/R est:6000-9000
£3631 $6500 €5301 Indian with rifle (28x18cm-11x7in) mono. W/C. 16-Mar-4 Matthew's, Oregon #67/R est:9000-12000
£8289 $15500 €12102 Hunting scene. On point (36x51cm-14x20in) s. W/C pair prov. 24-Jul-4 Coeur d'Alene, Hayden #253/R est:10000-20000
£8556 $16000 €12492 Wolf robe (28x23cm-11x9in) s. W/C. 24-Jul-4 Coeur d'Alene, Hayden #214/R est:5000-10000
£16043 $30000 €23423 Blackfoot chief (25x38cm-10x15in) s. W/C. 24-Jul-4 Coeur d'Alene, Hayden #174/R est:20000-30000
£32086 $60000 €46846 Schemers, Indian camp. Schemers, cowpuncher with grazing cattle (30x20cm-12x8in) s. gouache pair prov.lit. 24-Jul-4 Coeur d'Alene, Hayden #99/R est:30000 50000

SELTZER, W S (1955-) American
£933 $1615 €1362 Trespassers (64x94cm-25x37in) s. board. 9-Dec-3 Maynards, Vancouver #261 est:3000-4000 (C.D 2100)
£1765 $3000 €2577 Indian Chief (25x20cm-10x8in) s. canvas on masonite panel prov. 1-Nov-3 Santa Fe Art, Santa Fe #17/R est:2500-3500
£2647 $4500 €3865 Returning of the war party (46x61cm-18x24in) s. prov. 1-Nov-3 Santa Fe Art, Santa Fe #16/R est:4000-6000
Works on paper
£267 $461 €390 Blackfoot scouting party (33x38cm-13x15in) s. gouache on board. 9-Dec-3 Maynards, Vancouver #152 (C.D 600)
£444 $769 €648 Blackfoot encampment (36x53cm-14x21in) s. gouache on board. 9-Dec-3 Maynards, Vancouver #153 est:800-1000 (C.D 1000)
£889 $1538 €1298 Scouts (61x76cm-24x30in) s. gouache. 9-Dec-3 Maynards, Vancouver #262 est:3000-4000 (C.D 2000)

SELTZER, W Steve (1955-) American
£4545 $8500 €6636 Indian camp scene (61x91cm-24x36in) s. board. 24-Jul-4 Coeur d'Alene, Hayden #195/R est:6000-9000

SELTZER, William Steve (1955-) American
Works on paper
£826 $1496 €1206 Blackfoot scouting party (32x36cm-13x14in) s. gouache. 18-Apr-4 Levis, Calgary #215/R est:2000-2500 (C.D 2000)

SELVATICO, Lino (1872-1924) Italian
£1831 $3168 €2600 Lady (48x36cm-19x14in) s.d.24 board. 11-Dec-3 Christie's, Rome #144/R est:2800-3500

SELVE, W (19/20th C) German
£1133 $2051 €1700 Cows by water (19x40cm-7x16in) s. lit. 1-Apr-4 Frank Peege, Freiburg #1118/R est:800

SELWYN, William (1933-) British
Works on paper
£340 $554 €496 Seafront and jetty (26x36cm-10x14in) s. W/C. 23-Sep-3 Bonhams, Chester #897
£500 $815 €730 Winter landscape, Nant Gwynant (51x74cm-20x29in) W/C scratching out. 23-Sep-3 Bonhams, Chester #895

SEM (1863-1934) French
Works on paper
£828 $1382 €1200 La turfiste, portrait presume Lafitte (57x34cm-22x13in) s. W/C gouache. 17-Nov-3 Delorme & Bocage, Paris #143/R
£1586 $2649 €2300 Le cocktail (32x42cm-13x17in) s. W/C gouache. 17-Nov-3 Delorme & Bocage, Paris #144/R est:600-800

SEM, Anthon Hermanus Adrianus (attrib) (1821-c.1862) Dutch
£2715 $4697 €3964 Chateau Chillon (47x62cm-19x24in) indis.s. 9-Dec-3 Sotheby's, Zurich #9/R est:8000-12000 (S.FR 6000)

SEMEGHINI, Pio (1878-1964) Italian
£3056 $4828 €4400 Brunarella with pumpkin (35x26cm-14x10in) board. 6-Sep-3 Meeting Art, Vercelli #489 est:4000
£3356 $6007 €5000 Figures (30x33cm-12x13in) s. board painted 1930. 29-May-4 Farsetti, Prato #549/R est:4500-6000
£3497 $5944 €5000 Houses in Burano (25x34cm-10x13in) s.d.1940 board. 29-Nov-3 Farsetti, Prato #535/R est:3000
£4362 $7809 €6500 Portrait (31x47cm-12x19in) board painted c.1950. 29-May-4 Farsetti, Prato #436/R est:6000-7000
£6884 $11290 €9500 Still life with mask (39x47cm-15x19in) s.d.1935 board prov.exhib. 27-May-3 Sotheby's, Milan #131/R est:6000-8000
Works on paper
£476 $852 €700 Woman at bar. Burano (15x11cm-6x4in) sanguine double-sided. 16-Mar-4 Finarte Semenzato, Milan #238/R

SEMENOFF, Boris (1938-) Belgian
£400 $732 €600 Personnage vue de dos (80x63cm-31x25in) s.d.1981. 7-Jun-4 Palais de Beaux Arts, Brussels #384
£1000 $1830 €1500 Composition 3 (146x114cm-57x45in) s.d.1963 prov.exhib. 7-Jun-4 Palais de Beaux Arts, Brussels #142/R est:1500-2000

SEMENOWSKY, Eisman (?-1911) French
£559 $900 €816 Gypsy girl (33x23cm-13x9in) s. panel. 20-Aug-3 James Julia, Fairfield #1013/R
£1300 $2080 €1898 Elegant maidens on a terrace. Maidens in a boat (14x23cm-6x9in) one s. one init. panel pair. 18-Sep-3 Christie's, Kensington #212/R est:1200-1800
£1484 $2700 €2167 Young beauty adorned with flowers (30x25cm-12x10in) s. wood panel. 19-Jun-4 Jackson's, Cedar Falls #45/R est:1500-2500
£1655 $2764 €2400 Portrait d'une jeune fille. s.d.1887 panel. 17-Nov-3 Bernaerts, Antwerp #388 est:500-750
£2096 $3857 €3060 Portrait of young woman with hat (32x26cm-13x10in) s.i.d.1883. 14-Jun-4 Philippe Schuler, Zurich #4271/R est:3000-3500 (S.FR 4800)
£3521 $6162 €5000 Jeunes orientales. s.i. panel octagonal pair. 19-Dec-3 Pierre Berge, Paris #91/R est:4000-5000
£4000 $7000 €5840 Pretty young lady reclining on a sofa, masks and fans on the wall (30x36cm-12x14in) s. panel prov. 18-Dec-3 John Nicholson, Haslemere #1152/R est:4000-6000

SEMERAK, Zbynek (1919-1985) ?
Works on paper
£267 $491 €400 Untitled (33x17cm-13x7in) s.d.30.X.1997 gouache Indian ink lit. 9-Jun-4 Artcurial Briest, Paris #403

SEMINO, Giovanni Battista (1912-1987) Italian
£322 $602 €480 Ols teep road (42x34cm-17x13in) s.d.1956 board. 26-Feb-4 Cambi, Genoa #455/R

SEMMENCE, John (1930-1985) British
£300 $528 €438 Figures in a street (60x92cm-24x36in) s. board painting verso double-sided. 18-May-4 Bonhams, Knightsbridge #218/R

SEMPERE ESTEVE, Rafael (1928-) Spanish
Works on paper
£436 $772 €650 Ceramic market (49x70cm-19x28in) s.d.1988 W/C. 27-Apr-4 Duran, Madrid #21/R

SEMPERE, Eusebio (1924-) Spanish
Works on paper
£939 $1700 €1371 Untitled (58x36cm-23x14in) s.d.Sempere 1961 mixed media. 18-Apr-4 Bonhams & Butterfields, Los Angeles #7076 est:700-900
£4225 $7394 €6000 Composition (64x49cm-25x19in) s.d.1976 gouache. 16-Dec-3 Segre, Madrid #147/R est:4200

SEMPLE, William (19/20th C) British
£280 $524 €409 Lake Como. s. 22-Jul-4 Bonhams, Edinburgh #332

SEMPLICIO DA VERONA, Fra (1589-1654) Italian
Works on paper
£4200 $7686 €6132 Head of a man, turned to the left (16x11cm-6x4in) blk red chk htd white chk blue paper. 8-Jul-4 Sotheby's, London #38/R est:5000-7000

SEMPLICIO DA VERONA, Fra (attrib) (1589-1654) Italian
£2590 $4247 €3600 Annunciation (46x21cm-18x8in) copper. 4-Jun-3 Sotheby's, Milan #48/R est:4000-6000

SEMPREBON, Bruno (1906-) Italian
£1014 $1581 €1500 Interior with woman (45x34cm-18x13in) cardboard. 30-Mar-3 Adma, Formigine #659 est:1400-1500

SENAPE, Antonio (?-1842) Italian
Works on paper
£238 $397 €340 View of Girgenti (22x34cm-9x13in) i. ink. 24-Jun-3 Finarte Semenzato, Rome #11/R
£245 $409 €350 Dionisus' ear in Siracusa (40x24cm-16x9in) i. ink. 24-Jun-3 Finarte Semenzato, Rome #8/R
£550 $952 €803 Porte Maggiore. Sepoliro di Cicilia Metella (18x22cm-7x9in) i. ink pair. 10-Dec-3 Edgar Horn, Eastbourne #272/R
£1560 $2606 €2200 Views of Naples. pen ink Chinese ink pair. 15-Oct-3 Sotheby's, Paris #97/R est:1200
£2158 $3453 €3000 View of Naples (28x149cm-11x59in) i. Chinese ink on four sheets. 14-May-3 Finarte Semenzato, Milan #519 est:1300-1600

SENAT, Prosper L (1852-1925) American
£1600 $2912 €2336 Harbour scene with vessels, drying sails (69x48cm-27x19in) s. board. 17-Jun-4 Clevedon Sale Rooms #1015/R est:300-450
Works on paper
£251 $450 €366 Venice, venetian canal scene (69x48cm-27x19in) W/C. 21-Mar-4 Jeffery Burchard, Florida #63/R
£407 $700 €594 Bend in the stream (43x28cm-17x11in) s.d.1894 W/C. 7-Dec-3 Treadway Gallery, Cincinnati #529/R
£497 $900 €726 Seascape (74x53cm-29x21in) W/C. 2-Apr-4 Douglas, South Deerfield #27
£642 $1200 €937 Bermuda harbour view (23x43cm-9x17in) s.i.d.95 W/C. 29-Feb-4 Grogan, Boston #90/R
£1087 $2000 €1587 Palms at water's edge (69x48cm-27x19in) s.d.96 W/C. 25-Jun-4 Freeman, Philadelphia #28/R est:100-200

SENAVE, Jacques Albert (1758-1829) Belgian
£1049 $1804 €1500 La lecture des rebus (15x18cm-6x7in) panel. 8-Dec-3 Piasa, Paris #5 est:600-800

SENBERGS, Jan (1939-) Australian
£498 $832 €747 Study for Anxious Settlement (29x39cm-11x15in) s.d.84 i.verso. 27-Oct-3 Goodman, Sydney #58/R (A.D 1200)
£810 $1304 €1183 Houseboat (92x122cm-36x48in) s. board painted c.1960. 13-Oct-3 Joel, Victoria #379 est:2000-3000 (A.D 2000)
£813 $1276 €1179 Burnt bush, Moggs creek (72x106cm-28x42in) s.i.d.96 acrylic. 27-Aug-3 Christie's, Sydney #738/R est:2000-3000 (A.D 2000)
Works on paper
£413 $764 €603 Chicago 2 (65x94cm-26x37in) s.d.90 i.verso mixed media prov. 15-Mar-4 Sotheby's, Melbourne #183 est:200-300 (A.D 1000)
£992 $1835 €1448 Pittsburgh (140x174cm-55x69in) s.i.d.90 mixed media prov. 15-Mar-4 Sotheby's, Melbourne #81 est:1200-1800 (A.D 2400)

SENCHET, Victor (1879-1973) French
£629 $1000 €918 Port du Toulon (76x97cm-30x38in) s.d.1923 exhib. 9-Mar-3 William Jenack, New York #326

SENDLINGER, F (19/20th C) ?
£905 $1511 €1321 Still life of grapes, apples, pears and silver vessels (70x95cm-28x37in) s. board oval. 17-Nov-3 Waddingtons, Toronto #308/R est:700-1000 (C.D 2000)

SENE, Henry (1889-1961) French
£1711 $3147 €2600 Cavaliers se preparant pour la fantasia (40x70cm-16x28in) s. 25-Jun-4 Millon & Associes, Paris #78/R est:1500-2000
£6000 $11040 €9000 La fantasia aux environs de Marrakech (65x81cm-26x32in) s.d.1941 i.verso. 14-Jun-4 Gros & Delettrez, Paris #450/R est:8000-12000
Works on paper
£400 $716 €600 Mere et enfant boliviens (39x50cm-15x20in) s.d.1928 chl chk sanguine. 16-May-4 Thierry & Lannon, Brest #278

SENE, Louis (1747-c.1804) Swiss
Miniatures
£1700 $2941 €2482 Abbe de Rennepont (6cm-2in circular) s. 9-Dec-3 Christie's, London #87/R est:1000-1500

SENECHAL DE KERDREORET, Gustave Edouard le (1840-1920) French
£350 $584 €500 Nature morte aux fruits (32x41cm-13x16in) panel. 29-Jun-3 Eric Pillon, Calais #29/R
£467 $863 €700 Le port de Saint Malo (33x46cm-13x18in) s. cardboard. 14-Jul-4 Livinec, Gaudcheau & Jezequel, Rennes #166
£1944 $3072 €2800 Baai van Cansole (33x46cm-13x18in) s. 2-Sep-3 Christie's, Amsterdam #341/R est:2200-2600
Works on paper
£559 $1012 €850 Grands voiliers desarmes dans un bras de Rance (20x28cm-8x11in) s. W/C. 17-Apr-4 Deburaux, Boulogne #76

SENECHAL DE KERDREORET, Gustave Edouard le (attrib) (1840-1920) French
£490 $817 €700 Bateau et charettes (33x46cm-13x18in) 7-Oct-3 Livinec, Gaudcheau & Jezequel, Rennes #90

SENEQUE, Clement (1896-1930) South African
£328 $547 €479 Snow capped peaks (31x39cm-12x15in) s.d.20 board. 20-Oct-3 Stephan Welz, Johannesburg #599 est:4000-6000 (SA.R 3800)
£1724 $2879 €2517 Lake landscape with a jetty in the foreground (34x44cm-13x17in) canvas on board. 20-Oct-3 Stephan Welz, Johannesburg #329/R est:15000-20000 (SA.R 20000)
Works on paper
£238 $445 €347 View of Durban from Umbilo (19x29cm-7x11in) s. pastel. 24-Feb-4 Cannon & Cannon, Pietermaritzburg #281 (SA.R 3000)

SENET, Rafael (1856-1926) Spanish
£1678 $3087 €2500 Venice (35x19cm-14x7in) s. oil on board. 26-Mar-4 Ketterer, Hamburg #213/R est:3000-3500
£6338 $10965 €9000 Venetian canal (28x39cm-11x15in) s. 15-Dec-3 Ansorena, Madrid #312/R est:7500
£8000 $13600 €11680 Fisherwoman (96x52cm-38x20in) s. 18-Nov-3 Sotheby's, London #265/R
£9500 $17290 €13870 The gondoliers. Canal in Venice (51x31cm-20x12in) s. pair prov. 15-Jun-4 Sotheby's, London #180/R est:10000-15000
£10500 $19110 €15330 Promenade along the canal. View of Venice (31x51cm-12x20in) s. pair. 15-Jun-4 Sotheby's, London #181/R est:10000-15000
Works on paper
£1278 $2250 €1866 Venetian canal scene (53x33cm-21x13in) s. W/C. 18-May-4 Bonhams & Butterfields, San Francisco #135/R est:2000-3000
£1773 $2961 €2500 El Puente de Rialto, Venecia (19x30cm-7x12in) s. W/C. 23-Jun-3 Durán, Madrid #196/R est:1800
£3061 $5480 €4500 View of Venice (37x69cm-15x27in) s. W/C. 22-Mar-4 Durán, Madrid #170/R est:4500

SENFF, Adolf (1785-1863) German
£2133 $3819 €3200 Plant (22x17cm-9x7in) s.d.1825 paper. 13-May-4 Bassenge, Berlin #5662 est:400
Works on paper
£1004 $1828 €1506 Climbing plant with yellow flowers (29x19cm-11x7in) gouache prov. 17-Jun-4 Kornfeld, Bern #72/R (S.FR 2300)

SENGER, Ludwig von (1873-?) German
£533 $971 €800 Kaiser mountain in winter (70x100cm-28x39in) s.i. 1-Jul-4 Neumeister, Munich #2809
£733 $1335 €1100 Wintry mountain landscape (80x100cm-31x39in) s. 1-Jul-4 Neumeister, Munich #2808

SENGL, Peter (1945-) Austrian
£567 $1043 €850 Robot contacts (44x60cm-17x24in) s.d.70 tempera mixed media board. 9-Jun-4 Dorotheum, Salzburg #733/R
£671 $1235 €1000 Composition with figure (75x59cm-30x23in) s.i.d. acrylic pencil masonite. 26-Mar-4 Ketterer, Hamburg #649/R
£671 $1235 €1000 Wearing travelling clothes (90x70cm-35x28in) s.i.d. 26-Mar-4 Ketterer, Hamburg #650/R
£3691 $6607 €5500 Candle for you (120x100cm-47x39in) s.d.1985 prov. 25-May-4 Dorotheum, Vienna #364/R est:3000-4500
Works on paper
£563 $986 €800 Abstract composition (60x45cm-24x18in) s.i.d.94 mixed media. 19-Dec-3 Dorotheum, Vienna #421/R
£667 $1200 €1000 Artistic clerical couple (47x60cm-19x24in) s.i.d.79 mixed media. 21-Apr-4 Dorotheum, Vienna #231/R
£667 $1227 €1000 Scary screw (58x43cm-23x17in) s.d.1.7.70 Indian ink col pen. 9-Jun-4 Dorotheum, Salzburg #828/R

SENIOR, Mark (1864-1927) British
£1800 $3276 €2628 Moorland landscape, with farmlands (21x26cm-8x10in) board. 15-Jun-4 Bonhams, Leeds #175/R est:1200-1800
£2000 $3400 €2920 Daily news (69x44cm-27x17in) s. 18-Nov-3 Bonhams, Leeds #266/R est:2000-3000
£3000 $5460 €4380 Extensive moorland landscape (22x27cm-9x11in) i.indis.d.verso board. 15-Jun-4 Bonhams, Leeds #174/R est:1200-1800
£3800 $7106 €5548 Coastal scene with fishing boat off a beach (23x33cm-9x13in) s. panel. 22-Jul-4 Tennants, Leyburn #936/R est:2000-3000
£4200 $7644 €6132 Horse plough at work (20x25cm-8x10in) s. board. 15-Jun-4 Bonhams, Leeds #176/R est:2500-3500
£13500 $21465 €19710 Figures in a village square (51x61cm-20x24in) s.d.1904. 9-Sep-3 Gorringes, Lewes #2031/R est:3000-4000
Works on paper
£960 $1718 €1402 Pathway leading through a rose garden (25x34cm-10x13in) s. W/C. 16-Mar-4 Bonhams, Leeds #658/R

SENISE, Daniel (1955-) Brazilian
£2033 $3598 €3050 Untitled (70x124cm-28x49in) s.d.15/1/88 verso. 27-Apr-4 Bolsa de Arte, Rio de Janeiro #111/R (B.R 11100)
£6044 $10698 €9066 Pole people II (145x180cm-57x71in) s.d.1999 i.verso acrylic mixed media. 27-Apr-4 Bolsa de Arte, Rio de Janeiro #86/R (B.R 33000)
£6704 $12000 €9788 Tower of song (220x146cm-87x57in) s.i.d.1993 verso. 26-May-4 Sotheby's, New York #128/R est:15000-20000

SENNHAUSER, John (1907-1978) American/Swiss
Works on paper
£2059 $3500 €3006 Untitled (20x28cm-8x11in) s.d.1942 W/C. 9-Nov-3 Wright, Chicago #238 est:2000-3000

SENNO, Pietro (1831-1904) Italian
£2518 $4129 €3500 Cows at pasture (47x70cm-19x28in) s. canvas on card. 10-Jun-3 Pandolfini, Florence #84/R est:3200-3600
£43165 $70791 €60000 Re di Noce Beach, Elba island (130x170cm-51x67in) s. exhib.lit. 10-Jun-3 Pandolfini, Florence #96/R est:70000-80000

SENSEMANN, Susan (1949-) American
£273 $500 €399 Ouj-da (112x168cm-44x66in) 10-Jul-4 Hindman, Chicago #473/R
£301 $550 €439 Macondo x III (112x168cm-44x66in) 10-Jul-4 Hindman, Chicago #472/R

SENTIS, Juan Alfonso Carro (1920-) Spanish
£457 $850 €667 Interior (76x60cm-30x24in) s. 5-Mar-4 Skinner, Boston #516/R

SEOANE, Luis (1910-1979) Argentinian
£2685 $4805 €4000 Octopus (30x30cm-12x12in) s. 25-May-4 Durán, Madrid #129/R est:2900
£7017 $12700 €10245 Two faces (30x60cm-12x24in) 30-Mar-4 Arroyo, Buenos Aires #68
Works on paper
£342 $582 €500 Galicia (14x12cm-6x5in) s.d.1967 W/C. 4-Nov-3 Ansorena, Madrid #1000/R
£473 $832 €700 Galicia (13x11cm-5x4in) s.i.d.1967 W/C. 18-May-4 Segre, Madrid #314
£493 $863 €700 Blessing (36x25cm-14x10in) s.d.45 W/C dr lit. 16-Dec-3 Durán, Madrid #631/R
£526 $968 €800 Musicians (30x45cm-12x18in) s.d.1971 mixed media on metal. 22-Jun-4 Durán, Madrid #1253
£556 $906 €800 Warriors (36x24cm-14x9in) s.d.45 W/C lit. 23-Sep-3 Durán, Madrid #140/R
£556 $944 €800 Portrait of woman (13x13cm-5x5in) s.d.1977 bw. ink. 28-Oct-3 Segre, Madrid #218/R
£559 $1000 €816 Menu (35x20cm-14x8in) ink. 11-May-4 Arroyo, Buenos Aires #91
£578 $1035 €850 Woman and cat (28x19cm-11x7in) s.d.65 ink dr. 22-Mar-4 Durán, Madrid #99/R
£604 $1069 €900 Woman (20x15cm-8x6in) s. ink dr. 27-Apr-4 Durán, Madrid #653/R
£604 $1123 €900 Ambush (37x26cm-15x10in) s.d.45 mixed media lit. 2-Mar-4 Ansorena, Madrid #328/R
£621 $1037 €900 Woman reading (37x25cm-15x10in) s.d.45. 17-Nov-3 Durán, Madrid #603/R
£621 $1037 €900 Beating (36x26cm-14x10in) s.d.45 W/C dr. 17-Nov-3 Durán, Madrid #602/R
£634 $1096 €900 Goat (20x14cm-8x6in) s.d.43 dr. 15-Dec-3 Ansorena, Madrid #190/R
£638 $1066 €900 El descanso de los guerreros (37x25cm-15x10in) s.d.45 W/C lit. 23-Jun-3 Durán, Madrid #125/R
£660 $1049 €950 El recitador (37x25cm-15x10in) s.d.45 W/C lit. 29-Apr-3 Durán, Madrid #80/R
£669 $1171 €950 Peasant women (25x17cm-10x7in) s. pen. 16-Dec-3 Segre, Madrid #238/R
£671 $1255 €1000 Woman (27x36cm-11x14in) s.i.d.1961 ink W/C dr. 24-Feb-4 Durán, Madrid #125/R
£805 $1426 €1200 Woman holding basket on her head (36x25cm-14x10in) s. ink dr. 27-Apr-4 Durán, Madrid #629/R
£828 $1490 €1200 Pope audition (36x25cm-14x10in) s.d.45 dr W/C lit. 26-Jan-4 Durán, Madrid #16/R
£849 $1460 €1240 Portrait of woman (65x55cm-26x22in) s.d.49 mixed media. 3-Dec-3 Naón & Cia, Buenos Aires #90/R
£1074 $1901 €1600 Raphael painting a Madonna (36x25cm-14x10in) s.d.45 W/C ink lit. 27-Apr-4 Durán, Madrid #635/R est:1200

SEPESHY, Zoltan L (1898-1974) American
£1622 $3000 €2368 Rocky shore (46x61cm-18x24in) canvasboard. 13-Feb-4 Du Mouchelle, Detroit #2026/R est:3000-4000
£7784 $13000 €11365 Sandscape (63x76cm-25x30in) s. i.verso tempera masonite painted c.1938 prov.exhib.lit. 7-Oct-3 Sotheby's, New York #219 est:3000-5000

SEPP, Jan Christiaen (1739-1811) Dutch
Works on paper
£1689 $2973 €2500 Stork (41x29cm-16x11in) W/C col chk. 19-May-4 Sotheby's, Amsterdam #239/R est:1500-2000

SEQUEIRA, Domingos Antonio de (1768-1837) Portuguese
Works on paper
£4500 $8235 €6570 Young man gesturing to the right (18x23cm-7x9in) s.i. pen ink. 6-Jul-4 Christie's, London #94/R est:1500-2000

SERADOUR, Guy (1922-) French
£458 $792 €650 Le col blanc (35x24cm-14x9in) s. 13-Dec-3 Touati, Paris #168/R
£1818 $3127 €2600 Elegante a la robe bleue (73x54cm-29x21in) s. 8-Dec-3 Horta, Bruxelles #137 est:2500-3000
Works on paper
£409 $733 €597 Jeune femme au chapeau blanc (61x49cm-24x19in) s. pastel. 12-May-4 Dobiaschofsky, Bern #977/R (S.FR 950)

SERAFINI, Giuseppe (1915-1987) Italian
£296 $491 €420 Nude (30x20cm-12x8in) s. cardboard. 13-Jun-3 Farsetti, Prato #421
£333 $613 €500 Peasants (50x70cm-20x28in) cardboard prov. 14-Jun-4 Sant Agostino, Torino #237/R
£633 $1165 €950 Husband and wife (50x70cm-20x28in) s. cardboard. 11-Jun-4 Farsetti, Prato #495/R

SERANGELI, Giacchino Giuseppe (1768-1852) French
£118421 $217895 €180000 Portrait of Germaine Faipoult de Maisoncelle with her daughter Julie (192x128cm-76x50in) exhib.lit. 25-Jun-4 Piasa, Paris #43/R est:130000-150000

SERAPHINE DE SENLIS (1864-1942) French
£1600 $2880 €2400 Branche de fleurs (19x25cm-7x10in) s. panel. 26-Apr-4 Tajan, Paris #271/R est:2400-3000
£2098 $3608 €3000 Les cerises (36x49cm-14x19in) s. 3-Dec-3 Tajan, Paris #162 est:4000-5000
£2518 $4330 €3600 Vase de lilas (65x81cm-26x32in) s. 3-Dec-3 Tajan, Paris #163/R est:4000-5000

SEREBRIAKOV, Alexander (1907-1994) Russian
Works on paper
£1538 $2569 €2200 Projet de temple au bord du lac du Chateau de Groussay (44x64cm-17x25in) W/C. 26-Jun-3 Artcurial Briest, Paris #545 est:2000-3000
£1538 $2569 €2200 Projet de tente pour le mirador (39x63cm-15x25in) d.21 juillet 1967 W/C gouache graphite. 26-Jun-3 Artcurial Briest, Paris #546 est:2000-3000
£1538 $2569 €2200 Projet d'obelisque de face et de profil (50x39cm-20x15in) wax crayon graphite. 26-Jun-3 Artcurial Briest, Paris #547 est:2000-3000
£1958 $3270 €2800 Projet de mirador du parc du Chateau de Groussay (46x30cm-18x12in) W/C brown ink graphite. 26-Jun-3 Artcurial Briest, Paris #549 est:2000-3000
£2000 $3580 €2920 Blue interior (21x23cm-8x9in) s. W/C. 26-May-4 Sotheby's, Olympia #425/R est:2000-3000
£2448 $4088 €3500 Plan de la tente du mirador (43x63cm-17x25in) d.21 juillet 1967 brown chk graphite sold with a dr. 26-Jun-3 Artcurial Briest, Paris #553 est:2000-3000
£2797 $4671 €4000 Projet pour un obelisque (61x43cm-24x17in) crayon W/C gouache graphite. 26-Jun-3 Artcurial Briest, Paris #550 est:2000-3000
£2797 $4671 €4000 Projet pour un pavillon dans le parc du Chateau de Groussay (33x49cm-13x19in) W/C graphite. 26-Jun-3 Artcurial Briest, Paris #551 est:2000-3000
£2797 $4671 €4000 Avant projet de bateau a rames (43x63cm-17x25in) mono.d.1 septembre 1967 red chk W/C gouache graphite. 26-Jun-3 Artcurial Briest, Paris #554 est:2000-3000
£2867 $4789 €4100 Avant projet de la facade sur le grand lac du parc (29x43cm-11x17in) W/C gouache graphite. 26-Jun-3 Artcurial Briest, Paris #552 est:2000-3000
£2937 $4905 €4200 Avant projet l'embarcadere et debarcadere sur le parc (30x47cm-12x19in) mono.d.1 septembre 1967 black chk W/C gouache graphite. 26-Jun-3 Artcurial Briest, Paris #544 est:2000-3000
£3217 $5372 €4600 Projet du debarcadere et de l'embarcadere (30x43cm-12x17in) mono.i.d.1 septembre 1967 brown ink W/C gouache graphite. 26-Jun-3 Artcurial Briest, Paris #555 est:2000-3000
£3846 $7000 €5615 Elegant interior (34x53cm-13x21in) s.d.1943 W/C gouache htd gum arabic. 29-Jun-4 Sotheby's, New York #122/R est:7000-9000
£5000 $8950 €7300 Dining room at Beategui (38x49cm-15x19in) s.i.d.1950 W/C over pencil htd gouache. 26-May-4 Sotheby's, London #203/R est:6000-8000
£8000 $14320 €11680 Interior scene, Bestegui (38x57cm-15x22in) s.i.d.1950 W/C gouache over pencil. 26-May-4 Sotheby's, London #204/R est:8000-10000

SEREBRIAKOV, Alexander (attrib) (1907-1994) Russian
Works on paper
£532 $862 €750 Portrait d'interieur (21x23cm-8x9in) W/C. 23-May-3 Sotheby's, Paris #53/R
£1227 $2000 €1791 La Rue Mouffetard, Paris (48x64cm-19x25in) bears indis.sig.i.d.1929 gouache. 24-Sep-3 Doyle, New York #84/R est:2000-3000

SEREBRIAKOV, Alexievitch Vasili (1810-1886) Russian
£13846 $23815 €20215 Southern girl at the water fountain (65x55cm-26x22in) s.d.1853. 2-Dec-3 Bukowskis, Stockholm #276/R est:50000-60000 (S.KR 180000)

SEREBRIAKOVA, Zinaida (1884-1967) Russian
£70000 $119000 €102200 Basket of grapes and peaches (60x73cm-24x29in) s.d.1931. 19-Nov-3 Sotheby's, London #157/R est:70000-90000
Works on paper
£1690 $2924 €2400 Jeune fille assise devant un livre (35x25cm-14x10in) s. W/C. 15-Dec-3 Bailly Pommery, Paris #115 est:450-700
£8333 $15000 €12166 Study of three peasant women (44x37cm-17x15in) s.d.1915 graphite W/C gouache. 23-Apr-4 Sotheby's, New York #14/R est:18000-25000
£60897 $95000 € Young ballerinas (63x47cm-25x19in) s.cyrillic pastel exec. c.1921-24 unfinished sketch verso. 11-Apr-3 Christie's, Rockefeller NY #40/R est:80000-90000

SERENA, Luigi (1855-1911) Italian
£4765 $8530 €7100 Peasant woman (74x50cm-29x20in) s. 25-May-4 Finarte Semenzato, Milan #70/R est:3000-3500
£8451 $14620 €12000 Reading on the terrace (39x45cm-15x18in) s. 10-Dec-3 Sotheby's, Milan #129/R est:10000-15000

SERGEL, Johan Tobias (1740-1814) Swedish
Sculpture
£6462 $11114 €9435 Queen Lovisa Ulrika - face mask (19cm-7in) terracotta exhib.lit. 2-Dec-3 Bukowskis, Stockholm #442/R est:80000-100000 (S.KR 84000)
Works on paper
£778 $1400 €1136 Caricature of two dandies (24x22cm-9x9in) pen ink W/C exhib. 21-Jan-4 Sotheby's, New York #37/R est:1500-2000
£800 $1464 €1168 Portrait of a man in profile (28x20cm-11x8in) pen ink. 6-Jul-4 Christie's, London #197/R
£1848 $3307 €2698 Figure study for Raphael's Disputa (56x38cm-22x15in) red chk exec.c.1769 prov. 25-May-4 Bukowskis, Stockholm #537/R est:15000-20000 (S.KR 25000)
£1923 $3308 €2808 Study of a fountain (48x40cm-19x16in) Indian ink wash. 2-Dec-3 Bukowskis, Stockholm #438/R est:35000-40000 (S.KR 25000)
£1923 $3308 €2808 Study of a fountain (56x42cm-22x17in) Indian ink wash. 2-Dec-3 Bukowskis, Stockholm #439/R est:30000-35000 (S.KR 25000)

SERGEL, Johan Tobias (attrib) (1740-1814) Swedish
Works on paper
£776 $1389 €1133 Figure scenes (20x15cm-8x6in) Indian ink wash two. 25-May-4 Bukowskis, Stockholm #538/R (S.KR 10500)
£1385 $2382 €2022 Ariadne from Naxos with putti (35x55cm-14x22in) i. red chk. 3-Dec-3 AB Stockholms Auktionsverk #2343/R est:15000-18000 (S.KR 18000)
£1462 $2514 €2135 Hieronymous (57x38cm-22x15in) chk lit. 7-Dec-3 Uppsala Auktionskammare, Uppsala #82/R est:18000-20000 (S.KR 19000)

SERGER, Frederick B (1889-1965) American
£245 $450 €358 Red House (41x51cm-16x20in) s. 11-Jun-4 David Rago, Lambertville #247/R
£245 $450 €358 Roses (51x41cm-20x16in) s. 11-Jun-4 David Rago, Lambertville #248/R
£326 $600 €476 Still life of flowers and bowl of fruit (61x51cm-24x20in) s. 11-Jun-4 David Rago, Lambertville #331/R
£404 $650 €590 Garden path with sunflowers / A summer day (74x61cm-29x24in) s. 22-Feb-3 Bunte, Elgin #1204
£1061 $1900 €1549 Anemones (41x51cm-16x20in) s. prov. 6-May-4 Doyle, New York #121/R est:2000-3000
£1087 $2000 €1587 Still life (41x61cm-16x24in) s. 11-Jun-4 David Rago, Lambertville #332/R est:2200-2800

SERGEYEV, Nikolai (1908-1989) Russian
£54054 $96757 €80000 The sparkle (82x142cm-32x56in) s. 8-May-4 Bukowskis, Helsinki #441/R est:8000-12000

SERIE, Leopold (19th C) French
£397 $731 €580 Wooded landscape with woman bathing (45x32cm-18x13in) s. 14-Jun-4 Philippe Schuler, Zurich #5889 (S.FR 910)

SERIENT, Hermann (1935-) Austrian
£851 $1421 €1200 Utopia (29x23cm-11x9in) s.d.1991 s.d. verso panel. 14-Oct-3 Dorotheum, Vienna #294/R

SERIN, Harmen (1678-1765) Flemish
£3500 $6300 €5110 Portraits of gentlemen, one in a blue coat and one in a red coat (66x51cm-26x20in) one s. prov. pair. 23-Apr-4 Christie's, Kensington #108/R est:3000-5000

SERINI, G (1854-?) Italian
£1406 $2250 €2053 Venetian canal scene (53x86cm-21x34in) 19-Sep-3 Du Mouchelle, Detroit #2009/R est:2500-3500

SERINO, Vincenzo (1876-?) Italian
£366 $656 €534 Fishing boats in the Bay of Naples (33x48cm-13x19in) 12-May-4 Dobiaschofsky, Bern #980/R (S.FR 850)
£948 $1697 €1384 Fishing boats by the ruins of palazzo Donn'Anna, Nales (36x52cm-14x20in) s. 12-May-4 Dobiaschofsky, Bern #979/R est:1500 (S.FR 2200)

SERIS, Pierre (20th C) French
£352 $585 €500 La Temple de la Raison (115x146cm-45x57in) s. exhib. 16-Jun-3 E & Eve, Paris #87/R

SERISAWA, Sueo (1910-) Japanese
£1882 $3200 €2748 Study of a youngf girl (20x30cm-8x12in) s. i.verso canvas on board prov. 29-Oct-3 Christie's, Los Angeles #57/R est:2000-3000

SERITTI, Vincente (20th C) Italian
£220 $400 €321 Frutas y flores (16x21cm-6x8in) s. s.i.verso board. 7-Feb-4 Sloans & Kenyon, Bethesda #300/R

SERL, Jon (1894-?) American
£1000 $1800 €1460 Mother and child (30x41cm-12x16in) acrylic board. 24-Apr-4 Slotin Folk Art, Buford #322/R est:3000-5000
£2036 $3400 €2973 Three figures (61x46cm-24x18in) acrylic board. 15-Nov-3 Slotin Folk Art, Buford #151/R est:2000-4000
£2156 $3600 €3148 Mother and child (76x41cm-30x16in) board prov.lit. 15-Nov-3 Slotin Folk Art, Buford #152/R est:2000-4000
£2156 $3600 €3148 Man with fruit (53x43cm-21x17in) panel prov. 15-Nov-3 Slotin Folk Art, Buford #153/R est:2000-4000

SERNA, Ismael de la (1897-1968) Spanish
£694 $1159 €1000 Paysage de nuit (35x67cm-14x26in) s.d.1956 isorel panel lit. 21-Oct-3 Artcurial Briest, Paris #337
£1377 $2258 €1900 Nude horserider (27x37cm-11x15in) s. oil tempera exhib. 27-May-3 Durán, Madrid #291/R est:1800
£1736 $2899 €2500 Docks, la nuit (77x96cm-30x38in) s. tempera board. 21-Oct-3 Artcurial Briest, Paris #341/R est:2800-3500
£2057 $3332 €2900 Swan (26x35cm-10x14in) s. board. 20-May-3 Ansorena, Madrid #332/R est:2700
£2083 $3479 €3000 Gare (80x104cm-31x41in) s. panel. 21-Oct-3 Artcurial Briest, Paris #336/R est:3000-4000
£2500 $4525 €3650 Composition (74x60cm-29x24in) tempera isorel lit. 1-Apr-4 Christie's, Kensington #50/R est:800-1200
£2958 $5117 €4200 Saint Francis (73x45cm-29x18in) s. lit. 15-Dec-3 Ansorena, Madrid #95/R est:4200
£3659 $6000 €5342 Portal view, sailboats in harbour (64x56cm-25x22in) s. masonite. 1-Jun-3 William Jenack, New York #211 est:2000-3000
£3901 $6319 €5500 Toro (55x81cm-22x32in) s. 20-May-3 Ansorena, Madrid #313/R est:4800
£4138 $7448 €6000 Landscape with willows (75x69cm-30x27in) s. board. 26-Jan-4 Ansorena, Madrid #889/R est:6000
£4362 $8114 €6500 Composition (61x48cm-24x19in) s. cardboard. 2-Mar-4 Ansorena, Madrid #839/R est:6500
£4698 $8738 €7000 Guardia (88x60cm-35x24in) s. 2-Mar-4 Artcurial Briest, Paris #232/R est:8000-10000
£4861 $8021 €7000 Untitled (72x52cm-28x20in) s. 2-Jul-3 Ansorena, Madrid #882/R
£5034 $9363 €7500 Composition (75x52cm-30x20in) s. 2-Mar-4 Artcurial Briest, Paris #233/R est:6000-8000
£6000 $9540 €8700 Bodegon (58x71cm-23x28in) 11-Sep-3 Christie's, Kensington #101/R est:6000-8000
£6000 $10020 €8760 La fenetre ouverte (74x69cm-29x27in) board painted 1948 lit. 22-Oct-3 Sotheby's, Olympia #147/R est:4000-6000
£6250 $10313 €9000 Woman (88x60cm-35x24in) s. 2-Jul-3 Ansorena, Madrid #879/R
£6711 $12483 €10000 Vase of flowers (116x81cm-46x32in) st.sig. 2-Mar-4 Ansorena, Madrid #79/R est:10000
£7343 $12262 €10500 Panier de fruits a la pasteque (54x72cm-21x28in) s. paper on canvas. 30-Jun-3 Bailly Pommery, Paris #24/R
£7500 $12525 €10950 Nature morte aux fruits (54x73cm-21x29in) s. oil paper on canvas. 21-Oct-3 Sotheby's, London #130/R est:8000-12000
£8000 $13360 €11680 Nature morte (42x58cm-17x23in) s. board. 21-Oct-3 Sotheby's, London #129/R est:6000-8000
£8511 $13787 €12000 Woman with dog (94x71cm-37x28in) s.d.28. 20-May-3 Ansorena, Madrid #318/R est:12000
£9333 $16893 €14000 Still life with violin, cup and music sheets (65x54cm-26x21in) s. 30-Mar-4 Segre, Madrid #134/R est:12000
£9524 $17333 €14000 Still life with guitar and apple (80x60cm-31x24in) s. board. 3-Feb-4 Segre, Madrid #353/R est:13000
£9859 $17056 €14000 Mystery (72x128cm-28x50in) s.d.1927. 15-Dec-3 Ansorena, Madrid #315/R est:14000
£12752 $23718 €19000 Still life (73x93cm-29x37in) s.d.XXX. 2-Mar-4 Ansorena, Madrid #56/R est:18000
£13103 $21752 €19000 Still life of flowers with jug (60x80cm-24x31in) s. 30-Sep-3 Ansorena, Madrid #95/R est:19000
£19718 $34507 €28000 Still life (60x73cm-24x29in) s. 16-Dec-3 Segre, Madrid #113/R est:16500
£21127 $36550 €30000 Nature morte a la coupe de fruits (54x73cm-21x29in) s.d.1946 oil collage. 9-Dec-3 Artcurial Briest, Paris #270/R est:15000-20000
Works on paper
£268 $497 €400 Imploration (20x19cm-8x7in) st.sig. Chinese ink dr. 14-Mar-4 Eric Pillon, Calais #215/R
£268 $497 €400 Trois figures (20x18cm-8x7in) st.sig. graphite dr. 14-Mar-4 Eric Pillon, Calais #212/R
£268 $497 €400 Imploration (31x22cm-12x9in) st.sig. Chinese ink dr. 14-Mar-4 Eric Pillon, Calais #214/R
£268 $497 €400 Portrait d'homme de profil (20x18cm-8x7in) st.sig. Chinese ink wash dr. 14-Mar-4 Eric Pillon, Calais #211/R
£282 $487 €400 Portrait d'homme au chapeau (20x18cm-8x7in) st.sig. chl dr. 14-Dec-3 Eric Pillon, Calais #239/R
£302 $561 €450 Allegorie aux sciences (35x25cm-14x10in) st.sig. graphite ink. 2-Mar-4 Artcurial Briest, Paris #72
£302 $561 €450 Composition surrealiste (27x20cm-11x8in) st.sig. graphite. 2-Mar-4 Artcurial Briest, Paris #73
£433 $780 €650 Portrait of woman (33x25cm-13x10in) st.sig. pastel W/C lit. 24-Apr-4 Cornette de St.Cyr, Paris #404
£556 $928 €800 Profil d'homme (20x18cm-8x7in) st.sig. ink lead pencil prov. 21-Oct-3 Artcurial Briest, Paris #123
£559 $934 €800 Nature morte a la lampe a petrole (30x20cm-12x8in) s. chl dr. 29-Jun-3 Eric Pillon, Calais #279/R
£563 $975 €800 Nature morte aux fruits (22x30cm-9x12in) st.sig. Chinese ink chl. 14-Dec-3 Eric Pillon, Calais #241/R
£604 $1069 €900 Composition (32x25cm-13x10in) s. gouache. 27-Apr-4 Durán, Madrid #637/R
£629 $1051 €900 Cubist still life (33x43cm-13x17in) s. W/C. 30-Jun-3 Ansorena, Madrid #23/R
£909 $1518 €1300 Still life of fruit (33x42cm-13x17in) s. W/C. 30-Jun-3 Ansorena, Madrid #24/R
£1000 $1820 €1500 Horse and bull (26x37cm-10x15in) s. W/C Chinese ink. 4-Jul-4 Eric Pillon, Calais #293/R
£1189 $1985 €1700 Composition (31x24cm-12x9in) s. W/C. 24-Jun-3 Segre, Madrid #175/R est:1700
£1449 $2377 €2000 Higuera (49x32cm-19x13in) s. drawing W/C. 27-May-3 Durán, Madrid #91/R est:1800
£2035 $3500 €2971 Raffinerie de laco (73x95cm-29x37in) s.d.58 gouache oil col chk on masonite. 3-Dec-3 Doyle, New York #17/R est:2000-3000
£3200 $5344 €4672 Taureau (24x35cm-9x14in) s. W/C brush ink gouache prov. 22-Oct-3 Sotheby's, Olympia #185/R est:2000-3000
£3380 $5408 €4800 Still life of flowers (50x76cm-20x30in) s. gouache paper on board. 16-Sep-3 Segre, Madrid #172/R est:4800
£3467 $6275 €5200 Architecture fantastique aux marguerites (71x56cm-28x22in) s.d.1927 mixed media. 4-Apr-4 St-Germain-en-Laye Encheres #14/R est:1500-2000
£14085 $24366 €20000 Still life with violin (91x73cm-36x29in) s. mixed media board. 15-Dec-3 Ansorena, Madrid #974/R est:15000

SERNEELS, Antoine (1909-) Belgian
£382 $623 €550 Annonciation (100x90cm-39x35in) s. 23-Sep-3 Galerie Moderne, Brussels #773/R
£739 $1353 €1079 Female nude (60x73cm-24x29in) s. i.verso. 4-Jun-4 Zofingen, Switzerland #2520/R (S.FR 1700)
£750 $1388 €1095 Reclining nude (70x91cm-28x36in) s. 15-Jan-4 Christie's, Kensington #750/R

SERNEELS, Clement (1912-1991) Belgian
£991 $1774 €1447 Still life of roses (49x59cm-19x23in) s.d.62. 31-May-4 Stephan Welz, Johannesburg #508 (SA.R 12000)
£1092 $1878 €1594 Young African girl (59x40cm-23x16in) s.d.66 board. 3-Dec-3 Stephan Welz, Johannesburg #29/R est:3000-5000 (SA.R 12000)
£1274 $2191 €1860 Oriental girl (67x48cm-26x19in) s.d.67 canvas on board. 3-Dec-3 Stephan Welz, Johannesburg #28/R est:7000-10000 (SA.R 14000)
£1321 $2365 €1929 Spring time II (68x78cm-27x31in) s.d.84 prov. 31-May-4 Stephan Welz, Johannesburg #526 est:6000-9000 (SA.R 16000)
£1404 $2513 €2050 Still life of flowers in a green vase (59x49cm-23x19in) s.d.60 canvas on board. 31-May-4 Stephan Welz, Johannesburg #511/R est:7000-10000 (SA.R 17000)
£1486 $2661 €2170 Portrait of a young woman (59x49cm-23x19in) s.d.61. 31-May-4 Stephan Welz, Johannesburg #563 est:5000-8000 (SA.R 18000)
£1638 $2735 €2391 Still life of roses (51x41cm-20x16in) s.d.76. 20-Oct-3 Stephan Welz, Johannesburg #364 est:6000-8000 (SA.R 19000)

SERNER, Otto (1854-?) Swiss
Works on paper
£302 $556 €450 Southern coast in evening (17x38cm-7x15in) s.d.1.99 mixed media board. 26-Mar-4 Dorotheum, Vienna #244/R

SEROR, Lisa (20th C) ?
£699 $1189 €1000 L'appel (82x124cm-32x49in) s. acrylic pigments. 27-Nov-3 Calmels Cohen, Paris #105/R
£769 $1308 €1100 Composition a la chaise (107x79cm-42x31in) s. acrylic pigments. 27-Nov-3 Calmels Cohen, Paris #106/R

SEROV, V V (1941-) Russian
£435 $800 €635 Dinner in the field (44x69cm-17x27in) cardboard painted 1960. 27-Mar-4 Shishkin Gallery, Moscow #95/R
£598 $1100 €873 Mordovian chastooshkies (60x80cm-24x31in) painted 1990. 27-Mar-4 Shishkin Gallery, Moscow #97/R
£652 $1200 €952 Country women (40x79cm-16x31in) cardboard painted 1960. 27-Mar-4 Shishkin Gallery, Moscow #96/R

SEROV, Valentin Alexandrovitch (1865-1911) Russian
£10897 $17000 € Study of a Russian farm (26x33cm-10x13in) s.cyrillic i.verso cardboard. 11-Apr-3 Christie's, Rockefeller NY #20/R est:10000-15000
Works on paper
£3200 $5440 €4800 Portrait of young lady (58x45cm-23x18in) s.d.1905 pencil chk board. 25-Nov-3 Christie's, London #139/R est:2000-3000
£5319 $8404 €7500 Woman with book (50x17cm-20x7in) s.d.1902 chl pastel. 24-Jul-3 Claude Boisgirard, Paris #27/R

SERPAN (20th C) ?
£680 $1217 €1000 Lelanouct (73x92cm-29x36in) s. painted 1967 prov. 21-Mar-4 Calmels Cohen, Paris #145/R

SERPAN, Jaroslav (1922-1976) Czechoslovakian
£1133 $2074 €1700 Composition (81x100cm-32x39in) s. s.i.d.17.2.63 verso. 4-Jun-4 Lempertz, Koln #456/R est:2400
£1233 $2257 €1850 Imthsvuun (79x63cm-31x25in) s. s.i.d.16.5.1957 verso prov. 4-Jun-4 Lempertz, Koln #455/R est:2400
£1259 $2165 €1800 Seddummprc (92x73cm-36x29in) s.i.d.1967 verso oil acrylic. 4-Dec-3 Van Ham, Cologne #475/R est:2200

SERRA CASTELLET, Francisco (1909-) Spanish
£5141 $8894 €7300 Figure (65x35cm-26x14in) s. cardboard. 15-Dec-3 Ansorena, Madrid #327/R est:7300

SERRA DE RIVERA, Xavier (1946-) Spanish
£1111 $1889 €1600 House and stones (35x46cm-14x18in) s.d.1972 s.i.d.verso prov. 28-Oct-3 Segre, Madrid #325/R est:1400

SERRA MELGOSA, Joan (1899-1980) Spanish
£313 $575 €475 Landscape (50x65cm-20x26in) s. 22-Jun-4 Durán, Madrid #56/R
£2349 $4369 €3500 Still life with melon (72x100cm-28x39in) s. 2-Mar-4 Ansorena, Madrid #99/R est:3500

SERRA MELGOSA, Joan (attrib) (1899-1980) Spanish
£669 $1157 €950 Boats on the coast (46x56cm-18x22in) s. 15-Dec-3 Ansorena, Madrid #281/R

SERRA SANTA, Jose (1916-1998) Spanish/Argentinian
£403 $713 €600 Stormy day (19x30cm-7x12in) s. cardboard. 27-Apr-4 Durán, Madrid #700/R

SERRA Y AUQUE, Enrico (1859-1918) Spanish
£594 $993 €850 Lagoon near Rome (27x16cm-11x6in) s. canvas on board. 30-Jun-3 Ansorena, Madrid #249/R
£882 $1500 €1288 Pond with boats (43x80cm-17x31in) s. 20-Nov-3 Galeria y Remates, Montevideo #120/R
£1056 $1849 €1500 Lagoons (35x75cm-14x30in) s. 16-Dec-3 Segre, Madrid #85/R
£1761 $3081 €2500 Lagoons (75x45cm-30x18in) s. 16-Dec-3 Segre, Madrid #85b/R est:3000
£2355 $3862 €3250 Estatua de silfide (89x68cm-35x27in) s. 27-May-3 Durán, Madrid #248/R est:3250
£2657 $4517 €3800 Sunset over the Pontinian marshes (43x97cm-17x38in) s.d.1912 lit. 28-Nov-3 Schloss Ahlden, Ahlden #1436/R est:1600
£2721 $4871 €4000 Ruins by marsh (56x105cm-22x41in) s.i. 17-Mar-4 Neumeister, Munich #607/R est:4000
£7746 $13556 €11000 Saint Mary of Ripoll (113x61cm-44x24in) s. 16-Dec-3 Segre, Madrid #75/R est:11000

SERRA Y FARNES, Pedro (1890-1974) Spanish
£600 $1092 €900 Mountain landscape (21x31cm-8x12in) s. board. 29-Jun-4 Segre, Madrid #23/R
£987 $1786 €1500 View of San Cugat de Valles (65x81cm-26x32in) s.i. 14-Apr-4 Ansorena, Madrid #38/R

SERRA Y PORSON, Jose (1824-1910) Spanish
£664 $1109 €950 Guitar player (43x25cm-17x10in) s.d.85 board. 30-Jun-3 Ansorena, Madrid #319/R
Works on paper
£347 $566 €500 Bacchant (8x5cm-3x2in) s. Chinese ink dr. 23-Sep-3 Durán, Madrid #87/R
£382 $623 €550 Faune (9x6cm-4x2in) s. Chinese ink dr. 23-Sep-3 Durán, Madrid #86/R
£448 $749 €650 Studying plans (29x39cm-11x15in) s. W/C. 17-Nov-3 Durán, Madrid #29/R
£833 $1358 €1200 Horse watering (9x12cm-4x5in) s. Chinese ink gouache dr. 23-Sep-3 Durán, Madrid #88/R
£1910 $3113 €2750 Book lover (11x8cm-4x3in) s. Chinese ink gouache r. 23-Sep-3 Durán, Madrid #89/R

SERRA, Andreu (20th C) Spanish
£603 $977 €850 Town of Marreucos (62x46cm-24x18in) s. 20-May-3 Ansorena, Madrid #203/R

SERRA, Ernesto (1860-1915) Italian
£533 $981 €800 Girl with cat (50x36cm-20x14in) s. 14-Jun-4 Sant Agostino, Torino #122/R
£4604 $7551 €6400 Gentleman riding horse (300x143cm-118x56in) s.d.1899. 10-Jun-3 Pandolfini, Florence #129/R est:2200-2400

SERRA, Francisco (1912-1976) Spanish
£4667 $8493 €7000 Mujer junto al aparador (81x65cm-32x26in) s.d.1955. 29-Jun-4 Segre, Madrid #95/R est:6000

SERRA, Gustavo (20th C) Venezuelan?
£537 $875 €784 Horizontal composition I (90x120cm-35x47in) s. painted 1999. 20-Jul-3 Subastas Odalys, Caracas #66

SERRA, Luigi (1846-1888) Italian
Works on paper
£280 $476 €400 Sick (27x20cm-11x8in) s. pencil. 19-Nov-3 Finarte Semenzato, Milan #531/R

SERRA, Luigi (attrib) (1846-1888) Italian
Works on paper
£285 $450 €413 Roosting chickens (23x30cm-9x12in) W/C. 27-Jul-3 Simpson's, Houston #276

SERRA, Richard (1939-) American
£22346 $40000 €32625 Barge (89x79cm-35x31in) init.d.83 oilstick prov.exhib.lit. 13-May-4 Sotheby's, New York #186/R est:18000-25000
£34431 $57500 €50269 Untitled (76x103cm-30x41in) paintstick paper on board prov. 13-Nov-3 Sotheby's, New York #566/R est:20000-30000
£111732 $200000 €163129 The American flag is not an object of worship (287x376cm-113x148in) paintstick paper painted 1989 prov.exhib.lit. 13-May-4 Sotheby's, New York #183/R est:80000-120000
Prints
£1963 $3200 €2866 Hreppholar (89x114cm-35x45in) s.d.91 num.24/35 etching handmade paper. 24-Sep-3 Christie's, Rockefeller NY #380/R est:4000-6000
£2483 $4146 €3600 Paris (215x133cm-85x52in) s.d.1984 num.14/17 serigraph. 13-Nov-3 Finarte Semenzato, Rome #51/R est:2800-3500
£2761 $4500 €4031 Finkl Forge II (120x120cm-47x47in) s.d.1996 num.19/33 etching on Lanaquarelle. 24-Sep-3 Christie's, Rockefeller NY #382/R est:3000-4000
£5367 $9500 €7836 Vesturey I (181x90cm-71x35in) s.d.1991 num.18/35 relief etching aquatint clear coating spray. 28-Apr-4 Christie's, Rockefeller NY #401/R est:5000-7000
Sculpture
£47904 $80000 €69940 Vertical parallelogram (124x61x61cm-49x24x24in) steel edition 1 of 3 prov. 13-Nov-3 Sotheby's, New York #564/R est:60000-80000
£215569 $360000 €314731 Corner block (28x28x91cm-11x11x36in) hot rolled steel executed 1983 prov.lit. 12-Nov-3 Sotheby's, New York #42/R est:150000-200000
Works on paper
£435 $713 €600 Untitled (24x19cm-9x7in) s.d.92 pencil paper on card. 27-May-3 Sotheby's, Amsterdam #571/R
£453 $811 €680 Untitled (35x28cm-14x11in) mono.i. chl. 15-May-4 Dr Sturies, Dusseldorf #197/R

SERRA, Rosa (1944-) Dutch
Sculpture
£1333 $2453 €2000 Triangle (27cm-11in) s.num.1/7 bronze exec 2003. 8-Jun-4 Sotheby's, Amsterdam #241/R est:2000-3000
£1449 $2377 €2000 Alice (19cm-7in) i. num.1/7 green pat bronze lit. 27-May-3 Sotheby's, Amsterdam #525/R est:1500-2000
£1538 $2646 €2200 Fashion (47cm-19in) i num.6/7 brown pat. bronze lit. 2-Dec-3 Sotheby's, Amsterdam #288/R est:2000-3000
£1812 $2971 €2500 Arc (24cm-9in) i. num.3/7 brown pat bronze lit. 27-May-3 Sotheby's, Amsterdam #521/R est:2500-3500
£2000 $3680 €3000 Fusio (54x40x17cm-21x16x7in) s. num.1/7 marbleised bronze conceived 2002 one of seven lit. 9-Jun-4 Christie's, Amsterdam #279/R est:3500-4500
£2000 $3680 €3000 Expressio (35cm-14in) s.num.1/7 bronze exec 2003. 8-Jun-4 Sotheby's, Amsterdam #242/R est:2000-2500
£2378 $4090 €3400 Untitled (48cm-19in) i.num.3/7 brown pat. bronze. 2-Dec-3 Sotheby's, Amsterdam #287/R est:2000-3000
£2797 $4755 €4000 Jeanne (34cm-13in) s.num. bronze conceived 2002 lit. 25-Nov-3 Christie's, Amsterdam #143/R est:1500-2000
£3846 $6538 €5500 Fifth Avenue (64cm-25in) s.num.3/7 marbleized bronze incl bronze base conceived 2002 lit. 25-Nov-3 Christie's, Amsterdam #144/R est:2000-3000

SERRAFF, Luc Elysee (1936-) Algerian
£699 $1189 €1000 Est belle ce soir (81x100cm-32x39in) s.d.1992. 27-Nov-3 Calmels Cohen, Paris #111/R

SERRALUNGA, Luigi (1880-1940) Italian

£1241 $2061 €1800 Vase of tulips (75x57cm-30x22in) s. masonite. 1-Oct-3 Della Rocca, Turin #309/R
£1268 $2193 €1800 Vase of flowers (81x54cm-32x21in) s. 9-Dec-3 Finarte Semenzato, Milan #114/R
£2215 $4075 €3300 Flowers (100x80cm-39x31in) s.d.916 board. 24-Mar-4 Il Ponte, Milan #596/R est:3500-3800

SERRANO RUEDA, Santiago (1942-) Spanish

£338 $595 €500 Untitled IX (66x49cm-26x19in) s.d.1988 cardboard prov. 18-May-4 Segre, Madrid #234/R

SERRANO, Andres (1950-) American

Photographs
£2148 $3952 €3200 Lesa Lewis - Series big women (83x66cm-33x26in) s.i.d.1998 num.6/45 verso col photograph. 24-Mar-4 Joron-Derem, Paris #208/R est:2500-3000
£2600 $4732 €3796 Piss Discus (72x47cm-28x19in) s.i.d.1988 num.2/50 verso cibachrome. 4-Feb-4 Sotheby's, Olympia #266/R est:2500-3500
£3261 $6000 €4761 America, Playboy Buny Deanna Brooks (152x126cm-60x50in) s.i.num.3 verso cibachrome plexiglas prov. 10-Jun-4 Phillips, New York #468/R est:7000-9000
£3804 $7000 €5554 America, Snoop Dogg (166x139cm-65x55in) s.i.num.3 verso cibachrome plexiglas prov. 10-Jun-4 Phillips, New York #469/R est:7000-10000
£4491 $7500 €6557 Blood scape V (71x102cm-28x40in) s.d.1989 num.5 verso cibachrome mounted on plexiglas prov. 14-Nov-3 Phillips, New York #129/R est:8000-12000
£5000 $8350 €7300 History of sex, martyr (115x95cm-45x37in) s.i.num.2/7 verso cibachrome print edition 2 of 10 prov.lit. 22-Oct-3 Christie's, London #164/R est:5000-7000
£5689 $9500 €8306 Ascent (115x165cm-45x65in) cibachrome mounted on plexiglas executed 1983 prov. 14-Nov-3 Phillips, New York #128/R est:12000-18000
£7500 $12525 €10950 Black Rembrandt (41x31cm-16x12in) cibachrome prints aluminium edition of 15 three prov. 22-Oct-3 Christie's, London #165/R est:5000-7000
£7500 $13800 €10950 Budapest, young Hasid (100x81cm-39x32in) s.i. num.1/7 cibachrome executed 1994 prov.exhib. 25-Jun-4 Christie's, London #268/R est:7000-9000
£8000 $13360 €11680 Milk Cross (68x100cm-27x39in) s.i.num.2/10 verso cibachrome print exec 1987 lit. 21-Oct-3 Sotheby's, London #323/R est:8000-12000
£9396 $16819 €14000 Interpretations of dreams (102x83cm-40x33in) s.i.verso num.4/7 cibachrome exec.2001. 28-May-4 Farsetti, Prato #343/R est:14000-16000
£12291 $22000 €17945 Black Madonna (166x115cm-65x45in) s.i.num.3/4 verso Cibachrome print plexiglas prov.exhib. 12-May-4 Christie's, Rockefeller NY #357/R est:10000-15000
£12291 $22000 €17945 Blut und Boden, blood and soil (115x166cm-45x65in) s.i.d.1987 num.2/4 verso Cibachrome print plexiglas prov. 12-May-4 Christie's, Rockefeller NY #359/R est:12000-18000
£16760 $30000 €24470 Crucifixion (152x101cm-60x40in) s.i.d.1987 num.2/4 verso Cibachrome print plexiglas prov.exhib. 12-May-4 Christie's, Rockefeller NY #358/R est:22000-28000
£18994 $34000 €27731 Grey Moses (230x83cm-91x33in) cibachrome print two parts exec 1990 5 edn 10 prov. 13-May-4 Sotheby's, New York #391/R est:25000-35000
£31437 $52500 €45898 Black supper (102x470cm-40x185in) s.i.d.num.8/10 verso c-print 5 parts prov.lit. 13-Nov-3 Sotheby's, New York #519/R est:50000-70000
£32934 $55000 €48084 Red Pope (102x76cm-40x30in) s.i.num.1/10 d.1990 cibachrome prints triptych prov.exhib.lit. 12-Nov-3 Christie's, Rockefeller NY #539/R est:25000-35000

SERRANO, Emilio (1945-) Spanish

£1724 $3103 €2500 Integration (73x60cm-29x24in) s.i.verso board. 26-Jan-4 Durán, Madrid #72/R est:600

SERRANO, Jose Luis (20th C) Mexican?

Works on paper
£632 $1075 €923 Face tricks (60x80cm-24x31in) s.d.1987 pas. 30-Oct-3 Louis Morton, Mexico #134 (M.P 12000)

SERRANO, Julio (20th C) Spanish?

£280 $468 €409 Still life with roses (73x61cm-29x24in) s.i.d.58. 8-Oct-3 Christie's, Kensington #946

SERRANO, Pablo (1910-1985) Spanish

Sculpture
£4000 $7240 €6000 Guitar (38x10x12cm-15x4x5in) s. num.1/7 bronze steel base. 30-Mar-4 Segre, Madrid #230/R est:3500
£13103 $23586 €19000 Untitled (61cm-24in) stone iron lit. 26-Jan-4 Durán, Madrid #207/R est:14000

SERRASANTA, Jose (1916-2000) Argentinian

£451 $767 €650 Landscape with house (27x35cm-11x14in) s. 28-Oct-3 Segre, Madrid #355/R
£748 $1362 €1100 Spring (38x46cm-15x18in) s. board. 3-Feb-4 Segre, Madrid #341/R
£845 $1352 €1200 Couple by river (38x46cm-15x18in) s. board. 16-Sep-3 Segre, Madrid #272/R
£972 $1653 €1400 Landscape (46x55cm-18x22in) s. 28-Oct-3 Segre, Madrid #335/R
£1099 $1781 €1550 Landscape with shepherd and sheep (46x55cm-18x22in) s. 20-May-3 Ansorena, Madrid #199/R est:1450
£1383 $2240 €1950 Landscape with figures (38x55cm-15x22in) s. 20-May-3 Ansorena, Madrid #33/R est:1450
£1389 $2264 €2000 Spanish mountain village with man on donkey (60x73cm-24x29in) s. panel. 26-Sep-3 Bolland & Marotz, Bremen #683/R est:950
£3642 $6629 €5500 Flamenco (65x91cm-26x36in) s. 15-Jun-4 Rossini, Paris #175/R est:3000-4000
£4828 $8014 €7000 Rural scene (80x100cm-31x39in) s. board. 30-Sep-3 Ansorena, Madrid #99/R est:3600

SERRE, Alexandre (attrib) (1850-?) French

£1971 $3548 €2878 Still life of flowers in vase (60x40cm-24x16in) s.d.1882. 24-Apr-4 Rasmussen, Havnen #2119/R est:7000-10000 (D.KR 22000)

SERRES, Antony (1828-1898) French

£426 $711 €600 Petit garcon jouant (34x26cm-13x10in) cardboard. 23-Jun-3 Ribeyre & Baron, Paris #45/R
£2517 $4280 €3600 The audience (32x40cm-13x16in) s. 29-Nov-3 Bukowskis, Helsinki #393/R est:4000-6000

SERRES, Dominic (1722-1793) British

£23000 $42320 €33580 View of Portsmouth Harbour with man-o-war and other vessels (32x46cm-13x18in) s.d.1777 panel. 11-Jun-4 Christie's, London #47/R est:5000-8000
£72000 $124560 €105120 Panoramic view of Lewes from the south east with hunting party (90x182cm-35x72in) s. prov.exhib. 10-Dec-3 Bonhams, New Bond Street #36/R est:20000-30000

SERRES, Dominic Michael (fl.1783-1804) British

Works on paper
£800 $1432 €1168 Tintern Abbey on the Wye. A tranquil stretch of the river (43x59cm-17x23in) s.d.1778 pencil W/C pair. 26-May-4 Christie's, Kensington #370/R

SERRES, John Thomas (1759-1825) British

£2973 $5500 €4341 Shipping off Whitby (38x53cm-15x21in) s.d.1814 prov. 10-Feb-4 Christie's, Rockefeller NY #165a/R est:7000-10000
Works on paper
£1200 $2040 €1752 Port of Genoa (32x44cm-13x17in) s. pencil W/C. 20-Nov-3 Christie's, London #94/R est:800-1200
£1300 $2366 €1898 Highway by a Gothic villa (21x31cm-8x12in) s.d.1798 W/C over pencil. 1-Jul-4 Sotheby's, London #201/R est:1500-2000

SERRES, John Thomas (attrib) (1759-1825) British

£4000 $6800 €5840 English man-o-war off the coast of Dover. English man-o-war in a strong breeze (29x42cm-11x17in) pair. 27-Nov-3 Sotheby's, London #106/R est:3000-5000
Works on paper
£2400 $4440 €3504 English frigate in a heavy swell. English vessel de-rigging (25x30cm-10x12in) pair. 14-Jul-4 Sotheby's, Olympia #41/R est:800-1200

SERRES, John Thomas (circle) (1759-1825) British

£7500 $13500 €10950 English sixth rater and other shipping off a Continental port (63x85cm-25x33in) 21-Apr-4 Bonhams, New Bond Street #68/R est:3000-5000

SERRI, Alfredo (1897-1972) Italian

£243 $450 €355 Trompe l'oeil (15x28cm-6x11in) s. masonite. 24-Jan-4 Jeffery Burchard, Florida #6/R

SERRIER, Jean Pierre (1934-1989) French

£647 $1080 €945 Young woman with a red rose (53x44cm-21x17in) s. 20-Oct-3 Stephan Welz, Johannesburg #214/R est:8000-12000 (SA.R 7500)

SERRURE, Auguste (1825-1903) Flemish

£548 $932 €800 Portrait d'une jeune elegante (27x21cm-11x8in) s. panel. 4-Nov-3 Servarts Themis, Bruxelles #626/R
£805 $1442 €1200 Servante dans un interieur (54x39cm-21x15in) s. panel. 25-May-4 Campo & Campo, Antwerp #268
£1333 $2413 €2000 Vente aux encheres (12x21cm-5x8in) s. panel. 4-Apr-4 St-Germain-en-Laye Encheres #9/R est:2000-2500

SERRURE, Berthe (19/20th C) British

Works on paper
£676 $1209 €1000 Les jonquilles (48x48cm-19x19in) s. pastel. 10-May-4 Horta, Bruxelles #4

SERRUYS, Yvonne (1873-1953) Belgian

Sculpture
£1343 $2457 €2000 Jeune femme nue (57cm-22in) s.st.f.Hebrard pat bronze. 7-Jul-4 Tajan, Paris #119 est:2000-3000
£2069 $3455 €3000 Femme a la coupe (56cm-22in) s. brown pat bronze Cast Hebrard. 16-Nov-3 Muizon & Le Coent, Paris #116b

SERSE (1951-) Belgian?

Works on paper
£2013 $3564 €3000 Ai Sali d'Argenton (100x140cm-39x55in) crayon paper on aluminium. 27-Apr-4 Campo, Vlaamse Kaai #576 est:1200-1500

SERSTE, Paul (?) Belgian?

Sculpture
£1000 $1840 €1500 Enfant Africain (34cm-13in) s. terracotta stone socle. 14-Jun-4 Gros & Delettrez, Paris #286 est:800-1000

SERT, Henri (1938-1964) French

£476 $843 €695 Composition (49x84cm-19x33in) s.d.1960. 27-Apr-4 AB Stockholms Auktionsverk #1191/R (S.KR 6500)
£632 $1162 €923 Mask composition (50x65cm-20x26in) s.d.1960. 29-Mar-4 Rasmussen, Copenhagen #337/R (D.KR 7000)
£1625 $3038 €2373 Personage (54x65cm-21x26in) s.d.59. 25-Feb-4 Kunsthallen, Copenhagen #21/R est:10000 (D.KR 18000)
Works on paper
£916 $1667 €1337 Figure composition (63x49cm-25x19in) s.d.1959 pastel. 7-Feb-4 Rasmussen, Havnen #4195/R (D.KR 10000)

SERUSIER, Paul (1863-1927) French

£4296 $7518 €6100 Jeune femme en buste (26x13cm-10x5in) canvas on board. 21-Dec-3 Thierry & Lannon, Brest #206/R est:4000-6000
£7823 $14003 €11500 Paysage au chemin rouge (36x58cm-14x23in) s. paper on panel. 21-Mar-4 Calmels Cohen, Paris #164/R est:10000-12000
£10000 $17900 €15000 Le Huelgoat (38x26cm-15x10in) s.i.verso. 16-May-4 Thierry & Lannon, Brest #175/R est:5000-6000
£12353 $21000 €18035 La conteuse (81x130cm-32x51in) shaved board on canvas painted 1918 prov.lit. 5-Nov-3 Christie's, Rockefeller NY #257/R est:30000-40000
£14865 $26608 €22000 Eve cueillant une pomme (82x34cm-32x13in) mono. prov.exhib.lit. 7-May-4 Millon & Associes, Paris #97/R est:20000-30000
£34000 $62560 €49640 Soir, Avenue de Neuilly (50x63cm-20x25in) s. board on cradled panel painted c.1907 prov.exhib. 22-Jun-4 Sotheby's, London #140/R est:40000-60000
£52023 $90000 €75954 L'attente a la fontaine (110x69cm-43x27in) init. prov.exhib.lit. 11-Dec-3 Sotheby's, New York #114/R est:100000-150000
£70000 $125300 €105000 Les filles de Nanda (91x129cm-36x51in) 16-May-4 Thierry & Lannon, Brest #174/R est:90000-120000
£189944 $340000 €277318 Pecheur a la Laita (65x50cm-26x20in) s.d.90 tempera board on panel painted c.1890 prov.lit. 6-May-4 Sotheby's, New York #233a/R est:180000-220000
£190000 $349600 €277400 Mere et enfant dans un paysage breton (73x60cm-29x24in) s.d.90 prov. 22-Jun-4 Christie's, London #22/R est:200000-300000

Works on paper

£397 $727 €600 Jeune femme au papillon (34x46cm-13x18in) st.init. chl tracing paper. 7-Apr-4 Piasa, Paris #69
£433 $776 €650 Deux nus de dos et de face (64x46cm-25x18in) ink wash. 16-May-4 Thierry & Lannon, Brest #409
£520 $931 €780 Etude de nu, buste devoile (60x45cm-24x18in) chl wax graphite. 16-May-4 Thierry & Lannon, Brest #410
£669 $1171 €950 Arbre (30x23cm-12x9in) s. col crayons. 21-Dec-3 Thierry & Lannon, Brest #453b
£743 $1330 €1100 Bretonne en buste (30x27cm-12x11in) st.mono. black crayon. 7-May-4 Millon & Associes, Paris #95
£979 $1684 €1400 Paysage et portrait. Paysage (29x22cm-11x9in) pencil white chk double-sided. 5-Dec-3 Chochon-Barre & Allardi, Paris #148/R
£986 $1725 €1400 Etudes de Bretonnes (25x19cm-10x7in) studio st. wash. 21-Dec-3 Thierry & Lannon, Brest #121
£1149 $2056 €1700 Petites Bretonnes et rocher sur le Trieux (26x20cm-10x8in) s.i. pen black ink. 7-May-4 Millon & Associes, Paris #96/R est:1500-2000
£1200 $2148 €1800 L'Ankou sur son cheval (16x25cm-6x10in) chl col crayon. 16-May-4 Thierry & Lannon, Brest #411 est:600-800
£1258 $2353 €1900 Le bapteme du Christ (25x32cm-10x13in) chl pastel. 24-Jul-4 Thierry & Lannon, Brest #46 est:1500-2000
£2113 $3655 €3000 Bretonnes et chevre (10x18cm-4x7in) pastel prov. 15-Dec-3 Marc Kohn, Paris #87/R est:3000-4000
£2200 $3806 €3212 Les Remasseuses de Fougeres (20x24cm-8x9in) init. chl exhib. 11-Dec-3 Christie's, Kensington #20/R est:1500-2000
£3533 $6325 €5300 Portrait de jeune enfant (45x32cm-18x13in) mono. gouache. 16-May-4 Thierry & Lannon, Brest #97/R est:1500-2000
£4577 $8011 €6500 L'Annonciation (57x31cm-22x12in) col crayon. 21-Dec-3 Thierry & Lannon, Brest #122/R est:6000-7000
£14333 $25657 €21500 Les meules jaunes au Pouldu (41x56cm-16x22in) pastel exec. c.1890. 16-May-4 Thierry & Lannon, Brest #98/R est:20000-25000

SERVAES, Albert (1883-1966) Belgian

£1389 $2319 €2000 Fermettes (50x56cm-20x22in) s.d.1923. 21-Oct-3 Campo & Campo, Antwerp #272/R est:2500-3000
£3448 $6379 €5000 La nativite (59x79cm-23x31in) s.d.1919 exhib. 16-Feb-4 Horta, Bruxelles #178/R est:7000-9000
£6028 $10067 €8500 Harvest (45x52cm-18x20in) s. canvas on panel prov. 20-Oct-3 Bernaerts, Antwerp #215/R est:2000-2500

Works on paper

£300 $477 €435 Eucharistic Christ (60x49cm-24x19in) s.d.1936 chl paper on card. 11-Sep-3 Christie's, Kensington #68/R
£500 $895 €750 The Holy Family (58x43cm-23x17in) s.d.1937 chl lit. 15-May-4 De Vuyst, Lokeren #298
£922 $1540 €1300 Mother with child (76x61cm-30x24in) s.d.1961 chl chk wash. 14-Oct-3 Dorotheum, Vienna #192/R
£1118 $2058 €1700 Madonna and Child (68x58cm-27x23in) s.d.1956 mixed media. 22-Jun-4 Palais de Beaux Arts, Brussels #311/R est:2000-3000
£1184 $2179 €1800 Chemin de Croix (53x69cm-21x27in) s.d.1939 chl. 22-Jun-4 Palais de Beaux Arts, Brussels #315/R est:2000-3000
£1184 $2179 €1800 Chemin de Croix (53x69cm-21x27in) s.d.1939 chl. 22-Jun-4 Palais de Beaux Arts, Brussels #312/R est:2000-3000
£1184 $2179 €1800 Chemin de Croix (53x69cm-21x27in) s.d.1939 chl. 22-Jun-4 Palais de Beaux Arts, Brussels #313/R est:2000-3000
£1189 $2021 €1700 Le bapteme du Christ (68x50cm-27x20in) s.d.1938 chl exhib. 1-Dec-3 Palais de Beaux Arts, Brussels #127/R est:1750-2500
£1316 $2421 €2000 Chemin de Croix, fragment (53x69cm-21x27in) s.d.1939 chl. 22-Jun-4 Palais de Beaux Arts, Brussels #316/R est:2000-3000
£1600 $2864 €2400 Maria (77x64cm-30x25in) s.i.d.1935 chl prov.lit. 15-May-4 De Vuyst, Lokeren #297/R est:2400-2800
£1711 $3147 €2600 Chemin de Croix (53x69cm-21x27in) s.d.1939 chl. 22-Jun-4 Palais de Beaux Arts, Brussels #314/R est:2000-3000
£2685 $4752 €4000 Le Christ entoure de deux figures (98x155cm-39x61in) s.d.1937 chl. 27-Apr-4 Campo, Vlaamse Kaai #577 est:4000-4500

SERVAIS, Andre (1937-) Belgian

£308 $514 €440 Evening landscape with small fishing harbour (42x67cm-17x26in) s. board. 11-Oct-3 Hans Stahl, Hamburg #53/R

SERVAIS, Jacques Joseph (1803-1872) Belgian

£1127 $1949 €1600 Spa (61x71cm-24x28in) panel set of three. 10-Dec-3 Hotel des Ventes Mosan, Brussels #145 est:1400-1800

SERVANDONI, Jean Nicolas (attrib) (1695-1766) French

£2230 $3991 €3300 Arcadian landscape (45x55cm-18x22in) 8-May-4 Hans Stahl, Toestorf #114/R est:2500
£3020 $5557 €4500 Ruines d'un temple antique avec une statue (50x76cm-20x30in) 26-Mar-4 Piasa, Paris #42/R est:5000-7000
£15789 $29053 €24000 Figures au milieu de ruines antiques (75x101cm-30x40in) 24-Jun-4 Christie's, Paris #82/R est:12000-18000
£22000 $39600 €32120 Classical landscapes with figures resting beside cascades (772x64cm-304x25in) pair prov. 22-Apr-4 Sotheby's, London #115/R est:15000-20000

SERVEAU, Clement (1886-1972) French

£483 $869 €700 Nature morte a la tasse (61x50cm-24x20in) s. 25-Jan-4 Chayette & Cheval, Paris #248
£600 $1080 €900 Coquetier (41x33cm-16x13in) s. 24-Apr-4 Cornette de St.Cyr, Paris #343
£646 $1157 €950 Nature morte aux fruits (27x41cm-11x16in) s. 19-Mar-4 Oger, Dumont, Paris #9
£704 $1218 €1000 Bouquet de fleurs (35x26cm-14x10in) s.d.1942 panel. 13-Dec-3 Martinot & Savignat, Pontoise #30/R
£764 $1276 €1100 Composition au bouquet de fleurs (65x54cm-26x21in) s.d.46. 21-Oct-3 Artcurial Briest, Paris #178
£805 $1474 €1200 Bouquet of flowers (73x54cm-29x21in) s. 7-Jul-4 Artcurial Briest, Paris #154a
£897 $1614 €1300 Nature morte au pichet (27x41cm-11x16in) s. 25-Jan-4 Chayette & Cheval, Paris #249
£903 $1508 €1300 Femme lisant (71x68cm-28x27in) s. cardboard. 25-Oct-3 Cornette de St.Cyr, Paris #482
£934 $1680 €1400 Le livre ouvert (53x72cm-21x28in) s.d.1943 cardboard. 26-Apr-4 Tajan, Paris #188/R est:1500-2000
£1192 $2181 €1800 Composition a la fenetre (73x50cm-29x20in) s. 9-Apr-4 Claude Aguttes, Neuilly #96/R est:1800-2000
£1678 $2887 €2400 Nature morte a la cafetiere (65x54cm-26x21in) s. prov. 3-Dec-3 Oger, Dumont, Paris #10 est:2300
£2098 $3608 €3000 Nature morte au violon (73x92cm-29x36in) s. prov. 3-Dec-3 Oger, Dumont, Paris #9/R est:2300
£6500 $12090 €9490 Femme nue (46x15cm-18x6in) s. board. 4-Mar-4 Christie's, London #476/R est:700-1000

Works on paper

£322 $570 €480 Femme au repos (20x26cm-8x10in) s. gouache. 29-Apr-4 Claude Aguttes, Neuilly #113
£458 $792 €650 Musique cubiste (35x41cm-14x16in) s.d.1922 pastel chl. 13-Dec-3 Martinot & Savignat, Pontoise #250/R

SERVER, John William (1882-?) American

£520 $900 €759 Sunlit road way (30x18cm-12x7in) s.d.1903. 10-Dec-3 Alderfer's, Hatfield #491 est:300-500

SERVETTAR, G (19th C) Italian

£1448 $2404 €2100 Seascape (30x44cm-12x17in) s. 1-Oct-3 Della Rocca, Turin #203 est:500-550

SERVRANCKX, Victor (1897-1965) Belgian

£9790 $16643 €14000 Opus V (204x60cm-80x24in) s.d.1963 s.i.d.stretcher exhib.lit. 25-Nov-3 Christie's, Amsterdam #241/R est:15000-20000

SERWAZI, Albert B (1905-) American

£313 $500 €457 Masquerader (132x94cm-52x37in) s. 17-May-3 Bunte, Elgin #1317

SESEMANN, Elga (1922-) Finnish

£671 $1235 €1000 Still life (46x55cm-18x22in) s. 25-Mar-4 Hagelstam, Helsinki #993

SESIA DELLA MERLA, Gianni (1934-) Italian

£268 $497 €400 Girl on the sofa (50x40cm-20x16in) s. s.i.d.1999 verso masonite. 13-Mar-4 Meeting Art, Vercelli #518

SESSIONS, James (1882-1962) American

Works on paper

£359 $600 €524 Texas border, Ionk (20x23cm-8x9in) s. W/C. 14-Nov-3 Aspire, Cleveland #145
£378 $700 €552 Street scene, Quebec (20x25cm-8x10in) s. W/C. 16-Jan-4 Aspire, Cleveland #139/R
£509 $850 €743 Fiesta, Vera Cruz (20x23cm-8x9in) s. W/C. 14-Nov-3 Aspire, Cleveland #144
£531 $850 €775 Boat at dock (23x25cm-9x10in) s. W/C executed c.1945. 17-May-3 Bunte, Elgin #1307
£531 $850 €775 Children swimming, Haiti (23x25cm-9x10in) s. W/C executed 1945. 17-May-3 Bunte, Elgin #1308
£683 $1100 €997 Haitian sailboats (23x33cm-9x13in) s. W/C exec. c.1950. 22-Feb-3 Bunte, Elgin #1262
£870 $1400 €1270 Fisherman's home (33x48cm-13x19in) s. W/C prov. 22-Feb-3 Bunte, Elgin #1261 est:1500-2000
£1022 $1900 €1492 Boats at dock (23x26cm-9x10in) s.d.34 pencil W/C. 3-Mar-4 Christie's, Rockefeller NY #44/R est:1200-1800
£1080 $1900 €1577 Disaster at sea (48x61cm-19x24in) s. W/C exec.c.1940. 23-May-4 Treadway Gallery, Cincinnati #630/R est:2500-3500
£1628 $2800 €2377 Winter scene with horses and sled (51x69cm-20x27in) s. W/C exec.c.1950. 7-Dec-3 Treadway Gallery, Cincinnati #541/R est:3000-4000
£2186 $4000 €3192 Market day, New Orleans (20x33cm-8x13in) s.d.38 W/C. 5-Jun-4 Neal Auction Company, New Orleans #403/R est:1500-2500

SESSIONS, James (attrib) (1882-1962) American

Works on paper

£233 $400 €340 Caribbean sailboats at dock (23x25cm-9x10in) W/C exec.c.1950. 7-Dec-3 Treadway Gallery, Cincinnati #539/R
£320 $550 €467 Caribbean boathouse (23x25cm-9x10in) W/C exec.c.1950. 7-Dec-3 Treadway Gallery, Cincinnati #536/R
£378 $650 €552 Caribbean sailboat with figures (23x28cm-9x11in) W/C exec.c.1950. 7-Dec-3 Treadway Gallery, Cincinnati #535/R
£436 $750 €637 Caribbean women on the beach (23x25cm-9x10in) W/C exec.c.1950. 7-Dec-3 Treadway Gallery, Cincinnati #537/R

SESSLER, Alfred (1909-1963) American
£323 $600 €472 Standing man (15x8cm-6x3in) s.d.1953 masonite. 7-Mar-4 Treadway Gallery, Cincinnati #716/R

SESSLER, Stanley (1905-) American
£247 $450 €361 Madonna of the peonies (56x46cm-22x18in) s. d.60 verso canvasboard. 7-Feb-4 Dan Ripley, Indianapolis #9
£270 $500 €394 Potpourri (56x66cm-22x26in) s. masonite. 16-Jan-4 Aspire, Cleveland #58/R

SESSON, Shukei (attrib) (1504-1589) Japanese
Works on paper
£959 $1630 €1400 Eagle (108x57cm-43x22in) s. seals Indian ink. 8-Nov-3 Dr Fritz Nagel, Stuttgart #1851/R

SESTO, Cesare da (attrib) (1477-1523) Italian
£22069 $36634 €32000 Head of Christ (25x29cm-10x11in) oil tempera panel prov. 1-Oct-3 Dorotheum, Vienna #17/R est:6000-10000

SETELIK, Jaroslav (1881-1955) Polish
£1544 $2873 €2254 View of Lesser Town in Prague (45x75cm-18x30in) s. 6-Mar-4 Dorotheum, Prague #73/R est:40000-60000 (C.KR 75000)

SETHER, Gulbrand (1869-1910) American/Norwegian
£223 $400 €326 Isabella (64x84cm-25x33in) s. 10-Jan-4 Susanin's, Chicago #5060/R
£351 $650 €512 Midnight sun, Norway (48x66cm-19x26in) s. 13-Mar-4 Susanin's, Chicago #6070/R
£396 $650 €574 Winter scene with log houses (20x30cm-8x12in) s. 4-Jun-3 Alderfer's, Hatfield #284
£538 $1000 €785 Moonlit harbour village (56x99cm-22x39in) s. painted c.1910. 7-Mar-4 Treadway Gallery, Cincinnati #506/R est:1000-2000
£814 $1400 €1188 Blacksmith's shop (38x48cm-15x19in) s. painted c.1910. 7-Dec-3 Treadway Gallery, Cincinnati #608/R
Works on paper
£215 $400 €314 Snowy landscape (53x38cm-21x15in) s. W/C executed c.1910. 7-Mar-4 Treadway Gallery, Cincinnati #575/R
£430 $800 €628 Snowy night (36x66cm-14x26in) s. pastel executed c.1910. 7-Mar-4 Treadway Gallery, Cincinnati #518/R
£579 $950 €840 Winter nocturne (53x38cm-21x15in) s. gouache exec.c.1910. 7-Jun-3 Treadway Gallery, Cincinnati #1354

SETKOWICZ, Adam (1875-1945) Polish
£1172 $1957 €1711 Sleigh in front of cabin (45x41cm-18x16in) s. painted c.1930. 19-Oct-3 Agra, Warsaw #45/R est:7000 (P.Z 7500)

SETTERBERG, Carl (1897-?) American
Works on paper
£275 $475 €402 White sails (48x71cm-19x28in) s. W/C. 15-Dec-3 Winter Associates, Plainville #18/R

SETTI, Ercole (16th C) Italian
Works on paper
£1600 $2768 €2336 Group of tradesmen, two carrying platters on their heads (28x42cm-11x17in) i. black chk pen brown ink prov. 12-Dec-3 Christie's, Kensington #344/R est:1500-2000
£3946 $7063 €5800 Un paysan labourant, trois autres ramassant du ble (19x33cm-7x13in) red chk pen brown ink prov. 18-Mar-4 Christie's, Paris #52/R est:2000-3000

SETTLE, William F (1821-1897) British
£580 $945 €847 Port of Hull (23x30cm-9x12in) panel. 26-Sep-3 Dee Atkinson & Harrison, Driffield #543/R
Works on paper
£280 $465 €409 Yachts off Yarmouth (17x36cm-7x14in) mono.d.70 W/C. 1-Oct-3 Woolley & Wallis, Salisbury #151/R
£750 $1418 €1095 H M S Eurydice (22x33cm-9x13in) mono.d.76 W/C. 17-Feb-4 Bonhams, New Bond Street #3/R
£800 $1360 €1168 Yachts off Yarmouth (18x36cm-7x14in) mono.d.1870. 21-Nov-3 Dee Atkinson & Harrison, Driffield #776/R
£950 $1549 €1387 HMS Monarch of Caledonia. HMS Bacchante, Osborne and Volage (10x15cm-4x6in) s.d.85 beneath mount oval pair. 26-Sep-3 Dee Atkinson & Harrison, Driffield #585/R

SEUFFERT, Robert (1874-?) German
£1733 $3155 €2600 Mourning the death of Christ (117x228cm-46x90in) s.d.13. 1-Jul-4 Van Ham, Cologne #1618/R est:400

SEUPHOR, Michel (1901-1999) Belgian
Photographs
£2148 $3844 €3200 Atelier de Mondrian (20x25cm-8x10in) s.i. s.d.1929 verso gelatin silver print. 26-May-4 Christie's, Paris #148/R est:300-400
Works on paper
£387 $670 €550 Symmetric XXVI (65x49cm-26x19in) s.i.d.73 verso ink. 15-Dec-3 Bernaerts, Antwerp #1510/R
£503 $891 €750 Reine des sirenes (54x37cm-21x15in) s.i.d.28 dec. 54 verso Indian ink prov.exhib. 28-Apr-4 Charbonneaux, Paris #222
£1698 $2751 €2479 Fantaisie geometrique sur bleu roi avec jaune et vert (75x52cm-30x20in) s.i.d.15 janv81 verso Indian ink tempera collage board. 24-May-3 Burkhard, Luzern #150/R est:3500-4500 (S.FR 3600)

SEURAT, Georges (1859-1891) French
£823529 $1400000 €1202352 Femmes assises - Etude pour un dimanche apres midi a l'Ile de la grande jatte (16x25cm-6x10in) panel painted c.1884-85 prov.lit. 4-Nov-3 Christie's, Rockefeller NY #9/R est:1500000-2000000
Works on paper
£250000 $457500 €365000 A pas tremblants (32x24cm-13x9in) crayon exec.c.1884 prov.exhib.lit. 2-Feb-4 Christie's, London #4/R est:150000-250000

SEUSS, Dr (1904-1991) American
Works on paper
£3143 $5500 €4589 The Grinch (28x21cm-11x8in) s.i. col marker. 19-Dec-3 Sotheby's, New York #1141/R est:3000-5000

SEVE, Gilbert de (elder) (1615-1698) French
£11842 $21789 €18000 Portrait presume d'Anne-Marie-Louise d'Orleans (100x81cm-39x32in) exhib. 24-Jun-4 Christie's, Paris #36/R est:12000-18000

SEVEHON, Francky Boy (1954-) French
£417 $658 €600 Number one (100x81cm-39x32in) s.i.d.1988 acrylic. 27-Apr-3 Versailles Encheres #144
£417 $658 €600 Number two (100x81cm-39x32in) s.i.d.1988 acrylic. 27-Apr-3 Versailles Encheres #145
£629 $1070 €900 Bon weekend (46x56cm-18x22in) s. 20-Nov-3 Claude Aguttes, Neuilly #179
£839 $1427 €1200 Le jardin des plaisirs (81x100cm-32x39in) s. acrylic. 20-Nov-3 Claude Aguttes, Neuilly #260/R
£1888 $3210 €2700 Le pont Sully (81x100cm-32x39in) s. acrylic painted 1992. 29-Nov-3 Neret-Minet, Paris #131/R est:2550-2850

SEVELLEC, Jim (1897-1971) French
£845 $1479 €1200 Falaises a Kerlanne (32x40cm-13x16in) s. board. 21-Dec-3 Thierry & Lannon, Brest #360
£1333 $2387 €2000 Jeunes femmes de Plougastel a Landerneau (54x70cm-21x28in) s. 16-May-4 Thierry & Lannon, Brest #176/R est:1200-1400
Sculpture
£1867 $3341 €2800 Maison du vin (33x38cm-13x15in) s. pat bronze. 16-May-4 Renault-Aubry, Pontivy #126

SEVEN-SEVEN, Twins (1944-) Nigerian
Works on paper
£385 $654 €562 Chief Lisa (61x30cm-24x12in) s.d.72 s.i.d.verso mixed media on board. 4-Nov-3 Stephan Welz, Johannesburg #589 est:5000-8000 (SA.R 4500)

SEVENBOM, Johan (attrib) (18th C) Swedish
£1147 $1846 €1675 Ship wreck (45x68cm-18x27in) 25-Aug-3 Lilla Bukowskis, Stockholm #983 est:12000-15000 (S.KR 15000)

SEVERDONCK, Franz van (1809-1889) Belgian
£683 $1100 €997 Sheep and goat in a country landscape (23x31cm-9x12in) s. panel. 14-Jan-4 Christie's, Rockefeller NY #17/R est:1500-2000
£769 $1323 €1100 Sheep in a landscape (17x22cm-7x9in) s.d.1861 panel. 7-Dec-3 Sotheby's, Amsterdam #591
£824 $1400 €1203 Pasture, view with sheep, goat, chickens and a duck (18x24cm-7x9in) s.d.1840 i.verso panel. 21-Nov-3 Skinner, Boston #213/R est:1000-1500
£850 $1522 €1250 Cheval blanc a l'ecurie (17x22cm-7x9in) s.d.1858 panel. 16-Mar-4 Vanderkindere, Brussels #398
£966 $1786 €1400 Deux moutons, coq et poule dans un paysage (17x22cm-7x9in) s.d.1861 i.verso panel. 16-Feb-4 Horta, Bruxelles #86
£1133 $2029 €1700 Poultry yard (15x21cm-6x8in) s. panel lit. 14-May-4 Schloss Ahlden, Ahlden #2788/R est:1800
£1210 $2226 €1767 White horse, goat, sheep and poultry in a pasture (18x25cm-7x10in) s.d.1873 s.i.verso panel. 14-Jun-4 Waddingtons, Toronto #40/R est:2500-3500 (C.D 3000)
£1304 $2400 €1904 Sheep at rest with ducks and roosters (18x24cm-7x9in) s.d.1865 panel. 27-Jun-4 Freeman, Philadelphia #25/R est:1000-1500
£1351 $2419 €2000 Animaux de basse-cour pres d'une mare (18x24cm-7x9in) s. panel. 10-May-4 Horta, Bruxelles #173 est:2000-2500
£1400 $2324 €2044 Feeding time (17x25cm-7x10in) s.i.verso panel. 1-Oct-3 Sotheby's, Olympia #202/R est:800-1200
£1988 $3300 €2883 Sheep. s. board. 14-Jun-3 Fallon, Copake #64/R
£4362 $7809 €6500 Sheep and ducks in summer landscape (51x70cm-20x28in) s. i.verso. 27-May-4 Dorotheum, Vienna #211/R est:5500-6500

SEVERDONCK, Franz van (attrib) (1809-1889) Belgian
£660 $1221 €964 Cow and sheep in a meadow (34x49cm-13x19in) bears sig. panel. 14-Jul-4 Bonhams, Chester #501

SEVERDONCK, Franz van and MOREL, Jan Evert II (19th C) Belgian/Dutch
£1333 $2400 €2000 Shepherdess and her flock at rest (29x23cm-11x9in) s.i. 20-Apr-4 Sotheby's, Amsterdam #90/R est:2000-3000

SEVERDONCK, Joseph van (1819-1905) Belgian
£461 $847 €700 Jeune gamin et cheval (52x70cm-20x28in) s. 22-Jun-4 Palais de Beaux Arts, Brussels #324
£604 $1111 €900 Combat des cavaliers (16x22cm-6x9in) s. panel. 23-Mar-4 Galerie Moderne, Brussels #221/R
£738 $1366 €1100 Cavalier devant l'entree du chateau (50x86cm-20x34in) s. 15-Mar-4 Horta, Bruxelles #439
£1027 $1747 €1500 Cavalry battle (29x46cm-11x18in) s.d.1871 panel. 5-Nov-3 Hugo Ruef, Munich #1104/R est:900

£1342 $2470 €2000 Rue animee sous la pluie (38x54cm-15x21in) s. panel. 23-Mar-4 Galerie Moderne, Brussels #349/R est:400-600
Works on paper
£268 $494 €400 Deux enfants (57x46cm-22x18in) pastel. 23-Mar-4 Galerie Moderne, Brussels #158/R

SEVEREN, Dan van (1927-) Belgian
Works on paper
£563 $975 €800 Composition four-sided, oval, right angle (30x21cm-12x8in) s.d.1970 verso pencil wash. 13-Dec-3 De Vuyst, Lokeren #368
£2517 $4204 €3600 Composition with diamond (77x55cm-30x22in) s.d.1977 verso gouache Indian ink exhib. 11-Oct-3 De Vuyst, Lokeren #559/R est:2500-3000

SEVERIN, Jules (1888-1975) Belgian?
£270 $484 €400 Meule (60x70cm-24x28in) s. 10-May-4 Horta, Bruxelles #6

SEVERIN, Mark (1906-) British
Works on paper
£450 $716 €657 Marine border (28x23cm-11x9in) s. W/C. 10-Sep-3 Sotheby's, Olympia #285/R

SEVERINI, Gino (1883-1966) Italian
£3017 $5401 €4405 Jesus lying under cross (43x63cm-17x25in) s. behind glass. 12-May-4 Dobiaschofsky, Bern #981/R est:9000 (S.FR 7000)
£3103 $4966 €4500 Haed of Apostle (29x19cm-11x7in) tempera paper. 13-Mar-3 Galleria Pace, Milan #24/R est:5500-7000
£3986 $6776 €5700 Untitled (66x48cm-26x19in) s. tempera dr card painted 1949-50. 29-Nov-3 Farsetti, Prato #544/R est:3500
£4266 $7252 €6100 Untitled (66x48cm-26x19in) s. tempera dr card painted 1949-50 exhib.lit. 29-Nov-3 Farsetti, Prato #545/R est:3500
£5245 $8916 €7500 Saint-Pierre de Fribourg (20x32cm-8x13in) s. tempera card. 26-Nov-3 Pandolfini, Florence #19/R est:8000-9000
£6522 $10696 €9000 Natura morta con ruderi (20x21cm-8x8in) s. tempera paper on canvas exhib. 31-May-3 Farsetti, Prato #601/R est:5500-6500
£11189 $19021 €16000 Jeune pecheur (73x33cm-29x13in) i.verso board lit. 24-Nov-3 Christie's, Milan #247/R est:20000-30000
£14865 $26162 €22000 Danseuse (35x19cm-14x7in) s. s.i.verso tempera paper prov. 24-May-4 Christie's, Milan #290/R est:15000-20000
£23776 $40420 €34000 Still life with bowl (24x31cm-9x12in) s. cardboard painted 1947. 20-Nov-3 Finarte Semenzato, Milan #163/R est:25000-30000
£25676 $45189 €38000 Composition sur courbe algebrique (27x46cm-11x18in) s. s.i.d.1954 verso tempera masonite lit. 24-May-4 Christie's, Milan #306/R est:35000-40000
£36364 $61818 €52000 Still life with duck (50x61cm-20x24in) s. painted 1930 exhib. 29-Nov-3 Farsetti, Prato #432/R est:50000-60000
£42763 $78684 €65000 Nature morte aux jolies dentelles (33x40cm-13x16in) s. i.verso cardboard painted 1946 prov.lit. 23-Jun-4 Maigret, Paris #30/R est:30000-40000
£48951 $83217 €70000 Abstract dancer (70x49cm-28x19in) s. tempera paper on canvas exhib.lit. 29-Nov-3 Farsetti, Prato #472/R est:65000-75000
£52174 $85565 €72000 Livre vert et cafetiere orange (54x65cm-21x26in) s. s.i.d.1947 verso prov. 27-May-3 Sotheby's, Milan #234/R est:65000-80000
£73333 $134933 €110000 Composition with musical instruments (60x49cm-24x19in) s. prov.exhib.lit. 8-Jun-4 Finarte Semenzato, Milan #381/R est:100000-130000
£94595 $166486 €140000 Releve sur pointes 1 (65x46cm-26x18in) s. s.i.verso painted 1957 prov.exhib.lit. 24-May-4 Christie's, Milan #292/R est:130000-180000
£189944 $340000 €277318 Chatelard, paysage (100x74cm-39x29in) s. s.i.d.1918 stretcher prov.exhib.lit. 5-May-4 Christie's, Rockefeller NY #293/R est:250000-350000
£282353 $480000 €412235 Femme a la plante verte (100x81cm-39x32in) s.i. oil sand painted 1917 prov.exhib.lit. 5-Nov-3 Christie's, Rockefeller NY #262/R est:250000-350000
£318841 $522899 €440000 Still life (50x61cm-20x24in) s. i.d.1919 verso exhib.lit. 31-May-3 Farsetti, Prato #674/R
Prints
£1676 $3000 €2447 Arlecchino e pedrolino (65x50cm-26x20in) s.num.54/120 color lithograph. 6-May-4 Swann Galleries, New York #58/R est:2500-3500
£2000 $3400 €2920 Concert (35x49cm-14x19in) s.num.77/200 col lithograph. 6-Nov-3 Swann Galleries, New York #722/R est:2500-3500
£2118 $3600 €3092 Arlequins (38x28cm-15x11in) s.num.202/220 col lithograph. 6-Nov-3 Swann Galleries, New York #721/R est:2000-3000
£2570 $4600 €3752 Arlecchino e pedrolino (65x50cm-26x20in) s.num.26/120 color lithograph. 6-May-4 Swann Galleries, New York #579/R est:3000-5000
Sculpture
£8108 $15000 €11838 Arlequin (36cm-14in) s.i. painted glazed ceramic prov.lit. 11-Feb-4 Sotheby's, New York #48/R est:18000-22000
Works on paper
£385 $654 €550 Nature morte (16x24cm-6x9in) mono. ball point pen prov. 23-Nov-3 Cornette de St.Cyr, Paris #313
£959 $1784 €1430 Composition (20x13cm-8x5in) s. Chinese ink col pencil. 4-Mar-4 Babuino, Rome #455
£1034 $1728 €1500 Costumes (16x24cm-6x9in) init. pencil. 13-Nov-3 Finarte Semenzato, Rome #156/R
£1074 $2008 €1600 Still life (28x35cm-11x14in) s. gouache. 24-Feb-4 Durán, Madrid #628/R est:750
£1232 $2020 €1700 Dancer (29x22cm-11x9in) s. dr. 29-May-3 Galleria Pace, Milan #58 est:2500
£1342 $2497 €2000 Futuristic dancer (53x34cm-21x13in) s.i.d.1961 pencil. 4-Mar-4 Babuino, Rome #456
£1399 $2378 €2000 Girl with jug (36x25cm-14x10in) s.i. pencil. 20-Nov-3 Finarte Semenzato, Milan #135/R est:2000-2200
£2000 $3680 €3000 Fleurs et masques (37x26cm-15x10in) s. gouache pochoir exhib.lit. 11-Jun-4 Farsetti, Prato #312/R est:3000-4000
£2013 $3604 €3000 Danseuse (26x21cm-10x8in) s. pencil dr exec.c.1950. 29-May-4 Farsetti, Prato #415/R est:2000-3000
£2162 $3805 €3200 Collage de fer (22x27cm-9x11in) s. ink exec.1959. 24-May-4 Christie's, Milan #134/R est:3000-4000
£2238 $3804 €3200 Pigeons (18x25cm-7x10in) s. ink prov.exhib. 24-Nov-3 Christie's, Milan #125/R est:3000-4000
£2333 $4177 €3500 Still life with grapes and mandolin (30x25cm-12x10in) s. Chinese ink dr prov. 12-May-4 Stadion, Trieste #750/R est:2200-3200
£2500 $4600 €3800 Le gueridon au panier de noix, cruche et gateaux (20x27cm-8x11in) s.i. ink exec. 1946 prov. 23-Jun-4 Maigret, Paris #14/R est:2000-2500
£2552 $4261 €3700 Dance step (29x21cm-11x8in) s.d.64. 13-Nov-3 Finarte Semenzato, Rome #169/R est:3000-4000
£3691 $6607 €5500 Maternity (23x14cm-9x6in) s. pencil dr exec.1927. 29-May-4 Farsetti, Prato #403/R est:5500-6500
£4476 $7474 €6400 Adoration of the Magi (44x53cm-17x21in) s.i. chl. 26-Jun-3 Sant Agostino, Torino #195/R est:5000-6000
£8392 $14266 €12000 Music lesson (47x59cm-19x23in) s. chl pastel exec.1928 lit. 29-Nov-3 Farsetti, Prato #534/R est:5000
£10135 $17838 €15000 Musician (66x50cm-26x20in) s.i.d.1962 pastel paper on canvas prov.lit. 24-May-4 Christie's, Milan #288/R est:15000-20000
£12238 $20804 €17500 Composition (24x31cm-9x12in) s. pastel exhib. 26-Nov-3 Pandolfini, Florence #22/R est:18000-22000
£32866 $57516 €46670 Classical dancer 2 (70x33cm-28x13in) s. gouache cardboard prov.exhib.lit. 18-Dec-3 Tajan, Paris #42/R est:50000-60000
£43478 $71304 €60000 Costumes from Poitou (61x49cm-24x19in) s.d.MCMVIII s.i.verso pastel paper on cardboard prov.exhib.lit. 27-May-3 Sotheby's, Milan #218/R est:30000-40000

SEVERN, Joseph Arthur Palliser (1842-1931) British
Works on paper
£240 $400 €350 Breakers off the cliff. s.d.1885 W/C. 18-Oct-3 Harvey Clar, Oakland #1190
£350 $585 €511 Vesuvius - sunrise (25x36cm-10x14in) s.d.1906 W/C. 12-Nov-3 Halls, Shrewsbury #266
£400 $680 €584 Silver wood, shire (24x34cm-9x13in) s.i. 30-Oct-3 Bracketts, Tunbridge Wells #1037/R
£1300 $2366 €1898 Sunset over Coniston (16x23cm-6x9in) W/C over pencil htd bodycol prov. 1-Jul-4 Sotheby's, London #238/R est:1500-2000

SEVERN, Walter (1830-1904) British
Works on paper
£282 $519 €412 On the coast of Waterford (58x95cm-23x37in) s.i.d.1877 W/C. 14-Jun-4 Waddingtons, Toronto #77/R (C.D 700)

SEVERO DA RAVENNA (circle) (15th C) Italian
Sculpture
£14000 $24220 €20440 Kneeling Satyr (28cm-11in) greenish brown pat. black marble base lit. 11-Dec-3 Christie's, London #25/R est:15000-20000

SEVESTRE, Jules Marie (1834-1901) French
£3497 $6014 €5000 Femme a la riviere (86x105cm-34x41in) s. 2-Dec-3 Campo & Campo, Antwerp #330/R est:5500-6500

SEVILLA, Soledad (1944-) Spanish
£986 $1725 €1400 Engano XIV (50x70cm-20x28in) s. pastel prov. 16-Dec-3 Segre, Madrid #178/R

SEVILLANO, Angel (1942-1994) Spanish
£2778 $4528 €4000 Musicians (100x80cm-39x31in) s. board. 23-Sep-3 Durán, Madrid #110/R

SEVILLE SCHOOL (17th C) Spanish
£7092 $11844 €10000 Padre, aparte de me este caliz, Jesus en Getsemani (237x179cm-93x70in) 23-Jun-3 Durán, Madrid #221/R est:10000
£10067 $18725 €15000 Basket of flowers (75x156cm-30x61in) 2-Mar-4 Ansorena, Madrid #289/R est:8000

SEVILLE, Frederick William (19/20th C) British
Works on paper
£800 $1336 €1168 Shrewsbury from Castlefields (36x51cm-14x20in) s.d.1895 W/C. 12-Nov-3 Halls, Shrewsbury #241/R

SEWALL, Howard S (1899-1975) American
£307 $550 €448 Three heads in design (71x48cm-28x19in) s. oil paper over linen canvas painted c.1966. 16-Mar-4 Matthew's, Oregon #15/R
£349 $625 €510 Face and figures (51x41cm-20x16in) s. canvas on masonite painted c.1950. 16-Mar-4 Matthew's, Oregon #14/R

SEWARD, Coy Avon (1884-1939) American
£683 $1100 €997 Jessie Chisholm, founder of the Chisholm Trail (36x28cm-14x11in) s. 22-Feb-3 Bunte, Elgin #1251

SEWARD, Vivyan A (1902-1983) American
£208 $375 €304 North Tower, Golden Gate Bridge (61x45cm 24x18in) s. 25-Apr-4 Bonhams & Butterfields, San Francisco #5542/R
£240 $425 €350 Beach cliffs (51x61cm-20x24in) s.d.1965. 1-May-4 Harvey Clar, Oakland #1265
£272 $500 €397 View of Angel Island with sailboats on the bay (51x76cm-20x30in) s. masonite. 27-Jun-4 Bonhams & Butterfields, San Francisco #3836/R
£329 $550 €480 Sailing ship on the high seas (56x71cm-22x28in) s. 26-Oct-3 Bonhams & Butterfields, San Francisco #6533/R
£449 $750 €656 Burnt-out hamburger joint and whorehouse, Pittsburg, California (46x61cm-18x24in) s. i.stretcher. 26-Oct-3 Bonhams & Butterfields, San Francisco #6531/R

SEWELL, Amos (1901-) American
Works on paper
£214 $400 €312 Motorboat on the lake (56x33cm-22x13in) s. W/C. 28-Feb-4 Thomaston Place, Thomaston #252/R

SEWELL, Charles B (19/20th C) British
£280 $442 €409 Hooked trout (34x95cm-13x37in) indis.sig.d. 24-Jul-3 Lawrence, Crewkerne #954

SEWELL, Robert van Vorst (1860-1924) American

£475	$850	€694	Art nouveau mythological mural, Bacchantes (102x99cm-40x39in) 11-Jan-4 William Jenack, New York #372
£1732	$3100	€2529	Art nouveau mythological mural, Bacchantes (104x269cm-41x106in) s. 11-Jan-4 William Jenack, New York #360 est:2000-3000
£2116	$4000	€3089	Figure in vegetable garden (30x51cm-12x20in) prov. 17-Feb-4 John Moran, Pasadena #56/R est:3000-5000
£3267	$5750	€4901	Pre-Raphaelite painting of a mounted knight flanked by two angels (86x112cm-34x44in) s. 21-May-4 North East Auctions, Portsmouth #1519/R est:3000-5000

SEWELL, Robert van Vorst (attrib) (1860-1924) American

£535	$1000	€781	NYMPHS (79x76cm-31x30in) i.stretcher. 25-Feb-4 Doyle, New York #953/R

SEWOHL, Waldemar (1887-1967) German

£300	$549	€450	View of Altona (85x70cm-33x28in) s. 5-Jun-4 Arnold, Frankfurt #725

SEXTON, Frederick Lester (1889-?) American

£509	$850	€743	Niantic, Connecticut (30x41cm-12x16in) s. board. 26-Oct-3 Bonhams & Butterfields, San Francisco #6529/R

SEYDEL, Eduard (1822-1881) Luxembourger

£195	$349	€285	Returning home late (25x20cm-10x8in) s.d.48 paper on board. 22-Mar-4 Philippe Schuler, Zurich #6189 (S.FR 450)
£400	$732	€600	Maid and children in farm interior (18x26cm-7x10in) s. board. 5-Jun-4 Arnold, Frankfurt #727/R
£413	$756	€620	Midday rest under the village lime-tree (13x25cm-5x10in) s. panel. 5-Jun-4 Arnold, Frankfurt #726/R

SEYFERT (19th C) ?

£2128	$3553	€3000	Paysage de la campagne Suisse (38x60cm-15x24in) s.d.1816. 17-Oct-3 Tajan, Paris #119 est:3000-4000

SEYFFER, August (1774-1845) German

Works on paper

£280	$507	€420	Castle in Kirchheim unter Teck (30x46cm-12x18in) i. verso W/C Indian ink. 2-Apr-4 Winterberg, Heidelberg #547

SEYLBERGH, Jacques van den (1884-1960) Belgian

Works on paper

£295	$546	€440	Chaumiere dans un paysage enneige (44x38cm-17x15in) s. gouache cardboard. 15-Mar-4 Horta, Bruxelles #488

SEYLER, J (1873-1958) German

£987	$1816	€1500	Evening at the beach (24x29cm-9x11in) 28-Jun-4 Dr Fritz Nagel, Stuttgart #7094/R est:500

SEYLER, Julius (1873-1958) German

£278	$458	€400	Shrimp fishing in the shallows (70x100cm-28x39in) s. board on panel. 3-Jul-3 Van Ham, Cologne #1461
£310	$518	€453	Red Indians on horseback (30x38cm-12x15in) s. board. 20-Oct-3 Stephan Welz, Johannesburg #480/R est:4000-6000 (SA.R 3600)
£395	$726	€600	Lovers standing up under chestnut tree (30x22cm-12x9in) s. paper on panel. 24-Jun-4 Dr Fritz Nagel, Stuttgart #759/R
£403	$713	€600	Ramassage du varech (51x70cm-20x28in) s. cardboard. 30-Apr-4 Tajan, Paris #213
£417	$679	€600	Peasant ploughing (50x70cm-20x28in) s. panel. 25-Sep-3 Neumeister, Munich #2876/R
£433	$793	€650	Crab fishing on the coast (62x81cm-24x32in) s. board. 5-Jun-4 Arnold, Frankfurt #729/R
£461	$847	€700	Nude female figure (23x17cm-9x7in) s. board. 24-Jun-4 Dr Fritz Nagel, Stuttgart #757/R
£483	$806	€700	Extensive coastal landscape at low tide with lighthouse (45x71cm-18x28in) s. board lit. 10-Jul-3 Allgauer, Kempten #2681/R
£500	$915	€750	Fishermen on the beach (53x70cm-21x28in) s. board. 5-Jun-4 Arnold, Frankfurt #728/R
£503	$926	€750	Forest interior (45x70cm-18x28in) s. board. 24-Mar-4 Hugo Ruef, Munich #1105
£530	$964	€800	Fishing for crabs on the beach (73x100cm-29x39in) s. board. 18-Jun-4 Bolland & Marotz, Bremen #756/R
£563	$1025	€850	Saint-Tropez harbour (16x16cm-6x6in) s. cardboard. 16-Jun-4 Hugo Ruef, Munich #1078/R
£590	$962	€850	Bathers on beach (29x39cm-11x15in) s. board. 25-Sep-3 Neumeister, Munich #2877
£629	$1083	€900	Crab fishermen in Normandy (49x70cm-19x28in) s. cardboard prov. 5-Dec-3 Ketterer, Munich #19/R
£647	$1157	€945	Horse cart in country landscape (60x100cm-24x39in) s.d.18. 12-May-4 Dobiaschofsky, Bern #983/R est:1900 (S.FR 1500)
£658	$1211	€1000	Woman wearing hat in front of fence (52x34cm-20x13in) 24-Jun-4 Dr Fritz Nagel, Stuttgart #758/R
£658	$1211	€1000	Bridge over a river (14x18cm-6x7in) 28-Jun-4 Dr Fritz Nagel, Stuttgart #7093/R
£690	$1152	€1000	Female nude in sunlight (20x14cm-8x6in) s. canvas on fibreboard. 13-Nov-3 Neumeister, Munich #458/R
£800	$1456	€1200	Peasant ploughing (36x51cm-14x20in) s. board. 30-Jun-4 Neumeister, Munich #681/R
£878	$1546	€1300	Fishing for crabs (60x80cm-24x31in) board. 22-May-4 Sigalas, Stuttgart #476/R
£966	$1786	€1400	Horse drawn cart on mudflats (60x80cm-24x31in) s. 12-Feb-4 Weidler, Nurnberg #339/R
£986	$1706	€1400	Fishermen on beach with horses (60x91cm-24x36in) s. board. 11-Dec-3 Dr Fritz Nagel, Stuttgart #546/R
£1103	$1843	€1600	Vehicle pulled by oxen (49x70cm-19x28in) s. board. 13-Nov-3 Neumeister, Munich #457/R est:1800-2000
£1127	$1972	€1600	Fishermen with cart and horses (59x57cm-23x22in) s. panel. 19-Dec-3 Dorotheum, Vienna #145/R est:2000-2400
£1379	$2303	€2000	Potato harvest (22x30cm-9x12in) s. board. 13-Nov-3 Neumeister, Munich #459/R est:900-1000
£1724	$2879	€2500	Leda with the swan (31x24cm-12x9in) s. paper on canvas. 13-Nov-3 Neumeister, Munich #456/R est:2500-2800
£1800	$3222	€2700	Brittany (63x95cm-25x37in) s. paper on panel. 13-May-4 Neumeister, Munich #493/R est:2500-2800
£1867	$3341	€2800	Huts in the Rocky Mountains (21x27cm-8x11in) s. oil gouache. 13-May-4 Neumeister, Munich #494/R est:1800-2000
£2013	$3705	€3000	Countryfolk returning home (50x70cm-20x28in) s. board. 27-Mar-4 L & B, Essen #194/R est:900
£2533	$4560	€3800	Two Indians on horseback on hill (35x50cm-14x20in) s. board. 26-Apr-4 Rieber, Stuttgart #1289/R est:1600
£3020	$5406	€4500	Buffalo hunt (69x98cm-27x39in) s. board. 25-May-4 Karl & Faber, Munich #537/R est:5000-6000

Works on paper

£437	$696	€630	Shrimp fisherman with horse (18x25cm-7x10in) s. 11-Sep-3 Weidler, Nurnberg #354
£510	$913	€750	Shrimp fishing on mudflats (46x61cm-18x24in) s. gouache. 17-Mar-4 Neumeister, Munich #316/R

SEYMOUR, David (1911-1956) American

Photographs

£16667	$30000	€24334	Europe's children after the war (20x25cm-8x10in) album 100 gelatin silver print. 24-Apr-4 Phillips, New York #18/R est:40000-60000

SEYMOUR, George L (fl.1876-1916) British

£851	$1421	€1200	Marchang de volailles (50x35cm-20x14in) s. 16-Jun-3 Gros & Delettrez, Paris #510/R

SEYMOUR, James (1702-1752) British

£14205	$25000	€20739	Racing on Newmarket Heath (99x124cm-39x49in) prov.exhib. 18-May-4 Sotheby's, New York #207/R est:35000-45000

SEYMOUR, James (attrib) (1702-1752) British

Works on paper

£280	$518	€409	Horse race, two horse and jockeys (8x19cm-3x7in) pen ink sketch prov. 11-Mar-4 Morphets, Harrogate #326

SEYMOUR, James (style) (1702-1752) British

£10563	$18275	€15000	Black bay race horse and groom at the Bolton races (63x76cm-25x30in) i.d.1734 stretcher. 10-Dec-3 Christie's, Amsterdam #870/R est:6000-8000

SEYMOUR, Tom (19th C) British

£260	$416	€380	Mountainous lake landscape with deer (38x58cm-15x23in) s. 17-Sep-3 Brightwells, Leominster #858
£400	$736	€584	Figure fishing a lake in an extensive country landscape (36x50cm-14x20in) 8-Jun-4 Bonhams, Knightsbridge #240/R
£470	$799	€686	Highland cattle on the edge of a loch (29x49cm-11x19in) s. 4-Nov-3 Stephan Welz, Johannesburg #566/R est:4000-6000 (SA.R 5500)
£540	$929	€788	Rural landscapes with farmhouses in valley with figures (41x61cm-16x24in) s. pair. 2-Dec-3 Canterbury Auctions, UK #141/R
£550	$935	€803	When the fish comes in (40x60cm-16x24in) s. i.verso. 19-Nov-3 Tennants, Leyburn #1138
£860	$1600	€1256	North Wales - woman fetching water (49x74cm-19x29in) s. 2-Mar-4 Bearnes, Exeter #417/R
£2600	$4680	€3796	Autumn afternoon in Cumberland. Trout stream in Westmorland (41x61cm-16x24in) s. i.verso stretcher pair. 21-Apr-4 Tennants, Leyburn #1142 est:1200-1400

SEYPPEL, Hans (1886-?) German

£280	$476	€400	Vegetable field with tomatoes (55x56cm-22x22in) s. 22-Nov-3 Arnold, Frankfurt #641/R
£909	$1545	€1300	Figures working hard by river with passing bicycles and carriage (50x86cm-20x34in) s.d.1926. 22-Nov-3 Arnold, Frankfurt #640/R est:800

SEYSSAUD, René (1867-1952) French

£1757	$3145	€2600	Nu allonge (73x116cm-29x46in) s. 5-May-4 Coutau Begarie, Paris #82 est:1000-1200
£2222	$3511	€3200	Paysage aux oliviers (42x73cm-17x29in) s. 25-Apr-3 Etude de Provence, Marseille #89 est:3000-4000
£2979	$4974	€4200	Etang et cypres (46x38cm-18x15in) s. painted c.1910. 19-Jun-3 Millon & Associes, Paris #202/R est:2000-2500
£3357	$5774	€4800	Vue du midi (30x41cm-12x16in) s. panel. 3-Dec-3 Tajan, Paris #386/R est:3000-5000
£3404	$5685	€4800	Port du Midi (54x65cm-21x26in) s. 15-Oct-3 Claude Aguttes, Neuilly #24/R est:3000-4000
£4028	$6726	€5800	Terres rouges a Roussillon (46x55cm-18x22in) s. d.1937 verso. 25-Oct-3 Dianous, Marseille #416
£4094	$7533	€6100	Port en Mediterranee (55x46cm-22x18in) s. 29-Mar-4 Rieunier, Paris #49/R est:4000-5000

SEYSSES, Auguste (1862-?) French

Sculpture

£2800	$5124	€4088	Draped nude. Nude maiden (16cm-6in) indis sig. bronze two. 3-Jun-4 Sotheby's, Olympia #112/R est:750-850

SFORNI, G (19/20th C) Italian

£972	$1564	€1419	Sibilla Cumana (89x68cm-35x27in) s. canvasboard after Domenichino. 13-Oct-3 Joel, Victoria #434 est:800-1200 (A.D 2400)

SGRILLI, Roberto (1897-1985) Italian

£1408	$2437	€2000	View of Ponte Vecchio from the Arno (65x90cm-26x35in) s.d.25. 9-Dec-3 Pandolfini, Florence #84/R est:2000-3000

SHAA, Aqjangajuk (1937-) Canadian
Sculpture
£1081 $1838 €1578 Inuit drum dancer (38cm-15in) s. mottled green soapstone. 3-Nov-3 Waddingtons, Toronto #98/R est:2000-2500 (C.D 2400)
£1802 $3063 €2631 Dancing walrus with tusks (41cm-16in) mottled green soapstone. 3-Nov-3 Waddingtons, Toronto #343/R est:4000-6000 (C.D 4000)

SHAAR, Pinchas (1923-1996) Israeli
£382 $638 €550 Three masked figures (92x65cm-36x26in) s. d.1961 verso. 21-Oct-3 Campo & Campo, Antwerp #274

SHACKELFORD, Bud (1918-) American
Works on paper
£529 $1000 €772 Boats/harbour (51x69cm-20x27in) s. W/C prov. 17-Feb-4 John Moran, Pasadena #91/R

SHACKLETON, Keith (1923-) British
£380 $684 €555 Arctic terns (44x88cm-17x35in) s.d.75 board. 23-Apr-4 Charterhouse, Sherborne #695/R
£550 $869 €798 Black skimmer (61x44cm-24x17in) s.d.65 i.verso board. 3-Sep-3 Bonhams, Bury St Edmunds #406/R
£591 $1100 €863 Nesting eiders (45x91cm-18x36in) s.d.62 masonite. 5-Mar-4 Skinner, Boston #554/R
£798 $1300 €1165 Penguins of Antarctica (46x61cm-18x24in) s.d.70 masonite. 17-Jul-3 Doyle, New York #47/R
£1882 $3500 €2748 Icebergs, Greenland (51x61cm-20x24in) s.d.57 i.verso. 5-Mar-4 Skinner, Boston #523/R est:1200-1800

SHACKLETON, William (attrib) (1872-1933) British
£250 $463 €365 Standing draped female figure (62x30cm-24x12in) 13-Jul-4 Rosebery Fine Art, London #711
£850 $1335 €1233 Mermaid embracing before an underwater city (35x46cm-14x18in) canvas on panel. 28-Aug-3 Christie's, Kensington #364/R

SHADBOLT, Jack (1909-1998) Canadian
£402 $683 €587 Golden surprise (33x32cm-13x13in) s.d.1979 s.i.d.verso acrylic collage prov. 6-Nov-3 Heffel, Vancouver #106/R (C.D 900)
£3455 $6185 €5044 Blue falling (97x198cm-38x78in) s.d.1965 s.i.d.verso oil lucite prov. 27-May-4 Heffel, Vancouver #190/R est:9000-12000 (C.D 8500)
£4279 $7275 €6247 Navajo signal triptych (152x222cm-60x87in) s.d.1979 acrylic board triptych prov.exhib.lit. 27-Nov-3 Heffel, Vancouver #173/R est:9000-12000 (C.D 9500)
£5691 $10187 €8309 Presences in the field (102x124cm-40x49in) s.d.1960 s.i.d.verso oil lucite prov.exhib.lit. 6-May-4 Heffel, Vancouver #132/R est:8000-12000 (C.D 14000)
£6757 $11486 €9865 Rainy Island (149x203cm-59x80in) s.d.1978 i.verso acrylic board lit. 27-Nov-3 Heffel, Vancouver #171/R est:8000-10000 (C.D 15000)
£7317 $13098 €10683 Tuscan morning (99x125cm-39x49in) s.d.1964 s.i.verso lit. 27-May-4 Heffel, Vancouver #208/R est:25000-35000 (C.D 18000)
Sculpture
£1118 $2035 €1632 Sketch box easel (49x38x9cm-19x15x4in) s. wood prov.lit. 1-Jul-4 Heffel, Vancouver #27/R est:3000-5000 (C.D 2750)
Works on paper
£405 $689 €591 Italian town, 3 (41x56cm-16x22in) s.d.1962 s.i.d.verso ink wash prov. 27-Nov-3 Heffel, Vancouver #138 (C.D 900)
£721 $1225 €1053 Collioure (30x43cm-12x17in) s.i.d.May 1957 pencil prov. 27-Nov-3 Heffel, Vancouver #158/R (C.D 1600)
£901 $1532 €1315 Butterfly collage (29x33cm-11x13in) s.d.1961-1980 i.verso mixed media prov. 27-Nov-3 Heffel, Vancouver #174/R est:2000-2500 (C.D 2000)
£1220 $2183 €1781 Summer experience (57x74cm-22x29in) s.d.1960 s.i.d.verso ink gouache prov. 27-May-4 Heffel, Vancouver #209/R est:3000-4000 (C.D 3000)
£1228 $2087 €1793 Flowers and thorns (44x34cm-17x13in) s.d.1948 mixed media prov. 6-Nov-3 Heffel, Vancouver #105/R est:3000-4000 (C.D 2750)
£2027 $3446 €2959 Summer bouquet (38x56cm-15x22in) s.d.54 s.i.d. verso ink W/C prov.exhib. 18-Nov-3 Sotheby's, Toronto #142/R est:3000-5000 (C.D 4500)
£3333 $5467 €4866 Ritual form series (91x66cm-36x26in) s.d.1951 mixed media collage. 28-May-3 Maynards, Vancouver #90/R est:10000-12000 (C.D 7500)

SHAFER, Simon P (19/20th C) American
£432 $800 €631 Still life with cherries (25x41cm-10x16in) s.d.1897. 13-Mar-4 Susanin's, Chicago #6208/R
£462 $850 €675 Still life with cherries (25x41cm-10x16in) s.d.1897. 26-Jun-4 Susanin's, Chicago #6068/R

SHAFIK, Medhat (1956-) Egyptian
Works on paper
£3000 $5520 €4500 Buried towns I (100x70cm-39x28in) s. mixed media on canvas exec.1996. 8-Jun-4 Finarte Semenzato, Milan #182/R est:2000-3000

SHAHN, Ben (1898-1969) American
£3039 $5500 €4437 Scorched earth (15x32cm-6x13in) s. tempera prov. 31-Mar-4 Sotheby's, New York #139/R est:3000-5000
Prints
£1955 $3500 €2854 Pleiades (53x66cm-21x26in) s. col serigraph gold leaf rice paper one of 54 lit. 16-May-4 Wright, Chicago #350/R est:3000-4000
£2011 $3600 €2936 Deserted fairground (29x38cm-11x15in) color screenprint. 6-May-4 Swann Galleries, New York #581/R est:5000-8000
£3529 $6000 €5152 Deserted fairground (29x38cm-11x15in) s. col screenprint. 6-Nov-3 Swann Galleries, New York #723/R est:5000-8000
Works on paper
£405 $750 €591 Lincoln, 1940 (30x23cm-12x9in) s. 15-Jul-4 Doyle, New York #75/R
£870 $1600 €1270 Life new life (94x64cm-37x25in) pencil red conte crayon exec. c.1960. 10-Jun-4 Swann Galleries, New York #211/R est:1000-1500
£950 $1700 €1387 Mother and child (28x20cm-11x8in) s. ink wash. 16-May-4 Wright, Chicago #176/R est:1000-2000
£1044 $1900 €1524 Man reclining (41x58cm-16x23in) s.i. ink executed c.1955. 29-Jun-4 Sotheby's, New York #313/R est:2500-3500
£1196 $2200 €1746 Hickman. Valvena studying (20x15cm-8x6in) i. brush ink exec. 1948 two. 10-Jun-4 Swann Galleries, New York #213/R est:1500-2500
£1413 $2600 €2063 Gas station. Telegraph poles and platform. Table with framed picture. brush ink three. 10-Jun-4 Swann Galleries, New York #214/R est:1500-2500
£2096 $3500 €3060 Heron of Calvary, No 3 (58x86cm-23x34in) s. gouache gold paint board prov. 7-Oct-3 Sotheby's, New York #208 est:4000-6000
£3892 $6500 €5682 Self portrait (30x22cm-12x9in) ink prov.exhib. 11-Nov-3 Christie's, Rockefeller NY #169/R est:3000-5000
£4571 $8000 €6674 Man playing a cithere, Psalm 150 (101x65cm-40x26in) s.i. ink prov. 19-Dec-3 Sotheby's, New York #1049/R est:5000-7000
£5405 $10000 €7891 Three penny opera (36x36cm-14x14in) s. pen ink W/C paper on board prov. 11-Mar-4 Christie's, Rockefeller NY #82/R est:4000-6000
£10811 $20000 €15784 Atomic tables (46x213cm-18x84in) s. gouache gold leaf paper on board prov.lit. 11-Mar-4 Christie's, Rockefeller NY #84/R est:25000-35000

SHAKESPEARE, Percy (1906-) British
£1700 $3009 €2482 View of a street from a window with figure. 27-Apr-4 Lawrences, Bletchingley #1602/R est:500-700

SHALDERS, George (1826-1873) British
£307 $550 €517 Landscape with four children (23x33cm-9x13in) s. panel. 20-Mar-4 Pook & Pook, Downington #588
£850 $1581 €1241 Highland scene with a woman standing beside a man on horseback (61x86cm-24x34in) s. 4-Mar-4 Amersham Auction Rooms, UK #295
£900 $1467 €1314 Cattle watering at a lake (33x54cm-13x21in) s. 24-Sep-3 Dreweatt Neate, Newbury #145/R
£1374 $2500 €2006 View in North Wales (28x43cm-11x17in) s.d.58 i.verso board. 19-Jun-4 Jeffery Burchard, Florida #32
£2000 $3580 €2920 Hesitation before crossing (61x86cm-24x34in) s. 27-May-4 Christie's, Kensington #167/R est:2000-3000
Works on paper
£1500 $2505 €2190 Shepherd with his flock in a moorland landscape (22x50cm-9x20in) s.d.1871 pencil W/C bodycol prov. 16-Oct-3 Christie's, Kensington #137/R est:600-800
£2067 $3370 €3018 Through woodland pastures (48x71cm-19x28in) s.d.1870 W/C. 17-Jul-3 Naón & Cia, Buenos Aires #9/R
£8000 $13600 €11680 Through woodland pastures (50x71cm-20x28in) s.d.1870 W/C htd bodycol prov. 27-Nov-3 Sotheby's, London #354/R est:8000-12000

SHALDERS, George (attrib) (1826-1873) British
£600 $1002 €876 Cattle watering in a wooded landscape (46x61cm-18x24in) 12-Nov-3 Halls, Shrewsbury #312
£1154 $1985 €1685 Near Esher, Surrey (61x89cm-24x35in) 3-Dec-3 AB Stockholms Auktionsverk #2549/R est:12000-15000 (S.KR 15000)

SHANE, Frederick (1907-) American
£1437 $2400 €2098 Meandering road (81x66cm-32x26in) s. 19-Oct-3 Susanin's, Chicago #6065/R est:1200-2400

SHANGJUN (17th C) Chinese
Sculpture
£5019 $8382 €7328 Figure of Sakyamuni as an ascetic (14cm-6in) with sig soapstone. 27-Oct-3 Christie's, Hong Kong #773/R est:60000-80000 (HK.D 65000)

SHANKS, Duncan F (1937-) British
£2000 $3140 €2900 Winter night (112x112cm-44x44in) s. i.verso board. 27-Aug-3 Sotheby's, London #1151/R est:2000-3000
£2800 $4676 €4088 Culter burn (126x126cm-50x50in) s.i.d. 16-Oct-3 Bonhams, Edinburgh #9/R est:3000-5000
£3700 $6290 €5402 Shower over the Clyde valley (152x122cm-60x48in) s. s.i.d.1978 verso exhib. 19-Nov-3 Tennants, Leyburn #1298/R est:2000-3000

SHANKS, Nelson (1937-) American
£2035 $3500 €2971 Southern Lady (102x76cm-40x30in) s. 7-Dec-3 Freeman, Philadelphia #207 est:4000-6000
£2989 $5500 €4364 Portrait of a young woman (30x25cm-12x10in) s. board. 25-Jun-4 Freeman, Philadelphia #250/R est:500-800

SHANKS, William Somerville (1864-1951) British
£500 $915 €730 Three girls in a clearing (68x53cm-27x21in) s. board. 29-Jan-4 Bonhams, Edinburgh #302
£1100 $2013 €1606 Still life of irise and Japanese prints (75x62cm-30x24in) s. 8-Apr-4 Bonhams, Edinburgh #176 est:1000-1500

SHANNON, David Michael (1927-1993) Australian
£511 $883 €746 Industry (51x76cm-20x30in) s.d.54 i.verso hardboard. 10-Dec-3 Shapiro, Sydney #11 (A.D 1200)
£621 $968 €900 Autumn landscape (50x60cm-20x24in) s.d.78 canvasboard. 1-Aug-2 Joel, Victoria #283 est:2000-2500 (A.D 1800)
£813 $1276 €1179 Queenslander (89x105cm-35x41in) s.d.68. 26-Aug-3 Lawson Menzies, Sydney #391 est:2500-3500 (A.D 2000)
£1106 $1881 €1615 The red door (49x60cm-19x24in) s.d.69. 25-Nov-3 Christie's, Melbourne #213/R (A.D 2600)
£3659 $5744 €5306 Lilydale Quarry no 1 (90x182cm-35x72in) s.d.83 prov. 27-Aug-3 Christie's, Sydney #538/R est:6000-9000 (A.D 9000)
£3894 $6152 €5685 Marshalling yards IV (91x76cm-36x30in) s.d.71 prov. 2-Sep-3 Deutscher-Menzies, Melbourne #159/R est:6000-8000 (A.D 9500)
£4132 $7645 €6033 Edge of the city (91x71cm-36x28in) s.d.56 s.i.verso prov. 15-Mar-4 Sotheby's, Melbourne #100/R est:10000-15000 (A.D 10000)
£4545 $8409 €6636 Jugiong landscape No.3 (121x151cm-48x59in) s.d.87 prov.exhib. 15-Mar-4 Sotheby's, Melbourne #127/R est:8000-12000 (A.D 11000)
£5285 $8297 €7663 Untitled, city (121x182cm-48x72in) s. painted c.1966 exhib. 27-Aug-3 Christie's, Sydney #527/R est:15000-20000 (A.D 13000)
£6198 $11467 €9049 Road to Costerfield No.4 (122x152cm-48x60in) s.d.85 i.verso prov.exhib. 15-Mar-4 Sotheby's, Melbourne #122/R est:8000-12000 (A.D 15000)

Works on paper
£267 $486 €390 Boy (24x18cm-9x7in) s.d.56 gouache. 16-Jun-4 Deutscher-Menzies, Melbourne #571/R (A.D 700)
£366 $575 €534 Calendulas (65x50cm-26x20in) s.d.76 pastel. 26-Aug-3 Lawson Menzies, Sydney #129 est:1000-2000 (A.D 900)
£366 $575 €534 Anemonies (65x50cm-26x20in) s.d.76 pastel. 26-Aug-3 Lawson Menzies, Sydney #130 est:1000-2000 (A.D 900)
£537 $994 €784 Fisherman jetty (53x73cm-21x29in) s.d.73 i.verso pastel prov. 10-Mar-4 Deutscher-Menzies, Melbourne #550/R est:1000-1500 (A.D 1300)
£744 $1376 €1086 Figure at a window (29x19cm-11x7in) s.d.71 i.verso W/C pen ink. 10-Mar-4 Deutscher-Menzies, Melbourne #549/R est:400-600 (A.D 1800)
£826 $1405 €1206 Flowers (84x58cm-33x23in) s.d.78 pastel chl. 29-Oct-3 Lawson Menzies, Sydney #176/R est:1000-1500 (A.D 2000)

SHANNON, Sir James Jebusa (1862-1923) British/American
£380 $703 €555 Portrait of a lady, head and shoulders, with long plaited hair (43x34cm-17x13in) s.d.1898 oval. 14-Jul-4 Bonhams, Chester #513
£4800 $8640 €7008 Portrait of Pierre Collins, seated three-quarter length in a white dress (110x83cm-43x33in) 21-Apr-4 Christie's, Kensington #154/R est:4000-6000
£6000 $10740 €8760 Portrait of Lady Grace Dance, in a white dress with blue waistband (101x76cm-40x30in) sketch. 27-May-4 Christie's, Kensington #107/R est:3000-5000

SHAO MI (1594-1642) Chinese
Works on paper
£6757 $12162 €9865 Landscape (111x29cm-44x11in) s.i.d.1634 ink hanging scroll. 25-Apr-4 Christie's, Hong Kong #345/R est:50000-70000 (HK.D 95000)

SHAPIRO, David (1916-) American
£1258 $2000 €1837 Suki series (145x180cm-57x71in) 14-Sep-3 Susanin's, Chicago #6034/R est:1000-1500

SHAPIRO, Joel (1941-) American
£2778 $5000 €4056 Untitled (9x9cm-4x4in) s.d.1972 verso. 24-Apr-4 David Rago, Lambertville #393/R est:600-1200
£9000 $16560 €13140 Untitled (152x102cm-60x40in) oil pastel on paper prov. 25-Jun-4 Christie's, London #179/R est:5000-7000
Sculpture
£14970 $25000 €21856 Untitled (14x17x13cm-6x7x5in) s.d.1973-74 wood exhib. 13-Nov-3 Sotheby's, New York #125/R est:9000-12000
£17964 $30000 €26227 Untitled, JS 113 (18x18x18cm-7x7x7in) iron prov.exhib. 13-Nov-3 Sotheby's, New York #130/R est:10000-15000
£19461 $32500 €28413 Untitled (16x17x14cm-6x7x6in) bronze exhib. 13-Nov-3 Sotheby's, New York #126/R est:12000-16000
£19553 $35000 €28547 Untitled (22x36x19cm-9x14x7in) sig. st.d.80 num.1/3 cast iron paint prov.exhib. 13-May-4 Sotheby's, New York #182/R est:14000-18000
£20000 $36800 €29200 Untitled (18x19x9cm-7x7x4in) d.75 num.1/1 cast iron executed 1975 prov.exhib.lit. 25-Jun-4 Christie's, London #180/R est:20000-30000
£41899 $75000 €61173 Untitled (24x42x29cm-9x17x11in) with sig. st.d.90-91 num.2/6 dark brown pat bronze 2 parts prov. 13-May-4 Sotheby's, New York #178/R est:50000-70000
£89820 $150000 €131137 Untitled, JS 354 (8x62x50cm-3x24x20in) s.d.79 num.1/3 cast bronze prov.exhib. 13-Nov-3 Sotheby's, New York #122/R est:60000-80000
£89820 $150000 €131137 Untitled (91x143x102cm-36x56x40in) bronze executed 1985 prov. 13-Nov-3 Phillips, New York #25/R est:100000-150000
Works on paper
£3846 $7000 €5615 Untitled (37x48cm-15x19in) chk chl pastel executed 1991 prov. 29-Jun-4 Sotheby's, New York #611/R est:6000-8000
£7821 $14000 €11419 Untitled (41x51cm-16x20in) s.d.85 verso chl prov. 13-May-4 Sotheby's, New York #177/R est:6000-8000
£8982 $15000 €13114 Untitled (88x116cm-35x46in) chl prov. 13-Nov-3 Sotheby's, New York #577/R est:6000-8000
£9581 $16000 €13988 Untitled (81x102cm-32x40in) chl rag paper prov.exhib. 13-Nov-3 Sotheby's, New York #576/R est:8000-12000

SHAPIRO, Miriam (1923-) Canadian
£2083 $3750 €3041 Anonymous was a woman (29x21cm-11x8in) s.i.d.1976 verso acrylic collage. 24-Apr-4 David Rago, Lambertville #395/R est:300-600

SHAPIRO, Shmuel (1924-1985) American
£326 $597 €476 Tete bleu (30x24cm-12x9in) s.d.1967 tempera cardboard. 4-Jun-4 Zofingen, Switzerland #2960/R (S.FR 750)
£633 $1077 €924 Untitled (85x60cm-33x24in) s.d.1968 oilstick paper. 22-Nov-3 Burkhard, Luzern #18/R (S.FR 1400)

SHAPLAND, John (1865-1929) British
£900 $1674 €1314 On the Lynn (46x61cm-18x24in) indis sig. 4-Mar-4 Christie's, Kensington #479/R
Works on paper
£340 $622 €496 Totnes (28x45cm-11x18in) s. W/C. 7-Apr-4 Woolley & Wallis, Salisbury #46/R
£550 $974 €803 Moorland scenes (25x76cm-10x30in) s. W/C pair. 29-Apr-4 Gorringes, Lewes #2355

SHAPLEIGH, Frank Henry (1842-1906) American
£1075 $2000 €1570 Autumn, Jackson, NH (35x25cm-14x10in) s. s.i.verso. 5-Mar-4 Skinner, Boston #286/R est:800-1200
£1695 $3000 €2475 On Thorn Hill Road, Jackson, New Hampshire (41x25cm-16x10in) s.d.1887. 2-May-4 Grogan, Boston #67/R
£1882 $3500 €2748 Autumn view of a New England village with lake (51x76cm-20x30in) s.d.1883. 6-Mar-4 North East Auctions, Portsmouth #549/R est:3500-4500
£2016 $3750 €2943 Above the tree line - View of the White Mountains Presidential range (36x61cm-14x24in) s.d.1894. 6-Mar-4 North East Auctions, Portsmouth #228/R
£2096 $3500 €3060 Winter sunset at Lebanon, Maine (25x41cm-10x16in) s.d.1878 s.i.verso. 20-Jun-3 Freeman, Philadelphia #187/R est:1000-1500
£2554 $4750 €3729 Mount Washington from the Glen Road (36x61cm-14x24in) i.d.1877 stretcher. 6-Mar-4 North East Auctions, Portsmouth #230/R
£2874 $4800 €4196 Mt Washington and Ellis river at Jacks (18x30cm-7x12in) board. 16-Nov-3 CRN Auctions, Cambridge #9/R
£3210 $5200 €4687 Wooden bridge in Jackson, NH and Carter Notch (25x41cm-10x16in) s.d.1886 s.i. verso prov. 1-Aug-3 North East Auctions, Portsmouth #947/R est:4000-6000
£5040 $9274 €7358 In Charlotte Street, St. Augustine, Fla (18x31cm-7x12in) s.d.1891 s.i.verso board. 14-Jun-4 Waddingtons, Toronto #21/R est:6000-8000 (C.D 12500)
£5882 $10000 €8588 Hospital Street, St. Augustine, Florida (19x32cm-7x13in) s.d.1883 s.i.verso board. 21-Nov-3 Skinner, Boston #274/R est:800-1200

SHAPOSHNIKOV, Boris V (1890-1956) Russian
£7000 $12740 €10220 Musician (40x54cm-16x21in) d.1916 card prov. 21-Jun-4 Bonhams, New Bond Street #27/R est:4000-5000

SHAQU, Mannumi (1917-) North American
Sculpture
£1261 $2144 €1841 Woman with her child in an amaut, tending a kudlik (28cm-11in) s. mottled green soapstone. 3-Nov-3 Waddingtons, Toronto #114/R est:2500-3500 (C.D 2800)

SHARADIN, Henry W (1872-1966) American
£795 $1400 €1161 Landscape (56x66cm-22x26in) s. 21-May-4 Pook & Pook, Downington #89 est:700-1000

SHARAKU, Toshusai (fl.1794-1795) Japanese
Prints
£24867 $42273 €35560 Otani Hiroji III (31x14cm-12x6in) s. col print exec.1794 lit. 25-Nov-3 Sotheby's, Paris #117/R est:40000-50000
£40001 $73601 €60000 Actor. s. print. 11-Jun-4 Tajan, Paris #134/R est:60000-65000
£46196 $85000 €67446 Segawa kikunojo III as Oschizu - wife of Tanabe Bunzo (37x24cm-15x9in) s. print prov. 23-Mar-4 Christie's, Rockefeller NY #13/R est:100000-150000
£84720 $144025 €121150 Nakamura Narazo (32x22cm-13x9in) s. col print exec.1794 prov.exhib.lit. 25-Nov-3 Sotheby's, Paris #121/R est:80000-100000

SHARP, Dorothea (1874-1955) British
£2400 $4224 €3504 Bedtime (27x35cm-11x14in) panel. 19-May-4 Sotheby's, Olympia #180/R est:2500-3500
£3600 $6444 €5256 Still life of summer flowers (45x36cm-18x14in) s. board. 28-May-4 Lyon & Turnbull, Edinburgh #84/R est:3000-5000
£4000 $7480 €5840 Vase of summer flowers on a window sill (60x50cm-24x20in) s. 26-Feb-4 Lane, Penzance #270/R est:4000-5000
£4500 $7740 €6570 Children playing in the sea (31x41cm-12x16in) s. panel. 2-Dec-3 Bonhams, New Bond Street #15/R est:5000-7000
£4500 $7740 €6570 Young girl with child by the water's edge (31x41cm-12x16in) s. panel prov. 2-Dec-3 Bonhams, New Bond Street #16/R est:4000-6000
£5000 $8800 €7300 Studio flowers (35x45cm-14x18in) s. board. 19-May-4 Sotheby's, Olympia #139/R est:4000-6000
£7500 $12750 €10950 Little goatherd (51x61cm-20x24in) s. 21-Nov-3 Christie's, London #44/R est:8000-12000
£8000 $13360 €11680 Mother and child at the water's edge (28x38cm-11x15in) s. panel. 14-Oct-3 David Lay, Penzance #629/R est:6000-8000
£8368 $15146 €12217 Painting by the seaside (26x34cm-10x13in) s. board double-sided prov. 1-Apr-4 Heffel, Vancouver #92a/R est:8000-12000 (C.D 20000)
£8500 $14450 €12410 Playing in the shallows (30x40cm-12x16in) init. board. 26-Nov-3 Sotheby's, Olympia #70/R est:3000-5000
£10500 $19215 €15330 On the clifftop (36x46cm-14x18in) s. 2-Jun-4 Sotheby's, London #30/R est:10000-15000
£12000 $21960 €17520 Springtime (51x61cm-20x24in) s. 4-Jun-4 Christie's, London #63/R est:7000-10000
£12000 $21840 €17520 Child with birds (61x51cm-24x20in) 15-Jun-4 Bonhams, New Bond Street #21/R est:10000-15000
£14000 $25760 €20440 Children with dog (48x58cm-19x23in) s. 14-Jun-4 Louis Taylor, Stoke on Trent #1255
£18000 $30600 €26280 Children on the rocky shore (51x61cm-20x24in) s. 21-Nov-3 Christie's, London #46/R est:20000-30000
£30000 $54900 €43800 Summer day on the cliffs (89x67cm-35x26in) s. double-sided. 2-Jun-4 Sotheby's, London #31/R est:30000-50000
£30000 $54900 €43800 Daisy pickers (56x51cm-22x20in) s. 4-Jun-4 Christie's, London #62/R est:15000-20000

SHARP, John O Robert (20th C) American
£9756 $16000 €14244 Southern landscape with stormy sky, figure and cabin (71x107cm-28x42in) s. prov.exhib. 31-May-3 Brunk, Ashville #476/R est:2000-4000

SHARP, Joseph Henry (1859-1953) American
£1093 $2000 €1596 Children on a path (61x41cm-24x16in) s.d.1882. 5-Jun-4 Treadway Gallery, Cincinnati #624/R est:3000-5000
£1279 $2200 €1867 Portrait of James Stark Wayne (69x56cm-27x22in) s. painted c.1910 prov. 7-Dec-3 Treadway Gallery, Cincinnati #572/R est:2000-3000
£6952 $13000 €10150 Big Horn Mountains, Crow Reservation, Montana (23x33cm-9x13in) s. board painted c.1905 prov. 24-Jul-4 Coeur d'Alene, Hayden #127/R est:10000-15000
£6952 $13000 €10150 Purple Mountains (23x30cm-9x12in) s. s.d.1910 verso board prov. 24-Jul-4 Coeur d'Alene, Hayden #237/R est:6000-9000
£8021 $15000 €11711 Montana landscape (30x46cm-12x18in) s. prov. 24-Jul-4 Coeur d'Alene, Hayden #259/R est:10000-20000
£9091 $17000 €13273 Laguna twilight (15x20cm-6x8in) s. board prov. 24-Jul-4 Coeur d'Alene, Hayden #43/R est:10000-20000
£10056 $18000 €14682 Taos Valley (25x41cm-10x16in) 15-May-4 Altermann Galleries, Santa Fe #76/R
£10227 $18000 €14931 From Studio door (30x23cm-12x9in) s.i. canvas on masonite prov. 19-May-4 Sotheby's, New York #206/R est:10000-15000
£15436 $28403 €23000 Winter river landscape with boats (52x72cm-20x28in) s. 24-Mar-4 Hugo Ruef, Munich #1256/R est:1200
£17045 $30000 €24886 Aspens - Twining (51x61cm-20x24in) s. i.verso prov. 19-May-4 Sotheby's, New York #205/R est:30000-50000
£20053 $37500 €29277 Indians by firelight (25x30cm-10x12in) s. board prov. 24-Jul-4 Coeur d'Alene, Hayden #41/R est:20000-30000
£20588 $35000 €30058 Hunting son - firelight (30x41cm-12x16in) 1-Nov-3 Altermann Galleries, Santa Fe #43a
£21739 $40000 €31739 Young man of Taos, New Mexico (22x17cm-9x7in) s. i.verso canvasboard prov. 8-Jun-4 Bonhams & Butterfields, San Francisco #4124/R est:20000-25000
£23864 $42000 €34841 Aspens at Twining (63x76cm-25x30in) s. 18-May-4 Christie's, Rockefeller NY #52/R est:60000-80000

£24064	$45000	€35133	Taos backyard (36x43cm-14x17in) s. prov.lit. 24-Jul-4 Coeur d'Alene, Hayden #45/R est:20000-30000
£29412	$55000	€42942	Blackfeet teepees, Glacier Park (23x33cm-9x13in) s. board prov. 24-Jul-4 Coeur d'Alene, Hayden #103/R est:25000-45000
£31250	$55000	€45625	Red stone pipe (51x41cm-20x16in) s.i. prov. 19-May-4 Sotheby's, New York #199/R est:50000-70000
£34759	$65000	€50748	Landscape with teepee (23x33cm-9x13in) s. board prov. 24-Jul-4 Coeur d'Alene, Hayden #42/R est:30000-50000
£42614	$75000	€62216	Black Deer (130x104cm-51x41in) s.i. prov. 19-May-4 Sotheby's, New York #200/R est:50000-70000
£42781	$80000	€62460	Indian in his solitude (41x51cm-16x20in) s. prov.lit. 24-Jul-4 Coeur d'Alene, Hayden #102/R est:50000-75000
£43605	$75000	€63663	Chief Washakie (46x30cm-18x12in) s. prov. 3-Dec-3 Sotheby's, New York #148/R est:25000-35000
£48128	$90000	€70267	Blackfeet teepees, Glacier Park, Montana (23x33cm-9x13in) s. board prov. 24-Jul-4 Coeur d'Alene, Hayden #202/R est:25000-45000
£50802	$95000	€74171	Waterhole, Blackfoot Country (28x20cm-11x8in) s. board prov. 24-Jul-4 Coeur d'Alene, Hayden #166/R est:30000-50000
£69767	$120000	€101860	Early winter on Crow Reservation, Montana (44x65cm-17x26in) s. s.i.d.1908 verso prov. 4-Dec-3 Christie's, Rockefeller NY #72/R est:70000-90000
£70588	$120000	€103058	Taos Indians in the sunlight (18x24cm-7x9in) s. prov. 18-Nov-3 John Moran, Pasadena #114b est:75000-100000
£74866	$140000	€109304	Hunting son (41x30cm-16x12in) s. prov.lit. 24-Jul-4 Coeur d'Alene, Hayden #199/R est:30000-50000
£96257	$180000	€140535	Winter camp (46x61cm-18x24in) s. 24-Jul-4 Coeur d'Alene, Hayden #101/R est:200000-300000
£508021	$950000	€741711	Squaw winter (76x71cm-30x28in) s. prov.exhib.lit. 24-Jul-4 Coeur d'Alene, Hayden #40/R est:250000-450000
Works on paper			
£232	$425	€339	Portrait of a baby (28cm-11in circular) s. pastel executed 1880. 5-Jun-4 Treadway Gallery, Cincinnati #634/R
£11173	$20000	€16313	Taos Indians (25x36cm-10x14in) gouache board. 15-May-4 Altermann Galleries, Santa Fe #77/R

SHARP, Louis H (1875-1946) American

£635	$1200	€927	Autumn woods (51x66cm-20x26in) s. s.i. verso prov. 17-Feb-4 John Moran, Pasadena #148/R

SHARP, Peter (1964-) Australian

£391	$708	€571	Further down - goes on forever (121x121cm-48x48in) i.verso acrylic oil on canvas. 30-Mar-4 Lawson Menzies, Sydney #183/R est:600-800 (A.D 950)

SHARPE, Alfred (1830-1912) Australian

Works on paper			
£30970	$53578	€45216	Bridle track, new Zealand (57x95cm-22x37in) s.d.1889 W/C. 9-Dec-3 Peter Webb, Auckland #47/R est:90000-120000 (NZ.D 83000)

SHARPE, Eliza (1796-1874) British

Works on paper			
£260	$434	€380	Children and mistress in a schoolroom (48x61cm-19x24in) s.d.1855 W/C. 10-Jul-3 Gorringes, Worthing #716

SHARPE, Wendy (1960-) Australian

£1240	$2293	€1810	Mex in the garden (73x57cm-29x22in) s. s.i.verso. 10-Mar-4 Deutscher-Menzies, Melbourne #364/R est:2000-3000 (A.D 3000)
£1322	$2446	€1930	Masquerade (55x45cm-22x18in) s. 10-Mar-4 Deutscher-Menzies, Melbourne #363/R est:1800-2500 (A.D 3200)

SHARPLES, Ellen (1769-1849) British

Works on paper			
£1400	$2338	€2044	Portrait of John Claremont Whiteman, commander in the Hon East India Company's Service (23x21cm-9x8in) pastel. 14-Oct-3 Sotheby's, London #155/R est:800-1200

SHARPLES, George (1797-1849) British

Works on paper			
£838	$1500	€1223	Portraits of gentleman and his wife (25x18cm-10x7in) s.d.1819 pastel pair. 16-May-4 CRN Auctions, Cambridge #18/R

SHARPLES, James (1752-1811) American

Works on paper			
£360	$569	€522	Portrait of a lady in a grey dress and bonnet (23x17cm-9x7in) s.i.verso pastel. 24-Jul-3 Lawrence, Crewkerne #831
£865	$1600	€1263	Portrait of a lady in blue dress (21x18cm-8x7in) pastel executed c.1780. 17-Jan-4 Sotheby's, New York #1058/R est:800-1200
£1364	$2400	€1991	Portrait of two young children seated on an empire soda (25x23cm-10x9in) pastel prov. 21-May-4 Pook & Pook, Downington #206/R est:1000-1500
£1892	$3500	€2762	Portrait of a woman in a white lace cap, Miss Davis (24x19cm-9x7in) pastel oval. 17-Jan-4 Sotheby's, New York #1057/R est:2000-3000

SHATTER, Susan (1943-) American

Works on paper			
£552	$1000	€806	Colorado river, Indian summer (64x173cm-25x68in) W/C. 16-Apr-4 American Auctioneer #367/R
£635	$1150	€927	Virgin river II (102x71cm-40x28in) W/C. 16-Apr-4 American Auctioneer #368/R

SHATTUCK, Aaron Draper (1832-1928) American

£4469	$8000	€6525	New York sunset landscape (36x51cm-14x20in) s. 8-Jan-4 James Julia, Fairfield #665/R est:6000-8000
£4969	$8000	€7255	The wading pool (30x51cm-12x20in) s. 20-Aug-3 James Julia, Fairfield #1410/R est:9000-12000

SHATWELL, Helen (?) ?

£299	$475	€437	Still life of flowers, teapot and bowl of apples on blue cloth (61x76cm-24x30in) s. board. 10-Sep-3 Alderfer's, Hatfield #292

SHATZ, Shaul (1944-) Israeli

£824	$1500	€1236	Woman by the door (130x102cm-51x40in) s. s.d.1986 verso. 1-Jul-4 Ben-Ami, Tel Aviv #4933/R est:2000-3000

SHAW, Arthur Winter (1869-1948) British

£1200	$2232	€1752	Domestic chores (42x52cm-17x20in) s. 4-Mar-4 Christie's, Kensington #608/R est:1200-1800

SHAW, Barbara (1924-) British

£300	$555	€438	Cockerel (61x30cm-24x12in) mono.d.1998 verso canvasboard. 13-Feb-4 Sworder & Son, Bishops Stortford #136/R

SHAW, Bob (?) American

Works on paper			
£278	$500	€406	Patriotic fish art (30x41cm-12x16in) ink. 24-Apr-4 Slotin Folk Art, Buford #243/R

SHAW, Charles E (fl.1879-1899) British

Works on paper			
£260	$426	€380	Springtime (24x38cm-9x15in) s.i. W/C. 3-Jun-3 Fellows & Sons, Birmingham #97/R

SHAW, Charles Green (1892-1974) American

£5988	$10000	€8742	Fish and plants (23x30cm-9x12in) s.d.1941 verso canvasboard exhib. 9-Oct-3 Christie's, Rockefeller NY #110/R est:10000-15000
£8235	$14000	€12023	Kite abstraction (51x41cm-20x16in) s.d.1942. 9-Nov-3 Wright, Chicago #232 est:20000-30000
£11176	$19000	€16317	Still life with rye (28x20cm-11x8in) s. with sig.i.verso board. 9-Nov-3 Wright, Chicago #229 est:12000-15000
Sculpture			
£7263	$13000	€10604	Abstract composition (28x41cm-11x16in) painted wood prov. 16-May-4 Wright, Chicago #240/R est:18000-22000
Works on paper			
£5090	$8500	€7431	Today (51x38cm-20x15in) s.d.1940 collage ink prov.exhib. 11-Nov-3 Christie's, Rockefeller NY #170/R est:5000-7000

SHAW, Charles L (19th C) British

£580	$1038	€847	Wollaton Church, near Nottingham (29x45cm-11x18in) s. 18-Mar-4 Neales, Nottingham #737/R
£1163	$2000	€1698	On the Trent (64x104cm-25x41in) s.d.77. 6-Dec-3 Neal Auction Company, New Orleans #396/R est:2000-3000

SHAW, Charles S (19th C) British

£800	$1480	€1168	Cattle watering in a tranquil river (51x76cm-20x30in) s.d.1884. 15-Jan-4 Christie's, Kensington #891/R
£1000	$1670	€1460	Glen Kinlas (58x89cm-23x35in) s.d.1878 i.verso. 17-Oct-3 Keys, Aylsham #726

SHAW, Clare E (1866-1951) American

£264	$450	€385	California spring landscape with figures (28x36cm-11x14in) s. 22-Nov-3 Jackson's, Cedar Falls #87/R

SHAW, Dennis Orme (?) Irish?

£320	$550	€467	Still life with two apples (22x15cm-9x6in) s.d.1995 verso board. 3-Dec-3 John Ross, Belfast #179
£400	$656	€584	Hayfield (50x76cm-20x30in) s. 4-Jun-3 John Ross, Belfast #130
£460	$856	€672	Evening light, Knockinder Bay, Ards Peninsula (50x61cm-20x24in) s. 3-Mar-4 John Ross, Belfast #227

SHAW, Duncan Alexander (1840-1903) American?

£223	$415	€326	Gathering storm (29x41cm-11x16in) s.d.99 s.i.d.99 verso. 2-Mar-4 Ritchie, Toronto #39/R (C.D 555)

SHAW, Ellen S (fl.1938-1939) British

£525	$950	€767	Pekingese (22x18cm-9x7in) s. 30-Mar-4 Bonhams & Butterfields, San Francisco #112/R

SHAW, George (1843-1915) British

£300	$516	€438	Ponape off Bishops Rock (59x90cm-23x35in) s. 6-Dec-3 Shapes, Edinburgh #511/R
£380	$695	€555	Teign Head and Clapper Bridge, Dartmoor (62x127cm-24x50in) s. 3-Jun-4 Lane, Penzance #176

SHAW, J H (19th C) British

£1200	$2208	€1752	Grey racehorse in a loose box (56x79cm-22x31in) s.d.1887. 10-Jun-4 Christie's, Kensington #70/R est:1500-2000

SHAW, Jim (1952-) American
Works on paper
£1445 $2500 €2110 Dream drawing, sheep rustlers had taken over. Untitled (29x23cm-11x9in) graphite one exec.1999 one exec.2000 two prov. 10-Dec-3 Phillips, New York #596/R est:2000-3000
£1739 $3200 €2539 Dream drawing. Untitled (30x23cm-12x9in) s. one d.1995 one d.2001 verso graphite pair prov. 10-Jun-4 Phillips, New York #484/R est:2000-3000
£1911 $3250 €2790 Untitled - from the 65 distorted faces (36x28cm-14x11in) pencil prov.exhib. 9-Nov-3 Bonhams & Butterfields, Los Angeles #4068/R est:2000-4000
£2514 $4500 €3670 Untitled, Bing Crosby. Untitled, bird text. Untitled, dream drawing (43x36cm-17x14in) s. one d.1995 two d.2001 graphite three prov. 14-May-4 Phillips, New York #317/R est:5000-7000
£2515 $4200 €3672 Televised Chinese H-Bom. Untitled. Well, it was really an unequal contest (43x36cm-17x14in) graphite three framed dr. prov. 14-Nov-3 Phillips, New York #283/R est:4000-6000

SHAW, John Byam (1872-1919) British
£3500 $5810 €5110 For he cometh in with vanity and departeth in darkness (40x30cm-16x12in) s.d.1901 panel exhib. 1-Oct-3 Sotheby's, Olympia #179/R est:1500-2500
£3800 $6308 €5548 God is in heaven and thou upon earth, therefore let thy words by few (40x30cm-16x12in) panel prov. 1-Oct-3 Sotheby's, Olympia #180/R est:1500-2500
£5000 $8300 €7300 There is an evil which I have seen under the sun (25x40cm-10x16in) s. panel exhib. 1-Oct-3 Sotheby's, Olympia #178/R est:1500-2000
£24000 $40800 €35040 Time and chance happeneth to all I returned, and saw under the sun (86x61cm-34x24in) s.d.1901 exhib. 25-Nov-3 Christie's, London #149/R est:15000-25000
Works on paper
£300 $546 €438 Beauty and the beast (25x21cm-10x8in) mono.i. pencil black ink. 1-Jul-4 Christie's, Kensington #490/R
£600 $1080 €876 Adventures of Akbar (34x21cm-13x8in) s.i. ink W/C. 21-Jan-4 Sotheby's, Olympia #257/R
£700 $1190 €1022 Final embrace (13x9cm-5x4in) mono. W/C. 4-Nov-3 Bonhams, New Bond Street #150/R

SHAW, Joshua (1776-1860) American/British
£3039 $5500 €4437 Extensive mountainous landscape with a figure resting by a tree (55x80cm-22x31in) s.d.1818. 30-Mar-4 Christie's, Rockefeller NY #34/R est:3000-5000
£37000 $68080 €54020 View of Dinting Vale, Glossop, Derbyshire (122x168cm-48x66in) prov. 11-Jun-4 Christie's, London #40/R est:20000-30000

SHAW, Noel (20th C) British
£320 $595 €467 Boys fishing (28x35cm-11x14in) s. 3-Mar-4 John Ross, Belfast #101
Works on paper
£250 $465 €365 Viewing the sheep (30x38cm-12x15in) s. W/C. 3-Mar-4 John Ross, Belfast #84
£270 $502 €394 Sheep farmer with his dog (30x25cm-12x10in) s. W/C. 3-Mar-4 John Ross, Belfast #71
£350 $651 €511 At the fair (30x35cm-12x14in) s. pastel. 3-Mar-4 John Ross, Belfast #209

SHAW, Richard H (1832-?) Australian
Works on paper
£305 $556 €445 Aboriginal camp (24x29cm-9x11in) s. W/C. 16-Jun-4 Deutscher-Menzies, Melbourne #212/R (A.D 800)

SHAW, Tim (1964-) British
Sculpture
£2800 $4928 €4088 Dancer and Bull II (24x23cm-9x9in) s. num.1/8 slate base. 18-May-4 Woolley & Wallis, Salisbury #349/R est:600-800

SHAW, Walter (1851-1933) British
£1635 $2600 €2387 Star Point (61x107cm-24x42in) s. 13-Sep-3 Weschler, Washington #672/R est:1500-2000

SHAW, William (18th C) British
£4830 $8500 €7052 Groom with a race horse (71x90cm-28x35in) init.d.17. 18-May-4 Sotheby's, New York #208/R est:7000-9000

SHAWCROSS, Neal (1940-) British
£420 $722 €613 Landscape (101x152cm-40x60in) s.d.62. 4-Dec-3 Mellors & Kirk, Nottingham #884
£1184 $2179 €1800 The red mug (21x28cm-8x11in) s.d.2001 board. 22-Jun-4 De Veres Art Auctions, Dublin #14/R est:1500-2000
£1382 $2542 €2100 Nude study (43x30cm-17x12in) s. paper. 22-Jun-4 De Veres Art Auctions, Dublin #116/R est:1500-2000
£1382 $2542 €2100 Still life (43x43cm-17x17in) s. paper. 22-Jun-4 De Veres Art Auctions, Dublin #117/R est:1500-2000
£2432 $4597 €3600 Yellow teacup (51x51cm-20x20in) s. acrylic board. 17-Feb-4 Whyte's, Dublin #99/R est:3000-4000
£2500 $4150 €3650 Still life, poppies in a vase (76x56cm-30x22in) s.d.13 June 1998 oil on paper. 1-Oct-3 John Ross, Belfast #89 est:2250-2500
£4336 $7371 €6200 Basket of apples (59x74cm-23x29in) s.d.1999 oil on paper. 25-Nov-3 De Veres Art Auctions, Dublin #42/R est:4000-6000
£5705 $10097 €8500 Red and green still life (91x112cm-36x44in) s.d.2003 acrylic. 27-Apr-4 Whyte's, Dublin #156/R est:8000-10000
Works on paper
£550 $913 €803 Cat (35x30cm-14x12in) s.d.1976 W/C. 1-Oct-3 John Ross, Belfast #235
£850 $1581 €1241 Still life (45x68cm-18x27in) s.d.73 mixed media. 3-Mar-4 John Ross, Belfast #193
£1200 $2064 €1752 Fireplace (55x45cm-22x18in) s.d.1985 W/C. 3-Dec-3 John Ross, Belfast #50 est:1200-1500
£1400 $2296 €2044 Red barns (43x50cm-17x20in) s.d.1986 W/C. 4-Jun-3 John Ross, Belfast #73
£1400 $2296 €2044 Letter to 5, Short Strand, Belfast (55x76cm-22x30in) s.d.1988 W/C. 4-Jun-3 John Ross, Belfast #110 est:1800
£1400 $2324 €2044 Still life (55x71cm-22x28in) s.d.1996 mixed media. 1-Oct-3 John Ross, Belfast #123 est:1500-1800
£1400 $2408 €2044 A bottle of Tennents lager (61x43cm-24x17in) s.d.1990 mixed media. 3-Dec-3 John Ross, Belfast #160 est:1200-1500
£1579 $2905 €2400 Chair (50x38cm-20x15in) s.d.2003 W/C. 22-Jun-4 De Veres Art Auctions, Dublin #106/R est:2000-3000
£1700 $3111 €2482 Still life (76x56cm-30x22in) s.d.1963 W/C. 2-Jun-4 John Ross, Belfast #110 est:1200-1400
£1800 $3096 €2628 Still life (45x35cm-18x14in) s.d.1997 mixed media. 3-Dec-3 John Ross, Belfast #121 est:1200-1500
£2013 $3564 €3000 Pink fireplace. Recumbant nude (30x36cm-12x14in) s. W/C pastel pair. 27-Apr-4 Whyte's, Dublin #171/R est:2000-3000
£2148 $3801 €3200 Fruit dish in blue (51x76cm-20x30in) s.d.1974 W/C. 27-Apr-4 Whyte's, Dublin #180/R est:3000-4000
£2267 $4103 €3400 Vase of flowers (59x46cm-23x18in) s.d.83 W/C bodycol. 30-Mar-4 De Veres Art Auctions, Dublin #11/R est:3000-4000
£2368 $4358 €3600 Bowl of oranges (76x84cm-30x33in) s.d.1990 gouache prov. 22-Jun-4 De Veres Art Auctions, Dublin #24/R est:3500-5000
£2600 $4472 €3796 Reclining nude (76x91cm-30x36in) s.d.1992 mixed media. 3-Dec-3 John Ross, Belfast #119 est:2500-3000
£2703 $5108 €4000 Figure study (51x46cm-20x18in) s.d.2001 W/C ink prov. 17-Feb-4 Whyte's, Dublin #80/R est:3000-4000
£3800 $6954 €5548 Table top still life (129x94cm-51x37in) s.d.1989 mixed media. 2-Jun-4 John Ross, Belfast #106 est:4500-5000
£5405 $10216 €8000 Red nude (107x89cm-42x35in) s.d.1983 W/C. 17-Feb-4 Whyte's, Dublin #79/R est:7000-9000
£6500 $11635 €9490 Poppies (131x91cm-52x36in) s.d.1994 W/C acrylic. 14-May-4 Christie's, Kensington #396/R est:4000-6000

SHAWE, George (1915-1995) ?
£217 $350 €315 St. Florent le vieil (61x76cm-24x30in) s. s.i.verso. 24-Aug-3 Bonhams & Butterfields, Los Angeles #7033

SHAY, Ed (1947-) American
£273 $500 €399 Trip ia a fall (168x257cm-66x101in) 10-Jul-4 Hindman, Chicago #476/R

SHAYER, Charles (c.1826-1914) British
£900 $1647 €1314 Cattle resting by a river (29x0cm-11x0in) s.d.1847. 3-Jun-4 Lane, Penzance #252

SHAYER, Charles (attrib) (c.1826-1914) British
£500 $895 €730 Fisherfolk on a beach (36x46cm-14x18in) with sig. 27-May-4 Christie's, Kensington #225/R

SHAYER, Henry (c.1825-1864) British
£800 $1448 €1168 Busy rural landscape with numerous figures and cattle (56x89cm-22x35in) 16-Apr-4 Keys, Aylsham #711/R

SHAYER, Henry (attrib) (c.1825-1864) British
£901 $1622 €1315 Landscape with horse and rider (50x76cm-20x30in) indis sig. 26-Jan-4 Lilla Bukowskis, Stockholm #314 (S.KR 12000)

SHAYER, Henry and Charles (19th C) British
£2600 $4420 €3796 Figures and livestock by a riverside farmhouse (31x41cm-12x16in) with sig. 25-Nov-3 Christie's, London #65/R est:3000-5000
£3000 $5100 €4380 Woodland landscape with horses and figures (40x61cm-16x24in) prov. 19-Nov-3 Bonhams, New Bond Street #55/R est:2000-3000
£3000 $5520 €4380 Interior of a stable with farm animals (31x41cm-12x16in) s. prov. 23-Mar-4 Bonhams, New Bond Street #35/R est:3000-5000

SHAYER, W (19th C) British
£1304 $2400 €1904 Fishermen (33x46cm-13x18in) s.d.1850. 26-Jun-4 Susanin's, Chicago #6058/R est:800-1200

SHAYER, William (attrib) (19th C) British
£998 $1627 €1457 Coastal landscape with figures and horses (65x90cm-26x35in) s.indis.d.1821. 29-Sep-3 Lilla Bukowskis, Stockholm #155 (S.KR 13000)
£2500 $4650 €3650 Outside the inn (51x69cm-20x27in) indis.sig.d.18. 4-Mar-4 Christie's, Kensington #481/R est:3000-5000
£2700 $4401 €3942 The afternoon meal; a ploughman and his son with a team of horses (91x84cm-36x33in) s. 23-Sep-3 Anderson & Garland, Newcastle #402/R est:2000-3000
£5000 $8300 €7300 Fisherfolk on the shore (44x57cm-17x22in) s.d.1860 pair. 1-Oct-3 Woolley & Wallis, Salisbury #265/R est:3000-5000

SHAYER, William (snr) (1787-1879) British
£920 $1500 €1343 Fisherman on the beach (51x61cm-20x24in) s. 28-Sep-3 Simpson's, Houston #385/R
£1600 $2880 €2336 Collecting the day's catch (24x34cm-9x13in) panel. 21-Apr-4 Christie's, Kensington #27/R est:1500-2000
£1700 $3162 €2482 Gypsy encampment (36x30cm-14x12in) 4-Mar-4 Christie's, Kensington #464/R est:1200-1800
£1983 $3550 €2895 Picnic, young child on top of a horse, mother figure and a small donkey (64x76cm-25x30in) s. 19-Mar-4 Aspire, Cleveland #1/R est:2000-4000
£2300 $4255 €3358 Old farmstead (49x59cm-19x23in) s.d.1837 panel. 11-Mar-4 Morphets, Harrogate #292/R est:2000-3000
£2300 $4255 €3358 Farmyard in Hampshire (34x45cm-13x18in) s.d.1847. 11-Mar-4 Morphets, Harrogate #293/R est:2500-3000
£2400 $4416 €3504 Fisherfolk chatting on the shore, Alum Bay (43x35cm-17x14in) s. board. 8-Jun-4 Bonhams, Knightsbridge #254/R est:1000-1500
£4396 $8000 €6418 Fishermen at the coast (76x102cm-30x40in) s.d.1846. 7-Feb-4 Neal Auction Company, New Orleans #184/R est:8000-12000
£4469 $8000 €6525 Fisherman's cottages (75x101cm-30x40in) s. prov. 27-May-4 Sotheby's, New York #248/R est:10000-15000

£4700 $8789 €7050 Sorting the catch on the beach (75x100cm-30x39in) s.d.1854. 26-Jul-4 Bonhams, Bath #94/R est:4000-6000
£5000 $8500 €7300 Flower seller (43x53cm-17x21in) bears sig.d.1833. 19-Nov-3 Bonhams, New Bond Street #17/R est:4000-6000
£5000 $9200 €7300 Peasant family outside a woodland cottage (36x30cm-14x12in) s. prov. 23-Mar-4 Bonhams, New Bond Street #32/R est:5000-7000
£5000 $9200 €7300 Milking time (71x91cm-28x36in) s. 8-Jun-4 Bonhams, Knightsbridge #193/R est:5000-7000
£5000 $9250 €7300 Rest on the highway (56x51cm-22x20in) s. 14-Jul-4 Sotheby's, Olympia #32/R est:4000-6000
£5200 $9724 €7800 Returning from market (60x50cm-24x20in) s. 26-Jul-4 Bonhams, Bath #93/R est:3000-5000
£5400 $9180 €7884 Fisherfolk, boats and horses on the foreshore (62x112cm-24x44in) s. 29-Oct-3 Hampton & Littlewood, Exeter #614/R est:6000-8000
£5691 $10187 €8309 Hampshire farmer, home (86x109cm-34x43in) indis i. prov. 4-May-4 Ritchie, Toronto #10/R est:15000-20000 (C.D 14000)
£7500 $12750 €10950 Travelers in an extensive landscape, identified as Perlieu Common near Southampton (42x62cm-17x24in) s. 25-Nov-3 Christie's, London #67/R est:6000-8000
£9000 $15030 €13140 New Forest landscape with travelers, white pony, donkey and dog (44x58cm-17x23in) s. panel. 14-Oct-3 Bearnes, Exeter #356/R est:7000-9000
£9500 $16150 €13870 Gypsy encampment in a wooded landscape by a river with several figures (71x92cm-28x36in) s. 25-Nov-3 Christie's, London #62/R est:10000-15000
£12000 $22080 €17520 Watering place (71x91cm-28x36in) s.d.1864. 26-Mar-4 Sotheby's, London #45/R est:12000-18000
£15000 $27600 €21900 Fisherfolk in a coastal landscape (71x92cm-28x36in) s. indis d.1838. 11-Jun-4 Christie's, London #62/R est:15000-20000
£18000 $32400 €26280 Itinerant fishmonger. Interior of a fisherman's cottage (35x43cm-14x17in) board pair. 21-Apr-4 Cheffins, Cambridge #496/R est:15000-20000

SHAYER, William (snr-attrib) (1787-1879) British
£880 $1390 €1276 Fisherfolk on a beach (71x91cm-28x36in) with sig. 4-Sep-3 Christie's, Kensington #290/R
£2300 $4232 €3358 Fisherfolk on the beach (70x90cm-28x35in) bears sig.d.1842. 29-Mar-4 Bonhams, Bath #60/R est:2500-3500
£3000 $5400 €4380 Bargaining for fish (75x102cm-30x40in) bears sig.d.1833. 21-Jan-4 Sotheby's, Olympia #275/R est:3000-5000
£3374 $5500 €4892 Tending the flock. Going to market (53x43cm-21x17in) one s.d.1849 i. pair. 19-Jul-3 New Orleans Auction, New Orleans #211/R est:4500-7000

SHAYER, William (19th C) British
£700 $1141 €1022 Fisherfolk on the shore (24x34cm-9x13in) s.d.45. 23-Sep-3 Anderson & Garland, Newcastle #415/R

SHAYER, William J (1811-1892) British
£450 $766 €657 Figure on a horse drawn cart (28x23cm-11x9in) s. panel. 21-Nov-3 Walker's, Ottawa #258/R (C.D 1000)
£650 $1209 €949 Dogs resting by a hay stook. Goat and a terrier in a landscape (23x30cm-9x12in) s. indis d. board pair. 4-Mar-4 Christie's, Kensington #513/R
£893 $1536 €1304 Vessel on shore at low tide (30x51cm-12x20in) s.d.1842. 2-Dec-3 Ritchie, Toronto #43/R est:2500-3500 (C.D 2000)
£1042 $1646 €1500 Traders on English coast (48x64cm-19x25in) s.d.1869. 6-Sep-3 Schopman, Hamburg #702/R est:1250
£1500 $2370 €2175 Timber cart (71x91cm-28x36in) bears sig.d.1830. 3-Sep-3 Bonhams, Bury St Edmunds #423/R est:1500-2000
£1958 $3329 €2800 On the beach Hastings (51x66cm-20x26in) s.indis.d. 26-Nov-3 James Adam, Dublin #58/R est:3000-5000
£2900 $4843 €4234 Pastoral river landscape with milkmaid, cattle and distant tower (36x61cm-14x24in) s.d.1887. 16-Nov-3 Desmond Judd, Cranbrook #1045

SHAYER, William J (attrib) (1811-1892) British
£1343 $2457 €1961 Fishermen working on the English coast (68x103cm-27x41in) s.indis.d.59. 9-Jun-4 Rasmussen, Copenhagen #1789/R est:15000 (D.KR 15000)

SHAYER, William and Charles (19th C) British
£3000 $5160 €4380 Returning home (46x61cm-18x24in) s. 3-Dec-3 Bonhams, Knightsbridge #102/R est:3000-5000

SHAYEVITZ, Stephan (1952-) ?
£979 $1664 €1400 Trois Rabbins au fond rose (92x73cm-36x29in) s. 27-Nov-3 Calmels Cohen, Paris #79/R

SHCHERBAKOV, V I (1904-1991) Russian
£251 $450 €366 Self-portrait in red dressing gown (32x25cm-13x10in) oil paper on cardboard painted 1920's. 29-May-4 Shishkin Gallery, Moscow #15/R
Works on paper
£246 $440 €359 Pocket fashion album, the cover sketch (21x15cm-8x6in) gouache exec. 1937. 29-May-4 Shishkin Gallery, Moscow #17/R

SHEA, Frank (20th C) American
£565 $1000 €825 Vermont landscape in summer (41x51cm-16x20in) s. canvasboard. 2-May-4 Grogan, Boston #87/R
£566 $900 €826 East Gloucester (51x61cm-20x24in) s. 10-Sep-3 Alderfer's, Hatfield #465

SHEA, William (20th C) American
£220 $375 €321 Still life (41x51cm-16x20in) s. board. 9-Nov-3 Outer Cape Auctions, Provincetown #100/R
£613 $1000 €895 Peter Hunt studio with Frances Shea painting (48x61cm-19x24in) s. board. 19-Jul-3 Outer Cape Auctions, Provincetown #132/R

SHEAD, Garry (1942-) Australian
£2553 $4341 €3727 Queen (35x24cm-14x9in) s. oil paper on board. 26-Nov-3 Deutscher-Menzies, Melbourne #154/R est:6000-8000 (A.D 6000)
£4149 $6929 €6224 Model (27x20cm-11x8in) s. 27-Oct-3 Goodman, Sydney #191/R est:10000-14000 (A.D 10000)
£5085 $8644 €7424 Degas' other muse (27x19cm-11x7in) s. bears i.verso oil collage paper. 24-Nov-3 Sotheby's, Melbourne #76/R est:12000-16000 (A.D 12000)
£5508 $9364 €8042 Rembrandt and Model (29x21cm-11x8in) s. i.verso oil collage paper. 24-Nov-3 Sotheby's, Melbourne #49/R est:12000-16000 (A.D 13000)
£5785 $9835 €8446 Brumby (91x121cm-36x48in) s.d.88 board prov. 29-Oct-3 Lawson Menzies, Sydney #128/R est:18000-25000 (A.D 14000)
£6073 $9777 €8867 Old master and young model (27x19cm-11x7in) s. bears i.verso oil collage paper. 25-Aug-3 Sotheby's, Paddington #121/R est:15000-20000 (A.D 15000)
£11450 $20840 €16717 Tango teacher (60x45cm-24x18in) s. board prov. 16-Jun-4 Deutscher-Menzies, Melbourne #66/R est:35000-45000 (A.D 30000)
£11570 $21405 €16892 Morning light (58x58cm-23x23in) s. board prov. 10-Mar-4 Deutscher-Menzies, Melbourne #17/R est:32000-40000 (A.D 28000)
£17176 $31260 €25077 Artist and muse (76x61cm-30x24in) s. board painted c.2003. 16-Jun-4 Deutscher-Menzies, Melbourne #12/R est:38000-48000 (A.D 45000)
£18699 $33472 €27301 Velasquez and muse - homage to Las Meninas (74x58cm-29x23in) s. board prov. 4-May-4 Sotheby's, Melbourne #43/R est:50000-70000 (A.D 46000)
£22541 $35614 €32910 ER (75x60cm-30x24in) s.d.97 i. verso board. 2-Sep-3 Deutscher-Menzies, Melbourne #59/R est:48000-55000 (A.D 55000)
£22541 $36516 €32910 D H Lawrence series (46x61cm-18x24in) s. board prov. 30-Jul-3 Goodman, Sydney #74/R est:40000-50000 (A.D 55000)
£22901 $41679 €33435 Presentation (106x91cm-42x36in) s.d.95. 16-Jun-4 Deutscher-Menzies, Melbourne #68/R est:65000-85000 (A.D 60000)
£24590 $38852 €35901 Royal family (51x59cm-20x23in) s.d.96 s.i. verso board. 2-Sep-3 Deutscher-Menzies, Melbourne #75/R est:38000-45000 (A.D 60000)
£24809 $45153 €36221 Reflection - Rembrandt (90x122cm-35x48in) s.d.2000 s.d.verso board prov. 16-Jun-4 Deutscher-Menzies, Melbourne #54/R est:70000-90000 (A.D 65000)
£25532 $43404 €37277 Second Landing (59x75cm-23x30in) s.d.95 i.verso composition board lit. 26-Nov-3 Deutscher-Menzies, Melbourne #28/R est:50000-60000 (A.D 60000)
£36170 $61489 €52808 Visitation (91x122cm-36x48in) s.d.96 s.i.d.verso composition board prov.lit. 26-Nov-3 Deutscher-Menzies, Melbourne #45/R est:70000-90000 (A.D 85000)
£40650 $63821 €58943 1922 (90x121cm-35x48in) s.d.93 board prov.lit. 26-Aug-3 Christie's, Sydney #28/R est:100000-120000 (A.D 100000)
£42553 $72340 €62127 Knighthoods (91x121cm-36x48in) s.d.95 board prov.exhib.lit. 25-Nov-3 Christie's, Melbourne #17/R est:90000-120000 (A.D 100000)
£49587 $84298 €72397 Dance (92x122cm-36x48in) s. i.verso board. 29-Oct-3 Lawson Menzies, Sydney #30/R est:70000-80000 (A.D 120000)
Works on paper
£744 $1264 €1086 Fox in a box (68x75cm-27x30in) mixed media fox fur plastic magazine prov.exhib.lit. 29-Oct-3 Lawson Menzies, Sydney #151/R est:1200-1500 (A.D 1800)
£744 $1264 €1086 Springwood Bacchanal (55x75cm-22x30in) s.d.14/7/99 ink wash. 29-Oct-3 Lawson Menzies, Sydney #154/R est:2500-3500 (A.D 1800)
£992 $1686 €1448 Untitled (36x26cm-14x10in) s.d.8.1.76 ink W/C. 29-Oct-3 Lawson Menzies, Sydney #153/R est:1500-2000 (A.D 2400)

SHEAN, Charles M (?-1925) American
£1857 $3250 €2711 Portrait of Abraham Lincoln (84x76cm-33x30in) s.d.1912. 19-Dec-3 Sotheby's, New York #1089/R est:2000-3000

SHEARBON, Andrew (fl.1860s) British
£1040 $1800 €1518 Mother and children at seashore (91x71cm-36x28in) 12-Dec-3 Du Mouchelle, Detroit #2099/R est:2000-3000

SHEARD, Charlie (1960-) Australian
£351 $650 €512 Desert drawing 5 (101x152cm-40x60in) s.d.1991 i.verso prov. 15-Mar-4 Sotheby's, Melbourne #95 est:400-600 (A.D 850)

SHEARER, Christopher H (1840-1926) American
£261 $450 €381 Wooded landscape (43x58cm-17x23in) s.d.1895. 6-Dec-3 Neal Auction Company, New Orleans #1354
£563 $900 €822 Wooded autumnal landscape with stream (53x89cm-21x35in) s.d.1904. 20-Sep-3 Pook & Pook, Downington #179/R
£578 $1000 €844 Sylvan landscape (81x102cm-32x40in) s.d.1922. 10-Dec-3 Alderfer's, Hatfield #431/R est:3000-5000
£968 $1800 €1413 Sylvan landscape (81x102cm-32x40in) s.d.1922. 3-Mar-4 Alderfer's, Hatfield #425/R est:2000-2500
£1006 $1600 €1469 Landscape with stream in sylvan setting (61x51cm-24x20in) s.d.1913. 10-Sep-3 Alderfer's, Hatfield #406/R est:1500-2500
£1132 $1800 €1653 Sylvan landscape (81x102cm-32x40in) s.d.1922. 10-Sep-3 Alderfer's, Hatfield #403/R est:3000-5000
£1196 $2200 €1746 Figures on a pathway (51x84cm-20x33in) s.d.1886 board. 25-Jun-4 Freeman, Philadelphia #173/R est:1500-2500
£1209 $2250 €1765 Winter landscape at sunset with figures (51x76cm-20x30in) s.d.1888. 3-Mar-4 Alderfer's, Hatfield #424/R est:2500-3000
£1243 $2250 €1815 Landscape with river (76x64cm-30x25in) s. 16-Apr-4 James Julia, Fairfield #776/R est:2500-3500
£1389 $2500 €2028 Homestead (43x61cm-17x24in) s. 23-Jan-4 Freeman, Philadelphia #114/R est:1200-1300
£1730 $2750 €2526 Landscape with bare gnarled trees on rocky promontory in foreground (56x46cm-22x18in) s. 10-Sep-3 Alderfer's, Hatfield #407/R est:1500-2000
£1750 $2800 €2555 Summer landscape with cottages, cows and figure by a creek (33x41cm-13x16in) s.d.1879. 20-Sep-3 Pook & Pook, Downington #181/R est:2000-2500
Works on paper
£427 $700 €619 Barnyard scene with woman feeding chickens (33x48cm-13x19in) s. W/C. 4-Jun-3 Alderfer's, Hatfield #414

SHEARER, Donald M (20th C) British
£260 $424 €380 Near Broadford from Slegachan (30x58cm-12x23in) s. board. 25-Sep-3 Gorringes, Worthing #692

SHEARER, James Elliot (1858-?) British
Works on paper
£569 $950 €831 Rest along a country road (64x99cm-25x39in) s.d.1886 W/C. 18-Jun-3 Doyle, New York #73/R

SHEDLETSKY, Stuart (20th C) American
£475 $850 €694 Day shift (152x229cm-60x90in) oil on linen. 13-May-4 Dallas Auction Gallery, Dallas #261/R

SHEE, Sir Martin Archer (1769-1850) British
£1100 $1870 €1606 Portrait of Mrs Charlotte Picton of Iscoed (76x63cm-30x25in) i.on stretcher lit. 18-Nov-3 Sotheby's, Olympia #174/R est:1000-1500

£2000 $3400 €2920 Portrait of William Senhouse, standing beside a memorial to Lord Nelson (213x150cm-84x59in) 27-Nov-3 Sotheby's, London #160/R est:2500-4000
£2096 $3500 €3060 Portrait of John Fawcett (76x64cm-30x25in) 17-Oct-3 Du Mouchelle, Detroit #2006/R est:4000-8000
£2200 $4114 €3300 Postman (22x19cm-9x7in) s.d.September 1799 panel. 26-Jul-4 Bonhams, Bath #50/R est:600-800
£2817 $4873 €4000 Portrait of Anthony Morris Storer (75x63cm-30x25in) s.d.1795. 10-Dec-3 Bonhams & James Adam, Dublin #30/R est:4000-6000
£3378 $6385 €5000 Portrait of John Fawcett (76x64cm-30x25in) prov. 17-Feb-4 Whyte's, Dublin #154/R est:6000-8000
£4469 $8000 €6525 Portrait of Miss Elizabeth Johnson (76x63cm-30x25in) prov. 27-May-4 Sotheby's, New York #260/R est:6000-8000
£5921 $10895 €9000 Full length portrait of William Senhouse (213x150cm-84x59in) 22-Jun-4 Mealy's, Castlecomer #355/R est:8000-12000
£6627 $11000 €9675 Portrait of Captain Sir Charles Hastings Doyle in uniform (76x63cm-30x25in) prov. 30-Sep-3 Christie's, Rockefeller NY #339/R est:8000-12000
£7500 $12450 €10950 Portrait of George Watson Taylor of Erlestoke Park, Wiltshire (74x61cm-29x24in) 30-Sep-3 Sotheby's, London #353/R est:2000-3000
£10000 $17000 €14600 Portrait of a lady in a white dress holding a draw string purse, by a tree in a landscape (127x102cm-50x40in) 25-Nov-3 Christie's, London #45/R est:10000-15000

SHEEHAN, Charles A (fl.1901-1926) British
£319 $521 €460 Careful stitch (43x41cm-17x16in) s.d.02 canvas on board. 23-Sep-3 De Veres Art Auctions, Dublin #131/R

SHEELER, Charles (1883-1965) American
£39773 $70000 €58069 Vermont landscape - Peacham, Vermont (46x62cm-18x24in) s. painted 1924 prov.exhib.lit. 18-May-4 Christie's, Rockefeller NY #91/R est:40000-60000
£147727 $260000 €215681 San Francisco - Fisherman's Wharf (79x53cm-31x21in) s.d.1956 prov.exhib.lit. 19-May-4 Sotheby's, New York #147/R est:250000-350000
£153409 $270000 €223977 Ballarvale revisited (38x36cm-15x14in) s.d.49 tempera board prov. 19-May-4 Sotheby's, New York #142/R est:200000-300000
Photographs
£3757 $6500 €5485 Interior with plants (22x16cm-9x6in) silver print. 9-Dec-3 Swann Galleries, New York #581/R est:5000-6000
£4830 $8500 €7052 View of New York (23x17cm-9x7in) with sig. silver print. 20-May-4 Swann Galleries, New York #357/R est:8000-10000
£5291 $10000 €7725 American interior (21x18cm-8x7in) silver print. 17-Feb-4 Swann Galleries, New York #34/R est:10000-15000
£5820 $11000 €8497 Pennsylvania Barn (22x16cm-9x6in) silver print. 17-Feb-4 Swann Galleries, New York #33/R est:8000-12000
Prints
£5389 $9000 €7868 Roses (41x29cm-16x11in) s.i. lithograph prov. 11-Nov-3 Christie's, Rockefeller NY #171/R est:10000-12000
Works on paper
£3514 $6500 €5130 Landscape of rural town. s. gouache. 14-Jan-4 Dallas Auction Gallery, Dallas #101/R est:12000-15000
£8000 $14000 €11680 Horses (28x35cm-11x14in) gouache over pencil prov. 19-Dec-3 Sotheby's, New York #1151/R est:8000-12000
£22727 $40000 €33181 Electric power (14x14cm-6x6in) pencil exec c.1941 prov.lit. 18-May-4 Christie's, Rockefeller NY #137/R est:25000-35000
£24709 $42500 €36075 Tulip (51x38cm-20x15in) pastel chl prov. 3-Dec-3 Sotheby's, New York #55/R est:40000-60000

SHEERER, Mary Given (1865-1954) American
Works on paper
£233 $400 €340 Still life of roses (28x25cm-11x10in) s.d.1893 W/C. 6-Dec-3 Neal Auction Company, New Orleans #597

SHEETS, Millard (1907-1989) American
£2500 $4000 €3650 Untitled (53x66cm-21x26in) 19-Sep-3 Du Mouchelle, Detroit #48/R est:800-1000
Works on paper
£1321 $2100 €1929 Religious scenes (76x63cm-30x25in) s. W/C gouache board pair. 12-Sep-3 Skinner, Boston #532/R
£2910 $5500 €4249 Houses in landscape - Near Upland (38x56cm-15x22in) s. W/C prov. 17-Feb-4 John Moran, Pasadena #80/R est:5000-7000
£2989 $5500 €4364 Old church, Oaxca, Mexico (55x74cm-22x29in) s. W/C. 8-Jun-4 Bonhams & Butterfields, San Francisco #3477/R est:3000-5000
£3439 $6500 €5021 Fish Rock Islands from Havens Neck (38x56cm-15x22in) s. s.i.d.1974 verso prov. 17-Feb-4 John Moran, Pasadena #81/R est:4000-6000
£4412 $7500 €6442 Moorea, girls arranging flowers (53x74cm-21x29in) s.i.d.May 1977 verso W/C. 18-Nov-3 John Moran, Pasadena #82 est:5000-7000
£4891 $9000 €7141 Upper road, Hawaii (57x77cm-22x30in) s. i.d.1951 verso W/C prov. 8-Jun-4 Bonhams & Butterfields, San Francisco #4379/R est:7000-10000
£5294 $9000 €7729 Girl with roosters (53x74cm-21x29in) s.d.1983 W/C prov. 18-Nov-3 John Moran, Pasadena #83 est:7000-9000
£5435 $10000 €7935 Mending nests, Cook Bay Moorea (55x75cm-22x30in) s.i.d.1977 verso W/C. 8-Jun-4 Auctions by the Bay, Alameda #1116/R
£5650 $10000 €8249 The magic hour, Mendocino (55x75cm-22x30in) s.d.1981 W/C prov. 28-Apr-4 Christie's, Los Angeles #76/R est:10000-15000
£6471 $11000 €9448 Fisherman's house (53x74cm-21x29in) s. W/C prov. 18-Nov-3 John Moran, Pasadena #80 est:8000-10000
£7692 $14000 €11230 Connomorra ponies in panoramic landscape (53x74cm-21x29in) s. i.d.1969 verso W/C prov. 15-Jun-4 John Moran, Pasadena #81 est:15000-20000
£8235 $14000 €12023 Old coconut grove, Hawaii (56x74cm-22x29in) s. W/C prov. 18-Nov-3 John Moran, Pasadena #81 est:8000-10000
£10286 $18000 €15018 Kahanna Bay (35x58cm-14x23in) s.d.1935 W/C prov. 19-Dec-3 Sotheby's, New York #1035/R est:4000-7000
£11429 $20000 €16686 Windswept (57x76cm-22x30in) s.d.1941 W/C prov. 19-Dec-3 Sotheby's, New York #1137/R est:5000-7000
£16484 $30000 €24067 Lava Beach, Hawaii (56x76cm-22x30in) s.d.1968 i.verso W/C prov. 15-Jun-4 John Moran, Pasadena #80 est:15000-20000

SHEFFERS, Peter W (1894-1949) American
£802 $1275 €1171 In the Cascades (53x74cm-21x29in) s. 12-Sep-3 Aspire, Cleveland #51
£1129 $2100 €1648 Rockbound, coast near Ogunquit, Maine (75x101cm-30x40in) 5-Mar-4 Skinner, Boston #579/R est:2500-4500

SHEFFIELD, George (1839-1892) British
Works on paper
£700 $1190 €1022 Oriental fantasy, sailing boats on river before East Roman basilicas (24x34cm-9x13in) W/C. 26-Nov-3 Peter Wilson, Nantwich #138/R
£900 $1530 €1314 Moonlight attack (50x74cm-20x29in) s.d.1867 W/C. 24-Nov-3 Tiffin King & Nicholson, Carlisle #207/R
£900 $1611 €1314 Lock (59x93cm-23x37in) s.d.1867 W/C. 17-Mar-4 Bonhams, Chester #248 est:1000-1500
£1800 $3060 €2628 Common scene with cattle and sheep. River landscape with figures (61x91cm-24x36in) s.d.1882 pair. 5-Nov-3 John Nicholson, Haslemere #465/R est:2500-3000

SHELBOURNE, Anita (20th C) British
£729 $1145 €1050 Wild flowers (25x30cm-10x12in) s. 26-Aug-3 James Adam, Dublin #154/R est:1000-1200
£743 $1405 €1100 Sand and sea (38x38cm-15x15in) s. board. 17-Feb-4 Whyte's, Dublin #71/R est:1200-1500
£767 $1380 €1150 Landscape (25x30cm-10x12in) s. 20-Apr-4 James Adam, Dublin #131/R

SHELL STUDIOS (20th C) British?
Works on paper
£4800 $7632 €7008 Quick starting pair, Shell Oil and Shell petrol (51x76cm-20x30in) i. gouache lit. 10-Sep-3 Sotheby's, Olympia #67/R est:2000-3000

SHELLEY, John (1938-) British
£2200 $4070 €3212 Surrey cottage (61x76cm-24x30in) s.i.d.1981 board. 11-Mar-4 Christie's, Kensington #276/R est:1500-2000

SHELLEY, Samuel (c.1750-1808) British
Miniatures
£1100 $1969 €1606 Portrait of a naval officer in royal blue uniform (5cm-2in) W/C ivory plaited hair. 22-Mar-4 Bonhams & Brooks, Norfolk #74/R est:200-300
£1500 $2595 €2190 Young gentleman (4cm-2in) oval. 9-Dec-3 Christie's, London #154 est:1200-1500
£1650 $2970 €2409 Gentleman, in a dark cerise coat (4cm-2in) gold frame oval exhib. 22-Apr-4 Bonhams, New Bond Street #35 est:600-800
£1800 $3114 €2628 Wisdom and the fiend (17x14cm-7x6in) s. s.i.d.1798 verso exhib. 9-Dec-3 Christie's, London #186/R est:2000-3000
£2400 $3984 €3504 Portrait of a lady wearing a white dress (7cm-3in) gold frame. 2-Oct-3 Sotheby's, Olympia #12/R est:1500-2000
£3000 $5190 €4380 Young gentleman (4cm-2in) oval. 9-Dec-3 Christie's, London #164/R est:1500-2500
£3200 $5600 €4672 Naval Officer, possibly Archibald, 9th Earl of Dundonald (7cm-3in) gold frame blue glass reserve with hair oval. 18-Dec-3 Sotheby's, Olympia #6/R est:2000-3000
£4865 $9000 €7103 Young girl (5x3cm-2x1in) exec.c.1780 oval. 12-Mar-4 Du Mouchelle, Detroit #2036/R est:1000-2000

SHELTON, Margaret D (1915-1984) Canadian
£200 $366 €292 Mountain river (33x50cm-13x20in) s.d.1981 W/C. 1-Jun-4 Hodgins, Calgary #466/R (C.D 500)
£310 $561 €453 Untitled - artist's garden (31x41cm-12x16in) indis sig.d.1962 hard board. 18-Apr-4 Levis, Calgary #111/R (C.D 750)
£315 $536 €460 Mount Hector (41x51cm-16x20in) s.d.1974 i.verso canvasboard. 23-Nov-3 Levis, Calgary #124/R (C.D 700)
£320 $586 €467 Dahlias and calendulas (40x50cm-16x20in) s.i.d.1970 board. 1-Jun-4 Hodgins, Calgary #54/R (C.D 800)
£320 $586 €467 Nasturtiums (40x50cm-16x20in) s.i.d.1981 board. 1-Jun-4 Hodgins, Calgary #367/R (C.D 800)
£339 $567 €495 River flats, MT. Kitchener (30x40cm-12x16in) s.i.d.1981 board. 17-Nov-3 Hodgins, Calgary #162/R (C.D 750)
£428 $727 €625 Giant dahlias (41x51cm-16x20in) s.d.1968 i.verso board. 23-Nov-3 Levis, Calgary #125/R (C.D 950)
£440 $805 €642 Mt Bogart (30x40cm-12x16in) s.i. board. 1-Jun-4 Hodgins, Calgary #303/R (C.D 1100)
£473 $804 €691 Hector Lake (46x61cm-18x24in) i.verso canvasboard. 23-Nov-3 Levis, Calgary #123/R (C.D 1050)
£586 $995 €856 Waterfowl lake (51x61cm-20x24in) s.d.1971 board. 23-Nov-3 Levis, Calgary #122/R (C.D 1300)
£744 $1346 €1086 Untitled - bow river and backside of Tunnel Mountain (30x41cm-12x16in) oil on paper board. 18-Apr-4 Levis, Calgary #110/R est:1000-1200 (C.D 1800)
£1033 $1870 €1508 Untitled - high in the Rockies (37x46cm-15x18in) s. hard board. 18-Apr-4 Levis, Calgary #109/R est:1500-2000 (C.D 2500)
Works on paper
£203 $344 €296 Mount Rundle (25x36cm-10x14in) s.d.1980 W/C. 23-Nov-3 Levis, Calgary #127/R (C.D 450)
£207 $374 €302 Untitled - big sky county (25x36cm-10x14in) d.June 10.81 W/C. 18-Apr-4 Levis, Calgary #556/R (C.D 500)
£222 $369 €324 Slopes of Rundle (24x34cm-9x13in) estate st.verso W/C prov. 5-Oct-3 Levis, Calgary #105/R (C.D 500)
£226 $378 €330 Untitled - active skies over the farmyard (24x35cm-9x14in) W/C. 17-Nov-3 Hodgins, Calgary #314/R (C.D 500)
£226 $378 €330 Untitled - Bow Valley (25x33cm-10x13in) s.d.1974 W/C. 17-Nov-3 Hodgins, Calgary #374/R (C.D 500)
£260 $476 €380 Cascade Mountain (24x34cm-9x13in) W/C. 1-Jun-4 Hodgins, Calgary #57/R (C.D 650)
£260 $476 €380 Police Creek, Canmore (24x34cm-9x13in) W/C. 1-Jun-4 Hodgins, Calgary #102/R (C.D 650)
£300 $549 €438 Farm south east of Calgary (23x33cm-9x13in) W/C. 1-Jun-4 Hodgins, Calgary #147/R (C.D 750)
£313 $538 €457 Devil's Head Mountain (33x49cm-13x19in) s. W/C. 2-Dec-3 Joyner Waddington, Toronto #327/R (C.D 700)
£339 $567 €495 Untitled - pine in the mountains (26x36cm-10x14in) W/C. 17-Nov-3 Hodgins, Calgary #166/R (C.D 750)

SHELTON, Peter (1951-) American
Works on paper
£359 $600 €524 Belly (44x61cm-17x24in) chl. 19-Oct-3 Bonhams & Butterfields, Los Angeles #7093

SHEMI, Menachem (1896-1951) Israeli
£13855 $23000 €20228 Figure in landscape, Haifa Bay (65x92cm-26x36in) s.d.1938 prov. 2-Oct-3 Christie's, Tel Aviv #50/R est:25000-35000

SHEN FU WEN (20th C) Chinese
£419 $700 €612 Cranes (89x74cm-35x29in) s. lacquer. 11-Oct-3 Nadeau, Windsor #127/R

SHEN QUAN (1682-c.1760) Chinese
Works on paper
£19000 $31730 €27740 Peonies, birds and magnolia (191x96cm-75x38in) st.sig. ink col on silk exec.c.1750. 13-Nov-3 Sotheby's, Olympia #698/R est:4000-6000
£84942 $141853 €124015 Cranes of longevity (155x56cm-61x22in) one s.i. ink col on screen in 6 parts lit. 26-Oct-3 Christie's, Hong Kong #481/R (HK.D 1100000)

SHEN XIANG (16/17th C) Chinese
Works on paper
£7112 $12802 €10384 Plum blossoms in ink (144x50cm-57x20in) s.i. ink hanging scroll silk prov. 25-Apr-4 Christie's, Hong Kong #338/R est:120000-150000 (HK.D 100000)

SHEN ZENGZHI (1850-1922) Chinese
Works on paper
£1565 $2817 €2285 Calligraphy in standard script (116x34cm-46x13in) s.i. ink scroll. 25-Apr-4 Christie's, Hong Kong #14/R est:10000-12000 (HK.D 22000)

SHEN ZHOU (1427-1509) Chinese
Works on paper
£5405 $9027 €7891 Mountains after the rain (122x22cm-48x9in) s.i. ink. 26-Oct-3 Christie's, Hong Kong #417a/R (HK.D 70000)
£7336 $12251 €10711 Under the shade of pine (130x49cm-51x19in) s.i. ink on silk. 26-Oct-3 Christie's, Hong Kong #413/R (HK.D 95000)
£15444 $25792 €22548 Coxcomb and hen (151x72cm-59x28in) s.i. ink. 26-Oct-3 Christie's, Hong Kong #426/R (HK.D 200000)
£24893 $44808 €36344 Bamboo and plum blossoms in ink (31x264cm-12x104in) s.i.d.1501 ink handscroll. 25-Apr-4 Christie's, Hong Kong #344/R est:400000-500000 (HK.D 350000)

SHENG MOU (attrib) (19th C) Chinese
Works on paper
£2703 $4757 €4000 Landscape (87x35cm-34x14in) Indian ink. 21-May-4 Dr Fritz Nagel, Stuttgart #1670 est:250

SHENTON, Annie F (fl.1900-1906) British
£1250 $2250 €1825 Portrait of a Yorkshire terrier (41x51cm-16x20in) s.d.1908. 21-Jan-4 Sotheby's, New York #227/R est:3000-4000

SHEPARD, E H (1879-1976) British
Works on paper
£15000 $27450 €21900 Winnie the Pooh and Tigger with honey-pot at the table (9x11cm-4x4in) s.d.1929 ink. 8-Jul-4 Sotheby's, London #375/R est:15000-20000

SHEPARD, Ernest Howard (1879-1976) British
Works on paper
£250 $418 €365 Sirmione Castle, Lake Garda (25x36cm-10x14in) i.d.1915 pencil W/C. 16-Oct-3 Neales, Nottingham #883
£340 $585 €496 Glad news (35x26cm-14x10in) i. pencil black ink. 3-Dec-3 Christie's, Kensington #254
£380 $619 €555 May I have the peasure of this dance (35x26cm-14x10in) s. pencil. 24-Sep-3 Dreweatt Neate, Newbury #53
£400 $648 €580 Best of all ways to Lengthen our days is to borrow an hour from the night (35x2cm-14x1in) s. pen ink. 30-Jul-3 Hamptons Fine Art, Godalming #42
£500 $915 €730 Regrets (28x21cm-11x8in) init. pen wash prov. 27-Jan-4 Bonhams, Knightsbridge #13/R
£750 $1388 €1095 Dalmatian hound in Dalmatia (37x26cm-15x10in) s.i. pencil pen ink. 11-Feb-4 Sotheby's, Olympia #99/R
£750 $1320 €1095 Hippolyte pere in a ricketty cart, drawn by a vicious mule (19x26cm-7x10in) init.i. s.i.verso pen ink sold with another by same hand. 19-May-4 Sotheby's, Olympia #84/R
£2800 $4816 €4088 Roman road. Golden age. Falling out (38x27cm-15x11in) s.i. one init.i. black ink three sold with five by the same hand. 3-Dec-3 Christie's, Kensington #251/R est:800-1200
£2800 $4844 €4088 Bust of Winnie-the-Pooh wearing laurel wreath (4x3cm-2x1in) i.verso ink. 11-Dec-3 Sotheby's, London #319/R est:2000-3000
£3200 $5536 €4672 The King's breakfast. pencil two double-sided ten on 3 sheets 12. 11-Dec-3 Sotheby's, London #320/R est:1500-2000
£4000 $6880 €5840 Piglet (5x8cm-2x3in) s. brown ink. 3-Dec-3 Christie's, Kensington #255/R est:500-700
£4100 $7667 €5986 Studies of Pooh, Piglet and Eeyore (23x21cm-9x8in) i. pencil. 29-Feb-4 Wilkinson, Doncaster #189
£58000 $105560 €84680 So Winnie the Pooh pushed and pushed. He started to shunt out of the hole (15x18cm-6x7in) one i. one init.i. pencil black ink pair lit. 1-Jul-4 Christie's, Kensington #482/R est:60000-80000

SHEPELEV, L V (1937-) Russian
£1333 $2400 €1946 Fishermen, repairing the nets (55x78cm-22x31in) tempera. 24-Apr-4 Shishkin Gallery, Moscow #77/R est:1400-1600
£1556 $2800 €2272 At the work (60x80cm-24x31in) tempera on paper. 24-Apr-4 Shishkin Gallery, Moscow #79/R est:1200-1400
£1833 $3300 €2676 Conversation (54x77cm-21x30in) tempera. 24-Apr-4 Shishkin Gallery, Moscow #78/R est:1200-1400
Works on paper
£272 $500 €397 Welder (58x82cm-23x32in) gouache painted 1959. 27-Mar-4 Shishkin Gallery, Moscow #83/R
£380 $700 €555 In the dispatcher room (58x88cm-23x35in) gouache painted 1959. 27-Mar-4 Shishkin Gallery, Moscow #87/R
£408 $750 €596 The rest (57x80cm-22x31in) gouache painted1961. 27-Mar-4 Shishkin Gallery, Moscow #86/R
£489 $900 €714 Moscow, south west district (59x83cm-23x33in) gouache painted 1959. 27-Mar-4 Shishkin Gallery, Moscow #85/R
£598 $1100 €873 Concrete worker (82x59cm-32x23in) gouache painted 1964. 27-Mar-4 Shishkin Gallery, Moscow #84/R
£1111 $2000 €1622 Fisherman (56x78cm-22x31in) mixed media cardboard. 24-Apr-4 Shishkin Gallery, Moscow #80/R est:1200-1400

SHEPHARD, Clarence E (1869-1949) American
£601 $1100 €902 Haystacks (56x69cm-22x27in) 9-Jul-4 Du Mouchelle, Detroit #2166/R

SHEPHERD, David (1931-) British
£800 $1280 €1160 View of Purley Park, Berks (40x56cm-16x22in) s. 16-Sep-3 Bonhams, Knightsbridge #185
£1700 $3009 €2482 HMS Phoebe laying off Haifa (40x61cm-16x24in) s.d.69. 27-Apr-4 Henry Adams, Chichester #721/R est:1000-1500
£4000 $7360 €5840 Elephant by a pool (11x18cm-4x7in) s.d.85. 24-Mar-4 Hamptons Fine Art, Godalming #294/R
£4500 $8325 €6570 Rhinoceros (15x15cm-6x6in) s. sold with a Wedgwood plate of the same subject. 11-Feb-4 Sotheby's, Olympia #243/R est:3000-5000
£5000 $8600 €7300 Elephants (30x51cm-12x20in) s.d.98. 2-Dec-3 Gorringes, Lewes #2349/R est:5000-7000
£6000 $10320 €8760 Bull elephant (15x15cm-6x6in) s.d.96. 2-Dec-3 Gorringes, Lewes #2350/R est:4000-6000
£6000 $11040 €8760 Elephant at a water hole (13x18cm-5x7in) s.d.85 i.verso. 10-Jun-4 Christie's, Kensington #284/R est:5000-7000
£7000 $12320 €10220 Head of a lion (17x25cm-7x10in) s.d.83 overlap. 19-May-4 Sotheby's, Olympia #224/R est:3000-5000
£7200 $12672 €10512 Head of a tiger (18x25cm-7x10in) s.d.83 s.d.overlap. 19-May-4 Sotheby's, Olympia #225/R est:3000-5000
£8000 $13760 €11680 Elephants (20x30cm-8x12in) s. 2-Dec-3 Gorringes, Lewes #2345/R est:6000-8000
£14706 $27500 €21471 Resting tiger (36x56cm-14x22in) s. 24-Jul-4 Coeur d'Alene, Hayden #91/R est:15000-25000
£18000 $31680 €26280 Elephants (55x106cm-22x42in) s.d.02. 19-May-4 Sotheby's, Olympia #226/R est:20000-30000
£18605 $32000 €27163 Water buffalo (41x56cm-16x22in) s.d.70 prov. 5-Dec-3 Christie's, Rockefeller NY #98/R est:15000-20000
£20000 $34400 €29200 Elephants (51x102cm-20x40in) s.d.99. 2-Dec-3 Gorringes, Lewes #2347/R est:20000-25000
£22093 $38000 €32256 Bull elephant (41x56cm-16x22in) s. 5-Dec-3 Christie's, Rockefeller NY #99/R est:18000-25000
Works on paper
£1200 $2148 €1752 Study of an elephant (9x16cm-4x6in) s. pencil. 14-May-4 Christie's, Kensington #579/R est:600-800
£2500 $4625 €3650 Elephant in the undergrowth (19x23cm-7x9in) s.d.96 pencil. 11-Mar-4 Christie's, Kensington #137/R est:800-1200

SHEPHERD, George Sydney (1784-c.1858) British
Works on paper
£700 $1295 €1022 At the window (34x25cm-13x10in) s.d.1832 W/C. 10-Mar-4 Sotheby's, Olympia #46/R
£900 $1638 €1314 Royal dockyard and Chatham Kent (17x26cm-7x10in) pencil W/C htd white. 5-Feb-4 Mellors & Kirk, Nottingham #492

SHEPHERD, George Sydney (attrib) (1784-c.1858) British
Works on paper
£220 $407 €321 Fisherman on the jetty (10x19cm-4x7in) W/C pencil. 10-Mar-4 Sotheby's, Olympia #40/R
£1400 $2562 €2044 Guildford Castle, Surrey (35x30cm-14x12in) with i. pencil W/C prov. 3-Jun-4 Christie's, London #115/R est:1000-1500

SHEPHERD, J Clinton (1888-1963) American
£597 $950 €872 Hunt scene (51x61cm-20x24in) s. 10-Sep-3 Alderfer's, Hatfield #349/R

SHEPHERD, John (19th C) British
£580 $1073 €847 View at Claydon, Suffolk (25x20cm-10x8in) s. 11-Feb-4 Cheffins, Cambridge #435/R

SHEPHERD, Michael (1950-) New Zealander
£746 $1291 €1089 Souvenirs of time (24x37cm-9x15in) d.1988. 9-Dec-3 Peter Webb, Auckland #2/R (NZ.D 2000)
£1083 $1765 €1581 Landscape looking towards Mt Albert Grammar (27x49cm-11x19in) d.1985 board. 23-Sep-3 Peter Webb, Auckland #110/R est:3000-5000 (NZ.D 3000)
£1642 $2840 €2397 Landscape with too few lovers (29x44cm-11x17in) i.d.1991 board. 9-Dec-3 Peter Webb, Auckland #3/R est:3000-4000 (NZ.D 4400)
£1696 $3071 €2476 Self and Rangiriri (22x31cm-9x12in) i.d.1990 oil on plywood. 30-Mar-4 Peter Webb, Auckland #9/R est:3500-4500 (NZ.D 4750)
Works on paper
£362 $583 €529 Still life with suitcase (31x43cm-12x17in) ink collage. 12-Aug-3 Peter Webb, Auckland #180 (NZ.D 1000)

£752 $1278 €1098 Maungapohatu (37x68cm-15x27in) i.d.1986 ink acrylic. 27-Nov-3 International Art Centre, Auckland #34/R (NZ.D 2000)

SHEPHERD, S Horne (1909-1993) British

Works on paper

£600 $1002 €876 Female nude with reflection (38x26cm-15x10in) s. W/C bodycol. 16-Oct-3 Christie's, Kensington #585/R

SHEPHERD, Thomas Hosmer (1792-1864) British

Works on paper

£1000 $1830 €1460 Vintner's hall and St. Luke's, Old Street, London (12x20cm-5x8in) s. W/C. 7-Apr-4 Bonhams, Bury St Edmunds #423 est:800-1200
£1500 $2775 €2190 Pall Mall (12x19cm-5x7in) W/C. 9-Mar-4 Bonhams, New Bond Street #60/R est:1500-2500
£12000 $20400 €17520 Views of London. s.i. brown wash over pencil folio. 27-Nov-3 Sotheby's, London #269/R est:12000-15000

SHEPPARD, Faith (1920-) British

£260 $458 €380 Suffolk coast (40x58cm-16x23in) s. board. 18-May-4 Bonhams, Knightsbridge #145
£500 $920 €730 Malta - Scene of women washing (36x46cm-14x18in) s. 12-Jun-4 Dickins, Middle Claydon #83
£750 $1178 €1095 Village canal with bridge and boat to the foreground (19x23cm-7x9in) 31-Aug-3 Paul Beighton, Rotherham #531/R
£880 $1619 €1285 Malta - Scene of a Maltese House (61x61cm-24x24in) s. indis.i.verso board. 12-Jun-4 Dickins, Middle Claydon #81
£950 $1720 €1387 Malta - view of church at Msida Creek (46x69cm-18x27in) s. 17-Apr-4 Dickins, Middle Claydon #130
£950 $1748 €1387 Venice - Scene with gondolas at canals edge with buildings in background (41x58cm-16x23in) s. board. 12-Jun-4 Dickins, Middle Claydon #84
£1000 $1840 €1460 Malta - Town square with trees and fountain (46x69cm-18x27in) s. board. 12-Jun-4 Dickins, Middle Claydon #77
£1000 $1840 €1460 Malta - Scene of a cafe in Gozo Street (41x61cm-16x24in) s. board. 12-Jun-4 Dickins, Middle Claydon #78
£1000 $1840 €1460 Malta - Maltese cafe scene (41x61cm-16x24in) s. board. 12-Jun-4 Dickins, Middle Claydon #79
£1000 $1840 €1460 Venice - Venetian canal by Ruskin's House (41x56cm-16x22in) s. board. 12-Jun-4 Dickins, Middle Claydon #85
£1100 $1991 €1606 Malta - view of harbour with boats and buildings (41x58cm-16x23in) s. board. 17-Apr-4 Dickins, Middle Claydon #133
£1200 $2172 €1752 Yachts at Msida Creek, Malta (41x58cm-16x23in) s. board. 17-Apr-4 Dickins, Middle Claydon #131
£1200 $2208 €1752 Malta - Early morning - view of harbour (30x46cm-12x18in) s. board. 12-Jun-4 Dickins, Middle Claydon #68
£1200 $2208 €1752 Malta - Grand Harbour, Valletta (25x36cm-10x14in) s. board. 12-Jun-4 Dickins, Middle Claydon #73
£1200 $2208 €1752 Venice - Rialto Bridge (48x69cm-19x27in) board. 12-Jun-4 Dickins, Middle Claydon #86
£1300 $2392 €1898 Venice - Scene of a canal with launches (41x61cm-16x24in) s. board. 12-Jun-4 Dickins, Middle Claydon #87
£1450 $2668 €2117 Kelp gatherers at Concarneau, Brittany (71x89cm-28x35in) s. 12-Jun-4 Dickins, Middle Claydon #88
£1500 $2715 €2190 Venetian canal scene with gondolas (46x69cm-18x27in) s. board. 17-Apr-4 Dickins, Middle Claydon #134
£1600 $2896 €2336 Malta - view of harbour side and buildings and church upon a hill (46x61cm-18x24in) s. 17-Apr-4 Dickins, Middle Claydon #132
£1650 $2987 €2409 Malta a harbour scene with boats and buildings (51x76cm-20x30in) s. canvasboard. 17-Apr-4 Dickins, Middle Claydon #129
£1700 $3128 €2482 Malta - St Julian's Bay (46x58cm-18x23in) s. board. 12-Jun-4 Dickins, Middle Claydon #67
£1700 $3128 €2482 Malta - Sunday Trotter, Medina (25x36cm-10x14in) s. board. 12-Jun-4 Dickins, Middle Claydon #71
£1800 $3312 €2628 Malta - Scene across harbour with church on hill top to background (48x76cm-19x30in) 12-Jun-4 Dickins, Middle Claydon #75
£2200 $4048 €3212 Malta - Fishing boats at Msida Creek (36x46cm-14x18in) s. 12-Jun-4 Dickins, Middle Claydon #82
£2300 $4232 €3358 Swan flying over St Katherine's Dock (38x58cm-15x23in) s. board. 12-Jun-4 Dickins, Middle Claydon #65
£2500 $4600 €3650 Malta - Scene overlooking harbour with church on hill top to background (41x56cm-16x22in) s. board. 12-Jun-4 Dickins, Middle Claydon #72
£3700 $6808 €5402 Malta - Msida Creek with boats and the Trinity Evangelical Church (41x58cm-16x23in) s. board. 12-Jun-4 Dickins, Middle Claydon #80
£4100 $7544 €5986 Malta - By the British Hotel, Valletta (41x58cm-16x23in) s. board. 12-Jun-4 Dickins, Middle Claydon #66
£4600 $8464 €6716 Malta - St Julian's Bay (41x64cm-16x25in) s. board exhib. 12-Jun-4 Dickins, Middle Claydon #76

SHEPPARD, Herbert Charles (1859-1931) British

£350 $641 €511 Flying Dutchman in a swell (39x29cm-15x11in) oil sketch board sold with a letter. 6-Apr-4 Bristol Auction Rooms #444/R

SHEPPARD, Joseph (1930-) American

£528 $950 €771 After fight (41x51cm-16x20in) s.d.80 masonite. 23-Jan-4 Freeman, Philadelphia #124/R
£719 $1200 €1050 Merry - go - round (30x41cm-12x16in) s. board. 20-Jun-3 Freeman, Philadelphia #142/R
£1667 $3000 €2434 Windy evening (76x91cm-30x36in) s. masonite. 23-Jan-4 Freeman, Philadelphia #252/R est:3000-5000

SHEPPARD, Maurice (1947-) British

£450 $824 €657 To CW Owl Dream (37x75cm-15x30in) s.d.1975/6 board exhib. 7-Apr-4 Woolley & Wallis, Salisbury #253/R

SHEPPARD, Nancy (1890-?) British

£250 $453 €365 Furnace, Loch Fyne (48x61cm-19x24in) s. canvasboard. 17-Apr-4 Dickins, Middle Claydon #87
£250 $453 €365 Mrs Smilies Cottage, Loch Fyne (51x41cm-20x16in) s. canvasboard painted 1938. 17-Apr-4 Dickins, Middle Claydon #90
£250 $453 €365 Harvest time, Berkshire Downs (41x51cm-16x20in) s. board. 17-Apr-4 Dickins, Middle Claydon #93
£250 $453 €365 View of a river running through a wood (61x51cm-24x20in) s. 17-Apr-4 Dickins, Middle Claydon #128
£300 $543 €438 View of loch with castle and highlands behind (51x61cm-20x24in) s. 17-Apr-4 Dickins, Middle Claydon #86
£300 $543 €438 Scottish village scene with cottages (41x51cm-16x20in) s. canvasboard. 17-Apr-4 Dickins, Middle Claydon #88
£300 $543 €438 Switzerland, view of moored boats on Lake Geneva (41x51cm-16x20in) s. 17-Apr-4 Dickins, Middle Claydon #115
£300 $543 €438 Still life of dahlias in a vase (51x41cm-20x16in) s. canvasboard. 17-Apr-4 Dickins, Middle Claydon #126
£320 $579 €467 Still life of flowers in a vase (51x41cm-20x16in) board. 17-Apr-4 Dickins, Middle Claydon #127
£330 $597 €482 Small Scottish fishing harbour, view from the shore (51x61cm-20x24in) s. 17-Apr-4 Dickins, Middle Claydon #89
£340 $615 €496 Krail, Kingdom of Fife (51x61cm-20x24in) s. 17-Apr-4 Dickins, Middle Claydon #85
£340 $615 €496 Cambridge, scene of bridge over the Cam with figures in a punt (51x61cm-20x24in) s. 17-Apr-4 Dickins, Middle Claydon #112
£340 $615 €496 Bruges, view of river with figures rowing and figures crossing a bridge (51x61cm-20x24in) s. 17-Apr-4 Dickins, Middle Claydon #117
£350 $634 €511 Old Mill, Blewbury, Berkshire (51x41cm-20x16in) s. board. 17-Apr-4 Dickins, Middle Claydon #92
£360 $652 €526 Maltese scene of a stone fountain with figures and balcony looking over (61x51cm-24x20in) s. 17-Apr-4 Dickins, Middle Claydon #125
£380 $688 €555 Cambridge, view of bridge over River Cam (51x61cm-20x24in) s. 17-Apr-4 Dickins, Middle Claydon #113
£380 $688 €555 Delft, view of converging canals (51x61cm-20x24in) s. 17-Apr-4 Dickins, Middle Claydon #118
£420 $760 €613 Interior Berindene, Blewbury, Berkshire (51x41cm-20x16in) s.d.1936 board. 17-Apr-4 Dickins, Middle Claydon #91
£440 $796 €642 Old Cottage interior (51x41cm-20x16in) canvasboard. 17-Apr-4 Dickins, Middle Claydon #97
£460 $833 €672 Old cottage doorways, scene depicting interior view of a cottage (51x41cm-20x16in) canvasboard. 17-Apr-4 Dickins, Middle Claydon #98
£500 $905 €730 Beach at Wissant Pas-de Calis (41x51cm-16x20in) s. board painted 1939. 17-Apr-4 Dickins, Middle Claydon #114
£520 $941 €759 Switzerland, view of Lake Geneva depicting rowers and boats (51x61cm-20x24in) s. 17-Apr-4 Dickins, Middle Claydon #116
£520 $941 €759 Delft (51x61cm-20x24in) s. 17-Apr-4 Dickins, Middle Claydon #119
£540 $977 €788 Portrait of a seated woman wearing a black hat, red cape and black gloves (76x64cm-30x25in) s. 17-Apr-4 Dickins, Middle Claydon #80
£620 $1122 €905 Two nude studies of ladies. one s.d.1913 verso two. 17-Apr-4 Dickins, Middle Claydon #83
£620 $1122 €905 Bruges, view of bridge over canal with buildings behind (51x41cm-20x16in) s. board. 17-Apr-4 Dickins, Middle Claydon #120
£700 $1267 €1022 Casis Harbour (51x61cm-20x24in) s. 17-Apr-4 Dickins, Middle Claydon #124
£720 $1303 €1051 Portrait of the young Faith Sheppard wearing a red dress sat upon a sofa (76x64cm-30x25in) s. 17-Apr-4 Dickins, Middle Claydon #79
£880 $1593 €1285 Casis Harbour (51x61cm-20x24in) s. 17-Apr-4 Dickins, Middle Claydon #122
£1000 $1810 €1460 At Digswell (61x51cm-24x20in) s. canvasboard. 17-Apr-4 Dickins, Middle Claydon #111
£1000 $1810 €1460 Casis Harbour (51x61cm-20x24in) s. 17-Apr-4 Dickins, Middle Claydon #123
£1650 $2987 €2409 Passing Chelsea (114x86cm-45x34in) s. exhib. 17-Apr-4 Dickins, Middle Claydon #101

SHEPPARD, Peter Clapham (1882-1965) Canadian

£1280 $2342 €1869 Crating vegetables for market day, Humber River, Ontario (21x26cm-8x10in) s. panel. 1-Jun-4 Joyner Waddington, Toronto #280/R est:3000-4000 (C.D 3200)
£1360 $2489 €1986 Interior, Muskoka boathouse (21x26cm-8x10in) s. panel sketch verso double-sided. 1-Jun-4 Joyner Waddington, Toronto #207/R est:3000-4000 (C.D 3400)
£1440 $2635 €2102 Cherry Beach (21x26cm-8x10in) s. panel. 1-Jun-4 Joyner Waddington, Toronto #125/R est:3000-4000 (C.D 3600)
£1440 $2635 €2102 Toronto waterfront - Near Parliament Street (21x26cm-8x10in) s. panel sketch verso. 1-Jun-4 Joyner Waddington, Toronto #150/R est:3000-4000 (C.D 3600)

SHEPPARD, Warren W (1858-1937) American

£1173 $2100 €1713 Santa Maria Della Salute (41x61cm-16x24in) s.d.90. 14-May-4 Skinner, Boston #143/R est:800-1200
£1613 $3000 €2355 Off the coast (50x76cm-20x30in) s. 5-Mar-4 Skinner, Boston #319/R est:3000-5000
£3352 $6000 €4894 Gondolas under a bridge, Venice (61x41cm-24x16in) s. prov. 6-May-4 Shannon's, Milford #87/R est:6000-8000
£3827 $6200 €5549 Clipper ship (77x62cm-30x24in) s. 8-Aug-3 Barridorf, Portland #73/R est:5000-7000
£4630 $7500 €6714 On the river (38x56cm-15x22in) s. 8-Aug-3 Barridorf, Portland #82/R est:9000-12000
£8939 $16000 €13051 Twilight over the Isles of shoals (18x30cm-7x12in) indis.sig. prov. 6-May-4 Shannon's, Milford #115/R est:8000-12000

SHEPPERSON, Claude Allin (1867-1921) British

Works on paper

£1200 $2004 €1752 Stage Ball, at the Albert Hall (31x19cm-12x7in) s. mixed media sold with a letter. 7-Oct-3 Bonhams, Knightsbridge #41/R est:500-700

SHERIDAN, Noel (20th C) Irish

£296 $512 €420 Landscape (15x61cm-6x24in) s. board prov. 10-Dec-3 Bonhams & James Adam, Dublin #168/R
£915 $1584 €1300 Moon (36x40cm-14x16in) s. prov. 10-Dec-3 Bonhams & James Adam, Dublin #170/R
£1208 $2138 €1800 Kerry landscapes (20x30cm-8x12in) s. i.verso board pair prov. 27-Apr-4 Whyte's, Dublin #64/R est:1500-2000
£1268 $2028 €1800 Table top still life with fruit and blue bottle (58x85cm-23x33in) s. prov. 16-Sep-3 Whyte's, Dublin #5/R est:2000-3000
£1419 $2682 €2100 Composition (51x61cm-20x24in) s. prov. 17-Feb-4 Whyte's, Dublin #212/R est:1800-2200

SHERINGHAM, George (1884-1937) British
Works on paper
£260 $447 €380 Auriculas (41x33cm-16x13in) s. W/C. 3-Dec-3 Andrew Hartley, Ilkley #1051

SHERLINGH, Michael (19/20th C) American
£1324 $2250 €1933 Lake in wooded atmospheric landscape (64x76cm-25x30in) s. prov. 18-Nov-3 John Moran, Pasadena #183 est:2000-3000

SHERLOCK, Marjorie (1897-1973) British
£320 $544 €467 Seated nude female (46x36cm-18x14in) s. 29-Oct-3 Hampton & Littlewood, Exeter #545/R
£1800 $3330 €2628 At the bus stop (61x76cm-24x30in) s. 11-Feb-4 Sotheby's, Olympia #183/R est:600-800
Works on paper
£260 $476 €380 Bampton Fair, wet day (43x56cm-17x22in) s. W/C. 3-Jun-4 Lane, Penzance #139

SHERLOCK, Siriol (20th C) British?
Works on paper
£420 $739 €613 Heiconia Marginata (52x35cm-20x14in) s. W/C. 18-May-4 Woolley & Wallis, Salisbury #193/R
£680 $1197 €993 Group of Bromeliaceae (62x48cm-24x19in) s. W/C. 18-May-4 Woolley & Wallis, Salisbury #195/R
£700 $1232 €1022 Passiflora quadrangularis (63x49cm-25x19in) s. W/C htd white. 18-May-4 Woolley & Wallis, Salisbury #192/R

SHERLOCK, William P (1780-?) British
£608 $1100 €888 In the Welsh hills (69x89cm-27x35in) 16-Apr-4 Du Mouchelle, Detroit #2039/R est:800-1500

SHERMAN, Albert (1882-1971) Australian
£300 $555 €438 Thatched cottage (46x30cm-18x12in) s.d.1907. 10-Feb-4 David Lay, Penzance #220/R
£573 $1042 €837 Roses (40x45cm-16x18in) s. board. 16-Jun-4 Deutscher-Menzies, Melbourne #560/R est:1000-2000 (A.D 1500)
£1025 $1660 €1497 Sydney Harbour (31x24cm-12x9in) s. board. 30-Jul-3 Goodman, Sydney #94/R (A.D 2500)
£1057 $1659 €1543 Untitled, still life with daisies (36x32cm-14x13in) s. canvasboard. 1-Sep-3 Shapiro, Sydney #342/R est:1000-2000 (A.D 2600)
£1434 $2324 €2094 Still life (66x55cm-26x22in) s board prov. 30-Jul-3 Goodman, Sydney #97/R est:3500-4500 (A.D 3500)
£1446 $2676 €2111 Zinnias (47x52cm-19x20in) s. canvasboard. 10-Mar-4 Deutscher-Menzies, Melbourne #340/R est:5000-7500 (A.D 3500)
£1545 $2765 €2256 White blossoms in a Chinese vase (53x44cm-21x17in) s. board. 4-May-4 Sotheby's, Melbourne #271 est:3000-5000 (A.D 3800)
£1702 $2894 €2485 Gum blossom (51x61cm-20x24in) s. canvas on board painted 1930. 26-Nov-3 Deutscher-Menzies, Melbourne #272/R est:4500-5500 (A.D 4000)
£3112 $5197 €4668 Camellias (51x66cm-20x26in) s. 27-Oct-3 Goodman, Sydney #214/R est:4000-6000 (A.D 7500)

SHERMAN, Beatrix (20th C) American
£213 $375 €311 Still life with doll, book, and sewing stand (61x56cm-24x22in) s. i.verso. 22-May-4 Pook & Pook, Downington #468

SHERMAN, Cindy (1954-) American
Photographs
£1351 $2500 €1972 Untitled (43x28cm-17x11in) s.d.1990-91 num.22/125 colour photograph. 12-Feb-4 Sotheby's, New York #358/R est:3000-4000
£1667 $3066 €2500 Untitled (16x32cm-6x13in) s.d.1986/93 num.191/200 verso cibachrome prov. 9-Jun-4 Artcurial Briest, Paris #568/R est:2500-3000
£1796 $3000 €2622 Ancestor (71x43cm-28x17in) s. num.51/72 verso chromogenic col print exec.1985 prov. 17-Oct-3 Phillips, New York #291/R est:4000-6000
£2210 $4000 €3227 Untitled, Marilyn Monroe (39x23cm-15x9in) init.d.1982 num.41/125 chromogenic print prov. 19-Apr-4 Bonhams & Butterfields, San Francisco #486/R est:5000-7000
£2222 $3778 €3200 Ancestor (71x43cm-28x17in) s.i.d. verso col Kodacolor. 31-Oct-3 Lempertz, Koln #396/R est:4000
£2515 $4200 €3672 Ancestor (71x43cm-28x17in) with sig.i.d.1985 num.38/72 verso chromogenic print. 21-Oct-3 Swann Galleries, New York #330/R est:5000-7000
£2600 $4784 €3796 Untitled, Lucille Ball (26x21cm-10x8in) s.d.1975/2001 verso black white photo lit. 24-Jun-4 Sotheby's, Olympia #613/R est:1000-1500
£3370 $6200 €4920 Untitled, doll (98x65cm-39x26in) s.d.1999 num.10 verso black white photo prov. 10-Jun-4 Phillips, New York #429/R est:8000-12000
£3400 $6188 €4964 Untitled (18x13cm-7x5in) s.i.d.1980/2001 num.35/100 verso blk white photo. 4-Feb-4 Sotheby's, Olympia #61/R est:1000-1500
£7000 $11690 €10220 Untitled, no 269 (101x69cm-40x27in) cibachrome print prov. 22-Oct-3 Christie's, London #151/R est:8000-12000
£7500 $13650 €10950 Untitled (25x20cm-10x8in) s.d.1976/2000 num.12/20 verso blk white photo prov.lit. 5-Feb-4 Christie's, London #211/R est:7000-9000
£7821 $14000 €11419 Untitled, num 117 (88x62cm-35x24in) s.d.1983 num.16/18 verso col coupler print prov.exhib.lit. 12-May-4 Christie's, Rockefeller NY #384/R est:15000-20000
£8380 $15000 €12235 Untitled, num 304 (152x102cm-60x40in) s.d.1994 num.6/6 col coupler print foamcore prov. 12-May-4 Christie's, Rockefeller NY #382/R est:15000-20000
£8380 $15000 €12235 Untitled, num 328 (101x145cm-40x57in) s.d.1996 num.2/6 Cibachrome print foamcore prov. 12-May-4 Christie's, Rockefeller NY #383/R est:20000-30000
£8939 $16000 €13051 Untitled - The actress (25x20cm-10x8in) s.d.1976/00 verso blk white photo exec 1976 prov. 13-May-4 Sotheby's, New York #415/R est:12000-15000
£9000 $16380 €13140 Untitled (25x20cm-10x8in) s.d.76/00 num.4/20 blk white photo prov.lit. 5-Feb-4 Christie's, London #210/R est:7000-9000
£11377 $19000 €16610 Untitled no.124 (62x84cm-24x33in) s.d.1983 num.18 verso colour photograph prov. 14-Nov-3 Phillips, New York #154/R est:18000-22000
£11500 $19205 €16790 Untitled, no 174 (186x126cm-73x50in) cibachrome print prov.lit. 22-Oct-3 Christie's, London #150/R est:10000-15000
£12667 $23307 €19000 Untitled 124 (63x82cm-25x32in) num.16/18 cibachrome exec 1983 prov.exhib.lit. 8-Jun-4 Artcurial Briest, Paris #297/R est:18000-22000
£14525 $26000 €21207 Untitled, num 397 (114x84cm-45x33in) s.d.2000 num.5/6 col coupler print Cintra prov. 12-May-4 Christie's, Rockefeller NY #381/R est:35000-45000
£14970 $25000 €21856 Untitled, no 106 (122x61cm-48x24in) col photo edition 1 of 10 prov. 13-Nov-3 Sotheby's, New York #451/R est:25000-35000
£16766 $28000 €24478 Untitled no. 267 (67x102cm-26x40in) s.num.2/6 d.1992 verso colour coupler print prov.lit. 12-Nov-3 Christie's, Rockefeller NY #527/R est:15000-20000
£17877 $32000 €26100 Untitled film still 1 (25x20cm-10x8in) s.d.1977 num.2/10 verso black white photograph prov.exhib.lit. 13-May-4 Sotheby's, New York #341/R est:20000-30000
£19000 $34960 €27740 Untitled filmstill No.26 (68x95cm-27x37in) gelatin silver print executed 1979 prov.lit. 24-Jun-4 Christie's, London #46/R est:20000-30000
£19461 $32500 €28413 Untitled, no 357 (89x64cm-35x25in) s.d.2000 num.5/6 verso col photo prov.exhib.lit. 13-Nov-3 Sotheby's, New York #408/R est:20000-30000
£20958 $35000 €30599 Untitled, no 115 (116x76cm-46x30in) col photo prov.exhib. 13-Nov-3 Sotheby's, New York #458/R est:30000-40000
£23952 $40000 €34970 Untitled, film still no 42 (20x25cm-8x10in) s.num.5/10 verso gelatin silver print prov.lit. 13-Nov-3 Sotheby's, New York #501/R est:30000-40000
£28000 $51520 €40880 Untitled film still 1 (25x20cm-10x8in) s.d.77 num. 1/10 gelatin silver print prov.lit. 24-Jun-4 Sotheby's, London #103/R est:10000-15000
£33520 $60000 €48939 Untitled, num 226 (122x76cm-48x30in) s.d.1990 num.5/6 verso col coupler print foamcore prov.lit. 12-May-4 Christie's, Rockefeller NY #377/R est:50000-70000
£35928 $60000 €52455 Untitled film still no. 11 (20x25cm-8x10in) s.num.3/10 d.1978 verso gelatin silver print prov.exhib.lit. 12-Nov-3 Christie's, Rockefeller NY #525/R est:30000-40000
£35928 $60000 €52455 Untitled no. 152 (184x126cm-72x50in) s.d.1985 verso colour coupler print prov.exhib.lit. 12-Nov-3 Christie's, Rockefeller NY #526/R est:40000-60000
£39106 $70000 €57095 Untitled, num 220 (162x101cm-64x40in) s.d.1990 num.4/6 col coupler print foamcore prov.exhib.lit. 12-May-4 Christie's, Rockefeller NY #372/R est:70000-90000
£40503 $72500 €59134 Untitled film still 32 (41x51cm-16x20in) s.d.1979 num.2/3 verso gelatin silver print prov.exhib.lit. 13-May-4 Sotheby's, New York #340/R est:60000-80000
£41899 $75000 €61173 Untitled, film still no 49 (76x102cm-30x40in) s.d.1979 num.3/3 verso gelatin silver print board prov.exhib.lit. 12-May-4 Christie's, Rockefeller NY #371/R est:60000-80000
£44910 $75000 €65569 Untitled 220. s.d.1990 num.6 color coupler print prov.exhib.lit. 13-Nov-3 Phillips, New York #40/R est:90000-120000
£47486 $85000 €69330 Untitled no.211 (117x102cm-46x40in) s.d.1989 num.6 verso c-print prov.exhib. 13-May-4 Phillips, New York #17/R est:80000-120000
£71856 $120000 €104910 Untitled film still (41x51cm-16x20in) s.d.1979 v, gelatin silver print prov.exhib.lit. 13-Nov-3 Phillips, New York #38/R est:50000-70000
£86826 $145000 €126766 Untitled film still No. 21 (40x51cm-16x20in) s. num.2/3 d.1978 verso gelatin silver print prov.exhib.lit. 12-Nov-3 Christie's, Rockefeller NY #520/R est:80000-120000
£104790 $175000 €152993 Untitled film still no 54 (20x25cm-8x10in) s.d.1980 verso gelatin silver print prov.exhib.lit. 11-Nov-3 Christie's, Rockefeller NY #5/R est:150000-200000
£156425 $280000 €228381 Untitled film still 48 (41x51cm-16x20in) s.d.1979 black and white photograph prov.exhib.lit. 12-May-4 Sotheby's, New York #38/R est:200000-300000

SHERRIFFS, R S (1906-1960) British
Works on paper
£350 $648 €525 Caricatures of leading actors and actresses of the MGM film (35x44cm-14x17in) s. ink pencil exec. c.1932. 13-Jul-4 Bonhams, Knightsbridge #40/R

SHERRIN, D (19/20th C) British
Works on paper
£1081 $2000 €1578 Clipper ship at sea (51x71cm-20x28in) s. W/C gouache. 24-Jan-4 Jeffery Burchard, Florida #112/R

SHERRIN, Daniel (1868-1940) British
£260 $473 €380 Sandy Bay (39x59cm-15x23in) s. 5-Feb-4 Mellors & Kirk, Nottingham #526
£313 $500 €457 Landscape with cattle in distance (30x41cm-12x16in) s. painted c.1910. 20-Sep-3 Bunte, Elgin #1426
£320 $531 €467 Harvest time (30x48cm-12x19in) s. 2-Oct-3 Neales, Nottingham #785
£322 $599 €480 Coast with seagull (27x39cm-11x15in) s. cardboard. 2-Mar-4 Ansorena, Madrid #189/R
£360 $565 €522 Waves breaking on rocky coastline (43x61cm-17x24in) s. i.verso. 15-Dec-2 Desmond Judd, Cranbrook #849
£360 $655 €526 Highland cattle by a Scottish loch (61x51cm-24x20in) s. 15-Jun-4 Canterbury Auctions, UK #93/R
£376 $700 €549 Coastal scene (51x91cm-20x36in) s. painted c.1910. 7-Mar-4 Treadway Gallery, Cincinnati #500/R
£400 $680 €584 Waves (61x107cm-24x42in) s. 5-Nov-3 John Nicholson, Haslemere #613
£400 $728 €584 Country scene in summer with a horsecart on a track and workers relaxing (50x75cm-20x30in) s.d.92. 29-Jun-4 Anderson & Garland, Newcastle #379/R
£400 $732 €584 Highland cattle by a loch (59x91cm-23x36in) s. 6-Jul-4 Bonhams, Knightsbridge #153/R
£420 $697 €613 Cattle watering in a highland landscape (59x105cm-23x41in) s. 2-Oct-3 Locke & England, Leamington Spa #171
£450 $810 €657 River landscape at dusk (51x76cm-20x30in) s. 21-Apr-4 Tennants, Leyburn #1126
£460 $846 €672 Thatched country cottages in summer (23x34cm-9x13in) s. 11-Jun-4 Keys, Aylsham #719/R
£500 $850 €730 Rural landscape scene at sunset (49x75cm-19x30in) s. 28-Oct-3 Dickinson, Davy & Markham, Brigg #1079
£500 $935 €730 Sheep and shepherd in a landscape (102x76cm-40x30in) s. 26-Feb-4 Lane, Penzance #288
£529 $1000 €772 River landscape (61x66cm-24x26in) s. 22-Feb-4 Bonhams & Butterfields, Los Angeles #7035 est:1500-2500
£538 $1000 €785 Portrait of sailing vessel under way (46x61cm-18x24in) s.d. 3-Mar-4 Alderfer's, Hatfield #282/R est:700-900
£550 $1018 €803 Shepherd and his flock in a winter landscape - dawn (91x70cm-36x28in) s. 14-Jul-4 Christie's, Kensington #837/R
£580 $945 €847 Seashore (41x61cm-16x24in) s. i.verso. 24-Sep-3 Dreweatt Neate, Newbury #166/R
£600 $1002 €876 Near Bisley Heath, Surrey (51x76cm-20x30in) 21-Oct-3 Gorringes, Lewes #1956/R
£600 $960 €876 Highland cattle watering (60x90cm-24x35in) s. 18-Sep-3 Bonhams, Edinburgh #329a/R
£700 $1274 €1022 Highland cattle in a landscape (29x49cm-11x19in) s. 5-Feb-4 Mellors & Kirk, Nottingham #555/R
£720 $1346 €1051 Tranquil coastal view (50x76cm-20x30in) s. 24-Feb-4 Bonhams, Knowle #60/R

£765 $1300 €1117 Country path (91x61cm-36x24in) s. 22-Nov-3 Jackson's, Cedar Falls #16/R est:1500-2500
£950 $1758 €1387 Gathering hay at dusk (61x107cm-24x42in) s. 15-Jan-4 Christie's, Kensington #867/R
£1050 $1817 €1533 On the banks of the Avon, a summer evening with figures and punt (48x74cm-19x29in) s. 11-Dec-3 Neales, Nottingham #638/R est:1000-1200
£1100 $1870 €1606 River landscape with figures beside trees, and hills beyond (41x61cm-16x24in) s. 19-Nov-3 Tennants, Leyburn #1112 est:700-900
£1600 $2976 €2336 River in a mountainous landscape (51x76cm-20x30in) s. 4-Mar-4 Christie's, Kensington #463/R est:2000-3000
£1750 $2818 €2538 Near Abinger, Surrey (58x102cm-23x40in) s. 15-Aug-3 Keys, Aylsham #697/R est:1800-2500
£5000 $9150 €7300 Sand Dunes (49x76cm-19x30in) s. 28-Jan-4 Henry Adams, Chichester #294/R est:2000-3000
£5000 $9350 €7300 Summer's afternoon, river landscape with figures seated (61x107cm-24x42in) s.i. 22-Jul-4 Tennants, Leyburn #852/R est:3000-4000

SHERRIN, Daniel (attrib) (1868-1940) British
£700 $1253 €1022 Evening over the river (51x76cm-20x30in) with sig,. 27-May-4 Christie's, Kensington #197/R
£1100 $2035 €1606 Extensive wooded landscape with figures (74x125cm-29x49in) bears sig. 14-Jul-4 Bonhams, Chester #461/R est:1200-1800

SHERRIN, David (19/20th C) British
£980 $1813 €1431 Sand dunes (51x76cm-20x30in) s. 10-Mar-4 Sotheby's, Olympia #204/R est:600-800

SHERRIN, John (1819-1896) British
Works on paper
£480 $840 €701 Still life of spray of plums, apple and redcurrants against a mossy bank (30x23cm-12x9in) s. W/C. 16-Dec-3 Capes Dunn, Manchester #736/R
£1900 $3230 €2774 Jug of roses (29x23cm-11x9in) s. bodycol. 4-Nov-3 Bonhams, New Bond Street #130/R est:1000-1500
£2000 $3320 €2920 Still life of plums, an apple and cobnuts (26x37cm-10x15in) s. W/C. 1-Oct-3 Woolley & Wallis, Salisbury #87/R est:1000-1500
£3100 $5735 €4526 Primroses and a bird's nest against a mossy bank (31x42cm-12x17in) s. W/C htd bodycol. 14-Jan-4 Lawrence, Crewkerne #1335/R est:800-1200

SHERRIN, Reginald D (1891-1971) British
Works on paper
£280 $456 €406 Beach scene (40x101cm-16x40in) s. bodycol. 23-Sep-3 Bonhams, Knightsbridge #78/R
£280 $515 €409 Moorland landscape (36x53cm-14x21in) s. bodycol. 22-Jun-4 Bonhams, Knightsbridge #75/R
£300 $477 €438 Holywell Bay (51x81cm-20x32in) s. gouache. 9-Sep-3 Gorringes, Lewes #2088
£320 $573 €467 River Taw, Dartmoor (38x99cm-15x39in) s. i. gouache. 16-Mar-4 Bearnes, Exeter #393
£330 $591 €482 On Lydford Moors, Dartmoor (38x99cm-15x39in) s.i. gouache. 16-Mar-4 Bearnes, Exeter #394
£440 $810 €642 Lydford Moor Dartmoor (40x100cm-16x39in) s.d.1960 gouache. 8-Jun-4 Bearnes, Exeter #419

SHERRINGTON, Charles Robert (1778-1859) British
Works on paper
£260 $460 €380 Dartmouth Lakes, Halifax, Novia Scotia (11x15cm-4x6in) s. i.verso W/C. 27-Apr-4 Bonhams, New Bond Street #108

SHERWIN, John Keyse (1751-1790) British
Prints
£6200 $11098 €9052 Installation banquet of the Knights of St Patrick in the Great Hall, Dublin Castle (61x80cm-24x31in) engraving lit. 13-May-4 Sotheby's, London #7a/R est:2000-3000

SHERWOOD, Maud Winifred (1880-1956) Australian
£545 $856 €796 Farm building along riverbank (35x41cm-14x16in) s. acrylic. 27-Aug-3 Dunbar Sloane, Wellington #56/R (NZ.D 1500)
£1786 $3286 €2608 Reclining nude (30x44cm-12x17in) s. 25-Mar-4 International Art Centre, Auckland #118/R est:2500-3500 (NZ.D 5000)
Works on paper
£677 $1150 €988 Spanish shepherd (32x25cm-13x10in) s.i. ink W/C. 26-Nov-3 Dunbar Sloane, Wellington #111 est:2000-3000 (NZ.D 1800)
£5536 $9910 €8083 Part of fishing fleet, 1913 (44x45cm-17x18in) s. W/C. 12-May-4 Dunbar Sloane, Wellington #20/R est:12000-16000 (NZ.D 16000)

SHERWOOD, Walter J (1865-?) American
£600 $1074 €876 Portrait of a lady in a turquoise dress and hat (76x63cm-30x25in) s. 27-May-4 Christie's, Kensington #105/R

SHERWOOD, William Albert (19/20th C) Canadian
£333 $577 €486 Lower Town, Quebec (25x36cm-10x14in) s.d.98. 9-Dec-3 Pinneys, Montreal #163 (C.D 750)

SHI HU (1946-) Chinese
£4902 $8873 €7157 Laying a rainbow (70x51cm-28x20in) s. 3-Apr-4 Glerum, Singapore #52/R est:14000-17000 (S.D 15000)
£6250 $10438 €9125 Three Balinese Girls (87x69cm-34x27in) s. acrylic paper. 12-Oct-3 Sotheby's, Singapore #162/R est:15000-20000 (S.D 18000)

SHI LU (1919-1982) Chinese
Works on paper
£7824 $14083 €11423 Flowers (32x45cm-13x18in) s.i.d. ink col three scroll mounted as handscroll. 25-Apr-4 Christie's, Hong Kong #126/R est:70000-90000 (HK.D 110000)
£8535 $15363 €12461 Lotus (66x65cm-26x26in) s. ink col hanging scroll lit. 26-Apr-4 Sotheby's, Hong Kong #644/R est:120000-150000 (HK.D 120000)
£14225 $25605 €20769 Plum blossoms at West Lake (80x54cm-31x21in) s.i. ink col hanging scroll. 26-Apr-4 Sotheby's, Hong Kong #639/R est:200000-300000 (HK.D 200000)
£20077 $33529 €29312 Flowers in bloom (125x67cm-49x26in) s. ink hanging scroll. 27-Oct-3 Sotheby's, Hong Kong #252/R est:250000-350000 (HK.D 260000)

SHIBRAIN, Ahmad (1931-) Sudanese
Works on paper
£1900 $3363 €2774 Calligraphy (49x37cm-19x15in) s. W/C pen ink bodycol. 29-Apr-4 Bonhams, New Bond Street #597/R est:1500-2000

SHIELDS, Beckwith A (attrib) (20th C) American
Works on paper
£377 $600 €550 Movement study to Beethoven's Symphony 7 (28x87cm-11x34in) init. pastel. 12-Sep-3 Skinner, Boston #376/R

SHIELDS, Frederic (1833-1911) British
£1900 $3154 €2774 Sister Helen (55x37cm-22x15in) panel prov.exhib. 1-Oct-3 Sotheby's, Olympia #167/R est:500-700
£3500 $6405 €5110 Cartoon for the High Altar Chapel of the Ascension, Bayswater Road London (112x64cm-44x25in) 6-Apr-4 Capes Dunn, Manchester #711/R
Works on paper
£520 $868 €759 Letter (10x13cm-4x5in) s.i. W/C. 14-Oct-3 David Lay, Penzance #159/R
£2200 $4026 €3212 Head study of a young girl (38x33cm-15x13in) with i. blk red white chks. 3-Jun-4 Christie's, London #172/R est:1500-2000

SHIELDS, Irion (1895-1983) American
£556 $1000 €812 La Jolla Headland (51x61cm-20x24in) s.d.46 i.verso canvasboard. 25-Jan-4 Bonhams & Butterfields, San Francisco #3589/R

SHIELDS, Mark (20th C) Irish?
£1700 $2788 €2482 Forres (61x61cm-24x24in) s.d.90 board. 4-Jun-3 John Ross, Belfast #106 est:1200

SHIFU QIUYING (?) Chinese
£972 $1604 €1400 Palais et bateaux animes de personnages au bord de l'eau (44x72cm-17x28in) s. silk. 1-Jul-3 Lemoine & Ferrando, Paris #164

SHIGENAGA, Nishimura (c.1697-1756) Japanese
Prints
£3600 $6624 €5256 Ichikawa Danjuro II as Soga No Goro and Bando Hikosaburo I as Kudo Suketsune (32x14cm-13x6in) s. print exec. 1733. 8-Jun-4 Sotheby's, London #37/R est:900-1200
£6800 $12512 €9928 Landscape view of the Susaki Saiten by the Fukagawa in Edo (32x45cm-13x18in) s. print exec. c.1750's. 8-Jun-4 Sotheby's, London #39/R est:3000-4000

SHIKLER, Aaron (1922-) American
£539 $900 €787 Portrait of fashion designer Elizabeth Kiendl in her studio (30x36cm-12x14in) s.d.56. 20-Jun-3 Freeman, Philadelphia #145/R
£549 $1000 €802 Portrait of a girl (33x25cm-13x10in) s.d.1946. 7-Feb-4 Sloans & Kenyon, Bethesda #1303/R

SHILLING, Arthur (1941-1986) Canadian
£600 $1098 €876 Canadian fall (40x30cm-16x12in) s. canvasboard. 1-Jun-4 Joyner Waddington, Toronto #490 (C.D 1500)
£760 $1391 €1110 Portrait of a native girl (65x50cm-26x20in) s. 1-Jun-4 Joyner Waddington, Toronto #458 est:2000-3000 (C.D 1900)
£1680 $3074 €2453 Portrait of a young boy (62x52cm-24x20in) s. board prov. 1-Jun-4 Joyner Waddington, Toronto #309/R est:3000-5000 (C.D 4200)
£1728 $3092 €2523 Millie and Beewabon (61x55cm-24x22in) s.d.1979 masonite prov. 6-May-4 Heffel, Vancouver #133/R est:2200-2400 (C.D 4250)
£2045 $3334 €2986 Christine (46x40cm-18x16in) s.d.86 acrylic masonite prov. 23-Sep-3 Ritchie, Toronto #170/R est:3000-4000 (C.D 4500)
£3125 $5375 €4563 Woman at work in a field (75x60cm-30x24in) s. board. 2-Dec-3 Joyner Waddington, Toronto #223/R est:4000-5000 (C.D 7000)

SHINN, Everett (1876-1953) American
£16304 $30000 €23804 Flapper (76x55cm-30x22in) s.d.26 prov. 8-Jun-4 Bonhams & Butterfields, San Francisco #4060/R est:10000-15000
£31250 $55000 €45625 Clown - no laughs (91x107cm-36x42in) s.d.1935 prov.exhib.lit. 19-May-4 Sotheby's, New York #117/R est:30000-50000
Works on paper
£675 $1100 €986 Sirens (41x60cm-16x24in) s. ink. 28-Sep-3 Bonhams & Butterfields, Los Angeles #7002 est:1000-1500
£838 $1400 €1223 Old Joe at his shop (43x10cm-17x4in) init. i.verso pen ink board. 18-Jun-3 Doyle, New York #74/R
£1117 $2000 €1631 Court jester (51x38cm-20x15in) W/C pencil board. 26-May-4 Doyle, New York #98/R est:3000-5000
£1142 $2100 €1667 Lady angler (35x42cm-14x17in) s. indis.i.d.1910 sanguine conte htd white buff paper. 27-Jun-4 Freeman, Philadelphia #114/R est:4000-6000
£1257 $2250 €1835 Two women in a garden (36x28cm-14x11in) pencil wash board. 26-May-4 Doyle, New York #96/R est:3000-5000
£1257 $2250 €1835 Flight into Egypt (46x69cm-18x27in) s.d.1943 W/C pencil board. 26-May-4 Doyle, New York #97/R est:3000-5000
£1304 $2400 €1904 Landscape with a figure (30x43cm-12x17in) s.d.1902 pencil paper on card. 10-Jun-4 Swann Galleries, New York #215/R est:800-1200
£1705 $3000 €2489 Nude in bed (30x36cm-12x14in) s.d.1907 conte crayon. 18-May-4 Sotheby's, New York #92/R est:3000-5000
£2023 $3500 €2954 Flight into Egypt (38x61cm-15x24in) s.d.1943 W/C. 10-Dec-3 Alderfer's, Hatfield #340/R est:5000-7000

£2273 $4000 €3319 Afternoon idyll (30x44cm-12x17in) s.d.1907 conte crayon. 18-May-4 Sotheby's, New York #99/R est:3000-5000
£2841 $5000 €4148 It was the night before Christmas (36x28cm-14x11in) W/C pair lit. 3-Jan-4 Collins, Maine #43/R est:6000-8000
£2973 $5500 €4341 Argument (18x11cm-7x4in) s.d.1908 W/C ink pencil. 11-Mar-4 Christie's, Rockefeller NY #45/R est:5000-7000
£3714 $6500 €5422 Lovers in a park. Two beauties in a park (49x79cm-19x31in) s.d.1912 conte crayon board pair. 19-Dec-3 Sotheby's, New York #1001/R est:6000-8000
£5398 $9500 €7881 Reclining nude (24x46cm-9x18in) s.d.1907 conte crayon. 18-May-4 Sotheby's, New York #91/R est:3000-5000
£6630 $12000 €9680 Magician (15x20cm-6x8in) s.d.1907 chl board exhib. 31-Mar-4 Sotheby's, New York #1/R est:8000-12000
£11364 $20000 €16591 Into the bath (29x30cm-11x12in) s.d.1906 pastel htd white. 18-May-4 Sotheby's, New York #94/R est:6000-8000
£14857 $26000 €21691 By the fire (34x27cm-13x11in) s.d.1906 chl. 19-Dec-3 Sotheby's, New York #1003/R est:1500-2500
£21802 $37500 €31831 Evicted (69x96cm-27x38in) s.d.1913 chl board. 3-Dec-3 Sotheby's, New York #44/R est:40000-60000
£60694 $105000 €88613 Backstage at the start of Act III (30x52cm-12x20in) s.d.1906 pencil W/C chl paper board prov. 10-Dec-3 Bonhams & Butterfields, San Francisco #6056/R est:20000-30000

SHINN, Everett (attrib) (1876-1953) American
Works on paper
£636 $1100 €929 Garden landscape with figures of nude and partialy draped women (36x23cm-14x9in) s. W/C. 10-Dec-3 Alderfer's, Hatfield #342/R est:800-1200
£1590 $2750 €2321 Genre painting of costumed figures watching a dwarf (46x33cm-18x13in) i.verso W/C. 10-Dec-3 Alderfer's, Hatfield #341/R est:3000-4000
£1590 $2750 €2321 Two woodsmen with infant in the snow (46x33cm-18x13in) W/C. 10-Dec-3 Alderfer's, Hatfield #342a/R est:3000-4000

SHINNORS, John (1950-) Irish
£4895 $8322 €7000 Dolmens, Co. Clare (51x52cm-20x20in) s.d.77 board. 25-Nov-3 De Veres Art Auctions, Dublin #171 est:6000-9000
£7394 $11831 €10500 Kites and cliff (21x23cm-8x9in) s. s.i.d.1986 verso board prov. 16-Sep-3 Whyte's, Dublin #51/R est:6000-8000
£7692 $13077 €11000 Female still life calendar, April (61x61cm-24x24in) s. exhib. 18-Nov-3 Whyte's, Dublin #84/R est:10000-15000
£8451 $13521 €12000 Dance (38x51cm-15x20in) s. oil crayon board prov. 16-Sep-3 Whyte's, Dublin #50/R est:10000-12000

SHINODA, Morio (1931-) Japanese
Sculpture
£815 $1500 €1190 Front back (28x38x43cm-11x15x17in) init.d.1967 machined steel wire prov. 28-Mar-4 Wright, Chicago #579/R est:1000-1500

SHINODA, Toko (1913-) Japanese
£3352 $6000 €4894 Abstract (130x97cm-51x38in) s. 14-May-4 Du Mouchelle, Detroit #2285/R est:6000-8000

SHINSAI, Ryuryukyo (fl.1789-1820) Japanese
Prints
£3400 $6256 €4964 Still life of three horsemackerel (19x52cm-7x20in) s.i. print exec. early 1810's. 8-Jun-4 Sotheby's, London #442/R est:1000-1500

SHIPSIDES, Frank (1908-) British
Works on paper
£330 $535 €482 The Royal yacht, Victoria and Albert, July 9th 1908 (37x27cm-15x11in) s.d.1981 W/C. 27-Jan-3 Bristol Auction Rooms #523
£500 $850 €730 Welsh back, Bristol, early morning, Princes Street swing bridge (24x36cm-9x14in) s.i. W/C pair. 4-Nov-3 Bristol Auction Rooms #571

SHIRAGA, Kazuo (1924-) Japanese
£22819 $40389 €34000 Chimanesei Gyokuhankan (162x131cm-64x52in) s.i.d.1961 verso. 28-Apr-4 Artcurial Briest, Paris #272/R est:20000-25000
£23611 $38958 €34000 Chizosei shomenko (162x130cm-64x51in) s.d.1961 prov.exhib. 2-Jul-3 Cornette de St.Cyr, Paris #26/R est:35000-40000

SHIRAISHI, Yuko (1956-) British/Japanese
£1245 $2204 €1818 Field painted - 48 (51x46cm-20x18in) s.d.1989 verso. 27-Apr-4 AB Stockholms Auktionsverk #1094/R est:12000-15000 (S.KR 17000)
Prints
£733 $1297 €1070 Green sandwich (91x81cm-36x32in) s.d.1991. 27-Apr-4 AB Stockholms Auktionsverk #1140/R (S.KR 10000)

SHIRLOW, Florence (1903-1987) Australian
£287 $453 €419 Footballers (61x91cm-24x36in) s.d.1972 board prov. 2-Sep-3 Deutscher-Menzies, Melbourne #323/R (A.D 700)

SHIRREFF, Charles (c.1750-?) British
Miniatures
£1200 $2208 €1752 Officer, of the Calcutta Volunteer Cavalry (7cm-3in) s.d.1799 verso. 24-Jun-4 Bonhams, New Bond Street #73/R est:800-1200
£1300 $2340 €1898 Gentleman wearing a dark coat (6cm-2in) mono.verso pearl enamel gold fausse-montre frame oval exhib. 22-Apr-4 Bonhams, New Bond Street #61/R est:1200-1800
£1600 $2880 €2336 Miss Lydia White (6cm-2in) mono.verso gold frame oval exhib.lit. 22-Apr-4 Bonhams, New Bond Street #58/R est:1500-2000

SHIRREFFS, John (fl.1890-1898) British
Works on paper
£300 $516 €438 Domestic economy, cottage interior with seated figures of an elderly woman with her cat (36x25cm-14x10in) s. W/C prov. 2-Dec-3 Canterbury Auctions, UK #183
£360 $619 €526 Hesitation, cottage interior with seated figure of a woman darning a sock (36x25cm-14x10in) s. prov. 2-Dec-3 Canterbury Auctions, UK #184/R

SHISHKIN, Ivan Ivanovich (1832-1898) Russian
£8621 $14397 €12500 Paysage fluvial au crepuscule (48x55cm-19x22in) s.d. 17-Nov-3 Claude Boisgirard, Paris #10/R est:7000-8000
£11000 $18700 €16500 Pool in a forest (35x31cm-14x12in) init. canvas on board. 25-Nov-3 Christie's, London #152/R est:6000-8000
£16000 $27200 €24000 Wooded landscape (44x24cm-17x9in) s.d.1867 canvas on board. 25-Nov-3 Christie's, London #151/R est:8000-12000
£26000 $44200 €39000 Study of summer in Belovezh Forest (43x56cm-17x22in) s.i.d.1892. 25-Nov-3 Christie's, London #153/R est:10000-15000
£80000 $136000 €120000 Study of woodland glade in summer (30x57cm-12x22in) s.d.1870 paper on cardboard exhib. 25-Nov-3 Christie's, London #141/R est:35000-45000
Works on paper
£12195 $21829 €17805 Edge of the forest (27x38cm-11x15in) s.d.1877 mixed media. 28-May-4 Uppsala Auktionskammare, Uppsala #164/R est:15000-18000 (S.KR 165000)

SHISHKIN, Ivan Ivanovich (after) (1832-1898) Russian
£10000 $17900 €14600 Forest (183x130cm-72x51in) bears sig. 26-May-4 Sotheby's, London #41 est:5000-7000

SHISHKIN, Ivan Ivanovich (attrib) (1832-1898) Russian
£810 $1295 €1175 Dark wood (22x17cm-9x7in) bears sig.d.84 board. 15-May-3 Stuker, Bern #117 est:2500-3000 (S.FR 1700)
£1322 $2247 €1930 Sunlit stream in trees (56x36cm-22x14in) mono. 5-Nov-3 Dobiaschofsky, Bern #966/R est:3500 (S.FR 3000)
£2400 $4416 €3504 Forest scene (48x34cm-19x13in) board. 25-Mar-4 Christie's, Kensington #188/R est:1200-1800

SHITAO (1642-1707) Chinese
Works on paper
£19915 $35846 €29076 Scenes of Gucheng River (33x55cm-13x22in) s.i. ink col hanging scroll lit. 25-Apr-4 Christie's, Hong Kong #422/R est:300000-400000 (HK.D 280000)
£99573 $179232 €145377 Landscapes (24x18cm-9x7in) d.1695 one s. nine i. ink leaves ten album. 25-Apr-4 Christie's, Hong Kong #435/R est:1200000-1500000 (HK.D 1400000)
£393822 $657683 €574980 Listening to the sound of waterfall (223x76cm-88x30in) s.i.d.1684 ink col hanging scroll prov. 27-Oct-3 Sotheby's, Hong Kong #324/R (HK.D 5100000)

SHODO SAKU (19th C) Japanese
Sculpture
£1370 $2329 €2000 Old peasant (37cm-15in) i. bronze. 8-Nov-3 Dr Fritz Nagel, Stuttgart #1873a/R est:2300

SHOKLER, Harry (1896-1978) American
Works on paper
£1304 $2400 €1904 Wonder wheel (15x20cm-6x8in) s.i. pencil exec. c.1940. 10-Jun-4 Swann Galleries, New York #216/R est:1800-2200

SHOKO (19th C) Japanese
Sculpture
£1644 $2795 €2400 Samurai (28cm-11in) s. bronze. 8-Nov-3 Dr Fritz Nagel, Stuttgart #1836/R est:2200

SHOKOSAI, Hanbei (fl.1795-1809) Japanese
Prints
£2200 $4048 €3212 Arashi Kichisaburo II as Tsukushi Gonroku (30x14cm-12x6in) s. print lit. 8-Jun-4 Sotheby's, London #341/R est:1000-1500

SHOLOKHOV, B A (1919-) Russian
£223 $400 €326 Marina's portrait (75x50cm-30x20in) cardboard painted 1964. 29-May-4 Shishkin Gallery, Moscow #51/R
£223 $400 €326 Sketch for school choir (32x26cm-13x10in) cardboard painted 1950's. 29-May-4 Shishkin Gallery, Moscow #52/R
£447 $800 €653 School choir (80x100cm-31x39in) painted 1950's. 29-May-4 Shishkin Gallery, Moscow #50/R

SHOLOKHOV, P I (1899-1989) Russian
£444 $800 €648 Old houses, Borisoglebsk (25x29cm-10x11in) oil on cardboard. 24-Apr-4 Shishkin Gallery, Moscow #12/R
£447 $800 €653 Sketch of a house on a grey day (31x43cm-12x17in) painted 1930's. 29-May-4 Shishkin Gallery, Moscow #19/R
£447 $800 €653 Evening (21x30cm-8x12in) cardboard painted 1930's. 29-May-4 Shishkin Gallery, Moscow #21/R
£559 $1000 €816 House at sunset (26x35cm-10x14in) painted 1930's. 29-May-4 Shishkin Gallery, Moscow #18/R
£615 $1100 €898 Sketch with a house (31x34cm-12x13in) painted 1930's. 29-May-4 Shishkin Gallery, Moscow #20/R
£667 $1200 €974 Houses at the sunset (22x27cm-9x11in) oil on cardboard. 24-Apr-4 Shishkin Gallery, Moscow #14/R est:1500-1800
£833 $1500 €1216 House in Borisoglebsk (26x31cm-10x12in) oil on cardboard. 24-Apr-4 Shishkin Gallery, Moscow #15/R est:2000-3000
£889 $1600 €1298 Landscape with the red gates (25x29cm-10x11in) oil cardboard sketch. 24-Apr-4 Shishkin Gallery, Moscow #13/R est:2000-3000

SHONBORN, John Lewis (1852-1931) Hungarian
£1056 $1827 €1500 Cavalier de fantasia (44x37cm-17x15in) s. 15-Dec-3 Gros & Delettrez, Paris #88/R est:1500-2000

£1972 $3411 €2800 Chevaux au campement (73x92cm-29x36in) bears sig. 15-Dec-3 Gros & Delettrez, Paris #89/R est:2500-3500
£2482 $4145 €3500 Jeune fille a la riviere (38x55cm-15x22in) s. 16-Jun-3 Gros & Delettrez, Paris #192/R est:3800-4500

SHONIBARE, Yinka (1962-) British
£2000 $3340 €2920 Untitled (69cm-27in circular) acrylic emulsion textile prov. 22-Oct-3 Christie's, London #129/R est:4000-6000

SHOPE, Irvin (1900-1977) American
£284 $475 €415 Hero cowboy lassos the bad guy with gun in fall gallop (51x64cm-20x25in) mono. 27-Oct-3 O'Gallerie, Oregon #162/R

SHOPEN, Kenneth (1902-1967) American
£349 $600 €510 Green fields, Vermont (46x61cm-18x24in) s.d.1944 i.verso board. 7-Dec-3 Treadway Gallery, Cincinnati #700/R
Works on paper
£398 $700 €581 Positions (33x48cm-13x19in) s.d.1964 i.verso ink prov. 23-May-4 Treadway Gallery, Cincinnati #754/R

SHOR, Zvi (1898-1979) Israeli
£601 $1100 €877 Still life (56x46cm-22x18in) s. 1-Feb-4 Ben-Ami, Tel Aviv #4387/R
£820 $1500 €1197 Street scene (65x50cm-26x20in) prov. 1-Jun-4 Ben-Ami, Tel Aviv #4867/R est:2000-3000

SHORE, Arnold Joseph Victor (1897-1963) Australian
£621 $968 €900 Afternoon, Wattle Lodge (59x49cm-23x19in) s.d.37 s.i.verso. 1-Aug-2 Joel, Victoria #175 est:1000-2000 (A.D 1800)
£1653 $2810 €2413 Bush forms (38x29cm-15x11in) s.d.46 canvas on board. 29-Oct-3 Lawson Menzies, Sydney #108/R est:4000-6000 (A.D 4000)

SHORE, Jack (?) ?
£380 $646 €555 Still life of objects on a table top (73x53cm-29x21in) s. board. 29-Oct-3 Bonhams, Chester #352

SHORE, Merle (?) American
Works on paper
£686 $1200 €1002 Painting a playmate (51x31cm-20x12in) s. s.i.d.9/60 verso gouache acrylic crayon. 17-Dec-3 Christie's, Rockefeller NY #59/R

SHORE, Steven (1947-) American
Photographs
£2275 $3800 €3322 Miami Beach, Florida (35x45cm-14x18in) i.d.11/13/77 verso chromogenic col print. 17-Oct-3 Phillips, New York #195/R est:2500-3500
£2378 $4042 €3400 21st St and Spruce St, Philadelphia, Pennsylvania, 6/12/74 (20x25cm-8x10in) s.i.d. verso col photo. 27-Nov-3 Villa Grisebach, Berlin #1398/R est:1500-1800
£2667 $4907 €4000 Holden St, North Adams, MA 7/13/74 (20x25cm-8x10in) s.i.d. verso col photo. 10-Jun-4 Villa Grisebach, Berlin #1283/R est:1500-2000
£5090 $8500 €7431 Merced River, Yosemite Park, California (101x127cm-40x50in) num.3 chromogenic col print exec.1979 one of eight prov. 17-Oct-3 Phillips, New York #2/R est:8000-10000
£16216 $29027 €24000 Portfolio (25x20cm-10x8in) s.i. verso col photos 12. 8-May-4 Lempertz, Koln #367/R est:14000-16000

SHORT, Frederick Golden (1863-1936) British
£260 $478 €380 Beech trees in a glade (15x20cm-6x8in) s.d.1934 board. 14-Jun-4 Bonhams, Bath #84
£280 $465 €409 Trees in a forest (21x28cm-8x11in) s.d.1932 board. 1-Oct-3 Woolley & Wallis, Salisbury #284/R
£300 $498 €438 Trees in a forest (26x36cm-10x14in) board. 1-Oct-3 Woolley & Wallis, Salisbury #285/R
£300 $549 €438 Moorland landscape (31x46cm-12x18in) s.d.1914. 7-Apr-4 Bonhams, Bury St Edmunds #434
£300 $549 €438 Woodland scene (35x46cm-14x18in) s.d.1919. 7-Apr-4 Bonhams, Bury St Edmunds #441
£320 $589 €467 Sunny glade (15x21cm-6x8in) s.d.1935 board. 14-Jun-4 Bonhams, Bath #80
£325 $530 €475 Welsh mountainscape (18x28cm-7x11in) s.i. 27-Sep-3 Rogers Jones, Clwyd #97
£340 $626 €496 Woodland pond (15x20cm-6x8in) s.d.1935 board. 14-Jun-4 Bonhams, Bath #83
£350 $630 €511 Garden terrace (27x51cm-11x20in) s.d.1906. 22-Apr-4 Mellors & Kirk, Nottingham #1067/R
£350 $641 €511 New Forest heathland (21x29cm-8x11in) s. 7-Apr-4 Woolley & Wallis, Salisbury #185/R
£350 $641 €511 Rural landscape (21x29cm-8x11in) s. board. 7-Apr-4 Woolley & Wallis, Salisbury #186/R
£350 $644 €511 Stream through a beech wood (15x20cm-6x8in) s.d.1834 board. 14-Jun-4 Bonhams, Bath #81
£360 $601 €526 Pittenweem, Fifeshire, fishing boat at the quay (20x15cm-8x6in) s.d.1903 board. 20-Oct-3 Bonhams, Bath #126
£360 $637 €526 Forest scene in summer (27x37cm-11x15in) s. indis d. board. 28-Apr-4 George Kidner, Lymington #216/R
£360 $662 €526 Distant view from the woods (15x20cm-6x8in) s.d.1935 board. 14-Jun-4 Bonhams, Bath #82
£420 $697 €613 Tree in a forest (20x14cm-8x6in) s. board. 1-Oct-3 Woolley & Wallis, Salisbury #283/R
£500 $900 €730 Lady resting in an arboretum (75x55cm-30x22in) s.d.1908. 22-Apr-4 Mellors & Kirk, Nottingham #1066
£550 $913 €803 Stream in a forest (21x29cm-8x11in) s. board. 1-Oct-3 Woolley & Wallis, Salisbury #281/R
£650 $1079 €949 Forest clearing (22x38cm-9x15in) s. 1-Oct-3 Woolley & Wallis, Salisbury #286/R
£650 $1079 €949 River landscape with a hay cart (27x53cm-11x21in) s.d.95. 1-Oct-3 Woolley & Wallis, Salisbury #287/R
£700 $1190 €1022 Hampshire heathland (23x29cm-9x11in) canvasboard sold with another by the same hand. 26-Nov-3 Hamptons Fine Art, Godalming #171
£900 $1593 €1314 Forest scene, in autumn (51x76cm-20x30in) s. 28-Apr-4 George Kidner, Lymington #215

SHORT, George Anderson (1856-1945) British
Works on paper
£250 $425 €365 Hounds in pursuit of a hare with figures nearby (25x35cm-10x14in) s. pencil W/C. 19-Nov-3 Tennants, Leyburn #907

SHORT, Obadiah (1803-1886) British
£600 $1032 €876 Norfolk wooded landscape with horse watering at a stream (28x38cm-11x15in) prov. 5-Dec-3 Keys, Aylsham #590/R

SHORT, Richard (1841-1916) British
£380 $646 €555 Porthcawl, a gale (35x61cm-14x24in) s. i.d.1904 verso. 19-Nov-3 Tennants, Leyburn #1043
£4500 $7515 €6570 Istanbul from the Bosphorus (43x71cm-17x28in) s. 14-Oct-3 Sotheby's, London #10/R est:5000-7000

SHORT, Sir Frank (1857-1945) British
Works on paper
£260 $450 €380 Newhaven Head from Splash Point, Seaford (23x33cm-9x13in) s.d.1925 W/C. 12-Dec-3 Halls, Shrewsbury #625
£440 $757 €642 Pegwell Bay (28x43cm-11x17in) s. W/C. 2-Dec-3 Gorringes, Lewes #2395/R

SHORT, William (19/20th C) Australian
£1600 $2864 €2336 Portrait of a greyhound (25x30cm-10x12in) s. s.i.verso. 22-Mar-4 Bonhams & Brooks, Norfolk #242/R est:200-300

SHORT, William (jnr) (1875-1947) Australian
£2024 $3259 €2955 Evening on the Olinda track. Working on the Olinda track (79x56cm-31x22in) s.d.1894 pair. 13-Oct-3 Joel, Victoria #363/R est:3000-5000 (A.D 5000)

SHORT, William (snr-attrib) (1833-1917) Australian/British
£324 $521 €473 Lovers path in the great divide (19x29cm-7x11in) board. 13-Oct-3 Joel, Victoria #398 (A.D 800)

SHORTHOUSE, Arthur Charles (1870-1953) British
Works on paper
£300 $561 €438 Jolly Sailor Inn, Looe (43x54cm-17x21in) s.i.d.7.7.27 W/C. 24-Feb-4 Bonhams, Knowle #39
£420 $773 €613 Fragrant rose (45x38cm-18x15in) s. W/C. 23-Mar-4 Bonhams, Knightsbridge #36/R

SHOWALTER, C E (20th C) American?
£2044 $3700 €3066 Mallets (91x122cm-36x48in) 16-Apr-4 American Auctioneer #372/R est:3000-4500

SHPOLANSKY, Grigory Jefimowitsch (1899-1980) Russian
£2198 $4000 €3209 Maxim Gorky and theater group (160x132cm-63x52in) s. 7-Feb-4 Sloans & Kenyon, Bethesda #1267/R est:4000-6000

SHRADER, Edwin Roscoe (1879-1960) American
£1984 $3750 €2897 California landscape (51x66cm-20x26in) s. 17-Feb-4 John Moran, Pasadena #32/R est:2500-3500

SHRAND, Dr Hyman (?) American
£307 $500 €448 Provincetown carnival (122x58cm-48x23in) s. acrylic. 19-Jul-3 Outer Cape Auctions, Provincetown #121/R

SHROPSHIRE, George E (20th C) American
£442 $800 €645 New England countryside (20x25cm-8x10in) canvasboard pair. 3-Apr-4 Neal Auction Company, New Orleans #415/R

SHRUBSOLE, Sarah (19th C) British
Works on paper
£1008 $1855 €1472 Florinda (60x84cm-24x33in) s.d.1863 W/C exhib. 14-Jun-4 Waddingtons, Toronto #95/R est:2500-3000 (C.D 2500)

SHUCHO, Tamagawa (fl.1790-1803) Japanese
Prints
£6400 $11776 €9344 Spring (38x25cm-15x10in) s. print lit. 8-Jun-4 Sotheby's, London #267/R est:3000-5000

SHUERMANS, Elie (1896-1974) Belgian
£4196 $7133 €6000 Pheasants in landscape (138x225cm-54x89in) s. on glass. 26-Nov-3 Christie's, Paris #26/R est:6000-8000

SHUFELT, Robert (1935-) American
Works on paper
£294 $500 €429 Calf roping (18x28cm-7x11in) init. chl prov. 1-Nov-3 Santa Fe Art, Santa Fe #252/R
£324 $550 €473 Cowboy watching the herd (18x28cm-7x11in) init. chl prov. 1-Nov-3 Santa Fe Art, Santa Fe #253/R

£5080 $9500 €7417 Ropin off a horse (51x69cm-20x27in) s. pencil. 24-Jul-4 Coeur d'Alene, Hayden #189/R est:8000-12000

SHUKHAEV, Vasili (1887-1973) Russian
£48000 $85920 €70080 Picnic in cassis (60x100cm-24x39in) prov. 26-May-4 Sotheby's, London #135/R est:20000-30000
Works on paper
£1198 $2000 €1749 Standing nude (61x44cm-24x17in) s.d.1964 red chl. 21-Oct-3 Christie's, Rockefeller NY #101 est:2000-3000

SHULTSE, R (19th C) French?
£1208 $2138 €1800 Mountainous landscape (65x97cm-26x38in) s. 30-Apr-4 Tajan, Paris #113 est:1800-2000

SHULZ, Adolph Robert (1869-1963) American
£259 $425 €376 Autumn landscape (6x10cm-2x4in) canvas on board painted c.1910 prov. 7-Jun-3 Treadway Gallery, Cincinnati #1421

SHUNCHO, Yushido (fl.1770-1790) Japanese
Prints
£3000 $5520 €4380 Portrait of the strong boy Kintoki (68x11cm-27x4in) s. print exec. mid 1790's. 8-Jun-4 Sotheby's, London #259/R est:750-1000
£4200 $7728 €6132 An actor off stage with two women (32x22cm-13x9in) s. print exec. c.1789 prov. 8-Jun-4 Sotheby's, London #260/R est:4200-4800
£4545 $7727 €6500 Averse (38x25cm-15x10in) s. col print triptych lit. 25-Nov-3 Sotheby's, Paris #123/R est:7500-8500

SHUNEI, Katsukawa (c.1762-1819) Japanese
Prints
£2200 $4048 €3212 Ichikawa Yaozo III (34x22cm-13x9in) s. print exec. c.1794. 8-Jun-4 Sotheby's, London #178/R est:2200-2800
£3200 $5888 €4672 Actor Sawamura Sojuro III (36x24cm-14x9in) s. print exec. c.1791. 8-Jun-4 Sotheby's, London #176/R est:2200-2800

SHUNGYO, Katsukawa (fl.1789-1843) Japanese
Works on paper
£10870 $20000 €15870 Beauty holding a pipe (92x29cm-36x11in) s. col ink hanging scroll. 23-Mar-4 Christie's, Rockefeller NY #120/R est:10000-15000

SHUNMAN, Kubo (1757-1820) Japanese
Prints
£6800 $12512 €9928 Kinuta No Tamagawa in Mishima province (38x25cm-15x10in) s. print one sheet from a hexaptych exec. early 1790's lit. 8-Jun-4 Sotheby's, London #272/R est:3000-4000

SHUNSEN, Katsukawa Seijiro (c.1762-1830) Japanese
Prints
£2500 $4600 €3650 Two ladies beside a mosquito net (38x26cm-15x10in) s. print exec. c.1811. 8-Jun-4 Sotheby's, London #265/R est:2500-3500

SHUNSHO, Katsukawa (1726-1792) Japanese
Prints
£2000 $3680 €2920 Otani Hiroji III as Onio (31x15cm-12x6in) s. print exec. 1770 prov. 8-Jun-4 Sotheby's, London #162/R est:2000-3000
£2000 $3680 €2920 Nakamura Nakazo I as Mikawaya Giheiji and Nakamura Sukegoro II as Danshichi Kurobei (28x21cm 11x8in) s. print exec. 1768 prov.lit. 8-Jun-4 Sotheby's, London #159/R est:2000-2500
£2000 $3680 €2920 View of enjoying the cool of the evening breeze at Ryogoku Bridge (54x40cm-21x16in) s. print exec. c.1770. 8-Jun-4 Sotheby's, London #168/R est:2000-2500
£2200 $4048 €3212 Matsumoto Koshiro III as Shichibyoe (30x14cm-12x6in) s. print exec. 1771. 8-Jun-4 Sotheby's, London #164/R est:1000-1500
£3000 $5520 €4380 Ichikawa Danzo III as Fuwa Banzaemon (29x14cm-11x6in) s. print exec. 1768 prov.lit. 8-Jun-4 Sotheby's, London #155/R est:1200-1500

SHURTLEFF, Roswell Morse (1838-1915) American
£270 $500 €394 Landscape with cows (51x41cm-20x16in) s. 18-Jul-4 William Jenack, New York #381
£447 $800 €653 Keene valley. Woodland interior, Keene valley (20x25cm-8x10in) one s.i.d.1901 one panel pair. 26-May-4 Doyle, New York #43/R
£1136 $2000 €1659 Landscape of a woodland scene (28x38cm-11x15in) s. 3-Jan-4 Cobbs, Peterborough #189/R
£3429 $6000 €5006 New York view (41x51cm-16x20in) s. 19-Dec-3 Sotheby's, New York #1071/R est:4000-6000
Works on paper
£238 $450 €347 Autumn woodland riverbank scene (20x38cm-8x15in) s. W/C gouache. 22-Feb-4 Skinner, Boston #543/R

SHUSTER, William Howard (1893-1969) American
£4706 $8000 €6871 Hyde Park picnic (61x46cm-24x18in) s. s.i.verso canvas on board prov.lit. 1-Nov-3 Santa Fe Art, Santa Fe #200/R est:12000-15000

SHUTE, Ruth W and Samuel A (19th C) American
Works on paper
£14865 $27500 €21703 Portrait of Miss Adeline Bartlett of Lowell Massachusetts (13x12cm-5x5in) W/C pencil executed c.1830 prov.lit. 16-Jan-4 Sotheby's, New York #27/R est:10000-15000
£43243 $80000 €63135 Portrait of Miss Adeline Bartlett holding a letter (73x63cm-29x25in) W/C pencil ink executed c.1832 prov.exhib.lit. 16-Jan-4 Sotheby's, New York #26/R est:40000-60000

SHUTE, Samuel Addison (1803-1836) American
Works on paper
£18919 $35000 €27622 Portrait of a young lady wearing striped belt (71x56cm-28x22in) W/C pencil gouache executed c.1835 prov.exhib.lit. 16-Jan-4 Sotheby's, New York #28/R est:30000-50000

SHVEDOV, Ivan Alexandrovich (1917-1996) Russian
£400 $704 €584 Game of cards on the beach (34x47cm-13x19in) s. board. 18-May-4 Bonhams, Knightsbridge #106/R

SIAN, Fernand (19th C) Belgian
Sculpture
£1074 $1987 €1600 Trois enfants surpris par un crabe (35cm-14in) s. terracotta. 15-Mar-4 Horta, Bruxelles #378 est:800-1200
£3158 $5716 €4800 Deux amours (59x50cm-23x20in) s. terracotta. 19-Apr-4 Horta, Bruxelles #59/R est:6000-8000

SIAUW TIK KWIE (1913-1988) Javanese
£2174 $3370 €3174 Orchids (65x55cm-26x22in) s.d.83. 6-Oct-2 Sotheby's, Singapore #168/R est:4000-6000 (S.D 6000)

SIBBONS, Gudron (20th C) ?
£250 $455 €365 Brining in the sheaves (39x50cm-15x20in) s. 4-Jul-4 Lots Road Auctions, London #359
£360 $662 €526 Low tide (41x50cm-16x20in) s. panel. 23-Jun-4 Bonhams, Bury St Edmunds #361/R
£380 $673 €555 Cathedral view with figures to the foreground (29x39cm-11x15in) s. board. 28-Apr-4 George Kidner, Lymington #223/R
£480 $878 €701 Harvest time, Holland (30x41cm-12x16in) s. board. 7-Apr-4 Bonhams, Bury St Edmunds #452/R
£520 $962 €759 Loading a hay barge (40x50cm-16x20in) s. 16-Feb-4 Bonhams, Bath #104
£600 $1098 €876 Twilight Dutch landscape with windmill (30x41cm-12x16in) s. board pair. 7-Apr-4 Bonhams, Bury St Edmunds #454
£635 $1200 €927 Genre scenes with figures (41x51cm-16x20in) s. masonite pair. 21-Feb-4 Jeffery Burchard, Florida #56/R
£680 $1244 €993 Unloading the catch, Holland (41x51cm-16x20in) s. board. 7-Apr-4 Bonhams, Bury St Edmunds #453
£860 $1565 €1256 Coastal scene, fishermen loading at low tide (28x38cm-11x15in) s. board. 15-Jun-4 Bonhams, Leeds #129
£980 $1803 €1431 Horses crossing the river (30x40cm-12x16in) s. board pair. 23-Jun-4 Bonhams, Bury St Edmunds #362/R

SIBERDT, Eugène (1851-1931) Belgian
£270 $484 €400 Ramasseuse de bois (37x23cm-15x9in) painted 1891. 10-May-4 Amberes, Antwerp #321
£552 $1021 €800 Joueuse de tambourin (26x17cm-10x7in) s. panel. 16-Feb-4 Horta, Bruxelles #22
£552 $1021 €800 La marchande de fruits (27x17cm-11x7in) s. panel. 16-Feb-4 Horta, Bruxelles #23
£1399 $2378 €2000 Le cabinet de travail de Christophe Plantin Moretus a Anvers (61x40cm-24x16in) s.i.d.1880 panel. 18-Nov-3 Vanderkindere, Brussels #37 est:1250-1750
£2958 $5117 €4200 Portrait of a gentleman. Portrait of a lady (73x58cm-29x23in) s.i.d.1882 panel pair. 10-Dec-3 Christie's, Amsterdam #179/R est:2500-3500
£3716 $6652 €5500 Ramasseuse de bois (116x85cm-46x33in) 10-May-4 Amberes, Antwerp #322/R
£13000 $20800 €18850 Les Jojaux d'un Harem (134x103cm-53x41in) s.d.1921. 18-Sep-3 Christie's, Kensington #209/R est:8000-12000

SIBERECHTS, J (1627-1703) Flemish
£1379 $2552 €2000 La traie des vaches (58x78cm-23x31in) s. 16-Feb-4 Horta, Bruxelles #85 est:2500-2600

SIBERECHTS, Jan (1627-1703) Flemish
£13889 $25000 €20278 Figures with cart and horses fording stream (97x112cm-38x44in) mono. prov. 22-Jan-4 Sotheby's, New York #4/R est:30000-50000
£18000 $32400 €26280 Departure for the market (161x219cm-63x86in) s.d.1661. 21-Apr-4 Christie's, London #27/R est:18000-25000

SIBERECHTS, Jan (attrib) (1627-1703) Flemish
£1250 $2000 €1825 Pastoral scene (56x51cm-22x20in) 20-Sep-3 Bunte, Elgin #1424 est:6000-8000

SIBIYA, Lucky (1942-1999) South African
Sculpture
£1681 $3042 €2454 African figures (91x122cm-36x48in) s. carved wood. 30-Mar-4 Stephan Welz, Johannesburg #516/R est:14000-18000 (SA.R 20000)

SIBLEY, Andrew (1933-) Australian
£407 $638 €590 Untitled (67x105cm-26x41in) s.d.62 board. 27-Aug-3 Christie's, Sydney #713 (A.D 1000)
£426 $736 €622 Homage to Lorca (76x84cm-30x33in) i.verso prov. 10-Dec-3 Shapiro, Sydney #97 (A.D 1000)
£511 $883 €746 Hotel Mt Garnet (61x86cm-24x34in) s.d.61 i.verso board. 10-Dec-3 Shapiro, Sydney #83 (A.D 1200)
£1033 $1756 €1508 Lady of the cello. board. 29-Oct-3 Lawson Menzies, Sydney #129/R est:4000-6000 (A.D 2500)

£2273 $4022 €3319 All's well in the zoo (91x98cm-36x39in) s.d.2000 acrylic. 3-May-4 Christie's, Melbourne #225/R est:5000-8000 (A.D 5500)
Works on paper
£331 $612 €483 Two figures (74x54cm-29x21in) s.i.d.89 W/C ink. 10-Mar-4 Deutscher-Menzies, Melbourne #596 (A.D 800)
£638 $1085 €931 Tight rope (74x55cm-29x22in) W/C ink prov. 26-Nov-3 Deutscher-Menzies, Melbourne #134/R est:800-1200 (A.D 1500)
£744 $1376 €1086 Alice in the looking glass (72x45cm-28x18in) s.i.d.90 col ink prov. 15-Mar-4 Sotheby's, Melbourne #82 est:1000-1500 (A.D 1800)

SIBURNEY, Alex (20th C) ?
£1172 $1958 €1700 State sign Georgia. State sign Florida. State sign North Carolina (50x50cm-20x20in) s.i.d.1973 verso acrylic cardboard set of 3 exhib. 13-Nov-3 Finarte Semenzato, Rome #435/R est:1800-2200

SICARD, Francois Léon (1862-1934) French
Sculpture
£7000 $12810 €10220 Winged victory (91cm-36in) s.st.f.Thiebaut pat bronze. 9-Jul-4 Sotheby's, London #144/R est:6000-8000
£8276 $13738 €12000 Saint Michel terrassant le dragon (115cm-45in) s. brown pat bronze. 2-Oct-3 Sotheby's, Paris #18/R est:18000
£11858 $21225 €17313 Oedipe Vainqueur du Sphinx (65cm-26in) s. st.f Barbedienne bronze prov. 15-May-4 Christie's, Sydney #116/R est:30000-40000 (A.D 30000)

SICARD, Pierre (1900-1980) French
£220 $350 €321 Fruit (41x61cm-16x24in) s. 10-Sep-3 Alderfer's, Hatfield #299
£559 $951 €800 L'Indonesie (73x60cm-29x24in) s. 23-Nov-3 Cornette de St.Cyr, Paris #626

SICARDI, Louis Marie (1746-1825) French
£2000 $3400 €2920 Entrevue de Tilsitt (19x14cm-7x6in) s. ivory panel. 31-Oct-3 Moore Allen & Innocent, Cirencester #556/R est:2000-3000
Miniatures
£2081 $3828 €3100 Un homme de qualite en habit de Cour gris (5x4cm-2x2in) oval exec. c.1770 lit. 26-Mar-4 Pierre Berge, Paris #84/R est:600-800
£7000 $12600 €10220 Lady in a white dress and corsage (6cm-2in) s.d.1790 enamel silver gilt reverbere frame prov.exhib.lit. 22-Apr-4 Bonhams, New Bond Street #84/R est:6000-8000

SICBALDI, Adriano (1911-) Italian
£336 $594 €500 Flowers in grey background (49x34cm-19x13in) s. card on masonite. 1-May-4 Meeting Art, Vercelli #209
£374 $670 €550 Riomaggiore (57x80cm-22x31in) s.i.d.1956 cardboard exhib.lit. 22-Mar-4 Sant Agostino, Torino #535/R
£867 $1595 €1300 Santa Margherita Ligure (53x78cm-21x31in) s.d.1958 card. 14-Jun-4 Sant Agostino, Torino #177/R

SICHEL, Ernest Leopold (1862-1941) British
£280 $456 €406 Portrait of a gentleman wearing a grey suit, reading a newspaper (223x128cm-88x50in) s. 17-Jul-3 Tennants, Leyburn #802
Works on paper
£2300 $4255 €3358 A pool in the world (30x39cm-12x15in) s. pastel. 16-Feb-4 Bonhams, Bath #69 est:100-200

SICHEL, Nathaniel (1843-1907) German
£2657 $4517 €3800 Portrait of Oriental woman (74x52cm-29x20in) s. 20-Nov-3 Van Ham, Cologne #1869/R est:3800

SICHEL, Pierre (1899-1983) French
£3448 $6310 €5000 Portrait de Suzy Solidor (110x60cm-43x24in) s. prov. 28-Jan-4 Piasa, Paris #18/R est:4000-4200

SICHEL, Stefano (1950-) Italian
£400 $736 €600 Untitled (100x80cm-39x31in) s. s.verso painted 2000. 12-Jun-4 Meeting Art, Vercelli #253

SICHULSKI, Kazimierz (1879-1942) Polish
Works on paper
£1362 $2356 €1989 Portrait of a man wearing a costume (76x55cm-30x22in) pastel W/C cardboard exec. c.1905. 14-Dec-3 Agra, Warsaw #12/R est:9000 (P.Z 9000)
£2118 $3664 €3092 Solitary fir tree (97x61cm-38x24in) s.d.07 pastel cardboard. 14-Dec-3 Agra, Warsaw #32/R est:14000 (P.Z 14000)

SICILIA SOBRINO, J Alfonso (1963-) Spanish
Works on paper
£448 $749 €650 Vanity (150x200cm-59x79in) s.d.88 verso mixed media collage on canvas. 17-Nov-3 Durán, Madrid #63/R

SICILIA, Jose Maria (1954-) Spanish
£1150 $1990 €1679 Untitled (45x37cm-18x15in) s.d.85 acrylic paper. 11-Dec-3 Christie's, Kensington #250/R est:600-800
£9202 $15000 €13435 Black flower (127x81cm-50x32in) s.i.d.86 verso acrylic diptych prov. 23-Sep-3 Christie's, Rockefeller NY #155/R est:10000-15000
£11404 $20982 €16650 Lijadora azul (146x114cm-57x45in) s.i.d.1983 verso prov. 23-Jun-4 Koller, Zurich #3135/R est:8000-12000 (S.FR 26000)
£17483 $29196 €25000 Soller (240x240cm-94x94in) s.i.d.1989 verso white titanium acrylic canvas on panel prov. 11-Oct-3 Cornette de St.Cyr, Paris #20/R est:28000-32000
£21557 $36000 €31473 Pivezi Coreen (155x198cm-61x78in) painted 1985 prov. 12-Nov-3 Christie's, Rockefeller NY #606/R est:15000-20000
£25140 $45000 €36704 Flor 16 (332x190cm-131x75in) s.d.8.85 verso acrylic 2 parts prov.exhib. 13-May-4 Sotheby's, New York #443/R est:25000-35000
Works on paper
£4790 $8000 €6993 Untitled (39x34cm-15x13in) pigment paper encased in wax in five parts prov. 14-Nov-3 Phillips, New York #313/R est:10000-15000
£5000 $8350 €7300 Multi flower painting, D (30x100cm-12x39in) init.d.97 verso beeswax oil paper on board prov. 22-Oct-3 Christie's, London #118/R est:6000-8000
£7270 $11777 €10250 Aspirador (80x80cm-31x31in) s.d.83 mixed media canvas round. 20-May-3 Ansorena, Madrid #327/R est:10250

SICILIANO, Bernardo (1969-) Italian
£4930 $8627 €7000 Facory (122x152cm-48x60in) s.i.d.2000 prov. 16-Dec-3 Finarte Semenzato, Milan #222/R est:6800-7200
£5634 $9859 €8000 Sugar 4 (183x153cm-72x60in) s.i.d.1999 verso prov. 16-Dec-3 Finarte Semenzato, Milan #223/R est:7300-7700

SICKERT, Bernhard (1863-1932) British
£340 $551 €493 River scene with moored boats by jetty (38x51cm-15x20in) s.d.1920. 26-Jan-3 Desmond Judd, Cranbrook #817

SICKERT, W R (1860-1942) British
£400 $668 €584 Figures in an alley way (51x33cm-20x13in) 8-Oct-3 Andrew Hartley, Ilkley #1132

SICKERT, Walter Richard (1860-1942) British
£950 $1615 €1387 Le Vieux Colombier (38x32cm-15x13in) painted 1913 prov.exhib.lit. 21-Nov-3 Christie's, London #100/R
£3200 $5984 €4672 Cross at Chagford (23x15cm-9x6in) s.i. panel painted c.1915 panel. 26-Feb-4 Lane, Penzance #311/R est:3000-5000
£8108 $15000 €11838 Market place in Dieppe (71x91cm-28x36in) 13-Feb-4 Du Mouchelle, Detroit #2187/R est:20000-25000
£9500 $16340 €13870 Nude behind flowers (45x35cm-18x14in) s. painted c.1905-6 prov.exhib.lit. 3-Dec-3 Sotheby's, London #36/R est:10000-15000
£11000 $20020 €16060 Street scene (61x50cm-24x20in) prov. 15-Jun-4 Bonhams, New Bond Street #6/R est:12000-18000
£19000 $34770 €27740 Oeuillade (49x39cm-19x15in) s. prov.exhib.lit. 2-Jun-4 Sotheby's, London #19/R est:12000-18000
£20000 $36600 €29200 Yvonne (91x71cm-36x28in) s. painted c.1917 prov. 4-Jun-4 Christie's, London #21/R est:20000-30000
£22000 $37400 €32120 Santa Maria della Salute (25x20cm-10x8in) s. panel squared for transfer painted c.1901 prov.exhib.lit. 21-Nov-3 Christie's, London #56/R est:12000-18000
£23000 $39560 €33580 Divine Peggy - Lady Teazle (127x61cm-50x24in) s.i. prov.exhib. 3-Dec-3 Sotheby's, London #35/R est:15000-20000
£25000 $44750 €36500 Balcony (21x27cm-8x11in) s. board prov. 16-Mar-4 Bonhams, New Bond Street #16/R est:4000-6000
£32000 $54400 €46720 Rio de Mendicant, Venice (41x27cm-16x11in) s. painted c.1895-96 prov.exhib.lit. 21-Nov-3 Christie's, London #55/R est:30000-50000
Works on paper
£550 $919 €803 Old Middlesex, Drury Lane (20x29cm-8x11in) s. pencil htd white prov. 22-Oct-3 Cheffins, Cambridge #464
£650 $1118 €949 Horse and cart (21x30cm-8x12in) pencil. 3-Dec-3 Christie's, Kensington #456/R
£750 $1193 €1095 Old Middlesex (28x23cm-11x9in) init.i. pencil exhib. 10-Sep-3 Sotheby's, Olympia #120/R
£800 $1456 €1168 La Giuseppina (30x22cm-12x9in) s. pencil. 15-Jun-4 Bonhams, New Bond Street #4/R
£938 $1753 €1407 Somers Town (35x26cm-14x10in) s.i. conte prov.exhib. 20-Jul-4 Goodman, Sydney #45/R (A.D 2400)
£1300 $2236 €1898 Brighton (14x22cm-6x9in) s.i. pencil chk. 3-Dec-3 Christie's, Kensington #455/R est:800-1200
£1700 $3043 €2482 Dieppe (15x22cm-6x9in) s.i. pencil chk. 16-Mar-4 Bonhams, New Bond Street #7/R est:800-1200
£2200 $3674 €3212 Trapeze (30x11cm-12x4in) s.i. pencil. 16-Oct-3 Christie's, Kensington #228/R est:1000-1500
£3200 $5632 €4672 Middlesex cinema (24x24cm-9x9in) init.i. pen ink black white chk. 19-May-4 Sotheby's, Olympia #74/R est:800-1200

SICKERT, Walter Richard (attrib) (1860-1942) British
£291 $500 €425 Figures in a dark forest (25x20cm-10x8in) bears sig. verso. 6-Dec-3 Neal Auction Company, New Orleans #237

SIDANER, Henri le (1862-1939) French
£2683 $4750 €3917 Rue Flamande (15x20cm-6x8in) s. board painted c.1903. 2-May-4 Bonhams & Butterfields, Los Angeles #3002/R est:3000-5000
£4899 $9064 €7300 Reflets sur le canal en hiver (16x22cm-6x9in) s. panel exhib. 14-Mar-4 St-Germain-en-Laye Encheres #111/R est:7000-8000
£9375 $15656 €13594 Fisherman's daughter (45x32cm-18x13in) s.i. 17-Jun-3 Pinneys, Montreal #50 est:18000-24000 (C.D 21000)
£18156 $32500 €26508 Bruleuses d'herbes, etaples (43x55cm-17x22in) s.d.1889. 6-May-4 Sotheby's, New York #212/R est:15000-20000
£18156 $32500 €26508 Rue de l'Eglise au clair de lune, Villefranche-sur-mer (25x41cm-10x16in) s. board painted 1929 prov.exhib.lit. 6-May-4 Sotheby's, New York #270/R est:20000-30000
£25503 $45651 €38000 Le bassin (81x51cm-32x20in) s. 25-May-4 Chambelland & Giafferi, Paris #49/R est:20000-30000
£33520 $60000 €48939 Tour aux lanternes (92x72cm-36x28in) s. painted 1926 prov.exhib.lit. 6-May-4 Sotheby's, New York #268a/R est:70000-90000
£36313 $65000 €53017 Le Pont - Crepuscule (75x65cm-30x26in) s. painted 1903 prov.exhib.lit. 5-May-4 Christie's, Rockefeller NY #275/R est:40000-60000
£38235 $65000 €55823 Place sous la neige, Gerberoy (60x74cm-24x29in) s. painted 1910 prov.exhib.lit. 6-Nov-3 Sotheby's, New York #160/R est:40000-60000
£41177 $70000 €60118 Le bassin du parterre d'eau, Versailles (65x81cm-26x32in) s. prov.exhib.lit. 19-Nov-3 Bonhams & Butterfields, San Francisco #122/R est:75000-100000
£47486 $85000 €69330 Reflets, fenetres du Palais, Versailles (65x81cm-26x32in) s. painted 1917 prov.exhib.lit. 6-May-4 Sotheby's, New York #266/R est:80000-120000
£49296 $85282 €70000 Fenetre sur le ciel, Gerberoy (91x73cm-36x29in) s. exhib.lit. 12-Dec-3 Piasa, Paris #10/R est:70000-90000
£78212 $140000 €114190 L'Eveche, Chartres (66x97cm-26x38in) s. painted 1903 prov.exhib.lit. 6-May-4 Sotheby's, New York #261/R est:80000-120000
£80000 $145600 €116800 Le soir sur la maison (81x100cm-32x39in) s. painted 1925 prov.exhib.lit. 3-Feb-4 Christie's, London #151/R est:80000-120000

£80000	$147200	€116800	La chambre bleue, Villefranche-sur-Mer (46x54cm-18x21in) s. painted c.1927. 23-Jun-4 Christie's, London #190/R est:40000-60000
£85294	$145000	€124529	Matin, soleil, Venise (55x66cm-22x26in) s. painted 1917 prov.lit. 6-Nov-3 Sotheby's, New York #152/R est:80000-120000
£96026	$174768	€145000	Promenade sur un canal de Quimperle (73x60cm-29x24in) s. 18-Jun-4 Piasa, Paris #20/R est:60000-80000
£115000	$209300	€167900	Le jet d'eau (73x59cm-29x23in) s. painted 1905 prov. 3-Feb-4 Christie's, London #254/R est:120000-160000
£130000	$236600	€189800	La lanterne, gerberoy (100x81cm-39x32in) painted 1928 prov.exhib.lit. 4-Feb-4 Sotheby's, London #219/R est:140000-180000
£178771	$320000	€261006	Maison aux roses (80x100cm-31x39in) s. painted 1925 prov.lit. 6-May-4 Sotheby's, New York #246/R est:300000-400000
Works on paper			
£3911	$7000	€5710	Le portail (20x26cm-8x10in) s. pencil paper on board exec 1902 prov.exhib.lit. 5-May-4 Christie's, Rockefeller NY #102/R est:5000-7000
£4000	$6680	€5840	Le portail de la maison rose, Gerberoy (32x29cm-13x11in) s. col crayon pen ink pencil executed 1925. 21-Oct-3 Sotheby's, London #2/R est:4000-6000
£4384	$7452	€6400	Etaples (39x61cm-15x24in) s. pastel. 9-Nov-3 Eric Pillon, Calais #63/R
£6145	$11000	€8972	Facade de la maison de Gerberoy (32x23cm-13x9in) s. W/C pen ink exhib. paper on board prov. 5-May-4 Christie's, Rockefeller NY #103/R est:8000-12000
£6644	$11427	€9500	Etude pour le Dimanche (34x34cm-13x13in) s. exec.c.1898. 3-Dec-3 Tajan, Paris #4/R est:10000-15000

SIDDELL, Peter (1935-) New Zealander

£1339	$2464	€1955	Mercers Bay (22x38cm-9x15in) one s.d.1978 acrylic board sold with a sketch exhib. 25-Mar-4 International Art Centre, Auckland #29/R est:3500-4500 (NZ.D 3750)
£2500	$4600	€3650	View through a window (42x26cm-17x10in) s.d.1981 board exhib. 25-Mar-4 International Art Centre, Auckland #54/R est:6000-9000 (NZ.D 7000)
£3901	$6904	€5695	Green/white house (39x29cm-15x11in) s.d.1976 board. 28-Apr-4 Dunbar Sloane, Auckland #37/R est:15000-22000 (NZ.D 11000)
£5674	$10043	€8284	The bach (54x79cm-21x31in) s.d.1973 board. 28-Apr-4 Dunbar Sloane, Auckland #31/R est:30000-40000 (NZ.D 16000)
£9375	$14906	€13688	Brick house (52x41cm-20x16in) s.d.1991 prov. 1-May-3 Dunbar Sloane, Wellington #22/R est:12000-18000 (NZ.D 27000)
£12411	$21968	€18120	Hilltop and houses (137x98cm-54x39in) s.d.1974 board. 28-Apr-4 Dunbar Sloane, Auckland #24/R est:50000-70000 (NZ.D 35000)

SIDIBE, Malick (1935-) American

Photographs			
£1667	$3000	€2434	Nuit de noel - happy club (34x35cm-13x14in) s.i.d.2003 i.verso gelatin silver print prov. 23-Apr-4 Phillips, New York #18/R est:2000-3000
£2238	$3849	€3200	Yokoro (47x41cm-19x16in) s.i.d.1970/1999 silver print card printed later lit. 3-Dec-3 Sotheby's, Amsterdam #485/R est:1000-1500

SIDLER, Alfred (1905-1992) Swiss

£263	$439	€384	Flowers in glass vase (38x29cm-15x11in) s. panel prov. 15-Nov-3 Galerie Gloggner, Luzern #101/R (S.FR 600)

SIDLEY, Samuel (1829-1896) British

£900	$1665	€1314	Portrait of Mrs Frederick Cheere. Portrait of Rev Frederick Cheere (74x61cm-29x24in) s.d.1872 pair prov. 11-Feb-4 Cheffins, Cambridge #426/R
£900	$1665	€1314	Portrait of Ethel Marion Sidley (31x26cm-12x10in) s.i.d.1872 board. 14-Jul-4 Sotheby's, Olympia #78/R
£20000	$34000	€29200	Challenge (152x103cm-60x41in) s. exhib.lit. 25-Nov-3 Christie's, London #130/R est:20000-30000

SIDNEY, Herbert (1858-1923) British

Works on paper			
£3200	$5344	€4672	In Roman room (86x70cm-34x28in) s.d.MCMXVI. 12-Nov-3 Sotheby's, Olympia #110/R est:1000-1500

SIDNEY, Thomas (19th C) British

Works on paper			
£280	$512	€420	Study of Kingsdown beach in Kent (64x23cm-25x9in) s. pencil W/C. 30-Jul-4 Jim Railton, Durham #360
£400	$692	€584	Off the Mumbles with shipping (24x69cm-9x27in) s.i. W/C. 9-Dec-3 Bonhams, Oxford #65/R
£475	$850	€797	Coastal scene, Minehead, Somerset (23x46cm-9x18in) s. W/C. 20-Mar-4 Pook & Pook, Downington #275
£500	$830	€730	Robin Hood's Bay, Near Whiby, Yorks. Barmburgh Castle, Northumberland (23x68cm-9x27in) s.i.d.1908 W/C two. 1-Oct-3 Woolley & Wallis, Salisbury #159/R

SIDOLI, Nazzareno (1879-1970) Italian

£1056	$1827	€1500	Bunch of flowers (37x27cm-15x11in) s. panel. 11-Dec-3 Christie's, Rome #48/R est:1700-1900

SIDOLI, Pacifico (1868-1963) Italian

£667	$1213	€1000	Portrait of girl (45x37cm-18x15in) s.d.1927. 12-Jul-4 Il Ponte, Milan #455
£878	$1546	€1300	Shepherdess with herd (50x35cm-20x14in) s. board. 19-May-4 Il Ponte, Milan #651 est:1000-1200
Works on paper			
£400	$716	€600	Beauty (35x42cm-14x17in) s. mixed media card. 12-May-4 Stadion, Trieste #751/R

SIDORENKO, Sergei (1968-) Russian

£340	$619	€500	Sous l'ombrelle. s. 8-Feb-4 Lesieur & Le Bars, Le Havre #140

SIEBELIST, Arthur (1870-1945) ?

£14685	$24524	€21000	Farmstead in evening (59x86cm-23x34in) s. 11-Oct-3 Hans Stahl, Hamburg #124/R est:7000

SIEBEN, Gottfried (1856-1918) Austrian

Works on paper			
£599	$1000	€875	Starlet in dressing room, evidence of gentlemen callers (46x25cm-18x10in) s. W/C gouache en grisaille exec.c.1890. 15-Nov-3 Illustration House, New York #33/R

SIEBER, Hans Ruedi (1926-) Swiss

£405	$697	€591	Still life with fruit and watering can (61x65cm-24x26in) s. 8-Dec-3 Philippe Schuler, Zurich #5959 (S.FR 900)

SIEBERT, Fritz Anton (1878-?) German

£561	$863	€880	Altona fish market (62x48cm-24x19in) s. panel. 4-Sep-2 Schopman, Hamburg #264/R

SIEBERT, Georg (1896-1984) German

£1200	$2160	€1800	In the kitchen (56x46cm-22x18in) s.d. s.i.d. verso board. 24-Apr-4 Dr Lehr, Berlin #441/R est:2000
Works on paper			
£268	$475	€400	Having lunch (60x97cm-24x38in) s.d. chl W/C tempera board. 30-Apr-4 Dr Fritz Nagel, Stuttgart #449/R

SIEBNER, Arthur J (1875-1948) German

£302	$553	€450	Venice, music group in a gondola in front of noble gathering (62x44cm-24x17in) s.d.1923 lit. 8-Jul-4 Allgauer, Kempten #2220/R

SIEBURGER, Frida (1862-?) Czechoslovakian

£1536	$2612	€2243	Landscape with lake (99x74cm-39x29in) s. 29-Nov-3 Dorotheum, Prague #104/R est:70000-110000 (C.KR 70000)

SIECK, Rudolf (1877-1957) German

£1259	$2140	€1800	Early spring (80x70cm-31x28in) s.d.1944 tempera. 20-Nov-3 Weidler, Nurnberg #381
£2133	$3861	€3200	High summer landscape (63x72cm-25x28in) s. s.i. verso lit. 1-Apr-4 Frank Peege, Freiburg #1192/R est:600
£3691	$6792	€5500	June morning B (66x81cm-26x32in) s. i. verso panel. 26-Mar-4 Bolland & Marotz, Bremen #646/R
Works on paper			
£298	$542	€450	View of Lake Chiem (12x16cm-5x6in) s. W/C pen. 16-Jun-4 Hugo Ruef, Munich #1180
£302	$556	€450	Chiemsee landscape (21x32cm-8x13in) s. col. 24-Mar-4 Hugo Ruef, Munich #1264/R

SIEFF, Jeanloup (1933-2000) French

Photographs			
£2147	$3800	€3135	Derriere Anglais no.2, 1969 (48x32cm-19x13in) s.i.d.1969 gelatin silver print. 27-Apr-4 Christie's, Rockefeller NY #372/R est:4000-6000
£2222	$3778	€3200	Nude in mirror (30x20cm-12x8in) s.d. i.d. verso gelatin silver lit. 31-Oct-3 Lempertz, Koln #321/R est:2500

SIEFFERT, Paul (1874-1957) French

£652	$1193	€952	Femme nue au miroir (22x27cm-9x11in) s. panel. 4-Jun-4 Zofingen, Switzerland #2521/R (S.FR 1500)
£1208	$2138	€1800	Nu a sa lecture (55x46cm-22x18in) s. s.i.verso. 30-Apr-4 Tajan, Paris #175/R est:3000
£1700	$3145	€2482	Reclining nude (24x35cm-9x14in) s. 10-Mar-4 Sotheby's, Olympia #310/R est:1500-2000
£2098	$3566	€3000	Nu de dos (38x55cm-15x22in) s. 20-Nov-3 Gioffredo, Nice #40/R
£3289	$6053	€5000	Femme nue endormie (46x61cm-18x24in) s. 24-Jun-4 Christie's, Paris #158/R est:4000-6000
£3600	$6660	€5256	Jeune femme nue (60x81cm-24x32in) s. 14-Jul-4 Sotheby's, Olympia #273a/R est:4000-6000
£4000	$6880	€5840	Reclining female nude (16x26cm-6x10in) s. i.verso panel. 3-Dec-3 AB Stockholms Auktionsverk #2650/R est:8000-10000 (S.KR 52000)
£5000	$9100	€7300	Reclining nude (46x62cm-18x24in) s. 16-Jun-4 Christie's, Kensington #265/R est:5000-7000
£5200	$8632	€7592	Le dos de la nude (48x61cm-19x24in) s. prov. 10-Jun-3 Canterbury Auctions, UK #100/R
£6000	$10800	€8760	Reclining nude (74x100cm-29x39in) s. s.i.verso. 21-Jan-4 Sotheby's, Olympia #492/R est:6000-8000
£6000	$11100	€8760	Reclining nude (54x81cm-21x32in) s. 14-Jul-4 Sotheby's, Olympia #263/R est:4000-6000

SIEGARD, Par (1877 1961) Swedish

£879	$1556	€1283	Still life of flowers II (57x44cm-22x17in) s. panel. 27-Apr-4 AB Stockholms Auktionsverk #654/R (S.KR 12000)
Works on paper			
£1172	$2075	€1711	The female circus rider (35x24cm-14x9in) W/C painted c.1919-20 prov. 27-Apr-4 AB Stockholms Auktionsverk #743/R est:18000-20000 (S.KR 16000)

SIEGEL, Arthur (1913-1979) American

Photographs			
£2260	$4000	€3300	Right of assembly, 1939 (28x35cm-11x14in) s.d.1939 gelatin silver print. 27-Apr-4 Christie's, Rockefeller NY #223/R est:5000-7000
£7222	$13000	€10544	Glassware class I no.1 (34x26cm-13x10in) init.d.1937 gelatin silver print. 22-Apr-4 Phillips, New York #37/R est:10000-15000

SIEGEL, Leo Dink (1910-2003) American

Works on paper

£227	$425	€331	Shapely blonde skier attracts attention (28x23cm-11x9in) s. ink pencil. 26-Feb-4 Illustration House, New York #161

SIEGEL, Richard (20th C) American

Works on paper

£228	$425	€333	Rocky shore (80x109cm-31x43in) s.d.85 W/C. 5-Mar-4 Skinner, Boston #569/R
£228	$425	€333	Maine coast (106x162cm-42x64in) s.d.84 W/C. 5-Mar-4 Skinner, Boston #571/R

SIEGEN, August (19th C) German

£567	$948	€800	Pantheon in Paris (15x31cm-6x12in) s. panel. 17-Oct-3 Berlinghof, Heidelberg #1101/R
£909	$1545	€1300	Dutch harbour (71x97cm-28x38in) s. 20-Nov-3 Dorotheum, Salzburg #153/R
£1042	$1719	€1500	Monks working in winter monastery ruins (74x101cm-29x40in) s. 3-Jul-3 Van Ham, Cologne #1464 est:1900
£1042	$1698	€1500	Bacino di San Marco, Venice (15x31cm-6x12in) s. panel. 25-Sep-3 Dr Fritz Nagel, Stuttgart #1416/R est:1600
£1111	$1811	€1600	Rome (15x31cm-6x12in) s. panel. 25-Sep-3 Dr Fritz Nagel, Stuttgart #1415/R est:1600
£1447	$2663	€2200	View of Antwerp (100x75cm-39x30in) s. panel lit. 26-Jun-4 Karrenbauer, Konstanz #1761/R est:2000
£1607	$2780	€2346	Fady Bay Mosque, Cairo (53x41cm-21x16in) s. panel. 9-Dec-3 Rasmussen, Copenhagen #1502/R est:12000-15000 (D.KR 17000)
£1800	$3276	€2700	Venice - Doges Palace and Piazzetta (52x79cm-20x31in) s. 30-Jun-4 Neumeister, Munich #683/R est:2300
£2000	$3260	€2880	Town Hall, Danzig (54x41cm-21x16in) s. panel. 25-Sep-3 Dr Fritz Nagel, Stuttgart #1417/R est:3300
£2000	$3260	€2880	Old town of Lisbon (52x41cm-20x16in) s. panel. 25-Sep-3 Dr Fritz Nagel, Stuttgart #1418/R est:3300
£2000	$3340	€2920	Ansicht von Siegen (49x81cm-19x32in) s. 12-Nov-3 Sotheby's, Olympia #180/R est:2000-3000
£2000	$3700	€2920	Harbour view (74x100cm-29x39in) 10-Mar-4 Sotheby's, Olympia #256/R est:2000-3000
£2059	$3500	€3006	Italian market square with numerous figures (52x41cm-20x16in) s. panel. 19-Nov-3 Bonhams & Butterfields, San Francisco #43a/R
£2465	$4264	€3500	Cremona street (53x42cm-21x17in) s. panel. 11-Dec-3 Dr Fritz Nagel, Stuttgart #552/R est:1800
£3030	$5424	€4424	Harbour town with figures (75x101cm-30x40in) s. 25-May-4 Bukowskis, Stockholm #368/R est:50000-60000 (S.KR 41000)
£3077	$5231	€4400	Outing in Edermunde (100x74cm-39x29in) s. lit. 28-Nov-3 Schloss Ahlden, Ahlden #1509/R est:3500
£3077	$5231	€4400	Outing in Amsterdam (100x74cm-39x29in) s. lit. 28-Nov-3 Schloss Ahlden, Ahlden #1510/R est:3500
£3167	$5385	€4624	Piazza dei Signori in Vicenza (53x42cm-21x17in) s. panel. 19-Nov-3 Fischer, Luzern #1152/R est:2000-2500 (S.FR 7000)

SIEGER, Frederik (1902-1999) Dutch

£839	$1401	€1200	Untitled (135x140cm-53x55in) s. d.1984 verso acrylic. 30-Jun-3 Sotheby's, Amsterdam #399

SIEGER, Viktor (1843-1905) Austrian

£400	$688	€584	Girl picking flowers (33x23cm-13x9in) s. board. 4-Dec-3 Richardson & Smith, Whitby #474/R

SIEGERT, August (1786-1869) German

£850	$1521	€1241	Doge's Palace, Venice (32x41cm-13x16in) s. panel. 26-May-4 Sotheby's, Olympia #271/R est:1000-1500

SIEGFRIED, Edwin C (1889-1955) American

Works on paper

£404	$650	€586	California wetlands. s. pastel. 23-Aug-3 Harvey Clar, Oakland #1218

SIEGFRIED, Walter (1931-) Swiss

£390	$697	€569	Composition (34x39cm-13x15in) i.d. stretcher mixed media. 22-Mar-4 Philippe Schuler, Zurich #6048 (S.FR 900)

SIEGRIEST, Louis Bassi (1899-1989) American

£556	$1000	€812	Dead trees (41x51cm-16x20in) s. i.d.1949 verso board. 25-Jan-4 Bonhams & Butterfields, San Francisco #3590/R
£608	$1100	€888	Old hay barges (46x61cm-18x24in) i.verso. 3-Apr-4 Harvey Clar, Oakland #1244
£659	$1100	€962	Street, Virginia City. s. board. 18-Oct-3 Harvey Clar, Oakland #1482
£2023	$3500	€2954	Old House (56x71cm-22x28in) prov.exhib. 10-Dec-3 Bonhams & Butterfields, San Francisco #6264/R est:2000-3000
£26099	$47500	€38105	Mount Diablo landscape (28x38cm-11x15in) s.i.d.22 verso prov.exhib. 15-Jun-4 John Moran, Pasadena #45 est:40000-60000
£31792	$55000	€46416	Interior of Gile's House on Chabot Road, Oakland, California (30x40cm-12x16in) board prov.exhib. 10-Dec-3 Bonhams & Butterfields, San Francisco #6257/R est:45000-55000

SIEGRIEST, Lundy (1925-1985) American

£221	$400	€323	Untitled (30x41cm-12x16in) 3-Apr-4 Harvey Clar, Oakland #1230
£226	$400	€330	Resort (25x66cm-10x26in) s. i.verso masonite. 1-May-4 Harvey Clar, Oakland #1358
£234	$425	€342	Landscape (20x25cm-8x10in) 7-Feb-4 Harvey Clar, Oakland #1351
£235	$425	€343	Untitled (30x41cm-12x16in) 3-Apr-4 Harvey Clar, Oakland #1229
£237	$425	€346	Still life with fruit (56x71cm-22x28in) s. board. 10-Jan-4 Harvey Clar, Oakland #1201
£240	$400	€350	Back of farm, Bolinas. s. 15-Nov-3 Harvey Clar, Oakland #1221
£241	$425	€352	June landscape (91x61cm-36x24in) s. masonite. 22-May-4 Harvey Clar, Oakland #2251
£251	$450	€366	Untitled 136 (20x25cm-8x10in) 10-Jan-4 Harvey Clar, Oakland #1197
£254	$450	€371	Untitled No.52 (41x51cm-16x20in) 1-May-4 Harvey Clar, Oakland #1243
£255	$475	€372	Untitled, no 194 (20x25cm-8x10in) 6-Mar-4 Harvey Clar, Oakland #1268
£261	$475	€381	Landscape (20x25cm-8x10in) 7-Feb-4 Harvey Clar, Oakland #1352
£262	$475	€383	Untitled (20x25cm-8x10in) 3-Apr-4 Harvey Clar, Oakland #1234
£268	$475	€391	Untitled no.146 (25x36cm-10x14in) 1-May-4 Harvey Clar, Oakland #1247
£275	$500	€402	Landscape (30x41cm-12x16in) 7-Feb-4 Harvey Clar, Oakland #1349
£275	$500	€402	Landscape (30x41cm-12x16in) 7-Feb-4 Harvey Clar, Oakland #1350
£275	$500	€402	Landscape (30x41cm-12x16in) 7-Feb-4 Harvey Clar, Oakland #1348
£279	$500	€407	Untitled 164 (20x25cm-8x10in) 10-Jan-4 Harvey Clar, Oakland #1195
£282	$500	€412	Town scene - Untitled no.124 (41x51cm-16x20in) 1-May-4 Harvey Clar, Oakland #1244
£311	$550	€454	Untitled no.180/43 (23x30cm-9x12in) 1-May-4 Harvey Clar, Oakland #1249
£329	$550	€480	Forest lake. s. 15-Nov-3 Harvey Clar, Oakland #1219
£330	$600	€482	Landscape (30x41cm-12x16in) 7-Feb-4 Harvey Clar, Oakland #1347
£330	$600	€482	Blue landscape (48x20cm-19x8in) s. indis.d.6/13/60 verso masonite. 7-Feb-4 Harvey Clar, Oakland #1353
£330	$600	€482	Untitled no.95 (41x51cm-16x20in) prov. 19-Jun-4 Harvey Clar, Oakland #2211
£349	$650	€510	Untitled, no 214 (41x51cm-16x20in) 6-Mar-4 Harvey Clar, Oakland #1266
£359	$600	€524	Portrait of a boy. s. 18-Oct-3 Harvey Clar, Oakland #1261
£363	$650	€530	Untitled 212 (20x25cm-8x10in) 10-Jan-4 Harvey Clar, Oakland #1198
£376	$700	€549	Untitled, no 18 (41x51cm-16x20in) 6-Mar-4 Harvey Clar, Oakland #1265
£385	$700	€562	Untitled (23x30cm-9x12in) 7-Feb-4 Harvey Clar, Oakland #1356
£385	$700	€562	Untitled (23x30cm-9x12in) 7-Feb-4 Harvey Clar, Oakland #1357
£391	$700	€571	Untitled 104 (20x25cm-8x10in) 10-Jan-4 Harvey Clar, Oakland #1196
£403	$750	€588	Untitled, no 78 (41x51cm-16x20in) 6-Mar-4 Harvey Clar, Oakland #1267
£407	$700	€594	Sierra foothills. 6-Dec-3 Harvey Clar, Oakland #1182
£447	$800	€653	Untitled 54 (41x51cm-16x20in) 10-Jan-4 Harvey Clar, Oakland #1199
£494	$850	€721	Untitled, O. s. 6-Dec-3 Harvey Clar, Oakland #1184
£495	$900	€723	D Street Virginia City. s. 7-Feb-4 Harvey Clar, Oakland #1354
£523	$900	€764	Cows in the countryside. 6-Dec-3 Harvey Clar, Oakland #1185
£531	$850	€775	Along the Yuba. s. 20-Sep-3 Harvey Clar, Oakland #1304
£531	$950	€775	Gerry, portrait of Geraldine Politeau. s. 10-Jan-4 Harvey Clar, Oakland #1202
£569	$950	€831	Volcano, California. s. 15-Nov-3 Harvey Clar, Oakland #1458
£615	$1100	€898	Untitled 18 (41x51cm-16x20in) 10-Jan-4 Harvey Clar, Oakland #1203
£769	$1400	€1123	Town Scene (61x51cm-24x20in) 7-Feb-4 Harvey Clar, Oakland #1355
£879	$1600	€1283	Boy frightened by scream of his mother. s.i.verso. 7-Feb-4 Harvey Clar, Oakland #1471
£914	$1700	€1334	Flowers in vase no 2 (46x51cm-18x20in) s. board. 6-Mar-4 Harvey Clar, Oakland #1264
£934	$1700	€1364	Flowers no 1 (61x46cm-24x18in) s. board. 7-Feb-4 Harvey Clar, Oakland #1344
£1018	$1700	€1486	Southwestern sunrise. s. 15-Nov-3 Harvey Clar, Oakland #1459
£1117	$2000	€1631	Christmas tree. s. d.1940 verso. 10-Jan-4 Harvey Clar, Oakland #1200
£1198	$2000	€1749	Aftermath. s. 18-Oct-3 Harvey Clar, Oakland #1481
£1406	$2250	€2053	Backyard craps game. s. 20-Sep-3 Harvey Clar, Oakland #1521
£1847	$3250	€2697	Temple and jungle birds (91x124cm-36x49in) s. painted c.1960. 23-May-4 Treadway Gallery, Cincinnati #744/R est:2000-3000
£2326	$4000	€3396	Mt Lassen. s. acrylic board. 6-Dec-3 Harvey Clar, Oakland #1366
£2762	$5000	€4033	Fishing boat (122x64cm-48x25in) s. masonite. 3-Apr-4 Harvey Clar, Oakland #1353
£2793	$5000	€4078	Let's build a house. s. i.d.1950 verso. 10-Jan-4 Harvey Clar, Oakland #1564

Works on paper

£247	$450	€361	Golden morning (94x71cm-37x28in) s. mixed media prov. 19-Jun-4 Harvey Clar, Oakland #2218
£297	$475	€434	Untitled. s.d.1962 mixed media. 20-Sep-3 Harvey Clar, Oakland #1307
£385	$700	€562	Lava flow. s. mixed media canvas. 7-Feb-4 Harvey Clar, Oakland #1497
£531	$950	€775	Mirage. i.verso mixed media. 10-Jan-4 Harvey Clar, Oakland #1452
£621	$1100	€907	Blue and red image (124x94cm-49x37in) s. i.verso mixed media. 1-May-4 Harvey Clar, Oakland #1363

SIEGUMFELDT, Hermann Carl (1833-1912) Danish
£766 $1418 €1118 Portrait of Maria baroness Caroline Bille, and Johan baron Christian Bille (70x57cm-28x22in) s.d.1883 pair oval prov. 15-Mar-4 Rasmussen, Vejle #398/R (D.KR 8500)

SIEMIRADZKI, Hendrik (1843-1902) Polish
£48000 $85920 €70080 Rus burial in Bulgaria, 1883-1884 (31x42cm-12x17in) s.d.1907 board. 26-May-4 Sotheby's, London #21/R est:25000-35000
£260000 $478400 €379600 Nero's torches (94x174cm-37x69in) s.d.1882 prov. 23-Mar-4 Bonhams, New Bond Street #44/R est:120000-180000
Works on paper
£20921 $37866 €30545 Untitled (25x47cm-10x19in) s.i.d.1897 W/C go vellum prov. 1-Apr-4 Heffel, Vancouver #93/R est:15000-20000 (C.D 50000)

SIENESE SCHOOL (14th C) Italian
£11000 $20130 €16060 Crucifixion with Madonna and Saint John the Evangelist (20x14cm-8x6in) tempera panel. 8-Jul-4 Sotheby's, London #147/R est:12000-18000
£238889 $430000 €348778 Madonna and Child enthroned (33x29cm-13x11in) gold tempera panel painted c.1320-45. 22-Jan-4 Sotheby's, New York #9/R est:50000-70000

SIENESE SCHOOL (16th C) Italian
£5592 $10289 €8500 Adam and Eve (44x43cm-17x17in) panel oval. 24-Jun-4 Christie's, Paris #68/R est:2000-4000

SIENESE SCHOOL (17th C) Italian
£6338 $11092 €9000 Holy Family (160x108cm-63x43in) painted c.1630. 17-Dec-3 Piasa, Paris #49/R est:10000-12000
£14789 $23810 €21000 Sacred family with angels (90x123cm-35x48in) 8-May-3 Farsetti, Prato #397/R est:23000-28000
Works on paper
£6803 $12177 €10000 Des femmes agenouillees, entourees de figures, devant un palais (28x28cm-11x11in) i. pen grey was ink prov. 18-Mar-4 Christie's, Paris #16/R est:700-1000

SIENICKI, Jacek (1928-) Polish
£690 $1152 €1000 Bust of a man with white cloud around his head (99x69cm-39x27in) s.d.80 board. 16-Nov-3 Agra, Warsaw #89/R
£872 $1447 €1273 Head (61x50cm-24x20in) painted 1991. 2-Oct-3 Agra, Warsaw #10/R (P.Z 5700)

SIEPMAN VAN DEN BERG, Eja (1943-) Dutch
Sculpture
£4667 $8587 €7000 Staande jongen (73cm-29in) s.d.1988 st.f.Bronsgieterij blk pat bronze incl. base prov. 9-Jun-4 Christie's, Amsterdam #281/R est:7000-9000

SIEPMANN, Heinrich (1904-) German
£733 $1342 €1100 Untitled (70x50cm-28x20in) s.d.81 oil pencil paper on board. 4-Jun-4 Lempertz, Koln #458/R
£867 $1551 €1300 Composition (48x63cm-19x25in) s.d.57 oil Indian ink prov. 15-May-4 Van Ham, Cologne #931/R
£1000 $1830 €1500 Bordered area (62x44cm-24x17in) s.d.65 tempera graphite chk prov.exhib. 4-Jun-4 Lempertz, Koln #457/R est:1500
£1259 $2165 €1800 Vertically boxed in (90x70cm-35x28in) s.d.60 verso. 4-Dec-3 Van Ham, Cologne #477/R est:2000

SIERHUIS, Jan (1928-) Dutch
£340 $619 €500 Female figures (76x54cm-30x21in) s.d.76 black chk. 3-Feb-4 Christie's, Amsterdam #551
£611 $1100 €892 De Vrienden (89x127cm-35x50in) s.i.d.59 verso. 23-Jan-4 Freeman, Philadelphia #274/R
£658 $1211 €1000 Maanziek Paard (80x60cm-31x24in) s.d.80 s.i. verso. 28-Jun-4 Sotheby's, Amsterdam #297/R
£658 $1211 €1000 Landscape with car (40x60cm-16x24in) s.d.95. 28-Jun-4 Sotheby's, Amsterdam #297a/R
£710 $1300 €1037 Gate in Amsterdam (79x99cm-31x39in) s.d.59. 31-Jul-4 Sloans & Kenyon, Bethesda #300/R
£930 $1600 €1358 Mens en machine (61x74cm-24x29in) s.d.60 s.i.d.verso prov. 7-Dec-3 Freeman, Philadelphia #73 est:700-1000
£1570 $2700 €2292 Cyprus (119x150cm-47x59in) s.d.64 s.i.d.verso prov. 7-Dec-3 Freeman, Philadelphia #75 est:1200-1800
£2430 $3961 €3500 In the afternoon (90x102cm-35x40in) s.d.63. 29-Sep-3 Sotheby's, Amsterdam #366/R
£3043 $4991 €4200 Composition (130x150cm-51x59in) s.d.63. 27-May-3 Sotheby's, Amsterdam #537/R est:3000-5000

SIERON, Maurice (20th C) Belgian
Works on paper
£476 $852 €700 Le chargement des briques (54x79cm-21x31in) s.d.08 pastel paper on canvas. 16-Mar-4 Vanderkindere, Brussels #116

SIESTRZENCEWICZ, Stanislaw Bohusz (1869-1927) Polish
£5469 $9133 €7985 Harmless flirting (53x78cm-21x31in) s.indis.d.907. 19-Oct-3 Agra, Warsaw #12/R est:33000 (P.Z 35000)

SIEURIN, Jean (1931-) French
£379 $633 €550 Bras de Seine a Duclair (33x55cm-13x22in) s. cardboard. 11-Nov-3 Lesieur & Le Bars, Le Havre #104
£448 $749 €650 Brume a Villequier (54x81cm-21x32in) s. 11-Nov-3 Lesieur & Le Bars, Le Havre #105

SIEW HOCK MENG (1942-) Malaysian
£3105 $5619 €4533 Model (82x60cm-32x24in) s.d.1999 oil hardpaper. 3-Apr-4 Glerum, Singapore #16/R est:10000-12000 (S.D 9500)
£4167 $6958 €6084 Nude (80x60cm-31x24in) s.d.2001. 12-Oct-3 Sotheby's, Singapore #54/R est:12000-15000 (S.D 12000)
£19608 $35490 €28628 Resting (92x127cm-36x50in) s.d.1998 s.d.verso. 4-Apr-4 Sotheby's, Singapore #123/R est:40000-60000 (S.D 60000)
£19915 $35846 €29076 Dancer with gamelan orchestra (91x183cm-36x72in) s.d.1998. 25-Apr-4 Christie's, Hong Kong #568/R est:220000-260000 (HK.D 280000)
Works on paper
£4125 $7425 €6023 Two reclining nudes (50x65cm-20x26in) s.d.1990 pastel. 25-Apr-4 Christie's, Hong Kong #565/R est:20000-30000 (HK.D 58000)

SIEWERT, Clara (1862-?) German
£294 $490 €420 Elegant figures in ballroom (32x50cm-13x20in) s.d.1896. 28-Jun-3 Dannenberg, Berlin #779/R

SIGAFOOS, Richard G (20th C) American
£353 $650 €515 Windjammers (41x51cm-16x20in) s. board. 9-Jun-4 Alderfer's, Hatfield #430/R

SIGALON, Xavier (1787-1837) French
£1408 $2465 €2000 Portrait d'homme a la toque verte (55x46cm-22x18in) mono.d.1817. 17-Dec-3 Piasa, Paris #107 est:3000-4000

SIGARD, Eliahu (1901-1975) Israeli
£2000 $3580 €2920 Afternoon in the village (60x73cm-24x29in) s. 11-May-4 Sotheby's, Olympia #611/R est:2500-3500

SIGG, Fredy (20th C) Swiss
£541 $930 €790 Harlequin with a barrel-organ (95x83cm-37x33in) s.d.1967. 8-Dec-3 Philippe Schuler, Zurich #3360 (S.FR 1200)

SIGG, Hermann-Alfred (1924-) Swiss
£688 $1149 €998 River in rice fields II (81x116cm-32x46in) s.d. acrylic. 23-Jun-3 Philippe Schuler, Zurich #3429 (S.FR 1500)
£814 $1409 €1188 View of village in North Africa (65x92cm-26x36in) s.d.1980. 9-Dec-3 Sotheby's, Zurich #135/R est:1800-2500 (S.FR 1800)
£1310 $2345 €1913 Barbary girl (162x60cm-64x24in) s.d.1960 prov. 26-May-4 Sotheby's, Zurich #70/R est:3000-4000 (S.FR 3000)
£1629 $2769 €2378 River traces II (73x130cm-29x51in) s.d.1984 i. verso acrylic. 25-Nov-3 Germann, Zurich #57/R est:3000-5000 (S.FR 3600)
£1900 $3231 €2774 Flight over islands (92x146cm-36x57in) s.d.1970 acrylic prov.exhib.lit. 25-Nov-3 Germann, Zurich #86/R est:4000-5000 (S.FR 4200)

SIGMUND, Benjamin D (fl.1880-1904) British
Works on paper
£411 $699 €600 Enfants ramassant des brindilles (36x53cm-14x21in) s.d.84 W/C. 6-Nov-3 Sotheby's, Paris #135/R
£560 $952 €818 Picking wildflowers (26x36cm-10x14in) s. W/C. 29-Oct-3 Bonhams, Chester #399
£1100 $2002 €1606 Girls feeding chickens and calves beside cottages (25x36cm-10x14in) s. W/C sold with W/C coastal scene by Shapland two. 5-Feb-4 Gorringes, Worthing #472 est:150-200
£1100 $2024 €1606 Woman standing by a cottage with the sea beyond (34x23cm-13x9in) s.d.95 W/C. 23-Mar-4 Rosebery Fine Art, London #866/R est:500-800

SIGMUND, Karel Jan (1897-?) Czechoslovakian
£359 $631 €539 Winter (46x56cm-18x22in) s. canvas on cardboard. 22-May-4 Dorotheum, Prague #81/R est:8000-14000 (C.KR 17000)

SIGNAC, Paul (1863-1935) French
£50000 $91000 €73000 Saint-Briac, cour a la ville Hue (33x46cm-13x18in) s.i. painted 1885 prov.exhib.lit. 3-Feb-4 Christie's, London #118/R est:50000-70000
£217877 $390000 €318100 Saint-Briac, Le Bechet (46x65cm-18x26in) s.d.1885 prov.exhib.lit. 5-May-4 Christie's, Rockefeller NY #213/R est:200000-300000
£352941 $600000 €515294 Bassin a flots, Saint Malo (46x65cm-18x26in) s.d.1928 prov.exhib.lit. 4-Nov-3 Christie's, Rockefeller NY #37/R est:700000-900000
£520000 $951600 €759200 Port de Barfleur (73x92cm-29x36in) s.d.1931 prov.exhib.lit. 2-Feb-4 Christie's, London #17/R est:600000-800000
£520000 $956800 €759200 Mont Saint-Michel, brume et soleil (47x56cm-19x22in) s.d.97 prov.exhib.lit. 22-Jun-4 Christie's, London #14/R est:300000-450000
£530726 $950000 €774860 Collioure, le Mohamed-El-Sadok (26x34cm-10x13in) s. s.i.verso panel painted 1887 prov.exhib.lit. 5-May-4 Sotheby's, New York #8/R est:500000-700000
£740000 $1354200 €1080400 Saint-Tropez apres l'orage (65x81cm-26x32in) s.d.95 prov.exhib.lit. 2-Feb-4 Christie's, London #44/R est:400000-600000
£1550000 $2852000 €2263000 Balises, Saint-Briac (65x82cm-26x32in) s.d.90 prov.exhib.lit. 22-Jun-4 Christie's, London #17/R est:1800000-2200000
Prints
£3911 $7000 €5710 Le port de Veere (24x33cm-9x13in) s.i. etching drypoint. 6-May-4 Swann Galleries, New York #324/R est:12000-18000
£11096 $18863 €16200 Saint-Tropez, le port. s.i. lithograph. 6-Nov-3 Piasa, Paris #154/R
Sculpture
£2238 $3804 €3200 Young dromedary (14cm-6in) mono. bronze Cast.H Noack Berlin exhib.lit. 26-Nov-3 Lempertz, Koln #983/R est:3000
Works on paper
£552 $1021 €800 Chateau de Chinon (20x12cm-8x5in) s.d.1912 dr. 16-Feb-4 Giraudeau, Tours #30
£773 $1400 €1129 Landscape. W/C. 19-Apr-4 Caddigan, Hanover #4/R
£833 $1392 €1200 Marine (21x13cm-8x5in) s. blue ink drawing. 21-Oct-3 Artcurial Briest, Paris #36 est:1200-1500
£1467 $2640 €2200 Etude de ciel au coucher de soleil, Saint Tropez (15x20cm-6x8in) s.i. W/C exec. 1902. 26-Apr-4 Tajan, Paris #6/R est:2000-3000

£2254 $3899 €3200 Voiliers aux environs de Rouen (14x18cm-6x7in) st.sig. crayon ink wash. 15-Dec-3 Bailly Pommery, Paris #120/R est:1000-1500
£2324 $4020 €3300 Trois mats a Venise (16x21cm-6x8in) s. ink wash prov. 15-Dec-3 Bailly Pommery, Paris #119/R est:1500-1800
£2378 $4042 €3400 Paris, pont sur la Seine ave la Tour Eiffel (11x15cm-4x6in) s.mono. W/C pencil. 26-Nov-3 Lempertz, Koln #981/R est:3000
£2465 $4264 €3500 Barges sur la riviere (14x22cm-6x9in) st.sig. crayon W/C. 15-Dec-3 Bailly Pommery, Paris #117/R est:2500-3500
£2500 $4175 €3650 La Rochelle (9x13cm-4x5in) s.i. W/C gouache over chl. 22-Oct-3 Sotheby's, Olympia #55/R est:3000-4000
£2535 $4386 €3600 Voiliers a quai (16x24cm-6x9in) st.sig. crayon W/C. 15-Dec-3 Bailly Pommery, Paris #118/R est:2000-3000
£2961 $5447 €4500 Trois mats sortant du port (12x20cm-5x8in) s.i. W/C. 23-Jun-4 Maigret, Paris #16/R est:1500-2000
£3333 $5567 €4800 Seine a Suresnes (19x29cm-7x11in) st.sig.i.d.25.2.25 ink drawing. 21-Oct-3 Artcurial Briest, Paris #37/R est:5000-6000
£3400 $6256 €4964 Les balises (14x11cm-6x4in) s.i.d.1925 pencil W/C prov. 24-Mar-4 Sotheby's, Olympia #1/R est:3000-4000
£3521 $6092 €5000 Portrieux (22x40cm-9x16in) s.i.d.29 sepia ink wash crayon. 9-Dec-3 Artcurial Briest, Paris #81/R est:3000-4000
£4578 $7920 €6500 Voiliers dans l'entree du port (19x43cm-7x17in) s. sepia ink wash crayon. 9-Dec-3 Artcurial Briest, Paris #80/R est:5000-7000
£4688 $7500 €6844 Seine river, Paris (25x36cm-10x14in) W/C. 19-Sep-3 Du Mouchelle, Detroit #2235/R est:10000-15000
£5594 $9622 €8000 View at Rotterdam (11x15cm-4x6in) s.i. W/C pencil prov. 2-Dec-3 Sotheby's, Amsterdam #92/R est:8000-12000
£5867 $10795 €8800 Bourg Saint-Andeol (19x25cm-7x10in) s.i. W/C prov. 14-Jun-4 Tajan, Paris #43/R est:8000-10000
£5906 $10572 €8800 Voiliers sortant du port de La Rochelle (20x26cm-8x10in) s.i.d.1926 W/C graphite prov. 26-May-4 Christie's, Paris #42/R est:8000-12000
£6135 $10000 €8957 Samois, la peniche (17x25cm-7x10in) st.sig. W/C gouache black conte crayon prov. 25-Sep-3 Christie's, Rockefeller NY #503/R est:10000-15000
£6667 $10667 €9667 Seine landscape in Paris (21x27cm-8x11in) s.d.Juin 1910 W/C over pencil. 15-May-3 Stuker, Bern #1495/R est:12000-16000 (S.FR 14000)
£6757 $11622 €9865 Bridge in Geneva (21x28cm-8x11in) s. chl W/C bodycol. 2-Dec-3 Koller, Zurich #3050/R est:15000-20000 (S.FR 15000)
£7558 $13000 €11035 Le port de Rotterdam (18x25cm-7x10in) W/C chl prov. 3-Dec-3 Doyle, New York #122/R est:8000-12000
£7647 $13000 €11165 Paris (18x25cm-7x10in) s.d.1913 W/C gouache chl paper on paper prov. 5-Nov-3 Christie's, Rockefeller NY #109/R est:12000-16000
£7821 $14000 €11419 Bord de Seine (23x31cm-9x12in) st.sig. W/C chl. 6-May-4 Sotheby's, New York #415/R est:8000-12000
£8000 $14560 €11680 Vue de Venise (9x25cm-4x10in) s.d.1904 W/C pencil exec 1904. 5-Feb-4 Christie's, London #313/R est:8000-12000
£8235 $14000 €12023 Vaison (27x41cm-11x16in) s.d.33 W/C pencil prov. 6-Nov-3 Sotheby's, New York #110/R est:15000-20000
£9000 $16560 €13500 Scuola della Misericordia, Venice (20x25cm-8x10in) s.i.d.08 W/C black chk paper on card prov. 11-Jun-4 Villa Grisebach, Berlin #1518/R est:4000-6000
£9130 $16709 €13330 Les sables d'Olonne (21x26cm-8x10in) s.i. chl W/C. 4-Jun-4 Zofingen, Switzerland #2522/R est:18000 (S.FR 21000)
£10000 $18200 €14600 Pont des Arts (22x28cm-9x11in) s. W/C gouache chl. 5-Feb-4 Christie's, London #319/R est:8000-12000
£10056 $18000 €14682 Lomato (20x28cm-8x11in) s.i.d.22 gouache W/C over chl buff paper on board prov.exhib. 5-May-4 Christie's, Rockefeller NY #101/R est:18000-25000
£11189 $19245 €16000 Le Port de Marseille (53x63cm-21x25in) s. wash Indian ink brush over pencil col pen. 2-Dec-3 Hauswedell & Nolte, Hamburg #622/R est:10000
£11500 $20930 €16790 Tarascon (29x43cm-11x17in) init. pencil W/C gouache exec.c.1926 prov. 4-Feb-4 Sotheby's, London #402/R est:12000-15000
£11888 $20448 €17000 Le port de St. Tropez (17x22cm-7x9in) s. W/C black chk prov. 2-Dec-3 Sotheby's, Amsterdam #89/R est:12000-15000
£12000 $22080 €17520 Concarneau, thoniers (26x37cm-10x15in) s.d.25 W/C crayon prov. 22-Jun-4 Sotheby's, London #405/R est:8000-12000
£12081 $21624 €18000 Thonier a l'ancre (29x43cm-11x17in) sts.ig. W/C. 30-May-4 Eric Pillon, Calais #26/R
£13000 $23920 €18980 Pont des Arts, Paris (29x42cm-11x17in) s.d.1913 W/C pencil prov. 22-Jun-4 Sotheby's, London #403/R est:10000-15000
£13000 $23920 €18980 Voiliers au port de Saint Vaast La Hougue (27x43cm-11x17in) st.sig. W/C pencil exhib. 22-Jun-4 Sotheby's, London #427/R est:8000-12000
£13514 $25000 €19730 Bourg Saint-Andre (26x44cm-10x17in) s.i. W/C over chl. 12-Feb-4 Sotheby's, New York #29/R est:12000-18000
£14000 $25760 €20440 Effet de contrejour a Samois (17x25cm-7x10in) s.d.1900 W/C chl prov. 22-Jun-4 Sotheby's, London #428/R est:8000-12000
£14765 $26430 €22000 Sables d'Olonne (32x46cm-13x18in) s.i.d.1920 gouache W/C graphite prov. 26-May-4 Christie's, Paris #3/R est:20000-30000
£15000 $27300 €21900 Les sables d'Olonne (29x44cm-11x17in) s.d.1929 W/C over black crayon prov. 4-Feb-4 Sotheby's, London #401/R est:12000-15000
£15000 $27600 €21900 Goelette espagnole (30x45cm-12x18in) s.i.d.22 nov 30 W/C pencil prov. 24-Jun-4 Christie's, London #301/R est:15000-20000
£15882 $27000 €23188 Le port de Nice (25x40cm-10x16in) s.i.d.1922 W/C gouache blk chk paper on paper. 5-Nov-3 Christie's, Rockefeller NY #118/R est:20000-30000
£16000 $26720 €23360 Le port a St. Malo (27x19cm-11x7in) init.i. W/C black crayon prov. 21-Oct-3 Sotheby's, London #1/R est:12000-15000
£16000 $29440 €23360 Treguier (28x45cm-11x18in) s.i.d.24 W/C pencil. 22-Jun-4 Sotheby's, London #407/R est:18000-25000
£16471 $28000 €24048 Conarneau (18x38cm-7x15in) s.i.d.25 W/C gouache blk chk paper on paper. 5-Nov-3 Christie's, Rockefeller NY #108/R est:15000-20000
£16779 $30034 €25000 Trois-mats sortant du port de Saint-Malo (27x41cm-11x16in) s.i.d.1928 W/C gouache graphite prov. 26-May-4 Christie's, Paris #39/R est:25000-35000
£17105 $31474 €26000 Paris, la Seine au Pont Neuf (27x43cm-11x17in) s.d.1925 W/C prov. 23-Jun-4 Maigret, Paris #17/R est:15000-20000
£17647 $30000 €25765 Sur la Seine (28x42cm-11x17in) s.d.29 W/C blk chk paper on board prov. 5-Nov-3 Christie's, Rockefeller NY #119/R est:18000-22000
£19369 $33315 €28279 Sulaiman and Istanbul harbour (20x26cm-8x10in) s.i. W/C prov. 2-Dec-3 Koller, Zurich #3049/R est:20000-28000 (S.FR 43000)
£22000 $40040 €32120 Saint Tropez (44x30cm-17x12in) s.i.d.01 W/C chl pencil exec 1901 prov. 5-Feb-4 Christie's, London #315/R est:25000-35000
£25000 $45500 €36500 Dunkerque (28x44cm-11x17in) s.i.d.1930 W/C chl exec.1930 prov. 5-Feb-4 Christie's, London #318/R est:18000-25000
£25000 $45500 €36500 Retour de peche a Concarneau (29x45cm-11x18in) d.Juin 29 W/C chl prov. 5-Feb-4 Christie's, London #301/R est:25000-35000
£26667 $47733 €40000 Le port de Paimpol, Bretagne (26x42cm-10x17in) s.d.29 W/C chl. 15-May-4 De Vuyst, Lokeren #460/R
£34000 $61880 €49640 Palais des Papes, Avignon (28x44cm-11x17in) s.d.28 gouache W/C chl exec 1928 prov. 5-Feb-4 Christie's, London #317/R est:20000-30000
£55882 $95000 €81588 Mosquee de Sainte Sophie (89x116cm-35x46in) s. brush ink wash gouache paper on card. 6-Nov-3 Sotheby's, New York #112/R est:40000-60000

SIGNAC, Pierre (c.1624-1684) French
Miniatures
£49000 $84770 €71540 Christina, Queen of Sweden in white robes and black ribbon (7cm-3in) on gold oval prov. 9-Dec-3 Christie's, London #16/R est:10000-15000

SIGNORE, Littorio del (1938-) Canadian
£625 $1075 €913 Montreal, l'Ancien et Nouveau (75x60cm-30x24in) s. painted 1993. 2-Dec-3 Joyner Waddington, Toronto #263/R (C.D 1400)

SIGNORET, Charles Louis (1867-1932) French
£780 $1303 €1100 Marine au couchant (38x45cm-15x18in) s. 19-Jun-3 Millon & Associes, Paris #176/R
£1100 $2024 €1650 Pecheurs au couchant (74x101cm-29x40in) 9-Jun-4 Oger, Dumont, Paris #76 est:1000-1200

SIGNORET-LEDIEU, Lucie (1858-1904) French
Sculpture
£1119 $1924 €1600 Diane chasseresse se tenant assise sur un rocher (66cm-26in) s. bronze. 8-Dec-3 Rossini, Paris #244/R est:1000-1500

SIGNORI, Carlo Sergio (c.1906-) Italian
Sculpture
£2817 $4676 €4000 Torse feminin (77cm-30in) s. marble. 16-Jun-3 E & Eve, Paris #111/R

SIGNORINI, Francesco (19th C) Italian
Works on paper
£1389 $2500 €2028 Young nobleman (88x60cm-35x24in) s.i. W/C. 21-Jan-4 Sotheby's, New York #170/R est:3000-5000

SIGNORINI, Giuseppe (1857-1932) Italian
Works on paper
£541 $1000 €790 Cardinals playing chess (43x33cm-17x13in) W/C. 13-Feb-4 Du Mouchelle, Detroit #2020/R
£5882 $10000 €8588 The serenade (77x53cm-30x21in) s. i.verso W/C gouache board. 29-Oct-3 Christie's, Rockefeller NY #223/R est:10000-15000

SIGNORINI, T (19th C) Italian
£2000 $3640 €2920 Young girl on a path carrying a basket of flowers (20x30cm-8x12in) s. 3-Feb-4 Gorringes, Bexhill #1079/R est:1500-2000

SIGNORINI, Telemaco (1835-1901) Italian
£1000 $1790 €1500 In the wood (16x9cm-6x4in) board. 12-May-4 Stadion, Trieste #693 est:1000-1500
£2600 $4238 €3796 River landscape with early evening sunshine (8x17cm-3x7in) board prov. 24-Sep-3 Dreweatt Neate, Newbury #153/R est:1000-1500
£3000 $4890 €4380 Street scene with laundry hanging between buildings (18x11cm-7x4in) canvas board prov. 24-Sep-3 Dreweatt Neate, Newbury #154/R est:1500-2000
£5168 $9250 €7700 Motherly love (9x6cm-4x2in) canvas on cardboard prov. 25-May-4 Finarte Semenzato, Milan #218/R est:8000-9000
£6000 $9780 €8760 Landscape with town beyond (31x46cm-12x18in) prov. 24-Sep-3 Dreweatt Neate, Newbury #151/R est:4000-6000
£17000 $28900 €24820 View of Vinci (17x12cm-7x5in) s.d.73 board prov. 18-Nov-3 Sotheby's, London #330/R
£23333 $42933 €35000 Settignano (27x17cm-11x7in) s. cardboard prov. 10-Jun-4 Christie's, Rome #174/R est:23000-28000
£2500000 $4250000 €3650000 Tow-path (58x173cm-23x68in) s. prov.exhib.lit. 18-Nov-3 Sotheby's, London #328/R est:180000-250000
Works on paper
£863 $1416 €1200 Interior with women (18x13cm-7x5in) pencil. 10-Jun-3 Pandolfini, Florence #34/R
£1277 $2132 €1800 Children in Riomaggiore (20x13cm-8x5in) mono.i. pencil lit. 14-Oct-3 Finarte Semenzato, Milan #155/R
£1418 $2369 €2000 Portrait of girl (27x15cm-11x6in) init. pencil lit. 14-Oct-3 Finarte Semenzato, Milan #149/R
£1761 $3046 €2500 Autumn dream (30x25cm-12x10in) init. pencil card. 9-Dec-3 Finarte Semenzato, Milan #73/R est:2000-2500
£2695 $4501 €3800 Arcola street (19x12cm-7x5in) s.i. pencil W/C. 14-Oct-3 Finarte Semenzato, Milan #157/R

SIGNOVERT, Jean (1919-1981) French
£456 $853 €680 Composition (50x61cm-20x24in) s. prov. 29-Feb-4 Versailles Encheres #313/R
Works on paper
£349 $618 €520 Composition (50x59cm-20x23in) s.d.1956 mixed media isorel. 28-Apr-4 Charbonneaux, Paris #223

SIGNY, A (19th C) French
£1200 $2184 €1752 Resting livestock at the river (29x36cm-11x14in) s.d.47 panel. 16-Jun-4 Christie's, Kensington #17/R est:1500-2000

SIGRIST, Franz I (1727-1803) Austrian
£3974 $7232 €6000 Susannah and the Elders (60x77cm-24x30in) prov.lit. 16-Jun-4 Dorotheum, Vienna #179/R est:8000-12000

SIGRISTE, Guido (1864-1915) Swiss
£317 $538 €463 Hussar attack (16x23cm-6x9in) s. panel. 28-Nov-3 Zofingen, Switzerland #3181 (S.FR 700)
£559 $934 €800 An amourous couple seated on a garden bench (21x15cm-8x6in) s.d.89 panel. 30-Jun-3 Sotheby's, Amsterdam #110
£2489 $3982 €3634 General Rapp (54x73cm-21x29in) s.d.1894 bears i. verso. 19-Sep-3 Koller, Zurich #3117/R est:6000-8000 (S.FR 5500)

SIGUENZA ALONSO, Manuel (1870-?) Spanish
£282 $487 €400 Coastal view (64x93cm-25x37in) 15-Dec-3 Ansorena, Madrid #260/R

SIGURDSSON, Sigurdur (1916-) Icelandic
£599 $1018 €875 Still life of fruit on cloth (82x70cm-32x28in) s.d.1964. 10-Nov-3 Rasmussen, Vejle #674/R (D.KR 6500)

SIHLALI, Durant Basi (1935-) South African?
Works on paper
£388 $648 €566 Washday (52x74cm-20x29in) s. W/C. 20-Oct-3 Stephan Welz, Johannesburg #616 est:4000-6000 (SA.R 4500)
£431 $720 €629 Miner with coco pan (53x36cm-21x14in) s.d.75 W/C. 20-Oct-3 Stephan Welz, Johannesburg #614 est:4000-6000 (SA.R 5000)

SIHVONEN, Oli (1921-1991) American
£1006 $1800 €1469 Three by 3, red, light red, violet (76x76cm-30x30in) s.i.verso acrylic. 16-May-4 Wright, Chicago #285/R est:2000-3000
£1285 $2300 €1876 Three by 3, dark green, scarlet, blue (91x91cm-36x36in) s.i.verso acrylic. 16-May-4 Wright, Chicago #284/R est:2500-3500
£1397 $2500 €2040 Three by 3, 3 blues and dark green (76x76cm-30x30in) s.i.verso. 16-May-4 Wright, Chicago #286/R est:2000-3000
£1676 $3000 €2447 Matrix-on orange, sextet in orange (76x76cm-30x30in) s. s.i.d.1966 masonite. 16-May-4 Wright, Chicago #287/R est:2000-3000
£1676 $3000 €2447 Origin (61x91cm-24x36in) s. masonite. 16-May-4 Wright, Chicago #288/R est:900-1200
£2500 $4250 €3650 Ascendant (81x104cm-32x41in) s.on stretcher masonite. 9-Nov-3 Wright, Chicago #382 est:2000-3000
£2500 $4250 €3650 Symmetric variance no.8 (91x91cm-36x36in) s.verso masonite. 9-Nov-3 Wright, Chicago #381 est:3000-4000
£2654 $4750 €3875 Sextet (132x107cm-52x42in) s. 16-May-4 Wright, Chicago #289/R est:3000-4000
£2941 $5000 €4294 Configuration (150x84cm-59x33in) s.verso masonite. 9-Nov-3 Wright, Chicago #383 est:2000-3000
£2941 $5000 €4294 Vernal equinox (48x94cm-19x37in) s. masonite. 9-Nov-3 Wright, Chicago #380 est:2000-3000

SIIKAMAKI, Arvo (1943-) Finnish
Sculpture
£1351 $2419 €2000 Stranger (81cm-32in) s.d.75 bronze. 8-May-4 Bukowskis, Helsinki #225/R est:1000-2000
£1689 $3024 €2500 Nefertiti (46x66cm-18x26in) s.d.97 num.1/1 bronze. 8-May-4 Bukowskis, Helsinki #218/R est:2500-3500
£3716 $6652 €5500 Nocturne V (42x60x20cm-17x24x8in) s.d.1986 num.1/1 spectrolite. 8-May-4 Bukowskis, Helsinki #215/R est:5500-6500
£5245 $8916 €7500 Looking towards the future (69x71cm-27x28in) s.d.95 marble. 29-Nov-3 Bukowskis, Helsinki #241/R est:5000-7000

SIJTHOFF, Gisbertus Jan (1867-1949) Dutch
£360 $613 €526 Preparing tea (47x36cm-19x14in) s. 21-Nov-3 Walker's, Ottawa #203/R (C.D 800)
£1447 $2620 €2200 Larens interior with a mother gazing at a new-born in a basket (39x49cm-15x19in) s. 19-Apr-4 Glerum, Amsterdam #240/R est:2500-3000

SIKA, Jutta (1877-?) Swiss
Works on paper
£690 $1145 €1000 Flowers (36x50cm-14x20in) s.d.1932 mixed media. 30-Sep-3 Dorotheum, Vienna #366/R

SIKSTROM, Cecilia (1962) Swedish
£2644 $4494 €3860 Grey boudoir (100x60cm-39x24in) s.d.1994 verso. 4-Nov-3 Bukowskis, Stockholm #604/R est:18000-20000 (S.KR 35000)

SILAS, Ellis (fl.1916-1935) British
Works on paper
£300 $510 €438 Polperro Harbour, Cornwall (24x35cm-9x14in) s. W/C bodycol. 4-Nov-3 Dreweatt Neate, Newbury #68/R

SILAS, Louis (19th C) French
£6538 $11246 €9545 Scenes with cupids, flowers and parrots (206x342cm-81x135in) oil on canvas on screen in six parts. 3-Dec-3 AB Stockholms Auktionsverk #2574/R est:60000-80000 (S.KR 85000)

SILBER, Esther (20th C) American
£252 $400 €368 Southwest landscape (20x30cm-8x12in) s. masonite painted c.1940-50's. 13-Sep-3 Selkirks, St. Louis #58

SILBERBAUER, Fritz (1883-1974) Austrian
Works on paper
£350 $601 €500 Scenery (81x52cm-32x20in) mono. chl. 4-Dec-3 Dorotheum, Graz #167/R

SILBERMANN, Jean Claude (1935-) French
Works on paper
£590 $986 €850 Ils se souvient bien (62x47cm-24x19in) s.d.1975 W/C. 21-Oct-3 Campo, Vlaamse Kaai #1074

SILBERSTEIN, Nathan (1884-?) Polish
£348 $637 €508 Still life with fruit, flowers and urns (48x61cm-19x24in) s.d.1918. 4-Jun-4 Zofingen, Switzerland #2523 (S.FR 800)

SILBERT, Max (1871-?) French
£2060 $3750 €3008 Lacemakers (55x46cm-22x18in) s. 29-Jun-4 Sotheby's, New York #120/R est:3000-5000
£3843 $6880 €5611 Le jardin du Luxembourg (64x53cm-25x21in) s. 26-May-4 AB Stockholms Auktionsverk #2420/R est:25000-30000 (S.KR 52000)

SILDAR, William (20th C) American
Works on paper
£227 $400 €331 Untitled (51x135cm-20x53in) collage mixed media wall relief exec 1968. 23-May-4 Hindman, Chicago #1093/R

SILFONE, Gianni (20th C) American
£266 $425 €388 Brown county home (30x41cm-12x16in) s. canvasboard. 17-May-3 Bunte, Elgin #1298

SILKE, Eris (1907-) South African
Works on paper
£336 $608 €491 Two women (25x20cm-10x8in) s.d.85 mixed media on board. 30-Mar-4 Stephan Welz, Johannesburg #481 est:3000-5000 (SA.R 4000)

SILLEMANS, Experiens (attrib) (1611-1653) Dutch
Works on paper
£4000 $7160 €6000 Shipping in a harbour with figures on a quay (15x21cm-6x8in) s.d.1652 ink pen oil panel. 17-May-4 Christie's, Amsterdam #98/R est:6000-8000

SILLEN, Herman (1857-1908) Swedish
£707 $1223 €1032 Fishing boats off the Rock of Gibraltar (34x46cm-13x18in) s/. 15-Dec-3 Lilla Bukowskis, Stockholm #1011 (S.KR 9000)
£1256 $2249 €1834 Coastal landscape with sailing boat, Arildslage (41x61cm-16x24in) s.d.91. 26-May-4 AB Stockholms Auktionsverk #2094/R est:12000-15000 (S.KR 17000)
£3231 $5557 €4717 Vessels off Kronborg Palace (30x48cm-12x19in) s.d.91. 2-Dec-3 Bukowskis, Stockholm #123/R est:40000-50000 (S.KR 42000)
Works on paper
£1404 $2514 €2050 Rocks and breakers (29x52cm-11x20in) s.d.96 pastel. 26-May-4 AB Stockholms Auktionsverk #2243/R est:18000-20000 (S.KR 19000)
£2308 $3969 €3370 Sailing vessel on Blekinge coast (29x52cm-11x20in) s.d.96 pastel canvas. 3-Dec-3 AB Stockholms Auktionsverk #2450/R est:25000-30000 (S.KR 30000)

SILLMAN, Amy (1966-) American
£3374 $5500 €4926 River (107x117cm-42x46in) s.i.d.1997 stretcher oil gouache collage panel prov. 23-Sep-3 Christie's, Rockefeller NY #67/R est:5000-7000

SILO, Adam (1674-1772) Dutch
Works on paper
£1900 $3268 €2774 Dutch men-o-war and other shipping at a harbour mouth (21x30cm-8x12in) s. gouache. 4-Dec-3 Mellors & Kirk, Nottingham #841/R est:2000-2500

SILSETH, Eli (1927-1991) Norwegian
£244 $449 €366 Beach, sea and sky (80x64cm-31x25in) s. 14-Jun-4 Blomqvist, Lysaker #1359 (N.KR 3000)

SILVA BRUHNS, Ivan da (1881-1980) French
Works on paper
£4942 $8500 €7215 Design for a carpet for Maharani's bedroom in the Maharaja of Indore's Manik Bagh Palace (35x25cm-14x10in) s. gouache lit. 8-Dec-3 Phillips, New York #105/R est:6000-8000

SILVA, Carlos (1930-1987) Argentinian
£1676 $3000 €2447 Pirogne (70x62cm-28x24in) s.i.d.1979 verso acrylic cardboard. 4-May-4 Arroyo, Buenos Aires #13/R est:3000

SILVA, Francis Augustus (1835-1886) American
£5308 $9500 €7750 Landscape. 6-May-4 Shannon's, Milford #20/R
£5882 $10000 €8588 Venetian scene (58x43cm-23x17in) s. painted c.1879 prov. 30-Oct-3 Phillips, New York #47/R est:10000-15000
£7453 $12000 €10881 Coastal seascape (10x25cm-4x10in) s. panel. 20-Aug-3 James Julia, Fairfield #1308/R est:15000-20000
£12011 $21500 €17536 Sailboats off rocky coast (18x43cm-7x17in) s. panel. 8-Jan-4 James Julia, Fairfield #514/R est:12500-17500
£15116 $26000 €22069 Rocky coast (23x46cm-9x18in) init. prov. 4-Dec-3 Christie's, Rockefeller NY #12/R
£31977 $55000 €46686 Coastal sunset (51x91cm-20x36in) s.d.73. 4-Dec-3 Christie's, Rockefeller NY #7/R
£58140 $100000 €84884 On the Hudson (51x91cm-20x36in) s.d.86 prov.lit. 3-Dec-3 Sotheby's, New York #106/R est:100000-150000
£272727 $480000 €398181 Hudson river looking toward the Catskills (51x102cm-20x40in) s.d.1871 prov.exhib.lit. 18-May-4 Christie's, Rockefeller NY #36/R est:500000-700000
Works on paper
£1934 $3500 €2824 New England coastline (30x51cm-12x20in) s. W/C. 16-Apr-4 James Julia, Fairfield #552/R est:5000-10000

SILVA, Jerald (20th C) American
Works on paper
£326 $600 €476 Diana (119x119cm-47x47in) s.d.77 W/C. 28-Mar-4 Bonhams & Butterfields, San Francisco #2754 est:800-1200

SILVA, Jose Antonio da (1909-) Brazilian
£567 $1020 €850 Le panier de fruits (41x60cm-16x24in) s. 26-Apr-4 Tajan, Paris #274
£3297 $6033 €4946 Reindeer sleigh transporting wood (60x100cm-24x39in) s.d.1987. 6-Jul-4 Bolsa de Arte, Rio de Janeiro #145/R (B.R 18000)

SILVA, Oscar Pereira da (1867-1939) Brazilian
£2198 $4022 €3297 Landscape (60x50cm-24x20in) s. 6-Jul-4 Bolsa de Arte, Rio de Janeiro #129/R (B.R 12000)
£4212 $7456 €6318 Country landscape (37x92cm-15x36in) s. 27-Apr-4 Bolsa de Arte, Rio de Janeiro #18/R (B.R 23000)
£5495 $9725 €8243 Portrait of a slave girl (42x29cm-17x11in) s.i.d.1892. 27-Apr-4 Bolsa de Arte, Rio de Janeiro #31/R (B.R 30000)

SILVA, William P (1859-1948) American
£635 $1200 €927 Del Monte Hotel (20x25cm-8x10in) s. canvasboard. 17-Feb-4 John Moran, Pasadena #10b/R
£1455 $2750 €2124 The tranquil hour (25x20cm-10x8in) i. verso canvasboard prov. 17-Feb-4 John Moran, Pasadena #7/R est:3000-4000
£1500 $2400 €2190 Wind blown pines (51x61cm-20x24in) s. 20-Sep-3 Nadeau, Windsor #164/R
£1648 $3000 €2406 Eucalyptus, Southern California (30x38cm-12x15in) s. canvasboard. 15-Jun-4 John Moran, Pasadena #64b est:3000-4000
£1858 $3400 €2713 Bridge magnolia gardens (25x20cm-10x8in) s. canvasboard. 5-Jun-4 Neal Auction Company, New Orleans #355/R est:1500-2500
£2581 $4750 €3768 A blue day near Carmel, 17 Mile Drive (50x61cm-20x24in) s. i.verso panel. 8-Jun-4 Bonhams & Butterfields, San Francisco #4326/R est:4000-6000
£3297 $6000 €4814 Fountain in the Garden of Versailles (28x36cm-11x14in) s. i.verso canvasboard. 15-Jun-4 John Moran, Pasadena #64a est:3500-5000
£13736 $25000 €20055 Morning light in the garden of dreams (41x51cm-16x20in) s. i.d.1921 verso canvasboard prov.exhib. 15-Jun-4 John Moran, Pasadena #64 est:10000-15000
Works on paper
£503 $950 €734 Castle of Segovia, Spain (20x13cm-8x5in) i. verso pastel. 17-Feb-4 John Moran, Pasadena #12/R

SILVAIN, Christian (1950-) Belgian
Works on paper
£530 $964 €800 L'avion (106x75cm-42x30in) s. i.verso mixed media. 16-Jun-4 Hotel des Ventes Mosan, Brussels #286

SILVANI, F (1823-1899) Italian
£1119 $1869 €1600 Venice in the sunshine (25x43cm-10x17in) s. board. 11-Oct-3 Hans Stahl, Hamburg #68/R est:1400
£2222 $3778 €3200 Sailing boats off Venice (41x69cm-16x27in) s. 28-Oct-3 Dorotheum, Vienna #30/R est:3000-3500

SILVANI, Ferdinando (1823-1899) Italian
£676 $1162 €987 Venice (25x42cm-10x17in) s. board. 8-Dec-3 Philippe Schuler, Zurich #3435 (S.FR 1500)
£2308 $3923 €3300 Fishing boats on the Lagoon, Venice (56x88cm-22x35in) s. 20-Nov-3 Van Ham, Cologne #1871/R est:3000

SILVER, William W (19th C) American
Photographs
£10582 $20000 €15450 Panorama of New York City (32x39cm-13x15in) one i. albumen nine. 17-Feb-4 Swann Galleries, New York #18/R est:14000-18000

SILVERMAN, Burton (1928-) American
Works on paper
£276 $500 €403 Shoka (38x25cm-15x10in) W/C. 16-Apr-4 American Auctioneer #373/R
£552 $1000 €806 Biker (46x53cm-18x21in) W/C. 16-Apr-4 American Auctioneer #374/R

SILVERS, Robert (1968-) British?
Photographs
£4800 $8688 €7008 Flandrin - jeune homme (122x122cm-48x48in) s. cibachrome mounted on aluminium executed c.1999. 1-Apr-4 Christie's, Kensington #309/R est:1500-2000

SILVERSTEIN, Shel (1932-1999) American
Works on paper
£1143 $2000 €1669 But it's not as if we were stealing the song Charlie (28x24cm-11x9in) s. ink paper on board exec Aug 1956. 17-Dec-3 Christie's, Rockefeller NY #40/R est:2000-3000
£1714 $3000 €2502 Tell me, Mr Silverstein, is it true what they say about American women ? (30x21cm-12x8in) s. ink paper on board exec May 1957. 17-Dec-3 Christie's, Rockefeller NY #41/R est:3000-4000
£31429 $55000 €45886 Silverstein among the hippies (43x28cm-17x11in) pen ink twelve exec Sept 1968. 17-Dec-3 Christie's, Rockefeller NY #118/R est:6000-8000

SILVESTRE, Albert (1869-1954) Swiss
£1009 $1685 €1463 Savieze (37x45cm-15x18in) s.d. i.verso. 21-Jun-3 Galerie du Rhone, Sion #425/R est:2000-3000 (S.FR 2200)

SILVESTRE, Louis (17/18th C) French
£3020 $5557 €4500 Child portrait of Princess Theresia Benedicta von Sachsen (102x82cm-40x32in) prov. 25-Mar-4 Dr Fritz Nagel, Stuttgart #672/R est:5800
£3169 $5482 €4500 Portrait of Princess Theresia Benedicta von Sachsen as a child (102x82cm-40x32in) prov. 11-Dec-3 Dr Fritz Nagel, Stuttgart #484/R est:8500

SILVESTRE, Louis (younger-attrib) (1675-1760) French
£2715 $4344 €3964 Girl (117x92cm-46x36in) bears mono. 19-Sep-3 Koller, Zurich #3036/R est:6000-9000 (S.FR 6000)
Works on paper
£738 $1358 €1100 Paysage boise avec paysans au repos (43x32cm-17x13in) sanguine. 24-Mar-4 Claude Boisgirard, Paris #24/R

SILVESTRE, Nicolas Charles de (1699-1767) French
Works on paper
£1778 $3200 €2596 Two shepherds sitting under a tree in a landscape (35x25cm-14x10in) red chk. 22-Jan-4 Christie's, Rockefeller NY #100/R est:3000-5000

SILVESTRE, Paul (1884-?) French
Sculpture
£1643 $2744 €2350 Jeune fille aux oies (48x45x24cm-19x18x9in) s.st.f.Susses green pat bronze. 25-Jun-3 Maigret, Paris #206/R est:2300-2500

SILVESTRI, Tullio (1880-1963) Italian
£1748 $3007 €2500 Quiet village (90x80cm-35x31in) s. board. 3-Dec-3 Stadion, Trieste #973/R est:2000-3000

SILVY, Camille (1834-1910) British
Photographs
£7237 $13316 €11000 Lecture du premier ordre du jour de l'Armee d'Italie (25x18cm-10x7in) st.sig. albumen print. 23-Jun-4 Rieunier, Paris #45/R est:6000-7000

SIMA, Joseph (1891-1971) Czechoslovakian
£7002 $13023 €10223 Landscape (27x35cm-11x14in) s.d.934. 6-Mar-4 Dorotheum, Prague #127/R est:300000-450000 (C.KR 340000)
£12500 $20625 €18000 Toile grise-graphique gris (81x100cm-32x39in) s.d.1960 prov. 2-Jul-3 Cornette de St.Cyr, Paris #19/R est:18000-22000
£14966 $26790 €22000 Untitled (81x65cm-32x26in) s.d.1957. 21-Mar-4 Calmels Cohen, Paris #47/R est:10000-12000
£15172 $28069 €22000 Terre-lumiere (100x81cm-39x32in) s.d.1965 i.verso prov.exhib. 13-Feb-4 Charbonneaux, Paris #80/R est:10000-12000
Works on paper
£2252 $4098 €3400 Paysage sous un ciel jaune (58x73cm-23x29in) s.d.23 gouache. 18-Jun-4 Charbonneaux, Paris #114/R est:2500-3000
£2857 $5114 €4200 Pouvoir de la Betise (43x29cm-17x11in) s.d.51 crayon prov. 21-Mar-4 Calmels Cohen, Paris #25/R est:4000-6000
£3061 $5480 €4500 Untitled (65x50cm-26x20in) s.d.58 W/C graphite. 21-Mar-4 Calmels Cohen, Paris #24/R est:5000-6000
£6434 $11066 €9200 Le corps d'une femme dans un decor (33x38cm-13x15in) s.d.1927 W/C. 6-Dec-3 Renaud, Paris #322/R

SIMAK, Lev (1896-?) Czechoslovakian
£439 $746 €641 Girl from Hodonin (65x51cm-26x20in) s.d.49. 29-Nov-3 Dorotheum, Prague #76/R est:20000-30000 (C.KR 20000)

SIMARD, Marie Louise (?) French
Sculpture
£19500 $31005 €28470 Stallion (39x35cm-15x14in) st.f.La Stele i. bronze exec.c.1925. 9-Sep-3 Sotheby's, Olympia #375/R est:12000-18000

SIMBARI, Nicola (1927-) Italian
£530 $970 €800 Arbre en bord de mer (81x54cm-32x21in) s. 7-Apr-4 Piasa, Paris #115
£695 $1300 €1015 Fiumicino (41x51cm-16x20in) s.indis.d. 25-Feb-4 Doyle, New York #53/R
£856 $1600 €1250 Liguanea, girl with parasol (46x61cm-18x24in) s.d.64 i.stretcher. 25-Feb-4 Doyle, New York #54/R est:3000-5000
£1283 $2400 €1873 Coastal scene, Tampico (76x91cm-30x36in) s.d.64. 25-Feb-4 Doyle, New York #55/R est:3000-5000
£1730 $3200 €2526 Italian coast (46x61cm-18x24in) 12-Mar-4 Du Mouchelle, Detroit #2114/R est:4000-6000
£1838 $3400 €2683 Lebeccio (79x104cm-31x41in) 12-Mar-4 Du Mouchelle, Detroit #2116/R est:5000-6000
£2148 $3500 €3136 Woman at the beach (95x104cm-37x41in) s. 28-Sep-3 Bonhams & Butterfields, Los Angeles #7073 est:2000-3000
£2162 $4000 €3157 Turquoise marine (61x81cm-24x32in) 12-Mar-4 Du Mouchelle, Detroit #2115/R est:5000-6000
£2198 $4000 €3209 Ischitana (70x100cm-28x39in) s. acrylic prov. 29-Jun-4 Sotheby's, New York #368/R est:3000-5000
£2747 $5000 €4011 Seated girl, patio (90x99cm-35x39in) s. prov. 29-Jun-4 Sotheby's, New York #367/R est:3000-5000
£2987 $4750 €4361 Tournasol (71x51cm-28x20in) s.d.67 prov. 9-Sep-3 Arthur James, Florida #108
£2994 $5000 €4371 Procidana (131x160cm-52x63in) s.i.stretcher acrylic painted c.1983. 7-Oct-3 Sotheby's, New York #329 est:6000-8000
£3293 $5500 €4808 Nude in scarlet (130x161cm-51x63in) s. s.d.1983 verso acrylic. 7-Oct-3 Sotheby's, New York #328 est:6000-8000
£3297 $6000 €4814 Squall (70x100cm-28x39in) s. acrylic prov. 29-Jun-4 Sotheby's, New York #369/R est:3000-5000
£4324 $8000 €6313 Foce Verde (90x110cm-35x43in) s. s.i.d.1980 verso acrylic. 12-Feb-4 Sotheby's, New York #63/R est:4000-6000

£5405 $10000 €7891 Pescadora (101x130cm-40x51in) s. s.d.1984 verso acrylic. 12-Feb-4 Sotheby's, New York #62/R est:4000-6000
£6667 $12000 €9734 Porto d'Ischia (61x79cm-24x31in) s.d.66 prov. 20-Jan-4 Arthur James, Florida #44
Works on paper
£671 $1100 €973 Figure of a young girl standing next to an sunlit wall (76x53cm-30x21in) s.d.68 gouache. 31-May-3 Brunk, Ashville #110/R

SIMBERG, Hugo (1873-1917) Finnish
£2162 $3870 €3200 Coastal meadow (26x35cm-10x14in) s. board. 8-May-4 Bukowskis, Helsinki #192/R est:2500-3000
£2667 $4773 €4000 Waterfall (42x52cm-17x20in) s. 15-May-4 Hagelstam, Helsinki #96/R est:4000
£2797 $4755 €4000 View of Outokumpo (42x52cm-17x20in) s. board lit. 29-Nov-3 Bukowskis, Helsinki #107/R est:5000-5500
£5035 $8559 €7200 Mountain landscape from Kaukasien (31x20cm-12x8in) s. board. 29-Nov-3 Bukowskis, Helsinki #183/R est:6000-7000
£5070 $8772 €7200 Beach, Niemenlautta (26x35cm-10x14in) cardboard. 13-Dec-3 Hagelstam, Helsinki #69/R est:5000
£5270 $9434 €7800 The Royal yacht in Helsingfors Harbour (41x50cm-16x20in) s. board lit. 8-May-4 Bukowskis, Helsinki #177/R est:5000-8000
£7343 $12483 €10500 Tooth-ache (7x5cm-3x2in) s. board. 29-Nov-3 Bukowskis, Helsinki #195/R est:5000-6000
£9567 $17124 €14350 Borgaa river (37x47cm-15x19in) s.d.1912 lit. 15-May-4 Hagelstam, Helsinki #97/R est:15000
£10667 $19093 €16000 Figure on skies (20x16cm-8x6in) s. panel. 15-May-4 Hagelstam, Helsinki #98/R est:12000
£20423 $35331 €29000 Beach, Brittany (54x69cm-21x27in) s.d.1910. 13-Dec-3 Hagelstam, Helsinki #68/R est:30000
£54054 $96757 €80000 Sunny day in July - woman feeding chicken (223x183cm-88x72in) s.d.1911 lit. 8-May-4 Bukowskis, Helsinki #129/R est:80000-120000
Prints
£2133 $3819 €3200 Waves in summer (7x12cm-3x5in) s. col line etching lit. 15-May-4 Hagelstam, Helsinki #99/R est:1000
Works on paper
£394 $631 €560 Restlessness in the wood (9x23cm-4x9in) s. Indian ink exec.c.1896. 18-Sep-3 Hagelstam, Helsinki #806
£1761 $3046 €2500 Tree and cliff (24x32cm-9x13in) s.d.1898 Indian ink. 13-Dec-3 Hagelstam, Helsinki #61/R est:500
£11268 $19493 €16000 Fantasy scene - girl and animals (24x37cm-9x15in) s. W/C lit. 13-Dec-3 Hagelstam, Helsinki #67/R est:15000

SIMCOCK, Alice J (19/20th C) British
£800 $1304 €1168 Lion and Lioness resting (60x90cm-24x35in) s.d.1908. 24-Sep-3 Peter Wilson, Nantwich #1

SIMCOCK, Jack (1929-) British
£480 $773 €701 Rural Barn (31x49cm-12x19in) s.d.1965 board. 19-Feb-3 Peter Wilson, Nantwich #58

SIMELLI, Carlo Baldassare (19th C) Italian
Photographs
£1944 $3500 €2838 Cloud study, near Rome (21x28cm-8x11in) albumen print. 22-Apr-4 Phillips, New York #153/R est:5000-7000

SIMEN, Clothilde (attrib) (19th C) ?
£933 $1671 €1400 La Reine Marie-Antoinette conduite a l'echafaud (133x104cm-52x41in) indis.sig.d.1875. 11-May-4 Vanderkindere, Brussels #104

SIMENON, Regine Renchon (1906-) Belgian
£685 $1164 €1000 Boulevard anime en hiver (101x75cm-40x30in) s. 10-Nov-3 Horta, Bruxelles #372

SIMENSEN, Sigvald (?-1920) Norwegian
£334 $557 €488 Winter storm along the coast (56x99cm-22x39in) s. 17-Nov-3 Blomqvist, Lysaker #1299 (N.KR 4000)
£571 $1051 €834 Figures and boats by Vestland's fjord (85x64cm-33x25in) s. 29-Mar-4 Blomqvist, Lysaker #1304 (N.KR 7200)
£719 $1337 €1050 Landscape from Lofoten, Norway (100x129cm-39x51in) s. 2-Mar-4 Rasmussen, Copenhagen #1413/R (D.KR 8000)

SIMETI, Turi (1929-) Italian
£915 $1520 €1300 Untitled Bianco (50x50cm-20x20in) s.d.1998 verso. 14-Jun-3 Meeting Art, Vercelli #62/R
£1149 $2022 €1700 Composition (69x99cm-27x39in) s.d.1963 enamel paper on canvas. 22-May-4 Galleria Pananti, Florence #418/R est:1800-2000
£1361 $2476 €2000 Untitled (40x50cm-16x20in) s.verso prov. 6-Feb-4 Galleria Rosenberg, Milan #125/R est:1000
£1544 $2856 €2300 Extroflexion (50x40cm-20x16in) s.d.1972 acrylic. 11-Mar-4 Galleria Pace, Milan #134/R est:1500-2000
£1549 $2572 €2200 Untitled - Black (80x80cm-31x31in) s.d.2000 verso. 14-Jun-3 Meeting Art, Vercelli #557/R est:2000
£1745 $3123 €2600 Untitled (77x48cm-30x19in) s.d.2002 verso canvas on board. 30-May-4 Meeting Art, Vercelli #4 est:2000
£3049 $5000 €4452 Untitled (40x40cm-16x16in) s.d.65 verso oil wood on canvas two. 28-May-3 Sotheby's, Amsterdam #21/R est:5000-7000
£4573 $7500 €6677 Forme ovali al negativo (70x60cm-28x24in) s.d.66 verso canvas on panel prov. 28-May-3 Sotheby's, Amsterdam #51/R est:5000-7000
Works on paper
£867 $1595 €1300 Four white ovals (50x70cm-20x28in) s.d.78 mixed media card. 8-Jun-4 Finarte Semenzato, Milan #256/R est:900-1400

SIMIL, Emilcar (1944-) Canadian
£1133 $2029 €1700 Portrait de femme (60x60cm-24x24in) s. panel. 17-May-4 Rogeon, Paris #79/R

SIMILA, Seppo (?) Finnish
£278 $464 €400 Rowan berries (50x46cm-20x18in) s.d.84. 26-Oct-3 Bukowskis, Helsinki #499/R

SIMKIN, Richard (1840-1926) British
Works on paper
£380 $612 €551 Piper and quarter master sergeant, Black watch (24x16cm-9x6in) s. W/C. 21-Aug-3 Bonhams, Edinburgh #1221
£380 $631 €555 Band of the Royal Welsh Fusiliers (21x37cm-8x15in) s. W/C. 1-Oct-3 Woolley & Wallis, Salisbury #69/R

SIMM, Franz Xaver (1853-1918) Austrian
£4054 $6973 €5919 Distinguished lady wearing a black hat while sewing (47x31cm-19x12in) s. board prov. 8-Dec-3 Philippe Schuler, Zurich #3436/R est:12000-16000 (S.FR 9000)

SIMM, William Norris (?) British
£480 $859 €701 Lilac time (48x61cm-19x24in) 13-May-4 Mitchells, Cockermouth #1097

SIMMEN, Henri (20th C) ?
Sculpture
£1748 $2920 €2500 Tete de femme (28cm-11in) s. col sandstone. 24-Jun-3 Millon & Associes, Paris #220/R est:2800-3500
£5455 $9109 €7800 Tete cubiste (16x17x6cm-6x7x2in) s. brown sandstone. 24-Jun-3 Millon & Associes, Paris #221/R est:2500-3000
£6294 $10510 €9000 Tete de femme cubiste (23x19x6cm-9x7x2in) s. col sandstone. 24-Jun-3 Millon & Associes, Paris #219/R est:3500-4000

SIMMERS, Connie (1941-) British
£600 $1116 €876 Winter feeding (61x71cm-24x28in) s. prov. 4-Mar-4 Christie's, Kensington #238/R

SIMMLER, Friedrich Karl Joseph (1801-1872) German
£1806 $3015 €2600 Romantic landscape (32x39cm-13x15in) mono. lit. 25-Oct-3 Bergmann, Erlangen #920/R
Works on paper
£232 $425 €339 Wild horses gathering during a storm (21x27cm-8x11in) s. black chk pencil. 29-Jan-4 Swann Galleries, New York #328/R

SIMMLER, Wilhelm (1840-1914) German
£276 $461 €400 Young girl with boy in wood (31x44cm-12x17in) s. board. 9-Jul-3 Hugo Ruef, Munich #201
£2824 $4800 €4123 Hunting party (36x33cm-14x13in) mono. 22-Nov-3 Jackson's, Cedar Falls #12/R est:7000-9000
£3497 $5944 €5000 On the right track (80x116cm-31x46in) s. 24-Nov-3 Dorotheum, Vienna #202/R est:3500-4500

SIMMONS, Charles Eyres (?-1955) British
Works on paper
£440 $695 €638 Figures conversing in an English village (25x36cm-10x14in) s. W/C. 17-Nov-2 Desmond Judd, Cranbrook #864

SIMMONS, Edward Emerson (1852-1931) American
£968 $1800 €1413 On the river, New York (30x40cm-12x16in) s.i. canvasboard. 5-Mar-4 Skinner, Boston #585/R est:2000-3000
£1257 $2250 €1835 Europa and the bull (33x41cm-13x16in) s.stretcher. 26-May-4 Doyle, New York #44/R est:1500-2500
£2800 $4676 €4088 Low tide, St. Ives harbour (30x46cm-12x18in) s.d.1887 verso. 14-Oct-3 David Lay, Penzance #78 est:1000-2000
£9434 $15000 €13774 Spanish town (54x34cm-21x13in) s.d.1884. 12-Sep-3 Skinner, Boston #309/R est:25000
£34091 $60000 €49773 Contemplation - Portrait of Mrs Fisher (91x61cm-36x24in) s.d.1913 s.i.d.verso prov. 18-May-4 Christie's, Rockefeller NY #61/R est:60000-80000
£116279 $200000 €169767 September afternoon (55x35cm-22x14in) s.d.1891 i.verso. 3-Dec-3 Doyle, New York #177/R est:40000-60000

SIMMONS, Eyres (fl.1902-1914) British
Works on paper
£260 $450 €380 Fishing boat under full sail in an estuary (12x17cm-5x7in) s. W/C. 11-Dec-3 Lane, Penzance #121
£272 $501 €397 High Street, St. Peter Port (34x25cm-13x10in) s.i. W/C. 14-Jun-4 Waddingtons, Toronto #53/R (C.D 675)
£300 $525 €438 West country coastal scene (36x53cm-14x21in) s. W/C. 16-Dec-3 Gorringes, Bexhill #1181
£300 $558 €438 West country coastal scene with beached boats and church tower (23x12cm-9x5in) s. W/C. 4-Mar-4 Bonhams, Cornwall #227/R
£330 $597 €482 Harbour scene with boats at anchor (25x41cm-10x16in) s. W/C. 31-Mar-4 Brightwells, Leominster #870
£580 $1067 €847 View along a beach. View of a harbour (25x35cm-10x14in) s. W/C pair. 23-Mar-4 Bonhams, Knightsbridge #73/R

SIMMONS, Gary (1964-) American
£1133 $2029 €1700 Le lustre (61x61cm-24x24in) 12-May-4 Chochon-Barre & Allardi, Paris #27 est:150-200
£1667 $2983 €2500 Oddles of bows (122x152cm-48x60in) 12-May-4 Chochon-Barre & Allardi, Paris #24 est:150-200
£1800 $3222 €2700 Composition sur tableau d'ecolier (115x144cm-45x57in) d.1992 oil chl panel. 12-May-4 Chochon-Barre & Allardi, Paris #23 est:150-200

Works on paper
£267 $477 €400 Untitled (23x15cm-9x6in) pastel. 12-May-4 Chochon-Barre & Allardi, Paris #29
£767 $1372 €1150 Swamp drawning no 5 (103x70cm-41x28in) pastel exhib. 12-May-4 Chochon-Barre & Allardi, Paris #22
£1400 $2506 €2100 Untitled (122x152cm-48x60in) mixed media. 12-May-4 Chochon-Barre & Allardi, Paris #25 est:150-200

SIMMONS, J C (19th C) British
£1900 $3173 €2774 Figures conversing in south eastern coastal landscape (61x91cm-24x36in) s.d.1845. 16-Nov-3 Desmond Judd, Cranbrook #1041

SIMMONS, Laurie (1949-) American
Photographs
£9040 $16000 €13198 Walking camera, Jimmy the camera (163x122cm-64x48in) s.d.1987 num.2/10 verso cibachrome print prov. 27-Apr-4 Sotheby's, New York #40/R est:7000-10000

SIMMONS, William St Clair (fl.1878-1899) British
Works on paper
£950 $1758 €1387 Washing clothes in a stream (28x20cm-11x8in) s.i. 9-Mar-4 Gorringes, Lewes #1993

SIMOLDI, A (20th C) Italian?
£1100 $1936 €1606 Watering the horses (102x76cm-40x30in) s. board. 19-May-4 Dreweatt Neate, Newbury #78 est:1000-1500

SIMON, Armand (1906-1981) Belgian
Works on paper
£433 $793 €650 Composition surrealiste (31x28cm-12x11in) s.d.48 pen. 7-Jun-4 Palais de Beaux Arts, Brussels #194

SIMON, Claude (1913-) French
Works on paper
£1133 $2085 €1700 La table de travail de l'ecrivain (21x22cm-8x9in) s. crayon. 9-Jun-4 Piasa, Paris #238/R est:1000-1200

SIMON, Émile (1890-1976) French
£1007 $1652 €1400 Bretonne dans un interieur (38x46cm-15x18in) s. panel. 3-Jun-3 Livinec, Gaudcheau & Jezequel, Rennes #60/R
£1329 $2259 €1900 Vue de l'eglise de Languiana, Finistere (38x46cm-15x18in) s. panel. 28-Nov-3 Drouot Estimations, Paris #151
£1987 $3715 €3000 Procession en Bretagne (38x46cm-15x18in) s. panel. 24-Jul-4 Thierry & Lannon, Brest #214/R est:2000-3000
£2113 $3697 €3000 Pecheurs sur la cote pres de la chaumiere (46x55cm-18x22in) s. 21-Dec-3 Thierry & Lannon, Brest #210b/R est:1200-1500
£2133 $3819 €3200 Scene de marche a Douarnenez (45x54cm-18x21in) s. panel. 16-May-4 Thierry & Lannon, Brest #370/R est:1200-1500
£2333 $4317 €3500 Bruleurs de Goemon a Notre Dame de la Joie (27x35cm-11x14in) s. 14-Jul-4 Livinec, Gaudcheau & Jezequel, Rennes #193/R
£2394 $4190 €3400 Jour de pardon a Ste Anne La Palud (33x41cm-13x16in) s. panel. 21-Dec-3 Thierry & Lannon, Brest #361 est:2000-2500
£3521 $6162 €5000 Pardon de Ste Anne la Palud (81x65cm-32x26in) s. 21-Dec-3 Thierry & Lannon, Brest #219c est:4000-4600

SIMON, François (1818-1896) French
£4967 $9089 €7500 Le retour du troupeau (115x207cm-45x81in) s. pair. 9-Apr-4 Claude Aguttes, Neuilly #73/R est:7000-9000

SIMON, Gustav (19th C) Austrian
£829 $1410 €1210 Portrait of woman wearing red hat (46x36cm-18x14in) s. oval. 10-Nov-3 Rasmussen, Vejle #371/R (D.KR 9000)

SIMON, Hermann Gustave (1846-1895) American
£5000 $8500 €7300 Monarchs of peace (114x76cm-45x30in) s.d.1886 i.stretcher prov. 18-Nov-3 John Moran, Pasadena #159a est:3000-5000
Works on paper
£3779 $6500 €5517 English setter putting up woodcock. s.d.1896 pencil W/C bodycol. 5-Dec-3 Christie's, Rockefeller NY #85/R est:4000-6000

SIMON, Herve (1888-?) Belgian
£510 $913 €750 Nature morte aux oranges (40x50cm-16x20in) s. 16-Mar-4 Vanderkindere, Brussels #396

SIMON, Jacques (1885-1965) French
Works on paper
£521 $844 €740 Cows at pasture (75x54cm-30x21in) s.d.1921 W/C. 11-Aug-3 Boscher, Cherbourg #794

SIMON, Lucien (1861-1945) French
£530 $991 €800 Baigneuse a la pointe Ste Marine (24x19cm-9x7in) panel double-sided. 24-Jul-4 Thierry & Lannon, Brest #218/R
£530 $991 €800 St Guenole (20x35cm-8x14in) 24-Jul-4 Thierry & Lannon, Brest #407
£667 $1193 €1000 Les soeurs a la plage. Portrait de religieuse (33x40cm-13x16in) cardboard double-sided. 16-May-4 Thierry & Lannon, Brest #186/R
£733 $1313 €1100 Joueurs de quilles (19x26cm-7x10in) panel. 16-May-4 Thierry & Lannon, Brest #178
£795 $1486 €1200 Le mur de Marrakech (23x33cm-9x13in) panel. 24-Jul-4 Thierry & Lannon, Brest #219/R
£927 $1734 €1400 Interieur d'eglise, la messe (32x39cm-13x15in) s. 24-Jul-4 Thierry & Lannon, Brest #221/R
£1000 $1790 €1500 Sortie de messe a Ste-Marine (41x32cm-16x13in) i. paper double-sided. 16-May-4 Thierry & Lannon, Brest #179/R est:1500-2000
£1761 $3081 €2500 Bapteme de Penhors (22x28cm-9x11in) panel double-sided. 21-Dec-3 Thierry & Lannon, Brest #209/R est:2500-3000
£2133 $3819 €3200 Les bruleurs de goemon (23x33cm-9x13in) panel. 16-May-4 Thierry & Lannon, Brest #181/R est:3000-4000
£2185 $4087 €3300 Couple de Bigouden pres du Semaphore (27x35cm-11x14in) s. panel. 24-Jul-4 Thierry & Lannon, Brest #217/R est:3000-4000
£2817 $4930 €4000 Barque sous voile devant le Chateau rose, Ste Marine (36x48cm-14x19in) 21-Dec-3 Thierry & Lannon, Brest #210/R est:4000-5000
£2848 $5325 €4300 La fermiere (46x55cm-18x22in) s. 24-Jul-4 Thierry & Lannon, Brest #216/R est:4000-5000
£3000 $5010 €4380 Bretons aux costumes de fete (37x45cm-15x18in) board prov. 22-Oct-3 Sotheby's, Olympia #96/R est:1200-1800
£4138 $7655 €6000 Sortie de messe en Pays Bigouden (16x22cm-6x9in) s. panel. 16-Feb-4 Giraudeau, Tours #105
£4539 $7580 €6400 Circus horses (73x92cm-29x36in) s. 14-Oct-3 Finarte Semenzato, Milan #82/R est:8000
£4966 $8243 €7200 Saltimbanques (69x83cm-27x33in) s. 2-Oct-3 Sotheby's, Paris #115/R
£5634 $9859 €8000 Famille bidougene (49x60cm-19x24in) s. 21-Dec-3 Thierry & Lannon, Brest #362/R est:8000-10000
£11258 $21053 €17000 Le menhir (38x50cm-15x20in) 24-Jul-4 Thierry & Lannon, Brest #215/R est:10000-15000
£18000 $32220 €27000 Soir de noce en Bretagne (73x92cm-29x36in) s. 16-May-4 Thierry & Lannon, Brest #182/R est:15000-20000
£22069 $36634 €32000 Mascarade (131x178cm-52x70in) s. lit. 2-Oct-3 Sotheby's, Paris #161/R est:50000
£29333 $52507 €44000 Procession a Penhors (116x195cm-46x77in) s. exhib. 16-May-4 Thierry & Lannon, Brest #183/R est:28000-30000
Works on paper
£662 $1238 €1000 Cote rocheuses, la lueur jaune (20x26cm-8x10in) s. W/C gouache. 24-Jul-4 Thierry & Lannon, Brest #78/R
£795 $1486 €1200 Promeneurs dans la campagne enneigee (31x21cm-12x8in) s. W/C gouache. 24-Jul-4 Thierry & Lannon, Brest #81/R
£795 $1486 €1200 Place animee sur fond de montagne (22x33cm-9x13in) s. W/C gouache. 24-Jul-4 Thierry & Lannon, Brest #338/R
£993 $1858 €1500 Charette de foin (28x22cm-11x9in) s. W/C gouache. 24-Jul-4 Thierry & Lannon, Brest #80/R est:1500-2000
£1056 $1849 €1500 Jeune Bretonne et enfants sur la plage (13x25cm-5x10in) s. wash. 21-Dec-3 Thierry & Lannon, Brest #454 est:1200-1400
£1200 $2148 €1800 La brouette de foin (28x46cm-11x18in) gouache. 16-May-4 Thierry & Lannon, Brest #99/R est:1500-2000
£1391 $2601 €2100 Cheval devant un Penty breton (29x39cm-11x15in) s. W/C gouache. 24-Jul-4 Thierry & Lannon, Brest #337/R est:2000-3000
£1479 $2588 €2100 Portrait de jeune Bigouden (26x19cm-10x7in) s. W/C. 21-Dec-3 Thierry & Lannon, Brest #74 est:2100-2300
£1724 $2862 €2500 Laboureur (63x91cm-25x36in) s. gouache. 2-Oct-3 Sotheby's, Paris #131/R
£2119 $3963 €3200 Femme et enfant de Plougastel (31x22cm-12x9in) gouache prov. 24-Jul-4 Thierry & Lannon, Brest #113/R est:1500-2000
£2133 $3819 €3200 Jeune femme dans un interieur (46x32cm-18x13in) s. W/C. 16-May-4 Thierry & Lannon, Brest #78/R est:3000-3500
£4106 $7678 €6200 Interieur d'eglise aux flambeaux (69x91cm-27x36in) s. gouache. 24-Jul-4 Thierry & Lannon, Brest #112/R est:4000-5000
£4155 $7271 €5900 Retour de peche a la sardine, Douarnenez (37x45cm-15x18in) s. gouache wash. 21-Dec-3 Thierry & Lannon, Brest #267 est:2000-3000
£7815 $14613 €11800 Bigouden (58x44cm-23x17in) s. gouache. 24-Jul-4 Thierry & Lannon, Brest #111/R est:8000-10000
£10333 $18497 €15500 Les spectateurs au cirque (60x76cm-24x30in) s. W/C. 16-May-4 Thierry & Lannon, Brest #77/R est:7000-8000
£11268 $19718 €16000 Jour des Rameaux sur le chemin de l'eglise de Combrit (52x72cm-20x28in) s. gouache. 21-Dec-3 Thierry & Lannon, Brest #101/R est:9000-11000
£11724 $19462 €17000 Moisson en Bretagne (113x148cm-44x58in) s. W/C gouache chl. 2-Oct-3 Sotheby's, Paris #69/R est:9000
£13333 $23867 €20000 Jeune mere bigoudene et ses deux enfants (73x63cm-29x25in) s. W/C gouache. 16-May-4 Thierry & Lannon, Brest #76/R est:8000-10000
£14085 $24648 €20000 Sortie de messe en pays bigouden a Penmarch (58x93cm-23x37in) s. gouache. 21-Dec-3 Thierry & Lannon, Brest #102/R est:10000-12000
£27465 $48063 €39000 Batteuses de ble pres de la Tour Carree a St Guenole Penmarch (110x148cm-43x58in) s. W/C gouache. 21-Dec-3 Thierry & Lannon, Brest #103/R est:20000-25000

SIMON, Lucien (attrib) (1861-1945) French
£298 $542 €450 Jeune fille au blanc bonnet (40x32cm-16x13in) 16-Jun-4 Renaud, Paris #33

SIMON, Marc (1883-1964) French?
Works on paper
£3061 $5480 €4500 Salle de jeux du paquebot Normandie (65x75cm-26x30in) s. gouache lit. 21-Mar-4 St-Germain-en-Laye Encheres #13/R est:5000-6000

SIMON, Paul (1892-1979) French
Sculpture
£3356 $6275 €5000 Elephant et elephanteau. terracotta. 29-Feb-4 Osenat, Fontainebleau #43
Works on paper
£603 $1007 €850 Panthere devorant une antilope (22x37cm-9x15in) s. W/C. 19-Jun-3 Millon & Associes, Paris #26/R

SIMON, Tavik Frantisek (1877-1942) Czechoslovakian
£702 $1194 €1025 Marigold bouquet (37x45cm-15x18in) s.d.1912. 29-Nov-3 Dorotheum, Prague #50/R est:26000-38000 (C.KR 32000)
£1207 $2221 €1762 Sailing boats - southern France (28x40cm-11x16in) panel. 26-Mar-4 Koller, Zurich #524/R est:2000-3000 (S.FR 2800)

SIMON, Yohanan (1905-1976) Israeli
£860 $1462 €1256 Tropical garden (61x50cm-24x20in) s.i.d.60. 1-Dec-3 Koller, Zurich #6585 est:1500-2500 (S.FR 1900)

£873 $1607 €1275 Night of expectation (16x22cm-6x9in) s.i. i.d. verso board. 14-Jun-4 Philippe Schuler, Zurich #4343/R (S.FR 2000)
£1006 $1600 €1459 Kibbutz scene (33x38cm-13x15in) s.d.1968 canvas on board. 12-Sep-3 Aspire, Cleveland #106 est:3000-5000
£1967 $3600 €2872 Desert vegetation (33x41cm-13x16in) s.d.1964. 1-Jun-4 Ben-Ami, Tel Aviv #4892/R est:3500-4500
£9639 $16000 €14073 Divertissement vegetal (97x130cm-38x51in) s.d.68 i.stretcher. 2-Oct-3 Christie's, Tel Aviv #85/R est:16000-20000
£17470 $29000 €25506 Sabbath in the Kibbutz (96x70cm-38x28in) board. 2-Oct-3 Christie's, Tel Aviv #57/R est:25000-35000
Works on paper
£323 $550 €472 The sailors (25x16cm-10x6in) s. chl exec. 1947. 1-Dec-3 Ben-Ami, Tel Aviv #4341/R
£341 $580 €498 The first independence parade (21x19cm-8x7in) init. chl exec. 1947. 1-Dec-3 Ben-Ami, Tel Aviv #4340/R
£382 $650 €558 Men rowing the boat (23x18cm-9x7in) s. chl exec. 1947. 1-Dec-3 Ben-Ami, Tel Aviv #4339/R
£7263 $13000 €10604 Thirtieth anniversary of the October Revolution (69x49cm-27x19in) s. gouache lit. 18-Mar-4 Sotheby's, New York #10/R est:10000-15000

SIMON-AUGUSTE, Simon (1909-1987) French
£267 $491 €400 Bouquet de fleurs (55x46cm-22x18in) s. panel. 8-Jun-4 Livinec, Gaudcheau & Jezequel, Rennes #146/R
£329 $605 €500 Bateaux au port (73x30cm-29x12in) s. isorel. 27-Jun-4 Feletin, Province #123
£347 $566 €500 Yasmina (42x14cm-17x6in) s. i.verso prov. 29-Sep-3 Charbonneaux, Paris #280
£486 $792 €700 Le compotier bleu (27x46cm-11x18in) s. 29-Sep-3 Charbonneaux, Paris #281
£2238 $3849 €3200 Female nude on couch (40x71cm-16x28in) s. prov. 2-Dec-3 Sotheby's, Amsterdam #217/R est:1200-1500

SIMONAU, Gustave Adolphe (1810-1870) Belgian
Works on paper
£347 $565 €500 Town view (55x40cm-22x16in) s.indis.d. W/C. 29-Sep-3 Sotheby's, Amsterdam #27/R

SIMONE (?) ?
£510 $913 €750 Images d'atelier (74x64cm-29x25in) s. 17-Mar-4 Hotel des Ventes Mosan, Brussels #179

SIMONE, A de (19/20th C) Italian
£2448 $4161 €3500 The Marina Britannica in Naples harbour. s.d.86 pair. 18-Nov-3 Cambi, Genoa #376/R est:4000-5000
Works on paper
£650 $1105 €949 S.S. Madonna (42x64cm-17x25in) i. bodycol. 19-Nov-3 Christie's, Kensington #359/R
£700 $1190 €1022 Lufra (44x63cm-17x25in) s.i. bodycol. 19-Nov-3 Christie's, Kensington #356/R
£850 $1445 €1241 Eliza (42x58cm-17x23in) i. bodycol. 19-Nov-3 Christie's, Kensington #351/R
£1000 $1700 €1460 Schooner (41x62cm-16x24in) s.i. bodycol. 19-Nov-3 Christie's, Kensington #353/R
£1050 $1932 €1533 Steam yacht Onora at sea (43x58cm-17x23in) s.i. W/C bodycol. 23-Jun-4 Bonhams, Bury St Edmunds #319 est:400-600
£1500 $2415 €2175 Ships portrait R.V.V.C Chevy Chase (43x61cm-17x24in) s.d.90 gouache pair. 15-Aug-3 Keys, Aylsham #481/R est:600-800
£1700 $3043 €2482 Steam yacht Alberta in the Mediterranean off Naples (44x67cm-17x26in) s.i.d.1912 W/C bodycol. 26-May-4 Christie's, Kensington #447/R est:700-900
£1900 $3401 €2774 German liner Kaiser Wilhelm II in the Bay of Naples (43x65cm-17x26in) s.i.d.98 bodycol. 26-May-4 Christie's, Kensington #446/R est:800-1200
£1958 $3329 €2800 Boat by Naples harbour (41x66cm-16x26in) s.d. gouache. 18-Nov-3 Cambi, Genoa #428/R est:2500-3000
£2200 $3938 €3212 Twin-screw schooner Zoraide lying in the Bay of Naples (41x60cm-16x24in) s.i.d.95 bodycol. 26-May-4 Christie's, Kensington #445/R est:1000-1500
£2600 $4654 €3796 US steam yacht Iolanda in Neapolitan waters. At sea in a swell (38x63cm-15x25in) s.i.d.1908 bodycol pair. 26-May-4 Christie's, Kensington #443/R est:2000-3000
£3000 $5100 €4380 Chevy Chase (44x61cm-17x24in) s.i. bodycol pair. 19-Nov-3 Christie's, Kensington #358/R
£4000 $7160 €5840 Royal Thames Yacht Club schooner Marchesa. In heavy weather (43x61cm-17x24in) s.i.d.91 bodycol pair. 26-May-4 Christie's, Kensington #444/R est:1500-2500

SIMONE, Alfredo de (19/20th C) Italian
£1164 $2200 €1699 View of Southern area (17x23cm-7x9in) s. cardboard prov. 22-Feb-4 Galeria y Remates, Montevideo #67/R
£2841 $5000 €4148 South (26x35cm-10x14in) s. cardboard. 5-Jan-4 Galeria y Remates, Montevideo #79/R est:7000-9000

SIMONE, Antonio de (19th C) ?
£4865 $9000 €7103 American schooner lying at anchor in the Bay of Naples (35x51cm-14x20in) 15-Jan-4 Sotheby's, New York #292/R est:3000-5000

SIMONE, Nicolo de (17th C) Italian
£28369 $47376 €40000 Salomone adora gli idoli (174x237cm-69x93in) prov. 18-Jun-3 Christie's, Rome #419/R est:40000-60000

SIMONE, Tommaso de (19th C) Italian
£703 $1300 €1026 British Naval paddle sail steam ship off Stromboli (34x51cm-13x20in) s. 10-Feb-4 Christie's, Rockefeller NY #229/R
£2100 $3570 €3066 Royal Naval two-decker (38x48cm-15x19in) s.d.1863. 19-Nov-3 Christie's, Kensington #570/R
£2500 $4300 €3650 Schooner of the Royal yacht squadron (43x63cm-17x25in) s.d.1863. 2-Dec-3 Sotheby's, London #65/R est:1200-1800
£3600 $5760 €5256 British Mediterranean Squadron of the White arriving in Bay of Naples (45x66cm-18x26in) s.d.1861. 16-Sep-3 Bonhams, New Bond Street #17/R est:2000-3000
£4500 $8055 €6570 HMS Cressy lying at anchor off Naples (38x56cm-15x22in) s.d.1859. 26-May-4 Christie's, Kensington #651/R est:5000-7000
£12973 $24000 €18941 HMS Exmouth signaling her arrival at Naples (47x66cm-19x26in) s.d.1862 prov. 10-Feb-4 Christie's, Rockefeller NY #233/R est:12000-18000
Works on paper
£1271 $2250 €1856 Armed American clipper under sail (43x69cm-17x27in) s.i.d.1879 gouache prov. 27-Apr-4 Doyle, New York #12/R est:4000-6000
£2400 $4536 €3504 Schooner rigged steam yacht of the Royal Thames Yacht Club, Naples (37x53cm-15x21in) gouache pair. 17-Feb-4 Bonhams, New Bond Street #46/R est:1200-1800

SIMONE, de (19/20th C) Italian
£2000 $3320 €2920 Warships by dusk (46x65cm-18x26in) s.d.1861. 1-Oct-3 Bonhams, Knightsbridge #163/R est:2000-3000
Works on paper
£1067 $1941 €1600 Trois-mats mixte par gros temps (41x65cm-16x26in) s. gouache. 3-Jul-4 Neret-Minet, Paris #193/R est:2800-3000

SIMONET Y LOMBARDO, Enrique (1863-1927) Spanish
£2535 $4386 €3600 Procession (48x29cm-19x11in) s. 15-Dec-3 Ansorena, Madrid #345/R est:3600

SIMONETTI, A (19/20th C) Italian
£1800 $3186 €2628 Centre of attention (68x40cm-27x16in) s.d.1870. 28-Apr-4 Hampton & Littlewood, Exeter #569 est:1000-1500
£2000 $3400 €2920 Letter (64x49cm-25x19in) indis sig. 18-Nov-3 Bonhams, Leeds #179 est:2000-3000

SIMONETTI, Amedeo (1874-1922) Italian
Works on paper
£13333 $24400 €20000 Orientale a l'eventail (76x53cm-30x21in) s.i. W/C lit. 3-Jun-4 Tajan, Paris #342/R est:20000-25000

SIMONETTI, Attilio (1843-1925) Italian
£252 $413 €350 Alps (16x21cm-6x8in) s. board. 10-Jun-3 Pandolfini, Florence #144/R
£252 $413 €350 Alps (23x33cm-9x13in) s. board. 10-Jun-3 Pandolfini, Florence #143/R
£1439 $2360 €2000 Clown (24x30cm-9x12in) s. board. 10-Jun-3 Pandolfini, Florence #139/R est:2500-3000
£1799 $2950 €2500 Ladies chatting (40x31cm-16x12in) board. 10-Jun-3 Pandolfini, Florence #147/R est:1200-1500
£1942 $3186 €2700 View of temple in Tivoli (62x87cm-24x34in) s.d.1869. 10-Jun-3 Pandolfini, Florence #141/R est:1600-1800
Works on paper
£719 $1180 €1000 Alps (20x27cm-8x11in) s.i.d.1908 W/C. 10-Jun-3 Pandolfini, Florence #145/R
£935 $1534 €1300 Casamicciola (28x38cm-11x15in) s.i. W/C. 10-Jun-3 Pandolfini, Florence #142/R est:800-900
£1500 $2505 €2190 Duet (36x48cm-14x19in) s. W/C. 22-Oct-3 Cheffins, Cambridge #452/R est:1500-2000

SIMONETTI, Attilio (attrib) (1843-1925) Italian
£1511 $2478 €2100 Hunting scene along river (32x75cm-13x30in) 10-Jun-3 Pandolfini, Florence #140/R est:1100-1200

SIMONETTI, Ettore (19th C) Italian
£44118 $75000 €64412 Snake charmer (55x77cm-22x30in) s.i. 29-Oct-3 Christie's, Rockefeller NY #222/R est:80000-120000

SIMONI, Gustavo (1846-1926) Italian
£1594 $2614 €2200 Landscape with sheep and sheperds (29x61cm-11x24in) s. 27-May-3 Finarte Semenzato, Milan #56/R est:2500
£1773 $2961 €2500 Orientale sur une terrasse (24x17cm-9x7in) s.d.82 panel. 16-Jun-3 Gros & Delettrez, Paris #489/R est:2300-3000
Works on paper
£259 $463 €378 Russian market (50x36cm-20x14in) s.i. W/C. 13-May-4 Stuker, Bern #318/R (S.FR 600)
£1000 $1800 €1460 Italian beauty (43x31cm-17x12in) s. W/C. 21-Jan-4 Sotheby's, New York #172/R est:3000-5000
£1078 $1929 €1574 Two women with clay jugs (19x10cm-7x4in) s. gouache board. 13-May-4 Stuker, Bern #317/R est:2500-3500 (S.FR 2500)
£1800 $3096 €2628 Woman of the harem, Tlemcen, Algeria (35x22cm-14x9in) s.i.d.1881 pencil W/C. 4-Dec-3 Christie's, Kensington #221/R est:2000-3000
£3750 $6000 €5475 Busy market scene (53x86cm-21x34in) s.d.1901 W/C. 20-Sep-3 Pook & Pook, Downington #57/R est:3000-5000
£4000 $6800 €5840 Celebrations before an audience (42x60cm-17x24in) s.d.1917 W/C prov. 4-Nov-3 Bonhams, New Bond Street #96/R est:4000-6000

SIMONI, Scipione (19/20th C) Italian
Works on paper
£5594 $9343 €8000 View of Olevano. Barn (78x55cm-31x22in) s. W/C pair. 24-Jun-3 Finarte Semenzato, Rome #70/R est:9000

SIMONIDY, Michel (1870-1933) Rumanian
£268 $499 €400 Les rochers (38x48cm-15x19in) s. 3-Mar-4 Ferri, Paris #288
£282 $524 €420 Nu assis de dos (33x41cm-13x16in) panel. 3-Mar-4 Ferri, Paris #227
£282 $524 €420 Les rochers (32x41cm-13x16in) panel. 3-Mar-4 Ferri, Paris #228
£322 $599 €480 Nu rose dans un paysage (38x46cm-15x18in) s. 3-Mar-4 Ferri, Paris #222/R
£349 $649 €520 Baigneuse assise de dos (41x38cm-16x15in) s. 3-Mar-4 Ferri, Paris #287
£403 $749 €600 Paysage de mer et montagne (38x46cm-15x18in) s.d.26. 3-Mar-4 Ferri, Paris #219

£436	$811	€650	L'arbre au bord de l'eau (52x57cm-20x22in) cardboard. 3-Mar-4 Ferri, Paris #232
£503	$936	€750	Falaises et bateau (36x55cm-14x22in) s. 3-Mar-4 Ferri, Paris #286
£638	$1186	€950	Nu assise a la draperie (60x50cm-24x20in) s. 3-Mar-4 Ferri, Paris #283/R
£1007	$1872	€1500	Deux baigneuses au rocher (50x65cm-20x26in) s. 3-Mar-4 Ferri, Paris #284/R est:300-400
£1241	$2234	€1800	La lecture (54x65cm-21x26in) s.d.1910. 26-Jan-4 Gros & Delettrez, Paris #30/R est:1500-2500
£1259	$2165	€1800	Fille de pecheur a Quiberon gardant une vache (45x54cm-18x21in) s.d.1916 panel. 5-Dec-3 Chochon-Barre & Allardi, Paris #150/R est:2000-2500
£1409	$2621	€2100	Femme au sofa (50x55cm-20x22in) s. 3-Mar-4 Ferri, Paris #293/R est:1000-1500

Works on paper

£897	$1614	€1300	Voiliers au mouillage, Bretagne (48x60cm-19x24in) s. pastel. 26-Jan-4 Gros & Delettrez, Paris #29/R

SIMONIN, Victor (1877-1946) Belgian

£377	$640	€550	Kitchen still life (39x59cm-15x23in) s. 5-Nov-3 Vendue Huis, Gravenhage #313

SIMONINI, Francesco (1686-1753) Italian

£13333	$24000	€19466	Soldiers in rocky landscapes (47x36cm-19x14in) pair prov. 23-Jan-4 Christie's, Rockefeller NY #195/R est:12000-18000
£51007	$95383	€76000	Cavalry by town (117x161cm-46x63in) prov.lit. 25-Feb-4 Porro, Milan #50/R est:60000

Works on paper

£1892	$3330	€2800	Battle scene (37x47cm-15x19in) pen brown ink wash black chk lit. 19-May-4 Sotheby's, Amsterdam #150/R est:1500-2000
£2162	$3805	€3200	Cavaliers and infantrymen conversing. Sketch of a plan (27x37cm-11x15in) bears sig. pen brown ink wash black chk prov.exhib. 19-May-4 Sotheby's, Amsterdam #151/R est:4000-6000
£2432	$4281	€3600	Taking care of the wounded after a battle (34x52cm-13x20in) brown wash black chk prov.exhib.lit. 19-May-4 Sotheby's, Amsterdam #152/R est:3500-4500
£3061	$5480	€4500	Des soldats ramassant des blesses sur un champ de tabaille (39x67cm-15x26in) i. black chk pen brown ink grey wash prov. 18-Mar-4 Christie's, Paris #230/R est:4000-6000

SIMONINI, Francesco (attrib) (1686-1753) Italian

£3451	$5970	€4900	Choc de cavalerie au pied d'une ville fortifiee (36x67cm-14x26in) 12-Dec-3 Libert, Castor, Paris #31/R est:4000-5000

SIMONIS, Kazys (1887-1978) Lithuanian

Works on paper

£2513	$4498	€3669	Litauen coming forward through the ruins towards the light (50x72cm-20x28in) s.d.1918 W/C prov. 28-May-4 Uppsala Auktionskammare, Uppsala #283/R est:6000-8000 (S.KR 34000)

SIMONNET, Lucien (1849-1926) French

£470	$869	€700	Paysage (54x73cm-21x29in) s. 15-Mar-4 Blanchet, Paris #56/R
£2980	$5454	€4500	Paysage (96x145cm-38x57in) s. 9-Apr-4 Claude Aguttes, Neuilly #14/R est:1000-1200

SIMONS, Franz (1855-1919) Belgian

£805	$1498	€1200	Park lane in Brasschaat (60x80cm-24x31in) s. 8-Mar-4 Bernaerts, Antwerp #72/R
£1111	$1767	€1600	La consolation (65x50cm-26x20in) s. 9-Sep-3 Palais de Beaux Arts, Brussels #273/R est:700-1000
£1141	$2122	€1700	Girl with jug alongside water (94x70cm-37x28in) s. 4-Mar-4 Auction Maastricht #1051/R est:800-1200
£3974	$7232	€6000	Enfants dans un sous-bois (120x165cm-47x65in) s. 16-Jun-4 Hotel des Ventes Mosan, Brussels #172/R est:2400-2800
£4965	$8291	€7000	Petit joueur de cor (50x72cm-20x28in) s. 14-Oct-3 Vanderkindere, Brussels #16/R

SIMONS, Michiel (?-1673) Dutch

£14667	$26253	€22000	Rose, various fruit, glass flute, pheasant and other birds on a table (73x103cm-29x41in) s. 17-May-4 Christie's, Amsterdam #79/R est:12000-16000

SIMONS, Michiel (style) (?-1673) Dutch

£8000	$14640	€11680	Banketje still life with fruit, oysters and parrot arranged upon a stone ledge table top (92x122cm-36x48in) bears sig. 6-Jul-4 Sotheby's, Olympia #553/R est:4000-6000

SIMONSEN, Niels (1807-1885) Danish

£316	$591	€461	A monk (54x46cm-21x18in) s.d.1844. 25-Feb-4 Museumsbygningen, Copenhagen #178/R (D.KR 3500)
£748	$1181	€1085	Portrait of Commander Soren Ludvig Tuxen (60x48cm-24x19in) init.d.1837. 3-Sep-3 Museumsbygningen, Copenhagen #174 (D.KR 8000)
£985	$1802	€1438	From the camp - soldiers writing home (23x31cm-9x12in) s.d.1850 grisaille. 7-Jun-4 Museumsbygningen, Copenhagen #3/R (D.KR 11000)
£1418	$2453	€2070	Portrait of Commander Soren Ludvig Tuxen (60x48cm-24x19in) init.d.1837 prov. 9-Dec-3 Rasmussen, Copenhagen #1339/R est:15000 (D.KR 15000)
£1418	$2453	€2070	Flight of Bedouins on horseback (18x21cm-7x8in) prov. 9-Dec-3 Rasmussen, Copenhagen #1532/R est:10000-15000 (D.KR 15000)
£5415	$10126	€7906	Oriental men playing board game (27x36cm-11x14in) init.d.1859 exhib. 25-Feb-4 Museumsbygningen, Copenhagen #183/R est:30000-40000 (D.KR 60000)

SIMONSEN, Simon (1841-1928) Danish

£284	$491	€415	Roman shepherd (28x19cm-11x7in) s.i.d.1869. 9-Dec-3 Rasmussen, Copenhagen #1419/R (D.KR 3000)
£314	$585	€458	Reddish brown horse in field (18x25cm-7x10in) s. 2-Mar-4 Rasmussen, Copenhagen #1580/R (D.KR 3500)
£375	$625	€548	The stable at Circus Ehlers (27x35cm-11x14in) s.d.1895 cardboard. 25-Oct-3 Rasmussen, Havnen #2010/R (D.KR 4000)
£378	$700	€552	An unwelcome guest (18x23cm-7x9in) s. 10-Feb-4 Doyle, New York #209/R
£435	$778	€635	Stenrand farm with woman and two dogs in yard (23x36cm-9x14in) s.d.1905. 12-Jan-4 Rasmussen, Vejle #175/R (D.KR 4600)
£449	$709	€651	Summer landscape with gundogs (24x33cm-9x13in) s.i.d.13/9/1913. 2-Sep-3 Rasmussen, Copenhagen #1738/R (D.KR 4800)
£493	$887	€720	Donkey and cart (23x31cm-9x12in) s.d.1868. 24-Apr-4 Rasmussen, Havnen #2314/R (D.KR 5500)
£514	$812	€745	Autumn scene (20x25cm-8x10in) s.d.1893. 2-Sep-3 Rasmussen, Copenhagen #1891/R (D.KR 5500)
£537	$983	€784	Dachshund drinking from bowl by farm (37x29cm-15x11in) s.d.1884 i.stretcher. 9-Jun-4 Rasmussen, Copenhagen #1744/R (D.KR 6000)
£567	$981	€828	The pointer Tom (25x35cm-10x14in) s.d.1905. 9-Dec-3 Rasmussen, Copenhagen #1403/R (D.KR 6000)
£650	$1215	€949	Peasant boy on horseback near church (16x23cm-6x9in) init.d.1859. 25-Feb-4 Museumsbygningen, Copenhagen #127/R (D.KR 7200)
£794	$1255	€1151	Two in distress - batman with injured horse in farmyard (52x73cm-20x29in) s.d.1865 exhib. 2-Sep-3 Rasmussen, Copenhagen #1699/R (D.KR 8500)
£1125	$1833	€1643	Dachshund by stone wall (24x19cm-9x7in) s.d.1899 panel. 27-Sep-3 Rasmussen, Havnen #2267/R est:6000 (D.KR 12000)
£1312	$2349	€1916	Dogs waiting (9x11cm-4x4in) init. prov. 10-May-4 Rasmussen, Vejle #300/R est:6000-8000 (D.KR 14500)
£1348	$2507	€1968	Dog and cat in basket (25x33cm-10x13in) s.d.1866. 2-Mar-4 Rasmussen, Copenhagen #1603/R est:15000-20000 (D.KR 15000)
£1357	$2430	€1981	Dachshund watching chickens (30x42cm-12x17in) s.d.1890 prov. 10-May-4 Rasmussen, Vejle #301/R est:8000 (D.KR 15000)
£1418	$2538	€2070	Puppies at Gjoddinggaard (51x38cm-20x15in) s. 12-Jan-4 Rasmussen, Vejle #172/R est:20000-25000 (D.KR 15000)
£1512	$2707	€2208	Dachshund puppy on bench in garden (36x22cm-14x9in) s.d.1904. 12-Jan-4 Rasmussen, Vejle #173/R est:8000-12000 (D.KR 16000)
£1611	$2949	€2352	The pointer puppies asleep (23x33cm-9x13in) s.d.1915. 9-Jun-4 Rasmussen, Copenhagen #1649/R est:15000 (D.KR 18000)
£1617	$3008	€2361	Duck and ducklings (26x36cm-10x14in) s.d.1915. 2-Mar-4 Rasmussen, Copenhagen #1582/R est:15000-20000 (D.KR 18000)
£1869	$2953	€2710	The shore at Koisehusene, North Stevns - with hunter and two gun dogs (68x100cm-27x39in) s.d.1890 exhib. 2-Sep-3 Rasmussen, Copenhagen #1545/R est:30000-40000 (D.KR 20000)
£3781	$6541	€5520	Hunting dog and puppies (39x60cm-15x24in) s.d.1879. 9-Dec-3 Rasmussen, Copenhagen #1406/R est:50000-75000 (D.KR 40000)
£3800	$6460	€5548	Puppiers (23x40cm-9x16in) s.d.1898. 27-Nov-3 Christie's, Kensington #398/R est:2000-3000
£3970	$6868	€5796	Pointer and puppies (43x63cm-17x25in) s.d.1916. 9-Dec-3 Rasmussen, Copenhagen #1407/R est:75000-125000 (D.KR 42000)
£4299	$6793	€6234	Two pointer puppies resting (26x31cm-10x12in) s.d.1919. 2-Sep-3 Rasmussen, Copenhagen #1546/R est:15000-20000 (D.KR 46000)
£33645	$53159	€48785	Pointer and dachshund with many puppies (95x156cm-37x61in) s.i.d.1882 exhib. 2-Sep-3 Rasmussen, Copenhagen #1547/R est:100000-125000 (D.KR 360000)

SIMONSON, David (1831-1896) German

£909	$1545	€1300	Portrait d'une fillette tenant une rose (46x42cm-18x17in) s.d.1874. 18-Nov-3 Vanderkindere, Brussels #217

SIMONSON-CASTELLI, Ernst Oskar (1864-1929) German

£772	$1420	€1150	Men with wheelbarrow on beach (76x59cm-30x23in) s. 26-Mar-4 Bolland & Marotz, Bremen #494/R

SIMONSSON, Birger (1883-1938) Swedish

£350	$644	€525	The crow (59x74cm-23x29in) s. d.1934 verso. 14-Jun-4 Lilla Bukowskis, Stockholm #176 (S.KR 4800)
£350	$644	€525	Blue mountains (51x74cm-20x29in) s. d.1931 verso. 14-Jun-4 Lilla Bukowskis, Stockholm #177 (S.KR 4800)
£379	$697	€569	Road in summer (37x45cm-15x18in) s.d.1929 panel. 14-Jun-4 Lilla Bukowskis, Stockholm #61 (S.KR 5200)
£393	$679	€574	Coastal landscape (50x61cm-20x24in) s. panel. 15-Dec-3 Lilla Bukowskis, Stockholm #261 (S.KR 5000)
£508	$914	€762	Coastal landscape (40x48cm-16x19in) init. 25-Apr-4 Goteborg Auktionsverk, Sweden #416/R (S.KR 7000)
£580	$1044	€847	Landscape from Kungalv (48x60cm-19x24in) s. panel. 26-Apr-4 Bukowskis, Stockholm #40/R (S.KR 8000)

SIMONSSON, Konrad (1843-1916) Swedish

£1478	$2646	€2158	Summer landscape from Hastholmen (52x84cm-20x33in) s.d.1887 i.verso. 26-May-4 AB Stockholms Auktionsverk #2154/R est:20000-25000 (S.KR 20000)

SIMONY, Stefan (1860-1950) Austrian

£1042	$1698	€1500	Florisdorf (39x53cm-15x21in) s. 23-Sep-3 Wiener Kunst Auktionen, Vienna #116/R est:1500-3000
£1316	$2421	€2000	Study of Torbole at Lake Garda (25x35cm-10x14in) board. 22-Jun-4 Wiener Kunst Auktionen, Vienna #29/R est:2000
£2667	$4800	€4000	Kaiserpavillion (20x28cm-8x11in) s.d.1912 board. 21-Apr-4 Dorotheum, Vienna #1/R est:2000-2800
£2800	$4844	€4088	Austrian village (59x74cm-23x29in) s.d.1919. 11-Dec-3 Christie's, Kensington #17/R est:3000-5000
£4362	$7809	€6500	Working in the field with view of the fortress of Salzburg (73x110cm-29x43in) s.d.1903. 27-May-4 Dorotheum, Vienna #223/R est:6000-8000
£6250	$10625	€9000	Schonbrunn (64x94cm-25x37in) s.d.1912 prov. 28-Oct-3 Wiener Kunst Auktionen, Vienna #46/R est:7000-15000

Works on paper

£333	$600	€500	Coach by chapel with cows (56x74cm-22x29in) s.d.1912 W/C gouache canvas. 22-Apr-4 Allgauer, Kempten #3431/R

SIMPKINS, Henry J (1906-) Canadian

Works on paper

£580	$998	€847	Quebec City, Winter Carnival. Quebec Carnival (12x15cm-5x6in) W/C two. 2-Dec-3 Joyner Waddington, Toronto #352/R (C.D 1300)

SIMPKINS, John (20th C) American
£240 $400 €350 All my love (46x46cm-18x18in) s.d. acrylic. 11-Oct-3 Nadeau, Windsor #52/R
£719 $1200 €1050 Mrs. Tenderheart (117x76cm-46x30in) s. acrylic. 11-Oct-3 Nadeau, Windsor #54/R
£1018 $1700 €1486 Gold Falls (119x74cm-47x29in) s.d. acrylic. 11-Oct-3 Nadeau, Windsor #51/R est:6500-12000

SIMPOL, Claude (attrib) (c.1666-1716) French
Works on paper
£1127 $1949 €1600 Couronnement de la Vierge (25x17cm-10x7in) i. blk crayon brown wash htd white gouache prov. 10-Dec-3 Piasa, Paris #32 est:1000

SIMPSON, Alexander Brantingham (fl.1904-1931) British
£402 $651 €583 Butterflies - park landscape with nude woman (25x35cm-10x14in) s. panel exhib. 4-Aug-3 Rasmussen, Vejle #432/R (D.KR 4200)
Works on paper
£370 $592 €540 Bookworm (16x16cm-6x6in) s. W/C over pencil. 16-Sep-3 Bonhams, Knowle #52

SIMPSON, Charles Walter (1885-1971) British
£400 $704 €584 Moors, West Penwith (71x101cm-28x40in) s. 18-May-4 Rosebery Fine Art, London #733
£600 $1110 €876 Riding to the meet (53x76cm-21x30in) indis.sig. board. 9-Mar-4 Bonhams, Knightsbridge #246/R
£640 $1171 €934 Tug boats (26x34cm-10x13in) s.d.13 board prov. 1-Jun-4 Joyner Waddington, Toronto #373/R (C.D 1600)
£804 $1382 €1174 Tilling the field (14x19cm-6x7in) s.d.14 panel. 2-Dec-3 Joyner Waddington, Toronto #398 est:1000-12000 (C.D 1800)
£1071 $1843 €1564 Winter stream (45x60cm-18x24in) s. 2-Dec-3 Joyner Waddington, Toronto #213/R est:1500-1800 (C.D 2400)
£1357 $2267 €1981 Two golden retrievers in a landscape (45x61cm-18x24in) s. 17-Nov-3 Waddingtons, Toronto #106/R est:2000-3000 (C.D 3000)
£1400 $2380 €2044 Chestnut hunter with a lady up (75x100cm-30x39in) s. 27-Nov-3 Christie's, Kensington #150/R est:1500-2000
£2800 $4648 €4088 Mallard and five Aylesbury ducks by a stream (41x61cm-16x24in) s. 10-Jun-3 Canterbury Auctions, UK #104/R est:500-700
£16000 $29120 €23360 The tent (51x61cm-20x24in) s. i.stretcher. 15-Jun-4 Bonhams, New Bond Street #1/R est:5000-7000
Works on paper
£250 $408 €365 Harbour (30x27cm-12x11in) gouache. 23-Sep-3 Ritchie, Toronto #68 (C.D 550)
£750 $1365 €1095 Moorland sheep (36x53cm-14x21in) s. bodycol. 15-Jun-4 David Lay, Penzance #345
£850 $1590 €1275 Cattle in a farmyard (48x58cm-19x23in) s.d.1918 W/C. 22-Jul-4 Gorringes, Lewes #1939/R
£1550 $2589 €2263 Ducks at the water's edge (51x61cm-20x24in) s.d.1913 W/C. 14-Oct-3 David Lay, Penzance #210 est:1000-1400
£1700 $2839 €2482 Cows (51x61cm-20x24in) s.d.1913 W/C. 14-Oct-3 David Lay, Penzance #212/R est:700-900

SIMPSON, Jackson (?) ?
Works on paper
£550 $968 €803 Down towards a seaside town (32x43cm-13x17in) s. pencil W/C ink. 19-May-4 Christie's, Kensington #737/R

SIMPSON, James Alexander (1805-1880) American
£1059 $1800 €1546 Portrait of a young woman (53x43cm-21x17in) s.d.1850. 18-Nov-3 Doyle, New York #29 est:3000-5000

SIMPSON, Janet (fl.1910-1950) British
Works on paper
£300 $531 €438 Hop pickers paddock wood, Kent (27x17cm-11x7in) s. W/C. 28-Apr-4 Peter Wilson, Nantwich #138

SIMPSON, John (1782-1847) British
£900 $1422 €1305 Portrait of George Palmer at the age of 21 (76x63cm-30x25in) s. 3-Sep-3 Bonhams, Bury St Edmunds #453/R

SIMPSON, Lorna (1960-) American
£2874 $4800 €4196 Bed (90x51cm-35x20in) s.i.d.95 verso acrylic felt four panels prov. 12-Nov-3 Christie's, Rockefeller NY #530/R est:4000-6000
Photographs
£7263 $13000 €10604 Myths (109x347cm-43x137in) gelatin silver print four parts exec 1991 2 edn 3. 13-May-4 Sotheby's, New York #414/R est:10000-15000

SIMPSON, Peter (20th C) Australian?
£976 $1532 €1425 Shoreline (91x91cm-36x36in) diptych. 27-Aug-3 Christie's, Sydney #542 est:800-1500 (A.D 2400)

SIMPSON, William (1823-1899) British
Works on paper
£2200 $3740 €3212 Peshwari Mill (24x35cm-9x14in) s.i.d.1860 pencil W/C htd bodycol. 20-Nov-3 Christie's, London #118/R est:2500-3500
£2500 $4250 €3650 Lighthouse at Cape Chersonese looking south (23x35cm-9x14in) s.d.May 1855 W/C htd white. 4-Nov-3 Bonhams, New Bond Street #72/R est:2000-3000
£3400 $5780 €4964 Cotton transport, India (25x34cm-10x13in) s.i.d.1862 W/C prov. 4-Nov-3 Bonhams, New Bond Street #67/R est:2000-3000
£3400 $5780 €4964 Tomb of Omar Khayyam, Nishapur, Iran (34x23cm-13x9in) si.d.1886 W/C htd white. 4-Nov-3 Bonhams, New Bond Street #70/R est:2000-3000
£3500 $5705 €5110 Ghats at Mirzapore (33x51cm-13x20in) s.i.d.1864 pencil W/C touches bodycol htd white prov. 24-Sep-3 Christie's, London #49/R est:4000-6000
£4000 $6680 €5840 View of the fort of Chitor, India (25x35cm-10x14in) s. W/C over pencil htd bodycol. 14-Oct-3 Sotheby's, London #141/R est:4000-6000
£4000 $6800 €5840 Bazaar, Suez (68x47cm-27x19in) s.i.d.1884 W/C htd bodycol. 4-Nov-3 Bonhams, New Bond Street #91/R est:4000-6000
£4600 $7820 €6716 Rajgurh, central India (34x50cm-13x20in) i. W/C. 4-Nov-3 Bonhams, New Bond Street #66/R est:3000-5000
£5300 $9381 €7738 Chittorgarth, India (36x51cm-14x20in) s.i.d.1863 W/C. 27-Apr-4 Bonhams, New Bond Street #36/R est:5000-8000
£7800 $13260 €11388 New defences, Yenikale, Crimea (28x50cm-11x20in) s.d.3 June 1855 i.verso W/C htd white. 4-Nov-3 Bonhams, New Bond Street #71/R est:4000-6000
£8000 $13600 €11680 Sevastopol (29x50cm-11x20in) s.d.1855 pencil W/C htd white prov. 20-Nov-3 Christie's, London #124/R est:5000-7000
£12000 $19560 €17520 Leh, capital of Tibet, Kashmir (37x56cm-15x22in) s.i.d.1866 pencil W/C. 25-Sep-3 Christie's, London #463/R est:15000-20000
£13000 $21190 €18980 Buddhist Rock Cut Temple, Ajanta (33x51cm-13x20in) s.i.d.1875 pencil W/C htd white prov. 24-Sep-3 Christie's, London #50/R est:5000-8000

SIMROCK-MICHAEL, Margarete (1870-?) German
Works on paper
£280 $476 €400 Young woman in long dress on beach (26x13cm-10x5in) mono. gouache board. 21-Nov-3 Reiss & Sohn, Konigstein #308/R

SIMS, Agnes (1910-1990) American
£265 $475 €387 Three hounds. 13-May-4 Dallas Auction Gallery, Dallas #296/R
Sculpture
£765 $1300 €1117 Koshare (38x23x15cm-15x9x6in) s. clay turquoise stone prov. 1-Nov-3 Santa Fe Art, Santa Fe #155/R est:2000-3000
£882 $1500 €1288 Kachina (58x20x20cm-23x8x8in) s. clay wood rawhide prov. 1-Nov-3 Santa Fe Art, Santa Fe #156/R est:4000-6000

SIMS, Bernice (20th C) American
£306 $550 €447 Kids playing in the streets (41x51cm-16x20in) 24-Apr-4 Slotin Folk Art, Buford #594/R
£329 $550 €480 Hunting party (46x56cm-18x22in) acrylic board prov. 15-Nov-3 Slotin Folk Art, Buford #422/R
£333 $600 €486 Edmund Pettus Bridge (43x53cm-17x21in) 24-Apr-4 Slotin Folk Art, Buford #593/R
£359 $600 €524 Black bus (38x76cm-15x30in) acrylic. 15-Nov-3 Slotin Folk Art, Buford #423/R
£417 $750 €609 Civil rights march (48x64cm-19x25in) 24-Apr-4 Slotin Folk Art, Buford #592/R
£419 $700 €612 Brewton depot (61x91cm-24x36in) acrylic prov. 15-Nov-3 Slotin Folk Art, Buford #421/R

SIMS, Charles (1873-1926) British
£850 $1530 €1241 Study of figures and children on a beach (29x22cm-11x9in) i.verso oil paper. 21-Apr-4 Tennants, Leyburn #1220
£6800 $11560 €9928 Sunshine (40x51cm-16x20in) s. panel exhib. 26-Nov-3 Sotheby's, Olympia #71/R est:3500-5000

SIMS, Phil (1940-) ?
£865 $1600 €1263 Black Painting VI (170x152cm-67x60in) s.i.d.82 verso prov. 13-Jul-4 Christie's, Rockefeller NY #152/R est:400-600

SIMS, Sandy (20th C) British?
£380 $680 €555 Wadi Halfa steamer service (213x122cm-84x48in) s.d.67. 18-Mar-4 Christie's, Kensington #646

SIMSCH, Walter (20th C) German?
Works on paper
£486 $812 €700 Shore (48x72cm-19x28in) mono.d. W/C over pencil. 24-Oct-3 Ketterer, Hamburg #1087/R

SIMSON, William (1800-1847) British
£5500 $10230 €8030 Death of Edward V and his brother Richard, Duke of York, in the Tower, 1483 (91x127cm-36x50in) panel prov.exhib. 4-Mar-4 Christie's, Kensington #613/R est:6000-10000

SINCLAIR, Alfred Wadham (1866-1938) Australian
Works on paper
£420 $701 €613 Last gleam of sunshine, Kinloch, North Island, New Zealand (76x127cm-30x50in) s. W/C. 14-Oct-3 Bonhams, Knightsbridge #69/R

SINCLAIR, G (19th C) British
£1585 $2600 €2298 Boston harbour (25x33cm-10x13in) panel. 2-Jun-3 Grogan, Boston #633/R

SINCLAIR, Gerrit van W (1890-1955) American
£811 $1500 €1184 Switchman's shanty (61x51cm-24x20in) s.d.1945 s.i.d.verso board. 12-Mar-4 Jackson's, Cedar Falls #769/R est:500-750

SINCLAIR, Irving (1895-1969) American
£204 $375 €298 Portrait of a lady in a red dress (86x71cm-34x28in) s.d.47. 28-Mar-4 Bonhams & Butterfields, San Francisco #2756
£444 $769 €648 Portrait of Field Marshall (91x56cm-36x22in) s.d. 9-Dec-3 Maynards, Vancouver #176 (C.D 1000)

SINCLAIR, John (attrib) (fl.1872-1922) British
£5500 $10120 €8030 Match for 500 guineas between Mr Heathcote's Symmetry and Sir C Bunbury's Sorcerer (96x107cm-38x42in) with sig.d.1801 prov.lit. 10-Jun-4 Christie's, Kensington #11/R est:3000-5000

SINCLAIR, Mary (19/20th C) British
£280 $468 €409 Lincluden Abbey, Dumfries (25x45cm-10x18in) s.d.1880 i.verso. 13-Nov-3 Bonhams, Edinburgh #332a

SINCLAIR, Max (fl.1890-1910) British
£360 $619 €526 Arundel of Liverpool at anchor (43x35cm-17x14in) s. init.i.verso. 2-Dec-3 Sotheby's, London #98/R
£450 $752 €657 In the heart of the lake District, Cumberland (36x53cm-14x21in) s.d.96 i.verso. 13-Nov-3 Christie's, Kensington #184/R
£450 $720 €657 The wreck (30x46cm-12x18in) s.d.85 mono.i.verso. 16-Sep-3 Capes Dunn, Manchester #781/R
£600 $1020 €876 Windermere, mother and child on a mountain path (33x50cm-13x20in) s.d.1879. 19-Nov-3 Tennants, Leyburn #1077
£984 $1800 €1437 Coniston water (36x51cm-14x20in) s.d.1884. 10-Jul-4 Auctions by the Bay, Alameda #411/R
£2300 $4301 €3450 Crossing the Bar, Mantcamen. Home again, Glaucus (34x52cm-13x20in) s. mono.i.verso pair. 26-Jul-4 Bonhams, Bath #84/R est:1500-2000
£2365 $4234 €3453 Carrick Castle, Loch Goil (42x61cm-17x24in) s. 28-May-4 Uppsala Auktionskammare, Uppsala #117/R est:12000-15000 (S.KR 32000)

SINCLAIR, Olga (1957-) Panamanian
£8235 $14000 €12023 Bodegon en azul (200x200cm-79x79in) s.d.02 linen prov.exhib. 18-Nov-3 Christie's, Rockefeller NY #178/R est:14000-18000

SINCLAIR, William (19th C) British
£280 $451 €406 Valley of the Wharfe from cliff tops looking west (38x58cm-15x23in) 13-Aug-3 Andrew Hartley, Ilkley #858

SINDBERG, Adamine Marie Elisabeth (1840-1919) Danish
£3214 $5560 €4692 Windfall apples (22x28cm-9x11in) s.d.1865 exhib. 9-Dec-3 Rasmussen, Copenhagen #1581/R est:5000 (D.KR 34000)

SINDELAR, Charles (1885-1947) American
£258 $475 €387 Pastoral landscape (46x56cm-18x22in) s. painted 1925. 13-Jun-4 William Jenack, New York #132

SINDING CHRISTENSEN, Jens (1888-?) Danish
£276 $461 €400 Seascape (40x50cm-16x20in) s. 17-Nov-3 Durán, Madrid #146/R

SINDING, Elisabeth (1846-1930) Norwegian
£681 $1090 €987 Landscape from Jaeren (43x74cm-17x29in) s. 22-Sep-3 Blomqvist, Lysaker #1267/R (N.KR 8000)

SINDING, Knud (1875-1946) Danish
£271 $500 €396 Chickens in farmyard (80x110cm-31x43in) mono.d.1939. 15-Mar-4 Rasmussen, Vejle #471/R (D.KR 3000)
£276 $470 €403 Italian landscape with monastery (73x97cm-29x38in) mono.d.1924. 10-Nov-3 Rasmussen, Vejle #9/R (D.KR 3000)
£300 $489 €438 Peasants seated on ground next to calf and cow (80x94cm-31x37in) mono. 27-Sep-3 Rasmussen, Havnen #2140 (D.KR 3200)
£424 $784 €619 Interior (70x94cm-28x37in) mono.d.1944. 15-Mar-4 Rasmussen, Vejle #415 (D.KR 4700)
£492 $901 €718 Summer's day with small shepherd boy (43x58cm-17x23in) mono. 9-Jun-4 Rasmussen, Copenhagen #1675/R (D.KR 5500)
£543 $972 €793 Landscape with sheep and young shepherdboy (95x131cm-37x52in) mono.d.1933. 10-May-4 Rasmussen, Vejle #259/R (D.KR 6000)
£584 $1086 €853 Peasants resting on the heath (95x131cm-37x52in) mono.d.1920-21. 2-Mar-4 Rasmussen, Copenhagen #1596/R (D.KR 6500)
£895 $1638 €1307 Interior from the artist's sitting-room with own paintings on wall (70x91cm-28x36in) mono.d.1944. 9-Jun-4 Rasmussen, Copenhagen #1575/R (D.KR 10000)
£898 $1671 €1311 Figures on steps to the small Italian town Civita d'Antonio (60x101cm-24x40in) mono.d.1930. 2-Mar-4 Rasmussen, Copenhagen #1512/R (D.KR 10000)

SINDING, Otto Ludvig (1842-1909) Norwegian
£273 $436 €396 Seascape with sailing boat (31x47cm-12x19in) indis sig. 22-Sep-3 Blomqvist, Lysaker #1261/R (N.KR 3200)
£400 $692 €584 High mountains (30x65cm-12x26in) s. 13-Dec-3 Blomqvist, Lysaker #1343/R (N.KR 4600)
£2135 $3565 €3117 Rapids (38x50cm-15x20in) s. 13-Oct-3 Blomqvist, Oslo #264/R est:20000-25000 (N.KR 25000)
£7000 $12740 €10220 La Tarantella (100x187cm-39x74in) s.i.d.1880. 16-Jun-4 Christie's, Kensington #121/R est:8000-12000
£7341 $13140 €10718 Snow fall, view from Svolvaer, Lofoten (95x126cm-37x50in) s. s.i.stretcher lit. 25-May-4 Grev Wedels Plass, Oslo #20/R est:60000-80000 (N.KR 90000)
£7528 $12797 €10991 Spring day in Svolvaer (64x101cm-25x40in) s.i.d.1882 lit. 19-Nov-3 Grev Wedels Plass, Oslo #36/R est:80000-100000 (N.KR 88000)
£10693 $18178 €15612 Storm (83x143cm-33x56in) s.d.1875 s.i.stretcher. 19-Nov-3 Grev Wedels Plass, Oslo #35/R est:125000-150000 (N.KR 125000)
Works on paper
£513 $873 €749 Mountain landscape (31x47cm-12x19in) s. W/C. 19-Nov-3 Grev Wedels Plass, Oslo #114/R (N.KR 6000)
£941 $1600 €1374 Harbour in Lofoten (25x43cm-10x17in) s. pen wash. 19-Nov-3 Grev Wedels Plass, Oslo #115/R (N.KR 11000)

SINDING, Sigmund (1875-1936) Norwegian
£322 $588 €470 Rowing boat on land (59x60cm-23x24in) s. panel. 2-Feb-4 Blomqvist, Lysaker #1277/R (N.KR 4000)
£426 $681 €618 Out through the door - the door (60x50cm-24x20in) s. 22-Sep-3 Blomqvist, Lysaker #1269/R (N.KR 5000)

SINDING, Stephan (1846-1922) Norwegian
Sculpture
£1027 $1745 €1499 Caught mother (13cm-5in) s. bronze. 19-Nov-3 Grev Wedels Plass, Oslo #18/R (N.KR 12000)
£1601 $2866 €2337 Two people (26x27x19cm-10x11x7in) s.d.1889 bronze lit. 22-Mar-4 Blomqvist, Oslo #360/R est:25000-30000 (N.KR 20000)
£3250 $5525 €4745 Barbarian group, mother carrying her wounded son from battle (89cm-35in) s. white marble. 5-Nov-3 John Nicholson, Haslemere #1028 est:5000-6000
£3557 $6368 €5193 Amazon (80x80cm-31x31in) bronze cast 1908 prov. 15-May-4 Christie's, Sydney #67/R est:5000-8000 (A.D 9000)

SINEMUS, Willem Frederik (1903-1987) Dutch
£816 $1486 €1200 Untitled (53x45cm-21x18in) s.d.48 oil pastel collage cardboard. 3-Feb-4 Christie's, Amsterdam #610 est:1500-2000
Works on paper
£526 $968 €800 Composition with circles (60x48cm-24x19in) s.d.79 mixed media. 28-Jun-4 Sotheby's, Amsterdam #236/R
£658 $1211 €1000 Composition with circles and squares (62x68cm-24x27in) s.d.78 mixed media. 28-Jun-4 Sotheby's, Amsterdam #238/R
£671 $1242 €1000 Untitled (64x54cm-25x21in) s. gouache W/C ink. 15-Mar-4 Sotheby's, Amsterdam #279a est:1000-1500
£909 $1564 €1300 Composition (65x50cm-26x20in) s.d.63 mixed media. 8-Dec-3 Glerum, Amsterdam #158/R
£1049 $1783 €1500 Abstract Composition (68x50cm-27x20in) s.d.66 pastel. 25-Nov-3 Christie's, Amsterdam #104/R est:1500-2000

SINET, Andre (1867-?) French
Works on paper
£280 $481 €400 Street scene (32x25cm-13x10in) s. col chk. 3-Dec-3 Neumeister, Munich #431

SINET, Louis René Hippolyte (19th C) French
£496 $829 €700 Apprenti peintre endormi (27x35cm-11x14in) s.d.1882 panel. 14-Oct-3 Vanderkindere, Brussels #61

SINEZUBOV, Nikolai Vladimirovich (1891-1948) Russian
£470 $869 €700 Portrait de femme (73x60cm-29x24in) s.d.1949 isorel. 15-Mar-4 Claude Boisgirard, Paris #103
£3500 $6265 €5110 Still life with flowers and fruit (61x50cm-24x20in) s.d.44. 26-May-4 Sotheby's, Olympia #435/R est:3000-4000

SINGDAHLSEN, Andreas (1855-1947) Norwegian
£494 $790 €716 Haystacks near the fjord (36x59cm-14x23in) s. 22-Sep-3 Blomqvist, Lysaker #1273 (N.KR 5800)
£531 $978 €775 From Hemsedal (48x75cm-19x30in) s. 29-Mar-4 Blomqvist, Lysaker #1308 (N.KR 6700)
£1217 $2106 €1777 From Asker (55x87cm-22x34in) s. 13-Dec-3 Blomqvist, Lysaker #1345/R est:15000-18000 (N.KR 14000)
£1305 $2336 €1905 Man on bridge across weir, autumn landscape, Lier (54x86cm-21x34in) s. 25-May-4 Grev Wedels Plass, Oslo #51/R est:15000-20000 (N.KR 16000)

SINGER, Albert (1869-1922) German
£2254 $3899 €3200 Gemzen im gebirgte (177x119cm-70x47in) s.d.1904. 10-Dec-3 Christie's, Amsterdam #850/R est:2000-3000

SINGER, Clyde (1908-1999) American
£217 $400 €326 Self portrait (51x43cm-20x17in) masonite. 23-Mar-4 American Auctioneer #453783/R
£919 $1700 €1342 Two stage doormen discussing (41x30cm-16x12in) s.d.1979 panel. 13-Mar-4 DeFina, Austinburg #965/R est:300-500
Works on paper
£272 $455 €397 Two women standing on a busy street corner (20x15cm-8x6in) s.d.39 graphite. 14-Nov-3 Aspire, Cleveland #173
£284 $475 €415 New York street scene (25x36cm-10x14in) s. pencil dr. 25-Oct-3 Rachel Davis, Shaker Heights #290/R

SINGER, Gail (c.1924-) American
£832 $1415 €1190 Savant atomique (146x97cm-57x38in) s.d.1962 i.verso prov. 18-Nov-3 Babuino, Rome #302/R

SINGER-HIESSLEITNER, Emmi (1884-1980) Austrian
£1208 $2162 €1800 First snows - view of Gleinalm (46x64cm-18x25in) mono. 27-May-4 Dorotheum, Graz #62/R est:1800
Works on paper
£317 $526 €450 St Christoph am Arlberg (28x34cm-11x13in) mono. W/C. 12-Jun-3 Dorotheum, Graz #120/R

SINGH, Arpita (1937-) Indian
£11957 $22000 €17457 Untitled (85x81cm-33x32in) s.d.91 board. 25-Mar-4 Christie's, Rockefeller NY #231/R est:10000-15000
£15217 $28000 €22217 Pink flowers yellow flowers (86x76cm-34x30in) s.d.1989 i.d.1989 March verso. 25-Mar-4 Christie's, Rockefeller NY #229/R est:10000-15000

SINGH, Paramjit (1935-) Indian
£6046 $10882 €8827 Untitled (152x152cm-60x60in) s.d.2002. 25-Apr-4 Christie's, Hong Kong #609/R est:55000-75000 (HK.D 85000)

SINGIER, Gustave (1909-1985) French
£1118 $1900 €1632 Port Breton (23x15cm-9x6in) s. i.d.1956 verso prov. 22-Nov-3 Jackson's, Cedar Falls #387/R est:1000-2000

£4514 $7539 €6500 Nature morte (33x41cm-13x16in) s.d.44 s.i.d.verso. 21-Oct-3 Artcurial Briest, Paris #392/R est:6000-7000
£5600 $10080 €8400 Composition (56x44cm-22x17in) s.d.1966 paper on canvas prov.lit. 25-Apr-4 Versailles Encheres #65 est:6000-8000
£10211 $16440 €14500 Lovers (73x92cm-29x36in) s. paper on canvas painted 1947. 22-Aug-3 Deauville, France #128/R est:14000-16000
£13667 $24463 €20500 Le jeu d'echec. 16-May-4 Osenat, Fontainebleau #111/R est:15000-20000
£32000 $53440 €46720 Interieur flamand (149x170cm-59x67in) s.i.d.1951 stretcher prov.exhib.lit. 22-Oct-3 Christie's, London #18/R est:30000-40000

Works on paper
£679 $1154 €991 Lignes brisees (44x55cm-17x22in) s.d.1961 i.verso W/C ink. 22-Nov-3 Burkhard, Luzern #17/R (S.FR 1500)
£743 $1405 €1100 Composition (21x27cm-8x11in) s.d.1969 gouache W/C. 21-Feb-4 Cornette de St.Cyr, Paris #402/R
£789 $1453 €1200 Composition (49x31cm-19x12in) s.d.46 W/C graphite. 25-Jun-4 Millon & Associes, Paris #264/R
£905 $1511 €1321 Sans titre (43x55cm-17x22in) s.d.1958 W/C pastel prov. 24-Jun-3 Germann, Zurich #43/R (S.FR 2000)
£1049 $1752 €1500 Composition (44x55cm-17x22in) s. W/C prov. 29-Jun-3 Versailles Encheres #63/R
£1162 $2010 €1650 Maquette de decors pour Turcaret de Lesage (36x55cm-14x22in) st.sig.verso gouache collage. 14-Dec-3 Versailles Encheres #71/R est:2000-2500
£1267 $2280 €1900 Composition (54x43cm-21x17in) s.d.1973 W/C prov. 25-Apr-4 Versailles Encheres #38 est:1500-2000
£1300 $2340 €1950 Composition (44x55cm-17x22in) s.d.1962 W/C prov. 25-Apr-4 Versailles Encheres #21 est:2000-2200
£1333 $2400 €2000 Migration, sable et eau (45x55cm-18x22in) s.d.1960 W/C prov. 25-Apr-4 Versailles Encheres #22 est:2200-2500
£1333 $2400 €2000 Brume, sabler et eau (45x56cm-18x22in) s.d.1960 W/C exhib. 25-Apr-4 Versailles Encheres #23 est:2200-2500
£1667 $3000 €2500 Composition (37x56cm-15x22in) s.d.1968 W/C prov. 25-Apr-4 Versailles Encheres #46 est:1500-2000
£2237 $4116 €3400 Vestige marin II (44x55cm-17x22in) s.d.1960 W/C prov.exhib. 27-Jun-4 Versailles Encheres #68/R est:2000-2500
£2797 $4671 €4000 Enfant dans la campagne (36x26cm-14x10in) s.d.1943 W/C prov. 29-Jun-3 Versailles Encheres #66/R

SINGLETON, Henry (1766-1839) British
£35000 $64400 €51100 West End of the town. East End of the town (38x44cm-15x17in) pair. prov. 11-Jun-4 Christie's, London #34/R est:15000-20000

Works on paper
£1500 $2760 €2190 Portrait of Benjamin Franklin (23x17cm-9x7in) i. pencil. 26-Mar-4 Sotheby's, London #90/R est:2000-3000

SINGLETON, Henry (attrib) (1766-1839) British
£6500 $11895 €9490 Portrait of gentleman standing beside a tree (53x41cm-21x16in) i.verso prov. 8-Jul-4 Duke & Son, Dorchester #281/R

SINGLETON, Herbert (1945-) American
Sculpture
£1557 $2600 €2273 New Orleans funeral (41x137cm-16x54in) painted wood. 15-Nov-3 Slotin Folk Art, Buford #239/R est:1000-3000
£6257 $10450 €9135 The way we was, self-portrait (130x48cm-51x19in) oil wood prov. 15-Nov-3 Slotin Folk Art, Buford #238/R est:2000-4000

SINGLETON, Judi (1963-) Australian
£1296 $2086 €1892 Untitled (149x131cm-59x52in) s.d.1987 verso prov. 25-Aug-3 Sotheby's, Paddington #281/R est:3000-4000 (A.D 3200)

SINGRY, Jean Baptiste (1782-1824) French
Miniatures
£1000 $1730 €1460 Young gentleman in black coat yellow waistcoat and knotted cravat (6cm-2in) s. gilt-metal mount oval. 9-Dec-3 Christie's, London #140/R est:400-600
£1500 $2700 €2190 Gentleman in a dark blue coat (5cm-2in) s.d.1817 gold frame oval exhib. 22-Apr-4 Bonhams, New Bond Street #130/R est:800-1200
£1700 $2822 €2482 Portrait of a young lady wearing a black dress (7cm-3in) s. gilt metal mount rec. wood frame. 2-Oct-3 Sotheby's, Olympia #22/R est:1200-1800

SINGRY, Jean Baptiste (attrib) (1782-1824) French
Miniatures
£1064 $1723 €1500 Portrait de Isabelle du Neubourg, Baronne Mugnier (7x5cm-3x2in) s.d.1813 gold frame oval. 21-May-3 Daguerre, Paris #229 est:300-400

SINIBALDI, Jean Paul (1857-1909) French
£1034 $1914 €1500 La robe bayadere (81x65cm-32x26in) s. 11-Feb-4 Beaussant & Lefèvre, Paris #174/R est:1500-2000
£1184 $2179 €1800 Jeune femme brune en buste avec des plumes d'oiseaux dans les cheveux (27x21cm-11x8in) s. panel. 25-Jun-4 Rossini, Paris #72/R est:900-1100
£1586 $2934 €2300 La robe rose (73x60cm-29x24in) s. 11-Feb-4 Beaussant & Lefèvre, Paris #207/R est:1500-2000
£4545 $7727 €6500 La visite de la serre (66x46cm-26x18in) s. 1-Dec-3 Palais de Beaux Arts, Brussels #380/R est:6500-8000

SINICKI, René (20th C) French
£300 $500 €438 Les pasteques (12x15cm-5x6in) board. 19-Oct-3 Bonhams & Butterfields, Los Angeles #7065
£889 $1538 €1298 La chaise blanche (65x54cm-26x21in) isorel. 15-Dec-3 Iegor de Saint Hippolyte, Montreal #102 (C.D 2000)
£1689 $2922 €2466 Femme au divan (61x50cm-24x20in) 15-Dec-3 Iegor de Saint Hippolyte, Montreal #101 (C.D 3800)

SINNOTT, Kevin (1947-) British
£550 $990 €803 Woman with horse (19x27cm-7x11in) init. board. 20-Jan-4 Bonhams, Knightsbridge #232

SINT-JANS, Geert tot (circle) (?-1495) Dutch
£19737 $36316 €30000 Virgin of the Apocalypse (38x27cm-15x11in) panel. 24-Jun-4 Christie's, Paris #2/R est:3000-5000

SINTENIS, Renée (1888-1965) German
Sculpture
£1121 $2062 €1637 Galloping foal (23cm-9in) bronze lit. 25-Mar-4 Koller, Zurich #170 est:2500-3500 (S.FR 2600)
£1200 $2148 €1800 Foal lying down (8cm-3in) st.mono. dark brown pat.bronze lit. 14-May-4 Schloss Ahlden, Ahlden #1983/R est:1800
£1300 $2366 €1898 Selbstportrat - self portrait (7cm-3in) mono. bronze st.f.H.Noack executed c.1916 lit. 4-Feb-4 Sotheby's, London #265/R est:2000-3000
£1667 $3067 €2500 Sitting terrier puppy (8cm-3in) st.mono.st.f. Noack brown pat. bronze exec. 1925. 12-Jun-4 Villa Grisebach, Berlin #321/R est:2500-3500
£2000 $3680 €3000 Shetland pony running in the wind (7cm-3in) st.mono.st.f. Noack black pat bronze incl. black marble base. 12-Jun-4 Villa Grisebach, Berlin #154/R est:3500-4500
£2000 $3680 €3000 Self portrait (33cm-13in) stucco wooden base. 12-Jun-4 Villa Grisebach, Berlin #292/R est:3000-4000
£2098 $3608 €3000 Grazing foal (8x3x9cm-3x1x4in) st.mono. brown pat bronze marble base one of 25 prov.exhib.lit. 5-Dec-3 Ketterer, Munich #73/R est:5000-7000
£2448 $4161 €3500 Foal scratching face with hoof (6x7cm-2x3in) mono. bronze. 29-Nov-3 Bassenge, Berlin #6983/R est:4500
£2500 $4600 €3750 Dog begging (13x7x6cm-5x3x2in) bronze. 10-Jun-4 Hauswedell & Nolte, Hamburg #645/R est:5000
£2533 $4661 €3800 Shetland pony (8cm-3in) st.mono.st.f. Noack brown pat. bronze incl. green marble base. 12-Jun-4 Villa Grisebach, Berlin #153/R est:3000-4000
£2657 $4571 €3800 Jumping Shetland pony (7x3x14cm-3x1x6in) st.mono. st.f.Noack brown pat bronze marble base prov.exhib.lit. 5-Dec-3 Ketterer, Munich #69/R est:4000-5000
£2667 $4907 €4000 Pony glancing sideways (10cm-4in) st.mono.st.f. Noack black pat bronze. 12-Jun-4 Villa Grisebach, Berlin #156/R est:4000-6000
£2708 $4279 €3900 Grazing foal (7cm-3in) mono. brown pat.bronze. 6-Sep-3 Schopman, Hamburg #360/R est:4900
£2797 $4811 €4000 Foal with raised back leg (11x8x2cm-4x3x1in) bonze. 2-Dec-3 Hauswedell & Nolte, Hamburg #625/R est:4000
£2933 $5251 €4400 Self portrait (27cm-11in) mono. dark brown pat.bronze Cast.H.Noack Berlin. 15-May-4 Bassenge, Berlin #7136/R
£3147 $5350 €4500 Ill deer (7cm-3in) st.mono. brown green pat.bronze. 29-Nov-3 Villa Grisebach, Berlin #190/R est:5000-7000
£3147 $5413 €4500 Shetland pony (10x4x13cm-4x2x5in) st.mono. st.f.Noack dark brown pat bronze marble base exhib.lit. 5-Dec-3 Ketterer, Munich #72/R est:6000-7000
£3221 $5928 €4800 Golden bear (18cm-7in) mono.i. pat.bronze Cast.Noack, Berlin lit. 27-Mar-4 Auktionhaus Herr, Cologne #187/R est:5000
£3333 $5967 €5000 Young bear (13x7x7cm-5x3x3in) s.mono. brown pat.bronze prov.lit. 14-May-4 Ketterer, Munich #219/R est:4000-5000
£3356 $6174 €5000 Newborn foal (4x13x5cm-2x5x2in) mono. pat.bronze Cast.R Noack Berlin lit. 27-Mar-4 Auktionhaus Herr, Cologne #188/R est:5500
£3497 $6014 €5000 Two deer resting (6x10x7cm-2x4x3in) st.mono st.f.Noack auburn pat bronze marble base prov.lit. 5-Dec-3 Ketterer, Munich #74/R est:5000-7000
£3867 $7115 €5800 Foal lying down (6x12x7cm-2x5x3in) bronze. 10-Jun-4 Hauswedell & Nolte, Hamburg #646/R est:4500
£4000 $7160 €6000 Pony with head down (8x13x3cm-3x5x1in) st.mono. brown pat.bronze lit. 14-May-4 Ketterer, Munich #188/R est:6000-8000
£4000 $7360 €6000 Foal lying down (7x10x6cm-3x4x2in) bronze. 10-Jun-4 Hauswedell & Nolte, Hamburg #647/R est:7000
£4200 $7518 €6300 Jumping Shetland pony (12cm-5in) mono. goldbrown pat.bronze Cast.H.Noack Berlin Friedenau. 15-May-4 Bassenge, Berlin #7137/R est:7500
£4895 $8322 €7000 Newborn foal (12x12cm-5x5in) mono. gold brown pat.bronze Cast.H.Noack Berlin. 29-Nov-3 Bassenge, Berlin #6984/R est:8000
£4895 $8322 €7000 Miniature donkey (13cm-5in) mono. gold brown pat.bronze Cast.H.Noack. 29-Nov-3 Bassenge, Berlin #6985/R est:8000
£5594 $9510 €8000 Young seated terrier (8cm-3in) mono. bronze Cast.H.Noack Berlin exhib.lit. 26-Nov-3 Lempertz, Koln #982/R est:3000-3500
£6294 $10825 €9000 Young donkey (112x12x3cm-44x5x1in) bronze. 2-Dec-3 Hauswedell & Nolte, Hamburg #626/R est:7500
£6993 $11888 €10000 Proud foal (18cm-7in) mono. dark brown pat.bronze marble socle exhib.lit. 26-Nov-3 Lempertz, Koln #985/R est:6000-7000
£7692 $13077 €11000 Little Daphne (29cm-11in) st.mono. yellow brown pat.bronze Cast.Noack Berlin stone socle. 29-Nov-3 Villa Grisebach, Berlin #224/R est:12000-15000
£8333 $15333 €12500 Seated boy (14x18x11cm-6x7x4in) bronze. 10-Jun-4 Hauswedell & Nolte, Hamburg #649/R est:8000
£13333 $24533 €20000 Trotting elephant (10cm-4in) st.mono.st.f.Noack brown pat. bronze. 12-Jun-4 Villa Grisebach, Berlin #287/R est:12000-14000
£21678 $36853 €31000 Polo player II (43cm-17in) s.i. bronze Cast.H. Noack Berlin Friedenau prov.lit. 26-Nov-3 Lempertz, Koln #984/R est:35000
£54667 $100587 €82000 Rearing pony (116cm-46in) st.mono. st.f.H Noack greyish green pat bronze one of 4 prov. 11-Jun-4 Villa Grisebach, Berlin #44/R est:60000-80000

Works on paper
£568 $1045 €829 Foal lying down (25x16cm-10x6in) mono. Indian ink wash. 14-Jun-4 Philippe Schuler, Zurich #4024 (S.FR 1300)

SINTENIS, Renée (attrib) (1888-1965) German
Sculpture
£1064 $1777 €1500 Self portrait (37cm-15in) s. pat.bronze. 21-Jun-3 Hans Stahl, Hamburg #274/R est:1500

SION, Peeter (attrib) (1649-1695) Flemish
£3000 $4890 €4380 Virgin and Child in Glory with attendant Saints (28x35cm-11x14in) copper. 26-Sep-3 Christie's, Kensington #4/R est:3000-4000

SIOPIS, Penelope (1953-) South African
£588 $1065 €858 An overgrown farm (39x49cm-15x19in) s. 30-Mar-4 Stephan Welz, Johannesburg #467 est:3000-5000 (SA.R 7000)
£798 $1445 €1165 Still life of apples and a glass (39x49cm-15x19in) s. 30-Mar-4 Stephan Welz, Johannesburg #520/R est:3000-5000 (SA.R 9500)
£1849 $3346 €2700 Bedroom interior with a cat (90x100cm-35x39in) s. 30-Mar-4 Stephan Welz, Johannesburg #524/R est:7000-10000 (SA.R 22000)

SIQUEIROS, David (1896-1974) Mexican
£2568 $4750 €3749 Five mourning women (91x64cm-36x25in) s. 14-Jan-4 Dallas Auction Gallery, Dallas #109 est:10000-15000

£3194	$5271	€4600	Abstract (42x29cm-17x11in) s. acrylic card. 2-Jul-3 Ansorena, Madrid #870/R
£9444	$17000	€13788	Nahual (99x66cm-39x26in) s.d.65 acrylic board prov. 20-Jan-4 Arthur James, Florida #104
£13966	$25000	€20390	Nahuatl (102x66cm-40x26in) s.d.65 acrylic mixed media paper on wood prov. 26-May-4 Sotheby's, New York #132/R est:25000-35000
£20000	$34000	€29200	Hombre remando (119x84cm-47x33in) s. pyroxylin on masonite. 9-Nov-3 Bonhams & Butterfields, Los Angeles #4133/R est:40000-60000
£20588	$35000	€30058	Nenufar-medusa gigante (60x45cm-24x18in) s.d.3-64 i.verso acrylic on board prov.exhib. 19-Nov-3 Sotheby's, New York #112/R est:40000-60000
£26471	$45000	€38648	Kaktos (61x46cm-24x18in) s. s.i.d.1963 verso pyroxylin on pa, prov. 19-Nov-3 Sotheby's, New York #107/R est:30000-40000
£47059	$80000	€68706	Campesino - Peasant (84x69cm-33x27in) s.d.60 pyroxiline on masonite prov.exhib. 18-Nov-3 Christie's, Rockefeller NY #34/R est:80000-120000
£88235	$150000	€128823	Sin Titulo (80x61cm-31x24in) s.d.1965 pyroxylin on panel prov. 19-Nov-3 Sotheby's, New York #6/R est:50000-60000
Prints			
£2395	$4000	€3497	Zapata (51x38cm-20x15in) num.39/50 lithograph. 17-Oct-3 Du Mouchelle, Detroit #2029/R est:1300-2300
Works on paper			
£500	$900	€730	Bones (33x20cm-13x8in) shoe polish. 24-Apr-4 Du Mouchelle, Detroit #3264/R
£1836	$3250	€2681	Bailador (34x26cm-13x10in) s. gouache pyroxylin paper on board exec.c.1967 prov. 2-May-4 Bonhams & Butterfields, Los Angeles #3121/R est:3000-4000

SIRAK, Carol (1906-1976) American

£1037	$1700	€1504	Meadows in autumn (48x58cm-19x23in) estate st.verso board. 4-Jun-3 Alderfer's, Hatfield #371/R est:2000-3000
£2023	$3500	€2954	Along the river, winter landscape (51x61cm-20x24in) s. board. 10-Dec-3 Alderfer's, Hatfield #432/R est:2750-3250
£2767	$4400	€4040	Winter landscape with streamside buildings on snow-covered banks (61x61cm-24x24in) s. 10-Sep-3 Alderfer's, Hatfield #435/R est:4000-6000
£5308	$9500	€7750	Pennsylvania village (64x76cm-25x30in) s. 6-May-4 Shannon's, Milford #6/R est:8000-12000
£7784	$13000	€11365	Bucks County Village (91x91cm-36x36in) s. 23-Oct-3 Shannon's, Milford #51/R est:8000-12000

SIRANI, Elisabetta (1638-1665) Italian

£5034	$9262	€7500	St Jerome (102x84cm-40x33in) 24-Mar-4 Dorotheum, Vienna #77/R est:6000-9000
£11511	$18878	€16000	Sleeping putto (79x90cm-31x35in) 4-Jun-3 Sotheby's, Milan #117/R est:15000-20000
£19014	$30423	€27000	Cupid (117x147cm-46x58in) 21-Sep-3 Finarte, Venice #22/R
£63758	$114128	€95000	Putto in seascape (89x70cm-35x28in) prov.exhib.lit. 26-May-4 Porro, Milan #29/R est:120000-150000

SIRANI, Elisabetta (circle) (1638-1665) Italian

£10800	$18684	€15768	Saint Cecilia (27x22cm-11x9in) i. copper oval prov. 9-Dec-3 Sotheby's, Olympia #387/R est:4000-6000

SIRANI, Giovanni Andrea (1610-1670) Italian

£8054	$14980	€12000	Holy Family (99x73cm-39x29in) 2-Mar-4 Ansorena, Madrid #273/R est:17000
£15000	$27450	€21900	Allegory of Astrology (116x75cm-46x30in) prov. 8-Jul-4 Sotheby's, London #315/R est:15000-20000

SIRANI, Giovanni Andrea (attrib) (1610-1670) Italian

£6623	$12053	€10000	Christ with thorn crown (56x46cm-22x18in) 16-Jun-4 Christie's, Rome #263/R est:10000-15000

SIRONI, Mario (1885-1961) Italian

£671	$1248	€1000	Composition (25x16cm-10x6in) s. tempera paper. 4-Mar-4 Babuino, Rome #51
£738	$1373	€1100	Project for decoration (28x21cm-11x8in) tempera lit. 4-Mar-4 Babuino, Rome #37
£872	$1623	€1300	Faces of man (35x27cm-14x11in) i. tempera chk. 4-Mar-4 Babuino, Rome #4
£872	$1623	€1300	Crocodile (20x31cm-8x12in) d.1950 tempera ink paper. 4-Mar-4 Babuino, Rome #75
£872	$1623	€1300	Four tales (16x22cm-6x9in) tempera ink lit. 4-Mar-4 Babuino, Rome #92
£986	$1725	€1400	Vase with pansies (15x15cm-6x6in) s. tempera pencil paper. 16-Dec-3 Finarte Semenzato, Milan #297/R est:1200-1600
£1007	$1872	€1500	Parade (21x24cm-8x9in) tempera pencil paper. 4-Mar-4 Babuino, Rome #516 est:1000-1500
£1074	$1922	€1600	Blood is money (21x13cm-8x5in) s.i. tempera lead ink paper prov. 25-May-4 Sotheby's, Milan #64/R est:1500
£1141	$2122	€1700	Mime (18x14cm-7x6in) s. tempera ink pencil. 4-Mar-4 Babuino, Rome #24
£1141	$2122	€1700	Knife (20x15cm-8x6in) tempera paper on canvas lit. 4-Mar-4 Babuino, Rome #512 est:800-1000
£1141	$2122	€1700	Composition (18x33cm-7x13in) tempera ink card. 4-Mar-4 Babuino, Rome #526 est:1300-1500
£1208	$2247	€1800	Composition (20x25cm-8x10in) tempera paper. 4-Mar-4 Babuino, Rome #498
£1275	$2372	€1900	Composition (13x36cm-5x14in) mixed media tempera pencil ink. 4-Mar-4 Babuino, Rome #23
£1342	$2497	€2000	Composition with figure (16x24cm-6x9in) s. tempera ink. 4-Mar-4 Babuino, Rome #100 est:600-800
£1408	$2338	€2000	Composition and figure (33x23cm-13x9in) tempera paper double-sided. 11-Jun-3 Finarte Semenzato, Milan #613/R
£1409	$2621	€2100	Composition with figures (16x22cm-6x9in) tempera ink paper lit. 4-Mar-4 Babuino, Rome #101
£1477	$2643	€2200	Untitled (19x13cm-7x5in) s. tempera lead ink paper. 25-May-4 Sotheby's, Milan #65/R est:1500
£1477	$2643	€2200	Composition (22x19cm-9x7in) s. tempera pencil paper on card. 25-May-4 Sotheby's, Milan #111/R
£1477	$2746	€2200	Composition (19x18cm-7x7in) tempera pencil. 4-Mar-4 Babuino, Rome #523 est:1800-2200
£1611	$2996	€2400	Landscape with houses (15x20cm-6x8in) s. tempera pencil card exhib. 4-Mar-4 Babuino, Rome #406 est:1000-1200
£1611	$2996	€2400	Man and woman (18x11cm-7x4in) tempera ink wax crayon paper. 4-Mar-4 Babuino, Rome #454 est:1800-2200
£1622	$2854	€2400	Composition (16x22cm-6x9in) s. paper on canvas. 19-May-4 Il Ponte, Milan #1087 est:2500-3000
£1678	$3121	€2500	Composition with figure (17x21cm-7x8in) tempera ink. 4-Mar-4 Babuino, Rome #52
£1745	$3246	€2600	Mountainous landscape (36x43cm-14x17in) tempera paint double-sided. 4-Mar-4 Babuino, Rome #495 est:1500-2000
£1748	$2972	€2500	Studies of heads (32x25cm-13x10in) s. tempera chl paper prov. 20-Nov-3 Finarte Semenzato, Milan #130/R est:2500-3000
£1812	$3370	€2700	Composition (37x50cm-15x20in) s. tempera card. 4-Mar-4 Babuino, Rome #6
£1812	$3370	€2700	Arm with sword (33x40cm-13x16in) tempera paper. 4-Mar-4 Babuino, Rome #515 est:1800-2200
£1862	$3110	€2700	Drinker (27x26cm-11x10in) s. tempera paper lit. 14-Nov-3 Farsetti, Prato #78/R est:2100-2400
£1946	$3620	€2900	Landscape (13x21cm-5x8in) s. tempera pencil paper. 4-Mar-4 Babuino, Rome #50
£2013	$3745	€3000	Untitled (22x16cm-9x6in) s. tempera ink pencil paper. 4-Mar-4 Babuino, Rome #49
£2013	$3745	€3000	Composition (55x47cm-22x19in) tempera pencil wax crayon card. 4-Mar-4 Babuino, Rome #134 est:800-1200
£2013	$3745	€3000	Seated woman (21x11cm-8x4in) tempera paper exhib. 4-Mar-4 Babuino, Rome #156 est:1000-1200
£2013	$3745	€3000	Composition with figures (23x33cm-9x13in) s. tempera pencil paper exhib. 4-Mar-4 Babuino, Rome #524 est:2000-2500
£2133	$3925	€3200	Three figures (23x31cm-9x12in) tempera ink paper. 11-Jun-4 Farsetti, Prato #301/R est:3200-3600
£2148	$3995	€3200	Red flag (6x15cm-2x6in) tempera ink paper on card. 4-Mar-4 Babuino, Rome #120
£2162	$3805	€3200	Loneliness (33x24cm-13x9in) s. tempera ink paper painted 1924. 24-May-4 Christie's, Milan #28/R est:3500-5000
£2333	$4200	€3406	Untitled (25x33cm-10x13in) s. board prov. 25-Jan-4 Hindman, Chicago #1094/R est:1800-2400
£2349	$4369	€3500	Composition (23x29cm-9x11in) i.verso tempera paper. 4-Mar-4 Babuino, Rome #99 est:1500-2000
£2432	$4281	€3600	Skier (32x23cm-13x9in) tempera paper painted 1925 lit. 24-May-4 Christie's, Milan #30/R est:3000-4000
£2550	$4744	€3800	Composition (16x22cm-6x9in) s. tempera pencil card. 4-Mar-4 Babuino, Rome #511 est:700-900
£2550	$4744	€3800	Figure (31x21cm-12x8in) s. tempera lead paper. 4-Mar-4 Babuino, Rome #513 est:2000-2500
£2685	$4993	€4000	Untitled (49x60cm-19x24in) s. tempera paper. 4-Mar-4 Babuino, Rome #135
£2685	$4993	€4000	Anarchy (31x22cm-12x9in) i. tempera lead pencil card. 4-Mar-4 Babuino, Rome #423 est:1800-2200
£2819	$5243	€4200	Woman in evening gown (37x49cm-15x19in) tempera ink card. 4-Mar-4 Babuino, Rome #3
£2899	$4754	€4000	Nudes (35x38cm-14x15in) s. tempera pencil double-sided prov. 27-May-3 Sotheby's, Milan #175/R est:3500-4000
£2933	$5397	€4400	Jacopone da Todi and Pope Bonifcio VIII (45x36cm-18x14in) s. tempera paper on canvas prov. 8-Jun-4 Finarte Semenzato, Milan #376/R est:4500-5000
£3043	$4991	€4200	Figure (28x17cm-11x7in) s. tempera paper on canvas. 29-May-3 Galleria Pace, Milan #148/R est:6500
£3154	$5867	€4700	Composition (22x28cm-9x11in) s tempera pencil paper. 4-Mar-4 Babuino, Rome #36
£3221	$5766	€4800	Roman figure (39x26cm-15x10in) s. tempera pencil paper on canvas. 25-May-4 Sotheby's, Milan #29/R est:4000
£3356	$6007	€5000	Study (45x30cm-18x12in) init. tempera collage paper on cardboard. 25-May-4 Sotheby's, Milan #28/R est:6000
£3490	$6491	€5200	Composition with figures (27x32cm-11x13in) s. tempera ink lit. 4-Mar-4 Babuino, Rome #428 est:2000-2500
£3667	$6563	€5500	Composition (36x53cm-14x21in) s. tempera paper prov. 12-May-4 Stadion, Trieste #717/R est:4200-5200
£4054	$7135	€6000	Composition. Solicitor (25x34cm-10x13in) s. oil tempera paper double-sided. 24-May-4 Christie's, Milan #142/R est:4000-6000
£4196	$7133	€6000	Man (58x39cm-23x15in) s. tempera collage masonite. 25-Nov-3 Sotheby's, Milan #76/R est:6000-8000
£4362	$8114	€6500	Compositions (38x34cm-15x13in) s. tempera ink pencil paint paper. 4-Mar-4 Babuino, Rome #91 est:2000-2500
£4545	$7727	€6500	Landscape with figures (35x50cm-14x20in) tempera paper on canvas. 24-Nov-3 Christie's, Milan #249/R est:5000-7000
£4595	$8086	€6800	Composition (53x72cm-21x28in) tempera paper. 22-May-4 Galleria Pananti, Florence #463/R est:6000-7000
£4667	$8587	€7000	Study of figure (19x15cm-7x6in) s. tempera pencil ink prov. 14-Jun-4 Porro, Milan #8/R est:7000-8000
£4698	$8738	€7000	Composition with figures (13x25cm-5x10in) tempera ink wax crayon paper. 4-Mar-4 Babuino, Rome #387 est:1500-2000
£4698	$8738	€7000	Outside (65x43cm-26x17in) tempera ink paper lit. 4-Mar-4 Babuino, Rome #427 est:1500-2000
£4730	$8324	€7000	Two figures (60x50cm-24x20in) s. tempera ink chk paper on cardboard. 24-May-4 Christie's, Milan #140/R est:6000-8000
£5000	$8800	€7400	Composition (40x51cm-16x20in) s. tempera paper. 22-May-4 Galleria Pananti, Florence #469/R est:8000-9000
£5072	$8319	€7000	Trees (25x50cm-10x20in) s. tempera ink paper on canvas prov. 27-May-3 Sotheby's, Milan #179/R est:7000-9000
£5072	$8319	€7000	Landscape with houses (43x29cm-17x11in) s. tempera paper on canvas. 27-May-3 Sotheby's, Milan #174/R est:7000-9000
£5245	$8916	€7500	Mountains (41x59cm-16x23in) s. tempera pencil paper on canvas. 24-Nov-3 Christie's, Milan #165/R est:7000-10000
£5369	$9987	€8000	Fiat 1500 (53x38cm-21x15in) tempera ink paper. 4-Mar-4 Babuino, Rome #466 est:4000-4500
£5435	$8913	€7500	Interno metafisico (34x24cm-13x9in) s. tempera paper on canvas. 31-May-3 Farsetti, Prato #605/R est:5500-6500
£5594	$9510	€8000	Mountainous landscape (33x53cm-13x21in) 24-Nov-3 Christie's, Milan #21/R est:5000-7000
£5797	$9507	€8000	Composition (15x22cm-6x9in) tempera pencil paper on canvas prov. 27-May-3 Sotheby's, Milan #133/R est:7000-9000
£6711	$12483	€10000	Figures (19x44cm-7x17in) lit. 4-Mar-4 Babuino, Rome #426 est:4000-5000
£6757	$11892	€10000	Landscape with tree (39x49cm-15x19in) s. s.i.verso tempera ink chk paper on canvas exec.c.1955 prov. 24-May-4 Christie's, Milan #296/R est:10000-15000
£6993	$11888	€10000	Two figures (53x43cm-21x17in) s. 29-Nov-3 Farsetti, Prato #428/R est:10000-15000
£7047	$13107	€10500	Composition (22x29cm-9x11in) i. tempera ink pencil. 4-Mar-4 Babuino, Rome #110 est:3500-4000
£7246	$11884	€10000	Composition (33x49cm-13x19in) s. tempera pencil double-sided. 27-May-3 Sotheby's, Milan #180/R est:7000-9000
£7971	$13072	€11000	Landscape with statue (44x65cm-17x26in) s. tempera pencil chk paper on masonite. 27-May-3 Sotheby's, Milan #237/R est:10000-15000

£9420	$15449	€13000	Nude (61x58cm-24x23in) tempera paper on canvas painted 1940. 27-May-3 Sotheby's, Milan #182/R est:13000-18000
£9790	$16643	€14000	Rock, Alpine lake (30x38cm-12x15in) s. s.verso. 20-Nov-3 Finarte Semenzato, Milan #10/R est:14000-16000
£10000	$18400	€15000	Drinker (32x28cm-13x11in) paper on board. 8-Jun-4 Finarte Semenzato, Milan #377/R est:15000-18000
£10204	$18265	€15000	Archeological figure (35x21cm-14x8in) tempera paper. 16-Mar-4 Finarte Semenzato, Milan #467/R est:19000
£10490	$17832	€15000	Composition with horse and figures (71x54cm-28x21in) s. tempera oil paper on canvas prov. 25-Nov-3 Sotheby's, Milan #193/R est:15000-20000
£10839	$18427	€15500	Italy and the arts (27x53cm-11x21in) s. tempera paper on canvas. 20-Nov-3 Finarte Semenzato, Milan #181/R est:5500-6500
£11000	$20240	€16500	Figures (50x70cm-20x28in) s. painted 1957. 8-Jun-4 Finarte Semenzato, Milan #434/R est:18000-20000
£11189	$19021	€16000	Mountains (34x47cm-13x19in) s. cardboard. 29-Nov-3 Farsetti, Prato #436/R est:16000-20000
£11594	$19014	€16000	Houses and bell tower (54x59cm-21x23in) s. tempera paper on canvas prov. 27-May-3 Sotheby's, Milan #178/R est:13000-18000
£11957	$19609	€16500	Montagne a Cortina, fine anni '50 (24x52cm-9x20in) s. board on canvas exhib. 31-May-3 Farsetti, Prato #630/R est:15000-20000
£12752	$23718	€19000	Warriors and Balbo's plane (22x28cm-9x11in) tempera ink pastel paper exhib. 4-Mar-4 Babuino, Rome #106 est:5000-6000
£13423	$24966	€20000	Minerva (65x47cm-26x19in) tempera card. 4-Mar-4 Babuino, Rome #25 est:5000-6000
£14667	$26840	€22000	Idoli (66x50cm-26x20in) s. prov. 5-Jun-4 Lempertz, Koln #1003/R est:15000-20000
£14685	$24965	€21000	Metaphysical figures (24x30cm-9x12in) tempera ink paper on canvas painted 1918. 29-Nov-3 Farsetti, Prato #407/R est:20000-24000
£15217	$24957	€21000	Mountains and figures (40x50cm-16x20in) s. 27-May-3 Sotheby's, Milan #235/R est:22000-30000
£16892	$29730	€25000	Composition (50x40cm-20x16in) s. painted c.1950. 24-May-4 Christie's, Milan #291/R est:25000-30000
£18116	$29710	€25000	Composition (43x51cm-17x20in) s. board on canvas. 31-May-3 Farsetti, Prato #698/R est:20000-25000
£23776	$40420	€34000	Landscape with red figure (50x60cm-20x24in) d.1953 prov. 24-Nov-3 Christie's, Milan #242/R est:20000-30000
£37681	$61797	€52000	Il cavaliere dello scandalismo (84x59cm-33x23in) s. tempera collage paper on canvas lit. 31-May-3 Farsetti, Prato #647/R est:45000-55000
£39855	$65362	€55000	Composition (75x90cm-30x35in) s. 31-May-3 Farsetti, Prato #640/R est:55000-65000
£40268	$72081	€60000	Interior and suburbs (32x41cm-13x16in) s. painted 1932. 29-May-4 Farsetti, Prato #525/R est:60000-70000
£57047	$102114	€85000	Figure and wall (84x92cm-33x36in) painted 1939-40 exhib.lit. 29-May-4 Farsetti, Prato #500/R est:80000-100000
£310345	$518276	€450000	Engineer (106x90cm-42x35in) s. painted 1928 exhib.lit. 17-Nov-3 Sant Agostino, Torino #247/R est:450000-550000
£405797	$665507	€560000	Il cavallo sellato (90x72cm-35x28in) s. oil collage paper on canvas painted 1917 exhib.lit. 31-May-3 Farsetti, Prato #664/R

Prints

£2685	$4993	€4000	Mountainous landscape (11x39cm-4x15in) s. monotype ink. 4-Mar-4 Babuino, Rome #496 est:3500-4000

Works on paper

£268	$499	€400	Satirical figure (14x17cm-6x7in) pencil double-sided. 4-Mar-4 Babuino, Rome #2
£470	$874	€700	Untitled (14x15cm-6x6in) pencil. 4-Mar-4 Babuino, Rome #33
£537	$999	€800	Two figures (12x10cm-5x4in) ink wax crayon. 4-Mar-4 Babuino, Rome #442
£604	$1123	€900	Emperor (15x151cm-6x59in) ink exec.c.1924. 4-Mar-4 Babuino, Rome #1/R
£604	$1123	€900	Two figures (11x12cm-4x5in) ink wax crayon. 4-Mar-4 Babuino, Rome #434
£604	$1123	€900	Weight lifting (17x15cm-7x6in) pencil. 4-Mar-4 Babuino, Rome #437
£633	$1165	€950	Study of figures (18x11cm-7x4in) pencil dr card. 11-Jun-4 Farsetti, Prato #11/R
£738	$1373	€1100	To let (16x15cm-6x6in) pencil exec.1922. 4-Mar-4 Babuino, Rome #161
£759	$1267	€1100	Wall (23x30cm-9x12in) graphite. 13-Nov-3 Finarte Semenzato, Rome #196
£805	$1498	€1200	Nail (15x14cm-6x6in) ink. 4-Mar-4 Babuino, Rome #34
£805	$1498	€1200	Figures on stool (14x12cm-6x5in) lead wax crayon lit. 4-Mar-4 Babuino, Rome #435
£805	$1498	€1200	Winged figure (29x16cm-11x6in) ink lead wax crayon. 4-Mar-4 Babuino, Rome #438
£872	$1623	€1300	Landscape with trees (13x18cm-5x7in) ink pencil paper on card. 4-Mar-4 Babuino, Rome #385
£872	$1623	€1300	Don Sturzo (13x13cm-5x5in) pencil ink lit. 4-Mar-4 Babuino, Rome #439
£940	$1748	€1400	Woman with basket (14x20cm-6x8in) ink paper on card. 4-Mar-4 Babuino, Rome #155
£1000	$1800	€1500	Study of costume (28x20cm-11x8in) s. pencil tempera. 22-Apr-4 Finarte Semenzato, Rome #71/R est:1400-1700
£1007	$1802	€1500	Study (20x14cm-8x6in) s. ink lead. 25-May-4 Sotheby's, Milan #59/R est:1500
£1007	$1802	€1500	Study (31x22cm-12x9in) s. Indian ink paper on canvas prov. 25-May-4 Dorotheum, Vienna #168/R est:1500-2000
£1007	$1872	€1500	Mountainous landscape (26x18cm-10x7in) s. pencil. 4-Mar-4 Babuino, Rome #403 est:500-600
£1007	$1872	€1500	Figures in fantasy landscape (31x29cm-12x11in) pencil wax crayon paper on card. 4-Mar-4 Babuino, Rome #490 est:1400-1600
£1007	$1872	€1500	Death penalty (20x15cm-8x6in) pencil double-sided lit. 4-Mar-4 Babuino, Rome #491 est:600-800
£1034	$1655	€1500	Untitled (15x28cm-6x11in) s. pencil paper on canvas exec c.1950. 13-Mar-3 Galleria Pace, Milan #74/R est:1650-2100
£1074	$1997	€1600	Landscape with bull and figure (20x14cm-8x6in) s. ink. 4-Mar-4 Babuino, Rome #74
£1074	$1997	€1600	Corriere della Sera (23x23cm-9x9in) lead ink W/C card. 4-Mar-4 Babuino, Rome #440 est:1500-2000
£1087	$1783	€1500	Study (29x20cm-11x8in) s. i.verso Chinese ink. 27-May-3 Sotheby's, Milan #132 est:1500-2000
£1141	$2122	€1700	Landscape (15x20cm-6x8in) ink W/C lit. 4-Mar-4 Babuino, Rome #404 est:600-800
£1156	$2070	€1700	Composition (18x14cm-7x6in) s. pen exec.1960 prov.lit. 16-Mar-4 Finarte Semenzato, Milan #241/R est:1100
£1172	$1958	€1700	Harmony (22x17cm-9x7in) s. mixed media paper on card. 13-Nov-3 Finarte Semenzato, Rome #132/R est:1400-1600
£1172	$1958	€1700	Cannon (24x17cm-9x7in) s. pencil paper on canvas. 13-Nov-3 Finarte Semenzato, Rome #193/R est:1400-1600
£1268	$2104	€1800	Composition (12x20cm-5x8in) pencil dr. 13-Jun-3 Farsetti, Prato #90/R
£1275	$2372	€1900	Sironi's daughters (27x22cm-11x9in) s. pencil paper on card. 4-Mar-4 Babuino, Rome #159 est:1200-1400
£1342	$2403	€2000	Three figures (26x20cm-10x8in) s. ink two. 25-May-4 Sotheby's, Milan #67/R est:2000
£1342	$2403	€2000	Face to face (27x35cm-11x14in) s. chl pencil two. 25-May-4 Sotheby's, Milan #63/R est:3000
£1342	$2497	€2000	Coliseum (31x19cm-12x7in) ink W/C wax crayon. 4-Mar-4 Babuino, Rome #108 est:1000-1500
£1342	$2497	€2000	Soldiers (21x30cm-8x12in) s. mixed media tempera pencil. 4-Mar-4 Babuino, Rome #131
£1342	$2497	€2000	Urban landscape (11x9cm-4x4in) s. ink lit. 4-Mar-4 Babuino, Rome #405 est:300-400
£1361	$2435	€2000	Composition (21x29cm-8x11in) s. ink. 22-Mar-4 Sant Agostino, Torino #431/R est:2500
£1379	$2303	€2000	Seated female nude (38x28cm-15x11in) s. pencil chk. 13-Nov-3 Finarte Semenzato, Rome #161/R est:2000-2500
£1399	$2378	€2000	Figure (21x30cm-8x12in) s. pencil W/C paper on card prov. 25-Nov-3 Sotheby's, Milan #100 est:2500-3000
£1409	$2495	€2100	Annonciation (44x32cm-17x13in) s. crayon chl. 28-Apr-4 Charbonneaux, Paris #224/R est:1200-1500
£1409	$2621	€2100	Untitled (33x40cm-13x16in) pencil card lit. 4-Mar-4 Babuino, Rome #441 est:800-1200
£1409	$2621	€2100	Figures (22x29cm-9x11in) s. pencil. 4-Mar-4 Babuino, Rome #480
£1409	$2621	€2100	Mountainous landscape (10x23cm-4x9in) mixed media. 4-Mar-4 Babuino, Rome #525 est:600-800
£1477	$2746	€2200	Compositions (16x12cm-6x5in) s. pencil paper on card. 4-Mar-4 Babuino, Rome #109 est:600-800
£1477	$2746	€2200	Figures (29x22cm-11x9in) pencil paper on card. 4-Mar-4 Babuino, Rome #481 est:500-600
£1477	$2746	€2200	Puppy (28x36cm-11x14in) wax crayon double-sided lit. 4-Mar-4 Babuino, Rome #489 est:600-700
£1611	$2883	€2400	Three figures (28x20cm-11x8in) s. pencil ink two. 25-May-4 Sotheby's, Milan #61/R est:3000
£1611	$2996	€2400	Figures in landscape (31x23cm-12x9in) pencil. 4-Mar-4 Babuino, Rome #370 est:1200-1800
£1611	$2996	€2400	Figure with horse (13x16cm-5x6in) s. pencil. 4-Mar-4 Babuino, Rome #384 est:400-500
£1611	$2996	€2400	Horses (23x16cm-9x6in) pencil exec.1920. 4-Mar-4 Babuino, Rome #458 est:700-900
£1611	$2996	€2400	Mannequin (15x12cm-6x5in) s. ink lit. 4-Mar-4 Babuino, Rome #492 est:300-400
£1678	$3121	€2500	Figures (29x13cm-11x5in) pencil card lit. 4-Mar-4 Babuino, Rome #76
£1678	$3121	€2500	Maternity (34x24cm-13x9in) pencil tempera paper on card. 4-Mar-4 Babuino, Rome #157 est:300-400
£1745	$3246	€2600	Woman (29x20cm-11x8in) s. pencil W/C. 4-Mar-4 Babuino, Rome #154 est:800-1200
£1745	$3246	€2600	Office (20x28cm-8x11in) ink pencil lit. 4-Mar-4 Babuino, Rome #436 est:1600-1800
£1745	$3246	€2600	Plans (31x21cm-12x8in) pencil lit. 4-Mar-4 Babuino, Rome #493 est:800-1200
£1793	$2994	€2600	Interior (15x17cm-6x7in) s. pencil. 13-Nov-3 Finarte Semenzato, Rome #149/R est:2500-3000
£1812	$3370	€2700	Composition with six figures (14x23cm-6x9in) pencil card. 4-Mar-4 Babuino, Rome #160 est:500-600
£1879	$3495	€2800	Landscape with figures (32x22cm-13x9in) s. pencil wax crayon. 4-Mar-4 Babuino, Rome #85
£2013	$3745	€3000	Faces and figure (20x14cm-8x6in) ink. 4-Mar-4 Babuino, Rome #121
£2013	$3745	€3000	Seated man (29x21cm-11x8in) s. mixed media W/C Chinese ink pencil card. 4-Mar-4 Babuino, Rome #164 est:1500-2000
£2013	$3745	€3000	Suburbs with building sites (12x15cm-5x6in) s. ink. 4-Mar-4 Babuino, Rome #465 est:400-500
£2013	$3745	€3000	Exhibition (23x17cm-9x7in) pencil exhib. 4-Mar-4 Babuino, Rome #477 est:1000-1500
£2083	$3542	€3000	Boxer (15x10cm-6x4in) s. mixed media prov. 28-Oct-3 Il Ponte, Milan #276/R
£2083	$3292	€3000	After death (24x19cm-9x7in) mixed media. 6-Sep-3 Meeting Art, Vercelli #410 est:3000
£2148	$3844	€3200	Two figures at table (19x40cm-7x16in) s. pencil Chinese ink. 25-May-4 Sotheby's, Milan #66/R est:3000
£2148	$3995	€3200	Suburbs (13x14cm-5x6in) s. ink paper on card. 4-Mar-4 Babuino, Rome #5
£2148	$3995	€3200	Tram (21x13cm-8x5in) s. ink paper on card. 4-Mar-4 Babuino, Rome #112 est:200-300
£2148	$3995	€3200	Composition (32x23cm-13x9in) s. ink. 4-Mar-4 Babuino, Rome #119 est:1000-1500
£2148	$3995	€3200	Smoky suburbs (11x15cm-4x6in) ink W/C. 4-Mar-4 Babuino, Rome #132
£2148	$3995	€3200	Seated woman (10x12cm-4x5in) s. pencil paper on card. 4-Mar-4 Babuino, Rome #141 est:800-1000
£2148	$3995	€3200	Figures (27x29cm-11x11in) s. pencil wax crayon. 4-Mar-4 Babuino, Rome #146 est:1200-1800
£2148	$3995	€3200	Railway (17x9cm-7x4in) s. ink W/C paper on card. 4-Mar-4 Babuino, Rome #165 est:600-700
£2148	$3995	€3200	Composition (19x32cm-7x13in) wax crayon. 4-Mar-4 Babuino, Rome #388 est:1000-1200
£2148	$3995	€3200	Suburbs and crane (20x9cm-8x4in) s. ink. 4-Mar-4 Babuino, Rome #424 est:600-800
£2148	$3995	€3200	Arch (27x19cm-11x7in) wax crayon. 4-Mar-4 Babuino, Rome #479 est:800-1200
£2282	$4244	€3400	Composition (30x38cm-12x15in) s. mixed media W/C tempera Chinese ink. 4-Mar-4 Babuino, Rome #73
£2282	$4244	€3400	Landscape (22x25cm-9x10in) pencil. 4-Mar-4 Babuino, Rome #167 est:600-800
£2349	$4369	€3500	Suburbs (15x11cm-6x4in) s. pencil. 4-Mar-4 Babuino, Rome #422 est:1000-1200
£2416	$4494	€3600	Untitled (24x21cm-9x8in) Chinese ink lead lit. 4-Mar-4 Babuino, Rome #35
£2416	$4494	€3600	Composition with figures (31x24cm-12x9in) pencil lit. 4-Mar-4 Babuino, Rome #84
£2416	$4494	€3600	Composition with figures (22x28cm-9x11in) pencil. 4-Mar-4 Babuino, Rome #482 est:600-700
£2533	$4661	€3800	Maternity (13x11cm-5x4in) s. pencil tempera prov. 14-Jun-4 Porro, Milan #2/R est:4000-5000

£2550 $4744 €3800 Composition with figures (27x24cm-11x9in) pencil. 4-Mar-4 Babuino, Rome #93 est:1500-2000
£2685 $4805 €4000 Composition with figures (30x37cm-12x15in) s. chl tempera paper on canvas. 25-May-4 Sotheby's, Milan #32/R est:3000
£2685 $4993 €4000 Figures (43x28cm-17x11in) pencil. 4-Mar-4 Babuino, Rome #142 est:1500-2000
£2685 $4993 €4000 Suburbs (19x14cm-7x6in) s. pencil. 4-Mar-4 Babuino, Rome #409 est:600-800
£2685 $4993 €4000 Face and woman (44x32cm-17x13in) mixed media tempera pencil. 4-Mar-4 Babuino, Rome #453 est:1000-1500
£2685 $4993 €4000 Fighters (27x19cm-11x7in) s. pencil exhib. 4-Mar-4 Babuino, Rome #497 est:600-800
£2721 $4871 €4000 Unstable throne (38x33cm-15x13in) s. mixed media collage exec.1937 lit. 16-Mar-4 Finarte Semenzato, Milan #292/R est:4400
£2953 $5493 €4400 Man riding horse (17x20cm-7x8in) s. wax crayon. 4-Mar-4 Babuino, Rome #459 est:1000-1500
£3020 $5617 €4500 Suburbs and train (9x26cm-4x10in) pencil card. 4-Mar-4 Babuino, Rome #464
£3087 $5742 €4600 Figures (40x53cm-16x21in) pencil wax crayon. 4-Mar-4 Babuino, Rome #386 est:1600-2000
£3154 $5867 €4700 Suburbs (8x12cm-3x5in) s. ink paper on card. 4-Mar-4 Babuino, Rome #407 est:700-900
£3221 $5992 €4800 Suburbs (14x12cm-6x5in) s. ink paper on card lit. 4-Mar-4 Babuino, Rome #133 est:600-800
£3221 $5992 €4800 Triennale (29x21cm-11x8in) pencil exhib. 4-Mar-4 Babuino, Rome #478 est:1000-1400
£3289 $6117 €4900 Seated in an office (20x22cm-8x9in) s. ink. 4-Mar-4 Babuino, Rome #372 est:1000-1500
£3357 $5706 €4800 Self-portrait (24x20cm-9x8in) s.i. Chinese ink lit. 26-Nov-3 Pandolfini, Florence #9 est:6000-6200
£3490 $6491 €5200 Landscape with figures (22x28cm-9x11in) s. pencil chk lit. 4-Mar-4 Babuino, Rome #425 est:1800-2200
£3691 $6866 €5500 Metaphysical horse (11x21cm-4x8in) s. ink. 4-Mar-4 Babuino, Rome #457 est:800-1200
£4027 $7490 €6000 Rider (18x13cm-7x5in) s. ink paper on card exhib. 4-Mar-4 Babuino, Rome #113 est:1200-1600
£4295 $7989 €6400 Man at window (12x12cm-5x5in) s. pencil card exhib. 4-Mar-4 Babuino, Rome #122 est:1000-1500
£4295 $7989 €6400 Quarry (25x22cm-10x9in) s. ink W/C pencil card. 4-Mar-4 Babuino, Rome #152 est:1000-1500
£4698 $8738 €7000 Covers (28x22cm-11x9in) mixed media exhib. 4-Mar-4 Babuino, Rome #102 est:2000-2500
£4733 $8473 €7100 Landscape (29x45cm-11x18in) s. Chinese ink W/C prov. 12-May-4 Stadion, Trieste #718/R est:4200-5200
£4832 $8988 €7200 Allegory (20x14cm-8x6in) i. ink lit. 4-Mar-4 Babuino, Rome #499 est:1800-2200
£4895 $8322 €7000 Mountains (57x42cm-22x17in) s. mixed media paper on canvas prov. 24-Nov-3 Christie's, Milan #123/R est:7000-10000
£5369 $9987 €8000 Suburbs (21x29cm-8x11in) pencil. 4-Mar-4 Babuino, Rome #410 est:1200-1800
£5594 $9510 €8000 Composition (27x37cm-11x15in) s. mixed media paper on canvas. 20-Nov-3 Finarte Semenzato, Milan #182/R est:4500-5500
£5705 $10611 €8500 Minerva Italica (34x23cm-13x9in) mixed media double-sided. 4-Mar-4 Babuino, Rome #514 est:3800-4200
£6376 $11413 €9500 Composition with landscapes and figures (32x44cm-13x17in) gouache Chinese ink paper on canvas. 29-May-4 Farsetti, Prato #420/R est:7000-10000
£6552 $10941 €9500 Rider (41x25cm-16x10in) s. chl dr paper on canvas. 14-Nov-3 Farsetti, Prato #297/R est:2600-3000
£6711 $12483 €10000 Figures (30x23cm-12x9in) s. mixed media. 4-Mar-4 Babuino, Rome #90 est:1500-2000
£7931 $13245 €11500 Builder (39x29cm-15x11in) s. chl Chinese ink tempera paper on canvas. 17-Nov-3 Sant Agostino, Torino #196/R est:10000-14000
£10563 $18486 €15000 Landscape (45x60cm-18x24in) s. mixed media card on canvas prov. 16-Dec-3 Porro, Milan #1/R est:15000-20000
£12245 $21918 €18000 Composition with figures (48x70cm-19x28in) s. chl paper on canvas lit. 22-Mar-4 Sant Agostino, Torino #520/R est:22000
£13287 $22587 €19000 Figure in urban landscape (28x21cm-11x8in) s. ink tempera collage paper on canvas. 29-Nov-3 Farsetti, Prato #408/R est:12000-16000
£15436 $28711 €23000 Italian 20th Century (34x25cm-13x10in) mixed media ink pencil exec.1925 lit. 4-Mar-4 Babuino, Rome #94 est:2000-2500
£25352 $44366 €36000 Little theatre (43x49cm-17x19in) s. mixed media paper on canvas prov.lit. 16-Dec-3 Porro, Milan #12/R est:18000-22000

SISKIND, Aaron (1903-1991) American

Photographs
£2111 $3800 €3082 Kentucky (40x31cm-16x12in) s.d.1951 gelatin silver print prov. 23-Apr-4 Phillips, New York #250/R est:4000-6000
£2273 $4000 €3319 Martha's vineyard (25x33cm-10x13in) with sig. silver print. 20-May-4 Swann Galleries, New York #443/R est:5000-7500
£2695 $4500 €3935 Chicago (32x41cm-13x16in) s.i.d.verso gelatin silver print lit. 16-Oct-3 Phillips, New York #147/R est:3000-5000
£3593 $6000 €5246 New York (42x34cm-17x13in) sig.i.d.1951 verso silver print. 21-Oct-3 Swann Galleries, New York #227/R est:3500-5500
£3713 $6200 €5421 Pleasures and terrors of levitation (26x26cm-10x10in) s.i.d.1957 verso gelatin silver print. 17-Oct-3 Phillips, New York #85/R est:4000-6000
£4046 $7000 €5907 Chicago (42x34cm-17x13in) with sig.i. silver print. 9-Dec-3 Swann Galleries, New York #583/R est:2500-3500

SISLEY, Alfred (1839-1899) French

£117647 $200000 €171765 La meule de paille (38x56cm-15x22in) s.d.77 prov.exhib. 5-Nov-3 Christie's, Rockefeller NY #202/R est:200000-300000
£160000 $294400 €233600 Le brochet (42x80cm-17x31in) s. painted 1888 prov.exhib.lit. 23-Jun-4 Christie's, London #112/R est:100000-150000
£200000 $364000 €292000 Un chemin a Louveciennes (49x65cm-19x26in) s. painted 1876 prov.exhib.lit. 3-Feb-4 Christie's, London #114/R est:200000-300000
£247059 $420000 €360706 Chemin montant au Mont Valerien (50x65cm-20x26in) s. painted 1880 prov.exhib.lit. 5-Nov-3 Christie's, Rockefeller NY #209/R est:300000-400000
£251397 $450000 €367040 Saint-Mammes et les bords du Loing (46x56cm-18x22in) s. painted c.1885 prov.exhib. 4-May-4 Christie's, Rockefeller NY #4/R est:450000-650000
£280000 $509600 €408800 Storr rock, Lady's cove, le soir (65x81cm-26x32in) s. painted 1897 prov.exhib.lit. 21-Jun-4 Sotheby's, London #11/R est:300000-400000
£320000 $585600 €467200 Prairie et coteaux de Veneaux-Nadon (54x73cm-21x29in) s. painted 1881 prov.exhib.lit. 2-Feb-4 Christie's, London #19/R est:350000-450000
£323529 $550000 €472352 La berge a saint Mammes (50x65cm-20x26in) s. painted 1880 prov.exhib.lit. 4-Nov-3 Christie's, Rockefeller NY #10/R est:600000-800000
£580000 $1067200 €846800 Enfants jouant dans la prairie (50x73cm-20x29in) s.d.73 prov.exhib.lit. 22-Jun-4 Christie's, London #10/R est:700000-1000000
£670391 $1200000 €978771 Moulins de Moret en hiver (55x74cm-22x29in) s. painted 1890 prov.exhib.lit. 4-May-4 Christie's, Rockefeller NY #12/R est:800000-1200000
£850000 $1564000 €1241000 Pont de Moret, effet du matin (54x72cm-21x28in) s.d.91 prov.exhib.lit. 22-Jun-4 Christie's, London #8/R est:1000000-1500000
£882353 $1500000 €1288235 Le matin, le long du bois, au ,oid de juin (60x73cm-24x29in) s. painted 1883 prov.exhib.lit. 4-Nov-3 Christie's, Rockefeller NY #22/R est:1000000-1500000
£1300000 $2379000 €1898000 Route de Marly-le-Roi (60x73cm-24x29in) s.d.75 prov.exhib.lit. 2-Feb-4 Christie's, London #9/R est:1000000-1500000
£1400000 $2548000 €2044000 Route a Louveciennes (65x54cm-26x21in) s.d.74 prov.exhib.lit. 21-Jun-4 Sotheby's, London #4/R est:1500000-2000000
Works on paper
£56338 $97465 €80000 Effets de neige (31x44cm-12x17in) s. pastel paper on canvas. 12-Dec-3 Piasa, Paris #11/R est:80000-120000

SISMORE, Charles Porter (20th C) British

£993 $1808 €1500 Marine (30x45cm-12x18in) s. 15-Jun-4 Vanderkindere, Brussels #163 est:1500-2000

SISSON, Laurence P (1928-) American

£753 $1400 €1099 Beached Dory (42x57cm-17x22in) s. board. 5-Mar-4 Skinner, Boston #570/R est:800-1200
£1243 $2200 €1815 Winter harbour scene with trees in the foreground (24x44cm-9x17in) s. masonite. 2-May-4 Bonhams & Butterfields, San Francisco #1085/R est:3000-5000
£1412 $2400 €2062 Maine coastline (61x91cm-24x36in) s. masonite. 21-Nov-3 Skinner, Boston #578/R est:2500-3500
£1429 $2300 €2086 Maine coastal scene (53x71cm-21x28in) s. masonite. 20-Aug-3 James Julia, Fairfield #1361/R est:2250-2750
£2547 $4100 €3719 Waterfront (76x102cm-30x40in) board. 22-Aug-3 Altermann Galleries, Santa Fe #165
£5062 $8200 €7340 On the Maine coast (75x168cm-30x66in) s.d.65 board. 8-Aug-3 Barridorf, Portland #239/R est:6000-9000
Works on paper
£645 $1200 €942 Harbour view (55x73cm-22x29in) s. W/C. 5-Mar-4 Skinner, Boston #574/R
£960 $1700 €1402 Coastal Maine inlet in winter, mossy grey clouds above (51x74cm-20x29in) s. W/C. 1-May-4 Thomaston Place, Thomaston #644/R

SISTI, Anthony (1901-1983) American

Works on paper
£279 $500 €407 Boxer (25x33cm-10x13in) s.d.1939 ink. 16-May-4 Wright, Chicago #174/R

SITE, Mino delle (1914-1996) Italian

£7432 $13081 €11000 Portrait of Gianni Caproni from above (30x40cm-12x16in) s.d.37 prov.exhib. 24-May-4 Christie's, Milan #280/R est:9500-10000

SITHOLE, Lucas (1931-1994) South African

Sculpture
£2064 $3695 €3013 Wounded buffalo III (24x60cm-9x24in) steel. 31-May-4 Stephan Welz, Johannesburg #539/R est:15000-20000 (SA.R 25000)

SITNIKOV, Vassili (1915-1987) Russian

£728 $1362 €1100 Eglises sous la neige (95x144cm-37x57in) 20-Jul-4 Gioffredo, Nice #39

SITTE, Willi (1921-) German?

£2267 $4171 €3400 Man playing with a ball (60x54cm-24x21in) s.d.65 card. 12-Jun-4 Villa Grisebach, Berlin #418/R est:3000-4000
Works on paper
£867 $1560 €1300 Reclining figure (38x52cm-15x20in) s.d. Indian ink brush pen board. 24-Apr-4 Dr Lehr, Berlin #444/R

SITTER, Inger (1929-) Norwegian

£1724 $3190 €2500 Jeune fille au bas de l'escalier (52x57cm-20x22in) s.d.47. 19-Jan-4 Horta, Bruxelles #94/R est:2500-3000
Works on paper
£1281 $2139 €1870 Snow (46x55cm-18x22in) s. s.i.d.64 verso collage canvas. 13-Oct-3 Blomqvist, Oslo #320/R est:18000-20000 (N.KR 15000)

SITTHIKHET, Vasan (1957-) Thai

£417 $696 €609 Burning desires (71x50cm-28x20in) s. 12-Oct-3 Sotheby's, Singapore #180/R est:1200-1800 (S.D 1200)

SITU MIAN (1953-) Chinese

£1856 $3100 €2710 Feeding little brother (76x71cm-30x28in) s.d. 11-Oct-3 Nadeau, Windsor #29/R est:2000-3000
£11173 $20000 €16313 Village market (81x102cm-32x40in) 15-May-4 Altermann Galleries, Santa Fe #151/R
£14118 $24000 €20612 Sharing a lite (81x102cm-32x40in) 1-Nov-3 Altermann Galleries, Santa Fe #87

SITU, W Jason (20th C) American

£1301 $2250 €1899 Sunset in Finger rock (56x71cm-22x28in) s.i. i.stretcher exhib. 10-Dec-3 Bonhams & Butterfields, San Francisco #6345/R est:3000-5000

SITZLER, Fred (1949-) American

£821 $1370 €1199 Portrait of a champion dog, le petit Marquise da la France II (33x38cm-13x15in) s. 14-Nov-3 Aspire, Cleveland #79

SITZMAN, Edward R (1874-1949) American
£344 $550 €502 Autumn frost (41x30cm-16x12in) s. board. 21-Sep-3 William Jenack, New York #324
£989 $1800 €1444 Autumn forest (30x41cm-12x16in) s.i.d.1930 board. 20-Jun-4 Charlton Hall, Columbia #563/R est:800-1200
Works on paper
£583 $950 €851 Fall forest (33x48cm-13x19in) s. W/C. 27-Sep-3 Charlton Hall, Columbia #304/R

SIVELL, Robert (1888-1958) British
£2000 $3400 €2920 Portrait of a young girl (101x75cm-40x30in) s. 30-Oct-3 Christie's, London #188/R est:2000-3000

SIVERS, Clara von (1854-1924) German
£600 $1080 €900 Still life with pink chrysanthemums (52x92cm-20x36in) s.i. lit. 22-Apr-4 Allgauer, Kempten #3720/R
£1867 $3360 €2800 Morning dew on pink roses (24x34cm-9x13in) s.d.1880 canvas on cardboard. 21-Apr-4 Christie's, Amsterdam #23/R est:3000-5000
£3000 $5400 €4500 Colourful zinnias in a copper pot (88x110cm-35x43in) s. 21-Apr-4 Christie's, Amsterdam #54/R est:4000-6000
£3767 $6404 €5500 Still life with roses (24x34cm-9x13in) s.d.1886 canvas on board. 8-Nov-3 Hans Stahl, Toestorf #84/R est:6800

SIVESIND, Bengt (1947-) Norwegian
£415 $688 €602 Woman resting (100x100cm-39x39in) s. 16-Jun-3 Blomqvist, Lysaker #1217/R (N.KR 4800)

SIVIERO, Carlo (1882-) Italian
£933 $1671 €1400 Model (50x40cm-20x16in) s.d.1915 cardboard. 12-May-4 Stadion, Trieste #650/R est:1400-1800

SJAHWIL (1936-) Indonesian?
£942 $1460 €1375 Figure (70x70cm-28x28in) s.d.63. 6-Oct-2 Sotheby's, Singapore #134/R est:2500-3500 (S.D 2600)
£1993 $3089 €2910 Mother (90x90cm-35x35in) s.d.63. 6-Oct-2 Sotheby's, Singapore #133/R est:3000-4000 (S.D 5500)

SJAMAAR, Pieter Geerard (1819-1876) Dutch
£496 $829 €700 Recluse by lamplight (26x20cm-10x8in) s. panel. 20-Oct-3 Glerum, Amsterdam #50/R
£724 $1310 €1100 Greengrocer by candlelight (21x15cm-8x6in) s. panel. 19-Apr-4 Glerum, Amsterdam #88/R
£1068 $1816 €1560 Visitor at the workplace (25x35cm-10x14in) s. panel. 5-Nov-3 Vendue Huis, Gravenhage #72/R est:1500-2000
£1379 $2303 €2000 Men playing draughts by candle light (35x44cm-14x17in) s. panel lit. 10-Jul-3 Allgauer, Kempten #2682/R est:2000

SJOBERG, Axel (1866-1950) Swedish
£808 $1389 €1180 Seascape with cormorant on cliffs (81x105cm-32x41in) s.d.1900. 3-Dec-3 AB Stockholms Auktionsverk #2241/R (S.KR 10500)
£961 $1720 €1403 The ice is breaking up (76x110cm-30x43in) s.d.1921 exhib.prov. 26-May-4 AB Stockholms Auktionsverk #2108/R est:12000-15000 (S.KR 13000)
£3178 $5689 €4640 Archipelago (101x145cm-40x57in) s.i.d.1903 prov. 25-May-4 Bukowskis, Stockholm #93/R est:20000-25000 (S.KR 43000)
Works on paper
£388 $647 €566 Korso lighthouse in snow (36x54cm-14x21in) s.d.1923 W/C. 12-Oct-3 Uppsala Auktionskammare, Uppsala #445 (S.KR 5000)

SJOBERG, Bertil (1914-) Swedish
£451 $753 €658 Figure composition (97x130cm-38x51in) s.d.1976 prov. 7-Oct-3 Rasmussen, Copenhagen #261/R (D.KR 4800)

SJOLANDER, Waldemar (1906-1988) Swedish
£283 $509 €425 Woman in yellow (59x66cm-23x26in) s.i.d.1949. 25-Apr-4 Goteborg Auktionsverk, Sweden #334/R (S.KR 3900)
£290 $522 €435 Town scape, Gothenburg (33x27cm-13x11in) s. 25-Apr-4 Goteborg Auktionsverk, Sweden #371/R (S.KR 4000)
£355 $640 €533 Street scene, Gothenburg (64x70cm-25x28in) s. 25-Apr-4 Goteborg Auktionsverk, Sweden #392/R (S.KR 4900)
£355 $640 €533 Still life of flowers and dish with fish (90x95cm-35x37in) s/. 25-Apr-4 Goteborg Auktionsverk, Sweden #409/R (S.KR 4900)
£366 $648 €534 Still life of flowers (69x92cm-27x36in) s. 27-Apr-4 AB Stockholms Auktionsverk #863/R (S.KR 5000)
£563 $941 €822 Composition (85x60cm-33x24in) s. painted c.1960. 7-Oct-3 Rasmussen, Copenhagen #217/R (D.KR 6000)
£3172 $5393 €4631 Summer flowers in evening sunshine (110x105cm-43x41in) s.d.16.5.1941. 4-Nov-3 Bukowskis, Stockholm #108/R est:50000-60000 (S.KR 42000)

SJOLIE, Ole (Fauske) Norwegian
£884 $1618 €1291 Abstract composition (150x200cm-59x79in) s. 2-Feb-4 Blomqvist, Lysaker #1280/R (N.KR 11000)

SJOLUND, Stig (1955-) Swedish
£718 $1220 €1048 Untitled (71x100cm-28x39in) s.d.1987 verso diptych oil cibachrome prov.lit. 4-Nov-3 Bukowskis, Stockholm #572/R (S.KR 9500)

SJOSTEDT, Hans Eiler (1914-1983) Danish
£578 $1052 €867 Female nude and male model (139x112cm-55x44in) mono. exhib. 19-Jun-4 Rasmussen, Havnen #4114/R (D.KR 6500)

SJOSTROM, Hakan (20th C) Finnish
Works on paper
£417 $696 €600 Ariadne (44x59cm-17x23in) s.d.1965 gouache. 23-Oct-3 Hagelstam, Helsinki #885/R

SJOSTROM, Ina (1883-1969) Finnish
£322 $593 €480 Landscape (33x48cm-13x19in) s. 25-Mar-4 Hagelstam, Helsinki #1080
£333 $613 €500 Reflections (32x48cm-13x19in) s. 9-Jun-4 Bukowskis, Helsinki #548/R
£423 $676 €600 Red house by lake (48x66cm-19x26in) s. 21-Sep-3 Bukowskis, Helsinki #469/R
£671 $1235 €1000 View from the mountains (76x101cm-30x40in) 25-Mar-4 Hagelstam, Helsinki #1016

SJOSTROM, Vilho (1873-1944) Finnish
£556 $928 €800 Pine trees (55x38cm-22x15in) s. 23-Oct-3 Hagelstam, Helsinki #824
£671 $1235 €1000 Red house with garden (39x46cm-15x18in) s.d.1924. 25-Mar-4 Hagelstam, Helsinki #802/R
£676 $1082 €960 Villa in Tusby (43x38cm-17x15in) s. 21-Sep-3 Bukowskis, Helsinki #470/R
£872 $1623 €1300 Autumn (50x74cm-20x29in) s. 7-Mar-4 Bukowskis, Helsinki #448/R
£1259 $2140 €1800 View towards the sea (65x55cm-26x22in) s.d.1943. 29-Nov-3 Bukowskis, Helsinki #199/R est:1800-2000
£1338 $2315 €1900 Man smoking pipe (80x61cm-31x24in) s.d.1894. 13-Dec-3 Hagelstam, Helsinki #135/R est:2000
£1351 $2419 €2000 Man with pipe (61x50cm-24x20in) s. 8-May-4 Bukowskis, Helsinki #39/R est:2000-2300
£1408 $2437 €2000 Tree in autumn colours (57x75cm-22x30in) s. 13-Dec-3 Hagelstam, Helsinki #134/R est:1500
£1565 $2848 €2300 Winter's day (55x47cm-22x19in) s.d.1933. 8-Feb-4 Bukowskis, Helsinki #457/R est:1200
£1667 $2783 €2400 Landscape from Borgaa (54x41cm-21x16in) s.d.1912. 23-Oct-3 Hagelstam, Helsinki #835/R est:1500
£2000 $3580 €3000 Bay on lake (65x82cm-26x32in) s. 15-May-4 Hagelstam, Helsinki #140/R est:3000
£2162 $3870 €3200 Bench in the park (36x47cm-14x19in) board. 8-May-4 Bukowskis, Helsinki #118/R est:1200-1500
£3311 $5926 €4900 Woman on beach (42x50cm-17x20in) board. 8-May-4 Bukowskis, Helsinki #34/R est:1400-1700
£4930 $8528 €7000 Winter landscape, Vitasaari (61x50cm-24x20in) s.d.1922. 13-Dec-3 Hagelstam, Helsinki #133/R est:3000

SKAGERFORS, Olle (1920-1997) Swedish
£725 $1305 €1059 Grove (41x48cm-16x19in) init.d.1961. 26-Apr-4 Bukowskis, Stockholm #45/R (S.KR 10000)
Works on paper
£696 $1232 €1016 Self-portrait (41x33cm-16x13in) init. chl. 27-Apr-4 AB Stockholms Auktionsverk #752/R (S.KR 9500)

SKANBERG, Carl (1850-1883) Swedish
£691 $1127 €1009 Landscape with cottage by water (28x36cm-11x14in) s.d.72 canvas on panel. 29-Sep-3 Lilla Bukowskis, Stockholm #689 (S.KR 9000)
£1183 $2117 €1727 Summer landscape with lady on shore (70x107cm-28x42in) with sig. 26-May-4 AB Stockholms Auktionsverk #2188/R est:20000-25000 (S.KR 16000)
£1552 $2778 €2266 Coastal landscape with reeds, summer (19x34cm-7x13in) s.d.73. 26-May-4 AB Stockholms Auktionsverk #2211/R est:8000-10000 (S.KR 21000)
£1692 $2911 €2470 French landscape (65x94cm-26x37in) s.i.d.79. 3-Dec-3 AB Stockholms Auktionsverk #2249/R est:30000-35000 (S.KR 22000)
£2462 $4234 €3595 Canal scene, Venice (45x34cm-18x13in) st.sig. canvas on board. 3-Dec-3 AB Stockholms Auktionsverk #2487/R est:30000-35000 (S.KR 32000)
Works on paper
£268 $431 €391 Town gate in Taormina (17x12cm-7x5in) s.d.Mars 81 W/C. 25-Aug-3 Lilla Bukowskis, Stockholm #707 (S.KR 3500)

SKARBINA, Franz (1849-1910) German
£1134 $2030 €1656 Street scene with woman carrying water jug and milk jug by canal (68x44cm-27x17in) s.d.1894 prov. 12-Jan-4 Rasmussen, Vejle #341/R est:15000 (D.KR 12000)
£1944 $3169 €2800 Southern terrace with woman and cat (36x26cm-14x10in) s.i.d.1883 WC paper on board. 27-Sep-3 Dr Fritz Nagel, Stuttgart #9621/R est:2800
£2867 $4874 €4100 Cloister (70x56cm-28x22in) s. 20-Nov-3 Van Ham, Cologne #1872/R est:4400
£3472 $5799 €5000 Courtyard in the snow (50x35cm-20x14in) s.d. i. stretcher 1905. 24-Oct-3 Ketterer, Hamburg #106/R est:6000-8000
Works on paper
£1189 $2021 €1700 Potsdam station (43x60cm-17x24in) s. pastel panel. 27-Nov-3 Bassenge, Berlin #5651 est:1800
£1357 $2308 €1981 German soldier from Napoleonic era (36x24cm-14x9in) s.d.1884 W/C. 19-Nov-3 Fischer, Luzern #2488/R est:500-700 (S.FR 3000)
£6000 $11040 €9000 Young lady on the terrace (36x27cm-14x11in) s.i.d.83 W/C gouache. 12-Jun-4 Villa Grisebach, Berlin #107/R est:6000-8000

SKARI, Edvard (1839-1903) Norwegian
£1200 $2040 €1752 Congested shipping lanes (79x124cm-31x49in) s. 19-Nov-3 Christie's, Kensington #587/R

SKATCHKOV, Denis (?) Russian
£408 $743 €600 Petite fleuriste. s. 8-Feb-4 Lesieur & Le Bars, Le Havre #120
£1054 $1919 €1550 Bouquet de fete. s. 8-Feb-4 Lesieur & Le Bars, Le Havre #90

SKAW, Al (1951-) Australian
£1138 $1787 €1661 Trapeze (92x153cm-36x60in) s.d.95 prov.exhib. 27-Aug-3 Christie's, Sydney #808 est:300-500 (A.D 2800)
£1245 $2079 €1868 Tumbling in Sienna (167x91cm-66x36in) s.d.95 i.d.verso. 27-Oct-3 Goodman, Sydney #99/R est:3000-4000 (A.D 3000)

SKEAPING, John (1901-1980) British
Sculpture
£2000 $3400 €2920 Over the hurdle (38x25cm-15x10in) s. brown pat bronze wood plinth. 19-Nov-3 Sotheby's, Olympia #170/R est:2000-3000
£2000 $3440 €2920 The J B Whisky Trophy (28cm-11in) s. black pat. bronze. 2-Dec-3 Bonhams, New Bond Street #18/R est:2000-3000
£25000 $42500 €36500 Mill Reef (25x32cm-10x13in) s.i. brown pat bronze 6 of 10. 19-Nov-3 Sotheby's, Olympia #171/R est:20000-25000
Works on paper
£360 $637 €526 Bellerina (63x48cm-25x19in) s.d.76 pastel. 27-Apr-4 Bonhams, Knightsbridge #255
£450 $752 €657 Portrait of a pony (40x48cm-16x19in) s. pastel. 9-Oct-3 Greenslade Hunt, Taunton #485/R
£520 $900 €759 Race horse with jockey and trainer (39x32cm-15x13in) s. W/C. 9-Dec-3 Anderson & Garland, Newcastle #252/R
£550 $1007 €803 Out in front (45x63cm-18x25in) s.d.74 pastel prov.exhib. 7-Apr-4 Woolley & Wallis, Salisbury #82/R
£955 $1643 €1394 To the finish (54x73cm-21x29in) s.d.64 W/C. 3-Dec-3 Stephan Welz, Johannesburg #5/R est:7000-10000 (SA.R 10500)
£1000 $1720 €1460 Studies of antelopes (30x37cm-12x15in) s. pencil black ink col chk pair sold with print by the same hand. 3-Dec-3 Christie's, Kensington #212/R est:1200-1800
£1200 $2184 €1752 Out into the open, horse racing scene (53x72cm-21x28in) s.d.67 W/C htd bodycol prov. 30-Jun-4 Mervyn Carey, Tenterden #149/R
£1400 $2590 €2044 Horse and jockey, Arles (33x48cm-13x19in) s.i. col chk ink brush. 14-Jan-4 Lawrence, Crewkerne #1355 est:500-700
£1600 $2672 €2336 Trotting (41x58cm-16x23in) s.d.64 W/C. 18-Jun-3 John Nicholson, Haslemere #661/R est:1000-2000

SKEELE, Hannah Brown (1829-1901) American
£1975 $3200 €2864 Prize catch (30x46cm-12x18in) s. 8-Aug-3 Barridorf, Portland #248/R est:3000-5000

SKELL, Ludwig (1843-1905) German
£403 $749 €600 Two reindeer searching for food in a winter landscape (40x30cm-16x12in) s. 5-Mar-4 Wendl, Rudolstadt #3875/R
£655 $1094 €950 Stag with deer in mountain pasture (70x100cm-28x39in) s. 9-Jul-3 Hugo Ruef, Munich #202/R
£660 $1036 €950 Misty morning in Isar valley (55x71cm-22x28in) s. 30-Aug-3 Hans Stahl, Toestorf #19/R

SKELTON, John (fl.1735-1759) British
Works on paper
£514 $950 €771 Croydon Church and part of the Archbishop's Palace, Surrey (13x20cm-5x8in) s.i. pencil W/C exec. 1754 prov. 14-Jul-4 American Auctioneer #490478/R

SKELTON, John (1923-1999) British
£3851 $7279 €5700 At the start (41x51cm-16x20in) s. prov. 17-Feb-4 Whyte's, Dublin #94/R est:5000-7000
Works on paper
£764 $1245 €1100 Still life study with cheese and wine (46x26cm-18x10in) s. W/C. 24-Sep-3 James Adam, Dublin #95/R est:100-1500

SKELTON, John (20th C) Irish
£526 $968 €800 Open road, Connemara (24x30cm-9x12in) s. canvasboard. 22-Jun-4 De Veres Art Auctions, Dublin #173/R
£1477 $2613 €2200 Bellewstown, County Meath (46x61cm-18x24in) s. canvasboard. 27-Apr-4 Whyte's, Dublin #63/R est:2000-3000
£2937 $4993 €4200 Homesteads on Clew bay, Co. Mayo (64x76cm-25x30in) s. s.i.verso. 25-Nov-3 De Veres Art Auctions, Dublin #221 est:3000-4000
£3087 $5464 €4600 Raising the currach, three man currach, Inishbofin Island (36x46cm-14x18in) s. 27-Apr-4 Whyte's, Dublin #38/R est:3500-4500
£3497 $5944 €5000 Still life with blue jug (56x76cm-22x30in) s.i.verso board. 25-Nov-3 De Veres Art Auctions, Dublin #219/R est:5000-7000

SKEMP, Robert Oliver (1910-1984) American
£1611 $2883 €2400 No milk today (83x62cm-33x24in) s. lit. 27-May-4 Sotheby's, Paris #137/R est:1000-1500
£2416 $4325 €3600 Hanging (92x76cm-36x30in) s. lit. 27-May-4 Sotheby's, Paris #138/R est:900-1200

SKENE OF RUBISLAW, James (1775-1864) British
Works on paper
£3000 $5250 €4380 Interior of the Parthenon (33x59cm-13x23in) s.i.d.1841 W/C. 16-Dec-3 Bonhams, New Bond Street #2/R est:3000-5000

SKILLING, William (20th C) British/American
£1038 $1900 €1515 White horse in a landscape (91x122cm-36x48in) s. 10-Apr-4 Brunk, Ashville #62/R

SKIPWORTH, Frank Markham (1854-1929) British
£700 $1295 €1022 Portrait of a lady, seated in a chair (30x24cm-12x9in) 9-Mar-4 Bonhams, Knightsbridge #179/R

SKIRVING, Archibald (1749-1819) British
Miniatures
£6000 $10800 €8760 Gentleman wearing a blue coat with black collar (7cm-3in) mono.d.1798 gold frame oval prov.exhib.lit. 22-Apr-4 Bonhams, New Bond Street #141/R est:1500-2500

SKJOLDEBRAND, Eric (1816-1868) Swedish
£1256 $2249 €1834 View of Hogantorp's farm, Sodertalje (49x65cm-19x26in) init.d.1866. 26-May-4 AB Stockholms Auktionsverk #2312/R est:12000-15000 (S.KR 17000)

SKLAR, Dorothy (20th C) American
£635 $1200 €927 Zinnias and daffodils (41x30cm-16x12in) s. s.i. verso prov. 17-Feb-4 John Moran, Pasadena #112/R
Works on paper
£471 $800 €688 Bunker Hill Victorian (46x56cm-18x22in) s.d.49 W/C prov. 18-Nov-3 John Moran, Pasadena #91
£516 $950 €753 Oil derricks at Signal Hill (41x53cm-16x21in) s. W/C. 8-Jun-4 Auctions by the Bay, Alameda #1120/R
£769 $1400 €1123 Coastal scene with figures, Palisades Walk (36x51cm-14x20in) s.d.46 i.verso W/C. 15-Jun-4 John Moran, Pasadena #89a est:1000-2000

SKLAVOS, Yerassimos (1927-1967) Greek
Sculpture
£2848 $5183 €4300 Station spatiale 2 (49x22x12cm-19x9x5in) s. num.4/8 black pat bronze Cast Landowsky. 18-Jun-4 Charbonneaux, Paris #199/R est:4000-4500
£5000 $8950 €7300 Platre (44cm-17in) s. num.2/8 bronze exhib.lit. 10-May-4 Sotheby's, Olympia #99/R est:5000-7000

SKOCZYLAS, Wladyslaw (1883-1934) Polish
£919 $1618 €1342 Nativity scene (71x102cm-28x40in) s. W/C oil. 23-May-4 Agra, Warsaw #38/R (P.Z 6500)

SKOGBERG, Fanny Maria (1865-?) Finnish
£367 $669 €540 Stones on beach (23x25cm-9x10in) s. 8-Feb-4 Bukowskis, Helsinki #458/R

SKOGLUND, Sandy (1946-) American
Photographs
£3000 $5460 €4380 Walking on eggshells (121x152cm-48x60in) cibachrome print exec 1997 prov. 4-Feb-4 Sotheby's, Olympia #265/R est:3000-4000
£8383 $14000 €12239 Fox games (119x161cm-47x63in) s.i.d.num.9/30 dye-destruction print. 20-Oct-3 Christie's, Rockefeller NY #233/R est:15000-20000

SKOLD, Otte (1894-1958) Swedish
£1126 $2027 €1644 Odegard, Varmland (94x145cm-37x57in) s. panel exhib. 26-Jan-4 Lilla Bukowskis, Stockholm #198 est:20000-25000 (S.KR 15000)
£7553 $12840 €11027 Model wearing red dress (46x42cm-18x17in) s. painted 1930 lit. 4-Nov-3 Bukowskis, Stockholm #131/R est:100000-125000 (S.KR 100000)
Works on paper
£1450 $2611 €2117 Bull fighting in Collioure (15x23cm-6x9in) s. W/C htd white. 26-Apr-4 Bukowskis, Stockholm #54/R est:25000-30000 (S.KR 20000)

SKOTNES, Cecil (1926-) South African
£388 $648 €566 Three kings (89x120cm-35x47in) s.d.62 board. 20-Oct-3 Stephan Welz, Johannesburg #380/R est:5000-8000 (SA.R 4500)
£427 $726 €623 Figurative forms in a landscape (20x30cm-8x12in) s. 4-Nov-3 Stephan Welz, Johannesburg #639 est:4000-6000 (SA.R 5000)
£1652 $2956 €2412 Head (112x87cm-44x34in) s.d.September 67 canvas incised painted wood panel. 31-May-4 Stephan Welz, Johannesburg #604/R est:20000-30000 (SA.R 20000)

SKOULAKIS, Dimos (1939-) Greek
£4000 $7160 €5840 Omonia (120x150cm-47x59in) s. exhib. 10-May-4 Sotheby's, Olympia #83/R est:4000-6000

SKOVGAARD, Joakim (1856-1933) Danish
£271 $486 €396 Mother nursing baby (29x25cm-11x10in) init.d.1883. 10-May-4 Rasmussen, Vejle #208/R (D.KR 3000)
£316 $591 €461 Landscape with large trees (32x37cm-13x15in) init.d.1910. 25-Feb-4 Museumsbygningen, Copenhagen #187 (D.KR 3500)
£410 $644 €599 Landscape from Italy (34x41cm-13x16in) init.d.1931 paper on canvas. 30-Aug-3 Rasmussen, Havnen #2258 (D.KR 4400)
£567 $981 €828 Woman and chickens in front of farmhouse (33x40cm-13x16in) init.d.1897. 9-Dec-3 Rasmussen, Copenhagen #1556/R (D.KR 6000)
£1253 $2294 €1829 Fragment of Raphael's loft decoration in Villa Farnesina (162x103cm-64x41in) init.d.1914 exhib. 9-Jun-4 Rasmussen, Copenhagen #1538/R est:15000-20000 (D.KR 14000)
£1636 $2584 €2372 View from Pompeii (28x42cm-11x17in) s.i.d.1886 prov. 2-Sep-3 Rasmussen, Copenhagen #1663/R est:20000-25000 (D.KR 17500)
£5372 $9830 €7843 The large tree by Tjibodas (75x100cm-30x39in) mono.i.d.1908 exhib. 9-Jun-4 Rasmussen, Copenhagen #1750/R est:60000-80000 (D.KR 60000)

SKOVGAARD, Niels (1858-1938) Danish
£1176 $2106 €1717 Swedish landscape with elks (64x103cm-25x41in) mono.d.1915. 10-May-4 Rasmussen, Vejle #245/R est:15000 (D.KR 13000)

SKOVGAARD, P C (1817-1875) Danish
£716 $1311 €1045 Path through the wood (26x34cm-10x13in) indis.i.d.30 juni 1860. 9-Jun-4 Rasmussen, Copenhagen #1666/R (D.KR 8000)
£842 $1533 €1229 Figure on the outskirts of wood (32x36cm-13x14in) indis sig. panel prov. 7-Feb-4 Rasmussen, Havnen #2241/R (D.KR 9200)
£1495 $2363 €2168 Italian landscape with dried up riverbed, mountains in background (37x56cm-15x22in) 2-Sep-3 Rasmussen, Copenhagen #1551/R est:20000 (D.KR 16000)

SKOVGAARD, Peter Christian (1817-1875) Danish
£1121 $1772 €1625 Coastal landscape near Helsingor (30x40cm-12x16in) painted c.1844. 2-Sep-3 Rasmussen, Copenhagen #1741/R est:15000-20000 (D.KR 12000)
£1617 $3008 €2361 View of the sea at Moens Klint (34x50cm-13x20in) i.stretcher. 2-Mar-4 Rasmussen, Copenhagen #1391/R est:20000-25000 (D.KR 18000)
£2079 $3597 €3035 Washing day at Skaaninge pond (33x48cm-13x19in) s.d.1873 exhib.prov. 9-Dec-3 Rasmussen, Copenhagen #1211/R est:30000-40000 (D.KR 22000)

£2370 $3791 €3460 Landscape (30x52cm-12x20in) mono. exhib. 22-Sep-3 Rasmussen, Vejle #342/R est:15000-20000 (D.KR 25000)
£3581 $6553 €5228 The road to the bathing huts at Nyso (35x58cm-14x23in) s.25 august 1850 exhib.prov. 9-Jun-4 Rasmussen, Copenhagen #1478/R est:50000-60000 (D.KR 40000)
£4726 $8176 €6900 Moens cliff (53x42cm-21x17in) 9-Dec-3 Rasmussen, Copenhagen #1398/R est:30000-40000 (D.KR 50000)
£5000 $9000 €7300 Village pond at Hellebaek (78x98cm-31x39in) init. prov. 23-Apr-4 Sotheby's, New York #209/R est:10000-15000
£7162 $13107 €10457 Landscape with clouds near Jyderup (22x33cm-9x13in) i.verso. 9-Jun-4 Rasmussen, Copenhagen #1442/R est:80000-120000 (D.KR 80000)
£9452 $16352 €13800 Landscape with clouds at Jyderup (22x33cm-9x13in) i.verso. 9-Dec-3 Rasmussen, Copenhagen #1212/R est:40000-50000 (D.KR 100000)

SKRAMLIK, Johannes Ritter von (?) Czechoslovakian?
£596 $1091 €900 Connoisseur (70x50cm-28x20in) s. 8-Apr-4 Dorotheum, Vienna #43/R

SKRAMSTAD, Ludwig (1855-1912) Norwegian
£391 $615 €571 Landscape with figure on path (52x71cm-20x28in) s. 30-Aug-3 Rasmussen, Havnen #2249/R (D.KR 4200)
£407 $748 €611 Hazy landscape (41x31cm-16x12in) panel. 14-Jun-4 Blomqvist, Lysaker #1369/R (N.KR 5000)
£482 $883 €704 Spring thaw (40x65cm-16x26in) s. panel. 2-Feb-4 Blomqvist, Lysaker #1283 (N.KR 6000)
£493 $853 €700 Mountainous river landscape (32x47cm-13x19in) s. canvas on canvas. 10-Dec-3 Hugo Ruef, Munich #2493/R
£688 $1150 €1004 Landscape from Ongs (76x125cm-30x49in) s. 20-Oct-3 Blomqvist, Lysaker #1299/R (N.KR 8000)
£704 $1218 €1000 River landscape (33x52cm-13x20in) s. panel. 10-Dec-3 Hugo Ruef, Munich #2494/R
£804 $1471 €1174 Winter's day (58x100cm-23x39in) s. 2-Feb-4 Blomqvist, Lysaker #1282 (N.KR 10000)
£884 $1618 €1291 Rowing the hay across the fjord (111x160cm-44x63in) s. 2-Feb-4 Blomqvist, Lysaker #1284/R (N.KR 11000)
£1373 $2403 €2005 Fjord landscape from the west coast in moonlight (61x90cm-24x35in) s. i.stretcher. 16-Dec-3 Grev Wedels Plass, Oslo #371/R est:20000-30000 (N.KR 16000)
£2000 $3640 €2920 Early morning on the fjord (81x132cm-32x52in) s. 4-Feb-4 John Nicholson, Haslemere #159/R est:2000-3000
£2215 $3809 €3234 Mountain landscape with rapids and bird (66x110cm-26x43in) s. 8-Dec-3 Blomqvist, Oslo #440/R est:25000-30000 (N.KR 26000)

SKREDSVIG, Christian (1854-1924) Norwegian
£1448 $2491 €2114 Winter landscape with horse by house (47x29cm-19x11in) i.verso. 8-Dec-3 Blomqvist, Oslo #408/R est:20000-25000 (N.KR 17000)
£1626 $2992 €2439 Morning landscape (26x34cm-10x13in) s. panel. 14-Jun-4 Blomqvist, Lysaker #1371/R est:12000-15000 (N.KR 20000)
£2439 $4463 €3561 Flowers from Paris (28x32cm-11x13in) s.i. panel. 7-Jun-4 Blomqvist, Oslo #364/R est:40000-45000 (N.KR 30000)
£3416 $5705 €4987 Landscape with cows (40x54cm-16x21in) init.d.77. 13-Oct-3 Blomqvist, Oslo #261/R est:35000-45000 (N.KR 40000)
£3577 $6546 €5222 Woodland tarn (33x43cm-13x17in) s. panel. 7-Jun-4 Blomqvist, Oslo #325/R est:45000-55000 (N.KR 44000)
£5041 $9224 €7360 Landscape from Eggedal (57x80cm-22x31in) s. lit. 7-Jun-4 Blomqvist, Oslo #346/R est:50000-60000 (N.KR 62000)
£14412 $25797 €21042 An April evening in Eggedal (65x80cm-26x31in) s. i.stretcher lit. 22-Mar-4 Blomqvist, Oslo #310/R est:140000-160000 (N.KR 180000)
£20392 $36501 €29772 Spring in Eggedal (63x48cm-25x19in) s. i.stretcher. 25-May-4 Grev Wedels Plass, Oslo #10/R est:150000-200000 (N.KR 250000)
£20530 $34902 €29974 Beautiful Norefjell, pastoral landscape (101x127cm-40x50in) s.d.1903 i.stretcher. 19-Nov-3 Grev Wedels Plass, Oslo #44/R est:200000-250000 (N.KR 240000)
£25000 $45500 €36500 Norwegian poetry (120x95cm-47x37in) painted 1897 prov.exhib.lit. 15-Jun-4 Sotheby's, London #311/R est:25000-35000
Works on paper
£1441 $2580 €2104 Landscape from Eggedal (65x48cm-26x19in) s. mixed media. 22-Mar-4 Blomqvist, Oslo #363/R est:24000-26000 (N.KR 18000)
£1626 $2992 €2439 The brook (48x62cm-19x24in) s. mixed media. 14-Jun-4 Blomqvist, Lysaker #1372 est:16000-20000 (N.KR 20000)

SKREDSVIG, Christian (attrib) (1854-1924) Norwegian
Works on paper
£488 $898 €732 Winter in the mountains. pastel. 14-Jun-4 Blomqvist, Lysaker #1373/R (N.KR 6000)

SKRICKA, Ernst (1946-) Austrian
Works on paper
£329 $605 €500 One for all (70x55cm-28x22in) s.i.d.1975 ink W/C. 22-Jun-4 Wiener Kunst Auktionen, Vienna #344/R

SKROBISZEWSKA, Kararzyna (1976-) Polish
£552 $921 €800 Darkness (115x140cm-45x55in) s.i.d.02 verso. 16-Nov-3 Agra, Warsaw #98/R

SKUBKO, S M (1933-) Russian
£503 $900 €734 In Hiva (80x69cm-31x27in) oil cardboard painted 1960's. 29-May-4 Shishkin Gallery, Moscow #28/R

SKUBKO-KARPAS, L Y (1923-) Russian
£389 $700 €568 Young hockey player (70x50cm-28x20in) oil on cardboard. 24-Apr-4 Shishkin Gallery, Moscow #67/R
£25556 $46000 €37312 Interesting radio translation (143x117cm-56x46in) 24-Apr-4 Shishkin Gallery, Moscow #68/R est:50000-60000
Works on paper
£389 $700 €568 Girl in yellow (49x39cm-19x15in) pastel. 24-Apr-4 Shishkin Gallery, Moscow #65/R

SKULASON, Thorvaldur (1906-1984) Icelandic
£3159 $5812 €4612 Model (95x65cm-37x26in) s. painted c.1935 exhib.prov. 29-Mar-4 Rasmussen, Copenhagen #229/R est:40000-50000 (D.KR 35000)
£3249 $5978 €4744 Mountain landscape, Iceland (64x78cm-25x31in) s.d.31 prov. 29-Mar-4 Rasmussen, Copenhagen #251/R est:20000 (D.KR 36000)

SKULME, Uga (1895-1963) Russian
£800 $1416 €1168 Landscape with haystacks (65x81cm-26x32in) s.d.35. 27-Apr-4 Bonhams, Knightsbridge #274/R

SKUM, Nils Nilsson (1872-1951) Swedish
Works on paper
£517 $926 €755 Mountain landscape with flock of reindeer (25x34cm-10x13in) s.d.1947 mixed media. 28-May-4 Uppsala Auktionskammare, Uppsala #255/R (S.KR 7000)
£554 $1019 €831 Mountain landscape with reindeer (25x34cm-10x13in) s.d.1909 mixed media. 14-Jun-4 Lilla Bukowskis, Stockholm #254 (S.KR 7600)
£578 $1041 €844 Reindeer on the mountain (25x35cm-10x14in) s.d.1944 pencil chk. 26-Jan-4 Lilla Bukowskis, Stockholm #244 (S.KR 7700)
£654 $1125 €955 Mountain landscape with reindeer and tents (25x35cm-10x14in) s. col crayon pencil. 3-Dec-3 AB Stockholms Auktionsverk #2480/R (S.KR 8500)
£692 $1191 €1010 Bear hunt (26x33cm-10x13in) s.d.maj 1911 chk pencil. 2-Dec-3 Bukowskis, Stockholm #146a/R (S.KR 9000)
£714 $1314 €1071 The journey to the church (25x34cm-10x13in) s. pencil crayon. 14-Jun-4 Lilla Bukowskis, Stockholm #685 (S.KR 9800)
£1146 $2051 €1673 Moving the flock of reindeer (24x32cm-9x13in) s.d.1908 chk pencil exhib. 25-May-4 Bukowskis, Stockholm #200/R est:8000-10000 (S.KR 15500)
£1183 $2117 €1727 Laplander leading his flock of reindeer (26x34cm-10x13in) s.d.1942 chk pencil. 25-May-4 Bukowskis, Stockholm #199/R est:8000-10000 (S.KR 16000)
£1404 $2514 €2050 Mountain landscape with flock of reindeer (26x32cm-10x13in) s.d.1945 pencil col.chk. 26-May-4 AB Stockholms Auktionsverk #2322/R est:8000-10000 (S.KR 19000)

SKUTEZKY, Dominik (1850-1921) Hungarian
£9000 $16380 €13140 He who sleeps catches no fish (82x112cm-32x44in) s.i. prov.exhib.lit. 15-Jun-4 Sotheby's, London #50/R est:10000-15000

SLABBINCK, Rik (1914-1991) Belgian
£483 $893 €700 Paysage de Provence (27x38cm-11x15in) s. panel. 13-Jan-4 Vanderkindere, Brussels #35
£521 $870 €750 Marine (16x29cm-6x11in) s. panel. 21-Oct-3 Campo, Vlaamse Kaai #568
£521 $828 €750 Le chateau de Loppem (60x80cm-24x31in) s. 9-Sep-3 Palais de Beaux Arts, Brussels #274
£979 $1664 €1400 Village en Flandres (32x50cm-13x20in) s. panel. 18-Nov-3 Vanderkindere, Brussels #185
£993 $1808 €1500 Mon atelier avec poele (78x65cm-31x26in) s.d.45 exhib. 21-Jun-4 Bernaerts, Antwerp #262/R est:1800-2200
£1181 $1877 €1700 Provence ensoleillee (35x47cm-14x19in) s. panel. 15-Sep-3 Horta, Bruxelles #352 est:1200-1800
£1200 $2208 €1800 Jeune femme nue couchee (60x73cm-24x29in) s. 14-Jun-4 Horta, Bruxelles #57 est:1800-2200
£1379 $2552 €2000 Paysage sous la neige (38x55cm-15x22in) s. 13-Jan-4 Vanderkindere, Brussels #5 est:625-875
£1477 $2613 €2200 Nature morte au bouddha noir (60x74cm-24x29in) s. 27-Apr-4 Campo & Campo, Antwerp #212/R est:2500-3000
£1806 $3015 €2600 Still life on table (47x38cm-19x15in) s. 21-Oct-3 Campo & Campo, Antwerp #281 est:2750-3250
£2083 $3479 €3000 Floraison printaniere (60x73cm-24x29in) s. 21-Oct-3 Campo, Vlaamse Kaai #571/R est:1800-2200
£2098 $3503 €3000 Spring shrubs (55x38cm-22x15in) s. 11-Oct-3 De Vuyst, Lokeren #331/R est:1800-2200
£2238 $3804 €3200 Cafetiere, coupe et bouteilles (60x73cm-24x29in) s. 1-Dec-3 Palais de Beaux Arts, Brussels #128/R est:3000-5000
£2778 $4639 €4000 Paysage aux saules (75x92cm-30x36in) s. 21-Oct-3 Campo, Vlaamse Kaai #569 est:6000-7000
£3067 $5612 €4600 Paysage avec maison (60x73cm-24x29in) s. 7-Jun-4 Palais de Beaux Arts, Brussels #298/R est:3500-5000
£3125 $5219 €4500 Nature morte (78x53cm-31x21in) s. panel. 21-Oct-3 Campo, Vlaamse Kaai #570/R est:3000-4000
£5944 $9927 €8500 Nuages noirs (97x130cm-38x51in) s. exhib.lit. 11-Oct-3 De Vuyst, Lokeren #470/R est:8500-10000
Works on paper
£347 $580 €500 Rochers en Normandie (27x36cm-11x14in) s. pastel. 21-Oct-3 Campo & Campo, Antwerp #282/R

SLADDEN, Tom (20th C) New Zealander
£345 $542 €500 Paremata Bridge (37x50cm-15x20in) s.d.1993. 27-Aug-3 Dunbar Sloane, Wellington #144 (NZ.D 950)

SLADE, Caleb Arnold (1882-1961) American
£220 $375 €321 Jam pot (38x33cm-15x13in) s. 9-Nov-3 Outer Cape Auctions, Provincetown #98/R
£297 $550 €434 Landscape with red house (33x41cm-13x16in) s.d.1939 board. 17-Jul-4 Outer Cape Auctions, Provincetown #24/R
£409 $650 €597 Middle Eastern street scene (27x22cm-11x9in) s. 12-Sep-3 Skinner, Boston #310/R
£586 $950 €856 Landscape with tree lined stream and house in background (74x91cm-29x36in) s. 31-Jul-3 Eldred, East Dennis #852/R
£613 $1000 €895 Untitled fish (74x102cm-29x40in) s. 19-Jul-3 Outer Cape Auctions, Provincetown #100/R
£1852 $3000 €2704 Rocky seascape (23x28cm-9x11in) s. 31-Jul-3 Eldred, East Dennis #1088/R est:3000-5000
£2374 $4250 €3466 Boats on La Conche, France (33x41cm-13x16in) s.d.1914 verso board. 16-May-4 CRN Auctions, Cambridge #3/R
£3086 $5000 €4506 Couple harvesting wheat (44x56cm-17x22in) s. 31-Jul-3 Eldred, East Dennis #993/R est:6000-8000

SLAGER, Frederic François (1876-1953) Dutch
£582 $990 €850 Old farmhouse in Breugel. Forest (16x19cm-6x7in) s. panel two. 5-Nov-3 Vendue Huis, Gravenhage #205

£1736 $2899 €2500 Oude sacristie der kathedraal te's Bosch (43x67cm-17x26in) s.i.d.1911. 21-Oct-3 Sotheby's, Amsterdam #104/R est:3000-5000
£2133 $3840 €3200 Malle jan in the snow (56x101cm-22x40in) s.d.46. 20-Apr-4 Sotheby's, Amsterdam #124/R est:2000-3000

SLAGER, Jeanette (1881-1945) Dutch
£1900 $3268 €2774 Summer flowers in an oriental bowl on a draped table (93x108cm-37x43in) s. 4-Dec-3 Christie's, Kensington #105/R est:1200-1500

SLANEY, M Noel (1915-) British
£260 $476 €380 Vase and flowers (35x17cm-14x7in) s. board. 29-Jan-4 Bonhams, Edinburgh #325

SLANGENBURGH, Carel Jacob Baar van (1783-c.1850) Dutch
Works on paper
£685 $1164 €1000 Studies of a boy, a young woman, and pair of hands holding a pencil (18x21cm-7x8in) init. red black chk prov. 4-Nov-3 Sotheby's, Amsterdam #158/R

SLATAPER, Alberto (1870-1935) Italian
£600 $1074 €900 Important evening (49x34cm-19x13in) s.d.1909 cardboard. 12-May-4 Stadion, Trieste #711/R

SLATER, Charles H (fl.1860-1870) British
£680 $1231 €993 Grapes and roses (60x50cm-24x20in) s.d.68. 30-Mar-4 Sworder & Son, Bishops Stortford #560/R
Works on paper
£480 $864 €701 Spray of spring flowers on a shelf (17x24cm-7x9in) s. W/C htd white. 20-Apr-4 Hutchinson, Boroughbridge #305/R
£650 $1170 €949 Primroses, bluebells and daisies by a birds nest (33x25cm-13x10in) W/C htd white. 20-Apr-4 Hutchinson, Boroughbridge #304/R
£800 $1376 €1168 Still life of fruit, ewer and glass on a table (44x37cm-17x15in) s. W/C bodycol. 3-Dec-3 Christie's, Kensington #66/R
£900 $1638 €1314 Still life of grapes, pineapple and plums. Still life of grapes, apple, plum, pomegranate (23x33cm-9x13in) s. pencil W/C htd white. 1-Jul-4 Christie's, Kensington #263/R

SLATER, J F (1857-1937) British
£390 $706 €569 Landscape with shepherd and sheep in gateway beneath trees (48x74cm-19x29in) s. 17-Apr-4 Jim Railton, Durham #1723

SLATER, John Falconar (1857-1937) British
£250 $450 €365 Waves rolling on to a coastline in squally weather (49x63cm-19x25in) s. board. 21-Apr-4 Tennants, Leyburn #1112
£271 $453 €396 Evening glow, Whitby coast (50x76cm-20x30in) s. i.verso. 17-Nov-3 Waddingtons, Toronto #91/R (C.D 600)
£284 $475 €415 Seascape (51x76cm-20x30in) s. 20-Jun-3 Freeman, Philadelphia #141/R
£300 $477 €438 Trees by a river at evening (37x56cm-15x22in) s. 18-Mar-3 Anderson & Garland, Newcastle #483
£300 $510 €438 Moorland river with sheep grazing beside trees (40x56cm-16x22in) board. 19-Nov-3 Tennants, Leyburn #1129
£320 $582 €467 Poultry in a farmyard (25x34cm-10x13in) board. 29-Jun-4 Anderson & Garland, Newcastle #400
£360 $587 €526 Farmyard scene with duck pond in the foreground and haystack nearby (28x38cm-11x15in) s. millboard. 23-Sep-3 Anderson & Garland, Newcastle #365
£380 $695 €555 Whitley Park (35x47cm-14x19in) s. canvas on board. 6-Jul-4 Bonhams, Knightsbridge #154/R
£400 $692 €584 Potted plant on a windowsill (60x45cm-24x18in) s. board. 9-Dec-3 Anderson & Garland, Newcastle #397/R
£400 $740 €584 Queen Anne houses, fish quay, North Shields (51x35cm-20x14in) s. i.verso. 11-Mar-4 Morphets, Harrogate #275
£400 $728 €584 Poultry in a farmyard (25x34cm-10x13in) board. 29-Jun-4 Anderson & Garland, Newcastle #399
£450 $765 €657 Moorland landscape (76x102cm-30x40in) s. 19-Nov-3 Tennants, Leyburn #1132a
£480 $874 €701 Poultry in a farmyard (23x29cm-9x11in) board. 29-Jun-4 Anderson & Garland, Newcastle #398
£480 $874 €701 Poultry and a coop (21x30cm-8x12in) s. board. 29-Jun-4 Anderson & Garland, Newcastle #405
£500 $850 €730 Landscape with figure, horse and cart approaching farm buildings (55x81cm-22x32in) s. board. 19-Nov-3 Tennants, Leyburn #1130/R
£500 $850 €730 Country lane at dusk with figures by a wooden fence (56x39cm-22x15in) s. board. 19-Nov-3 Tennants, Leyburn #1132
£520 $915 €759 Moored boat (40x52cm-16x20in) s. board. 18-May-4 Bonhams, Knightsbridge #115/R
£561 $932 €813 Harbour scene with steamboats (76x127cm-30x50in) s. 16-Jun-3 Blomqvist, Lysaker #1353/R (N.KR 6500)
£600 $1002 €876 Moorland landscape (47x58cm-19x23in) s. board sold with a companion. 7-Oct-3 Bonhams, Knightsbridge #251/R
£600 $1104 €876 Sunshine and shadow on rocks by the sea (53x79cm-21x31in) s. 23-Mar-4 Anderson & Garland, Newcastle #370/R
£680 $1081 €993 Horse-drawn cart in a snow storm (38x51cm-15x20in) s. 18-Mar-3 Anderson & Garland, Newcastle #479
£680 $1136 €993 Riding under the apple tree (23x32cm-9x13in) init. board. 12-Nov-3 Sotheby's, Olympia #130/R
£680 $1238 €993 Cockerel and hens (19x46cm-7x18in) s. board. 29-Jun-4 Anderson & Garland, Newcastle #407
£700 $1211 €1022 Thatched cottage with a woman feeding poultry in the yard (61x91cm-24x36in) s. 9-Dec-3 Anderson & Garland, Newcastle #398/R
£700 $1190 €1022 Figure in a horse and cart passing a blacksmith's workshop at dusk (51x61cm-20x24in) s. board. 19-Nov-3 Tennants, Leyburn #1131
£880 $1602 €1285 Sunny shore (60x90cm-24x35in) s. board. 29-Jun-4 Anderson & Garland, Newcastle #401/R
£950 $1634 €1387 Mountain pass under cloud. Horses and cart on a riverside track by a cottage (46x56cm-18x22in) s. pair. 5-Dec-3 Keys, Aylsham #658/R
£960 $1747 €1402 Farmer with a pair of draught horses on a country road (23x32cm-9x13in) init. board. 29-Jun-4 Anderson & Garland, Newcastle #409
£1000 $1840 €1460 Cullercoats Bay (32x92cm-13x36in) s. 23-Mar-4 Anderson & Garland, Newcastle #372 est:400-600
£1200 $1992 €1752 Clydesdales at work (46x62cm-18x24in) s. board. 1-Oct-3 Sotheby's, Olympia #148/R est:1000-2000
£1200 $2184 €1752 Man and woman conversing in a cottage garden with poultry in sunlight (45x68cm-18x27in) board. 29-Jun-4 Anderson & Garland, Newcastle #410/R est:600-1000
£1400 $2548 €2044 Turkey and poultry in a yard (26x60cm-10x24in) s. 29-Jun-4 Anderson & Garland, Newcastle #406/R est:1000-1600
£1500 $2730 €2190 Sunshine on the North sea (74x125cm-29x49in) s. 29-Jun-4 Anderson & Garland, Newcastle #402 est:1500-2500
£1600 $2912 €2336 In a greenhouse (81x56cm-32x22in) s. i. verso board. 29-Jun-4 Anderson & Garland, Newcastle #404/R est:400-600
£2300 $4186 €3358 Horse-cart fording a river with a farm and windmill in the distance (60x90cm-24x35in) s. 29-Jun-4 Anderson & Garland, Newcastle #403/R est:2000-3000
£2600 $4108 €3770 Returning with the catch (69x96cm-27x38in) s. board. 4-Sep-3 Christie's, Kensington #193/R est:700-900
£2600 $4706 €3796 Fishing cobble off Staithes (48x74cm-19x29in) s. 19-Apr-4 British Auctioneer #499/R
£2800 $5040 €4088 North Shields from Newcastle (77x128cm-30x50in) s.d.1910. 21-Jan-4 Sotheby's, Olympia #381/R est:2500-3500
£3100 $5270 €4526 Garden scene with lupins and other flowers, cold frames beyond (61x91cm-24x36in) s. board. 19-Nov-3 Tennants, Leyburn #1132b/R est:800-1000
Works on paper
£260 $413 €380 River landscape with a horse-cart approaching a bridge (25x34cm-10x13in) s. gouache. 18-Mar-3 Anderson & Garland, Newcastle #252
£300 $540 €438 Garden scene with stone steps leading to a rose bower (46x61cm-18x24in) s. pastel prov. 21-Apr-4 Tennants, Leyburn #1058
£370 $588 €540 Waves breaking on a rocky shore (18x26cm-7x10in) s. gouache. 18-Mar-3 Anderson & Garland, Newcastle #254
£400 $728 €584 Bright cloud over a sunlit sea (49x73cm-19x29in) s. gouache. 29-Jun-4 Anderson & Garland, Newcastle #189
£550 $935 €803 Country house garden with herbaceous borders, fish pond and trees (46x62cm-18x24in) s. pastel prov. 19-Nov-3 Tennants, Leyburn #872
£780 $1349 €1139 Garden in summer with pool and fountain in the foreground (53x71cm-21x28in) s. pastel. 9-Dec-3 Anderson & Garland, Newcastle #191/R

SLAUGHTER, William A (1923-) American
£1916 $3200 €2797 West Texas (76x61cm-30x24in) 18-Oct-3 David Dike, Dallas #252/R est:1500-3000

SLAVICEK, Jan (1900-) Czechoslovakian
£366 $656 €534 Portrait of Emil Zatopek (50x39cm-20x15in) s. panel. 12-May-4 Dobiaschofsky, Bern #986/R (S.FR 850)
£658 $1119 €961 Dead little dove (51x43cm-20x17in) s.indis.d. plywood. 29-Nov-3 Dorotheum, Prague #91/R est:30000-45000 (C.KR 30000)
£700 $1163 €1022 Plate with apples (38x46cm-15x18in) mono.d.28. 4-Oct-3 Dorotheum, Prague #104/R (C.KR 32000)
£927 $1724 €1353 Bowl with apples (37x45cm-15x18in) s.d.1934 panel. 6-Mar-4 Dorotheum, Prague #124/R est:40000-60000 (C.KR 45000)
£1532 $2543 €2237 Flower (45x29cm-18x11in) s. panel. 4-Oct-3 Dorotheum, Prague #129/R est:50000-70000 (C.KR 70000)
£1647 $3064 €2405 Still life with fruit and beer bottle (65x81cm-26x32in) s.d.1926. 6-Mar-4 Dorotheum, Prague #102/R est:80000-120000 (C.KR 80000)
Works on paper
£372 $618 €543 Prague (44x54cm-17x21in) s.d.1942 sepia W/C. 4-Oct-3 Dorotheum, Prague #347/R est:12000-18000 (C.KR 17000)

SLEATOR, James Sinton (1889-1950) British
£1500 $2685 €2190 Young girl in blue (42x30cm-17x12in) board. 14-May-4 Christie's, Kensington #387a est:1500-2500
£1800 $2952 €2628 Still life (50x40cm-20x16in) s. 4-Jun-3 John Ross, Belfast #70 est:2500
£7000 $12530 €10220 Still life with flowers in a vase (70x54cm-28x21in) board prov. 14-May-4 Christie's, Kensington #387/R est:4000-6000

SLEEBE, Ferdinand Joseph (1907-1994) Dutch
£336 $577 €480 Still life of flowers (78x66cm-31x26in) s. maroufle. 8-Dec-3 Glerum, Amsterdam #281/R
Works on paper
£294 $505 €420 Nets drying (23x32cm-9x13in) s. gouache. 8-Dec-3 Glerum, Amsterdam #253/R

SLEIGH, Bernard (1872-1954) British
£2000 $3400 €2920 Garden of Enna (30x39cm-12x15in) mono. tempera on board. 25-Nov-3 Christie's, London #179/R est:2000-3000
Works on paper
£960 $1738 €1402 Architects and workmen constructing a timber framed church (110x143cm-43x56in) s. chl pastel. 2-Apr-4 Moore Allen & Innocent, Cirencester #759/R

SLEPCHENKO, Alexei (20th C) Russian
£367 $660 €550 Dance (80x95cm-31x37in) mono. 26-Apr-4 Millon & Associes, Paris #235/R
£367 $660 €550 Interrupted match (120x180cm-47x71in) 26-Apr-4 Millon & Associes, Paris #242/R

SLEPKOV, Anatou (?) Russian?
Works on paper
£300 $555 €438 Lady on a horse riding side saddle (50x40cm-20x16in) s.d.97 pencil W/C htd white. 13-Feb-4 Sworder & Son, Bishops Stortford #57/R

SLETTEMARK, Kjartan (1932-) Swedish
Sculpture
£1964 $3338 €2867 Theatre (65x85x15cm-26x33x6in) s. mixed media exec.c.1970. 4-Nov-3 Bukowskis, Stockholm #567/R est:8000-10000 (S.KR 26000)

SLEVENSZKY, Lajos (1910-1975) Hungarian
£2240 $4054 €3270 Nagybanya (94x109cm-37x43in) s. 16-Apr-4 Mu Terem Galeria, Budapest #64/R (H.F 850000)

SLEVOGT, M (1868-1932) German
£1042 $1698 €1500 Landscape (26x33cm-10x13in) 29-Sep-3 Dr Fritz Nagel, Stuttgart #6919/R

SLEVOGT, Max (1868-1932) German
£625 $1044 €900 Putto (6x6cm-2x2in) s. silk on paper. 24-Oct-3 Ketterer, Hamburg #544/R
£1800 $3294 €2700 After Watteau (21x28cm-8x11in) s. col chks. 5-Jun-4 Lempertz, Koln #1005/R est:3000
£3297 $6000 €4814 Portrait (49x30cm-19x12in) s.d.88 board prov. 29-Jun-4 Sotheby's, New York #124/R est:4000-6000
£4000 $7360 €6000 Marietta di Rigado (40x26cm-16x10in) s.d.1904 board. 10-Jun-4 Hauswedell & Nolte, Hamburg #652/R est:8000
£63380 $109648 €90000 Summer landscape in the Pfalz (69x88cm-27x35in) s.d.30 lit. 13-Dec-3 Lempertz, Koln #186/R est:35000-40000
£75000 $136500 €109500 Gartenweg zum Sommerhaus (62x77cm-24x30in) s.d.1912 prov.exhib.lit. 3-Feb-4 Christie's, London #181/R est:40000-60000
Works on paper
£267 $491 €400 Death escapes the harmony (10x10cm-4x4in) mono.i.d.17 black brush prov. 12-Jun-4 Villa Grisebach, Berlin #649/R
£567 $1043 €850 Children's concert (10x14cm-4x6in) s. brown pen prov. 12-Jun-4 Villa Grisebach, Berlin #651/R
£694 $1160 €1000 Untitled (31x38cm-12x15in) s. Indian ink. 25-Oct-3 Dr Lehr, Berlin #481/R
£733 $1349 €1100 Byron (33x23cm-13x9in) i. ink brush pen over pencil double-sided prov. 12-Jun-4 Villa Grisebach, Berlin #648/R
£800 $1472 €1200 Sleeping horses (17x24cm-7x9in) s. W/C on pencil. 10-Jun-4 Hauswedell & Nolte, Hamburg #655/R
£1800 $3312 €2628 La cirque (40x46cm-16x18in) s. pastel. 24-Mar-4 Sotheby's, Olympia #32/R est:2000-3000
£1800 $3312 €2700 Penthesilea (26x36cm-10x14in) s. W/C gouache pencil over lithograph. 10-Jun-4 Hauswedell & Nolte, Hamburg #684/R est:4000
£4133 $7605 €6200 Dance of Morgiane with Dolche (17x31cm-7x12in) s.i. W/C Indian ink bodycol htd gold. 10-Jun-4 Hauswedell & Nolte, Hamburg #657/R est:6000

SLEVOGT, Max (attrib) (1868-1932) German
£6643 $11094 €9500 Moonlit valley and mountains (53x73cm-21x29in) s. 11-Oct-3 Hans Stahl, Hamburg #33/R est:6000

SLEWINSKY, Wladyslaw (1854-1918) Polish
£30000 $51000 €43800 Still life of fruit (49x60cm-19x24in) s. prov.exhib. 18-Nov-3 Sotheby's, London #357/R
£37821 $65431 €55219 Jug with flowers (61x50cm-24x20in) s. painted c.1909 lit. 14-Dec-3 Agra, Warsaw #75/R (P.Z 250000)

SLINGELANDT, Pieter van (1640-1691) Dutch
£23000 $42090 €33580 Portrait of man (16x12cm-6x5in) s.d.1668 copper prov. 8-Jul-4 Sotheby's, London #268/R est:8000-12000

SLINGENEYER, Ernest (1820-1894) Belgian
£1342 $2497 €2000 At the forge (70x52cm-28x20in) s. panel. 8-Mar-4 Bernaerts, Antwerp #114/R est:2000-2500

SLINGSBY, Robert (1955-) South African
£444 $756 €648 Pillars of knowledge (40x40cm-16x16in) s.d.1997. 4-Nov-3 Stephan Welz, Johannesburg #687/R est:4000-6000 (SA.R 5200)
£940 $1598 €1372 Green mythological beast with petroglyphs (99x109cm-39x43in) s.d.1989. 4-Nov-3 Stephan Welz, Johannesburg #689/R est:12000-16000 (SA.R 11000)

SLIPPER, Gary P (1934-) Canadian
£560 $1025 €818 Mouth of time (45x35cm-18x14in) s.d.65 board. 1-Jun-4 Joyner Waddington, Toronto #528 (C.D 1400)
Works on paper
£440 $805 €642 Man contemplating plants. Prisoners (18x12cm-7x5in) one s.d.73 other s. first pencil second oil on plexiglass two pro. 1-Jun-4 Joyner Waddington, Toronto #498 (C.D 1100)

SLOAN, Jeanette Pasin (1946-) American
Works on paper
£874 $1600 €1276 Untitled (89x114cm-35x45in) col pencil gouache. 10-Jul-4 Hindman, Chicago #485/R est:500-700

SLOAN, John (1871-1951) American
£870 $1600 €1270 Landscape with bridge and house with red chimney (20x25cm-8x10in) s. card on canvas. 10-Jun-4 Swann Galleries, New York #219/R est:2000-3000
£3824 $6500 €5583 Nude asleep, green couch (41x51cm-16x20in) s.i.d.43 board. 31-Oct-3 North East Auctions, Portsmouth #1888
£8939 $16000 €13051 Willows and rocks (41x51cm-16x20in) s. i.d.56 verso prov. 6-May-4 Shannon's, Milford #77/R est:15000-20000
£12791 $22000 €18675 Tailored hat (56x46cm-22x18in) s. s.i.d.35 verso panel prov.lit. 4-Dec-3 Christie's, Rockefeller NY #93/R est:25000-35000
£14535 $25000 €21221 Picture of woe (61x51cm-24x20in) s.i.d.1918. 3-Dec-3 Doyle, New York #291/R est:8000-12000
£15337 $25000 €22392 Nude at piano (71x61cm-28x24in) s. tempera oil panel painted c.1933 prov.exhib.lit. 27-Sep-3 Charlton Hall, Columbia #106/R est:20000-30000
£26946 $45000 €39341 Looking west, Santa Fe, New Mexico (46x56cm-18x22in) s. s.i.d.23 stretcher prov.exhib.lit. 9-Oct-3 Christie's, Rockefeller NY #86/R est:15000-25000
£34091 $60000 €49773 Blonde rock and blue sea (51x61cm-20x24in) s. s.i.stretcher painted 1914 prov.exhib.lit. 19-May-4 Sotheby's, New York #107/R est:40000-60000
£63953 $110000 €93371 High tide, Gloucester (51x61cm-20x24in) s. s.i.d.1914 on stretcher prov.lit. 3-Dec-3 Sotheby's, New York #42/R est:80000-120000
Prints
£2353 $4000 €3435 Snowstorm in the village (17x13cm-7x5in) s. etching exec.1925. 31-Oct-3 Sotheby's, New York #198/R
£5085 $9000 €7424 Barber shop (25x30cm-10x12in) s.i. etching aquatint. 30-Apr-4 Sotheby's, New York #28/R est:10000-12000
Works on paper
£320 $550 €467 Two fashionable ladies conversing (18x15cm-7x6in) s.d.1916 pencil. 7-Dec-3 Freeman, Philadelphia #167
£497 $900 €726 Bust of a young woman (18x15cm-7x6in) ink. 16-Apr-4 Du Mouchelle, Detroit #2114/R
£633 $1058 €924 Santa Cruz Valley, New Mexico (34x48cm-13x19in) s.i. W/C. 17-Nov-3 Waddingtons, Toronto #9/R (C.D 1400)
£698 $1200 €1019 Thunder Heads (20x25cm-8x10in) s.i. d.1921 pencil. 7-Dec-3 Freeman, Philadelphia #168 est:500-800
£1514 $2800 €2271 Tesuque Augly (23x30cm-9x12in) init.i. crayon prov. 14-Jul-4 American Auctioneer #490219/R est:3000-4000
£1780 $3275 €2599 Gossip (13x10cm-5x4in) i.d.1909 black conte prov.exhib. 25-Jun-4 Freeman, Philadelphia #12/R est:1000-1500
£2935 $5400 €4285 Nude (33x23cm-13x9in) s.i.d.1930 pencil. 10-Jun-4 Swann Galleries, New York #218/R est:3000-5000
£5587 $10000 €9381 Central Park with mother and child in carriage (33x48cm-13x19in) s. W/C. 20-Mar-4 Pook & Pook, Downington #555/R est:2500-3500

SLOANE, Eric (1910-1985) American
£1000 $1600 €1460 Harbour scene (53x64cm-21x25in) s. board. 20-Sep-3 Pook & Pook, Downington #526 est:3500-5500
£1625 $2600 €2373 Cloud study (51x61cm-20x24in) s. board. 20-Sep-3 Nadeau, Windsor #81/R
£2096 $3500 €3060 Clearing sky, Peconic Bay (33x38cm-13x15in) s.i. board. 29-Jun-3 William Jenack, New York #244 est:4000-6000
£3529 $6000 €5152 Shore sky (55x102cm-22x40in) s.i. board prov. 21-Nov-3 Skinner, Boston #487/R est:12000-18000
£3824 $6500 €5583 Above the clouds (122x122cm-48x48in) s. board. 21-Nov-3 Skinner, Boston #477/R est:5000-7000
£3911 $7000 €5710 Dawn, Brookfield Connecticut (41x64cm-16x25in) board. 15-May-4 Altermann Galleries, Santa Fe #136/R
£4790 $8000 €6993 Vermont Spring (61x107cm-24x42in) s. masonite prov. 23-Oct-3 Shannon's, Milford #159/R est:9000-12000
£6417 $12000 €9369 New England (43x56cm-17x22in) s. board prov. 24-Jul-4 Coeur d'Alene, Hayden #116/R est:8000-12000
£7910 $14000 €11549 Santa Fe aspens (58x45cm-23x18in) s.i.verso masonite prov. 28-Apr-4 Christie's, Los Angeles #70/R est:10000-15000
£8556 $16000 €12492 Autumn (43x58cm-17x23in) s. board prov. 24-Jul-4 Coeur d'Alene, Hayden #117/R est:8000-12000
£9581 $16000 €13988 Barn in winter (43x61cm-17x24in) s. panel prov. 9-Oct-3 Christie's, Rockefeller NY #74/R est:15000-25000
£12849 $23000 €18760 Taow recollection (33x109cm-13x43in) board. 15-May-4 Altermann Galleries, Santa Fe #135/R
£15432 $25000 €22376 Autumn shadows (61x91cm-24x36in) s. masonite. 8-Aug-3 Barridorf, Portland #254/R est:15000-25000
£20053 $37500 €29277 Kansas sky (61x91cm-24x36in) s. board prov. 24-Jul-4 Coeur d'Alene, Hayden #115/R est:10000-20000
Works on paper
£745 $1200 €1088 Covered bridge (23x33cm-9x13in) s. ink exec. c.1950's. 22-Feb-3 Bunte, Elgin #1284

SLOANE, Phyllis (20th C) American
£297 $550 €434 Spring day, a wonderful rooftop vista overlooking a Cleveland neighbourhood (61x51cm-24x20in) s. d.1987 acrylic. 16-Jan-4 Aspire, Cleveland #78/R
Works on paper
£270 $450 €394 Alcazar 2 (74x53cm-29x21in) s.d.1930 pastel. 14-Nov-3 Aspire, Cleveland #188

SLOBODKINA, Esphyr (1908-) American
£2500 $4475 €3650 Abstract composition (31x53cm-12x21in) s.d.50. 26-May-4 Sotheby's, Olympia #504/R est:2500-3500
£5294 $9000 €7729 Mural sketch no.4 (18x48cm-7x19in) s.i.d.1938 board prov. 9-Nov-3 Wright, Chicago #241 est:10000-15000

SLODKI, Marceli (?) Italian?
£265 $482 €400 Nu couche (27x35cm-11x14in) s. cardboard. 16-Jun-4 Claude Boisgirard, Paris #145

SLOMAN, Bodil (1884-1954) Danish
Works on paper
£587 $1097 €857 Still life of flowers, gourds and grapes (74x91cm-29x36in) init.d.28 W/C gouache. 25-Feb-4 Museumsbygningen, Copenhagen #98/R (D.KR 6500)

SLOMAN, Joseph (1883-?) American
£483 $850 €705 City scene (25x20cm-10x8in) s. board painted c.1930. 23-May-4 Treadway Gallery, Cincinnati #656/R

SLONE, Sandi (20th C) American
£419 $750 €612 Jason's voyage. acrylic. 18-Mar-4 Skinner, Bolton #561/R

SLOODTS, Jean Baptiste (1843-?) French
Sculpture
£7400 $12062 €10804 Peacock (165cm-65in) golden pat bronze incl pedestal. 28-Sep-3 Wilkinson, Doncaster #11/R

SLOOVERE, Georges de (1873-1970) Belgian
£362 $648 €529 Street scene with figures (33x47cm-13x19in) s. panel. 10-May-4 Rasmussen, Vejle #460/R (D.KR 4000)
£1049 $1783 €1500 Fillette accoudee sur la rampe d'un canal a Bruges (60x70cm-24x28in) s. 1-Dec-3 Palais de Beaux Arts, Brussels #43/R est:600-900

SLOTT-MOLLER, Agnes (1862-1937) Danish
£284 $508 €415 From a garden (36x27cm-14x11in) s.d.1929. 12-Jan-4 Rasmussen, Vejle #74/R (D.KR 3000)
£328 $547 €479 Field landscape (32x50cm-13x20in) s. 25-Oct-3 Rasmussen, Havnen #2178/R (D.KR 3500)
£335 $543 €486 Summer's day at Lovenholm (56x80cm-22x31in) s.d.1922. 4-Aug-3 Rasmussen, Vejle #332/R (D.KR 3500)
£922 $1567 €1346 Scene from a ballad (100x140cm-39x55in) 10-Nov-3 Rasmussen, Vejle #234/R (D.KR 10000)
£48000 $87360 €70080 Dying betrothed (82x135cm-32x53in) s.d.1906 exhib.lit. 17-Jun-4 Christie's, London #41/R est:30000-50000

SLOTT-MOLLER, Harald (1864-1937) Danish
£313 $533 €457 Evening peace - woman in profile (18x17cm-7x7in) 10-Nov-3 Rasmussen, Vejle #237/R (D.KR 3400)
£679 $1215 €991 Greenhouse seen through open door, cat in foreground (64x44cm-25x17in) s. 10-May-4 Rasmussen, Vejle #473/R (D.KR 7500)
£2050 $3219 €2993 Summer's day in the wood with Mrs Myllius and Mrs Scholl (64x75cm-25x30in) s.d.1917. 30-Aug-3 Rasmussen, Havnen #2104/R est:20000-30000 (D.KR 22000)

SLOUN, Frank van (1879-1938) American
£882 $1500 €1288 In the tropics (61x33cm-24x13in) s. pressed wood board on press board. 20-Nov-3 Auctions by the Bay, Alameda #1091/R
£1087 $2000 €1587 The vision (35x40cm-14x16in) s. i.verso board prov. 8-Jun-4 Bonhams & Butterfields, San Francisco #4250/R est:3000-5000

SLOVAK, Milos (20th C) ?
£2500 $4300 €3650 Oriental model (140x60cm-55x24in) mono. 4-Dec-3 Christie's, Kensington #160/R est:3000-5000

SLUIS, George Vander (1915-) American
Works on paper
£260 $450 €380 Pike's Peak, Colorado (30x41cm-12x16in) s.d.41 gouache. 13-Dec-3 Weschler, Washington #564

SLUIS, Marianne (1940-) Dutch
£594 $1022 €850 Marrakech (100x100cm-39x39in) s. 8-Dec-3 Glerum, Amsterdam #421/R

SLUIS, Peter (1929-) Irish/Dutch
£805 $1426 €1200 Still life with onions (25x30cm-10x12in) s. canvasboard. 27-Apr-4 Whyte's, Dublin #145/R
£1748 $2972 €2500 The violin player (58x41cm-23x16in) s. i.verso board. 18-Nov-3 Whyte's, Dublin #136/R est:2000-3000
Works on paper
£320 $576 €480 Psychedelic plane (27x40cm-11x16in) s.d.97 W/C. 20-Apr-4 James Adam, Dublin #186/R
£403 $721 €600 Sailor boy (23x26cm-9x10in) s. gouache. 31-May-4 Hamilton Osborne King, Dublin #54/R
£480 $869 €720 Coming together (25x24cm-10x9in) s.d.1994 W/C. 30-Mar-4 De Veres Art Auctions, Dublin #190/R
£738 $1321 €1100 Portrait of a girl (50x40cm-20x16in) s.d.2004 mixed media. 31-May-4 Hamilton Osborne King, Dublin #237

SLUITER, Willy (1873-1949) Dutch
£884 $1583 €1300 Balinese silver smith (23x31cm-9x12in) s.d.23 gouache W/C chk pencil. 16-Mar-4 Christie's, Amsterdam #14/R est:1500-2000
£1301 $2212 €1900 Schevening beach with wooden boats (32x21cm-13x8in) s.d.1895 panel. 5-Nov-3 Vendue Huis, Gravenhage #122/R est:2000-2500
£1316 $2421 €2000 Lady reading (81x63cm-32x25in) s.d.6/98. 28-Jun-4 Sotheby's, Amsterdam #74/R est:2000-3000
Works on paper
£272 $487 €400 Dunes (16x24cm-6x9in) s. W/C. 17-Mar-4 Hotel des Ventes Mosan, Brussels #130
£382 $603 €550 New Year's wish, warm welcome in Volendam (20x13cm-8x5in) s.i.d.Dec 1910 black ink. 2-Sep-3 Christie's, Amsterdam #289
£496 $829 €700 Above the water (24x32cm-9x13in) s. W/C htd white. 20-Oct-3 Glerum, Amsterdam #124/R
£804 $1343 €1150 Girl knitting in front of a farm (49x38cm-19x15in) s. pastel. 30-Jun-3 Sotheby's, Amsterdam #212/R
£1259 $2140 €1800 May Annie (38x30cm-15x12in) s.i.d.1918 pastel. 24-Nov-3 Glerum, Amsterdam #21/R est:1200-1800
£1361 $2476 €2000 Laren, Gooi 1913 - poster design (11x8cm-4x3in) s. pencil chk W/C set of three. 3-Feb-4 Christie's, Amsterdam #312/R est:1200-1600
£1507 $2562 €2200 Young mother (48x38cm-19x15in) s. pastel. 5-Nov-3 Vendue Huis, Gravenhage #116/R est:2500-3000
£1974 $3632 €3000 Beachcomber in Katwijk (48x39cm-19x15in) s. s.i.verso pencil W/C htd white. 22-Jun-4 Christie's, Amsterdam #257/R est:3000-5000
£2177 $3962 €3200 Carrying cheese, Edam (18x23cm-7x9in) s. pencil pastel set of five. 3-Feb-4 Christie's, Amsterdam #309/R est:1500-2000
£2763 $5084 €4200 A walk on the beach with granddad (57x45cm-22x18in) s.i. chl pastel. 22-Jun-4 Christie's, Amsterdam #284/R est:1000-1500
£2857 $5200 €4200 Van vollenhoven's bieren - poster design (21x13cm-8x5in) init. pencil ink col chk set of 10. 3-Feb-4 Christie's, Amsterdam #310/R est:1500-2000
£3000 $5400 €4500 Coachdriver waiting for passengers (23x29cm-9x11in) s.d.04 pastel black chk. 20-Apr-4 Sotheby's, Amsterdam #132/R est:5000-7000
£6178 $10317 €9020 Baraboedoer (75x80cm-30x31in) s.i.d.1923 pastel prov.exhib.lit. 26-Oct-3 Christie's, Hong Kong #14/R est:80000-100000 (HK.D 80000)

SLUYS, Jacob van der (1660-1732) Dutch
£2154 $3705 €3145 At the fishmarket (28x24cm-11x9in) s. panel. 7-Dec-3 Uppsala Auktionskammare, Uppsala #12/R est:20000-25000 (S.KR 28000)

SLUYS, Remy van (1907-1994) Belgian
£405 $714 €600 Altar of Church of Our Lady in Antwerp (104x82cm-41x32in) s.d.72. 24-May-4 Bernaerts, Antwerp #471/R

SLUYTERMANN VON LANGEWEYDE, Georg (1903-1978) German
£517 $957 €750 Maize field (44x54cm-17x21in) s. board. 14-Feb-4 Hans Stahl, Hamburg #56/R
£1389 $2319 €2000 Hunting still life (71x61cm-28x24in) s. masonite. 24-Oct-3 Ketterer, Hamburg #107/R est:2500-3000

SLUYTERS, Jan (1881-1957) Dutch
£6667 $12267 €10000 A square in Avignon (59x79cm-23x31in) s.d.1953. 9-Jun-4 Christie's, Amsterdam #197/R est:8000-12000
£8696 $14261 €12000 Cyclamen (56x47cm-22x19in) s. 27-May-3 Sotheby's, Amsterdam #311/R est:15000-20000
£13333 $24533 €20000 Hoek Leidsestraat met zicht of het Koningsplein te Amsterdam (50x75cm-20x30in) s. s. stretcher painted c.1958. 8-Jun-4 Sotheby's, Amsterdam #172/R est:8000-12000
£20979 $36084 €30000 Boerderij te Heeze (33x29cm-13x11in) s.i.d.09 oil on card prov. 2-Dec-3 Sotheby's, Amsterdam #11/R est:28000-35000
£24476 $41608 €35000 Still life with flowers in a vase (87x72cm-34x28in) painted c.1938. 25-Nov-3 Christie's, Amsterdam #180/R est:30000-50000
£31469 $53497 €45000 Elegant lady in Spanish dress (100x77cm-39x30in) s. painted c.1925 prov. 25-Nov-3 Christie's, Amsterdam #181/R est:45000-60000
£52448 $90210 €75000 Herfst stilleven (95x107cm-37x42in) s. prov.exhib. 2-Dec-3 Sotheby's, Amsterdam #16/R est:60000-80000
£94203 $154493 €130000 Nude with pearls (96x66cm-38x26in) s. painted c.1925 lit. 27-May-3 Sotheby's, Amsterdam #315/R est:120000-180000
£94203 $154493 €130000 Corner of studio with model (86x66cm-34x26in) s. painted c.1912 prov.exhib. 27-May-3 Sotheby's, Amsterdam #319/R est:130000-190000
Works on paper
£317 $555 €450 Maternite. mono. col crayon. 16-Dec-3 Galerie Moderne, Brussels #693
£699 $1203 €1000 Study modinettes (12x6cm-5x2in) init. pencil. 2-Dec-3 Sotheby's, Amsterdam #15/R est:1200-1500
£1141 $2099 €1700 Interior with covered table (19x25cm-7x10in) s. mixed media. 29-Mar-4 Glerum, Amsterdam #108 est:1000-1500
£1958 $3368 €2800 St. Gerard le puy (16x23cm-6x9in) s.i.d.49 col crayon pencil. 2-Dec-3 Sotheby's, Amsterdam #233/R est:1200-1500
£2609 $4278 €3600 Reclining nude (24x42cm-9x17in) s. black red chk prov. 27-May-3 Sotheby's, Amsterdam #473/R est:2000-3000
£2800 $5152 €4200 Le lecteur (26x20cm-10x8in) s.i.d.06 col pencil W/C prov. 9-Jun-4 Christie's, Amsterdam #2/R est:4000-6000
£3691 $6829 €5500 Mother with two children (46x35cm-18x14in) s. pastel. 15-Mar-4 Sotheby's, Amsterdam #193/R est:1500-2000
£4196 $7133 €6000 Horse and wagon in Paris (25x19cm-10x7in) mono. col crayons W/C gouache. 25-Nov-3 Christie's, Amsterdam #25/R est:6000-8000
£4895 $8322 €7000 Seated nude (68x44cm-27x17in) s. chl W/C. 25-Nov-3 Christie's, Amsterdam #159/R est:8000-12000
£8667 $15947 €13000 Dancing nude (30x28cm-12x11in) gouache exec c.1920. 8-Jun-4 Sotheby's, Amsterdam #170/R est:4000-6000
£9333 $17173 €14000 Reclining nude (25x39cm-10x15in) s. W/C pastel pencil. 8-Jun-4 Sotheby's, Amsterdam #184/R est:5000-7000
£10490 $18042 €15000 Female nude seated (29x19cm-11x7in) s. W/C ink pencil prov. 2-Dec-3 Sotheby's, Amsterdam #94/R est:6000-8000
£19580 $33678 €28000 Les Parisiennes (26x19cm-10x7in) s.d.06 W/C ink pencil prov.lit. 2-Dec-3 Sotheby's, Amsterdam #93/R est:10000-15000

SLUYTERS, Jan (jnr) (1914-) Dutch
£909 $1545 €1300 View of Amsterdam canal in autumn (60x70cm-24x28in) s. 24-Nov-3 Glerum, Amsterdam #60/R
£10490 $18042 €15000 De spuistraat met het bodecentrum te Amsterdam (97x89cm-38x35in) s. s.i.stretcher painted c.1938 prov. 2-Dec-3 Sotheby's, Amsterdam #21/R est:15000-25000
£17391 $28522 €24000 View of city of Amsterdam (66x80cm-26x31in) s. 27-May-3 Sotheby's, Amsterdam #313/R est:15000-25000

SMALL, David (1846-1927) British
Works on paper
£250 $400 €365 Crail (24x34cm-9x13in) s. W/C. 15-May-3 Bonhams, Edinburgh #367

SMALL, William (1843-1929) British
£680 $1238 €993 Logger returns (16x31cm-6x12in) init. board. 3-Feb-4 Sworder & Son, Bishops Stortford #300/R

SMALLFIELD, Frederick (1829-1915) British
Works on paper
£6719 $12028 €9810 Tartini (40x68cm-16x27in) init.i.d.1863 i.verso W/C prov. 15-May-4 Christie's, Sydney #52/R est:12000-18000 (A.D 17000)

SMALLFIELD, Jessica (19th C) British
Works on paper
£280 $442 €409 Portrait of a girl wearing a white bonnet and reading a book (24x18cm-9x7in) s.d.1858. 3-Sep-3 Bonhams, Bury St Edmunds #338/R

SMARGIASSI, Gabriele (1798-1882) Italian
£408 $649 €600 Femme de Tivoli cousant (26x22cm-10x9in) i.verso. 21-Mar-3 Bailly Pommery, Paris #85
£1611 $2883 €2400 Landscape (24x19cm-9x7in) s.d.1839. 25-May-4 Finarte Semenzato, Milan #118/R est:1800-2000

Works on paper

£2113	$3507	€3000	Landscape with trees (30x42cm-12x17in) s. W/C cardboard. 11-Jun-3 Christie's, Rome #226 est:3500-4500

SMART, Edmund Hodgson (1873-1942) British

£480	$763	€701	Portrait of Mrs. E S Nutt (74x61cm-29x24in) s.d.1924 i.verso. 12-Sep-3 Gardiner & Houlgate, Bath #143/R

SMART, Jeffrey (1921-) Australian

£10656	$16836	€15558	The little church at Hindmarsh (51x61cm-20x24in) s. hessian prov.exhib. 2-Sep-3 Deutscher-Menzies, Melbourne #43/R est:30000-35000 (A.D 26000)
£11382	$20374	€16618	Study for the arrow carriers (24x25cm-9x10in) s. canvas on board painted 1978 prov.lit. 4-May-4 Sotheby's, Melbourne #2/R est:30000-40000 (A.D 28000)
£14227	$22338	€24141	Old boilers, lakeside (49x60cm-19x24in) s. prov.lit. 26-Aug-3 Christie's, Sydney #48/R est:35000-45000 (A.D 35000)
£15702	$27793	€22925	Study for the yellow truck, Helsinki (32x23cm-13x9in) s. prov. 3-May-4 Christie's, Melbourne #89/R est:38000-45000 (A.D 38000)
£20763	$35297	€30314	Study for Hide and Seek (30x45cm-12x18in) s. painted 1969/70 prov.exhib. 24-Nov-3 Sotheby's, Melbourne #44/R est:32000-38000 (A.D 49000)
£22901	$41679	€33435	Study for truck and trailer approaching city (24x64cm-9x25in) s. canvas on board. 16-Jun-4 Deutscher-Menzies, Melbourne #53/R est:60000-80000 (A.D 60000)
£24793	$43884	€36198	Study for motel swimming pool (41x29cm-16x11in) s. canvas on board prov.exhib.lit. 3-May-4 Christie's, Melbourne #68/R est:45000-55000 (A.D 60000)
£26423	$41484	€38313	First study for service station, Calabria (35x28cm-14x11in) s. board prov.lit. 26-Aug-3 Christie's, Sydney #76/R est:45000-65000 (A.D 65000)
£30534	$55573	€44580	Second study for portrait of Clive James (39x51cm-15x20in) s. canvas on board prov.exhib. 16-Jun-4 Deutscher-Menzies, Melbourne #78/R est:50000-70000 (A.D 80000)
£32520	$51057	€47154	Study for skaters (37x9cm-15x4in) s. prov.exhib. 26-Aug-3 Christie's, Sydney #41/R est:60000-80000 (A.D 80000)
£38168	$69466	€55725	Slides, Cinecitta (72x91cm-28x36in) s.i.verso. 16-Jun-4 Deutscher-Menzies, Melbourne #20/R est:100000-140000 (A.D 100000)
£41322	$76446	€60330	Second study for railway bridge 1996 (32x91cm-13x36in) s. board prov.exhib. 10-Mar-4 Deutscher-Menzies, Melbourne #22/R est:60000-80000 (A.D 100000)
£48729	$82839	€71144	Piazza d'Esedra (54x74cm-21x29in) s.d.1965 bears i.verso board prov.exhib. 24-Nov-3 Sotheby's, Melbourne #7/R est:120000-150000 (A.D 115000)
£68702	$125038	€100305	Hitch-hiker (68x89cm-27x35in) s. s.i.stretcher verso prov.exhib. 16-Jun-4 Deutscher-Menzies, Melbourne #19/R est:120000-150000 (A.D 180000)
£70248	$129959	€102562	Skaters 1999 (65x85cm-26x33in) s. prov.exhib. 10-Mar-4 Deutscher-Menzies, Melbourne #27/R est:160000-200000 (A.D 170000)
£138211	$216992	€200406	Near Pisa Airport (98x75cm-39x30in) indis.sig. prov. 27-Aug-3 Christie's, Sydney #548/R est:280000-350000 (A.D 340000)

Prints

£3099	$5485	€4525	Directors (12x74cm-5x29in) s.i.num.34/90 etching. 3-May-4 Christie's, Melbourne #364/R est:6000-8000 (A.D 7500)
£3719	$6880	€5430	Directors (12x75cm-5x30in) s.num.29/90 etching aquatint. 10-Mar-4 Deutscher-Menzies, Melbourne #254/R est:6500-8500 (A.D 9000)
£3817	$6947	€5573	Dome (43x43cm-17x17in) col etching prov. 16-Jun-4 Deutscher-Menzies, Melbourne #439/R est:4000-6000 (A.D 10000)

Works on paper

£2542	$4322	€3711	Landscape with tree (38x48cm-15x19in) s.i. pastel prov. 24-Nov-3 Sotheby's, Melbourne #166/R est:10000-15000 (A.D 6000)

SMART, John (snr) (1742-1811) British

Miniatures

£1900	$3287	€2774	Young lady (5cm-2in) W/C pencil on card oval prov. 9-Dec-3 Christie's, London #104/R est:1000-1500
£2000	$3460	€2920	Young lady (3cm-1in) gold frame oval prov. 9-Dec-3 Christie's, London #78 est:1500-2500
£2300	$4232	€3358	Lady Mary Lowther, wearing a white dress (6cm-2in) W/C pencil on card rectangular prov.lit. 24-Jun-4 Bonhams, New Bond Street #3/R est:1000-1500
£2800	$4844	€4088	Young lady (4cm-2in) init.d.1769 gilt metal frame oval. 9-Dec-3 Christie's, London #70/R est:2000-3000
£4000	$7160	€5840	Richard Twining in blue coat (4cm 2in) init.d.1771 silver gilt frame cut diamonds. 25-May-4 Christie's, London #175 est:4000-6000
£4500	$8055	€6570	Young gentleman in a grey coat (4cm-2in) init.d.1777 silver gilt frame prov. 25-May-4 Christie's, London #104/R est:4000-6000
£5000	$9000	€7300	Gentleman wearing black coat and white cravat (4cm-2in) s.d.1780 diamond gold bracelet clasp mount oval exhib.lit. 22-Apr-4 Bonhams, New Bond Street #55/R est:5000-7000
£7568	$14000	€11049	Sir Archibal Hope (3x3cm-1x1in) oval. 12-Mar-4 Du Mouchelle, Detroit #2013/R est:2000-3000
£8000	$14320	€11680	Young officer, in red coat, powdered hair en queue (3cm-1in) init.d.1774 silver gilt frame. 25-May-4 Christie's, London #132/R est:6000-8000
£9000	$16200	€13140	Gentleman wearing gold edged grey coat (5cm-2in) s.d.1779 gold frame oval exhib.lit. 22-Apr-4 Bonhams, New Bond Street #54/R est:6000-8000
£9500	$17100	€13870	Lady, wearing gold trimmed blue dress (4cm-2in) init.d.1768 gold frame oval prov.exhib.lit. 22-Apr-4 Bonhams, New Bond Street #47/R est:8000-12000
£9500	$17100	€13870	Lady, wearing white dress with pink stripes (4cm-2in) s.d.1779 gold frame oval exhib. 22-Apr-4 Bonhams, New Bond Street #49/R est:8000-12000
£10000	$17300	€14600	Officer (4cm-2in) init.d.1781 oval. 9-Dec-3 Christie's, London #82/R est:8000-12000
£10500	$17850	€15330	John Spottiswoode (4cm-2in) init.d.1779 oval prov. 18-Nov-3 Bonhams, New Bond Street #68/R est:10000-15000
£12000	$21480	€17520	Miss Gascoine in gold bordered white dress (6cm-2in) pencil W/C on card silver gilt metal frame prov.lit. 25-May-4 Christie's, London #176/R est:5000-6000
£13000	$23920	€18980	Thomas Russell wearing a pale grey coat (4cm-2in) s.d.1771 gold frame plaited hair seed pearls. 24-Jun-4 Bonhams, New Bond Street #90/R est:8000-12000
£13514	$25000	€19730	Sarah Tyssen (5x5cm-2x2in) oval. 12-Mar-4 Du Mouchelle, Detroit #2014/R est:2000-3000
£14000	$25060	€20440	Miss Loraine Smith, in blue bordered white silk dress (5cm-2in) init.d.1781. 25-May-4 Christie's, London #156/R est:12000-15000
£15000	$26850	€21900	Miss Mary Lewin, later Mrs. Ralph Jackson (5cm-2in) init.d.1776 prov.exhib.lit. 25-May-4 Christie's, London #84/R est:10000-15000
£17000	$28900	€24820	Charlotte Palmer (4cm-2in) init.d.1770 oval prov.lit. 18-Nov-3 Bonhams, New Bond Street #67/R est:12000-18000
£18000	$32400	€26280	Portraits of Robert Williams and his wife Ivey Williams (8cm-3in) s.d.1801 mono.i.verso gold frame oval pair prov.exhib.lit. 22-Apr-4 Bonhams, New Bond Street #116/R est:20000-30000
£22000	$38060	€32120	Young lady (5cm-2in) init.d.1776 prov.exhib.lit. 9-Dec-3 Christie's, London #83/R est:12000-15000
£22000	$38060	€32120	Miss Twining (8cm-3in) init.d.1801 silver-gilt frame oval. 9-Dec-3 Christie's, London #157/R est:15000-20000
£22000	$39380	€32120	Mrs Walter Bracebridge, wearing a blue blue dress (5cm-2in) init.d.1781 god frame plaited hair. 25-May-4 Christie's, London #155/R est:12000-15000
£26000	$46540	€37960	Lieutenant General John Richardson, wearing red coat (7cm-3in) s.d.1794 init. gold fausse montre frame plaited hair. 25-May-4 Christie's, London #129/R est:15000-20000
£28000	$50120	€40880	Mr. John Chamier in a white silk dress, purple short sleeves (6cm-2in) s.d.1786 silver gilt frame plaited hair prov. 25-May-4 Christie's, London #131/R est:12000-15000
£32000	$57280	€46720	Mra John Richardson, in white dress and green sash (7cm-3in) s.d.1974 gold frame plaited hair prov. 25-May-4 Christie's, London #130/R est:12000-15000
£35000	$63000	€51100	Peeress, in ermine trimmed mauve satin robe (5cm-2in) init.d.1775 mono.verso pearl diamond gold frame oval exhib.lit. 22-Apr-4 Bonhams, New Bond Street #44/R est:12000-18000

Works on paper

£306	$550	€447	Study of a seaman on the Melville (16x15cm-6x6in) red chk prov. 21-Jan-4 Doyle, New York #12

SMART, John (1838-1899) British

£340	$541	€496	View in the Highlands with a figure and sheep by a stream in the foreground (28x43cm-11x17in) s. 18-Mar-3 Anderson & Garland, Newcastle #410/R

Works on paper

£350	$662	€511	Highland landscape (43x66cm-17x26in) s. W/C. 19-Feb-4 Lyon & Turnbull, Edinburgh #108

SMART, Sally (1960-) Australian

£1721	$2719	€2513	X-ray vanitas: identity skirt (166x121cm-65x48in) s.i.d.1988 oil enamel prov.exhib. 2-Sep-3 Deutscher-Menzies, Melbourne #190/R est:4000-5000 (A.D 4200)
£1860	$3440	€2716	Mad house history painting series no.1 (173x60cm-68x24in) s.d.1990 i.verso oil on woolen blanket. 15-Mar-4 Sotheby's, Melbourne #52/R est:4000-6000 (A.D 4500)
£3512	$6498	€5128	Mad house history painting series No.8 (173x58cm-68x23in) s.i.verso oil on felt painted 1990. 15-Mar-4 Sotheby's, Melbourne #83/R est:4000-6000 (A.D 8500)

Prints

£1951	$3063	€2829	Equisite dress (150x135cm-59x53in) s.i.d.1991 num.9/22 printed collage. 27-Aug-3 Christie's, Sydney #518/R est:2000-4000 (A.D 4800)

SMEALL, William (1790-1883) British

£250	$473	€365	Figures by a Doocot (24x32cm-9x13in) s.i. panel. 19-Feb-4 Lyon & Turnbull, Edinburgh #143

SMEATON, James (20th C) Australian?

£650	$1164	€949	Jetty (195x298cm-77x117in) painted c.1988. 10-May-4 Joel, Victoria #308 est:2000-4000 (A.D 1600)
£1983	$3669	€2895	Edge (213x334cm-84x131in) s.d.89 synthetic polymer two panel prov.exhib. 15-Mar-4 Sotheby's, Melbourne #112/R est:4000-6000 (A.D 4800)

SMEDLEY, Will Larrymore (1871-1958) American

£250	$400	€365	Landscape with snowy woodland interior (41x58cm-16x23in) s. board. 20-Sep-3 Nadeau, Windsor #179/R

SMEDLEY, William Thomas (1858-1920) American

Works on paper

£750	$1328	€1095	I saw tall Derricks by the Hundreds Rise (35x24cm-14x9in) s.d.1886 W/C. 27-Apr-4 Bonhams, New Bond Street #118/R
£1053	$1695	€1537	Sunday morning, Collins Street, Melbourne (50x34cm-20x13in) s.i. W/C htd white. 13-Oct-3 Joel, Victoria #306 est:800-1200 (A.D 2600)

SMEERS, Frans (1873-1960) Belgian

£282	$487	€400	Le corsage rouge (50x40cm-20x16in) s. panel. 10-Dec-3 Hotel des Ventes Mosan, Brussels #163
£671	$1235	€1000	Costume portugais (60x40cm-24x16in) s. 23-Mar-4 Galerie Moderne, Brussels #176/R
£1277	$2132	€1800	Promenade en barque (23x33cm-9x13in) s. panel. 14-Oct-3 Vanderkindere, Brussels #98
£3472	$5799	€5000	Day at the beach (32x50cm-13x20in) s. 21-Oct-3 Sotheby's, Amsterdam #97/R est:5000-7000
£5556	$9278	€8000	Girl leaning out of the window (46x38cm-18x15in) s. panel. 21-Oct-3 Sotheby's, Amsterdam #118/R est:5000-7000

Works on paper

£490	$832	€700	Cannes, la croisette. d.21 crayon. 18-Nov-3 Galerie Moderne, Brussels #622/R
£769	$1323	€1100	Vue de parc de Bruxelles (31x37cm-12x15in) s. chl. 8-Dec-3 Horta, Bruxelles #49

SMEERS, Frans (attrib) (1873-1960) Belgian

£767	$1372	€1150	Estuaire anime (35x55cm-14x22in) panel. 11-May-4 Vanderkindere, Brussels #14
£1608	$2734	€2300	Madame Morichar sur la digue a Ostende (46x27cm-18x11in) panel. 18-Nov-3 Vanderkindere, Brussels #97 est:625-875
£3262	$5448	€4600	Maternite (70x50cm-28x20in) 17-Jun-3 Galerie Moderne, Brussels #178/R est:3000-5000

SMELLIE, J (19/20th C) British

£1200	$2208	€1752	Log cart (85x144cm-33x57in) s.d.28. 25-Mar-4 Bonhams, Edinburgh #363 est:1000-1500

SMET, Frederic de (1876-1943) Belgian
£594 $1010 €850 Woodland with stream (61x91cm-24x36in) mono.d. 21-Nov-3 Reiss & Sohn, Konigstein #31/R

SMET, Gustave de (1877-1943) Belgian
£470 $832 €700 Nature morte aux fleurs (45x64cm-18x25in) s. 27-Apr-4 Campo & Campo, Antwerp #74/R
£2535 $4386 €3600 Pier-Spal mill in Afsnee (15x22cm-6x9in) mono. i.d.1912 verso. 13-Dec-3 De Vuyst, Lokeren #117/R est:3500-4500
£2933 $5251 €4400 Beguinage of Bruges (46x55cm-18x22in) mono. lit. 15-May-4 De Vuyst, Lokeren #453/R est:5000-7000
£14667 $26987 €22000 The Vondelpark, Amsterdam (46x34cm-18x13in) s. panel painted c.1915 prov. 9-Jun-4 Christie's, Amsterdam #100/R est:15000-20000
£17483 $30070 €25000 Stillleven met anemonen (37x25cm-15x10in) s. painted 1915 prov.lit. 2-Dec-3 Sotheby's, Amsterdam #106/R est:15000-20000
£19014 $32894 €27000 Farm (42x51cm-17x20in) s. 13-Dec-3 De Vuyst, Lokeren #480/R
Works on paper
£2200 $3938 €3300 Woman standing (66x46cm-26x18in) s. sanguine. 15-May-4 De Vuyst, Lokeren #569/R est:5000-6000
£69930 $118881 €100000 At the window (64x49cm-25x19in) s. gouache chl cardboard exec c.1931 prov.exhib.lit. 25-Nov-3 Christie's, Amsterdam #211/R est:80000-120000

SMET, Henri de (1865-1940) Belgian
£385 $662 €550 Moulin dans un paysage (24x28cm-9x11in) s. 2-Dec-3 Campo & Campo, Antwerp #111
£833 $1492 €1250 L'attente (50x32cm-20x13in) s.indis.d. panel. 11-May-4 Vanderkindere, Brussels #600
£1711 $3096 €2600 Gentleman sitting in a neo-renaissance interior (48x37cm-19x15in) s.d.1901. 19-Apr-4 Glerum, Amsterdam #296/R est:2000-2500
£3691 $6755 €5500 A l'auberge (91x70cm-36x28in) s. 8-Jul-4 Campo, Vlaamse Kaai #89/R est:4000-6000

SMET, Léon de (1881-1966) Belgian
£3846 $6538 €5500 Arbres au printemps (65x50cm-26x20in) s. panel. 1-Dec-3 Palais de Beaux Arts, Brussels #44/R est:4000-5000
£4667 $8587 €7000 Claire in a summer dress in front of the mirror (60x70cm-24x28in) s. painted c.1943-44. 9-Jun-4 Christie's, Amsterdam #77/R est:8000-12000
£5500 $10120 €8030 Paysage (65x80cm-26x31in) s. prov. 24-Mar-4 Sotheby's, Olympia #47/R est:5000-7000
£5594 $9510 €8000 Paysage de Flandres (60x60cm-24x24in) mono. 18-Nov-3 Vanderkindere, Brussels #118 est:8000-10000
£7000 $12110 €10220 On the riverbank (38x46cm-15x18in) mono. 11-Dec-3 Lyon & Turnbull, Edinburgh #79/R est:4000-6000
£11594 $19014 €16000 Santa Margareta (60x75cm-24x30in) s. board exhib. 27-May-3 Sotheby's, Amsterdam #331/R est:15000-20000
£17000 $28390 €24820 Saint Jean-Cap-Ferrat (61x74cm-24x29in) s.d.1925 prov. 21-Oct-3 Sotheby's, London #128/R est:18000-25000
£18243 $32655 €27000 Composition au vase fleuri et objets precieux sur fond de gravure (65x75cm-26x30in) s. 10-May-4 Horta, Bruxelles #135/R est:30000-40000
£19118 $32500 €27912 Nature morte (77x103cm-30x41in) s.d.1960 exhib. 6-Nov-3 Sotheby's, New York #344/R est:35000-45000
£25175 $42042 €36000 Still life (80x101cm-31x40in) s. lit. 11-Oct-3 De Vuyst, Lokeren #440/R
£30986 $53606 €44000 Le bouquet de fleurs aux coquelicots (72x92cm-28x36in) s.d.1921. 12-Dec-3 Piasa, Paris #12/R est:25000-30000
Works on paper
£9333 $16707 €14000 Mirrored view (47x63cm-19x25in) s.d.1914 pastel. 15-May-4 De Vuyst, Lokeren #459/R est:16000-18000

SMETS, Albert (fl.1880`s) Belgian
£1017 $1800 €1485 Barn interior with sheep (23x38cm-9x15in) s. i.verso panel. 2-May-4 Bonhams & Butterfields, San Francisco #1033/R est:2500-3500

SMETS, Louis (1840-1896) Belgian
£6000 $11220 €8760 Frozen winter landscape with figures skating on the ice (46x63cm-18x25in) s.d.1857. 22-Jul-4 Tennants, Leyburn #831/R est:2800-3200

SMIBERT, John (attrib) (1688-1751) American
£2361 $4250 €3447 Portrait of a young lady (76x63cm-30x25in) prov. 21-Jan-4 Sotheby's, New York #94/R est:5000-7000

SMIDT, Emil Leonhard (1878-1954) German
£567 $948 €800 Florence (18x25cm-7x10in) s.d.1919 canvas panel prov. 21-Jun-3 Hans Stahl, Hamburg #113/R
£660 $1102 €950 Poultry (29x38cm-11x15in) s.d. paper on panel. 24-Oct-3 Ketterer, Hamburg #108/R
£1418 $2369 €2000 Figures in Umberto Park, Rome (18x25cm-7x10in) s.d.1944 canvas board. 21-Jun-3 Hans Stahl, Hamburg #112/R est:900

SMIDTH, Hans (1839-1917) Danish
£270 $501 €394 Railway compartment (30x35cm-12x14in) s. 2-Mar-4 Rasmussen, Copenhagen #1551/R (D.KR 3000)
£293 $524 €428 Heath landscape (23x38cm-9x15in) s. prov. 12-Jan-4 Rasmussen, Vejle #312 (D.KR 3100)
£303 $485 €442 White farm house (40x34cm-16x13in) s. 22-Sep-3 Rasmussen, Vejle #143/R (D.KR 3200)
£379 $607 €553 Heath landscape with peasant (33x44cm-13x17in) s. 22-Sep-3 Rasmussen, Vejle #1450/R (D.KR 4000)
£398 $637 €581 Interior (29x34cm-11x13in) s. 22-Sep-3 Rasmussen, Vejle #139/R (D.KR 4200)
£452 $810 €660 Farm yard with cows and chickens (30x43cm-12x17in) s. exhib. 10-May-4 Rasmussen, Vejle #328/R (D.KR 5000)
£496 $917 €724 Landscape with farm (25x49cm-10x19in) s. 15-Mar-4 Rasmussen, Vejle #476/R (D.KR 5500)
£562 $967 €821 Marsh landscape (31x47cm-12x19in) s. 2-Dec-3 Kunsthallen, Copenhagen #539/R (D.KR 6000)
£587 $1097 €857 Figures in marshy landscape (36x29cm-14x11in) s. 25-Feb-4 Kunsthallen, Copenhagen #504 (D.KR 6500)
£667 $1234 €974 Young girl picking berries on the heath (22x28cm-9x11in) s. 15-Mar-4 Rasmussen, Vejle #475/R (D.KR 7400)
£711 $1137 €1038 Danish summer landscape with thatched house (37x47cm-15x19in) s. 22-Sep-3 Rasmussen, Vejle #142/R (D.KR 7500)
£806 $1289 €1177 Landscape with lime burner (38x65cm-15x26in) s. 22-Sep-3 Rasmussen, Vejle #152/R (D.KR 8500)
£839 $1317 €1225 Farmyard with figures, poultry and cows (30x47cm-12x19in) s.d.93. 30-Aug-3 Rasmussen, Havnen #2146/R (D.KR 9000)
£985 $1802 €1438 On the way home from market in oxen drawn cart (37x62cm-15x24in) s. prov. 9-Jun-4 Rasmussen, Copenhagen #1670/R (D.KR 11000)
£1083 $2025 €1581 Summer's day with birch trees (47x68cm-19x27in) s.d.1890 exhib. 25-Feb-4 Kunsthallen, Copenhagen #542/R est:15000 (D.KR 12000)
£1258 $2340 €1837 Gypsies on the heath (36x50cm-14x20in) s. 2-Mar-4 Rasmussen, Copenhagen #1637/R est:15000 (D.KR 14000)
£1611 $2949 €2352 Boy sitting barefoot on stone steps (39x38cm-15x15in) s. 7-Jun-4 Museumsbygningen, Copenhagen #141/R est:6000 (D.KR 18000)
£1623 $3003 €2370 Coastal landscape with boat coming ashore (26x35cm-10x14in) 15-Mar-4 Rasmussen, Vejle #474/R est:20000 (D.KR 18000)
£1682 $2658 €2439 Field landscape with peasants and sheep (38x70cm-15x28in) s.d.92 exhib. 2-Sep-3 Rasmussen, Copenhagen #1604/R est:20000 (D.KR 18000)
£1751 $2977 €2556 Figures and cows in farmyard (30x46cm-12x18in) s.d.93. 10-Nov-3 Rasmussen, Vejle #335/R est:20000-25000 (D.KR 19000)
£2991 $4725 €4337 Fire on the heath (64x114cm-25x45in) s. exhib.prov. 2-Sep-3 Rasmussen, Copenhagen #1605/R est:20000-25000 (D.KR 32000)

SMILLIE, George H (1840-1921) American
£296 $550 €432 Autumnal landscape with distant mountains (50x76cm-20x30in) 5-Mar-4 Skinner, Boston #303/R
£1537 $2750 €2244 Summer landscape with farmhouse (33x43cm-13x17in) s.d.1910 board. 8-Jan-4 James Julia, Fairfield #831/R est:2500-3500
£2059 $3500 €3006 Eveing among the cedars (23x38cm-9x15in) s.d.1883. 21-Nov-3 Skinner, Boston #263/R est:2500-3500
£3106 $5000 €4535 Magnolia, Mass July 1879 (20x36cm-8x14in) s. i.d. i. stretcher. 20-Aug-3 James Julia, Fairfield #1382/R est:2000-4000
£5096 $8000 €7440 Cows in a meadow. s. 30-Aug-3 Fallon, Copake #22 est:12000-15000

SMILLIE, George H (attrib) (1840-1921) American
£1117 $2000 €1631 Woodland stream (84x53cm-33x21in) prov. 26-May-4 Doyle, New York #45/R est:1000-1500

SMILLIE, James (1807-1885) American
£62500 $110000 €91250 Lake Placid and the Adirondack Mountains from Whiteface (58x102cm-23x40in) mono.d.1878 canvas on board prov.exhib. 18-May-4 Christie's, Rockefeller NY #4/R est:80000-120000

SMIRNOFF, Boris (1895-?) French
£426 $711 €600 Corrida (19x24cm-7x9in) s. cardboard. 20-Jun-3 Drouot Estimations, Paris #219
£426 $711 €600 Corrida (19x23cm-7x9in) s. cardboard. 20-Jun-3 Drouot Estimations, Paris #220

SMIRNOFF, Fedor (1896-1979) Russian
£350 $594 €500 Coastline with boats and figures (49x63cm-19x25in) s. board. 29-Nov-3 Arnold, Frankfurt #494/R

SMISSAERT, Frans (1862-1944) Dutch
£355 $592 €500 Net repairers on the dunes (47x52cm-19x20in) s.d.06. 20-Oct-3 Glerum, Amsterdam #79/R

SMISSEN, Jacob (1735-1813) German
Works on paper
£328 $600 €479 Peasants resting among classical ruins (17x22cm-7x9in) s.i. brush black ink gray wash. 29-Jan-4 Swann Galleries, New York #304/R

SMISSEN, Léon van der (1900-1966) Belgian
£1342 $2483 €2000 Returning farmer with cows (170x200cm-67x79in) s. 13-Mar-4 De Vuyst, Lokeren #338/R est:2000-3000

SMIT, Aernout (1641-1710) Dutch
£1500 $2550 €2190 Dutch Admiralty (37x45cm-15x18in) init. 19-Nov-3 Christie's, Kensington #445/R
£2273 $4000 €3319 Shipping offshore in rough seas (23x30cm-9x12in) s. panel. 18-May-4 Bonhams & Butterfields, San Francisco #25/R est:4000-6000
£2857 $5200 €4200 Three master in a gale off a rocky coast (62x91cm-24x36in) s. 3-Feb-4 Christie's, Amsterdam #42/R est:3000-5000
£23973 $40753 €35000 Man-o-war, possibly Het Wapen van Utrech, a wijdschip in a stiff breeze (86x112cm-34x44in) s.d.1671 prov.lit. 5-Nov-3 Christie's, Amsterdam #61/R est:15000-20000

SMIT, Aernout (attrib) (1641-1710) Dutch
£2778 $4389 €4000 Frigate and other shipping in a stiff breeze (57x80cm-22x31in) panel. 2-Sep-3 Christie's, Amsterdam #108/R est:4000-6000

SMIT, Arie (1916-) Dutch
£1307 $2366 €1908 Evening at the temple (20x25cm-8x10in) s.d.94 acrylic canvas on board lit. 3-Apr-4 Glerum, Singapore #19/R est:4500-5500 (S.D 4000)
£1503 $2721 €2194 Taman bunga (26x36cm-10x14in) s.d.96 acrylic. 3-Apr-4 Glerum, Singapore #20/R est:5000-6000 (S.D 4600)
£1797 $3253 €2624 Padi fields (31x34cm-12x13in) s.d.91 s.d.verso acrylic lit. 4-Apr-4 Sotheby's, Singapore #2/R est:5000-7000 (S.D 5500)
£2614 $4732 €3816 Land descends in terrace (30x30cm-12x12in) s.d.91 s.i.d.verso acrylic. 4-Apr-4 Sotheby's, Singapore #1/R est:4000-6000 (S.D 8000)

£2721	$4871	€4000	Balines landscape (33x38cm-13x15in) s.i.d.85. 16-Mar-4 Christie's, Amsterdam #99/R est:3000-5000
£3201	$5761	€4673	Pura - temple (30x30cm-12x12in) s.i.d.94 acrylic. 25-Apr-4 Christie's, Hong Kong #501/R est:20000-28000 (HK.D 45000)
£3226	$5161	€4710	Harvest time (28x37cm-11x15in) s.d.91 s.i.d.1991 verso acrylic lit. 18-May-3 Sotheby's, Singapore #1/R est:5000-7000 (S.D 9000)
£3623	$5616	€5290	Landscape (50x60cm-20x24in) s.d.94 acrylic. 6-Oct-2 Sotheby's, Singapore #3/R est:8000-10000 (S.D 10000)
£3986	$6178	€5820	Padi field (23x35cm-9x14in) s.d.94. 6-Oct-2 Sotheby's, Singapore #5/R est:6000-8000 (S.D 11000)
£4422	$7915	€6500	Jungle with temple ruins, Bali (42x48cm-17x19in) s.i. 16-Mar-4 Christie's, Amsterdam #129/R est:3000-5000
£4422	$7915	€6500	Balinese landscape (80x125cm-31x49in) s. 16-Mar-4 Christie's, Amsterdam #132 est:4000-6000
£4633	$7737	€6764	Coastal landscape (60x48cm-24x19in) s.i.d.72. 26-Oct-3 Christie's, Hong Kong #3/R est:35000-55000 (HK.D 60000)
£5161	$8258	€7535	Landscape (50x60cm-20x24in) s.d.99 s.i.d.99 verso acrylic. 18-May-3 Sotheby's, Singapore #11/R est:7000-9000 (S.D 14400)
£5229	$9464	€7634	In front of the temple (52x58cm-20x23in) s.d.03 s.i.d.2003 verso acrylic. 3-Apr-4 Glerum, Singapore #26/R est:14000-18000 (S.D 16000)
£5792	$9672	€8456	Temple (56x56cm-22x22in) s.i.d.72. 26-Oct-3 Christie's, Hong Kong #2/R est:35000-55000 (HK.D 75000)
£5797	$8986	€8464	Tanah Lot (60x68cm-24x27in) s.d.97 s.i.d.verso acrylic lit. 6-Oct-2 Sotheby's, Singapore #19/R est:15000-20000 (S.D 16000)
£6022	$9634	€8792	Pura (41x51cm-16x20in) s.d.91 acrylic. 18-May-3 Sotheby's, Singapore #2/R est:6000-8000 (S.D 16800)
£6452	$10323	€9420	Landscape (55x57cm-22x22in) s.d.91 acrylic prov. 18-May-3 Sotheby's, Singapore #3/R est:8000-10000 (S.D 18000)
£6884	$10670	€10051	Three women in the Pura (36x46cm-14x18in) s.d.96 s.i.d.1996 verso lit. 6-Oct-2 Sotheby's, Singapore #4/R est:7000-9000 (S.D 19000)
£7609	$11793	€11109	Good morning (40x40cm-16x16in) s.d.88 s.i.d.1988 verso acrylic lit. 6-Oct-2 Sotheby's, Singapore #1/R est:7000-9000 (S.D 21000)
£8333	$12917	€12166	Pura Merah (32x43cm-13x17in) s.d.90 s.i.d.verso oil acrylic lit. 6-Oct-2 Sotheby's, Singapore #20/R est:10000-12000 (S.D 23000)
£8535	$15363	€12461	Flowers (106x86cm-42x34in) s.d.93 acrylic lit. 25-Apr-4 Christie's, Hong Kong #571/R est:90000-140000 (HK.D 120000)
£8602	$13763	€12559	View of the Borobudur (60x48cm-24x19in) s. 18-May-3 Sotheby's, Singapore #21/R est:6000-8000 (S.D 24000)
£8696	$13478	€12696	Hari Galungan (45x50cm-18x20in) s.d.93 s.i.d.verso acrylic lit. 6-Oct-2 Sotheby's, Singapore #21/R est:15000-20000 (S.D 24000)
£9032	$14452	€13187	Ceremony on Bali Island (82x61cm-32x24in) s. 18-May-3 Sotheby's, Singapore #10/R est:20000-30000 (S.D 25200)
£9804	$17745	€14314	Enam kuntum (70x70cm-28x28in) s.d.90 acrylic lit. 4-Apr-4 Sotheby's, Singapore #22/R est:30000-50000 (S.D 30000)
£13900	$23212	€20294	Balinese temple (63x76cm-25x30in) s.i.d.76 acrylic on canvas. 26-Oct-3 Christie's, Hong Kong #1/R est:60000-90000 (HK.D 180000)
£19097	$31892	€27882	Red trees (100x71cm-39x28in) s.d.66 lit. 12-Oct-3 Sotheby's, Singapore #22/R est:30000-40000 (S.D 55000)
£25605	$46088	€37383	Tangkolak (62x89cm-24x35in) s.i.d.59 s.i.d.verso prov. 25-Apr-4 Christie's, Hong Kong #505/R est:200000-300000 (HK.D 360000)

Works on paper

£1020	$1827	€1500	Composition (19x26cm-7x10in) s.i.d.62 gouache. 16-Mar-4 Christie's, Amsterdam #135/R est:2000-3000
£1377	$2134	€2010	Seated boy (39x32cm-15x13in) s.d.79 mixed media canvas. 6-Oct-2 Sotheby's, Singapore #7/R est:1500-2000 (S.D 3800)
£2381	$4262	€3500	Women approaching a temple (16x21cm-6x8in) s.i.d.84 gouache paper on plywood prov. 16-Mar-4 Christie's, Amsterdam #98/R est:2000-3000

SMITH OF CHICHESTER, George (attrib) (1714-1776) British

£4000	$6800	€5840	Still life of meat, fruit and vegetables on a table (61x90cm-24x35in) 27-Nov-3 Sotheby's, London #199/R est:4000-6000

SMITH OF CHICHESTER, William (attrib) (1707-1764) British

£6944	$11458	€10000	Still life with grapes, peaches and plums (62x75cm-24x30in) i.d.1760. 2-Jul-3 Neumeister, Munich #580/R est:5000

SMITH OF DERBY, Thomas (?-1767) British

£12000	$21840	€17520	View of shipping on the river Avon from Durdham Down, near Bristol (49x117cm-19x46in) 1-Jul-4 Sotheby's, London #136/R est:15000-20000
£25000	$45500	€36500	Church procession entering Furness Abbey (68x110cm-27x43in) prov. 1-Jul-4 Sotheby's, London #139/R est:25000-30000

SMITH, Albert (1896-1940) American

Works on paper

£734	$1300	€1072	Untitled (76x76cm-30x30in) s.d.85 s.verso mixed media. 2-May-4 Bonhams & Butterfields, Los Angeles #3043/R est:2000-4000

SMITH, Albert E (1929-) American

Works on paper

£227	$400	€331	Abstract (25x21cm-10x8in) s. mixed media triptich prov. 23-May-4 Bonhams & Butterfields, Los Angeles #7078/R

SMITH, Alfred (1853-1946) French

£1467	$2625	€2200	Le moulin Barat a Crozant (47x56cm-19x22in) 16-May-4 Osenat, Fontainebleau #113/R est:2000-2500
£4000	$7160	€5840	Arc de Triomphe (75x52cm-30x20in) s.i.d.94. 26-May-4 Sotheby's, Olympia #330/R est:4000-6000

Works on paper

£387	$708	€580	Moutons dans la bergerie (19x31cm-7x12in) d.1875 graphite dr htd white chk. 6-Jun-4 Osenat, Fontainebleau #12

SMITH, Alice Ravenel Huger (1876-1945) American

Works on paper

£2202	$3500	€3215	On the water (36x47cm-14x19in) s. W/C paper on board. 12-Sep-3 Skinner, Boston #523/R
£17296	$27500	€25252	Dusk landscape of cypress swamp, buildings with lighted windows in distance (53x30cm-21x12in) s. W/C. 10-Sep-3 Alderfer's, Hatfield #341/R est:3000-4000
£17296	$27500	€25252	Landscape with sun setting behing building, tall trees in foreground (53x33cm-21x13in) s. W/C. 10-Sep-3 Alderfer's, Hatfield #342/R est:3000-4000
£18868	$30000	€27547	Southern pines (54x35cm-21x14in) s. W/C gouache. 12-Sep-3 Skinner, Boston #417/R est:35000

SMITH, Annie (20th C) American

£757	$1400	€1105	Playful kittens (36x48cm-14x19in) s.d.1883 verso. 13-Mar-4 Susanin's, Chicago #6173/R

SMITH, Arthur Reginald (1871-1934) British

Works on paper

£420	$701	€613	View of upper Wharfedale (15x25cm-6x10in) s.i.verso W/C. 8-Oct-3 Andrew Hartley, Ilkley #1093
£500	$935	€730	Neal Capel Curig, North Wales (26x37cm-10x15in) s. pencil W/C prov. 22-Jul-4 Tennants, Leyburn #775
£540	$902	€788	Bridge in Langstrothdale (36x51cm-14x20in) s. W/C. 8-Oct-3 Andrew Hartley, Ilkley #1092
£560	$1019	€818	Early morning, Kettlewell (38x53cm-15x21in) s.d.1913 W/C pencil. 15-Jun-4 Bonhams, Leeds #30
£600	$1104	€876	An Uplands road (25x37cm-10x15in) s. W/C. 23-Mar-4 Rosebery Fine Art, London #864
£720	$1202	€1051	Winter twilight, Grassington (23x38cm-9x15in) s. W/C. 8-Oct-3 Andrew Hartley, Ilkley #1091

SMITH, Austin (20th C) British

Works on paper

£320	$544	€467	Fishing boats leaving Scarborough harbour (17x23cm-7x9in) s.d.1912 W/C. 1-Dec-3 David Duggleby, Scarborough #285
£360	$680	€526	Off Flamboro (26x36cm-10x14in) s.d.1924 W/C. 23-Feb-4 David Duggleby, Scarborough #696/R
£380	$604	€551	Scarborough, fishing boat on the shoreline (22x42cm-9x17in) s.d.1914 W/C. 9-Sep-3 David Duggleby, Scarborough #183
£440	$832	€642	North Bay, Scarborough (26x36cm-10x14in) s.d.1924 W/C. 23-Feb-4 David Duggleby, Scarborough #695/R
£600	$1086	€876	Arguments yard. Tin ghaut (23x14cm-9x6in) s.i. W/C pair. 30-Mar-4 David Duggleby, Scarborough #41/R
£720	$1202	€1051	Fishing Boat entering Whitby Harbour in heavy seas (36x53cm-14x21in) s.d.1925 W/C. 10-Oct-3 Richardson & Smith, Whitby #105/R

SMITH, Blaise (20th C) Irish?

£839	$1427	€1200	Bramblestown, summer, County Kilkenny (24x30cm-9x12in) s.i.d.1998 verso board. 18-Nov-3 Whyte's, Dublin #94/R

SMITH, Bradley (1910-1997) American

Works on paper

£353	$650	€515	Cowboy (66x51cm-26x20in) s.d.1921 pastel. 26-Jun-4 Sloans & Kenyon, Bethesda #1024/R

SMITH, Brett James (20th C) American

£13369	$25000	€19519	Laid back (66x91cm-26x36in) s. 24-Jul-4 Coeur d'Alene, Hayden #192/R est:12000-18000

SMITH, Carl Fritjof (1859-1917) Norwegian

£284	$474	€415	Norwegian landscape (28x21cm-11x8in) s. 20-Oct-3 Blomqvist, Lysaker #1300 (N.KR 3300)

SMITH, Carlton A (1853-1946) British

£860	$1393	€1247	Dying embers (51x61cm-20x24in) 25-May-3 Desmond Judd, Cranbrook #1071
£11000	$18700	€16060	Blackberry picking (77x51cm-30x20in) s.d.1904. 19-Nov-3 Bonhams, New Bond Street #111/R est:10000-15000
£13000	$23660	€18980	Shelling peas (77x51cm-30x20in) s.d.1892 prov. 16-Jun-4 Bonhams, New Bond Street #69/R est:15000-20000

Works on paper

£400	$732	€600	Cottage interior scene (35x25cm-14x10in) s. W/C. 27-Jul-4 Henry Adams, Chichester #382
£2100	$3465	€3066	At the spinning wheel (42x46cm-17x18in) s.d.1894 W/C. 4-Jul-3 Honiton Galleries, Honiton #55/R est:2500-3500
£2800	$5096	€4088	Returning home from school (40x53cm-16x21in) s. pencil W/C bodycol. 1-Jul-4 Christie's, Kensington #175/R est:3000-5000
£3533	$5759	€5158	Girl by slate (26x17cm-10x7in) s.d.1903 W/C. 29-Sep-3 Lilla Bukowskis, Stockholm #650 est:8000-10000 (S.KR 46000)
£3800	$7182	€5548	Secret (25x18cm-10x7in) s.d.1907 W/C. 19-Feb-4 Grant, Worcester #414/R est:400-600
£8500	$15640	€12410	Shelling peas (39x28cm-15x11in) s.d.1892 W/C exhib. 8-Jun-4 Bonhams, New Bond Street #109/R est:5000-8000
£10121	$16296	€14777	Broken hoop (46x66cm-18x26in) s. W/C. 13-Oct-3 Joel, Victoria #303/R est:6000-8000 (A.D 25000)

SMITH, Carlton A (attrib) (1853-1946) British

£900	$1647	€1350	Cottage interior scene (34x55cm-13x22in) 27-Jul-4 Henry Adams, Chichester #450/R

SMITH, Carrita (20th C) American

£299	$500	€437	Flowers by a window (91x76cm-36x30in) s.d.81. 20-Jun-3 Freeman, Philadelphia #113a/R

SMITH, Cedric (20th C) American

£479	$800	€699	Julep mints (51x61cm-20x24in) acrylic canvas with photographic images. 15-Nov-3 Slotin Folk Art, Buford #385/R

SMITH, Charles (fl.1857-1908) British

£400 $668 €584 Cleaver Church near Windsor (49x76cm-19x30in) 12-Nov-3 Sotheby's, Olympia #69/R

£900 $1611 €1314 Extensive landscape with sheep and figures and castle in background (100x75cm-39x30in) s. i.verso board. 22-Mar-4 Mullucks Wells, Bishop's Stortford #504/R

SMITH, Charles L A (1871-1937) American

Works on paper

£978 $1800 €1428 Live oaks and pasture land, Santa Maria Valley, California (48x62cm-19x24in) s.d.1910 W/C prov. 8-Jun-4 Bonhams & Butterfields, San Francisco #4232/R est:3000-5000

SMITH, Claude (20th C) American

Works on paper

£914 $1600 €1334 Be well-rounded (43x38cm-17x15in) s. W/C paper on ills board exec Nov 1962. 17-Dec-3 Christie's, Rockefeller NY #95/R est:2000-3000

SMITH, Colonel Robert (1787-1873) British

£13000 $21190 €18980 Attack on an Indian Fort, probably Bharatpore (66x107cm-26x42in) prov.lit. 24-Sep-3 Christie's, London #28/R est:15000-25000

Works on paper

£1500 $2655 €2190 Ferry at Calsuna (39x49cm-15x19in) i.verso pencil W/C after Thomas Daniell. 29-Apr-4 Christie's, Kensington #93 est:1500-2500

£8500 $13855 €12410 Dwellings in the Himalayan foothills (25x41cm-10x16in) s.d.1814 pencil W/C scratching out prov. 24-Sep-3 Christie's, London #25/R est:2500-3500

£18000 $29340 €26280 View of the Qutb complex (86x173cm-34x68in) init.d.1860. 24-Sep-3 Christie's, London #85/R est:20000-25000

£34000 $55420 €49640 Crossing the River Son with the Hill Fort at Rhotasgarh, Shahabad District (33x51cm-13x20in) s.i. pencil W/C htd white prov.lit. 24-Sep-3 Christie's, London #26/R est:8000-12000

SMITH, Colvin (1795-1875) British

£600 $1116 €876 Portrait of Sir James Gibson. Portrait of Dr. John Gillies (61x51cm-24x20in) two. 4-Mar-4 Christie's, Kensington #13/R

£6500 $11635 €9490 Full length portrait of George Patrick Skene and his son with guns and dog (240x152cm-94x60in) prov.lit. 28-May-4 Lyon & Turnbull, Edinburgh #51/R est:5000-8000

Works on paper

£520 $967 €759 Portrait of Hon William Maule of Panmure MP (53x43cm-21x17in) 4-Mar-4 Christie's, Kensington #15/R

SMITH, Dan (?) ?

Works on paper

£475 $750 €694 Pioneer family (38x38cm-15x15in) s. W/C ink on board. 26-Jul-3 Harvey Clar, Oakland #1208

SMITH, David (1906-1965) American

£69832 $125000 €101955 Open window (244x33cm-96x13in) s.d.1959 spray enamel prov.exhib.lit. 12-May-4 Christie's, Rockefeller NY #111/R est:100000-150000

Sculpture

£47904 $80000 €69940 Picture between doors (28x21x11cm-11x8x4in) s. iron steel exec 1934 prov.exhib.lit. 12-Nov-3 Christie's, Rockefeller NY #305/R est:100000-150000

£446927 $800000 €652513 Little Albany IX (46x52x11cm-18x20x4in) s.i.d.7-11-60 painted steel prov.exhib.lit. 11-May-4 Christie's, Rockefeller NY #16/R est:400000-600000

£658683 $1100000 €961677 Family Totem (81x56x15cm-32x22x6in) s.i.d.1951 painted steel prov.exhib.lit. 11-Nov-3 Christie's, Rockefeller NY #22/R est:700000-900000

£778443 $1300000 €1136527 Walking dida (72x53x13cm-28x21x5in) s.d,10-19-59 green pat. bronze prov.exhib.lit. 12-Nov-3 Sotheby's, New York #17/R est:450000-650000

£1508380 $2700000 €2202235 Untitled (251x88x22cm-99x35x9in) welded steel exec 1960 prov.exhib.lit. 12-May-4 Sotheby's, New York #21/R est:2500000-3500000

Works on paper

£6000 $11040 €9000 Untitled (50x65cm-20x26in) s.d. Indian ink brush. 11-Jun-4 Hauswedell & Nolte, Hamburg #1533/R est:10000

£17877 $32000 €26100 Untitled (69x102cm-27x40in) init.d.1957 ink prov.exhib. 12-May-4 Christie's, Rockefeller NY #117/R est:25000-35000

SMITH, David (1920-1998) British

£340 $602 €496 Town with bridge. Still life (35x46cm-14x18in) board two. 27-Apr-4 Bonhams, Knightsbridge #50

£1700 $3094 €2482 Hong Kong Hong Kong (76x102cm-30x40in) s.d.97. 4-Feb-4 Sotheby's, Olympia #135/R est:300-500

SMITH, David Murray (1865-1952) British

£520 $868 €759 Extensive landscape (86x112cm-34x44in) 21-Oct-3 Gorringes, Lewes #2143/R

Works on paper

£300 $483 €435 Quiet mere (20x25cm-8x10in) s. W/C. 15-Aug-3 Keys, Aylsham #495/R

SMITH, E Boyd (1860-1943) American

£588 $1100 €858 Tranquil sea (25x28cm-10x11in) s. board. 29-Feb-4 Grogan, Boston #64/R

£1076 $1700 €1571 Haystacks near Auvers (30x36cm-12x14in) s. canvas on board. 7-Sep-3 Treadway Gallery, Cincinnati #576/R est:3000-5000

Works on paper

£428 $800 €625 Procession of prehistoric animals in blizzard (20x28cm-8x11in) ink gouache. 26-Feb-4 Illustration House, New York #162

SMITH, E Leslie (20th C) American

£328 $600 €479 Black child shelling peas, seated near a barrel (51x61cm-20x24in) s.d.98. 10-Apr-4 Cobbs, Peterborough #154/R

SMITH, Edith Agnes (1867-1954) Canadian

Works on paper

£222 $369 €324 On the Bedford basin (16x21cm-6x8in) s.d.1908 W/C. 5-Oct-3 Levis, Calgary #301/R (C.D 500)

SMITH, Edward (19/20th C) British

Works on paper

£450 $824 €657 Dairy maid with ducks outside a country cottage (28x18cm-11x7in) s. W/C. 28-Jul-4 Mallams, Oxford #222/R

SMITH, Ella B (20th C) American

£303 $500 €442 Untitled, impressionistic landscape with water/buildings, summer (71x76cm-28x30in) s. 7-Jul-3 Schrager Galleries, Milwaukee #1629

SMITH, Emily Guthrie (1909-1986) American

£299 $500 €437 Roland S Jary (28x25cm-11x10in) canvasboard. 18-Oct-3 David Dike, Dallas #140/R

£1647 $2750 €2405 New Mexico landscape (61x91cm-24x36in) 18-Oct-3 David Dike, Dallas #143/R est:3000-6000

Works on paper

£359 $600 €524 Young girl (28x18cm-11x7in) pastel. 18-Oct-3 David Dike, Dallas #134/R

SMITH, Ernest Beach (19/20th C) American

£359 $600 €524 Harper Hospital group of 1908 (89x180cm-35x71in) 17-Oct-3 Du Mouchelle, Detroit #2121/R

SMITH, Ernest Browning (1866-1951) American

£549 $900 €796 California coast (10x12cm-4x5in) s. canvas on board painted c.1930. 7-Jun-3 Treadway Gallery, Cincinnati #1476

SMITH, F Ford (19/20th C) British

£320 $544 €467 Study of a white dog in an interior (30x40cm-12x16in) s. 19-Nov-3 Tennants, Leyburn #1204

SMITH, Francis (1881-1961) Portuguese

£13014 $22123 €19000 Paris, Montmartre, rue animee (38x55cm-15x22in) s. 9-Nov-3 Eric Pillon, Calais #126/R

Works on paper

£367 $656 €550 Le reverbere (314x8cm-124x3in) dr. 16-May-4 Osenat, Fontainebleau #48

£2937 $4993 €4200 Jean Cocteau a l'Institut (43x26cm-17x10in) s. pen, ink W/C gouache. 28-Nov-3 Blanchet, Paris #136/R est:4000-5000

£6667 $11933 €10000 La maison bleue (31x23cm-12x9in) gouache. 16-May-4 Osenat, Fontainebleau #47/R est:2000-3000

£9396 $17383 €14000 Maison rose a Montmartre (38x55cm-15x22in) s. stump. 14-Mar-4 Eric Pillon, Calais #130/R

£10432 $16691 €14500 Street with figures in Portugal (48x38cm-19x15in) s. W/C gouache. 18-May-3 Salle des ventes Pillet, Lyon la Foret #92/R

£12081 $22349 €18000 Rue anime a Lisbonne (46x38cm-18x15in) s.d.1924 gouache cardboard. 15-Mar-4 Claude Boisgirard, Paris #104/R est:10000-12000

£12766 $20680 €18000 Printemps au Portugal (74x50cm-29x20in) s. gouache. 23-May-3 Sotheby's, Paris #59/R est:5000-7000

£15385 $26462 €22000 Le bord de mer (62x46cm-24x18in) s.d.30 gouache oil board. 2-Dec-3 Christie's, Paris #249/R est:300-500

SMITH, Francis Hopkinson (1838-1915) American

Works on paper

£1259 $2330 €1889 Landscape with bridge (30x58cm-12x23in) s.i. W/C prov. 14-Jul-4 American Auctioneer #490404/R est:1500-2500

£1750 $2800 €2555 Canal scene (64x41cm-25x16in) s. W/C gouache. 20-Sep-3 Pook & Pook, Downington #559/R est:1200-1800

£1788 $3200 €3002 The afterglow, canal scene (74x48cm-29x19in) s. gouache. 20-Mar-4 Pook & Pook, Downington #345/R est:1500-2500

£1934 $3500 €2824 Dieppe, France (31x45cm-12x18in) s. W/C graphite. 31-Mar-4 Sotheby's, New York #42/R est:2000-3000

£1955 $3500 €2854 Bayou (43x66cm-17x26in) s. W/C gouache board exec.c.1880 prov. 26-May-4 Doyle, New York #33/R est:3000-5000

£4000 $7080 €5840 El Cerro, Havana, Cuba (23x41cm-9x16in) s.i.d.3.81 W/C bodycol. 27-Apr-4 Bonhams, New Bond Street #119/R est:2000-3000

SMITH, Francis Wilford (1927-) American

Works on paper

£571 $1000 €834 I call it 'fore-play' (42x32cm-17x13in) s. ink W/C ills board exec 1973 exhib. 17-Dec-3 Christie's, Rockefeller NY #248/R

£1143 $2000 €1669 And then I get this almost paranoid jealousy. (41x31cm-16x12in) s. ink W/C ills board exec 1872 exhib. 17-Dec-3 Christie's, Rockefeller NY #244/R est:2000-3000

£1143 $2000 €1669 Mirror, Mirror on the wall, whose is the largest. (42x32cm-17x13in) s.i. ink W/C ills board exec 1978 exhib. 17-Dec-3 Christie's, Rockefeller NY #246/R est:2000-3000

SMITH, Frank Vining (1879-1967) American

£226 $400 €330 Evening forest (41x51cm-16x20in) s. 2-May-4 Grogan, Boston #71/R

£556	$900	€812	Seascape (18x24cm-7x9in) s. board. 31-Jul-3 Eldred, East Dennis #1090/R
£4824	$8200	€7043	American clipper ship under sail (61x76cm-24x30in) s. board. 21-Nov-3 Eldred, East Dennis #558/R est:2000-3000
£7263	$13000	€10604	Clipper ship (67x107cm-26x42in) s. 14-May-4 Skinner, Boston #124/R est:1500-2000

SMITH, Frederick Carl (1868-1955) American

£529	$1000	€772	Probably the French countryside (15x23cm-6x9in) bears sig. board prov. 17-Feb-4 John Moran, Pasadena #183/R
£815	$1500	€1190	Western desert landscape (36x46cm-14x18in) s. 9-Jun-4 Alderfer's, Hatfield #431/R est:2000-3000
£824	$1400	€1203	Ohio river, near Cincinnati, probably near Smith's Landing (41x33cm-16x13in) prov. 18-Nov-3 John Moran, Pasadena #195 est:1000-1500
£930	$1600	€1358	California mission courtyard scene (28x38cm-11x15in) s.i. 6-Dec-3 Pook & Pook, Downington #298 est:1200-1800
£1176	$2000	€1717	Desert spring (30x41cm-12x16in) s. i.verso board prov. 18-Nov-3 John Moran, Pasadena #194 est:800-1200
£1190	$2250	€1737	Lingering snow - High Sierras (64x76cm-25x30in) s. i. stretcher prov. 17-Feb-4 John Moran, Pasadena #182/R est:2500-3500
£1511	$2750	€2206	Coastal landscape (46x61cm-18x24in) s. masonite prov. 15-Jun-4 John Moran, Pasadena #180 est:2000-3000
£1765	$3000	€2577	Flowers of the Desert Antelope Valley, Mojave, Calif (41x56cm-16x22in) s. board prov. 18-Nov-3 John Moran, Pasadena #193 est:1500-2500

SMITH, Frithjof (19th C) Norwegian

£2402	$4299	€3507	At the mountain farm in summer (39x55cm-15x22in) s.d.70. 22-Mar-4 Blomqvist, Oslo #308/R est:30000-60000 (N.KR 30000)

SMITH, Frog (fl.1928-1944) American

£500	$900	€730	Dowling camp mill at Slator (43x64cm-17x25in) panel on board. 24-Apr-4 Slotin Folk Art, Buford #367/R

SMITH, G R (19th C) British

Works on paper

£1400	$2240	€2044	Cowes (16x23cm-6x9in) init.i.d.1866 W/C htd white. 16-Sep-3 Bonhams, New Bond Street #19/R est:800-1200

SMITH, Gary Ernest (20th C) American

£276	$500	€403	Universal order, mountain landscape (30x41cm-12x16in) s.i.d.July 71. 18-Apr-4 Bonhams & Butterfields, Los Angeles #7034

SMITH, Gean (1851-1928) American

£428	$800	€625	Escape (61x51cm-24x20in) s.d.15 i.stretcher. 25-Feb-4 Doyle, New York #84/R

SMITH, George (1829-1901) British

£400	$708	€584	Hearth (51x61cm-20x24in) s. 29-Apr-4 Christie's, Kensington #122/R
£560	$935	€818	Small Arran harbour scene. 19-Jun-3 Bonhams, Edinburgh #388
£1400	$2226	€2044	Straw plaiting (30x35cm-12x14in) mono.d.1854 panel. 9-Sep-3 Bonhams, Knightsbridge #57/R est:1500-2000
£1800	$3348	€2628	Straw plaiting (31x36cm-12x14in) mono.d.1854 panel. 4-Mar-4 Christie's, Kensington #604/R est:2000-3000
£2000	$3400	€2920	Love letter (25x20cm-10x8in) s. panel. 19-Nov-3 Bonhams, New Bond Street #24/R est:2000-3000
£2000	$3440	€2920	Shire horses watering at a trough (30x40cm-12x16in) s. board. 6-Dec-3 Shapes, Edinburgh #410/R est:600-800
£12500	$22750	€18250	Lacemaker (61x50cm-24x20in) s.d.1865 panel prov. 16-Jun-4 Bonhams, New Bond Street #31/R est:12000-18000

SMITH, George (1870-1934) British

£550	$919	€803	Ploughman (29x39cm-11x15in) board. 16-Oct-3 Bonhams, Edinburgh #227
£837	$1515	€1222	Bruges, figures in the park (17x25cm-7x10in) s.i.verso panel prov. 1-Apr-4 Heffel, Vancouver #94/R est:600-800 (C.D 2000)
£850	$1556	€1241	Busy harbour (39x49cm-15x19in) s. canvasboard. 8-Apr-4 Bonhams, Edinburgh #88
£950	$1615	€1387	Landscape with sheep (31x40cm-12x16in) s. board. 10-Nov-3 Thomson Roddick & Medcalf, Edinburgh #213/R
£1200	$2232	€1752	Blackwaterfoot, Arran (39x29cm-15x11in) s. s.i.d.1914 verso canvasboard. 2-Mar-4 Bristol Auction Rooms #353/R est:200-300
£1300	$2171	€1898	Cow and calf (30x40cm-12x16in) s. board. 16-Oct-3 Bonhams, Edinburgh #136 est:800-1200
£2093	$3600	€3056	Arrival at Blenheim Palace (66x51cm-26x20in) s. 7-Dec-3 Hindman, Chicago #762/R est:2500-3500
£2600	$4420	€3796	Arrival at the fair (68x88cm-27x35in) s. board. 30-Oct-3 Christie's, London #126/R est:3000-5000

SMITH, George (?) British?

£500	$930	€730	Bruges, entrance to River Bridge (16x23cm-6x9in) s. board. 6-Mar-4 Shapes, Edinburgh #421/R
£540	$1004	€788	Vegetable market, Bruges (16x23cm-6x9in) s.board exhib. 6-Mar-4 Shapes, Edinburgh #422/R

SMITH, George (?) Canadian?

£3333	$5533	€4866	Logging (102x127cm-40x50in) 2-Oct-3 Heffel, Vancouver #38 (C.D 7500)

SMITH, George Dee (1944-) American

£355	$650	€533	Herd bulls on Speciman Ridge (23x30cm-9x12in) s. board prov. 7-Jun-4 Everard, Savannah #476471/R

SMITH, Gerard Arnold Christiaan (1905-1995) Dutch

£582	$990	€850	Still life (30x40cm-12x16in) s. board. 5-Nov-3 Vendue Huis, Gravenhage #453/R

SMITH, Gordon Appelby (1919-) Canadian

£244	$401	€356	Pacific rim trees (30x53cm-12x21in) s. acrylic paper. 28-May-3 Maynards, Vancouver #81a (C.D 550)
£407	$728	€594	Ninstints (31x49cm-12x19in) s.i. acrylic paper exec. c.1988 prov. 27-May-4 Heffel, Vancouver #138/R (C.D 1000)
£446	$759	€651	Untitled (33x46cm-13x18in) s. acrylic. 6-Nov-3 Heffel, Vancouver #109/R (C.D 1000)
£1111	$1922	€1622	Untitled (102x102cm-40x40in) s.verso. 9-Dec-3 Maynards, Vancouver #212 (C.D 2500)
£1520	$2782	€2219	Landscape (75x90cm-30x35in) s. painted 1981 prov. 1-Jun-4 Joyner Waddington, Toronto #184/R est:3000-3500 (C.D 3800)
£1802	$3063	€2631	Cormorants (74x33cm-29x13in) s. i.verso board painted 1949-1950 prov.lit. 27-Nov-3 Heffel, Vancouver #179 est:2500-3500 (C.D 4000)
£2033	$3699	€2968	P1 (91x107cm-36x42in) s. acrylic prov. 1-Jul-4 Heffel, Vancouver #28/R est:3000-4000 (C.D 5000)
£2252	$3829	€3288	Painting, 5 (152x81cm-60x32in) i.d.1994 verso acrylic tarpaulin lit. 27-Nov-3 Heffel, Vancouver #178/R est:3500-4500 (C.D 5000)
£3348	$5759	€4888	Pond painting FS VII (167x100cm-66x39in) s. acrylic prov. 2-Dec-3 Joyner Waddington, Toronto #394 est:4000-6000 (C.D 7500)
£3862	$6913	€5639	Howe Sound (54x69cm-21x27in) s. s.i.verso painted c.1948 prov. 27-May-4 Heffel, Vancouver #152/R est:4000-6000 (C.D 9500)

Works on paper

£407	$728	€594	Gwa-Yas-Dum (46x33cm-18x13in) s.i.d.1947 pencil. 27-May-4 Heffel, Vancouver #139/R (C.D 1000)

SMITH, Grace Cossington (1892-1984) Australian

£2033	$3191	€2948	Sea (17x20cm-7x8in) s. canvas on board painted c.1919 prov. 26-Aug-3 Christie's, Sydney #324/R est:5000-8000 (A.D 5000)
£2686	$4754	€3922	House by the road (23x18cm-9x7in) s. s.i.d.June 1978 verso board. 3-May-4 Christie's, Melbourne #356/R est:5000-7000 (A.D 6500)
£6098	$9573	€8842	Sea beyond (43x53cm-17x21in) s. board prov. 26-Aug-3 Christie's, Sydney #65/R est:15000-20000 (A.D 15000)
£6198	$10971	€9049	Rocky bush (52x41cm-20x16in) s. board prov. 3-May-4 Christie's, Melbourne #120/R est:15000-20000 (A.D 15000)
£6504	$10211	€9431	Bush scene (45x26cm-18x10in) s. board prov. 26-Aug-3 Christie's, Sydney #210/R est:12000-15000 (A.D 16000)
£7317	$11488	€10610	Sussex Downs (25x34cm-10x13in) s.i.d.49 board prov. 26-Aug-3 Christie's, Sydney #118/R est:14000-18000 (A.D 18000)
£8085	$13745	€11804	After fire (44x38cm-17x15in) s.i.d.51 board exhib.prov. 25-Nov-3 Christie's, Melbourne #31/R est:17000-20000 (A.D 19000)
£8097	$13036	€11822	From the dining room window (37x24cm-15x9in) s.d.47 board prov. 25-Aug-3 Sotheby's, Paddington #125/R est:20000-30000 (A.D 20000)
£8130	$12764	€11789	Landscape with pond, Sussex (46x37cm-18x15in) s. board painted c.1950 prov. 26-Aug-3 Christie's, Sydney #49/R est:18000-22000 (A.D 20000)
£9091	$16818	€13273	Blue Mountains (45x42cm-18x17in) board painted c.1933 prov. 10-Mar-4 Deutscher-Menzies, Melbourne #76/R est:25000-35000 (A.D 22000)
£31915	$54255	€46596	Tea Tray (47x54cm-19x21in) s.d.45 s.i.d.verso board prov. 26-Nov-3 Deutscher-Menzies, Melbourne #17/R est:65000-85000 (A.D 75000)
£46809	$79574	€68341	Winter Tree, Turramurra (61x51cm-24x20in) s.d.35 board prov.exhib.lit. 26-Nov-3 Deutscher-Menzies, Melbourne #16/R est:65000-85000 (A.D 110000)
£70248	$124339	€102562	Still life with jugs (79x54cm-31x21in) s.d.63 board prov.exhib. 3-May-4 Christie's, Melbourne #103/R est:140000-180000 (A.D 170000)

SMITH, Graham (20th C) British

Works on paper

£340	$568	€496	Waiting at cover (27x36cm-11x14in) s. W/C bodycol. 20-Oct-3 Bonhams, Bath #96
£390	$651	€569	The Devon and Somerset above Dunkery Hill (28x38cm-11x15in) s.i. W/C bodycol. 9-Oct-3 Greenslade Hunt, Taunton #476/R

SMITH, Grant B (20th C) American

£380	$700	€555	Ghost town in the Rockies (119x61cm-47x24in) s.i. board. 25-Mar-4 Doyle, New York #63/R

SMITH, Harry C (?) American

£281	$450	€410	Desert near Palm Springs. s. 20-Sep-3 Harvey Clar, Oakland #1327

SMITH, Harry Craig (1882-1957) American

£735	$1250	€1073	Mountain view with desert scrub brush (51x61cm-20x24in) s. 31-Oct-3 North East Auctions, Portsmouth #1733

SMITH, Harry Leslie (1900-1974) Canadian

Works on paper

£335	$576	€489	Heavy Snow (37x49cm-15x19in) s.d.40 W/C exhib. 2-Dec-3 Joyner Waddington, Toronto #372/R (C.D 750)

SMITH, Henry Pember (1854-1907) American

£469	$750	€685	Passing storm in mid ocean (28x43cm-11x17in) s. 20-Sep-3 Pook & Pook, Downington #284
£741	$1200	€1082	Coastal village scene with houses and trees (25x36cm-10x14in) s. 31-Jul-3 Eldred, East Dennis #281/R
£1125	$1800	€1643	American country landscape (33x48cm-13x19in) s. 20-Sep-3 Pook & Pook, Downington #285 est:1000-1500
£1173	$2100	€1713	Houses on a country lane (35x51cm-14x20in) s. 14-May-4 Skinner, Boston #69/R est:1500-2500
£2791	$4800	€4075	Mid-summer landscape (51x71cm-20x28in) s. 2-Dec-3 Christie's, Rockefeller NY #67/R est:3000-5000
£3294	$5500	€4809	Last Gleam, East Lyme, Connecticut (51x71cm-20x28in) s. 23-Oct-3 Shannon's, Milford #206/R est:1500-2500
£3533	$6500	€5158	Farm house by a pond in a lush landscape (25x35cm-10x14in) s. 8-Jun-4 Bonhams & Butterfields, San Francisco #4041/R est:3000-5000
£4000	$7000	€5840	Spring morning (51x71cm-20x28in) s. 19-Dec-3 Sotheby's, New York #1123/R est:5000-7000
£4076	$7500	€5951	Reflections on a river (51x71cm-20x28in) s. 27-Jun-4 Freeman, Philadelphia #93/R est:5000-8000

£4749	$8500	€6934	Garden gate (56x76cm-22x30in) s. canvas on masonite prov. 6-May-4 Shannon's, Milford #246/R est:5000-7000
£6704	$12000	€9788	Venetian canal (89x64cm-35x25in) s. 26-May-4 Doyle, New York #41/R est:6000-8000
Works on paper			
£377	$687	€570	Houses on the water's edge (24x20cm-9x8in) s.d.1883 W/C. 17-Jun-4 Frank Peege, Freiburg #1220/R

SMITH, Henry Pember (attrib) (1854-1907) American

£438	$700	€639	Reading tea leaves (36x43cm-14x17in) 21-Sep-3 William Jenack, New York #279

SMITH, Herbert Luther (1809-1869) British

Works on paper			
£260	$442	€380	Portrait of a gentleman, in a buff waistcoat (53x37cm-21x15in) s.d.1856 W/C. 26-Nov-3 Hamptons Fine Art, Godalming #95

SMITH, Hobbe (1862-1942) Dutch

£694	$1132	€1000	Polder landscape with a windmill (32x26cm-13x10in) s. panel. 29-Sep-3 Sotheby's, Amsterdam #41/R
£724	$1231	€1057	Windmill by canal (83x49cm-33x19in) s.d.03. 19-Nov-3 Fischer, Luzern #1096/R (S.FR 1600)
£987	$1786	€1500	Potato harvest (54x45cm-21x18in) s. 19-Apr-4 Glerum, Amsterdam #121/R est:1000-1500
£1156	$2105	€1700	Portrait of a girl, said to br the artist's daughter (40x30cm-16x12in) with sig.d.86. 3-Feb-4 Christie's, Amsterdam #296 est:600-800
£1319	$2085	€1900	Sailing vessels in a stiff breeze (33x43cm-13x17in) s. 2-Sep-3 Christie's, Amsterdam #330/R est:2000-3000
£2222	$3511	€3200	Koepelkerk on the Singel, Amsterdam (43x35cm-17x14in) s. s.verso. 2-Sep-3 Christie's, Amsterdam #275/R est:2000-3000
£8000	$14400	€12000	Festive fleet on the Zuiderzee (228x184cm-90x72in) s. 21-Apr-4 Christie's, Amsterdam #146/R est:15000-20000

SMITH, J Christopher (1891-1943) American

£307	$500	€448	San Pedro Harbour (30x40cm-12x16in) s. board double-sided. 28-Sep-3 Bonhams & Butterfields, Los Angeles #7013
£399	$650	€583	Park picnic, Los Angeles (45x55cm-18x22in) s. board painted c.1924 board. 28-Sep-3 Bonhams & Butterfields, Los Angeles #7011
£399	$650	€583	Lunna-nah-a-gia-camu - Portrait of an Indian (6x6cm-2x2in) s. board. 28-Sep-3 Bonhams & Butterfields, Los Angeles #7014
£460	$750	€672	Early Cambria (30x41cm-12x16in) s. board double-sided. 28-Sep-3 Bonhams & Butterfields, Los Angeles #7012
£2116	$4000	€3089	House and figures in landscape (30x41cm-12x16in) s. board. 17-Feb-4 John Moran, Pasadena #60c/R est:2000-3000
£2174	$4000	€3174	Fishermen at San Pedro (76x101cm-30x40in) s. painted c.1925 prov. 8-Jun-4 Bonhams & Butterfields, San Francisco #4270/R est:4000-6000
£4046	$7000	€5907	Navajo Group (76x102cm-30x40in) s. i.verso. 10-Dec-3 Bonhams & Butterfields, San Francisco #6337/R est:3000-5000

SMITH, J R (19th C) British

Works on paper			
£1477	$2600	€2156	View from the back parlour of Col Godwin's Hotel at Paterson (20x30cm-8x12in) i. W/C. 21-May-4 Pook & Pook, Downington #355/R est:2000-2500

SMITH, Jack (1928-) British

£43000	$78690	€62780	Baby in sink (109x126cm-43x50in) s. board prov.exhib. 2-Jun-4 Sotheby's, London #80/R est:20000-30000

SMITH, Jack Carrington (1908-) Australian

£488	$873	€712	Pear tree (71x84cm-28x33in) s.d.58 board. 10-May-4 Joel, Victoria #306 (A.D 1200)
£1220	$1915	€1769	Boating (55x70cm-22x28in) s.d.44. 26-Aug-3 Christie's, Sydney #325/R est:2000-3000 (A.D 3000)

SMITH, Jack W (1873-1949) American

£329	$550	€480	Canoe on a lake (11x15cm-4x6in) s.i. 16-Nov-3 Bonhams & Butterfields, Los Angeles #7001/R
£714	$1300	€1042	Lake in mountain landscape (10x13cm-4x5in) s. canvasboard. 15-Jun-4 John Moran, Pasadena #6
£1984	$3750	€2897	High Sierras landscape - probably around Bishop, CA (41x51cm-16x20in) s. masonite prov. 17-Feb-4 John Moran, Pasadena #144a/R est:3000-5000
£4706	$8000	€6871	Riders in a valley (51x61cm-20x24in) s. 29-Oct-3 Christie's, Los Angeles #5/R est:8000-12000
£5163	$9500	€7538	Rocks on the California coast, sunset (45x60cm-18x24in) s. masonite. 8-Jun-4 Bonhams & Butterfields, San Francisco #4266/R est:10000-15000
£8824	$15000	€12883	Silver surf (71x86cm-28x34in) s. i.verso. 29-Oct-3 Christie's, Los Angeles #53/R est:15000-25000
£10405	$18000	€15191	Winter solitude, High Sierras (61x76cm-24x30in) s. i.verso prov. 10-Dec-3 Bonhams & Butterfields, San Francisco #6248a/R est:20000-30000
£10582	$20000	€15450	Minaret Range - High Sierras (51x61cm-20x24in) s. i. verso prov. 17-Feb-4 John Moran, Pasadena #144/R est:6000-9000
£10870	$20000	€15870	Marine, Laguna (45x61cm-18x24in) s.d.1921 i.verso board prov. 8-Jun-4 Bonhams & Butterfields, San Francisco #4237/R est:7000-10000
£14550	$27500	€21243	The Sentinel of the Coast (61x76cm-24x30in) s. 17-Feb-4 John Moran, Pasadena #97/R est:15000-20000
£90395	$160000	€131977	Along the Pacific coast (83x106cm-33x42in) s.d.1922 prov. 28-Apr-4 Christie's, Los Angeles #25/R est:40000-60000

SMITH, James Burrell (1824-1897) British

£1900	$3496	€2774	Extensive rural landscape with figure crossing a stone bridge (28x61cm-11x24in) mono. 8-Jun-4 Lawrences, Bletchingley #1408/R est:2000-3000
Works on paper			
£250	$415	€365	Fingle bridge (17x31cm-7x12in) s.d.1844 W/C. 30-Sep-3 Bristol Auction Rooms #537/R
£320	$573	€467	Two figures before a large country house (23x31cm-9x12in) s.d.1873 W/C. 17-Mar-4 Bonhams, Chester #344
£400	$668	€584	Hermitage Castle, near Hawick (25x41cm-10x16in) s.d.1860 pencil W/C bodycol. 16-Oct-3 Christie's, Kensington #109/R
£450	$828	€657	Cows in a mountainous landscape (46x66cm-18x26in) i. pencil W/C. 25-Mar-4 Christie's, Kensington #152/R
£1000	$1700	€1460	Continental village scene (36x54cm-14x21in) s.d.1864 W/C. 4-Nov-3 Bonhams, New Bond Street #80/R est:1000-1500
£1200	$2040	€1752	On the Rhine. In the lakes (18x48cm-7x19in) s.d.1870 W/C bodycol. 4-Nov-3 Bonhams, New Bond Street #84/R est:1200-1800

SMITH, James Burrell (attrib) (?-1897) British

£400	$680	€584	Figure by a highland croft (42x34cm-17x13in) 4-Nov-3 Rowley Fine Art, Newmarket #411

SMITH, James William Garrett (fl.1878-1887) British

£1000	$1600	€1460	Dutch fishing boats on the sands at Scheveningen (36x46cm-14x18in) i.verso. 21-Sep-3 Desmond Judd, Cranbrook #1026

SMITH, Jesse Willcox (1863-1935) American

£1390	$2600	€2029	Child lighting candle in Christmas Eve window (23x20cm-9x8in) board. 26-Feb-4 Illustration House, New York #163 est:2000-4000
£19767	$34000	€28860	Children at the beach (53x38cm-21x15in) s. oil mixed media chl board prov. 7-Dec-3 Freeman, Philadelphia #170 est:25000-40000
£34884	$60000	€50931	Young tennis player (53x38cm-21x15in) s. oil mixed media chl board prov. 7-Dec-3 Freeman, Philadelphia #171 est:25000-40000
£44693	$80000	€65252	Little Bo Peep has lost her sheep (46x64cm-18x25in) s. oil chl board. 15-May-4 Illustration House, New York #71/R est:50000-70000
£59140	$110000	€86344	In the garden (59x39cm-23x15in) s. oil gouache chl board lit. 5-Mar-4 Skinner, Boston #401/R est:20000-30000
£65868	$110000	€96167	The goose girl (56x36cm-22x14in) s. oil chl board. 15-Nov-3 Illustration House, New York #69/R est:50000-70000
Works on paper			
£450	$774	€657	Sympathy is hard to find amongst ones former victims (11x15cm-4x6in) init.d.12 pencil W/C. 3-Dec-3 Christie's, Kensington #270/R
£2326	$4000	€3396	Washday (51x23cm-20x9in) W/C chl prov. 7-Dec-3 Freeman, Philadelphia #172 est:5000-8000
£2762	$4750	€4033	Curtsey (13x15cm-5x6in) init. pen blk ink wash. 7-Dec-3 Freeman, Philadelphia #173 est:2500-4000
£7263	$13000	€10604	Young woman at the piano (48x28cm-19x11in) s. chl. 15-May-4 Illustration House, New York #87/R est:7000-10000
£26347	$44000	€38467	Boy sitting on a hobby horse (56x38cm-22x15in) s. mixed media board. 15-Nov-3 Illustration House, New York #73/R est:30000-40000

SMITH, Jim (?) American

£949	$1500	€1386	Bull dogging (25x43cm-10x17in) acrylic board. 7-Sep-3 Treadway Gallery, Cincinnati #770/R est:5000-7000
Works on paper			
£285	$450	€416	Portrait (30x43cm-12x17in) s. pencil board. 7-Sep-3 Treadway Gallery, Cincinnati #779/R
£633	$1000	€924	Cowboy leaning against wall with lasso (48x25cm-19x10in) s. pencil board. 7-Sep-3 Treadway Gallery, Cincinnati #773/R est:800-1200

SMITH, Joachim (fl.1760-1813) British

Miniatures			
£2000	$3680	€2920	Portrait of Samuel Beachcroft and his wife Elizabeth (12cm-5in) s.d.1782 oval pair prov. 24-Jun-4 Bonhams, New Bond Street #2/R est:2000-3000

SMITH, John (fl.1854-1876) British

£379	$697	€553	Midlands stream (12x19cm-5x7in) board. 8-Jun-4 Dales, Durban #4 (SA.R 4500)

SMITH, John Brandon (fl.1859-1884) British

£350	$644	€511	Pass of Glencoe (43x53cm-17x21in) s.indis.d. 23-Mar-4 Rosebery Fine Art, London #904
£1000	$1700	€1460	Waterfall and bridges, Wales (66x51cm-26x20in) s.d.1872. 29-Oct-3 Bonhams, Chester #496 est:1000-1400
£1000	$1730	€1460	Dunolly Castle, Argyllshire (60x75cm-24x30in) s.d.1880. 11-Dec-3 Lyon & Turnbull, Edinburgh #96/R est:1500-2000
£1300	$2210	€1898	River landscape with boy with fishing net (61x49cm-24x19in) s.d.1863. 29-Oct-3 Bonhams, Chester #453/R est:1400-1800
£2700	$5022	€3942	Near Capel Curig, Wales. Welsh waterfall (25x20cm-10x8in) s. board pair. 4-Mar-4 Christie's, Kensington #443/R est:2000-3000
£3000	$5100	€4380	Waterfall. Mountain stream (46x36cm-18x14in) s. one d.1869 one indis.i. pair prov. 19-Nov-3 Bonhams, New Bond Street #28/R est:3000-5000
£3500	$6510	€5110	Angler on a riverbank. Waterfall in a river landscape (46x36cm-18x14in) pair prov. 4-Mar-4 Christie's, Kensington #442/R est:2000-3000
£3500	$6265	€5110	Falls of Foyen (76x61cm-30x24in) s.d.1872. 27-May-4 Christie's, Kensington #165/R est:4000-6000
£3600	$6696	€5256	Figures by a waterfall (66x51cm-26x20in) s.d.1874 prov. 4-Mar-4 Christie's, Kensington #444/R est:2500-3500
£3800	$6308	€5548	Waterfall near Onllwyn, South Wales (44x34cm-17x13in) s.d.1879. 1-Oct-3 Sotheby's, Olympia #126/R est:2500-3500
£4800	$8592	€7008	Near Capel Curig, North Wales (46x36cm-18x14in) s.d.1872 pair. 28-May-4 Lyon & Turnbull, Edinburgh #81/R est:2000-3000
£5800	$9164	€8410	Falls of the Parthen, South Wales, waterfall with a plunge pool in a landscape (45x34cm-18x13in) s.d.1880. 2-Sep-3 Bonhams, Oxford #102/R est:1000-1500

SMITH, John Guthrie Spence (1880-1951) British

£270	$432	€394	Trees. morning (36x46cm-14x18in) s.d.10. 18-Sep-3 Bonhams, Edinburgh #353

SMITH, John Henry (fl.1852-1893) British

£1100	$1980	€1606	The chase (30x41cm-12x16in) s.d.1889. 21-Jan-4 Sotheby's, Olympia #269/R est:600-800

SMITH, John Noel (1952-) Irish
£476 $843 €695 Studio interior (65x59cm-26x23in) s/d/88 acrylic prov. 27-Apr-4 AB Stockholms Auktionsverk #1115/R (S.KR 6500)

SMITH, John Raphael (1752-1812) British
£4581 $8200 €6688 Soldier's farewell on the eve of a battle (38x30cm-15x12in) wood panel sold with a framed print exhib. 18-Mar-4 Richard Opfer, Timonium #62/R
Works on paper
£7000 $12810 €10220 Portrait of the Right Honourable Charles James Fox MP seated in his study (61x44cm-24x17in) pastel. 3-Jun-4 Christie's, London #50/R est:2500-3500

SMITH, John Raphael (attrib) (1752-1812) British
Works on paper
£780 $1396 €1139 Portrait of Henry Dawkins reading a book. Portrait of a child with a rabbit (48x32cm-19x13in) pastel two. 22-Mar-4 Bonhams & Brooks, Norfolk #185/R

SMITH, John Rubens (1775-1849) British/American
£1875 $3000 €2738 Fishermen by a river (74x91cm-29x36in) s.d.1837. 21-Sep-3 Grogan, Boston #53/R

SMITH, John Thomas (1766-1833) British
Prints
£3549 $5750 €5182 Private signals of the Merchants of Boston. chromolithograph exec.c.1830. 26-Jul-3 Thomaston Place, Thomaston #63/R

SMITH, John Warwick (1749-1831) British
£580 $1061 €847 Vale of Meifod, North Wales (15x23cm-6x9in) 7-Apr-4 Gardiner & Houlgate, Bath #159/R
Works on paper
£580 $1085 €870 Cascade on the margin of Lake of Lugano (42x30cm-17x12in) s.d.1806 W/C pencil. 26-Jul-4 Bonhams, Bath #8/R
£800 $1360 €1168 Isola Bella, Lago Maggiore. View of Lago Maggiore, Italy (30x44cm-12x17in) d.1792 verso W/C pair. 4-Nov-3 Bonhams, New Bond Street #73/R
£1800 $3060 €2628 Lake with mountains beyond (31x43cm-12x17in) W/C over pencil prov. 27-Nov-3 Sotheby's, London #296/R est:2000-3000
£2000 $3700 €2920 Pass from Tyrol into Italy, near Verona. Cortona (18x30cm-7x12in) one i. W/C pair. 9-Mar-4 Gorringes, Lewes #2277 est:2000-2500
£3800 $6460 €5548 View near the head of Lake Thun, Switzerland (35x52cm-14x20in) s.d.1788 pencil W/C htd bodycol prov. 20-Nov-3 Christie's, London #87/R est:3000-5000

SMITH, John Warwick (attrib) (1749-1831) British
Works on paper
£360 $659 €526 From the race ground near the starting post (10x33cm-4x13in) i.verso pen ink grey wash. 28-Jul-4 Mallams, Oxford #121/R

SMITH, Jori (1907-) Canadian
£363 $668 €530 Nice (10x15cm-4x6in) s. board. 9-Jun-4 Walker's, Ottawa #105/R (C.D 900)
£1577 $2680 €2302 Scene de village, St Urbain (19x24cm-7x9in) s.d.36 s.i.verso board. 21-Nov-3 Walker's, Ottawa #64/R est:1200-1600 (C.D 3500)

SMITH, Joseph B (1798-1876) American
£29570 $55000 €43172 American clipper Ocean Express entering the Golden Gate (81x112cm-32x44in) painted c.1855-1860 prov.lit. 6-Mar-4 North East Auctions, Portsmouth #672/R est:25000-40000

SMITH, Joseph Lindon (1863-1950) American
£1022 $1900 €1492 Tomb of Siptah, Valley of the Kings (69x59cm-27x23in) s. canvasboard prov. 5-Mar-4 Skinner, Boston #337/R est:700-900
£1505 $2800 €2197 Tomb of Siptah, Valley of the Kings (69x59cm-27x23in) s. canvasboard prov. 5-Mar-4 Skinner, Boston #336/R est:700-900
£2151 $4000 €3140 Egyptian figure, Tomb of Siptah, Valley of the Kings (69x59cm-27x23in) s. canvasboard prov. 5-Mar-4 Skinner, Boston #335/R est:700-900

SMITH, Joshua (1905-1995) Australian
£1235 $2235 €1803 Dora Toovey sketching, Manly (26x40cm-10x16in) s. i.verso board painted c.1979/80. 31-Mar-4 Goodman, Sydney #491/R est:2000-3000 (A.D 3000)

SMITH, Keith C (1924-2000) Canadian
£640 $1171 €934 River near Banff, Alberta (55x70cm-22x28in) s.i. 1-Jun-4 Hodgins, Calgary #337/R (C.D 1600)
£880 $1610 €1285 Howe Sound (80x104cm-31x41in) s. 1-Jun-4 Hodgins, Calgary #59/R est:3000-5000 (C.D 2200)
£3213 $5976 €4691 Black Tusk (127x243cm-50x96in) s. s.i.d.1991 verso prov. 4-Mar-4 Heffel, Vancouver #42/R est:3000-5000 (C.D 8000)

SMITH, Ken (?) ?
£1557 $2523 €2273 Seawall, objects, ocean 1 (96x138cm-38x54in) acrylic panel. 30-Jul-3 Goodman, Sydney #76/R est:3800-4200 (A.D 3800)

SMITH, Kiki (1954-) American
£865 $1600 €1263 Self Portrait (55x90cm-22x35in) fabric paint linen painted 1982. 12-Feb-4 Sotheby's, New York #275/R est:4000-6000
£865 $1600 €1263 A B C (55x70cm-22x28in) fabric paint linen. 12-Feb-4 Sotheby's, New York #276/R est:4000-6000
Sculpture
£11377 $19000 €16610 Double Head II (25x46x18cm-10x18x7in) with sig.d.1994 cast phosphorus bronze steel prov. 12-Nov-3 Christie's, Rockefeller NY #612/R est:30000-40000
£22754 $38000 €33221 Meat Arm (80x30x23cm-31x12x9in) with sig.d.1992 cast phosphorous bronze steel prov. 12-Nov-3 Christie's, Rockefeller NY #613/R est:20000-30000
£35928 $60000 €52455 Arm and leg. with sig.d.1991 cast iron bronze chain prov. 12-Nov-3 Christie's, Rockefeller NY #611/R est:60000-80000

SMITH, Kimber (1922-1981) American
£596 $996 €864 Composition rouge-jaune sur fond blanc (80x51cm-31x20in) mono. acrylic. 23-Jun-3 Philippe Schuler, Zurich #3571 (S.FR 1300)
£1810 $3023 €2643 Le fleuve - Hochfelden (82x300cm-32x118in) mono.i.d.1977 verso. 24-Jun-3 Germann, Zurich #4/R est:5000-7000 (S.FR 4000)
Works on paper
£362 $605 €529 Study for shadow screen II (30x45cm-12x18in) gouache prov. 24-Jun-3 Germann, Zurich #1048 (S.FR 800)

SMITH, Lance (1950-) British
£2254 $3763 €3291 A las cince de las tarde - At five in the afternoon II (183x153cm-72x60in) s.d.1986-87 verso acrylic collage prov. 7-Oct-3 Rasmussen, Copenhagen #118/R est:25000 (D.KR 24000)

SMITH, Lawrence Beall (1909-) American
Works on paper
£220 $400 €321 T.V (33x25cm-13x10in) s. dr. 19-Jun-4 Rachel Davis, Shaker Heights #375

SMITH, Leon Polk (1906-1996) American
£706 $1200 €1031 Untitled (30x23cm-12x9in) s.d.1959 verso board. 9-Nov-3 Wright, Chicago #386 est:1000-1500
£2616 $4500 €3819 Untitled (76x57cm-30x22in) s.d.72 acrylic. 3-Dec-3 Doyle, New York #88/R est:5000-7000
£4268 $7000 €6189 To be hungry at an angle (64x64cm-25x25in) i.verso prov. 31-May-3 Brunk, Ashville #443/R est:2000-4000
£7547 $12000 €11019 Untitled (107x51cm-42x20in) 14-Sep-3 Wright, Chicago #160/R est:15000-20000
£25449 $42500 €37156 Constellation no 12 purple orange streak (295x152cm-116x60in) init.i.d.1973 verso acrylic two parts prov. 13-Nov-3 Sotheby's, New York #231/R est:12000-18000
Works on paper
£588 $1000 €858 Untitled (48x38cm-19x15in) s.d.1967 gouache. 9-Nov-3 Wright, Chicago #387 est:1000-1500
£1351 $2500 €1972 Untitled (101x66cm-40x26in) s.d.60 cut paper collage prov. 12-Feb-4 Sotheby's, New York #110/R est:3500-4500

SMITH, Leonard John (1885-?) British
Works on paper
£850 $1420 €1241 Female nude studies (33x23cm-13x9in) s. W/C pair. 17-Oct-3 Keys, Aylsham #502

SMITH, Lewis Edward (1871-1926) Canadian?
£360 $659 €526 Ship in Halifax harbour (14x20cm-6x8in) s. panel prov.lit. 1-Jun-4 Joyner Waddington, Toronto #355/R (C.D 900)
£489 $812 €714 Untitled, lake with green hills (30x37cm-12x15in) s. canvasboard. 5-Oct-3 Levis, Calgary #113/R (C.D 1100)

SMITH, Lowell Ellsworth (1924-) American
Works on paper
£203 $375 €296 Beach scene with bathers (20x25cm-8x10in) s. W/C. 16-Jan-4 Aspire, Cleveland #161/R

SMITH, Ludvig August (1820-1906) Danish
£37807 $65406 €55198 The model Florentine in front of mirror (120x93cm-47x37in) s.d.1841 exhib. 9-Dec-3 Rasmussen, Copenhagen #1225/R est:400000-500000 (D.KR 400000)

SMITH, Marcella (1887-1963) British
£800 $1512 €1168 Fishing boats in harbour at St Ives (15x21cm-6x8in) s. board. 18-Feb-4 John Bellman, Billingshurst #1830
£980 $1852 €1431 Old buildings in St Ives (15x22cm-6x9in) s. board. 18-Feb-4 John Bellman, Billingshurst #1829

SMITH, Marie Cockrell (20th C) American
£569 $950 €831 Shadows (61x76cm-24x30in) 18-Oct-3 David Dike, Dallas #171/R

SMITH, Marshall D (1874-1973) American
£1744 $3000 €2546 Muzzin's call to prayer, Salee (91x74cm-36x29in) s.i. painted c.1930. 7-Dec-3 Treadway Gallery, Cincinnati #490/R est:2000-3000

SMITH, Mary (1842-1878) American
£1395 $2400 €2037 Rabbits (15x20cm-6x8in) i.verso paper. 7-Dec-3 Freeman, Philadelphia #163 est:1000-1500
£8939 $16000 €13051 Feeding her chicks (51x61cm-20x24in) s.d.1872. 14-May-4 Skinner, Boston #109/R est:3000-5000

SMITH, Mary Tillman (1904-1995) American
£359 $600 €524 Five faces on red (69x140cm-27x55in) Household paint roofing tin. 15-Nov-3 Slotin Folk Art, Buford #210/R
£359 $600 €524 Two people in green (61x81cm-24x32in) Household paint board. 15-Nov-3 Slotin Folk Art, Buford #212/R
£419 $700 €612 Blue man on red background (61x61cm-24x24in) household paint board prov. 15-Nov-3 Slotin Folk Art, Buford #211/R

£500 $900 €730 Purple face (61x61cm-24x24in) housepaint on board. 24-Apr-4 Slotin Folk Art, Buford #407/R
£528 $950 €771 Three green and yellow figures (81x104cm-32x41in) housepaint on board. 24-Apr-4 Slotin Folk Art, Buford #405/R
£556 $1000 €812 I am the (71x53cm-28x21in) board. 24-Apr-4 Slotin Folk Art, Buford #408/R est:500-1000
£556 $1000 €812 Seven blue figures on yellow (94x127cm-37x50in) housepaint on board. 24-Apr-4 Slotin Folk Art, Buford #406/R est:1000-2000
£694 $1250 €1013 Mr Ron, Miss Bettie and Mrs Sonne (48x51cm-19x20in) housepaint on tin. 24-Apr-4 Slotin Folk Art, Buford #404/R est:1000-2000
£750 $1350 €1095 Pupp dog Miss Bettie (53x66cm-21x26in) housepaint on tin prov. 24-Apr-4 Slotin Folk Art, Buford #403/R est:1000-2000
Sculpture
£1347 $2250 €1967 Blue man on yellow (114x66cm-45x26in) household paint cutout roofing tin prov. 15-Nov-3 Slotin Folk Art, Buford #208/R est:1000-2000

SMITH, Matt Read (1960-) American
£2353 $4000 €3435 January evening - Grand Canyon (41x76cm-16x30in) oil on linen. 1-Nov-3 Altermann Galleries, Santa Fe #189

SMITH, Miller (fl.1885-1920) British
Works on paper
£260 $481 €380 Meadows at Grantchester (28x48cm-11x19in) s.d.1908 i.verso W/C. 13-Feb-4 Keys, Aylsham #249/R
£680 $1251 €993 Sheep grazing in landscape (14x9cm-6x4in) s. W/C. 11-Jun-4 Keys, Aylsham #429
£800 $1472 €1168 Shepherd in hut with lambs (15x10cm-6x4in) s.d.90 W/C. 11-Jun-4 Keys, Aylsham #431/R

SMITH, Mortimer L (?) American
£1719 $2750 €2510 Winter landscape (30x46cm-12x18in) 19-Sep-3 Du Mouchelle, Detroit #2144/R est:2000-3000

SMITH, Norman (1910-) British
Works on paper
£650 $1060 €949 Doons House, Uffington (52x72cm-20x28in) s. i.verso pastel. 24-Sep-3 Dreweatt Neate, Newbury #8/R

SMITH, Oliver Phelps (1867-1953) American
Works on paper
£522 $950 €762 Merry widow, stage design (35x43cm-14x17in) one s. i. W/C pencil pair prov. 29-Jun-4 Sotheby's, New York #291/R

SMITH, Paki (20th C) Irish
£533 $960 €800 Holy Spirit arrives at one of the twelve gates (142x122cm-56x48in) s.d.1990. 20-Apr-4 James Adam, Dublin #43/R

SMITH, Peter James (20th C) New Zealander
£1950 $3452 €2847 Detecting the motion of the Earth relative to the ether (31x168cm-12x66in) s.d.1999 oil acrylic prov.exhib. 28-Apr-4 Dunbar Sloane, Auckland #65a/R est:6000-10000 (NZ.D 5500)
£2000 $3680 €2920 Traces of history (92x61cm-36x24in) s.d.2002. 25-Mar-4 International Art Centre, Auckland #125/R est:7000-9000 (NZ.D 5600)
£2182 $3425 €3164 Magnitude (60x121cm-24x48in) s.d.2001. 27-Aug-3 Dunbar Sloane, Wellington #61/R est:5000-8000 (NZ.D 6000)
£3195 $5432 €4665 Chrometic dispersion, Alexander's Dark Island (38x185cm-15x73in) s.i.d.1997. 26-Nov-3 Dunbar Sloane, Wellington #40 est:5000-7000 (NZ.D 8500)

SMITH, Philip (1952-) American
£1514 $2800 €2210 Before Paris (147x187cm-58x74in) i.d.1992 verso oil wax prov. 13-Jul-4 Christie's, Rockefeller NY #158/R est:1500-2000

SMITH, Ray (1959-) American
Works on paper
£324 $600 €473 Untitled (42x37cm-17x15in) s.d.89 W/C prov. 13-Jul-4 Christie's, Rockefeller NY #137/R

SMITH, Reginald (1855-1925) British
£380 $692 €555 Pentire Point (20x36cm-8x14in) s. panel. 15-Jun-4 David Lay, Penzance #496
Works on paper
£250 $448 €365 View from the cliffs across Ladram Bay, Devon (87x58cm-34x23in) s.d.1888 W/C. 28-May-4 Dreweatt Neate, Newbury #41/R
£280 $510 €409 Sheep near a track leading to a West Country cove (70x90cm-28x35in) s. W/C. 6-Feb-4 Honiton Galleries, Honiton #294
£500 $825 €730 View from the cliffs across Ladram Bay, Devon (87x58cm-34x23in) s.d.188 W/C. 4-Jul-3 Honiton Galleries, Honiton #43/R

SMITH, Richard (1931-) British
£1387 $2400 €2025 You was never lovlier (89x89cm-35x35in) prov. 15-Dec-3 Hindman, Chicago #98 est:1000-1500

SMITH, Rosamund Lombard (1876-1948) American
£642 $1150 €937 Flowered dress (114x84cm-45x33in) s. 8-Jan-4 James Julia, Fairfield #1077/R est:800-1000
£818 $1300 €1194 Young woman with flowers (20x15cm-8x6in) init. d.1923 verso canvas on board. 12-Sep-3 Skinner, Boston #350/R est:300-500

SMITH, Rosemary (20th C) Irish
£347 $566 €500 Backyards, Irishtown, Dublin (50x61cm-20x24in) s.d.1973. 24-Sep-3 James Adam, Dublin #150/R

SMITH, Rufus Way (1854-?) American
£2273 $4000 €3319 Forest landscape (86x66cm-34x26in) s.d.1888 board. 23-May-4 Treadway Gallery, Cincinnati #512/R est:3000-5000

SMITH, Rupert Jasen (20th C) American
Prints
£1977 $3500 €2886 Hommage to Andy Warhol (91x91cm-36x36in) s. screenprint. 30-Apr-4 Sotheby's, New York #464/R est:2000-3000

SMITH, Russell (1812-1896) American
£2353 $4000 €3435 Near Mt. Loudon (30x46cm-12x18in) s. 21-Nov-3 Eldred, East Dennis #881/R est:2000-4000
£2395 $4000 €3497 Corn sheaves and buggy (20x30cm-8x12in) init.d.68 s.d.1868 verso oil paper prov. 9-Oct-3 Christie's, Rockefeller NY #1/R est:5000-7000
£7527 $14000 €10989 View of a valley, springtime (30x46cm-12x18in) 30. 3-Mar-4 Christie's, Rockefeller NY #17/R est:3000-5000

SMITH, Russell (attrib) (1812-1896) American
£1078 $1800 €1574 Camp on the marsh, evening glow (33x58cm-13x23in) s. 29-Jun-3 William Jenack, New York #219 est:2000-3000

SMITH, Sir Matthew (1879-1959) British
£800 $1272 €1168 Vase of roses (51x61cm-20x24in) 12-Sep-3 Gardiner & Houlgate, Bath #187/R
£2000 $3580 €2920 Leaf study (51x30cm-20x12in) prov. 16-Mar-4 Bonhams, New Bond Street #32/R est:2000-3000
£8000 $13760 €11680 Dieppe Harbour (33x40cm-13x16in) board prov.exhib. 3-Dec-3 Sotheby's, London #20/R est:5000-7000
£10000 $18300 €14600 Girl (40x51cm-16x20in) init. init.d.31 verso. 2-Jun-4 Sotheby's, London #65/R est:10000-15000
£13000 $23270 €18980 Approaching storm (31x36cm-12x14in) prov. 16-Mar-4 Bonhams, New Bond Street #33/R est:5000-8000
£15000 $27450 €21900 Still life with clay figure (46x92cm-18x36in) init. i.d.4/1939 verso. 4-Jun-4 Christie's, London #22/R est:20000-30000
£17000 $28900 €24820 Tulips (61x38cm-24x15in) painted 1926. 21-Nov-3 Christie's, London #93/R est:15000-20000
£25000 $44750 €36500 The plaster cast (73x96cm-29x38in) prov.exhib.lit. 16-Mar-4 Bonhams, New Bond Street #13/R est:15000-20000
£26000 $46540 €37960 Nu couchee (60x73cm-24x29in) prl. 16-Mar-4 Bonhams, New Bond Street #30/R est:15000-25000
£26000 $47580 €37960 Reclining nude (58x74cm-23x29in) prov. 8-Jul-4 Duke & Son, Dorchester #285/R est:15000-25000
£35000 $60200 €51100 Barn with trees, Varengeville (55x46cm-22x18in) s. prov.exhib. 3-Dec-3 Sotheby's, London #11/R est:30000-40000
Works on paper
£850 $1360 €1241 Still life of vase of flowers (30x23cm-12x9in) s. W/C. 16-Sep-3 Gorringes, Bexhill #1612/R
£1500 $2775 €2190 Still life with flowers (31x24cm-12x9in) s. W/C. 11-Mar-4 Christie's, Kensington #318/R est:1200-1800
£1500 $2775 €2190 Still life with pheasants (49x34cm-19x13in) s. W/C. 11-Mar-4 Christie's, Kensington #320/R est:1500-2000

SMITH, Stephen Catterson (19/20th C) British
£330 $521 €479 Portrait of a young man (35x26cm-14x10in) canvas on board prov. 24-Jul-3 Lawrence, Crewkerne #930
£3867 $7000 €5646 Irish royalty (102x76cm-40x30in) s. 3-Apr-4 Dan Ripley, Indianapolis #3179/R est:9000-12000

SMITH, Stephen Catterson (attrib) (19/20th C) British
£313 $509 €450 Portrait of Joseph Burke (76x63cm-30x25in) 24-Sep-3 James Adam, Dublin #28/R

SMITH, Stephen Catterson (elder) (1806-1872) British
£16500 $29535 €24090 Portrait of Marianne Gage, full-length, seated on a red cloak, feeding a dog (154x122cm-61x48in) 14-May-4 Christie's, London #120/R est:10000-15000

SMITH, Thomas (?) British
£320 $509 €467 Naples (25x38cm-10x15in) s.i.indis.d.1848 canvas on board. 12-Sep-3 Gardiner & Houlgate, Bath #125/R
£805 $1506 €1200 Chasse au tigre (61x50cm-24x20in) 1-Mar-4 Coutau Begarie, Paris #119/R

SMITH, Tony (1912-1980) American
Sculpture
£18000 $30060 €26280 We lost (45x45x45cm-18x18x18in) st.sig.d.1962 black pat. bronze prov.exhib. 22-Oct-3 Bonhams, New Bond Street #102/R est:18000-22000
£23313 $38000 €34037 Duck (27x32x22cm-11x13x9in) s.num.5/9 black pat bronze prov. 23-Sep-3 Christie's, Rockefeller NY #27/R est:7000-9000
£26000 $47320 €37960 Marriage (51x51x61cm-20x20x24in) st.sig.d.1961 num.6/9 black pat bronze prov. 6-Feb-4 Sotheby's, London #137/R est:12000-18000
£71856 $120000 €104910 Tau (114x178x109cm-45x70x43in) s.i.d.1965 num.5/6 painted aluminium prov.lit. 12-Nov-3 Christie's, Rockefeller NY #363/R est:60000-80000
Works on paper
£9816 $16000 €14331 Untitled (30x45cm-12x18in) d.4-22-61 ink prov.exhib. 23-Sep-3 Christie's, Rockefeller NY #55/R est:7000-9000

SMITH, Tony Brummell (20th C) British
Works on paper
£400 $652 €580 Glass topped table (57x64cm-22x25in) s. pastel. 17-Jul-3 Tennants, Leyburn #782

SMITH, Vernon B (1894-?) American

£276	$500	€403	Overseer (33x25cm-13x10in) s.d.1945 board. 3-Apr-4 Outer Cape Auctions, Provincetown #83/R
£337	$550	€492	Untitled (25x33cm-10x13in) s. board. 19-Jul-3 Outer Cape Auctions, Provincetown #153/R

SMITH, W Eugene (1918-1978) American

Photographs

£1587	$3000	€2317	Self portrait (34x18cm-13x7in) i. verso silver print. 17-Feb-4 Swann Galleries, New York #87/R est:3500-4500
£2000	$3680	€3000	Migrant children, Michigan (27x34cm-11x13in) i. verso silver gelatin. 10-Jun-4 Villa Grisebach, Berlin #1284/R est:2000-2500
£2119	$3750	€3094	Pittsburgh (34x23cm-13x9in) studio st. verso photo board prov. 28-Apr-4 Sotheby's, New York #157/R est:3000-5000
£2395	$4000	€3497	Nurse midwife (26x34cm-10x13in) silver print. 21-Oct-3 Swann Galleries, New York #220/R est:3500-4500
£2545	$4250	€3716	Rail yards, Pittsburgh (34x23cm-13x9in) estate st.verso photo board exec.1955-56 printed later prov. 17-Oct-3 Sotheby's, New York #146/R est:3000-5000
£3390	$6000	€4949	Selected images (22x33cm-9x13in) one s.d.1959 one s.i.d.1950 photo two printed later prov. 28-Apr-4 Sotheby's, New York #155/R est:4000-6000
£5090	$8500	€7431	Schweitzer with lamp at his desk. First Communion dress (22x34cm-9x13in) s. photos one board exec.1950-54 printed later two prov. 17-Oct-3 Sotheby's, New York #170/R est:3500-5000
£11299	$20000	€16497	The walk to paradise garden (37x37cm-15x15in) s. i.verso photo printed later. 28-Apr-4 Sotheby's, New York #206/R est:15000-25000

SMITH, Wallace Herndon (1901-) American

£2174	$4000	€3174	Interior of the artist's studio (36x46cm-14x18in) s. board. 26-Jun-4 Selkirks, St. Louis #153/R est:2000-3000

Works on paper

£313	$575	€457	Street scene with cyclist (36x51cm-14x20in) s. W/C. 26-Jun-4 Selkirks, St. Louis #152

SMITH, William Collingwood (1815-1887) British

Works on paper

£345	$538	€500	Fairlight Bay, Hastings (34x61cm-13x24in) s. W/C. 1-Aug-2 Joel, Victoria #184 est:800-1200 (A.D 1000)
£360	$644	€526	Extensive Alpine landscape with figures and horses on a mountain path (30x55cm-12x22in) s. W/C htd white. 17-Mar-4 Bonhams, Chester #362
£450	$765	€657	Shipping in secluded harbour (34x62cm-13x24in) s. pencil W/C. 19-Nov-3 Christie's, Kensington #334/R
£750	$1275	€1095	Windmill at harvest time (36x51cm-14x20in) s. W/C. 26-Nov-3 Hamptons Fine Art, Godalming #82/R
£900	$1467	€1314	Stokesay Castle Shropshire. Mountain village (32x49cm-13x19in) s. W/C htd white pair. 25-Sep-3 Mellors & Kirk, Nottingham #731/R
£3600	$6624	€5256	Dogana and the church of Santa Maria Della Salute, Venice (14x42cm-6x17in) W/C over pencil htd bodycol. 26-Mar-4 Sotheby's, London #85/R est:2000-3000
£8500	$14450	€12410	Bay of Uri, Lake Lucerne from the left bank (76x129cm-30x51in) s. W/C htd bodycol scratching out prov.exhib. 27-Nov-3 Sotheby's, London #310/R est:3000-5000

SMITH, William Harding (1848-1922) British

£800	$1376	€1168	Still life of fruit, birds nest and cob nuts (25x36cm-10x14in) s.d.1877 pair. 2-Dec-3 Gorringes, Lewes #2512
£1765	$3000	€2577	Still life with fruit (51x61cm-20x24in) s.d. 21-Nov-3 Skinner, Boston #242/R est:3000-5000

Works on paper

£380	$692	€555	Gondoliers conversing before the Doge's Palace (61x44cm-24x17in) s. pencil W/C scratching out. 1-Jul-4 Christie's, Kensington #370/R
£400	$736	€584	Bell ringing at the Church of St Mary de Haura, New Shoreham, Sussex (43x33cm-17x13in) pencil W/C. 25-Mar-4 Christie's, Kensington #131/R
£1600	$2720	€2336	Kensington High Street on Queen Victoria's Diamond Jubilee 1897 (17x22cm-7x9in) init. W/C. 4-Nov-3 Bonhams, New Bond Street #132/R est:1000-1500

SMITH, William St Thomas (1862-1926) Canadian

Works on paper

£360	$613	€526	Cottage by a stream, evening (27x36cm-11x14in) s. W/C. 21-Nov-3 Walker's, Ottawa #95/R (C.D 800)
£1071	$1843	€1564	Village with two people chatting. Cottage with farmer and sheep (24x34cm-9x13in) s. W/C two. 2-Dec-3 Joyner Waddington, Toronto #489 est:600-800 (C.D 2400)

SMITH, Xanthus (1838-1929) American

£813	$1300	€1187	Susquehanna scene (18x53cm-7x21in) s. indis d. 19-Sep-3 Freeman, Philadelphia #100/R est:1000-1500
£2326	$4000	€3396	Coastal landscape with a couple standing on the cliffs (41x64cm-16x25in) s.d.1885. 6-Dec-3 Pook & Pook, Downington #97/R est:4000-5000
£2326	$4000	€3396	Hope (53x84cm-21x33in) s. s.i.verso. 7-Dec-3 Freeman, Philadelphia #165 est:1500-2500
£2825	$5000	€4125	USS frigate Saranac off Panama. i.verso. 1-May-4 Thomaston Place, Thomaston #90/R
£4063	$6500	€5932	Paddle steamer at full steam (23x30cm-9x12in) s. i.verso. 19-Sep-3 Freeman, Philadelphia #206/R est:800-1200

Works on paper

£411	$650	€600	Harbour scene with moored sailing vessels (10x18cm-4x7in) s. chl. 6-Sep-3 Brunk, Ashville #733

SMITH-HALD, Frithjof (1846-1903) Norwegian

£818	$1365	€1194	Winter light. Northern Norway (28x40cm-11x16in) s. panel. 20-Oct-3 Blomqvist, Lysaker #1302/R (N.KR 9500)
£16253	$27630	€23729	Young boys fishing (60x100cm-24x39in) s.i.d.89. 19-Nov-3 Grev Wedels Plass, Oslo #22/R est:150000-200000 (N.KR 190000)

SMITHEMAN, S Francis (20th C) British

£1500	$2685	€2190	Mariquita, Octavia and Noroda racing in the Solent 1911 (56x91cm-22x36in) s. 26-May-4 Christie's, Kensington #513/R est:2000-3000
£3200	$5440	€4672	H.M.S. Victory (61x91cm-24x36in) s. 19-Nov-3 Christie's, Kensington #468/R

SMITHER, Michael (1939-) New Zealander

£362	$587	€525	Untitled bush scene (18x40cm-7x16in) s.d.1996 board. 31-Jul-3 International Art Centre, Auckland #143/R est:1100-1600 (NZ.D 1000)
£692	$1239	€1010	Cloudy mountain top landscape (43x71cm-17x28in) init.d.2/4/1976. 11-May-4 Peter Webb, Auckland #61/R est:3000-4000 (NZ.D 2000)
£764	$1215	€1115	Train on New Plymouth Coast (35x25cm-14x10in) s.verso painted c.1964. 1-May-3 Dunbar Sloane, Wellington #16/R est:800-1500 (NZ.D 2200)
£1038	$1858	€1515	Evening at Daves Bay (41x22cm-16x9in) board. 12-May-4 Dunbar Sloane, Wellington #142 est:3000-6000 (NZ.D 3000)
£1128	$1917	€1647	In praise of fathers (40x24cm-16x9in) init.d.1988 board. 26-Nov-3 Dunbar Sloane, Wellington #21/R est:1500-2500 (NZ.D 3000)
£1359	$2201	€1971	Paddle boats (28x50cm-11x20in) s.d.1996 board. 31-Jul-3 International Art Centre, Auckland #27/R est:2800-4000 (NZ.D 3750)
£1596	$2824	€2330	At the beach (37x48cm-15x19in) board double-sided prov. 28-Apr-4 Dunbar Sloane, Auckland #65/R est:2000-4000 (NZ.D 4500)
£2128	$3766	€3107	Untitled (70x81cm-28x32in) board prov. 28-Apr-4 Dunbar Sloane, Auckland #75/R est:6000-8000 (NZ.D 6000)
£2632	$4474	€3843	Cloud series 3 (70x82cm-28x32in) s.d.1988 board. 27-Nov-3 International Art Centre, Auckland #126/R est:8000-11000 (NZ.D 7000)
£4104	$7101	€5992	Istrom Nadas at the piano in Dunedin (45x31cm-18x12in) init.d.1970 board. 9-Dec-3 Peter Webb, Auckland #167/R est:7000-10000 (NZ.D 11000)
£4887	$8308	€7135	Rock pool, New Plymouth (55x55cm-22x22in) s.d.1972 board. 27-Nov-3 International Art Centre, Auckland #49/R est:10000-15000 (NZ.D 13000)
£5776	$9415	€8433	Headlands and seascape (30x122cm-12x48in) s.d.1970 board prov. 23-Sep-3 Peter Webb, Auckland #83/R est:15000-20000 (NZ.D 16000)
£7463	$12910	€10896	Mountain range with green hill (21x91cm-8x36in) s.d.1969 board. 9-Dec-3 Peter Webb, Auckland #57/R est:25000-35000 (NZ.D 20000)
£7836	$13556	€11441	Stones in blue bottle (34x38cm-13x15in) init.d.1996 board exhib. 9-Dec-3 Peter Webb, Auckland #56/R est:18000-24000 (NZ.D 21000)
£8696	$14087	€12609	Rocks, The Gables, New Plymouth (67x76cm-26x30in) s.d.1965 board. 31-Jul-3 International Art Centre, Auckland #20/R est:25000-40000 (NZ.D 24000)
£9441	$17182	€13784	Stones in blue bottle (33x37cm-13x15in) init.d.1969 board. 29-Jun-4 Peter Webb, Auckland #43/R est:20000-30000 (NZ.D 27000)
£20522	$35504	€29962	Rock pools (120x90cm-47x35in) s.d.1968 board. 9-Dec-3 Peter Webb, Auckland #76/R est:45000-65000 (NZ.D 55000)
£22727	$41364	€33181	Thomas on the potty (62x53cm-24x21in) init.d.2001 board exhib. 29-Jun-4 Peter Webb, Auckland #41/R est:75000-95000 (NZ.D 65000)
£34586	$58797	€50496	Sarah eating baked beans (70x54cm-28x21in) s.d.1967 board exhib. 26-Nov-3 Dunbar Sloane, Wellington #20/R est:50000-70000 (NZ.D 92000)
£34965	$63636	€51049	Doubting Thomas (91x76cm-36x30in) s.d.1968 board. 29-Jun-4 Peter Webb, Auckland #58/R est:90000-120000 (NZ.D 100000)
£35461	$62766	€51773	Dreamer (71x179cm-28x70in) s.d.78 board. 28-Apr-4 Dunbar Sloane, Auckland #29/R est:135000-155000 (NZ.D 100000)
£57836	$100056	€84441	Sarah with cat (91x103cm-36x41in) s.d.1967 board. 9-Dec-3 Peter Webb, Auckland #33/R est:90000-130000 (NZ.D 155000)

Works on paper

£532	$941	€777	Rocks and pylons at new Plymouth (42x40cm-17x16in) mixed media prov. 28-Apr-4 Dunbar Sloane, Auckland #87/R (NZ.D 1500)
£709	$1255	€1035	Along the road (44x59cm-17x23in) s.d.1960 W/C prov. 28-Apr-4 Dunbar Sloane, Auckland #42/R est:2000-4000 (NZ.D 2000)
£1000	$1840	€1460	Artists mother (37x26cm-15x10in) s.d.1965 W/C pencil. 25-Mar-4 International Art Centre, Auckland #39/R (NZ.D 2800)
£1958	$3564	€2859	Portrait study of a man (84x55cm-33x22in) init.d.1969 W/C. 29-Jun-4 Peter Webb, Auckland #189/R est:3000-5000 (NZ.D 5600)

SMITHSON, Robert (1938-1973) American

Works on paper

£16760	$30000	€24470	Island of coal (45x61cm-18x24in) s.i.d.1969 col marker col crayons pencil prov. 13-May-4 Sotheby's, New York #191/R est:18000-25000
£39106	$70000	€57095	Spiral jetty, Great Salt Lake - Movie treatment (72x60cm-28x24in) s.i.d.1970 pencil paperboard two parts prov.exhib. 13-May-4 Sotheby's, New York #192/R est:45000-55000

SMITS, Jakob (1856-1928) Belgian

£822	$1529	€1225	Farmhouse in landscape (23x26cm-9x10in) s. canvas on panel. 8-Mar-4 Bernaerts, Antwerp #827/R
£42667	$78080	€64000	Rue de hameau (120x140cm-47x55in) s. exhib. 7-Jun-4 Palais de Beaux Arts, Brussels #104/R est:30000-40000

Works on paper

£267	$483	€400	Esquisse de figure (14x11cm-6x4in) s. dr. 30-Mar-4 Campo, Vlaamse Kaai #162
£395	$714	€600	Maternite. Etude de fileuse (26x34cm-10x13in) st.sig. chl double-sided. 19-Apr-4 Horta, Bruxelles #436
£458	$792	€650	Mother and child (34x24cm-13x9in) s. dr. 15-Dec-3 Bernaerts, Antwerp #1503
£490	$842	€700	Les bergers (43x56cm-17x22in) red chk executed c.1924. 2-Dec-3 Sotheby's, Amsterdam #37/R
£490	$842	€700	En campine (32x37cm-13x15in) s. red chk executed c.1924. 2-Dec-3 Sotheby's, Amsterdam #38/R
£1399	$2406	€2000	La femme adultere (26x35cm-10x14in) red chk exhib. 2-Dec-3 Sotheby's, Amsterdam #40/R est:3000-4000
£1399	$2406	€2000	Le Christ en croix (43x36cm-17x14in) red chk W/C exhib. 2-Dec-3 Sotheby's, Amsterdam #41/R est:3000-4000
£1399	$2406	€2000	Le Christ en croix (54x45cm-21x18in) s. W/C executed c.1924 exhib. 2-Dec-3 Sotheby's, Amsterdam #42/R est:2000-2500
£1748	$3007	€2500	Sitting woman at the window (21x24cm-8x9in) s. black chk executed c.1924. 2-Dec-3 Sotheby's, Amsterdam #35/R est:2000-3000
£1867	$3341	€2800	Motherhood (34x31cm-13x12in) s. sanguine gold background. 15-May-4 De Vuyst, Lokeren #303/R est:3000-3500
£1958	$3368	€2800	Christ a table (33x44cm-13x17in) W/C executed c.1924 exhib. 2-Dec-3 Sotheby's, Amsterdam #33/R est:1000-1500
£2098	$3608	€3000	Le bapteme (32x45cm-13x18in) s.d.1910 red chk exhib. 2-Dec-3 Sotheby's, Amsterdam #34/R est:3500-4500
£2128	$3553	€3000	Self portrait (55x44cm-22x17in) s. W/C pastel gouache. 20-Oct-3 Bernaerts, Antwerp #49 est:3000-4000
£2937	$4993	€4200	Mother and children in front of a farm (24x29cm-9x11in) s. blk chk exhib. 25-Nov-3 Christie's, Amsterdam #222/R est:4000-6000
£3846	$6538	€5500	Mere et enfant (39x32cm-15x13in) s. mixed media. 1-Dec-3 Palais de Beaux Arts, Brussels #316/R est:3000-4000

SMITS, Jan Gerard (1823-1910) Dutch

£382	$623	€550	Evening landscape (13x14cm-5x6in) s. panel. 29-Sep-3 Sotheby's, Amsterdam #49/R
£1208	$2235	€1800	View of the Rijksmuseum, Amsterdam (24x18cm-9x7in) s. 15-Mar-4 Sotheby's, Amsterdam #95/R est:750-900
£3061	$5571	€4500	View on the Damrak and the Beurs van Berlage, Amsterdam (50x100cm-20x39in) s. 3-Feb-4 Christie's, Amsterdam #319/R est:1500-2000
£4762	$8667	€7000	Damrak entree Amstredam (61x91cm-24x36in) s. s.i.stretcher. 3-Feb-4 Christie's, Amsterdam #334/R est:2500-3500

SMITZ, Gaspar (1635-1707) Dutch

£3000	$5460	€4500	Still life (49x40cm-19x16in) mono. 1-Jul-4 Van Ham, Cologne #1162/R est:8000

SMOLDERS, Pol (1921-1997) Belgian

£2361	$3943	€3400	Arlequin (68x48cm-27x19in) s. 21-Oct-3 Campo, Vlaamse Kaai #574/R est:1200-1500

SMOORENBERG, Dirk (1883-1960) Dutch

£1544	$2856	€2300	Cows near the waterside (50x65cm-20x26in) s. 15-Mar-4 Sotheby's, Amsterdam #255/R est:2000-3000
£1579	$2905	€2400	Dutch water-landscape (53x62cm-21x24in) s. 22-Jun-4 Christie's, Amsterdam #464/R est:1500-2000
£1678	$2853	€2400	Lake with waterlillies and a village in the background (18x24cm-7x9in) s. board. 24-Nov-3 Glerum, Amsterdam #55/R est:1500-2000
£2000	$3660	€3000	Lake scene in winter (25x30cm-10x12in) s. 7-Jun-4 Glerum, Amsterdam #23/R est:1000-1500
£2632	$4842	€4000	Sailing boats off a rocky coast, possibly England (40x30cm-16x12in) s. 22-Jun-4 Christie's, Amsterdam #586/R est:4000-6000
£2632	$4842	€4000	A summer bouquet (50x50cm-20x20in) s. 22-Jun-4 Christie's, Amsterdam #587/R est:4000-6000
£2899	$4754	€4000	View of the water in winter (50x60cm-20x24in) s. 27-May-3 Sotheby's, Amsterdam #484/R est:4000-6000
£3611	$5885	€5200	Still life with apples in a basket (54x74cm-21x29in) s.d.11 prov. 29-Sep-3 Sotheby's, Amsterdam #192/R
£4861	$7681	€7000	Waterlily in a pond (39x54cm-15x21in) s.d.23. 2-Sep-3 Christie's, Amsterdam #356/R est:8000-12000
£6159	$10101	€8500	Still life with flowers (55x70cm-22x28in) s.d.25. 27-May-3 Sotheby's, Amsterdam #481/R est:3000-4000
£6803	$12381	€10000	Waterlilies (45x50cm-18x20in) s. 3-Feb-4 Christie's, Amsterdam #473/R est:5000-7000
£6993	$12028	€10000	Water landscape (42x65cm-17x26in) s. 2-Dec-3 Sotheby's, Amsterdam #2/R est:6000-8000

SMOUDI, Abdullatif (1948-) Syrian

£1400	$2478	€2044	Yellow figure (78x58cm-31x23in) 29-Apr-4 Bonhams, New Bond Street #573/R est:800-1200

SMOUT, Lucas (younger) (1671-1713) Flemish

£2600	$4498	€3796	Elegant figures inspecting the catch on a beach with sailing barges and shipping beyond (40x54cm-16x21in) s. 10-Dec-3 Bonhams, New Bond Street #63/R est:2000-3000

SMY, Wolfgang (1952-) German

£556	$928	€800	Speed swimming II (73x102cm-29x40in) s.i.d. verso acrylic board. 25-Oct-3 Dr Lehr, Berlin #482/R
£556	$928	€800	Bang (73x102cm-29x40in) s.i.d. verso acrylic chk board. 25-Oct-3 Dr Lehr, Berlin #483/R

SMYTH, Emily (?) British?

Works on paper

£360	$666	€526	Scottish family outside a hovel (46x71cm-18x28in) s. W/C. 11-Mar-4 Duke & Son, Dorchester #85

SMYTH, George H (20th C) British?

£460	$754	€672	Sublimity (30x30cm-12x12in) s.d.2001 verso. 4-Jun-3 John Ross, Belfast #251

SMYTH, Henry (19th C) British

£550	$919	€803	Haddon Hall, Derbyshire (65x90cm-26x35in) s.i.verso. 20-Oct-3 Bonhams, Bath #43
£900	$1530	€1314	Kidwelly (31x41cm-12x16in) s. s.i.d.1882 verso set of 3. 18-Nov-3 Sotheby's, Olympia #37/R

SMYTH, Norman (20th C) Irish

£280	$459	€409	Reflection (30x40cm-12x16in) s. 4-Jun-3 John Ross, Belfast #203
£1133	$2051	€1700	Two gentlemen of Sorrento (31x41cm-12x16in) s. panel. 30-Mar-4 De Veres Art Auctions, Dublin #33/R est:1500-2000

SMYTH, Rosemary (20th C) Irish

£338	$592	€480	Donegal field patterns (50x60cm-20x24in) s. 16-Dec-3 James Adam, Dublin #188/R

SMYTH, William (1813-1878) Irish

Works on paper

£950	$1739	€1387	Settlement at Port Louis (15x30cm-6x12in) i.d.1834 pencil wash prov. 7-Apr-4 Christie's, London #67/R

SMYTHE, Edward Robert (1810-1899) British

£400	$668	€584	Figures and pony (28x23cm-11x9in) s. 17-Oct-3 Keys, Aylsham #692
£500	$835	€730	Figures resting under oak tree (30x23cm-12x9in) s. 17-Oct-3 Keys, Aylsham #693
£900	$1503	€1314	Children before a riverside cottage (91x71cm-36x28in) s. 13-Nov-3 Christie's, Kensington #78/R
£2500	$3950	€3625	Cherry tree inn, Woodbridge (30x41cm-12x16in) s. 4-Sep-3 Christie's, Kensington #141/R est:3000-5000

Works on paper

£800	$1480	€1168	Norfolk coastal view with fisherfolk by the waterside with horses (28x41cm-11x16in) s. W/C. 13-Feb-4 Keys, Aylsham #598/R

SMYTHE, Edward Robert (attrib) (1810-1899) British

£1250	$2088	€1825	Mid day rest (46x61cm-18x24in) 12-Nov-3 Halls, Shrewsbury #317/R est:1200-1800

SMYTHE, Eugene Leslie (1857-1932) American

£347	$549	€500	Cape Cod, New York (25x35cm-10x14in) s.d.1896 i. verso. 6-Sep-3 Schopman, Hamburg #703/R
£464	$850	€677	Twilight (30x41cm-12x16in) 31-Jan-4 South Bay, Long Island #248
£1630	$3000	€2380	View over rooftops, Pasadena (26x36cm-10x14in) s.d.92. 8-Jun-4 Bonhams & Butterfields, San Francisco #4315/R est:3000-5000

SMYTHE, Leslie (19th C) British

£440	$695	€638	Highland landscape with cows and figures by a loch (60x105cm-24x41in) s.d.1873. 24-Jul-3 Dominic Winter, Swindon #124/R

SMYTHE, Lionel Percy (1839-1913) British

£793	$1467	€1150	Paysage ecossais avec un lac (76x128cm-30x50in) s. 13-Jan-4 Vanderkindere, Brussels #168

Works on paper

£490	$833	€715	Fishergirl by the rock pool (27x37cm-11x15in) s.d.98 W/C. 1-Dec-3 David Duggleby, Scarborough #250/R
£1000	$1830	€1460	Cornfield (24x34cm-9x13in) s. W/C scratching out. 3-Jun-4 Christie's, London #39/R est:1200-1800
£1500	$2745	€2190	Children playing with a greyhound at the edge of a meadow (15x27cm-6x11in) pencil W/C htd touches bodycol prov. 3-Jun-4 Christie's, London #35/R est:2000-3000
£1500	$2745	€2190	Farmyard at the Chateau d'Honvault, Wimereux (18x31cm-7x12in) s. pencil W/C scratching out prov.exhib. 3-Jun-4 Christie's, London #37/R est:2000-3000
£1800	$3294	€2628	Hero of our Century (23x16cm-9x6in) s.d.1874 W/C gum arabic scratching out prov.exhib. 3-Jun-4 Christie's, London #44/R est:1500-2500
£2000	$3660	€2920	Sea nymphs (27x16cm-11x6in) s.d.1910 pencil W/C scratching out prov.exhib. 3-Jun-4 Christie's, London #40/R est:2500-3500
£2800	$5124	€4088	Gathering corn (23x33cm-9x13in) pencil W/C scratching out prov. 3-Jun-4 Christie's, London #38/R est:2000-3000
£3000	$5460	€4380	The harvesters (21x33cm-8x13in) s.d.1883 pencil W/C htd white. 1-Jul-4 Christie's, Kensington #209/R est:3000-5000
£3500	$6405	€5110	Garden Gateway (46x27cm-18x11in) s. pencil W/C htd touches bodycol prov.exhib.lit. 3-Jun-4 Christie's, London #34/R est:4000-6000
£4500	$8235	€6570	Digging potatoes (25x32cm-10x13in) s.d.1895 pencil W/C scratching out prov.exhib. 3-Jun-4 Christie's, London #36/R est:2500-3500
£6000	$10740	€8760	Fruit d'amour (78x56cm-31x22in) s.d.1910 W/C. 26-May-4 Sotheby's, Olympia #183/R est:6000-9000

SMYTHE, Thomas (1825-1906) British

£550	$919	€803	Working horses resting (20x25cm-8x10in) 14-Oct-3 David Lay, Penzance #422
£600	$1038	€876	Figure with chickens on a footbridge before a thatched cottage (12x18cm-5x7in) panel. 10-Dec-3 Bonhams, Bury St Edmunds #571/R
£750	$1373	€1095	Ducks by the pond before a thatched cottage (30x40cm-12x16in) with sig. 7-Apr-4 Bonhams, Bury St Edmunds #429/R
£900	$1530	€1314	Mare and foal beneath a tree (30x40cm-12x16in) s. 1-Dec-3 Bonhams, Bath #122/R
£900	$1557	€1314	At the cottage door (28x36cm-11x14in) s. panel. 10-Dec-3 Bonhams, Bury St Edmunds #559
£1200	$2160	€1752	Returning from the fields (32x43cm-13x17in) s. 21-Apr-4 Christie's, Kensington #29/R
£1300	$2340	€1898	Farmyard friends (32x42cm-13x17in) s. 21-Apr-4 Christie's, Kensington #28/R
£1800	$3060	€2628	Over the water (30x46cm-12x18in) s. 27-Nov-3 Christie's, Kensington #178/R est:1000-1500
£1850	$2923	€2683	Horse outside the inn on a wintry day (30x46cm-12x18in) s. 3-Sep-3 Bonhams, Bury St Edmunds #461/R est:1200-1800
£2000	$3640	€2920	Autumn landscape, figures plough and dog (33x41cm-13x16in) s. 30-Jun-4 Neal & Fletcher, Woodbridge #268 est:2000-4000
£2200	$4004	€3212	Landscape harvest scene with figures (30x41cm-12x16in) s. 30-Jun-4 Neal & Fletcher, Woodbridge #267
£3300	$6105	€4818	Haywain at a country pool (44x59cm-17x23in) s. 14-Jan-4 Lawrence, Crewkerne #1429/R est:1500-2500
£7600	$13832	€11096	Donkey race (36x46cm-14x18in) i. 30-Jun-4 Neal & Fletcher, Woodbridge #279/R
£8000	$13600	€11680	Outside the village inn. Haymaking (30x41cm-12x16in) s. pair. 25-Nov-3 Christie's, London #142/R est:10000-15000
£9200	$16928	€13432	Dinning chair sledge (50x76cm-20x30in) s. 11-Jun-4 Christie's, London #137/R est:8000-12000

Works on paper

£460	$837	€672	East Anglian landscape, two figures gossiping outside cottages (20x28cm-8x11in) s. W/C. 30-Jun-4 Neal & Fletcher, Woodbridge #276
£720	$1138	€1044	Figures on a bridge with windmill beyond (27x43cm-11x17in) s. W/C. 3-Sep-3 Bonhams, Bury St Edmunds #303/R

SMYTHE, Thomas (attrib) (1825-1906) British

£900	$1620	€1314	Well-earned rest (30x41cm-12x16in) 21-Apr-4 Christie's, Kensington #30/R

SNABILLE, Maria Gertruida (attrib) (1776-1839?) German
Works on paper
£2838 $4995 €4200 Studies of flies and beetles (15x15cm-6x6in) pen brown black ink W/C. 19-May-4 Sotheby's, Amsterdam #130/R est:800-1200

SNAPE, Martin (fl.1874-1901) British
Works on paper
£280 $510 €409 View near Valletta (22x29cm-9x11in) s. pencil W/C htd white. 1-Jul-4 Mellors & Kirk, Nottingham #704

SNAPE, Sue McCartney (20th C) British
Works on paper
£250 $455 €365 The polo wife (37x25cm-15x10in) init.i.d.98 pencil black ink W/C lit. 1-Jul-4 Christie's, Kensington #541/R
£300 $546 €438 The hangover (34x28cm-13x11in) init.i.d.99 pencil black ink W/C lit. 1-Jul-4 Christie's, Kensington #528/R
£300 $546 €438 The American banker (40x34cm-16x13in) init.i.d.98 pencil black ink W/C lit. 1-Jul-4 Christie's, Kensington #539/R
£300 $546 €438 The home tutor (35x34cm-14x13in) init.i.d.99 pencil W/C lit. 1-Jul-4 Christie's, Kensington #542/R
£350 $602 €511 Travel rep (53x33cm-21x13in) init.i.d.98 pencil W/C lit. 3-Dec-3 Christie's, Kensington #354/R
£350 $602 €511 Man to fix the washing machine (51x40cm-20x16in) init.i.d.99 pencil black ink W/C lit. 3-Dec-3 Christie's, Kensington #367/R
£350 $637 €511 The male shop assistant (44x33cm-17x13in) init.i.d.98 pencil crayon black ink W/C lit. 1-Jul-4 Christie's, Kensington #537/R
£380 $654 €555 Food allergy sufferer (40x36cm-16x14in) int.i.d.01 pencil black ink W/C lit. 3-Dec-3 Christie's, Kensington #376/R
£400 $688 €584 Used car dealer (46x38cm-18x15in) init.i.d.98 pencil black ink W/C lit. 3-Dec-3 Christie's, Kensington #361/R
£400 $728 €584 Network marketeer (53x40cm-21x16in) init.i.d.96 pencil black ink W/C gold leaf lit. 1-Jul-4 Christie's, Kensington #527/R
£400 $728 €584 The dog wrangler (57x39cm-22x15in) init.i.d.01 pencil black ink W/C lit. 1-Jul-4 Christie's, Kensington #530/R
£420 $764 €613 The village shop lady (45x38cm-18x15in) init.i. pencil black ink W/C lit. 1-Jul-4 Christie's, Kensington #524/R
£450 $774 €657 Cyclist (47x25cm-19x10in) init.i.d.00 pencil black ink W/C crayon lit. 3-Dec-3 Christie's, Kensington #358/R
£450 $774 €657 Vegetable prize winner (48x29cm-19x11in) init. pencil W/C. 3-Dec-3 Christie's, Kensington #363/R
£450 $774 €657 Long married couple (49x34cm-19x13in) init.i.d.98 pencil black ink W/C lit. 3-Dec-3 Christie's, Kensington #364/R
£450 $774 €657 Pop stars cook (42x38cm-17x15in) init.i.d.00 pencil W/C lit. 3-Dec-3 Christie's, Kensington #365/R
£450 $774 €657 Doctor's receptionist (46x33cm-18x13in) init.i.d.97 pencil crayon W/C lit. 3-Dec-3 Christie's, Kensington #366/R
£480 $826 €701 President of the Oxford Union (51x35cm-20x14in) init.i.d.99 pencil pen black ink W/C crayon lit. 3-Dec-3 Christie's, Kensington #347/R
£480 $826 €701 Bed and breakfast landlady (43x28cm-17x11in) init.i.d.96 pen black ink W/C lit. 3-Dec-3 Christie's, Kensington #353/R
£480 $826 €701 Swimmer (55x34cm-22x13in) init. pencil black ink W/C. 3-Dec-3 Christie's, Kensington #360/R
£500 $910 €730 The spinster aunt (53x23cm-21x9in) init.i.d.96 pencil black ink W/C collage lit. 1-Jul-4 Christie's, Kensington #529/R
£520 $894 €759 Ethnic jewelry designer (48x29cm-19x11in) init.i.d.96 pencil black ink W/C lit. 3-Dec-3 Christie's, Kensington #350/R
£550 $946 €803 Magazine editor (46x32cm-18x13in) init.i.d.99 pencil black ink W/C lit. 3-Dec-3 Christie's, Kensington #370/R
£550 $946 €803 Bodyguard (38x28cm-15x11in) init.i.d.99 pencil felt tip pen W/C lit. 3-Dec-3 Christie's, Kensington #373/R
£580 $998 €847 Barbecue host (41x29cm-16x11in) init.i. pencil black ink W/C lit. 3-Dec-3 Christie's, Kensington #345/R
£580 $998 €847 Groundsman (49x34cm-19x13in) init.i.d.02 pencil black ink W/C lit. 3-Dec-3 Christie's, Kensington #355/R
£600 $1032 €876 Arts patron (56x37cm-22x15in) init.i.d.99 pencil black ink W/C lit. 3-Dec-3 Christie's, Kensington #352/R
£600 $1032 €876 Office smoker (52x30cm-20x12in) init.d. pencil black ink W/C crayon lit. 3-Dec-3 Christie's, Kensington #356/R
£600 $1032 €876 Young married shopping for the house (44x34cm-17x13in) init.i.d.01 pencil black ink W/C crayon lit. 3-Dec-3 Christie's, Kensington #368/R
£600 $1032 €876 Textile designer (43x32cm-17x13in) init.i.d.01 pencil crayon W/C lit. 3-Dec-3 Christie's, Kensington #371/R
£600 $1092 €876 The ski instructor (34x25cm-13x10in) init.i.d.98 pencil black ink W/C lit. 1-Jul-4 Christie's, Kensington #533/R
£650 $1118 €949 Eclipse of the sun (51x37cm-20x15in) init.i. pencil black ink W/C. 3-Dec-3 Christie's, Kensington #369/R
£650 $1183 €949 The House of Lords (75x53cm-30x21in) pencil W/C prov. 1-Jul-4 Christie's, Kensington #522/R
£700 $1204 €1022 Computer fixer (43x37cm-17x15in) init.i.d.97 pencil W/C lit. 3-Dec-3 Christie's, Kensington #377/R
£750 $1365 €1095 The middle class football fan (44x29cm-17x11in) init.i.d.99 pencil W/C collage lit. 1-Jul-4 Christie's, Kensington #574
£780 $1342 €1139 Jolly ex-pat (42x40cm-17x16in) init.i.d.1997 pencil black ink W/C lit. 3-Dec-3 Christie's, Kensington #351/R
£800 $1376 €1168 Film and TV researcher (38x28cm-15x11in) init.i.d.98 pencil black ink W/C lit. 3-Dec-3 Christie's, Kensington #375/R
£850 $1462 €1241 Pregnant woman (56x33cm-22x13in) init.i.d.00 pencil crayon W/C lit. 3-Dec-3 Christie's, Kensington #372/R
£850 $1462 €1241 Lady Ludgrove's progress through the water (55x32cm-22x13in) init.i.d.00 pencil black ink W/C lit. 3-Dec-3 Christie's, Kensington #374/R
£900 $1638 €1314 The St Andrew's Sloane (45x33cm-18x13in) init.i.d.00 pencil black ink W/C lit. 1-Jul-4 Christie's, Kensington #536/R
£1100 $1892 €1606 Teetotaler (51x33cm-20x13in) init.i.d.01 pencil black ink W/C crayon lit. 3-Dec-3 Christie's, Kensington #348/R est:600-800
£1200 $2064 €1752 Spoilt IVF brats (53x39cm-21x15in) init.i.d.01 pencil black ink crayon W/C lit. 3-Dec-3 Christie's, Kensington #362/R est:600-800
£1300 $2236 €1898 Shooting wife (53x30cm-21x12in) init.i.d.98 pencil black ink W/C crayon lit. 3-Dec-3 Christie's, Kensington #346/R est:700-1000
£1300 $2236 €1898 Career nanny (43x37cm-17x15in) init.i.d.98 pencil black ink W/C crayon lit. 3-Dec-3 Christie's, Kensington #349/R est:600-800

SNAPE, William H (fl.1885-1892) British
£300 $567 €438 Fisher's Row, Oxford (28x20cm-11x8in) s. board. 19-Feb-4 Richardson & Smith, Whitby #54
£7500 $13650 €10950 Chopping firewood (40x30cm-16x12in) s. panel prov. 1-Jul-4 Sotheby's, London #324/R est:6000-8000

SNAPP, Frank (20th C) American
Works on paper
£305 $500 €442 Dressing the bride (28x20cm-11x8in) s.d. W/C board. 7-Jun-3 Treadway Gallery, Cincinnati #1465

SNAYERS, Peeter (1592-1666) Flemish
£6111 $11000 €8922 Conversion of Saint Paul (71x89cm-28x35in) copper. 23-Jan-4 Christie's, Rockefeller NY #23/R est:10000-15000
£19000 $34770 €27740 Landscape with cavalry engagement (80x107cm-31x42in) indis.sig. prov. 8-Jul-4 Sotheby's, London #294/R est:12000-18000

SNAYERS, Peeter (attrib) (1592-1666) Flemish
£1399 $2336 €2000 La conversion de Saint Paul (28x33cm-11x13in) panel. 26-Jun-3 Artcurial Briest, Paris #475 est:2000-3000
£1923 $3308 €2808 Battle scene (17x23cm-7x9in) 3-Dec-3 AB Stockholms Auktionsverk #2661/R est:30000-40000 (S.KR 25000)

SNEBUR (1964-) Italian
£699 $1189 €1000 Fog on Mars (50x50cm-20x20in) s.i.d.2002 verso prov.exhib. 24-Nov-3 Christie's, Milan #92/R
£1351 $2378 €2000 Spatial fields (80x60cm-31x24in) s.i.d.2002 verso acrylic prov.exhib. 24-May-4 Christie's, Milan #108/R est:2200-2800

SNEE, Christopher (1957-) Australian
£763 $1389 €1114 Dunder Funk (100x100cm-39x39in) s. i.d.99 verso enamel on board. 16-Jun-4 Deutscher-Menzies, Melbourne #253/R est:2500-4000 (A.D 2000)

SNEL, Han (1925-1998) Dutch
£1323 $2289 €1932 Girl from Bali (54x41cm-21x16in) s.i.d.54. 9-Dec-3 Rasmussen, Copenhagen #1530/R est:12000 (D.KR 14000)
£1569 $2839 €2291 Village scene (37x29cm-15x11in) s.d.53 panel. 4-Apr-4 Sotheby's, Singapore #39/R est:3000-4000 (S.D 4800)
£1613 $2968 €2355 Portrait of Siti, the artist's wife (50x45cm-20x18in) s.i. prov. 9-Jun-4 Walker's, Ottawa #311/R est:2000-3000 (C.D 4000)
£3125 $5219 €4563 Two Baliese women (50x59cm-20x23in) s.d.89 lit. 12-Oct-3 Sotheby's, Singapore #32/R est:8000-10000 (S.D 9000)
£4301 $6882 €6279 Blue market (48x60cm-19x24in) s.d.69. 18-May-3 Sotheby's, Singapore #4/R est:7000-9000 (S.D 12000)
£4422 $7915 €6500 Portrait of Siti, wife of the artist (60x43cm-24x17in) s.d.63. 16-Mar-4 Christie's, Amsterdam #105/R est:2500-3500
£5442 $9741 €8000 Balinese beauties (38x76cm-15x30in) s.d.57. 16-Mar-4 Christie's, Amsterdam #133/R est:2000-3000
£5556 $9278 €8112 Women (70x60cm-28x24in) s.d.90. 12-Oct-3 Sotheby's, Singapore #36/R est:7000-9000 (S.D 16000)
£22222 $40222 €32444 Balinese women at the market (144x74cm-57x29in) s.d.75 canvas on board. 4-Apr-4 Sotheby's, Singapore #14/R est:15000-20000 (S.D 68000)
£52288 $94641 €76340 Balinese woman (179x240cm-70x94in) s.d.77 canvas on board. 4-Apr-4 Sotheby's, Singapore #28/R est:40000-60000 (S.D 160000)
Works on paper
£1293 $2314 €1900 Portrait of a seated girl (57x47cm-22x19in) s.d.64 pencil htd white sold with a woodcut by same hand. 16-Mar-4 Christie's, Amsterdam #104 est:800-1200
£1389 $2319 €2028 Balinese woman (55x35cm-22x14in) s.d.57 chl. 12-Oct-3 Sotheby's, Singapore #17/R est:4000-6000 (S.D 4000)

SNELL, Henry Bayley (1858-1943) American
£1816 $3250 €2651 Adobe home. s.i. board. 13-May-4 Dallas Auction Gallery, Dallas #166/R est:2000-4000

SNELL, James Herbert (1861-1935) British
£280 $515 €409 Village street (25x35cm-10x14in) s. 23-Jun-4 Bonhams, Bury St Edmunds #372
£300 $549 €450 Coastal view with girl mending nets (33x23cm-13x9in) s.d.1884. 30-Jul-4 Jim Railton, Durham #966
£320 $576 €467 Angler at Twyford bridge, Yalding (30x39cm-12x15in) s. s.verso. 22-Apr-4 Lawrence, Crewkerne #932
£360 $655 €526 Fishermen and boats in a cove (56x76cm-22x30in) s. i.verso. 15-Jun-4 Bonhams, Oxford #113
£380 $703 €555 Country road (24x34cm-9x13in) s. board. 9-Mar-4 Bonhams, Knightsbridge #294/R
£380 $692 €555 Sheep grazing by hurdles in a river landscape (25x35cm-10x14in) s. panel. 15-Jun-4 Bonhams, Oxford #117
£400 $736 €584 Picking primroses (39x39cm-15x15in) s. canvasboard. 23-Jun-4 Bonhams, Bury St Edmunds #373/R
£420 $722 €600 Moored boats with a village in the background (23x33cm-9x13in) s. panel. 7-Dec-3 Sotheby's, Amsterdam #653a
£440 $810 €642 Harvest time (42x55cm-17x22in) s. 23-Jun-4 Bonhams, Bury St Edmunds #369
£450 $806 €657 Farnham Common (35x51cm-14x20in) s. s.i.verso board. 14-May-4 Christie's, Kensington #517/R
£460 $796 €672 An Essex windmill (38x51cm-15x20in) s. 14-Dec-3 Desmond Judd, Cranbrook #1125
£550 $990 €803 Old mill, Golden Green. Storm cloud, Yalding (29x39cm-11x15in) s. s.i.verso. 22-Apr-4 Lawrence, Crewkerne #931
£680 $1129 €993 Old Orchard (47x64cm-19x25in) s.d.1890. 1-Oct-3 Sotheby's, Olympia #157/R
£700 $1204 €1022 Young girl in a country lane in summer (33x23cm-13x9in) 5-Dec-3 Keys, Aylsham #708/R

SNELL, Nyilpirr Spider (c.1925-) Australian
Works on paper
£1423 $2248 €2078 Untitled (75x90cm-30x35in) i.verso synthetic polymer paint canvas prov. 28-Jul-3 Sotheby's, Paddington #497/R est:3000-5000 (A.D 3500)

SNELL, Rudolf (1823-1898) Swiss
£391 $716 €571 Summer landscape (61x40cm-24x16in) cardboard. 4-Jun-4 Zofingen, Switzerland #2366 (S.FR 900)

SNELLING, Henry Hunt (1817-1897) American
Photographs
£13889 $25000 €20278 Union Square, New York (29x41cm-11x16in) salt print collodion negative. 22-Apr-4 Phillips, New York #24/R est:30000-40000

SNELLING, Lilian (20th C) American
Works on paper
£3200 $5920 €4672 Lily (54x36cm-21x14in) s.i. pencil W/C. 15-Jul-4 Bonhams, New Bond Street #42/R est:2000-3000
£3400 $6290 €4964 Lily (54x36cm-21x14in) s.i. pencil W/C. 15-Jul-4 Bonhams, New Bond Street #43/R est:2000-3000

SNELLING, Matthew (1621-1678) British
Miniatures
£5000 $9200 €7300 King Charles II of England, wearing amour (7cm-3in) W/C on vellum rec. tortoiseshell frame prov.lit. 24-Jun-4 Bonhams, New Bond Street #41/R est:5000-7000

SNELLMAN, Anita (1924-) Finnish
£733 $1313 €1100 Catalina (100x80cm-39x31in) s.d.1961. 15-May-4 Hagelstam, Helsinki #175/R
£2400 $4296 €3600 Still life of fruit (90x123cm-35x48in) s.d.1978. 15-May-4 Hagelstam, Helsinki #174/R est:2400

SNELLMAN, Anna (1884-1962) Finnish
£333 $597 €500 Flowers (41x33cm-16x13in) s. 15-May-4 Hagelstam, Helsinki #144/R
£465 $744 €660 Flowers (61x50cm-24x20in) s. 18-Sep-3 Hagelstam, Helsinki #945
£544 $990 €800 Still life of flowers (46x38cm-18x15in) s. 8-Feb-4 Bukowskis, Helsinki #459/R
£676 $1209 €1000 Still life of fruit (38x46cm-15x18in) s.d.1919. 8-May-4 Bukowskis, Helsinki #149/R
£1067 $1909 €1600 Lady in white dress (41x42cm-16x17in) s.d.1915 board. 15-May-4 Hagelstam, Helsinki #145/R est:400

SNELLMAN, Christina (1928-) Finnish
£436 $803 €650 Girl with sunflowers (55x39cm-22x15in) s.d.1963. 25-Mar-4 Hagelstam, Helsinki #1059
£1014 $1814 €1500 Drying hurdles (38x60cm-15x24in) s/d/60. 8-May-4 Bukowskis, Helsinki #273/R est:700-1000

SNELLMAN, Eero (1890-1951) Finnish
£667 $1227 €1000 Landscape from Hogland (50x39cm-20x15in) s.d.1919. 9-Jun-4 Bukowskis, Helsinki #551/R
£915 $1465 €1300 Winter landscape with river (51x66cm-20x26in) s. 21-Sep-3 Bukowskis, Helsinki #474/R

SNELSON, Kenneth (1927-) American
Prints
£2297 $4250 €3354 East River Drive (50x297cm-20x117in) s.d.1980 num.9/10 gelatin silver print felt tip pen. 12-Feb-4 Sotheby's, New York #266/R est:2500-3500
Sculpture
£4335 $7500 €6329 Untitled (36x36x36cm-14x14x14in) porcelainized aluminum stainless steel maquettes four prov. 15-Dec-3 Hindman, Chicago #39/R est:6000-8000
£4396 $8000 €6418 Stage five (92x30cm-36x12in) aluminum coated wire executed 1966 prov.exhib. 29-Jun-4 Sotheby's, New York #562/R est:8000-10000

SNIDOW, Gordon (1936-) British
£14706 $27500 €21471 Red Mackinaw (76x91cm-30x36in) s. prov. 24-Jul-4 Coeur d'Alene, Hayden #205/R est:20000-30000
Works on paper
£1294 $2200 €1889 Standing cowboy (20x15cm-8x6in) gouache on board. 1-Nov-3 Altermann Galleries, Santa Fe #132
£2329 $3750 €3377 Saddle up (13x15cm-5x6in) chl. 22-Aug-3 Altermann Galleries, Santa Fe #121

SNOECK, Jacques (1881-1921) Dutch
£850 $1420 €1241 Sewing in the nursery (41x32cm-16x13in) s. 8-Oct-3 Christie's, Kensington #825/R

SNOW, Edward Taylor (1844-1913) American
£756 $1300 €1104 Autumn landscape (43x58cm-17x23in) s. canvas on board painted c.1900. 7-Dec-3 Treadway Gallery, Cincinnati #509/R
Works on paper
£488 $800 €708 Dutch woman (36x28cm-14x11in) s.d. W/C. 7-Jun-3 Treadway Gallery, Cincinnati #1321

SNOW, John (1911-) Canadian
£578 $959 €844 Untitled, river (38x48cm-15x19in) s.d.1974 canvasboard exhib. 5-Oct-3 Levis, Calgary #115/R (C.D 1300)
£840 $1537 €1226 Church at Dubrovnik (35x40cm-14x16in) s.d.1975 canvas on board prov.exhib. 1-Jun-4 Hodgins, Calgary #455/R est:1500-2000 (C.D 2100)
£880 $1610 €1285 Mountain Valley (60x85cm-24x33in) s.i.d.1986 prov. 1-Jun-4 Hodgins, Calgary #400/R est:2000-3000 (C.D 2200)
Works on paper
£331 $598 €483 Untitled - mother and child (64x48cm-25x19in) s.verso mixed media. 18-Apr-4 Levis, Calgary #112/R (C.D 800)
£856 $1455 €1250 Laundry (26x36cm-10x14in) s. W/C double-sided prov. 23-Nov-3 Levis, Calgary #134/R est:1200-1500 (C.D 1900)

SNOW, John Wray (1801-1854) British
£400 $704 €584 Snow, the kill (61x92cm-24x36in) 18-May-4 Rosebery Fine Art, London #702

SNOW, Michael (1929-) Canadian
£10811 $18378 €15784 Trane (89x128cm-35x50in) s.i.d.1959 prov. 18-Nov-3 Sotheby's, Toronto #109/R est:15000-20000 (C.D 24000)
£11261 $19144 €16441 Bracket I (152x102cm-60x40in) s.d.60 s.i.d.1960 stretcher verso lit. 18-Nov-3 Sotheby's, Toronto #82/R est:25000-35000 (C.D 25000)
Sculpture
£5357 $9214 €7821 Phold (36cm-14in) s.d.62 cut paper shadow box relief prov.lit. 2-Dec-3 Joyner Waddington, Toronto #82/R est:8000-12000 (C.D 12000)

SNOWMAN, Isaac (1874-?) Israeli
£30000 $55200 €43800 Good news (133x89cm-52x35in) s. exhib. 11-Jun-4 Christie's, London #110/R est:30000-50000
£70588 $120000 €103058 Busy idleness (92x137cm-36x54in) s. prov.exhib. 29-Oct-3 Christie's, Rockefeller NY #65/R est:150000-200000

SNYDER, Clarence W (1873-?) American
£311 $500 €454 The girl and the pool (76x64cm-30x25in) s. s.i. stretcher. 20-Aug-3 James Julia, Fairfield #1715/R

SNYDER, Peter Etril (1944-) Canadian
£428 $728 €625 Horses near the barn (45x61cm-18x24in) s. board. 27-Nov-3 Heffel, Vancouver #76/R (C.D 950)

SNYDER, William McKendree (1848-1930) American
£1105 $1900 €1613 Southern Indiana beech forest (25x36cm-10x14in) s. painted c.1900. 7-Dec-3 Treadway Gallery, Cincinnati #514/R est:2000-3000
£1209 $2200 €1765 Beechwood forest with winding path (23x43cm-9x17in) s. 21-Jun-4 Winter Associates, Plainville #60/R est:750-1500
£1395 $2400 €2037 Southern Indiana beech forest (23x38cm-9x15in) s. painted c.2400. 7-Dec-3 Treadway Gallery, Cincinnati #513/R est:2000-3000
£3125 $5500 €4563 Path through a Southern Indiana beech woods (46x71cm-18x28in) s. painted c.1890. 23-May-4 Treadway Gallery, Cincinnati #491/R est:5000-7000

SNYDER, William McKinley (19/20th C) American
£1018 $1700 €1486 Wooded landscape (23x36cm-9x14in) 14-Nov-3 Du Mouchelle, Detroit #46/R est:750-850

SNYDERS, Frans (1579-1657) Dutch
£9722 $15847 €14000 Heron in reeds (132x116cm-52x46in) prov. 24-Sep-3 Neumeister, Munich #342/R est:10000
£12000 $21960 €18000 Bird concert (102x140cm-40x55in) 1-Jun-4 Sotheby's, Milan #159/R est:10000-15000
£160000 $276800 €233600 Melon, grapes, apples and pears with other fruit in a basket, wine glass and a Diana monkey on table (96x147cm-38x58in) prov.exhib.lit. 10-Dec-3 Christie's, London #23/R est:40000-60000
£170000 $311100 €248200 Deer, fawn and other dead game suspended on hooks (178x137cm-70x54in) s. prov.lit. 7-Jul-4 Christie's, London #30/R est:200000-300000
£200000 $366000 €292000 Still life of fruit with bowls and sparrow (54x85cm-21x33in) s. i.verso panel prov.lit. 7-Jul-4 Sotheby's, London #27/R est:200000-300000

SNYDERS, Frans (circle) (1579-1657) Dutch
£6711 $12349 €10000 Six parakeets in tree (30x21cm-12x8in) panel. 25-Mar-4 Dr Fritz Nagel, Stuttgart #598/R est:1000

SNYDERS, Frans (studio) (1579-1657) Dutch
£7500 $12975 €10950 Still life of peacock, roe deer, lobster on a Wan-Li porcelain plate (120x186cm-47x73in) 11-Dec-3 Sotheby's, London #170/R est:8000-12000
£24000 $43920 €35040 Dead hare and other game, lobster and fruit on a wooden table top (98x127cm-39x50in) panel. 7-Jul-4 Bonhams, New Bond Street #72/R est:15000-20000

SNYDERS, Frans (style) (1579-1657) Dutch
£5988 $10000 €8742 Boar hunt (120x168cm-47x66in) prov.exhib.lit. 7-Oct-3 Sotheby's, New York #39/R est:2000-4000

SNYERS, Pieter (1681-1752) Flemish
£3133 $5734 €4574 Battle scene from the 30 years war (74x62cm-29x24in) s. 9-Jun-4 Rasmussen, Copenhagen #1547/R est:50000-75000 (D.KR 35000)
£6849 $11644 €10000 Flower garland surrounding a German silver-gilt and ivory tankard (93x77cm-37x30in) s. 4-Nov-3 Sotheby's, Amsterdam #30/R est:4000-6000
£15000 $27000 €21900 Courtship scene, young lady being presented by young men with flowers (85x68cm-33x27in) s. prov. 22-Apr-4 Sotheby's, London #103/R est:15000-20000
£15123 $26163 €22080 Still life of dead game and guns in landscape (110x173cm-43x68in) s. exhib.prov. 9-Dec-3 Rasmussen, Copenhagen #1214/R est:200000-250000 (D.KR 160000)

SOAN, Hazel (20th C) British
Works on paper
£1200 $2004 €1752 Pride of elephants walking from trees towards an opening (56x71cm-22x28in) s. W/C. 18-Jun-3 John Nicholson, Haslemere #647/R est:750-1500

SOARES, Valeska (1957-) Brazilian

Sculpture			
£3667	$6747	€5500	Model after vanishing point (34x34x2cm-13x13x1in) steel perfume exec.1998 prov.lit. 10-Jun-4 Christie's, Paris #85/R est:4000-5500

SOBALVARRO, Orlando (20th C) Latin American

£178	$295	€258	Petroglifo (104x50cm-41x20in) d.1974 oil mixed triplay. 12-Jun-3 Louis Morton, Mexico #38/R est:1000-1200 (M.P 3100)
£218	$362	€316	Retrato de mujer (140x160cm-55x63in) d.1977 triplay. 12-Jun-3 Louis Morton, Mexico #162/R est:1400-1600 (M.P 3800)
£316	$524	€458	Caballo encanto de Amerrisque (114x140cm-45x55in) d.1986. 12-Jun-3 Louis Morton, Mexico #158/R est:1500-1700 (M.P 5500)
£430	$714	€624	Los circenses (114x178cm-45x70in) d.1995. 12-Jun-3 Louis Morton, Mexico #97/R est:2000-2400 (M.P 7500)

SOBERA, Vicente (20th C) Spanish?

£362	$594	€500	Ventana (54x54cm-21x21in) s.d.79. 27-May-3 Durán, Madrid #730/R
£362	$594	€500	Meditacion (53x42cm-21x17in) s.d.79 masonite. 27-May-3 Durán, Madrid #1294/R

SOBLE, John Jacob (20th C) American

£223	$400	€326	Woman at the mirror (25x20cm-10x8in) s. 16-May-4 Wright, Chicago #169/R

SOBRADO, Pedro (1936-) Spanish

£694	$1132	€1000	Maternidad (73x60cm-29x24in) s. exhib.lit. 16-Jul-3 Durán, Madrid #137/R
£890	$1514	€1300	In the field (55x46cm-22x18in) s. 4-Nov-3 Ansorena, Madrid #891/R
£942	$1545	€1300	Marionetas (73x60cm-29x24in) s. 27-May-3 Durán, Madrid #92/R
£972	$1604	€1400	Walking hand in hand (73x60cm-29x24in) s. 2-Jul-3 Ansorena, Madrid #928/R
£1034	$1862	€1500	Dame of the rose (65x81cm-26x32in) s. 26-Jan-4 Durán, Madrid #88/R est:1500
£1034	$1862	€1500	Visit (65x81cm-26x32in) s. 26-Jan-4 Ansorena, Madrid #912/R est:1500
£1275	$2283	€1900	From the quay (73x92cm-29x36in) s. board. 25-May-4 Durán, Madrid #104/R est:1500
£1342	$2376	€2000	Figures (93x122cm-37x48in) s. board. 27-Apr-4 Durán, Madrid #134/R est:1900
£1846	$3378	€2750	Interior (122x92cm-48x36in) s. board. 12-Jul-4 Durán, Madrid #146/R est:1900
Works on paper			
£289	$524	€440	Masks (65x50cm-26x20in) s. W/C. 14-Apr-4 Ansorena, Madrid #381/R

SOBRAT, Anak Agung Gede (1911-1992) Balinese

£4082	$7306	€6000	Selling bananas (68x45cm-27x18in) s.i.d.1958. 16-Mar-4 Christie's, Amsterdam #115/R est:4000-6000
£5435	$8424	€7935	Market in Bali (79x59cm-31x23in) s.i.verso. 6-Oct-2 Sotheby's, Singapore #140/R est:15000-18000 (S.D 15000)
£6944	$11597	€10138	Festival in Bali (98x58cm-39x23in) s.d.1980 tempera cloth. 12-Oct-3 Sotheby's, Singapore #160/R est:22000-28000 (S.D 20000)
£8163	$14612	€12000	Market scene (121x81cm-48x32in) s.i. 16-Mar-4 Christie's, Amsterdam #112/R est:10000-15000
Works on paper			
£1797	$3253	€2624	Balinese beauty (60x47cm-24x19in) s.i. pastel. 3-Apr-4 Glerum, Singapore #5/R est:5000-6000 (S.D 5500)

SOBRERO, Emilio (1890-1964) Italian

£769	$1285	€1100	Building site (31x29cm-12x11in) s. i.d.1928 verso board. 26-Jun-3 Sant Agostino, Torino #263/R

SOBRILE, Giuseppe (1879-1956) Italian

£979	$1635	€1400	Morning in Sea Valley (33x40cm-13x16in) s.d.1939 board. 26-Jun-3 Sant Agostino, Torino #82/R est:1800
£2267	$4171	€3400	Snowfall (48x75cm-19x30in) s.d.1930 board. 8-Jun-4 Della Rocca, Turin #221/R est:2500-3500
£2292	$3896	€3300	Lights in landscape covered in snow (38x49cm-15x19in) s.d.1943 board. 1-Nov-3 Meeting Art, Vercelli #309/R est:1500
£2797	$4671	€4000	Village under snow (33x42cm-13x17in) s.d.1931 board. 26-Jun-3 Sant Agostino, Torino #290/R est:2500-3500
£3103	$5152	€4500	Landscape covered in snow (47x75cm-19x30in) s.d.1933 board. 1-Oct-3 Della Rocca, Turin #214/R
£4698	$8315	€7000	Alpi Graie in winter (22x27cm-9x11in) s. board two. 1-May-4 Meeting Art, Vercelli #103 est:6000
£5600	$10304	€8400	Snow (52x44cm-20x17in) s.d.1933 board. 14-Jun-4 Sant Agostino, Torino #295/R est:2500-3000

SOCHA, Dan (20th C) American

Works on paper			
£410	$750	€615	Ranchette (46x64cm-18x25in) pastel gouache. 10-Jul-4 Hindman, Chicago #492/R

SOCHACZEWSKI, Alexander (1843-1923) Polish

£9220	$15397	€13000	Criee (170x240cm-67x94in) mono. 14-Oct-3 Vanderkindere, Brussels #60/R est:7500-12500

SOCHACZEWSKI, Alexander (attrib) (1843-1923) Polish

£887	$1480	€1250	Portrait de sous-officier cosaque assis (160x98cm-63x39in) 14-Oct-3 Vanderkindere, Brussels #28
£887	$1480	€1250	Portrait d'officier cosaque (99x61cm-39x24in) 14-Oct-3 Vanderkindere, Brussels #24

SOCRATE, Carlo (1889-1967) Italian

£2797	$4755	€4000	Double portrait (80x70cm-31x28in) s.d.1949. 24-Nov-3 Christie's, Milan #101/R est:3500-4000

SODERGREN, Sigfrid (1920-) Swedish

£474	$763	€692	Kalhygge (51x70cm-20x28in) s.d.90 exhib. 25-Aug-3 Lilla Bukowskis, Stockholm #593 (S.KR 6200)

SODERMARK, Johan Per (1822-1889) Swedish

£961	$1720	€1403	Portraits of Count Erik Josias Sparre and his wife (77x62cm-30x24in) s.d.1880 oval pair prov.lit. 26-May-4 AB Stockholms Auktionsverk #2130/R (S.KR 13000)

SOEBORG, Axel (1872-1939) Danish

£301	$512	€439	Spring day in a Swedish village (39x44cm-15x17in) mono.d.29. 29-Nov-3 Rasmussen, Havnen #2263 (D.KR 3200)

SOEDARSONO, Srihadi (1931-) Javanese

£22876	$41405	€33399	Spirits of Legong (100x147cm-39x58in) s.d.92 s.i.d.1992 verso. 3-Apr-4 Glerum, Singapore #70/R est:70000-90000 (S.D 70000)
£32680	$59150	€47713	Pura Gunung Lebak (100x130cm-39x51in) s.d.1986. 3-Apr-4 Glerum, Singapore #33/R est:60000-80000 (S.D 100000)

SOEDIBIO (1912-1980) Indonesian?

£2174	$3370	€3174	Still life (88x64cm-35x25in) s.d.69. 6-Oct-2 Sotheby's, Singapore #169/R est:3000-4000 (S.D 6000)

SOEDJOJONO, S (1914-1986) Indonesian

£4248	$7690	€6202	Guru dan Muridnya (48x68cm-19x27in) s.i.d.Jan 1984. 3-Apr-4 Glerum, Singapore #39/R est:14000-18000 (S.D 13000)
£10145	$15725	€14812	Self portrait (61x46cm-24x18in) s.d.1965 board. 6-Oct-2 Sotheby's, Singapore #121/R est:25000-30000 (S.D 28000)
£10417	$17396	€15209	Pengantin anak negeri (51x61cm-20x24in) s.i.d.1978. 12-Oct-3 Sotheby's, Singapore #158/R est:30000-40000 (S.D 30000)
£10458	$18928	€15269	Ratu laut selatan (70x50cm-28x20in) mono.d.1984. 4-Apr-4 Sotheby's, Singapore #153/R est:30000-50000 (S.D 32000)
£11380	$20484	€16615	Tukang becak - Becak driver (89x68cm-35x27in) init.i.d.1981. 25-Apr-4 Christie's, Hong Kong #582/R est:120000-160000 (HK.D 160000)
£11438	$20703	€16699	Layang-layangku bargus (90x60cm-35x24in) mono.d.1975. 4-Apr-4 Sotheby's, Singapore #152/R est:35000-55000 (S.D 35000)
£12903	$20645	€18838	Waktu ada es di gorkum, ned (60x80cm-24x31in) s.i.d.1976 canvas on board. 18-May-3 Sotheby's, Singapore #134/R est:30000-40000 (S.D 36000)
£13900	$23212	€20294	Landscape (52x59cm-20x23in) s.d.1989 board. 26-Oct-3 Christie's, Hong Kong #67/R est:55000-80000 (HK.D 180000)
£17204	$27527	€25118	Kembang kembang buatan (90x100cm-35x39in) s.i.d.1976. 18-May-3 Sotheby's, Singapore #156/R est:25000-30000 (S.D 48000)
£22394	$37398	€32695	Gunung massigit, West Java - Massig Mountain , West Java (90x125cm-35x49in) s.i.d.1971. 26-Oct-3 Christie's, Hong Kong #49/R est:70000-90000 (HK.D 290000)
£27778	$50278	€40556	Monas (70x90cm-28x35in) mono.d.1980. 4-Apr-4 Sotheby's, Singapore #151/R est:80000-120000 (S.D 85000)
£27799	$46425	€40587	Mawar mawar putih - white roses (70x59cm-28x23in) s.i.d.1959. 26-Oct-3 Christie's, Hong Kong #48/R est:55000-65000 (HK.D 360000)
£28450	$51209	€41537	Pemandangan dekat lido - landscape near Lido (80x120cm-31x47in) init.i.d.1976. 25-Apr-4 Christie's, Hong Kong #581/R est:90000-140000 (HK.D 400000)
£35562	$64011	€51921	De alam bebas - Portrait of a nude amidst a green landscape (143x101cm-56x40in) s.i.d.1962. 25-Apr-4 Christie's, Hong Kong #583/R est:180000-350000 (HK.D 500000)
£35562	$64011	€51921	Legend Ramayana (138x91cm-54x36in) s.i.d.1963. 25-Apr-4 Christie's, Hong Kong #584/R est:160000-200000 (HK.D 500000)
£36458	$60885	€53229	Kuda-Kuda Berlarian (100x140cm-39x55in) s.d.1969. 12-Oct-3 Sotheby's, Singapore #130/R est:38000-48000 (S.D 105000)

SOEHLKE, Gerhard (attrib) (19th C) German?

£1133	$2085	€1700	Study of a male head (59x49cm-23x19in) bears sig.d.1847. 9-Jun-4 Beaussant & Lefèvre, Paris #216/R est:1200-1500

SOELEN, Theodore van (1890-1964) American

£5000	$8500	€7300	Adobe with Ristras (25x33cm-10x13in) s.d.17 board prov.lit. 1-Nov-3 Santa Fe Art, Santa Fe #215/R est:25000-30000
£17647	$30000	€25765	Cienega in spring (89x114cm-35x45in) oil egg tempera. 1-Nov-3 Altermann Galleries, Santa Fe #158
£23529	$40000	€34352	Cowboys (51x61cm-20x24in) s. board prov.lit. 1-Nov-3 Santa Fe Art, Santa Fe #131/R est:50000-70000

SOER, Chris (1882-1961) Dutch

£316	$572	€480	Beguinage of Bruges (18x24cm-7x9in) s. 19-Apr-4 Glerum, Amsterdam #25[illegible]/R
£748	$1362	€1100	View of the wetstraat, Brussels, in winter (40x50cm-16x20in) s. 3-Feb-4 Christie's, Amsterdam #270/R est:1000-1500

SOEST, Gerard van (c.1637-1681) British

£10000	$17000	€14600	Double portrait of a lady and her son with his arm resting on a hound, in a landscape (146x121cm-57x48in) s. prov.lit. 25-Nov-3 Christie's, London #9/R est:15000-25000

SOEST, Gerard van (circle) (c.1637-1681) British

£5000	$8950	€7300	Portrait of Anne Buck, seated in brown gown, with her daughter (127x101cm-50x40in) 22-Mar-4 Bonhams & Brooks, Norfolk #337/R est:2500-3500
£11173	$20000	€16313	Portrait of four children (144x113cm-57x44in) 27-May-4 Sotheby's, New York #214/R est:20000-30000

SOEST, Louis W van (1867-1948) Dutch
£420 $701 €600 Forest pond in the afternoon light (49x65cm-19x26in) s. board. 30-Jun-3 Sotheby's, Amsterdam #260/R
£461 $834 €700 Farm in a landscape (39x33cm-15x13in) s. 19-Apr-4 Glerum, Amsterdam #227
£780 $1303 €1100 Garden in winter (24x17cm-9x7in) s. canvas on panel prov.exhib. 20-Oct-3 Glerum, Amsterdam #164/R
£2098 $3503 €3000 In the snow of Amsterdam (66x77cm-26x30in) s. prov. 30-Jun-3 Sotheby's, Amsterdam #275/R
£4333 $7800 €6500 Atmospheric winters day (99x121cm-39x48in) s. 21-Apr-4 Christie's, Amsterdam #151/R est:3000-5000

SOEST, Pierre Gerardus Cornelis van (1930-2001) Dutch
£667 $1220 €1000 Abstract composition (170x190cm-67x75in) s.d.72. 7-Jun-4 Glerum, Amsterdam #223/R

SOEST, Pieter Cornelisz van (17th C) Dutch
£95000 $161500 €138700 Dutch attack on English fleet in the Medway (69x110cm-27x43in) prov. 19-Nov-3 Christie's, Kensington #436/R est:30000-50000

SOETERIK, Theodoor (1810-1883) Dutch
£694 $1097 €1000 Cattle on a forest path (80x57cm-31x22in) s. 2-Sep-3 Christie's, Amsterdam #198/R est:1000-1500
Works on paper
£260 $475 €380 Boaters on a lake (37x35cm-15x14in) s. W/C. 29-Jan-4 Swann Galleries, New York #202/R

SOETOPO (1931-) Indonesia
£2703 $4514 €3946 Burung betet - parrot (140x100cm-55x39in) s.d.1966. 26-Oct-3 Christie's, Hong Kong #71/R est:45000-65000 (HK.D 35000)

SOFFA, Orville (20th C) American?
£694 $1200 €1013 Living instructions (43x58cm-17x23in) s. board. 15-Dec-3 Hindman, Chicago #11/R

SOFFIANTINO, Giacomo (1929-) Italian
£621 $1037 €900 Untitled (60x50cm-24x20in) s.d.1977. 17-Nov-3 Sant Agostino, Torino #135/R
£1259 $2102 €1800 Flea market (70x70cm-28x28in) s. d.1978 on stretcher. 26-Jun-3 Sant Agostino, Torino #227/R est:1800-2200
Works on paper
£272 $487 €400 Untitled (70x50cm-28x20in) s.d.1962 pastel card. 22-Mar-4 Sant Agostino, Torino #343/R
£340 $609 €500 Untitled (48x61cm-19x24in) s.d.1965 mixed media. 22-Mar-4 Sant Agostino, Torino #346/R

SOFFICI, Ardengo (1879-1964) Italian
£8054 $14416 €12000 Seascape (35x50cm-14x20in) s.d.1950 cardboard lit. 30-May-4 Meeting Art, Vercelli #88 est:10000
£10135 $17838 €15000 Summer landscape (37x26cm-15x10in) s.d.47 paper on canvas lit. 24-May-4 Christie's, Milan #294/R est:15000-20000
£26174 $46852 €39000 Landscape in Poggio (60x50cm-24x20in) s. i.verso painted 1959. 29-May-4 Farsetti, Prato #441/R est:30000-40000
£26846 $48054 €40000 On the road to Carmignano (45x55cm-18x22in) s. painted 1950. 29-May-4 Farsetti, Prato #501/R est:40000-50000
£28667 $52747 €43000 Landscape (70x50cm-28x20in) s. cardboard painted 1950 lit. 8-Jun-4 Finarte Semenzato, Milan #445/R est:42000-50000
£57971 $95072 €80000 Trofeino (65x50cm-26x20in) tempera board lit. 31-May-3 Farsetti, Prato #668/R est:80000-90000
£57971 $95072 €80000 Paesaggio a Poggia a Caiano (70x70cm-28x28in) s.d.32 exhib. 31-May-3 Farsetti, Prato #739/R est:80000-90000
£63758 $114128 €95000 Sunset in Tuscan countryside (64x48cm-25x19in) s.d.23 cardboard exhib.lit. 29-May-4 Farsetti, Prato #527/R est:80000-100000
Works on paper
£1338 $2315 €1900 Farm (6x10cm-2x4in) s.i. pencil. 9-Dec-3 Pandolfini, Florence #348/R est:2000-2200
£1439 $2360 €2000 Oxen (23x32cm-9x13in) pencil. 10-Jun-3 Pandolfini, Florence #346/R est:2000-2300
£5405 $9514 €8000 Tuscan landscape (23x32cm-9x13in) s. W/C paper on cardboard exec.c.1963 prov. 24-May-4 Christie's, Milan #295 est:8000-12000
£6000 $11040 €9000 Si vous les volez, qu'est-ce qu'ils me donneront apres ? (29x22cm-11x9in) s. pencil pastel W/C exec.1904. 11-Jun-4 Farsetti, Prato #567/R est:4800-5800
£7609 $12478 €10500 Landscape (23x31cm-9x12in) s. W/C exhib. 31-May-3 Farsetti, Prato #611/R est:10000-12000

SOFRONOVA, Antonina (1892-1966) Russian
Works on paper
£861 $1567 €1300 Composition (23x16cm-9x6in) W/C. 16-Jun-4 Claude Boisgirard, Paris #146/R

SOGARO, Oscar (1888-1967) Italian
£473 $894 €700 Village square (33x26cm-13x10in) s.d.48 cardboard. 20-Feb-4 Stadion, Trieste #66/R

SOGLOBOV, A (1897-1943) Russian
£627 $1147 €915 Coastal landscape (24x33cm-9x13in) s.d.1924. 9-Jun-4 Rasmussen, Copenhagen #1616/R (D.KR 7000)

SOGLOW, Otto (1900-1975) ?
Works on paper
£958 $1600 €1399 Woman's visit to museum is rewarded by a falling fig leaf (36x23cm-14x9in) s. pen ink sequential drawing exec.c.1950. 15-Nov-3 Illustration House, New York #52/R est:2000-3000

SOHIER, Alice Ruggles (1880-?) American
Works on paper
£250 $400 €365 Child sipping her soda (46x28cm-18x11in) s. W/C en grisaille. 21-Sep-3 Grogan, Boston #70/R

SOHL, Will (1906-1969) German
£733 $1320 €1100 Summer flowers in vase (70x70cm-28x28in) s.d.1927. 26-Apr-4 Rieber, Stuttgart #1246/R
£1049 $1783 €1500 Sylt. Seascape. Houses (49x68cm-19x27in) s.d.1948 1949 gouache Indian ink three prov. 26-Nov-3 Lempertz, Koln #989/R est:1500
Works on paper
£839 $1401 €1200 Coastal landscape (50x64cm-20x25in) s.d.6 II 48 W/C. 10-Oct-3 Winterberg, Heidelberg #2005/R
£1268 $2193 €1800 Waterlilies (51x72cm-20x28in) s.d.11.VI.1958 gouache Indian ink. 13-Dec-3 Lempertz, Koln #356/R est:1000

SOHLBERG, Harald (1869-1935) Norwegian
£4390 $8034 €6409 Winter night in Rondane (52x60cm-20x24in) s.d.1917 col lithograph. 7-Jun-4 Blomqvist, Oslo #395/R est:50000-70000 (N.KR 54000)

SOHN, Hermann (1895-1971) German
£470 $832 €700 Still life of flowers and fruit (110x65cm-43x26in) s.d. 30-Apr-4 Dr Fritz Nagel, Stuttgart #452/R

SOHN, Hermann (attrib) (1895-1971) German
£470 $832 €700 Mettingen (60x50cm-24x20in) 30-Apr-4 Dr Fritz Nagel, Stuttgart #451/R

SOHN, John August Wilhelm (1830-1899) German
£8235 $14000 €12023 Elegant lady with fan wearing a black shawl (135x101cm-53x40in) s. oval. 29-Oct-3 Christie's, Rockefeller NY #35/R est:15000-20000

SOHN, Niclaes (1767-1825) German
Works on paper
£2654 $4246 €3875 The dovecote (64x91cm-25x36in) s.d.1814 gouache paper on slate. 22-Sep-3 Rasmussen, Vejle #94/R est:10000-15000 (D.KR 28000)

SOHN-RETHEL, Otto (1877-1949) German
£433 $789 €650 Portrait of a young girl sitting at a table with a yellow duck and teddy bear (68x57cm-27x22in) 1-Jul-4 Van Ham, Cologne #1622/R
£567 $1031 €850 Portrait of a young girl sitting at a table with her teddy bear (70x60cm-28x24in) s.d.1915. 1-Jul-4 Van Ham, Cologne #1621/R

SOISSON, Jacques (20th C) ?
£451 $844 €658 Composition (33x24cm-13x9in) mono.d.92 prov. 25-Feb-4 Kunsthallen, Copenhagen #180/R (D.KR 5000)

SOKO, Hayashi (1777-1813) Japanese
Works on paper
£2600 $4342 €3770 Crane (130x29cm-51x11in) s. ink slight colour hanging scroll. 18-Jun-3 Christie's, London #288/R est:1500-2000

SOKOL, Erich (1933-) American
Works on paper
£1257 $2200 €1835 Well if this doesn't work we'd damn sure better get the net ready (44x32cm-17x13in) s. gouache ills board exec May 1962. 17-Dec-3 Christie's, Rockefeller NY #139/R est:3000-4000
£1796 $3000 €2622 Brigitte Bardot, France Nuyen, Rita Hayworth, Sophia Loren, Jane Mansfield (20x13cm-8x5in) pen ink gouache pencil en grisaille five. 15-Nov-3 Illustration House, New York #51/R est:4000-6000
£3429 $6000 €5006 It must be fate, my wife and your husband breaking their legs on the same day (51x38cm-20x15in) s. gouache ink illus board exec Dec 1959. 17-Dec-3 Christie's, Rockefeller NY #43/R est:4000-6000
£3429 $6000 €5006 Gosh - you mean some girls have zones that aren't erogenous (48x36cm-19x14in) s. gouache ills board exec 1973. 17-Dec-3 Christie's, Rockefeller NY #247/R est:4000-6000
£4000 $7000 €5840 Royalty at dinner (71x56cm-28x22in) s. gouache ink ills board exec Feb 1960 exhib.lit. 17-Dec-3 Christie's, Rockefeller NY #198/R est:4000-6000
£4571 $8000 €6674 Yes, Virginia there is a Santa Claus (42x31cm-17x12in) s. gouache ills board exec Jan 1963. 17-Dec-3 Christie's, Rockefeller NY #142/R est:5000-7000

SOKOLE, Miron (1901-) American
Works on paper
£353 $600 €515 Person inside (18x13cm-7x5in) s. mixed media. 9-Nov-3 Wright, Chicago #345

SOKOLOFF, A (19/20th C) Russian
£19444 $35000 €28388 Festivities in the square (70x100cm-28x39in) s. 23-Apr-4 Sotheby's, New York #21/R est:20000-30000

SOKOLOFF, Anatolio (1891-1971) Russian
£588 $1100 €882 First job of an immigrant (30x41cm-12x16in) s.d.62. 25-Jul-4 Bonhams & Butterfields, San Francisco #6101/R

SOKOLOFF, Ivan Ivanovitch (1823-1918) Russian
£3500 $5950 €5250 Young girl at stream (21x29cm-8x11in) s.d.1901 paper on board. 25-Nov-3 Christie's, London #167/R est:2000-3000

SOKOLOFF, Piotr Petrovitch (1821-1899) Russian
Works on paper
£600 $1074 €900 Two men greeting on the road to church (27x36cm-11x14in) s.d.1841 mixed media. 15-May-4 Hagelstam, Helsinki #41/R
£1100 $1870 €1606 Huntsman with two Borzoi (26x23cm-10x9in) s. W/C over pencil. 19-Nov-3 Sotheby's, London #67/R est:1000-1500

SOKOLOV, Pavel Petrovich (1826-1905) Russian
Works on paper
£1552 $2778 €2266 Horseplay in salon (30x38cm-12x15in) s.d.1881 W/C. 12-May-4 Dobiaschofsky, Bern #988/R est:3500 (S.FR 3600)

SOKOLOV, Pavel Petrovich (attrib) (1826-1905) Russian
Works on paper
£275 $500 €402 View of Hermitage, St Petersburg (18x23cm-7x9in) W/C. 8-Feb-4 William Jenack, New York #337

SOKOLOV, Pavel Petrovich (1899-1961) Russian
£556 $1000 €812 Portrait of the peoples's artist of Russian Federation L F Sovranskiy (55x45cm-22x18in) 24-Apr-4 Shishkin Gallery, Moscow #35/R est:1400-1600
£6389 $11500 €9328 Flowers (110x76cm-43x30in) 24-Apr-4 Shishkin Gallery, Moscow #36/R est:8000-10000
Works on paper
£389 $700 €568 Borodin opera Prince Igor decorations (28x43cm-11x17in) W/C. 24-Apr-4 Shishkin Gallery, Moscow #34/R

SOKOLOVSKAYA, Oxana D (1917-) Russian
£782 $1400 €1142 House on Point overlooking sea (41x53cm-16x21in) s.d.1948 board. 20-Mar-4 Sloans & Kenyon, Bethesda #1166/R

SOLANGE, E (19/20th C) French?
£1000 $1830 €1500 Fellahin au bord du canal (38x46cm-15x18in) s. 3-Jun-4 Tajan, Paris #339/R est:1200-1500

SOLANO, Nelsa (1921-) Spanish
£471 $800 €688 Dam (46x56cm-18x22in) s. 20-Nov-3 Galeria y Remates, Montevideo #107/R

SOLANO, Susana (1946-) Spanish
Sculpture
£7186 $12000 €10492 Que Duda Cabe no 3 (77x75x79cm-30x30x31in) steel lead exec 1987 prov. 12-Nov-3 Christie's, Rockefeller NY #574/R est:15000-20000

SOLARI, Achille (1835-?) Italian
£1056 $1690 €1500 Landscape near Naples (28x48cm-11x19in) s. 18-Sep-3 Rieber, Stuttgart #1348 est:1650
£5775 $9990 €8200 Naples from Sorrento. Capri from Sorrento (27x40cm-11x16in) one s. pair. 10-Dec-3 Finarte Semenzato, Rome #222/R est:8200-8700

SOLARI, Luis A (1918-1993) Uruguayan
£802 $1300 €1163 Fray Bentos (66x90cm-26x35in) s. 29-Jul-3 Galeria y Remates, Montevideo #105/R
Works on paper
£265 $500 €387 Toreador (46x36cm-18x14in) s.d.1950 mixed media. 22-Feb-4 Galeria y Remates, Montevideo #115/R
£408 $750 €596 Woman (24x16cm-9x6in) s. collage on fabric. 22-Jun-4 Galeria y Remates, Montevideo #143/R
£427 $700 €623 Branch (32x25cm-13x10in) s. collage prov. 3-Jun-3 Galeria y Remates, Montevideo #48

SOLARIO, Andrea (attrib) (1460-1522) Italian
£20000 $34600 €29200 Christ carrying the Cross (33x27cm-13x11in) panel. 11-Dec-3 Sotheby's, London #14/R est:20000-30000

SOLAVAGGIONE, Piero (1899-1979) Italian
£533 $981 €800 Bali (50x50cm-20x20in) s. s.verso. 14-Jun-4 Sant Agostino, Torino #116/R
£884 $1583 €1300 Trees along the Meletta (50x60cm-20x24in) s.d.1964. 22-Mar-4 Sant Agostino, Torino #369/R
£952 $1705 €1400 Landscape along the Po (50x60cm-20x24in) s.d.1966 s.i.verso. 22-Mar-4 Sant Agostino, Torino #536/R
£1103 $1843 €1600 Still life with peppers (44x47cm-17x19in) s. paper. 17-Nov-3 Sant Agostino, Torino #124/R est:1600
£1122 $2009 €1650 River landscape (50x60cm-20x24in) s. 22-Mar-4 Sant Agostino, Torino #537/R est:2000
£1333 $2453 €2000 Along the Po in Turin (30x40cm-12x16in) s.i.d.1975 s.i.d.verso. 14-Jun-4 Sant Agostino, Torino #334/R est:800-1000
£1379 $2303 €2000 Landscape (52x61cm-20x24in) s. s.i.d.1957 verso. 17-Nov-3 Sant Agostino, Torino #119/R est:1500-2000
£1517 $2534 €2200 Rural road (69x53cm-27x21in) s.d.1959 s.i.d.verso exhib. 17-Nov-3 Sant Agostino, Torino #126/R est:1800-2200
£1667 $3067 €2500 Autumnal landscape (53x70cm-21x28in) s. s.i.d.1954 verso. 14-Jun-4 Sant Agostino, Torino #333/R est:1500-2000

SOLBERG, Morten (1935-) American
£1463 $2400 €2136 Solitude, polar bear on iceberg (56x76cm-22x30in) s.i. s.verso acrylic on W/C board prov. 31-May-3 Brunk, Ashville #649/R est:4000-8000

SOLBES, Rafael (1940-1981) Spanish
£4483 $8069 €6500 Workmen eating (92x102cm-36x40in) s.d.62. 26-Jan-4 Ansorena, Madrid #888/R est:6000

SOLDAN, Uuno (1883-1954) Finnish
£302 $562 €450 Sunny winter's day (69x101cm-27x40in) s. 7-Mar-4 Bukowskis, Helsinki #450/R
£634 $1014 €900 Sunny winter's day (68x100cm-27x39in) s. 21-Sep-3 Bukowskis, Helsinki #475/R

SOLDAN-BROFELDT, Venny (1863-1945) Finnish
£805 $1482 €1200 Winter (20x31cm-8x12in) init. 25-Mar-4 Hagelstam, Helsinki #859
£1400 $2506 €2100 Flowers (22x16cm-9x6in) s. board. 15-May-4 Hagelstam, Helsinki #66/R est:1000
£1408 $2254 €2000 Flowers (22x15cm-9x6in) s. 18-Sep-3 Hagelstam, Helsinki #1017 est:600
£1429 $2600 €2100 Crocuses (19x24cm-7x9in) s.d.44. 8-Feb-4 Bukowskis, Helsinki #461/R est:700
£1469 $2497 €2100 The railway station in Viborg (15x17cm-6x7in) s. board. 29-Nov-3 Bukowskis, Helsinki #169/R est:1800-2000
£2081 $3870 €3100 Friends (43x30cm-17x12in) s.d.1928. 7-Mar-4 Bukowskis, Helsinki #451/R est:2000
£3239 $5604 €4600 Still life of flowers and potatoes (62x46cm-24x18in) s.d.1943. 13-Dec-3 Hagelstam, Helsinki #146/R est:4000
£5634 $9746 €8000 View in the skerries (35x71cm-14x28in) s. 13-Dec-3 Hagelstam, Helsinki #147/R est:4000
£27972 $47552 €40000 Girl seated on beach (40x35cm-16x14in) s.d.19 board. 29-Nov-3 Bukowskis, Helsinki #101/R est:2500-3000
Works on paper
£867 $1551 €1300 Child sleeping (14x13cm-6x5in) s. Indian ink pencil. 15-May-4 Hagelstam, Helsinki #67/R

SOLDATI, Atanasio (1896-1953) Italian
£301 $479 €439 Untitled (27x40cm-11x16in) s. 29-Apr-3 Louis Morton, Mexico #61/R (M.P 5000)
£486 $768 €700 Lively big city street (24x18cm-9x7in) s. board. 6-Sep-3 Arnold, Frankfurt #661/R
£2113 $3507 €3000 Composition (31x20cm-12x8in) tempera paper on canvas. 11-Jun-3 Finarte Semenzato, Milan #621/R
£3472 $5486 €5000 Composition (23x17cm-9x7in) tempera cardboard. 6-Sep-3 Meeting Art, Vercelli #351 est:5000
£4545 $7727 €6500 Untitled (19x29cm-7x11in) s. tempera card. 24-Nov-3 Christie's, Milan #154/R est:4000-6000
£7639 $12069 €11000 Untitled (16x24cm-6x9in) tempera board painted 1944. 6-Sep-3 Meeting Art, Vercelli #595 est:10000
£8784 $15459 €13000 Still life (50x40cm-20x16in) s.d.IX cardboard prov.exhib. 24-May-4 Christie's, Milan #222/R est:14000-18000
£14765 $26430 €22000 Composition (54x31cm-21x12in) s. board painted 1950. 29-May-4 Farsetti, Prato #486/R est:20000-25000
£17483 $29720 €25000 Stuck bird (70x70cm-28x28in) s. s.i.verso prov.exhib. 24-Nov-3 Christie's, Milan #263/R est:30000-40000
£22222 $37778 €32000 Small composition (46x33cm-18x13in) s. prov. 28-Oct-3 Il Ponte, Milan #251/R
£23448 $39159 €34000 Composition (50x50cm-20x20in) s. painted 1940-43. 17-Nov-3 Sant Agostino, Torino #277/R est:34000-40000
Works on paper
£1119 $1869 €1600 Composition (7x7cm-3x3in) s. mixed media. 26-Jun-3 Sant Agostino, Torino #203/R est:1000
£3356 $6208 €5000 Landscape (16x20cm-6x8in) s. col pencil. 11-Mar-4 Galleria Pace, Milan #128/R est:6000-8000

SOLDATI, Massimo (1959-) Italian
£878 $1546 €1300 Dream (80x80cm-31x31in) s.i.d.1998 verso exhib. 24-May-4 Christie's, Milan #104/R
£1818 $3091 €2600 Flight 2 (100x100cm-39x39in) s.i.d.1998 verso prov. 24-Nov-3 Christie's, Milan #73/R est:2500-3000

SOLDATICZ, Giorgio (1873-1955) Italian
£4000 $7360 €6000 Self-portrait with Giacomo Balla's wife (70x53cm-28x21in) s.i.d.1914. 8-Jun-4 Sotheby's, Milan #131/R est:6000-8000

SOLDE, Alexandre (1822-1893) French
£21053 $38737 €32000 Trophees de chasse (191x218cm-75x86in) s.d.1877. 24-Jun-4 Tajan, Paris #81/R est:8000-12000

SOLDENHOFF, Alexander Leo (1882-1951) Swiss
£452 $724 €660 Crouching figure (63x48cm-25x19in) s. s.i.d.1945 verso. 16-Sep-3 Philippe Schuler, Zurich #5637 (S.FR 1000)
£524 $964 €765 Flora in garden with watering can (46x38cm-18x15in) s. 14-Jun-4 Philippe Schuler, Zurich #5750 (S.FR 1200)

SOLDERA, Emilio (1874-1955) Italian
£306 $548 €450 Rural scene (30x40cm-12x16in) s. board. 22-Mar-4 Sant Agostino, Torino #42/R
£458 $792 €650 Ortica Station, Milan (30x37cm-12x15in) s. s.i.verso board. 9-Dec-3 Finarte Semenzato, Milan #11/R
£500 $920 €750 Stream (40x50cm-16x20in) s. board. 14-Jun-4 Sant Agostino, Torino #132/R

£872 $1562 €1300 Landscape in Lombardy (56x88cm-22x35in) s. 25-May-4 Finarte Semenzato, Milan #87/R est:1300-1500

SOLDI, Andrea (1703-1771) Italian
£1489 $2785 €2174 Portrait of gentleman (61x50cm-24x20in) s.d.1755. 25-Feb-4 Kunsthallen, Copenhagen #553/R est:10000 (D.KR 16500)
£9790 $16643 €14000 Portrait of lady, seated (172x101cm-68x40in) prov. 25-Nov-3 Hamilton Osborne King, Dublin #153/R est:15000-25000

SOLDI, Raul (1905-1994) Argentinian
£3516 $6400 €5133 Cuba. Glew (23x17cm-9x7in) s. paper pair. 29-Jun-4 Arroyo, Buenos Aires #107/R est:2500
£3552 $6500 €5186 Formosa (25x35cm-10x14in) board. 1-Jun-4 Arroyo, Buenos Aires #91
£4918 $9000 €7180 Village street (27x35cm-11x14in) board. 1-Jun-4 Arroyo, Buenos Aires #90
£5307 $9500 €7748 Figure (23x14cm-9x6in) s. tempera paper. 4-May-4 Arroyo, Buenos Aires #11/R est:5000
£5587 $10000 €8157 Landscape in Glew (17x22cm-7x9in) s. board. 4-May-4 Arroyo, Buenos Aires #73/R est:3400
£13260 $24000 €19360 Car (35x45cm-14x18in) canvas on cardboard. 30-Mar-4 Arroyo, Buenos Aires #84
£13966 $25000 €20390 Figure (52x42cm-20x17in) s. board. 4-May-4 Arroyo, Buenos Aires #84/R est:24000
£24590 $45000 €35901 Figure (55x65cm-22x26in) 1-Jun-4 Arroyo, Buenos Aires #68
£43716 $80000 €63825 Girl with scarf (55x45cm-22x18in) 1-Jun-4 Arroyo, Buenos Aires #81
Works on paper
£894 $1600 €1305 Reading (37x30cm-15x12in) ink. 11-May-4 Arroyo, Buenos Aires #94
£1319 $2400 €1926 Dream (37x29cm-15x11in) s. ink. 5-Jul-4 Arroyo, Buenos Aires #35/R est:1100
£8242 $15000 €12033 On the mountains (31x50cm-12x20in) s.d.38 W/C. 29-Jun-4 Arroyo, Buenos Aires #57/R est:15000

SOLE, Giovan Gioseffo dal (1654-1719) Italian
£13245 $24106 €20000 Arianna abandoned (50x51cm-20x20in) lit. 16-Jun-4 Christie's, Rome #422/R est:10000-15000

SOLENGHI, Giuseppe (1879-1944) Italian
£272 $487 €400 Lake Maggiore (33x45cm-13x18in) s. s.i.d.1934 board. 22-Mar-4 Sant Agostino, Torino #152/R
£317 $548 €450 Snowfall in Milan (16x11cm-6x4in) s. board. 10-Dec-3 Finarte Semenzato, Rome #216
£458 $792 €650 The Naviglio in Milan (61x46cm-24x18in) 9-Dec-3 Finarte Semenzato, Milan #115/R
£680 $1218 €1000 19th Century Milan (15x25cm-6x10in) s. board. 22-Mar-4 Sant Agostino, Torino #185/R
£1007 $1802 €1500 Old Milan with carriages (17x12cm-7x5in) s. board. 25-May-4 Finarte Semenzato, Milan #165/R est:500-600
£1087 $1783 €1500 Market in Chioggia (60x80cm-24x31in) s. s.i.verso. 27-May-3 Il Ponte, Milan #953/R
£4422 $7915 €6500 Chioggia (80x110cm-31x43in) s.i.d.1920. 22-Mar-4 Sant Agostino, Torino #263/R est:7000

SOLER GILL, Domingo (1871-1951) Spanish
£532 $862 €750 Landscape (33x38cm-13x15in) board. 20-May-3 Ansorena, Madrid #208/R
£940 $1748 €1400 Garden (28x36cm-11x14in) s. board. 2-Mar-4 Ansorena, Madrid #35/R
£1056 $1827 €1500 Lady and girl (70x50cm-28x20in) s.d.1918. 10-Dec-3 Castellana, Madrid #119/R

SOLER PUIG, Juan (1906-1984) Spanish
£303 $545 €442 Still life (64x80cm-25x31in) s. 25-Apr-4 Subastas Odalys, Caracas #73
£350 $585 €511 Rest as the world goes by (33x41cm-13x16in) s. 8-Oct-3 Christie's, Kensington #929/R
£420 $659 €613 At the flower stall (27x22cm-11x9in) s. 28-Aug-3 Christie's, Kensington #343
£480 $845 €701 Parisian street scene (40x32cm-16x13in) s. 18-May-4 Fellows & Sons, Birmingham #96/R
£500 $785 €730 Figures congregated before a statue on a Parisian street (38x46cm-15x18in) s. 28-Aug-3 Christie's, Kensington #340/R
£500 $785 €730 Elegant figures on a Parisian boulevard (60x81cm-24x32in) s. 28-Aug-3 Christie's, Kensington #341/R
£537 $950 €800 Pot maker (81x65cm-32x26in) s. 27-Apr-4 Durán, Madrid #62/R
£650 $1183 €949 Croquet on the beach (38x46cm-15x18in) s. 16-Jun-4 Christie's, Kensington #71/R
£738 $1307 €1100 Fishermen (66x81cm-26x32in) s. 27-Apr-4 Durán, Madrid #63/R
£750 $1178 €1095 Carriages and figures before the Arc de Triomphe (46x55cm-18x22in) s. 28-Aug-3 Christie's, Kensington #342/R
£1000 $1790 €1460 Elegant figures before a carriage in a Parisienne square (46x55cm-18x22in) s. 18-Mar-4 Christie's, Kensington #678/R est:1000-1500
£1100 $1969 €1606 Parisienne departure (46x55cm-18x22in) s. 18-Mar-4 Christie's, Kensington #676/R est:1000-1500
£1200 $1884 €1752 Elegant figures and carriages on a bustling Parisian boulevard (45x55cm-18x22in) s. 28-Aug-3 Christie's, Kensington #345/R est:800-1200
£1241 $2110 €1812 Still life with peppers (61x91cm-24x36in) s. 23-Nov-3 Subastas Odalys, Caracas #130/R
£1600 $2672 €2336 Figures before the Moulin Rouge (65x81cm-26x32in) s. 8-Oct-3 Christie's, Kensington #930/R est:1500-2000
£1800 $3330 €2628 Figures in a Parisian street scene (27x22cm-11x9in) s. sold with another by same hand. 14-Jul-4 Christie's, Kensington #1244/R est:800-1200
£1900 $3515 €2774 Lady on a Parisian street with a parasol (46x54cm-18x21in) s. 14-Jul-4 Christie's, Kensington #1232/R est:1000-1500
£1900 $3515 €2774 Snow at the opera house (46x53cm-18x21in) s. 14-Jul-4 Christie's, Kensington #1240/R est:1000-1500
£2382 $4050 €3478 Still life with bread (100x80cm-39x31in) s. 23-Nov-3 Subastas Odalys, Caracas #59/R est:3000

SOLIMENA, Francesco (1657-1747) Italian
£3500 $6055 €5110 Christ and the woman of Samria (47x61cm-19x24in) 12-Dec-3 Christie's, Kensington #236/R est:2500-3500
£16107 $29638 €24000 Vanitas - skull with ivy and books (23x38cm-9x15in) prov. 24-Mar-4 Dorotheum, Vienna #76/R est:14000-17000
£30000 $54900 €43800 Humility. Faith (48x37cm-19x15in) pair prov. 8-Jul-4 Sotheby's, London #158/R est:25000-35000
£32394 $56690 €46000 Eliah (102x77cm-40x30in) prov. 17-Dec-3 Christie's, Rome #511/R est:40000-60000
£33557 $62752 €50000 Scipio's continence (44x56cm-17x22in) exhib.lit. 25-Feb-4 Porro, Milan #66/R est:50000
£43000 $77400 €62780 Noli me Tangere (68x50cm-27x20in) 21-Apr-4 Christie's, London #85/R est:15000-20000
Works on paper
£927 $1687 €1400 L'apparition du Christ a Saint Francois (14x13cm-6x5in) black crayon prov. sold with sketch. 16-Jun-4 Piasa, Paris #35

SOLIMENA, Francesco (attrib) (1657-1747) Italian
£9864 $17656 €14500 Annonciation (82x63cm-32x25in) 19-Mar-4 Beaussant & Lefèvre, Paris #56/R est:4000-5000

SOLIMENA, Francesco (studio) (1657-1747) Italian
£8803 $15229 €12500 Portrait of the Cardinal Carlo Antonio De Luca (195x144cm-77x57in) 12-Dec-3 Finarte, Venice #357/R est:10000-12000
£13889 $25000 €20278 Rebecca and Eliezer at the well (151x114cm-59x45in) 22-Jan-4 Sotheby's, New York #188/R est:30000-50000

SOLIS, Juan Rodriquez de (attrib) (?) Spanish
£1205 $2000 €1759 Martyrs of Mount Ararat (25x51cm-10x20in) panel prov.lit. 30-Sep-3 Christie's, Rockefeller NY #376/R est:4000-6000

SOLLIER, Henri Alexandre (1886-?) French
£800 $1280 €1168 Still life dans l'atelier (40x32cm-16x13in) s. 17-Sep-3 Bonhams, Brooks & Langlois, Jersey #72/R
£850 $1522 €1250 Rocher de Ru (50x45cm-20x18in) s. 18-Mar-4 Peschetau-Badin Godeau & Leroy, Paris #54

SOLMAN, Joseph (1909-) American
£1816 $3250 €2651 Portrait (48x28cm-19x11in) s. 16-May-4 Wright, Chicago #151/R est:1000-1500
£2826 $5200 €4126 Portrait of a woman (61x41cm-24x16in) init. 10-Jun-4 Swann Galleries, New York #220/R est:6000-9000
£5000 $8000 €7300 Tonia (102x51cm-40x20in) s. 17-May-3 Bunte, Elgin #1311 est:800-1200

SOLODKOV, Alexei M (1880-1953) Russian
£1229 $2200 €1794 Sea and surf (132x93cm-52x37in) painted 1949. 29-May-4 Shishkin Gallery, Moscow #100/R est:6000-8000

SOLOGAUB, Leonida (1884-1956) Russian/Dutch
£600 $1092 €900 Farm, Bezuidenhout (73x59cm-29x23in) s. 30-Jun-4 Vendue Huis, Gravenhage #627

SOLOMKO, Sergei (1859-1926) Russian
£3231 $5557 €4717 Portrait of woman (41x26cm-16x10in) 3-Dec-3 AB Stockholms Auktionsverk #2654/R est:20000-25000 (S.KR 42000)
£7000 $12530 €10220 Russian beauty in headress (42x27cm-17x11in) s. 26-May-4 Sotheby's, London #96/R est:8000-12000
Works on paper
£1200 $2148 €1752 Costume design (33x25cm-13x10in) s.i. pencil W/C set of five. 26-May-4 Sotheby's, Olympia #407/R est:1500-2000
£5500 $9845 €8030 Young lovers (30x40cm-12x16in) s. W/C over panel oval. 26-May-4 Sotheby's, Olympia #442/R est:2000-3000

SOLOMON, Abraham (1824-1862) British
£700 $1281 €1022 Portrait of a lady wearing a pink dress (30x24cm-12x9in) s.i. panel. 6-Jul-4 Bonhams, Knightsbridge #170/R

SOLOMON, David (1945-) Canadian
Works on paper
£1136 $1852 €1659 Abstract (206x65cm-81x26in) mixed media five paneled folding screen. 23-Sep-3 Ritchie, Toronto #183/R est:3000-4000 (C.D 2500)

SOLOMON, Hyde (1911-1982) American
£240 $400 €350 Abstract composition (74x51cm-29x20in) s.d.1951 s.i.stretcher. 25-Oct-3 David Rago, Lambertville #1015

SOLOMON, Lance Vaiben (1913-1989) Australian
£826 $1405 €1206 Jetty, Booker Bay, Woy Woy (25x21cm-10x8in) s.d.1948 s.i.d.verso canvas on board. 29-Oct-3 Lawson Menzies, Sydney #103/R est:1500-2000 (A.D 2000)
£1145 $2084 €1672 Along the creek (61x76cm-24x30in) s. i.verso canvas on board. 16-Jun-4 Deutscher-Menzies, Melbourne #347/R est:3000-5000 (A.D 3000)

SOLOMON, Simeon (1840-1905) British
Works on paper
£778 $1300 €1136 Christ and St John (33x37cm-13x15in) s.d.1892 red chk board. 7-Oct-3 Sotheby's, New York #137
£900 $1656 €1314 Tormented conscience (39x30cm-15x12in) mono.i.d.1889 red pencil. 25-Mar-4 Christie's, Kensington #123/R

£2000 $3400 €2920 Study of a woman, bust-length in profile wearing a brown and blue dress (33x27cm-13x11in) s.d.22.12.94 W/C. 20-Nov-3 Christie's, London #141/R est:2000-3000
£2500 $4150 €3650 Head of a girl (35x26cm-14x10in) pencil. 1-Oct-3 Sotheby's, Olympia #163/R est:2500-3500
£2767 $4953 €4040 Good and Evil (27x40cm-11x16in) init.d.1889 brown white chk grey paper prov. 15-May-4 Christie's, Sydney #328/R est:6000-8000 (A.D 7000)
£3200 $5440 €4672 Spirit of Shelley (32x25cm-13x10in) init.i.d.1885 pencil col chks oval. 20-Nov-3 Christie's, London #140/R est:3000-5000
£5000 $9200 €7300 Head study of a girl (46x30cm-18x12in) bears init.d.1874 pencil. 8-Jun-4 Bonhams, New Bond Street #64/R est:5000-8000
£9800 $18032 €14308 Ophelia (41x46cm-16x18in) ink wash prov. 26-Mar-4 Sotheby's, London #71/R est:3000-5000

SOLOMONS, Estella Frances (1882-1968) Irish

£625 $1150 €950 West Donegal (25x33cm-10x13in) init. canvasboard. 22-Jun-4 De Veres Art Auctions, Dublin #123/R
£694 $1132 €1000 Coastal mountain landscape (24x34cm-9x13in) board prov. 24-Sep-3 James Adam, Dublin #137/R est:1000-1200
£1149 $2171 €1700 From the back strand, Marble Hall, Conty Donegal (25x34cm-10x13in) i.verso canvasboard. 17-Feb-4 Whyte's, Dublin #132/R est:1200-1500
£1181 $1924 €1700 Green Hollows (30x39cm-12x15in) board prov. 24-Sep-3 James Adam, Dublin #85/R est:1500-2000
£1275 $2257 €1900 Figures on the Strand, Kerry (30x39cm-12x15in) s. i.verso panel. 27-Apr-4 Whyte's, Dublin #23/R est:2000-3000
£1351 $2554 €2000 Sunset, Breaghy, County Donegal (24x34cm-9x13in) s. canvasboard. 17-Feb-4 Whyte's, Dublin #66/R est:2000-3000
£1479 $2558 €2100 Sea, West Kerry (34x44cm-13x17in) init.verso board. 10-Dec-3 Bonhams & James Adam, Dublin #189/R est:1500-2000
£1620 $2802 €2300 Seascape, Ballymoss, Co Donegal (31x38cm-12x15in) s. canvasboard. 10-Dec-3 Bonhams & James Adam, Dublin #190/R est:1500-2000
£2657 $4517 €3800 Seascape, Donegal (27x34cm-11x13in) s.indis.d.193 canvas on board. 18-Nov-3 Whyte's, Dublin #108/R est:2000-3000
£2958 $4732 €4200 Dublin Bay (30x38cm-12x15in) s.i. panel. 16-Sep-3 Whyte's, Dublin #18/R est:2000-3000
£3514 $6641 €5200 Self portrait in blue coat (34x27cm-13x11in) init.d.1926 panel prov.exhib. 17-Feb-4 Whyte's, Dublin #46/R est:4000-6000
£5282 $9137 €7500 View of Howth harbour (33x43cm-13x17in) s.d.1908 s.i.verso. 10-Dec-3 Bonhams & James Adam, Dublin #94/R est:6000-8000

SOLONEN, Jouko (1920-) Finnish

£405 $726 €600 Resting (90x80cm-35x31in) s.d.83. 8-May-4 Bukowskis, Helsinki #285/R

SOLOVIEV, A L (1938-) Russian

£1389 $2500 €2028 Nikuliha country (22x79cm-9x31in) oil on cardboard. 24-Apr-4 Shishkin Gallery, Moscow #85/R est:1400-1600

SOLOWEY, Ben (1900-1978) American

£4403 $7000 €6428 Still life with peonies and fern in blue and white coffee pot on draped table (76x51cm-30x20in) s. 10-Sep-3 Alderfer's, Hatfield #386/R est:5000-7000

SOLTAU, Hermann Wilhelm (1812-1861) German

Works on paper
£267 $477 €400 Illustration of a Goethe poem (63x46cm-25x18in) s.d.1845 gouache. 13-May-4 Bassenge, Berlin #5664/R

SOLTAU, Nicolaus (1877-1956) German

£510 $785 €800 Boat entering Cuxhaven harbour in the rain (46x65cm-18x26in) s. 4-Sep-2 Schopman, Hamburg #265/R

SOMAINI, Francesco (1926-) Italian

Sculpture
£2238 $3804 €3200 Untitled (42x12x30cm-17x5x12in) s.d.1962 metal. 24-Nov-3 Christie's, Milan #219/R est:1800-2200
£2238 $3804 €3200 Spring (55x55x50cm-22x22x20in) s.d.63 bronze. 24-Nov-3 Christie's, Milan #218/R est:3000-4000
£2754 $4516 €3800 Absolute (118x75cm-46x30in) concrete wood rust iron exhib.lit. 27-May-3 Il Ponte, Milan #555/R
£4056 $6895 €5800 Composition (67x38x30cm-26x15x12in) s.d.61 bronze iron. 20-Nov-3 Finarte Semenzato, Milan #205/R est:2500-2800
£8392 $14266 €12000 Untitled (29x48x39cm-11x19x15in) s.d.1977 bronze concrete. 24-Nov-3 Christie's, Milan #220/R est:3000-4000
£41844 $67787 €59000 L'education. L'amour (65x130cm-26x51in) s.d.1829 bas relief marble pair lit. 21-May-3 Daguerre, Paris #294/R est:45000-60000
£60000 $110400 €87600 Classical lovers with Cupid. Domestic scene with classical figures (63x128cm-25x50in) i.d.1829 marble relief pair. 10-Jun-4 Christie's, London #78/R est:30000-50000

SOMARE, Guido (1923-2003) Italian

Works on paper
£333 $613 €500 Nude (45x38cm-18x15in) s. pen. 8-Jun-4 Finarte Semenzato, Milan #257/R

SOMELLI, Guido (1881-?) Italian

£324 $531 €450 View of Venice (28x38cm-11x15in) 5-Jun-3 Adma, Formigine #202

SOMER, Hendrik van (1615-1685) Dutch

£38889 $70000 €56778 Saint John the Baptist (185x151cm-73x59in) 22-Jan-4 Sotheby's, New York #81/R est:80000-120000

SOMER, Hendrik van (attrib) (1615-1685) Dutch

£4930 $8627 €7000 Saint Jerome (92x71cm-36x28in) i. oval. 17-Dec-3 Christie's, Rome #447/R est:7000-10000

SOMER, Paul van II (c.1649-1694) Flemish

Works on paper
£656 $1200 €958 Putti parading with the attributes of war among classical ruins (19x28cm-7x11in) pen brown ink card stock. 29-Jan-4 Swann Galleries, New York #177/R

SOMERS, Louis (1813-1880) Belgian

£2000 $3660 €3000 Compagnie musicale dans une auberge (38x46cm-15x18in) s. panel. 7-Jun-4 Palais de Beaux Arts, Brussels #105/R est:3500-5000
£2013 $3725 €3000 The chat (63x47cm-25x19in) s. panel. 13-Mar-4 De Vuyst, Lokeren #299/R est:1500-2000

SOMERSCALES, Thomas (1842-1927) British

£350 $601 €500 Village in sunny landscape (6x16cm-2x6in) mono.d.1892 panel. 5-Dec-3 Michael Zeller, Lindau #796
£7000 $13090 €10220 Marine study of French fishing boats (28x46cm-11x18in) s.d.1917. 24-Feb-4 Tayler & Fletcher, Cheltenham #6
£13000 $20800 €18980 Under small canvas (61x107cm-24x42in) s.d.05 bears i.verso prov. 16-Sep-3 Bonhams, New Bond Street #74/R est:10000-15000
£21000 $39690 €30660 Windjammer heaving to off Valparaiso (49x76cm-19x30in) s.d.1905 lit. 17-Feb-4 Bonhams, New Bond Street #77/R est:2500-35000
Works on paper
£460 $869 €672 Three masted clipper and tug boat on choppy sea (24x19cm-9x7in) s. W/C. 17-Feb-4 Fellows & Sons, Birmingham #104/R

SOMERSCALES, Thomas (attrib) (1842-1927) British

£2200 $3674 €3212 Steamship off the coast (41x57cm-16x22in) 14-Oct-3 Sotheby's, London #245/R est:1500-2000

SOMERSET, Richard Gay (1848-1928) British

£360 $601 €526 Path though woods (69x51cm-27x20in) s. i.verso. 11-Nov-3 Bonhams, Knightsbridge #33/R
£1739 $2800 €2539 View of the Roman Theatre at Aries with figures seated amongst the ruins (25x36cm-10x14in) s. board. 14-Jan-4 Christie's, Rockefeller NY #81/R est:1500-2500

SOMERVILLE, Edith Oenone (1858-1949) British

£1100 $2035 €1606 Upper Lake, Killarney (41x51cm-16x20in) s. i. verso. 14-Jul-4 Christie's, Kensington #1053/R est:1000-1500
£2162 $4086 €3200 Torry Bay, County Donegal (46x61cm-18x24in) s. s.i.verso prov.exhib. 17-Feb-4 Whyte's, Dublin #150/R est:2000-3000
£3846 $6538 €5500 At Etaples (41x33cm-16x13in) s. i.d.1898 verso. 25-Nov-3 De Veres Art Auctions, Dublin #63/R est:5000-7000
Works on paper
£338 $639 €500 Sleeping infant with mother and child keeping watch (15x47cm-6x19in) d.Ocotber 1903 pencil. 17-Feb-4 Whyte's, Dublin #148
£574 $1085 €850 Man seated with arms folded across his chest. Man seated at a rool top desk (18x18cm-7x7in) chl pencil two. 17-Feb-4 Whyte's, Dublin #145
£642 $1213 €950 An artist seated at her easel (22x14cm-9x6in) studio st. panel. 17-Feb-4 Whyte's, Dublin #143
£642 $1213 €950 Woman standing by a window. Landscape with quayside building and boats (36x22cm-14x9in) indis i. chl two. 17-Feb-4 Whyte's, Dublin #147
£676 $1277 €1000 Hunting scenes (9x13cm-4x5in) pencil set of four. 17-Feb-4 Whyte's, Dublin #144 est:500-700
£878 $1660 €1300 Woman asleep in a chair, thought to be Violet Martin (15x23cm-6x9in) mono.d.22 May 1888 pencil double-sided. 17-Feb-4 Whyte's, Dublin #142/R est:800-1200

SOMERVILLE, Stuart (1908-1983) British

£400 $708 €584 Arrangement of mixed roses (18x38cm-7x15in) s. board. 27-Apr-4 Bonhams, Knightsbridge #129/R
£400 $732 €584 Figure on a sunny mountain track (39x49cm-15x19in) s.d.1932 board. 8-Jul-4 Lawrence, Crewkerne #1661
£407 $728 €594 Floral still life (51x71cm-20x28in) s.d.50. 4-May-4 Ritchie, Toronto #47/R est:1500-2000 (C.D 1000)
£550 $974 €803 Still life of clematis and other flowers (26x20cm-10x8in) s. sold with another by same hand. 27-Apr-4 Bonhams, Knightsbridge #47
£600 $1122 €876 Still life of flowers (30x36cm-12x14in) s. board. 20-Jul-4 Sworder & Son, Bishops Stortford #683/R
£680 $1204 €993 Still life of hollyhocks. Still life of mixed flowers (34x24cm-13x9in) s. pair. 27-Apr-4 Bonhams, Knightsbridge #133/R
£850 $1420 €1241 Flowerpiece (76x63cm-30x25in) s.d.52 exhib. 8-Oct-3 Christie's, Kensington #961/R
£980 $1774 €1431 Still life of flowers in a glass vase on a ledge (48x38cm-19x15in) s.d.50. 16-Apr-4 Keys, Aylsham #679/R
£1000 $1620 €1450 Mixed flowers in a vase on a marble ledge (61x51cm-24x20in) s.d.49 two. 30-Jul-3 Hamptons Fine Art, Godalming #256 est:700-1000

SOMM, Henry (1844-1907) French

£3600 $6588 €5400 Elegantes chez le chapelier (55x38cm-22x15in) s. 6-Jun-4 Osenat, Fontainebleau #242/R est:3000-3500
Works on paper
£493 $893 €750 Elegante appelant un fiacre (19x27cm-7x11in) s. ink. 19-Apr-4 Boscher, Cherbourg #815
£544 $974 €800 Une elegante dans la rue (31x21cm-12x8in) s. W/C pen black ink. 19-Mar-4 Piasa, Paris #179
£680 $1217 €1000 Portrait d'une Japonaise en costume traditionnel (22x14cm-9x6in) s. W/C gouache pen brown ink. 17-Mar-4 Tajan, Paris #150
£769 $1308 €1100 Elegante appelant un fiacre (19x27cm-7x11in) s. ink pseudonyme of Francois Sommier. 24-Nov-3 Boscher, Cherbourg #764/R
£800 $1432 €1200 Elegante au moulin ruge. W/C. 16-May-4 Osenat, Fontainebleau #49/R
£867 $1595 €1300 La Japonaise (20x15cm-8x6in) s. W/C. 9-Jun-4 Beaussant & Lefèvre, Paris #215/R
£1530 $2800 €2234 Elegantly dressed woman at a door (25x20cm-10x8in) s. W/C. 29-Jan-4 Swann Galleries, New York #272/R est:800-1200
£2100 $3507 €3066 Elegante sur la plage dans le vent (30x17cm-12x7in) s.d.1883 W/C. 22-Oct-3 Bonhams, New Bond Street #17/R est:1800-2500

SOMME, Jacob (1862-1940) Norwegian
£5988 $10180 €8742 Interior (55x67cm-22x26in) s.indis.i.d.16. 19-Nov-3 Grev Wedels Plass, Oslo #5/R est:50000 (N.KR 70000)

SOMME, Theophile (1871-1952) French
Sculpture
£1000 $1570 €1460 Semi draped young beauty. bronze. 15-Dec-2 Desmond Judd, Cranbrook #544
£2400 $4080 €3504 Figure of a maiden (34cm-13in) s. gilt bronze. 25-Nov-3 Sotheby's, Olympia #156/R est:1800-2200

SOMMER, Carl August (1829-?) German
£1056 $1827 €1500 Hudson high mountains. Sunset in New York (22x31cm-9x12in) s. i. verso two. 12-Dec-3 Altus, Berlin #574/R est:1500
£3125 $5219 €4500 Holstein (66x102cm-26x40in) s. 24-Oct-3 Ketterer, Hamburg #110/R est:5500-6000

SOMMER, Carl Wilhelm August (1839-1921) German
Sculpture
£1329 $2219 €1900 Bacchantal figure (61cm-24in) i. bronze. 27-Jun-3 Michael Zeller, Lindau #2054/R est:1900
£1453 $2500 €2121 Harvest (79cm-31in) s.st.f.Fondnelli Roma brown pat bronze exec.c.1880. 7-Dec-3 Treadway Gallery, Cincinnati #510/R est:2500-3500
£15000 $25950 €21900 Beelzebub, Lord of the Flies (123cm-48in) s. green brown pat bronze col marble base lit. 12-Dec-3 Sotheby's, London #266/R est:15000-20000

SOMMER, Charles A (19th C) American
£5294 $9000 €7729 Catskill Mountain (51x91cm-20x36in) s. 31-Oct-3 North East Auctions, Portsmouth #1734

SOMMER, Elke (1940-) German
£399 $678 €570 Three women (100x74cm-39x29in) s.d.1980. 20-Nov-3 Weidler, Nurnberg #7198
£455 $773 €650 Dancing girl (90x59cm-35x23in) s.d.1990. 20-Nov-3 Weidler, Nurnberg #7197

SOMMER, F (1822-1901) Swiss
£1413 $2600 €2063 Italian scene (46x61cm-18x24in) s. 28-Mar-4 Carlsen Gallery, Greenville #374/R

SOMMER, Frederick (1905-1999) American
Photographs
£2825 $5000 €4125 Anatomy of an atlas, 1985 (14x12cm-6x5in) s.i.d.1985 verso gelatin silver print prov. 27-Apr-4 Christie's, Rockefeller NY #299/R est:5500-6500
£2910 $5500 €4249 Pottery collage (25x31cm-10x12in) s.d.1992 gelatin silver print. 17-Feb-4 Christie's, Rockefeller NY #254/R est:5000-7000
£4790 $8000 €6993 Circumnavigation of the blood (11x15cm-4x6in) s.i.d.1950 verso gelatin silver print printed c.1970 prov.lit. 20-Oct-3 Christie's, Rockefeller NY #121/R est:5000-7000
£4802 $8500 €7011 Arizona landscape (19x24cm-7x9in) s.i.d.1943 gelatin silver print lit. 27-Apr-4 Christie's, Rockefeller NY #301/R est:6000-8000
£5988 $10000 €8742 Moon culmination (24x19cm-9x7in) s.i.d.1951 verso gelatin silver print printed later lit. 20-Oct-3 Christie's, Rockefeller NY #120/R est:7000-9000
£6780 $12000 €9899 Cut paper (23x19cm-9x7in) s.i.d.1970 verso photo. 28-Apr-4 Sotheby's, New York #189/R est:7000-10000
£11299 $20000 €16497 Arizona landscape (19x24cm-7x9in) s.i.d.1943 verso photo printed later prov. 28-Apr-4 Sotheby's, New York #150/R est:8000-12000
£19209 $34000 €28045 Livia (19x24cm-7x9in) s.i.d.1948 verso photo prov.lit. 27-Apr-4 Sotheby's, New York #19/R est:15000-25000
£22599 $40000 €32995 Selected images from chicken parts (24x19cm-9x7in) s.d.1990 gelatin silver print set of six prov.lit. 27-Apr-4 Christie's, Rockefeller NY #302/R est:30000-40000
Prints
£5650 $10000 €8249 Collage (37x42cm-15x17in) s.d.1992 hand col lithograph collage prov. 27-Apr-4 Christie's, Rockefeller NY #300/R est:5000-7000

SOMMER, Georg (19th C) German
£350 $584 €500 Departing fishing boats (80x120cm-31x47in) s. 28-Jun-3 Bolland & Marotz, Bremen #734

SOMMER, William (1867-1949) American
Works on paper
£270 $500 €394 Portrait of a girl (48x30cm-19x12in) estate st. W/C pen ink. 13-Mar-4 DeFina, Austinburg #724/R
£338 $625 €493 Vase with flowers and sleeping cat (36x25cm-14x10in) s. W/C graphite. 16-Jan-4 Aspire, Cleveland #44/R
£346 $620 €505 Flower pots and vases (58x43cm-23x17in) s.d.Feb 23 91 pencil dr. 19-Mar-4 Aspire, Cleveland #73/R
£489 $900 €714 Clown and horse (28x38cm-11x15in) W/C pen ink. 10-Jun-4 Swann Galleries, New York #221/R
£545 $975 €796 Seated young boy (38x28cm-15x11in) with sig. W/C. 19-Mar-4 Aspire, Cleveland #71 est:800-1200
£569 $950 €831 Circus horse and ringmaster (28x38cm-11x15in) s. W/C ink. 14-Nov-3 Aspire, Cleveland #140
£628 $1125 €917 Seated young boy with curly golden hair (38x28cm-15x11in) with sig. W/C. 19-Mar-4 Aspire, Cleveland #72/R est:800-1200
£649 $1200 €948 Country lane (30x46cm-12x18in) s.d.1942 W/C. 13-Mar-4 DeFina, Austinburg #618a/R
£734 $1225 €1072 Cubist style landscape scene with cattle grazing (41x25cm-16x10in) s. W/C. 14-Nov-3 Aspire, Cleveland #141
£811 $1500 €1184 Brandywine landscape (48x64cm-19x25in) s.d.1936 W/C. 13-Mar-4 DeFina, Austinburg #726/R est:2000-3000
£865 $1600 €1263 Country hillside landscape with buildings and pond (30x43cm-12x17in) s.d.1942 W/C. 13-Mar-4 DeFina, Austinburg #619/R est:800-1000
£1648 $3000 €2406 Fruit and floral still life with picture (41x36cm-16x14in) s. W/C pen ink. 19-Jun-4 Rachel Davis, Shaker Heights #381 est:1200-1800
£2994 $5000 €4371 Artist's studio (25x36cm-10x14in) s. W/C. 25-Oct-3 Rachel Davis, Shaker Heights #299/R

SOMMERFELD, William (1906-) American
£225 $375 €326 High View Hotel porch, Block Island (38x56cm-15x22in) s. canvasboard. 30-Jun-3 Winter Associates, Plainville #78/R

SOMMERS, Otto (19th C) American
£1096 $1863 €1600 Herd of cows returning home in mountain landscape (93x117cm-37x46in) s.d.1873. 5-Nov-3 Hugo Ruef, Munich #1106/R est:1200
£1512 $2600 €2208 Idyllic landscape of the voyage of life, youth (66x91cm-26x36in) s. 6-Dec-3 Pook & Pook, Downington #415/R est:2500-3500

SOMOGYI, Daniel (1837-1890) Hungarian
£833 $1317 €1200 Dachstein in evening (78x110cm-31x43in) s.d.1879. 6-Sep-3 Arnold, Frankfurt #663
£1667 $2633 €2400 Konigsee with St Bartholoma (77x111cm-30x44in) s.i.d.1879. 6-Sep-3 Arnold, Frankfurt #662/R est:1200
£3311 $6060 €5000 Mountain landscape (77x111cm-30x44in) s.i.d.1879. 8-Apr-4 Dorotheum, Vienna #273/R est:3000-3500

SOMOGYI, Istvan (1897-) Hungarian
£347 $549 €500 Pussta landscape with horses (60x70cm-24x28in) s. lit. 19-Sep-3 Schloss Ahlden, Ahlden #1555/R
£347 $549 €500 Galloping horses (60x80cm-24x31in) s. lit. 19-Sep-3 Schloss Ahlden, Ahlden #1554/R
£556 $878 €800 Horses in pasture (49x69cm-19x27in) s. board lit. 19-Sep-3 Schloss Ahlden, Ahlden #1556/R

SOMOV, Konstantin (1869-1939) Russian
Works on paper
£2685 $4966 €4000 Les amoureux sur un banc (22x28cm-9x11in) s.d.1912 gouache. 15-Mar-4 Claude Boisgirard, Paris #105 est:1800-2000
£5988 $10000 €8742 Two ladies in the country (10x8cm-4x3in) s.d.22 W/C. 21-Oct-3 Christie's, Rockefeller NY #106 est:7000-9000
£6000 $10200 €9000 Miniature landscape with rainbow (4x8cm-2x3in) init. W/C. 25-Nov-3 Christie's, London #211/R est:5000-7000
£15894 $28927 €24000 Lady with veil (13x9cm-5x4in) s.d.1928 W/C gouache oval. 15-Jun-4 Rossini, Paris #67 est:1000-1500
£105556 $190000 €154112 Puppet theatre (27x32cm-11x13in) s.i.d.1931 gouache. 23-Apr-4 Sotheby's, New York #104/R est:40000-60000

SOMVILLE (1923-) Belgian
Works on paper
£1678 $2803 €2400 Femme au chapeau fleuri (70x53cm-28x21in) s.d.1968 pastel. 11-Oct-3 De Vuyst, Lokeren #341/R est:2000-2400

SOMVILLE, Roger (1923-) Belgian
£1528 $2551 €2200 Femme a la plante (40x50cm-16x20in) s. 21-Oct-3 Campo, Vlaamse Kaai #575 est:4000-5000
£3931 $7272 €5700 Arlequin (80x100cm-31x39in) s. 16-Feb-4 Horta, Bruxelles #27/R est:1200-1500
£4276 $7868 €6500 Visage de femme (60x72cm-24x28in) s. 22-Jun-4 Palais de Beaux Arts, Brussels #318/R est:4500-6000
£7333 $13420 €11000 La sevillane (92x73cm-36x29in) s.d.1977 verso. 7-Jun-4 Palais de Beaux Arts, Brussels #387/R est:6000-8000
Works on paper
£276 $510 €400 Tete d'homme (19x20cm-7x8in) s.d.1969. 19-Jan-4 Horta, Bruxelles #325
£329 $605 €500 Deux figures (53x71cm-21x28in) s.d.1969 Chinese ink wash. 22-Jun-4 Palais de Beaux Arts, Brussels #317
£336 $614 €500 Le peintre et son modele (37x55cm-15x22in) s.d.1972 mixed media. 8-Jul-4 Campo, Vlaamse Kaai #239
£372 $654 €550 Tete de profil (36x26cm-14x10in) s. ink. 18-May-4 Galerie Moderne, Brussels #251
£417 $696 €600 Un des roles de peintre (55x72cm-22x28in) s.d.1979 ink. 21-Oct-3 Campo, Vlaamse Kaai #576
£430 $783 €650 Baigneuse (36x27cm-14x11in) s. india ink. 16-Jun-4 Hotel des Ventes Mosan, Brussels #283
£439 $830 €650 Le hibou (64x47cm-25x19in) s.i.d.61 ink. 17-Feb-4 Galerie Moderne, Brussels #141/R
£467 $859 €700 Arlequin (71x53cm-28x21in) s.i.d.1966 india ink wash. 14-Jun-4 Horta, Bruxelles #285
£473 $832 €700 Femme (41x37cm-16x15in) s. gouache. 18-May-4 Galerie Moderne, Brussels #247/R
£541 $951 €800 Self-portrait (48x59cm-19x23in) s.d.1975 dr. 18-May-4 Galerie Moderne, Brussels #133/R
£604 $1105 €900 Arlequin (75x55cm-30x22in) s. pastel. 8-Jul-4 Campo, Vlaamse Kaai #238/R
£634 $1096 €900 Deux femmes (46x58cm-18x23in) s.d.1967 wash Indian ink. 13-Dec-3 De Vuyst, Lokeren #295
£1342 $2483 €2000 Composition with horse's head and figure (48x63cm-19x25in) s.d.1965 Indian ink. 13-Mar-4 De Vuyst, Lokeren #300/R est:2000-3000
£1689 $3024 €2500 Simone a la digue (54x72cm-21x28in) s.d.1963 wash. 10-May-4 Horta, Bruxelles #31 est:1000-1200

SON, Johannes (1859-?) French
£940 $1729 €1400 Nature morte (65x105cm-26x41in) s. 28-Mar-4 Anaf, Lyon #244

SON, Joris van (1623-1667) Flemish
£27778 $50000 €40556 Peaches and oysters on a silver platter with grapes and lobster on a table (34x44cm-13x17in) prov. 23-Jan-4 Christie's, Rockefeller NY #152/R est:50000-70000
£28000 $51240 €40880 Still life with grapes, plums, apricots and other fruit (61x76cm-24x30in) s.d.1663 prov. 8-Jul-4 Sotheby's, London #142/R est:15000-20000

SONDERBORG, Karl Horst (20th C) German
Works on paper
£369 $687 €550 Composition (66x50cm-26x20in) s.d.64 Indian ink. 3-Mar-4 Artcurial Briest, Paris #517
£403 $749 €600 Composition (108x75cm-43x30in) s.d.65 Indian ink. 3-Mar-4 Artcurial Briest, Paris #521
£503 $936 €750 Composition (78x57cm-31x22in) s.d.64 Indian ink. 3-Mar-4 Artcurial Briest, Paris #518
£537 $999 €800 Composition (65x50cm-26x20in) s.d.62 Indian ink paper on cardboard prov. 3-Mar-4 Artcurial Briest, Paris #515
£537 $999 €800 Composition (108x75cm-43x30in) s.d.65 Indian ink. 3-Mar-4 Artcurial Briest, Paris #520/R
£604 $1124 €900 Composition (101x64cm-40x25in) s.i.d.65 Indian ink prov. 3-Mar-4 Artcurial Briest, Paris #519/R

SONDERBORG, Kurt R H (1923-) Danish
£3020 $5406 €4500 15.8.90 21.05-21 27 h (101x73cm-40x29in) s.i.d.90 acrylic. 25-May-4 Karl & Faber, Munich #540/R est:6000
£11189 $19245 €16000 2.VIII.55 19:47 - 21:39 h (52x67cm-20x26in) s.d. s.i.d. verso egg tempera prov.exhib. 5-Dec-3 Ketterer, Munich #318/R est:15000-20000
£13287 $22587 €19000 June 16-61 (109x71cm-43x28in) s.d. 61 oil tempera foil panel exhib. 29-Nov-3 Villa Grisebach, Berlin #341/R est:15000-20000
Works on paper
£700 $1113 €1015 Rigg II (116x89cm-46x35in) s.d.68 pencil brush ink on canvas prov. 11-Sep-3 Christie's, Kensington #198/R est:3000-4000

SONDERGAARD, Jens (1895-1957) Danish
£305 $548 €445 Female nude (35x30cm-14x12in) cardboard prov. 24-Apr-4 Rasmussen, Havnen #4192/R (D.KR 3400)
£812 $1519 €1186 Woodland picture (90x100cm-35x39in) s.d.28-29 maj 56. 25-Feb-4 Kunsthallen, Copenhagen #251/R (D.KR 9000)
£948 $1744 €1384 Landscape with fields and pine trees (39x39cm-15x15in) s. canvas on panel. 29-Mar-4 Rasmussen, Copenhagen #472/R (D.KR 10500)
£1353 $2502 €1975 View across Limfjorden (66x78cm-26x31in) s. exhib. 15-Mar-4 Rasmussen, Vejle #659/R est:20000 (D.KR 15000)
£1517 $2427 €2200 Summer landscape (65x75cm-26x30in) s. 17-Sep-3 Kunsthallen, Copenhagen #293/R est:15000 (D.KR 16000)
£1690 $2823 €2467 Fishing village (89x105cm-35x41in) s.indis.d.31. 7-Oct-3 Rasmussen, Copenhagen #307/R est:20000-25000 (D.KR 18000)
£1690 $2823 €2467 Boasts on beach (73x90cm-29x35in) s.d.45. 7-Oct-3 Rasmussen, Copenhagen #365/R est:20000-25000 (D.KR 18000)
£1894 $3503 €2765 Dune landscape with houses (85x118cm-33x39in) s. 15-Mar-4 Rasmussen, Vejle #658/R est:25000 (D.KR 21000)
£2076 $3819 €3031 View of Hundested Harbour (90x118cm-35x46in) d.maj1953 1956. 29-Mar-4 Rasmussen, Copenhagen #214/R est:25000 (D.KR 23000)
£2330 $4194 €3402 Landscape with man walking, trees and view towards water (90x100cm-35x39in) s.d.1944. 24-Apr-4 Rasmussen, Havnen #4248/R est:25000-30000 (D.KR 26000)
£2437 $4484 €3558 Hilly landscape with cow in foreground (78x90cm-31x35in) s. 29-Mar-4 Rasmussen, Copenhagen #571/R est:20000-25000 (D.KR 27000)
£2527 $4726 €3689 Landscape (80x100cm-31x39in) s. 25-Feb-4 Kunsthallen, Copenhagen #236/R est:25000 (D.KR 28000)
£2938 $4701 €4260 Evening landscape (100x120cm-39x47in) s.d.49. 17-Sep-3 Kunsthallen, Copenhagen #287/R est:20000 (D.KR 31000)
£3167 $5670 €4624 Landscape with Heltborg Church in background (87x103cm-34x41in) s. 10-May-4 Rasmussen, Vejle #574/R est:30000 (D.KR 35000)
£3226 $5484 €4710 Fishing boats by the west coast (80x100cm-31x39in) s. 10-Nov-3 Rasmussen, Vejle #633/R est:25000-30000 (D.KR 35000)
£4739 $7583 €6872 Figures on the beach, sailing vessels on the fjord (100x122cm-39x48in) s. 17-Sep-3 Kunsthallen, Copenhagen #65/R est:50000 (D.KR 50000)
£9025 $16606 €13177 Two figures (138x150cm-54x59in) s.d.47 s.d.1947 verso prov. 29-Mar-4 Rasmussen, Copenhagen #37/R est:100000 (D.KR 100000)
Works on paper
£478 $894 €698 Houses in Stenbjerg (40x50cm-16x20in) s.d.1950 W/C exhib. 25-Feb-4 Kunsthallen, Copenhagen #194 (D.KR 5300)

SONDERGAARD, Ole (19/20th C) Danish
£538 $968 €785 Interior scene with girl (59x44cm-23x17in) s. 24-Apr-4 Rasmussen, Havnen #2330 (D.KR 6000)

SONDERGAARD, Poul (1905-1986) Danish
Sculpture
£6318 $11814 €9224 Standing girl (140cm-55in) s. bronze prov. 24-Feb-4 Rasmussen, Copenhagen #55/R est:75000 (D.KR 70000)
£8574 $16033 €12518 Standing girl (203cm-80in) bronze prov. 24-Feb-4 Rasmussen, Copenhagen #57/R est:75000 (D.KR 95000)
£10830 $20253 €15812 Seated girl (140cm-55in) bronze prov. 24-Feb-4 Rasmussen, Copenhagen #56/R est:50000 (D.KR 120000)

SONDERLAND, Fritz (1836-1896) German
£1133 $2063 €1700 Postillon d'Amour (30x24cm-12x9in) s. panel. 1-Jul-4 Van Ham, Cologne #1623/R est:1800
£1544 $2840 €2300 Kittens playing (66x44cm-26x17in) s.d.85 verso. 26-Mar-4 Bolland & Marotz, Bremen #591a/R est:2200

SONDERMANN, Hermann (1832-1901) German
£909 $1518 €1300 Children playing with kittens (21x24cm-8x9in) s.d.1864. 30-Jun-3 Sotheby's, Amsterdam #301/R

SONG MAOJIN (fl.1585-1620) Chinese
Works on paper
£2059 $3500 €3006 Landscapes (79x99cm-31x39in) s. ink col hanging scrolls pair prov. 4-Nov-3 Bonhams & Butterfields, San Francisco #3432/R est:4000-6000

SONG QIXIANG (1917-) Chinese
Works on paper
£1500 $2685 €2190 New Years painting (46x69cm-18x27in) s.i. col in hanging scroll prov. 6-May-4 Sotheby's, London #102/R est:1400-1800

SONG WENZHI (1918-1999) Chinese
Works on paper
£2200 $4048 €3212 Zhangnan in early spring (42x37cm-17x15in) s. ink hanging scroll. 8-Jun-4 Bonhams, New Bond Street #60 est:800-1200

SONGA, Arturo (20th C) Italian
£298 $542 €450 Rural (52x46cm-20x18in) s.d.921 board. 17-Jun-4 Finarte Semenzato, Milan #290

SONIMATI DI MOMBELLI, Giulio (1858-?) Italian
£733 $1349 €1100 Gressoney Valley in October (35x50cm-14x20in) s.d.1899 board exhib. 14-Jun-4 Sant Agostino, Torino #218/R

SONJE, Jan Gabrielsz (1625-1707) Dutch
£1457 $2652 €2200 Southern river landscape with shepherds and their flock (49x37cm-19x15in) i. panel. 16-Jun-4 Dorotheum, Vienna #499/R est:2000-3000

SONNE, Jorgen Valentin (1801-1890) Danish
£374 $591 €542 Two soldiers on horseback on the look-out (21x27cm-8x11in) 2-Sep-3 Rasmussen, Copenhagen #1697/R (D.KR 4000)
£1121 $1772 €1625 Thatched house with garden (33x50cm-13x20in) s.stretcher prov. 2-Sep-3 Rasmussen, Copenhagen #1662/R est:15000 (D.KR 12000)
£1186 $1921 €1732 Arabs on guard duty (23x17cm-9x7in) init.i.d.1835 verso panel prov. 9-Aug-3 Hindemae, Ullerslev #148/R est:12000 (D.KR 12500)
£2059 $3768 €3006 Going out for a ride - the key to the gate (78x79cm-31x31in) s.d.1870 exhib. 9-Jun-4 Rasmussen, Copenhagen #1639/R est:30000 (D.KR 23000)
£4476 $8192 €6535 Shepherds on the Roman Campagna (57x71cm-22x28in) painted c.1836 exhib. 9-Jun-4 Rasmussen, Copenhagen #1424/R est:50000-75000 (D.KR 50000)
£7188 $13369 €10494 Italian shepherd family (50x62cm-20x24in) s.i.d.1833 exhib.prov. 2-Mar-4 Rasmussen, Copenhagen #1284/R est:100000 (D.KR 80000)
£8411 $13290 €12196 Peasant boy about to pick water lilies for his girlfriend one summer's day (71x88cm-28x35in) s.d.1860. 2-Sep-3 Rasmussen, Copenhagen #1502/R est:100000 (D.KR 90000)

SONNEGA, Auke (1910-1963) Dutch
£4301 $6882 €6279 Made Purna (57x47cm-22x19in) s.d.57. 18-May-3 Sotheby's, Singapore #39/R est:12000-15000 (S.D 12000)
£6564 $10961 €9583 Balinese beauty (35x30cm-14x12in) s.d.55. 26-Oct-3 Christie's, Hong Kong #12/R est:38000-48000 (HK.D 85000)
£7742 $12387 €11303 Tintja dewa figure (66x55cm-26x22in) s. 18-May-3 Sotheby's, Singapore #12/R est:20000-30000 (S.D 21600)
£30888 $51583 €45096 Between dream and reality (60x40cm-24x16in) s. prov.exhib.lit. 26-Oct-3 Christie's, Hong Kong #11/R est:160000-200000 (HK.D 400000)
Works on paper
£10870 $16848 €15870 Collection of portraits. pencil black crayon gouache album of 24 prov.exhib. 6-Oct-2 Sotheby's, Singapore #23/R est:18000-20000 (S.D 30000)

SONNLEITHNER, Ludwig (1817-?) German
Sculpture
£5534 $9905 €8080 Cherub riding a deer, blowing a trumpet (39cm-15in) s. bronze marble base prov. 15-May-4 Christie's, Sydney #147/R est:3000-5000 (A.D 14000)

SONNTAG, William L (1822-1900) American
£3750 $6000 €5475 River landscape with fisherman (25x30cm-10x12in) s. 20-Sep-3 Jeffery Burchard, Florida #88/R
£4192 $7000 €6120 Morning Light (25x30cm-10x12in) s.i. 23-Oct-3 Shannon's, Milford #128/R est:7000-9000
£7059 $12000 €10306 Woodland waterfall (31x26cm-12x10in) s. 30-Oct-3 Phillips, New York #48/R est:15000-20000
£7059 $12000 €10306 Sprawling mountain landscape (79x119cm-31x47in) s. 21-Nov-3 Skinner, Boston #271/R est:12000-18000
£8383 $14000 €12239 Autumn landscape (20x30cm-8x12in) s. 9-Oct-3 Christie's, Rockefeller NY #2/R est:5000-7000
£13408 $24000 €19576 Old mill on the Androscoggin (51x79cm-20x31in) s. i.verso prov.exhib. 6-May-4 Shannon's, Milford #76/R est:20000-30000
£17010 $31128 €24835 Arcadian landscape with temple ruins and river (88x138cm-35x54in) s. prov. 9-Jun-4 Rasmussen, Copenhagen #1546/R est:75000-100000 (D.KR 190000)
£18156 $32500 €26508 Mist in the mountains (119x99cm-47x39in) s.d.1886 canvas on panel. 26-May-4 Doyle, New York #19/R est:15000-25000
£25926 $42000 €37593 Golden sunlight (48x56cm-19x22in) s. prov. 8-Aug-3 Barridorf, Portland #131/R est:20000-30000

SONNTAG, William L (jnr) (1869-1898) American
£3177 $5750 €4638 Hudson Valley (41x61cm-16x24in) s. exhib. 3-Apr-4 Neal Auction Company, New Orleans #669/R est:6000-9000
Works on paper
£1613 $3000 €2355 Lighthouse on shore (8x17cm-3x7in) s. W/C bodycol. 3-Mar-4 Christie's, Rockefeller NY #24/R est:1200-1800
£2601 $4500 €3797 Grove of trees on a stormy day. Ruins at Sunset (25x33cm-10x13in) s.d.93 s.d.92 pencil W/C pair prov. 10-Dec-3 Bonhams & Butterfields, San Francisco #6008/R est:5000-7000
£2941 $5000 €4412 Bridge at night (102x76cm-40x30in) gouache. 29-Nov-3 Carlsen Gallery, Greenville #117/R
£2994 $5000 €4371 Likely Pool (36x53cm-14x21in) s.d.92 i.verso W/C. 23-Oct-3 Shannon's, Milford #154/R est:5000-7000
£5882 $10000 €8823 New York scene. s. W/C. 29-Nov-3 Carlsen Gallery, Greenville #118/R

SONREL, Elisabeth (1874-1953) French
Works on paper
£552 $900 €800 Nymph robed in white with floral garlands (30x41cm-12x16in) s. W/C gouache. 19-Jul-3 New Orleans Auction, New Orleans #540
£658 $1211 €1000 La gardeuse d'oie a Lavardin (43x29cm-17x11in) s. W/C. 28-Jun-4 Rossini, Paris #64/R
£1267 $2331 €1900 La jeune dentelliere de pont l'abbe (46x28cm-18x11in) s. W/C. 14-Jun-4 Tajan, Paris #115 est:2000-3000
£3333 $6133 €5000 La chavauchee fantastique (32x48cm-13x19in) s. W/C. 11-Jun-4 Claude Aguttes, Neuilly #66/R est:3000-5000
£5138 $9198 €7501 Portrait of a young girl (42x26cm-17x10in) s.d.1896 W/C prov. 15-May-4 Christie's, Sydney #374/R est:10000-15000 (A.D 13000)
£9538 $16500 €13925 Female spirits in a canyon (54x39cm-21x15in) s.d.1893 W/C ink gold paint. 11-Dec-3 Sotheby's, New York #181/R est:8000-12000

SONTGENS, Johann Jakob (17th C) German
£3667 $6600 €5500 Venus and Cupid resting (118x200cm-46x79in) mono.d.1685. 26-Apr-4 Rieber, Stuttgart #1284/R est:9900

SOOLMAKER, Jan Frans (1635-1685) Flemish
£2113 $3380 €3000 Landscape with herder and travellers by fountain (40x51cm-16x20in) s. panel lit. 19-Sep-3 Karlheinz Kaupp, Staufen #1906/R est:3000

SOOLMAKER, Jan Frans (attrib) (1635-1685) Flemish
£1900 $3002 €2755 Couple with cattle and goats in an Arcadian landscape (32x43cm-13x17in) pair. 3-Sep-3 Bonhams, Bury St Edmunds #455/R est:2000-3000

SOONIUS, Louis (1883-1956) Dutch
£333 $607 €500 Milkmaid (49x69cm-19x27in) s. 30-Jun-4 Vendue Huis, Gravenhage #13
£374 $670 €550 Mere et enfants dans un interieur (78x67cm-31x26in) 22-Mar-4 Amberes, Antwerp #252
£385 $662 €550 Farmyard (25x34cm-10x13in) s. panel. 8-Dec-3 Glerum, Amsterdam #87/R
£445 $757 €650 House by the water (59x39cm-23x15in) s. 5-Nov-3 Vendue Huis, Gravenhage #290/R
£3947 $7263 €6000 Summertime: elegant bathing (40x61cm-16x24in) s. 22-Jun-4 Christie's, Amsterdam #299/R est:6000-8000
£13699 $23288 €20000 Children playing on the beach (58x88cm-23x35in) s.d.1921. 5-Nov-3 Vendue Huis, Gravenhage #361/R est:20000-25000
Works on paper
£8667 $15600 €13000 Beach fun at Scheveningen (35x46cm-14x18in) s. pastel. 20-Apr-4 Sotheby's, Amsterdam #205/R est:4000-6000

SOOT, Berit (?) Norwegian
Works on paper
£317 $584 €463 Untitled (104x122cm-41x48in) collage oil panel. 29-Mar-4 Blomqvist, Lysaker #1311/R (N.KR 4000)

SOPER, Eileen A (1905-1990) British
£260 $465 €380 Summer flowers in lustre jug (59x49cm-23x19in) s.verso prov. 25-May-4 Sworder & Son, Bishops Stortford #398/R

SOPER, George (1870-1942) British
Works on paper
£450 $774 €657 Horses ploughing (24x34cm-9x13in) s. W/C. 2-Dec-3 Sworder & Son, Bishops Stortford #520/R

SOPER, Thomas James (1836-1890) British
Works on paper
£300 $558 €438 Mill pool in river landscape (36x53cm-14x21in) s. W/C. 2-Mar-4 Bearnes, Exeter #372/R
£440 $818 €642 Figures resting in country lane (48x66cm-19x26in) s. W/C. 2-Mar-4 Bearnes, Exeter #386/R

SOPHER, Bernhard (1879-1949) American/Syrian
Sculpture
£1867 $3341 €2800 Water carrier (37cm-15in) s. dark brown pat.bronze marble socle lit. 14-May-4 Schloss Ahlden, Ahlden #1985/R est:2400

SOPHIANOPULO, Cesare C (1889-1968) Italian
£979 $1684 €1400 Portrait (19x17cm-7x7in) s. lit. 3-Dec-3 Stadion, Trieste #1030/R

SORA, Orlando (1903-?) Italian
Works on paper
£3357 $5773 €4800 Madonna and Child in lake landscape (70x50cm-28x20in) s.d.35 mixed media board. 3-Dec-3 Stadion, Trieste #1019/R est:3500-4500

SORBI, Raffaello (1844-1931) Italian
£1389 $2361 €2000 Light amongst the trees (9x5cm-4x2in) s. board. 1-Nov-3 Meeting Art, Vercelli #403/R est:2000
£2013 $3765 €3000 Field in the morning (15x10cm-6x4in) s. board. 25-Feb-4 Porro, Milan #28/R est:4000
£2158 $3540 €3000 Woman holding flowers (15x8cm-6x3in) board. 10-Jun-3 Pandolfini, Florence #47/R est:3000-4000
£2198 $4000 €3209 Landscapes (4x8cm-2x3in) s. panel pair. 29-Jun-4 Sotheby's, New York #111/R est:2000-3000
£3000 $4980 €4380 Lunchtime tales (10x8cm-4x3in) both s. board pair. 1-Oct-3 Sotheby's, Olympia #245/R est:3000-5000
£5235 $9789 €7800 Tuscan cow-boy (11x7cm-4x3in) s. board prov. 25-Feb-4 Porro, Milan #1/R est:5000
£19310 $32248 €28000 Lady waiting (15x19cm-6x7in) s. 14-Nov-3 Farsetti, Prato #550/R est:28000-32000
£140000 $254800 €204400 Sunlit osteria (61x86cm-24x34in) painted 1913 prov. 17-Jun-4 Christie's, London #81/R est:140000-180000

SORDET, Eugène Etienne (1836-1915) Swiss
£275 $460 €399 Cervin depuis Zermatt (24x36cm-9x14in) s. i.d.verso paper on wood exhib. 21-Jun-3 Galerie du Rhone, Sion #300/R (S.FR 600)
£286 $487 €418 Sunlit castle (17x24cm-7x9in) s. board exhib. 5-Nov-3 Dobiaschofsky, Bern #3737 (S.FR 650)
£368 $659 €537 Valere a Sion (30x45cm-12x18in) s.i.d. board on masonite. 22-Mar-4 Philippe Schuler, Zurich #4361 (S.FR 850)

SOREAU, Isaak (circle) (1604-?) Dutch
£10000 $18300 €14600 Grapes, pear and apples on a silver salver, bowl of raspberries (49x64cm-19x25in) panel. 7-Jul-4 Bonhams, New Bond Street #73/R est:10000-15000

SOREAU, Pieter (17th C) Dutch
£4054 $7135 €6000 Still life of apples, black and white grapes and a walnut in a porcelain bowl (52x65cm-20x26in) s.d.1652. 18-May-4 Sotheby's, Amsterdam #96/R est:6000-8000

SOREDA, Juan (16th C) Spanish
£2303 $4237 €3500 Saint Christopher and Saint Nicholas of Bari (27x25cm-11x10in) panel. 24-Jun-4 Tajan, Paris #32/R est:4000-6000

SORENSEN, Anna Klint (1899-1985) Danish
Works on paper
£542 $996 €791 Cubist mirror reflection of a man smoking (35x25cm-14x10in) s.i.d.1932 Indian ink W/C. 29-Mar-4 Rasmussen, Copenhagen #537/R (D.KR 6000)

SORENSEN, C F (1818-1879) Danish
£485 $761 €708 Coastal landscape from Marstrand (28x41cm-11x16in) s.d.22 juli 1852 paper on cardboard. 30-Aug-3 Rasmussen, Havnen #2004/R (D.KR 5200)
£553 $940 €807 Southern coastal landscape with vessels (26x37cm-10x15in) s. 10-Nov-3 Rasmussen, Vejle #298/R (D.KR 6000)
£629 $1170 €918 Sailing vessels at Oresund (16x28cm-6x11in) s. 2-Mar-4 Rasmussen, Copenhagen #1247/R (D.KR 7000)
£671 $1229 €980 Coastal landscape from Marstrand in Sweden (27x41cm-11x16in) i.d.22 juli 1852 with sig. verso. 9-Jun-4 Rasmussen, Copenhagen #1642/R (D.KR 7500)
£794 $1421 €1159 Coastal landscape with cliffs and angler (27x33cm-11x13in) s. 12-Jan-4 Rasmussen, Vejle #42/R (D.KR 8400)
£895 $1638 €1307 Sailing vessels at sea in fresh breeze (23x33cm-9x13in) s. 9-Jun-4 Rasmussen, Copenhagen #1801/R (D.KR 10000)
£898 $1671 €1311 Two men in rowing boat on calm waters (21x32cm-8x13in) mono.d.juni 1870. 2-Mar-4 Rasmussen, Copenhagen #1245/R (D.KR 10000)
£1134 $1962 €1656 Fishing boats at water's edge (30x40cm-12x16in) init.d.76. 9-Dec-3 Rasmussen, Copenhagen #1467/R est:6000-8000 (D.KR 12000)
£1477 $2703 €2156 Italian coastal cliffs with sailing boats at sea (31x46cm-12x18in) init.d.August 1864. 7-Jun-4 Museumsbygningen, Copenhagen #21/R est:12000-15000 (D.KR 16500)
£1522 $2785 €2222 Summer morning at Arildsleje, Kullen (31x38cm-12x15in) init.i.d.1867. 9-Jun-4 Rasmussen, Copenhagen #1788/R est:15000 (D.KR 17000)
£1984 $3670 €2897 Fishermen and boats at Skagen Strand (32x45cm-13x18in) init.d.1860 exhib. 15-Mar-4 Rasmussen, Vejle #70/R est:25000 (D.KR 22000)

SORENSEN, Carl Frederick (1818-1879) Danish
£1300 $2392 €1898 Shipping in choppy waters (23x30cm-9x12in) init.d.8 May 1876. 23-Mar-4 Bonhams, New Bond Street #21/R
£1300 $2392 €1898 Off the coast of Kinn, Norway (25x42cm-10x17in) init.i.d.9 Jun 1871. 23-Mar-4 Bonhams, New Bond Street #22/R
£1319 $2085 €1900 Fishermen with catch (17x23cm-7x9in) s.i.d.54 lit. 19-Sep-3 Schloss Ahlden, Ahlden #1574/R est:1900
£1422 $2275 €2076 Seascape with sailing vessels, North Sea (58x85cm-23x33in) s.d.1874. 22-Sep-3 Rasmussen, Vejle #271/R est:18000-20000 (D.KR 15000)
£1617 $3008 €2361 Fishermen landing the catch (43x59cm-17x23in) s.d.57. 2-Mar-4 Rasmussen, Copenhagen #1441/R est:18000-20000 (D.KR 18000)
£1701 $2943 €2483 Seascape with two sailing vessels (26x40cm-10x16in) s.i.d.1859. 9-Dec-3 Rasmussen, Copenhagen #1459/R est:15000-20000 (D.KR 18000)
£1810 $3240 €2643 Seascape with sailing vessels and rowing boat in a calm (21x24cm-8x9in) s. 10-May-4 Rasmussen, Vejle #335/R est:20000-25000 (D.KR 20000)
£1977 $3677 €2886 Fishing boats off the coast at Hornbaek (44x64cm-17x25in) s.i.d.16 august. 2-Mar-4 Rasmussen, Copenhagen #1215/R est:15000-20000 (D.KR 22000)
£2291 $4101 €3345 Oresund avec Helsingor, Kroneborg etc du sud (36x53cm-14x21in) s. 25-May-4 Bukowskis, Stockholm #327a/R est:20000-25000 (S.KR 31000)
£2363 $4088 €3450 From a Norwegian ship builders (32x46cm-13x18in) i.d.Juli 1872 exhib.prov. 9-Dec-3 Rasmussen, Copenhagen #1456/R est:12000-15000 (D.KR 25000)
£2457 $4251 €3587 Coastal landscape with Antwerp in background (27x40cm-11x16in) s.i.d.1893 Sept. 9-Dec-3 Rasmussen, Copenhagen #1444/R est:30000-40000 (D.KR 26000)
£2695 $5013 €3935 Sailing vessel off coast with snow covered mountains (42x57cm-17x22in) s.d.1872. 2-Mar-4 Rasmussen, Copenhagen #1230/R est:25000-35000 (D.KR 30000)
£3055 $5682 €4460 Waves crashing on breakwater (16x24cm-6x9in) s.i.d.1846. 2-Mar-4 Rasmussen, Copenhagen #1407/R est:15000 (D.KR 34000)
£3214 $5560 €4692 Seascape with sailing vessels on a grey day (102x155cm-40x61in) s. 9-Dec-3 Rasmussen, Copenhagen #1487/R est:30000 (D.KR 34000)
£3400 $6290 €4964 Amsterdam harbour by the Rokin (32x48cm-13x19in) s.i.d.Juli 1953 prov. 10-Mar-4 Sotheby's, Olympia #238/R est:2000-3000
£3774 $7019 €5510 Pair of Nordland's fishing boats along the Norwegian coast (46x75cm-18x30in) s.d.1878 prov. 2-Mar-4 Rasmussen, Copenhagen #1429/R est:30000-40000 (D.KR 42000)
£5372 $9830 €7843 Seascape with beached boats (60x88cm-24x35in) s.d.1860. 9-Jun-4 Rasmussen, Copenhagen #1827/R est:40000 (D.KR 60000)
£8535 $15876 €12461 Many figures on a pier in the Bay of Naples (44x60cm-17x24in) s.d.1867. 2-Mar-4 Rasmussen, Copenhagen #1291/R est:40000 (D.KR 95000)

£10397 $17987 €15180 Morning in Madeira with the town Funchal in background (80x113cm-31x44in) s.d.1848 exhib. 9-Dec-3 Rasmussen, Copenhagen #1219/R est:50000-75000 (D.KR 110000)
£35939 $66846 €52471 The straight between Helsingor and Helsingborg (154x222cm-61x87in) s.d.1859 exhib.prov. 2-Mar-4 Rasmussen, Copenhagen #1213/R est:200000-250000 (D.KR 400000)
Works on paper
£674 $1126 €984 The Liner Stockholm at Rive Fjord (134x205cm-53x81in) s.d.24 august 1866 W/C crayon. 25-Oct-3 Rasmussen, Havnen #2605/R (D.KR 7200)

SORENSEN, Carl Frederick (attrib) (1818-1879) Danish
£332 $538 €485 Coastal landscape from Bornholm (25x40cm-10x16in) 9-Aug-3 Hindemae, Ullerslev #27/R (D.KR 3500)
£671 $1188 €1000 After the storm (48x71cm-19x28in) 28-Apr-4 Schopman, Hamburg #677/R

SORENSEN, Eiler (1869-1953) Danish
£271 $462 €396 Candle lit interior (82x86cm-32x34in) s.d.1910. 19-Nov-3 Fischer, Luzern #2304/R (S.FR 600)
£672 $1210 €981 Two girls playing outside (39x44cm-15x17in) s. 24-Apr-4 Rasmussen, Havnen #4193 (D.KR 7500)
£841 $1329 €1219 Three children on frozen lake (49x58cm-19x23in) s.d.1917. 2-Sep-3 Rasmussen, Copenhagen #1936/R (D.KR 9000)

SORENSEN, Henrik (1882-1962) Norwegian
£706 $1136 €1031 From Edsborg, Telemark (37x46cm-15x18in) s. panel. 25-Aug-3 Blomqvist, Lysaker #1318 (N.KR 8200)
£731 $1222 €1067 Landscape from Holmsbu (54x50cm-21x20in) s. panel exhib.prov. 20-Oct-3 Blomqvist, Lysaker #1317 (N.KR 8500)
£732 $1346 €1069 Copper beach (27x35cm-11x14in) init.d.44 s.i.d. verso panel. 10-Jun-4 Grev Wedels Plass, Oslo #223/R (N.KR 9000)
£858 $1502 €1253 Pouring with rain, Smorklep (50x58cm-20x23in) init.d.39 panel exhib. 16-Dec-3 Grev Wedels Plass, Oslo #227/R (N.KR 10000)
£872 $1605 €1273 Wood (24x33cm-9x13in) mono.d.41 s.d.1941 verso panel. 29-Mar-4 Blomqvist, Lysaker #1327 (N.KR 11000)
£1601 $2866 €2337 Landscape from Vinje (55x46cm-22x18in) mono. i.d.1961 verso panel. 22-Mar-4 Blomqvist, Oslo #401/R est:20000-25000 (N.KR 20000)
£1826 $3159 €2666 Summer landscape, Stoea (24x33cm-9x13in) s. panel. 13-Dec-3 Blomqvist, Lysaker #1376/R est:10000-15000 (N.KR 21000)
£2114 $3868 €3086 Portrait of Gudrun (54x46cm-21x18in) init.d.31. 7-Jun-4 Blomqvist, Oslo #376/R est:18000-22000 (N.KR 26000)
£2162 $3869 €3157 Portrait of Tone Veli (48x38cm-19x15in) mono.d.40 panel. 22-Mar-4 Blomqvist, Oslo #395/R est:20000-25000 (N.KR 27000)
£2811 $4835 €4104 Mountain landscape, Haukeli (46x55cm-18x22in) init.d.47 s.i.d.verso panel. 8-Dec-3 Blomqvist, Oslo #495/R est:30000-35000 (N.KR 33000)
Works on paper
£317 $529 €463 Comforting son (54x50cm-21x20in) s. mixed media. 17-Nov-3 Blomqvist, Lysaker #1335 (N.KR 3800)

SORENSEN, Jens (1887-1953) Danish
£284 $455 €412 Constitution day at Bakken (52x55cm-20x22in) s. 17-Sep-3 Kunsthallen, Copenhagen #278 (D.KR 3000)
£302 $550 €453 Landscape from Dyrehavsbakken (33x48cm-13x19in) s. 19-Jun-4 Rasmussen, Havnen #2349 (D.KR 3400)
£343 $634 €501 Peacock Theatre at Tivoli with many figures (22x27cm-9x11in) mono. 15-Mar-4 Rasmussen, Vejle #650/R (D.KR 3800)
£466 $732 €680 Summer's day with figures by Dyrehaven Hill (134x200cm-53x79in) s. 30-Aug-3 Rasmussen, Havnen #4395/R (D.KR 5000)

SORENSEN, Jorgen (1861-1894) Norwegian
£2033 $3720 €2968 House by the sea (57x100cm-22x39in) s.indis.d. 7-Jun-4 Blomqvist, Oslo #324/R est:35000-40000 (N.KR 25000)

SORENSEN, Jorgine (19th C) Danish
£2778 $4639 €4000 Summer flowers in basket (32x40cm-13x16in) mono.d. 24-Oct-3 Ketterer, Hamburg #109/R est:4500-5000

SORENSEN, Laurits (1882-?) Danish
£200 $374 €300 Ship portrait of Nora Danemark (63x96cm-25x38in) s. 25-Jul-4 Bonhams & Butterfields, San Francisco #6041/R
£376 $677 €549 Seascape with sailing ship (62x96cm-24x38in) s. 24-Apr-4 Rasmussen, Havnen #2131 (D.KR 4200)
£1000 $1810 €1500 Sinner (60x40cm-24x16in) s. 1-Apr-4 Van Ham, Cologne #1646 est:1000
£1549 $2572 €2200 Autumn river (80x120cm-31x47in) 16-Jun-3 Dorotheum, Vienna #252/R est:2200-2600

SORENSEN, Soren (1885-1937) Danish
£317 $567 €463 Woman in doorway, garden behind (60x51cm-24x20in) init.d.1911. 10-May-4 Rasmussen, Vejle #315/R (D.KR 3500)

SORGATO, Oscar (1902-1941) Italian
£504 $826 €700 Gardener in the park (64x25cm-25x10in) s.d.1925. 10-Jun-3 Pandolfini, Florence #226
£935 $1534 €1300 Rialto Bridge, Venice (60x79cm-24x31in) s.d.MCMXXII board. 10-Jun-3 Pandolfini, Florence #265/R est:600-700

SORGH, Hendrik Martensz (1611-1670) Dutch
£1342 $2470 €2000 Two peasants drinking at table (33x39cm-13x15in) s. bears d. lit. 25-Mar-4 Karlheinz Kaupp, Staufen #2311/R est:1000
£5120 $8500 €7475 Interior of a barn with woman spinning (40x57cm-16x22in) s. panel prov. 30-Sep-3 Christie's, Rockefeller NY #420/R est:10000-15000
£6000 $10380 €8760 Barn interior with various pots, barrels, baskets and cat, boors seated beyond (37x32cm-15x13in) panel prov. 11-Dec-3 Sotheby's, London #133/R est:4000-6000
£15000 $27000 €21900 Interior of an inn with peasants drinking and conversing before a fire (28x39cm-11x15in) s. panel prov. 21-Apr-4 Christie's, London #35/R est:6000-8000
£16667 $30000 €24334 Peasant couple in an interior (25x19cm-10x7in) panel prov. 23-Jan-4 Christie's, Rockefeller NY #148/R est:15000-20000
£19000 $34200 €27740 Interior of a barn with two women (52x83cm-20x33in) panel prov. 22-Apr-4 Sotheby's, London #36/R est:10000-15000

SORGH, Hendrik Martensz (attrib) (1611-1670) Dutch
£540 $859 €788 Dutch peasants in kitchen larder (33x41cm-13x16in) i. 23-Mar-3 Desmond Judd, Cranbrook #1025
£3020 $5557 €4500 Still life with kitchen instruments (45x37cm-18x15in) panel. 24-Mar-4 Dorotheum, Vienna #152/R est:5000-7000

SORIA SANTA CRUZ, Enrique de (19th C) Spanish
£426 $711 €600 Horse race (56x100cm-22x39in) s.d.94. 20-Oct-3 Durán, Madrid #584/R

SORIA, Eduardo (19/20th C) Italian?
£909 $1518 €1300 Portrait of the Countess of Artal (50x35cm-20x14in) s. 10-Oct-3 Stadion, Trieste #809
£1064 $1723 €1500 Portrait of a Breton woman (41x33cm-16x13in) s. 20-May-3 Ansorena, Madrid #113/R est:1500

SORIANO, Juan (1920-) Mexican
£11064 $18809 €16153 Cats (80x115cm-31x45in) s. oil tempera. 30-Oct-3 Louis Morton, Mexico #84/R est:165000-175000 (M.P 210000)
£18824 $32000 €27483 La nina con corona de rosa - Girl with a crown of flowers (74x59cm-29x23in) s.d.40 prov. 18-Nov-3 Christie's, Rockefeller NY #99/R est:25000-30000
Works on paper
£2500 $4500 €3650 Girl (64x51cm-25x20in) W/C gouache on board. 24-Apr-4 Du Mouchelle, Detroit #3273/R est:4000-7000

SORINE, Saveli (1878-1953) Russian
£3333 $6000 €4866 Portrait of Pavel Maliukov (46x38cm-18x15in) s.d.1922 prov. 23-Apr-4 Sotheby's, New York #99/R est:8000-12000
Works on paper
£10067 $18321 €15100 Portrait de musicien, chef d'orchestre au compositeur (87x72cm-34x28in) s. pastel htd paper on canvas. 29-Jun-4 Gioffredo, Nice #40/R
£20333 $37007 €30500 Jeune femme et son chien (120x89cm-47x35in) s.d.1944 pastel htd. paper on canvas. 29-Jun-4 Gioffredo, Nice #41/R

SORIO, Enrico (1838-1909) Italian
£20833 $37500 €30416 La Piazza delle Erbe, Verona (150x93cm-59x37in) s. prov. 23-Apr-4 Sotheby's, New York #84/R est:20000-30000

SORIO, Luigi (1838-1909) Italian
£940 $1682 €1400 Girl at mirror (39x30cm-15x12in) s. 25-May-4 Finarte Semenzato, Milan #145 est:1500-2000

SORLIER, Charles (1887-1985) French?
Prints
£2393 $4307 €3494 Die Zauberflote (100x66cm-39x26in) s. col lithograph after Marc Chagall lit. 26-Apr-4 Bukowskis, Stockholm #321/R est:12000-15000 (S.KR 33000)
£3474 $5906 €5072 L'ange du jugement (51x43cm-20x17in) s.num.40/200 col lithograph after Marc Chagall lit. 4-Nov-3 Bukowskis, Stockholm #349/R est:45000-50000 (S.KR 46000)
£3927 $6677 €5733 La tribu de Gad - Douze Maquettes de vitraux pour Jerusalem (62x46cm-24x18in) s.num.99/150 col lit. after Marc Chagall lit. 4-Nov-3 Bukowskis, Stockholm #348/R est:35000-40000 (S.KR 52000)
£3977 $7000 €5806 Tripe of Simeon (61x46cm-24x18in) s. col lithograph after Chagall. 23-May-4 Hindman, Chicago #124/R est:300-500
£4351 $7832 €6352 L'ange du jugement (52x43cm-20x17in) s.num.168/200 col lithograph after Marc Chagall lit. 26-Apr-4 Bukowskis, Stockholm #318/R est:30000-35000 (S.KR 60000)
£4641 $8354 €6776 La beie des anges au bouquet de roses (61x46cm-24x18in) s.num.102/150 col lithograph after Marc Chagall lit. 26-Apr-4 Bukowskis, Stockholm #312/R est:60000-80000 (S.KR 64000)
£4908 $8688 €7166 Champs Elysees (60x42cm-24x17in) s.num.31/200 col lithograph after Marc Chagall lit. 27-Apr-4 AB Stockholms Auktionsverk #1257/R est:60000-70000 (S.KR 67000)
£4931 $8876 €7199 Avenue de la Victoire a Nice (61x46cm-24x18in) s.num.LX/LXXV col lithograph after Marc Chagall lit. 26-Apr-4 Bukowskis, Stockholm #313/R est:50000-60000 (S.KR 68000)
£5085 $9000 €7424 Bouquet (71x53cm-28x21in) s.num.38/300 col lithograph after Marc Chagall. 30-Apr-4 Sotheby's, New York #78/R est:6000-8000
£5287 $8988 €7719 Les coquelicots (55x41cm-22x16in) s.num.246/400 col lithograph after Marc Chagall lit. 4-Nov-3 Bukowskis, Stockholm #346/R est:50000-60000 (S.KR 70000)
£5588 $9500 €8158 Fight between Jacob and the angel (52x41cm-20x16in) s. col lithograph after Chagall. 31-Oct-3 Sotheby's, New York #232/R
£5650 $10000 €8249 Carmen (102x66cm-40x26in) s.num.111/150 col lithograph after Marc Chagall. 30-Apr-4 Sotheby's, New York #80/R est:7000-10000
£5656 $10181 €8258 Fiances dans le ciel de Nice (62x46cm-24x18in) s.num.115/150 col lithograph after Marc Chagall lit. 26-Apr-4 Bukowskis, Stockholm #316/R est:60000-80000 (S.KR 78000)
£6091 $10964 €8893 Bataille des fleurs (62x46cm-24x18in) s.num.II/LXXV col lithograph after Marc Chagall lit. 26-Apr-4 Bukowskis, Stockholm #314/R est:60000-70000 (S.KR 84000)
£6647 $11299 €9705 Romeo et Juliette (64x100cm-25x39in) s.num.65/200 col lithograph after Marc Chagall lit. 4-Nov-3 Bukowskis, Stockholm #347/R est:100000-120000 (S.KR 88000)
£7910 $14000 €11549 Magic flute (101x66cm-40x26in) s.num.48/200 col lithograph after Marc Chagall. 30-Apr-4 Sotheby's, New York #81/R est:10000-12000
£8000 $14560 €11680 Les coquelicots (64x48cm-25x19in) s.num.9/400 col lithograph after Marc Chagall. 1-Jul-4 Sotheby's, London #148/R est:6000-8000

£10877 $19579 €15880 La flute enchantee (100x65cm-39x26in) s.num.196/200 col lithograph after Marc Chagall lit. 26-Apr-4 Bukowskis, Stockholm #317/R est:175000-200000 (S.KR 150000)
£18681 $33066 €27274 Carmen (102x66cm-40x26in) s.num.14/200 col lithograph after Marc Chagall lit. 27-Apr-4 AB Stockholms Auktionsverk #1261/R est:200000-250000 (S.KR 255000)

SORMANI, Marino (1926-1996) Italian
£524 $902 €750 Beach (35x60cm-14x24in) s.d.1970 tempera board. 3-Dec-3 Stadion, Trieste #954/R

SORNUM, Borge (1920-) Danish
£300 $537 €438 Homage to Khachaturian (49x45cm-19x18in) s. prov. 16-Mar-4 Bonhams, Knightsbridge #154/R

SOROLLA Y BASTIDA, J (1863-1923) Spanish
Works on paper
£2083 $3396 €3000 Desnudo academico (43x31cm-17x12in) s. drawing. 16-Jul-3 Durán, Madrid #508/R est:600

SOROLLA Y BASTIDA, Joaquin (1863-1923) Spanish
£3830 $6204 €5400 Apunte de paisaje (10x17cm-4x7in) panel. 20-May-3 Ansorena, Madrid #169/R est:5400
£4069 $7324 €5900 Study for landscape (10x17cm-4x7in) board. 26-Jan-4 Ansorena, Madrid #191/R est:5400
£4545 $7591 €6500 Palace door (21x17cm-8x7in) board. 30-Jun-3 Ansorena, Madrid #444/R est:6500
£4577 $7919 €6500 Court scene (20x26cm-8x10in) cardboard. 15-Dec-3 Ansorena, Madrid #50/R est:6500
£4658 $7918 €6800 Head of Magdalene (25x16cm-10x6in) board. 4-Nov-3 Ansorena, Madrid #149/R est:5800
£5137 $8733 €7500 Allegory (20x33cm-8x13in) cardboard. 4-Nov-3 Ansorena, Madrid #146/R est:7500
£5245 $8759 €7500 Boy (19x15cm-7x6in) board. 30-Jun-3 Ansorena, Madrid #445/R
£5263 $9526 €8000 Study of flowers (21x30cm-8x12in) 14-Apr-4 Ansorena, Madrid #77/R est:8000
£6207 $10303 €9000 Blue landscape (11x26cm-4x10in) board. 30-Sep-3 Ansorena, Madrid #82/R est:9000
£7237 $13099 €11000 Head of elderly man (45x24cm-18x9in) 14-Apr-4 Ansorena, Madrid #63/R est:11000
£8276 $13738 €12000 Old man with glasses (45x26cm-18x10in) painted c.1888. 30-Sep-3 Ansorena, Madrid #86/R est:12000
£8369 $13557 €11800 Arco del Triunfo (20x24cm-8x9in) panel. 20-May-3 Ansorena, Madrid #164/R est:10800
£8966 $16138 €13000 Gate (22x17cm-9x7in) board. 26-Jan-4 Ansorena, Madrid #198/R est:6500
£10563 $18275 €15000 Cafe de Paris (19x31cm-7x12in) card. 15-Dec-3 Ansorena, Madrid #323/R est:15000
£10738 $19973 €16000 Roman Forum (23x34cm-9x13in) board. 2-Mar-4 Ansorena, Madrid #60/R est:14000
£12587 $21021 €18000 Portrait of young girl (33x27cm-13x11in) oval prov. 24-Jun-3 Segre, Madrid #107/R est:15000
£14085 $22535 €20000 Valencia beach (7x8cm-3x3in) cardboard prov.exhib. 16-Sep-3 Segre, Madrid #293/R est:5000
£16783 $28028 €24000 Capea en Torrente (12x7cm-5x3in) s. panel prov. 24-Jun-3 Segre, Madrid #108/R est:6000
£16901 $29239 €24000 Boats and fishermen (13x21cm-5x8in) 15-Dec-3 Ansorena, Madrid #39/R est:18000
£20000 $34000 €29200 Sewing nets, Valencia beach (10x13cm-4x5in) prov. 18-Nov-3 Sotheby's, London #212/R
£33566 $56056 €48000 Estudio de las figuras de la Virgen Maria y San Juan (92x62cm-36x24in) s.i.verso prov. 24-Jun-3 Segre, Madrid #105/R est:18000
£38732 $61972 €55000 Valencia beach (14x9cm-6x4in) s.i.verso board prov. 16-Sep-3 Segre, Madrid #294/R est:30000
£39855 $65362 €55000 Portrait of Martina Lorente de Rodriguez (112x79cm-44x31in) s. painted 1898 lit. 27-May-3 Durán, Madrid #270/R est:37500
£41176 $70000 €60117 Net menders in Valencia (38x57cm-15x22in) bears sig.d.1909 canvas on board prov. 29-Oct-3 Christie's, Rockefeller NY #201/R est:100000-150000
£41958 $70070 €60000 Primer apunte para el cuadro "La Vuelta de la Pesca" (7x12cm-3x5in) s.i. panel prov. 24-Jun-3 Segre, Madrid #109/R est:9000
£52000 $88400 €75920 Biarritz beach (16x22cm-6x9in) s.d.1906 board prov.exhib.lit. 18-Nov-3 Sotheby's, London #213/R
£75000 $127500 €109500 On the deck (25x37cm-10x15in) s. prov.lit. 18-Nov-3 Sotheby's, London #219/R
£220000 $374000 €321200 Laura de San Telmo dancing (205x140cm-81x55in) prov.lit. 18-Nov-3 Sotheby's, London #234/R
£280000 $476000 €408800 Beached boats (44x54cm-17x21in) s.d.1909 prov. 18-Nov-3 Sotheby's, London #245/R
£350000 $595000 €511000 Young girl eating apples (46x59cm-18x23in) s.i.d.1899 prov.lit. 18-Nov-3 Sotheby's, London #214/R
£3300000 $5610000 €4818000 Bathing time (84x119cm-33x47in) s.d.1904 prov.exhib.lit. 18-Nov-3 Sotheby's, London #221/R est:3000000-4000000
Works on paper
£839 $1401 €1200 Estudio de patas de bueyes (16x19cm-6x7in) pencil paper on vellum prov. 24-Jun-3 Segre, Madrid #93/R
£1259 $2102 €1800 Alegoria, Dos damas a la moda clasica (15x23cm-6x9in) pencil prov. 24-Jun-3 Segre, Madrid #94/R est:600
£1329 $2219 €1900 El Padre Jofre (29x45cm-11x18in) s.i. pencil drawing grain paper prov. 24-Jun-3 Segre, Madrid #100/R est:600
£1338 $2141 €1900 Beaching the boat. i. pencil dr double-sided prov. 16-Sep-3 Segre, Madrid #292/R est:1000
£1467 $2655 €2200 Study for fisherwomen (16x21cm-6x8in) s. pencil prov. 30-Mar-4 Segre, Madrid #109a/R est:1800
£2378 $3971 €3400 Huertano valenciano (27x19cm-11x7in) s.i. pencil beige paper prov. 24-Jun-3 Segre, Madrid #96/R est:1000
£2797 $4671 €4000 Estudio de figuras para "El Padre Jofre protegiendo a un loco" (45x30cm-18x12in) s.i. pencil drawing prov. 24-Jun-3 Segre, Madrid #98/R est:1300
£2937 $4905 €4200 Damas con mantilla, joven lanzando una piedra, y hombre de espaldas (36x24cm-14x9in) s.i.d.Octubre 87 pencil beige grain paper prov. 24-Jun-3 Segre, Madrid #99/R est:1300
£3287 $5489 €4700 Boat on the beach with fishermen (21x16cm-8x6in) pencil drawing paper vellum double-sided prov. 24-Jun-3 Segre, Madrid #103/R est:1600
£3497 $5839 €5000 Clotilde and Matilda Sorolla (13x20cm-5x8in) s.i. pen sepia prov. 24-Jun-3 Segre, Madrid #97/R est:2100
£4196 $7007 €6000 Cara de nino (50x35cm-20x14in) s.i. chl thick grain paper double-sided prov. 24-Jun-3 Segre, Madrid #92/R est:2400
£4667 $8447 €7000 Fisherwomen in Valencia (16x21cm-6x8in) s. pencil prov. 30-Mar-4 Segre, Madrid #110/R est:4200
£6993 $11678 €10000 Pescador con sombrero de paja (22x32cm-9x13in) s.i.d.1894 pencil drawing prov. 24-Jun-3 Segre, Madrid #101/R est:1300
£8392 $14014 €12000 Nino desnudo sentado en una silla (32x22cm-13x9in) s.i.d.1893 blk ink grain paper prov. 24-Jun-3 Segre, Madrid #95/R est:3000
£8392 $14014 €12000 Remeros y pescador de espaldas (24x32cm-9x13in) s. pencil drawing prov. 24-Jun-3 Segre, Madrid #102/R est:2100
£18182 $30364 €26000 Esperando la pesca, playa de Valencia (16x22cm-6x9in) s.i. pencil drawing prov. 24-Jun-3 Segre, Madrid #104/R est:4200
£20979 $35035 €30000 Tio de Sagunto con guitarra (68x36cm-27x14in) s.d.1886 W/C gouache prov. 24-Jun-3 Segre, Madrid #106/R est:12600

SORRELL, Alan (1904-1974) British
Works on paper
£320 $554 €467 New College Garden and St Peter's Church (30x46cm-12x18in) s.d.1964 W/C. 9-Dec-3 Bonhams, Oxford #67
£340 $629 €496 Hadrians Wall, looking west towards Chollerford (23x38cm-9x15in) s. W/C. 9-Mar-4 Gorringes, Lewes #2238

SORRELL, Elizabeth (1916-) British
Works on paper
£1200 $1908 €1752 Fisherman's bouquet (73x53cm-29x21in) s.d.64 W/C prov.exhib. 10-Sep-3 Sotheby's, Olympia #148/R est:800-1200

SORRIBES MANZANA, Julio (1933-) Spanish
£3442 $5645 €4750 Fiesta campestre (89x116cm-35x46in) s.d.51. 27-May-3 Durán, Madrid #230/R est:4750

SORRO, Ilta (1911-) Finnish
£1678 $3121 €2500 Town among mountains (23x43cm-9x17in) s.i.d.04. 7-Mar-4 Bukowskis, Helsinki #452/R est:2000

SORTET, Paul (1905-1966) Belgian
£497 $904 €750 Danse africaine (33x23cm-13x9in) s. panel. 15-Jun-4 Galerie Moderne, Brussels #363/R
£497 $904 €750 Le Lac Kivu (70x80cm-28x31in) s. 15-Jun-4 Galerie Moderne, Brussels #160
£800 $1472 €1200 Danseur africain (80x70cm-31x28in) s.i.d.39. 10-Jun-4 Camard, Paris #126/R

SOSETSU, Mori (fl.1818-1830) Japanese
Works on paper
£598 $1100 €873 Monkey on rock (118x38cm-46x15in) s. col ink hanging scroll. 23-Mar-4 Christie's, Rockefeller NY #125/R est:3000-4000

SOSNO, Sacha (1937-) French
Sculpture
£4895 $8420 €7000 Double tete (45cm-18in) one s.d.80 num.3/8 pat bronze Cast Guyot pair prov. 4-Dec-3 Piasa, Paris #77/R est:2000-3000
£5455 $9273 €7800 Golfeurs (42cm-17in) s.d.91 num.1/1, 4/8, 5/8, 6/8 brown pat bronze st.f.Guyot four. 20-Nov-3 Gioffredo, Nice #29/R
£6667 $12333 €10000 Quelle est la question ? (55x34x38cm-22x13x15in) marble exec.1996 prov. 18-Jul-4 Sotheby's, Paris #165/R est:6000-8000

SOSPIZIO, Seve (1908-1962) Italian
£298 $542 €450 Seashore (35x45cm-14x18in) s. i.d.1955 verso. 17-Jun-4 Galleria Pananti, Florence #563/R

SOSSON, L (20th C) French
Sculpture
£1905 $3467 €2800 Woman (20cm-8in) ivory marble base. 4-Feb-4 Segre, Madrid #631/R est:480
£2069 $3228 €3000 Standing nude female with flowing robes (28cm-11in) incised sig. bronze marble base. 1-Aug-2 Joel, Victoria #500 est:6000-8000 (A.D 6000)

SOSSON, Louis (20th C) French
Sculpture
£1200 $2208 €1800 Le reveil (26cm-10in) s. ivory onyx base. 9-Jun-4 Beaussant & Lefèvre, Paris #274/R est:1500-1800
£1667 $3067 €2500 Danseuse au cerceau (21cm-8in) s. ivory brass onyx base. 9-Jun-4 Beaussant & Lefèvre, Paris #275/R est:1200-1500

SOTATSU, Tawaraya (studio) (17th C) Japanese
Works on paper
£40761 $75000 €59511 Utsusemi - shell of the locust (29x36cm-11x14in) ink silver gold leaf folding screen prov. 23-Mar-4 Christie's, Rockefeller NY #97/R est:25000-35000

SOTO (?) ?
Sculpture
£2235 $4000 €3263 34 steel panels (51x66x13cm-20x26x5in) metal wood. 13-May-4 Dallas Auction Gallery, Dallas #344/R est:3000-6000

SOTO, Eduardo de (20th C) Spanish
£322 $537 €460 Selva harbour, Costa Brava (55x65cm-22x26in) s. s.i.d.1957 verso. 30-Jun-3 Ansorena, Madrid #281/R

SOTO, Jesus Rafael (1923-) Venezuelan
£1847 $3435 €2697 Double spiral (39x39cm-15x15in) s.verso acrylic. 14-Mar-4 Subastas Odalys, Caracas #35/R est:3300
£9756 $16000 €14244 Cercle et rectangle (35x52cm-14x20in) s.i.d.1968 verso panel wooden nylon hanging element exhib. 28-May-3 Sotheby's, Amsterdam #117/R est:14000-16000
£10000 $18400 €14600 Circulo pequeno (60cm-24in circular) s.i.d.1971 verso oil panel metal nylon wire prov. 25-Jun-4 Christie's, London #133/R est:12000-15000
£12000 $21840 €17520 50 and 50 Azul y negro (100x102cm-39x40in) s.i.d.1976 verso oil metal wood prov. 5-Feb-4 Christie's, London #131/R est:12000-16000
£15500 $28210 €22630 L'Oeil-de-Boeuf (70x70cm-28x28in) s.d.1963 verso oil steel nylon wood round prov.exhib. 5-Feb-4 Christie's, London #132/R est:15000-20000
£19118 $32500 €27912 Tes blancas (102x102cm-40x40in) s.i.d.1971 verso painted wood metal elements lit. 19-Nov-3 Sotheby's, New York #13/R est:25000-35000
£23529 $40000 €34352 Carres noirs sur noir (107x107cm-42x42in) s.i.d.1968 verso oil panel metal nylon hanging elements prov. 19-Nov-3 Sotheby's, New York #144/R est:25000-35000
Sculpture
£915 $1500 €1336 Squares and curves (50x50x9cm-20x20x4in) s.verso acrylic. 1-Jun-3 Subastas Odalys, Caracas #90
£915 $1500 €1336 Vibrant squares (39x39x9cm-15x15x4in) s.verso acrylic exec.2000. 1-Jun-3 Subastas Odalys, Caracas #110
£1259 $2140 €1800 Untitled (50cm-20in) s.i. serigraphed plexiglass metal. 27-Nov-3 Lempertz, Koln #447/R est:1000
£2371 $4031 €3462 Untitled (27x27x9cm-11x11x4in) metal resin. 30-Oct-3 Louis Morton, Mexico #48/R est:50000-80000 (M.P 45000)
£2600 $4732 €3796 Quadrato (44x40x49cm-17x16x19in) st.sig.i. num.44/75 silkscreen steel nylon wood spokes prov. 4-Feb-4 Sotheby's, Olympia #84/R est:2000-3000
£4054 $7500 €5919 Tiratura 45 no 5 (65x17x17cm-26x7x7in) st.sig.i.d.1966 painted wood construction. 13-Jul-4 Christie's, Rockefeller NY #37/R est:2000-3000
£5405 $10000 €7891 Carre Vert (39x39x15cm-15x15x6in) i. verso painted wood metal construction prov. 13-Jul-4 Christie's, Rockefeller NY #38/R est:1000-1500
£7444 $12655 €10868 Untitled (52x60x43cm-20x24x17in) num.1/8 bronze. 23-Nov-3 Subastas Odalys, Caracas #138/R est:16000
£7821 $14000 €11419 Vibrant parallels (47x32x14cm-19x13x6in) s.i.d.1965 verso painted wood metal prov. 26-May-4 Sotheby's, New York #109/R est:12000-18000
£8791 $16000 €12835 Gabon (32x38x14cm-13x15x6in) s.d.1965 verso mixed media construction prov. 29-Jun-4 Sotheby's, New York #422/R est:8000-12000
£11173 $20000 €16313 Untitled (25x92x48cm-10x36x19in) s.d.969 painted wood painted metal nylon wire. 26-May-4 Sotheby's, New York #49/R est:20000-25000
£12849 $23000 €18760 Ronde et jaune (60x60x21cm-24x24x8in) s.i.d.1969 verso acrylic felt tip pen monofilament board prov.lit. 14-May-4 Phillips, New York #263/R est:30000-40000
£12937 $21993 €18500 Untitled (87x102x23cm-34x40x9in) s.d.1972 verso painted wood metal nylon. 24-Nov-3 Christie's, Milan #269/R est:15000-20000
£15000 $25050 €21900 Curvas blancas B (100x100x25cm-39x39x10in) s.i.d.1975 verso wire metal paint wood prov. 22-Oct-3 Christie's, London #37/R est:10000-15000
£16084 $27343 €23000 Blanc a gauche (103x102x17cm-41x40x7in) s.i.d.1994 verso acrylic metal panel prov. 19-Nov-3 Tajan, Paris #26/R est:25000-30000
£17000 $31280 €24820 Colour inferior (154x76x17cm-61x30x7in) s.i.d.1998 verso painted wood. 24-Jun-4 Sotheby's, London #150/R est:10000-15000
£21635 $39375 €32453 Purple in the middle (80x80x40cm-31x31x16in) s.verso mixed media panel exec.1976. 21-Jun-4 Subastas Odalys, Caracas #84/R est:45000
£22000 $36740 €32120 Three horizontal colours (100x100x30cm-39x39x12in) s.i.d.1988 verso painted wood nylon wire metal prov. 21-Oct-3 Sotheby's, London #337/R est:10000-15000
£30000 $50100 €43800 Black and white square (60x60x30cm-24x24x12in) s.d.1959 verso painted wood metal prov. 21-Oct-3 Sotheby's, London #332/R est:12000-18000
£38000 $69920 €55480 Black and white square (60x60x30cm-24x24x12in) s.d.1959 verso painted wood metal prov. 24-Jun-4 Sotheby's, London #154/R est:12000-18000
Works on paper
£1290 $2400 €1883 Vibracion rosa (35x25cm-14x10in) s. collage. 2-Mar-4 Swann Galleries, New York #636/R est:2000-3000

SOTO, Rafael Fernandez de (1915-1984) Spanish
£671 $1248 €1000 Gypsy caravan (60x73cm-24x29in) s. s.verso. 2-Mar-4 Ansorena, Madrid #181/R

SOTO, Raphael de (1904-1987) ?
£5034 $9010 €7500 Cafe set (43x66cm-17x26in) s. cardboard painted c.1960. 27-May-4 Sotheby's, Paris #150/R est:2000-3000

SOTOMAYOR Y ZARAGOZA, Fernando (1875-1960) Spanish
£940 $1663 €1400 Faces (21x15cm-8x6in) dr in 4 parts exhib. 27-Apr-4 Durán, Madrid #131/R
£3882 $7026 €5900 Galician woman (20x14cm-8x6in) s. cardboard. 14-Apr-4 Ansorena, Madrid #60b/R est:2900
£4138 $6910 €6000 Portrait of lady (60x50cm-24x20in) s. 11-Nov-3 Castellana, Madrid #157/R est:5500
£14789 $25880 €21000 Portrait of lady (146x115cm-57x45in) s. 16-Dec-3 Durán, Madrid #204/R est:21000
£120000 $204000 €175200 Festival of Saint Filomena (129x108cm-51x43in) s. prov.exhib. 18-Nov-3 Sotheby's, London #207/R est:50000-70000
Works on paper
£470 $832 €700 Black boy (39x27cm-15x11in) s.d.1889 chl dr. 27-Apr-4 Durán, Madrid #694/R
£993 $1658 €1400 Male nude (58x46cm-23x18in) s. chl dr prov. 20-Oct-3 Durán, Madrid #48/R

SOTTER, George William (1879-1953) American
£2987 $4750 €4361 Seagull cove (25x30cm-10x12in) s. canvasboard. 10-Sep-3 Alderfer's, Hatfield #402/R est:5000-7000
£3659 $6000 €5306 View of London skyline (20x28cm-8x11in) board prov. 4-Jun-3 Alderfer's, Hatfield #363/R est:6000-8000
£5031 $8000 €7345 Autumn landscape (25x30cm-10x12in) s. masonite. 10-Sep-3 Alderfer's, Hatfield #401/R est:5000-7000
£5435 $10000 €7935 Still life of jug, tumbler and oranges in front of green drape (25x30cm-10x12in) s. canvasboard. 9-Jun-4 Alderfer's, Hatfield #530/R est:5000-7000
£5435 $10000 €7935 Pennsylvania landscape (46x58cm-18x23in) s. 11-Jun-4 David Rago, Lambertville #250/R est:10000-15000
£9140 $17000 €13344 Nocturnal winter landscape with a quarry (18x23cm-7x9in) s. board. 3-Mar-4 Alderfer's, Hatfield #426/R est:3000-5000
£11561 $20000 €16879 Landscape rolling hills with trees and buildings extensive blue sky (25x30cm-10x12in) s.d.1923 board. 10-Dec-3 Alderfer's, Hatfield #509/R est:10000-15000
£12903 $24000 €18838 Open pastures (25x30cm-10x12in) s. canvasboard. 5-Mar-4 Skinner, Boston #447/R est:3000-5000
£20380 $37500 €29755 New Hope Pa top house nocturnal (23x23cm-9x9in) s.i.verso board. 11-Jun-4 David Rago, Lambertville #350/R est:15000-20000
£31792 $55000 €46416 Bucks County barn in moonlight (25x30cm-10x12in) board. 10-Dec-3 Alderfer's, Hatfield #508/R est:20000-25000
£34682 $60000 €50636 Nocturnal winter landscape with farmhouse (20x25cm-8x10in) s. canvasboard. 10-Dec-3 Alderfer's, Hatfield #507/R est:20000-25000
£46196 $85000 €67446 Impressionist spring landscape, figures in front of stone building (25x30cm-10x12in) s. canvasboard. 9-Jun-4 Alderfer's, Hatfield #529 est:40000-60000

SOTTOCORNOLA, Giovanni (1855-1917) Italian
Works on paper
£10667 $19627 €16000 Anita and Mariuccia, first lessons (85x70cm-33x28in) s. pastel. 8-Jun-4 Sotheby's, Milan #143/R est:15000-25000

SOTTSASS, Ettore (1917-) Austrian
£1538 $2615 €2200 Study for fabric (46x65cm-18x26in) s.verso tempera paper. 26-Nov-3 Pandolfini, Florence #514 est:1900-2000
£2657 $4517 €3800 Study for fabric (48x64cm-19x25in) s.verso tempera paper. 26-Nov-3 Pandolfini, Florence #515/R est:2000-2200

SOUBRE, Charles (1821-1895) Belgian
£350 $584 €500 Le berger et son troupeau avant l'orage (41x72cm-16x28in) s.d.1871. 13-Oct-3 Horta, Bruxelles #449
£629 $1070 €900 Portrait Orientaliste (32x26cm-13x10in) s. panel. 18-Nov-3 Galerie Moderne, Brussels #820/R
£694 $1104 €1000 Drinking man (115x88cm-45x35in) s. 15-Sep-3 Bernaerts, Antwerp #206/R

SOUCH, John (attrib) (c.1593-1645) British
£26000 $47580 €37960 Portrait of Lord and lady Poulett of Hinton Saint George (197x160cm-78x63in) 7-Jul-4 Bonhams, New Bond Street #98/R est:20000-30000

SOUDAN, Maurice (1878-1948) Belgian
£3448 $6379 €5000 Azalees sur fond de riviere (60x64cm-24x25in) s. 19-Jan-4 Horta, Bruxelles #164/R est:5000-7000

SOUDEIKINE, Olga (20th C) Russian
Works on paper
£2013 $3705 €3000 Scene galante dans un paysage champetre (38x28cm-15x11in) s.d.1929 W/C gouache. 29-Mar-4 Lombrail & Teucquam, Paris #114/R

SOUDEIKINE, Sergei (1883-1946) Russian
£50000 $91000 €75000 Still life (81x107cm-32x42in) s.d.1927. 29-Jun-4 Gioffredo, Nice #39/R
Works on paper
£2500 $4500 €3650 Le rossignol - hight priest and young priest (36x24cm-14x9in) s.i. pencil W/C gouache silver htd on board pair. 23-Apr-4 Sotheby's, New York #102/R est:4000-6000
£2593 $4200 €3760 Untitled (61x51cm-24x20in) s.d.1938 mixed media. 8-Aug-3 Barridorf, Portland #155/R est:4000-6000
£5556 $10000 €8112 Set design (38x30cm-15x12in) s. pencil gouache. 23-Apr-4 Sotheby's, New York #105/R est:6000-8000
£27778 $50000 €40556 Traveling circus (51x76cm-20x30in) s. mixed media on board prov. 23-Apr-4 Sotheby's, New York #107/R est:50000-70000

SOUGEZ, Emmanuel (1889-1972) French?
Photographs
£4000 $7040 €6000 Assia se peignant (39x27cm-15x11in) s.i.verso gelatin silver print. 21-May-4 Bloomsbury, London #104/R est:2000-3000

SOUILLET, Georges François (1861-1957) French
£464 $867 €700 Le vieux port de Loctudy, vu de Kerazan (24x33cm-9x13in) s. board. 24-Jul-4 Thierry & Lannon, Brest #222/R

SOUINES, Mentor (20th C) Venezuelan
£503 $840 €734 Landscape (60x75cm-24x30in) s. masonite. 19-Oct-3 Subastas Odalys, Caracas #146

SOULACROIX, F (1825-1879) French
£10053 $19000 €14677 Portrait of a lady, in an interior wearing a satin gown (58x33cm-23x13in) s. 21-Feb-4 Brunk, Ashville #116/R est:10000-20000

SOULACROIX, Frederic (1825-1879) French
£6000 $10200 €8760 Promenade dans le jardin (42x28cm-17x11in) s. panel prov. 18-Nov-3 Sotheby's, London #347/R
£9146 $15000 €13262 Lady in an interior wearing a satin gown (58x33cm-23x13in) s.d.1886 prov. 31-May-3 Brunk, Ashville #179/R est:8000-15000
£18056 $32500 €26362 Proposal (61x46cm-24x18in) s. prov. 23-Apr-4 Sotheby's, New York #189/R est:12000-18000
£22000 $40040 €32120 La proposition (87x61cm-34x24in) s. prov. 15-Jun-4 Sotheby's, London #186/R est:15000-20000
£24706 $42000 €36071 Entrance (91x53cm-36x21in) s. 29-Oct-3 Christie's, Rockefeller NY #140/R est:30000-40000
£33000 $56760 €48180 Young lady reading a book (57x32cm-22x13in) s. 3-Dec-3 Christie's, London #21/R est:30000-40000

£36000 $64440 €52560 Reverie (72x42cm-28x17in) s. 7-Jan-4 George Kidner, Lymington #216/R est:20000-30000
£102000 $185640 €148920 Meditation (75x43cm-30x17in) s. prov. 16-Jun-4 Bonhams, New Bond Street #98/R est:30000-50000

SOULAGES, Pierre (1919-) French
£20271 $35677 €30000 Composition in black and brown (55x42cm-22x17in) s. acrylic vinyl paper on canvas painted 1976 prov.lit. 18-May-4 Tajan, Paris #65/R est:18000-20000
£20423 $35331 €29000 Untitled (64x50cm-25x20in) s.d.68 oil Indian ink. 13-Dec-3 Lempertz, Koln #188/R est:12000
£38666 $71146 €58000 Peinture 65 x 100 cm 11 Juillet 1987 (66x101cm-26x40in) s.i.d.1987 verso acrylic canvas prov. 8-Jun-4 Artcurial Briest, Paris #276/R est:60000-80000
£39161 $65399 €56000 Sans titre, 7/4/81 (130x97cm-51x38in) s. d.1981 verso prov. 11-Oct-3 Cornette de St.Cyr, Paris #8/R est:60000-80000
£49650 $82916 €71000 Peinture (63x102cm-25x40in) s.i.d.89 verso prov.lit. 29-Jun-3 Versailles Encheres #104/R
£55556 $91667 €80000 Peinture (130x92cm-51x36in) s.i.d.29 mars 88 verso prov.lit. 2-Jul-3 Cornette de St.Cyr, Paris #33/R est:80000-100000
£63889 $100944 €92000 Peinture (46x38cm-18x15in) s. painted 1951 prov.exhib.lit. 27-Apr-3 Versailles Encheres #40 est:90000
£64429 $118550 €96000 Peinture (55x38cm-22x15in) s.d.1952 prov.lit. 29-Mar-4 Cornette de St.Cyr, Paris #13/R est:100000-120000
£82000 $149240 €119720 17 Juillet 1963 (91x73cm-36x29in) s.d.63 s.i.verso prov.exhib.lit. 4-Feb-4 Christie's, London #13/R est:35000-55000
£100000 $158000 €144000 Peinture (162x114cm-64x45in) s. d.1972 verso prov.exhib.lit. 27-Apr-3 Versailles Encheres #47
£100000 $185000 €150000 Peinture (202x159cm-80x63in) s. s.i.d.1967 verso prov.exhib.lit. 18-Jul-4 Sotheby's, Paris #237/R est:120000-150000
£100559 $180000 €146816 Peinture 130 x 97 cm 18 fevrier 1969 (130x97cm-51x38in) s. s.i.d.1969 verso prov.lit. 12-May-4 Christie's, Rockefeller NY #127/R est:80000-120000
£110000 $200200 €160600 Peinture (96x129cm-38x51in) s.i.d.5 Juin 62 verso prov.lit. 6-Feb-4 Sotheby's, London #178/R est:60000-80000
£150000 $273000 €219000 Peinture (92x65cm-36x26in) s. s.d.6.12.54 verso prov.exhib.lit. 6-Feb-4 Sotheby's, London #175/R est:50000-70000
£150000 $276000 €219000 Peinture, 30 Septembre 1963 (202x163cm-80x64in) s.d.63 s.d.verso prov.exhib.lit. 23-Jun-4 Sotheby's, London #26/R est:150000-200000
£210526 $387368 €320000 Peinture (89x116cm-35x46in) s.d.1958 prov.exhib.lit. 27-Jun-4 Versailles Encheres #83/R est:250000-300000
Prints
£2183 $3624 €3100 Riviere IX (66x50cm-26x20in) s.num.89/100 col etching. 13-Jun-3 Calmels Cohen, Paris #61/R est:2300-2500
£2535 $4208 €3600 Riviere I (66x50cm-26x20in) s.num.1/100 col etching. 13-Jun-3 Calmels Cohen, Paris #53/R est:2300-2500
£2535 $4208 €3600 Riviere XXII (95x94cm-37x37in) s.num.44/90 col etching. 13-Jun-3 Calmels Cohen, Paris #75/R est:3500-4000
£2817 $4676 €4000 Riviere XX (50x65cm-20x26in) s.num.100 col etching. 13-Jun-3 Calmels Cohen, Paris #73/R est:2000-2200
£2877 $4890 €4200 Untitled. s.d.52 col aquatint drypoint. 6-Nov-3 Piasa, Paris #155/R
Works on paper
£5000 $9200 €7300 Projet pour une couverture (34x25cm-13x10in) i. ink prov. 24-Jun-4 Sotheby's, Olympia #537/R est:3500-4500
£6500 $11960 €9490 Projet pour une couverture (34x24cm-13x9in) i. ink prov. 24-Jun-4 Sotheby's, Olympia #536/R est:3500-4500
£7105 $13074 €10800 Composition (21x17cm-8x7in) s.i. ink wash prov. 27-Jun-4 Versailles Encheres #85/R est:8000-10000
£7500 $13800 €10950 Untitled (32x24cm-13x9in) s. ink exec c.1962-64 prov. 24-Jun-4 Sotheby's, London #184/R est:6000-8000
£14000 $22260 €20300 Sans titre (63x51cm-25x20in) s. gouache paper on canvas prov. 11-Sep-3 Christie's, Kensington #190/R est:10000-15000
£15000 $23850 €21750 Sans titre (105x75cm-41x30in) s. gouache paper on canvas prov. 11-Sep-3 Christie's, Kensington #185/R est:12000-18000
£22378 $38042 €32000 Untitled (75x50cm-30x20in) s.d.1955 i. verso gouache Indian ink brush. 27-Nov-3 Lempertz, Koln #450/R est:20000
£27273 $46364 €39000 1977 A-40 (109x75cm-43x30in) s.d.77 gouache vinyl paper on canvas. 28-Nov-3 Blanchet, Paris #218/R est:40000-50000
£27632 $50842 €42000 Composition (65x52cm-26x20in) s.d.1973 ink prov.exhib.lit. 27-Jun-4 Versailles Encheres #103/R est:40000-45000
£106667 $196267 €160000 Peinture 202 x125 (202x125cm-80x49in) s. walnut stain acrylic vinyl canvas exec 1975 prov.exhib.lit. 8-Jun-4 Artcurial Briest, Paris #275/R est:140000-180000

SOULEN, Henry James (1888-1965) American
£689 $1150 €1006 Workers hoeing an rocky field around a central female figure (38x74cm-15x29in) s. board. 14-Nov-3 Aspire, Cleveland #68 est:1000-2000
Works on paper
£250 $450 €365 Girl with watering jug (36x22cm-14x9in) s. gouache board. 25-Apr-4 Bonhams & Butterfields, San Francisco #5520/R

SOULIE, Paul (19th C) French
Works on paper
£828 $1382 €1200 Portrait du bateau de Phenix (45x61cm-18x24in) s.d.1856 W/C. 12-Nov-3 Chassaing Rivet, Toulouse #212

SOULIE, Tony (1955-) French
Works on paper
£872 $1544 €1300 Composition (100x100cm-39x39in) s.d.1990 verso mixed media. 28-Apr-4 Artcurial Briest, Paris #305 est:1500-1800

SOULIMENKO, Piotr (1914-) Russian
£300 $552 €438 Market at Basur, guinea (26x48cm-10x19in) s.d.1962 board. 28-Mar-4 Lots Road Auctions, London #344

SOUPAULT, Philippe (1897-1990) French
Works on paper
£300 $552 €450 Est-ce la mort ou la folie (29x21cm-11x8in) s.i.d.1983 felt tip pen prov. 9-Jun-4 Piasa, Paris #242/R

SOURDILLON, Berthe (1895-1976) French
£482 $805 €680 New York (81x116cm-32x46in) panel isorel. 23-Jun-3 Lombrail & Teucquam, Paris #289

SOUSTRE, A (?) ?
£1901 $3289 €2700 Concert de chambre (34x25cm-13x10in) s. porcelain. 9-Dec-3 Vanderkindere, Brussels #220 est:1000-1500

SOUTER, Camille (1929-) British
£1611 $2883 €2400 From a hillside (36x18cm-14x7in) s.d.1964 oil on paper prov. 26-May-4 James Adam, Dublin #111/R est:2000-3000
£3333 $6033 €5000 Fish (14x19cm-6x7in) s.indis.d.56 oil paper prov. 31-Mar-4 James Adam, Dublin #74/R est:3000-5000
£3867 $6999 €5800 Fish cut in two (65x48cm-26x19in) s.i.d.1989 oil paper. 30-Mar-4 De Veres Art Auctions, Dublin #103/R est:6000-9000
£5986 $9577 €8500 London again (46x61cm-18x24in) s.d. s.verso oil paper prov. 16-Sep-3 Whyte's, Dublin #41/R est:7000-9000
£14685 $24965 €21000 Long evening (58x71cm-23x28in) s.i.d.1963 oil paper on board. 25-Nov-3 De Veres Art Auctions, Dublin #56/R est:18000-22000
£15000 $26850 €21900 Iron gates (62x101cm-24x40in) s.indis.i.d.1962 oil paper on board prov. 14-May-4 Christie's, Kensington #409/R est:6000-8000
£17333 $31373 €26000 Poppies from the old garden in Blackrock (32x37cm-13x15in) s.d.1973 oil paper on board. 30-Mar-4 De Veres Art Auctions, Dublin #32/R est:7000-10000
£21333 $38613 €32000 Musical clown at Duffy's Circus (59x52cm-23x20in) s.verso oil paper on board exhib. 30-Mar-4 De Veres Art Auctions, Dublin #30/R est:20000-30000
Works on paper
£5503 $9851 €8200 Abstract (46x31cm-18x12in) s.d.1956 mixed media. 26-May-4 James Adam, Dublin #67/R est:3000-5000
£11500 $20585 €16790 The dead basking shark, Achill, waiting to be carved (51x39cm-20x15in) s.d.1965 black ink oil prov.exhib. 14-May-4 Christie's, London #96/R est:4000-6000

SOUTER, John Bulloch (1890-1972) British
£300 $480 €438 Pink roses in white vase with two handles in dark background (38x27cm-15x11in) s. board. 16-Sep-3 Rosebery Fine Art, London #620
£700 $1169 €1022 Self portrait (43x36cm-17x14in) s.d.1958 board. 8-Oct-3 Andrew Hartley, Ilkley #1140
£750 $1365 €1095 Still life of pink roses in a white jug (38x30cm-15x12in) s. board prov. 15-Jun-4 Bonhams, Knightsbridge #87/R
£2000 $3440 €2920 Chelsea conversation (38x51cm-15x20in) board sold with two similar by same hand prov. 2-Dec-3 Bonhams, New Bond Street #42/R est:2000-3000

SOUTH AMERICAN SCHOOL, 17th C
£17483 $30070 €25000 Monks by the Virgin (96x75cm-38x30in) 8-Dec-3 Claude Aguttes, Neuilly #22/R est:6000-8000

SOUTH AMERICAN SCHOOL, 18th C
£7200 $12744 €10512 Eruption of a volcano, Antigua, Guatemala, Central America (94x124cm-37x49in) i. prov. 27-Apr-4 Bonhams, New Bond Street #129/R est:2500-3000

SOUTH GERMAN SCHOOL, 15th C
£7718 $14201 €11500 St Agnes (147x55cm-58x22in) panel. 24-Mar-4 Hugo Ruef, Munich #873/R est:6500

SOUTH GERMAN SCHOOL, 16th C
£11921 $21695 €18000 Scenes from the Life of the Virgin with donors and their patron saints (109x88cm-43x35in) panel prov. 16-Jun-4 Dorotheum, Vienna #137/R est:18000-25000

SOUTH GERMAN SCHOOL, 18th C
£5000 $8650 €7300 Sliced melon with grapes and tomatoes on a ledge (35x51cm-14x20in) 10-Dec-3 Bonhams, New Bond Street #97/R est:1500-2500
Sculpture
£11000 $20240 €16060 St Michael slaying the Devil (18cm-7in) i.d.1742 fruitwood plinth. 10-Jun-4 Christie's, London #121/R est:3000-5000

SOUTH ITALIAN SCHOOL, 18th C
£15603 $26057 €22000 Still life with flowers and fruit (108x148cm-43x58in) 17-Jun-3 Finarte Semenzato, Milan #632/R est:25000-35000

SOUTHALL, Joseph Edward (1861-1944) British
£6500 $12025 €9490 Blue shed (27x19cm-11x7in) mono.d.1923 tempera on silk prov.exhib. 11-Mar-4 Christie's, Kensington #83/R est:5000-8000

SOUTHARD, Don (1955-) American
£1477 $2600 €2156 Day at the beach (206x180cm-81x71in) init. acrylic painted c.1990. 23-May-4 Treadway Gallery, Cincinnati #719/R est:5000-7000

SOUTHERN, Clara (1861-1940) Australian
£2893 $5120 €4224 Old shed (35x27cm-14x11in) s. prov. 3-May-4 Christie's, Melbourne #291/R est:7000-10000 (A.D 7000)
£3862 $6063 €5600 Back of the barn (46x30cm-18x12in) s. 27-Aug-3 Christie's, Sydney #549/R est:12000-16000 (A.D 9500)
£4580 $8336 €6687 Yarra at Warrandyte (64x34cm-25x13in) s. board exhib. 16-Jun-4 Deutscher-Menzies, Melbourne #151/R est:15000-20000 (A.D 12000)

SOUTHERN, Donald (c.1900-?) British
Works on paper
£260 $432 €380 Bassenthwaite lake and Skiddaw (23x36cm-9x14in) s.d.1970 W/C. 2-Oct-3 Mitchells, Cockermouth #804
£280 $465 €409 Ennerdale water (18x25cm-7x10in) s. W/C. 2-Oct-3 Mitchells, Cockermouth #803/R
£400 $664 €584 Windermere (36x48cm-14x19in) s.d.1969 W/C. 2-Oct-3 Mitchells, Cockermouth #802/R

SOUTHGATE, Frank (1872-1916) British

£1670 $3039 €2438 Sparrow hawk attacking a brood of ducklings (42x63cm-17x25in) s. 29-Jun-4 Rowley Fine Art, Newmarket #379/R
£1800 $2988 €2628 Mallard taking flight (19x28cm-7x11in) s. prov. 2-Oct-3 Ewbank, Send #827 est:1500-2500
Works on paper
£300 $501 €438 Norfolk mill (33x48cm-13x19in) s. W/C. 17-Oct-3 Keys, Aylsham #661/R
£424 $720 €619 Pheasants (39x57cm-15x22in) s.d.1900 W/C prov. 24-Nov-3 Sotheby's, Melbourne #317/R (A.D 1000)
£500 $920 €730 Warm vorner on the outlying beat (28x49cm-11x19in) s. W/C. 10-Jun-4 Christie's, Kensington #249/R
£715 $1301 €1044 Shooting from amongst the reeds (30x47cm-12x19in) s.d.1902 pen ink W/C. 29-Jun-4 Rowley Fine Art, Newmarket #380/R
£800 $1336 €1168 Richmond Castle (28x41cm-11x16in) s. W/C. 17-Oct-3 Keys, Aylsham #662
£860 $1522 €1256 Mallards taking off (27x57cm-11x22in) s. W/C htd white over pencil. 27-Apr-4 Bonhams, Knowle #65
£1050 $1743 €1533 Snipe on the edge of sand dunes (11x19cm-4x7in) s. W/C. 2-Oct-3 Ewbank, Send #825/R est:1000-1500
£1350 $2390 €1971 Herring gulls on a shore (26x46cm-10x18in) s. W/C htd white over pencil. 27-Apr-4 Bonhams, Knowle #64 est:600-800
£1400 $2478 €2044 Rowing boat at low tide (26x57cm-10x22in) s. W/C htd white over pencil. 27-Apr-4 Bonhams, Knowle #66 est:500-700
£1550 $2589 €2263 Bamburgh Castle (23x33cm-9x13in) s. W/C. 17-Oct-3 Keys, Aylsham #663

SOUTINE, Chaim (1893-1943) Russian

£35000 $64400 €51100 Herrings and a bottle of Chianti (68x40cm-27x16in) s. painted c.1917 prov.exhib.lit. 22-Jun-4 Sotheby's, London #169/R est:60000-80000
£42000 $77280 €61320 Femme couchee (21x34cm-8x13in) panel painted c.1940 prov.exhib.lit. 22-Jun-4 Sotheby's, London #170/R est:30000-40000
£64706 $110000 €94471 Still life with herrings and onions (38x61cm-15x24in) s. painted c.1917 prov.exhib.lit. 5-Nov-3 Christie's, Rockefeller NY #300/R est:100000-150000
£75000 $136500 €109500 Banlieue parisienne (65x54cm-26x21in) s. painted c.1919 prov.lit. 3-Feb-4 Christie's, London #287/R est:70000-100000
£110000 $202400 €160600 Portrait of a young woman - Paulette Jourdain (35x36cm-14x14in) s. painted c.1928 prov.exhib.lit. 22-Jun-4 Sotheby's, London #167/R est:70000-90000
£110000 $202400 €160600 Arbres a Auxerre (73x60cm-29x24in) s. painted c.1939 prov.exhib.lit. 23-Jun-4 Christie's, London #196/R est:120000-180000
£140000 $257600 €204400 Portrait of Charlot (30x25cm-12x10in) s. painted c.1937 prov.exhib.lit. 22-Jun-4 Sotheby's, London #168/R est:80000-120000
£162011 $290000 €236536 Paysage avec des personnages (64x54cm-25x21in) s. painted c.1920 prov.exhib.lit. 5-May-4 Christie's, Rockefeller NY #283/R est:250000-350000
£235294 $400000 €343529 La jeune Polonaise (65x50cm-26x20in) painted 1929 prov.exhib.lit. 5-Nov-3 Christie's, Rockefeller NY #276/R est:150000-250000
£617647 $1050000 €901765 Le route folle a cagnes - la gaude (82x65cm-32x26in) s. painted c.1923 prov.exhib.lit. 4-Nov-3 Christie's, Rockefeller NY #38/R est:1200000-1600000
£720000 $1317600 €1051200 Arbre de Vence (75x52cm-30x20in) painted c.1929 prov.lit. 2-Feb-4 Christie's, London #22/R est:500000-700000
£820000 $1492400 €1197200 Sieste (73x92cm-29x36in) painted c.1934 prov.exhib.lit. 21-Jun-4 Sotheby's, London #45/R est:500000-700000
£850000 $1547000 €1241000 Arbre de Vence (93x65cm-37x26in) painted c.1929 prov.exhib.lit. 21-Jun-4 Sotheby's, London #44/R est:500000-700000
£1200000 $2184000 €1752000 Femme entrant dan sl'eau (113x72cm-44x28in) painted c.1931 prov.exhib.lit. 21-Jun-4 Sotheby's, London #46/R est:350000-500000

SOUTO, Alfredo (1862-1940) Spanish

Works on paper
£2641 $4621 €3750 Cabaret (60x90cm-24x35in) s. wash. 16-Dec-3 Durán, Madrid #150/R est:3500

SOUTO, Arturo (1901-1964) Spanish

£1127 $1972 €1600 Man with hat (51x40cm-20x16in) s. canvas on cardboard. 16-Dec-3 Durán, Madrid #148/R
£1197 $2095 €1700 Woman (70x55cm-28x22in) s. cardboard. 16-Dec-3 Durán, Madrid #149/R est:1500
£1408 $2465 €2000 Mexican harbour (37x44cm-15x17in) 16-Dec-3 Durán, Madrid #147/R est:2000
£2289 $4005 €3250 Two women (36x46cm-14x18in) s. 16-Dec-3 Durán, Madrid #145/R est:3000
£3521 $6162 €5000 Village (60x80cm-24x31in) s. 16-Dec-3 Durán, Madrid #146/R est:3000
Works on paper
£352 $616 €500 Study of hands (20x29cm-8x11in) s. ink. 16-Dec-3 Segre, Madrid #236/R
£816 $1486 €1200 Boats by the sea (23x29cm-9x11in) s. W/C. 3-Feb-4 Segre, Madrid #169/R
£897 $1614 €1300 Peasant family (30x24cm-12x9in) W/C. 26-Jan-4 Ansorena, Madrid #299/R est:1100
£1007 $1802 €1500 Young woman (61x45cm-24x18in) s. dr. 25-May-4 Durán, Madrid #95/R est:1200
£1316 $2382 €2000 Stroll (61x91cm-24x36in) s. W/C. 14-Apr-4 Ansorena, Madrid #354/R est:2000
£2113 $3655 €3000 Stroll (61x91cm-24x36in) s. W/C. 15-Dec-3 Ansorena, Madrid #158/R est:3000

SOUTTER, Jean Jacques (1765-1842) Swiss

Miniatures
£3400 $6086 €4964 Young auditor at the French Conseil d'Etat (3cm-1in) init. enamel on copper. 25-May-4 Christie's, London #15/R est:1500-2000

SOUTTER, Louis (1871-1942) Swiss

£1357 $2348 €1981 Bosquets (17x22cm-7x9in) i. pencil prov.lit. 9-Dec-3 Sotheby's, Zurich #70/R est:3000-5000 (S.FR 3000)
Works on paper
£1485 $2658 €2168 Caupole surmontee d'une croix (20x13cm-8x5in) ink prov.exhib.lit. 26-May-4 Sotheby's, Zurich #62/R est:3000-4000 (S.FR 3400)
£1572 $2814 €2295 Boudry (26x20cm-10x8in) i.d.1930 ink prov.lit. 26-May-4 Sotheby's, Zurich #61/R est:2000-3000 (S.FR 3600)
£1834 $3283 €2678 Horreurs chretiennes (22x17cm-9x7in) ink prov.exhib.lit. 26-May-4 Sotheby's, Zurich #64/R est:3000-4000 (S.FR 4200)
£2183 $3974 €3187 Du rivage je regardais (21x17cm-8x7in) i. Indian ink. 17-Jun-4 Kornfeld, Bern #755/R est:6000 (S.FR 5000)
£2183 $3974 €3187 Imitation de la Vierge de Raffael (22x17cm-9x7in) i. Indian ink. 17-Jun-4 Kornfeld, Bern #760/R est:5000 (S.FR 5000)
£2183 $3974 €3187 Les deux tombeaux (22x17cm-9x7in) i. Indian ink. 17-Jun-4 Kornfeld, Bern #753/R est:6000 (S.FR 5000)
£2183 $3974 €3187 Maria della Stella (22x17cm-9x7in) i. pencil. 17-Jun-4 Kornfeld, Bern #757 est:6000 (S.FR 5000)
£2183 $3974 €3187 Cherubin aile (22x18cm-9x7in) i. pencil quatered paper. 17-Jun-4 Kornfeld, Bern #758/R est:6000 (S.FR 5000)
£2294 $3830 €3326 Christ au tombeau (18x21cm-7x8in) i. prov. Indian ink. 19-Jun-3 Kornfeld, Bern #944 est:6000 (S.FR 5000)
£2620 $4769 €3825 La gare international (22x17cm-9x7in) i. Indian ink. 17-Jun-4 Kornfeld, Bern #754/R est:6000 (S.FR 6000)
£2838 $5166 €4143 Grues roses (21x27cm-8x11in) i. Indian ink. 17-Jun-4 Kornfeld, Bern #751/R est:7500 (S.FR 6500)
£3057 $5563 €4463 Mater vivantis (22x17cm-9x7in) i. pencil quartered paper. 17-Jun-4 Kornfeld, Bern #756/R est:7500 (S.FR 7000)
£3057 $5563 €4463 Michel Ange les avait jetes dans le souffre (22x18cm-9x7in) i. Indian ink. 17-Jun-4 Kornfeld, Bern #759/R est:6000 (S.FR 7000)
£3167 $5480 €4624 Fleurs (27x43cm-11x17in) mono. ink prov.lit. 9-Dec-3 Sotheby's, Zurich #86/R est:8000-12000 (S.FR 7000)
£3239 $5604 €4600 Untitled (25x3cm-10x1in) mono. Chinese ink prov. 9-Dec-3 Artcurial Briest, Paris #476/R est:3500-4000
£3493 $6253 €5100 Les lys et les vierges folles (21x28cm-8x11in) col pen prov.exhib.lit. 26-May-4 Sotheby's, Zurich #63/R est:8000-12000 (S.FR 8000)
£5963 $9959 €8646 Composition d'apres Giotto (27x19cm-11x7in) s. pen brush. 19-Jun-3 Kornfeld, Bern #946/R est:15000 (S.FR 13000)

SOUVARINE, Joshua (19/20th C) American/Italian

£514 $950 €750 Genre scene depicting hooded figure clipping wings of a kneeling female fairy (76x51cm-30x20in) s. 24-Jan-4 Jeffery Burchard, Florida #56/R

SOUVERAIN, R (20th C) Haitian

£273 $500 €399 Horse drinking (61x82cm-24x32in) s.i. board. 3-Jun-4 Christie's, Rockefeller NY #1129/R

SOUVERBIE (20th C) French

£1597 $2635 €2300 Toreador et Picadors dans l'arene (43x33cm-17x13in) 3-Jul-3 Claude Aguttes, Neuilly #156 est:1200-1800

SOUVERBIE, Jean (1891-1981) French

£1208 $2235 €1800 Paysage boise (46x55cm-18x22in) s. isorel. 15-Mar-4 Blanchet, Paris #105 est:1000-1200
£1611 $2980 €2400 Jeune femme au jardin (52x42cm-20x17in) s.d.18 isorel. 15-Mar-4 Blanchet, Paris #106/R est:1200-1500
£1835 $3064 €2661 Portrait of blonde haired woman carrying fruit dish (46x38cm-18x15in) 23-Jun-3 Philippe Schuler, Zurich #3572/R est:3000-3500 (S.FR 4000)
£2333 $4293 €3500 Village en bord de mer (31x40cm-12x16in) s.d.1925. 14-Jun-4 Tajan, Paris #80/R est:4000-5000
£2361 $3943 €3400 L'aurore et la nuit (38x46cm-15x18in) s.d.1946 s.i.d.46 verso. 23-Oct-3 Credit Municipal, Paris #68 est:1500-2000
£3893 $7201 €5800 La fenetre ouverte (38x29cm-15x11in) s.d.1930 isorel. 15-Mar-4 Blanchet, Paris #107/R est:1500-1800
£4138 $7448 €6000 Coiffure (35x24cm-14x9in) s. s.i.d.1933 verso. 25-Jan-4 Chayette & Cheval, Paris #244/R est:2000-2500
£9722 $16236 €14000 Baigneuses (73x100cm-29x39in) s.d. s.i.d. verso. 25-Oct-3 Dr Lehr, Berlin #487/R est:4000
£10333 $18807 €15500 Nu dans les ruines (50x74cm-20x29in) s.d.67. 29-Jun-4 Gioffredo, Nice #37
£11888 $19853 €17000 Assiette de fruits (38x46cm-15x18in) s. 7-Oct-3 Livinec, Gaudcheau & Jezequel, Rennes #143
£14765 $27315 €22000 Nature morte aux fruits (31x57cm-12x22in) s. 15-Mar-4 Blanchet, Paris #104/R est:4000-5000
£26846 $48054 €40000 Deux baigneuses (73x100cm-29x39in) s.d.1963. 30-May-4 Eric Pillon, Calais #216/R
£34000 $62560 €51000 Femme a la pasteque (100x80cm-39x31in) s. prov.exhib. 8-Jun-4 Artcurial Briest, Paris #172/R est:15000-20000
Works on paper
£366 $608 €520 La musique (7x9cm-3x4in) s. black crayon htd col. 10-Jun-3 Renaud, Paris #38
£450 $797 €657 Mother and children (25x17cm-10x7in) s.d.26 pen ink. 27-Apr-4 Bonhams, Knightsbridge #112/R
£479 $815 €700 Couple (20x26cm-8x10in) s.d.30 crayon chl dr. 5-Nov-3 Tajan, Paris #13/R

SOUZA, Francis Newton (1924-2002) British/Indian

£3800 $6042 €5548 Bubbles under water (60x74cm-24x29in) s.d.61 board. 10-Sep-3 Sotheby's, Olympia #329/R est:1500-2000
£8152 $15000 €11902 Girl and two men in a landscape (104x96cm-41x38in) s.d.63 exhib. 24-Mar-4 Sotheby's, New York #166/R est:15000-20000
£9000 $15030 €13140 Untitled (58x73cm-23x29in) s.d.58 verso board prov. 17-Oct-3 Christie's, Kensington #510/R est:6000-8000
£13043 $24000 €19043 Small landscape (5x65cm-2x26in) canvas on board. 25-Mar-4 Christie's, Rockefeller NY #205/R est:20000-25000
£16000 $26720 €23360 Untitled (71x95cm-28x37in) s.verso board prov. 17-Oct-3 Christie's, Kensington #508/R est:8000-12000
£16304 $30000 €23804 Evolution of Apollo (138x109cm-54x43in) s.d.63 i.d.1963 verso. 24-Mar-4 Sotheby's, New York #168/R est:20000-25000
£16304 $30000 €23804 St Francis (84x61cm-33x24in) s.d.61. 25-Mar-4 Christie's, Rockefeller NY #209/R est:12000-18000
£19022 $35000 €27772 Untitled (71x60cm-28x24in) s.d.1950 board. 25-Mar-4 Christie's, Rockefeller NY #210/R est:12000-15000
£24457 $45000 €35707 Untitled (85x179cm-33x70in) s.d.89 acrylic. 25-Mar-4 Christie's, Rockefeller NY #239/R est:45000-50000
£70652 $130000 €103152 Mystic repast (125x152cm-49x60in) s.d.1953 s.i.d.1953 verso board prov.lit. 24-Mar-4 Sotheby's, New York #165/R est:50000-70000

Works on paper
£300 $531 €438 Still life (20x25cm-8x10in) s.d.45 ink. 27-Apr-4 Bonhams, Knightsbridge #297/R
£950 $1682 €1387 Landscape (20x32cm-8x13in) s.d.59 pen sold with a book. 27-Apr-4 Bonhams, Knightsbridge #294/R
£1087 $2000 €1587 Standing nude (33x20cm-13x8in) s.d.58 pencil black ink W/C. 24-Mar-4 Sotheby's, New York #167/R est:3000-5000
£1200 $2004 €1752 Nude (37x23cm-15x9in) s. black ink. 17-Oct-3 Christie's, Kensington #521/R est:1000-1500
£1422 $2560 €2076 Reclining nude (28x43cm-11x17in) s.d.1966 i.verso W/C ink paper on card. 25-Apr-4 Christie's, Hong Kong #600/R est:16000-20000 (HK.D 20000)
£1495 $2750 €2183 Head of man (25x20cm-10x8in) s.d.1955 pen ink. 24-Mar-4 Sotheby's, New York #170/R est:1500-2000
£1766 $3250 €2578 Priest with monstrance (53x36cm-21x14in) s.d.1954 s.i.d.1954 verso pencil gouache. 24-Mar-4 Sotheby's, New York #169/R est:1200-1600
£3912 $7041 €5712 Woman with a nose ring (56x38cm-22x15in) s.d.1951 gouache pencil paper on card. 25-Apr-4 Christie's, Hong Kong #595/R est:55000-75000 (HK.D 55000)
£4979 $8962 €7269 Nude (38x56cm-15x22in) s.d.1951 mixed media paper on card. 25-Apr-4 Christie's, Hong Kong #594/R est:55000-75000 (HK.D 70000)

SOUZA-PINTO, Jose Giulio (1856-1939) Portuguese
£3221 $5928 €4800 Etude de femme nue debout dans la prairie (30x13cm-12x5in) 28-Mar-4 Anaf, Lyon #247/R est:3000-4000
£5705 $10497 €8500 Marguerite, fille de l'artiste, vue de profil (24x17cm-9x7in) 28-Mar-4 Anaf, Lyon #249/R est:3000-4000
£8242 $14588 €12363 Cow drinking water (24x32cm-9x13in) s. 27-Apr-4 Bolsa de Arte, Rio de Janeiro #23/R (B.R 45000)
£8500 $15640 €12410 Bather (34x24cm-13x9in) s.d.1895. 23-Mar-4 Bonhams, New Bond Street #96/R est:10000-15000
£16107 $29638 €24000 Femme nue debout se relevant les cheveux (52x36cm-20x14in) 28-Mar-4 Anaf, Lyon #248/R est:6000-7000
Works on paper
£8974 $15885 €13461 Peasant (30x23cm-12x9in) d. august 1913 pastel. 27-Apr-4 Bolsa de Arte, Rio de Janeiro #28/R (B.R 49000)

SOUZY, Bernard de (1945-) French?
£352 $585 €500 Ayrton Senna sur Mac Laren Honda (60x92cm-24x36in) s.i. s.d.25/4/2000 verso acrylic. 15-Jun-3 Artcurial Briest, Paris #130/R
£352 $585 €500 De Portago, 12 heures de Sebring (61x92cm-24x36in) s.i. s.d.31/3/00 verso acrylic. 15-Jun-3 Artcurial Briest, Paris #138/R
£387 $643 €550 Eddy Irvine, 57 Gd Prix d'Italie, Monza (60x92cm-24x36in) s.i. s.d.18 september 97 verso acrylic. 15-Jun-3 Artcurial Briest, Paris #128/R
£423 $701 €600 Portrait de Ayrton Senna (92x78cm-36x31in) s.i. s.d.20/2/00 verso acrylic. 15-Jun-3 Artcurial Briest, Paris #124
£423 $701 €600 Ayrton Senna en course (91x144cm-36x57in) s. i.d.8 mai 2000 verso acrylic. 15-Jun-3 Artcurial Briest, Paris #139
£493 $818 €700 Michael Schumacher, Ferrari, et Mika Hakinen a la lutte (60x120cm-24x47in) s.i. s.d.25 mai 2000 verso acrylic. 15-Jun-3 Artcurial Briest, Paris #133
£493 $818 €700 La Ferrari F 333 SP de Moretti et Theys (62x103cm-24x41in) s.i. s.d.verso. 15-Jun-3 Artcurial Briest, Paris #140
£493 $818 €700 Enzo Ferrari sur Alfa-Romeo 40/60 HP, tipo Corsa (60x92cm-24x36in) s.i. s.d.30/11/99 verso. 15-Jun-3 Artcurial Briest, Paris #148/R
£599 $994 €850 Michael Schumacher sur Ferrari (69x93cm-27x37in) mono.i. s.verso acrylic. 15-Jun-3 Artcurial Briest, Paris #141/R

SOVIG, Theodor (1840-1892) Norwegian
£7526 $13472 €10988 Bergen seen from the sea (49x76cm-19x30in) s.d.1880 i.stretcher. 22-Mar-4 Blomqvist, Oslo #355/R est:100000-120000 (N.KR 94000)

SOWERBY, John G (1850-1914) British
Works on paper
£360 $673 €540 Woodland scene (23x36cm-9x14in) s. W/C htd gouache. 22-Jul-4 Dominic Winter, Swindon #96/R
£600 $978 €876 Chrysanthemums, a young woman and her cat in an English country garden (16x25cm-6x10in) s. W/C. 23-Sep-3 Anderson & Garland, Newcastle #303/R

SOYA-JENSEN, C M (1860-1912) Danish
£287 $516 €419 Landscape with tree by river (45x68cm-18x27in) init.d.1929. 24-Apr-4 Rasmussen, Havnen #2199 (D.KR 3200)
£316 $591 €461 Coastal landscape with boathouses (20x32cm-8x13in) init. 25-Feb-4 Museumsbygningen, Copenhagen #163 (D.KR 3500)
£1164 $2130 €1699 Summer morning at Vejle fjord (65x110cm-26x43in) init.indis.d.87 exhib. 9-Jun-4 Rasmussen, Copenhagen #1786/R est:8000-10000 (D.KR 13000)

SOYER, Moses (1899-1974) American
£543 $1000 €793 Still life (41x51cm-16x20in) s. canvasboard. 25-Jun-4 Freeman, Philadelphia #301/R
£604 $1100 €906 Portrait of a young woman with long brown hair (91x20cm-36x8in) board. 16-Jun-4 Wolf's, New York #487430/R
£814 $1400 €1188 Duet (51x41cm-20x16in) s. i.stretcher. 7-Dec-3 Freeman, Philadelphia #149
£1099 $2000 €1605 Landscape (41x51cm-16x20in) s. i.stretcher. 29-Jun-4 Sotheby's, New York #245/R est:3000-5000
£1125 $1800 €1643 Avi (64x51cm-25x20in) s. painted c.1972. 20-Sep-3 Bunte, Elgin #1205 est:1000-1500
£1625 $2600 €2373 Pensive girl (46x36cm-18x14in) s. 20-Sep-3 Bunte, Elgin #1206 est:800-1200
£2160 $3500 €3132 Dance studio (86x76cm-34x30in) s. prov. 8-Aug-3 Barridorf, Portland #359/R est:5000-7000
£2188 $3500 €3194 Girl at the window (51x41cm-20x16in) s. sold with a letter. 21-Sep-3 Grogan, Boston #65d/R
Works on paper
£233 $400 €340 Piano player (18x25cm-7x10in) s. pencil pen W/C. 2-Dec-3 Christie's, Rockefeller NY #92/R
£326 $600 €476 Couple in interior (36x53cm-14x21in) s. W/C chl. 25-Jun-4 Freeman, Philadelphia #48/R

SOYER, Paul Constant (1823-1903) French
£431 $772 €629 Kitchen still life (24x32cm-9x13in) s.d.51 panel. 12-May-4 Dobiaschofsky, Bern #990/R (S.FR 1000)
£532 $888 €750 Vase de fleurs (23x17cm-9x7in) s. panel. 17-Jun-3 Vanderkindere, Brussels #48
Works on paper
£1200 $2004 €1752 Young girl at her writing desk (20x15cm-8x6in) s. pencil W/C prov. 16-Oct-3 Christie's, Kensington #91/R est:800-1200

SOYER, Raphael (1899-1987) American
£889 $1600 €1298 Seated nude (69x48cm-27x19in) s. board. 25-Apr-4 Bonhams & Butterfields, San Francisco #5537/R est:2000-3000
£1111 $2000 €1622 Nude female near screen (64x41cm-25x16in) s. masonite. 20-Jan-4 Arthur James, Florida #746
£2054 $3800 €2999 Rockport (41x61cm-16x24in) s. i.stretcher prov. 11-Mar-4 Christie's, Rockefeller NY #81/R est:4000-6000
£2286 $3750 €3315 Artist at easel, David Burliuk painting portrait of a woman (30x36cm-12x14in) s. painted c.1951. 4-Jun-3 Alderfer's, Hatfield #288 est:300-500
£2703 $5000 €3946 Rockport landscape (51x67cm-20x26in) s. i.d.1955 verso prov. 11-Mar-4 Christie's, Rockefeller NY #79/R est:4000-6000
£3804 $7000 €5554 Woman in a doorway (23x18cm-9x7in) s. masonite. 10-Jun-4 Sotheby's, New York #315/R est:2000-3000
£3867 $7000 €5646 Reclining nude (30x46cm-12x18in) s. prov. 31-Mar-4 Sotheby's, New York #172 est:4000-6000
£4054 $7500 €5919 Melancholy (30x31cm-12x12in) s. 11-Mar-4 Christie's, Rockefeller NY #80/R est:4000-6000
£4324 $8000 €6313 Young woman braiding her hair (30x23cm-12x9in) s. prov. 11-Mar-4 Christie's, Rockefeller NY #78/R est:5000-7000
£4396 $8000 €6418 Two women changing (43x28cm-17x11in) s. panel painted c.1960. 29-Jun-4 Sotheby's, New York #279/R est:4000-6000
£6286 $11000 €9178 Self-portrait (64x71cm-25x28in) s. prov. 19-Dec-3 Sotheby's, New York #1054/R est:7000-10000
£11765 $20000 €17177 Young lady on a bed (102x127cm-40x50in) s. prov. 29-Oct-3 Christie's, Los Angeles #37/R est:25000-35000
£36932 $65000 €53921 Room mates (81x66cm-32x26in) s. painted 1935 prov.exhib.lit. 19-May-4 Sotheby's, New York #168/R est:50000-70000
Prints
£1788 $3200 €2610 Springtime (36x44cm-14x17in) s.i. lithograph. 6-May-4 Swann Galleries, New York #587/R est:4000-6000
Works on paper
£222 $400 €324 Female nude (30x18cm-12x7in) s. pencil W/C. 23-Jan-4 Freeman, Philadelphia #52/R
£254 $425 €371 Studies of female nudes (44x53cm-17x21in) s. ink W/C. 26-Oct-3 Bonhams & Butterfields, San Francisco #6589/R
£272 $500 €397 Head studies of Dikran Kelekian (36x23cm-14x9in) s.i. pen ink W/C. 25-Mar-4 Doyle, New York #64/R
£305 $546 €445 Couple (20x25cm-8x10in) s.i.d.1971 graphite w,. 4-May-4 Ritchie, Toronto #56/R (C.D 750)
£370 $600 €540 Reclining nude (33x43cm-13x17in) s. pastel. 2-Aug-3 Neal Auction Company, New Orleans #197
£392 $650 €568 Seated nude (36x36cm-14x14in) s. chl exec.c.1970. 14-Jun-3 Rachel Davis, Shaker Heights #468
£500 $900 €730 In a triple mirror in a European hotel (20x25cm-8x10in) s.i.d.1964 graphite W/C. 23-Jan-4 Freeman, Philadelphia #7/R
£503 $900 €734 Three reclining nudes (18x20cm-7x8in) s. pen ink. 20-Mar-4 Rachel Davis, Shaker Heights #316/R est:600-900
£512 $850 €742 Reclining female nude (28x46cm-11x18in) s. col pastel exec.c.1970. 14-Jun-3 Rachel Davis, Shaker Heights #467
£707 $1300 €1032 Woman with brown skirt and jacket (38x28cm-15x11in) s. W/C pencil. 10-Jun-4 Swann Galleries, New York #223/R

SOYLAND, Ingrid Nordby (1917-) Norwegian
£310 $517 €453 Flowers in vase (100x110cm-39x43in) s. 20-Oct-3 Blomqvist, Lysaker #1320 (N.KR 3600)

SPACAGNA, Jacques (1936-) French
Works on paper
£884 $1583 €1300 Chevaliers aux bouclier (65x54cm-26x21in) s.d.72-73 mixed media canvas prov. 21-Mar-4 Calmels Cohen, Paris #146/R est:800-1200

SPACAL, Luigi (1907-2000) Italian
£3401 $6088 €5000 Untitled (59x49cm-23x19in) s.d.53 s.d.verso. 16-Mar-4 Finarte Semenzato, Milan #338/R est:4000-4200
Works on paper
£559 $934 €800 Suspended town (40x34cm-16x13in) s.d.58 mm. 10-Oct-3 Stadion, Trieste #533/R

SPACKMAN, Cyril Saunders (1887-1963) American
Sculpture
£1885 $3394 €2752 Woman (99cm-39in) mono. stone. 26-Apr-4 Bukowskis, Stockholm #264/R est:25000-30000 (S.KR 26000)

SPACKMAN, Isaac (attrib) (?-1771) British
Works on paper
£6471 $11000 €9448 Birds (39x46cm-15x18in) embossed gouache set of 5. 25-Nov-3 Christie's, Rockefeller NY #151/R est:4000-6000
£6471 $11000 €9448 Birds (34x27cm-13x11in) embossed gouache five sold with other two. 25-Nov-3 Christie's, Rockefeller NY #150/R est:5000-8000

SPADA, Lionello (1576-1622) Italian
£57931 $96166 €84000 St Jerome (106x163cm-42x64in) 1-Oct-3 Dorotheum, Vienna #270/R est:30000-50000

Works on paper
£1064 $1777 €1500 Frate girato con le braccia alzate in preghiera. Frate girato verso la destra (33x21cm-13x8in) chl white chk brown paper prov. 18-Jun-3 Christie's, Rome #402/R est:1500-2000

SPADA, Valerio (1613-1688) Italian
Works on paper
£950 $1644 €1387 Panther leaping from an arabesque between two baskets of grapes (11x30cm-4x12in) pen brown ink prov. 12-Dec-3 Christie's, Kensington #362
£3200 $5856 €4672 Allegory of Victory on a oak tree (29x43cm-11x17in) i. pen ink on vellum. 6-Jul-4 Christie's, London #62/R est:2000-3000

SPADA, Valerio (attrib) (1613-1688) Italian
Works on paper
£252 $403 €350 Tree (33x23cm-13x9in) pen ink on letter. 14-May-3 Finarte Semenzato, Milan #494/R

SPADARI, Gian Giacomo (1938-) Italian
£400 $736 €600 Dedicated to (70x70cm-28x28in) s.i.d.70 verso prov. 8-Jun-4 Finarte Semenzato, Milan #258/R
£694 $1160 €1000 Eric von Stroheim, le grande illusion (73x60cm-29x24in) s.i.d.1990 verso acrylic prov. 25-Oct-3 Cornette de St.Cyr, Paris #461/R

SPADINI, Armando (1883-1925) Italian
£63380 $105211 €90000 Little girl on wooden horse. Wooden horse (100x80cm-39x31in) prov.exhib.lit. double-sided. 11-Jun-3 Christie's, Rome #276/R est:60000-70000
Works on paper
£414 $691 €600 Founding of Moses (16x20cm-6x8in) Chinese ink. 13-Nov-3 Finarte Semenzato, Rome #136/R

SPADINO, Bartolomeo (18th C) Italian
£8500 $14705 €12410 Peaches, apples, pears and grapes on ledge. Grapes, pears and melon on ledge (11x27cm-4x11in) bears sig copper pair. 10-Dec-3 Bonhams, New Bond Street #34/R est:4000-6000

SPADINO, Giovanni Paolo (17th C) Italian
£8511 $14213 €12000 Still life with various fruit and rabbit (63x83cm-25x33in) i. 18-Jun-3 Christie's, Rome #331/R est:14000-18000
£12752 $23463 €19000 Still life of fruit with grapes and pomegranates (64x49cm-25x19in) 24-Mar-4 Finarte Semenzato, Rome #106/R est:22000
£27333 $48927 €41000 Still life of flowers and fruit in landscape (101x101cm-40x40in) exhib.lit. 17-May-4 Finarte Semenzato, Rome #126/R est:45000-55000

SPADINO, Giovanni Paolo (attrib) (17th C) Italian
£6623 $12053 €10000 Peaches, plums and figs (27x47cm-11x19in) 16-Jun-4 Christie's, Rome #382/R est:10000-12000

SPADINO, Giovanni Paolo (circle) (17th C) Italian
£14000 $24220 €20440 Marble bust surrounded by flowers, fruit and a parrot in a landscape (109x168cm-43x66in) 12-Dec-3 Christie's, Kensington #265/R est:6000-8000

SPAENDONCK, Cornelis van (1756-1840) French
£15385 $28000 €22462 Peaches, grapes, melon and a pineapple with peonies in an urn on a ledge (68x53cm-27x21in) s. panel. 4-Feb-4 Christie's, Rockefeller NY #77/R est:10000-15000
Works on paper
£1370 $2329 €2000 Bunch of flowers with jasmine, forget-me-nots and violets (23x15cm-9x6in) mono. gouache prov.lit. 4-Nov-3 Sotheby's, Amsterdam #147/R est:2000-4000

SPAENDONCK, Cornelis van (attrib) (1756-1840) French
£3667 $6637 €5500 Guirlande de roses (31x45cm-12x18in) 30-Mar-4 Rossini, Paris #49/R est:4000-6000
£26000 $47060 €39000 Grand bouquet de fleurs (81x56cm-32x22in) 30-Mar-4 Gioffredo, Nice #117/R
Works on paper
£1382 $2170 €2004 Still life with bee (35x45cm-14x18in) s. W/C. 26-Aug-3 Lawson Menzies, Sydney #127 est:4000-6000 (A.D 3400)

SPAENDONCK, Gerard van (1746-1822) French
£12000 $20400 €17520 Tulips, primroses and forget-me-nots in a basketd with a dunnock;s nest on a stone ledge (62x51cm-24x20in) s. oval prov.lit. 29-Oct-3 Christie's, London #42/R est:15000-20000
£527778 $950000 €770556 Still life of flowers in basket with two butterflies by alabaster urn (100x81cm-39x32in) s.d.1787 prov.exhib.lit. 22-Jan-4 Sotheby's, New York #123/R est:800000-1200000
Works on paper
£959 $1630 €1400 Tulip (24x18cm-9x7in) s.verso pen brown ink prov.lit. 4-Nov-3 Sotheby's, Amsterdam #149/R
£20548 $34932 €30000 Self portrait seated at a table (37x29cm-15x11in) black white chk htd white prov.lit. 5-Nov-3 Christie's, Amsterdam #144/R est:6000-8000

SPAENDONCK, Gerard van (after) (1746-1822) French
£7394 $12792 €10500 Bouquet de fleurs et de fruits (131x99cm-52x39in) 10-Dec-3 Maigret, Paris #45/R est:6000-7000

SPAGNA, Lo (c.1450-1528) Italian
£30921 $56895 €47000 Madonna and Child (35x27cm-14x11in) tempera panel prov.exhib. 24-Jun-4 Christie's, Paris #56/R est:25000-35000

SPAGNULO, Giuseppe (1936-) Italian
Sculpture
£9396 $16819 €14000 Broken iron (41x86x83cm-16x34x33in) s.d.68 iron exhib. 25-May-4 Sotheby's, Milan #179/R est:5000-6000
Works on paper
£738 $1366 €1100 White head (50x35cm-20x14in) s.d.1987 mixed media. 11-Mar-4 Galleria Pace, Milan #42/R

SPAHN, Victor (1949-) French
£671 $1201 €1000 Skier (65x54cm-26x21in) s. 30-May-4 Eric Pillon, Calais #154/R

SPALA, Vaclav (1885-1946) Czechoslovakian
£4640 $8167 €6960 Flowers in a vase (31x24cm-12x9in) s.d.38. 22-May-4 Dorotheum, Prague #161/R est:160000-240000 (C.KR 220000)
Works on paper
£658 $1119 €961 Still life with pears and apples (15x25cm-6x10in) s.i.d.1944 W/C. 29-Nov-3 Dorotheum, Prague #107/R est:15000-25000 (C.KR 30000)
£802 $1411 €1203 Landscape (27x41cm-11x16in) init.d.13 W/C. 22-May-4 Dorotheum, Prague #201/R est:28000-45000 (C.KR 38000)

SPALDING, Charles B (attrib) (fl.1832-1875) British
£280 $440 €406 On the scent (25x30cm-10x12in) 28-Aug-3 Christie's, Kensington #117/R

SPALDING, Frank (20th C) American
£539 $900 €787 Encounter of crusaders with Saracens (71x97cm-28x38in) s.i.verso. 20-Jun-3 Freeman, Philadelphia #225/R

SPALLETTI, Ettore (1940-) Italian
£10145 $16638 €14000 Untitled (150x110cm-59x43in) oil mixed media panel painted 1974 prov.exhib. 27-May-3 Sotheby's, Milan #287/R est:15000-20000

SPAMAAR, Pieter Gerardus (19th C) Dutch
£1512 $2600 €2208 Card game by candlelight (18x23cm-7x9in) s. panel. 6-Dec-3 Neal Auction Company, New Orleans #181/R

SPAMPINATO, Clemente (1912-) American
Sculpture
£1497 $2500 €2186 At the gate (17x43cm-7x17in) s.d.1934 green pat bronze prov. 7-Oct-3 Sotheby's, New York #199 est:3000-5000

SPANGENBERG, Paul (1843-1918) German
£333 $613 €500 Autumn pond (63x80cm-25x31in) s.d.1907. 9-Jun-4 Dorotheum, Salzburg #575/R

SPANI, Dominik (1811-1896) Swiss
£298 $498 €432 Man's portrait (55x41cm-22x16in) s.d.1847. 23-Jun-3 Philippe Schuler, Zurich #8476 (S.FR 650)

SPANISH COLONIAL SCHOOL, 18th C
£3704 $7000 €5408 Madonna with Christ as Salvator Mundi (61x42cm-24x17in) 21-Feb-4 Weschler, Washington #254 est:7000-9000

SPANISH SCHOOL
£9589 $16301 €14000 Unbelieving Thomas (111x149cm-44x59in) after Caravaggio. 9-Nov-3 Finarte, Venice #30/R est:16000-20000
£11409 $20423 €17000 Saint JOhn the Baptist (235x162cm-93x64in) 25-May-4 Durán, Madrid #689/R est:1200
Sculpture
£8800 $14960 €12848 Saint John (150cm-59in) painted wood. 28-Oct-3 Sotheby's, London #3/R

SPANISH SCHOOL, 15th C
£5208 $8854 €7500 Crucifixion (100x77cm-39x30in) board lit. 29-Oct-3 Il Ponte, Milan #814/R
£42254 $67606 €60000 Madonna of Charity (136x145cm-54x57in) board triptych. 21-Sep-3 Finarte, Venice #56/R est:60000

SPANISH SCHOOL, 16th C
£5634 $9859 €8000 Portement de Croix. Christ a l acolonne. Christ au roseau (79x94cm-31x37in) panel triptych. 17-Dec-3 Piasa, Paris #1/R est:8000-10000
£7237 $13316 €11000 Madonna and Child (145x120cm-57x47in) panel painted c.1580. 25-Jun-4 Piasa, Paris #53/R est:4000-6000
£7500 $13725 €10950 Madonna and Child (37x26cm-15x10in) panel. 9-Jul-4 Christie's, Kensington #114/R est:4000-6000

SPANISH SCHOOL, 17th C
£5000 $8000 €7300 Assumption of Mary (119x84cm-47x33in) 20-Sep-3 Sloans & Kenyon, Bethesda #1158/R est:12000-15000
£5220 $9500 €7621 Architectural capriccio with figures among ruins (172x123cm-68x48in) prov. 29-Jun-4 Sotheby's, New York #24/R est:6000-8000
£5333 $9547 €8000 Holy Family and Saint Nicholas (73x84cm-29x33in) board. 12-May-4 Finarte Semenzato, Milan #35/R est:8000-12000
£5705 $10497 €8500 Il Principe di Danimarca (70x52cm-28x20in) i. verso. 25-Mar-4 Karlheinz Kaupp, Staufen #2267/R est:6000

£7639 $12604 €11000 Portrait of Don Antonio de Moncada (36x26cm-14x10in) copper. 3-Jul-3 Dr Fritz Nagel, Stuttgart #466/R est:2500
£8156 $13621 €11500 Portrait de Charles II d'Espagne enfant (127x102cm-50x40in) painted c.1670. 17-Oct-3 Tajan, Paris #28/R est:6000-8000
£11620 $20102 €16500 Portrait of Jean Baptiste de Nuvolara. Portrait of Isabelle de Nuvolara (131x89cm-52x35in) bears i.d.1632 pair prov. 9-Dec-3 Vanderkindere, Brussels #325/R est:10000-15000
£12414 $22966 €18000 Still life of fruit (47x62cm-19x24in) 14-Jan-4 Castellana, Madrid #232/R est:20000
£17333 $31720 €26000 Portrait of lady (214x115cm-84x45in) 1-Jun-4 Sotheby's, Milan #106/R est:10000-15000
£24434 $41538 €35674 Basket with peaches, plums, apricots and berries (62x87cm-24x34in) 19-Nov-3 Fischer, Luzern #101/R est:20000-24000 (S.FR 54000)
£33557 $60067 €50000 Figs, bread and glass of wine. Cherries and flowers (32x41cm-13x16in) one i.verso board pair. 26-May-4 Porro, Milan #2/R est:40000-50000
£126667 $233067 €190000 Nature morte aux raisins et grenades (57x86cm-22x34in) 11-Jun-4 Maigret, Paris #45/R est:30000-40000
Sculpture
£8000 $13600 €11680 Sleeping Christ child (23cm-9in) ivory. 28-Oct-3 Sotheby's, London #40/R
Works on paper
£6000 $10980 €8760 Penitent Magdalene with angels (25x18cm-10x7in) pen brown ink prov. 8-Jul-4 Sotheby's, London #53/R est:6000-8000

SPANISH SCHOOL, 17th/18th C
£8333 $13583 €12000 Balthazar's dinner (145x198cm-57x78in) 23-Sep-3 Durán, Madrid #245/R est:7500
Sculpture
£21000 $35700 €30660 Saint Francis of Assisi (33cm-13in) ivory. 28-Oct-3 Sotheby's, London #36/R

SPANISH SCHOOL, 18th C
£6471 $11000 €9448 Santa Lucia (106x84cm-42x33in) i. prov. 18-Nov-3 Christie's, Rockefeller NY #65/R est:8000-10000
£12500 $23000 €19000 Village celebrations (74x131cm-29x52in) pair. 25-Jun-4 Piasa, Paris #55/R est:8000-10000
£20000 $33400 €29200 View of Havana (65x103cm-26x41in) 14-Oct-3 Sotheby's, London #238/R est:20000-30000
£32258 $60000 €47097 Ornate still life with flowers and vegetables (92x114cm-36x45in) 5-Mar-4 Skinner, Boston #211/R est:3000-5000

SPANISH SCHOOL, 19th C
£6250 $10188 €9000 Vessel Providencia entering harbour (73x91cm-29x36in) 23-Sep-3 Durán, Madrid #171/R est:8500

SPANISH SCHOOL, 20th C
£13158 $23816 €20000 Exit (24x19cm-9x7in) s. board. 14-Apr-4 Ansorena, Madrid #225 est:200

SPANISH-FRENCH SCHOOL, 19th C
£20690 $34345 €30000 Portrait of bearded man (60x48cm-24x19in) i. i. verso. 1-Oct-3 Dorotheum, Vienna #277/R est:8000-12000

SPANISH-NEAPOLITAN SCHOOL, 17th C
£107692 $185231 €157230 Wine harvest (157x187cm-62x74in) prov.exhib.lit. 2-Dec-3 Bukowskis, Stockholm #345/R est:300000-400000 (S.KR 1400000)

SPANJAERT, Jan (17th C) Dutch
£2466 $4192 €3600 Barn interior with a peasant family (46x63cm-18x25in) mono. indis d. panel. 5-Nov-3 Christie's, Amsterdam #40/R est:4000-6000
£2685 $4940 €4000 Peasants in barn (32x47cm-13x19in) mono.d.1637 panel prov. 24-Mar-4 Dorotheum, Vienna #155/R est:4000-6000

SPANO, Luciano (20th C) Mexican
Works on paper
£527 $896 €769 Two figures (120x100cm-47x39in) s.d.2001 mixed media on canvas. 30-Oct-3 Louis Morton, Mexico #136/R (M.P 10000)

SPANOGHE, Léon (1874-1955) Belgian?
£800 $1432 €1200 Moored boat on the River Scheld (70x80cm-28x31in) s. 15-May-4 De Vuyst, Lokeren #316
£933 $1671 €1400 Boat at the quay (90x70cm-35x28in) s. 15-May-4 De Vuyst, Lokeren #315/R
£1133 $2029 €1700 The mill of Baasrode under snow (97x73cm-38x29in) s. 15-May-4 De Vuyst, Lokeren #314/R est:2000-2400
£1333 $2387 €2000 The Scheld dike of Dendermonde (115x94cm-45x37in) s. 15-May-4 De Vuyst, Lokeren #313/R est:2200-2800
£1338 $2315 €1900 Winter along the Scheldt (81x71cm-32x28in) s. 13-Dec-3 De Vuyst, Lokeren #296 est:1800-2200

SPANYI, Bela von (1852-1914) Hungarian
£566 $900 €826 Autumn landscape (36x60cm-14x24in) s. 12-Sep-3 Skinner, Boston #451/R
£979 $1635 €1400 Storks on rivershore on misty morning (39x50cm-15x20in) s. 9-Oct-3 Michael Zeller, Lindau #765/R
£1054 $1908 €1539 Small houses on the hillside (34x45cm-13x18in) s. 16-Apr-4 Mu Terem Galeria, Budapest #44/R (H.F 400000)
£1300 $2340 €1898 Cattle watering (70x80cm-28x31in) s. 21-Jan-4 Sotheby's, Olympia #405/R est:1000-1500
£1581 $2861 €2308 Watering (64x36cm-25x14in) s.i. 16-Apr-4 Mu Terem Galeria, Budapest #96/R (H.F 600000)
£1757 $3145 €2600 Evening lake landscape with storks on shore (75x105cm-30x41in) s. 6-May-4 Michael Zeller, Lindau #885/R est:1600
£3000 $5400 €4380 Moonlit landscape with stork (50x60cm-20x24in) s. 21-Jan-4 Sotheby's, Olympia #404/R est:4000-6000
£3162 $5723 €4617 Meadow full of poppies (110x65cm-43x26in) s. 16-Apr-4 Mu Terem Galeria, Budapest #94/R (H.F 1200000)
£3258 $5408 €4757 Sunset by lake Balaton (96x117cm-38x46in) s. 4-Oct-3 Kieselbach, Budapest #40/R (H.F 1200000)

SPANYI, Kornel (1858-?) Hungarian
£215 $400 €314 Wooded landscape with stream and birch trees (30x41cm-12x16in) s. 3-Mar-4 Alderfer's, Hatfield #285
£229 $425 €334 Landscape with stream and wading birds (30x41cm-12x16in) s. 3-Mar-4 Alderfer's, Hatfield #284

SPARE, Austin Osman (1888-1956) British
Works on paper
£450 $734 €657 Female nude seated (22x17cm-9x7in) init. pastel. 24-Sep-3 Dreweatt Neate, Newbury #20/R
£680 $1170 €993 Seated female nudes (55x40cm-22x16in) init. chl red white chk double-sided. 3-Dec-3 Christie's, Kensington #659/R
£750 $1320 €1095 Redundant Isle (23x30cm-9x12in) init.i. pen ink board prov.lit. 19-May-4 Sotheby's, Olympia #185/R
£1600 $2752 €2336 Derivation of Ginger Rogers (29x30cm-11x12in) init.i.d.'51-54 pencil W/C. 3-Dec-3 Christie's, Kensington #657/R est:1200-1800
£1700 $2924 €2482 Seated female nude (42x52cm-17x20in) init.d.35 pastel. 3-Dec-3 Christie's, Kensington #658/R est:800-1200

SPARFVENFELDT, Gustaf Victor (20th C) Swedish
£1843 $3005 €2691 The battle at Lutzen (100x150cm-39x59in) after Carl Wahlbom. 29-Sep-3 Lilla Bukowskis, Stockholm #617 est:10000-15000 (S.KR 24000)

SPARKS, Herbert Blande (fl.1892-1893) British
£450 $824 €657 Portrait of a Grecian lady with lyre (89x51cm-35x20in) s.d.1894. 27-Jan-4 Peter Francis, Wales #7/R
Works on paper
£330 $600 €482 Pre-Raphaelite beauty and roses (43x28cm-17x11in) s. W/C. 7-Feb-4 Sloans & Kenyon, Bethesda #1250/R

SPARKS, Will (1862-1937) American
£1514 $2800 €2210 Twilight, old mining town, Nevada, now Arizona (51x61cm-20x24in) s. 13-Mar-4 DeFina, Austinburg #833/R est:2000-4000
£1923 $3500 €2808 Tree in sunset landscape (36x43cm-14x17in) s. prov. 15-Jun-4 John Moran, Pasadena #123a est:3000-4000
£2206 $3750 €3221 Adobe at dusk (28x36cm-11x14in) s. 20-Nov-3 Auctions by the Bay, Alameda #1068/R
£2473 $4500 €3611 Sunshine and adobe (13x25cm-5x10in) s. i.d.1920 verso board. 15-Jun-4 John Moran, Pasadena #123 est:4000-5000
£2910 $5500 €4249 Nocturnal coastal bay (28x36cm-11x14in) s.d.1914 prov. 17-Feb-4 John Moran, Pasadena #166/R est:1500-2500
£4324 $8000 €6313 Settlers home, twilight in the Napa valley, California (76x102cm-30x40in) s.d.1923 i.verso. 13-Mar-4 DeFina, Austinburg #653/R est:3000-5000

SPARRE, Emma (1851-1913) Swedish
£692 $1191 €1010 Vanitas still life (65x53cm-26x21in) s.d.1886. 3-Dec-3 AB Stockholms Auktionsverk #2535/R (S.KR 9000)

SPARRE, Louis (1863-1964) Finnish/Swedish
£629 $1070 €900 The Countess (78x52cm-31x20in) s.i.d.1892 lit. 29-Nov-3 Bukowskis, Helsinki #102/R
£714 $1164 €1042 Lion hill (60x44cm-24x17in) s.i. prov. 29-Sep-3 Lilla Bukowskis, Stockholm #193 (S.KR 9300)
£1147 $1846 €1675 Coastal landscape with figures by fishing village (39x55cm-15x22in) s. panel. 25-Aug-3 Lilla Bukowskis, Stockholm #1091 est:15000 (S.KR 15000)
£1231 $2117 €1797 View from Reimersholmsberget over buildings of the alcohol central (33x36cm-13x14in) s.d.1937 panel. 3-Dec-3 AB Stockholms Auktionsverk #2613/R est:12000-15000 (S.KR 16000)
£1240 $2071 €1810 Fishing boats by harbour entrance (57x71cm-22x28in) s.d.1916. 12-Oct-3 Uppsala Auktionskammare, Uppsala #420 est:8000-10000 (S.KR 16000)
£1895 $3487 €2843 Girl wearing pink dress (112x86cm-44x34in) s.d.1930. 14-Jun-4 Lilla Bukowskis, Stockholm #533 est:10000-15000 (S.KR 26000)
Works on paper
£300 $537 €450 Dagger Bank (19x25cm-7x10in) s.d.25.2.1905 W/C. 15-May-4 Hagelstam, Helsinki #90/R
£367 $656 €550 Beach houses in Borgaa (15x16cm-6x6in) s.d.1904 pencil. 15-May-4 Hagelstam, Helsinki #89/R

SPARRE, Victor (1919-) Norwegian
£1334 $2148 €1948 Meeting under the street lamp (54x65cm-21x26in) s. painted c.1984/1992. 25-Aug-3 Blomqvist, Lysaker #1290/R est:25000-30000 (N.KR 15500)
£1707 $3124 €2492 Cathedral (95x62cm-37x24in) s.d.62 s.i.d. verso panel. 7-Jun-4 Blomqvist, Oslo #427/R est:18000-22000 (N.KR 21000)

SPARROW, Simon (1914-2000) American
£240 $400 €350 Aliens (56x41cm-22x16in) oil pastel paper prov. 15-Nov-3 Slotin Folk Art, Buford #366/R
Works on paper
£1111 $2000 €1622 Untitled assemblage. glitter mixed media jewelry bullet cases prov. 24-Apr-4 Slotin Folk Art, Buford #362/R est:3000-5000

SPARS, Eylert (1903-) German
£872 $1544 €1300 Falkenstein shore, Hamburg Blankensee (44x50cm-17x20in) s.d.48. 28-Apr-4 Schopman, Hamburg #650/R

SPAT, Gabriel (1890-1967) French
£330 $600 €482 Circus performers (14x11cm-6x4in) s. 7-Feb-4 Sloans & Kenyon, Bethesda #882/R
£559 $1000 €816 Still life (13x10cm-5x4in) s. board. 14-May-4 Skinner, Boston #348/R
£1351 $2500 €1972 Place Vendome (26x21cm-10x8in) s. board. 12-Feb-4 Sotheby's, New York #84/R est:1200-1500

SPAULDING, Henry Plympton (1868-?) American
Works on paper
£486 $900 €710 Field of daisies (46x71cm-18x28in) s.d.1908 gouache white paperboard. 10-Mar-4 Doyle, New York #48/R
£549 $950 €802 View of Ogunquit, Maine (24x34cm-9x13in) s.d.1900 W/C. 13-Dec-3 Weschler, Washington #548

SPAUN, Paul von (1876-1932) Austrian
£1267 $2331 €1900 Southern coastal landscape (81x110cm-32x43in) s. 11-Jun-4 Wendl, Rudolstadt #4281/R est:160
£1800 $3096 €2628 Coast off Dubrovnik (68x136cm-27x54in) s.d.1905. 4-Dec-3 Christie's, Kensington #76/R est:2000-3000

SPAZZAPAN, Luigi (1890-1958) Italian
£1408 $2338 €2000 Cavallo imbardato (36x40cm-14x16in) s. tempera W/C paper on canvas painted 1940-41. 14-Jun-3 Meeting Art, Vercelli #408/R est:2000
£1497 $2679 €2200 Along the river (35x25cm-14x10in) tempera cardboard lit. 22-Mar-4 Sant Agostino, Torino #475/R est:2600
£2113 $3507 €3000 Landscape with figure (45x55cm-18x22in) board. 11-Jun-3 Finarte Semenzato, Milan #531/R
£2381 $4262 €3500 In the study (50x38cm-20x15in) s. tempera Chinese ink paper prov.lit. 22-Mar-4 Sant Agostino, Torino #416/R est:3500
£2414 $4031 €3500 Woman and cat (50x37cm-20x15in) s. tempera paper on canvas. 17-Nov-3 Sant Agostino, Torino #176/R est:3000-4000
£2690 $4492 €3900 Mum (36x40cm-14x16in) s. tempera paper on canvas. 17-Nov-3 Sant Agostino, Torino #168/R est:4000
£2759 $4607 €4000 Landscape in pink (37x45cm-15x18in) s. tempera exhib. 17-Nov-3 Sant Agostino, Torino #104/R est:4500
£2819 $5046 €4200 Nude of woman at mirror (99x65cm-39x26in) s. paper on board painted 1928-30 exhib.lit. 29-May-4 Farsetti, Prato #561/R est:4000-6000
£5517 $9214 €8000 Self-portrait (65x43cm-26x17in) cardboard prov.exhib.lit. 17-Nov-3 Sant Agostino, Torino #204/R est:8000-10000
£6122 $10959 €9000 Bar in the park (48x38cm-19x15in) cardboard painted c.1935. 22-Mar-4 Sant Agostino, Torino #521/R est:9000-12000
£6207 $10366 €9000 Shipwreck (47x73cm-19x29in) tempera paper on canvas prov.exhib.lit. 17-Nov-3 Sant Agostino, Torino #217/R est:8000-10000
£7692 $12846 €11000 Fish on the tables (49x69cm-19x27in) s.d.1947 tempera paper on canvas. 26-Jun-3 Sant Agostino, Torino #254/R est:9000-12000
£8966 $14972 €13000 Arlequins (92x100cm-36x39in) tempera cardboard. 17-Nov-3 Sant Agostino, Torino #203/R est:13000-16000
Works on paper
£1034 $1728 €1500 Bull (35x25cm-14x10in) s. col Chinese ink paper on canvas. 17-Nov-3 Sant Agostino, Torino #137/R est:2000
£1379 $2303 €2000 Figure (50x37cm-20x15in) s. Chinese ink W/C. 17-Nov-3 Sant Agostino, Torino #178/R est:2000-2500
£2759 $4607 €4000 Idol (50x37cm-20x15in) s. mixed media paper on canvas. 17-Nov-3 Sant Agostino, Torino #299/R est:3500-4500

SPEAKMAN, Anna Weatherby (?-1937) American
£1471 $2500 €2148 Scene of a seaside cottage and flower garden (51x61cm-20x24in) s. 31-Oct-3 North East Auctions, Portsmouth #1729

SPEAR, Arthur Prince (1879-1959) American
Works on paper
£220 $400 €330 Nymph (56x38cm-22x15in) s.d.1921 pastel. 16 Jun 4 Wolf's, New York #486579/R
£262 $470 €383 View of Annisquam Point, March 22d (23x36cm-9x14in) s. 8-Jan-4 James Julia, Fairfield #929/R

SPEAR, Ruskin (1911-1990) British
£500 $900 €730 Macbeth (104x107cm-41x42in) s. board. 20-Jan-4 Bonhams, Knightsbridge #308/R
£500 $910 €730 After rain - The Lizard (35x71cm-14x28in) board. 21-Jun-4 Bonhams, Bath #400/R
£700 $1260 €1022 Thames at Hammersmith (21x31cm-8x12in) s. board. 20-Jan-4 Bonhams, Knightsbridge #287/R
£900 $1503 €1314 Two boys with a black cat (61x51cm-24x20in) s. board. 21-Oct-3 Bonhams, Knightsbridge #4/R
£950 $1549 €1387 Still life with sardines (29x38cm-11x15in) s. indis.i.verso canvasboard. 24-Sep-3 Dreweatt Neate, Newbury #205
£1000 $1630 €1460 Girl resting (34x45cm-13x18in) paper. 24-Sep-3 Dreweatt Neate, Newbury #196 est:600-800
£1000 $1720 €1460 Road to Roche Station (24x39cm-9x15in) s. board. 2-Dec-3 Bonhams, New Bond Street #105/R est:1100-1500
£1100 $1892 €1606 Isleworth (13x27cm-5x11in) s. board. 2-Dec-3 Bonhams, New Bond Street #100/R est:800-1200
£1300 $2236 €1898 Beach, Gorran Haven (20x32cm-8x13in) s. board. 2-Dec-3 Bonhams, New Bond Street #104/R est:1500-2000
£1300 $2340 €1898 Foreshore and Chiswick Ayot (15x29cm-6x11in) s.board. 20-Jan-4 Bonhams, Knightsbridge #284/R est:1200-1800
£1300 $2392 €1898 Portrait of a young lady (76x64cm-30x25in) init. 8-Jun-4 Gorringes, Lewes #2254 est:600-800
£1800 $3006 €2628 Hogarth's cat (61x51cm-24x20in) s. board. 21-Oct-3 Bonhams, Knightsbridge #3/R est:2000-3000
£1800 $3006 €2628 Ginger cat (63x76cm-25x30in) s. 21-Oct-3 Bonhams, Knightsbridge #38/R est:2000-2500
£3600 $6336 €5256 Woman with cat (61x51cm-24x20in) s.d.65 board. 19-May-4 Sotheby's, Olympia #179/R est:4000-6000
£3850 $6776 €5621 Cat (61x74cm-24x29in) s. 19-May-4 Sotheby's, Olympia #177/R est:4000-6000
£4000 $6880 €5840 Blue harbour (63x76cm-25x30in) s. board. 2-Dec-3 Bonhams, New Bond Street #97/R est:4000-5000
£4000 $7400 €5840 Still life of sardines (30x39cm-12x15in) s. s.i.d.1971 verso board. 11-Feb-4 Sotheby's, Olympia #174/R est:4000-6000
£4000 $7040 €5840 Lord George Brown in the Memorial Hall, Farringdon Street, below a portrait of William III (91x71cm-36x28in) s. sold with letters from the artist. 19-May-4 Sotheby's, Olympia #182/R est:3000-4000
£5500 $9680 €8030 At the bar (66x31cm-26x12in) s.d.62 oil on paper. 19-May-4 Sotheby's, Olympia #170/R est:3000-5000
£14000 $25620 €20440 South Kensington (47x61cm-19x24in) s. board. 2-Jun-4 Sotheby's, London #88/R est:10000-15000
£28000 $47600 €40880 Arty tie (89x91cm-35x36in) s. board prov.exhib. 21-Nov-3 Christie's, London #15/R est:15000-25000
Works on paper
£270 $494 €394 Study of hands (29x39cm-11x15in) s. chl. 3-Jun-4 Lane, Penzance #113
£350 $616 €511 Hammersmith Broadway (23x12cm-9x5in) chl W/C prov. 18-May-4 Bonhams, Knightsbridge #155
£620 $1091 €905 Time to get up (17x17cm-7x7in) pen ink. 18-May-4 Bonhams, Knightsbridge #157
£900 $1584 €1314 Doves (61x61cm-24x24in) pencil gouache prov. 19-May-4 Sotheby's, Olympia #171/R
£4500 $8325 €6570 Music lesson (63x90cm-25x35in) s.d.1950 col chk W/C gouache oil. 11-Feb-4 Sotheby's, Olympia #178/R est:4000-6000

SPEAR, Ruskin (attrib) (1911-1990) British
£250 $438 €365 Densely wooded landscape (38x48cm-15x19in) 19-Dec-3 Mallams, Oxford #246/R

SPEAR, Thomas Truman (1803-1882) American
£370 $650 €540 St. Peter (76x64cm-30x25in) mono.d.1866 i.verso. 22-May-4 New Orleans Auction, New Orleans #562
£1111 $1800 €1622 Two women in music room (36x29cm-14x11in) 31-Jul-3 Eldred, East Dennis #1203/R est:2000-3000

SPEARS, Ethel (1903-1974) American
Works on paper
£659 $1100 €962 Punch and Judy Tuilleries Garden, Paris (43x58cm-17x23in) W/C. 18-Oct-3 David Dike, Dallas #249/R
£898 $1500 €1311 Carousel (33x43cm-13x17in) W/C. 18-Oct-3 David Dike, Dallas #280/R est:800-1200

SPEARS, Frank (1906-1991) South African
£274 $465 €400 Still life with a bowl of lemons (51x66cm-20x26in) s. board. 4-Nov-3 Stephan Welz, Johannesburg #704 est:3500-5000 (SA.R 3200)
£310 $518 €453 White roses in a glass (48x42cm-19x17in) s. board. 20-Oct-3 Stephan Welz, Johannesburg #600 est:3500-5000 (SA.R 3600)
£513 $872 €749 Still life with a tea pot (44x54cm-17x21in) s. board. 4-Nov-3 Stephan Welz, Johannesburg #703 est:3000-5000 (SA.R 6000)
£862 $1440 €1259 Still life of flowers (66x46cm-26x18in) s. board. 20-Oct-3 Stephan Welz, Johannesburg #632 est:3000-4000 (SA.R 10000)

SPECHT, August (1849-?) German
£933 $1680 €1400 Orang-utan as artist (36x28cm-14x11in) s. board. 26-Apr-4 Rieber, Stuttgart #1251/R

SPECHT, August Friedrich (1814-1903) German
Works on paper
£1778 $3200 €2596 Scenes with dogs and kittens (13x21cm-5x8in) s. black chk W/C bodycol five. 22-Jan-4 Christie's, Rockefeller NY #199/R est:4000-6000

SPECK, August (1898-1977) Swiss
£262 $482 €383 Rhine at Ellikon (26x37cm-10x15in) s. i.d. verso panel. 14-Jun-4 Philippe Schuler, Zurich #5751 (S.FR 600)

SPECK, Loran (1944-) American
£3352 $6000 €4894 Indian pottery with onions and peppers (30x41cm-12x16in) board. 15-May-4 Altermann Galleries, Santa Fe #131/R
£5882 $10000 €8588 Acoma pottery with rattle (56x46cm-22x18in) board. 1-Nov-3 Altermann Galleries, Santa Fe #125

SPECKAERT, Hans (attrib) (?-c.1577) Flemish
Works on paper
£2260 $3843 €3300 Flagellation du Christ (25x23cm-10x9in) pen ink over crayon prov. 6-Nov-3 Tajan, Paris #9/R

SPEECKAERT, Michel Joseph (1748-1838) Belgian
£1769 $3219 €2600 Hunter's prize (46x38cm-18x15in) s.d.1822. 3-Feb-4 Christie's, Amsterdam #83/R est:1000-1500
£3691 $6829 €5500 Still life with game and fruit (45x65cm-18x26in) s.d.1829 panel. 13-Mar-4 De Vuyst, Lokeren #307/R est:1500-2000
£8667 $15513 €13000 A peach, a pear and grapes in a basket on a covered ledge (35x44cm-14x17in) s.i. panel prov. 17-May-4 Glerum, Amsterdam #52/R est:3500-5000
£10000 $17300 €14600 Basket of peaches and grapes on a relief marble ledge. Roses and morning glory on a ledge (54x43cm-21x17in) s.d.1831 panel pair. 10-Dec-3 Bonhams, New Bond Street #112/R est:10000-15000
£11000 $18700 €16060 Parrot tulip, roses and other flowers in an urn on a stone ledge with starlings in a nest (71x57cm-28x22in) s. panel. 29-Oct-3 Bonhams, New Bond Street #99/R est:10000-15000
£18792 $34577 €28000 Bouquet of flowers with roses, tulips, poppy and other blossoms (71x56cm-28x22in) s.d.1810. 24-Mar-4 Dorotheum, Vienna #166/R est:35000-45000

SPEED, Harold (1872-1957) British

£280	$493	€409	Moonlit bridge (18x15cm-7x6in) init.d.1897 board prov. 18-May-4 Bonhams, Knightsbridge #22/R
£489	$900	€714	Nude woman with back to artist in garden setting with two men and cherubs (91x91cm-36x36in) s. 9-Jun-4 Alderfer's, Hatfield #366/R est:3000-5000
£1000	$1670	€1460	Waves (28x41cm-11x16in) s. board. 16-Oct-3 Christie's, Kensington #402/R est:5000-7000
£2654	$4750	€3875	Lawn tennis (89x102cm-35x40in) s. 26-May-4 Doyle, New York #148/R est:5000-7000
£18000	$33120	€26280	Portrait of John Ellison McCartney holding a football (157x67cm-62x26in) s.d.1911 prov. 11-Jun-4 Christie's, London #189/R est:7000-10000
£22000	$40480	€32120	Vale of Leutha (135x151cm-53x59in) s. prov.exhib.lit. 11-Jun-4 Christie's, London #101/R est:20000-30000
Works on paper			
£250	$430	€365	Angler (25x20cm-10x8in) chl prov. 3-Dec-3 Christie's, Kensington #454

SPEED, Ulysses Grant (1930-) American

Sculpture			
£932	$1500	€1361	Bronc rider (12cm-5in) bronze edition of 100. 22-Aug-3 Altermann Galleries, Santa Fe #124
£1176	$2000	€1717	Picnic (23cm-9in) bronze. 1-Nov-3 Altermann Galleries, Santa Fe #145
£2358	$3750	€3443	Opening up new country (38cm-15in) s.d.1971 num.25 golden brown pat bronze walnut base. 13-Sep-3 Selkirks, St. Louis #60/R est:4000-5000
£2390	$3800	€3489	Following the bell mare (56cm-22in) brown pat bronze walnut base. 13-Sep-3 Selkirks, St. Louis #59/R est:4000-5000
£3616	$5750	€5279	In the wake of the mountain men (81cm-32in) s.d.1977 num.30 bronze walnut base. 13-Sep-3 Selkirks, St. Louis #61/R est:7000-8000
£15882	$27000	€23188	Half breed (305cm-120in) bronze. 1-Nov-3 Altermann Galleries, Santa Fe #32

SPEELMAN, Adriana Gerarda (attrib) (1801-1847) Dutch

£1000	$1810	€1500	Nature morte aux fleurs (45x35cm-18x14in) s. panel. 30-Mar-4 Campo & Campo, Antwerp #271/R est:2000-2500

SPEER, Martin (attrib) (1700-1765) German

£2416	$4446	€3600	Death of Simon the Magician (99x75cm-39x30in) 25-Mar-4 Dr Fritz Nagel, Stuttgart #664/R est:2800

SPEICHER, Eugene (1883-1962) American

£699	$1300	€1021	Nocturnal landscape with trees (61x81cm-24x32in) s. 3-Mar-4 Alderfer's, Hatfield #366/R est:800-1200
£898	$1500	€1311	Landscape, Eddyville (33x25cm-13x10in) s. prov. 20-Jun-3 Freeman, Philadelphia #175/R est:800-1200
£1329	$2100	€1940	Autumn landscape (76x114cm-30x45in) s. 7-Sep-3 Treadway Gallery, Cincinnati #683/R est:3000-5000
£1366	$2500	€1994	Autumn landscape (76x114cm-30x45in) s. painted c.1940 exhib. 5-Jun-4 Treadway Gallery, Cincinnati #756/R est:2000-3000
£2571	$4500	€3754	Bouquet in a blue and white vase (42x34cm-17x13in) s. prov. 19-Dec-3 Sotheby's, New York #1135/R est:2500-3500
£2907	$5000	€4244	Blonde nude (92x77cm-36x30in) s. i.stretcher prov.lit. 3-Dec-3 Doyle, New York #284/R est:4000-6000
£6977	$12000	€10186	Peonies (55x45cm-22x18in) s. 3-Dec-3 Doyle, New York #285/R est:3000-5000
Works on paper			
£211	$390	€308	Head of a man (30x48cm-12x19in) s. pencil. 16-Jan-4 Aspire, Cleveland #140/R

SPEIGHT, Francis (1896-1989) American

£1890	$3250	€2759	Factories by a river (30x41cm-12x16in) i. canvasboard. 7-Dec-3 Freeman, Philadelphia #200 est:1500-2500

SPELLER, Henry (1902-) American

Works on paper			
£278	$500	€406	Like mother. like daughter (64x46cm-25x18in) col pencil. 24-Apr-4 Slotin Folk Art, Buford #410/R
£389	$650	€568	Woman in red dress (61x48cm-24x19in) pencil crayon prov. 15-Nov-3 Slotin Folk Art, Buford #331/R
£444	$800	€648	Woman with fancy headdress (61x48cm-24x19in) col pencil prov. 24-Apr-4 Slotin Folk Art, Buford #411/R
£444	$800	€648	Dressed to kill (61x51cm-24x20in) col pencil prov. 24-Apr-4 Slotin Folk Art, Buford #412/R
£569	$950	€831	Cowboy couple (61x46cm-24x18in) crayon pencil. 15-Nov-3 Slotin Folk Art, Buford #330/R

SPELMAN, John A (1880-1941) American

£989	$1800	€1444	Brown County, Indiana (69x79cm-27x31in) s. 7-Feb-4 Harvey Clar, Oakland #1576
£1076	$1700	€1571	Rocky coast (71x81cm-28x32in) s. 7-Sep-3 Treadway Gallery, Cincinnati #589/R est:2500-3500
£1344	$2500	€1962	Rocky coast (71x81cm-28x32in) s. painted c.1920. 7-Mar-4 Treadway Gallery, Cincinnati #616/R est:2000-3000
£2557	$4500	€3733	Western landscape. s. painted c.1930. 23-May-4 Treadway Gallery, Cincinnati #498/R est:2500-3500

SPELT, Adriaen van der (attrib) (1630-1670) Dutch

£5800	$10614	€8468	Garland of tulips, roses, poppies and other flowers in a niche (51x39cm-20x15in) panel. 7-Jul-4 Bonhams, New Bond Street #43/R est:5000-7000

SPELTDOOREN, Henri (19th C) Belgian

£1958	$3368	€2800	Mere et fill au rouet (55x46cm-22x18in) s.d.1869 panel. 2-Dec-3 Campo & Campo, Antwerp #332/R est:1800-2200

SPENCE, Andrew (1947-) American

£1514	$2800	€2210	Sleeping bag (179x122cm-70x48in) canvas on panel prov. 13-Jul-4 Christie's, Rockefeller NY #15/R est:2000-3000

SPENCE, Charles (19/20th C) British?

£407	$744	€594	Ship's portrait of Royal Edward (27x57cm-11x22in) s.d.1911 canvas on panel. 7-Jun-4 Blomqvist, Oslo #225/R (N.KR 5000)

SPENCE, Percy Frederick Seaton (1868-1933) Australian

£6356	$10805	€9280	Stockmen mustering sheep (90x136cm-35x54in) s. prov. 24-Nov-3 Sotheby's, Melbourne #252/R est:12000-18000 (A.D 15000)
Works on paper			
£300	$528	€438	Three quarter length portrait of a young lady with a blue ribbon in her hair (28x43cm-11x17in) s.d.Oct 1911 W/C. 18-May-4 Fellows & Sons, Birmingham #167/R
£600	$1062	€876	Joy of life (19cm-7in circular) s.d.1924 W/C bodycol. 27-Apr-4 Bonhams, New Bond Street #15/R
£1000	$1700	€1460	Horses with riders on a coastal track (48x38cm-19x15in) s.d.1924 W/C pair. 28-Oct-3 Lawrences, Bletchingley #1406
£1734	$3000	€2532	Design for a poster for Vickers aircraft (77x39cm-30x15in) s.d.1923 gouache. 11-Dec-3 Sotheby's, New York #231/R est:3000-5000

SPENCELAYH, Charles (1865-1958) British

£1600	$2608	€2336	Good day but little profit (49x58cm-19x23in) s.d.1956 i.verso prov. 25-Sep-3 Mellors & Kirk, Nottingham #740/R est:2000-3000
£2500	$4300	€3650	A good day but little profit (51x61cm-20x24in) s.d.1956. 5-Dec-3 Chrystals Auctions, Isle of Man #282 est:3000-5000
£2800	$5012	€4088	In front of the fire (17x22cm-7x9in) 26-May-4 Sotheby's, Olympia #185/R est:1000-1500
£4200	$7686	€6132	Portrait of a lady (48x38cm-19x15in) s.d.1933. 28-Jan-4 Ibbett Mosely, Sevenoaks #2
£5500	$9350	€8030	Old man's pleasure (63x51cm-25x20in) s. i.verso. 19-Nov-3 Bonhams, New Bond Street #52/R est:7000-10000
£8500	$15640	€12410	Fifty years ago (35x25cm-14x10in) s. canvas on board prov. 23-Mar-4 Bonhams, New Bond Street #126/R est:12000-18000
£9000	$14760	€13140	Grannies tea (36x54cm-14x21in) s. i.verso. 3-Jun-3 Fellows & Sons, Birmingham #81/R est:8000-12000
£19000	$34200	€27740	Leaden coin (25x18cm-10x7in) s. board. 21-Jan-4 Sotheby's, Olympia #298/R est:10000-15000
£20000	$36800	€29200	Natures beauties, known and unknown (61x47cm-24x19in) s.d.1951 prov.exhib.lit. 26-Mar-4 Sotheby's, London #75/R est:20000-30000
£25000	$42500	€36500	Good tonic (41x25cm-16x10in) s.d.1946. 19-Nov-3 Bonhams, New Bond Street #114/R est:12000-18000
£28000	$47600	€40880	Grandmother's portrait (15x20cm-6x8in) s. panel lit. 19-Nov-3 Bonhams, New Bond Street #115/R est:25000-35000
£48000	$88320	€70080	Filling the lamp (41x36cm-16x14in) s. 23-Mar-4 Bonhams, New Bond Street #127/R est:40000-60000
£60000	$102000	€87600	Telegram (40x51cm-16x20in) s.d.1946. 19-Nov-3 Bonhams, New Bond Street #112/R est:60000-80000
£64000	$117760	€93440	Empty chair (59x48cm-23x19in) s.d.1947 exhib. 26-Mar-4 Sotheby's, London #76/R est:30000-50000
£83000	$141100	€121180	Old gold (25x20cm-10x8in) s. panel. 19-Nov-3 Bonhams, New Bond Street #120/R est:30000-50000
Works on paper			
£250	$450	€365	Wake up England, the Mousetrap (26x15cm-10x6in) i. W/C. 22-Apr-4 Lawrence, Crewkerne #811
£260	$486	€380	Second childhood, man with toy (15x10cm-6x4in) s. pencil. 26-Feb-4 Lane, Penzance #48
£7800	$14352	€11388	All his worldly wealth (6x8cm-2x3in) s. W/C on ivorine. 26-Mar-4 Sotheby's, London #77/R est:6000-8000
£8400	$14028	€12264	Departing spirits (24x34cm-9x13in) s.d.1894 W/C prov. 16-Oct-3 Lawrence, Crewkerne #663/R
£14000	$23800	€20440	Much noise, little music (27x37cm-11x15in) s. s.i.backboard pencil W/C htd bodycol prov. 20-Nov-3 Christie's, London #114/R est:15000-20000
£18000	$29340	€26280	Interior scene with elderly bearded gentleman plucking a pheasant (30x25cm-12x10in) s. W/C. 27-Sep-3 Rogers Jones, Clwyd #117/R
£20000	$34000	€29200	Latest addition (22x17cm-9x7in) s.i. W/C. 19-Nov-3 Bonhams, New Bond Street #113/R est:8000-12000
£20000	$36400	€29200	Touch of Rheumatism (22x16cm-9x6in) s. W/C prov. 16-Jun-4 Bonhams, New Bond Street #73/R est:8000-12000

SPENCER, Arthur (19th C) British

£381	$610	€552	Moor landscape at dusk (62x31cm-24x12in) s. 15-May-3 Stuker, Bern #1501 (S.FR 800)
£658	$1211	€1000	Venetian view with the Rialto and gondolas (32x39cm-13x15in) s. board. 22-Jun-4 Mealy's, Castlecomer #319/R est:500-700

SPENCER, Claire (1937-) British

Works on paper			
£800	$1432	€1168	Landscape with distant hills, Clemt, Worcestershire (48x67cm-19x26in) s. gouache. 14-May-4 Christie's, Kensington #594/R

SPENCER, Edward (?) British

Works on paper			
£340	$568	€493	Gem at Horning ferry (18x34cm-7x13in) i. W/C gouache. 25-Jun-3 Dreweatt Neate, Newbury #1335/R

SPENCER, Fred (fl.1891-1924) British

£480	$763	€701	Still life study of apples and grapes (16x25cm-6x10in) s. 18-Mar-3 Anderson & Garland, Newcastle #320/R
Works on paper			
£410	$668	€599	Still life of apples and grapes (1x23cm-0x9in) s. W/C. 23-Sep-3 Anderson & Garland, Newcastle #249
£450	$828	€657	Still life of fruit in a bowl (18x31cm-7x12in) s. W/C. 8-Jun-4 Bonhams, Knightsbridge #70/R
£820	$1394	€1197	Apples in a basket (17x24cm-7x9in) s. W/C. 1-Dec-3 Bonhams, Bath #70/R

£1300 $2067 €1898 Selection of books (20x30cm-8x12in) s. W/C. 9-Sep-3 Gorringes, Lewes #1849/R est:1200-1500

SPENCER, Frederick R (attrib) (1806-1875) American
£535 $850 €781 Portrait of a young girl in burgundy dress (61x53cm-24x21in) board. 10-Sep-3 Alderfer's, Hatfield #257

SPENCER, Gervase (1700-1763) British
Miniatures
£1500 $2760 €2190 Lady wearing ermine trimmed cerise robe over a white dress (4cm-2in) init.d.1760 enamel set in a fishskin case. 24-Jun-4 Bonhams, New Bond Street #5/R est:1500-2500

SPENCER, Gilbert (1892-1979) British
£2100 $3423 €3066 Cottager at Aldworth (33x46cm-13x18in) init. board prov.exhib. 24-Sep-3 Dreweatt Neate, Newbury #91/R est:400-600
£2800 $5096 €4088 Descent from the cross (54x58cm-21x23in) s.d.1915-60 board. 1-Jul-4 Christie's, Kensington #33/R est:1500-2000
£4500 $7650 €6570 Artist's garden, Burdens Farm House (61x76cm-24x30in) s. 21-Nov-3 Christie's, London #138/R est:5000-8000
£5000 $7950 €7300 Winter landscape (51x66cm-20x26in) s. 10-Sep-3 Sotheby's, Olympia #176/R est:3000-5000
£9000 $16110 €13140 Fontwell Vale (68x102cm-27x40in) s.d.1936 prov. 16-Mar-4 Bonhams, New Bond Street #48/R est:9000-12000
Works on paper
£240 $437 €360 Head of a young girl (36x25cm-14x10in) s.d. pencil paper on board. 2-Jul-4 Bloomsbury, London #245/R
£310 $490 €450 Man who picked up sticks on the Sabbath (52x35cm-20x14in) pen black ink over pencil. 24-Jul-3 Lawrence, Crewkerne #880
£550 $919 €803 Portrait of Hilda Carline (29x18cm-11x7in) s.i.d.1925 pencil prov.exhib. 16-Oct-3 Christie's, Kensington #543/R

SPENCER, John Clinton (1861-1919) American
£376 $700 €549 Still life of two woodcocks (51x36cm-20x14in) s.d.1884. 6-Mar-4 North East Auctions, Portsmouth #1132/R

SPENCER, Niles (1893-1952) American
£559 $1000 €816 Landscape with a church (33x36cm-13x14in) s. board. 8-May-4 Susanin's, Chicago #6078/R est:2000-3000
£590 $950 €861 The yellow house (23x30cm-9x12in) s. i. verso board. 20-Aug-3 James Julia, Fairfield #1690/R
£139535 $240000 €203721 Behind the square (61x45cm-24x18in) s. canvasboard prov.exhib.lit. 4-Dec-3 Christie's, Rockefeller NY #95/R est:60000-80000

SPENCER, Richard B (fl.1840-1870) British
£3000 $4980 €4380 Battle of the Nile 1789 (50x76cm-20x30in) indis.s. 1-Oct-3 George Kidner, Lymington #180/R est:3500-5000
£3006 $5500 €4389 Ship William Pictured off Dover (56x91cm-22x36in) s. 6-Jun-4 Skinner, Boston #90a/R est:6000-8000
£5495 $10000 €8023 Celebrated Battle of Trafalgar (60x98cm-24x39in) exhib. 29-Jun-4 Sotheby's, New York #164/R est:10000-15000

SPENCER, Richard B (attrib) (fl.1840-1870) British
£1800 $3222 €2628 H.M.S Victory being towed into Gibraltar on hr way home after the Battle of Trafalgar (61x91cm-24x36in) 11-May-4 Bonhams, Knightsbridge #243/R est:2000-3000

SPENCER, Sir Stanley (1891-1959) British
£300 $501 €438 Portrait of Patricia Preece (15x10cm-6x4in) 21-Oct-3 Gorringes, Lewes #1947/R
£400 $668 €584 Children on a beach (15x10cm-6x4in) 21-Oct-3 Gorringes, Lewes #1948
£7500 $12900 €10950 Roofs and clouds (13x16cm-5x6in) board painted c.1913-1915 prov. 3-Dec-3 Sotheby's, London #5/R est:6000-8000
£15000 $25800 €21900 Portrait of Patricia Preece (50x40cm-20x16in) oil pencil prov.exhib.lit. 3-Dec-3 Sotheby's, London #37/R est:10000-15000
£70000 $119000 €102200 Cottage garden, Leonard Stanley (51x76cm-20x30in) painted April 1940 prov.lit. 21-Nov-3 Christie's, London #139/R est:70000-100000
£95000 $163400 €138700 Saint Oeter escaping from prison (36x36cm-14x14in) prov.lit. 2-Dec-3 Sotheby's, London #70/R est:50000-70000
£1100000 $2013000 €1606000 Christ preaching at Cookham Regatta; listening from punts (97x145cm-38x57in) prov.exhib.lit. 2-Jun-4 Sotheby's, London #81/R est:1000000-1500000
Works on paper
£377 $682 €550 Male figure studies (54x36cm-21x14in) pencil double-sided prov. 1-Apr-4 Heffel, Vancouver #95/R (C.D 900)
£500 $935 €730 Portrait of a woman (33x23cm-13x9in) s.d.1925 pencil. 26-Feb-4 Lane, Penzance #107
£1400 $2520 €2044 Study for Hyacinths (35x25cm-14x10in) pencil prov. 20-Jan-4 Bonhams, Knightsbridge #115/R est:1000-1500
£1400 $2590 €2044 Girl's head (35x25cm-14x10in) pencil exhib. 11-Feb-4 Sotheby's, Olympia #102/R est:700-900
£3906 $7305 €5859 Design for mural (12x89cm-5x35in) pencil prov. 20-Jul-4 Goodman, Sydney #43/R est:2000-3000 (A.D 10000)

SPENCER, T (1700-1763) British
£1500 $2385 €2175 Clipper passing the Isle of Wight (61x92cm-24x36in) 9-Sep-3 David Duggleby, Scarborough #302 est:1500-2000

SPENCER, Thomas (1700-1763) British
£13000 $23920 €18980 Portrait of Dormouse, a bay racehorse led by a jockey (48x64cm-19x25in) i. 26-Mar-4 Sotheby's, London #41/R est:6000-8000
£17000 $28390 €24820 Bay and a grey hunter in a landscape belonging to Thomas Watson, 3rd earl of Rockingham (87x98cm-34x39in) 14-Oct-3 Sotheby's, London #428/R est:8000-12000
£22000 $38720 €32120 Bay Bolton held by a groom in a parkland setting (102x127cm-40x50in) prov. 21-May-4 Christie's, London #11/R est:25000-40000

SPENCER, William Barnett (19th C) British
£3200 $6048 €4672 Battle of Trafalgar (61x91cm-24x36in) s. 17-Feb-4 Bonhams, New Bond Street #76/R est:2000-3000

SPENCER, William G (?) Irish
Works on paper
£570 $1021 €850 Avonmore River, Vale of Clara. River near Foulks Mill County Wexford (39x47cm-15x19in) both s. W/C pair. 31-May-4 Hamilton Osborne King, Dublin #96/R

SPENCER-BOWER, Olivia (1905-1884) New Zealander
£1636 $2569 €2372 Young ladies playing recorders (41x35cm-16x14in) init. board painted c.1945. 27-Aug-3 Dunbar Sloane, Wellington #47/R est:4000-6000 (NZ.D 4500)
Works on paper
£414 $703 €604 Wellington Harbour from Eastbourne (45x33cm-18x13in) s. W/C. 26-Nov-3 Dunbar Sloane, Wellington #77 est:1000-2000 (NZ.D 1100)
£818 $1285 €1186 Untitled, landscape (52x73cm-20x29in) s. W/C. 27-Aug-3 Dunbar Sloane, Wellington #120 (NZ.D 2250)
£865 $1548 €1263 Still life with jug of daffodils (50x57cm-20x22in) s. W/C. 12-May-4 Dunbar Sloane, Wellington #119/R est:2500-4000 (NZ.D 2500)
£893 $1616 €1304 Figure under Nikau Palms (47x37cm-19x15in) s. W/C. 30-Mar-4 Peter Webb, Auckland #152/R est:2500-3500 (NZ.D 2500)
£909 $1655 €1327 Coastal landscape (38x57cm-15x22in) s. W/C prov. 29-Jun-4 Peter Webb, Auckland #93/R est:2000-3000 (NZ.D 2600)
£1444 $2354 €2108 Punakaiki, West Coast (40x34cm-16x13in) s. W/C. 23-Sep-3 Peter Webb, Auckland #132/R est:3000-4000 (NZ.D 4000)

SPENDER, Humphrey (1910-) British
£300 $555 €438 Lock gate III (48x76cm-19x30in) s.d.58 board. 11-Mar-4 Christie's, Kensington #186
£450 $819 €657 Blackriver pool (39x58cm-15x23in) s.d.64 board. 1-Jul-4 Christie's, Kensington #193
£4600 $8096 €6716 Traffic landscapes, Arterial Road en Route to Bolton (51x68cm-20x27in) s. s.i.verso board prov.exhib.lit. 19-May-4 Sotheby's, Olympia #302/R est:1200-1800
Works on paper
£260 $442 €380 Red path (40x57cm-16x22in) s.d.1972 chl W/C gouache. 26-Nov-3 Sotheby's, Olympia #122/R
£700 $1295 €1022 Still life with a lamp, mushroom and fruit (39x53cm-15x21in) chl W/C pen ink. 11-Mar-4 Christie's, Kensington #187

SPENGLER, Clemens (1903-) German
£2222 $3711 €3200 Garden (60x80cm-24x31in) s. s.i.d. verso. 25-Oct-3 Dr Lehr, Berlin #488/R est:1200

SPERANTZAS, Vassilis (1938-) Greek
£5000 $8950 €7300 Couple in an interior (35x45cm-14x18in) s. 11-May-4 Bonhams, New Bond Street #123/R est:2000-3000
£9500 $17005 €13870 Woman (98x131cm-39x52in) s. 10-May-4 Sotheby's, Olympia #105/R est:7000-10000

SPERL, Johann (attrib) (1840-1914) German
£714 $1300 €1042 Genre scene with young boy in red coat (25x18cm-10x7in) panel. 7-Feb-4 Sloans & Kenyon, Bethesda #1235a/R

SPERLICH, Josef (20th C) German
£699 $1189 €1000 Pair of kittens playing (15x21cm-6x8in) s.i. panel. 28-Nov-3 Schloss Ahlden, Ahlden #1443/R

SPERLICH, Sophie (1863-1906) German
£345 $576 €500 Two kittens (16x21cm-6x8in) s. panel. 9-Jul-3 Hugo Ruef, Munich #203
£430 $783 €650 Four young cats playing on the floor (8x22cm-3x9in) panel lit. 19-Jun-4 Bergmann, Erlangen #807
£451 $713 €650 Two kittens (15x21cm-6x8in) s. panel painted c.1900. 5-Sep-3 Wendl, Rudolstadt #3634/R
£793 $1442 €1158 Two kittens (15x21cm-6x8in) s. panel. 20-Jun-4 Agra, Warsaw #44/R (P.Z 5500)
£845 $1513 €1200 Garden scene with two cats (16x22cm-6x9in) s.i. panel lit. 8-Jan-4 Allgauer, Kempten #2521/R

SPERLING, Heinrich (1844-1924) German
£460 $828 €672 Saddled grey horse and a hound in a brick floored stable (19x27cm-7x11in) s. board. 20-Apr-4 Rowley Fine Art, Newmarket #414/R
£1258 $2290 €1900 Two horses by a wooden fence (61x49cm-24x19in) s. 19-Jun-4 Hans Stahl, Hamburg #98/R est:1700
£1381 $2500 €2016 Manne junior (19x15cm-7x6in) s.d.06 i.verso. 30-Mar-4 Bonhams & Butterfields, San Francisco #130a est:2500-3500
£1389 $2194 €2000 Radis Rouge (48x60cm-19x24in) s.d.1916 i. verso lit. 19-Sep-3 Schloss Ahlden, Ahlden #1696/R est:1900
£1844 $3079 €2600 Horse and dog in stable (19x27cm-7x11in) s.d.1917 panel. 21-Jun-3 Hans Stahl, Hamburg #58/R est:900
£2200 $3982 €3300 Two pointers in field (65x88cm-26x35in) s.d.1900. 1-Apr-4 Van Ham, Cologne #1649/R est:3000

SPERLING-HECKEL, Catharina (attrib) (1699-1741) German
Miniatures
£15000 $27000 €21900 Prince Charles Edward Stuart, the young pretender (9cm-4in) i. gilt metal frame oval prov.exhib.lit. 22-Apr-4 Bonhams, New Bond Street #19/R est:15000-18000

SPERO, Nancy (1926-) American?
£1806 $3250 €2637 Untitled (15x17cm-6x7in) s.d.1984 acrylic. 24-Apr-4 David Rago, Lambertville #399/R est:200-400

£2083 $3750 €3041 Untitled (18x23cm-7x9in) s.d.1984 acrylic paper. 24-Apr-4 David Rago, Lambertville #509/R est:300-500
Prints
£2083 $3750 €3041 Untitled (20x21cm-8x8in) s.d.1982 monoprint W/C pastel. 24-Apr-4 David Rago, Lambertville #562/R est:300-500
Works on paper
£1000 $1800 €1460 To the revolution (7x28cm-3x11in) s.d.1983 ink. 24-Apr-4 David Rago, Lambertville #541/R est:400-600
£1167 $2100 €1704 Untitled (15x20cm-6x8in) s.d.1983 ink. 24-Apr-4 David Rago, Lambertville #334/R est:300-500
£1389 $2500 €2028 Untitled (10x25cm-4x10in) s.d.1982 ink W/C. 24-Apr-4 David Rago, Lambertville #274/R est:400-800
£2222 $4000 €3244 Untitled (18x23cm-7x9in) s.d.1965 W/C ink. 24-Apr-4 David Rago, Lambertville #524/R est:200-400
£2500 $4500 €3650 Pilot-eagle-skull (39x25cm-15x10in) s.i.d.1968 collage. 24-Apr-4 David Rago, Lambertville #475/R est:200-400
£3611 $6500 €5272 Eligy I (18x23cm-7x9in) s.i.d.1966 W/C. 24-Apr-4 David Rago, Lambertville #175/R est:200-400
£5278 $9500 €7706 I died at Rodez under electroshock, Artoud (27x19cm-11x7in) s.i.d.1969 W/C. 24-Apr-4 David Rago, Lambertville #75/R est:200-400

SPESCHA, Mathias (1925-) Swiss
£5882 $10000 €8588 Untitled (136x141cm-54x56in) s. jute prov. 25-Nov-3 Germann, Zurich #22/R est:15000-20000 (S.FR 13000)
£6987 $12856 €10201 Untitled (104x100cm-41x39in) s.d.1965 verso jute. 8-Jun-4 Germann, Zurich #105/R est:7000-10000 (S.FR 16000)
Works on paper
£679 $1133 €991 Untitled (37x28cm-15x11in) s.d.2002 verso gouache on panel. 24-Jun-3 Germann, Zurich #23/R (S.FR 1500)
£679 $1133 €991 Untitled (37x28cm-15x11in) s.d.2002 verso gouache on panel. 24-Jun-3 Germann, Zurich #25 (S.FR 1500)
£905 $1511 €1321 Untitled (52x49cm-20x19in) s.d.1962 gouache. 24-Jun-3 Germann, Zurich #28/R (S.FR 2000)
£1448 $2462 €2114 Untitled (63x62cm-25x24in) s.d.92 gouache paper on canvas. 22-Nov-3 Burkhard, Luzern #197/R est:3500-4000 (S.FR 3200)
£2613 $4494 €3815 Untitled (89x79cm-35x31in) s.d.1964 gouache. 8-Dec-3 Philippe Schuler, Zurich #3231 est:2500-3500 (S.FR 5800)

SPETHMANN, Albert (1894-?) German
£461 $783 €673 Landscape with figures and houses (90x80cm-35x31in) s.d.1915 exhib. 10-Nov-3 Rasmussen, Vejle #363/R (D.KR 5000)
£548 $932 €800 The Isar near Bad Tolz (83x60cm-33x24in) s. 5-Nov-3 Hugo Ruef, Munich #1107

SPICER, Henry (1743-1804) British
Miniatures
£1300 $2327 €1898 Gentleman in a blue coat, powdered hair (7cm-3in) enamel on copper. 25-May-4 Christie's, London #33/R est:600-800

SPICER, Peggy (c.1900-1982) New Zealander
£543 $875 €793 Rural landscape, Taupo (37x49cm-15x19in) s. board. 12-Aug-3 Peter Webb, Auckland #235/R (NZ.D 1500)
£595 $1023 €869 The mouth of the Awakino river (63x80cm-25x31in) s. board. 7-Dec-3 International Art Centre, Auckland #265/R (NZ.D 1600)
Works on paper
£294 $550 €429 Liverpool Street (33x46cm-13x18in) s. W/C. 24-Feb-4 Peter Webb, Auckland #9/R (NZ.D 800)
£294 $550 €429 Cottage in Queen's Road, Panmure (27x39cm-11x15in) s. ink. 24-Feb-4 Peter Webb, Auckland #56/R (NZ.D 800)
£301 $518 €439 Hulme Cottage, Parnell (29x40cm-11x16in) s. W/C. 7-Dec-3 International Art Centre, Auckland #367/R (NZ.D 810)
£335 $575 €489 Howe Street, Ponsonby (35x45cm-14x18in) s. W/C. 7-Dec-3 International Art Centre, Auckland #418 (NZ.D 900)
£344 $585 €502 Landscape with farmers, Ruatoria (35x51cm-14x20in) s. ink W/C. 4-Nov-3 Peter Webb, Auckland #13/R (NZ.D 950)
£368 $688 €537 House in Symond Street (23x30cm-9x12in) s. ink. 24-Feb-4 Peter Webb, Auckland #76/R (NZ.D 1000)
£551 $1031 €804 France Street, Ponsonby (39x34cm-15x13in) s. W/C. 24-Feb-4 Peter Webb, Auckland #142/R (NZ.D 1500)

SPICER, Peter (fl.1900-1910) British
£300 $567 €438 Foxes mask and brush hung from a nail upon a wall (48x38cm-19x15in) s. 20-Feb-4 Dickins, Middle Claydon #73

SPICKETT, Ronald (1926-) Canadian
£800 $1464 €1168 Rider (135x75cm-53x30in) painted 1967. 1-Jun-4 Hodgins, Calgary #36/R est:2000-3000 (C.D 2000)

SPICUZZA, Francesco J (1883-1962) American
£299 $500 €437 Floral still life (76x61cm-30x24in) s. board. 27-Oct-3 Schrager Galleries, Milwaukee #1057/R
£444 $800 €648 Floral still life (58x74cm-23x29in) s. board. 26-Jan-4 Schrager Galleries, Milwaukee #1427
£509 $850 €743 Birds at bird bath (61x46cm-24x18in) s. board. 27-Oct-3 Schrager Galleries, Milwaukee #1105/R
£599 $1000 €875 Still life with summer blooming flowers (76x61cm-30x24in) s. 26-Oct-3 Bonhams & Butterfields, San Francisco #6519/R
£865 $1600 €1263 Flowers in blossom (74x58cm-29x23in) s. board. 19-Jul-4 Schrager Galleries, Milwaukee #772/R
£2471 $4250 €3608 Small town gas station (46x61cm-18x24in) s. board prov. 3-Dec-3 Doyle, New York #293/R est:3000-5000
£7778 $14000 €11356 Bradford beach (61x79cm-24x31in) s. board. 26-Apr-4 Schrager Galleries, Milwaukee #1435/R
Works on paper
£278 $500 €406 Penney Island, Cedar Lake, Wisconsin (43x64cm-17x25in) s. pastel. 26-Apr-4 Schrager Galleries, Milwaukee #606/R

SPIEGEL, Louis (1901-1975) American
£301 $550 €439 After couse (61x76cm-24x30in) s.i. canvasboard painted c.1960. 5-Jun-4 Treadway Gallery, Cincinnati #606/R

SPIEGELEIR, Marthe de (1897-?) Belgian
£704 $1218 €1000 Orphans (121x61cm-48x24in) s. 15-Dec-3 Bernaerts, Antwerp #479

SPIEGLER, Franz Josef (attrib) (1691-1757) German
Works on paper
£655 $1192 €956 The Mother of God appearing to the monks (39x37cm-15x15in) red chk. 16-Jun-4 Fischer, Luzern #2547/R (S.FR 1500)

SPIELBERG, Hertha (1890-1977) German?
Works on paper
£270 $484 €400 Girl with green hat (46x39cm-18x15in) mono.d.32 gouache. 8-May-4 Hans Stahl, Toestorf #95/R

SPIELMANN, Oscar (1901-1974) Austrian
£371 $676 €542 Young Algerian girl (41x32cm-16x13in) s.i. panel. 16-Jun-4 Fischer, Luzern #2387 (S.FR 850)

SPIELTER, Carl Johann (1851-1922) German
£298 $542 €450 Portrait of the artist's mother (60x50cm-24x20in) s.i.d.1897. 18-Jun-4 Bolland & Marotz, Bremen #758/R
£315 $541 €450 Washerwoman from Capri (30x50cm-12x20in) d.1880 canvas on panel. 5-Dec-3 Bolland & Marotz, Bremen #643
£331 $603 €500 Portrait of Yerony de Gravenda (57x44cm-22x17in) s.i.d.83. 18-Jun-4 Bolland & Marotz, Bremen #757/R
£699 $1203 €1000 Small girl from Capri (46x27cm-18x11in) s.d.80. 5-Dec-3 Bolland & Marotz, Bremen #637/R
£699 $1203 €1000 Hotel Pagano in Capri (30x51cm-12x20in) d.1880 canvas on panel. 5-Dec-3 Bolland & Marotz, Bremen #642
£1333 $2413 €2000 Two old people reading letter from son at table (100x126cm-39x50in) s.d.1914. 1-Apr-4 Van Ham, Cologne #1650/R est:1800
£1888 $3248 €2700 Half-figure portrait of young woman in front of a landscape (100x69cm-39x27in) s.d.05. 5-Dec-3 Bolland & Marotz, Bremen #635/R est:2000
£2517 $4330 €3600 Girl with doll (140x83cm-55x33in) s.d.1892. 5-Dec-3 Bolland & Marotz, Bremen #632/R est:3300
£2937 $5052 €4200 Ottoman village above the coast. Mountain village with Mosque (66x158cm-26x62in) one s.d.1889 one s.d.1898 two. 5-Dec-3 Bolland & Marotz, Bremen #634/R est:2100
£6643 $11427 €9500 Venus with cupid making music (104x175cm-41x69in) s.d.82 indis.i.verso. 5-Dec-3 Bolland & Marotz, Bremen #633/R est:2700

SPIERINCKS, Karel Philips (1608-1639) Flemish
£3289 $6053 €5000 Christ charpentier (94x69cm-37x27in) 23-Jun-4 Sotheby's, Paris #2/R est:5000-7000

SPIERS, Albert van (1666-1718) Dutch
Works on paper
£7778 $14000 €11356 Design for a floral frontispiece with a portrait medallion of Agnes Block (44x32cm-17x13in) s.i. black chk W/C bodycol htd gold prov. 22-Jan-4 Christie's, Rockefeller NY #129/R est:3000-5000

SPIERS, Benjamin Walter (fl.1875-1893) British
Works on paper
£850 $1335 €1233 Still life with a jug, glass and apples (16x24cm-6x9in) s.d.1876 pencil W/C. 28-Aug-3 Christie's, Kensington #471/R
£5000 $8500 €7300 High Life. Low Life (22x31cm-9x12in) both s.d.87 pencil W/C one htd white scratching out two exhib. 20-Nov-3 Christie's, London #113/R est:6000-8000

SPIERS, Charlotte H (fl.1880-1914) British
Works on paper
£500 $935 €750 Sunny lane, Long Wittenham, Oxfordshire (22x35cm-9x14in) s. W/C. 22-Jul-4 Dominic Winter, Swindon #98/R

SPIERS, Harry (1869-1934) American
Works on paper
£253 $400 €369 Landscape with birch trees on hill (38x51cm-15x20in) s. W/C. 6-Sep-3 Brunk, Ashville #1109
£329 $550 €480 Rushing woodland stream (51x66cm-20x26in) s. W/C. 16-Nov-3 CRN Auctions, Cambridge #7/R

SPIES, S (19th C) Scandinavian?
£440 $800 €642 Young girl with flowers (47x60cm-19x24in) s.d.1897. 7-Feb-4 Rasmussen, Havnen #2089/R (D.KR 4800)

SPIESS, Walter (1895-1942) Russian
£154839 $247742 €226065 Thuringerwald (60x75cm-24x30in) mono. lit. 18-May-3 Sotheby's, Singapore #48/R est:280000-350000 (S.D 432000)
£199275 $308877 €290942 Banyan with two young Balinese (72x57cm-28x22in) mono. prov.lit. 6-Oct-2 Sotheby's, Singapore #38/R est:500000-700000 (S.D 550000)
Works on paper
£12091 $21764 €17653 Seated man (32x26cm-13x10in) s.d.29 pencil prov. 25-Apr-4 Christie's, Hong Kong #525/R est:120000-200000 (HK.D 170000)

SPILHACZEK, Max (1876-1961) Austrian
£704 $1232 €1000 In Kaunitzgasse in Vienna (38x31cm-15x12in) s.d.1918 panel. 19-Dec-3 Dorotheum, Vienna #26/R

SPILHAUS, Nita (1878-1967) German
£382 $603 €550 Street scene (39x27cm-15x11in) s. 5-Sep-3 Wendl, Rudolstadt #3635/R
£769 $1308 €1123 Interior (39x30cm-15x12in) mono. canvas on board. 4-Nov-3 Stephan Welz, Johannesburg #688 est:5000-8000 (SA.R 9000)
£840 $1521 €1226 Flowers in a vase (46x40cm-18x16in) mono. board. 30-Mar-4 Stephan Welz, Johannesburg #533 est:7000-10000 (SA.R 10000)
£855 $1453 €1248 Ravine (50x37cm-20x15in) mono.i. i.verso. 4-Nov-3 Stephan Welz, Johannesburg #630/R est:7000-10000 (SA.R 10000)
£2064 $3695 €3013 Mountainous landscape (32x42cm-13x17in) mono. board. 31-May-4 Stephan Welz, Johannesburg #534/R est:10000-15000 (SA.R 25000)

SPILIMBERGO, Adriano (1908-1975) Italian
£397 $723 €600 Portrait of man (115x66cm-45x26in) s.d.30. 18-Jun-4 Stadion, Trieste #328
£2448 $4161 €3500 Landscape (26x41cm-10x16in) s.d.53. 25-Nov-3 Sotheby's, Milan #98/R est:3500-4500
£6711 $12013 €10000 Landscape (80x100cm-31x39in) s.d.52 exhib. 29-May-4 Farsetti, Prato #560/R est:10000-15000

SPILIMBERGO, Lino Eneas (1896-1964) Argentinian
£2732 $5000 €3989 San Nicola's Church, Bari (20x17cm-8x7in) tempera. 1-Jun-4 Arroyo, Buenos Aires #74
£13812 $25000 €20166 Landscape in the pampa (40x60cm-16x24in) 30-Mar-4 Arroyo, Buenos Aires #83
£15470 $28000 €22586 Boy (61x40cm-24x16in) board. 30-Mar-4 Arroyo, Buenos Aires #90
Prints
£3736 $6800 €5455 Nudes (42x26cm-17x10in) s. print exhib.lit. 29-Jun-4 Arroyo, Buenos Aires #15/R est:5000

SPILLAR, Jaroslav (1869-1917) Czechoslovakian
£1750 $3256 €2555 Girl in room (37x28cm-15x11in) bears sig. 6-Mar-4 Dorotheum, Prague #42/R est:40000-60000 (C.KR 85000)

SPILLAR, Karel (1871-1939) Czechoslovakian
£439 $746 €641 Motherhood (60x49cm-24x19in) s.d.1930 canvas on cardboard. 29-Nov-3 Dorotheum, Prague #42 (C.KR 20000)
£2548 $3924 €4000 Arcadian autumn (45x62cm-18x24in) s.d.1911. 4-Sep-2 Schopman, Hamburg #111/R est:4200
£7171 $12622 €10757 Micareme (54x64cm-21x25in) s.i. 22-May-4 Dorotheum, Prague #148/R est:250000-380000 (C.KR 340000)
Works on paper
£1042 $1698 €1500 Seated female nude (50x40cm-20x16in) s.d.1926 pastel oil chk. 26-Sep-3 Bolland & Marotz, Bremen #619/R est:1000

SPILLER, David (1942-) British
£400 $732 €600 No snow in Africa (58x41cm-23x16in) s.i.d.84-93 col chk acrylic board. 4-Jun-4 Lempertz, Koln #463/R

SPILLIAERT, L (1881-1946) Belgian
Works on paper
£26056 $45077 €37000 Hens and chickens (68x97cm-27x38in) s.d.1917 W/C Indian ink col pencil gouache pastel prov.exhib.lit. 13-Dec-3 De Vuyst, Lokeren #461/R

SPILLIAERT, Léon (1881-1946) Belgian
Works on paper
£1067 $1952 €1600 Emile Verhaeren (17x25cm-7x10in) s.i.d.1905 verso crayon. 7-Jun-4 Palais de Beaux Arts, Brussels #302/R est:1200-1800
£1733 $3172 €2600 Jeunes filles au chapeau (25x17cm-10x7in) s. india ink crayon exec. 1910-1912. 7-Jun-4 Palais de Beaux Arts, Brussels #300/R est:2000-3000
£2550 $4718 €3800 Woman with checked shawl (39x27cm-15x11in) s. pastel col chk. 13-Mar-4 De Vuyst, Lokeren #549/R est:4000-5000
£2800 $5124 €4200 Fermes blanches dans un paysage (16x24cm-6x9in) s.d.1929 W/C. 7-Jun-4 Palais de Beaux Arts, Brussels #301/R est:2800-3500
£3020 $5346 €4500 Travaux des champs (33x25cm-13x10in) s. pastel. 27-Apr-4 Campo & Campo, Antwerp #217/R est:5000-5500
£3087 $5464 €4600 Figurine aux coquillages (47x34cm-19x13in) s.d.1932 W/C prov.exhib. 27-Apr-4 Campo & Campo, Antwerp #216/R est:4250-4750
£3133 $5609 €4700 View of a lake through trees (42x32cm-17x13in) s.d.1920 W/C exhib. 15-May-4 De Vuyst, Lokeren #469/R est:4500-5500
£3667 $6747 €5500 Het Sparrenbos (23x30cm-9x12in) s. W/C exec 1934 prov. 8-Jun-4 Sotheby's, Amsterdam #177/R est:5000-7000
£3867 $6960 €5800 Portrait of Jan Lancsweert, nephew of the artist, age five (30x17cm-12x7in) s. mixed media. 26-Apr-4 Bernaerts, Antwerp #287/R est:2500-3000
£4167 $6625 €6000 Marine aux trois barques (17x26cm-7x10in) s. W/C. 9-Sep-3 Vanderkindere, Brussels #194/R
£4545 $7727 €6500 Heures ternes (53x27cm-21x11in) wash. 1-Dec-3 Palais de Beaux Arts, Brussels #133/R est:6300-8000
£5333 $9547 €8000 Landscape (29x22cm-11x9in) s.d.1919 W/C. 15-May-4 De Vuyst, Lokeren #464/R est:8500-9500
£5600 $10248 €8400 Le chemin du village (54x38cm-21x15in) s.d.1927 W/C gouache crayon. 7-Jun-4 Palais de Beaux Arts, Brussels #299/R est:8700-14000
£5667 $10143 €8500 Landscape (53x74cm-21x29in) s.d.1930 W/C. 15-May-4 De Vuyst, Lokeren #570/R est:9000-12000
£6000 $11040 €9000 Vanitas (55x77cm-22x30in) s. W/C gouache pastel prov.exhib.lit. 8-Jun-4 Sotheby's, Amsterdam #41/R est:10000-15000
£6522 $10696 €9000 Village (62x50cm-24x20in) s.d.1930 gouache. 27-May-3 Sotheby's, Amsterdam #333/R est:6000-8000
£6993 $11888 €10000 Bouquet de narcisses (49x65cm-19x26in) s.d.1936 W/C. 1-Dec-3 Palais de Beaux Arts, Brussels #135/R est:10000-15000
£7333 $13127 €11000 Paysage (29x47cm-11x19in) s.d.1930 W/C. 11-May-4 Vanderkindere, Brussels #155/R est:7500-10000
£7667 $13723 €11500 Park scene with pond and boat (55x76cm-22x30in) s.d.1928 gouache W/C. 15-May-4 De Vuyst, Lokeren #471/R est:12000-14000
£7746 $13556 €11000 Les futs (50x34cm-20x13in) s.d.1938 W/C gouache pen prov. 16-Dec-3 Claude Aguttes, Neuilly #31/R est:7000-9000
£8725 $16141 €13000 River landscape with trees (37x55cm-15x22in) s.d.1931 W/C. 13-Mar-4 De Vuyst, Lokeren #465/R est:12000-14000
£16783 $28531 €24000 Seascape (49x64cm-19x25in) s.d.1919 gouache W/C. 25-Nov-3 Christie's, Amsterdam #235/R est:18000-22000
£22917 $38271 €33000 Promenade a la plage (48x87cm-19x34in) s.d.1920 W/C. 21-Oct-3 Campo, Vlaamse Kaai #579/R est:24000-35000

SPILSBURY, Maria (1777-c.1823) British
£700 $1106 €1015 At the well (43x53cm-17x21in) indis s.d.1812. 4-Sep-3 Christie's, Kensington #300/R
£1800 $3330 €2628 At the well (43x53cm-17x21in) s. 13-Jan-4 Bonhams, Knightsbridge #100/R est:2000-3000

SPIN, Jacob (1806-1885) Dutch
Works on paper
£339 $566 €495 The George E Thatcher, Boston (29x41cm-11x16in) s.i.d.1870 W/C. 17-Nov-3 Waddingtons, Toronto #169/R (C.D 750)
£1477 $2717 €2200 Portrait of the three-mast Robertus Hendrikus Rotterdam (18x28cm-7x11in) one s.d.1860 W/C one s.d.1872 two. 29-Mar-4 Glerum, Amsterdam #133 est:2000-3000

SPINDLER, Charles (1865-1938) German
£940 $1663 €1400 Village d'Alsace (51x75cm-20x30in) s. panel. 27-Apr-4 Claude Aguttes, Neuilly #246/R

SPINDLER, Walter (19th C) French
Works on paper
£400 $692 €584 Night (21x27cm-8x11in) s.i.d.MDCCCXCVIII col chk pen ink W/C after Michelangelo prov. 12-Dec-3 Christie's, Kensington #508/R

SPINELLI, Gian Battista (?-1647) Italian
Works on paper
£987 $1816 €1500 Putto (15x11cm-6x4in) pen ink. 22-Jun-4 Sotheby's, Milan #47/R est:1500-2000

SPINELLI, Niccolo (attrib) (1430-1514) Italian
Sculpture
£7343 $12262 €10500 Crucifixion (118x53cm-46x21in) painted wood lit. 7-Oct-3 Pandolfini, Florence #680/R est:7500-8000

SPINETTI, Mario (19/20th C) Italian
Works on paper
£1708 $2750 €2494 Interior scene with figures (51x74cm-20x29in) s. W/C exec. c.1920. 22-Feb-3 Bunte, Elgin #1260 est:3000-4000

SPINKS, T (19th C) British
£1100 $2013 €1650 River landscape (50x75cm-20x30in) s.d.1887. 12-Jul-4 Mullucks Wells, Bishop's Stortford #411/R est:400-500

SPINKS, Thomas (19th C) British
£276 $470 €403 English landscape with waterway (41x61cm-16x24in) s. 10-Nov-3 Rasmussen, Vejle #31 (D.KR 3000)
£537 $1004 €800 Angler by mountain river (36x54cm-14x21in) s.d.1880. 24-Feb-4 Dorotheum, Vienna #91/R
£800 $1432 €1168 English landscapes, cattle, trees and a river. s. pair. 5-May-4 John Nicholson, Haslemere #537
£850 $1547 €1241 Welsh river (40x60cm-16x24in) s.i.d.1900 pair. 5-Feb-4 Mellors & Kirk, Nottingham #528/R
£950 $1710 €1387 River Conway looking up the Lledyr (29x44cm-11x17in) s.d.1885. 22-Apr-4 Lawrence, Crewkerne #914/R
£950 $1758 €1387 Sheep grazing in parkland (45x61cm-18x24in) s.d.1901. 14-Jul-4 Sotheby's, Olympia #81/R
£1000 $1820 €1460 Meeting of the Conway and the Machno, south of Betws-y-Coed (50x90cm-20x35in) s.d.1879. 21-Jun-4 Bonhams, Bath #330/R est:1500-2000
£1300 $2210 €1898 Summer river landscape with sheep grazing in meadows (25x35cm-10x14in) s.d.1910 panel. 19-Nov-3 Tennants, Leyburn #1060/R est:700-800
£1400 $2520 €2044 River landscapes (38x58cm-15x23in) pair. 21-Apr-4 Cheffins, Cambridge #478 est:1000-1500
£1657 $3000 €2419 Landscape with a fisherman by a stream (71x91cm-28x36in) s.d.1878. 30-Mar-4 Christie's, Rockefeller NY #35/R est:4000-6000
£1800 $3006 €2628 Bend of the river (51x76cm-20x30in) s.d.1895. 13-Nov-3 Christie's, Kensington #103/R est:1800-2200
£1887 $3000 €2755 Fisherman on the Dee (51x91cm-20x36in) s.d.1877. 9-Mar-3 William Jenack, New York #72 est:3000-5000
£2100 $3570 €3066 River landscape with an angler beside trees (51x76cm-20x30in) s.d.1891. 19-Nov-3 Tennants, Leyburn #1061/R est:1000-1500
£2200 $4070 €3212 Extensive river landscape with cattle watering (49x74cm-19x29in) s.d.1896. 10-Feb-4 Bonhams, Knightsbridge #344/R est:2000-3000
£2800 $5152 €4200 Welsh river landscapes (30x46cm-12x18in) s.d.1887 pair. 23-Jun-4 Byrne's, Chester #675/R est:2500-3500
£4000 $6800 €5840 River landscapes (25x35cm-10x14in) s.indis.d. i.verso pair. 19-Nov-3 Tennants, Leyburn #1059/R est:1100-1400

SPINKS, Thomas (attrib) (19th C) British
£1694 $3116 €2473 Welsh river landscape (62x91cm-24x36in) s.d.1892 prov. 14-Jun-4 Waddingtons, Toronto #137/R est:2000-3000 (C.D 4200)

SPINNLER, Rolf (1927-) Swiss
£500 $830 €725 Flowers (100x70cm-39x28in) s.d.1960 verso. 13-Jun-3 Zofingen, Switzerland #3035 (S.FR 1100)
Works on paper
£545 $905 €790 Green composition (58x70cm-23x28in) mono.d.1975 mixed media. 13-Jun-3 Zofingen, Switzerland #3034/R (S.FR 1200)

SPIRIDON, Ignace (fl.1869-1900) Italian
£10667 $19520 €16000 Divertissement matinal (56x47cm-22x19in) s. 5-Jun-4 Gros & Delettrez, Paris #70/R est:15000-20000

SPIRIN, Gennady (1948-) Russian
Works on paper
£299 $500 €437 The first Thanksgiving (36x56cm-14x22in) W/C. 11-Oct-3 Nadeau, Windsor #76/R

SPIRO, Eugen (1874-1972) German
£1534 $2869 €2240 Surrealistic landscape (62x81cm-24x32in) s. masonite. 25-Feb-4 Kunsthallen, Copenhagen #146/R est:25000 (D.KR 17000)
£1844 $3079 €2600 Sleeping nude (28x35cm-11x14in) s. lit. 16-Oct-3 Dorotheum, Salzburg #594/R est:4400-5000
£1944 $3247 €2800 Boy on beach (38x46cm-15x18in) s.i.d. s.i. verso board prov. 24-Oct-3 Ketterer, Hamburg #547/R est:2800-3400
£2000 $3600 €3000 Woman athlete (47x39cm-19x15in) s. board. 26-Apr-4 Rieber, Stuttgart #1261/R est:4500
£2734 $4483 €3800 Group of friends (65x55cm-26x22in) s.d. 4-Jun-3 Ketterer, Hamburg #877/R est:4500-5500
£3497 $5944 €5000 Still life with apples (38x44cm-15x17in) s.d.08 board prov. 29-Nov-3 Villa Grisebach, Berlin #152/R est:5000-6000
£6294 $10699 €9000 Reading - model in Paris (60x73cm-24x29in) s. bears d.1909 prov.exhib. 26-Nov-3 Lempertz, Koln #992/R est:5000-7000

SPIRO, Georges (1909-1994) French
£308 $524 €450 Surreal composition (61x50cm-24x20in) s. 5-Nov-3 Dobiaschofsky, Bern #974 (S.FR 700)
£349 $643 €510 Surreal composition (33x40cm-13x16in) s. 14-Jun-4 Philippe Schuler, Zurich #5892 (S.FR 800)
£385 $654 €562 Quodlibet with photos by Picasso, Modigliani and Matisse (54x45cm-21x18in) s.d.54 prov. 19-Nov-3 Fischer, Luzern #2307/R (S.FR 850)
£490 $832 €700 Nature morte, au mouches prisonnieres (23x18cm-9x7in) s. 20-Nov-3 Gioffredo, Nice #68/R
£537 $988 €800 La planete (19x24cm-7x9in) s. 28-Mar-4 Anaf, Lyon #246
£621 $1117 €900 Jeux du soleil (61x50cm-24x20in) s. 25-Jan-4 Chayette & Cheval, Paris #258
£732 $1200 €1061 Paysage Lunaire (46x38cm-18x15in) s. painted c.1970. 7-Jun-3 Treadway Gallery, Cincinnati #1522
£786 $1446 €1148 Untitled (60x50cm-24x20in) s.d.1960. 8-Jun-4 Germann, Zurich #881/R (S.FR 1800)
£806 $1426 €1177 Surrealistic composition (22x26cm-9x10in) s. cardboard. 27-Apr-4 AB Stockholms Auktionsverk #1182/R (S.KR 11000)
£831 $1412 €1213 Paysage aux fleurs (19x24cm-7x9in) s. panel. 5-Nov-3 AB Stockholms Auktionsverk #1101/R (S.KR 11000)
£1467 $2625 €2200 Figure on unicycle (65x54cm-26x21in) s.d.58. 15-May-4 Van Ham, Cologne #938/R est:2200
£1573 $2500 €2297 Franz Kafka (81x66cm-32x26in) s. masonite. 12-Sep-3 Skinner, Boston #842/R est:6000
£2870 $4879 €4190 La femme sterile (60x50cm-24x20in) s. 5-Nov-3 AB Stockholms Auktionsverk #1104/R est:12000-15000 (S.KR 38000)
£3021 $5136 €4411 Le peintre (73x60cm-29x24in) s. panel. 5-Nov-3 AB Stockholms Auktionsverk #1105/R est:18000-20000 (S.KR 40000)

SPITZ, Karl (1853-?) German
£276 $461 €400 Eschbach (30x43cm-12x17in) s. s.i. verso board lit. 10-Jul-3 Allgauer, Kempten #2688/R

SPITZER, Walter (1927-) Polish
£552 $900 €806 Jewish wedding. Circus scene (24x33cm-9x13in) s.verso two. 28-Sep-3 Bonhams & Butterfields, Los Angeles #7045 est:500-750
£839 $1401 €1200 Le peintre et son modele (97x130cm-38x51in) s. 29-Jun-3 Feletin, Province #105/R

SPITZNER, Sigmund J (?) German
£1154 $1962 €1650 Madonna with child (64x53cm-25x21in) s. 20-Nov-3 Weidler, Nurnberg #333/R est:1200

SPITZWEG, Carl (1808-1885) German
£2685 $4940 €4000 Fisherman (10x13cm-4x5in) panel lit. 25-Mar-4 Karlheinz Kaupp, Staufen #2737/R est:4000
£3333 $6067 €5000 Thistle (30x16cm-12x6in) i.d.1871 canvas on board lit. 30-Jun-4 Neumeister, Munich #686/R est:3000
£5594 $9622 €8000 Rocky outcrop (29x25cm-11x10in) cardboard prov. 5-Dec-3 Ketterer, Munich #17/R est:4000-5000
£6207 $11483 €9000 Couple in forest clearing (13x10cm-5x4in) s.rhombus panel. 12-Feb-4 Weidler, Nurnberg #329/R est:9000
£7947 $14464 €12000 The master of witches (31x19cm-12x7in) panel painted c. 1870-75. 18-Jun-4 Bolland & Marotz, Bremen #772/R est:13000
£10490 $18042 €15000 Country scene with village church under darkening skies (13x32cm-5x13in) board. 3-Dec-3 Neumeister, Munich #746/R est:12000
£12500 $20625 €18000 Don Quixote with horse in gorge (22x11cm-9x4in) i. panel prov.lit. 2-Jul-3 Neumeister, Munich #778/R est:14000
£13889 $22639 €20000 Arrival at Seeshaupt on Starnberger See (65x47cm-26x19in) oil over pen paper on board lit.exhib. 25-Sep-3 Dr Fritz Nagel, Stuttgart #1422/R
£13986 $23776 €20000 Two boys by mountain top fire (25x18cm-10x7in) s.rhombus canvas on board. 24-Nov-3 Dorotheum, Vienna #55/R est:16000-18000
£18000 $32760 €26280 A Turk in a narrow lane (38x26cm-15x10in) board prov.lit. 15-Jun-4 Sotheby's, London #36/R est:10000-15000
£43333 $78867 €65000 Hunter with girl on woodland path (31x23cm-12x9in) i. 30-Jun-4 Neumeister, Munich #685/R est:45000
£51724 $95172 €75517 Harvesting hay in the mountains (45x32cm-18x13in) 26-Mar-4 Koller, Zurich #3122/R est:150000-200000 (S.FR 120000)
£55556 $91667 €80000 The forbidden road (32x26cm-13x10in) s.rhombus bears d.184 lit. 2-Jul-3 Neumeister, Munich #776/R est:75000
£64220 $107248 €93119 Arcadian landscape (50x43cm-20x17in) s. lit.prov. 23-Jun-3 Philippe Schuler, Zurich #3550/R est:100000-140000 (S.FR 140000)
Works on paper
£333 $597 €500 Tree study (21x33cm-8x13in) pencil. 14-May-4 Bassenge, Berlin #6226
£395 $726 €600 Knight in armour (22x11cm-9x4in) pencil. 25-Jun-4 Michael Zeller, Lindau #795/R
£550 $985 €803 Backward glance (28x18cm-11x7in) s. pencil black ink. 18-Mar-4 Christie's, Kensington #740
£552 $916 €800 Figure studies (21x33cm-8x13in) pencil. 30-Sep-3 Dorotheum, Vienna #172/R
£559 $934 €800 Grand Bazar a Alexandrie (21x17cm-8x7in) i. pencil. 10-Oct-3 Winterberg, Heidelberg #775/R
£629 $1070 €900 Fallen tree (20x25cm-8x10in) pencil study. 20-Nov-3 Dorotheum, Salzburg #230/R
£634 $1135 €900 Building facade (28x22cm-11x9in) st.sig. pencil. 8-Jan-4 Allgauer, Kempten #2167/R
£662 $1212 €1000 Seated figure with legs crossed at ankles (33x21cm-13x8in) st.sig. pencil. 7-Apr-4 Dorotheum, Salzburg #186/R
£811 $1427 €1200 Steps (24x20cm-9x8in) pencil. 22-May-4 Lempertz, Koln #1464/R
£833 $1375 €1200 Girl thinking (24x19cm-9x7in) pencil. 2-Jul-3 Neumeister, Munich #492/R
£845 $1513 €1200 Landscape scene with houses (28x21cm-11x8in) st.sig. i.d.30 Aug 39 lit. 8-Jan-4 Allgauer, Kempten #2166/R
£1133 $2051 €1700 Couple out walking with three daughters (22x27cm-9x11in) pencil. 2-Apr-4 Winterberg, Heidelberg #548/R est:1200
£1216 $2141 €1800 Studies of figures (21x33cm-8x13in) pencil prov. two. 22-May-4 Lempertz, Koln #14763/R est:2000

SPITZWEG, Carl (attrib) (1808-1885) German
£1049 $1783 €1500 Extensive landscape (9x24cm-4x9in) panel. 20-Nov-3 Weidler, Nurnberg #316/R est:1500

SPITZWEG, Carl (style) (1808-1885) German
£306 $504 €440 Fisherman (23x17cm-9x7in) canvas on board. 3-Jul-3 Neumeister, Munich #2919

SPLIETH, Heinrich (1877-1929) German
Sculpture
£1319 $2085 €1900 Horse and rider (43x61x14cm-17x24x6in) s.d.1919 bronze lit. 19-Sep-3 Schloss Ahlden, Ahlden #785/R est:2300

SPLITGERBER, August (1844-1918) German
£280 $476 €400 Going for a walk (9x17cm-4x7in) s. panel. 28-Nov-3 Schloss Ahlden, Ahlden #1471/R
£397 $723 €600 Shepherds in a sunset landscape (13x23cm-5x9in) s. panel. 18-Jun-4 Bolland & Marotz, Bremen #773/R
£596 $1085 €900 Winter landscape with a stream and ducks (19x31cm-7x12in) s. cardboard. 17-Jun-4 Frank Peege, Freiburg #1136/R
£638 $1141 €950 Dune landscape (22x30cm-9x12in) paper. 25-May-4 Karl & Faber, Munich #137/R
£800 $1432 €1200 Winter landscape (13x26cm-5x10in) s. panel lit. 14-May-4 Schloss Ahlden, Ahlden #2787/R
£2038 $3750 €2975 Children playing with goats by a stream (81x115cm-32x45in) s. 27-Jun-4 Freeman, Philadelphia #41/R est:2000-3000

SPODE, Samuel (19th C) British
£800 $1304 €1168 Jemmy and Topsy, a horse and terrier in a loosebox (49x59cm-19x23in) s.i. 24-Sep-3 Peter Wilson, Nantwich #5
£4200 $7728 €6132 John Dawson Duckett on Lad (71x91cm-28x36in) s.i.d.1856. 10-Jun-4 Christie's, Kensington #57/R est:1000-1500

SPODE, Samuel (attrib) (19th C) British
£1181 $1924 €1700 Greyhounds in landscapes (30x44cm-12x17in) pair. 28-Sep-3 Hamilton Osborne King, Dublin #124/R est:2000-3000
£1620 $2802 €2300 Bay hunter and chestnut hunter (15x19cm-6x7in) pair. 10-Dec-3 Bonhams & James Adam, Dublin #25/R est:2000-3000
£4651 $8000 €6790 Lord Wilton's Gladiator, with Bill Scott up (71x91cm-28x36in) prov. 5-Dec-3 Christie's, Rockefeller NY #3/R est:10000-15000

SPOEL, Hendrik van der (1904-1987) Dutch
Works on paper
£347 $549 €500 Composition (86x64cm-34x25in) s.d.78 gouache. 2-Sep-3 Christie's, Amsterdam #474

SPOERER, Eduard (1841-1898) German
£665 $1191 €971 Coastal landscape, Normandy (47x59cm-19x23in) s.d.80 panel. 26-May-4 AB Stockholms Auktionsverk #2460/R (S.KR 9000)
£4476 $7608 €6400 Coastal landscape with sailing boat (107x151cm-42x59in) s.d.1889 lit. 28-Nov-3 Schloss Ahlden, Ahlden #1493/R est:4500

SPOERRI, Daniel (1930-) Swiss
Sculpture
£3490 $6247 €5200 Belles et la bete (160x162x125cm-63x64x49in) accumulation panel exec.1990 exhib. 26-May-4 Christie's, Paris #113/R est:8000-12000
£4800 $8640 €7200 Guerrier (82cm-32in) wood assemblage metal exec.c.1982. 25-Apr-4 Versailles Encheres #160 est:10000-12000
£6522 $12000 €9522 Tableau piege (71x71x33cm-28x28x13in) s.i.d.1972 num.verso glassware cigarette butts plates box prov. 10-Jun-4 Phillips, New York #622/R est:4000-6000

£8000 $14480 €11680 Relief de la fete footballeurs (95x73x15cm-37x29x6in) wood glass china metal plastic prov.exhib. 1-Apr-4 Christie's, Kensington #260/R est:5000-7000
£10000 $16700 €14600 Tableau piege (101x101x40cm-40x40x16in) s.i.d.1963 glasses plates spoons knifes forks board prov.exhib. 21-Oct-3 Sotheby's, London #343/R est:6000-8000
£16000 $29120 €23360 Hammer-tisch (80x200x53cm-31x79x21in) s.d.Oct 78 ceramic metal objects linen board prov.exhib. 6-Feb-4 Sotheby's, London #224/R est:12000-15000

Works on paper

£528 $877 €750 Untitled (19x20cm-7x8in) s. mixed media collage cardboard. 14-Jun-3 Meeting Art, Vercelli #44/R
£634 $1052 €900 Untitled (19x21cm-7x8in) s. mixed media collage cardboard. 14-Jun-3 Meeting Art, Vercelli #102/R
£634 $1052 €900 Untitled (19x21cm-7x8in) s. mixed media colage cardboard. 14-Jun-3 Meeting Art, Vercelli #320/R
£676 $1189 €1000 T'en as unoeil (20x18cm-8x7in) s. collage exec 1994 exhib. 18-May-4 Tajan, Paris #110/R est:1200-1300
£805 $1474 €1200 Brote (56x56cm-22x22in) s. num.80/100 assemblage of objects on panel. 7-Jul-4 Artcurial Briest, Paris #347
£811 $1427 €1200 Jacob's medicines (18x20cm-7x8in) s. collage cardboard. 22-May-4 Galleria Pananti, Florence #374/R
£845 $1403 €1200 Untitled (19x20cm-7x8in) s. mixed media collage board. 14-Jun-3 Meeting Art, Vercelli #514/R
£940 $1719 €1400 Brote (56x56cm-22x22in) s. num.85/100 verso assemblage of objects on panel prov. 7-Jul-4 Artcurial Briest, Paris #346 est:800-1200
£2517 $4280 €3600 Tableau piege: Cavigliano - Aachen Express (30x30cm-12x12in) s.i.d.69 69 verso collage wood ceramic glass plastic. 27-Nov-3 Lempertz, Koln #453/R est:2500-3000
£3873 $6701 €5500 Danger de la multiplication (60x60cm-24x24in) s.i.d.1970-71 verso assemblage mixed media panel prov.lit. 9-Dec-3 Artcurial Briest, Paris #532/R est:4000-6000
£4578 $7920 €6500 Tableau piege (70x70cm-28x28in) s.i.d.1974 mixed media panel. 9-Dec-3 Artcurial Briest, Paris #524/R est:6000-8000

SPOHLER, Jan Jacob (1811-1866) Dutch

£592 $1072 €900 Icy landscape with mill by a canal (30x22cm-12x9in) init. panel. 19-Apr-4 Glerum, Amsterdam #35/R
£1343 $2470 €2000 Vue des canaux d'Amsterdam (20x16cm-8x6in) s. panel. 24-Mar-4 Tajan, Paris #87 est:2000-3000
£2400 $4296 €3600 River landscape with mill (45x64cm-18x25in) s. 11-May-4 Vendu Notarishuis, Rotterdam #120/R est:4000-5000
£2517 $4204 €3600 Winter in Dutch harbour (21x27cm-8x11in) s.d.47 panel. 28-Jun-3 Bolland & Marotz, Bremen #735/R est:400
£3147 $5413 €4500 Winter in a Dutch harbour (21x27cm-8x11in) s.d.47 panel. 5-Dec-3 Bolland & Marotz, Bremen #656/R est:4800
£3200 $5760 €4800 Travelers on a path, Haarlem in the distance (28x36cm-11x14in) s. indis d. panel. 20-Apr-4 Sotheby's, Amsterdam #16/R est:6000-8000
£3611 $5742 €5200 Dutch landscape with figures (27x36cm-11x14in) s.d.1840 panel. 9-Sep-3 Vanderkindere, Brussels #37/R
£5263 $9684 €8000 Skaters on a frozen waterway (62x86cm-24x34in) s. 22-Jun-4 Christie's, Amsterdam #49/R est:8000-12000
£5333 $9600 €8000 Skating figures by a windmill (16x22cm-6x9in) s. panel. 20-Apr-4 Sotheby's, Amsterdam #48/R est:8000-12000
£10588 $18000 €15458 Dutch winter landscape with skaters (38x52cm-15x20in) s. panel prov. 19-Nov-3 Bonhams & Butterfields, San Francisco #59/R
£15000 $27600 €21900 Winter scene with figures on the ice (60x82cm-24x32in) s. 23-Mar-4 Bonhams, New Bond Street #9/R est:6000-9000
£16107 $29638 €24000 River landscape in winter with figures on frozen river (70x98cm-28x39in) s. bears d. panel. 25-Mar-4 Dr Fritz Nagel, Stuttgart #769/R est:25000
£20833 $34792 €30000 Winter landscape with skaters near a koek en zopie (60x80cm-24x31in) s.d.64. 21-Oct-3 Sotheby's, Amsterdam #205/R est:25000-35000
£24476 $41608 €35000 Extensive Dutch canal landscape in winter (35x47cm-14x19in) s. panel. 20-Nov-3 Van Ham, Cologne #1875/R est:40000
£32000 $57920 €48000 Winter canal (80x104cm-31x41in) s. panel. 1-Apr-4 Van Ham, Cologne #1651/R est:40000
£36000 $64800 €54000 Figures on frozen waterway near a koek en zopie (52x70cm-20x28in) s. 20-Apr-4 Sotheby's, Amsterdam #179/R est:60000-80000

SPOHLER, Jan Jacob (attrib) (1811-1866) Dutch

£479 $800 €699 Winter landscape with figures by a frozen stream (46x66cm-18x26in) 20-Jun-3 Freeman, Philadelphia #217/R
£1325 $2411 €2000 Landscape near Amstel, Amsterdam (46x65cm-18x26in) s.i. 18-Jun-4 Bolland & Marotz, Bremen #774/R est:2700

SPOHLER, Jan Jacob Coenraad (1837-1923) Dutch

£488 $800 €708 Village canal scene (20x15cm-8x6in) s. panel. 2-Jun-3 Grogan, Boston #653/R
£612 $1096 €900 Dutch landscape in summer (30x46cm-12x18in) s. 17-Mar-4 Neumeister, Munich #613/R
£893 $1536 €1304 Figures on the frozen river in the late afternoon (40x60cm-16x24in) s. panel. 2-Dec-3 Ritchie, Toronto #118/R est:5000-7000 (C.D 2000)
£2093 $3600 €3056 Dutch canal scene (35x44cm-14x17in) s. 3-Dec-3 Doyle, New York #102/R est:4000-6000
£2159 $3670 €3152 Dutch river landscape (46x65cm-18x26in) s. 5-Nov-3 Dobiaschofsky, Bern #976/R est:6000 (S.FR 4900)
£2431 $3840 €3500 Summer, windmills along a river (21x27cm-8x11in) s. panel. 2-Sep-3 Christie's, Amsterdam #165/R est:3000-4000
£2778 $4722 €4000 Early morning. Sunset over Zaandam (12x9cm-5x4in) both init. s.i.verso panel pair. 28-Oct-3 Christie's, Amsterdam #51/R est:4000-6000
£5000 $9100 €7500 Winter evening landscape with a windmill and skaters on a frozen canal (43x67cm-17x26in) s. 1-Jul-4 Van Ham, Cologne #1628/R est:8500
£5655 $9444 €8200 River landscape with mills and flat-bottomed boats (68x84cm-27x33in) s. 11-Nov-3 Vendu Notarishuis, Rotterdam #12/R est:8000-10000
£8000 $14560 €11680 The river crossing (26x35cm-10x14in) s. panel. 15-Jun-4 Sotheby's, London #150/R est:7000-9000
£9200 $16744 €13432 Figures skating on a frozen river near a windmill (26x35cm-10x14in) s. panel. 15-Jun-4 Sotheby's, London #151/R est:7000-9000
£10000 $18000 €15000 Winter landscape with figure on a frozen waterway (33x48cm-13x19in) s.d.69. 20-Apr-4 Sotheby's, Amsterdam #188/R est:15000-20000
£13889 $23194 €20000 Winter landscape with figures on frozen river (37x55cm-15x22in) s. 21-Oct-3 Sotheby's, Amsterdam #174/R est:12000-18000

SPOHLER, Johannes Franciscus (1853-1894) Dutch

£3472 $5799 €5000 Town scene in winter, Utrecht (13x9cm-5x4in) s. panel. 21-Oct-3 Sotheby's, Amsterdam #16/R est:5000-7000
£4167 $6958 €6000 Figures in a Dutch town (18x14cm-7x6in) s. panel. 21-Oct-3 Sotheby's, Amsterdam #50/R est:6000-8000
£4200 $6720 €6090 Dutch town in summer (21x16cm-8x6in) s. panel. 18-Sep-3 Christie's, Kensington #58/R est:3500-4500
£4800 $8880 €7008 By the canal, Amsterdam (16x20cm-6x8in) s. panel. 10-Mar-4 Sotheby's, Olympia #251/R est:2000-3000
£6000 $10860 €9000 Off the coast at Katwijk (46x62cm-18x24in) s. 1-Apr-4 Van Ham, Cologne #1652/R est:8000
£8000 $14400 €12000 Villagers in the streets of a Dutch town (20x16cm-8x6in) s. panel. 20-Apr-4 Sotheby's, Amsterdam #3/R est:5000-7000
£10000 $18400 €14600 Continental town in winter (27x21cm-11x8in) s. panel. 23-Mar-4 Bonhams, New Bond Street #1/R est:3000-5000
£17361 $29514 €25000 Daily activities along a canal in a Dutch city, Amsterdam (48x62cm-19x24in) s. prov. 28-Oct-3 Christie's, Amsterdam #238/R est:20000-30000
£20000 $36000 €30000 Zuiderhavendijk in Enkhuizen (70x90cm-28x35in) s. 20-Apr-4 Sotheby's, Amsterdam #177/R est:20000-30000
£21528 $35951 €31000 Villagers in the streets of a wintry town (33x26cm-13x10in) s. panel. 21-Oct-3 Sotheby's, Amsterdam #179/R est:25000-35000
£50000 $83000 €73000 Dutch canal scene (70x90cm-28x35in) s. 1-Oct-3 Sotheby's, Olympia #200/R est:8000-12000

SPOHLER, Johannes Franciscus (attrib) (1853-1894) Dutch

£3121 $5055 €4400 Lively Amsterdam street (44x34cm-17x13in) s. panel lit. 23-May-3 Karlheinz Kaupp, Staufen #1769/R est:500

SPOHN, Rudolf (1905-1975) Austrian

Works on paper

£387 $643 €550 Untitled (45x33cm-18x13in) s.d.81 W/C. 12-Jun-3 Dorotheum, Graz #121/R

SPOLDI, Aldo (1950-) Italian

£345 $576 €500 Study (66x17cm-26x7in) s.verso tempera cardboard. 13-Nov-3 Galleria Pace, Milan #68/R

SPOLTORE, Federico (1902-) Italian

£3901 $6514 €5500 Portrait of children with dog (160x173cm-63x68in) s. 17-Jun-3 Finarte Semenzato, Milan #520/R est:6000

SPOLVERINI, Ilario (1657-1734) Italian

£48611 $79236 €70000 Cavalry battles (91x130cm-36x51in) pair. 25-Sep-3 Dr Fritz Nagel, Stuttgart #1223/R

SPOLVERINI, Ilario (attrib) (1657-1734) Italian

£5235 $9632 €7800 Battle scene (45x60cm-18x24in) lit. 29-Mar-4 Pandolfini, Florence #692/R est:9000

SPOLVERINI, Ilario (school) (1657-1734) Italian

£6954 $12656 €10500 Battle scene (106x172cm-42x68in) 17-Jun-4 Finarte Semenzato, Milan #394/R est:10000-12000

SPONGBERG, Grace (1906-) American

Works on paper

£219 $400 €320 Old house (36x41cm-14x16in) s. W/C executed c.1940 exhib. 5-Jun-4 Treadway Gallery, Cincinnati #752/R

SPONZA, Nicola (1914-1996) Italian

£350 $584 €500 Boats in Grado (50x70cm-20x28in) s. 10-Oct-3 Stadion, Trieste #435/R
£426 $711 €600 Ponterosso, Trieste (30x50cm-12x20in) s. oil faesite. 21-Jun-3 Stadion, Trieste #196/R

SPOONER, Arthur (1873-1962) British

£460 $796 €672 St Malo, Britanny, sunlit square with carts beneath tall trees (30x38cm-12x15in) 11-Dec-3 Neales, Nottingham #658/R
£550 $1018 €803 Turkeys (24x32cm-9x13in) panel. 11-Feb-4 Sotheby's, Olympia #152/R
£600 $1092 €876 Clifton near Nottingham (30x37cm-12x15in) s. 1-Jul-4 Mellors & Kirk, Nottingham #806/R
£700 $1120 €1015 Mare and foal under a tree (36x43cm-14x17in) s. board. 16-Sep-3 Bonhams, Knightsbridge #116/R
£700 $1169 €1022 Horse and hay wagon. Shire horses resting in a field (29x39cm-11x15in) s. board. 16-Oct-3 Christie's, Kensington #379/R
£750 $1403 €1095 Figures beside a frozen fountain in a winter landscape (33x39cm-13x15in) s. canvasboard. 22-Jul-4 Tennants, Leyburn #834
£900 $1665 €1314 Break from ploughing. Mare and foal (45x50cm-18x20in) s. board pair. 11-Feb-4 Sotheby's, Olympia #151/R est:1000-1500
£1000 $1630 €1460 Porlock (31x33cm-12x13in) s.i.d.1922 canvas board. 24-Sep-3 Dreweatt Neate, Newbury #123/R est:600-800
£1050 $1785 €1533 The lesson (23x32cm-9x13in) s.indis.i. board. 27-Nov-3 Greenslade Hunt, Taunton #1018/R est:250-350
£3500 $6265 €5110 Sunlight and shadow (39x49cm-15x19in) s. 18-Mar-4 Neales, Nottingham #739/R est:800-1200
£4400 $8008 €6424 Haymaking (36x40cm-14x16in) s. canvas on board. 1-Jul-4 Mellors & Kirk, Nottingham #827/R est:800-1200
£20000 $36800 €29200 Nottingham Old Market (114x129cm-45x51in) s. prov.exhib. 9-Jun-4 Christie's, London #45/R est:10000-15000
£190000 $349600 €277400 Goose Fair, Nottingham (183x245cm-72x96in) s.d.1926 prov.exhib. 9-Jun-4 Christie's, London #44/R est:60000-80000

SPOONER, Arthur (attrib) (1873-1962) British

£420 $777 €613 Portrait of seated young woman in ball gown (58x48cm-23x19in) 12-Feb-4 Andrew Hartley, Ilkley #830

SPORRI, Eduard (1901-1995) Swiss

Sculpture

£1045 $1735 €1515 Dove of peace (31cm-12in) s. bronze. 13-Jun-3 Zofingen, Switzerland #2251/R est:1200 (S.FR 2300)

£1448 $2462 €2114 Bather (35cm-14in) i. brown pat.bronze. 19-Nov-3 Fischer, Luzern #1462/R est:2500-3500 (S.FR 3200)

SPRADLING, Frank (20th C) American

£299 $500 €437 Jim Thorpe fumble, by mistake (69x102cm-27x40in) s.i.verso. 20-Jun-3 Freeman, Philadelphia #248/R

SPRAGUE, Amelia (?) American

£366 $600 €531 Woodland interior (20x25cm-8x10in) s. board. 7-Jun-3 Treadway Gallery, Cincinnati #496

SPRAGUE, Edith (fl.1883-1903) British

£400 $664 €584 New College, Oxford (15x23cm-6x9in) s.d.1992. 3-Oct-3 Mallams, Oxford #234/R

SPRANGER, Bartholomaeus (attrib) (1546-1611) Flemish

Works on paper

£1692 $2911 €2470 Mythological figure scene (18x13cm-7x5in) bears sig.d.1580 Indian ink wash. 2-Dec-3 Bukowskis, Stockholm #451/R est:12000-15000 (S.KR 22000)

SPRANGER, Bartholomaeus (circle) (1546-1611) Flemish

£6000 $10380 €8760 Venus and cupid (25x18cm-10x7in) copper prov.exhib. 12-Dec-3 Christie's, Kensington #9/R est:3000-5000

£9060 $16037 €13500 Women at Jesus' grave (105x88cm-41x35in) 27-Apr-4 Porro, Milan #285/R est:13500

SPRANGER, R W (19th C) ?

£6338 $10965 €9000 View of Florence (35x53cm-14x21in) s.d.1871. 9-Dec-3 Pandolfini, Florence #53/R est:3000-4000

SPREAFICO, Leonardo (1907-1974) Italian

£528 $877 €750 Composition (45x56cm-18x22in) s. i.d.1970 verso. 14-Jun-3 Meeting Art, Vercelli #423/R

SPREEUWEN, Jacob van (1611-?) Dutch

£5173 $9518 €7553 Bathseba and her maid (72x56cm-28x22in) s.d.1633 panel lit. 26-Mar-4 Koller, Zurich #3019/R est:15000-25000 (S.FR 12000)

SPRENGEL, Knut Verner (1877-1926) Swedish?

£292 $536 €438 Riddarholmen and Town Hall (58x65cm-23x26in) s. 14-Jun-4 Lilla Bukowskis, Stockholm #676 (S.KR 4000)

SPRETER, Roy (1899-1967) American

£719 $1200 €1050 But Mom, I DID beat Tom wrestlin (79x79cm-31x31in) s. 15-Nov-3 Illustration House, New York #163/R

SPRINCHORN, Carl (1887-1971) American

Works on paper

£463 $750 €671 Pauline lord as Anna Christie (27x18cm-11x7in) s. s.i.verso W/C. 8-Aug-3 Barridorf, Portland #305/R

£932 $1500 €1361 Fall panoramic landscape (28x38cm-11x15in) s.i. W/C. 20-Aug-3 James Julia, Fairfield #1689/R est:1500-2500

£3086 $5000 €4475 Foothills at la Canada, California (42x60cm-17x24in) pastel. 8-Aug-3 Barridorf, Portland #110/R est:5000-7000

SPRING, Ernest W (20th C) American

Works on paper

£251 $450 €366 House (33x46cm-13x18in) s. W/C. 7-May-4 Sloans & Kenyon, Bethesda #1119/R

£447 $800 €653 House on the hill (53x74cm-21x29in) s. W/C. 7-May-4 Sloans & Kenyon, Bethesda #1121/R

SPRINGAEL, Antoine (1871-1928) Belgian

£667 $1200 €1000 Before the execution (105x155cm-41x61in) s. 20-Apr-4 Sotheby's, Amsterdam #84/R est:4000-6000

SPRINGER, Charles Henry (1857-1920) American

£782 $1400 €1142 Eastons beach-west side (41x71cm-16x28in) s.d.1913 prov. 8-Jan-4 James Julia, Fairfield #967/R est:1000-1500

SPRINGER, Cornelis (1817-1891) Dutch

£20690 $37034 €30207 Market fountain in Hildesheim (25x20cm-10x8in) s.d.69 panel. 12-May-4 Dobiaschofsky, Bern #992/R est:32000 (S.FR 48000)

£27778 $46389 €40000 Figures behind the church, Woerden (25x20cm-10x8in) s. panel. 21-Oct-3 Sotheby's, Amsterdam #164/R est:20000-30000

£28235 $48000 €41223 View of the South entrance of the St Pancras Church, Enkhuizen (25x20cm-10x8in) s.d.69 s.i.st.verso panel prov. 28-Oct-3 Sotheby's, New York #80/R est:60000-80000

£76667 $138000 €115000 Busy street in Bremen with the Saint Johann church in the background (57x47cm-22x19in) s.d.1864 prov.lit. 20-Apr-4 Sotheby's, Amsterdam #190/R est:120000-180000

£93333 $168000 €140000 Many figures on a market square in front of the Martinikirche Braunschweig (80x65cm-31x26in) s.d.1874 panel prov.lit. 20-Apr-4 Sotheby's, Amsterdam #178/R est:150000-200000

£145833 $243542 €210000 View of Grote market, Zwolle (54x44cm-21x17in) mono.d.69 panel prov.exhib.lit. 21-Oct-3 Sotheby's, Amsterdam #187/R est:160000-200000

£147222 $245861 €212000 Fishmarket in a Dutch town (66x56cm-26x22in) s. canvas on panel. 21-Oct-3 Sotheby's, Amsterdam #199/R est:180000-220000

£156667 $282000 €235000 View of the Wijnhuistoren, Zutphen (46x58cm-18x23in) s.d.1857 panel prov.lit. 20-Apr-4 Sotheby's, Amsterdam #163/R est:180000-220000

Works on paper

£2800 $5180 €4088 Heerengraacht, Amsterdam (43x57cm-17x22in) s. black chk wash. 14-Jul-4 Sotheby's, Olympia #164/R est:3000-5000

SPRINGER, Leendert (jnr) (1831-1894) Dutch

£490 $842 €700 Dutch canal in early morning light (32x50cm-13x20in) s. 4-Dec-3 Schopman, Hamburg #645/R

SPRONKEN, Arthur (1930-) Dutch

Sculpture

£1449 $2377 €2000 Horse's head (15cm-6in) mono. bronze marble base. 27-May-3 Sotheby's, Amsterdam #378/R est:2000-3000

£2754 $4516 €3800 Horse (17cm-7in) mono. bronze. 27-May-3 Sotheby's, Amsterdam #384/R est:2200-2800

£3333 $6133 €5000 Horse (40cm-16in) init. bronze exec 1960. 8-Jun-4 Sotheby's, Amsterdam #243/R est:5000-7000

£3623 $5942 €5000 Rider (33cm-13in) mono. bronze marble base. 27-May-3 Sotheby's, Amsterdam #377/R est:5000-7000

£4895 $8322 €7000 Amazone (50cm-20in) bronze excl marble base. 25-Nov-3 Christie's, Amsterdam #134/R est:6500-8000

£46667 $85867 €70000 Paard (300cm-118in) bronze cast c.1970 prov. 8-Jun-4 Sotheby's, Amsterdam #20/R est:18000-25000

SPRONSEN, Jan van (1932-) Dutch

£451 $713 €650 Toreador (17x23cm-7x9in) s.d.2000 acrylic pencil. 26-Apr-3 Auction Maastricht #140/R

£486 $768 €700 Bullfight (24x34cm-9x13in) s.d.2002 acrylic pen. 26-Apr-3 Auction Maastricht #139/R

SPROSSE, Carl (1819-1874) German

Works on paper

£1447 $2663 €2200 View of the Moritz Dam (38x49cm-15x19in) s. W/C pencil board oval. 26-Jun-4 C & K, Leipzig #774/R est:800

SPROTTE, Siegward (1913-) German

£769 $1285 €1123 Jellyfish (43x43cm-17x17in) s. s.i.d.1985 oil sand. 24-Jun-3 Germann, Zurich #130/R (S.FR 1700)

£995 $1692 €1453 Landscape (63x83cm-25x33in) s.d.1994 s.i.d. verso panel prov. 25-Nov-3 Germann, Zurich #90/R est:2000-3000 (S.FR 2200)

£1223 $2250 €1786 Kampen cycle - Hommage a Turner (74x104cm-29x41in) s.d.1987 s.i.d. masonite prov. 8-Jun-4 Germann, Zurich #155/R est:3500-4500 (S.FR 2800)

£1267 $2331 €1900 Haus meiner Nachbarin - my neighbour's house (41x48cm-16x19in) s.d.81 i. stretcher prov. 9-Jun-4 Christie's, Amsterdam #44/R est:2000-3000

£1357 $2267 €1981 Untitled (61x60cm-24x24in) s.d.1981. 24-Jun-3 Germann, Zurich #133/R est:2000-3000 (S.FR 3000)

£2715 $4615 €3964 Grasses growing on sand (100x125cm-39x49in) s.d.1991 s.i.d. verso prov. 25-Nov-3 Germann, Zurich #87/R est:8000-12000 (S.FR 6000)

Works on paper

£333 $613 €500 Beach (31x41cm-12x16in) s.d. W/C. 11-Jun-4 Hauswedell & Nolte, Hamburg #1540/R

£570 $1050 €850 Country composition (37x27cm-15x11in) s.d.68 W/C gouache. 26-Mar-4 Bolland & Marotz, Bremen #707/R

SPRUANCE, Benton (1904-1967) American

Prints

£1933 $3500 €2822 Subway shift, the second front (26x41cm-10x16in) s.d.1943 lithograph. 19-Apr-4 Bonhams & Butterfields, San Francisco #60/R est:1500-2500

£3038 $5500 €4435 Road from the shore (26x37cm-10x15in) s.d.1936 lithograph edition of 25. 19-Apr-4 Bonhams & Butterfields, San Francisco #55/R est:1500-2500

Works on paper

£299 $500 €437 Winged lion (48x64cm-19x25in) init. gouache. 20-Jun-3 Freeman, Philadelphia #15/R

SPRUANCE, Benton (attrib) (1904-1967) American

£396 $650 €578 Still life with birds and flowers (76x89cm-30x35in) 4-Jun-3 Alderfer's, Hatfield #325/R

SPRUCE, Everett (1908-) American

£6936 $12000 €10127 Desert at night (61x76cm-24x30in) s.i.verso masonite prov.exhib. 10-Dec-3 Bonhams & Butterfields, San Francisco #6129/R est:500-7000

£7186 $12000 €10492 Untitled (178x61cm-70x24in) burlap panel pair. 18-Oct-3 David Dike, Dallas #182/R est:8000-12000

£7609 $14000 €11109 Desert at night (61x76cm-24x30in) s. i.verso masonite prov.exhib. 8-Jun-4 Bonhams & Butterfields, San Francisco #4156/R est:5000-7000

Works on paper

£299 $500 €437 Whippoorwill (23x33cm-9x13in) W/C exhib. 18-Oct-3 David Dike, Dallas #99/R

£599 $1000 €875 Sandpiper (23x36cm-9x14in) W/C exhib. 18-Oct-3 David Dike, Dallas #100/R

SPRUNGLI, Hans Jakob (c.1559-1637) Swiss

Works on paper

£306 $562 €447 Female nude (26x19cm-10x7in) i. chk htd white. 14-Jun-4 Philippe Schuler, Zurich #4453/R (S.FR 700)

SPURR, Barbara (fl.1914) British
Works on paper
£380 $604 €555 Last man in - ten minutes left to play (28x21cm-11x8in) s. W/C. 10-Sep-3 Cheffins, Cambridge #497/R

SPURRIER, Steven (1878-1961) British
£1900 $3458 €2774 Men's dressing tent (44x61cm-17x24in) s. pencil W/C brush blk ink exhib. 1-Jul-4 Christie's, Kensington #57/R est:1000-1500
£2200 $4004 €3212 In the studio (71x56cm-28x22in) prov. 1-Jul-4 Christie's, Kensington #58/R est:1500-2000
£2600 $4732 €3796 Ebb tide (52x67cm-20x26in) s. canvas on board prov.exhib. 1-Jul-4 Christie's, Kensington #54/R est:2000-3000
£3800 $6916 €5548 Flunkeys (81x51cm-32x20in) s.d.45. 1-Jul-4 Christie's, Kensington #59/R est:4000-6000
£5200 $8840 €7592 Juggler practicing (69x56cm-27x22in) s. 30-Oct-3 Duke & Son, Dorchester #258/R
Works on paper
£290 $458 €421 Portrait of a seated girl (45x30cm-18x12in) s. W/C gouache. 7-Sep-3 Lots Road Auctions, London #369
£400 $708 €584 Artist's wife reading by the fire (24x35cm-9x14in) s. W/C bodycol. 27-Apr-4 Bonhams, Knowle #41
£400 $728 €584 Comforts of travelling in Spain (22x34cm-9x13in) s. pencil pen brush blk ink prov. 1-Jul-4 Christie's, Kensington #62
£720 $1274 €1051 Artist's wife walking on a beach (25x13cm-10x5in) s. W/C bodycol. 27-Apr-4 Bonhams, Knowle #68
£750 $1365 €1095 On the beach (24x35cm-9x14in) s. W/C bodycol prov. 1-Jul-4 Christie's, Kensington #56/R

SPYRATOU, Fani Floka (1924-) Greek
£1000 $1790 €1460 Spring flowers (60x50cm-24x20in) s. 11-May-4 Bonhams, New Bond Street #44/R est:1000-1500

SPYROPOULOS, Jannis (1912-1990) Greek
£2953 $5463 €4400 Perasma no 3 (54x65cm-21x26in) s. i.d.1962 verso. 13-Mar-4 De Vuyst, Lokeren #566/R est:4500-6500
£3672 $6500 €5361 Parenthesis C (48x58cm-19x23in) s. oil paper board prov. 2-May-4 Bonhams & Butterfields, Los Angeles #3081/R est:3000-4000
£5496 $9729 €8024 Greek village scene (47x57cm-19x22in) s.i.verso board. 28-Apr-4 Dunbar Sloane, Auckland #59/R est:4500-6500 (NZ.D 15500)
£6000 $10740 €8760 Page number 5 (65x54cm-26x21in) s. s.i.d.1972 stretcher oil collage. 11-May-4 Bonhams, New Bond Street #106/R est:5000-7000
£7000 $11900 €10220 Hydra (49x56cm-19x22in) s. paper. 18-Nov-3 Sotheby's, London #48/R est:7000-9000
£7200 $12600 €10512 Page 13 (65x54cm-26x21in) s. s.i.d.1968 stretcher oil collage prov.exhib. 16-Dec-3 Bonhams, New Bond Street #117/R est:5000-7000
£13287 $22853 €19000 Strophi (114x162cm-45x64in) s. i. stretcher prov. 5-Dec-3 Ketterer, Munich #329/R est:18000-24000
£15000 $25500 €21900 House on hill (60x80cm-24x31in) s. 18-Nov-3 Sotheby's, London #47/R est:7000-9000
£15254 $27000 €22271 Untitled (96x157cm-38x62in) s. oil collage prov. 2-May-4 Bonhams & Butterfields, Los Angeles #3082/R est:6000-8000
£33000 $57750 €48180 Strophe no 3 (114x145cm-45x57in) s. s.i.d.1969 stretcher oil collage. 16-Dec-3 Bonhams, New Bond Street #113/R est:20000-25000
Works on paper
£1695 $2881 €2475 Page No 5 (65x24cm-26x9in) s. bears i.d.1972 verso mixed media canvas. 24-Nov-3 Sotheby's, Melbourne #351/R est:4000-6000 (A.D 4000)
£1800 $3060 €2628 Orossimo (48x38cm-19x15in) s. mixed media board prov. 18-Nov-3 Sotheby's, London #114/R est:2000-3000
£5369 $9933 €8000 Astros L (81x65cm-32x26in) s. i.d.1964 verso collage canvas prov. 13-Mar-4 De Vuyst, Lokeren #484/R est:6000-10000
£6000 $10200 €8760 Abstract (41x24cm-16x9in) s. 18-Nov-3 Sotheby's, London #113/R est:1500-2500
£7000 $11900 €10220 Parnassus (53x42cm-21x17in) s.d.45 mixed media board prov. 18-Nov-3 Sotheby's, London #115/R est:3000-5000

SQUIBB, Ruth (1928-) South African
£259 $432 €378 Hydrangeas in a glass vase (70x80cm-28x31in) s. board. 20-Oct-3 Stephan Welz, Johannesburg #899 est:2000-3000 (SA.R 3000)
£259 $432 €378 Cape Town Harbour (50x75cm-20x30in) s. board. 20-Oct-3 Stephan Welz, Johannesburg #916 est:1800-2400 (SA.R 3000)
£276 $461 €403 Shebeen, Hubert Street, Johannesburg (52x70cm-20x28in) s. board. 20-Oct-3 Stephan Welz, Johannesburg #883 est:2000-3000 (SA.R 3200)

SQUILLANTINI, Remo (1920-1996) Italian
£867 $1569 €1300 Figures (18x23cm-7x9in) s. canvas on cardboard. 2-Apr-4 Farsetti, Prato #461
£1733 $3137 €2600 Little concert (49x35cm-19x14in) s. 2-Apr-4 Farsetti, Prato #613/R est:2200-2700
£2778 $4389 €4000 Karl Valentin (50x40cm-20x16in) board. 6-Sep-3 Meeting Art, Vercelli #481 est:4000
£3034 $5068 €4400 At the seaside (40x30cm-16x12in) s. s.i.verso board. 13-Nov-3 Finarte Semenzato, Rome #432/R est:4000-4500
£3448 $5759 €5000 Fiances (40x30cm-16x12in) s. board. 14-Nov-3 Farsetti, Prato #493/R est:4400-4800
£3691 $6829 €5500 Difficult breakfast (60x60cm-24x24in) s.s.i.verso board. 13-Mar-4 Meeting Art, Vercelli #557 est:5000
£3819 $6035 €5500 Friends (50x60cm-20x24in) board. 6-Sep-3 Meeting Art, Vercelli #497 est:5000
£3873 $6430 €5500 Perplexity (60x50cm-24x20in) s. s.i.verso painted 1992. 11-Jun-3 Finarte Semenzato, Milan #527/R est:6500
£4467 $8219 €6700 Derby (70x50cm-28x20in) s. board painted 1990. 11-Jun-4 Farsetti, Prato #501/R est:6500-7500
£5369 $9611 €8000 Jazz (70x60cm-28x24in) s. s.i.verso board painted 1987. 30-May-4 Meeting Art, Vercelli #74 est:8000
£7639 $12069 €11000 Jazz (100x100cm-39x39in) board. 6-Sep-3 Meeting Art, Vercelli #729 est:10000
Works on paper
£805 $1490 €1200 Courtship (26x19cm-10x7in) s. pastel. 13-Mar-4 Meeting Art, Vercelli #479
£828 $1382 €1200 Portrait of woman with hat (17x12cm-7x5in) s. mixed media cardboard. 14-Nov-3 Farsetti, Prato #435/R

SQUIRE, Anne (20th C) American
£233 $375 €340 Orange roofs through the trees (46x39cm-18x15in) s.d.25 canvasboard. 17-Aug-3 Bonhams & Butterfields, San Francisco #5821

SQUIRE, John (fl.1880-1896) British
£550 $935 €803 Swansea Bay towards Mumbles (20x33cm-8x13in) s.d.1885 board. 18-Nov-3 Sotheby's, Olympia #41/R

SQUIRRELL, Leonard (1893-1979) British
Works on paper
£520 $900 €759 Rushing stream through autumnal trees (22x33cm-9x13in) s.d.1933 W/C over pencil. 10-Dec-3 Bonhams, Bury St Edmunds #458
£580 $1003 €847 Horse and cart before a ruined tower (23x35cm-9x14in) s.d.1933 W/C over pencil. 10-Dec-3 Bonhams, Bury St Edmunds #464/R
£590 $1074 €861 Landscape, Beaucaire, Provence (20x36cm-8x14in) s.d.1974 W/C. 30-Jun-4 Neal & Fletcher, Woodbridge #231
£620 $1135 €905 At Vaison, Provence (29x43cm-11x17in) s. pastel. 7-Apr-4 Bonhams, Bury St Edmunds #417
£880 $1610 €1285 Old Houses by the Shirehall, Woodbridge, Suffolk (21x22cm-8x9in) s.d.1958 pencil W/C. 28-Jan-4 Dreweatt Neate, Newbury #8/R
£880 $1575 €1285 Stopham bridge Sussex (23x34cm-9x13in) s.d.1955 W/C. 20-Mar-4 Lacy Scott, Bury St.Edmunds #460/R

SQUITIERI, Italo (20th C) Italian
£400 $716 €600 Red fruit (70x50cm-28x20in) s. s.i.d.1959 verso. 12-May-4 Stadion, Trieste #830/R

SRETENSKI, Georgi A (1899-1973) Russian
£870 $1600 €1270 Harvesting the hay (80x123cm-31x48in) painted 1957. 27-Mar-4 Shishkin Gallery, Moscow #49/R est:4000-5000

STAACKMAN, Heinrich Maria (1852-1940) German
£1589 $2893 €2400 Arabian horse rider (90x140cm-35x55in) s.d.98. 16-Jun-4 Hugo Ruef, Munich #1096/R est:1000
£3800 $6080 €5510 Gathering of Arab horsemen (64x96cm-25x38in) s.d.92. 18-Sep-3 Christie's, Kensington #215/R est:2000-3000

STAATEN, L van (1836-1909) Dutch
Works on paper
£280 $442 €409 Dutch panoramic landscape scene with figures, boats and buildings (36x51cm-14x20in) s. W/C. 26-Apr-3 Hogben, Folkstone #241
£290 $461 €423 Papen Drecht (58x37cm-23x15in) s. W/C. 9-Sep-3 Bonhams, Leeds #194
£390 $698 €569 Near Rotterdam (39x59cm-15x23in) s.i.on mount W/C. 26-May-4 Outhwaite & Litherland, Liverpool #289/R

STAATEN, Louis van (1836-1909) Dutch
£373 $600 €545 Dutch harbour scene (38x61cm-15x24in) s. 24-Aug-3 Bonhams & Butterfields, Los Angeles #7036
£1100 $1738 €1595 Dordrecht (29x23cm-11x9in) s. 4-Sep-3 Locke & England, Leamington Spa #137
£1161 $1996 €1695 View of Leyden (41x61cm-16x24in) s. i. on stretcher prov. 2-Dec-3 Ritchie, Toronto #124/R est:2000-2500 (C.D 2600)
Works on paper
£224 $400 €327 Near Overschie (38x55cm-15x22in) s.i. W/C. 4-May-4 Ritchie, Toronto #62/R (C.D 550)
£250 $443 €365 Dutch harbour scene with windmill (28x38cm-11x15in) s. W/C. 28-Apr-4 Peter Wilson, Nantwich #114
£260 $424 €380 Veere Harbour (38x59cm-15x23in) s. W/C. 23-Sep-3 Anderson & Garland, Newcastle #263/R
£260 $478 €380 Canal scene with fishing boats (40x30cm-16x12in) s. W/C. 8-Jun-4 Bonhams, Chester #836
£260 $476 €390 Dutch canal scene with barge and church (40x30cm-16x12in) s. W/C. 12-Jul-4 Mullucks Wells, Bishop's Stortford #401/R
£270 $494 €405 Dutch canal scene with windmill (30x40cm-12x16in) s. W/C. 12-Jul-4 Mullucks Wells, Bishop's Stortford #400/R
£280 $529 €409 Near Monnikendam, Holland (60x39cm-24x15in) s. pencil W/C. 19-Feb-4 Christie's, Kensington #160
£290 $542 €423 Near Amsterdam (53x36cm-21x14in) s. W/C bodycol. 24-Feb-4 Bonhams, Knowle #40
£292 $538 €426 Dutch harbour scene (40x59cm-16x23in) s. W/C. 14-Jun-4 Waddingtons, Toronto #212/R (C.D 725)
£300 $567 €438 Haarlem, Holland (60x39cm-24x15in) s. pencil W/C htd bodycol. 19-Feb-4 Christie's, Kensington #161
£320 $522 €467 Dutch canal scene with a barge moored near a tower in the foreground (59x39cm-23x15in) s. W/C. 23-Sep-3 Anderson & Garland, Newcastle #262
£320 $579 €467 Dutch river landscape with boats by a windmill, Amsterdam in distance (28x36cm-11x14in) s. W/C. 16-Apr-4 Keys, Aylsham #497
£320 $586 €467 Near Rotterdam (36x54cm-14x21in) s.i. W/C htd white. 10-Jun-4 Neales, Nottingham #552
£330 $604 €482 On the Canal, Dordrecht (36x54cm-14x21in) s.i. W/C htd white. 10-Jun-4 Neales, Nottingham #551/R
£350 $571 €511 Papendrecht (59x40cm-23x16in) s. W/C. 23-Sep-3 Anderson & Garland, Newcastle #261/R
£350 $627 €511 Near Dortrecht (36x54cm-14x21in) s. W/C. 11-May-4 Dreweatt Neate, Newbury #465/R
£360 $659 €526 Dordrecht, canal scene with shipping and buildings (49x74cm-19x29in) s.i. W/C htd bodycol. 6-Apr-4 Bonhams, Chester #885
£420 $664 €609 Sailing barges moored in a Dutch town (40x29cm-16x11in) s. W/C. 2-Sep-3 Bristol Auction Rooms #554/R
£420 $689 €613 Dutch river landscape with windmill (60x39cm-24x15in) s. W/C htd white. 3-Jun-3 Fellows & Sons, Birmingham #183/R
£440 $700 €638 Haarlem canal (38x28cm-15x11in) s. W/C. 12-Sep-3 Aspire, Cleveland #166
£560 $1036 €818 Papendrecht. Amsterdam (59x39cm-23x15in) both s. W/C pair. 14-Jul-4 Bonhams, Chester #417

£600	$1032	€876	Dordrecht, a Dutch canal scene with figures, shipping and buildings (34x75cm-13x30in) s. W/C. 2-Dec-3 Sworder & Son, Bishops Stortford #485/R
£850	$1445	€1241	Vollendam. Middendam (50x75cm-20x30in) s. W/C bodycol pair. 1-Dec-3 Bonhams, Bath #78/R
£950	$1720	€1387	Haarlem. Monnikendam (56x38cm-22x15in) s. W/C pair. 16-Apr-4 Keys, Aylsham #510/R
£1000	$1600	€1460	Dutch canal scenes (40x60cm-16x24in) s. W/C pair. 17-Sep-3 Bonhams, Brooks & Langlois, Jersey #97/R

STABELL, Allan (1943-) Danish?

£812	$1519	€1186	Composition (162x130cm-64x51in) s.d.2000 verso. 25-Feb-4 Kunsthallen, Copenhagen #135 (D.KR 9000)

STABELL, Harald Krohg (1874-1963) Norwegian

Works on paper

£2232	$3906	€3259	Mountain farm, possibly in Moere (55x76cm-22x30in) s. gouache. 16-Dec-3 Grev Wedels Plass, Oslo #105/R est:8000-10000 (N.KR 26000)

STABLI, Adolf (1842-1901) Swiss

£606	$1085	€885	Wooded landscape (59x88cm-23x35in) s. canvas on panel. 22-Mar-4 Philippe Schuler, Zurich #4362 (S.FR 1400)
£1233	$2096	€1800	Track with birch trees (38x48cm-15x19in) s.d.1893. 5-Nov-3 Hugo Ruef, Munich #1138/R est:1800
£2915	$4751	€4256	Storm clouds over lake (85x110cm-33x43in) s.d.91. 29-Sep-3 Christie's, Zurich #9/R est:5000-7000 (S.FR 6500)
£5240	$9380	€7650	Seascape with storm (110x140cm-43x55in) s. 26-May-4 Sotheby's, Zurich #13/R est:8000-12000 (S.FR 12000)
£9955	$16923	€14534	Lakeshore in evening (38x46cm-15x18in) s. 28-Nov-3 Zofingen, Switzerland #2488/R est:3000 (S.FR 22000)

STABROWSKI, Kazimierz (1869-1929) Polish

Works on paper

£622	$1151	€908	Three birds (49x68cm-19x27in) pastel. 14-Mar-4 Agra, Warsaw #50/R (P.Z 4500)

STACEY, Anna Lee (1871-1943) American

£698	$1200	€1019	Moonlight (25x18cm-10x7in) s.i.verso board painted c.1910. 7-Dec-3 Treadway Gallery, Cincinnati #548/R

STACEY, Walter S (1846-1929) British

£3500	$6300	€5110	Haunted grange (77x57cm-30x22in) s.d.1888. 21-Jan-4 Sotheby's, Olympia #293/R est:1000-2000

STACHE, Adolphe (1823-1862) Belgian

£2900	$4930	€4234	Letter- study of two ladies in an interior taking tea (65x51cm-26x20in) s. panel. 31-Oct-3 Moore Allen & Innocent, Cirencester #785/R est:1500-2500

STACHELSCHEID, Karl (1917-) German

£699	$1203	€1000	Street scene (90x76cm-35x30in) s.d.52. 4-Dec-3 Van Ham, Cologne #487/R
£1067	$1931	€1600	Circus in winter camp (60x80cm-24x31in) s. 1-Apr-4 Van Ham, Cologne #1653/R est:1800

STACHIEWICZ, Piotr (1858-1938) Polish

Works on paper

£313	$489	€457	Madonna and Child (20x15cm-8x6in) s. W/C gouache. 30-Mar-3 Agra, Warsaw #53/R (P.Z 2000)
£756	$1309	€1104	Two young ladies in love (43x59cm-17x23in) s. pastel exec. c.1920. 14-Dec-3 Agra, Warsaw #11/R (P.Z 5000)
£756	$1309	€1104	Portrait of a female head (43x59cm-17x23in) s. pastel exec. c.1920. 14-Dec-3 Agra, Warsaw #10/R (P.Z 5000)
£1202	$2116	€1755	Portrait of lady (60x44cm-24x17in) s. pastel cardboard. 23-May-4 Agra, Warsaw #27/R (P.Z 8500)
£1411	$2201	€2060	Portrait of a young woman (45x61cm-18x24in) s. pastel exec.c.1920. 30-Mar-3 Agra, Warsaw #36/R est:5000 (P.Z 9000)

STACK, Josef Magnus (1812-1868) Swedish

£554	$992	€809	Landscape with trees (41x27cm-16x11in) s. 28-May-4 Uppsala Auktionskammare, Uppsala #115 (S.KR 7500)

STACK, Michael (1947-) American

£1955	$3500	€2854	Red sky over the Rio Grande (61x102cm-24x40in) 15-May-4 Altermann Galleries, Santa Fe #168/R
£5028	$9000	€7341	Summer evening fields of hatch (61x51cm-24x20in) 15-May-4 Altermann Galleries, Santa Fe #167/R

STACQUET, Henri (1838-1907) Belgian

Works on paper

£338	$595	€500	Canal de Katwijck (35x44cm-14x17in) s. W/C. 18-May-4 Galerie Moderne, Brussels #111
£967	$1730	€1450	Bord de mer anime en Hollande (60x52cm-24x20in) s. gouache cardboard. 11-May-4 Vanderkindere, Brussels #18

STADELHOFER, Helmut (1914-) German

£552	$1021	€800	Chiemsee fishing (78x97cm-31x38in) s. 12-Feb-4 Weidler, Nurnberg #4511/R
£629	$1070	€900	Chiemsee fishermen by Fraueninsel (68x78cm-27x31in) s.i. 20-Nov-3 Weidler, Nurnberg #311/R

STADEMANN, Adolf (1824-1895) German

£524	$876	€750	Evening winter walk (34x58cm-13x23in) mono. 10-Oct-3 Winterberg, Heidelberg #776/R
£600	$954	€876	Sleigh ride ina winter landscape (14x27cm-6x11in) s. panel. 10-Sep-3 Edgar Horn, Eastbourne #371/R
£933	$1708	€1400	Moonlit coast with fishing boats and windmills (23x37cm-9x15in) s. panel. 5-Jun-4 Arnold, Frankfurt #732/R
£940	$1729	€1400	Winter landscape (21x27cm-8x11in) s. panel lit. 25-Mar-4 Karlheinz Kaupp, Staufen #2743/R
£1422	$2546	€2076	Enjoying the ice in the evening (9x48cm-4x19in) s. panel. 12-May-4 Dobiaschofsky, Bern #993/R est:3800 (S.FR 3300)
£1678	$2887	€2400	Dutch winter landscape in evening light (28x54cm-11x21in) s. 3-Dec-3 Neumeister, Munich #751/R est:3000
£1702	$2757	€2400	Peasants with horse drawn sled in front of tent (24x33cm-9x13in) mono. lit. 23-May-3 Karlheinz Kaupp, Staufen #1746/R est:1500
£1762	$2996	€2573	Enjoying the ice in the evening (12x38cm-5x15in) s. panel. 5-Nov-3 Dobiaschofsky, Bern #977/R est:2200 (S.FR 4000)
£2000	$3640	€3000	Winter river (28x43cm-11x17in) s. canvas on panel. 30-Jun-4 Neumeister, Munich #689/R est:3200
£2000	$3660	€3000	Moonlight over lake bank with camp-fire and fishermen (66x120cm-26x47in) s. 5-Jun-4 Arnold, Frankfurt #731/R est:3000
£2098	$3608	€3000	Walkers in a winter landscape with frozen pond and town in distance (31x47cm-12x19in) s. board. 3-Dec-3 Neumeister, Munich #752/R est:3000
£2168	$3729	€3100	Children having fun on a frozen lake (31x47cm-12x19in) s. board. 3-Dec-3 Neumeister, Munich #750/R est:3000
£2200	$4004	€3300	Late winter landscape (28x45cm-11x18in) s. canvas on panel. 30-Jun-4 Neumeister, Munich #690/R est:3200
£2262	$3846	€3303	Winter landscapes (21x16cm-8x6in) mono. panel two. 1-Dec-3 Koller, Zurich #6450/R est:5000-7000 (S.FR 5000)
£2381	$4262	€3500	Winter pleasures outside village (31x47cm-12x19in) s. board. 17-Mar-4 Neumeister, Munich #614/R est:3000
£2535	$4386	€3600	Landscape (18x24cm-7x9in) board. 13-Dec-3 Lempertz, Koln #49/R est:2000
£2817	$4873	€4000	Ice pleasures (30x36cm-12x14in) s. 13-Dec-3 Lempertz, Koln #256/R est:2000
£2939	$4907	€4291	Frozen river (32x40cm-13x16in) s. panel prov.lit. 15-Nov-3 Galerie Gloggner, Luzern #103/R est:8000-8500 (S.FR 6700)
£3000	$5160	€4380	Dutch winter skating view (28x39cm-11x15in) s. card. 4-Dec-3 Christie's, Kensington #182/R est:3000-5000
£3000	$5160	€4380	Skaters in a winter landscape. Crossing in a winter landscape (29x46cm-11x18in) s. canvas on board pair. 4-Dec-3 Christie's, Kensington #183/R est:3000-5000
£3846	$6615	€5500	Evening winter landscape with children playing on a frozen lake (58x88cm-23x35in) s. 3-Dec-3 Neumeister, Munich #747/R est:4000
£4070	$7000	€5942	Winter scene with skaters, Holland (48x71cm-19x28in) s. 7-Dec-3 Freeman, Philadelphia #21 est:7000-10000

STADLER, Toni (1888-1982) German

Sculpture

£1748	$3007	€2500	Head of French woman - Christine (34x24x18cm-13x9x7in) bonze. 2-Dec-3 Hauswedell & Nolte, Hamburg #634/R est:3000
£1958	$3368	€2800	Boy, one arm behind back (28x8x7cm-11x3x3in) bronze exhib. 2-Dec-3 Hauswedell & Nolte, Hamburg #635/R est:4000

STADLER, Toni von (1850-1917) Austrian

£634	$1096	€900	Autumn landscape (30x40cm-12x16in) s.d.06 fibreboard. 10-Dec-3 Hugo Ruef, Munich #2502/R
£2238	$3737	€3200	Extensive landscape (51x65cm-20x26in) s.i.d.1916. 10-Oct-3 Winterberg, Heidelberg #777/R est:3000
£3000	$5520	€4500	French woodland scene (47x53cm-19x21in) s.d.1902 panel i.verso. 12-Jun-4 Villa Grisebach, Berlin #103/R est:3000-5000

STADLIN, Adolf W (19th C) ?

Sculpture

£2013	$3765	€3000	Johanna Maria Stebenmann. Hans Jakob Guyer (30x26x4cm-12x10x2in) wax relief exec.1859 two. 29-Feb-4 Finarte, Venice #18/R est:2500-3000

STADNIK, A M (1916-1998) Russian

£894	$1600	€1305	At the dacha, portrait of an actress (70x81cm-28x32in) painted 1956. 29-May-4 Shishkin Gallery, Moscow #54/R est:2500-3500

STADSKLEIV, Thorleif (1865-1946) Norwegian

£2529	$4526	€3692	Mountain landscape with lake (114x135cm-45x53in) s. 25-May-4 Grev Wedels Plass, Oslo #68/R est:20000-30000 (N.KR 31000)

STADTLANDER, Barbara (1928-) American

£591	$1100	€863	Joe's things (74x61cm-29x24in) s.i. masonite. 7-Mar-4 William Jenack, New York #245 est:2000-3000

STAECK, Klaus (1938-) German

Sculpture

£427	$700	€623	Christliches abendland (43x63x13cm-17x25x5in) s.i.d.1969 num.3/15 verso mixed media board in plexiglass frame. 28-May-3 Sotheby's, Amsterdam #90/R

STAEHR-NIELSEN, Erik (1890-1921) Danish

£469	$764	€685	Fuerta Ventura, Canary Islands (46x63cm-18x25in) s.d.1914. 27-Sep-3 Rasmussen, Havnen #2275 (D.KR 5000)
£469	$764	€685	Spring woods (48x48cm-19x19in) s. 27-Sep-3 Rasmussen, Havnen #2276 (D.KR 5000)
£544	$886	€794	The Spanish Ocean - Canary Islands in background (34x54cm-13x21in) s. 27-Sep-3 Rasmussen, Havnen #2274 (D.KR 5800)
£2015	$3667	€2942	Figure composition (63x87cm-25x34in) s.d.1916 artists board exhib. 7-Feb-4 Rasmussen, Havnen #4228/R est:10000-15000 (D.KR 22000)

STAEHR-OLSEN, Fritz (1858-1922) Danish

£1418	$2453	€2070	Windy day off Kronborg (80x120cm-31x47in) s. 9-Dec-3 Rasmussen, Copenhagen #1493/R est:15000-20000 (D.KR 15000)

Works on paper

£2238	$4096	€3267	From Copenhagen's Customs house (43x92cm-17x36in) s.d.1891 gouache. 9-Jun-4 Rasmussen, Copenhagen #1607/R est:5000 (D.KR 25000)

STAEL, Nicolas de (1914-1955) French

£53333	$98133	€80000	Composition (46x61cm-18x24in) painted c.1947 lit. 8-Jun-4 Artcurial Briest, Paris #210/R est:80000-100000
£55000	$100100	€80300	Composition (81x54cm-32x21in) s.d.46 verso prov.exhib.lit. 5-Feb-4 Christie's, London #115/R est:50000-70000
£60000	$109200	€87600	Composition (54x73cm-21x29in) s. prov.lit. 6-Feb-4 Sotheby's, London #180/R est:25000-35000
£110000	$202400	€160600	Composition (33x46cm-13x18in) s. painted 1949 exhib.lit. 25-Jun-4 Christie's, London #103/R est:20000-30000
£240000	$436800	€350400	Livres (46x61cm-18x24in) s. painted 1954 prov.exhib.lit. 4-Feb-4 Christie's, London #17/R est:120000-160000
£311377	$520000	€454610	Paysage de Provence (50x61cm-20x24in) s. painted 1953 prov.exhib.lit. 12-Nov-3 Sotheby's, New York #60/R est:400000-600000
£340000	$618800	€496400	Composition (81x116cm-32x46in) s. painted 1950 prov.exhib.lit. 5-Feb-4 Sotheby's, London #32/R est:180000-250000
£420000	$772800	€613200	Paysage Mediterranean (60x81cm-24x32in) s. painted 1954 prov.exhib.lit. 24-Jun-4 Christie's, London #11/R est:300000-400000
£620000	$1140800	€905200	Nature morte (54x73cm-21x29in) s. painted 1952 prov.exhib. 23-Jun-4 Sotheby's, London #19/R est:350000-450000
£1150000	$2093000	€1679000	Mediterranee (96x146cm-38x57in) s. painted 1954 prov.exhib.lit. 5-Feb-4 Sotheby's, London #31/R est:700000-1000000

Works on paper

£2684	$4993	€4000	Composition (19x24cm-7x9in) s.d.49 black Indian ink. 3-Mar-4 Artcurial Briest, Paris #522 est:4000-6000
£10135	$17838	€15000	Vase de flours (54x41cm-21x16in) s. felt pen exec 1954 prov.lit. 18-May-4 Tajan, Paris #25/R est:15000-20000
£32000	$58880	€46720	Femme assise (100x146cm-39x57in) chl paper on canvas exec c.1955 prov. 24-Jun-4 Sotheby's, London #199/R est:10000-15000

STAFFORD, Lawrence (1938-) American

£833	$1392	€1200	Untitled (61x153cm-24x60in) s.i.d. verso acrylic. 24-Oct-3 Ketterer, Hamburg #548/R

STAFFORD, Simeon (1956-) British

£400	$664	€584	St Ives, a day on the sands (44x60cm-17x24in) s.d.02. 2-Oct-3 Lane, Penzance #21
£400	$664	€584	Traffic by the docks (44x60cm-17x24in) s.d.02 board. 2-Oct-3 Lane, Penzance #22
£440	$805	€642	By the sea, Cornwall (43x60cm-17x24in) s.d.2003. 3-Jun-4 Lane, Penzance #107

STAGER, Balz (1861-1937) Swiss

£271	$462	€396	Selbsanft from Hotel Todi (47x36cm-19x14in) s.d.1897 board. 25-Nov-3 Germann, Zurich #898 (S.FR 600)
£286	$487	€418	Near Netstal (35x52cm-14x20in) s.mono.d.1885 i. verso canvas on board. 5-Nov-3 Dobiaschofsky, Bern #980 (S.FR 650)
£295	$490	€428	Old stone hut near Netstal (30x40cm-12x16in) s.i. verso board. 13-Jun-3 Zofingen, Switzerland #3039 (S.FR 650)
£371	$631	€542	Walensee in summer (42x34cm-17x13in) s.d.1904. 28-Nov-3 Zofingen, Switzerland #3182 (S.FR 820)
£480	$884	€701	Storm near Quinten (70x90cm-28x35in) s.d. 14-Jun-4 Philippe Schuler, Zurich #5753 (S.FR 1100)
£485	$824	€708	Upper Murg (36x44cm-14x17in) mono.d1892 i. verso board. 5-Nov-3 Dobiaschofsky, Bern #979/R (S.FR 1100)
£1126	$1937	€1644	In Klonthal looking towards the Glarnisch (46x54cm-18x21in) s.d.1911. 8-Dec-3 Philippe Schuler, Zurich #3361 est:2000-2500 (S.FR 2500)
£1928	$3220	€2815	Walensee in the morning (70x90cm-28x35in) s.d.1908. 24-Oct-3 Hans Widmer, St Gallen #128/R est:2000-4200 (S.FR 4300)

STAGURA, Albert (1866-1947) German

£548	$932	€800	Matterhorn from Riffelhaus (25x36cm-10x14in) s.i. board lit. 6-Nov-3 Allgauer, Kempten #3584/R
£753	$1281	€1100	Moor landscape with jetty (60x65cm-24x26in) s. board. 5-Nov-3 Hugo Ruef, Munich #1139/R

Works on paper

£1197	$2071	€1700	Moor landscape (45x65cm-18x26in) s.d.1924 pastel. 10-Dec-3 Hugo Ruef, Munich #2564/R est:1200
£2069	$3455	€3000	Beuerberg in Isar valley (55x70cm-22x28in) s. pastel. 9-Jul-3 Hugo Ruef, Munich #300/R est:400
£2431	$4059	€3500	Early spring (44x60cm-17x24in) s. i. verso pastel lit. 25-Oct-3 Bergmann, Erlangen #959/R
£2695	$4500	€3935	Peonies (79x71cm-31x28in) s.i.d.1923 pastel prov. 7-Oct-3 Sotheby's, New York #158 est:3000-5000
£2917	$4813	€4200	Schloss Umkirch - Fulwell Park near Freiburg (60x70cm-24x28in) s.i.d.26.11.1926 i. verso. 2-Jul-3 Neumeister, Munich #493/R est:1400

STAHL, Benjamin Albert (1910-1987) American

£1796	$3000	€2622	Woman with basket of flowers pausing in Italian landscape (56x69cm-22x27in) s.d.1950. 15-Nov-3 Illustration House, New York #135/R est:3000-5000
£2824	$4800	€4123	New girl in town (51x61cm-20x24in) s.d.78 prov.lit. 1-Nov-3 Santa Fe Art, Santa Fe #181/R est:8000-12000
£2941	$5000	€4294	New customer. Study for the New Customer (46x61cm-18x24in) one s.d.78 oil one s.i.verso chl two prov.lit. 1-Nov-3 Santa Fe Art, Santa Fe #182/R est:8000-12000
£2941	$5000	€4294	Dutch Annie (61x51cm-24x20in) s.d.77 s.i.d.Aug 1977 verso prov.lit. 1-Nov-3 Santa Fe Art, Santa Fe #183/R est:8000-12000

STAHL, Friedrich (1863-1940) German

£2838	$4995	€4200	Young woman from Rome (27x22cm-11x9in) s. panel. 22-May-4 Lempertz, Koln #1609/R est:2000
£5068	$8919	€7500	Boccaccio telling story from Decamerone (91x96cm-36x38in) prov. 22-May-4 Lempertz, Koln #1610/R est:6000-8000

STAHLEY, Joseph (c.1900) American

£1618	$2750	€2362	New colt (69x84cm-27x33in) s.d.35 prov. 1-Nov-3 Santa Fe Art, Santa Fe #234/R est:3000-5000

STAHLI, Johannes (1778-1861) Swiss

Works on paper

£330	$562	€482	Mill in Bernese Oberland (27x41cm-11x16in) s. W/C. 5-Nov-3 Dobiaschofsky, Bern #1349/R (S.FR 750)
£560	$1003	€818	River landscape near Interlaken with view of Jungfrau (30x41cm-12x16in) W/C gouache on pencil. 13-May-4 Stuker, Bern #9411 (S.FR 1300)

STAIGG, Richard Morrell (1817-1881) American

£2358	$3750	€3443	Daily news (47x32cm-19x13in) s. board. 12-Sep-3 Skinner, Boston #228/R est:700-900

STAINER-KNITTEL, Anna (1841-1915) Austrian

£2254	$3899	€3200	Bunch of alpine flowers (24x39cm-9x15in) s.d.1907 board. 10-Dec-3 Dorotheum, Vienna #265/R est:2000-2400

STAINTON, George (fl.1860-1890) British

£1500	$2760	€2190	Ships at anchor in a calm sea (41x61cm-16x24in) s. 8-Jun-4 Gorringes, Lewes #1995/R est:800-1200
£1600	$2928	€2336	Leaving port (41x56cm-16x22in) s. 7-Apr-4 Gardiner & Houlgate, Bath #258/R est:1700-2550
£1800	$3366	€2628	Gillingham Reach (41x61cm-16x24in) s. 24-Feb-4 Bonhams, Knowle #46 est:400-600

Works on paper

£380	$604	€555	Busy river estuary with numerous vessels (29x46cm-11x18in) s. W/C. 10-Sep-3 Edgar Horn, Eastbourne #359/R
£450	$810	€657	Fishing boats and a wreck in choppy seas (29x45cm-11x18in) s. W/C over pencil. 21-Jan-4 Sotheby's, Olympia #159/R
£621	$1148	€900	Coastal landscape with figures on beach and sialing boats in the distance (21x32cm-8x13in) s. W/C. 11-Feb-4 Woodwards, Cork #6/R
£740	$1339	€1080	Off the coast (19x31cm-7x12in) s. W/C. 30-Mar-4 David Duggleby, Scarborough #183/R

STAINTON, George (attrib) (fl.1860-1890) British

£1900	$3268	€2774	On the medway (74x48cm-29x19in) s. i.verso. 3-Dec-3 Cheffins, Cambridge #620/R est:800-1200

STAJESSI, Valentino (19th C) Italian?

£437	$803	€638	Madonna with Child (68x55cm-27x22in) s.i. verso. 14-Jun-4 Philippe Schuler, Zurich #5894 (S.FR 1000)

STAJUDA, Jerzy (1936-1992) Polish

£636	$1150	€929	Untitled (51x35cm-20x14in) d.1957-1966 paper board. 4-Apr-4 Agra, Warsaw #22/R (P.Z 4500)

Works on paper

£260	$431	€380	Untitled (27x40cm-11x16in) W/C exec.1983. 2-Oct-3 Agra, Warsaw #25/R (P.Z 1700)
£310	$518	€450	Untitled (76x54cm-30x21in) s.i. W/C. 16-Nov-3 Agra, Warsaw #75/R

STALBEMT, Adriaen van (1580-1662) Flemish

£15790	$29053	€24000	Midas ecoutant Apollon (60x76cm-24x30in) s.d.1639 panel. 24-Jun-4 Tajan, Paris #13/R est:25000-30000
£18121	$32436	€27000	Diane et Neptune (28cm-11in circular) copper prov. 25-May-4 Palais de Beaux Arts, Brussels #91/R est:16500-20000

STALBEMT, Adriaen van (attrib) (1580-1662) Flemish

£2700	$4401	€3942	Wooded landscape with a cavalryman and other figures on a track (24x30cm-9x12in) st.verso panel. 26-Sep-3 Christie's, Kensington #27/R est:1500-2500

STALLER, Gerard Johan (1880-1956) Dutch

£1342	$2483	€2000	View of the Oude Kerk, Amsterdam (23x32cm-9x13in) s. panel. 15-Mar-4 Sotheby's, Amsterdam #134/R est:2000-3000
£4027	$7450	€6000	Market scene (32x24cm-13x9in) s.d.1919 panel. 15-Mar-4 Sotheby's, Amsterdam #153/R est:1600-2200

Works on paper

£833	$1358	€1200	Viskoopman - Fish merchant (50x30cm-20x12in) s. pastel. 29-Sep-3 Sotheby's, Amsterdam #181/R
£2763	$5084	€4200	View of the Uilenburgersteeg (72x44cm-28x17in) s.d.33 pastel. 28-Jun-4 Sotheby's, Amsterdam #65/R est:4000-6000

STAMFORD, Everard (18th C) British

£27907	$48000	€40744	Venus and Painter, two hounds owned by Thomas Noel and the Earl of Gainsborough (90x98cm-35x39in) s.i. pair prov. 5-Dec-3 Christie's, Rockefeller NY #9/R est:20000-30000

STAMMBACH, Eugen (1876-1966) German

£366	$586	€520	Roses in vase (44x32cm-17x13in) canvas on board. 18-Sep-3 Rieber, Stuttgart #1075/R

STAMMEL, Eberhard (1833-1906) German

£1111	$1811	€1600	Morning sun (26x31cm-10x12in) s.d.1877 canvas on board. 24-Sep-3 Neumeister, Munich #561/R est:2000

STAMMEL, Josef Thaddaus (1695-1765) Austrian

Sculpture

£10067	$18523	€15000	St Peter (95cm-37in) painted gilded wood prov. 25-Mar-4 Dorotheum, Vienna #69/R est:16000-18000

STAMOS, Theodoros (1922-1997) American

£1176	$2000	€1717	Infinity field - Jerusalem series (76x58cm-30x23in) s.i.d.1984 verso acrylic. 9-Nov-3 Wright, Chicago #330 est:1500-2000
£2315	$3750	€3380	Abstract study in blue and red (76x79cm-30x31in) 3-Aug-3 North East Auctions, Portsmouth #1981/R
£3374	$5500	€4926	Double green sun box (41x183cm-16x72in) acrylic prov. 23-Sep-3 Christie's, Rockefeller NY #24/R est:6000-8000
£3784	$7000	€5525	Thaw (59x49cm-23x19in) s. board prov. 13-Jul-4 Christie's, Rockefeller NY #31/R est:2000-3000
£3988	$6500	€5822	Torino series VI (137x127cm-54x50in) s.i.d.1988 stretcher prov.exhib. 23-Sep-3 Christie's, Rockefeller NY #23/R est:8000-12000
£5000	$8650	€7300	Infinity Field, Lefkadas Series (82x51cm-32x20in) s.i.d.1980 overlap acrylic. 11-Dec-3 Christie's, Kensington #247/R est:5000-7000
£5882	$10000	€8588	Infinity field, Lefkada series (153x61cm-60x24in) s.d.1977 verso acrylic. 22-Nov-3 Burkhard, Luzern #194/R est:14000-18000 (S.FR 13000)
£8649	$16000	€12628	Infinity field Sunion Night Refraction (203x76cm-80x30in) s.i.d.1971 verso prov. 13-Jul-4 Christie's, Rockefeller NY #30/R est:4000-6000
£9605	$17000	€14023	Abstract composition (41x51cm-16x20in) s.indis.d.1946 masonite. 2-May-4 Bonhams & Butterfields, Los Angeles #3036/R est:6000-8000
£10270	$19000	€14994	Red Sun Box (152x127cm-60x50in) s. s.i.d.1964-65 stretcher prov. 13-Jul-4 Christie's, Rockefeller NY #29/R est:4000-6000
£33520	$60000	€48939	Very low sun (175x102cm-69x40in) s. s.i.d.1963-1964 stretcher prov.lit. 13-May-4 Sotheby's, New York #112/R est:20000-30000

STAMPFLI, Peter (1937-) Swiss

Works on paper

£2817	$4930	€4000	M and S Contact (119x96cm-47x38in) s.d.1977 prov. 18-Dec-3 Cornette de St.Cyr, Paris #110/R est:4000-5000

STAMPFLI, Pierre Victor (1916-1975) Swiss

£409	$733	€597	Summer landscape (24x55cm-9x22in) s.d.54. 12-May-4 Dobiaschofsky, Bern #1000/R (S.FR 950)

STAN, Vladimir (?) ?

£979	$1664	€1400	Visages (100x100cm-39x39in) s. 20-Nov-3 Claude Aguttes, Neuilly #272/R

STANCHI, Giovanni (c.1645-?) Italian

£11173	$20000	€16313	Putti surrounded by garland of flowers (98x77cm-39x30in) 27-May-4 Sotheby's, New York #105/R est:20000-30000
£13793	$22897	€20000	Still life of flowers including tulips, primroses and other flowers (86x70cm-34x28in) 1-Oct-3 Dorotheum, Vienna #52/R est:20000-30000
£35000	$64050	€51100	Still lives with garlands of flowers (135x119cm-53x47in) pair. 8-Jul-4 Sotheby's, London #166/R est:30000-50000

STANCHI, Giovanni (attrib) (c.1645-?) Italian

£5592	$10289	€8500	Putto surrounded by garland of flowers (72x84cm-28x33in) 24-Jun-4 Tajan, Paris #40/R est:6000-8000

STANCHI, Giovanni (circle) (c.1645-?) Italian

£7394	$12939	€10500	Nature morte au vase de fleurs sur en entablement (73x92cm-29x36in) 18-Dec-3 Tajan, Paris #63/R est:4000-6000
£13423	$23758	€20000	Putti in flower garland (70cm-28in circular) 27-Apr-4 Porro, Milan #281/R est:20000

STANCHI, Giovanni (school) (c.1645-?) Italian

£12000	$21480	€18000	Vase of flowers (111x76cm-44x30in) exhib.lit. 17-May-4 Finarte Semenzato, Rome #103/R est:22000-24000

STANCHI, Nicolo (1623-1690) Italian

£44737	$82316	€68000	Guirlande de fleurs entourant un vase. Corbeille de fleurs. (171x120cm-67x47in) pair. 25-Jun-4 Doutrebente, Paris #7/R est:15000-20000

STANCIN, James (20th C) American?

£625	$1100	€913	Lone Rider (61x91cm-24x36in) s. 23-May-4 Hindman, Chicago #1034/R

STANDING, Henry William (19/20th C) British

£520	$931	€759	Figures in a horse drawn phaeton (23x46cm-9x18in) s. 11-Jan-4 Desmond Judd, Cranbrook #727
Works on paper			
£550	$935	€803	Shire horses (33x63cm-13x25in) s.d.1896 W/C. 19-Nov-3 Sotheby's, Olympia #63/R

STANDING, William (20th C) American

£5080	$9500	€7417	Horse on a hill (48x76cm-19x30in) s.d.1932 canvas on board prov. 24-Jul-4 Coeur d'Alene, Hayden #283/R est:4000-6000

STANDISH, William (19th C) ?

£3700	$6660	€5402	Groom and grey hunter waiting at the covert (76x107cm-30x42in) s.d.1849. 21-Apr-4 Christie's, Kensington #17/R est:3000-5000

STANFIELD, Clarkson (1793-1867) British

£399	$650	€583	Fishing port (41x30cm-16x12in) s.d.1836 board. 24-Sep-3 Doyle, New York #86/R
£2431	$4132	€3500	Under the vines, view on the Bay of Naples with the castle of Ischia (38x56cm-15x22in) s.d.1854. 28-Oct-3 Christie's, Amsterdam #27/R est:3000-5000
£3000	$5100	€4380	Barges (41x61cm-16x24in) s.d.1853. 19-Nov-3 Christie's, Kensington #534/R
£3000	$4920	€4380	Venetian canal scene with figures and gondolas to the foreground (50x29cm-20x11in) s.i.d.1853. 3-Jun-3 Fellows & Sons, Birmingham #43/R est:1000-1500
£30000	$53700	€43800	Castle Cornet, Guernsey (74x117cm-29x46in) i. prov. 26-May-4 Christie's, Kensington #608/R est:20000-30000
Works on paper			
£400	$716	€584	Hulks lying in the Medway (23x34cm-9x13in) pencil W/C htd bodycol prov. 26-May-4 Christie's, Kensington #406/R
£480	$888	€701	Distant view of Southampton (12x18cm-5x7in) W/C prov. 14-Jul-4 Sotheby's, Olympia #45/R
£1100	$2024	€1606	Aldbar Castle, Scotland with sporting figures (27x23cm-11x9in) init.i.d.1861 pencil W/C htd white. 8-Jun-4 Holloways, Banbury #248/R est:600-800
£3200	$5440	€4672	French man-o-war off Spithead (33x43cm-13x17in) mono. W/C over pencil htd bodycol prov. 27-Nov-3 Sotheby's, London #264/R est:1500-2000

STANFIELD, Clarkson (attrib) (1793-1867) British

£1028	$1624	€1491	Sailing vessels in rough seas off rocky coast (76x127cm-30x50in) 2-Sep-3 Rasmussen, Copenhagen #1642/R (D.KR 11000)

STANFIELD, George Clarkson (1828-1878) British

£900	$1683	€1314	Isola Lecchi Lago de Guarda (32x42cm-13x17in) i.verso board. 22-Jul-4 Tennants, Leyburn #832
£1374	$2500	€2006	View of a town with fortress by the river (60x107cm-24x42in) s.d.1872. 29-Jun-4 Sotheby's, New York #156/R est:3000-5000
£3400	$5882	€4964	Richmond Castle, Yorkshire, landscape with castle above town with figures (64x99cm-25x39in) 11-Dec-3 Ewbank, Send #449/R est:3500-5000

STANG, Joseph (19/20th C) ?

£1469	$2452	€2100	Morale. Histoire. Philosophie. Eloquence (41x32cm-16x13in) s.i.d.1900 set of 4 in one frame. 7-Oct-3 Livinec, Gaudcheau & Jezequel, Rennes #120/R

STANGE, Bernhard (1807-1880) German

£860	$1574	€1256	Contemplation by moonlight (49x39cm-19x15in) 8-Apr-4 Christie's, Kensington #84/R

STANGERUS, Cornelis (1616-1667) Dutch

£12667	$22673	€19000	Earthenware tankard, tobacco, bun and other objects on a table (54x59cm-21x23in) s.d.1664 prov.lit. 17-May-4 Christie's, Amsterdam #82/R est:7000-10000

STANGL, Heinz (1942-) Austrian

£1111	$1811	€1600	Untitled (49x29cm-19x11in) s.d.68. 23-Sep-3 Wiener Kunst Auktionen, Vienna #164/R est:2000-3500

STANGRET, Maria (1929-) Polish

£1585	$2885	€2314	Abstract composition (99x71cm-39x28in) s.d.1962 panel. 20-Jun-4 Agra, Warsaw #45/R (P.Z 11000)

STANHOPE, John Roddam Spencer (1829-1908) British

£80925	$140000	€118151	Shulamite (94x125cm-37x49in) i. prov.exhib.lit. 11-Dec-3 Sotheby's, New York #39/R est:150000-200000

STANIER, H (19th C) British

£1100	$2057	€1606	Spanish village girl holding fan (66x50cm-26x20in) s.i.d.1892. 22-Jul-4 Martel Maides, Guernsey #228/R

STANIER, Henry (?-1892) British

Works on paper

£1450	$2465	€2117	Watch tower at the Alhambra. Tower of Comares. Grenada. Alhambra (32x23cm-13x9in) three s.i.d.1865 one s.d.1870 W/C over pencil bodycol four. 25-Nov-3 Bonhams, Knowle #186 est:200-300

STANKIEWICZ, Richard (1922-) American

£10086	$18357	€14726	Two men and a dog (121x97cm-48x38in) s. 20-Jun-4 Agra, Warsaw #46/R (P.Z 70000)
Sculpture			
£1357	$2308	€1981	Untitled (114x43x32cm-45x17x13in) mono.d.1965 iron prov. 25-Nov-3 Germann, Zurich #84/R est:4000-8000 (S.FR 3000)
£4192	$7000	€6120	Young lady with flowers (124x58x41cm-49x23x16in) welded scrap metal exec.c.1955 prov.exhib. 13-Nov-3 Sotheby's, New York #106/R est:10000-15000
£4595	$8500	€6709	Family with pet (49x36x23cm-19x14x9in) iron steel exec 1957 prov.exhib. 12-Feb-4 Sotheby's, New York #176/R est:7000-9000
£8589	$14000	€12540	Untitled (77x63x35cm-30x25x14in) welded steel prov. 23-Sep-3 Christie's, Rockefeller NY #33/R est:7000-9000

STANKO, Leszek (20th C) ?

£350	$648	€511	Cattle grazing by a sunlit steam (48x69cm-19x27in) s. 15-Jan-4 Christie's, Kensington #984/R

STANKOWSKI, Anton (1906-) ?

Photographs

£8333	$14167	€12000	Suring. Suring. Window, doors. Spiral movement (23x17cm-9x7in) s.d. verso silver gelatin four lit. 31-Oct-3 Lempertz, Koln #324/R est:12000-15000

STANLAWS, Penhryn (1877-1957) American

£272	$500	€397	Portrait of a lady (23x18cm-9x7in) s. board. 10-Jun-4 Swann Galleries, New York #228/R
Works on paper			
£4192	$7000	€6120	Moonlight fancies (122x56cm-48x22in) s. pastel sandpaper canvas. 15-Nov-3 Illustration House, New York #146/R est:4000-6000

STANLEY, Bob (1932-) American
Works on paper
£1000 $1800 €1460 YA Tittle, Fall (32x26cm-13x10in) s.i.d.1964 verso liquitex canvas. 24-Apr-4 David Rago, Lambertville #418/R est:200-400

STANLEY, Caleb Robert (1795-1868) British
£550 $1012 €825 Penarth seafront (23x33cm-9x13in) s. 24-Jun-4 Ewbank, Send #605/R

STANLEY, Carl Frederik (1738-1813) British
Works on paper
£2336 $4345 €3411 Audience at Ove Hoegh-Guldberg's at the Prince's Palace (31x42cm-12x17in) s.i.d.1777 pencil wash. 2-Mar-4 Rasmussen, Copenhagen #1675/R est:30000-40000 (D.KR 26000)

STANLEY, John Mix (1814-1872) American
£468750 $825000 €684375 Deerslayer (61x51cm-24x20in) s.d.1868 prov. 19-May-4 Sotheby's, New York #194/R est:250000-350000

STANLEY, Robert (20th C) American
£1390 $2600 €2029 Cowboy firing gun while holding reins (46x33cm-18x13in) board. 26-Feb-4 Illustration House, New York #167 est:3000-5000

STANNARD OF NORWICH, Emily (1803-1885) British
£1346 $2329 €1965 Still life with flowers and nest (49x59cm-19x23in) s.d.1871. 9-Dec-3 Louis Morton, Mexico #378/R est:5000-8000 (M.P 26000)
Works on paper
£550 $1029 €825 Bedfordshire landscape. Willow trees beside a stream (24x33cm-9x13in) s. pencil W/C pair. 22-Jul-4 Tennants, Leyburn #760

STANNARD, Alexander Molyneux (1878-1975) British
Works on paper
£260 $471 €380 Shepherd and sheep in a country lane (13x15cm-5x6in) W/C. 16-Apr-4 Keys, Aylsham #487/R
£280 $484 €409 Young girl with chickens outside a thatched cottage (24x30cm-9x12in) s. W/C. 10-Dec-3 Bonhams, Bury St Edmunds #528
£320 $550 €467 Thatched cottages beside a lane (18x25cm-7x10in) s. W/C. 2-Dec-3 Gorringes, Lewes #2231
£330 $525 €479 Poultry feeding before thatched cottages in rural English landscape (18x25cm-7x10in) s.d.1898. 23-Mar-3 Desmond Judd, Cranbrook #1046
£400 $644 €580 Figure by a thatched cottage (23x33cm-9x13in) s. W/C. 13-Aug-3 Andrew Hartley, Ilkley #732/R
£400 $720 €584 Bedfordshire cottages with a flower garden (34x49cm-13x19in) s. pencil W/C. 21-Apr-4 Tennants, Leyburn #1043
£420 $769 €613 Devon cottage, child and kitten before a cottage (24x35cm-9x14in) s. W/C. 3-Jun-4 Bonhams, Cornwall #224
£500 $860 €730 Shepherd with sheep in a country (15x20cm-6x8in) s. W/C. 5-Dec-3 Keys, Aylsham #415
£500 $925 €730 Thatched cottage with young girl passing. Thatched cottage (16x23cm-6x9in) s. W/C pair. 16-Jul-4 Charterhouse, Sherborne #619/R
£700 $1211 €1022 Young girl with chickens outside a thatched country cottage (23x34cm-9x13in) s. W/C. 10-Dec-3 Bonhams, Bury St Edmunds #495
£1300 $2327 €1898 Country lane, a young girl with a hoop (18x25cm-7x10in) s. W/C. 5-May-4 John Nicholson, Haslemere #374/R est:1000-1500

STANNARD, Alfred (1806-1889) British
£565 $1039 €825 Cattle on a riverbank (14x18cm-6x7in) s.d.1880 panel. 14-Jun-4 Waddingtons, Toronto #117/R est:1500-1800 (C.D 1400)
£1000 $1860 €1460 On the Yare at snset (23x30cm-9x12in) s.d.1873. 4-Mar-4 Christie's, Kensington #428/R est:1000 1500
£4000 $7160 €5840 On the Yare (33x48cm-13x19in) s. panel. 27-May-4 Christie's, Kensington #131/R est:2000-3000

STANNARD, Alfred (attrib) (1806-1889) British
£380 $711 €555 View near Norwich (7x8cm-3x3in) panel. 25-Feb-4 Mallams, Oxford #374/R

STANNARD, Eloise Harriet (c.1828-1915) British
£250 $460 €365 Partially peeled banana (3x6cm-1x2in) s. 11-Jun-4 Keys, Aylsham #606/R
£2994 $5000 €4371 Untitled (30x37cm-12x15in) s.d.1870. 20-Oct-3 Sotheby's, New York #410/R est:5000-7000
£2994 $5000 €4371 Untitled (30x37cm-12x15in) s.d.1872. 20-Oct-3 Sotheby's, New York #411/R est:5000-7000
£5200 $8216 €7540 Fruit and flowers in season (23x18cm-9x7in) s. set of four. 3-Sep-3 Bonhams, Bury St Edmunds #468/R est:6000-8000
£6000 $10020 €8760 Basket of strawberries (27x32cm-11x13in) s.d.1886. 13-Nov-3 Christie's, Kensington #354/R est:5000-7000
£12000 $22080 €17520 Poppies in a vase, with white lilac on marble ledge (51x43cm-20x17in) s.d.1891. 11-Jun-4 Christie's, London #95/R est:10000-15000

STANNARD, Henry (1844-1920) British
Works on paper
£380 $688 €555 Pheasant foraging for berries in a snowscape (69x59cm-27x23in) s. W/C. 31-Mar-4 Bonhams, Knightsbridge #20/R
£480 $850 €701 River landscape with distant church (23x36cm-9x14in) s. W/C. 28-Apr-4 Halls, Shrewsbury #439/R
£700 $1211 €1022 Conversation at the cottage gate (24x34cm-9x13in) s. W/C. 10-Dec-3 Bonhams, Bury St Edmunds #455
£720 $1174 €1051 Sheltered corner (42x85cm-17x33in) s. W/C. 24-Sep-3 Dreweatt Neate, Newbury #45/R
£894 $1600 €1305 Bedfordshire cottage. Out in the cold (24x34cm-9x13in) s.i.verso W/C pencil htd white pair. 6-May-4 Doyle, New York #26/R est:3000-5000
£1100 $2024 €1606 Early morning. Eventide (25x36cm-10x14in) s. W/C pair. 8-Jun-4 Bonhams, New Bond Street #125/R est:1000-1500

STANNARD, Henry Sylvester (1870-1951) British
£1050 $1754 €1533 Hay carts in a landscape. 21-Oct-3 Gorringes, Lewes #2083
Works on paper
£260 $471 €380 Rural path with silver birches (23x33cm-9x13in) s. W/C. 30-Mar-4 Sworder & Son, Bishops Stortford #549/R
£280 $515 €409 Near Waddenhow, Wadenhoe, Northants (37x73cm-15x29in) s. W/C. 23-Mar-4 Rosebery Fine Art, London #806
£280 $493 €409 Shepherd and companion with flock (23x33cm-9x13in) s. W/C. 20-May-4 Richardson & Smith, Whitby #658
£290 $484 €421 Devon coastline (24x34cm-9x13in) W/C exhib. 21-Jun-3 Lacy Scott, Bury St.Edmunds #485
£320 $586 €467 Sheep in an autumn landscape (25x36cm-10x14in) s. W/C. 6-Jul-4 Bearnes, Exeter #424/R
£330 $624 €482 Horse and rider by cottages at sunset (33x60cm-13x24in) s. W/C. 17-Feb-4 Rosebery Fine Art, London #581
£360 $619 €526 Lush coastal view (25x36cm-10x14in) s. W/C. 4-Dec-3 Richardson & Smith, Whitby #422/R
£400 $636 €584 Chickens and ducks on a path outside a cottage (15x25cm-6x10in) s. W/C. 9-Sep-3 Rowley Fine Art, Newmarket #459/R
£400 $720 €584 Country girl fetching water, ducks by a rustic bridge (25x35cm-10x14in) s. W/C. 22-Apr-4 Lawrence, Crewkerne #781/R
£500 $915 €730 Dreaming Pool, Erlestoke Park, Wiltshire (34x50cm-13x20in) s. i.verso W/C. 28-Jan-4 Dreweatt Neate, Newbury #26/R
£500 $900 €730 Cottage near Wantage (26x37cm-10x15in) s. pencil W/C htd white. 22-Apr-4 Mellors & Kirk, Nottingham #1029
£500 $885 €730 Rural scene, haymaking with corn stooks. W/C. 27-Apr-4 Lawrences, Bletchingley #1549
£550 $919 €803 Farm at Cardington Cross (25x35cm-10x14in) s. W/C. 22-Oct-3 Cheffins, Cambridge #458
£600 $1002 €876 Rural landscape (25x35cm-10x14in) s. W/C. 14-Oct-3 Bonhams, Knightsbridge #57/R
£700 $1120 €1022 Thatched country cottage in summer (25x36cm-10x14in) W/C. 15-May-3 Mitchells, Cockermouth #1062/R
£700 $1295 €1022 Children on the beach (25x34cm-10x13in) s. W/C. 10-Mar-4 Sotheby's, Olympia #172/R
£750 $1223 €1095 Sussex village pond (26x37cm-10x15in) s. W/C. 24-Sep-3 Dreweatt Neate, Newbury #33/R
£780 $1349 €1139 Hay gathering in the water meadows (21x32cm-8x13in) s. W/C. 10-Dec-3 Bonhams, Bury St Edmunds #456
£800 $1336 €1168 River landscapes (12x24cm-5x9in) one s. W/C pair. 14-Oct-3 Bonhams, Knightsbridge #206/R
£800 $1360 €1168 Bedfordshire landscape, with ploughed field and trees (22x32cm-9x13in) s.i. pencil W/C. 19-Nov-3 Tennants, Leyburn #974
£800 $1456 €1168 Autumnal river scene (36x25cm-14x10in) s. W/C. 16-Jun-4 Andrew Hartley, Ilkley #985/R
£800 $1472 €1168 Cottage garden (23x34cm-9x13in) s. W/C. 8-Jun-4 Bonhams, New Bond Street #126/R
£1000 $1800 €1460 Bluebells by the Queen's cottage, Kew Gardens (24x34cm-9x13in) s. W/C. 21-Jan-4 Sotheby's, Olympia #205/R est:500-700
£1000 $1830 €1460 View towards Bisham Abbey (24x34cm-9x13in) s. W/C. 27-Jan-4 Bonhams, Knightsbridge #224/R est:800-1200
£1000 $1870 €1460 Sheep Lane. W/C. 26-Feb-4 Ambrose, Loughton #978/R est:1200-1500
£1000 $1840 €1460 Old Alesford, Hants (26x35cm-10x14in) s. W/C. 8-Jun-4 Bonhams, New Bond Street #124/R est:1000-1500
£1100 $1870 €1606 Cottage scene, Maulden, Bedfordshire (24x35cm-9x14in) s.d.08 W/C. 4-Nov-3 Bonhams, New Bond Street #143/R est:1000-1500
£1100 $2024 €1606 Near Sharnbrook, Bedfordshire (24x34cm-9x13in) s. W/C. 8-Jun-4 Bonhams, New Bond Street #122/R est:1200-1800
£1200 $2148 €1752 Near Kimbolton, Bedfordshire (24x35cm-9x14in) s. W/C. 25-May-4 Bonhams, Knightsbridge #162b/R est:1200-1800
£1300 $2210 €1898 Changing pastures (33x54cm-13x21in) s. W/C pair. 18-Nov-3 Sotheby's, Olympia #27/R est:1000-1500
£1300 $2327 €1898 Tulip bed (34x48cm-13x19in) s. W/C. 26-May-4 Sotheby's, Olympia #103/R est:1000-2000
£1300 $2366 €1898 Landscape with haymakers in the distance (25x36cm-10x14in) s. W/C. 16-Jun-4 Andrew Hartley, Ilkley #984/R est:1200-1500
£1350 $2457 €1971 Country cottage in summer (25x36cm-10x14in) s. W/C. 16-Jun-4 Andrew Hartley, Ilkley #983/R est:1500-1800
£1400 $2590 €2044 Shepherd and his flock at sunset (25x34cm-10x13in) s. W/C. 10-Mar-4 Sotheby's, Olympia #147/R est:1000-1500
£1500 $2550 €2190 Shepherd and his flock on a river bank near Flitwick, Bedfordshire (24x34cm-9x13in) s. W/C sold with a companion. 1-Dec-3 Bonhams, Bath #58/R est:700-900
£1500 $2550 €2190 Figures by a field gate, said to be near Ampthill, Bedfordshire (27x36cm-11x14in) s. W/C sold with one W/C and one oil by different hands. 26-Nov-3 Hamptons Fine Art, Godalming #37 est:500-700
£1500 $2775 €2190 Bletsoe Garden, Bedfordshire. Cottage scene, Bedfordshire (26x36cm-10x14in) s. W/C pair. 9-Mar-4 Bonhams, New Bond Street #109/R est:1500-2000
£1550 $2589 €2263 English thatched cottage (25x36cm-10x14in) s. W/C. 18-Jun-3 John Nicholson, Haslemere #586 est:1500-1800
£1600 $2944 €2336 Best of friends (25x35cm-10x14in) s. pencil W/C. 25-Mar-4 Christie's, Kensington #137/R est:1000-2000
£1600 $2864 €2336 Thurleigh, Bedfordshire (25x34cm-10x13in) s. W/C. 25-May-4 Bonhams, Knightsbridge #162a/R est:1200-1800
£1700 $3094 €2482 Windsor Castle from Cooper's Hill (34x49cm-13x19in) s. pencil W/C htd white prov. 1-Jul-4 Christie's, Kensington #137/R est:1500-2500
£1800 $3312 €2628 Near Stratford on Avon (24x34cm-9x13in) s. W/C. 8-Jun-4 Bonhams, New Bond Street #117/R est:2000-3000
£1900 $3496 €2774 Rye Bridge, Ashtead Common (24x34cm-9x13in) s. W/C. 8-Jun-4 Bonhams, New Bond Street #123/R est:1200-1800
£2000 $3600 €2920 Wood wagon at Warbleton, Sussex (35x25cm-14x10in) s. W/C. 21-Jan-4 Sotheby's, Olympia #208/R est:2000-3000
£2000 $3440 €2920 Children on a path by a thatched cottage (36x25cm-14x10in) s. W/C. 5-Dec-3 Chrystals Auctions, Isle of Man #235/R est:2000-3000
£2400 $4440 €3504 Lace seller at Bolnhurst, Beds (25x36cm-10x14in) s.i.verso W/C bodycol. 11-Mar-4 Duke & Son, Dorchester #110/R est:500-1000
£2400 $4464 €3504 An important letter - mother and child approaching post office (48x75cm-19x30in) s. W/C. 2-Mar-4 Bearnes, Exeter #323/R est:800-1200
£2400 $4416 €3504 In the time of roses (25x35cm-10x14in) s. W/C. 8-Jun-4 Bonhams, New Bond Street #116/R est:2000-3000
£2650 $4214 €3843 In the time of roses, Gipsy Lane, Bedford (25x35cm-10x14in) s. W/C. 9-Sep-3 Sworder & Son, Bishops Stortford #385/R est:250-350

£2800 $4760 €4088 By the shepherd's cottage, Flitwick, Bedfordshire (25x37cm-10x15in) s. i.verso W/C. 4-Nov-3 Bonhams, New Bond Street #144/R est:1500-2000
£2900 $4727 €4234 Country scene with cottage and young girl holding a kitten (29x23cm-11x9in) s. W/C. 24-Sep-3 Peter Wilson, Nantwich #117
£3100 $5704 €4526 Driving home the flock. Rural idyll (32x51cm-13x20in) s. W/C pair. 24-Mar-4 Hamptons Fine Art, Godalming #243/R
£3200 $5888 €4672 Home at last (35x24cm-14x9in) s. W/C. 8-Jun-4 Bonhams, New Bond Street #129/R est:2000-3000
£3800 $6460 €5548 At Cuxham, Oxfordshire. In September at Keysoe, Bedfordshire (24x34cm-9x13in) one s. W/C htd bodycol pair. 27-Nov-3 Sotheby's, London #410/R est:3000-5000
£4000 $7400 €5840 Young children by the cottage gate (25x36cm-10x14in) s. W/C. 9-Mar-4 Bonhams, New Bond Street #108/R est:2000-3000
£4600 $8602 €6716 Bringing in the ducks (33x48cm-13x19in) s. i.verso pencil W/C. 22-Jul-4 Tennants, Leyburn #764/R est:1500-2500

STANNARD, Joseph (1797-1830) British
Works on paper
£450 $716 €657 Tower near Bristol with coach and horses (16x12cm-6x5in) mono. pencil W/C. 9-Sep-3 Rowley Fine Art, Newmarket #400/R

STANNARD, Lilian (1877-1944) British
Works on paper
£600 $1122 €876 Cottage with flowers to the foreground. W/C. 26-Feb-4 Ambrose, Loughton #979/R
£780 $1303 €1139 Cottage garden (24x34cm-9x13in) s. pencil W/C. 16-Oct-3 Christie's, Kensington #201/R
£1150 $1840 €1679 View of a summer cottage garden (33x23cm-13x9in) s. W/C. 8-Jan-3 Biddle & Webb, Birmingham #901
£1800 $3060 €2628 Cottage near Haslemere, Surrey (17x24cm-7x9in) s. pencil W/C htd white scratching out prov. 20-Nov-3 Christie's, London #102/R est:1800-2500
£1900 $3496 €2774 Peaceful walk (25x36cm-10x14in) s. W/C. 8-Jun-4 Bonhams, New Bond Street #127/R est:2000-3000

STANNARD, Theresa Sylvester (1898-1947) British
Works on paper
£350 $644 €511 Mother and daughter in a rural landscape (24x35cm-9x14in) s. W/C. 22-Jun-4 Bonhams, Knightsbridge #38/R
£520 $884 €759 Gardens of the Old Palace, Buckden, Hants (17x26cm-7x10in) W/C. 27-Nov-3 Clevedon Sale Rooms #158/R
£620 $1159 €905 Landscape with cottage (27x37cm-11x15in) s. W/C. 20-Jul-4 Sworder & Son, Bishops Stortford #695/R
£650 $1086 €949 English garden with rose arbour and river frontage (33x23cm-13x9in) s. W/C. 18-Jun-3 John Nicholson, Haslemere #587/R
£650 $1177 €949 Formal garden in summer (18x25cm-7x10in) s. W/C. 16-Apr-4 Keys, Aylsham #486/R
£700 $1169 €1022 At the cottage door (36x25cm-14x10in) s. pencil W/C. 16-Oct-3 Christie's, Kensington #204/R
£725 $1167 €1059 Country cottage (35x25cm-14x10in) s. W/C. 20-Aug-3 Dunbar Sloane, Auckland #70/R est:1500-3000 (NZ.D 2000)
£800 $1464 €1168 An old Warwickshire garden (51x35cm-20x14in) W/C. 29-Jan-4 Ambrose, Loughton #1111
£900 $1647 €1314 Hollyhocks in a Warwickshire garden (36x25cm-14x10in) s. W/C bodycol. 27-Jan-4 Bonhams, Knightsbridge #52/R
£1000 $1840 €1460 Rose garden (33x48cm-13x19in) s. pencil W/C bodycol. 25-Mar-4 Christie's, Kensington #242/R est:1000-1500
£1000 $1820 €1460 Summertime, Bedfordshire, young girl feedting a cat (25x36cm-10x14in) s. 16-Jun-4 John Nicholson, Haslemere #658/R est:1000-1500
£1200 $2208 €1752 Cottage garden (34x24cm-13x9in) s. W/C. 8-Jun-4 Bonhams, New Bond Street #128/R est:1200-1800

STANOWSKY, Mikael (1883-1935) Finnish
£381 $693 €560 Winter landscape (40x50cm-16x20in) s. 8-Feb-4 Bukowskis, Helsinki #462/R
£436 $803 €650 Evening in the skerries (50x61cm-20x24in) s. 25-Mar-4 Hagelstam, Helsinki #823
£738 $1373 €1100 Seascape (62x94cm-24x37in) s. H Bjerke. 7-Mar-4 Bukowskis, Helsinki #455/R

STANSFIELD, John Heber (1878-1953) American
£462 $800 €675 Utah landscape (18x26cm-7x10in) s.d.1945 board. 13-Dec-3 Auctions by the Bay, Alameda #1830/R

STANTON, Clark (1832-1894) British
Works on paper
£350 $585 €511 Highland gentleman caught on the moors in a shower (53x36cm-21x14in) s. W/C. 8-Oct-3 Halls, Shrewsbury #88/R

STANTON, Elizabeth (1894-?) American
£485 $800 €708 Untitled, nude female, seated with back to observer (43x36cm-17x14in) s. 7-Jul-3 Schrager Galleries, Milwaukee #1614

STANZIONE, Massimo (1585-1656) Italian
£34000 $61200 €49640 Madonna and Child in a landscape (47x36cm-19x14in) init. canvas on panel. 22-Apr-4 Sotheby's, London #63/R est:10000-15000

STANZIONE, Massimo (attrib) (1585-1656) Italian
£16667 $30500 €25000 Le martyr de Sainte Agathe (98x75cm-39x30in) 6-Jun-4 Anaf, Lyon #189/R est:40000-50000
Works on paper
£1316 $2421 €2000 Figures (11x8cm-4x3in) pen ink pair prov. 22-Jun-4 Sotheby's, Milan #46/R est:2000-3000
£2303 $4237 €3500 Study (12x17cm-5x7in) pen ink over sanguine exhib. 22-Jun-4 Sotheby's, Milan #39/R est:3500-4500

STANZIONE, Massimo (circle) (1585-1656) Italian
£5500 $10065 €8030 Saint Laurence (63x39cm-25x15in) prov. 9-Jul-4 Christie's, Kensington #159/R est:5000-7000

STAP, Jan J van der (1874-1940) Dutch
£241 $425 €352 Dutch farmhouse in polder landscape (36x46cm-14x18in) s.d.1910. 22-May-4 Harvey Clar, Oakland #2195

STAPEL, Dick (1942-) Dutch
£903 $1426 €1300 Still life (40x50cm-16x20in) s.d.1997. 26-Apr-3 Auction Maastricht #118/R

STAPLEAUX, Michel (1799-1881) Belgian
£29333 $52507 €44000 Portrait of Madame de Satel (155x173cm-61x68in) s. 17-May-4 Finarte Semenzato, Rome #88/R est:50000-60000

STAPLES, Clayton (1892-1978) American
£342 $550 €499 Harry LaMont (76x81cm-30x32in) s. 22-Feb-3 Bunte, Elgin #1209
Works on paper
£941 $1600 €1374 Walsenberg, Colorado (46x64cm-18x25in) s. W/C prov. 1-Nov-3 Santa Fe Art, Santa Fe #137/R est:1000-2000

STAPLES, Sir Robert Ponsonby (1853-1943) British
£1184 $2179 €1800 Coastal view (31x46cm-12x18in) s.d.1901 board prov. 22-Jun-4 De Veres Art Auctions, Dublin #113/R est:1500-2500
£2500 $4175 €3650 Jealousy (131x91cm-52x36in) prov. 13-Nov-3 Christie's, Kensington #326/R est:3000-5000
Works on paper
£380 $635 €555 Haidee, the pirate's daughter, finding the body of Don Juan (63x43cm-25x17in) s. pencil bodycol board. 16-Oct-3 Christie's, Kensington #210/R
£574 $1085 €850 Portrait of H John Dix. In train to Dungannon with Bob. In Belfast tram (23x34cm-9x13in) s.i.d.1909-1924 col pencil crayon ink W/C htd white set of three. 17-Feb-4 Whyte's, Dublin #157/R
£769 $1308 €1100 Head and shoulders of a woman (39x29cm-15x11in) mono.s.1900 pastel. 18-Nov-3 Whyte's, Dublin #119/R

STAPPEN, Charles van der (1843-1910) Belgian
Sculpture
£1544 $2856 €2300 Pacing horse (37x50cm-15x20in) s.d.1909 black pat bronze st.f.A van Aerschodt lit. 13-Mar-4 De Vuyst, Lokeren #339/R est:1500-2000

STAPPERS, Julien (1875-1960) Belgian
£278 $464 €400 Vase de fleurs et Vierge (100x80cm-39x31in) s. 21-Oct-3 Galerie Moderne, Brussels #278
£313 $491 €450 Homme en priere (80x60cm-31x24in) s. 26-Aug-3 Galerie Moderne, Brussels #344
£359 $663 €520 Composition au vase fleuri et a la figurine (85x95cm-33x37in) s. 16-Feb-4 Horta, Bruxelles #369
£367 $675 €550 La Gaulette (80x60cm-31x24in) s. 14-Jun-4 Horta, Bruxelles #9
£379 $702 €550 Vase fleuri d'orchidees (50x58cm-20x23in) s. 16-Feb-4 Horta, Bruxelles #370
£417 $654 €600 Vase garni de fleurs (40x32cm-16x13in) s. 26-Aug-3 Galerie Moderne, Brussels #306
£521 $870 €750 Nature morte aux fleurs (75x65cm-30x26in) s. 21-Oct-3 Campo & Campo, Antwerp #646
£556 $928 €800 Panier garni (75x64cm-30x25in) s. 21-Oct-3 Galerie Moderne, Brussels #382
£590 $986 €850 Entablement garni (87x120cm-34x47in) s. 21-Oct-3 Galerie Moderne, Brussels #216
£660 $1036 €950 Paysage de la mediterranee (45x60cm-18x24in) s. 26-Aug-3 Galerie Moderne, Brussels #360/R
£811 $1451 €1200 Vase fleuri de pivoines (33x41cm-13x16in) s. 10-May-4 Horta, Bruxelles #278
£1259 $2165 €1800 Marabout au bois sacre de Blida (38x50cm-15x20in) s. panel exhib. 8-Dec-3 Tajan, Paris #332/R est:2000-3000
£1600 $2672 €2336 Orchids in a silver bowl on a table draped in lace (50x60cm-20x24in) s. 8-Oct-3 Christie's, Kensington #956/R est:1200-1800
£1958 $3368 €2800 Baie d'Alger (60x80cm-24x31in) s. 8-Dec-3 Tajan, Paris #331/R est:3000-4000

STAPRANS, Raymond (1926-) American
£938 $1500 €1369 On our kitchen table (142x160cm-56x63in) s. 18-May-3 Auctions by the Bay, Alameda #1154/R
£3022 $5500 €4412 Boats no.1 (56x64cm-22x25in) s.d.1959 prov. 19-Jun-4 Harvey Clar, Oakland #2213

STAR, Andrew (?) British
£250 $465 €365 Sky pilot (29x40cm-11x16in) s.i. 2-Mar-4 Bearnes, Exeter #408

STARCK, Julien Josephus Gaspard (1814-1884) Belgian
£1200 $2148 €1800 Deux jeunes filles sous la pluie (73x57cm-29x22in) s. 11-May-4 Vanderkindere, Brussels #29 est:1750-2500

STARCK, Julien Josephus Gaspard (attrib) (1814-1884) Belgian
£1277 $2132 €1800 La chasse dans le bois (30x23cm-12x9in) 17-Jun-3 Christie's, Paris #33/R est:1000-1500
£1667 $2717 €2400 Attic room with mourning woman by empty bed (79x92cm-31x36in) s.d.187. 25-Sep-3 Dr Fritz Nagel, Stuttgart #1424/R est:2800

STARCKE, Richard (1864-1945) German
£308 $514 €440 Medieval street, possibly Rothenburg (22x14cm-9x6in) s.d.13 canvas on board. 9-Oct-3 Michael Zeller, Lindau #767

STARING, Willem Constantijn (1847-1916) Dutch
Works on paper
£1049 $1804 €1500 Queen Wilhelmina riding (50x76cm-20x30in) s.d.1912 W/C. 8-Dec-3 Glerum, Amsterdam #8/R est:2000-3000

STARK, Arthur James (1831-1902) British
£1600 $2864 €2336 Haymaking (29x44cm-11x17in) 27-May-4 Christie's, Kensington #136/R est:700-1000

STARK, H and TODTSCHINDER, F (19th C) German
Sculpture
£1678 $3087 €2500 Grape harvester (28cm-11in) d.1894. 25-Mar-4 Dr Fritz Nagel, Stuttgart #937/R est:800

STARK, James (1794-1859) British
£750 $1275 €1095 Cattle and figures in a river landscape (20x35cm-8x14in) bears sig. prov. 27-Nov-3 Greenslade Hunt, Taunton #997/R
£1736 $2760 €2535 Sluice, possibly North Wales (45x60cm-18x24in) indis sig. verso. 1-May-3 Dunbar Sloane, Wellington #80/R est:7000-10000 (NZ.D 5000)
£2200 $3938 €3212 Shepherd and his flock by a brook at Allswater (27x42cm-11x17in) i.verso panel. 27-May-4 Christie's, Kensington #135/R est:1800-2200
Works on paper
£300 $510 €438 River landscape with a wooden millhouse (22x31cm-9x12in) i.verso W/C over pencil. 29-Oct-3 Hampton & Littlewood, Exeter #496/R

STARK, James (attrib) (1794-1859) British
£345 $617 €504 Evening river landscape (46x61cm-18x24in) i. 12-May-4 Dobiaschofsky, Bern #1001/R (S.FR 800)
£660 $1122 €964 Rural river landscapes with figures on pathways in foreground (30x60cm-12x24in) 31-Oct-3 Moore Allen & Innocent, Cirencester #764/R
£4400 $7084 €6380 Landscape with peasants cooking over an open fire, and animals (43x58cm-17x23in) i. 13-Aug-3 Rupert Toovey, Partridge Green #10/R est:1000-1500
£5500 $9900 €8030 View in Windsor Great Park (43x58cm-17x23in) s. i.d.1845 verso. 20-Apr-4 Clarke Gammon, Guildford #18/R est:1000-1500

STARK, Karl (1921-) Austrian
£3691 $6534 €5500 Untitled (76x80cm-30x31in) s.d.1978. 28-Apr-4 Wiener Kunst Auktionen, Vienna #212/R est:5000-10000
£6944 $11806 €10000 Dahlias (80x96cm-31x38in) s.d.68 lit. 28-Oct-3 Wiener Kunst Auktionen, Vienna #119/R est:10000-18000
£7639 $12986 €11000 Back yard in Nussdorf (66x87cm-26x34in) s.d.1966. 28-Oct-3 Wiener Kunst Auktionen, Vienna #117/R est:8000-15000
Works on paper
£1958 $3329 €2800 Flowers (62x46cm-24x18in) s.d.61 W/C. 28-Nov-3 Wiener Kunst Auktionen, Vienna #503/R est:2000-5000
£2105 $3874 €3200 Female nude (64x47cm-25x19in) s.d.1988 gouache. 22-Jun-4 Wiener Kunst Auktionen, Vienna #338/R est:3000

STARK, Melville F (1904-1987) American
£1572 $2500 €2295 Near Easton, figures and boats (41x51cm-16x20in) s. board. 10-Sep-3 Alderfer's, Hatfield #288/R est:1500-1800
£1686 $2900 €2462 Winter landscape (41x51cm-16x20in) canvasboard. 7-Dec-3 Freeman, Philadelphia #202 est:3000-5000

STARK, Otto (1859-1926) American
£302 $550 €441 Plein air (33x25cm-13x10in) s. sold with letter. 1-Jul-4 Dan Ripley, Indianapolis #150

STARK, Zora (20th C) ?
£403 $749 €600 Untitled. 8-Mar-4 Rieunier, Paris #190

STARKER, Erwin (1872-1938) German
£369 $679 €550 Bodensee (82x61cm-32x24in) s. panel. 25-Mar-4 Dr Fritz Nagel, Stuttgart #770/R
£396 $645 €570 Landscape near Ditzingen (443x56cm-174x22in) s. 27-Sep-3 Dr Fritz Nagel, Stuttgart #9370/R
£578 $1052 €850 Evening near Ditzingen (36x49cm-14x19in) s. i.d.1930 verso board. 3-Feb-4 Sigalas, Stuttgart #523/R
£733 $1320 €1100 Bathers on the Neckar with distant town (90x130cm-35x51in) s. prov. 24-Apr-4 Reiss & Sohn, Konigstein #5377/R
£775 $1340 €1100 Ditzingen with Solitude mountains in evening (36x49cm-14x19in) s. i. verso board. 11-Dec-3 Dr Fritz Nagel, Stuttgart #545/R
£833 $1358 €1200 Fishing boats on Bodensee (40x56cm-16x22in) s. board prov.lit. 27-Sep-3 Dr Fritz Nagel, Stuttgart #9649/R
£1042 $1719 €1500 Early autumn in the Wurm valley (90x130cm-35x51in) s. 3-Jul-3 Dr Fritz Nagel, Stuttgart #517/R
Works on paper
£403 $741 €600 Wooded river in afternoon sun (79x102cm-31x40in) s. pastel. 25-Mar-4 Dr Fritz Nagel, Stuttgart #771/R

STARKWEATHER, William Edward (1879-1969) American
£297 $550 €434 Sunset at Entry Island, Magdalen Islands, PQ, Canada (30x41cm-12x16in) s. i.d.1938 verso canvas on masonite. 10-Mar-4 Doyle, New York #49/R
£1536 $2750 €2243 Cliff at Entry Island, PQ, Canada, Magdalen Islands (30x41cm-12x16in) s. i.d.1938 verso canvas on masonite. 26-May-4 Doyle, New York #60/R est:1500-2500
£2907 $5000 €4244 Cliff at Cape St. Mary (40x50cm-16x20in) s. i.verso canvasboard. 3-Dec-3 Doyle, New York #179/R est:1500-2000
£6977 $12000 €10186 Outdoor painter, Karl Larsen (27x35cm-11x14in) s. i.verso canvas on masonite prov. 3-Dec-3 Doyle, New York #215/R est:3000-5000

STARN TWINS (1961-) American
Photographs
£1359 $2500 €2039 Siamese twins, yellow (107cm-42in) silicon tape toner film prov. 10-Jun-4 Phillips, New York #433/R est:3000-4000
£4802 $8500 €7011 Attracted to light - H (127x127cm-50x50in) s.d.1996-2000 num.3/3 photo four parts lit. 27-Apr-4 Sotheby's, New York #37/R est:6000-8000
Works on paper
£3243 $6000 €4735 Black and Red Square - 508 (244x244cm-96x96in) mixed media two parts exec 1986 prov.exhib.lit. 12-Feb-4 Sotheby's, New York #322a/R est:4000-6000

STARNDECKER, Peter (20th C) American
£649 $1200 €948 Barges setting out at sunset (20x25cm-8x10in) s. panel. 10-Feb-4 Christie's, Rockefeller NY #244/R

STAROWIEYSKI, Franciszek (1930-) Polish
Works on paper
£216 $393 €315 Portrait of a man's head (29x41cm-11x16in) s.d.1994 pastel cardboard. 20-Jun-4 Agra, Warsaw #47/R (P.Z 1500)
£240 $435 €350 Person (63x46cm-25x18in) s. gouache pastel. 4-Apr-4 Agra, Warsaw #72/R (P.Z 1700)
£240 $435 €350 Glowy (67x49cm-26x19in) s. pastel. 4-Apr-4 Agra, Warsaw #73/R (P.Z 1700)
£255 $456 €372 Untitled (67x49cm-26x19in) pastel exec.1987. 6-May-4 Agra, Warsaw #43/R (P.Z 1800)
£255 $456 €372 Composition with figures (62x49cm-24x19in) wash. 6-May-4 Agra, Warsaw #60/R (P.Z 1800)
£260 $431 €380 Divine Poland raped by profane Europe (35x25cm-14x10in) pencil chk exec.1998. 2-Oct-3 Agra, Warsaw #44/R (P.Z 1700)
£368 $659 €537 Portrait of man (57x44cm-22x17in) pastel. 6-May-4 Agra, Warsaw #25/R (P.Z 2600)
£480 $869 €701 Male nude (69x49cm-27x19in) s.d.98 pastel W/C. 4-Apr-4 Agra, Warsaw #81/R (P.Z 3400)
£521 $896 €761 Poster for a car (67x49cm-26x19in) s. pastel. 4-Dec-3 Agra, Warsaw #25/R (P.Z 3500)
£536 $921 €783 Group of nude woman in various poses (41x31cm-16x12in) s.i.d.98 pastel. 4-Dec-3 Agra, Warsaw #20/R (P.Z 3600)
£625 $1075 €913 Nude woman with spider crawling on her knee (99x68cm-39x27in) s.i.d.98 pastel. 4-Dec-3 Agra, Warsaw #19/R (P.Z 4200)
£3058 $5076 €4465 Untitled (250x600cm-98x236in) pastel exec.1985. 2-Oct-3 Agra, Warsaw #63/R est:10000 (P.Z 20000)
£3602 $6556 €5259 Untitled (185x145cm-73x57in) s.d.1981 pastel. 20-Jun-4 Agra, Warsaw #48/R (P.Z 25000)

STARR, Sidney (1857-1925) American/British
£380 $695 €555 Sailing vessel off a coast (14x23cm-6x9in) s. panel. 6-Apr-4 Bonhams, Knightsbridge #146/R

STARRETT, Jim (1937-) American
Works on paper
£528 $950 €771 Drawing num 5 (14x11cm-6x4in) graphite prov. 24-Apr-4 David Rago, Lambertville #400/R

STARREVELD, Pieter (1911-1989) Dutch?
Sculpture
£1053 $1937 €1600 Torso (33cm-13in) bronze stone base. 28-Jun-4 Sotheby's, Amsterdam #279/R est:1800-2200
£1189 $2045 €1700 Torso (26cm-10in) green pat. bronze marble base. 2-Dec-3 Sotheby's, Amsterdam #279/R est:1200-1500
£1304 $2139 €1800 Torso (33cm-13in) bronze stone base. 27-May-3 Sotheby's, Amsterdam #510/R est:2000-3000
£1304 $2139 €1800 Leda and the swan (49cm-19in) mono. bronze marble base. 27-May-3 Sotheby's, Amsterdam #512/R est:2000-3000
£1399 $2406 €2000 Paard (58cm-23in) bronze marble base. 2-Dec-3 Sotheby's, Amsterdam #276/R est:3000-4000
£1739 $2852 €2400 Woman playing cello (19cm-7in) mono. bronze marble base. 27-May-3 Sotheby's, Amsterdam #513/R est:1800-2200
£2319 $3803 €3200 Pair on a bench (22cm-9in) mono. bronze marble base. 27-May-3 Sotheby's, Amsterdam #509/R est:1800-2200
£5435 $8913 €7500 Jumping filly (145cm-57in) bronze marble base. 27-May-3 Sotheby's, Amsterdam #514/R est:8000-12000
Works on paper
£245 $421 €350 Horses (50x70cm-20x28in) mono.d.1936 W/C. 2-Dec-3 Sotheby's, Amsterdam #282a

STASESON, Joan Hall (20th C) Canadian
£226 $378 €330 Lilacs (20x15cm-8x6in) s.d.2003. 17-Nov-3 Hodgins, Calgary #358/R (C.D 500)

STASHEVETCH, Joseph (1958-) American
Works on paper
£2059 $3500 €3006 Thunderbolt no.9 (96x122cm-38x48in) chl conte crayon W/C prov. 9-Nov-3 Bonhams & Butterfields, Los Angeles #4057/R est:2000-3000

STASIO, Stefano di (1948-) Italian
Works on paper
£1000 $1800 €1500 Figures (30x40cm-12x16in) s. pastel exec.1998 exhib. 22-Apr-4 Finarte Semenzato, Rome #90/R est:1200-1400

STASSEN, Franz (1869-?) German

£4000	$6640	€5840	Creation of man (25x41cm-10x16in) init. panel. 30-Sep-3 Sotheby's, London #103/R est:1500-2500
Works on paper			
£331	$553	€480	Man's portrait (52x45cm-20x18in) s.d.1930 chl col chk. 14-Nov-3 Altus, Berlin #591

STATOM, Thermon (20th C) American

Sculpture			
£5587	$10000	€8157	Glass ladder (213x91cm-84x36in) s.d.1988 glass wood prov. 16-May-4 Wright, Chicago #335/R est:10000-15000

STATTLER, J (19th C) German?

£822	$1397	€1200	Madonna and Infant Jesus on cloud (116x70cm-46x28in) s.i.d.1872. 6-Nov-3 Allgauer, Kempten #3585/R

STAUB, Josef (1931-) Swiss

Sculpture			
£12227	$21886	€17851	Large swing (158x192x150cm-62x76x59in) mono.d.1973 chrome lit. 26-May-4 Sotheby's, Zurich #151/R est:10000-15000 (S.FR 28000)

STAUDACHER, Hans (1923-) Swiss

£486	$812	€700	Untitled (50x70cm-20x28in) s.d. mixed media board. 25-Oct-3 Dr Lehr, Berlin #491/R
£2128	$3553	€3000	Untitled (40x50cm-16x20in) s.d. stretcher. 14-Oct-3 Dorotheum, Vienna #197/R est:6000-9000
£3103	$5679	€4500	Untitled (66x39cm-26x15in) s. mono.d.59 verso masonite. 27-Jan-4 Dorotheum, Vienna #155/R est:6000-8500
£4027	$7208	€6000	Squares and circles (50x100cm-20x39in) s. s.d.1980-88 verso prov. 25-May-4 Dorotheum, Vienna #365/R est:6000-8000
£5705	$10211	€8500	Untitled (70x100cm-28x39in) s.d.55 s.d.58 verso. 25-May-4 Dorotheum, Vienna #222/R est:8000-10000
£6993	$11888	€10000	Untitled (130x140cm-51x55in) s.d.86 oil acrylic prov. 26-Nov-3 Dorotheum, Vienna #300/R est:10000-14000
£7895	$14526	€12000	Untitled (110x110cm-43x43in) s.d.1967. 22-Jun-4 Wiener Kunst Auktionen, Vienna #324/R est:12000
£11111	$18889	€16000	My head (117x85cm-46x33in) s. i.d.58 verso panel. 28-Oct-3 Wiener Kunst Auktionen, Vienna #232/R est:16000-25000
£18056	$30694	€26000	The earth (200x155cm-79x61in) s.i.d.61. 28-Oct-3 Wiener Kunst Auktionen, Vienna #237/R est:25000-42000
Works on paper			
£775	$1356	€1100	Untitled (60x44cm-24x17in) s.d.1993 mixed media. 19-Dec-3 Dorotheum, Vienna #423/R
£800	$1440	€1200	Little packet (16x16cm-6x6in) s. Indian ink W/C. 21-Apr-4 Dorotheum, Vienna #259/R
£805	$1490	€1200	Untitled (30x22cm-12x9in) s.d.1989 mixed media. 9-Mar-4 Dorotheum, Vienna #200/R
£933	$1671	€1400	Untitled (41x57cm-16x22in) s.d.93 mixed media. 13-May-4 Dorotheum, Linz #582/R
£966	$1767	€1400	Composition (21x31cm-8x12in) s.i.d.50 verso mixed media two. 27-Jan-4 Dorotheum, Vienna #148/R
£987	$1816	€1500	Untitled (50x70cm-20x28in) s.d.1988 mixed media. 22-Jun-4 Wiener Kunst Auktionen, Vienna #334/R est:1500
£1056	$1849	€1500	Untitled (62x46cm-24x18in) s.d.1977 mixed media. 19-Dec-3 Dorotheum, Vienna #309/R est:2000-2600
£1074	$1976	€1600	Composition (64x48cm-25x19in) s.d. gouache Indian ink. 26-Mar-4 Ketterer, Hamburg #660/R est:1800-2200
£1184	$2179	€1800	Untitled (64x48cm-25x19in) s.d.1971 mixed media. 22-Jun-4 Wiener Kunst Auktionen, Vienna #404/R est:1800
£1208	$2235	€1800	Untitled (30x33cm-12x13in) s.d.58 mixed media. 9-Mar-4 Dorotheum, Vienna #154/R est:1800-2400
£1241	$2272	€1800	Untitled (64x48cm-25x19in) s.d.83 mixed media. 27-Jan-4 Dorotheum, Vienna #243/R est:1800-2600
£1329	$2259	€1900	Self portrait with animals and heart (21x31cm-8x12in) s.mono. mixed media pen Indian ink two. 26-Nov-3 Dorotheum, Vienna #194/R est:1700-2400
£1477	$2732	€2200	Heaven on earth (49x34cm-19x13in) s.i.d.59 mixed media. 9-Mar-4 Dorotheum, Vienna #145/R est:2000-2800
£1745	$3228	€2600	Apple tree (69x49cm-27x19in) s.i.d.1982 mixed media. 9-Mar-4 Dorotheum, Vienna #199/R est:2000-2800
£2013	$3564	€3000	Untitled (60x81cm-24x32in) s. mixed media. 28-Apr-4 Wiener Kunst Auktionen, Vienna #245/R est:2500-4000

STAUDACHER, Vitus (1850-1925) German

£352	$563	€500	Landscape study with figures (20x33cm-8x13in) s.d.1893 board lit. 19-Sep-3 Karlheinz Kaupp, Staufen #1977/R
£921	$1695	€1400	Figures on village street (53x35cm-21x14in) s.d.1893. 24-Jun-4 Dr Fritz Nagel, Stuttgart #761/R

STAUDT, Klaus (1932-) German

£1586	$2696	€2316	Vier Stellungen (42x42cm-17x17in) s.verso dispersion wood prov. 5-Nov-3 AB Stockholms Auktionsverk #1153/R est:12000-15000 (S.KR 21000)

STAUFFER, Fred (1892-1980) Swiss

£181	$308	€264	Brown still life (85x130cm-33x51in) s.d.40 s.i. stretcher study verso lit. 18-Nov-3 Hans Widmer, St Gallen #1205 (S.FR 400)
£386	$641	€560	River landscape (59x99cm-23x39in) s.d.1933. 13-Jun-3 Zofingen, Switzerland #3037 (S.FR 850)
£419	$711	€612	Hay harvest (35x50cm-14x20in) s.i.d.70 panel. 5-Nov-3 Dobiaschofsky, Bern #982/R (S.FR 950)
£476	$762	€690	Village (64x86cm-25x34in) s.d.25. 15-May-3 Stuker, Bern #1502/R (S.FR 1000)
£573	$974	€837	Narrow village street in Wallis (69x41cm-27x16in) s.d.63 i. verso panel. 5-Nov-3 Dobiaschofsky, Bern #983/R (S.FR 1300)
£661	$1123	€965	Autumn near Muttenz (70x65cm-28x26in) s.d.36 i. stretcher. 7-Nov-3 Dobiaschofsky, Bern #156/R (S.FR 1500)
£690	$1234	€1007	Hay harvest (62x80cm-24x31in) mono.d.23 i. stretcher. 13-May-4 Stuker, Bern #328/R est:3000-4000 (S.FR 1600)
£724	$1158	€1057	Moon rising near Egg (99x122cm-39x48in) s.d.1975 i. verso masonite. 16-Sep-3 Philippe Schuler, Zurich #3255 est:1800-2400 (S.FR 1600)
£762	$1273	€1113	Houses in winter landscape (91x76cm-36x30in) s.d.46. 24-Oct-3 Hans Widmer, St Gallen #119/R est:1400-3500 (S.FR 1700)
£807	$1348	€1178	White smoke (87x112cm-34x44in) s.d.50 s.i. stretcher. 24-Oct-3 Hans Widmer, St Gallen #88/R est:1400-3800 (S.FR 1800)
£837	$1423	€1222	Grape harvest (50x39cm-20x15in) s.d.42 i. verso. 5-Nov-3 Dobiaschofsky, Bern #981/R (S.FR 1900)
£1076	$1797	€1571	Hamlet in mountain landscape (65x94cm-26x37in) s.d.35. 24-Oct-3 Hans Widmer, St Gallen #120/R est:1400-3500 (S.FR 2400)
£1101	$1872	€1607	Signpost in Emmental (89x112cm-35x44in) s.d.73 panel. 7-Nov-3 Dobiaschofsky, Bern #154/R est:5000 (S.FR 2500)
£1310	$2384	€1913	At the foot of Riggisberg (73x122cm-29x48in) s.d.74 masonite. 16-Jun-4 Fischer, Luzern #1332/R est:3500-4500 (S.FR 3000)
£1762	$2996	€2573	Emmental (90x149cm-35x59in) s.d.70 panel. 7-Nov-3 Dobiaschofsky, Bern #150/R est:8000 (S.FR 4000)

STAUFFER-BERN, Karl (1857-1891) Swiss

£3879	$6944	€5663	Nude study of old man (104x85cm-41x33in) s. 14-May-4 Dobiaschofsky, Bern #54/R est:14000 (S.FR 9000)
Prints			
£1940	$3569	€2832	Portrait of Gottfried Keller (39x30cm-15x12in) s.i. etching. 26-Mar-4 Koller, Zurich #3388 est:2500-3500 (S.FR 4500)
£7240	$11584	€10570	Portrait of Gottfried Keller (39x30cm-15x12in) s.i. etching. 19-Sep-3 Koller, Zurich #3256/R est:5000-7000 (S.FR 16000)

STAVEREN, Jan van (1625-1668) Dutch

£6164	$10479	€9000	Flagellation of Christ (62x48cm-24x19in) s.d.1642 panel prov. 4-Nov-3 Sotheby's, Amsterdam #108/R est:4000-6000

STAVEREN, Jan van (attrib) (1625-1668) Dutch

£1075	$1935	€1570	Portrait of an academic in his study (41x29cm-16x11in) panel. 24-Apr-4 Rasmussen, Havnen #2312/R est:7000-10000 (D.KR 12000)

STAVINOHA, Eduard (1903-?) American

£219	$350	€320	Still life (41x33cm-16x13in) s.d.32. 21-Sep-3 Bonhams & Butterfields, San Francisco #2844/R

STAVRIANOS, Wendy (1941-) Australian

£1145	$2084	€1672	Threads of memory (136x137cm-54x54in) s.d.1941. 16-Jun-4 Deutscher-Menzies, Melbourne #396/R est:3500-5500 (A.D 3000)

STAVROWSKY, Oleg (1927-) American

£932	$1500	€1351	Stayin with him (16x20cm-6x8in) 22-Aug-3 Altermann Galleries, Santa Fe #129
£1955	$3500	€2854	Shadow (71x51cm-28x20in) 15-May-4 Altermann Galleries, Santa Fe #107/R
£2857	$4600	€4143	Mountain lion (76x127cm-30x50in) 22-Aug-3 Altermann Galleries, Santa Fe #24
£2941	$5000	€4294	Skyliner (76x61cm-30x24in) 1-Nov-3 Altermann Galleries, Santa Fe #20
£3073	$5500	€4487	Taking a break (51x61cm-20x24in) 15-May-4 Altermann Galleries, Santa Fe #109/R
£6704	$12000	€9788	Spot repairs (122x91cm-48x36in) 15-May-4 Altermann Galleries, Santa Fe #93/R

STAZEWSKI, Henryk (1894-1988) Polish

£1220	$2099	€1781	Composition (42x42cm-17x17in) s.d.1980 acrylic board. 4-Dec-3 Agra, Warsaw #36/R est:8000 (P.Z 8200)
£1836	$3323	€2681	Untitled (30x30cm-12x12in) s.d.1981. 4-Apr-4 Agra, Warsaw #42/R (P.Z 13000)
£1958	$3329	€2800	Untitled (35x35cm-14x14in) s.d.1984 verso acrylic panel prov. 27-Nov-3 Lempertz, Koln #456/R est:2200
£2133	$3904	€3200	Untitled (47x47cm-19x19in) s.d.1984 verso acrylic masonite prov. 4-Jun-4 Lempertz, Koln #464/R est:2000
£2168	$3685	€3100	Untitled (35x35cm-14x14in) s.d.1984 verso acrylic panel prov. 27-Nov-3 Lempertz, Koln #455/R est:2200
£2621	$4377	€3800	NR 80 (33x29cm-13x11in) s.i.d.1974 verso acrylic metal. 16-Nov-3 Agra, Warsaw #28/R est:1000
£2691	$4817	€3929	Untitled (44x44cm-17x17in) painted 1981. 6-May-4 Agra, Warsaw #55/R (P.Z 19000)
£2882	$5245	€4208	Composition abstract III (27x40cm-11x16in) s.d.1958 oil felt board. 20-Jun-4 Agra, Warsaw #49/R (P.Z 20000)
£3586	$5989	€5200	Relief (50x50cm-20x20in) s.d.1975 verso acrylic. 16-Nov-3 Agra, Warsaw #6/R est:2000
£3670	$6092	€5358	Number 111 (43x43cm-17x17in) d.1976 board. 2-Oct-3 Agra, Warsaw #19/R est:10000 (P.Z 24000)
Works on paper			
£847	$1534	€1237	Figures (32x27cm-13x11in) s. gouache pencil paper board. 4-Apr-4 Agra, Warsaw #9/R (P.Z 6000)

STEAD, Fred (1863-1940) British

£560	$1002	€818	Still life of flowers (59x49cm-23x19in) s. 16-Mar-4 Bonhams, Leeds #646
£1050	$1785	€1533	Mother and child (59x49cm-23x19in) s. 18-Nov-3 Bonhams, Leeds #160/R est:700-900
Works on paper			
£3000	$5610	€4380	Extensive Dales landscape with village in foreground (120x173cm-47x68in) s. pastel. 22-Jul-4 Tennants, Leyburn #779/R est:1500-2000

STEADMAN, E (20th C) American

£313	$500	€457	Orientalist beauty (76x61cm-30x24in) s.d.1929 board. 20-Sep-3 Sloans & Kenyon, Bethesda #1186a/R

STEADMAN, Ralph Idris (1936-) British
Works on paper
£550 $919 €803 Smoker's dream of paradise (83x58cm-33x23in) s.d.26 Feb 91 pen ink W/C wash. 14-Oct-3 Bonhams, New Bond Street #256/R

STEARNS, Junius Brutus (attrib) (1810-1885) American
£2049 $3750 €2992 Portrait of Stephen Brewer (71x58cm-28x23in) prov. 6-Jun-4 Skinner, Boston #14/R est:1500-2500

STECK, Leo (1883-1960) Swiss
£658 $1211 €1000 L'Invocation (110x87cm-43x34in) s. i.d.1917 verso. 28-Jun-4 Joron-Derem, Paris #108

STEDING, Konny (1963-) ?
£333 $543 €480 Deux figures (160x110cm-63x43in) s.verso acrylic. 29-Sep-3 Charbonneaux, Paris #287

STEEL, George Hammond (1900-1960) British
£500 $915 €730 Old houses, Saffron Walden (35x50cm-14x20in) s. board prov. 7-Apr-4 Dreweatt Neate, Newbury #129
£600 $948 €870 Lobster pot, Mousehole (25x30cm-10x12in) s. board. 3-Sep-3 Bonhams, Bury St Edmunds #401

STEEL, Kenneth (1906-1973) British
£280 $445 €409 Durham Castle and Cathedral from the river (38x54cm-15x21in) s.d.11. 18-Mar-3 Anderson & Garland, Newcastle #134/R

STEELE, E (19/20th C) British
£1200 $2232 €1752 Still life of fruit in dish (58x48cm-23x19in) s.d.1902. 8-Mar-4 Louis Taylor, Stoke on Trent #988/R est:300-400

STEELE, Edwin (19th C) British
£280 $459 €409 Still life of chrysanthemums (30x51cm-12x20in) s. 29-May-3 Neales, Nottingham #836/R
£280 $521 €409 Still life of fruit on a slab (38x48cm-15x19in) s. 5-Mar-4 Dee Atkinson & Harrison, Driffield #627
£320 $518 €467 Still life study of soft fruit (36x48cm-14x19in) s.d.1887 panel. 7-Aug-3 Amersham Auction Rooms, UK #281
£320 $589 €467 Still life of flowers and fruit (32x42cm-13x17in) s. 8-Jun-4 Bonhams, Knightsbridge #99
£360 $666 €526 Still life of grapes, peaches, plums, lemon and various flowers and foliage (29x39cm-11x15in) board. 14-Jul-4 Bonhams, Chester #518
£500 $915 €730 Still life with fruit (44x60cm-17x24in) s.d.1899. 1-Feb-4 Lots Road Auctions, London #366
£550 $1012 €803 Still life of fruit and vines on a ledge (44x60cm-17x24in) s. 8-Jun-4 Bonhams, Knightsbridge #235/R
£600 $1098 €876 Floral still life (44x60cm-17x24in) s.d.1909. 1-Feb-4 Lots Road Auctions, London #365
£880 $1619 €1285 Mixed garden flowers on a shelf. Fruit on a shelf (50x60cm-20x24in) both s.d.1880 pair. 14-Jun-4 Bonhams, Bath #157
£980 $1813 €1431 Still life with flowers (74x61cm-29x24in) s. 12-Feb-4 Andrew Hartley, Ilkley #819
£1250 $2000 €1825 Still life with a basket of flowers with fruit (24x31cm-9x12in) s. 16-Sep-3 Woolley & Wallis, Salisbury #71/R est:800-1200

STEELE, Louis John (1843-1918) New Zealander
£3986 $6457 €5780 Evening sunset. Maori spear fishing (20x30cm-8x12in) s.d.1913 pair. 31-Jul-3 International Art Centre, Auckland #49/R est:14000-18000 (NZ.D 11000)
£4135 $7030 €6037 The Thelma on the Waitemata (44x34cm-17x13in) s.d.1906 prov. 27-Nov-3 International Art Centre, Auckland #91/R est:12000-16000 (NZ.D 11000)
Works on paper
£338 $575 €493 Boat at rest (19x32cm-7x13in) s.d.1885 gouache. 26-Nov-3 Dunbar Sloane, Wellington #154 (NZ.D 900)

STEELE, Marian Williams (1916-2001) American
£601 $1100 €902 Survival (76x102cm-30x40in) s. masonite. 2-Aug-4 Grogan, Boston #105
Works on paper
£300 $550 €450 State House, Beacon Hill (76x56cm-30x22in) s. W/C. 2-Aug-4 Grogan, Boston #106

STEELE, Theodore Clement (1847-1926) American
£14535 $25000 €21221 Landscape (51x71cm-20x28in) s.d.1906. 7-Dec-3 Susanin's, Chicago #6011/R est:3000-5000
£37791 $65000 €55175 Quiet forest (46x71cm-18x28in) s.d.1900 prov. 7-Dec-3 Freeman, Philadelphia #130 est:25000-40000
£50847 $90000 €74237 Summer camp (55x81cm-22x32in) s. 28-Apr-4 Christie's, Los Angeles #2/R est:12000-18000

STEELINK, Willem (1826-1913) Dutch
£738 $1373 €1100 Sheep near farm (27x36cm-11x14in) s. 8-Mar-4 Bernaerts, Antwerp #847/R
£1622 $3000 €2368 Sheep grazing (33x46cm-13x18in) s. 13-Mar-4 Susanin's, Chicago #6152/R est:1000-1500
£1700 $3179 €2482 Return of the flock (40x28cm-16x11in) s. 21-Jul-4 Lyon & Turnbull, Edinburgh #123/R est:1500-2500
Works on paper
£461 $847 €700 Peasant woman with her child returning home from church (36x57cm-14x22in) s. W/C. 28-Jun-4 Sotheby's, Amsterdam #125/R

STEELINK, Willem (jnr) (1856-1928) Dutch
£500 $885 €730 Sheep at the edge of a pond (47x34cm-19x13in) s. 29-Apr-4 Christie's, Kensington #165/R
£559 $934 €800 Still life with apples (15x30cm-6x12in) s. canvas on panel. 30-Jun-3 Sotheby's, Amsterdam #120/R
£1800 $3006 €2628 Returning home (46x30cm-18x12in) s. 12-Nov-3 Halls, Shrewsbury #323/R est:1000-1500
£1946 $3601 €2900 Trois enfants a la construction du chateau de sable (29x21cm-11x8in) s. 15-Mar-4 Horta, Bruxelles #97 est:3000-4000
Works on paper
£413 $690 €603 Changing pastures (30x53cm-12x21in) W/C. 17-Jun-3 Maynards, Vancouver #323 (C.D 925)
£909 $1563 €1300 Shepherd and his flock (39x55cm-15x22in) s. W/C. 7-Dec-3 Sotheby's, Amsterdam #607/R

STEELINK, Willem (jnr-attrib) (1856-1928) Dutch
£300 $549 €438 Herding sheep on a path (44x66cm-17x26in) 8-Jul-4 Lawrence, Crewkerne #1612

STEELL, David George (1856-1930) British
£850 $1445 €1241 Clockwork (51x41cm-20x16in) s.i.d.April 27th 1905 painted oval. 27-Nov-3 Christie's, Kensington #138/R

STEELL, David George (attrib) (1856-1930) British
£400 $704 €584 Young wild cat (19cm-7in) mono. bears i.verso board. 18-May-4 Rosebery Fine Art, London #782

STEELL, David George and Gourlay (19th C) British
£4500 $8370 €6570 Prize bull (63x76cm-25x30in) s.d.1879. 4-Mar-4 Christie's, Kensington #536/R est:2000-3000

STEELL, Gourlay (1819-1894) British
£1500 $2505 €2190 Burns at the plough (30x40cm-12x16in) s.indis.d. board. 12-Nov-3 Sotheby's, Olympia #87/R est:800-1200
Works on paper
£1381 $2500 €2016 Jamie (39x31cm-15x12in) s.indis.d. i.verso W/C col chk htd white. 30-Mar-4 Bonhams & Butterfields, San Francisco #85/R est:1500-2200
£6500 $11960 €9490 West Highland terrier (37x30cm-15x12in) s. W/C bodycol. 10-Jun-4 Christie's, Kensington #380/R est:2000-3000

STEELL, Gourlay (attrib) (1819-1894) British
£2600 $4784 €3796 Two dandie dinmont terriers in an interior (30x36cm-12x14in) indis sig.d.1855 arched top. 10-Jun-4 Christie's, Kensington #385/R est:1000-1500

STEEN, Jan (c.1626-1679) Dutch
£6757 $11892 €10000 Seated peasant with herring (19x14cm-7x6in) s. panel prov. 22-May-4 Lempertz, Koln #1135/R est:10000-12000
£11620 $18592 €16500 Merry company (47x55cm-19x22in) panel. 19-Sep-3 Sigalas, Stuttgart #428/R est:15000
£19178 $32603 €28000 Woman counting coins at a table (33x21cm-13x8in) s. panel painted with studio prov. 5-Nov-3 Christie's, Amsterdam #45/R est:15000-25000
£230000 $420900 €335800 Feast of the Chamber of Rethoricians (64x84cm-25x33in) s. 7-Jul-4 Sotheby's, London #17/R est:60000-80000

STEEN, Jan (attrib) (c.1626-1679) Dutch
£21000 $37800 €30660 Winter landscape with figures skating and playing on a frozen river (35x48cm-14x19in) panel prov. 22-Apr-4 Sotheby's, London #88/R est:8000-12000

STEEN, Knut (1924-) Norwegian
Sculpture
£1281 $2139 €1870 Two figures (17x18x29cm-7x7x11in) metal incl.plinth. 13-Oct-3 Blomqvist, Oslo #345/R est:18000-20000 (N.KR 15000)

STEEN-JOHNSEN, Soren (1903-1979) Norwegian
£435 $752 €635 Winter landscape, Svardalshogda (81x100cm-32x39in) s. 13-Dec-3 Blomqvist, Lysaker #1356 (N.KR 5000)

STEENBERGEN, Elke van (19/20th C) Belgian
Works on paper
£345 $638 €500 La mere attendrie (28x37cm-11x15in) mono.d.1918 i.verso W/C. 13-Jan-4 Vanderkindere, Brussels #66

STEENE, Augustus van den (1803-1870) Belgian
£2550 $4744 €3800 Farmer's wife on donkey at edge of wood with windmill (55x76cm-22x30in) s.d.1841 panel. 8-Mar-4 Bernaerts, Antwerp #71/R est:4000-4500

STEENE, William (1888-1965) American
£482 $800 €704 Seascape (41x51cm-16x20in) s. canvasboard. 4-Oct-3 Neal Auction Company, New Orleans #590/R
£714 $1300 €1042 Snowy day in the woods (41x51cm-16x20in) s. 7-Feb-4 Neal Auction Company, New Orleans #513/R est:1200-1800

STEENHOLT, A de (18/19th C) Dutch
£4200 $7686 €6132 Still life with roses, poppies and other flowers and fruit on a marble ledge (43x33cm-17x13in) s. panel. 6-Jul-4 Sotheby's, Olympia #600/R est:2000-3000

STEENHOUWER, P C (20th C) Dutch
£580 $969 €847 Dutch town scene with figures before a shop (41x32cm-16x13in) s. oil wood. 24-Jun-3 Bonhams, Chester #942

STEENWEGEN, Gustave van (1905-1986) Belgian

£278	$464	€400	Vase de fleurs (39x33cm-15x13in) s.d.1966 cardboard. 21-Oct-3 Campo, Vlaamse Kaai #1164
£347	$580	€500	Nature morte aux fleurs dans un vase (70x92cm-28x36in) s. 21-Oct-3 Campo & Campo, Antwerp #338

STEENWYCK, Hendrik van (elder-attrib) (1550-1603) Dutch

£704	$1232	€1000	Scene d'interieur d'eglise (43x33cm-17x13in) panel. 17-Dec-3 Piasa, Paris #5

STEENWYCK, Hendrik van (younger) (1580-1649) Flemish

£12000	$21600	€17520	Interior with church (14x10cm-6x4in) init.indis.d.16 copper. 22-Apr-4 Sotheby's, London #68/R est:4000-6000
£13000	$23400	€18980	Interior of a church crypt with figures by torchlight (27x36cm-11x14in) s.d.1602 panel. 22-Apr-4 Sotheby's, London #69/R est:8000-12000
£22000	$40260	€32120	Interior of a cathedral with gentlemen and beggars (27cm-11in circular) s.d.1621 panel prov. 7-Jul-4 Christie's, London #25/R est:10000-15000

STEEPLE, John (1816-1887) British

Works on paper

£350	$595	€511	South Downs Way, Sussex, with woman walking her dog (25x33cm-10x13in) s.d.1877. 5-Nov-3 John Nicholson, Haslemere #492
£350	$641	€525	Coastal landscape with cows (51x30cm-20x12in) s.d.1879 W/C. 30-Jul-4 Jim Railton, Durham #843
£370	$681	€540	Travelers on a riverside path (13x19cm-5x7in) s.d.1856 W/C. 11-Jun-4 Keys, Aylsham #441/R
£420	$773	€613	In the highlands (7x15cm-3x6in) s.d.68 W/C. 11-Jun-4 Keys, Aylsham #425/R

STEER, Henry Reynolds (1858-1928) British

Works on paper

£300	$549	€438	Good impression (33x30cm-13x12in) s. W/C pencil exhib. 8-Jul-4 Lawrence, Crewkerne #1552/R
£302	$504	€441	Travelers and a jester in a wooded landscape (34x25cm-13x10in) s. W/C. 20-Oct-3 Stephan Welz, Johannesburg #446 est:1600-2000 (SA.R 3500)
£600	$948	€876	Figures meeting in a manor garden (46x27cm-18x11in) s. W/C. 2-Sep-3 Gildings, Market Harborough #402/R
£650	$1164	€949	Lover's tryst (43x25cm-17x10in) s. W/C. 5-May-4 Goldings, Lincolnshire #492
£800	$1512	€1168	Coastal view with figures carrying smuggled goods nearing the shore (36x54cm-14x21in) s. W/C htd gouache. 18-Feb-4 Rupert Toovey, Partridge Green #6/R
£1600	$2864	€2336	Solo (25x17cm-10x7in) s.d.92 W/C. 26-May-4 Sotheby's, Olympia #170/R est:700-900

STEER, Philip Wilson (1860-1942) British

£732	$1128	€1150	English landscape in early spring. s. 4-Sep-2 Schopman, Hamburg #112/R
£850	$1590	€1241	Buildwas Abbey (25x36cm-10x14in) panel. 26-Feb-4 Mallams, Cheltenham #241/R
£1200	$2184	€1752	Poplars near Buildwas (26x36cm-10x14in) board prov. 15-Jun-4 Bonhams, Knightsbridge #12/R est:800-1200
£1800	$3060	€2628	Canal and towpath through the woods (60x85cm-24x33in) s.d.90. 1-Dec-3 Bonhams, Bath #32/R est:2000-3000
£14000	$23800	€20440	Dusk on the beach (61x61cm-24x24in) s.d.91 prov. 21-Nov-3 Christie's, London #124/R est:15000-20000
£50000	$91500	€73000	Fisher children, Etaples (46x62cm-18x24in) painted 1887 prov.exhib.lit. 4-Jun-4 Christie's, London #11/R est:30000-50000

Works on paper

£280	$496	€409	Deal pier (23x30cm-9x12in) s.d.1934 W/C. 27-Apr-4 Bonhams, Knightsbridge #261
£280	$510	€409	View of Southwood from Walberswick (11x27cm-4x11in) s. W/C. 15-Jun-4 Bonhams, Knightsbridge #143/R
£300	$531	€438	Beach at Walmer (18x29cm-7x11in) W/C prov. 27-Apr-4 Bonhams, Knightsbridge #18/R
£380	$695	€555	Ironbridge (22x34cm-9x13in) W/C pencil prov. 8-Jul-4 Lawrence, Crewkerne #1566/R
£420	$773	€613	View in Naresfoot Park 1915 (24x34cm-9x13in) W/C bodycol. 29-Mar-4 Bonhams, Bath #36/R
£600	$1122	€876	Beach scene with fishing boats, thought to be Whitstable, Kent (8x12cm-3x5in) s.d.1931 sepia W/C. 24-Feb-4 Canterbury Auctions, UK #170/R
£620	$1091	€905	Boats on the estuary (24x34cm-9x13in) s.d.1922 W/C. 18-May-4 Bonhams, Knightsbridge #220/R
£620	$1135	€905	Coastal scene with fishing vessels (23x33cm-9x13in) s.d.1920 pencil W/C. 28-Jul-4 Mallams, Oxford #83/R
£750	$1290	€1095	River at Bridgenorth, Shropshire (22x33cm-9x13in) W/C exhib. 3-Dec-3 Christie's, Kensington #227/R
£840	$1537	€1226	Cranes unloading at Green Hythe (20x30cm-8x12in) W/C exec. 1932 prov.exhib. 28-Jul-4 Mallams, Oxford #108/R

STEER, Philip Wilson (attrib) (1860-1942) British

£260	$476	€380	Racing yachts off the coast (29x50cm-11x20in) 6-Jun-4 Lots Road Auctions, London #363
£5000	$9150	€7300	Girl sewing (63x48cm-25x19in) lit. 2-Jun-4 Sotheby's, London #8/R est:5000-7000

STEFAN, Ross (1934-1999) American

£324	$600	€473	White River Apache girl (41x30cm-16x12in) s. 15-Jul-4 Sotheby's, New York #58/R
£649	$1200	€948	Trail beautiful-lively may I walk-navajo (41x56cm-16x22in) s. i. stretcher. 15-Jul-4 Sotheby's, New York #72/R
£1486	$2750	€2170	Get along little Nellie (46x61cm-18x24in) s. s.i.d.1969 stretcher. 15-Jul-4 Sotheby's, New York #53/R est:1500-2000
£2800	$5040	€4088	Dutch winter landscape scenes with cottages (28x59cm-11x23in) s. pair. 20-Apr-4 Hutchinson, Boroughbridge #317/R est:800-1200
£2941	$5000	€4294	Trails of the windmill (66x102cm-26x40in) 1-Nov-3 Altermann Galleries, Santa Fe #112
£2973	$5500	€4341	Legendary trail of the spider clan (71x127cm-28x50in) s. 15-Jul-4 Sotheby's, New York #57/R est:3000-5000
£3243	$6000	€4735	Passing parade (71x102cm-28x40in) s. 15-Jul-4 Sotheby's, New York #56/R est:3000-5000
£6704	$12000	€9788	Yawning Deer Spring (61x91cm-24x36in) 15-May-4 Altermann Galleries, Santa Fe #114/R

STEFANI, Pierre (1938-) French?

£267	$477	€400	Figures on the beach near Britany (17x23cm-7x9in) s. panel. 11-May-4 Vendu Notarishuis, Rotterdam #678
£290	$484	€420	Haamstede Castle (14x24cm-6x9in) panel. 11-Nov-3 Vendu Notarishuis, Rotterdam #656/R
£313	$500	€457	Seashore landscape, barques e maree basse (56x69cm-22x27in) s. board. 18-May-3 Auctions by the Bay, Alameda #1005/R
£320	$573	€480	Beach near Knokke (17x23cm-7x9in) s. panel. 11-May-4 Vendu Notarishuis, Rotterdam #688
£331	$553	€480	Veere Campveerse tower (13x18cm-5x7in) s. panel. 11-Nov-3 Vendu Notarishuis, Rotterdam #637
£336	$561	€480	Beach near Zoutelande (29x39cm-11x15in) panel. 24-Jun-3 Vendu Notarishuis, Rotterdam #256
£533	$955	€800	Beach near Ostend (17x23cm-7x9in) s. panel. 11-May-4 Vendu Notarishuis, Rotterdam #689

STEFANI, Vincenzo de (1859-1937) Italian

£4082	$7306	€6000	Figure in the wood (79x57cm-31x22in) s.d.1901. 22-Mar-4 Sant Agostino, Torino #238/R est:8000

STEFANO, Armando de (1926-) Italian

£497	$904	€750	Bernardina (50x60cm-20x24in) s.d.1973. 17-Jun-4 Galleria Pananti, Florence #80/R

STEFANONI, Tino (1937-) Italian

£1111	$1756	€1600	Composition (36x36cm-14x14in) painted 2002. 6-Sep-3 Meeting Art, Vercelli #577 est:1600
£1333	$2453	€2000	Untitled (32x46cm-13x18in) s.d.2003 verso acrylic. 12-Jun-4 Meeting Art, Vercelli #479/R est:2000
£1333	$2453	€2000	Untitled (32x42cm-13x17in) s.d.2002 acrylic. 12-Jun-4 Meeting Art, Vercelli #845/R est:2000
£1389	$2194	€2000	Untitled (32x46cm-13x18in) acrylic painted 2002. 6-Sep-3 Meeting Art, Vercelli #741 est:2000
£1477	$2732	€2200	Interior (30x45cm-12x18in) s.d.1987 verso. 11-Mar-4 Galleria Pace, Milan #80/R est:2300-3000
£1477	$2732	€2200	Untitled (32x42cm-13x17in) s.d.2003 acrylic. 13-Mar-4 Meeting Art, Vercelli #327
£1745	$3123	€2600	Untitled (32x42cm-13x17in) s.d.2003 acrylic. 30-May-4 Meeting Art, Vercelli #16 est:2000
£1905	$3410	€2800	Landscape with still life (32x46cm-13x18in) s.d.2003 verso. 16-Mar-4 Finarte Semenzato, Milan #357/R est:3000
£1972	$3451	€2800	Things (30x40cm-12x16in) s.d.1979 acrylic graphite. 16-Dec-3 Finarte Semenzato, Milan #214/R est:1800-2200
£2113	$3697	€3000	Houses and trees (32x42cm-13x17in) s.d.2003 verso. 16-Dec-3 Finarte Semenzato, Milan #260/R est:2000-2500
£2564	$4538	€3743	Senza titolo F35 and F36 (30x240cm-12x94in) s.d.1996 verso acrylic diptych. 27-Apr-4 AB Stockholms Auktionsverk #1206/R est:40000-50000 (S.KR 35000)

STEFANOU, Nikos (1933-) Greek

£2000	$3580	€2920	Village scene (26x36cm-10x14in) s. 10-May-4 Sotheby's, Olympia #81/R est:1200-1800
£2200	$3938	€3212	Cityscape (52x72cm-20x28in) s. 11-May-4 Bonhams, New Bond Street #112/R est:2200-3200
£3100	$5425	€4526	View of Gazi, Athens (30x50cm-12x20in) s. 16-Dec-3 Bonhams, New Bond Street #141/R est:2000-2500

STEFANSSEN, Jon (1881-1962) Icelandic

£2275	$3640	€3322	View over the sea, Iceland (58x80cm-23x31in) s. 22-Sep-3 Rasmussen, Vejle #597/R est:2000 (D.KR 24000)

STEFFAN, Johann Gottfried (1815-1905) Swiss

£382	$630	€550	Landscape (25x37cm-10x15in) s. panel. 5-Jul-3 Geble, Radolfzell #485/R
£606	$1085	€885	Bavarian landscape (35x45cm-14x18in) s.d. 22-Mar-4 Philippe Schuler, Zurich #4363 (S.FR 1400)
£2489	$3982	€3634	Summers day in Tierfehd (65x75cm-26x30in) s.d.1888. 19-Sep-3 Koller, Zurich #3125/R est:5000-7000 (S.FR 5500)
£4279	$7360	€6247	Meiringen (39x58cm-15x23in) s.d.1850 paper on canvas. 2-Dec-3 Koller, Zurich #3004/R est:8000-12000 (S.FR 9500)

STEFFAN, Johann Gottfried (attrib) (1815-1905) Swiss

£614	$1025	€896	Summer landscape (27x35cm-11x14in) prov. 15-Nov-3 Galerie Gloggner, Luzern #104/R (S.FR 1400)
£1111	$1811	€1600	Cows in ford watched by herders (56x46cm-22x18in) bears sig.i. 25-Sep-3 Dr Fritz Nagel, Stuttgart #1425/R est:900

STEFFANI, Luigi (1827-1898) Italian

£2837	$4738	€4000	Low tide (32x54cm-13x21in) init. 14-Oct-3 Finarte Semenzato, Milan #102 est:7000

STEFFELAAR, Cornelis (1795-1861) Dutch

Works on paper

£410	$750	€599	Wooded landscape near Haarlem (44x33cm-17x13in) s. brush black gray ink wash. 29-Jan-4 Swann Galleries, New York #201/R

STEFFEN, Eduard (19th C) Austrian

£816	$1461	€1200	Architectural landscape (64x87cm-25x34in) s.d.1887. 20-Mar-4 Bergmann, Erlangen #1126

STEFFEN, Walter Arnold (1924-1982) Swiss
£317 $538 €463 Houses in Saanen in Bernese Oberland (48x121cm-19x48in) board. 25-Nov-3 Germann, Zurich #902 (S.FR 700)
£485 $824 €708 Woman's head (36x38cm-14x15in) s. 5-Nov-3 Dobiaschofsky, Bern #986/R (S.FR 1100)
£498 $831 €727 Snake theatre (61x87cm-24x34in) s.i. verso panel. 24-Jun-3 Germann, Zurich #1050 (S.FR 1100)
£543 $907 €793 Landscape (40x60cm-16x24in) s. board. 24-Jun-3 Germann, Zurich #1051 (S.FR 1200)
£588 $982 €858 Flowers in vase (43x58cm-17x23in) prov.exhib. 24-Jun-3 Germann, Zurich #1055 (S.FR 1300)
£948 $1697 €1384 Flowers in bowl (55x77cm-22x30in) s.d.59 board exhib. 14-May-4 Dobiaschofsky, Bern #264/R est:4000 (S.FR 2200)
£1176 $1965 €1717 Woman's head (70x55cm-28x22in) s.d.1974. 24-Jun-3 Germann, Zurich #1056 est:1400-1800 (S.FR 2600)

STEFFENSEN, Hans Voigt (1941-) Danish
£301 $512 €439 Oxen and cart by Volga (50x60cm-20x24in) s. painted c.1976/77. 26-Nov-3 Kunsthallen, Copenhagen #93 (D.KR 3200)
£2076 $3819 €3031 Bali (80x90cm-31x35in) s. d.85 verso. 29-Mar-4 Rasmussen, Copenhagen #335/R est:15000 (D.KR 23000)
£4327 $7357 €6317 Ballet dancers (200x230cm-79x91in) s. 26-Nov-3 Kunsthallen, Copenhagen #120/R est:50000 (D.KR 46000)

STEFFENSEN, Poul (1866-1923) Danish
£287 $465 €416 Geese grazing (19x35cm-7x14in) init. 4-Aug-3 Rasmussen, Vejle #105/R (D.KR 3000)
£360 $576 €526 Heather landscape with oxen and cart on road (59x85cm-23x33in) s. 22-Sep-3 Rasmussen, Vejle #239/R (D.KR 3800)
£369 $627 €539 Landscape with cattle grazing (31x48cm-12x19in) init.d.99. 10-Nov-3 Rasmussen, Vejle #121/R (D.KR 4000)
£421 $704 €615 Horse and foal (33x49cm-13x19in) init.d.16. 25-Oct-3 Rasmussen, Havnen #2130 (D.KR 4500)
£466 $750 €676 Cows and herdsman (66x99cm-26x39in) 15-Aug-3 Douglas, South Deerfield #1
£537 $983 €784 Sheep in the meadow (64x100cm-25x39in) s.d.1917 prov. 9-Jun-4 Rasmussen, Copenhagen #1959/R (D.KR 6000)
£701 $1107 €1016 Milkmaid watering the calves (34x51cm-13x20in) s. 2-Sep-3 Rasmussen, Copenhagen #1769/R (D.KR 7500)
£716 $1311 €1045 Farmer with cattle in meadow (35x50cm-14x20in) s. prov. 9-Jun-4 Rasmussen, Copenhagen #1661 (D.KR 8000)
£718 $1163 €1041 Cattle by river (71x101cm-28x40in) s. 4-Aug-3 Rasmussen, Vejle #136/R (D.KR 7500)
£761 $1393 €1111 A cow licking the eye of another cow (30x50cm-12x20in) s. prov. 9-Jun-4 Rasmussen, Copenhagen #1709/R (D.KR 8500)
£813 $1455 €1187 Cattle in the shallows (73x93cm-29x37in) s. 10-May-4 Joel, Victoria #274 est:2000-3000 (A.D 2000)
£1028 $1624 €1491 Brining the cows out, farm in Emborg, Jylland (64x102cm-25x40in) s. 2-Sep-3 Rasmussen, Copenhagen #1768/R (D.KR 11000)
£1244 $2015 €1804 Girl with three calves (58x72cm-23x28in) s. 4-Aug-3 Rasmussen, Vejle #135/R est:8000-10000 (D.KR 13000)
£1970 $3604 €2876 Young man flirting with maid in the harvest time (23x34cm-9x13in) init.d.05 prov. 9-Jun-4 Rasmussen, Copenhagen #1674/R est:20000-25000 (D.KR 22000)

STEFULA, Dorothea (1914-) Swiss?
£331 $553 €480 The three girls or a holiday (45x35cm-18x14in) s.d.1955 i.d.1955 verso. 13-Nov-3 Neumeister, Munich #464
£759 $1267 €1100 Young girls at the window (29x36cm-11x14in) s.d.1956 board. 13-Nov-3 Neumeister, Munich #465/R

STEFULA, Giorgio (1913-) German
£905 $1511 €1321 Le pont neuf a Chartres (66x93cm-26x37in) s. s.i.d.1968 verso. 24-Jun-3 Germann, Zurich #166 est:3000-4000 (S.FR 2000)

STEGEMANN, Heinrich (1888-1945) German
£298 $542 €450 Portrait of a woman (64x73cm-25x29in) s.d.1920 canvas on board. 19-Jun-4 Quittenbaum, Hamburg #97/R

STEGER, Milly (1881-1948) German
Sculpture
£2000 $3580 €3000 Small kneeling figure (44x20x24cm-17x8x9in) i. brown pat.bronze prov.lit. 15-May-4 Van Ham, Cologne #941/R est:3500
£2448 $4161 €3500 Head (41cm-16in) mono. black pat.bronze Cast.Schmake Dusseldorf. 29-Nov-3 Villa Grisebach, Berlin #212/R est:3000-4000
£4895 $8420 €7000 Experiencing pain (110x25x18cm-43x10x7in) wood exec. 1947-48 prov.lit. 4-Dec-3 Van Ham, Cologne #489/R est:7000

STEGGLES, Harold (fl.1930-1938) British
£449 $750 €656 Untitled. s. panel prov. 20-Oct-3 Sotheby's, New York #206/R

STEGLICH, Julius (1839-1913) German
£3020 $5557 €4500 Jeune femme et son bebe (65x55cm-26x22in) s.i.d.1864 oval exhib. 28-Mar-4 Anaf, Lyon #250/R est:4500-5500

STEHLI, Jean Claude (1923-) Swiss
£409 $679 €593 Portrait Marie (54x81cm-21x32in) s.d.1954 i. verso. 13-Jun-3 Zofingen, Switzerland #3046 (S.FR 900)

STEIB, Josef (1898-1957) German
£246 $425 €359 Landscape with farm scene, horse and plow (48x56cm-19x22in) s.d.1926. 10-Dec-3 Alderfer's, Hatfield #308/R
£333 $600 €500 Narrow Tunisian street (150x126cm-59x50in) s.d.1934-1937. 26-Apr-4 Rieber, Stuttgart #930/R
£660 $1075 €950 Summer village street (61x71cm-24x28in) s.d.1930. 25-Sep-3 Neumeister, Munich #2884
£699 $1189 €1000 Eifel landscape near Mayen (60x71cm-24x28in) s.d.1934/1937. 20-Nov-3 Van Ham, Cologne #1877/R
Works on paper
£367 $667 €550 Study of a head (29x20cm-11x8in) s.d.1956 W/C lit. 1-Jul-4 Van Ham, Cologne #1630
£400 $724 €600 Harbour worker, Venezuela (28x20cm-11x8in) s.i.d.17.1.56 W/C pen lit. 1-Apr-4 Van Ham, Cologne #1654
£417 $688 €600 Head studies (28x20cm-11x8in) s.d.1956 W/C. 3-Jul-3 Van Ham, Cologne #1467

STEICHEN, Edward J (1879-1973) American
Photographs
£1791 $3350 €2687 James J Dooley, Vanity Fair, November, Tammany Hall Leader (254x204cm-100x80in) photo. 25-Jul-4 Bonhams & Butterfields, San Francisco #6235/R est:300-500
£2174 $3565 €3000 Frances Farmer (34x25cm-13x10in) i. verso vintage carbro col by N Deeks. 30-May-3 Villa Grisebach, Berlin #1366/R est:3000-5000
£2373 $4200 €3465 Brancusi's bird in space in Steichen's studio (28x27cm-11x11in) i.d.1957 gelatin silver print. 27-Apr-4 Christie's, Rockefeller NY #44/R est:3000-5000
£3439 $6500 €5021 Henri Matisse (20x24cm-8x9in) silver print. 17-Feb-4 Swann Galleries, New York #52/R est:6000-9000
£4790 $8000 €6993 Pear on a plate, France (35x27cm-14x11in) i. photo exec.1920 printed later prov. 17-Oct-3 Sotheby's, New York #154/R est:6000-9000
£31073 $55000 €45367 Dixie Ray for Woodbury Soap (24x19cm-9x7in) i.d.1935 verso photo prov. 27-Apr-4 Sotheby's, New York #32/R est:20000-30000
£53672 $95000 €78361 Three pears and an apple (24x19cm-9x7in) i.verso photo exec.c.1921 prov.lit. 27-Apr-4 Sotheby's, New York #26/R est:30000-50000
£73446 $130000 €107231 Gloria Swanson (24x19cm-9x7in) i.num.verso warm-toned photo prov.lit. 27-Apr-4 Sotheby's, New York #24/R est:20000-30000
Works on paper
£755 $1200 €1102 Winter landscape, Wisconsin (23x33cm-9x13in) s. exec.c.1890 W/C. 4-May-3 William Jenack, New York #166

STEICHER, Eugene (20th C) American?
Works on paper
£542 $900 €786 Portrait of a girl (30x20cm-12x8in) mixed media. 13-Jun-3 Du Mouchelle, Detroit #2435/R

STEIG, William (1907-) American
Works on paper
£1006 $1800 €1469 Dramatic operatic scene (23x25cm-9x10in) s. pen ink W/C en grisaille. 15-May-4 Illustration House, New York #136/R est:2000-3000

STEIGER, Karl Gustav (1867-1935) Swiss
£573 $974 €837 Neuenburgersee landscape (72x106cm-28x42in) s. 5-Nov-3 Dobiaschofsky, Bern #987 (S.FR 1300)

STEIGER, William (20th C) American
£667 $1200 €974 Untitled. Sold with one by Jerrold Turner (35x45cm-14x18in) one s.d.83 one s.i.d.1986 verso two. 25-Apr-4 Bonhams & Butterfields, San Francisco #5625/R

STEIN, Alwyn von (1848-1919) Austrian
£3017 $5552 €4405 Two gypsy children (120x150cm-47x59in) 26-Mar-4 Koller, Zurich #3132/R est:7000-10000 (S.FR 7000)

STEIN, Anna (1936-) ?
£496 $829 €700 Qumran, Jordanie, mer Morte (110x90cm-43x35in) s.d.1989 s.verso exhib. 19-Oct-3 Charbonneaux, Paris #131/R
Sculpture
£1206 $2013 €1700 La tour (95x26x20cm-37x10x8in) s.d.1/1 bronze. 19-Oct-3 Charbonneaux, Paris #183/R est:4000

STEIN, Georges (1870-?) French
£1141 $2020 €1700 Bordeaux, le port (38x61cm-15x24in) s.d.XIV. 30-Apr-4 Tajan, Paris #219 est:2000-2500
£1781 $2974 €2600 Place Palud a Lausanne (64x53cm-25x21in) s. 16-Nov-3 Koller, Geneva #1275/R est:2500-3500 (S.FR 4060)
£1793 $2995 €2600 La corniche de moulleau a Arachon (37x52cm-15x20in) s.i.d.1915. 17-Nov-3 Tajan, Paris #162/R est:1800-2000
£2267 $4125 €3400 Elegantes et cavaliers sur les Champs-Elysees (17x22cm-7x9in) s. panel. 4-Jul-4 Eric Pillon, Calais #56/R
£2817 $4676 €4000 Place des Cordeliers (25x41cm-10x16in) s.d. panel. 15-Jun-3 Peron, Melun #55a
£3000 $5460 €4380 Avenue de l'opera at dusk, Paris (38x55cm-15x22in) s.i. 16-Jun-4 Christie's, Kensington #7/R est:3000-5000
£5423 $8730 €7700 Paris, Cafe rue de la Paix (27x35cm-11x14in) s.i. 22-Aug-3 Deauville, France #39/R est:8000-10000
£5500 $9900 €8030 L'Opera de Paris (46x65cm-18x26in) s.i. 21-Jan-4 Sotheby's, Olympia #517/R est:3000-4000
£5814 $10000 €8488 Evening in Paris (48x74cm-19x29in) s. 7-Dec-3 Freeman, Philadelphia #30 est:10000-15000
Works on paper
£600 $942 €870 Walking in St. Jacques, Paris (25x36cm-10x14in) s.i. pencil W/C bodycol htd white. 28-Aug-3 Christie's, Kensington #495/R
£750 $1343 €1095 Horsedrawn carriages with the Arc de Triomphe in the background (18x23cm-7x9in) s. W/C gouache pencil. 7-May-4 Mallams, Oxford #299/R
£850 $1335 €1233 Evening stroll through Paris (24x33cm-9x13in) s.i. pencil W/C bodycol htd white. 28-Aug-3 Christie's, Kensington #496/R
£993 $1808 €1500 L'Avenue de Wagram et l'Arc de Triomphe (23x40cm-9x16in) s.i. pastel W/C. 18-Jun-4 Piasa, Paris #93/R est:1500-2000
£2013 $3725 €3000 Paris, Grands Boulevards (37x53cm-15x21in) s. gouache W/C. 14-Mar-4 Eric Pillon, Calais #53/R

STEIN, Henri (?) ?
£822 $1513 €1250 Moulin Rouge (27x35cm-11x14in) s. 25-Jun-4 Millon & Associes, Paris #170/R

STEIN, Janos (?) ?
£1336 $2365 €1951 Nymph and faun (108x100cm-43x39in) 28-Apr-4 Kieselbach, Budapest #144/R (H.F 500000)

STEIN, Joel (1926-) French
£867 $1595 €1300 Petite cadence trichrome (25x25cm-10x10in) s.i.d.1994 verso acrylic. 12-Jun-4 Meeting Art, Vercelli #484/R

STEIN, Otto Th W (1877-1958) German
£600 $1080 €900 Hidden (25x51cm-10x20in) board. 24-Apr-4 Dr Lehr, Berlin #448/R

STEIN, Peter (1922-) Swiss
£658 $1211 €961 Composition (65x60cm-26x24in) s.d.71 acrylic. 23-Jun-4 Koller, Zurich #3092/R (S.FR 1500)
£1078 $1929 €1574 Composition in grey (90x75cm-35x30in) s.d.67. 14-May-4 Dobiaschofsky, Bern #277/R est:3000 (S.FR 2500)
£1448 $2462 €2114 Two tracks (140x70cm-55x28in) prov. 22-Nov-3 Burkhard, Luzern #207/R est:3000-4000 (S.FR 3200)

STEINACH, Anton Victor Alexander (1819-1891) German
£590 $974 €850 Sunlit woodland track (46x58cm-18x23in) canvas on board one of pair. 3-Jul-3 Dr Fritz Nagel, Stuttgart #518/R
£590 $974 €850 Trees on edge of wood (46x58cm-18x23in) one of pair. 3-Jul-3 Dr Fritz Nagel, Stuttgart #519/R
£660 $1042 €950 Trees at edge of wood (45x58cm-18x23in) lit. 19-Sep-3 Schloss Ahlden, Ahlden #1592/R

STEINACKER, Alfred (1838-1914) Austrian
£331 $603 €500 Market near Komorn in Hungary (18x31cm-7x12in) s. panel. 19-Jun-4 Bergmann, Erlangen #856
£729 $1145 €1050 Course (16x42cm-6x17in) s. panel. 29-Aug-3 Deauville, France #153/R
£1056 $1754 €1500 Meeting on the Pussta (25x39cm-10x15in) s. panel. 16-Jun-3 Dorotheum, Vienna #93/R est:1800-2200
£1268 $2193 €1800 Hungarian market scene with melon seller (16x32cm-6x13in) s. panel. 10-Dec-3 Dorotheum, Vienna #153/R est:1800-2200

STEINBERG, Irina Valerianovna (1905-1985) Russian
Works on paper
£16000 $27200 €23360 Collection of drawings, illustrations and sketches. most s. various d.1920s 30s W/C pencil twenty five. 19-Nov-3 Sotheby's, London #183/R est:18000-25000

STEINBERG, J (19th C) German?
£4054 $7135 €6000 Still life of fruit with parrot and swallow (59x70cm-23x28in) s.d.1837. 22-May-4 Lempertz, Koln #1611/R est:6000

STEINBERG, Nathaniel P (1893-1966) American
£349 $600 €510 Repose (25x30cm-10x12in) s. painted c.1930. 7-Dec-3 Treadway Gallery, Cincinnati #615/R

STEINBERG, Saul (1914-1999) American
£8589 $14000 €12540 Leningrad table (53x41cm-21x16in) s.d.1973 oil ink W/C collage board prov. 23-Sep-3 Christie's, Rockefeller NY #50/R est:12000-18000
Prints
£1977 $3500 €2886 Tree nine variation (50x59cm-20x23in) s.d.1969 num.1/1 lithograph. 30-Apr-4 Sotheby's, New York #465/R est:4000-6000
£5689 $9500 €8306 Head (51x67cm-20x26in) s. zincograph executed c.1946 prov. 11-Nov-3 Christie's, Rockefeller NY #172/R est:1500-2000
Sculpture
£1081 $2000 €1578 Untitled (6x23x9cm-2x9x4in) s.i.d.1981 music box instrument graphite blk felt tip pen wood. 13-Jul-4 Christie's, Rockefeller NY #88/R est:1500-2000
£17361 $28646 €25000 Writing table (66x50cm-26x20in) s.d.1972 wood collage prov. 2-Jul-3 Cornette de St.Cyr, Paris #100/R est:25000-35000
Works on paper
£507 $958 €750 Happy birthday to Moucha (25x33cm-10x13in) s.d.1951 ink stamps. 21-Feb-4 Cornette de St.Cyr, Paris #403
£1912 $3250 €2792 Untitled (58x38cm-23x15in) s.d.1948 ink. 9-Nov-3 Wright, Chicago #328 est:3000-5000
£1957 $3600 €2857 Letter D (13x15cm-5x6in) s. pen ink. 10-Jun-4 Swann Galleries, New York #229/R est:800-1200
£2432 $4500 €3551 Baseball (37x58cm-15x23in) s.d.1954 blk blue ink col crayons prov. 12-Feb-4 Sotheby's, New York #131/R est:5000-7000
£2500 $4175 €3650 Grosvenor Hotel (38x30cm-15x12in) pen ink W/C rubber stamps. 22-Oct-3 Bonhams, New Bond Street #90/R est:3000-4000
£2616 $4500 €3819 Up and down (53x36cm-21x14in) s.d.1965 s.i.d.verso pen ink prov. 3-Dec-3 Doyle, New York #31/R est:3000-5000
£2994 $5000 €4371 Statement for a museum catalogue (9x20cm-4x8in) ink executed 1946 exhib. 11-Nov-3 Christie's, Rockefeller NY #173/R est:1000-2000
£3681 $6000 €5374 Newspaper still life (38x51cm-15x20in) s.d.1973 crayon graphite prov. 23-Sep-3 Christie's, Rockefeller NY #49/R est:7000-9000
£4396 $8000 €6418 La pluie (76x101cm-30x40in) s.d.1969 ink. 29-Jun-4 Sotheby's, New York #444/R est:8000-12000
£5988 $10000 €8742 Graph paper building (30x22cm-12x9in) s.d.1950 ink graph paper collage prov.exhib. 13-Nov-3 Sotheby's, New York #160/R est:10000-15000
£7000 $11690 €10220 Napeagne, the fish factory (49x62cm-19x24in) s.d.1969 W/C ink prov. 22-Oct-3 Christie's, London #64/R est:7000-10000
£7558 $13000 €11035 Today - cover b (49x35cm-19x14in) s.i. W/C pen ink pencil pastel prov. 3-Dec-3 Doyle, New York #30/R est:4000-6000
£14054 $26000 €20519 Nose drypoint table (41x53cm-16x21in) s.d.1976 assemblage prov. 12-Feb-4 Sotheby's, New York #105/R est:12000-18000

STEINBOECK, Carl (19th C) Austrian
£3497 $5944 €5000 Dobling (78x110cm-31x43in) one of pair. 24-Nov-3 Dorotheum, Vienna #21/R est:6000-8000
£4895 $8322 €7000 View over Donau toward Kahlenberg and leopoldsberg (78x110cm-31x43in) s.d.1823 one of pair. 24-Nov-3 Dorotheum, Vienna #22/R est:6000-8000

STEINBRUK, Eduard (1802-1882) German
Works on paper
£952 $1705 €1400 Vue du Colisee a Rome depuis la fenetre de la chambre de l'artiste (13x21cm-5x8in) s.i.d.1827 graphite W/C. 18-Mar-4 Christie's, Paris #267/R

STEINBUCHLER, Rudolf (1901-2003) Austrian
Works on paper
£420 $713 €600 Fresco sketch (23x19cm-9x7in) s. W/C pencil. 27-Nov-3 Dorotheum, Linz #588

STEINER, Albert (1877-1965) Swiss?
Photographs
£2155 $3858 €3146 Silsersee in the evening (17x23cm-7x9in) s. photo. 14-May-4 Dobiaschofsky, Bern #227/R est:1400 (S.FR 5000)
£3167 $5480 €4624 Piz Bernina, Oberengadin, Graubunden (29x23cm-11x9in) s.i. silver gelatin. 9-Dec-3 Sotheby's, Zurich #114/R est:2500-3500 (S.FR 7000)
£7240 $12525 €10570 Evening over Silvaplaner and Silsersee, Oberengadin (23x29cm-9x11in) s.i. silver gelatin. 9-Dec-3 Sotheby's, Zurich #113/R est:3000-4000 (S.FR 16000)
£8734 $15633 €12752 Evening at Silsersee (22x28cm-9x11in) s.i. gelatin silver print. 26-May-4 Sotheby's, Zurich #110/R est:6000-8000 (S.FR 20000)
£9170 $16415 €13388 Summer day at Silvaplanersee (22x29cm-9x11in) s.i. gelatin silver print. 26-May-4 Sotheby's, Zurich #113/R est:5000-7000 (S.FR 21000)

STEINER, Ernst (1864-1934) Austrian
Sculpture
£3500 $5950 €5110 Tyrolean interior scene (30x40cm-12x16in) s. limewood relief. 28-Oct-3 Sotheby's, London #204/R est:2500-3000

STEINER, Heinz (1905-) Austrian
Works on paper
£352 $616 €500 Market stall in Kalvarienberg (60x42cm-24x17in) s.i.d.1957 gouache. 19-Dec-3 Dorotheum, Vienna #134

STEINER, Josef Kamenitzky (1910-1981) Austrian
£458 $792 €650 Large bunch of flowers (49x40cm-19x16in) s. panel. 10-Dec-3 Dorotheum, Vienna #72
£458 $792 €650 Large bunch of flowers (49x40cm-19x16in) s. panel. 10-Dec-3 Dorotheum, Vienna #71

STEINER, Lilly (1884-1962) Austrian
£320 $550 €467 Trees beside a road (91x74cm-36x29in) s.d.1933. 7-Dec-3 Treadway Gallery, Cincinnati #642/R

STEINER, Michael (20th C) ?
Sculpture
£3000 $5490 €4500 Nuba (30x105x57cm-12x41x22in) brown pat.bronze. 4-Jun-4 Lempertz, Koln #470/R est:6000

STEINER, Minou (1940-) British?
£500 $910 €730 Swans (56x76cm-22x30in) s. board. 15-Jun-4 David Lay, Penzance #638
Works on paper
£360 $601 €526 Cat (38x56cm-15x22in) s. mixed media. 14-Oct-3 David Lay, Penzance #476

STEINER, Ralph (1899-1986) American
Photographs
£2994 $5000 €4371 After the rehearsal of the Chase of Clyde Griffiths (24x19cm-9x7in) s.i.d.1936 verso gelatin silver print prov. 20-Oct-3 Christie's, Rockefeller NY #8/R est:4000-6000

STEINERT, Otto (1915-1978) German
Photographs
£5333 $9813 €8000 Luminogramm 1 (30x40cm-12x16in) bromide silver gelatin lit.exhib. 10-Jun-4 Villa Grisebach, Berlin #1285/R est:8000-12000

STEINERT, R (?) ?
£1333 $2413 €2000 Snowy river landscape with farmsteads and windmill at sunset (54x80cm-21x31in) s. 1-Apr-4 Van Ham, Cologne #1655/R est:2000

STEINERT, Vida (1906-) New Zealander
£536 $970 €783 Landscape. Two female figures in landscape (45x57cm-18x22in) canvas on board double-sided. 30-Mar-4 Peter Webb, Auckland #186/R est:2500-3500 (NZ.D 1500)
£1143 $2069 €1669 Children at the beach (47x55cm-19x22in) board. 30-Mar-4 Peter Webb, Auckland #188/R est:2500-3500 (NZ.D 3200)
£2393 $4331 €3494 Maori and model T (50x54cm-20x21in) board. 30-Mar-4 Peter Webb, Auckland #187/R est:2500-3500 (NZ.D 6700)

STEINFELD, Franz (1787-1868) Austrian
Works on paper
£1342 $2470 €2000 Mountain lake (16x24cm-6x9in) bears sig.d.28/6 848 W/C. 26-Mar-4 Dorotheum, Vienna #177/R est:800-1000

STEINFELD, Franz (attrib) (1787-1868) Austrian
£486 $826 €700 Mountain lake (30x37cm-12x15in) d.859 paper on board. 28-Oct-3 Dorotheum, Vienna #223

STEINFELD, Wilhelm (1816-1854) Austrian
£2797 $4755 €4000 Gosau mill (60x47cm-24x19in) s.d.853. 24-Nov-3 Dorotheum, Vienna #170/R est:4500-5500

STEINFURTH, Hermann (1823-1880) German
£450 $733 €657 Portrait of a youth (68x56cm-27x22in) s. 27-Sep-3 Rasmussen, Havnen #2162/R (D.KR 4800)

STEINHART, Anton (1889-1964) Austrian
Works on paper
£267 $491 €400 Walker on Monchsberg with view of Salzburg (31x24cm-12x9in) s.d.1950 Indian ink wash. 9-Jun-4 Dorotheum, Salzburg #843/R

STEINIKE, Heinrich (1825-1909) German
£1181 $1948 €1700 Two monks taking a walk by Italian lake (149x122cm-59x48in) s. 2-Jul-3 Neumeister, Munich #781/R est:800
£1888 $3248 €2700 Alpine lake landscape in the late evening sun (90x125cm-35x49in) s. 5-Dec-3 Bolland & Marotz, Bremen #660/R est:1800

STEININGER, Hermann (1915-) ?
£267 $491 €400 Wachau landscape with view of church (55x69cm-22x27in) s. masonite. 9-Jun-4 Dorotheum, Salzburg #634/R
£486 $792 €700 Vineyard in the Wachau (75x85cm-30x33in) s. chipboard. 23-Sep-3 Wiener Kunst Auktionen, Vienna #126/R

STEINKE, Bettina (1913-1999) American
£1056 $1700 €1531 Happy Tattlers, Guatemala (30x23cm-12x9in) 22-Aug-3 Altermann Galleries, Santa Fe #194

STEINLE, Bartholomaus (attrib) (?-1628) German
Sculpture
£7394 $12792 €10500 Holy Michael (106cm-42in) col wood. 10-Dec-3 Hugo Ruef, Munich #2768/R est:8500

STEINLE, Edward Jakob von (1810-1886) Austrian/German
Works on paper
£873 $1590 €1275 Christ in the Cross with six scenes of the life of Christ (22x28cm-9x11in) W/C over pencil prov. 17-Jun-4 Kornfeld, Bern #75/R (S.FR 2000)

STEINLE, Franz Xaver (1810-1874) German
£615 $1028 €880 Christ with angel in Garden of Gethsemane (68x52cm-27x20in) s.i.d.1839. 9-Oct-3 Michael Zeller, Lindau #768/R

STEINLEN, Christian Gottlieb (1779-1847) Swiss
Works on paper
£280 $502 €409 Chateau de Villard near Vevey with Dents du Midi (24x35cm-9x14in) s. W/C over pencil. 12-May-4 Dobiaschofsky, Bern #1291/R (S.FR 650)

STEINLEN, Marguerite (1899-?) Swiss
£727 $1207 €1054 Zurich sous la neige Noel 1942 (51x42cm-20x17in) s.d.1954 i. verso masonite. 13-Jun-3 Zofingen, Switzerland #3047/R est:2000 (S.FR 1600)

STEINLEN, Theophile Alexandre (1859-1923) Swiss
£882 $1500 €1288 Group of soldiers in an open landscape (27x29cm-11x11in) s.d.1915 black chk paper on board. 19-Nov-3 Bonhams & Butterfields, San Francisco #110/R
£1057 $1797 €1543 Woman in dark clothes (21x16cm-8x6in) s. 5-Nov-3 Dobiaschofsky, Bern #989/R est:4000 (S.FR 2400)
£2013 $3745 €3000 Trois vases de fleurs (73x54cm-29x21in) mono. 3-Mar-4 Tajan, Paris #24/R est:3000-4000
£12670 $21158 €18498 Deux chats se reposant dans un fauteuil (65x80cm-26x31in) s. 24-Jun-3 Germann, Zurich #61/R est:30000-50000 (S.FR 28000)
Prints
£2397 $4075 €3500 Chat sur le plancher. s. aquatint. 6-Nov-3 Piasa, Paris #157/R
£2432 $4500 €3551 Two cats (59x46cm-23x18in) s. pochoir silk exec.c.1895. 9-Mar-4 Christie's, Rockefeller NY #237/R est:5000-7000
£2941 $5000 €4294 Modele lisant (25x34cm-10x13in) s. etching aquatint drypoint exec.1898. 4-Nov-3 Christie's, Rockefeller NY #207/R est:4000-6000
£3000 $5160 €4380 Tournee du chat noir de rodolphe salis (56x36cm-22x14in) black red lithograph. 2-Dec-3 Christie's, London #313/R est:3000-5000
£3000 $5460 €4380 L'hiver, chat sure un coussin (50x61cm-20x24in) s. col lithograph edition of 250. 1-Jul-4 Sotheby's, London #313/R est:3000-3500
£5882 $10000 €8588 Compagnie francaise des chocolats et des thes (80x60cm-31x24in) col lithograph. 31-Oct-3 Sotheby's, New York #461/R
£13333 $24400 €20000 Motorcycles comiot (198x140cm-78x55in) mono.d.1899 col lithograph two parts. 7-Jun-4 Sotheby's, Amsterdam #2/R est:6000-8000
Sculpture
£2258 $4200 €3297 Le chat (8x5x4cm-3x2x2in) i. dark brown pat. bronze. 2-Mar-4 Swann Galleries, New York #643/R est:4000-6000
£3867 $7115 €5800 Deux chats dos a dos (19x5cm-7x2in) s. num.2 red brown pat bronze. 10-Jun-4 Camard, Paris #45/R est:6000-8000
Works on paper
£282 $487 €400 Tete de trois-quarts (61x45cm-24x18in) s. chl chk. 12-Dec-3 Piasa, Paris #95/R
£299 $500 €437 Figure study (61x46cm-24x18in) s. chl. 19-Oct-3 Susanin's, Chicago #6062/R
£312 $521 €450 Regrets a Ninon, projet d'illustration (39x29cm-15x11in) s. chl crayon ink blue crayon. 21-Oct-3 Artcurial Briest, Paris #29
£331 $603 €500 Personnage observant un tableau assis sur une chaise (32x28cm-13x11in) init. chl. 18-Jun-4 Charbonneaux, Paris #115
£403 $741 €600 Femme de profil (27x21cm-11x8in) s. lead pencil. 24-Mar-4 Joron-Derem, Paris #52
£420 $722 €600 Etudes de chats (35x25cm-14x10in) chl. 5-Dec-3 Chochon-Barre & Allardi, Paris #151/R
£423 $731 €600 Le chat et la grenouille (43x31cm-17x12in) s. pen black ink wash. 13-Dec-3 Martinot & Savignat, Pontoise #134
£658 $1211 €1000 Jeune femme de profil (62x46cm-24x18in) s. chl htd white chk. 28-Jun-4 Joron-Derem, Paris #99/R
£733 $1342 €1100 La vieille des ruines (53x38cm-21x15in) s.i.d. chl. 5-Jun-4 Lempertz, Koln #1008/R
£754 $1281 €1100 Le 18 Mars au Pere-Lachaise (35x52cm-14x20in) s.i. chl wash W/C. 6-Nov-3 Tajan, Paris #249/R
£769 $1308 €1100 Marchands de marrons (30x25cm-12x10in) s. col crayon dr. 28-Nov-3 Drouot Estimations, Paris #136
£905 $1448 €1312 Two women in bistro (43x55cm-17x22in) s. pencil pastel. 15-May-3 Stuker, Bern #1511/R (S.FR 1900)
£979 $1664 €1400 Au cafe concert (30x25cm-12x10in) s. col crayon dr. 28-Nov-3 Drouot Estimations, Paris #137/R
£1049 $1783 €1500 Mere et enfants (37x26cm-15x10in) s. fusain. 28-Nov-3 Blanchet, Paris #48/R est:1000-1200
£1667 $3000 €2434 Midinettes (50x65cm-20x26in) s. chl. 21-Jan-4 Sotheby's, New York #199/R est:3500-4500
£1678 $2853 €2400 Danseuse en pleure (22x15cm-9x6in) st. pastel. 1-Dec-3 Camard, Paris #18/R est:2500-2800
£1733 $3189 €2600 Seated lady wearing a hat (62x48cm-24x19in) s. pastel chl. 11-Jun-4 Villa Grisebach, Berlin #1520/R est:1400-1800
£1779 $3290 €2650 Apres le theatre (31x25cm-12x10in) s. chl col crayon dr. 14-Mar-4 Eric Pillon, Calais #57/R
£1905 $3410 €2800 Deux etudes de femmes vues de dos (54x41cm-21x16in) st.init. chl white chk. 19-Mar-4 Piasa, Paris #189/R est:1500-1600
£2151 $4000 €3140 Chat endormie (22x25cm-9x10in) s. blue crayon. 2-Mar-4 Swann Galleries, New York #642/R est:4000-6000
£3200 $5888 €4800 Les trottins (45x30cm-18x12in) s. blue crayon. 11-Jun-4 Claude Aguttes, Neuilly #26b/R est:3000-5000
£3497 $6014 €5000 Le marche (47x61cm-19x24in) s. chl prov.exhib. 5-Dec-3 Ketterer, Munich #31/R est:5000-7000
£5500 $10120 €8030 Aux Folies Bergeres (32x25cm-13x10in) s. chl col crayon pen ink exec c.1894 prov.exhib. 24-Jun-4 Christie's, London #302/R est:6000-8000

STEINLEN, Theophile Alexandre (attrib) (1859-1923) Swiss
Works on paper
£629 $1000 €918 Ribbons (30x41cm-12x16in) s. chl. 12-Sep-3 Skinner, Boston #327/R

STEINMANN, Heinz (1943-) Australian
£391 $707 €571 Journey to port (82x106cm-32x42in) board. 31-Mar-4 Goodman, Sydney #458 (A.D 950)

STEINMETZ-NORIS, Fritz (1860-?) German
£1497 $2679 €2200 Fatherly advice (22x17cm-9x7in) s.i. panel. 17-Mar-4 Neumeister, Munich #615/R est:2600

STEIR, Pat (1940-) American
Works on paper
£1333 $2400 €1946 Same space dreaming remembering (19x26cm-7x10in) s.d.1972 pencil ink wash crayon. 24-Apr-4 David Rago, Lambertville #559/R est:1000-2000

STEKELENBURG, Jan (1922-1977) Dutch
£972 $1585 €1400 Still life (31x43cm-12x17in) s. board. 29-Sep-3 Sotheby's, Amsterdam #385

STELL, Tom (1898-1981) American
Works on paper
£1018 $1700 €1486 Portrait of Janet Kendal (46x30cm-18x12in) pencil. 18-Oct-3 David Dike, Dallas #74/R est:500-1000

STELLA, Frank (1936-) American
£9412 $16000 €13742 Puerto Rican blue pigeon no.8 (55x77cm-22x30in) init.i.d.1976 oil glitter lacquer on aluminium. 21-Nov-3 Swann Galleries, New York #201/R est:20000-30000
£19000 $31730 €27740 Ravy II (49x202cm-19x80in) s.i.d.70 paper prov. 21-Oct-3 Sotheby's, London #352/R est:15000-20000
£36313 $65000 €53017 Brazilian Merganser (216x155cm-85x61in) oil col crayon glitter foil mylar collage Tycore exec 1980 prov. 13-May-4 Sotheby's, New York #222/R est:35000-45000
£47486 $85000 €69330 Green solitaire (155x223cm-61x88in) s.d.80 oil col crayon glitter mylar collage Tycore prov.exhib. 13-May-4 Sotheby's, New York #221/R est:35000-45000
£53892 $90000 €78682 Untitled (23x23cm-9x9in) s.d.1960 stretcher prov.lit. 13-Nov-3 Sotheby's, New York #223/R est:40000-60000
£119760 $200000 €174850 Honduras Lottery Co, smaller version (60x60cm-24x24in) alkyd painted c.1962. 13-Nov-3 Sotheby's, New York #224/R est:60000-80000
£131737 $220000 €192336 I. Scramble - Ascending Yellow Values - Descending Spectrum (175x175cm-69x69in) s.i.d.78 stretcher acrylic prov. 12-Nov-3 Christie's, Rockefeller NY #354/R est:200000-300000
£156425 $280000 €228381 Scramble - Ascending spectrum ascending red values (175x175cm-69x69in) s.i.d.78 stretcher acrylic prov. 13-May-4 Sotheby's, New York #167/R est:250000-350000

£212291	$380000	€309945	Scramble - Violet double/left V right 12 (175x350cm-69x138in) acrylic painted 1977 prov.exhib. 12-May-4 Sotheby's, New York #54/R est:350000-450000
£217877	$390000	€318100	Sacramento No 6 (262x262cm-103x103in) acrylic linen painted 1978 prov. 12-May-4 Christie's, Rockefeller NY #161/R est:280000-320000

Prints

£1676	$3000	€2447	York factory 1 (35x102cm-14x40in) s.d.1971 num.8/100 col screenprint. 4-May-4 Doyle, New York #267/R est:3000-4000
£1840	$3000	€2686	Then came a fire and burnt the stick, Plate 5 (129x134cm-51x53in) s.d.84 num.26/60 lithograph linocut col screenprint collage. 24-Sep-3 Christie's, Rockefeller NY #399/R est:5000-7000
£1840	$3000	€2686	East Euralia (55x125cm-22x49in) s.d.1995 num.3/28 lithograph screenprint etching aquatint relief. 24-Sep-3 Christie's, Rockefeller NY #400/R est:3500-4500
£1872	$3239	€2733	Shards V (99x113cm-39x44in) s.d.88 num.APXIV screenprint. 10-Dec-3 Shapiro, Sydney #72/R est:4500-5500 (A.D 4400)
£1977	$3500	€2886	Star of Persia II (57x66cm-22x26in) s.d.1967 num. T.P.II col lithograph. 28-Apr-4 Christie's, Rockefeller NY #403/R est:3000-4000
£1977	$3500	€2886	Illustration after el lissitzky's had gadya, hungry cat ate up the goat (115x136cm-45x54in) s.d.84 num.34/60 lithograph linocut. 30-Apr-4 Sotheby's, New York #481/R est:4000-6000
£1977	$3500	€2886	Squeeze of the hand (184x139cm-72x55in) s.d.88 num.56/60 screenprint lithograph. 30-Apr-4 Sotheby's, New York #484/R est:4000-6000
£2100	$3822	€3066	Shards II (101x115cm-40x45in) s.d.1982 num.19/100 col offset lithograph screenprint. 21-Jun-4 Bonhams, New Bond Street #102/R est:2000-3000
£2147	$3500	€3135	Shards Variant Ia (114x101cm-45x40in) s.d.1982 num.PP II offset lithograph col screenprint Arches. 24-Sep-3 Christie's, Rockefeller NY #397/R est:3500-4500
£2147	$3800	€3135	Shards (100x115cm-39x45in) s.d.1982 num.46/60 col offset lithograph screenprint. 28-Apr-4 Christie's, Rockefeller NY #415/R est:3000-4000
£2147	$3800	€3135	Shards (101x114cm-40x45in) s.d.1982 num.46/100 col offset lithograph screenprint. 28-Apr-4 Christie's, Rockefeller NY #416/R est:3000-4000
£2206	$3750	€3221	Stranz (189x106cm-74x42in) s. col screenprint. 31-Oct-3 Sotheby's, New York #784/R
£2260	$4000	€3300	Swan engraving circle (131cm-52in circular) s.i.d.1983 etching relief. 30-Apr-4 Sotheby's, New York #479/R est:2000-3000
£2260	$4000	€3300	Extracts (85x107cm-33x42in) s.d.1993 num.11/40 etching relief. 30-Apr-4 Sotheby's, New York #486/R est:3000-5000
£2353	$4000	€3435	Cantahar (133x133cm-52x52in) s. lithograph screenprint intaglio. 31-Oct-3 Sotheby's, New York #782/R
£2353	$4000	€3435	Fattiburg (78cm-31in circular) s. lithograph screenprint intaglio. 31-Oct-3 Sotheby's, New York #777/R
£2401	$4250	€3505	Cantahar (133x133cm-52x52in) s.i.d.1998 lithograph screenprint. 30-Apr-4 Sotheby's, New York #496/R est:4000-5000
£2500	$4250	€3650	Limanora (61x53cm-24x21in) s. lithograph etching aquatint. 31-Oct-3 Sotheby's, New York #773/R
£2542	$4500	€3711	Illustration after el lissitzky's had gadya, one small goat papa bought for two zuzim (133x130cm-52x51in) s.d.1982-84 col lithograph linocut. 30-Apr-4 Sotheby's, New York #480/R est:5000-7000
£2542	$4500	€3711	Quarter deck (190x141cm-75x56in) s.d.89 num.60/60 screenprint lithograph linocut. 30-Apr-4 Sotheby's, New York #483/R est:4000-6000
£2647	$4500	€3865	Nemrik (112x82cm-44x32in) s. screenprint etching lithograph engraving. 31-Oct-3 Sotheby's, New York #785/R
£2684	$4750	€3919	Bower in the Arsacides (148x126cm-58x50in) s.d.1993 num.8/38 lithograph etching relief. 30-Apr-4 Sotheby's, New York #488/R est:4500-5500
£2684	$4750	€3919	Spectralia (68x83cm-27x33in) s.d.1995 num.37/75 etching lithograph relief. 30-Apr-4 Sotheby's, New York #490/R est:4000-5000
£2703	$5000	€3946	Shards III (116x102cm-46x40in) s.d.1982 num.RTP IX offset lithograph col screenprint. 12-Feb-4 Christie's, Rockefeller NY #239/R est:3000-4000
£2761	$4500	€4031	Sinjerli Variation IV (81x108cm-32x43in) s.d.77 num.97/100 offset lithograph col screenprint Arches. 24-Sep-3 Christie's, Rockefeller NY #395/R est:5000-7000
£2825	$5000	€4125	Guifa e la beretta rossa (147x170cm-58x67in) s.d.1989 num.20/50 col relief printed etching aquatint. 28-Apr-4 Christie's, Rockefeller NY #420/R est:8000-12000
£2825	$5000	€4125	Bene come il sale (193x150cm-76x59in) s.d.1989 num.18/50 col etching aquatint. 28-Apr-4 Christie's, Rockefeller NY #421/R est:5000-7000
£2825	$5000	€4125	Feneralia (117x106cm-46x42in) s.i. lithograph etching aquatint relief. 30-Apr-4 Sotheby's, New York #489/R est:3500-4500
£2825	$5000	€4125	Libertinia (54x125cm-21x49in) s.d.1995 num.50/50 screenprint etching relief. 30-Apr-4 Sotheby's, New York #491/R est:3500-4500
£2830	$4585	€4132	River of ponds IV (81x81cm-32x32in) s.i.d71 col lithograph. 24-May-3 Burkhard, Luzern #116/R est:4500-5500 (S.FR 6000)
£2941	$5000	€4294	Sinjerli variation (81x107cm-32x42in) s. offset lithograph. 31-Oct-3 Sotheby's, New York #764/R
£2941	$5000	€4294	Battering ram (150x88cm-59x35in) s. lithograph etching aquatint screenprint. 31-Oct-3 Sotheby's, New York #770/R
£2973	$5500	€4341	Shards variant IVa (101x115cm-40x45in) s.d.1982 num.46/49 offset lithograph col screenprint. 12-Feb-4 Christie's, Rockefeller NY #240/R est:2500-3500
£3107	$5500	€4536	River of ponds II (81x81cm-32x32in) s.d.1971 num.39/78 col lithograph. 28-Apr-4 Christie's, Rockefeller NY #404/R est:4000-5000
£3235	$5500	€4723	Figlefia (61x53cm-24x21in) s. col etching aquatint lithograph. 31-Oct-3 Sotheby's, New York #774/R
£3390	$6000	€4949	River of ponds III (81x81cm-32x32in) s.d.1971 num.A.P.IV col lithograph. 28-Apr-4 Christie's, Rockefeller NY #405/R est:4000-5000
£3390	$6000	€4949	Polar co-ordinates (98x97cm-39x38in) s.d.1980 num.6/100 col offset lithograph screenprint. 28-Apr-4 Christie's, Rockefeller NY #411/R est:6000-8000
£3529	$6000	€5152	Fossil whale (186x136cm-73x54in) s. etching aquatint engraving. 31-Oct-3 Sotheby's, New York #769/R
£3529	$6000	€5152	Estoril three (168x131cm-66x52in) s. etching woodcut. 31-Oct-3 Sotheby's, New York #766/R
£3529	$6000	€5152	Egyplosis relief (81x81cm-32x32in) s. col etching aquatint. 31-Oct-3 Sotheby's, New York #776/R
£3529	$6000	€5152	Swoonarie (107x132cm-42x52in) s. etching aquatint lithograph screenprint. 31-Oct-3 Sotheby's, New York #771/R
£3824	$6500	€5583	Sinjerli variation (81x81cm-32x32in) s. offset lithograph. 31-Oct-3 Sotheby's, New York #765/R
£3842	$6800	€5609	Sinjerli variation (64x64cm-25x25in) s.d.77 num.97/100 col offset lithograph screenprint. 28-Apr-4 Christie's, Rockefeller NY #408/R est:5000-7000
£3867	$7000	€5646	Sinjerli variation squared with coloured ground (81x81cm-32x32in) s.i.d.1981 col offset lithograph silkscreen. 19-Apr-4 Bonhams & Butterfields, San Francisco #310/R est:6000-8000
£3911	$7000	€5710	Puerto rican blue pelican (83x11cm-33x4in) s.i.d.1977 offset lithograph. 6-May-4 Swann Galleries, New York #589/R est:10000-15000
£3955	$7000	€5774	Sinjerli variation squared with colored ground II (81x81cm-32x32in) s.d.1981 num.41/50 col offset lithograph screenprint. 28-Apr-4 Christie's, Rockefeller NY #412/R est:5000-7000
£3955	$7000	€5774	One small goat papa bought for two zuzim (133x130cm-52x51in) s.d.84 num.24/60 col lithograph linocut screenprint collage. 28-Apr-4 Christie's, Rockefeller NY #417/R est:5000-7000
£3955	$7000	€5774	Polar co-ordinates VI (97x96cm-38x38in) s.d.1980 num.83/100 offset lithograph. 30-Apr-4 Sotheby's, New York #472/R est:6000-8000
£3955	$7000	€5774	Whale watch (184x185cm-72x73in) s.d.1993 num.12/26 lithograph etching relief. 30-Apr-4 Sotheby's, New York #487/R est:6000-8000
£4118	$7000	€6012	Variation (81x81cm-32x32in) s.d.1981 offset lithograph col screenprint. 4-Nov-3 Christie's, Rockefeller NY #348/R est:3000-4000
£4118	$7000	€6012	Juam (198x152cm-78x60in) s.d.1997 etching aquatint woodcut relief. 4-Nov-3 Christie's, Rockefeller NY #351/R est:5000-7000
£4237	$7500	€6186	Polar co-odinates VIII (97x96cm-38x38in) s.d.1980 num.16/100 offset lithograph. 30-Apr-4 Sotheby's, New York #473/R est:6000-8000
£4324	$8000	€6313	One small goat papa bought for two zuzim (133x130cm-52x51in) s.d.84 num.37/60 col lithograph linocut screenprint. 12-Feb-4 Christie's, Rockefeller NY #241/R est:4000-6000
£4412	$7500	€6442	Juam (202x156cm-80x61in) s. etching aquatint lithograph screenprint. 31-Oct-3 Sotheby's, New York #779/R
£4706	$8000	€6871	Penna di Hu (140x166cm-55x65in) s. screenprint woodcut etching. 31-Oct-3 Sotheby's, New York #768/R
£4802	$8500	€7011	Eskimo (86x116cm-34x46in) s.d.1977 num.39/50 offset lithograph. 30-Apr-4 Sotheby's, New York #469/R est:6000-8000
£4802	$8500	€7011	La penna di hu (167x139cm-66x55in) s.d.1988 num.1/42 etching relief. 30-Apr-4 Sotheby's, New York #482/R est:6000-8000
£5500	$9460	€8030	Juam, from imaginary places (199x154cm-78x61in) s.d.1997 woodcut etching lithograph relief. 2-Dec-3 Christie's, London #311/R est:3000-5000
£5650	$10000	€8249	Estoril three II (168x131cm-66x52in) s.d.1982 num.5/30 col etching woodcut. 28-Apr-4 Christie's, Rockefeller NY #414/R est:10000-15000
£5650	$10000	€8249	Polar co-codinates I (97x96cm-38x38in) s.d.1980 num.83/100 col offset lithograph. 30-Apr-4 Sotheby's, New York #470/R est:6000-8000
£5650	$10000	€8249	Polar co-codinates V (97x96cm-38x38in) s.i.d.1980 num.83/100 col offset lithograph. 30-Apr-4 Sotheby's, New York #471/R est:6000-8000
£5650	$10000	€8249	Imola three IV (167x132cm-66x52in) s.i.d.1984 screenprint relief. 30-Apr-4 Sotheby's, New York #477/R est:10000-15000
£6215	$11000	€9074	Polar co-ordinates (99x97cm-39x38in) s.d.1980 num.15/100 col offset lg screenprint. 28-Apr-4 Christie's, Rockefeller NY #410/R est:8000-10000
£6215	$11000	€9074	Talladega five I (167x129cm-66x51in) s.i.d.1982 woodcut relief. 30-Apr-4 Sotheby's, New York #475/R est:10000-15000
£6780	$12000	€9899	Jonah historically regarded (183x133cm-72x52in) s.i.d.1992 hand col etching relief. 30-Apr-4 Sotheby's, New York #485/R est:5000-7000
£11765	$20000	€17177	Double gray (59x109cm-23x43in) s. col screenprint. 31-Oct-3 Sotheby's, New York #762/R
£12429	$22000	€18146	Wake island rail (157x217cm-62x85in) s.d.1979 num.8/10 col screenprint acrylic oilsticks glitter. 28-Apr-4 Christie's, Rockefeller NY #409/R est:15000-25000
£12429	$22000	€18146	Imola five II (169x127cm-67x50in) s.d.1983 num.30/30 col relief printed woodcut. 28-Apr-4 Christie's, Rockefeller NY #418/R est:12000-15000
£12712	$22500	€18560	Double gray scramble (59x109cm-23x43in) s.d.1973 num.47/100 col screenprint. 30-Apr-4 Sotheby's, New York #468/R est:20000-30000
£25424	$45000	€37119	Pergusa three, state I (170x131cm-67x52in) s.i.d.1983 num.2/10 col relief printed woodcut etching. 28-Apr-4 Christie's, Rockefeller NY #419/R est:50000-70000
£28249	$50000	€41244	Talladega three II (168x131cm-66x52in) s.d.1982 num.2/30 col etching. 28-Apr-4 Christie's, Rockefeller NY #413/R est:55000-65000

Sculpture

£19553	$35000	€28547	Untitled (138x91x48cm-54x36x19in) metal painted metal Tycore bronze garden hose steel prov. 13-May-4 Sotheby's, New York #241/R est:40000-60000
£50898	$85000	€74311	Pequod meets the Rachel (163x133x43cm-64x52x17in) acrylic enamel on aluminum executed 1988 prov.lit. 13-Nov-3 Phillips, New York #24/R est:90000-120000
£77844	$130000	€113652	Quadrant (254x212x116cm-100x83x46in) mixed media cast aluminum prov.exhib. 13-Nov-3 Sotheby's, New York #255/R est:150000-200000
£80000	$148000	€120000	Cutting in (365x357x137cm-144x141x54in) mixed media on aluminium exec.1990 prov.exhib. 18-Jul-4 Sotheby's, Paris #228/R est:100000-150000
£80000	$148000	€120000	Zolder (199x179x32cm-78x70x13in) mixed media aluminium exec.1982 prov.exhib. 18-Jul-4 Sotheby's, Paris #233/R est:80000-120000
£323353	$540000	€472095	Does the Whale diminish (197x366x77cm-78x144x30in) oil oilstick enamel on aluminium exec 1988 prov. 12-Nov-3 Christie's, Rockefeller NY #412/R est:100000-150000

Works on paper

£2000	$3400	€2920	Painting at Leo Castelli Gallery (26x26cm-10x10in) s.i.d.1966 pen ink. 21-Nov-3 Swann Galleries, New York #198/R est:2000-3000
£3944	$6823	€5600	Jundapur (71cm-28in circular) s.i.d.96 mixed media collage. 13-Dec-3 Lempertz, Koln #189/R est:3000-3500
£16760	$30000	€24470	Triple Stack - Newport Beach (102x71cm-40x28in) s.d.69 ink W/C prov. 13-May-4 Sotheby's, New York #136/R est:15000-20000
£25449	$42500	€37156	Jerdon's courser (46x58cm-18x23in) mixed media tycore prov.exhib. 13-Nov-3 Sotheby's, New York #288/R est:30000-40000
£458101	$820000	€668827	Slieve roe (198x226cm-78x89in) s.i.stretcher metallic powder polymer emulsion on canvas. 13-May-4 Phillips, New York #45/R est:600000-800000

STELLA, Jacques de (1596-1657) French

£24000	$42960	€36000	Madonna and Child. on slate. 15-May-4 other European Auctioneer #130

STELLA, Jacques de (attrib) (1596-1657) French

£563	$986	€800	Madonna and Child (18x15cm-7x6in) panel octagonal. 19-Dec-3 Pierre Berge, Paris #51

Works on paper

£552	$921	€800	Levitation of St Joseph of Copertino during mass (27x33cm-11x13in) mono. pen over graphite wash prov. double-sided. 15-Nov-3 Lempertz, Koln #1407/R
£1549	$2711	€2200	Bethsabee au bain (14x11cm-6x4in) black chk pen brown ink wash prov. 17-Dec-3 Christie's, Paris #39/R est:1500-2000

STELLA, Joseph (1879-1946) American/Italian

£882	$1500	€1288	Green forest (13x18cm-5x7in) s. canvasboard. 9-Nov-3 Wright, Chicago #133 est:1000-1500
£1765	$3000	€2577	Landscape with smokestack (13x20cm-5x8in) 9-Nov-3 Wright, Chicago #134 est:2500-3500
£10588	$18000	€15458	In the garden of Eden (28x38cm-11x15in) s. s.i.verso. 9-Nov-3 Wright, Chicago #139 est:12000-18000
£11364	$20000	€16591	Pink roses (36x41cm-14x16in) prov. 19-May-4 Sotheby's, New York #165/R est:15000-20000
£14205	$25000	€20739	Green palms (43x46cm-17x18in) s. prov. 19-May-4 Sotheby's, New York #166/R est:15000-20000

£28409 $50000 €41477 Pink flower (43x30cm-17x12in) s. prov. 19-May-4 Sotheby's, New York #156/R est:18000-24000
Works on paper
£265 $475 €387 Study of flowers (23x28cm-9x11in) s. ink pencil. 8-May-4 Susanin's, Chicago #6072/R
£279 $475 €407 Man at a window (20x10cm-8x4in) s. pencil. 9-Nov-3 Wright, Chicago #112
£305 $500 €442 Pear (23x30cm-9x12in) s. col pencil. 4-Jun-3 Alderfer's, Hatfield #302/R
£380 $700 €555 Floral study (18x23cm-7x9in) s. W/C pencil. 10-Jun-4 Swann Galleries, New York #235/R
£435 $800 €635 Portrait of a lady wearing a hat (15x10cm-6x4in) s. pencil. 10-Jun-4 Swann Galleries, New York #230/R
£435 $800 €635 Head of a young woman (20x13cm-8x5in) s. pen ink. 10-Jun-4 Swann Galleries, New York #231/R
£447 $800 €653 Tree study (64x48cm-25x19in) pastel lit. 16-May-4 Wright, Chicago #107/R
£571 $1000 €834 Swan (18x13cm-7x5in) W/C prov. 19-Dec-3 Sotheby's, New York #1004/R
£670 $1200 €978 Luncheon by the sea (23x20cm-9x8in) W/C pencil. 16-May-4 Wright, Chicago #106/R
£1059 $1800 €1546 Tree with bird (36x28cm-14x11in) silverpoint col pencil exhib. 9-Nov-3 Wright, Chicago #120 est:1800-2200
£1167 $2100 €1704 Old woman resting (135x122cm-53x48in) s. gouache pencil paper on board. 24-Apr-4 Weschler, Washington #640/R est:2000-3000
£1286 $2250 €1878 Flower (16x15cm-6x6in) studio st. col pencil paper on board. 19-Dec-3 Sotheby's, New York #1014/R est:1000-2000
£2374 $4250 €3466 Untitled (23x15cm-9x6in) s. mixed media collage prov. 16-May-4 Wright, Chicago #139/R est:4000-6000
£2793 $5000 €4078 Lotus flower (25x33cm-10x13in) s.d.1943 silverpoint crayon exhib. 16-May-4 Wright, Chicago #101/R est:5000-7000
£2794 $4750 €4079 Untitled - view through the valley (33x48cm-13x19in) W/C. 9-Nov-3 Wright, Chicago #123 est:3000-5000
£3533 $6500 €5158 Flower (36x25cm-14x10in) s.d.1940 col pastel silverpoint. 10-Jun-4 Swann Galleries, New York #233/R est:4000-6000
£3889 $7000 €5678 Still life of books and Chinese lanterns (60x44cm-24x17in) s. pastel prov. 24-Apr-4 Weschler, Washington #641/R est:6000-8000
£5028 $9000 €7341 Waterlily and woodduck (36x51cm-14x20in) s. W/C gouache pencil. 26-May-4 Doyle, New York #160/R est:8000-12000
£5163 $9500 €7538 Palmette (43x30cm-17x12in) s. col pastel. 10-Jun-4 Swann Galleries, New York #232/R est:4000-6000
£5398 $9500 €7881 Barbados (48x63cm-19x25in) s. pastel prov. 18-May-4 Christie's, Rockefeller NY #141/R est:20000-30000
£11364 $20000 €16591 Collage 7 (25x20cm-10x8in) s. collage pasted papers on paper exec c.1921 prov.exhib. 18-May-4 Christie's, Rockefeller NY #143/R est:10000-15000

STELLETSKY, Dimitri (1875-1947) Russian
£28000 $50120 €40880 Martha Posadnitsa (163x60cm-64x24in) tempera on paper. 26-May-4 Sotheby's, London #205/R est:15000-20000
Works on paper
£40000 $68000 €58400 Young Boyarina (163x60cm-64x24in) i.verso gouache paper on canvas prov.exhib.lit. 19-Nov-3 Sotheby's, London #140/R est:20000-30000

STELLINGWERFF, Jacobus (?-1736) Dutch
Works on paper
£676 $1189 €1000 Chapel of Souburg at Walcheren (17x23cm-7x9in) i. black chk brown wash prov. 19-May-4 Sotheby's, Amsterdam #255/R

STEMATSKY, Avigdor (1908-1989) Israeli
£8065 $15000 €11775 Abstracted figure (64x49cm-25x19in) s.d.60. 5-Mar-4 Skinner, Boston #602/R est:1000-2000
£10056 $18000 €14682 Untitled (91x117cm-36x46in) s.d.70 verso. 18-Mar-4 Sotheby's, New York #33/R est:15000-20000
Works on paper
£1786 $3250 €2608 Untitled (50x70cm-20x28in) s. W/C chl. 29-Jun-4 Sotheby's, New York #403/R est:4000-6000

STEN, Helge (1923-1965) Finnish
£300 $552 €450 The last snow (60x90cm-24x35in) s.d.61. 9-Jun-4 Bukowskis, Helsinki #558/R

STEN, John (1879-1922) Swedish
£831 $1412 €1213 Cubist model (40x34cm-16x13in) i.indis.d.191. verso. 4-Nov-3 Bukowskis, Stockholm #163a/R (S.KR 11000)

STENBERG, Emerik (1873-1927) Swedish
£398 $640 €581 Hol-Per from Aakero (68x51cm-27x20in) i.verso. 25-Aug-3 Lilla Bukowskis, Stockholm #644 (S.KR 5200)

STENBERG, Ron (1919-) New Zealander?
£664 $1209 €969 Auld Reekie - Edinburgh (38x47cm-15x19in) s.i. s.i.verso canvasboard prov. 29-Jun-4 Peter Webb, Auckland #90/R est:2000-3000 (NZ.D 1900)
£874 $1591 €1276 New Zealand houses (42x60cm-17x24in) s. board prov. 29-Jun-4 Peter Webb, Auckland #89/R est:3000-5000 (NZ.D 2500)
£1165 $1981 €1701 Waiting for repairs, Tayport, Scotland (38x66cm-15x26in) s. board painted c.1960. 27-Nov-3 International Art Centre, Auckland #4/R est:2000-3000 (NZ.D 3100)

STENERSEN, Gudmund (1863-1934) Norwegian
£344 $575 €502 Under Bitihorn (65x80cm-26x31in) s. 20-Oct-3 Blomqvist, Lysaker #1304 (N.KR 4000)
£601 $1052 €877 Winter landscape with man rowing (40x61cm-16x24in) s. 16-Dec-3 Grev Wedels Plass, Oslo #221/R (N.KR 7000)
£1033 $1725 €1508 Landscape from Gol (65x80cm-26x31in) s. 20-Oct-3 Blomqvist, Lysaker #1305/R est:15000-18000 (N.KR 12000)

STENGEL, George J (1872-1937) American
£2295 $4200 €3351 Now comes still evening (30x41cm-12x16in) s. 10-Apr-4 Brunk, Ashville #95/R est:500-1000

STENGL, Walter (1902-1980) Austrian
£2797 $4755 €4000 Procession of bird handlers in traditional dress (66x265cm-26x104in) s. 20-Nov-3 Dorotheum, Salzburg #211/R est:2800-3600

STENIUS, Per (1922-) Finnish
£507 $907 €750 Mountain landscape (46x65cm-18x26in) s.d.67. 8-May-4 Bukowskis, Helsinki #288/R
£634 $1014 €900 Forest (62x76cm-24x30in) s.d.1976. 18-Sep-3 Hagelstam, Helsinki #814/R
£1268 $2028 €1800 February sunshine (54x65cm-21x26in) s.d.1997. 18-Sep-3 Hagelstam, Helsinki #1009 est:2000
£1333 $2387 €2000 Town in India (115x80cm-45x31in) s.d.1965. 15-May-4 Hagelstam, Helsinki #201/R est:1800
£1333 $2387 €2000 Street scene in India (61x52cm-24x20in) s.d.1984. 15-May-4 Hagelstam, Helsinki #203/R est:1200
£1549 $2680 €2200 Street scene with figures (60x75cm-24x30in) s.d.1966. 13-Dec-3 Hagelstam, Helsinki #181/R est:1500
£4133 $7399 €6200 Interior (72x100cm-28x39in) s.d.1959. 15-May-4 Hagelstam, Helsinki #202/R est:1800

STENNEBERG, Piet (1902-1972) Dutch
£395 $726 €600 City of London (40x30cm-16x12in) init. s.i.d.1969 verso prov. 22-Jun-4 Christie's, Amsterdam #597/R
£428 $787 €650 Studio, Bergen (37x38cm-15x15in) s. s.i.d.1944 prov. 22-Jun-4 Christie's, Amsterdam #596/R
£461 $847 €700 La reve du vieux marin (43x45cm-17x18in) s.i.d.1951 burlap. 22-Jun-4 Christie's, Amsterdam #599/R

STENNER, Hermann (1891-1914) German
Works on paper
£1600 $2864 €2400 Taking down from the cross (34x26cm-13x10in) s.d. bears i. chl. 15-May-4 Bassenge, Berlin #7144/R est:1500

STENSTADVOLD, Hakon (1912-1977) Norwegian
£238 $438 €347 August evening (60x75cm-24x30in) s. 29-Mar-4 Blomqvist, Lysaker #1316 (N.KR 3000)
£338 $618 €493 Summer night, Engervann (71x115cm-28x45in) s/. 2-Feb-4 Blomqvist, Lysaker #1289/R (N.KR 4200)

STENVALL, Kaj (1951-) Finnish
£5634 $9746 €8000 How much on the Richter scale? (90x120cm-35x47in) s.d.1995 lit. 13-Dec-3 Hagelstam, Helsinki #198/R est:6500

STENVERT, Curt (1920-1994) Austrian
£533 $976 €800 House concert (73x88cm-29x35in) s.d.1985 i.d. verso panel. 4-Jun-4 Lempertz, Koln #472/R

STENVINKEL, Jan (1933-1989) Swedish
£487 $843 €711 Seascape (73x92cm-29x36in) s. 15-Dec-3 Lilla Bukowskis, Stockholm #391 (S.KR 6200)

STEPANOV, Daniil Klavdievich (1882-1937) Russian
£22000 $39380 €32120 Bay of Samarkand (34x38cm-13x15in) s.i.d.1923 oil on wood prov. 26-May-4 Sotheby's, London #288/R est:5000-7000

STEPANOVA, Varvara (1894-1958) Russian
Works on paper
£12000 $21840 €17520 Collage (19x13cm-7x5in) collage exec c.1919 prov. 5-Feb-4 Christie's, London #351/R est:5000-7000
£35000 $64400 €51100 Three figures (28x35cm-11x14in) s.d.21 gouache W/C brush India ink col pencil prov.exhib. 24-Jun-4 Christie's, London #371/R est:5000-7000

STEPHAN, August (1868-1936) Austrian
£694 $1097 €1000 Marriage proposal. s. panel. 6-Sep-3 Schopman, Hamburg #704/R

STEPHAN, Gary (1942-) American
£1056 $1900 €1542 Invitation. Hand mirror. Wealth of knowledge. 1 s.i.d.1978 verso 1 d.1979 verso 1 s.i.d.1979 verso acrylic 3. 24-Apr-4 David Rago, Lambertville #426/R est:200-400

STEPHAN, Joseph (1709-1786) German
£26000 $47580 €37960 Boar hunt. Stag hunt. Stag hunt the kill (75x108cm-30x43in) one s. set of three prov. 7-Jul-4 Christie's, London #63/R est:25000-35000

STEPHANIE, Serge (1943-) French
Works on paper
£476 $852 €700 Gifle (65x50cm-26x20in) s. s.i.verso mixed media board prov. 21-Mar-4 Calmels Cohen, Paris #147/R

STEPHANOFF, Francis Philip (1788-1860) British
£700 $1169 €1022 At the opera (31x25cm-12x10in) panel. 22-Oct-3 Cheffins, Cambridge #528
£1100 $1969 €1606 Trial of Algernon Sydney in 1683, feel my pulse my lord (71x91cm-28x36in) panel. 22-Mar-4 Bonhams & Brooks, Norfolk #315/R est:400-600

STEPHANOFF, James (1787-1874) British
Works on paper
£250 $448 €365 Two young boys with a falcon. s.d.1855. 17-Mar-4 John Nicholson, Haslemere #666

STEPHENS, David (20th C) New Zealander?
Works on paper
£293 $542 €428 Queenstown (56x73cm-22x29in) s. W/C. 9-Mar-4 Watson's, Christchurch #196 (NZ.D 800)

STEPHENSON, Ian (1934-) British
£8000 $13600 €11680 Early diorama (102x204cm-40x80in) in 2 parts painted 1962. 26-Nov-3 Sotheby's, Olympia #178/R est:600-800

STEPHENSON, Lionel Macdonald (1854-1907) Canadian
£720 $1318 €1051 Indian encampment (25x47cm-10x19in) board. 1-Jun-4 Joyner Waddington, Toronto #255/R est:1200-1500 (C.D 1800)
£804 $1382 €1174 Fort Garry in winter (27x46cm-11x18in) init.i.d.1869 board. 2-Dec-3 Joyner Waddington, Toronto #306/R est:1500-2000 (C.D 1800)
£804 $1382 €1174 Fort Garry in summer (27x44cm-11x17in) init.i.d.1869 board. 2-Dec-3 Joyner Waddington, Toronto #307/R est:1500-2000 (C.D 1800)

STEPHENSON, Peter (1823-1860) American
£1322 $2446 €1930 Target figure (167x167cm-66x66in) s.d.89 s.i.d.verso oil collage on canvas prov. 15-Mar-4 Sotheby's, Melbourne #65 est:800-1200 (A.D 3200)
£1489 $2532 €2174 Message sticks (137x137cm-54x54in) s.d.94 s.i.d.1994 verso. 25-Nov-3 Christie's, Melbourne #131/R est:3500-4500 (A.D 3500)
Works on paper
£851 $1447 €1242 Red Code (77x112cm-30x44in) s.i.d.02 pastel chl pencil. 26-Nov-3 Deutscher-Menzies, Melbourne #164/R (A.D 2000)

STEPHENSON, Willie (fl.1893-1938) British
£260 $481 €380 View of the Orme, Llandudno, with woman stood on a cliff top (24x38cm-9x15in) mono. W/C. 14-Jul-4 Bonhams, Chester #326
£280 $476 €409 On the Conway, Bettws-y-Coed, North Wales (41x56cm-16x22in) s. i.verso. 18-Nov-3 Bonhams, Leeds #218
£720 $1224 €1051 Old Welsh cottage. Autumn afternoon. s W/C pair. 29-Oct-3 Bonhams, Chester #312
Works on paper
£280 $456 €409 Sunset seascape with boats (30x20cm-12x8in) s. W/C. 27-Sep-3 Rogers Jones, Clwyd #9
£300 $501 €438 Rural landscape with figures walking across a bridge (37x27cm-15x11in) s. W/C. 7-Oct-3 Fellows & Sons, Birmingham #491/R
£580 $963 €847 Wyddfyd cottage, Great Orme Llandudno with figures (36x56cm-14x22in) s. W/C. 30-Sep-3 Rogers Jones, Clwyd #122

STEPPE, R (19th C) Belgian
£2177 $3897 €3200 Apres-midi, cote Anglaise (100x170cm-39x67in) 22-Mar-4 Amberes, Antwerp #253/R

STEPPE, Romain (1859-1927) Belgian
£276 $458 €400 Ostende (25x24cm-10x9in) panel. 6-Oct-3 Amberes, Antwerp #270
£304 $544 €450 Bord de l'Escaut (14x10cm-6x4in) cardboard. 10-May-4 Amberes, Antwerp #159
£306 $548 €450 Vue d'un village (23x16cm-9x6in) panel. 22-Mar-4 Amberes, Antwerp #255
£333 $613 €500 Barque de peche (48x69cm-19x27in) 14-Jun-4 Amberes, Antwerp #125
£338 $605 €500 Moulin a vent (68x48cm-27x19in) 10-May-4 Amberes, Antwerp #327
£349 $649 €520 Seascape with two yachts (16x24cm-6x9in) s. panel. 8-Mar-4 Bernaerts, Antwerp #256/R
£350 $594 €500 Bord de l'Escaut au coucher du soleil (50x40cm-20x16in) s. 18-Nov-3 Vanderkindere, Brussels #31
£352 $609 €500 Estacade (37x52cm-15x20in) s. 15-Dec-3 Bernaerts, Antwerp #249
£367 $656 €550 Coin de plage Flamande, apres-midi de Septembre (50x40cm-20x16in) s. 15-May-4 De Vuyst, Lokeren #320
£385 $654 €550 Marine (15x23cm-6x9in) canvas laid down. 1-Dec-3 Amberes, Antwerp #353/R
£420 $713 €600 Voiliers en pleine mer (47x69cm-19x27in) 1-Dec-3 Amberes, Antwerp #355
£426 $711 €600 Cargo en mer (50x62cm-20x24in) s. 17-Jun-3 Vanderkindere, Brussels #143
£464 $844 €700 Marine avec trois-mats (70x50cm-28x20in) indis.s. 21-Jun-4 Bernaerts, Antwerp #453
£473 $847 €700 Barques de peche (48x68cm-19x27in) 10-May-4 Amberes, Antwerp #326
£473 $847 €700 Mer du Nord (59x78cm-23x31in) 10-May-4 Amberes, Antwerp #324
£486 $812 €700 Moulin a St Amands, Baasrode (45x58cm-18x23in) s. 21-Oct-3 Campo, Vlaamse Kaai #580
£490 $832 €700 Soir a Terneuzen (48x69cm-19x27in) 1-Dec-3 Amberes, Antwerp #352
£493 $853 €700 Sur l'Escaut, soir de septembre (26x15cm-10x6in) s. panel. 9-Dec-3 Campo, Vlaamse Kaai #438
£510 $913 €750 Marine (70x49cm-28x19in) s. 16-Mar-4 Vanderkindere, Brussels #235
£533 $965 €800 La baie de Naples (26x35cm-10x14in) s.d.1912. 30-Mar-4 Campo, Vlaamse Kaai #166
£595 $1100 €869 Boat in rough seas (18x23cm-7x9in) s. panel. 17-Jul-4 New Orleans Auction, New Orleans #731/R
£667 $1207 €1000 Bateau a la tombee de la nuit (24x32cm-9x13in) s. panel. 30-Mar-4 Campo, Vlaamse Kaai #167
£676 $1189 €1000 Marine (70x100cm-28x39in) s. 18-May-4 Galerie Moderne, Brussels #288
£775 $1340 €1100 Claire de lune sur l'Escaut (50x80cm-20x31in) s. 9-Dec-3 Campo, Vlaamse Kaai #429
£828 $1374 €1200 Rentree au port (102x88cm-40x35in) 6-Oct-3 Amberes, Antwerp #271
£828 $1531 €1200 Coucher de soleil sur l'Escaut (32x24cm-13x9in) s. panel. 16-Feb-4 Horta, Bruxelles #491
£979 $1635 €1400 De Schelde de Baasrode (50x40cm-20x16in) s. i.verso. 11-Oct-3 De Vuyst, Lokeren #344
£1000 $1810 €1500 Petits bateaux en mer (60x80cm-24x31in) 30-Mar-4 Campo & Campo, Antwerp #276/R est:1200-1400
£1733 $3137 €2600 Een gevaarlijk ogenblik (110x150cm-43x59in) s. 30-Mar-4 Campo & Campo, Antwerp #275/R est:4000-5000
£1800 $3294 €2700 On the river (79x91cm-31x36in) i.verso. 27-Jul-4 Henry Adams, Chichester #478/R est:2000-3000
£2517 $4280 €3600 Voiliers en pleine mer (125x174cm-49x69in) 1-Dec-3 Amberes, Antwerp #354/R
£2857 $5114 €4200 Apres-midi de printemps (119x178cm-47x70in) 22-Mar-4 Amberes, Antwerp #254

STEPPES, Edmund (1873-1968) German
£372 $665 €550 Schmiechetal in spring (12x20cm-5x8in) s.i.d.1931 i. verso oil tempera panel. 6-May-4 Michael Zeller, Lindau #889

STERCHI, Eda Elizabeth (1885-?) American
£215 $400 €314 Muslim cemetery (38x46cm-15x18in) s. board painted c.1910. 7-Mar-4 Treadway Gallery, Cincinnati #634/R
£274 $450 €397 Tunis architecture (38x46cm-15x18in) s. board painted c.1910. 7-Jun-3 Treadway Gallery, Cincinnati #1373
£291 $500 €425 Desert oasis (38x46cm-15x18in) s. board painted c.1910. 7-Dec-3 Treadway Gallery, Cincinnati #626/R
£341 $600 €498 Portrait of a woman (66x51cm-26x20in) s. painted c.1930. 23-May-4 Treadway Gallery, Cincinnati #617/R
£465 $800 €679 Street in Tunis (46x38cm-18x15in) s. painted c.1911. 7-Dec-3 Treadway Gallery, Cincinnati #491/R
£610 $1000 €885 Portrait of an Indian woman (91x66cm-36x26in) s. painted c.1940. 7-Jun-3 Treadway Gallery, Cincinnati #1394

STERIS, Gerasimos (1895-1985) Greek
£6000 $10200 €8760 Joshua tree (56x41cm-22x16in) prov. 18-Nov-3 Sotheby's, London #42/R est:6000-8000
£7500 $13425 €10950 Homeric shore (39x47cm-15x19in) s. prov. 10-May-4 Sotheby's, Olympia #33/R est:3000-5000
£8000 $14320 €11680 Dream figure (54x37cm-21x15in) oil paper prov. 11-May-4 Bonhams, New Bond Street #84/R est:6000-8000
£9500 $17005 €13870 Happy mountains (122x157cm-48x62in) s. prov. 10-May-4 Sotheby's, Olympia #120/R est:7000-9000
£17000 $30430 €24820 Sexism (100x80cm-39x31in) board prov. 10-May-4 Sotheby's, Olympia #47/R est:15000-20000
£24000 $40800 €35040 Greek fishermen (101x81cm-40x32in) prov. 18-Nov-3 Sotheby's, London #40/R est:15000-20000
£24000 $40800 €35040 Fishing village (61x92cm-24x36in) s. prov. 18-Nov-3 Sotheby's, London #43/R est:15000-20000
£34000 $57800 €49640 Galatea (73x63cm-29x25in) prov. 18-Nov-3 Sotheby's, London #38/R est:18000-25000
Works on paper
£1800 $3222 €2628 Portrait of a woman (69x39cm-27x15in) pastel gouache prov. 10-May-4 Sotheby's, Olympia #117/R est:2000-3000
£1800 $3222 €2628 Abstract study of a woman (71x38cm-28x15in) pastel gouache prov. 10-May-4 Sotheby's, Olympia #119/R est:3000-5000
£2800 $5012 €4088 Four nudes in a landscape (24x30cm-9x12in) pastel blue paper prov. 10-May-4 Sotheby's, Olympia #32/R est:1000-1500
£3500 $6265 €5110 Clown (54x39cm-21x15in) pastel prov. 10-May-4 Sotheby's, Olympia #118/R est:2000-3000
£4000 $7160 €5840 Greek Island (25x91cm-10x36in) pencil blk crayon prov. 10-May-4 Sotheby's, Olympia #156/R est:3000-5000
£26000 $44200 €37960 Dream (50x130cm-20x51in) s. pastel prov. 18-Nov-3 Sotheby's, London #39/R est:8000-12000

STERKENBURG, Piet (1900-?) Dutch
£804 $1342 €1174 Fishing vessels (51x61cm-20x24in) s. 17-Jun-3 Maynards, Vancouver #318 est:1500-2000 (C.D 1800)
£875 $1400 €1278 Dutch harbour scene. s. 20-Sep-3 Harvey Clar, Oakland #1370

STERL, Robert Hermann (1867-1932) German
Works on paper
£1200 $2172 €1800 Summer landscape (48x60cm-19x24in) mono.d.93 pastel. 1-Apr-4 Van Ham, Cologne #1656 est:1300

STERLING, Marc (1898-1976) Russian
£1007 $1782 €1500 Nature morte aux poissons (50x61cm-20x24in) s. 27-Apr-4 Artcurial Briest, Paris #146 est:1500-2000
£1745 $3228 €2600 Nature morte au poisson et a la cruche (54x65cm-21x26in) s. 15-Mar-4 Claude Boisgirard, Paris #109 est:1000-1200
£2819 $5215 €4200 Nature morte au coq (50x61cm-20x24in) s. 15-Mar-4 Claude Boisgirard, Paris #108/R est:2500-3000
Works on paper
£464 $844 €700 Nature morte aux poissons et a la bouteille (45x54cm-18x21in) s. 16-Jun-4 Claude Boisgirard, Paris #149

STERN, Bernhard (1920-) American
£250 $463 €375 Mysterious art dealer (102x92cm-40x36in) s.i.d.87 verso. 13-Jul-4 Rosebery Fine Art, London #659
£552 $916 €800 Crowd noise (146x114cm-57x45in) s. i.d.1981 verso. 30-Sep-3 Blanchet, Paris #335

STERN, Bert (1930-) American
Photographs
£2174 $4000 €3174 Marilyn Monroe-crucifix II (110x111cm-43x44in) s.i.d.1962 num.3 col coupler print prov. 10-Jun-4 Phillips, New York #569/R est:7000-9000
£2700 $4590 €3942 Marilyn Monroe with necklace (51x61cm-20x24in) s.d.1982 verso silver print exec.1962 lit. 19-Nov-3 Sotheby's, Olympia #181/R est:3000-4000
£2994 $5000 €4371 Marilyn acclaimed (64x62cm-25x24in) s.num.3/6 chromogenic print exec.1962 printed later. 17-Oct-3 Sotheby's, New York #282/R est:5000-7000
£3593 $6000 €5246 Marilyn Monroe, the last sitting (48x48cm-19x19in) s.num.64/250 chromogenic prints 10 folio sold with magazine. 20-Oct-3 Christie's, Rockefeller NY #89/R est:5000-7000

STERN, Emma (1878-1970) German
£403 $713 €600 Cyclist (40x75cm-16x30in) s. panel. 30-Apr-4 Dr Fritz Nagel, Stuttgart #952/R

STERN, Ignaz (1680-1748) German
£4054 $7135 €6000 Guardian angel (26x19cm-10x7in) panel oval. 18-May-4 Sotheby's, Milan #477/R est:6000-8000
£30000 $54900 €45000 Saint John Nepomuceno (172x123cm-68x48in) 1-Jun-4 Sotheby's, Milan #45/R est:10000-15000

STERN, Ignaz (attrib) (1680-1748) German
£805 $1482 €1200 Madeleine (31x26cm-12x10in) oval. 26-Mar-4 Pierre Berge, Paris #16

STERN, Ignaz (circle) (1680-1748) German
£10791 $17698 €15000 Nativity (75x101cm-30x40in) 4-Jun-3 Sotheby's, Milan #38/R est:7000-10000

STERN, Irma (1894-1966) South African
£11207 $18716 €16362 Still life of flowers in a vase (47x35cm-19x14in) init.d.1931 board. 20-Oct-3 Stephan Welz, Johannesburg #365/R est:120000-150000 (SA.R 130000)
£12069 $20155 €17621 Bare breasted woman in a window (78x59cm-31x23in) s.d.1932. 20-Oct-3 Stephan Welz, Johannesburg #325/R est:180000-240000 (SA.R 140000)
£17949 $30513 €26206 Tree, Switzerland (86x68cm-34x27in) s.d.1959 i.verso. 4-Nov-3 Stephan Welz, Johannesburg #633/R est:250000-350000 (SA.R 210000)
£26891 $48672 €39261 Fishermen repairing nets with a harbour in the background (89x69cm-35x27in) s.d.1963. 30-Mar-4 Stephan Welz, Johannesburg #434/R est:300000-500000 (SA.R 320000)
£30172 $50388 €44051 Still life of lilies in a jug by the artist (87x87cm-34x34in) s.d.1944. 20-Oct-3 Stephan Welz, Johannesburg #279/R est:400000-600000 (SA.R 350000)
Prints
£3621 $6047 €5287 Seated nude (40x32cm-16x13in) s.d.1943 monotype. 20-Oct-3 Stephan Welz, Johannesburg #326/R est:12000-16000 (SA.R 42000)
Works on paper
£337 $620 €492 Woman holding container on her head (25x21cm-10x8in) pen ink. 8-Jun-4 Dales, Durban #5 (SA.R 4000)
£600 $1002 €876 Head and shoulder study of African lady (28x20cm-11x8in) s.d.1939 chl dr. 17-Oct-3 Keys, Aylsham #504/R
£798 $1445 €1165 Group of four musicians (12x17cm-5x7in) brush ink lit. 30-Mar-4 Stephan Welz, Johannesburg #493/R est:7000-10000 (SA.R 9500)
£900 $1593 €1314 Group of figures (29x26cm-11x10in) s.d.1931 ink W/C. 27-Apr-4 Bonhams, Knightsbridge #191/R
£1261 $2282 €1841 Three Malay women (18x17cm-7x7in) s.d.1932 pen ink wash. 30-Mar-4 Stephan Welz, Johannesburg #483/R est:7000-10000 (SA.R 15000)
£1724 $2879 €2517 Seated woman with a book (44x27cm-17x11in) s.d.1944 pen ink. 20-Oct-3 Stephan Welz, Johannesburg #347/R est:9000-12000 (SA.R 20000)
£1817 $3252 €2653 Workers in the field (29x20cm-11x8in) s.d.1961 ball-point pen. 31-May-4 Stephan Welz, Johannesburg #478/R est:9000-12000 (SA.R 22000)
£2642 $4730 €3857 Portrait of a woman (42x33cm-17x13in) s.d.1941 pencil. 31-May-4 Stephan Welz, Johannesburg #575/R est:20000-30000 (SA.R 32000)
£2890 $5173 €4219 Portrait of a woman with elaborate coiffure (47x33cm-19x13in) s.d.1935 chl. 31-May-4 Stephan Welz, Johannesburg #574/R est:20000-30000 (SA.R 35000)
£4274 $7265 €6240 Cape orchard with houses (35x48cm-14x19in) s.d.1933 W/C gouache. 4-Nov-3 Stephan Welz, Johannesburg #614/R est:12000-18000 (SA.R 50000)

STERN, Jonasz (1904-1987) Polish
£9655 $16124 €14000 Composition (70x53cm-28x21in) painted c.1948. 16-Nov-3 Agra, Warsaw #18/R est:6000
Works on paper
£372 $640 €543 Abstract composition (31x22cm-12x9in) W/C exec. c.1950. 4-Dec-3 Agra, Warsaw #44/R (P.Z 2500)
£625 $1075 €913 Abstract composition (29x20cm-11x8in) s.i. W/C exec.1953. 4-Dec-3 Agra, Warsaw #38/R (P.Z 4200)
£1517 $2534 €2200 Composition of a head (31x23cm-12x9in) gouache W/C exec. c.1950. 16-Nov-3 Agra, Warsaw #62/R est:500
£2825 $5113 €4125 Tablica X (55x44cm-22x17in) s.d.1977 collage. 4-Apr-4 Agra, Warsaw #60/R (P.Z 20000)

STERN, Max (1872-?) German
£1100 $1749 €1595 Couple on a beach by moonlight (39x58cm-15x23in) s.d.1898 prov. 9-Sep-3 Bonhams, Knightsbridge #234/R est:1200-1800
Works on paper
£1241 $2061 €1800 Cornelius Square in Dusseldorf (33x41cm-13x16in) s. i. verso pastel. 30-Sep-3 Dorotheum, Vienna #377/R est:2000-2400

STERNBERG, Harry (1904-) American
£688 $1100 €1004 Palm springs (61x76cm-24x30in) s. board painted c.1968. 17-May-3 Bunte, Elgin #1314 est:800-1200

STERNBERG, Nicolas (1901-) Hungarian
£284 $474 €400 Clowns (35x27cm-14x11in) cardboard on canvas. 14-Oct-3 Millon & Associes, Paris #294
£284 $474 €400 Jazzmen (55x46cm-22x18in) cardboard on canvas. 14-Oct-3 Millon & Associes, Paris #310
£319 $533 €450 Spectacle de rue (41x33cm-16x13in) cardboard. 14-Oct-3 Millon & Associes, Paris #300/R
£319 $533 €450 Portrait d'homme (35x27cm-14x11in) cardboard on canvas. 14-Oct-3 Millon & Associes, Paris #295/R
£355 $592 €500 Clowns (65x54cm-26x21in) s. 14-Oct-3 Millon & Associes, Paris #315/R
£369 $616 €520 Clown a la guitare (73x50cm-29x20in) mono. 14-Oct-3 Millon & Associes, Paris #316
£426 $711 €600 Clown (81x54cm-32x21in) 14-Oct-3 Millon & Associes, Paris #320
£482 $805 €680 Auto-portrait (73x60cm-29x24in) 14-Oct-3 Millon & Associes, Paris #319
£532 $888 €750 Clowns (55x46cm-22x18in) cardboard on canvas. 14-Oct-3 Millon & Associes, Paris #305/R
£638 $1066 €900 Jardin anime (61x50cm-24x20in) cardboard on canvas. 14-Oct-3 Millon & Associes, Paris #313/R
Works on paper
£270 $484 €400 Portrait de Nicolas Sternberg dessinant. s.d.1924 pen. 7-May-4 Millon & Associes, Paris #116
£284 $474 €400 Portrait de femme (79x58cm-31x23in) W/C. 14-Oct-3 Millon & Associes, Paris #284/R
£324 $581 €480 Portrait de Miche (49x32cm-19x13in) s.i.d.juillet 1929 black chk. 7-May-4 Millon & Associes, Paris #113
£387 $670 €550 Autoportrait (50x32cm-20x13in) mono.d.1926 chl. 10-Dec-3 Millon & Associes, Paris #38/R
£459 $822 €680 Portrait de Vital dans Volpone (49x32cm-19x13in) s.d.1929 black chk. 7-May-4 Millon & Associes, Paris #105/R
£743 $1330 €1100 Autoportrait (49x39cm-19x15in) s.d.1926 W/C black ink. 7-May-4 Millon & Associes, Paris #102/R
£1056 $1754 €1500 Portrait de femme (105x73cm-41x29in) s.d.1929 crayon dr prov.exhib. 13-Jun-3 Renaud, Paris #46/R est:700
£1081 $1935 €1600 L'aubade du clown blanc (49x32cm-19x13in) s.d.octobre 1929 graphite. 7-May-4 Millon & Associes, Paris #115/R est:200-250
£1149 $2056 €1700 Bijou (63x48cm-25x19in) s.i.d.octobre 1931 black chk W/C gouache. 7-May-4 Millon & Associes, Paris #107/R est:200-300

STERNE, Maurice (1878-1957) American
£315 $500 €460 Taos woman (55x30cm-22x12in) s. i.verso paper. 12-Sep-3 Skinner, Boston #317a/R
£615 $1100 €898 Along the Ganges, Benares (71x79cm-28x31in) s. 26-May-4 Doyle, New York #107/R
£615 $1100 €898 Pilgrimage, Benares (51x69cm-20x27in) s. 26-May-4 Doyle, New York #108/R

STERNER, Albert Edward (1863-1946) American
£950 $1700 €1387 Still life of fruit, flowers and sculpture of bust of a child (76x64cm-30x25in) s.d.38 s.i.stretcher exhib. 8-Jan-4 James Julia, Fairfield #978/R est:800-1200
Works on paper
£800 $1256 €1160 Introduction (43x34cm-17x13in) s.i.d.1903 pencil W/C bodycol. 28-Aug-3 Christie's, Kensington #493/R

STERNFELD, Joel (1944-) American
Photographs
£1693 $3200 €2472 Coeburn, Virginia, April 1981 (38x48cm-15x19in) dye transfer print. 17-Feb-4 Christie's, Rockefeller NY #164/R est:2000-3000
£3704 $7000 €5408 Lake Oswego, Oregon , June 1979 (34x43cm-13x17in) s.i.d.1982 dye transfer print. 17-Feb-4 Christie's, Rockefeller NY #165/R est:2000-3000
£3704 $7000 €5408 After the flash flood, Rancho Mirage, California, July 1979 (38x48cm-15x19in) s.i.d.1981 num.3/50 dye transfer print. 17-Feb-4 Christie's, Rockefeller NY #166/R est:2000-3000
£73446 $130000 €107231 On this site, landscape in memoriam (47x60cm-19x24in) s.i.d.1994-2000 53 color coupler prints prov.lit. 27-Apr-4 Christie's, Rockefeller NY #342/R est:90000-120000

STERRE DE JONG, Jacobus (1866-1920) Dutch
£541 $919 €790 Mealtime (46x36cm-18x14in) s. prov. 21-Nov-3 Walker's, Ottawa #202/R (C.D 1200)
£1316 $2382 €2000 Girl knitting with a small child, at the surf (44x33cm-17x13in) s. 19-Apr-4 Glerum, Amsterdam #125/R est:2500-3000
Works on paper
£724 $1332 €1100 Mother and daughter (30x40cm-12x16in) s. W/C. 28-Jun-4 Sotheby's, Amsterdam #21/R
£987 $1816 €1500 Feeding the goats (41x35cm-16x14in) s. W/C htd white exhib. 22-Jun-4 Christie's, Amsterdam #165/R est:1500-2000

STERREN, John van der (1938-) Dutch/Indonesian
£588 $1065 €858 Cathedral of the Good Shepherd Singapore (40x50cm-16x20in) s.d.96 i.d.Sept 96 verso. 3-Apr-4 Glerum, Singapore #6/R (S.D 1800)

STERRER, Karl (1885-1960) Austrian
£1133 $2040 €1700 You (155x89cm-61x35in) s.i.d.1964 masonite. 21-Apr-4 Dorotheum, Vienna #190/R est:2000-2600

STETSON, Charles Walter (1858-1911) American
£652 $1200 €952 Ladies in a forest interior (61x41cm-24x16in) s.d.94. 25-Jun-4 Freeman, Philadelphia #325/R

STETTEN, Carl von (attrib) (1857-?) German
Works on paper
£521 $859 €750 Mexican landscape (27x21cm-11x8in) i. verso W/C htd white. 2-Jul-3 Neumeister, Munich #494/R

STETTER, Dora (1881-1968) German
£940 $1729 €1400 Still life with potted geraniums (59x53cm-23x21in) s. 26-Mar-4 Bolland & Marotz, Bremen #631/R

STETTLER, Johann Bernhard (1778-1858) Swiss?
Works on paper
£603 $1080 €880 Insects (26x21cm-10x8in) s. W/C. 13-May-4 Stuker, Bern #9116/R (S.FR 1400)

STETTLER, Marthe (1870-1945) Swiss
£265 $485 €400 Paysage du Valais (26x33cm-10x13in) s.i.d.1914 panel. 7-Apr-4 Piasa, Paris #99

STETTNER, Louis (1922-) American
£1941 $3571 €2950 Femme au crepuscule (116x89cm-46x35in) s.d.2004. 27-Jun-4 Versailles Encheres #194/R est:1200-1500

STEUDEL, Max (1873-?) German
£423 $676 €600 Gladioli (80x70cm-31x28in) s. 18-Sep-3 Rieber, Stuttgart #1087

STEUERWALDT, Wilhelm II (attrib) (1815-1871) German
£1133 $2063 €1700 Monks on their way to church in a snowy church courtyard (29x38cm-11x15in) 1-Jul-4 Van Ham, Cologne #1632/R est:1500

STEVAN, Jean (1896-1962) Belgian
£310 $536 €440 Orchard with hen (30x39cm-12x15in) s. board. 13-Dec-3 De Vuyst, Lokeren #304
£338 $585 €480 Landscape with farm (40x50cm-16x20in) s. panel. 13-Dec-3 De Vuyst, Lokeren #305

STEVENS, Agapit (1849-1917) Belgian
£473 $847 €700 Jeune fille aux colombes (68x52cm-27x20in) s. 10-May-4 Horta, Bruxelles #327
£625 $1019 €900 Fileuses (76x58cm-30x23in) s. 23-Sep-3 Galerie Moderne, Brussels #721/R
£1007 $1862 €1500 Allegorie (80x62cm-31x24in) s. canvas on panel. 15-Mar-4 Horta, Bruxelles #279 est:800-1000
£1467 $2655 €2200 Joueuse de mandoline (75x55cm-30x22in) s. 30-Mar-4 Campo & Campo, Antwerp #277/R est:2200-2500
£4000 $7280 €6000 Full length portrait of a young woman dressed in finery adjusting her hair (75x51cm-30x20in) s.d.1873 panel. 20-Jun-4 Wilkinson, Doncaster #336 est:6000-8000

STEVENS, Aime (1879-?) Belgian
£405 $766 €600 La danseuse de flamenco (60x40cm-24x16in) s. 17-Feb-4 Galerie Moderne, Brussels #255/R

STEVENS, Albert George (1863-1925) British
Works on paper
£430 $740 €628 Gossips (24x33cm-9x13in) s. W/C. 2-Dec-3 Sworder & Son, Bishops Stortford #485b/R
£440 $700 €638 Breakers on the shore at Sandsend (30x45cm-12x18in) s.i.verso W/C. 9-Sep-3 David Duggleby, Scarborough #150
£480 $763 €696 Thatched cottages with gossips (26x38cm-10x15in) s. W/C. 9-Sep-3 David Duggleby, Scarborough #20/R
£3200 $5792 €4672 Study of an old woman knitting (28x18cm-11x7in) s.d.1909 W/C. 15-Apr-4 Richardson & Smith, Whitby #116/R est:400-600

STEVENS, Albert George (attrib) (1863-1925) British
Works on paper
£620 $1122 €905 Whitby from Bog Hall (24x36cm-9x14in) W/C. 30-Mar-4 David Duggleby, Scarborough #93/R

STEVENS, Alfred (1823-1906) Belgian
£430 $800 €628 Untitled (23x28cm-9x11in) board. 6-Mar-4 Page, Batavia #139
£662 $1205 €1000 Marine au clair de lune (41x33cm-16x13in) s. panel. 15-Jun-4 Blanchet, Paris #139/R
£1702 $2843 €2400 Marine (19x24cm-7x9in) mono. panel. 14-Oct-3 Vanderkindere, Brussels #23
£1800 $3240 €2628 Leaving port (40x33cm-16x13in) s. 21-Jan-4 Sotheby's, Olympia #402/R est:2000-3000
£2000 $3680 €3000 Barque de peche avant l'orage (32x24cm-13x9in) s. panel. 14-Jun-4 Horta, Bruxelles #97 est:3500-5500
£2113 $3782 €3000 Marine (18x11cm-7x4in) mono. panel. 11-Jan-4 Rouillac, Vendome #396
£2649 $4954 €4000 Voilier en mer soleil couchant (33x24cm-13x9in) s. paper. 24-Jul-4 Thierry & Lannon, Brest #223/R est:2500-3000
£3104 $5183 €4500 Promenade au pied d'une falaise en Normandie (40x60cm-16x24in) s. 17-Nov-3 Tajan, Paris #158/R est:4600-6000
£3289 $6053 €5000 Marine (31x41cm-12x16in) s. panel. 24-Jun-4 Claude Boisgirard, Paris #10/R est:5000-6000
£3333 $5967 €5000 Buste de femme (27x22cm-11x9in) mono. panel prov. 15-May-4 De Vuyst, Lokeren #435/R est:5000-7000
£3493 $6428 €5100 Honfleur (31x41cm-12x16in) s.d.91 i.d.Sept 91 verso panel. 14-Jun-4 Philippe Schuler, Zurich #4329/R est:3000-5000 (S.FR 8000)
£3819 $6302 €5500 Steam ship and sailing ships at sea (41x32cm-16x13in) s. panel. 2-Jul-3 Neumeister, Munich #782/R est:2500
£3916 $6540 €5600 Seascape (32x24cm-13x9in) s. panel. 29-Jun-3 Eric Pillon, Calais #35/R
£3972 $6633 €5600 Portrait de Solange de Biancourt (57x42cm-22x17in) s.d.1886. 14-Oct-3 Vanderkindere, Brussels #31/R
£4040 $7352 €6100 Le Treport (35x26cm-14x10in) s. panel. 20-Jun-4 Versailles Encheres #48/R est:2500-3000
£4828 $8931 €7000 Vapeur et voilier avant l'orage (41x33cm-16x13in) s. 19-Jan-4 Horta, Bruxelles #185/R est:4000-6000
£4895 $8420 €7000 Vapeur au clair de lune (56x46cm-22x18in) s. 3-Dec-3 Beaussant & Lefèvre, Paris #76/R est:7500-8000
£4965 $8291 €7000 Le Treport (32x41cm-13x16in) s. i.d.octobre 1890 verso panel. 17-Jun-3 Christie's, Paris #125/R est:4000-6000
£5600 $9128 €8176 Three quarter portrait of a girl holding a book (99x72cm-39x28in) 28-Sep-3 Wilkinson, Doncaster #278/R
£5667 $10143 €8500 Seascape (46x38cm-18x15in) s. panel exhib. 15-May-4 De Vuyst, Lokeren #436/R est:7000-9000
£5882 $10000 €8588 Jeune femme regardant la mer (32x24cm-13x9in) s. panel. 29-Oct-3 Christie's, Rockefeller NY #178/R est:20000-30000
£6040 $11174 €9000 Vue sur la plage (26x35cm-10x14in) s. panel lit. 13-Mar-4 De Vuyst, Lokeren #430/R est:7500-8500
£6993 $11888 €10000 La sortie de port (65x53cm-26x21in) s. 27-Nov-3 Millon & Associes, Paris #127/R est:10000-12000
£15363 $27500 €22430 Two women by the sea (25x35cm-10x14in) s. i.verso panel. 6-May-4 Doyle, New York #55/R est:30000-40000
£20000 $36400 €29200 Le bouquet (58x48cm-23x19in) s.d.57 prov.exhib.lit. 15-Jun-4 Sotheby's, London #182/R est:20000-30000
£28000 $51520 €40880 Sa Majeste La Parisienne (92x60cm-36x24in) s.d.1880 prov.lit. 23-Mar-4 Bonhams, New Bond Street #13/R est:30000-50000
£30000 $51600 €43800 An aspiring connoisseur (124x46cm-49x18in) s. prov. 3-Dec-3 Christie's, London #19/R est:30000-50000
Works on paper
£276 $510 €400 Deux elegantes (25x18cm-10x7in) mono. drawing wash. 19-Jan-4 Horta, Bruxelles #186
£530 $964 €800 Etude d'enfant pour le Mercredi des Cendres (32x20cm-13x8in) st.sig. chl stump white chk. 16-Jun-4 Piasa, Paris #229
£25000 $42500 €36500 Portrait of La Baronne du Mesnil de Saint-Front (194x84cm-76x33in) s.d.87 pastel prov.exhib.lit. 19-Nov-3 Bonhams, New Bond Street #11/R est:25000-35000

STEVENS, Alfred (attrib) (1823-1906) Belgian
£986 $1706 €1400 Portrait of young woman (45x32cm-18x13in) s.d.1886 board. 11-Dec-3 Dr Fritz Nagel, Stuttgart #549/R
£2993 $5358 €4400 Portrait de Solange de Briancourt (57x42cm-22x17in) s. 16-Mar-4 Vanderkindere, Brussels #169 est:700-1000

STEVENS, Edith Briscoe (1896-1931) American
£659 $1100 €962 October (41x51cm-16x20in) s. exhib. 20-Jun-3 Freeman, Philadelphia #117/R
£670 $1200 €978 Noon light, Gloucester, Mass (20x25cm-8x10in) s. i.verso canvasboard. 14-May-4 Skinner, Boston #253/R
£1954 $3125 €2853 Sailing ships at dock (76x64cm-30x25in) s. 16-Mar-3 Provenance, Pittstown #1325/R

STEVENS, Eion (1952-) New Zealander
£294 $526 €429 Glove (58x52cm-23x20in) s.i.d.2000 board. 12-May-4 Dunbar Sloane, Wellington #211 (NZ.D 850)
£319 $590 €466 Catching the 10.15 (91x75cm-36x30in) s.d.1989 i.verso. 13-Jul-4 Watson's, Christchurch #15/R (NZ.D 900)
£346 $619 €505 Prodigy (38x62cm-15x24in) s.i.d.6/92 verso board. 12-May-4 Dunbar Sloane, Wellington #9/R est:1000-2000 (NZ.D 1000)
£515 $963 €752 Bar Chords (72x64cm-28x25in) i. s.d.1994 verso board. 24-Feb-4 Peter Webb, Auckland #86/R (NZ.D 1400)
£692 $1239 €1010 Minstrel (80x69cm-31x27in) s.d.12/97 verso board. 11-May-4 Watson's, Christchurch #17/R (NZ.D 2000)
£868 $1380 €1267 Annunciation (76x76cm-30x30in) s.i.d.1.88 verso. 1-May-3 Dunbar Sloane, Wellington #46/R est:2000-3000 (NZ.D 2500)

STEVENS, George (19th C) British
£600 $1098 €876 Dead game and a basket on a ledge (20x25cm-8x10in) s.d.1842 mahogany panel. 7-Apr-4 Woolley & Wallis, Salisbury #280/R
£1000 $1850 €1460 Still life of game (76x63cm-30x25in) s.i. 14-Jul-4 Sotheby's, Olympia #52/R est:1000-1500
£1350 $2376 €1971 Blackcock in a landscape (20x25cm-8x10in) s.d.verso prov. 18-May-4 Woolley & Wallis, Salisbury #99/R est:3000-5000
£1923 $3500 €2808 Greyhound and a springer spaniel in a landscape (130x170cm-51x67in) s. 29-Jun-4 Peter Webb, Auckland #102/R est:8000-12000 (NZ.D 5500)

STEVENS, Gustav Max (1871-1946) German
£629 $1083 €900 Portrait of a small girl's head in profile (32x24cm-13x9in) s. board. 5-Dec-3 Bolland & Marotz, Bremen #661/R

STEVENS, John (1793-1868) British
£380 $703 €555 A lady and child out walking (79x40cm-31x16in) s. board. 13-Jan-4 Bonhams, Ipswich #268

STEVENS, John Calvin (1855-?) American
£1235 $2000 €1791 Coastal Maine in winter (30x41cm-12x16in) 8-Aug-3 Barridorf, Portland #208/R est:1000-1500

STEVENS, Joseph (1819-1892) Belgian
£839 $1427 €1200 Scene animaliere (21x15cm-8x6in) s.d.1869 panel. 18-Nov-3 Vanderkindere, Brussels #108
£1000 $1820 €1500 Two dogs waiting for their masters (32x25cm-13x10in) s. canvas on board. 1-Jul-4 Van Ham, Cologne #1633/R est:1200
£10000 $18000 €14600 Best friends (121x76cm-48x30in) s. prov. 22-Apr-4 Christie's, Rockefeller NY #160/R est:18000-22000

STEVENS, Leopold (1866-1935) French
£331 $606 €500 Port (40x60cm-16x24in) s. 7-Apr-4 Piasa, Paris #45

STEVENS, Mary L (19/20th C) American
£611 $1100 €892 View of San Joaquin Valley (33x54cm-13x21in) s.d.1905 prov. 24-Apr-4 Weschler, Washington #609/R

STEVENS, Nelson (1935-) American
£359 $600 €524 Song of a native son (76x117cm-30x46in) acrylic. 14-Nov-3 Du Mouchelle, Detroit #2104/R

STEVENS, Pieter (1567-1624) Flemish
Works on paper
£6081 $10703 €9000 Fantasy mountain landscape with buildings and ruins (19x31cm-7x12in) pen brown ink col wash red chk prov.exhib. 19-May-4 Sotheby's, Amsterdam #12/R est:10000-15000

STEVENS, Pieter (attrib) (1567-1624) Flemish
£17730 $29610 €25000 Cavalier et promeneurs en bord de foret. Depart pour le marche (77x113cm-30x44in) one bears sig pair prov. 22-Jun-3 Versailles Encheres #36/R est:22000

STEVENS, Stanford P (1897-1974) American
£329 $550 €480 Western landscape with Indians attacking a stage coach (64x102cm-25x40in) s. panel. 27-Oct-3 O'Gallerie, Oregon #78/R

STEVENS, Vera (1895-?) American
£1946 $3250 €2841 Boothbay Harbour (58x69cm-23x27in) s. i.stretcher prov.exhib. 23-Oct-3 Shannon's, Milford #2/R est:1500-2500

STEVENS, Will Henry (1881-1949) American
£1625 $2600 €2373 Stream in deep woods (51x41cm-20x16in) s. 20-Sep-3 New Orleans Auction, New Orleans #859/R
Works on paper
£1061 $1900 €1549 Untitled (56x43cm-22x17in) s. pastel. 16-May-4 Wright, Chicago #143/R est:2000-3000

STEVENS, William Capling (1870-1912) British
£300 $510 €438 Druids altar, Bingley (49x75cm-19x30in) s. 18-Nov-3 Bonhams, Leeds #222

STEVENS, William Lester (1888-1969) American
£824 $1400 €1203 Landscape (76x61cm-30x24in) s. board. 21-Nov-3 Eldred, East Dennis #694/R est:600-900
£1117 $2000 €1631 Lanesville harbour, Cape Ann (31x35cm-12x14in) s. i.verso masonite prov. 14-May-4 Skinner, Boston #249/R est:1500-2500
£1117 $2000 €1631 Winter brook (56x46cm-22x18in) 7-May-4 Douglas, South Deerfield #23
£1297 $2400 €1894 Rockport Marsh with boat (51x61cm-20x24in) s. 13-Feb-4 David Rago, Lambertville #13/R
£1564 $2800 €2283 Boats at dockside (58x51cm-23x20in) 7-May-4 Douglas, South Deerfield #8
£1564 $2800 €2283 Ocean and shore (74x56cm-29x22in) 7-May-4 Douglas, South Deerfield #9
£1732 $3100 €2529 Cliff, sailboats and shack (71x61cm-28x24in) 7-May-4 Douglas, South Deerfield #4
£1732 $3100 €2529 Apple blossoms, sheep and shepherd (61x51cm-24x20in) 7-May-4 Douglas, South Deerfield #10
£2011 $3600 €2936 Rocky shore and sailboat (56x51cm-22x20in) 7-May-4 Douglas, South Deerfield #7
£2210 $4000 €3227 Wilderness (91x76cm-36x30in) masonite. 2-Apr-4 Douglas, South Deerfield #1
£2402 $4300 €3507 Ocean sailboat and rocks (102x76cm-40x30in) 7-May-4 Douglas, South Deerfield #1
£2626 $4700 €3834 Fall impressions (51x51cm-20x20in) 7-May-4 Douglas, South Deerfield #6
£2849 $5100 €4160 Marsh with cows and sailboat (76x51cm-30x20in) 7-May-4 Douglas, South Deerfield #21
£2961 $5300 €4323 Barn, house in fall (61x51cm-24x20in) 7-May-4 Douglas, South Deerfield #5
£3022 $5500 €4412 Port scene, Vinal Haven, Maine (64x76cm-25x30in) s. 7-Feb-4 Sloans & Kenyon, Bethesda #1312/R est:4000-6000
£3039 $5500 €4437 Coastal with tree and lighthouse (89x76cm-35x30in) masonite. 2-Apr-4 Douglas, South Deerfield #2
£3184 $5700 €4649 Pigean Cove (61x51cm-24x20in) 7-May-4 Douglas, South Deerfield #3
£3315 $6000 €4840 Upland road (36x30cm-14x12in) masonite. 2-Apr-4 Douglas, South Deerfield #4
£3495 $6500 €5103 North shore wharf (60x76cm-24x30in) s. 5-Mar-4 Skinner, Boston #536/R est:1500-2500
£3632 $6500 €5303 Road to the farm (81x91cm-32x36in) s. exhib. 6-May-4 Shannon's, Milford #220/R est:6000-8000
£4190 $7500 €6117 Lone maple (74x91cm-29x36in) s. i.verso. 6-May-4 Shannon's, Milford #162/R est:6000-8000
£4190 $7500 €6117 Sunlit sea, Vinal Haven, Maine (61x91cm-24x36in) s. i.verso prov. 14-May-4 Skinner, Boston #238/R est:2500-3500
£4469 $8000 €6525 Cliffs of Grand Manan (86x96cm-34x38in) s. i.verso masonite prov. 14-May-4 Skinner, Boston #177/R est:4000-6000
£4749 $8500 €6934 Berkshire snow (91x61cm-36x24in) 7-May-4 Douglas, South Deerfield #2
£6145 $11000 €8972 Bridge (81x91cm-32x36in) s. masonite prov. 14-May-4 Skinner, Boston #228/R est:4000-6000
£11173 $20000 €16313 Canal lock New Hope, Pennsylvania (36x36cm-14x14in) s. painted c.1927-1929. 6-May-4 Shannon's, Milford #135/R est:20000-30000
Works on paper
£279 $500 €407 Pond with arch bridge (48x38cm-19x15in) W/C. 7-May-4 Douglas, South Deerfield #17
£279 $500 €407 Rocky shore with Freighter (36x25cm-14x10in) W/C. 7-May-4 Douglas, South Deerfield #30
£313 $500 €457 Harbour scene with village (43x53cm-17x21in) s. W/C. 20-Sep-3 Pook & Pook, Downington #177
£335 $600 €489 Light on the sea (69x53cm-27x21in) W/C. 7-May-4 Douglas, South Deerfield #14
£447 $800 €653 Village with shacks (56x46cm-22x18in) W/C. 7-May-4 Douglas, South Deerfield #26
£559 $1000 €816 Village with church (56x46cm-22x18in) W/C. 7-May-4 Douglas, South Deerfield #12
£588 $1000 €858 Hillside landscape, winter (46x71cm-18x28in) s. W/C gouache. 21-Nov-3 Skinner, Boston #498/R est:500-700
£670 $1200 €978 Boats at dockside (71x53cm-28x21in) W/C. 7-May-4 Douglas, South Deerfield #28
£754 $1350 €1101 Seacoast village (46x56cm-18x22in) s. W/C. 8-Jan-4 James Julia, Fairfield #934/R est:800-1200
£782 $1400 €1142 Village with bridge, hills (56x46cm-22x18in) W/C. 7-May-4 Douglas, South Deerfield #13
£950 $1700 €1387 Boat at dockside (61x51cm-24x20in) W/C. 7-May-4 Douglas, South Deerfield #22
£950 $1700 €1387 Farm with hills (64x51cm-25x20in) W/C. 7-May-4 Douglas, South Deerfield #27
£1117 $2000 €1631 Building entrance (28x33cm-11x13in) gouache. 7-May-4 Douglas, South Deerfield #20
£1173 $2100 €1713 On the Aron (38x30cm-15x12in) gouache. 7-May-4 Douglas, South Deerfield #19
£1211 $1950 €1768 Morning light (36x43cm-14x17in) s. W/C. 20-Aug-3 James Julia, Fairfield #1656/R est:1500-2500
£1453 $2600 €2121 Winter brook and bridge (28x23cm-11x9in) gouache. 7-May-4 Douglas, South Deerfield #15
£1620 $2900 €2365 Church and house (43x53cm-17x21in) W/C. 7-May-4 Douglas, South Deerfield #11
£1620 $2900 €2365 Lighthouse on rocks (64x48cm-25x19in) W/C. 7-May-4 Douglas, South Deerfield #18
£1934 $3500 €2824 Charcoal kilns at Leverett, Mass (51x71cm-20x28in) W/C. 2-Apr-4 Douglas, South Deerfield #3
£2793 $5000 €4078 Village Brittany (28x23cm-11x9in) gouache. 7-May-4 Douglas, South Deerfield #16

STEVENS, William Lester (attrib) (1888-1969) American
£435 $700 €635 Bass rocks (51x61cm-20x24in) 20-Aug-3 James Julia, Fairfield #1657/R

STEVENSON, Florence Ezzell (1894-?) American
£375 $600 €548 Flowers arrangement (61x51cm-24x20in) s. canvasboard painted c.1940. 17-May-3 Bunte, Elgin #1343

STEVENSON, Harold (1929-) American
£347 $600 €507 Thumb (53x36cm-21x14in) prov. 15-Dec-3 Hindman, Chicago #103/R
Works on paper
£347 $549 €500 Untitled (73x53cm-29x21in) s. mixed media prov. 27-Apr-3 Versailles Encheres #78

STEVENSON, Patric (1909-1983) Irish
£340 $558 €496 Rhododendrons in the Mournes (30x45cm-12x18in) s.d.1963 verso egg tempera. 4-Jun-3 John Ross, Belfast #195
£450 $805 €670 Lighthouse (33x25cm-13x10in) s. board prov. 26-May-4 James Adam, Dublin #166/R
£878 $1660 €1300 Down cathedral, and Southwell school, Downpatrick (46x33cm-18x13in) s. board. 17-Feb-4 Whyte's, Dublin #172/R est:2000-3000

STEVENSON, Robert Macaulay (1860-1952) British
£700 $1099 €1015 Pastoral landscape (45x61cm-18x24in) s. prov. 27-Aug-3 Sotheby's, London #1043/R
£1400 $2338 €2044 Bend in the river (70x90cm-28x35in) s. 16-Oct-3 Lyon & Turnbull, Edinburgh #94 est:400-600

STEVENSON, William Grant (1849-1919) British
£700 $1169 €1022 Kitten and a frog (20x28cm-8x11in) s.d.1881 board. 16-Oct-3 Bonhams, Edinburgh #159

STEVENSON, William Leroy (1905-1966) Canadian
£297 $550 €434 Landscape with trees (61x76cm-24x30in) s. board. 12-Mar-4 Jackson's, Cedar Falls #1013/R
£307 $500 €448 Landscape with trees (61x76cm-24x30in) s. board. 24-Sep-3 Jackson's, Cedar Falls #757/R
£432 $721 €631 In Queen Elizabeth Park (40x50cm-16x20in) s.i. board. 17-Nov-3 Hodgins, Calgary #288/R est:1000-1500 (C.D 955)
£543 $907 €793 Shady pool (40x50cm-16x20in) s.i. board. 17-Nov-3 Hodgins, Calgary #46/R est:1000-1500 (C.D 1200)
£588 $982 €858 Flowers (50x40cm-20x16in) s.i. board prov. 17-Nov-3 Hodgins, Calgary #140/R est:1000-1500 (C.D 1300)

STEVER, Jorge (1940-) German
£366 $648 €534 Untitled (140x112cm-55x44in) s. acrylic chk prov. 27-Apr-4 AB Stockholms Auktionsverk #1190/R (S.KR 5000)
Works on paper
£534 $845 €780 Tulips (180x20cm-71x8in) mixed media panel diptych. 27-Apr-3 Subastas Odalys, Caracas #82

STEWARD, Seth W (1844-1924) American
£279 $500 €407 Maine landscape (15x33cm-6x13in) s.d.1919 board. 8-Jan-4 James Julia, Fairfield #873/R

STEWART, Allan (1865-1951) British
£500 $790 €725 Cavalier in an interior (36x26cm-14x10in) s. prov. 4-Sep-3 Christie's, Kensington #251/R

STEWART, Allison (20th C) American
Works on paper
£441 $750 €644 Path 17. 1988 (61x91cm-24x36in) mixed media. 22-Nov-3 New Orleans Auction, New Orleans #1265
£441 $750 €644 Path 7, 1987 (61x91cm-24x36in) mixed media. 22-Nov-3 New Orleans Auction, New Orleans #1266
£588 $1000 €858 Path 11, 1988 (61x91cm-24x36in) mixed media. 22-Nov-3 New Orleans Auction, New Orleans #1264/R est:800-1200

STEWART, Cecil Thornley (1881-1967) South African
£345 $576 €504 Ceightley's Krantz (67x100cm-26x39in) s. board. 20-Oct-3 Stephan Welz, Johannesburg #781 est:4000-6000 (SA.R 4000)

STEWART, Charles Edward (fl.1890-1930) British
£2800 $4760 €4088 Midwinter steeplechase (46x61cm-18x24in) s. 19-Nov-3 Sotheby's, Olympia #73/R est:3000-5000
Works on paper
£650 $1105 €949 Huntsmen and hounds on a woodland track (30x39cm-12x15in) init. W/C. 19-Nov-3 Sotheby's, Olympia #71/R

STEWART, F A (1877-1945) British
£560 $1025 €818 Laneway, Corktown (44x31cm-17x12in) s. canvas on board. 1-Jun-4 Joyner Waddington, Toronto #353/R (C.D 1400)
Works on paper
£1800 $3240 €2628 Cheshire hunting in the Wirrall at Winsham Gorse (23x36cm-9x14in) s. W/C. 21-Apr-4 Brightwells, Leominster #756/R est:1200-1600

STEWART, Frank Algernon (1877-1945) British
Works on paper
£340 $530 €496 Cottesmore, hark to hounds (15x28cm-6x11in) init. i.verso pen ink over pencil. 28-Mar-3 Greenslade Hunt, Taunton #487/R
£1500 $2700 €2190 Pytchley hunt away from Waterloo Gorse (28x42cm-11x17in) s. W/C. 23-Apr-4 Charterhouse, Sherborne #654/R
£7500 $13875 €10950 Hunting by the ocean, Cattistock (43x64cm-17x25in) s.i.d.1938 W/C bodycol. 11-Mar-4 Duke & Son, Dorchester #64/R est:5000-8000

STEWART, Grace Bliss (1895-?) American
£234 $425 €351 Fishing boats (20x23cm-8x9in) s. painted c.1940-1950. 16-Jun-4 Wolf's, New York #487308/R

STEWART, Ida Lillie Strother (c.1890-1965) British
£950 $1511 €1387 Isabella and Lorenzo (45x56cm-18x22in) s.i. panel. 18-Mar-3 Anderson & Garland, Newcastle #504/R

STEWART, James (1791-1863) British
£350 $613 €511 Children by the coast (40x55cm-16x22in) 18-Dec-3 Bonhams, Edinburgh #367

STEWART, James (attrib) (1791-1863) British
Works on paper
£300 $549 €438 View of Holyrood Palace (15x23cm-6x9in) pen ink wash. 28-Jul-4 Mallams, Oxford #117/R

STEWART, James Lawson (fl.1883-1889) British
Works on paper
£280 $515 €409 Village street scene (63x98cm-25x39in) s. W/C. 23-Mar-4 Rosebery Fine Art, London #815
£310 $546 €453 Old London Bridge (92x76cm-36x30in) s. W/C. 19-May-4 John Bellman, Billingshurst #1819
£400 $640 €584 View of the Old Council House of the Marches of Wales (51x76cm-20x30in) s. W/C. 17-Sep-3 Brightwells, Leominster #839
£450 $832 €657 Factory worker (12x22cm-5x9in) s. W/C. 10-Mar-4 Sotheby's, Olympia #85/R
£450 $828 €657 Study of a 16th Century Farmhouse with figure and duck pond (36x51cm-14x20in) s. W/C. 8-Jun-4 Peter Francis, Wales #37/R
£450 $819 €657 Village cross (64x93cm-25x37in) s. pencil W/C htd white. 1-Jul-4 Mellors & Kirk, Nottingham #713
£500 $835 €730 Stone building by a river (49x75cm-19x30in) s. W/C. 21-Oct-3 Sworder & Son, Bishops Stortford #301/R
£520 $957 €759 On a river-way in a Continental town (63x102cm-25x40in) s. W/C. 24-Mar-4 Hamptons Fine Art, Godalming #265/R
£600 $1074 €876 Chingford Church (64x99cm-25x39in) s. W/C. 25-May-4 Bonhams, Knightsbridge #87/R
£650 $1196 €949 Tutbury Castle, Staffordshire (51x71cm-20x28in) s. W/C. 8-Jun-4 Peter Francis, Wales #36/R
£850 $1420 €1241 St Paul's wharf (47x69cm-19x27in) s. W/C. 7-Oct-3 Bonhams, Knightsbridge #32/R
£1000 $1730 €1460 The Westgate and Leicester Hospital (64x97cm-25x38in) s. W/C. 11-Dec-3 Ewbank, Send #411/R est:400-600

STEWART, John (19/20th C) British
Works on paper
£250 $415 €365 Saturnia and Andrew Doria, off Gibralta (52x77cm-20x30in) s. gouache. 1-Oct-3 Bonhams, Knightsbridge #103/R
£280 $465 €409 Leviathon, being towed into port (37x55cm-15x22in) s. gouache. 1-Oct-3 Bonhams, Knightsbridge #102/R
£300 $498 €438 United States, leaving the Cherbourg Peninsular (38x56cm-15x22in) s. gouache. 1-Oct-3 Bonhams, Knightsbridge #101/R
£320 $544 €467 The Achille Lauro departing from Genoa (37x55cm-15x22in) s. W/C bodycol. 19-Nov-3 Christie's, Kensington #399/R
£1530 $2800 €2234 R M S Titanic embarking on her maiden voyage with the Needles off to port (60x95cm-24x37in) s. W/C gouache. 29-Jul-4 Christie's, Rockefeller NY #215/R est:1500-2000

STEWART, John (19/20th C) British
Works on paper
£450 $765 €657 Mount Stewart in heavy swell (46x70cm-18x28in) s.d.1970 W/C htd gouache. 25-Nov-3 Bonhams, Knightsbridge #45/R

STEWART, Julius L (1855-1919) American
£3521 $6162 €5000 Jeune femme de profil (41cm-16in circular) s.d.1903. 17-Dec-3 Rabourdin & Choppin de Janvry, Paris #80 est:8000-10000
£56667 $104267 €85000 Conversation venitienne (73x101cm-29x40in) s.i.d.1891 lit. 11-Jun-4 Claude Aguttes, Neuilly #28/R est:50000-60000
Works on paper
£2695 $4500 €3935 Fashionable lady (49x29cm-19x11in) s.d.79 chl. 7-Oct-3 Sotheby's, New York #192 est:5000-7000

STEWART, Mark (1951-) American
Works on paper
£311 $500 €451 Rock Island (64x97cm-25x38in) W/C. 22-Aug-3 Altermann Galleries, Santa Fe #168

STEWART, Robert W (20th C) American
Works on paper
£262 $450 €383 Central Park (28x36cm-11x14in) s. W/C exec.c.1930. 7-Dec-3 Treadway Gallery, Cincinnati #624/R

STEWART, Ron (1941-) Canadian
Works on paper
£683 $1100 €990 Trapper's loss (38x76cm-15x30in) W/C. 22-Aug-3 Altermann Galleries, Santa Fe #70

STEWART, William (?) British
Works on paper
£250 $400 €365 Harbour with sailing barges and other shipping at anchor (26x49cm-10x19in) s. W/C. 16-Sep-3 Holloways, Banbury #266

STEYAERT, Anton Pieter (1788-1863) Flemish
£3401 $6088 €5000 Landscape with trees, herder and cattle (53x67cm-21x26in) s.d.1826 panel. 17-Mar-4 Neumeister, Munich #616/R est:4800

STEYAERT, Francois (1863-1948) Belgian
£1007 $1862 €1500 Farm houses in a winter landscape (55x60cm-22x24in) s. 15-Mar-4 Sotheby's, Amsterdam #213/R est:750-850

STEYER, Chester L (20th C) American
£546 $1000 €797 Winter stream (53x69cm-21x27in) s. painted c.1920. 5-Jun-4 Treadway Gallery, Cincinnati #567/R est:1250-1750

STEYN, Stella (1907-1987) British/Irish
£572 $1053 €870 Fruit on a table (33x46cm-13x18in) prov. 22-Jun-4 De Veres Art Auctions, Dublin #201/R
£1067 $1931 €1600 Daffodils in a jug (51x35cm-20x14in) board prov. 30-Mar-4 De Veres Art Auctions, Dublin #240/R est:1000-1500
£2098 $3566 €3000 Model seated on a Bentwood chair (83x48cm-33x19in) prov. 18-Nov-3 Whyte's, Dublin #132/R est:3000-4000
£2098 $3566 €3000 Still life composition (51x69cm-20x27in) studio st. 25-Nov-3 De Veres Art Auctions, Dublin #141/R est:3000-4000
£2517 $4280 €3600 Reclining female nude (36x69cm-14x27in) 25-Nov-3 De Veres Art Auctions, Dublin #137/R est:3500-5000
£4895 $8322 €7000 Still life (87x81cm-34x32in) studio st. 25-Nov-3 De Veres Art Auctions, Dublin #138/R est:7000-9000
Works on paper
£260 $442 €380 Red C (21x14cm-8x6in) mixed media. 18-Nov-3 Bonhams, Knightsbridge #186/R
£333 $603 €500 Admiring the view (16x19cm-6x7in) ink prov. 30-Mar-4 De Veres Art Auctions, Dublin #219/R
£573 $975 €820 My poor husband always considered (26x21cm-10x8in) pen ink. 25-Nov-3 De Veres Art Auctions, Dublin #140/R
£633 $1146 €950 Boring group (18x24cm-7x9in) wash prov. 30-Mar-4 De Veres Art Auctions, Dublin #218/R
£946 $1788 €1400 Acrobats (14x13cm-6x5in) studio st. gouache crayon exhib. 17-Feb-4 Whyte's, Dublin #1/R est:800-1200

STEYNBERG, Coert (1905-1982) South African
Sculpture
£1552 $2591 €2266 Op die strand (41cm-16in) s.d.79 bronze. 20-Oct-3 Stephan Welz, Johannesburg #786 est:2000-3000 (SA.R 18000)

STIACCINI, U (19/20th C) Italian
Sculpture
£4167 $7500 €6084 Young girl seated on a cushioned stool, looking at a mouse (49cm-19in) s. ormolu alabaster marble base. 23-Apr-4 Christie's, Rockefeller NY #103/R est:4000-6000

STICK, Frank (1884-1966) American
£14706 $27500 €21471 Prize catch (66x91cm-26x36in) s. lit. 24-Jul-4 Coeur d'Alene, Hayden #11/R est:10000-20000

STICKS, George Blackie (1843-1938) British
£260 $478 €380 Ruined castle by a loch at sunset (13x13cm-5x5in) s.d.80 board round. 23-Mar-4 Anderson & Garland, Newcastle #369
£420 $752 €613 Loch Gail, Scotland (58x41cm-23x16in) s.d.1894 i.verso. 17-Mar-4 Bonhams, Chester #360
£440 $735 €642 In the highlands (30x25cm-12x10in) s.d.1871. 16-Oct-3 Bonhams, Edinburgh #198
£800 $1440 €1168 Glengarry Castle, evening (46x38cm-18x15in) s.i.d.1893. 21-Apr-4 Tennants, Leyburn #1139
£820 $1369 €1197 Bambrough Castle (35x46cm-14x18in) s. i.verso. 12-Nov-3 Sotheby's, Olympia #67/R
£850 $1505 €1241 Glen Coe and bridge of the three waters (50x74cm-20x29in) s.d.1880 i.verso. 28-Apr-4 Peter Wilson, Nantwich #82
£900 $1611 €1314 Island of Bute, moonrise (24x49cm-9x19in) s.d.1878 s.i.d.verso. 18-Mar-4 Neales, Nottingham #763/R
£1050 $1911 €1533 Dunstarn Castle, Canty Bay, South Berwick (20x30cm-8x12in) s. i.d.1873 verso pair. 15-Jun-4 Bonhams, Leeds #112/R
£1500 $2445 €2190 Marsden Bay, a figure salvaging rigging after a storm (89x68cm-35x27in) s.d.1895 s.indis.i. verso. 23-Sep-3 Anderson & Garland, Newcastle #320/R est:900-1300
£1600 $2560 €2336 Dunstanburgh Castle (91x71cm-36x28in) s. indis.i.d.1894. 16-Sep-3 Bonhams, Knowle #93/R est:800-1200
£6993 $12028 €10000 Troupeau dans un paturage sur fond de Grampions Hills (78x153cm-31x60in) s.d.1891. 8-Dec-3 Horta, Bruxelles #219/R est:15000-20000

STICKS, George Blackie (attrib) (1843-1938) British
£640 $1088 €934 Loch Ard (40x55cm-16x22in) 18-Nov-3 Bonhams, Leeds #214/R

STICKS, Harry (1867-1938) British
£760 $1201 €1110 Mountainous Highland scene with raging river (41x66cm-16x26in) s. 23-Jul-3 Grant, Worcester #484/R
£1450 $2509 €2117 Comb Hill, Borrowdale (40x65cm-16x26in) s. i.verso. 9-Dec-3 Anderson & Garland, Newcastle #418/R est:700-1100
Works on paper
£680 $1251 €993 Country road curving past a farmhouse. Sunlit coastal view (19x27cm-7x11in) s. W/C pair. 23-Mar-4 Anderson & Garland, Newcastle #245

STIDHAM, Michael (20th C) American
£554 $925 €809 Mako shark (58x89cm-23x35in) s. 11-Oct-3 Nadeau, Windsor #156/R

STIEF, Sebastian (1811-1889) Austrian
£986 $1706 €1400 View of Salzburg (24x41cm-9x16in) s.d.1871. 10-Dec-3 Dorotheum, Vienna #6/R
£1818 $3091 €2600 Arrival of St Rupert with Chuniald and Gislar at ruins of Iuvavums (81x117cm-32x46in) s.d.1885. 20-Nov-3 Dorotheum, Salzburg #142/R est:5200-7000

STIEFEL, Eduard (1875-1968) Swiss
£633 $1014 €924 Shepherd scene near Ebnat-Kappel (111x111cm-44x44in) s. prov. 16-Sep-3 Philippe Schuler, Zurich #3256/R (S.FR 1400)

STIEGEL, Eduard (1818-1879) German
Works on paper
£270 $484 €400 Hesslar in Hessen (20x31cm-8x12in) s.d. w/C. 4-May-4 Hartung & Hartung, Munich #4078/R

STIEGLITZ, Alfred (1864-1946) American
Photographs
£2540 $4800 €3708 Three steerage (19x15cm-7x6in) num.36 photogravure. 17-Feb-4 Christie's, Rockefeller NY #35/R est:5000-7000
£2762 $5000 €4033 Steerage (19x15cm-7x6in) num.36 photogravure. 19-Apr-4 Bonhams & Butterfields, San Francisco #329/R est:2000-3000
£3107 $5500 €4536 Hand of man (16x21cm-6x8in) s.d.04 photogravure tissue. 28-Apr-4 Sotheby's, New York #108/R est:5000-7000
£4491 $7500 €6557 Equivalent. Study at Lake George (9x11cm-4x4in) photos mounted back to back exec.c.1930. 17-Oct-3 Sotheby's, New York #189/R est:10000-15000
£5689 $9500 €8306 Steerage (33x26cm-13x10in) photogravure exec.1907 printed c.1915 prov. 17-Oct-3 Sotheby's, New York #135/R est:10000-15000
£6215 $11000 €9074 Steerage (33x26cm-13x10in) photogravure vellum. 28-Apr-4 Sotheby's, New York #110/R est:10000-15000
£7345 $13000 €10724 Steerage, 1907 (32x26cm-13x10in) large format photogravure lit. 27-Apr-4 Christie's, Rockefeller NY #244/R est:10000-15000
£10180 $17000 €14863 Spring showers (31x13cm-12x5in) photogravure board exec.1899 printed later. 17-Oct-3 Sotheby's, New York #186/R est:8000-12000
£10734 $19000 €15672 Spring showers (31x13cm-12x5in) photogravure printed 1903-4. 28-Apr-4 Sotheby's, New York #111/R est:10000-20000
£25000 $45000 €36500 Poplars lake George. Equivalent W5. Lake George (12x9cm-5x4in) gelatin silver print mounted on board set of three prov.lit. 23-Apr-4 Phillips, New York #65/R est:40000-60000

STIELER, Joseph Karl (1781-1858) German
£805 $1482 €1200 Portrait d'homme au foulard blanc (33x27cm-13x11in) mono.d.824. 24-Mar-4 Tajan, Paris #76

STIELER, Joseph Karl (attrib) (1781-1858) German
£3364 $5316 €4878 Portraits of Goethe and Schiller, two German poets (36x29cm-14x11in) indis.sig.one d.1837 pair. 2-Sep-3 Rasmussen, Copenhagen #1586/R est:30000 (D.KR 36000)

STIELER, Joseph Karl (studio) (1781-1858) German
£10333 $18910 €15500 Portrait de Ludovika et Maximilien de Baviere (72x51cm-28x20in) prov. 6-Jun-4 Rouillac, Vendome #15

STIELER, Robert (1847-1908) German
£451 $754 €650 Village street (63x45cm-25x18in) s. canvas on board. 24-Oct-3 Ketterer, Hamburg #234/R

STIEPEVICH, Vincent G (1841-1910) Russian
£898 $1500 €1311 Good news (61x51cm-24x20in) s. 20-Jun-3 Freeman, Philadelphia #116/R est:400-600
£1111 $1800 €1611 Harem favorite II (51x41cm-20x16in) s. canvas on board prov. 8-Aug-3 Barridorf, Portland #356/R est:3000-5000
£8025 $13000 €11636 Harem favorite (76x51cm-30x20in) s. 8-Aug-3 Barridorf, Portland #89/R est:15000-20000

STIERHOUT, Joop (1911-1997) Dutch
£510 $929 €750 Blaubrug, Amsterdam (60x50cm-24x20in) s. prov. 3-Feb-4 Christie's, Amsterdam #340/R
£680 $1238 €1000 Still life with tulips and cherry blossom (80x100cm-31x39in) s. 3-Feb-4 Christie's, Amsterdam #505 est:1000-1500
£748 $1362 €1100 Galerij aan de stadhouderskade, Amsterdam (60x80cm-24x31in) s. i.stretcher prov. 3-Feb-4 Christie's, Amsterdam #343 est:700-900
£884 $1610 €1300 Pink roses (15x13cm-6x5in) s. sold with four others by same hand. 3-Feb-4 Christie's, Amsterdam #506 est:500-700
£952 $1733 €1400 Paleis op de dam (50x60cm-20x24in) s. two. 3-Feb-4 Christie's, Amsterdam #338/R est:600-800
£1156 $2105 €1700 Building of the Stopera, Amsterdam (51x71cm-20x28in) s.d.82 prov. 3-Feb-4 Christie's, Amsterdam #339/R est:800-1200
£1156 $2105 €1700 Court of Justice, Prinsengracht, Amsterdam (60x90cm-24x35in) s. prov. 3-Feb-4 Christie's, Amsterdam #341 est:600-800
£3265 $5943 €4800 View of the Amstel with Carree theatre in the distance (80x130cm-31x51in) s. prov. 3-Feb-4 Christie's, Amsterdam #337/R est:3000-5000

STIERLE, Edmund (20th C) ?
£324 $571 €480 Sailing boats and gondolas in Venice (99x82cm-39x32in) s.d.24. 21-May-4 Mehlis, Plauen #15190/R

STIFTER, Moritz (1857-1905) Austrian
£3200 $5504 €4672 Elegant women in interiors (21x13cm-8x5in) s. panel pair. 4-Dec-3 Christie's, Kensington #130/R est:1500-2000
£11364 $20000 €16591 Rhamazan Bride (58x36cm-23x14in) s. panel prov. 23-May-4 Hindman, Chicago #19/R est:5000-7000

STIFTER, Moritz (attrib) (1857-1905) Austrian
£369 $679 €550 Girl in traditional old German dress (18x13cm-7x5in) s. lit. 25-Mar-4 Karlheinz Kaupp, Staufen #2749/R

STIGLMAIER, Johann Baptist (1791-1844) German
£743 $1308 €1100 Mountainous landscape with lake (14x20cm-6x8in) s.verso board. 18-May-4 Segre, Madrid #76/R

STIGLMAYER, Johann (19th C) German
£455 $773 €650 Fishermen on Gosausee (14x20cm-6x8in) s. board. 20-Nov-3 Dorotheum, Salzburg #159/R

STIHA, Vladan (1908-1992) American
£559 $900 €811 Indian in snow (30x41cm-12x16in) board. 22-Aug-3 Altermann Galleries, Santa Fe #55

STIKVOORT, Koos (1891-?) Dutch
£417 $658 €600 Dead sparrow (12x16cm-5x6in) s.d.1973 panel. 2-Sep-3 Christie's, Amsterdam #431

STILL, Clyfford (1904-1980) American
£628743 $1050000 €917965 1950-T (140x112cm-55x44in) painted 1950 prov.exhib. 11-Nov-3 Christie's, Rockefeller NY #24/R est:1200000-1600000
£1017964 $1700000 €1486227 1945-R (88x79cm-35x31in) with sig.i.d.45 prov.exhib. 11-Nov-3 Christie's, Rockefeller NY #23/R est:1200000-1600000
£1564246 $2800000 €2283799 1960-F (285x368cm-112x145in) s.i.d.1960 verso prov.exhib.lit. 12-May-4 Sotheby's, New York #20/R est:3000000-4000000

STILLING, H C (?) ?
Works on paper
£1106 $1880 €1615 View of Venice (35x26cm-14x10in) i.d.1851 verso W/C. 10-Nov-3 Rasmussen, Vejle #4/R est:15000 (D.KR 12000)

STILLING, Harald (1815-1891) Danish
Works on paper
£284 $508 €415 Mother and child seated at a farm in Sorent (24x17cm-9x7in) init.i. 12-Jan-4 Rasmussen, Vejle #296 (D.KR 3000)
£425 $761 €621 Ruins at Pompeii (22x29cm-9x11in) init.i. W/C. 12-Jan-4 Rasmussen, Vejle #368 (D.KR 4500)

STILLMAN, Marie Spartali (1844-1927) British
Works on paper
£2400 $4008 €3504 Angel holing a white lily (28x53cm-11x21in) mono.d.91 W/C. 7-Oct-3 Fellows & Sons, Birmingham #490/R est:1500-2500
£7000 $12950 €10220 Autumn (38x28cm-15x11in) mono. W/C bodycol. 9-Mar-4 Bonhams, New Bond Street #68/R est:6000-8000
£50000 $85000 €73000 Childhood of Saint Cecily (10x74cm-4x29in) mono.d.83 pencil W/C bodycol. 26-Nov-3 Christie's, London #23/R est:60000-80000

STIMM, Thomas (1948-) Austrian
Sculpture
£2632 $4842 €4000 Large flower with leaf (109x60x30cm-43x24x12in) clay lit. 22-Jun-4 Wiener Kunst Auktionen, Vienna #448/R est:4000

STINE, Al (20th C) American
Works on paper
£857 $1500 €1251 Babs, are we members of the beat generation (55x38cm-22x15in) s. W/C ills board exec c.1960. 17-Dec-3 Christie's, Rockefeller NY #102/R est:3000-4000

STINGEL, Rudolf (1956-) Austrian
£2874 $4800 €4196 Untitled (81x81cm-32x32in) s.d.98 oil enamel prov. 14-Nov-3 Phillips, New York #288/R est:4000-6000

STINTON, Harry I (1882-1968) British
Works on paper
£1600 $2768 €2336 Mountainous landscape with grazing sheep, church and house beyond (41x29cm-16x11in) s. W/C. 10-Dec-3 Rupert Toovey, Partridge Green #101/R est:600-900
£1700 $3145 €2482 Highland cattle a landscape (30x43cm-12x17in) s. W/C bodycol. 11-Mar-4 Duke & Son, Dorchester #80/R est:300-500

STINTON, J (1870-1961) British
Works on paper
£1300 $2249 €1898 Mountainous landscape with highland cattle on a path near pool (17x24cm-7x9in) s. W/C htd white. 10-Dec-3 Rupert Toovey, Partridge Green #100/R est:600-900

STINTON, James (1870-1961) British
Works on paper
£300 $555 €438 Brace of pheasants in winter landscape. s. W/C. 14-Jan-4 Brightwells, Leominster #861
£300 $555 €438 Brace of pheasants in an autumn landscape. s. W/C. 14-Jan-4 Brightwells, Leominster #862
£600 $1092 €876 Pair of pheasants on heath ground (13x20cm-5x8in) s. W/C. 16-Jun-4 Brightwells, Leominster #843/R
£600 $1092 €876 Pair of pheasants in overcast skies (13x20cm-5x8in) W/C. 16-Jun-4 Brightwells, Leominster #844/R
£1220 $2306 €1781 Pheasants in a grassy landscape (23x36cm-9x14in) s. W/C pair. 19-Feb-4 Grant, Worcester #398/R est:1200-1500

STINTON, John (20th C) British
Works on paper
£280 $440 €409 Highland cattle (10x13cm-4x5in) s. W/C. 10-Dec-2 Bamfords, Derby #724

STIRLING, David (1889-1971) American
£262 $450 €383 Autumn, Estes Park, Colorado (74x89cm-29x35in) s. board painted c.1930. 7-Dec-3 Treadway Gallery, Cincinnati #580/R
£389 $650 €568 Estes Park (41x51cm-16x20in) board. 17-Oct-3 Du Mouchelle, Detroit #68/R
£389 $650 €568 Autumn scene (41x51cm-16x20in) board. 17-Oct-3 Du Mouchelle, Detroit #69/R
£635 $1200 €927 River pool (74x58cm-29x23in) s. i. verso board prov. 17-Feb-4 John Moran, Pasadena #189/R
£795 $1400 €1161 Forest inteiror (46x61cm-18x24in) s. board painted c.1930. 23-May-4 Treadway Gallery, Cincinnati #604/R

STIRNBRAND, Franz Seraph (1788-1882) Austrian
£451 $736 €650 Portrait of woman wearing blue dress (67x60cm-26x24in) 25-Sep-3 Dr Fritz Nagel, Stuttgart #1427/R
£592 $1089 €900 Portrait of Freifrau von Brand (66x53cm-26x21in) s.d.1829. 24-Jun-4 Dr Fritz Nagel, Stuttgart #765/R
£789 $1453 €1200 Portrait of Karl Freiherr von Ronder (70x54cm-28x21in) i.1833 verso paper on canvas. 24-Jun-4 Dr Fritz Nagel, Stuttgart #764/R
£872 $1605 €1300 Grandmother in chair with girl (70x60cm-28x24in) s. i. stretcher. 25-Mar-4 Dr Fritz Nagel, Stuttgart #773/R
£1690 $2924 €2400 Grandmother and granddaughter reading (70x60cm-28x24in) s. 11-Dec-3 Dr Fritz Nagel, Stuttgart #550/R est:2900
£1712 $2911 €2500 Man and woman's portraits (78x58cm-31x23in) i.d.1839 verso pair. 5-Nov-3 Hugo Ruef, Munich #1141/R est:2000
£1733 $3172 €2600 Girl with bunch of summer flowers (56x47cm-22x19in) s.d.1860 board oval. 5-Jun-4 Arnold, Frankfurt #736/R est:800

STIRNBRAND, Franz Seraph (attrib) (1788-1882) Austrian
£1736 $2830 €2500 Portrait of officer. Portrait of woman in pink dress (66x52cm-26x20in) pair. 25-Sep-3 Dr Fritz Nagel, Stuttgart #1428/R est:3500

STIRNER, Karl (1882-1943) German
£278 $453 €400 Horse market (16x28cm-6x11in) s.d.1924 tempera Indian ink prov. 27-Sep-3 Dr Fritz Nagel, Stuttgart #9636/R
£347 $566 €500 The athletes (17x15cm-7x6in) s.i.d.1912 tempera over pencil paper on board prov. 27-Sep-3 Dr Fritz Nagel, Stuttgart #9640/R
£382 $623 €550 Christ in front of the high court (25x31cm-10x12in) mono.i.d.1927 tempera pencil W/C board. 27-Sep-3 Dr Fritz Nagel, Stuttgart #9638/R
£403 $713 €600 Southern landscape (24x30cm-9x12in) mono.i.d. tempera. 30-Apr-4 Dr Fritz Nagel, Stuttgart #946/R
£451 $736 €650 Satyr family (15x12cm-6x5in) mono.d.1916 s.i.d. verso tempera board prov. 27-Sep-3 Dr Fritz Nagel, Stuttgart #9642/R
£590 $962 €850 Tightrope walkers (15x17cm-6x7in) mono.i. tempera board prov. 27-Sep-3 Dr Fritz Nagel, Stuttgart #9639/R
£662 $1205 €1000 Sailing boats on a lake (135x200cm-53x79in) s. tempera oil board. 19-Jun-4 Quittenbaum, Hamburg #48/R
£694 $1132 €1000 Painting school (12x18cm-5x7in) s.d.1913 i. verso tempera pencil prov. 27-Sep-3 Dr Fritz Nagel, Stuttgart #9641/R
£906 $1604 €1350 Vineyard in spring (22x27cm-9x11in) mono.d. tempera. 30-Apr-4 Dr Fritz Nagel, Stuttgart #945/R
£940 $1663 €1400 Landscape with house (24x30cm-9x12in) s.d. tempera. 30-Apr-4 Dr Fritz Nagel, Stuttgart #943/R
£1007 $1782 €1500 Mountain road near Siracusa (29x34cm-11x13in) tempera paper on board. 30-Apr-4 Dr Fritz Nagel, Stuttgart #947/R est:1800
£1208 $2138 €1800 Nazareth (23x31cm-9x12in) s.i.d. tempera. 30-Apr-4 Dr Fritz Nagel, Stuttgart #944/R est:1350
£1875 $3056 €2700 Garden party (24x30cm-9x12in) s. tempera chl paper on board prov. 27-Sep-3 Dr Fritz Nagel, Stuttgart #9637/R est:1000
£1944 $3169 €2800 Carnival procession in decorated street (35x25cm-14x10in) mono.d.1924 tempera prov. 27-Sep-3 Dr Fritz Nagel, Stuttgart #9643/R est:1600
£2292 $3735 €3300 Couple reading love letter in garden (22x26cm-9x10in) s.d.1930 tempera prov. 27-Sep-3 Dr Fritz Nagel, Stuttgart #9644/R est:1800
£3125 $5094 €4500 Siracusa (30x35cm-12x14in) mono.i.d.XII 33 tempera prov. 27-Sep-3 Dr Fritz Nagel, Stuttgart #9645/R est:1500
Works on paper
£278 $453 €400 Oktoberfest in Munich (15x16cm-6x6in) s. Indian ink tempera prov. 27-Sep-3 Dr Fritz Nagel, Stuttgart #9635/R
£313 $509 €450 Rooftop view (18x14cm-7x6in) mono.d.1924 col pen pencil gouache paper on board prov. 27-Sep-3 Dr Fritz Nagel, Stuttgart #9633/R
£521 $849 €750 Peasant woman working in fields (14x14cm-6x6in) s. pencil col pen gouache paper on board prov. 27-Sep-3 Dr Fritz Nagel, Stuttgart #9634/R
£590 $962 €850 Fortress (27x21cm-11x8in) s.d.1926 verso col pen chl. 27-Sep-3 Dr Fritz Nagel, Stuttgart #9632/R

STIRNIMANN, Friedrich (1841-1900) Swiss
£271 $462 €396 Young woman (59x43cm-23x17in) s. 19-Nov-3 Fischer, Luzern #2311/R (S.FR 600)
£652 $1200 €952 Darning the sock (34x41cm-13x16in) s.d.1881. 27-Jun-4 Freeman, Philadelphia #26/R

STIRNWEIS, Shannon (1931-) American
£278 $500 €406 Indian horsemen on a rocky bluff (50x76cm-20x30in) s.d.79 masonite. 25-Apr-4 Bonhams & Butterfields, San Francisco #5567/R

STITCHBURY, Peter (20th C) New Zealander
Works on paper
£692 $1239 €1010 Untitled - secrets (69x100cm-27x39in) s.i.d.1997 verso graphite. 11-May-4 Peter Webb, Auckland #166/R est:2500-3500 (NZ.D 2000)

STITT, Moritz (1843-1911) Austrian
£1189 $1985 €1700 Triumph of Galatea (65x110cm-26x43in) s.d.1872. 26-Jun-3 Weidler, Nurnberg #6683

STIVERS, Don (20th C) American
£4469 $8000 €6525 Military man and woman (91x58cm-36x23in) board. 15-May-4 Altermann Galleries, Santa Fe #85/R

STIXRUD, Chr (1900-1968) Norwegian
£311 $516 €451 Storgaten in Oslo (27x35cm-11x14in) s. panel. 16-Jun-3 Blomqvist, Lysaker #1228 (N.KR 3600)

STJEPANOFF, Alexei (1858-1911) Russian
£6579 $11908 €10000 Russian military resting in the barracks (63x76cm-25x30in) s. 19-Apr-4 Glerum, Amsterdam #303/R est:400-600

STOBBAERTS, Jan (1838-1914) Belgian
£288 $489 €420 Interieur d'etable (40x60cm-16x24in) s. 10-Nov-3 Horta, Bruxelles #348
£420 $722 €600 Ruelle a Anvers (39x29cm-15x11in) panel. 2-Dec-3 Campo & Campo, Antwerp #337
£559 $951 €800 Farms (18x33cm-7x13in) s. canvas on panel. 25-Nov-3 Christie's, Amsterdam #239/R
£600 $1074 €900 Interieur d'etable animee (31x41cm-12x16in) s. panel. 11-May-4 Vanderkindere, Brussels #5
£709 $1184 €1000 Cour de ferme animee (25x30cm-10x12in) s. exhib. 14-Oct-3 Vanderkindere, Brussels #585
£745 $1244 €1050 Interieur de l'etable (21x29cm-8x11in) s. 14-Oct-3 Vanderkindere, Brussels #583
£2000 $3680 €3000 Jeune fille rentrant dans l'etable (48x75cm-19x30in) s. 14-Jun-4 Horta, Bruxelles #79 est:1800-2200

STOBBAERTS, Marcel (c.1899-1979) Belgian
£278 $442 €400 Jeune femme nue allongee (38x46cm-15x18in) s. 15-Sep-3 Horta, Bruxelles #9
£374 $670 €550 Moissons en Brabant (80x100cm-31x39in) s.d.1943. 16-Mar-4 Vanderkindere, Brussels #232/R
Works on paper
£319 $533 €450 Port industriel (36x41cm-14x16in) s. gouache ink dr. 17-Jun-3 Vanderkindere, Brussels #191

STOBBAERTS, Pieter (1865-1948) Belgian
£270 $511 €400 Cour de ferme (50x63cm-20x25in) s.d.1899. 17-Feb-4 Vanderkindere, Brussels #97
£433 $780 €650 Interior (58x64cm-23x25in) s. 26-Apr-4 Bernaerts, Antwerp #286/R
£470 $832 €700 Jardin derriere la maison (72x101cm-28x40in) s. 27-Apr-4 Campo & Campo, Antwerp #219/R
£541 $968 €800 Etang en automne (42x62cm-17x24in) s. one d.1918 pair. 10-May-4 Horta, Bruxelles #333
£607 $1123 €880 Etang en automne (42x62cm-17x24in) both s. one d.1918 two. 19-Jan-4 Horta, Bruxelles #487

STOBER, Franz (1760-1834) Austrian
£3947 $7263 €6000 Hilly landscape with trees and peasants (28x38cm-11x15in) s. panel. 24-Jun-4 Dr Fritz Nagel, Stuttgart #679/R est:10000

STOCK, Dennis (1928-) American
Photographs
£1667 $3000 €2434 Venice Beach Rock Festival (22x34cm-9x13in) gelatin silver print. 24-Apr-4 Phillips, New York #86/R est:3000-5000
£2500 $4500 €3650 Audrey Hepburn during the filming of Sabrina (34x22cm-13x9in) i.verso gelatin silver print. 24-Apr-4 Phillips, New York #32/R est:6000-9000

STOCK, Henri Charles (1826-1885) French?
£320 $550 €467 Sailboat in country landscape (18x33cm-7x13in) s. panel. 7-Dec-3 Grogan, Boston #65/R

STOCK, Ignatius van der (17th C) Dutch
£16107 $29638 €24000 Wooded landscape with figures (135x185cm-53x73in) prov. 24-Mar-4 Dorotheum, Vienna #182/R est:16000-20000

STOCK, Ignatius van der (attrib) (17th C) Dutch
£2800 $5040 €4088 Wooded landscape with travelers on a path and figures resting nearby (72x111cm-28x44in) 21-Apr-4 Bonhams, New Bond Street #27/R est:2500-3500

STOCK, Johann Friedrich (?-1866) German
£3467 $6205 €5200 Landscape near Palermo (50x72cm-20x28in) s.d.1861 s.i.d.verso. 13-May-4 Babuino, Rome #360 est:1500-2000

STOCK, Joseph Whiting (1815-1855) American
£3243 $6000 €4735 Portrait of a child wearing a double strand coral and gold necklace (55x67cm-22x26in) 15-Jan-4 Sotheby's, New York #304/R est:5000-7000
£8824 $15000 €12883 Double portrait of the Marshall children, boy with riding crop and girl in pink with book (76x91cm-30x36in) i. 31-Oct-3 North East Auctions, Portsmouth #1743 est:8000-12000

STOCK, Joseph Whiting (attrib) (1815-1855) American
£8743 $16000 €12765 Portraits of the Thayer twins (76x64cm-30x25in) pair. 6-Jun-4 Skinner, Boston #243/R est:30000-50000

STOCKFLETH, J (19th C) German?
£1149 $2056 €1700 Village street in Oevenum on the Fohr (22x30cm-9x12in) s.d.1913 i. verso. 8-May-4 Hans Stahl, Toestorf #87/R est:2200

STOCKHOLDER, Jessica (1959-) American
Sculpture
£3681 $6000 €5374 Untitled, JS no 058 (129x228x109cm-51x90x43in) wood oil acrylic fabric metal papier mache cloth glue prov. 23-Sep-3 Christie's, Rockefeller NY #157/R est:4000-6000
Works on paper
£1026 $1815 €1498 Untitled (42x35cm-17x14in) s.d.June 87 verso mixed media. 27-Apr-4 AB Stockholms Auktionsverk #1083/R (S.KR 14000)

STOCKLEIN, Christian (1741-1795) Swiss
£3000 $5400 €4380 Church interior with elegant company (26x44cm-10x17in) s.d.1774 panel. 23-Apr-4 Christie's, Kensington #10/R est:3000-5000
£14084 $24648 €20000 Vue de l'interieur d'une synagogue (31x48cm-12x19in) s.d.177 panel. 18-Dec-3 Tajan, Paris #20/R est:10000-12000

STOCKLER, Emanuel (1819-1893) German
Works on paper
£3691 $6792 €5500 Horse lovers living room (34x43cm-13x17in) s.d.1856 W/C. 26-Mar-4 Dorotheum, Vienna #183/R est:3000-3500

STOCKMAN, Billy (1925-) Australian
£813 $1455 €1187 Carpet snake (61x50cm-24x20in) s. acrylic canvas on board. 10-May-4 Joel, Victoria #378 est:1500-2000 (A.D 2000)
Works on paper
£352 $657 €528 Men's ceremony (60x45cm-24x18in) synthetic polymer canvas exec. 1993 prov. 21-Jul-4 Shapiro, Sydney #63/R (A.D 900)
£625 $1169 €938 Bush potato yam, yala, dreaming (76x56cm-30x22in) synthetic polymer paint canvasboard prov. 26-Jul-4 Sotheby's, Melbourne #568 (A.D 1600)
£2157 $3861 €3149 Wild Bush Potato (61x76cm-24x30in) synthetic polymer paint composition board exec 1983 prov. 25-May-4 Lawson Menzies, Sydney #65/R est:6000-7000 (A.D 5500)
£8130 $12846 €11789 Yala, bush potato, dreaming (84x55cm-33x22in) i.verso synthetic polymer paint composition board prov. 28-Jul-3 Sotheby's, Paddington #172/R est:20000-30000 (A.D 20000)

STOCKMAN, Oliver (?) ?
£460 $750 €672 Children feeding swans (38x51cm-15x20in) s. 28-Sep-3 Simpson's, Houston #134/R

STOCKMANN, Anton (1868-1940) Swiss
£441 $750 €644 Winter landscape (41x51cm-16x20in) s. 22-Nov-3 Jackson's, Cedar Falls #86/R
£1140 $1904 €1664 Self portrait (25x20cm-10x8in) s.d.1909 paper on board prov. 15-Nov-3 Galerie Gloggner, Luzern #106/R est:600-800 (S.FR 2600)

STOCKMANN, Hermann (1867-1939) German
£470 $832 €700 Wolf tower in Esslingen (45x34cm-18x13in) s.i. board. 30-Apr-4 Dr Fritz Nagel, Stuttgart #462/R
£486 $792 €700 Fishing harbour and church on the Maper (28x37cm-11x15in) s.d.96 bears i. verso canvas on board. 26-Sep-3 Bolland & Marotz, Bremen #622/R
£2381 $4262 €3500 Extensive Dachau moorland (34x49cm-13x19in) s.i.d.1928 i. stretcher. 17-Mar-4 Neumeister, Munich #617/R est:1000
£3333 $6067 €5000 Hay harvest in Dachau (51x94cm-20x37in) s.i.d.1922. 30-Jun-4 Neumeister, Munich #694/R est:5000
Works on paper
£317 $567 €450 Caricature of men eating and conversing at a table (30x33cm-12x13in) s.d.1902 pencil pen lit. 8-Jan-4 Allgauer, Kempten #2171/R

STOCKS, Arthur (1846-1889) British
£620 $1073 €905 Old lady at her spinning wheel (46x35cm-18x14in) s.d.1870 panel. 10-Dec-3 Bonhams, Bury St Edmunds #567
£3200 $5760 €4672 Penny whistle (58x41cm-23x16in) s.d.1879 panel. 22-Apr-4 Mellors & Kirk, Nottingham #1116/R est:2000-3000

STOCKS, Minna (1846-1928) German
£699 $1168 €1000 Mealtime (52x42cm-20x17in) s. 28-Jun-3 Bolland & Marotz, Bremen #737/R
£993 $1658 €1400 Nature morte aux chats (52x41cm-20x16in) s. 15-Oct-3 Hotel des Ventes Mosan, Brussels #145

STOCKS, Walter Fryer (fl.1862-1903) British
Works on paper
£850 $1572 €1241 Stile (25x35cm-10x14in) s.d.1865 W/C gouache. 10-Mar-4 Sotheby's, Olympia #61/R est:400-600

STOCKUM, Hilda van (1908-) Dutch
£1477 $2643 €2200 Still life study of flowers in a copper bowl (30x25cm-12x10in) init. board. 26-May-4 James Adam, Dublin #148/R est:1000-1500
£3611 $5886 €5200 Four duck eggs (49x59cm-19x23in) init. i.d.1989 verso board exhib. 24-Sep-3 James Adam, Dublin #40/R est:5000-8000

STOCQUART, Ildephonse (1819-1889) Belgian
£650 $1086 €949 Young bull with a sheep in a landscape (39x33cm-15x13in) s. panel. 22-Oct-3 Cheffins, Cambridge #522
£872 $1562 €1300 Personnages dans un paysage (35x44cm-14x17in) s. panel. 25-May-4 Campo & Campo, Antwerp #278/R

STODDARD, Alice Kent (1893-1976) American
£335 $550 €486 Seascape (30x41cm-12x16in) st.sig. board. 4-Jun-3 Alderfer's, Hatfield #344/R
£457 $750 €663 Seascape with rocky shoreline (41x51cm-16x20in) st.sig. canvasboard. 4-Jun-3 Alderfer's, Hatfield #343/R
£1195 $1900 €1745 Morning Mist (61x89cm-24x35in) s. 10-Sep-3 Alderfer's, Hatfield #441/R est:3000-4000
£1882 $3500 €2748 Seascape with rocky shoreline (64x76cm-25x30in) s. 3-Mar-4 Alderfer's, Hatfield #427/R est:3000-4000
Works on paper
£229 $375 €332 Landscape with large guarded building flying American and French flags (15x3cm-6x1in) st.sig. W/C. 4-Jun-3 Alderfer's, Hatfield #345

STODDARD, Herbert C (1910-) American
£278 $450 €406 Blind Pass, Sarasota (30x41cm-12x16in) s.i. canvasboard. 2-Aug-3 Neal Auction Company, New Orleans #564

STODDART, Margaret Olrog (1865-1934) New Zealander
Works on paper
£797 $1291 €1156 Gum trees (48x32cm-19x13in) s.d.1894 W/C. 31-Jul-3 International Art Centre, Auckland #91/R est:2500-3500 (NZ.D 2200)
£1455 $2284 €2110 Landscape with wooden hut (25x35cm-10x14in) init.d.1891 W/C. 27-Aug-3 Dunbar Sloane, Wellington #127 est:800-1200 (NZ.D 4000)
£1504 $2556 €2196 Harvest field, North Canterbury (24x34cm-9x13in) s. W/C. 27-Nov-3 International Art Centre, Auckland #84/R est:4500-6500 (NZ.D 4000)
£2015 $3727 €2942 Autumn in Canterbury (35x24cm-14x9in) s. W/C. 9-Mar-4 Watson's, Christchurch #25 est:6500-8000 (NZ.D 5500)
£2174 $3522 €3152 Mediterranean lane (35x24cm-14x9in) s.d.1905 W/C. 31-Jul-3 International Art Centre, Auckland #51/R est:7000-10000 (NZ.D 6000)
£2182 $3425 €3164 Cottage and orchard (24x35cm-9x14in) s. W/C. 27-Aug-3 Dunbar Sloane, Wellington #13/R est:5000-7000 (NZ.D 6000)
£2545 $3996 €3690 Cornwall street scene (25x35cm-10x14in) s. W/C. 27-Aug-3 Dunbar Sloane, Wellington #14/R est:5000-7000 (NZ.D 7000)
£2820 $4793 €4117 Cherry blossom (24x34cm-9x13in) s. W/C. 26-Nov-3 Dunbar Sloane, Wellington #34/R est:6000-8000 (NZ.D 7500)
£2857 $5257 €4171 Daffodils (55x38cm-22x15in) s.d.1896 W/C. 25-Mar-4 International Art Centre, Auckland #108/R est:5000-7500 (NZ.D 8000)
£2899 $4696 €4204 White chrysanthemums (33x50cm-13x20in) s.d.1892 W/C. 31-Jul-3 International Art Centre, Auckland #65/R est:10000-15000 (NZ.D 8000)

£7895 $13421 €11527 Roses (38x56cm-15x22in) s.d.1894 W/C. 27-Nov-3 International Art Centre, Auckland #95/R est:12000-18000 (NZ.D 21000)
£9398 $15977 €13721 White roses (38x50cm-15x20in) s. W/C. 27-Nov-3 International Art Centre, Auckland #83/R est:25000-35000 (NZ.D 25000)

STOEBEL, Edgar (1909-2001) French
£300 $537 €450 Composition (50x65cm-20x26in) s. 17-May-4 Chayette & Cheval, Paris #160
£336 $621 €500 Composition abstraite (37x27cm-15x11in) s. cardboard. 15-Mar-4 Blanchet, Paris #134
£594 $1010 €850 Composition abstraite (61x46cm-24x18in) s. 28-Nov-3 Blanchet, Paris #90
£769 $1308 €1100 Composition au masque (38x55cm-15x22in) s. 28-Nov-3 Blanchet, Paris #89
£805 $1490 €1200 Figurasynthese au chien et au buste de femme (65x50cm-26x20in) s. 15-Mar-4 Blanchet, Paris #135
£1141 $2111 €1700 Composition symbolique (50x61cm-20x24in) s. 15-Mar-4 Blanchet, Paris #132/R est:1500-2000
£1309 $2421 €1950 Figurasynthese a l'oiseau (50x61cm-20x24in) s. 15-Mar-4 Blanchet, Paris #133 est:2000-2500

STOECKL, Rupert (1923-1995) German
Works on paper
£353 $640 €530 Abstract composition (21x44cm-8x17in) s.d. 2-Apr-4 Winterberg, Heidelberg #1654

STOECKLI, Paul (1906-1992) Swiss
£339 $577 €495 Scratching out (21x21cm-8x8in) s. tempera scratching out board. 22-Nov-3 Burkhard, Luzern #38/R (S.FR 750)
£498 $846 €727 City (33x40cm-13x16in) s. 19-Nov-3 Fischer, Luzern #2312/R (S.FR 1100)
£995 $1692 €1453 Collage (29x29cm-11x11in) s. tempera collage board. 22-Nov-3 Burkhard, Luzern #53/R (S.FR 2200)
£1267 $2154 €1850 Collage (35x33cm-14x13in) s. tempera collage board. 22-Nov-3 Burkhard, Luzern #40/R est:1800-2400 (S.FR 2800)
£2264 $3668 €3305 Composition (89x116cm-35x46in) s. prov. 24-May-3 Burkhard, Luzern #51/R est:3500-4500 (S.FR 4800)
£2941 $5000 €4294 Fish market (80x65cm-31x26in) s. 25-Nov-3 Germann, Zurich #130/R est:3000-5000 (S.FR 6500)
Works on paper
£294 $500 €429 Collage (15x12cm-6x5in) s. collage board relief. 22-Nov-3 Burkhard, Luzern #54/R (S.FR 650)
£302 $489 €441 Untitled (23x15cm-9x6in) s. gouache Indian ink. 24-May-3 Burkhard, Luzern #1/R (S.FR 640)
£362 $615 €529 Collage (19x19cm-7x7in) s. collage ink. 22-Nov-3 Burkhard, Luzern #37/R (S.FR 800)
£362 $615 €529 Collage (22x22cm-9x9in) mono. W/C collage board exec. 1979 prov. 22-Nov-3 Burkhard, Luzern #55/R (S.FR 800)
£401 $650 €585 Untitled (29x42cm-11x17in) s. gouache. 24-May-3 Burkhard, Luzern #4/R (S.FR 850)
£474 $849 €692 Diary page - Composition (20x17cm-8x7in) s. collage. 12-May-4 Dobiaschofsky, Bern #1004/R (S.FR 1100)
£1538 $2615 €2245 Page of a diary (100x70cm-39x28in) s. collage gouache ink board exec. 1982 prov. 22-Nov-3 Burkhard, Luzern #56/R est:3000-4000 (S.FR 3400)
£1810 $3077 €2643 Page of a diary (100x70cm-39x28in) s. collage gouache ink tempera board prov. 22-Nov-3 Burkhard, Luzern #39/R est:4000-5000 (S.FR 4000)

STOECKLIN, Niklaus (1896-1982) Swiss
£2691 $4386 €3929 Still live with rose and beetle (27x19cm-11x7in) s.d.42 canvas on panel. 29-Sep-3 Christie's, Zurich #86/R est:6000-8000 (S.FR 6000)
£4130 $7559 €6030 Oak moth (31x28cm-12x11in) s.d.39 canvas on masonite. 7-Jun-4 Christie's, Zurich #127/R est:7000-9000 (S.FR 9500)
£5217 $9548 €7617 Still life with plums and mountain crystal (28x22cm-11x9in) s.d.1917 board prov.exhib. 7-Jun-4 Christie's, Zurich #124/R est:12000-15000 (S.FR 12000)
£7826 $14322 €11426 Solitude (39x33cm-15x13in) mono.d.20 board prov.exhib.lit. 7-Jun-4 Christie's, Zurich #126/R est:12000-15000 (S.FR 18000)
£10480 $19074 €15301 Acrobat (44x31cm-17x12in) mono. board. 17-Jun-4 Kornfeld, Bern #769/R est:20000 (S.FR 24000)
Works on paper
£409 $679 €593 Saint Tropez (19x26cm-7x10in) s.d.1934 Indian ink board. 13-Jun-3 Zofingen, Switzerland #3049 (S.FR 900)
£793 $1348 €1158 Farmstead in Schuls (17x22cm-7x9in) mono.i. sepia. 7-Nov-3 Dobiaschofsky, Bern #175/R (S.FR 1800)
£830 $1510 €1212 Blue fish (12x22cm-5x9in) s.d.52 W/C on Indian ink. 17-Jun-4 Kornfeld, Bern #772 est:1500 (S.FR 1900)
£1310 $2384 €1913 Christmas tree decorations (15x21cm-6x8in) s.d.60 W/C. 17-Jun-4 Kornfeld, Bern #774 est:2000 (S.FR 3000)
£1528 $2782 €2231 Snowdrops in jug. Alpine flowers. Toys from Basel (17x26cm-7x10in) mono. col pen W/C three. 17-Jun-4 Kornfeld, Bern #771 est:5000 (S.FR 3500)
£3930 $7153 €5738 Clus Ironworks (127x90cm-50x35in) mono.i. bodycol on pencil. 17-Jun-4 Kornfeld, Bern #770/R est:10000 (S.FR 9000)
£6335 $10959 €9249 View of Sils Baselgia towards the Fextal (28x36cm-11x14in) s.d.1947 chl oil masonite exhib. 9-Dec-3 Sotheby's, Zurich #103/R est:8000-12000 (S.FR 14000)

STOFF, Alois (1846-?) Austrian
£2685 $4752 €4000 Kaiser Karl I von Osterreich (48x39cm-19x15in) s.d.1918 board. 29-Apr-4 Dorotheum, Vienna #180/R est:1800-2600

STOFFE, Jan van der (attrib) (1611-1682) Dutch
£2817 $4930 €4000 Cavalry battle (44x65cm-17x26in) indis.sig. board. 17-Dec-3 Christie's, Rome #345/R est:2500-3000

STOHL, Michael (1813-1881) Austrian
Works on paper
£400 $740 €584 Portrait of an old lady praying (49x36cm-19x14in) s.d.1874 W/C. 9-Mar-4 Bonhams, Knightsbridge #13/R
£420 $777 €613 Madonna and Child, holding fruit and flowers accompanied by Saints (63x63cm-25x25in) s.i. pencil W/C scratching out after Titian. 14-Jul-4 Christie's, Kensington #820/R

STOHLMANN, Friedrich (18/19th C) German
£250 $400 €365 Fides caritas specs - faith charity hope (84x71cm-33x28in) s.d.1816 i.verso. 19-Sep-3 Freeman, Philadelphia #128/R

STOHNER, Karl (1894-?) German
£451 $736 €650 Still life of fruit (63x85cm-25x33in) s. bears d. 27-Sep-3 Dr Fritz Nagel, Stuttgart #9372/R
£1831 $3168 €2600 Tulips in vase (62x51cm-24x20in) s.d.1913. 13-Dec-3 Lempertz, Koln #190/R est:1500

STÖHR, Ernst (1865-1917) Austrian
£2254 $3944 €3200 Interior (73x54cm-29x21in) s.d.1910 panel. 19-Dec-3 Dorotheum, Vienna #13/R est:3800-5500

STOHR, Julia W Collins (1866-?) American
Works on paper
£621 $1100 €907 Summer landscape with a cottage and roses (20x28cm-8x11in) s. pastel board. 2-May-4 Bonhams & Butterfields, San Francisco #1127/R

STÖHRER, Walter (1937-2000) German
£4196 $7133 €6000 Untitled (113x75cm-44x30in) s.d.November 1981 oil chks W/C Indian ink. 29-Nov-3 Villa Grisebach, Berlin #376/R est:6000-8000
£8741 $15035 €12500 Figure red (200x120cm-79x47in) s.d. s.i.d. verso prov. 5-Dec-3 Ketterer, Munich #351/R est:20000-24000
£11000 $19690 €16500 History of the eye (201x221cm-79x87in) s.d.77 oil mixed media. 15-May-4 Van Ham, Cologne #942/R est:22000
Prints
£2168 $3685 €3100 Untitled (79x54cm-31x21in) s.d.1984 w/C col wax chk over etching drypoint. 29-Nov-3 Villa Grisebach, Berlin #915/R est:2500-3000
Works on paper
£629 $1070 €900 Cyankali I. Cyankali II (15x10cm-6x4in) s.i.d.1977 verso chk Indian ink board two prov. 27-Nov-3 Lempertz, Koln #462/R
£1119 $1924 €1600 Untitled (62x84cm-24x33in) s.d.67 acrylic W/C wax crayon pencil ink. 4-Dec-3 Van Ham, Cologne #494 est:1800
£1133 $2074 €1700 Untitled (53x70cm-21x28in) s.d.1977 W/C oil chk Indian ink brush on etching. 4-Jun-4 Lempertz, Koln #467/R est:2000
£1259 $2165 €1800 Untitled (70x100cm-28x39in) s.i.d.27/9/81 collage acrylic wax crayon W/C. 4-Dec-3 Van Ham, Cologne #493/R est:2000
£1867 $3416 €2800 Untitled (75x55cm-30x22in) s.d.1993 varnish gouache oil chk Indian ink on etching prov. 4-Jun-4 Lempertz, Koln #466/R est:2000

STOILOFF, C (1850-1924) Austrian/Russian
£993 $1808 €1500 Galloping troika (21x32cm-8x13in) s. panel. 21-Jun-4 Dorotheum, Vienna #241/R est:1700-1900
£1736 $2951 €2500 Horses and riders in the snow (37x58cm-15x23in) s.pseudonym Stoiloff. 28-Oct-3 Dorotheum, Vienna #61/R est:2500-2800
£3642 $6629 €5500 Journey of the governors (31x47cm-12x19in) s. i.verso panel. 21-Jun-4 Dorotheum, Vienna #89/R est:5000-6000

STOILOFF, Constantin (1850-1924) Austrian/Russian
£247 $450 €361 Encampment (30x15cm-12x6in) s. board. 19-Jun-4 Jackson's, Cedar Falls #251/R
£271 $486 €396 Landscape with riders and horses by water (58x79cm-23x31in) s. 10-May-4 Rasmussen, Vejle #36 (D.KR 3000)
£282 $487 €400 Fisherman on the beach (80x49cm-31x19in) s. 12-Dec-3 Berlinghof, Heidelberg #995/R
£607 $1123 €880 Three men in horse drawn sledge fighting wolves (16x32cm-6x13in) s. panel. 14-Feb-4 Hans Stahl, Hamburg #96
£699 $1189 €1000 Enjoying the speed - man with horses and sleigh (16x32cm-6x13in) s. board. 29-Nov-3 Bukowskis, Helsinki #401/R
£746 $1245 €1089 Riders in winter landscape (31x48cm-12x19in) i. pane lp. 15-Nov-3 Galerie Gloggner, Luzern #8/R (S.FR 1700)
£867 $1569 €1300 Horse drawn sledge in evening (15x29cm-6x11in) s. panel. 1-Apr-4 Van Ham, Cologne #1282/R
£870 $1600 €1270 Carrying the catch home (81x130cm-32x51in) s. painted c.1880. 26-Jun-4 Susanin's, Chicago #6130/R est:2000-4000
£1014 $1581 €1500 Wolves attacking horse drawn sleigh (65x45cm-26x18in) 28-Mar-3 Behringer, Furth #1293/R est:1000
£1034 $1914 €1500 Young fisherwomen on the seashore (68x105cm-27x41in) s. 14-Feb-4 Meeting Art, Vercelli #296/R est:1500
£1148 $1860 €1665 Watering the horses (50x82cm-20x32in) s. 4-Aug-3 Rasmussen, Vejle #424/R est:12000-15000 (D.KR 12000)
£1291 $2350 €1950 Russian peasants working in the fields (80x130cm-31x51in) s. 19-Jun-4 Dannenberg, Berlin #547/R est:1300
£1294 $2225 €1850 Gold transport in the Siberian Taiga snow (68x55cm-27x22in) s. 6-Dec-3 Dannenberg, Berlin #768/R est:800
£1528 $2597 €2200 Vorwarts - the courageous advance (26x47cm-10x19in) s. panel. 28-Oct-3 Christie's, Amsterdam #22/R est:3000-5000
£1818 $2945 €2636 Winter landscape with Cossacks and horses (69x106cm-27x42in) s. 4-Aug-3 Rasmussen, Vejle #423/R est:6000-8000 (D.KR 19000)
£1934 $3500 €2824 Charge of Cossacks in snow (30x48cm-12x19in) panel. 16-Apr-4 Du Mouchelle, Detroit #2304/R est:3500-4500
£2148 $4016 €3200 Covered horse drawn cart (31x48cm-12x19in) s.i. panel. 24-Feb-4 Dorotheum, Vienna #127/R est:300-3200
£2156 $4011 €3148 Three men in rowing boat fighting with polar bears (90x124cm-35x49in) s.d.1912. 2-Mar-4 Rasmussen, Copenhagen #1414/R est:15000 (D.KR 24000)
£2262 $3846 €3303 Cossack wedding (31x47cm-12x19in) s. panel. 28-Nov-3 Zofingen, Switzerland #2686/R est:2000 (S.FR 5000)
£2517 $4330 €3600 Russian army procession in a winter landscape (31x47cm-12x19in) s. i.verso panel. 3-Dec-3 Neumeister, Munich #755/R est:3000
£2800 $5096 €4088 Pferdetross (30x47cm-12x19in) s. panel. 16-Jun-4 Christie's, Kensington #210/R est:3000-5000
£2980 $5424 €4500 Transporting gold in Russia (32x47cm-13x19in) s. panel. 16-Jun-4 Hugo Ruef, Munich #1097/R est:2000
£3000 $5550 €4380 Siberian gold convoy (54x43cm-21x17in) s. panel. 15-Jan-4 Christie's, Kensington #834/R est:1500-2000

£3214	$5560	€4692	Many figures in fishing village (83x130cm-33x51in) s. 9-Dec-3 Rasmussen, Copenhagen #1644/R est:20000-25000 (D.KR 34000)
£3217	$5469	€4600	Watering the horses (50x82cm-20x32in) s. 29-Nov-3 Bukowskis, Helsinki #400/R est:2000-3000
£3280	$6035	€4920	Landscape with horse and carriage (50x81cm-20x32in) s. 14-Jun-4 Lilla Bukowskis, Stockholm #1126 est:15000-20000 (S.KR 45000)
£3378	$5946	€5000	Mounted Cossacks accompanying gold transport in Siberia (31x47cm-12x19in) s. panel. 22-May-4 Lempertz, Koln #1612/R est:1500
£4138	$6910	€6000	Troikas and wild riders in winter evening landscape (173x269cm-68x106in) s. lit. 12-Jul-3 Bergmann, Erlangen #644/R est:6000
£4189	$7499	€6200	Sledge ride (69x105cm-27x41in) s. 8-May-4 Bukowskis, Helsinki #410/R est:3000-4000
£6291	$11450	€9500	Governor's trip (69x106cm-27x42in) s. i. stretcher. 19-Jun-4 Dannenberg, Berlin #548/R est:2000
£8500	$14450	€12410	Huntsman chasing through the snow (69x106cm-27x42in) s. 19-Nov-3 Sotheby's, London #53/R est:4000-6000
£9000	$16110	€13140	Cavalrymen with spears (37x58cm-15x23in) s. 26-May-4 Sotheby's, London #81/R est:5000-7000
£10000	$17000	€14600	Hunting the wolf (69x105cm-27x41in) s. 19-Nov-3 Sotheby's, London #54/R est:4000-6000
£12000	$21480	€17520	Cossack cavalry charge through snow (52x79cm-20x31in) s. 26-May-4 Sotheby's, London #82/R est:6000-8000
£12000	$21480	€17520	Racing sledge (69x106cm-27x42in) s. 26-May-4 Sotheby's, London #84/R est:7000-9000
£14000	$25060	€20440	Battle scene (68x105cm-27x41in) s. 26-May-4 Sotheby's, London #85/R est:7000-9000
£16000	$28640	€23360	Siberian gold convoy (69x105cm-27x41in) s. 26-May-4 Sotheby's, London #83/R est:6000-8000
Works on paper			
£500	$895	€750	Muhlviertel farmsteads (31x44cm-12x17in) s. w/C. 13-May-4 Dorotheum, Linz #545/R

STOILOFF, Constantin (attrib) (1850-1924) Austrian/Russian

£1600	$2720	€2336	Hunting scenes (19x29cm-7x11in) each bears sig. panel pair. 19-Nov-3 Sotheby's, London #57/R est:1000-1500

STOITZNER, A (19/20th C) Austrian?

£1135	$1895	€1600	Still life with flowers and fruit (54x67cm-21x26in) s. 15-Oct-3 Dorotheum, Vienna #10/R est:1100

STOITZNER, Carl (1866-1943) Austrian

£769	$1308	€1123	Reading in the wine cellar (58x50cm-23x20in) s. panel. 1-Dec-3 Koller, Zurich #6488/R est:1700-2300 (S.FR 1700)

STOITZNER, Constantin (1863-1934) Austrian

£223	$400	€326	Tavern scene with men gambling (53x41cm-21x16in) s. 29-May-4 Brunk, Ashville #540/R
£278	$450	€406	Die Weinprobe (20x15cm-8x6in) s. i.verso panel. 2-Aug-3 Neal Auction Company, New Orleans #710/R
£301	$517	€430	Man with glasses grinning at the Journal Amusant (20x15cm-8x6in) s. panel. 6-Dec-3 Dannenberg, Berlin #830/R
£301	$517	€430	Farmer with a wine bottle and glass in his hand (20x15cm-8x6in) s. panel. 6-Dec-3 Dannenberg, Berlin #831/R
£341	$566	€494	Connoisseur (21x15cm-8x6in) s. panel. 13-Jun-3 Zofingen, Switzerland #2535/R (S.FR 750)
£493	$818	€700	A warm drop (21x16cm-8x6in) s. 16-Jun-3 Dorotheum, Vienna #236/R
£577	$992	€842	Still life of flowers (55x68cm-22x27in) s. 3-Dec-3 AB Stockholms Auktionsverk #2553/R (S.KR 7500)
£634	$1052	€900	Latest news (20x15cm-8x6in) s.i. panel. 16-Jun-3 Dorotheum, Vienna #233/R
£903	$1535	€1300	Fruit seller (64x80cm-25x31in) s. 28-Oct-3 Dorotheum, Vienna #230/R
£923	$1588	€1348	Zechbruder (20x15cm-8x6in) one s. panel pair. 3-Dec-3 AB Stockholms Auktionsverk #2575/R (S.KR 12000)
£1268	$2193	€1800	Reading. Drinking (21x6cm-8x2in) s. panel pair. 10-Dec-3 Christie's, Amsterdam #666/R est:1500-2000
£1879	$3477	€2800	Peasant room (29x90cm-11x35in) 9-Mar-4 Dorotheum, Vienna #33/R est:3000-4500

STOITZNER, Josef (1884-1951) Austrian

£1974	$3632	€3000	Farm garden (33x42cm-13x17in) board. 22-Jun-4 Wiener Kunst Auktionen, Vienna #63/R est:3000
£2381	$4262	€3500	Harbour (63x93cm-25x37in) s. panel. 17-Mar-4 Neumeister, Munich #618/R est:2800
£3357	$5773	€4800	On the balcony of an old farm house (60x50cm-24x20in) s. 3-Dec-3 Neumeister, Munich #756/R est:3000
£3618	$6658	€5500	Still life of flowers (43x33cm-17x13in) s. 22-Jun-4 Wiener Kunst Auktionen, Vienna #61/R est:4000
£5963	$9959	€8646	Farmstead with fruit trees (67x57cm-26x22in) s. board. 23-Jun-3 Philippe Schuler, Zurich #3573/R est:7000-9000 (S.FR 13000)
£6028	$10067	€8500	Interior with oven (100x90cm-39x35in) s. 14-Oct-3 Dorotheum, Vienna #63/R est:9000-13000
£21477	$38013	€32000	Autumn landscape (79x143cm-31x56in) s. 28-Apr-4 Wiener Kunst Auktionen, Vienna #69/R est:11500-16000

STOITZNER, Rudolf (1873-1933) Austrian

£349	$649	€520	Still life with flowers and fruit (69x55cm-27x22in) s. 5-Mar-4 Wendl, Rudolstadt #3880/R
£539	$1003	€787	Still life of apples, pears, grapes and yellow roses (82x121cm-32x48in) s. 2-Mar-4 Rasmussen, Copenhagen #1564/R (D.KR 6000)
£1389	$2292	€2000	Still life of flowers (76x73cm-30x29in) s. 2-Jul-3 Neumeister, Munich #785/R est:1800

STOITZNER, Siegfried (1892-1976) Austrian

£407	$692	€594	Hunter with dead dear (14x18cm-6x7in) s.d.1943 panel. 19-Nov-3 Fischer, Luzern #2313/R (S.FR 900)
£2621	$4796	€3800	St Michael in der Wachau (60x70cm-24x28in) s. 27-Jan-4 Dorotheum, Vienna #95/R est:2200-3600
£3356	$6208	€5000	Durnstein (56x74cm-22x29in) s. panel. 9-Mar-4 Dorotheum, Vienna #69/R est:3000-4000
£4196	$7133	€6000	Spitz (72x95cm-28x37in) s. 28-Nov-3 Wiener Kunst Auktionen, Vienna #471/R est:6000-12000
Works on paper			
£1986	$3316	€2800	Street in Durnstein (37x30cm-15x12in) s.d.1923 gouache. 16-Oct-3 Dorotheum, Salzburg #855/R est:1200-1600

STOJANOW, Pjotr (fl.1887-1894) Russian

£979	$1664	€1400	Winter bride trip (22x35cm-9x14in) s. panel. 20-Nov-3 Van Ham, Cologne #1878
£1944	$3169	€2800	Napoleon in troika returning to Moscow (61x100cm-24x39in) s. 25-Sep-3 Dr Fritz Nagel, Stuttgart #1430/R est:3000
£2431	$4010	€3500	Bride's journey in the snow (55x90cm-22x35in) s. 3-Jul-3 Van Ham, Cologne #1472/R est:3600
£2518	$4129	€3500	Bride travelling by sleigh (56x69cm-22x27in) s. 4-Jun-3 Ketterer, Hamburg #102/R est:3500-4500
£3472	$5903	€5000	Frochliche Fahrt - a wedding party in a carriage in winter (56x90cm-22x35in) s. 28-Oct-3 Christie's, Amsterdam #33/R est:6000-8000
£3793	$7017	€5500	Chariot attele avec noceurs sur fond de paysage enneige (57x70cm-22x28in) s. 16-Feb-4 Horta, Bruxelles #150/R est:5000-7000

STOJAROV, Vladimir (attrib) (1926-1973) Russian

£278	$500	€406	In the country (44x51cm-17x20in) 24-Apr-4 Shishkin Gallery, Moscow #44/R

STOJKOV, Sava (19/20th C) Yugoslavian

£229	$383	€332	Le printemps (39x49cm-15x19in) s.d. oil glass exhib. 21-Jun-3 Galerie du Rhone, Sion #152 (S.FR 500)

STOK, Jacobus van der (1795-1864) Dutch

£465	$800	€679	Village at the water's edge (11x14cm-4x6in) s. panel. 3-Dec-3 Doyle, New York #103/R
£5333	$9600	€8000	Country idyll (56x70cm-22x28in) s. panel prov. 21-Apr-4 Christie's, Amsterdam #41/R est:8000-12000

STOK, Jacobus van der (attrib) (1795-1864) Dutch

£1053	$1905	€1600	Sailing ship on choppy seas in front of a fortress tower (24x29cm-9x11in) indis.s. panel. 19-Apr-4 Glerum, Amsterdam #15/R est:800-1200

STOKES, Adrian (1854-1935) British

£250	$458	€365	Trees, Monte Verita (45x60cm-18x24in) exhib. 8-Jul-4 Lawrence, Crewkerne #91663
£400	$720	€584	Sunset through trees (20x27cm-8x11in) s.i.verso panel prov.exhib. 20-Apr-4 Rosebery Fine Art, London #432
£1242	$2000	€1813	Two terriers (41x53cm-16x21in) s. 20-Aug-3 James Julia, Fairfield #1003/R est:3000-4000

STOKES, Constance (1906-1991) Australian

Works on paper			
£405	$652	€591	Draped nude (37x27cm-15x11in) s.d.82 pencil conte exhib. 13-Oct-3 Joel, Victoria #309/R est:1000-1500 (A.D 1000)
£661	$1223	€965	Woman with flowers (37x27cm-15x11in) s.d.69 W/C pastel pen ink. 10-Mar-4 Deutscher-Menzies, Melbourne #539/R est:1000-1500 (A.D 1600)

STOKES, Frank Wilbert (1858-1927) American

£3500	$5424	€5110	Antarctic berg off King Oscar II Land, Weddell Sea (30x39cm-12x15in) s.i.d.1914 canvasboard. 25-Sep-2 Christie's, London #109/R est:3000-4000

STOKES, George Vernon (1873-1954) British

£1400	$2506	€2044	Joyo, German Spitz dog standing in a garden (51x61cm-20x24in) s. 22-Mar-4 Bonhams & Brooks, Norfolk #265/R est:600-800
Works on paper			
£400	$680	€584	Bulldog (41x33cm-16x13in) s. pencil W/C. 27-Nov-3 Christie's, Kensington #351/R
£1550	$2465	€2263	Study of the heads of two otter hounds (35x27cm-14x11in) s. W/C. 12-Sep-3 Jacobs & Hunt, Petersfield #330/R est:300-500

STOKES, Jim (1959-) Canadian

£260	$476	€380	Field sketch (20x90cm-8x35in) s.i.d.1990 acrylic. 1-Jun-4 Hodgins, Calgary #205/R (C.D 650)

STOLERENKO, Piotr (1925-) Russian

£1103	$1843	€1600	Vase with red roses (78x100cm-31x39in) s. 17-Nov-3 Durán, Madrid #682/R est:1600
£1724	$2879	€2500	Mediterranean terrace (82x100cm-32x39in) s. 17-Nov-3 Durán, Madrid #681/R est:1800

STOLKER, Jan (attrib) (1724-1785) Dutch

£1035	$1852	€1511	Portrait of an artist colleague (18x13cm-7x5in) copper oval. 26-May-4 AB Stockholms Auktionsverk #2579/R (S.KR 14000)

STOLL, Artur (1947-) ?

Works on paper			
£276	$461	€400	Untitled (43x60cm-17x24in) s.d.1978 pencil. 13-Nov-3 Neumeister, Munich #639/R
£563	$901	€800	Expressive abstract composition (60x85cm-24x33in) s.d.82 gouache lit. 19-Sep-3 Karlheinz Kaupp, Staufen #2163/R

STOLL, Fredy (20th C) French?
Sculpture
£13287 $22587 €19000 Daphne (94cm-37in) s.st.f. bronze sold with base prov. 18-Nov-3 Sotheby's, Paris #119/R est:15000-20000

STOLL, George (1954-) American
Sculpture
£1734 $3000 €2532 Untitled (53x28x28cm-21x11x11in) beeswax, paraffin pigment prov. 10-Dec-3 Phillips, New York #561/R est:2000-3000

STOLL, Leopold (1792-1850) German
£815 $1500 €1190 Still life of mixed flowers (42x29cm-17x11in) s.d.1878. 27-Jun-4 Freeman, Philadelphia #34/R est:3000-5000
£1631 $2725 €2300 Nature morte de jete de fleurs (21x26cm-8x10in) s. paper on canvas. 17-Oct-3 Tajan, Paris #67/R est:2000-3000
£1690 $2924 €2400 Flowers in a vase (66x52cm-26x20in) s.d.1840. 10-Dec-3 Dorotheum, Vienna #226/R est:2500-3000
£2378 $4042 €3400 Flowers in vase with pomegranate and bird (69x56cm-27x22in) s.d.1846. 24-Nov-3 Dorotheum, Vienna #206/R est:3000-3500
£14444 $26000 €21088 Still life of flowers in a vase with bunches of grapes and peaches (72x57cm-28x22in) s.d.1828. 22-Jan-4 Sotheby's, New York #237/R est:30000-40000
Works on paper
£699 $1189 €1000 Etude du grappe de raisin. s. W/C. 24-Nov-3 E & Eve, Paris #83/R
£719 $1151 €1000 Grappe de raisin (17x23cm-7x9in) s. W/C htd white gouache. 16-May-3 Tajan, Paris #206
£2200 $4048 €3212 Peonies. Tulips (50x35cm-20x14in) s.d.1874 W/C pair. 25-Mar-4 Christie's, Kensington #81/R est:3000-5000

STOLLREITHER, Paul (1886-1973) German
£276 $461 €400 Tegernsee landscape (65x80cm-26x31in) s. 9-Jul-3 Hugo Ruef, Munich #218

STOLTENBERG, Mattias (1799-1871) Norwegian
£5204 $9315 €7598 Dusgaard - Hedmark landscape with fence (28x36cm-11x14in) panel exhib. 22-Mar-4 Blomqvist, Oslo #342/R est:80000-100000 (N.KR 65000)

STOLTZ, Jette Birgitta (1923-) Swedish
£591 $1058 €863 Love-flowers - Still life of doves and bleeding hearts (115x103cm-45x41in) s. 28-May-4 Uppsala Auktionskammare, Uppsala #342/R (S.KR 8000)

STOLTZ, Sam (1876-1952) American
£243 $450 €355 Smoky mountains - new found gap (51x58cm-20x23in) s.i. masonite. 17-Jan-4 New Orleans Auction, New Orleans #739

STOLZ SEGUI, Ramon (1872-1924) Spanish
£537 $999 €800 Study of landscape (45x34cm-18x13in) s. 2-Mar-4 Ansorena, Madrid #185/R
£805 $1498 €1200 Head of angels (27x30cm-11x12in) s. 2-Mar-4 Ansorena, Madrid #215/R

STOLZ VICIANO, Ramon (1903-1958) Spanish
£2958 $4732 €4200 Woman from Valencia in a garden (60x75cm-24x30in) s.i. 16-Sep-3 Segre, Madrid #89/R est:3500
Works on paper
£276 $458 €400 Girl in profile (37x28cm-15x11in) s. chl sanguine. 1-Oct-3 Ansorena, Madrid #488/R

STOM, Antonio (18th C) Italian
£7394 $11905 €10500 Paesaggio con piramide e rovine antiche (30x43cm-12x17in) 8-May-3 Farsetti, Prato #483 est:14000-18000

STOMER, Matthias I (attrib) (c.1600-c.1650) Flemish
£17808 $30274 €26000 Penitent Magdalen (148x114cm-58x45in) 5-Nov-3 Christie's, Amsterdam #38/R est:8000-10000

STOMER, Matthias I (style) (c.1600-c.1650) Flemish
£27000 $49410 €39420 Nocturnal scene with a man holding a candle, pointing to a crab on a table (95x70cm-37x28in) 6-Jul-4 Sotheby's, Olympia #540/R est:8000-12000

STOMNE, Arne (1918-1995) Norwegian
£912 $1678 €1332 Composition (90x73cm-35x29in) s. painted c.1962/63. 29-Mar-4 Blomqvist, Lysaker #1325 (N.KR 11500)

STONE, A (19th C) British?
£393 $657 €574 Wooded landscape (62x51cm-24x20in) s. 25-Oct-3 Rasmussen, Havnen #2016/R (D.KR 4200)

STONE, Albert (19/20th C) British
£650 $1086 €949 Wooded track. River landscape (25x44cm-10x17in) s. pair. 13-Nov-3 Christie's, Kensington #154/R

STONE, Don (1929-) American
£1795 $3250 €2621 Homeward bound (38x71cm-15x28in) s.i. 16-Apr-4 James Julia, Fairfield #711/R est:2000-3000
Works on paper
£559 $1000 €816 Milkweeds (25x38cm-10x15in) s. W/C gouache. 14-May-4 Skinner, Boston #158/R
£663 $1200 €968 Woman with raincoat (18x23cm-7x9in) s. W/C. 16-Apr-4 James Julia, Fairfield #712/R est:500-1000
£813 $1300 €1187 Fisherman with dinghy (36x51cm-14x20in) s. W/C. 21-Sep-3 Grogan, Boston #86/R

STONE, Fern Cunningham (1889-?) American
£279 $500 €407 California landscape (61x76cm-24x30in) s. prov. 20-Mar-4 Sloans & Kenyon, Bethesda #1193/R

STONE, Frank (1800-1859) British
£850 $1445 €1241 Portrait of a gentleman, said to be Heathcliffe (12x16cm-5x6in) board. 19-Nov-3 Tennants, Leyburn #1153
£5500 $9350 €8030 Voyage out. The return (39x51cm-15x20in) s. pair. 25-Nov-3 Christie's, London #169/R est:3000-5000
£7000 $11620 €10220 Missing boat (76x64cm-30x25in) s.d.58 exhib. 1-Oct-3 Sotheby's, Olympia #125/R est:8000-12000

STONE, J R (?) ?
£828 $1500 €1209 Figures in a coach on a country lane (42x69cm-17x27in) s. 18-Apr-4 Bonhams & Butterfields, Los Angeles #7043 est:2000-3000

STONE, Louis K (1902-1984) American
£484 $900 €707 Spring river landscape with mountains (36x41cm-14x16in) s.d.1935 board. 3-Mar-4 Alderfer's, Hatfield #428 est:600-800
Works on paper
£246 $425 €359 Abstract composition (15x8cm-6x3in) s. W/C. 10-Dec-3 Alderfer's, Hatfield #418/R
£457 $750 €667 Abstract composition (15x13cm-6x5in) s.d.1939 W/C. 4-Jun-3 Alderfer's, Hatfield #317/R

STONE, Marcus (1840-1921) British
£500 $900 €730 Vole with berries. The bird and snail (14x18cm-6x7in) s. board pair. 21-Apr-4 Rupert Toovey, Partridge Green #150/R
£3700 $6808 €5402 Vase of flowers (43x25cm-17x10in) s. 25-Mar-4 Mallams, Cheltenham #296/R est:3000-4000
£15000 $25500 €21900 Summer fruit. Winter berries (94x32cm-37x13in) s. i.stretcher pair exhib. 19-Nov-3 Bonhams, New Bond Street #76/R est:10000-15000
£20588 $35000 €30058 Married for love (38x61cm-15x24in) s.d.81 panel. 29-Oct-3 Christie's, Rockefeller NY #72/R est:40000-60000
£36000 $65520 €52560 End of the story. s.d.1900 prov.exhib. 1-Jul-4 Sotheby's, London #314/R est:30000-50000
Works on paper
£608 $1089 €900 Spring (32x11cm-13x4in) s.d.1894 W/C. 8-May-4 Dawo, Saarbrucken #145/R
£5800 $9860 €8468 Portrait of Kate Macready Dickens (20x25cm-8x10in) s.d.August 65 W/C. 4-Nov-3 Bonhams, New Bond Street #108/R est:1500-2000

STONE, Marcus (attrib) (1840-1921) British
£850 $1573 €1241 Chairs in a corridor, believed to be at Knole House, Kent (12x22cm-5x9in) bears i.verso board. 10-Feb-4 Bonhams, Knightsbridge #116/R

STONE, Paul (20th C) American
Works on paper
£250 $425 €365 Sneaking a smoke (43x66cm-17x26in) s. W/C exec.c.1964. 9-Nov-3 Outer Cape Auctions, Provincetown #134/R

STONE, R (fl.1900) British
£2000 $3700 €3000 The meet. Full cry (15x35cm-6x14in) s. panel pair. 16-Jul-4 Charterhouse, Sherborne #630/R

STONE, Rudolf (19/20th C) British
£750 $1388 €1125 Coaching subjects (15x23cm-6x9in) s. panel pair. 14-Jul-4 Brightwells, Leominster #663/R
£1600 $2944 €2336 Moving off. On the scent (42x68cm-17x27in) s. set of three. 10-Jun-4 Christie's, Kensington #54/R est:2000-3000
£2500 $4250 €3650 Meet. Setting off. Over the fence. Kill (16x31cm-6x12in) s. set of four. 27-Nov-3 Christie's, Kensington #16/R est:3000-5000

STONE, Sasha (20th C) ?
Photographs
£2386 $4200 €3484 Female nude (23x29cm-9x11in) with sig. silver print. 20-May-4 Swann Galleries, New York #354/R est:4000-5000

STONE, Thomas Albert (1897-1978) Canadian
£313 $538 €457 Yankee Dame Falls (35x45cm-14x18in) s. board. 2-Dec-3 Joyner Waddington, Toronto #342/R (C.D 700)
£446 $768 €651 Bear Lake and Creek (35x45cm-14x18in) s. board. 2-Dec-3 Joyner Waddington, Toronto #321/R est:800-1200 (C.D 1000)
£670 $1152 €978 Lumber Camp, Haliburton (30x40cm-12x16in) s. 2-Dec-3 Joyner Waddington, Toronto #439 (C.D 1500)
£759 $1305 €1108 Sunrise, Algonquin Park (55x75cm-22x30in) s. board. 2-Dec-3 Joyner Waddington, Toronto #486 (C.D 1700)

STONE, W (19/20th C) British
£1200 $2196 €1752 Figures before a cottage in landscape. Figures on a track in a landscape (45x82cm-18x32in) s. pair. 6-Jul-4 Bonhams, Knightsbridge #205/R est:1000-1500

STONE, Walter King (1875-1949) American
£272 $500 €397 The red barn (41x51cm-16x20in) s. board. 25-Jun-4 Freeman, Philadelphia #224/R

£407 $750 €594 Winter landscape (76x122cm-30x48in) s.d.130 masonite. 25-Jun-4 Freeman, Philadelphia #220/R
£462 $850 €675 Overlooking a valley (76x122cm-30x48in) s. masonite. 25-Jun-4 Freeman, Philadelphia #222/R

STONE, William (19/20th C) British
£314 $500 €455 Old cottage on the roadside near Solihull in winter (36x46cm-14x18in) s. s.i.verso. 12-Sep-3 Aspire, Cleveland #48
£400 $728 €584 Habberley Valley, near Kidderminster, winter (74x124cm-29x49in) s.d.1879. 16-Jun-4 Andrew Hartley, Ilkley #1083
£500 $885 €730 Travelers in summer. Winter landscape (51x76cm-20x30in) s. one d.1911 pair. 29-Apr-4 Gorringes, Lewes #2365
£900 $1701 €1314 Harvester's return (75x125cm-30x49in) s. 19-Feb-4 Lyon & Turnbull, Edinburgh #73 est:300-500

STONE, William R (19th C) British
£550 $913 €803 Fleeing the storm (77x128cm-30x50in) s. 1-Oct-3 Sotheby's, Olympia #63/R

STONECIPHER, Barbara (20th C) American
£324 $600 €473 Factories in the East Bay (46x61cm-18x24in) init. canvasboard. 13-Mar-4 Auctions by the Bay, Alameda #488/R

STONELAKE, Frank P (1879-1929) British
£700 $1169 €1022 End of the day, a hunt passes a coach and four (30x41cm-12x16in) s. 9-Oct-3 Greenslade Hunt, Taunton #496/R

STONES, Anthony (20th C) New Zealander?
£679 $1249 €991 Read bowling (40x49cm-16x19in) s. exhib. 25-Mar-4 International Art Centre, Auckland #166/R (NZ.D 1900)

STONES, Elsie Margaret (1920-) Australian
Works on paper
£237 $425 €356 Lily Redstart (44x30cm-17x12in) s.i.d.1969 W/C. 17-May-4 Sotheby's, Melbourne #593 (A.D 600)
£395 $708 €593 Botanical study (29x21cm-11x8in) s.i. W/C. 17-May-4 Sotheby's, Melbourne #591 (A.D 1000)

STOOF, J B (19th C) Dutch
£1333 $2387 €2000 Fortune-teller (100x135cm-39x53in) s.d.1850. 11-May-4 Vendu Notarishuis, Rotterdam #138 est:2000-3000

STOOP, Dirk (1618-1681) Dutch
£2365 $4162 €3500 Hilly landscape with sportsmen, horses and hounds resting after the hunt (47x63cm-19x25in) bears sig panel. 18-May-4 Sotheby's, Amsterdam #82/R est:4000-6000
£6000 $10200 €8760 Landscape with hunters resting by a path (43x51cm-17x20in) panel. 29-Oct-3 Christie's, London #27/R est:6000-8000
£6000 $10380 €8760 Italianate river landscape with a muleteer on a track and a horseman watering his horse (89x114cm-35x45in) 10-Dec-3 Bonhams, New Bond Street #51/R est:5000-7000
£8000 $14400 €11680 Cavalry skirmish (50x69cm-20x27in) init. panel. 21-Apr-4 Christie's, London #40/R est:8000-12000
£8904 $15137 €13000 Siege of a fortified castle (49x70cm-19x28in) s. 4-Nov-3 Sotheby's, Amsterdam #64/R est:6000-8000

STOOP, Maerten (1620-1647) Dutch
£6040 $11114 €9000 Officer with girl in billeted quarters (41x61cm-16x24in) panel. 25-Mar-4 Dr Fritz Nagel, Stuttgart #604/R est:10000

STOOP, Maerten (attrib) (1620-1647) Dutch
£2098 $3503 €3000 Scene de pedicure (39x31cm-15x12in) panel. 12-Oct-3 Salle des ventes Pillet, Lyon la Foret #35/R est:2500-3000

STOOPENDAAL, Georg (1866-1953) Swedish
£512 $958 €748 Ploughing a field (38x61cm-15x24in) s.d.1925. 29-Feb-4 Uppsala Auktionskammare, Uppsala #28 (S.KR 7000)

STOOPENDAAL, Mosse (1901-1948) Swedish
£612 $985 €894 Ducks landing (33x41cm-13x16in) s.d.33. 25-Aug-3 Lilla Bukowskis, Stockholm #165 (S.KR 8000)
£692 $1191 €1010 Birds in snow (34x49cm-13x19in) s. 7-Dec-3 Uppsala Auktionskammare, Uppsala #206/R (S.KR 9000)
£786 $1359 €1148 Winter landscape with crows (41x51cm-16x20in) s. 15-Dec-3 Lilla Bukowskis, Stockholm #675 (S.KR 10000)
£802 $1475 €1203 Sjoeorre (69x86cm-27x34in) s.d.1929. 14-Jun-4 Lilla Bukowskis, Stockholm #524 (S.KR 11000)
£1021 $1767 €1491 Greater black-backed gulls (50x73cm-20x29in) s. s.d.39 verso. 15-Dec-3 Lilla Bukowskis, Stockholm #15 (S.KR 13000)
£1088 $1958 €1632 Wooded landscape with fox (36x51cm-14x20in) s.d.1932. 25-Apr-4 Goteborg Auktionsverk, Sweden #222/R est:18000 (S.KR 15000)
£1231 $2117 €1797 Eiderducks (40x56cm-16x22in) s,. 7-Dec-3 Uppsala Auktionskammare, Uppsala #205/R est:12000-15000 (S.KR 16000)
£1256 $2249 €1834 Winter landscape with squirrels (31x25cm-12x10in) s. 26-May-4 AB Stockholms Auktionsverk #2162/R est:8000-10000 (S.KR 17000)
£1335 $2310 €1949 Bullfinches (41x33cm-16x13in) s. 15-Dec-3 Lilla Bukowskis, Stockholm #445/R est:8000-10000 (S.KR 17000)
£1385 $2382 €2022 Eiderducks in flight (50x70cm-20x28in) s. 3-Dec-3 AB Stockholms Auktionsverk #2246/R est:15000-18000 (S.KR 18000)
£1615 $2778 €2358 Squirrel (55x46cm-22x18in) s. 2-Dec-3 Bukowskis, Stockholm #48/R est:15000-20000 (S.KR 21000)
£1700 $3043 €2482 Great-tits in flowering bush (30x40cm-12x16in) s.d.45. 26-May-4 AB Stockholms Auktionsverk #2295/R est:22000-25000 (S.KR 23000)
£1813 $3263 €2720 Herring gulls (60x80cm-24x31in) s.d.1943. 25-Apr-4 Goteborg Auktionsverk, Sweden #230/R est:20000 (S.KR 25000)
£1848 $3307 €2698 Wooded scene in winter with bullfinches (34x14cm-13x6in) s.d.1938 panel. 26-May-4 AB Stockholms Auktionsverk #2294/R est:15000-20000 (S.KR 25000)
£1922 $3440 €2806 Bullfinches in bush in winter (41x33cm-16x13in) s. 26-May-4 AB Stockholms Auktionsverk #2296/R est:25000-30000 (S.KR 26000)
£1923 $3308 €2808 Winter landscape with fox (45x68cm-18x27in) s. 3-Dec-3 AB Stockholms Auktionsverk #2364/R est:30000-35000 (S.KR 25000)
£2069 $3704 €3021 Family of seagulls (90x145cm-35x57in) s.d.1945. 26-May-4 AB Stockholms Auktionsverk #2235/R est:30000-40000 (S.KR 28000)
£2143 $3837 €3129 Wild geese (38x46cm-15x18in) s.d.1939. 26-May-4 AB Stockholms Auktionsverk #2289/R est:20000-25000 (S.KR 29000)
£2462 $4234 €3595 Small birds in winter (43x50cm-17x20in) s. 3-Dec-3 AB Stockholms Auktionsverk #2283/R est:25000-30000 (S.KR 32000)
£2538 $4569 €3807 Bullfinches (51x60cm-20x24in) s.d.1939. 25-Apr-4 Goteborg Auktionsverk, Sweden #174/R est:25000 (S.KR 35000)
£2809 $5027 €4101 Duck having a dip (116x87cm-46x34in) s. s.d.1927 verso. 25-May-4 Bukowskis, Stockholm #29/R est:40000-50000 (S.KR 38000)
£2923 $5028 €4268 Ducks in flight (55x81cm-22x32in) s. 3-Dec-3 AB Stockholms Auktionsverk #2285/R est:20000-25000 (S.KR 38000)
£2956 $5292 €4316 Mallards by ice-hole in winter (98x126cm-39x50in) s.d.1928. 25-May-4 Bukowskis, Stockholm #28/R est:35000-40000 (S.KR 40000)
£2956 $5292 €4316 Seagulls (73x110cm-29x43in) s.d.1940. 25-May-4 Bukowskis, Stockholm #33/R est:30000-40000 (S.KR 40000)
£2956 $5292 €4316 Seagulls in winter (80x125cm-31x49in) s.d.36. 25-May-4 Bukowskis, Stockholm #181/R est:35000-40000 (S.KR 40000)
£3030 $5424 €4424 Ducks in flight at sunset (75x153cm-30x60in) s. 25-May-4 Bukowskis, Stockholm #32/R est:35000-40000 (S.KR 41000)
£3400 $6086 €4964 Frosty landscape with blackgrouse in bush (72x93cm-28x37in) s. 25-May-4 Bukowskis, Stockholm #175/R est:30000-35000 (S.KR 46000)
£3615 $6218 €5278 Swans on wintry waterway (95x145cm-37x57in) s.i.d.1942 panel. 3-Dec-3 AB Stockholms Auktionsverk #2323/R est:50000-60000 (S.KR 47000)
£3695 $6615 €5395 Seagulls on rocks in morning (76x120cm-30x47in) s.d.1940. 26-May-4 AB Stockholms Auktionsverk #2297/R est:50000-60000 (S.KR 50000)
£4065 $7276 €5935 Attendant grouse in bushy landscape (60x92cm-24x36in) s.d.30. 26-May-4 AB Stockholms Auktionsverk #2298/R est:60000-80000 (S.KR 55000)
£4065 $7276 €5935 Winter landscape with bullfinches (46x54cm-18x21in) s.d.1946 panel. 26-May-4 AB Stockholms Auktionsverk #2338/R est:35000-40000 (S.KR 55000)
Works on paper
£2615 $4498 €3818 Crows in pine branches (30x47cm-12x19in) s. W/C. 2-Dec-3 Bukowskis, Stockholm #53/R est:15000-18000 (S.KR 34000)

STOOPS, Herbert Morton (1887-1948) American
£3352 $6000 €4894 Indians sending smoke signals as pioneers look on (81x53cm-32x21in) 15-May-4 Illustration House, New York #32/R est:4000-6000

STOPFORD, Robert Lowe (1813-1898) British
Works on paper
£880 $1390 €1285 Thirkin Abbey, Baltimore harbour, Cork (35x51cm-14x20in) s.i.verso W/C. 23-Jul-3 Hampton & Littlewood, Exeter #380/R
£1800 $3258 €2700 Thirkin Abbey, Balti More harbour, Co Cork (33x50cm-13x20in) W/C. 31-Mar-4 James Adam, Dublin #59/R est:1400-1800
£5839 $10452 €8700 Entrance to Baltimore Harbour. Sherkin Island off Cork Coast (34x51cm-13x20in) W/C pair. 26-May-4 James Adam, Dublin #7/R est:2500-3500

STOPPANI, Maurice (1921-) French
£300 $540 €450 Les chardons mauves (61x38cm-24x15in) s.d.1988 panel. 20-Apr-4 Chenu & Scrive, Lyon #157/R
£300 $540 €450 La bouteille grise (55x38cm-22x15in) s. 20-Apr-4 Chenu & Scrive, Lyon #158/R

STOPPOLONI, Augusto (1855-1936) Italian
Works on paper
£700 $1120 €1022 Cupid and Putti frolicking in the clouds (42x75cm-17x30in) s.i. pastel. 17-Sep-3 Bonhams, Brooks & Langlois, Jersey #102/R
£1192 $2170 €1800 Portrait of a fashionable woman, seated in a chair. Portrait of a seated gentleman (86x65cm-34x26in) s. pastel pair. 17-Jun-4 Hamilton Osborne King, Dublin #216/R est:1500-2500

STORCH, Frederik (1805-1883) Danish
£376 $677 €549 Portrait of young woman from Rome (27x19cm-11x7in) s.i.d.46 canvas on paper. 24-Apr-4 Rasmussen, Havnen #2048/R (D.KR 4200)
£486 $802 €700 Brother and sisters in rowing boat on mountain lake (40x50cm-16x20in) s.d.1839. 3-Jul-3 Van Ham, Cologne #1474/R
£986 $1706 €1400 Part of Sorrent (24x31cm-9x12in) s. canvas on panel. 10-Dec-3 Dorotheum, Vienna #166/R
£2085 $3336 €3044 Portrait of Sophia Sehsted-Jull, aged 4 (63x55cm-25x22in) s.i.d.1858 verso. 22-Sep-3 Rasmussen, Vejle #80/R est:20000 (D.KR 22000)
£2238 $4096 €3267 Mother and child by table with toys (47x38cm-19x15in) 9-Jun-4 Rasmussen, Copenhagen #1587/R est:30000 (D.KR 25000)

STORCH, Frederik (attrib) (1805-1883) Danish
£2836 $4905 €4141 Neapolitan fisherfamily on the beach (75x61cm-30x24in) 9-Dec-3 Rasmussen, Copenhagen #1237/R est:40000 (D.KR 30000)

STORCH, Karl (elder) (1864-1954) German
£671 $1235 €1000 Landscape with village and windmill near Segeberg (50x70cm-20x28in) s.d.1948 panel. 26-Mar-4 Bolland & Marotz, Bremen #596/R
£1042 $1698 €1500 Farmstead by Segeberger See (39x59cm-15x23in) s.d.1946 panel. 26-Sep-3 Bolland & Marotz, Bremen #623/R est:1600

STORCK, Abraham (c.1635-c.1710) Dutch
£20139 $33632 €29000 Strollers on Dutch quay (12x11cm-5x4in) s. canvas on panel prov. 21-Oct-3 Fraysse & Associes, Paris #11/R
£50000 $86500 €73000 Coastal landscape with pinks, state barge amd man-o-war in a calm (32x38cm-13x15in) s. canvas on panel. 10-Dec-3 Bonhams, New Bond Street #9/R est:20000-30000

£63889 $115000 €93278 Capriccio of the Grand Canal (56x76cm-22x30in) s.d.1696 prov. 22-Jan-4 Sotheby's, New York #118/R est:120000-150000

STORCK, Abraham (after) (c.1635-c.1710) Dutch
£6849 $11644 €10000 Dutch ships sailing on the IJ, Amsterdam (51x64cm-20x25in) i. 5-Nov-3 Christie's, Amsterdam #59/R est:4000-6000

STORCK, Jacob (1641-1687) Dutch
£20000 $34600 €29200 River landscape with figures in a ferry before an imaginary town (65x97cm-26x38in) remains of sig prov.lit. 11-Dec-3 Sotheby's, London #153/R est:8000-12000

STORCK, Jacob (circle) (1641-1687) Dutch
£9000 $16200 €13140 River Amstel, looking towards the Hoog Sluis (85x127cm-33x50in) prov. 23-Apr-4 Christie's, Kensington #56/R est:4000-6000

STORCK, Johannes (17th C) Dutch
Works on paper
£1020 $1827 €1500 Un paysage fluvial, une eglise sur la droite et une ville a l'arrier plan (19x31cm-7x12in) s. pen brown ink grey wash prov. 18-Mar-4 Christie's, Paris #322/R est:2000-3000

STORELLI, Felix Marie Ferdinand (1778-1854) Italian
£833 $1417 €1200 Castle (25x34cm-10x13in) s. cardboard. 1-Nov-3 Meeting Art, Vercelli #180/R
£8882 $16343 €13500 Mort d'Adonis (113x146cm-44x57in) exhib. 24-Jun-4 Tajan, Paris #44/R est:15000-20000
Works on paper
£3200 $5760 €4672 Chateau seen with formal gardens and across parkland with sheep (23x32cm-9x13in) s. W/C black chk pair. 20-Apr-4 Sotheby's, Olympia #118/R est:3000-4000

STORELLI, Ferdinand Michel (1805-?) French
£22378 $37371 €32000 La maison du Tasse. Danseurs Napolitains devant le Vesuve (102x160cm-40x63in) s.d.1877 pair. 26-Jun-3 Artcurial Briest, Paris #511 est:30000-40000

STORER, Charles (1817-1907) American
Works on paper
£335 $550 €486 Homestead (41x56cm-16x22in) s.d.1892 W/C. 2-Jun-3 Grogan, Boston #649/R

STOREY, George Adolphus (1834-1919) British
£1800 $3348 €2628 Pandora (50x40cm-20x16in) mono. 4-Mar-4 Christie's, Kensington #583/R est:2000-3000
Works on paper
£500 $895 €730 Kilburn looking towards Hampstead (12x24cm-5x9in) mono.d.1858 W/C prov. 11-May-4 Sotheby's, Olympia #615/R

STOREY, George Adolphus (attrib) (1834-1919) British
£4000 $7160 €5840 Letter (127x101cm-50x40in) 26-May-4 Sotheby's, Olympia #146/R est:3000-4000

STOREY, Paul (1957-) British
£3000 $5370 €4380 Penelope Grotesque (200x200cm-79x79in) acrylic prov. 16-Mar-4 Bonhams, Knightsbridge #157/R est:1000-1500

STORK, Mary (1938-) British
Works on paper
£280 $484 €409 Aquarius (43x30cm-17x12in) s.d.2002 pastel. 11-Dec-3 Lane, Penzance #147
£300 $555 €438 Muse (69x46cm-27x18in) s.d. mixed media. 10-Feb-4 David Lay, Penzance #250
£400 $692 €584 Meeting (89x61cm-35x24in) s.d.1998 pastel mixed media. 11-Dec-3 Lane, Penzance #146

STORM VAN S'GRAVENSANDE, Carel Nicolaas (1841-1924) Dutch
£395 $714 €600 Winter day in the Hague with view of Nassau Street (55x45cm-22x18in) mono. panel. 19-Apr-4 Glerum, Amsterdam #272/R

STORM, Juan (1927-1995) Uruguayan
£941 $1600 €1374 Figure with horse and tree (58x79cm-23x31in) s.d.73. 25-Nov-3 Galeria y Remates, Montevideo #70/R
£1323 $2500 €1932 Woman in red (90x60cm-35x24in) s.d.95. 22-Feb-4 Galeria y Remates, Montevideo #103/R est:2800
£1882 $3200 €2748 Molles Station (80x93cm-31x37in) s. lit. 25-Nov-3 Galeria y Remates, Montevideo #68/R
£1989 $3500 €2904 Nude and cowboy at dusk (108x176cm-43x69in) s.d.87. 5-Jan-4 Galeria y Remates, Montevideo #54/R est:3800-4500
£2118 $3600 €3092 Lagoon (83x103cm-33x41in) s. 25-Nov-3 Galeria y Remates, Montevideo #69/R
£3333 $6300 €4866 Nude (120x190cm-47x75in) s.d.91. 22-Feb-4 Galeria y Remates, Montevideo #102/R est:5200

STORM, Per Palle (1910-1994) Norwegian
Sculpture
£1057 $1934 €1543 Seated man (63x31x33cm-25x12x13in) plaster. 7-Jun-4 Blomqvist, Oslo #393/R est:12000-15000 (N.KR 13000)

STORMONT, Howard Gull (fl.1884-1923) British
Works on paper
£950 $1720 €1387 Landscapes with figures (30x47cm-12x19in) s.d.1890 W/C set of three. 30-Mar-4 Sworder & Son, Bishops Stortford #594/R

STORR, Chris (1963-) American
£213 $375 €311 Ocean's Solitude II (30x30cm-12x12in) s. 3-Jan-4 Outer Cape Auctions, Provincetown #42/R
£239 $375 €349 Provincetown distant light (15x61cm-6x24in) s. board. 20-Apr-3 Outer Cape Auctions, Provincetown #53/R
£250 $425 €365 Provincetown, beach town (25x25cm-10x10in) s. board. 9-Nov-3 Outer Cape Auctions, Provincetown #92/R
£262 $475 €383 Coastal inlet (61x61cm-24x24in) s.verso. 3-Apr-4 Outer Cape Auctions, Provincetown #70/R

STORRIER, Tim (1949-) Australian
£851 $1447 €1242 Horizon (91x91cm-36x36in) s. 25-Nov-3 Christie's, Melbourne #150/R (A.D 2000)
£2881 $5214 €4206 Untitled - flying fort series (111x153cm-44x60in) s. 30-Mar-4 Lawson Menzies, Sydney #149/R est:3000-5000 (A.D 7000)
£4508 $7123 €6582 At the end of the hall (50x39cm-20x15in) s.i.d.1989 board prov. 2-Sep-3 Deutscher-Menzies, Melbourne #137/R est:8000-12000 (A.D 11000)
£4878 $7659 €7073 Heap II (102x131cm-40x52in) s.i.d.28-2-85 acrylic W/C pencil pl. 26-Aug-3 Christie's, Sydney #2/R est:9000-12000 (A.D 12000)
£4959 $8430 €7240 Nile evening (35x50cm-14x20in) s.i.d.27.5.84 acrylic pencil prov.lit. 29-Oct-3 Lawson Menzies, Sydney #5/R est:10000-15000 (A.D 12000)
£5691 $8935 €8252 Vulcan's shield for Achilles (151x11cm-59x4in) s.i.d.89 acrylic prov. 27-Aug-3 Christie's, Sydney #595/R est:18000-25000 (A.D 14000)
£6198 $10971 €9049 Departure (102x152cm-40x60in) s. oil paper prov. 3-May-4 Christie's, Melbourne #21/R est:18000-28000 (A.D 15000)
£8130 $12764 €11789 Un petit dejeuner a Cairo (152x152cm-60x60in) s.d.78 acrylic pencil. 26-Aug-3 Christie's, Sydney #111/R est:20000-30000 (A.D 20000)
£8714 $14552 €13071 Still life (115x113cm-45x44in) s.d.78. 27-Oct-3 Goodman, Sydney #187/R est:12000-18000 (A.D 21000)
£12245 $22531 €17878 Cherry bar and smoke (51x91cm-20x36in) s. i.verso. 29-Mar-4 Goodman, Sydney #91/R est:30000-35000 (A.D 30000)
£14050 $25992 €20513 Rose crossing (91x183cm-36x72in) s. i.d.1999 verso synthetic polymer on canvas. 10-Mar-4 Deutscher-Menzies, Melbourne #72/R est:40000-60000 (A.D 34000)
£20492 $33197 €29918 Burning rope series (60x183cm-24x72in) s.d.1998 acrylic mixed media prov. 30-Jul-3 Goodman, Sydney #32/R est:45000-55000 (A.D 50000)
£22267 $35850 €32510 Boundary (136x200cm-54x79in) s.i.d.1988 prov.lit. 25-Aug-3 Sotheby's, Paddington #109/R est:45000-65000 (A.D 55000)
£24793 $43884 €36198 Evening line (107x243cm-42x96in) s. s.i.verso acrylic rope prov. 3-May-4 Christie's, Melbourne #135/R est:65000-85000 (A.D 60000)
£37190 $68802 €54297 Dawn of the new day (122x152cm-48x60in) s.d.1997 prov. 10-Mar-4 Deutscher-Menzies, Melbourne #104/R est:65000-85000 (A.D 90000)
£39592 $72849 €57804 Evening water line (106x244cm-42x96in) s.d.1999 i.verso acrylic prov.lit. 29-Mar-4 Goodman, Sydney #83/R est:80000-120000 (A.D 97000)
£44262 $71705 €64623 Dawn - still life (106x243cm-42x96in) s. i.d.2001 verso acrylic prov. 30-Jul-3 Goodman, Sydney #75/R est:65000-85000 (A.D 108000)
Sculpture
£4959 $9174 €7240 Boot and apple (50x41x9cm-20x16x4in) s. bronze. 10-Mar-4 Deutscher-Menzies, Melbourne #206a/R est:5000-8000 (A.D 12000)
Works on paper
£1053 $1695 €1537 Thoughts on our Camp no.5 (70x100cm-28x39in) s.i.d.78 mixed media prov.exhib. 25-Aug-3 Sotheby's, Paddington #264/R est:3000-5000 (A.D 2600)
£1276 $2170 €1863 Bottle with red cap (29x20cm-11x8in) s.i.d.1987 synthetic polymer paint pencil string collage prov. 26-Nov-3 Deutscher-Menzies, Melbourne #15/R est:4000-6000 (A.D 3000)
£1322 $2446 €1930 Studies of saddle and bags (20x23cm-8x9in) s. pencil. 10-Mar-4 Deutscher-Menzies, Melbourne #509/R est:1000-1500 (A.D 3200)
£2331 $3962 €3403 Juggernaut (164x165cm-65x65in) s. synthetic polymer paint painted c.1969. 24-Nov-3 Sotheby's, Melbourne #82/R est:5000-7000 (A.D 5500)
£3306 $6116 €4827 Approach to Nune (57x57cm-22x22in) s. synthetic polymer executed c.1977. 10-Mar-4 Deutscher-Menzies, Melbourne #206/R est:9000-12000 (A.D 8000)
£4198 $7641 €6129 Evening (30x91cm-12x36in) s. synthetic polymer on canvas. 16-Jun-4 Deutscher-Menzies, Melbourne #173/R est:10000-15000 (A.D 11000)
£6147 $9713 €8975 Indado ruins (111x52cm-44x20in) s. synthetic polymer paint. 2-Sep-3 Deutscher-Menzies, Melbourne #90/R est:16000-20000 (A.D 15000)
£6198 $11467 €9049 Dream landscape (152x152cm-60x60in) mono. synthetic polymer. 10-Mar-4 Deutscher-Menzies, Melbourne #131/R est:25000-35000 (A.D 15000)
£7252 $13198 €10588 Lord sky (40x50cm-16x20in) s. synthetic polymer. 16-Jun-4 Deutscher-Menzies, Melbourne #10/R est:15000-20000 (A.D 19000)
£7692 $12385 €11230 Pacific drift - the gesture (103x151cm-41x59in) s.i.d.1997 synthetic polymer paint lit. 25-Aug-3 Sotheby's, Paddington #148/R est:20000-30000 (A.D 19000)
£8130 $14553 €11870 Tank (93x150cm-37x59in) s.i.d.1990 W/C. 4-May-4 Sotheby's, Melbourne #95/R est:20000-30000 (A.D 20000)
£8511 $14468 €12426 Night lament (51x152cm-20x60in) s.i.d.1995 synthetic polymer paint exhib. 26-Nov-3 Deutscher-Menzies, Melbourne #53/R est:20000-25000 (A.D 20000)
£9836 $15541 €14361 Altitude landscape (200x198cm-79x78in) s.d.77 synthetic polymer prov. 2-Sep-3 Deutscher-Menzies, Melbourne #91/R est:25000-30000 (A.D 24000)
£11570 $19669 €16892 Evening - point-point (89x120cm-35x47in) s.d.1986 mixed media rope prov. 29-Oct-3 Lawson Menzies, Sydney #15/R est:20000-30000 (A.D 28000)
£17073 $26805 €24756 Burning rope (103x151cm-41x59in) s.d.1988 W/C acrylic rope. 26-Aug-3 Christie's, Sydney #13/R est:30000-40000 (A.D 42000)
£20038 $36469 €29255 Summer evening (66x152cm-26x60in) s. s.i.d.1994 stretcher synthetic polymer. 16-Jun-4 Deutscher-Menzies, Melbourne #13/R est:45000-65000 (A.D 52500)
£20992 $38206 €30648 Point to point (61x183cm-24x72in) synthetic polymer prov. 16-Jun-4 Deutscher-Menzies, Melbourne #62/R est:50000-70000 (A.D 55000)
£24590 $38852 €35901 Evening fire line at the seven mile - morning run (71x366cm-28x144in) s.i. synthetic polymer. 2-Sep-3 Deutscher-Menzies, Melbourne #35/R est:55000-75000 (A.D 60000)
£26860 $49690 €39216 Centurion - the night runner (152x244cm-60x96in) s.i.d.1992 synthetic polymer on canvas. 10-Mar-4 Deutscher-Menzies, Melbourne #80/R (A.D 65000)
£36585 $65488 €53414 Incendiary monument - The burning of the gifts (152x305cm-60x120in) s.i.d.1989 prov.exhib. 4-May-4 Sotheby's, Melbourne #80/R est:90000-120000 (A.D 90000)
£56911 $101870 €83090 Garland, water line (106x244cm-42x96in) s.d.1999 synthetic polymer canvas lit. 4-May-4 Sotheby's, Melbourne #1/R est:100000-140000 (A.D 140000)

STORSTEIN, Aage (1900-1983) Norwegian
£550 $919 €803 Landscape (46x55cm-18x22in) s. panel. 17-Nov-3 Blomqvist, Lysaker #1322/R (N.KR 6600)
£601 $1052 €877 Pine trees (55x46cm-22x18in) s.d.46 panel. 16-Dec-3 Grev Wedels Plass, Oslo #222 (N.KR 7000)
£1193 $1908 €1730 Landscape from Ronna with boathouse (50x70cm-20x28in) s. panel painted c.1970-1072. 22-Sep-3 Blomqvist, Lysaker #1293/R est:15000-18000 (N.KR 14000)
£2121 $3796 €3097 View towards Ronsholmen, Justoy (60x73cm-24x29in) s.d.63 s.i.d. verso panel. 25-May-4 Grev Wedels Plass, Oslo #71/R est:15000-20000 (N.KR 26000)
£2726 $4688 €3980 Study for The Norwegian wall, West Gallery, Oslo Town Hall (96x110cm-38x43in) s. lit. 8-Dec-3 Blomqvist, Oslo #514/R est:35000-45000 (N.KR 32000)

STORTENBEKER, Pieter (1828-1898) Dutch
£544 $990 €800 Cattle in a landscape (45x32cm-18x13in) s. panel. 3-Feb-4 Christie's, Amsterdam #145
£940 $1738 €1400 Landscape with a little girl (56x89cm-22x35in) s. 15-Mar-4 Sotheby's, Amsterdam #99/R est:1000-1500
Works on paper
£403 $741 €600 Meadow by Voorburg (20x31cm-8x12in) s.i. black chk. 29-Mar-4 Glerum, Amsterdam #48
£995 $1662 €1453 Cows in a sunlit polder landscape (36x59cm-14x23in) s. W/C. 17-Nov-3 Waddingtons, Toronto #153/R est:800-1200 (C.D 2200)

STORY, George H (1835-1923) American
£1308 $2250 €1910 New Haven fall (17x30cm-7x12in) i.verso board painted c.1870. 3-Dec-3 Doyle, New York #167/R est:1500-2500

STORY, Julian Russell (1850-1919) American
£2797 $4811 €4000 Portrait d'une elegante a l'eventail (55x35cm-22x14in) s.d.90 panel. 2-Dec-3 Christie's, Paris #522/R est:3000-5000

STOSKOPFF, Sebastien (1597-1657) German
£14483 $24186 €21000 Girl with dog and pretzel (152x118cm-60x46in) prov.lit. 15-Nov-3 Lempertz, Koln #1145/R est:15000-20000

STOSKOPFF, Sebastien (attrib) (1597-1657) German
£7237 $13316 €11000 Still life with oranges (30x50cm-12x20in) 24-Jun-4 Tajan, Paris #52/R est:12000-15000
£11111 $20000 €16222 Still life of a carp in a bowl placed on a wooden box, all resting on a table (50x62cm-20x24in) 22-Jan-4 Sotheby's, New York #198/R est:20000-30000

STOTHARD, Thomas (1755-1834) British
£300 $549 €438 Love and War (28x15cm-11x6in) wooden panel. 27-Jan-4 Gorringes, Lewes #1667
£1500 $2685 €2190 Passage of the Duoro, Oporto liberated, 1809, a design for an outer compartment of the Wellington Sh (15x25cm-6x10in) oil ink bodycol. 27-May-4 Christie's, Kensington #266/R est:400-600
£3200 $5888 €4672 Illustration to a novel (29x95cm-11x37in) prov. 11-Jun-4 Christie's, London #33/R est:4000-6000
£7500 $13800 €10950 View of Seringapatam, with English soldiers overlooking Indian cavalry (34x51cm-13x20in) 11-Jun-4 Christie's, London #56/R est:7000-10000
Works on paper
£500 $835 €730 Street in Southall (13x9cm-5x4in) s.i. pen black ink. 16-Oct-3 Christie's, Kensington #50/R
£811 $1427 €1200 Interior with woman seated on a chair and man entering the room (17x13cm-7x5in) s. brush col ink wash black lead prov.exhib.lit. 19-May-4 Sotheby's, Amsterdam #182/R

STOTT OF OLDHAM, William (1857-1900) British
£12000 $22080 €17520 Queen Iseult (98x109cm-39x43in) s. s.i.stretcher exhib. 11-Jun-4 Christie's, London #160/R est:12000-18000

STOTT, Edward (1859-1918) British
£5800 $9860 €8468 Moonrise over a stackyard (26x36cm-10x14in) s. 21-Nov-3 Christie's, London #31/R est:4000-6000
Works on paper
£700 $1204 €1022 Hagar and Ishmael beside a well in the desert (25x36cm-10x14in) mono. col chk. 3-Dec-3 Christie's, Kensington #145/R
£720 $1310 €1051 Corner of the orchard (31x24cm-12x9in) mono. pastel. 15-Jun-4 Bonhams, New Bond Street #15/R
£1100 $1837 €1606 Calf in a summer meadow (25x17cm-10x7in) mono. col chk prov. 16-Oct-3 Christie's, Kensington #212/R est:600-800

STOTZ, Otto (1805-1873) German
£526 $968 €800 Oriental warrior on a galloping horse (22x28cm-9x11in) s.d.1840. 22-Jun-4 Christie's, Amsterdam #75/R
£7601 $12618 €11097 Galloping horses, house of prince Schonborn (64x86cm-25x34in) s.d.1838. 4-Oct-3 Kieselbach, Budapest #93/R (H.F 2800000)

STOTZER, Werner (1931-) German
Sculpture
£2569 $4291 €3700 Seated figure (30x10x12cm-12x4x5in) mono.i. bronze Cast.Guss Barth/Elmenhorst. 25-Oct-3 Dr Lehr, Berlin #496/R est:3000

STOUPE, Seamus (1872-?) British
Works on paper
£400 $664 €584 Figures on a beach (28x38cm-11x15in) s. W/C. 1-Oct-3 John Ross, Belfast #266

STOUT, Myron (1908-1987) American
Works on paper
£7362 $12000 €10749 Untitled (15x20cm-6x8in) s.verso pencil exec.c.1970 prov.exhib. 23-Sep-3 Christie's, Rockefeller NY #54/R est:10000-15000

STOVER, Dieter (1922-1984) German
£1042 $1740 €1500 Langeland (140x110cm-55x43in) s.d. acrylic. 24-Oct-3 Ketterer, Hamburg #550/R est:1500-2000
£1042 $1740 €1500 White traces (140x120cm-55x47in) s.d. acrylic cotton hessian. 24-Oct-3 Ketterer, Hamburg #551/R est:1500-2000

STOWARD, F (19th C) ?
£1300 $2171 €1898 Shorthorn in landscape (52x64cm-20x25in) s.d.1859. 16-Oct-3 Lawrence, Crewkerne #718/R

STOWELL, Flaxney (19/20th C) ?
£700 $1204 €1022 Pooilvash Bay. s. s.i.verso. 5-Dec-3 Chrystals Auctions, Isle of Man #299h
Works on paper
£520 $894 €759 Bradda Head (15x23cm-6x9in) s. W/C. 5-Dec-3 Chrystals Auctions, Isle of Man #260
£600 $1002 €876 Castletown Harbour (25x30cm-10x12in) s. W/C. 20-Jun-3 Chrystals Auctions, Isle of Man #207/R
£1100 $1892 €1606 Entrance to Castletown harbour (25x36cm-10x14in) s. W/C. 5-Dec-3 Chrystals Auctions, Isle of Man #259 est:900-1200
£1200 $2064 €1752 Pulpits Rock (33x51cm-13x20in) s.d.1882 W/C. 5-Dec-3 Chrystals Auctions, Isle of Man #261 est:800-1200

STOWER, Willy (1864-1931) German
Works on paper
£432 $708 €600 Royal yacht Hohenzoller off Istanbul (15x23cm-6x9in) s.i. W/C gouache bodycol over pencil. 4-Jun-3 Ketterer, Hamburg #22/R
£576 $944 €800 Royal yacht Hohenzoller off Venice (19x32cm-7x13in) s. W/C bodycol board. 4-Jun-3 Ketterer, Hamburg #23/R
£576 $944 €800 Cruise ship off African coast (19x32cm-7x13in) s. W/C gouache bodycol over pencil board. 4-Jun-3 Ketterer, Hamburg #28/R
£791 $1298 €1100 Three masted bark off coast (19x32cm-7x13in) s. W/C bodycol over pencil board. 4-Jun-3 Ketterer, Hamburg #27/R
£1056 $1827 €1500 Royal yacht Hohenzollern sailing off the coast of Syrakus, Sicily (32x45cm-13x18in) s.i.d.1904 pencil W/C bodycol pair prov. 10-Dec-3 Christie's, Amsterdam #181/R est:1200-1600

STOWEROFFSKI, Ernst Friedrich (1816-1878) German
Works on paper
£694 $1097 €1000 Horse and rider (17x19cm-7x7in) s. W/C lit. 19-Sep-3 Schloss Ahlden, Ahlden #1454/R

STRAATEN, H van (1665-1722) Dutch
£284 $500 €415 Three generation (61x81cm-24x32in) s. 22-May-4 Harvey Clar, Oakland #2206

STRACHAN, Claude (1865-1929) British
£880 $1496 €1285 View of Warwick Castle (28x44cm-11x17in) s.d.97 canvasboard. 25-Nov-3 Bonhams, Knowle #230/R
£950 $1549 €1387 Coastal country landscape with milk maid on a path (31x44cm-12x17in) s.d.94. 24-Sep-3 Peter Wilson, Nantwich #15
Works on paper
£300 $537 €438 Coastal harvest field, with a sleeping girl (20x30cm-8x12in) s. W/C. 25-May-4 Sworder & Son, Bishops Stortford #416/R
£500 $835 €730 Rural landscape with horse grazing (52x37cm-20x15in) s.d.1885 W/C htd white. 7-Oct-3 Fellows & Sons, Birmingham #480/R
£1200 $2064 €1752 On the way home (43x28cm-17x11in) s. pencil W/C bodycol. 3-Dec-3 Christie's, Kensington #76/R est:1500-2000
£1200 $2208 €1752 Gathering primroses, possibly near Thorrington, Suffolk (33x48cm-13x19in) s. pencil W/C bodycol. 25-Mar-4 Christie's, Kensington #136/R est:1500-2500
£1300 $2392 €1898 At the cottage gate (17x26cm-7x10in) s. W/C bodycol. 8-Jun-4 Bonhams, New Bond Street #101/R est:1500-2000
£1350 $2457 €1971 Bratton, Somerset (35x49cm-14x19in) s. W/C bodycol. 21-Jun-4 Bonhams, Bath #460/R est:1500-2000
£1450 $2639 €2117 West Porlock Road, Somerset (25x35cm-10x14in) s. W/C bodycol. 21-Jun-4 Bonhams, Bath #461/R est:1500-2000
£1500 $2550 €2190 Country cottage (44x59cm-17x23in) s. W/C htd bodycol. 4-Nov-3 Bonhams, New Bond Street #157/R est:1500-2000
£1800 $3006 €2628 Cottage steps (42x28cm-17x11in) s. W/C. 12-Nov-3 Sotheby's, Olympia #62/R est:1000-1500
£2000 $3680 €2920 Thatched woodland cottage (17x26cm-7x10in) s. W/C bodycol. 8-Jun-4 Bonhams, New Bond Street #100/R est:2000-3000
£3500 $6265 €5110 Mother and child seated on the cottage gate (19x26cm-7x10in) s. W/C. 16-Mar-4 Bonhams, Leeds #615/R est:2000-3000
£4200 $7770 €6132 At Llanfair (29x47cm-11x19in) s. W/C. 9-Mar-4 Bonhams, New Bond Street #130/R est:4000-6000
£4500 $8280 €6570 Lame duck (17x26cm-7x10in) s. W/C bodycol. 8-Jun-4 Bonhams, New Bond Street #99/R est:3000-5000
£7800 $14352 €11388 Statue in a romantic garden (27x45cm-11x18in) s. W/C. 8-Jun-4 Bonhams, New Bond Street #97/R est:5000-8000

STRACHAN, David Edgar (1919-1970) British
£324 $521 €473 Lovers (14x19cm-6x7in) i.verso board. 13-Oct-3 Joel, Victoria #378 (A.D 800)
£744 $1376 €1086 Portrait of Bill Beresford (37x35cm-15x14in) s. i.d.1935 verso. 10-Mar-4 Deutscher-Menzies, Melbourne #465/R est:2000-4000 (A.D 1800)
£2979 $5064 €4349 Still life with fish (45x30cm-18x12in) s. board prov. 26-Nov-3 Deutscher-Menzies, Melbourne #148/R est:7000-9000 (A.D 7000)
£3252 $5106 €4715 Adam and Eve (33x19cm-13x7in) s. board prov.exhib. 26-Aug-3 Christie's, Sydney #132/R est:8000-12000 (A.D 8000)

£5319 $9202 €7766 Untitled, landscape with still life and boy's head (41x51cm-16x20in) s. board prov. 10-Dec-3 Shapiro, Sydney #1/R est:8000-12000 (A.D 12500)

STRACHAN, Robert Douglas (1875-1950) British
£850 $1607 €1241 Portrait of a lady in white dress (127x100cm-50x39in) 19-Feb-4 Lyon & Turnbull, Edinburgh #138

STRACK, Ludwig Philipp (attrib) (1761-1836) German
Works on paper
£1757 $3092 €2600 Aqueduct in Villa des Maecenas near Tivoli (43x56cm-17x22in) brush gouache prov. 22-May-4 Lempertz, Koln #1465/R est:2600

STRADONE, Giovanni (1911-1981) Italian
£521 $885 €750 Ruins (60x80cm-24x31in) s. s.i.d.1957 verso. 28-Oct-3 Il Ponte, Milan #338/R
£1000 $1800 €1500 Passiflora (45x35cm-18x14in) s.i.d.41 verso. 22-Apr-4 Finarte Semenzato, Rome #157/R est:1400-1700
£1333 $2400 €2000 Young man with guitar (40x36cm-16x14in) board exhib. 22-Apr-4 Finarte Semenzato, Rome #220/R est:1800-2000
£2467 $4440 €3700 Marcello with straw hat (43x34cm-17x13in) s. painted 1930 exhib. 22-Apr-4 Finarte Semenzato, Rome #221/R est:2800-3200

STRAETEN, George van der (1856-1928) Belgian
Sculpture
£757 $1400 €1136 Lady with a lyre (51cm-20in) s. bronze prov. 17-Jul-4 Skinner, Boston #758/R est:1500-2500
£1138 $1900 €1661 Bust of a young girl (28cm-11in) s. brown pat. bronze marble base. 19-Oct-3 Susanin's, Chicago #6004/R est:800-1200
£2215 $4075 €3300 Woman feeding chicks (32cm-13in) s. gold pat.bronze ivory Cast.Societe des bronzes de Paris. 25-Mar-4 Dr Fritz Nagel, Stuttgart #947/R est:2500

STRAETEN, van der (?) ?
Sculpture
£2260 $4000 €3300 Merveilleuse (25cm-10in) i. brown pat bronze exec.c.1900. 2-May-4 Bonhams & Butterfields, San Francisco #1524/R est:2000-3000

STRAFFORD, Henry (19th C) British
£10563 $18275 €15000 Portraits of cows and bulls (36x46cm-14x18in) mono.d.1830 s.i.d.1830 verso five. 11-Dec-3 Dr Fritz Nagel, Stuttgart #448/R est:2000

STRAHALM, Franz (1879-1935) American/Austrian
£11976 $20000 €17485 Evening glow (91x107cm-36x42in) exhib. 18-Oct-3 David Dike, Dallas #254/R est:10000-20000

STRAHAN, Geoffrey (?-1916) British
£1500 $2550 €2190 Busy day in the Upper Pool, London (89x122cm-35x48in) s.d.1903. 19-Nov-3 Christie's, Kensington #593/R est:800-1200

STRAHN, Peter Josef (1904-) German
£267 $485 €400 Two children by cow hut (25x37cm-10x15in) s. fibreboard. 1-Jul-4 Neumeister, Munich #2816
£1259 $2140 €1800 Sheep in meadow (60x80cm-24x31in) s. 20-Nov-3 Van Ham, Cologne #1879/R est:2000

STRAMPP, Adriane Beth (1960-) Australian/American
£620 $1147 €905 Long summer (108x30cm-43x12in) s.d.1991 i.verso prov. 15-Mar-4 Sotheby's, Melbourne #189 est:300-600 (A.D 1500)
£1352 $2191 €1974 Still life (122x152cm-48x60in) s.d.99. 30-Jul-3 Goodman, Sydney #78/R est:3800-4500 (A.D 3300)
£3049 $4786 €4452 Villandry (182x167cm-72x66in) s.d.96 verso prov. 27-Aug-3 Christie's, Sydney #611/R est:1500-2500 (A.D 7500)
£3455 $5425 €5044 In absentia (182x213cm-72x84in) s.d.96 verso. 27-Aug-3 Christie's, Sydney #692/R est:1500-2500 (A.D 8500)

STRAND, Paul (1890-1976) American
Photographs
£1587 $3000 €2317 Untitled (24x19cm-9x7in) s. gelatin silver print executed c.1928. 17-Feb-4 Christie's, Rockefeller NY #41/R est:4000-6000
£2646 $5000 €3863 Ranchos de Taos church, New Mexico (19x25cm-7x10in) gelatin silver print. 17-Feb-4 Christie's, Rockefeller NY #92/R est:6000-8000
£6587 $11000 €9617 Woman, Patzcuaro, Mexico (24x19cm-9x7in) s. silver print sold with a letter. 21-Oct-3 Swann Galleries, New York #154/R est:9000-12000
£8000 $14080 €11680 Driftwood (24x19cm-9x7in) vintage gelatin silver print. 18-May-4 Bonhams, New Bond Street #227/R est:10000-12000
£8475 $15000 €12374 San Antonio, Texas, 1918 (18x23cm-7x9in) platinum print prov. 27-Apr-4 Christie's, Rockefeller NY #315/R est:20000-30000
£14815 $28000 €21630 New York, 1916 (25x32cm-10x13in) num.81/100 platinum palladium print printed 1976-77. 17-Feb-4 Christie's, Rockefeller NY #37/R est:12000-18000
£15873 $30000 €23175 Chris-to, Tlacochoya, Oxaca, Mexico (24x19cm-9x7in) s.i.d. verso varnished platinum print. 17-Feb-4 Swann Galleries, New York #59/R est:35000-45000
£53672 $95000 €78361 Toadstool, Maine (25x19cm-10x7in) s.i.d.1928 verso varnished platinum print prov. 27-Apr-4 Sotheby's, New York #23/R est:80000-120000

STRAND, Svein (1934-) Norwegian
£12810 $22930 €18703 Table, mirror, window (147x114cm-58x45in) s. i.d.1988-89 stretcher exhib. 22-Mar-4 Blomqvist, Oslo #618/R est:100000-120000 (N.KR 160000)

STRANG, Michael J (1942-) British
£650 $1086 €949 Gulval sunflower field by moonlight (91x122cm-36x48in) s.i.d.1996/7 verso board. 14-Oct-3 David Lay, Penzance #617/R

STRANG, William (1859-1921) British
£4000 $6680 €5840 Bath (122x104cm-48x41in) s.d.1904 prov.exhib. 16-Oct-3 Bonhams, Edinburgh #115/R est:3000-5000
Works on paper
£450 $747 €657 Edward Pryor (25x21cm-10x8in) s.d.1907 pencil. 1-Oct-3 Woolley & Wallis, Salisbury #157/R
£580 $1073 €847 Portrait of Arthur Whitelegge (38x24cm-15x9in) s.i.d.1912 black crayon sanguine htd white. 14-Jan-4 Lawrence, Crewkerne #1349

STRANGE, Albert (1855-1917) British
£1000 $1610 €1450 Whitby harbour (43x33cm-17x13in) s. 15-Aug-3 Keys, Aylsham #692/R est:800-1200

STRANOVER, Tobias (1684-1735) Czechoslovakian
£2069 $3455 €3000 Still life with bird and grapes (51x41cm-20x16in) s. canvas on panel. 15-Nov-3 Lempertz, Koln #1147/R est:3500
£8500 $15300 €12410 Fruits with a parrot and a goldfinch on a ledge (58x65cm-23x26in) 23-Apr-4 Christie's, Kensington #137/R est:6000-8000
£13382 $23418 €19000 Natures mortes de fruites et de fleurs (116x152cm-46x60in) pair. 18-Dec-3 Tajan, Paris #34/R est:20000-25000
£22000 $38060 €32120 Peaches on a silver tazza with a melon, an apple and other fruit on a stone ledge (48x61cm-19x24in) 10-Dec-3 Bonhams, New Bond Street #11/R est:4000-6000

STRANOVER, Tobias (attrib) (1684-1735) Czechoslovakian
£9500 $17100 €13870 Peaches, grapes, plums and a melon, parrot and goldfinch, landscape beyond (76x62cm-30x24in) 21-Apr-4 Bonhams, New Bond Street #95/R est:4000-6000

STRANSKY, Ferdinand (1904-) Austrian
£1611 $2980 €2400 Sleeping figure (46x61cm-18x24in) s.d.65 oil masonite. 9-Mar-4 Dorotheum, Vienna #131/R est:2800-3400
£3472 $5903 €5000 Still life (45x59cm-18x23in) s. panel. 28-Oct-3 Wiener Kunst Auktionen, Vienna #110/R est:5000-10000

STRASBOURG SCHOOL, French
£6800 $12444 €9928 Peaches, wine glass and round loaf (49x65cm-19x26in) prov.lit. 9-Jul-4 Christie's, Kensington #118/R est:7000-10000

STRASSER, Benjamin (1888-1955) Austrian
£260 $465 €380 Still life with flowers, fruit and wine glasses (46x56cm-18x22in) s. 22-Mar-4 Philippe Schuler, Zurich #6193 (S.FR 600)
£862 $1543 €1259 Young ballet dancer (86x69cm-34x27in) s. 12-May-4 Dobiaschofsky, Bern #1009/R est:2200 (S.FR 2000)
£1333 $2440 €2000 Portrait of Ernestine Farber-Strasser (98x80cm-39x31in) s.d.1928 prov. 5-Jun-4 Lempertz, Koln #1010/R est:2000
£1700 $3145 €2482 Portrait of a young girl, seated half length in a green dress holding an orange (79x69cm-31x27in) s.d.1914. 14-Jul-4 Christie's, Kensington #896/R est:1200-1800

STRASSER, Conrad (1878-?) Swiss
£281 $504 €410 Still life with orchids (42x34cm-17x13in) s. panel. 22-Mar-4 Philippe Schuler, Zurich #6049 (S.FR 650)
£420 $773 €613 Still life of roses in a vase (58x74cm-23x29in) 23-Jun-4 Cheffins, Cambridge #436/R

STRASSER, Jakob (1896-1978) Swiss
£317 $538 €463 Riverside houses (41x34cm-16x13in) s.d.1953. 28-Nov-3 Zofingen, Switzerland #3189 (S.FR 700)
£362 $615 €529 Border guards (35x35cm-14x14in) s.d.1940. 28-Nov-3 Zofingen, Switzerland #3192 (S.FR 800)
£385 $654 €562 Lucern (60x65cm-24x26in) s.i.d.1955. 28-Nov-3 Zofingen, Switzerland #3193 (S.FR 850)
£520 $885 €759 Fruit trees in bloom (45x50cm-18x20in) s.i.d.1935 verso. 28-Nov-3 Zofingen, Switzerland #3190 (S.FR 1150)

STRASSER, Roland (1892-1974) Austrian
Works on paper
£1497 $2679 €2200 Reclining Balinese nude (38x26cm-15x10in) s.i. black chk pastel W/C gouache sold with two others by same ha. 16-Mar-4 Christie's, Amsterdam #17 est:800-1200
£1701 $3044 €2500 Seated geisha (60x48cm-24x19in) s.i.d.30 gouache. 16-Mar-4 Christie's, Amsterdam #74/R est:1500-2000
£1849 $3329 €2700 Dancing girl with fan. Japanese woman. Two Balinese girl dancing (32x22cm-13x9in) s.i. pencil htd set of seven. 25-Apr-4 Christie's, Hong Kong #513/R est:6500-9500 (HK.D 26000)
£2288 $4141 €3340 Peasant girl (50x33cm-20x13in) s. crayon. 4-Apr-4 Sotheby's, Singapore #7/R est:6000-8000 (S.D 7000)

STRATEMEYER, George (19th C) American
£8500 $14195 €12410 Traveller on horseback on the Pali Road, Hawaii (36x51cm-14x20in) prov. 14-Oct-3 Sotheby's, London #189/R est:3000-4000

STRATHMANN, Carl (1866-1939) German
Works on paper
£1329 $2285 €1900 King Nebucadnezzar in the forest (45x79cm-18x31in) s. W/C. 3-Dec-3 Neumeister, Munich #435/R est:2000

STRATHMANN, Carl (attrib) (1866-1939) German
£590 $962 €850 Moonlit Tegernsee (20x28cm-8x11in) panel. 26-Sep-3 Bolland & Marotz, Bremen #624/R

STRATIGOS, Georgios (1880-1944) Greek
£4000 $6800 €5840 Boats at sea (115x101cm-45x40in) s. prov. 18-Nov-3 Sotheby's, London #93/R est:4000-6000

Works on paper
£2200 $3938 €3212 Oriental Beauty (32x23cm-13x9in) s. W/C gouache. 10-May-4 Sotheby's, Olympia #4/R est:1000-1500

STRATMANN, Robert (1877-?) German
£280 $467 €400 First sun (67x88cm-26x35in) s. i. verso. 28-Jun-3 Bolland & Marotz, Bremen #807/R

STRATTA, Carlo (1852-1936) Italian
Works on paper
£504 $826 €700 Young woman (28x21cm-11x8in) W/C. 5-Jun-3 Adma, Formigine #283
£603 $1007 €850 Parisian profile (29x22cm-11x9in) s. W/C card. 20-Oct-3 Sant Agostino, Torino #250/R

STRAUBE, William (1871-1954) German
Works on paper
£959 $1630 €1400 Espasingen in winter (37x50cm-15x20in) s.d.1929 W/C. 8-Nov-3 Geble, Radolfzell #843/R
£2333 $4177 €3500 Trees (26x35cm-10x14in) s.d. W/C prov. 14-May-4 Ketterer, Munich #80/R est:1500-2000
£5467 $9785 €8200 Berlin street (38x45cm-15x18in) s.d. pastel prov. 14-May-4 Ketterer, Munich #79/R est:1800-2400

STRAUBINGER, Klaus (1839-?) German
£331 $603 €500 Bouquet of flowers (47x63cm-19x25in) mono.d.88 board. 18-Jun-4 Bolland & Marotz, Bremen #957/R

STRAUCH, Ludwig Karl (1875-1959) Austrian
Works on paper
£267 $500 €390 Ready for church service (53x36cm-21x14in) s. W/C. 24-Feb-4 Arthur James, Florida #12
£361 $675 €527 Mountain landscape, Austria (51x69cm-20x27in) s.d.1918 pastel. 25-Feb-4 Museumsbygningen, Copenhagen #106/R (D.KR 4000)

STRAUGH, Julian M (20th C) British
Works on paper
£700 $1113 €1022 The Spurs' double winners' parade (96x65cm-38x26in) s. col pastel. 11-Sep-3 Sotheby's, Olympia #106/R

STRAUS, Meyer (1831-1905) American/German
£549 $900 €802 Mt. Hood (38x56cm-15x22in) s.i.d.June 30 1880 panel. 9-Jun-3 O'Gallerie, Oregon #839/R
£667 $1200 €974 Trees by a lake (17x12cm-7x5in) s.i.d.1876 paper on board arched top. 25-Apr-4 Bonhams & Butterfields, San Francisco #5497/R est:1000-1500
£756 $1300 €1104 Mated in death. s. linen. 6-Dec-3 Harvey Clar, Oakland #1146
£2824 $4800 €4123 Bayou Teche, Louisiana (36x48cm-14x19in) s.d.1871 canvas on panel. 22-Nov-3 New Orleans Auction, New Orleans #1065/R est:5000-8000

STRAUSER, Sterling (1907-1995) American
£625 $1000 €913 Clown (61x46cm-24x18in) s. board. 20-Sep-3 Sloans & Kenyon, Bethesda #638/R est:2000-2500
£1006 $1600 €1469 Tiger ladies (81x122cm-32x48in) s.d.73 masonite. 13-Sep-3 Weschler, Washington #796/R est:2000-3000
£1173 $2100 €1713 Pink chrysanthemums (61x51cm-24x20in) s. board. 7-May-4 Sloans & Kenyon, Bethesda #1205a/R est:700-900

STRAUSS, Andre (1885-1971) French
£333 $613 €500 Bord de riviere (46x61cm-18x24in) s. 9-Jun-4 Beaussant & Lefèvre, Paris #219/R

STRAWSER, Barbara (20th C) American
£258 $475 €377 The black rooster (51x41cm-20x16in) s.d.2000 board. 25-Jun-4 Freeman, Philadelphia #116/R

STREATFIELD, Kathleen (fl.1906-1927) British
Works on paper
£260 $442 €380 Study of a boy (30x24cm-12x9in) s.d.1916 pencil W/C. 19-Nov-3 Tennants, Leyburn #939

STREATOR, Harold A (1861-1926) American
£1176 $2000 €1717 Stream in a landscape (41x51cm-16x20in) i.verso prov. 18-Nov-3 John Moran, Pasadena #48 est:2000-2500

STREBEL, Richard Hermann (1861-?) German
£426 $689 €600 Hunting near Billwurder (92x125cm-36x49in) s. i. verso lit. 23-May-3 Karlheinz Kaupp, Staufen #1777/R

STREBELLE, Jean Marie (1916-) Belgian
Works on paper
£280 $501 €420 Fresque d'animaux d'Africque (36x108cm-14x43in) s. gouache. 11-May-4 Vanderkindere, Brussels #234
£479 $815 €700 Reverie (72x54cm-28x21in) s. mixed media. 10-Nov-3 Horta, Bruxelles #244
£1241 $2297 €1800 Elegante sur fond de paysage (72x110cm-28x43in) s. 19-Jan-4 Horta, Bruxelles #316 est:700-900

STREBELLE, Rodolphe (1880-1959) Belgian
£280 $467 €400 Jeune fille au collier (70x65cm-28x26in) s. 13-Oct-3 Horta, Bruxelles #515
£855 $1548 €1300 Composition au vase fleuri (60x70cm-24x28in) s. 19-Apr-4 Horta, Bruxelles #29
£1549 $2711 €2200 Fillette, au panier, dans un paysage (70x65cm-28x26in) s. 16-Dec-3 Galerie Moderne, Brussels #803/R est:500-700
Works on paper
£294 $499 €420 Nieuport. s. W/C. 18-Nov-3 Galerie Moderne, Brussels #809

STRECHINE, Stephanie de (1858-?) German
£450 $833 €657 Figures on a country road (16x23cm-6x9in) s.d.1879 panel. 10-Feb-4 Bonhams, Knightsbridge #74/R
£1007 $1852 €1500 Wood near Gaisach (90x130cm-35x51in) s. 24-Mar-4 Hugo Ruef, Munich #1126 est:600

STRECKENBACH, Max T (1865-1936) German
£519 $950 €758 Still life with flowers (55x70cm-22x28in) s. oil on cardboard. 1-Jun-4 Ben-Ami, Tel Aviv #4923/R est:1000-1500
£699 $1286 €1021 Still life with poppies (72x60cm-28x24in) s. canvas on masonite. 14-Jun-4 Philippe Schuler, Zurich #4344 (S.FR 1600)
£733 $1320 €1100 Pansies in vase (23x27cm-9x11in) s. board. 23-Apr-4 Altus, Berlin #559/R
£1096 $1863 €1600 Poppy (58x47cm-23x19in) s. 8-Nov-3 Hans Stahl, Toestorf #85/R est:900
£1528 $2414 €2200 Poppies in Delft vase (60x75cm-24x30in) s. 6-Sep-3 Schopman, Hamburg #775/R est:1400
£1600 $2896 €2400 Still life with poppies (66x50cm-26x20in) s. 3-Apr-4 Hans Stahl, Hamburg #89/R est:2600
£1611 $2964 €2400 Still life with lilac (70x80cm-28x31in) i. 29-Mar-4 Dr Fritz Nagel, Stuttgart #6914/R est:900
£2119 $3857 €3200 Still life with artichokes, tomatoes and a basket (50x80cm-20x31in) s. 18-Jun-4 Bolland & Marotz, Bremen #776/R est:3500
£2168 $3729 €3100 Still life with poppies (54x80cm-21x31in) s. 6-Dec-3 Hans Stahl, Toestorf #91/R est:3600

STRECKER, Emil (1841-1925) German
£1389 $2292 €2000 Young girl reading at table (32x26cm-13x10in) s. 3-Jul-3 Dr Fritz Nagel, Stuttgart #521/R

STREEFKERK, Carl August (1884-1968) Dutch
£325 $581 €475 Harbour (40x80cm-16x31in) s. 22-Mar-4 Philippe Schuler, Zurich #4459 (S.FR 750)
£1150 $1955 €1679 Canalside flower market, Amsterdam (58x99cm-23x39in) s. 29-Oct-3 Bonhams, Chester #475 est:1200-1800

STREET, Evelyn (20th C) Irish
£265 $482 €400 Home in mountain landscape (60x75cm-24x30in) board. 15-Jun-4 James Adam, Dublin #173/R
£400 $720 €600 River landscape (30x60cm-12x24in) mono. board. 20-Apr-4 James Adam, Dublin #104/R
£433 $780 €650 Mountain landscape (50x64cm-20x25in) mono. board. 20-Apr-4 James Adam, Dublin #45/R
£500 $900 €750 Travelling figure in mountain landscape (59x74cm-23x29in) mono. 20-Apr-4 James Adam, Dublin #44/R

STREET, George Edmund (1824-1881) British
Works on paper
£1200 $2064 €1752 Palazzo Orfei, Venice (28x21cm-11x8in) i.d.1868 pencil black ink W/C sold with a dr by another hand. 3-Dec-3 Christie's, Kensington #105/R est:1200-1800

STREET, Robert (1796-1865) American
£2732 $5000 €3989 Portrait of a man. Portrait of a woman (76x64cm-30x25in) s.d.1837 pair. 7-Jun-4 Bonhams & Butterfields, San Francisco #2019/R est:6000-8000
£14865 $27500 €21703 Portrait of Ann Marie Vick and her infant daughter (76x66cm-30x26in) s.d.1836 prov. 15-Jan-4 Sotheby's, New York #311/R est:10000-15000
£17442 $30000 €25465 Village in winter (76x91cm-30x36in) s.d.1849-51 prov. 3-Dec-3 Sotheby's, New York #108/R est:40000-60000

STREET, Robert (attrib) (1796-1865) American
£663 $1100 €961 Portrait. board. 14-Jun-3 Fallon, Copake #55

STREETON, Sir Arthur Ernest (1867-1943) Australian
£6870 $12504 €10030 Bomb officers quarters, Glisy (76x63cm-30x25in) s.i.d.1918 prov.exhib. 16-Jun-4 Deutscher-Menzies, Melbourne #48/R est:18000-25000 (A.D 18000)
£11885 $19254 €17352 Chrysanthemums (61x51cm-24x20in) s. 30-Jul-3 Goodman, Sydney #95/R est:20000-30000 (A.D 29000)
£13223 $24463 €19306 Canterbury bells, purple and white (61x51cm-24x20in) s. prov.exhib. 10-Mar-4 Deutscher-Menzies, Melbourne #100/R est:32000-40000 (A.D 32000)
£14050 $25992 €20513 Tobacco jar and billy (40x34cm-16x13in) s.acrylic canvas on board prov.exhib. 10-Mar-4 Deutscher-Menzies, Melbourne #194/R est:12000-18000 (A.D 34000)
£15385 $24769 €22462 Foxgloves and stocks (60x50cm-24x20in) s. bears i.verso prov.exhib.lit. 25-Aug-3 Sotheby's, Paddington #139/R est:30000-50000 (A.D 38000)
£18595 $32913 €27149 Hobart from the slopes of Mount Wellington (60x50cm-24x20in) s. painted c.1938 prov.exhib. 3-May-4 Christie's, Melbourne #60/R est:45000-55000 (A.D 45000)
£19068 $32415 €27839 Cairo (50x60cm-20x24in) s.i. painted c.1898 prov.exhib. 24-Nov-3 Sotheby's, Melbourne #26/R est:45000-65000 (A.D 45000)
£21138 $37837 €30861 Roses in a cream vase (58x48cm-23x19in) s. prov. 4-May-4 Sotheby's, Melbourne #74/R est:40000-60000 (A.D 52000)
£22358 $35102 €32419 Hills and clouds (63x75cm-25x30in) s. painted c.1928 prov. 26-Aug-3 Christie's, Sydney #70/R est:60000-80000 (A.D 55000)
£22901 $41679 €33435 Melbourne (20x66cm-8x26in) s. oil cedar panel pencil. 16-Jun-4 Deutscher-Menzies, Melbourne #94/R est:65000-85000 (A.D 60000)
£24390 $43659 €35609 Roses, La France (58x48cm-23x19in) s. prov. 4-May-4 Sotheby's, Melbourne #75/R est:40000-60000 (A.D 60000)

£26271 $44661 €38356 Sherbrooke (51x76cm-20x30in) s. painted 1921 prov.exhib. 24-Nov-3 Sotheby's, Melbourne #52/R est:50000-70000 (A.D 62000)
£32839 $55826 €47945 Railway bridge over the Derwent (50x76cm-20x30in) s.d.37 prov.exhib. 24-Nov-3 Sotheby's, Melbourne #14/R est:50000-60000 (A.D 77500)
£57377 $90656 €83770 North Shore, Sydney (16x42cm-6x17in) s.d.92 panel prov. 2-Sep-3 Deutscher-Menzies, Melbourne #32/R est:140000-180000 (A.D 140000)
Works on paper
£405 $652 €591 Bridge and landscape (24x33cm-9x13in) init.d.1901 pencil. 25-Aug-3 Sotheby's, Paddington #420 (A.D 1000)
£447 $702 €653 Facade of the North Transept of Kelso Abbey, Scotland (24x35cm-9x14in) s. pencil wash. 1-Sep-3 Shapiro, Sydney #390 (A.D 1100)
£658 $1192 €961 Artist at work (15x18cm-6x7in) s. pen ink. 1-Apr-4 Joel, Victoria #166 (A.D 1600)
£1818 $3091 €2727 Middle Harbour, France (34x49cm-13x19in) s.i.d.1918 W/C. 28-Oct-3 Goodman, Sydney #388/R (A.D 4400)
£2834 $4563 €4138 View of Windsor Castle (28x32cm-11x13in) s. W/C. 25-Aug-3 Sotheby's, Paddington #469/R est:5000-8000 (A.D 7000)
£3306 $5851 €4827 Sunday at home, Streeton Home (32x26cm-13x10in) s.d. i.verso W/C prov.exhib.lit. 3-May-4 Christie's, Melbourne #380/R est:9000-12000 (A.D 8000)
£3435 $6252 €5015 Bay of Naples (18x25cm-7x10in) W/C prov. 16-Jun-4 Deutscher-Menzies, Melbourne #152/R est:10000-15000 (A.D 9000)
£3470 $6384 €5066 Guildford (50x34cm-20x13in) s. W/C prov. 29-Mar-4 Goodman, Sydney #113/R est:6000-8000 (A.D 8500)
£3846 $6192 €5615 Windsor Forest (48x34cm-19x13in) s.i.d.1903 W/C exhib. 25-Aug-3 Sotheby's, Paddington #338/R est:5000-8000 (A.D 9500)
£4545 $8045 €6636 Cairo (43x24cm-17x9in) s.i. W/C prov. 3-May-4 Christie's, Melbourne #309/R est:8000-12000 (A.D 11000)
£5263 $8474 €7684 Camouflaged siege gun, Querrieu (35x53cm-14x21in) s.i.d.1918 exhib. 25-Aug-3 Sotheby's, Paddington #458/R est:6000-9000 (A.D 13000)
£6612 $11702 €9654 Still life, Georgian silver (30x46cm-12x18in) s. W/C prov. 3-May-4 Christie's, Melbourne #63/R est:10000-15000 (A.D 16000)

STREICHMAN, Yehezkel (1906-1993) Israeli
£21658 $40500 €31621 Sunset (131x130cm-52x51in) init. s.indis.d.verso painted c.1960 exhib. 1-Mar-4 Ben-Ami, Tel Aviv #4677/R est:40000-50000
£25140 $45000 €36704 Composition (100x136cm-39x54in) init.d.61 s.verso. 18-Mar-4 Sotheby's, New York #28/R est:35000-45000
Works on paper
£795 $1400 €1161 Abstract (27x34cm-11x13in) s.d.1960. 1-Jan-4 Ben-Ami, Tel Aviv #4396/R est:1400-1800
£1130 $2000 €1650 Blue composition (70x50cm-28x20in) s.d.1965 W/C. 1-May-4 Ben-Ami, Tel Aviv #4778/R est:3000-4000
£1176 $2000 €1717 The next door neighbour (61x45cm-24x18in) s.d.1991 mixed media. 1-Dec-3 Ben-Ami, Tel Aviv #4356/R est:2500-3500
£1807 $3000 €2638 Veranda (45x60cm-18x24in) s.d.1981 W/C pencil. 2-Oct-3 Christie's, Tel Aviv #77/R est:3000-5000
£1955 $3500 €2854 Composition (48x68cm-19x27in) s.d.74 W/C pastel. 18-Mar-4 Sotheby's, New York #32/R est:4000-6000
£2596 $4750 €3790 Abstract (69x99cm-27x39in) s.d.1966 W/C. 1-Jun-4 Ben-Ami, Tel Aviv #4897/R est:6000-8000
£3088 $5250 €4508 Abstract composition (71x126cm-28x50in) s. W/C collage mixed media. 1-Dec-3 Ben-Ami, Tel Aviv #4357/R est:7000-10000

STREIT, Carl (1852-?) German
£403 $749 €600 Hessen landscape (50x60cm-20x24in) s. i. verso. 6-Mar-4 Arnold, Frankfurt #855/R

STREIT, Frances Norris (20th C) American
£2198 $4000 €3209 Portrait of a boxer (71x58cm-28x23in) s. with maiden name verso. 7-Feb-4 Dan Ripley, Indianapolis #8

STREITT, Franciszek (1839-1890) Polish
£6376 $11413 €9500 The doll doctor (43x33cm-17x13in) s.d.876 panel. 27-May-4 Dorotheum, Vienna #24/R est:5000-7000
£7500 $13875 €10950 Accident, travelers surveying cart with a broken wheel, in winter landscape (42x82cm-17x32in) s. 11-Mar-4 Morphets, Harrogate #284/R est:5500-6500
£16571 $30159 €24194 Three children (43x33cm-17x13in) s.d.1876 panel. 20-Jun-4 Agra, Warsaw #50/R (P.Z 115000)
£21944 $34232 €32038 Group of people with wagon (44x76cm-17x30in) s. painted c.1887. 30-Mar-3 Agra, Warsaw #2/R est:80000 (P.Z 140000)

STRELE, Martha (1889-?) ?
Works on paper
£195 $349 €285 Girl with long plaits (49x34cm-19x13in) s.d. pastel chk. 22-Mar-4 Philippe Schuler, Zurich #5722 (S.FR 450)

STRELLET, Ephraim (fl.1900-1935) British
Miniatures
£2500 $4250 €3650 Young lady in white robes and strand of pearls (10cm-4in) s.verso gilt wood frame oval. 18-Nov-3 Bonhams, New Bond Street #167/R est:700-900

STREMEL, Max Arthur (1859-1928) German
£3947 $7263 €6000 Lakeside scene (76x67cm-30x26in) s. 25-Jun-4 Michael Zeller, Lindau #595/R est:800

STREMPEL, Horst (1904-1975) German
£699 $1189 €1000 Listeners (68x89cm-27x35in) s.i. verso panel. 29-Nov-3 Bassenge, Berlin #6991/R
£1200 $2148 €1800 Still life with oranges and bottle (61x51cm-24x20in) s.d. panel. 15-May-4 Bassenge, Berlin #7145/R est:1500
Works on paper
£500 $900 €750 Girl with red sun (34x58cm-13x23in) s.d. gouache board. 24-Apr-4 Dr Lehr, Berlin #463/R

STREMPLER (?) ?
Works on paper
£172 $288 €249 Gallo (75x55cm-30x22in) s.d.1977 mixed media wood. 24-Jun-3 Louis Morton, Mexico #173 (M.P 3000)

STRETTON, Philip Eustace (fl.1884-1919) British
£850 $1556 €1241 A corner of Robert Ferrer's dining room. The drawing room (43x29cm-17x11in) one s. board two. 7-Apr-4 Woolley & Wallis, Salisbury #332/R
£3521 $6092 €5000 Pet (40x50cm-16x20in) s.d.1900. 9-Dec-3 Pandolfini, Florence #214/R est:2000-2200
£5536 $10020 €8083 Qui Vive (75x62cm-30x24in) s.d.1909. 30-Mar-4 Peter Webb, Auckland #118/R est:8000-12000 (NZ.D 15500)
£6000 $10200 €8760 Coming events cast their shadows before (51x41cm-20x16in) s. prov. 27-Nov-3 Christie's, Kensington #292/R est:3000-4000
£6500 $11050 €9490 Companions (44x59cm-17x23in) s.d.1907 oval pair. 27-Nov-3 Christie's, Kensington #388/R est:6000-8000
£7568 $14000 €11049 Terrier at rest (41x51cm-16x20in) s.d.1900. 10-Feb-4 Doyle, New York #273/R est:15000-25000

STREULI, Beat (1957-) Swiss
Photographs
£4333 $7973 €6500 Untitled (137x200cm-54x79in) s.d.97 num.AP3 verso col photograph under plexiglas prov. 8-Jun-4 Artcurial Briest, Paris #292/R est:5000-7000
£6597 $11215 €9500 Sydney/Melbourne (151x201cm-59x79in) s.i.d. verso C-print plexiglas. 30-Oct-3 Van Ham, Cologne #252/R est:12000
£6757 $12095 €10000 Untitled (138x202cm-54x80in) s.i.d. verso col photo. 8-May-4 Lempertz, Koln #271/R est:10000-12000

STREVENS, John (1902-1990) British
£300 $531 €438 Birthday picnic (40x50cm-16x20in) s.i. 27-Apr-4 Bonhams, Knightsbridge #228/R
£380 $684 €555 Au Cafe (26x46cm-10x18in) s. s.i.verso. 20-Jan-4 Bonhams, Knightsbridge #258/R
£389 $700 €568 Blue dress (46x36cm-18x14in) s.d.53 prov. 23-Jan-4 Freeman, Philadelphia #230/R
£400 $648 €580 Spring in the Boulevardes (41x36cm-16x14in) s. 7-Aug-3 Amersham Auction Rooms, UK #290
£450 $747 €657 Promenade aux jardins (49x75cm-19x30in) s. i.verso. 30-Sep-3 Bristol Auction Rooms #573
£486 $900 €710 Madame X (51x41cm-20x16in) s. s.i. verso. 15-Jul-4 Sotheby's, New York #67/R
£500 $920 €730 Children in the snow (60x50cm-24x20in) s. 24-Mar-4 Hamptons Fine Art, Godalming #290/R
£550 $1018 €803 Les jardins du Louvre (45x36cm-18x14in) s. i. verso. 14-Jul-4 Christie's, Kensington #1228/R
£595 $1100 €869 Promenade d'autres jours (61x51cm-24x20in) s. s.i.verso. 24-Jan-4 Jeffery Burchard, Florida #68/R
£611 $1100 €892 Winter walk (61x76cm-24x30in) s. s.i.verso. 23-Jan-4 Freeman, Philadelphia #96/R
£680 $1156 €993 Vers le theatre (49x75cm-19x30in) s. s.i.verso. 29-Oct-3 Bonhams, Chester #465
£700 $1274 €1022 Promenade d'Autres Jours (61x51cm-24x20in) s. s.i. verso. 1-Jul-4 Christie's, Kensington #28/R
£750 $1365 €1095 Robe rouge (46x35cm-18x14in) s. s.i. verso. 1-Jul-4 Christie's, Kensington #27/R
£800 $1408 €1168 Julie (46x35cm-18x14in) i.verso. 19-May-4 Christie's, Kensington #702/R

STRIBBLING, David (1959-) British
£750 $1380 €1095 Tiger (41x51cm-16x20in) s. 10-Jun-4 Christie's, Kensington #283/R

STRIBRNY, Vladimir (1905-) Czechoslovakian
£351 $597 €512 Girl nude (34x20cm-13x8in) s. canvas on cardboard. 29-Nov-3 Dorotheum, Prague #49/R est:16000-25000 (C.KR 16000)

STRICH-CHAPELL, Walter (1877-1960) German
£313 $494 €450 Hohenhaslach (75x88cm-30x35in) s.d.52 panel. 6-Sep-3 Arnold, Frankfurt #667
£400 $724 €600 Swabian Alps in autumn (54x68cm-21x27in) s. lit. 1-Apr-4 Frank Peege, Freiburg #1163/R
£810 $1296 €1150 Swabian landscape after the rain (100x80cm-39x31in) s.d.1943 panel. 18-Sep-3 Rieber, Stuttgart #1244/R
£915 $1465 €1300 Winter landscape with trees (61x61cm-24x24in) s. panel. 18-Sep-3 Rieber, Stuttgart #1249/R
£1127 $1803 €1600 After the rain - near Sersheim (80x100cm-31x39in) s. panel. 18-Sep-3 Rieber, Stuttgart #914/R est:1600
£1408 $2254 €2000 Untitled (28x22cm-11x9in) s.d.1957 pastel. 18-Sep-3 Rieber, Stuttgart #944 est:2980
£2215 $3920 €3300 Swabian Alps in spring (60x80cm-24x31in) s. prov. 30-Apr-4 Dr Fritz Nagel, Stuttgart #950/R est:4000

STRICKER, Fifo (1952-) Swiss
Works on paper
£1595 $2855 €2329 Elephant and parrot (61x50cm-24x20in) mono.d.1990 col pen Indian ink lit. 14-May-4 Dobiaschofsky, Bern #280/R est:5500 (S.FR 3700)

STRICKLAND, Anthony (1920-) South African?
£588 $1065 €858 Five Xhosa women (49x75cm-19x30in) s. canvasboard. 30-Mar-4 Stephan Welz, Johannesburg #226 est:2000-3000 (SA.R 7000)

STRID, Hardy (1921-) Swedish
£525 $966 €788 The girl who loved Kandinsky (166x160cm-65x63in) s.d.83 verso prov. 14-Jun-4 Lilla Bukowskis, Stockholm #63 (S.KR 7200)

STRIDER, Marjorie Virginia (1934-) American
£1285 $2300 €1876 Dutch iris (61x61cm-24x24in) triptych prov. 16-May-4 Wright, Chicago #445/R est:1000-1500

STRIENING, Jan (1827-1903) Dutch
Works on paper
£411 $699 €600 Halberstadt cathedral square and cellar (55x37cm-22x15in) s. W/C. 5-Nov-3 Vendue Huis, Gravenhage #150

STRIGEL, Bernhard (studio) (1460-1528) German
£26667 $49067 €40000 Portrait of Maximilian I (77x42cm-30x17in) panel. 11-Jun-4 Hauswedell & Nolte, Hamburg #913/R est:25000

STRIGEL, Hans (younger-circle) (fl.1450-1479) German
£9000 $16200 €13140 Nativity (110x103cm-43x41in) panel. 21-Apr-4 Christie's, London #55/R est:10000-15000

STRIK, Berend (1960-) Dutch
Works on paper
£1304 $2139 €1800 Juice up (39x56cm-15x22in) s.i.d.1997 verso mixed media embroidery canvas on board exhib.lit. 27-May-3 Sotheby's, Amsterdam #462/R est:1500-2000

STRIK, Lou (1921-) Dutch
£800 $1464 €1200 Farmer in front of a landscape with farm and trees (39x48cm-15x19in) s.d.44 panel. 7-Jun-4 Glerum, Amsterdam #332/R

STRINDBERG, August (1849-1912) Swedish
£199557 $357206 €291353 The recluse (30x19cm-12x7in) cardboard painted 1892 prov.exhib.lit. 26-May-4 AB Stockholms Auktionsverk #2127/R est:1200000-1500000 (S.KR 2700000)

STRINDBERG, Tore (1882-1968) Swedish
Sculpture
£2882 $5160 €4208 The Russian eagle attacking the Swedish lion (70cm-28in) s. green pat.bronze. 26-May-4 AB Stockholms Auktionsverk #2232/R est:15000-20000 (S.KR 39000)

STRINGER, Terry (1946-) New Zealander
£347 $552 €507 Rose (38x33cm-15x13in) s.d.1979 acrylic on board. 1-May-3 Dunbar Sloane, Wellington #134 est:800-1500 (NZ.D 1000)
Sculpture
£2985 $5164 €4358 Marmaduke, study of a sleeping cat (40x23cm-16x9in) s.d.1979 num.2/6 brown pat bronze. 9-Dec-3 Peter Webb, Auckland #28/R est:7000-9000 (NZ.D 8000)
Works on paper
£357 $646 €521 Untitled, nude (56x38cm-22x15in) s.d.1979 W/C. 4-Apr-4 International Art Centre, Auckland #288 (NZ.D 1000)

STRINGER, Thomas (attrib) (1722-1790) British
£20000 $33400 €29200 Two hunters with their grooms accompanied by hounds (100x124cm-39x49in) 14-Oct-3 Sotheby's, London #429/R est:8000-12000

STRINGFELLOW, Carl (1954-) Australian
£254 $475 €381 Sydney harbour storm (44x52cm-17x20in) s board. 25-Jul-4 Lawson Menzies, Sydney #89/R (A.D 650)
£494 $894 €721 River boats (56x71cm-22x28in) s. 31-Mar-4 Goodman, Sydney #514/R (A.D 1200)

STRISIK, Paul (1918-1998) American
£323 $600 €472 First light (20x25cm-8x10in) s.d.80 board prov. 5-Mar-4 Skinner, Boston #460/R
£591 $1100 €863 Lane in Provence. Village church, San Miguel, Mexico (25x30cm-10x12in) s. board two prov. 5-Mar-4 Skinner, Boston #506/R
£699 $1300 €1021 Valley aspens (30x40cm-12x16in) s.d.80 prov. 5-Mar-4 Skinner, Boston #435/R est:1000-1500
£765 $1300 €1117 Hillside maple (41x51cm-16x20in) s. prov. 21-Nov-3 Skinner, Boston #439/R est:1000-1500
£941 $1600 €1374 Sparkling light, covered bridge view (30x41cm-12x16in) s.d.78 prov. 21-Nov-3 Skinner, Boston #446/R est:1000-1500
£1294 $2200 €1889 Hollow (41x61cm-16x24in) s. prov. 21-Nov-3 Skinner, Boston #442/R est:1500-2000
£1294 $2200 €1889 Silver light (30x41cm-12x16in) s. masonite prov. 21-Nov-3 Skinner, Boston #491/R est:1000-1500
£1559 $2900 €2276 Turkey Point (30x40cm-12x16in) s. prov. 5-Mar-4 Skinner, Boston #439/R est:1000-1500
£1647 $2800 €2405 St. Joachim's church, Rockport (50x76cm-20x30in) s. prov. 21-Nov-3 Skinner, Boston #546/R est:1500-2000
£1795 $3250 €2621 Bass Rocks (30x41cm-12x16in) s. board. 16-Apr-4 James Julia, Fairfield #533/R est:1200-1500
£2059 $3500 €3006 Yellow barn, Vermont (41x51cm-16x20in) s. prov. 21-Nov-3 Skinner, Boston #444/R est:1200-1800
£2101 $3760 €3067 Pebble cove (25x36cm-10x14in) s. board prov. 8-Jan-4 James Julia, Fairfield #757/R est:1500-2500
£2545 $4250 €3716 Gloucester Fishing Boats (51x41cm-20x16in) s. i.verso prov. 23-Oct-3 Shannon's, Milford #43/R est:3000-5000
£2654 $4750 €3875 Rockport harbour (20x30cm-8x12in) s. prov. 6-May-4 Shannon's, Milford #138/R est:3000-5000

STRNAD, Oskar (20th C) Austrian
Sculpture
£3243 $6000 €4735 Adam und Eva (60cm-24in) s.d. bronze marble. 11-Mar-4 Sotheby's, New York #187/R est:5000-7000

STRNADEL, Antonin (1910-1975) Czechoslovakian
£675 $1188 €1013 Beskydy Mountains (39x70cm-15x28in) s. 22-May-4 Dorotheum, Prague #91/R est:12000-18000 (C.KR 32000)

STROBEL, J (19/20th C) ?
£617 $1048 €901 Snowy landscape near DAvos (54x95cm-21x37in) s.i.d.09. 7-Nov-3 Dobiaschofsky, Bern #158/R (S.FR 1400)

STROBEL, Oscar A (1891-1967) American
Works on paper
£252 $450 €368 Desert mountains (37x49cm-15x19in) s. gouache canvasboard. 14-May-4 Skinner, Boston #202/R

STRODE, Thaddeus (1964-) American
Works on paper
£1412 $2500 €2062 Killer of the soul (91x91cm-36x36in) s.i.d.90 verso mixed media canvas. 2-May-4 Bonhams & Butterfields, Los Angeles #3063/R est:2000-3000

STROEBEL, Johann Anthonie Balthasar (1821-1905) Dutch
£1250 $2088 €1800 In the wine cellar (35x38cm-14x15in) s. 21-Oct-3 Sotheby's, Amsterdam #66/R est:3000-5000
£1333 $2427 €2000 Artist and his family in a domestic interior (14x19cm-6x7in) s.d.67 panel. 1-Jul-4 Christie's, Amsterdam #714/R est:3000-5000
£2262 $3620 €3303 Art dealer (58x47cm-23x19in) s. 19-Sep-3 Koller, Zurich #3119/R est:4000-5000 (S.FR 5000)
£4800 $8736 €7200 Light lunch (90x69cm-35x27in) s. prov. 1-Jul-4 Christie's, Amsterdam #699/R est:8000-12000

STROHLING, Peter Eduard (1768-1826) Russian
£3030 $5424 €4424 Scene from the life of Peter The Great (45x60cm-18x24in) s. copper on panel. 22-Mar-4 Philippe Schuler, Zurich #4430/R est:6000-8000 (S.FR 7000)
£5220 $9500 €7621 Hebe (61x48cm-24x19in) s. copper exhib. 4-Feb-4 Christie's, Rockefeller NY #116/R est:4000-6000
Miniatures
£3700 $6808 €5402 Young gentleman wearing a black cape (8cm-3in) gold frame prov. 24-Jun-4 Bonhams, New Bond Street #128/R est:2000-3000
£11500 $20125 €16790 Thomas, 10th Earl of Dundonald (7cm-3in) gold frame glazed hair reserve verso oval. 18-Dec-3 Sotheby's, Olympia #1/R est:2500-3500

STROM, Charles W (1886-1967) Norwegian
£559 $934 €816 August in Hjartdal (116x131cm-46x52in) s. exhib. 20-Oct-3 Blomqvist, Lysaker #1308/R (N.KR 6500)

STROM, Gerda Elisabeth Blom (1886-1959) Danish
£412 $672 €602 Still life of wild flowers (86x94cm-34x37in) s.d.1919. 27-Sep-3 Rasmussen, Havnen #2094 (D.KR 4400)

STROM, Halfdan (1863-1949) Norwegian
£2600 $4680 €3796 Young girl by the water (55x80cm-22x31in) s.d.08. 21-Jan-4 Sotheby's, Olympia #473/R est:2000-3000

STROMME, Olav (1909-1978) Norwegian
£254 $467 €371 Heads (30x60cm-12x24in) panel. 29-Mar-4 Blomqvist, Lysaker #1324 (N.KR 3200)
£258 $431 €377 Portrait of man (33x24cm-13x9in) s. panel. 20-Oct-3 Blomqvist, Lysaker #1312 (N.KR 3000)
£258 $431 €377 Composition (38x46cm-15x18in) s. panel. 20-Oct-3 Blomqvist, Lysaker #1313 (N.KR 3000)
£301 $485 €439 Landscape (50x61cm-20x24in) s. panel. 25-Aug-3 Blomqvist, Lysaker #1307/R (N.KR 3500)
£386 $676 €564 Coastal landscape (33x41cm-13x16in) s.d.67 panel. 16-Dec-3 Grev Wedels Plass, Oslo #224/R (N.KR 4500)
£396 $637 €578 Composition (50x61cm-20x24in) S. PA. 25-Aug-3 Blomqvist, Lysaker #1308 (N.KR 4600)
£473 $790 €691 Composition (38x45cm-15x18in) s. panel. 20-Oct-3 Blomqvist, Lysaker #1311/R (N.KR 5500)
£482 $883 €704 At the racecourse (27x35cm-11x14in) s. panel. 2-Feb-4 Blomqvist, Lysaker #1294/R (N.KR 6000)
£522 $903 €762 Herring fishing (20x46cm-8x18in) panel. 13-Dec-3 Blomqvist, Lysaker #1366 (N.KR 6000)
£645 $1078 €942 Joint V (80x68cm-31x27in) s. exhib. 20-Oct-3 Blomqvist, Lysaker #1309/R (N.KR 7500)
£648 $1075 €940 Composition (33x24cm-13x9in) s. panel. 16-Jun-3 Blomqvist, Lysaker #1229 (N.KR 7500)
£648 $1075 €940 Theatre scene (49x60cm-19x24in) s. panel. 16-Jun-3 Blomqvist, Lysaker #1230/R (N.KR 7500)
£652 $1128 €952 Composition (50x70cm-20x28in) s. panel. 13-Dec-3 Blomqvist, Lysaker #1367 (N.KR 7500)
£688 $1150 €1004 Figure with wings (50x70cm-20x28in) s. panel. 20-Oct-3 Blomqvist, Lysaker #1310/R (N.KR 8000)
£696 $1203 €1016 Composition (70x49cm-28x19in) s. 13-Dec-3 Blomqvist, Lysaker #1370/R (N.KR 8000)
£699 $1280 €1021 Composition (16x46cm-6x18in) s. panel. 2-Feb-4 Blomqvist, Lysaker #1293 (N.KR 8700)
£961 $1720 €1403 Compositions (38x60cm-15x24in) s.d.68 one panel two. 22-Mar-4 Blomqvist, Oslo #600/R est:15000-20000 (N.KR 12000)
£1022 $1758 €1492 Town scene, possibly Aalesund (80x85cm-31x33in) s.d.32. 8-Dec-3 Blomqvist, Oslo #518/R est:15000-18000 (N.KR 12000)
£1130 $1956 €1650 Composition with orange (60x61cm-24x24in) s. panel. 13-Dec-3 Blomqvist, Lysaker #1368/R est:6000-8000 (N.KR 13000)
£1537 $2567 €2244 Theatre stage from Rigoletto (53x73cm-21x29in) s. i.stretcher. 13-Oct-3 Blomqvist, Oslo #311/R est:25000-30000 (N.KR 18000)
£1652 $2858 €2412 Doge Palace (50x65cm-20x26in) s. 13-Dec-3 Blomqvist, Lysaker #1365/R est:25000-30000 (N.KR 19000)
£3578 $6153 €5224 Herring fishing (49x69cm-19x27in) s.d.60 panel. 8-Dec-3 Blomqvist, Oslo #550/R est:40000-50000 (N.KR 42000)

Works on paper
£348 $602 €508 Collage (49x61cm-19x24in) s. mixed media. 13-Dec-3 Blomqvist, Lysaker #1369/R (N.KR 4000)
£417 $722 €609 Composition (17x24cm-7x9in) s. mixed media. 13-Dec-3 Blomqvist, Lysaker #1371/R (N.KR 4800)

STROMME, Tove (20th C) Norwegian
£577 $928 €842 Horizon (70x100cm-28x39in) s. 25-Aug-3 Blomqvist, Lysaker #1309 (N.KR 6700)

STRONG, C E (19th C) British
£1200 $2004 €1752 Breezy day, shipping in an estuary (61x91cm-24x36in) s.indis.d. 26-Jun-3 Greenslade Hunt, Taunton #524/R est:1000-1500

STRONG, Elizabeth (1855-1941) American
£508 $900 €742 Two young puppy dogs peering out from a basket (33x41cm-13x16in) s. 3-May-4 O'Gallerie, Oregon #724/R
£535 $1000 €781 Landscape with pond and mountain (58x46cm-23x18in) s.d.1920. 29-Feb-4 Grogan, Boston #67/R
£1587 $3000 €2317 Carmel coastal (36x25cm-14x10in) s. prov. 17-Feb-4 John Moran, Pasadena #110/R est:1000-2000

STRONG, Joseph Dwight (jnr) (1852-1899) American
£4913 $8500 €7173 Second Artillery NGC at the opening of the Hotel del Monte, Camp Crocker (91x118cm-36x46in) s.i.d.1880 prov.exhib. 10-Dec-3 Bonhams & Butterfields, San Francisco #6137/R est:6000-8000

STRONG, Ray Stanford (1905-) American
£1236 $2250 €1805 Mountain landscape (30x41cm-12x16in) s. 15-Jun-4 John Moran, Pasadena #165 est:1500-2000

STRONG, William M (19/20th C) Irish
£300 $516 €438 Fourth Tele (25x25cm-10x10in) s. board. 3-Dec-3 John Ross, Belfast #246
£350 $641 €511 Blue chair (56x56cm-22x22in) s. board. 2-Jun-4 John Ross, Belfast #180

STROOBANT, François (attrib) (1819-1916) Belgian
£294 $490 €420 Portrait of young woman (40x30cm-16x12in) mono.d.93. 28-Jun-3 Dannenberg, Berlin #783/R

STROPPA, Leonardo (1900-1991) Italian
£295 $502 €425 Portobello Road (50x60cm-20x24in) s. s.i.verso. 1-Nov-3 Meeting Art, Vercelli #107
£340 $609 €500 Vase of flowers (60x40cm-24x16in) s. 22-Mar-4 Sant Agostino, Torino #383/R
£426 $711 €600 Turin Duomo (40x50cm-16x20in) s. masonite. 20-Oct-3 Sant Agostino, Torino #127/R
£933 $1717 €1400 Vase of flowers (60x80cm-24x31in) s. 14-Jun-4 Sant Agostino, Torino #374/R
Works on paper
£355 $592 €500 Flowers (40x30cm-16x12in) s. W/C. 20-Oct-3 Sant Agostino, Torino #113/R

STROUDLEY, James (1906-1985) British
£600 $1092 €876 Market scene (71x92cm-28x36in) board. 3-Feb-4 Sworder & Son, Bishops Stortford #264/R
£700 $1274 €1022 Abstract, red yellow and green (76x61cm-30x24in) s. verso board. 1-Jul-4 Christie's, Kensington #394/R
£1000 $1820 €1460 Abstract (122x76cm-48x30in) board. 1-Jul-4 Christie's, Kensington #393/R est:1000-1500
£1100 $2002 €1606 Abstract (76x61cm-30x24in) s. verso. 1-Jul-4 Christie's, Kensington #392/R est:800-1200
£1500 $2505 €2190 Afternoon in the shade, Regents Park (52x62cm-20x24in) s. board. 7-Oct-3 Bonhams, Knightsbridge #68/R est:1500-2000
£1500 $2775 €2190 Abstract (122x76cm-48x30in) s.verso board. 11-Mar-4 Christie's, Kensington #357/R est:1000-1500
Works on paper
£750 $1320 €1095 Study for games (99x291cm-39x115in) s. triptych. 19-May-4 Sotheby's, Olympia #92/R

STROZZI, Bernardo (1581-1644) Italian
£59310 $99048 €86000 Christ and Caifah (110x148cm-43x58in) prov.lit. 15-Nov-3 Porro, Milan #242/R est:70000

STRUBE, Hermann (1879-1960) German
£287 $519 €430 Sunset on the Baar (44x58cm-17x23in) s.mono.d.1923 i. verso. 1-Apr-4 Frank Peege, Freiburg #1222/R
Works on paper
£284 $460 €400 The Blauen (14x23cm-6x9in) mono.i.d.50 W/C lit. 23-May-3 Karlheinz Kaupp, Staufen #1788

STRUBIN, Robert (1897-1965) Swiss
Works on paper
£1900 $3174 €2774 Mandala - rosette (48x57cm-19x22in) s.d.1941 goauche Indian. 24-Jun-3 Germann, Zurich #176/R est:3000-4000 (S.FR 4200)

STRUCK, Herman (1887-1954) American
£1902 $3500 €2853 Ready for anything (61x81cm-24x32in) s. prov. 8-Jun-4 Bonhams & Butterfields, San Francisco #4376/R est:5000-7000

STRUCK, Hermann (1876-1944) German
£490 $817 €700 Match seller (44x31cm-17x12in) s. i. verso panel. 28-Jun-3 Bolland & Marotz, Bremen #738/R

STRUDWICK, John Melhuish (1849-1937) British
£43353 $75000 €63295 When sorrow comes in summer (89x54cm-35x21in) 11-Dec-3 Sotheby's, New York #36/R est:80000-120000
£125000 $230000 €182500 Ten virgins (74x152cm-29x60in) prov.exhib.lit. 9-Jun-4 Christie's, London #21/R est:100000-150000
£450000 $765000 €657000 Music, faintly, dies away, thy dear eyes dream that love will live for ave, G F Bodley (77x39cm-30x15in) init.d.1893 prov.exhib.lit. 26-Nov-3 Christie's, London #13/R est:500000-700000
Works on paper
£1200 $2040 €1752 Head of a woman (25x19cm-10x7in) pencil. 20-Nov-3 Christie's, London #152/R est:1500-2000
£1900 $3477 €2774 Study of figure and subsidiary study of a figure. Study of Church (35x25cm-14x10in) with i. pencil prov. double-sided prov. 3-Jun-4 Christie's, London #170/R est:800-1200
£2400 $4392 €3504 Study for an angel in a green dress (71x26cm-28x10in) pencil two joined sheets prov. 3-Jun-4 Christie's, London #171/R est:1500-2000
£3800 $6954 €5548 Study of a young girl in profile to the right (36x25cm-14x10in) mono. pencil prov. 3-Jun-4 Christie's, London #168/R est:2000-3000

STRUPLER, Hans Rudolf (1935-) Swiss
Works on paper
£390 $697 €569 Composition (28x34cm-11x13in) mono. gouache. 22-Mar-4 Philippe Schuler, Zurich #4227 (S.FR 900)
£390 $697 €569 Untitled (17x21cm-7x8in) W/C. 22-Mar-4 Philippe Schuler, Zurich #4228 (S.FR 900)
£617 $1048 €901 Fire dragon (28x30cm-11x12in) mono. mixed media. 7-Nov-3 Dobiaschofsky, Bern #255/R (S.FR 1400)
£705 $1198 €1029 Dragon resting (56x68cm-22x27in) mono. W/C bodycol. 7-Nov-3 Dobiaschofsky, Bern #253/R (S.FR 1600)

STRUSS, Karl (1886-1981) American
Photographs
£4790 $8000 €6993 Untitled, boat in harbour (9x11cm-4x4in) s.d.1911 platinum print board on paper prov. 17-Oct-3 Phillips, New York #32/R est:10000-15000
£4790 $8000 €6993 Untitled, car (8x11cm-3x4in) s.d.1911 platinum print board on paper prov. 17-Oct-3 Phillips, New York #33/R est:10000-15000
£5090 $8500 €7431 Untitled, sky (10x8cm-4x3in) s.d.1911 platinum print board on paper prov. 17-Oct-3 Phillips, New York #34/R est:10000-15000

STRUTH, Thomas (1954-) German
Photographs
£2235 $4000 €3263 Jiangxi Zhong Lu Shanghai (41x61cm-16x24in) s.i.d.1997 num.59/60 cibachrome print prov. 13-May-4 Sotheby's, New York #437/R est:3000-4000
£2333 $4200 €3406 Via Sanita, Naples (70x86cm-28x34in) gelatin silver print. 23-Apr-4 Phillips, New York #90/R est:4000-6000
£2400 $4416 €3504 Traditional Japanese house 1, Yamasuchi (43x54cm-17x21in) s.i.d.1991 num.4/10 gelatin silver print. 24-Jun-4 Sotheby's, Olympia #633/R est:2500-3500
£2465 $4313 €3500 Via Guglielmo, Naples (57x42cm-22x17in) s.num.verso black white photograph exec 1988/1990. 18-Dec-3 Cornette de St.Cyr, Paris #171/R est:3000-4000
£2465 $4313 €3500 Overbruckstrasse, Duisberg (43x59cm-17x23in) s.num.verso black white photograph exec 1985/1990. 18-Dec-3 Cornette de St.Cyr, Paris #172/R est:3000-4000
£2500 $4175 €3650 Hubertusstrasse, Duisburg (43x60cm-17x24in) s.i.d.1989 num.5/10 verso gelatin silver print prov. 22-Oct-3 Christie's, London #139/R est:2000-3000
£2778 $5000 €4056 Rue de l'Hotel de Ville, Geneve (70x86cm-28x34in) num.1/10 gelatin silver print prov. 23-Apr-4 Phillips, New York #89/R est:4000-6000
£2793 $5000 €4078 Zhe jiang zhong lu, shanghai (49x61cm-19x24in) s.i.d.1997 verso col coupler print prov. 14-May-4 Phillips, New York #310/R est:5000-7000
£2817 $4930 €4000 Via Celliglo, Naples (58x42cm-23x17in) s. num.verso black white photograph exec 1988/1990. 18-Dec-3 Cornette de St.Cyr, Paris #170/R est:3000-4000
£3000 $5010 €4380 Am Kreuzacker, Duisburg (45x59cm-18x23in) s.i.d.1985 1989 num.4/10 verso gelatin silver print prov. 22-Oct-3 Christie's, London #140/R est:2000-3000
£3114 $5200 €4546 Plant no 46, Canna (45x58cm-18x23in) s.verso num.3 chromogenic col print exec.1993 one of ten prov.lit. 17-Oct-3 Phillips, New York #275/R est:5000-7000
£3352 $6000 €4894 Avenue du Devin du Village, Geneva (70x86cm-28x34in) gelatin silver print edition of ten prov.exhib. 14-May-4 Phillips, New York #307/R est:6000-8000
£3600 $6012 €5256 Haunghe fe - die frebgasse (51x59cm-20x23in) s.i.verso colour photograph executed 1997. 22-Oct-3 Bonhams, New Bond Street #124/R est:3500-4500
£3713 $6200 €5421 Zhe jiang zhong Lu, Shanghai (44x55cm-17x22in) s.i.d.1997 verso colour coupler print prov. 14-Nov-3 Phillips, New York #285/R est:4000-6000
£5000 $9000 €7300 City tracks, Tokyo (77x117cm-30x46in) s.d.1991 verso chromogenic col print prov.lit. 23-Apr-4 Phillips, New York #5/R est:10000-15000
£6000 $10200 €8760 South Lasalla Street, Chicago (44x58cm-17x23in) gelatin silver print. 18-Nov-3 Christie's, Kensington #251/R est:3000-5000
£7263 $13000 €10604 Huanghe Lue, Shanghai (93x116cm-37x46in) col photo edition of ten prov.exhib. 14-May-4 Phillips, New York #183/R est:10000-15000
£7821 $14000 €11419 Via Monte Cardonet, Rome (43x56cm-17x22in) s.i.d.1988 num.verso gelatin silver print three prov.exhib. 12-May-4 Christie's, Rockefeller NY #442/R est:12000-18000
£10056 $18000 €14682 Landschaft no 22 landschaft Mais-Acher winterthur (100x118cm-39x46in) col coupler print edition 6 of 10 prov. 12-May-4 Christie's, Rockefeller NY #440/R est:20000-30000
£14371 $24000 €20982 Chicago 1990 (67x86cm-26x34in) gelatin silver prints exec 1990 four prov. 12-Nov-3 Christie's, Rockefeller NY #580/R est:15000-20000
£17000 $28390 €24820 Waldstrasse au dem Lindberg - Landscape No.3 - Winterhur (81x102cm-32x40in) s.i.d.1992 num.2/10 verso cibachrome print prov.lit. 21-Oct-3 Sotheby's, London #317/R est:18000-25000
£20556 $37000 €30012 Paradise (146x186cm-57x73in) chromogenic color print prov. 23-Apr-4 Phillips, New York #62/R est:40000-60000

£21334 $39254 €32000 Boats at Wushan, Yangtse Gorge, China (142x182cm-56x72in) s. num.7/10 verso cibachrome exec 1997 prov.lit. 8-Jun-4 Artcurial Briest, Paris #290/R est:25000-30000
£23464 $42000 €34257 Chicago Board Trade, Chicago (120x102cm-47x40in) s.i.d.1990 num.3/10 verso col coupler print prov.exhib. 12-May-4 Christie's, Rockefeller NY #446/R est:12000-18000
£30726 $55000 €44860 Paradise 2 (185x233cm-73x92in) s.verso c-print mounted of plexiglas prov.exhib.lit. 13-May-4 Phillips, New York #64/R est:40000-60000
£36313 $65000 €53017 Paradise 15 Yakushima Japan (188x295cm-74x116in) col coupler print edition 1 of 10 prov.exhib. 12-May-4 Christie's, Rockefeller NY #431/R est:60000-80000
£37989 $68000 €55464 Paradise 8, Blumfield Track, Daintree/Australien (172x216cm-68x85in) s. gelatin silver print edition of 10 prov.lit. 14-May-4 Phillips, New York #187/R est:40000-60000
£40719 $68000 €59450 Paradise 10 (182x227cm-72x89in) s. c-print on plexiglas executed 1999 prov.exhib.lit. 13-Nov-3 Phillips, New York #52/R est:40000-60000
£42000 $76440 €61320 Todai-Ji, interior Nara (170x231cm-67x91in) cibachrome print edn 6/10 exec 1999 prov. 5-Feb-4 Sotheby's, London #46/R est:40000-60000
£51676 $92500 €75447 Todai-Ji interior - Nara (176x238cm-69x94in) cibachrome print exec 1999 7 edn 10 prov. 13-May-4 Sotheby's, New York #388/R est:60000-80000
£61453 $110000 €89721 Musee Louvre 2 Paris 1989 (218x180cm-86x71in) s.i.d.1989 verso color coupler print prov.exhib.lit. 13-May-4 Phillips, New York #63/R est:120000-180000
£95808 $160000 €139880 Musee du Louvre 3 Paris (152x168cm-60x66in) s.i.num.3/10 d.1989 verso colour coupler print prov.exhib. 12-Nov-3 Christie's, Rockefeller NY #579/R est:70000-90000
£117318 $210000 €171284 Milan Duomo - Interior (175x220cm-69x87in) cibachrome print exec 1998 edn 8/10 prov. 12-May-4 Sotheby's, New York #57/R est:120000-180000
£220000 $367400 €321200 Pantheon, Rome (137x194cm-54x76in) s.i.d.13.12.1990 num.1/10 verso cibachrome print. 21-Oct-3 Sotheby's, London #313/R est:100000-150000

Works on paper
£4000 $7240 €5840 Janice Guy, Napoli (59x44cm-23x17in) s.i.d.1988 num.4/10 verso gelatin silver print prov. 1-Apr-4 Christie's, Kensington #306/R est:2000-3000

STRUTT, Alfred William (1856-1924) British
£4200 $7140 €6132 Do your worst (84x142cm-33x56in) s. 27-Nov-3 Christie's, Kensington #25/R est:3000-5000
£13834 $24763 €20198 In a fix (92x144cm-36x57in) s. prov. 15-May-4 Christie's, Sydney #427/R est:50000-80000 (A.D 35000)
£15500 $28210 €22630 Sweet tooth (62x46cm-24x18in) s. i.verso. 16-Jun-4 Bonhams, New Bond Street #51/R est:5000-7000

STRUTT, Jacob George (1784-1867) British
£800 $1496 €1200 St Peter's from Villa Pamphili, Rome (14x22cm-6x9in) s.d.1841 oil paper. 26-Jul-4 Bonhams, Bath #59/R
£800 $1496 €1200 Ischia with a group of dancers on a promontory in the foreground (15x23cm-6x9in) s.d.1841 oil paper. 26-Jul-4 Bonhams, Bath #60/R
£1600 $2960 €2336 Arch of Titus, entrance to the Forum, Rome (12x18cm-5x7in) s. oil paper. 13-Jan-4 Bonhams, Knightsbridge #310/R est:800-1200
£3200 $5728 €4672 Log cart in lake landscape (72x90cm-28x35in) s. 27-May-4 Christie's, Kensington #126/R est:2000-3000

STRUTT, Jacob George (attrib) (1784-1867) British
£1006 $1800 €1469 Roman ruins (30x47cm-12x19in) 14-May-4 Skinner, Boston #27/R est:700-900

STRUTT, William (1826-1915) British
£10277 $18395 €15004 Coming Race - empty plate of food (45x75cm-18x30in) prov. 15-May-4 Christie's, Sydney #9/R est:20000-30000 (A.D 26000)
£20243 $32591 €29555 David's first victory (94x54cm-37x21in) s. prov. 25-Aug-3 Sotheby's, Paddington #5/R est:80000-120000 (A.D 50000)

Works on paper
£7287 $11733 €10639 Bolting horse (26x36cm-10x14in) s. gouache oil sold with a preparatory sketch prov. 25-Aug-3 Sotheby's, Paddington #13/R est:20000-30000 (A.D 18000)

STRUTT, William (attrib) (1826-1915) British
£391 $700 €571 Lion and lioness (61x74cm-24x29in) mono.d.1904. 8-May-4 Susanin's, Chicago #6121/R

STRUTZEL, Otto (1855-1930) German
£533 $971 €800 Hilly landscape (30x41cm-12x16in) s.d.17.4.1916 bears i. board. 30-Jun-4 Neumeister, Munich #699
£541 $1000 €790 Landscape with rolling hills, forest and mountains beyond (30x36cm-12x14in) s.d.9.9.29 board. 17-Jan-4 New Orleans Auction, New Orleans #512/R est:1200-1800
£629 $1145 €950 Isar-Wasser (63x43cm-25x17in) s.d.08. 19-Jun-4 Bergmann, Erlangen #861
£704 $1169 €1000 Dachsund sitting down (27x32cm-11x13in) mono.d.2.8.99 canvas on board. 16-Jun-3 Dorotheum, Vienna #121/R
£845 $1462 €1200 Shepherd with his flock (60x80cm-24x31in) s.i. 10-Dec-3 Christie's, Amsterdam #669/R
£952 $1705 €1400 Winter landscape - road to Gern. i.d.7.11.89 canvas on board. 17-Mar-4 Neumeister, Munich #623/R
£1000 $1800 €1500 Flock of sheep in extensive cloudy landscape (31x36cm-12x14in) s.mono.d.1.2.V.18 canvas on board lit. 22-Apr-4 Allgauer, Kempten #3731/R est:1500
£1117 $2000 €1631 Shepherdess with goats in a forest clearing (61x51cm-24x20in) s.d.1901. 21-Mar-4 Jeffery Burchard, Florida #18
£1333 $2427 €2000 Ducks on stream (51x36cm-20x14in) s. 30-Jun-4 Neumeister, Munich #698/R
£1719 $2923 €2510 Horse and cart on bridge over Amper (35x51cm-14x20in) s. 19-Nov-3 Fischer, Luzern #1161/R est:3000-4000 (S.FR 3800)
£2349 $4205 €3500 Vehicle on the Mitterndorfer Bridge over the Amper (35x51cm-14x20in) s. 27-May-4 Dorotheum, Vienna #230/R est:5000-5600
£3221 $5928 €4800 Shepherd with flock beneath trees (76x100cm-30x39in) s. lit. 25-Mar-4 Karlheinz Kaupp, Staufen #2755/R est:1500
£3333 $5500 €4800 Girls in boats on Bodensee (30x39cm-12x15in) s. board. 5-Jul-3 Geble, Radolfzell #486/R est:3900

STRUTZEL, Otto (attrib) (1855-1930) German
£285 $518 €430 Extensive landscape with shepherd, his dog and herd (45x55cm-18x22in) s.i.d.94. 19-Jun-4 Bergmann, Erlangen #849

STRUWER, Ardy (1939-) Swedish
£1478 $2646 €2158 Cubist's longing (98x131cm-39x52in) s. i.d.1999 verso. 28-May-4 Uppsala Auktionskammare, Uppsala #356/R est:15000-18000 (S.KR 20000)

STRUYK, Hubert (20th C) New Zealander?
£761 $1210 €1111 Cubist landscape (49x80cm-19x31in) s.d.61 acrylic. 9-Sep-3 Watson's, Christchurch #100 (NZ.D 2100)

STRUYKEN, Peter (1939-) Dutch
£6667 $12267 €10000 Cluster 2 (200x133cm-79x52in) ac perspex panel exec. 1971-1975 two exhib.lit. 9-Jun-4 Christie's, Amsterdam #334/R est:7000-9000

STRUYS, Alexander (19th C) Dutch?
£282 $487 €400 Artist's studio (45x35cm-18x14in) s. 9-Dec-3 Vanderkindere, Brussels #9

STRY, Abraham van (18/19th C) Dutch
£5755 $9439 €8000 Bouquet de fleurs pres d'un faisan de Mongolie dans un paysage (74x60cm-29x24in) s.d.1774. 6-Jun-3 Drouot Estimations, Paris #19/R est:8000-10000

STRY, Abraham van (elder) (1753-1826) Dutch
£34247 $58219 €50000 Interior with a seated child in a high chair teasing a dog, servant washing by the window (63x53cm-25x21in) s. panel prov.exhib. 5-Nov-3 Christie's, Amsterdam #73/R est:20000-30000

Works on paper
£1164 $1979 €1700 Butcher at his block, side of beef to his right (53x37cm-21x15in) black chk W/C prov.lit. 5-Nov-3 Christie's, Amsterdam #142/R est:2000-3000
£14685 $24965 €21000 Joies de l'hiver (34x51cm-13x20in) s. pen Chinese ink wash. 21-Nov-3 Lombrail & Teucquam, Paris #96/R est:2500-3000

STRY, Jacob van (1756-1815) Dutch
£2000 $3640 €3000 Dutch river landscape with cows (104x158cm-41x62in) mono. panel. 30-Jun-4 Neumeister, Munich #483a/R est:4000
£2956 $5292 €4316 Stable with sheep and cow (39x31cm-15x12in) s. panel. 28-May-4 Uppsala Auktionskammare, Uppsala #15/R est:20000-25000 (S.KR 40000)
£3425 $5822 €5000 Pastoral landscape with cattle by a river bank, with herdsmen and a horseman (59x91cm-23x36in) panel. 5-Nov-3 Christie's, Amsterdam #74/R est:6000-8000
£9459 $16649 €14000 Winter landscape with a farmstead near a frozen river and a couple conversing (65x83cm-26x33in) s. 18-May-4 Sotheby's, Amsterdam #117/R est:15000-20000
£39726 $67534 €58000 Winter landscape with wood gatherers, merchantmen and their sledge (65x81cm-26x32in) s. panel. 4-Nov-3 Sotheby's, Amsterdam #106/R est:20000-30000

Works on paper
£411 $699 €600 Seated man resting his hands on a cane (43x32cm-17x13in) s. black chk ink W/C. 5-Nov-3 Christie's, Amsterdam #143
£548 $932 €800 Landscape with herdsman and cows resting (20x32cm-8x13in) mono.bears i.verso pen black grey ink col wash prov. 4-Nov-3 Sotheby's, Amsterdam #117/R
£946 $1665 €1400 Sheep (15x21cm-6x8in) s. W/C black chk exhib. 19-May-4 Sotheby's, Amsterdam #276/R
£1389 $2500 €2028 Extensive river landscape with peasants and cattle (18x27cm-7x11in) black chk pen brown ink W/C. 22-Jan-4 Christie's, Rockefeller NY #250/R est:3000-5000
£1689 $2973 €2500 Study of the head of a sheep (12x15cm-5x6in) s. W/C black chk exhib. 19-May-4 Sotheby's, Amsterdam #277/R est:1000-1500
£2466 $4192 €3600 River landscape with rider conversing with shepherd, with cows and sheep (25x47cm-10x19in) s. black ink grey wash over black chk. 4-Nov-3 Sotheby's, Amsterdam #115/R est:4000-6000

STRY, Jacob van (attrib) (1756-1815) Dutch
£420 $713 €600 La nettoyeuse de cuivres (44x36cm-17x14in) panel. 18-Nov-3 Vanderkindere, Brussels #225
£1600 $2896 €2400 Repos en bordure de riviere (82x105cm-32x41in) s. 30-Mar-4 Campo, Vlaamse Kaai #214 est:2500-3500
£2128 $3553 €3000 Berger et troupeau pres d'un cours d'eau (97x116cm-38x46in) bears sig. 15-Oct-3 Rabourdin & Choppin de Janvry, Paris #45/R est:4000-5000

STRYDONCK, Guillaume van (1861-1937) Belgian
£733 $1320 €1100 Hilly landscape (54x63cm-21x25in) s.d.94. 26-Apr-4 Bernaerts, Antwerp #123/R
£980 $1764 €1431 Indian carriage (50x119cm-20x47in) s.i.d.94. 21-Jan-4 Sotheby's, Olympia #515/R est:1000-2000
£1329 $2259 €1900 Maharadja (47x25cm-19x10in) s.i.d.1894. 1-Dec-3 Palais de Beaux Arts, Brussels #329/R est:750-1000
£2083 $3312 €3000 Nature morte aux fruits de mer (84x146cm-33x57in) s.d.1901. 9-Sep-3 Vanderkindere, Brussels #87

STRZEMINSKI, Wladyslaw (1893-1952) Polish

Works on paper
£2897 $4837 €4200 The harvester (50x35cm-20x14in) pencil ink pen exec. 1950 lit. 16-Nov-3 Agra, Warsaw #4/R est:1000

STUART, Alexander Charles (1831-1898) American
£435 $800 €635 Boat along the shore, evening (10x23cm-4x9in) s. board. 25-Jun-4 Freeman, Philadelphia #229/R
£4372 $8000 €6383 Philadelphia waterfront - 1860 (76x127cm-30x50in) s. prov. 29-Jul-4 Christie's, Rockefeller NY #248/R est:10000-15000

STUART, Charles (19th C) British
£300 $501 €438 Parkland view, with small bridge and gazebo by the lake (44x29cm-17x11in) s. 7-Oct-3 Fellows & Sons, Birmingham #399/R

£800 $1488 €1168 Crossing the burn (61x51cm-24x20in) s.d.1881. 4-Mar-4 Christie's, Kensington #46/R
£1500 $2805 €2190 Highland loch (46x61cm-18x24in) s.i.d.1884 prov. 22-Jul-4 Tennants, Leyburn #846 est:600-800
£3394 $5667 €4955 Haymaking among the mountains. The home of the red deer (61x45cm-24x18in) one s.d.1892 i. stretcher one s. i. stretcher two. 17-Nov-3 Waddingtons, Toronto #119/R est:4000-6000 (C.D 7500)
£6000 $9420 €8700 Sunlight in the glen. Vantage (61x46cm-24x18in) s.d. pair. 27-Aug-3 Sotheby's, London #947/R est:4000-6000
£6000 $10380 €8760 A rift in the clouds. s. 14-Dec-3 Desmond Judd, Cranbrook #1119
£7000 $11900 €10220 Sheep dipping (77x128cm-30x50in) s.d.1890. 30-Oct-3 Christie's, London #84/R est:7000-10000
£7000 $11900 €10220 Highland landscape, with cattle and sheep before a loch (71x91cm-28x36in) s. 30-Oct-3 Christie's, London #82/R est:7000-10000

STUART, Derek M (20th C) Canadian
Sculpture
£3444 $5959 €5028 Fraydal (94cm-37in) d.1979 bronze. 9-Dec-3 Maynards, Vancouver #241 est:1500-2000 (C.D 7750)

STUART, Ernest (fl.1889-1903) British
Works on paper
£280 $456 €409 Big breaker near Start Point (26x74cm-10x29in) s. W/C. 25-Sep-3 Clevedon Sale Rooms #181
£290 $464 €423 Trawlers in a calm (35x53cm-14x21in) s. W/C. 18-Sep-3 Bearnes, Exeter #445
£540 $950 €788 Clearing after a gale, north Cornwall (36x99cm-14x39in) s. W/C. 31-Dec-3 Lambrays, Wadebridge #654
£950 $1777 €1387 Stormy coastal scene (29x86cm-11x34in) s. W/C. 22-Jul-4 Martel Maides, Guernsey #226/R
£1477 $2717 €2200 Wave (28x76cm-11x30in) s. W/C. 25-Mar-4 Hagelstam, Helsinki #901 est:100

STUART, Gilbert (1755-1828) American
£13966 $25000 €20390 Portrait of man said to be Theophilus Jones (76x63cm-30x25in) prov. 27-May-4 Sotheby's, New York #261/R est:15000-20000
£15607 $27000 €22786 Portrait of Hannah More (76x64cm-30x25in) prov.exhib. 13-Dec-3 Sloans & Kenyon, Bethesda #819/R est:25000-30000
£24000 $42960 €35040 Portrait of Philadelphia Hannah, Lady Cremore, half-length (74x61cm-29x24in) oval prov. 13-May-4 Sotheby's, London #4/R est:20000-30000

STUART, Gilbert (after) (1755-1828) American
£3804 $7000 €5554 Lansdowne portrait of George Washington (76x51cm-30x20in) 26-Jun-4 Sloans & Kenyon, Bethesda #1091/R est:5000-7000

STUART, Gilbert (attrib) (1755-1828) American
£9290 $17000 €13563 Portrait of Colonel Thomas Dawes (81x91cm-32x36in) panel prov. 6-Jun-4 Skinner, Boston #97/R est:10000-15000
£12568 $23000 €18349 Portrait of Judge Thomas Dawes Jr. (81x64cm-32x25in) panel prov. 6-Jun-4 Skinner, Boston #98/R est:10000-15000

STUART, Gilbert (style) (1755-1828) American
£7800 $14430 €11388 Portrait of Sir Thomas Taylor (126x98cm-50x39in) 14-Jan-4 Lawrence, Crewkerne #1389/R est:1000-1500

STUART, Guy Frank (1942-) Australian
£244 $383 €354 From Savoy Park Plaza (111x151cm-44x59in) s. s.d.89 verso prov.exhib. 27-Aug-3 Christie's, Sydney #746 (A.D 600)

STUART, James Everett (1852-1941) American
£355 $650 €518 Sunset glow Mt. Tacoma (56x36cm-22x14in) s. 7-Jun-4 O'Gallerie, Oregon #806/R
£432 $800 €631 Among the trees, Lake Geneva (60x51cm-24x20in) 18-Jan-4 Bonhams & Butterfields, Los Angeles #7001/R
£459 $850 €670 Mount Hood (23x41cm-9x16in) s.d.1901 board. 13-Mar-4 Susanin's, Chicago #6130/R
£503 $950 €734 Crater Lake, Oregon (36x56cm-14x22in) s. panel. 22-Feb-4 Bonhams & Butterfields, Los Angeles #7004 est:600-800
£636 $1100 €929 Sunset glow, Mt Shasta (18x12cm-7x5in) s.d.Oct 30 1921 board. 13-Dec-3 Auctions by the Bay, Alameda #1893/R
£659 $1100 €962 Late afternoon near Morristown, NJ (43x74cm-17x29in) s.d.July 17 1923 board. 19-Jun-3 Shelley, Hendersonville #978
£757 $1400 €1105 Indian camp with ocean going canoes (46x76cm-18x30in) s.d.Sept 4 1885. 19-Jan-4 O'Gallerie, Oregon #130/R est:1000-1400
£765 $1300 €1117 Oak trees about one mile south of Camp Curry, Yosemite National Park (51x61cm-20x24in) s.d.Sept 5 1918 i.d.verso. 18-Nov-3 John Moran, Pasadena #176a
£850 $1350 €1241 Sunset glow Mount Tacoma from the Pugallup river, Washington (36x56cm-14x22in) s.d.1904. 14-Sep-3 Susanin's, Chicago #6092/R est:800-1200
£941 $1600 €1374 Storm at sunset, Watsonville, California (51x61cm-20x24in) s.i.d.Nov 17 1918. 18-Nov-3 John Moran, Pasadena #176 est:1500-2000
£1190 $2250 €1737 Houses in atmospheric lake/landscape (30x46cm-12x18in) s.d.Jan 17, 1935 panel prov. 17-Feb-4 John Moran, Pasadena #169/R est:1000-2000
£1323 $2500 €1932 Rocks near Monterey California, June 3 1886 (53x76cm-21x30in) s. i.d. verso. 17-Feb-4 John Moran, Pasadena #106/R est:1500-2500
£1647 $2750 €2405 Sunset glow Mt. Hood (51x61cm-20x24in) s.verso. 27-Oct-3 O'Gallerie, Oregon #140/R est:1500-2000
£1872 $3500 €2733 Piscataqua river above the Woolen Mill Dam, Dover, ME (43x74cm-17x29in) s. i.d.Oct 6 1906 verso. 28-Feb-4 Thomaston Place, Thomaston #148/R

STUART, Michelle (1940-) American
Works on paper
£472 $764 €689 Project color/time/landform transformations (62x77cm-24x30in) s.i.d.1977 mixed media collage paper muslin earth dust prov. 24-May-3 Burkhard, Luzern #124/R (S.FR 1000)
£611 $1100 €892 Drawing 23/31. Untitled (22x30cm-9x12in) one s. one pastel graphite one graphite staples collage two. 24-Apr-4 David Rago, Lambertville #429/R

STUART, R Easton (fl.1890-1940) British
£250 $400 €365 Joiner's workshop (35x45cm-14x18in) s. s.i.verso. 18-Sep-3 Bonhams, Edinburgh #346

STUART, W E D (19th C) British
£600 $1056 €876 Grapes, apples, roses and other fruit, ceramic jug on wooden ledge (51x61cm-20x24in) 19-May-4 Christie's, Kensington #591/R
£1757 $3250 €2565 Still life with fruit, urn and tankard (61x91cm-24x36in) s.d.1856. 15-Jul-4 Sotheby's, New York #27/R est:2000-3000
£2400 $4296 €3504 Grapes, peaches and other fruit salver and a bejeweled cup (63x63cm-25x25in) with sig.d.1851. 27-May-4 Christie's, Kensington #340/R est:1000-1500

STUBBS, George (1724-1806) British
£27933 $50000 €40782 Two bay mares and grey pony in landscape (62x75cm-24x30in) s.i.d.1793 prov.lit. 27-May-4 Sotheby's, New York #251/R est:50000-70000

STUBBS, Ralph Reuben (1820-1879) British
£250 $450 €365 A ship in a storm beside a cliff side (39x54cm-15x21in) s.d.1861. 20-Jan-4 Bonhams, Leeds #160
£400 $636 €580 Beggars Bridge Glaisdale River scene with fisherman in the foreground (29x43cm-11x17in) i.verso. 9-Sep-3 David Duggleby, Scarborough #384
£400 $748 €584 View of Scarborough from the south bay looking towards the town (23x35cm-9x14in) s.d.1855 indis.i.verso stretcher. 22-Jul-4 Tennants, Leyburn #811
Works on paper
£320 $525 €467 Moorland scene with figures (33x51cm-13x20in) d.1869 W/C. 6-Jun-3 Biddle & Webb, Birmingham #24

STUBBS, William P (1842-1909) American
£938 $1500 €1369 Double masted schooner Marye Dana (142x231cm-56x91in) s. canvas on plywood. 18-May-3 Auctions by the Bay, Alameda #1042/R
£1984 $3750 €2897 Portrait of steam trawler in coastal waters (58x13cm-23x5in) s. 22-Feb-4 Skinner, Boston #377 est:1500-2500
£4070 $7000 €5942 Ship portrait, J Henry Edmunds (56x76cm-22x30in) 6-Dec-3 South Bay, Long Island #100/R
£6831 $12500 €10247 American three-master schooner W S Jordan under full sail (56x91cm-22x36in) s. prov. 29-Jul-4 Eldred, East Dennis #287/R est:3000-5000
£7104 $13000 €10372 Fishing schooner - Helen H Benedict off the new England coast (66x107cm-26x42in) s.d.1884. 29-Jul-4 Christie's, Rockefeller NY #247/R est:7000-9000
£12575 $21000 €18360 The gardener, C Reynolds (56x91cm-22x36in) s. 16-Nov-3 CRN Auctions, Cambridge #40/R
£15135 $28000 €22097 Dauntless and Mohawk rounding the mark (65x91cm-26x36in) prov. 10-Feb-4 Christie's, Rockefeller NY #200/R est:15000-25000

STUBEL, Ermanno (19/20th C) Italian
£567 $919 €800 Via dei Colombi, Trieste (45x38cm-18x15in) s. panel. 22-May-3 Stadion, Trieste #342/R

STUBENRAUCH, Hans (1875-1941) German
£671 $1235 €1000 Man kissing woman's hand (40x50cm-16x20in) s. i. verso panel. 24-Mar-4 Hugo Ruef, Munich #1128/R

STUBER, Dedrick B (1878-1954) American
£802 $1500 €1203 Old thatched bungalow (46x61cm-18x24in) s. canvas over board. 25-Jul-4 Bonhams & Butterfields, San Francisco #6091/R est:2000-3000
£1006 $1600 €1469 Sunlit wooded landscape (38x48cm-15x19in) s. panel. 13-Sep-3 Selkirks, St. Louis #62/R est:2000-3000
£1511 $2750 €2206 Early view of Silverlake (33x48cm-13x19in) s. board. 15-Jun-4 John Moran, Pasadena #34 est:3000-4000
£1618 $2750 €2362 Stream meandering in California landscape, probably Owens Valley (28x36cm-11x14in) s. board. 18-Nov-3 John Moran, Pasadena #11 est:2000-3000
£1618 $2750 €2362 Gallant ships (64x76cm-25x30in) s. prov. 18-Nov-3 John Moran, Pasadena #58 est:3000-4000
£1902 $3500 €2777 Desert in bloom (50x61cm-20x24in) s. masonite prov. 8-Jun-4 Bonhams & Butterfields, San Francisco #4351/R est:4000-6000

STUBLEY, Trevor Hugh (1932-) British
Works on paper
£280 $476 €409 Dales landscape with mills and other buildings beside a stream (60x79cm-24x31in) s. pen ink W/C gouache. 19-Nov-3 Tennants, Leyburn #934

STUBNER, Robert Emil (1874-1931) German
£275 $506 €410 Still life with fruit, candlestick and chrysanthemums (90x109cm-35x43in) s.d.1913. 27-Mar-4 Dannenberg, Berlin #628/R
£658 $1211 €1000 Three-quarter length portrait of young woman with hat (85x90cm-33x35in) s. 25-Jun-4 Altus, Berlin #494/R
£1556 $2738 €2272 Still life (90x110cm-35x43in) s. oval. 23-May-4 Agra, Warsaw #22/R (P.Z 11000)

STUBNER, Robert Emil (attrib) (1874-1931) German
£263 $484 €400 Flower park at a villa (63x87cm-25x34in) 25-Jun-4 Altus, Berlin #477/R

STUCK, Franz von (1863-1928) German
£8333 $13583 €12000 Daughter Mary in profile (31x31cm-12x12in) s. panel prov. 27-Sep-3 Dr Fritz Nagel, Stuttgart #9651/R est:6000
£9500 $17290 €13870 Faun und Bacchus (24x22cm-9x9in) board octagon painted c.1905. 21-Jun-4 Bonhams, New Bond Street #14/R est:10000-15000
£9655 $16124 €14000 Portrait of Lotte Harburger (30x30cm-12x12in) s. panel. 9-Jul-3 Hugo Ruef, Munich #222/R est:9000
£14583 $23771 €21000 Portrait of Margot Szanto (64x60cm-25x24in) s.d.1918 canvas on panel prov. 27-Sep-3 Dr Fritz Nagel, Stuttgart #9652/R est:25000

£14667	$26987	€22000	Evening landscape (35x43cm-14x17in) s. 10-Jun-4 Hauswedell & Nolte, Hamburg #697/R est:18000
£216763	$375000	€316474	Inferno (128x209cm-50x82in) s.d.1908 prov.exhib.lit. 11-Dec-3 Sotheby's, New York #169/R est:400000-600000
Sculpture			
£1931	$3225	€2800	Amazone (13cm-5in) dark pat.bronze copper. 15-Nov-3 Von Zezschwitz, Munich #51/R est:1500
£2069	$3455	€3000	Beethoven mask (46x46cm-18x18in) s. brown pat bronze st.f.C Leyrer. 13-Nov-3 Neumeister, Munich #470/R est:5000-6000
£4308	$7409	€6290	Athlete (64cm-25in) s. dark pat.bronze. 2-Dec-3 Bukowskis, Stockholm #253/R est:35000-40000 (S.KR 56000)
£4667	$8353	€7000	Athlete (66x32x28cm-26x13x11in) i. black brown pat.bronze Cast.C.Leyrer Munich prov.exhib.lit. 14-May-4 Ketterer, Munich #122/R est:8000-12000
£7000	$12740	€10220	Mask of Beethoven (47x47cm-19x19in) s.i. dark brown pat bronze st.f.C Leyrer prov.lit. 17-Jun-4 Christie's, London #63/R est:8000-12000
£7543	$13502	€11013	Amazone (65cm-26in) s. pat.bronze. 13-May-4 Stuker, Bern #6753/R est:4000-6000 (S.FR 17500)
£8276	$13821	€12000	Hostile enemy (71cm-28in) i. dark brown pat bronze st.f.Guss C Leyrer exhib. 13-Nov-3 Neumeister, Munich #471/R est:10000-12000
£12667	$22673	€19000	Dancer (63x23x32cm-25x9x13in) i. black brown pat.bronze Cast.C.Leyrer Munich prov.exhib.lit. 14-May-4 Ketterer, Munich #121/R est:17000-19000
Works on paper			
£1310	$2188	€1900	Female nude bending over (44x38cm-17x15in) s. red ochre white chk. 13-Nov-3 Neumeister, Munich #469/R est:1000-1200
£2759	$4607	€4000	Portrait of a girl in three-quarter profile (54x48cm-21x19in) s. pastel over pencil board. 13-Nov-3 Neumeister, Munich #467/R est:5000-6000
£3448	$5759	€5000	Portrait of a woman (53x45cm-21x18in) s. pastel bodycol pencil board. 13-Nov-3 Neumeister, Munich #468/R est:5000-5500
£27778	$47222	€40000	Tilla Durieux as Circe (53x46cm-21x18in) s.i. mixed media lit. 28-Oct-3 Wiener Kunst Auktionen, Vienna #63/R est:35000-70000

STUCKELBERG, Ernst (1831-1903) Swiss

£273	$453	€396	Hilltop fortress (13x22cm-5x9in) mono. panel. 13-Jun-3 Zofingen, Switzerland #3053 (S.FR 600)
£419	$711	€612	Portrait of Adele Jenny Backofen (39x35cm-15x14in) s.d.1858 i. stretcher. 5-Nov-3 Dobiaschofsky, Bern #993/R (S.FR 950)
£498	$846	€727	Bride from Anticoli (47x37cm-19x15in) s.i.d.1857 verso. 28-Nov-3 Zofingen, Switzerland #2489/R (S.FR 1100)
£526	$879	€768	Landscape near Sigriswyl (13x23cm-5x9in) mono. i.d.1893 verso panel prov. 15-Nov-3 Galerie Gloggner, Luzern #107/R (S.FR 1200)
£568	$1045	€829	Capri coast (31x41cm-12x16in) s.d. 14-Jun-4 Philippe Schuler, Zurich #4238/R (S.FR 1300)
£1135	$2066	€1657	Italian girl (40x35cm-16x14in) s.d.1869. 16-Jun-4 Fischer, Luzern #1312/R est:2000-2500 (S.FR 2600)

STUCKELBERG, Ernst (attrib) (1831-1903) Swiss

£452	$769	€660	Neapolitan herder with child (61x50cm-24x20in) 28-Nov-3 Zofingen, Switzerland #3196/R (S.FR 1000)

STUCKENBERG, Fritz (1881-1944) German

Works on paper			
£671	$1201	€1000	Cosmic (39x28cm-15x11in) s. W/C col chk lit. 25-May-4 Karl & Faber, Munich #545/R
£993	$1808	€1500	Untitled (38x29cm-15x11in) s.d.1924 W/C. 18-Jun-4 Bolland & Marotz, Bremen #958 est:1600
£1342	$2403	€2000	Abstract composition "S 12 1 20" (50x36cm-20x14in) s.i.d.20 W/C Indian ink lit. 25-May-4 Karl & Faber, Munich #544/R est:2800

STUCKENBERG, Fritz (attrib) (1881-1944) German

Works on paper			
£600	$1002	€876	Untitled (26x20cm-10x8in) chl crayon sold with another by Albert Magnell. 21-Oct-3 Bonhams, Knightsbridge #200

STUDDY, George Ernest (1878-1948) British

Works on paper			
£800	$1472	€1168	Studies for illustrations including Bonzo (34x27cm-13x11in) s. W/C. 22-Jun-4 Bonhams, Knightsbridge #89/R
£1000	$1840	€1460	Just to remind you, when are we going to the movies (36x24cm-14x9in) s.i.verso W/C. 22-Jun-4 Bonhams, Knightsbridge #88/R est:1000-1500
£1000	$1840	€1460	Keep your end up (21x34cm-8x13in) s.i.verso W/C. 22-Jun-4 Bonhams, Knightsbridge #89a/R est:1000-1500
£1100	$2024	€1606	Bitten on the tail by a crab (36x24cm-14x9in) s. W/C prov. 22-Jun-4 Bonhams, Knightsbridge #87/R
£1900	$3268	€2774	My mistake (37x28cm-15x11in) s.d.22 pencil W/C. 3-Dec-3 Christie's, Kensington #274/R est:1200-1800

STUDE, Alvin (20th C) American

£228	$425	€333	Winter magic (71x91cm-28x36in) s. painted c.1920. 7-Mar-4 Treadway Gallery, Cincinnati #641/R

STUDER, Harold (1942-) Swiss

Works on paper			
£352	$599	€514	Surreal work of a man (50x50cm-20x20in) s.d.31.1.91 verso W/C oil glaze. 5-Nov-3 Dobiaschofsky, Bern #1923 (S.FR 800)

STUEMPFIG, Walter (1914-1970) American/German

£1117	$2000	€1876	Street scene of several children standing before a cathedral (56x71cm-22x28in) prov. 20-Mar-4 Pook & Pook, Downington #134/R est:2000-3000
£2312	$4000	€3376	Portrait of a young man (46x46cm-18x18in) s. 11-Dec-3 Sotheby's, New York #218/R est:4000-6000
£3179	$5500	€4641	Figure by the seaside (96x107cm-38x42in) s. prov. 10-Dec-3 Bonhams & Butterfields, San Francisco #6063/R est:5000-7000
£4412	$7500	€6442	Canal (51x66cm-20x26in) s. prov. 31-Oct-3 North East Auctions, Portsmouth #1887 est:4000-6000

STUHLMANN, Heinrich (1803-1886) German

£1467	$2699	€2200	Woman and child in a small boot on a mountain lake (35x43cm-14x17in) s.d.1844. 11-Jun-4 Wendl, Rudolstadt #4291/R est:1200
£6944	$11597	€10000	Country market (87x115cm-34x45in) s. prov. 24-Oct-3 Ketterer, Hamburg #112/R est:12000-14000

STUHLMULLER, Karl (1858-1930) German

£1029	$1750	€1502	Winter scene of peasants leaving a home stead (33x56cm-13x22in) s.i. panel. 31-Oct-3 North East Auctions, Portsmouth #1202
£2215	$4075	€3300	Returning home from the fields. 26-Mar-4 Karrenbauer, Konstanz #1773/R est:3000
£2610	$4750	€3811	Feeding time (33x64cm-13x25in) s.i. panel. 7-Feb-4 Auctions by the Bay, Alameda #1517/R
£3000	$5460	€4500	Hay harvest (19x40cm-7x16in) s.i. 30-Jun-4 Neumeister, Munich #702/R est:4500
£3819	$6302	€5500	Peasants outside village tavern (18x26cm-7x10in) s.i. 2-Jul-3 Neumeister, Munich #788/R est:3500
£9524	$17048	€14000	Winter cattle market outside town (25x29cm-10x11in) s.i. 17-Mar-4 Neumeister, Munich #624/R est:12000

STUHR, William (1882-1958) Danish

£276	$470	€403	Fetching water, Tozeur in North Africa (80x105cm-31x41in) s.i.d.30. 10-Nov-3 Rasmussen, Vejle #596/R (D.KR 3000)

STULER, August (1800-1865) German

Works on paper			
£700	$1267	€1050	War memorial (44x30cm-17x12in) s.i.d.11/49 W/C pencil. 2-Apr-4 Winterberg, Heidelberg #554

STULL, Henry (1851-1913) American

£2159	$3800	€3152	Dead heat between Dobbins and Domino in their great match (38x30cm-15x12in) s.d.1893. 21-May-4 North East Auctions, Portsmouth #531/R est:4000-6000
£3267	$5750	€4770	Jockey and horse (46x61cm-18x24in) s.d.1890. 21-May-4 North East Auctions, Portsmouth #530/R est:4000-6000
£4913	$8500	€7173	Horse and jockey (46x61cm-18x24in) s.d.1888 prov. 10-Dec-3 Bonhams & Butterfields, San Francisco #6004/R est:6000-8000
£9677	$18000	€14128	General Harding, Imp Great Tom - Liza Davis by Whirlwind - Belle Meade (41x61cm-16x24in) s.d.1883. 6-Mar-4 North East Auctions, Portsmouth #1124/R est:2500-3500
£15116	$26000	€22069	Margrave, winner of the Preakness Stakes in 1896, with jockey up (58x72cm-23x28in) s. 5-Dec-3 Christie's, Rockefeller NY #136/R est:12000-18000

STULTUS, Dyalma (1902-1977) Italian

£1600	$2864	€2400	Path to the church (45x55cm-18x22in) s. s.i.verso board. 12-May-4 Stadion, Trieste #657/R est:2000-3000
Works on paper			
£265	$482	€400	Houses on the road (50x34cm-20x13in) s.d.74 W/C. 18-Jun-4 Stadion, Trieste #111/R
£336	$577	€480	Beggar (61x47cm-24x19in) s.d.26 chl lead. 3-Dec-3 Stadion, Trieste #1095/R

STUMP, Samuel John (c.1783-1863) British

Miniatures			
£1500	$2760	€2190	Midshipman, wearing blue uniform (7cm-3in) s. rec. papier mache frame. 24-Jun-4 Bonhams, New Bond Street #123/R est:500-700

STUNDER, Johann Jakob (1759-1811) Danish

£1000	$1810	€1500	Portrait of woman with flower in hair (77x60cm-30x24in) s. 1-Apr-4 Van Ham, Cologne #1660a/R est:2200

STUNTZ, Electrina (attrib) (1797-1847) German

£2207	$3686	€3200	Mary with Christ child before extensive landscape (44x34cm-17x13in) panel. 9-Jul-3 Hugo Ruef, Munich #223 est:900

STUPAR, Marko (1936-) ?

£389	$697	€580	Vue de Honfleur (22x27cm-9x11in) s. 25-May-4 Chambelland & Giafferi, Paris #22/R
£521	$869	€750	Nature morte au pichet (53x40cm-21x16in) s. oil gouache paper. 21-Oct-3 Artcurial Briest, Paris #356
£10490	$17518	€15000	La brasserie (130x161cm-51x63in) 30-Jun-3 Artcurial Briest, Paris #759/R est:15000-20000
Works on paper			
£268	$494	€400	Enfant (45x45cm-18x18in) s. gouache. 24-Mar-4 Joron-Derem, Paris #192
£322	$596	€480	Le jardin public (18x24cm-7x9in) s. pastel. 15-Mar-4 Blanchet, Paris #148
£336	$617	€500	Bateau a quai (46x59cm-18x23in) s. gouache. 24-Mar-4 Joron-Derem, Paris #191
£342	$630	€510	Rue de Paris (65x50cm-26x20in) s. gouache. 24-Mar-4 Joron-Derem, Paris #187
£342	$630	€510	Rue de Paris (65x50cm-26x20in) s. gouache. 24-Mar-4 Joron-Derem, Paris #188
£342	$630	€510	Rue de Paris (65x50cm-26x20in) s. gouache. 24-Mar-4 Joron-Derem, Paris #189
£364	$663	€550	Terrasse de cafe a Paris (19x16cm-7x6in) s. gouache. 15-Jun-4 Blanchet, Paris #201/R
£397	$723	€600	Une rue animee a Paris (20x23cm-8x9in) s. gouache. 15-Jun-4 Blanchet, Paris #200/R
£432	$800	€631	Sur la plage (25x53cm-10x21in) s. mixed media. 17-Jan-4 New Orleans Auction, New Orleans #524

STUPLE, Charles (20th C) American
£353 $600 €515 View of Motif no.1 and Rock Port Harbour (64x76cm-25x30in) 21-Nov-3 Eldred, East Dennis #520/R

STURANI, Mario (20th C) Italian
Works on paper
£629 $1051 €900 Lady with veiled hat (30x25cm-12x10in) pencil card. 26-Jun-3 Sant Agostino, Torino #152/R

STURGE, F W (19/20th C) British
Works on paper
£330 $551 €479 Tintagel castle (64x89cm-25x35in) s. W/C. 14-Jul-3 Trembath Welch, Great Dunmow #554

STURGEON, Eric (20th C) British
Works on paper
£680 $1081 €986 St Anne's Gate, Salisbury with figures (52x70cm-20x28in) s. i.verso W/C. 12-Sep-3 ELR Auctions, Sheffield #295/R

STURGEON, Josiah (20th C) British
£450 $752 €657 Autumn evening, Chelsea (31x41cm-12x16in) s. board. 7-Oct-3 Bonhams, Knightsbridge #60/R

STURGES, Jock (1947-) American
Photographs
£1640 $3100 €2394 Danielle, Montavivet, France (45x32cm-18x13in) s.i.d.1989 num.6/40 gelatin silver print. 17-Feb-4 Christie's, Rockefeller NY #232/R est:2500-3500

STURGESS, John (fl.1869-1903) British
£570 $986 €832 A lady's hack (35x25cm-14x10in) s.d.1895. 11-Dec-3 Lane, Penzance #310
£640 $1126 €934 Study for a portrait of XII Duke of York (26x40cm-10x16in) 18-May-4 Woolley & Wallis, Salisbury #167/R
£2900 $5191 €4234 Hunting scenes with riders and hounds in full cry (16x34cm-6x13in) panel set of six. 16-Mar-4 Bonhams, Oxford #80/R est:2000-3000

STURGESS, R W (1890-1932) Australian
Works on paper
£289 $535 €422 Kookaburra (17x16cm-7x6in) s. W/C. 10-Mar-4 Deutscher-Menzies, Melbourne #531/R (A.D 700)
£382 $695 €558 River landscape (24x38cm-9x15in) s. W/C. 16-Jun-4 Deutscher-Menzies, Melbourne #595/R est:1000-1500 (A.D 1000)

STURGIS, Mabel Russell (attrib) (1865-?) American
£342 $550 €499 Landscape (25x46cm-10x18in) s.d.1910. 10-May-3 Auctions by the Bay, Alameda #1296/R

STURLA, Michel (19/20th C) ?
£1986 $3316 €2800 Port d'Alger (54x73cm-21x29in) s. 19-Oct-3 Rabourdin & Choppin de Janvry, Paris #30/R est:3000-3500

STURM, Friedrich (attrib) (1822-1898) Austrian
£1009 $1685 €1463 Harem woman (100x73cm-39x29in) 23-Jun-3 Philippe Schuler, Zurich #3551/R est:3000-4000 (S.FR 2200)

STURM, Fritz Ludwig Christian (1834-1906) German
£4392 $7861 €6500 Summer's day on the coast (78x130cm-31x51in) s.i.d.1886 lit. 8-May-4 Schloss Ahlden, Ahlden #784/R est:6500

STURM, Helmut (1932-) German
£664 $1143 €950 Composition (43x56cm-17x22in) s.d.78 oil paper. 4-Dec-3 Van Ham, Cologne #498/R
£1667 $3067 €2500 Composition in blue (99x84cm-39x33in) s.d. acrylic dispersion col chk paper collage. 11-Jun-4 Hauswedell & Nolte, Hamburg #1546/R est:2500
£2069 $3455 €3000 In between play (115x125cm-45x49in) s.d.1977 sack. 13-Nov-3 Neumeister, Munich #641/R est:2000-2500
£7136 $11917 €10419 Figure composition (120x100cm-47x39in) s. painted c.1961 prov. 7-Oct-3 Rasmussen, Copenhagen #75/R est:100000 (D.KR 76000)
Works on paper
£863 $1416 €1200 Composition (100x74cm-39x29in) s.d. mixed media board. 4-Jun-3 Ketterer, Hamburg #891/R

STURM, Josef (1858-?) Austrian
£966 $1612 €1400 Wooden bridge in winter landscape with Zugspitze (80x100cm-31x39in) s. lit. 10-Jul-3 Allgauer, Kempten #2692/R

STURM, Pierre Henri (1785-1869) French
Miniatures
£1300 $2392 €1898 Louis XVIII (5cm-2in) s. enamel. 24-Jun-4 Bonhams, New Bond Street #17/R est:800-1200

STURROCK, Alick Riddell (1885-1953) British
£600 $1032 €876 Suburban January (72x61cm-28x24in) s. 4-Dec-3 Bonhams, Edinburgh #82/R
£4000 $6440 €5800 Suburban January (72x61cm-28x24in) s. i.on overlap. 21-Aug-3 Bonhams, Edinburgh #1187/R est:700-1000

STURSA, Jan (1880-1925) Czechoslovakian
Sculpture
£1100 $1837 €1606 Man (54cm-21in) s. pat bronze. 13-Nov-3 Christie's, Kensington #271/R

STURTEVANT, Elaine (1926-) American
£13287 $22189 €19000 Peinture a haute tension (162x96cm-64x38in) acrylic flocage neon after Martial Raysee. 11-Oct-3 Cornette de St.Cyr, Paris #108/R est:20000-25000
£14685 $24524 €21000 Warhol, gold Marylin Monroe (46cm-18in circular) s.i.d.1973 verso acrylic ink screenprint. 11-Oct-3 Cornette de St.Cyr, Paris #109/R est:8000-10000
£30726 $55000 €44860 Study for Warhol flowers (56x56cm-22x22in) s.i.d.1971 verso acrylic silkscreen ink prov. 12-May-4 Christie's, Rockefeller NY #376/R est:15000-20000

STURTEVANT, Helena (1872-1946) American
£1075 $2000 €1570 International race week (50x76cm-20x30in) s.d.1937 i.d.verso. 5-Mar-4 Skinner, Boston #578/R est:1500-2000
£2514 $4500 €3670 Second beach (56x66cm-22x26in) s. 26-May-4 Doyle, New York #61/R est:2000-3000

STURZENEGGER, Hans (1875-1943) Swiss
£1121 $2006 €1637 Bielersee (81x75cm-32x30in) s.d.32 i. stretcher. 14-May-4 Dobiaschofsky, Bern #217/R est:3600 (S.FR 2600)

STUTTERHEIM, Lodewyk Philippus (1873-1943) Dutch
£377 $640 €550 Roses in a vase (44x30cm-17x12in) s. 5-Nov-3 Vendue Huis, Gravenhage #318
£382 $603 €550 Red flowers in a jug (44x35cm-17x14in) s. oil paper on panel. 2-Sep-3 Christie's, Amsterdam #282
£526 $968 €800 A farmhouse by a stream (50x65cm-20x26in) s. s.i.verso. 22-Jun-4 Christie's, Amsterdam #241/R
£1328 $2285 €1900 Town view with windmills (40x50cm-16x20in) s. 7-Dec-3 Sotheby's, Amsterdam #623/R

STUVEN, Ernst (1660-1712) German
£18000 $31140 €26280 Still life of flowers in a glass vase on a stone ledge (85x67cm-33x26in) prov. 11-Dec-3 Sotheby's, London #168/R est:15000-20000

STYKA, Adam (1890-1959) French
£1591 $2800 €2323 Portrait of a young Indian boy on a mule by the shore (25x33cm-10x13in) s. board oval. 21-May-4 Pook & Pook, Downington #377/R est:3500-4500
£3200 $5888 €4800 Le marche des oranges (50x61cm-20x24in) s. i.verso. 11-Jun-4 Pierre Berge, Paris #237/R est:4000-5000
£4846 $8238 €7075 La rencontre (80x64cm-31x25in) s. 5-Nov-3 Dobiaschofsky, Bern #995/R est:13000 (S.FR 11000)
£5918 $10594 €8700 Jeune egyptien et son buffle (65x81cm-26x32in) s. prov.lit. 21-Mar-4 St-Germain-en-Laye Encheres #36/R est:6000-8000
£7353 $12500 €10735 Collier Promis (81x65cm-32x26in) s. prov. 28-Oct-3 Sotheby's, New York #95/R est:20000-30000
£11315 $19915 €16520 Couple (65x81cm-26x32in) painted 1930. 23-May-4 Agra, Warsaw #7/R (P.Z 80000)
£13732 $23757 €19500 Rencontre (81x65cm-32x26in) s. 15-Dec-3 Gros & Delettrez, Paris #188/R est:9000-12000
£14336 $24658 €20500 Tois amis au campement (60x73cm-24x29in) s. 8-Dec-3 Tajan, Paris #334/R est:12000-15000
£21127 $36549 €30000 Parure de la fiancee (81x65cm-32x26in) s. 15-Dec-3 Gros & Delettrez, Paris #78/R est:30000-35000

STYKA, Jan (1858-1925) French
£1135 $1895 €1600 Pierre l'Apotre (81x54cm-32x21in) s.i.d.1916. 19-Oct-3 Charbonneaux, Paris #145/R est:1200
£2724 $4549 €3950 Portrait de Henri Rochefort (80x65cm-31x26in) s. cardboard. 17-Nov-3 Claude Boisgirard, Paris #89/R est:2500-3000
£9444 $17000 €13788 Officers on horseback (147x143cm-58x56in) s.d.1898. 21-Jan-4 Sotheby's, New York #246/R est:8000-12000

STYKA, Tade (1889-1954) French
£688 $1100 €1004 Portrait of a lady with a fur stole, Mae Bourne Strassburger (81x64cm-32x25in) s. 19-Sep-3 Freeman, Philadelphia #76/R est:400-600
£940 $1663 €1400 Portrait de femme (46x38cm-18x15in) s. cardboard. 30-Apr-4 Tajan, Paris #168/R est:1200-1500

STYRING, Elizabeth (fl.1911-1938) British
£360 $612 €526 Quayside, Whitby (50x76cm-20x30in) board. 18-Nov-3 Bonhams, Leeds #145
Works on paper
£280 $484 €409 Continental canal scene (48x33cm-19x13in) s. W/C. 12-Dec-3 Halls, Shrewsbury #631

SU CHUNSHENG (?) Chinese
Works on paper
£608 $1070 €900 Clouds in the Hanshuang mountains (68x45cm-27x18in) s.i. seal Indian ink col hanging scroll. 21-May-4 Dr Fritz Nagel, Stuttgart #1113/R

SU XINPING (1960-) Oriental
£7190 $13013 €10497 Holiday no 5 (190x160cm-75x63in) s. 3-Apr-4 Glerum, Singapore #53/R est:15000-18000 (S.D 22000)

SUANDI, Gusti Ketut (1932-) Balinese
£695 $1161 €1015 Penari - profile of a dancer (29x29cm-11x11in) s.i.d.90 oil gold paint on plywood. 26-Oct-3 Christie's, Hong Kong #74/R est:9000-14000 (HK.D 9000)

£725 $1123 €1059 Dance (60x90cm-24x35in) s.d.87. 6-Oct-2 Sotheby's, Singapore #154/R (S.D 2000)
£1699 $2837 €2481 Offering rites (61x50cm-24x20in) s.i.d.88. 26-Oct-3 Christie's, Hong Kong #75/R est:14000-18000 (HK.D 22000)

SUAREZ LLANOS, Ignacio (1830-1881) Spanish
£764 $1299 €1100 Portrait of Don Anselmo Cifuentes (115x85cm-45x33in) s.d.1871. 28-Oct-3 Segre, Madrid #52/R

SUAREZ, Antonio (1923-) Spanish
£423 $739 €600 Untitled (27x20cm-11x8in) s. paper. 16-Dec-3 Segre, Madrid #223/R
£567 $1026 €850 Shape (33x50cm-13x20in) s. cardboard. 30-Mar-4 Segre, Madrid #185/R
£775 $1356 €1100 Still life (27x35cm-11x14in) s.d.1974. 16-Dec-3 Segre, Madrid #218/R
£870 $1426 €1200 Still life with window (70x50cm-28x20in) s.d.74 paper exhib. 27-May-3 Durán, Madrid #100/R
£1118 $2058 €1700 Composition (35x49cm-14x19in) s.d.99. 22-Jun-4 Durán, Madrid #50/R
£1678 $2970 €2500 Still life (30x42cm-12x17in) s. board painted 1948. 27-Apr-4 Durán, Madrid #72/R est:2000
Works on paper
£301 $503 €425 Floers (24x16cm-9x6in) s.d.72 mixed media. 20-Oct-3 Durán, Madrid #591/R
£303 $546 €440 Untitled (16x24cm-6x9in) s. mixed media board. 26-Jan-4 Ansorena, Madrid #856/R
£319 $533 €450 Composition (17x26cm-7x10in) s. mixed media board. 20-Oct-3 Durán, Madrid #593/R
£319 $533 €450 Composition (16x26cm-6x10in) s. mixed media board. 20-Oct-3 Durán, Madrid #594/R
£336 $571 €490 Untitled (28x39cm-11x15in) s.d.2000 mixed media. 4-Nov-3 Ansorena, Madrid #1003/R
£345 $621 €500 Untitled (24x30cm-9x12in) s. mixed media cardboard. 26-Jan-4 Ansorena, Madrid #933/R
£493 $908 €750 Composition (19x24cm-7x9in) s. mixed media. 22-Jun-4 Durán, Madrid #552/R

SUAREZ, Aurelio (1911-) Spanish
£9420 $15449 €13000 Endemoniado (38x46cm-15x18in) s. i.d.mayo 1949 verso. 27-May-3 Durán, Madrid #169/R est:10000
£18621 $31097 €27000 Smell (46x38cm-18x15in) s. s.i.d.1947 verso. 17-Nov-3 Durán, Madrid #236/R est:27000

SUBANI, Rahmat (1949-2003) Oriental
£1562 $2609 €2281 Dibalik Kegelapan (94x124cm-37x49in) s.d.1996 s.i.d.verso. 12-Oct-3 Sotheby's, Singapore #190/R est:3000-4000 (S.D 4500)
£2536 $3931 €3703 Behind the Bilik (125x95cm-49x37in) s.d.1998. 6-Oct-2 Sotheby's, Singapore #188/R est:5000-7000 (S.D 7000)
£2778 $4639 €4056 Dilema (120x90cm-47x35in) s.d.1998 s.i.d.verso. 12-Oct-3 Sotheby's, Singapore #191/R est:4000-6000 (S.D 8000)
£3441 $5505 €5024 Nanas and bengkoang (110x80cm-43x31in) mono.d.2002 s.i.d.2000-2002 verso. 18-May-3 Sotheby's, Singapore #196/R est:3000-5000 (S.D 9600)
£4710 $7301 €6877 Pelaku pasar (120x90cm-47x35in) s.d.2000 s.i.d.verso. 6-Oct-2 Sotheby's, Singapore #177/R est:3000-5000 (S.D 13000)
£4731 $7570 €6907 Distributor Dunia Gelombang Ke III (120x90cm-47x35in) mono.d.2001-2003 i.d.2001-2003 verso. 18-May-3 Sotheby's, Singapore #189/R est:3000-5000 (S.D 13200)

SUBERO, Oswaldo (1934-) Venezuelan
£266 $495 €388 Untitled (17x13cm-7x5in) panel painted 1983. 14-Mar-4 Subastas Odalys, Caracas #73/R
£804 $1310 €1174 Bi-dimensional picture (80x70cm-31x28in) s.verso painted 1979. 28-Sep-3 Subastas Odalys, Caracas #29/R

SUBIRA-PUIG (1926-) Spanish
Sculpture
£2105 $3874 €3200 Petit Ivry (24x23x18cm-9x9x7in) wood exec.1979 exhib. 27-Jun-4 Versailles Encheres #167/R est:2000-2500

SUBIRA-PUIG, Jose (1926-) Spanish
Sculpture
£1352 $2419 €2000 Winner (62x42x16cm-24x17x6in) s. wood exec.2001. 4-May-4 Calmels Cohen, Paris #211/R est:1500-2000

SUBIRANA, Ismael (1937-) Spanish
£326 $535 €450 Aldea (46x65cm-18x26in) s. 27-May-3 Durán, Madrid #626/R

SUBLEYRAS, Pierre (attrib) (1699-1749) French
£6154 $10585 €8985 Female saint with palm leaf (114x89cm-45x35in) 7-Dec-3 Uppsala Auktionskammare, Uppsala #57/R est:80000-100000 (S.KR 80000)

SUBLEYRAS-TIBALDI, Maria Felice (1707-1770) Italian
Works on paper
£9444 $17000 €13788 Banquet at the house of Simon (23x50cm-9x20in) gouache on parchment. 21-Jan-4 Sotheby's, New York #124/R est:15000-20000

SUCH, W T (fl.1847-1857) British
£2899 $4754 €4000 Marsh with flying birds (70x90cm-28x35in) s.d.1857. 27-May-3 Finarte Semenzato, Milan #136/R est:1000-1500

SUCHET, Joseph François (1824-1896) French
£602 $1000 €879 Steep Coast line (30x46cm-12x18in) s. 4-Oct-3 Neal Auction Company, New Orleans #912/R

SUCHODOLSKI, Janvier (1797-1875) Polish
£3357 $5706 €4800 Cossacks in village (66x88cm-26x35in) s. 20-Nov-3 Van Ham, Cologne #1880/R est:2800

SUCHODOLSKI, Piotr (1829-?) Polish
£12766 $21319 €18000 Landscape with gathering storm (31x56cm-12x22in) s.cyrillic.d.91. 21-Jun-3 Hans Stahl, Hamburg #59/R est:3200

SUCHY, Adalbert (1783-1849) Austrian
£3356 $5940 €5000 Kaiser Franz I von Osterreich (74x60cm-29x24in) s.d.820. 29-Apr-4 Dorotheum, Vienna #40/R est:5000-7000
Miniatures
£5500 $9625 €8030 Lady and Gentleman (10cm-4in) both s. latter d.1830 rec cut corners gilt metal mounts pair. 18-Dec-3 Sotheby's, Olympia #23/R est:10000-15000

SUCKOW, Alexander von (1855-?) German
£1192 $2181 €1800 Fishing boats on stormy sea (42x58cm-17x23in) s. board. 8-Apr-4 Dorotheum, Vienna #232/R est:1800-2000

SUDARSO (20th C) Indonesian
£2162 $3611 €3157 Two girls (118x75cm-46x30in) s.d.87. 26-Oct-3 Christie's, Hong Kong #58/R est:32000-40000 (HK.D 28000)
£2471 $4127 €3608 Wanita baju merah - girl wearing a red dress (115x80cm-45x31in) s.d.77. 26-Oct-3 Christie's, Hong Kong #57/R est:35000-65000 (HK.D 32000)

SUDARSONO, Shrihadi (1931-) Indonesian
£10145 $15725 €14812 Two dancers (101x85cm-40x33in) s.d.1972. 6-Oct-2 Sotheby's, Singapore #153/R est:25000-30000 (S.D 28000)
£12153 $20295 €17743 Dancer (60x55cm-24x22in) s.d.2000 s.i.d.verso. 12-Oct-3 Sotheby's, Singapore #148/R est:28000-35000 (S.D 35000)
£13763 $22022 €20094 Pantai (140x108cm-55x43in) s.d.1966 s.i.d.1966 verso. 18-May-3 Sotheby's, Singapore #179/R est:18000-25000 (S.D 38400)
£16340 $29575 €23856 Balinese dancer (128x100cm-50x39in) s.d.85 lit. 4-Apr-4 Sotheby's, Singapore #160/R est:50000-70000 (S.D 50000)
£17070 $30725 €24922 View of a landscape with a windmill (120x100cm-47x39in) s.d.78 s.d.verso. 25-Apr-4 Christie's, Hong Kong #570/R est:120000-160000 (HK.D 240000)
£20833 $34792 €30416 Penari (130x100cm-51x39in) s.d.89 s.i.d.verso. 12-Oct-3 Sotheby's, Singapore #147/R est:40000-60000 (S.D 60000)
£21505 $34409 €31397 Women (130x130cm-51x51in) s.d.1966. 18-May-3 Sotheby's, Singapore #165/R est:35000-55000 (S.D 60000)
£27174 $42120 €39674 Krakatau (90x244cm-35x96in) s.d.1984 s.i.d.verso. 6-Oct-2 Sotheby's, Singapore #162/R est:40000-60000 (S.D 75000)
Works on paper
£1307 $2366 €1908 Costa Del Sol (35x51cm-14x20in) s. W/C. 4-Apr-4 Sotheby's, Singapore #172/R est:3000-4000 (S.D 4000)

SUDARYONO (1952-) Indonesian
£516 $826 €753 Sumptuous planet (140x140cm-55x55in) s.d.2002. 18-May-3 Sotheby's, Singapore #195/R (S.D 1440)

SUDDABY, Rowland (1912-1973) British
£450 $752 €657 Still life with fruit and flowers (46x31cm-18x12in) s.d.35 board. 21-Oct-3 Bonhams, Knightsbridge #79/R
£450 $792 €657 Still life with butterflies (63x76cm-25x30in) s. board. 18-May-4 Bonhams, Knightsbridge #177/R
£500 $835 €730 View in Suffolk (30x37cm-12x15in) s. board prov. 21-Oct-3 Bonhams, Knightsbridge #17/R
£500 $860 €730 Lane near Cornard, Suffolk (51x61cm-20x24in) s. board. 2-Dec-3 Sworder & Son, Bishops Stortford #522/R
£600 $1110 €876 Figure in a marsh landscape with trees, sky clearing (33x44cm-13x17in) s. indis d. board. 14-Jan-4 Lawrence, Crewkerne #1437/R
£660 $1181 €964 Wooded landscape with buildings beyond (46x55cm-18x22in) s. board. 16-Mar-4 Bonhams, Leeds #563
£760 $1292 €1110 Still life items on a table before a window. 28-Oct-3 Lawrences, Bletchingley #1756
£1800 $3060 €2628 Surreal landscape (39x56cm-15x22in) s. board. 26-Nov-3 Sotheby's, Olympia #72/R est:800-1200
Works on paper
£340 $629 €496 Sussex landscape (41x56cm-16x22in) s.d.49 W/C ink. 9-Mar-4 Gorringes, Lewes #2218
£420 $685 €613 Fallen Elm (28x41cm-11x16in) s.i. pen ink W/C. 24-Sep-3 Dreweatt Neate, Newbury #67
£460 $837 €672 Still life of assorted flowers with pears, apple and grapes (56x67cm-22x26in) s. mixed media prov. 15-Jun-4 Bonhams, Leeds #75
£500 $925 €730 Autumn landscape (45x55cm-18x22in) s. pen brush ink wax crayon W/C. 11-Mar-4 Christie's, Kensington #178
£520 $894 €759 Still life with fruit (43x56cm-17x22in) s. W/C bodycol. 2-Dec-3 Sworder & Son, Bishops Stortford #522a/R
£1350 $2376 €1971 Bathers (54x75cm-21x30in) s.d.1938 pencil. 19-May-4 Sotheby's, Olympia #91/R est:1000-1500

SUDDUTH, Jimmy Lee (1910-) American
£236 $425 €345 Football player (122x91cm-48x36in) paint stain mud on plywood. 24-Apr-4 Slotin Folk Art, Buford #438/R
£240 $400 €350 Self-portrait in blue overalls (122x61cm-48x24in) household paint mud panel prov. 15-Nov-3 Slotin Folk Art, Buford #253/R
£250 $450 €365 Boxing match (61x61cm-24x24in) paint mud on board. 24-Apr-4 Slotin Folk Art, Buford #440/R
£299 $500 €437 Woman in hat milking cow (61x122cm-24x48in) household paint mud panel prov. 15-Nov-3 Slotin Folk Art, Buford #252/R
£333 $600 €486 Large ferris wheel (122x61cm-48x24in) paint mud on board. 24-Apr-4 Slotin Folk Art, Buford #441/R

£419 $700 €612 Portrait of Jesus. household paint mud board prov. 15-Nov-3 Slotin Folk Art, Buford #256/R
£472 $850 €689 Three woman (61x61cm-24x24in) paint mud on wood board. 24-Apr-4 Slotin Folk Art, Buford #445/R
£556 $1000 €812 Large house (122x117cm-48x46in) paint over mud on wood. 24-Apr-4 Slotin Folk Art, Buford #442/R est:1000-2000
£778 $1400 €1136 Group of three car (46x61cm-18x24in) paint mud set of three. 24-Apr-4 Slotin Folk Art, Buford #446/R est:500-1000
£889 $1600 €1298 Self portrait (132x66cm-52x26in) housepaint mud prov. 24-Apr-4 Slotin Folk Art, Buford #443/R est:1000-2000
£2056 $3700 €3002 Self portrait (122x61cm-48x24in) mud chk white paint wood board. 24-Apr-4 Slotin Folk Art, Buford #437/R est:1000-2000

Works on paper
£240 $400 €350 Ferris wheel (122x61cm-48x24in) mud paint panel. 15-Nov-3 Slotin Folk Art, Buford #255/R
£389 $700 €568 Santas in front of skyscrapers (122x122cm-48x48in) mud paint on board. 24-Apr-4 Slotin Folk Art, Buford #444/R
£479 $800 €699 Woman and wine (86x97cm-34x38in) pure mud chk board. 15-Nov-3 Slotin Folk Art, Buford #250/R
£539 $900 €787 Dolly Parton (86x76cm-34x30in) mud paint headboard. 15-Nov-3 Slotin Folk Art, Buford #254/R
£599 $1000 €875 Can can dancers (91x122cm-36x48in) mud chalk board. 15-Nov-3 Slotin Folk Art, Buford #248/R
£719 $1200 €1050 Large cow (91x122cm-36x48in) mud paint board. 15-Nov-3 Slotin Folk Art, Buford #251/R
£1557 $2600 €2273 Spiked hair triplets (152x38cm-60x15in) mud paint board. 15-Nov-3 Slotin Folk Art, Buford #249/R est:1000-1500

SUDEIKIN, Sergei Yurievich (1882-1946) Russian
£3293 $5500 €4808 Country houses (34x31cm-13x12in) s. board. 21-Oct-3 Christie's, Rockefeller NY #119 est:3000-4000
£8500 $14450 €12410 Dancer with yellow shawl (35x24cm-14x9in) bears init. board. 19-Nov-3 Sotheby's, London #191/R est:4000-6000
£11976 $20000 €17485 Portrait of a woman (46x36cm-18x14in) s. board prov. 21-Oct-3 Christie's, Rockefeller NY #118 est:10000-15000
£39310 $65648 €57000 Apple harvest (138x201cm-54x79in) s. 9-Jul-3 Hugo Ruef, Munich #204/R est:8500
£40000 $71600 €58400 Dinner party (51x61cm-20x24in) s. 26-May-4 Sotheby's, London #265/R est:25000-35000

Works on paper
£3000 $5370 €4380 Costume designs for the opera Mavra (33x75cm-13x30in) s. gouache. 26-May-4 Sotheby's, London #215/R est:3000-5000
£5000 $8500 €7300 Set design for the Marriage of Figaro (29x46cm-11x18in) s.i.d.1915 W/C gouache over pencil. 19-Nov-3 Sotheby's, London #197/R est:4000-6000
£12000 $20400 €17520 Stage set design of a rainbow above a grotto (30x49cm-12x19in) s.i. gouache card. 19-Nov-3 Sotheby's, London #198/R est:3000-5000
£21000 $37590 €30660 Stage set design (50x68cm-20x27in) s.d.1915 mixed media on card. 26-May-4 Sotheby's, London #214/R est:8000-12000
£135000 $229500 €197100 Georgian cabaret, Tiflis (68x66cm-27x26in) s.d.1919 gouache board. 19-Nov-3 Sotheby's, London #149/R est:30000-40000

SUDEK, Josef (1896-1976) Czechoslovakian
Photographs
£1808 $3200 €2640 In the cathedral, 1942 (38x28cm-15x11in) s. gelatin silver print. 27-Apr-4 Christie's, Rockefeller NY #72/R est:4000-6000
£1808 $3200 €2640 From the Vicinity of Zebrak Castle (16x24cm-6x9in) i.d. gelatin silver print executed c.1929 lit. 27-Apr-4 Christie's, Rockefeller NY #73/R est:4000-6000
£1916 $3200 €2797 Untitled - landscape (11x8cm-4x3in) with sig. pigment print. 21-Oct-3 Swann Galleries, New York #251a/R est:4000-6000
£1916 $3200 €2797 Untitled, sheep grazing (17x28cm-7x11in) s. gelatin silver print exec.c.1920 prov. 20-Oct-3 Christie's, Rockefeller NY #255/R est:3000-5000
£2260 $4000 €3300 Prague panorama (8x28cm-3x11in) s.i.d. gelatin silver print executed c.1955. 27-Apr-4 Christie's, Rockefeller NY #76/R est:4000-6000
£2646 $5000 €3863 Still life - glass (16x11cm-6x4in) s. i. verso silver print. 17-Feb-4 Swann Galleries, New York #77/R est:5000-7000
£2695 $4500 €3935 Untitled, egg and decanter (15x11cm-6x4in) s. pigment print. 20-Oct-3 Christie's, Rockefeller NY #256/R est:5000-7000
£3713 $6200 €5421 Studio of the sculptor, Hana Wichterlov (16x22cm-6x9in) pigment print exec.1953 prov.lit. 17-Oct-3 Phillips, New York #269/R est:8000-12000

SUDKOVSKY, Rufin (1850-1885) Russian
£31000 $55490 €45260 Stranded derelict at dusk (51x103cm-20x41in) s. Cyrillic. 26-May-4 Christie's, Kensington #676/R est:10000-15000

SUDRE, Pierre (?) French
£533 $955 €800 Le Mont Ventoux (60x81cm-24x32in) s. 16-May-4 Thierry & Lannon, Brest #371/R

SUE, Louis (1875-1968) French
£2098 $3504 €3000 Interieur Japonisant (65x81cm-26x32in) s. 30-Jun-3 Artcurial Briest, Paris #729/R est:3000-4000

SUETIN, Nikolai Mikhailovich (1897-1954) Russian
Works on paper
£16667 $30500 €25000 Suprematist composition (22x15cm-9x6in) W/C prov. 5-Jun-4 Lempertz, Koln #1012/R est:8000-10000

SUGAI, Kumi (1919-1996) Japanese
£2817 $4873 €4000 Ligue (99x81cm-39x32in) s.d.67 s.i.d.1967 verso prov. 13-Dec-3 Lempertz, Koln #359/R est:4000
£5743 $10108 €8500 Untitled (61x38cm-24x15in) s. s.d.1956 verso prov. 18-May-4 Tajan, Paris #31/R est:5000-6000
£6579 $12105 €10000 Ligue (100x81cm-39x32in) s.d.1967 s.i.d.verso. 27-Jun-4 Versailles Encheres #101/R est:10000-12000
£7333 $13200 €11000 Marche d'autoroute 3 (100x81cm-39x32in) s.d.1965 s.i.d.verso prov. 25-Apr-4 Versailles Encheres #206 est:12000-15000
£7821 $14000 €11419 Novembre (198x198cm-78x78in) s.i.d.verso oil acrylic. 7-May-4 Sloans & Kenyon, Bethesda #416/R est:20000-30000
£8389 $15017 €12500 Beach (100x81cm-39x32in) s. painted 1956 prov. 26-May-4 Christie's, Paris #73/R est:10000-15000
£11732 $21000 €17129 Chrysanthemum (119x104cm-47x41in) prov. 20-Mar-4 Sloans & Kenyon, Bethesda #1190/R est:15000-20000

Works on paper
£933 $1680 €1400 Untitled (18x13cm-7x5in) s.i.d.89 gouache ink. 25-Apr-4 Versailles Encheres #191 est:500-600

SUGHI, Alberto (1928-) Italian
£699 $1203 €1000 Neptune (37x58cm-15x23in) s. tempera paper. 3-Dec-3 Stadion, Trieste #1065/R
£874 $1503 €1250 Friends (50x71cm-20x28in) s. tempera mixed media paper on canvas. 3-Dec-3 Stadion, Trieste #989/R
£900 $1593 €1314 Couple (60x50cm-24x20in) s. 27-Apr-4 Bonhams, Knightsbridge #120/R
£1342 $2497 €2000 Starter (83x63cm-33x25in) s.i. oil W/C pastel card. 4-Mar-4 Babuino, Rome #95
£1458 $2304 €2100 Man and woman (50x70cm-20x28in) tempera card on on canvas painted 1998. 6-Sep-3 Meeting Art, Vercelli #676
£1538 $2615 €2200 Woman (51x35cm-20x14in) s. s.i.verso. 24-Nov-3 Christie's, Milan #99 est:2000-3000
£1812 $3352 €2700 Patio (70x50cm-28x20in) s.i. tempera paper on canvas. 13-Mar-4 Meeting Art, Vercelli #227 est:2500
£1972 $3273 €2800 Seated girl (70x50cm-28x20in) s. i.verso. 13-Jun-3 Farsetti, Prato #63/R
£2600 $4680 €3900 In the evening atthe yellow house (40x50cm-16x20in) s. painted 1992. 22-Apr-4 Finarte Semenzato, Rome #304/R est:3800-4200
£2685 $4966 €4000 Woman with boy (70x60cm-28x24in) s.d.1966. 11-Mar-4 Galleria Pace, Milan #142/R est:5000-6500
£2703 $4757 €4000 Lady with tidy hair (70x50cm-28x20in) s. painted 1975. 19-May-4 Il Ponte, Milan #1099 est:5000-6000
£2828 $4722 €4100 Figures at bar (50x70cm-20x28in) s. board. 13-Nov-3 Finarte Semenzato, Rome #310/R est:3000-3500
£2933 $5397 €4400 Girl at window (100x80cm-39x31in) s. on vellum. 12-Jun-4 Meeting Art, Vercelli #625/R est:4000
£2937 $4993 €4200 Untitled (70x50cm-28x20in) s. prov. 25-Nov-3 Sotheby's, Milan #6/R est:1500-2000
£3129 $5601 €4600 Portrait of man (70x49cm-28x19in) s. 16-Mar-4 Finarte Semenzato, Milan #244/R est:1700
£3310 $5528 €4800 Couple in landscape (40x50cm-16x20in) s. 13-Nov-3 Galleria Pace, Milan #61/R est:5000-6500
£3357 $5706 €4800 Car crash (70x120cm-28x47in) s. prov. exhib. 26-Nov-3 Pandolfini, Florence #63 est:5500-6000
£3467 $6240 €5200 Visiting the museum (38x60cm-15x24in) s. 22-Apr-4 Finarte Semenzato, Rome #222/R est:3800-4200
£3691 $6607 €5500 Composition with figures (100x130cm-39x51in) s. 25-May-4 Sotheby's, Milan #43/R est:6000
£4082 $7306 €6000 Man at cinema (65x45cm-26x18in) s. prov. 16-Mar-4 Finarte Semenzato, Milan #245/R est:1700
£4196 $7217 €6000 Man and woman (98x76cm-39x30in) s. s.i.verso oil mixed media. 3-Dec-3 Stadion, Trieste #993/R est:4000-5000
£4452 $7568 €6500 Figures (50x70cm-20x28in) s. painted 2000. 7-Nov-3 Galleria Rosenberg, Milan #62/R est:6500
£5634 $9352 €8000 Racconto Nero n.1 (80x60cm-31x24in) s. s.i.verso painted 1998. 14-Jun-3 Meeting Art, Vercelli #485/R est:8000

Works on paper
£336 $624 €500 The secret of waiting (40x30cm-16x12in) s.i. pencil. 4-Mar-4 Babuino, Rome #449
£541 $951 €800 Figures (90x60cm-35x24in) s. chl. 19-May-4 Il Ponte, Milan #1125
£733 $1327 €1100 Figures (60x56cm-24x22in) s. mixed media exec.1968. 2-Apr-4 Farsetti, Prato #247
£946 $1665 €1400 Pierrot (45x55cm-18x22in) s. mixed media. 19-May-4 Il Ponte, Milan #1118 est:1200-1400
£1067 $1963 €1600 Face of woman (50x35cm-20x14in) s. chl mixed media paper on canvas. 12-Jun-4 Meeting Art, Vercelli #262/R est:1000
£1074 $1997 €1600 Waiting at the bar (60x73cm-24x29in) s. 4-Mar-4 Babuino, Rome #59
£1319 $2085 €1900 Girl at table (70x50cm-28x20in) mixed media card on canvas. 6-Sep-3 Meeting Art, Vercelli #447 est:1500
£1931 $3090 €2800 Reclining figure (50x70cm-20x28in) s. mixed media paper on canvas. 13-Mar-3 Galleria Pace, Milan #148/R est:4000-5000
£1958 $3368 €2800 On the pillow (50x80cm-20x31in) s. mixed media on canvas. 3-Dec-3 Stadion, Trieste #1169/R est:800-1200
£2013 $3725 €3000 For Saint Giuliano (90x60cm-35x24in) s.i. chl tempera. 13-Mar-4 Meeting Art, Vercelli #258 est:3000
£2153 $3401 €3100 Figure in landscape (70x90cm-28x35in) pastel tempera paper on canvas exec.1988. 6-Sep-3 Meeting Art, Vercelli #705 est:2000

SUGIMOTO, Hiroshi (1948-) Japanese
Photographs
£3293 $5500 €4808 White Mantled Colobus (36x59cm-14x23in) s.i.d.1980 num.6/25 verso gelatin silver print. 20-Oct-3 Christie's, Rockefeller NY #253/R est:7000-9000
£4192 $7000 €6120 Palace, Pennsylvania (42x52cm-17x20in) s.i.d.1978 num.5/25 verso gelatin silver print. 20-Oct-3 Christie's, Rockefeller NY #251/R est:10000-15000
£4192 $7000 €6120 Palms, Detroit (42x51cm-17x20in) s.i.d.1980 num.5/25 verso gelatin silver print. 20-Oct-3 Christie's, Rockefeller NY #252/R est:10000-15000
£5090 $8500 €7431 Midland NY (51x61cm-20x24in) s.i.num.1/25 d.1976 gelatin silver print prov. 12-Nov-3 Christie's, Rockefeller NY #531/R est:10000-15000
£5389 $9000 €7868 Irish sea, Isle of Man II (51x61cm-20x24in) s.i.num.16/25 338 gelatin silver print prov. 13-Nov-3 Sotheby's, New York #497/R est:12000-18000
£5988 $10000 €8742 Sea of Japan, Rebun Island (51x61cm-20x24in) i.d.1996 num.461 gelatin silver print prov. 14-Nov-3 Phillips, New York #244/R est:12000-18000
£6587 $11000 €9617 VA Fox NY (51x61cm-20x24in) s.i.num.1/25 d.1976 verso gelatin silver print. 12-Nov-3 Christie's, Rockefeller NY #532/R est:10000-15000
£6667 $12000 €9734 Winnetka Drive in , Paramount (51x61cm-20x24in) i.d.1993 num.20/25 gelatin silver print. 23-Apr-4 Phillips, New York #9/R est:12000-18000
£7345 $13000 €10724 Dead Sea, En Gedi (43x54cm-17x21in) i.d.1992 num.10/25 and 375 photo. 28-Apr-4 Sotheby's, New York #235/R est:10000-20000
£7784 $13000 €11365 United Nations headquarters, New York (58x47cm-23x19in) s. gelatin silver print lit. 20-Oct-3 Christie's, Rockefeller NY #249/R est:10000-15000
£7784 $13000 €11365 Bay of Sagami, Atami (51x61cm-20x24in) s.i.d.1998 num.3/25 505 gelatin silver print prov.exhib. 13-Nov-3 Sotheby's, New York #496/R est:14000-18000
£7821 $14000 €11419 Proctor's Theatre New York (51x61cm-20x24in) s.i.d.1996 num.1/25 gelatin silver print board prov. 12-May-4 Christie's, Rockefeller NY #452/R est:12000-18000

£8000	$14560	€11680	Guggenheim Museum, Bilbao (61x49cm-24x19in) s. num.12/25 953 gelatin silver print prov.lit. 5-Feb-4 Christie's, London #208/R est:10000-15000
£8000	$14560	€11680	Lake Superior, Cascade river (42x54cm-17x21in) s.mount i.d.1995 num.14/25 gelatin silver print prov. 6-Feb-4 Sotheby's, London #270/R est:6000-8000
£8000	$14480	€11680	Simi Valley drive-in Simi Valley (48x56cm-19x22in) i.d.1993 gelatine silver print prov. 1-Apr-4 Christie's, Kensington #332/R est:8000-12000
£8500	$14195	€12410	Bay of Sagami, Atami (47x60cm-19x24in) impressed i.d.1997 num.3/25 gelatin silver print prov. 21-Oct-3 Sotheby's, London #311/R est:6000-8000
£8500	$15470	€12410	Civic, New Zealand (42x54cm-17x21in) s.mount i.d.1991 num.11/25 gelatin silver print prov. 6-Feb-4 Sotheby's, London #103/R est:6000-8000
£8696	$14261	€12000	Gulf of Bothnia (50x63cm-20x25in) num9/25 silver print. 30-May-3 Farsetti, Prato #414/R
£8982	$15000	€13114	Baltic sea (51x61cm-20x24in) i.d.1996 num.450 gelatin silver print prov. 14-Nov-3 Phillips, New York #208/R est:12000-18000
£8982	$15000	€13114	Orinda Theatre, Orinda (42x55cm-17x22in) s.i.d.1992 num.7/25 gelatin silver print prov. 17-Oct-3 Phillips, New York #24/R est:15000-20000
£9000	$16380	€13140	Polar bear (42x54cm-17x21in) s.mount i.d.1976 num.20/25 gelatin silver print prov.lit. 6-Feb-4 Sotheby's, London #280/R est:4000-6000
£9000	$16560	€13140	U A Little neck, New York (42x54cm-17x21in) impressed i.d.1977 num.1/25 gelatin silver print lit. 24-Jun-4 Sotheby's, London #107/R est:6000-8000
£9497	$17000	€13866	Ionian Sea, Santa Cesaria (51x61cm-20x24in) s. mount i.d.1993 num.5/25 424 gelatin silver print exhib. 13-May-4 Sotheby's, New York #395/R est:10000-15000
£9500	$17290	€13870	Sea of Japan Oki III (51x61cm-20x24in) s.i.d.1987 num.OKI III gelatin silver print prov. 5-Feb-4 Christie's, London #205/R est:7000-10000
£9605	$17000	€14023	Bay of Sagami, Atami (42x54cm-17x21in) i.d.1997 num.14/25 and 504 photo. 28-Apr-4 Sotheby's, New York #236/R est:10000-20000
£9605	$17000	€14023	Alhambra, San Francisco (42x54cm-17x21in) i.d.1992 num.7/25 and 237 photo. 28-Apr-4 Sotheby's, New York #237/R est:10000-20000
£10000	$18400	€14600	South Bay drive in, San Diego (47x60cm-19x24in) i.d.1993 num.17/25 gelatin silver print prov.lit. 25-Jun-4 Christie's, London #237/R est:8000-12000
£10180	$17000	€14863	Sea of Japan, Hokkaido I (51x61cm-20x24in) s.i.num.9/25 d.1988 verso gelatin silver print. 12-Nov-3 Christie's, Rockefeller NY #533/R est:10000-15000
£10615	$19000	€15498	Imperial - Montreal (51x61cm-20x24in) i.d.1995 num.3/25 257 gelatin silver print prov.lit. 13-May-4 Sotheby's, New York #329/R est:14000-18000
£11377	$19000	€16610	El Capitan, Hollywood (42x54cm-17x21in) s.i.d.1993 num.9/25 245 gelatin silver print prov. 20-Oct-3 Christie's, Rockefeller NY #250/R est:15000-20000
£11732	$21000	€17129	101 Drive-in, Ventura (51x61cm-20x24in) s.i.d.1993 num.714 gelatin silver print on paper prov.exhib. 14-May-4 Phillips, New York #176/R est:10000-15000
£12000	$20400	€17520	Tyrrhenian sea, Conca (42x54cm-17x21in) s.i.d.1994 s.i.dv. num5/25 gelatin silver print. 18-Nov-3 Christie's, Kensington #250/R est:8000-12000
£12000	$21840	€17520	Sea of Japan Rebun Island (50x63cm-20x25in) s. st.i. num.4/25 460 gelatin silver print exec 1996 lit. 5-Feb-4 Christie's, London #206/R est:7000-10000
£12291	$22000	€17945	Draken Goteborg (51x61cm-20x24in) s.i.d.2001 num.9.25 273 gelatin silver print on paper prov. 13-May-4 Sotheby's, New York #331/R est:12000-18000
£12575	$21000	€18360	Hi-way 39 drive in orange (47x58cm-19x23in) i.d.1993 num.715 gelatin silver print prov. 14-Nov-3 Phillips, New York #204/R est:12000-18000
£12575	$21000	€18360	Metropolitan state, Los Angeles (45x63cm-18x25in) i.d.1993 num.248 gelatin silver print prov.exhib.lit. 14-Nov-3 Phillips, New York #205/R est:12000-18000
£13408	$24000	€19576	Rockefeller Center (60x49cm-24x19in) s.num.5/25 gelatin silver print paper prov. 12-May-4 Christie's, Rockefeller NY #451/R est:12000-18000
£13473	$22500	€19671	Mediterannean sea, Crete II (51x61cm-20x24in) s.i.d.1990 num.2/25 347 gelatin silver print prov. 13-Nov-3 Sotheby's, New York #498/R est:12000-18000
£14000	$25760	€20440	Rosecrans drive-in, Paramount (42x54cm-17x21in) impressed i.d.1993 num 13/25 gelatin silver print prov.lit. 24-Jun-4 Sotheby's, London #108/R est:7000-9000
£14525	$26000	€21207	Regency, San Francisco (47x60cm-19x24in) s.i.d.1992 num.239 gelatin silver print on paperboard prov.exhib. 14-May-4 Phillips, New York #175/R est:15000-20000
£16000	$29120	€23360	Compton Drive-In, Compton (42x54cm-17x21in) s.mount i.d.1994 num.12/25 gelatin silver print prov.lit. 6-Feb-4 Sotheby's, London #104/R est:7000-9000
£19553	$35000	€28547	Cinerama Dome - Hollywood (51x61cm-20x24in) i.d.1993 num.5.25 250 gelatin silver print prov.lit. 13-May-4 Sotheby's, New York #330/R est:12000-18000
£19553	$35000	€28547	Proctors Theatre New York (48x57cm-19x22in) s.i.d.1996 num.10/25 gelatin silver print lit. 13-May-4 Sotheby's, New York #332/R est:12000-18000
£19553	$35000	€28547	Brooklyn Bridge (83x66cm-33x26in) s.num.12/25 gelatin silver print paper prov.exhib. 12-May-4 Christie's, Rockefeller NY #450/R est:15000-20000
£23952	$40000	€34970	El Capitan Hollywood (51x61cm-20x24in) s.i.d.1993 num. gelatin silver print edition of 25 prov.exhib.lit. 13-Nov-3 Sotheby's, New York #439/R est:15000-20000
£25449	$42500	€37156	Chrysler building, William van Alen (61x51cm-24x20in) gelatin silver print edition of 25 prov.exhib. 13-Nov-3 Sotheby's, New York #436/R est:18000-22000
£78212	$140000	€114190	Chrysler Building (182x152cm-72x60in) gelatin silver print paper edition 2 of 5 prov.exhib. 12-May-4 Christie's, Rockefeller NY #449/R est:50000-70000

SUGITO, Hiroshi (20th C) Japanese?

£7362	$12000	€10749	Enter (142x218cm-56x86in) s.i.d.1996-97 verso acrylic pigment prov. 23-Sep-3 Christie's, Rockefeller NY #84/R est:8000-12000

SUHR, Christoph (1771-1842) German

£4514	$7358	€6500	Portrait of brothers and sisters (130x101cm-51x40in) s.i.d.1814. 25-Sep-3 Dr Fritz Nagel, Stuttgart #1426/R est:8000

SUHRLANDT, Carl (1828-1919) German

£2000	$3640	€3000	Prussian soldiers in a battle (64x84cm-25x33in) s. 1-Jul-4 Van Ham, Cologne #1637/R est:3500
£8287	$15000	€12099	Dandie Dinmonts, Weasel, Mr Mustard and Pepper (63x97cm-25x38in) s.i.d.1885. 30-Mar-4 Bonhams & Butterfields, San Francisco #62/R est:15000-20000

SUHS, Josef (19/20th C) ?

£786	$1431	€1148	The shrine of Venus (82x35cm-32x14in) s. 16-Jun-4 Fischer, Luzern #1224/R (S.FR 1800)

SUINER, Max (19/20th C) German?

£369	$679	€550	Group of men. 26-Mar-4 Karrenbauer, Konstanz #1775/R est:550

SUIRE, Herman von le (1861-1926) German

£1959	$3507	€2900	Chiemsee shore on summer's day (50x76cm-20x30in) s.i. 6-May-4 Michael Zeller, Lindau #756/R est:2400

SUISHO, Nishiyama (1879-1958) Japanese

Works on paper

£930	$1600	€1358	Spring. Autumn (128x26cm-50x10in) s. ink col on silk pair. 2-Dec-3 Christie's, Rockefeller NY #235/R est:2000-3000

SUISSE, Gaston (1896-1988) French

£1678	$2970	€2500	Tanagras dans les orchidees (35x16cm-14x6in) s. panel painted 1939. 27-Apr-4 Claude Aguttes, Neuilly #39/R est:1800-2300
£2053	$3736	€3100	Oiseau dans les branchages (69x33cm-27x13in) s. lacquer panel. 19-Jun-4 St-Germain-en-Laye Encheres #166/R est:2000-3000
£2349	$4158	€3500	Ecureuils (70x40cm-28x16in) panel. 3-May-4 Giraudeau, Tours #46
£4336	$7371	€6200	Oiseaux et cactees (149x50cm-59x20in) s. panel. 28-Nov-3 Drouot Estimations, Paris #79/R est:5000-6000
£6081	$10703	€9000	Colins de Virginie (44x55cm-17x22in) s. panel prov. 18-May-4 Christie's, Paris #20/R est:4000-6000
£25175	$42797	€36000	Paysage (100x200cm-39x79in) s. 18-Nov-3 Sotheby's, Paris #92/R est:20000-25000

Works on paper

£333	$613	€500	Boa (36x46cm-14x18in) s. chl col crayon. 10-Jun-4 Camard, Paris #140
£400	$736	€600	Chimpanze (20x14cm-8x6in) s. graphite. 10-Jun-4 Camard, Paris #137
£426	$711	€600	Jeunes merles (21x36cm-8x14in) s. pencil chl oil pastel lit. 12-Oct-3 St-Germain-en-Laye Encheres #98/R
£600	$1104	€900	Panthere noire (26x17cm-10x7in) s. graphite. 10-Jun-4 Camard, Paris #138
£629	$1151	€950	Anhinga branche (21x26cm-8x10in) s. crayon Chinese ink htd W/C. 7-Apr-4 Maigret, Paris #2/R
£629	$1151	€950	Zebu agenouille (23x28cm-9x11in) s. crayon htd pastel. 7-Apr-4 Maigret, Paris #1/R
£733	$1349	€1100	Tigre (17x26cm-7x10in) s. graphite htd white chk. 10-Jun-4 Camard, Paris #139
£745	$1244	€1050	Garulax (38x20cm-15x8in) s. chk pencil wax pastel exec.c.1940 exhib.lit. 12-Oct-3 St-Germain-en-Laye Encheres #93/R
£759	$1267	€1100	Jeune merle (23x16cm-9x6in) mono. crayon. 14-Nov-3 Claude Boisgirard, Paris #24/R
£828	$1514	€1200	Zebu (22x31cm-9x12in) s. Wolf wax crayon. 28-Jan-4 Piasa, Paris #17/R
£897	$1497	€1300	Mouflon (12x12cm-5x5in) mono. crayon. 14-Nov-3 Claude Boisgirard, Paris #23/R
£1014	$1814	€1500	Taureau (31x24cm-12x9in) s. wax crayon. 5-May-4 Claude Boisgirard, Paris #23 est:800-1000
£1034	$1728	€1500	Aigles branches (28x22cm-11x9in) s. crayon pastel lit. 14-Nov-3 Claude Boisgirard, Paris #22/R est:1200-1500
£1208	$2138	€1800	Lion couche (15x28cm-6x11in) s. crayon. 27-Apr-4 Claude Aguttes, Neuilly #40/R est:1200
£1342	$2161	€2000	Les huppes (43x36cm-17x14in) s. pastel gold background. 23-Feb-3 St-Germain-en-Laye Encheres #117/R est:1800
£1467	$2699	€2200	Poissons rouges (57x16cm-22x6in) s. chl col crayon dr. 11-Jun-4 Piasa, Paris #10 est:1500-2000
£1517	$2534	€2200	Tigre couche (15x23cm-6x9in) s. crayon. 14-Nov-3 Claude Boisgirard, Paris #21/R est:1500-2000
£1554	$2782	€2300	Jeune merle branche (40x19cm-16x7in) s. chl chk lit. 5-May-4 Claude Boisgirard, Paris #25/R est:1500-2000
£1554	$2782	€2300	Merle branche (40x19cm-16x7in) s. chl chk lit. 5-May-4 Claude Boisgirard, Paris #24/R est:2000-2500
£1745	$3089	€2600	Ignicolores (70x31cm-28x12in) s. pastel oil exhib.lit. 27-Apr-4 Claude Aguttes, Neuilly #41/R est:2500-3000
£1748	$2972	€2500	Lion couche (13x20cm-5x8in) s. crayon. 27-Nov-3 Claude Aguttes, Neuilly #58 est:800-1000
£1800	$3312	€2700	Couple de fennecs (44x48cm-17x19in) s.d.1925 sanguine dr. 8-Jun-4 Camard, Paris #17/R est:2000-2500
£1867	$3435	€2800	Oiseaux branches (50x26cm-20x10in) s. chl col crayon. 11-Jun-4 Piasa, Paris #8/R
£1888	$3248	€2700	Faisans (40x110cm-16x43in) s. pastel oil. 3-Dec-3 Coutau Begarie, Paris #104 est:2000-2500
£2267	$4171	€3400	Singe dormant (27x20cm-11x8in) s. wax crayon dr. 11-Jun-4 Piasa, Paris #9 est:1200-1500
£2308	$3923	€3300	Ignicolor et hirondelle de chine (34x32cm-13x13in) s. pastel oil. 24-Nov-3 Tajan, Paris #23/R est:2000-2500
£2551	$4566	€3800	Ecureuils roux (53x33cm-21x13in) s.d.1935 pastel oil. 27-May-4 Tajan, Paris #26/R est:3000-3500
£2800	$5012	€4200	Colins de Virginie, rossignol et moineaux (50x98cm-20x39in) s. pastel oil. 12-May-4 Coutau Begarie, Paris #180/R est:2000-3000

SUIZL, Louis (?) French?

£804	$1383	€1150	Loix, Ile de Re (46x55cm-18x22in) s.i. panel. 2-Dec-3 Claude Aguttes, Neuilly #14

SUKER, Arthur (1857-?) British

£1500	$2505	€2190	Off the rocks (126x101cm-50x40in) mono. 11-Nov-3 Bonhams, Knightsbridge #92/R est:1000-1500

Works on paper

£260	$411	€377	Moorland Tors (29x47cm-11x19in) s. W/C. 2-Sep-3 Bristol Auction Rooms #547/R
£270	$491	€394	West country coast (48x74cm-19x29in) s. W/C. 15-Jun-4 David Lay, Penzance #615
£280	$456	€409	On the River Dart Devon (23x34cm-9x13in) s. pencil W/C. 25-Sep-3 Mellors & Kirk, Nottingham #726
£280	$510	€409	Lizard (41x70cm-16x28in) s. W/C. 21-Jun-4 Bonhams, Bath #406
£300	$561	€438	Coastal scene, Sark (35x68cm-14x27in) s. wash. 22-Jul-4 Martel Maides, Guernsey #204
£400	$680	€584	Summers day on the river Lune (46x34cm-18x13in) s. pencil W/C prov. 19-Nov-3 Tennants, Leyburn #977
£560	$1030	€818	Shafts of sunlight over the sea (54x89cm-21x35in) s. W/C. 23-Mar-4 Anderson & Garland, Newcastle #269/R
£580	$1073	€870	Coastal scene (48x74cm-19x29in) s. W/C. 15-Jul-4 Rendalls, Ashburton #1896
£700	$1211	€1022	St Michael's Mount, Cornwall evening in Mount's Bay, with fishing boats (28x46cm-11x18in) s. W/C htd white. 11-Dec-3 Neales, Nottingham #519/R

SUKHOROVSKY, Martsely Gavrilovich (1840-1908) Russian

£14000	$23800	€21000	Portrait of lady (39x30cm-15x12in) s. board. 25-Nov-3 Christie's, London #163/R est:10000-15000

SUKKERT, Adolf (19th C) German
£4014 $6423 €5700 Venice, St Maria della Salute in evening sunshine (65x80cm-26x31in) s.d.1858. 18-Sep-3 Rieber, Stuttgart #856/R est:1200

SUKOKU, Ko (1730-1804) Japanese
Works on paper
£408 $750 €596 Dancing puppeteer and child (72x25cm-28x10in) s. ink hanging scroll. 23-Mar-4 Christie's, Rockefeller NY #102/R

SULLIVAN, William (20th C) American
£464 $850 €696 Rapidan - Criglersville Road (51x137cm-20x54in) 10-Jul-4 Hindman, Chicago #522/R est:500-700

SULLIVAN, William Holmes (?-1908) British
£2500 $4250 €3650 King Lear and the fool (93x71cm-37x28in) s.d.1877. 25-Nov-3 Christie's, London #183/R est:3000-5000
£3000 $4770 €4380 Tender Chord (44x29cm-17x11in) s.d.1890 i.verso. 18-Mar-3 Anderson & Garland, Newcastle #552/R est:3000-5000

SULLY, Frank (20th C) British
£280 $496 €409 Blue bird and fruit (45x55cm-18x22in) s. board. 27-Apr-4 Bonhams, Knightsbridge #224/R

SULLY, Thomas (1783-1872) American/British
£1676 $3000 €2447 Theatrical studies (23x15cm-9x6in) paper on board pair. 6-May-4 Shannon's, Milford #203/R est:3000-5000
£2793 $5000 €4078 Sisters (30x25cm-12x10in) oil paper. 6-May-4 Shannon's, Milford #205/R est:5000-7000
£3297 $6000 €4814 Portrait of Susan Hall (51x43cm-20x17in) s.d.1837 board prov. 29-Jun-4 Sotheby's, New York #183/R est:8000-12000
£4891 $9000 €7141 Portrait of a lady believed to be Marion French (61x51cm-24x20in) prov. 27-Jun-4 Freeman, Philadelphia #71/R est:8000-12000
£5028 $9000 €8442 Portrait of Lord Byron (74x61cm-29x24in) init.d.1839. 20-Mar-4 Pook & Pook, Downington #574/R est:4000-6000
£8333 $15000 €12166 Portrait of Thomas Livezey (38x48cm-15x19in) init.d.1826 canvas on canvas prov.lit. 24-Apr-4 Freeman, Philadelphia #318/R est:12000-18000
£9605 $17000 €14023 Portrait of Fanny Kemble (76x64cm-30x25in) mono. 27-Apr-4 Doyle, New York #30/R est:8000-12000
£27273 $48000 €39819 Portrait of Mrs C Ford (48x38cm-19x15in) init.d.1830 canvas on panel prov.lit. 18-May-4 Christie's, Rockefeller NY #9/R est:40000-60000
£28409 $50000 €41477 Mr and Mrs Hamilton (76x61cm-30x24in) init.d.1850 verso oval pair prov.lit. 19-May-4 Sotheby's, New York #99/R est:20000-30000
£48864 $86000 €71341 Self portrait (76x62cm-30x24in) mono.i.d.June 1850 prov.exhib.lit. 18-May-4 Christie's, Rockefeller NY #8/R est:30000-50000
Works on paper
£240 $400 €350 Figure in an interior (8x8cm-3x3in) W/C prov. 29-Jun-3 William Jenack, New York #135
£1512 $2600 €2208 View of the Schuylkill River (10x18cm-4x7in) s. W/C ink. 6-Dec-3 Pook & Pook, Downington #251/R est:1000-1500

SULLY, Thomas (attrib) (1783-1872) American/British
£1216 $2250 €1775 Portrait of young child (48x42cm-19x17in) oval prov. 18-Jan-4 Bonhams & Butterfields, Los Angeles #7016a/R est:1500-2500
£5682 $10000 €8296 Portrait of George Frederick Cooke (79x64cm-31x25in) painted 1811 prov. 23-May-4 Hindman, Chicago #127/R est:10000-20000
£8235 $14000 €12023 Girl in red dress with a dog (76x64cm-30x25in) prov. 18-Nov-3 Doyle, New York #30/R est:6000-8000

SULTAN, Donald (1951-) American
£800 $1448 €1168 Wall flowers (21x29cm-8x11in) init.i.d.Jan 18 1994 tempera on paper prov. 1-Apr-4 Christie's, Kensington #284/R est:1000-1500
£2703 $5000 €3946 Black eggs and tomatoes (32x33cm-13x13in) init.i.d.98 oil tar plaster over wood panel. 12-Feb-4 Sotheby's, New York #322/R est:8000-12000
£4335 $7500 €6329 Iris (124x123cm-49x48in) i.d.1981 tar oil vinyl on wood prov. 10-Dec-3 Phillips, New York #468/R est:3000-5000
£4865 $9000 €7103 Cigarette with smoke ring (122x122cm-48x48in) init.i.verso linoleum tile oil spackle compound tar wood prov. 12-Feb-4 Sotheby's, New York #257/R est:8000-12000
£5000 $9100 €7300 Three peaches and two melons (32x34cm-13x13in) init.i.d.July 21 1988 tar panel sold with two chl and one ink 4. 4-Feb-4 Sotheby's, Olympia #6/R est:5000-7000
£10778 $18000 €15736 Three pears (33x32cm-13x13in) init.i.d.May 12 1989 verso oil tar panel prov. 13-Nov-3 Sotheby's, New York #148/R est:8000-12000
Prints
£1695 $3000 €2475 Four red flowers (70x91cm-28x36in) init. num.5/40 woodcut. 30-Apr-4 Sotheby's, New York #501/R est:2000-3000
£1977 $3500 €2886 Six red flowers October 28 1999 (71x90cm-28x35in) init.i. num.3/40 woodcut. 30-Apr-4 Sotheby's, New York #502/R est:2000-3000
£2119 $3750 €3094 Four blue flowers May 19 1999 (70x91cm-28x36in) init.i. num.3/40 woodcut. 30-Apr-4 Sotheby's, New York #503/R est:2000-3000
£2353 $4000 €3435 Black lemons and egg (161x124cm-63x49in) s.i.d.1987 aquatint. 4-Nov-3 Christie's, Rockefeller NY #352/R est:3000-5000
£3529 $6000 €5152 Black lemon (156x119cm-61x47in) init.i. aquatint. 31-Oct-3 Sotheby's, New York #787/R
£3529 $6000 €5152 Black eggs and roses (173x175cm-68x69in) init. col woodcut. 31-Oct-3 Sotheby's, New York #791/R
£4412 $7500 €6442 Six yellows July 24 (58x78cm-23x31in) init. col screenprint. 31-Oct-3 Sotheby's, New York #792/R
£5367 $9500 €7836 Untitled (160x370cm-63x146in) ini.i.d.1987 num.5 verso col aquatint print 6 panel screen. 28-Apr-4 Christie's, Rockefeller NY #422/R est:10000-15000
Works on paper
£1156 $2000 €1688 Three cigarettes (22x15cm-9x6in) init.i.d.1997 pen ink gouache prov. 10-Dec-3 Phillips, New York #467/R est:3000-4000
£2162 $4000 €3157 Doughy relief (144x144cm-57x57in) s.i.d.1988 stretcher latex tar canvas prov. 13-Jul-4 Christie's, Rockefeller NY #84/R est:6000-8000
£4670 $8500 €6818 Three black eggs (152x122cm-60x48in) init.i.d.Oct 21 1988 chl prov. 29-Jun-4 Sotheby's, New York #590/R est:5000-7000
£5220 $9500 €7621 Black lemons July 30 1985 (127x96cm-50x38in) init.i. chl prov. 29-Jun-4 Sotheby's, New York #561/R est:8000-12000
£5946 $11000 €8681 Black lemons March 19 1985 (127x96cm-50x38in) init.i. chl prov. 12-Feb-4 Sotheby's, New York #255/R est:8000-12000

SULZER, Julius von (1818-1889) Swiss
£326 $554 €476 Portrait of boy with dog before lake landscape (24x18cm-9x7in) s. panel. 19-Nov-3 Fischer, Luzern #2316 (S.FR 720)

SUMIDA, Gregory (20th C) American?
Works on paper
£407 $700 €594 Innuit wearing tov'toka (27x37cm-11x15in) s.i. gouache on board. 3-Dec-3 Doyle, New York #252/R

SUMMERS, Robert (1940-) American
£1912 $3250 €2792 Great job (23x30cm-9x12in) s.d.1998 board prov. 1-Nov-3 Santa Fe Art, Santa Fe #102/R est:3000-4000
Sculpture
£1176 $2000 €1717 Buffalo soldier (335cm-132in) bronze. 1-Nov-3 Altermann Galleries, Santa Fe #14
£1397 $2500 €2040 Spirit of the West (41cm-16in) bronze edn of 40. 15-May-4 Altermann Galleries, Santa Fe #96/R

SUMNER, Laura W Y (20th C) American
£441 $700 €644 Passengers and drivers (35x25cm-14x10in) 12-Sep-3 Skinner, Boston #480/R

SUMNER, Maud (1902-1985) South African
£647 $1080 €945 Desert landscape (90x70cm-35x28in) s. 20-Oct-3 Stephan Welz, Johannesburg #409 est:8000-12000 (SA.R 7500)
£690 $1152 €1007 Dune landscape (22x60cm-9x24in) s. 20-Oct-3 Stephan Welz, Johannesburg #576 est:2500-4000 (SA.R 8000)
£940 $1598 €1372 Sunrise over water (59x80cm-23x31in) s. 4-Nov-3 Stephan Welz, Johannesburg #824 est:8000-10000 (SA.R 11000)
£1638 $2735 €2391 Mystica, young woman (65x54cm-26x21in) s. 20-Oct-3 Stephan Welz, Johannesburg #265/R est:20000-30000 (SA.R 19000)
£1817 $3252 €2653 Nightscape of a village over the trees (49x64cm-19x25in) s. 31-May-4 Stephan Welz, Johannesburg #530/R est:15000-20000 (SA.R 22000)
£2946 $5421 €4301 Still life of fruit with jug (41x48cm-16x19in) board. 8-Jun-4 Dales, Durban #7 (SA.R 35000)
£3448 $5759 €5034 Thames (52x63cm-20x25in) s. 20-Oct-3 Stephan Welz, Johannesburg #301/R est:25000-35000 (SA.R 40000)
Works on paper
£537 $961 €784 Bay (46x59cm-18x23in) pen W/C. 31-May-4 Stephan Welz, Johannesburg #129 (SA.R 6500)
£598 $1017 €873 Village in Warwickshire (46x60cm-18x24in) s. pen ink W/C. 4-Nov-3 Stephan Welz, Johannesburg #686/R est:7000-10000 (SA.R 7000)
£637 $1096 €930 Winter landscape with ice skaters (46x61cm-18x24in) W/C. 3-Dec-3 Stephan Welz, Johannesburg #33 est:3000-5000 (SA.R 7000)
£728 $1252 €1063 Winter landscape (46x61cm-18x24in) s. W/C. 3-Dec-3 Stephan Welz, Johannesburg #32/R est:5000-8000 (SA.R 8000)
£784 $1404 €1145 Two bridges on the Thames (43x61cm-17x24in) s. pen W/C. 31-May-4 Stephan Welz, Johannesburg #483/R (SA.R 9500)
£991 $1774 €1447 Thames (45x62cm-18x24in) s. pen W/C. 31-May-4 Stephan Welz, Johannesburg #484 (SA.R 12000)

SUN KEHONG (1532-1610) Chinese
Works on paper
£10669 $19203 €15577 Haiyue studio (28x121cm-11x48in) s.i. d.1594 ink col handscroll. 25-Apr-4 Christie's, Hong Kong #333/R est:70000-90000 (HK.D 150000)

SUN KEHONG (attrib) (1532-1610) Chinese
Works on paper
£559 $962 €800 Four birds on an autumn branch (136x44cm-54x17in) i. ink silk hanging scroll. 5-Dec-3 Lempertz, Koln #235/R

SUN QUA (c.1830-1870) Chinese
Works on paper
£16500 $26895 €24090 View of Mount Erskine and Pulo Ticoose Bay, Prince of Wales Island (51x65cm-20x26in) i. W/C after William Daniell prov. 25-Sep-3 Christie's, London #465/R est:3000-5000

SUN RIXIAO (20th C) Chinese
Works on paper
£377 $640 €550 Rain in Jialing (56x38cm-22x15in) s.d.1978 Indian ink col. 7-Nov-3 Dr Fritz Nagel, Stuttgart #962/R

SUN YU (19th C) Chinese
Works on paper
£2098 $3608 €3000 Mountain landscape with craggy rocks, waterfall and footpath (270x97cm-106x38in) s.i. ink hanging scroll. 5-Dec-3 Lempertz, Koln #242/R est:2900

SUNARYO (20th C) Indonesian
£6022 $9634 €8792 Kandang burung (75x75cm-30x30in) s.d.99. 18-May-3 Sotheby's, Singapore #182/R est:12000-15000 (S.D 16800)
Works on paper
£2778 $5028 €4056 Legong dancer (55x55cm-22x22in) s.d.94 mixed media canvas. 3-Apr-4 Glerum, Singapore #48/R est:5000-7000 (S.D 8500)

£3922 $7098 €5726 Kupu Kupu (75x75cm-30x30in) s.d.99 mixed media canvas. 3-Apr-4 Glerum, Singapore #43/R est:12000-15000 (S.D 12000)

SUNARYO, Edi (1951-) Indonesian
£1319 $2203 €1926 Imagi Setitiga (100x120cm-39x47in) s.d.2000. 12-Oct-3 Sotheby's, Singapore #194/R est:3000-4000 (S.D 3800)

SUNDBLAD, Fanny (1858-1918) Finnish
£1867 $3341 €2800 Cabin life (41x44cm-16x17in) s.d.1887 canvas on board. 15-May-4 Hagelstam, Helsinki #94/R est:3000

SUNDBLOM, Haddon Hubbard (1899-1976) American
£2096 $3500 €3060 Boy with sword kneeling on couch (84x79cm-33x31in) s.verso. 15-Nov-3 Illustration House, New York #162/R est:6000-9000
£3352 $6000 €4894 Couple at banister surrounded by flowers (94x76cm-37x30in) 15-May-4 Illustration House, New York #120/R est:5000-7000
£11976 $20000 €17485 Woman amidst tree branches watches man depart (89x71cm-35x28in) s. 15-Nov-3 Illustration House, New York #121/R est:25000-35000
£25946 $48000 €37881 Coca Cola Santa (122x96cm-48x38in) lit. 11-Mar-4 Christie's, Rockefeller NY #87/R est:20000-30000

SUNDBYE, Nina (1944-) Norwegian
Sculpture
£1022 $1758 €1492 Per Aabel as Jean de France (46x20x20cm-18x8x8in) s.d.96 num.2/7 on socle. 8-Dec-3 Blomqvist, Oslo #531/R est:25000-35000 (N.KR 12000)

SUNDELL, Thure (1864-1924) Finnish
£1000 $1790 €1500 Coastal landscape with large rocks (24x34cm-9x13in) s. canvas on board. 15-May-4 Hagelstam, Helsinki #88/R est:1500
£1389 $2319 €2000 Winter landscape (33x45cm-13x18in) s. 23-Oct-3 Hagelstam, Helsinki #851 est:1200
£1549 $2680 €2200 Winter landscape (23x31cm-9x12in) s. 13-Dec-3 Hagelstam, Helsinki #122/R est:1500
£1972 $3411 €2800 Landscape, Narpes (30x20cm-12x8in) s. 13-Dec-3 Hagelstam, Helsinki #121/R est:1500
£2958 $5117 €4200 Kasko harbour (32x45cm-13x18in) s. 13-Dec-3 Hagelstam, Helsinki #123/R est:2000
£4595 $8224 €6800 Coastal landscape from Kaskot area (56x92cm-22x36in) s. 8-May-4 Bukowskis, Helsinki #141/R est:5000-6000
£4930 $8528 €7000 Evening landscape (58x88cm-23x35in) s. 13-Dec-3 Hagelstam, Helsinki #120/R est:5000

SUNDERLAND, Thomas (1744-1828) British
Works on paper
£450 $752 €657 View of Goldsbro Grounds, Yorkshire, from the house (22x29cm-9x11in) pencil pen black ink wash exhib. 16-Oct-3 Christie's, Kensington #24/R
£500 $920 €730 Lake Windermere from Curwen's Island (24x35cm-9x14in) pencil pen ink grey wash prov. 23-Mar-4 Bonhams, Knightsbridge #165/R
£3600 $6552 €5256 Lake District view with a fisherman (34x48cm-13x19in) W/C over pencil. 1-Jul-4 Sotheby's, London #202/R est:1500-2000

SUNDSTROM, Harriet (1872-1961) Swedish
£420 $713 €600 Fishing huts (40x32cm-16x13in) s. lit. 28-Nov-3 Schloss Ahlden, Ahlden #1503/R

SUNDT-HANSEN, Carl (1841-1907) Norwegian
Works on paper
£28022 $50160 €40912 Girl seated on chair by the weave (50x66cm-20x26in) s.d.1886 pastel paper on canvas lit. 22-Mar-4 Blomqvist, Oslo #325/R est:100000-120000 (N.KR 350000)

SUNDT-OHLSEN, Thoralv (1884-1948) Norwegian
£450 $824 €657 Ice thawing, Grondola (53x48cm-21x19in) s. canvas on panel. 2-Feb-4 Blomqvist, Lysaker #1298 (N.KR 5600)

SUNER, Francisco (1925-) Spanish
£1678 $3121 €2500 Man holding tray (81x65cm-32x26in) s. 2-Mar-4 Ansorena, Madrid #832/R est:2500

SUNESSON, Stina (1925-1998) Swedish
Works on paper
£1183 $2117 €1727 A day in spring (18x22cm-7x9in) s. gouache. 26-May-4 AB Stockholms Auktionsverk #2304/R est:12000-15000 (S.KR 16000)
£1330 $2381 €1942 Flowering time (20x25cm-8x10in) s.i. gouache. 26-May-4 AB Stockholms Auktionsverk #2326/R est:20000-25000 (S.KR 18000)
£1552 $2778 €2266 Apple tree in blossom (20x24cm-8x9in) s. gouache. 25-May-4 Bukowskis, Stockholm #133/R est:15000-18000 (S.KR 21000)

SUNYER, Joachim (1875-1956) Spanish
£6000 $10200 €8760 Girl at mirror (46x38cm-18x15in) s. prov.lit. 18-Nov-3 Sotheby's, London #222/R
£11594 $19014 €16000 Desnudo en el campo (46x38cm-18x15in) s. 27-May-3 Durán, Madrid #183/R est:15000
£15862 $26331 €23000 Field (47x63cm-19x25in) s. painted 1890 prov. 30-Sep-3 Ansorena, Madrid #88/R est:23000
£120000 $204000 €175200 Mountains in Sitges (96x121cm-38x48in) s. prov.lit. 18-Nov-3 Sotheby's, London #211/R
Works on paper
£2098 $3503 €3000 Small village on the hill (31x44cm-12x17in) s. gouache. 29-Jun-3 Eric Pillon, Calais #221/R

SUPANCHICH, Konrad von (1858-1935) Hungarian
Works on paper
£317 $526 €450 Fishing boats off Venice (34x40cm-13x16in) s.d.1912 pastel chk board. 12-Jun-3 Dorotheum, Graz #144/R

SUPISICHE, Ricardo (1912-1992) Argentinian
£1381 $2500 €2016 Jockey (50x75cm-20x30in) 30-Mar-4 Arroyo, Buenos Aires #26
£2123 $3800 €3100 Women chatting (50x75cm-20x30in) s.d.967. 4-May-4 Arroyo, Buenos Aires #62/R est:3200
£2235 $4000 €3263 Couple talking (50x75cm-20x30in) s.d.968 i.verso. 4-May-4 Arroyo, Buenos Aires #63/R est:3200
£3799 $6800 €5547 Women on the seashore (50x75cm-20x30in) s.d.966. 4-May-4 Arroyo, Buenos Aires #61/R est:3200
£4696 $8500 €6856 Woman (100x70cm-39x28in) 30-Mar-4 Arroyo, Buenos Aires #86
Works on paper
£615 $1100 €898 Figure in landscape (34x47cm-13x19in) W/C. 11-May-4 Arroyo, Buenos Aires #96

SUPPANTSCHITSCH, Max (1865-1953) Austrian
Works on paper
£483 $801 €700 Wachau street (28x22cm-11x9in) s. mixed media. 30-Sep-3 Dorotheum, Vienna #306/R
£789 $1453 €1200 Idyllic landscape (20x36cm-8x14in) mono.d.1900 mixed media. 22-Jun-4 Wiener Kunst Auktionen, Vienna #215/R
£1379 $2290 €2000 Narrow street in Emmersdorf/Wachau (19x25cm-7x10in) s. W/C. 30-Sep-3 Dorotheum, Vienna #278/R est:2000-2400
£2069 $3434 €3000 Durnstein in Wachau (18x29cm-7x11in) s.d.29 W/C. 30-Sep-3 Dorotheum, Vienna #279/R est:2400-2800

SUPRIA, Dede Eri (1956-) Indonesian
£2604 $4349 €3802 Business Clown (69x79cm-27x31in) s.d.2001. 12-Oct-3 Sotheby's, Singapore #193/R est:6000-8000 (S.D 7500)
£2614 $4732 €3816 Unvealing the mask (100x70cm-39x28in) s.d.2001. 3-Apr-4 Glerum, Singapore #58/R est:8000-10000 (S.D 8000)
£3623 $5616 €5290 Clown (115x121cm-45x48in) s.d.2000. 6-Oct-2 Sotheby's, Singapore #187/R est:10000-12000 (S.D 10000)
£3986 $6178 €5820 Dancer (100x120cm-39x47in) s.d.2001. 6-Oct-2 Sotheby's, Singapore #179/R est:1000-12000 (S.D 11000)
£8602 $13763 €12559 Surf back to Bali (110x90cm-43x35in) s.d.2002. 18-May-3 Sotheby's, Singapore #194/R est:12000-15000 (S.D 24000)

SURAND, Gustave (1860-1937) French
£420 $701 €613 Female nude in a landscape (40x23cm-16x9in) s.i.d.1887 panel. 7-Oct-3 Bonhams, Knightsbridge #119/R
£430 $788 €650 Lion et femme morte (46x65cm-18x26in) s.i.d.1909. 7-Apr-4 Piasa, Paris #57
£568 $1033 €829 Red haired nude. Study for a mythological scene (33x26cm-13x10in) s. cardboard double-sided. 16-Jun-4 Fischer, Luzern #2394/R (S.FR 1300)
£2400 $4416 €3600 Tigre rugissant (32x40cm-13x16in) s.i.d.1932. 11-Jun-4 Claude Aguttes, Neuilly #32/R est:3000-4000
£2887 $4995 €4100 Tigre rugissant (46x61cm-18x24in) s. 10-Dec-3 Rossini, Paris #111/R
Works on paper
£600 $1104 €900 Elephant (30x37cm-12x15in) s.i. W/C. 11-Jun-4 Claude Aguttes, Neuilly #34/R
£867 $1595 €1300 Lion couche (27x41cm-11x16in) s.i.d.1932 pastel. 11-Jun-4 Claude Aguttes, Neuilly #33/R

SURBEK, Victor (1885-1975) Swiss
£441 $749 €644 Field flowers with blossoming cherry tree (65x100cm-26x39in) s. i.verso. 7-Nov-3 Dobiaschofsky, Bern #149/R (S.FR 1000)
£485 $824 €708 Wooded landscape with small wooden bridge (23x39cm-9x15in) s. i. verso panel. 7-Nov-3 Dobiaschofsky, Bern #147/R (S.FR 1100)
£837 $1423 €1222 Garden with poppies (75x51cm-30x20in) s. i. verso. 7-Nov-3 Dobiaschofsky, Bern #148/R (S.FR 1900)
£2172 $3692 €3171 Bernese landscape (96x110cm-38x43in) s.d.1908. 25-Nov-3 Germann, Zurich #101/R est:5000-8000 (S.FR 4800)
Works on paper
£333 $533 €483 Arth-Goldau am Rigi (48x62cm-19x24in) s.i.138 W/C Indian ink. 15-May-3 Stuker, Bern #1518 (S.FR 700)
£661 $1123 €965 Farmstead (46x61cm-18x24in) s.i.d.1938 Indian ink brush wash. 5-Nov-3 Dobiaschofsky, Bern #996/R (S.FR 1500)

SURDI, Luigi (1897-1959) Italian
£336 $594 €500 Still life with watermelon (51x63cm-20x25in) s.d.1942 board. 1-May-4 Meeting Art, Vercelli #438
£347 $621 €520 Portrait of woman with hat (42x34cm-17x13in) s. 13-May-4 Babuino, Rome #542
£400 $720 €600 Vase with chrysanthemums (64x52cm-25x20in) s.d.42 board. 22-Apr-4 Finarte Semenzato, Rome #258

SUREAU (20th C) French
£1035 $1852 €1511 Still life of flowers and fruit (54x48cm-21x19in) s. 25-May-4 Bukowskis, Stockholm #383/R (S.KR 14000)

SUREDA, Andre (1872-1930) French
Works on paper
£600 $1104 €900 Etude de personnages (61x44cm-24x17in) mono. mixed media prov. 11-Jun-4 Claude Aguttes, Neuilly #120/R
£1141 $2042 €1700 L'Algerienne. s.i.d.1911 chl htd gouache. 25-May-4 Chambelland & Giafferi, Paris #30/R est:1200-1500
£4965 $8291 €7000 Jeune femme au foulard vert (63x48cm-25x19in) s.d.1912 W/C gouache. 16-Jun-3 Gros & Delettrez, Paris #533/R est:6000-8000

SURENDORF, Charles (1906-1979) American
£223 $400 €326 Self portrait (61x51cm-24x20in) s.d.54 masonite. 8-May-4 Auctions by the Bay, Alameda #489/R

SURIE, Jacoba (1879-1970) Dutch
£267 $488 €400 Still life of fruit (29x39cm-11x15in) s. 7-Jun-4 Glerum, Amsterdam #33/R
£451 $713 €650 Fruit and bottles. indis sig. 2-Sep-3 Christie's, Amsterdam #223
£903 $1426 €1300 Apples (30x40cm-12x16in) s. 2-Sep-3 Christie's, Amsterdam #227/R est:1200-1600
£2041 $3714 €3000 Grapes, pears, pumpkins on a draped kitten table (42x56cm-17x22in) s. 3-Feb-4 Christie's, Amsterdam #165/R est:3000-5000

SURIKOV, Vasilii Ivanovich (1848-1916) Russian
£2069 $3828 €3000 Bojarin with father (134x61cm-53x24in) 12-Feb-4 Weidler, Nurnberg #317/R est:3300
£3630 $6171 €5300 Paysanne russe (21x17cm-8x7in) s.d.1882. 9-Nov-3 Eric Pillon, Calais #96/R
£28000 $47600 €42000 Study of the head of God's Fool (25x20cm-10x8in) canvas on board lit. 25-Nov-3 Christie's, London #150/R est:10000-15000

SURPRISE, Wakartu Cory (1929-) Australian
Works on paper
£813 $1285 €1179 Untitled (110x76cm-43x30in) i.verso synthetic polymer paint prov. 28-Jul-3 Sotheby's, Paddington #496/R est:2000-3000 (A.D 2000)

SURREY, Philip Henry (1910-1990) Canadian
£4018 $6911 €5866 Motorcyclists (51x75cm-20x30in) s. board prov. 2-Dec-3 Joyner Waddington, Toronto #126/R est:8000-10000 (C.D 9000)
£5200 $9516 €7592 Summer by the water (30x40cm-12x16in) s.d.44 board prov. 1-Jun-4 Joyner Waddington, Toronto #111/R est:8000-10000 (C.D 13000)
Works on paper
£289 $500 €422 Boston Bruins hit the ice (19x28cm-7x11in) s. mixed media prov. 9-Dec-3 Pinneys, Montreal #14 (C.D 650)
£543 $852 €793 Rue la nuit (30x40cm-12x16in) pastel. 26-Aug-3 Iegor de Saint Hippolyte, Montreal #146 (C.D 1200)
£667 $1153 €974 St Andrews, New Brunswick (46x32cm-18x13in) s. s.i.verso mixed media. 9-Dec-3 Pinneys, Montreal #147 (C.D 1500)
£1760 $3221 €2570 Winter pattern (44x57cm-17x22in) s. pastel prov. 1-Jun-4 Joyner Waddington, Toronto #77/R est:2500-4000 (C.D 4400)

SURTEES, John (1819-1915) British
£302 $556 €441 On the Lledr, Carnarvonshire, North Wales (41x66cm-16x26in) s.d.71. 14-Jun-4 Waddingtons, Toronto #129/R (C.D 750)
£805 $1498 €1200 Peasant with girl in Scottish landscape (61x51cm-24x20in) s.d.57. 6-Mar-4 Arnold, Frankfurt #856/R
£1000 $1720 €1460 The stepping stones (49x75cm-19x30in) s. s.i.verso. 4-Dec-3 Mellors & Kirk, Nottingham #933/R est:700-900
Works on paper
£500 $865 €730 Tynemouth Priory under an evening sky (44x65cm-17x26in) W/C. 9-Dec-3 Anderson & Garland, Newcastle #288/R

SURTEES, Robert (?-1802) British
£3600 $6444 €5256 Bandit encampment in a forest (149x100cm-59x39in) s.i.d.1775. 11-May-4 Bonhams, Knightsbridge #107/R est:3000-4000

SURTEL, Paul (1893-1985) French
£461 $770 €650 Le mas provencal (33x41cm-13x16in) s. cardboard. 20-Jun-3 Drouot Estimations, Paris #184
£699 $1189 €1000 Bas de la Caromb (33x41cm-13x16in) s. masonite. 28-Nov-3 Drouot Estimations, Paris #203
£733 $1335 €1100 Village provencal (32x41cm-13x16in) s. masonite. 29-Jun-4 Chenu & Scrive, Lyon #172/R

SURVAGE, Leopold (1879-1968) French
£1608 $2734 €2300 Village (38x46cm-15x18in) s. prov. 23-Nov-3 Cornette de St.Cyr, Paris #319/R est:200-300
£1946 $3445 €2900 Les poissons (17x13cm-7x5in) s.d.55 casein panel. 27-Apr-4 Artcurial Briest, Paris #63/R est:2000-3000
£2013 $3564 €3000 Portrait de Marcelle Montagne (65x54cm-26x21in) s.d.31. 27-Apr-4 Artcurial Briest, Paris #62 est:2000-3000
£2039 $3753 €3100 Feuillage et ville (27x41cm-11x16in) s.d.55. 25-Jun-4 Millon & Associes, Paris #233/R est:1800-2200
£2416 $4470 €3600 Village et eglise en Provence (33x41cm-13x16in) s.d.1926 panel. 14-Mar-4 Eric Pillon, Calais #236/R
£3889 $7000 €5678 Leaf (36x28cm-14x11in) 24-Apr-4 Du Mouchelle, Detroit #3281/R est:2000-3000
£4362 $7721 €6500 Bouquet de fleurs (46x38cm-18x15in) s.d.33. 27-Apr-4 Artcurial Briest, Paris #53/R est:4000-6000
£6000 $10860 €8760 Figure (35x28cm-14x11in) s.d.29.9.36 prov. 1-Apr-4 Christie's, Kensington #58/R est:6000-8000
£8553 $15737 €13000 Untitled (65x81cm-26x32in) s.d.1927 prov. 27-Jun-4 Versailles Encheres #131/R est:12000-15000
£8824 $15000 €12883 Untitled (55x46cm-22x18in) s.d.30 prov. 5-Nov-3 Christie's, Rockefeller NY #307/R est:25000-35000
£9211 $16947 €14000 Parole (170x105cm-67x41in) s. s.i.d.1946 casein panel. 25-Jun-4 Millon & Associes, Paris #232/R est:12000-15000
£9333 $16800 €14000 Hands (65x80cm-26x31in) s.d.1935. 24-Apr-4 Cornette de St.Cyr, Paris #406/R est:20000
£10695 $20000 €15615 Portrait de nonnes (81x105cm-32x41in) s.d.29. 25-Feb-4 Christie's, Rockefeller NY #92/R est:10000-15000
£10860 $18462 €15856 Composition cubiste (34x22cm-13x9in) s. indis.i. d.1919 verso panel prov. 22-Nov-3 Burkhard, Luzern #99/R est:13000-16000 (S.FR 24000)
£11268 $19493 €16000 Les presences (65x80cm-26x31in) s.d.56 exhib.lit. 13-Dec-3 De Vuyst, Lokeren #496/R est:16000-20000
£12587 $21021 €18000 Composition (65x81cm-26x32in) s.d.1934. 11-Oct-3 De Vuyst, Lokeren #460/R est:18000-22000
£15200 $27512 €22800 Homme dans la ville et fleurs (33x24cm-13x9in) s. panel. 1-Apr-4 Credit Municipal, Paris #43/R est:400-600
£15436 $27322 €23000 Presence (61x51cm-24x20in) s.d.56 lit. 27-Apr-4 Artcurial Briest, Paris #187/R est:25000-30000
£19901 $36618 €29852 Allegorie de la femme (46x112cm-18x44in) s.d.1936 exhib.lit. 8-Jun-4 Artcurial Briest, Paris #95/R est:30000-40000
£20806 $38699 €31000 Oiseau dans la ville (54x73cm-21x29in) s.d.20. 2-Mar-4 Artcurial Briest, Paris #144/R est:25000-35000
£22667 $41480 €34000 Le coq (34x25cm-13x10in) s. panel painted 1914 lit. 7-Jun-4 Artcurial Briest, Paris #40/R est:25000-30000
£22819 $42444 €34000 Composition (55x46cm-22x18in) s.d.30 prov. 2-Mar-4 Artcurial Briest, Paris #151/R est:25000-35000
£24667 $45387 €37000 Femmes de collioure (81x105cm-32x41in) s.d.29 lit. 8-Jun-4 Artcurial Briest, Paris #99/R est:28000-35000
£36000 $65520 €52560 Le port (92x73cm-36x29in) s. painted 1919-21 prov. 4-Feb-4 Sotheby's, London #258/R est:25000-35000
£39474 $72632 €60000 Homme dans la ville (220x110cm-87x43in) s. oil canvas on panel prov. 25-Jun-4 Millon & Associes, Paris #234/R est:40000-60000
£45455 $77274 €65000 Taureau echappe (160x239cm-63x94in) s.i.d.1928 prov.exhib.lit. 19-Nov-3 Tajan, Paris #115/R est:70000-80000
£64335 $110657 €92000 Paysage a la porteuse (135x90cm-53x35in) s.d.26 lit. 8-Dec-3 Artcurial Briest, Paris #35/R est:90000-130000
Works on paper
£280 $481 €400 Visage (24x19cm-9x7in) s.d.43 dr. 3-Dec-3 Tajan, Paris #63
£280 $481 €400 Les baigneurs et l'oiseau (26x21cm-10x8in) s.d.30 graphite. 3-Dec-3 Tajan, Paris #62
£296 $545 €450 Paysage a l'eglise (36x46cm-14x18in) s.d.45 W/C graphite. 25-Jun-4 Millon & Associes, Paris #228
£304 $575 €450 Femme et mains (21x15cm-8x6in) s.d.1943 prov. 21-Feb-4 Cornette de St.Cyr, Paris #222
£329 $605 €500 Village (31x45cm-12x18in) s.d.52 W/C. 25-Jun-4 Millon & Associes, Paris #217
£336 $621 €500 Quatre portraits (12x12cm-5x5in) studio st. Chinese ink dr. 14-Mar-4 Eric Pillon, Calais #239/R
£336 $594 €500 Portrait de Marcelle Montagne (26x19cm-10x7in) s. crayon drawing. 27-Apr-4 Artcurial Briest, Paris #54/R
£395 $726 €600 Saint Paul Square (37x45cm-15x18in) s.d.37 W/C. 25-Jun-4 Millon & Associes, Paris #220
£403 $713 €600 La mine (26x38cm-10x15in) s.d.51 bears studio st. W/C. 27-Apr-4 Artcurial Briest, Paris #65
£420 $713 €600 Composition abstraite (28x75cm-11x30in) s.d.1947 W/C prov. 23-Nov-3 Cornette de St.Cyr, Paris #323
£490 $832 €700 Femmes et paysage (28x22cm-11x9in) mono. graphite prov. 23-Nov-3 Cornette de St.Cyr, Paris #318
£530 $964 €800 Route (47x63cm-19x25in) s.d.1930 W/C. 15-Jun-4 Rossini, Paris #155/R
£537 $999 €800 Paysage de Provence (43x63cm-17x25in) s.d.50 W/C. 2-Mar-4 Artcurial Briest, Paris #65
£537 $950 €800 Scene animee (34x48cm-13x19in) mono. crayon tracing paper. 27-Apr-4 Artcurial Briest, Paris #56
£579 $1065 €880 Maille bois (22x23cm-9x9in) s.i. W/C. 25-Jun-4 Millon & Associes, Paris #223
£604 $1069 €900 Personnages (52x43cm-20x17in) s.d.40 bears studio st. crayon. 27-Apr-4 Artcurial Briest, Paris #58/R
£604 $1069 €900 Visage (30x20cm-12x8in) s.d.12 bears studio st. crayon. 27-Apr-4 Artcurial Briest, Paris #60/R
£658 $1211 €1000 Jardin boise et ville (24x33cm-9x13in) s.indis.d. W/C. 25-Jun-4 Millon & Associes, Paris #222
£671 $1248 €1000 Composition aux visages (18x28cm-7x11in) s.d.50 bears studio st. W/C. 3-Mar-4 Tajan, Paris #146
£671 $1235 €1000 Paysage (52x62cm-20x24in) s. W/C. 29-Mar-4 Lombrail & Teucquam, Paris #142/R
£671 $1201 €1000 Homme a la pomme (43x61cm-17x24in) s.d.1951 W/C gouache. 30-May-4 Eric Pillon, Calais #207/R
£699 $1189 €1000 Femme et mains (21x15cm-8x6in) s.d.1943 graphite prov. 23-Nov-3 Cornette de St.Cyr, Paris #315/R
£724 $1332 €1100 Paysage situe a Vichy (62x45cm-24x18in) s.d.1930 W/C. 28-Jun-4 Joron-Derem, Paris #165
£769 $1308 €1100 Le fil a plomb (37x49cm-15x19in) s.i.d.1955 graphite prov. 23-Nov-3 Cornette de St.Cyr, Paris #322/R
£795 $1446 €1200 Abbaye aux cypres (31x39cm-12x15in) s.i. mixed media panel. 15-Jun-4 Rossini, Paris #153/R
£833 $1392 €1200 Architecutre et personnage (15x11cm-6x4in) s.d.41 studio st. W/C traces of crayon. 21-Oct-3 Artcurial Briest, Paris #104
£839 $1427 €1200 Composition aux personnages (27x45cm-11x18in) s.d.1938 Indian ink prov. 23-Nov-3 Cornette de St.Cyr, Paris #314/R
£867 $1595 €1300 La Guadeloupe (63x87cm-25x34in) W/C crayon prov. 8-Jun-4 Artcurial Briest, Paris #96/R est:4000-6000
£872 $1614 €1300 Passant dans la ville (8x9cm-3x4in) init. W/C gouache. 14-Mar-4 Eric Pillon, Calais #238/R
£1067 $1920 €1600 L'arbre de vie (27x21cm-11x8in) s.d.39 gouache. 26-Apr-4 Tajan, Paris #52/R est:1300-1500
£1189 $2021 €1700 Paysannes (28x41cm-11x16in) s. graphite Indian ink wash prov. 23-Nov-3 Cornette de St.Cyr, Paris #321/R est:200-300
£1379 $2290 €2000 Village (33x41cm-13x16in) s.d.1926 W/C panel. 1-Oct-3 Millon & Associes, Paris #31/R
£1608 $2734 €2300 Personnage dans la ville (41x32cm-16x13in) s.d.1956 W/C prov. 23-Nov-3 Cornette de St.Cyr, Paris #316/R est:200-300
£1667 $3067 €2500 La route vers Amboise (45x54cm-18x21in) s.i.d.30 W/C. 14-Jun-4 Tajan, Paris #68/R est:2500-3500
£1678 $2970 €2500 Visage (29x20cm-11x8in) s. bears studio st. crayon. 27-Apr-4 Artcurial Briest, Paris #59/R est:1500-2000
£2013 $3685 €3000 Personnages attables (54x75cm-21x30in) s.i.d.51 W/C. 7-Jul-4 Artcurial Briest, Paris #69/R est:3500-4500
£2083 $3479 €3000 L'eau (49x67cm-19x26in) s.i.d.50 studio st. W/C prov. 21-Oct-3 Artcurial Briest, Paris #112/R est:3000-4000
£2517 $4280 €3600 Paysage, maison et arbres (40x26cm-16x10in) s. Indian ink wash prov. 23-Nov-3 Cornette de St.Cyr, Paris #317 est:100-150
£2533 $4661 €3800 L'oiseau de la pense en naissant s'eleve (14x11cm-6x4in) s.i.d.45 casein panel prov.lit. 8-Jun-4 Artcurial Briest, Paris #80/R est:3000-4000
£2667 $4800 €4000 Le ciel dans la ville (24x31cm-9x12in) s.d.25 gouache. 26-Apr-4 Tajan, Paris #50 est:3000-3800
£2778 $4639 €4000 Deux personnages aux feuilles (27x21cm-11x8in) s.d.34 studio st. gouache W/C. 21-Oct-3 Artcurial Briest, Paris #120/R est:2000-3000
£3667 $6747 €5500 Rythmes colores (23x113cm-9x44in) mono. gouache prov. 8-Jun-4 Artcurial Briest, Paris #90/R est:4000-6000

£4363 $8115 €6500 Vache (65x81cm-26x32in) s. W/C varnish canvas. 3-Mar-4 Tajan, Paris #144/R est:7000-9000
£6333 $11653 €9500 L'homme (183x149cm-72x59in) gouache prov. 8-Jun-4 Artcurial Briest, Paris #91/R est:12000-15000
£8451 $13691 €12000 La vache (65x81cm-26x32in) s. W/C varnish canvas. 5-Aug-3 Tajan, Paris #36/R est:8000-10000
£8667 $15860 €13000 Serie des paysages cosmiques, le fil a plomb (80x100cm-31x39in) s.d.55 casein panel lit. 7-Jun-4 Artcurial Briest, Paris #39/R est:20000-30000

SUS, Gustav Konrad (1823-1881) German
£862 $1345 €1259 Chickens (14x17cm-6x7in) s. panel. 30-Mar-3 Agra, Warsaw #47/R (P.Z 5500)

SUSAT, Alberto (1898-1977) Austrian
Works on paper
£319 $533 €450 Salzach shore with Hotel Stein and Mullner Church (36x51cm-14x20in) s.d.30 w/C. 16-Oct-3 Dorotheum, Salzburg #938/R

SUSENIER, Abraham (attrib) (1620-1664) Dutch
£9500 $16150 €13870 Oysters and partly peeled lemon on a pewter dish, bread and other oysters on a draped table (55x46cm-22x18in) init. panel. 31-Oct-3 Christie's, Kensington #40/R est:6000-8000

SUSILUOTO, Ahti (1940-) Finnish
Works on paper
£340 $619 €500 Woman on table (62x36cm-24x14in) s. mixed media. 8-Feb-4 Bukowskis, Helsinki #465/R
£442 $805 €650 An artist's life (65x45cm-26x18in) s.d.99 mixed media. 8-Feb-4 Bukowskis, Helsinki #467/R

SUSINI, Antonio (circle) (?-1624) Italian
Sculpture
£39437 $69014 €56000 Statuette equestre (25x22x10cm-10x9x4in) after Jean de Bologne pat bronze lit. 17-Dec-3 Delorme & Bocage, Paris #60/R est:15000-20000

SUSS, Josef (elder) (1867-1937) Austrian
£1284 $2298 €1900 Pater cellar master (52x41cm-20x16in) s. i. verso panel. 6-May-4 Michael Zeller, Lindau #892/R est:1900

SUSSER, Frantisek (1890-?) Austrian
£1756 $2985 €2564 Female nude (85x67cm-33x26in) s. 29-Nov-3 Dorotheum, Prague #87/R est:80000-120000 (C.KR 80000)

SUSSI, Anton Giulio (1858-?) Italian
£284 $443 €420 Seascape (46x31cm-18x12in) 30-Mar-3 Adma, Formigine #677

SUSTERMANS, Justus (1597-1681) Flemish
£4577 $8011 €6500 Portrait de gentilhomme a la collerette de dentelle (64x49cm-25x19in) 18-Dec-3 Tajan, Paris #86/R est:7000-8000
£17000 $30600 €24820 Portrait of Leopoldo di Cosimo II de Medici (67x50cm-26x20in) 21-Apr-4 Christie's, London #75/R est:8000-12000

SUSTERMANS, Justus (attrib) (1597-1681) Flemish
£1847 $3250 €2697 Portrait of a man with collar (60x48cm-24x19in) 19-May-4 Doyle, New York #6047 est:2000-3000
£2416 $4446 €3600 Portrait of elegant lady with golden necklace (86x71cm-34x28in) prov. 24-Mar-4 Dorotheum, Vienna #338/R est:3000-5000
£3803 $6655 €5400 Portrait of gentleman (74x59cm-29x23in) 17-Dec-3 Christie's, Rome #362/R est:4000-6000

SUSTERMANS, Justus (circle) (1597-1681) Flemish
£10000 $16300 €14600 Portrait of a gentleman, small bust-length (35x35cm-14x14in) canvas on panel round. 26-Sep-3 Christie's, Kensington #120/R est:2000-3000

SUSTERMANS, Justus (studio) (1597-1681) Flemish
£5634 $9070 €8000 Ritratto di giovane di casa Medici (79x63cm-31x25in) oval. 8-May-3 Farsetti, Prato #788/R est:9000-10000

SUSTRIS, Lambert (c.1515-1568) Dutch
£536913 $1004027 €800000 Venus and Love (96x66cm-38x26in) lit. 29-Feb-4 Finarte, Venice #48/R

SUSTRIS, Lambert (attrib) (c.1515-1568) Dutch
£70000 $128100 €102200 Mystic marriage of Saint Catherine (48x65cm-19x26in) prov. 8-Jul-4 Sotheby's, London #154/R est:20000-30000

SUSTRIS, Lambert (circle) (c.1515-1568) Dutch
£26923 $46308 €39308 Infant Jesus' betrothal to Saint Catherine (99x135cm-39x53in) 2-Dec-3 Bukowskis, Stockholm #327/R est:200000-250000 (S.KR 350000)
£46000 $82800 €67160 Portrait of a gentleman, wearing an embroidered doublet (116x90cm-46x35in) i. panel prov. 22-Apr-4 Sotheby's, London #40/R est:25000-35000

SUTCLIFFE, Elizabeth Trevor (fl.1886-1928) British
£540 $967 €788 Still life of primroses and forget-me-nots in a blue glazed jug (28x43cm-11x17in) s. 16-Mar-4 Bonhams, Leeds #648/R

SUTCLIFFE, Frank Meadow (1853-1941) British
Photographs
£2200 $3872 €3212 Dock End, Whitby (57x74cm-22x29in) s.i. carbon print prov.lit. 19-May-4 Christie's, London #81/R est:2500-3500

SUTCLIFFE, Geoffrey (20th C) British
£500 $945 €730 Caves, Warren Beach, Hartland Quay no.1 (122x122cm-48x48in) init. board. 19-Feb-4 Christie's, Kensington #237/R

SUTCLIFFE, J (19th C) British
£2000 $3580 €2920 Three children with fruit and flowers in a landscape setting (124x100cm-49x39in) s.d.July 11 1860. 11-May-4 Bonhams, Knightsbridge #178/R est:2000-3000

SUTCLIFFE, John (19th C) British
£350 $651 €511 Figures before cottage (20x30cm-8x12in) 4-Mar-4 Christie's, Kensington #523/R

SUTCLIFFE, Lester (1848-1933) British
£250 $463 €365 Seaweed gatherer (25x36cm-10x14in) indis.s. 14-Jul-4 Christie's, Kensington #907
Works on paper
£290 $473 €423 Coastal scene, fishing boats in middle distance (38x61cm-15x24in) s.d.1881 W/C. 26-Sep-3 Dee Atkinson & Harrison, Driffield #562/R

SUTER, Jakob (1805-1874) Swiss
Works on paper
£550 $919 €798 Landscape near Nice (31x43cm-12x17in) s.i.d.1843 W/C. 23-Jun-3 Philippe Schuler, Zurich #3920 (S.FR 1200)

SUTERMEISTER, Carl Jakob (attrib) (1809-1853) Swiss
£617 $1048 €901 Portrait of couple (63x49cm-25x19in) 5-Nov-3 Dobiaschofsky, Bern #3750 (S.FR 1400)

SUTHERLAND, David (1883-1973) British
£460 $805 €672 Estuary, Plockton (36x44cm-14x17in) s.i.verso board. 18-Dec-3 Bonhams, Edinburgh #313
£900 $1449 €1305 Flower piece (51x39cm-20x15in) s. canvasboard exhib. 21-Aug-3 Bonhams, Edinburgh #1166
£1200 $2040 €1752 Figures bathing in a harbour by a quayside (24x28cm-9x11in) s. panel. 19-Nov-3 Tennants, Leyburn #1258/R est:700-900
£1350 $2174 €1958 Plockton, Lochcarron (36x44cm-14x17in) s. board double-sided. 21-Aug-3 Bonhams, Edinburgh #1112/R est:1200-1800

SUTHERLAND, Graham (1903-1980) British
£4500 $8235 €6570 Bee hatching (30x24cm-12x9in) init.d.79 pencil W/C bodycol ink squared for transfer prov.exhib. 4-Jun-4 Christie's, London #47/R est:2000-3000
£5500 $8745 €8030 Landscape with palms (19x27cm-7x11in) init.d.Aug 1961 i.verso prov. 10-Sep-3 Sotheby's, Olympia #273/R est:6000-8000
£58000 $106140 €84680 Cypress cones (102x76cm-40x30in) s.d.1956 exhib.lit. 4-Jun-4 Christie's, London #45/R est:40000-60000
£105000 $178500 €153300 Vine pergola (46x56cm-18x22in) s.d.47 i.d.verso prov.exhib. 21-Nov-3 Christie's, London #82/R est:30000-50000
£135000 $247050 €197100 Toad (143x122cm-56x48in) painted 1961-62 prov.exhib.lit. 4-Jun-4 Christie's, London #46/R est:60000-80000
Prints
£2200 $4026 €3212 Thorn cross (46x64cm-18x25in) s.num.76/100 col lithograph. 3-Jun-4 Christie's, Kensington #199 est:400-600
Works on paper
£300 $546 €438 Dog (13x20cm-5x8in) ink htd white. 15-Jun-4 David Lay, Penzance #675
£400 $728 €584 Crucifixion study (28x20cm-11x8in) chl. 1-Jul-4 Christie's, Kensington #216/R
£400 $728 €584 Leg study for the Northampton Crucifixion (28x20cm-11x8in) chl. 1-Jul-4 Christie's, Kensington #231/R
£700 $1274 €1022 Crucifixion foot study (28x20cm-11x8in) chl brown crayon. 1-Jul-4 Christie's, Kensington #229/R
£750 $1253 €1095 Untitled (16x10cm-6x4in) pencil W/C prov. 16-Oct-3 Christie's, Kensington #686/R
£800 $1400 €1168 Special greeting (28x20cm-11x8in) pastel. 18-Dec-3 John Nicholson, Haslemere #1094/R
£900 $1665 €1314 Study for the frontispiece for lithograph (28x31cm-11x12in) s.i.d.1973 pencil pen brush ink prov. 11-Mar-4 Christie's, Kensington #301/R est:600-800
£900 $1638 €1314 Crucifixion leg study (28x20cm-11x8in) chl study verso double-sided. 1-Jul-4 Christie's, Kensington #220/R
£900 $1638 €1314 Double crucifixion study (28x20cm-11x8in) pencil bodycol. 1-Jul-4 Christie's, Kensington #232/R
£1000 $1820 €1460 Crucifixion study (28x20cm-11x8in) chl study verso double-sided. 1-Jul-4 Christie's, Kensington #234/R est:1500-2000
£1100 $2035 €1606 Gateway (25x17cm-10x7in) init. pencil brush ink. 11-Mar-4 Christie's, Kensington #300/R est:600-800
£1100 $2002 €1606 Crucifixion study (28x20cm-11x8in) chl sketch verso double-sided. 1-Jul-4 Christie's, Kensington #222/R est:1500-2000
£1100 $2002 €1606 Crucifixion study (28x20cm-11x8in) chl. 1-Jul-4 Christie's, Kensington #227/R est:800-1200
£1200 $2184 €1752 Study for Crucifixion (37x21cm-15x8in) init. pencil biro brush blk ink squared. 1-Jul-4 Christie's, Kensington #233/R est:1000-1500
£1361 $2435 €2000 Three studies (16x11cm-6x4in) s.d.1973 mixed media. 22-Mar-4 Sant Agostino, Torino #493/R est:2500
£1600 $2912 €2336 Study for the Northampton Crucifixion (28x20cm-11x8in) chl. 1-Jul-4 Christie's, Kensington #221/R est:1500-2000
£2000 $3400 €2920 Study for origins of the land (11x25cm-4x10in) init. ink W/C col crayon. 21-Nov-3 Christie's, London #79/R est:1500-2500
£2400 $4080 €3504 Poster design (75x49cm-30x19in) s.d.50 ink pencil gouache collage. 26-Nov-3 Sotheby's, Olympia #175/R est:1000-1500
£2500 $4625 €3650 Birds (49x34cm-19x13in) gouache prov. 11-Mar-4 Christie's, Kensington #230/R est:2000-3000

£3000 $5460 €4380 Still life with flaming urn (24x37cm-9x15in) s.d.1978 pencil W/C pen black ink. 1-Jul-4 Christie's, Kensington #368/R est:2500-3500
£4225 $7394 €6000 Untitled (36x41cm-14x16in) s.d.1974 W/C Chinese ink. 16-Dec-3 Finarte Semenzato, Milan #299/R est:7500-8500
£5000 $9200 €7500 Banana leaves and wall (22x28cm-9x11in) s.d. gouache Indian ink col chks. 11-Jun-4 Hauswedell & Nolte, Hamburg #1548/R est:6000
£7800 $13728 €11388 Monkey (30x22cm-12x9in) s.d.53 col chk gouache pen ink prov.exhib. 18-May-4 Woolley & Wallis, Salisbury #115/R est:2000-3000
£8500 $14620 €12410 Origins of the land (26x50cm-10x20in) s.i. W/C gouache pencil. 2-Dec-3 Bonhams, New Bond Street #153/R est:4000-6000
£9000 $16470 €13140 Study for form in estuary. Two studies for road mounting between hedges. Cairn (9x9cm-4x4in) W/C bodycol ink col crayon squared for transfer common mount. 4-Jun-4 Christie's, London #48/R est:5000-7000
£13000 $23790 €18980 Standing form against red background (41x17cm-16x7in) s.d.51 black crayon W/C bodycol pencil prov.exhib. 4-Jun-4 Christie's, London #49/R est:8000-12000
£14500 $26535 €21170 Landscape with uprushing wind (66x46cm-26x18in) s.d.1940 pen ink wash W/C wax crayon prov.exhib. 2-Jun-4 Sotheby's, London #74/R est:15000-20000
£16000 $27520 €23360 Standing form against a wall (57x24cm-22x9in) init.d.1952 gouache col chks blk ink prov.exhib. 3-Dec-3 Sotheby's, London #57/R est:12000-15000
£16500 $28050 €24090 Pembroke landscape (30x24cm-12x9in) s.d.1940 ink W/C bodycol prov.exhib. 21-Nov-3 Christie's, London #80/R est:10000-15000
£18056 $30153 €26000 Study for bestiary (76x56cm-30x22in) s. s.i.d.1964 verso Chinese ink W/C pastel paper on canvas. 21-Oct-3 Sotheby's, Milan #382/R est:16500-18000
£21000 $38430 €30660 Origins of the land (28x50cm-11x20in) s.d.1950 W/C gouache chk pencil prov. 2-Jun-4 Sotheby's, London #73/R est:8000-12000
£26000 $44200 €37960 Precipitous road to hill (49x70cm-19x28in) s.d.MCMXXXX ink W/C bodycol collage prov.exhib.lit. 21-Nov-3 Christie's, London #83/R est:15000-20000

SUTHERLAND, Jane (1855-1928) Australian
Works on paper
£1463 $2620 €2136 Young woman in a garden (40x21cm-16x8in) s. pastel. 4-May-4 Sotheby's, Melbourne #326/R est:4000-6000 (A.D 3600)

SUTHERLAND, Jean P (1902-1978) Australian
£744 $1376 €1086 Thames (30x15cm-12x6in) board. 10-Mar-4 Deutscher-Menzies, Melbourne #526/R est:500-700 (A.D 1800)

SUTHERS, Leghe (1855-1924) British
£2850 $5187 €4161 Village street with man on horseback and sheep before a cottage (51x41cm-20x16in) s. 16-Jun-4 John Nicholson, Haslemere #778/R est:3000-5000

SUTTER, David (1811-1880) French
£2238 $3849 €3200 Le grand chene a Barbizon (42x32cm-17x13in) s. panel. 7-Dec-3 Osenat, Fontainebleau #141

SUTTER, Jules de (1895-1970) Belgian
£674 $1125 €950 La chambre a coucher (80x80cm-31x31in) s.d.29. 17-Jun-3 Vanderkindere, Brussels #175
£2207 $4083 €3200 Madame Desutter contemplant une oeuvre de son mari. s. 19-Jan-4 Horta, Bruxelles #209 est:4000-6000
£3947 $7145 €6000 Madame Desutter contemplant une oeuvre de son mari (125x81cm-49x32in) s. 19-Apr-4 Horta, Bruxelles #64 est:2500-3500
Works on paper
£268 $475 €400 Petit garcon sur une chaise jaune (35x27cm-14x11in) mono. mixed media. 27-Apr-4 Campo & Campo, Antwerp #78
£417 $663 €600 Nu assis (35x25cm-14x10in) mono. pastel. 9-Sep-3 Palais de Beaux Arts, Brussels #205
£470 $832 €700 Jeune homme assis (36x26cm-14x10in) s. mixed media. 27-Apr-4 Campo & Campo, Antwerp #76
£470 $832 €700 Nu assis (36x27cm-14x11in) s.d.1966 mixed media. 27-Apr-4 Campo & Campo, Antwerp #79

SUTTERLIN, Johann (1823-1872) Swiss
£1136 $1886 €1647 Jura village (41x63cm-16x25in) s. 13-Jun-3 Zofingen, Switzerland #2380/R est:4500 (S.FR 2500)

SUTTON, Ivan (1944-) Irish?
£389 $634 €560 Musicians (26x31cm-10x12in) s. canvas on board. 23-Sep-3 De Veres Art Auctions, Dublin #130
£909 $1545 €1300 Roundstone Harbour with Twelve Pins in background (34x43cm-13x17in) s. i.verso canvas on board. 18-Nov-3 Whyte's, Dublin #164/R
£951 $1664 €1350 Trawlers berth at Kilmore Quay (40x51cm-16x20in) s. canvasboard. 16-Dec-3 James Adam, Dublin #234/R
£979 $1664 €1400 Low tide Carraroe (51x41cm-20x16in) s. canvasboard. 25-Nov-3 De Veres Art Auctions, Dublin #163 est:1400-1800
£1133 $2040 €1700 Inisheer village, Aran Islands, Co Galway (39x49cm-15x19in) s. board. 20-Apr-4 James Adam, Dublin #109/R est:1500-2000
£1200 $2160 €1800 Card players (50x59cm-20x23in) s. board. 20-Apr-4 James Adam, Dublin #151/R est:1800-2500
£1333 $2413 €2000 Hunter 707's racing in Dublin bay (51x77cm-20x30in) s. 30-Mar-4 De Veres Art Auctions, Dublin #93/R est:2000-3000
£1447 $2663 €2200 Becalmed before Galway Hooker Race Carraroe (51x76cm-20x30in) s. canvasboard. 22-Jun-4 De Veres Art Auctions, Dublin #182/R est:2000-3000
£1711 $3147 €2600 Sunny evening, low tide, Roundstone, County Galway (57x76cm-22x30in) s. canvasboard. 22-Jun-4 De Veres Art Auctions, Dublin #156/R est:2000-3000
£1745 $3123 €2600 Launching the Currach, Inishmaan, Co Galway (50x75cm-20x30in) s. i. verso board. 31-May-4 Hamilton Osborne King, Dublin #113/R est:2500-3500
£1818 $3091 €2600 Carraroe (51x76cm-20x30in) s. canvasboard. 25-Nov-3 De Veres Art Auctions, Dublin #162 est:2000-3000
£1892 $3576 €2800 Johnny Bailey's Galway Hooker, Capall, off Carraroe, County Galway (51x76cm-20x30in) s. s.i.verso board. 17-Feb-4 Whyte's, Dublin #235/R est:2500-3500
£2431 $3962 €3500 Roundstone (51x76cm-20x30in) s. board. 23-Sep-3 De Veres Art Auctions, Dublin #234/R est:2000-3000
£2617 $4633 €3900 New Raleigh (51x76cm-20x30in) s. i.verso canvasboard. 27-Apr-4 Whyte's, Dublin #194/R est:2500-3500
£2800 $5068 €4200 Launching the Currach at Inisheer, Aran Islands, Co Galway (51x77cm-20x30in) s. 30-Mar-4 De Veres Art Auctions, Dublin #189/R est:2500-3500
£2817 $4507 €4000 Low tide, Roundstone, County Galway (51x76cm-20x30in) s. s.i.verso board. 16-Sep-3 Whyte's, Dublin #212/R est:2000-3000
£2937 $4993 €4200 Becalmed Galway hookers off Carraroe, County Galway (64x91cm-25x36in) s. s.i.verso board. 18-Nov-3 Whyte's, Dublin #173/R est:4000-5000

SUTTON, John (1935-) British
£320 $554 €467 Early morning on Waxham Cut (50x66cm-20x26in) s. i.verso. 10-Dec-3 Bonhams, Bury St Edmunds #557
£800 $1384 €1168 Unloading cargo, the Pool of London, Blackfriars Bridge and St Pauls (48x74cm-19x29in) s. 11-Dec-3 Ewbank, Send #402/R
Works on paper
£250 $463 €365 Amber Fort, Jaipur (33x48cm-13x19in) s. W/C. 13-Feb-4 Keys, Aylsham #617
£300 $501 €438 View of the Thames at Greenwich (33x51cm-13x20in) s. W/C htd bodycol. 12-Nov-3 Halls, Shrewsbury #262/R
£340 $629 €496 Corn exchange, Leeds (33x48cm-13x19in) s. W/C executed c.1900. 13-Feb-4 Keys, Aylsham #618
£380 $703 €555 Clock Tower, Leicester (33x51cm-13x20in) s. W/C. 13-Feb-4 Keys, Aylsham #619
£420 $773 €613 London Street, Norwich (14x20cm-6x8in) s. W/C. 11-Jun-4 Keys, Aylsham #594
£430 $778 €628 Summer shadows, Pin Mill, Suffolk (36x48cm-14x19in) s. W/C. 16-Apr-4 Keys, Aylsham #603/R
£550 $1012 €803 Low tide, Pin Mill (13x20cm-5x8in) s. W/C executed c.1900. 11-Jun-4 Keys, Aylsham #593/R

SUTTON, Philip (1928-) British
£600 $1110 €876 Bouquet in a vase (45x45cm-18x18in) s.d.1974 verso prov. 11-Mar-4 Christie's, Kensington #317/R
£650 $1170 €949 Landscape at Snape (30x51cm-12x20in) s.i.d.1958 verso board. 20-Jan-4 Bonhams, Knightsbridge #133/R
£700 $1169 €1022 Fish on a plate (41x51cm-16x20in) init. s.d.1959 verso. 16-Oct-3 Christie's, Kensington #685/R
£800 $1440 €1168 Cristina (99x99cm-39x39in) s.i.verso. 20-Jan-4 Bonhams, Knightsbridge #238/R
£1500 $2505 €2190 Landscape with telegraph pole (41x41cm-16x16in) s.d.1958 stretcher prov. 16-Oct-3 Christie's, Kensington #655/R est:800-1200
£1700 $3043 €2482 Flowers (102x102cm-40x40in) s.i.d.1967 verso prov. 14-May-4 Christie's, Kensington #587/R est:1500-2000
£1938 $3295 €2829 Flowers for Chopin (120x120cm-47x47in) s.i. verso. 5-Nov-3 Dobiaschofsky, Bern #999/R est:4000 (S.FR 4400)
£2000 $3580 €2920 Lux (117x117cm-46x46in) s.i.d.1984 verso prov. 14-May-4 Christie's, Kensington #566/R est:2000-3000
£2200 $3938 €3212 Heathers gate (76x76cm-30x30in) s.i.d.1990 verso. 14-May-4 Christie's, Kensington #584/R est:1000-1500

SUTTON, William A (1917-2000) New Zealander
£903 $1435 €1318 Canterbury University (35x30cm-14x12in) s.d.1955 canvas on board. 1-May-3 Dunbar Sloane, Wellington #117 est:500-1000 (NZ.D 2600)
£1173 $1912 €1713 Down the river (30x37cm-12x15in) s.d.1947 canvas on board. 23-Sep-3 Peter Webb, Auckland #148/R est:2500-3500 (NZ.D 3250)
£1389 $2208 €2028 Arthurs Pass (29x38cm-11x15in) s.d.1947 canvas on board. 1-May-3 Dunbar Sloane, Wellington #68/R est:5000-7000 (NZ.D 4000)
£1455 $2284 €2110 Composition 10 (29x73cm-11x29in) s.d.1972 board. 27-Aug-3 Dunbar Sloane, Wellington #49/R est:1000-2000 (NZ.D 4000)
£13986 $25455 €20420 Te Tihi O Kahukura and sky no.2 (152x244cm-60x96in) s.d.1977. 29-Jun-4 Peter Webb, Auckland #68/R est:45000-65000 (NZ.D 40000)
£33929 $61411 €49536 Country church (51x61cm-20x24in) s.d.1953 prov.exhib. 30-Mar-4 Peter Webb, Auckland #38/R est:65000-85000 (NZ.D 95000)

SUVERO, Mark di (1933-) American
Sculpture
£1667 $3000 €2434 Delivered word (44x29cm-17x11in) s. num.40/75 copperplated aluminium exec. 1981. 25-Apr-4 Bonhams & Butterfields, San Francisco #5638/R est:800-1200
£12637 $23000 €18450 Untitled (24cm-9in) s. welded steel kinetic in two parts executed c.1979 prov. 29-Jun-4 Sotheby's, New York #498/R est:15000-20000
£22346 $40000 €32625 Kik (37x52x31cm-15x20x12in) s. steel polished steel exec 1990 prov.exhib.lit. 13-May-4 Sotheby's, New York #218/R est:15000-20000
£22455 $37500 €32784 Untitled (33x41x28cm-13x16x11in) painted rusted steel iron two parts prov. 13-Nov-3 Sotheby's, New York #178/R est:20000-30000
£22647 $38500 €33065 Split piece (46x28x43cm-18x11x17in) steel mobile exec. 1982 prov. 7-Nov-3 Selkirks, St. Louis #552/R est:45000-55000
£23952 $40000 €34970 Van Gogh's ear (40x34x31cm-16x13x12in) steel two parts exhib. 13-Nov-3 Sotheby's, New York #107/R est:20000-30000
£25140 $45000 €36704 Untitled (56x99x61cm-22x39x24in) steel stainless steel aluminium stone wire string prov. 12-May-4 Christie's, Rockefeller NY #183/R est:35000-45000
£30726 $55000 €44860 Mayakovsky (69x102x53cm-27x40x21in) rusted steel four parts exec 1976 prov.exhib. 13-May-4 Sotheby's, New York #139/R est:15000-20000
£33520 $60000 €48939 Untitled (84x99x94cm-33x39x37in) galvanised steel polished steel exec 1968 prov.exhib. 13-May-4 Sotheby's, New York #113/R est:40000-60000
£71856 $120000 €104910 Departure 2001 (91x124x109cm-36x49x43in) wood steel prov.exhib. 13-Nov-3 Sotheby's, New York #108/R est:40000-60000

SUWAGE, Agus (1959-) Indonesian?
£3261 $5054 €4761 Newun Sewu (150x140cm-59x55in) s.d.2002. 6-Oct-2 Sotheby's, Singapore #189/R est:4000-6000 (S.D 9000)

SUYDAM, James Augustus (1819-1865) American
£14525 $26000 €21207 Casting the nets (6x11cm-2x4in) init. canvas on board prov. 6-May-4 Shannon's, Milford #123/R est:20000-30000
£88235 $150000 €128823 Conway meadows (28x51cm-11x20in) s. prov.exhib. 30-Oct-3 Phillips, New York #33/R est:150000-250000

SUZOR-COTE, Marc-Aurele de Foy (1869-1937) Canadian
£1013 $1723 €1479 Le chasseur (37x29cm-15x11in) s. conte prov.lit. 21-Nov-3 Walker's, Ottawa #100/R est:1000-1500 (C.D 2250)
£1339 $2304 €1955 Thatched roof cottage in summer (20x22cm-8x9in) s. paper on board. 2-Dec-3 Joyner Waddington, Toronto #405 est:3000-4000 (C.D 3000)
£1583 $2898 €2311 Perdrix (33x24cm-13x9in) s.d.95. 27-Jan-4 Iegor de Saint Hippolyte, Montreal #33 (C.D 3800)
£1728 $3093 €2523 Temps gris Arthabaska , PQ (6x10cm-2x4in) s. s.indis d. board prov. 31-May-4 Sotheby's, Toronto #147/R est:2500-3500 (C.D 4250)

£1829 $3274 €2670 Arthabaska (9x14cm-4x6in) s. board prov. 31-May-4 Sotheby's, Toronto #186/R est:3000-4000 (C.D 4500)
£2033 $3638 €2968 Jeune paysanne Canadienne (24x20cm-9x8in) s. s.i.verso panel prov.exhib. 31-May-4 Sotheby's, Toronto #183/R est:5000-7000 (C.D 5000)
£2160 $3953 €3154 Beauce, France (6x11cm-2x4in) s.i.d. verso painted 1901 panel prov. 1-Jun-4 Joyner Waddington, Toronto #307/R est:3000-5000 (C.D 5400)
£3862 $6913 €5639 Etude Espagne, Fuenterrabia (22x15cm-9x6in) s.d.1907 i.verso panel prov.lit. 27-May-4 Heffel, Vancouver #83/R est:6000-8000 (C.D 9500)
£4065 $7276 €5935 Fuenterrabia (22x15cm-9x6in) s.d.1907 i.d.verso panel prov. 27-May-4 Heffel, Vancouver #84/R est:6000-8000 (C.D 10000)
£4878 $8732 €7122 Paysage environs d'arthabaska, PQ (21x27cm-8x11in) s. s.i.d.1921 verso panel. 31-May-4 Sotheby's, Toronto #187/R est:5000-7000 (C.D 12000)
£169643 $291786 €247679 Autumn ploughing, Arthabaska (62x86cm-24x34in) s.d.1909 prov.exhib.lit. 2-Dec-3 Joyner Waddington, Toronto #50/R est:200000-250000 (C.D 380000)
Sculpture
£1220 $2183 €1781 Le remmancheur (19x18x12cm-7x7x5in) s.i.d.1922 num.2/10 bronze wood base prov. 6-May-4 Heffel, Vancouver #137/R est:4000-5000 (C.D 3000)
£1321 $2365 €1929 Le pere Fleury (26x29x24cm-10x11x9in) s.d.1908 num.8/10 bronze prov. 6-May-4 Heffel, Vancouver #136/R est:4000-5000 (C.D 3250)
£1515 $2712 €2212 Maria Chapdelaine (25x24x11cm-10x9x4in) s.i.d.1925 num.7/10 bronze Cast Inverness, Quebec prov. 8-Jan-4 Heffel, Vancouver #032 est:4000-5000 (C.D 3500)
£2165 $3874 €3161 Vieux Cocher (46x20x23cm-18x8x9in) s.i.d.1937 num.1/8 bronze Cast Inverness, Quebec prov. 8-Jan-4 Heffel, Vancouver #031 est:4000-5000 (C.D 5000)
£2236 $4002 €3265 Glaneuse (40x22cm-16x9in) s. num.3/10 bronze wood base prov. 6-May-4 Heffel, Vancouver #135/R est:4000-5000 (C.D 5500)
£4054 $6892 €5919 Caughnawaga Indian woman (39x25x26cm-15x10x10in) s.i.verso bronze prov. 23-Nov-3 Levis, Calgary #136/R est:9000-12000 (C.D 9000)
Works on paper
£338 $574 €493 Landscape near Ottawa (10x20cm-4x8in) s.d.1905 sepia. 21-Nov-3 Walker's, Ottawa #99/R (C.D 750)
£982 $1689 €1434 Portrait of a man (39x27cm-15x11in) s.d.07 chl htd white. 2-Dec-3 Joyner Waddington, Toronto #255/R est:1500-1800 (C.D 2200)
£1000 $1630 €1460 Nude (46x30cm-18x12in) s. chl prov. 23-Sep-3 Ritchie, Toronto #65/R est:2000-3000 (C.D 2200)
£1126 $1914 €1644 Study of an Indian (44x28cm-17x11in) s.d.1923 chl paper on paperboard. 23-Nov-3 Levis, Calgary #137/R est:2500-3000 (C.D 2500)
£1171 $1991 €1710 Quebec stream. Hay stooks (27x41cm-11x16in) s. i.d.7 verso col chk double-sided prov. 21-Nov-3 Walker's, Ottawa #37/R est:3000-4000 (C.D 2600)
£1674 $2879 €2444 Seated female nude (60x42cm-24x17in) s. chl. 2-Dec-3 Joyner Waddington, Toronto #247/R est:1000-1500 (C.D 3750)
£2439 $4366 €3561 Apres midi de Septembre - Arthabaska, PQ (11x18cm-4x7in) s.i.d.1918 i.verso pastel prov.exhib. 31-May-4 Sotheby's, Toronto #146/R est:2500-3500 (C.D 6000)
£3348 $5759 €4888 Riverside farmhouses in winter (29x37cm-11x15in) s. pastel. 2-Dec-3 Joyner Waddington, Toronto #347/R est:3000-5000 (C.D 7500)
£15244 $27287 €22256 La source - the spring (61x45cm-24x18in) s. pastel prov.lit. 31-May-4 Sotheby's, Toronto #188/R est:18000-22000 (C.D 37500)

SUZUKI, Kason (1860-1919) Japanese
Works on paper
£600 $1002 €876 Fox. Badger (109x28cm-43x11in) s. ink pair. 12-Nov-3 Christie's, London #10/R

SUZUKI, Shonen (1849-1918) Japanese
Works on paper
£1119 $1924 €1600 White fox under a cedar tree (118x49cm-46x19in) s. ink col silk hanging scroll. 5-Dec-3 Lempertz, Koln #782/R est:1200

SUZZONI, Romain (20th C) French?
£336 $628 €500 La chaise (100x81cm-39x32in) s. exhib. 29-Feb-4 Versailles Encheres #316

SVABINSKY, Max (1873-1962) Czechoslovakian
Works on paper
£285 $472 €416 Sitting man figure with hat (11x12cm-4x5in) s.mono. pencil. 4-Oct-3 Dorotheum, Prague #220/R est:10000-15000 (C.KR 13000)
£329 $613 €480 Before the dusk (47x64cm-19x25in) s.i. chl. 6-Mar-4 Dorotheum, Prague #180/R est:14000-22000 (C.KR 16000)
£700 $1163 €1022 Portrait of Mrs Palkovska (40x20cm-16x8in) s.d.1918 pencil W/C. 4-Oct-3 Dorotheum, Prague #223/R est:28000-40000 (C.KR 32000)
£788 $1308 €1150 Lady portrait (102x85cm-40x33in) s. chk. 4-Oct-3 Dorotheum, Prague #225/R est:36000-55000 (C.KR 36000)
£1055 $1856 €1583 Kiss (50x28cm-20x11in) s. pencil white chk. 22-May-4 Dorotheum, Prague #202/R est:20000-30000 (C.KR 50000)

SVANBERG, Max Walter (1912-1995) Swedish
£806 $1426 €1177 Wood nymph (38x75cm-15x30in) s. 27-Apr-4 AB Stockholms Auktionsverk #677/R (S.KR 11000)
£943 $1631 €1377 Queen of the Ocean (70x50cm-28x20in) s.d.42. 15-Dec-3 Lilla Bukowskis, Stockholm #216 (S.KR 12000)
£2198 $3890 €3209 Listening love (33x44cm-13x17in) s.d.50 mixed media panel exhib. 27-Apr-4 AB Stockholms Auktionsverk #780/R est:40000-50000 (S.KR 30000)
Works on paper
£476 $843 €695 Surrealistic composition with heads (33x26cm-13x10in) s.d.41 pencil. 27-Apr-4 AB Stockholms Auktionsverk #820/R (S.KR 6500)
£731 $1257 €1067 Composition with birdwoman and lion (36x21cm-14x8in) s.d.50 mixed media. 7-Dec-3 Uppsala Auktionskammare, Uppsala #235 (S.KR 9500)
£1099 $1945 €1605 20 phases of Kristina (41x20cm-16x8in) s.d.68 collage exhib.lit. 27-Apr-4 AB Stockholms Auktionsverk #778/R est:8000-10000 (S.KR 15000)
£1284 $2183 €1875 20 phases of Kristina (46x52cm-18x20in) s.d.69 collage exhib.lit. 5-Nov-3 AB Stockholms Auktionsverk #903/R est:18000-20000 (S.KR 17000)
£2238 $3849 €3200 Cinq chanteurs et musiciens entours de personnages d'esprit surrealiste (44x61cm-17x24in) s.d.1938 mixed media. 6-Dec-3 Renaud, Paris #333/R
£2417 $4109 €3529 In the symbol of the flowering dresses (46x38cm-18x15in) s.d.63 mixed media exhib. 5-Nov-3 AB Stockholms Auktionsverk #767/R est:25000-30000 (S.KR 32000)
£3741 $6697 €5500 Femme - Oiseau (45x37cm-18x15in) s.d.60 gouache. 21-Mar-4 Calmels Cohen, Paris #21/R est:5000-6000

SVANLUND, Olle (1909-1996) Swedish
£261 $470 €392 Harbour scene with fisherman and wife (70x80cm-28x31in) s.d.47. 25-Apr-4 Goteborg Auktionsverk, Sweden #1270/R (S.KR 3600)

SVEDBERG, Lena (1946-1972) Swedish
Works on paper
£1208 $2054 €1764 Nixon and Palme (50x64cm-20x25in) s. Indian ink collage htd white. 4-Nov-3 Bukowskis, Stockholm #542/R est:20000-25000 (S.KR 16000)

SVENDSEN, Bjarke Regn (1949-) Danish
£351 $561 €509 Composition (81x122cm-32x48in) s.d.80-82 verso masonite. 17-Sep-3 Kunsthallen, Copenhagen #124 (D.KR 3700)
£679 $1215 €991 Composition with rope and reflexes (99x99cm-39x39in) s.d.85. 10-May-4 Rasmussen, Vejle #800y/R (D.KR 7500)

SVENDSEN, Svend (1864-1934) Norwegian/American
£219 $400 €320 Path through the snow (46x61cm-18x24in) s. painted c.1900. 5-Jun-4 Treadway Gallery, Cincinnati #608/R
£252 $400 €368 Winter landscape at evening with birches and houses on distant hillside (56x66cm-22x26in) s. 5-May-3 O'Gallerie, Oregon #753/R
£313 $500 €457 Fire light nocturnal scene (76x51cm-30x20in) s. 20-Sep-3 Jeffery Burchard, Florida #16/R
£380 $700 €555 Winter landscape (56x76cm-22x30in) s. 26-Jun-4 Susanin's, Chicago #6129/R
£447 $800 €653 Path to the mountains (46x61cm-18x24in) s. 14-May-4 Skinner, Boston #223/R
£581 $1000 €848 Winter landscape (25x30cm-10x12in) s. painted c.1920. 7-Dec-3 Treadway Gallery, Cincinnati #524/R
£615 $1100 €898 Winter's night (44x60cm-17x24in) s. canvasboard. 14-May-4 Skinner, Boston #224/R

SVENSSON, Christian Fredrik (1834-1909) Swedish
£336 $542 €491 Sailing boat with red sails (27x21cm-11x8in) s. cardboard. 25-Aug-3 Lilla Bukowskis, Stockholm #507 (S.KR 4400)
£435 $783 €653 Seascape with sailing boats (42x31cm-17x12in) s. 25-Apr-4 Goteborg Auktionsverk, Sweden #207/R (S.KR 6000)
£526 $946 €768 Seascape (86x146cm-34x57in) s. 26-Jan-4 Lilla Bukowskis, Stockholm #428 (S.KR 7000)
£665 $1191 €971 Seascape with sailing boats (53x104cm-21x41in) s. 28-May-4 Uppsala Auktionskammare, Uppsala #129 (S.KR 9000)
£802 $1475 €1203 Seascape with boats (33x62cm-13x24in) s. 14-Jun-4 Lilla Bukowskis, Stockholm #328 (S.KR 11000)
£956 $1539 €1396 Seascape (56x106cm-22x42in) s. 25-Aug-3 Lilla Bukowskis, Stockholm #355 (S.KR 12500)
£1606 $2585 €2345 Seascape (45x100cm-18x39in) s. 25-Aug-3 Lilla Bukowskis, Stockholm #494 est:20000-25000 (S.KR 21000)
£1774 $3175 €2590 Ship's portrait of Aeolus in Copenhagen Harbour (40x60cm-16x24in) s.d.1890. 25-May-4 Bukowskis, Stockholm #156/R est:15000-20000 (S.KR 24000)
£1848 $3307 €2698 Seascape with vessels having Dutch flags (66x97cm-26x38in) s. 25-May-4 Bukowskis, Stockholm #157/R est:15000-20000 (S.KR 25000)
£3154 $5425 €4605 Shipwreck (110x180cm-43x71in) s. 2-Dec-3 Bukowskis, Stockholm #124/R est:30000-35000 (S.KR 41000)

SVENSSON, Gunnar (1892-1977) Swedish
£334 $600 €501 Summer garden (55x66cm-22x26in) s/. 25-Apr-4 Goteborg Auktionsverk, Sweden #315/R (S.KR 4600)
£437 $805 €656 Paalsundet (65x46cm-26x18in) s. 14-Jun-4 Lilla Bukowskis, Stockholm #49 (S.KR 6000)
£733 $1297 €1070 View of Stockholm with Katarinahissen (61x50cm-24x20in) s. 27-Apr-4 AB Stockholms Auktionsverk #698/R (S.KR 10000)

SVENSSON, Kari (1954-) Danish
£993 $1827 €1450 Stormy seas, Faroe Islands (125x140cm-49x55in) init.d.95 i.stretcher. 29-Mar-4 Rasmussen, Copenhagen #272/R (D.KR 11000)

SVENSSON, Otto H (1917-) Danish
£282 $480 €412 Composition S II (79x74cm-31x29in) s.d.59 verso. 29-Nov-3 Rasmussen, Havnen #4054/R (D.KR 3000)

SVENSSON, Roland (1910-2003) Swedish
£487 $843 €711 River landscape (23x32cm-9x13in) s.d.39. 15-Dec-3 Lilla Bukowskis, Stockholm #700 (S.KR 6200)
£9790 $17621 €14293 Archipelago in winter (121x70cm-48x28in) s.d.1965. 26-Apr-4 Bukowskis, Stockholm #196/R est:50000-70000 (S.KR 135000)
Works on paper
£307 $501 €448 View of Puetro de Andraitx (33x45cm-13x18in) s. bears i. W/C. 29-Sep-3 Lilla Bukowskis, Stockholm #517 (S.KR 4000)
£333 $595 €486 Self-portrait in the seaward skerries (29x22cm-11x9in) s. mixed media. 26-May-4 AB Stockholms Auktionsverk #2324/R (S.KR 4500)
£538 $926 €785 Mountain landscape from the Atlan coast (44x27cm-17x11in) s.d.55 W/C chl. 3-Dec-3 AB Stockholms Auktionsverk #2446/R (S.KR 7000)
£538 $926 €785 Dunotter Castle, Kincardine, Scotland (41x30cm-16x12in) s. W/C chl. 3-Dec-3 AB Stockholms Auktionsverk #2447/R (S.KR 7000)
£1692 $2911 €2470 Archipelago, Gilloga (30x43cm-12x17in) s.i.d.43 pastel. 3-Dec-3 AB Stockholms Auktionsverk #2277/R est:12000-15000 (S.KR 22000)
£2462 $4234 €3595 From Gill Island, dusk (26x41cm-10x16in) s. mixed media. 3-Dec-3 AB Stockholms Auktionsverk #2445/R est:15000-18000 (S.KR 32000)
£3695 $6615 €5395 From the skerries - Store Nasa (34x46cm-13x18in) s. mixed media. 26-May-4 AB Stockholms Auktionsverk #2109/R est:25000-30000 (S.KR 50000)

SVENSSON, Uno (1929-) Swedish
Works on paper
£340 $608 €500 Untitled (80x58cm-31x23in) s.d.90 mixed media paper on panel. 21-Mar-4 Calmels Cohen, Paris #148/R

SVENSSON, Wiking (1915-1979) Swedish
£254 $457 €381 Figure (44x56cm-17x22in) s. 25-Apr-4 Goteborg Auktionsverk, Sweden #402/R (S.KR 3500)

SVENUNGSSON, Jan (1961-) Swedish
Works on paper
£879 $1556 €1283 Gas II (49x129cm-19x51in) s.d.1990 verso collage. 27-Apr-4 AB Stockholms Auktionsverk #1143/R (S.KR 12000)

SVERTSCHKOFF, Nicolas Gregorovitch (1817-1898) Russian
£18000 $30600 €26280 Huntsmen resting before the chase (46x65cm-18x26in) s.d.1890. 19-Nov-3 Sotheby's, London #31/R est:25000
£20000 $34000 €30000 Horse drawn sledge (49x71cm-19x28in) s. 25-Nov-3 Christie's, London #105/R est:6000-8000
£30000 $53700 €43800 Still life with Balalaika (52x74cm-20x29in) 26-May-4 Sotheby's, London #19/R est:5000-7000
£120000 $214800 €175200 Attacked by wolves (80x130cm-31x51in) s. 26-May-4 Sotheby's, London #36/R est:40000-60000
Works on paper
£634 $995 €926 Winter landscape with figures in sleigh with horses (22x31cm-9x12in) s.d.1855 i.verso pencil crayon. 30-Aug-3 Rasmussen, Havnen #2012 (D.KR 6800)
£1064 $1681 €1500 Horses. s. graphite. 24-Jul-3 Claude Boisgirard, Paris #67
£1700 $3043 €2482 Winter sleigh ride (22x32cm-9x13in) s.i.d.1859 pencil W/C. 26-May-4 Sotheby's, Olympia #376/R est:800-1000
£2600 $4420 €3900 Winter troika in snowstorm (23x32cm-9x13in) s.d.1855 pencil htd white. 25-Nov-3 Christie's, London #106/R est:4000-6000
£2695 $5013 €3935 Russian soldier on horseback with two dogs on a lead (32x24cm-13x9in) s. W/C. 2-Mar-4 Rasmussen, Copenhagen #1323/R est:4000 (D.KR 30000)

SVERTSCHKOFF, Vladimir Dimitrievitch (attrib) (1820-1888) Russian
£2667 $4773 €4000 Roses (75x60cm-30x24in) s.verso. 15-May-4 Hagelstam, Helsinki #38/R est:4000

SVETOSLAVSKY, Sergei Ivanovich (1857-1931) Russian
£1021 $1634 €1450 Woodland glade (44x63cm-17x25in) s. 18-Sep-3 Hagelstam, Helsinki #982
£13245 $24106 €20000 Scene de marche en Russie (42x62cm-17x24in) s. 16-Jun-4 Claude Boisgirard, Paris #156/R est:20000-22000
£22000 $37400 €33000 Oriental market scene (47x62cm-19x24in) s. canvas on board. 25-Nov-3 Christie's, London #119/R est:12000-15000

SVIRIDOV, Sergei (1964-) Russian
£278 $453 €400 Still life in Venice (54x65cm-21x26in) s. 23-Sep-3 Durán, Madrid #673/R
£417 $663 €600 Merienda sobre mentel rosa (56x71cm-22x28in) s. 29-Apr-3 Durán, Madrid #816/R

SVOBODA, Josef (1901-) Czechoslovakian
£702 $1194 €1025 Lake in a forest (89x88cm-35x35in) s. 29-Nov-3 Dorotheum, Prague #60/R est:15000-25000 (C.KR 32000)
£1476 $2599 €2214 Fishing barges (90x90cm-35x35in) s. 22-May-4 Dorotheum, Prague #136/R est:40000-60000 (C.KR 70000)

SVOLINSKY, Karel (1896-1986) Czechoslovakian?
£300 $540 €450 Clown portrait (28x22cm-11x9in) s. oil tempera board. 24-Apr-4 Reiss & Sohn, Konigstein #5709/R

SWABIAN SCHOOL (15th C) German
£6000 $10200 €8760 Dormition of the Virgin (110x91cm-43x36in) panel. 29-Oct-3 Christie's, London #46/R est:6000-8000

SWABIAN SCHOOL (16th C) German
£5500 $9900 €8030 Dormition of the Virgin (101x70cm-40x28in) panel prov. 21-Apr-4 Christie's, London #52/R est:6000-8000

SWAGEMAKERS, Theo (1898-1994) Dutch
£476 $808 €680 Poor woman (100x80cm-39x31in) s.d.39 exhib. 24-Nov-3 Glerum, Amsterdam #117/R
£476 $867 €700 Still life with a pear and two lemons (28x33cm-11x13in) s.d.78 board prov. 3-Feb-4 Christie's, Amsterdam #420
£556 $878 €800 Still life with a candlestick, fruit and a wine glass (30x40cm-12x16in) s.d.83 canvasboard. 2-Sep-3 Christie's, Amsterdam #436
£556 $906 €800 Flowers in a white ceramic vase (50x60cm-20x24in) s.d.69. 29-Sep-3 Sotheby's, Amsterdam #309/R
£764 $1207 €1100 Still life with yellow jug (48x55cm-19x22in) s.d.69 plywood. 2-Sep-3 Christie's, Amsterdam #438 est:1000-1500
£833 $1358 €1200 View of the Blauwburgwal, Amsterdam (60x80cm-24x31in) s.i.verso. 29-Sep-3 Sotheby's, Amsterdam #281/R

SWAGERS, Frans (1756-1836) Dutch
£592 $1089 €900 Paysage fluvial avec un troupeau et des paysans (32x40cm-13x16in) s. 25-Jun-4 Rossini, Paris #56
£1879 $3495 €2800 Paysage fluvial anime d'un troupeau et personnages (40x32cm-16x13in) s. 7-Mar-4 Livinec, Gaudcheau & Jezequel, Rennes #46
£2639 $4169 €3800 River landscape with a damlooper and figures on the shore by a windmill (49x66cm-19x26in) s.d.1790. 2-Sep-3 Christie's, Amsterdam #110/R est:2500-3500
£3767 $6404 €5500 Troupeau dans un paysage (83x107cm-33x42in) s. 10-Nov-3 Horta, Bruxelles #112
£7400 $13468 €11100 Cattle, goat, dog and figures in high winds. Resting on a calm day by a river (29x38cm-11x15in) pair. 20-Jun-4 Wilkinson, Doncaster #338 est:8000-12000

SWAGERS, Frans (attrib) (1756-1836) Dutch
£1626 $2911 €2374 Pastoral landscape in harvest time (74x98cm-29x39in) 26-May-4 AB Stockholms Auktionsverk #2564/R est:25000-30000 (S.KR 22000)

SWAINE, Francis (1740-1782) British
£600 $954 €870 Moonlight river landscape (15x19cm-6x7in) s. copper. 9-Sep-3 Bonhams, Knightsbridge #64/R
£2000 $3580 €2920 Ships of the Red Squadron at sea. An Admiralty yacht off a Channel port (20x25cm-8x10in) s. copper pair. 26-May-4 Christie's, Kensington #569/R est:2000-4000
£2100 $3759 €3066 Dutch warship running into harbour under reduced sail. Dutch warship heading out to sea (15x19cm-6x7in) s. panel pair. 26-May-4 Christie's, Kensington #568/R est:2000-4000
£5345 $8926 €7804 British men-o-war (75x135cm-30x53in) 20-Oct-3 Stephan Welz, Johannesburg #184/R est:50000-70000 (SA.R 62000)
£9000 $14400 €13140 Ships of the fleet in the Hamoaze, with a view of Dock across the water (49x65cm-19x26in) s. 16-Sep-3 Bonhams, New Bond Street #73/R est:10000-15000

SWAINSON, William (fl.1884-1888) British
£4000 $6200 €5840 Portrait of artist son Edwin Swainson, in Brazilian landscape, holding a bow and arrow (83x69cm-33x27in) prov. 26-Sep-2 Christie's, London #108/R est:3000-5000

SWALLEY, John F (1887-?) American
£241 $425 €352 Maumee river scene (61x76cm-24x30in) s. painted c.1940. 23-May-4 Treadway Gallery, Cincinnati #731/R
£909 $1600 €1327 Industrial harbour scene (61x76cm-24x30in) s. painted c.1940. 23-May-4 Treadway Gallery, Cincinnati #727/R est:800-1200

SWALLOW, Ricky (1974-) Australian
Works on paper
£1221 $2223 €1783 Head disguise (28x19cm-11x7in) s.d.99 W/C two. 16-Jun-4 Deutscher-Menzies, Melbourne #185/R est:2500-4500 (A.D 3200)

SWALLOW, William Weldon (1912-) American
£1258 $2000 €1837 Landscape with farm buildings on hilly terrain (41x51cm-16x20in) s. board. 10-Sep-3 Alderfer's, Hatfield #421/R est:500-700

SWAMINATHAN, Jagdish (1928-1993) Indian
£5163 $9500 €7538 Untitled (56x82cm-22x32in) s.d.93 verso. 24-Mar-4 Sotheby's, New York #194/R est:8000-12000
£19022 $35000 €27772 Untitled (81x115cm-32x45in) s.d.91. 25-Mar-4 Christie's, Rockefeller NY #228/R est:15000-20000
£35326 $65000 €51576 Untitled (146x226cm-57x89in) 25-Mar-4 Christie's, Rockefeller NY #227/R est:50000-60000
Works on paper
£1902 $3500 €2777 Untitled (52x29cm-20x11in) s.indis.d. black ink. 24-Mar-4 Sotheby's, New York #191/R est:3500-4500

SWAN, Cuthbert Edmund (1870-1931) British
£780 $1303 €1139 Black panther (13x24cm-5x9in) init. panel. 11-Nov-3 Bonhams, Knightsbridge #40/R
£1800 $3330 €2628 Panther guarding his kill (51x76cm-20x30in) s.d.1899. 14-Jul-4 Christie's, Kensington #925/R est:2000-3000

SWAN, Douglas (1930-2001) American
£288 $472 €400 Air sock (26x38cm-10x15in) s.i.d. verso canvs on masonite plexiglas. 4-Jun-3 Ketterer, Hamburg #899/R
£995 $1692 €1453 Road and air aspects (70x70cm-28x28in) s.i.d.1976 verso acrylic. 22-Nov-3 Burkhard, Luzern #193/R (S.FR 2200)

SWAN, Edward (?) British
Works on paper
£280 $510 €420 The innocence of youth (25x17cm-10x7in) init. pencil W/C. 1-Jul-4 Christie's, Kensington #473/R
£400 $680 €584 Maid and poultry outside a cottage (25x36cm-10x14in) mono. W/C bodycol. 30-Oct-3 Duke & Son, Dorchester #91/R

SWAN, Edwin (1873-?) Irish
£5369 $9933 €8000 Portrait of a lady, seated wearing a blue dress (156x112cm-61x44in) s.d.1900. 10-Mar-4 James Adam, Dublin #15/R est:8000-12000

SWAN, John (20th C) American
£10695 $20000 €15615 River Tea (61x91cm-24x36in) s. 24-Jul-4 Coeur d'Alene, Hayden #255/R est:15000-20000

SWAN, John Macallan (1847-1910) British
£1400 $2338 €2044 Flight to Egypt (61x92cm-24x36in) s. 12-Nov-3 Sotheby's, Olympia #104/R est:800-1200

SWAN, Yvette (1970-) Australian
£17021 $28936 €24851 Going home (152x137cm-60x54in) s.d.02 s.i.d.2002 verso oil pastel graphite pencil. 25-Nov-3 Christie's, Melbourne #84/R est:8000-12000 (A.D 40000)
Works on paper
£5668 $9126 €8275 Reflections (198x137cm-78x54in) s.d.02 i.verso mixed media canvas. 25-Aug-3 Sotheby's, Paddington #307/R est:4000-7000 (A.D 14000)

SWANE, Christine (1876-1960) Danish
£611 $1040 €892 Pine forest (50x60cm-20x24in) init.d.1956 exhib. 26-Nov-3 Kunsthallen, Copenhagen #344 (D.KR 6500)

£656	$1069	€958	Swan windmill, Kjertеminde (84x72cm-33x28in) init. 28-Sep-3 Hindemae, Ullerslev #212/R (D.KR 7000)
£995	$1782	€1453	Still life of objects on table (65x64cm-26x25in) mono. 10-May-4 Rasmussen, Vejle #633/R (D.KR 11000)
£1596	$2666	€2330	Still life of plants and vases on window ledge (80x60cm-31x24in) mono. s.d.1947 verso. 7-Oct-3 Rasmussen, Copenhagen #317/R est:12000 (D.KR 17000)
£2160	$3607	€3154	Still life of flowers (75x65cm-30x26in) mono. s.d.1960 verso. 7-Oct-3 Rasmussen, Copenhagen #301/R est:15000 (D.KR 23000)
£2164	$3678	€3159	Still life of green plants (100x100cm-39x39in) init.d.1925. 29-Nov-3 Rasmussen, Havnen #4392/R est:25000 (D.KR 23000)
£2268	$4060	€3311	Landscape with buildings (63x78cm-25x31in) init.d.1948 prov. 12-Jan-4 Rasmussen, Vejle #537/R est:4000-8000 (D.KR 24000)
£4061	$7473	€5929	Still life of plants (131x101cm-52x40in) init.d.1944 s.d.1944 verso prov.exhib.lit. 29-Mar-4 Rasmussen, Copenhagen #215/R est:25000-30000 (D.KR 45000)

SWANE, Lars (1913-2002) Danish

£321	$583	€469	Fishing village with beached boats (63x80cm-25x31in) init.d.48. 7-Feb-4 Rasmussen, Havnen #4086 (D.KR 3500)
£326	$583	€476	From Maarup harbour (61x75cm-24x30in) s.d.1976. 10-May-4 Rasmussen, Vejle #696/R (D.KR 3600)
£378	$677	€552	Landscape from Nivaa Bay (45x55cm-18x22in) s.d.58 i.stretcher. 12-Jan-4 Rasmussen, Vejle #505 (D.KR 4000)
£452	$810	€660	Four cows in field (92x115cm-36x45in) init.d.47. 10-May-4 Rasmussen, Vejle #701/R (D.KR 5000)
£473	$846	€691	Coastal landscape (60x75cm-24x30in) s.d.58. 12-Jan-4 Rasmussen, Vejle #591 (D.KR 5000)
£478	$775	€693	Dune landscape with houses and sea (65x75cm-26x30in) s. 4-Aug-3 Rasmussen, Vejle #586 (D.KR 5000)
£633	$1134	€924	Still life of bouquet of flowers on table (70x60cm-28x24in) s.d.1955. 10-May-4 Rasmussen, Vejle #632/R (D.KR 7000)
£637	$1039	€930	Interior scene with many potted plants (86x67cm-34x26in) init.d.44. 28-Sep-3 Hindemae, Ullerslev #239/R (D.KR 6800)

SWANE, Sigurd (1879-1973) Danish

£284	$455	€412	Portrait of vicar Bechmann's wife (60x56cm-24x22in) prov. 17-Sep-3 Kunsthallen, Copenhagen #276 (D.KR 3000)
£302	$550	€453	Landscape from Kullen, Bjorkerod (47x60cm-19x24in) init. 19-Jun-4 Rasmussen, Havnen #4080/R (D.KR 3400)
£358	$645	€523	Outside a small town, Padules in Sierra Nevada, Spain (47x63cm-19x25in) s. d.juli 1966 verso. 24-Apr-4 Rasmussen, Havnen #4174 (D.KR 4000)
£373	$585	€545	Summer's day by small house (39x45cm-15x18in) init. 30-Aug-3 Rasmussen, Havnen #4335 (D.KR 4000)
£376	$677	€549	Autumn landscape (47x55cm-19x22in) init. 24-Apr-4 Rasmussen, Havnen #4044/R (D.KR 4200)
£498	$806	€722	Southern landscape with figures on mountain path (50x49cm-20x19in) init. 4-Aug-3 Rasmussen, Vejle #655/R (D.KR 5200)
£506	$844	€739	Green landscape (60x60cm-24x24in) init. 25-Oct-3 Rasmussen, Havnen #4054/R (D.KR 5400)
£560	$1046	€818	Flower picture (68x50cm-27x20in) init. 25-Feb-4 Kunsthallen, Copenhagen #235 (D.KR 6200)
£640	$1087	€934	Danish autumn landscape in sunshine (62x82cm-24x32in) init. 29-Nov-3 Rasmussen, Havnen #4357 (D.KR 6800)
£711	$1137	€1031	The outskirts of Jalon, Alicante (49x61cm-19x24in) init. 17-Sep-3 Kunsthallen, Copenhagen #289/R (D.KR 7500)
£753	$1279	€1099	Interior scene with small girl wearing red dress (82x65cm-32x26in) init. 26-Nov-3 Kunsthallen, Copenhagen #334/R (D.KR 8000)
£790	$1343	€1153	Danish autumn landscape (62x73cm-24x29in) init.d.41. 29-Nov-3 Rasmussen, Havnen #4313/R (D.KR 8400)
£812	$1495	€1186	Cow in landscape (61x84cm-24x33in) init.d.44. 29-Mar-4 Rasmussen, Copenhagen #454/R (D.KR 9000)
£939	$1568	€1371	Autumn forest (94x74cm-37x29in) init. 7-Oct-3 Rasmussen, Copenhagen #330/R (D.KR 10000)
£941	$1694	€1374	Hyacinths (59x52cm-23x20in) mono. 24-Apr-4 Rasmussen, Havnen #4102 (D.KR 10500)
£948	$1517	€1375	Irises in white jug (60x40cm-24x16in) init. 17-Sep-3 Kunsthallen, Copenhagen #291/R (D.KR 10000)
£1067	$1941	€1601	The music lesson (100x94cm-39x37in) s.d.1911 exhib. 19-Jun-4 Rasmussen, Havnen #4179/R est:10000-15000 (D.KR 12000)
£1185	$1896	€1718	Still life of hyacinths and tulips on table (85x70cm-33x28in) init. 17-Sep-3 Kunsthallen, Copenhagen #307/R est:15000 (D.KR 12500)
£2437	$4484	€3558	Still life of flowers (65x51cm-26x20in) init.d.31. 29-Mar-4 Rasmussen, Copenhagen #189/R est:30000 (D.KR 27000)
£7220	$13285	€10541	At her toilet - nude female model (94x72cm-37x28in) init.d.1915 s.stretcher prov. 29-Mar-4 Rasmussen, Copenhagen #197/R est:80000 (D.KR 80000)

SWANENBURGH, Isaac Claesz van (1538-1614) Flemish

£10345	$17276	€15000	Portrait of Marytge Dedel, wife of the artist (95x71cm-37x28in) d.i.1570 panel prov.lit. 15-Nov-3 Lempertz, Koln #1151/R est:15000-20000

SWANENBURGH, Jacob Isaacsz (1571-1638) Flemish

£2961	$5448	€4500	Christ aux Limbes (19x50cm-7x20in) panel. 24-Jun-4 Tajan, Paris #6/R est:6000-8000

SWANEVELT, Herman van (1600-1655) Dutch

£32000	$58560	€46720	Italianate landscape with travellers on path (47x64cm-19x25in) s.d.1649 panel prov. 8-Jul-4 Sotheby's, London #119/R est:15000-20000
£37162	$65405	€55000	Itailianate landscape with figures, man on a donkey and fishermen near a river (71x100cm-28x39in) indis sig.i. prov.exhib. 18-May-4 Sotheby's, Amsterdam #72/R est:20000-30000
Works on paper			
£61644	$104795	€90000	Landscape with Balaam and the ass (23x32cm-9x13in) i. pen brown ink brown grey wash over col chk prov. 4-Nov-3 Sotheby's, Amsterdam #99/R est:20000-30000

SWANEVELT, Herman van (attrib) (1600-1655) Dutch

£4225	$7394	€6000	Rural landscape (32x26cm-13x10in) panel. 17-Dec-3 Piasa, Paris #18/R est:2000-3000

SWANN, James (1905-1985) American

Works on paper			
£240	$400	€350	Reclining nude (23x23cm-9x9in) pencil. 18-Oct-3 David Dike, Dallas #50/R

SWANSON, Garry R (1941-) American

£6395	$11000	€9337	Serengeti mid-day (60x120cm-24x47in) s.i. prov. 3-Dec-3 Doyle, New York #255/R est:8000-12000

SWANSON, George Alan (1908-) American

£274	$450	€400	Wooded landscape (46x41cm-18x16in) s. prov. 31-May-3 Brunk, Ashville #224/R

SWANSON, Ray (1937-) American

£2353	$4000	€3435	Returning with news of Indians (61x91cm-24x36in) canvasboard. 1-Nov-3 Altermann Galleries, Santa Fe #106
£2795	$4500	€4053	Slippers are too big, fountain is too high (51x41cm-20x16in) board. 22-Aug-3 Altermann Galleries, Santa Fe #40
£3631	$6500	€5301	Caught again (71x91cm-28x36in) board. 15-May-4 Altermann Galleries, Santa Fe #31/R
£8696	$14000	€12609	Navajo mother and child (102x76cm-40x30in) 22-Aug-3 Altermann Galleries, Santa Fe #39
£8824	$15000	€12883	Final touches (61x97cm-24x38in) board. 1-Nov-3 Altermann Galleries, Santa Fe #94
£12291	$22000	€17945	Land of the eagle (127x76cm-50x30in) 15-May-4 Altermann Galleries, Santa Fe #29/R

SWANSTROM, Verna (20th C) American

£735	$1250	€1073	River landscape (46x61cm-18x24in) s. board prov. 18-Nov-3 John Moran, Pasadena #191

SWANWICK, Betty (1915-1989) British

Works on paper			
£1600	$2816	€2336	Joshua and Angelica at the Royal Academy (58x51cm-23x20in) W/C pencil. 19-May-4 Sotheby's, Olympia #272/R est:800-1200

SWANWICK, Harold (1866-1929) British

£38000	$69920	€55480	Drinking trough (123x183cm-48x72in) s. exhib.lit. 11-Jun-4 Christie's, London #127/R est:30000-50000
Works on paper			
£605	$1113	€883	Wildflowers on the coast (65x110cm-26x43in) s.d.1892 W/C. 14-Jun-4 Waddingtons, Toronto #71/R est:2000-2500 (C.D 1500)
£780	$1435	€1139	Droving sheep in the afternoon sun (17x25cm-7x10in) W/C. 23-Mar-4 Rosebery Fine Art, London #729/R
£1100	$2035	€1606	Weary beasts returning from the plough (33x42cm-13x17in) s.d.94 W/C. 14-Jul-4 Sotheby's, Olympia #116/R est:1000-2000
£1815	$3339	€2650	Tilling the uplands (24x40cm-9x16in) s. W/C. 9-Jun-4 Walker's, Ottawa #365/R est:3000-3500 (C.D 4500)
£2800	$4760	€4088	Shepherd and sheep in an extensive downland landscape (74x124cm-29x49in) s.i. W/C. 30-Oct-3 Duke & Son, Dorchester #118/R est:300-600

SWANZY, Mary (1882-1978) Irish

£1678	$2853	€2400	Ladies in a window. Table set with wine and bread (25x30cm-10x12in) s. panel double-sided. 18-Nov-3 Whyte's, Dublin #24/R est:6000-8000
£4161	$7448	€6200	Swan (24x33cm-9x13in) s. board prov. 26-May-4 James Adam, Dublin #107/R est:6000-8000
£7042	$11268	€10000	Figures at market, Czechoslovakia (30x41cm-12x16in) s. 16-Sep-3 Whyte's, Dublin #12/R est:7000-9000
£7047	$12473	€10500	Fishermen, Kilkeel, County Down (40x31cm-16x12in) s. board prov. 27-Apr-4 Whyte's, Dublin #112/R est:10000-12000
£8889	$16000	€12978	Portrait of a woman wearing a black hat (43x30cm-17x12in) i. verso board. 23-Apr-4 Weschler, Washington #134/R est:600-800
£9000	$16110	€13140	Banana tree, Samoa (76x56cm-30x22in) s. i.verso prov.exhib. 14-May-4 Christie's, London #9/R est:10000-15000
£38000	$68020	€55480	Two young girls among banana trees (76x63cm-30x25in) s. i.verso prov.exhib. 13-May-4 Sotheby's, London #32/R est:40000-60000
Works on paper			
£700	$1253	€1022	Male standing figure wearing a garland (27x19cm-11x7in) chl pastel prov. 14-May-4 Christie's, Kensington #406/R

SWART VAN GRONINGEN, Jan (c.1495-1560) Dutch

£88889	$160000	€129778	Baptism of Christ (95x49cm-37x19in) panel prov.exhib. 23-Jan-4 Christie's, Rockefeller NY #17/R est:200000-300000
Works on paper			
£6419	$11297	€9500	Biblical scene, possibly seeking refuge with Samuel (25x18cm-10x7in) bears i.verso pen grey ink brown wash black chk prov.exhib. 19-May-4 Sotheby's, Amsterdam #16/R est:12000-18000

SWART VAN GRONINGEN, Jan (attrib) (c.1495-1560) Dutch

Works on paper			
£2585	$4627	€3800	Tobie recevant des excrements d'oiseaux sur les yeux et devenant aveugle (24x14cm-9x6in) pen brown ink black crayon brown wash htd gouache. 19-Mar-4 Piasa, Paris #11/R est:2500

SWART, Cristianus Hendricus de (1818-1897) Dutch

£664	$1110	€950	The hay harvest (15x20cm-6x8in) s.d.1846 panel. 30-Jun-3 Sotheby's, Amsterdam #74

SWART, Jan de (20th C) American

Sculpture			
£1639	$3000	€2459	Untitled, two heads (30x30x13cm-12x12x5in) carved satinwood. 6-Jun-4 Wright, Chicago #343/R est:3000-5000

SWARTZ, Johan David (attrib) (1678-c.1729) Swedish
£5692 $9791 €8310 Portrait of Queen Ulrika Eleonora the younger (145x117cm-57x46in) bears sig.d.1725 verso. 3-Dec-3 AB Stockholms Auktionsverk #2494/R est:40000-50000 (S.KR 74000)

SWARTZ, John (19/20th C) American
Photographs
£19886 $35000 €29034 Wild bunch (18x21cm-7x8in) silver print executed c.1900. 20-May-4 Swann Galleries, New York #277/R est:50000-70000

SWARTZLANDER, Frank (20th C) American
£518 $850 €756 Autumn landscape with house (23x23cm-9x9in) s. 4-Jun-3 Alderfer's, Hatfield #389
£549 $900 €802 Landscape with house and barn (23x25cm-9x10in) s. board. 4-Jun-3 Alderfer's, Hatfield #390/R

SWAYHOOVER, Albert (1931-) American
£409 $650 €597 Landscape with lakeside house on hill, sailboat moored at shore (122x91cm-48x36in) s. 10-Sep-3 Alderfer's, Hatfield #344/R

SWEARINGEN, Johnnie (1908-1993) American
£1317 $2200 €1923 Farm scene with man, dog and bulls (41x61cm-16x24in) masonite prov. 15-Nov-3 Slotin Folk Art, Buford #145/R est:2000-4000
£1737 $2900 €2536 Choppin' cotton (48x58cm-19x23in) canvasboard prov. 15-Nov-3 Slotin Folk Art, Buford #147/R est:2000-4000
£2096 $3500 €3060 Watermelon farming (76x102cm-30x40in) acrylic prov. 15-Nov-3 Slotin Folk Art, Buford #146/R est:2000-4000

SWEBACH, Bernard Edouard (1800-1870) French
£2254 $3899 €3200 Halte de militaires pres d'une maison (36x47cm-14x19in) s.d.1825. 10-Dec-3 Maigret, Paris #33/R est:4000-5000
£4503 $8196 €6800 Scene de chasse a courre au cerf (22x44cm-9x17in) s.d.1821. 16-Jun-4 Beaussant & Lefèvre, Paris #4/R est:4000-5000
£5775 $10106 €8200 Combat de chevaux sauvages (37x44cm-15x17in) s.d.1853. 17-Dec-3 Piasa, Paris #104/R est:8000-12000
£14765 $27168 €22000 Jewish horse market (56x78cm-22x31in) mono.d.1823 lit. 25-Mar-4 Karlheinz Kaupp, Staufen #2758/R est:3900
Works on paper
£496 $829 €700 Scene de chasse a courre (7x14cm-3x6in) s.d.1838 W/C. 20-Jun-3 Drouot Estimations, Paris #52
£1310 $2188 €1900 Hussard a cheval (12x16cm-5x6in) s. W/C. 16-Nov-3 Muizon & Le Coent, Paris #26

SWEBACH-DESFONTAINES (18/19th C) French
Works on paper
£476 $852 €700 Cavaliers au repos (13x13cm-5x5in) black crayon. 17-Mar-4 Tajan, Paris #97

SWEBACH-DESFONTAINES, Jacques François (1769-1823) French
£1268 $2104 €1800 Cavaliers (24x33cm-9x13in) 10-Jun-3 Adjug'art, Brest #116/R
£30000 $54900 €43800 Military encampment in landscape (28x57cm-11x22in) mono. panel prov. 8-Jul-4 Sotheby's, London #337/R est:15000-20000

SWEBACH-DESFONTAINES, Jacques François (attrib) (1769-1823) French
£3448 $6172 €5034 Men and horses (54x45cm-21x18in) panel. 12-May-4 Dobiaschofsky, Bern #1010/R est:6500 (S.FR 8000)

SWEDISH SCHOOL, 18th C
£9231 $15877 €13477 Table of monarchs from Gustaf Vasa to Gustaf III (28x21cm-11x8in) folio of 18. 2-Dec-3 Bukowskis, Stockholm #298/R est:80000 (S.KR 120000)

SWEDISH SCHOOL, 19th C
Sculpture
£6800 $12171 €9928 Portrait bust of King Karl XII (74cm-29in) white marble incl. socle. 26-May-4 AB Stockholms Auktionsverk #2263/R est:20000-30000 (S.KR 92000)

SWEDLUND, Pelle (1865-1947) Swedish
£1154 $1985 €1685 The knight and the dragon (63x75cm-25x30in) init. 2-Dec-3 Bukowskis, Stockholm #154/R est:20000-25000 (S.KR 15000)
£2231 $3837 €3257 Girl dressed in blue, summer evening, Visby (85x70cm-33x28in) init. lit. 2-Dec-3 Bukowskis, Stockholm #153/R est:25000-30000 (S.KR 29000)
£2365 $4234 €3453 Lighting the fire, autumn evening (122x93cm-48x37in) panel. 25-May-4 Bukowskis, Stockholm #219/R est:25000-30000 (S.KR 32000)

SWEELINK, Gerrit Pietersz (1566-1645) Dutch
Works on paper
£8904 $15137 €13000 Saint Francis receiving the Stigmata (14x18cm-6x7in) mono.i.d.14 Oct 1608 i.verso pen brown ink col wash prov.exhib.li. 4-Nov-3 Sotheby's, Amsterdam #20/R est:1500-2000

SWEERTS, Michiel (1618-1664) Flemish
£328947 $605263 €500000 Portrait de jeune garcon au chapeau (34x26cm-13x10in) 25-Jun-4 Rossini, Paris #40/R est:10000-12000

SWEERTS, Michiel (attrib) (1618-1664) Flemish
£3693 $6500 €5392 Self portrait wearing a red turban (48x41cm-19x16in) oil paper on panel. 28-May-4 Aspire, Cleveland #12/R est:7000-12000
£13000 $23400 €18980 Burial (82x64cm-32x25in) prov.lit. 21-Apr-4 Christie's, London #25/R est:10000-15000
£17219 $31338 €26000 Portrait of young man (65x49cm-26x19in) 16-Jun-4 Christie's, Rome #435/R est:10000-15000
£20000 $33400 €29200 Portrait of a young boys head and shoulders wearing brown coat (20x15cm-8x6in) prov. 18-Jun-3 John Nicholson, Haslemere #746/R est:1000-2000

SWEERTS, Michiel (circle) (1618-1664) Flemish
£13158 $24211 €20000 Portrait d'homme (12x9cm-5x4in) panel octagonal prov. 24-Jun-4 Christie's, Paris #41/R est:800-1200
£18000 $32400 €26280 Portrait of a young artist holding a drawing (20x14cm-8x6in) panel. 22-Apr-4 Sotheby's, London #38/R est:5000-7000

SWEET, Francis E (20th C) American
£1111 $2000 €1622 Launch Site (91x61cm-36x24in) s.d.1989 board. 26-Jan-4 Schrager Galleries, Milwaukee #1394

SWEET, Pat (20th C) American?
£359 $600 €524 Ascot (91x61cm-36x24in) masonite. 18-Oct-3 David Dike, Dallas #260/R

SWEET, Walter H (1889-1943) British
Works on paper
£400 $668 €584 Donald Falls, Newcastle (35x25cm-14x10in) s. W/C htd white. 14-Oct-3 Bearnes, Exeter #347
£400 $748 €584 St Michael's Mount from the foreshore Marazion (25x36cm-10x14in) s. W/C. 26-Feb-4 Lane, Penzance #74
£400 $748 €584 Mousehole harbour (18x28cm-7x11in) s. W/C. 26-Feb-4 Lane, Penzance #91
£480 $898 €701 Coastal landscape near Land's End, Cornwall (25x36cm-10x14in) s. 26-Feb-4 Lane, Penzance #73
£950 $1757 €1387 Unravelling the nets (35x53cm-14x21in) s. W/C. 10-Mar-4 Sotheby's, Olympia #173/R est:600-800
£1100 $1826 €1606 Cottages at Mousehole harbour (24x36cm-9x14in) s. W/C. 2-Oct-3 Lane, Penzance #185/R est:850-950
£1400 $2324 €2044 Newlyn Slip and harbour (25x35cm-10x14in) s. W/C. 2-Oct-3 Lane, Penzance #10/R est:900-1200

SWEETLEY, Denby (20th C) British?
£600 $954 €876 Birds amongst poppies, sunflowers and lilies (81x74cm-32x29in) panel pair. 9-Sep-3 Gorringes, Lewes #1977/R

SWENNEN, Walter (20th C) ?
£2500 $4175 €3600 After Matthew (190x180cm-75x71in) s. d.1988 verso. 21-Oct-3 Campo & Campo, Antwerp #290/R est:3000-3500

SWIESZEWSKI, Alexander (1839-1895) Polish
£1766 $2931 €2578 Landscape with tall pinetrees (12x19cm-5x7in) s. canvas on board painted c.1880. 15-Jun-3 Agra, Warsaw #22/R est:9000 (P.Z 11000)
£2031 $3392 €2965 Sunset over Jeziorem Gosausee (15x26cm-6x10in) mono. board painted c.1890. 19-Oct-3 Agra, Warsaw #33/R est:5000 (P.Z 13000)
£2098 $3608 €3000 Walkers on the banks of the Isar (13x32cm-5x13in) s. panel. 3-Dec-3 Neumeister, Munich #761/R est:1500
£4539 $7852 €6627 Landscape with lake and fishing boat with mountains in background (34x65cm-13x26in) s. painted c.1880. 14-Dec-3 Agra, Warsaw #33/R est:22000 (P.Z 30000)

SWIFT, John Warkup (1815-1869) British
£880 $1628 €1285 Narrow escape (53x77cm-21x30in) s. 10-Feb-4 Bonhams, Knightsbridge #24
£900 $1575 €1314 Fishing and other boats with a man-o-war on the rocks (38x61cm-15x24in) s.d.1869. 18-Dec-3 John Nicholson, Haslemere #1128
£2841 $5000 €4148 Rescue at sea (62x90cm-24x35in) s.d.1849. 18-May-4 Bonhams & Butterfields, San Francisco #153/R est:3000-5000
£2973 $5500 €4341 The Amoor running under reduced sail in the Channel off Dover (61x91cm-24x36in) s.d.1868 prov. 10-Feb-4 Christie's, Rockefeller NY #228/R est:6000-8000

SWIFT, John Warkup (attrib) (1815-1869) British
£627 $1009 €915 Ship wreck (38x61cm-15x24in) 25-Aug-3 Lilla Bukowskis, Stockholm #264 (S.KR 8200)

SWIFT, Kate (20th C) Irish
£577 $1011 €820 Lovers (54x45cm-21x18in) s.d.03. 16-Dec-3 James Adam, Dublin #63/R

SWIFT, Patrick (1927-1983) Irish
£1486 $2809 €2200 London plane tree with building beyond (33x24cm-13x9in) d.1956-59 verso prov. 17-Feb-4 Whyte's, Dublin #18/R est:2000-3000
£9396 $16819 €14000 Bridge through trees (81x58cm-32x23in) board prov. 26-May-4 James Adam, Dublin #73/R est:14000-16000
£9859 $17056 €14000 Farmhouse through trees, Algarve, Portugal (72x90cm-28x35in) studio st.verso exhib. 10-Dec-3 Bonhams & James Adam, Dublin #92/R est:14000-16000

SWINBURNE, Edward (1765-1847) British
£400 $632 €580 Continental landscape, with lake, figures and goats (25x34cm-10x13in) s. card. 24-Jul-3 Dominic Winter, Swindon #70/R

SWINDEN, Henri Etienne van (1801-1836) Dutch
£1189 $2045 €1700 Fishing boat on the Dutch coast in the morning (52x66cm-20x26in) s.d.1831 canvas on canvas. 5-Dec-3 Bolland & Marotz, Bremen #663/R est:1700

SWINNERTON, Frederick (19th C) British
£1300 $2418 €1898 Milkmaid (51x91cm-20x36in) s. 4-Mar-4 Christie's, Kensington #648/R est:1000-1500

SWINNERTON, James G (1875-1974) American
£682 $1200 €996 On the edge of the canyon (21x20cm-8x8in) s. canvasboard. 23-May-4 Bonhams & Butterfields, San Francisco #6610/R
£765 $1300 €1117 Outline of Agatha Needle, Navaho Country (41x30cm-16x12in) s.i. canvas on board prov.lit. 1-Nov-3 Santa Fe Art, Santa Fe #80/R est:1000-2000
£882 $1500 €1288 Window Rock, New Mexico, Navaho Reservation (30x41cm-12x16in) s.i. canvas on board prov.lit. 1-Nov-3 Santa Fe Art, Santa Fe #79/R est:1500-2500
£1040 $1800 €1518 View of the Grand Canyon (25x30cm-10x12in) s. canvas board. 10-Dec-3 Bonhams & Butterfields, San Francisco #6135/R est:2000-3000
£1445 $2500 €2110 Palo Verde tree in bloom (71x86cm-28x34in) s. prov. 10-Dec-3 Bonhams & Butterfields, San Francisco #6334/R est:3000-5000
£2198 $4000 €3209 Monument Valley (63x76cm-25x30in) s. 29-Jun-4 Sotheby's, New York #251/R est:6000-9000
£3468 $6000 €5063 Sunset, Navajo reservation (41x36cm-16x14in) canvasboard prov. 10-Dec-3 Bonhams & Butterfields, San Francisco #6335/R est:4000-6000
£5028 $9000 €7341 Fingers of the desert (71x86cm-28x34in) 15-May-4 Altermann Galleries, Santa Fe #178/R
£5587 $10000 €8157 Monument Valley thunderstorm (76x102cm-30x40in) 15-May-4 Altermann Galleries, Santa Fe #179/R

SWISS SCHOOL, 16th C
£4751 $7935 €6936 Portrait de Abraham von Graffenried (18x14cm-7x6in) copper prov. 16-Nov-3 Koller, Geneva #1235/R est:14000-18000 (S.FR 10835)

SWISS SCHOOL, 18th C
£5172 $9517 €7551 Portrait of Seigneur de Rumligen, Bailli de Konitz (79x63cm-31x25in) d.1722 verso. 26-Mar-4 Koller, Zurich #3057/R est:4000-7000 (S.FR 12000)

SWISS SCHOOL, 19th C
£1702 $2928 €2485 Boy with gun (73x57cm-29x22in) 2-Dec-3 Koller, Zurich #3011/R est:8000-10000 (S.FR 3780)
Works on paper
£2398 $4076 €3500 Paysan suisse (24x16cm-9x6in) pen ink double-sided. 6-Nov-3 Tajan, Paris #215/R

SWITZER, Scott (20th C) American
£190 $350 €277 Reclining woman in a white dress (61x76cm-24x30in) s. 27-Jun-4 Bonhams & Butterfields, San Francisco #3865/R

SWOBODA, Josef Maria (1918-) Austrian
£355 $592 €500 Old wine cellar (40x50cm-16x20in) s. 14-Oct-3 Dorotheum, Vienna #121/R

SWOBODA, Rudolf (elder) (1819-1859) Austrian
£1379 $2303 €2000 Hunting party resting by mountain lake (145x203cm-57x80in) s. tin lit. 12-Jul-3 Bergmann, Erlangen #652/R est:3000

SWOBODA, Rudolf (younger) (1859-1914) Austrian
£867 $1551 €1300 Traunkirchen with Traunstein (75x91cm-30x36in) s. 13-May-4 Dorotheum, Linz #442/R

SWORD, James Brade (1839-1915) American
£706 $1200 €1031 Rocky inlet (46x76cm-18x30in) s.d.86 exhib. 18-Nov-3 Doyle, New York #30a est:2000-3000
£921 $1500 €1345 Cattle eating at rivers edge, autumn (38x56cm-15x22in) s. prov. 28-Sep-3 Bonhams & Butterfields, Los Angeles #7018a est:2000-3000
£1341 $2400 €1958 Cows by a stream (61x51cm-24x20in) s. 7-May-4 Sloans & Kenyon, Bethesda #1177/R est:3000-4000
£2045 $3600 €2986 Road Home - Wagon ride (51x71cm-20x28in) s. 23-May-4 Hindman, Chicago #156/R est:4000-6000
Works on paper
£329 $550 €480 Landscape with house (38x58cm-15x23in) s. W/C prov. 18-Jun-3 Doyle, New York #76/R

SWYNCOP, Charles (1895-1970) Belgian
£350 $584 €500 Marche couvert (46x38cm-18x15in) s. 13-Oct-3 Horta, Bruxelles #27
£397 $723 €600 Enfant au ballon (47x37cm-19x15in) s. 15-Jun-4 Galerie Moderne, Brussels #319

SWYNCOP, Philippe (1878-1949) Belgian
£302 $559 €450 La marchande de fleurs (46x38cm-18x15in) s. 15-Mar-4 Horta, Bruxelles #143
£526 $968 €800 Beach scene (37x46cm-15x18in) s.d.1954 panel. 22-Jun-4 Christie's, Amsterdam #509/R
£596 $1085 €900 La belle de Grenade (100x80cm-39x31in) s.i.d.1924. 15-Jun-4 Vanderkindere, Brussels #60
£671 $1235 €1000 Portrait d'espagnole (70x55cm-28x22in) s.d.1941. 23-Mar-4 Galerie Moderne, Brussels #149/R
£1127 $1949 €1600 Elegante a l'eventail (100x80cm-39x31in) s.d.1932. 14-Dec-3 St-Germain-en-Laye Encheres #78/R est:1500-2000
£2282 $4221 €3400 Nature morte au homard (100x150cm-39x59in) s. 15-Mar-4 Horta, Bruxelles #142 est:1800-2000
£3034 $5462 €4400 Fillette au chapeau fleuri (60x50cm-24x20in) s.d.21. 20-Jan-4 Galerie Moderne, Brussels #310/R est:1500-2000
£6400 $11456 €9344 Repose (98x123cm-39x48in) s.d.1927. 26-May-4 Sotheby's, Olympia #334/R est:5000-7000

SWYNNERTON, Annie (1844-1933) British
£2766 $4702 €4038 Portrait of Colwyn E A Philipps - eldest son of Viscount St Davids, G B E (84x82cm-33x32in) indis sig i. exhib. 26-Nov-3 Deutscher-Menzies, Melbourne #296c/R est:7000-10000 (A.D 6500)

SWYNNERTON, Frederick (19th C) British?
£19277 $32000 €28144 Maharaja of Kapurthala (234x130cm-92x51in) s.i.d.1890. 4-Oct-3 Neal Auction Company, New Orleans #388/R est:30000-50000

SYBERG, Ernst (1906-1981) Danish
£376 $627 €549 Autumn landscape, Snogekjaergaard, august (67x97cm-26x38in) s. exhib. 7-Oct-3 Rasmussen, Copenhagen #338 (D.KR 4000)
£427 $682 €619 Summer landscape (70x100cm-28x39in) s.d.1949. 17-Sep-3 Kunsthallen, Copenhagen #238 (D.KR 4500)

SYBERG, Fritz (1862-1939) Danish
£282 $470 €412 Landscape with water and reeds (46x66cm-18x26in) s. 7-Oct-3 Rasmussen, Copenhagen #318 (D.KR 3000)
£339 $576 €495 Landscape (20x28cm-8x11in) mono.d.1884. 29-Nov-3 Rasmussen, Havnen #4014 (D.KR 3600)
£562 $938 €821 Field landscape with farms (64x84cm-25x33in) mono.d.1917 18. 25-Oct-3 Rasmussen, Havnen #4005/R (D.KR 6000)
£587 $1079 €857 Wooded landscape (32x44cm-13x17in) mono.d.1916. 29-Mar-4 Rasmussen, Copenhagen #518/R (D.KR 6500)
£812 $1501 €1186 Autumn landscape with houses (66x90cm-26x35in) mono.d.1927. 15-Mar-4 Rasmussen, Vejle #671/R (D.KR 9000)
£900 $1441 €1314 Woman enjoying the view of lake (69x86cm-27x34in) s. 22-Sep-3 Rasmussen, Vejle #150/R (D.KR 9500)
£995 $1592 €1453 Seagulls in field by fjord (26x56cm-10x22in) mono. 22-Sep-3 Rasmussen, Vejle #151/R (D.KR 10500)
£1376 $2229 €2009 View across fields (48x66cm-19x26in) mono.d.1935. 9-Aug-3 Hindemae, Ullerslev #75/R est:12000 (D.KR 14500)
£1493 $2673 €2180 Summer landscape with sheep (56x66cm-22x26in) mono.d.1937. 10-May-4 Rasmussen, Vejle #551/R est:12000-15000 (D.KR 16500)
£1986 $3653 €2900 Chair and table in garden (215x150cm-85x59in) mono.d.1921-25. 29-Mar-4 Rasmussen, Copenhagen #499/R est:25000 (D.KR 22000)
£3280 $5347 €4789 Small girl with doll's pram, flowering bush in background (80x101cm-31x40in) init.d.1917. 28-Sep-3 Hindemae, Ullerslev #165/R est:10000-15000 (D.KR 35000)
Works on paper
£267 $485 €401 Dunes, beach and sea (58x73cm-23x29in) mono.d.1919 W/C. 19-Jun-4 Rasmussen, Havnen #4222 (D.KR 3000)

SYCHKOV, Feodor Vasilievich (1870-1958) Russian
£24575 $42514 €35880 Happy children on a sledge carousel (75x108cm-30x43in) s.d.1917. 9-Dec-3 Rasmussen, Copenhagen #1287/R est:100000-150000 (D.KR 260000)
£28000 $47600 €42000 Girl in flower garden (81x64cm-32x25in) s.d.1939. 25-Nov-3 Christie's, London #220/R est:3500-4500
£32000 $57280 €46720 Day off the Kolkhoz (65x78cm-26x31in) s.d.1937. 26-May-4 Sotheby's, London #307/R est:18000-25000

SYDNEY BIRD PAINTER (fl.1790) Australian
Works on paper
£8642 $15642 €12617 Parroquet from Botany Bay (39x28cm-15x11in) i. W/C lit. 30-Mar-4 Christie's, Melbourne #358/R est:10000-15000 (A.D 21000)

SYDNEY, Grahame (1948-) New Zealander
£2899 $4696 €4204 Nude on chair (48x28cm-19x11in) s.d.1969 board. 31-Jul-3 International Art Centre, Auckland #17/R est:8000-12000 (NZ.D 8000)
Works on paper
£714 $1214 €1042 Study of Caroline Kaunda (33x44cm-13x17in) s.d.15/12/1974 pencil. 27-Nov-3 International Art Centre, Auckland #55/R (NZ.D 1900)
£2068 $3515 €3019 Standing (53x54cm-21x21in) s.i.d.20.August 1987 pencil dr. 26-Nov-3 Dunbar Sloane, Wellington #31/R est:1500-2500 (NZ.D 5500)
£6294 $11455 €9189 Ida valley landscape (53x74cm-21x29in) s.d.2001 W/C. 29-Jun-4 Peter Webb, Auckland #26/R est:20000-30000 (NZ.D 18000)
£11278 $19173 €16466 Water tank on the Maniototo (55x75cm-22x30in) s.d.1989 W/C. 27-Nov-3 International Art Centre, Auckland #54/R est:20000-30000 (NZ.D 30000)

SYER, John (1815-1885) British
£420 $760 €613 Ruswarp (30x43cm-12x17in) s.verso oil on card. 15-Apr-4 Richardson & Smith, Whitby #126/R
£600 $1020 €876 Tranquil river landscape (27x38cm-11x15in) s. board. 26-Nov-3 Hamptons Fine Art, Godalming #195
£850 $1573 €1241 At the old watermill (68x91cm-27x36in) s.d.1852. 14-Jul-4 Christie's, Kensington #923
£1500 $2490 €2190 Figures in a wooded landscape (28x40cm-11x16in) s. board. 1-Oct-3 Sotheby's, Olympia #35/R est:800-1200
£1700 $3060 €2482 Resting in the hay stacks (31x46cm-12x18in) 21-Jan-4 Sotheby's, Olympia #380/R est:1000-1500
£2215 $4075 €3300 Dunstanborough Castle in Northumberland (104x152cm-41x60in) s.d.1876. 27-Mar-4 L & B, Essen #204/R est:1500
£4000 $6360 €5800 Panoramic view of Whitby (75x126cm-30x50in) s.d.1883. 9-Sep-3 David Duggleby, Scarborough #396/R est:4000-5000
£11500 $20930 €16790 Low tide (102x138cm-40x54in) s. 16-Jun-4 Bonhams, New Bond Street #72/R est:7000-10000
Works on paper
£280 $440 €406 Drover with cattle by a thatched cottage (23x35cm-9x14in) s.d.81 pencil W/C htd white. 28-Aug-3 Christie's, Kensington #481/R
£280 $476 €409 On the Esk (30x48cm-12x19in) s. W/C. 30-Oct-3 Richardson & Smith, Whitby #352
£300 $549 €438 Trawlers and fisherfolk, Whitby (35x63cm-14x25in) s.d.1883 W/C htd white scratching out. 6-Jul-4 Bearnes, Exeter #418/R
£350 $634 €511 Staithes (23x30cm-9x12in) W/C. 15-Apr-4 Richardson & Smith, Whitby #136
£450 $828 €657 Suspension Bridge at Bristol (36x57cm-14x22in) pencil W/C prov. 25-Mar-4 Christie's, Kensington #149/R
£550 $1012 €803 Whitby harbour (48x72cm-19x28in) s. W/C. 23-Mar-4 Bonhams, Knightsbridge #69/R

£700 $1169 €1022 Brock-a-Beck, Goathland High Moor (41x71cm-16x28in) s. W/C. 10-Oct-3 Richardson & Smith, Whitby #95

SYER, John C (1846-1913) British
£543 $1000 €793 Gothic landscape (28x43cm-11x17in) s. panel. 26-Jun-4 Susanin's, Chicago #6057/R est:600-1000
£550 $990 €803 Estuary at Whitby (41x53cm-16x21in) s. 21-Jan-4 Sotheby's, Olympia #343/R
£2300 $4186 €3358 Haymaking (74x125cm-29x49in) s. 3-Feb-4 Sworder & Son, Bishops Stortford #270/R est:1500-1800
Works on paper
£500 $925 €730 Newlyn Harbour, Cornwall. Cadwich Cove,Cornwall (40x28cm-16x11in) both s. W/C pair. 14-Jul-4 Bonhams, Chester #451

SYKES, Aubrey F (1910-1995) British
£300 $510 €438 Copper and Gold - a still life of fruit and copper pans (66x53cm-26x21in) s. 30-Oct-3 Grant, Worcester #551

SYKES, Charles (1875-1950) British
Sculpture
£1000 $1620 €1450 Lovers (41cm-16in) s.verso bronze exec.c.1890-1920. 26-Jan-3 Desmond Judd, Cranbrook #531

SYKES, Henry (1855-1921) British
Works on paper
£280 $454 €409 Moorish gateway, with figures and donkey (36x53cm-14x21in) s. W/C. 7-Aug-3 Neales, Nottingham #472
£1173 $1900 €1701 Distant village, summer (34x27cm-13x11in) s. W/C prov.exhib. 8-Aug-3 Barridorf, Portland #151/R est:1800-2200

SYKES, John Gutteridge (1866-1941) British
Works on paper
£320 $512 €467 Figure with donkey walking in a lane (18x27cm-7x11in) s. W/C. 17-Sep-3 Bonhams, Brooks & Langlois, Jersey #99/R
£580 $1038 €847 Pudding Hill, St Ives. Felak Village, Cornwall (36x18cm-14x7in) s. W/C pair. 7-May-4 Chrystals Auctions, Isle of Man #285
£600 $1104 €876 Geese and ducks before a mill and haystack (10x14cm-4x6in) s. W/C pair. 11-Jun-4 Keys, Aylsham #420
£750 $1253 €1095 Preparing nets (30x43cm-12x17in) s. W/C. 14-Oct-3 David Lay, Penzance #205

SYKES, Peace (fl.1870-1900) British
£700 $1295 €1022 Busy market scene (51x71cm-20x28in) i.d.1850 verso. 13-Jan-4 Bonhams, Knightsbridge #230/R

SYKORA, Gustav (1889-?) Czechoslovakian?
£790 $1343 €1153 Girl semi-nude (65x80cm-26x31in) s. 29-Nov-3 Dorotheum, Prague #59/R est:14000-25000 (C.KR 36000)
£3593 $6000 €5246 Odalisque (86x124cm-34x49in) s. prov. 7-Oct-3 Sotheby's, New York #91 est:1000-1500

SYKORA, Zdenek (1920-) Czechoslovakian
£6000 $10980 €9000 Line No 32 (150x150cm-59x59in) s.d.85 verso s.i.d.1985 stretcher prov.exhib. 4-Jun-4 Lempertz, Koln #474a/R est:8000-10000
£9333 $17080 €14000 Square structure (126x100cm-50x39in) s.d.63 verso s.i.d.1963 stretcher acrylic prov.exhib. 4-Jun-4 Lempertz, Koln #474/R est:8000-10000

SYLVESTER, Frederick Oakes (1869-1915) American
£427 $700 €619 Summer landscape (13x18cm-5x7in) i.verso board painted c.1910. 7-Jun-3 Treadway Gallery, Cincinnati #1390
£5959 $10250 €8700 View of Grafton heights (51x64cm-20x25in) s.d.1913. 6-Dec-3 Selkirks, St. Louis #177/R est:10000-12000

SYLVESTER, Harry Elliot (1860-1921) American
£881 $1400 €1286 Egg Rock, Nahant (36x46cm-14x18in) s.d.1915 i.verso. 12-Sep-3 Skinner, Boston #497/R

SYLVESTER, Leif (1940-) Danish
£337 $550 €492 May be it will rain (40x40cm-16x16in) s.d.94 acrylic. 27-Sep-3 Rasmussen, Havnen #4015/R (D.KR 3600)

SYME, Eveline W (1888-1961) Australian
£336 $578 €491 Nude study, seated. 7-Dec-3 Joel, Victoria #62/R (A.D 800)
£336 $578 €491 Female nude standing. 7-Dec-3 Joel, Victoria #51 (A.D 800)
£455 $773 €664 Fruit seller (33x25cm-13x10in) board. 29-Oct-3 Lawson Menzies, Sydney #167/R est:1000-1500 (A.D 1100)
Prints
£3688 $5828 €5384 The bay (16x26cm-6x10in) s.i.d.1932 col linocut. 2-Sep-3 Deutscher-Menzies, Melbourne #236/R est:6500-8500 (A.D 9000)

SYME, Sue (20th C) New Zealander?
Works on paper
£403 $746 €588 Bottom up (51x39cm-20x15in) s. W/C. 9-Mar-4 Watson's, Christchurch #63 est:1100-1500 (NZ.D 1100)

SYMONDS, Eyres (?) British?
Works on paper
£550 $1007 €825 Boats on the shore (34x54cm-13x21in) s. W/C. 3-Jun-4 Lane, Penzance #321

SYMONDS, William Robert (1851-1934) British
£1000 $1580 €1450 Portrait of Hon Lady Violet Agar-Roberts of Lanhdrock, Cornwall (43x30cm-17x12in) init. 4-Sep-3 Christie's, Kensington #79/R est:1500-2500
£6600 $10758 €9636 Family portrait (217x150cm-85x59in) s.d.1887. 28-Sep-3 Wilkinson, Doncaster #271/R

SYMONS, George Gardner (1863-1930) American
£726 $1300 €1060 Lily pond (20x25cm-8x10in) s. i.verso canvasboard. 8-Jan-4 Doyle, New York #43/R
£1445 $2500 €2110 View of the Bronx River, New York (30x41cm-12x16in) init.i. canvasboard. 10-Dec-3 Bonhams & Butterfields, San Francisco #6029/R est:5000-7000
£1553 $2500 €2267 Hilltop barn (76x91cm-30x36in) s. s.i. stretcher. 20-Aug-3 James Julia, Fairfield #1629/R est:2500-3500
£1648 $3000 €2406 Figures in atmospheric farming landscape (15x23cm-6x9in) s. board prov. 15-Jun-4 John Moran, Pasadena #12 est:2500-3500
£1708 $2750 €2494 Along Westfield River 1930 (23x30cm-9x12in) s. i.d. verso board. 20-Aug-3 James Julia, Fairfield #1630/R est:2000-3000
£3892 $6500 €5682 Hillside and deep ravine (51x63cm-20x25in) s. 9-Oct-3 Christie's, Rockefeller NY #40/R est:5000-7000
£4545 $8000 €6636 Mission of San Juan Capastrano (53x36cm-21x14in) painted 1883. 23-May-4 Hindman, Chicago #951/R est:8000-12000
£4749 $8500 €6934 Connecticut river (30x38cm-12x15in) s. panel prov. 6-May-4 Shannon's, Milford #52/R est:5000-7000
£10983 $19000 €16035 Moonlight in Winter (33x41cm-13x16in) s. prov. 10-Dec-3 Bonhams & Butterfields, San Francisco #6031/R est:20000-25000

SYMONS, George Gardner (attrib) (1863-1930) American
£615 $1100 €898 Pines (56x51cm-22x20in) s.i. 14-May-4 Skinner, Boston #154/R
£1647 $2800 €2405 Winter landscape (76x91cm-30x36in) s.i. 21-Nov-3 Skinner, Boston #494/R est:3000-5000

SYMONS, Mark Lancelot (1887-1935) British
£4800 $8256 €7008 Crucifixion (68x68cm-27x27in) s. 2-Dec-3 Bonhams, New Bond Street #69/R est:2000-3000
£40000 $71600 €58400 Were you there when they crucified My Lord (210x148cm-83x58in) s. prov.exhib. 16-Mar-4 Bonhams, New Bond Street #49/R est:6000-8000

SYMONS, William Christian (1845-1911) British
Works on paper
£250 $418 €365 Reading the sad news (33x26cm-13x10in) s. pencil W/C. 16-Oct-3 Christie's, Kensington #45
£380 $707 €555 Still life of roses in glass vase (35x24cm-14x9in) s. bodycol htd gum arabic. 2-Mar-4 Bearnes, Exeter #366

SYNAVE, Tancrede (1860-?) French
£2980 $5424 €4500 Une repetition de la mort du cygne de St Saens (55x81cm-22x32in) s.i. cardboard. 19-Jun-4 Quittenbaum, Hamburg #49/R est:4400
£8067 $14843 €12100 La sortie de l'Opera (102x102cm-40x40in) s.i. 11-Jun-4 Pierre Berge, Paris #177/R est:12000-15000

SYPKENS, Ferdinand Hendrik (1813-1860) Dutch
£1748 $2919 €2500 Figures skating on the ice (48x59cm-19x23in) s. 30-Jun-3 Sotheby's, Amsterdam #127

SYROVY, Josef (1879-1956) Czechoslovakian
£464 $817 €696 Prague (95x115cm-37x45in) s. 22-May-4 Dorotheum, Prague #117/R est:12000-18000 (C.KR 22000)

SYS, Maurice (1880-1972) Belgian
£2676 $4630 €3800 Latem farm (39x40cm-15x16in) s. 13-Dec-3 De Vuyst, Lokeren #553/R est:4500-5500
£3288 $5589 €4800 Vase fleuri sur fond de paysage (39x40cm-15x16in) s.d.1910. 10-Nov-3 Horta, Bruxelles #193/R
£10490 $17517 €15000 Winter morning in the Netherlands (61x71cm-24x28in) s. exhib.lit. 11-Oct-3 De Vuyst, Lokeren #441/R est:14000-16000
Works on paper
£3356 $6208 €5000 Volendam shipbuilding yard in the winter (31x31cm-12x12in) s. W/C gouache. 13-Mar-4 De Vuyst, Lokeren #537/R est:5000-6000

SYSANG, Johanna Dorothea (1729-1791) German
Works on paper
£420 $713 €600 Parrot (30x37cm-12x15in) bears i. bodycol. 27-Nov-3 Bassenge, Berlin #5509

SZABO, Laszlo (1917-) Hungarian
Sculpture
£2517 $4204 €3600 Form (174x69cm-69x27in) s. bronze iron base incl. base. 11-Oct-3 De Vuyst, Lokeren #347/R est:3500-4000

SZABO, Vladimir (1905-1991) Hungarian
£5220 $9031 €7621 Budapest is 100 years old (90x120cm-35x47in) s.d.1973 fibreboard. 12-Dec-3 Kieselbach, Budapest #65/R (H.F 2000000)
£6948 $12298 €10144 Old confectionery (70x80cm-28x31in) s.d.1973 board. 28-Apr-4 Kieselbach, Budapest #85/R (H.F 2600000)
£7377 $13353 €10770 Young lady with cat (63x44cm-25x17in) s. 16-Apr-4 Mu Terem Galeria, Budapest #175/R (H.F 2800000)

SZAFRAN, Sam (1930-) French

Works on paper			
£1275	$2334	€1900	Homme et son chien (64x49cm-25x19in) s.i.d.65 sanguine drawing brown ink wash. 7-Jul-4 Artcurial Briest, Paris #349 est:2000-3000
£1736	$2743	€2500	Rider (48x63cm-19x25in) s.i. chl ink wash prov. 27-Apr-3 Versailles Encheres #59
£2817	$4873	€4000	Homme au repos (77x57cm-30x22in) s. chl. 9-Dec-3 Artcurial Briest, Paris #550/R est:3000-4000
£4196	$7007	€6000	Escalier (30x27cm-12x11in) s. W/C. 29-Jun-3 Versailles Encheres #139/R
£4698	$8315	€7000	Philodendron (38x26cm-15x10in) s. pastel prov. 28-Apr-4 Artcurial Briest, Paris #257/R est:7500-8000
£4861	$8021	€7000	L'escalier (30x10cm-12x4in) s. W/C silk prov. 2-Jul-3 Cornette de St.Cyr, Paris #52/R est:8000-10000
£7333	$13200	€11000	Escalier (30x25cm-12x10in) s. W/C on silk. 25-Apr-4 Versailles Encheres #154 est:12000-15000
£11225	$20092	€16500	Untitled (73x47cm-29x19in) s. W/C prov.exhib. 21-Mar-4 Calmels Cohen, Paris #183/R est:10000-15000
£17450	$31235	€26000	Charpente (77x58cm-30x23in) s. chl wax crayon paper on card. 26-May-4 Christie's, Paris #93/R est:2000-3000
£19048	$34096	€28000	Untitled (36x48cm-14x19in) s. W/C prov.exhib. 21-Mar-4 Calmels Cohen, Paris #182/R est:10000-15000
£19333	$35574	€29000	L'artiste dans son atelier (100x70cm-39x28in) s.d. pastel chl prov. 8-Jun-4 Artcurial Briest, Paris #260/R est:30000-40000
£34899	$62470	€52000	Escalier (41x33cm-16x13in) s. pastel paper on panel. 26-May-4 Christie's, Paris #94/R est:1500-2000
£210884	$377483	€310000	Atelier au feuillage avec personnage (120x80cm-47x31in) s. pastel exec. c.1978 prov. 21-Mar-4 Calmels Cohen, Paris #181/R est:200000-300000

SZANCENBACH, Jan (1928-1999) Polish

£2276	$3801	€3300	Landscape with trees, river and house (65x75cm-26x30in) s.i.d.1995. 16-Nov-3 Agra, Warsaw #47/R est:3000

SZANKOWSKI, Boleslaw von (1873-1953) Polish

£694	$1160	€1000	Portrait of woman with shawl (79x55cm-31x22in) s. 22-Oct-3 Neumeister, Munich #767/R
£800	$1472	€1168	Portrait of Helene, the artist's daughter (83x67cm-33x26in) board. 23-Mar-4 Rosebery Fine Art, London #912/R
£933	$1689	€1400	Portrait of brunette beauty with rose in hand (85x70cm-33x28in) s. 1-Apr-4 Van Ham, Cologne #1664
£1873	$3409	€2735	Portrait of a woman (885x70cm-348x28in) s. painted 1930. 20-Jun-4 Agra, Warsaw #51/R (P.Z 13000)
£2465	$4264	€3500	Spanish beauty in red (90x71cm-35x28in) s. 10-Dec-3 Christie's, Amsterdam #664/R est:2000-3000
Works on paper			
£1453	$2600	€2121	Reclining gypsy beauty (56x74cm-22x29in) s. pastel conte crayon. 11-Jan-4 William Jenack, New York #82 est:800-1200

SZANTHO, Maria (1898-1984) Hungarian

£355	$592	€500	Girl with banjo (80x60cm-31x24in) s. 14-Oct-3 Dorotheum, Vienna #153/R
£479	$800	€699	Young girl with violin (84x64cm-33x25in) 14-Nov-3 Du Mouchelle, Detroit #2108/R
£608	$1089	€900	Bare breasted red haired beauty (79x62cm-31x24in) s. 6-May-4 Michael Zeller, Lindau #893/R
£700	$1169	€1022	Portrait of a female nude (80x60cm-31x24in) s. board. 21-Oct-3 Bonhams, Knightsbridge #81/R
£734	$1226	€1050	Still life (100x70cm-39x28in) 10-Oct-3 Stadion, Trieste #113/R
£800	$1256	€1160	Bather in contemplation (80x60cm-31x24in) s. 28-Aug-3 Christie's, Kensington #258/R
£865	$1600	€1263	Reclining nude (51x79cm-20x31in) s. 17-Jan-4 New Orleans Auction, New Orleans #522/R est:1200-1800
£1216	$2177	€1800	Portrait of dark haired beauty (79x59cm-31x23in) s. 6-May-4 Michael Zeller, Lindau #894/R est:1600

SZATHOS, Maria (1898-?) ?

£500	$860	€730	Ballerina with tambourine (78x59cm-31x23in) s. 7-Dec-3 Lots Road Auctions, London #349

SZCEZESNY, Stefan (1951-) German

£1389	$2319	€2000	Submarine I (100x130cm-39x51in) s.d. verso i.d. stretcher acrylic metallic cols pebbles collage. 24-Oct-3 Ketterer, Hamburg #553/R est:3000-5000

SZCZEPANSKI, Stanislaw (1895-1973) Polish

£1881	$2934	€2746	Still life with silverware (57x46cm-22x18in) s.d.1945. 30-Mar-3 Agra, Warsaw #28/R est:11000 (P.Z 12000)

SZCZESNIAK, Ted (?) American

£359	$600	€524	Shimmering golden light, marshes around Giverny, France (43x58cm-17x23in) s.i.d.01-03. 14-Nov-3 Aspire, Cleveland #88

SZEKELY, Bertalan (1835-1910) Hungarian

£1958	$3386	€2859	Sunset (34x44cm-13x17in) cardboard. 12-Dec-3 Kieselbach, Budapest #117/R (H.F 750000)
£3258	$5408	€4757	Garden in Szada (38x75cm-15x30in) panel. 4-Oct-3 Kieselbach, Budapest #36/R (H.F 1200000)
£3801	$6309	€5549	Female portrait (50x40cm-20x16in) s. 4-Oct-3 Kieselbach, Budapest #65/R (H.F 1400000)
£5879	$10406	€8583	Twilight in the park in Szada (42x64cm-17x25in) cardboard. 28-Apr-4 Kieselbach, Budapest #37/R (H.F 2200000)

SZEKELY, Pierre (1923-2001) Hungarian

Sculpture			
£1275	$2372	€1900	Voyage indicible (21x15x15cm-8x6x6in) s.i.d.base bolster onyx exec 1987-1988. 3-Mar-4 Tajan, Paris #260 est:2000-2500

SZEKESSY, Zoltan (1899-1968) Hungarian

Sculpture			
£1538	$2615	€2200	Child's head (22cm-9in) s. mid brown green pat.bronze. 26-Nov-3 Lempertz, Koln #996/R est:2000

SZEMADAM, Gyorgy (1947-) Hungarian

£543	$901	€793	Pohja (50x60cm-20x24in) init. canvas on board. 4-Oct-3 Kieselbach, Budapest #135/R (H.F 200000)
£574	$993	€838	Bogey - Self Portrait (92x59cm-36x23in) s.verso fibreboard. 12-Dec-3 Kieselbach, Budapest #108/R (H.F 220000)

SZENDY, Arisztid (20th C) Hungarian?

£594	$993	€850	Still life (60x80cm-24x31in) 10-Oct-3 Stadion, Trieste #131/R

SZENES, Arpad (1897-1985) French

£25001	$41751	€36000	Grand Ciel (54x81cm-21x32in) s. painted c.1978-1980 prov. 21-Oct-3 Artcurial Briest, Paris #384a/R est:40000-45000
Works on paper			
£458	$838	€687	Portrait of Ione Saldanha (30x22cm-12x9in) s. mixed media exec. 1940. 6-Jul-4 Bolsa de Arte, Rio de Janeiro #29/R (B.R 2500)
£604	$1105	€900	Old man with a pipe (23x16cm-9x6in) s.d.944 brown ink paper on board. 7-Jul-4 Artcurial Briest, Paris #108
£5556	$9167	€8000	Banquet journal (20x27cm-8x11in) s. gouache newspaper lit. 2-Jul-3 Cornette de St.Cyr, Paris #24/R est:8000-10000
£6643	$11294	€9500	Vieira da Silva peignant (26x35cm-10x14in) s. Indian ink prov. 23-Nov-3 Cornette de St.Cyr, Paris #324/R est:500-700
£9790	$16643	€14000	Paysage abstrait (51x32cm-20x13in) s.d.1970 gouache prov. 23-Nov-3 Cornette de St.Cyr, Paris #325/R est:1000-1500

SZERBAKOW, Fedor (1911-) German?

£265	$482	€400	Winter landscape (61x80cm-24x31in) s. i.verso board. 18-Jun-4 Bolland & Marotz, Bremen #387
£278	$453	€400	Moor canal in the evening (60x50cm-24x20in) s. panel. 26-Sep-3 Bolland & Marotz, Bremen #380/R
£313	$509	€450	Hamme on a rainy day (50x70cm-20x28in) s. i.d. 1994 verso panel. 26-Sep-3 Bolland & Marotz, Bremen #379/R
£331	$603	€500	Landscape with river and houses (80x70cm-31x28in) s. i.verso board. 18-Jun-4 Bolland & Marotz, Bremen #386/R
£344	$627	€520	Early spring landscape (42x52cm-17x20in) s. i.verso board. 18-Jun-4 Bolland & Marotz, Bremen #388
£347	$566	€500	Hamme landscape with boats (60x79cm-24x31in) s.d.1948 panel. 26-Sep-3 Bolland & Marotz, Bremen #376
£350	$601	€500	Old cottage in the moor (50x60cm-20x24in) s. i.verso fibreboard. 5-Dec-3 Bolland & Marotz, Bremen #424/R
£397	$723	€600	Trees on the banks of a canal (60x95cm-24x37in) s.d.78 board. 18-Jun-4 Bolland & Marotz, Bremen #385/R
£417	$679	€600	Storm on the Teufelsmoor (70x60cm-28x24in) s.d.75 canvas on panel. 26-Sep-3 Bolland & Marotz, Bremen #378/R
£420	$722	€600	Farm in autumn (50x60cm-20x24in) s.d.79 i.verso. 5-Dec-3 Bolland & Marotz, Bremen #423
£486	$792	€700	Evening on the Hamme (70x60cm-28x24in) s.d.78 canvas on panel. 26-Sep-3 Bolland & Marotz, Bremen #377/R
£521	$849	€750	Moorland in evening (70x99cm-28x39in) s.i. verso panel. 26-Sep-3 Bolland & Marotz, Bremen #375/R
£570	$1050	€850	Moorland canal (60x50cm-24x20in) s. panel. 26-Mar-4 Bolland & Marotz, Bremen #375/R
£594	$1022	€850	Farmhouse in winter (50x62cm-20x24in) s.d.79 fibreboard. 5-Dec-3 Bolland & Marotz, Bremen #420/R
£629	$1083	€900	Winter with snow covered cottages and large clouds (70x100cm-28x39in) s. i.verso fibreboard. 5-Dec-3 Bolland & Marotz, Bremen #421/R
£909	$1564	€1300	Sheep shed in moor in autumn (81x113cm-32x44in) s. i.verso fibreboard. 5-Dec-3 Bolland & Marotz, Bremen #419/R

SZERNER, Vladyslav (1836-1915) Polish

£3194	$5271	€4600	Mounted cossack in mountain landscape (43x31cm-17x12in) s. 2-Jul-3 Neumeister, Munich #789/R est:1000
£3356	$6174	€5000	Young Cossack flower seller on horseback (60x40cm-24x16in) s. lit. 25-Mar-4 Karlheinz Kaupp, Staufen #2772/R est:2500
£3695	$6615	€5395	The goosegirl making a garland of flowers (68x56cm-27x22in) s.d.1873. 28-May-4 Uppsala Auktionskammare, Uppsala #90/R est:50000-60000 (S.KR 50000)

SZERNER, Vladyslav (attrib) (1836-1915) Polish

£4749	$8500	€6934	Stopping for a conversation (41x33cm-16x13in) s. 8-Jan-4 James Julia, Fairfield #502/R est:4000-8000

SZETO, Nigel (20th C) Canadian?

Works on paper			
£240	$400	€350	Bird and flowers (38x38cm-15x15in) s.d. W/C. 11-Oct-3 Nadeau, Windsor #125/R

SZIKSZAY, Ferenc (1871-1908) Hungarian

£347	$573	€500	Pecheurs de crevettes (46x61cm-18x24in) s.d.1907. 5-Jul-3 Neret-Minet, Paris #151/R

SZILAGYI, Jolan (1895-1971) Hungarian

£594	$993	€850	Still life with lemon and china (80x60cm-31x24in) 10-Oct-3 Stadion, Trieste #120
£629	$1051	€900	Still life on the table (60x80cm-24x31in) 10-Oct-3 Stadion, Trieste #117

SZINYEI MERSE, Pal von (1845-1920) Hungarian

£70585	$117171	€103054	Eruption of Vesuv (63x87cm-25x34in) s.d.1863 verso. 4-Oct-3 Kieselbach, Budapest #128/R (H.F 26000000)

SZLANYI, Lajos (1869-?) Hungarian
£516 $856 €753 Market in Szolnok (20x39cm-8x15in) s. board. 4-Oct-3 Kieselbach, Budapest #5/R (H.F 190000)

SZOBEL, Geza (1905-) Czechoslovakian
£243 $406 €350 Defile bleu (35x29cm-14x11in) s. panel. 21-Oct-3 Artcurial Briest, Paris #359
£521 $869 €750 Orphee (130x97cm-51x38in) s.d.59 panel. 21-Oct-3 Artcurial Briest, Paris #361
£1399 $2336 €2000 Composition (92x65cm-36x26in) s. prov. 29-Jun-3 Versailles Encheres #23/R
£1793 $2994 €2600 Composition rouge (195x100cm-77x39in) s.d.1939 panel. 17-Nov-3 Claude Boisgirard, Paris #90/R est:2500-3000
Works on paper
£490 $832 €700 Composition (63x48cm-25x19in) s. pastel prov. 23-Nov-3 Cornette de St.Cyr, Paris #330
£490 $832 €700 Composition (63x47cm-25x19in) s. pastel prov. 23-Nov-3 Cornette de St.Cyr, Paris #331
£517 $859 €750 Femme assise (50x35cm-20x14in) s. graphite W/C. 30-Sep-3 Blanchet, Paris #336/R

SZOBOTKA, Imbre (1890-1961) Hungarian
£2371 $4292 €3462 Fishers at the lake Balaton (76x100cm-30x39in) s. 16-Apr-4 Mu Terem Galeria, Budapest #126/R (H.F 900000)
£5973 $9914 €8721 Summer day (55x69cm-22x27in) s. 4-Oct-3 Kieselbach, Budapest #68/R (H.F 2200000)

SZOLNAY, Sandor (1893-1950) Hungarian
£869 $1442 €1269 View of Nagybanya (57x77cm-22x30in) s.d.924. 4-Oct-3 Kieselbach, Budapest #12/R (H.F 320000)

SZONYI, Istvan (1894-1960) Hungarian
£1069 $1892 €1561 Zebegeny hillside (29x42cm-11x17in) s. tempera. 28-Apr-4 Kieselbach, Budapest #6/R (H.F 400000)
£4344 $7211 €6342 Mother and child in classical landscape (68x56cm-27x22in) s. 4-Oct-3 Kieselbach, Budapest #110/R (H.F 1600000)
£6787 $11266 €9909 Meeting (60x80cm-24x31in) s. tempera. 4-Oct-3 Kieselbach, Budapest #155/R (H.F 2500000)
£12292 $21757 €17946 Bend of the Danube (70x100cm-28x39in) s. 28-Apr-4 Kieselbach, Budapest #55/R (H.F 4600000)
£13574 $22533 €19818 Via Aureliana (71x92cm-28x36in) s.d.1929 tempera. 4-Oct-3 Kieselbach, Budapest #39/R (H.F 5000000)
£22000 $40040 €32120 View of the Danube bend at Zebegeny (71x80cm-28x31in) s. prov. 15-Jun-4 Sotheby's, London #63/R est:10000-15000
Works on paper
£418 $722 €610 Landscape (37x54cm-15x21in) s.d.1918 pencil. 12-Dec-3 Kieselbach, Budapest #166/R (H.F 160000)
£923 $1532 €1348 Red bloused model in shadow (42x30cm-17x12in) d.1922 W/C. 4-Oct-3 Kieselbach, Budapest #31/R (H.F 340000)

SZOPOS, Sandor (1881-1954) Hungarian
£896 $1621 €1308 In front of the mirror (92x114cm-36x45in) s. 16-Apr-4 Mu Terem Galeria, Budapest #115/R (H.F 340000)

SZWACZ, Boguslaw (1912-) Polish
£226 $409 €339 Abstract (60x46cm-24x18in) s.d.1961 oil Indian ink gouache W/C. 4-Apr-4 Agra, Warsaw #15/R (P.Z 1600)

SZYDLOWSKI, Henryk (1950-) New Zealander
£489 $831 €714 The Yellow Bridge over the Green Meadow (78x98cm-31x39in) s.d.1991. 27-Nov-3 International Art Centre, Auckland #131/R (NZ.D 1300)
£688 $1170 €1004 Owl from the windmill (20x20cm-8x8in) s.d.1999 s.d.verso. 4-Nov-3 Peter Webb, Auckland #138/R est:1200-2000 (NZ.D 1900)
£797 $1355 €1164 Magic of the visible bird (20x20cm-8x8in) s.d.1999 s.d.verso. 4-Nov-3 Peter Webb, Auckland #139/R est:1200-2000 (NZ.D 2200)
£2750 $5060 €4015 Red door to the puppet paradise (75x100cm-30x39in) s. 25-Mar-4 International Art Centre, Auckland #95/R est:7000-10000 (NZ.D 7700)

SZYK, Arthur (1894-1951) Polish
£2131 $3900 €3111 Had Gadia (30x24cm-12x9in) s. tempera. 1-Feb-4 Ben-Ami, Tel Aviv #4571/R est:2500-3500
Works on paper
£645 $1200 €942 Things to come (21x15cm-8x6in) s.d.1942 pen ink. 2-Mar-4 Swann Galleries, New York #646/R est:1500-2500
£645 $1200 €942 Not impressed (23x18cm-9x7in) s.d.1942 pen ink. 2-Mar-4 Swann Galleries, New York #647/R est:1500-2500
£875 $1400 €1278 Give our love to Yamamoto (15x10cm-6x4in) s.i.d.1943 pen ink card. 18-Sep-3 Swann Galleries, New York #630/R
£938 $1500 €1369 Antisemitic propaganda is the best softener of democracy (15x13cm-6x5in) s.id.1942 pen ink. 18-Sep-3 Swann Galleries, New York #629/R est:1800-2200
£1381 $2500 €2016 Nazi satire (20x15cm-8x6in) W/C. 16-Apr-4 American Auctioneer #389/R est:3500-4000
£1500 $2731 €2250 Racial humiliation (14x9cm-6x4in) s.i.d. pen ink pencil. 2-Jul-4 Bloomsbury, London #333/R est:1500-2000
£2125 $3400 €3103 To the glorious memory of Colonel Mickey Marcus (13x11cm-5x4in) s.i.d.1948 pen ink card. 18-Sep-3 Swann Galleries, New York #631/R est:1800-2200
£5742 $9934 €8383 Riders (13x23cm-5x9in) s. mixed media. 12-Dec-3 Kieselbach, Budapest #61/R (H.F 2200000)

SZYKIER, Ksawery (1860-1895) Polish
£986 $1706 €1400 Winter landscape with carriage and horse (10x15cm-4x6in) s.i.d.93 panel. 10-Dec-3 Dorotheum, Vienna #78/R

SZYMANSKI, Rolf (1928-) German
Sculpture
£1267 $2267 €1900 Small figure Nr IV: Ephesus (21x6x4cm-8x2x2in) mono. bronze. 15-May-4 Dr Sturies, Dusseldorf #206/R
£1400 $2506 €2100 Small figure Nr 1 (21x7x4cm-8x3x2in) mono.i. bronze. 15-May-4 Dr Sturies, Dusseldorf #205/R
£3944 $6823 €5600 Open figure (33cm-13in) mono.i. verso Cast.Barth Berlin. 13-Dec-3 Lempertz, Koln #360/R est:1500

SZYMKOWICZ, Charles (1948-) Belgian
£537 $950 €800 L'enfant eclate (122x180cm-48x71in) s.d.1974 paper on panel. 27-Apr-4 Campo, Vlaamse Kaai #593
£1600 $2864 €2400 Autoportrait se chipotant la barbe (130x120cm-51x47in) s.d.89 s.i.verso. 15-May-4 De Vuyst, Lokeren #325 est:2000-2400
Works on paper
£604 $1069 €900 Fil jaune (71x52cm-28x20in) s.d.1979 mixed media. 27-Apr-4 Campo, Vlaamse Kaai #591

SZYSKOWITZ, Rudolf (1905-1976) Austrian
Works on paper
£563 $935 €800 Mausoleum in Graz (31x23cm-12x9in) mono. ochre. 12-Jun-3 Dorotheum, Graz #187

SZYSZLO, Fernando de (1925-) Peruvian
£4571 $8000 €6674 Mar de lurin (49x69cm-19x27in) s. acrylic prov. 19-Dec-3 Sotheby's, New York #1180/R est:10000-15000
£9412 $16000 €13742 Camino a Orrantia (119x150cm-47x59in) s. s.i.d.1983 verso acrylic prov. 18-Nov-3 Christie's, Rockefeller NY #145/R est:10000-15000

TAAFFE, Philip (1955-) American
£2703 $4757 €4000 Double cascade (66x101cm-26x40in) s.d.2002 verso tempera paper prov. 24-May-4 Christie's, Milan #76/R est:5000-6000
£22455 $37500 €32784 Christus, fire-eater (110x65cm-43x26in) s.i.d.1990 verso oil paper collage prov.exhib. 13-Nov-3 Sotheby's, New York #597/R est:20000-30000
Prints
£14525 $26000 €21207 Bizerte (167x129cm-66x51in) linoleum block print acrylic linen prov. 14-May-4 Phillips, New York #222/R est:30000-40000
£23952 $40000 €34970 Totem (427x60cm-168x24in) s.i. verso monoprint collage acrylic enamel linen exec 1989 prov. 12-Nov-3 Christie's, Rockefeller NY #626/R est:50000-70000
Works on paper
£398 $725 €597 Untitled (33x25cm-13x10in) s.d.1995 mixed media. 30-Jun-4 Daniel Cooney, Brooklyn #487359/R
£1739 $3200 €2539 Untitled (43x56cm-17x22in) s.d.1988 verso W/C gouache chk prov. 10-Jun-4 Phillips, New York #489/R est:2500-3500
£9581 $16000 €13988 Untitled (113x149cm-44x59in) s. verso acrylic paper on canvas prov. 14-Nov-3 Phillips, New York #166/R est:20000-30000
£19553 $35000 €28547 Via Toledo (101x125cm-40x49in) s.i.d.1991 verso gouache ac/ chl fixative linen prov. 14-May-4 Phillips, New York #223/R est:35000-45000
£41916 $70000 €61197 Conflagration (290x298cm-114x117in) s.i.d.1990-91 verso mixed media canvas prov. 12-Nov-3 Christie's, Rockefeller NY #625/R est:70000-90000

TAANMAN, Jacob (1836-1923) Dutch
£538 $926 €785 Interior scene with carpenter at his bench (32x23cm-13x9in) s. panel. 7-Dec-3 Uppsala Auktionskammare, Uppsala #90/R (S.KR 7000)
£550 $946 €803 Butterflies (22x19cm-9x7in) s. board. 4-Dec-3 Bonhams, Edinburgh #105/R
Works on paper
£403 $745 €600 Portrait of a young lady with her little dog (60x45cm-24x18in) s.d.January 1855 black chk htd white. 15-Mar-4 Sotheby's, Amsterdam #112a/R
£470 $850 €686 Quiet moment (30x41cm-12x16in) s.d.1905. 3-Apr-4 Neal Auction Company, New Orleans #313/R

TABACCHI, Odoardo (1831-1905) Italian
Sculpture
£2958 $5117 €4200 Diver (77cm-30in) s. bronze. 10-Dec-3 Finarte Semenzato, Rome #206/R est:4000-4500
£7394 $13679 €10795 Tuffolina - bathing girl (112cm-44in) s.i.d.1879 marble. 15-Mar-4 Rasmussen, Vejle #949/R est:75000-100000 (D.KR 82000)

TABACCO, Wilma (1953-) Australian/Italian
£331 $612 €483 Making time (51x120cm-20x47in) s.d.1991 i.verso on three panel. 15-Mar-4 Sotheby's, Melbourne #89 (A.D 800)
£496 $917 €724 Surface to surface (91x137cm-36x54in) s.d.1989 i.verso prov. 15-Mar-4 Sotheby's, Melbourne #155 est:900-1200 (A.D 1200)
£909 $1682 €1327 Surface to air (121x152cm-48x60in) s.d.1988 i.verso prov. 15-Mar-4 Sotheby's, Melbourne #53 est:1500-2500 (A.D 2200)
£992 $1755 €1448 Altarpiece (111x152cm-44x60in) s.i.d.1988 stretcher prov. 3-May-4 Christie's, Melbourne #265/R est:2000-3000 (A.D 2400)
Works on paper
£492 $777 €718 Opium (92x92cm-36x36in) s.i. verso s.d.1994 stretcher synthetic polymer prov. 2-Sep-3 Deutscher-Menzies, Melbourne #339/R (A.D 1200)

TABARA, Enrique Luis (1930-) Ecuadorian
Works on paper
£483 $869 €700 Untitled (38x46cm-15x18in) s.d.1957 verso. 26-Jan-4 Ansorena, Madrid #872/R

TABARD, Maurice (1897-1984) French
Photographs
£2963 $5600 €4326 Solarised portrait of a woman (35x5cm-14x2in) solarised silver print. 17-Feb-4 Swann Galleries, New York #64/R est:6000-9000

£4859 $8406 €6900 Composition (19x14cm-7x6in) s.d.31 photograph. 10-Dec-3 Artcurial Briest, Paris #24/R est:5000-7000
£6667 $12000 €9734 Surimpression and solarization (36x29cm-14x11in) s.d.1947 num.3 gelatin silver print prov.lit. 22-Apr-4 Phillips, New York #204/R est:12000-18000

TABBOO, Stephen (20th C) ?
Works on paper
£3200 $5312 €4672 New York (51x137cm-20x54in) s.d.1993 verso mixed media canvas. 30-Sep-3 Sotheby's, London #345/R est:700-900

TABNER, Len (1936-) British
Works on paper
£880 $1602 €1285 Looking towards Redcar Blast Furnace from Saltburn (17x35cm-7x14in) s.i.d.31.1.83 pencil wash htd bodycol. 29-Jun-4 Anderson & Garland, Newcastle #122/R

TABUCHI, Yasse (1921-) Japanese
£473 $894 €700 La nuit de givre (120x74cm-47x29in) s.d.1959 verso. 21-Feb-4 Cornette de St.Cyr, Paris #407
£814 $1458 €1188 La pentre ensoreile (46x38cm-18x15in) mono. s.d.1980 verso. 10-May-4 Rasmussen, Vejle #774/R (D.KR 9000)
£3893 $7162 €5800 Porte du sud (146x97cm-57x38in) s.d.1972 s.i.d.verso acrylic. 24-Mar-4 Joron-Derem, Paris #176 est:1300-1500

TABUENA, Romeo (1921-) Mexican
£850 $1538 €1241 Mother and child (42x30cm-17x12in) s.d.1959 cardboard. 4-Apr-4 Sotheby's, Singapore #118/R est:2000-3000 (S.D 2600)
£1307 $2366 €1908 Carabao (31x53cm-12x21in) s.d.56 board. 4-Apr-4 Sotheby's, Singapore #99/R est:4000-6000 (S.D 4000)
£1853 $3095 €2705 Farmers with buffaloes (44x59cm-17x23in) s.d.1966 board. 26-Oct-3 Christie's, Hong Kong #32/R est:16000-26000 (HK.D 24000)
£2431 $4059 €3549 Man and cockerel (84x54cm-33x21in) s.d.1967. 12-Oct-3 Sotheby's, Singapore #67/R est:4000-6000 (S.D 7000)
£2581 $4129 €3768 Gallo y carabao (48x39cm-19x15in) s.d.1967 acrylic masonite. 18-May-3 Sotheby's, Singapore #85/R est:6000-8000 (S.D 7200)
£3529 $6000 €5152 La familia (67x93cm-26x37in) s.d.1956 board prov. 19-Nov-3 Sotheby's, New York #114/R est:10000-15000
£3922 $7098 €5726 Village scene (40x70cm-16x28in) s.d.1963 board. 4-Apr-4 Sotheby's, Singapore #98/R est:4500-6500 (S.D 12000)
£3993 $6668 €5830 Village scene (55x37cm-22x15in) s.d.1960 cardboard. 12-Oct-3 Sotheby's, Singapore #82/R est:4000-6000 (S.D 11500)
£4731 $7570 €6907 Three women (76x67cm-30x26in) s.d.1977 acrylic. 18-May-3 Sotheby's, Singapore #57/R est:12000-18000 (S.D 13200)
Works on paper
£2778 $4639 €4056 River Scene. Carabao (47x54cm-19x21in) s.d.1960 s.d.54 mixed media cardboard second W/C two. 12-Oct-3 Sotheby's, Singapore #81/R est:3000-4000 (S.D 8000)

TABUSSO, Francesco (1930-) Italian
£1119 $1869 €1600 Model (60x50cm-24x20in) s. 26-Jun-3 Sant Agostino, Torino #261/R est:1500-2000
£2897 $4837 €4200 Village fair (31x56cm-12x22in) s. masonite. 17-Nov-3 Sant Agostino, Torino #233/R est:3500-4500
£3310 $5528 €4800 By the lake (50x60cm-20x24in) init.d.1965 s.i.d.verso. 17-Nov-3 Sant Agostino, Torino #234/R est:3500-4500
£3357 $5606 €4800 Trout (60x80cm-24x31in) init. i.on stretcher. 26-Jun-3 Sant Agostino, Torino #264/R est:4000-5000
£4138 $6910 €6000 Offering nature (30x50cm-12x20in) init. board prov.exhib.lit. 17-Nov-3 Sant Agostino, Torino #232/R est:3500-4500
£4577 $7599 €6500 Viaggiatore tedesco (70x100cm-28x39in) s. s.i.d.1975 verso. 14-Jun-3 Meeting Art, Vercelli #496/R est:5000
£5102 $9133 €7500 Shelves (70x60cm-28x24in) s.s.i.verso. 22-Mar-4 Sant Agostino, Torino #530/R est:7500-9500
£5782 $10350 €8500 Popina (100x120cm-39x47in) s. painted 1999 exhib.lit. 22-Mar-4 Sant Agostino, Torino #532/R est:8000-10000
Works on paper
£690 $1152 €1000 Mushrooms with flowers (56x75cm-22x30in) s.i. W/C. 17-Nov-3 Sant Agostino, Torino #133/R
£897 $1497 €1300 Interior of brothel (41x33cm-16x13in) s. mixed media card. 17-Nov-3 Sant Agostino, Torino #108/R
£952 $1705 €1400 Riverbank and hills (57x76cm-22x30in) s.i. mixed media. 22-Mar-4 Sant Agostino, Torino #331/R
£1034 $1728 €1500 Towards pleasure (41x32cm-16x13in) s. mixed media card. 17-Nov-3 Sant Agostino, Torino #107/R est:700

TACCA, Ferdinando (studio) (1619-1686) Italian
Sculpture
£24000 $41520 €35040 Two wrestling woman (46cm-18in) brown pat. bronze lit. 11-Dec-3 Christie's, London #49/R est:20000-30000

TACCHI, Cesare (1940-) Italian
£1056 $1849 €1500 Painting mark (71x100cm-28x39in) s.d.1989 temperapaper. 16-Dec-3 Finarte Semenzato, Milan #358/R est:1300-1700
Works on paper
£5797 $9507 €8000 Portrait on printed fabric (100x100cm-39x39in) s.i.d.1965 verso ink on padded canvas prov. 27-May-3 Sotheby's, Milan #209c/R est:5000-6000
£21014 $34464 €29000 Joyful spring (210x300cm-83x118in) s.i.d.1965 ink mixed media fabric on board in 3 parts prov.exhib. 27-May-3 Sotheby's, Milan #209a/R est:12000-15000

TACK, Augustus Vincent (1870-1949) American
£625 $1000 €913 Portrait of Mrs Tuttle (71x56cm-28x22in) prov. 20-Sep-3 Sloans & Kenyon, Bethesda #972/R est:1000-1200
£688 $1100 €1004 Desert landscape (53x91cm-21x36in) canvas on board prov. 20-Sep-3 Sloans & Kenyon, Bethesda #981/R est:2250-2500
£750 $1200 €1095 Mother and Child. Study for Holy Mother and Child (61x58cm-24x23in) s. one oil one graphite. 20-Sep-3 Sloans & Kenyon, Bethesda #982/R est:2500-3000
£1438 $2300 €2099 Head of a young girl, wearing brown (64x61cm-25x24in) s.i.verso board prov. 20-Sep-3 Sloans & Kenyon, Bethesda #973/R est:1500-1750
£1688 $2700 €2464 Deerfield after sunset (38x76cm-15x30in) s. canvas on board. 20-Sep-3 Sloans & Kenyon, Bethesda #975/R est:1800-2200
£2625 $4200 €3833 Landscape and clouds (61x46cm-24x18in) s. prov. 20-Sep-3 Sloans & Kenyon, Bethesda #979/R est:2000-2250
£2813 $4500 €4107 Sea with sailboat (46x61cm-18x24in) prov. 20-Sep-3 Sloans & Kenyon, Bethesda #978/R est:1750-2250
£2813 $4500 €4107 Hawaiian cliffs (56x46cm-22x18in) s. prov. 20-Sep-3 Sloans & Kenyon, Bethesda #980/R est:2750-3000
£2969 $4750 €4335 Deerfield River, early spring (46x61cm-18x24in) s.i. prov. 20-Sep-3 Sloans & Kenyon, Bethesda #974/R est:1500-2000
£2969 $4750 €4335 Rocks and sea (30x46cm-12x18in) s. prov. 20-Sep-3 Sloans & Kenyon, Bethesda #977/R est:1200-1500
£3125 $5000 €4563 End of Deerfield Street, moonrise (46x61cm-18x24in) s. prov. 20-Sep-3 Sloans & Kenyon, Bethesda #976/R est:2500-2750
£8287 $15000 €12099 Decorative panel (79x89cm-31x35in) s. canvas on masonite prov. 31-Mar-4 Sotheby's, New York #40/R est:12000-18000

TADDEL, Luigi (1898-1992) Swiss
£430 $731 €628 Monte Bre (59x68cm-23x27in) s. 1-Dec-3 Koller, Zurich #6561 (S.FR 950)

TADEUSZ, Norbert (1940-) German
£467 $835 €700 Female nude on table (16x12cm-6x5in) s.d. oil on pencil. 15-May-4 Dr Sturies, Dusseldorf #207/R
£5000 $9150 €7500 Untitled - sleeping figure (95x130cm-37x51in) s.i.d.74 verso. 4-Jun-4 Lempertz, Koln #477/R est:7600
Works on paper
£420 $713 €600 Sunbather (41x30cm-16x12in) s.d.1967 gouache over pencil. 29-Nov-3 Arnold, Frankfurt #506/R
£2000 $3580 €3000 Cavalli (170x11cm-67x4in) s.d.1997 s.d. verso mixed media. 15-May-4 Van Ham, Cologne #948/R est:3500

TADINI, Emilio (1927-2002) Italian
£621 $993 €900 Untitled (50x70cm-20x28in) s. acrylic pencil paper painted 1997. 13-Mar-3 Galleria Pace, Milan #43/R
£690 $1152 €1000 Figure (42x33cm-17x13in) s.i.verso acrylic painted 1982. 13-Nov-3 Galleria Pace, Milan #58/R
£738 $1366 €1100 Voltaire's life (36x30cm-14x12in) s.d.1967 cardboard on canvas. 13-Mar-4 Meeting Art, Vercelli #46
£764 $1207 €1100 Untitled (33x32cm-13x13in) acrylic collage cardboard. 6-Sep-3 Meeting Art, Vercelli #540
£933 $1699 €1400 Untitled (35x44cm-14x17in) s.d.1965 acrylic canvas on board prov. 12-Jul-4 Il Ponte, Milan #989 est:1300-1400
£1172 $1958 €1700 Landscape with shaver (54x65cm-21x26in) s.i. verso painted 1980. 13-Nov-3 Galleria Pace, Milan #50/R est:1600
£1333 $2453 €2000 Nowhere (50x71cm-20x28in) s. acrylic card. 12-Jun-4 Meeting Art, Vercelli #78/R est:1500
£1333 $2453 €2000 Fairy tale (38x46cm-15x18in) s.i.verso. 12-Jun-4 Meeting Art, Vercelli #480/R est:2000
£1477 $2732 €2200 Domestic mythology (38x46cm-15x18in) s.i.verso acrylic. 11-Mar-4 Galleria Pace, Milan #103/R est:2200-3000
£1479 $2588 €2100 Player (32x44cm-13x17in) s. 17-Dec-3 Il Ponte, Milan #1119/R est:1800-2000
£1611 $2980 €2400 Fairy tale (38x46cm-15x18in) s.i.verso acrylic. 13-Mar-4 Meeting Art, Vercelli #302 est:1500
£1678 $3003 €2500 Notes for another story (82x64cm-32x25in) s.i.d.1972 verso acrylic prov. 25-May-4 Sotheby's, Milan #164/R est:3000
£2414 $4031 €3500 Unreal city (46x38cm-18x15in) s.verso. 13-Nov-3 Finarte Semenzato, Rome #431/R est:3500-4000
£2568 $4519 €3800 Untitled (99x150cm-39x59in) s. acrylic pencil painted 1985 prov. 24-May-4 Christie's, Milan #39/R est:3500-5000
£2690 $4303 €3900 Portrait D (81x65cm-32x26in) s.i.d.1977 verso acrylic. 13-Mar-3 Galleria Pace, Milan #152/R est:4800-6200
£3194 $5335 €4600 Viva de Voltaire, il letture (74x60cm-29x24in) s.i.d.1968 verso. 25-Oct-3 Cornette de St.Cyr, Paris #816/R est:1200-1500
£3333 $6133 €5000 Fairy tale (60x73cm-24x29in) s.i. acrylic painted 2001 lit. 12-Jun-4 Meeting Art, Vercelli #862/R est:5000
£3356 $6208 €5000 Fairy tale (60x73cm-24x29in) s.i.verso. 13-Mar-4 Meeting Art, Vercelli #121
£3889 $6494 €5600 L'uotto dell organizzazione (128x97cm-50x38in) s.i.d.1968 verso. 25-Oct-3 Cornette de St.Cyr, Paris #817/R est:2000-3000
£4027 $7208 €6000 Fairy tale (92x73cm-36x29in) s.i.verso acrylic painted 2001 lit. 30-May-4 Meeting Art, Vercelli #38 est:5000
£4167 $6583 €6000 Fairy tale (73x92cm-29x36in) acrylic. 6-Sep-3 Meeting Art, Vercelli #363 est:5000
£4225 $7014 €6000 Fiaba (60x73cm-24x29in) s.i.verso acrylic. 14-Jun-3 Meeting Art, Vercelli #112/R est:5000
£4895 $8322 €7000 Town (98x130cm-39x51in) s.i.verso. 20-Nov-3 Finarte Semenzato, Milan #223/R est:5000-6000
£5245 $8916 €7500 Unruly holiday (73x60cm-29x24in) s.d.65 s.i.d.verso prov. 25-Nov-3 Sotheby's, Milan #41/R est:5000-7000
£5436 $10003 €8100 L'uotto dell Organizzazione (128x97cm-50x38in) s.i.d.1968 verso. 29-Mar-4 Cornette de St.Cyr, Paris #79/R est:3000-4000
£6419 $11297 €9500 Trip to Italy (162x130cm-64x51in) s.i.d.1971 acrylic prov. 24-May-4 Christie's, Milan #187/R est:5000-7000
£9732 $17419 €14500 Parade (130x195cm-51x77in) s.i.d.1975 acrylic. 28-May-4 Farsetti, Prato #318/R est:14500-16500
£12195 $20000 €17805 Ventilatore 1-8 (42x60cm-17x24in) s.i.d.1972 verso acrylic eight prov. 28-May-3 Sotheby's, Amsterdam #150/R est:12000-15000
Works on paper
£417 $658 €600 Fairy tale (50x35cm-20x14in) mixed media. 6-Sep-3 Meeting Art, Vercelli #730
£667 $1227 €1000 Untitled (50x35cm-20x14in) s. mixed media. 10-Jun-4 Galleria Pace, Milan #50/R
£759 $1214 €1100 Untitled (70x50cm-28x20in) s.i. mixed media. 13-Mar-3 Galleria Pace, Milan #1/R
£1931 $3225 €2800 Composition (100x150cm-39x59in) s. mixed media paper on canvas. 13-Nov-3 Galleria Pace, Milan #139/R est:3800

TAELEMANS, Jean François (1851-1931) Belgian

£336 $571 €480 Vue de village en hiver (50x38cm-20x15in) s. 1-Dec-3 Palais de Beaux Arts, Brussels #314/R
£1081 $2043 €1600 Village anime sous la neige (38x50cm-15x20in) s. 17-Feb-4 Vanderkindere, Brussels #42 est:800-1200

TAEUBER-ARP, Sophie (1889-1943) Swiss

£110000 $196900 €165000 Six espaces distincts (64x87cm-25x34in) s. exhib.prov. 15-May-4 Hagelstam, Helsinki #52/R est:150000
£111888 $192448 €160000 Composition a cinq cercles (33x41cm-13x16in) st.sig.verso painted 1931 prov.exhib. 8-Dec-3 Artcurial Briest, Paris #44/R est:160000-200000
Works on paper
£3930 $7153 €5738 Shells (32x24cm-13x9in) s.d.1937 verso chk. 17-Jun-4 Kornfeld, Bern #783/R est:10000 (S.FR 9000)
£33000 $60060 €48180 Bandes, cercles et lignes (26x35cm-10x14in) s.verso distemper exec.1932 prov.lit. 4-Feb-4 Sotheby's, London #512/R est:30000-40000
£46000 $84640 €67160 Taches quadrangulaires evoquant un groupe de personnages (26x35cm-10x14in) st.sig. gouache over pencil prov.lit. 22-Jun-4 Sotheby's, London #479/R est:15000-20000

TAEYE, Camille de (1938-) Belgian

£604 $1105 €900 Opera III (115x145cm-45x57in) s.d.1995 panel. 8-Jul-4 Campo, Vlaamse Kaai #90
£1477 $2613 €2200 Le libellule (92x74cm-36x29in) s. 27-Apr-4 Campo, Vlaamse Kaai #388 est:300-400
Works on paper
£331 $603 €500 Art graphique (73x55cm-29x22in) s.d.74 chl pastel. 15-Jun-4 Vanderkindere, Brussels #108
£1267 $2318 €1900 Composition surrealiste avec poireaux (44x100cm-17x39in) s.d.90 mixed media. 7-Jun-4 Palais de Beaux Arts, Brussels #355 est:500-700

TAFLINGER, Elmer E (1891-?) American

£376 $650 €549 Girl with still life. painted c.1940. 12-Dec-3 Du Mouchelle, Detroit #2450/R

TAFURI, Clemente (1903-1971) Italian

£734 $1263 €1050 Figures on the beach (32x46cm-13x18in) s. board. 3-Dec-3 Stadion, Trieste #1028/R
£1060 $1928 €1600 In the wood (33x44cm-13x17in) board. 17-Jun-4 Finarte Semenzato, Milan #265/R est:1800-2000
£1812 $3244 €2700 Female nude (35x23cm-14x9in) s. 25-May-4 Finarte Semenzato, Milan #128/R est:1500-2000
£1879 $3364 €2800 Young lady in purple (35x25cm-14x10in) s. 25-May-4 Finarte Semenzato, Milan #126/R est:1500-2000
£1879 $3364 €2800 Red scarf (40x30cm-16x12in) s. 25-May-4 Finarte Semenzato, Milan #127/R est:1500-2000

TAFURI, Felice (1939-) Italian

£1745 $3089 €2600 Thoughtful (50x60cm-20x24in) s. s.verso cardboard on canvas. 1-May-4 Meeting Art, Vercelli #363 est:2000

TAFURI, Raffaele (1857-1929) Italian

£1333 $2453 €2000 Roses on armchair (39x49cm-15x19in) s. cardboard prov. 10-Jun-4 Christie's, Rome #189/R est:1500-2000
£1418 $2298 €2000 A la orilla del rio (37x51cm-15x20in) s. 20-May-3 Ansorena, Madrid #195/R est:2000

TAGGART, Elizabeth (20th C) British

£1000 $1720 €1460 County Down landscape (129x96cm-51x38in) s.d.70. 3-Dec-3 John Ross, Belfast #107 est:500-600
Works on paper
£1268 $2028 €1800 Magical landscape (57x83cm-22x33in) s.d.1969 pen ink W/C gold paint. 16-Sep-3 Whyte's, Dublin #199/R est:1000-1500

TAGGER, Siona (1900-1988) Israeli

£367 $650 €536 Seter, gate of the synagogue of Rabbi Shimon Bar-Yochia (65x50cm-26x20in) s. oil on perspex prov. 1-May-4 Ben-Ami, Tel Aviv #4798/R
£535 $1000 €781 Purim, Haman and Mordechai (49x64cm-19x25in) s. oil perspex prov.exhib. 1-Mar-4 Ben-Ami, Tel Aviv #4698/R
£1824 $3100 €2663 Coffee house in Jerusalem (44x54cm-17x21in) s. i.d.1975 verso cardboard. 1-Dec-3 Ben-Ami, Tel Aviv #4369/R est:3500-4500
£2322 $4250 €3390 My tent in Tira (55x38cm-22x15in) s. i.d.1947 verso. 1-Jun-4 Ben-Ami, Tel Aviv #4896/R est:6000-8000
£2529 $4300 €3692 Courtyard in the old city of Zaffed (46x38cm-18x15in) s. i.verso painted early 1960's. 1-Dec-3 Ben-Ami, Tel Aviv #4372/R est:5000-7000
£4765 $8100 €6957 Jerusalem (38x55cm-15x22in) s. i.d.1979 verso. 1-Dec-3 Ben-Ami, Tel Aviv #4338/R est:6000-8000
£4866 $9100 €7104 Still life with pomegranates and landscape of Zaffed through the window (38x46cm-15x18in) s. i.d.verso exhib. 1-Mar-4 Ben-Ami, Tel Aviv #4713/R est:10000-15000
£6354 $11500 €9277 The gate (66x46cm-26x18in) i. verso painted 1928 exhib. 1-Apr-4 Ben-Ami, Tel Aviv #4761/R est:12000-16000
£8305 $14700 €12125 Portrait of Lea Levin (46x38cm-18x15in) s. i.d.1932 verso. 1-May-4 Ben-Ami, Tel Aviv #4799/R est:8000-12000
£10383 $19000 €15159 Village in France (46x38cm-18x15in) s. d.1931 verso prov.exhib.lit. 1-Jun-4 Ben-Ami, Tel Aviv #4912/R est:24000-32000
Works on paper
£275 $500 €413 Dinosaurs struggle (65x50cm-26x20in) s. mixed media Perspex exhib. 1-Jul-4 Ben-Ami, Tel Aviv #4986/R
£291 $530 €437 Chamber orchestra (50x65cm-20x26in) s. mixed media Perspex exhib. 1-Jul-4 Ben-Ami, Tel Aviv #4985/R
£308 $560 €462 Folk festival (65x50cm-26x20in) s. mixed media Perspex exhib. 1-Jul-4 Ben-Ami, Tel Aviv #4984/R
£454 $850 €663 Somal (29x38cm-11x15in) s.i.d.1932 chl prov.exhib. 1-Mar-4 Ben-Ami, Tel Aviv #4693/R
£642 $1200 €937 Orange pickers (34x49cm-13x19in) s. W/C exec.c.1940 exhib. 1-Mar-4 Ben-Ami, Tel Aviv #4694/R
£904 $1600 €1320 Ein Karem (50x64cm-20x25in) s. d.1970 verso W/C. 1-May-4 Ben-Ami, Tel Aviv #4838/R est:1800-2400
£963 $1800 €1406 Village in the Sharon Valley (30x40cm-12x16in) s.d.1941 W/C. 1-Mar-4 Ben-Ami, Tel Aviv #4676/R est:2000-3000
£1136 $2000 €1659 Landscape of Tiberias (46x65cm-18x26in) s. W/C exec.c.1950. 1-Jan-4 Ben-Ami, Tel Aviv #4390/R est:2000-3000
£1658 $3100 €2421 Landscape of Saffed (54x38cm-21x15in) s. W/C exec.c.1940 prov. 1-Mar-4 Ben-Ami, Tel Aviv #4691/R est:3000-4000

TAGGESELLE, Max (19/20th C) German

Works on paper
£347 $566 €500 Boy in sailor suit (101x66cm-40x26in) s.i.d.1908 pastel. 27-Sep-3 Dannenberg, Berlin #617/R

TAGLIABUE, Carlo Costantino (1880-1960) Italian

£699 $1203 €1000 Sunset in Portofino (21x15cm-8x6in) s. board. 3-Dec-3 Stadion, Trieste #1057/R
£1067 $1963 €1600 Alpine lake in Valsesia (50x60cm-20x24in) s. i.verso board. 8-Jun-4 Sotheby's, Milan #39/R est:1500-2500
£1479 $2558 €2100 Marine (50x70cm-20x28in) s.d.1930 board. 9-Dec-3 Finarte Semenzato, Milan #42/R est:2200-2500
£1538 $2646 €2200 Summer afternoon (30x50cm-12x20in) s. s.i.verso board. 3-Dec-3 Stadion, Trieste #1017/R est:1600-2000

TAGORE, Rabindra Nath (1861-1941) Indian

Works on paper
£16000 $26720 €23360 Portrait (35x21cm-14x8in) s.d.9 Nov 28 verso pencil black ink prov. 17-Oct-3 Christie's, Kensington #506/R est:5000-7000

TAGTSTROM, David (1894-) Swedish

£254 $457 €381 Lars-Eric - Interior scene with boy (29x34cm-11x13in) init.d.28 panel. 25-Apr-4 Goteborg Auktionsverk, Sweden #203/R (S.KR 3500)

TAHON, Andre (1907-1985) Belgian

£2000 $3680 €3000 Getting dressed (159x90cm-63x35in) s. canvas on plywood. 9-Jun-4 Christie's, Amsterdam #79/R est:3000-5000

TAHON, Johan (1965-) Belgian

Sculpture
£5034 $9312 €7500 Standing figure (138x32cm-54x13in) s. brown pat bronze one of one. 13-Mar-4 De Vuyst, Lokeren #512/R est:7500-9500
£6711 $12416 €10000 An-sich (136x114cm-54x45in) num.1/3 brown pat bronze. 13-Mar-4 De Vuyst, Lokeren #507/R est:10000-12000

TAHSEEN, Said (1904-1985) Syrian

£1400 $2478 €2044 Portrait of the poet Al-Maari (51x51cm-20x20in) s. 29-Apr-4 Bonhams, New Bond Street #566/R est:1500-2000

TAHSIN, Diyarbakirli (1875-1937) Turkish

£6333 $11653 €9500 Marine, vue d'Istanbul (90x71cm-35x28in) s.d.1929. 11-Jun-4 Claude Aguttes, Neuilly #175/R est:5000-7000

TAIBO GONZALEZ, German (1889-1919) Spanish

£3345 $5854 €4750 Cornered (50x30cm-20x12in) s. 16-Dec-3 Durán, Madrid #194/R

TAILFEATHERS, Gerald (1925-1975) Canadian

Works on paper
£203 $344 €296 Just a Ridin', Blackfoot (13x15cm-5x6in) s.d.1959 ink prov. 23-Nov-3 Levis, Calgary #573/R (C.D 450)

TAILLANDIER, Yvon (1926-) French

£223 $400 €326 Tracteur a propolsion centaurique (51x66cm-20x26in) s. i.stretcher acrylic prov. 20-Mar-4 Sloans & Kenyon, Bethesda #355/R
£267 $480 €400 Ce rond est un grand aeroplane (40x50cm-16x20in) s. acrylic. 24-Apr-4 Cornette de St.Cyr, Paris #720
£268 $491 €400 Personnages (48x63cm-19x25in) s. mixed media. 7-Jul-4 Artcurial Briest, Paris #351
£315 $535 €450 Composition aux avions (50x65cm-20x26in) s. acrylic paper on canvas. 28-Nov-3 Blanchet, Paris #235
£333 $600 €500 Reves reciproques (41x33cm-16x13in) s. acrylic painted 1992-2000. 24-Apr-4 Cornette de St.Cyr, Paris #722
£343 $583 €490 New Delhi (58x43cm-23x17in) s. paper on canvas. 20-Nov-3 Claude Aguttes, Neuilly #97/R
£467 $840 €700 Jules Verne (64x54cm-25x21in) s. acrylic. 24-Apr-4 Cornette de St.Cyr, Paris #723/R
£600 $1080 €900 Tsar de toutes les filles (65x81cm-26x32in) s.d.1999 acrylic. 24-Apr-4 Cornette de St.Cyr, Paris #724
£764 $1276 €1100 Petit diable ingenieur (89x119cm-35x47in) s. 25-Oct-3 Cornette de St.Cyr, Paris #818
Sculpture
£2013 $3564 €3000 Groom appelant un taxi (135cm-53in) mono. polychrome acrylic cardboard. 29-Apr-4 Claude Aguttes, Neuilly #186/R est:3000-3500
Works on paper
£236 $431 €350 Projet d'affiche pour le Salon de Mai1983 (60x44cm-24x17in) s. mixed media. 7-Jul-4 Artcurial Briest, Paris #352
£369 $661 €550 Biscottes (46x62cm-18x24in) s.i.d.1986 mixed media paper on canvas. 25-May-4 Chambelland & Giafferi, Paris #85/R

£470 $841 €700 Personnage fantastique (62x46cm-24x18in) s.d.1988 mixed media paper on canvas. 25-May-4 Chambelland & Giafferi, Paris #86/R

TAINBERT, Geo (19/20th C) ?
£263 $476 €400 Vase de fleurs (73x54cm-29x21in) s. 19-Apr-4 Boscher, Cherbourg #910/R

TAIPANA, Simon Manigyogihok (20th C) North American
Sculpture
£2928 $4977 €4275 Musk ox carved with arctic animals and scenes from arctic life (38cm-15in) s. mottled dark soapstone. 3-Nov-3 Waddingtons, Toronto #190/R est:5000-6000 (C.D 6500)

TAIT, Agnes Gabrielle McNulty (1894-1981) American
£1117 $2000 €1631 Horse ranch in Texas Hill Country. s. 13-May-4 Dallas Auction Gallery, Dallas #23/R est:500-800
£1156 $2000 €1688 Begin the Beguine (44x36cm-17x14in) s.i.verso canvasboard prov. 10-Dec-3 Bonhams & Butterfields, San Francisco #6079/R est:3000-5000
Works on paper
£216 $360 €315 Sleeping small cat (25x36cm-10x14in) s. W/C. 14-Nov-3 Aspire, Cleveland #167
£217 $350 €317 Portrait of Carol Habberley at age 10 (48x34cm-19x13in) s. W/C. 24-Aug-3 Bonhams & Butterfields, Los Angeles #7005
£273 $500 €399 Woman in summer evening formal dress (28x23cm-11x9in) s. W/C gouache chl. 10-Apr-4 Auctions by the Bay, Alameda #1642/R

TAIT, Arthur Fitzwilliam (1819-1905) American
£4595 $8500 €6709 Sheep in a field (36x53cm-14x21in) s.d.1901. 13-Mar-4 DeFina, Austinburg #834/R est:2000-3000
£8523 $15000 €12444 Dan Catlin home, Adirondacks Long Lake NY (30x38cm-12x15in) s.d.87 i.verso prov.lit. 19-May-4 Sotheby's, New York #92/R est:15000-25000
£10000 $17000 €14600 Quail (28x39cm-11x15in) s.i.d.1867 s.i.d.verso board prov. 21-Nov-3 Skinner, Boston #292/R est:6000-8000
£10270 $19000 €14994 Pointer retrieving woodcock (74x58cm-29x23in) s. verso. 10-Feb-4 Doyle, New York #243/R est:20000-30000
£10976 $18000 €15915 Sheep in a rocky landscape (51x76cm-20x30in) s.d.85 i.verso prov. 31-May-3 Brunk, Ashville #554/R est:8000-15000

TAIT, Arthur Fitzwilliam (attrib) (1819-1905) American
Works on paper
£311 $500 €454 Dog portrait 'Duncan Grey' (15x23cm-6x9in) s.i. W/C. 20-Aug-3 James Julia, Fairfield #1001/R

TAJIRI, Shinkichi (1923-) Dutch
Sculpture
£9420 $15449 €13000 Obiit (33cm-13in) bronze wooden base exec.1962. 27-May-3 Sotheby's, Amsterdam #436/R est:10000-15000

TAKA (1941-) Japanese
£691 $1271 €1050 Composition (74x63cm-29x25in) s. mixed media collage. 28-Jun-4 Joron-Derem, Paris #208

TAKAHASHI, Oshin (19th C) Japanese
Works on paper
£380 $695 €555 Kacho e of the four seasons (90x75cm-35x30in) s. col ink on silk. 7-Apr-4 Sotheby's, Olympia #2/R

TAKAHASHI, Shotei (1871-1945) Japanese
Prints
£9500 $17005 €13870 Awabitori (53x38cm-21x15in) s. woodblock. 6-May-4 Sotheby's, London #1/R est:2000-3000

TAKALA, Veikko (1923-) Finnish
£451 $754 €650 Listener (40x60cm-16x24in) s.d.89. 26-Oct-3 Bukowskis, Helsinki #511/R
£567 $1043 €850 Like an icon (83x53cm-33x21in) s. oil mixed media. 9-Jun-4 Bukowskis, Helsinki #561/R

TAKANEN, Johannes (1849-1885) Finnish
Sculpture
£1141 $2099 €1700 Andromeda (91cm-36in) s.d.1878 plaster. 25-Mar-4 Hagelstam, Helsinki #767/R

TAKIS (1925-) Greek
Sculpture
£1334 $2454 €2000 Indicateur I (54x10x12cm-21x4x5in) s. num.6/40 base plexiglass aeronautic parts prov. 9-Jun-4 Artcurial Briest, Paris #498/R est:2000-2500
£1486 $2661 €2200 Indicator I (63cm-25in) plexiglas exec.1970. 4-May-4 Calmels Cohen, Paris #251/R est:1500-2000
£1667 $3066 €2500 Musical I (100x31x6cm-39x12x2in) plexiglas steel piano cord other objects exec 1967 exhib. 9-Jun-4 Artcurial Briest, Paris #496/R est:3000-4000
£2200 $3740 €3212 Signals - Series 2 (210cm-83in) d.1968 metal light bulbs electrical components. 18-Nov-3 Bonhams, Knightsbridge #190/R est:1000-1500
£2333 $4293 €3500 Signals (153cm-60in) num.2/16 multiple with traffic lights electrical system exec 1967. 8-Jun-4 Sotheby's, Amsterdam #121/R est:3000-5000
£2349 $4158 €3500 Signal (210cm-83in) s.d.1968 collage. 27-Apr-4 Campo, Vlaamse Kaai #595 est:1300-3500
£2800 $4452 €4060 Teleumiere (78x41x34cm-31x16x13in) glass metal painted wood lamp dry vapour electrical components. 11-Sep-3 Christie's, Kensington #244/R est:3000-4000
£2937 $4993 €4200 Croix (90cm-35in) s.d.89 iron lead. 18-Nov-3 Pierre Berge, Paris #25/R est:3000-3500
£3000 $5100 €4380 Gong (178x178cm-70x70in) bronze. 18-Nov-3 Sotheby's, London #55/R est:3000-4000
£3667 $6747 €5500 Double signal (230x23x26cm-91x9x10in) editions unlimited Bath exec 1967. 9-Jun-4 Artcurial Briest, Paris #497/R est:4000-5000
£8000 $13600 €11680 Signals (325cm-128in) pat bronze. 18-Nov-3 Sotheby's, London #112/R est:8000-12000
£8000 $14320 €11680 Fleur (260cm-102in) s. num.3/4 st.f. black pat metal. 10-May-4 Sotheby's, Olympia #53/R est:7000-9000
£10500 $17850 €15330 Fleur (315cm-124in) st.f.Tesconi Pietrasanta i. num.4/4 pat bronze. 18-Nov-3 Sotheby's, London #54/R est:8000-12000
£11000 $20020 €16060 Signal (125x20x14cm-49x8x6in) steel iron exec.c.1955-56 prov. 6-Feb-4 Sotheby's, London #196/R est:4500-5500
£15333 $27907 €23000 Sculpture magnetique (223x130x70cm-88x51x28in) s. iron porcelan prov. 29-Jun-4 Cornette de St.Cyr, Paris #60/R est:20000-25000
£16000 $28640 €23360 Music (257x90cm-101x35in) s.i.d.1973 verso wood metal magnets speakers three parts. 10-May-4 Sotheby's, Olympia #92/R est:15000-20000
£18056 $30153 €26000 Signal (300cm-118in) s. base iron. 21-Oct-3 Artcurial Briest, Paris #610/R est:20000-25000
Works on paper
£800 $1432 €1168 Lignes paralleles (79x58cm-31x23in) s.i. cardboard wood magnets metal. 10-May-4 Sotheby's, Olympia #90/R

TAKIS, Nicholas (1903-1965) American
Works on paper
£309 $525 €451 Couple on the beach (51x61cm-20x24in) s. gouache on card. 5-Nov-3 Doyle, New York #75/R

TAKKIRUQ, Nelson (1930-) North American
Sculpture
£5180 $8806 €7563 Inuit archer with bow (53cm-21in) s. mottled soapstone antler sinew. 3-Nov-3 Waddingtons, Toronto #402/R est:7000-9000 (C.D 11500)

TAL COAT, Pierre (1905-1985) French
£1000 $1730 €1460 Nature morte au pichet et raisins (33x41cm-13x16in) s. 11-Dec-3 Christie's, Kensington #198/R est:600-800
£1000 $1840 €1500 Paysage du midi (24x35cm-9x14in) s. canvas on panel painted c.1941. 9-Jun-4 Le Roux & Morel, Paris #21/R est:1500-1800
£1149 $2056 €1700 Untitled (10x14cm-4x6in) mono. cardboard. 4-May-4 Calmels Cohen, Paris #153/R est:1000-1500
£1476 $2746 €2200 Composition (33x24cm-13x9in) s. isorel. 3-Mar-4 Artcurial Briest, Paris #525 est:1800-2200
£2168 $3729 €3100 Femme assise (65x50cm-26x20in) s. painted 1935 prov.exhib. 8-Dec-3 Christie's, Paris #69/R est:1800-2400
£2448 $4161 €3500 Terres, eaux, sous-jacentes (55x65cm-22x26in) mono. prov. 18-Nov-3 Pierre Berge, Paris #39/R est:3000-4500
£2667 $4853 €4000 Femme allongee (27x41cm-11x16in) s. prov. 29-Jun-4 Sotheby's, Paris #22/R est:4000-6000
£2817 $4873 €4000 Vers le haut (33x41cm-13x16in) mono. i.d.1983 verso panel. 9-Dec-3 Artcurial Briest, Paris #423/R est:4000-6000
£2905 $5200 €4300 Untitled (61x50cm-24x20in) mono. d.1938 on stretcher paper on canvas. 4-May-4 Calmels Cohen, Paris #170/R est:2500-3000
£3000 $5190 €4380 Composition (99x99cm-39x39in) s. prov.exhib. 11-Dec-3 Christie's, Kensington #231/R est:2000-3000
£3020 $5618 €4500 Composition (161x129cm-63x51in) 3-Mar-4 Artcurial Briest, Paris #524 est:4000-5000
£3147 $5350 €4500 Paroi (65x81cm-26x32in) mono. prov. 18-Nov-3 Pierre Berge, Paris #40/R est:4500-6000
£3427 $5722 €4900 Poissons (49x59cm-19x23in) s. paper on canvas. 29-Jun-3 Versailles Encheres #51/R
£3521 $6092 €5000 Basses terres (60x73cm-24x29in) mono. prov. 14-Dec-3 Versailles Encheres #70/R est:4500-5500
£3667 $6747 €5500 En Drome II (60x73cm-24x29in) mono. painted 1981-1982 prov.exhib. 8-Jun-4 Artcurial Briest, Paris #225/R est:8000-12000
£3695 $6615 €5395 L'aqvarium (129x96cm-51x38in) sold with letter painted c.1945. 28-May-4 Uppsala Auktionskammare, Uppsala #311/R est:50000-60000 (S.KR 50000)
£3750 $5925 €5400 Composition (60x74cm-24x29in) mono. 27-Apr-3 Versailles Encheres #25
£3793 $7017 €5500 Nature morte, sur la table (117x102cm-46x40in) init. exhib. 13-Feb-4 Charbonneaux, Paris #75/R est:5000-6000
£5473 $10344 €8100 Sous-jacent (97x130cm-38x51in) mono. i.d.1970 verso prov. 21-Feb-4 Cornette de St.Cyr, Paris #408/R est:10000-12000
£6667 $12267 €10000 Glauque (81x116cm-32x46in) mono. painted 1972 prov.exhib. 8-Jun-4 Artcurial Briest, Paris #224/R est:10000-15000
£8000 $14720 €12000 Carriere (97x130cm-38x51in) s. i.d.1968-69 verso prov. 8-Jun-4 Artcurial Briest, Paris #223/R est:12000-15000
£8054 $14416 €12000 Passage rapide (95x129cm-37x51in) init. painted 1952. 26-May-4 Christie's, Paris #79/R est:5000-8000
Works on paper
£302 $534 €450 Joueurs de cartes (30x43cm-12x17in) s. lead pencil exec c.1930. 27-Apr-4 Artcurial Briest, Paris #91
£500 $900 €750 Self-portrait (43x21cm-17x8in) s.d.1977 graphite. 25-Apr-4 Versailles Encheres #7
£541 $968 €800 Clivages (10x28cm-4x11in) s. s.i.d.1984 verso W/C. 4-May-4 Calmels Cohen, Paris #207
£671 $1248 €1000 Portrait de Gertrude Stein (26x21cm-10x8in) s. graphite paper on cardboard exec.c.1930. 2-Mar-4 Artcurial Briest, Paris #70
£872 $1544 €1300 Composition (49x64cm-19x25in) s.d.4.72 Indian ink ink wash. 28-Apr-4 Artcurial Briest, Paris #259 est:800-1200
£1127 $1949 €1600 Paysage (39x47cm-15x19in) mono.d.79 W/C prov. 9-Dec-3 Artcurial Briest, Paris #498 est:1500-2000

TALBERG, Boris (20th C) Russian?
Works on paper
£442 $791 €650 Finale des Jeux Olympiques de Cortina d'Ampezzo (26x11cm-10x4in) W/C. 21-Mar-4 Rossini, Paris #210
£676 $1189 €1000 Projet de fresque (10x16cm-4x6in) gouache prov. 19-May-4 Camard, Paris #35

TALBOT, William Henry Fox (1800-1877) British
Photographs
£2778 $5000 €4056 Fine grass study (9x6cm-4x2in) experimental photographic engraving prov. 22-Apr-4 Phillips, New York #33/R est:8000-12000

TALCOTT, Fern (20th C) American
£214 $400 €312 Still life with fruit, mask and jug (119x72cm-47x28in) s.d.1951 verso board. 29-Feb-4 Bonhams & Butterfields, San Francisco #4590

TALICHKIN, Sergey (20th C) ?
£596 $1085 €900 Odyssey of the mind (100x120cm-39x47in) s. 15-Jun-4 James Adam, Dublin #69/R
£662 $1205 €1000 Voice of silence (100x150cm-39x59in) s. 15-Jun-4 James Adam, Dublin #71/R

TALIRUNILI, Joe (1906-1976) North American
Sculpture
£811 $1378 €1184 Owl (9cm-4in) mottled dark soapstone. 3-Nov-3 Waddingtons, Toronto #80/R est:700-1000 (C.D 1800)
£901 $1532 €1315 Owl (9cm-4in) s. mottled grey soapstone. 3-Nov-3 Waddingtons, Toronto #83/R est:1500-2000 (C.D 2000)
£1712 $2910 €2500 Owl (20cm-8in) s. mottled grey soapstone. 3-Nov-3 Waddingtons, Toronto #85/R est:2000-3000 (C.D 3800)

TALLANT, Richard H (1853-1934) American
£214 $350 €312 Sheep Lake, National Park, Colorado (30x46cm-12x18in) s. s.i.verso. 24-Sep-3 Jackson's, Cedar Falls #760/R
£1278 $2300 €1866 Colorado mountain lake (83x56cm-33x22in) s. 24-Apr-4 Weschler, Washington #620/R est:1000-1500

TALLENTIRE, Anne (1949-) British
£350 $594 €500 Figures on horseback in a wood (37x75cm-15x30in) s. 18-Nov-3 Mealy's, Castlecomer #1394
£533 $960 €800 Fishermen in port archway (61x52cm-24x20in) s. canvasboard. 20-Apr-4 James Adam, Dublin #194/R
£676 $1277 €1000 Road to Roundstone (38x76cm-15x30in) s. 17-Feb-4 Whyte's, Dublin #181 est:1000-1200
£867 $1569 €1300 Illusion (40x61cm-16x24in) s.i. 30-Mar-4 De Veres Art Auctions, Dublin #154/R

TALLEZ, H (20th C) ?
£1216 $2141 €1800 In cabaret (75x50cm-30x20in) s.d.1928 board. 21-May-4 Mehlis, Plauen #15223/R est:1800

TALLMAN, John (19th C) American
£2060 $3750 €3008 Still life with strawberries (51x61cm-20x24in) s.d.1874. 29-Jun-4 Sotheby's, New York #194/R est:2500-3500

TALLONE, Anna Nascimbene (1901-1961) Italian
£816 $1461 €1200 Checrouit Lake (70x100cm-28x39in) s. 22-Mar-4 Sant Agostino, Torino #179/R

TALLONE, Cesare (1853-1919) Italian
£336 $594 €500 Portrait of girl in profile (70x38cm-28x15in) 1-May-4 Meeting Art, Vercelli #44
£1549 $2572 €2200 Mountain landscape scene (36x50cm-14x20in) s. panel. 11-Jun-3 Christie's, Rome #122/R est:2500-3500

TALLONE, Guido (1894-1967) Italian
£1056 $1754 €1500 Ca' del Bado' (61x76cm-24x30in) s.d.52. 11-Jun-3 Finarte Semenzato, Milan #518/R
£1761 $2923 €2500 Chiusa sul fiume (48x66cm-19x26in) s. 14-Jun-3 Meeting Art, Vercelli #148/R est:2500
£3077 $5231 €4492 Still life with fish and brass bowl (69x80cm-27x31in) s. bears d. panel prov. 19-Nov-3 Fischer, Luzern #1125/R est:2500-3500 (S.FR 6800)

TALMA, Francois Joseph (1763-1826) French
Works on paper
£851 $1379 €1200 Croquis de costume de soldat Romain (33x19cm-13x7in) W/C black crayon. 21-May-3 Daguerre, Paris #98/R

TALMAGE, Algernon (1871-1939) British
£250 $408 €365 Sheep in pasture (14x23cm-6x9in) panel. 26-Sep-3 Bigwood, Stratford on Avon #427
£280 $468 €409 Sheep grazing (15x22cm-6x9in) s. 19-Jun-3 Bonhams, Edinburgh #370
£320 $534 €467 Sheep in autumn landscape (51x66cm-20x26in) 12-Nov-3 Sotheby's, Olympia #125/R
£650 $1105 €949 Sheep grazing in a meadow (13x23cm-5x9in) s. panel. 30-Oct-3 Duke & Son, Dorchester #210/R
£2400 $4440 €3504 Summer time (63x76cm-25x30in) s.d.23. 10-Mar-4 Sotheby's, Olympia #222/R est:1000-2000
£3000 $5490 €4380 Kingdom of the winds (74x99cm-29x39in) s.d.1936 prov. 3-Jun-4 Lane, Penzance #155/R est:4000-5000
£6400 $11712 €9344 St Ives harbour (61x76cm-24x30in) s.d.1903. 3-Jun-4 Lane, Penzance #215/R est:4000-6000

TALPAZAN, Ionel (1955-) Rumanian
Works on paper
£264 $475 €385 Spaceship and face (71x56cm-28x22in) mixed media on posterboard. 24-Apr-4 Slotin Folk Art, Buford #792/R
£361 $650 €527 Spaceship landing (71x56cm-28x22in) mixed media on posterboard. 24-Apr-4 Slotin Folk Art, Buford #793/R

TALWINSKI, Igor (1907-) Polish
£300 $501 €438 Portrait of a girl with blue necklace (56x46cm-22x18in) s. 21-Oct-3 Bonhams, Knightsbridge #161/R
£360 $644 €526 Nude with red ribbon and mirror (53x44cm-21x17in) s. 22-Mar-4 Bearnes, Exeter #36
£480 $859 €701 Nude on a white sheet (44x52cm-17x20in) s. 22-Mar-4 Bearnes, Exeter #35
£550 $1012 €803 Green necklace (56x46cm-22x18in) s. 8-Jun-4 Gorringes, Lewes #2096
£563 $935 €800 Portrait de jeune fille (55x45cm-22x18in) 15-Jun-3 Teitgen, Nancy #99
£650 $1151 €949 La baigneuse (55x46cm-22x18in) s. prov. 27-Apr-4 Bonhams, Knightsbridge #217/R

TAM, Reuben (1916-) American
£1852 $3000 €2685 Days towards landfall (56x76cm-22x30in) s. board prov. 8-Aug-3 Barridorf, Portland #316/R est:2000-3000

TAMANOUCHI, Mitsuo (1928-) Japanese
Works on paper
£254 $425 €371 Mount Fuji (30x48cm-12x19in) s. W/C. 20-Jun-3 Freeman, Philadelphia #33/R

TAMAYO, Rufino (1899-1991) Mexican
£35294 $60000 €51529 Tete - Head (53x46cm-21x18in) s.d.58 prov.exhib. 18-Nov-3 Christie's, Rockefeller NY #140/R est:60000-80000
£43605 $75000 €63663 Dos personajes (46x55cm-18x22in) s.d.59 oil sand. 3-Dec-3 Doyle, New York #21/R est:100000-150000
£58824 $100000 €85883 Autorretrato (41x33cm-16x13in) s.d.31 panel prov. 19-Nov-3 Sotheby's, New York #19/R est:50000-70000
£211765 $360000 €309177 Hombre en rojo (80x100cm-31x39in) s.d.0-76 d.verso oil sans prov.exhib. 19-Nov-3 Sotheby's, New York #17/R est:300000-350000
£213333 $392533 €320000 Smoker (76x59cm-30x23in) s.d.45 prov.exhib. 10-Jun-4 Christie's, Paris #19/R est:285000-325000
£217877 $390000 €318100 Bowl full of bowl (67x47cm-26x19in) s.d.28 prov.exhib.lit. 26-May-4 Sotheby's, New York #4/R est:300000-400000
£446927 $800000 €652513 New York from a terrace (52x87cm-20x34in) s.d.37 prov.exhib.lit. 26-May-4 Sotheby's, New York #10/R est:800000-1000000
£573333 $1054933 €860000 Claustrophobia (81x73cm-32x29in) s.d.54 prov.exhib.lit. 10-Jun-4 Christie's, Paris #29/R est:650000-800000
Prints
£1657 $3000 €2419 Quetzacoatl (61x122cm-24x48in) s.num.20/70 col mixograph. 19-Apr-4 Bonhams & Butterfields, San Francisco #78/R est:4000-6000
£1765 $3000 €2577 Red mask (54x70cm-21x28in) s. col lithograph. 31-Oct-3 Sotheby's, New York #202
£1912 $3250 €2792 Figure (76x56cm-30x22in) s. num.66/140 col etching. 31-Oct-3 Sotheby's, New York #204/R
£2031 $3250 €2965 Virgin of Guadalupe (18x23cm-7x9in) s. woodcut executed c.1928-30. 20-Sep-3 Sloans & Kenyon, Bethesda #1013/R est:4000-5000
£2118 $3600 €3092 Sandias (77x57cm-30x22in) s.num.35/150 col lithograph. 6-Nov-3 Swann Galleries, New York #733/R est:2000-3000
£2118 $3600 €3092 Hombre negro en fondo rojo (77x58cm-30x23in) s.num.50/140 col mixograph. 6-Nov-3 Swann Galleries, New York #736/R est:2000-3000
£2260 $4000 €3300 Perro (60x79cm-24x31in) s.num.64/100 col lithograph. 30-Apr-4 Sotheby's, New York #31/R est:3000-4000
£2624 $4750 €3831 Hombre con baston (85x64cm-33x25in) s.d.1980 num.85/100 col mixograph. 19-Apr-4 Bonhams & Butterfields, San Francisco #79/R est:4000-5000
£5882 $10000 €8588 Two figures attcked by dogs (152x249cm-60x98in) s. col mixograph. 4-Nov-3 Christie's, Rockefeller NY #353/R est:8000-12000
£6077 $11000 €8872 Sandias con manzana (69x88cm-27x35in) s.num.33/90 col mixograph. 19-Apr-4 Bonhams & Butterfields, San Francisco #80/R est:6000-8000
Sculpture
£39106 $70000 €57095 Monument to the unknown hero (203x60x50cm-80x24x20in) st.sig. num.2/3 steel prov.exhib. 26-May-4 Sotheby's, New York #44/R est:90000-120000
Works on paper
£8824 $15000 €12883 Dos banistas - Two women bathing (27x21cm-11x8in) s.d.34 gouache prov. 18-Nov-3 Christie's, Rockefeller NY #97/R est:20000-25000
£9412 $16000 €13742 Mujer con canasta (23x18cm-9x7in) s.d.42 gouache prov. 19-Nov-3 Sotheby's, New York #100/R est:20000-25000
£19118 $32500 €27912 La familla (30x20cm-12x8in) s.d.26 gouache prov.exhib.lit. 19-Nov-3 Sotheby's, New York #102/R est:25000-35000
£30588 $52000 €44658 Mujer con naranja - Woman with orange (61x46cm-24x18in) s. W/C gouache pencil exec. c.1940 prov. 18-Nov-3 Christie's, Rockefeller NY #36/R est:40000-60000
£35294 $60000 €51529 Virgen de Guadalupe (25x17cm-10x7in) s.d.26 gouache W/C prov.lit. 19-Nov-3 Sotheby's, New York #1/R est:40000-60000
£39106 $70000 €57095 Nude (75x55cm-30x22in) s.d.47 graphite col pencil lit. 26-May-4 Sotheby's, New York #40a/R est:60000-80000
£105882 $180000 €154588 Mujer arreglandose el pelo (73x58cm-29x23in) s.d.44 s.i.d.verso gouache prov.exhib.lit. 19-Nov-3 Sotheby's, New York #18/R est:125000-175000

TAMBURI, Orfeo (1910-1994) Italian
£629 $1070 €900 Madonna and Child (28x22cm-11x9in) s. tempera paper on canvas. 24-Nov-3 Christie's, Milan #97
£667 $1227 €1000 Roman hills (46x37cm-18x15in) s. tempera paper. 12-Jun-4 Meeting Art, Vercelli #260/R
£667 $1227 €1000 Paris (32x24cm-13x9in) s. tempera paper on canvas. 12-Jun-4 Meeting Art, Vercelli #719/R
£680 $1218 €1000 Painter (43x34cm-17x13in) s. tempera paper painted1948. 16-Mar-4 Finarte Semenzato, Milan #295/R
£759 $1267 €1100 Houses on the beach (24x31cm-9x12in) s. tempera W/C pencil paper. 13-Nov-3 Finarte Semenzato, Rome #143
£1497 $2679 €2200 Portrait (50x72cm-20x28in) s. 16-Mar-4 Finarte Semenzato, Milan #299/R est:2200
£1724 $2879 €2500 Rocks in Maratea (20x34cm-8x13in) s. i.d.1960 verso. 13-Nov-3 Finarte Semenzato, Rome #265 est:2000-2500
£1800 $3258 €2700 Paris (20x15cm-8x6in) s. on canvas on cardboard. 2-Apr-4 Farsetti, Prato #91/R est:1600-1900

£1905 $3410 €2800 Roman landscape (44x46cm-17x18in) s. 16-Mar-4 Finarte Semenzato, Milan #304/R est:3000
£2000 $3680 €3000 Landscape (27x39cm-11x15in) s. canvas on masonite. 12-Jun-4 Meeting Art, Vercelli #615/R est:3000
£2041 $3653 €3000 Bather by the sea (100x65cm-39x26in) s. prov. 16-Mar-4 Finarte Semenzato, Milan #294/R est:4000
£2069 $3455 €3000 Landscape. s. 13-Nov-3 Galleria Pace, Milan #40/R est:4000
£3147 $5350 €4500 Roofs (30x40cm-12x16in) s. 20-Nov-3 Finarte Semenzato, Milan #213/R est:4500-4800
£3514 $6184 €5200 Yellow and black walls (26x32cm-10x13in) s. canvas on cardboard painted c.1962 prov. 24-May-4 Christie's, Milan #56/R est:3000-4000
£3691 $6607 €5500 Paris (30x39cm-12x15in) s. 29-May-4 Farsetti, Prato #552/R est:4500-6000
£3691 $6829 €5500 Houses in Paris (30x20cm-12x8in) s. 11-Mar-4 Galleria Pace, Milan #66/R est:6500-8500
£3691 $6607 €5500 Houses in Paris (30x40cm-12x16in) s. 30-May-4 Meeting Art, Vercelli #65 est:5000
£3846 $6538 €5500 Paris (30x40cm-12x16in) s. canvas on board prov. 25-Nov-3 Sotheby's, Milan #81/R est:4000-5000
£3916 $6657 €5600 Untitled (40x30cm-16x12in) s. masonite. 24-Nov-3 Christie's, Milan #76/R est:3500-5000
£4027 $7208 €6000 Houses (29x38cm-11x15in) s. painted 1984 prov. 25-May-4 Sotheby's, Milan #33/R est:6000
£4698 $8409 €7000 Paris (30x40cm-12x16in) s. 29-May-4 Farsetti, Prato #556/R est:6000-9000
£5369 $9933 €8000 Houses in Paris (40x30cm-16x12in) s. 11-Mar-4 Galleria Pace, Milan #148/R est:9500-12000
£8054 $14416 €12000 Paris (50x70cm-20x28in) s. 29-May-4 Farsetti, Prato #551/R est:11500-13000
£11000 $19910 €16500 Paris (50x70cm-20x28in) s. 2-Apr-4 Farsetti, Prato #293/R est:16000-18000
Works on paper
£268 $497 €400 Composition (42x32cm-17x13in) s.d.1963 W/C. 13-Mar-4 Meeting Art, Vercelli #346
£336 $621 €500 Study (32x24cm-13x9in) s. Chinese ink. 13-Mar-4 Meeting Art, Vercelli #217
£349 $648 €520 View of town (28x22cm-11x9in) s. ink. 4-Mar-4 Babuino, Rome #408
£397 $723 €600 Windows (38x23cm-15x9in) s. W/C paper on canvas. 17-Jun-4 Galleria Pananti, Florence #400/R
£400 $724 €600 Landscape (12x9cm-5x4in) s. W/C felt-tip pen paper on canvas exec.1968. 2-Apr-4 Farsetti, Prato #39
£403 $745 €600 Windows in Paris (31x24cm-12x9in) s.d.1959. 13-Mar-4 Meeting Art, Vercelli #480
£493 $863 €700 Paris square (17x21cm-7x8in) s. W/C tempera card. 16-Dec-3 Finarte Semenzato, Milan #159
£503 $931 €750 Composition (42x32cm-17x13in) s. W/C. 13-Mar-4 Meeting Art, Vercelli #215
£897 $1497 €1300 Houses in Paris (50x35cm-20x14in) s. W/C. 13-Nov-3 Galleria Pace, Milan #108/R
£1042 $1646 €1500 Black and white windows (21x27cm-8x11in) wash exec.1960. 6-Sep-3 Meeting Art, Vercelli #670 est:1500
£1477 $2643 €2200 Landscape. Root. Bush (32x42cm-13x17in) s.d.60 Chinese ink W/C two oils three. 25-May-4 Sotheby's, Milan #40 est:2000
£1905 $3410 €2800 Moulin ROuge (30x36cm-12x14in) s. W/C paper on canvas. 16-Mar-4 Finarte Semenzato, Milan #250/R est:1200

TAMBURINI, Arnaldo (1843-1901) Italian
£889 $1600 €1298 Serenade (18x23cm-7x9in) s. panel. 20-Jan-4 Arthur James, Florida #642
£1236 $2100 €1805 Preparing for the journey (56x69cm-22x27in) bears sig.i. 21-Nov-3 Skinner, Boston #236/R est:1800-2200
£1500 $2775 €2190 Monk holding a cockerel (30x25cm-12x10in) s. 10-Feb-4 Bonhams, Knightsbridge #178/R
£3693 $6500 €5392 Kittle more salt? (31x25cm-12x10in) s.i. 18-May-4 Bonhams & Butterfields, San Francisco #54/R est:3000-5000

TAMBURINI, Jose Maria (1856-1932) Spanish
£423 $731 €600 Night landscape with river (29x38cm-11x15in) s. 15-Dec-3 Ansorena, Madrid #265/R
£428 $787 €650 Landscape at night (29x38cm-11x15in) s. 22-Jun-4 Durán, Madrid #163/R

TAMBURRINI, Amerigo (19/20th C) Italian?
£669 $1111 €950 Vaso con fiori (65x53cm-26x21in) s. wood. 11-Jun-3 Christie's, Rome #54/R

TAMLIN, J H P (fl.1903-1911) British
£1850 $3275 €2701 King's Lynn fishing boats (61x46cm-24x18in) s.d.1912. 27-Apr-4 Bonhams, Knowle #105 est:300-500

TAMM, Franz Werner (1658-1724) German
£15000 $25950 €21900 Peonies, chrysanthemums, rose and other flowers in a sculpted urn (115x90cm-45x35in) 10-Dec-3 Bonhams, New Bond Street #37/R est:8000-12000
£20000 $36000 €29200 Still life with putti, fruit and flowers in an exotic landscape. s. 22-Apr-4 Sotheby's, London #106/R est:20000-30000
£72000 $128880 €108000 Pumpkins, grapes and pomegranates. Watermelon, grapes and figs (74x100cm-29x39in) pair. 12-May-4 Finarte Semenzato, Milan #103/R est:40000-60000

TAMM, Franz Werner (attrib) (1658-1724) German
£2825 $5000 €4125 Putto with a watermelon and flowers (76x64cm-30x25in) 2-May-4 Bonhams & Butterfields, San Francisco #1024/R est:4000-6000

TAMM, Franz Werner (circle) (1658-1724) German
£6711 $12349 €10000 Still life with fruit, vegetables, birds and rabbit (61x76cm-24x30in) 24-Mar-4 Dorotheum, Vienna #223/R est:2000-3500

TAMMARO, Francesco (1939-) Italian
£613 $1000 €895 Street and market (36x66cm-14x26in) s. board. 27-Sep-3 Charlton Hall, Columbia #108/R
£663 $1200 €968 Parisian street scene (30x61cm-12x24in) s. board. 3-Apr-4 Charlton Hall, Columbia #120/R est:1000-1500
£900 $1413 €1305 Carriages and elegant figures on a bustling Parisian boulevard (30x60cm-12x24in) s. panel. 28-Aug-3 Christie's, Kensington #338/R

TAMMI, Pasi (20th C) Finnish?
Works on paper
£403 $741 €600 And it is spring again (24x21cm-9x8in) s.d.1998 W/C gouache. 25-Mar-4 Hagelstam, Helsinki #976

TAN CHOH TEE (1942-) Chinese
£1961 $3549 €2863 Chinatown (50x65cm-20x26in) s.d.83. 4-Apr-4 Sotheby's, Singapore #108/R est:4000-6000 (S.D 6000)

TAN, Humen (20th C) American
Works on paper
£800 $1400 €1168 Dining Room from the Playboy Town House (51x32cm-20x13in) gouache ink ills board exec May 1962. 17-Dec-3 Christie's, Rockefeller NY #163/R
£1143 $2000 €1669 Three images from Playboys Patio Terrace (38x51cm-15x20in) ink W/C ills board three exec Aug 1963. 17-Dec-3 Christie's, Rockefeller NY #165/R est:4000-6000
£1371 $2400 €2002 Street view of the Facade (44x37cm-17x15in) gouache ink ills board exec May 1962. 17-Dec-3 Christie's, Rockefeller NY #161/R est:2000-3000
£1600 $2800 €2336 Playboy Patio Terrace (50x91cm-20x36in) gouache ink ills board exec Aug 1963. 17-Dec-3 Christie's, Rockefeller NY #164/R est:4000-6000
£5143 $9000 €7509 Living Room from Playboy Town House (51x75cm-20x30in) gouache ink ills board exec May 1962. 17-Dec-3 Christie's, Rockefeller NY #162/R est:5000-7000

TANABE, Takao (1926-) Canadian
£442 $822 €645 The land sketch 0 (40x50cm-16x20in) s. acrylic painted 1972 prov. 4-Mar-4 Heffel, Vancouver #44/R (C.D 1100)
£496 $902 €724 Prairie Hills (51x66cm-20x26in) s.i.verso acrylic prov. 5-Feb-4 Heffel, Vancouver #59/R (C.D 1200)
£1440 $2635 €2102 Queen Charlotte summer (64x150cm-25x59in) s. acrylic. 1-Jun-4 Joyner Waddington, Toronto #129/R est:4000-6000 (C.D 3600)
£2236 $4002 €3265 Foothills (157x139cm-62x55in) s.i.d.97 verso acrylic prov. 6-May-4 Heffel, Vancouver #138/R est:3000-4000 (C.D 5500)
£2455 $4223 €3584 White horse near Cherhill, Wiltshire (90x176cm-35x69in) s.d.95 acrylic. 2-Dec-3 Joyner Waddington, Toronto #303/R est:3000-4000 (C.D 5500)
£4800 $8784 €7008 Sunset 11/86 - View from Lasqueti (94x240cm-37x94in) s. acrylic prov. 1-Jun-4 Joyner Waddington, Toronto #118/R est:12000-15000 (C.D 12000)
£5430 $8525 €7874 Land (114x300cm-45x118in) s. s.i.verso prov. 30-Aug-3 Heffel, Vancouver #28 est:4000-6000 (C.D 12000)
£7200 $13176 €10512 Errington, Axel Heiberg island, High Arctic (105x240cm-41x94in) s. painted 1990 prov. 1-Jun-4 Joyner Waddington, Toronto #119/R est:12000-15000 (C.D 18000)

TANAKA, Atouko (20th C) Japanese
Works on paper
£889 $1600 €1298 Untitled (7x6cm-3x2in) s.d.1970 verso gouache. 24-Apr-4 David Rago, Lambertville #436/R est:100

TANCK, Walter (1894-1954) German
£436 $803 €650 Self portrait (24x18cm-9x7in) s.d.25. 27-Mar-4 L & B, Essen #205/R
£859 $1521 €1280 Holstein stream (40x51cm-16x20in) s.d.43. 28-Apr-4 Schopman, Hamburg #653/R

TANCREDI (1927-1964) Italian
£10490 $17832 €15000 Untitled (100x80cm-39x31in) tempera painted 1962 prov.lit. 25-Nov-3 Sotheby's, Milan #170/R est:12000-15000
£13043 $21391 €18000 Untitled (130x97cm-51x38in) tempera collage painted 1962 lit. 27-May-3 Sotheby's, Milan #202/R est:16000-18000
£15385 $26154 €22000 Untitled (155x165cm-61x65in) tempera paper on canvas prov.lit. 25-Nov-3 Sotheby's, Milan #229/R est:23000-28000
£19463 $36007 €29000 Composition (50x65cm-20x26in) s. painted 1952 lit. 13-Mar-4 Meeting Art, Vercelli #123 est:20000
£20000 $36000 €30000 Untitled (59x40cm-23x16in) i.verso prov. 22-Apr-4 Finarte Semenzato, Rome #350/R est:12000-14000
£20280 $34476 €29000 Untitled (162x130cm-64x51in) oil fabric collage painted 1961 prov.exhib.lit. 25-Nov-3 Sotheby's, Milan #230/R est:35000-45000
£24161 $43248 €36000 Untitled (100x81cm-39x32in) tempera casein masonite painted 1960 prov.exhib.lit. 25-May-4 Sotheby's, Milan #272/R est:15000-20000
£32168 $54685 €46000 Untitled (70x100cm-28x39in) s. s.d.58 verso prov. 25-Nov-3 Sotheby's, Milan #218/R est:40000-50000
£97315 $174195 €145000 Untitled (121x140cm-48x55in) painted 1953 prov.exhib.lit. 25-May-4 Sotheby's, Milan #281/R est:50000-60000
Works on paper
£1043 $1668 €1512 Composition (43x35cm-17x14in) gouache paper on canvas. 17-Sep-3 Kunsthallen, Copenhagen #41/R (D.KR 11000)
£1087 $1783 €1500 Untitled (48x33cm-19x13in) pencil exec.1961 exhib.lit. 27-May-3 Sotheby's, Milan #138 est:1000-1500
£1327 $2123 €1924 Composition (65x50cm-26x20in) gouache paper on canvas. 17-Sep-3 Kunsthallen, Copenhagen #52/R est:18000 (D.KR 14000)
£1399 $2378 €2000 Untitled (54x36cm-21x14in) s.d.62 pencil tempera prov. 24-Nov-3 Christie's, Milan #60/R est:2500-3000
£2536 $4159 €3500 Untitled (46x38cm-18x15in) i. mixed media exec.1959 prov.lit. 27-May-3 Sotheby's, Milan #139/R est:2000-3000
£2897 $4634 €4200 Composition (20x29cm-8x11in) pastel. 13-Mar-3 Galleria Pace, Milan #32/R est:5000-6500
£3043 $4991 €4200 Untitled (41x33cm-16x13in) pencil exec.1960 prov.lit. 27-May-3 Sotheby's, Milan #140/R est:2000-3000
£12081 $21624 €18000 Untitled (70x100cm-28x39in) s. mixed media paper on canvas exec.1952 prov.lit. 25-May-4 Sotheby's, Milan #291/R est:13000-18000
£12667 $23307 €19000 Untitled (71x101cm-28x40in) s. mixed media paper on canvas exec.1953 prov.exhib.lit. 8-Jun-4 Finarte Semenzato, Milan #396/R est:12500-15000
£14493 $23768 €20000 Mad (151x171cm-59x67in) mixed media paper on canvas exec.1960 exhib.lit. 27-May-3 Sotheby's, Milan #267/R est:25000-30000

TANCULA-NIELSEN, J René (1949-) Scandinavian
£376 $640 €549 Still life (75x130cm-30x51in) s.d.1989 verso. 26-Nov-3 Kunsthallen, Copenhagen #179 (D.KR 4000)

TANDA, Ausonio (20th C) Italian
£800 $1440 €1200 Ships at sea (65x80cm-26x31in) s. painted 1959. 22-Apr-4 Finarte Semenzato, Rome #224/R
£1067 $1920 €1600 Landscape in Sardinia (60x100cm-24x39in) s.verso. 22-Apr-4 Finarte Semenzato, Rome #223/R est:1200-1500

TANDBERG, Odd (1924-) Norwegian
£1631 $2920 €2381 Seated female nude (99x73cm-39x29in) s.d.1945 verso panel. 25-May-4 Grev Wedels Plass, Oslo #93/R est:20000-30000 (N.KR 20000)

TANG HAIWEN (1929-1991) Chinese
Works on paper
£772 $1290 €1127 Abstract landscapes (18x18cm-7x7in) s. W/C triptych. 26-Oct-3 Christie's, Hong Kong #158/R est:12000-24000 (HK.D 10000)
£800 $1432 €1168 Untitled (13x17cm-5x7in) s. col ink set of three. 6-May-4 Sotheby's, London #137/R
£927 $1547 €1353 Abstract landscapes (18x18cm-7x7in) s. W/C. 26-Oct-3 Christie's, Hong Kong #159/R est:15000-30000 (HK.D 12000)
£1200 $2148 €1752 Untitled (69x45cm-27x18in) s. ink diptych two lit. 6-May-4 Sotheby's, London #132/R est:1500-2500
£1500 $2685 €2190 Untitled (70x50cm-28x20in) s. ink on card diptych two lit. 6-May-4 Sotheby's, London #133/R est:2000-3000
£1500 $2685 €2190 Untitled (70x49cm-28x19in) s. ink diptych lit. 6-May-4 Sotheby's, London #143/R est:2000-3000
£1800 $3222 €2628 View of Antibes (32x46cm-13x18in) s. W/C. 6-May-4 Sotheby's, London #138/R est:2000-3000
£2400 $4296 €3504 Untitled (70x59cm-28x23in) s. ink diptych lit. 6-May-4 Sotheby's, London #144/R est:2000-3000
£3912 $7041 €5712 Green valley (99x70cm-39x28in) s. W/C prov. 25-Apr-4 Christie's, Hong Kong #759/R est:45000-85000 (HK.D 55000)

TANG MULI (1947-) Chinese
£500 $835 €730 Deer and stag on hillside (75x138cm-30x54in) s.d.80. 14-Nov-3 Christie's, Kensington #275/R
£2747 $5000 €4121 Nude woman seated on a rug with a basket of apples (102x69cm-40x27in) s.d.89 s.d.1989 verso. 16-Jun-4 Wolf's, New York #487288/R est:10000-15000

TANG YIN (1470-1523) Chinese
Works on paper
£3089 $5158 €4510 Hibiscus (111x30cm-44x12in) s.i. ink. 26-Oct-3 Christie's, Hong Kong #425/R (HK.D 40000)
£4267 $7681 €6230 Birds on bamboo branches (79x29cm-31x11in) s.i. ink hanging scroll. 25-Apr-4 Christie's, Hong Kong #337/R est:45000-65000 (HK.D 60000)
£46332 $77375 €67645 Enjoying the evening breeze on fishing boat (160x85cm-63x33in) s.i. ink on silk prov. 26-Oct-3 Christie's, Hong Kong #427/R (HK.D 600000)

TANG, Raili (1950-) Finnish
£559 $951 €800 Composition (55x40cm-22x16in) s.d.87 acrylic. 29-Nov-3 Bukowskis, Helsinki #304/R

TANGEN, Olof (1903-1997) Norwegian
£3089 $5654 €4510 Summer in Kragero (140x185cm-55x73in) s.i. verso. 7-Jun-4 Blomqvist, Oslo #419/R est:25000-30000 (N.KR 38000)

TANGI, Myriam (20th C) ?
Works on paper
£559 $951 €800 Minyan 6397 (15x45cm-6x18in) s. W/C. 27-Nov-3 Calmels Cohen, Paris #138/R

TANGO, Camillo (19th C) Italian
£439 $830 €650 Oriental woman (80x60cm-31x24in) s.d.1905. 20-Feb-4 Stadion, Trieste #150/R

TANGRY, Morel de (1857-1930) French
£839 $1427 €1200 Saint Jean cap Ferrat (65x92cm-26x36in) s. 20-Nov-3 Gioffredo, Nice #127/R

TANGUY, Yves (1900-1955) American/French
£88235 $150000 €128823 Untitled (26x35cm-10x14in) s.d.38 canvasboard prov. 5-Nov-3 Christie's, Rockefeller NY #321/R est:150000-200000
£180505 $332130 €263537 Repondre - Extraneous matter (35x27cm-14x11in) s.d.38 artists board prov.lit. 29-Mar-4 Rasmussen, Copenhagen #30/R est:1000000-1500000 (D.KR 2000000)
£394558 $706259 €580000 Entre l'herve et le vent (45x37cm-18x15in) s.d.34 prov.exhib.lit. 21-Mar-4 Calmels Cohen, Paris #154/R est:600000-800000
Prints
£3824 $6500 €5583 Rhabdomance (30x22cm-12x9in) s. etching aquatint. 31-Oct-3 Sotheby's, New York #462/R
Works on paper
£2752 $4596 €3990 Surreal composition (25x19cm-10x7in) s. Indian ink. 19-Jun-3 Kornfeld, Bern #967/R est:5000 (S.FR 6000)
£2937 $4993 €4200 Composition (32x24cm-13x9in) s.d.35 Indian ink. 29-Nov-3 Villa Grisebach, Berlin #299/R est:5000-7000
£4367 $7948 €6376 Composition (32x24cm-13x9in) s.d.35 Indian ink. 17-Jun-4 Kornfeld, Bern #784/R est:10000 (S.FR 10000)
£5443 $9742 €8000 Untitled (27x20cm-11x8in) i.d.37 ink. 21-Mar-4 Calmels Cohen, Paris #45/R est:5000-6000
£7000 $12600 €10500 Composition mecanique (21x13cm-8x5in) s. ink. 26-Apr-4 Tajan, Paris #83/R est:3000-4000
£9500 $17290 €13870 Grand Passage (35x28cm-14x11in) s.d.53 felt tip pen collage prov.lit. 5-Feb-4 Christie's, London #396/R est:8000-12000
£11000 $20240 €16060 Composition (45x29cm-18x11in) s. pencil prov. 22-Jun-4 Sotheby's, London #483/R est:8000-12000
£16892 $29730 €25000 Cadavre exquis (31x20cm-12x8in) wax crayon exec c.1937 with V Brauner R Ubac J Herold prov. 18-May-4 Tajan, Paris #2/R est:15000-18000
£50000 $91000 €73000 For Sonia (28x21cm-11x8in) s.i.d.44 gouache W/C pencil exec 1944 prov. 5-Feb-4 Christie's, London #397/R est:30000-40000

TANJORE SCHOOL (19th C) Indian
Works on paper
£9783 $18000 €14283 Hindu Deities (25x20cm-10x8in) i. pencil pen ink W/C board one hundred album exec.c.1840. 24-Mar-4 Sotheby's, New York #139/R est:10000-15000

TANKARD, Allan P (?) British?
Works on paper
£690 $1235 €1007 Pier head Liverpool under snow (58x58cm-23x23in) s.i. W/C. 26-May-4 Outhwaite & Litherland, Liverpool #292

TANNAES, Marie (1854-1939) Norwegian
£488 $898 €732 Winter in Hurdal (66x86cm-26x34in) s. 14-Jun-4 Blomqvist, Lysaker #1396 (N.KR 6000)
£539 $992 €787 Tarn (26x42cm-10x17in) s. 29-Mar-4 Blomqvist, Lysaker #1330/R (N.KR 6800)
£816 $1460 €1191 Landscape from Holmestrand (25x36cm-10x14in) s. 25-May-4 Grev Wedels Plass, Oslo #48/R (N.KR 10000)
£1022 $1758 €1492 Summer time - house near water (51x65cm-20x26in) s. 8-Dec-3 Blomqvist, Oslo #466a/R est:20000-25000 (N.KR 12000)
£1057 $1945 €1586 Evening landscape near Mjosen (39x57cm-15x22in) s. 14-Jun-4 Blomqvist, Lysaker #1395/R est:15000-20000 (N.KR 13000)
£1260 $2306 €1840 Summer landscape (51x60cm-20x24in) s. 7-Jun-4 Blomqvist, Oslo #360/R est:15000-18000 (N.KR 15500)
£1717 $3004 €2507 Snowing, Stensparken (86x58cm-34x23in) s. i.stretcher. 16-Dec-3 Grev Wedels Plass, Oslo #373/R est:30000 (N.KR 20000)
£2129 $3663 €3108 Fjord landscape, possibly near Kragero (50x81cm-20x32in) s.d.81. 8-Dec-3 Blomqvist, Oslo #423/R est:25000-30000 (N.KR 25000)
£4770 $8204 €6964 Oslofjord with Akershus Fort (55x81cm-22x32in) s. 8-Dec-3 Blomqvist, Oslo #404/R est:25000-30000 (N.KR 56000)

TANNARD, J C (19/20th C) British?
£865 $1600 €1263 Irish setter (51x66cm-20x26in) s. bears d.19 prov. 10-Feb-4 Doyle, New York #198/R est:1500-2500

TANNER, C (?) ?
£1000 $1700 €1460 Bay hunter in a stable (51x62cm-20x24in) s.d.1840. 29-Oct-3 Hampton & Littlewood, Exeter #583/R est:500-600

TANNER, Edwin (1920-1980) Australian
£13115 $20721 €19148 Shipyard (109x94cm-43x37in) s. board. 2-Sep-3 Deutscher-Menzies, Melbourne #77/R est:38000-45000 (A.D 32000)
£18033 $28492 €26328 Waterpower persons (80x98cm-31x39in) s.d.54 i. verso prov.exhib. 2-Sep-3 Deutscher-Menzies, Melbourne #44/R est:45000-55000 (A.D 44000)
Works on paper
£1138 $2037 €1661 White line bouncing and surging beneath an orange squeak (65x49cm-26x19in) s.i.d.1967 pastel prov. 4-May-4 Sotheby's, Melbourne #118 (A.D 2800)

TANNER, Rudolf (1781-1853) Swiss/German
£452 $769 €660 Portraits of Kaspar and Anna Magdalena Landis-Bleuler (65x51cm-26x20in) s.mono.d.1821 verso pair. 19-Nov-3 Fischer, Luzern #2319/R (S.FR 1000)
£543 $923 €793 Portraits of Hans Georg and Victoire Wild-Fleury (57x44cm-22x17in) s.d.1829 verso pair. 19-Nov-3 Fischer, Luzern #2320/R (S.FR 1200)

TANNER, W (?) ?
£1850 $3386 €2701 Half portrait of a country boy (50x40cm-20x16in) s. 3-Jun-4 Lane, Penzance #40/R est:2000-3000

TANNERT, Volker (1955-) German
Works on paper
£524 $892 €750 Untitled (132x100cm-52x39in) chl. 27-Nov-3 Lempertz, Koln #464/R

TANNEUR, Philippe (1795-1878) French
£897 $1497 €1300 Coup de vent (27x40cm-11x16in) mono. panel. 11-Nov-3 Lesieur & Le Bars, Le Havre #107

TANNING, Dorothea (1910-) American
Works on paper
£1223 $2225 €1786 L'ecuyere (32x25cm-13x10in) s.d.59 W/C bodycol over pencil. 17-Jun-4 Kornfeld, Bern #785 est:2500 (S.FR 2800)
£1266 $2305 €1848 L'oiseau rapace (32x25cm-13x10in) s. W/C bodycol on pencil. 17-Jun-4 Kornfeld, Bern #787 est:2500 (S.FR 2900)

TANOBE, Miyuki (1937-) Canadian
£676 $1149 €987 Restaurant S Dubois, Montreal (20x25cm-8x10in) s. s.i.verso paper on panel. 21-Nov-3 Walker's, Ottawa #114/R (C.D 1500)
Works on paper
£361 $672 €527 Jeux d'enfant (30x25cm-12x10in) s. s.i.d.23-07-80 verso mixed media prov. 2-Mar-4 Ritchie, Toronto #202/R (C.D 900)
£640 $1171 €934 Miller Sweets (30x40cm-12x16in) s.i.d.1976 mixed media panel. 1-Jun-4 Hodgins, Calgary #72/R (C.D 1600)

TANOUX, Adrien Henri (1865-1923) French

£596 $1085 €900 Jeune homme avec chien (33x22cm-13x9in) s. 17-Jun-4 Marie & Robert, Paris #64
£1135 $1895 €1600 Prisonniere du harem (35x19cm-14x7in) s. panel. 19-Oct-3 Rabourdin & Choppin de Janvry, Paris #83/R est:1700-2000
£3357 $5773 €4800 La pause (55x46cm-22x18in) s. 7-Dec-3 Osenat, Fontainebleau #156 est:5000-6000
£6383 $10660 €9000 Odalisque reveuse (80x50cm-31x20in) s.d.1901. 19-Oct-3 Rabourdin & Choppin de Janvry, Paris #82/R est:15000

TANSEY, Francis (1959-) Irish

£1391 $2531 €2100 Fire and ice (102x102cm-40x40in) s.i.verso. 15-Jun-4 James Adam, Dublin #184/R est:2000-3000

TANSHIN, Kano (1785-1835) Japanese

Works on paper
£789 $1429 €1200 Landscape (58x98cm-23x39in) s. Indian ink col gold silk. 16-Apr-4 Dorotheum, Vienna #313/R

TANTTU, Erkki (1907-1985) Finnish

£1056 $1827 €1500 Night in Helsinki (51x60cm-20x24in) s.d.1936. 13-Dec-3 Hagelstam, Helsinki #155/R est:2500

TANYU, Kano (attrib) (1602-1674) Japanese

Works on paper
£1630 $3000 €2380 Mount Fuji. Miho no matsubara (151x351cm-59x138in) s. ink gold wash pair six panel screens. 23-Mar-4 Christie's, Rockefeller NY #68/R est:3000-4000

TANZI, Léon Louis Antoine (1846-1913) French

£403 $753 €600 Ploughing (40x72cm-16x28in) 26-Feb-4 Cambi, Genoa #430/R

TANZIO DA VARALLO, Antonio d'Enrico (style) (1575-1635) Italian

£16000 $27200 €23360 Saint Romuald. saint Benedict (220x132cm-87x52in) prov. 29-Oct-3 Christie's, London #89/R est:10000-15000

TAO LENGYUE (1895-1985) Chinese

Works on paper
£19915 $35846 €29076 Plum blossoms (149x40cm-59x16in) s.i. ink hanging scrolls four prov.exhib.lit.. 26-Apr-4 Sotheby's, Hong Kong #621/R est:30000-50000 (HK.D 280000)
£20077 $33529 €29312 Orchid (68x132cm-27x52in) s. ink col prov.exhib. 27-Oct-3 Sotheby's, Hong Kong #295/R est:30000-50000 (HK.D 260000)

TAPIES, Antonio (1923-) Spanish

£1250 $2088 €1800 Papeles de son Armadans (3x11cm-1x4in) s.i. verso oil chk pencil. 24-Oct-3 Ketterer, Hamburg #554/R est:1800-2000
£3200 $5792 €4800 Untitled (95x124cm-37x49in) s. eau forte. 30-Mar-4 Segre, Madrid #197/R est:4000
£5986 $10475 €8500 Key of fire series 10 (33x41cm-13x16in) s. paper on board prov.lit. 16-Dec-3 Segre, Madrid #132/R est:4000
£7067 $12932 €10600 Untitled (38x55cm-15x22in) s. oil chk paper double-sided two prov. 4-Jun-4 Lempertz, Koln #482/R est:10000
£8000 $13360 €11680 Linea vermeja (40x54cm-16x21in) s. oil chl paper prov.lit. 22-Oct-3 Christie's, London #4/R est:9000-12000
£11268 $19718 €16000 Cross and signs (23x17cm-9x7in) s. acrylic col wax crayon prov. 16-Dec-3 Segre, Madrid #136/R est:12000
£11538 $19615 €16500 Untitled (36x49cm-14x19in) paint chk marble powder painted 1979 exhib. 28-Nov-3 Farsetti, Prato #146/R est:15000-18000
£18023 $31000 €26314 Untitled (49x62cm-19x24in) s.d.1953 oil mixed media on board. 3-Dec-3 Doyle, New York #49/R est:30000-50000
£23000 $42320 €33580 Clavos y cuerda (89x146cm-35x57in) s. oil rope nails on canvas painted 1969 prov.exhib.lit. 25-Jun-4 Christie's, London #171/R est:20000-30000
£26000 $43420 €37960 Pintura, collage oxido rojizo (73x73cm-29x29in) s. s.d.1960 verso oil paper collage on canvas prov.lit. 22-Oct-3 Christie's, London #3/R est:30000-40000
£27333 $49200 €41000 Drawing (73x92cm-29x36in) s.verso painted 1976 prov.exhib.lit. 25-Apr-4 Versailles Encheres #115 est:35000-40000
£28188 $50456 €42000 Papier et ficelle (85x54cm-33x21in) s. oil paper string painted 1964 prov.lit. 25-May-4 Sotheby's, Milan #290/R est:15000-20000
£30000 $55200 €43800 Manta (156x212cm-61x83in) oil sand blanket ropes nails painted 1973 prov.exhib.lit. 25-Jun-4 Christie's, London #172/R est:30000-50000
£33520 $60000 €48939 Blue on blotting paper (49x65cm-19x26in) s.d.1961 s.d.verso oil paperboard collage lit. 13-May-4 Sotheby's, New York #118/R est:40000-60000
£38000 $69920 €55480 Composition (70x94cm-28x37in) s.d.1956 oil sand. 25-Jun-4 Christie's, London #144/R est:22000-28000
£40000 $73600 €58400 Papel sobre lienzo marron (100x100cm-39x39in) s.d.1960 verso oil paper on canvas prov.lit. 25-Jun-4 Christie's, London #168/R est:50000-70000
£44000 $80960 €64240 A (38x52cm-15x20in) s.d.1961 verso oil sand prov.exhib.lit. 25-Jun-4 Christie's, London #145/R est:22000-28000
£52448 $89161 €75000 Composition (105x75cm-41x30in) s. s.d.1959 verso oil mixed media board on canvas prov.exhib.lit. 26-Nov-3 Dorotheum, Vienna #61/R est:80000-100000
£55000 $91850 €80300 Pintura con cartones (131x163cm-52x64in) s.verso oil sand card resin prov.lit. 22-Oct-3 Christie's, London #12/R est:70000-90000
£100000 $182000 €146000 El accidente (89x116cm-35x46in) s.verso painted 1951 prov.exhib.lit. 4-Feb-4 Christie's, London #24/R est:60000-80000
£140000 $254800 €204400 Materia sobre lienzo y papel collage (171x196cm-67x77in) s.verso oil sand newspaper collage on canvas painted 1964 prov. 4-Feb-4 Christie's, London #32/R est:60000-70000
£150000 $273000 €219000 L'infern (96x129cm-38x51in) s.verso painted 1951 prov.lit. 3-Feb-4 Sotheby's, London #84/R est:150000-200000

Prints
£2013 $3564 €3000 Untitled (90x63cm-35x25in) s.i. lithograph. 28-Apr-4 Wiener Kunst Auktionen, Vienna #284/R est:3000-5000
£2138 $3549 €3100 Carmi 3 (56x76cm-22x30in) s. num.4/75 carborundum. 1-Oct-3 Ansorena, Madrid #422/R est:2900
£2333 $4177 €3500 Cobert de roig (75x75cm-30x30in) s. etching relief scratching. 15-May-4 Van Ham, Cologne #957/R est:2000
£2333 $4293 €3500 Als Mestres de Catalunya (78x119cm-31x47in) s. num.80/100 col lithograph exec 1974. 8-Jun-4 Sotheby's, Amsterdam #327/R est:3500-4500
£2533 $4535 €3800 A damunt vermell (56x76cm-22x30in) s. col etching. 15-May-4 Van Ham, Cologne #954/R est:4200
£2600 $4680 €3900 Carre rouge (63x90cm-25x35in) s. num.18/50 col eau forte. 24-Apr-4 Cornette de St.Cyr, Paris #268/R est:3000

Works on paper
£1161 $1800 €1695 Fan (23x42cm-9x17in) s. mixed media. 3-Nov-2 Subastas Odalys, Caracas #40/R
£1288 $2100 €1880 Fan (25x42cm-10x17in) s. mixed media. 20-Jul-3 Subastas Odalys, Caracas #92
£1379 $2303 €2000 Hand and foot (23x32cm-9x13in) s. pencil wax crayon. 13-Nov-3 Finarte Semenzato, Rome #115 est:1800-2400
£1379 $2483 €2000 Witness of the silence (26x25cm-10x10in) s.i.d.1970 dr. 26-Jan-4 Ansorena, Madrid #309/R est:2000
£2036 $3462 €2973 Untitled (24x19cm-9x7in) s. chk prov. 22-Nov-3 Burkhard, Luzern #142/R est:5500-7500 (S.FR 4500)
£6667 $12000 €10000 Untitled (34x48cm-13x19in) s. mixed media. 25-Apr-4 Versailles Encheres #88 est:8000-9000
£8333 $13750 €12000 Marshall bean (24x35cm-9x14in) s. mixed media. 2-Jul-3 Ansorena, Madrid #863/R
£8392 $14266 €12000 Untitled (52x75cm-20x30in) s.d.Juin 1984 mixed media. 26-Nov-3 Dorotheum, Vienna #90/R est:10000-15000
£14094 $26215 €21000 Cos dibuixat (36x52cm-14x20in) s. ink mixed media prov. 3-Mar-4 Artcurial Briest, Paris #527 est:12000-15000
£14765 $27463 €22000 Poems from the Catalan VII (76x57cm-30x22in) s. ink wax crayon collage. 2-Mar-4 Ansorena, Madrid #847/R est:22000
£18056 $28528 €26000 Carton-matiere (44x77cm-17x30in) s. paint crayon prov.exhib.lit. 27-Apr-3 Versailles Encheres #57
£19000 $31730 €27740 Friso I (39x316cm-15x124in) s. mixed media terracotta eight parts exec 1981 prov.exhib.lit. 21-Oct-3 Sotheby's, London #376/R est:15000-20000
£28521 $49342 €40500 Papier gaufre en forme de croix (54x74cm-21x29in) s. crayon gaufrage prov.lit. 14-Dec-3 Versailles Encheres #129/R est:30000-35000
£33557 $60067 €50000 Composition (96x124cm-38x49in) s.i.d.1985 verso mixed media. 28-May-4 Farsetti, Prato #41/R est:46000-52000
£38000 $69160 €55480 Materia-codo, matter-elbow (82x66cm-32x26in) s.verso mixed media prov.exhib.lit. 6-Feb-4 Sotheby's, London #191/R est:25000-35000
£60000 $109200 €87600 Inscriptions and four strokes on sackcloth (200x270cm-79x106in) s. mixed media collage canvas prov.exhib.lit. 6-Feb-4 Sotheby's, London #189/R est:60000-80000
£85000 $141950 €124100 Blanca con iniciales (65x100cm-26x39in) init. mixed media canvas on wood prov.exhib.lit. 22-Oct-3 Christie's, London #6/R est:50000-70000

TAPIRO Y BARO, Jose (1830-1913) Spanish

Works on paper
£1316 $2421 €2000 Pensive moment (41x26cm-16x10in) s. W/C. 28-Jun-4 Sotheby's, Amsterdam #27/R est:2000-3000
£2013 $3604 €3000 Bust of black man (42x29cm-17x11in) s. W/C. 25-May-4 Durán, Madrid #114/R est:2500
£2817 $4930 €4000 Bust of Arab man (42x29cm-17x11in) s. W/C. 16-Dec-3 Durán, Madrid #52/R est:650
£3310 $5495 €4800 Young man in local costume (38x26cm-15x10in) s. W/C. 30-Sep-3 Ansorena, Madrid #8/R est:1300
£4000 $7240 €6000 Oriental figure (44x30cm-17x12in) s. W/C. 30-Mar-4 Segre, Madrid #75/R est:2700
£4400 $8096 €6424 Falconer (34x24cm-13x9in) s.i. W/C bodycol. 8-Jun-4 Bonhams, New Bond Street #1/R est:1000-1500
£4400 $8096 €6424 Lady in an ancient theatre (40x25cm-16x10in) s. W/C bodycol. 8-Jun-4 Bonhams, New Bond Street #2/R est:1200-1800

TAPLIN, Guy (1939-) British

Sculpture
£1050 $1659 €1523 Swan (122cm-48in) s.i. painted wood. 3-Sep-3 Bonhams, Bury St Edmunds #404/R est:1200-1800
£1300 $2067 €1898 Crow (48x46cm-19x18in) painted wood metal. 10-Sep-3 Sotheby's, Olympia #255/R est:1000-1500
£1400 $2590 €2044 Curlew (42x40cm-17x16in) s.i.d.1980 painted wood metal. 11-Feb-4 Sotheby's, Olympia #245/R est:1500-2000
£1600 $2672 €2336 Canada goose (28cm-11in) i. paint wood. 16-Oct-3 Christie's, Kensington #337/R est:1000-1500
£1800 $3330 €2628 Egret (110cm-43in) s.i.num.15 painted wood steel rod. 11-Feb-4 Sotheby's, Olympia #244/R est:1500-2000
£2000 $3180 €2920 Preening grebe. Grebe (30x61cm-12x24in) one s.i. painted wood pair. 10-Sep-3 Sotheby's, Olympia #254/R est:2000-3000
£3000 $5460 €4380 Three curlews (49x52x300cm-19x20x118in) s. painted wood. 1-Jul-4 Christie's, Kensington #261/R est:3000-5000

TAPPER, Garth (1927-1999) New Zealander

£543 $924 €793 Kathleen (59x49cm-23x19in) s.d.1965 board. 4-Nov-3 Peter Webb, Auckland #211 est:1000-1500 (NZ.D 1500)
£564 $959 €823 Study of the artist's daughter (41x39cm-16x15in) s. board. 27-Nov-3 International Art Centre, Auckland #122/R (NZ.D 1500)
£893 $1643 €1304 Jackie (67x56cm-26x22in) s. board. 25-Mar-4 International Art Centre, Auckland #144/R (NZ.D 2500)
£940 $1598 €1372 Jill (36x27cm-14x11in) s. board. 27-Nov-3 International Art Centre, Auckland #88/R (NZ.D 2500)
£1034 $1758 €1510 Sun showers (36x27cm-14x11in) s. board. 27-Nov-3 International Art Centre, Auckland #46/R (NZ.D 2750)
£1429 $2629 €2086 Card players (28x38cm-11x15in) s. board. 25-Mar-4 International Art Centre, Auckland #13/R est:3000-5000 (NZ.D 4000)
£1643 $2991 €2399 Still life with jug and vase (39x43cm-15x17in) s. board. 29-Jun-4 Peter Webb, Auckland #129/R est:4000-6000 (NZ.D 4700)
£2128 $3766 €3107 Night workers (40x60cm-16x24in) s.d.74 board. 28-Apr-4 Dunbar Sloane, Auckland #39/R est:6000-8000 (NZ.D 6000)
£3287 $5982 €4799 Tuakau (26x35cm-10x14in) s.d.1975 board prov. 29-Jun-4 Peter Webb, Auckland #80/R est:4000-6000 (NZ.D 9400)
£5245 $9545 €7658 Wooded rural landscape (111x186cm-44x73in) s.d.1988 canvasboard. 29-Jun-4 Peter Webb, Auckland #128/R est:15000-20000 (NZ.D 15000)
£9790 $17818 €14293 Card players (78x80cm-31x31in) s. s.i.verso board. 29-Jun-4 Peter Webb, Auckland #78/R est:25000-35000 (NZ.D 28000)

TAPPER, Kain (1930-) Finnish
Works on paper
£1399 $2378 €2000 Skull (35x50cm-14x20in) s.d.79 mixed media. 29-Nov-3 Bukowskis, Helsinki #234/R est:1700-2000

TAPPERT, Georg (1880-1957) German
£2098 $3566 €3000 Toeplitz, summer evening (34x49cm-13x19in) s.i. verso. 29-Nov-3 Villa Grisebach, Berlin #246/R est:3000-4000
£125874 $213986 €180000 Female - seated, wearing red turban (120x109cm-47x43in) s. prov.exhib. 26-Nov-3 Lempertz, Koln #1000/R est:200000-250000
Works on paper
£278 $464 €400 Couple (17x10cm-7x4in) chl W/C. 24-Oct-3 Ketterer, Hamburg #1109/R
£347 $580 €500 Revue (6x15cm-2x6in) Indian ink transparent paper. 25-Oct-3 Dr Lehr, Berlin #504/R
£594 $1010 €850 Wood III - woodland interior Baltic I (45x34cm-18x13in) s. pastel. 29-Nov-3 Villa Grisebach, Berlin #677/R est:500-700
£933 $1717 €1400 Snake charmer (33x25cm-13x10in) s. W/C pen sepia. 12-Jun-4 Villa Grisebach, Berlin #653/R est:1400-1800
£1151 $1888 €1600 Reclining figure with red blouse and feather boa (23x24cm-9x9in) W/C over pencil. 4-Jun-3 Ketterer, Hamburg #915/R

TAQUOY, Maurice (1878-1952) French
Works on paper
£870 $1426 €1200 Chasse a courre, Amazone (25x34cm-10x13in) W/C htd gouache. 28-May-3 Coutau Begarie, Paris #168/R
£937 $1472 €1350 Course (21x31cm-8x12in) s.d.1929 W/C htd gouache. 29-Aug-3 Deauville, France #132/R
£1049 $1804 €1500 A l'entrainement (9x20cm-4x8in) W/C. 3-Dec-3 Coutau Begarie, Paris #213 est:1500-1600

TARASIEWICZ, Leon (1957-) Polish
£2492 $4237 €3638 Untitled (130x190cm-51x75in) s.d.96 verso. 5-Nov-3 AB Stockholms Auktionsverk #935/R est:20000-25000 (S.KR 33000)

TARASIN, Jan (1926-) Polish
£3823 $6346 €5582 Derby (114x129cm-45x51in) painted 1995. 2-Oct-3 Agra, Warsaw #12/R est:8000 (P.Z 25000)
Works on paper
£363 $628 €530 Untitled (33x49cm-13x19in) s.d.98 gouache. 10-Dec-3 Agra, Warsaw #36/R (P.Z 2400)
£690 $1152 €1000 Various objects (46x54cm-18x21in) s.d.97 W/C board. 16-Nov-3 Agra, Warsaw #37/R

TARAVAL, Hugues (1729-1785) French
£9540 $17553 €14500 Diseuse de bonne aventure (86x64cm-34x25in) 24-Jun-4 Tajan, Paris #65/R est:15000-18000

TARAVAL, Hugues (attrib) (1729-1785) French
Works on paper
£1118 $1900 €1632 Reclining female nude (43x53cm-17x21in) chk prov. 25-Nov-3 Christie's, Rockefeller NY #505/R est:4000-6000

TARAZONA, Manolo (1937-) Spanish
£1513 $2784 €2300 Hommage a Turner (149x89cm-59x35in) s.d.1987 lit. 28-Jun-4 Joron-Derem, Paris #196/R est:3000-3500

TARBELL, Edmund C (1862-1938) American
£46512 $80000 €67908 Study of girl with sailboat (46x36cm-18x14in) prov.exhib. 3-Dec-3 Sotheby's, New York #31/R est:30000-50000
£142045 $250000 €207386 Contemplation (76x64cm-30x25in) s. painted c.1900 prov.lit. 19-May-4 Sotheby's, New York #33/R est:250000-350000

TARBET, Graham Henderson (?) British
Works on paper
£260 $481 €380 Cattle by a slow moving river landscape (33x48cm-13x19in) W/C. 15-Jul-4 Mitchells, Cockermouth #594
£300 $480 €438 Highland scene with snow covered hills (25x36cm-10x14in) s. W/C. 16-Sep-3 Gorringes, Bexhill #1521

TARDIA, Enzo (1960-) Italian
£333 $613 €500 Far away from the world (100x100cm-39x39in) s.i.d.2001. 12-Jun-4 Meeting Art, Vercelli #207/R
£333 $613 €500 Painting (100x100cm-39x39in) s.i.d.2001-03 verso oil brush spatula tube. 12-Jun-4 Meeting Art, Vercelli #537/R
£333 $613 €500 Between fire and terror (100x100cm-39x39in) s. painted 1998-2003. 12-Jun-4 Meeting Art, Vercelli #909/R
£436 $807 €650 Changes at sunset (100x100cm-39x39in) s.i.d.2002 verso. 13-Mar-4 Meeting Art, Vercelli #329

TARDIEU, Henri Simon (attrib) (1688-1741) French?
Works on paper
£1056 $1849 €1500 Portrait de l'Abee Jean Antoine de Maroulle, tenant un livre (34x26cm-13x10in) i. black chk pen brown ink col wash after Charles Coypel. 17-Dec-3 Christie's, Paris #61/R est:600-800

TARDIEU, Victor François (1870-1937) French
£6863 $12422 €10020 Les tombeaux de hue (21x26cm-8x10in) s. panel painted c.1923. 4-Apr-4 Sotheby's, Singapore #79/R est:12000-15000 (S.D 21000)

TARENGHI, Enrico (1848-?) Italian
Works on paper
£600 $1074 €876 Game of chess (73x54cm-29x21in) s. W/C. 26-May-4 Sotheby's, Olympia #280/R
£1117 $2000 €1631 Nuns of St. Terses after a ceremony (71x51cm-28x20in) s. W/C. 16-May-4 CRN Auctions, Cambridge #39/R
£3200 $5440 €4672 After prayers (76x53cm-30x21in) s. W/C. 4-Nov-3 Bonhams, New Bond Street #92/R est:3000-5000

TARGETT, Thomas G (fl.1869-1879) British
£850 $1547 €1241 Speckled trout lying across a landscape net (25x43cm-10x17in) i. 29-Jun-4 Capes Dunn, Manchester #754/R

TARKAY, Itzchak (1935-) Yugoslavian/Israeli
£2529 $4300 €3692 Cafe scene (114x145cm-45x57in) s. 7-Nov-3 Selkirks, St. Louis #657/R est:5000-7000

TARKHOFF, Nicolas (1871-1930) Russian
£4041 $6870 €5900 Branche de fleurs (46x36cm-18x14in) s. 9-Nov-3 Eric Pillon, Calais #115/R
£5500 $9845 €8030 Beach (27x35cm-11x14in) s. 26-May-4 Sotheby's, London #186/R est:5000-7000
£6667 $12267 €10000 Madame Tarkhoff allaitant son bebe (42x35cm-17x14in) s. prov. 8-Jun-4 Artcurial Briest, Paris #157/R est:8000-10000
£7000 $12530 €10220 Gladioli (46x36cm-18x14in) s. paper on canvas. 26-May-4 Sotheby's, London #164/R est:7000-9000
£12583 $22901 €19000 Nature morte aux bouquets de fleurs (95x75cm-37x30in) s. 16-Jun-4 Claude Boisgirard, Paris #157/R est:10000-12000
£17450 $30886 €26000 Coq (79x54cm-31x21in) s. prov. 27-Apr-4 Artcurial Briest, Paris #147/R est:12000-15000
£38889 $70000 €56778 Artist's two children (60x73cm-24x29in) s. lit. 23-Apr-4 Sotheby's, New York #50/R est:40000-60000
Works on paper
£811 $1427 €1200 Maternity (49x31cm-19x12in) studio st. crayon double-sided. 19-May-4 Camard, Paris #17
£3600 $6444 €5256 Mother and child (21x27cm-8x11in) s. crayon. 26-May-4 Sotheby's, Olympia #452/R est:2000-3000
£22000 $37400 €32120 Storm clouds gathering over the orchard (75x103cm-30x41in) s. gouache card prov.lit. 19-Nov-3 Sotheby's, London #204/R est:3000-4000

TARNOCZY, Bertha von (1846-1936) Austrian
£704 $1218 €1000 A mountain in Tyrol (33x57cm-13x22in) s. 10-Dec-3 Dorotheum, Vienna #7/R

TARNOGROCKI, Otto (1875-?) German
£1126 $2049 €1700 Waiting for an excursion by boat. Farmhouse (63x69cm-25x27in) s.i.d.1913 double-sided. 19-Jun-4 Quittenbaum, Hamburg #50/R est:1600

TARR, James (1905-1996) British
£550 $946 €803 Self portrait with wife. Landscape (56x76cm-22x30in) board double-sided. 3-Dec-3 Christie's, Kensington #403
£1300 $2405 €1898 Chess player (56x76cm-22x30in) 11-Mar-4 Christie's, Kensington #40/R est:600-800

TARRANT, Margaret W (1888-1959) British
Works on paper
£950 $1739 €1387 Pond fairies on the riverbank, with bulrushes and mountains beyond (16x11cm-6x4in) s. W/C over pencil htd bodycol. 6-Jul-4 Peter Wilson, Nantwich #60/R

TARREGA, Ricardo (1904-1999) Spanish
£552 $993 €800 Landscape with bridge (90x113cm-35x44in) s. s.verso. 26-Jan-4 Ansorena, Madrid #146/R

TARRIT, Jean (1865-1950) French
Sculpture
£2329 $3959 €3400 Cat with green eyes sitting on wooden books with a mouse (47cm-19in) s. bronze. 5-Nov-3 Vendue Huis, Gravenhage #4029/R est:750-1000

TARULLI, D Stefano (19th C) Italian
£378 $700 €552 Man holding holy book (61x48cm-24x19in) 13-Feb-4 Du Mouchelle, Detroit #2267/R

TASKOVSKI, Vasko (1937-) Macedonian
£508 $950 €762 Rocks by the shore (81x99cm-32x39in) s.d.93. 21-Jul-4 Goodman, Sydney #155 (A.D 1300)
£781 $1461 €1172 Floating fish (81x99cm-32x39in) s.d.93. 21-Jul-4 Goodman, Sydney #154 (A.D 2000)
£899 $1680 €1349 Untitled (114x144cm-45x57in) s.d.93. 21-Jul-4 Goodman, Sydney #153 (A.D 2300)

TASLITZKY, Boris (1911-) French
£1325 $2411 €2000 Tete de gericault d'apres le buste de Jacques Lipchitz (50x73cm-20x29in) s.d.1937 prov.exhib. 18-Jun-4 Piasa, Paris #229/R est:3000-4000

TASMANIAN SCHOOL (19th C)
£15385 $24769 €22462 Cricket match believed to be between England 11 and 22 of Tasmania (36x59cm-14x23in) prov. 25-Aug-3 Sotheby's, Paddington #183/R est:25000-35000 (A.D 38000)

TASSAERT, Octave (1800-1874) French
£2863 $4868 €4180 Reclining Odaliske (14x22cm-6x9in) 5-Nov-3 Dobiaschofsky, Bern #1001/R est:2200 (S.FR 6500)

TASSAERT, Octave (attrib) (1800-1874) French
£538 $876 €785 Interior scene with two women (49x38cm-19x15in) 29-Sep-3 Lilla Bukowskis, Stockholm #189 (S.KR 7000)

TASSAERT, Philippe Joseph (1732-1803) Flemish
Works on paper
£1781 $3027 €2600 Drawing academy (33x40cm-13x16in) s.d.1764 pen brown ink wash over black chk. 4-Nov-3 Sotheby's, Amsterdam #138 est:1500-2000

TASSEL, Jean (attrib) (1608-1667) French
£2649 $4821 €4000 Jeune femme plumant une volaille dans un interieur de cuisine (73x56cm-29x22in) 21-Jun-4 Tajan, Paris #85/R est:4000-4500
£4000 $7200 €5840 Madonna and Child (23x17cm-9x7in) copper. 20-Apr-4 Sotheby's, Olympia #320/R est:4000-6000

TASSI, Agostino (1565-1644) Italian
Works on paper
£1093 $2000 €1596 Scene of Christ tempted (21x16cm-8x6in) i. pen brown ink gray wash. 29-Jan-4 Swann Galleries, New York #37/R est:1500-2500

TASSI, Agostino (attrib) (1565-1644) Italian
£800 $1328 €1168 Drover and cattle in a landscape (36x46cm-14x18in) 3-Oct-3 Mallams, Oxford #212/R
£6338 $10965 €9000 Harbour with arcades (42x73cm-17x29in) 14-Dec-3 Finarte, Venice #96/R est:9000
Works on paper
£252 $403 €350 Two lovers playing (9x11cm-4x4in) pen brown ink brown wash traces of blk crayon. 16-May-3 Tajan, Paris #3
£1844 $3079 €2600 Enlevement de Janire. pen ink wash prov. 15-Oct-3 Sotheby's, Paris #129/R

TASSIE, James (1735-1799) British
Miniatures
£1750 $2765 €2538 Portraits of Archibald Grahame (9x6cm-4x2in) i. pair oval. 3-Sep-3 Bonhams, Bury St Edmunds #257/R est:1000-1500

TASTSIOGLOU, Nakis (1955-) Greek
Sculpture
£1600 $2864 €2336 Untitled (80x95cm-31x37in) s.d.1999 Plexiglas iron light prov.exhib. 10-May-4 Sotheby's, Olympia #100/R est:1500-2000

TATAFIORE, Ernesto (1943-) Italian
£2933 $5368 €4400 Vendicante (226x226cm-89x89in) s.i. i.verso acrylic graphite. 4-Jun-4 Lempertz, Koln #486/R est:4000
Works on paper
£294 $505 €420 Man in hat (51x67cm-20x26in) s. pencil bodycol. 3-Dec-3 Hauswedell & Nolte, Hamburg #1019/R
£294 $505 €420 La vertu ou la mort (51x67cm-20x26in) s. pencil bodycol. 3-Dec-3 Hauswedell & Nolte, Hamburg #1020/R
£302 $514 €441 Isolato nei tuoi pensieri (36x17cm-14x7in) s. mixed media prov. 5-Nov-3 AB Stockholms Auktionsverk #1040/R (S.KR 4000)
£340 $578 €496 Vive la Montagne (20x18cm-8x7in) s. mixed media prov.lit. 5-Nov-3 AB Stockholms Auktionsverk #1039/R (S.KR 4500)
£453 $770 €661 Casa duplay (20x23cm-8x9in) s. mixed media prov.lit. 5-Nov-3 AB Stockholms Auktionsverk #1038/R (S.KR 6000)
£1000 $1790 €1500 Untitled (216x30cm-85x12in) s.i. pencil bodycol oil canvas. 15-May-4 Dr Sturies, Dusseldorf #210/R

TATANIQ, George (1910-) North American
Sculpture
£901 $1532 €1315 Inuit drummer holding a drum and beater (16cm-6in) s. mottled dark grey soapstone antler exec.c.1975. 3-Nov-3 Waddingtons, Toronto #161/R est:2000-2500 (C.D 2000)
£1081 $1838 €1578 Musk ox with horns with an Inuit hunter on its back (20cm-8in) s. mottled grey soapstone. 3-Nov-3 Waddingtons, Toronto #179/R est:1500-2000 (C.D 2400)
£3491 $5934 €5097 Musk ox with horns (13cm-5in) s. mottled dark soapstone exec.c.1970. 3-Nov-3 Waddingtons, Toronto #171/R est:600-900 (C.D 7750)
£5405 $9189 €7891 Standing Inuk looking over his shoulder (51cm-20in) mottled dark soapstone prov. 3-Nov-3 Waddingtons, Toronto #170/R est:10000-15000 (C.D 12000)

TATARNIKOV, Georgui (1914-1971) Russian
£251 $450 €366 Landscape with farmhouse (33x46cm-13x18in) s. board. 11-Jan-4 William Jenack, New York #219

TATE, Gayle B (1944-) American
£284 $500 €415 Sweet tooth, trompe l'oeil (28x33cm-11x13in) s. s.i.verso board. 28-May-4 Aspire, Cleveland #40/R
£299 $550 €437 Cows grazing in a valley (25x38cm-10x15in) i. paper. 10-Jun-4 Swann Galleries, New York #238/R
£500 $850 €730 Black cat (51x40cm-20x16in) s.d.Nov 1988 verso panel. 21-Nov-3 Skinner, Boston #70/R
£538 $1000 €785 Time is money (15x20cm-6x8in) s. board painted c.2000. 7-Mar-4 Treadway Gallery, Cincinnati #700/R est:1000-1500
£647 $1100 €945 Pure gold (20x25cm-8x10in) s.i. panel. 21-Nov-3 Skinner, Boston #431/R est:500-700
£756 $1300 €1104 Hidden assets (25x20cm-10x8in) s. panel. 6-Dec-3 Selkirks, St. Louis #194/R
£943 $1500 €1367 Cash cow (13x18cm-5x7in) s. trompe l'oeil panel. 12-Sep-3 Aspire, Cleveland #118 est:1200-1800
£973 $1800 €1421 Funny money (30x23cm-12x9in) s. panel. 16-Jan-4 Aspire, Cleveland #76/R est:1500-2000
£988 $1700 €1442 Do not touch (13x18cm-5x7in) s. panel. 6-Dec-3 Selkirks, St. Louis #195/R est:1200-1800
£1006 $1600 €1459 Freedom (28x33cm-11x13in) s. trompe l'oeil panel. 12-Sep-3 Aspire, Cleveland #119 est:1800-2500
£2095 $3750 €3059 Letter rack with picture of the artist's daughter (61x51cm-24x20in) s. i.verso panel prov. 26-May-4 Doyle, New York #109/R est:5000-7000

TATE, Nairne (20th C) ?
£550 $919 €803 At the seaside (51x61cm-20x24in) s. board. 8-Oct-3 Christie's, Kensington #652/R

TATHAM, Agnes Clara (1893-?) British
£18000 $30600 €26280 Idol (99x57cm-39x22in) s. exhib.lit. 26-Nov-3 Sotheby's, Olympia #35/R est:10000-15000

TATO (1896-1974) Italian
£2703 $4757 €4000 Comacchio (60x74cm-24x29in) s. board exhib. 24-May-4 Christie's, Milan #201/R est:4000-6000
£3103 $5183 €4500 Urbanisms (70x70cm-28x28in) s. board. 13-Nov-3 Finarte Semenzato, Rome #306/R est:3000-3500
£3406 $5586 €4700 Il garrir dei gagliardetti II (21x31cm-8x12in) s. i.d.1928 verso panel. 31-May-3 Farsetti, Prato #657/R est:2000-3000
£3497 $5944 €5000 Atomic explosion (101x73cm-40x29in) s.d.1955 oil enamel cardboard. 24-Nov-3 Christie's, Milan #308/R est:5000-7000
£10204 $18265 €15000 Flying over the Rhein (70x50cm-28x20in) s. board painted c.1935 prov.exhib.lit. 16-Mar-4 Finarte Semenzato, Milan #460/R est:14000

TATOSSIAN, Armand (1948-) Canadian
£221 $411 €323 St Urbain (51x61cm-20x24in) s. s.i.verso. 2-Mar-4 Ritchie, Toronto #155/R (C.D 550)
£292 $534 €426 Ete Indien (25x30cm-10x12in) s. i.verso. 27-Jan-4 Iegor de Saint Hippolyte, Montreal #34 (C.D 700)
£428 $727 €625 Laurentian village (46x61cm-18x24in) s. s.i.verso. 21-Nov-3 Walker's, Ottawa #17/R (C.D 950)
£583 $1068 €851 Charlevoix en hiver (51x61cm-20x24in) s. 27-Jan-4 Iegor de Saint Hippolyte, Montreal #35 (C.D 1400)
£625 $1044 €906 Nature morte (76x61cm-30x24in) s. 17-Jun-3 Pinneys, Montreal #118 est:1200-1500 (C.D 1400)
£670 $1152 €978 Rue Comsol (50x40cm-20x16in) s. 2-Dec-3 Joyner Waddington, Toronto #362/R (C.D 1500)
£714 $1229 €1042 Autumn landscape, St Donat (40x50cm-16x20in) s. 2-Dec-3 Joyner Waddington, Toronto #346/R (C.D 1600)
£720 $1318 €1051 Printemps (75x100cm-30x39in) s. 1-Jun-4 Joyner Waddington, Toronto #251/R est:3000-4000 (C.D 1800)
£720 $1318 €1051 Montreal street scene (50x60cm-20x24in) s. 1-Jun-4 Joyner Waddington, Toronto #340/R est:2000-2500 (C.D 1800)
£720 $1318 €1051 Forest path (75x100cm-30x39in) s. 1-Jun-4 Joyner Waddington, Toronto #390/R est:3000-4000 (C.D 1800)
£720 $1318 €1051 Spring, Doncaster (60x75cm-24x30in) s. painted 1991. 1-Jun-4 Joyner Waddington, Toronto #398/R est:2500-3000 (C.D 1800)
£759 $1267 €1101 Bouquet de fleurs (40x51cm-16x20in) s. s.i.verso. 17-Jun-3 Pinneys, Montreal #141 est:900-1200 (C.D 1700)
£804 $1382 €1174 Rigaud Degel (50x60cm-20x24in) s. 2-Dec-3 Joyner Waddington, Toronto #210/R est:2000-2500 (C.D 1800)
£889 $1538 €1298 Sous bois (76x76cm-30x30in) s.i.verso. 9-Dec-3 Pinneys, Montreal #143 est:1800-2400 (C.D 2000)
£1300 $2379 €1898 Plateau (75x100cm-30x39in) s. 1-Jun-4 Joyner Waddington, Toronto #267/R est:3000-4000 (C.D 3250)
£1333 $2440 €1946 Trois maisons (76x102cm-30x40in) s. 27-Jan-4 Iegor de Saint Hippolyte, Montreal #36 (C.D 3200)
£1339 $2237 €1942 Village view in winter (76x102cm-30x40in) s. 17-Jun-3 Pinneys, Montreal #137 est:3000-4000 (C.D 3000)
£1360 $2489 €1986 Townships in winter (60x75cm-24x30in) s. 1-Jun-4 Joyner Waddington, Toronto #381/R est:2500-3500 (C.D 3400)
£1429 $2457 €2086 Queen Street, Toronto (60x75cm-24x30in) s. 2-Dec-3 Joyner Waddington, Toronto #146/R est:2500-3000 (C.D 3200)
£1429 $2457 €2086 Fall Colours (60x75cm-24x30in) s. 2-Dec-3 Joyner Waddington, Toronto #354/R est:2500-3000 (C.D 3200)
£1518 $2611 €2216 Old Quebec (50x60cm-20x24in) s. 2-Dec-3 Joyner Waddington, Toronto #337/R est:2000-2500 (C.D 3400)
£1520 $2782 €2219 Sous-bois, ete (100x75cm-39x30in) s. 1-Jun-4 Joyner Waddington, Toronto #296/R est:3000-4000 (C.D 3800)
£2846 $5093 €4155 Les champions du bassin (76x102cm-30x40in) s. s.i.verso prov. 31-May-4 Sotheby's, Toronto #63/R est:4500-5500 (C.D 7000)
£3348 $5759 €4888 Children playing (75x100cm-30x39in) s. 2-Dec-3 Joyner Waddington, Toronto #238/R est:4500-5500 (C.D 7500)
£4400 $8052 €6424 Mi-Septembre (120x150cm-47x59in) s. 1-Jun-4 Joyner Waddington, Toronto #232/R est:6000-8000 (C.D 11000)
£5285 $9459 €7716 Charlevois in winter (76x101cm-30x40in) s. prov. 31-May-4 Sotheby's, Toronto #19/R est:4500-5500 (C.D 13000)

TATTEGRAIN, Francis (1852-1915) French
£867 $1569 €1300 Entree de village la nuit. Etude d'eglise (21x34cm-8x13in) s. panel double-sided. 30-Mar-4 Rossini, Paris #1057

TATTERSFIELD, Shirley (20th C) American
£838 $1500 €1223 Twin bridges, a bird's eye view mural of Georgetown (102x132cm-40x52in) s. 21-Mar-4 Jeffery Burchard, Florida #66/R

TAUBE, Eugen (1860-1913) Finnish
£704 $1127 €1000 Moonlight (17x35cm-7x14in) s. 18-Sep-3 Hagelstam, Helsinki #1005
£1399 $2378 €2000 Sunset in the skerries (39x63cm-15x25in) s. 29-Nov-3 Bukowskis, Helsinki #190/R est:2500-3000
£1812 $3334 €2700 Coastal landscape (45x65cm-18x26in) s/. 25-Mar-4 Hagelstam, Helsinki #907 est:3000
£1946 $3581 €2900 Landscape (36x85cm-14x33in) s. 25-Mar-4 Hagelstam, Helsinki #982 est:2400
£2113 $3655 €3000 Moonlight (37x22cm-15x9in) s. panel. 13-Dec-3 Hagelstam, Helsinki #85/R est:1600
£3028 $5239 €4300 Summer (100x67cm-39x26in) s. 13-Dec-3 Hagelstam, Helsinki #84/R est:4500
£3378 $6047 €5000 Lights in the windows (86x68cm-34x27in) s. 8-May-4 Bukowskis, Helsinki #86/R est:5000-7000
Works on paper
£943 $1697 €1415 Coastal landscape (21x29cm-8x11in) s.d.1939 crayon. 25-Apr-4 Goteborg Auktionsverk, Sweden #362/R (S.KR 13000)

TAUBES, Frederic (1900-1981) American
£324 $600 €473 Still life with flowers and musical instruments (71x112cm-28x44in) s. 15-Jul-4 Doyle, New York #78/R
£591 $1100 €863 Houses along a coastal inlet (66x81cm-26x32in) s. 3-Mar-4 Christie's, Rockefeller NY #34/R

TAUNAY, Nicolas Antoine (1755-1830) French
£5495 $10055 €8243 Battle scene (16x28cm-6x11in) s. panel. 6-Jul-4 Bolsa de Arte, Rio de Janeiro #157/R (B.R 30000)
£6690 $11708 €9500 Enfants ramassants des noix (23x18cm-9x7in) s.verso panel lit. 17-Dec-3 Piasa, Paris #66a est:5000-6000
£8667 $15860 €13000 Les comediens italiens. Le charlatan (21x12cm-8x5in) paper on panel pair prov. 6-Jun-4 Anaf, Lyon #190/R est:12000-15000
£20000 $34600 €29200 Quay with stevedores and peasants conversing, boat-builders at work, fortress beyond (54x65cm-21x26in) s. prov. 11-Dec-3 Sotheby's, London #35/R est:20000-30000
Works on paper
£1361 $2435 €2000 Deux scenes de la Comedia dell'Arte (10x20cm-4x8in) W/C ink wash pair. 22-Mar-4 Digard, Paris #27/R est:2500-3000

TAUNAY, Nicolas Antoine (attrib) (1755-1830) French
£3000 $5490 €4500 Magicien devant la porte d'une ville (34x46cm-13x18in) 5-Jun-4 Gros & Delettrez, Paris #64/R est:4500-6000

TAUNTON, Adrian (?) British
Works on paper
£370 $596 €540 Evening tide, Blakeney (38x53cm-15x21in) s.d.03 W/C. 15-Aug-3 Keys, Aylsham #667

TAUPIN, Jules (1863-1932) French
£2465 $4264 €3500 Koubba a Laghouat (95x127cm-37x50in) s.i. 15-Dec-3 Gros & Delettrez, Paris #471/R est:3600-4200
£8054 $14899 €12000 Les tisseuses (73x60cm-29x24in) s. lit. 15-Mar-4 Gros & Delettrez, Paris #233/R est:12000-15000
£10638 $17766 €15000 Les fileuses (81x65cm-32x26in) s. 16-Jun-3 Gros & Delettrez, Paris #437/R est:15000-20000

TAUREL, Henri (1843-?) French
£616 $962 €900 Little girl along on a path (60x108cm-24x43in) s.d.1900. 10-Apr-3 Weidler, Nurnberg #301/R

TAURELLE, Bernard (20th C) ?
£337 $550 €492 Landscape (80x115cm-31x45in) s. 28-Sep-3 Bonhams & Butterfields, Los Angeles #7072
£489 $846 €714 Apres le bain (116x89cm-46x35in) 15-Dec-3 Iegor de Saint Hippolyte, Montreal #105 (C.D 1100)
£1689 $2922 €2466 Le collier (116x89cm-46x35in) 15-Dec-3 Iegor de Saint Hippolyte, Montreal #104 (C.D 3800)
£2667 $4613 €3894 La barriere blanche (100x100cm-39x39in) 15-Dec-3 Iegor de Saint Hippolyte, Montreal #103 (C.D 6000)

TAUSS, Herbert (1929-2001) American
£267 $500 €390 Couple on porch swing, younger sister peeking around corner (33x53cm-13x21in) s. oil paper board. 26-Feb-4 Illustration House, New York #173

TAUSZKY, David Anthony (1878-1972) American
£952 $1800 €1390 The little artist, 1917 (61x41cm-24x16in) s.d.1917. 17-Feb-4 John Moran, Pasadena #107/R est:3000-5000

TAUZIN, Louis (fl.1867-1914) French
£1064 $1777 €1500 Elegante en crinoline sur le bord de mer, Royan (38x56cm-15x22in) s. i.verso. 20-Jun-3 Drouot Estimations, Paris #65 est:1500-2000

TAVAGNACCO, Guido (20th C) Italian
£594 $1022 €850 Study of women (40x50cm-16x20in) s. 3-Dec-3 Stadion, Trieste #962/R

TAVARES, Cristina (1961-) Portuguese
£333 $607 €500 Untitled (117x90cm-46x35in) s.d.99. 29-Jun-4 Chenu & Scrive, Lyon #173/R

TAVARONE, Lazzaro (attrib) (1556-1641) Dutch
£2667 $4773 €4000 Saint Lawrence's martyrdom (21x25cm-8x10in) copper. 12-May-4 Finarte Semenzato, Milan #86/R est:6000-8000
Works on paper
£1667 $3000 €2434 Christ in the house of Simon the Pharisee (36x28cm-14x11in) black chk pen ink wash squared for transfer exhib. 21-Jan-4 Sotheby's, New York #17/R est:3500-4500

TAVE, Georgette (1925-) French
£2098 $3608 €3000 Le chemin au petit citronier (116x89cm-46x35in) s. s.i.verso prov. 2-Dec-3 Sotheby's, Amsterdam #216/R est:1200-1500
£3147 $5413 €4500 Odalisque a la toilette (78x38cm-31x15in) s. s.i.verso prov. 2-Dec-3 Sotheby's, Amsterdam #213/R est:1000-1500

TAVELLA, Carlo Antonio (attrib) (1668-1738) Italian
£4930 $8528 €7000 Arcadian landscape with shepherds bathing (54x73cm-21x29in) 11-Dec-3 Dr Fritz Nagel, Stuttgart #495/R est:3000

TAVENIER, Hendrik (1734-1807) Dutch
Works on paper
£291 $495 €425 View of Thiel (10x25cm-4x10in) i. pen brown ink. 4-Nov-3 Sotheby's, Amsterdam #160/R
£291 $495 €425 View of the church at Almelo (13x18cm-5x7in) i. pen brown ink. 4-Nov-3 Sotheby's, Amsterdam #161/R
£291 $495 €425 Oudorp by Alkmaar (10x24cm-4x9in) i. pen brown ink. 4-Nov-3 Sotheby's, Amsterdam #162/R

TAVENRAAT, Johannes (1809-1881) Dutch
£833 $1317 €1200 Working the land (24x18cm-9x7in) s. s.i.verso panel. 2-Sep-3 Christie's, Amsterdam #162a est:1200-1600

TAVERNA, Gaudenz (1814-1878) Swiss
£452 $769 €660 Two children (29x23cm-11x9in) s.d.1846. 28-Nov-3 Zofingen, Switzerland #2490 (S.FR 1000)

TAVERNARO, Guglielmo (1909-1989) Swiss
Works on paper
£452 $756 €660 Composition (38x47cm-15x19in) mono.d.1984 mixed media board. 24-Jun-3 Germann, Zurich #1060 (S.FR 1000)

TAVERNE, Amedee Jean Nicolas de (1816-1871) French
Works on paper
£603 $1007 €850 Portrait d'un Turc (20x17cm-8x7in) i.d4 novembre 1843 W/C sold with two W/C in the same frame. 20-Jun-3 Drouot Estimations, Paris #33
£674 $1125 €950 Portrait d'un Grec (20x17cm-8x7in) i.d.1843 W/C crayon. 20-Jun-3 Drouot Estimations, Paris #31

TAVERNE, Louis (1859-1934) Belgian
£451 $718 €650 Pecheur sur l'etang (80x181cm-31x71in) s. 9-Sep-3 Vanderkindere, Brussels #243

TAVERNIER, Andrea (1858-1932) Italian
£5369 $9503 €8000 Summer green (27x37cm-11x15in) s. board. 1-May-4 Meeting Art, Vercelli #254 est:8000
£6014 $10043 €8600 Lake (27x37cm-11x15in) s. board. 26-Jun-3 Sant Agostino, Torino #300/R est:9000-11000
£8333 $15333 €12500 Village (26x37cm-10x15in) s. board. 14-Jun-4 Sant Agostino, Torino #300/R est:6000-8000
£10345 $17172 €15000 Green cloister (65x55cm-26x22in) s. exhib. 1-Oct-3 Della Rocca, Turin #315/R est:18000
£11702 $19543 €16500 Gabiet plain (52x65cm-20x26in) cardboard exhib.lit. 20-Oct-3 Sant Agostino, Torino #296/R est:16000
£15000 $27600 €22500 Last light on the peaks (28x37cm-11x15in) s. board prov. 14-Jun-4 Sant Agostino, Torino #306/R est:10000-14000
Works on paper
£1361 $2435 €2000 Nymph at the source (22x24cm-9x9in) s. pastel. 22-Mar-4 Sant Agostino, Torino #265/R est:2000-2500

TAVERNIER, Armand (1899-1991) Belgian
£1773 $2961 €2500 Village sous la neige (70x70cm-28x28in) s. i.d.avril 1947 verso. 17-Jun-3 Vanderkindere, Brussels #137/R est:2500-3500
£2411 $4027 €3400 Paysage enneige (80x100cm-31x39in) s. 14-Oct-3 Vanderkindere, Brussels #105
£2483 $4593 €3600 Paysage enneige (80x100cm-31x39in) s. 13-Jan-4 Vanderkindere, Brussels #480/R est:3000-4000

TAVERNIER, Jules (1844-1899) French
£4348 $8000 €6348 Light falling in the redwoods (66x40cm-26x16in) s. prov. 8-Jun-4 Bonhams & Butterfields, San Francisco #4160/R est:6000-8000

TAVERNIER, Julien Louis (1879-?) French
£496 $829 €700 Le grand canal (33x41cm-13x16in) s. isorel. 19-Jun-3 Millon & Associes, Paris #101
£2036 $3462 €2973 Nu au fauteuil bleu (92x73cm-36x29in) s. 19-Nov-3 Fischer, Luzern #1118/R est:5000-7000 (S.FR 4500)

TAVERNIER, Paul (1852-?) French
£786 $1431 €1148 Taking a rest from reading (55x38cm-22x15in) s.d.1880. 16-Jun-4 Fischer, Luzern #1158/R (S.FR 1800)

£3636 $6255 €5200 Scene de chasse a courre a Fontainebleau (65x92cm-26x36in) s. 7-Dec-3 Osenat, Fontainebleau #197 est:5500-6000

Works on paper

£839 $1443 €1200 Beaute Algeroise (36x22cm-14x9in) s. W/C. 8-Dec-3 Tajan, Paris #326/R

£2246 $3684 €3100 Chasse a courre du cerf, Bat l'eau (38x56cm-15x22in) W/C. 28-May-3 Coutau Begarie, Paris #320/R est:2500-3000

TAWNEY, Lenore (1925-) American

Works on paper

£2515 $4200 €3672 Impetus (16x16cm-6x6in) init. printed paper collage on printed paper executed 1967 prov. 11-Nov-3 Christie's, Rockefeller NY #176/R est:500-700

TAY BAK KOI (1939-) Singaporean

£2796 $4473 €4082 Buffaloes (81x117cm-32x46in) s. canvas on board. 18-May-3 Sotheby's, Singapore #56/R est:6000-8000 (S.D 7800)

Works on paper

£1075 $1720 €1570 Cranes (46x50cm-18x20in) s. mixed media. 18-May-3 Sotheby's, Singapore #58/R est:2500-3500 (S.D 3000)

TAYLER, D (?) ?

£820 $1500 €1230 Clipper ship (61x91cm-24x36in) s. 29-Jul-4 Eldred, East Dennis #466/R est:2000-3000

£943 $1500 €1377 Schooner at sea (51x61cm-20x24in) s. 9-Sep-3 Arthur James, Florida #409

TAYLER, E Easton (20th C) British?

£320 $573 €467 Portrait of a seated young lady in riding attire, holding a whip (74x48cm-29x19in) s.d.1933 board. 7-May-4 Mallams, Oxford #383/R

TAYLER, Edward (1828-1906) British

Miniatures

£5500 $10120 €8030 Young boy, called Alick, possibly Alexander Hohenlohe (7cm-3in) s. gilt metal frame prov. 24-Jun-4 Bonhams, New Bond Street #190/R est:700-900

Works on paper

£300 $552 €438 Portrait of a young girl, wearing a blue necklace (32x26cm-13x10in) s. pencil W/C oval. 25-Mar-4 Christie's, Kensington #231

£1000 $1700 €1460 Portrait of Countess of Carnarvon, nee lady Evelyn Stanhope (41x30cm-16x12in) bears sig.i. W/C prov.exhib. 4-Nov-3 Bonhams, New Bond Street #109/R est:800-1200

TAYLER, John Frederick (1802-1889) British

Works on paper

£330 $584 €482 The Downs (29x46cm-11x18in) W/C over pencil. 28-Apr-4 Hampton & Littlewood, Exeter #529

£700 $1169 €1022 Resting by the wayside (14x22cm-6x9in) pencil W/C. 16-Oct-3 Christie's, Kensington #101

£939 $1700 €1371 Foxhounds in a stable (45x58cm-18x23in) init.d.1859 W/C htd white. 30-Mar-4 Bonhams & Butterfields, San Francisco #65/R est:1500-2200

£5442 $9741 €8000 Waiting for the ferry, Isle of Skye (26x59cm-10x23in) s.d.1855 W/C htd gouache. 17-Mar-4 Maigret, Paris #18/R est:1200-1500

TAYLOR, Alfred Henry (?-1868) British

Works on paper

£550 $1001 €803 Portrait of Richard Myddelton Biddulph, aged four years (30x21cm-12x8in) s.d.72 i.verso pencil W/C pair. 21-Jun-4 Christie's, London #464

TAYLOR, Ben (1960-) Australian

£350 $633 €511 Tank (152x122cm-60x48in) s. i.d.1989 verso. 30-Mar-4 Lawson Menzies, Sydney #50 est:1000-1500 (A.D 850)

£823 $1490 €1202 Overflowing tank (122x152cm-48x60in) i.verso. 30-Mar-4 Lawson Menzies, Sydney #153b/R est:1000-1500 (A.D 2000)

TAYLOR, Charles (19th C) British

Works on paper

£800 $1432 €1168 Mouth of the harbour, Great Yarmouth (39x75cm-15x30in) s. W/C. 25-May-4 Sworder & Son, Bishops Stortford #420/R

TAYLOR, Charles (jnr) (fl.1841-1883) British

Works on paper

£520 $894 €759 Ships in rough sea (24x57cm-9x22in) W/C. 2-Dec-3 Sotheby's, London #73/R

£750 $1275 €1095 Big class cutter (35x53cm-14x21in) pencil W/C bodycol. 19-Nov-3 Christie's, Kensington #425/R

£1500 $2580 €2190 American merchantman off the Dutch coast (37x56cm-15x22in) W/C. 2-Dec-3 Sotheby's, London #72/R est:1500-2500

TAYLOR, Dennis (?) New Zealander?

Works on paper

£321 $582 €469 Awatea approaching Wellington (35x54cm-14x21in) s. W/C. 4-Apr-4 International Art Centre, Auckland #252/R (NZ.D 900)

£372 $639 €543 Cambria (35x55cm-14x22in) s. W/C. 7-Dec-3 International Art Centre, Auckland #338 (NZ.D 1000)

TAYLOR, E Mervyn (20th C) New Zealander

Works on paper

£484 $867 €707 Silence (38x54cm-15x21in) s.d.1952 mixed media prov. 12-May-4 Dunbar Sloane, Wellington #175 est:750-1500 (NZ.D 1400)

£779 $1394 €1137 Headland Te Kaha (36x53cm-14x21in) s.d.1964 W/C prov. 12-May-4 Dunbar Sloane, Wellington #176/R est:1500-3000 (NZ.D 2250)

TAYLOR, Edward R (1838-1912) British

£920 $1444 €1334 River scene with Victorian figures conversing and figures in punts. s. 15-Dec-2 Desmond Judd, Cranbrook #921

TAYLOR, Edwin (fl.1882-84) British

£260 $471 €380 Sheep track (30x40cm-12x16in) s. 4-Apr-4 Lots Road Auctions, London #361/R

TAYLOR, Ernest Archibald (1874-1952) British

£950 $1530 €1378 Firth of Clyde (49x59cm-19x23in) s.verso panel. 21-Aug-3 Bonhams, Edinburgh #1140

TAYLOR, Francis (1899-?) British

£2717 $5000 €3967 Landscape with tree (30x41cm-12x16in) s. board. 11-Jun-4 David Rago, Lambertville #238/R est:6000-9000

£10063 $16000 €14692 Winter scene of stream in woods (28x38cm-11x15in) s.d.35. 10-Sep-3 Alderfer's, Hatfield #385/R est:5000-7000

TAYLOR, Frank (fl.1980s) British

Works on paper

£260 $458 €380 King for a day (24x30cm-9x12in) s. mixed media. 18-May-4 Woolley & Wallis, Salisbury #290/R

£500 $880 €730 Temples, peacocks and palms (35x43cm-14x17in) s. mixed media. 18-May-4 Woolley & Wallis, Salisbury #130/R

TAYLOR, Frederick Bourchier (1906-1987) Canadian

£246 $457 €359 Buildings in the harbour, Cheticamp, Cape Breton NS (16x20cm-6x8in) s.d.79 s.i.verso panel. 2-Mar-4 Ritchie, Toronto #113/R (C.D 610)

£290 $499 €423 Mixed flowers in a blue glass vase (40x35cm-16x14in) s. 2-Dec-3 Joyner Waddington, Toronto #538 (C.D 650)

£320 $586 €467 At the edge of a cedar swamp, Kirk's Ferry P, Quebec (27x35cm-11x14in) s. verso canvas on board. 1-Jun-4 Joyner Waddington, Toronto #379/R (C.D 800)

£379 $652 €553 Still life with grapes, mango and white mug (30x40cm-12x16in) s. board. 2-Dec-3 Joyner Waddington, Toronto #340/R (C.D 850)

£714 $1229 €1042 Cluster of fish houses - Gabarus, Cape Breton (30x50cm-12x20in) s.d.75 prov. 2-Dec-3 Joyner Waddington, Toronto #265/R (C.D 1600)

£759 $1305 €1108 On the long trail, Branley Mountain near Manchester, Vermont (21x26cm-8x10in) s.d.54 panel. 2-Dec-3 Joyner Waddington, Toronto #524 (C.D 1700)

£811 $1378 €1184 In the town centre, San Miguel (102x81cm-40x32in) s. s.i.d.1961 verso lit. 21-Nov-3 Walker's, Ottawa #129/R est:1500-2000 (C.D 1800)

£3213 $5976 €4691 Looking down St Urbain St, Montreal (27x22cm-11x9in) s. panel prov. 2-Mar-4 Ritchie, Toronto #112/R est:600-800 (C.D 8000)

£4800 $8784 €7008 In Percy Walters Park (50x60cm-20x24in) s. board painted April 1950 prov. 1-Jun-4 Joyner Waddington, Toronto #146/R est:8000-12000 (C.D 12000)

TAYLOR, George F (fl.1925) British

Works on paper

£360 $572 €526 What is it? (23x15cm-9x6in) s.d.1925 brown ink panel. 10-Sep-3 Cheffins, Cambridge #443/R

TAYLOR, H (19th C) British

£750 $1275 €1095 Rural scene with woman feeding chickens. Figure making a haystack (30x25cm-12x10in) s. board pair. 19-Nov-3 Tennants, Leyburn #1076

TAYLOR, Henry King (fl.1857-1869) British

£900 $1611 €1314 Fishermen pulling in their nets off a fortified headland (41x61cm-16x24in) 26-May-4 Christie's, Kensington #686/R

£5800 $10614 €8468 Sailing vessels in a stiff breeze off a harbour (91x127cm-36x50in) s. prov. 8-Jul-4 Duke & Son, Dorchester #169/R

TAYLOR, Henry Weston (1881-?) American

Works on paper

£188 $350 €274 Interior scene with figures (56x74cm-22x29in) s. chl. 3-Mar-4 Alderfer's, Hatfield #432

TAYLOR, Howard (1918-) Australian

£22901 $41679 €33435 Tree lined green paddock (61x122cm-24x48in) s.d.93 s.i.verso board prov.exhib. 16-Jun-4 Deutscher-Menzies, Melbourne #57/R est:60000-80000 (A.D 60000)

Sculpture

£4527 $8193 €6609 Small forest group (41x35x31cm-16x14x12in) painted carved wood. 30-Mar-4 Lawson Menzies, Sydney #292 est:400-600 (A.D 11000)

TAYLOR, Ida (fl.1884-1893) British

£2800 $4760 €4088 Dutch flower sellers, with other figures nearby (85x99cm-33x39in) s. 19-Nov-3 Tennants, Leyburn #1241/R est:3000-4000

TAYLOR, J Behenna (?) British?

Works on paper

£520 $900 €759 Jacob journeying to Egypt (29x70cm-11x28in) mono. W/C. 9-Dec-3 Anderson & Garland, Newcastle #272/R

TAYLOR, James (1930-) British

£250 $463 €365 Paysage (58x118cm-23x46in) s.d.1959 board. 10-Mar-4 Cheffins, Cambridge #103/R

£320 $512 €467 Figure with dressing gown (59x36cm-23x14in) s. panel prov. 16-Sep-3 Rosebery Fine Art, London #402/R
£500 $861 €730 Grey landscape with houses (49x72cm-19x28in) s. prov. 3-Dec-3 Stephan Welz, Johannesburg #19/R est:6000-9000 (SA.R 5500)
£637 $1096 €930 Farmhouse with trees (58x80cm-23x31in) s. prov. 3-Dec-3 Stephan Welz, Johannesburg #18/R est:6000-9000 (SA.R 7000)
£682 $1174 €996 Farmhouse (49x99cm-19x39in) s. prov. 3-Dec-3 Stephan Welz, Johannesburg #17/R est:7000-10000 (SA.R 7500)
£1183 $2035 €1727 Conversation (88x115cm-35x45in) s.d.1962 prov. 3-Dec-3 Stephan Welz, Johannesburg #16/R est:10000-15000 (SA.R 13000)

TAYLOR, John Austin (?) American
Works on paper
£364 $575 €531 Yacht Mirimad (36x48cm-14x19in) s. gouache on board. 25-Jul-3 Eldred, East Dennis #291d/R

TAYLOR, John C E (1902-) American
£2374 $4250 €3466 Magnolia flower (76x63cm-30x25in) s.d.1935. 14-May-4 Skinner, Boston #367/R est:700-900

TAYLOR, John D (fl.1880-1900) British
£1000 $1700 €1460 Trawlers landing their nets, Tarbert (66x102cm-26x40in) s.d.1880. 19-Nov-3 Tennants, Leyburn #1030/R est:1000-1200

TAYLOR, Josiah (fl.1846-1877) British
£2432 $4500 €3551 Royal Yacht Squadron racing lugger New Moon in the Channel off Dover (51x92cm-20x36in) prov. 10-Feb-4 Christie's, Rockefeller NY #218/R est:5000-7000

TAYLOR, Leonard Campbell (1874-1963) British
£580 $963 €847 Grand Canal, Venice (9x13cm-4x5in) s. board. 1-Oct-3 Woolley & Wallis, Salisbury #214/R
£949 $1700 €1386 Moonrise by the sea (25x30cm-10x12in) s.d.98 i.verso panel. 16-Mar-4 Bonhams & Butterfields, San Francisco #6168/R est:2000-3000
£3125 $5000 €4563 Town square in France with figures (71x91cm-28x36in) s. 20-Sep-3 Sloans & Kenyon, Bethesda #1174/R est:5000-6000
£4600 $8142 €6716 Rain it raineth every day (36x27cm-14x11in) s.i.d.1906 panel. 27-Apr-4 Bonhams, Knightsbridge #136/R est:2500-3500
£15000 $27300 €21900 Rain in raineth every day (37x27cm-15x11in) s.d.1906 panel. 1-Jul-4 Sotheby's, London #327/R est:15000-20000
£52000 $95160 €75920 Mother love (46x61cm-18x24in) s. exhib. 2-Jun-4 Sotheby's, London #2/R est:30000-50000

TAYLOR, Maeve (20th C) Irish
£282 $493 €400 Ice cream break (30x40cm-12x16in) s. board. 16-Dec-3 James Adam, Dublin #162/R
£345 $604 €490 Summer, Glenshalene (34x44cm-13x17in) s. board. 16-Dec-3 James Adam, Dublin #218/R

TAYLOR, Michael (1950-) Australian
£424 $720 €619 Seamarks (91x91cm-36x36in) s.d.77 bears i.verso. 24-Nov-3 Sotheby's, Melbourne #229 (A.D 1000)
£741 $1341 €1082 Bredbo nocturine (51x61cm-20x24in) s.d.76 i.verso. 30-Mar-4 Lawson Menzies, Sydney #163 est:2000-3000 (A.D 1800)
£1646 $2979 €2403 Starry night (182x152cm-72x60in) s.d.76. 30-Mar-4 Lawson Menzies, Sydney #171/R est:2500-3500 (A.D 4000)
£2439 $3829 €3561 Gulf waters (151x183cm-59x72in) s.d.80 i.verso prov. 27-Aug-3 Christie's, Sydney #715/R est:2000-3000 (A.D 6000)
£2881 $5214 €4206 Blackened trees (150x110cm-59x43in) i.verso. 30-Mar-4 Lawson Menzies, Sydney #156b/R est:2000-3000 (A.D 7000)

TAYLOR, Michael Franklin (1933-) Australian
£260 $416 €380 Reclining nude (53x99cm-21x39in) s.d.1989. 19-May-3 Bruton Knowles, Cheltenham #252/R
£702 $1300 €1025 Figure in a cave (122x183cm-48x72in) s.d.12.10.89 i.verso prov. 15-Mar-4 Sotheby's, Melbourne #171 est:400-600 (A.D 1700)

TAYLOR, Rolla S (1872-1970) American
£689 $1150 €1006 Sunset with country road (20x25cm-8x10in) canvasboard. 18-Oct-3 David Dike, Dallas #271/R
£898 $1500 €1311 San Antonio river (25x36cm-10x14in) board. 18-Oct-3 David Dike, Dallas #229/R est:1500-2000
£1290 $2400 €1883 Texas bluebonnets (25x36cm-10x14in) s. board painted 1940. 7-Mar-4 Treadway Gallery, Cincinnati #572/R est:3000-5000
£1497 $2500 €2186 Spring, Texas (41x51cm-16x20in) canvasboard. 18-Oct-3 David Dike, Dallas #201/R est:2000-2500
£2326 $4000 €3396 Hacienda in south Texas (41x61cm-16x24in) s. painted c.1940. 7-Dec-3 Treadway Gallery, Cincinnati #560/R est:2500-4500

TAYLOR, Samuel Connolly (1870-1944) British
Works on paper
£428 $787 €650 On the Lagan (28x38cm-11x15in) s.i.d.1894 W/C prov. 22-Jun-4 De Veres Art Auctions, Dublin #252

TAYLOR, Sarah (20th C) British
£300 $501 €438 Faded history (150cm-59in) 16-Nov-3 Lots Road Auctions, London #14

TAYLOR, T (19th C) ?
Works on paper
£700 $1274 €1022 Tinker Tailor Soldier Sailor Apothecary Ploughboy Thief (53x41cm-21x16in) i.verso W/C. 3-Feb-4 Gorringes, Bexhill #936

TAYLOR, Walter (1875-1965) British
Works on paper
£538 $1000 €785 Study of a woman (43x30cm-17x12in) s. black col chk. 3-Mar-4 Christie's, Rockefeller NY #47/R

TAYLOR, Walter (1860-1943) British
£600 $1110 €876 View from a window, Brunswick Square, Brighton (66x46cm-26x18in) s. verso. 11-Mar-4 Christie's, Kensington #99/R
Works on paper
£450 $774 €657 View across the rooftops from a window (46x33cm-18x13in) s. W/C. 3-Dec-3 Cheffins, Cambridge #588/R
£1200 $2148 €1752 Parliament, Athens (31x38cm-12x15in) s. blk chk W/C. 10-May-4 Sotheby's, Olympia #139/R est:600-800

TAYLOR, William Lindsey (20th C) American
£405 $700 €591 Weehawken stone quarry (61x75cm-24x30in) s. i.d.1928 verso. 13-Dec-3 Weschler, Washington #576

TAYLOR, William S (1882-?) American
£300 $501 €438 At the market (25x49cm-10x19in) board. 16-Oct-3 Christie's, Kensington #331

TAYLOR-BUCKLEY, Maura (20th C) Irish?
£563 $986 €800 Composition with teapot, ceramics and book (46x61cm-18x24in) s. 16-Dec-3 James Adam, Dublin #229/R

TAYLOR-GHEE, Robert Eagar (1869-1951) Australian
£1619 $2607 €2364 Frankston from Oliver's Hill (29x38cm-11x15in) s. board. 13-Oct-3 Joel, Victoria #307/R est:4000-6000 (A.D 4000)

TAYLOR-WOOD, Sam (1967-) British
Photographs
£1900 $3496 €2774 Looking out (16x55cm-6x22in) s.i.d.2002 num.12/200 C-type col photo prov. 24-Jun-4 Sotheby's, Olympia #635/R est:800-1200
£26816 $48000 €39151 Soliloquy II (224x256cm-88x101in) two c-prints diptych prov.exhib.lit. 13-May-4 Phillips, New York #59/R est:40000-60000

TAYMANS, Louis (1826-1877) Belgian
£3448 $6379 €5000 La fileuse et le petit marchand de fruits (60x47cm-24x19in) s.d.1854 panel. 16-Feb-4 Horta, Bruxelles #133/R est:6000-8000

TCHEKHONINE, Sergei (1878-1936) Russian
Works on paper
£2200 $3740 €3300 Costume design for 'In 1825' (32x19cm-13x7in) s.d.1925 pencil W/C. 25-Nov-3 Christie's, London #202/R est:1500-2000
£3103 $5152 €4500 Arlequin (31x21cm-12x8in) s. gouache. 6-Oct-3 Blanchet, Paris #250/R
£6000 $10740 €8760 Costume design for a female dancer (29x21cm-11x8in) s.d.1926 pencil pen W/C. 11-May-4 Sotheby's, Olympia #527/R est:2000-3000
£7000 $12530 €10220 Costume design for a Spanish dancer (28x20cm-11x8in) s.d.1926 pen brush ink W/C. 11-May-4 Sotheby's, Olympia #528/R est:3000-5000
£19231 $30000 € Landscape (70x48cm-28x19in) s.cyrillic W/C gouache. 11-Apr-3 Christie's, Rockefeller NY #52/R est:30000-40000

TCHELITCHEV, Pavel (1898-1957) American/Russian
£3548 $6600 €5180 Les oeufs (32x38cm-13x15in) s. prov. 5-Mar-4 Skinner, Boston #426/R est:3000-5000
£6000 $10920 €8760 Study for inacheve (97x130cm-38x51in) painted 1956 prov. 4-Feb-4 Sotheby's, London #288/R est:7000-9000
£7586 $12669 €11000 Nature morte aux pores (63x52cm-25x20in) s.d.1927 oil sand. 17-Nov-3 Claude Boisgirard, Paris #91/R est:10000-12000
£8092 $14000 €11814 Head (64x48cm-25x19in) exhib. 15-Dec-3 Hindman, Chicago #16/R est:5000-7000
Works on paper
£400 $728 €584 Femme allongee. Femme endormie (54x42cm-21x17in) studio st.verso Indian ink double-sided prov. 21-Jun-4 Bonhams, New Bond Street #57/R
£414 $750 €604 Leaf study (41x34cm-16x13in) s.d.39 pen ink. 18-Apr-4 Bonhams & Butterfields, Los Angeles #7086
£432 $800 €631 Hand and apples (27x29cm-11x11in) i.verso sepia ink prov. 12-Feb-4 Sotheby's, New York #70/R
£535 $850 €781 Figural study (26x20cm-10x8in) s.d.31 ink wash. 13-Sep-3 Weschler, Washington #706/R
£543 $869 €793 Femmes et spahis (26x20cm-10x8in) sepia Indian ink pen wash. 16-Sep-3 Philippe Schuler, Zurich #3058/R (S.FR 1200)
£543 $1000 €793 Surreal landscape with children (20x28cm-8x11in) s.d.1940 pen ink wash. 10-Jun-4 Swann Galleries, New York #242/R
£650 $1151 €949 Portrait of a young girl (30x20cm-12x8in) s.i.d.34 pen ink. 27-Apr-4 Bonhams, Knightsbridge #52
£650 $1183 €949 Studies of jugglers, acrobats and horses (45x28cm-18x11in) studio st.verso Indian ink exec.c.1929 prov. 21-Jun-4 Bonhams, New Bond Street #56/R
£870 $1600 €1270 Head of a woman (30x18cm-12x7in) s.d.1934 brush brown ink. 10-Jun-4 Swann Galleries, New York #240/R est:1200-1800
£950 $1729 €1387 Portrait of Jacques Stettiner (56x45cm-22x18in) studio st.verso Indian ink prov. 21-Jun-4 Bonhams, New Bond Street #54/R
£1117 $2000 €1631 Nude in hammock. s.i. W/C. 13-May-4 Dallas Auction Gallery, Dallas #337/R est:1000-2000
£1200 $2124 €1752 Costume design for oriental dancer (44x28cm-17x11in) i.d.1921 pencil W/C gouache prov. 27-Apr-4 Bonhams, Knightsbridge #29/R est:600-800
£1486 $2750 €2170 Jeune pecheur (44x27cm-17x11in) s.i.d.30 brown ink wash thin paper prov. 12-Feb-4 Sotheby's, New York #73/R est:3000-5000
£1711 $3200 €2498 Dessins pour costumes (46x28cm-18x11in) s. gouache pair. 25-Feb-4 Christie's, Rockefeller NY #73/R est:2000-3000
£1744 $3000 €2546 Design for a male dancer costume (26x21cm-10x8in) s. pen ink wash executed c.1932 prov.exhib.lit. 3-Dec-3 Doyle, New York #75/R est:2000-3000
£1848 $3400 €2698 Anatomical study, head (33x25cm-13x10in) s.d.1940 pencil. 10-Jun-4 Swann Galleries, New York #241/R est:1000-1500

£2000	$3640	€2920	Study for Adam (31x21cm-12x8in) W/C exec.1928 prov. 4-Feb-4 Sotheby's, London #553/R est:2000-3000
£3892	$6500	€5682	Interior landscape (35x28cm-14x11in) s.d.46 ink wash. 7-Oct-3 Sotheby's, New York #287 est:4000-6000
£6936	$12000	€10127	Spangled head (76x51cm-30x20in) s.i.verso W/C gouache sequins board prov. 11-Dec-3 Sotheby's, New York #213/R est:12000-15000
£12270	$20000	€17914	Spiral head III (50x35cm-20x14in) s.d.50 pastel over black W/C prov.exhib. 25-Sep-3 Christie's, Rockefeller NY #611/R est:14000-18000

TCHERINA, Ludmila (20th C) ?

Works on paper

£216	$387	€315	Ballet nude (56x39cm-22x15in) s. mixed media pastel. 22-Mar-4 Philippe Schuler, Zurich #4054 (S.FR 500)

TCHERNIAWSKY, Charles (1900-) Russian

Works on paper

£900	$1656	€1314	Artist and his model (57x40cm-22x16in) s. model pen black ink chl sold with an oil by A T Zverev. 23-Mar-4 Rosebery Fine Art, London #944

TCHERNJAEV, Anatole (1937-) Russian

£1127	$1949	€1600	Friend of the artist with woman (98x105cm-39x41in) s.i.d.83 lit. 13-Dec-3 De Vuyst, Lokeren #310 est:1700-2500

TCHERNOV, Eugueni (1948-) Russian

£272	$495	€400	Rue de Moscou. s. 8-Feb-4 Lesieur & Le Bars, Le Havre #101
£306	$557	€450	Kazatchok. s. canvas on cardboard. 8-Feb-4 Lesieur & Le Bars, Le Havre #102
£306	$557	€450	La peche miraculeuse. s. canvas on cardboard. 8-Feb-4 Lesieur & Le Bars, Le Havre #149
£340	$619	€500	Quai de Sebastopol. s. canvas on cardboard. 8-Feb-4 Lesieur & Le Bars, Le Havre #62
£340	$619	€500	Apres la peche. s. 8-Feb-4 Lesieur & Le Bars, Le Havre #64
£340	$619	€500	Peintre du dimanche. s. 8-Feb-4 Lesieur & Le Bars, Le Havre #148
£422	$768	€620	Horizon. s. canvas on cardboard. 8-Feb-4 Lesieur & Le Bars, Le Havre #61
£422	$768	€620	Deux bouquets. s. 8-Feb-4 Lesieur & Le Bars, Le Havre #150
£442	$805	€650	Boutons d'or. s. cardboard. 8-Feb-4 Lesieur & Le Bars, Le Havre #103
£476	$867	€700	Toits rouges. s. 8-Feb-4 Lesieur & Le Bars, Le Havre #63
£918	$1671	€1350	Bicyclette. s. 8-Feb-4 Lesieur & Le Bars, Le Havre #100
£1769	$3219	€2600	Crepuscule doree. s. 8-Feb-4 Lesieur & Le Bars, Le Havre #147

TCHETCHET, Victor (1891-1974) ?

Works on paper

£802	$1500	€1171	Woman lounging at beach pavilion (97x71cm-38x28in) s. pastel exec.c.1930. 26-Feb-4 Illustration House, New York #174 est:3000-5000

TCHISTOVSKI, Lew (1902-) Russian

£369	$653	€550	Nature morte aux fleurs et coquillages (31x40cm-12x16in) s. panel. 28-Apr-4 Charbonneaux, Paris #226
£400	$716	€584	Orchids (23x18cm-9x7in) s. board. 11-May-4 Bonhams, Knightsbridge #84/R
£845	$1462	€1200	Danseuse (65x50cm-26x20in) canvas on isorel. 13-Dec-3 Martinot & Savignat, Pontoise #239
£1000	$1770	€1460	Still life of vase of delphiniums, gladioli and other flowers (55x47cm-22x19in) board. 27-Apr-4 Henry Adams, Chichester #682 est:900-1200

TCHOUKOV, Nikolai (1923-) Russian

£1408	$2437	€2000	Tale (89x133cm-35x52in) s. 15-Dec-3 Ansorena, Madrid #58/R est:2000

TCHUBANOV, Boris (1946-) Russian

£4577	$7919	€6500	Jeune fille a l'ombrelle (73x54cm-29x21in) s. 14-Dec-3 Rabourdin & Choppin de Janvry, Paris #27/R est:8000-9000

TCVETKOV, Viktor (1920-) Russian

£4167	$7500	€6084	Two boys bathing (99x131cm-39x52in) s.d.48. 23-Apr-4 Sotheby's, New York #120/R est:12000-18000
£12000	$20400	€17520	The Finish (144x215cm-57x85in) s. s.i.verso. 19-Nov-3 Sotheby's, London #237/R est:12000-18000
£35000	$59500	€51100	Bicycle ride (129x104cm-51x41in) s.d.1965. 19-Nov-3 Sotheby's, London #238/R est:8000-12000

TEAGUE, David (20th C) British

Works on paper

£260	$476	€380	Pheasants in snow (42x64cm-17x25in) s.d.1991 gouache. 6-Apr-4 Bristol Auction Rooms #412/R

TEAGUE, Donald (1897-1991) American

£3107	$5500	€4536	Rue de l'Abbaye, Paris (35x27cm-14x11in) s.i. board sketch verso. 28-Apr-4 Christie's, Los Angeles #60/R est:3000-5000

Works on paper

£311	$500	€451	Lady drinking tea (61x25cm-24x10in) gouache. 22-Aug-3 Altermann Galleries, Santa Fe #238
£3955	$7000	€5774	Gypsy quarter, Ronda (15x24cm-6x9in) s. s.i.verso W/C graphite paper on board. 28-Apr-4 Christie's, Los Angeles #29/R est:2500-3500
£4545	$8500	€6636	Paris hotel (15x23cm-6x9in) s. W/C. 24-Jul-4 Coeur d'Alene, Hayden #37/R est:7000-10000

TEAGUE, Violet Helen (1872-1951) Australian

£552	$861	€800	Lovers lane, Lockmaben, Tasmania (27x35cm-11x14in) s. panel. 1-Aug-2 Joel, Victoria #229 est:1500-2000 (A.D 1600)

TEASDALE, John (1848-1926) British

£260	$413	€380	Plummer Tower, Newcastle city walls (30x23cm-12x9in) s.d.1887. 18-Mar-3 Anderson & Garland, Newcastle #259/R

TEASDALE, Noel (1941-) Australian

Works on paper

£393	$726	€574	Boulder mine site (84x112cm-33x44in) s.d.89 i.verso synthetic polymer mixed media on canvas. 15-Mar-4 Sotheby's, Melbourne #153 est:200-400 (A.D 950)

TEASDALE, Percy Morton (1870-?) British

£310	$493	€453	Houses by a river with punts moored in the foreground and ruined castle (34x43cm-13x17in) s. 18-Mar-3 Anderson & Garland, Newcastle #534
£1800	$3366	€2628	Figures thatching the corn pikes, other figures and a horse and cart nearby (63x76cm-25x30in) s. 22-Jul-4 Tennants, Leyburn #932 est:2000-3000

TEBBITT, Henri (1852-1926) Australian

Works on paper

£250	$393	€365	Ancient tree, still waters (34x48cm-13x19in) s. W/C. 24-Nov-2 Goodman, Sydney #84 (A.D 700)
£386	$606	€560	Untitled - lake scene with castle (44x75cm-17x30in) s. W/C. 26-Aug-3 Lawson Menzies, Sydney #69 est:800-1000 (A.D 950)
£458	$834	€669	Quiet landscape (22x36cm-9x14in) s. W/C. 16-Jun-4 Deutscher-Menzies, Melbourne #594/R est:1000-2000 (A.D 1200)
£552	$861	€800	Meandering morning stream (59x11cm-23x4in) s. W/C. 1-Aug-2 Joel, Victoria #192 est:1000-1500 (A.D 1600)
£813	$1455	€1187	Old Farmhouse (60x116cm-24x46in) s. W/C htd white. 10-May-4 Joel, Victoria #265 est:1500-2500 (A.D 2000)

TEBBY, Arthur Kemp (1865-1935) British

£344	$616	€502	Dolls and toadstool on woodland (25x35cm-10x14in) s. 10-May-4 Rasmussen, Vejle #415/R (D.KR 3800)

TEED, Douglas Arthur (1864-1929) American

£503	$800	€734	Moroccan market scene (40x24cm-16x9in) s.d.1912 board. 13-Sep-3 Weschler, Washington #750/R
£738	$1300	€1077	Desert sandstorm (51x63cm-20x25in) s.d.1922. 23-May-4 Bonhams & Butterfields, Los Angeles #7065a/R
£818	$1300	€1194	Strolling through St Mark's Square, Venice (36x25cm-14x10in) s.i.d.1895. 13-Sep-3 Weschler, Washington #752/R
£881	$1400	€1286	Farmyard (69x94cm-27x37in) s.d.1900. 13-Sep-3 Weschler, Washington #751/R est:2000-3000
£1006	$1600	€1469	Autumn landscape with farmhouse in a clearing (36x51cm-14x20in) s.d.1912. 13-Sep-3 Weschler, Washington #753/R est:1200-1800
£1081	$2000	€1578	Arab merchant scene (66x58cm-26x23in) 13-Feb-4 Du Mouchelle, Detroit #2135/R est:2000-2500
£1445	$2500	€2110	Landscape with cattle near a river (51x41cm-20x16in) s.d.1900 prov. 10-Dec-3 Bonhams & Butterfields, San Francisco #6009/R est:3000-5000

TEEL, Lewis Woods (1883-1948) American

£1796	$3000	€2622	West Texas landscape (25x38cm-10x15in) 18-Oct-3 David Dike, Dallas #288/R est:1000-2000
£2695	$4500	€3935	Big bend (66x89cm-26x35in) masonite. 18-Oct-3 David Dike, Dallas #217/R est:5000-10000

TEGIN, D K (1914-1988) Russian

£326	$600	€476	Sketch of the young Komosol men for the painting of Lenin's speech (83x58cm-33x23in) painted 1950's. 27-Mar-4 Shishkin Gallery, Moscow #3/R
£353	$650	€515	At the Moscow river, in the Peski (25x36cm-10x14in) cardboard painted 1958. 27-Mar-4 Shishkin Gallery, Moscow #1/R
£652	$1200	€952	Windy day, Palanga (35x50cm-14x20in) cardboard painted 1950. 27-Mar-4 Shishkin Gallery, Moscow #2/R

TEGNER, Christian Martin (1803-1881) Danish

£851	$1472	€1242	Norwegian landscape with lake (29x40cm-11x16in) s.i.d.1869 verso. 9-Dec-3 Rasmussen, Copenhagen #1479/R (D.KR 9000)

TEGNER, Rudolph (1873-1950) Danish

Sculpture

£1217	$2033	€1777	Seated girl (29cm-11in) s. bronze marble base. 25-Oct-3 Rasmussen, Havnen #4073/R est:5000-7000 (D.KR 13000)
£8500	$15300	€12410	Aphrodite guiding the arrow of Eros (102cm-40in) s. st.f.Siot green pat bronze lit. 22-Apr-4 Christie's, Kensington #531/R est:5000-8000
£23121	$40000	€33757	Victory (92x35x23cm-36x14x9in) with sig. bronze prov. 11-Dec-3 Sotheby's, New York #166/R est:12000-15000

TEIBLER, Georg (1854-1911) Austrian

£397	$723	€600	Portrait of Wilhelm Wollanchs (74x58cm-29x23in) s.d.1885 i.verso. 21-Jun-4 Dorotheum, Vienna #262/R

TEICHEL, Franz (1816-?) German

Works on paper

£300	$540	€438	Mother and children beside a cottage door (17x22cm-7x9in) s.d.1842 pencil W/C htd white. 21-Apr-4 Tennants, Leyburn #972
£369	$679	€550	Dachshund (23x31cm-9x12in) s. pastel. 25-Mar-4 Hagelstam, Helsinki #819

TEICHMANN, Alfred (1903-1980) German
£295 $543 €440 Peasants loading sailing ship with hay (73x93cm-29x37in) s. 27-Mar-4 Dannenberg, Berlin #630/R

TEIXEIRA DE MATTOS, Henri (1856-1908) Dutch
£347 $600 €507 Potato peeler (56x48cm-22x19in) s. 12-Dec-3 Eldred, East Dennis #714/R
£362 $655 €550 Young mother from Schevening with child (42x30cm-17x12in) s. canvas on panel. 19-Apr-4 Glerum, Amsterdam #128/R

TEIXEIRA, Floriano (20th C) Brazilian?
£13736 $24313 €20604 Market scene (140x200cm-55x79in) s.i.d.1968. 27-Apr-4 Bolsa de Arte, Rio de Janeiro #67/R (B.R 75000)

TEIXIDOR, Jordi (1941-) Spanish
£667 $1207 €1000 Untitled (80x58cm-31x23in) s.d.1975 prov. 30-Mar-4 Segre, Madrid #150/R
£2241 $4034 €3250 Orange window (200x117cm-79x46in) s.i.d.1973 verso board. 26-Jan-4 Durán, Madrid #646/R est:3000
£2535 $4437 €3600 3-45/79-4 (85x85cm-33x33in) s.i.d.1979 verso prov. 16-Dec-3 Segre, Madrid #171/R est:2900

TEIXIDOR, Modest (1854-1927) Spanish
£1974 $3572 €3000 Church (80x108cm-31x43in) s. 14-Apr-4 Ansorena, Madrid #165/R est:3000

TEJADA, P Joaquin (19/20th C) Spanish
£345 $621 €500 Landscape (32x46cm-13x18in) s.i.d.1902 on palette. 26-Jan-4 Durán, Madrid #571/R

TEJEO, Rafael (1798-1856) Spanish
£2181 $3904 €3250 Portrait of young woman (46x35cm-18x14in) s. 25-May-4 Durán, Madrid #183/R est:700

TELARIK, Alois (1884-1961) ?
£4673 $7383 €6776 Young girl wearing Arabic costume (123x80cm-48x31in) s. 2-Sep-3 Rasmussen, Copenhagen #1561/R est:60000 (D.KR 50000)

TELARO, Rino (1950-) Italian
£521 $870 €750 Arrogance makes us deaf (39x49cm-15x19in) s. d.1998 verso. 21-Oct-3 Campo & Campo, Antwerp #293
£556 $928 €800 Untitled (49x39cm-19x15in) s. d.1998 verso. 21-Oct-3 Campo & Campo, Antwerp #292

TELCS, Ede (1872-1948) Hungarian
Sculpture
£2000 $3780 €2920 Buddah and a naked acaite (86cm-34in) pink veined marble prov. 17-Feb-4 Sotheby's, Olympia #64/R est:2000-3000
£3200 $5536 €4672 St Christopher carrying the Christ Child (71x41x24cm-28x16x9in) s. white marble. 12-Dec-3 Sotheby's, London #248/R est:3000-5000

TELEMAQUE, Herve (1937-) Haitian
£3356 $6175 €5000 Boites et poids (50x50cm-20x20in) s.i.d.1971 verso. 29-Mar-4 Cornette de St.Cyr, Paris #76/R est:4000-5000
£6376 $11732 €9500 Usages-Manches (60x92cm-24x36in) s.i.d.1975 verso. 29-Mar-4 Cornette de St.Cyr, Paris #75/R est:10000-12000
Works on paper
£6338 $10965 €9000 A son habitude (130x200cm-51x79in) mono.d.84 s.i.d.verso mixed media panel on on canvas. 9-Dec-3 Artcurial Briest, Paris #382/R est:12000-15000

TELEPY, Karoly (1828-1906) Hungarian
£695 $1230 €1015 Hilly landscape (16x24cm-6x9in) cardboard. 28-Apr-4 Kieselbach, Budapest #36/R (H.F 260000)
£1976 $3577 €2885 Swift mountain river (25x19cm-10x7in) s. 16-Apr-4 Mu Terem Galeria, Budapest #106/R (H.F 750000)
£2036 $3380 €2973 Landscape with a mountain brook (18x24cm-7x9in) s. panel. 4-Oct-3 Kieselbach, Budapest #35/R (H.F 750000)

TELIGA, Stanley Frederick de (1924-1998) Australian
£386 $606 €560 Closing dark (122x101cm-48x40in) s.d.69 acrylic board prov.exhib. 26-Aug-3 Christie's, Sydney #403 (A.D 950)
£569 $893 €825 Warm surf IV (137x123cm-54x48in) s.d.67 s.i.verso acrylic board prov.exhib. 26-Aug-3 Christie's, Sydney #294 est:600-800 (A.D 1400)
£894 $1404 €1296 Across the Kydra (130x90cm-51x35in) s.d.77 s.i.d.77 verso acrylic prov.exhib. 26-Aug-3 Christie's, Sydney #409 est:600-800 (A.D 2200)
£1138 $1787 €1661 Untitled, Maclaughlin river (176x132cm-69x52in) s.d.74 prov.exhib. 27-Aug-3 Christie's, Sydney #747 est:800-1000 (A.D 2800)

TELKESSY, Valeria (1870-?) Hungarian
£431 $720 €629 Still life of a bowl of flowers and pot plants (58x78cm-23x31in) s. 20-Oct-3 Stephan Welz, Johannesburg #477 est:3000-5000 (SA.R 5000)

TELLA, Garcia (1906-1938) ?
Works on paper
£336 $628 €500 La mouffe (73x54cm-29x21in) s. i.d.1968 verso mixed media isorel panel. 29-Feb-4 Versailles Encheres #186/R

TELLA, Jose Garcia (1905-1983) Spanish
£282 $454 €400 Untitled (60x50cm-24x20in) s. panel. 11-May-3 Versailles Encheres #151
£2113 $3655 €3000 Street in Paris (50x61cm-20x24in) s. board. 15-Dec-3 Ansorena, Madrid #950/R est:3000
Works on paper
£738 $1306 €1100 Scene Parisienne (44x32cm-17x13in) s.d.950 i.verso W/C Indian ink. 27-Apr-4 Artcurial Briest, Paris #120

TELLANDER, Frederic A (1878-?) American
£528 $950 €771 Venetian scene (53x61cm-21x24in) s. prov. 23-Jan-4 Freeman, Philadelphia #168/R

TELLER, Grif (20th C) American
£449 $750 €656 Autumn landscape with stream (30x41cm-12x16in) s. canvasboard. 20-Jun-3 Freeman, Philadelphia #102/R

TELLES, Sergio (1936-) French?
£336 $601 €500 Quai des Grands-Augustins (30x50cm-12x20in) s. panel. 25-May-4 Chambelland & Giafferi, Paris #32/R
£448 $807 €650 Children on the beach (21x29cm-8x11in) s. cardboard. 26-Jan-4 Durán, Madrid #4/R
£685 $1164 €1000 Boys on the seashore (21x29cm-8x11in) s. cardboard. 4-Nov-3 Ansorena, Madrid #418/R
£1391 $2545 €2100 Courses a Beyrouth (31x51cm-12x20in) s. panel. 7-Apr-4 Piasa, Paris #219 est:1000-1200
£1761 $3046 €2500 Scene de marche (33x41cm-13x16in) s.i.d.1998 panel. 15-Dec-3 Charbonneaux, Paris #205/R est:2000-2500
£2148 $3801 €3200 L'hotel des Francs (42x51cm-17x20in) s. 29-Apr-4 Claude Aguttes, Neuilly #94 est:2300-2500
£2483 $4593 €3600 Mon atelier au Bresil (65x54cm-26x21in) s. s.i.d.1991 verso. 13-Feb-4 Charbonneaux, Paris #98/R est:3000-4000
£2781 $5062 €4200 Ouro Preto (54x73cm-21x29in) s. s.i.d.1991 verso. 18-Jun-4 Charbonneaux, Paris #167/R est:4000-4500

TELLIER, Jean Baptiste Joseph le (fl.1759-1812) French
Miniatures
£1800 $3222 €2628 Marie Claude Morliere, in pink and brown striped dress (6cm-2in circular) ormolu frame beaded border. 25-May-4 Christie's, London #92/R est:600-800

TELLIER, Raymond (1897-1985) French
£292 $525 €426 Figures outside a cathedral (33x41cm-13x16in) s. 23-Jan-4 Freeman, Philadelphia #232/R
£1667 $3067 €2500 Portrait de jeune Africaine (46x38cm-18x15in) cardboard. 14-Jun-4 Gros & Delettrez, Paris #289/R est:2500-3500

TEMINE, Emile (19/20th C) ?
£638 $1066 €900 Personnage dans un ruelle (33x21cm-13x8in) s. 16-Jun-3 Gros & Delettrez, Paris #216/R

TEMMERMAN, Jean Pierre (20th C) Belgian?
Works on paper
£302 $535 €450 Composition (36x47cm-14x19in) mixed media. 27-Apr-4 Campo, Vlaamse Kaai #597
£369 $653 €550 Composition (49x66cm-19x26in) mixed media. 27-Apr-4 Campo, Vlaamse Kaai #598

TEMMINCK, Henrietta Christina (1813-1886) Dutch
£822 $1397 €1200 Interior with two ladies and a man (23x18cm-9x7in) s. 5-Nov-3 Vendue Huis, Gravenhage #137

TEMPE, Wil (1920-) American
£1359 $2500 €2039 Santa Fe Trail (50x61cm-20x24in) canvasboard. 8-Jun-4 Bonhams & Butterfields, San Francisco #4151/R est:3000-5000

TEMPEST, Cyril (19/20th C) British
£375 $600 €548 Sunset sail (36x25cm-14x10in) s. 21-Sep-3 Grogan, Boston #92/R

TEMPEST, Margaret (1892-1982) British
£300 $528 €438 Still life of flowers against a red background (98x78cm-39x31in) s.d.97 board. 18-May-4 Bonhams, Knightsbridge #211/R

TEMPESTA, Antonio (1555-1630) Italian
Works on paper
£900 $1557 €1314 Allegorical figures and angels holding garlands around a cartouche (34x27cm-13x11in) black chk pen brown ink wash. 12-Dec-3 Christie's, Kensington #327/R

TEMPESTA, Antonio (attrib) (1555-1630) Italian
£4467 $8085 €6700 Flora (96x134cm-38x53in) 30-Mar-4 Babuino, Rome #75/R est:4000

TEMPESTINO (17/18th C) Italian
£4161 $7073 €5950 Landscape with stream and village (49x74cm-19x29in) 1-Dec-3 Babuino, Rome #33/R est:3000-4000

TEMPLE, Edwyn (1835-1920) British
Works on paper
£600 $1074 €876 Rakaia Gorge, Takamatu. Akaroa Harbour, New Zealand (24x35cm-9x14in) one init. W/C two. 26-May-4 Sotheby's, Olympia #133/R

TEMPLE, Hans (1857-1931) Austrian

£1690 $2806 €2400 Still life of shells and necklace (43x59cm-17x23in) s. i. verso board. 16-Jun-3 Dorotheum, Vienna #151/R est:2400-2800

TEMPLE, Robert Scott (fl.1874-1900) British

Works on paper

£300 $552 €438 Street scene (22x29cm-9x11in) s. W/C. 23-Jun-4 Bonhams, Bury St Edmunds #350

TEMPLE, Ruth Anderson (1884-1939) American

£452 $800 €660 Still life with flowers (30x25cm-12x10in) s. 2-May-4 Bonhams & Butterfields, San Francisco #1152/R
£806 $1500 €1177 Floral still life in pink and purple (76x91cm-30x36in) s. 5-Mar-4 Skinner, Boston #370/R est:1800-2200
£950 $1700 €1387 Figures with umbrellas on a bridge (20x28cm-8x11in) s. board. 7-May-4 Sloans & Kenyon, Bethesda #1692a/R est:700-900
£960 $1700 €1402 Gladiolas in a vase (36x30cm-14x12in) s. exhib. 2-May-4 Bonhams & Butterfields, San Francisco #1150/R est:2500-3500
£2825 $5000 €4125 Portrait of a young girl (51x41cm-20x16in) s. 2-May-4 Bonhams & Butterfields, San Francisco #1068/R est:800-1200

TEMPLE, Vere (20th C) British

Works on paper

£320 $586 €467 Three bloodhounds (38x32cm-15x13in) pen ink. 7-Apr-4 Woolley & Wallis, Salisbury #95/R

TEMPLETON, John (19th C) British

£943 $1500 €1377 Two women playing a lyre (91x71cm-36x28in) s.d.1860. 13-Sep-3 Selkirks, St. Louis #228 est:500-700

TEMPLIN, Victor (1920-1994) Russian

£280 $504 €420 Under-growth in spring (50x64cm-20x25in) s. 26-Apr-4 Millon & Associes, Paris #101/R
£333 $600 €500 Arbre aux tons pastels (49x64cm-19x25in) s.d.85. 26-Apr-4 Millon & Associes, Paris #98/R
£387 $696 €580 Blue horse (59x79cm-23x31in) s. 26-Apr-4 Millon & Associes, Paris #99/R
£733 $1320 €1100 Under-growth in spring (56x78cm-22x31in) s.d.83. 26-Apr-4 Millon & Associes, Paris #102/R
£1400 $2548 €2044 Flowers in the field (43x58cm-17x23in) s. board painted 1966. 20-Jun-4 Lots Road Auctions, London #384/R est:1000-1500
£2000 $3640 €2920 Red Cardigan (75x51cm-30x20in) s. board painted 1966. 20-Jun-4 Lots Road Auctions, London #371a/R est:1600-2200

TEMPSKY, Major Gustavus Ferdinand von (1828-1868) German

Works on paper

£11348 $20085 €16568 Untitled, Paterangi pa in background (13x22cm-5x9in) init. W/C. 28-Apr-4 Dunbar Sloane, Auckland #17/R est:12000-18000 (NZ.D 32000)
£17021 $30128 €24851 Paterangi (13x22cm-5x9in) s. W/C. 28-Apr-4 Dunbar Sloane, Auckland #16/R est:15000-20000 (NZ.D 48000)

TEN BERGE, Bernardus Gerardus (1825-1875) Dutch

£347 $565 €500 Stable interior with a little girl feeding the chickens (37x47cm-15x19in) s.d.1864. 29-Sep-3 Sotheby's, Amsterdam #29/R
£2083 $3542 €3000 Sheep in landscape (51x69cm-20x27in) s. 28-Oct-3 Dorotheum, Vienna #69/R est:3600-4000

TEN BOSCH, Lena Cornelia (1890-1945) Dutch

£1399 $2336 €2000 Roses in an urn-shaped vase (60x80cm-24x31in) s. 30-Jun-3 Sotheby's, Amsterdam #218/R

TEN CATE, Johannes Marinus (1859-1896) Dutch

£4514 $7538 €6500 Sorting the catch (29x37cm-11x15in) s. panel prov. 21-Oct-3 Sotheby's, Amsterdam #2/R est:3000-5000

Works on paper

£800 $1360 €1168 Children playing in the wood (24x36cm-9x14in) s. W/C. 4-Nov-3 Bonhams, New Bond Street #3/R
£2200 $4070 €3212 Children rescuing a cat trapped in a tree (15x23cm-6x9in) W/C. 9-Mar-4 Bonhams, New Bond Street #11/R est:1000-1500
£4600 $8510 €6716 Children in a snowy landscape (15x24cm-6x9in) W/C. 9-Mar-4 Bonhams, New Bond Street #12/R est:1000-1500

TEN CATE, Pieter (1868-1937) Dutch

£320 $550 €467 Wooded landscape with a stream (30x43cm-12x17in) s. 6-Dec-3 Pook & Pook, Downington #289f
£979 $1664 €1400 Still life with wild roses and jug (25x32cm-10x13in) s. panel. 20-Nov-3 Van Ham, Cologne #1511/R est:1200

TEN CATE, Siebe Johannes (1858-1908) Dutch

£1121 $2062 €1637 Seine landscape (28x42cm-11x17in) s.d.1904 chk. 26-Mar-4 Koller, Zurich #3115/R est:2500-3500 (S.FR 2600)
£2237 $4116 €3400 View of Dordrecht (39x32cm-15x13in) s.i.d.1905. 25-Jun-4 Millon & Associes, Paris #60/R est:3000-4000
£4832 $8553 €7200 Overschie (55x46cm-22x18in) s.d.1903. 30-Apr-4 Tajan, Paris #217/R est:4000-6000

Works on paper

£699 $1168 €1000 Toledo (32x40cm-13x16in) s.d.86 W/C. 13-Oct-3 Horta, Bruxelles #391
£700 $1190 €1022 Lucerne, fireworks from the chateau (30x41cm-12x16in) s.i.d.98 pastel. 5-Nov-3 John Nicholson, Haslemere #490/R
£780 $1303 €1100 Pecheur pres du pont Moret (27x35cm-11x14in) s.i.d.1903 pastel. 19-Jun-3 Millon & Associes, Paris #178/R
£786 $1431 €1148 Lucerne, fireworks from the Chateau (29x40cm-11x16in) s.i.d.98 pastel. 16-Jun-4 Fischer, Luzern #2612/R (S.FR 1800)
£800 $1432 €1200 Mill by river (30x43cm-12x17in) s. pastel. 12-May-4 Brissoneau, France #101/R
£3741 $6697 €5500 Une rue dans un village, un homme marchant avec une canne (26x34cm-10x13in) s.i.d.93 pastel. 18-Mar-4 Christie's, Paris #188/R est:1000-1500

TEN COMPE, Jan (1713-1761) Dutch

£5667 $10143 €8500 Cappricio view of The Hague, with figures along a river and barge (27x37cm-11x15in) s. panel. 17-May-4 Christie's, Amsterdam #107/R est:8000-12000

TEN HOVEN, H (19/20th C) Dutch

£307 $500 €448 Canal scene, Amsterdam (41x30cm-16x12in) s. 27-Sep-3 Charlton Hall, Columbia #671/R
£451 $713 €650 View of the Montelbaanstoren on the Oudeschans, Amsterdam (55x86cm-22x34in) s. 2-Sep-3 Christie's, Amsterdam #250

TEN KATE, Herman (1822-1891) Dutch

£2098 $3503 €3000 The conversation (18x26cm-7x10in) s. panel prov. 30-Jun-3 Sotheby's, Amsterdam #67/R
£3472 $5799 €5000 At the inn (20x26cm-8x10in) s.d.1850 panel. 21-Oct-3 Sotheby's, Amsterdam #20/R est:4000-6000
£4762 $8667 €7000 Humble question (29x41cm-11x16in) s. panel. 3-Feb-4 Christie's, Amsterdam #124/R est:5000-7000
£6759 $11287 €9800 Old Dutch interior with troupe of nobility (38x58cm-15x23in) s. panel. 11-Nov-3 Vendu Notarishuis, Rotterdam #160/R est:10000-15000
£13000 $23920 €18980 Musical evening (65x98cm-26x39in) s. panel. 25-Mar-4 Christie's, Kensington #73/R est:7000-10000
£26389 $44069 €38000 Merry company at the inn (52x77cm-20x30in) s.d.64 panel. 21-Oct-3 Sotheby's, Amsterdam #208/R est:20000-30000

Works on paper

£400 $668 €584 Mending the nets (20x29cm-8x11in) s. W/C. 13-Nov-3 Bonhams, Edinburgh #394
£600 $1002 €876 Soldiers carousing and playing dice in an interior (23x33cm-9x13in) s.d.1861 W/C. 8-Oct-3 Andrew Hartley, Ilkley #1040
£1000 $1810 €1500 Discussion in tavern (12x18cm-5x7in) s.d.1855 W/C. 1-Apr-4 Van Ham, Cologne #1469/R est:1500
£1350 $2471 €2025 Interior scenes with figures (23x33cm-9x13in) s.d. W/C pair. 27-Jul-4 Henry Adams, Chichester #409/R est:1000-1500
£1579 $2858 €2400 Men in dress-coats and drinking figures in an Inn (21x30cm-8x12in) s. W/C prov. 19-Apr-4 Glerum, Amsterdam #93/R est:2000-3000
£1900 $3287 €2774 Artist's studio (21x30cm-8x12in) s.indis.d. W/C. 11-Dec-3 Lyon & Turnbull, Edinburgh #35/R est:1000-1500

TEN KATE, J M (1831-1910) Dutch

£360 $655 €526 Portrait of a Dutch girl (25x20cm-10x8in) bears sig. board. 5-Feb-4 Gorringes, Worthing #461

TEN KATE, Jan Jacob Lodewijk (1850-1929) Dutch

Works on paper

£1353 $2300 €1975 Snowball fight (48x63cm-19x25in) s. W/C gouache on board. 21-Nov-3 Skinner, Boston #240/R est:300-500

TEN KATE, Johan Mari (1831-1910) Dutch

£816 $1461 €1200 In the Kampong (33x48cm-13x19in) s. 16-Mar-4 Christie's, Amsterdam #4/R est:1000-1500
£2778 $4639 €4056 Landscape (49x72cm-19x28in) s. 12-Oct-3 Sotheby's, Singapore #44/R est:8000-12000 (S.D 8000)
£5229 $9464 €7634 Village scene (16x23cm-6x9in) s.i.verso. 4-Apr-4 Sotheby's, Singapore #42/R est:7000-9000 (S.D 16000)
£5369 $9933 €8000 Vegetable saleswoman (67x56cm-26x22in) s. 13-Mar-4 De Vuyst, Lokeren #527/R est:8000-10000
£7333 $13200 €11000 Taking care of baby brother (27x37cm-11x15in) s. panel. 20-Apr-4 Sotheby's, Amsterdam #166/R est:10000-15000
£12000 $21600 €18000 Fisherman's family, Marken (59x89cm-23x35in) s. 20-Apr-4 Sotheby's, Amsterdam #180/R est:15000-20000

Works on paper

£559 $962 €800 Enfants a la chasse au lapin (17x24cm-7x9in) W/C. 3-Dec-3 Coutau Begarie, Paris #209/R
£1333 $2400 €2000 Chasing the rabbit (24x35cm-9x14in) s. W/C. 20-Apr-4 Sotheby's, Amsterdam #14/R est:2000-3000
£1389 $2319 €2000 Fisherman bringing in the catch (26x36cm-10x14in) s. W/C. 21-Oct-3 Sotheby's, Amsterdam #49/R est:2000-3000

TEN KATE, Johan Mari (attrib) (1831-1910) Dutch

£350 $595 €511 Dutch canal scene with a figure fishing from a boat (34x51cm-13x20in) s. 19-Nov-3 Tennants, Leyburn #1035/R
£1156 $2070 €1700 Indonesian landscape (48x238cm-19x94in) 16-Mar-4 Christie's, Amsterdam #3a est:800-1200

TEN KLOOSTER, Johannes Frederik Englebert (1873-1940) Dutch

£544 $974 €800 Indonesian river landscape. Beach (54x67cm-21x26in) mono. two prov. 16-Mar-4 Christie's, Amsterdam #80
£1020 $1827 €1500 Tropical beach. Ox cart on the beach (60x20cm-24x8in) mono. panel two prov. 16-Mar-4 Christie's, Amsterdam #76/R est:800-1200

TENCY, Jan-Baptiste (1755-1808) Flemish

£3497 $5944 €5000 Fete dans un village. s.d.1771. 21-Nov-3 Coutau Begarie, Paris #130/R est:6000-8000

TENERANI, Pietro (1789-1869) Italian

Sculpture

£9932 $16884 €14500 Love (92cm-36in) s.verso marble. 8-Nov-3 Finarte, Venice #207/R est:8000-10000

£13423 $24027 €20000 Putto hunting (92cm-36in) s.verso white marble. 27-May-4 Semenzato, Florence #156/R est:8000-10000

TENG NEE CHEONG (1951-) Singaporean

£1242 $2248 €1813 Emerald butterflies with hibiscus (64x79cm-25x31in) s.d.92 s.i.d.verso. 4-Apr-4 Sotheby's, Singapore #188/R est:3800-4800 (S.D 3800)

TENGGREN, Gustaf Adolf (1896-1981) Swedish

£305 $548 €458 Portrait of Grandmother (37x27cm-15x11in) s.d.14. 25-Apr-4 Goteborg Auktionsverk, Sweden #183/R (S.KR 4200)

Works on paper

£268 $483 €402 Eugene (17x11cm-7x4in) s.d.1915 W/C htd white. 25-Apr-4 Goteborg Auktionsverk, Sweden #194/R (S.KR 3700)
£276 $496 €414 Water in grotto (29x22cm-11x9in) s.d.15 W/C. 25-Apr-4 Goteborg Auktionsverk, Sweden #185/R (S.KR 3800)
£290 $522 €435 Pirates attacking (53x32cm-21x13in) s. gouache grisaille. 25-Apr-4 Goteborg Auktionsverk, Sweden #191/R (S.KR 4000)
£363 $653 €545 Interior scene with two figures (29x23cm-11x9in) s. W/C. 25-Apr-4 Goteborg Auktionsverk, Sweden #188/R (S.KR 5000)
£1182 $2128 €1773 Interior scene with armour (68x48cm-27x19in) s.d.1913 W/C. 25-Apr-4 Goteborg Auktionsverk, Sweden #184/R est:8000 (S.KR 16300)
£2248 $4046 €3372 The Pied Piper (32x29cm-13x11in) s.d.1930 W/C. 25-Apr-4 Goteborg Auktionsverk, Sweden #193/R est:10000 (S.KR 31000)
£2308 $3969 €3370 From Among gnomes and trolls (28x22cm-11x9in) s.d.18 W/C. 2-Dec-3 Bukowskis, Stockholm #42/R est:8000-10000 (S.KR 30000)

TENIERS, David (17th C) Flemish

£7447 $12436 €10500 Vue de village anime (34x49cm-13x19in) bears sig. panel. 17-Jun-3 Vanderkindere, Brussels #437 est:3500-5000
£20000 $36800 €30000 Nature morte au gibier (152x183cm-60x72in) mono. 11-Jun-4 Maigret, Paris #44/R est:35000-40000

TENIERS, David (attrib) (17th C) Flemish

£1400 $2534 €2100 Danse villageoise (23x28cm-9x11in) s.d.1672 panel. 5-Apr-4 Deburaux, Boulogne #61 est:1400-1600
£3057 $5563 €4463 The four church fathers, Gregor, Hieronymus, Ambrosius and Augustin (20x26cm-8x10in) panel. 16-Jun-4 Fischer, Luzern #1029/R est:8000-12000 (S.FR 7000)
£4138 $6869 €6000 River landscape with castle and peasants (34x46cm-13x18in) mono. panel prov. 1-Oct-3 Dorotheum, Vienna #34/R est:6000-9000

TENIERS, David (circle) (17th C) Flemish

£7383 $13584 €11000 Alchemists's workshop (73x92cm-29x36in) 24-Mar-4 Dorotheum, Vienna #402/R est:8000-12000
£9607 $16908 €14026 Village festival (83x120cm-33x47in) prov. 22-May-4 Galerie Gloggner, Luzern #101/R est:14000-16000 (S.FR 22000)

TENIERS, David (elder) (1582-1649) Flemish

£26207 $47172 €38000 Landscape with travellers and buildings (107x138cm-42x54in) 26-Jan-4 Ansorena, Madrid #58/R est:30000

TENIERS, David (style) (17th C) Flemish

£38462 $65385 €55000 Sugar factory (149x200cm-59x79in) 21-Nov-3 Coutau Begarie, Paris #131/R est:30000-40000

TENIERS, David (younger) (1610-1690) Flemish

£10000 $18000 €14600 Mystic marriage of Saint Catherine (31x23cm-12x9in) panel after Domenico Fetti prov.lit. 22-Apr-4 Sotheby's, London #52/R est:10000-15000
£32000 $57600 €46720 Pastoral landscape with a washerwoman and a herdsman with cattle and sheep (39x59cm-15x23in) s. panel prov. 21-Apr-4 Christie's, London #10/R est:20000-30000
£34965 $58392 €50000 Men chatting outside inn (19x24cm-7x9in) board. 30-Jun-3 Ansorena, Madrid #179/R
£144737 $266317 €220000 Singerie (15x21cm-6x8in) copper prov. 24-Jun-4 Tajan, Paris #20/R est:80000-100000

TENIERS, David (younger-attrib) (1610-1690) Flemish

£3500 $6055 €5110 Landscape with hunter returning with his game (69x51cm-27x20in) indis.mono. 12-Dec-3 Christie's, Kensington #37/R est:4000-6000
£3846 $6615 €5615 The Flight into Egypt (56x77cm-22x30in) bears mono. copper prov. 2-Dec-3 Bukowskis, Stockholm #381/R est:30000-40000 (S.KR 50000)

Works on paper

£582 $1065 €850 Study for Peasants. Study of female nudes posing (10x15cm-4x6in) i. red chk double-sided. 9-Jun-4 Rasmussen, Copenhagen #2058/R (D.KR 6500)

TENIERS, David (younger-circle) (1610-1690) Flemish

£7784 $13000 €11365 Interior with monkeys seated around a table, others in the background (25x34cm-10x13in) copper prov. 7-Oct-3 Sotheby's, New York #56/R est:6000-8000
£11000 $18700 €16060 Tavern interior with monkeys drinking and smoking (24x33cm-9x13in) copper. 31-Oct-3 Christie's, Kensington #38/R est:5000-7000
£13000 $22100 €18980 Figures conversing outside a country house (107x138cm-42x54in) 31-Oct-3 Christie's, Kensington #32/R est:7000-10000

TENIERS, David (younger-style) (1610-1690) Flemish

£6240 $10795 €9110 Village kermesse (71x102cm-28x40in) bears sig. 9-Dec-3 Sotheby's, Olympia #353/R est:3000-5000
£6500 $11895 €9490 Village scene with figures merry making and dancing (36x48cm-14x19in) oil paper on canvas. 6-Jul-4 Sotheby's, Olympia #535/R est:2000-3000
£7500 $13725 €10950 Tavern interior with peasants drinking smoking and merry making (49x64cm-19x25in) panel. 6-Jul-4 Sotheby's, Olympia #536/R est:3000-5000
£9868 $18158 €15000 Singerie (28x37cm-11x15in) bears sig. 24-Jun-4 Christie's, Paris #17/R est:6000-8000

TENIERS, David III (1638-1685) Flemish

£13103 $21752 €19000 Peasant celebrating. s. board. 30-Sep-3 Ansorena, Madrid #53/R est:14000
£18621 $30910 €27000 Ball game (24x33cm-9x13in) s. board. 30-Sep-3 Ansorena, Madrid #52/R est:25000

TENJU, Nakagawa (?-1795) Japanese

Works on paper

£800 $1336 €1168 Landscape with Chinese poem (120x26cm-47x10in) s. ink col pair. 12-Nov-3 Christie's, London #21/R

TENMYOUYA, Hisashi (1966-) Japanese?

£4469 $8000 €6525 Tatoo man's battle (60x41cm-24x16in) acrylic paper on board exhib.lit. 12-May-4 Christie's, Rockefeller NY #301/R est:10000-15000

TENNANT, Dorothy (1855-1926) British

£480 $758 €696 Eve (62x49cm-24x19in) s.d.1883 i.verso. 4-Sep-3 Christie's, Kensington #229/R
£600 $1074 €876 Cupid with two cherubs (25x35cm-10x14in) oil on paper prov. 27-May-4 Christie's, Kensington #322/R
£650 $1164 €949 Nymph with two cherubs (20x15cm-8x6in) mono. i.verso panel prov. 27-May-4 Christie's, Kensington #320/R

TENNANT, John F (1796-1872) British

£300 $474 €435 Rustic travellers around a camp (30x38cm-12x15in) i.verso panel. 27-Jul-3 Desmond Judd, Cranbrook #1037
£500 $850 €730 Looking for the boats (22x16cm-9x6in) s. panel. 27-Nov-3 Morphets, Harrogate #422/R

TENNANT, Stephen (1906-1987) British

Works on paper

£400 $664 €584 Polynesian and Malaysian taya (55x35cm-22x14in) i. W/C. 1-Oct-3 Woolley & Wallis, Salisbury #153/R
£450 $819 €657 Suitor (29x18cm-11x7in) pencil W/C. 1-Jul-4 Christie's, Kensington #12/R

TENNER, Eduard (1830-1901) German

£2292 $3781 €3300 Upper Rhine landscape (87x160cm-34x63in) s. 3-Jul-3 Dr Fritz Nagel, Stuttgart #514/R est:1500

TENNIEL, John (1820-1914) British

Works on paper

£260 $424 €377 Mr Birrell as Gulliver (16x20cm-6x8in) mono. pencil. 23-Sep-3 Bonhams, Knightsbridge #167/R
£350 $602 €511 Saucy Jacks scrap book of drawings on board the yacht Amethyst (16x23cm-6x9in) init.d.1844-1847 pencil album. 3-Dec-3 Christie's, Kensington #261

TENREIRO (?) ?

Sculpture

£4579 $8104 €6869 Tape (21x151cm-8x59in) s.verso painted wood. 27-Apr-4 Bolsa de Arte, Rio de Janeiro #97/R (B.R 25000)

Works on paper

£1282 $2269 €1923 Landscape (37x54cm-15x21in) s. gouache. 27-Apr-4 Bolsa de Arte, Rio de Janeiro #17/R (B.R 7000)
£1648 $3016 €2472 Portrait of a young girl (30x28cm-12x11in) s. graphite col crayon. 6-Jul-4 Bolsa de Arte, Rio de Janeiro #30/R (B.R 9000)

TEPPER, Saul (1899-1987) American

£1337 $2500 €1952 Couple attending to injured man in small boat (76x64cm-30x25in) s.d.1936. 26-Feb-4 Illustration House, New York #175 est:2500-4000
£3892 $6500 €5682 Pilot and civilian lighting up, bags of mail (89x64cm-35x25in) s. 15-Nov-3 Illustration House, New York #157/R est:5000-7000

TEPPING, Jean Marc Benjamin (1803-1871) Swiss

£2262 $3846 €3303 Urnersee with view of Urirotstock (26x20cm-10x8in) s. panel. 19-Nov-3 Fischer, Luzern #1243/R est:3500-5000 (S.FR 5000)
£2500 $4475 €3650 Mountain landscape with lake and sailing boat (28x37cm-11x15in) s. 17-May-4 Beurret, Zurich #12/R est:1500-2000 (S.FR 5800)

TER MEULEN, Frans Pieter (1843-1927) Dutch

£537 $993 €800 Ox drawn cart with peasant woman nearby (35x50cm-14x20in) s. canvas on panel. 15-Mar-4 Sotheby's, Amsterdam #168/R
£1389 $2194 €2000 Sheep grazing (54x81cm-21x32in) s. 2-Sep-3 Christie's, Amsterdam #285 est:1200-1600
£2121 $3648 €3097 Sheep grazing in a sunny meadow (68x105cm-27x41in) s. prov. 2-Dec-3 Ritchie, Toronto #121/R est:6000-8000 (C.D 4750)

Works on paper

£340 $569 €480 In the sheep pen (20x15cm-8x6in) s. gouache. 20-Oct-3 Glerum, Amsterdam #37
£847 $1500 €1237 Sheep grazing in a thicket (41x56cm-16x22in) s. pencil W/C. 2-May-4 Bonhams & Butterfields, San Francisco #1035/R est:1000-1500

TERA, Teppo (1935-) Finnish

£2838 $5080 €4200 Pair of capercaillies (50x60cm-20x24in) s.d.73. 8-May-4 Bukowskis, Helsinki #167/R est:5000-6000
£7692 $13077 €11000 Winter landscape with grouse (80x95cm-31x37in) s.d.78. 29-Nov-3 Bukowskis, Helsinki #149/R est:10000-12000

TERAOKA, Masami (1936-) American
Prints
£1648 $3000 €2406 Kunisada eclipsed (66x116cm-26x46in) s.d.1993 num.14/30 woodcut etching. 29-Jun-4 Sotheby's, New York #648/R est:2500-3500
Works on paper
£424 $750 €619 Study for Tampon Series, self portrait (16x9cm-6x4in) i.d.1982 pencil tracing paper. 2-May-4 Bonhams & Butterfields, Los Angeles #3060/R

TERBORCH, Gerard (1617-1681) Dutch
£48276 $80621 €70000 Portrait of man (66x49cm-26x19in) prov.lit. 15-Nov-3 Lempertz, Koln #1154/R est:65000-70000
£52448 $90210 €75000 Couple in an interior served by a page (67x56cm-26x22in) prov.lit. 2-Dec-3 Christie's, Paris #717/R est:10000-15000

TERBORCH, Gerard (attrib) (1617-1681) Dutch
£479 $800 €699 Portrait of man in blue (25x23cm-10x9in) copper. 19-Oct-3 Susanin's, Chicago #6038/R
Works on paper
£662 $1205 €1000 Portrait of a young woman (24x17cm-9x7in) sanguine. 18-Jun-4 Bolland & Marotz, Bremen #473/R

TERBRUGGHEN, Hendrick (attrib) (1588-1629) Dutch
£5000 $8500 €7300 Laughing bravo with a bass viol and roemer (48x34cm-19x13in) 31-Oct-3 Christie's, Kensington #23/R est:2000-4000
Works on paper
£4167 $7500 €6084 Study of the head of a smiling girl (19x16cm-7x6in) black red chk htd white prov. 21-Jan-4 Sotheby's, New York #69/R est:5000-7000

TERBRUGGHEN, Hendrick (style) (1588-1629) Dutch
£23364 $36916 €33878 Card players (102x118cm-40x46in) 2-Sep-3 Rasmussen, Copenhagen #1588/R est:30000-50000 (D.KR 250000)

TERECHKOVITCH, Costia (1902-1978) French
£590 $950 €861 Circus couple (61x47cm-24x19in) s. pastel W/C chl. 17-Aug-3 Bonhams & Butterfields, San Francisco #5832
£699 $1168 €1000 Still life (27x35cm-11x14in) s. board. 11-Oct-3 De Vuyst, Lokeren #348
£933 $1671 €1400 Les poissons de Belle Ile (33x65cm-13x26in) d.36 isorel. 16-May-4 Osenat, Fontainebleau #116/R
£1379 $2483 €2000 Vase de fleurs sur fond rouge (35x27cm-14x11in) s. 25-Jan-4 Chayette & Cheval, Paris #212 est:600-800
£1549 $2494 €2200 Ballerine (49x23cm-19x9in) s. cardboard. 22-Aug-3 Deauville, France #111/R est:2000-2500
£2177 $3897 €3200 Bas noirs (36x18cm-14x7in) s. board. 19-Mar-4 Millon & Associes, Paris #75/R est:500-800
£2586 $4629 €3776 Woman and boy at window (81x60cm-32x24in) s.d.33. 13-May-4 Stuker, Bern #344/R est:6000-8000 (S.FR 6000)
£2980 $5424 €4500 Fillette en rouge (27x16cm-11x6in) s. cardboard. 15-Jun-4 Rossini, Paris #84/R est:1500-2500
£3169 $5102 €4500 Femme au chapeau (73x54cm-29x21in) s. prov. 22-Aug-3 Deauville, France #110/R est:4500-5000
£3200 $5792 €4672 Femme au chapeau (65x54cm-26x21in) s. 1-Apr-4 Christie's, Kensington #130/R est:2500-3500
£3356 $6275 €5000 Paysage au bord de l'eau (60x79cm-24x31in) s.d.1929 prov. 29-Feb-4 Versailles Encheres #188/R est:6000-8000
£3448 $6172 €5034 Le homard (60x81cm-24x32in) s. 12-May-4 Dobiaschofsky, Bern #1017/R est:9500 (S.FR 8000)
£3800 $6346 €5548 Still life with flowers (65x50cm-26x20in) s. paper on canvas prov. 22-Oct-3 Sotheby's, Olympia #123/R est:2500-3500
£5000 $8950 €7500 La fille de l'artiste dans le parc (52x72cm-20x28in) 16-May-4 Osenat, Fontainebleau #117/R est:8000-10000
£6000 $10200 €8760 Ladies on the terrace (54x75cm-21x30in) s. 19-Nov-3 Sotheby's, London #227/R est:6000-8000
Works on paper
£336 $621 €500 Jeune femme au chapeau (62x47cm-24x19in) s.d.1927 graphite exhib. 15-Mar-4 Claude Boisgirard, Paris #112
£446 $746 €647 La jeune fille (34x26cm-13x10in) s.d.1952 W/C. 17-Jun-3 Pinneys, Montreal #52 est:900-1200 (C.D 1000)
£850 $1521 €1241 Dushetchka by Chekhov (36x28cm-14x11in) i.d.1962 W/C over pencil sold with two others. 26-May-4 Sotheby's, Olympia #441/R est:800-1200
£1074 $1997 €1600 Femme accoudee (60x38cm-24x15in) s. gouache. 3-Mar-4 Tajan, Paris #120 est:1500-2000
£1408 $2268 €2000 Femme au bibi (61x45cm-24x18in) s.d.1930 W/C gouache. 22-Aug-3 Deauville, France #22 est:2000-2500
£1604 $3000 €2342 Personnages de cirque (61x47cm-24x19in) s. pastel pencil. 25-Feb-4 Christie's, Rockefeller NY #81/R est:2500-3500
£1879 $3495 €2800 Hammamet, Tunisie (53x40cm-21x16in) s.i.d.1959 W/C gouache. 3-Mar-4 Tajan, Paris #119/R est:1000-1200
£1974 $3632 €3000 Jeune fille au chapeau (63x50cm-25x20in) s. W/C prov. 22-Jun-4 Ribeyre & Baron, Paris #62/R est:1000-1200

TERESZCZUK, P (20th C) Austrian
Sculpture
£2667 $4773 €4000 Woman with umbrella (54cm-21in) s. bronze ivory. 13-May-4 Dorotheum, Linz #332/R est:1600-2000

TERLIKOWSKI, Vladimir de (1873-1951) Polish
£596 $1085 €900 Paysage aux peupliers (27x34cm-11x13in) s. panel. 16-Jun-4 Claude Boisgirard, Paris #158
£604 $1124 €900 Portrait de Marie-Lucie a la blouse rose (46x38cm-18x15in) s.d.1930. 3-Mar-4 Tajan, Paris #122
£671 $1248 €1000 Cypres (46x61cm-18x24in) s.d.29. 3-Mar-4 Tajan, Paris #121
£724 $1202 €1050 Nature morte aux fleurs (54x66cm-21x26in) s. 1-Oct-3 Millon & Associes, Paris #154/R
£724 $1209 €1050 Jeune fille brune (46x38cm-18x15in) s.indis.d.1917. 17-Nov-3 Claude Boisgirard, Paris #93/R
£855 $1574 €1300 Bouquet de fleurs (55x38cm-22x15in) s.d.1938. 23-Jun-4 Maigret, Paris #24
£1074 $1987 €1600 Village en Auvergne (33x41cm-13x16in) s.d.1913. 15-Mar-4 Claude Boisgirard, Paris #114 est:800-1000
£1611 $2980 €2400 Jardin (60x73cm-24x29in) s.d.1911. 15-Mar-4 Claude Boisgirard, Paris #113/R est:2500-3000
£1724 $2879 €2500 Bouquet de fleurs (61x46cm-24x18in) s.d. 17-Nov-3 Claude Boisgirard, Paris #95/R est:2500-3000
£1748 $2920 €2500 Vase de fleurs (65x54cm-26x21in) s. 29-Jun-3 Eric Pillon, Calais #180/R
£2138 $3570 €3100 Bateaux dans la lagune (54x73cm-21x29in) s.indis.d.1933. 17-Nov-3 Claude Boisgirard, Paris #100/R est:2500-3000
£2483 $4594 €3700 Bouquet de roses (54x65cm-21x26in) s. 15-Mar-4 Claude Boisgirard, Paris #115/R est:2500-3000
£2621 $4377 €3800 Paysage. Un village (55x65cm-22x26in) s.d.1925 double-sided. 17-Nov-3 Claude Boisgirard, Paris #96 est:3000-4000
£2819 $5215 €4200 Vase de roses (60x91cm-24x36in) s. 14-Mar-4 Eric Pillon, Calais #173/R
£2828 $4722 €4100 Pont St Michel (54x73cm-21x29in) s.d.1933. 17-Nov-3 Claude Boisgirard, Paris #94/R est:3500-4000
£5000 $8350 €7300 Masks (129x160cm-51x63in) s.d.20. 22-Oct-3 Sotheby's, Olympia #124/R est:6000-8000

TERLOUW, Kees (1890-1948) Dutch
£273 $500 €399 Canal Holland (50x72cm-20x28in) s. board. 10-Jul-4 Auctions by the Bay, Alameda #414/R
£333 $613 €500 Riviere a travers un village des Flandres (50x100cm-20x39in) s. 14-Jun-4 Tajan, Paris #71
£380 $680 €555 Barges on a Dutch canal, with bridge in distance (48x60cm-19x24in) indis sig.i. 16-Mar-4 Gildings, Market Harborough #451/R
£400 $680 €584 Evening river landscape, boats moored beside a cottage (25x33cm-10x13in) s. 5-Nov-3 John Nicholson, Haslemere #551
£420 $722 €600 Autumn's reflections by the waterfall (60x120cm-24x47in) s. triplex. 7-Dec-3 Sotheby's, Amsterdam #610
£616 $1048 €900 Still life with roses (39x58cm-15x23in) s. 5-Nov-3 Vendue Huis, Gravenhage #218
£671 $1235 €1000 Automne au bois de vincennes (65x81cm-26x32in) s. 28-Mar-4 Anaf, Lyon #267/R
£671 $1235 €1000 Riviere en automne, foret de Prinsenhage, Brabant (65x81cm-26x32in) s. 28-Mar-4 Anaf, Lyon #268
£699 $1202 €1000 Interieur Flamand (52x82cm-20x32in) s. panel. 3-Dec-3 Tajan, Paris #371
£828 $1382 €1200 Still life of flowers with roses (59x79cm-23x31in) s. 11-Nov-3 Vendu Notarishuis, Rotterdam #153/R
£952 $1733 €1400 Moored barges at dusk. Dahlia in a vase (33x41cm-13x16in) s. two. 3-Feb-4 Christie's, Amsterdam #295 est:600-800
£1538 $2646 €2200 Bouquet de fleurs dans un cuivre (65x99cm-26x39in) s. 3-Dec-3 Tajan, Paris #370 est:2000-3000

TERNI, A L (?) Italian
£851 $1523 €1242 Mountain landscape with figures, horse and cart, Italy (69x106cm-27x42in) s. 12-Jan-4 Rasmussen, Vejle #456/R (D.KR 9000)
£1333 $2453 €2000 View of Lake Garda (67x103cm-26x41in) s. canvas on board. 10-Jun-4 Christie's, Rome #159/R est:2200-2500

TERNO, Nina (1935-) Finnish
Sculpture
£2095 $3749 €3100 The last shirt (60cm-24in) s. bronze. 8-May-4 Bukowskis, Helsinki #221/R est:1500-1800
£2973 $5322 €4400 Baesse (34cm-13in) s.d.1988 bronze. 8-May-4 Bukowskis, Helsinki #223/R est:4000-5000

TERNUS, Aubert (19th C) French?
£9800 $15484 €14308 Full length portrait of Emperor Napoleon III in ceremonial uniform (224x157cm-88x62in) s. 27-Apr-3 Wilkinson, Doncaster #287/R

TERPENING, Sonya (1954-) American
£3352 $6000 €4894 View from the top (61x76cm-24x30in) 15-May-4 Altermann Galleries, Santa Fe #156/R

TERPNING, Howard A (1927-) American
£1955 $3500 €2854 Hunter taking aim at rabbit, dog ready to retrieve (38x53cm-15x21in) s. board. 15-May-4 Illustration House, New York #10/R est:2000-3000
£69519 $130000 €101498 Winter blanket (76x61cm-30x24in) s. 24-Jul-4 Coeur d'Alene, Hayden #208/R est:100000-200000
£106952 $200000 €156150 Shoshone visitors (71x81cm-28x32in) s. prov.exhib.lit. 24-Jul-4 Coeur d'Alene, Hayden #180/R est:200000-300000
£149733 $280000 €218610 Crows in Yellowstone (112x81cm-44x32in) s. prov.exhib. 24-Jul-4 Coeur d'Alene, Hayden #133/R est:250000-350000
£156012 $265220 €227778 Cooling off the hard way (84x112cm-33x44in) 1-Nov-3 Altermann Galleries, Santa Fe #88
Works on paper
£5080 $9500 €7417 Choppy waters (46x56cm-18x22in) s. gouache on board. 24-Jul-4 Coeur d'Alene, Hayden #271/R est:6000-9000
£8939 $16000 €13051 Indian portrait (30x23cm-12x9in) mixed media. 15-May-4 Altermann Galleries, Santa Fe #42a/R
£117647 $220000 €171765 Guardians (71x74cm-28x29in) s. gouache. 24-Jul-4 Coeur d'Alene, Hayden #46/R est:150000-250000

TERRAIRE, Clovis (19/20th C) French
£333 $607 €500 Cows out at pasture in the Alps (38x55cm-15x22in) s. 1-Jul-4 Van Ham, Cologne #1639/R
£387 $643 €550 Paysage a Laffrey, Isere (46x61cm-18x24in) s. panel. 10-Jun-3 Renaud, Paris #31/R
£845 $1403 €1200 Calanques (33x46cm-13x18in) s. 15-Jun-3 Peron, Melun #116

TERRELL, Terry (20th C) American

£333 $600 €486 Abstract tree (20x13cm-8x5in) oil on paper. 24-Apr-4 Slotin Folk Art, Buford #499/R
£556 $1000 €812 Imaginary portrait 2002 (43x46cm-17x18in) board. 24-Apr-4 Slotin Folk Art, Buford #497/R est:1000-1500
£556 $1000 €812 Boy's face (18x13cm-7x5in) oil on paper. 24-Apr-4 Slotin Folk Art, Buford #498/R est:500-800

TERRINI, Alberto (?) Italian?

£550 $919 €803 Venetian canal scene (31x41cm-12x16in) s. board. 7-Oct-3 Bonhams, Knightsbridge #128/R

TERRIS, Adolphe (1820-1900) French

Photographs
£1958 $3270 €2800 Etude d'elements (29x37cm-11x15in) cyanotype exec.c.1865. 10-Oct-3 Tajan, Paris #163/R est:3000-3500
£2448 $4088 €3500 Etude de modeles (30x37cm-12x15in) cyanotype exec.c.1865. 10-Oct-3 Tajan, Paris #176/R est:4500-6000
£3497 $5840 €5000 Etudes de modeles (28x37cm-11x15in) cyanotypes pair exec.c.1865. 10-Oct-3 Tajan, Paris #162/R est:5000-6000
£7343 $12263 €10500 Etude de vestiges antiques (31x38cm-12x15in) cyanotype exec.c.1865. 10-Oct-3 Tajan, Paris #167/R est:4500-5500

TERRIS, John (1865-1914) British

Works on paper
£311 $557 €454 Village people waiting for the boats (29x44cm-11x17in) s. W/C. 11-May-4 Watson's, Christchurch #31/R (NZ.D 900)
£360 $634 €526 Continental town scene (54x38cm-21x15in) s. W/C. 20-May-4 Bonhams, Edinburgh #364
£550 $919 €803 Old Rouen, France (74x49cm-29x19in) s. W/C exhib. 16-Oct-3 Bonhams, Edinburgh #163

TERRUELLA, Joaquim (1891-1957) Spanish

£408 $731 €600 Bull in the field (18x33cm-7x13in) s. board. 22-Mar-4 Durán, Madrid #589/R
£1074 $1997 €1600 Boats on the coast (17x20cm-7x8in) s. cardboard. 2-Mar-4 Ansorena, Madrid #125/R est:1200
£1418 $2298 €2000 Pase taurino (36x44cm-14x17in) s. 20-May-3 Ansorena, Madrid #206/R est:900
£1573 $2628 €2250 Beached boats (27x35cm-11x14in) s. board. 30-Jun-3 Ansorena, Madrid #232/R
£2013 $3745 €3000 Toreador (39x55cm-15x22in) s. 2-Mar-4 Ansorena, Madrid #42/R est:3000
£2535 $4386 €3600 Vicente Barrera toreador (54x65cm-21x26in) s.d.1932. 15-Dec-3 Ansorena, Madrid #346/R est:3600
£6972 $12061 €9900 Beach scene (24x27cm-9x11in) s. board. 15-Dec-3 Ansorena, Madrid #49/R est:4500
£7047 $13107 €10500 Landscape (35x35cm-14x14in) s. cardboard. 2-Mar-4 Ansorena, Madrid #70/R est:9650
£8310 $14376 €11800 Beached boats (46x55cm-18x22in) s. 15-Dec-3 Ansorena, Madrid #42/R est:10800
£11034 $19862 €16000 Beach scene (46x54cm-18x21in) s. 26-Jan-4 Ansorena, Madrid #206/R est:16000
Works on paper
£1342 $2497 €2000 Bull scene (48x58cm-19x23in) s.i. chl lead dr. 2-Mar-4 Ansorena, Madrid #323/R est:1500

TERRUSO, Saverio (1939-2003) Italian

£342 $582 €500 Figures (50x70cm-20x28in) s. tempera over serigraph. 7-Nov-3 Galleria Rosenberg, Milan #141/R
£433 $797 €650 From the window (20x20cm-8x8in) s. s.i.d.199 verso. 12-Jun-4 Meeting Art, Vercelli #208/R
£452 $756 €660 Corrida (80x60cm-31x24in) s. 24-Jun-3 Germann, Zurich #1063/R (S.FR 1000)
£517 $864 €750 Musical instruments (20x20cm-8x8in) s. s.i.verso. 13-Nov-3 Galleria Pace, Milan #65/R
£600 $1104 €900 Still life (40x50cm-16x20in) s. s.i.verso board. 12-Jun-4 Meeting Art, Vercelli #212/R
£621 $1037 €900 Night lovers (50x35cm-20x14in) s. s.i.verso acrylic. 13-Nov-3 Galleria Pace, Milan #15/R
£633 $1165 €950 Praying (30x40cm-12x16in) s. 12-Jun-4 Meeting Art, Vercelli #556/R
£667 $1227 €1000 Praying (40x30cm-16x12in) s. s.i.verso board painted 1983. 12-Jun-4 Meeting Art, Vercelli #897
£733 $1349 €1100 Still life with window (26x30cm-10x12in) s. s.verso. 10-Jun-4 Galleria Pace, Milan #144/R
£738 $1366 €1100 Landscape in Romagna (40x50cm-16x20in) s.s.i.verso. 11-Mar-4 Galleria Pace, Milan #15/R
£759 $1267 €1100 Still life with fish (20x30cm-8x12in) s. s.i.verso. 13-Nov-3 Galleria Pace, Milan #28/R
£759 $1267 €1100 At the table (30x20cm-12x8in) s. painted 2002. 13-Nov-3 Galleria Pace, Milan #90/R
£800 $1472 €1200 Trees in Calabria (49x70cm-19x28in) s.d.72 masonite. 8-Jun-4 Finarte Semenzato, Milan #269/R
£800 $1472 €1200 Bar (30x40cm-12x16in) s. s.i.verso. 12-Jun-4 Meeting Art, Vercelli #662/R
£828 $1324 €1200 Composition (40x30cm-16x12in) s. 13-Mar-3 Galleria Pace, Milan #5/R
£915 $1520 €1300 Sicilian landscape (38x50cm-15x20in) s. s.i.d.1980 verso panel. 14-Jun-3 Meeting Art, Vercelli #145/R
£933 $1671 €1400 Procession (50x70cm-20x28in) s. 12-May-4 Stadion, Trieste #702/R
£966 $1612 €1400 Praying (20x30cm-8x12in) s. s.i.verso painted 2001. 13-Nov-3 Galleria Pace, Milan #75/R est:2300
£1014 $1664 €1400 Working (70x50cm-28x20in) s. s.i.verso. 29-May-3 Galleria Pace, Milan #19 est:1700-2200
£1042 $1646 €1500 Stormy nature (72x100cm-28x39in) acrylic paper on canvas painted 1997. 6-Sep-3 Meeting Art, Vercelli #688 est:1500
£1141 $2111 €1700 Praying during procession (40x50cm-16x20in) s.d.1971 tempera cardboard. 11-Mar-4 Galleria Pace, Milan #132/R est:2000-2600
£1208 $2235 €1800 Life tree (50x70cm-20x28in) s. i.d.1999 verso acrylic. 13-Mar-4 Meeting Art, Vercelli #447 est:1000
£1232 $2020 €1700 Still life with plane (40cm-16in circular) s. 29-May-3 Galleria Pace, Milan #75/R est:2600
£1310 $2097 €1900 Lovers (50x60cm-20x24in) s. s.i.verso panel. 13-Mar-3 Galleria Pace, Milan #55/R est:2100-2700
£1477 $2732 €2200 Trees (30x40cm-12x16in) s. s.i.d.1984 verso board. 13-Mar-4 Meeting Art, Vercelli #162 est:750
£1477 $2732 €2200 Towards th evillage (40x60cm-16x24in) s. s.i.verso. 13-Mar-4 Meeting Art, Vercelli #224 est:1000
£1544 $2763 €2300 Harvest (60x80cm-24x31in) s. board. 30-May-4 Meeting Art, Vercelli #69 est:2000
£1611 $2980 €2400 Composition (50x70cm-20x28in) s. 13-Mar-4 Meeting Art, Vercelli #193 est:1500
£1690 $2806 €2400 Still life in a landscape (60x68cm-24x27in) s. panel. 14-Jun-3 Meeting Art, Vercelli #626/R est:2000
£1745 $3228 €2600 Landscape in Sicily (50x70cm-20x28in) s. s.i.verso. 13-Mar-4 Meeting Art, Vercelli #542 est:1500
£1793 $2869 €2600 Strong nature (60x80cm-24x31in) s. s.verso. 13-Mar-3 Galleria Pace, Milan #120/R est:2000-3000
£1800 $3312 €2700 Procession in Monreale (50x80cm-20x31in) s.d.1971 board. 12-Jun-4 Meeting Art, Vercelli #634/R est:2500
£2000 $3680 €3000 At the table (100x80cm-39x31in) s. on vellum. 12-Jun-4 Meeting Art, Vercelli #741/R est:3000
Sculpture
£1074 $1987 €1600 Praying (54cm-21in) s. painted wood. 11-Mar-4 Galleria Pace, Milan #69/R est:1900-2400

TERRY, David (20th C) American

£299 $500 €437 Coming in (30x41cm-12x16in) 18-Oct-3 David Dike, Dallas #237/R

TERRY, Henry (fl.1879-1920) British

Works on paper
£360 $666 €526 Cottage interior with an old woman and a child (30x23cm-12x9in) s. W/C. 11-Mar-4 Duke & Son, Dorchester #96
£600 $978 €876 Top-hatted gentleman at a Church doorway (36x25cm-14x10in) s.i. W/C. 27-Sep-3 Rogers Jones, Clwyd #116
£600 $1110 €876 An old man smoking a clay pipe (25x20cm-10x8in) s.verso W/C. 11-Mar-4 Duke & Son, Dorchester #95
£840 $1378 €1226 Reflections (33x48cm-13x19in) s.d.1891 i.verso W/C. 3-Jun-3 Fellows & Sons, Birmingham #95/R
£1400 $2576 €2044 Studies concentration (19x17cm-7x7in) s.d.1881 W/C. 8-Jun-4 Bonhams, Knightsbridge #11/R est:500-700
£1500 $2790 €2190 Threading the needle, interior scene (43x30cm-17x12in) s. 5-Mar-4 Dee Atkinson & Harrison, Driffield #686/R est:300-500

TERRY, Joseph Alfred (1872-1939) British

£500 $850 €730 Nymphs (44x30cm-17x12in) s. i.verso board. 26-Nov-3 Hamptons Fine Art, Godalming #130
£550 $897 €803 Landscape at sunset with travellers (16x24cm-6x9in) paper. 24-Sep-3 Dreweatt Neate, Newbury #204
£720 $1303 €1051 Evening return home, North Yorkshire (29x34cm-11x13in) s.d.1906. 30-Mar-4 David Duggleby, Scarborough #184/R
£1800 $3330 €2628 Two ladies in an interior (61x51cm-24x20in) s. prov. 11-Mar-4 Christie's, Kensington #25/R est:2000-3000
£3000 $5370 €4380 At the cafe-concert (71x91cm-28x36in) s. prov. 14-May-4 Christie's, Kensington #491/R est:3000-4000
Works on paper
£1700 $2703 €2465 Figures promenading by the sea (28x21cm-11x8in) W/C. 9-Sep-3 David Duggleby, Scarborough #39/R est:1000-1500
£1750 $2783 €2538 Summer at Scarborough (28x21cm-11x8in) W/C. 9-Sep-3 David Duggleby, Scarborough #38/R est:1500-2000

TERSLOSE, A C (?) ?

£397 $734 €580 Cottage interior with old gentleman (53x62cm-21x24in) s.d.1907. 15-Mar-4 Rasmussen, Vejle #422/R (D.KR 4400)

TERTOOLEN, Ellis (1951-) Dutch

Works on paper
£972 $1536 €1400 Little girl (38x27cm-15x11in) s.d.2003 oil distemper panel. 26-Apr-3 Auction Maastricht #100/R

TERUZ (20th C) Brazilian

£5311 $9401 €7967 Seated woman (55x46cm-22x18in) s.d.1962 i.d.verso. 27-Apr-4 Bolsa de Arte, Rio de Janeiro #51/R (B.R 29000)
£7051 $12904 €10577 Children playing (81x100cm-32x39in) s.d.1984 s.i.d.verso. 6-Jul-4 Bolsa de Arte, Rio de Janeiro #133/R (B.R 38500)

TERVAKORPI, Nikolaj (20th C) Finnish

£625 $1044 €900 Good day's hunting (65x108cm-26x43in) s.d.1922. 26-Oct-3 Bukowskis, Helsinki #513/R

TERWESTEN, Augustin (17/18th C) Dutch

£12162 $21770 €18000 Melancholy (67x78cm-26x31in) s. 8-May-4 Hans Stahl, Toestorf #115/R est:18000

TERWESTEN, Matheus (1670-1757) Dutch

£1060 $1928 €1600 Adoration of the Magi (63x54cm-25x21in) s. 16-Jun-4 Dorotheum, Vienna #500/R est:2000-3000
£3593 $6000 €5246 Susanna and the Elders (53x44cm-21x17in) s.d.1719. 7-Oct-3 Sotheby's, New York #54/R est:6000-8000
£5405 $9514 €8000 Ceres holing a silver gilt bowl surrounded by putti (65x55cm-26x22in) s.d.1732 prov. 18-May-4 Sotheby's, Amsterdam #125/R est:8000-12000

TERWEY, Jan Pieter (1883-1965) Dutch
£280 $502 €409 Summer Ligerz on Bielersee (51x69cm-20x27in) s. 12-May-4 Dobiaschofsky, Bern #1018/R (S.FR 650)
£432 $717 €626 Spring in the country (64x45cm-25x18in) s. 13-Jun-3 Zofingen, Switzerland #3056 (S.FR 950)
£455 $755 €660 Bielersee with St Peterinsel (39x78cm-15x31in) s. 13-Jun-3 Zofingen, Switzerland #3055 (S.FR 1000)

TERZI, Aleardo (1870-1943) Italian
£16779 $31376 €25000 Female nude (71x52cm-28x20in) init.d.1919 prov.exhib.lit. 25-Feb-4 Porro, Milan #37/R est:22000-25000
Works on paper
£671 $1201 €1000 Study for toiletry line (50x30cm-20x12in) init.d.1905 Chinese ink W/C. 25-May-4 Sotheby's, Milan #21/R

TERZIC, Mario (1945-) Austrian
Works on paper
£267 $480 €400 On the search for lost culture (68x98cm-27x39in) s.i.d.Marz 84 pencil col pen W/C. 21-Apr-4 Dorotheum, Vienna #289/R

TESA, Gioseppe (?) Italian
£645 $1097 €942 Venetian scene (30x46cm-12x18in) s. 10-Nov-3 Rasmussen, Vejle #20/R (D.KR 7000)

TESCHENDORFF, Emil (1833-1894) German
£1258 $2340 €1837 Brother and sister playing on a terrace (125x96cm-49x38in) s.d.1870. 2-Mar-4 Rasmussen, Copenhagen #1539/R est:15000-20000 (D.KR 14000)
£2431 $4010 €3500 Portrait of brother and sister with favourite toys (125x96cm-49x38in) s.d.1870. 3-Jul-3 Dr Fritz Nagel, Stuttgart #524/R est:5900

TESDORPF-EDENS, Ilse (1892-1966) German
£490 $817 €700 Still life of autumn flowers (41x31cm-16x12in) s. panel. 11-Oct-3 Hans Stahl, Hamburg #128/R
£538 $899 €770 Still life with red flowers in vase (41x31cm-16x12in) s. panel. 11-Oct-3 Hans Stahl, Hamburg #127
£596 $1085 €900 Still life with flowers (24x17cm-9x7in) s. i.verso board. 19-Jun-4 Quittenbaum, Hamburg #51/R
£633 $1146 €950 Still life with red and blue anenomes (36x30cm-14x12in) s. board. 3-Apr-4 Hans Stahl, Hamburg #181/R
£734 $1226 €1050 Street and gardens in Hamburg-Nienstedten (39x35cm-15x14in) s. board. 11-Oct-3 Hans Stahl, Hamburg #126/R

TESHIGAHARA, Sofu (1900-1979) Japanese
Works on paper
£2000 $3680 €3000 Getsu-ko (172x387cm-68x152in) st.sig blk ink gold paper six panel folding screen exec. 1970. 9-Jun-4 Christie's, Amsterdam #291/R est:1500-2000
£2000 $3680 €3000 Untitled (172x387cm-68x152in) st.sig. blk ink gold paper six panel folding screen. 9-Jun-4 Christie's, Amsterdam #295/R est:1800-2200
£2667 $4907 €4000 Untitled (172x375cm-68x148in) st.sig. blk ink gold leaf six panel folding screen. 9-Jun-4 Christie's, Amsterdam #292/R est:1800-2200

TESI, Mauro Antonio (1730-1766) Italian
Works on paper
£350 $594 €500 Sketch for altar canopy (32x37cm-13x15in) pen. 28-Nov-3 Bassenge, Berlin #6059

TESI, Mauro Antonio (attrib) (1730-1766) Italian
Works on paper
£410 $750 €599 Design for a pitcher (24x13cm-9x5in) pen brown ink col wash. 29-Jan-4 Swann Galleries, New York #133/R

TESKEY, Donald (20th C) Irish?
£2937 $4993 €4200 Waste ground (30x30cm-12x12in) s. s.i.d.2002 verso prov. 18-Nov-3 Whyte's, Dublin #76/R est:3000-4000
£3691 $6534 €5500 Broken gate (29x39cm-11x15in) s. canvas on board. 27-Apr-4 Whyte's, Dublin #36/R est:4000-5000
£4189 $7918 €6200 Grand Canal place II (30x38cm-12x15in) s. i.d.1998 verso prov. 17-Feb-4 Whyte's, Dublin #40/R est:3000-4000
£4336 $7371 €6200 Figure on a path (51x38cm-20x15in) s.d.95 oil on paper. 25-Nov-3 De Veres Art Auctions, Dublin #146/R est:2500-3500
£6081 $11493 €9000 Street shadows, Ship Street (60x76cm-24x30in) s.i.d.2001. 17-Feb-4 Whyte's, Dublin #69/R est:10000-12000
£7832 $13315 €11200 Fruit market, early morning (109x122cm-43x48in) s.i.verso. 25-Nov-3 De Veres Art Auctions, Dublin #109/R est:9000-12000
£8000 $14480 €12000 Portobello (109x122cm-43x48in) s. exhib. 30-Mar-4 De Veres Art Auctions, Dublin #90/R est:10000-15000

TESSANDORI, Luis (1897-1974) Argentinian
£12849 $23000 €18760 Horses in the fields (117x154cm-46x61in) s.d.36. 4-May-4 Arroyo, Buenos Aires #87/R est:15000

TESSARI, Romolo (1868-?) Italian
£33803 $54423 €48000 Pensieri (110x140cm-43x55in) s.d.96. 8-May-3 Farsetti, Prato #267/R est:55000-65000
Works on paper
£439 $830 €650 Summer in Venice (46x28cm-18x11in) s. W/C. 20-Feb-4 Stadion, Trieste #560/R
£467 $835 €700 Rainy day (44x29cm-17x11in) s. W/C. 12-May-4 Stadion, Trieste #753/R

TESSARI, Vittorio (1860-1947) Italian
£775 $1286 €1100 Signora in interno (30x23cm-12x9in) s. canvas on board. 11-Jun-3 Christie's, Rome #49
£1333 $2387 €2000 Portrait of lady in interior (33x16cm-13x6in) s.d.1884 board. 13-May-4 Babuino, Rome #357/R est:800-1200

TESSIER (?) French
Sculpture
£4605 $8474 €7000 Honore-Gabriel Riqueti (47cm-19in) pat terracotta lit. 23-Jun-4 Sotheby's, Paris #115/R est:6000-8000

TESSIER, O L (?) French
£498 $806 €722 Evening in town with rain (65x92cm-26x36in) s. 4-Aug-3 Rasmussen, Vejle #435/R (D.KR 5200)
£756 $1308 €1104 The Cathedral in Milan at night (65x92cm-26x36in) s. 9-Dec-3 Rasmussen, Copenhagen #1665/R (D.KR 8000)

TESTA, Angelo (20th C) American?
Works on paper
£1676 $3000 €2447 Untitled (74x48cm-29x19in) s.d.1962 W/C board prov. 16-May-4 Wright, Chicago #328/R est:3500-4500

TESTA, Pietro (1611-1650) Italian
£16667 $30000 €24334 Four cardinal virtues appearing to saint Jerome (111x149cm-44x59in) 23-Jan-4 Christie's, Rockefeller NY #126/R est:30000-40000

TESTAS, Willem de Famars (1834-1896) Dutch
Works on paper
£349 $583 €500 The defeat (19x28cm-7x11in) s. W/C. 30-Jun-3 Sotheby's, Amsterdam #300/R
£2378 $4042 €3400 Idylle Orientale (34x25cm-13x10in) s. W/C. 1-Dec-3 Palais de Beaux Arts, Brussels #350/R est:500-700

TESTER, Jefferson (1900-) American
£540 $965 €788 Portrait of a girl with black hair (46x36cm-18x14in) s. oil paper. 16-Mar-4 Matthew's, Oregon #20/R

TESTI, Alfonso (1842-1919) Italian
£1007 $1652 €1400 Street in Florence (38x20cm-15x8in) s. s.i.verso. 10-Jun-3 Pandolfini, Florence #168/R est:1300-1500

TETAR VAN ELVEN (19/20th C) Dutch
£276 $451 €403 Church interior (18x11cm-7x4in) s. panel. 29-Sep-3 Lilla Bukowskis, Stockholm #533 (S.KR 3600)

TETAR VAN ELVEN, Jan Baptist (1805-1889) Dutch
£780 $1303 €1100 Interior of a church (20x15cm-8x6in) s. panel. 20-Oct-3 Glerum, Amsterdam #92/R

TETAR VAN ELVEN, Pierre Henri Theodore (1828-1908) Dutch
£943 $1500 €1377 Town square with figures and fountain (41x51cm-16x20in) 14-Sep-3 Susanin's, Chicago #6111/R est:2000-3000
£2000 $3400 €2920 Arabian bazaar (79x51cm-31x20in) s. 22-Nov-3 New Orleans Auction, New Orleans #660/R est:6000-9000
£2000 $3400 €2920 Arabian street scene (79x51cm-31x20in) s. 22-Nov-3 New Orleans Auction, New Orleans #661/R est:6000-9000
£10667 $19200 €16000 Cappricio view in a Dutch town (43x56cm-17x22in) s. panel. 21-Apr-4 Christie's, Amsterdam #207/R est:7000-9000
Works on paper
£530 $964 €800 Interior of a mosque (36x27cm-14x11in) s.i. W/C. 16-Jun-4 Hugo Ruef, Munich #1133/R

TETE, Maurice Louis (1880-1948) French
Works on paper
£533 $960 €800 Mere a l'enfant. Faune a la flute de pan (61x38cm-24x15in) s. pastel double-sided. 20-Apr-4 Chenu & Scrive, Lyon #159/R

TETMAJER-NAIMSKA, Jadwiga (1891-1975) Polish
£1254 $1956 €1831 Country manor in Bronowicach (66x50cm-26x20in) s. 30-Mar-3 Agra, Warsaw #39/R est:8000 (P.Z 8000)

TETMAYER, Wlodzimierz (1862-1923) Polish
£1873 $3409 €2735 Road and houses (64x43cm-25x17in) s. cardboard painted 1910. 20-Jun-4 Agra, Warsaw #52/R (P.Z 13000)
£8213 $14948 €11991 People seated in a field (70x96cm-28x38in) s. painted 1910. 20-Jun-4 Agra, Warsaw #53/R (P.Z 57000)
£14890 $23229 €21739 Easter in Bronowicach (75x100cm-30x39in) s.d.190. 30-Mar-3 Agra, Warsaw #3/R est:80000 (P.Z 95000)

TETRODE, Willem Danielsz van (16th C) Dutch
Sculpture
£222222 $400000 €324444 Rome or Florence (44cm-17in) bronze lit. 22-Jan-4 Sotheby's, New York #160/R est:200000-300000

TETRODE, Willem Danielsz van (attrib) (16th C) Dutch
Sculpture
£11000 $20130 €16060 Flagellation (25cm-10in) bronze prov.lit. 9-Jul-4 Sotheby's, London #72/R est:10000-15000

TETSIS, Panayiotis (1925-) Greek
£6000 $10740 €8760 Landscape (38x81cm-15x32in) s. 10-May-4 Sotheby's, Olympia #58/R est:6000-8000
£12000 $21480 €17520 Still life (55x84cm-22x33in) s. 10-May-4 Sotheby's, Olympia #59/R est:10000-15000
Works on paper
£7500 $13425 €10950 Still life (62x100cm-24x39in) s. W/C. 10-May-4 Sotheby's, Olympia #35/R est:5000-7000

TETSUGYU (19th C) Japanese
Works on paper
£1100 $1837 €1595 Tsu - insight (27x61cm-11x24in) s. ink hanging scroll. 18-Jun-3 Christie's, London #305/R est:1500-2000

TETTAMANTI, Ampelio (1914-1961) Italian
£333 $613 €500 By the fire (38x55cm-15x22in) s. painted 1954. 8-Jun-4 Finarte Semenzato, Milan #270/R
£400 $736 €600 Helsinki harbour (50x70cm-20x28in) s.d.1955. 12-Jun-4 Meeting Art, Vercelli #264
£570 $1055 €850 Interior (60x80cm-24x31in) s.d.1955 lit. 13-Mar-4 Meeting Art, Vercelli #513

TETZNER, Heinz (1920-) German?
Works on paper
£320 $576 €480 Two gnus (50x73cm-20x29in) s. W/C board. 24-Apr-4 Dr Lehr, Berlin #469/R
£333 $600 €500 Self portrait (71x49cm-28x19in) s.d. W/C board. 24-Apr-4 Dr Lehr, Berlin #470/R

TEUBER, Hermann (1894-1985) German
£1538 $2615 €2200 Still life with pine cone (36x47cm-14x19in) s.d.1964 board exhib. 29-Nov-3 Villa Grisebach, Berlin #259/R est:3000-4000
£2517 $4280 €3600 Still life (60x80cm-24x31in) s.d.1960 s.i.d.5/60 verso panel. 29-Nov-3 Villa Grisebach, Berlin #258/R est:4500-5500

TEUBER, Hermann (attrib) (1894-1985) German
£1467 $2684 €2200 Street in a district of Dresden with figures on either side of the road (52x65cm-20x26in) mono. i.verso. 5-Jun-4 Arnold, Frankfurt #737/R est:600

TEUNINK, Walter (1941-) Belgian
£694 $1160 €1000 Paysage a Wallekauter (70x80cm-28x31in) s. 21-Oct-3 Campo & Campo, Antwerp #294/R

TEVET, Nachum (1946-) Israeli
Sculpture
£3073 $5500 €4487 Still life with strips (55cm-22in) s.i.d.1992 verso acrylic wood exhib. 18-Mar-4 Sotheby's, New York #45/R est:5000-7000

TEW, Helen Louise (?) American?
£317 $575 €463 Clam house, Nauset Harbour (41x30cm-16x12in) s. board. 3-Apr-4 Outer Cape Auctions, Provincetown #15/R

TEW, Justin (1969-) British
£500 $835 €730 View of Venice (49x67cm-19x26in) s. 21-Oct-3 Bonhams, Knightsbridge #141/R
£600 $1110 €876 Santa Maria Della Salute, Venice (62x84cm-24x33in) s. board. 11-Mar-4 Christie's, Kensington #296/R
£650 $1086 €949 Venetian promenade (61x86cm-24x34in) s. oil paper. 16-Oct-3 Christie's, Kensington #435/R
£800 $1480 €1168 Venetian panorama (70x135cm-28x53in) s. 11-Mar-4 Christie's, Kensington #294/R
£850 $1420 €1241 Salute (61x86cm-24x34in) s. oil paper. 16-Oct-3 Christie's, Kensington #436/R

TEWKSBURY, Fanny B Wallace (1852-?) American
Works on paper
£323 $550 €472 Orchard (42x52cm-17x20in) s. W/C. 21-Nov-3 Skinner, Boston #463/R

TEXIER, Richard (1955-) French
£1241 $2297 €1800 Le navire etait blanc (56x46cm-22x18in) s.i.d.1933 verso. 13-Feb-4 Charbonneaux, Paris #88/R est:1500-2000
£1400 $2520 €2100 Terre (54x22cm-21x9in) s.verso mixed media panel. 24-Apr-4 Cornette de St.Cyr, Paris #727/R est:1200-1500
£1771 $2957 €2550 Nord (62x50cm-24x20in) init.d.1990. 25-Oct-3 Cornette de St.Cyr, Paris #821/R est:2000-3000
£2292 $3827 €3300 Petite mecanique celeste (81x65cm-32x26in) s.d.12 novembre 1989 s.i.d.verso oil screenprint. 25-Oct-3 Cornette de St.Cyr, Paris #822/R est:2500-3000
£2400 $4320 €3600 Untitled (130x130cm-51x51in) s.d.1986 verso acrylic. 24-Apr-4 Cornette de St.Cyr, Paris #725 est:3000-4000
Works on paper
£743 $1405 €1100 Trois ou quatre solutions possibles (68x48cm-27x19in) s.i.d.1989 mixed media panel. 21-Feb-4 Cornette de St.Cyr, Paris #411/R
£1316 $2421 €2000 Untitled (73x92cm-29x36in) mono.d.1990 mixed media on canvas. 27-Jun-4 Versailles Encheres #189/R est:2000-2500
£1544 $2825 €2300 Rivage superieur (92x73cm-36x29in) s.d.1997 i. verso mixed media canvas. 7-Jul-4 Artcurial Briest, Paris #354 est:1200-1500
£2000 $3600 €3000 Terra Ionga (100x50cm-39x20in) s.i.d.1996 mixed media on canvas. 24-Apr-4 Cornette de St.Cyr, Paris #726/R est:2500-3000

TEYLER, Johan (1648-?) Dutch
Prints
£2667 $4773 €4000 View of the Amstel from Blue Bridge (39x52cm-15x20in) col etching. 13-May-4 Bassenge, Berlin #5320 est:4500

THACKWRAY, James Vicary (1919-) South African
£299 $509 €437 Cape landscape with labourers and a barn (59x74cm-23x29in) s. 4-Nov-3 Stephan Welz, Johannesburg #303 est:1000-1500 (SA.R 3500)

THADDEUS, Henry Jones (1860-1929) British
£2533 $4535 €3800 Interieur de ferme, la fileuse (43x59cm-17x23in) s.d.1881. 16-May-4 Thierry & Lannon, Brest #187/R est:4000-5000
£3380 $5848 €4800 Portrait of a bearded gentleman (69x54cm-27x21in) s.d.1889. 10-Dec-3 Bonhams & James Adam, Dublin #31/R est:5000-7000
£5800 $10440 €8468 Casbah Gate, Tangier (30x25cm-12x10in) s.d.1884. 21-Jan-4 Sotheby's, Olympia #376/R est:1200-1800

THADEN, Barbara (20th C) ?
£267 $480 €400 Untitled (170x170cm-67x67in) s.i.d.1986 acrylic. 24-Apr-4 Cornette de St.Cyr, Paris #728

THAI NGO (20th C) Vietnamese
£950 $1587 €1387 Movement (90x60cm-35x24in) s.i. 17-Nov-3 Hodgins, Calgary #16/R est:1500-1800 (C.D 2100)

THAIDAY, Ken (snr) (c.1950-) Australian
Sculpture
£1545 $2441 €2256 Trevall, Erub Island, Darnley Island (120x111cm-47x44in) plywood enamel paint metal wire glass exec.c.1993 prov. 28-Jul-3 Sotheby's, Paddington #188/R est:4000-6000 (A.D 3800)
£3320 $6209 €4980 Beizam, shark dance mask (74x53x26cm-29x21x10in) plywood PVC metal enamel paint rope shells feathers exec.c.1990. 26-Jul-4 Sotheby's, Melbourne #299/R est:10000-15000 (A.D 8500)
£4065 $6423 €5935 Beizam, hammerhead shark, headdress (19x92x95cm-7x36x37in) plywood enamel paint metal wire plastic glass bamboo prov. 28-Jul-3 Sotheby's, Paddington #187/R est:10000-15000 (A.D 10000)
£6098 $9634 €8903 Beizam, shark dance mask (73x25x53cm-29x10x21in) plywood pvc metal enamel paint rope glass feathers prov. 28-Jul-3 Sotheby's, Paddington #185/R est:5000-7000 (A.D 15000)

THALASSOUDIS, Jim (1962-) Australian
£992 $1806 €1448 Evening sky at Pelican point (91x198cm-36x78in) s.i.d.2001 gold leaf oil canvas board two prov. 16-Jun-4 Deutscher-Menzies, Melbourne #187/R est:2500-3500 (A.D 2600)

THALINGER, E Oscar (1885-?) American
£756 $1300 €1104 Carnival (56x97cm-22x38in) s. masonite. 7-Dec-3 Susanin's, Chicago #6048/R est:800-1200
£1818 $3200 €2654 Fruit vendor (61x76cm-24x30in) s. board. 22-May-4 Selkirks, St. Louis #663/R est:2000-2500

THALMANN, Peter (1926-) Swiss?
£432 $717 €626 Winter sun (31x40cm-12x16in) mono.d.1974. 13-Jun-3 Zofingen, Switzerland #3057 (S.FR 950)

THAMM, Adolf (1859-1925) German
£490 $842 €700 Figures on the path towards the harbour (30x19cm-12x7in) s. i.verso board. 6-Dec-3 Hans Stahl, Toestorf #63/R
£667 $1207 €1000 Houses by river in southern German town (51x60cm-20x24in) s. 1-Apr-4 Van Ham, Cologne #1667
£1275 $2257 €1900 Dresden (43x33cm-17x13in) s.d.96 board. 28-Apr-4 Schopman, Hamburg #504/R est:1000

THANH VAN (1970-) Vietnamese?
£3623 $5616 €5290 Street scene (80x94cm-31x37in) s.d.2000. 6-Oct-2 Sotheby's, Singapore #107/R est:2500-3500 (S.D 10000)

THANS, Willem (1816-?) Dutch
£2797 $4755 €4000 Trois personnages autour de la bougie dans une auberge (39x27cm-15x11in) s. panel. 18-Nov-3 Vanderkindere, Brussels #36/R est:4000-6000

THAREL, Léon (?-1902) French
Sculpture
£834 $1500 €1218 Idle fiddle (25cm-10in) incised sig. bronze. 24-Jan-4 Skinner, Boston #618 est:800-1200

THARRATS, Juan Jose (1918-2001) Spanish
£452 $769 €660 Composition (28x50cm-11x20in) s. 25-Nov-3 Germann, Zurich #905 (S.FR 1000)

£	$	€	Description
£452	$769	€660	Composition (35x50cm-14x20in) s. prov. 25-Nov-3 Germann, Zurich #906 (S.FR 1000)
£511	$900	€746	Paisaje transfigurado (61x203cm-24x80in) s.i.d.1956 verso. 22-May-4 Selkirks, St. Louis #809
£568	$1000	€829	Ladamalai (112x145cm-44x57in) s. s.i.d.1959-60 verso oil linen. 22-May-4 Selkirks, St. Louis #810
£987	$1816	€1500	Composition (65x81cm-26x32in) s.d.67. 22-Jun-4 Durán, Madrid #59/R est:700
£1193	$2100	€1742	Num 10 astre noir (130x97cm-51x38in) oil linen. 22-May-4 Selkirks, St. Louis #810a/R est:1000-1500
Works on paper			
£483	$801	€700	Shapes (24x35cm-9x14in) s. mixed media cardboard. 1-Oct-3 Ansorena, Madrid #545/R
£590	$962	€850	Formas (23x34cm-9x13in) s. mixed media collage. 16-Jul-3 Durán, Madrid #48/R
£674	$1091	€950	Formas (25x34cm-10x13in) s. mixed media collage. 20-May-3 Ansorena, Madrid #345/R

THARRATS, Juan Vidal (20th C) Spanish

£	$	€	Description
£1479	$2558	€2100	Sur fond rouge (59x72cm-23x28in) s. s.i.d.1959 verso. 14-Dec-3 Versailles Encheres #33/R est:1000-1500

THAUBERGER, David (1948-) Canadian

£	$	€	Description
£543	$907	€793	Rail line (24x50cm-9x20in) s.i.d.2000 acrylic on board. 17-Nov-3 Hodgins, Calgary #300/R est:1000-1250 (C.D 1200)
£600	$1098	€876	Hysham Hardware (43x55cm-17x22in) acrylic letraset painted September 1991. 1-Jun-4 Joyner Waddington, Toronto #316/R (C.D 1500)
£1118	$2001	€1632	Devil's house (109x142cm-43x56in) s.verso acrylic glitter letraset painted 1988 prov. 6-May-4 Heffel, Vancouver #139/R est:2000-3000 (C.D 2750)
£1220	$2183	€1781	Crossroads store (113x144cm-44x57in) s.i.d.1990 verso acrylic glitter letraset prov. 27-May-4 Heffel, Vancouver #54/R est:3000-4000 (C.D 3000)

THAULOW, F (1847-1906) Norwegian

£	$	€	Description
£6405	$11465	€9351	From the outskirts of Cordoba (47x56cm-19x22in) s. 22-Mar-4 Blomqvist, Oslo #347/R est:100000-150000 (N.KR 80000)

THAULOW, Fritz (1847-1906) Norwegian

£	$	€	Description
£1789	$2862	€2594	Village in Correze (45x57cm-18x22in) s. oil sketch exhib. 22-Sep-3 Blomqvist, Lysaker #1299/R est:20000-25000 (N.KR 21000)
£6281	$11242	€9170	Figures on the pier (57x83cm-22x33in) s.d.76. 25-May-4 Grev Wedels Plass, Oslo #63/R est:60000-80000 (N.KR 77000)
£8869	$15876	€12949	Paysage et riviere (47x56cm-19x22in) s. exhib. 25-May-4 Bukowskis, Stockholm #325/R est:150000-200000 (S.KR 120000)
£8889	$16000	€12978	Market place in Dieppe, after a rain storm (66x88cm-26x35in) s. indis d.94. 23-Apr-4 Sotheby's, New York #38/R est:20000-30000
£14324	$26213	€20913	River landscape with whirlpool, France (60x80cm-24x31in) s. painted c.1896 prov. 9-Jun-4 Rasmussen, Copenhagen #1472/R est:150000-250000 (D.KR 160000)
£16260	$29106	€23740	Verona Bridge (74x94cm-29x37in) s. 25-May-4 Bukowskis, Stockholm #328/R est:250000-300000 (S.KR 220000)
£18310	$31676	€26000	La rue de Caumartin a Paris, la nuit (28x47cm-11x19in) s.i. 12-Dec-3 Piasa, Paris #77/R est:22000-25000
£19444	$35000	€28388	Midnight mass (90x117cm-35x46in) s. prov. 23-Apr-4 Sotheby's, New York #39/R est:30000-40000
£22912	$41013	€33452	Autumn landscape with rapids (66x82cm-26x32in) s. 25-May-4 Bukowskis, Stockholm #329/R est:300000-350000 (S.KR 310000)
£26423	$48354	€38578	From the frozen channel near Christiania (93x155cm-37x61in) s.i.d.76 i.stretcher exhib. 7-Jun-4 Blomqvist, Oslo #331/R est:350000-400000 (N.KR 325000)
£30743	$51341	€44885	River running through village, possibly Abbeville (74x59cm-29x23in) s. lit. 13-Oct-3 Blomqvist, Oslo #293/R est:400000-500000 (N.KR 360000)
£32520	$59512	€47479	Landscape from Farsund's jetty (83x144cm-33x57in) s.d.79. 7-Jun-4 Blomqvist, Oslo #344/R est:350000-400000 (N.KR 400000)
£33077	$56892	€48292	French townscene with watercourse (65x81cm-26x32in) s. painted c.1900. 3-Dec-3 AB Stockholms Auktionsverk #2564/R est:500000-600000 (S.KR 430000)
£42000	$76440	€61320	Bord de riviere, vue d'Abbeville (61x73cm-24x29in) s.i.d.94 exhib. 15-Jun-4 Sotheby's, London #347/R est:40000-60000
£55000	$100100	€80300	Winter sun (67x82cm-26x32in) s. canvas on board painted c.1900-01 prov. 15-Jun-4 Sotheby's, London #310/R est:40000-60000
£70000	$127400	€102200	Rowing (54x96cm-21x38in) s.i.d.1892 prov.lit. 15-Jun-4 Sotheby's, London #344/R est:40000-60000
Works on paper			
£301	$550	€439	Summer landscape with stream (20x30cm-8x12in) s. W/C. 7-Jun-4 O'Gallerie, Oregon #781/R
£19444	$35000	€28388	Winter on the Isle of Stord (48x65cm-19x26in) s.d.89 pastel prov.exhib. 22-Apr-4 Christie's, Rockefeller NY #11/R est:40000-60000

THAULOW, Fritz (attrib) (1847-1906) Norwegian

£	$	€	Description
£958	$1600	€1399	Winter river scene (28x44cm-11x17in) bears sig.indis.d.1893. 26-Oct-3 Bonhams & Butterfields, San Francisco #6445/R
£3356	$6242	€5000	Pecheurs a la riviere (55x45cm-22x18in) 3-Mar-4 Ferri, Paris #393/R est:6000-7000

THAXTER, Edward R (?-1881) American

£	$	€	Description
Sculpture			
£1058	$2000	€1545	Young girl (69x48cm-27x19in) s. marble relief wood stand oval. 23-Feb-4 Winter Associates, Plainville #80/R est:1500-2000

THAYER, Abbott H (1849-1921) American

£	$	€	Description
£1061	$1900	€1549	Evergreen (28x33cm-11x13in) s. 8-Jan-4 Doyle, New York #44/R est:1500-2000
£3846	$7000	€5615	Study of a horse (62x51cm-24x20in) s. 4-Feb-4 Christie's, Rockefeller NY #38/R est:200-300

THAYER, Abbott H (attrib) (1849-1921) American

£	$	€	Description
£382	$650	€558	Head of a girl (21x15cm-8x6in) oil on paper. 21-Nov-3 Skinner, Boston #395/R

THAYER, Emma Beach (1850-1924) American

£	$	€	Description
£6358	$11000	€9283	Zinnias (36x30cm-14x12in) s. i.verso board prov. 10-Dec-3 Bonhams & Butterfields, San Francisco #6059/R est:3000-5000

THAYER, Sanford (1820-1880) American

£	$	€	Description
£1387	$2400	€2025	Red box with grapes (20x25cm-8x10in) i.verso board. 13-Dec-3 Weschler, Washington #541

THE TOUT (20th C) British

£	$	€	Description
Works on paper			
£1400	$2590	€2044	Chasing at Lingfield Park (49x71cm-19x28in) s.i.d.1934 pencil pen in, W/C. 10-Mar-4 Sotheby's, Olympia #223/R est:800-1200

THEATRE, Henri (1913-) Belgian

£	$	€	Description
£226	$378	€330	Les Bohemiens (83x103cm-33x41in) s.i. 17-Nov-3 Hodgins, Calgary #402/R (C.D 500)

THEER, Adolf (1811-1868) Austrian

£	$	€	Description
£833	$1392	€1200	Biedermeier woman's portrait (16x10cm-6x4in) s. i. verso gouache ivory lit. 25-Oct-3 Bergmann, Erlangen #917/R

THEER, Albert (1815-1902) Austrian

£	$	€	Description
Works on paper			
£671	$1235	€1000	Young man with moustache and beard (8x6cm-3x2in) s.d.1841 i. verso W/C ivory one of pair. 26-Mar-4 Dorotheum, Vienna #367/R
£2013	$3705	€3000	Young woman wearing black dress (13x10cm-5x4in) s.d.1852. 26-Mar-4 Dorotheum, Vienna #366/R est:1500-2000

THEGERSTROM, Robert (1857-1919) Swedish

£	$	€	Description
£1100	$1969	€1606	Orange sellers, Cairo (65x54cm-26x21in) s.i.d.1888. 18-Mar-4 Christie's, Kensington #648/R est:1000-1500
£1769	$3043	€2583	Soir d'ete, landscape with waterway (114x182cm-45x72in) s.d.1890. 7-Dec-3 Uppsala Auktionskammare, Uppsala #180/R est:12000-15000 (S.KR 23000)
£2692	$4631	€3930	On the shore of the Nile (38x46cm-15x18in) s. exhib.prov. 3-Dec-3 AB Stockholms Auktionsverk #2404/R est:35000-40000 (S.KR 35000)
Works on paper			
£3462	$5954	€5055	The violinist - possibly self portrait (95x75cm-37x30in) s.d.1886 mixed media canvas. 3-Dec-3 AB Stockholms Auktionsverk #2488/R est:50000-60000 (S.KR 45000)
£4000	$7360	€5840	Elegant lady wearing a veil (46x38cm-18x15in) s.i.d.1885 pastel paper on canvas. 23-Mar-4 Bonhams, New Bond Street #28/R est:3000-5000

THEIJ, Yves (20th C) Belgian

£	$	€	Description
£294	$550	€429	Nude in repose (61x74cm-24x29in) s. 25-Feb-4 Doyle, New York #67/R

THEILGAARD, Sophus (1845-1923) Danish

£	$	€	Description
£414	$704	€604	Coastal landscape with children bathing (63x84cm-25x33in) mono.d.1871. 29-Nov-3 Rasmussen, Havnen #3280/R (D.KR 4400)
£733	$1320	€1100	Paysage de campagne, l'ete (53x74cm-21x29in) s.d.14. 20-Apr-4 Chenu & Scrive, Lyon #160/R
£945	$1692	€1380	Coastal landscape with woman knitting and boy at water's edge (63x81cm-25x32in) mono.d.1871. 12-Jan-4 Rasmussen, Vejle #54/R (D.KR 10000)

THEIS, Heinz (1894-) German

£	$	€	Description
£278	$442	€400	Startled horse with peasant (53x72cm-21x28in) s.d.1940. 11-Sep-3 Weidler, Nurnberg #6599

THEK, Paul (1933-) American

£	$	€	Description
£6333	$11337	€9500	Untitled - red and green marks (45x61cm-18x24in) acrylic canvasboard. 15-May-4 Dr Sturies, Dusseldorf #212/R

THELANDER, Par Gunnar (1936-) Swedish

£	$	€	Description
Works on paper			
£806	$1426	€1177	Untitled (55x65cm-22x26in) s. mixed media prov. 27-Apr-4 AB Stockholms Auktionsverk #948/R (S.KR 11000)

THELOT, Antoine Charles (1798-1853) French

£	$	€	Description
£805	$1498	€1200	Portrait of Caroline Schilling of Constatt (36x29cm-14x11in) mono.d.1833. 5-Mar-4 Wendl, Rudolstadt #3883/R

THELWELL, Norman (1923-2004) British

£	$	€	Description
Works on paper			
£275	$492	€402	Racehorse with jockey up after the race with owner (17x14cm-7x6in) s. pen ink. 11-May-4 Dreweatt Neate, Newbury #439/R
£340	$568	€496	Cross country run (18x26cm-7x10in) s. pen ink. 16-Oct-3 Lawrence, Crewkerne #679
£400	$668	€584	Eskimo and dogs (31x26cm-12x10in) s. pen ink wash. 16-Oct-3 Lawrence, Crewkerne #680
£750	$1388	€1095	How many trading stamps did they give you with him? (18x25cm-7x10in) s.s.i. pen ink htd white. 11-Mar-4 Duke & Son, Dorchester #106/R
£1000	$1670	€1460	As much spirit of adventure (18x13cm-7x5in) s.i. pen ink. 16-Oct-3 Lawrence, Crewkerne #698/R
£1100	$1837	€1606	I'm sorry Mrs Chadwick but when your daughter fell, I'm afraid she broke a leg (18x13cm-7x5in) s.i. ink crayon pen. 16-Oct-3 Lawrence, Crewkerne #699

THEOBALD, Renee (1926-) French

£	$	€	Description
£272	$500	€397	Villa in the sun (23x28cm-9x11in) s. 23-Jun-4 Doyle, New York #5072/R

THEODORE, Francois Jean (attrib) (1762-1825) ?
£1000 $1840 €1460 Cattle watering with castle beyond (63x76cm-25x30in) 23-Jun-4 Bonhams, Bury St Edmunds #382/R est:1500-2500

THEODOROPOULOS, Angelos (1889-1965) Greek
£1500 $2685 €2190 Greek landscape (37x51cm-15x20in) s. hardboard. 11-May-4 Bonhams, New Bond Street #72/R est:1500-2000

THEOFILAKTOPOULOS, Makis (1939-) Greek
£4800 $8400 €7008 Space, blue. Space, grey (120x80cm-47x31in) one s.d.82 verso one s.verso pair. 16-Dec-3 Bonhams, New Bond Street #144/R est:4000-6000

THEOTOCOPULI, Jorge Manuel (1578-1631) Spanish
Works on paper
£601 $1100 €877 Martyrdom of St Bartholomew (19x14cm-7x6in) pen brown ink wash. 29-Jan-4 Swann Galleries, New York #342/R

THERIAT, Charles James (1860-1934) American
£3911 $7000 €5710 Hunter in the desert (56x109cm-22x43in) prov. 26-May-4 Doyle, New York #130/R est:6000-8000

THERKILDSEN, Michael (1850-1925) Danish
£537 $983 €784 A white mare (39x52cm-15x20in) init.d.94. 9-Jun-4 Rasmussen, Copenhagen #1708/R (D.KR 6000)
£1797 $3342 €2624 Landscape with horses by fjord (90x126cm-35x50in) init.d.11. 2-Mar-4 Rasmussen, Copenhagen #1298/R est:15000-25000 (D.KR 20000)
£1985 $3434 €2898 Cattle in landscape (52x76cm-20x30in) init. exhib.prov. 9-Dec-3 Rasmussen, Copenhagen #1599/R est:7000-10000 (D.KR 21000)
Prints
£387 $658 €565 Watering the cattle (21x32cm-8x13in) init. 10-Nov-3 Rasmussen, Vejle #539 (D.KR 4200)

THERKILDSEN, Michael (attrib) (1850-1925) Danish
£1109 $1984 €1619 Herderboy with cattle (49x69cm-19x27in) mono.indis.d. 28-May-4 Uppsala Auktionskammare, Uppsala #143/R est:15000-20000 (S.KR 15000)

THERMIGNON, Carlo (1857-1938) Italian
£952 $1705 €1400 View of Usseglio with figures (41x18cm-16x7in) s. cardboard. 22-Mar-4 Sant Agostino, Torino #191/R

THERRATS, Joan (1947-) American?
£722 $1300 €1054 Abstraction (51x99cm-20x39in) 24-Apr-4 Du Mouchelle, Detroit #3290/R est:500-800

THERRIEN, Robert (1947-) American
Sculpture
£20950 $37500 €30587 Cathedral (244x65x10cm-96x26x4in) painted wood prov. 13-May-4 Sotheby's, New York #181/R est:40000-60000
Works on paper
£528 $924 €750 Untitled (48x35cm-19x14in) crayon pasted paper prov. 18-Dec-3 Cornette de St.Cyr, Paris #96/R

THERULON, F Z (19th C) French
£2800 $4480 €4088 Summer's afternoon (124x89cm-49x35in) s. 18-Sep-3 Christie's, Kensington #153/R est:3000-5000

THESONNIER, Alfred (20th C) French
£230 $375 €336 Still life with cheese, salami, bread (55x46cm-22x18in) s. 28-Sep-3 Bonhams & Butterfields, Los Angeles #7029

THEURILLAT, Herbert Léon (1896-1987) Swiss
£388 $694 €566 Street (101x91cm-40x36in) s. 13-May-4 Stuker, Bern #346 (S.FR 900)
£570 $952 €832 La pluie (54x65cm-21x26in) s. 16-Nov-3 Koller, Geneva #1242 (S.FR 1300)

THEVENET, Louis (1874-1930) Belgian
£350 $594 €500 Coin de riviere (30x35cm-12x14in) s. 18-Nov-3 Galerie Moderne, Brussels #649/R
£350 $584 €500 Cafetiere sur une table (26x38cm-10x15in) s.d.1925 verso cardboard. 7-Oct-3 Palais de Beaux Arts, Brussels #588
£417 $696 €600 Nature morte a l'estampe. s. w. 21-Oct-3 Galerie Moderne, Brussels #456
£927 $1687 €1400 Interieur a Nieuport (34x30cm-13x12in) s.d.1930. 15-Jun-4 Vanderkindere, Brussels #36
£1000 $1790 €1500 Nature morte (40x30cm-16x12in) s.d.1930. 15-May-4 De Vuyst, Lokeren #328/R est:1500-1800
£1076 $1711 €1550 Chapeau de paille (22x27cm-9x11in) s.d.1920 panel. 9-Sep-3 Vanderkindere, Brussels #78
£1972 $3411 €2800 De leuvense stoof (37x31cm-15x12in) s.d.1921 prov.exhib. 13-Dec-3 De Vuyst, Lokeren #311/R est:3000-4000
£2027 $3831 €3000 Moules frites (32x46cm-13x18in) s. 17-Feb-4 Galerie Moderne, Brussels #257/R est:2000-3000
£3020 $5346 €4500 Interieur (50x60cm-20x24in) s.d.1926. 27-Apr-4 Campo, Vlaamse Kaai #599 est:3000-3500
£4196 $7007 €6000 Dans le jardin (46x55cm-18x22in) s.d.1908. 11-Oct-3 De Vuyst, Lokeren #438/R
£5000 $8950 €7500 Still life with shell fish (60x70cm-24x28in) s.d.1919 mono.verso prov.exhib. 15-May-4 De Vuyst, Lokeren #562/R est:6500-7500
£5315 $8876 €7600 Composition a la commode et au voiloncelle (47x37cm-19x15in) s.d.1919 mono.verso. 13-Oct-3 Horta, Bruxelles #129 est:8000-12000
£7237 $13099 €11000 L'interieur du Cheval Blanc a Hal (70x61cm-28x24in) s.d.1928 mono.verso. 19-Apr-4 Horta, Bruxelles #112/R est:12000-15000
£7333 $13127 €11000 Interior with sleeping cat, an early summer morning (70x61cm-28x24in) s.d.1928 exhib. 15-May-4 De Vuyst, Lokeren #470/R est:13000-15000
£8054 $14899 €12000 Interior of The Greve (70x60cm-28x24in) s.d.1920 exhib.lit. 13-Mar-4 De Vuyst, Lokeren #547/R est:12500-15000

THEVENET, Pierre (1870-1937) Belgian
£331 $603 €500 Avant l'orage (21x26cm-8x10in) s. cardboard. 21-Jun-4 Bernaerts, Antwerp #455
£350 $594 €500 Paris, Quai Bonte (22x26cm-9x10in) s. panel. 18-Nov-3 Galerie Moderne, Brussels #690
£436 $772 €650 Serres sur fond de village (37x48cm-15x19in) s. 27-Apr-4 Campo, Vlaamse Kaai #600
£490 $832 €700 Paris, Tour Saint-Severin (23x27cm-9x11in) s. cardboard. 18-Nov-3 Galerie Moderne, Brussels #830/R
£2113 $3655 €3000 Menton, vu des hauteurs du cap Martin (50x61cm-20x24in) s. s.i.verso. 13-Dec-3 De Vuyst, Lokeren #312/R est:2400-2800
Works on paper
£367 $664 €550 La Meuse a Anseremme (45x65cm-18x26in) s. mixed media. 30-Mar-4 Palais de Beaux Arts, Brussels #700

THEVENIN, Henri (?) French
Works on paper
£251 $475 €366 Pointers in a landscape (15x23cm-6x9in) s. W/C. 21-Feb-4 Jeffery Burchard, Florida #10a/R

THEVENOT, Adrien (20th C) French
£3617 $6040 €5100 Femme nue au drape blanc assise sur la plage (81x65cm-32x26in) s. 19-Oct-3 Peron, Melun #339
£4043 $6751 €5700 Paris et oehone (163x131cm-64x52in) s. 19-Oct-3 Peron, Melun #336
Works on paper
£799 $1318 €1150 Jeune femme assise (100x80cm-39x31in) pastel. 1-Jul-3 Lemoine & Ferrando, Paris #66

THEYS, Conrad (1940-) South African
£342 $581 €499 Still life with pomegranates (24x32cm-9x13in) s.d.1970 board. 4-Nov-3 Stephan Welz, Johannesburg #702 est:2500-3500 (SA.R 4000)
£1008 $1825 €1472 District six (43x56cm-17x22in) s.d.69 board. 30-Mar-4 Stephan Welz, Johannesburg #504 est:3000-5000 (SA.R 12000)
Works on paper
£314 $562 €458 Philipi (25x30cm-10x12in) s.d.1995 s.i.d.verso pastel. 31-May-4 Stephan Welz, Johannesburg #157 (SA.R 3800)
£372 $665 €543 Saron (25x30cm-10x12in) s.d.1995 s.i.d.verso pastel. 31-May-4 Stephan Welz, Johannesburg #156 (SA.R 4500)

THEYS, Ivan (1936-) Belgian
£1538 $2615 €2200 Gestreepte peren no.3 (65x92cm-26x36in) s.d.1970 i.,stretcher. 25-Nov-3 Christie's, Amsterdam #110/R est:2000-3000
£1667 $3067 €2500 View from a window (81x65cm-32x26in) s.d.73. 9-Jun-4 Christie's, Amsterdam #193/R est:2500-3000
£1748 $2972 €2500 De Verzoeking (65x54cm-26x21in) s. s.d.1974 verso i.stretcher. 25-Nov-3 Christie's, Amsterdam #102/R est:1800-2200

THIAUCOURT, Guy (?) French
£315 $526 €450 Le cirque. s. 29-Jun-3 Feletin, Province #153

THIBAULT, Marcel (20th C) French
£2113 $3655 €3000 Souk a TUnis (46x55cm-18x22in) 15-Dec-3 Gros & Delettrez, Paris #152/R est:3000-4000
£2113 $3655 €3000 Cafe a Tunis (38x46cm-15x18in) 15-Dec-3 Gros & Delettrez, Paris #151/R est:3000-4000

THIBESART, Raymond (1874-?) French
£267 $491 €400 Amandier en fleurs (24x32cm-9x13in) s. cardboard. 14-Jun-4 Tajan, Paris #53
£570 $1050 €850 Bord de l'eau (75x100cm-30x39in) s. 24-Mar-4 Joron-Derem, Paris #56
£802 $1300 €1163 Lime trees in flower (65x81cm-26x32in) s. 29-Jul-3 Galeria y Remates, Montevideo #36/R
£1197 $2071 €1700 Pommiers en fleur (63x100cm-25x39in) s. 13-Dec-3 Martinot & Savignat, Pontoise #232/R est:1800-2000
£1208 $2235 €1800 Brume printaniere sur l'etang (65x81cm-26x32in) s. 15-Mar-4 Horta, Bruxelles #386 est:1800-2200

THIBODEAU, Virginia (20th C) ?
£663 $1100 €961 Floral still life (58x48cm-23x19in) painted c.1960. 14-Jun-3 Du Mouchelle, Detroit #1082/R
Works on paper
£331 $550 €480 Floral still life (30x41cm-12x16in) W/C. 14-Jun-3 Du Mouchelle, Detroit #1086/R

THIBON DE LIBIAN, Valentin (1889-1931) Argentinian
£14118 $24000 €20612 Carbonero de puerto - Harbour coal merchant (73x60cm-29x24in) s.d.930 prov.exhib. 18-Nov-3 Christie's, Rockefeller NY #92/R est:30000-40000
Works on paper
£994 $1800 €1451 Bohemian (11x10cm-4x4in) ink. 30-Mar-4 Arroyo, Buenos Aires #31

THIEBAUD, Wayne (1920-) American

£137725 $230000 €201079 Cafe rose (30x20cm-12x8in) s.d.1962 prov. 13-Nov-3 Sotheby's, New York #195/R est:250000-350000
£215569 $360000 €314731 Five Eating Figures (25x36cm-10x14in) s.d.1963 s.i.d.stretcher prov.exhib. 12-Nov-3 Christie's, Rockefeller NY #326/R est:240000-320000

Prints

£1808 $3200 €2640 Candy counter (47x64cm-19x25in) s.d.70 num.15/50 col linocut. 28-Apr-4 Christie's, Rockefeller NY #427/R est:2500-3500
£1892 $3500 €2762 Peppermints (12x15cm-5x6in) s.d.1964 num.11/15 etching. 12-Feb-4 Christie's, Rockefeller NY #247/R est:1500-2500
£2147 $3800 €3135 Sandwich (14x27cm-6x11in) s.d.71 num.15/50 col linocut. 28-Apr-4 Christie's, Rockefeller NY #430/R est:2000-3000
£2270 $4200 €3314 Nine candied apples (13x15cm-5x6in) s.d.1964 num.21/25 etching aquatint. 12-Feb-4 Christie's, Rockefeller NY #246/R est:2500-3500
£2500 $4250 €3650 Eyeglasses (21x28cm-8x11in) s. etching drypoint. 31-Oct-3 Sotheby's, New York #798/R
£2712 $4800 €3960 Toy counter (46x61cm-18x24in) s.d.70 num.15/50 col screenprint. 28-Apr-4 Christie's, Rockefeller NY #432/R est:3000-4000
£2844 $4750 €4152 Black suckers (45x55cm-18x22in) s.i.d.1970-71 aquatint. 21-Oct-3 Bonhams & Butterfields, San Francisco #1434/R
£3107 $5500 €4536 Chocolate cake (45x34cm-18x13in) s.d.71 num.15/50 col lithograph. 28-Apr-4 Christie's, Rockefeller NY #426/R est:2500-3500
£3352 $6000 €4894 Steep Street (74x53cm-29x21in) s.d.1989 num.21/50 aquatint drypoint soft ground etching prov. 7-May-4 Sloans & Kenyon, Bethesda #1754/R est:5000-7000
£3374 $5500 €4926 Downgrade (76x57cm-30x22in) s.d.1979 num.12/50 etching aquatint on Somerset. 24-Sep-3 Christie's, Rockefeller NY #403/R est:2000-3000
£3374 $5500 €4926 Sardines (30x23cm-12x9in) s.d.1982 num.42/50 etching col aquatint on Kozo paper. 24-Sep-3 Christie's, Rockefeller NY #404/R est:2500-3500
£3390 $6000 €4949 Glasses (37x50cm-15x20in) s.d.70 num.15/50 col lithograph. 28-Apr-4 Christie's, Rockefeller NY #429/R est:2000-3000
£4520 $8000 €6599 Dark country city (55x80cm-22x31in) s.d.1988 num.13/25 aquatint softground. 30-Apr-4 Sotheby's, New York #506/R est:4000-6000
£5085 $9000 €7424 Lipstick rows (13x58cm-5x23in) s.d.70 num.15/50 col screenprint. 28-Apr-4 Christie's, Rockefeller NY #428/R est:4000-6000
£5689 $9500 €8306 Paint cans (76x59cm-30x23in) s.d.1990 num.50/100 col lithograph. 21-Oct-3 Bonhams & Butterfields, San Francisco #1436/R
£10000 $17000 €14600 Dark cake (38x44cm-15x17in) s. col woodcut. 31-Oct-3 Sotheby's, New York #797/R
£10169 $18000 €14847 Rabbit (31x47cm-12x19in) s.d.71 num.15/50 col lithograph. 28-Apr-4 Christie's, Rockefeller NY #431/R est:2000-3000
£11299 $20000 €16497 Big suckers (44x56cm-17x22in) s.d.71 num.15/50 col aquatint. 28-Apr-4 Christie's, Rockefeller NY #425/R est:7000-9000
£15819 $28000 €23096 Candy apples (39x42cm-15x17in) s.d.1981 num.89/200 col woodcut. 28-Apr-4 Christie's, Rockefeller NY #433/R est:15000-20000

Works on paper

£41899 $75000 €61173 Cake slices (16x25cm-6x10in) s.d.1964 India ink double-sided prov. 13-May-4 Sotheby's, New York #147/R est:60000-80000

THIEL, Frank (20th C) German

Photographs

£7778 $14000 €11356 Stadt 5/02.A Berlin (190x163cm-75x64in) s.i.d.1996 chromogenic colour print prov. 23-Apr-4 Phillips, New York #6/R est:7000-10000
£9497 $17000 €13866 Stadt 7/11/A Berlin (175x240cm-69x94in) s.i.d.99 verso col photo Plexiglas edition of 4 prov. 14-May-4 Phillips, New York #306/R est:8000-12000

THIELE, Alexander (1924-) German

£268 $491 €400 Munich beer garden (51x61cm-20x24in) s.i.verso lit. 8-Jul-4 Allgauer, Kempten #2233/R
£268 $491 €400 Munich beer garden (51x61cm-20x24in) s. i.verso. 8-Jul-4 Allgauer, Kempten #2234/R
£268 $491 €400 Munich beer garden (51x61cm-20x24in) s. i.verso. 8-Jul-4 Allgauer, Kempten #2235/R
£278 $453 €400 Dinner party (60x50cm-24x20in) s. s.i. verso. 27-Sep-3 Dannenberg, Berlin #619/R
£302 $553 €450 Figures in beer garden (61x51cm-24x20in) s. 8-Jul-4 Allgauer, Kempten #2236/R
£403 $741 €600 Cafe garden in Berlin (50x60cm-20x24in) s. s.i. verso. 27-Mar-4 Dannenberg, Berlin #633/R
£455 $759 €650 Munich beer garden (60x50cm-24x20in) s. i. verso. 9-Oct-3 Michael Zeller, Lindau #772/R
£493 $882 €700 Ducks in the reeds (40x60cm-16x24in) s. lit. 8-Jan-4 Allgauer, Kempten #2532
£538 $899 €770 Cafe garden Berlin Wannsee (50x60cm-20x24in) s.i. 27-Jun-3 Michael Zeller, Lindau #681/R
£541 $968 €800 Garden cafe on Starnberger See (50x60cm-20x24in) s. i. verso. 8-May-4 Hans Stahl, Toestorf #37/R
£552 $921 €800 Cafe garden by Starnberger See (50x60cm-20x24in) s. 9-Jul-3 Hugo Ruef, Munich #225
£615 $1028 €880 Munich beer garden (60x50cm-24x20in) s.i. 27-Jun-3 Michael Zeller, Lindau #682/R
£664 $1109 €950 Cafe garden on Starnberger See (50x60cm-20x24in) s. i. verso. 9-Oct-3 Michael Zeller, Lindau #771/R

THIELE, Anton (1838-1902) Danish

£316 $591 €461 Hilly spring landscape with flowering meadow (42x63cm-17x25in) s.d.98. 25-Feb-4 Museumsbygningen, Copenhagen #193 (D.KR 3500)
£3214 $5560 €4692 Young girl wearing classic costume picking roses (79x53cm-31x21in) s. prov. 9-Dec-3 Rasmussen, Copenhagen #1570/R est:15000-20000 (D.KR 34000)

THIELE, Arthur (1841-1919) German

£377 $640 €550 Deer in winter landscape (15x23cm-6x9in) s. panel. 5-Nov-3 Hugo Ruef, Munich #1150/R
£724 $1332 €1100 Winter landscape with dead rabbit and crow (92x114cm-36x45in) s.d.1863. 25-Jun-4 Michael Zeller, Lindau #511/R

THIELE, Johann Alexander (1685-1752) German

Works on paper

£3169 $5546 €4500 Paysage fluvial au grand pins (14x25cm-6x10in) mono. gouache. 17-Dec-3 Delorme & Bocage, Paris #14/R est:5000-6000

THIELE, Johann Alexander (attrib) (1685-1752) German

£4333 $7843 €6500 View of city on river, possibly Dresden (48x61cm-19x24in) panel. 1-Apr-4 Van Ham, Cologne #1252/R est:7500

THIELE, Otto (1870-1955) German

£359 $668 €524 Street scene with women in front of pastel coloured house (59x48cm-23x19in) s. 2-Mar-4 Rasmussen, Copenhagen #1356/R (D.KR 4000)
£1042 $1771 €1500 At the stonecutters (50x65cm-20x26in) s. 28-Oct-3 Dorotheum, Vienna #268/R est:1800-2000
£1200 $2148 €1800 Berlin flower market (46x38cm-18x15in) s. board. 13-May-4 Neumeister, Munich #506/R est:1500-1800

THIELEN, Jan Philips van (1618-1667) Flemish

£3642 $6666 €5500 Still life of flowers and annunciation to Mary (121x101cm-48x40in) 7-Apr-4 Dorotheum, Salzburg #64/R est:8000-10000
£6000 $10200 €8760 Still life of tulips, roses and other flowers in a glass vase (63x53cm-25x21in) prov. 30-Oct-3 Sotheby's, Olympia #5/R est:3000-4000
£6000 $10380 €8760 Still life of roses, tulips and other flowers in a glass vase on a stone ledge (63x53cm-25x21in) fragment prov. 9-Dec-3 Sotheby's, Olympia #337/R est:3500-4500
£14765 $27168 €22000 Bouquet of flowers with carnatiosn, roses, tulips (63x53cm-25x21in) prov. 24-Mar-4 Dorotheum, Vienna #168/R est:22000-26000

THIELER, Fred (1916-1999) German

£1200 $2208 €1800 SG K3/57 (65x100cm-26x39in) s.d.57 s.i.d.1957 verso board. 12-Jun-4 Villa Grisebach, Berlin #845/R est:1800-2400
£1667 $2983 €2500 Composition (100x80cm-39x31in) s.d.81 s.d. verso oil gouache board. 15-May-4 Van Ham, Cologne #964/R est:3300
£1799 $2950 €2500 7 S B 59 (65x50cm-26x20in) s.d. board on canvas. 4-Jun-3 Ketterer, Hamburg #923/R est:2500-3500
£2083 $3479 €3000 K.M.P. 10.57 (50x65cm-20x26in) s.d. s.i. verso resin dispersion. 24-Oct-3 Ketterer, Hamburg #560/R est:3000-4000
£2083 $3479 €3000 S.W. 12/57 (68x95cm-27x37in) s. s.i.d. verso resin dispersion. 24-Oct-3 Ketterer, Hamburg #561/R est:3000-4000
£2083 $3479 €3000 72-H-K/15 (59x80cm-23x31in) s.d. i.d. verso resin dispersion. 24-Oct-3 Ketterer, Hamburg #563/R est:3000-3500
£4000 $6680 €5840 St.M. 12/58 (96x68cm-38x27in) s.d.58 s.i.d.verso oil board on cellutex exhib. 22-Oct-3 Bonhams, New Bond Street #75/R est:4500-5500
£4514 $7538 €6500 H. 20/85 (90x110cm-35x43in) s.d. s.i. stretcher acrylic tempera. 24-Oct-3 Ketterer, Hamburg #559/R est:7000-9000
£5000 $8950 €7500 B.I.58 (68x95cm-27x37in) s.i. verso board on panel. 15-May-4 Van Ham, Cologne #963/R est:7500
£10667 $19520 €16000 0 - 26-55 or 26/55 blue/red (85x125cm-33x49in) s.d.55 s.i. verso hessian exhib.lit. 4-Jun-4 Lempertz, Koln #488/R est:16000-18000
£20000 $35800 €30000 Untitled (198x168cm-78x66in) s.d. s.d. verso. 13-May-4 Neumeister, Munich #774/R est:30000-35000

Prints

£2431 $4059 €3500 XIII.D.57 (68x96cm-27x38in) s. s.i.d. verso silkcut board. 24-Oct-3 Ketterer, Hamburg #562/R est:3500-4500
£3497 $6014 €5000 I.K.57 (100x65cm-39x26in) s.d. s.i.d. verso silkcut board. 5-Dec-3 Ketterer, Munich #305/R est:4800-5800

Works on paper

£1333 $2453 €2000 Composition (47x66cm-19x26in) Mixed media. 12-Jun-4 Villa Grisebach, Berlin #846/R est:1800-2400
£2667 $4907 €4000 Untitled (100x78cm-39x31in) s.d.81 mixed media. 12-Jun-4 Villa Grisebach, Berlin #355/R est:4000-6000
£3356 $5940 €5000 Untitled (115x135cm-45x53in) s.d. mixed media canvas. 30-Apr-4 Dr Fritz Nagel, Stuttgart #960/R est:6000
£6294 $10699 €9000 Galaxy II (100x110cm-39x43in) s.d.73 s.i.d. stretcher mixed media. 29-Nov-3 Villa Grisebach, Berlin #359/R est:7000-9000
£6993 $11888 €10000 K III/80 (110x150cm-43x59in) mixed media. 29-Nov-3 Villa Grisebach, Berlin #380/R est:10000-15000

THIELKE, Henry Daniel (1789-?) ?

£600 $1074 €876 Portrait of a lady, seated in a black dress with lace trim (76x65cm-30x26in) i.verso. 27-May-4 Christie's, Kensington #92/R

THIEM, Paul (1858-1922) German

£480 $874 €720 Portrait of Julius Bohler (117x87cm-46x34in) s.d.19. 1-Jul-4 Neumeister, Munich #2820
£493 $908 €750 People walking along the canal (38x49cm-15x19in) 28-Jun-4 Dr Fritz Nagel, Stuttgart #6982/R
£833 $1375 €1200 Waterfall (121x96cm-48x38in) s.d.15. 2-Jul-3 Neumeister, Munich #790
£1800 $3276 €2700 Sailing boat on Starnberger See (87x166cm-34x65in) s. 30-Jun-4 Neumeister, Munich #707/R est:1800

THIEMANN, Hans (1910-) German

Works on paper

£333 $613 €500 Saint Georg (44x37cm-17x15in) s.d.44 pen ink. 12-Jun-4 Villa Grisebach, Berlin #847/R

THIEME, Anthony (1888-1954) American/Dutch

£2018 $3250 €2946 Still life (76x64cm-30x25in) s. 20-Aug-3 James Julia, Fairfield #1332/R est:4000-7000
£2419 $4500 €3532 Village street (63x76cm-25x30in) s. 3-Mar-4 Christie's, Rockefeller NY #35/R est:4000-6000
£2717 $5000 €3967 Unloading cargo (29x39cm-11x15in) s. prov. 8-Jun-4 Bonhams & Butterfields, San Francisco #4096/R est:4000-6000
£2989 $5500 €4364 The old farmhouse (40x50cm-16x20in) s. i.verso canvasboard prov. 8-Jun-4 Bonhams & Butterfields, San Francisco #4095/R est:6000-8000
£2989 $5500 €4364 Break of day (76x91cm-30x36in) s. i.verso prov. 8-Jun-4 Bonhams & Butterfields, San Francisco #4098/R est:4000-6000
£2994 $5000 €4371 Silver Light (64x76cm-25x30in) s. i.verso prov. 23-Oct-3 Shannon's, Milford #3/R est:5000-7000
£3297 $6000 €4814 Pigeon Cove (63x76cm-25x30in) s. s.i.stretcher. 29-Jun-4 Sotheby's, New York #242/R est:6000-8000
£3571 $6500 €5214 Delft, Holland (62x75cm-24x30in) s.i. i.verso. 29-Jun-4 Sotheby's, New York #241/R est:7000-10000

£3693 $6500 €5392 Last snow in Connecticut (46x56cm-18x22in) s. i.verso. 21-May-4 North East Auctions, Portsmouth #828/R
£3771 $6750 €5506 Boats and old fortress (28x38cm-11x15in) s. i.verso panel. 20-Mar-4 Selkirks, St. Louis #160/R est:8000-10000
£3771 $6750 €5506 Italian neighbors, Pozzuoli (28x38cm-11x15in) s. i.verso panel. 20-Mar-4 Selkirks, St. Louis #161/R est:8000-10000
£3915 $7400 €5716 New England harbour with boats at dock (41x51cm-16x20in) s. canvasboard. 21-Feb-4 Brunk, Ashville #444/R est:5000-10000
£4545 $8000 €6636 Seaport (48x61cm-19x24in) s. prov. 23-May-4 Hindman, Chicago #159/R est:8000-12000
£4938 $8000 €7209 Main St, Rockport, MA (20x24cm-8x9in) i. verso canvas panel. 31-Jul-3 Eldred, East Dennis #1007/R est:6000-8000
£5645 $10500 €8242 Vermont landscape (64x76cm-25x30in) s. 6-Mar-4 North East Auctions, Portsmouth #561/R est:8000-12000
£6630 $12000 €9680 New England harbor (56x46cm-22x18in) s. 16-Apr-4 James Julia, Fairfield #530/R est:8000-12000
£6818 $12000 €9954 Rockport waterfront (76x91cm-30x36in) s. prov. 23-May-4 Hindman, Chicago #158/R est:12000-18000
£7186 $12000 €10492 Transparent Sail, France (64x76cm-25x30in) s. prov. 23-Oct-3 Shannon's, Milford #191/R est:12000-18000
£7735 $14000 €11293 Harbour scene (30x41cm-12x16in) s. s.i.verso canvas on board painted c.1930 prov.exhib. 31-Mar-4 Sotheby's, New York #25/R est:6000-8000
£12346 $20000 €17902 Home with the catch (76x91cm-30x36in) s. 8-Aug-3 Barridorf, Portland #244/R est:20000-30000
£38462 $70000 €56155 St. George Street, St Augustine, Florida (76x91cm-30x36in) s.i.verso. 29-Jun-4 Sotheby's, New York #240/R est:20000-30000

Works on paper
£198 $350 €289 Fishing boats in a harbour (18x14cm-7x6in) s. ink black wash. 2-May-4 Bonhams & Butterfields, San Francisco #1138/R
£282 $500 €412 Figures in St Mark's Square, Venice (13x17cm-5x7in) s. pencil W/C. 2-May-4 Bonhams & Butterfields, San Francisco #1165/R
£339 $600 €495 Sun-dappled house with chef in the doorway (8x10cm-3x4in) s. W/C. 2-May-4 Bonhams & Butterfields, San Francisco #1166/R
£455 $850 €683 Waves crashing on a beach (37x49cm-15x19in) s. mixed media prov. 25-Jul-4 Bonhams & Butterfields, San Francisco #6100/R
£508 $900 €742 Street scene in Boston (19x14cm-7x6in) s. pencil W/C. 2-May-4 Bonhams & Butterfields, San Francisco #1105/R
£508 $900 €742 European street scene (13x18cm-5x7in) s. pencil W/C. 2-May-4 Bonhams & Butterfields, San Francisco #1108/R
£791 $1400 €1155 Galleons on the high seas (38x48cm-15x19in) s. mixed media. 2-May-4 Bonhams & Butterfields, San Francisco #1079/R est:600-800
£1130 $2000 €1650 Chinatown, new York (13x18cm-5x7in) pencil W/C. 2-May-4 Bonhams & Butterfields, San Francisco #1107/R est:1000-1500
£1977 $3500 €2886 Winter town square with fountain (14x19cm-6x7in) s. mixed media. 2-May-4 Bonhams & Butterfields, San Francisco #1104/R est:2000-3000
£3390 $6000 €4949 Fishing boat with figures (56x79cm-22x31in) s. pencil W/C sold with a companion. 2-May-4 Bonhams & Butterfields, San Francisco #1077/R est:5000-7000
£3827 $6200 €5549 Punto barrios, Guatemala (39x56cm-15x22in) W/C. 8-Aug-3 Barridorf, Portland #243/R est:5000-7000

THIEME, Anthony (attrib) (1888-1954) American/Dutch
£1073 $1900 €1567 View of an Italian port (36x46cm-14x18in) bears sig. board. 2-May-4 Bonhams & Butterfields, San Francisco #1083/R est:300-500

THIENON, Louis (1812-?) French
Works on paper
£590 $944 €820 Personnages dans les fosses d'un chateau (20x27cm-8x11in) s.d.1840 W/C htd white gouache traces blk crayon. 16-May-3 Tajan, Paris #184

THIERBACH, Richard (1860-1931) German
£347 $638 €520 View of Stolberg-im-Harz (73x89cm-29x35in) s. 11-Jun-4 Wendl, Rudolstadt #4293/R

THIERFELDER, Vivian (1929-) Canadian
Works on paper
£946 $1608 €1381 Iris Cameo (36cm-14in circular) s.d.1983 W/C prov. 23-Nov-3 Levis, Calgary #138/R est:3000-3500 (C.D 2100)

THIERRIAT, Augustin Alexandre (1789-1870) French
£6897 $11448 €10000 Still life of flower (73x60cm-29x24in) 1-Oct-3 Dorotheum, Vienna #144/R est:12000-17000

THIERRY, Jacques Étienne (1750-1832) French
Works on paper
£850 $1471 €1241 View of an arcade at the Palais-Royal. Theatre de l'Odeon, Paris (25x36cm-10x14in) i. pencil W/C pair. 12-Dec-3 Christie's, Kensington #474/R

THIERRY, Joseph François Desire (1812-1866) French
Works on paper
£578 $1035 €850 L'orangerie de Versailles, un couple au premier plan (16x16cm-6x6in) indis.sig.i. pen black ink W/C. 18-Mar-4 Christie's, Paris #299/R

THIERY DE SAINT COLOMBE, Luc Vincent (1734-c.1811) French
Works on paper
£850 $1556 €1241 Figure on a terrace overlooking the sea (20x26cm-8x10in) i. pen ink wash over pencil. 7-Jul-4 Bonhams, Knightsbridge #27/R

THIJSEN, Carolus Johannes (1867-1917) Dutch
£978 $1750 €1428 Mother with child (18x22cm-7x9in) board. 9-Jan-4 Du Mouchelle, Detroit #2006/R est:1500-2000

THIL, Jeanne (1887-1968) French
£7800 $14196 €11388 Camel train outside Sousse (99x99cm-39x39in) s. 16-Jun-4 Christie's, Kensington #274/R est:1000-1500
Works on paper
£2270 $3790 €3200 Chameau devant l'amphitheatre Romain d'El Djem (32x55cm-13x22in) s. gouache. 16-Jun-3 Gros & Delettrez, Paris #455/R est:1500-2000

THIOLAT, Dominique (1946-) French
£599 $1036 €850 Untitled (245x200cm-96x79in) acrylic. 15-Dec-3 Charbonneaux, Paris #265/R

THIOLLET, Alexandre (1824-1895) French
£1218 $1986 €1778 Rural landscape with milkmaid and cow (44x65cm-17x26in) s. prov. 28-Sep-3 Hindemae, Ullerslev #28/R est:8000-10000 (D.KR 13000)

THIRION, Eugène Romain (attrib) (1839-1910) French
£2270 $3790 €3200 La republique protectrice (116x89cm-46x35in) 17-Jun-3 Christie's, Paris #21/R est:2500-3500

THIRION, Victor Charles (1833-1878) French
£19444 $35000 €28388 Une jeune fille aux fleurs (114x76cm-45x30in) s. prov. 23-Apr-4 Sotheby's, New York #57/R est:30000-40000

THIRKETTLE, Robert Frank (1849-1916) British
Works on paper
£500 $850 €730 Harbour scene, fishing boats at the quay (76x56cm-30x22in) s. 5-Nov-3 John Nicholson, Haslemere #511

THIRKETTLE, Sharon (20th C) Canadian
£311 $516 €454 Seven peaks (20x40cm-8x16in) s. s.i.verso board. 5-Oct-3 Levis, Calgary #306/R (C.D 700)

THIRTLE, Janet (19/20th C) British
£550 $1007 €803 Catching up (43x56cm-17x22in) s.d.1916. 7-Apr-4 Bonhams, Bury St Edmunds #432

THIRTLE, John (1777-1839) British
Works on paper
£290 $470 €421 Port of Thorndon, Wellington (11x17cm-4x7in) s. W/C. 31-Jul-3 International Art Centre, Auckland #72/R (NZ.D 800)
£290 $470 €421 Bluff, New Zealand (11x17cm-4x7in) s. W/C. 31-Jul-3 International Art Centre, Auckland #73/R (NZ.D 800)
£600 $1098 €876 Wooded river landscape with a herdsman and cattle (21x29cm-8x11in) pencil W/C gum arabic htd bodycol scratching prov.exhib. 3-Jun-4 Christie's, London #138/R
£1100 $2013 €1606 Farmyard with timber drag (24x34cm-9x13in) d.1806 pencil grey wash prov. 3-Jun-4 Christie's, London #107/R est:500-700

THIRY, Rene (1870-1960) French
£9028 $15980 €13181 Breton harbour scene with fisherman in the foreground (132x160cm-52x63in) s.d.07. 2-May-4 Bonhams & Butterfields, San Francisco #1042/R est:6000-8000

THIVET, Yvonne (1888-1972) French
£851 $1421 €1200 Rue de la casbah (35x27cm-14x11in) s.i.d.1941 cardboard. 19-Oct-3 Rabourdin & Choppin de Janvry, Paris #84/R
Works on paper
£534 $976 €800 Dans le vieux Biskra (37x45cm-15x18in) s. gouache. 3-Jun-4 Tajan, Paris #340/R

THOL, Hendrick Otto von (1859-1902) Dutch
£2585 $4705 €3800 Winter, wood gatherer on a snow covered path at dusk (59x78cm-23x31in) s. 3-Feb-4 Christie's, Amsterdam #273/R est:2000-3000

THOLE, Karel (1914-2000) Dutch?
£667 $1200 €1000 Nightwings (30x25cm-12x10in) s. i.verso tempera card. 22-Apr-4 Finarte Semenzato, Rome #87/R

THOLEN, Willem Bastiaan (1860-1931) Dutch
£496 $829 €700 Farm in between the trees (31x39cm-12x15in) s. 20-Oct-3 Glerum, Amsterdam #74/R
£724 $1310 €1100 Church of Spankeren (25x35cm-10x14in) s. canvas on panel. 19-Apr-4 Glerum, Amsterdam #113/R
£884 $1610 €1300 Dune landscape (30x50cm-12x20in) s. 3-Feb-4 Christie's, Amsterdam #140/R est:1500-2000
£1206 $2013 €1700 Fishing boat on the Zuiderzee (15x41cm-6x16in) s. canvas on panel. 20-Oct-3 Glerum, Amsterdam #167/R est:600-800
£1528 $2414 €2200 Vaartje, Giethoorn (31x51cm-12x20in) s. 2-Sep-3 Christie's, Amsterdam #208/R est:2500-3500
£1748 $3007 €2500 Willows at the edge of a ditch (32x48cm-13x19in) marouflе. 8-Dec-3 Glerum, Amsterdam #49/R est:2500-2800
£2639 $4169 €3800 Bringing in the eel traps (28x42cm-11x17in) s.d.06 panel. 2-Sep-3 Christie's, Amsterdam #206/R est:2200-2600
£4514 $7674 €6500 Moonlit bend in the river Ussel near Kampen (97x119cm-38x47in) s. prov.exhib. 28-Oct-3 Christie's, Amsterdam #188/R est:7000-9000
£6944 $11597 €10000 Figures strolling on a quay (32x51cm-13x20in) s.d.16 canvas on panel. 21-Oct-3 Sotheby's, Amsterdam #89/R est:6000-8000
£7639 $12986 €11000 Clouds over a calm lake (72x102cm-28x40in) s. 28-Oct-3 Christie's, Amsterdam #165/R est:7000-9000
£17333 $31200 €26000 Winter, Scheveningen beach in the snow (38x59cm-15x23in) s.d.92 prov. 21-Apr-4 Christie's, Amsterdam #118/R est:7000-9000

Works on paper
£745 $1200 €1088 Wooded landscape (56x67cm-22x26in) s. W/C bodycol. 14-Jan-4 Christie's, Rockefeller NY #28/R est:2000-3000
£921 $1695 €1400 Two studies of children and their nannies (25x33cm-10x13in) s. black chalk two. 22-Jun-4 Christie's, Amsterdam #158/R est:800-1200
£1118 $2058 €1700 Portrait of Peronne Arntzenius (32x25cm-13x10in) s. black chk sold with 2 sketchbooks and family photo album prov. 22-Jun-4 Christie's, Amsterdam #156/R est:700-900
£1733 $3120 €2600 Farm on the waterfront, Kaag (44x68cm-17x27in) s. W/C. 20-Apr-4 Sotheby's, Amsterdam #104/R est:3000-5000
£2778 $4722 €4000 Activities by the water, Giethoorn (42x33cm-17x13in) s. pencil W/C htd white exhib.lit. 28-Oct-3 Christie's, Amsterdam #174/R est:5000-7000

THOLLANDER, Earl (1922-2001) American
Works on paper
£272 $500 €397 Money loaned (42x51cm-17x20in) s. casein. 27-Jun-4 Bonhams & Butterfields, San Francisco #3849/R

THOM, James Crawford (1835-1898) American
£363 $650 €530 Two children resting on a rock, distant church (48x43cm-19x17in) s. 29-May-4 Brunk, Ashville #479/R
£441 $750 €644 Boatman with three passengers (30x46cm-12x18in) s. board. 21-Nov-3 Eldred, East Dennis #698/R
£516 $950 €753 Cabin interior with mother and children (25x36cm-10x14in) s. 11-Jun-4 David Rago, Lambertville #231/R
£586 $950 €856 Boatman with three passengers (30x46cm-12x18in) s. board. 31-Jul-3 Eldred, East Dennis #879/R
£894 $1600 €1305 Landscape with grazing cows in distance (28x41cm-11x16in) s. 16-May-4 CRN Auctions, Cambridge #10/R
£934 $1700 €1364 Woman along forest path (20x13cm-8x5in) s. board. 7-Feb-4 Sloans & Kenyon, Bethesda #1288/R est:600-800
£1087 $2000 €1587 Figures in a landscape by a river (18x36cm-7x14in) s. panel prov. 25-Jun-4 Freeman, Philadelphia #240/R est:1000-1500
Works on paper
£283 $450 €413 Landscape with figures (43x71cm-17x28in) s. W/C. 9-Mar-3 William Jenack, New York #401

THOMA, Hans (1839-1924) German
£369 $679 €550 Trees on shore of Lago di Bracciano near Rome (29x43cm-11x17in) bears i.d.1874 pen wash. 26-Mar-4 Bolland & Marotz, Bremen #429/R
£838 $1500 €1223 Luncheon (27x34cm-11x13in) s.i.d.91 board. 14-May-4 Skinner, Boston #32/R est:1000-1500
£1389 $2292 €2000 Holy Family (42x42cm-17x17in) mono.d.93. 5-Jul-3 Geble, Radolfzell #487/R est:2000
£1500 $2550 €2190 Ortler, with mountaineers in the foreground (49x68cm-19x27in) 26-Nov-3 Peter Wilson, Nantwich #93 est:1500-1800
£2617 $4868 €3900 Birth of Christ (133x99cm-52x39in) s.i.d.1915. 6-Mar-4 Arnold, Frankfurt #864/R est:3000
£8099 $14011 €11500 Angler near Sackingen (44x76cm-17x30in) mono.d.1870. 13-Dec-3 Lempertz, Koln #50/R est:10000
Prints
£599 $958 €850 Siegfried striding through wood (49x35cm-19x14in) mono.d.1912 print technique zinc. 19-Sep-3 Karlheinz Kaupp, Staufen #1983

THOMA, Hans (attrib) (1839-1924) German
£1724 $3172 €2517 Two cats (12x18cm-5x7in) mono.d.1864 paper on board. 26-Mar-4 Koller, Zurich #3112/R est:2500-3500 (S.FR 4000)

THOMA, Josef (1828-1899) Austrian
£986 $1577 €1400 Stream in the Alps (97x141cm-38x56in) s. 18-Sep-3 Rieber, Stuttgart #929/R
£1034 $1728 €1500 High mountain landscape with peasant girl (77x95cm-30x37in) s.d.1875. 15-Nov-3 Lempertz, Koln #1705/R est:1500
£1200 $2064 €1752 Mountainous Swiss lake landscape (31x48cm-12x19in) s.d.1874 board. 4-Dec-3 Christie's, Kensington #179/R est:1500-2000
£1399 $2336 €2000 Fishermen on shore by moonlight (70x105cm-28x41in) s. 28-Jun-3 Bolland & Marotz, Bremen #741/R est:3300
£1584 $2692 €2313 Waterfall with washerwoman (74x199cm-29x78in) s.d.1875. 19-Nov-3 Fischer, Luzern #1157/R est:3500-5000 (S.FR 3500)
£1645 $3026 €2500 Winter landscape (26x47cm-10x19in) s. panel. 22-Jun-4 Wiener Kunst Auktionen, Vienna #10/R est:2000
£2349 $4205 €3500 Mountain torrent in the Alps (97x141cm-38x56in) s. 27-May-4 Dorotheum, Vienna #49/R est:3800-4200
£2617 $4816 €3900 Mont Blanc in Switzerland (69x106cm-27x42in) s. lit. 25-Mar-4 Karlheinz Kaupp, Staufen #2776/R est:1800
£3497 $5944 €5000 Peasant girl with goat on woodland path (79x60cm-31x24in) s. 24-Nov-3 Dorotheum, Vienna #115/R est:5000-6000
£13429 $24575 €19606 Alpine landscape with mountains near lake (90x123cm-35x48in) s. 9-Jun-4 Rasmussen, Copenhagen #1522/R est:25000 (D.KR 150000)

THOMA, Sepp (1883-1963) Austrian
£400 $720 €600 Farmstead in hilly landscape (51x42cm-20x17in) s. panel. 22-Apr-4 Dorotheum, Graz #27/R

THOMANN, Adolf (1874-1961) Swiss
£870 $1591 €1270 Montee a l'alpage, les Hauderes (51x55cm-20x22in) s.d.27. 5-Jun-4 Galerie du Rhone, Sion #400 (S.FR 2000)

THOMAS, Adolph (1834-1887) German
£1259 $2140 €1800 Fountain in Italy (44x60cm-17x24in) s. board. 22-Nov-3 Arnold, Frankfurt #652/R
£1408 $2437 €2000 Mountain alpine meadow with grazing cows in Bavaria (98x147cm-39x58in) s.d.1870 canvas on fibreboard. 10-Dec-3 Hugo Ruef, Munich #2507/R est:1200

THOMAS, Alain (20th C) French
£1189 $2200 €1784 Gathering hay in the fields (76x102cm-30x40in) s. 17-Jul-4 New Orleans Auction, New Orleans #234/R est:3000-5000

THOMAS, Alice Blair (1857-1945) American/Canadian
£204 $375 €298 View of a palace with small boats in foreground (23x30cm-9x12in) s. canvasboard. 27-Jun-4 Bonhams & Butterfields, San Francisco #3826/R
£552 $1000 €806 Flock of sheep (93x77cm-37x30in) s.d.1917. 18-Apr-4 Bonhams & Butterfields, Los Angeles #7049 est:1000-1500
£559 $950 €816 Floral still life (61x76cm-24x30in) s. canvas on canvas prov. 18-Nov-3 John Moran, Pasadena #172

THOMAS, Alma Woolsey (1891-1978) American
£10778 $18000 €15736 Untitled (99x35cm-39x14in) s. acrylic painted c.1965-70 prov. 13-Nov-3 Sotheby's, New York #260/R est:10000-15000
£14724 $24000 €21497 Azaleas in spring (51x61cm-20x24in) s.d.68 s.i.verso prov. 23-Sep-3 Christie's, Rockefeller NY #26/R est:3000-5000
£16467 $27500 €24042 Untitled (99x35cm-39x14in) s. acrylic painted c.1965-70 prov. 13-Nov-3 Sotheby's, New York #259/R est:10000-15000
£23699 $41000 €34601 Sparkling leaves among pink roses (76x114cm-30x45in) s.d.73 acrylic prov. 13-Dec-3 Weschler, Washington #601 est:20000-30000
£35294 $60000 €51529 Splashdown of Apollo (165x129cm-65x51in) init. acrylic. 21-Nov-3 Swann Galleries, New York #203/R est:10000-15000
Works on paper
£2973 $5500 €4341 Untitled (56x75cm-22x30in) s. W/C ink exec c.1970 prov. 12-Feb-4 Sotheby's, New York #132/R est:4000-6000
£3757 $6500 €5485 Untitled (57x76cm-22x30in) s.d.71 W/C prov. 13-Dec-3 Weschler, Washington #600 est:4000-6000
£4324 $8000 €6313 Untitled (56x75cm-22x30in) s. W/C ink exec c.1970 prov. 12-Feb-4 Sotheby's, New York #133/R est:4000-6000
£5780 $10000 €8439 Untitled (56x76cm-22x30in) s.d.67 W/C ink prov. 13-Dec-3 Weschler, Washington #599 est:3000-5000

THOMAS, Barry (1961-) American
£2353 $4000 €3435 Summertime fun (76x102cm-30x40in) 1-Nov-3 Altermann Galleries, Santa Fe #196

THOMAS, Billy (1920-) Australian
Works on paper
£938 $1753 €1407 Untitled (45x60cm-18x24in) bears name.verso earth pigments bush gum. 26-Jul-4 Sotheby's, Melbourne #120/R est:2500-3500 (A.D 2400)
£1220 $1927 €1769 Waterholes, Ludun country (80x60cm-31x24in) i.verso earth pigments binders canvas prov.exhib. 28-Jul-3 Sotheby's, Paddington #285/R est:2000-3000 (A.D 3000)
£1220 $1927 €1769 Untitled (59x99cm-23x39in) i.verso earth pigments binder linen prov. 28-Jul-3 Sotheby's, Paddington #410/R est:3000-5000 (A.D 3000)
£1484 $2776 €2226 Untitled (60x80cm-24x31in) bears name.verso earth pigments synthetic binder prov. 26-Jul-4 Sotheby's, Melbourne #458/R est:4000-6000 (A.D 3800)
£1484 $2776 €2226 Untitled (60x90cm-24x35in) bears name.verso earth pigments synthetic binder canvas prov. 26-Jul-4 Sotheby's, Melbourne #459/R est:4000-6000 (A.D 3800)
£1829 $2890 €2652 Yimbooro. Giidjooridja (80x60cm-31x24in) i.verso earth pigments binder canvas pair prov.exhib. 28-Jul-3 Sotheby's, Paddington #284/R est:4000-6000 (A.D 4500)
£3252 $5138 €4715 Marminijoo waterhole (140x100cm-55x39in) i.verso earth pigments binder canvas prov.exhib. 28-Jul-3 Sotheby's, Paddington #286/R est:8000-12000 (A.D 8000)
£3252 $5138 €4715 Minyalga (140x100cm-55x39in) i.verso earth pigments binder canvas prov.exhib. 28-Jul-3 Sotheby's, Paddington #287/R est:8000-12000 (A.D 8000)
£3320 $6209 €4980 Balgoo balgoo (80x100cm-31x39in) bears name.verso earth pigments bush gum canvas prov. 26-Jul-4 Sotheby's, Melbourne #119/R est:8000-10000 (A.D 8500)
£3711 $6939 €5567 Mindijarra waterhole (149x100cm-59x39in) bears name.verso synthetic polymer paint canvas prov. 26-Jul-4 Sotheby's, Melbourne #121/R est:12000-18000 (A.D 9500)
£6911 $10919 €10021 Untitled (120x90cm-47x35in) i.verso earth pigments binder canvas prov. 28-Jul-3 Sotheby's, Paddington #199/R est:10000-15000 (A.D 17000)
£7114 $11240 €10315 Young women's corroboree (90x121cm-35x48in) i.verso earth pigments binder canvas prov.exhib. 28-Jul-3 Sotheby's, Paddington #200/R est:8000-12000 (A.D 17500)

THOMAS, Conrad Arthur (1858-1932) American
£2514 $4500 €3670 The trade (59x414cm-23x163in) s.d.1899. 14-May-4 Skinner, Boston #211/R est:1000-1500

THOMAS, David (?) British
£248 $459 €362 Untitled (193x127cm-76x50in) s.d.1989-91 i.verso prov. 15-Mar-4 Sotheby's, Melbourne #85 (A.D 600)
£500 $925 €730 Blackfriars Bridge, London (67x117cm-26x46in) indis sig.d.1909. 11-Mar-4 Christie's, Kensington #270/R
£1600 $2752 €2336 Delamere Terrace, Little Venice, London (113x143cm-44x56in) s. board. 3-Dec-3 Christie's, Kensington #696/R est:800-1200
Works on paper
£450 $752 €657 Views of Soho (16x56cm-6x22in) s. gouache. 7-Oct-3 Bonhams, Knightsbridge #32a

THOMAS, Edgar Herbert (fl.1888-1926) British
£350 $595 €511 River bend (23x15cm-9x6in) s.d.1926 verso board. 18-Nov-3 Sotheby's, Olympia #43/R

THOMAS, Emma Louise Osman (19th C) British
Works on paper
£400 $652 €584 Young woman greeted by the figure of an angel at a garden gateway (55x37cm-22x15in) i. W/C. 28-Sep-3 Wilkinson, Doncaster #330

THOMAS, Francis Wynne (1907-) British
£850 $1352 €1241 Lobster. Vegetables (51x61cm-20x24in) s. pair. 10-Sep-3 Sotheby's, Olympia #192/R
£1500 $2385 €2190 After the air raid. Ruined church (51x61cm-20x24in) s. pair. 10-Sep-3 Sotheby's, Olympia #191/R est:1000-1500

THOMAS, Gerard (attrib) (1663-1720) Flemish
£2587 $4399 €3700 Painter in studio (50x60cm-20x24in) 22-Nov-3 Arnold, Frankfurt #651/R est:3000

THOMAS, Gerard (style) (1663-1720) Flemish
£6711 $12013 €10000 L'atelier du peintre (150x200cm-59x79in) 25-May-4 Palais de Beaux Arts, Brussels #543/R est:12500-17500

THOMAS, Grosvenor (1856-1923) British
£340 $622 €496 Woodland stream (36x46cm-14x18in) s. 6-Apr-4 Bonhams, Knightsbridge #133/R
£1200 $1884 €1740 Burst of colour (25x35cm-10x14in) s. 27-Aug-3 Sotheby's, London #1047/R est:1500-2000
£1800 $3348 €2628 Mill pond (39x59cm-15x23in) s. 4-Mar-4 Christie's, Kensington #476/R est:2000-3000

THOMAS, Henri Joseph (1878-1972) Belgian
£333 $597 €500 Bouquet d'anemones sechees (36x46cm-14x18in) s. 11-May-4 Vanderkindere, Brussels #24
£550 $995 €803 Still life of vase of roses and plate of cherries (58x48cm-23x19in) s. 31-Mar-4 Brightwells, Leominster #902
£759 $1403 €1100 Pensive (34x26cm-13x10in) s. panel. 16-Feb-4 Horta, Bruxelles #237
£800 $1432 €1200 Femme accoudee (35x26cm-14x10in) s. panel. 15-May-4 De Vuyst, Lokeren #333/R
£1049 $1752 €1500 Nu couche (70x100cm-28x39in) s.d.1924. 13-Oct-3 Horta, Bruxelles #223 est:2000-3000
£1200 $2184 €1752 Dressed for the ball (34x27cm-13x11in) s. 16-Jun-4 Christie's, Kensington #255/R est:1500-2500
£2533 $4535 €3800 La danseuse nue (65x38cm-26x15in) s. canvas on panel. 11-May-4 Vanderkindere, Brussels #16 est:4000-6000
Works on paper
£267 $488 €400 Danseuse (39x25cm-15x10in) s.i. pastel. 7-Jun-4 Palais de Beaux Arts, Brussels #306

THOMAS, J M (20th C) British
£292 $461 €420 Aiguille verte - autumn in the Chamonix Valley (41x51cm-16x20in) s. s.i.on stretcher. 2-Sep-3 Christie's, Amsterdam #417

THOMAS, James Havard (1854-1921) British
Sculpture
£2500 $4150 €3650 Castagnettes (35cm-14in) dark brown pat bronze. 30-Sep-3 Sotheby's, London #124/R est:1000-1500

THOMAS, Karl (1948-) American
£683 $1100 €990 Winter sunset (22x30cm-9x12in) 22-Aug-3 Altermann Galleries, Santa Fe #149
£3529 $6000 €5152 Morning glow tetons (102x152cm-40x60in) 1-Nov-3 Altermann Galleries, Santa Fe #108
£6983 $12500 €10195 Golden Canyon (102x152cm-40x60in) 15-May-4 Altermann Galleries, Santa Fe #170/R

THOMAS, Les (1962-) Canadian
Works on paper
£300 $549 €438 Pineapple (39x51cm-15x20in) mixed media board. 1-Jun-4 Hodgins, Calgary #333/R (C.D 750)
£320 $586 €467 Flowers (40x37cm-16x15in) s.i.d.1997 mixed media board. 1-Jun-4 Hodgins, Calgary #332/R (C.D 800)

THOMAS, Louis (?) French
£1000 $1830 €1500 Paysage symboliste (54x73cm-21x29in) s. 6-Jun-4 Anaf, Lyon #496/R est:1500-2000

THOMAS, Margaret (1916-) British
£480 $845 €701 Pail of roses (40x52cm-16x20in) mono. board exhib. 18-May-4 Bonhams, Knightsbridge #113/R
£550 $974 €803 Still life with roses (80x45cm-31x18in) mono.d.60 board. 27-Apr-4 Bonhams, Knightsbridge #150

THOMAS, Mrs Vernon (1894-?) American
£1117 $2000 €1631 New year's baby holding 1936 horseshoe (69x51cm-27x20in) s. canvasboard. 15-May-4 Illustration House, New York #75/R est:1800-2400
£1257 $2100 €1835 Young girl and dog chasing her hat on a blustery day (69x51cm-27x20in) s. canvasboard sold with magazine. 15-Nov-3 Illustration House, New York #74/R est:1800-2400

THOMAS, Paul (1859-1910) French
£284 $455 €415 Landscape from Heimatdorf in Norway (40x50cm-16x20in) s. panel. 22-Sep-3 Rasmussen, Vejle #193/R (D.KR 3000)
£421 $664 €610 By the duck pond (42x50cm-17x20in) s. 2-Sep-3 Rasmussen, Copenhagen #1770/R (D.KR 4500)
£5333 $9653 €8000 La toilette des communiantes (139x103cm-55x41in) s. exhib. 31-Mar-4 Sotheby's, Paris #131/R est:8000-12000

THOMAS, Paul (1868-1910) French
£346 $620 €505 North African village (23x38cm-9x15in) mono. 22-Mar-4 Philippe Schuler, Zurich #6196 (S.FR 800)

THOMAS, Paul Kirk Middlebrook (1875-1962) American
£217 $375 €317 Woodland landscape in springtime (25x36cm-10x14in) s. board. 10-Dec-3 Alderfer's, Hatfield #369/R

THOMAS, Pieter Hendrik (1814-1866) Dutch
£1053 $1937 €1600 Fishermen in a mountainous river landscape (23x33cm-9x13in) s. panel. 28-Jun-4 Sotheby's, Amsterdam #40/R est:1600-1800
£1382 $2542 €2100 Sailing vessels offshore (23x32cm-9x13in) s. panel. 28-Jun-4 Sotheby's, Amsterdam #39/R est:1600-1800
£1468 $2452 €2100 Sailing vessel at sea (20x28cm-8x11in) s. panel prov. 30-Jun-3 Sotheby's, Amsterdam #153/R

THOMAS, Richard D (1935-) American
£1056 $1700 €1542 Flathead (15x11cm-6x4in) board. 22-Aug-3 Altermann Galleries, Santa Fe #116
£8235 $14000 €12023 Moving the 7th cavalry (76x102cm-30x40in) 1-Nov-3 Altermann Galleries, Santa Fe #100

THOMAS, Rover (c.1926-1998) Australian
£15702 $26694 €22925 Canning stock route (107x202cm-42x80in) natural earth pigment acrylic binders on canvas prov. 29-Oct-3 Lawson Menzies, Sydney #56/R est:40000-50000 (A.D 38000)
Prints
£2033 $3211 €2948 Baroogoo country (113x135cm-44x53in) s.i.num.13/20 lithograph prov. 28-Jul-3 Sotheby's, Paddington #292/R est:4000-6000 (A.D 5000)
£2734 $5113 €4101 Punmu, the universe (112x77cm-44x30in) num.12 of 50 serigraph print. 26-Jul-4 Sotheby's, Melbourne #463/R est:2000-3000 (A.D 7000)
£3455 $5459 €5010 Mt Newman (79x70cm-31x28in) s.i.num.11/50 etching exec.c.1996 prov.exhib.lit. 28-Jul-3 Sotheby's, Paddington #291/R est:6000-8000 (A.D 8500)
Works on paper
£4314 $7722 €6298 Cyclone Tracy - Lightening (92x60cm-36x24in) s. verso natural earth pigments linen prov. 25-May-4 Lawson Menzies, Sydney #152/R est:12000-15000 (A.D 11000)
£4706 $8424 €6871 Cyclone Tracy (51x71cm-20x28in) s. verso natural earth pigments linen exec 1995. 25-May-4 Lawson Menzies, Sydney #173/R est:8000-12000 (A.D 12000)
£5285 $8350 €7663 Waterfall, Nindjirramangin country (80x100cm-31x39in) i.verso earth pigments binder canvas prov. 28-Jul-3 Sotheby's, Paddington #294/R est:7000-10000 (A.D 13000)
£6098 $9634 €8842 Untitled (51x71cm-20x28in) s.verso earth pigments binder linen exec.c.1996 prov. 28-Jul-3 Sotheby's, Paddington #414/R est:4000-6000 (A.D 15000)
£6641 $12418 €9962 Mirrilinggi Hill (40x60cm-16x24in) i.verso pigment canvas exec. c.1995 prov. 21-Jul-4 Shapiro, Sydney #20/R est:12000-18000 (A.D 17000)
£7843 $14039 €11451 Claypen (91x90cm-36x35in) i. verso natural earth pigments linen exec 1995 prov. 25-May-4 Lawson Menzies, Sydney #20/R est:25000-30000 (A.D 20000)
£7843 $14039 €11451 Crossroads (92x122cm-36x48in) natural earth pigments linen exec 1995. 25-May-4 Lawson Menzies, Sydney #155/R est:30000-40000 (A.D 20000)
£8264 $14050 €12065 Mounthouse Station homestead (100x183cm-39x72in) s.verso natural earth pigment synthetic binders on canvas prov. 29-Oct-3 Lawson Menzies, Sydney #81/R est:30000-40000 (A.D 20000)
£8594 $16070 €12891 Untitled (92x124cm-36x49in) bears name earth pigments bush gum prov. 26-Jul-4 Sotheby's, Melbourne #222/R est:40000-60000 (A.D 22000)
£8943 $14130 €12967 Balabudd country (50x70cm-20x28in) earth pigments binders canvas prov.exhib. 28-Jul-3 Sotheby's, Paddington #125/R est:30000-40000 (A.D 22000)
£10744 $18264 €15686 Gundimulul, Wolf Creek (120x160cm-47x63in) natural earth pigment brush resins on board prov. 29-Oct-3 Lawson Menzies, Sydney #53/R est:25000-30000 (A.D 26000)
£12195 $19268 €17683 Crossroads (93x125cm-37x49in) i.verso earth pigments binder linen exec.c.1996 prov. 28-Jul-3 Sotheby's, Paddington #417/R est:30000-40000 (A.D 30000)
£19531 $36523 €29297 Barragoo, Lake Gregory (94x104cm-37x41in) earth pigments bush gum prov. 26-Jul-4 Sotheby's, Melbourne #221/R est:50000-80000 (A.D 50000)
£19919 $31472 €28883 Owl (67x58cm-26x23in) s.verso earth pigments binders composition board prov. 28-Jul-3 Sotheby's, Paddington #123/R est:50000-80000 (A.D 49000)
£23577 $37252 €34187 Roads cross (76x91cm-30x36in) s.verso natural earth pigments binders canvas exec.c.1987 prov. 28-Jul-3 Sotheby's, Paddington #105/R est:30000-50000 (A.D 58000)
£24390 $38537 €35366 Willy willy (61x106cm-24x42in) s.verso earth pigments binder prov. 28-Jul-3 Sotheby's, Paddington #203/R est:40000-60000 (A.D 60000)
£25957 $44906 €37897 Black rock at well (80x160cm-31x63in) i.verso natural pigment canvas prov. 10-Dec-3 Shapiro, Sydney #181/R est:60000-90000 (A.D 61000)
£27451 $49137 €40078 Lake Gregory (99x179cm-39x70in) i. verso natural earth pigment linen exec 1995. 25-May-4 Lawson Menzies, Sydney #36/R est:40000-60000 (A.D 70000)
£32520 $51382 €47154 Junction of the Ord river (90x120cm-35x47in) i.verso earth pigments bush gum canvas prov.exhib. 28-Jul-3 Sotheby's, Paddington #126/R est:80000-120000 (A.D 80000)
£37109 $69395 €55664 Dumbun, owls (60x59cm-24x23in) s. verso earth pigments bush gum plywood prov. 26-Jul-4 Sotheby's, Melbourne #29/R est:70000-100000 (A.D 95000)
£37109 $69395 €55664 Bunkangrill creek (92x102cm-36x40in) bears i.verso earth pigments bush gum canvas prov. 26-Jul-4 Sotheby's, Melbourne #219/R est:120000-160000 (A.D 95000)
£44531 $83273 €66797 Owl (76x50cm-30x20in) s. verso earth pigments bush gum prov. 26-Jul-4 Sotheby's, Melbourne #27/R est:70000-100000 (A.D 114000)
£48828 $91309 €73242 Juntarkal rainbow serpent (60x122cm-24x48in) earth pigments bush gum board prov. 26-Jul-4 Sotheby's, Melbourne #122/R est:80000-120000 (A.D 125000)
£50980 $91255 €74431 Crossroads (200x266cm-79x105in) natural earth pigments linen exec 1995 prov. 25-May-4 Lawson Menzies, Sydney #41/R est:150000-200000 (A.D 130000)
£82031 $153398 €123047 Untitled (60x120cm-24x47in) earth pigments bush gum plywood prov. 26-Jul-4 Sotheby's, Melbourne #128/R est:120000-180000 (A.D 210000)
£97561 $154146 €141463 Massacre site, Old Texas Downs (100x168cm-39x66in) s.verso earth pigments bush gums linen prov. 28-Jul-3 Sotheby's, Paddington #201/R est:250000-350000 (A.D 240000)

£132114 $208740 €191565 Yillimbiddi country (100x140cm-39x55in) i.verso earth pigments bush gum canvas prov.exhib.lit. 28-Jul-3 Sotheby's, Paddington #127/R est:200000-300000 (A.D 325000)
£166667 $263333 €241667 Burago, Lake Gregory (121x162cm-48x64in) i.verso earth pigments bush gum canvas prov.exhib. 28-Jul-3 Sotheby's, Paddington #106/R est:150000-250000 (A.D 410000)
£263672 $493066 €395508 Uluru, Ayers Rock (90x180cm-35x71in) i. earth pigments bush gum prov. 26-Jul-4 Sotheby's, Melbourne #129/R est:700000-1000000 (A.D 675000)

THOMAS, Stephen Seymour (1868-1956) American
£1190 $2250 €1737 Boys with sailboat at water's edge (25x33cm-10x13in) s. i. verso panel. 17-Feb-4 John Moran, Pasadena #40a/R est:1200-1800

THOMAS, Thomas (19th C) British
£300 $510 €438 Cattle watering in an extensive landscape (41x66cm-16x26in) s. 30-Oct-3 Duke & Son, Dorchester #153a
£550 $902 €803 River landscape with cottages (38x48cm-15x19in) s. 6-Jun-3 Biddle & Webb, Birmingham #228
£1000 $1840 €1460 Homewards, travelers on a wooded lane (51x76cm-20x30in) s. 8-Jun-4 Gorringes, Lewes #2013/R est:1000-1500

THOMAS, Thomas Henry (1839-1915) British
£414 $691 €600 English landscape with farmstead (30x45cm-12x18in) s. 9-Jul-3 Hugo Ruef, Munich #228
£556 $928 €800 Landscape with farmstead (30x45cm-12x18in) s. 24-Oct-3 Ketterer, Hamburg #240/R

THOMAS, Victor (1854-?) German
Works on paper
£454 $785 €663 Quiet reflections (32x23cm-13x9in) s. ink exec. 1890-1900. 14-Dec-3 Agra, Warsaw #9/R (P.Z 3000)

THOMAS, Walter (1894-1971) British
£700 $1253 €1022 Booth Line tanker Hubert at sea (81x107cm-32x42in) s. 26-May-4 Christie's, Kensington #540/R
Works on paper
£1000 $1790 €1460 Booth Line vessel Hildebrand in various locations (37x49cm-15x19in) s. pencil W/C htd white four. 26-May-4 Christie's, Kensington #541/R est:1200-1800

THOMAS, William (19th C) British
£24000 $40080 €35040 Portrait of George Morgan standing wearing uniform of the 2nd Royal Hussars (126x100cm-50x39in) s. 14-Oct-3 Sotheby's, London #466/R est:4000-6000

THOMAS, William Barton (1877-1947) British
Works on paper
£260 $442 €380 Boston from the Scalp (20x27cm-8x11in) s.i. W/C. 18-Nov-3 Bonhams, Leeds #78

THOMASSE, A (1850-1930) French
£1918 $3260 €2800 Sangliers s'abreuvant (60x73cm-24x29in) s.d.1926. 5-Nov-3 Rabourdin & Choppin de Janvry, Paris #76/R est:1200-1500

THOMASSE, Adolphe (1850-1930) French
£1103 $2041 €1600 Arlequins festoyant (24x32cm-9x13in) s.d.1872 panel. 19-Jan-4 Horta, Bruxelles #93 est:1800-2200

THOMASSIN, Desire (1858-1933) Austrian
£276 $461 €400 Peasant with horses (35x24cm-14x9in) s. board. 9-Jul-3 Hugo Ruef, Munich #229
£915 $1584 €1300 Haymaking (48x58cm-19x23in) s. cardboard. 10-Dec-3 Hugo Ruef, Munich #2508/R
£966 $1612 €1400 Flock of sheep in heath landscape (14x18cm-6x7in) s. panel prov. 15-Nov-3 Lempertz, Koln #1706/R est:2000
£1000 $1820 €1500 Peasant with wagon on track (20x26cm-8x10in) s. panel. 30-Jun-4 Neumeister, Munich #712/R
£1310 $2188 €1900 Herder with animals in autumnal landscape (122x94cm-48x37in) s. board lit. 12-Jul-3 Bergmann, Erlangen #657/R est:2200
£1389 $2208 €2000 Peasant with horse and cart on country road (15x23cm-6x9in) s. panel. 11-Sep-3 Weidler, Nurnberg #315 est:2000
£1467 $2625 €2200 Village street with horse drawn cart in Upper Bavaria (13x17cm-5x7in) s. panel. 13-May-4 Bassenge, Berlin #5673 est:900
£1633 $2922 €2400 Hay harvest (26x42cm-10x17in) s. panel. 17-Mar-4 Neumeister, Munich #632/R est:2200
£1678 $2887 €2400 Haymaking in farm landscape (12x48cm-5x19in) s. panel. 3-Dec-3 Neumeister, Munich #767/R est:2500
£1747 $3179 €2551 Hunting party in a winter woodland landscape (75x55cm-30x22in) s.d.1896. 16-Jun-4 Fischer, Luzern #1101/R est:3000-4000 (S.FR 4000)
£2041 $3653 €3000 Upper Bavarian moorland (100x120cm-39x47in) s.i.d.1928 i. stretcher. 17-Mar-4 Neumeister, Munich #630/R est:2500
£2361 $3896 €3400 Harvesting hay in the pre-alps (27x36cm-11x14in) s. board. 3-Jul-3 Van Ham, Cologne #1480/R est:2200
£2778 $4417 €4000 Enjoying the ice in the evening. Winter landscape with windmill (14x22cm-6x9in) s.d.1899 panel two. 11-Sep-3 Weidler, Nurnberg #4918
£2817 $4507 €4000 Peasant couple with horse drawn wagon (30x40cm-12x16in) s. panel lit. 19-Sep-3 Sigalas, Stuttgart #431/R est:4500
£3691 $6792 €5500 Fishmarket on beach (40x54cm-16x21in) s.i.d.1918. 27-Mar-4 L & B, Essen #207/R est:2500
£3819 $6493 €5500 Dorf im Winter bei Morgendammerung (46x75cm-18x30in) s.i.d.1897. 28-Oct-3 Christie's, Amsterdam #82/R est:6000-8000

THOMASSIN, Louise (20th C) French
£667 $1207 €1000 Still life of flowers with asters, mimosa, and berries in copper pot (51x75cm-20x30in) s.d.16 board on canvas. 1-Apr-4 Van Ham, Cologne #1668/R

THOME, Verner (1878-1953) Finnish
£517 $941 €760 Bridge in Rutumi (27x34cm-11x13in) s.d.1926. 8-Feb-4 Bukowskis, Helsinki #470/R
£664 $1129 €950 Rapids (41x34cm-16x13in) s.d.1931 exhib. 29-Nov-3 Bukowskis, Helsinki #65/R
£811 $1451 €1200 Pine tree in summer (52x41cm-20x16in) s.d.1930 board exhib. 8-May-4 Bukowskis, Helsinki #90/R
£2000 $3580 €3000 Archipelago (42x69cm-17x27in) s.d.1913. 15-May-4 Hagelstam, Helsinki #168/R est:3000
£3446 $6168 €5100 Children playing (54x71cm-21x28in) 8-May-4 Bukowskis, Helsinki #194/R est:2500-3500
£15000 $25800 €21900 Boys bathing in strong sunshine (141x230cm-56x91in) s.d.1913. 7-Dec-3 Uppsala Auktionskammare, Uppsala #173/R est:80000-100000 (S.KR 195000)
Works on paper
£633 $1165 €950 Boy on beach (25x27cm-10x11in) s. W/C gouache. 9-Jun-4 Bukowskis, Helsinki #567/R
£804 $1367 €1150 Finnish boy (56x34cm-22x13in) s. W/C exhib. 29-Nov-3 Bukowskis, Helsinki #55/R

THOMING, Frederik Christian (1802-1873) Danish
£3194 $5015 €4600 Bay of Naples near Castellamare in evening (27x39cm-11x15in) mono.d.1847 panel. 30-Aug-3 Hans Stahl, Toestorf #93/R est:3600
£16115 $29490 €23528 Italian fishermen in their boats off Naples (55x72cm-22x28in) s.d.1848 prov. 9-Jun-4 Rasmussen, Copenhagen #1419/R est:150000-200000 (D.KR 180000)

THOMIRE, Pierre Philippe (attrib) (1751-1843) French
Sculpture
£8633 $14158 €12000 Bacchus et une lionne. Ceres tenant une gerbe de ble (37x13x13cm-15x5x5in) gilt bronze pair. 6-Jun-3 Maigret, Paris #181/R est:11000-15000

THOMKINS, Andre (1930-1985) Swiss
Works on paper
£1055 $1762 €1530 Moraine near Eriswil (21x12cm-8x5in) s.i.d.1973 pencil. 19-Jun-3 Kornfeld, Bern #976 est:3000 (S.FR 2300)

THOMMESEN, Erik (1916-) Danish
Sculpture
£4883 $8154 €7129 Figure (181cm-71in) s.d.1945 carved oak. 7-Oct-3 Rasmussen, Copenhagen #37/R est:40000-60000 (D.KR 52000)

THOMON, Thomas de (1754-1813) French
Works on paper
£432 $691 €600 Landscape with anglers (18x23cm-7x9in) s. i.verso pencil card. 14-May-3 Finarte Semenzato, Milan #514/R

THOMOPOULOS, Epaminondas (1878-1974) Greek
£900 $1611 €1314 Figure in a landscape (26x16cm-10x6in) s. canvasboard. 11-May-4 Bonhams, New Bond Street #37/R
£1500 $2625 €2190 Hunters in a mountainous winter landscape (33x42cm-13x17in) s. canvas on board. 16-Dec-3 Bonhams, New Bond Street #73/R est:1500-2000
£2400 $4344 €3504 Farm girl tending turkeys (41x70cm-16x28in) s. 1-Apr-4 Christie's, Kensington #129/R est:2000-3000
£3000 $5370 €4380 Seascape (30x30cm-12x12in) s. canvas on hardboard. 11-May-4 Bonhams, New Bond Street #69/R est:2000-3000
£6000 $10500 €8760 Mythological scene (47x123cm-19x48in) s. 16-Dec-3 Bonhams, New Bond Street #84/R est:6000-8000
£6000 $10740 €8760 Snowy day (61x90cm-24x35in) 10-May-4 Sotheby's, Olympia #137/R est:6000-8000
£6000 $10740 €8760 A shepherdess with her flock (57x93cm-22x37in) s.d.1923. 11-May-4 Bonhams, New Bond Street #38/R est:6000-8000
£11000 $19250 €16060 In the country, near Patras (45x64cm-18x25in) s.d.1905. 16-Dec-3 Bonhams, New Bond Street #28/R est:6000-8000

THOMPSON, Alfred Wordsworth (1840-1896) American
£3629 $6750 €5298 The ox cart (22x35cm-9x14in) s. 5-Mar-4 Skinner, Boston #288/R est:1000-1500

THOMPSON, Algernon (1880-1944) British
£300 $489 €438 Study of a bay horse (35x41cm-14x16in) s.d.1905. 25-Sep-3 Clevedon Sale Rooms #198

THOMPSON, Bob (1937-1966) American
Works on paper
£2400 $3912 €3504 A Portrait Negroid (56x43cm-22x17in) s.i.d.July 1964 col wash. 23-Sep-3 John Nicholson, Haslemere #178/R est:500-1000

THOMPSON, Cephas Giovanni (1809-1888) American
£629 $1000 €918 Portrait of John Gray (71x61cm-28x24in) 10-Sep-3 Sotheby's, New York #333/R

THOMPSON, E (19/20th C) ?
Works on paper
£691 $1147 €1002 Ship's portrait, Aster of Fredrikshald (37x54cm-15x21in) s. gouache. 16-Jun-3 Blomqvist, Lysaker #1351/R (N.KR 8000)

THOMPSON, Edward (?) ?
Works on paper
£580 $922 €847 Extensive river landscape (21cm-8in circular) s.d.1922 W/C. 9-Sep-3 Bamfords, Derby #1088

THOMPSON, Edward H (1866-1949) British
£420 $727 €613 Eagle Crag (33x58cm-13x23in) s.d.1903. 11-Dec-3 Mitchells, Cockermouth #869/R
Works on paper
£270 $500 €394 Coniston Lake (18x25cm-7x10in) s.d.1913 W/C. 15-Jul-4 Mitchells, Cockermouth #874/R
£380 $699 €555 Wastwater and Great Gable (30x44cm-12x17in) s. W/C. 14-Jun-4 Bonhams, Bath #21
£400 $644 €580 Landscape with cottages in the distance (28x38cm-11x15in) s. W/C. 15-Aug-3 Keys, Aylsham #450
£400 $632 €584 Misty lake and mountain scene (15x23cm-6x9in) s. W/C. 24-Jul-3 Mitchells, Cockermouth #906
£400 $740 €584 Quiet evening, Bassenthwaite Lake and Skiddaw (18x25cm-7x10in) s. W/C. 15-Jul-4 Mitchells, Cockermouth #624/R
£420 $752 €613 After rain, Loch Katrine (24x35cm-9x14in) s. W/C. 25-May-4 Bonhams, Knightsbridge #268/R
£420 $785 €630 Swelling seas up a rocky inlet (50x40cm-20x16in) s. W/C. 26-Jul-4 Bonhams, Bath #17/R
£460 $764 €672 Buttermere (18x23cm-7x9in) s.d.1924 W/C. 2-Oct-3 Mitchells, Cockermouth #859
£460 $842 €672 Loch Lomond (18x25cm-7x10in) s.d.04 W/C. 27-Jan-4 Gorringes, Lewes #1595
£500 $790 €730 Derwentwater with Causey Pike and Grisdale Pike from Broomhill Point (23x33cm-9x13in) s. 24-Jul-3 Mitchells, Cockermouth #847
£500 $915 €730 Sunset on Luch Lomond (17x25cm-7x10in) s. W/C. 8-Apr-4 Bonhams, Edinburgh #132
£500 $910 €730 Misty Highland loch with sheep grazing (24x39cm-9x15in) s. W/C. 15-Jun-4 Rosebery Fine Art, London #614
£540 $999 €788 Lake District farmhouse with attached barn (20x33cm-8x13in) s.d.1919 W/C. 15-Jul-4 Mitchells, Cockermouth #573/R
£550 $913 €803 Mountainous lake scene with fisher folk and birds flying (38x25cm-15x10in) s. W/C. 2-Oct-3 Biddle & Webb, Birmingham #877
£580 $916 €847 Thirlmere and Helvellyn (20x25cm-8x10in) s.d.1928 W/C. 24-Jul-3 Mitchells, Cockermouth #891/R
£580 $916 €847 Ashness Bridge (20x25cm-8x10in) s.d.1928 W/C. 24-Jul-3 Mitchells, Cockermouth #892/R
£600 $1038 €876 River, silver birch and mountain scene (25x18cm-10x7in) s.d.1925 W/C. 11-Dec-3 Mitchells, Cockermouth #930/R
£600 $1074 €876 Waterlily Bay, Derwentwater (23x33cm-9x13in) s.d.1919 W/C. 13-May-4 Mitchells, Cockermouth #1018/R
£620 $1073 €905 Scale Force near Crummock Water. Dungeon Ghyll near Ambleside (25x18cm-10x7in) s. W/C pair. 11-Dec-3 Mitchells, Cockermouth #924
£680 $1224 €993 The sweetest hour of eve, Coniston from Water Head (18x24cm-7x9in) s.d.1925 pencil W/C htd white. 21-Apr-4 Tennants, Leyburn #1026
£700 $1211 €1022 Rising Mists - Loch Kating. W/C. 9-Dec-3 Lawrences, Bletchingley #1831
£700 $1295 €1022 Eventide, Coniston Lake (17x24cm-7x9in) s.d.1922 W/C. 14-Jul-4 Bonhams, Chester #308/R
£720 $1325 €1080 In autumn (25x33cm-10x13in) s. W/C bodycol. 23-Jun-4 Byrne's, Chester #667/R
£740 $1369 €1080 Watendlath House (20x33cm-8x13in) s.d.1919 W/C. 15-Jul-4 Mitchells, Cockermouth #576/R
£750 $1253 €1095 An August morning (17x25cm-7x10in) s. W/C. 16-Oct-3 Bonhams, Edinburgh #169
£750 $1298 €1095 Ennerdale (23x36cm-9x14in) s.d.1922 W/C. 11-Dec-3 Mitchells, Cockermouth #868/R
£750 $1185 €1095 Windermere from near Wrea (25x36cm-10x14in) s.d.1928 W/C. 24-Jul-3 Mitchells, Cockermouth #904/R
£750 $1403 €1125 View of the Langdale Pikes from across Lake Windermere (30x46cm-12x18in) s. W/C. 26-Jul-4 Bonhams, Bath #18/R
£780 $1459 €1170 Wastwater (26x36cm-10x14in) s. W/C. 26-Jul-4 Bonhams, Bath #16/R
£800 $1336 €1168 Scene in the Lake District (26x36cm-10x14in) s. W/C paper on board. 16-Oct-3 Lawrence, Crewkerne #665/R
£800 $1384 €1168 Sweet peace of the early morn, river Derwent near Bassenthwaite lake (30x58cm-12x23in) s. W/C. 11-Dec-3 Mitchells, Cockermouth #922/R
£800 $1384 €1168 Crummock and Buttermere with Honister Crag, the Haystack and High Crag (21x26cm-8x10in) s. W/C. 9-Dec-3 Anderson & Garland, Newcastle #332
£800 $1480 €1168 Newlands Valley (25x46cm-10x18in) s. W/C. 15-Jul-4 Mitchells, Cockermouth #497/R
£850 $1411 €1241 Late afternoon on Windermere (23x38cm-9x15in) W/C. 2-Oct-3 Mitchells, Cockermouth #856/R
£900 $1611 €1314 Scafell from Great Gable (23cm-9in circular) s.d.1923 W/C. 13-May-4 Mitchells, Cockermouth #1003/R
£900 $1611 €1314 Haweswater (23cm-9in circular) s.d.1923 W/C. 13-May-4 Mitchells, Cockermouth #1004/R
£900 $1665 €1314 River, mountains and forest (36x48cm-14x19in) s. W/C. 15-Jul-4 Mitchells, Cockermouth #515/R
£900 $1665 €1314 Ennerdale Lake (25x36cm-10x14in) W/C. 15-Jul-4 Mitchells, Cockermouth #553/R
£950 $1501 €1387 Lake District scene, possibly Wastwater (23x38cm-9x15in) s. W/C. 24-Jul-3 Mitchells, Cockermouth #843/R
£950 $1777 €1387 Head of Derwentwater, the Shepherd Crag and Loclose from Waterlily Bay (9x16cm-4x6in) s.d.29 i.verso W/C. 25-Feb-4 Mallams, Oxford #310/R
£950 $1710 €1387 Lakeland landscape with a stone bridge, cottages nearby, mountains beyond (21x26cm-8x10in) s. pencil W/C. 21-Apr-4 Tennants, Leyburn #1025
£1000 $1580 €1460 Bassenthwaite Lake (28x48cm-11x19in) s. W/C. 24-Jul-3 Mitchells, Cockermouth #844/R est:1000-1500
£1000 $1580 €1460 Ashness Bridge (28x43cm-11x17in) s. W/C. 24-Jul-3 Mitchells, Cockermouth #845/R est:1000-1500
£1000 $1580 €1460 Foxglove time, Bassenthwaite Lake and Skiddaw from the Wythop Fell (23x38cm-9x15in) s. W/C. 24-Jul-3 Mitchells, Cockermouth #905/R est:800-1200
£1000 $1580 €1460 Ennerdale (28x43cm-11x17in) s.d.1925 W/C. 24-Jul-3 Mitchells, Cockermouth #917/R est:1000-1500
£1000 $1860 €1460 Spring time, River Derwent in Borrowdale. s. W/C. 4-Mar-4 Mitchells, Cockermouth #846 est:500-800
£1050 $1880 €1533 Lake District scene with bullrushes and silver birch (18x23cm-7x9in) s.d.1924 W/C. 13-May-4 Mitchells, Cockermouth #1002/R est:200-400
£1150 $1921 €1679 Blue and russet of October, the Trossachs above Ardlui (35x25cm-14x10in) s. W/C. 16-Oct-3 Bonhams, Edinburgh #180 est:600-800
£1200 $2040 €1752 Lakescene in October with Bassenthwaite Lake from Armathwaite (29x50cm-11x20in) s. W/C. 24-Nov-3 Tiffin King & Nicholson, Carlisle #220/R est:1000-1500
£1200 $2208 €1752 When the light is veiled, Rydal Water (19x30cm-7x12in) s.d.1928 W/C. 8-Jun-4 Bonhams, Knightsbridge #71/R est:500-800
£1220 $2184 €1781 Near Dockray, Ullswater (18x25cm-7x10in) s.d.1924 W/C. 13-May-4 Mitchells, Cockermouth #1001/R est:300-500
£1250 $2163 €1825 Buttermere with haystacks (23x33cm-9x13in) s.d.1922 W/C. 11-Dec-3 Mitchells, Cockermouth #867/R est:700-1000
£1300 $2457 €1898 Blue bells in a Lake District landscape with fells beyond (15x23cm-6x9in) s. W/C. 19-Feb-4 Richardson & Smith, Whitby #39
£1300 $2431 €1898 The budding year, Keswick. Spring time, Keswick (25x35cm-10x14in) s. pencil W/C pair. 22-Jul-4 Tennants, Leyburn #738/R est:1000-1500
£1350 $2511 €1971 View from Fleetwith Pike (28x20cm-11x8in) s. W/C. 4-Mar-4 Mitchells, Cockermouth #777/R est:250-350
£1700 $2686 €2482 An autumn morning, Derwentwater and Bassenthwaite Lake with Skiddaw (25x38cm-10x15in) s. W/C. 24-Jul-3 Mitchells, Cockermouth #925/R est:600-800
£1800 $2880 €2628 Windermere (23x46cm-9x18in) s. W/C. 15-May-3 Mitchells, Cockermouth #1021/R est:1000-1500
£1900 $3230 €2774 Passing gleams, Derwentwater and the Borrowdale Fells from Friars Crag (28x44cm-11x17in) s.d.1921 pencil W/C. 19-Nov-3 Tennants, Leyburn #992/R est:1000-1500
£1950 $3120 €2847 Ennerdale (43x58cm-17x23in) s.d.1923 W/C. 15-May-3 Mitchells, Cockermouth #1050/R est:1000-1500
£2000 $3640 €2920 Crab apple blossom near Ambleside. Early summer, the River Brathay, Ambleside (23x28cm-9x11in) s. W/C pair. 20-Jun-4 Lawrences, Bletchingley #1311 est:2000-2500
£2100 $3570 €3066 Lakescene at heather time with Crummock Water and Buttermere (29x49cm-11x19in) s. W/C. 24-Nov-3 Tiffin King & Nicholson, Carlisle #219/R est:1000-1500
£2200 $3476 €3212 When summer wanes, Crummock Water with Red Pike, High Crag, High Stile and Rannerdale Knott (25x51cm-10x20in) s. W/C. 24-Jul-3 Mitchells, Cockermouth #908/R est:1000-1500
£2300 $4117 €3358 Fine afternoon, Bassenthwaite Lake from the Armathwaite shore (36x51cm-14x20in) s. W/C. 13-May-4 Mitchells, Cockermouth #998/R est:1200-1800
£2300 $4048 €3358 Views at Derwentwater (42x57cm-17x22in) s.d.1922 W/C pair. 19-May-4 John Bellman, Billingshurst #1853/R est:600-900

THOMPSON, Francis Roy (1896-1967) Australian
£830 $1386 €1245 Moored boats (49x54cm-19x21in) s. 27-Oct-3 Goodman, Sydney #167/R (A.D 2000)

THOMPSON, G (?) ?
£718 $1300 €1048 English landscape with cottage (41x51cm-16x20in) s. sold with painting by Charles G Morris and another hand. 18-Apr-4 Bonhams & Butterfields, Los Angeles #7042 est:500-750

THOMPSON, Gabriel (fl.1889-1908) British
£270 $459 €394 Mountain river landscape (35x50cm-14x20in) s. board. 25-Nov-3 Bonhams, Knowle #249/R

THOMPSON, J T (19th C) British
£460 $768 €672 A sharp between two flats (77x63cm-30x25in) s.d.1852 i.verso. 14-Oct-3 Bonhams, Ipswich #309

THOMPSON, Jerome (1814-1886) American
£442 $800 €645 Portrait of a seated girl wearing a pink dress and holding a book (76x64cm-30x25in) painted 1837. 2-Apr-4 Eldred, East Dennis #881a
£723 $1200 €1048 Landscape. 14-Jun-3 Fallon, Copake #114/R
£904 $1500 €1311 Landscape. s. 14-Jun-3 Fallon, Copake #369/R

THOMPSON, Maureen (20th C) Australian
Works on paper
£255 $456 €372 Old Way for Aboriginal people (53x56cm-21x22in) synthetic polymer paint canvas exec 2002. 25-May-4 Lawson Menzies, Sydney #297/R (A.D 650)

THOMPSON, Mrs Jerome (19th C) American
£798 $1300 €1197 Child with puppy (61x46cm-24x18in) s.d.1883. 28-Sep-3 Carlsen Gallery, Greenville #106/R

THOMPSON, Pauline (1942-) New Zealander
£870 $1400 €1270 Burning St Thomas' Church, Napier (45x60cm-18x24in) init.d.1984 s.i.verso. 12-Aug-3 Peter Webb, Auckland #115/R (NZ.D 2400)

THOMPSON, Richard Earl (attrib) (1914-1991) American
£811 $1500 €1217 Quiet playground, two children picking flowers in a landscape (46x61cm-18x24in) s. 19-Jul-4 Schrager Galleries, Milwaukee #755/R

THOMPSON, Sydney Lough (1877-1973) New Zealander
£347 $552 €507 Storm over Manapouri (16x26cm-6x10in) s. 1-May-3 Dunbar Sloane, Wellington #91 est:1000-2000 (NZ.D 1000)
£486 $773 €710 Snow covered landscape (16x26cm-6x10in) s. canvas on board. 1-May-3 Dunbar Sloane, Wellington #110 est:2000-3000 (NZ.D 1400)
£1656 $3096 €2500 Marche breton pres des halles (22x27cm-9x11in) s. board. 24-Jul-4 Thierry & Lannon, Brest #226/R est:1200-1500
£1684 $2981 €2459 Harbour at Quimper, Brittany (15x18cm-6x7in) s. canvasboard oval. 28-Apr-4 Dunbar Sloane, Auckland #40/R est:3500-5500 (NZ.D 4750)
£3200 $5728 €4800 Chapelle de Locmaria An Hent (46x61cm-18x24in) s. 16-May-4 Thierry & Lannon, Brest #188/R est:5000-6000
£3571 $6571 €5214 Rocky hill from across the Matukituki river (36x44cm-14x17in) s. board. 25-Mar-4 International Art Centre, Auckland #79/R est:10000-15000 (NZ.D 10000)
£4286 $7886 €6258 Loading, Concarneau (22x27cm-9x11in) s. board. 25-Mar-4 International Art Centre, Auckland #73/R est:14000-18000 (NZ.D 12000)
£5000 $9200 €7300 Plage des Dames, Concarneau (21x27cm-8x11in) s. board exhib. 25-Mar-4 International Art Centre, Auckland #72/R est:14000-18000 (NZ.D 14000)

£6522 $10565 €9457 Garden at Glaciere (31x40cm-12x16in) s. 31-Jul-3 International Art Centre, Auckland #23/R est:18000-26000 (NZ.D 18000)
£6767 $11504 €9880 Pardon near Penmarch, Brittany (31x40cm-12x16in) s. board exhib. 27-Nov-3 International Art Centre, Auckland #75/R est:20000-28000 (NZ.D 18000)
£6920 $12388 €10103 Tourette sur Loupe, France (45x54cm-18x21in) s. 11-May-4 Watson's, Christchurch #16/R est:14000-20000 (NZ.D 20000)
£7785 $13936 €11366 Les vignes en automne (65x50cm-26x20in) s. 11-May-4 Watson's, Christchurch #24/R est:20000-35000 (NZ.D 22500)
£8700 $16094 €12702 Lake Pearson, Canterbury (50x61cm-20x24in) s. 9-Mar-4 Watson's, Christchurch #46 est:11000-20000 (NZ.D 23750)
£9890 $18296 €14439 Porte en Provence (61x50cm-24x20in) s. 9-Mar-4 Watson's, Christchurch #14 est:16000-24000 (NZ.D 27000)
£15977 $27162 €23326 Fisherman, Concarneau (45x54cm-18x21in) s. 27-Nov-3 International Art Centre, Auckland #70/R est:40000-50000 (NZ.D 42500)
Works on paper
£1681 $3042 €2454 An old stone church (36x44cm-14x17in) s. gouache. 30-Mar-4 Stephan Welz, Johannesburg #167 est:2000-3000 (SA.R 20000)
£2455 $3854 €3560 Winter sunlight (38x56cm-15x22in) s. gouache. 27-Aug-3 Dunbar Sloane, Wellington #44/R est:6500-9000 (NZ.D 6750)

THOMPSON, Tim (1951-) British
£420 $785 €613 Sailing ship (24x19cm-9x7in) s. oval. 22-Jul-4 Martel Maides, Guernsey #196/R
£700 $1169 €1022 H.M.S Ferret preparing for action off Cape Griz Nez (76x101cm-30x40in) s.i.d.1978. 11-Nov-3 Bonhams, Knightsbridge #228/R
£1639 $3000 €2393 British and American schooners off St Catherine's Point, Isle of Wight (24x30cm-9x12in) s. 29-Jul-4 Christie's, Rockefeller NY #311/R est:5000-7000
£3514 $6500 €5130 J-class yachts racing in the light airs off the Brenton lightship (30x41cm-12x16in) s. 10-Feb-4 Christie's, Rockefeller NY #249/R est:10000-15000
£7500 $14175 €10950 Britannia off the Royal Yacht Squadron (76x102cm-30x40in) s. 17-Feb-4 Bonhams, New Bond Street #52/R est:8000-12000

THOMPSON, Walter W (1881-1948) American
£732 $1200 €1069 Now the day is over (51x76cm-20x30in) s. 4-Jun-3 Alderfer's, Hatfield #270/R

THOMS, Ernst (1896-1983) German
£8000 $14720 €12000 Cowhead (38x38cm-15x15in) s.i.d.1924 cardboard exhib. 12-Jun-4 Villa Grisebach, Berlin #237/R est:12000-15000

THOMSEN, August Carl Wilhelm (1813-1886) Danish
£478 $775 €693 Wooded landscape with lake and deer (69x97cm-27x38in) s. 4-Aug-3 Rasmussen, Vejle #310/R (D.KR 5000)
£6075 $9598 €8809 Thyra Dannebod telling King Gorm that his son Knud has died (140x116cm-55x46in) s. exhib.prov. 2-Sep-3 Rasmussen, Copenhagen #1621/R est:30000-40000 (D.KR 65000)

THOMSEN, Emma Augusta (1822-1897) Danish
£606 $951 €885 Branch of gooseberries (19x17cm-7x7in) s. cardboard. 30-Aug-3 Rasmussen, Havnen #2102 (D.KR 6500)
£9883 $18383 €14429 Flowers in a basket (41x51cm-16x20in) s.d.1853 panel exhib.prov. 2-Mar-4 Rasmussen, Copenhagen #1260/R est:70000-80000 (D.KR 110000)

THOMSEN, Frederik Gotfred (1819-1891) Danish
£867 $1361 €1266 Interior scene with young girl with parrot, cat and dog (77x64cm-30x25in) s. 30-Aug-3 Rasmussen, Havnen #2058/R (D.KR 9300)

THOMSEN, Jorgen (1905-1959) Danish
£517 $837 €750 Cubist landscape (80x103cm-31x41in) s.d.33. 4-Aug-3 Rasmussen, Vejle #691 (D.KR 5400)

THOMSEN, René (1897-1976) French
£664 $1143 €950 Baigneuses (50x65cm-20x26in) s.d.22. 5-Dec-3 Gros & Delettrez, Paris #75

THOMSEN, Valdemar (?) ?
Works on paper
£995 $1782 €1453 A swan (88x114cm-35x45in) init. W/C pastel. 10-May-4 Rasmussen, Vejle #260/R (D.KR 11000)

THOMSON OF DUDDINGTON, Rev John (1778-1840) British
£340 $629 €496 Scottish landscape (17x24cm-7x9in) indis.i.d.1833 verso panel. 9-Mar-4 Bonhams, Knightsbridge #133/R
£2000 $3580 €2920 Fast Castle (36x50cm-14x20in) lit.exhib. 28-May-4 Lyon & Turnbull, Edinburgh #54/R est:2000-3000

THOMSON, Adam Bruce (1885-1976) British
£4500 $8505 €6570 Old Dean Bridge (75x90cm-30x35in) s. 19-Feb-4 Lyon & Turnbull, Edinburgh #145 est:1000-1500
Works on paper
£380 $635 €555 Loch Leven and Glencoe (34x52cm-13x20in) s. W/C en grisaille. 16-Oct-3 Bonhams, Edinburgh #207
£780 $1326 €1139 Path to Duncraig, Plockton. s. W/C. 10-Nov-3 Thomson Roddick & Medcalf, Edinburgh #216/R
£1200 $2064 €1752 Cuillins from the Mainland (32x48cm-13x19in) s. pencil W/C. 4-Dec-3 Bonhams, Edinburgh #23/R est:1500-2000
£1200 $2064 €1752 Plockton Village (33x41cm-13x16in) s. pencil W/C. 4-Dec-3 Bonhams, Edinburgh #52/R est:1200-1500
£1300 $2093 €1885 Path down to Plockton (19x23cm-7x9in) s. W/C. 21-Aug-3 Bonhams, Edinburgh #1131/R est:1200-1800
£1500 $2580 €2190 Autumn, Peeblesshire (49x61cm-19x24in) s. W/C. 4-Dec-3 Bonhams, Edinburgh #28/R est:1500-2500
£2800 $4508 €4060 Strand, Calva, Iona (29x40cm-11x16in) s. W/C. 21-Aug-3 Bonhams, Edinburgh #1132/R est:1500-2500

THOMSON, Alastair W (20th C) British
£380 $635 €555 Slioch, Loch Maree (49x74cm-19x29in) s. 16-Oct-3 Bonhams, Edinburgh #59
£380 $635 €555 September day, Colonsay (50x75cm-20x30in) s. 16-Oct-3 Bonhams, Edinburgh #62

THOMSON, Alfred Reginald (1895-1979) British
Works on paper
£325 $553 €475 Back view of a reclining nude (36x48cm-14x19in) s.d.38 crayon. 5-Nov-3 John Nicholson, Haslemere #565

THOMSON, Ann (1933-) Australian
£3292 $5959 €4806 Subterfuge (200x300cm-79x118in) s.d.88 verso. 30-Mar-4 Lawson Menzies, Sydney #115 est:5000-7000 (A.D 8000)
£3306 $6116 €4827 Primavera (196x243cm-77x96in) s.d.87 i.verso prov.exhib. 15-Mar-4 Sotheby's, Melbourne #8/R est:5000-10000 (A.D 8000)
Works on paper
£243 $391 €355 Journey (34x42cm-13x17in) s.d.86 i.verso crayon chl prov. 25-Aug-3 Sotheby's, Paddington #429/R (A.D 600)
£309 $559 €451 Instinct series XI (80x60cm-31x24in) s.d.90 i.verso mixed media. 30-Mar-4 Lawson Menzies, Sydney #139/R (A.D 750)

THOMSON, Carl Christian Frederik Jakob (1847-1912) Danish
£430 $774 €628 Portrait of Elise Dieckmann (22x17cm-9x7in) 24-Apr-4 Rasmussen, Havnen #2093 (D.KR 4800)
£629 $1170 €918 Wooded landscape (41x30cm-16x12in) init.d.87. 2-Mar-4 Rasmussen, Copenhagen #1339 (D.KR 7000)
£717 $1290 €1047 Portraits of the vicar and his wife from Stubbekobing (56x45cm-22x18in) init.d.1872 pair. 24-Apr-4 Rasmussen, Havnen #2096 (D.KR 8000)
£941 $1694 €1374 Portrait of the artist's daughter Elise (81x65cm-32x26in) mono. 24-Apr-4 Rasmussen, Havnen #2095/R (D.KR 10500)

THOMSON, George (1868-1965) Canadian
£1915 $3255 €2796 Shore road, Georgian Bay (63x76cm-25x30in) s.d.1935 s.i.verso. 27-Nov-3 Heffel, Vancouver #188/R est:2500-3500 (C.D 4250)

THOMSON, Henry (1773-1843) British
£2000 $3340 €2920 Lady holding up a bowl of fruit and flowers (104x86cm-41x34in) after Titian. 8-Oct-3 Halls, Shrewsbury #91/R est:1200-1800
£4000 $7280 €5840 Sleeping child (100x125cm-39x49in) prov.exhib. 1-Jul-4 Sotheby's, London #154/R est:4000-6000

THOMSON, Henry Grinnell (1850-1939) American
£2232 $3839 €3259 Lambert House, Wilton (42x51cm-17x20in) s. prov. 2-Dec-3 Ritchie, Toronto #89/R est:2500-4000 (C.D 5000)

THOMSON, Jeff (20th C) New Zealander
Sculpture
£2431 $3865 €3549 Cow (122cm-48in) s.d.1993 corrugated iron mixed media. 1-May-3 Dunbar Sloane, Wellington #19/R est:3000-5000 (NZ.D 7000)
£3014 $5335 €4400 Elephant (121cm-48in) s.d.1986 verso oil corrugated iron. 28-Apr-4 Dunbar Sloane, Auckland #30/R est:6000-8000 (NZ.D 8500)

THOMSON, John Murray (1885-1974) British
£260 $434 €380 Goat, kids in a barn (50x75cm-20x30in) s. 23-Oct-3 Bonhams, Edinburgh #355
£750 $1253 €1095 Highland ponies (60x90cm-24x35in) s. 16-Oct-3 Bonhams, Edinburgh #123
£2000 $3460 €2920 Highland shepherd (91x51cm-36x20in) s. 11-Dec-3 Lyon & Turnbull, Edinburgh #89/R est:2000-3000

THOMSON, Nigel (1945-) Australian
£658 $1192 €961 Untitled - man and child (163x247cm-64x97in) s.d.81 acrylic. 30-Mar-4 Lawson Menzies, Sydney #196 est:300-500 (A.D 1600)

THOMSON, Tom (1877-1917) Canadian
£9910 $16847 €14469 Nocturne, camp in the woods (23x36cm-9x14in) prov. 18-Nov-3 Sotheby's, Toronto #101/R est:15000-18000 (C.D 22000)
£13514 $22973 €19730 Summer landscape (24x32cm-9x13in) board prov.lit. 18-Nov-3 Sotheby's, Toronto #119/R est:25000-30000 (C.D 30000)
£14228 $25467 €20773 On the Sydenham River (29x37cm-11x15in) s. prov. 31-May-4 Sotheby's, Toronto #189/R est:35000-40000 (C.D 35000)
£38000 $69540 €55480 Spring, Algonquin Park (21x26cm-8x10in) panel prov.lit. 1-Jun-4 Joyner Waddington, Toronto #51/R est:100000-150000 (C.D 95000)
£40179 $69107 €58661 Moonlight nocturne (20x25cm-8x10in) board painted c.1913-1914 prov.lit. 2-Dec-3 Joyner Waddington, Toronto #49/R est:50000-70000 (C.D 90000)
£54054 $91892 €78919 Islands, Canoe Lake (18x25cm-7x10in) i.verso canvasboard prov. 18-Nov-3 Sotheby's, Toronto #12/R est:50000-70000 (C.D 120000)
Works on paper
£596 $1085 €900 Un carrefour (29x22cm-11x9in) mono. W/C. 16-Jun-4 Renaud, Paris #46

THON, Fernand (1892-1981) Belgian
£333 $610 €500 Still life with anemones (33x38cm-13x15in) s. 7-Jun-4 Glerum, Amsterdam #42/R

THON, Miltiadis (1875-1945) Greek
Works on paper
£25000 $43750 €36500 Views of Greece. fifteen s.d.1895 to 1937 W/C 135 album. 16-Dec-3 Bonhams, New Bond Street #19/R est:25000-30000

THON, Sixt (1817-1901) German

£3438	$5741	€5019	Two children (85x85cm-33x33in) s.d.1851. 19-Oct-3 Agra, Warsaw #20/R est:12000 (P.Z 22000)

THON, William (1916-2000) American

£556	$1000	€812	Beached boat (20x33cm-8x13in) s. canvas on cardboard. 23-Jan-4 Freeman, Philadelphia #163/R
£761	$1400	€1111	Trees and arches (55x90cm-22x35in) s. oil mixed media board. 27-Jun-4 Freeman, Philadelphia #131/R est:1000-1500
£944	$1700	€1378	Composition (91x91cm-36x36in) s. 23-Jan-4 Freeman, Philadelphia #108/R est:600-800
£1359	$2500	€1984	Golden autumn (122x58cm-48x23in) s. i. verso board prov.exhib. 27-Jun-4 Freeman, Philadelphia #133/R est:3000-5000
£1728	$2800	€2506	Ancient architecture (51x77cm-20x30in) s. prov. 8-Aug-3 Barridorf, Portland #186/R est:3000-5000
£3827	$6200	€5549	Waterfall (55x89cm-22x35in) s. board prov.exhib. 8-Aug-3 Barridorf, Portland #234/R est:3000-5000
Works on paper			
£438	$700	€639	Bird Island (51x66cm-20x26in) s. W/C acrylic. 17-May-3 Bunte, Elgin #1270
£1235	$2000	€1791	Hadrian's Villa (46x70cm-18x28in) s. W/C. 8-Aug-3 Barridorf, Portland #21/R est:2000-3000
£1728	$2800	€2506	Grand Canal (5x76cm-2x30in) s. W/C gouache. 8-Aug-3 Barridorf, Portland #317/R est:3000-5000

THONING, Lars (1949-1996) Danish

£360	$576	€526	Surrealistic landscape with eagle (40x50cm-16x20in) s. 22-Sep-3 Rasmussen, Vejle #643/R (D.KR 3800)

THONY, Wilhelm (1888-1949) Austrian

£23490	$41577	€35000	Meeting (34x45cm-13x18in) panel lit. 28-Apr-4 Wiener Kunst Auktionen, Vienna #113/R est:25000-50000
£34965	$59441	€50000	Eggenberg Castle (34x56cm-13x22in) s. board double-sided. 25-Nov-3 Hassfurther, Vienna #69/R est:50000-70000
£38462	$65385	€55000	The Brooklyn Bridge (46x60cm-18x24in) s. board. 26-Nov-3 Lempertz, Koln #1001/R est:50000-60000
Works on paper			
£1174	$2102	€1750	In the restaurant (25x31cm-10x12in) s. pen wash. 27-May-4 Hassfurther, Vienna #73/R est:2500-3500
£1645	$3026	€2500	New York (28x34cm-11x13in) pencil. 22-Jun-4 Wiener Kunst Auktionen, Vienna #142/R est:2500
£3758	$6728	€5600	Paris (33x41cm-13x16in) s. pencil. 27-May-4 Hassfurther, Vienna #72/R est:2500-3500
£4027	$7208	€6000	Paris, street scene - Rue Suresne (32x35cm-13x14in) s. Indian ink pen brush wash. 25-May-4 Dorotheum, Vienna #186/R est:3400-4500

THOPAS, Johannes (c.1630-c.1700) Dutch

Works on paper			
£11111	$20000	€16222	Portrait of a seated old lady holding a book (24x19cm-9x7in) gouache prov.exhib. 21-Jan-4 Sotheby's, New York #60/R est:20000-30000

THORBJORN, Einar (?) Scandinavian?

£375	$600	€548	Saddle Iceberg, Greenland (68x97cm-27x38in) s.indis.i. 21-Sep-3 Bonhams & Butterfields, San Francisco #2816/R

THORBURN, Archibald (1860-1935) British

£1500	$2715	€2190	Portrait of a bearded gentleman holding a gun (74x61cm-29x24in) s.d.1858. 31-Mar-4 Bonhams, Knightsbridge #24a/R est:1500-2000
£5114	$9000	€7466	Seascape with a polar bear standing on the ice flow (69x117cm-27x46in) s. i.stretcher. 3-Jan-4 Cobbs, Peterborough #34/R
Works on paper			
£550	$935	€803	Scottish mountain hare, summer (13x9cm-5x4in) s.i.verso pencil W/C gouache oval prov. 19-Nov-3 Tennants, Leyburn #913
£650	$1047	€943	Wildcat prowling (11x16cm-4x6in) pencil. 21-Aug-3 Bonhams, Edinburgh #1034
£800	$1464	€1168	Woodcock (13x19cm-5x7in) init. W/C. 28-Jul-4 Bonhams, Knightsbridge #73/R
£1600	$2672	€2336	Ring plover (9x12cm-4x5in) s. W/C gouache. 12-Nov-3 Sotheby's, Olympia #134/R est:1000-1500
£1806	$2979	€2600	Flying sea eagle over surf (39x29cm-15x11in) s.d.1921 W/C. 3-Jul-3 Van Ham, Cologne #1481 est:400
£2400	$4080	€3504	Golden Eagle on a dead stag (16x25cm-6x10in) s. grisaille. 30-Oct-3 Christie's, London #40/R est:1500-2000
£2800	$5152	€4088	Birds (8x11cm-3x4in) one s.i. pen ink pencil sketches set of eight. 10-Jun-4 Christie's, Kensington #258/R est:700-1000
£3600	$6624	€5256	Rough legged buzzard, Buteo lagopus (26x17cm-10x7in) s.d.1917 W/C. 8-Jun-4 Bonhams, New Bond Street #74/R est:4000-6000
£3600	$6588	€5256	Grouse in flight (38x46cm-15x18in) s.d.87 W/C. 28-Jul-4 Bonhams, Knightsbridge #70/R est:4000-6000
£3800	$6460	€5548	Honey Buzzard (27x18cm-11x7in) s.d.1917 pencil W/C bodycol gum arabic. 30-Oct-3 Christie's, London #38/R est:4000-6000
£3800	$6954	€5548	Mallard on the water's edge (45x67cm-18x26in) s.d.1882 W/C htd white. 28-Jul-4 Bonhams, Knightsbridge #72/R est:4000-6000
£5000	$8800	€7300	Cock pheasant in flight (48x63cm-19x25in) s. pencil W/C htd bodycol buff paper. 21-May-4 Christie's, London #63/R est:6000-8000
£5500	$9350	€8030	Gyr Falcon (27x18cm-11x7in) s.d.1917 pencil W/C bodycol gum arabic. 30-Oct-3 Christie's, London #32/R est:6000-8000
£5500	$9350	€8030	Montagu's Harrier (27x18cm-11x7in) s.d.1917 pencil W/C bodycol gum arabic. 30-Oct-3 Christie's, London #39/R est:5000-7000
£5800	$9860	€8468	Goshawk (27x18cm-11x7in) s.d.1917 pencil W/C bodycol gum arabic buff paper. 30-Oct-3 Christie's, London #33/R est:5000-7000
£6200	$10540	€9052	Marsh Harrier (27x19cm-11x7in) s.d.1917 pencil W/C bodycol gum arabic. 30-Oct-3 Christie's, London #36/R est:5000-7000
£6200	$10540	€9052	Kestrel (28x18cm-11x7in) s.d.1917 pencil W/C bodycol. 30-Oct-3 Christie's, London #37/R est:4000-6000
£6400	$11008	€9344	Sentinel (20x26cm-8x10in) s.d.1900 W/C pencil htd gouache. 3-Dec-3 Bonhams, Knightsbridge #48/R est:4000-6000
£6500	$11895	€9490	Pheasants in a bluebell wood (19x26cm-7x10in) s.d.1932 W/C htd bodycol. 28-Jul-4 Bonhams, Knightsbridge #67/R est:3000-5000
£7200	$12384	€10512	Flushed pheasants, autumn (53x74cm-21x29in) s.d.1899 W/C bodycol. 3-Dec-3 Bonhams, Knightsbridge #47/R est:7000-9000
£7200	$13176	€10512	Peregrine Falcon (53x36cm-21x14in) s.d.1901 W/C htd white. 28-Jul-4 Bonhams, Knightsbridge #71/R est:3000-5000
£7500	$12750	€10950	Capercaillie on a Scot's Pine (33x24cm-13x9in) s.d.1926 pencil W/C bodycol prov.exhib. 30-Oct-3 Christie's, London #27/R est:7000-10000
£8000	$13600	€11680	Red grouse on moorland (18x26cm-7x10in) s.d.1933 pencil W/C bodycol prov. 30-Oct-3 Christie's, London #28/R est:8000-12000
£8000	$14640	€11680	Golden plovers in flight (37x55cm-15x22in) s.d.1928 W/C htd white. 28-Jul-4 Bonhams, Knightsbridge #66/R est:2000-3000
£8200	$13940	€11972	Sparrowhawk in winter (27x18cm-11x7in) s.d.1917 pencil W/C bodycol gum arabic. 30-Oct-3 Christie's, London #30/R est:7000-10000
£8200	$15006	€11972	Frost-bound spring, snipe in winter (27x37cm-11x15in) s.d.1913 W/C htd bodycol. 28-Jul-4 Bonhams, Knightsbridge #64/R est:2000-3000
£8500	$14450	€12410	Peregrine Falcon (27x19cm-11x7in) s.d.1917 pencil W/C bodycol gum arabic buff paper. 30-Oct-3 Christie's, London #31/R est:7000-10000
£8500	$14450	€12410	Merlin (26x18cm-10x7in) s.d.1917 pencil W/C bodycol gum arabic buff paper. 30-Oct-3 Christie's, London #35/R est:6000-8000
£8500	$15470	€12410	Golden Eagle (26x18cm-10x7in) s.d.1916 W/C htd bodcol prov.exhib.lit. 1-Jul-4 Sotheby's, London #341/R est:7000-10000
£8800	$14960	€12848	Hobby (27x18cm-11x7in) s.d.1916 pencil W/C bodycol gum arabic buff paper. 30-Oct-3 Christie's, London #34/R est:5000-7000
£9000	$14130	€13050	Pintail ducks (33x55cm-13x22in) s. W/C. 27-Aug-3 Sotheby's, London #991/R est:10000-15000
£9500	$16150	€13870	Pheasant in winter (53x36cm-21x14in) s.d.1899 pencil W/C bodycol gum arabic scratching out prov. 30-Oct-3 Christie's, London #26/R est:10000-15000
£9500	$17385	€13870	Pheasants in a wood, a cock and a hen (18x27cm-7x11in) s.d.1932 W/C htd. bodycol. 28-Jul-4 Bonhams, Knightsbridge #65/R est:2500-3000
£10000	$18200	€14600	Red partridges (26x35cm-10x14in) s.d.1913 W/C htd bodcol. 1-Jul-4 Sotheby's, London #340/R est:10000-15000
£10000	$18200	€14600	Common eider ducks (51x41cm-20x16in) s.d.1912 W/C bodycol prov.lit. 1-Jul-4 Sotheby's, London #343/R est:7000-10000
£10800	$19764	€15768	Nesting Grey Partridge in clover (18x27cm-7x11in) s. W/C bodycol. 28-Jul-4 Bonhams, Knightsbridge #68/R est:3000-5000
£11000	$18700	€16060	Goldenye and tufted duck (27x36cm-11x14in) s.d.1919 pencil W/C bodycol gum arabic buff paper prov. 30-Oct-3 Christie's, London #29/R est:5000-8000
£11800	$21594	€17228	Woodcock and it's young (18x27cm-7x11in) s.d.1933 W/C htd bodycol. 28-Jul-4 Bonhams, Knightsbridge #69/R est:2500-3000
£12000	$18840	€17400	Evening roost, black game (36x53cm-14x21in) s. W/C htd white. 27-Aug-3 Sotheby's, London #989/R est:12000-18000
£12000	$21840	€17520	Woodcock nesting on a beach (26x37cm-10x15in) s.d.1910 W/C htd bodycol prov. 1-Jul-4 Sotheby's, London #342/R est:10000-15000
£13000	$20410	€18850	Golden eagle (56x37cm-22x15in) s.d.1828 W/C. 27-Aug-3 Sotheby's, London #987/R est:8000-12000
£15000	$23550	€21750	Red grouse in flight (33x55cm-13x22in) s.d.1926 W/C. 27-Aug-3 Sotheby's, London #988/R est:10000-15000
£16000	$29120	€23360	Common Snipe, Jack Snipe, Broad Billed Great Snipe and other birds in landscape setting (46x36cm-18x14in) s.d.1915 W/C. 4-Feb-4 John Nicholson, Haslemere #40/R est:15000-20000
£17000	$28900	€24820	Mallard and Teal in the snow (48x75cm-19x30in) s.d.1906 pencil W/C bodycol gum arabic. 30-Oct-3 Christie's, London #25/R est:12000-18000
£17000	$29920	€24820	Ptarmigan in winter plumage (28x49cm-11x19in) s. pencil W/C htd bodycol grey paper. 21-May-4 Christie's, London #62/R est:10000-15000
£18000	$30600	€26280	Dusting Partridge (28x39cm-11x15in) s. pencil W/C bodycol buff paper. 30-Oct-3 Christie's, London #53/R est:2000-3000
£24000	$42240	€35040	Lost roe (74x53cm-29x21in) s.d.1905 i.verso pencil W/C gum Arabic htd bodycol scratching out. 21-May-4 Christie's, London #61/R est:18000-25000
£26000	$40820	€37700	Ptarmigan in the snow (36x56cm-14x22in) s.i. W/C. 27-Aug-3 Sotheby's, London #990/R est:15000-20000
£28000	$47600	€40880	The lost hind (69x114cm-27x45in) s.d.1894 pencil W/C htd bodycol gum arabic exhib. 30-Oct-3 Christie's, London #50/R est:30000-50000
£30000	$51600	€43800	Grouse in flight across an extensive highland landscape (41x54cm-16x21in) s.d.1892 W/C htd. 3-Dec-3 Bonhams, Knightsbridge #50/R est:25000-30000
£80000	$140800	€116800	Bridle Path (56x76cm-22x30in) s.d.1910 pencil W/C htd bodycol gum Arabic lit. 21-May-4 Christie's, London #60/R est:60000-80000

THORBURN, Robert (1818-1885) British

Works on paper			
£320	$554	€467	Portrait of a lady (22x14cm-9x6in) W/C bodycol ivory. 11-Dec-3 Lyon & Turnbull, Edinburgh #103/R

THOREN, Esaias (1901-1981) Swedish

£292	$536	€438	The black fish (21x46cm-8x18in) s. panel. 14-Jun-4 Lilla Bukowskis, Stockholm #53 (S.KR 4000)
£398	$640	€581	Atoms (24x35cm-9x14in) s. panel. 25-Aug-3 Lilla Bukowskis, Stockholm #335 (S.KR 5200)
£474	$763	€692	The red fish (23x32cm-9x13in) s. 25-Aug-3 Lilla Bukowskis, Stockholm #62 (S.KR 6200)
£614	$1002	€896	Geometric composition with purple background (51x37cm-20x15in) s.d.1980 panel. 29-Sep-3 Lilla Bukowskis, Stockholm #936 (S.KR 8000)
£628	$1087	€917	Vasformer (45x30cm-18x12in) s. panel. 15-Dec-3 Lilla Bukowskis, Stockholm #48 (S.KR 8000)
£659	$1167	€962	The blue bird (29x37cm-11x15in) s.d.68 panel. 27-Apr-4 AB Stockholms Auktionsverk #661/R (S.KR 9000)
£660	$1142	€964	Geometric composition (22x61cm-9x24in) s.d.1971 panel. 15-Dec-3 Lilla Bukowskis, Stockholm #608/R (S.KR 8400)
£739	$1323	€1079	Composition with red background (37x71cm-15x28in) s.d.1961 panel. 28-May-4 Uppsala Auktionskammare, Uppsala #310/R (S.KR 10000)
£906	$1541	€1323	Geometric composition I (55x46cm-22x18in) s. panel prov. 5-Nov-3 AB Stockholms Auktionsverk #752/R (S.KR 12000)
£943	$1697	€1415	Surrealistic statues (46x55cm-18x22in) s. panel. 25-Apr-4 Goteborg Auktionsverk, Sweden #322/R (S.KR 13000)
£982	$1699	€1434	Jug and head (38x46cm-15x18in) s.d.56 panel. 15-Dec-3 Lilla Bukowskis, Stockholm #54 (S.KR 12500)
£994	$1600	€1451	Surrealistic beach scene (32x41cm-13x16in) s. panel. 25-Aug-3 Lilla Bukowskis, Stockholm #761 (S.KR 13000)
£1100	$1903	€1606	Surrealistic beach scene with shells (38x46cm-15x18in) s. panel. 15-Dec-3 Lilla Bukowskis, Stockholm #580 (S.KR 14000)
£1231	$2117	€1797	One tattered and one whole sculpture (38x45cm-15x18in) s.d.1956 panel. 7-Dec-3 Uppsala Auktionskammare, Uppsala #268/R est:15000-18000 (S.KR 16000)
£1523	$2741	€2224	Surrealistic landscape (48x82cm-19x32in) s. panel. 26-Apr-4 Bukowskis, Stockholm #80/R est:30000-35000 (S.KR 21000)
£1538	$2723	€2245	Lergoekar - composition with birds (24x33cm-9x13in) s.d.47 panel. 27-Apr-4 AB Stockholms Auktionsverk #662/R est:15000-18000 (S.KR 21000)

£1813 $3082 €2647 Still life of toy ocarinas (38x46cm-15x18in) s.d.1946 panel. 5-Nov-3 AB Stockholms Auktionsverk #800/R est:25000-30000 (S.KR 24000)
£2870 $4879 €4190 Composition in yellow (86x120cm-34x47in) s.d.62. 4-Nov-3 Bukowskis, Stockholm #52/R est:25000-30000 (S.KR 38000)
£5076 $9137 €7411 Prehistoric age (65x92cm-26x36in) s.d.1939 prov. 26-Apr-4 Bukowskis, Stockholm #83/R est:70000-80000 (S.KR 70000)
£6164 $11095 €8999 Surrealistic landscape with cypress (40x30cm-16x12in) s.d.1937 panel. 26-Apr-4 Bukowskis, Stockholm #153/R est:80000-100000 (S.KR 85000)
£7326 $12455 €10696 Judgement of Paris (61x51cm-24x20in) s.d.1926. 5-Nov-3 AB Stockholms Auktionsverk #776/R est:80000-100000 (S.KR 97000)
£12690 $22843 €18527 Torso and jugs (60x81cm-24x32in) s.d.1931 exhib.lit. 26-Apr-4 Bukowskis, Stockholm #149/R est:175000-200000 (S.KR 175000)
£47861 $86149 €69877 Dancers (86x51cm-34x20in) s.d.30. 26-Apr-4 Bukowskis, Stockholm #16/R est:300000-350000 (S.KR 660000)
Works on paper
£2271 $4020 €3316 Woman in landscape (50x30cm-20x12in) s.d.33 gouache. 27-Apr-4 AB Stockholms Auktionsverk #689/R est:20000-25000 (S.KR 31000)

THOREN, Gunnar (1931-2002) Swedish
£363 $653 €545 Tree by the Mediterranean (97x50cm-38x20in) s. 25-Apr-4 Goteborg Auktionsverk, Sweden #421/R (S.KR 5000)
£725 $1305 €1088 Composition with horizontal line (130x150cm-51x59in) s. 25-Apr-4 Goteborg Auktionsverk, Sweden #422/R (S.KR 10000)

THOREN, Otto von (1828-1889) Austrian
£826 $1379 €1198 River landscape (46x65cm-18x26in) s. 23-Jun-3 Philippe Schuler, Zurich #8638 (S.FR 1800)
£1007 $1883 €1500 Wild ride (24x45cm-9x18in) s. panel. 24-Feb-4 Dorotheum, Vienna #233/R est:2000-2500
£9790 $16643 €14000 Bringing in the hay before the storm (115x200cm-45x79in) s. 24-Nov-3 Dorotheum, Vienna #117/R est:16000-20000

THOREN, Otto von (attrib) (1828-1889) Austrian
£1119 $1869 €1600 Landscape with cows and peasants (47x70cm-19x28in) prov. 10-Oct-3 Stadion, Trieste #557/R est:1200-1600
£3947 $7263 €6000 Les bains a Trouville (28x42cm-11x17in) indis.mono. 25-Jun-4 Daguerre, Paris #133/R est:6000-8000

THORENFELD, Anton Erik (1839-1907) Danish
£656 $1128 €958 Landscape from Svendborg with sheep in summer (56x84cm-22x33in) s.d.1860 prov. 3-Dec-3 Museumsbygningen, Copenhagen #121/R (D.KR 7000)

THORESEN, Dag (1953-) Norwegian
£1281 $2293 €1870 Dripping dreamer (100x130cm-39x51in) init. i.d.1987-90 v,. 22-Mar-4 Blomqvist, Oslo #629/R est:24000-28000 (N.KR 16000)

THORJUSSEN, Kjell (1942-) Norwegian
£322 $588 €470 From Lofoten (79x110cm-31x43in) s. 2-Feb-4 Blomqvist, Lysaker #1307/R (N.KR 4000)
£459 $766 €670 From Lofoten (79x110cm-31x43in) s. 17-Nov-3 Blomqvist, Lysaker #1340 (N.KR 5500)

THORKILDSEN, Michael (1850-1925) Danish
£281 $458 €410 Cattle grazing in outskirts of wood (19x29cm-7x11in) init. 27-Sep-3 Rasmussen, Havnen #2206 (D.KR 3000)

THORLAKSON, Thorarinn Benedikt (1867-1924) Icelandic
£3430 $6310 €5008 Flade hills, Frederikshavn (35x45cm-14x18in) i.d.Juli 1901. 29-Mar-4 Rasmussen, Copenhagen #227/R est:40000 (D.KR 38000)
£3430 $6310 €5008 Landscape with snow covered mountains (23x35cm-9x14in) s.d.1902 i.stretcher. 29-Mar-4 Rasmussen, Copenhagen #249/R est:15000-20000 (D.KR 38000)
£4152 $7639 €6062 Flade church, Frederikshavn (31x47cm-12x19in) s.d.1901. 29-Mar-4 Rasmussen, Copenhagen #248/R est:40000 (D.KR 46000)
£4332 $7971 €6325 View of a blue lake with trees in foreground (22x32cm-9x13in) s.d.1901 lit. 29-Mar-4 Rasmussen, Copenhagen #228/R est:15000 (D.KR 48000)

THORMA, Janos (1870-1937) Hungarian
£2503 $4530 €3654 Lying woman (60x75cm-24x30in) s. 16-Apr-4 Mu Terem Galeria, Budapest #57/R (H.F 950000)

THORNAM, Emmy (1852-1935) Danish
£313 $573 €457 Bouquet of stocks (41x38cm-16x15in) s. 9-Jun-4 Rasmussen, Copenhagen #1866 (D.KR 3500)
£374 $591 €542 Forget-me-nots and beech leaves (43x57cm-17x22in) s. 2-Sep-3 Rasmussen, Copenhagen #1726/R (D.KR 4000)
£400 $756 €584 Daisies, lilac and other summer flowers in a pottery jug (41x46cm-16x18in) s. 19-Feb-4 Christie's, Kensington #264/R
£473 $818 €691 White hawthorn flowers (42x49cm-17x19in) s. exhib. 9-Dec-3 Rasmussen, Copenhagen #1582/R (D.KR 5000)
£670 $1085 €972 Chrysanthemums (52x45cm-20x18in) s. 4-Aug-3 Rasmussen, Vejle #149/R (D.KR 7000)
£670 $1085 €972 Flowers in basket (26x36cm-10x14in) s. 4-Aug-3 Rasmussen, Vejle #150/R (D.KR 7000)
£1083 $2025 €1581 Still life of red and white pelargoniums in jugs (50x60cm-20x24in) s. exhib. 25-Feb-4 Museumsbygningen, Copenhagen #157 est:6000-8000 (D.KR 12000)
£6250 $10438 €9000 Flowers and bush (93x74cm-37x29in) s. 24-Oct-3 Ketterer, Hamburg #114/R est:10000-11000

THORNAM, Maria Elise (1857-1901) Danish
£276 $470 €403 Landscape from Bagsvaerd Lake (47x40cm-19x16in) mono. exhib. 10-Nov-3 Rasmussen, Vejle #91/R (D.KR 3000)

THORNBERY, Hubert Anslow (19th C) British
£3000 $5670 €4380 Fishing fleet entering harbour (36x30cm-14x12in) s. 17-Feb-4 Bonhams, New Bond Street #32/R est:2000-3000

THORNDIKE, Charles Hall (1875-1935) American
£658 $1211 €1000 Vence (75x130cm-30x51in) s.i.d.1928 verso. 28-Jun-4 Joron-Derem, Paris #115
£1358 $2539 €2050 Bord de mer (32x41cm-13x16in) s.d.1910 panel. 24-Jul-4 Thierry & Lannon, Brest #227/R est:2000-2500

THORNE, Alfred (1850-1916) Swedish
£612 $985 €894 Summer landscape (39x61cm-15x24in) s.d.1891. 25-Aug-3 Lilla Bukowskis, Stockholm #122 (S.KR 8000)
£863 $1554 €1260 Landscape with figure (27x23cm-11x9in) s.d.77. 26-Jan-4 Lilla Bukowskis, Stockholm #352 (S.KR 11500)
£943 $1631 €1377 Still late summer (55x88cm-22x35in) s. 15-Dec-3 Lilla Bukowskis, Stockholm #663 (S.KR 12000)
£961 $1720 €1403 Summer landscape with Breven's work (38x60cm-15x24in) s.i.d.1891. 26-May-4 AB Stockholms Auktionsverk #2119/R est:15000-18000 (S.KR 13000)
£1846 $3175 €2695 Summer landscape with rapids (38x61cm-15x24in) s.d.1902. 3-Dec-3 AB Stockholms Auktionsverk #2520/R est:18000-20000 (S.KR 24000)
£3077 $5292 €4492 Spring landscape with figure and apple-tree in blossom (80x134cm-31x53in) s.d.1889. 2-Dec-3 Bukowskis, Stockholm #162/R est:50000-70000 (S.KR 40000)

THORNE, Anna Louise (1878-?) American
£6325 $10500 €9235 Blue eyes (69x89cm-27x35in) s. 4-Oct-3 Neal Auction Company, New Orleans #557/R est:6000-9000

THORNELEY, Charles (fl.1858-1898) British
£1150 $2128 €1679 Moored fishing vessels by a lighthouse (35x30cm-14x12in) s. 13-Jul-4 Rosebery Fine Art, London #650
£1397 $2500 €2040 Docks, early morning (45x61cm-18x24in) s. indis d. 6-May-4 Doyle, New York #30/R est:2000-3000
£1450 $2422 €2117 Off the Kentish Coast (28x38cm-11x15in) s. 10-Oct-3 Richardson & Smith, Whitby #84/R est:2000-2500
£2300 $3910 €3358 French fishing vessels preparing to head out to sea (25x41cm-10x16in) s. 25-Nov-3 Bonhams, Knowle #241/R est:800-1200

THORNELEY, Charles (attrib) (fl.1858-1898) British
£1900 $3515 €2774 Rochester (38x76cm-15x30in) indis sig.i. 11-Mar-4 Duke & Son, Dorchester #229/R est:800-1500

THORNHILL, Sir James (1675-1734) British
£7000 $12880 €10220 Neptune and Amphritrite (122x76cm-48x30in) prov. 11-Jun-4 Christie's, London #10/R est:4000-6000
Works on paper
£3000 $5100 €4380 Design for a ceiling (14x21cm-6x8in) pen ink wash over red chk. 27-Nov-3 Sotheby's, London #242/R est:1000-1500

THORNLEY (?) ?
£1100 $2079 €1606 Coastal scene with fishing folk (29x49cm-11x19in) s. 18-Feb-4 John Bellman, Billingshurst #1895 est:400-600
£1478 $2646 €2158 Harbour entrance with fishing boats and light house (25x41cm-10x16in) s. 26-May-4 AB Stockholms Auktionsverk #2394/R est:20000-25000 (S.KR 20000)
£1500 $2415 €2175 Moonlit harbour scene (33x30cm-13x12in) s. 13-Aug-3 Andrew Hartley, Ilkley #831/R est:500-800
£2289 $4167 €3342 Low tide (25x41cm-10x16in) indis.sig. 7-Feb-4 Rasmussen, Havnen #2013 est:4000-5000 (D.KR 25000)
£2900 $4669 €4205 Coastal scene with fishing boats (33x28cm-13x11in) s. 13-Aug-3 Andrew Hartley, Ilkley #830/R est:500-800

THORNLEY, Georges W (1857-1935) French
£2414 $4031 €3500 Les dunes (45x61cm-18x24in) s. 17-Nov-3 Delorme & Bocage, Paris #121/R est:3000-3500
Prints
£4520 $8000 €6599 Meules (22x26cm-9x10in) lithograph after Claude Monet. 30-Apr-4 Sotheby's, New York #161/R est:3000-5000
£6471 $11000 €9448 Repetition de danse (24x31cm-9x12in) s. lithograph after Degas. 31-Oct-3 Sotheby's, New York #241/R
£8000 $14560 €11680 Repetition (48x62cm-19x24in) s. black lithograph exec.c.1888 signed by and after Edgar Degas. 1-Jul-4 Sotheby's, London #157/R est:3000-4000

THORNLEY, Hubert (19th C) British
£400 $688 €584 Shipping at the mouth of the Thames (36x51cm-14x20in) s. 2-Dec-3 Gorringes, Lewes #2442/R
£1457 $2666 €2200 A fresh breeze (22x40cm-9x16in) s.i. verso. 8-Apr-4 Dorotheum, Vienna #215/R est:1800-2000
£2600 $4680 €3796 Off Greenwich, on the Thames (25x40cm-10x16in) s. i.verso. 21-Apr-4 Tennants, Leyburn #1101 est:1000-1500
£2923 $5028 €4268 Return of the fishing boat (36x30cm-14x12in) s. prov. 2-Dec-3 Bukowskis, Stockholm #296/R est:25000-30000 (S.KR 38000)
£3000 $4800 €4380 Margate (25x20cm-10x8in) s.i. panel. 16-Sep-3 Bonhams, New Bond Street #56/R est:2000-3000
£3500 $6475 €5250 Shipping off Scarborough (25x41cm-10x16in) s. 14-Jul-4 Sotheby's, Olympia #75/R est:1000-1500
£3800 $6080 €5548 Scarborough (25x20cm-10x8in) s.i. panel. 16-Sep-3 Bonhams, New Bond Street #55/R est:2000-3000
£3846 $6615 €5615 Sunrise, Collier Brig, Hastings (40x61cm-16x24in) s. 7-Dec-3 Uppsala Auktionskammare, Uppsala #113/R est:8000-10000 (S.KR 50000)
£6500 $10400 €9490 Low tide at Scarborough at sunrise (36x61cm-14x24in) s.i. i.verso. 16-Sep-3 Bonhams, New Bond Street #11/R est:3000-5000

THORNLEY, W (19/20th C) British
£1000 $1700 €1460 Fishing harbour scenes with various boats and distant church (43x33cm-17x13in) s. 5-Nov-3 John Nicholson, Haslemere #615/R est:1000-1500
£1600 $2512 €2320 Coastal scene with boats and fisherman (19x39cm-7x15in) s. 27-Aug-3 Dunbar Sloane, Wellington #95/R est:500-1500 (NZ.D 4400)

THORNLEY, William (19/20th C) British

£250 $448 €365 Hay barges and other shipping in the harbour (25x41cm-10x16in) s. 26-May-4 Christie's, Kensington #715/R
£600 $1116 €876 Moonlit harbour (20cm-8in circular) board. 4-Mar-4 Christie's, Kensington #549/R
£733 $1313 €1100 View of Antibes (56x67cm-22x26in) s. 12-May-4 Brissoneau, France #18/R
£800 $1464 €1168 Coastal scene with fisherfolk (19x39cm-7x15in) s. 6-Jul-4 Bonhams, Knightsbridge #234/R
£850 $1445 €1241 Meadway at dusk (25x20cm-10x8in) s. panel. 19-Nov-3 Christie's, Kensington #549/R
£860 $1436 €1256 Shipping at sunset (25x20cm-10x8in) mono i.verso panel. 17-Nov-3 Waddingtons, Toronto #87/R est:800-1200 (C.D 1900)
£900 $1548 €1314 U.S.S Chicago off Gravesend (36x31cm-14x12in) s.i. 2-Dec-3 Sotheby's, London #46/R
£1200 $2148 €1752 Old hulks on the Medway at dusk (25x20cm-10x8in) panel. 26-May-4 Christie's, Kensington #707/R est:1200-1800
£1277 $2132 €1800 Bateaux a maree basse (46x61cm-18x24in) s. 19-Jun-3 Millon & Associes, Paris #182/R est:2000-2500
£1300 $2210 €1898 Crowded waters off Dover (41x61cm-16x24in) s. 19-Nov-3 Christie's, Kensington #550
£1400 $2380 €2044 Fishing boats off a coastline, with a buoy and sea birds (20x41cm-8x16in) s. i.verso. 19-Nov-3 Tennants, Leyburn #1019 est:1500-2000
£1500 $2490 €2190 Shipping vessels in rough waters (30x46cm-12x18in) mono. 1-Oct-3 Bonhams, Knightsbridge #169/R est:1500-2000
£1500 $2550 €2190 Early morning. Early evening (35x30cm-14x12in) s. pair. 19-Nov-3 Christie's, Kensington #556/R
£1500 $2550 €2190 Busy shipping lanes (25x41cm-10x16in) s. 19-Nov-3 Christie's, Kensington #548/R
£1500 $2835 €2190 Dusk (36x30cm-14x12in) s. 17-Feb-4 Bonhams, New Bond Street #30/R est:1500-2000
£1500 $2685 €2190 Hulks in the Medway at dusk (35x30cm-14x12in) s. 26-May-4 Christie's, Kensington #709/R est:1500-2000
£1500 $2685 €2190 Fresh breeze off Margate (36x30cm-14x12in) s. 26-May-4 Christie's, Kensington #710/R est:1500-2000
£1600 $2656 €2336 Unloading the catch (25x20cm-10x8in) s. panel. 1-Oct-3 Bonhams, Knightsbridge #166/R est:800-1200
£1600 $2720 €2336 Fishing vessels (35x30cm-14x12in) s. 19-Nov-3 Christie's, Kensington #555/R
£1600 $2880 €2336 Figures and fishing boats on an estuary by moonlight (25x45cm-10x18in) i. 21-Apr-4 Tennants, Leyburn #1102 est:800-1200
£1650 $3086 €2409 Shipping in a harbour at dusk (31x25cm-12x10in) s. 20-Jul-4 Sworder & Son, Bishops Stortford #771/R est:500-800
£2000 $3400 €2920 Sunset over Whitby (25x41cm-10x16in) indis.sig. 19-Nov-3 Christie's, Kensington #551/R
£2000 $3780 €2920 Fishing boats making for Port (36x30cm-14x12in) s. 17-Feb-4 Bonhams, New Bond Street #31/R est:2000-3000
£2300 $3657 €3335 Estuary with sailing barges (25x45cm-10x18in) s. 9-Sep-3 David Duggleby, Scarborough #310/R est:2000-3000
£2400 $4488 €3600 Fishing boats off the coast and entering harbour by moonlight (15x20cm-6x8in) s. board pair. 22-Jul-4 Gorringes, Lewes #1862/R est:400-600
£2600 $4472 €3796 Whitby by moonlight (24x39cm-9x15in) s. 4-Dec-3 Mellors & Kirk, Nottingham #881/R est:2500-3000
£2600 $4654 €3796 Scarborough, fishing boats on the beach outside the harbour (34x39cm-13x15in) i. 17-May-4 David Duggleby, Scarborough #694/R est:1000-1500
£2623 $4800 €3830 Shipping in a calm at dusk (20x30cm-8x12in) s. 29-Jul-4 Christie's, Rockefeller NY #264/R est:6000-8000
£2750 $4373 €3988 Fishing boats outside Scarborough harbour (35x30cm-14x12in) s. 9-Sep-3 David Duggleby, Scarborough #334/R est:3000-4000
£2844 $4750 €4152 Ships off the coast (25x41cm-10x16in) s. prov. 23-Oct-3 Shannon's, Milford #242/R est:2000-3000
£3000 $5580 €4380 Coastal sunset with fishing boats (24x39cm-9x15in) s. 2-Mar-4 Bristol Auction Rooms #352/R est:2200-2500
£3000 $5370 €4380 Shipping in the Channel off the south coast. Crowded waters off the harbour mouth (25x41cm-10x16in) s. pair. 26-May-4 Christie's, Kensington #713/R est:3000-6000
£3200 $6048 €4672 Off Harwich (20x41cm-8x16in) s. bears i.verso. 17-Feb-4 Bonhams, New Bond Street #41/R est:1500-2000
£3600 $5976 €5256 Fishing before St Michael's Mount, Cornwall (34x28cm-13x11in) s. 2-Oct-3 Lane, Penzance #85/R est:2750-3500
£3800 $6460 €5548 Shoreham, Kent, with figures and boats at sunset (25x41cm-10x16in) s. i.verso. 19-Nov-3 Tennants, Leyburn #1018/R est:2500-3500
£4144 $7500 €6050 Harbour scenes (36x30cm-14x12in) s.i. pair. 3-Apr-4 Neal Auction Company, New Orleans #144/R est:5000-7000
£4595 $8500 €6709 Unloading the day's catch on the foreshore (25x41cm-10x16in) s. pair prov. 10-Feb-4 Christie's, Rockefeller NY #238/R est:6000-8000

Works on paper

£467 $849 €700 Mill along the river (24x34cm-9x13in) s. W/C. 4-Jul-4 Eric Pillon, Calais #71/R
£533 $971 €800 Wind mill (24x34cm-9x13in) s. W/C. 4-Jul-4 Eric Pillon, Calais #70/R
£690 $1262 €1000 Bord de village anime (34x49cm-13x19in) s. W/C. 1-Feb-4 Feletin, Province #124

THORNLEY, William (attrib) (19/20th C) British

£1300 $2158 €1898 Fishing boats in choppy waters off the coast (23x43cm-9x17in) bears sig.d.91 sold with a companion. 3-Oct-3 Mallams, Oxford #222/R est:800-1200

THORNTON, Leslie (1925-) British

Sculpture

£1200 $2184 €1752 Rising Sun (23x23cm-9x9in) s.d.1977 num.3/6 polished bronze. 4-Feb-4 Sotheby's, Olympia #91/R est:500-700

THORNTON, Mildred Valley (1890-1967) Canadian

£393 $711 €574 Wascana Park (20x25cm-8x10in) s. i.verso oil on paper board prov. 18-Apr-4 Levis, Calgary #114/R (C.D 950)
£528 $946 €771 Stanley Park (63x76cm-25x30in) s. i.verso canvasboard prov. 6-May-4 Heffel, Vancouver #142/R (C.D 1300)
£533 $875 €778 BC coast (23x25cm-9x10in) s. board. 28-May-3 Maynards, Vancouver #71 (C.D 1200)
£1198 $2169 €1749 Untitled - coastal fishermen (51x61cm-20x24in) s. prov. 18-Apr-4 Levis, Calgary #113/R est:2000-2500 (C.D 2900)
£1600 $2928 €2336 Arriving at the Potlatch (75x100cm-30x39in) s. card. 1-Jun-4 Joyner Waddington, Toronto #362/R est:4000-6000 (C.D 4000)
£2642 $4730 €3857 Mountain landscape (71x91cm-28x36in) s. prov. 6-May-4 Heffel, Vancouver #141/R est:2500-3500 (C.D 6500)

Works on paper

£196 $355 €286 Untitled - afternoon at the beach (16x18cm-6x7in) s. W/C prov. 18-Apr-4 Levis, Calgary #116/R (C.D 475)
£285 $509 €416 Indian village with totem (36x27cm-14x11in) s. W/C prov. 6-May-4 Heffel, Vancouver #140/R (C.D 700)

THORNTON, R (?) British?

Works on paper

£420 $701 €613 Woman outside a cottage overlooking a lake (36x51cm-14x20in) s. W/C. 20-Jun-3 Chrystals Auctions, Isle of Man #234

THORNTON, Robert John (1768-1837) British

Prints

£1639 $3000 €2393 Temple of flora, Superb lily (76x61cm-30x24in) col mezzotint aquatint executed 1800. 3-Jun-4 Christie's, Rockefeller NY #672/R est:1500-2000
£2077 $3800 €3032 Temple of flora, night blooming cereus (76x61cm-30x24in) col mezzotint aquatint executed c.1800 prov. 3-Jun-4 Christie's, Rockefeller NY #671/R est:4000-6000

THORNTON, Valerie (1931-1991) British

£600 $1074 €876 Entry in Jerusalem (78x102cm-31x40in) 16-Mar-4 Bonhams, Knightsbridge #160

THORNTON-CLARK, Emanuele (?) British?

£700 $1169 €1022 Portrait of a lady, in a chair (81x60cm-32x24in) 7-Oct-3 Bonhams, Knightsbridge #152/R

THORNYCROFT, Hamo (1850-1925) British

Sculpture

£2400 $4128 €3504 General Gordon (37cm-15in) s.i.d.1888 dark brown pat bronze. 4-Dec-3 Mellors & Kirk, Nottingham #1020/R est:1800-2500
£2800 $5012 €4088 Lieutenant Norman Donaldson (38cm-15in) s.d.1915 bronze. 16-Mar-4 Woolley & Wallis, Salisbury #104/R est:800-1200
£4500 $8280 €6570 Maquette for the mower (20cm-8in) init.d.1884 dark brown pat. bronze prov.lit. 11-Jun-4 Christie's, London #78/R est:5000-8000
£18000 $33120 €26280 Mower (59cm-23in) s.d.1884 brown black pat. bronze lit. 11-Jun-4 Christie's, London #171/R est:8000-12000

THORNYCROFT, Helen (1848-1912) British

£250 $395 €363 Maiden in a wood (24x19cm-9x7in) mono.d.66 board. 4-Sep-3 Christie's, Kensington #287
£260 $465 €380 Gathering seaweed (51x68cm-20x27in) mono. i.verso. 11-May-4 Bonhams, Knightsbridge #244b

THORP, Carl (1912-) American

£216 $400 €315 Cathedral from Chartres, New Orleans (48x69cm-19x27in) s.i.1959 masonite. 17-Jan-4 New Orleans Auction, New Orleans #744
£250 $425 €365 New Orleans city dump (51x61cm-20x24in) s.i.d.1969 verso board. 22-Nov-3 New Orleans Auction, New Orleans #1250
£307 $550 €448 South Street, Rockport, Mass (51x61cm-20x24in) s. s.i.d.Aug 1970 verso masonite. 14-May-4 Skinner, Boston #261/R

THORP, William Eric (1901-1993) British

£450 $752 €657 Thames tug, with Battersea bridge beyond (25x34cm-10x13in) s. board. 7-Oct-3 Bonhams, Knightsbridge #64/R
£480 $859 €701 Fishing trawlers in the harbour at Mevagissey (25x30cm-10x12in) s. board. 26-May-4 Christie's, Kensington #748/R
£1189 $2200 €1736 Towing out to sea (70x81cm-28x32in) s. masonite. 10-Feb-4 Christie's, Rockefeller NY #245/R est:3000-5000

THORPE, Hilda (1920-2000) American

£563 $900 €822 Blue divide (145x244cm-57x96in) s.i.d.76 verso acrylic. 20-Sep-3 Sloans & Kenyon, Bethesda #686/R

THORPE, Mackenzie (20th C) British

£280 $493 €409 Pink footed geese (61x61cm-24x24in) s.d.1941. 18-May-4 Woolley & Wallis, Salisbury #143/R
£380 $669 €555 Pink footed geese over the Lincolnshire coast (51x76cm-20x30in) s.d.1968. 18-May-4 Woolley & Wallis, Salisbury #144/R

Works on paper

£3500 $6405 €5110 Sheep swimming (58x51cm-23x20in) init.d.2000. 7-Apr-4 Andrew Hartley, Ilkley #1128 est:4000-6000
£3800 $6840 €5548 Study of two sheep on a hillside in distant landscape (46x31cm-18x12in) mono.i.d.92 pastel crayon. 21-Apr-4 Tennants, Leyburn #999/R est:1500-2000

THORPE, William Eric (1901-1993) British

£1600 $2880 €2336 View of Tower Bridge from the Thames (23x28cm-9x11in) s. board sold with four others by same hand five. 20-Jan-4 Bonhams, Knightsbridge #126/R est:500-700

THORRISEN, Jon (1951-) Norwegian

£402 $736 €587 Landscape (40x50cm-16x20in) s. 2-Feb-4 Blomqvist, Lysaker #1311 (N.KR 5000)

THORS, Joseph (fl.1863-1900) British

£260 $434 €380 Old Banks Farm (26x21cm-10x8in) s. 22-Oct-3 Cheffins, Cambridge #516
£340 $622 €496 Stream and cottages at sunset (28x38cm-11x15in) s. 7-Apr-4 Gardiner & Houlgate, Bath #311/R

£400	$720	€584	Landscape with a figure near a windmill (23x30cm-9x12in) s. 22-Apr-4 Mellors & Kirk, Nottingham #1061
£440	$695	€638	Pastoral river landscape (28x16cm-11x6in) canvasboard. 4-Sep-3 Bonhams, Cornwall #477
£500	$810	€725	In a forest (51x41cm-20x16in) s. 30-Jul-3 Hamptons Fine Art, Godalming #280
£500	$920	€730	Rural landscape with an angler seated beneath a willow tree (61x51cm-24x20in) s. 8-Jun-4 Lawrences, Bletchingley #1396
£580	$986	€847	Country barns with figure and two horses (52x42cm-20x17in) s. 1-Dec-3 David Duggleby, Scarborough #324/R
£600	$1002	€876	Figure and birds (38x48cm-15x19in) s. 17-Oct-3 Keys, Aylsham #703
£700	$1309	€1050	Farmyard scene with figures and distant sea view (40x60cm-16x24in) s. 26-Jul-4 Bonhams, Bath #65/R
£814	$1360	€1188	Sussex homestead (20x30cm-8x12in) s. i.stretcher. 17-Nov-3 Waddingtons, Toronto #102/R est:1500-2000 (C.D 1800)
£880	$1461	€1285	Figures on a path by a thatched cottage (56x70cm-22x28in) s. 1-Oct-3 Woolley & Wallis, Salisbury #293/R
£1000	$1790	€1460	Returning to the farm (40x61cm-16x24in) s. 27-May-4 Christie's, Kensington #171/R est:500-700
£1041	$1738	€1520	Woman and children outside a thatched cottage (25x35cm-10x14in) bears sig. 17-Nov-3 Waddingtons, Toronto #103/R est:2500-3500 (C.D 2300)
£1102	$1873	€1609	View near Guildford (45x60cm-18x24in) s. s.i.verso prov.exhib. 24-Nov-3 Sotheby's, Melbourne #306/R (A.D 2600)
£1300	$2418	€1898	Returning home (66x51cm-26x20in) s. 4-Mar-4 Christie's, Kensington #510/R est:500-800
£1344	$2500	€1962	Bradgate Park (36x45cm-14x18in) s.i. 5-Mar-4 Skinner, Boston #256/R est:2500-3000
£1467	$2625	€2200	Farmhouse on the lakeside (20x28cm-8x11in) s. panel. 14-May-4 Behringer, Furth #1569/R est:3000
£1500	$2790	€2190	Shepherd and his flock in a wooded landscape, near Leamington (20x30cm-8x12in) s. board. 4-Mar-4 Christie's, Kensington #445/R est:1500-2000
£1500	$2700	€2190	Wooded landscapes scene with figures on a path (46x35cm-18x14in) s.i.verso. 20-Apr-4 Hutchinson, Boroughbridge #322/R est:1000-1500
£1600	$2976	€2336	At the waters edge (39x60cm-15x24in) s. 4-Mar-4 Christie's, Kensington #440/R est:2000-3000
£1700	$2686	€2465	Returning home (61x76cm-24x30in) s. 4-Sep-3 Christie's, Kensington #301 est:1800-2200
£1700	$3162	€2482	Farmyard, Berkshire (53x43cm-21x17in) s. prov. 4-Mar-4 Christie's, Kensington #448/R est:700-900
£1800	$2988	€2628	Berkswell, Warwickshire (24x35cm-9x14in) s. panel. 1-Oct-3 Woolley & Wallis, Salisbury #321/R est:800-1200
£1800	$3006	€2628	Rural landscape with cattle grazing beside a stream, thatched cottage (44x29cm-17x11in) s.i. 7-Oct-3 Fellows & Sons, Birmingham #415/R est:700-1000
£1848	$3400	€2698	Landscape with cottages (30x46cm-12x18in) s. prov. 27-Jun-4 Hindman, Chicago #794/R est:3000-5000
£1950	$3608	€2847	Figure in a small boat on a wooded river (14x22cm-6x9in) s. board. 14-Jan-4 Lawrence, Crewkerne #1417/R est:500-700
£2000	$3640	€2920	Rural landscapes showing figures walking along a track beside farm buildings (23x33cm-9x13in) board pair. 4-Feb-4 Brightwells, Leominster #1007 est:1000-1500
£2300	$3910	€3358	Figures beside a pond with extensive landscape beyond (25x36cm-10x14in) s. 19-Nov-3 Tennants, Leyburn #1056/R est:2500-3000
£2400	$3984	€3504	Country lane with a herdsman and cattle, cottage nearby (29x39cm-11x15in) s. 1-Oct-3 Woolley & Wallis, Salisbury #320/R est:800-1200
£2500	$4150	€3650	Lake landscape (30x40cm-12x16in) s. 1-Oct-3 Sotheby's, Olympia #42/R est:1500-2500
£2500	$4250	€3650	Figures by a rustic cottage, beyond a pool (76x63cm-30x25in) s. 25-Nov-3 Bonhams, Knowle #262/R est:3000-5000
£2500	$4725	€3650	View of a village with two figures and chickens in the foreground (33x23cm-13x9in) s. 17-Feb-4 Fellows & Sons, Birmingham #34/R est:2000-3000
£2600	$4420	€3796	Mother and child beside a thatched cottage with chickens nearby (25x36cm-10x14in) s. 19-Nov-3 Tennants, Leyburn #1057/R est:2500-3000
£2703	$4838	€4000	Farmstead by cornfield (35x51cm-14x20in) s. 6-May-4 Michael Zeller, Lindau #899/R est:900
£2800	$5292	€4088	Burnham Beeches - two figures gathering wood in a forest clearing (62x75cm-24x30in) s. i.verso. 17-Feb-4 Fellows & Sons, Birmingham #66/R est:1500-2500
£3111	$5382	€4542	Country scenes (41x61cm-16x24in) s. pair. 9-Dec-3 Maynards, Vancouver #173 est:5000-7000 (C.D 7000)
£3300	$5907	€4818	Old farm (18x24cm-7x9in) s. 18-Mar-4 Neales, Nottingham #746/R est:1000-1500
£3800	$6992	€5548	Country road (25x36cm-10x14in) s. panel. 11-Jun-4 Christie's, London #135/R est:2000-3000
£4000	$6800	€5840	Lock at Pangbourne on Thames (61x91cm-24x36in) s. s.i.d.1888 verso. 25-Nov-3 Christie's, London #140/R est:3000-5000
£4000	$6680	€5840	Feeding the chickens. Wooded landscape (25x35cm-10x14in) s. pair. 12-Nov-3 Sotheby's, Olympia #36/R est:4000-6000

THORS, Joseph (attrib) (fl.1863-1900) British

£320	$589	€467	Wooded landscape with travellers on a path (24x34cm-9x13in) s. 23-Jun-4 Cheffins, Cambridge #493
£550	$919	€803	Figures in a landscape (38x38cm-15x15in) bears another sig. board. 7-Oct-3 Bonhams, Knightsbridge #248/R
£703	$1300	€1026	River near Hertford (61x107cm-24x42in) indis.sig. 10-Mar-4 Doyle, New York #50/R
£2200	$4070	€3212	Country landscape with timbered cottage and figure on a track (22x30cm-9x12in) 9-Mar-4 Bonhams, Knightsbridge #240/R est:1000-1500

THORSEN, Lars (1876-1952) American?

£1676	$3000	€2447	Mast, schooner and sailboat (61x76cm-24x30in) s. 14-May-4 Skinner, Boston #133/R est:1000-1500

THORVALDSEN, Bertel (1770-1844) Danish

Sculpture

£1700	$3128	€2482	The Phrygian boy (48x56cm-19x22in) alabaster. 23-Jun-4 Bonhams, Bury St Edmunds #515/R est:800-1200

Works on paper

£378	$654	€552	Old man with four wings resting his tired head on stick (17x11cm-7x4in) i. Indian ink brown wash lit. 9-Dec-3 Rasmussen, Copenhagen #1742/R (D.KR 4000)

THORVALDSEN, Bertel (after) (1770-1844) Danish

Sculpture

£11888	$20210	€17000	L'Empereur Napoleon 1er en Cesar (81cm-32in) white marble. 1-Dec-3 Coutau Begarie, Paris #312/R est:5000-6000

THOUY, Marc (1946-) French

£362	$626	€529	Compotier de fraises et poires (46x55cm-18x22in) s. i.verso exhib. 12-Dec-3 Galerie du Rhone, Sion #139 (S.FR 800)
£385	$665	€562	Pomme, noix et pichet (22x27cm-9x11in) s. s.i.verso exhib. 12-Dec-3 Galerie du Rhone, Sion #140 (S.FR 850)

THRANE, Ragnhild (1853-1913) Norwegian

£652	$1128	€952	Apple tree in blossom (100x80cm-39x31in) s. 13-Dec-3 Blomqvist, Lysaker #1381/R (N.KR 7500)
£870	$1504	€1270	Portrait of Martha Kristine Thrane (90x61cm-35x24in) s. 13-Dec-3 Blomqvist, Lysaker #1382/R (N.KR 10000)

THRASHER, J W (1962-) American

£351	$650	€512	Pheasants in the esnow. s. 14-Jul-4 Dallas Auction Gallery, Dallas #467/R
£459	$850	€670	Quail in flight. s. 14-Jul-4 Dallas Auction Gallery, Dallas #215/R
£541	$1000	€790	Ducks in flight. s. 14-Jul-4 Dallas Auction Gallery, Dallas #214/R
£1135	$2100	€1657	In days gone by (61x91cm-24x36in) s.i. 14-Jan-4 Dallas Auction Gallery, Dallas #424/R est:2500-3500

THRASHER, Leslie (1889-1936) American

£455	$800	€664	Burned supper (43x39cm-17x15in) s. 23-May-4 Bonhams & Butterfields, Los Angeles #7028/R
£540	$950	€788	Domestic squabble (46x33cm-18x13in) s. 23-May-4 Bonhams & Butterfields, Los Angeles #7027/R
£966	$1700	€1410	Bather (39x33cm-15x13in) s. 23-May-4 Bonhams & Butterfields, Los Angeles #7026/R
£1079	$1900	€1575	I quit (52x44cm-20x17in) s. 23-May-4 Bonhams & Butterfields, Los Angeles #7029/R

THRASHER, W R (1908-1997) American

£541	$1000	€790	Landscape with quail. s. 14-Jul-4 Dallas Auction Gallery, Dallas #446/R
£958	$1600	€1399	Ducks in flight (61x91cm-24x36in) 18-Oct-3 David Dike, Dallas #321/R est:1500-2000
£1757	$3250	€2565	Landscape of bluebonnets (61x91cm-24x36in) s. 14-Jan-4 Dallas Auction Gallery, Dallas #135/R est:3000-5000
£2545	$4250	€3716	Texas wildflowers (61x91cm-24x36in) 18-Oct-3 David Dike, Dallas #92/R est:3000-6000

THRONE-HOLST, Wanda (1965-) Swedish

Works on paper

£1922	$3440	€2806	Wandering (130x150cm-51x59in) indis.sig. mixed media canvas. 22-Mar-4 Blomqvist, Oslo #653/R est:18000-22000 (N.KR 24000)

THUE, Henry (1890-1921) Norwegian?

£473	$790	€691	Man thinking (100x81cm-39x32in) s. 20-Oct-3 Blomqvist, Lysaker #1331 (N.KR 5500)

THUILLIER, Pierre (attrib) (1799-1858) French

Works on paper

£333	$603	€500	Paysage Mediterraneen, El Biar, d'Alger (19x29cm-7x11in) brown wash W/C exhib.lit. 30-Mar-4 Rossini, Paris #1059

THUILLIER-MORNARD, Louise (1829-?) French

£1600	$2928	€2400	Seaweed gatherers on the Brittany coast (71x108cm-28x43in) s. 5-Jun-4 Arnold, Frankfurt #743/R est:300

THULDEN, Theodor van (1606-1669) Dutch

£4452	$7568	€6500	Holy Family with Saint Catherine and Saint Barbara (66x54cm-26x21in) 4-Nov-3 Ansorena, Madrid #37/R est:8500

THULDEN, Theodor van (attrib) (1606-1669) Dutch

£1351	$2378	€2000	Medea and her two children (48x62cm-19x24in) panel. 24-May-4 Bernaerts, Antwerp #93/R est:2000-3000
£2676	$4683	€3800	Orphee venant chercher Eurydice (64x79cm-25x31in) 17-Dec-3 Piasa, Paris #13/R est:3000-4000

THULIN, Jons Truedsson (20th C) Swedish

£668	$1155	€975	Takblafond (182x162cm-72x64in) s.d.1950. 15-Dec-3 Lilla Bukowskis, Stockholm #224 (S.KR 8500)

THUM, Christian (1625-1696) Swedish

£2365	$4234	€3453	Hermit with perishable symbols (96x135cm-38x53in) 28-May-4 Uppsala Auktionskammare, Uppsala #48/R est:30000-40000 (S.KR 32000)

THUM, Erich (1886-?) German

£403	$749	€600	Men with crane (60x50cm-24x20in) s. 6-Mar-4 Arnold, Frankfurt #865/R

THUNMAN, Olof (1879-1944) Swedish

£480	$860	€701	Lake landscape (52x90cm-20x35in) s.d.1912. 28-May-4 Uppsala Auktionskammare, Uppsala #228 (S.KR 6500)

THUR, Franz Felix (1890-1978) Austrian
Works on paper
£400 $720 €600 Schlossberg (34x41cm-13x16in) s.d.1946 W/C. 22-Apr-4 Dorotheum, Graz #72/R

THURAU, Friedrich (?-1888) German
£3017 $5401 €4405 River in evening (80x107cm-31x42in) s. 12-May-4 Dobiaschofsky, Bern #1019/R est:6500 (S.FR 7000)

THURBER, James Grover (1894-1961) American
Works on paper
£5090 $8500 €7431 Woman (15x6cm-6x2in) s. ink. 11-Nov-3 Christie's, Rockefeller NY #177/R est:6000-8000
£5090 $8500 €7431 Don't let's spoil everything by you being sick (20x25cm-8x10in) s. pen ink board. 15-Nov-3 Illustration House, New York #46/R est:4000-6000

THURBURN, Lee (20th C) American
£363 $650 €530 Vincent's sunflowers (76x102cm-30x40in) i. 13-May-4 Dallas Auction Gallery, Dallas #353/R

THURBURN, Percy C (fl.1930-1935) British
£400 $732 €584 Felucca, boat building on the Nile (91x120cm-36x47in) init. board exhib. 6-Jul-4 Bearnes, Exeter #482/R

THURLBY, Fred (20th C) British
£1000 $1840 €1460 Sawgate Royal Duke and Saxby Fashion, heavy horses (41x51cm-16x20in) s.i. i.verso. 10-Jun-4 Christie's, Kensington #109/R est:1000-1500
£1100 $2024 €1606 Belvoir Trojan (30x41cm-12x16in) s.i.d.1936. 10-Jun-4 Christie's, Kensington #421/R est:700-900
£1600 $2944 €2336 Mina of Crossing, a heavy horse (46x61cm-18x24in) s.i.d.1918. 10-Jun-4 Christie's, Kensington #104/R est:1000-1500
£1600 $2944 €2336 Rose of Crossing, a heavy horse (46x61cm-18x24in) s.i.d.1918. 10-Jun-4 Christie's, Kensington #105/R est:1000-1500
£1800 $3312 €2628 Bonnie Favourite, a heavy horse (51x61cm-20x24in) s.i.d.1918. 10-Jun-4 Christie's, Kensington #103/R est:1000-1500
£2200 $4048 €3212 Rose of Ashhill, a heavy horse (46x61cm-18x24in) s.i.d.1918. 10-Jun-4 Christie's, Kensington #102/R est:1000-1500
£4800 $8160 €7008 Quality, grey shire horse in a paddock (55x60cm-22x24in) init.i.d.1910. 27-Nov-3 Christie's, Kensington #151/R est:2500-3500
£5000 $8500 €7300 Norbury Juno, shire horse with a foal in a stable (44x59cm-17x23in) s.i.d.1912. 27-Nov-3 Christie's, Kensington #152/R est:2500-3500

THURMAN, Peder (1839-1919) Norwegian
£402 $736 €587 Fjord landscape with rowing boat (45x69cm-18x27in) s. 2-Feb-4 Blomqvist, Lysaker #1309/R (N.KR 5000)

THURMAND, E (19/20th C) Norwegian
£400 $669 €584 From Drobak (67x88cm-26x35in) s. 17-Nov-3 Blomqvist, Lysaker #1344 (N.KR 4800)

THURMANN, Oystein (1925-1988) Norwegian
£528 $972 €792 Figure in the room (95x115cm-37x45in) s. 14-Jun-4 Blomqvist, Lysaker #1400/R (N.KR 6500)
£542 $905 €791 Composition (70x80cm-28x31in) s. 17-Nov-3 Blomqvist, Lysaker #1343 (N.KR 6500)
£1168 $1950 €1705 Soft encounter (130x119cm-51x47in) s. 17-Nov-3 Blomqvist, Lysaker #1342 est:15000-20000 (N.KR 14000)

THURMOND, Ethel Dora (1905-1988) American
Works on paper
£337 $550 €492 Bluebonnets and oak trees with Spanish moss (30x51cm-12x20in) s.d.1930 pastel board. 28-Sep-3 Simpson's, Houston #79/R

THURSTON, Rosalie Winifred (20th C) British
£280 $493 €409 Alhambra, Grenade. s. 18-May-4 Bonhams, Knightsbridge #171

THYGESEN, Rudolf (1880-1953) Norwegian
£238 $438 €347 Autumn landscape (60x73cm-24x29in) s. 29-Mar-4 Blomqvist, Lysaker #1335 (N.KR 3000)
£488 $898 €732 House in winter (37x46cm-15x18in) s. 14-Jun-4 Blomqvist, Lysaker #1402 (N.KR 6000)
£555 $1021 €810 Sea view (66x81cm-26x32in) s. 29-Mar-4 Blomqvist, Lysaker #1334 (N.KR 7000)
£650 $1197 €949 Winter landscape with house (33x41cm-13x16in) init. i.verso. 10-Jun-4 Grev Wedels Plass, Oslo #224/R (N.KR 8000)
£684 $1163 €999 Study for Leda (51x66cm-20x26in) init.i.d.1915 lit. 19-Nov-3 Grev Wedels Plass, Oslo #75/R (N.KR 8000)
£852 $1465 €1244 Landscape by the coast (48x57cm-19x22in) init.indis.d. 8-Dec-3 Blomqvist, Oslo #491/R (N.KR 10000)
£858 $1502 €1253 Winter at Hadeland (60x73cm-24x29in) init.d.40 panel exhib. 16-Dec-3 Grev Wedels Plass, Oslo #228/R (N.KR 10000)
£1025 $1711 €1497 Trees (60x72cm-24x28in) init.d.32. 13-Oct-3 Blomqvist, Oslo #312/R (N.KR 12000)
£2395 $4072 €3497 Winter in Oslo (61x73cm-24x29in) init.d.51 exhib. 19-Nov-3 Grev Wedels Plass, Oslo #14/R est:20000-30000 (N.KR 28000)
£2575 $4506 €3760 Landscape from Orsey, Normandy (85x94cm-33x37in) init.indis.d.29 i.verso exhib. 16-Dec-3 Grev Wedels Plass, Oslo #374/R est:20000-30000 (N.KR 30000)
£4065 $7439 €5935 Spring landscape (164x244cm-65x96in) init.d.34 prov. 7-Jun-4 Blomqvist, Oslo #384/R est:50000-60000 (N.KR 50000)
£11382 $20829 €16618 Autumn landscape (164x244cm-65x96in) init.d.33 prov. 7-Jun-4 Blomqvist, Oslo #382/R est:90000-110000 (N.KR 140000)

THYS, Gaston (1863-1893) French
£961 $1720 €1403 Nu a l'eventail (27x41cm-11x16in) s. 26-May-4 AB Stockholms Auktionsverk #2366/R (S.KR 13000)
£1277 $2132 €1800 Diogene et sa lanterne (257x150cm-101x59in) s. 19-Oct-3 St-Germain-en-Laye Encheres #27/R est:3000-3500

THYS, Susy Kathy (1936-) Swiss
£273 $453 €396 The conversation (19x23cm-7x9in) s.i. verso. 13-Jun-3 Zofingen, Switzerland #3059 (S.FR 600)
£283 $517 €413 Still life with bottles (65x54cm-26x21in) s. 4-Jun-4 Zofingen, Switzerland #2975 (S.FR 650)
£603 $1080 €880 Winter scene (30x30cm-12x12in) s. 12-May-4 Dobiaschofsky, Bern #1020/R (S.FR 1400)
£1454 $2471 €2123 Andalusia (89x116cm-35x46in) s. i. verso. 7-Nov-3 Dobiaschofsky, Bern #236/R est:5000 (S.FR 3300)

THYSEBAERT, Émile (1873-1962) Belgian
£280 $476 €400 La sortie de la messe. Vue Orientaliste (5x80cm-2x31in) s. double-sided. 18-Nov-3 Galerie Moderne, Brussels #852
£390 $651 €550 Temps orageux (60x50cm-24x20in) s.d.1925. 14-Oct-3 Vanderkindere, Brussels #66
£603 $1007 €850 Kermesse a Bruxelles (35x52cm-14x20in) s. panel. 17-Jun-3 Vanderkindere, Brussels #39

TIARINI, Alessandro (attrib) (1577-1668) Italian
Works on paper
£500 $865 €730 Scene from the life of Saint Francis (32x51cm-13x20in) red chk pen brown ink wash prov. 12-Dec-3 Christie's, Kensington #337

TIBALDI, Pellegrino (attrib) (1527-1596) Italian
Works on paper
£5333 $9813 €8000 Susanna and the elders (25x21cm-10x8in) Indian ink on bodycol htd white. 11-Jun-4 Hauswedell & Nolte, Hamburg #915/R est:3000

TIBBLE, Geoffrey (1909-1952) British
Works on paper
£2200 $3740 €3212 Figures in an interior (24x33cm-9x13in) s. pencil W/C bodycol sold with a painting by Denis Matthews. 21-Nov-3 Christie's, London #62/R est:800-1200

TIBBO, Teuane (1893-1984) New Zealander
£670 $1139 €978 Harbour scene. s.d.1968 board. 4-Nov-3 Peter Webb, Auckland #113/R est:1500-2500 (NZ.D 1850)
£939 $1530 €1371 Kava ceremony, Fiji (60x75cm-24x30in) s.d.1967 i.verso canvas on board. 23-Sep-3 Peter Webb, Auckland #120/R (NZ.D 2600)

TIBERTELLI DE PISIS, Bona (1926-2000) Italian
£612 $1096 €900 Chambre de la peur (100x73cm-39x29in) s. painted 1974 prov.exhib. 21-Mar-4 Calmels Cohen, Paris #84/R
Works on paper
£2041 $3653 €3000 Wotan (114x144cm-45x57in) s. patchwork canvas exec 1966 exhib. 21-Mar-4 Calmels Cohen, Paris #81/R est:3000-4000

TIBETAN SCHOOL, 12th/13th C
£11957 $22000 €17457 Buddha, Sadaksari, Acala and Tara (20x14cm-8x6in) distemper cloth. 24-Mar-4 Sotheby's, New York #56/R est:25000-35000
£13043 $24000 €19043 Portrait of two lamas (19x14cm-7x6in) distemper cloth. 24-Mar-4 Sotheby's, New York #57/R est:25000-35000

TIBETAN SCHOOL, 13th/14th C
£43478 $80000 €63478 Bon Deities and Masters (49x39cm-19x15in) distemper cloth. 24-Mar-4 Sotheby's, New York #58/R est:80000-120000

TIBETAN SCHOOL, 14th C
£59783 $110000 €87283 Amitabha (57x48cm-22x19in) distemper cloth. 24-Mar-4 Sotheby's, New York #59/R est:80000-120000

TIBETAN SCHOOL, 15th C
£27174 $50000 €39674 Tikshna-Manjusri (63x53cm-25x21in) distemper cloth. 24-Mar-4 Sotheby's, New York #64/R est:50000-80000

TIBETAN SCHOOL, 18th C
£4076 $7500 €5951 Vanavasin and Kalika (71x41cm-28x16in) i. distemper cloth. 24-Mar-4 Sotheby's, New York #97/R est:8000-12000
£7609 $14000 €11109 Kapaladhara Hevajra (64x39cm-25x15in) distemper cloth. 24-Mar-4 Sotheby's, New York #101/R est:4000-6000
£9783 $18000 €14283 Mahakala (74x51cm-29x20in) distemper cloth. 24-Mar-4 Sotheby's, New York #102/R est:25000-35000
Works on paper
£6522 $12000 €9522 Untitled (35x23cm-14x9in) distemper cloth wood diptych exhib.lit. 24-Mar-4 Sotheby's, New York #94/R est:12000-15000

TIBOR, Erno (1885-1945) Hungarian
£790 $1431 €1153 Provincial central square (64x89cm-25x35in) s. oil on card. 16-Apr-4 Mu Terem Galeria, Budapest #142/R (H.F 300000)

TICE, George A (1938-) American
Photographs
£1796 $3000 €2622 Petit's Mobil station (27x34cm-11x13in) s. gelatin silver print. 20-Oct-3 Christie's, Rockefeller NY #153/R est:2500-3500
£2116 $4000 €3089 Petit's Mobil station (39x49cm-15x19in) s.i.d.1980 gelatin silver print. 17-Feb-4 Christie's, Rockefeller NY #255/R est:2500-3500

TICHO, Anna (1894-1980) Israeli
Works on paper
£2793 $5000 €4078 Hills of Jerusalem (23x29cm-9x11in) s. pencil. 18-Mar-4 Sotheby's, New York #9/R est:3000-4000
£3373 $5600 €4925 Jericho (25x30cm-10x12in) s. pencil prov. 2-Oct-3 Christie's, Tel Aviv #4/R est:4000-6000
£12651 $21000 €18470 Old Jerusalem (51x37cm-20x15in) s. chl pencil lit. 2-Oct-3 Christie's, Tel Aviv #1/R est:9000-12000

TICHY, Frantisek (1896-1961) Czechoslovakian
Works on paper
£1204 $1998 €1758 Artiste (33x19cm-13x7in) s.d.53 col pencil. 4-Oct-3 Dorotheum, Prague #298/R est:50000-75000 (C.KR 55000)

TICHY, Josef (1922-) Austrian
Works on paper
£439 $773 €650 Karnten landscape (46x63cm-18x25in) s.d.63 W/C. 19-May-4 Dorotheum, Klagenfurt #59

TICKNER, Michael (?) Canadian?
£234 $398 €342 Up in the air (41x51cm-16x20in) s.d.1989 acrylic on masonite. 19-Nov-3 Maynards, Vancouver #32 (C.D 520)

TICULIN, Mario (19/20th C) Italian
£340 $569 €480 Canale a Chioggia (50x65cm-20x26in) s. plywood. 21-Jun-3 Stadion, Trieste #407/R

TIDEMAND, Adolph (1814-1876) Norwegian
£15825 $26903 €23105 Woman and child resting on mountain path (26x26cm-10x10in) s.d.1852 panel lit. 19-Nov-3 Grev Wedels Plass, Oslo #12/R est:200000-300000 (N.KR 185000)
£35073 $59624 €51207 Going to the cheese farm (31x27cm-12x11in) s. 19-Nov-3 Grev Wedels Plass, Oslo #68/R est:500000-700000 (N.KR 410000)
£109756 $200854 €160244 The mother by the cradle - Thora Ingebrigtsdatter and baby (33x44cm-13x17in) s.d.1857 prov.lit. 7-Jun-4 Blomqvist, Oslo #320/R est:1500000-1800000 (N.KR 1350000)
£150897 $270106 €220310 Wolf hunters resting at the outfarm (50x46cm-20x18in) s.d.1854 lit. 25-May-4 Grev Wedels Plass, Oslo #21/R est:1500000-2000000 (N.KR 1850000)

TIDEMAND, Adolph Claudius (1854-1919) Norwegian
£1138 $2094 €1707 Portrait of Caroline Gundersen. Portrait of man. two sold with book. 14-Jun-4 Blomqvist, Lysaker #1405 est:5000-6000 (N.KR 14000)

TIDEMANN, Philipp (1657-1705) German
Works on paper
£480 $874 €701 Elandia Nova (10x26cm-4x10in) red chk. 16-Jun-4 Fischer, Luzern #2549 (S.FR 1100)
£3716 $6541 €5500 Infant Hercules wrestling with snakes (29x37cm-11x15in) s.d.1690 pen black ink grey wash black chk prov.exhib.lit. 19-May-4 Sotheby's, Amsterdam #113/R est:4000-6000

TIDEY, Alfred (1808-1892) British
Works on paper
£374 $637 €546 Stuart and mother (35x30cm-14x12in) i. verso W/C bodycol. 5-Nov-3 Dobiaschofsky, Bern #1006/R (S.FR 850)

TIDMARSH, H E (fl.1880-1927) British
Works on paper
£2900 $5423 €4234 Panoramic view of London (6x33cm-2x13in) s. W/C. 25-Feb-4 Mallams, Oxford #325/R est:600-800

TIEBERT, Hermann (1895-) German
£304 $544 €450 Autumn wood with figures in sunlight (32x27cm-13x11in) s.d.1955 canvas on board. 6-May-4 Michael Zeller, Lindau #900
£405 $726 €600 Summer landscape in Westallgau (35x47cm-14x19in) s.d.1955 board. 6-May-4 Michael Zeller, Lindau #901/R
£474 $849 €692 Portrait of young man (48x35cm-19x14in) s.d.1924. 12-May-4 Dobiaschofsky, Bern #1021/R (S.FR 1100)

TIECHE, Adolf (1877-1957) Swiss
£333 $533 €483 Animated Bubenberg square in Berne (73x98cm-29x39in) s.d.1948. 15-May-3 Stuker, Bern #1534/R (S.FR 700)
Works on paper
£498 $846 €727 Villa in Lenzburg (56x73cm-22x29in) s. i.d.1924 verso. 28-Nov-3 Zofingen, Switzerland #3200 (S.FR 1100)

TIEDJEN, Willy (1881-1950) German
£278 $464 €400 Coast landscape (45x60cm-18x24in) s. board. 22-Oct-3 Neumeister, Munich #768/R
£417 $658 €600 Five ducks in reeds (41x60cm-16x24in) s.i.d.1912. 6-Sep-3 Arnold, Frankfurt #673
£486 $812 €700 Feeding horses in front of Tyrolean tavern (100x131cm-39x52in) s.d.1921. 24-Oct-3 Ketterer, Hamburg #241/R
£490 $832 €700 Cattle grazing (42x48cm-17x19in) s. panel. 29-Nov-3 Bukowskis, Helsinki #381/R
£933 $1680 €1400 Shepherd with flock under trees (62x100cm-24x39in) s.d.23 lit. 22-Apr-4 Allgauer, Kempten #3734/R
£940 $1719 €1400 Herd of sheep in extensive landscape (70x95cm-28x37in) s.i.verso. 8-Jul-4 Allgauer, Kempten #2243/R
£1042 $1698 €1500 Summer day (90x144cm-35x57in) s. i. verso. 24-Sep-3 Neumeister, Munich #571/R est:1250

TIEL, Quiryn Martinus Adrianus van (1900-1967) Dutch
£1449 $2377 €2000 Two cocks (95x109cm-37x43in) s.d.64 prov. 27-May-3 Sotheby's, Amsterdam #325/R est:4000-6000
£2667 $4880 €4000 Shepherd and shepherdess with farm in the background (90x90cm-35x35in) s. 7-Jun-4 Glerum, Amsterdam #128/R est:4000-6000
£5594 $9510 €8000 Town in winter (95x104cm-37x41in) s.d.35 prov.exhib. 25-Nov-3 Christie's, Amsterdam #191/R est:8000-12000

TIELENS, Alexandre (1868-1959) Belgian
£289 $533 €440 Marche a Place Sainte Catherine (26x35cm-10x14in) s. cardboard. 22-Jun-4 Palais de Beaux Arts, Brussels #319
£389 $720 €580 Vase fleuri de roses (55x45cm-22x18in) s. 15-Mar-4 Horta, Bruxelles #348
£455 $773 €650 Nature morte aux roses et fraises (60x80cm-24x31in) s. 18-Nov-3 Vanderkindere, Brussels #228
£490 $817 €700 Ruelle Mediterraneene (44x55cm-17x22in) s. 13-Oct-3 Horta, Bruxelles #497
£699 $1168 €1000 Marche provencal (46x96cm-18x38in) s. 13-Oct-3 Horta, Bruxelles #496
£1250 $2125 €1800 Yellow and pink roses in glass vase (28x36cm-11x14in) s. 28-Oct-3 Dorotheum, Vienna #163/R est:2000-2400

TIELING, Lodewyck (17th C) ?
£2113 $3380 €3000 Evening landscape with herders resting with cattle (56x74cm-22x29in) s. lit. 19-Sep-3 Karlheinz Kaupp, Staufen #1877/R est:2500

TIEMANN, Walter (1876-1951) German
£521 $823 €750 Extensive summer landscape (65x50cm-26x20in) s.d.1913. 5-Sep-3 Wendl, Rudolstadt #3648/R

TIEPOLO, Giovanni Battista (1696-1770) Italian
£35461 $59220 €50000 San Clemente Papa adora la Trinita (106x57cm-42x22in) 17-Jun-3 Finarte Semenzato, Milan #671/R est:50000-70000
£80537 $142550 €120000 Rebecca at well (28x39cm-11x15in) 27-Apr-4 Porro, Milan #310/R est:120000
Works on paper
£2676 $4630 €3800 Study for allegorical statue (28x19cm-11x7in) pencil lead. 14-Dec-3 Finarte, Venice #16/R est:4000-5000
£2676 $4630 €3800 Study for allegorical statue (28x19cm-11x7in) pencil lead. 14-Dec-3 Finarte, Venice #15/R est:4000-5000
£3000 $5490 €4380 Standing soldier, with studies of heads and figures. Two studies of heads (28x20cm-11x8in) chk pen ink double-sided corner cut. 6-Jul-4 Christie's, London #73/R est:3000-5000
£8333 $15000 €12166 Heads of satyrs, women and other studies (18x18cm-7x7in) i. pen black brown ink grey wash prov. 22-Jan-4 Christie's, Rockefeller NY #67/R est:20000-30000
£11000 $20130 €16060 Caricature of a man seen from behind wearing a tricorn and a long coat (19x10cm-7x4in) pen brown ink wash corners cut prov. 6-Jul-4 Christie's, London #71/R est:12000-18000
£11644 $19794 €17000 Study of Oriental man (21x14cm-8x6in) pen ink wash. 6-Nov-3 Tajan, Paris #53/R
£12000 $21960 €17520 Study of the head of a bearded man (21x17cm-8x7in) red chk htd white chk blue paper. 8-Jul-4 Sotheby's, London #107/R est:5000-7000
£19000 $34770 €27740 Angel seated on a cloud seen di sotto in su (19x16cm-7x6in) black chk pen ink wash. 6-Jul-4 Christie's, London #72/R est:12000-16000
£23611 $42500 €34472 Farm buildings behind a wall (8x24cm-3x9in) pen ink wash prov.lit. 21-Jan-4 Sotheby's, New York #93/R est:20000-30000
£58000 $106140 €84680 Holy Family resting by an urn (27x20cm-11x8in) black chk pen ink wash prov.lit. 6-Jul-4 Christie's, London #70/R est:60000-80000
£109589 $186301 €160000 Caricature (20x13cm-8x5in) ink wash dr. 4-Nov-3 Ansorena, Madrid #132/R est:16000

TIEPOLO, Giovanni Battista (circle) (1696-1770) Italian
£5369 $9611 €8000 Jeune femme au chien entouree de serviteurs (72x55cm-28x22in) 25-May-4 Palais de Beaux Arts, Brussels #83/R est:6000-8000

TIEPOLO, Giovanni Battista (style) (1696-1770) Italian
£19200 $31872 €28032 Allegory of the transition to death (46x61cm-18x24in) 3-Oct-3 Mallams, Oxford #215/R est:400-600

TIEPOLO, Giovanni Domenico (1727-1804) Italian
Works on paper
£3333 $6000 €4866 Iphegenia led to the Council of Agamemnon (19x28cm-7x11in) black chk pen brown ink wash. 22-Jan-4 Christie's, Rockefeller NY #68/R est:6000-10000
£3592 $6213 €5100 Centaurs (17x24cm-7x9in) pencil pen lead. 14-Dec-3 Finarte, Venice #17/R est:5000-6000
£3889 $7000 €5678 Dogs playing in a landscape (16x19cm-6x7in) s. black chk pen grey ink wash prov. 22-Jan-4 Christie's, Rockefeller NY #70/R est:5000-7000
£4444 $8000 €6488 Dogs attacking chickens in a landscape (16x20cm-6x8in) black chk pen grey ink wash prov. 22-Jan-4 Christie's, Rockefeller NY #71/R est:5000-7000
£4800 $8784 €7008 Saint Peter and Saint John healing the Paralytic (21x29cm-8x11in) s.i. pen ink wash prov. 6-Jul-4 Christie's, London #79/R est:5000-8000
£6463 $11568 €9500 Saint Laurent entoure d'anges montant au ciel (27x19cm-11x7in) s. pen grey ink wash prov. 18-Mar-4 Christie's, Paris #46/R est:7000-10000

£6803 $12177 €10000 L'Assomption de la Vierge (25x18cm-10x7in) s. pen brown ink wash prov. 18-Mar-4 Christie's, Paris #47/R est:5000-7000
£7692 $13231 €11000 Trois figures (26x18cm-10x7in) d.1744 sanguine exhib. 8-Dec-3 Horta, Bruxelles #91 est:1500-2000
£8333 $15000 €12166 Crowd watching a charlatan. Flying angel (21x28cm-8x11in) pen ink chk double-sided lt. 21-Jan-4 Sotheby's, New York #96/R est:14000-18000
£8500 $15555 €12410 Putti playing with a crown of laurels, Cupid blindfolded to the left (19x21cm-7x8in) s. black chk pen ink wash prov. 6-Jul-4 Christie's, London #78/R est:5000-7000
£8889 $16000 €12978 Centaur drawing a bow in a landscape (20x28cm-8x11in) s. black chk pen brown ink grey wash prov. 22-Jan-4 Christie's, Rockefeller NY #69/R est:5000-7000
£9167 $16500 €13384 St. Mark the Evangelist (27x20cm-11x8in) pen ink wash over chk. 21-Jan-4 Sotheby's, New York #98/R est:12000-16000
£10000 $18300 €14600 Female figure in the clouds, surrounded by putti with a bow and arrows (28x19cm-11x7in) s. bears i. verso pen brown ink grey-brown wash prov. 8-Jul-4 Sotheby's, London #108/R est:12000-18000
£11111 $20000 €16222 Two clocked figures seen from the rear (24x19cm-9x7in) pen ink wash over black chk. 21-Jan-4 Sotheby's, New York #95/R est:7000-9000
£14000 $25620 €20440 Zephyr, standing in profile to the right, holding a cornucopia (28x11cm-11x4in) s. i.verso black chk pen brown ink grey wash. 6-Jul-4 Christie's, London #81/R est:7000-10000
£14966 $26789 €22000 Venus debout sur un entablement, un putto a ses pieds (27x15cm-11x6in) s.i. black chk pen brown ink grey wash prov. 18-Mar-4 Christie's, Paris #69/R est:10000-15000
£15541 $27351 €23000 Hercules and Antaeus (20x14cm-8x6in) s. pen black ink grey wash black chk prov.exhib. 19-May-4 Sotheby's, Amsterdam #171/R est:12000-18000
£17687 $31660 €26000 Bacchus tenant une draperie et une guirlande (28x18cm-11x7in) s.i. black chk pen brown ink grey wash prov. 18-Mar-4 Christie's, Paris #68/R est:10000-15000
£22000 $40260 €32120 Neptune, Amphitrite and time with a Nereid (19x27cm-7x11in) s. black chk pen ink wash prov. 6-Jul-4 Christie's, London #80/R est:20000-30000
£34247 $58219 €50000 Cenature and nymph (27x30cm-11x12in) s. pen wash ink prov.lit. 4-Nov-3 Ansorena, Madrid #127/R est:50000
£125000 $228750 €182500 Scene in a Venetian Campo (35x38cm-14x15in) s.d.1791 pen brown blk ink grey wash over blk chk. 8-Jul-4 Sotheby's, London #110/R est:80000-120000

TIEPOLO, Giovanni Domenico (attrib) (1727-1804) Italian
£419 $772 €625 Bearded man (55x43cm-22x17in) lit. 25-Mar-4 Karlheinz Kaupp, Staufen #2315/R
£15068 $25616 €22000 Allegory (49x60cm-19x24in) paper on canvas. 7-Nov-3 Farsetti, Prato #536/R est:22000-26000

TIEPOLO, Giovanni Domenico (circle) (1727-1804) Italian
£161972 $280211 €230000 St Dominicus (44x34cm-17x13in) 13-Dec-3 Lempertz, Koln #260/R est:2000

TIEPOLO, Lorenzo (attrib) (1736-1776) Italian
Works on paper
£1316 $2421 €2000 Head of Oriental man (30x20cm-12x8in) pencil. 22-Jun-4 Sotheby's, Milan #88/R est:1500-2000
£1974 $3632 €3000 Portrait of painter (30x21cm-12x8in) pencil. 22-Jun-4 Sotheby's, Milan #91/R est:1500-2000

TIFFANY, Louis Comfort (1848-1933) American
£11111 $18556 €16000 Market day in a town in Brittany (25x41cm-10x16in) s. 21-Oct-3 Sotheby's, Amsterdam #34/R est:5000-7000
£11892 $22000 €17362 European landscape with chateau (16x36cm-6x14in) s. 9-Mar-4 Christie's, Rockefeller NY #49/R est:10000-15000
£22099 $40000 €32265 North African town (67x51cm-26x20in) s. 31-Mar-4 Sotheby's, New York #39/R est:7000-10000
£25946 $48000 €37881 Port of Piraeus, Greece (23x37cm-9x15in) s. prov. 11-Mar-4 Christie's, Rockefeller NY #22/R est:10000-15000
£25946 $48000 €37881 Church in a mountain landscape (19x52cm-7x20in) s.d.68 board. 9-Mar-4 Christie's, Rockefeller NY #48/R est:20000-30000
Works on paper
£1630 $3000 €2380 North African courtyard (25x18cm-10x7in) W/C pencil paper on card. 10-Jun-4 Swann Galleries, New York #243/R est:1500-2500
£4324 $8000 €6313 Architectural studies (16x11cm-6x4in) s. pencil pair. 9-Mar-4 Christie's, Rockefeller NY #51/R est:4000-6000
£8982 $15000 €13114 Market scene (25x16cm-10x6in) s. W/C gouache paper on board. 9-Oct-3 Christie's, Rockefeller NY #16/R est:4000-6000
£18919 $35000 €27622 Shanty town, New York (27x53cm-11x21in) s.i. gouache pencil paper on board prov. 11-Mar-4 Christie's, Rockefeller NY #5/R est:5000-7000

TIFFANY, Louis Comfort (attrib) (1848-1933) American
£3784 $7000 €5525 Waterfront landscape (30x41cm-12x16in) painted c.1870. 9-Mar-4 Christie's, Rockefeller NY #50/R est:6000-8000

TIGHE, Francis Browne (fl.1885-1926) British
Works on paper
£600 $1092 €876 View of Manchester (43x28cm-17x11in) s.d.1896m W/C. 29-Jun-4 Capes Dunn, Manchester #807

TIGLIO, Marcos (1903-1976) Argentinian
£1031 $1680 €1505 Study (29x34cm-11x13in) s. i.on stretcher cardboard. 17-Jul-3 Naón & Cia, Buenos Aires #77/R
£2732 $5000 €3989 Three flowers (35x29cm-14x11in) cardboard. 1-Jun-4 Arroyo, Buenos Aires #20
£9066 $16500 €13236 Village street (62x52cm-24x20in) s.d.58 cardboard. 29-Jun-4 Arroyo, Buenos Aires #93/R est:12000

TIHANYI, Lajos (1885-1939) Hungarian
£40722 $67599 €59454 Portrait of Mrs Kar (76x64cm-30x25in) 4-Oct-3 Kieselbach, Budapest #115/R (H.F 15000000)

TIHMENEV, Evgeni (20th C) Russian
Works on paper
£10563 $18275 €15000 Dog and bear (60x47cm-24x19in) s. pastel. 13-Dec-3 Hagelstam, Helsinki #31/R est:8000

TIKHMENOV, Efim (19/20th C) Russian
£18000 $32220 €26280 Hunting the wild cat (61x46cm-24x18in) s. 26-May-4 Sotheby's, London #76/R est:5000-7000

TIKHOMIROV, Ivan (20th C) Russian
£259 $463 €378 Landscape with path by water (42x55cm-17x22in) s. panel. 28-May-4 Uppsala Auktionskammare, Uppsala #181 (S.KR 3500)

TIKKANEN, Ulf (1920-1969) Finnish
Sculpture
£1972 $3411 €2800 The bird girl (108cm-43in) bronze granite. 13-Dec-3 Hagelstam, Helsinki #8/R est:2000

TIKTAK, John (1916-1981) North American
Sculpture
£13514 $22973 €19730 Two Inuit figures standing back to back (41cm-16in) s. mottled grey soapstone. 3-Nov-3 Waddingtons, Toronto #230/R est:15000-20000 (C.D 30000)
£24775 $42117 €36172 Head of an Inuk (14cm-6in) mottled dark soapstone exec.c.1968. 3-Nov-3 Waddingtons, Toronto #225/R est:5000-6000 (C.D 55000)

TILBORCH, Gillis van (c.1625-1678) Flemish
£8380 $15000 €12235 Figures drinking and gambling in courtyard (91x75cm-36x30in) 27-May-4 Sotheby's, New York #27/R est:15000-20000
£13793 $22897 €20000 Peasants quarrelling after game of cards (87x71cm-34x28in) s.d.166 panel prov. 1-Oct-3 Dorotheum, Vienna #176/R est:25000-35000

TILBORCH, Gillis van (attrib) (c.1625-1678) Flemish
£1600 $2864 €2400 Portrait of a man with hat (16x13cm-6x5in) copper oval. 17-May-4 Glerum, Amsterdam #35/R est:1000-1500
£7947 $14464 €12000 Reunion de buveurs et fumeurs devant un auberge (57x81cm-22x32in) bears sig. 21-Jun-4 Tajan, Paris #80/R est:6000-8000

TILBORCH, Gillis van (style) (c.1625-1678) Flemish
£8741 $14860 €12500 Village festival (200x380cm-79x150in) 20-Nov-3 Van Ham, Cologne #1426/R est:3500

TILBURG, Karel Cornelis van (1885-1961) Dutch?
£559 $934 €800 Spring landscape with river (60x79cm-24x31in) s. 9-Oct-3 Michael Zeller, Lindau #777/R

TILCHE, Otto (19/20th C) British
Works on paper
£260 $416 €380 Mending boats on the Norfolk Broads (23x48cm-9x19in) s. W/C exec.c.1880-1890. 21-Sep-3 Desmond Judd, Cranbrook #1074

TILDEN, Douglas (1860-1935) American
Sculpture
£10839 $18427 €15500 The boxer (75cm-30in) s. dark brown pat bronze st.f. Gruet. 28-Nov-3 Schloss Ahlden, Ahlden #514/R est:5500

TILEMAN-PETERSEN, Christian (1874-1926) Danish
£284 $455 €415 Interior from Lerchenborg (60x48cm-24x19in) s.d.1925. 22-Sep-3 Rasmussen, Vejle #45/R (D.KR 3000)
£450 $824 €657 Interior, believed to be the Writing Room at the Royal Palce Rosenberg (38x32cm-15x13in) s.d.1922 s.verso. 6-Apr-4 Bonhams, Knightsbridge #88/R

TILGNER, Victor Oskar (1844-1896) Austrian
Sculpture
£5484 $9652 €8226 Bust of the Emperor Elisabeth (62cm-24in) s. pat bronze sold with wooden base. 22-May-4 Dorotheum, Prague #305/R est:100000-150000 (C.KR 260000)

TILIPAU-KISTLER, Maria (1884-1963) Austrian
£284 $474 €400 Monte Cristallo with Durensee in Ampezzo valley (33x48cm-13x19in) s.d.1938 canvas on panel. 16-Oct-3 Dorotheum, Salzburg #628/R
£433 $797 €650 Flowers in vase (25x32cm-10x13in) s.d.1927. 9-Jun-4 Dorotheum, Salzburg #631/R
£524 $892 €750 White roses, willow catkin and violets (33x21cm-13x8in) s. panel in shape of palette. 27-Nov-3 Dorotheum, Linz #510/R
£524 $892 €750 Alpine flowers (28x19cm-11x7in) s. panel. 27-Nov-3 Dorotheum, Linz #511/R
£559 $951 €800 Globe-flower and forget-me-nots (24x17cm-9x7in) s. board. 27-Nov-3 Dorotheum, Linz #465/R

TILIUS, Jan (1660-1719) Italian
£1773 $2961 €2500 Un jeune homme montrant un chardonneret (20x16cm-8x6in) panel. 17-Oct-3 Tajan, Paris #89 est:2500-3000
£2400 $4392 €3504 Diogenes of Sinope throwing away his bowl on witnessing a young child drinking water from a fountain (30x24cm-12x9in) bears sig.d.1671 panel. 7-Jul-4 Bonhams, New Bond Street #89/R est:2000-3000

TILL, Johann (jnr) (1827-1894) Austrian
£530 $964 €800 Flower greeting (26x32cm-10x13in) s.d.862. 21-Jun-4 Dorotheum, Vienna #158

TILL, Josef (1927-) Yugoslavian

Works on paper

£537 $961 €800 Untitled (22x30cm-9x12in) s. col pen pencil board double-sided prov. 25-May-4 Dorotheum, Vienna #307/R

TILL, Leopold (1830-1893) Austrian

£961 $1720 €1403 Snowball fight (42x53cm-17x21in) s. 26-May-4 AB Stockholms Auktionsverk #2379/R (S.KR 13000)

TILLBERG, Harald (1877-?) German

£366 $586 €520 Mediterranean landscape (96x115cm-38x45in) s. 18-Sep-3 Rieber, Stuttgart #1037

TILLEMANS, J (18th C) Flemish

£3500 $6405 €5110 Italianate landscape with drovers and their animals (100x169cm-39x67in) 6-Jul-4 Sotheby's, Olympia #485/R est:4000-6000

£3600 $6588 €5256 Italianate landscape with drovers watering their animals at a well (69x91cm-27x36in) s. 6-Jul-4 Sotheby's, Olympia #484/R est:3000-4000

TILLEMANS, Peter (1684-1734) Flemish

£5500 $9900 €8030 Italianate harbour with peasants and elegant figures by a frigate (38x52cm-15x20in) s.d.1708 prov. 23-Apr-4 Christie's, Kensington #114/R est:5000-7000

Works on paper

£16000 $29120 €23360 View of Chirk Castle from the garden (20x39cm-8x15in) pen ink wash exhib. 21-Jun-4 Christie's, London #22/R est:5000-8000

TILLER, Lars (1924-1994) Norwegian

£961 $1720 €1403 Still life of fruit and vase (45x37cm-18x15in) s.d.53 panel. 22-Mar-4 Blomqvist, Oslo #604/R (N.KR 12000)

£1220 $2232 €1781 Blue composition (60x73cm-24x29in) init.d.76-77. 7-Jun-4 Blomqvist, Oslo #430/R est:18000-22000 (N.KR 15000)

£1841 $3296 €2688 In the middle of town (80x102cm-31x40in) s.d.79 i.stretcher. 22-Mar-4 Blomqvist, Oslo #611/R est:20000-25000 (N.KR 23000)

£4878 $8927 €7122 Brown composition (70x110cm-28x43in) s.d.61 exhib. 7-Jun-4 Blomqvist, Oslo #428/R est:70000-90000 (N.KR 60000)

£8518 $14651 €12436 Composition (100x80cm-39x31in) s.d.1963 lit. 8-Dec-3 Blomqvist, Oslo #538/R est:60000-80000 (N.KR 100000)

TILLERS, Imants (1950-) Australian

£9016 $14246 €13163 Dievturi (152x152cm-60x60in) oil synthetic polymer paint gesso graphite board. 2-Sep-3 Deutscher-Menzies, Melbourne #62/R est:18000-24000 (A.D 22000)

£10744 $19017 €15686 Horizon (101x141cm-40x56in) six canvasboards prov. 3-May-4 Christie's, Melbourne #75/R est:18000-25000 (A.D 26000)

£14498 $24937 €21167 Bonegilla (225x210cm-89x83in) acrylic gouache on 54 canvasboards. 3-Dec-3 Dunbar Sloane, Auckland #45/R est:35000-45000 (NZ.D 39000)

Works on paper

£9160 $16672 €13374 Preparation for a journey into the unknown I 1996 (229x229cm-90x90in) synthetic polymer oil stick gouache 54 panel prov.exhib. 16-Jun-4 Deutscher-Menzies, Melbourne #4/R est:30000-40000 (A.D 24000)

TILLMANS, Wolfgang (1968-) German

Photographs

£1630 $3000 €2380 Park (61x51cm-24x20in) s.i.num.3 verso c-print exec.1999 printed 2001 prov. 10-Jun-4 Phillips, New York #499/R est:1500-2000

£2200 $4048 €3212 Alex (40x30cm-16x12in) s.i.d.97 num.10/10 verso col photo lit. 24-Jun-4 Sotheby's, Olympia #637/R est:1000-1500

£2778 $5000 €4056 Mental picture no.26 (60x51cm-24x20in) s.i.d. num.126/26 chromogenic print exhib.lit. 23-Apr-4 Phillips, New York #233/R est:2000-3000

£3200 $5824 €4672 Paula typewriter looking (56x38cm-22x15in) s.i.d.94 verso colour photograph prov.lit. 4-Feb-4 Sotheby's, Olympia #269/R est:2500-3500

£3370 $6200 €4920 Mental picture no 10 (51x61cm-20x24in) s.i.d.2000 verso c-print prov. 10-Jun-4 Phillips, New York #510/R est:1500-2000

£3593 $6000 €5246 Turnhouse (61x91cm-24x36in) s.i. num.1/3 verso chromogenic col print exec.1995 prov.lit. 17-Oct-3 Phillips, New York #292/R est:6000-8000

£4046 $7000 €5907 John and Paula, Hay cx1000 (26x39cm-10x15in) s.i.d.1994 verso chromogenic photograph lit. 12-Dec-3 Sotheby's, New York #479/R est:4000-6000

£4500 $8190 €6570 Wanking (40x30cm-16x12in) s.i.d.Aug91 num.5/10 1 verso gelatin silver print lit. 4-Feb-4 Sotheby's, Olympia #64/R est:1000-1500

£9239 $17000 €13489 Waterloo Bridge (145x215cm-57x85in) c-print prov. 10-Jun-4 Phillips, New York #506/R est:1500-2000

£10615 $19000 €15498 Night swimmer (210x138cm-83x54in) inkjet print prov.exhib. 14-May-4 Phillips, New York #172/R est:10000-15000

£20958 $35000 €30599 White jeans on white (150x200cm-59x79in) c-print executed 1991 prov.lit. 13-Nov-3 Phillips, New York #48/R est:20000-30000

TILLY, Vilhelm Eyvind (1860-1935) Danish

£2457 $4251 €3587 Young lady and her black horse and dog in the farmyard (63x72cm-25x28in) s. 9-Dec-3 Rasmussen, Copenhagen #1443/R est:10000 (D.KR 26000)

TILLYER, William (1938-) British

£3000 $4770 €4380 Courthope (153x122cm-60x48in) s.verso acrylic prov. 10-Sep-3 Sotheby's, Olympia #305/R est:3000-4000

£6000 $10980 €8760 Study for the romantic section of Arcadia, Gesture, form and illusion (76x91cm-30x36in) s. acrylic prov.exhib. 4-Jun-4 Christie's, London #130/R est:4000-6000

TILMOUTH, Sheila (1949-) British

£260 $465 €380 Tea with the cat (36x41cm-14x16in) on gesso exhib. 27-May-4 Mallams, Cheltenham #228

TILSON, Joe (1928-) British

£2200 $3674 €3212 Geometry (61x61cm-24x24in) s.d.1964 acrylic panel. 16-Oct-3 Christie's, Kensington #699/R est:2000-3000

£2600 $4342 €3796 Collage 17/W 1961 (152x101cm-60x40in) s.i.d.1961 verso acrylic wood collage board prov. 16-Oct-3 Christie's, Kensington #697/R est:2000-3000

£25000 $43000 €36500 Colour chart (156x207cm-61x81in) s.i.d.1969-1971 verso canvas on wood relief prov. 3-Dec-3 Sotheby's, London #85/R est:10000-15000

Sculpture

£46980 $84094 €70000 Navona I (177x46x5cm-70x18x2in) s.i.verso wood iron screws exec.1961-65 prov.exhib. 25-May-4 Sotheby's, Milan #176/R est:7000-9000

Works on paper

£400 $728 €584 Stardome (43x56cm-17x22in) s.i.d.1967 pencil collage. 30-Jun-4 Christie's, Kensington #86/R

£450 $819 €657 Big bird envelope (45x56cm-18x22in) s.i.d.1967 pencil pen black ink collage. 30-Jun-4 Christie's, Kensington #83/R

£500 $910 €730 Thumb (45x58cm-18x23in) i.d.1967 pencil pen black ink collage. 30-Jun-4 Christie's, Kensington #84/R

£600 $1092 €876 New York (76x56cm-30x22in) s.d.1967 pencil pen brush black ink. 30-Jun-4 Christie's, Kensington #85/R

£1200 $2184 €1752 Jet matchbox (45x56cm-18x22in) s.i.d.1967 pencil pen black ink bodycol. 30-Jun-4 Christie's, Kensington #88/R est:400-600

£1500 $2775 €2190 New York Decals (90x100cm-35x39in) s. collage silkscreen. 13-Jul-4 Bonhams, Knightsbridge #137/R est:1000-1500

£1600 $2912 €2336 Clip-matic lips (45x55cm-18x22in) s.i.d.1967 pencil pen black ink collage. 30-Jun-4 Christie's, Kensington #87/R est:600-800

TIMICO, Benno (?) Italian

£260 $478 €380 Figures and two oxen (15x25cm-6x10in) indis.sig. board. 29-Mar-4 Thomson Roddick & Medcalf, Edinburgh #258/R

TIMKOV, Nikolai (1912-1993) Russian

£11111 $20000 €16222 Fall (60x80cm-24x31in) s.d.64 s.i.d.verso. 23-Apr-4 Sotheby's, New York #119/R est:20000-30000

£11667 $21000 €17034 Landscape with Torshok village in the distance (50x60cm-20x24in) s.d.78 s.i.d.verso board. 23-Apr-4 Sotheby's, New York #118/R est:20000-30000

TIMLIN, William M (1893-1943) South African

£264 $473 €385 Landscape with a house (36x51cm-14x20in) s.d.1913 board. 31-May-4 Stephan Welz, Johannesburg #114 (SA.R 3200)

£733 $1224 €1070 Spring, Natal (42x42cm-17x17in) s. board. 20-Oct-3 Stephan Welz, Johannesburg #239/R est:7000-10000 (SA.R 8500)

£948 $1584 €1384 Winter, Natal (50x80cm-20x31in) s. i.verso. 20-Oct-3 Stephan Welz, Johannesburg #244 est:6000-9000 (SA.R 11000)

Works on paper

£289 $517 €422 Mountainous landscape (23x36cm-9x14in) s. pastel. 31-May-4 Stephan Welz, Johannesburg #203 (SA.R 3500)

£414 $691 €604 Snow on the Drakensberg, Natal (37x52cm-15x20in) s. i.verso pastel. 20-Oct-3 Stephan Welz, Johannesburg #505 est:2000-4000 (SA.R 4800)

£769 $1308 €1123 Fantasy (27x37cm-11x15in) W/C. 4-Nov-3 Stephan Welz, Johannesburg #698/R est:9000-12000 (SA.R 9000)

£2393 $4068 €3494 Fairy embroideries (28x22cm-11x9in) mono.i. W/C. 4-Nov-3 Stephan Welz, Johannesburg #699/R est:10000-15000 (SA.R 28000)

TIMM, Vassili Fedorovich (1820-1895) Russian

Works on paper

£1149 $2056 €1700 A married couple (20x16cm-8x6in) s.d.1843 mixed media. 8-May-4 Bukowskis, Helsinki #440/R est:1000-1200

TIMMEL, Vito (1886-1949) Austrian

£2133 $3819 €3200 Lady in red (59x49cm-23x19in) s. lit. 12-May-4 Stadion, Trieste #840/R est:2500-3500

£2533 $4535 €3800 Landscape with tree (40x50cm-16x20in) s. board. 12-May-4 Stadion, Trieste #794/R est:2000-3000

£15333 $27447 €23000 View of Trieste (100x100cm-39x39in) s.d.42 lit. 12-May-4 Stadion, Trieste #677/R est:15000-20000

Works on paper

£1000 $1790 €1500 Woman in interior (14x15cm-6x6in) W/C lit. 12-May-4 Stadion, Trieste #707/R est:500-700

£1267 $2267 €1900 Dancer (51x37cm-20x15in) s.d.1927 mixed media. 12-May-4 Stadion, Trieste #661/R est:2000-3000

£1267 $2267 €1900 Games on the beach (51x37cm-20x15in) s.d.1927 mixed media. 12-May-4 Stadion, Trieste #660/R est:2000-3000

TIMMERMAHN, Peter Klein (1942-) Swiss

£2270 $3904 €3314 Three Graces (162x130cm-64x51in) s.d.94 acrylic. 2-Dec-3 Koller, Zurich #3112/R est:5000-7000 (S.FR 5040)

TIMMERMANS (?) ?

£1806 $3015 €2600 Marine Hollandaise (84x131cm-33x52in) s. 21-Oct-3 Thierry & Lannon, Brest #77

TIMMERMANS, Felix (1886-1947) Belgian

Works on paper

£544 $974 €800 Twee oogjes zo blauw (27x20cm-11x8in) col chk. 22-Mar-4 Amberes, Antwerp #257

TIMMERMANS, Henri (1858-1942) Belgian

£470 $860 €700 Interieur (30x40cm-12x16in) s. panel. 8-Jul-4 Campo, Vlaamse Kaai #248

£570 $1021 €850 A l'auberge (34x50cm-13x20in) s. 25-May-4 Campo & Campo, Antwerp #287/R

£800 $1440 €1200 Woman reading (55x75cm-22x30in) s. 26-Apr-4 Bernaerts, Antwerp #436/R

£1000 $1790 €1500 La lettre d'amour (28x45cm-11x18in) s. 11-May-4 Vanderkindere, Brussels #58 est:1000-1500

£1408 $2437 €2000 En conversation (66x82cm-26x32in) s. 9-Dec-3 Campo, Vlaamse Kaai #446/R est:1500-1700

£2148 $3995 €3200 Farmer's interior with pipe smokers and card players (118x98cm-46x39in) s. 8-Mar-4 Bernaerts, Antwerp #115/R est:2000-3000
£2148 $3844 €3200 Voor ne kus (153x113cm-60x44in) 25-May-4 Campo & Campo, Antwerp #286/R est:6000-10000
£27660 $46191 €39000 Carnival (230x215cm-91x85in) s. 20-Oct-3 Bernaerts, Antwerp #132/R est:25000-35000
£35000 $63700 €51100 Festival (223x216cm-88x85in) s.d.1891. 17-Jun-4 Christie's, London #7/R est:40000-60000

TIMMERMANS, Jean (1899-1986) Belgian
Works on paper
£226 $385 €330 Provence (54x73cm-21x29in) s. W/C. 18-Nov-3 Hans Widmer, St Gallen #1213 (S.FR 500)
£319 $508 €460 Jeux d'enfants (53x66cm-21x26in) s. W/C. 15-Sep-3 Horta, Bruxelles #326

TIMMERMANS, Louis (1846-1910) French
£1344 $2500 €1962 Moonlit harbour (76x127cm-30x50in) s. 5-Mar-4 Skinner, Boston #322/R est:2000-3000
£3125 $5313 €4500 Choppy surf (60x73cm-24x29in) s. 28-Oct-3 Christie's, Amsterdam #80/R est:4500-5500
£3846 $6615 €5500 Dutch fishing boat at the coast in the evening (76x128cm-30x50in) s. canvas on canvas. 5-Dec-3 Bolland & Marotz, Bremen #669/R est:4400
£5634 $9746 €8000 Fishing boats at sunset (50x65cm-20x26in) s.d.1907. 13-Dec-3 De Vuyst, Lokeren #446/R est:8500-10000
Works on paper
£862 $1440 €1250 Navires au Havre (32x49cm-13x19in) s. W/C. 11-Nov-3 Lesieur & Le Bars, Le Havre #109
£1275 $2372 €1900 Voiliers amares et quais animes (33x48cm-13x19in) s. W/C. 7-Mar-4 Lesieur & Le Bars, Le Havre #133/R

TIMMERMANS, Louis (attrib) (1846-1910) French
£3830 $6396 €5400 La jetee du Treport (37x46cm-15x18in) bears sig. panel. 19-Oct-3 Anaf, Lyon #280/R est:6000-7000

TIMMONS, Brendan (?) Irish?
£345 $631 €500 Near Letterfrack (71x48cm-28x19in) s. 28-Jan-4 Woodwards, Cork #255

TIMMS, Freddy (1948-) Australian
£6504 $10211 €9431 Sugar bag (180x230cm-71x91in) s.d.verso acrylic prov. 26-Aug-3 Christie's, Sydney #53a/R est:15000-20000 (A.D 16000)
Works on paper
£2549 $4563 €3722 Black Creek (122x122cm-48x48in) i.verso synthetic polymer paint canvas exec 1997. 25-May-4 Lawson Menzies, Sydney #172/R est:7000-9000 (A.D 6500)
£3252 $5138 €4715 Lissadell station (101x163cm-40x64in) i.d.March 1997 verso synthetic polymer paint linen prov. 28-Jul-3 Sotheby's, Paddington #418/R est:6000-8000 (A.D 8000)
£3333 $5967 €4866 Humpy (122x183cm-48x72in) synthetic polymer paint canvas exec 1996. 25-May-4 Lawson Menzies, Sydney #47/R est:8000-10000 (A.D 8500)
£5691 $8992 €8252 Untitled (120x240cm-47x94in) synthetic polymer paint board prov. 28-Jul-3 Sotheby's, Paddington #206/R est:15000-20000 (A.D 14000)
£11328 $21184 €16992 Lake Argyle country (91x242cm-36x95in) synthetic polymer paint prov.exhib.lit. 26-Jul-4 Sotheby's, Melbourne #220/R est:15000-20000 (A.D 29000)

TIMMS, Tiger Jupurrurla (20th C) Australian
Works on paper
£1446 $2459 €2111 Duck and water (116x196cm-46x77in) synthetic polymer paint on canvas. 29-Oct-3 Lawson Menzies, Sydney #63/R est:2000-2500 (A.D 3500)

TIMOTEO DA COSTA, Artur (1882-1923) Brazilian?
£1099 $2011 €1649 Landscape (17x19cm-7x7in) s.i.d.1920 cardboard. 6-Jul-4 Bolsa de Arte, Rio de Janeiro #121/R (B.R 6000)
£5128 $9077 €7692 Self portrait (50x61cm-20x24in) 27-Apr-4 Bolsa de Arte, Rio de Janeiro #25/R (B.R 28000)

TIMOTEO DA COSTA, Joao (1879-1932) Brazilian?
£1832 $3352 €2748 In the studio (170x100cm-67x39in) s.i.d.1929. 6-Jul-4 Bolsa de Arte, Rio de Janeiro #114/R (B.R 10000)

TIMYM, William (20th C) British
Sculpture
£993 $1818 €1500 Two chimpanzees (15cm-6in) s.num.8/9 brown pat. bronze. 6-Apr-4 Sotheby's, Olympia #96/R est:800-1200
£1000 $1800 €1460 Study of an African bull elephant. s. num.4/9 bronze. 25-Jan-4 Desmond Judd, Cranbrook #531
£1060 $1939 €1600 Pug dog (20x24cm-8x9in) s. dark brown pat. bronze. 6-Apr-4 Sotheby's, Olympia #88/R est:800-1200

TINAM-BARBIER, Madame (19th C) French?
£1141 $2111 €1700 L'escalier bleu (56x39cm-22x15in) s. 15-Mar-4 Gros & Delettrez, Paris #268/R est:1500-1800

TINDLE, David (1932-) British
£370 $651 €540 Umbrella and chair (11x14cm-4x6in) init. egg tempera board. 18-May-4 Bonhams, Knightsbridge #63/R
£600 $1062 €876 Madame le Golher's garden (30x30cm-12x12in) init. egg tempera board. 27-Apr-4 Bonhams, Knightsbridge #235/R
£600 $1056 €876 Rowing boats Oxford (50x45cm-20x18in) s.d.59 s.i.d.overlap. 18-May-4 Bonhams, Knightsbridge #93/R
£700 $1239 €1022 Corner of the studio (30x30cm-12x12in) init. 27-Apr-4 Bonhams, Knightsbridge #238/R
£800 $1480 €1168 Beach, Seaford (20x23cm-8x9in) board. 10-Mar-4 Cheffins, Cambridge #109
£900 $1431 €1314 Still life of fruit and a teasil plant (76x63cm-30x25in) s.d.1955 s.i.verso sold with another by the same hand. 10-Sep-3 Sotheby's, Olympia #200/R
£950 $1682 €1387 Rolling egg (25x25cm-10x10in) s.i.d.97 egg tempera. 27-Apr-4 Bonhams, Knightsbridge #197/R
£1000 $1820 €1460 Tea (81x100cm-32x39in) s.i.d. verso acrylic. 1-Jul-4 Christie's, Kensington #350/R est:1000-1500
£1600 $2912 €2336 View from David's House,Tuscany (56x73cm-22x29in) init. tempera. 1-Jul-4 Christie's, Kensington #286/R est:1000-1500
£1800 $3006 €2628 Young dog (60x81cm-24x32in) i.d.1982 verso egg tempera. 21-Oct-3 Gildings, Market Harborough #443 est:2000-3000
£3500 $6020 €5110 Apple tree (48x73cm-19x29in) s. tempera board. 2-Dec-3 Bonhams, New Bond Street #148/R est:3000-5000
Works on paper
£340 $602 €496 View from the Berkshire Downs (22x33cm-9x13in) s.d.1988 W/C. 27-Apr-4 Bonhams, Knightsbridge #21/R
£800 $1440 €1168 Table by the window (43x33cm-17x13in) W/C bodycol. 20-Jan-4 Bonhams, Knightsbridge #77/R

TING, Walasse (1929-1998) Chinese
£805 $1490 €1200 Cat (23x38cm-9x15in) st.sig. acrylic paper. 13-Mar-4 De Vuyst, Lokeren #317
£1569 $2839 €2291 Women with parrots (35x48cm-14x19in) s. acrylic on rice paper. 4-Apr-4 Sotheby's, Singapore #191/R est:3000-5000 (S.D 4800)
£1745 $3228 €2600 Four women (40x40cm-16x16in) st.sig. acrylic paper. 13-Mar-4 De Vuyst, Lokeren #316/R est:2200-2500
£2268 $4060 €3311 A sleep in the garden tonight (76x102cm-30x40in) s.d.1970. 12-Jan-4 Rasmussen, Vejle #582/R est:15000-20000 (D.KR 24000)
£2500 $4175 €3650 Grasshopper (33x47cm-13x19in) s.d.60 verso. 12-Oct-3 Sotheby's, Singapore #14/R est:4000-6000 (S.D 7200)
£2533 $4535 €3800 Red Chinese calligraphy (81x100cm-32x39in) s.i.d. s.i.d. verso. 13-May-4 Neumeister, Munich #775/R est:2000-2200
£2841 $5000 €4148 Black and White (160x180cm-63x71in) i. verso painted 1958 prov. 23-May-4 Hindman, Chicago #075/R est:3000-5000
£3791 $6975 €5535 I am still the same old virgin (86x127cm-34x50in) s.d.74 verso acrylic. 29-Mar-4 Rasmussen, Copenhagen #145/R est:40000 (D.KR 42000)
£4525 $8100 €6607 My girlfriend (70x100cm-28x39in) s. prov. 10-May-4 Rasmussen, Vejle #595/R est:30000-40000 (D.KR 50000)
£5019 $8382 €7328 I hug my cat everyday (51x75cm-20x30in) s.d.1985 acrylic. 26-Oct-3 Christie's, Hong Kong #116/R est:65000-90000 (HK.D 65000)
£6250 $10438 €9125 Catch me a grasshopper (102x127cm-40x50in) s.i.d.79 verso acrylic. 12-Oct-3 Sotheby's, Singapore #13/R est:18000-25000 (S.D 18000)
£6667 $12267 €10000 Three Geishas (177x96cm-70x38in) s.d.1988 acrylic Japanese paper. 8-Jun-4 Sotheby's, Amsterdam #287/R est:10000-15000
£7246 $11884 €10000 Jeune fille au pull turquoise (96x176cm-38x69in) acrylic paper on canvas prov. 27-May-3 Sotheby's, Amsterdam #402/R est:10000-15000
£17204 $27527 €25118 My life is a red rose (71x107cm-28x42in) s.i.d.75 verso acrylic. 18-May-3 Sotheby's, Singapore #15/R est:18000-28000 (S.D 48000)
Works on paper
£632 $1162 €923 Reclining woman among flowers (15x20cm-6x8in) gouache Indian ink. 29-Mar-4 Rasmussen, Copenhagen #425/R (D.KR 7000)
£632 $1162 €923 Reclining woman among flowers (16x22cm-6x9in) gouache Indian ink. 29-Mar-4 Rasmussen, Copenhagen #426/R (D.KR 7000)
£632 $1162 €923 Woman among flowers (15x21cm-6x8in) gouache Indian ink. 29-Mar-4 Rasmussen, Copenhagen #427/R (D.KR 7000)
£764 $1276 €1100 Femmes aux perroquets (35x47cm-14x19in) studio st. W/C. 21-Oct-3 Campo, Vlaamse Kaai #583/R
£1377 $2258 €1900 Untitled (38x48cm-15x19in) st.sig. W/C. 27-May-3 Sotheby's, Amsterdam #554/R est:1500-2000
£1422 $2560 €2076 Girls (15x20cm-6x8in) W/C hanging scroll. 26-Apr-4 Sotheby's, Hong Kong #598/R est:4000-6000 (HK.D 20000)
£1449 $2377 €2000 Untitled (38x48cm-15x19in) st.sig. W/C. 27-May-3 Sotheby's, Amsterdam #553/R est:1500-2000
£1594 $2614 €2200 Untitled (38x48cm-15x19in) st.sig. W/C. 27-May-3 Sotheby's, Amsterdam #564/R est:1500-2000
£1884 $3090 €2600 Untitled (38x48cm-15x19in) st.sig. W/C. 27-May-3 Sotheby's, Amsterdam #552/R est:1500-2000
£1961 $3549 €2863 Two women (50x71cm-20x28in) s.i. W/C rice paper on canvas. 4-Apr-4 Sotheby's, Singapore #190/R est:3000-5000 (S.D 6000)
£2448 $4210 €3500 Reclining nude with cat (59x88cm-23x35in) s. W/C. 2-Dec-3 Sotheby's, Amsterdam #309/R est:3000-4000
£2899 $4754 €4000 Untitled (73x113cm-29x44in) st.sig. W/C. 27-May-3 Sotheby's, Amsterdam #563/R est:3000-4000
£3125 $5219 €4563 Flowers (176x95cm-69x37in) s. W/C. 12-Oct-3 Sotheby's, Singapore #11/R est:10000-15000 (S.D 9000)
£3268 $5915 €4771 Women with parrots (37x49cm-15x19in) s. W/C rice paper on canvas. 4-Apr-4 Sotheby's, Singapore #189/R est:3000-5000 (S.D 10000)
£3986 $6536 €5500 Untitled (70x109cm-28x43in) st.sig. W/C. 27-May-3 Sotheby's, Amsterdam #550/R est:3000-4000
£4902 $8873 €7157 Guilin landscape (69x159cm-27x63in) s. W/C rice paper. 4-Apr-4 Sotheby's, Singapore #194/R est:6000-8000 (S.D 15000)
£5161 $8258 €7535 Girl in kimono (44x59cm-17x23in) seal sig. W/C. 18-May-3 Sotheby's, Singapore #42/R est:10000-15000 (S.D 14400)
£7190 $13013 €10497 Three ladies with flowers (175x95cm-69x37in) s. W/C on rice paper. 4-Apr-4 Sotheby's, Singapore #187/R est:15000-20000 (S.D 22000)
£9104 $14566 €13292 Girl with flowers (76x96cm-30x38in) seal sig. W/C paper on canvas. 18-May-3 Sotheby's, Singapore #41/R est:9000-12000 (S.D 25400)
£11594 $17971 €16927 Woman with flowers and parrot (179x96cm-70x38in) s. W/C paper on canvas. 6-Oct-2 Sotheby's, Singapore #39/R est:12000-18000 (S.D 32000)
£18667 $34347 €28000 Geisha with cat (96x177cm-38x70in) s. W/C paper on canvas. 8-Jun-4 Sotheby's, Amsterdam #296/R est:8000-10000
£21333 $39253 €32000 Nude (69x180cm-27x71in) s. mixed media paper on canvas prov. 8-Jun-4 Sotheby's, Amsterdam #286/R est:7000-10000

TINGUELY, Jean (1925-1991) Swiss
£11468 $19151 €16629 Meta extra and super leggera (60x113cm-24x44in) s. oil gouache W/C. 19-Jun-3 Kornfeld, Bern #981/R est:30000 (S.FR 25000)
Prints
£3275 $5961 €4782 Liberte (68x88cm-27x35in) s. num.38/100 col lithograph collage. 16-Jun-4 Fischer, Luzern #2825/R est:6000-7000 (S.FR 7500)
Sculpture
£1259 $2140 €1800 Untitled (44x14x7cm-17x6x3in) s.i.d.12.Mai 86 plastic paper string metal prov. 26-Nov-3 Dorotheum, Vienna #294/R est:2000-3000
£10860 $18136 €15856 Composition (65x65cm-26x26in) s.d. verso painted wood metal prov.lit. 24-Jun-3 Germann, Zurich #17/R est:18000-22000 (S.FR 24000)

£24017	$42991	€35065	Nietzsche thinking hard (109x107x76cm-43x42x30in) metal wood motor exhib.lit. 26-May-4 Sotheby's, Zurich #161/R est:35000-45000 (S.FR 55000)
£36000	$66600	€54000	Bouc de Rene (160x110x190cm-63x43x75in) iron horns engine exhaust exec.1990 prov.exhib. 18-Jul-4 Sotheby's, Paris #263/R est:40000-50000
£40000	$73600	€58400	Le perforateur (53x103x62cm-21x41x24in) welded iron painted rubber electric motor wire transformer. 25-Jun-4 Christie's, London #128/R est:40000-60000
£65000	$118300	€94900	Casoar (193x64x47cm-76x25x19in) iron elec motor metal rod feather paint exec 1963 prov.exhib.lit. 5-Feb-4 Christie's, London #157/R est:50000-70000
£73333	$135667	€110000	Fontaine V (205x96x77cm-81x38x30in) metal iron light engine exec.1963 prov.exhib.lit. 18-Jul-4 Sotheby's, Paris #156/R est:80000-120000
£120000	$222000	€180000	Odalisk. metal iron rubber engines exec.1989 prov.exhib.lit. 18-Jul-4 Sotheby's, Paris #255/R est:150000-250000
Works on paper			
£385	$654	€562	Untitled (38x28cm-15x11in) s. biro on offset print prov. 25-Nov-3 Germann, Zurich #908 (S.FR 850)
£467	$835	€700	Composition (41x36cm-16x14in) s.d.62 feltip pen. 15-May-4 De Vuyst, Lokeren #334
£814	$1360	€1188	Recherches pour un relief sonore (23x30cm-9x12in) s.i.d.1969 felt pen pencil. 24-Jun-3 Germann, Zurich #174/R est:2000-2500 (S.FR 1800)
£917	$1532	€1330	Lettre-dessin a Henriette Grindat. Dessin (23x37cm-9x15in) black felt pen ball point pen cardboard double-sided. 21-Jun-3 Galerie du Rhone, Sion #439 est:2000-2500 (S.FR 2000)
£1055	$1762	€1530	Est ce que je pourrait avoir quelques photo's d'Eureka (26x21cm-10x8in) s.d. mixed media. 21-Jun-3 Galerie du Rhone, Sion #440/R est:2500-3000 (S.FR 2300)
£1121	$2006	€1637	Untitled (27x30cm-11x12in) s.i.d.26.VI.1989 mixed media. 14-May-4 Dobiaschofsky, Bern #266/R est:5000 (S.FR 2600)
£1135	$1895	€1600	Untitled (25x16cm-10x6in) s.i.d.18.VII.91 mixed media prov. 14-Oct-3 Dorotheum, Vienna #284/R est:1000-1500
£1570	$2558	€2292	Abstract compositions (21x15cm-8x6in) s.d.89 felt pen biro two. 29-Sep-3 Christie's, Zurich #101/R est:4000-6000 (S.FR 3500)
£1606	$2681	€2329	J'arrive pas en ce moment a faire un dessin (29x20cm-11x8in) s.d. mixed media. 21-Jun-3 Galerie du Rhone, Sion #438/R est:2500-3000 (S.FR 3500)
£1796	$3000	€2622	Untitled (25x36cm-10x14in) s.d.1964 collage ink. 7-Oct-3 Sotheby's, New York #362 est:4000-5000
£1806	$2979	€2600	Sans titre (29x20cm-11x8in) s. gouache collage prov. 2-Jul-3 Cornette de St.Cyr, Paris #74/R est:3000-4000
£1927	$3217	€2794	Love W B letter (32x38cm-13x15in) s.d.8.Sept 87 collage drawing script. 19-Jun-3 Kornfeld, Bern #980/R est:5000 (S.FR 4200)
£2333	$4177	€3500	Hannibal (30x40cm-12x16in) s.i.d. ball pen feltpen ink prov. 14-May-4 Ketterer, Munich #258/R est:3000-4000
£2371	$4244	€3462	Meta (41x58cm-16x23in) s.i.d.1988 mixed media. 14-May-4 Dobiaschofsky, Bern #265/R est:7500 (S.FR 5500)
£2412	$4439	€3522	Picture document (30x40cm-12x16in) s. mixed media collage text. 23-Jun-4 Koller, Zurich #3083/R est:5800-7000 (S.FR 5500)
£2467	$4489	€3700	Micheline (19x31cm-7x12in) s. gouache acrylic ink felt-tip pen prov. 29-Jun-4 Cornette de St.Cyr, Paris #68/R est:3000-4000
£2708	$4982	€3954	Decorated letter to Knud W Jensen from the artist (29x21cm-11x8in) s.d.1974 collage. 29-Mar-4 Rasmussen, Copenhagen #172/R est:12000-15000 (D.KR 30000)
£2708	$4982	€3954	Decorated letter to Knud W Jensen (21x30cm-8x12in) s. collage prov. 29-Mar-4 Rasmussen, Copenhagen #173/R est:12000-15000 (D.KR 30000)
£2708	$4982	€3954	Decorated letter to Knud W Jensen from the artist (30x40cm-12x16in) s.d.1986 collage prov. 29-Mar-4 Rasmussen, Copenhagen #175/R est:15000-20000 (D.KR 30000)
£2797	$4755	€4000	Untitled (21x29cm-8x11in) s.d.26 Juli 1982 gouache col pen pencil biro feather. 27-Nov-3 Lempertz, Koln #480/R est:2200
£3041	$5351	€4500	Meta Pandemonium (61x44cm-24x17in) s.i.d.1990 verso mixed media prov. 18-May-4 Tajan, Paris #93/R est:5000-6000
£3125	$5219	€4500	Tinguely in Munche (29x21cm-11x8in) s.i. mixed media collage prov.exhib. 21-Oct-3 Artcurial Briest, Paris #543/R est:3500-4000
£4189	$7374	€6200	Untitled (21x29cm-8x11in) s. ink collage ball pen col crayons prov.exhib. 18-May-4 Tajan, Paris #90/R est:4000-5000
£4324	$8000	€6313	Vive il Trovatore - collaboration with Niki De Saint Phalle (35x42cm-14x17in) s.i. pencil crayon pastel felt tip pen pall point collage prov. 12-Feb-4 Sotheby's, New York #149/R est:4000-5000
£4392	$7730	€6500	Untitled (23x29cm-9x11in) s. ink collage ball pen col crayons exec 1975 prov.exhib. 18-May-4 Tajan, Paris #89/R est:5000-6000
£4800	$8832	€7008	Co-operation imaginaire avec Yves Klein (65x85cm-26x33in) s.i.d.1988 gouache pastel felt-tip pen cardboard prov. 24-Jun-4 Sotheby's, London #257/R est:5000-7000
£10196	$17334	€14886	Chaos No.1 (47x65cm-19x26in) s.d.1965 mixed media cardboard prov.exhib.lit. 5-Nov-3 AB Stockholms Auktionsverk #1085/R est:100000-120000 (S.KR 135000)

TINGUELY, Jean Louis (1937-) ?

£286	$487	€418	Hilly countryside with farmsteads (27x39cm-11x15in) s. canvas on board. 5-Nov-3 Dobiaschofsky, Bern #3757 (S.FR 650)

TINGUELY, Jean and AEPPLI, Eva (20th C) Swiss/French

Sculpture			
£7333	$13567	€11000	Mirha (62cm-24in) iron mixed media exec.1991 prov. 18-Jul-4 Sotheby's, Paris #251/R est:8000-10000

TINMAN, Dorothy (20th C) British

£300	$492	€438	Still life with oranges (35x45cm-14x18in) s. board. 4-Jun-3 John Ross, Belfast #234
£350	$641	€511	Lough shore, Strangford (30x40cm-12x16in) s.d.04 verso. 2-Jun-4 John Ross, Belfast #72
£380	$695	€555	Shorelines, Tramore (35x45cm-14x18in) s.d.04 board. 2-Jun-4 John Ross, Belfast #124
£400	$688	€584	Mac Reds (35x45cm-14x18in) s.d.03 verso board. 3-Dec-3 John Ross, Belfast #138
£500	$830	€730	Teelin, Donegal (40x50cm-16x20in) s.d.2003 verso board. 1-Oct-3 John Ross, Belfast #229

TINNING, George Campbell (1910-) Canadian

£335	$576	€489	Near Sutton in the Eastern townships, Quebec (40x50cm-16x20in) s. board. 2-Dec-3 Joyner Waddington, Toronto #459 (C.D 750)

TINTORE, Simone del (attrib) (1630-1708) Italian

£5629	$10245	€8500	Enfant pres d'une nature morte de fleurs et de fruits dans un paysage (70x99cm-28x39in) 21-Jun-4 Tajan, Paris #6 est:1500-2000
£100671	$185235	€150000	Melons, grapes, quinces, figs and other fruit with woman and putti (123x149cm-48x59in) 26-Mar-4 Bolland & Marotz, Bremen #475/R est:10000

TINTORE, Simone del (circle) (1630-1708) Italian

£9155	$16021	€13000	Mushrooms, apples and basket (57x106cm-22x42in) prov. 17-Dec-3 Christie's, Rome #470/R est:10000-15000

TINTORETTO (style) (16/17th C) Italian

£6923	$11908	€10108	Portrait of gentleman (127x94cm-50x37in) 3-Dec-3 AB Stockholms Auktionsverk #2723/R est:18000-20000 (S.KR 90000)

TINTORETTO, Domenico (1560-1635) Italian

£13966	$25000	€20390	Penitent Magdalene (134x101cm-53x40in) 27-May-4 Sotheby's, New York #86/R est:30000-50000
£15000	$27450	€21900	Pandora, allegory of Generosity (113x102cm-44x40in) prov.lit. 8-Jul-4 Sotheby's, London #305/R est:15000-20000
£30201	$55570	€45000	Portrait of the Venetian procurator Michele Priuli (127x109cm-50x43in) i. 24-Mar-4 Dorotheum, Vienna #3/R est:30000-40000
£40268	$74094	€60000	Portrait of a gentleman (114x95cm-45x37in) lit.exhib.prov. 24-Mar-4 Dorotheum, Vienna #58/R est:50000-70000
Works on paper			
£2585	$4627	€3800	Un homme endormi (27x20cm-11x8in) black white chk prov.lit. 18-Mar-4 Christie's, Paris #3/R est:800-1200

TINTORETTO, Domenico (attrib) (1560-1635) Italian

£13889	$25000	€20278	Baptism of Christ (119x86cm-47x34in) prov.lit. 22-Jan-4 Sotheby's, New York #137/R est:10000-15000

TINTORETTO, Domenico (circle) (1560-1635) Italian

£6000	$10200	€8760	Madonna and Child with infant Saint John the Baptist, Saint Elizabeth (96x122cm-38x48in) prov. 31-Oct-3 Christie's, Kensington #110/R est:6000-8000

TINTORETTO, Jacopo (1518-1594) Italian

£9932	$16884	€14500	Crucifixion (41x56cm-16x22in) board. 9-Nov-3 Finarte, Venice #59/R est:9000-12000
£30000	$51900	€43800	Portrait of a bearded gentleman, wearing an ermine-lined black coat (68x56cm-27x22in) lit. 11-Dec-3 Sotheby's, London #15/R est:30000-40000
£68966	$114483	€100000	Portrait of the Doge Girolamo Priuli (100x81cm-39x32in) prov.lit. 30-Sep-3 Ansorena, Madrid #40/R est:100000
£83333	$150000	€121666	Portrait of bearded Venetian nobleman (112x90cm-44x35in) s.i. prov.lit. 22-Jan-4 Sotheby's, New York #16/R est:150000-200000
£125000	$225000	€182500	Agony in the garden (148x177cm-58x70in) prov.exhib.lit. 22-Jan-4 Sotheby's, New York #47/R est:200000-300000
£130000	$237900	€189800	Deposition (104x134cm-41x53in) lit. 7-Jul-4 Sotheby's, London #45/R est:150000-200000
£133333	$244000	€200000	Portrait of Sebastiano Veniero (194x132cm-76x52in) prov.exhib.lit. 1-Jun-4 Sotheby's, Milan #189/R est:200000-300000

TINTORETTO, Jacopo (circle) (1518-1594) Italian

£15000	$27000	€21900	Resurrection (85x99cm-33x39in) fragment. 21-Apr-4 Christie's, London #90/R est:15000-20000

TINTORETTO, Jacopo (studio) (1518-1594) Italian

£15000	$27000	€21900	Portrait of a cardinal, thought to be Cardinal Giovanni Grimani (115x101cm-45x40in) prov. 21-Apr-4 Christie's, London #92/R est:6000-8000

TINYAN, Chan (1942-) Canadian

£280	$512	€409	Floral still life (75x60cm-30x24in) s. 1-Jun-4 Hodgins, Calgary #186/R (C.D 700)

TIPARY, Dezso (1887-?) Hungarian

£992	$1716	€1448	Walk in the park (58x64cm-23x25in) s. 12-Dec-3 Kieselbach, Budapest #15/R (H.F 380000)

TIPPENS, Jack Duane (20th C) American

£818	$1300	€1194	Wire (122x152cm-48x60in) s.d.1976 verso. 14-Sep-3 Susanin's, Chicago #6060/R est:500-700

TIPPETT, William Vivian (1833-1910) British

£340	$632	€496	Cattle resting under a tree (31x40cm-12x16in) s. 2-Mar-4 Bristol Auction Rooms #305
£500	$830	€730	Horses and foal in a meadow (29x49cm-11x19in) s. 2-Oct-3 Lane, Penzance #106
£520	$863	€759	Horses in a water meadow (29x49cm-11x19in) s. 2-Oct-3 Lane, Penzance #107

TIPUNGWUTI, Benny (c.1916-1979) Australian

Works on paper			
£407	$642	€594	Turtle and fish (36x92cm-14x36in) earth pigments eucalyptus bark exec.c.1972 prov. 28-Jul-3 Sotheby's, Paddington #260 (A.D 1000)

TIQUET, F (19/20th C) French

£2372	$4245	€3463	Interior of the Louvre, Paris (99x81cm-39x32in) s.d.1903 prov. 15-May-4 Christie's, Sydney #485/R est:5000-7000 (A.D 6000)

TIRADO Y CARDONA, Fernando (1862-1907) Spanish

£1379	$2469	€2013	Man in interior (20x10cm-8x4in) s. panel. 13-May-4 Stuker, Bern #347/R est:3500-4500 (S.FR 3200)

TIRATELLI, Aurelio (1842-1900) Italian
Works on paper
£1690 $2806 €2400 Lotta di tori nel paesaggio. Bovini al pascolo (25x37cm-10x15in) one s. one s.d.1876 ink W/C cardboard second by E Coleman two. 11-Jun-3 Christie's, Rome #168 est:2300-2800

TIRATELLI, Cesare (1864-1933) Italian
£41667 $75000 €60834 Village procession (62x136cm-24x54in) s.i. 22-Apr-4 Christie's, Rockefeller NY #223/R est:50000-70000

TIREFORT, J E (20th C) American?
£1279 $2200 €1867 Flat iron building (61x51cm-24x20in) s.d.1936. 7-Dec-3 Treadway Gallery, Cincinnati #499/R est:1500-2000
£1570 $2700 €2292 Broadway (61x51cm-24x20in) s.d.1936. 7-Dec-3 Treadway Gallery, Cincinnati #500/R est:1500-2000

TIRELLI, Marco (1956-) Italian
£1049 $1783 €1500 Untitled (70x98cm-28x39in) s.d.1988 verso oil tempera paper on canvas. 25-Nov-3 Sotheby's, Milan #56 est:1500-2000
Works on paper
£3913 $6417 €5400 Untitled XII (140x60cm-55x24in) mixed media board. 30-May-3 Farsetti, Prato #244/R

TIREN, Gerda (1858-1928) Swedish
£505 $812 €737 Summer idyll (22x27cm-9x11in) s. canvas on panel prov. 25-Aug-3 Lilla Bukowskis, Stockholm #959 (S.KR 6600)

TIREN, Johan (1853-1911) Swedish
£3252 $5821 €4748 In the studio (131x82cm-52x32in) s. 25-May-4 Bukowskis, Stockholm #42/R est:30000-40000 (S.KR 44000)
Works on paper
£1166 $2146 €1749 Girl and goat (36x52cm-14x20in) s. W/C. 14-Jun-4 Lilla Bukowskis, Stockholm #85 est:6000-8000 (S.KR 16000)
£1848 $3307 €2698 Laplander and fallen reindeer (31x46cm-12x18in) s. gouache. 25-May-4 Bukowskis, Stockholm #197/R est:30000-35000 (S.KR 25000)

TIREN, Nils (1885-1935) Swedish
Works on paper
£281 $503 €410 Owl landing (45x57cm-18x22in) s.d.1921. 28-May-4 Uppsala Auktionskammare, Uppsala #246 (S.KR 3800)

TIRINNANZI, Nino (1923-) Italian
£300 $552 €450 Landscape (20x28cm-8x11in) s.d.1996 board. 11-Jun-4 Farsetti, Prato #464
£468 $767 €650 Farms (20x30cm-8x12in) s. tempera pastel cardboard on canvas. 10-Jun-3 Pandolfini, Florence #387/R
£1067 $1931 €1600 Landscape (20x28cm-8x11in) s.d.955 canvas on cardboard. 2-Apr-4 Farsetti, Prato #508/R est:1200-1500
£1622 $2854 €2400 Trees and houses (50x40cm-20x16in) s. 22-May-4 Galleria Pananti, Florence #447/R est:2000-3000
£1972 $3411 €2800 Tuscan farms (50x70cm-20x28in) s.d.969. 9-Dec-3 Pandolfini, Florence #391/R est:2100-2200
£1987 $3616 €3000 Circus (90x55cm-35x22in) s.d.1957. 17-Jun-4 Galleria Pananti, Florence #613/R est:3000-3500
£2568 $4519 €3800 Still life with bottles (36x50cm-14x20in) s.d.1942 cardboard. 22-May-4 Galleria Pananti, Florence #517/R est:3500-4000
£3642 $6629 €5500 Landscape with farm (50x70cm-20x28in) s.d.964. 21-Jun-4 Pandolfini, Florence #372/R est:6200-6500
Works on paper
£458 $792 €650 Square with figures (18x26cm-7x10in) s.d.960 W/C. 9-Dec-3 Pandolfini, Florence #324

TIRODE, Léon (1873-?) French
£320 $579 €480 Drague (24x32cm-9x13in) s. canvas on cardboard. 3-Apr-4 Gerard, Besancon #71
£333 $603 €500 Le Doubs vers Avanne (23x38cm-9x15in) oil paper on panel. 3-Apr-4 Gerard, Besancon #73
£418 $710 €610 Lavandieres au bord du Mercurot a Beure (61x46cm-24x18in) s. isorel. 8-Nov-3 Gerard, Besancon #109
£1027 $1747 €1500 Portrait de femme (73x60cm-29x24in) s. 8-Nov-3 Gerard, Besancon #110

TIRONI, Francesco (attrib) (?-1800) Italian
£6711 $12349 €10000 Rio dei Mendicanti in Venice (51x70cm-20x28in) 24-Mar-4 Dorotheum, Vienna #20/R est:12000-15000
£19205 $35146 €29000 Vue de Venise (59x86cm-23x34in) 7-Apr-4 Libert, Castor, Paris #9/R est:20000-30000
£50993 $92808 €77000 Grand Canal and Church of the Scalzi (54x85cm-21x33in) 15-Jun-4 Claude Aguttes, Neuilly #14/R est:25000-30000

TISCHBACH, Dupetz (19/20th C) ?
Works on paper
£276 $461 €400 Artisan fabriquant des eventails (25x19cm-10x7in) s.i.d.1912 W/C. 14-Nov-3 Piasa, Paris #310

TISCHBEIN, August Anton (1805-1867) German
£1800 $3222 €2628 Mother and child (47x33cm-19x13in) s.d.1836. 26-May-4 Sotheby's, Olympia #316/R est:2000-3000

TISCHBEIN, August Anton (attrib) (1805-1867) German
£467 $738 €677 Portrait of young man with arms crossed (20x17cm-8x7in) s.d.1850. 2-Sep-3 Rasmussen, Copenhagen #1928/R (D.KR 5000)

TISCHBEIN, Johann Friedrich August (1750-1812) German
£7586 $12669 €11000 Portrait of young girl with dove (65x50cm-26x20in) s.i.d.1778 prov. 15-Nov-3 Lempertz, Koln #1156/R est:12000

TISCHBEIN, Johann Friedrich August (attrib) (1750-1812) German
£5500 $8800 €7975 Mystery suitor (46x39cm-18x15in) indis.sig. indis.i.stretcher. 18-Sep-3 Christie's, Kensington #167/R est:4000-6000

TISCHBEIN, Johann Heinrich (elder) (1722-1789) German
£4366 $7554 €6200 Young woman with parrot (22x19cm-9x7in) mono. panel. 13-Dec-3 Lempertz, Koln #51/R est:2000

TISCHBEIN, Johann Heinrich Wilhelm (1751-1829) German
£56000 $102480 €81760 Conradin of Swabia (67x94cm-26x37in) s.d.1788 prov. 8-Jul-4 Sotheby's, London #172/R est:40000-60000
Works on paper
£280 $476 €400 Sketches of bison and antelopes (21x33cm-8x13in) bears i. pencil pen. 27-Nov-3 Bassenge, Berlin #5522
£544 $990 €800 Steps to S Maria Aracoll in Rome (16x24cm-6x9in) i. sepia over pencil W/C double-sided. 6-Feb-4 Paul Kieffer, Pforzhiem #8268
£680 $1238 €1000 Near Terracina with the road goes through the fortress (22x32cm-9x13in) i. sepia over pencil W/C. 6-Feb-4 Paul Kieffer, Pforzhiem #8269/R
£952 $1733 €1400 Farmstead near Foro Traiano (21x33cm-8x13in) i. Indian ink W/C over pencil double-sided. 6-Feb-4 Paul Kieffer, Pforzhiem #8270/R
£1497 $2724 €2200 Campo Vaccino (22x36cm-9x14in) i. Indian ink brush W/C over pencil double-sided. 6-Feb-4 Paul Kieffer, Pforzhiem #8267/R est:2400
£2133 $3861 €3200 Wolf tearing at dead deer watched by hidden fox (21x33cm-8x13in) W/C htd white Indian ink. 2-Apr-4 Winterberg, Heidelberg #370/R est:4500

TISCHBEIN, Johann Heinrich Wilhelm (attrib) (1751-1829) German
£10403 $19141 €15500 Portrait d'homme tenant un oeuvre de Newton (60x47cm-24x19in) 24-Mar-4 Tajan, Paris #85/R est:12000-15000

TISCHENDORF, Fritz (1891-?) German?
£1034 $1893 €1500 Sunny Istanbul (40x34cm-16x13in) s.d.28. 27-Jan-4 Dorotheum, Vienna #45/R est:1500-1700

TISDALL, Hans (1910-1997) British
£4000 $7400 €5840 Strand landschaft - shorescape (183x198cm-72x78in) s. s.i.verso. 11-Mar-4 Christie's, Kensington #356/R est:4000-6000
£4000 $7400 €5840 Portlights (183x198cm-72x78in) s. exhib. 11-Mar-4 Christie's, Kensington #358/R est:4000-6000

TISIO, Benvenuto da Garofalo (1481-1559) Italian
Works on paper
£26389 $47500 €38528 Bishop seated on a throne, with two standing figures (18x12cm-7x5in) black chk pen brown ink wash prov.lit. 22-Jan-4 Christie's, Rockefeller NY #15/R est:50000-70000

TISIO, Benvenuto da Garofalo (circle) (1481-1559) Italian
£7000 $12810 €10220 Madonna and Child with Saint John the Baptist (42x27cm-17x11in) i. panel arched top. 6-Jul-4 Sotheby's, Olympia #413/R est:7000-10000

TISIO, Benvenuto da Garofalo (studio) (1481-1559) Italian
£12931 $23793 €18879 Anna and Joachim with Infant St John visiting Mary, Joseph and Christ child (62x81cm-24x32in) prov.lit. 26-Mar-4 Koller, Zurich #3082/R est:30000-50000 (S.FR 30000)

TISNIKAR, Joze (1928-1998) ?
Works on paper
£372 $654 €550 Drunk (50x43cm-20x17in) s.d.94 chl W/C wash. 19-May-4 Dorotheum, Klagenfurt #94/R

TISSANDIER, Albert (1839-1906) French
Works on paper
£1000 $1810 €1500 Tours et toits de Notre-Dame de Paris (66x88cm-26x35in) s.i.d.aout 1872 chl black crayon htd white gouache exhib. 31-Mar-4 Sotheby's, Paris #119/R est:1500-2000

TISSERAND, Jerome (1948-) French
£313 $522 €450 Composition (100x87cm-39x34in) s. s.d.1990 verso. 25-Oct-3 Cornette de St.Cyr, Paris #824

TISSIER, A (1814-1876) French
£1343 $2457 €1961 Young Italian woman with tambourine (73x60cm-29x24in) s.d.1867. 9-Jun-4 Rasmussen, Copenhagen #1927/R est:20000 (D.KR 15000)

TISSOT, James Jacques Joseph (1836-1902) French
£26761 $46831 €38000 Le bal (62x42cm-24x17in) s. oil gouache paper lit. 16-Dec-3 Claude Aguttes, Neuilly #96/R est:25000-30000
£150000 $270000 €219000 Visiteurs etrangers au Louvre (36x26cm-14x10in) s. panel prov.lit. 23-Apr-4 Sotheby's, New York #108/R est:200000-300000

£920000 $1564000 €1343200 Spring (141x53cm-56x21in) s. prov.exhib.lit. 26-Nov-3 Christie's, London #21/R est:600000-800000
Prints
£1765 $3000 €2577 Promenade dans la neige (56x27cm-22x11in) mono. etching drypoint. 31-Oct-3 Sotheby's, New York #463/R
£1836 $3250 €2681 Le dimanche matin (40x19cm-16x7in) s. etching drypoint. 30-Apr-4 Sotheby's, New York #227 est:3000-5000
£2000 $3680 €3000 Berthe (35x27cm-14x11in) s. etching drypoint. 11-Jun-4 Villa Grisebach, Berlin #1501/R est:2000-3000
£2353 $4000 €3435 Entre les deux mon coueur balance (25x36cm-10x14in) etching drypoint. 6-Nov-3 Swann Galleries, New York #430/R est:5000-8000
£2454 $4000 €3583 The Hammock (37x28cm-15x11in) etching drypoint executed 1880. 24-Sep-3 Christie's, Rockefeller NY #176/R est:3000-5000
£2534 $4308 €3700 Journal. eau forte drypoint. 6-Nov-3 Piasa, Paris #158a/R
£2817 $4873 €4000 Promenade dans la neige (57x27cm-22x11in) etching drypoint. 11-Dec-3 Piasa, Paris #156/R
£3667 $6637 €5500 Querelle d'Amoureux (30x18cm-12x7in) etching drypoint. 2-Apr-4 Winterberg, Heidelberg #559/R est:740
£4118 $7000 €6012 Le journal (38x29cm-15x11in) artist st. etching drypoint. 6-Nov-3 Swann Galleries, New York #435/R est:6000-9000
£4190 $7500 €6117 Le journal (38x29cm-15x11in) s. etching drypoint. 6-May-4 Swann Galleries, New York #326/R est:6000-9000
£4749 $8500 €6934 Le journal (38x29cm-15x11in) etching drypoint. 6-May-4 Swann Galleries, New York #330/R est:6000-9000
£5307 $9500 €7748 L'ete (37x21cm-15x8in) etching drypoint. 6-May-4 Swann Galleries, New York #329/R est:5000-8000
£15254 $27000 €22271 October, Wentworth (55x28cm-22x11in) s. etching. 30-Apr-4 Sotheby's, New York #225/R est:20000-30000
Works on paper
£1633 $2922 €2400 Execution de deux communards par les versaillais (24x17cm-9x7in) s.i.d.1871 wash W/C. 17-Mar-4 Maigret, Paris #102/R est:2200-3000
£2235 $4000 €3263 Sadducee (17x8cm-7x3in) s. W/C gouache on card executed c.1895. 18-Mar-4 Sotheby's, New York #268/R est:4000-6000
£3600 $6120 €5256 Sadducee (17x8cm-7x3in) s. W/C bodycol. 4-Nov-3 Bonhams, New Bond Street #82/R est:2500-3500
£30000 $51000 €43800 Au louvre (41x22cm-16x9in) s. pencil W/C prov.exhib. 27-Nov-3 Sotheby's, London #324/R est:30000-40000

TISSOT, Laurent (20th C) French
£1040 $1841 €1550 Autoroute (10x81cm-4x32in) s. acrylic. 29-Apr-4 Claude Aguttes, Neuilly #257 est:1600-1800

TITCOMB, William Henry (attrib) (1824-1888) American
£4301 $8000 €6279 Ice skating, Mt Chocorus, New Hampshire (56x76cm-22x30in) prov. 6-Mar-4 North East Auctions, Portsmouth #1136/R est:8000-12000

TITCOMB, William Holt Yates (1858-1930) British
£650 $1183 €949 Viaticum (46x81cm-18x32in) s. 15-Jun-4 David Lay, Penzance #486
£2000 $3320 €2920 Unity, a family group gathered around a fire in a Cornish cottage (24x34cm-9x13in) s. prov. 2-Oct-3 Lane, Penzance #319 est:2000-2500
£2554 $4750 €3729 View near Claremont, New Hampshire (46x66cm-18x26in) 6-Mar-4 North East Auctions, Portsmouth #550/R est:2500-3500

TITI, Tiberio di (1573-1627) Italian
£22378 $38042 €32000 Portraits de Giovanni et de Piero Bini (89x69cm-35x27in) i.d.1588 panel pair. 1-Dec-3 Millon & Associes, Paris #5/R est:30000-45000
£24000 $43920 €35040 Portrait of a group of three children (116x165cm-46x65in) 7-Jul-4 Bonhams, New Bond Street #119/R est:15000-20000

TITIAN (c.1488-1576) Italian
£1952055 $3318493 €2850000 Saint Mary Magdalene (105x95cm-41x37in) prov.lit. 9-Nov-3 Finarte, Venice #156/R

TITIAN (after) (c.1488-1576) Italian
£5000 $9000 €7300 Penitent Magalene (116x96cm-46x38in) prov. 20-Apr-4 Sotheby's, Olympia #221/R est:5000-7000
£10000 $18000 €14600 Danae (115x166cm-45x65in) 20-Apr-4 Sotheby's, Olympia #219/R est:8000-12000
£44400 $76812 €64824 Venus of Urbino (120x165cm-47x65in) prov. 9-Dec-3 Sotheby's, Olympia #370/R est:6000-8000

TITIAN (circle) (c.1488-1576) Italian
£11189 $19245 €16000 Portrait ofgentleman (90x107cm-35x42in) 2-Dec-3 Sotheby's, Milan #62/R est:12000-16000
Works on paper
£38000 $69540 €55480 Fallen warrior twisting around to the left holding a sword and shield (20x31cm-8x12in) i. black white chk prov. 6-Jul-4 Christie's, London #13/R est:40000-60000

TITIAN (school) (c.1488-1576) Italian
£55432 $99224 €80931 Madonna and Child (170x112cm-67x44in) prov.lit. 25-May-4 Bukowskis, Stockholm #427/R est:800000-1000000 (S.KR 750000)

TITIAN (style) (c.1488-1576) Italian
£5500 $10065 €8030 Reclining Venus with a Satyr (118x190cm-46x75in) 6-Jul-4 Sotheby's, Olympia #424/R est:5000-7000
£10526 $19368 €16000 Scene from the life of Saint Anthony (68x58cm-27x23in) prov.exhib.lit. 24-Jun-4 Christie's, Paris #63/R est:5000-7000

TITO, Ettore (1859-1941) Italian
£3077 $5138 €4400 Peasant family (34x28cm-13x11in) s. s.verso board. 26-Jun-3 Sant Agostino, Torino #281/R est:1600
£13245 $24768 €20000 Jeune femme de profil avec fichu (35x23cm-14x9in) s. panel. 20-Jul-4 Gioffredo, Nice #9/R
£18056 $32500 €26362 Zingare in riva al mare - Gypsy women by the sea (23x32cm-9x13in) s.d.1881 panel. 23-Apr-4 Sotheby's, New York #73/R est:18000-25000
£24138 $40069 €35000 Bathers in the sun (130x130cm-51x51in) s. 1-Oct-3 Della Rocca, Turin #321/R est:30000-40000
£29139 $54490 €44000 Jeune femme a la robe rouge (100x50cm-39x20in) s. panel. 20-Jul-4 Gioffredo, Nice #8/R

TITO, Ettore (attrib) (1859-1941) Italian
Works on paper
£1549 $2572 €2200 The woman with black hair (58x41cm-23x16in) s.i.d.1907 pastel cardboard exhib. 11-Jun-3 Christie's, Rome #185/R est:700-1000

TITO, Santi di (attrib) (1536-1603) Italian
Works on paper
£1769 $3166 €2600 Des soldats attaquant un camp, une ville dans le lointain a gauche (23x31cm-9x12in) i. pen brown ink wash htd white. 18-Mar-4 Christie's, Paris #13/R est:2000-3000
£4474 $8232 €6800 Study of man (36x24cm-14x9in) sanguine. 22-Jun-4 Sotheby's, Milan #6/R est:3000-3500

TITONEL, Angelo (1938-) Italian
£533 $965 €800 Aquarium (69x41cm-27x16in) s.d.1975 s.i.d.verso. 2-Apr-4 Farsetti, Prato #94

TITOV, Eugene (1969-) Russian
£1361 $2476 €2000 Aurore. s. 8-Feb-4 Lesieur & Le Bars, Le Havre #156
Works on paper
£633 $1140 €950 Queen of Sabba (65x54cm-26x21in) s. mixed media. 26-Apr-4 Millon & Associes, Paris #151
£733 $1320 €1100 Wisdom (46x38cm-18x15in) s. mixed media. 26-Apr-4 Millon & Associes, Paris #149/R
£733 $1320 €1100 Dawn (61x50cm-24x20in) s. mixed media. 26-Apr-4 Millon & Associes, Paris #150/R

TITOV, Konstantin (1913-1998) Russian
£7600 $13604 €11096 Beaties of Astrakhan (130x130cm-51x51in) s.d.1979. 26-May-4 Sotheby's, London #309/R est:8000-12000

TITOV, Vladimir (?-) Russian
£422 $768 €620 Fleurs blanches. s. 8-Feb-4 Lesieur & Le Bars, Le Havre #113

TITTELBACH, Voitech (1900-1971) Czechoslovakian
£560 $1003 €818 Youth games (70x100cm-28x39in) s. 12-May-4 Dobiaschofsky, Bern #1024/R (S.FR 1300)

TITUS-CARMEL, Gerard (1942-) French
Works on paper
£270 $483 €400 Eclats-petit chrome I (61x80cm-24x31in) s.d.1982 crayon chl pastel prov. 4-May-4 Calmels Cohen, Paris #220
£407 $680 €594 L'usage du necessaire (74x103cm-29x41in) s.i.d.1972 prov. 24-Jun-3 Germann, Zurich #73 (S.FR 900)
£709 $1341 €1050 Inscription de la sphere initiale (77x77cm-30x30in) s.i.d.1972 graphite collage. 21-Feb-4 Cornette de St.Cyr, Paris #413/R
£1049 $1752 €1500 Summer sticks (73x103cm-29x41in) s.i.d.1974 crayon collage dr exhib. 29-Jun-3 Versailles Encheres #229/R

TITZ, Carlo Giorgio (1928-1958) Italian
£900 $1611 €1350 Urban landscape (55x70cm-22x28in) s. 12-May-4 Stadion, Trieste #828/R est:800-1200

TITZ, Louis (1859-1932) Belgian
Works on paper
£769 $1308 €1123 Snow storm (45x31cm-18x12in) s.d.1891 W/C. 25-Nov-3 Germann, Zurich #909/R est:1500-2000 (S.FR 1700)
£978 $1692 €1428 Malines (43x66cm-17x26in) s. W/C. 9-Dec-3 Maynards, Vancouver #150 est:3000-3500 (C.D 2200)
£1831 $3168 €2600 Impasse Hilaire, Bruxelles (69x45cm-27x18in) s.i.d.1921 W/C. 13-Dec-3 De Vuyst, Lokeren #318 est:1000-1250

TIUTRIUMOV, Nikanor Leontevich (1821-1877) Russian
£6294 $10699 €9000 Portrait of girl (65x55cm-26x22in) s.d.1862 oval. 29-Nov-3 Bukowskis, Helsinki #423/R est:9000-10000

TIVOLI, Giuseppe (1845-?) Italian
Works on paper
£944 $1577 €1350 La lectura (33x22cm-13x9in) s.d.1898 W/C. 24-Jun-3 Segre, Madrid #20/R

TIVOLI, Serafino de (1826-1892) Italian
£9155 $15838 €13000 Cows grazing (53x78cm-21x31in) s.d.1858. 10-Dec-3 Sotheby's, Milan #88/R est:8000-10000

TIZARD, Frances (20th C) New Zealander
Works on paper
£674 $1193 €984 Mt Taranaki with homestead (11x16cm-4x6in) pencil exec.c.1880. 28-Apr-4 Dunbar Sloane, Auckland #219 (NZ.D 1900)

TJAKAMARA, Freddy West (c.1940-1995) Australian
Works on paper
£1736 $2950 €2535 Nunkari kutjarra - two doctors 1976 (60x75cm-24x30in) synthetic polymer paint on canvas. 29-Oct-3 Lawson Menzies, Sydney #59/R est:4000-6000 (A.D 4200)
£2642 $4175 €3831 Untitled (153x122cm-60x48in) i.d.1991 verso synthetic polymer paint linen prov. 28-Jul-3 Sotheby's, Paddington #482/R est:5000-7000 (A.D 6500)

TJAKAMARRA, Alan Winderoo (c.1920-) Australian
Works on paper
£4688 $8766 €7032 Impirrkarawarnu (119x90cm-47x35in) bears name.verso synthetic polymer paint canvas prov.exhib. 26-Jul-4 Sotheby's, Melbourne #70/R est:12000-18000 (A.D 12000)

TJAKAMARRA, Anatjari (c.1930-1992) Australian
Works on paper
£3125 $5844 €4688 Origins of soakages (92x22cm-36x9in) synthetic polymer paint board prov. 26-Jul-4 Sotheby's, Melbourne #410/R est:8000-12000 (A.D 8000)
£3252 $5138 €4715 Lizard story (61x46cm-24x18in) synthetic polymer paint composition board prov. 28-Jul-3 Sotheby's, Paddington #230/R est:8000-12000 (A.D 8000)
£5882 $10529 €8588 Tingari Site (153x183cm-60x72in) synthetic polymer paint linen exec 1988 prov. 25-May-4 Lawson Menzies, Sydney #45/R est:12000-15000 (A.D 15000)
£39063 $73047 €58595 Yarranyanga (152x122cm-60x48in) bears name.verso synthetic polymer paint linen prov. 26-Jul-4 Sotheby's, Melbourne #108/R est:100000-150000 (A.D 100000)
£40650 $64228 €58943 Tingari men's travels from Kulkuta toward Lake Macdonald (182x152cm-72x60in) synthetic polymer paint linen prov.exhib.lit. 28-Jul-3 Sotheby's, Paddington #178/R est:100000-150000 (A.D 100000)

TJAKAMARRA, Barney Wakuri (?-1994) Australian
Works on paper
£372 $633 €543 Tingarri 1997 (92x46cm-36x18in) synthetic polymer paint on Belgian linen prov. 29-Oct-3 Lawson Menzies, Sydney #58/R est:1200-1500 (A.D 900)

TJAKAMARRA, Charlie Gordon (c.1930-) Australian
Works on paper
£275 $491 €402 Wannupurku (100x75cm-39x30in) synthetic polymer paint canvas exec 1990 prov. 25-May-4 Lawson Menzies, Sydney #138/R (A.D 700)
£1301 $2055 €1899 Lake Karli near Lappi Lappi (106x73cm-42x29in) i.verso synthetic polymer paint canvas prov.exhib. 28-Jul-3 Sotheby's, Paddington #409/R est:3000-5000 (A.D 3200)

TJAKAMARRA, Ginger (20th C) Australian
Works on paper
£650 $1028 €949 Untitled (152x60cm-60x24in) synthetic polymer paint linen prov. 28-Jul-3 Sotheby's, Paddington #481 est:1000-2000 (A.D 1600)

TJAKAMARRA, Jackie (c.1935-c.1993) Australian
Works on paper
£2539 $4748 €3809 Tjunpul (120x89cm-47x35in) bears name.verso synthetic polymer paint linen prov. 26-Jul-4 Sotheby's, Melbourne #484/R est:7000-10000 (A.D 6500)

TJAKAMARRA, John (c.1930-2003) Australian
Works on paper
£5469 $10227 €8204 Untitled (61x56cm-24x22in) synthetic polymer paint board prov. 26-Jul-4 Sotheby's, Melbourne #98/R est:15000-25000 (A.D 14000)
£5859 $10957 €8789 Untitled (64x54cm-25x21in) synthetic polymer powder paint board exec.c.1972 prov. 26-Jul-4 Sotheby's, Melbourne #99/R est:10000-15000 (A.D 15000)

TJAKAMARRA, Long Jack Phillipus (1932-1993) Australian
Works on paper
£1255 $2246 €1832 Rain Dreaming (59x151cm-23x59in) synthetic polymer paint linen exec 1986 prov. 25-May-4 Lawson Menzies, Sydney #63/R est:3000-5000 (A.D 3200)
£1563 $2922 €2345 Untitled (43x23cm-17x9in) synthetic polymer powder paint board prov. 26-Jul-4 Sotheby's, Melbourne #411/R est:2000-3000 (A.D 4000)
£1829 $2890 €2652 Snake at Laru Laru (75x54cm-30x21in) synthetic polymer paint board prov.lit. 28-Jul-3 Sotheby's, Paddington #266/R est:7000-10000 (A.D 4500)
£3252 $5138 €4715 Kangaroo dreaming (65x35cm-26x14in) synthetic polymer paint composition board exec.c.1971/2 prov. 28-Jul-3 Sotheby's, Paddington #271/R est:8000-12000 (A.D 8000)
£4688 $8766 €7032 Possum story (55x26cm-22x10in) synthetic polymer paint board prov. 26-Jul-4 Sotheby's, Melbourne #203/R est:10000-15000 (A.D 12000)
£8594 $16070 €12891 Corroboree for young men (45x64cm-18x25in) synthetic polymer paint board prov. 26-Jul-4 Sotheby's, Melbourne #204/R est:20000-30000 (A.D 22000)

TJAKAMARRA, Long Jack Phillipus (attrib) (1932-1993) Australian
Works on paper
£1725 $3089 €2519 Water dreaming (30x61cm-12x24in) synthetic polymer paint exec 1975 three prov. 25-May-4 Lawson Menzies, Sydney #60/R est:1500-2500 (A.D 4400)

TJAKAMARRA, Mick Gill (1919-) Australian
Works on paper
£938 $1753 €1407 Untitled (100x50cm-39x20in) bears name.verso synthetic polymer paint canvas prov.exhib.lit. 26-Jul-4 Sotheby's, Melbourne #422/R (A.D 2400)
£1301 $2055 €1886 Water dreaming at Lappi Lappi (149x75cm-59x30in) i.verso synthetic polymer paint canvas prov. 28-Jul-3 Sotheby's, Paddington #408/R est:3000-4000 (A.D 3200)

TJAKAMARRA, Old Mick Wallankarri (c.1900-1996) Australian
Works on paper
£1647 $2948 €2405 Mens site (54x37cm-21x15in) i. verso synthetic polymer paint board exec c.1975 prov. 25-May-4 Lawson Menzies, Sydney #67/R est:5000-7000 (A.D 4200)

TJAKAMARRA, Ronnie Lawson (c.1930-) Australian
Works on paper
£813 $1276 €1179 Bush onion (126x125cm-50x49in) synthetic polymer paint canvas. 27-Aug-3 Christie's, Sydney #745 est:2000-3000 (A.D 2000)

TJAKAMARRA, Simon (c.1946-1990) Australian
Works on paper
£1133 $2118 €1700 Untitled (71x56cm-28x22in) synthetic polymer paint linen prov. 26-Jul-4 Sotheby's, Melbourne #573/R (A.D 2900)

TJAKAMARRA, Tommy Skeen (c.1930-) Australian
Works on paper
£8594 $16070 €12891 Undalarra (121x91cm-48x36in) bears name.verso synthetic polymer paint canvas prov.exhib.lit. 26-Jul-4 Sotheby's, Melbourne #78/R est:8000-12000 (A.D 22000)

TJAMATJI, Paddy (c.1912-1996) Australian
Works on paper
£8130 $12846 €11789 Nest for owls and birds at Drowney Gorge (70x110cm-28x43in) earth pigments bush gum canvas prov.exhib. 28-Jul-3 Sotheby's, Paddington #128/R est:10000-15000 (A.D 20000)
£10569 $16699 €15325 Turkey Creek Junction - Warmun Hole (71x111cm-28x44in) i.verso earth pigments binder composition board prov. 28-Jul-3 Sotheby's, Paddington #163/R est:25000-35000 (A.D 26000)
£15625 $29219 €23438 Tawurr the kangaroo at Kanmanturr (60x59cm-24x23in) earth pigments bush gum plywood prov. 26-Jul-4 Sotheby's, Melbourne #28/R est:25000-35000 (A.D 40000)

TJAMPITJIN, Boxer Milner (c.1934-) Australian
Works on paper
£2539 $4748 €3809 Untitled (149x74cm-59x29in) bears name.verso synthetic polymer paint linen prov. 26-Jul-4 Sotheby's, Melbourne #253/R est:8000-12000 (A.D 6500)
£3027 $5661 €4541 Rainbow dreaming near Purwirr, Sturt creek (149x100cm-59x39in) bears name.verso synthetic polymer paint canvas prov.exhib. 26-Jul-4 Sotheby's, Melbourne #448/R est:5000-8000 (A.D 7750)
£8984 $16801 €13476 Tjirrwangu naparlan (150x75cm-59x30in) bears name.verso synthetic polymer paint linen prov. 26-Jul-4 Sotheby's, Melbourne #254/R est:10000-15000 (A.D 23000)

TJAMPITJIN, Sam (c.1930-) Australian
Works on paper
£471 $842 €688 Wilkinkarra (80x30cm-31x12in) synthetic polymer canvas exec 2000 prov. 25-May-4 Lawson Menzies, Sydney #15/R (A.D 1200)
£1563 $2922 €2345 Wirtjinpiyi (100x75cm-39x30in) bears name.verso synthetic polymer paint canvas prov.exhib. 26-Jul-4 Sotheby's, Melbourne #428/R est:4000-6000 (A.D 4000)
£1626 $2569 €2358 Mitjungarti (91x61cm-36x24in) i.verso synthetic polymer paint linen prov. 28-Jul-3 Sotheby's, Paddington #492/R est:4000-6000 (A.D 4000)
£5078 $9496 €7617 Wirtjinpiyi (90x61cm-35x24in) bears name.verso synthetic polymer paint canvas prov.exhib. 26-Jul-4 Sotheby's, Melbourne #76/R est:7000-10000 (A.D 13000)

TJAMPITJIN, Sunfly (c.1916-1996) Australian
Works on paper
£14118 $25271 €20612 Two women at Yataru (113x83cm-44x33in) synthetic polymer paint canvas exec 1987 prov. 25-May-4 Lawson Menzies, Sydney #32/R est:25000-35000 (A.D 36000)
£66406 $124180 €99609 Yapinti, pinki dreaming (118x84cm-46x33in) bears name.verso synthetic polymer paint canvas prov.exhib.lit. 26-Jul-4 Sotheby's, Melbourne #71/R est:70000-100000 (A.D 170000)

TJAMPITJINPA, Anatjari (1929-) Australian
Works on paper
£1563 $2922 €2345 Karrilwarra (91x70cm-36x28in) bears name.verso synthetic polymer paint linen prov. 26-Jul-4 Sotheby's, Melbourne #571/R est:5000-8000 (A.D 4000)
£1626 $2569 €2358 Minmantja (91x46cm-36x18in) i.verso synthetic polymer paint linen prov. 28-Jul-3 Sotheby's, Paddington #483/R est:4000-6000 (A.D 4000)
£1875 $3506 €2813 Untitled (151x91cm-59x36in) bears name.verso synthetic polymer paint linen prov. 26-Jul-4 Sotheby's, Melbourne #276/R est:7000-10000 (A.D 4800)
£2539 $4748 €3809 Tingari story at Ngaariwlada (152x122cm-60x48in) bears name.verso synthetic polymer paint linen prov. 26-Jul-4 Sotheby's, Melbourne #277/R est:8000-12000 (A.D 6500)
£3711 $6939 €5567 Untitled (168x89cm-66x35in) bears name.verso synthetic polymer paint linen prov. 26-Jul-4 Sotheby's, Melbourne #106/R est:12000-15000 (A.D 9500)
£4297 $8035 €6446 Tingari events at Panmapalinya (121x75cm-48x30in) synthetic polymer paint linen prov. 26-Jul-4 Sotheby's, Melbourne #105/R est:10000-15000 (A.D 11000)
£6098 $9634 €8842 Untitled (183x122cm-72x48in) synthetic polymer paint linen prov. 28-Jul-3 Sotheby's, Paddington #176/R est:15000-20000 (A.D 15000)

TJAMPITJINPA, Dini Campbell (c.1940-) Australian
Works on paper
£2266 $4237 €3399 Untitled (137x93cm-54x37in) bears name.verso synthetic polymer paint linen prov. 26-Jul-4 Sotheby's, Melbourne #509/R est:6000-8000 (A.D 5800)

TJAMPITJINPA, Dinny Nolan (c.1922-) Australian
Works on paper
£2745 $4914 €4008 Preparing for Ceremony - Male Kangaroo (55x71cm-22x28in) bears s.i. verso synthetic polymer paint canvasboard prov. 25-May-4 Lawson Menzies, Sydney #64/R est:8000-12000 (A.D 7000)
£3906 $7305 €5859 Water and kampurrarpa (78x68cm-31x27in) synthetic polymer paint board prov. 26-Jul-4 Sotheby's, Melbourne #103/R est:10000-15000 (A.D 10000)

TJAMPITJINPA, Kaapa Mbitjana (c.1920-1989) Australian
Works on paper
£1641 $3068 €2462 Untitled (60x40cm-24x16in) bears name.verso synthetic polymer paint board prov. 26-Jul-4 Sotheby's, Melbourne #493/R est:4000-6000 (A.D 4200)
£1860 $3161 €2716 Secret/sacred 1975 (55x71cm-22x28in) synthetic polymer paint on board exhib. 29-Oct-3 Lawson Menzies, Sydney #82/R est:6000-8000 (A.D 4500)
£2539 $4748 €3809 Untitled (76x60cm-30x24in) name.i.d.1975 verso synthetic polymer paint canvasboard prov. 26-Jul-4 Sotheby's, Melbourne #494/R est:3000-4000 (A.D 6500)
£3319 $5742 €4846 Untitled (79x199cm-31x78in) i.verso synthetic polymer paint canvas prov. 10-Dec-3 Shapiro, Sydney #166/R est:8000-12000 (A.D 7800)
£5691 $8992 €8252 Untitled (75x55cm-30x22in) s. i.verso synthetic polymer paint board prov. 28-Jul-3 Sotheby's, Paddington #165/R est:7000-10000 (A.D 14000)
£8203 $15340 €12305 Emu story (61x45cm-24x18in) synthetic polymer paint board prov.lit. 26-Jul-4 Sotheby's, Melbourne #208/R est:20000-30000 (A.D 21000)
£31250 $58438 €46875 Untitled, kangaroo ceremony (122x91cm-48x36in) s. synthetic polymer paint board prov.lit. 26-Jul-4 Sotheby's, Melbourne #209/R est:80000-120000 (A.D 80000)

TJAMPITJINPA, Kenny Williams (c.1950-) Australian
Works on paper
£732 $1156 €1069 Untitled, tjuntulpul (122x91cm-48x36in) i.verso synthetic polymer paint linen prov. 28-Jul-3 Sotheby's, Paddington #396 est:2000-3000 (A.D 1800)

TJAMPITJINPA, Maxie (1945-1997) Australian
Works on paper
£371 $694 €557 Untitled (120x91cm-47x36in) bears name.d.1984 verso synthetic polymer paint canvas prov. 26-Jul-4 Sotheby's, Melbourne #468 (A.D 950)
£1172 $2191 €1758 Untitled (112x55cm-44x22in) bears name.verso synthetic polymer paint linen prov. 26-Jul-4 Sotheby's, Melbourne #301/R est:3000-5000 (A.D 3000)
£2353 $4212 €3435 Country in flood (120x180cm-47x71in) s. verso synthetic polymer paint linen exec 1997 prov. 25-May-4 Lawson Menzies, Sydney #79/R est:8000-10000 (A.D 6000)
£3125 $5844 €4688 Untitled (183x122cm-72x48in) bears name.verso synthetic polymer paint linen prov. 26-Jul-4 Sotheby's, Melbourne #302/R est:8000-12000 (A.D 8000)
£3125 $5844 €4688 Fire at Warlukurlangu (137x91cm-54x36in) bears name.verso synthetic polymer paint linen prov. 26-Jul-4 Sotheby's, Melbourne #515/R est:8000-12000 (A.D 8000)
£3418 $6392 €5127 Untitled (122x122cm-48x48in) bears name.verso synthetic polymer paint linen prov. 26-Jul-4 Sotheby's, Melbourne #514/R est:7000-10000 (A.D 8750)

TJAMPITJINPA, Milner Sturt (c.1926-) Australian
Works on paper
£469 $877 €704 Piriyul (90x60cm-35x24in) bears name.verso synthetic polymer paint canvas prov.exhib. 26-Jul-4 Sotheby's, Melbourne #438/R (A.D 1200)

TJAMPITJINPA, Old Walter (1912-1980) Australian
Works on paper
£3125 $5844 €4688 Water story (64x30cm-25x12in) synthetic polymer powder paint board prov. 26-Jul-4 Sotheby's, Melbourne #409/R est:8000-12000 (A.D 8000)
£4297 $8035 €6446 Women collecting kampurrarpa (43x23cm-17x9in) name.i.verso synthetic polymer paint board exec.c.1973 prov. 26-Jul-4 Sotheby's, Melbourne #206/R est:5000-8000 (A.D 11000)
£6641 $12418 €9962 Water dreaming (71x21cm-28x8in) synthetic polymer paint board prov. 26-Jul-4 Sotheby's, Melbourne #202/R est:10000-15000 (A.D 17000)

TJAMPITJINPA, Pegleg (1920-) Australian
Works on paper
£2353 $4212 €3435 Tingari (91x66cm-36x26in) synthetic polymer paint linen exec 2002 prov. 25-May-4 Lawson Menzies, Sydney #87/R est:8000-9000 (A.D 6000)
£5882 $10529 €8588 Tingari Cycle (143x92cm-56x36in) synthetic polymer paint canvas exec 2002 prov. 25-May-4 Lawson Menzies, Sydney #88/R est:10000-12000 (A.D 15000)

TJAMPITJINPA, Ronnie (c.1943-) Australian
Works on paper
£1172 $2191 €1758 Claypan site of Tjungaringya (91x61cm-36x24in) bears name.verso synthetic polymer paint linen prov. 26-Jul-4 Sotheby's, Melbourne #512/R est:3000-5000 (A.D 3000)
£1484 $2776 €2226 Tingari (122x46cm-48x18in) s.verso synthetic polymer linen exec. 2003 prov. 21-Jul-4 Shapiro, Sydney #45/R est:4000-6000 (A.D 3800)
£1626 $2569 €2358 Untitled (107x28cm-42x11in) i.verso synthetic polymer paint linen prov. 28-Jul-3 Sotheby's, Paddington #386/R est:2000-3000 (A.D 4000)
£1626 $2569 €2358 Water dreaming at Lappi Lappi (92x61cm-36x24in) i.verso synthetic polymer paint linen prov. 28-Jul-3 Sotheby's, Paddington #490/R est:4000-6000 (A.D 4000)
£1653 $2810 €2413 Tingari (181x90cm-71x35in) synthetic polymer paint on Belgian linen prov. 29-Oct-3 Lawson Menzies, Sydney #61/R est:3000-5000 (A.D 4000)
£1875 $3506 €2813 Tjintjintjinna (91x91cm-36x36in) bears name.verso synthetic polymer paint canvas prov. 26-Jul-4 Sotheby's, Melbourne #500/R est:5000-7000 (A.D 4800)
£2148 $4018 €3222 Yunala (122x122cm-48x48in) bears name.verso synthetic polymer paint linen prov. 26-Jul-4 Sotheby's, Melbourne #274/R est:6000-8000 (A.D 5500)
£2553 $4417 €3727 Untitled, designs associated with the emu dreaming site (152x122cm-60x48in) i.verso synthetic polymer paint linen prov. 10-Dec-3 Shapiro, Sydney #174/R est:7000-9000 (A.D 6000)
£2656 $4967 €3984 Untitled (122x122cm-48x48in) bears name.verso wpp. canvas prov. 26-Jul-4 Sotheby's, Melbourne #499/R est:7000-10000 (A.D 6800)
£5488 $9823 €8012 Tingari painting (132x194cm-52x76in) s.verso synthetic polymer linen canvas prov. 4-May-4 Sotheby's, Melbourne #63/R est:10000-15000 (A.D 13500)
£6224 $10394 €9336 Tingari cycle (153x213cm-60x84in) i.verso synthetic polymer paint. 27-Oct-3 Goodman, Sydney #47/R est:15000-18000 (A.D 15000)
£6301 $9955 €9136 Untitled (91x152cm-36x60in) synthetic polymer paint linen prov. 28-Jul-3 Sotheby's, Paddington #111/R est:12000-18000 (A.D 15500)
£7813 $14609 €11720 Old woman and her two children, thunder and lightning (152x122cm-60x48in) bears name.verso synthetic polymer paint linen prov. 26-Jul-4 Sotheby's, Melbourne #191/R est:25000-35000 (A.D 20000)
£10331 $19112 €15083 Untitled (152x122cm-60x48in) synthetic polymer linen on canvas prov.exhib. 15-Mar-4 Sotheby's, Melbourne #23/R est:18000-25000 (A.D 25000)
£16260 $25691 €23577 Yarryarrunya (183x153cm-72x60in) i.verso synthetic polymer paint linen prov. 28-Jul-3 Sotheby's, Paddington #112/R est:40000-60000 (A.D 40000)

TJAMPITJINPA, Shorty Jackson (c.1950-) Australian
Works on paper
£511 $868 €746 Owl - dreaming from Kurruktu (164x48cm-65x19in) i.verso synthetic polymer paint linen prov. 25-Nov-3 Christie's, Melbourne #193 (A.D 1200)

TJANGALA, David Hall (c.1930-) Australian
Works on paper
£2148 $4018 €3222 Kurtal (99x49cm-39x19in) s.verso synthetic polymer paint canvas prov.exhib. 26-Jul-4 Sotheby's, Melbourne #421/R est:3000-4000 (A.D 5500)

TJANGALA, George Wallaby (c.1939-) Australian
Works on paper
£664 $1242 €996 Lake Gregory (119x60cm-47x24in) bears name.verso synthetic polymer paint canvas prov.exhib. 26-Jul-4 Sotheby's, Melbourne #444/R (A.D 1700)

TJANGALA, George Yapa (c.1950-) Australian
Works on paper
£1484 $2776 €2226 Pukarta rockhole (167x47cm-66x19in) synthetic polymer paint linen prov. 26-Jul-4 Sotheby's, Melbourne #506/R est:4000-6000 (A.D 3800)
£1563 $2922 €2345 Tjukartu (122x61cm-48x24in) bears name.verso synthetic polymer paint linen prov. 26-Jul-4 Sotheby's, Melbourne #505/R est:4000-6000 (A.D 4000)

TJANGALA, Ray James (c.1958-) Australian
Works on paper
£859 $1607 €1289 Yunala (91x46cm-36x18in) bears name.verso synthetic polymer paint linen prov. 26-Jul-4 Sotheby's, Melbourne #572/R (A.D 2200)
£2846 $4496 €4127 Tjuntupul (92x137cm-36x54in) i.verso synthetic polymer paint linen prov. 28-Jul-3 Sotheby's, Paddington #282/R est:7000-10000 (A.D 7000)
£4492 $8400 €6738 Yunala (153x122cm-60x48in) bears name.verso synthetic polymer paint linen prov. 26-Jul-4 Sotheby's, Melbourne #189/R est:8000-12000 (A.D 11500)

TJANGALA, Riley Major (c.1948-) Australian
Works on paper
£1138 $1787 €1650 Ancestor snake men, dreaming (122x121cm-48x48in) synthetic polymer paint canvas prov. 26-Aug-3 Christie's, Sydney #253/R est:2000-3000 (A.D 2800)

TJANGALA, Toby (c.1941-) Australian
Works on paper
£4472 $7065 €6529 Emus at Watulpunyu (122x91cm-48x36in) synthetic polymer paint composition board prov.exhib.lit. 28-Jul-3 Sotheby's, Paddington #265/R est:5000-8000 (A.D 11000)

TJANGALA, Uta Uta (1920-1990) Australian
Works on paper
£1367 $2557 €2051 Crow at Muyinga (45x38cm-18x15in) bears name.verso synthetic polymer paint canvasboard prov. 26-Jul-4 Sotheby's, Melbourne #495/R est:1500-2500 (A.D 3500)
£1423 $2248 €2063 Untitled (77x61cm-30x24in) i.verso synthetic polymer paint canvasboard. 28-Jul-3 Sotheby's, Paddington #486/R est:4000-6000 (A.D 3500)
£5488 $8671 €7958 Two travelling women (105x183cm-41x72in) synthetic polymer paint linen prov. 28-Jul-3 Sotheby's, Paddington #384/R est:12000-15000 (A.D 13500)
£5859 $10957 €8789 Old man story (166x97cm-65x38in) synthetic polymer paint linen prov. 26-Jul-4 Sotheby's, Melbourne #278/R est:15000-20000 (A.D 15000)
£7724 $12203 €11200 Medicine story (46x36cm-18x14in) earth pigments enamel synthetic polymer paint board prov. 28-Jul-3 Sotheby's, Paddington #169/R est:15000-25000 (A.D 19000)
£7813 $14609 €11720 Untitled (65x26cm-26x10in) bears name.verso synthetic polymer powder paint board prov. 26-Jul-4 Sotheby's, Melbourne #95/R est:22000-28000 (A.D 20000)
£35569 $56199 €51575 Women's dreaming (60x45cm-24x18in) synthetic polymer paint composition board prov. 28-Jul-3 Sotheby's, Paddington #108/R est:80000-120000 (A.D 87500)

TJAPALTJARI, Clifford Possum (1934-2002) Australian

£752 $1278 €1098 Wari Wari (78x49cm-31x19in) s.i.verso acrylic board prov. 27-Nov-3 International Art Centre, Auckland #184/R (NZ.D 2000)
£6015 $10226 €8782 Honey ants dreaming (120x92cm-47x36in) s.verso acrylic prov. 27-Nov-3 International Art Centre, Auckland #183/R est:15000-20000 (NZ.D 16000)

Works on paper

£703 $1315 €1055 Emu dreaming at Mt Allen (55x40cm-22x16in) s.verso synthetic polymer canvas exec. c. 1989 prov. 21-Jul-4 Shapiro, Sydney #61/R (A.D 1800)
£781 $1461 €1172 Eagle dreaming at Mt Allen (51x40cm-20x16in) s.verso synthetic polymer canvas exec. c.1989 prov. 21-Jul-4 Shapiro, Sydney #60/R est:2500-4000 (A.D 2000)
£1012 $1630 €1478 Hunting ceremony (89x58cm-35x23in) s. synthetic polymer on canvas prov. 13-Oct-3 Joel, Victoria #379a est:5000-7000 (A.D 2500)
£1797 $3360 €2696 Untitled (122x92cm-48x36in) synthetic polymer canvas exec. 1988 prov. 21-Jul-4 Shapiro, Sydney #59/R est:4000-6000 (A.D 4600)
£2549 $4563 €3722 Worm dreaming (112x50cm-44x20in) synthetic polymer paint canvas exec 1996 prov. 25-May-4 Lawson Menzies, Sydney #81/R est:7000-9000 (A.D 6500)
£2734 $5113 €4101 Water track dreaming (61x45cm-24x18in) name.i.d.1981 verso synthetic polymer paint canvasboard prov. 26-Jul-4 Sotheby's, Melbourne #513/R est:4000-6000 (A.D 7000)
£3137 $5616 €4580 Bush Plums (135x78cm-53x31in) s. verso synthetic polymer paint linen exec 1998 prov. 25-May-4 Lawson Menzies, Sydney #80/R est:12000-18000 (A.D 8000)
£3516 $6574 €5274 Untitled (70x50cm-28x20in) s.d.1983 verso synthetic polymer paint board prov. 26-Jul-4 Sotheby's, Melbourne #497/R est:10000-15000 (A.D 9000)
£4297 $8035 €6446 Narripi, worm, dreaming (120x89cm-47x35in) s.d.1996 verso synthetic polymer paint linen prov. 26-Jul-4 Sotheby's, Melbourne #498/R est:5000-8000 (A.D 11000)
£5691 $8992 €8252 Narripi worm dreaming (96x125cm-38x49in) s.i.d.1994 verso synthetic polymer paint linen prov. 28-Jul-3 Sotheby's, Paddington #502/R est:3000-5000 (A.D 14000)
£10196 $18251 €14886 Honey Ant Dreaming (120x200cm-47x79in) synthetic polymer paint linen exec 1994 prov. 25-May-4 Lawson Menzies, Sydney #68/R est:25000-35000 (A.D 26000)
£39063 $73047 €58595 Untitled, ceremony (39x92cm-15x36in) synthetic polymer powder paint board exec.c.1971 prov. 26-Jul-4 Sotheby's, Melbourne #97/R est:80000-120000 (A.D 100000)

TJAPALTJARRI, Benny (20th C) Australian

Works on paper

£732 $1156 €1061 Untitled, wilkipakanu (122x92cm-48x36in) i.verso synthetic polymer paint linen prov. 28-Jul-3 Sotheby's, Paddington #397 est:2000-3000 (A.D 1800)

TJAPALTJARRI, David Corby (c.1945-1980) Australian

Works on paper

£938 $1753 €1407 Untitled, emu dance (37x39cm-15x15in) bears name.verso synthetic polymer paint board prov. 26-Jul-4 Sotheby's, Melbourne #556/R (A.D 2400)
£2033 $3211 €2948 Katata (46x46cm-18x18in) s.i.verso synthetic polymer paint composition board prov. 28-Jul-3 Sotheby's, Paddington #480/R est:5000-8000 (A.D 5000)

TJAPALTJARRI, Joseph Jurra (c.1950-) Australian

Works on paper

£1804 $3229 €2634 Water site at Kirritjina (90x140cm-35x55in) synthetic polymer paint canvas exec 2002 prov. 25-May-4 Lawson Menzies, Sydney #70/R est:5500-7000 (A.D 4600)
£3906 $7305 €5859 Timalnja (122x137cm-48x54in) bears name.verso synthetic polymer paint linen prov. 26-Jul-4 Sotheby's, Melbourne #197/R est:15000-20000 (A.D 10000)

TJAPALTJARRI, Mick Namerari (1926-1998) Australian

Works on paper

£273 $511 €410 Blue wren fire story (25x35cm-10x14in) name.i.d.1982 verso synthetic polymer paint canvasboard prov. 26-Jul-4 Sotheby's, Melbourne #551/R (A.D 700)
£371 $694 €557 Yankutanya, crow tracks (30x24cm-12x9in) bears name.i.verso synthetic polymer paint canvasboard prov. 26-Jul-4 Sotheby's, Melbourne #553 (A.D 950)
£859 $1607 €1289 Untitled (46x38cm-18x15in) bears name.verso synthetic polymer paint linen. 26-Jul-4 Sotheby's, Melbourne #558/R (A.D 2200)
£1872 $3239 €2733 Mouse dreaming (120x90cm-47x35in) s.i.verso synthetic polymer paint linen exec.c.1995 prov. 10-Dec-3 Shapiro, Sydney #186/R est:4000-6000 (A.D 4400)
£1953 $3652 €2930 Untitled (105x28cm-41x11in) bears name.verso synthetic polymer paint linen prov. 26-Jul-4 Sotheby's, Melbourne #268/R est:4000-6000 (A.D 5000)
£2439 $3854 €3537 Untitled (122x61cm-48x24in) i.verso synthetic polymer paint linen prov. 28-Jul-3 Sotheby's, Paddington #393/R est:7000-10000 (A.D 6000)
£2846 $4496 €4127 Mulpingyu rock hole (122x61cm-48x24in) i.verso synthetic polymer paint linen prov. 28-Jul-3 Sotheby's, Paddington #387/R est:7000-10000 (A.D 7000)
£3252 $5138 €4715 Narrkulynga dreaming site (81x100cm-32x39in) synthetic polymer paint linen prov.exhib.lit. 28-Jul-3 Sotheby's, Paddington #272/R est:8000-12000 (A.D 8000)
£4297 $8035 €6446 Untitled, Tingari story (150x120cm-59x47in) bears name.verso synthetic polymer paint linen prov. 26-Jul-4 Sotheby's, Melbourne #279/R est:15000-25000 (A.D 11000)
£5469 $10227 €8204 Tjakalpa, bandicoot dreaming (91x61cm-36x24in) bears name.verso synthetic polymer paint linen prov. 26-Jul-4 Sotheby's, Melbourne #262/R est:18000-25000 (A.D 14000)
£6250 $11688 €9375 Water dreaming in the Sandhills (29x29cm-11x11in) synthetic polymer powder paint board prov. 26-Jul-4 Sotheby's, Melbourne #205/R est:12000-18000 (A.D 16000)
£6809 $11779 €9941 Mouse dreaming (130x174cm-51x69in) i.verso synthetic polymer paint canvas prov. 10-Dec-3 Shapiro, Sydney #187/R est:15000-25000 (A.D 16000)
£9375 $17531 €14063 Kutunga at Mintjilpirri (182x122cm-72x48in) bears name.verso synthetic polymer paint linen prov. 26-Jul-4 Sotheby's, Melbourne #199/R est:30000-40000 (A.D 24000)
£12195 $19268 €17683 Bandicoot dreaming (75x121cm-30x48in) i.verso synthetic polymer paint linen prov. 28-Jul-3 Sotheby's, Paddington #273/R est:20000-30000 (A.D 30000)
£13008 $20553 €18862 Untitled (45x37cm-18x15in) i.verso synthetic polymer paint composition board prov. 28-Jul-3 Sotheby's, Paddington #107/R est:20000-30000 (A.D 32000)
£27344 $51133 €41016 Marnpi rockhole (153x122cm-60x48in) bears name.verso synthetic polymer paint linen prov. 26-Jul-4 Sotheby's, Melbourne #111/R est:70000-100000 (A.D 70000)
£73171 $115610 €106098 Tjunginpa, mouse dreaming (182x152cm-72x60in) i.verso synthetic polymer paint linen prov. 28-Jul-3 Sotheby's, Paddington #116/R est:100000-150000 (A.D 180000)

TJAPALTJARRI, Paddy Sims (c.1916-) Australian

Works on paper

£1328 $2484 €1992 Walpa jukurrpa, wind dreaming (90x76cm-35x30in) bears name.verso synthetic polymer paint linen prov. 26-Jul-4 Sotheby's, Melbourne #273/R est:1000-6000 (A.D 3400)
£1406 $2630 €2109 Karnta jukurrpa, women dreaming (122x77cm-48x30in) i.verso synthetic polymer linen exec. 2000 prov. 21-Jul-4 Shapiro, Sydney #110/R est:3500-5000 (A.D 3600)
£1569 $2808 €2291 Possum dreaming (122x46cm-48x18in) synthetic polymer paint linen exec 1994 prov. 25-May-4 Lawson Menzies, Sydney #12/R est:3500-5000 (A.D 4000)

TJAPALTJARRI, Tim Leura (1936-1984) Australian

Works on paper

£1211 $2264 €1817 Water dreaming (57x43cm-22x17in) synthetic polymer paint canvasboard prov. 26-Jul-4 Sotheby's, Melbourne #569/R est:1000-1500 (A.D 3100)
£2439 $3854 €3537 Bush fire over kangaroo camp (57x43cm-22x17in) i.verso synthetic polymer paint composition board exec.c.1974 pro. 28-Jul-3 Sotheby's, Paddington #269/R est:5000-8000 (A.D 6000)
£2846 $4496 €4127 Untitled, death spirit dreaming (56x45cm-22x18in) synthetic polymer paint canvasboard exec.c.1979 prov. 28-Jul-3 Sotheby's, Paddington #268/R est:3000-5000 (A.D 7000)
£5859 $10957 €8789 Alpalyparranjka (56x76cm-22x30in) bears name i.verso synthetic polymer paint board exec.c.1977 prov. 26-Jul-4 Sotheby's, Melbourne #101/R est:12000-18000 (A.D 15000)
£8594 $16070 €12891 Father/son/grandfather dreaming (47x62cm-19x24in) synthetic polymer powder paint board exec.c.1978 prov. 26-Jul-4 Sotheby's, Melbourne #102/R est:20000-30000 (A.D 22000)
£23438 $43828 €35157 Untitled, feeding the children (151x155cm-59x61in) synthetic polymer paint linen prov. 26-Jul-4 Sotheby's, Melbourne #104/R est:60000-80000 (A.D 60000)

TJAPALTJARRI, Walala (c.1960-) Australian

Works on paper

£703 $1315 €1055 Tingari (92x156cm-36x61in) i.verso synthetic polymer linen exec. 2002 prov. 21-Jul-4 Shapiro, Sydney #34/R (A.D 1800)
£1426 $2666 €2151 Tingari (212x136cm-83x54in) i.verso synthetic polymer linen exec. 2003 prov. 21-Jul-4 Shapiro, Sydney #47/R est:4000-6000 (A.D 3650)
£1804 $3229 €2634 Tingarri cycle (151x91cm-59x36in) synthetic polymer paint linen exec 2002 prov. 25-May-4 Lawson Menzies, Sydney #93/R est:5000-7000 (A.D 4600)

TJAPALTJARRI, Warlimpirrnga (c.1959-) Australian

Works on paper

£1931 $3051 €2800 Untitled (122x122cm-48x48in) i.verso synthetic polymer paint linen prov. 28-Jul-3 Sotheby's, Paddington #114/R est:4000-6000 (A.D 4750)
£2439 $3854 €3537 Untitled (91x122cm-36x48in) i.verso synthetic polymer paint linen prov. 28-Jul-3 Sotheby's, Paddington #113/R est:4000-6000 (A.D 6000)
£2930 $5479 €4395 Untitled (122x184cm-48x72in) bears name.verso synthetic polymer paint linen prov. 26-Jul-4 Sotheby's, Melbourne #269/R est:10000-15000 (A.D 7500)
£2941 $5265 €4294 Tingari (92x180cm-36x71in) synthetic polymer paint linen exec 2001 prov. 25-May-4 Lawson Menzies, Sydney #86/R est:8000-10000 (A.D 7500)
£3906 $7305 €5859 Untitled (153x122cm-60x48in) bears name.verso synthetic polymer paint linen prov. 26-Jul-4 Sotheby's, Melbourne #263/R est:12000-18000 (A.D 10000)

TJAPANANGKA, Bob Dingle (c.1933-) Australian

Works on paper

£1328 $2484 €1992 Tilgar (119x85cm-47x33in) bears name.verso synthetic polymer paint prov. 26-Jul-4 Sotheby's, Melbourne #434/R est:4000-6000 (A.D 3400)

TJAPANANGKA, Dick Lechleitner (1944-) Australian

Works on paper

£511 $868 €746 Sugar ant dreaming (122x91cm-48x36in) i.verso synthetic polymer paint canvas prov. 25-Nov-3 Christie's, Melbourne #239 (A.D 1200)

TJAPANANGKA, George (c.1938-) Australian

Works on paper

£1563 $2922 €2345 Untitled (162x46cm-64x18in) bears name.verso synthetic polymer paint linen prov. 26-Jul-4 Sotheby's, Melbourne #511/R est:4000-6000 (A.D 4000)

TJAPANANGKA, Johnny Scobie (attrib) (c.1935-1999) Australian

Works on paper

£610 $963 €891 Emu story at Mitukatjiri (74x54cm-29x21in) i.verso synthetic polymer paint canvasboard exec.c.1974. 28-Jul-3 Sotheby's, Paddington #548 est:2000-3000 (A.D 1500)

TJAPANANGKA, Long Tom (c.1930-) Australian

Works on paper

£392 $702 €572 Sand Goanna (92x33cm-36x13in) synthetic polymer paint masonite exec 1995. 25-May-4 Lawson Menzies, Sydney #102/R (A.D 1000)

£1016	$1606	€1473	Untitled (90x60cm-35x24in) earth pigments binder linen prov. 28-Jul-3 Sotheby's, Paddington #383/R est:2500-3500 (A.D 2500)
£2383	$4123	€3479	Haasts Bluff Mountain (91x150cm-36x59in) synthetic polymer paint prov. 10-Dec-3 Shapiro, Sydney #138/R est:5000-7000 (A.D 5600)
£2439	$3854	€3537	Ulampawarru and Mereeni ranges (81x182cm-32x72in) synthetic polymer paint linen prov. 28-Jul-3 Sotheby's, Paddington #381/R est:5000-8000 (A.D 6000)
£2439	$3854	€3537	Untitled (173x182cm-68x72in) i.verso synthetic polymer paint linen prov. 28-Jul-3 Sotheby's, Paddington #382/R est:6000-8000 (A.D 6000)
£3719	$6880	€5430	Untitled (136x182cm-54x72in) synthetic polymer executed 1995 prov. 15-Mar-4 Sotheby's, Melbourne #116/R est:5000-7000 (A.D 9000)

TJAPANANGKA, Pinta Pinta (20th C) Australian

Works on paper

£1569	$2808	€2291	Tingari dreaming (91x45cm-36x18in) synthetic polymer paint linen exec 1998 prov. 25-May-4 Lawson Menzies, Sydney #5/R est:2500-3000 (A.D 4000)
£1911	$3019	€2771	Untitled, (56x61cm-22x24in) i.verso synthetic polymer paint linen pair prov. 28-Jul-3 Sotheby's, Paddington #279/R est:4000-6000 (A.D 4700)
£2539	$4748	€3809	Untitled (90x46cm-35x18in) bears name.verso synthetic polymer paint linen prov. 26-Jul-4 Sotheby's, Melbourne #110/R est:3000-5000 (A.D 6500)

TJAPANANGKA, Tjumpo (c.1930-) Australian

Works on paper

£703	$1315	€1055	Untitled (35x45cm-14x18in) i.verso synthetic polymer canvasboard two panels exec.1999 prov. 21-Jul-4 Shapiro, Sydney #109/R (A.D 1800)
£1094	$2045	€1641	Untitled (35x45cm-14x18in) i.verso synthetic polymer canvasboard three panels prov. 21-Jul-4 Shapiro, Sydney #108/R est:3000-5000 (A.D 2800)
£2734	$5113	€4101	Ngunkanapilka (152x76cm-60x30in) bears name.verso synthetic polymer paint canvas prov. 26-Jul-4 Sotheby's, Melbourne #251/R est:6000-8000 (A.D 7000)
£3516	$6574	€5274	Wangapanta (120x85cm-47x33in) bears name.verso synthetic polymer paint canvas prov.exhib.lit. 26-Jul-4 Sotheby's, Melbourne #85/R est:8000-12000 (A.D 9000)
£11382	$17984	€16504	Wirramanu luurnpa (180x296cm-71x117in) i.verso synthetic polymer paint linen multi artists prov. 28-Jul-3 Sotheby's, Paddington #196/R est:15000-20000 (A.D 28000)

TJAPANGATI, Charlie (1949-) Australian

Works on paper

£1412	$2527	€2062	Tingari Dreaming at Karrilwalla (46x91cm-18x36in) synthetic polymer paint linen exec 2001 prov. 25-May-4 Lawson Menzies, Sydney #74/R est:2500-4000 (A.D 3600)

TJAPANGATI, John John Bennett (20th C) Australian

Works on paper

£1707	$2698	€2475	Untitled (91x61cm-36x24in) i.verso synthetic polymer paint linen prov. 28-Jul-3 Sotheby's, Paddington #485 est:2000-3000 (A.D 4200)

TJAPANGATI, John Mosquito (c.1920-) Australian

Works on paper

£2236	$3533	€3242	Marloo (89x60cm-35x24in) i.verso synthetic polymer paint linen prov. 28-Jul-3 Sotheby's, Paddington #491/R est:3000-5000 (A.D 5500)
£2734	$5113	€4101	Tjintjamatju (100x50cm-39x20in) bears name.verso synthetic polymer paint canvas prov.exhib. 26-Jul-4 Sotheby's, Melbourne #77/R est:6000-8000 (A.D 7000)

TJAPANGATI, Kanya (c.1950-) Australian

Works on paper

£1787	$3092	€2609	Untitled, body paint designs associated with Tingari ceremonies (122x91cm-48x36in) i.verso synthetic polymer paint linen prov. 10-Dec-3 Shapiro, Sydney #189/R est:3500-5000 (A.D 4200)

TJAPANGATI, Old Tutuma (c.1915-1987) Australian

Works on paper

£3516	$6574	€5274	Eagle dreaming (122x93cm-48x37in) synthetic polymer paint board prov.lit. 26-Jul-4 Sotheby's, Melbourne #260/R est:10000-15000 (A.D 9000)
£3906	$7305	€5859	Payiyarrnganya (90x60cm-35x24in) synthetic polymer paint board exec.c.1979 prov.exhib. 26-Jul-4 Sotheby's, Melbourne #261/R est:10000-15000 (A.D 10000)
£4297	$8035	€6446	Ngawaya II (91x71cm-36x28in) bears name.verso synthetic polymer paint canvas prov.exhib. 26-Jul-4 Sotheby's, Melbourne #257/R est:6000-8000 (A.D 11000)
£4688	$8766	€7032	Mushroom and kangaroo dreaming (122x91cm-48x36in) synthetic polymer paint board exec.c.1975 prov.lit. 26-Jul-4 Sotheby's, Melbourne #259/R est:15000-20000 (A.D 12000)
£6641	$12418	€9962	Untitled (54x25cm-21x10in) synthetic polymer paint artboard prov. 26-Jul-4 Sotheby's, Melbourne #94/R est:8000-12000 (A.D 17000)

TJAPANGATI, Timmy Payungka (c.1942-2000) Australian

Works on paper

£586	$1096	€879	Wilkinkarra, Lake Mackay (61x30cm-24x12in) bears name.i.verso synthetic polymer paint canvasboard prov. 26-Jul-4 Sotheby's, Melbourne #557 (A.D 1500)
£625	$1169	€938	Untitled (112x55cm-44x22in) bears name synthetic polymer paint linen prov. 26-Jul-4 Sotheby's, Melbourne #548/R (A.D 1600)
£938	$1753	€1407	Untitled (91x61cm-36x24in) bears name.verso synthetic polymer paint linen prov. 26-Jul-4 Sotheby's, Melbourne #549/R (A.D 2400)
£1138	$1798	€1650	Untitled, fire maker man (40x30cm-16x12in) synthetic polymer paint canvasboard. 28-Jul-3 Sotheby's, Paddington #547 est:1500-2500 (A.D 2800)
£1301	$2055	€1886	Untitled (107x28cm-42x11in) i.verso synthetic polymer paint linen prov. 28-Jul-3 Sotheby's, Paddington #392/R est:2000-3000 (A.D 3200)
£1341	$2120	€1944	Payari (112x55cm-44x22in) i.verso synthetic polymer paint canvasboard prov. 28-Jul-3 Sotheby's, Paddington #278 est:1500-2500 (A.D 3300)
£1569	$2808	€2291	Tingari (91x46cm-36x18in) synthetic polymer paint linen exec 1997 prov. 25-May-4 Lawson Menzies, Sydney #85/R est:5000-6000 (A.D 4000)
£3125	$5844	€4688	Untitled (71x55cm-28x22in) bears name.verso synthetic polymer paint canvasboard prov. 26-Jul-4 Sotheby's, Melbourne #555/R est:3000-5000 (A.D 8000)
£10938	$20453	€16407	Untitled, kangaroo story (104x58cm-41x23in) synthetic polymer paint board exec.c.1972 prov. 26-Jul-4 Sotheby's, Melbourne #210/R est:30000-40000 (A.D 28000)

TJAPANGATI, Wimmitji (c.1925-) Australian

Works on paper

£6098	$9634	€8842	Tingari at Kurra (91x61cm-36x24in) i.verso synthetic polymer paint canvas prov. 28-Jul-3 Sotheby's, Paddington #195/R est:15000-20000 (A.D 15000)
£6641	$12418	€9962	Water dreaming (91x61cm-36x24in) bears name.verso synthetic polymer paint canvas prov.exhib. 26-Jul-4 Sotheby's, Melbourne #68/R est:15000-20000 (A.D 17000)
£10938	$20453	€16407	Karlingawi (120x90cm-47x35in) bears name.verso synthetic polymer paint canvas prov.exhib. 26-Jul-4 Sotheby's, Melbourne #74/R est:30000-50000 (A.D 28000)
£11719	$21914	€17579	Kutu (120x60cm-47x24in) bears name.verso synthetic polymer paint canvas prov.exhib. 26-Jul-4 Sotheby's, Melbourne #69/R est:30000-40000 (A.D 30000)

TJARKIN, A (19th C) Russian

£1495	$2363	€2168	Horses in the farmyard (58x72cm-23x28in) s.d.1875. 2-Sep-3 Rasmussen, Copenhagen #1698/R est:15000 (D.KR 16000)

TJUNGARRAYI, Charlie Tarawa (c.1921-1999) Australian

Works on paper

£1057	$1670	€1533	Untitled (76x61cm-30x24in) synthetic polymer paint canvasboard prov. 28-Jul-3 Sotheby's, Paddington #479/R est:2500-3500 (A.D 2600)
£3252	$5138	€4715	Wichetty grub dreaming at Nurapalangunja (79x61cm-31x24in) synthetic polymer paint composition board prov. 28-Jul-3 Sotheby's, Paddington #478/R est:8000-12000 (A.D 8000)
£70313	$131484	€105470	The trial (76x40cm-30x16in) synthetic polymer paint board prov. 26-Jul-4 Sotheby's, Melbourne #96/R est:70000-100000 (A.D 180000)

TJUNGARRAYI, Charlie Tarawa (attrib) (c.1921-1999) Australian

Works on paper

£2032	$3211	€2967	Camps of men (58x14cm-23x6in) synthetic polymer paint composition board. 28-Jul-3 Sotheby's, Paddington #270/R est:5000-7000 (A.D 5000)

TJUNGARRAYI, Shorty Lungkarda (1920-1987) Australian

Works on paper

£9350	$14772	€13558	Untitled (79x61cm-31x24in) i.verso synthetic polymer paint composition board prov. 28-Jul-3 Sotheby's, Paddington #171/R est:15000-20000 (A.D 23000)
£37109	$69395	€55664	Untitled (50x35cm-20x14in) synthetic polymer paint earth pigments board prov.exhib.lit. 26-Jul-4 Sotheby's, Melbourne #100/R est:100000-150000 (A.D 95000)

TJUNGARRAYI, Two Bob (c.1938-) Australian

£650	$1028	€943	Untitled (126x100cm-50x39in) i.verso. 22-Jul-3 Lawson Menzies, Sydney #69/R est:2000-3000 (A.D 1600)

Works on paper

£1373	$2457	€2005	Men's dreaming (137x90cm-54x35in) synthetic polymer paint linen exec 1990 prov. 25-May-4 Lawson Menzies, Sydney #91/R est:2000-3000 (A.D 3500)

TJUNGARRAYI, Yala Yala Gibbs (c.1925-) Australian

Works on paper

£1172	$2191	€1758	Tingari cycle (152x51cm-60x20in) bears name.verso synthetic polymer paint linen prov. 26-Jul-4 Sotheby's, Melbourne #507/R est:3000-5000 (A.D 3000)
£1250	$2338	€1875	Untitled (132x59cm-52x23in) bears name.verso synthetic polymer paint linen prov. 26-Jul-4 Sotheby's, Melbourne #508/R est:4000-6000 (A.D 3200)
£1829	$2890	€2652	Kanparrka, centipede dreaming (90x45cm-35x18in) i.verso synthetic polymer paint linen prov. 28-Jul-3 Sotheby's, Paddington #276/R est:4000-6000 (A.D 4500)
£1953	$3652	€2930	Ngatatjula (92x61cm-36x24in) bears name.verso synthetic polymer paint linen prov. 26-Jul-4 Sotheby's, Melbourne #109/R est:6000-8000 (A.D 5000)
£2344	$4383	€3516	Wapintjinna (90x46cm-35x18in) bears name.verso synthetic polymer paint linen prov. 26-Jul-4 Sotheby's, Melbourne #267/R est:5000-7000 (A.D 6000)
£4878	$7707	€7073	Wirlpi (122x121cm-48x48in) i.verso synthetic polymer paint linen prov. 28-Jul-3 Sotheby's, Paddington #274/R est:12000-18000 (A.D 12000)
£5859	$10957	€8789	Irrirrinki (152x121cm-60x48in) bears name.verso synthetic polymer paint linen prov. 26-Jul-4 Sotheby's, Melbourne #198/R est:18000-25000 (A.D 15000)

TJUNGURRAYI, Brandy (c.1930-) Australian

Works on paper

£537	$914	€784	Artist's country (119x179cm-47x70in) synthetic polymer paint on canvas. 29-Oct-3 Lawson Menzies, Sydney #83/R est:1500-2000 (A.D 1300)
£1563	$2922	€2345	Untitled (120x61cm-47x24in) bears name.verso synthetic polymer paint linen prov. 26-Jul-4 Sotheby's, Melbourne #196/R est:4000-6000 (A.D 4000)
£2157	$3861	€3149	Tingari at Palal Palal (122x91cm-48x36in) synthetic polymer paint linen exec 2000 prov. 25-May-4 Lawson Menzies, Sydney #98/R est:7000-8500 (A.D 5500)
£7813	$14609	€11720	Palal palal (153x182cm-60x72in) bears name.verso synthetic polymer paint linen prov. 26-Jul-4 Sotheby's, Melbourne #193/R est:20000-30000 (A.D 20000)

TJUNGURRAYI, Charlie Marshall (20th C) Australian

Works on paper

£894	$1404	€1296	Kunatjarrayi (122x183cm-48x72in) synthetic polymer paint linen prov. 26-Aug-3 Christie's, Sydney #236 est:2000-3000 (A.D 2200)

TJUNGURRAYI, Charlie Tjaruru (c.1920-) Australian

Works on paper

£332	$621	€498	Emu dreaming (35x45cm-14x18in) bears name.i.verso synthetic polymer paint canvasboard prov. 26-Jul-4 Sotheby's, Melbourne #561 (A.D 850)

£625 $1169 €938 Untitled (40x30cm-16x12in) bears name.verso synthetic polymer paint board exec.c.1973 prov. 26-Jul-4 Sotheby's, Melbourne #559 (A.D 1600)
£2846 $4496 €4127 Legend of Tingari at Pirmarlyna (78x61cm-31x24in) synthetic polymer paint composition board prov.exhib.lit. 28-Jul-3 Sotheby's, Paddington #264/R est:7000-10000 (A.D 7000)

TJUNGURRAYI, George (c.1947-) Australian
£2857 $5257 €4171 Tali (122x172cm-48x68in) acrylic linen sold with photo. 29-Mar-4 Goodman, Sydney #42/R est:8000-10000 (A.D 7000)
Works on paper
£294 $526 €429 Sand Hills (45x91cm-18x36in) synthetic polymer paint linen exec 1998. 25-May-4 Lawson Menzies, Sydney #96/R (A.D 750)
£745 $1334 €1088 Tingari Site (61x91cm-24x36in) synthetic polymer canvas exec 2002 prov.exhib. 25-May-4 Lawson Menzies, Sydney #6/R (A.D 1900)
£1172 $2191 €1758 Kantapintinya (107x28cm-42x11in) bears name.verso synthetic polymer paint linen prov. 26-Jul-4 Sotheby's, Melbourne #485/R est:3000-5000 (A.D 3000)
£2033 $3211 €2948 Untitled (91x46cm-36x18in) i.verso synthetic polymer paint linen prov. 28-Jul-3 Sotheby's, Paddington #283/R est:3000-5000 (A.D 5000)
£2734 $5113 €4101 Sandhill country (91x91cm-36x36in) bears name.verso synthetic polymer paint linen prov. 26-Jul-4 Sotheby's, Melbourne #195/R est:7000-10000 (A.D 7000)
£3617 $6258 €5281 Men's story, Tingari (152x112cm-60x44in) i.verso synthetic polymer paint linen prov. 10-Dec-3 Shapiro, Sydney #214/R est:8000-12000 (A.D 8500)
£8943 $14130 €12967 Mululuangulngy (183x152cm-72x60in) i.verso synthetic polymer paint linen prov. 28-Jul-3 Sotheby's, Paddington #181/R est:22000-28000 (A.D 22000)
£12195 $19268 €17683 Tingari cycle at Paykapungkunya (152x183cm-60x72in) synthetic polymer paint linen prov.exhib. 28-Jul-3 Sotheby's, Paddington #115/R est:20000-30000 (A.D 30000)

TJUNGURRAYI, Helicopter (c.1946-) Australian
£2341 $4049 €3418 Untitled (120x180cm-47x71in) synthetic polymer paint linen triptych multiple artists prov. 10-Dec-3 Shapiro, Sydney #144/R est:4000-6000 (A.D 5500)
Works on paper
£2353 $4212 €3435 Mamakarra Soakage (150x75cm-59x30in) synthetic polymer paint linen exec 2000 prov. 25-May-4 Lawson Menzies, Sydney #127/R est:5000-7000 (A.D 6000)

TJUNGURRAYI, Paddy Carroll (c.1927-) Australian
Works on paper
£16260 $25691 €23577 Ancestral map of the artist's country (217x258cm-85x102in) synthetic polymer paint linen sold with documentation prov. 28-Jul-3 Sotheby's, Paddington #182/R est:35000-45000 (A.D 40000)

TJUNGURRAYI, Willy (c.1930-) Australian
Works on paper
£732 $1156 €1061 Karukarungya (91x91cm-36x36in) i.verso synthetic polymer paint linen prov. 28-Jul-3 Sotheby's, Paddington #500 est:2000-4000 (A.D 1800)
£3252 $5138 €4715 Winwinpa (153x91cm-60x36in) i.verso synthetic polymer paint linen prov. 28-Jul-3 Sotheby's, Paddington #398/R est:8000-12000 (A.D 8000)

TJUNGURRAYI, Yumpululu (c.1925-) Australian
Works on paper
£6250 $11688 €9375 Man and two wives, rocks (49x29cm-19x11in) bears name i.verso synthetic polymer powder paint board prov. 26-Jul-4 Sotheby's, Melbourne #93/R est:8000-12000 (A.D 16000)

TJUPURRULA, Billy Rowe (c.1955-) Australian
Works on paper
£392 $702 €572 Spear straightening (122x61cm-48x24in) synthetic polymer paint canvas exec 1999 prov. 25-May-4 Lawson Menzies, Sydney #99/R (A.D 1000)

TJUPURRULA, Dominic Martin (c.1938-) Australian
Works on paper
£391 $730 €587 Untitled (99x75cm-39x30in) bears name.verso synthetic polymer paint linen prov. 26-Jul-4 Sotheby's, Melbourne #488 (A.D 1000)
£1172 $2191 €1758 Near Kiwirrkura (90x61cm-35x24in) bears name.verso synthetic polymer paint canvas prov.exhib. 26-Jul-4 Sotheby's, Melbourne #431/R est:3000-5000 (A.D 3000)
£1255 $2246 €1832 Murrua (90x60cm-35x24in) synthetic polymer paint canvas exec 1994 prov. 25-May-4 Lawson Menzies, Sydney #29/R est:4000-6000 (A.D 3200)
£1563 $2922 €2345 Muyunpa (99x76cm-39x30in) bears name.verso synthetic polymer paint canvas prov.exhib.lit. 26-Jul-4 Sotheby's, Melbourne #429/R est:3000-4000 (A.D 4000)

TJUPURRULA, Donkeyman Lee (c.1925-1993) Australian
Works on paper
£7031 $13148 €10547 Native cat dreaming (159x79cm-63x31in) bears name.verso synthetic polymer paint canvas prov.exhib.lit. 26-Jul-4 Sotheby's, Melbourne #79/R est:20000-30000 (A.D 18000)
£11719 $21914 €17579 Wala wala (118x178cm-46x70in) bears name.verso synthetic polymer paint canvas prov.exhib.lit. 26-Jul-4 Sotheby's, Melbourne #80/R est:30000-40000 (A.D 30000)

TJUPURRULA, Johnny Warrangula (1932-2001) Australian
£1215 $1955 €1774 Fire dreaming (128x182cm-50x72in) acrylic. 13-Oct-3 Joel, Victoria #429 est:3000-5000 (A.D 3000)
Works on paper
£3125 $5844 €4688 Tingari cycle (124x71cm-49x28in) bears name.i.verso synthetic polymer paint linen prov. 26-Jul-4 Sotheby's, Melbourne #510/R est:8000-12000 (A.D 8000)
£4065 $6382 €5894 Events at Tjikari (152x182cm-60x72in) synthetic polymer paint canvas prov.exhib.lit. 27-Aug-3 Christie's, Sydney #583 est:1000-1500 (A.D 10000)
£4681 $8098 €6834 Untitled, events associated with the soakage site of Tjikari (122x183cm-48x72in) i.verso synthetic polymer paint linen prov. 10-Dec-3 Shapiro, Sydney #169/R est:12000-18000 (A.D 11000)
£4688 $8766 €7032 Goanna dreaming (53x36cm-21x14in) bears name.i.d.4/4/74 verso synthetic polymer paint board prov. 26-Jul-4 Sotheby's, Melbourne #412/R est:15000-20000 (A.D 12000)
£7422 $13879 €11133 Mala, wallaby, dreaming (23x34cm-9x13in) synthetic polymer paint board prov. 26-Jul-4 Sotheby's, Melbourne #91/R est:15000-25000 (A.D 19000)
£9375 $17531 €14063 Water dreaming at Kalipinypa (54x24cm-21x9in) synthetic polymer paint paperboard prov. 26-Jul-4 Sotheby's, Melbourne #92/R est:25000-35000 (A.D 24000)
£10547 $19723 €15821 Old man's fire story (30x51cm-12x20in) i.verso synthetic polymer board exec. 1972. 21-Jul-4 Shapiro, Sydney #66/R est:30000-40000 (A.D 27000)
£12500 $23375 €18750 Yulpini, white egret dreaming at Kalipinypa (125x160cm-49x63in) synthetic polymer paint canvas prov. 26-Jul-4 Sotheby's, Melbourne #200/R est:40000-60000 (A.D 32000)
£13281 $24836 €19922 Emu men at Kalipinypa (51x33cm-20x13in) bears name.verso synthetic polymer powder paint board prov. 26-Jul-4 Sotheby's, Melbourne #207/R est:40000-60000 (A.D 34000)
£14844 $27758 €22266 Bush tucker dreaming (202x130cm-80x51in) synthetic polymer paint linen prov. 26-Jul-4 Sotheby's, Melbourne #201/R est:50000-70000 (A.D 38000)
£40650 $64228 €58943 Water and bush tucker dreaming (57x56cm-22x22in) synthetic polymer paint composition board prov. 28-Jul-3 Sotheby's, Paddington #110/R est:100000-150000 (A.D 100000)
£119919 $189472 €173883 Spearing of Matingpilangu (203x173cm-80x68in) synthetic polymer paint linen prov. 28-Jul-3 Sotheby's, Paddington #184/R est:300000-500000 (A.D 295000)

TJUPURRULA, Johnny Warrangula (attrib) (1932-2001) Australian
£392 $702 €572 Hare Wallaby Dreaming (26x19cm-10x7in) poster paint hardboard painted c.1975 prov. 25-May-4 Lawson Menzies, Sydney #61/R (A.D 1000)
£471 $842 €688 Hare Wallaby Dreaming (49x20cm-19x8in) poster paint hardboard painted c.1975 prov. 25-May-4 Lawson Menzies, Sydney #62/R (A.D 1200)
Works on paper
£2642 $4175 €3831 Untitled (77x56cm-30x22in) synthetic polymer paint canvasboard exec.c.1974 prov. 28-Jul-3 Sotheby's, Paddington #488 est:3000-5000 (A.D 6500)

TJUPURRULA, Johnny Yungut (c.1930-) Australian
Works on paper
£579 $983 €845 Tingarri cycle (122x62cm-48x24in) synthetic polymer paint on Belgian linen. 29-Oct-3 Lawson Menzies, Sydney #67/R est:1600-2000 (A.D 1400)
£1172 $2191 €1758 Ngaminya (91x91cm-36x36in) bears name.verso synthetic polymer paint linen prov. 26-Jul-4 Sotheby's, Melbourne #275/R est:3000-5000 (A.D 3000)

TJUPURRULA, Mekini (1932-) Australian
Works on paper
£1057 $1670 €1543 Emu dreaming (157x56cm-62x22in) synthetic polymer paint linen prov. 28-Jul-3 Sotheby's, Paddington #501/R est:1500-2500 (A.D 2600)

TJUPURRULA, Richard Tax (c.1938-) Australian
Works on paper
£1953 $3652 €2930 Kurtal (99x74cm-39x29in) bears name.verso synthetic polymer paint canvas prov.exhib.lit. 26-Jul-4 Sotheby's, Melbourne #86/R est:4000-6000 (A.D 5000)

TJUPURRULA, Sandy Gordon (c.1934-) Australian
Works on paper
£1074 $1826 €1568 Artist's birthplace (76x100cm-30x39in) synthetic polymer paint on canvas. 29-Oct-3 Lawson Menzies, Sydney #85/R est:800-1000 (A.D 2600)

TJUPURRULA, Turkey Tolson (c.1938-2001) Australian
£2236 $4002 €3265 Spear dreaming (86x136cm-34x54in) i. verso acrylic canvas prov.exhib. 10-May-4 Joel, Victoria #346 est:6000-8500 (A.D 5500)
Works on paper
£1176 $2106 €1717 Watikutjara at Lampintja, Pintupi (61x30cm-24x12in) synthetic polymer paint canvasboard exec 1984 prov. 25-May-4 Lawson Menzies, Sydney #66/R est:1500-2500 (A.D 3000)
£1563 $2922 €2345 Straightening spears (92x61cm-36x24in) i.verso synthetic polymer paint exec. 1999 prov. 21-Jul-4 Shapiro, Sydney #72/R est:4000-6000 (A.D 4000)
£3125 $5844 €4688 Two men at Warrulunga (180x74cm-71x29in) synthetic polymer paint linen prov. 26-Jul-4 Sotheby's, Melbourne #492/R est:8000-12000 (A.D 8000)
£3252 $5138 €4715 Kungka kuntjarra, two women (91x122cm-36x48in) i.verso synthetic polymer paint linen prov. 28-Jul-3 Sotheby's, Paddington #280/R est:7000-10000 (A.D 8000)
£4339 $8027 €6335 Straightening spears (147x91cm-58x36in) s.d.May 1996 verso synthetic polymer on line canvas. 15-Mar-4 Sotheby's, Melbourne #22 est:6000-8000 (A.D 10500)
£4609 $8620 €6914 Rockhole site of Willinya (152x87cm-60x34in) bears name.verso synthetic polymer paint linen prov. 26-Jul-4 Sotheby's, Melbourne #491/R est:12000-18000 (A.D 11800)
£4878 $7707 €7073 Straightening spears at Ilyingaungau (122x122cm-48x48in) i.verso synthetic polymer paint linen prov. 28-Jul-3 Sotheby's, Paddington #281/R est:8000-12000 (A.D 12000)
£18750 $35063 €28125 Mitukatjirri (181x121cm-71x48in) bears name.verso synthetic polymer paint linen prov. 26-Jul-4 Sotheby's, Melbourne #182/R est:60000-80000 (A.D 48000)
£23438 $43828 €35157 Straightening spears at Illyingaungau (122x152cm-48x60in) bears name.verso synthetic polymer paint linen prov. 26-Jul-4 Sotheby's, Melbourne #194/R est:50000-80000 (A.D 60000)

£25000 $46750 €37500 Straightening spears at Illyingaungau (152x183cm-60x72in) bears name.verso synthetic polymer paint linen prov. 26-Jul-4 Sotheby's, Melbourne #107/R est:60000-80000 (A.D 64000)
£28455 $44959 €41260 Straightening spears at Ilyingaungau (152x183cm-60x72in) synthetic polymer paint linen prov.exhib. 28-Jul-3 Sotheby's, Paddington #179/R est:70000-100000 (A.D 70000)

TKACHEV, Aleksei Petrovich (1922-) Russian
£5500 $9845 €8030 Studies of children (30x20cm-12x8in) oil on card set of three. 26-May-4 Sotheby's, London #308/R est:3000-5000

TKACHEV, Aleksei and Sergei (20th C) Russian
£30000 $53700 €43800 In the years of collectivisation (90x97cm-35x38in) s. s.d.1972 verso. 26-May-4 Sotheby's, London #310/R est:10000-15000

TO NGOC VAN (1906-1954) Vietnamese
£7285 $13331 €11000 Angkor (53x62cm-21x24in) s.d.1935. 7-Apr-4 Piasa, Paris #160/R est:6000-8000
Works on paper
£75269 $120430 €109893 Disillusionment (93x57cm-37x22in) s.d.1932 gouache ink silk. 18-May-3 Sotheby's, Singapore #110/R est:150000-200000 (S.D 210000)

TOBEEN, Felix-Elie (1880-1938) French
£1788 $3254 €2700 Still life (17x20cm-7x8in) s. cardboard. 19-Jun-4 St-Germain-en-Laye Encheres #152/R est:1500-1800
£2119 $3857 €3200 Bouquet de fleurs dans un vase jaune (41x33cm-16x13in) s. 18-Jun-4 Piasa, Paris #102 est:500-600
£2318 $4219 €3500 Vase de fleurs et pommes (31x39cm-12x15in) s. cardboard. 18-Jun-4 Piasa, Paris #103 est:500-600
£2500 $3975 €3625 Nu endormi (42x85cm-17x33in) s. board painted c.1920. 11-Sep-3 Christie's, Kensington #70/R est:2500-3500
£2500 $3975 €3650 Nu allonge (42x85cm-17x33in) s. board painted c.1920. 11-Sep-3 Christie's, Kensington #67/R est:2500-3500
£2517 $4580 €3800 Nature morte aux pommes et couteau (24x29cm-9x11in) s. cardboard. 18-Jun-4 Piasa, Paris #104 est:300-400

TOBEY, Mark (1890-1976) American
£559 $962 €800 Composition (11x15cm-4x6in) i. verso tempera foam. 3-Dec-3 Hauswedell & Nolte, Hamburg #1023/R
£1412 $2400 €2062 Sign no.263 (28x33cm-11x13in) s.d.61 tempera on paper prov.exhib. 9-Nov-3 Bonhams & Butterfields, Los Angeles #4090/R est:3000-5000
£1810 $3077 €2643 Untitled (29x20cm-11x8in) s.d.1962 W/C. 25-Nov-3 Germann, Zurich #18/R est:5000-6000 (S.FR 4000)
£1813 $3082 €2647 Untitled (15x10cm-6x4in) s.d.66 painting on monoprint. 5-Nov-3 AB Stockholms Auktionsverk #1176/R est:8000-10000 (S.KR 24000)
£3329 $5659 €4760 Untitled (17x11cm-7x4in) s.d.1965 tempera paper on canvas. 18-Nov-3 Babuino, Rome #47/R est:4500-5500
£3439 $5846 €5021 Untitled (15x11cm-6x4in) s. tempera paper painted 1967. 22-Nov-3 Burkhard, Luzern #121/R est:8000-9000 (S.FR 7600)
£4196 $7217 €6000 Composition (100x50cm-39x20in) s. verso tempera styropor. 3-Dec-3 Hauswedell & Nolte, Hamburg #1022/R est:7000
£7746 $12859 €11000 Etoile (28x22cm-11x9in) d.54 tempera paper exhib.lit. 11-Jun-3 Finarte Semenzato, Milan #626/R est:15000
£8380 $15000 €12235 Untitled (40x28cm-16x11in) s.d.1970 tempera paper double-sided prov. 12-May-4 Christie's, Rockefeller NY #211/R est:10000-15000
£12570 $22500 €18352 Untitled (15x12cm-6x5in) both s.d.68 tempera other tempera paper on board two prov. 13-May-4 Sotheby's, New York #107/R est:8000-12000
£19553 $35000 €28547 Untitled (15x6cm-6x2in) s.d.59 tempera paper painted 1959 prov. 12-May-4 Christie's, Rockefeller NY #120/R est:10000-15000
Prints
£4305 $7319 €6285 Untitled (99x50cm-39x20in) s. col monoprint. 5-Nov-3 AB Stockholms Auktionsverk #1294/R est:8000-12000 (S.KR 57000)
Works on paper
£524 $892 €750 Personnages (17x11cm-7x4in) s.d.1960 gouache prov. 23-Nov-3 Cornette de St.Cyr, Paris #333/R
£664 $1129 €950 Personnages (24x15cm-9x6in) s.d.1960 gouache prov. 23-Nov-3 Cornette de St.Cyr, Paris #334/R
£864 $1434 €1253 Composition (24x10cm-9x4in) s. bears d.61 mixed media. 13-Jun-3 Zofingen, Switzerland #2536/R est:2000 (S.FR 1900)
£1357 $2308 €1981 Untitled (20x28cm-8x11in) s.d.66 W/C. 22-Nov-3 Burkhard, Luzern #93/R est:2800-3400 (S.FR 3000)
£1385 $2480 €2022 Untitled composition (25x35cm-10x14in) s.d. bears i. verso mixed media silk paper on paper. 22-Mar-4 Philippe Schuler, Zurich #5731 est:1000-1500 (S.FR 3200)
£1964 $3338 €2867 Untitled (24x13cm-9x5in) s.d.68 W/C. 5-Nov-3 AB Stockholms Auktionsverk #1175/R est:18000-20000 (S.KR 26000)
£2133 $3925 €3200 Man's face (31x27cm-12x11in) s.d. W/C. 11-Jun-4 Hauswedell & Nolte, Hamburg #1560/R est:1800
£2267 $4171 €3400 Abstract composition (12x17cm-5x7in) s.d. W/C oil monotype. 11-Jun-4 Hauswedell & Nolte, Hamburg #1562/R est:1000
£2312 $4000 €3376 Travellers (46x30cm-18x12in) W/C prov. 15-Dec-3 Hindman, Chicago #28/R est:8000-12000
£2800 $5152 €4200 Abstract composition (15x11cm-6x4in) s.d. W/C monotype. 11-Jun-4 Hauswedell & Nolte, Hamburg #1563/R est:1200
£3208 $5196 €4684 Untitled (29x22cm-11x9in) s.d.68 W/C tempera prov. 24-May-3 Burkhard, Luzern #75/R est:2500-3500 (S.FR 6800)
£5263 $9684 €7684 Untitled (70x48cm-28x19in) s. mixed media. 23-Jun-4 Koller, Zurich #3141/R est:7000-9000 (S.FR 12000)
£5333 $9813 €8000 Untitled (19x10cm-7x4in) s.d.68 gouache cardboard. 12-Jun-4 Villa Grisebach, Berlin #400/R est:5000-7000
£5389 $9000 €7868 Released energy (58x87cm-23x34in) s.d.57 ink prov. 7-Oct-3 Sotheby's, New York #346 est:3000-5000
£5882 $10000 €8588 Untitled (33x22cm-13x9in) s.d.1970 gouache tempera paper prov.exhib. 22-Nov-3 Burkhard, Luzern #190/R est:13000-15000 (S.FR 13000)
£6114 $10943 €8926 Composition, gentle ways (29x22cm-11x9in) s.d.1969 mixed media. 26-May-4 Sotheby's, Zurich #150/R est:8000-12000 (S.FR 14000)
£7042 $12324 €10000 Yellow fall (56x78cm-22x31in) s.d.52 mixed media card prov. 16-Dec-3 Porro, Milan #35/R est:12000-14000
£7333 $13493 €11000 Untitled (54x75cm-21x30in) s.d. Indian ink brush. 11-Jun-4 Hauswedell & Nolte, Hamburg #1559/R est:4000
£9189 $17000 €13784 Nomadia (41x56cm-16x22in) s.d.50 W/C prov. 14-Jul-4 American Auctioneer #490214/R est:4000-6000
£18667 $34347 €28000 Ancient empires (24x40cm-9x16in) s.d. gouache. 11-Jun-4 Hauswedell & Nolte, Hamburg #1558/R est:3000
£26946 $45000 €39341 All together on Earth (23x30cm-9x12in) s.d.54 gouache ink wax crayon graphite prov.exhib. 12-Nov-3 Christie's, Rockefeller NY #314/R est:20000-30000

TOBIAS, Ben (c.1901-1985) Canadian
£450 $752 €657 St. Ives Bay (40x50cm-16x20in) s.i.d.1957 board. 21-Oct-3 Bonhams, Knightsbridge #99/R
£1300 $2171 €1898 Punch and Judy show, Cornwall (41x51cm-16x20in) s.i.d.1957 panel. 14-Oct-3 David Lay, Penzance #598 est:900-1200
£2000 $3640 €2920 Penzance (41x51cm-16x20in) s.i.d.1960 panel. 15-Jun-4 David Lay, Penzance #109/R est:1200-1400

TOBIASSE, Theo (1927-) Israeli
£3020 $5346 €4500 Petit pastel pour un homme (35x51cm-14x20in) s.i.d.XII 80 oil W/C gouache collage pastel paper. 27-Apr-4 Artcurial Briest, Paris #249c/R est:2500-3000
£3200 $5888 €4800 La theiere bleue (33x24cm-13x9in) s.i. 13-Jun-4 Lombrail & Teucquam, Paris #120/R
£3819 $6378 €5500 Venise d'amour (26x34cm-10x13in) s.i. prov. 21-Oct-3 Artcurial Briest, Paris #24 est:3000-4000
£4000 $7360 €6000 Le grand cirque de la vie (24x66cm-9x26in) s.i. oil gouache W/C collage paper on canvas diptych. 9-Jun-4 Christie's, Amsterdam #137/R est:4000-6000
£4206 $7571 €6141 Je deviens comme une espece de songe (46x38cm-18x15in) s.d.76. 26-Apr-4 Bukowskis, Stockholm #249/R est:25000-30000 (S.KR 58000)
£4909 $8346 €7167 Rien ne me rattache a la terra (60x73cm-24x29in) s.d.73 prov. 5-Nov-3 AB Stockholms Auktionsverk #1099/R est:35000-40000 (S.KR 65000)
£5467 $10059 €8200 Les filles de Loth (54x65cm-21x26in) s.i. 13-Jun-4 Lombrail & Teucquam, Paris #118/R
£6333 $11653 €9500 Les filles de Loth (73x91cm-29x36in) s.i. oil collage. 9-Jun-4 Christie's, Amsterdam #147/R est:6000-8000
£7000 $11130 €10150 Tout ce que j'aime est loin de moi (64x79cm-25x31in) s.i. 11-Sep-3 Christie's, Kensington #164/R est:6000-8000
£7500 $12975 €10950 Le montreur de moutons (71x58cm-28x23in) s.i. 11-Dec-3 Christie's, Kensington #211/R est:5000-7000
£8000 $12720 €11600 Le printemps a Venise (91x72cm-36x28in) s.i. 11-Sep-3 Christie's, Kensington #159/R est:8000-12000
£8000 $14720 €12000 Portrait de dame en bleu (61x91cm-24x36in) s.i. 9-Jun-4 Christie's, Amsterdam #141/R est:4000-6000
£9500 $17195 €13870 Paris, vivait en creux sur les bords de la Seine (89x116cm-35x46in) s.i. 1-Apr-4 Christie's, Kensington #137/R est:7000-9000
£10429 $17000 €15226 Jeune fille sur un oiseau (74x58cm-29x23in) s.i.d.68 prov. 25-Sep-3 Christie's, Rockefeller NY #641/R est:8000-12000
£10695 $20000 €15615 Ceux qui chantent le Duomo de Firenze (50x61cm-20x24in) s.i.d.67 prov. 25-Feb-4 Christie's, Rockefeller NY #88/R est:6000-8000
£10811 $20000 €15784 Les 2 Odalisques (81x116cm-32x46in) s.i.d.61. 12-Feb-4 Sotheby's, New York #52/R est:12000-18000
£11500 $19895 €16790 Le petit cycliste devant la synagogue (89x89cm-35x35in) s.i.d.68. 11-Dec-3 Christie's, Kensington #203/R est:7000-9000
£12000 $20760 €17520 Symphonie pour les gens qui n'ont pas de maison (80x89cm-31x35in) s.i.d.68. 11-Dec-3 Christie's, Kensington #210/R est:5000-7000
£13904 $26000 €20300 Des murs remplis d'une ivresse etrange (65x81cm-26x32in) s.i.d.69 prov. 25-Feb-4 Christie's, Rockefeller NY #87/R est:8000-12000
£15000 $23850 €21750 Les fruits sont des mots de lumiere (71x90cm-28x35in) s.i. 11-Sep-3 Christie's, Kensington #158/R est:8000-12000
£15035 $25860 €21500 Dis moi viens-tu chercher mon ame (73x92cm-29x36in) s. 3-Dec-3 Tajan, Paris #393 est:8000-10000
£16783 $28867 €24000 L'orange et la maternite a la fenetre (116x89cm-46x35in) s.i. prov. 2-Dec-3 Sotheby's, Amsterdam #100/R est:8000-12000
Sculpture
£3867 $7115 €5800 Myriam (50cm-20in) s.i. num.8/8 bronze incl. stone base. 9-Jun-4 Christie's, Amsterdam #138/R est:3000-5000
Works on paper
£933 $1717 €1400 Au bord des fleurs de Babylone (49x68cm-19x27in) s.i. W/C pastel pencil. 9-Jun-4 Christie's, Amsterdam #142/R
£1000 $1840 €1500 Gens de la bible (50x69cm-20x27in) s.i.d.88 pencil. 9-Jun-4 Christie's, Amsterdam #145/R est:1200-1600
£2193 $4035 €3202 Je suis le terebinthe de Sichem (49x64cm-19x25in) s.i.d.1973 gouache. 23-Jun-4 Koller, Zurich #3119/R est:6000-8000 (S.FR 5000)
£2917 $4871 €4200 Fleurs de Neguev (100x58cm-39x23in) s.d.85 mixed media collage prov. 21-Oct-3 Artcurial Briest, Paris #25 est:1000-1500
£3000 $5520 €4500 Le desir a l'heure des arabesques (50x69cm-20x27in) s.i. gouache W/C wax crayon. 9-Jun-4 Christie's, Amsterdam #139/R est:2500-3500
£3067 $5000 €4478 Un songe lointain aux quatre vents de memoire (68x101cm-27x40in) s.i. pastel gouache exec.c.1979. 25-Sep-3 Christie's, Rockefeller NY #636/R est:5000-7000
£3467 $6379 €5200 Ballet pour une dame au bord d'un puits (50x68cm-20x27in) s.i. gouache. 9-Jun-4 Christie's, Amsterdam #140/R est:2500-3500
£4435 $8161 €6475 Quand Israel sortit (63x47cm-25x19in) s.d.66 mixed media. 14-Jun-4 Waddingtons, Toronto #317/R est:4000-5000 (C.D 11000)
£4800 $8304 €7008 Les bergers de Florence (51x66cm-20x26in) s. pen brush black ink gouache. 11-Dec-3 Christie's, Kensington #201/R est:3000-5000
£10352 $17909 €14700 Le poete sur une poire (100x65cm-39x26in) s.i. mixed media canvas prov. 13-Dec-3 Touati, Paris #157/R est:12000

TOBIN, G (1768-1838) British
Works on paper
£1150 $2151 €1679 Man-o-war and other sailing ships in a harbour (22x34cm-9x13in) s.d.1815 W/C. 20-Jul-4 Sworder & Son, Bishops Stortford #770/R est:300-500

TOBLER, Victor (1846-1915) German
£921 $1695 €1400 Peasant interior with mother and children (39x49cm-15x19in) s. 24-Jun-4 Dr Fritz Nagel, Stuttgart #763/R

TOCI, Luigi Salsiccioni (20th C) Italian
£375 $600 €548 Tuscan landscape (36x48cm-14x19in) s. board. 20-Sep-3 Sloans & Kenyon, Bethesda #132/R
£1063 $1700 €1552 Woman hanging laundry in Tuscan field (58x119cm-23x47in) s. s.verso. 20-Sep-3 Sloans & Kenyon, Bethesda #133/R est:1750-2000

TOCORNAL, Antonio (1964-) Spanish
£476 $867 €700 357 (100x100cm-39x39in) s.d.1988 verso oil mixed media prov.exhib. 3-Feb-4 Segre, Madrid #213/R
£510 $929 €750 M/T 360 (100x100cm-39x39in) s.i.d.88 verso prov. 3-Feb-4 Segre, Madrid #214/R

TOCQUE, Louis (after) (1696-1772) French
£7761 $13891 €11331 Count Carl Gustaf Tessin (80x65cm-31x26in) canvas on panel. 25-May-4 Bukowskis, Stockholm #514/R est:50000-60000 (S.KR 105000)

TOCQUE, Louis (attrib) (1696-1772) French
Works on paper
£442 $791 €650 Une main tenant le pommeau d'une epee, un autre un baton. Draperie (27x18cm-11x7in) red white chk double-sided. 18-Mar-4 Christie's, Paris #244/R
£884 $1583 €1300 Portrait d'homme de profil en habit bleu (54x30cm-21x12in) pastel. 19-Mar-4 Piasa, Paris #76/R

TOCQUE, Louis (school) (1696-1772) French
£5674 $9475 €8000 Portrait of the Prince of Conde (137x98cm-54x39in) 14-Oct-3 Finarte Semenzato, Rome #135/R est:6000-7000

TOD, Joanne (20th C) Canadian
£4505 $7658 €6577 Elixir (127x114cm-50x45in) s.i.d.1997 verso prov. 18-Nov-3 Sotheby's, Toronto #112/R est:10000-15000 (C.D 10000)
£4878 $8732 €7122 144w. 55th, 9th floor (61x91cm-24x36in) s. i.d.1997 verso prov. 31-May-4 Sotheby's, Toronto #157/R est:6000-9000 (C.D 12000)
Works on paper
£1464 $2489 €2137 Liftings (21x28cm-8x11in) one s.d.1997 col pencil vellum two prov.exhib. 18-Nov-3 Sotheby's, Toronto #67/R est:3000-5000 (C.D 3250)

TODARO, Vincenzo (1855-1926) Italian
£1098 $1900 €1603 Young girl feeding rabbits (28x36cm-11x14in) s.d.1880. 13-Dec-3 Sloans & Kenyon, Bethesda #783/R est:1800-2200

TODD, Arthur Ralph Middleton (1891-c.1967) British
£520 $972 €759 Morwanna (41x33cm-16x13in) s. board prov.exhib. 24-Feb-4 Bonhams, Knowle #144
£5000 $9250 €7300 Wild flowers (46x38cm-18x15in) s. exhib. 11-Feb-4 Sotheby's, Olympia #119/R est:800-1200
Works on paper
£1400 $2618 €2044 Music hat chrms, man playing a wind instrument (24x18cm-9x7in) s.d.1911. 26-Feb-4 Lane, Penzance #238 est:1000-1200

TODD, Henry George (1846-1898) British
£700 $1267 €1022 Still life study of grapes, peach, cherries and white currants on a bank (23x18cm-9x7in) s.d.1896. 16-Apr-4 Keys, Aylsham #691/R
£2000 $3680 €2920 Still life of fruit on a marble shelf (19cm-7in circular) s.d.1893 oil card pair. 23-Jun-4 Bonhams, Bury St Edmunds #399/R est:2000-3000
£3463 $5784 €5021 Still life of grapes and plums. Still life of grapes and strawberries (18x22cm-7x9in) s.d.1878 pair. 23-Jun-3 Philippe Schuler, Zurich #3552 est:3500-4000 (S.FR 7550)

TODD, Henry Stanley (1872-1941) American
£298 $525 €435 Football scene (33x43cm-13x17in) s.i.d.1930 board. 24-May-4 Winter Associates, Plainville #137/R
£384 $675 €561 Portrait of a young woman standing (135x86cm-53x34in) s. 24-May-4 Winter Associates, Plainville #36

TODD, Milan (1922-) Yugoslavian
£483 $753 €700 Chattering Iiy (58x88cm-23x35in) s. 1-Aug-2 Joel, Victoria #232 est:2500-3000 (A.D 1400)
£574 $930 €838 Midnight mating dance - plumed egret (91x106cm-36x42in) s.d.81 i.verso acrylic. 30-Jul-3 Goodman, Sydney #119/R (A.D 1400)

TODD, Ralph (1856-1932) British
£1450 $2683 €2117 Hosking's old dairy (51x69cm-20x27in) 10-Feb-4 David Lay, Penzance #441/R est:1000-1500
Works on paper
£380 $700 €555 Portrait of a early woman (25x18cm-10x7in) W/C. 11-Jun-4 Du Mouchelle, Detroit #2084/R
£1300 $2392 €1898 Repairing the net, Cornish lass (38x26cm-15x10in) s. W/C. 10-Jun-4 Morphets, Harrogate #530/R est:1000-1500
£1500 $2505 €2190 Inspecting Granddaughter's needlework prowess (51x33cm-20x13in) s. W/C. 10-Oct-3 Richardson & Smith, Whitby #63/R est:1500-2000
£1500 $2805 €2190 Quiet smoke by the harbour wall (42x28cm-17x11in) s. W/C. 26-Feb-4 Lane, Penzance #170/R est:1500-2000
£1650 $3069 €2409 Who'll buy my caller herrings (35x25cm-14x10in) s. W/C. 2-Mar-4 Bristol Auction Rooms #337/R est:1500-1800
£1991 $3324 €2907 Awaitinf the fleet's return, Newlyn, Cornwall (40x30cm-16x12in) s. W/C. 17-Nov-3 Waddingtons, Toronto #70/R est:1500-2000 (C.D 4400)
£2000 $3340 €2920 Waiting for the boats (38x28cm-15x11in) s.i. W/C. 14-Oct-3 Bearnes, Exeter #337/R est:800-1200
£2036 $3400 €2973 Arranging the nets, Newlyn, Cornwall (29x39cm-11x15in) s. W/C. 17-Nov-3 Waddingtons, Toronto #71/R est:1500-2000 (C.D 4500)
£4500 $7650 €6570 Fishermen's thoughts (51x35cm-20x14in) s. W/C scratching out. 27-Nov-3 Sotheby's, London #424/R est:5000-7000
£4500 $7470 €6570 Watching the fleet set out (47x33cm-19x13in) s. W/C. 2-Oct-3 Lane, Penzance #75/R est:3500-3750

TODE, Knut Gustaf Waldemar (1859-1900) Swedish
£1216 $2177 €1800 Dancing elves (58x96cm-23x38in) s. 8-May-4 Bukowskis, Helsinki #388/R est:1000-1200

TODERI, Grazia (1963-) Italian?
Photographs
£8000 $13360 €11680 London (125x190cm-49x75in) s.d.2001 num.2/5 verso cibachrome on plexiglass prov. 20-Oct-3 Sotheby's, London #52/R est:8000-12000

TODESCHINI, Lucio (1892-1969) Italian
£725 $1188 €1000 Fabbri Bridge, Porta Genova (102x70cm-40x28in) s.i. 27-May-3 Il Ponte, Milan #951/R
£1812 $3207 €2700 Peasant woman with goat (140x100cm-55x39in) s. lit. 1-May-4 Meeting Art, Vercelli #93 est:2500

TODESCHINI, Piero (19/20th C) Italian?
£435 $713 €600 Portrait of woman (70x50cm-28x20in) s.d.XI. 27-May-3 Il Ponte, Milan #937/R
£725 $1188 €1000 Hail Mary (70x60cm-28x24in) s.i. board. 27-May-3 Finarte Semenzato, Milan #141/R est:1000-1300
£725 $1188 €1000 Gallantry (70x60cm-28x24in) s.i. board. 27-May-3 Finarte Semenzato, Milan #142/R est:1000-1300

TODHUNTER, Francis Augustus (1884-1963) American
£250 $400 €365 The picnic. s. canvasboard. 20-Sep-3 Harvey Clar, Oakland #1320
£659 $1100 €962 Repair yard. 18-Oct-3 Harvey Clar, Oakland #1255

TODO GARCIA, Francisco (1922-) Spanish
£1538 $2569 €2200 Buganvillas de Cadaques (40x40cm-16x16in) s.d.1990 s.i.d. prov. 24-Jun-3 Segre, Madrid #173/R est:2500
£2535 $4056 €3600 Columbia coffee (60x60cm-24x24in) s.d.1993 s.i.d.verso prov. 16-Sep-3 Segre, Madrid #165/R

TOEPUT, Lodewyk (1550-1603) Flemish
£3944 $6823 €5600 Portrait of lady (85x68cm-33x27in) 14-Dec-3 Finarte, Venice #71/R est:5500-6500
Works on paper
£1600 $2880 €2336 Woodland scene with buildings in the distance (19x26cm-7x10in) pen brown ink wash black chk. 20-Apr-4 Sotheby's, Olympia #53/R est:2000-3000
£3000 $5490 €4380 River by the edge of a wood, with the sun setting to the left (17x27cm-7x11in) pen brown ink brown blue wash over traces blk chk prov.exhib. 8-Jul-4 Sotheby's, London #14/R est:4000-6000

TOEPUT, Lodewyk (attrib) (1550-1603) Flemish
Works on paper
£361 $650 €527 Fantastic landscape (11x21cm-4x8in) pen ink wash. 21-Jan-4 Doyle, New York #25
£2585 $4627 €3800 Un retable avec des sculptures encadrant un tableau avec une ville (64x49cm-25x19in) i.verso black chk pen brown ink wash prov. 18-Mar-4 Christie's, Paris #17/R est:4000-6000

TOEPUT, Lodewyk (circle) (1550-1603) Flemish
£7931 $13245 €11500 La visitation dans un parc Venitien (102x141cm-40x56in) painted c.1600. 17-Nov-3 Delorme & Bocage, Paris #48/R est:9000-12000

TOFANARI, Sirio (1886-1969) Italian
Sculpture
£14500 $25085 €21170 Female monkey with its young (51x40cm-20x16in) s.d.1933 brown pat bronze black marble base st.f.Lazzeri Firenze. 12-Dec-3 Sotheby's, London #265/R est:10000-15000

TOFANO, Edouardo (attrib) (1838-1920) Italian
£3356 $6007 €5000 Morning in the mountains (33x49cm-13x19in) s. 25-May-4 Finarte Semenzato, Milan #110/R est:5000-6000

TOFFOLI, Louis (1907-1999) French
£922 $1540 €1300 Nature morte (16x22cm-6x9in) s. 20-Jun-3 Drouot Estimations, Paris #173
£1096 $1863 €1600 Paysage du Bresil (27x46cm-11x18in) s. painted 1962. 9-Nov-3 Eric Pillon, Calais #242/R
£1250 $2088 €1800 Attente (33x24cm-13x9in) s. i.verso. 25-Oct-3 Dianous, Marseille #444
£1597 $2668 €2300 Travail (46x27cm-18x11in) s. s.i.d.58 verso. 21-Oct-3 Artcurial Briest, Paris #339/R est:1500-2000
£3357 $5773 €4800 Paysage safed (60x92cm-24x36in) s. 2-Dec-3 Sotheby's, Amsterdam #204/R est:2500-3500
£4396 $7780 €6418 Grande Mere (72x50cm-28x20in) s.i. verso. 27-Apr-4 AB Stockholms Auktionsverk #1173/R est:40000-50000 (S.KR 60000)
£4483 $7486 €6500 Rabbin lisant (74x50cm-29x20in) s. i.verso. 11-Jul-3 Rabourdin & Choppin de Janvry, Paris #29/R
£6164 $9678 €9000 Etameur rouge (73x60cm-29x24in) s. i.verso painted 1980 lit. 20-Apr-3 Deauville, France #140/R est:9000-12000
£6598 $11018 €9500 Moment de reflexion (73x54cm-29x21in) s. 21-Oct-3 Artcurial Briest, Paris #340 est:5000-6000
£6623 $12053 €10000 Les jattes (73x54cm-29x21in) s. painted c.1985 lit. 18-Jun-4 Piasa, Paris #218/R est:10000-15000
£7947 $14464 €12000 Bresil, Bahiane au fournil (73x92cm-29x36in) s. painted 1964 lit. 18-Jun-4 Piasa, Paris #219/R est:12000-15000
£9669 $17694 €14600 Femme a l'ombrelle (73x60cm-29x24in) s. 9-Apr-4 Claude Aguttes, Neuilly #90/R est:8000-10000

TOFT, Albert (1862-1949) British

Sculpture

£4500	$8280	€6570	Hagar (22cm-9in) s. brown pat. bronze verde marble plinth prov.lit. 11-Jun-4 Christie's, London #72/R est:3000-5000

TOFT, Alfonso (1866-1964) British

£1050	$1659	€1523	Extensive landscape in Romney Marsh with cattle and castle (71x100cm-28x39in) s. pair. 2-Sep-3 Bonhams, Oxford #103 est:1000-1500

TOFT-HANSEN, Hans (1888-?) Danish

£251	$450	€366	Snow covered village street (61x79cm-24x31in) s.d.37. 16-Mar-4 Matthew's, Oregon #54/R

TOGNI, Ponziano (1906-) Italian

£950	$1615	€1387	Landscape near Tinizong (54x72cm-21x28in) s.d.1944. 28-Nov-3 Zofingen, Switzerland #3201 est:2500 (S.FR 2100)

TOGORES, Jose de (1893-1970) Spanish

£7971	$13072	€11000	The slave (70x60cm-28x24in) s. 27-May-3 Durán, Madrid #241/R est:10000
£11034	$19862	€16000	Nude in the studio (122x83cm-48x33in) s.d.1951. 26-Jan-4 Ansorena, Madrid #219/R est:12000

TOHAN, Unkoku (1635-1724) Japanese

Works on paper

£2466	$4192	€3600	Landscapes (58x171cm-23x67in) s. Indian ink gold pair of six panel screens. 8-Nov-3 Dr Fritz Nagel, Stuttgart #1896/R est:1500
£42000	$70140	€61320	Spring. Summer (176x376cm-69x148in) ink col gold leaf in six parts pair lit. 12-Nov-3 Christie's, London #43/R est:50000-80000

TOHKA, Sakari (1911-1958) Finnish

Sculpture

£1275	$2372	€1900	Young woman (33cm-13in) s. bronze. 7-Mar-4 Bukowskis, Helsinki #278/R est:700

TOIT, Paul du (1922-1986) South African

£556	$944	€812	On the far end, op die uiterste rand (78x96cm-31x38in) s.d.82 i.verso. 4-Nov-3 Stephan Welz, Johannesburg #696 est:7000-10000 (SA.R 6500)
£756	$1369	€1104	Three aloes in a mountainous landscape (24x39cm-9x15in) s. canvasboard. 30-Mar-4 Stephan Welz, Johannesburg #455/R est:7000-10000 (SA.R 9000)
£769	$1308	€1123	Atmospheric landscape (45x63cm-18x25in) s.d.77 canvas on board. 4-Nov-3 Stephan Welz, Johannesburg #625/R est:10000-15000 (SA.R 9000)
£1176	$2129	€1717	Mountainous landscape with aloes and a tree (44x55cm-17x22in) s.d.1950. 30-Mar-4 Stephan Welz, Johannesburg #457/R est:15000-20000 (SA.R 14000)
£1552	$2591	€2266	Head (60x50cm-24x20in) s.d.99 acrylic. 20-Oct-3 Stephan Welz, Johannesburg #369/R est:6000-9000 (SA.R 18000)
£1817	$3252	€2653	Jester (80x80cm-31x31in) s.d.1999 i. stretcher. 31-May-4 Stephan Welz, Johannesburg #571/R est:10000-15000 (SA.R 22000)
£1880	$3197	€2745	Forest fire (37x62cm-15x24in) s.d.71 canvas on board. 4-Nov-3 Stephan Welz, Johannesburg #631/R est:12000-16000 (SA.R 22000)
£2051	$3487	€2994	Extensive landscape (42x50cm-17x20in) s. canvas on board. 4-Nov-3 Stephan Welz, Johannesburg #626/R est:14000-18000 (SA.R 24000)

TOJETTI, Virgilio (1851-1901) American

£993	$1808	€1500	Nude beauty at the fireplace (20x30cm-8x12in) s. 21-Jun-4 Dorotheum, Vienna #61/R est:1800-2000

TOJNER, Vibeke (20th C) ?

£549	$1000	€802	Abstract landscape (143x125cm-56x49in) 7-Feb-4 Rasmussen, Havnen #4223 (D.KR 6000)

TOKKIE, Rik (20th C) Belgian

£374	$670	€550	Trillingen (97x72cm-38x28in) 22-Mar-4 Amberes, Antwerp #259

TOL, Claes Jacobsz (attrib) (17th C) Dutch

£3819	$6035	€5500	Italianate landscape with a bacchanalia (38x47cm-15x19in) panel. 2-Sep-3 Christie's, Amsterdam #62/R est:3500-4500

TOL, Dominicus van (attrib) (1635-1676) Dutch

£2000	$3620	€3000	Lecon de dessin (29x23cm-11x9in) panel. 1-Apr-4 Credit Municipal, Paris #15/R est:4000-5000
£2083	$3437	€3000	Scholar reading (29x22cm-11x9in) paeln. 3-Jul-3 Dr Fritz Nagel, Stuttgart #463/R est:3900
£2083	$3437	€3000	Woman spinning yarn (28x22cm-11x9in) panel. 3-Jul-3 Dr Fritz Nagel, Stuttgart #464/R est:3900

TOLA, Jose (1943-) Peruvian

£10588	$18000	€15458	Un hombre solitario sin ti - A solitary man without you (150x180cm-59x71in) s.d. painted 2000 prov.exhib. 18-Nov-3 Christie's, Rockefeller NY #128/R est:18000-22000

TOLD, Heinrich (1861-1924) Austrian?

£780	$1303	€1100	Girl from southern Tyrol holding sickle (65x52cm-26x20in) s. 16-Oct-3 Dorotheum, Salzburg #570/R

TOLDT, Alois (19/20th C) Austrian

£307	$561	€460	At the city gate (26x21cm-10x8in) s. panel. 5-Jun-4 Arnold, Frankfurt #744/R
£528	$914	€750	Klausen on the Eisack (31x47cm-12x19in) s. panel. 10-Dec-3 Dorotheum, Vienna #51/R
£528	$914	€750	Mountain in Vintschgau near Meran (31x47cm-12x19in) s.i.verso panel. 10-Dec-3 Dorotheum, Vienna #52/R

TOLE, Charles (1903-1989) New Zealander

£1880	$3195	€2745	The brown house (34x39cm-13x15in) s. board. 27-Nov-3 International Art Centre, Auckland #17/R est:5000-8000 (NZ.D 5000)

TOLE, John (1890-1967) New Zealander

£543	$875	€793	Lillie and cannas (48x38cm-19x15in) s. 20-Aug-3 Dunbar Sloane, Auckland #65 est:2500-5000 (NZ.D 1500)
£1399	$2545	€2043	Maori Pa, Waihi (24x30cm-9x12in) board prov. 29-Jun-4 Peter Webb, Auckland #84/R est:4500-6500 (NZ.D 4000)
£1429	$2586	€2086	Still life with fruit and tulips (61x30cm-24x12in) s. board. 30-Mar-4 Peter Webb, Auckland #153/R est:5000-7000 (NZ.D 4000)

TOLEDO, Francisco (1940-) Mexican

£16471	$28000	€24048	Escarabajo (103x89cm-41x35in) oil sand canvas on masonite painted 1963 prov. 19-Nov-3 Sotheby's, New York #108/R est:35000-45000
£20588	$35000	€30058	Acuatico (102x91cm-40x36in) s.d.65 verso oil sand canvas on masonite prov. 19-Nov-3 Sotheby's, New York #39/R est:50000-60000
£29412	$50000	€42942	La cabra (73x92cm-29x36in) painted c.1965 prov. 19-Nov-3 Sotheby's, New York #109/R est:50000-60000
£32353	$55000	€47235	Mano ripap (56x76cm-22x30in) s. oil sand collage paper on masonite painted 1967 prov. 19-Nov-3 Sotheby's, New York #141/R est:60000-80000
£266667	$490667	€400000	Magician (104x263cm-41x104in) s.i. painted 1970. 10-Jun-4 Christie's, Paris #65/R est:365000-445000

Works on paper

£1800	$3006	€2628	Untitled (24x24cm-9x9in) s.d.63 pen ink W/C prov. 22-Oct-3 Bonhams, New Bond Street #71/R est:2000-3000
£2431	$4059	€3500	Personnage sur fond bleu (47x37cm-19x15in) s. gouache. 21-Oct-3 Artcurial Briest, Paris #631/R est:2000-2500
£3297	$6000	€4814	Cocodrilo y Conejo jugando a futbol (53x41cm-21x16in) s. W/C gouache ink prov. 29-Jun-4 Sotheby's, New York #414/R est:7000-9000
£5294	$9000	€7729	Sin titulo (25x33cm-10x13in) s. gouache executed c.1970. 19-Nov-3 Sotheby's, New York #164/R est:10000-15000
£6145	$11000	€8972	Chango II (18x27cm-7x11in) s. W/C gouache silver leaf exec.1987 prov.exhib. 26-May-4 Sotheby's, New York #178/R est:12000-18000
£8000	$14720	€12000	Primitive mask (21x26cm-8x10in) s. gouache collage W/C exec.c.1968 prov. 10-Jun-4 Christie's, Paris #41/R est:9500-13000
£26667	$49067	€40000	Deers not wanting to touch water (57x77cm-22x30in) s. W/C gouache paper on canvas exec.c.1970. 10-Jun-4 Christie's, Paris #63/R est:48000-65000
£67039	$120000	€97877	Self-portrait IV (81x61cm-32x24in) encaustic oil collage panel exec.1996 prov.exhib. 26-May-4 Sotheby's, New York #45/R est:90000-120000

TOLEDO, Irma Rafaela (1910-2002) Swiss

£1745	$3228	€2600	Still life with bottles, glasses and spoon (45x57cm-18x22in) s.d.53 tempera board. 9-Mar-4 Dorotheum, Vienna #111/R est:2000-2800

TOLL, Emma (1847-1917) Swedish

£654	$1125	€955	Summer landscape, Hemaan (21x15cm-8x6in) s.d.1895 panel. 3-Dec-3 AB Stockholms Auktionsverk #2376/R (S.KR 8500)

TOLLET, Tony (1857-?) French

£4895	$8322	€7000	Petite fille russe devant le kremlin (74x60cm-29x24in) s. 27-Nov-3 Millon & Associes, Paris #155/R est:8000-10000

TOLLI (1953-) Icelandic

£1221	$2038	€1783	Winter landscape (160x150cm-63x59in) s. prov. 7-Oct-3 Rasmussen, Copenhagen #255/R est:15000-18000 (D.KR 13000)

TOLLIVER, Mose (1919-) American

£222	$400	€324	Bird on a branch (61x43cm-24x17in) housepaint on board. 24-Apr-4 Slotin Folk Art, Buford #489/R
£222	$400	€324	Man riding a green horse (38x61cm-15x24in) housepaint on board prov. 24-Apr-4 Slotin Folk Art, Buford #493/R
£222	$400	€324	Freedom bus (36x58cm-14x23in) d.Jan 1993 housepaint on board prov. 24-Apr-4 Slotin Folk Art, Buford #494/R
£240	$400	€350	Purple devil (69x33cm-27x13in) household paint paperboard. 15-Nov-3 Slotin Folk Art, Buford #354/R
£250	$450	€365	Blue moose lady (61x61cm-24x24in) housepaint on board prov. 24-Apr-4 Slotin Folk Art, Buford #491/R
£278	$500	€406	Self portrait with carpet hair (81x41cm-32x16in) housepaint on board carpet scraps. 24-Apr-4 Slotin Folk Art, Buford #490/R
£299	$500	€437	Diane Long looking for food for children during slave times (81x61cm-32x24in) paint board. 15-Nov-3 Slotin Folk Art, Buford #355/R
£299	$500	€437	Man having sex with small woman (61x38cm-24x15in) household paint plywood prov. 15-Nov-3 Slotin Folk Art, Buford #351/R
£306	$550	€447	Sure foot rue (89x41cm-35x16in) housepaint on plywood prov. 24-Apr-4 Slotin Folk Art, Buford #492/R
£306	$550	€447	Hunting scene II (36x43cm-14x17in) housepaint on board prov. 24-Apr-4 Slotin Folk Art, Buford #495/R
£329	$550	€480	Red (64x58cm-25x23in) household paint wood board. 15-Nov-3 Slotin Folk Art, Buford #352/R
£333	$600	€486	Statue of Eve (81x61cm-32x24in) board. 24-Apr-4 Slotin Folk Art, Buford #488/R
£389	$650	€568	Blue face (69x66cm-27x26in) paint board. 15-Nov-3 Slotin Folk Art, Buford #358/R
£479	$800	€699	Erotic large lady with man (86x51cm-34x20in) paint board. 15-Nov-3 Slotin Folk Art, Buford #357/R
£500	$900	€730	On the cross with two birds (86x61cm-34x24in) housepaint on board. 24-Apr-4 Slotin Folk Art, Buford #487/R
£1078	$1800	€1574	Scooter lady (64x46cm-25x18in) household paint wood board prov. 15-Nov-3 Slotin Folk Art, Buford #350/R est:1000-1500

TOLMAN, Stacy (1860-1935) American

£1676	$3000	€2447	View from the First Baptist Church, Providence, Rhode Island (51x41cm-20x16in) prov. 14-May-4 Skinner, Boston #298/R est:3000-5000

TOLOMEO, Carla (1944-) Italian
Sculpture
£3087 $5526 €4600 Chair (162cm-64in) haberdashery sequin. 25-May-4 Sotheby's, Milan #55/R est:3000
£6993 $11888 €10000 Chair and lemons (187cm-74in) wood velvet exec.2003. 28-Nov-3 Farsetti, Prato #140/R est:10000-12000

TOLOSA ALSINA, Aurelio (1861-1938) Spanish
£3425 $5822 €5000 Garden (81x100cm-32x39in) s. exhib. 4-Nov-3 Ansorena, Madrid #350/R est:5000

TOLSON, Edgar (1904-1984) American
Sculpture
£2156 $3600 €3148 Dr Robert Siegel at his anvil (25cm-10in) s.d.1976 wood sold with base prov. 15-Nov-3 Slotin Folk Art, Buford #186/R est:2000-3000

TOLSTOI, Count Fiodr Petrovich (1783-1873) Russian
Sculpture
£2500 $4475 €3650 Scenes from homer's odyssey (16x26cm-6x10in) i. plaster relief set of three. 26-May-4 Sotheby's, London #342/R est:3000-5000

TOM, Jan Bedys (1813-1894) Dutch
£3691 $6534 €5500 Cattle by water (70x120cm-28x47in) s. 28-Apr-4 Schopman, Hamburg #506/R est:2800
£3819 $6378 €5500 Two goats (15x24cm-6x9in) s. panel. 21-Oct-3 Sotheby's, Amsterdam #58/R est:4000-6000

TOM, Jan Bedys (attrib) (1813-1894) Dutch
£629 $1082 €900 Cows in a landscape (14x18cm-6x7in) indis.s. panel. 7-Dec-3 Sotheby's, Amsterdam #594a/R

TOM-PETERSEN, Peter (1861-1926) Danish
£298 $468 €435 From Helsingor Harbour (30x34cm-12x13in) s.d.06. 30-Aug-3 Rasmussen, Havnen #2105 (D.KR 3200)
£476 $867 €695 Evening in a field (42x56cm-17x22in) s.d.1900. 7-Feb-4 Rasmussen, Havnen #2280 (D.KR 5200)
£809 $1504 €1181 Street scene, Vognmagergade, Copenhagen (42x34cm-17x13in) s. 2-Mar-4 Rasmussen, Copenhagen #1508/R (D.KR 9000)
£1253 $2294 €1829 Street in Aeroskobing (43x37cm-17x15in) s.d.1919. 9-Jun-4 Rasmussen, Copenhagen #1956/R est:5000 (D.KR 14000)
£1357 $2430 €1981 Sunny farm yard with woman and children playing (47x63cm-19x25in) s. i.stretcher. 10-May-4 Rasmussen, Vejle #59/R est:10000-12000 (D.KR 15000)

TOMA, Giovacchino (1836-1891) Italian
£2155 $3858 €3146 Portrait of Italian woman (57x38cm-22x15in) s. 12-May-4 Dobiaschofsky, Bern #1026/R est:8000 (S.FR 5000)

TOMA, Giovacchino (attrib) (1836-1891) Italian
£278 $500 €406 Mocking of Christ (61x51cm-24x20in) s.d.1851. 24-Apr-4 Skinner, Boston #190/R

TOMALTY, Terry (1935-) Canadian?
£269 $489 €393 Rosie St Lin (30x41cm-12x16in) s.i. board prov. 5-Feb-4 Heffel, Vancouver #60/R (C.D 650)
£305 $546 €445 Camden Yards (25x30cm-10x12in) s. s.i.verso. 6-May-4 Heffel, Vancouver #143/R (C.D 750)
£495 $842 €723 Hockey night (30x41cm-12x16in) s. s.i.verso prov. 23-Nov-3 Levis, Calgary #139/R (C.D 1100)
£586 $995 €856 The Big O (20x25cm-8x10in) s. i.verso prov. 27-Nov-3 Heffel, Vancouver #156/R (C.D 1300)
£680 $1244 €993 Diamonds at the Ritz (40x50cm-16x20in) s. prov. 1-Jun-4 Joyner Waddington, Toronto #157/R (C.D 1700)
£714 $1229 €1042 Reflections, The Ritz (30x40cm-12x16in) s. 2-Dec-3 Joyner Waddington, Toronto #159/R (C.D 1600)
£766 $1302 €1118 Rodick Gates, McGill (30x40cm-12x16in) s. s.i.verso prov. 27-Nov-3 Heffel, Vancouver #36/R est:1200-1600 (C.D 1700)
£1016 $1819 €1483 Rink de Gaspe Street (30x40cm-12x16in) s. s.i.verso. 27-May-4 Heffel, Vancouver #175/R est:1300-1600 (C.D 2500)
£1280 $2342 €1869 Rink, Baron Byng, Montreal (60x75cm-24x30in) s. 1-Jun-4 Joyner Waddington, Toronto #235/R est:3000-3500 (C.D 3200)
£1689 $2872 €2466 Centre Molson (40x50cm-16x20in) s. s.i.verso prov. 27-Nov-3 Heffel, Vancouver #154/R est:2000-2500 (C.D 3750)
£2642 $4730 €3857 Heritage Classic, Edmonton, Alberta (76x101cm-30x40in) s.i.d.2003. 27-May-4 Heffel, Vancouver #174/R est:4500-5500 (C.D 6500)

TOMANECK, Joseph (1889-?) American
£1125 $1800 €1643 Spring flowers (71x91cm-28x36in) s. s.i.verso on stretcher. 20-Sep-3 Jeffery Burchard, Florida #61/R

TOMASELLI, Fred (1956-) American?
£27933 $50000 €40782 Blue weave (15x25cm-6x10in) s.i.d.1900-95 verso hemp leaves acrylic resin wood panel prov. 12-May-4 Christie's, Rockefeller NY #317/R est:40000-60000
£32934 $55000 €48084 Green Light (122x122cm-48x48in) s.i.d.1993 verso acrylic hemp leaves resin panel prov. 12-Nov-3 Christie's, Rockefeller NY #564/R est:40000-60000
£34916 $62500 €50977 Home (122x122cm-48x48in) s.i.d.1993 verso acrylic pills hemp leaves resin panel prov.exhib. 13-May-4 Sotheby's, New York #396/R est:50000-70000
Works on paper
£3681 $6000 €5374 John-5-22-59 (36x44cm-14x17in) i.d.12-12-94 s.d.12-94 verso prismacolor gouache prov. 23-Sep-3 Christie's, Rockefeller NY #70/R est:3000-5000

TOMASELLO, Luis (1915-) Argentinian
Sculpture
£1360 $2311 €1986 Reflection No.2 (65x65cm-26x26in) polychrome painted wood relief exhib.prov. 5-Nov-3 AB Stockholms Auktionsverk #941/R est:15000-18000 (S.KR 18000)
£3958 $6531 €5700 Atmosphere chromoplastique no 257 (90x90cm-35x35in) s.d.1970 verso wood relief prov. 2-Jul-3 Cornette de St.Cyr, Paris #201/R est:4000-5000
£5495 $9725 €8023 Atmosphere cromoplastique Number 187 (121x121cm-48x48in) s.i.d.1968 painted wood relief prov. 27-Apr-4 AB Stockholms Auktionsverk #1235/R est:80000-100000 (S.KR 75000)
£6159 $10101 €8500 Atmosphere chromoplastique n (85x85x8cm-33x33x3in) s.i.d.1976 paint wood. 27-May-3 Sotheby's, Amsterdam #450/R est:5000-7000

TOMASSI, G (19th C) Italian
£1100 $2024 €1606 Still life of mixed flowers, fruit and nuts with other objects (73x100cm-29x39in) s. 29-Mar-4 Bonhams, Bath #96/R est:1000-1500

TOMASZEWSKI, Henryk (20th C) Polish
Works on paper
£260 $431 €380 Hommage a Jean Paul Sartre (19x12cm-7x5in) ink pen exec. 1961. 2-Oct-3 Agra, Warsaw #5/R (P.Z 1700)

TOMBA, Casimiro (1857-1929) Italian
Works on paper
£667 $1207 €1000 Girl at the park (76x58cm-30x23in) s.i. W/C. 30-Mar-4 Babuino, Rome #337/R
£4000 $7360 €6000 Esclave enfilant sa babouche (51x38cm-20x15in) s.i. W/C. 14-Jun-4 Gros & Delettrez, Paris #128/R est:6000-8000

TOMEA, Fiorenzo (1910-1960) Italian
£1517 $2534 €2200 Peasant woman from Cadore (51x32cm-20x13in) s. s.d.1951 verso board. 13-Nov-3 Finarte Semenzato, Rome #434 est:1800-2200
£2000 $3680 €3000 Candles (18x24cm-7x9in) s. cardboard on canvas. 8-Jun-4 Finarte Semenzato, Milan #429/R est:3000-3500
£3056 $4828 €4400 Candles (16x21cm-6x8in) cardboard. 6-Sep-3 Meeting Art, Vercelli #485 est:4000
£3623 $5942 €5000 Sunset (30x39cm-12x15in) s. s.i.d.1943 verso cardboard on canvas prov. 27-May-3 Sotheby's, Milan #141/R est:5000-6000
£3873 $6778 €5500 Still life with candles (33x45cm-13x18in) s. cardboard prov. 17-Dec-3 Il Ponte, Milan #1101/R est:5000-6000
£5035 $8559 €7200 Candles (40x50cm-16x20in) s. prov. 24-Nov-3 Christie's, Milan #173/R est:3500-5000
£5172 $8638 €7500 Lanterns (41x42cm-16x17in) s. s.i.d.1942 verso board. 17-Nov-3 Sant Agostino, Torino #230/R est:7000-9000
£5705 $10211 €8500 Landscape in Cadore (50x40cm-20x16in) s. s.i.verso exhib. 25-May-4 Sotheby's, Milan #56/R est:8000
£6207 $10366 €9000 Candles (48x59cm-19x23in) s. painted 1938. 17-Nov-3 Sant Agostino, Torino #239/R est:8000-10000
£6884 $11290 €9500 Pere e mele (40x60cm-16x24in) s. i.d.1951 verso. 31-May-3 Farsetti, Prato #622/R est:5000-7000
£6884 $11290 €9500 Candele (40x50cm-16x20in) s. 31-May-3 Farsetti, Prato #623/R est:4000-6000
£6993 $11888 €10000 Venice (32x44cm-13x17in) s. canvas on cardboard painted 1940. 29-Nov-3 Farsetti, Prato #430/R est:10000-12000
£7343 $12483 €10500 Still life (50x60cm-20x24in) s.d.1959. 24-Nov-3 Christie's, Milan #115/R est:4000-6000
£7692 $13077 €11000 Fresh flowers (50x40cm-20x16in) s. s.d.1942 verso board. 29-Nov-3 Farsetti, Prato #431/R est:10000-12000
£7971 $13072 €11000 Nevicata (40x50cm-16x20in) s. s.d.1957 verso. 31-May-3 Farsetti, Prato #625/R est:6500-7500
£16667 $27333 €23000 Finestra a Zoppe (71x61cm-28x24in) s. 31-May-3 Farsetti, Prato #621/R est:8000-10000
Works on paper
£811 $1427 €1200 Landscape (44x44cm-17x17in) s. W/C ink. 24-May-4 Christie's, Milan #31

TOMEC, Heinrich (1863-1928) Austrian
£1500 $2775 €2190 View of Prague (88x98cm-35x39in) s. 10-Mar-4 Sotheby's, Olympia #235/R est:1500-2000

TOMINETTI, Achille (1848-1917) Italian
£2781 $5062 €4200 Landscape (52x98cm-20x39in) s. 17-Jun-4 Finarte Semenzato, Milan #286/R est:2000-3000
£10490 $18042 €15000 Back to the barn (66x92cm-26x36in) s. 3-Dec-3 Stadion, Trieste #1014/R est:6000-8000

TOMINZ, Alfredo (1854-1936) Italian
£2797 $4811 €4000 Riders (60x40cm-24x16in) s. 3-Dec-3 Stadion, Trieste #981/R est:3500-4500
£8237 $15321 €12026 Roman contest (64x115cm-25x45in) s.d.05. 6-Mar-4 Dorotheum, Prague #19/R est:400000-600000 (C.KR 400000)
£8333 $14167 €12000 Al Trotto (58x37cm-23x15in) both s.d.97 pair. 28-Oct-3 Christie's, Amsterdam #196/R est:8000-12000
£12914 $23503 €19500 Horse market in Duino (56x115cm-22x45in) s.i. 18-Jun-4 Stadion, Trieste #464/R est:10000-15000

TOMINZ, Alfredo (attrib) (1854-1936) Italian
£1056 $1827 €1500 Travelling (63x40cm-25x16in) cardboard. 9-Dec-3 Finarte Semenzato, Milan #46/R est:1500-1800

TOMINZ, Giuseppe (attrib) (1790-1866) Italian
£8392 $14266 €12000 Family portrait (79x84cm-31x33in) 24-Nov-3 Dorotheum, Vienna #190/R est:3000-4000

TOMKIN, William Stephen (1861-1940) British
Works on paper
£320 $525 €467 Wind against tide (34x16cm-13x6in) s.d.1909 i.verso W/C. 3-Jun-3 Fellows & Sons, Birmingham #94/R
£340 $568 €493 Steam ship with sailing boats off the shore (18x34cm-7x13in) s.d.1910 W/C. 21-Jun-3 Lacy Scott, Bury St.Edmunds #440/R
£440 $726 €642 Sailing boats off Folkstone. North Sea. Ships moored of busy harbour (12x22cm-5x9in) s.d.1896 W/C three one frame. 4-Jul-3 Honiton Galleries, Honiton #37/R

TOMLIN, Bradley Walker (1899-1953) American
£125749 $210000 €183594 Number 14 (51x46cm-20x18in) s.verso painted 1949 prov.exhib. 11-Nov-3 Christie's, Rockefeller NY #19/R est:70000-90000

TOMLINSON, William (19th C) American
£378 $650 €552 Winter landscape (71x97cm-28x38in) s. 7-Dec-3 William Jenack, New York #366

TOMMASI FERRONI, Riccardo (1934-2000) Italian
£361 $600 €523 Studio fer un giolo Toruquivo. s. 14-Jun-3 Fallon, Copake #91/R
£1931 $3225 €2800 Landscape with Achilles and Chirone (35x50cm-14x20in) s. s.i.d.1994 verso copper. 13-Nov-3 Finarte Semenzato, Rome #238/R est:2000-2500
£2993 $5088 €4280 From the Orlando Furioso (35x50cm-14x20in) s. cardboard prov. 18-Nov-3 Babuino, Rome #377/R est:1600-1800
Works on paper
£552 $921 €800 Study (40x30cm-16x12in) s. ink. 13-Nov-3 Finarte Semenzato, Rome #181
£1241 $1986 €1800 Bull (23x33cm-9x13in) s. drawing. 13-Mar-3 Galleria Pace, Milan #67/R est:2100-2700

TOMMASI, Adolfo (1851-1933) Italian
£1364 $2318 €1950 Femme au chapeau. Jeune garcon dans la campagne (14x9cm-6x4in) s. pair. 27-Nov-3 Millon & Associes, Paris #178/R est:2000-2500
£3525 $5781 €4900 Houses on the canal (41x27cm-16x11in) s. s.i.verso board. 10-Jun-3 Pandolfini, Florence #162/R est:6000-7000
£5333 $9813 €8000 Street in San Gervasio (25x15cm-10x6in) s. board. 10-Jun-4 Christie's, Rome #171/R est:2000-3000
£33557 $60067 €50000 Maternity (170x113cm-67x44in) s. painted 1895 exhib.lit. 25-May-4 Finarte Semenzato, Milan #193/R est:60000-70000

TOMMASI, Angiolo (1858-1923) Italian
£500 $895 €750 Lady in courtyard (20x19cm-8x7in) s. board. 12-May-4 Stadion, Trieste #645/R
£1379 $2303 €2000 Portrait of girl (19x13cm-7x5in) s. board. 14-Nov-3 Farsetti, Prato #528/R est:1600-2000
£2759 $5103 €4000 Promenade en bord de mer. Pecheur avec son filet (10x16cm-4x6in) s. panel pair. 16-Feb-4 Horta, Bruxelles #153 est:2000-2500
£4027 $7530 €6000 In the woods (19x13cm-7x5in) s. board prov. 25-Feb-4 Porro, Milan #26/R est:7000
£10070 $17320 €14400 Paysage lacustre avec pecheurs (10x29cm-4x11in) two s. panel set of three. 8-Dec-3 Horta, Bruxelles #90 est:1800-2200
£11921 $21695 €18000 Lake landscapes (10x29cm-4x11in) s. board set of 3. 21-Jun-4 Pandolfini, Florence #132/R est:18000-19000

TOMMASI, Ghigo (1906-) Italian
£690 $1152 €1000 Hunters resting (58x68cm-23x27in) s. s.i.d.1954 verso board. 14-Nov-3 Farsetti, Prato #401/R

TOMMASI, Ludovico (1866-1941) Italian
£935 $1534 €1300 Women chatting (17x25cm-7x10in) s.i.d.1925 cardboard. 10-Jun-3 Pandolfini, Florence #164/R est:1500-1800
£1100 $1870 €1606 Figures in a wooded landscape (36x26cm-14x10in) s.d.909 board. 1-Dec-3 Bonhams, Bath #133 est:600-800
£1620 $2802 €2300 Study of geraniums (35x25cm-14x10in) s. board. 9-Dec-3 Pandolfini, Florence #255/R est:2500-2700
£1700 $2890 €2482 Woman seated in a garden terrace (30x18cm-12x7in) s.d.97 board. 1-Dec-3 Bonhams, Bath #132/R est:800-1200
£3380 $5848 €4800 Under trees (45x37cm-18x15in) s. cardboard. 11-Dec-3 Christie's, Rome #169/R
£4667 $8587 €7000 The Arno in Bellariva (32x60cm-13x24in) s.d.88. 10-Jun-4 Christie's, Rome #180/R est:5000-7000
£4965 $8291 €7000 Tuscan farms (31x45cm-12x18in) s. cardboard. 14-Oct-3 Finarte Semenzato, Milan #184/R
£8054 $14416 €12000 Market in Viareggio (47x45cm-19x18in) s. cardboard. 25-May-4 Finarte Semenzato, Milan #12/R est:4000-5000
£9060 $16943 €13500 Landscape with farm (13x21cm-5x8in) s. card prov. 25-Feb-4 Porro, Milan #6/R est:10000-12000
Works on paper
£347 $627 €520 Trees (33x25cm-13x10in) s. sanguine exhib.lit. 2-Apr-4 Farsetti, Prato #531
£483 $806 €700 Landscape (50x32cm-20x13in) s. pastel. 14-Nov-3 Farsetti, Prato #509

TOMMASI, Publio de (1849-1914) Italian
£1268 $2104 €1800 Country scenes (40x21cm-16x8in) s.d.1927 canvas on board two. 11-Jun-3 Christie's, Rome #116/R est:1500-2000
Works on paper
£1102 $1873 €1609 Suitor (72x51cm-28x20in) s.i.d.87. 24-Nov-3 Sotheby's, Melbourne #314/R (A.D 2600)
£2768 $4347 €4041 Untitled, the tarot card reader (74x131cm-29x52in) s. W/C. 1-Sep-3 Shapiro, Sydney #356/R est:10000-15000 (A.D 6810)
£2768 $4347 €4041 Untitled, the tavern serenade (74x106cm-29x42in) s. W/C. 1-Sep-3 Shapiro, Sydney #357/R est:10000-15000 (A.D 6810)
£4508 $7303 €6582 The toast (50x73cm-20x29in) s.i. W/C. 30-Jul-3 Goodman, Sydney #204/R est:9000-12000 (A.D 11000)

TOMMASI, T (19th C) ?
£1340 $2170 €1943 Interior scene with girl and parrot (58x48cm-23x19in) s. 4-Aug-3 Rasmussen, Vejle #161/R est:15000 (D.KR 14000)

TOMOS, Gwyneth (20th C) British
£260 $468 €380 Farmstead at Trawsfynydd (28x43cm-11x17in) s. board. 24-Apr-4 Rogers Jones, Clwyd #164

TOMS, Carel (20th C) British
Works on paper
£300 $543 €438 Fort Grey, Guernsey (18x30cm-7x12in) s.d.89 W/C. 1-Apr-4 Martel Maides, Guernsey #210/R

TOMS, Carl (20th C) ?
Works on paper
£400 $632 €580 Miss Vivien Leigh, costume design (37x25cm-15x10in) s.i. W/C. 3-Sep-3 Bonhams, Bury St Edmunds #375

TOMSCHICZEK, Peter (1940-) ?
Works on paper
£1233 $2096 €1800 Composition in brown (55x76cm-22x30in) s.d.88 mixed media collage. 5-Nov-3 Hugo Ruef, Munich #1262 est:1800
£1507 $2562 €2200 Composition in blue (50x50cm-20x20in) s.d.88 mixed media. 5-Nov-3 Hugo Ruef, Munich #1260 est:2000
£2270 $3790 €3200 Object picture with jeans (98x80cm-39x31in) s.i.d.75 verso collage mixed media. 16-Oct-3 Dorotheum, Salzburg #741/R est:4000-5000
£3425 $5822 €5000 Composition in red (15x13cm-6x5in) s.d.88/89 mixed media collage. 5-Nov-3 Hugo Ruef, Munich #1263/R est:3800

TOMSON, Clifton (1775-1828) British
£900 $1530 €1314 Carriage horse and dog (61x74cm-24x29in) s.indis.i.indis.d. 28-Oct-3 Henry Adams, Chichester #430/R
£4800 $8160 €7008 Fulford with jockey up (74x97cm-29x38in) s.i.d.1817 prov. 19-Nov-3 Sotheby's, Olympia #14/R est:3000-5000

TOMSON, Clifton (attrib) (1775-1828) British
£650 $1060 €949 Mare and foal beside a river (17x21cm-7x8in) 24-Sep-3 Dreweatt Neate, Newbury #111/R

TON, Konstantin Andreevich (1794-1881) Russian
Works on paper
£3000 $5370 €4380 Architectural drawing of the Monastery of San Patrizio and San Isidore, Rome (20x25cm-8x10in) W/C ink. 26-May-4 Sotheby's, London #8/R est:3000-4000

TONDINO, Tristan (20th C) Canadian
£258 $467 €377 Staten Island ferry (61x51cm-24x20in) s. s.i.verso. 18-Apr-4 Levis, Calgary #581/R (C.D 625)
£258 $467 €377 Did you see that? (13x18cm-5x7in) s. s.i.verso. 18-Apr-4 Levis, Calgary #583/R (C.D 625)

TONDOS, Stanislaw (1854-1917) Polish
Works on paper
£1556 $2738 €2272 Venice (72x51cm-28x20in) s. W/C cardboard exec.1885. 23-May-4 Agra, Warsaw #21/R (P.Z 11000)

TONDU, Andre (1903-1980) French
£946 $1693 €1400 L'attente (64x49cm-25x19in) s.d.30 cardboard. 5-May-4 Coutau Begarie, Paris #48a

TONELLI, Carlos (1937-) South American
£735 $1250 €1073 Copper jug and orchid (53x70cm-21x28in) s.d.86. 25-Nov-3 Galeria y Remates, Montevideo #25/R

TONEY, Anthony (1913-) American
£375 $600 €548 Decade of confrontation (102x152cm-40x60in) s.d.1970 s.d.verso. 20-Sep-3 Bunte, Elgin #1290
£734 $1300 €1072 Cityscape (91x152cm-36x60in) s.d. i.verso. 1-May-4 Harvey Clar, Oakland #1235

TONG KAI (17th C) Chinese
Works on paper
£11583 $19344 €16911 Various subjects (17x10cm-7x4in) artist seal ink col silk 23 leaves album. 27-Oct-3 Sotheby's, Hong Kong #308/R est:50000-70000 (HK.D 150000)

TONGE, Lammert van der (1871-1937) Dutch
£726 $1335 €1060 Toy horse (36x27cm-14x11in) s. 14-Jun-4 Waddingtons, Toronto #222/R est:1000-1500 (C.D 1800)
£2301 $4165 €3359 Mother and children by a window (45x54cm-18x21in) s. prov. 1-Apr-4 Heffel, Vancouver #100/R est:2500-3500 (C.D 5500)

TONGEREN, Jan van (1897-1991) Dutch
£5594 $9510 €8000 Still life with basket (55x70cm-22x28in) s.d.75 prov. 25-Nov-3 Christie's, Amsterdam #193/R est:6000-8000
£7692 $13231 €11000 Stilleven tegen rose fond (65x75cm-26x30in) s.d.1976 prov. 2-Dec-3 Sotheby's, Amsterdam #28/R est:4000-6000

TONGERLOO, Frans van (1882-) Belgian
£805 $1426 €1200 Rade d'Anvers (90x123cm-35x48in) s.d.1927. 27-Apr-4 Campo & Campo, Antwerp #262/R

TONIN, Rodolfo (1959-) Italian
£578 $1052 €850 Summer detail (70x80cm-28x31in) s. 6-Feb-4 Galleria Rosenberg, Milan #114/R

TONIOLO, Leopoldo (1833-1908) Italian
£18000 $32760 €26280 Beauty asleep in a hammock (294x127cm-116x50in) s.d.1877. 15-Jun-4 Sotheby's, London #137/R est:12000-18000

TONK, Ernest (1889-1968) American
£824 $1400 €1203 Hell raisers (61x76cm-24x30in) s.d.1943 prov. 1-Nov-3 Santa Fe Art, Santa Fe #101/R est:2000-3000
£837 $1515 €1222 Out of the western night (53x54cm-21x21in) s. i.verso board. 1-Apr-4 Heffel, Vancouver #98/R est:2500-3000 (C.D 2000)
£1324 $2250 €1933 Trail boss (61x76cm-24x30in) s.d.1953 canvas on masonite panel prov. 1-Nov-3 Santa Fe Art, Santa Fe #224/R est:2000-3000

TONKS, Henry (1862-1937) British
Works on paper
£1500 $2685 €2190 Resting among the sand hills (23x34cm-9x13in) s.d.1904 pencil W/C. 14-May-4 Christie's, Kensington #497/R est:700-1000
£1511 $2750 €2206 Conversation then turned on Tonks (32x40cm-13x16in) i. W/C ink pencil prov. 29-Jun-4 Sotheby's, New York #177/R est:1000-1500

TONNA, Jean Baptiste (18th C) French
Works on paper
£260 $478 €380 St, Sebastian (45x32cm-18x13in) i.verso black white chk htd white. 8-Jun-4 Bonhams, Knightsbridge #57/R

TONNANCOUR, Jacques de (1917-) Canadian
£1786 $3071 €2608 Winter landscape (44x58cm-17x23in) s.d.66 board. 2-Dec-3 Joyner Waddington, Toronto #200/R est:5000-6000 (C.D 4000)
Works on paper
£622 $1076 €908 Fossile 7 (61x61cm-24x24in) s.d.78 verso mixed media. 15-Dec-3 Iegor de Saint Hippolyte, Montreal #11 (C.D 1400)
£711 $1230 €1038 Le jongleur (51x51cm-20x20in) s.d.1968 mixed media. 15-Dec-3 Iegor de Saint Hippolyte, Montreal #12 (C.D 1600)

TONNESSEN, Bente (1944-) Norwegian
Works on paper
£516 $831 €753 Center piece (75x105cm-30x41in) s. W/C. 25-Aug-3 Blomqvist, Lysaker #1335/R (N.KR 6000)

TOOGOOD, Romeo (1902-1966) British
Works on paper
£400 $664 €584 Man with a burden (33x25cm-13x10in) s. W/C exhib. 1-Oct-3 John Ross, Belfast #269

TOORENVLIET, Abraham II (attrib) (1682-1735) Dutch
£498 $796 €727 Idyllic landscape with sheep and herders (46x37cm-18x15in) s. 16-Sep-3 Philippe Schuler, Zurich #5475 (S.FR 1100)

TOORENVLIET, Jacob (attrib) (1635-1719) Dutch
£4027 $7409 €6000 Cobbler family in workshop (111x90cm-44x35in) 25-Mar-4 Dr Fritz Nagel, Stuttgart #606/R est:7000
£6250 $10188 €9000 Cobbler and wife in workshop (111x90cm-44x35in) 25-Sep-3 Dr Fritz Nagel, Stuttgart #1257/R est:11000

TOOROP, Charley (1891-1955) Dutch
£7333 $13420 €11000 Landscape near Bergen (80x100cm-31x39in) s. exhib. 7-Jun-4 Glerum, Amsterdam #109/R est:12000-15000
£12587 $21650 €18000 Klein stilleven (40x38cm-16x15in) init. s.i.d.Dec 1927 verso. 2-Dec-3 Sotheby's, Amsterdam #19/R est:14000-18000
£62937 $108252 €90000 Beemster - bloeiende boom (76x105cm-30x41in) s. s.i.d.1940 verso prov.exhib.lit. 2-Dec-3 Sotheby's, Amsterdam #7/R est:25000-30000
Works on paper
£1141 $2099 €1700 Portrait of Madame Fauconnier (57x46cm-22x18in) mono. chl wash. 26-Mar-4 Ketterer, Hamburg #672/R est:1500-1800

TOOROP, Jan Th (1858-1928) Dutch
£18667 $33600 €28000 Preparing the mael (53x66cm-21x26in) s.d.83 prov. 20-Apr-4 Sotheby's, Amsterdam #236/R est:18000-25000
£38462 $66154 €55000 Interieur with a girl from Walcheren (30x38cm-12x15in) s.d.1904 canvas on panel prov.exhib.lit. 2-Dec-3 Sotheby's, Amsterdam #8/R est:35000-50000
Prints
£3716 $6541 €5500 Boy and girl digging potatoes in the dunes (14x19cm-6x7in) s.i.d.1904 col wash orange woodcut prov. 19-May-4 Sotheby's, Amsterdam #385/R est:800-1200
Works on paper
£800 $1448 €1200 Eglise St Joseph, Nimegue (40x14cm-16x6in) W/C. 30-Mar-4 Campo, Vlaamse Kaai #173
£966 $1612 €1400 Author and muse (60x47cm-24x19in) mono. mixed media lit. 10-Jul-3 Allgauer, Kempten #2368/R
£1007 $1862 €1500 Farmer returning home (9x18cm-4x7in) s. ink. 15-Mar-4 Sotheby's, Amsterdam #103/R est:1500-2500
£1051 $1850 €1534 Madonna and Child (30x20cm-12x8in) s.d.1922 graphite pencil. 28-May-4 Aspire, Cleveland #116/R est:1500-2500
£1164 $1979 €1700 Woman in profile (16x11cm-6x4in) pencil. 5-Nov-3 Vendue Huis, Gravenhage #396/R est:1200-1500
£1867 $3435 €2800 Portrait of a woman (18x14cm-7x6in) s.d.1925 pencil. 9-Jun-4 Christie's, Amsterdam #16/R est:2800-3500
£2657 $4571 €3800 View on Zierikzee (11x15cm-4x6in) s.d.1916 W/C black chk exhib. 2-Dec-3 Sotheby's, Amsterdam #232/R est:3000-5000
£2899 $4754 €4000 View of city (30x42cm-12x17in) s. pencil. 27-May-3 Sotheby's, Amsterdam #323/R est:6000-9000
£4000 $7360 €6000 Portrait of D Isna Zaratskij (24x19cm-9x7in) s.i.d.1927 gouache W/C pencil lit. 9-Jun-4 Christie's, Amsterdam #14/R est:6000-8000
£4000 $7360 €6000 Self portrait (25x19cm-10x7in) s.i.d.1926 pencil prov. 9-Jun-4 Christie's, Amsterdam #17/R est:4000-6000
£4667 $8587 €7000 Portrait of Jopie Jurriaan Kok (17x12cm-7x5in) s.i.d.1906 pencil W/C prov. 9-Jun-4 Christie's, Amsterdam #18/R est:5000-7000
£4667 $8540 €7000 Children at the pump (10x15cm-4x6in) s.d.1903 W/C gouache. 7-Jun-4 Glerum, Amsterdam #28/R est:3000-4000
£5072 $8319 €7000 View over the dunes (10x15cm-4x6in) s.d.1907 col chk pencil. 27-May-3 Sotheby's, Amsterdam #472/R est:1000-1500
£8696 $14261 €12000 Portrait of Lou Wiener (51x34cm-20x13in) s.i.d.1920 black chk pastel. 27-May-3 Sotheby's, Amsterdam #507/R est:3000-4000

TOOTILL, John (20th C) New Zealander
£1692 $2876 €2470 Kete (122x122cm-48x48in) s. oil paper on canvas painted 2001. 27-Nov-3 International Art Centre, Auckland #140/R est:4000-6000 (NZ.D 4500)

TOOVEY, Edwin (1835-1900) British
Works on paper
£1678 $2853 €2400 Paysage anglais vallonne avec ferme (38x59cm-15x23in) s.d.1862 W/C gouache. 1-Dec-3 Palais de Beaux Arts, Brussels #381/R est:2000-3000

TOPELIUS-ACKE, Eva (1855-1929) Finnish
£3472 $5799 €5000 From Brahestad (35x28cm-14x11in) s.d.26/3-1900. 26-Oct-3 Bukowskis, Helsinki #279/R est:1500

TOPETE, Juan Bautista (1936-) Spanish
£296 $545 €450 Peaks in the Sierra Telera (56x81cm-22x32in) s.d.98. 22-Jun-4 Durán, Madrid #88/R

TOPFFER, Rodolphe (1799-1846) Swiss
£432 $717 €626 Alpine excursion (26x22cm-10x9in) 13-Jun-3 Zofingen, Switzerland #2381/R (S.FR 950)

TOPFFER, Wolfgang Adam (1766-1847) Swiss
£4310 $7716 €6293 Paysage avec bergeres pres d'un etang (21x38cm-8x15in) board. 14-May-4 Dobiaschofsky, Bern #47/R est:12000 (S.FR 10000)
£7263 $13000 €10604 River landscape with view of Saleve (26x33cm-10x13in) i.verso paper on board. 27-May-4 Sotheby's, New York #113/R est:10000-15000
£11732 $21000 €17129 Washerwomen in a grotto (18x21cm-7x8in) panel. 27-May-4 Sotheby's, New York #114/R est:10000-15000
Works on paper
£430 $744 €628 Monsieur assis (32x21cm-13x8in) pencil. 9-Dec-3 Sotheby's, Zurich #3/R (S.FR 950)
£862 $1543 €1259 Le bonimenteur (12x19cm-5x7in) s. wash ink W/C. 13-May-4 Pierre Berge, Paris #2/R (S.FR 2000)
£1078 $1929 €1574 Tree in landscape (23x21cm-9x8in) mono. pen wash. 14-May-4 Dobiaschofsky, Bern #15/R est:1800 (S.FR 2500)
£1145 $1947 €1672 Young woman sitting on stone (23x18cm-9x7in) pencil W/C. 5-Nov-3 Dobiaschofsky, Bern #1205 est:450 (S.FR 2600)
£3524 $5991 €5145 Landscape with waterfall and woman (28x37cm-11x15in) mono. W/C. 7-Nov-3 Dobiaschofsky, Bern #14/R est:5000 (S.FR 8000)
£4846 $8238 €7075 Vue de Savoie (21x27cm-8x11in) gouache. 7-Nov-3 Dobiaschofsky, Bern #30/R est:9000 (S.FR 11000)

TOPFFER, Wolfgang Adam (attrib) (1766-1847) Swiss
£1457 $2651 €2200 Etude de cimes d'arbres (29x41cm-11x16in) paper on canvas. 21-Jun-4 Tajan, Paris #127/R est:2000-3000

TOPHAM, Francis William (1808-1877) British
£260 $458 €380 Blind beggar (24x18cm-9x7in) panel. 19-May-4 Christie's, Kensington #621
Works on paper
£1600 $2912 €2336 The flower seller (61x49cm-24x19in) s.d.1867 pencil W/C bodycol prov. 1-Jul-4 Christie's, Kensington #164/R est:700-900
£1800 $3330 €2628 Feeding the chicks (49x37cm-19x15in) s. W/C. 9-Mar-4 Bonhams, New Bond Street #113/R est:2000-3000
£3243 $6130 €4800 Late again! (27x20cm-11x8in) s.d.1856 i.verso W/C htd white. 17-Feb-4 Whyte's, Dublin #159/R est:2000-3000

TOPHAM, Frank William Warwick (1838-1929) British
£1700 $2720 €2482 Lady in waiting with a servant on a terrace with romanesque arcade beyond (104x79cm-41x31in) s.d.1896 canvas on canvas. 17-Sep-3 Brightwells, Leominster #906 est:2000-3000
Works on paper
£270 $483 €394 Mother at prayer with infant alongside (33x23cm-13x9in) s. W/C. 7-May-4 Mallams, Oxford #254/R
£300 $537 €438 Soldiers three (33x23cm-13x9in) s. W/C. 7-May-4 Mallams, Oxford #253/R

TOPHAM, William Thirston (1886-1967) Canadian
£215 $335 €312 Fishing on the Miramichi River (20x25cm-8x10in) s.i. oil on tin prov. 26-Mar-3 Walker's, Ottawa #420/R (C.D 500)
£473 $804 €691 Miramichi River (21x25cm-8x10in) s. s.i.verso prov. 23-Nov-3 Levis, Calgary #140/R (C.D 1050)

TOPIAK, Agnes (1905-?) North American
Sculpture
£1261 $2144 €1841 Standing Inuit woman (11cm-4in) s. mottled dark soapstone exec.c.1953. 3-Nov-3 Waddingtons, Toronto #44/R est:1500-2000 (C.D 2800)

TOPOLSKI, Feliks (1907-1989) Polish
Works on paper
£360 $601 €526 Tea drinkers in Lafanukao (34x26cm-13x10in) s.d.1944 pencil. 21-Oct-3 Bonhams, Knightsbridge #77/R
£500 $885 €730 Rehearsing Pinter (41x29cm-16x11in) s.i. pencil ink wax crayon. 27-Apr-4 Bonhams, Knightsbridge #31/R
£600 $1074 €876 Military brothel in Saigon (35x24cm-14x9in) s.i.d.1950 pencil. 14-May-4 Christie's, Kensington #556

TOPOR, Roland (1938-1997) French
Works on paper
£395 $726 €600 Chute (24x17cm-9x7in) s.i. ink dr prov. 27-Jun-4 Versailles Encheres #165
£537 $1004 €800 Sans titre (26x20cm-10x8in) s.d.1968 ink col ink. 29-Feb-4 Versailles Encheres #320/R
£4514 $7538 €6500 Homme debout (50x35cm-20x14in) s.d.1976 ink india ink col chk. 21-Oct-3 Christie's, Paris #118/R est:400-600

TOPORKOV, D A (1885-1937) Russian
£1944 $3500 €2838 In the port (34x60cm-13x24in) 24-Apr-4 Shishkin Gallery, Moscow #6/R est:4000-5000

TOPP, Arnold (1887-1945) German
Works on paper
£333 $600 €500 Constructivist composition (18x14cm-7x6in) mono.i.d. Indian ink on pencil. 24-Apr-4 Reiss & Sohn, Konigstein #5714/R
£5036 $8259 €7000 Southern landscape (29x25cm-11x10in) s. s.d. verso pastel. 4-Jun-3 Ketterer, Hamburg #930/R est:5000-7000

TOPPELIUS, Woldemar (1858-1933) Russian
£845 $1462 €1200 Coastal landscape from Aaland (39x55cm-15x22in) s. 13-Dec-3 Hagelstam, Helsinki #118/R
£909 $1545 €1300 Coastal landscape with breakers (30x48cm-12x19in) s.d.04. 29-Nov-3 Bukowskis, Helsinki #203/R
£1284 $2298 €1900 Seascape with vessels by the coast (44x67cm-17x26in) s.d.94. 8-May-4 Bukowskis, Helsinki #66/R est:1800-2200
£1333 $2387 €2000 Farmyard (33x48cm-13x19in) s. canvas on board. 15-May-4 Hagelstam, Helsinki #81/R est:2000
£1408 $2437 €2000 Beached boat (50x41cm-20x16in) s.d.1926. 13-Dec-3 Hagelstam, Helsinki #119/R est:2000
£2238 $3804 €3200 Skagerak (32x45cm-13x18in) s.d.1901 canvas on board exhib. 29-Nov-3 Bukowskis, Helsinki #207/R est:2000-2500

TOPPELIUS-KISELEFF, Marga (1862-1924) Finnish
Works on paper
£1007 $1872 €1500 Hollyhocks (37x61cm-15x24in) s.d.1895 W/C. 7-Mar-4 Bukowskis, Helsinki #461/R est:700

TOPPI, Mario (1934-) American/Italian
£270 $500 €394 Untitled (61x76cm-24x30in) s.i.verso tempera board painted c.1960. 13-Mar-4 DeFina, Austinburg #958/R
£270 $500 €394 Untitled (71x99cm-29x39in) s. tempera board. 13-Mar-4 DeFina, Austinburg #959/R
£1620 $2900 €2365 Idillio (64x84cm-25x33in) s. board. 20-Mar-4 Selkirks, St. Louis #522/R est:800-1200

TOPPING, James (1879-1949) American
£1061 $1900 €1549 Landscape (43x51cm-17x20in) s. board. 8-May-4 Susanin's, Chicago #6156/R est:1500-2500

TORAL, Cristobal (1938-) Spanish
£3867 $7000 €5646 Grapes (41x31cm-16x12in) board. 30-Mar-4 Arroyo, Buenos Aires #58
£6875 $11000 €10038 Nude with white flower (147x155cm-58x61in) s. painted c.1971. 17-May-3 Bunte, Elgin #1318 est:2000-3000
£15625 $25469 €22500 Nude with flower (146x148cm-57x58in) s. el. 23-Sep-3 Durán, Madrid #221/R est:9000

TORAL, Mario (1934-) Chilean
£1000 $1700 €1460 Sick woman in the sun (185x125cm-73x49in) s.d.1982. 25-Nov-3 Galeria y Remates, Montevideo #98/R

TORCHI, Angelo (1856-1915) Italian
£1056 $1754 €1500 Nell'aia (18x28cm-7x11in) s. panel. 11-Jun-3 Christie's, Rome #63 est:2000-3000

TORCIA, Francesco Saverio (1840-?) Italian
£493 $853 €700 Sailing boats (21x17cm-8x7in) s. board. 11-Dec-3 Christie's, Rome #64
£3448 $5759 €5000 Fishing in the Bay of Naples (64x104cm-25x41in) s. lit. 10-Jul-3 Allgauer, Kempten #2705/R est:1500

TORDI, Sinibaldo (1876-1955) Italian
£1197 $2071 €1700 Chess game (34x60cm-13x24in) s.verso board. 9-Dec-3 Pandolfini, Florence #215/R est:1200-1500
£1344 $2500 €1962 The cardinal. The guitar (26x17cm-10x7in) s. one panel one canvas two. 5-Mar-4 Skinner, Boston #218a/R est:1800-2200
£1872 $3500 €2733 Concert (51x41cm-20x16in) s.i. 25-Feb-4 Doyle, New York #22/R est:3000-5000

TORDI, Sinibaldo (attrib) (1876-1955) Italian
£650 $1021 €943 New arrival (40x51cm-16x20in) 28-Aug-3 Christie's, Kensington #333/R

TORDJMANN, Franck (20th C) ?
Sculpture
£4895 $8322 €7000 Violon, instrument du voyage (150x60x20cm-59x24x8in) s. plexiglas. 27-Nov-3 Calmels Cohen, Paris #132/R est:3500-4500

TORDOFF, Fred (20th C) American?
£240 $400 €350 Shad fishing, shipping on the Hudson (28x58cm-11x23in) s. panel. 29-Jun-3 William Jenack, New York #123
£259 $425 €378 Ships off Fort Lee, Palisades cliffs (28x53cm-11x21in) s. 1-Jun-3 William Jenack, New York #190
£265 $450 €387 Whaleship (51x61cm-20x24in) s. 21-Nov-3 Eldred, East Dennis #559/R
£282 $500 €412 Breezy day on the Hudson river (69x89cm-27x35in) s. 2-May-4 William Jenack, New York #286
£300 $550 €450 American warships at sea (56x76cm-22x30in) s. 29-Jul-4 Eldred, East Dennis #189/R
£300 $550 €450 Whaling ship and shipping off the West Point lighthouse (30x56cm-12x22in) s. 29-Jul-4 Eldred, East Dennis #449/R
£324 $550 €473 South seas whaling (51x66cm-20x26in) s. 21-Nov-3 Eldred, East Dennis #548/R
£366 $600 €534 Shipping off the Battery New York (20x53cm-8x21in) s. panel. 1-Jun-3 William Jenack, New York #265
£383 $700 €575 Shipping in Boston Harbour (25x46cm-10x18in) s. 29-Jul-4 Eldred, East Dennis #191/R
£469 $850 €685 Calm off the coast (20x36cm-8x14in) s. panel. 2-Apr-4 Eldred, East Dennis #659a/R
£475 $850 €694 Ship passing through the Nantucket Lightship (51x91cm-20x36in) s. 11-Jan-4 William Jenack, New York #90
£516 $950 €753 Ship Red Jacket, Captain S Reid (91x112cm-36x44in) s. 13-Jun-4 William Jenack, New York #207
£568 $1000 €829 Shipping off the Battery, N.Y (30x86cm-12x34in) s. 23-May-4 William Jenack, New York #272 est:800-1200
£594 $950 €867 Breezy day on the Hudson (56x89cm-22x35in) s. 21-Sep-3 William Jenack, New York #310
£601 $1100 €902 Ship Kit Carson, Captain Prince S Cowell (71x81cm-28x32in) s. 29-Jul-4 Eldred, East Dennis #188/R
£884 $1600 €1291 Whaling ships in the Arctic Regions (30x91cm-12x36in) s. 2-Apr-4 Eldred, East Dennis #642a/R est:1500-2000
£1022 $1900 €1492 Shipping off the Battery, New York Harbour (30x91cm-12x36in) s. 7-Mar-4 William Jenack, New York #263 est:500-700
Works on paper
£242 $450 €353 Mounted Atlantic salmon with fly (41x76cm-16x30in) s. W/C. 7-Mar-4 William Jenack, New York #66

TORELLI, Felice (1667-1748) Italian
£8054 $14819 €12000 Bishops (78x94cm-31x37in) 29-Mar-4 Pandolfini, Florence #777/R est:15000

TORELLI, Felice (attrib) (1667-1748) Italian
Works on paper
£1944 $3169 €2800 Holy Family with St Elisabeth and Infant St John (11x9cm-4x4in) pen wash. 26-Sep-3 Bolland & Marotz, Bremen #460/R est:3000

TORELLI, Giuseppe (1881-1959) Italian
£433 $776 €650 Mountains (71x70cm-28x28in) s.d.62 cardboard. 12-May-4 Stadion, Trieste #772

TORELLI, Vieri (1873-1959) Italian
Works on paper
£364 $663 €550 Cottage in the mountains (35x25cm-14x10in) s. W/C. 17-Jun-4 Galleria Pananti, Florence #476/R

TORENBEEK, John Louis (1927-) Dutch
Works on paper
£280 $481 €400 Close friend (48x31cm-19x12in) s.d.56 gouache lit. 8-Dec-3 Glerum, Amsterdam #225/R

TORETTI, P (19/20th C) Italian
£484 $900 €707 Mediterranean coastal landscape with figures and buildings (46x102cm-18x40in) s. 3-Mar-4 Alderfer's, Hatfield #319/R est:800-1200

TORGERSEN, Thorvald (1862-1943) Norwegian
£256 $409 €371 Village in summer (50x73cm-20x29in) s. 22-Sep-3 Blomqvist, Lysaker #1311/R (N.KR 3000)
£2733 $4564 €3990 Three children fishing for crabs (60x70cm-24x28in) s. 13-Oct-3 Blomqvist, Oslo #296/R est:25000-30000 (N.KR 32000)

TORGERSON, William (19th C) American
£984 $1800 €1437 Paddle steamer in an engagement (61x91cm-24x36in) s. 29-Jul-4 Christie's, Rockefeller NY #269/R est:300-5000

TORGGLER, Hermann (1878-1939) Austrian
£2639 $4486 €3800 Grafin Sigmund (222x150cm-87x59in) s. bears d. 28-Oct-3 Dorotheum, Vienna #132/R est:1800-2200

TORHAMN, Gunnar (1894-1955) Swedish
£1077 $1852 €1572 Coastal landscape with woman walking (50x60cm-20x24in) s. panel. 7-Dec-3 Uppsala Auktionskammare, Uppsala #260/R (S.KR 14000)
£1093 $2012 €1640 Examining the net (33x41cm-13x16in) s. panel. 14-Jun-4 Lilla Bukowskis, Stockholm #525 est:8000-10000 (S.KR 15000)
£1421 $2316 €2075 Interior scene with women (51x61cm-20x24in) s. panel. 29-Sep-3 Lilla Bukowskis, Stockholm #493 est:8000-10000 (S.KR 18500)
£1690 $2754 €2467 Fisherfolk (46x56cm-18x22in) s. panel. 29-Sep-3 Lilla Bukowskis, Stockholm #492 est:10000-12000 (S.KR 22000)
£1767 $2879 €2580 Fisher madams (53x66cm-21x26in) s. panel. 29-Sep-3 Lilla Bukowskis, Stockholm #488 est:12000-15000 (S.KR 23000)
£2930 $5187 €4278 The Tunisian woman (81x64cm-32x25in) s.d.26. 27-Apr-4 AB Stockholms Auktionsverk #749/R est:20000-25000 (S.KR 40000)

TORIN, Kano Hashin (1679-1754) Japanese
Works on paper
£312 $530 €455 Carp jumping up waterfall (85x34cm-33x13in) s. seal Indian ink silk hanging scroll prov. 8-Nov-3 Dr Fritz Nagel, Stuttgart #1859/R

TORLAKSON, Jim (1951-) American
Works on paper
£221 $400 €323 Campton Navajo (28x41cm-11x16in) W/C. 16-Apr-4 American Auctioneer #395/R
£516 $950 €753 Russ leifson rig (28x41cm-11x16in) s. W/C. 26-Jun-4 Susanin's, Chicago #6104/R

TORNA, Oscar (1842-1894) Swedish
£338 $608 €493 Landscape with cattle (33x42cm-13x17in) s. canvas on panel. 26-Jan-4 Lilla Bukowskis, Stockholm #570 (S.KR 4500)
£439 $821 €641 Fox by water's edge (35x26cm-14x10in) s.i.d.1884. 29-Feb-4 Uppsala Auktionskammare, Uppsala #306 (S.KR 6000)
£846 $1455 €1235 Rowing in moonlight (50x85cm-20x33in) s.d.1875. 7-Dec-3 Uppsala Auktionskammare, Uppsala #185/R (S.KR 11000)
£1130 $2079 €1695 Summer landscape with children playing by lake (114x80cm-45x31in) s.i.d.aug.1889. 14-Jun-4 Lilla Bukowskis, Stockholm #473 est:15000-20000 (S.KR 15500)
£1256 $2249 €1834 Rowing trip in moonlight (49x83cm-19x33in) s.d.1875. 26-May-4 AB Stockholms Auktionsverk #2240/R est:18000-20000 (S.KR 17000)
£1257 $2174 €1835 Farm view with red cottages (54x86cm-21x34in) s.d.1892. 15-Dec-3 Lilla Bukowskis, Stockholm #320 est:20000 (S.KR 16000)
£1626 $2911 €2374 The avenue, Schedevi (97x81cm-38x32in) s.i.d.Maj 1880. 26-May-4 AB Stockholms Auktionsverk #2276/R est:20000-25000 (S.KR 22000)
£2764 $5086 €4035 Autumn landscape (126x191cm-50x75in) s.i.d.Sept-Oct 1889 i.verso exhib. 10-Jun-4 Grev Wedels Plass, Oslo #230/R est:30000-50000 (N.KR 34000)

TORNABUONI, Lorenzo (1934-) Italian
£733 $1320 €1100 Rower (42x39cm-17x15in) s. 22-Apr-4 Finarte Semenzato, Rome #146/R

TORNAI, Gyula (1861-1928) Hungarian
£760 $1262 €1110 Yard with a blooming fruit tree (33x59cm-13x23in) s. panel. 4-Oct-3 Kieselbach, Budapest #182/R (H.F 280000)
£1172 $2169 €1700 Old Egyptian female fighter (74x45cm-29x18in) s. 14-Feb-4 Hans Stahl, Hamburg #101/R est:1800
£1629 $2704 €2378 Sunlit yard (34x25cm-13x10in) s. panel. 4-Oct-3 Kieselbach, Budapest #88/R (H.F 600000)
£2543 $4400 €3713 Study of a boy (74x73cm-29x29in) s. prov. 11-Dec-3 Sotheby's, New York #215/R est:4000-6000
£4887 $8112 €7135 Morroccan goldsmith with chanukka candle, seder plates and bsamin (27x21cm-11x8in) s. panel. 4-Oct-3 Kieselbach, Budapest #89/R (H.F 1800000)
£8551 $15135 €12484 Arabian scene (59x29cm-23x11in) s.d.1899 panel. 28-Apr-4 Kieselbach, Budapest #156/R (H.F 3200000)
£13333 $24000 €19466 Musical afternoon (114x104cm-45x41in) s. 23-Apr-4 Sotheby's, New York #97/R est:20000-30000
Works on paper
£527 $954 €769 Hookahing (33x25cm-13x10in) s. W/C. 16-Apr-4 Mu Terem Galeria, Budapest #88/R (H.F 200000)

TORNATSKY, Luke J (20th C) American
Works on paper
£359 $600 €524 At rest (107x84cm-42x33in) s. s.d.2001 verso pastel prov. 15-Nov-3 Sloans & Kenyon, Bethesda #111/R

TORNEMAN, Axel (1880-1925) Swedish
£2069 $3704 €3021 Still life of flowers and figureen (60x49cm-24x19in) s. panel. 26-May-4 AB Stockholms Auktionsverk #2282/R est:30000-40000 (S.KR 28000)
Works on paper
£2462 $4234 €3595 The factory gate (48x50cm-19x20in) s. W/C exhib. exec.c.1915. 2-Dec-3 Bukowskis, Stockholm #87a/R est:15000-20000 (S.KR 32000)
£2828 $5091 €4129 Night cafe in Paris (33x29cm-13x11in) s.i.d.06 Indian ink htd white prov. 26-Apr-4 Bukowskis, Stockholm #124/R est:40000-45000 (S.KR 39000)

TORNING, Tage (1925-) Swedish
£261 $470 €392 Landscape with trees (46x50cm-18x20in) s. 25-Apr-4 Goteborg Auktionsverk, Sweden #355/R (S.KR 3600)
£276 $496 €414 Portrait (55x45cm-22x18in) s. 25-Apr-4 Goteborg Auktionsverk, Sweden #354/R (S.KR 3800)
£334 $600 €501 Figure by the fire (54x64cm-21x25in) s. 25-Apr-4 Goteborg Auktionsverk, Sweden #325/R (S.KR 4600)

TORNO, Ken (20th C) American
£305 $500 €442 Autumn in Indiana (24x30cm-9x12in) s. painted c.1940. 7-Jun-3 Treadway Gallery, Cincinnati #1407
£579 $950 €840 Winter landscape (16x20cm-6x8in) s.d. 7-Jun-3 Treadway Gallery, Cincinnati #1410

TORNOE, Wenzel (1844-1907) Danish
£406 $689 €593 Danish summer landscape (37x60cm-15x24in) s.d.1903. 10-Nov-3 Rasmussen, Vejle #104/R (D.KR 4400)
£473 $818 €691 Child wearing white dress with red ribbon (22x22cm-9x9in) init. 9-Dec-3 Rasmussen, Copenhagen #1383/R (D.KR 5000)
£662 $1145 €967 Portrait of Kristian Zahrtmann (65x55cm-26x22in) painted c.1863. 9-Dec-3 Rasmussen, Copenhagen #1336/R (D.KR 7000)
£2695 $5013 €3935 The monk is being waited on (44x61cm-17x24in) s. 2-Mar-4 Rasmussen, Copenhagen #1279/R est:30000-40000 (D.KR 30000)
£5671 $9811 €8280 The studio - studying the day's work (50x37cm-20x15in) init.d.1884 exhib. 9-Dec-3 Rasmussen, Copenhagen #1261/R est:60000-80000 (D.KR 60000)
£34972 $60501 €51059 Aqua Alta - carnival in Venice (80x150cm-31x59in) s.d.1889. 9-Dec-3 Rasmussen, Copenhagen #1257/R est:100000-125000 (D.KR 370000)

TORNQUIST, Ellen (1871-?) Scandinavian
£333 $613 €500 In spring (71x65cm-28x26in) s. 9-Jun-4 Dorotheum, Salzburg #567/R

TORNQUIST, Herbert (20th C) New Zealander
£839 $1527 €1225 South of Tauranga (29x44cm-11x17in) s. board prov. 29-Jun-4 Peter Webb, Auckland #91/R est:2500-3500 (NZ.D 2400)

TORNQUIST, Jorrit (1938-) Austrian
£2685 $4805 €4000 Composition OP180 (79x79cm-31x31in) s.i.d.1970 verso acrylic prov. 25-May-4 Sotheby's, Milan #175/R est:1500-2000

TORNYAI, Janos (1869-1936) Hungarian
£597 $991 €872 In the room (19x25cm-7x10in) s. panel. 4-Oct-3 Kieselbach, Budapest #109/R (H.F 220000)
£626 $1084 €914 Boy on the terrace (48x42cm-19x17in) s. 12-Dec-3 Kieselbach, Budapest #213/R (H.F 240000)
£1283 $2270 €1873 Summer day (46x58cm-18x23in) s. canvas on cardboard. 28-Apr-4 Kieselbach, Budapest #126/R (H.F 480000)
£1827 $3161 €2667 Winter mood (42x53cm-17x21in) s. paper. 12-Dec-3 Kieselbach, Budapest #192/R (H.F 700000)
£3952 $7153 €5770 First reading (59x45cm-23x18in) s. oil on wood. 16-Apr-4 Mu Terem Galeria, Budapest #42/R (H.F 1500000)

TORO, Attilio (1892-1982) Italian
£986 $1706 €1400 Girl in interior (40x30cm-16x12in) s. cardboard. 11-Dec-3 Christie's, Rome #54/R
£1333 $2453 €2000 Woman n the sofa (27x23cm-11x9in) s. 8-Jun-4 Della Rocca, Turin #293/R est:300-400
£1409 $2636 €2100 Woman at mirror (49x34cm-19x13in) 26-Feb-4 Cambi, Genoa #462/R est:1200-1500
£1678 $3138 €2500 Woman on the sofa (49x34cm-19x13in) 26-Feb-4 Cambi, Genoa #464/R est:1200-1500

TORO, Elias (20th C) Venezuelan?
Sculpture
£3474 $5905 €5072 Kneeling woman (60x30x60cm-24x12x24in) s.verso num.6/8 bronze exec.1994. 23-Nov-3 Subastas Odalys, Caracas #77/R

TORO, Luigi (1836-1900) Italian
£437 $795 €638 Young woman with exposed shoulders (59x40cm-23x16in) s. 16-Jun-4 Fischer, Luzern #2398/R (S.FR 1000)

TOROSSIAN, Haroutioun (1933-) Lebanese
£2400 $4248 €3504 Woman in mirror (71x53cm-28x21in) s.verso. 29-Apr-4 Bonhams, New Bond Street #563/R est:2000-2500

TORRALLARDONA, Carlos (1913-1986) Argentinian
£824 $1500 €1203 Waiting (30x24cm-12x9in) s.d.74. 29-Jun-4 Arroyo, Buenos Aires #7/R est:1500
£1374 $2500 €2006 Dancing evening (50x61cm-20x24in) s.d.74. 5-Jul-4 Arroyo, Buenos Aires #23/R est:2500
Works on paper
£1117 $2000 €1631 In the bar (38x30cm-15x12in) s. mixed media. 4-May-4 Arroyo, Buenos Aires #39/R est:1800

TORRE, Bartolomeo (?-c.1554) Italian
Works on paper
£4444 $8000 €6488 Ecorche study of a right shoulder and arm, the bones, and five heads (21x22cm-8x9in) black chk pen brown ink wash prov. 22-Jan-4 Christie's, Rockefeller NY #8/R est:4000-6000

TORRE, Carlos de la (1856-1832) Argentinian
£1913 $3500 €2793 Beach (11x17cm-4x7in) cardboard. 1-Jun-4 Arroyo, Buenos Aires #29

TORRE, Enrico della (1931-) Italian
£2013 $3725 €3000 Landscape (47x76cm-19x30in) s.i.d.1976 verso card on canvas lit. 13-Mar-4 Meeting Art, Vercelli #75 est:3000

TORRE, Flaminio (attrib) (1621-1661) Italian

£28000	$51240	€40880	Saint Peter in penitence (86x99cm-34x39in) lit. 8-Jul-4 Sotheby's, London #215/R est:15000-20000

TORRE, Giulio del (1856-1932) Italian

£5200	$9308	€7592	Street urchins (25x15cm-10x6in) s.d.1894 panel pair. 7-May-4 Christopher Matthews, Yorkshire #309/R est:2500-3500

TORRENTS LLADO, Joaquin (1946-1993) Spanish

£3169	$5546	€4500	Tree in Son Oleza. s.d.1975. 16-Dec-3 Durán, Madrid #157/R est:3750

TORRES AGUERO, Leopoldo (1924-) Argentinian

£824	$1500	€1203	Rooftops (40x60cm-16x24in) s.d.56. 5-Jul-4 Arroyo, Buenos Aires #18/R est:1500

TORRES FUSTER, Antonio (1874-1945) Spanish

£846	$1455	€1235	La dama del manton (59x45cm-23x18in) s. 7-Dec-3 Uppsala Auktionskammare, Uppsala #116/R (S.KR 11000)
£12000	$21720	€18000	Interior with odalisk (89x132cm-35x52in) s. 30-Mar-4 Segre, Madrid #76/R est:15000
£18000	$30960	€26280	Tambourine player (89x131cm-35x52in) s. 3-Dec-3 Christie's, London #94/R est:18000-25000

TORRES GUARDIA, Jose (1932-) Spanish

£621	$1117	€900	Fish (49x63cm-19x25in) s.d.1980 board. 26-Jan-4 Ansorena, Madrid #914/R

TORRES NARVAEZ, Salvador (1927-) Spanish

£390	$651	€550	Puerto (60x73cm-24x29in) s. 23-Jun-3 Durán, Madrid #728/R

TORRES, Augusto (1913-1992) Uruguayan

£353	$600	€515	Houses and trees (45x33cm-18x13in) s. 20-Nov-3 Galeria y Remates, Montevideo #61/R
£824	$1400	€1203	Spanish village (34x46cm-13x18in) s. 25-Nov-3 Galeria y Remates, Montevideo #65/R
£1136	$2000	€1659	Italian landscape (33x45cm-13x18in) s. 5-Jan-4 Galeria y Remates, Montevideo #42/R est:3000
£1497	$2500	€2186	Still life (37x33cm-15x13in) s. canvas on cardboard. 7-Oct-3 Galeria y Remates, Montevideo #48/R
£1875	$3300	€2738	Still life (43x60cm-17x24in) s. s.verso prov. 5-Jan-4 Galeria y Remates, Montevideo #41/R est:3500-4000
£2123	$3800	€3100	Still life (30x41cm-12x16in) s. cardboard. 4-May-4 Arroyo, Buenos Aires #75/R est:3800
£2235	$3800	€3263	Street with tram (50x60cm-20x24in) s. 25-Nov-3 Galeria y Remates, Montevideo #64/R
£2548	$4000	€3720	Untitled (42x57cm-17x22in) s. masonite. 23-Nov-2 Subastas Odalys, Caracas #26/R
£2647	$4500	€3865	Figure and cart (40x53cm-16x21in) s.d.48 cardboard. 25-Nov-3 Galeria y Remates, Montevideo #63/R
£2994	$5000	€4371	Urban movements (48x74cm-19x29in) s. cardboard. 7-Oct-3 Galeria y Remates, Montevideo #47/R
£3636	$6400	€5309	Montparnasse (48x69cm-19x27in) s. cardboard prov. 5-Jan-4 Galeria y Remates, Montevideo #39/R est:6500-7500
£3693	$6500	€5392	Composition with woman (55x50cm-22x20in) s. cardboard. 5-Jan-4 Galeria y Remates, Montevideo #38/R est:8000-10000
£3864	$6800	€5641	Ancap harbour (64x41cm-25x16in) s. s.i.verso cardboard. 5-Jan-4 Galeria y Remates, Montevideo #40/R est:6000-8000
£5587	$10000	€8157	Composition (51x40cm-20x16in) s.d.1937 board. 26-May-4 Sotheby's, New York #105/R est:10000-15000
Works on paper			
£463	$750	€671	Paisaje Urbano Constructivo (16x22cm-6x9in) s. Indian ink. 29-Jul-3 Galeria y Remates, Montevideo #115/R

TORRES, Horacio (1924-1976) Uruguayan

£1603	$2950	€2340	New York (50x60cm-20x24in) s.d.1971. 22-Jun-4 Galeria y Remates, Montevideo #102/R est:3500-4500

TORRES, Luis (20th C) Venezuelan?

£255	$470	€383	Untitled (80x120cm-31x47in) acrylic. 27-Jun-4 Subastas Odalys, Caracas #36
£380	$600	€555	Cat and cup (87x103cm-34x41in) s. painted 2002. 1-Dec-2 Subastas Odalys, Caracas #102

TORRES, Ramon (18th C) ?

£3776	$6306	€5400	Still life with vegetables and eggs (47x77cm-19x30in) s.d.1729. 24-Jun-3 Segre, Madrid #54/R est:5400
£3776	$6306	€5400	Still life with dishes and pottery (47x77cm-19x30in) s.d.1729. 24-Jun-3 Segre, Madrid #55/R est:5400

TORRES-GARCIA, Joaquin (1874-1949) Uruguayan

£1646	$2700	€2403	Pedralbes Monastery, Barcelona (14x24cm-6x9in) s.d.1898 i.verso canvas on cardboard lit. 3-Jun-3 Galeria y Remates, Montevideo #60
£3380	$5408	€4800	Landscape (27x42cm-11x17in) painted c.1895. 16-Sep-3 Segre, Madrid #291/R est:4800
£12676	$20282	€18000	Still life with bottle and watermelon (27x45cm-11x18in) s.d.1928 cardboard. 16-Sep-3 Segre, Madrid #311/R est:18000
£13529	$23000	€19752	Iglesia (51x42cm-20x17in) s.d.40 prov. 19-Nov-3 Sotheby's, New York #93/R est:20000-25000
£15244	$25000	€22256	Still life with carrots (43x52cm-17x20in) s.d.44 cardboard. 3-Jun-3 Galeria y Remates, Montevideo #59
£19553	$35000	€28547	Three primitive figures (38x46cm-15x18in) s.d.28 prov. 26-May-4 Sotheby's, New York #107/R est:25000-30000
£22159	$39000	€32352	Florence Cathedral (50x40cm-20x16in) s.d.46 cardboard prov. 5-Jan-4 Galeria y Remates, Montevideo #32/R est:40000-50000
£26667	$49067	€40000	Amberes harbour (35x42cm-14x17in) s. cardboard painted c.1940 prov. 10-Jun-4 Christie's, Paris #52/R est:40000-55000
£27933	$50000	€40782	Figures en rouge et noir (38x46cm-15x18in) s.d.28 tempera prov.exhib.lit. 26-May-4 Sotheby's, New York #43/R est:60000-80000
£30000	$55200	€45000	Still life (34x58cm-13x23in) s.d.28 canvas on cardboard prov.exhib. 10-Jun-4 Christie's, Paris #50/R est:60000-75000
£32353	$55000	€47235	Three standing figures (72x40cm-28x16in) s.d.27. 19-Nov-3 Sotheby's, New York #99/R est:30000-40000
£64706	$110000	€94471	Grafismo metafisico (42x52cm-17x20in) s.d.43 board prov.exhib.lit. 19-Nov-3 Sotheby's, New York #48/R est:60000-80000
£93333	$171733	€140000	Two figures and composition (44x47cm-17x19in) s.d.46 cardboard prov. 10-Jun-4 Christie's, Paris #45/R est:140000-160000
£94118	$160000	€137412	Locomotive avec charette (50x61cm-20x24in) s.d.29 prov.exhib. 19-Nov-3 Sotheby's, New York #31/R est:100000-150000
£100000	$184000	€150000	Train on iron bridge (50x69cm-20x27in) s.d.43 cardboard prov.exhib.lit. 10-Jun-4 Christie's, Paris #46/R est:100000-150000
£123333	$225700	€185000	Constructivo a cinco tonos con elementos de puerto (49x68cm-19x27in) mono.i.d.43 cardboard prov.lit. 7-Jun-4 Artcurial Briest, Paris #27/R est:130000-180000
£167598	$300000	€244693	Constructive art (51x68cm-20x27in) s.d.1943 board prov.exhib.lit. 26-May-4 Sotheby's, New York #17/R est:275000-325000
Sculpture			
£2148	$3995	€3200	Toy horse (27x37x6cm-11x15x2in) s. polychrome wood. 2-Mar-4 Ansorena, Madrid #753/R est:3000
£3523	$6200	€5144	Dog (12x12x3cm-5x5x1in) painted wood exec.1919. 5-Jan-4 Galeria y Remates, Montevideo #34/R est:7000-9000
Works on paper			
£1280	$2100	€1869	Still life with jug and bottle (12x22cm-5x9in) pencil dr. 3-Jun-3 Galeria y Remates, Montevideo #62
£1377	$2300	€2010	Face of woman (15x21cm-6x8in) s.d.1921 Chinese ink. 7-Oct-3 Galeria y Remates, Montevideo #45/R
£1818	$3200	€2654	Head (16x23cm-6x9in) pencil dr prov. 5-Jan-4 Galeria y Remates, Montevideo #35/R est:3000-4000
£5096	$8000	€7440	Untitled (11x9cm-4x4in) s. chl. 23-Nov-2 Subastas Odalys, Caracas #23/R
£5102	$9286	€7500	Composition (19x13cm-7x5in) pencil dr exec.1940 double-sided. 3-Feb-4 Segre, Madrid #366/R est:6000
£7059	$12000	€10306	Constructivist (16x13cm-6x5in) ink gouache pencil paper on board exec. c.1935 prov. 18-Nov-3 Christie's, Rockefeller NY #110/R est:15000-20000
£10319	$16820	€15066	Strolling in Barcelona (35x27cm-14x11in) s. pencil W/C dr prov. 17-Jul-3 Naón & Cia, Buenos Aires #4/R
£10319	$16820	€15066	At the make-up (30x31cm-12x12in) s.d.1900 pencil W/C dr exhib. 17-Jul-3 Naón & Cia, Buenos Aires #5/R
£12216	$21500	€17835	Landscape with cart (24x42cm-9x17in) s.d.1917 ink pastel prov.exhib.lit. 5-Jan-4 Galeria y Remates, Montevideo #33/R est:14000-17000
£12353	$21000	€18035	Port composition. Constructivo with fish and mask (16x11cm-6x4in) three init.d.27-28-38 graphite set of five exhib. 19-Nov-3 Sotheby's, New York #142/R est:12000-18000
£13966	$25000	€20390	Composition (22x19cm-9x7in) s.d.38 pencil ink prov. 26-May-4 Sotheby's, New York #42/R est:22000-28000

TORRESPRAT, Enric (1938-) Spanish

£1087	$1783	€1500	Venice (60x73cm-24x29in) s. i.verso lit. 27-May-3 Durán, Madrid #126/R est:1500
£1259	$2102	€1800	Girls on the beach (94x64cm-37x25in) s. 30-Jun-3 Ansorena, Madrid #326/R

TORREY, Elliot Bouton (1867-1949) American

£2610	$4750	€3811	Young girl and roses (99x74cm-39x29in) s. 15-Jun-4 John Moran, Pasadena #92 est:5000-7000

TORREY, Hiram Dwight (1820-1900) American

£12791	$22000	€18675	Indians in a wooded landscape (130x178cm-51x70in) s.i.d.1856 prov. 7-Dec-3 Freeman, Philadelphia #107 est:3000-5000

TORRICINI, N (?) Italian

£1079	$1770	€1500	Night landscape (53x74cm-21x29in) s.d.1918 tempera paper. 10-Jun-3 Pandolfini, Florence #55/R est:1300-1600

TORRIGLIA, Giovanni Battista (1858-1937) Italian

£84000	$142800	€122640	Fisherman's family (74x110cm-29x43in) s. 19-Nov-3 Bonhams, New Bond Street #94/R est:80000-120000

TORRILHON, Amy (20th C) French?

£276	$458	€400	Chateau de Chillon la nuit (61x50cm-24x20in) s. 30-Sep-3 Blanchet, Paris #338

TORRINI, Pietro (1852-1920) Italian

£15294	$26000	€22329	Mouse in the trap (63x90cm-25x35in) s. prov. 28-Oct-3 Sotheby's, New York #141/R est:12000-18000
Works on paper			
£775	$1239	€1100	Italian soldier (35x25cm-14x10in) s. W/C. 16-Sep-3 Segre, Madrid #15/R

TORRISET, Kjell (1950-) Norwegian

£1452	$2424	€2120	From the series - 100 pictures (54x65cm-21x26in) s.d.2001-2002 panel exhib. 13-Oct-3 Blomqvist, Oslo #323/R est:15000-18000 (N.KR 17000)
£2033	$3720	€2968	Perspectives (30x30cm-12x12in) s. verso four. 7-Jun-4 Blomqvist, Oslo #446/R est:16000-20000 (N.KR 25000)

TORROJA, Enrique (20th C) Argentinian

Works on paper			
£385	$700	€562	Untitled (42x31cm-17x12in) s. pencil. 5-Jul-4 Arroyo, Buenos Aires #12/R

TORROME, Francisco J (19/20th C) ?
Works on paper
£250 $460 €365 Road from Pershore (13x19cm-5x7in) s.d.1918 W/C. 11-Jun-4 Keys, Aylsham #445/R

TORSCHENKO, Igor (1965-) Russian
£704 $1232 €1000 The sitter (160x130cm-63x51in) 19-Dec-3 Dorotheum, Vienna #397/R
£1007 $1862 €1500 Untitled (170x200cm-67x79in) mono.cyrillic d.01 verso. 9-Mar-4 Dorotheum, Vienna #257/R est:3000-5000
£1733 $3120 €2600 Untitled (155x175cm-61x69in) mono.d. verso. 21-Apr-4 Dorotheum, Vienna #333/R est:5000-6000
£1831 $3204 €2600 Blooming (91x111cm-36x44in) mono.i.Cyrillic d.98-2001 verso. 19-Dec-3 Dorotheum, Vienna #398/R est:1200-2200
£2148 $3973 €3200 Untitled (170x170cm-67x67in) mono.cyrillic.d. verso. 9-Mar-4 Dorotheum, Vienna #237/R est:3000-6000

TORSHEIM, Oddvar (1938-) Norwegian
Works on paper
£252 $464 €378 The shout in the room I (30x32cm-12x13in) s. W/C. 14-Jun-4 Blomqvist, Lysaker #1407/R (N.KR 3100)

TORSLEFF, August (1884-1968) Danish
£305 $548 €445 Interior scene with figures by child in crib (86x68cm-34x27in) s. 24-Apr-4 Rasmussen, Havnen #2248 (D.KR 3400)
£340 $623 €496 Two sisters wearing green dresses (62x66cm-24x26in) s.d.1923. 9-Jun-4 Rasmussen, Copenhagen #1998/R (D.KR 3800)

TORSO, Alessandro del (1883-?) Italian
£524 $876 €750 Old houses in Zuel, Cortina, Italy (40x53cm-16x21in) board. 10-Oct-3 Stadion, Trieste #600/R

TORSSLOW, Harald (1838-1909) Swedish
£1021 $1767 €1491 Landscape from Vanern with Lackso Palace (53x76cm-21x30in) s.d.1894. 15-Dec-3 Lilla Bukowskis, Stockholm #1060 (S.KR 13000)
£1130 $2079 €1695 Coastal landscape with figures and fishing huts (100x145cm-39x57in) s.d.1880. 14-Jun-4 Lilla Bukowskis, Stockholm #471 est:10000-12000 (S.KR 15500)
£3692 $6351 €5390 Fjord landscape with figures by fishing village (100x147cm-39x58in) s.d.1885. 3-Dec-3 AB Stockholms Auktionsverk #2401/R est:80000-100000 (S.KR 48000)

TORSTEINSON, Torstein L (1876-1966) Norwegian
£516 $831 €753 In the forest (99x64cm-39x25in) s. 25-Aug-3 Blomqvist, Lysaker #1329/R (N.KR 6000)
£950 $1577 €1378 Still life of the red mug (90x65cm-35x26in) s. 16-Jun-3 Blomqvist, Lysaker #1245 (N.KR 11000)
£1382 $2294 €2004 Memories (100x85cm-39x33in) s. 16-Jun-3 Blomqvist, Lysaker #1244 est:18000-20000 (N.KR 16000)

TORVUND, Gunnar (1948-) Norwegian
Sculpture
£3416 $5705 €4987 Pink with profile (150x100cm-59x39in) st.sig. wood bronze plexiglass exhib. 13-Oct-3 Blomqvist, Oslo #328/R est:50000-60000 (N.KR 40000)

TOSA SCHOOL, Japanese
Works on paper
£11644 $19795 €17000 Scenes from Genji Monogatari (152x56cm-60x22in) Indian ink goldleaf col six panel folding screen. 8-Nov-3 Dr Fritz Nagel, Stuttgart #1894/R est:11000

TOSA SCHOOL (16th C) Japanese
Works on paper
£12162 $21405 €18000 Landscape (123x45cm-48x18in) six panel screen. 22-May-4 Dr Fritz Nagel, Stuttgart #2100/R est:18000
£67935 $125000 €99185 Pine trees and Chinese black pines (147x350cm-58x138in) i. col ink gold leaf six panel screen. 23-Mar-4 Christie's, Rockefeller NY #65/R est:35000-45000

TOSANI, Patrick (20th C) ?
Photographs
£2098 $3503 €3000 Geographie I (162x162cm-64x64in) s.i.d.1988 num.1/3 verso cibachrome prov. 11-Oct-3 Cornette de St.Cyr, Paris #23/R est:3000-4000
£7186 $12000 €10492 Self portraits (51x41cm-20x16in) s.num.6/8 verso c-print 12 prov.exhib. 13-Nov-3 Sotheby's, New York #423/R est:15000-20000

TOSAR GRANADOS, Manuel (1945-) Spanish
£470 $879 €700 House in Cadiz (47x56cm-19x22in) s. 24-Feb-4 Durán, Madrid #57/R
£570 $1021 €850 Spot in Ibiza (46x57cm-18x22in) s. 25-May-4 Durán, Madrid #75/R

TOSCANO RICO, Maria (1919-) Portuguese
£1007 $1802 €1500 Cathedral in the fields (60x74cm-24x29in) s.d.1981 board. 31-May-4 Cabral Moncada Leiloes, Lisbon #248/R est:1500-2250

TOSCHI, Ermanno (1906-) Italian
£282 $487 €400 Marina di Carrara (20x30cm-8x12in) s. s.i.d.1967 verso. 9-Dec-3 Pandolfini, Florence #417/R

TOSCHIK, Larry (1922-) American
£221 $400 €323 Impending danger (71x112cm-28x44in) s. board. 16-Apr-4 James Julia, Fairfield #841/R

TOSHIMITSU, Imai (1928-2001) Japanese
£3333 $6133 €5000 Paris (50x63cm-20x25in) s.i.d.1962 cardboard. 12-Jun-4 Meeting Art, Vercelli #126/R est:5000

TOSI, Arturo (1871-1956) Italian
£2759 $4607 €4000 Winter landscape (17x25cm-7x10in) board. 13-Nov-3 Finarte Semenzato, Rome #328/R est:3500-4500
£5369 $9611 €8000 Little church amongst trees (31x38cm-12x15in) s. board painted c.1920. 29-May-4 Farsetti, Prato #433/R est:8000-10000
£6757 $11892 €10000 Landscape (49x60cm-19x24in) s. 24-May-4 Christie's, Milan #314/R est:10000-15000
£7971 $13072 €11000 Rovetta (50x60cm-20x24in) s.d.1949 oil pastel prov. 27-May-3 Sotheby's, Milan #187/R est:10000-15000
£8042 $13671 €11500 Oranges and grapes (50x60cm-20x24in) s. board. 25-Nov-3 Sotheby's, Milan #88/R est:12000-15000
£8276 $13821 €12000 Forthcoming spring (50x60cm-20x24in) s. s.d.1944 verso. 17-Nov-3 Sant Agostino, Torino #240/R est:11000-14000
£8503 $15221 €12500 Lake landscape (50x60cm-20x24in) s. 16-Mar-4 Finarte Semenzato, Milan #443/R est:12000
£8784 $15459 €13000 Winter in Rovetta (50x60cm-20x24in) s. painted 1951. 22-May-4 Galleria Pananti, Florence #518/R est:12000-14000
£10145 $16638 €14000 Venice (50x60cm-20x24in) s. prov. 27-May-3 Sotheby's, Milan #186/R est:12000-15000
Works on paper
£272 $487 €400 Landscape (20x25cm-8x10in) s. pencil. 16-Mar-4 Finarte Semenzato, Milan #260/R
£1871 $3349 €2750 Houses in Rovetta (42x55cm-17x22in) s. W/C. 22-Mar-4 Sant Agostino, Torino #432/R est:2000

TOSINI, Michele (1503-1577) Italian
£9929 $16582 €14000 Madonna con bambino e San Giovannino (92x70cm-36x28in) panel. 18-Jun-3 Christie's, Rome #444/R est:15000-20000
£11111 $20000 €16222 Saint Catherine of Alexandia (43x33cm-17x13in) panel prov. 22-Jan-4 Sotheby's, New York #136/R est:25000-35000
£16000 $27200 €23360 Madonna and Child with the infant Saint John the Baptist (107x79cm-42x31in) panel. 29-Oct-3 Christie's, London #83/R est:8000-12000
£55556 $100000 €81112 Allegorical figure (73x55cm-29x22in) panel prov. 22-Jan-4 Sotheby's, New York #15/R est:60000-80000

TOSSANI-SPINELLI, Alda (1880-1959) Italian
£385 $680 €562 Still life of roses in glass vase (61x81cm-24x32in) s. 22-May-4 Weschler, Washington #177

TOSSIGNANO, Bernardino da (fl.c.1515-1520) Italian
£47222 $85000 €68944 Saint Helena holding the Cross, with the Emperor Constantine (207x142cm-81x56in) s.d.9 April 1515 panel prov.lit. 23-Jan-4 Christie's, Rockefeller NY #4/R est:20000-30000

TOSTI, Riccardo (1910-1986) Italian
£507 $958 €750 Harvester (50x60cm-20x24in) s. s.i.verso. 20-Feb-4 Stadion, Trieste #224
£532 $888 €750 Porticciolo (50x80cm-20x31in) s. 21-Jun-3 Stadion, Trieste #199/R

TOSTRUP, Axel Olaf (1947-) Norwegian
£244 $449 €356 Still life of bottle, glass and bowl (100x70cm-39x28in) s. oil paper. 10-Jun-4 Grev Wedels Plass, Oslo #226/R (N.KR 3000)
£244 $449 €356 Composition (100x70cm-39x28in) s. oil paper. 10-Jun-4 Grev Wedels Plass, Oslo #227/R (N.KR 3000)

TOTH, Gyula (1891-1970) Hungarian
£1265 $2289 €1847 Presbyterian church in Nagybanya (67x53cm-26x21in) s. 16-Apr-4 Mu Terem Galeria, Budapest #59/R (H.F 480000)

TOTH, Jean (20th C) European
£530 $991 €800 Dimanche matin (100x119cm-39x47in) 24-Jul-4 Thierry & Lannon, Brest #1t/R
Works on paper
£298 $557 €450 Etude pour pardon (23x67cm-9x26in) dr. exec. 1995. 24-Jul-4 Thierry & Lannon, Brest #41t

TOTH, Laszlo (1869-1895) Hungarian
£251 $450 €377 Tavern with figures in back room (30x41cm-12x16in) s. canvas on panel. 29-May-4 Brunk, Ashville #104/R

TOTH, Menyhert (1904-1980) Hungarian
£1500 $2730 €2190 Landscape with mountains beyond (26x42cm-10x17in) init. s.i.d.1941 verso. 15-Jun-4 Bonhams, Knightsbridge #185/R est:1000-1500

TOTH, Sandor (1904-1980) Hungarian
Works on paper
£1336 $2365 €1951 Midinette (30x19cm-12x7in) s.i.d.1929 mixed media. 28-Apr-4 Kieselbach, Budapest #58/R (H.F 500000)

TOTH, Tibor (1962-2001) Hungarian
Works on paper
£333 $613 €500 Landscap weith red arch (63x75cm-25x30in) s.d.1991 mixed media paper on board. 9-Jun-4 Dorotheum, Salzburg #743/R

£467	$859	€700	Red is hope (73x104cm-29x41in) s.d.1992 mixed media masonite. 9-Jun-4 Dorotheum, Salzburg #742/R

TOTTIE, Sophie (1964-) Swedish

Works on paper

£302	$514	€441	G. Arkipelag (62x45cm-24x18in) s.d.1999 verso pencil prov. 4-Nov-3 Bukowskis, Stockholm #635/R (S.KR 4000)
£508	$914	€742	Untitled (32x30cm-13x12in) s.d.1993 verso pencil prov. 26-Apr-4 Bukowskis, Stockholm #465/R (S.KR 7000)
£544	$979	€794	To Tuscholsky I (32x30cm-13x12in) s.d.1993 verso pencil prov. 26-Apr-4 Bukowskis, Stockholm #464/R (S.KR 7500)
£604	$1027	€882	Untitled (123x103cm-48x41in) s. verso mixed media collage canvas. 4-Nov-3 Bukowskis, Stockholm #605/R (S.KR 8000)

TOUCHAGUES, Louis (1893-1974) French

Works on paper

£294	$505	€420	Femme nue allongee (50x65cm-20x26in) s. studio st.verso gouache board. 2-Dec-3 Christie's, Paris #437/R
£315	$541	€450	Promenade a Biarritz (31x24cm-12x9in) s.i. W/C gouache. 2-Dec-3 Christie's, Paris #439/R
£594	$1022	€850	Nu au fauteuil (47x34cm-19x13in) s. W/C ink. 2-Dec-3 Christie's, Paris #438/R

TOUDOUZE, Simon Alexandre (1850-1909) French

£428	$787	€650	Paysage (26x80cm-10x31in) s. s.d.1894 verso panel. 28-Jun-4 Joron-Derem, Paris #114

TOULLEC, Jean Louis le (20th C) French

£300	$537	€450	Marine a Concarneau (38x55cm-15x22in) s. 16-May-4 Thierry & Lannon, Brest #328
£563	$1053	€850	Discussion a Concarneau (54x65cm-21x26in) s. 24-Jul-4 Thierry & Lannon, Brest #274

TOULMOUCHE, Auguste (1829-1890) French

£600	$1092	€876	Reverie (30x35cm-12x14in) s. 16-Jun-4 Rupert Toovey, Partridge Green #131/R
£6704	$12000	€9788	Sweet memories (47x28cm-19x11in) s.d.1887. 6-May-4 Doyle, New York #52/R est:12000-18000

TOULOT, Jules (1863-?) French

£5800	$10672	€8468	Elegant au chapeau (81x65cm-32x26in) s.d.1903. 25-Mar-4 Christie's, Kensington #59/R est:4000-6000

TOULOUSE, Roger (1918-1994) French

£699	$1189	€1000	Nature morte a l'oeuf (47x56cm-19x22in) s.d.1942. 28-Nov-3 Drouot Estimations, Paris #196
£1325	$2411	€2000	Fleurs (55x38cm-22x15in) s. s.i.d.1938 verso lit. 19-Jun-4 Binoche, Orleans #26 est:2000-2500

TOULOUSE-LAUTREC, Henri de (1864-1901) French

£725	$1188	€1000	Loge (29x23cm-11x9in) s. mixed media cardboard prov. 27-May-3 Il Ponte, Milan #901
£7263	$13000	€10604	Cavalier. Silhouette (16x26cm-6x10in) pencil double-sided exec 1881 prov.lit. 6-May-4 Sotheby's, New York #229/R est:12000-18000
£83799	$150000	€122347	Cheval de chasse a courre (24x18cm-9x7in) s. panel prov.exhib.lit. 6-May-4 Sotheby's, New York #240/R est:60000-80000

Prints

£1613	$3000	€2355	Carnival (25x16cm-10x6in) col lithograph. 2-Mar-4 Swann Galleries, New York #656/R est:2000-3000
£1676	$3000	€2447	Aristide Bruant (81x60cm-32x24in) col lithograph. 4-May-4 Doyle, New York #272/R est:3000-5000
£1765	$3000	€2577	Luce Myres, de face (37x25cm-15x10in) artist st.num.3 green lithograph. 6-Nov-3 Swann Galleries, New York #443/R est:3500-5000
£1788	$3200	€2610	Folies Bergere, les pudeurs de monsieur Prudhomme (37x27cm-15x11in) lithograph. 6-May-4 Swann Galleries, New York #332/R est:3000-5000
£1902	$3500	€2777	Madame Rejane (28x23cm-11x9in) lithograph. 10-Jun-4 Sotheby's, New York #278/R est:3000-5000
£2011	$3600	€2936	Debauche (23x31cm-9x12in) color lithograph. 6-May-4 Swann Galleries, New York #340/R est:2500-3500
£2054	$3800	€2999	La tige, Moulin Rouge (30x24cm-12x9in) s. lithograph. 12-Feb-4 Christie's, Rockefeller NY #410/R est:2000-3000
£2059	$3500	€3006	Promenoir (46x35cm-18x14in) mono. lithograph. 31-Oct-3 Sotheby's, New York #469/R
£2095	$3750	€3059	Lender dans madam sutan (36x25cm-14x10in) lithograph. 14-May-4 Du Mouchelle, Detroit #2116/R est:1000-1500
£2123	$3610	€3100	Luce Myres, de profil. i. lithograph. 6-Nov-3 Piasa, Paris #167/R
£2235	$3800	€3263	Nuit blanche (36x27cm-14x11in) lithograph exec.1893. 4-Nov-3 Christie's, Rockefeller NY #209/R est:4500-5500
£2260	$4000	€3300	Le tocsin (57x45cm-22x18in) blue turquoise green lithograph. 30-Apr-4 Sotheby's, New York #265 est:5000-7000
£2347	$4318	€3427	Au Moulin Rouge - l'Union Franco-Russe (38x26cm-15x10in) s. lithograph lit. 29-Mar-4 Rasmussen, Copenhagen #62/R est:10000 (D.KR 26000)
£2374	$4250	€3466	May Belfort (81x61cm-32x24in) col lithograph card. 4-May-4 Doyle, New York #275/R est:3000-4000
£2401	$4250	€3505	Les vieilles histoires, Couverture (34x54cm-13x21in) mono. col lithograph. 30-Apr-4 Sotheby's, New York #232/R est:4000-6000
£2401	$4250	€3505	Femme sur le dos, lassitude (40x52cm-16x20in) reddish brown olive green lithograph. 30-Apr-4 Sotheby's, New York #252/R est:5000-7000
£2500	$4300	€3650	Lender dansant le pas du bolero, dans chilperic (37x27cm-15x11in) olive-green lithograph edition of 50. 4-Dec-3 Sotheby's, London #220/R est:3000-5000
£2527	$4650	€3689	Brandes et Leloir (56x38cm-22x15in) mono. lithograph printed in moss green lit. 29-Mar-4 Rasmussen, Copenhagen #56/R est:20000 (D.KR 28000)
£2527	$4650	€3689	Yvette Guilbert (39x31cm-15x12in) mono. lithograph lit. 29-Mar-4 Rasmussen, Copenhagen #58/R est:12000-15000 (D.KR 28000)
£2527	$4650	€3689	Sagesse (35x27cm-14x11in) s. lithograph in colour lit. 29-Mar-4 Rasmussen, Copenhagen #63/R est:10000 (D.KR 28000)
£2542	$4500	€3711	La coiffure (32x24cm-13x9in) col lithograph. 30-Apr-4 Sotheby's, New York #229/R est:3000-4000
£2542	$4500	€3711	Lender et lavalliere, dans une revue aux varietes (55x38cm-22x15in) mono. olive green lithograph. 30-Apr-4 Sotheby's, New York #238/R est:5000-7000
£2647	$4500	€3865	Elles (40x52cm-16x20in) i. lithograph. 31-Oct-3 Sotheby's, New York #467/R
£2647	$4500	€3865	Lender dansant le pas du Bolero, dans Chilperic (38x27cm-15x11in) artist st.num.11 lithograph. 6-Nov-3 Swann Galleries, New York #441/R est:6000-9000
£2740	$4658	€4000	Au Moulin Rouge. i. lithograph. 6-Nov-3 Piasa, Paris #162
£2752	$4596	€3990	Les vieux messieurs. st.mono. lithograph. 19-Jun-3 Kornfeld, Bern #985 est:10000 (S.FR 6000)
£2800	$5012	€4200	Au Moulin Rouge, un rude! Un vrai rude! (36x25cm-14x10in) st.mono. lithograph prov. 14-May-4 Ketterer, Munich #113/R est:4500-5500
£2800	$5096	€4088	Sagesse (36x28cm-14x11in) s.num.26 lithograph edition of 100. 1-Jul-4 Sotheby's, London #300/R est:3000-4000
£2825	$5000	€4125	May Belfort (79x60cm-31x24in) col lithograph. 30-Apr-4 Sotheby's, New York #262/R est:5000-7000
£2901	$5221	€4235	Mademoiselle Marcelle Lender, en buste (33x24cm-13x9in) col lithograph lit. 26-Apr-4 Bukowskis, Stockholm #447a/R est:50000-60000 (S.KR 40000)
£2905	$5200	€4241	Un monsieur et une dame, programme pour l'argent (32x23cm-13x9in) color lithograph. 6-May-4 Swann Galleries, New York #336/R est:7000-10000
£3000	$5160	€4380	Programme pour l'argent (32x24cm-13x9in) col lithograph. 4-Dec-3 Sotheby's, London #225/R est:4000-5000
£3073	$5500	€4487	Mademoiselle Marcelle Lender, en buste (33x24cm-13x9in) col lithograph. 4-May-4 Doyle, New York #274/R est:6000-8000
£3159	$5812	€4612	Yvette Guilbert (38x31cm-15x12in) mono. lithograph lit. 29-Mar-4 Rasmussen, Copenhagen #55/R est:20000-25000 (D.KR 35000)
£3467	$6275	€5200	Loge au mascaron dore (31x24cm-12x9in) col lithograph. 31-Mar-4 Tajan, Paris #334/R est:1500-2000
£3562	$6055	€5200	Souper a Londres. lithograph. 6-Nov-3 Piasa, Paris #169/R
£3667	$6710	€5500	Guy et Mealy dans Paris qui marche (28x23cm-11x9in) s. st.mono. lithograph. 5-Jun-4 Lempertz, Koln #1013/R est:4000-5000
£3672	$6500	€5361	Madame le Margoin, modiste (31x25cm-12x10in) lithograph. 30-Apr-4 Sotheby's, New York #259/R est:6000-8000
£3824	$6500	€5583	Chatelaine (57x45cm-22x18in) coll lithograph. 31-Oct-3 Sotheby's, New York #480/R
£3911	$7000	€5710	May Milton (79x61cm-31x24in) color lithograph. 6-May-4 Swann Galleries, New York #337/R est:7000-10000
£3944	$6586	€5758	Elles (63x47cm-25x19in) mono. col lithograph. 7-Oct-3 Rasmussen, Copenhagen #386/R est:30000-40000 (D.KR 42000)
£4061	$7473	€5929	Programme pour Une Faillite (42x32cm-17x13in) mono. lithograph printed in colour prov.lit. 29-Mar-4 Rasmussen, Copenhagen #54/R est:20000-25000 (D.KR 45000)
£4110	$6986	€6000	Lender et Lavalliere. lithograph. 6-Nov-3 Piasa, Paris #168/R
£4118	$7000	€6012	Di Ti Fellow, Anglaise au Cafe Concert (32x26cm-13x10in) s.num.19 violet lithograph. 6-Nov-3 Swann Galleries, New York #448/R est:8000-12000
£4532	$7704	€6617	Mademoiselle Marcelle Lender, en buste (32x24cm-13x9in) lithograph lit. 5-Nov-3 AB Stockholms Auktionsverk #1295/R est:60000-80000 (S.KR 60000)
£4706	$8000	€6871	Jane Avril (125x90cm-49x35in) col lithograph. 31-Oct-3 Sotheby's, New York #472/R
£4802	$8500	€7011	Mademoiselle Marcelle Lender en buste (35x27cm-14x11in) col lithograph. 30-Apr-4 Sotheby's, New York #237/R est:8000-12000
£5000	$9100	€7300	Femme qui se peigne (53x40cm-21x16in) num.16 col lithograph edition of 100. 1-Jul-4 Sotheby's, London #308/R est:5000-6000
£5248	$9500	€7662	Divan Japonais (78x61cm-31x24in) col transferred screen lithograph crayon brush spatter. 19-Apr-4 Bonhams & Butterfields, San Francisco #224/R est:6000-8000
£5650	$10000	€8249	Mademoiselle Marcelle Lender, en buste (33x24cm-13x9in) col lithograph. 28-Apr-4 Christie's, Rockefeller NY #244/R est:10000-15000
£6114	$11127	€8926	Au Hanneton. s. st.mono. lithograph. 17-Jun-4 Kornfeld, Bern #799/R est:12500 (S.FR 14000)
£6376	$11732	€9500	Femme au lit, profil, au petit lever (40x52cm-16x20in) col lithograph. 26-Mar-4 Ketterer, Hamburg #220/R est:12000-16000
£6471	$11000	€9448	Mademoiselle Marcelle Lender, en buste (33x24cm-13x9in) col lithograph. 6-Nov-3 Swann Galleries, New York #442/R est:12000-18000
£6575	$11178	€9600	Brandes dans sa loge. lithograph one of 25. 6-Nov-3 Piasa, Paris #164/R
£6704	$12000	€9788	Femme au lit, au petit lever (40x52cm-16x20in) color lithograph. 6-May-4 Swann Galleries, New York #339/R est:15000-20000
£6780	$12000	€9899	Miss May Belfort au bar achille (31x26cm-12x10in) lithograph. 30-Apr-4 Sotheby's, New York #242/R est:8000-10000
£7059	$12000	€10306	Troupe de mademoiselle Elegantine (62x80cm-24x31in) col lithograph. 31-Oct-3 Sotheby's, New York #481/R
£7110	$11874	€10310	Mademoiselle Marcelle Lender. col lithograph. 19-Jun-3 Kornfeld, Bern #991 est:12500 (S.FR 15500)
£7821	$14000	€11419	Mademoiselle Marcelle Lender (33x24cm-13x9in) color lithograph. 6-May-4 Swann Galleries, New York #335/R est:15000-20000
£8000	$14560	€11680	Mademoiselle Marcelle Lender en buste (36x27cm-14x11in) col lithograph. 1-Jul-4 Sotheby's, London #301/R est:5000-7000
£9040	$16000	€13198	Aux ambassadeurs (30x24cm-12x9in) s. col lithograph. 30-Apr-4 Sotheby's, New York #235/R est:20000-30000
£9862	$16470	€14300	Anna Held, dans 'Toutes ces dames au theatre'. lithograph. 19-Jun-3 Kornfeld, Bern #989 est:17500 (S.FR 21500)
£9928	$18267	€14495	Frontispiece pour Ellis (42x40cm-17x16in) s. lithograph in colour lit. 29-Mar-4 Rasmussen, Copenhagen #53/R est:50000 (D.KR 110000)
£10000	$17900	€15000	Mademoiselle Marcelle Lender, en buste (32x24cm-13x9in) col lithograph. 13-May-4 Bassenge, Berlin #5674a/R est:9000
£10044	$18279	€14664	Mademoiselle Marcelle Lender. col lithograph. 17-Jun-4 Kornfeld, Bern #795/R est:17500 (S.FR 23000)
£10734	$19000	€15672	La revue blanche (128x93cm-50x37in) col lithograph. 30-Apr-4 Sotheby's, New York #264/R est:18000-24000
£10870	$20000	€15870	Frontispiece pour Elles (64x48cm-25x19in) col lithograph. 10-Jun-4 Sotheby's, New York #277/R est:6000-8000
£11000	$20020	€16060	Divan Japonais (80x60cm-31x24in) col lithograph. 1-Jul-4 Sotheby's, London #307/R est:12000-15000
£11176	$19000	€16317	Troupe de M.lle Eglantine (62x80cm-24x31in) col lithograph exec. 1896. 4-Nov-3 Christie's, Rockefeller NY #211/R est:20000-30000
£12156	$20300	€17626	Debauche - deuxieme planche. s. col lithograph. 19-Jun-3 Kornfeld, Bern #993/R est:17500 (S.FR 26500)
£12228	$22500	€17853	May Belfort (79x61cm-31x24in) col lithograph. 10-Jun-4 Sotheby's, New York #279/R est:20000-30000
£12291	$22000	€17945	Aux ambassadeurs (30x25cm-12x10in) s. color lithograph. 6-May-4 Swann Galleries, New York #333/R est:30000-40000
£12429	$22000	€18146	Le Suisse, menu (37x27cm-15x11in) lithograph. 30-Apr-4 Sotheby's, New York #253/R est:20000-30000
£12667	$22673	€19000	Au Moulin Rouge (46x34cm-18x13in) s. col lithograph. 11-May-4 Christie's, Paris #150/R est:18000-25000

£13380 $23148 €19000 Aux ambassadeurs (41x57cm-16x22in) lithograph one of 100 exec. 1894. 14-Dec-3 Rabourdin & Choppin de Janvry, Paris #10/R est:22000-25000
£13559 $24000 €19796 Reine de Joie (134x95cm-53x37in) col lithograph on linen. 28-Apr-4 Christie's, Rockefeller NY #241/R est:6000-9000
£13595 $23112 €19849 Au Moulin Rouge, la goulue et sa saeur (46x35cm-18x14in) s.col lit. one of 100 col lithograph prov.exhib.lit. 4-Nov-3 Bukowskis, Stockholm #471/R est:200000-250000 (S.KR 180000)
£14118 $24000 €20612 Jane Avril (129x94cm-51x37in) col lithograph. 31-Oct-3 Sotheby's, New York #471/R
£14124 $25000 €20621 La loge au mascaron (37x29cm-15x11in) s.num.27 col lithograph. 30-Apr-4 Sotheby's, New York #230/R est:30000-40000
£15294 $26000 €22329 Le Troupe de Mademoiselle Eglantine (60x80cm-24x31in) col lithograph. 6-Nov-3 Swann Galleries, New York #444/R est:18000-22000
£15819 $28000 €23096 La Troupe de Mademoiselle Eglantine (62x80cm-24x31in) col lithograph on linen. 28-Apr-4 Christie's, Rockefeller NY #246/R est:20000-30000
£16594 $30201 €24227 Elles. lithograph. 17-Jun-4 Kornfeld, Bern #798/R est:20000 (S.FR 38000)
£16949 $30000 €24746 Jane Avril (130x95cm-51x37in) col lithograph. 28-Apr-4 Christie's, Rockefeller NY #242/R est:10000-15000
£17059 $29000 €24906 May Belfort (79x61cm-31x24in) col lithograph. 31-Oct-3 Sotheby's, New York #477/R
£17123 $29110 €25000 Jockey se rendant au poteau. lithograph. 6-Nov-3 Piasa, Paris #171/R
£17148 $31552 €25036 Le Jockey (51x36cm-20x14in) mono.d.1899 lithograph in black white print run of 100 prov.lit. 29-Mar-4 Rasmussen, Copenhagen #57/R est:40000 (D.KR 190000)
£18079 $32000 €26395 Divan Japonais (79x60cm-31x24in) col lithograph on linen. 28-Apr-4 Christie's, Rockefeller NY #243/R est:20000-30000
£18824 $32000 €27483 Aristide Bruant (139x95cm-55x37in) col lithograph exec.1893. 4-Nov-3 Christie's, Rockefeller NY #208/R est:35000-45000
£19118 $32500 €27912 May Belfort (81x60cm-32x24in) col lithograph. 31-Oct-3 Sotheby's, New York #479/R
£20000 $36400 €29200 Le pony philibert (37x26cm-15x10in) lithograph. 30-Jun-4 Christie's, London #321/R est:4000-6000
£20588 $35000 €30058 Aristide Bruant (139x98cm-55x39in) col lithograph. 31-Oct-3 Sotheby's, New York #475/R
£21765 $37000 €31777 Couverture (59x85cm-23x33in) s.i. lithograph. 31-Oct-3 Sotheby's, New York #465/R
£22353 $38000 €32635 Femme a glace, la glace a main (52x10cm-20x4in) i. col lithograph. 6-Nov-3 Swann Galleries, New York #445/R est:18000-22000
£22905 $41000 €33441 Au Moulin Rouge, la Goyloue et sa Soeur (46x35cm-18x14in) s. color lithograph. 6-May-4 Swann Galleries, New York #331/R est:40000-60000
£23529 $40000 €34352 Aristide Bruant (134x95cm-53x37in) col lithograph. 31-Oct-3 Sotheby's, New York #474/R
£25000 $42500 €36500 Sescau (61x80cm-24x31in) col lithograph. 31-Oct-3 Sotheby's, New York #476/R
£29412 $50000 €42942 Ambassadeurs (144x98cm-57x39in) col lithograph. 31-Oct-3 Sotheby's, New York #464/R
£30000 $48000 €43800 Mademoiselle Marcelle Lender, en buste (3x24cm-1x9in) col lithograph edition of 1100. 18-Sep-3 Swann Galleries, New York #659/R est:15000-20000
£44118 $75000 €64412 Jane Avril (55x38cm-22x15in) col lithograph. 31-Oct-3 Sotheby's, New York #482/R
£52941 $90000 €77294 Reine de joie (140x96cm-55x38in) col lithograph. 31-Oct-3 Sotheby's, New York #470/R
£169492 $300000 €247458 La clownesse assise (52x40cm-20x16in) col lithograph. 30-Apr-4 Sotheby's, New York #247/R est:300000-400000

Works on paper

£222 $384 €324 Moulin rouge, la goullie (69x41cm-27x16in) serigraph. 9-Dec-3 Maynards, Vancouver #193a (C.D 500)
£596 $1091 €900 Foret (23x18cm-9x7in) crayon drawing exec c.1881 lit. 7-Apr-4 Piasa, Paris #17
£1000 $1670 €1460 Tete de femme/homme de profil (17x10cm-7x4in) i.verso pencil lit. 22-Oct-3 Bonhams, New Bond Street #7/R est:1000-1500
£1447 $2663 €2113 Portrait of writers (15x10cm-6x4in) st.sig. ink prov.lit. 23-Jun-4 Koller, Zurich #3112 est:4000-7000 (S.FR 3300)
£1888 $3210 €2700 People and horse (17x11cm-7x4in) lead pencil drawing exec c.1880 prov.lit. 1-Dec-3 Camard, Paris #23/R est:2800-3000
£2055 $3493 €3000 Caricature erotique (12x20cm-5x8in) crayon prov. 6-Nov-3 Tajan, Paris #201/R
£2098 $3608 €3000 Cheval et chien. Chasseur (14x17cm-6x7in) black crayon double-sided exec.c.1878 prov.lit. 3-Dec-3 Beaussant & Lefèvre, Paris #75/R est:2000-3000
£2198 $4000 €3209 Femme (23x36cm-9x14in) ink executed 1894 prov.exhib.lit. 29-Jun-4 Sotheby's, New York #326/R est:4000-6000
£2260 $3843 €3300 Femme de dos (19x13cm-7x5in) pen ink prov. 6-Nov-3 Tajan, Paris #212/R
£2454 $4000 €3583 Le Chirurgien Pean (23x18cm-9x7in) pencil paper on board prov.lit. 25-Sep-3 Christie's, Rockefeller NY #505/R est:4000-6000
£2837 $4738 €4000 Les chevaux de cirque (10x16cm-4x6in) st.init. pencil pen double-sided. 15-Oct-3 Rabourdin & Choppin de Janvry, Paris #17/R est:5500-6000
£2837 $4738 €4000 L'espagnole (23x14cm-9x6in) graphite double-sided. 15-Oct-3 Rabourdin & Choppin de Janvry, Paris #18/R est:5500-6000
£2837 $4738 €4000 La rixe (19x30cm-7x12in) st. pencil double-sided. 15-Oct-3 Rabourdin & Choppin de Janvry, Paris #20/R est:5500-6000
£2851 $5246 €4162 Study of two heads (18x13cm-7x5in) pen paper on board lit. 23-Jun-4 Koller, Zurich #3111/R est:2500-4000 (S.FR 6500)
£3082 $5240 €4500 Caricature (23x17cm-9x7in) crayon prov. 6-Nov-3 Tajan, Paris #204/R
£3374 $5500 €4926 Cerfs et biches (15x20cm-6x8in) st.mono. pencil paper on board prov.lit. 25-Sep-3 Christie's, Rockefeller NY #501/R est:6000-8000
£3380 $5848 €4800 Souvenir de l'Exposition Universelle (16x10cm-6x4in) mono. ink prov.lit. 15-Dec-3 Marc Kohn, Paris #84/R est:6000-8000
£3688 $6159 €5200 Le lion Brutus (14x23cm-6x9in) i.d.16 avril 83 graphite double-sided. 15-Oct-3 Rabourdin & Choppin de Janvry, Paris #19/R est:5500-6000
£4192 $7000 €6120 Attelage au repos. Croquis de Cavaliers (13x21cm-5x8in) pencil double-sided exec.c.1879-81 lit. 7-Oct-3 Sotheby's, New York #249/R est:8000-10000
£4294 $7000 €6269 Sanglier (9x15cm-4x6in) pencil drs three prov.lit. 25-Sep-3 Christie's, Rockefeller NY #506/R est:6000-8000
£5380 $8500 €7855 Au circqu, travil des poids (36x25cm-14x10in) mono. W/C. 7-Sep-3 Treadway Gallery, Cincinnati #563/R est:5000-7000
£5517 $9159 €8000 Hure de sanglier (14x23cm-6x9in) st.mono. W/C gouache prov.exhib.lit. 2-Oct-3 Sotheby's, Paris #151/R est:6000
£10056 $18000 €14682 Cavalier sellant son cheval (23x17cm-9x7in) st.mono. pen ink pencil tracing paper on card prov.exhib.lit. 6-May-4 Sotheby's, New York #228/R est:15000-20000
£16000 $29440 €23360 Femmes dansant (35x23cm-14x9in) blue red crayon drawn circa 1894 prov.lit. 24-Jun-4 Christie's, London #311/R est:12000-15000

TOUMANOFF, Eileen (20th C) American

£219 $400 €329 Geometric shapes in brown, blue and grey (163x81cm-64x32in) acrylic. 31-Jul-4 Sloans & Kenyon, Bethesda #1209/R

TOUPIN, Fernand (1930-) Canadian

£533 $885 €778 Touches noires (36x28cm-14x11in) s.d.1963 i.d.verso prov. 5-Oct-3 Levis, Calgary #118/R (C.D 1200)

TOURETTE, P (?) ?

£2703 $5000 €3946 Setters on point (56x46cm-22x18in) s. 10-Feb-4 Doyle, New York #192/R est:4000-6000

TOURGUENEFF, Pierre Nicolas (1854-1912) Russian/French

Sculpture

£2000 $3400 €2920 English horse (47cm-19in) s. pat bronze. 20-Nov-3 Sotheby's, Olympia #197/R est:2000-3000

TOURIE (19th C) ?

£4698 $8409 €7000 Interieur de cabaret anime de nombreux personnages (80x121cm-31x48in) s. 25-May-4 Palais de Beaux Arts, Brussels #563/R est:7000-10000

TOURILLON, Alfred Edouard (19th C) French

£3217 $5533 €4600 Les chevreuils (72x91cm-28x36in) 3-Dec-3 Coutau Begarie, Paris #111/R est:1800-2000

TOURNACHON, Gaspard Felix (1820-1910) French

Photographs

£28169 $48732 €40000 Ambassade du Japon a Paris (23x31cm-9x12in) albumen print exec.1862 set of 13 prov. 10-Dec-3 Artcurial Briest, Paris #6/R est:40000-60000

TOURNEMINE, Charles Emile de (1812-1872) Italian

£1667 $3017 €2500 Ibis et Flamand (14x18cm-6x7in) mono. mono.i.d.30 mai 1861 exhib. 30-Mar-4 Rossini, Paris #1060 est:700-1200

Works on paper

£638 $1173 €950 Scene de campagne (15x25cm-6x10in) s. W/C ink prov. 24-Mar-4 Joron-Derem, Paris #237/R

TOURNIER, Jean Ulrich (?-c.1865) French

£1467 $2684 €2200 Bouquet champetre (32x25cm-13x10in) s. 6-Jun-4 Osenat, Fontainebleau #72a/R est:2000-2500

TOURNIER, Nicolas (1590-1657) French

£11409 $21221 €17000 David holding Goliath's head (122x94cm-48x37in) 2-Mar-4 Ansorena, Madrid #272/R est:15000

TOURNON, Georges (?) ?

£276 $458 €400 Clown a la parade (79x59cm-31x23in) s. cardboard painted 1920. 1-Oct-3 Millon & Associes, Paris #81

TOURNY, Joseph Gabriel (1817-1880) French

Works on paper

£1336 $2231 €1951 Young woman with a black headband (39x29cm-15x11in) s.i. W/C. 20-Oct-3 Stephan Welz, Johannesburg #197/R est:3000-5000 (SA.R 15500)

TOURNY, Léon Auguste (1835-?) French

Works on paper

£861 $1567 €1300 Madonna with Saints (59x51cm-23x20in) s. W/C. 21-Jun-4 Pandolfini, Florence #13/R

TOURRIER, Alfred Holst (1836-1892) British

£2699 $4750 €3941 Suing for mercy (80x130cm-31x51in) s. indis d. indis i.verso. 18-May-4 Bonhams & Butterfields, San Francisco #166/R est:4000-6000

TOURSKY, G de (19/20th C) ?

£2533 $4661 €3800 Odalisque au tigre (45x81cm-18x32in) s. 14-Jun-4 Gros & Delettrez, Paris #551/R est:3000-3500

TOURTEL, Mary (1897-1940) British

Works on paper

£750 $1298 €1095 Rupert the Bear (7x5cm-3x2in) s.d.Jan 12. 1943 one d. Jan 14. 1943 pencil pair. 11-Dec-3 Sotheby's, London #325/R

TOUSIGNANT, Claude (1932-) Canadian

£1920 $3514 €2803 Double (90x90cm-35x35in) s.i.d.6/73 acrylic round prov. 1-Jun-4 Joyner Waddington, Toronto #94/R est:5000-7000 (C.D 4800)
£2236 $4002 €3265 Bivalence multiple (30cm-12in circular) s.i.d.1971 diptych. 31-May-4 Sotheby's, Toronto #24/R est:4000-6000 (C.D 5500)
£2400 $4392 €3504 Double (90x90cm-35x35in) s.d.6/73 verso acrylic round prov. 1-Jun-4 Joyner Waddington, Toronto #93/R est:5000-7000 (C.D 6000)

TOUSSAINT, Fernand (1873-1956) Belgian

£448 $829 €650 Ruelle de Bruges animee (38x46cm-15x18in) s. canvas on cardboard. 13-Jan-4 Vanderkindere, Brussels #182
£1034 $1862 €1500 Nature morte aux roses (21x26cm-8x10in) s. panel. 20-Jan-4 Galerie Moderne, Brussels #146/R est:2000-3000
£1310 $2424 €1900 Portrait d'elegante (45x36cm-18x14in) s.d.33. 19-Jan-4 Horta, Bruxelles #206 est:2500-3500

£1316	$2382	€2000	Couple sur un pont (46x38cm-18x15in) s. panel. 19-Apr-4 Horta, Bruxelles #93 est:2000-2500
£1389	$2319	€2000	Marcheur dans la Dreve (46x38cm-18x15in) s. 21-Oct-3 Galerie Moderne, Brussels #347 est:1800-2400
£1528	$2429	€2200	Le fenaison (44x54cm-17x21in) s. canvas on cardboard. 15-Sep-3 Horta, Bruxelles #134 est:2200-2800
£1528	$2551	€2200	Reflets dans l'etang (37x45cm-15x18in) s. 21-Oct-3 Galerie Moderne, Brussels #355/R est:1800-2400
£2013	$3725	€3000	Still life with roses (65x81cm-26x32in) s. 13-Mar-4 De Vuyst, Lokeren #322/R est:4000-6000
£2414	$4031	€3500	Portrait of young woman wearing hat (27x31cm-11x12in) s.i. panel lit. 10-Jul-3 Allgauer, Kempten #2706/R est:3500
£2621	$4848	€3800	Elegant promenant son chien dans un parc (50x60cm-20x24in) s. 16-Feb-4 Horta, Bruxelles #177/R est:2500-3000
£3793	$7017	€5500	Elegante a la robe rose (46x37cm-18x15in) s. 19-Jan-4 Horta, Bruxelles #205/R est:5500-7000
£4027	$7450	€6000	Young woman with shawl (35x27cm-14x11in) s. canvas on board. 13-Mar-4 De Vuyst, Lokeren #448/R est:7000-8000
£5333	$9600	€8000	Elegant pose (45x37cm-18x15in) s. paintersboard. 21-Apr-4 Christie's, Amsterdam #193/R est:5000-7000
£5517	$10207	€8000	Elegante (46x37cm-18x15in) s. 13-Jan-4 Vanderkindere, Brussels #119/R est:3750-5000
£5960	$10848	€9000	Nature morte aux fleurs et fruits (45x55cm-18x22in) s. 15-Jun-4 Galerie Moderne, Brussels #334/R est:4000-6000
£6053	$10955	€9200	Composition au vase fleuri de pivoines, aux cerises et aux peches (65x81cm-26x32in) s. 19-Apr-4 Horta, Bruxelles #92/R est:10000-15000
£8667	$15600	€13000	Seductive pose (70x50cm-28x20in) s. 21-Apr-4 Christie's, Amsterdam #194/R est:4000-6000
£11888	$19853	€17000	Elegante a l'eventail et aux roses (99x80cm-39x31in) s. 13-Oct-3 Horta, Bruxelles #144/R est:9000-12000
£31042	$55565	€45321	Patiensen (94x73cm-37x29in) s. 26-May-4 AB Stockholms Auktionsverk #2367/R est:150000-200000 (S.KR 420000)
Works on paper			
£544	$974	€800	Deux scenes animees dans des maisons de mode (26x18cm-10x7in) s. one d.98 W/C htd gouache pair. 21-Mar-4 Muizon & Le Coent, Paris #44
£1931	$3476	€2800	Elegante (27x20cm-11x8in) s. W/C. 20-Jan-4 Galerie Moderne, Brussels #154/R est:2000-3000
£7273	$12364	€10400	L'heure du the (52x34cm-20x13in) s.d.06 W/C. 18-Nov-3 Vanderkindere, Brussels #104/R est:1000-1500

TOUSSAINT, Fernand (attrib) (1873-1956) Belgian

£5068	$8919	€7500	Elegante (80x65cm-31x26in) 18-May-4 Galerie Moderne, Brussels #138/R est:2000-3000

TOUSSAINT, Louis (1826-1887) German

£1599	$2750	€2335	Young artist (66x49cm-26x19in) s. indis i. 3-Dec-3 Doyle, New York #112/R est:5000-7000

TOUTENEL, Lodewijk Jan Petrus (1819-1883) Belgian

£1376	$2298	€1995	Portrait of Mayor (56x72cm-22x28in) s. panel. 23-Jun-3 Philippe Schuler, Zurich #3553 est:3500-4000 (S.FR 3000)

TOVAR, Ivan (1942-) Dominican

£658	$1211	€1000	Untitled (31x38cm-12x15in) s.d.1963. 27-Jun-4 Versailles Encheres #166
£3741	$6697	€5500	Tentative d'echappement (75x60cm-30x24in) s.d.1978 i.verso prov. 21-Mar-4 Calmels Cohen, Paris #90/R est:3000-3500
£10884	$19483	€16000	L'aiguille (97x130cm-38x51in) s.d.70 s.i.d.verso. 19-Mar-4 Millon & Associes, Paris #165/R est:10000-12000

TOVEY, Gordon (20th C) New Zealander

£319	$565	€466	Ships off Napier Hill (29x38cm-11x15in) board. 28-Apr-4 Dunbar Sloane, Auckland #95/R (NZ.D 900)

TOWERS, Samuel (1862-1943) British

£5600	$9520	€8176	Man goeth to his work and his labour, till the evening (75x125cm-30x49in) s.d.1903 W/C. 29-Oct-3 Bonhams, Chester #354/R est:2000-3000
Works on paper			
£280	$512	€409	Scene on the river Llugwy Betwsy-Coed, North Wales (30x38cm-12x15in) s. W/C. 6-Apr-4 Capes Dunn, Manchester #707/R
£320	$589	€467	Harvest scene (47x70cm-19x28in) W/C. 8-Jun-4 Holloways, Banbury #256
£950	$1549	€1378	Village well (27x40cm-11x16in) s. W/C. 23-Sep-3 Bonhams, Knightsbridge #49/R

TOWLE, H Ledyard (1890-?) ?

£1445	$2500	€2110	Girl and Macaw (128x102cm-50x40in) prov. 10-Dec-3 Bonhams & Butterfields, San Francisco #6068/R est:5000-7000

TOWN, Harold Barling (1924-1990) Canadian

£207	$329	€302	Park (38x53cm-15x21in) s.i. 15-Sep-3 Ritchie, Toronto #164/R (C.D 450)
£207	$329	€302	Muscle woman (66x51cm-26x20in) s.i.d.83 verso. 15-Sep-3 Ritchie, Toronto #173/R (C.D 450)
£218	$346	€318	Muscle lady (71x51cm-28x20in) s.i.verso. 15-Sep-3 Ritchie, Toronto #172/R (C.D 475)
£252	$401	€368	Muscle woman (115x79cm-45x31in) s.d.83. 15-Sep-3 Ritchie, Toronto #174/R (C.D 550)
£275	$438	€402	Untitled (28x38cm-11x15in) masonite. 15-Sep-3 Ritchie, Toronto #119/R (C.D 600)
£275	$438	€402	Portrait of woman (61x48cm-24x19in) masonite. 15-Sep-3 Ritchie, Toronto #70/R (C.D 600)
£275	$438	€402	Still life (30x41cm-12x16in) s.d.47 d.verso masonite. 15-Sep-3 Ritchie, Toronto #121/R (C.D 600)
£275	$438	€402	Circle lost (25x20cm-10x8in) s.i.d.59 verso. 15-Sep-3 Ritchie, Toronto #166/R (C.D 600)
£275	$438	€402	Eight (16x66cm-6x26in) s.i.d.1984 verso. 15-Sep-3 Ritchie, Toronto #201/R (C.D 600)
£298	$474	€435	No room at Mondrian's inn (32x85cm-13x33in) s.i.d.1959 verso. 15-Sep-3 Ritchie, Toronto #7/R (C.D 650)
£298	$474	€435	Silent light (30x15cm-12x6in) s.i.verso oil lucite. 15-Sep-3 Ritchie, Toronto #76/R (C.D 650)
£321	$511	€469	Toy horse (72x93cm-28x37in) s.i.d.verso acrylic masonite wood. 15-Sep-3 Ritchie, Toronto #49/R (C.D 700)
£321	$511	€469	Silent light (20x25cm-8x10in) s.d.1966. 15-Sep-3 Ritchie, Toronto #77/R (C.D 700)
£321	$511	€469	Homage to Turner (23x23cm-9x9in) s.i.d.59 verso oil lucite. 15-Sep-3 Ritchie, Toronto #95/R (C.D 700)
£390	$620	€569	Hidden letter (15x15cm-6x6in) s.i. 15-Sep-3 Ritchie, Toronto #67/R (C.D 850)
£390	$620	€569	Toy horse (58x70cm-23x28in) s.d.82 acrylic masonite wood relief. 15-Sep-3 Ritchie, Toronto #209/R (C.D 850)
£413	$656	€603	Silent light (41x41cm-16x16in) s. oil lucite prov. 15-Sep-3 Ritchie, Toronto #78/R (C.D 900)
£436	$693	€637	Untitled (96cm-38in circular) canvas on panel. 15-Sep-3 Ritchie, Toronto #42/R (C.D 950)
£436	$693	€637	Field edge (23x20cm-9x8in) s.i.d.58 verso oil lucite. 15-Sep-3 Ritchie, Toronto #66/R (C.D 950)
£436	$693	€637	Fence caper with hidden red (20x20cm-8x8in) s.i.verso. 15-Sep-3 Ritchie, Toronto #200/R (C.D 950)
£459	$729	€670	Toy horse (71x100cm-28x39in) s.d.82 acrylic masonite wood relief. 15-Sep-3 Ritchie, Toronto #140/R (C.D 1000)
£459	$729	€670	Muscle man (132x86cm-52x34in) s.i.d.83 verso prov. 15-Sep-3 Ritchie, Toronto #175/R (C.D 1000)
£459	$729	€670	Oh, how we danced (50x50cm-20x20in) s.i. prov. 15-Sep-3 Ritchie, Toronto #204/R (C.D 1000)
£550	$875	€803	Grey stretch (163x163cm-64x64in) s.i.verso oil lucite linen. 15-Sep-3 Ritchie, Toronto #147/R (C.D 1200)
£642	$1021	€937	Homage to Turner (25x20cm-10x8in) s.d.59 oil lucite. 15-Sep-3 Ritchie, Toronto #93/R (C.D 1400)
£734	$1167	€1072	Sp. (13x8cm-5x3in) masonite. 15-Sep-3 Ritchie, Toronto #69/R (C.D 1600)
£780	$1240	€1139	Homage to Turner (20x23cm-8x9in) s.i.d.58 verso. 15-Sep-3 Ritchie, Toronto #94/R (C.D 1700)
£780	$1240	€1139	Abstract (35x46cm-14x18in) s.d.52 masonite. 15-Sep-3 Ritchie, Toronto #120/R (C.D 1700)
£780	$1240	€1139	Break in Joe's wall (20x20cm-8x8in) s.i.d.58 verso oil lucite. 15-Sep-3 Ritchie, Toronto #153/R (C.D 1700)
£780	$1240	€1139	Blue tower (30x30cm-12x12in) s.d.59 oil lucite masonite. 15-Sep-3 Ritchie, Toronto #152/R (C.D 1700)
£780	$1240	€1139	Late gate (21x36cm-8x14in) s.i.d.58 verso oil lucite canvas on masonite. 15-Sep-3 Ritchie, Toronto #165/R (C.D 1700)
£826	$1313	€1206	Untitled (61x118cm-24x46in) masonite. 15-Sep-3 Ritchie, Toronto #55/R (C.D 1800)
£826	$1313	€1206	Trick reflection (30x30cm-12x12in) s. s.i.d.81-82 verso. 15-Sep-3 Ritchie, Toronto #163/R (C.D 1800)
£826	$1313	€1206	Untitled (122x122cm-48x48in) s. linen. 15-Sep-3 Ritchie, Toronto #180/R (C.D 1800)
£1004	$1867	€1466	Untitled, snap (61x61cm-24x24in) sig.handprint verso prov. 2-Mar-4 Ritchie, Toronto #170/R est:3000-5000 (C.D 2500)
£1009	$1605	€1473	Untitled (36x51cm-14x20in) masonite. 15-Sep-3 Ritchie, Toronto #54/R (C.D 2200)
£1220	$2183	€1781	Snap (76x76cm-30x30in) s.i. prov. 31-May-4 Sotheby's, Toronto #72/R est:4000-6000 (C.D 3000)
£1835	$2917	€2679	Stretch 28 (84x347cm-33x137in) s.d.71 prov. 15-Sep-3 Ritchie, Toronto #148/R (C.D 4000)
£2033	$3638	€2968	Optical stamp no.10 (152x137cm-60x54in) s.d.64 s.d.verso. 31-May-4 Sotheby's, Toronto #91/R est:6000-8000 (C.D 5000)
£2638	$4194	€3851	Mural studies (24x95cm-9x37in) masonite three. 15-Sep-3 Ritchie, Toronto #37/R (C.D 5750)
£3400	$6222	€4964	White time (60x64cm-24x25in) s.d.58 oil lucite prov. 1-Jun-4 Joyner Waddington, Toronto #88/R est:5000-7000 (C.D 8500)
£4279	$7275	€6247	Picture for Heather 3 (122x83cm-48x33in) s.d.60 s.i.d.73 verso oil lucite 44 masonite prov. 18-Nov-3 Sotheby's, Toronto #80/R est:8000-10000 (C.D 9500)
£4464	$7679	€6517	Snap (120x147cm-47x58in) s.d.73 oil lucite lit. 2-Dec-3 Joyner Waddington, Toronto #107/R est:12000-15000 (C.D 10000)
Works on paper			
£207	$329	€302	Heat seat (63x56cm-25x22in) s.i.d.79-80 verso mixed media collage panel. 15-Sep-3 Ritchie, Toronto #10/R (C.D 450)
£207	$329	€302	Untitled (27x36cm-11x14in) s.d.81 graphite. 15-Sep-3 Ritchie, Toronto #13/R (C.D 450)
£207	$329	€302	Untitled (18x13cm-7x5in) s.d.85 graphite board. 15-Sep-3 Ritchie, Toronto #46/R (C.D 450)
£207	$329	€302	Untitled (85x51cm-33x20in) paint tube tops on plywood. 15-Sep-3 Ritchie, Toronto #110/R (C.D 450)
£207	$329	€302	You cannot iron a drip (29x24cm-11x9in) i.verso mixed media collage panel. 15-Sep-3 Ritchie, Toronto #115/R (C.D 450)
£218	$346	€318	Sun bunker (48x37cm-19x15in) s.d.87 mixed media. 15-Sep-3 Ritchie, Toronto #81/R (C.D 475)
£218	$346	€318	Untitled (50x61cm-20x24in) gouache. 15-Sep-3 Ritchie, Toronto #141/R (C.D 475)
£218	$346	€318	Giuseppe Verdi (40x30cm-16x12in) s.d.85 graphite board prov. 15-Sep-3 Ritchie, Toronto #158/R (C.D 475)
£218	$346	€318	Model (18x11cm-7x4in) s.d.51 gouache card. 15-Sep-3 Ritchie, Toronto #159/R (C.D 475)
£229	$365	€334	Untitled (67x80cm-26x31in) mixed media collage plywood. 15-Sep-3 Ritchie, Toronto #6/R (C.D 500)
£229	$365	€334	Tripods (15x22cm-6x9in) s.d.73 ink prov. 15-Sep-3 Ritchie, Toronto #12/R (C.D 500)
£229	$365	€334	Untitled (24x22cm-9x9in) s.d.85 graphite. 15-Sep-3 Ritchie, Toronto #98/R (C.D 500)
£252	$401	€368	Untitled (12x17cm-5x7in) s.d.76 graphite. 15-Sep-3 Ritchie, Toronto #47/R (C.D 550)
£252	$401	€368	Untitled (196x45cm-77x18in) mixed media on wooden door. 15-Sep-3 Ritchie, Toronto #109/R (C.D 550)
£279	$444	€407	Untitled (32x52cm-13x20in) s.d.79 gouache ink. 15-Sep-3 Ritchie, Toronto #176/R (C.D 610)
£321	$511	€469	Toy horse (22x28cm-9x11in) s.d.79 ink gouache prov. 15-Sep-3 Ritchie, Toronto #17/R (C.D 700)
£321	$511	€469	Toy horse (76x106cm-30x42in) s.i.d.82 acrylic wood relief. 15-Sep-3 Ritchie, Toronto #50/R (C.D 700)
£321	$511	€469	Bug waslk (57x77cm-22x30in) s.d.83 graphite ink W/C prov. 15-Sep-3 Ritchie, Toronto #128/R (C.D 700)
£344	$547	€502	Untitled (70x59cm-28x23in) pair. 15-Sep-3 Ritchie, Toronto #51/R (C.D 750)
£366	$655	€534	Toy horse (22x30cm-9x12in) s.d.1979 s.i.d.verso gouache prov. 27-May-4 Heffel, Vancouver #187/R (C.D 900)

£413 $656 €603 Bug waslk (57x77cm-22x30in) s.d.1983 graphite ink W/C prov. 15-Sep-3 Ritchie, Toronto #129/R (C.D 900)
£1101 $1750 €1607 Toy horse (152x102cm-60x40in) s.d.82 gouache board prov. 15-Sep-3 Ritchie, Toronto #48/R (C.D 2400)

TOWNE, Charles (jnr) (1781-1854) British
£467 $850 €701 Landscape with cows and figure in front of a ruin (28x43cm-11x17in) s. board painted c.1840. 16-Jun-4 Wolf's, New York #486813/R

TOWNE, Charles (jnr-attrib) (1781-1854) British
£700 $1106 €1015 Horse tethered before an inn on a blustery day (15x22cm-6x9in) panel. 4-Sep-3 Christie's, Kensington #309/R

TOWNE, Charles (1763-1840) British
£1600 $2864 €2336 Drover, cattle and dogs crossing a bridge in a continental landscape (28x33cm-11x13in) s. 7-May-4 Mallams, Oxford #340 est:800-1200
£2400 $3864 €3480 Drover and his cattle on a path way in extensive landscape (25x38cm-10x15in) s.d.1805. 15-Aug-3 Keys, Aylsham #677/R est:1250-1500
£2600 $4836 €3796 Horsemen resting by an escarpment (51x63cm-20x25in) s.d.1820. 4-Mar-4 Christie's, Kensington #412/R est:2000-3000
£4000 $6800 €5840 View of Hawthornden Castle (21x16cm-8x6in) s.d.1823 panel prov. 30-Oct-3 Christie's, London #20/R est:2500-4000
£5587 $10000 €8157 Hunting party. Gentlemen with bag before house (12x14cm-5x6in) init.d.1823 panel pair. 27-May-4 Sotheby's, New York #20/R est:10000-15000
£6000 $10200 €8760 Fallow deer leaping across a field in a landscape (21x27cm-8x11in) i.d.1809 panel. 25-Nov-3 Christie's, London #86/R est:4000-6000

TOWNE, Charles (attrib) (1763-1840) British
£260 $478 €380 Cattle and sheep in a meadow (20x28cm-8x11in) i. verso board. 11-Jun-4 Halls, Shrewsbury #760/R
£2000 $3700 €2920 Horses and sheep in a landscape. Cattle by a river (11x15cm-4x6in) bear init.d. panel pair sold with a landscape with cattle. 14-Jul-4 Sotheby's, Olympia #21/R est:2000-3000
£4500 $8235 €6570 Drover and country girl passing on a track, a farmstead and ruin beyond (69x86cm-27x34in) 6-Jul-4 Bearnes, Exeter #495/R est:5000-7000

TOWNE, Charles (circle) (1763-1840) British
£3352 $6000 €4894 Dappled grey hunter (57x72cm-22x28in) 27-May-4 Sotheby's, New York #255/R est:6000-8000

TOWNE, Francis (1740-1816) British
Works on paper
£2800 $4816 €4088 Mill at Chudleigh, Suffolk (20x25cm-8x10in) s.d.1785 pencil brown ink W/C prov. 3-Dec-3 Christie's, Kensington #6/R est:1000-1500
£3427 $6306 €5003 At Dunford Bridge, Devon (23x14cm-9x6in) s.i. W/C pen prov. 14-Jun-4 Waddingtons, Toronto #97/R est:5000-7000 (C.D 8500)
£6000 $10200 €8760 Tothill, Devon (14x23cm-6x9in) i.verso pencil pen grey ink W/C. 20-Nov-3 Christie's, London #52/R est:2500-3500
£8000 $13600 €11680 James White's Estate at Fordland, Devon (17x39cm-7x15in) pencil pen blk ink W/C two joined sheets prov.exhib. 20-Nov-3 Christie's, London #41/R est:6000-8000
£9000 $16470 €13140 Durham with a view of the castle (17x50cm-7x20in) s.i.d.1811 verso pencil grey in, W/C two joined sheets prov. 3-Jun-4 Christie's, London #56/R est:3000-5000
£15000 $27450 €21900 Durham Cathedral (17x50cm-7x20in) s.i.d.1811 verso pencil W/C two joined sheets prov. 3-Jun-4 Christie's, London #55/R est:4000-6000
£16000 $27200 €23360 Bassenthwaite, Lake District (15x35cm-6x14in) i.verso pen ink W/C on two joined sheet prov. 27-Nov-3 Sotheby's, London #254/R est:7000-10000
£20000 $34000 €29200 Ruin by the road going to Pont Lamentana, Italy (31x47cm-12x19in) s.d.1786 pencil W/C prov. 20-Nov-3 Christie's, London #42/R est:7000-10000

TOWNE, Norman (1915-1988) British
Works on paper
£250 $463 €365 Autumn landscape (20x25cm-8x10in) s.d.54 gouache. 11-Mar-4 Christie's, Kensington #254
£350 $585 €511 Boats by a river (19x24cm-7x9in) W/C bodycol brush black ink. 16-Oct-3 Christie's, Kensington #660/R
£350 $648 €511 Still life with fruit and jug (20x25cm-8x10in) gouache. 11-Mar-4 Christie's, Kensington #308/R

TOWNSEND, Alfred O (1846-1917) British
Works on paper
£250 $433 €365 Phillack from across the water from Hayle, Cornwall (42x63cm-17x25in) s. W/C. 11-Dec-3 Lane, Penzance #101

TOWNSEND, Ernest (1880-1944) British
£260 $447 €380 Buttercups in a grey jug (38x30cm-15x12in) s. 5-Dec-3 Keys, Aylsham #265/R
£300 $483 €438 Nasturtiums (23x30cm-9x12in) s. 15-Aug-3 Keys, Aylsham #777
£420 $689 €613 Still life of vase of peonies (48x38cm-19x15in) s. 28-May-3 Brightwells, Leominster #1078
£2000 $3600 €2920 Portrait of Alfred Edward Goodey (156x142cm-61x56in) s.d.1942 i.verso sold with a photograph. 22-Apr-4 Mellors & Kirk, Nottingham #1135/R est:1500-2000

TOWNSEND, Ernest (attrib) (1880-1944) British
£340 $534 €496 Self portrait with half a mild (50x40cm-20x16in) 16-Apr-3 Bamfords, Derby #639

TOWNSEND, Graeme (1954-) Australian
£4545 $7727 €6636 Rooster in a wheelbarrow (180x240cm-71x94in) s. 29-Oct-3 Lawson Menzies, Sydney #173/R est:8000-10000 (A.D 11000)
Works on paper
£534 $973 €780 Full moon magpie patrol (80x100cm-31x39in) s.d.83 gouache. 16-Jun-4 Deutscher-Menzies, Melbourne #606/R est:1500-2500 (A.D 1400)

TOWNSEND, H William (1940-) Canadian
£294 $491 €429 Ottawa street scene (25x30cm-10x12in) s.i. panel. 17-Nov-3 Hodgins, Calgary #252/R (C.D 650)
£480 $878 €701 Bamfield, BC, Vancouver Island (40x50cm-16x20in) s.i. 1-Jun-4 Hodgins, Calgary #411/R (C.D 1200)
£588 $982 €858 Mountain view, Yoho National Park (55x70cm-22x28in) s.i. board. 17-Nov-3 Hodgins, Calgary #379/R est:2000-2500 (C.D 1300)
£679 $1133 €991 Kathleen Lake, The Yukon (50x60cm-20x24in) s.i. board. 17-Nov-3 Hodgins, Calgary #413/R est:1500-2000 (C.D 1500)
£769 $1285 €1123 Grand Canyon at sunset (40x50cm-16x20in) s.i. 17-Nov-3 Hodgins, Calgary #161/R est:1000-1500 (C.D 1700)

TOWNSHEND, Arthur Louis (fl.1880-1912) British
£900 $1530 €1314 Charibert, a chestnut racehorse in a stable (46x61cm-18x24in) s. 27-Nov-3 Christie's, Kensington #73/R
£1183 $2200 €1727 Portrait of a chestnut mare in a landscape (61x91cm-24x36in) s. 6-Mar-4 North East Auctions, Portsmouth #1121/R

TOWNSHEND, James A (?-1949) British
£260 $424 €380 Winter chill and drear, country land with a drop hunting gate (40x62cm-16x24in) s.verso. 31-Jan-3 Bigwood, Stratford on Avon #275
£450 $752 €657 Winter chill and drear (38x61cm-15x24in) s. 17-Oct-3 Keys, Aylsham #773

TOWNSLEY, Channel Pickering (1867-1921) American
£37838 $70000 €55243 By the pool (64x76cm-25x30in) s. 15-Jul-4 Sotheby's, New York #36/R est:1500-2000

TOXIC (1965-) American
£5369 $9611 €8000 Untitled (118x217cm-46x85in) s.d.2002 verso enamel acrylic. 28-May-4 Farsetti, Prato #322/R est:7000-9000

TOYEN (1902-1980) Czechoslovakian
£44219 $79151 €65000 Portrait d'Andre Breton (49x64cm-19x25in) s.i.d.1950 oil chl pastel collage prov. 21-Mar-4 Calmels Cohen, Paris #41/R est:6000-8000
Works on paper
£3265 $5845 €4800 Untitled (15x13cm-6x5in) s. ink exhib. 21-Mar-4 Calmels Cohen, Paris #13/R est:3000-4000
£4082 $7306 €6000 Untitled (16x12cm-6x5in) s. ink exhib. 21-Mar-4 Calmels Cohen, Paris #14/R est:3000-4000

TOYNBEE, Lawrence L (1922-2002) British
£340 $602 €496 Morning in the Eden Valley (23x35cm-9x14in) board. 27-Apr-4 Bonhams, Knightsbridge #182/R
£550 $946 €803 Half tide on Spekes Beach (61x76cm-24x30in) init.d.63 board exhib. 3-Dec-3 Christie's, Kensington #703
£1200 $2220 €1752 Bathers in the surf (101x122cm-40x48in) init.d.71 board. 11-Mar-4 Christie's, Kensington #263/R est:1000-1500
£2300 $3841 €3358 Skating in Oxford (91x122cm-36x48in) init.d.69 board. 16-Oct-3 Christie's, Kensington #324/R est:2500-3500

TOYOCHIKA, Takamura (1890-1972) Japanese
Sculpture
£1304 $2400 €1904 Seated hotei - God of good fortune (25x41cm-10x16in) s. bronze. 23-Mar-4 Christie's, Rockefeller NY #203/R est:3000-5000

TOYOHIKO, Okamoto (1773-1845) Japanese
Works on paper
£559 $962 €800 Straw hut on the coast in spring (31x55cm-12x22in) s. ink col hanging scroll. 5-Dec-3 Lempertz, Koln #766/R

TOYOKUNI (18/19th C) Japanese
Works on paper
£84459 $148649 €125000 Two Bijin (109x49cm-43x19in) s. seal hanging screen. 22-May-4 Dr Fritz Nagel, Stuttgart #2126/R est:3000

TOYOKUNI, Utagawa (1769-1825) Japanese
Prints
£2600 $4784 €3796 Kintaro showing off his strength (38x75cm-15x30in) s. print triptych exec. late 1790's prov. 8-Jun-4 Sotheby's, London #336/R est:1000-1500
£2800 $5152 €4088 Ichikawa Yaozo III and Iwai Hanshiro IV (38x25cm-15x10in) s. print exec. 1798. 8-Jun-4 Sotheby's, London #312/R est:2000-2500
£3400 $6256 €4964 Bijin-Ga (24x11cm-9x4in) s. print exec. late 1790's prov.lit. 8-Jun-4 Sotheby's, London #330/R est:1500-2000
£4200 $7728 €6132 Blossom wind (37x25cm-15x10in) s. print triptych exec. 1780's prov.lit. 8-Jun-4 Sotheby's, London #328/R est:2500-3500

TOYONOBU, Ishikawa (1711-1785) Japanese
Prints
£2000 $3680 €2920 Segawa Kikujiro I as Kumo No Taema (35x17cm-14x7in) s. print exec. 1755. 8-Jun-4 Sotheby's, London #49/R est:2000-3000
£4200 $7728 €6132 Segawa Kichiji II (43x30cm-17x12in) s. print exec. 1750 lit. 8-Jun-4 Sotheby's, London #42/R est:3000-4000
£16000 $29440 €23360 Courtesan with child attendant (48x31cm-19x12in) s.i. print exec. c.1750's. 8-Jun-4 Sotheby's, London #44/R est:10000-12000

TOZELLI, Felippo (1794-?) Italian

Works on paper

£1081	$1903	€1600	Portrait of a young woman (30x24cm-12x9in) pastel prov. 19-May-4 Sotheby's, Amsterdam #260/R est:2000-3000

TOZER, H Spernon (1864-c.1938) British

£550	$919	€803	Old lady with chicks in an interior (43x57cm-17x22in) s.d.1936 board. 21-Oct-3 Bonhams, Knightsbridge #102/R
£680	$1251	€993	Carpenter (51x36cm-20x14in) s.d.92. 24-Mar-4 Hamptons Fine Art, Godalming #315/R
£980	$1666	€1431	Evening meal (27x37cm-11x15in) s.d.1915 canvasboard. 25-Nov-3 Bonhams, Knowle #224/R
Works on paper			
£740	$1369	€1080	Ploughmans lunch (22x32cm-9x13in) s.d.1910 W/C. 14-Jul-4 Bonhams, Chester #484/R
£740	$1369	€1080	Shelling peas (22x29cm-9x11in) s.d.1910 W/C. 14-Jul-4 Bonhams, Chester #485
£750	$1343	€1095	Afternoon tea (20x30cm-8x12in) s.d.1905 W/C. 26-May-4 Sotheby's, Olympia #98/R
£1600	$2880	€2336	The patchwork quilt (25x32cm-10x13in) s.i.d.1933 pencil W/C. 21-Apr-4 Tennants, Leyburn #1011/R est:1000-1200
£2000	$3320	€2920	A musical interlude (35x49cm-14x19in) s. W/C. 2-Oct-3 Lane, Penzance #300/R est:2000-2500
£2350	$4160	€3525	Old woman peeling vegetables. Woman cooking at a fire (22x32cm-9x13in) s.d.99 W/C pair. 27-Apr-4 Holloways, Banbury #249/R est:1200-1800

TOZER, Henry E (fl.1889-1892) British

Works on paper

£280	$518	€409	Sail stream ship in rough water (18x51cm-7x20in) s.d.70 W/C. 13-Feb-4 Keys, Aylsham #411/R
£711	$1287	€1038	Sailing in rough seas (24x62cm-9x24in) s.d.1888 W/C two prov. 1-Apr-4 Heffel, Vancouver #99/R (C.D 1700)

TOZZI, Mario (1895-1979) Italian

£2115	$3595	€3088	Still life (1x28cm-0x11in) s. 5-Nov-3 Dobiaschofsky, Bern #1008/R est:9000 (S.FR 4800)
£3077	$5138	€4400	Deposition (41x51cm-16x20in) s. cardboard painted 1919 exhib.lit. 26-Jun-3 Sant Agostino, Torino #253/R est:4000-5000
£4225	$7014	€6000	Sl with bread and glass (33x25cm-13x10in) s. 13-Jun-3 Farsetti, Prato #574/R
£4483	$7486	€6500	Still life with apples and grapes (23x19cm-9x7in) s. 13-Nov-3 Finarte Semenzato, Rome #379/R est:6000-7000
£4698	$8691	€7000	Maternity (17x15cm-7x6in) s. painted 1942. 11-Mar-4 Galleria Pace, Milan #137/R est:8000-11000
£5594	$9510	€8000	Mountainous landscape (52x37cm-20x15in) s. painted 1918. 25-Nov-3 Sotheby's, Milan #82/R est:8000-10000
£5944	$9927	€8500	Mother and daughter (77x62cm-30x24in) s. prov. 29-Jun-3 St-Germain-en-Laye Encheres #13/R
£9091	$15455	€13000	Embarcadero (38x30cm-15x12in) s. s.verso painted 1920. 25-Nov-3 Sotheby's, Milan #130/R est:13000-18000
£9441	$16238	€13500	Riposo Nel Giardino (55x44cm-22x17in) s. cardboard prov.exhib.lit. 2-Dec-3 Calmels Cohen, Paris #55/R est:8000-10000
£10738	$19221	€16000	Still life (39x45cm-15x18in) s. painted 1943 prov. 25-May-4 Sotheby's, Milan #247/R est:20000-25000
£11189	$19245	€16000	Testina a fondo beige (35x27cm-14x11in) s. prov.exhib.lit. 2-Dec-3 Calmels Cohen, Paris #58/R est:8000-12000
£13103	$21883	€19000	Little head, lowered eyes (35x27cm-14x11in) s.d.1971 lit. 17-Nov-3 Sant Agostino, Torino #276/R est:18000-22000
£13986	$24056	€20000	Le pot et l'oeuf (55x46cm-22x18in) s. prov.exhib.lit. 2-Dec-3 Calmels Cohen, Paris #57/R est:10000-15000
£14493	$23768	€20000	Portrait (65x45cm-26x18in) s. 31-May-3 Farsetti, Prato #639/R est:20000-25000
£19463	$34839	€29000	Absence (56x46cm-22x18in) s. painted 1977 prov.lit. 25-May-4 Sotheby's, Milan #256/R est:25000-30000
£20290	$33275	€28000	Figures (55x46cm-22x18in) s. lit. 27-May-3 Sotheby's, Milan #249/R est:30000-40000
£20690	$34552	€30000	Still life with glasses and orange (60x40cm-24x16in) s.d.1959 lit. 13-Nov-3 Finarte Semenzato, Rome #445/R est:30000-35000
£23776	$40420	€34000	Prisoner (77x116cm-30x46in) s.d.966 exhib.lit. 29-Nov-3 Farsetti, Prato #533/R est:20000
£24638	$40406	€34000	Painter and model (81x49cm-32x19in) s. prov.exhib.lit. 27-May-3 Sotheby's, Milan #253/R est:20000-30000
£28188	$50456	€42000	Figure (64x53cm-25x21in) s.d.969 s.i.d.verso. 25-May-4 Sotheby's, Milan #262/R est:30000-40000
£29371	$50517	€42000	Proclamazione (55x46cm-22x18in) s. prov.exhib.lit. 2-Dec-3 Calmels Cohen, Paris #59/R est:20000-25000
£31884	$52290	€44000	Town by the sea (55x80cm-22x31in) s.d.1962 prov.exhib.lit. 27-May-3 Sotheby's, Milan #256/R est:40000-50000
£55944	$96224	€80000	Le peintre et sa femme (92x73cm-36x29in) s.d.1928 prov.exhib.lit. 2-Dec-3 Calmels Cohen, Paris #54/R est:40000-60000
£67832	$116671	€97000	Ritratto de Mia Moglie (121x77cm-48x30in) prov.exhib.lit. 2-Dec-3 Calmels Cohen, Paris #56/R est:25000-30000
Works on paper			
£1611	$2996	€2400	Woman in profile (39x22cm-15x9in) s. pastel card. 4-Mar-4 Babuino, Rome #430 est:3000-3500
£1905	$3410	€2800	Head (65x49cm-26x19in) s. sanguine prov. 16-Mar-4 Finarte Semenzato, Milan #261/R est:1200
£2174	$3565	€3000	Figura (65x50cm-26x20in) s.i. pastel ruled paper. 31-May-3 Farsetti, Prato #610/R est:2000-3000
£3401	$6088	€5000	Figures (72x50cm-28x20in) s. pencil paper on canvas prov. 16-Mar-4 Finarte Semenzato, Milan #321/R est:5500
£4828	$8062	€7000	Portrait and structure (70x50cm-28x20in) s.d.970 wax crayon prov. 13-Nov-3 Finarte Semenzato, Rome #172/R est:3800-4200

TRABACCHI, Giuseppe (1839-1909) Italian

Sculpture

£1006	$1800	€1469	Allegorical female figure wearing an acorn (89cm-35in) s. bronze black marble base. 20-Mar-4 Selkirks, St. Louis #554 est:900-1400

TRABUCCO, Alberto (1899-1990) Argentinian

£28415	$52000	€41486	Tea time (95x80cm-37x31in) board. 1-Jun-4 Arroyo, Buenos Aires #70

TRACEY, Liam (?) British?

£2083	$3396	€3000	Autumn sunlight, Grand Canal (64x76cm-25x30in) s. board. 23-Sep-3 De Veres Art Auctions, Dublin #175/R est:1800-2200

TRACHEL, Domenico (1830-1897) French

£764	$1245	€1100	Seascape in evening (26x41cm-10x16in) s. panel. 24-Sep-3 Neumeister, Munich #573/R
Works on paper			
£490	$832	€700	Pecheurs dans un crique (28x45cm-11x18in) s.d.1894 W/C. 20-Nov-3 Gioffredo, Nice #26/R

TRACHEL, Ercole (1820-1872) French

Works on paper

£500	$910	€750	Collines nicoises (24x33cm-9x13in) s. W/C. 29-Jun-4 Gioffredo, Nice #325

TRACHSEL, Albert (1863-1929) Swiss

Works on paper

£341	$566	€494	Lakeshore landscape (24x35cm-9x14in) s. W/C. 13-Jun-3 Zofingen, Switzerland #3062 (S.FR 750)

TRACY, John M (1844-1893) American

£203	$350	€296	Portrait of cow in field (38x58cm-15x23in) s. 10-Dec-3 Alderfer's, Hatfield #283

TRAFFELET, Fritz (1897-1954) Swiss

£955	$1585	€1385	Reclining female nude (48x70cm-19x28in) s. 13-Jun-3 Zofingen, Switzerland #3063/R est:1500 (S.FR 2100)

TRAGARDH, Carl (1861-1899) Swedish

£439	$821	€641	Landscape with house (44x60cm-17x24in) s. canvas on panel. 29-Feb-4 Uppsala Auktionskammare, Uppsala #360 (S.KR 6000)
£591	$1058	€863	Landscape with cows (55x72cm-22x28in) s. lit. 28-May-4 Uppsala Auktionskammare, Uppsala #198/R (S.KR 8000)
£734	$1182	€1072	French landscape (44x54cm-17x21in) s. 25-Aug-3 Lilla Bukowskis, Stockholm #447 (S.KR 9600)
£985	$1802	€1438	Cows at water hole in the forest (38x55cm-15x22in) s.d.1890. 9-Jun-4 Rasmussen, Copenhagen #1741/R (D.KR 11000)
£1192	$2051	€1740	Shepherd and flock in Cagnes (82x68cm-32x27in) s.i.d.1889 lit. 2-Dec-3 Bukowskis, Stockholm #89/R est:20000-25000 (S.KR 15500)
£2217	$3570	€3237	Parisian street scene (54x44cm-21x17in) s.i.d.89 lit. 25-Aug-3 Lilla Bukowskis, Stockholm #652 est:20000-25000 (S.KR 29000)
£3533	$5759	€5158	Summer landscape with man by cattle (74x100cm-29x39in) s.d.91 lit. 29-Sep-3 Lilla Bukowskis, Stockholm #17 est:40000-45000 (S.KR 46000)

TRAILL, Jessie Constance Alicia (1881-1967) Australian

Prints

£2642	$4729	€3857	Princes Bridge (14x42cm-6x17in) s.i.d.1913 num. 12/20 etching. 10-May-4 Joel, Victoria #252/R est:2000-2500 (A.D 6500)
£3441	$5540	€5024	Great arch (27x24cm-11x9in) s.i.d.1932 num.1/30 etching aquatint. 13-Oct-3 Joel, Victoria #440 est:800-1200 (A.D 8500)

TRAIN, Edward (1801-1866) British

£300	$567	€438	Figures in a highland landscape (23x36cm-9x14in) s.d.1854. 19-Feb-4 Christie's, Kensington #206
£680	$1265	€993	Figures in a loch landscape (38x58cm-15x23in) s.d.1853. 4-Mar-4 Christie's, Kensington #60/R
£990	$1802	€1445	Highland glen with travellers bridge in the foreground (50x50cm-20x20in) s.d.1858 round. 29-Jun-4 Anderson & Garland, Newcastle #393/R

TRAMPEDACH, Kurt (1943-) Danish

£6769	$12455	€9883	Yoko Ono (163x120cm-64x47in) s.d.88 acrylic on serigraph on canvas. 29-Mar-4 Rasmussen, Copenhagen #184/R est:80000 (D.KR 75000)
£7109	$11374	€10308	Self-portrait (195x132cm-77x52in) paper on panel. 17-Sep-3 Kunsthallen, Copenhagen #45/R est:100000 (D.KR 75000)
£7981	$13329	€11652	Annette (170x118cm-67x46in) init.d.83. 7-Oct-3 Rasmussen, Copenhagen #121/R est:100000 (D.KR 85000)
Works on paper			
£376	$627	€549	Double portrait - pages from Diary (33x44cm-13x17in) s.d.April-May 1976 pencil wash. 7-Oct-3 Rasmussen, Copenhagen #211/R (D.KR 4000)
£469	$784	€685	Double portrait - from a Diary (32x43cm-13x17in) s.d.marts 1976 pencil wash. 7-Oct-3 Rasmussen, Copenhagen #206/R (D.KR 5000)

TRAMPOTA, Jan (1889-1942) Czechoslovakian

£1094	$1817	€1597	In park (46x61cm-18x24in) board double-sided. 4-Oct-3 Dorotheum, Prague #101/R est:50000-80000 (C.KR 50000)

TRAN BA VANG, Nicole (1963-) ?

Photographs

£2098	$3503	€3000	Sans titre 06 (47x120cm-19x47in) s.num.3/5 verso col photo prov. 11-Oct-3 Cornette de St.Cyr, Paris #153/R est:2500-3000

TRAN CAN (20th C) Vietnamese

£868	$1450	€1267	Vietnamese girl (65x52cm-26x20in) s.d.37. 12-Oct-3 Sotheby's, Singapore #103/R est:2500-3800 (S.D 2500)

TRAN LUU HAU (1928-) Vietnamese
£1736 $2899 €2535 Still life (80x90cm-31x35in) s.d.02. 12-Oct-3 Sotheby's, Singapore #107/R est:5500-7500 (S.D 5000)
£1993 $3089 €2910 Still life (100x80cm-39x31in) s.d.01. 6-Oct-2 Sotheby's, Singapore #109/R est:5500-7500 (S.D 5500)
£2366 $3785 €3454 Still life (80x90cm-31x35in) s.d.99. 18-May-3 Sotheby's, Singapore #129/R est:4500-5500 (S.D 6600)
£2796 $4473 €4082 Still life with fruits (80x90cm-31x35in) s.d.02. 18-May-3 Sotheby's, Singapore #126/R est:4500-5500 (S.D 7800)
Works on paper
£1377 $2134 €2010 Ho Tay Lake (68x79cm-27x31in) s.d.95 gouache. 6-Oct-2 Sotheby's, Singapore #108/R est:3500-4500 (S.D 3800)
£2222 $4022 €3244 Peasant from the mountain (42x45cm-17x18in) s.d.82 gouache on silk prov. 4-Apr-4 Sotheby's, Singapore #177/R est:4000-6000 (S.D 6800)

TRAN TRONG VU (1964-) Vietnamese
£1333 $2387 €2000 Mon nom est vous (200x82cm-79x32in) s.d.2001 acrylic. 17-May-4 Marie & Robert, Paris #62 est:2000-3000

TRANKOVSKY (19th C) Russian
£6667 $12000 €9734 Oriental beauty (73x51cm-29x20in) s. 23-Apr-4 Sotheby's, New York #177/R est:8000-12000

TRAP, Dirk (1922-) Dutch
£296 $545 €450 Coffee bean place in Waddenzee (60x70cm-24x28in) s.d.1983. 22-Jun-4 Christie's, Amsterdam #608/R

TRAPMAN, Jan (1879-1943) Dutch
Sculpture
£2113 $3507 €3000 Sparrow-halk (21cm-8in) s. wood. 16-Jun-3 Glerum, Amsterdam #432/R est:3200-3800
£4000 $7320 €6000 Bison bull (27cm-11in) gold brown pat. bronze mono. incl. base st.f. Bloemendaal. 7-Jun-4 Sotheby's, Amsterdam #125/R est:3500-4500

TRAPP, Ludmilla (20th C) British?
Works on paper
£420 $752 €613 Roses in a glass (35x27cm-14x11in) s. W/C. 25-May-4 Bonhams, Knightsbridge #95a

TRAUB, Gustav (1885-1955) German
£333 $603 €500 Black Forest mill (68x64cm-27x25in) s. s.i.d.1940 verso lit. 1-Apr-4 Frank Peege, Freiburg #1204/R
£507 $907 €750 Werdenfelser Land (60x80cm-24x31in) s.i.d.1947 board. 6-May-4 Michael Zeller, Lindau #903/R

TRAUNWIESER, Wilhelm (1916-1998) Austrian
£284 $474 €400 Street (47x57cm-19x22in) mono. 16-Oct-3 Dorotheum, Salzburg #688/R

TRAUSCHKE, Christian (17/18th C) German
Works on paper
£329 $549 €470 Man making music by ruins (24x34cm-9x13in) s.i.d.1706 wash pen. 10-Oct-3 Winterberg, Heidelberg #517

TRAUTMANN, Johann Georg (1713-1769) German
£2148 $3952 €3200 Fire raging across town at night (18x22cm-7x9in) panel. 24-Mar-4 Dorotheum, Vienna #254/R est:3000-5000

TRAUTSCHOLD, Carl Friedrich Wilhelm (1815-1877) German
£4200 $7770 €6132 Portrait of Justus von Liebig (76x65cm-30x26in) oval prov.lit. 14-Jul-4 Sotheby's, Olympia #141/R est:2500-3000

TRAUTTWEILLER, Stefanie von (1888-?) German
£724 $1231 €1057 Biedermeier interior (60x75cm-24x30in) s. 28-Nov-3 Zofingen, Switzerland #2692/R est:1500 (S.FR 1600)

TRAVER, Charles Warde (1880-?) American
£1553 $2500 €2252 Just a song at twilight (76x97cm-30x38in) s. exhib. 17-Aug-3 Jeffery Burchard, Florida #56

TRAVER, George A (20th C) American
£374 $700 €546 Hudson river near Hadley (46x58cm-18x23in) s. 28-Feb-4 Thomaston Place, Thomaston #365/R
£374 $700 €546 Hudson River near Hadley (43x58cm-17x23in) s. 24-Jul-4 Thomaston Place, Thomaston #61/R
£503 $900 €734 Cottage across the river (30x41cm-12x16in) s. canvasboard. 14-May-4 Skinner, Boston #64/R est:600-800

TRAVERSARI, Ettore (19th C) Italian
£30882 $52500 €45088 Galerie d'Apollon au Louvre (71x107cm-28x42in) s.d.1883 exhib. 28-Oct-3 Sotheby's, New York #178/R est:30000-40000

TRAVERSE, Pierre (1892-1979) French
Sculpture
£5705 $10554 €8500 Femme nue au drape (62cm-24in) s. white marble. 14-Mar-4 St-Germain-en-Laye Encheres #121/R est:3000-4000
£6549 $11330 €9300 Femme nue au drape (62cm-24in) s. base white marble. 14-Dec-3 St-Germain-en-Laye Encheres #107/R est:3000-4000

TRAVERSI, Gaspare (?-1769) Italian
£41611 $77812 €62000 Beggar (74x102cm-29x40in) s.verso lit. 25-Feb-4 Porro, Milan #65/R est:50000
£59310 $99048 €86000 Beggar (74x102cm-29x40in) s.verso lit. 15-Nov-3 Porro, Milan #209/R est:50000

TRAVERSI, Gaspare (circle) (?-1769) Italian
£20950 $37500 €30587 Men gambling in interior (128x151cm-50x59in) 27-May-4 Sotheby's, New York #92/R est:6000-8000

TRAVIES, Edouard (1809-1870) French
Prints
£42000 $75180 €61320 Various dead game (60x43cm-24x17in) hand col lithograph 68 album exec.c.1854-62. 13-May-4 Sotheby's, London #49/R est:30000-40000
Works on paper
£345 $576 €500 Couple de pies grieches (36x48cm-14x19in) s.i. pen black ink black crayon two sheets. 13-Nov-3 Binoche, Paris #55/R
£380 $635 €555 Male woodchat shrike and great grey shrike (16x9cm-6x4in) s.d.1834 W/C. 14-Oct-3 Bonhams, Knightsbridge #14/R
£476 $852 €700 Deux canards colverts (17x26cm-7x10in) s. black crayon W/C htd gum arabic. 17-Mar-4 Maigret, Paris #119
£517 $864 €750 Perdrix de la Californie (30x44cm-12x17in) i. black crayon. 13-Nov-3 Binoche, Paris #58/R
£552 $921 €800 Geai, trophee (50x33cm-20x13in) W/C gouache black crayon. 13-Nov-3 Binoche, Paris #61/R
£586 $979 €850 Corbeau (43x32cm-17x13in) W/C gouache black crayon pen black ink. 13-Nov-3 Binoche, Paris #65/R
£621 $1037 €900 Poule d'eau (36x50cm-14x20in) i.verso W/C gouache black crayon. 13-Nov-3 Binoche, Paris #57/R
£690 $1152 €1000 Vautour royal (45x35cm-18x14in) i. W/C gouache black crayon pen black ink. 13-Nov-3 Binoche, Paris #54
£889 $1600 €1298 Arab stallion and carthorse (18x12cm-7x5in) s.d.1837 black lead pen brown ink W/C prov. 22-Jan-4 Christie's, Rockefeller NY #145/R est:2000-3000
£1241 $2073 €1800 Vautour pape, urubu noir (10x9cm-4x4in) s.d.1834 W/C varnish brush col wash black pencil. 13-Nov-3 Binoche, Paris #82 est:1200-1500
£1517 $2534 €2200 Various animals, one by Prevost, one by Oudot. two s. one d.1837 W/C gouache three sheets one mount. 13-Nov-3 Binoche, Paris #32/R est:2000
£1517 $2534 €2200 Pluvier dore, trophee (56x39cm-22x15in) s. W/C gouache black crayon pen black ink. 13-Nov-3 Binoche, Paris #63/R est:2500-3000
£1724 $2879 €2500 Lai a gorge blanche (22x30cm-9x12in) s.d.1842 W/C gouache varnish black crayon. 13-Nov-3 Binoche, Paris #112/R est:1000
£1793 $2994 €2600 Aigle royal (50x37cm-20x15in) i. W/C gouache black crayon pen black ink. 13-Nov-3 Binoche, Paris #56/R est:3000-3500
£1793 $2994 €2600 Vanneau (35x49cm-14x19in) i. W/C gouache black crayon pen black ink two sheets. 13-Nov-3 Binoche, Paris #64/R est:1500
£2000 $3340 €2900 Couple de traquets motteux au cul blanc (33x47cm-13x19in) s.i. W/C gouache crayon pen black ink sold with two oval studies. 13-Nov-3 Binoche, Paris #51/R est:3000-3500
£2069 $3455 €3000 Gypaete barbu (48x35cm-19x14in) s.i. W/C gouache black crayon pen black ink. 13-Nov-3 Binoche, Paris #44/R est:3500-4000
£2069 $3455 €3000 Tourne-pierre (32x47cm-13x19in) W/C gouache black crayon pen black ink. 13-Nov-3 Binoche, Paris #46/R est:3000
£2069 $3455 €3000 Perdrix rouge (34x47cm-13x19in) W/C gouache black crayon pen black ink. 13-Nov-3 Binoche, Paris #47/R est:3000
£2069 $3455 €3000 Pie grieche grise et pie treche rousse (28x43cm-11x17in) i. W/C black crayon. 13-Nov-3 Binoche, Paris #48/R est:3000-3500
£2069 $3455 €3000 Pygargue (51x39cm-20x15in) s.i. W/C gouache black crayon pen black ink. 13-Nov-3 Binoche, Paris #52/R est:3000-3500
£2414 $4031 €3500 Perdrix grise, trophee (46x35cm-18x14in) i. W/C gouache black crayon pen black ink. 13-Nov-3 Binoche, Paris #45/R est:2500-3000
£2414 $4031 €3500 Becasse, trophee (54x38cm-21x15in) W/C gouache black crayon pen black ink sold with another W/C. 13-Nov-3 Binoche, Paris #60/R est:2500-3000
£2621 $4377 €3800 Couple d'ortolans des roseaux (48x38cm-19x15in) s.i.d.16 juillet 1858 W/C gouache black crayon pen black ink. 13-Nov-3 Binoche, Paris #43/R est:4000
£3103 $5183 €4500 Lievre, trophee (59x36cm-23x14in) s.i.d.2 decembre 1868 i.verso W/C gouache black crayon. 13-Nov-3 Binoche, Paris #49/R est:4000-4500
£3448 $5759 €5000 Grive, becassine des marais et bouvreuil pivoine male, trophee (48x32cm-19x13in) i. W/C gouache varnish black crayon. 13-Nov-3 Binoche, Paris #86/R est:5500-6000
£30000 $53700 €43800 Zoologie, classification des animaux (40x29cm-16x11in) i. W/C bodycol card 27 album exec.c.1839. 13-May-4 Sotheby's, London #50/R est:30000-40000

TRAVIS, Kathryn Hail (1888-1972) American
£479 $800 €699 Hondo Calley, autumn (30x41cm-12x16in) canvasboard. 18-Oct-3 David Dike, Dallas #238/R
£539 $900 €787 New Mexico (25x36cm-10x14in) board. 18-Oct-3 David Dike, Dallas #235/R

TRAVIS, Olin Herman (1888-1975) American
£1123 $2100 €1640 Early spring Colorado (38x48cm-15x19in) s. masonite. 25-Feb-4 Dallas Auction Gallery, Dallas #48/R est:3000-5000
£1497 $2500 €2186 Sunny brook (36x51cm-14x20in) panel. 18-Oct-3 David Dike, Dallas #191/R est:3000-6000
£2216 $3700 €3235 Stream at white rock (30x41cm-12x16in) board. 18-Oct-3 David Dike, Dallas #316/R est:3000-5000
£2395 $4000 €3497 Portrait (51x41cm-20x16in) 18-Oct-3 David Dike, Dallas #265/R est:3000-6000
£2994 $5000 €4371 Dallas county wheat fields (30x41cm-12x16in) board. 18-Oct-3 David Dike, Dallas #230/R est:3000-5000
£4491 $7500 €6557 Cloud study, Arbuckle mountains (51x61cm-20x24in) board. 18-Oct-3 David Dike, Dallas #166/R est:8000-12000
£7485 $12500 €10928 Phony cripple beggar (61x46cm-24x18in) exhib. 18-Oct-3 David Dike, Dallas #202/R est:12000-18000
Works on paper
£1497 $2500 €2186 Little Mexico (33x43cm-13x17in) chl pastel gouache. 18-Oct-3 David Dike, Dallas #218/R est:2500-5000

TRAVIS, Olin Herman (attrib) (1888-1975) American
£391 $700 €571 Mountain landscape (38x48cm-15x19in) i. masonite. 13-May-4 Dallas Auction Gallery, Dallas #240/R

TRAYER, Jules (1824-1908) French
£2027 $3486 €2959 Governess helping a young girl to dress (35x26cm-14x10in) s. panel prov. 8-Dec-3 Philippe Schuler, Zurich #3438/R est:5000-7000 (S.FR 4500)

TRAZ, Edouard de (1832-1918) Swiss
£655 $1192 €956 Canal landscape with sailing boats (33x40cm-13x16in) s. 16-Jun-4 Fischer, Luzern #2400/R (S.FR 1500)

TREACY, Liam (1934-) Irish
£933 $1689 €1400 Still life with letters (19x24cm-7x9in) s. board. 30-Mar-4 De Veres Art Auctions, Dublin #224/R
£986 $1725 €1400 Off Grafton Street (34x43cm-13x17in) s. 16-Dec-3 James Adam, Dublin #143/R
£1208 $2162 €1800 Garden in bloom (20x25cm-8x10in) s. board. 26-May-4 James Adam, Dublin #171/R est:700-1000
£1259 $2140 €1800 Near Roundstone (30x39cm-12x15in) s. canvasboard. 25-Nov-3 De Veres Art Auctions, Dublin #2/R est:1400-1800
£1333 $2413 €2000 Blue morning (31x41cm-12x16in) s.d.1981 canvasboard. 30-Mar-4 De Veres Art Auctions, Dublin #34/R est:2000-3000
£1806 $2943 €2600 Avoca in winter (63x76cm-25x30in) s. board. 23-Sep-3 De Veres Art Auctions, Dublin #354/R est:1200-1600
£2238 $3804 €3200 Boats at harbour. Garden path (20x25cm-8x10in) s. canvas on board pair. 18-Nov-3 Whyte's, Dublin #170/R est:2500-3000
£2416 $4325 €3600 Mont Martre (35x24cm-14x9in) s. 26-May-4 James Adam, Dublin #175/R est:2000-3000
£3147 $5350 €4500 Summer garden, Delgany (41x48cm-16x19in) s. i.verso. 25-Nov-3 De Veres Art Auctions, Dublin #220/R est:2500-3500

TRECCANI, Ernesto (1920-1994) Italian
£275 $509 €410 Face (30x20cm-12x8in) s. s.verso. 13-Mar-4 Meeting Art, Vercelli #482
£278 $439 €400 Figure (40x20cm-16x8in) 6-Sep-3 Meeting Art, Vercelli #446
£282 $468 €400 Figura (40x20cm-16x8in) s. 14-Jun-3 Meeting Art, Vercelli #446
£282 $468 €400 Volto tra i fiori (40x30cm-16x12in) s. 14-Jun-3 Meeting Art, Vercelli #552
£287 $527 €430 Figure (35x25cm-14x10in) s. s.verso. 12-Jun-4 Meeting Art, Vercelli #751
£288 $489 €420 Faces of women (30x60cm-12x24in) s. 7-Nov-3 Tuttarte, Modena #808
£306 $548 €450 Female face (35x25cm-14x10in) s. 22-Mar-4 Sant Agostino, Torino #328/R
£317 $526 €450 Figura (40x20cm-16x8in) s. 14-Jun-3 Meeting Art, Vercelli #702
£331 $603 €500 Iris (60x20cm-24x8in) s. 17-Jun-4 Galleria Pananti, Florence #226/R
£331 $603 €500 Face (50x35cm-20x14in) s. 17-Jun-4 Galleria Pananti, Florence #404/R
£333 $547 €460 Face. s. s.verso. 29-May-3 Galleria Pace, Milan #82/R
£333 $603 €500 Face (49x35cm-19x14in) s. acrylic. 2-Apr-4 Farsetti, Prato #72
£336 $621 €500 Face (40x30cm-16x12in) s. s.verso. 13-Mar-4 Meeting Art, Vercelli #204
£340 $609 €500 Female face (35x25cm-14x10in) s. 22-Mar-4 Sant Agostino, Torino #326/R
£345 $576 €500 Figures (20x40cm-8x16in) s. s.verso. 13-Nov-3 Galleria Pace, Milan #23/R
£345 $576 €500 Figures (40x20cm-16x8in) s. s.verso. 13-Nov-3 Galleria Pace, Milan #66/R
£345 $576 €500 Figure (40x20cm-16x8in) s. 13-Nov-3 Galleria Pace, Milan #88/R
£347 $549 €500 Figure (35x25cm-14x10in) 6-Sep-3 Meeting Art, Vercelli #671
£366 $608 €520 Volto (50x35cm-20x14in) s. 14-Jun-3 Meeting Art, Vercelli #603
£367 $664 €550 Figure (50x35cm-20x14in) acrylic. 2-Apr-4 Farsetti, Prato #15
£374 $681 €550 Figures (35x50cm-14x20in) s.verso. 6-Feb-4 Galleria Rosenberg, Milan #129/R
£379 $607 €550 Figure (40x20cm-16x8in) s. s.verso. 13-Mar-3 Galleria Pace, Milan #114/R
£387 $643 €550 Flowers (70x50cm-28x20in) s. acrylic. 13-Jun-3 Farsetti, Prato #157
£403 $745 €600 Faces (50x35cm-20x14in) s.s.verso. 13-Mar-4 Meeting Art, Vercelli #13
£403 $745 €600 Figure (50x35cm-20x14in) s. s.verso. 13-Mar-4 Meeting Art, Vercelli #296
£407 $748 €610 Face amongst flowers (50x40cm-20x16in) s. s.verso. 12-Jun-4 Meeting Art, Vercelli #298/R
£409 $757 €610 Face (50x35cm-20x14in) s.s.verso. 13-Mar-4 Meeting Art, Vercelli #463
£409 $757 €610 Red rose (40x30cm-16x12in) s.s.verso. 13-Mar-4 Meeting Art, Vercelli #510
£417 $767 €625 Figure (50x35cm-20x14in) s. 12-Jun-4 Meeting Art, Vercelli #112
£433 $797 €650 Figures (50x35cm-20x14in) s. acrylic pair. 11-Jun-4 Farsetti, Prato #276
£433 $789 €650 Portrait of Miriam (40x30cm-16x12in) s. s.i.d.1964 verso. 12-Jul-4 Il Ponte, Milan #1017
£436 $807 €650 Figure (60x30cm-24x12in) s. 13-Mar-4 Meeting Art, Vercelli #143
£442 $805 €650 Family (40x60cm-16x24in) s. 6-Feb-4 Galleria Rosenberg, Milan #4/R
£445 $757 €650 Figures (35x50cm-14x20in) s. 7-Nov-3 Galleria Rosenberg, Milan #9/R
£448 $717 €650 Figure (50x35cm-20x14in) s. s.verso. 13-Mar-3 Galleria Pace, Milan #125/R
£503 $931 €750 Hedge (60x60cm-24x24in) s. 13-Mar-4 Meeting Art, Vercelli #77
£537 $993 €800 Cape d'Antibes (60x30cm-24x12in) s. 13-Mar-4 Meeting Art, Vercelli #311
£580 $951 €800 Face (50x35cm-20x14in) s. 29-May-3 Galleria Pace, Milan #39
£604 $1117 €900 Faces (60x40cm-24x16in) s. 13-Mar-4 Meeting Art, Vercelli #203
£604 $1117 €900 Figure (90x45cm-35x18in) s. 13-Mar-4 Meeting Art, Vercelli #324
£621 $1037 €900 Seascape with seagulls (40x60cm-16x24in) s. s.verso. 13-Nov-3 Galleria Pace, Milan #80/R
£634 $1052 €900 Winter edge (70x80cm-28x31in) s.verso acrylic. 13-Jun-3 Farsetti, Prato #204/R
£671 $1242 €1000 Face and flowers (60x40cm-24x16in) s. s.verso. 11-Mar-4 Galleria Pace, Milan #92/R
£690 $1103 €1000 Treasure (50x35cm-20x14in) s. s.verso. 13-Mar-3 Galleria Pace, Milan #160/R
£712 $1211 €1040 Four figures (50x70cm-20x28in) 7-Nov-3 Tuttarte, Modena #679/R
£725 $1188 €1000 Figure and hedge (70x50cm-28x20in) s. 29-May-3 Galleria Pace, Milan #3/R
£725 $1188 €1000 Figures (70x30cm-28x12in) s. s.verso. 29-May-3 Galleria Pace, Milan #77/R
£725 $1188 €1000 Figure (50x70cm-20x28in) s. 29-May-3 Galleria Pace, Milan #150/R
£725 $1188 €1000 Pan. Figure and duck (25x35cm-10x14in) s. s.on stretcher two. 27-May-3 Sotheby's, Milan #142
£772 $1428 €1150 Night in Cape d'Antibes (40x60cm-16x24in) s. s.verso. 13-Mar-4 Meeting Art, Vercelli #435
£800 $1472 €1200 Portrait of woman (80x70cm-31x28in) s. 8-Jun-4 Finarte Semenzato, Milan #279/R
£805 $1490 €1200 Three faces (60x40cm-24x16in) s.verso. 11-Mar-4 Galleria Pace, Milan #13/R
£828 $1382 €1200 Untitled (90x45cm-35x18in) s. s.verso. 13-Nov-3 Galleria Pace, Milan #147/R
£872 $1614 €1300 Face (90x45cm-35x18in) s. 11-Mar-4 Galleria Pace, Milan #140/R
£897 $1434 €1300 Guitar (50x70cm-20x28in) s. 13-Mar-3 Galleria Pace, Milan #29/R est:1200-1700
£915 $1465 €1300 Head of woman (49x39cm-19x15in) s. s.d.1971 verso paper on canvas. 19-Sep-3 Finarte, Venice #464/R
£940 $1738 €1400 Figure (110x35cm-43x14in) s.s.verso. 11-Mar-4 Galleria Pace, Milan #70/R est:1700-2200
£1087 $1783 €1500 Geraniums. Face of man. Face of woman (60x60cm-24x24in) s.i.d.1969 verso set of 3. 27-May-3 Sotheby's, Milan #143 est:1500-2000
£1103 $1843 €1600 Figure (100x70cm-39x28in) s. s.d.verso. 13-Nov-3 Galleria Pace, Milan #43/R est:2500
£1259 $2140 €1800 Hedge with daisies (75x100cm-30x39in) s.i.d.1971 verso. 24-Nov-3 Christie's, Milan #205 est:1200-1800
£1342 $2483 €2000 Plants (100x70cm-39x28in) s. s.verso. 13-Mar-4 Meeting Art, Vercelli #538 est:1000
£1667 $3067 €2500 Faces amongst flowers (120x80cm-47x31in) s. s.verso. 12-Jun-4 Meeting Art, Vercelli #598/R est:2500
£1678 $3104 €2500 Faces (120x100cm-47x39in) s. 13-Mar-4 Meeting Art, Vercelli #400 est:2500
£2083 $3292 €3000 Faces (150x100cm-59x39in) 6-Sep-3 Meeting Art, Vercelli #470 est:3000
Works on paper
£315 $535 €450 Study for cicada (49x50cm-19x20in) s. pencil tempera card on canvas double-sided prov. 26-Nov-3 Pandolfini, Florence #191/R
£340 $609 €500 Figure (50x35cm-20x14in) s. mixed media on canvas. 22-Mar-4 Sant Agostino, Torino #327/R
£397 $723 €600 Woman (70x30cm-28x12in) s. s.i.d.1977 verso mixed media on canvas. 21-Jun-4 Pandolfini, Florence #340
£600 $1104 €900 Flowers. Figure (40x30cm-16x12in) s. mixed media paper on canvas set of 2. 10-Jun-4 Galleria Pace, Milan #20/R

TRECHSLIN, Anne Marie (1927-) Swiss
Works on paper
£259 $463 €378 Rose in bloom (24x17cm-9x7in) s. W/C over pencil. 12-May-4 Dobiaschofsky, Bern #3977/R (S.FR 600)

TRECK, Jan Janssen (1606-1652) Dutch
£22973 $40432 €34000 Still life with a man-li porcelain bowl with grapes on a pewter plate, plums and nuts on draped tabl (53x45cm-21x18in) s. prov. 18-May-4 Sotheby's, Amsterdam #88/R est:40000-60000

TRECOURT, Giacomo (1812-1882) Italian
£8451 $14789 €12000 Self-portrait (50x41cm-20x16in) s. 17-Dec-3 Finarte Semenzato, Milan #112/R est:6000-7000

TREDUPP, Charles (19/20th C) American
£303 $500 €442 Marinescape (23x30cm-9x12in) s. academy board. 7-Jul-3 Schrager Galleries, Milwaukee #1545

TREGO, William Brooke Thomas (1859-1909) American
£815 $1500 €1190 Portrait of Walter Emersom Baum (30x20cm-12x8in) 9-Jun-4 Alderfer's, Hatfield #533/R est:1500-2000

TREMATOR (?) ?
£740 $1325 €1080 Spanish quartet (76x102cm-30x40in) s. 18-Mar-4 Christie's, Kensington #685/R

TREMBATH, Ernest (1943-) Australian
£310 $484 €450 Misty morning in the valley (62x86cm-24x34in) s. board. 1-Aug-2 Joel, Victoria #211 est:1200-1500 (A.D 900)

TREMBLAY, Claude (20th C) Canadian
£282 $519 €412 The artist's house, Quebec (76x76cm-30x30in) s. s.i.verso. 9-Jun-4 Walker's, Ottawa #180/R (C.D 700)
£338 $574 €493 Un moment important (30x61cm-12x24in) s. s.i.verso. 23-Nov-3 Levis, Calgary #142/R (C.D 750)
£379 $652 €553 Realite ne peut etre Cernee (75x90cm-30x35in) s. 2-Dec-3 Joyner Waddington, Toronto #529 (C.D 850)
£444 $738 €648 La vie nous aime (91x91cm-36x36in) s. s.i.verso acrylic. 5-Oct-3 Levis, Calgary #119/R (C.D 1000)
£495 $842 €723 En regardant couler le temps (91x76cm-36x30in) s. s.i.verso. 23-Nov-3 Levis, Calgary #141/R (C.D 1100)
£721 $1225 €1053 Dans la lumiere et melodie (76x91cm-30x36in) s. s.i.verso acrylic. 27-Nov-3 Heffel, Vancouver #166 (C.D 1600)
£950 $1587 €1387 Chanson tout relour (120x150cm-47x59in) s.i. 17-Nov-3 Hodgins, Calgary #102/R est:2250-2750 (C.D 2100)

TREMBLAY, Louis (1949-) Canadian
£260 $476 €380 Komauska (30x35cm-12x14in) s.i. 1-Jun-4 Hodgins, Calgary #410/R (C.D 650)
£269 $489 €393 Baie St Paul (61x76cm-24x30in) s. s.i.verso board prov. 5-Feb-4 Heffel, Vancouver #61/R (C.D 650)
£290 $485 €421 Le village au Printemps (51x61cm-20x24in) s. 17-Jun-3 Pinneys, Montreal #176 (C.D 650)
£536 $921 €783 Campe de peche sur la Riviere Malbaie (60x75cm-24x30in) s. 2-Dec-3 Joyner Waddington, Toronto #269/R (C.D 1200)

TREML, Johann Friedrich (1816-1852) Austrian
Works on paper
£738 $1307 €1100 Study (13x14cm-5x6in) s. W/C prov. 28-Apr-4 Wiener Kunst Auktionen, Vienna #25/R
£1048 $1907 €1530 The homecoming soldier (21x18cm-8x7in) s.d.1844 prov.exhib. W/C. 17-Jun-4 Kornfeld, Bern #76/R (S.FR 2400)

TREMLETT, David (1945-) British
Works on paper
£1800 $3006 €2628 Wall drawing sketch no 10b (90x102cm-35x40in) s.i.d.96 chl pencil paper collage prov. 22-Oct-3 Christie's, London #67/R est:2000-3000
£2200 $4004 €3212 No 100 (108x108cm-43x43in) s.d.90 pastel lit. 4-Feb-4 Sotheby's, Olympia #20/R est:2000-3000
£2800 $5152 €4088 India (110x110cm-43x43in) acrylic white chk paper on board exec.c.1988 prov. 24-Jun-4 Sotheby's, Olympia #471/R est:2000-3000
£3500 $6370 €5110 Front (66x212cm-26x83in) pastel exec 1989 lit. 4-Feb-4 Sotheby's, Olympia #16/R est:3000-4000
£3500 $6370 €5110 Side (66x212cm-26x83in) pastel exec 1989 lit. 4-Feb-4 Sotheby's, Olympia #15/R est:3000-4000
£5000 $9050 €7300 Writing for space (84x59cm-33x23in) s.i.d.92 pastel pencil three parts. 1-Apr-4 Christie's, Kensington #285/R est:6000-8000

TREMOHARS (?) French?
Works on paper
£563 $986 €800 Port anime a Concarneau (115x15cm-45x6in) s. gouache. 21-Dec-3 Thierry & Lannon, Brest #415

TREMOIS, Pierre Yves (1921-) French
Works on paper
£340 $541 €500 Chasseurs et chiens (29x34cm-11x13in) s. crayon. 21-Mar-3 Bailly Pommery, Paris #106
£476 $757 €700 Deux cerfs (36x28cm-14x11in) s.pen Chinese ink gouache. 21-Mar-3 Bailly Pommery, Paris #105

TREMOLIERE, Pierre Charles (1703-1739) French
Works on paper
£5102 $9133 €7500 Une allegoire de l'Asie, assise sur un chameau (27x31cm-11x12in) i. red chk. 18-Mar-4 Christie's, Paris #119/R est:3500-4500

TREMONT, Auguste (1893-?) Luxembourger
£6803 $12177 €10000 Panthere noire dans un arbre (39x62cm-15x24in) s. panel. 16-Mar-4 Vanderkindere, Brussels #229/R est:350-500
Sculpture
£12676 $21930 €18000 Cerf axis debout (51x45cm-20x18in) s. st.f.Valsuani brown pat bronze. 13-Dec-3 De Vuyst, Lokeren #466/R est:20000-25000
£13287 $22189 €19000 Cheval (30x38cm-12x15in) s. St.f.Valsuani dark brown bronze. 11-Oct-3 De Vuyst, Lokeren #533/R est:17000-20000
£13333 $23867 €20000 Panthere (17x42cm-7x17in) s. brown pat bronze Cast C Valsuani. 11-May-4 Vanderkindere, Brussels #473/R est:8000-12000
£13605 $24354 €20000 Babouin (26x17cm-10x7in) s. black pat bronze Cast C. Valsuani. 16-Mar-4 Vanderkindere, Brussels #150/R est:4000-5000

TRENCH, P C (19th C) British
Works on paper
£380 $635 €555 Breton town (35x20cm-14x8in) s. W/C. 20-Oct-3 Bonhams, Bath #62

TRENCHARD, Fred (1941-) American
£494 $800 €721 Kitchen (122x122cm-48x48in) s.d.1969. 2-Aug-3 Neal Auction Company, New Orleans #396

TRENK, Franz (1899-1960) Austrian
£775 $1286 €1100 Coastal landscape (80x90cm-31x35in) s.d.1940. 12-Jun-3 Dorotheum, Graz #79/R
£800 $1440 €1200 Early spring in the mountains (46x61cm-18x24in) s.d.1939. 22-Apr-4 Dorotheum, Graz #29/R
Works on paper
£528 $877 €750 Adriatic fishing harbour (46x58cm-18x23in) s.d.1956 W/C. 12-Jun-3 Dorotheum, Graz #69/R

TRENNERY, Horace Hurtle (1899-1958) Australian
£1362 $2315 €1989 Landscape, Flinders Range (20x25cm-8x10in) s.d.24 canvas on board prov. 26-Nov-3 Deutscher-Menzies, Melbourne #219/R est:2000-4000 (A.D 3200)
£2341 $3979 €3418 Hill Slopes (26x38cm-10x15in) s. canvasboard prov. 26-Nov-3 Deutscher-Menzies, Melbourne #218/R est:7000-9000 (A.D 5500)
£5328 $8418 €7779 Cottage, Port Willunga (25x29cm-10x11in) s.i. canvas on board prov.exhib. 2-Sep-3 Deutscher-Menzies, Melbourne #55/R est:14000-18000 (A.D 13000)
Works on paper
£1603 $2918 €2340 Aroona Valley (34x47cm-13x19in) chl. 16-Jun-4 Deutscher-Menzies, Melbourne #264/R est:5000-7000 (A.D 4200)

TRENTANOVE, Raimondo (1792-1832) Italian
Sculpture
£11000 $18700 €16060 Napoleone (49cm-19in) i. carved marble. 4-Nov-3 Woolley & Wallis, Salisbury #182/R est:4000-5000

TRENTI, Gerolamo (1828-1898) Italian
£3243 $5708 €4800 Trento, Italy (73x24cm-29x9in) 19-May-4 Il Ponte, Milan #542 est:1300-1400

TRENTINI, Guido (1889-?) Italian
£3041 $5351 €4500 Velia (44x38cm-17x15in) s.d.1935. 24-May-4 Christie's, Milan #211/R est:3500-5000
£3329 $5659 €4760 Carousel (49x60cm-19x24in) s. painted 1956 prov. 18-Nov-3 Babuino, Rome #432/R est:3000-4000

TREPP, Judith (1941-) American
£1223 $2250 €1786 Untitled (37x34cm-15x13in) s.d.2002 stretcher tempera oil Indian ink. 8-Jun-4 Germann, Zurich #135/R est:3500-3800 (S.FR 2800)

TRESGUERRAS, Francisco Eduardo (1759-1833) Mexican
£1193 $2183 €1742 Day in the fields I (42x57cm-17x22in) 27-Jan-4 Louis Morton, Mexico #275 est:25000-30000 (M.P 24000)
£1193 $2183 €1742 Day in the fields II (42x57cm-17x22in) 27-Jan-4 Louis Morton, Mexico #276 est:25000-30000 (M.P 24000)

TRETCHIKOFF, Vladimir (1913-) Russian
£1176 $2129 €1717 Portrait of a woman (55x42cm-22x17in) s. canvasboard. 30-Mar-4 Stephan Welz, Johannesburg #487/R est:5000-8000 (SA.R 14000)

TREU, Nicolaus (attrib) (1734-1786) German
£2837 $4738 €4000 Enfant au chat (59x49cm-23x19in) 17-Oct-3 Renaud, Paris #45/R est:1500-2000
£6711 $12349 €10000 Two children at window showing walnut to squirrel (61x47cm-24x19in) 24-Mar-4 Dorotheum, Vienna #228/R est:8000-10000

TREVELYAN, Judith (?) ?
£364 $571 €528 Pizzeria (85x109cm-33x43in) s. acrylic board. 27-Aug-3 Dunbar Sloane, Wellington #104 (NZ.D 1000)

TREVELYAN, Julian (1910-1989) British
£484 $867 €707 Lunch at the mall (86x119cm-34x47in) s. acrylic on board. 12-May-4 Dunbar Sloane, Wellington #146/R est:1800-2500 (NZ.D 1400)
£1800 $3060 €2628 Studies (15x20cm-6x8in) s.d.83 verso board set of 3. 26-Nov-3 Sotheby's, Olympia #172/R est:1000-1500
£2600 $4342 €3796 Red Square (76x92cm-30x36in) s.d.61 prov. 17-Nov-3 Trembath Welch, Great Dunmow #529/R est:3000-4000
£2700 $5049 €4050 Lulu (50x40cm-20x16in) s.d.86. 26-Jul-4 Bonhams, Bath #44/R est:1500-2500
£2900 $5220 €4234 Cretan surrealist landscape , view from an aircraft (39x49cm-15x19in) s.d.59. 22-Apr-4 Lawrence, Crewkerne #956/R est:3000-4000
£3200 $5728 €4672 Luberon foothills (51x61cm-20x24in) s.d.61 i.stretcher. 16-Mar-4 Bonhams, New Bond Street #74/R est:2000-3000
£3200 $5824 €4672 Man with oxen (30x40cm-12x16in) s.d.56 board. 15-Jun-4 Bonhams, Knightsbridge #3/R est:2500-3500
£4800 $8784 €7008 Self-portrait with cat (51x41cm-20x16in) s.d.76 prov. 2-Jun-4 Sotheby's, London #90/R est:5000-7000
£5500 $8745 €8030 Landscape with harvesters (28x48cm-11x19in) s.d.46. 10-Sep-3 Sotheby's, Olympia #218/R est:1000-1500
£5500 $9460 €8030 Towers and oxen (101x81cm-40x32in) s.d.62 s.i.verso board. 2-Dec-3 Bonhams, New Bond Street #147/R est:3000-5000
£5500 $9845 €8030 Ox stalls (54x65cm-21x26in) s.d.55. 16-Mar-4 Bonhams, New Bond Street #73/R est:3000-5000
£7000 $11900 €10220 Two birds (38x46cm-15x18in) s.d.32 board exhib. 21-Nov-3 Christie's, London #9/R est:7000-10000
£7500 $13875 €10950 Tug boats (25x32cm-10x13in) s.d.78 board. 11-Mar-4 Christie's, Kensington #245/R est:3000-5000
£7500 $13875 €10950 Life boats (60x76cm-24x30in) s.d.87 prov. 11-Mar-4 Christie's, Kensington #247/R est:4000-6000
£8000 $13760 €11680 Spring flowers (25x36cm-10x14in) s.d.44 prov. 2-Dec-3 Bonhams, New Bond Street #142/R est:3000-5000
£17000 $31110 €24820 Studio riot (60x73cm-24x29in) s.d.33 prov.exhib. 2-Jun-4 Sotheby's, London #109/R est:12000-18000
Works on paper
£600 $1122 €900 Spinnakers (15x23cm-6x9in) s.d.87 mixed media. 26-Jul-4 Bonhams, Bath #45/R
£800 $1480 €1168 Stud farm (15x23cm-6x9in) s.d.87 W/C pencil. 11-Feb-4 Sotheby's, Olympia #259/R
£1900 $3515 €2774 Reading Sartre before a harbour (28x38cm-11x15in) sd.1939 ink wash. 10-Feb-4 David Lay, Penzance #576/R est:1500-2000

£2000 $3440 €2920 Spanish park (34x52cm-13x20in) s.d.34 pencil gouache. 3-Dec-3 Christie's, Kensington #689/R est:1500-2000
£4200 $7686 €6132 Potteries (29x39cm-11x15in) s.d.1938 pencil ink wash. 4-Jun-4 Christie's, London #6/R est:2000-3000

TREVILLE, Richard de (1864-1929) American
£341 $550 €498 Waves on the shore (20x41cm-8x16in) s. canvas on board. 17-Aug-3 Bonhams & Butterfields, San Francisco #5801
£359 $650 €524 Panoramic landscape (41x89cm-16x35in) s. 3-Apr-4 Harvey Clar, Oakland #1240
£412 $700 €602 River mountain landscape (25x51cm-10x20in) init. canvasboard prov. 18-Nov-3 John Moran, Pasadena #99
£503 $900 €734 Poppies and lupines (15x25cm-6x10in) s. canvas on board. 16-Mar-4 Matthew's, Oregon #89/R

TREVISANI, Francesco (1656-1746) Italian
£3356 $6174 €5000 Penitent Magdalene (73x58cm-29x23in) 24-Mar-4 Dorotheum, Vienna #44/R est:5000-7000
£4861 $8118 €7000 Madonna and Child with Saint John (75cm-30in circular) 22-Oct-3 Finarte Semenzato, Milan #3/R
£5500 $9515 €8030 Penitent Magdalen (133x96cm-52x38in) 12-Dec-3 Christie's, Kensington #273/R est:6000-8000
£25000 $42500 €36500 Madonna and Child with the Infant Saint John the Baptist (78x69cm-31x27in) 29-Oct-3 Christie's, London #69/R est:15000-20000

TREVISANI, Francesco (attrib) (1656-1746) Italian
£4333 $7757 €6500 Lucrezia (90x69cm-35x27in) 12-May-4 Finarte Semenzato, Milan #32/R est:3000-4000
£16216 $28541 €24000 Madonna and Child (98x73cm-39x29in) 18-May-4 Sotheby's, Milan #478/R est:15000-20000

TREVISANI, Francesco (style) (1656-1746) Italian
£10200 $17646 €14892 Lucretia (99x69cm-39x27in) canvas on board. 9-Dec-3 Sotheby's, Olympia #397/R est:5000-7000

TREVOR, Helen Mabel (1831-1900) British
£1800 $3348 €2628 Fisherman (80x53cm-31x21in) s. 3-Mar-4 John Ross, Belfast #120 est:2000-3000

TREW, C J (18th C) German?
Prints
£2123 $3610 €3100 Flower (45x30cm-18x12in) col copperplate htd white. 4-Nov-3 Hartung & Hartung, Munich #3367/R est:800
£2329 $3959 €3400 Flower (45x30cm-18x12in) col copperplate htd white. 4-Nov-3 Hartung & Hartung, Munich #3369/R est:700

TREW, Christoph Jakob (18th C) German?
Prints
£34000 $60860 €49640 Hortus nitidissimis omnem per annum superbiens floribus (52x36cm-20x14in) hand col etching engraving 110 album after G D Ehret and others. 13-May-4 Sotheby's, London #52/R est:30000-40000

TRIANDAFYLLIDIS, Theofrastos (1881-1955) Greek
£11000 $19250 €16060 Figures on a street (29x38cm-11x15in) s. canvas on board. 16-Dec-3 Bonhams, New Bond Street #76/R est:7000-9000
£14000 $25060 €20440 Under the fig-tree (35x41cm-14x16in) s. cardboard prov.lit. 11-May-4 Bonhams, New Bond Street #93/R est:14000-18000
£18000 $31500 €26280 Bathers on a boat (30x18cm-12x7in) s. cardboard painted c.1925-30 prov.lit. 16-Dec-3 Bonhams, New Bond Street #93/R est:10000-15000

TRIBOUT, Georges Henri (1884-1962) French?
£280 $476 €400 Nature morte a l'amphore (100x81cm-39x32in) s.d.1926 prov. 23-Nov-3 Cornette de St.Cyr, Paris #335/R

TRICKER, Florence (20th C) American
£217 $375 €317 Clouds and landscape (10x15cm-4x6in) s. board. 10-Dec-3 Alderfer's, Hatfield #450
£629 $1000 €918 Mountainous landscape (30x25cm-12x10in) s. board. 10-Sep-3 Alderfer's, Hatfield #416/R
£692 $1100 €1010 Landscape with distant waterside villatge under cloudy sky (25x28cm-10x11in) s. board. 10-Sep-3 Alderfer's, Hatfield #417

TRICKETT, John (1952-) British
£270 $464 €394 Portrait of an English pointer (26x20cm-10x8in) board. 5-Dec-3 Honiton Galleries, Honiton #1b
£320 $582 €467 Spaniel in woodland (23x33cm-9x13in) s. 4-Feb-4 Brightwells, Leominster #960
£320 $550 €467 Portrait of a black Labrador (31x26cm-12x10in) board. 5-Dec-3 Honiton Galleries, Honiton #1a
£340 $585 €496 Man crossing a bridge with a gun dog (46x56cm-18x22in) board. 5-Dec-3 Honiton Galleries, Honiton #10
£380 $646 €555 Study of an English pointer (19x24cm-7x9in) s. i.verso. 19-Nov-3 Tennants, Leyburn #1196
£420 $794 €613 Study of a black Labrador puppy (30x25cm-12x10in) s. board. 23-Feb-4 David Duggleby, Scarborough #698/R
£1381 $2500 €2016 Spring spaniel (76x61cm-30x24in) s. 30-Mar-4 Bonhams & Butterfields, San Francisco #83/R est:1800-2800
£2200 $4048 €3212 Spaniel, evening light (51x76cm-20x30in) s. 10-Jun-4 Christie's, Kensington #414/R est:600-1000
£2800 $5152 €4088 Springer spaniel in the snow (61x76cm-24x30in) s. 10-Jun-4 Christie's, Kensington #413/R est:800-1200

TRIEBEL, Carl (1823-1885) German
£704 $1218 €1000 Achensee viewed from Achen Church in the village (33x52cm-13x20in) s. 10-Dec-3 Hugo Ruef, Munich #2509/R
£1176 $2175 €1717 Mountainous landscape (31x52cm-12x20in) 14-Mar-4 Agra, Warsaw #43/R (P.Z 8500)

TRIEBSCH, Franz (1870-?) German
£267 $483 €400 Still life with roses and apple (57x48cm-22x19in) s.d.34. 3-Apr-4 Hans Stahl, Hamburg #92
£294 $505 €420 Yellow chrysanthemum in brown vase (55x70cm-22x28in) s. 5-Dec-3 Bolland & Marotz, Bremen #670

TRIER, Hann (1915-1999) German
£1748 $2972 €2500 Twin I (50x64cm-20x25in) s.d.69 s.i.d.1969 verso acrylic. 27-Nov-3 Lempertz, Koln #483/R est:3500
£2000 $3680 €3000 Vortex (40x41cm-16x16in) mono.d. s.i.d. verso. 11-Jun-4 Hauswedell & Nolte, Hamburg #1565/R est:3500
£4225 $7310 €6000 Thrust V (100x65cm-39x26in) s.d.67 s.i.d. stretcher acrylic lit. 13-Dec-3 Lempertz, Koln #191/R est:7000
£7333 $13127 €11000 Seguiriya I (97x116cm-38x46in) s.d. 15-May-4 Bassenge, Berlin #7160/R est:9000
Works on paper
£294 $490 €420 Figuration (56x42cm-22x17in) mono.d.1994 W/C. 10-Oct-3 Winterberg, Heidelberg #2050/R
£367 $656 €550 Untitled (52x77cm-20x30in) s.d.73 W/C. 15-May-4 Van Ham, Cologne #977
£667 $1227 €1000 Sketch for ceiling painting in Schloss Charlottenburg (65x76cm-26x30in) mono.d. W/C. 11-Jun-4 Hauswedell & Nolte, Hamburg #1566/R
£867 $1551 €1300 Vibrations (73x51cm-29x20in) mono.d.59 W/C board exhib. 15-May-4 Van Ham, Cologne #976/R
£1007 $1852 €1500 Untitled (62x49cm-24x19in) s.d. W/c. 26-Mar-4 Ketterer, Hamburg #674/R est:1800-2500

TRIER, Hans A (1877-1962) British
£460 $764 €672 Old houses in the Plaza Segovia (14x20cm-6x8in) s. panel. 6-Oct-3 David Duggleby, Scarborough #191/R

TRIGA, Giacomo (?-1746) Italian
£3691 $6792 €5500 Dream of St Joseph (84x70cm-33x28in) oval prov. 24-Mar-4 Dorotheum, Vienna #68/R est:5000-7000

TRIGLAV, Matiya Jama (?) ?
£400 $668 €584 Mountain (46x64cm-18x25in) 21-Oct-3 Gorringes, Lewes #2116

TRIGOSO, Falcao (1879-1956) Portuguese
£6711 $12013 €10000 Landscape (26x35cm-10x14in) s.i.d.1939 panel. 31-May-4 Cabral Moncada Leiloes, Lisbon #83/R est:10000-15000

TRIMBORN, Hans (1891-1979) German
£638 $1173 €950 Cutter in northern harbour (70x89cm-28x35in) s. oil gouache board. 26-Mar-4 Bolland & Marotz, Bremen #377/R

TRINDALL, Gordon Lyall (1886-1965) Australian
£407 $638 €594 Untitled, still life with roses (53x46cm-21x18in) s. 1-Sep-3 Shapiro, Sydney #350/R (A.D 1000)
£488 $766 €712 Untitled, still life with gladioli and nerine lilies (96x82cm-38x32in) s. masonite. 1-Sep-3 Shapiro, Sydney #365/R (A.D 1200)

TRINER, Franz Xaver (1767-1824) Swiss
Works on paper
£667 $1207 €1000 Vue du Lac d'Oberalp prise du chemin (40x50cm-16x20in) s. W/C. 1-Apr-4 Van Ham, Cologne #1669
£800 $1448 €1200 Pont du Diable sur le Mont du St Gothard (48x37cm-19x15in) s. W/C. 1-Apr-4 Van Ham, Cologne #1670

TRINIDAD, Jose (1924-) Canadian
£190 $323 €277 Barns and tree (61x91cm-24x36in) s. i.verso prov. 6-Nov-3 Heffel, Vancouver #112/R (C.D 425)
£650 $1164 €949 The newcomer (50x61cm-20x24in) s.d.1979 i.verso. 6-May-4 Heffel, Vancouver #145/R (C.D 1600)
£1644 $2630 €2400 Tea garden (76x102cm-30x40in) s. 16-Sep-3 Maynards, Vancouver #359 est:3000-4000 (C.D 3600)

TRINQUESSE, Louis Rolland (1746-1800) French
Works on paper
£3311 $6026 €5000 Portrait de femme en pied, vue de cote (20x32cm-8x13in) s.d.1778 black crayon htd white chk. 16-Jun-4 Piasa, Paris #112/R est:4000-6000

TRINQUIER, Antonin (1833-?) French
£8333 $15000 €12166 Still life with dishes, vase, candlestick and other objects on a table (81x129cm-32x51in) s.d.1875. 22-Apr-4 Christie's, Rockefeller NY #140/R est:10000-15000

TRINQUIER, Louis Isaac (1853-1922) French
Works on paper
£554 $992 €820 Pierrot, Colombine et Arlequin (29x23cm-11x9in) s. W/C wash. 5-May-4 Coutau Begarie, Paris #24/R

TRIPE, Linnaeus (1822-1902) British
Photographs
£2300 $4048 €3358 No.67 Amerapoora, Ouk Kyoung (25x35cm-10x14in) mono. albumenized salt print. 18-May-4 Bonhams, New Bond Street #72/R est:2800-3200

£2700 $4752 €3942 No.64, Amerapoora, Mohdee Kyoung (25x34cm-10x13in) mono. albumenized salt print. 18-May-4 Bonhams, New Bond Street #71/R est:2000-2500
£2700 $4752 €3942 No.71 Amerapoora, street leading to the palace, 1855 (25x32cm-10x13in) mono. albumenized salt print. 18-May-4 Bonhams, New Bond Street #75/R est:1600-2000
£2963 $5600 €4326 Number 43, Amerapoora, Corner of Mugabboodee-tee Kyoung (28x35cm-11x14in) s. salted paper print from waxed calotype negative. 17-Feb-4 Swann Galleries, New York #2/R est:7000-10000
£3175 $6000 €4636 Number 52, Amerapoora, Mosque (33x27cm-13x11in) s. salted paper print from waxed calotype negative. 17-Feb-4 Swann Galleries, New York #3/R est:7000-10000
£3600 $6336 €5256 No.75 Amerapoora, street in the city, 1855 (26x35cm-10x14in) mono. albumenized salt print. 18-May-4 Bonhams, New Bond Street #77/R est:2000-2400
£3600 $6336 €5256 No.78 Amerapoora, entrance to the Aracan pagoda (25x34cm-10x13in) mono. albumenized salt print. 18-May-4 Bonhams, New Bond Street #78/R est:2800-3200

TRIPE, M E R (fl.1934-37) British
£1107 $1982 €1616 Study of tree in rural scene (36x28cm-14x11in) init. board. 12-May-4 Dunbar Sloane, Wellington #446 (NZ.D 3200)
Works on paper
£1880 $3195 €2745 Pastoral landscape with sheep (62x27cm-24x11in) s.d.1909 W/C. 26-Nov-3 Dunbar Sloane, Wellington #144/R est:2000-4000 (NZ.D 5000)

TRIPE, Mary Elizabeth (1867-1939) New Zealander
Works on paper
£1418 $2511 €2070 Portrait of a lady (57x45cm-22x18in) s. W/C. 28-Apr-4 Dunbar Sloane, Auckland #106/R est:4000-7000 (NZ.D 4000)

TRIPP, Sir Herbert Alker (1883-1954) British
Works on paper
£500 $835 €730 Metroppole Hotel, Brighton (56x99cm-22x39in) s. gouache. 10-Jul-3 Gorringes, Worthing #667/R

TRIPPEL, Albert Ludwig (1813-1854) German
£472 $750 €689 Pastoral scene (25x38cm-10x15in) s. 14-Sep-3 Susanin's, Chicago #6078/R
£946 $1665 €1400 Fortress ruins in rocky landscape (25x35cm-10x14in) s. 22-May-4 Lempertz, Koln #1617/R

TRIQUET, Jules-Octave (1867-1914) French
£559 $951 €800 Portrait de Raymond Poincare (61x53cm-24x21in) s. 27-Nov-3 Millon & Associes, Paris #112/R
£10588 $18000 €15458 Girl in a hammock (86x116cm-34x46in) s. 28-Oct-3 Sotheby's, New York #167/R est:12000-15000
Works on paper
£2057 $3435 €2900 L'heure du the (83x67cm-33x26in) s. pastel. 19-Jun-3 Millon & Associes, Paris #16/R est:3500-4000

TRIQUETI, Henri Joseph (1807-1874) French
Sculpture
£1300 $2236 €1898 Young woman in Renaissance style (76cm-30in) s.d.1859 marble relief ebonised plinth incl. base. 4-Dec-3 Mellors & Kirk, Nottingham #1015 est:800-1200

TRIRUM, Johannes Wouterus van (1924-) Dutch
£303 $507 €440 Two kittens playing (49x39cm-19x15in) s. 11-Nov-3 Vendu Notarishuis, Rotterdam #633/R
£420 $713 €600 Three kittens playing (30x40cm-12x16in) s. panel. 20-Nov-3 Van Ham, Cologne #1888
£420 $722 €600 Three cats playing with fruits (50x60cm-20x24in) s. 5-Dec-3 Bolland & Marotz, Bremen #671/R

TRISCOTT, Samuel Peter Rolt (1846-1925) American
Works on paper
£475 $850 €694 Water meadow (19x30cm-7x12in) s. W/C. 14-May-4 Skinner, Boston #84/R
£531 $950 €775 Quiet of the river bank (30x55cm-12x22in) s. W/C gouache. 14-May-4 Skinner, Boston #88/R
£1070 $2000 €1562 Fall stream (41x64cm-16x25in) W/C. 28-Feb-4 Thomaston Place, Thomaston #250/R
£1202 $2200 €1755 River scene (43x69cm-17x27in) s. W/C. 31-Jan-4 South Bay, Long Island #173

TRISTAN, Luis (attrib) (1586-1624) Spanish
£26316 $48421 €40000 Saint John the Evangelist (78x61cm-31x24in) i.verso prov. 24-Jun-4 Christie's, Paris #52/R est:15000-20000

TRISTRAM, J W (1872-1938) Australian
Works on paper
£305 $556 €445 Evening (20x30cm-8x12in) s.d.1922 W/C. 16-Jun-4 Deutscher-Menzies, Melbourne #596/R (A.D 800)
£344 $625 €502 Coastal cliffs, Narrabeen (25x44cm-10x17in) s.d.1927 W/C canvas-paper. 16-Jun-4 Deutscher-Menzies, Melbourne #597/R (A.D 900)

TRISTRAM, John W (1872-1938) Australian
Works on paper
£325 $511 €475 Untitled, coastal scene (28x35cm-11x14in) s.d.1908 W/C. 1-Sep-3 Shapiro, Sydney #370/R (A.D 800)
£366 $655 €534 Saplings (23x26cm-9x10in) s.d.1921 W/C. 10-May-4 Joel, Victoria #297 (A.D 900)
£579 $1070 €845 Moonlight reflection (24x35cm-9x14in) s.d.1924 W/C. 10-Mar-4 Deutscher-Menzies, Melbourne #527/R est:1500-2500 (A.D 1400)

TRITTEN, Gottfried (1923-) Swiss
Works on paper
£661 $1123 €965 Abstract composition in blue (31x79cm-12x31in) s. W/C bodycol. 5-Nov-3 Dobiaschofsky, Bern #1009/R (S.FR 1500)

TRIVIDIC, Pierre le (1898-1960) French
Works on paper
£667 $1227 €1000 Paysage (43x58cm-17x23in) s.d.1932 chl htd white prov. 11-Jun-4 Pierre Berge, Paris #258

TRIVIGNO, Helen (1920-1985) American
£392 $650 €572 Sunflowers (30x30cm-12x12in) s. enamel copper. 4-Oct-3 Neal Auction Company, New Orleans #1141
£652 $1200 €952 Sunflowers (33x43cm-13x17in) s. enaneled copper. 27-Mar-4 New Orleans Auction, New Orleans #818/R est:1200-1800

TRIVILINI, Armand (20th C) American
£489 $900 €714 Wintertime (20x25cm-8x10in) s. i.verso canvasboard. 25-Mar-4 Doyle, New York #67/R

TRNKA, Jiri (1912-) Czechoslovakian
£1313 $2180 €1917 Girl with jug (35x25cm-14x10in) s. board. 4-Oct-3 Dorotheum, Prague #103/R est:30000-45000 (C.KR 60000)

TROCKEL, Rosemarie (1952-) German
£17964 $30000 €26227 Untitled (193x150cm-76x59in) acrylic knit yarn prov.exhib. 13-Nov-3 Sotheby's, New York #512/R est:15000-20000
£22346 $40000 €32625 Untitled (200x100cm-79x39in) baked enamel steel three hotplates prov.lit. 14-May-4 Phillips, New York #241/R est:25000-35000
£22754 $38000 €33221 Musk (170x200cm-67x79in) oil spray enamel painted 1984 prov.exhib. 12-Nov-3 Christie's, Rockefeller NY #572/R est:10000-15000
Sculpture
£1333 $2440 €2000 Untitled (40x40x15cm-16x16x6in) s.i. varnish steel. 4-Jun-4 Lempertz, Koln #494/R est:2500
£43114 $72000 €62946 Gewohnheitstier 6 (55x110x17cm-22x43x7in) bronze executed 1996 prov.exhib.lit. 13-Nov-3 Phillips, New York #51/R est:50000-70000
£47486 $85000 €69330 Gewohnheitstier 5 (16x120x90cm-6x47x35in) bronze executed 1996 prov.exhib.lit. 13-May-4 Phillips, New York #15/R est:60000-80000
Works on paper
£284 $500 €415 World as man (23x15cm-9x6in) s.d.88 graphite. 23-May-4 Hindman, Chicago #1009/R
£13408 $24000 €19576 Kaschmir (57x77cm-22x30in) s.i.d.96 verso chl prov. 14-May-4 Phillips, New York #285/R est:3000-4000

TROELSTRA, Jelle (20th C) Scandinavian?
£979 $1664 €1400 Bridge over a river in front of a Spanish mountain village (60x72cm-24x28in) s. 24-Nov-3 Glerum, Amsterdam #631/R

TROGER (studio) (18th C) Austrian
Sculpture
£12667 $23307 €19000 Mendiants en guenilles (34x19cm-13x7in) ivory incl. base. 11-Jun-4 Maigret, Paris #174/R est:15000-20000

TROGER, Simon (1694-1768) Austrian
Sculpture
£11034 $18317 €16000 Beggar woman (38cm-15in) wood ivory glass. 30-Sep-3 Dorotheum, Vienna #48/R est:5000-7000

TROGER, Simon (attrib) (1694-1768) Austrian
Sculpture
£3611 $6500 €5272 Figure of the Pope Sylvester (47cm-19in) ivory and studio lit. 22-Jan-4 Sotheby's, New York #166/R est:6000-9000

TROIANI, Don (1949-) American
£8380 $15000 €12235 Gen Jeb Stuart (76x61cm-30x24in) 15-May-4 Altermann Galleries, Santa Fe #82/R
£19553 $35000 €28547 Cowpens (79x104cm-31x41in) 15-May-4 Altermann Galleries, Santa Fe #83/R

TROILI, Uno (1815-1875) Swedish
£1308 $2249 €1910 Boy with soap bubbles (73x62cm-29x24in) painted c.1847-1850 prov. 7-Dec-3 Uppsala Auktionskammare, Uppsala #118/R est:15000-20000 (S.KR 17000)

TROIVAUX, Jean Baptiste Desire (1788-1860) French
Miniatures
£3500 $6265 €5110 Young lady seated on a green upholstered sofa (7x6cm-3x2in) s.d.1838 rec. ormolu easel frame. 25-May-4 Christie's, London #213/R est:1500-2500

TROJANOWSKI, Wincenty (1859-1928) Polish
£1293 $2315 €1888 Female nude on rock (95x75cm-37x30in) s.i.d.1893. 12-May-4 Dobiaschofsky, Bern #1029/R est:5500 (S.FR 3000)

TROKES, Heinz (1913-1997) German

£1259	$2165	€1800	The red angel (40x50cm-16x20in) s.d. s.i.d. verso. 3-Dec-3 Hauswedell & Nolte, Hamburg #1025/R est:600
£1958	$3329	€2800	Bird on mountain (101x83cm-40x33in) s.d.70 i.d.1970 stretcher. 29-Nov-3 Villa Grisebach, Berlin #358/R est:3500-4500
£2667	$4907	€4000	Aladin (50x60cm-20x24in) s.d.50 s.i.d.verso. 12-Jun-4 Villa Grisebach, Berlin #340/R est:4000-6000
£2937	$4993	€4200	After the Karneval (66x74cm-26x29in) s.d.54 s.i.d. verso exhib. 27-Nov-3 Lempertz, Koln #489/R est:4500
£3333	$6133	€5000	Old project (58x49cm-23x19in) s.d.48 s.i.d.verso exhib. 12-Jun-4 Villa Grisebach, Berlin #341/R est:7000-9000
£8392	$14266	€12000	Paddle steamer (24x33cm-9x13in) mono.d.45 canvas on board. 29-Nov-3 Bassenge, Berlin #7010/R est:9000
Works on paper			
£490	$832	€700	Play figures (66x50cm-26x20in) s.d.76 i.d.7.5.76 verso W/C. 29-Nov-3 Villa Grisebach, Berlin #925/R
£667	$1227	€1000	Untitled (48x66cm-19x26in) s.d.60 W/C. 12-Jun-4 Villa Grisebach, Berlin #850/R
£667	$1227	€1000	Southern town (22x31cm-9x12in) W/C col chk. 12-Jun-4 Villa Grisebach, Berlin #848/R
£1200	$2208	€1800	Reflection in the garden (43x58cm-17x23in) s.d.58 s.i.d.verso W/C. 12-Jun-4 Villa Grisebach, Berlin #849/R est:1000-1500
£2000	$3580	€3000	Composition (50x64cm-20x25in) s.d. W/C. 15-May-4 Bassenge, Berlin #7161/R est:2500

TROLKOVSKII, O (19/20th C) Russian

£5988	$10000	€8742	Landscape with windmill (45x67cm-18x26in) s.d.1902. 21-Oct-3 Christie's, Rockefeller NY #93 est:10000-12000

TROLLE, Harald (1834-1882) Danish

£379	$701	€553	Autumn scene by Tjustrup Lake (29x43cm-11x17in) s. 15-Mar-4 Rasmussen, Vejle #472/R (D.KR 4200)

TROMBADORI, Francesco (1886-1961) Italian

£1580	$2687	€2260	Farms in the Roman countryside (13x18cm-5x7in) s.i. board. 18-Nov-3 Babuino, Rome #280/R est:1000-1200
£4828	$8062	€7000	Landscape (25x30cm-10x12in) s. board. 17-Nov-3 Sant Agostino, Torino #226/R est:3500-4500

TROMBINI, Giuliano (1953-) Italian

£387	$643	€550	Piano Bar (35x100cm-14x39in) s. 14-Jun-3 Meeting Art, Vercelli #645/R
£390	$651	€550	Cafe (70x100cm-28x39in) s. s.verso painted 2003. 20-Oct-3 Sant Agostino, Torino #122/R

TROMETTA, Nicolo (16/17th C) Italian

Works on paper			
£492	$900	€718	Study of a male scholar holding a scroll (25x13cm-10x5in) pencil. 29-Jan-4 Swann Galleries, New York #27/R

TROMETTA, Nicolo (attrib) (16/17th C) Italian

Works on paper			
£1918	$3260	€2800	Esprit Saint eclairant Saint Joseph avec l'enfant Jesus (27x19cm-11x7in) pen ink wash htd gouache. 6-Nov-3 Tajan, Paris #19/R

TROMKA, Abram (1896-1954) American

£1235	$2000	€1791	Monhegan (76x127cm-30x50in) s. board. 8-Aug-3 Barridorf, Portland #311/R est:2000-3000

TROMP, Jan Zoetelief (1872-1947) Dutch

£638	$1066	€900	Larens interior with mother and child (97x65cm-38x26in) 20-Oct-3 Glerum, Amsterdam #89/R
£1944	$3072	€2800	Zinnias in a pewter jar (53x46cm-21x18in) s. 2-Sep-3 Christie's, Amsterdam #216/R est:3000-5000
£6944	$11806	€10000	Feeding the kittens (44x56cm-17x22in) s. 28-Oct-3 Christie's, Amsterdam #121/R est:12000-16000
£6944	$11806	€10000	By the fire (18x26cm-7x10in) s. panel prov. 28-Oct-3 Christie's, Amsterdam #128/R est:10000-15000
£46667	$84000	€70000	Fun on the beach (31x40cm-12x16in) s. 21-Apr-4 Christie's, Amsterdam #105/R est:50000-70000
£69444	$115972	€100000	Sunny day at the beach (36x51cm-14x20in) s. s.verso prov. 21-Oct-3 Sotheby's, Amsterdam #245/R est:100000-150000
Works on paper			
£600	$1092	€876	On the quayside (16x22cm-6x9in) s. W/C. 15-Jun-4 Rosebery Fine Art, London #465
£1600	$2768	€2336	Hay cart (14x20cm-6x8in) s. W/C. 11-Dec-3 Lyon & Turnbull, Edinburgh #37/R est:600-800
£2800	$4844	€4088	Drying the laundry (14x18cm-6x7in) s. W/C. 11-Dec-3 Lyon & Turnbull, Edinburgh #36/R est:400-600
£3800	$6916	€5548	Mother and children at a swing (25x36cm-10x14in) s. W/C. 16-Jun-4 Andrew Hartley, Ilkley #966/R est:2500-3500
£4861	$8118	€7000	Beach stroll (15x22cm-6x9in) s. W/C htd white. 21-Oct-3 Sotheby's, Amsterdam #127/R est:6000-8000
£5000	$8650	€7300	Fisherman's return (18x25cm-7x10in) s. W/C. 11-Dec-3 Lyon & Turnbull, Edinburgh #38/R est:800-1200
£6597	$11215	€9500	Billygoat (25x35cm-10x14in) s. W/C htd white prov. 28-Oct-3 Christie's, Amsterdam #119/R est:10000-15000
£11111	$18556	€16000	Return from the catch (49x70cm-19x28in) s. W/C. 21-Oct-3 Sotheby's, Amsterdam #227/R est:12000-15000

TROMPIZ, Virgilio (1927-) Venezuelan

£233	$400	€340	Faces (33x41cm-13x16in) s. 7-Dec-3 Subastas Odalys, Caracas #1/R
£276	$475	€403	Figures (41x33cm-16x13in) s. 7-Dec-3 Subastas Odalys, Caracas #90/R
£296	$545	€444	Untitled (33x41cm-13x16in) s. 27-Jun-4 Subastas Odalys, Caracas #160
£319	$575	€466	Figure (33x41cm-13x16in) s. 25-Apr-4 Subastas Odalys, Caracas #1/R
£328	$525	€479	Untitled (33x41cm-13x16in) s. 21-Sep-3 Subastas Odalys, Caracas #1/R
£336	$625	€491	Figure (33x41cm-13x16in) s. 14-Mar-4 Subastas Odalys, Caracas #1/R
£357	$650	€536	Figures (50x45cm-20x18in) s. 21-Jun-4 Subastas Odalys, Caracas #1/R
£368	$580	€537	Faces (44x50cm-17x20in) s. 27-Apr-3 Subastas Odalys, Caracas #20
£506	$845	€739	Untitled (50x45cm-20x18in) s. 13-Jul-3 Subastas Odalys, Caracas #58
£616	$1145	€899	Figure (51x70cm-20x28in) s. 14-Mar-4 Subastas Odalys, Caracas #51/R
£718	$1220	€1048	Faces (45x50cm-18x20in) s. painted 1960. 23-Nov-3 Subastas Odalys, Caracas #1/R
£774	$1200	€1130	Blue nude (54x64cm-21x25in) s. 29-Sep-2 Subastas Odalys, Caracas #1/R
£1044	$1650	€1524	Figures (60x90cm-24x35in) s. 1-Dec-2 Subastas Odalys, Caracas #1/R
£1250	$2125	€1825	Figures (51x70cm-20x28in) s. painted c.1960. 23-Nov-3 Subastas Odalys, Caracas #145/R
£1806	$2800	€2637	Figure (71x51cm-28x20in) s. 29-Sep-2 Subastas Odalys, Caracas #45/R
£2707	$4520	€3952	Untitled (54x64cm-21x25in) s. canvas on panel. 19-Oct-3 Subastas Odalys, Caracas #98/R est:3000
Works on paper			
£239	$445	€349	Untitled (50x45cm-20x18in) s. mixed media exec.1968. 14-Mar-4 Subastas Odalys, Caracas #81

TRONCET, Antony (1879-1939) French

£667	$1220	€1000	Toilette (24x19cm-9x7in) s. canvas on cardboard prov. 6-Jun-4 Rouillac, Vendome #54
£15556	$28000	€22712	Reluctant model (205x117cm-81x46in) s. prov.lit. 23-Apr-4 Sotheby's, New York #204/R est:30000-40000

TROOD, W H H (1848-1899) British

£1000	$1670	€1460	Busy bodies and busy bees (25x36cm-10x14in) init. panel. 8-Oct-3 Andrew Hartley, Ilkley #1125/R est:3000-4000

TROOD, William Henry Hamilton (1848-1899) British

£5134	$8830	€7496	Watchful terriers (36x46cm-14x18in) s.d.1895 prov. 2-Dec-3 Ritchie, Toronto #57/R est:7000-10000 (C.D 11500)
£7200	$12960	€10512	Keeping watch (40x56cm-16x22in) s.d.1891. 21-Jan-4 Sotheby's, Olympia #360/R est:6000-9000
£7500	$12750	€10950	Favourite terrier (43x56cm-17x22in) s.d.1891. 26-Nov-3 Hamptons Fine Art, Godalming #240/R est:8000-10000
£9783	$18000	€14283	Nursing puppies (48x41cm-19x16in) s. 26-Jun-4 Selkirks, St. Louis #415/R est:10000-15000
£16000	$27200	€23360	Bashful and Freedom, two hounds before a kennel (46x61cm-18x24in) s.d.1893. 27-Nov-3 Christie's, Kensington #374/R est:3000-5000

TROOST, Cornelis (1697-1750) Dutch

Works on paper			
£1351	$2378	€2000	Battle scene, with cavalry and infantry before a hilltop church (13x19cm-5x7in) s.d.1742 pen black ink grey wsh prov.exhib.lit. 19-May-4 Sotheby's, Amsterdam #244/R est:2500-3500

TROPPA, Girolamo (1636-1706) Italian

£13245	$24106	€20000	Head of elderly bearded man (76x63cm-30x25in) 16-Jun-4 Christie's, Rome #434/R est:20000-30000

TROSCHKE, Wolfgang (1947-) German

£1667	$2717	€2400	Untitled (176x140cm-69x55in) s. mixed media linen plexiglas prov. 27-Sep-3 Dr Fritz Nagel, Stuttgart #9657/R est:1500

TROST, Carl (1811-1884) German

£604	$1111	€900	Chevalier devant un palais Gothique (59x48cm-23x19in) mono.d.1858. 24-Mar-4 Tajan, Paris #86

TROST, Friedrich (1844-1922) German

Works on paper			
£625	$1031	€900	Schloss Schillingsfurt (25x37cm-10x15in) s. Indian ink. 3-Jul-3 Van Ham, Cologne #1484/R
£769	$1308	€1100	Old Nurnberg with Thon (22x33cm-9x13in) s.d.1896 W/C pencil. 20-Nov-3 Weidler, Nurnberg #7004/R

TROTIN, Hector (1894-1966) French

£400	$736	€584	Ascension d;un ballon anglais (26x16cm-10x6in) s. board prov. 24-Mar-4 Sotheby's, Olympia #184/R
£400	$736	€584	Ascension de l'aigle (25x17cm-10x7in) s.i.verso board prov. 24-Mar-4 Sotheby's, Olympia #185/R

TROTT, F G (?) British

£480	$816	€701	Polperro, Cornwall (50x60cm-20x24in) s.i.d.1959 verso. 1-Dec-3 Bonhams, Bath #33

TROTTA, Vincent (20th C) American

Works on paper			
£340	$550	€496	Semi nude woman holding her hand to an earphone, atop the globe. s. chl gouache exec.c.1900 prov. 26-Jul-3 Thomaston Place, Thomaston #187/R

TROTTER, John (fl.1756-1792) Irish
£16201 $29000 €23653 Portrait of Robert Mack, architect (91x76cm-36x30in) s.d.1784 prov. 14-May-4 Skinner, Boston #48/R est:3000-5000
£55000 $91850 €80300 Portrait of Captain John Alston, standing in a landscape wearing uniform of the 100th Regiment (126x101cm-50x40in) prov.lit. 14-Oct-3 Sotheby's, London #457/R est:25000-35000

TROTTER, McKie (1874-1968) American
£299 $500 €437 Fields (38x25cm-15x10in) board. 18-Oct-3 David Dike, Dallas #161/R
£898 $1500 €1311 Mexican buildings at night (20x46cm-8x18in) board. 18-Oct-3 David Dike, Dallas #158/R est:1000-2000

TROTTER, Priscilla (20th C) American
£323 $600 €472 Harbour scene (20x25cm-8x10in) s. board painted c.1930. 7-Mar-4 Treadway Gallery, Cincinnati #559/R

TROTTEYN, Jos (1910-) Belgian
£909 $1545 €1300 La fauche (150x115cm-59x45in) s. 1-Dec-3 Palais de Beaux Arts, Brussels #325/R

TROTTI, Sandro (1934-) Italian
£622 $1058 €890 Portrait of Yoko (80x60cm-31x24in) s.i.verso. 18-Nov-3 Babuino, Rome #490/R

TROTZIG, Ulf (1925-) Norwegian
£287 $516 €419 Abstract composition in colour (66x55cm-26x22in) s.d.63. 24-Apr-4 Rasmussen, Havnen #4040 (D.KR 3200)

TROUBETZKOY, Prince Paolo (1866-1938) Russian
Sculpture
£2254 $3741 €3200 La cagna (30cm-12in) s.d.1897 pat bronze. 11-Jun-3 Christie's, Rome #10/R est:1300-1800
£2254 $3899 €3200 Ballerina (35cm-14in) s. bronze. 10-Dec-3 Sotheby's, Milan #152/R est:1000-1500
£3147 $5255 €4500 Dancer (36cm-14in) st.sig. bronze prov. 24-Jun-3 Finarte Semenzato, Rome #89/R est:2500
£4000 $7360 €6000 Rider (42x20x33cm-17x8x13in) s. bronze. 8-Jun-4 Sotheby's, Milan #153/R est:6000-8000
£4000 $7360 €6000 Young girl (48cm-19in) s. bronze. 8-Jun-4 Sotheby's, Milan #160/R est:5000-7000
£4028 $6847 €5800 Arab rider. s.d.1897 pat plaster. 29-Oct-3 Il Ponte, Milan #536/R
£15000 $27450 €21900 Seated lady (37x42cm-15x17in) s.d.1929 pat bronze prov. 9-Jul-4 Sotheby's, London #161/R est:15000-20000
£23000 $41400 €33580 Standing man with his pug dog (41cm-16in) s.i.d.1924 brown pat bronze st.f.A.A. Hebrard. 21-Apr-4 Sotheby's, London #149/R est:8000-12000

TROUILLE, Clovis (1889-1975) French
£20409 $36532 €30000 Musiciens (61x50cm-24x20in) s. painted c.1939 prov.exhib.lit. 21-Mar-4 Calmels Cohen, Paris #55/R est:30000-35000
£27211 $48708 €40000 Grand poeme d'Amiens (100x81cm-39x32in) s. painted c.1945-1963 prov.exhib.lit. 21-Mar-4 Calmels Cohen, Paris #52/R est:4000-60000
Works on paper
£105442 $188741 €155000 Voyeuse (46x38cm-18x15in) s. painted 1960 prov.exhib.lit. 21-Mar-4 Calmels Cohen, Paris #49/R est:60000-80000

TROUILLEBERT, Paul Desire (1829-1900) French
£493 $853 €700 Automne (32x16cm-13x6in) s. panel. 14-Dec-3 Eric Pillon, Calais #24/R
£669 $1070 €950 Portrait of girl (46x37cm-18x15in) s. 16-Sep-3 Segre, Madrid #32
£1333 $2413 €2000 Bouquet de violettes (11x19cm-4x7in) s. panel. 31-Mar-4 Sotheby's, Paris #109/R est:1000-1500
£1422 $2546 €2076 Portrait of young woman in turquoise dress (61x50cm-24x20in) s.d.1892. 12-May-4 Dobiaschofsky, Bern #1031/R est:5000 (S.FR 3300)
£1500 $2790 €2190 Wooded landscape with figure on track (45x60cm-18x24in) s. 2-Mar-4 Bearnes, Exeter #415/R est:1000-1500
£1846 $3138 €2640 Woodland walk (44x35cm-17x14in) s. 20-Nov-3 Weidler, Nurnberg #336/R est:2640
£2368 $4358 €3600 Rowing boats by wooded shore (28x40cm-11x16in) s. board. 24-Jun-4 Dr Fritz Nagel, Stuttgart #766/R est:4200
£2371 $4244 €3462 River landscape in summer (24x32cm-9x13in) s. 12-May-4 Dobiaschofsky, Bern #1032/R est:4600 (S.FR 5500)
£3467 $6309 €5200 Diane chasseresse (85x46cm-33x18in) s. lit. 4-Jul-4 Eric Pillon, Calais #36/R
£3624 $6741 €5400 Paysanne sur la route de l'etang (30x25cm-12x10in) s. 7-Mar-4 Lesieur & Le Bars, Le Havre #134/R
£3779 $6500 €5517 Repos sur le chemin (38x46cm-15x18in) s. 2-Dec-3 Christie's, Rockefeller NY #60/R est:8000-12000
£4072 $6923 €5945 Wood gatherer under trees (61x50cm-24x20in) s. 19-Nov-3 Fischer, Luzern #1069/R est:9000-12000 (S.FR 9000)
£4276 $7868 €6500 La villa a Saint Maur des Fosses (43x52cm-17x20in) s.i. 28-Jun-4 Rossini, Paris #68/R est:2000-2200
£4474 $8232 €6800 Gardienne d'oies (46x61cm-18x24in) s. 24-Jun-4 Christie's, Paris #149/R est:6000-8000
£4978 $8911 €7268 River landscape with rowing boat and distant town (21x26cm-8x10in) s. panel prov. 22-Mar-4 Philippe Schuler, Zurich #4431/R est:7000-9000 (S.FR 11500)
£5072 $8319 €7000 Bord de riviere avec des paysannes (38x45cm-15x18in) s. 11-May-3 Osenat, Fontainebleau #34/R est:8500-9000
£5235 $9737 €7800 Pecheur en barque (26x31cm-10x12in) s. prov. 3-Mar-4 Fraysse & Associes, Paris #21/R est:7000-9000
£5240 $9537 €7650 River landscape with a washerwoman (38x46cm-15x18in) s. 16-Jun-4 Fischer, Luzern #1130/R est:12000-15000 (S.FR 12000)
£5430 $9231 €7928 River landscape with trees and figures (38x46cm-15x18in) s. 19-Nov-3 Fischer, Luzern #1076/R est:10000-12000 (S.FR 12000)
£5603 $10030 €8180 La verite (42x69cm-17x27in) s. exhib. 17-May-4 Beurret, Zurich #20/R est:6000-8000 (S.FR 13000)
£5667 $10257 €8500 Canal a Venise (43x23cm-17x9in) s. 5-Apr-4 Deburaux, Boulogne #100/R est:7000-7500
£5862 $9790 €8500 Lavandiere (49x39cm-19x15in) s. lit. 17-Nov-3 Tajan, Paris #55/R est:8000-10000
£6111 $11000 €8922 Le fagoteur (61x50cm-24x20in) s. 23-Apr-4 Sotheby's, New York #152/R est:12000-15000
£6294 $10825 €9000 Paysage au moulin (38x46cm-15x18in) s. prov. 8-Dec-3 Artcurial Briest, Paris #6/R est:7000-9000
£6294 $10825 €9000 Andromede (48x27cm-19x11in) s. 8-Dec-3 Cornette de St.Cyr, Paris #73/R est:8000-10000
£6338 $10965 €9000 Pecheur en bord de riviere (20x33cm-8x13in) s. 12-Dec-3 Piasa, Paris #54/R est:9000-11000
£7746 $12859 €11000 Pecheurs en barque (39x31cm-15x12in) s. lit. 15-Jun-3 Peron, Melun #72
£7860 $14463 €11476 Boat and figures on shore (33x46cm-13x18in) s. prov. 14-Jun-4 Philippe Schuler, Zurich #4331/R est:10000-14000 (S.FR 18000)
£8278 $15149 €12500 Vaches au paturage (31x56cm-12x22in) s. 7-Apr-4 Piasa, Paris #21/R est:10000-12000
£8500 $14620 €12410 Woman washing clothes at the riverside (45x56cm-18x22in) s. 4-Dec-3 Christie's, Kensington #10/R est:4000-6000
£9868 $18158 €15000 Paysanne sur chemin (56x47cm-22x19in) s. 24-Jun-4 Christie's, Paris #161/R est:6000-8000
£10556 $19000 €15412 Bords de la Marne, pres d'Angers (61x74cm-24x29in) s. 23-Apr-4 Sotheby's, New York #151/R est:20000-30000
£10738 $19221 €16000 Paysanne au bord de lac (46x38cm-18x15in) s. 27-May-4 Christie's, Paris #116/R est:8000-12000
£11176 $19000 €16317 Boatman on a river landscape (61x75cm-24x30in) s. 28-Oct-3 Sotheby's, New York #126/R est:18000-25000
£11765 $18824 €17177 Washerwoman by lake (46x38cm-18x15in) s. 19-Sep-3 Koller, Zurich #3095/R est:14000-18000 (S.FR 26000)
£12222 $22000 €17844 Au bord d'une mare dans la foret (65x81cm-26x32in) s. 22-Apr-4 Christie's, Rockefeller NY #119/R est:20000-30000
£13406 $21986 €18500 Bord de riviere, la gardienne d'oie (46x55cm-18x22in) s. 11-May-3 Osenat, Fontainebleau #36/R est:16000-18000
£14430 $25540 €21500 Pont de pierres (46x61cm-18x24in) s. s.i.on stretcher prov. 30-Apr-4 Tajan, Paris #137/R est:12000-15000
£15436 $28712 €23000 Personnages au bord d'une riviere (61x50cm-24x20in) s. prov. 2-Mar-4 Artcurial Briest, Paris #104/R est:15000-20000
£16327 $25959 €24000 Small boat and house on waterside (37x55cm-15x22in) s. 23-Mar-3 Mercier & Cie, Lille #220/R est:23000-25000
£20588 $35000 €30058 Shoring the fishing boat (66x81cm-26x32in) s. 28-Oct-3 Sotheby's, New York #125/R est:30000-40000
£22222 $40000 €32444 Paysage au bord de l'eau (90x117cm-35x46in) s. 23-Apr-4 Sotheby's, New York #153/R est:30000-40000

TROUILLEBERT, Paul Desire (attrib) (1829-1900) French
£409 $733 €597 Paysage avec arbres a la riviere (26x35cm-10x14in) i. board. 12-May-4 Dobiaschofsky, Bern #1034/R (S.FR 950)
£1676 $3100 €2514 Dramatic coastal view (102x76cm-40x30in) s. 17-Jul-4 Skinner, Boston #538/R est:2000-4000

TROUVILLE, Henri-Charles (19th C) French
£2797 $4811 €4000 La mare aux Fees (37x61cm-15x24in) init. painted c.1885-90. 7-Dec-3 Osenat, Fontainebleau #142

TROVA, Ernest (1927-) American
£2198 $4000 €3209 Study, falling man series no.104 (96x96cm-38x38in) s.verso latex painted 1963 prov. 29-Jun-4 Sotheby's, New York #436/R est:2500-3500
Sculpture
£966 $1700 €1410 Study/falling man, double figures (18cm-7in) mono.d.1986 num.41/99 polished bronze plinth. 22-May-4 Selkirks, St. Louis #666/R est:1250-1500
£2568 $4750 €3749 Landscape 5 - Study, falling man series (36x39x44cm-14x15x17in) various objects exec 1964 prov. 12-Feb-4 Sotheby's, New York #181/R est:1200-1800
£3267 $5750 €4770 Study/falling man (38cm-15in) mono.num.413/46/1434 chrome plated bronze black pedestal. 22-May-4 Selkirks, St. Louis #667/R est:5000-6000
£6522 $12000 €9522 Profile canto IV (366x366x152cm-144x144x60in) st.sig.d.1974 steel edition of three prov. 10-Jun-4 Phillips, New York #422/R est:15000-20000
£18405 $30000 €26871 FM/72 (178x61x61cm-70x24x24in) s.d.80 silver plated polished metal 5 from edition of 6 prov. 23-Sep-3 Christie's, Rockefeller NY #184/R est:15000-20000

TROXLER, Georges (1867-1941) Swiss
£271 $493 €396 Male nude (81x54cm-32x21in) s.verso painted c.1890. 16-Jun-4 Fischer, Luzern #2402 (S.FR 620)
£349 $636 €510 Winter day in Arosa (47x57cm-19x22in) s. 16-Jun-4 Fischer, Luzern #2404 (S.FR 800)
£393 $715 €574 Snow covered Luzern, seen from Hitzlisberg (49x45cm-19x18in) s. painted c.1910. 16-Jun-4 Fischer, Luzern #2403/R (S.FR 900)

TROXLER, Georges Alfons (1901-1990) Swiss
£271 $462 €396 Autumn landscape (45x56cm-18x22in) s. 19-Nov-3 Fischer, Luzern #2236/R (S.FR 600)
£306 $556 €447 Allotments with church (63x50cm-25x20in) s.d.1969. 16-Jun-4 Fischer, Luzern #2407/R (S.FR 700)

TROY, François de (attrib) (1645-1730) French
£1888 $3248 €2700 Portrait de magistrat (92x73cm-36x29in) 7-Dec-3 Livinec, Gaudcheau & Jezequel, Rennes #112/R
£3007 $5172 €4300 Portrait de femme (92x73cm-36x29in) 7-Dec-3 Livinec, Gaudcheau & Jezequel, Rennes #111/R

TROY, François de (studio) (1645-1730) French
£7599 $13982 €11550 Portrait presume de la duchesse du Maine vue aux trois-quarts (130x100cm-51x39in) oval. 25-Jun-4 Doutrebente, Paris #9/R est:7000-8000

TROY, Jean François de (1679-1752) French
£83333 $150000 €121666 Allegory of painting (88x109cm-35x43in) s.d.1733 prov.lit. 23-Jan-4 Christie's, Rockefeller NY #66/R est:150000-200000
£211268 $365493 €300000 Angelique et Medor (156x121cm-61x48in) 10-Dec-3 Maigret, Paris #44/R est:30000-40000

TROYE, Edward (1808-1874) American
£14785 $27500 €21586 Major Winfield (79x99cm-31x39in) s.verso. 3-Mar-4 Alderfer's, Hatfield #303/R est:1500-2500

TROYEN, Michel (1875-1915) French
£1300 $2041 €1885 Rue de la Paix. Le Madelaine (41x33cm-16x13in) s. pair. 28-Aug-3 Christie's, Kensington #225/R est:1200-1800

TROYEN, Rombout van (1605-c.1650) Dutch
£1477 $2643 €2200 Landscape with figures by classical monument (33x49cm-13x19in) i. 25-May-4 Karl & Faber, Munich #73/R est:4000
£2483 $4146 €3600 Scene from the Old Testament (49x65cm-19x26in) s.d.16 panel prov. 15-Nov-3 Lempertz, Koln #1159/R est:4000
£11189 $18685 €16000 Worshipping Salomon (35x57cm-14x22in) board prov. 30-Jun-3 Ansorena, Madrid #174/R est:16000
£13158 $24211 €20000 Building Babel's Tower (38x51cm-15x20in) panel oval. 25-Jun-4 Piasa, Paris #23/R est:25000-30000
£15789 $28579 €24000 Biblical scene (36x49cm-14x19in) s.indis.d. board. 14-Apr-4 Ansorena, Madrid #136/R est:24000

TROYEN, Rombout van (attrib) (1605-c.1650) Dutch
£1441 $2652 €2104 Sacrifice in grotto (16x22cm-6x9in) copper. 14-Jun-4 Philippe Schuler, Zurich #4332/R est:3500-4000 (S.FR 3300)

TROYER, Prosper de (1880-1961) Belgian
£2394 $4142 €3400 La peche miraculeuse (120x90cm-47x35in) s.d.1925 panel. 9-Dec-3 Campo, Vlaamse Kaai #284/R est:2500-3000

TROYON, Constant (1810-1865) French
£493 $853 €700 Etude de fermiere avec sa vache (13x8cm-5x3in) s. panel. 10-Dec-3 Maigret, Paris #74
£800 $1512 €1168 Herders watering their cattle (8x17cm-3x7in) s. panel. 19-Feb-4 Christie's, Kensington #138/R
£1133 $2051 €1700 Chapelle (23x32cm-9x13in) mono.indis.d. panel. 30-Mar-4 Rossini, Paris #1063/R est:250-400
£1267 $2305 €1900 Crepuscule au bord de mer (23x30cm-9x12in) 5-Jul-4 Neret-Minet, Paris #34/R est:1000-1500
£1400 $2338 €2044 Cattle in a forest clearing (54x74cm-21x29in) s. 11-Nov-3 Bonhams, Knightsbridge #105/R est:1500-2000
£1651 $2758 €2394 Troupeau a l'etang (32x24cm-13x9in) s. panel prov. 21-Jun-3 Galerie du Rhone, Sion #93/R est:3500-4500 (S.FR 3600)
£1705 $3000 €2489 Cattle in wooded stream (20x18cm-8x7in) s. panel. 22-May-4 New Orleans Auction, New Orleans #124/R est:2500-4000
£2018 $3371 €2926 Paysage au falaises (62x89cm-24x35in) mono. painted c.1840. 21-Jun-3 Galerie du Rhone, Sion #505/R est:4000-6000 (S.FR 4400)
£2098 $3608 €3000 Vaches a la lisiere d'un bois (16x11cm-6x4in) init. panel exec.c.1840-45 exhib. 7-Dec-3 Osenat, Fontainebleau #46 est:3000-3200
£2586 $4629 €3776 Landscape with cow and cloudy skies (37x45cm-15x18in) s. 13-May-4 Stuker, Bern #349/R est:6000-8000 (S.FR 6000)
£2606 $4508 €3700 Les vendanges (32x46cm-13x18in) s. 12-Dec-3 Libert, Castor, Paris #62 est:400-600
£2837 $4738 €4000 Le retour du marche (38x46cm-15x18in) 17-Jun-3 Christie's, Paris #157/R est:4000-6000
£3022 $5500 €4412 Cattle grazing (37x46cm-15x18in) s. panel. 29-Jun-4 Sotheby's, New York #81/R est:5000-7000
£5000 $9200 €7600 Le retour du troupeau (41x33cm-16x13in) s. 23-Jun-4 Maigret, Paris #72/R est:5500-6000
£5594 $9622 €8000 Deux vaches couchees dans la prairie (32x45cm-13x18in) prov. 7-Dec-3 Osenat, Fontainebleau #45 est:8000
£6111 $11000 €8922 Deux chevaux atteles a une herse, conduits par un paysan (60x78cm-24x31in) st.sig. prov.lit. 22-Apr-4 Christie's, Rockefeller NY #105/R est:10000-15000
£6250 $10000 €9125 Two cows and ploughman (69x56cm-27x22in) prov. 20-Sep-3 Sloans & Kenyon, Bethesda #1179/R est:10000-12000
£6667 $12000 €9734 Retour de la vache (63x48cm-25x19in) s. prov. 22-Apr-4 Christie's, Rockefeller NY #106/R est:15000-20000
£13889 $25000 €20278 Les porteurs d'eau (70x95cm-28x37in) s. prov. 23-Apr-4 Sotheby's, New York #150/R est:20000-30000
£50000 $92000 €75000 Outdoor party (97x103cm-38x41in) s. painted 1855/60 prov. 11-Jun-4 Villa Grisebach, Berlin #3/R est:50000-70000
Works on paper
£280 $507 €420 Collines proches de Perpignan (25x36cm-10x14in) s. W/C. 30-Mar-4 Rossini, Paris #1062
£320 $550 €467 Shepherd and flock (12x16cm-5x6in) init. chl htd white. 3-Dec-3 Cheffins, Cambridge #562/R
£432 $691 €600 Paysans dans un champ (32x45cm-13x18in) mono. chl white chk beige paper. 16-May-3 Tajan, Paris #185
£680 $1218 €1000 Bouquet de fleurs (23x37cm-9x15in) s. W/C. 17-Mar-4 Maigret, Paris #109/R
£1789 $2988 €2594 Chiens de chasse (35x47cm-14x19in) s. W/C prov. 21-Jun-3 Galerie du Rhone, Sion #504/R est:4000-6000 (S.FR 3900)

TROYON, Constant (attrib) (1810-1865) French
£797 $1307 €1100 Paysage au soleil couchant (27x23cm-11x9in) cardboard. 11-May-3 Osenat, Fontainebleau #137

TROYON, Henry (19th C) French
£491 $800 €717 Bretonese mill scene (61x51cm-24x20in) s. 27-Sep-3 Thomaston Place, Thomaston #222

TRUB, Charles (1925-) Swiss
£271 $462 €396 Landscape with trees (45x60cm-18x24in) s. bears d. 18-Nov-3 Hans Widmer, St Gallen #1214 (S.FR 600)

TRUBBIANI, Valeriano (1937-) Italian
Sculpture
£1667 $3000 €2500 Siege (218cm-86in) iron aluminium unique exhib.lit. 22-Apr-4 Finarte Semenzato, Rome #226/R est:3000-3500

TRUBNER, Alice (1875-1916) German
£861 $1567 €1300 Still life with a Japanese doll (44x52cm-17x20in) s. i.verso stretcher. 18-Jun-4 Bolland & Marotz, Bremen #784/R

TRUBNER, Wilhelm (1851-1917) German
£1111 $1811 €1600 Young church server (91x78cm-36x31in) s.d.92. 25-Sep-3 Dr Fritz Nagel, Stuttgart #1432/R est:3000
£1208 $2162 €1800 Konigssee (25x28cm-10x11in) paper. 25-May-4 Karl & Faber, Munich #145/R est:2500
£1528 $2521 €2200 Small girl sitting on garden bench (84x49cm-33x19in) i. board. 2-Jul-3 Neumeister, Munich #793/R est:2200
£2000 $3200 €2900 Forest (24x36cm-9x14in) s. prov. 18-Sep-3 Christie's, Kensington #65/R est:3000-5000
£2078 $3719 €3034 Heidelberg Castle (21x27cm-8x11in) mono. panel. 22-Mar-4 Philippe Schuler, Zurich #4432/R est:3500-4500 (S.FR 4800)
£4000 $6400 €5800 Wooded lake landscape (60x74cm-24x29in) s. 18-Sep-3 Christie's, Kensington #64/R est:3000-5000
£6944 $11458 €10000 Island in the Starnberger See (62x80cm-24x31in) s. 2-Jul-3 Neumeister, Munich #792/R est:12000
£6944 $11319 €10000 Mausbachtal near Stift Neuburg (92x79cm-36x31in) s. lit. 25-Sep-3 Dr Fritz Nagel, Stuttgart #1433/R est:8000
£8333 $15333 €12500 Head of a goblin (58x43cm-23x17in) s. cardboard painted 1891 prov.exhib. 12-Jun-4 Villa Grisebach, Berlin #122/R est:4000-6000
£8803 $15229 €12500 View of Starnberger See through trees (59x44cm-23x17in) s. 13-Dec-3 Lempertz, Koln #52/R est:8000
£11000 $18920 €16060 Heidelberger Schloss (67x96cm-26x38in) s. 4-Dec-3 Christie's, Kensington #201/R est:12000-18000
£11111 $18333 €16000 Roses behind fence in park landscape of Possenhofen (75x61cm-30x24in) s. 2-Jul-3 Neumeister, Munich #791/R est:20000
Works on paper
£350 $584 €500 Church in Gutach (26x19cm-10x7in) mono. chk. 10-Oct-3 Winterberg, Heidelberg #790

TRUBUS (1926-1966) Indonesian
£9150 $16562 €13359 Dancer (65x75cm-26x30in) s.d.11/8/55 prov. 4-Apr-4 Sotheby's, Singapore #158/R est:25000-35000 (S.D 28000)

TRUE, Allen Tupper (1881-1955) American
Works on paper
£549 $1000 €802 His father's son (51x61cm-20x24in) s. gouache exec.c.1908. 19-Jun-4 Jackson's, Cedar Falls #179/R

TRUE, David (1942-) American
£919 $1700 €1342 Zen of Alarm (60x70cm-24x28in) acrylic ink paper on canvas exec 1988 prov. 12-Feb-4 Sotheby's, New York #212/R est:1000-1500
Works on paper
£240 $400 €350 Untitled (76x56cm-30x22in) W/C ink. 19-Oct-3 Bonhams & Butterfields, Los Angeles #7089
£270 $500 €394 Rite of Passage III (28x34cm-11x13in) s.d.80 mixed media diptych prov. 13-Jul-4 Christie's, Rockefeller NY #102/R

TRUEDSSON, Folke (1913-) Scandinavian
Sculpture
£1511 $2568 €2206 Split shape (120cm-47in) s.num.1/5 gold pat.bronze on stone socle lit. 4-Nov-3 Bukowskis, Stockholm #251/R est:25000-30000 (S.KR 20000)

TRUESDELL, Gaylord Sangston (1850-1899) American
Works on paper
£3842 $6800 €5609 Farmer with his cattle (26x35cm-10x14in) s. 2-May-4 Bonhams & Butterfields, San Francisco #1109/R est:3000-5000

TRUEX, Van Day (1904-1979) American
Works on paper
£408 $750 €596 Siesta, garden, Villa Aurelia, Rome (51x69cm-20x27in) ink. 23-Jun-4 Doyle, New York #5075/R

TRUFFAUT, Fernand (1866-1955) French
Works on paper
£272 $487 €400 Vue animee de la porte Saint-Martin (36x51cm-14x20in) s. W/C traces black crayon. 17-Mar-4 Tajan, Paris #170/R
£315 $541 €450 Port de Marseille (26x36cm-10x14in) s.i.d.1910 W/C. 8-Dec-3 Christie's, Paris #67/R
£552 $1021 €800 A TRouville (26x37cm-10x15in) s.i. W/C. 16-Feb-4 Giraudeau, Tours #34
£625 $1150 €950 Bruges, la tour des Halles (37x51cm-15x20in) s.i.d.1925 W/C exhib. 28-Jun-4 Joron-Derem, Paris #179
£933 $1689 €1400 Le port de Canes (38x52cm-15x20in) s. W/C gouache. 30-Mar-4 Rossini, Paris #1064/R

TRUITT, Anne (1921-) American
Sculpture
£3784 $7000 €5525 Toth (244x23x23cm-96x9x9in) s.d.29 June 83 base acrylic over wood prov. 12-Feb-4 Sotheby's, New York #303/R est:3000-4000

TRUMAN, Herbert (fl.1912-1933) British
£380 $707 €555 Babbacombe Beach, Torquay (30x44cm-12x17in) s. board exhib. 2-Mar-4 Bristol Auction Rooms #351/R
£1400 $2562 €2044 Low tide, St Ives harbour (32x39cm-13x15in) s.i.d.1937 verso canvasboard. 3-Jun-4 Lane, Penzance #165/R est:1400-1600

TRUMAN, J (?) British?
£3800 $6992 €5548 Lady Trespass, bay racehorse, with jockey up, owner and trainer by their side (58x77cm-23x30in) s.i.d.1866. 10-Jun-4 Christie's, Kensington #17/R est:3000-4000

TRUMBULL, John (1756-1843) American
Works on paper
£113636 $200000 €165909 Death of General Warren at Bunker's Hill (13x20cm-5x8in) s.i. d.1785-6 verso sepia ink wash prov. 19-May-4 Sotheby's, New York #100/R est:15000-30000

TRUMBULL, John (attrib) (1756-1843) American
£2285 $4250 €3336 Portrait of Captain Richardson (76x64cm-30x25in) 5-Mar-4 Skinner, Boston #273/R est:3000-5000

TRUMPER, August (1874-1956) German
£909 $1545 €1300 House between trees in garden (70x50cm-28x20in) s.d.1922. 20-Nov-3 Van Ham, Cologne #1889

TRUNDLEY, David (1949-) British
Works on paper
£280 $512 €409 Exercising on a cold morning (30x46cm-12x18in) s. W/C. 7-Apr-4 Woolley & Wallis, Salisbury #83/R

TRUNK, Herman (jnr) (1899-1963) American
£1294 $2200 €1889 Road with a telephone pole (38x28cm-15x11in) s. W/C prov. 9-Nov-3 Wright, Chicago #217 est:3000-4000

TRUPHEMUS, Jacques (1922-) French
£2800 $5040 €4200 Au bord de la mer (16x22cm-6x9in) s.d.62 cardboard. 20-Apr-4 Chenu & Scrive, Lyon #162/R est:2000-3000

TRUPPE, Karl (1887-1959) Austrian
£1067 $1931 €1600 Dream of youth (64x90cm-25x35in) s. lit. 1-Apr-4 Frank Peege, Freiburg #1144/R est:1500
£1208 $2162 €1800 Still life with hat and guitar (27x40cm-11x16in) s.d.1923 board. 25-May-4 Dorotheum, Vienna #157/R est:2200-3200
£1678 $2853 €2400 Werzer Bad in Portschach on Worthersee (27x38cm-11x15in) mono. bears d. board. 19-Nov-3 Dorotheum, Klagenfurt #35 est:1000
£1690 $3025 €2400 White and red chrysanthemums (44x31cm-17x12in) s.i. indis.d. board lit. 8-Jan-4 Allgauer, Kempten #2535/R est:600
£2448 $4161 €3500 Leda with the swan (21x29cm-8x11in) s.d.45 panel. 25-Nov-3 Hassfurther, Vienna #70/R est:3500-4500
£6993 $11888 €10000 Still life (45x59cm-18x23in) s. board. 25-Nov-3 Hassfurther, Vienna #71/R est:8000-10000
£10490 $17832 €15000 Peasant Madonna (131x200cm-52x79in) s.d.1924. 26-Nov-3 Dorotheum, Vienna #137/R est:22000-28000

TRUSLER, Peter (20th C) Australian
£569 $893 €831 Black swan (34x34cm-13x13in) s.d.91. 27-Aug-3 Christie's, Sydney #795 est:300-500 (A.D 1400)

TRUSS, Jonathan (1960-) British
£250 $415 €365 Head of a lion (44x33cm-17x13in) 1-Oct-3 Woolley & Wallis, Salisbury #185/R
£260 $481 €380 Pony club (38x120cm-15x47in) s.d.2001. 16-Jul-4 Charterhouse, Sherborne #562/R
£260 $481 €380 Three foals in a landscape (48x73cm-19x29in) s.d.2001. 16-Jul-4 Charterhouse, Sherborne #565/R
£280 $518 €409 Two elephants in an evening setting sun landscape (49x75cm-19x30in) s. 16-Jul-4 Charterhouse, Sherborne #564/R
£400 $664 €584 Elephant (51x76cm-20x30in) s. 1-Oct-3 Woolley & Wallis, Salisbury #187/R
£420 $769 €613 Two elephants watering (61x91cm-24x36in) s. 7-Apr-4 Woolley & Wallis, Salisbury #277/R
£480 $888 €701 Siberian tiger in a snowscape (60x90cm-24x35in) 16-Jul-4 Charterhouse, Sherborne #566/R
£800 $1328 €1168 Head of a tiger (44x54cm-17x21in) s. 1-Oct-3 Woolley & Wallis, Salisbury #186/R
£800 $1328 €1168 Elephant and calf (51x76cm-20x30in) s.d.99. 1-Oct-3 Woolley & Wallis, Salisbury #188/R

TRUSSARDI, Giacinto (1881-1947) Italian
Works on paper
£267 $478 €390 Portrait of a child (60x47cm-24x19in) s.i.d.1919 pastel. 12-May-4 Dobiaschofsky, Bern #3979 (S.FR 620)

TRUSTTUM, Philip (1940-) New Zealander
£435 $704 €631 Untitled (40x30cm-16x12in) s.d.1975 acrylic on paper. 31-Jul-3 International Art Centre, Auckland #87/R est:2000-3000 (NZ.D 1200)
£441 $825 €644 Still life with landscape (27x17cm-11x7in) init. board. 24-Feb-4 Peter Webb, Auckland #81/R (NZ.D 1200)
£543 $875 €793 Garden Painting (37x29cm-15x11in) s.d.1972 board. 12-Aug-3 Peter Webb, Auckland #37/R (NZ.D 1500)
£694 $1104 €1013 Untitled - abstract (75x55cm-30x22in) s. 1-May-3 Dunbar Sloane, Wellington #90/R est:2000-3000 (NZ.D 2000)
£1119 $1937 €1634 Abstracted view to terrace (138x99cm-54x39in) s.d.1970 board. 9-Dec-3 Peter Webb, Auckland #137/R est:3000-5000 (NZ.D 3000)
£1330 $2460 €1942 Disorder (230x174cm-91x69in) s.d.83 acrylic. 13-Jul-4 Watson's, Christchurch #63/R est:4000-5000 (NZ.D 3750)
£1389 $2208 €2028 Garden series no.5 9.30 (120x74cm-47x29in) s.d.1974 hardboard. 1-May-3 Dunbar Sloane, Wellington #32/R est:4000-7000 (NZ.D 4000)
£1673 $2877 €2443 Tennis series (178x63cm-70x25in) s.d.1944 verso prov. 3-Dec-3 Dunbar Sloane, Auckland #38/R est:4500-7000 (NZ.D 4500)
£2536 $4109 €3677 Mauve - line (141x119cm-56x47in) s. board prov. 31-Jul-3 International Art Centre, Auckland #19/R est:6000-9000 (NZ.D 7000)
£7143 $13143 €10429 No 30 trees and roof (152x122cm-60x48in) s.d.1974 board. 25-Mar-4 International Art Centre, Auckland #31/R est:25000-35000 (NZ.D 20000)
Works on paper
£3717 $6394 €5427 Ned Kelly (177x100cm-70x39in) s.d.1988 collage mixed media. 3-Dec-3 Dunbar Sloane, Auckland #67/R est:12000-20000 (NZ.D 10000)

TRUSZ, Ivan (1869-1940) Russian
£4035 $7343 €5891 Wooded landscape (70x98cm-28x39in) s. cardboard painted 1900. 20-Jun-4 Agra, Warsaw #54/R (P.Z 28000)

TRUSZKOWSKI, Jerzy (20th C) Polish
Works on paper
£588 $982 €858 Napoleon surveying French advance. Napoleon surveying Polish cavalry advance (28x48cm-11x19in) s. W/C pair. 17-Nov-3 Waddingtons, Toronto #283/R (C.D 1300)

TRUTAT, Felix (attrib) (1824-1848) French
£24138 $40069 €35000 Academie d'homme (46x38cm-18x15in) prov. 2-Oct-3 Sotheby's, Paris #113/R est:7000-10000

TRUTKOVSKY, Konstantin Alexandrovich (1827-1893) Russian
Works on paper
£6500 $11050 €9750 Three young Ukranian peasant girls (35x45cm-14x18in) s.d.1885 pencil W/C. 25-Nov-3 Christie's, London #130/R est:3000-5000

TRUYEN, Johannes Paulus Franciscus (1928-) Dutch
£1408 $2338 €2000 Winter landscape (70x90cm-28x35in) s.d.72. 12-Jun-3 Auction Maastricht #929/R est:2000-4000
£1867 $3435 €2800 De Vallei van Sint Franciscus (105x135cm-41x53in) s.d.98. 9-Jun-4 Christie's, Amsterdam #384/R est:2000-3000
Works on paper
£868 $1372 €1250 My secret garden (50x65cm-20x26in) s.d.2001 mixed media. 26-Apr-3 Auction Maastricht #105/R
£1268 $2104 €1800 Flower power (90x64cm-35x25in) s.d.68 mixed media collage fabric. 12-Jun-3 Auction Maastricht #923/R est:1800-2500

TRYGGELIN, Erik (1878-1962) Swedish
£522 $851 €762 Karlberg from Rorstrandgatan (32x45cm-13x18in) s.d.1924-25. 29-Sep-3 Lilla Bukowskis, Stockholm #329 (S.KR 6800)
£1538 $2646 €2245 Riddarfjarden, Stockholm (19x32cm-7x13in) s.d.1927. 3-Dec-3 AB Stockholms Auktionsverk #2234/R est:12000-15000 (S.KR 20000)
£1774 $3175 €2590 Weather clearing after rain - Klara Lake (32x48cm-13x19in) s.d.1919 1920. 26-May-4 AB Stockholms Auktionsverk #2093/R est:12000-15000 (S.KR 24000)
£7095 $12701 €10359 Men about town in evening, Ile de la Cite, Paris. s.d.okt.1916. 25-May-4 Bukowskis, Stockholm #40/R est:100000-125000 (S.KR 96000)

TRYNZ, Libby (20th C) American
£216 $400 €315 Abstract (69x69cm-27x27in) s. 15-Feb-4 Outer Cape Auctions, Provincetown #104/R

TRYON, Dwight W (1849-1925) American
£8383 $14000 €12239 Landscape, South Dartmouth, Massachusetts (36x51cm-14x20in) s.d.Oct. 1886 panel prov. 23-Oct-3 Shannon's, Milford #135/R est:8000-12000
£11976 $20000 €17485 Night (20x30cm-8x12in) s.i.d.1921 panel prov. 23-Oct-3 Shannon's, Milford #106/R est:8000-12000

TRZETRZEWINSKA, Irena (1934-) Polish
£282 $511 €423 Harenda (58x74cm-23x29in) s.d.58. 4-Apr-4 Agra, Warsaw #34/R (P.Z 2000)

TSAROUKHIS, Yannis (1910-1989) Greek
£4200 $7140 €6132 Reclining man (23x20cm-9x8in) s. paper prov. 18-Nov-3 Sotheby's, London #60/R
£12000 $20400 €17520 Portrait of model (100x73cm-39x29in) s.d.88 oil pastel paper prov. 18-Nov-3 Sotheby's, London #61/R est:12000-18000
£58000 $98600 €84680 Port of Pireaus (65x90cm-26x35in) s.d.56 prov.lit. 18-Nov-3 Sotheby's, London #23/R est:30000-40000
Works on paper
£1000 $1790 €1460 Portrait of a girl (34x24cm-13x9in) s.d.1966 pencil. 10-May-4 Sotheby's, Olympia #157/R est:1000-1500
£1200 $2100 €1752 Portrait of a woman, seated (33x23cm-13x9in) s. W/C. 16-Dec-3 Bonhams, New Bond Street #118/R est:1200-1800
£1500 $2625 €2190 Jeune modele demi-nu (29x24cm-11x9in) s.d.28-11-63 pencil exhib. 16-Dec-3 Bonhams, New Bond Street #129/R est:1500-2500
£1800 $3150 €2628 Portrait of a young man. Naked youth (26x17cm-10x7in) one s.d.19-6-79 pencil red chk one red ink chk pair prov. 16-Dec-3 Bonhams, New Bond Street #127/R est:2000-3000

TSARYK, Tetyana (20th C) Irish?
£267 $480 €400 Howth Yacht Club (64x54cm-25x21in) s.d.2003. 20-Apr-4 James Adam, Dublin #120/R
£833 $1500 €1250 Rainy day, Clarendon Street (66x93cm-26x37in) s.d.2003. 20-Apr-4 James Adam, Dublin #122/R
£951 $1664 €1350 Howth harbour, evening (51x75cm-20x30in) s.d.2003. 16-Dec-3 James Adam, Dublin #134/R
£1076 $1690 €1550 Ha penny bridge (88x75cm-35x30in) s. 26-Aug-3 James Adam, Dublin #172/R est:600-800

TSCHACBASOV, Nahum (1899-1984) Russian

£432	$800	€631	Abstract figure (110x68cm-43x27in) s.d.53 board prov. 13-Jul-4 Christie's, Rockefeller NY #125/R
£865	$1600	€1263	Mother and child (90x58cm-35x23in) s.d.55 board prov. 13-Jul-4 Christie's, Rockefeller NY #124/R est:1000-1500

TSCHAGGENY, Charles Philogene (1815-1894) Belgian

£574	$1028	€850	Vue des environs de Chimay (21x25cm-8x10in) s. panel. 10-May-4 Horta, Bruxelles #2
£600	$1074	€900	Paysage Ardennais a la riviere (37x54cm-15x21in) s. 11-May-4 Vanderkindere, Brussels #109
£811	$1427	€1200	Vaches dans les pres (20x50cm-8x20in) s. 18-May-4 Galerie Moderne, Brussels #231
£909	$1564	€1300	Jeune fermier avec cheval (30x26cm-12x10in) s.i.d.69. 2-Dec-3 Campo & Campo, Antwerp #353/R
£1389	$2194	€2000	Tending to the horse (20x25cm-8x10in) s.d.1850 panel. 2-Sep-3 Christie's, Amsterdam #194 est:1500-2000
£3265	$5943	€4800	Le demenagement, attelage devant la ferme (51x95cm-20x37in) 9-Feb-4 Amberes, Antwerp #296/R

TSCHAGGENY, Edmond (1818-1873) Belgian

£490	$817	€700	Brebis 3 ans (32x42cm-13x17in) mono.d.1857. 7-Oct-3 Palais de Beaux Arts, Brussels #589
£1329	$2259	€1900	Le bouc (23x35cm-9x14in) s. panel. 18-Nov-3 Galerie Moderne, Brussels #825/R est:800-1000
£2282	$4085	€3400	Idyllic meadow scene (20x25cm-8x10in) s.d.1850 panel. 27-May-4 Dorotheum, Vienna #164/R est:3600-4000
£3667	$6600	€5500	Shepherdess and her flock (36x30cm-14x12in) s.d.1854 panel. 20-Apr-4 Sotheby's, Amsterdam #88/R est:2000-3000
£6897	$12759	€10000	Conversation des bergers dans un paysage (42x53cm-17x21in) s. 19-Jan-4 Horta, Bruxelles #203 est:15000-20000
Works on paper			
£563	$975	€800	Shepherd and his flock in the snow (15x22cm-6x9in) mono.d.1863 W/C. 13-Dec-3 De Vuyst, Lokeren #322

TSCHAGGENY, Frederic (1851-1921) Belgian

£493	$893	€750	Portrait de Chloris (45x36cm-18x14in) s. 19-Apr-4 Horta, Bruxelles #388

TSCHANG-YEUL KIM (1929-) Korean

£7065	$13000	€10315	Untitled (81x71cm-32x28in) 23-Mar-4 Christie's, Rockefeller NY #356/R est:4000-5000

TSCHARNER, Johann Wilhelm von (1886-1946) Swiss

£405	$697	€591	Reading woman (20x24cm-8x9in) s. 8-Dec-3 Philippe Schuler, Zurich #5966 (S.FR 900)
£495	$852	€723	Still life with fruit (40x73cm-16x29in) s. 8-Dec-3 Philippe Schuler, Zurich #5965 (S.FR 1100)
£717	$1198	€1047	House in garden landscape with flowers and trees (50x65cm-20x26in) s. 24-Oct-3 Hans Widmer, St Gallen #146/R est:1600-3200 (S.FR 1600)
£1572	$2893	€2295	At the edge of the city (50x65cm-20x26in) s. 8-Jun-4 Germann, Zurich #890 est:2000-2500 (S.FR 3600)
£1584	$2740	€2313	Still life of fruit (39x56cm-15x22in) s. 9-Dec-3 Sotheby's, Zurich #29/R est:3500-4500 (S.FR 3500)

TSCHAUTSCH, Albert (1843-?) German

£500	$885	€730	Bite of the apple (47x36cm-19x14in) canvas on board. 29-Apr-4 Christie's, Kensington #129/R
£600	$1062	€876	Venetian backwater, late afternoon (41x33cm-16x13in) s. canvas on card. 29-Apr-4 Christie's, Kensington #251/R
£1733	$3155	€2600	Young shepherd boy in a mountainous landscape playing the panpipes (51x35cm-20x14in) s. 1-Jul-4 Van Ham, Cologne #1644/R est:1800

TSCHECH, Will (1891-?) German

£703	$1300	€1026	Impressionist restaurant scene with waiter and patrons (56x46cm-22x18in) s.d.1913. 24-Jan-4 Jeffery Burchard, Florida #32a/R

TSCHELAN, Hans (1873-1964) Austrian

£588	$1100	€858	Woman leaving church (51x46cm-20x18in) s. panel. 25-Feb-4 Doyle, New York #20/R
£695	$1300	€1015	Village festival (33x36cm-13x14in) s. panel. 25-Feb-4 Doyle, New York #19/R

TSCHINKEL, Augustin (1905-1983) Czechoslovakian

£8667	$15860	€13000	Workers (90x57cm-35x22in) mono. s.i.d.1932 verso exhib. 5-Jun-4 Lempertz, Koln #1017/R est:15000-20000

TSCHIRCH, Egon (1889-1948) German

£933	$1689	€1400	Still life with sunflowers (83x67cm-33x26in) s.d.1930. 1-Apr-4 Van Ham, Cologne #1571

TSCHIRTNER, Oswald (1920-) ?

Works on paper			
£467	$859	€700	Mensch au einem sessel sitzend (16x11cm-6x4in) s.d.1971 Indian ink prov. 9-Jun-4 Artcurial Briest, Paris #368
£800	$1472	€1200	Schwimmender Mensch (21x30cm-8x12in) s.i.d.1971 Indian ink prov.lit. 9-Jun-4 Artcurial Briest, Paris #365/R

TSCHUDI, Lill (1911-) German

Prints			
£2700	$4968	€3942	Sailor's holiday (20x26cm-8x10in) s.i. num.44/50 linocut. 28-Jun-4 Bonhams, New Bond Street #281/R est:2000-3000
£2900	$5336	€4234	French porters (28x26cm-11x10in) s.i. num.28/50 col linocut. 28-Jun-4 Bonhams, New Bond Street #282/R est:1500-2000

TSCHUDY, Herbert Bolivar (1874-1946) American

£4070	$7000	€5942	Fulton Street ferry, evening (50x40cm-20x16in) s. prov. 3-Dec-3 Doyle, New York #257/R est:3000-5000

TSCHUMI, Otto (1904-1985) Swiss

£1900	$3231	€2774	Truziluri bucimamba (30x21cm-12x8in) s.i.d.73 verso oil tempera board prov. 22-Nov-3 Burkhard, Luzern #29/R est:4500-5500 (S.FR 4200)
£1946	$3308	€2841	Shadows (21x30cm-8x12in) s.d.73 s.i.d.verso oil tempera board prov. 22-Nov-3 Burkhard, Luzern #30/R est:5000-6000 (S.FR 4300)
£1991	$3385	€2907	Humming bird (30x37cm-12x15in) s.d.49 tempera pastel paper prov. 22-Nov-3 Burkhard, Luzern #26/R est:5000-6000 (S.FR 4400)
£2036	$3462	€2973	Le chantier (30x23cm-12x9in) s.d.72 s.i.d.verso oil tempera board prov. 22-Nov-3 Burkhard, Luzern #28/R est:5000-6000 (S.FR 4500)
£2982	$4979	€4324	Bull (30x37cm-12x15in) s.d.49 paper. 19-Jun-3 Kornfeld, Bern #1006/R est:8000 (S.FR 6500)
Works on paper			
£204	$346	€298	Humming bird (27x37cm-11x15in) s.i.d.12/10/49 pencil prov. 22-Nov-3 Burkhard, Luzern #27/R (S.FR 450)
£321	$536	€465	Many sided bird (30x20cm-12x8in) s.i.d.30.5.78 W/C. 19-Jun-3 Kornfeld, Bern #1007 (S.FR 700)
£688	$1149	€998	Nighttime (27x15cm-11x6in) s.d.23 chl. 19-Jun-3 Kornfeld, Bern #1000 est:2000 (S.FR 1500)

TSCHURIKOFF, Feodor (19th C) Russian

£9459	$16932	€14000	Hunting the fox (65x109cm-26x43in) s.d.1912. 8-May-4 Bukowskis, Helsinki #413/R est:2800-3200

TSEITLIN, Grigori Izrailevich (20th C) Russian

£4500	$8055	€6570	Girl in a fur coat (80x65cm-31x26in) s.d.1962. 26-May-4 Sotheby's, Olympia #459/R est:4000-6000
£5000	$8950	€7300	Moment for music (97x70cm-38x28in) s.d.1949. 26-May-4 Sotheby's, Olympia #463/R est:5000-7000

TSIKOUDAKIS, Stavros (1945-2003) Greek

£4800	$8400	€7008	Trojan I (90x110cm-35x43in) s. exhib. 16-Dec-3 Bonhams, New Bond Street #142/R est:4000-6000

TSINGOS, Thanos (1914-1965) Greek

£699	$1189	€1000	Composition (33x26cm-13x10in) s. oil paper. 20-Nov-3 Claude Aguttes, Neuilly #251/R
£1800	$3222	€2628	Splashes of blue (130x89cm-51x35in) s.d.55 exhib. 10-May-4 Sotheby's, Olympia #28/R est:2000-3000
£2800	$4760	€4088	Flowers (61x74cm-24x29in) s.d.54 prov. 18-Nov-3 Sotheby's, London #149/R est:3000-4000
£2800	$5012	€4088	Red and white flowers (19x23cm-7x9in) s. canvasboard. 10-May-4 Sotheby's, Olympia #93/R est:1500-2500
£3200	$5728	€4672	Explosion (130x97cm-51x38in) s.d.55. 10-May-4 Sotheby's, Olympia #30/R est:2000-3000
£4545	$7591	€6500	Composition abstraite (46x55cm-18x22in) s.d.54. 25-Jun-3 Rabourdin & Choppin de Janvry, Paris #124/R est:7000-7500
£4600	$8050	€6716	La salamandre (92x60cm-36x24in) prov.lit. 16-Dec-3 Bonhams, New Bond Street #133/R est:4000-5000
£6000	$10200	€8760	Fond marin (93x73cm-37x29in) s. painted c.1956-57. 18-Nov-3 Sotheby's, London #150/R est:5000-7000
£6500	$11635	€9490	Red animals (89x130cm-35x51in) s.d.56. 10-May-4 Sotheby's, Olympia #27/R est:4000-6000
£7000	$12250	€10220	Fleurs (88x130cm-35x51in) s. 16-Dec-3 Bonhams, New Bond Street #124/R est:7000-9000
£7500	$12750	€10950	Fleurs sur fond bleu (89x116cm-35x46in) s.i.d.1959 verso. 18-Nov-3 Sotheby's, London #148/R est:5000-7000
£8500	$15215	€12410	Flowers on a white background (54x65cm-21x26in) s.d.57. 10-May-4 Sotheby's, Olympia #29/R est:4000-6000
£8500	$15215	€12410	Harmony in green (89x130cm-35x51in) s.d.56. 10-May-4 Sotheby's, Olympia #94/R est:3000-5000
Works on paper			
£1500	$2685	€2190	Composition (50x32cm-20x13in) s.indis.i.d.54 gouache. 11-May-4 Bonhams, New Bond Street #119/R est:1500-2000

TSIREH, Awa (1895-1955) American

Works on paper			
£1630	$3000	€2380	Untitled (61x48cm-24x19in) W/C three. 24-Jun-4 Sotheby's, New York #204/R est:2000-3000
£2174	$4000	€3174	Pueblo ceremonial dance (38x56cm-15x22in) s. gouache on board. 14-Jun-4 Bonhams & Butterfields, San Francisco #1109/R est:2000-3000

TSIRIGOTI, Nikolai Grigorievich (1864-?) Russian

£34000	$57800	€49640	Night on the Kazbek mountain (85x135cm-33x53in) s. 19-Nov-3 Sotheby's, London #79/R est:8000-12000

TSOCLIS, Costa (1930-) Greek

£10000	$17900	€14600	Fillosia (279x221cm-110x87in) s. oil paper wood on canvas prov.exhib. 10-May-4 Sotheby's, Olympia #63/R est:5000-7000
Sculpture			
£1500	$2685	€2190	Oranges (50x60x15cm-20x24x6in) s.i.d.1970 num.14/20 wood plastic. 11-May-4 Bonhams, New Bond Street #113/R est:1500-2000
£1600	$2800	€2336	Space with wooden plank (107x82x7cm-42x32x3in) s.num.40/50 wood nails print Plexiglas. 16-Dec-3 Bonhams, New Bond Street #146/R est:1000-1500
Works on paper			
£1056	$1849	€1500	Untitled (90x67cm-35x26in) s.i. polymer board. 16-Dec-3 Finarte Semenzato, Milan #207/R est:1300-1700
£3000	$5370	€4380	Mine c 1000 Midy (130x100cm-51x39in) s.d.1972 collage pencil tempera card exhib. 11-May-4 Bonhams, New Bond Street #125/R est:3000-4000

£11500 $20585 €16790 Rocks (135x110cm-53x43in) s. mixed media. 10-May-4 Sotheby's, Olympia #68/R est:7000-10000
£13000 $23270 €18980 Untitled (210x170cm-83x67in) s.d.76 wood mixed media panel three. 10-May-4 Sotheby's, Olympia #62/R est:8000-12000

TSUKIMARO, Kitagawa (fl.1801-1829) Japanese
Prints
£1818 $3091 €2600 Surimono: trois oiseaux en plein vol (19x18cm-7x7in) s. col print exec.1817 lit. 25-Nov-3 Sotheby's, Paris #133/R est:600-700

TSVETKOV, V A (1920-) Russian
£335 $600 €489 Christmas motif (50x40cm-20x16in) painted 1995. 29-May-4 Shishkin Gallery, Moscow #88/R
£503 $900 €734 Herder (47x29cm-19x11in) cardboard sketch. 29-May-4 Shishkin Gallery, Moscow #87/R
£615 $1100 €898 Carnations (48x33cm-19x13in) cardboard painted 1998. 29-May-4 Shishkin Gallery, Moscow #86/R
£726 $1300 €1060 Lenin proclaims the Soviet Power (55x80cm-22x31in) painted 1974. 29-May-4 Shishkin Gallery, Moscow #85/R
£1333 $2400 €1946 Dressmaker (50x45cm-20x18in) canvas on plywood. 24-Apr-4 Shishkin Gallery, Moscow #29/R est:3000-4000
£1444 $2600 €2108 Lilac bouquet (50x37cm-20x15in) 24-Apr-4 Shishkin Gallery, Moscow #32/R est:3000-4000
£1778 $3200 €2596 Dahlias (61x50cm-24x20in) 24-Apr-4 Shishkin Gallery, Moscow #30/R est:4000-5000
£2000 $3600 €2920 Annichkov Bridge view in St. Petersburg (57x48cm-22x19in) 24-Apr-4 Shishkin Gallery, Moscow #31/R est:4000-5000

TUBARO, Renzo (20th C) Italian
£629 $1083 €900 Still life with lemon (60x44cm-24x17in) s. canvas on board exhib. 3-Dec-3 Stadion, Trieste #1119/R

TUBBECKE, Paul (1848-1924) German
£490 $842 €700 Hilly summer landscape with farmhouse (45x60cm-18x24in) s. board. 4-Dec-3 Dorotheum, Graz #42/R
£621 $1037 €900 Autumnal river landscape with bridge (109x152cm-43x60in) s. canvas on board lit. 12-Jul-3 Bergmann, Erlangen #838/R
£940 $1748 €1400 Park landscape with stone bridge over a river (43x60cm-17x24in) s. i. stretcher canvas on board. 5-Mar-4 Wendl, Rudolstadt #3890/R
£2113 $3655 €3000 Farmyard with geese (32x44cm-13x17in) s. 10-Dec-3 Hugo Ruef, Munich #2511/R est:1100
£3380 $5848 €4800 Figures with geese on a sunlit hill (33x45cm-13x18in) s.i. canvas on cardboard exhib.lit. 10-Dec-3 Christie's, Amsterdam #170 est:800-1200

TUBKE, Angelika (20th C) German?
£867 $1569 €1300 Slovakian girl (24x16cm-9x6in) i. 2-Apr-4 Dr Fritz Nagel, Leipzig #4025/R

TUBKE, Werner (1929-) ?
£15385 $26154 €22000 St martin (50x70cm-20x28in) s.d.89 s. verso prov. 29-Nov-3 Villa Grisebach, Berlin #372/R est:18000-24000
Works on paper
£1200 $2208 €1800 Portrait of Schamow (63x48cm-25x19in) s.d.77 chk W/C. 12-Jun-4 Villa Grisebach, Berlin #852/R est:1800-2400

TUCCI, Giuseppe (attrib) (18/19th C) Italian
£1745 $3211 €2600 Animal studies of donkey and cow (23x30cm-9x12in) bears sig. verso. 24-Mar-4 Dorotheum, Vienna #277/R est:3000-4000

TUCEK, Karl (1889-?) Austrian
£490 $832 €700 Furnitz area (65x80cm-26x31in) s. 19-Nov-3 Dorotheum, Klagenfurt #36

TUCH, Kurt Otto (1877-1963) German
Works on paper
£286 $487 €418 Playing boule (33x45cm-13x18in) s. W/C on col chk. 5-Nov-3 Dobiaschofsky, Bern #3766 (S.FR 650)

TUCKER, Ada E (fl.1881-1928) British
£1550 $2852 €2263 Kittens regarding a snail (33x57cm-13x22in) s. 29-Mar-4 Bonhams, Bath #111/R est:800-1200

TUCKER, Albert (1914-1999) Australian
£3049 $5457 €4452 Parrot (30x40cm-12x16in) s. composition board. 4-May-4 Sotheby's, Melbourne #167/R est:8000-12000 (A.D 7500)
£4959 $8777 €7240 Ibis and bush (24x34cm-9x13in) s.d.63 board prov. 3-May-4 Christie's, Melbourne #313/R est:7000-9000 (A.D 12000)
£5106 $8681 €7455 Antipodean Head (33x24cm-13x9in) s.d.76 oil pastel prov. 26-Nov-3 Deutscher-Menzies, Melbourne #60/R est:9000-12000 (A.D 12000)
£6073 $9777 €8867 Ibis (60x76cm-24x30in) s.d.64 i.verso composition board prov. 25-Aug-3 Sotheby's, Paddington #144/R est:15000-20000 (A.D 15000)
£7660 $13021 €11184 The gully (60x80cm-24x31in) s.d.65 board prov. 25-Nov-3 Christie's, Melbourne #62/R est:25000-35000 (A.D 18000)
£8085 $13745 €11804 River dreaming (41x51cm-16x20in) s.d.71 s.i.d.1971 verso prov. 25-Nov-3 Christie's, Melbourne #82/R est:18000-25000 (A.D 19000)
£8264 $14628 €12065 Ibis at dusk (55x70cm-22x28in) s. board prov. 3-May-4 Christie's, Melbourne #14/R est:20000-30000 (A.D 20000)
£8898 $15127 €12991 Flying Ibis (69x90cm-27x35in) s.d.70 composition board. 24-Nov-3 Sotheby's, Melbourne #33/R est:20000-30000 (A.D 21000)
£9717 $15644 €14187 Parrots in flight (55x70cm-22x28in) s. composition board prov. 25-Aug-3 Sotheby's, Paddington #161/R est:25000-35000 (A.D 24000)
£16260 $25528 €23577 Faun and parrots (55x70cm-22x28in) s.d.70 board prov. 26-Aug-3 Christie's, Sydney #67/R est:40000-50000 (A.D 40000)
£34836 $55041 €50861 The card players (71x91cm-28x36in) s.d.73 board prov. 2-Sep-3 Deutscher-Menzies, Melbourne #105/R est:1000-140000 (A.D 85000)
Works on paper
£1653 $2926 €2413 Parrot flying through the bush (20x22cm-8x9in) s. pastel. 3-May-4 Christie's, Melbourne #206/R est:1500-2500 (A.D 4000)
£4545 $8409 €6636 Image of modern Evil (20x25cm-8x10in) s.d.43 W/C ink prov. 10-Mar-4 Deutscher-Menzies, Melbourne #108/R est:12000-15000 (A.D 11000)

TUCKER, Allen (1866-1939) American
£670 $1200 €978 Landscape with river (25x30cm-10x12in) indis.i.d.December 25th 1890. 8-Jan-4 James Julia, Fairfield #1040/R
£3824 $6500 €5583 Library window (61x51cm-24x20in) s. painted c.1920 prov.exhib. 30-Oct-3 Phillips, New York #93/R est:6000-8000

TUCKER, Arthur (1864-1929) British
£550 $880 €798 Dinham bridge, Ludlow (30x35cm-12x14in) s. 17-Sep-3 James Thompson, Kirby Lonsdale #178
Works on paper
£270 $443 €394 Cottages at Windermere (23x33cm-9x13in) s. W/C htd white. 29-May-3 Neales, Nottingham #770/R
£300 $528 €438 On the Greta, Cumberland (30x44cm-12x17in) s. W/C. 21-May-4 Bracketts, Tunbridge Wells #251/R
£370 $592 €537 Cottages at Windermere (23x34cm-9x13in) 17-Sep-3 James Thompson, Kirby Lonsdale #52
£376 $650 €549 Coastal scene (33x51cm-13x20in) s. W/C. 13-Dec-3 Charlton Hall, Columbia #364/R
£400 $644 €580 Windermere from Rayrigg (18x23cm-7x9in) i.verso W/C. 13-Aug-3 Andrew Hartley, Ilkley #769
£450 $810 €657 Rydal Water (16x34cm-6x13in) s. pencil W/C. 21-Apr-4 Tennants, Leyburn #1024
£550 $1012 €803 Highland fishing village, viewed from the sea (30x45cm-12x18in) s.i. W/C bodycol. 29-Mar-4 Bonhams, Bath #15/R
£580 $1067 €847 Richmond Castle (23x34cm-9x13in) s. W/C. 23-Mar-4 Anderson & Garland, Newcastle #258/R
£800 $1440 €1168 Extensive landscape with sheep grazing in foreground (34x70cm-13x28in) s. pencil W/C. 21-Apr-4 Tennants, Leyburn #1023
£2600 $4706 €3796 Robin Hood's Bay (33x51cm-13x20in) s. W/C. 15-Apr-4 Richardson & Smith, Whitby #148/R est:1500-2000

TUCKER, Edward (c.1825-1909) British
£1100 $1782 €1595 Fishing boats and other sailing craft off the Sussex coast (43x66cm-17x26in) s. painted c.1860-1880. 26-Jan-3 Desmond Judd, Cranbrook #828
Works on paper
£260 $434 €380 Busy Cathedral Harbour Town (28x43cm-11x17in) s. W/C. 10-Oct-3 Richardson & Smith, Whitby #245
£260 $434 €380 Mountainous path with figures and cart (30x51cm-12x20in) s. W/C. 16-Oct-3 Mallams, Cheltenham #204
£280 $501 €409 Lake District barn with fishermen by a stream (19x31cm-7x12in) s. W/C. 17-May-4 David Duggleby, Scarborough #639/R
£300 $540 €438 Scottish fishing village with beached boats and driving nets (37x55cm-15x22in) s. W/C. 21-Jan-4 James Thompson, Kirby Lonsdale #68
£300 $552 €438 Fishermen rowing out to sea before the squall (24x41cm-9x16in) s. pencil W/C. 25-Mar-4 Christie's, Kensington #252
£420 $680 €609 Fishing boats in a choppy sea (23x48cm-9x19in) s. W/C. 30-Jul-3 Hamptons Fine Art, Godalming #63
£440 $805 €642 Sheep on the shore of a lake (26x40cm-10x16in) s. W/C. 6-Jul-4 Bearnes, Exeter #432/R
£440 $805 €642 Ferry, Windermere (25x34cm-10x13in) s. W/C. 6-Jul-4 Bearnes, Exeter #459
£450 $792 €657 Windermere (23x39cm-9x15in) s. W/C. 19-May-4 James Thompson, Kirby Lonsdale #62
£580 $998 €847 Mill in Kentmere, near Kendal (28x43cm-11x17in) s. W/C. 3-Dec-3 Andrew Hartley, Ilkley #1037
£620 $1054 €905 Highland river landscape with fisherman and sheep in foreground (31x51cm-12x20in) s. pseudonym Edward Arden W/C scratching out. 31-Oct-3 Moore Allen & Innocent, Cirencester #521/R

TUCKER, Edward (jnr) (1847-1910) British
Works on paper
£280 $510 €409 Lakeland scene near Ambleside (20x33cm-8x13in) s. W/C. 16-Jun-4 Andrew Hartley, Ilkley #950
£320 $586 €467 Mountainous lake scene (25x46cm-10x18in) W/C. 31-Jan-4 Nigel Ward, Hereford #1387/R
£450 $824 €657 Mountainous lake scene with fishermen (30x48cm-12x19in) s. W/C. 31-Jan-4 Nigel Ward, Hereford #1388/R

TUCKER, Frederick (fl.1880-1915) British
Works on paper
£280 $442 €409 Farmyard view (38x51cm-15x20in) s. indis.d W/C. 5-Sep-3 Honiton Galleries, Honiton #33/R
£340 $619 €496 Extensive landscape with hay meadow in the foreground (36x61cm-14x24in) s. W/C. 16-Jun-4 Andrew Hartley, Ilkley #941
£700 $1169 €1022 Fishing smacks off the coast (38x56cm-15x22in) s. W/C. 16-Nov-3 Desmond Judd, Cranbrook #1075
£700 $1169 €1022 Fishing smacks off the coast (38x56cm-15x22in) s. W/C. 16-Nov-3 Desmond Judd, Cranbrook #1076
£3200 $5440 €4672 Extensive landscape with farmstead amongst trees (24x38cm-9x15in) s. W/C card sold with collection of W/C's by various hands. 26-Nov-3 Hamptons Fine Art, Godalming #34 est:2000-3000

TUCKER, James W (1898-1972) British
£1200 $2184 €1752 Looking towards the Severn Vale from Painswick (41x51cm-16x20in) s. 17-Jun-4 Clevedon Sale Rooms #1058/R est:200-300
Works on paper
£600 $1020 €876 Summer landscape (76x54cm-30x21in) s. W/C. 26-Nov-3 Sotheby's, Olympia #88/R

TUCKER, John Wallace (18/19th C) British

£360 $612 €526 Moonlight and early morning on the river Exe (22x29cm-9x11in) i.verso. 29-Oct-3 Hampton & Littlewood, Exeter #602/R
£650 $1086 €949 Exwick church and Haldon Beacon from Exwick fields, Devonshire (24x34cm-9x13in) s.i.d.1838 verso board. 13-Nov-3 Christie's, Kensington #96/R
£650 $1164 €949 Footbridge on the Teign (18x25cm-7x10in) panel. 26-May-4 Sotheby's, Olympia #73/R
£1400 $2338 €2044 Topsham from the old entrance to the Exeter canal (18x24cm-7x9in) panel sold with a companion. 26-Jun-3 Greenslade Hunt, Taunton #526/R est:800-1200
£1400 $2520 €2044 Man fishing in a gorge. Thatched cottage (32x24cm-13x9in) panel pair. 21-Apr-4 Tennants, Leyburn #1123 est:1500-2000

TUCKER, Raymond (19/20th C) British

Works on paper
£1900 $3420 €2774 Liverpool, beach scene (36x48cm-14x19in) W/C. 20-Apr-4 Canterbury Auctions, UK #162 est:200-300
£4000 $7480 €5840 Two young boys in a Clovelly fishing boat, off the coast of Devon (47x64cm-19x25in) pencil W/C gouache htd white. 22-Jul-4 Tennants, Leyburn #654/R est:4000-6000

TUCKER, William (1935-) American/British

Sculpture
£5405 $10000 €7891 Horse X (87x97x52cm-34x38x20in) init. num.1/6 bronze. 12-Feb-4 Sotheby's, New York #309/R est:1000-15000
£6500 $11180 €9490 Horse X (92cm-36in) init.num.5/6 dark grey pat bronze exec 1986 prov.exhib. 3-Dec-3 Sotheby's, London #78/R est:1200-1500

TUCKSON, John Anthony (1921-1973) Australian

£1148 $1813 €1676 Untitled - TD 491 (51x76cm-20x30in) paper prov. 2-Sep-3 Deutscher-Menzies, Melbourne #217/R est:2500-3500 (A.D 2800)
£2119 $3602 €3094 TP 503 (33x24cm-13x9in) cardboard painted c.1956/59 prov. 24-Nov-3 Sotheby's, Melbourne #87/R est:3500-5000 (A.D 5000)
£4918 $7770 €7180 Artist and model (44x55cm-17x22in) 2-Sep-3 Deutscher-Menzies, Melbourne #66/R est:12000-15000 (A.D 12000)
£28689 $45328 €41886 Big red W (122x152cm-48x60in) board exhib. 2-Sep-3 Deutscher-Menzies, Melbourne #26/R est:75000-95000 (A.D 70000)
Works on paper
£1157 $2048 €1689 Untitled, abstract with trees (51x76cm-20x30in) s.verso W/C gouache prov. 3-May-4 Christie's, Melbourne #256 est:2800-3800 (A.D 2800)
£1736 $3072 €2535 Untitled, breakfast, man eating (51x76cm-20x30in) W/C prov. 3-May-4 Christie's, Melbourne #240/R est:3000-5000 (A.D 4200)
£2227 $3585 €3251 TD 1605 (76x56cm-30x22in) gouache ink painted 1952-1956 prov.exhib. 25-Aug-3 Sotheby's, Paddington #246/R est:6000-8000 (A.D 5500)

TUCKWELL, George (1919-) British

£420 $743 €613 Abstract townscape (30x39cm-12x15in) mono. board. 27-Apr-4 Bonhams, Knightsbridge #279/R

TUDGAY, F (19th C) British

£10929 $20000 €15956 Byzantium off the cliffs of Dover with the castle in the distance (61x91cm-24x36in) s.d.1861. 29-Jul-4 Christie's, Rockefeller NY #254/R est:25000-35000

TUDGAY, I (19th C) British

£600 $1020 €876 Danish brig in two positions off Dover (60x90cm-24x35in) 19-Nov-3 Christie's, Kensington #578/R
£1676 $3000 €2447 Schooner-rigged Government steam yacht passing the Needles (53x81cm-21x32in) s.d.1871. 16-Mar-4 Bonhams & Butterfields, San Francisco #6129/R est:4000-6000

TUDGAY, J L (19th C) British

£1441 $2652 €2104 Battle of Trafalgar (92x163cm-36x64in) s. 14-Jun-4 Philippe Schuler, Zurich #4333/R est:4000-6000 (S.FR 3300)

TUDGAY, J and F (19th C) British

£18156 $32500 €26508 American Full-rigger Rose Standish rounding the South foreland near Dover (64x91cm-25x36in) s.d.1864. 16-Mar-4 Bonhams & Butterfields, San Francisco #6128/R est:10000-15000
£20541 $38000 €29990 Final moments of the engagement between CSS Alabama and USS Kearsage (71x107cm-28x42in) s.d.1864 prov. 10-Feb-4 Christie's, Rockefeller NY #195/R est:40000-60000

TUDLIK (1890-1966) North American

Prints
£2703 $4595 €3946 Bird dream forewarning blizzard (53x39cm-21x15in) num.16/30 stonecut. 3-Nov-3 Waddingtons, Toronto #290/R est:3000-4000 (C.D 6000)
Sculpture
£1171 $1991 €1710 Owl (9cm-4in) marbled green soapstone exec.c.1958. 3-Nov-3 Waddingtons, Toronto #344/R est:2500-3500 (C.D 2600)
£1441 $2450 €2104 Young owl (8cm-3in) marbled green soapstone. 3-Nov-3 Waddingtons, Toronto #334/R est:2500-3500 (C.D 3200)
£2793 $4748 €4078 Bird with upswept wings (10cm-4in) mottled green soapstone. 3-Nov-3 Waddingtons, Toronto #309/R est:2000-3000 (C.D 6200)
£3153 $5360 €4603 Owl (13cm-5in) mottled green soapstone. 3-Nov-3 Waddingtons, Toronto #331/R est:3000-5000 (C.D 7000)
Works on paper
£2477 $4212 €3616 Man killing seal (76x51cm-30x20in) stencil. 3-Nov-3 Waddingtons, Toronto #306/R est:4000-6000 (C.D 5500)

TUERENHOUT, Jef van (1926-) Belgian

£567 $948 €800 Venus (66x54cm-26x21in) s.d.65 panel. 20-Oct-3 Bernaerts, Antwerp #237
£1399 $2378 €2000 Les racines humaines (78x88cm-31x35in) 1-Dec-3 Amberes, Antwerp #364/R
£2778 $4639 €4000 Hello James (90x80cm-35x31in) s. 21-Oct-3 Campo, Vlaamse Kaai #609/R est:4500-5500
£4167 $6958 €6000 Reine (98x68cm-39x27in) s. 21-Oct-3 Campo, Vlaamse Kaai #608/R est:6000-7000
£6250 $10438 €9000 Les mauvais amis (120x100cm-47x39in) s. 21-Oct-3 Campo, Vlaamse Kaai #606/R est:9000-12000
£6250 $10438 €9000 De lente (120x100cm-47x39in) s. 21-Oct-3 Campo, Vlaamse Kaai #607/R est:9000-12000
Sculpture
£1745 $3089 €2600 Torse de femme au chapeau (41cm-16in) mono. bronze. 27-Apr-4 Campo & Campo, Antwerp #264/R est:2000-3000
Works on paper
£604 $1117 €900 Fisherman (48x62cm-19x24in) s.i.1958 wash. 13-Mar-4 De Vuyst, Lokeren #370
£972 $1624 €1400 Three women (53x73cm-21x29in) s.d.1975 col dr. 21-Oct-3 Campo & Campo, Antwerp #340 est:1500-1800
£2431 $4059 €3500 Femme en bleu avec chat (98x69cm-39x27in) s. gouache. 21-Oct-3 Campo & Campo, Antwerp #339/R est:4000-6000
£2550 $4514 €3800 Deux figures (78x58cm-31x23in) s. W/C. 27-Apr-4 Campo, Vlaamse Kaai #641/R est:3000-3500
£3028 $5239 €4300 Woman with flowers (100x70cm-39x28in) s. gouache. 13-Dec-3 De Vuyst, Lokeren #523/R est:3500-4500

TUFF, Richard (?) British?

Works on paper
£880 $1470 €1285 Mousehole (43x58cm-17x23in) s. gouache. 14-Oct-3 David Lay, Penzance #489

TUFFERY, Michael (20th C) New Zealander

£695 $1182 €1015 Moana Losi (9x48cm-4x19in) s. board. 27-Nov-3 International Art Centre, Auckland #62/R (NZ.D 1850)

TUFTA, Bjorn Sigurd (1956-) Norwegian

£1016 $1860 €1483 Landscape I. Landscape II (40x50cm-16x20in) s.i.d.90 verso pair. 7-Jun-4 Blomqvist, Oslo #453/R (N.KR 12500)

TUGEL, Otto (1892-1973) German

Works on paper
£273 $495 €410 Trees in storm (29x42cm-11x17in) s.d.1942 pencil. 3-Apr-4 Hans Stahl, Hamburg #110
£306 $498 €440 Death and the Maiden (25x24cm-10x9in) s. pencil. 26-Sep-3 Bolland & Marotz, Bremen #389
£333 $603 €500 Goat (49x38cm-19x15in) mono. pencil. 3-Apr-4 Hans Stahl, Hamburg #114
£347 $627 €520 Bridge on the moor in autumn storm (42x61cm-17x24in) s.d.1954 chl wash. 3-Apr-4 Hans Stahl, Hamburg #109
£375 $611 €540 Horse and cart on moor (24x24cm-9x9in) s. pencil. 26-Sep-3 Bolland & Marotz, Bremen #390
£400 $724 €600 Stormy day on moor (33x50cm-13x20in) s.i.d.1947 pen. 3-Apr-4 Hans Stahl, Hamburg #107/R
£400 $724 €600 Swallows in morning (25x21cm-10x8in) s.d.1952 W/C sepia Indian ink. 3-Apr-4 Hans Stahl, Hamburg #111
£436 $772 €650 River on the moor in autumn storm (47x65cm-19x26in) s. mixed media masonite. 30-Apr-4 Dr Fritz Nagel, Stuttgart #474/R
£440 $796 €660 Cattle under trees (45x62cm-18x24in) s. W/C paper on board. 3-Apr-4 Hans Stahl, Hamburg #108/R
£480 $869 €720 Forsythia and cats (45x34cm-18x13in) s. W/C. 3-Apr-4 Hans Stahl, Hamburg #103
£486 $792 €700 Hands of a moorland peasant (25x25cm-10x10in) s. mixed media panel. 26-Sep-3 Bolland & Marotz, Bremen #388/R
£587 $1062 €880 Spring evening on the moor (30x30cm-12x12in) mono. s.i.d.1944 verso mixed media board. 3-Apr-4 Hans Stahl, Hamburg #102
£587 $1062 €880 Self portrait in landscape (49x38cm-19x15in) mono.d.1943 W/C. 3-Apr-4 Hans Stahl, Hamburg #113
£629 $1145 €950 Still life with jug and flowers on a window sill (45x39cm-18x15in) s.d.1945 W/C. 18-Jun-4 Bolland & Marotz, Bremen #396/R
£667 $1207 €1000 Woman and child with paper lantern (64x50cm-25x20in) s. W/C sepia Indian ink board. 3-Apr-4 Hans Stahl, Hamburg #97/R
£859 $1607 €1289 Head study, purported to be a self portrait (29x23cm-11x9in) s.d.1916 pencil prov. 20-Jul-4 Goodman, Sydney #75/R est:600-800 (A.D 2200)
£933 $1689 €1400 Burial on winter moorland (47x61cm-19x24in) s.d.1946 pen. 3-Apr-4 Hans Stahl, Hamburg #96/R
£933 $1689 €1400 Girl seated by moorland hut (64x49cm-25x19in) s.d.1948 W/C gouache chk board. 3-Apr-4 Hans Stahl, Hamburg #104/R
£996 $1863 €1494 Baron Elizabeth von Manendorff (36x28cm-14x11in) s.d.1921 ink. 21-Jul-4 Goodman, Sydney #275 (A.D 2550)
£1000 $1810 €1500 Breakfast still life with catkins (45x62cm-18x24in) s.d.1947 W/C mixed media. 3-Apr-4 Hans Stahl, Hamburg #101/R est:500
£1000 $1810 €1500 Young woman writing letter in garden (89x60cm-35x24in) s.d.1957 W/C paper on panel. 3-Apr-4 Hans Stahl, Hamburg #98/R est:500
£1250 $2338 €1875 Man with a pipe (36x28cm-14x11in) s.d.1921 prov. 20-Jul-4 Goodman, Sydney #74/R est:500-700 (A.D 3200)
£1467 $2655 €2200 Young woman with fur hat in autumn landscape (68x50cm-27x20in) s.d.1946 W/C mixed media. 3-Apr-4 Hans Stahl, Hamburg #94/R est:600
£1600 $2896 €2400 Girl with bird (65x49cm-26x19in) mono. mixed media paper on panel. 3-Apr-4 Hans Stahl, Hamburg #95/R est:500

TUGGENER, Jakob (1904-1988) Swiss

Works on paper
£204 $346 €298 St Moritz from the balcony of the Palace Hotel (34x45cm-13x18in) s.d.44 s.i.d. verso W/C over pencil. 18-Nov-3 Hans Widmer, St Gallen #1216 (S.FR 450)

TUGWELL, Christopher (1938-) South African
£248 $443 €362 Secluded pool (44x59cm-17x23in) s. board. 31-May-4 Stephan Welz, Johannesburg #126 (SA.R 3000)
£248 $443 €362 Extensive landscape with farmstead and storm clouds (27x44cm-11x17in) s. board. 31-May-4 Stephan Welz, Johannesburg #135 (SA.R 3000)
£248 $443 €362 Still life with aubergines, a bottle of wine and apples (50x35cm-20x14in) s. board. 31-May-4 Stephan Welz, Johannesburg #183 (SA.R 3000)
£259 $432 €378 Figure with two pack donkeys (42x54cm-17x21in) s. board. 20-Oct-3 Stephan Welz, Johannesburg #882 est:2000-3000 (SA.R 3000)
£359 $610 €524 Breaking waves (50x75cm-20x30in) s. canvas on board. 4-Nov-3 Stephan Welz, Johannesburg #287 est:2000-3000 (SA.R 4200)
£404 $743 €590 Fisherman on beach (60x90cm-24x35in) 8-Jun-4 Dales, Durban #9 (SA.R 4800)
£431 $720 €629 Extensive landscape with windmill (25x35cm-10x14in) s. board. 20-Oct-3 Stephan Welz, Johannesburg #897 est:2000-3000 (SA.R 5000)
£431 $720 €629 Landscape with overcast sky (24x43cm-9x17in) s. canvas on board. 20-Oct-3 Stephan Welz, Johannesburg #917 est:1800-2400 (SA.R 5000)
£661 $1182 €965 Herdsmen and cattle in a field (44x59cm-17x23in) s. canvas on board. 31-May-4 Stephan Welz, Johannesburg #489/R (SA.R 8000)

TUKE, Henry Scott (1858-1929) British
£500 $915 €730 Napoleon reviewing his troops after the Battle of Lodi (59x98cm-23x39in) 6-Jul-4 Bearnes, Exeter #490/R
£12000 $19440 €17400 Boy on a beach (36x27cm-14x11in) s.d.1908 canvasboard. 30-Jul-3 Hamptons Fine Art, Godalming #232/R est:12000-15000
£24000 $43920 €35040 Rowing party, study of four boys and boats. s. prov. 3-Jun-4 Lane, Penzance #200/R est:20000-30000
£33000 $57090 €48180 After the bathe (40x31cm-16x12in) painted c.1921 prov. 11-Dec-3 Lane, Penzance #50/R est:18000-24000
£68000 $124440 €99280 Bather (39x32cm-15x13in) s.d.1924 panel prov. 4-Jun-4 Christie's, London #59/R est:25000-35000
Works on paper
£965 $1785 €1409 Italian hillside village (36x25cm-14x10in) s.d.1906 W/C. 10-Feb-4 David Lay, Penzance #6
£2000 $3740 €2920 View of Pennance Point, Falmouth, from below artists cottage (20x25cm-8x10in) init.d.1921 W/C. 26-Feb-4 Lane, Penzance #41 est:1000-1200
£2100 $3486 €3066 Evening departure (25x36cm-10x14in) s.d.1925 pastel prov.exhib. 1-Oct-3 Bonhams, Knightsbridge #89/R est:1000-1500
£2500 $4150 €3650 Shipping at Goa (24x44cm-9x17in) W/C. 2-Oct-3 Lane, Penzance #381 est:3500-4000
£3600 $6588 €5256 Finnish barque Favell in Falmouth Harbour (24x35cm-9x14in) s.d.1927 W/C. 7-Apr-4 Woolley & Wallis, Salisbury #166/R est:1200-1800
£4000 $6880 €5840 Portrait of a boy (33x24cm-13x9in) init.d.1893 pastel. 3-Dec-3 Christie's, Kensington #431/R est:4000-6000
£4000 $7480 €5840 Rusty barque, three masted ship at anchor with other shipping (36x49cm-14x19in) s.d.1913 prov. 26-Feb-4 Lane, Penzance #20/R est:5000-6000
£4500 $7740 €6570 Boy in a field (10x15cm-4x6in) init.d.96 W/C. 3-Dec-3 Christie's, Kensington #433/R est:1500-2000
£5000 $8350 €7300 At anchor at Trefusis (30x43cm-12x17in) s.d.1921 W/C. 14-Oct-3 David Lay, Penzance #104 est:5000-7000
£5400 $9882 €7884 Shipping at anchor in the Carrick Roads Falmouth (25x44cm-10x17in) s.d.1926. 3-Jun-4 Lane, Penzance #20/R est:4500-5500
£5500 $8800 €8030 Discovery at Falmouth (25x35cm-10x14in) s.i. W/C prov.exhib. 16-Sep-3 Bonhams, New Bond Street #44/R est:2000-3000
£18000 $32580 €26280 Portrait of W G Grace wearing Ranji's turban (24x17cm-9x7in) i. W/C sold with photograph prov. 19-Apr-4 Bonhams, Chester #630 est:10000-15000

TUKE, Henry Scott (attrib) (1858-1929) British
Works on paper
£280 $510 €409 Study of a boat at her moorings (34x24cm-13x9in) bears sig pencil crayon. 21-Jun-4 Bonhams, Bath #410
£1250 $2288 €1825 Two masted sailing boat (24x17cm-9x7in) indis sig. W/C. 7-Apr-4 Bonhams, Bury St Edmunds #385 est:250-350

TUKIAINEN, Aimo (1917-1996) Finnish
Sculpture
£1216 $2177 €1800 On the beach (47cm-19in) s. bronze. 8-May-4 Bukowskis, Helsinki #26/R est:1500-2500

TULLAT, Luc (20th C) French
£267 $461 €390 Les pavots (65x50cm-26x20in) 15-Dec-3 Iegor de Saint Hippolyte, Montreal #106 (C.D 600)

TULLI, Wladimiro (1922-2003) Italian
£467 $840 €700 Sea (50x67cm-20x26in) s. i.verso board. 22-Apr-4 Finarte Semenzato, Rome #182
Works on paper
£828 $1382 €1200 Landscape. Composition (50x71cm-20x28in) s.d.63 mixed media cardboard two. 13-Nov-3 Finarte Semenzato, Rome #433
£915 $1602 €1300 Composition (35x48cm-14x19in) s.d.1964 Chinese ink tempera. 16-Dec-3 Finarte Semenzato, Milan #94/R est:1300-1500
£979 $1664 €1400 Red cloud (39x50cm-15x20in) s. hydropaint cardboard on panel. 28-Nov-3 Farsetti, Prato #27

TULLOCH, Maurice (1894-1974) British
£1600 $2928 €2336 Polo match at Smith's Lawn Windsor (49x58cm-19x23in) s. 28-Jul-4 Bonhams, Knightsbridge #154/R est:800-1200

TULLY, Sidney Strickland (1860-1911) British
£643 $1195 €939 Working man (23x30cm-9x12in) mono. canvasboard exhib. 2-Mar-4 Ritchie, Toronto #71/R (C.D 1600)

TULP, Herman (1955-) Dutch
£1049 $1783 €1500 South European landscape with houses and a canal (29x50cm-11x20in) s.d.91 board. 24-Nov-3 Glerum, Amsterdam #263/R est:1500-2000

TUMARKIN, Igael (1933-) Israeli
£470 $879 €700 Composition (19x24cm-7x9in) s.d.1959 oil mixed media. 29-Feb-4 Versailles Encheres #323
£700 $1211 €1022 Composition (42x32cm-17x13in) s.d.60 oil gold paint sand board. 11-Dec-3 Christie's, Kensington #226/R
£900 $1557 €1314 Composition (79x28cm-31x11in) s.d.1960 oil gold paint sand board. 11-Dec-3 Christie's, Kensington #232/R
£1007 $1883 €1500 Composition (81x54cm-32x21in) s.verso oil mixed media. 29-Feb-4 Versailles Encheres #322/R est:1500-2000
Works on paper
£1267 $2331 €1900 Composition (81x65cm-32x26in) s.d.60 verso mixed media canvas. 11-Jun-4 Pierre Berge, Paris #59 est:1800-2000
£3000 $5460 €4380 Black Sun (130x110cm-51x43in) sd.61 s.i.d.1961 verso mixed media canvas prov. 4-Feb-4 Sotheby's, Olympia #225/R est:3000-4000

TUMICELLI, Jacopo (1764-1825) Italian
Miniatures
£1200 $2160 €1752 Gentleman in a blue coat (6cm-2in circular) s. gilt metal frame exhib. 22-Apr-4 Bonhams, New Bond Street #131/R est:500-700

TUNE, Geoff (20th C) New Zealander
£722 $1177 €1054 Piha Beach with Lion Rock (73x135cm-29x53in) s.i.verso board. 23-Sep-3 Peter Webb, Auckland #143/R est:2000-3000 (NZ.D 2000)

TUNGILIK, Mark (1913-1986) North American
Sculpture
£811 $1378 €1184 Musk ox with horns with an Inuk on it's back (6cm-2in) s. mottled dark soapstone bone ivory. 3-Nov-3 Waddingtons, Toronto #416/R est:400-600 (C.D 1800)

TUNICK, Spencer (1967-) American
Photographs
£6587 $11000 €9617 New York (127x152cm-50x60in) s.d.1997 num.6 verso gelatin silver print prov. 14-Nov-3 Phillips, New York #242/R est:10000-15000

TUNINETTO, Adriano (1930-2004) Italian
£336 $621 €500 Suburbs (80x70cm-31x28in) s. s.i.d.2002 verso. 13-Mar-4 Meeting Art, Vercelli #32
£352 $585 €500 Topologia (80x100cm-31x39in) s.i.d.1991 verso. 14-Jun-3 Meeting Art, Vercelli #589/R
£400 $736 €600 Untitled (70x80cm-28x31in) s. s.d.12002 verso. 12-Jun-4 Meeting Art, Vercelli #778/R
£455 $759 €650 Block (80x90cm-31x35in) s.i.d.2002 verso. 26-Jun-3 Sant Agostino, Torino #221/R
£533 $981 €800 Topology (70x80cm-28x31in) s. s.i.d.2002 verso. 12-Jun-4 Meeting Art, Vercelli #344/R

TUNNARD, John (1900-1971) British
£11000 $20020 €16060 Signal (45x19cm-18x7in) s.d.60 board exhib.lit. 15-Jun-4 Bonhams, New Bond Street #103/R est:4000-6000
£13800 $22908 €20148 Abstract (24x45cm-9x18in) s. oil glass painted c.1940's prov. 2-Oct-3 Lane, Penzance #200/R est:6000-8000
£21000 $38430 €30660 City lights (55x52cm-22x20in) s.i.d.61 s.i.d.verso board prov.exhib.lit. 2-Jun-4 Sotheby's, London #112/R est:10000-15000
£34000 $60860 €49640 Landmark (33x43cm-13x17in) s.d.45 board prov.lit. 16-Mar-4 Bonhams, New Bond Street #52/R est:10000-15000
Works on paper
£500 $850 €730 Untitled (42x48cm-17x19in) s.d.55 pastel. 18-Nov-3 Bonhams, Knightsbridge #201/R
£500 $850 €730 Figure in a landscape (36x53cm-14x21in) s. pastel. 18-Nov-3 Bonhams, Knightsbridge #200/R
£650 $1034 €949 Abstract composition (54x36cm-21x14in) studio st.verso W/C black chk. 10-Sep-3 Sotheby's, Olympia #276/R
£850 $1445 €1241 Abstract composition (14x19cm-6x7in) s.i.d.62 mixed media. 26-Nov-3 Sotheby's, Olympia #158/R
£1100 $1749 €1606 Abstract composition (13x18cm-5x7in) s.d.63-64 W/C gouache. 10-Sep-3 Sotheby's, Olympia #279/R est:1000-1500
£2200 $3872 €3212 Workforce (38x56cm-15x22in) pastel W/C pencil gouache. 19-May-4 Sotheby's, Olympia #279/R est:1500-2000
£2600 $4732 €3796 Yellow wagtail by a fish pond (38x53cm-15x21in) s.d.52 W/C bodycol. 15-Jun-4 David Lay, Penzance #360/R est:2000-3000
£4000 $7320 €5840 Stellar, abstract (38x55cm-15x22in) i.d.1967 mixed media. 3-Jun-4 Lane, Penzance #150/R est:4000-5000
£6500 $11180 €9490 Untitled (35x44cm-14x17in) s. pen blk ink W/C gouache col chks. 3-Dec-3 Sotheby's, London #56/R est:3000-4000
£7692 $14000 €11230 Head (56x38cm-22x15in) s.i.d.45 s.i.d.verso pastel ink prov. 29-Jun-4 Sotheby's, New York #508/R est:4000-6000

TUNNER, Joseph Ernst (1792-1877) Austrian
Works on paper
£629 $1151 €950 Scene from battle (20x25cm-8x10in) s.d.1827 pen. 7-Apr-4 Dorotheum, Salzburg #179/R

TUNNICLIFFE, Charles Frederick (1901-1979) British
Works on paper
£270 $486 €394 Waiting for the ebb (36x66cm-14x26in) s. W/C prov. 20-Apr-4 Canterbury Auctions, UK #159/R
£280 $476 €409 Mistlethrush (40x30cm-16x12in) s.i.d.1980 bodycol pencil tracing paper laid down. 1-Dec-3 Bonhams, Bath #55/R
£313 $584 €470 Circus elephants (36x54cm-14x21in) mono. W/C. 20-Jul-4 Goodman, Sydney #91/R (A.D 800)
£420 $769 €613 Lambs and birds (7x16cm-3x6in) W/C pencil. 7-Apr-4 Woolley & Wallis, Salisbury #99/R

£620 $1110 €905 Lakeland views (27x37cm-11x15in) s. pencil W/C pair. 25-May-4 Sworder & Son, Bishops Stortford #342/R
£650 $1190 €949 Genuine Homer Pigeon, First prize Royal Welsh Show 1958 (27x21cm-11x8in) i. W/C htd white. 28-Jul-4 Bonhams, Knightsbridge #60/R
£820 $1533 €1197 Mute swan in flight (9x11cm-4x4in) s.i. W/C prov. 24-Feb-4 Canterbury Auctions, UK #201/R
£900 $1647 €1314 Ringed Plover (17x28cm-7x11in) s. W/C. 28-Jul-4 Bonhams, Knightsbridge #62/R
£1000 $1820 €1460 Canada geese in flight (25x33cm-10x13in) s. pencil W/C. 1-Jul-4 Christie's, Kensington #272/R est:1000-2000
£1100 $2002 €1606 Siamese in catmint (75x51cm-30x20in) s. W/C. 15-Jun-4 Bonhams, New Bond Street #49/R est:1200-1800
£4000 $7320 €5840 Blue Gazzi Modena pigeons. Red Barred Schietti pigeon. Blue Argent pigeon (25x29cm-10x11in) i. pencil W/C bodycol four prov.exhib. 3-Jun-4 Christie's, London #189/R est:2000-3000
£4000 $7320 €5840 Four pigeon studies (25x29cm-10x11in) i. pencil W/C bodycol four prov.exhib. 3-Jun-4 Christie's, London #191/R est:2500-3500
£4800 $8784 €7008 Four pigeon studies (29x25cm-11x10in) i. pencil W/C bodycol four prov.exhib. 3-Jun-4 Christie's, London #190/R est:2500-3500
£6500 $11895 €9490 Five pigeon studies (25x32cm-10x13in) i. one d.1967 pencil W/C bodycol five prov.exhib. 3-Jun-4 Christie's, London #192/R est:3000-5000
£11000 $20130 €16060 Five pigeon studies (27x29cm-11x11in) i. pencil W/C bodycol five prov.exhib. 3-Jun-4 Christie's, London #193/R est:3000-5000

TUNNILLIE, Ashevak (1956-) North American
Sculpture
£723 $1345 €1056 Falcon with outstretched wings (27cm-11in) sig.syllabics green striated stone. 2-Mar-4 Ritchie, Toronto #241/R est:1500-2000 (C.D 1800)

TUNNILLIE, Ovilu (1949-) North American
Sculpture
£811 $1378 €1184 Arctic bird (51cm-20in) marbled green soapstone exec.c.1979. 3-Nov-3 Waddingtons, Toronto #118/R est:2000-3000 (C.D 1800)
£1332 $2264 €1945 Sedna (61cm-24in) s. mottled green soapstone. 3-Nov-3 Waddingtons, Toronto #94/R est:3500-4500 (C.D 2955)

TUNOLD, Bernt (1877-1946) Norwegian
£1022 $1635 €1482 Landscape with barn (65x55cm-26x22in) s. 22-Sep-3 Blomqvist, Lysaker #1312/R (N.KR 12000)
£1704 $2726 €2471 Landscape from Selje (60x84cm-24x33in) s. 22-Sep-3 Blomqvist, Lysaker #1313/R est:30000-40000 (N.KR 20000)
£1721 $2874 €2513 Landscape with barn (65x55cm-26x22in) s. 20-Oct-3 Blomqvist, Lysaker #1335 est:22000-25000 (N.KR 20000)
£6405 $11465 €9351 Landscape from Bjorndalen towards Laksevag (93x125cm-37x49in) s. exhib.lit. 22-Mar-4 Blomqvist, Oslo #394/R est:90000-110000 (N.KR 80000)

TUOHY, Patrick (attrib) (1894-1930) British
Works on paper
£336 $601 €500 Choir boy (51x35cm-20x14in) W/C. 31-May-4 Hamilton Osborne King, Dublin #212

TUPKE-GRANDE, Helene (1876-?) German
£278 $453 €400 River harbour with boats in evening (54x46cm-21x18in) s. bears i. verso canvas on panel. 26-Sep-3 Bolland & Marotz, Bremen #689

TUPPER, Alexander (1885-1950) American
£346 $550 €505 House with flower garden, probably Gloucester (61x71cm-24x28in) 25-Feb-3 Bunch, West Chester #438/R

TUPPER, Margaret (1887-1979) American
£479 $800 €699 Clothesline (30x36cm-12x14in) 18-Oct-3 David Dike, Dallas #299/R

TURA, Gianfrancesco (16th C) Italian
£25839 $45735 €38500 Saint Thomas (45x35cm-18x14in) board lit. 2-May-4 Finarte, Venice #57/R est:30000-40000
£46667 $84933 €70000 Nativity wth Saint Agnes and Saint Barbara (72x97cm-28x38in) prov.lit. 4-Jul-4 Finarte, Venice #52/R est:60000-80000

TURCATO, Giulio (1912-1995) Italian
£580 $951 €800 Untitled (11x28cm-4x11in) s.d.68 board. 27-May-3 Sotheby's, Milan #147
£1208 $2162 €1800 Comice (50x32cm-20x13in) s. tempera card. 28-May-4 Farsetti, Prato #267/R est:1600-1900
£1467 $2699 €2200 Net (52x68cm-20x27in) s. tempera paper. 11-Jun-4 Farsetti, Prato #114/R est:1900
£1517 $2534 €2200 Urban landscape (30x25cm-12x10in) s. 13-Nov-3 Finarte Semenzato, Rome #287 est:2000-3000
£1533 $2821 €2300 Changing blue (30x35cm-12x14in) s. oil mixed media. 12-Jun-4 Meeting Art, Vercelli #91/R est:1500
£1972 $3273 €2800 Changing green (69x50cm-27x20in) prov. 11-Jun-3 Finarte Semenzato, Milan #565/R
£2013 $3604 €3000 Composition (91x60cm-36x24in) s. acrylic W/C painted 1968 prov. 25-May-4 Sotheby's, Milan #81/R est:4000
£2174 $3565 €3000 Landscape (50x61cm-20x24in) s. prov. 27-May-3 Sotheby's, Milan #145/R est:4000
£2174 $3565 €3000 Landscape (50x61cm-20x24in) s. prov. 27-May-3 Sotheby's, Milan #146 est:3000-4000
£2260 $3842 €3300 Archipelagos (50x60cm-20x24in) s. s.verso. 7-Nov-3 Tuttarte, Modena #733 est:5000-6000
£2319 $3803 €3200 Untitled (60x80cm-24x31in) s. s.verso oil sand mixed media. 27-May-3 Sotheby's, Milan #148 est:2000-3000
£2465 $4092 €3500 Archipelagus (50x70cm-20x28in) s. acrylic mixed media. 13-Jun-3 Farsetti, Prato #239/R
£2483 $4146 €3600 Untitled (60x80cm-24x31in) s.verso oil sand mixed media. 13-Nov-3 Galleria Pace, Milan #56/R est:5500
£2617 $4842 €3900 Changing (50x70cm-20x28in) s. oil mixed media. 13-Mar-4 Meeting Art, Vercelli #105 est:3000
£2617 $4868 €3900 Venice, La Salute (100x70cm-39x28in) s. 4-Mar-4 Babuino, Rome #115 est:3000-3500
£2667 $4907 €4000 Changing blue (70x90cm-28x35in) s. oil mixed media. 12-Jun-4 Meeting Art, Vercelli #478/R est:4000
£2703 $4757 €4000 Untitled (50x70cm-20x28in) s. s.verso oil sand painted 1970 prov. 24-May-4 Christie's, Milan #93/R est:3000-4000
£2759 $4607 €4000 Fluorescent orange (60x80cm-24x31in) s. oil mixed media painted 1970 exhib.lit. 17-Nov-3 Sant Agostino, Torino #287/R est:2800-3200
£2887 $4793 €4100 Changing orange (50x70cm-20x28in) s. acrylic mixed media. 13-Jun-3 Farsetti, Prato #306/R
£3020 $5406 €4500 Archipelagus (50x70cm-20x28in) s. oil mixed media lit. 28-May-4 Farsetti, Prato #28/R est:3400-4400
£3041 $5351 €4500 Archipelagus (50x70cm-20x28in) s. s.verso prov. 24-May-4 Christie's, Milan #91/R est:3000-5000
£3356 $6007 €5000 Changing white, red (80x100cm-31x39in) s. s.i.verso oil mixed media. 30-May-4 Meeting Art, Vercelli #26 est:5000
£3356 $6242 €5000 Night scene (80x90cm-31x35in) canvas on plastic. 4-Mar-4 Babuino, Rome #522 est:3500-4000
£3497 $5944 €5000 Still life with vase of flowers and leeks (50x70cm-20x28in) s. 26-Nov-3 Pandolfini, Florence #55 est:5200-5500
£3716 $6541 €5500 Acropolis (50x70cm-20x28in) s.i.verso oil collage painted 1972 prov. 24-May-4 Christie's, Milan #92/R est:3500-5500
£3758 $6991 €5600 Guitar player (58x42cm-23x17in) s. s.i.verso. 4-Mar-4 Babuino, Rome #153 est:4000-5000
£3758 $6991 €5600 Prints (70x90cm-28x35in) s. oil dye. 4-Mar-4 Babuino, Rome #433 est:2500-3000
£3803 $6313 €5400 Cangiante blu notte (70x90cm-28x35in) s. oil mixed media. 14-Jun-3 Meeting Art, Vercelli #351/R est:4000
£4336 $7371 €6200 Composition (60x80cm-24x31in) s. 24-Nov-3 Christie's, Milan #170/R est:3000-4000
£4400 $8096 €6600 Itineraries (90x60cm-35x24in) s. oil mixed media. 12-Jun-4 Meeting Art, Vercelli #866/R est:5000
£4762 $8667 €7000 Changing blue (80x120cm-31x47in) s. 6-Feb-4 Galleria Rosenberg, Milan #51/R est:7000
£5825 $9903 €8330 Portrait of woman (40x30cm-16x12in) s. masonite prov. 18-Nov-3 Babuino, Rome #392/R est:4000-5000
£5972 $9436 €8600 Moon surface (80x50cm-31x20in) oilmm. on foam. 6-Sep-3 Meeting Art, Vercelli #614 est:8000
£6081 $10703 €9000 Cosmological (130x162cm-51x64in) oil sand prov. 24-May-4 Christie's, Milan #177 est:7000-10000
£6159 $10101 €8500 Net (70x100cm-28x39in) s. s.verso. 30-May-3 Farsetti, Prato #538/R
£6376 $11413 €9500 Chinese flies (90x70cm-35x28in) s.verso oil mixed media. 28-May-4 Farsetti, Prato #287/R est:7200-8200
£8392 $14266 €12000 Composition (120x59cm-47x23in) s. oil sand mixed media painted 1949 prov. 25-Nov-3 Sotheby's, Milan #223/R est:10000-15000
£8621 $14397 €12500 Architecture (60x80cm-24x31in) s. prov. 13-Nov-3 Finarte Semenzato, Rome #336/R est:18000-20000
£8725 $15617 €13000 Milky way (175x134cm-69x53in) s. s.verso oil mixed media. 28-May-4 Farsetti, Prato #134/R est:9000-11000
£9388 $16428 €13330 Composition (66x74cm-26x29in) s. painted 1955. 16-Dec-3 Porro, Milan #27/R est:15000-20000
£9396 $16819 €14000 Moon surface (146x56cm-57x22in) s. oil mixed media on foam on board painted 1968 prov. 25-May-4 Sotheby's, Milan #198/R est:13000-18000
£9573 $16275 €13690 Composition (50x70cm-20x28in) s. prov. 18-Nov-3 Babuino, Rome #483/R est:7000-9000
Works on paper
£642 $1091 €937 Senza titulo (47x67cm-19x26in) s. gouache prov. 5-Nov-3 AB Stockholms Auktionsverk #1096/R (S.KR 8500)
£1067 $1963 €1600 Five hundred lira (50x72cm-20x28in) s. mixed media collage. 8-Jun-4 Finarte Semenzato, Milan #282/R est:500-550
£1119 $1902 €1600 Seated nude (26x20cm-10x8in) s. Chinese ink W/C. 20-Nov-3 Finarte Semenzato, Milan #42/R est:1500-2000
£1267 $2280 €1900 Itineraries (55x73cm-22x29in) s. col Chinese ink prov. 22-Apr-4 Finarte Semenzato, Rome #95/R est:2000-2500
£2000 $3680 €3000 Itineraries (50x70cm-20x28in) s. waterpaint on canvas. 11-Jun-4 Farsetti, Prato #308/R est:2600-3000
£2333 $4293 €3500 Mechanic (70x100cm-28x39in) s. mixed media on canvas. 8-Jun-4 Finarte Semenzato, Milan #410/R est:2500-3000
£2667 $4800 €4000 Ruins in Warsaw. Mine entry (38x46cm-15x18in) s. Chinese ink card prov. two. 22-Apr-4 Finarte Semenzato, Rome #113/R est:2000-2500

TURCHI, Alessandro (1578-1649) Italian
£26389 $47500 €38528 Cephalus and Procris (187x266cm-74x105in) 22-Jan-4 Sotheby's, New York #208/R est:10000-15000
£84507 $147887 €120000 Christ entering Jerusalem (200x230cm-79x91in) i.on stretcher prov.lit. 17-Dec-3 Christie's, Rome #509/R est:120000-160000
£160000 $276800 €233600 Last Communion of the Magdalene (50x37cm-20x15in) silvered copper. 11-Dec-3 Sotheby's, London #18/R est:40000-60000

TURCHI, Alessandro (attrib) (1578-1649) Italian
£7821 $14000 €11419 Diana and Apollo slaying the children of Niobe (50x30cm-20x12in) i.verso copper. 14-May-4 Skinner, Boston #9/R est:600-800

TURCHI, Alessandro (circle) (1578-1649) Italian
£10000 $18700 €14600 Annunciation (19x14cm-7x6in) oil slate. 27-Feb-4 Christie's, Kensington #193/R est:1500-2500

TURCHIARO, Aldo (1929-) Italian
£349 $648 €520 Doves and dogs (70x50cm-28x20in) s.d.1963. 4-Mar-4 Babuino, Rome #21

TURINA Y AREAL, Joaquin (1847-1903) Spanish
£20134 $36040 €30000 Party in Seville garden (45x65cm-18x26in) s. board. 25-May-4 Durán, Madrid #202/R est:30000

TURKI, Yahia (1903-1968) Tunisian
£2183 $3777 €3100 Scene de souk (36x27cm-14x11in) s. panel. 15-Dec-3 Gros & Delettrez, Paris #155/R est:1500-2000
£4043 $6751 €5700 Echoppe a Tunis (60x50cm-24x20in) s. 16-Jun-3 Gros & Delettrez, Paris #93/R est:4500-6000

TURLETTI, Celestino (1845-1904) Italian
£722 $1300 €1054 Poodle messenger (25x20cm-10x8in) mono.i. 24-Apr-4 Weschler, Washington #582/R

TURNBULL, Jas (19th C) American
£1559 $2900 €2276 Panoramic view around Waverly NY (71x91cm-28x36in) s. 7-Mar-4 William Jenack, New York #233 est:1500-2000

TURNBULL, William (1922-) British
£750 $1320 €1095 Sea creatures (102x76cm-40x30in) s.d.1951 Feb overlap oil sand paper on canvas. 19-May-4 Sotheby's, Olympia #288/R
£1412 $2400 €2062 Untitled - walking figures (124x99cm-49x39in) s.d.1953 verso prov. 9-Nov-3 Wright, Chicago #415 est:3000-4000
£11333 $20853 €17000 Fifteen, 1963 (249x249cm-98x98in) s.i.d.1963 stretcher prov. 9-Jun-4 Christie's, Amsterdam #299/R est:6000-8000
Sculpture
£5294 $9000 €7729 Untitled - figure (109x48cm-43x19in) init.d.1947 welded steel green pat. plaster prov. 9-Nov-3 Wright, Chicago #248 est:5000-7000
£26000 $44720 €37960 Idol I (146cm-57in) s.d.55 num.1/4 green brown pat bronze exec 1955 prov.exhib.lit. 3-Dec-3 Sotheby's, London #75/R est:14000-18000
£29448 $48000 €42994 Standing female figure (160x40x61cm-63x16x24in) s.d.1957 green brown pat bronze prov. 23-Sep-3 Christie's, Rockefeller NY #4/R est:10000-15000

TURNER OF OXFORD, William (1789-1862) British
Works on paper
£340 $619 €496 Wychwood Fair, figures and horses by a tree (13x19cm-5x7in) s. pencil W/C. 15-Jun-4 Bonhams, Oxford #60
£420 $777 €613 Summer landscape (18x24cm-7x9in) W/C. 10-Mar-4 Sotheby's, Olympia #43/R
£494 $850 €721 Coastal seascape with flying gulls (18x25cm-7x10in) s. i.verso W/C. 6-Dec-3 Pook & Pook, Downington #340/R
£560 $1025 €818 Grange Fell, Borrowdale (23x33cm-9x13in) i. W/C. 28-Jul-4 Mallams, Oxford #174/R
£750 $1290 €1095 Country folk on a track with Cader Idris beyond (39x54cm-15x21in) pencil W/C. 3-Dec-3 Christie's, Kensington #109/R
£1200 $2244 €1752 Figures on a track with Cadr Idris beyond (15x21cm-6x8in) W/C. 25-Feb-4 Mallams, Oxford #210/R est:1200-1500
£1800 $3060 €2628 Near Minstead, New Forest, Hampshire, looking towards the Isle of Wight (19x27cm-7x11in) pencil W/C prov.exhib. 20-Nov-3 Christie's, London #50/R est:2000-3000
£2000 $3680 €2920 In the forest of Wychwood (59x73cm-23x29in) s. W/C over pencil htd stopping out. 26-Mar-4 Sotheby's, London #109/R est:2000-3000
£3000 $5490 €4380 Plains of Marathon, Greece (14x20cm-6x8in) i. verso pencil W/C. 3-Jun-4 Christie's, London #146/R est:3000-5000
£6000 $10200 €8760 View of London from Shooters Hill (25x74cm-10x29in) s. W/C over pencil htd white on two joined sheet prov. 27-Nov-3 Sotheby's, London #255/R est:7000-10000
£17500 $29050 €25550 Stonehenge at sunset (25x38cm-10x15in) W/C exhib. 3-Oct-3 Mallams, Oxford #113/R est:1000-1500
£26000 $44200 €37960 An April Shower (45x68cm-18x27in) s. pencil W/C gum arabic htd bodycol scratching out prov.exhib. 20-Nov-3 Christie's, London #76/R est:30000-50000

TURNER, Alan (20th C) ?
£722 $1300 €1054 La barca (70x40cm-28x16in) s.d.1988 prov. 24-Apr-4 David Rago, Lambertville #458/R
£889 $1600 €1298 Near-far (57x51cm-22x20in) s.d.1989 prov. 24-Apr-4 David Rago, Lambertville #454/R est:800-1200
Works on paper
£444 $800 €648 Study for a green barette. Untitled (30x22cm-12x9in) one init.d.1988 pencil one init.d.1984 chl collage 2 prov. 24-Apr-4 David Rago, Lambertville #456/R

TURNER, August D (?-1919) American
£278 $500 €406 Houses along a lake (58x76cm-23x30in) s. 23-Jan-4 Freeman, Philadelphia #117/R
£459 $850 €670 Blue Mountains (38x46cm-15x18in) s. s.i.stretcher. 10-Mar-4 Doyle, New York #51/R

TURNER, Ben (1912-1966) American
£2941 $5000 €4294 Floral (81x91cm-32x36in) 1-Nov-3 Altermann Galleries, Santa Fe #153
£3235 $5500 €4723 New Mexico landscape with lake in foreground (66x97cm-26x38in) 1-Nov-3 Altermann Galleries, Santa Fe #154

TURNER, Charles (1773-1857) British
Works on paper
£4000 $6800 €5840 Portrait of Joseph Mallord William Turner in profile wearing a black coat (26x20cm-10x8in) i. blk red white blue chk stump. 20-Nov-3 Christie's, London #29/R est:4000-6000

TURNER, Charles E (1883-1965) British
£700 $1260 €1022 Fairey Seafox above the Graf Spee in the South Atlantic (50x75cm-20x30in) s. 22-Apr-4 Lawrence, Crewkerne #954
Works on paper
£10000 $15900 €14600 Match (41x69cm-16x27in) s. W/C htd bodycol exhib. 11-Sep-3 Sotheby's, Olympia #105/R est:1000-1500

TURNER, Charles Henry (1848-1908) American
£256 $425 €374 Home alone from Buckburg market (71x53cm-28x21in) s. 4-Oct-3 Skinner, Boston #449
£500 $850 €730 From the balcony, Mt. Vernon Street, Boston (26x18cm-10x7in) panel. 21-Nov-3 Skinner, Boston #285/R
£591 $1100 €863 Woodland (60x92cm-24x36in) s. 5-Mar-4 Skinner, Boston #448/R

TURNER, Colin (?) British?
£282 $493 €400 Still life with oranges and apples (41x65cm-16x26in) s.d.73. 16-Dec-3 James Adam, Dublin #201/R

TURNER, Daniel (fl.1782-1817) British
£650 $1086 €949 Prospect view of Carisbrook Castle (45x69cm-18x27in) s. panel. 11-Nov-3 Bonhams, Knightsbridge #92g/R
£700 $1190 €1022 Blackfriars Bridge (22x29cm-9x11in) panel. 19-Nov-3 Christie's, Kensington #460/R
£850 $1343 €1233 Old London Bridge with the Thames partially frozen (28x36cm-11x14in) s. panel. 4-Sep-3 Christie's, Kensington #82/R

TURNER, Dennis Knight (1924-) New Zealander
£1818 $2855 €2636 Hone Heke (89x64cm-35x25in) s.d.1962 board. 27-Aug-3 Dunbar Sloane, Wellington #12/R est:1500-2500 (NZ.D 5000)
£2182 $3425 €3164 Untitled, fish and figures (39x44cm-15x17in) s.d.10-1952 canvas on board. 27-Aug-3 Dunbar Sloane, Wellington #2/R est:2000-4000 (NZ.D 6000)
Works on paper
£643 $1183 €939 Swanson and Queen Street (55x77cm-22x30in) s.d.1963 W/C. 25-Mar-4 International Art Centre, Auckland #132/R (NZ.D 1800)

TURNER, Desmond (20th C) Irish
£676 $1277 €1000 Farm by a river, County Down (36x46cm-14x18in) s. 17-Feb-4 Whyte's, Dublin #173/R est:1200-1500
£805 $1426 €1200 Cottages and hay stacks, west of Ireland coast (51x61cm-20x24in) s. 27-Apr-4 Whyte's, Dublin #58/R
Works on paper
£364 $663 €550 Figure and cottages by cliff (30x40cm-12x16in) s. W/C. 15-Jun-4 James Adam, Dublin #110/R

TURNER, Elisabeth (1845-1915) ?
Works on paper
£340 $636 €510 Four horses in a sunlit landscape beside trees (70x91cm-28x36in) s.d.92 pastel. 22-Jul-4 Tennants, Leyburn #702

TURNER, F C (1795-1865) British
£2500 $4600 €3650 In Full Cry (51x76cm-20x30in) s. i. prov. 12-Jun-4 Dickins, Middle Claydon #10

TURNER, Frances Calcott (1795-1865) British
£2000 $3400 €2920 Leamington steeplechase (35x43cm-14x17in) s.indis.d.183. 19-Nov-3 Sotheby's, Olympia #15/R est:2000-3000

TURNER, Francis Calcraft (c.1782-1846) British
£500 $900 €730 Breaking cover (30x37cm-12x15in) 21-Apr-4 Christie's, Kensington #95/R
£1300 $2210 €1898 Riding the storm (30x35cm-12x14in) panel. 27-Nov-3 Christie's, Kensington #59/R est:1000-1500

TURNER, George (1843-1910) British
£280 $465 €409 Barrow on Trent, Derby (30x38cm-12x15in) s.d.1902 verso board. 2-Oct-3 Mitchells, Cockermouth #881
£630 $1002 €920 Mill, Dale Abbey, Derbyshire, scene with figures and horses and carts (29x49cm-11x19in) s.i.d.1881 verso. 9-Sep-3 Bamfords, Derby #1142/R
£1000 $1670 €1460 Derbyshire lane scene (37cm-15in circular) s.i. 16-Oct-3 Lawrence, Crewkerne #735/R
£1100 $1837 €1606 Crossing the ford near Ticknall (30x46cm-12x18in) s.d.1879 i.verso. 13-Nov-3 Christie's, Kensington #157/R est:1000-1500
£1200 $2148 €1752 Near Little Eaton, Derbyshire (23x30cm-9x12in) s. s.i.d.97 verso board sold with another attrib to the same hand. 26-May-4 Sotheby's, Olympia #165/R est:1000-1500
£1600 $2928 €2336 Nearest way to the homestead (17x25cm-7x10in) s.i.d.1893 verso board. 6-Apr-4 Bonhams, Knightsbridge #196/R est:600-800
£1750 $3255 €2555 Stepping stone, Dovedale, Derbyshire (29x44cm-11x17in) s. board. 2-Mar-4 Bamfords, Derby #451/R est:1000-1500
£1800 $3222 €2628 Lane near Barrow-on-Trent, Derbyshire (36x54cm-14x21in) s. 18-Mar-4 Neales, Nottingham #740 est:1500-2000
£2200 $3454 €3212 Scene at Knowle Hills, Derbyshire (24x34cm-9x13in) s. s.d.1887 verso board. 10-Dec-2 Bamfords, Derby #766/R est:800-1200
£2300 $4071 €3358 Carter and dog along a country track. Driving sheep down an extensive valley (30x46cm-12x18in) s. board pair. 27-Apr-4 Bonhams, Knowle #120 est:2000-3000
£2400 $3768 €3504 Trent, near Barrow (39x65cm-15x26in) s. s.d.1889 verso. 10-Dec-2 Bamfords, Derby #764/R est:800-1200
£2500 $3925 €3650 Lane between Barrow abd Sinfin (26x24cm-10x9in) s. s.d.1880 verso board. 10-Dec-2 Bamfords, Derby #765/R est:800-1200
£2600 $4316 €3796 River scene with barge (50x76cm-20x30in) s. 1-Oct-3 George Kidner, Lymington #187/R est:3000-5000
£3000 $5580 €4380 Resting in the lane (51x76cm-20x30in) s. s.i.verso. 4-Mar-4 Christie's, Kensington #480/R est:3000-5000
£3100 $5270 €4526 Twyford lane, Derbyshire (28x51cm-11x20in) s.d.79 i.verso. 6-Nov-3 Biddle & Webb, Birmingham #901/R est:500-800
£3100 $5673 €4526 Highland Cattle - Near Glencoe (61x91cm-24x36in) s.i.d.1882. 10-Jun-4 Neales, Nottingham #591/R est:2000-3000
£3200 $5024 €4672 Near Cole Orton, Leicestershire (39x65cm-15x26in) s. s.d.1889 verso. 10-Dec-2 Bamfords, Derby #763/R est:1200-1800
£3200 $5024 €4672 On the hillside, near Windly, Derbyshire (30x41cm-12x16in) s. s.d.1899 verso board. 10-Dec-2 Bamfords, Derby #767/R est:800-1200
£3500 $5565 €5110 Highland drove in Glencoe (70x90cm-28x35in) s. s.i.verso. 9-Sep-3 Bamfords, Derby #1141/R est:3000-4000
£3600 $5652 €5256 Harvesting near Ingleby (39x44cm-15x17in) s. s.verso. 10-Dec-2 Bamfords, Derby #768/R est:800-1200
£4400 $7172 €6424 Blackberry Dell near Kirk Ireton (39x60cm-15x24in) s. s.i.d.1903 verso. 25-Sep-3 Mellors & Kirk, Nottingham #754/R est:3000-4000
£4500 $8280 €6570 The Trent near Ingleby (61x102cm-24x40in) s.d.1878 i.d.verso. 23-Mar-4 Bonhams, New Bond Street #64/R est:4000-6000

£4600 $7958 €6716 Quiet scene in Calke Park, wooded summer river landscape (51x76cm-20x30in) s. painted 1889. 11-Dec-3 Neales, Nottingham #624/R est:3000-4000
£4700 $7473 €6862 Scene near Stanto, Derbyshire (40x64cm-16x25in) s.d.1874 s.verso. 9-Sep-3 Bamfords, Derby #1145/R est:3000-5000
£5400 $10044 €7884 Shady lane in Derbyshire (75x121cm-30x48in) s.d.1892. 2-Mar-4 Bamfords, Derby #471/R est:5000-7000
£5500 $9900 €8030 Stepping stones at Hognaston Derbyshire (40x60cm-16x24in) s. s.i.verso. 22-Apr-4 Mellors & Kirk, Nottingham #1123/R est:4000-5000
£5500 $9900 €8030 Lane at Mackworth Derbyshire (29x44cm-11x17in) s.d.1900 board. 22-Apr-4 Mellors & Kirk, Nottingham #1125/R est:3000-4000
£5500 $9900 €8030 Cottage at Kirk Ireton (29x44cm-11x17in) s..i.d.1900 verso. 22-Apr-4 Mellors & Kirk, Nottingham #1126/R est:4000-5000
£5700 $10089 €8322 Shepherd and flock resting on a country track (61x92cm-24x36in) s.d.84. 27-Apr-4 Bonhams, Knowle #115 est:6000-8000
£6000 $10800 €8760 Gatherers. Stepping stones (51x81cm-20x32in) one s. pair. 21-Jan-4 Sotheby's, Olympia #335/R est:3000-5000
£6500 $11700 €9490 Fording the stream (60x90cm-24x35in) s. 22-Apr-4 Mellors & Kirk, Nottingham #1132/R est:4000-5000
£7500 $13500 €10950 At the crossroads (60x88cm-24x35in) s.i. 22-Apr-4 Mellors & Kirk, Nottingham #1133/R est:4000-5000
£8500 $15300 €12410 Mercaston brook Derbyshire (34x52cm-13x20in) s.d.1902 s.i.d.verso. 22-Apr-4 Mellors & Kirk, Nottingham #1137/R est:4000-5000

TURNER, George (attrib) (1843-1910) British
£720 $1296 €1051 Landscape with figures by a stream (46x31cm-18x12in) 21-Jan-4 Sotheby's, Olympia #317/R

TURNER, Graham (20th C) British
Works on paper
£1450 $2610 €2117 Blue Train Bentley versus Le Train Bleu (34x53cm-13x21in) gouache board. 26-Apr-4 Bonhams, New Bond Street #258

TURNER, Helen M (1858-1958) American
£249 $450 €364 Flowerpiece (69x53cm-27x21in) s. board. 3-Apr-4 Neal Auction Company, New Orleans #986/R
£600 $1020 €876 Daffodils, roses and lilac in a vase by apples on a table (69x56cm-27x22in) s. board. 6-Nov-3 Christie's, Kensington #947
£1923 $3500 €2808 Mexican quarters, Cuernavaca (63x76cm-25x30in) s. 29-Jun-4 Sotheby's, New York #252/R est:5000-7000

TURNER, J M W (1775-1851) British
£9000 $17010 €13140 Coastal scene with sailing barges beneath cliffs (76x30cm-30x12in) bears sig. 21-Feb-4 Nigel Ward, Hereford #1490/R

TURNER, James Alfred (?-1908) Australian
£1134 $1825 €1656 While the billy boils (17x17cm-7x7in) init. tin round prov. 25-Aug-3 Sotheby's, Paddington #330/R est:2000-3000 (A.D 2800)
£1465 $2286 €2124 In charge (21x28cm-8x11in) s. board. 1-Aug-2 Joel, Victoria #320 est:3500-4500 (A.D 4250)
£1951 $3493 €2848 Enjoying the Old friend (34x19cm-13x7in) s. board. 10-May-4 Joel, Victoria #248 est:2500-3500 (A.D 4800)
£2066 $3657 €3016 Droving sheep (25x40cm-10x16in) s. prov. 3-May-4 Christie's, Melbourne #279/R est:5000-7000 (A.D 5000)
£2236 $4002 €3265 In the kitchen (20x34cm-8x13in) s. board. 10-May-4 Joel, Victoria #416 est:3000-4000 (A.D 5500)
£2236 $4002 €3265 In the laundry (19x34cm-7x13in) s. board. 10-May-4 Joel, Victoria #417 est:3000-4000 (A.D 5500)
£2273 $4022 €3319 Woodcutters (38x23cm-15x9in) s.d.1906 prov. 3-May-4 Christie's, Melbourne #280/R est:4000-6000 (A.D 5500)
£3306 $5851 €4827 He shows fight (30x60cm-12x24in) s.d.1889 prov. 3-May-4 Christie's, Melbourne #289/R est:6000-8000 (A.D 8000)
£3441 $5540 €5024 Come here away back (24x29cm-9x11in) s.d.1887 prov.exhib. 25-Aug-3 Sotheby's, Paddington #482/R est:6000-10000 (A.D 8500)
£8097 $13036 €11822 Hauling timber (70x100cm-28x39in) s.d.1906 prov. 25-Aug-3 Sotheby's, Paddington #158/R est:20000-30000 (A.D 20000)
£35124 $62169 €51281 On guard (100x151cm-39x59in) s.d.1892 prov. 3-May-4 Christie's, Melbourne #58/R est:50000-70000 (A.D 85000)
Works on paper
£621 $968 €900 Coming home (23x16cm-9x6in) s. W/C. 1-Aug-2 Joel, Victoria #265 est:1200-1500 (A.D 1800)

TURNER, Jerrold (20th C) American
£208 $375 €304 Houses with a fence in foreground (35x45cm-14x18in) s.d.84. 25-Apr-4 Bonhams & Butterfields, San Francisco #5571/R
£667 $1200 €974 Benicia Bridge, trains diabolo. Temescal (40x50cm-16x20in) s.d.84 verso pair. 25-Apr-4 Bonhams & Butterfields, San Francisco #5626/R

TURNER, John (20th C) Irish?
£750 $1395 €1095 Village of Articlave, Co. L'derry (45x61cm-18x24in) s.d.68 board. 3-Mar-4 John Ross, Belfast #60

TURNER, John (fl. 1872-1880) British
Works on paper
£450 $842 €675 Study of a child seated beside a rock with a ball in an extensive landscape (19x24cm-7x9in) s.d.1871 pencil W/C oval. 22-Jul-4 Tennants, Leyburn #706/R

TURNER, John Davenall (1900-1980) Canadian
£317 $529 €463 Untitled - Northern lights (55x70cm-22x28in) s. 17-Nov-3 Hodgins, Calgary #325/R (C.D 700)

TURNER, Joseph Mallord William (1775-1851) British
£2200000 $4004000 €3212000 Fort Vimieux (71x112cm-28x44in) prov.exhib.lit. 1-Jul-4 Sotheby's, London #16/R est:2000000-3000000
Works on paper
£2600 $4420 €3796 Norbury Park, Surrey (14x26cm-6x10in) bears i. pencil wash prov. 4-Nov-3 Bonhams, New Bond Street #28/R est:4000-6000
£3200 $5440 €4672 Tellhurst Mill, Sussex (20x12cm-8x5in) i. pencil prov. 20-Nov-3 Christie's, London #44/R est:1200-1800
£3600 $6120 €5256 Saltwood Castle, Hythe, Kent (18x13cm-7x5in) pencil grey blue wash prov. 4-Nov-3 Bonhams, New Bond Street #27/R est:4000-6000
£3600 $6624 €5256 Sackville cottage, East Grinstead, Sussex (6x9cm-2x4in) W/C over pencil prov. 26-Mar-4 Sotheby's, London #110/R est:2000-3000
£4600 $8464 €6716 Edinburgh from Calton Hill (26x41cm-10x16in) pencil prov.lit. 26-Mar-4 Sotheby's, London #107/R est:3000-5000
£6000 $11100 €8760 Drydens Monument (23x18cm-9x7in) i. W/C over pencil bodycol. 11-Mar-4 Duke & Son, Dorchester #132/R
£34000 $62560 €49640 Norham Castle on the Tweed (19x14cm-7x6in) s.i. W/C over pencil htd stopping out prov.exhib.lit. 26-Mar-4 Sotheby's, London #112/R est:30000-50000
£175000 $297500 €255500 On the River Ouse, with a view of York Minster in the distance (51x72cm-20x28in) pencil W/C bodycol white chk scratching out prov.exhib.lit. 20-Nov-3 Christie's, London #82/R est:60000-100000
£200000 $368000 €292000 Oberhofen on Lake Thun, Switzerland (24x35cm-9x14in) pencil pen ink W/C scratching out prov.exhib.lit. 9-Jun-4 Christie's, London #13/R est:200000-300000
£230000 $391000 €335800 Study of a sea and sky off Margate (23x32cm-9x13in) i. W/C over pencil prov.lit. 27-Nov-3 Sotheby's, London #15/R est:50000-70000
£250000 $457500 €365000 From Rheinfels looking over St Goar to Burg Katz, Germany (19x31cm-7x12in) pencil W/C htd. touches bodycol scratching out wash prov.exhib. 3-Jun-4 Christie's, London #69/R est:70000-100000
£270000 $491400 €394200 Flint Castle, North Wales (23x32cm-9x13in) s. W/C over pencil htd bodycol scratching out prov.exhib.lit. 1-Jul-4 Sotheby's, London #17/R est:250000-400000

TURNER, Joseph Mallord William (after) (1775-1851) British
£4330 $7750 €6322 Waterway with large buildings on each side, figures and boats (46x81cm-18x32in) s. 8-Jan-4 James Julia, Fairfield #677/R est:1000-2000
£7500 $14025 €10950 Old Pier, Calais (80x120cm-31x47in) bears init. 21-Jul-4 Lyon & Turnbull, Edinburgh #126/R est:4000-6000

TURNER, Joseph Mallord William (attrib) (1775-1851) British
£5240 $8750 €7650 Queen Mabs Grotto (69x89cm-27x35in) 16-Nov-3 William Jenack, New York #189 est:10000-15000
Works on paper
£667 $1200 €974 Looking from Ulva to Mull, Scotland (22x32cm-9x13in) i. pencil. 23-Apr-4 Weschler, Washington #131a/R

TURNER, Joseph Mallord William and GIRTIN, Thomas (19th C) British
Works on paper
£3500 $5950 €5110 Italian landscape, possibly Frascati (16x23cm-6x9in) pencil W/C prov.lit. 20-Nov-3 Christie's, London #18/R est:4000-6000
£6000 $10200 €8760 Estuary, possibly Dartmouth (20x28cm-8x11in) pencil grey blue wash prov.lit. 20-Nov-3 Christie's, London #17/R est:5000-8000

TURNER, Kenneth (20th C) American
Works on paper
£519 $929 €758 Changing skyline, Wellington (50x73cm-20x29in) s. pencil pastel. 12-May-4 Dunbar Sloane, Wellington #51/R est:1500-3000 (NZ.D 1500)

TURNER, Marjorie (20th C) British
Works on paper
£514 $950 €750 Sealyham terriers (25x48cm-10x19in) s.d.1975 col chk paper on board. 10-Feb-4 Doyle, New York #178/R

TURNER, Maud M (fl.1891-1908) British
£3243 $6000 €4735 Spy, a dandie dinmont terrier (25x30cm-10x12in) s.i. canvasboard. 10-Feb-4 Doyle, New York #139/R est:2000-3000

TURNER, Paul (1904-1993) American
£1257 $2100 €1835 Texas bluebonnets (46x61cm-18x24in) board painted c.1950. 18-Oct-3 David Dike, Dallas #169/R est:750-1500

TURNER, Percival (20th C) British
£290 $464 €423 Seascape (35x50cm-14x20in) init.d.1923. 19-May-3 Bruton Knowles, Cheltenham #243

TURNER, Prudence (1930-) British
£250 $463 €365 Highland scene with lake and mountains (60x90cm-24x35in) s. 16-Jul-4 Charterhouse, Sherborne #471
£320 $582 €467 At the head of Loch Duich (50x76cm-20x30in) s. 15-Jun-4 Bonhams, Knightsbridge #104/R
£360 $644 €526 Glen Torridon (48x69cm-19x27in) s. 17-May-4 David Duggleby, Scarborough #659/R
£380 $635 €555 Seaweed gatherers (60x90cm-24x35in) s. 21-Oct-3 Bonhams, Knightsbridge #127
£540 $988 €788 Early morning, with deer before a Scottish loch (51x76cm-20x30in) s. i.verso. 6-Apr-4 Bonhams, Chester #986

TURNER, Ross Sterling (1847-1915) American
£4118 $7000 €6012 Still life, with potted flowers, lantern and covered Delft urn (76x112cm-30x44in) s.d.1888. 8-Nov-3 Van Blarcom, South Natick #153/R est:1000-1500
Works on paper
£1102 $1950 €1609 View of Singing Beach, Manchester-by-the-sea, Massachusetts (36x48cm-14x19in) s.d.97 W/C. 2-May-4 Van Blarcom, South Natick #8

TURNER, W H M (attrib) (fl.1850-1887) British
£1788 $3200 €3002 Portrait of a horse with lowlands and mountains in background (48x61cm-19x24in) 20-Mar-4 Pook & Pook, Downington #578/R est:3000-4000

TURNER, William (19th C) British
£400 $708 €584 Windy harbour between Siddington and Twemlow (50x45cm-20x18in) s.i.verso. 28-Apr-4 Peter Wilson, Nantwich #34
£450 $797 €657 High road with figures and a cart (19x21cm-7x8in) s.i.verso board. 28-Apr-4 Peter Wilson, Nantwich #17
£1250 $2213 €1825 Miners coming, home Bardford Colliery. s.d.1954 i.verso board. 28-Apr-4 Peter Wilson, Nantwich #22
Works on paper
£320 $592 €467 Fisherman (13x8cm-5x3in) s. s.i.d.1971 verso card. 14-Jul-4 Bonhams, Chester #386
£380 $695 €555 Adlington Road, solitary figure on wooded country lane (25x17cm-10x7in) s. i. verso W/C. 6-Jul-4 Peter Wilson, Nantwich #55/R
£865 $1600 €1298 Near Lochinver-Stack, Suilven and Quiang (20x48cm-8x19in) s. pencil W/C bodycol exec. 1838 prov. 14-Jul-4 American Auctioneer #490242/R est:2000-3000

TURNER, William Eddowes (c.1820-1885) British
£280 $504 €409 Study of the racehorse First Principle, held by a groom (33x43cm-13x17in) s. i.d.1902 verso. 21-Apr-4 Tennants, Leyburn #1176

TURNER, William Lakin (1867-1936) British
£300 $510 €438 Lakeland steam (25x19cm-10x7in) indis sig. s.i.d.verso board. 29-Oct-3 Bonhams, Chester #313
£320 $595 €467 Horned cattle grazing (32x42cm-13x17in) s. 2-Mar-4 Bamfords, Derby #452
£430 $744 €628 Autumnal wood (24x35cm-9x14in) s. 9-Dec-3 Bristol Auction Rooms #421/R
£520 $827 €759 Highlands (18x28cm-7x11in) s. board. 9-Sep-3 Bamfords, Derby #1161/R
£600 $1122 €876 Mountain tarn (28x43cm-11x17in) s. 27-Feb-4 Thomson, Roddick & Medcalf, Carlisle #286
£950 $1710 €1387 Derwentwater (25x25cm-10x10in) s.d.1897 s.d.Jully 1897 verso panel. 22-Apr-4 Mellors & Kirk, Nottingham #1084/R
£1400 $2646 €2044 Looking down Glen Turret, Crieff (36x51cm-14x20in) s.i. i.verso. 19-Feb-4 Lyon & Turnbull, Edinburgh #141 est:300-500
£1500 $2700 €2190 Gate Crag, Borrowdale (28x41cm-11x16in) s. i.verso prov. 21-Apr-4 Tennants, Leyburn #1140/R est:500-700

TURPIN DE CRISSE, Lancelot Theodore (1782-1859) French
£5263 $9684 €8000 Vue de l'interieur d'un cloitre (73x60cm-29x24in) mono. lit. 23-Jun-4 Rieunier, Paris #32/R est:10000-12000
£23529 $40000 €34352 Venice; preparations for the festival at the Campo di SS Giovanni e Paolo (96x128cm-38x50in) init.d.1840 canvas on board. 29-Oct-3 Christie's, Rockefeller NY #242/R est:40000-60000

TURPIN DE CRISSE, Lancelot Theodore (attrib) (1782-1859) French
£3867 $7037 €5800 Vue de la cote amalfitaine (27x35cm-11x14in) 30-Jun-4 Delvaux, Paris #165/R est:3000-4000

TURRELL, James (1943-) American
Prints
£12000 $22080 €18000 Still light (83x59cm-33x23in) some s.i. aquatint album of 8 exec. 1990 one of 40. 12-Jun-4 Villa Grisebach, Berlin #439/R est:6000-8000
£28000 $51520 €42000 First light (99x69cm-39x27in) some s.i. aquatint album of 20 exec. 1990 one of 10. 12-Jun-4 Villa Grisebach, Berlin #438/R est:10000-15000

TURRELL, Terry (20th C) American
£333 $600 €486 Inches and yards (61x61cm-24x24in) board prov. 24-Apr-4 Slotin Folk Art, Buford #603/R
£359 $600 €524 Face (25x25cm-10x10in) wood. 15-Nov-3 Slotin Folk Art, Buford #340/R
£599 $1000 €875 Two figures (30x25cm-12x10in) wood board. 15-Nov-3 Slotin Folk Art, Buford #341/R

TURSHANSKI, Leonid Viktorovitch (1875-1945) Russian
£1806 $2853 €2600 Farmer woman sitting in front of her house (35x61cm-14x24in) s. painted c.1900. 5-Sep-3 Wendl, Rudolstadt #3651/R est:1900

TURTIAINEN, Jorma (1936-) Finnish
£293 $532 €430 Picking flowers (70x90cm-28x35in) s.d.1980. 8-Feb-4 Bukowskis, Helsinki #472/R
£374 $681 €550 Girl on road by willows (90x120cm-35x47in) s.d.1984. 8-Feb-4 Bukowskis, Helsinki #473/R

TURTLE, Arnold E (1892-1954) American/British
£2711 $4500 €3958 Northshore Cabin under the pines (58x76cm-23x30in) s. 4-Oct-3 Neal Auction Company, New Orleans #1108/R est:3000-5000

TURVILLE, Serge de (1924-) French
£282 $487 €400 Paysage (80x80cm-31x31in) s.d.1924 oil collage. 15-Dec-3 Charbonneaux, Paris #206

TURZAK, Charles (1899-1985) American
£279 $500 €407 Abstract medley of rectangles (69x53cm-27x21in) s. linen. 16-May-4 Wright, Chicago #320/R

TUSAN, Nyoman (1933-2002) Indonesian?
£688 $1067 €1004 Dewi sri (51x42cm-20x17in) s. 6-Oct-2 Sotheby's, Singapore #135/R est:1500-2000 (S.D 1900)

TUSCAN SCHOOL (15th C) Italian
£15172 $25338 €22000 Angel kiss (48x36cm-19x14in) oil tempera panel prov. 15-Nov-3 Lempertz, Koln #1158/R est:10000
£16892 $29730 €25000 Christ as man of pain (61x46cm-24x18in) panel prov. 22-May-4 Lempertz, Koln #1149/R est:40000

TUSCAN SCHOOL (16th C) Italian
£5705 $10497 €8500 St Sebastian (36x13cm-14x5in) panel. 24-Mar-4 Dorotheum, Vienna #51/R est:6000-8000
£9155 $15838 €13000 Justice (100x76cm-39x30in) 14-Dec-3 Finarte, Venice #120/R est:12000-16000
£10417 $17708 €15000 Madonna and Child (75x60cm-30x24in) board. 29-Oct-3 Il Ponte, Milan #746/R

TUSCAN SCHOOL (17th C) Italian
£5342 $8334 €7800 Saint John beheaded (75x65cm-30x26in) board. 8-Apr-3 Il Ponte, Milan #179/R
£10638 $17766 €15000 Sacred Family (139x115cm-55x45in) 17-Jun-3 Finarte Semenzato, Milan #645/R est:10000-15000
£11268 $18141 €16000 Ritratto di un negromante (99x75cm-39x30in) 8-May-3 Farsetti, Prato #688/R est:10000-14000

TUSCAN SCHOOL (18th/19th C) Italian
£10738 $19758 €16000 Untitled (283x254cm-111x100in) tempera panel. 29-Mar-4 Pandolfini, Florence #733/R est:6000

TUSCAN SCHOOL (19th C) Italian
£6338 $11092 €9000 Saint Catherine (50x25cm-20x10in) tempera board. 17-Dec-3 Christie's, Rome #397/R est:10000-15000

TUSET TUSET, Salvador (1883-1951) Spanish
£1103 $1986 €1600 View of Venice (50x40cm-20x16in) s. board. 26-Jan-4 Durán, Madrid #132 est:1300

TUSQUELLAS CORBELLA, Miguel (1884-?) Spanish
£423 $739 €600 Nude (40x30cm-16x12in) s. paper. 16-Dec-3 Durán, Madrid #572

TUSQUETS Y MAIGNON, Ramon (1839-1904) Italian
£10145 $16638 €14000 Rincon de Venecia (63x41cm-25x16in) s. 27-May-3 Durán, Madrid #271/R est:12000
£23077 $38538 €33000 Playing by the fire (80x53cm-31x21in) s.i.d.1873. 30-Jun-3 Ansorena, Madrid #348/R est:33000
Works on paper
£355 $574 €500 View over Cordoba roofs (23x50cm-9x20in) s.i.d.1872 W/C lit. 23-May-3 Karlheinz Kaupp, Staufen #1827/R
£6159 $10101 €8500 Antes del concierto (60x39cm-24x15in) s. W/C. 27-May-3 Durán, Madrid #176/R est:8000

TUSQUETS, Eugenia (20th C) American
£217 $350 €317 Entre deux (122x91cm-48x36in) s.d.91 verso. 17-Aug-3 Bonhams & Butterfields, San Francisco #5843

TUTSWEETOK, Lucy Tasseor (1934-) North American
Sculpture
£1036 $1761 €1513 Inuit faces (20cm-8in) s. mottled dark soapstone. 3-Nov-3 Waddingtons, Toronto #794/R est:1000-1500 (C.D 2300)
£1171 $1991 €1710 Inuit figures (30cm-12in) mottled dark soapstone. 3-Nov-3 Waddingtons, Toronto #373/R est:1500-2000 (C.D 2600)
£1306 $2221 €1907 Inuit figures (29cm-11in) s. mottled dark soapstone. 3-Nov-3 Waddingtons, Toronto #370/R est:700-1000 (C.D 2900)

TUTTINE, Johann Baptist (1838-1889) German
£972 $1604 €1400 Black Forest scene (62x49cm-24x19in) s.d.1876. 3-Jul-3 Van Ham, Cologne #1486
£2465 $3944 €3500 First approach (63x49cm-25x19in) s.d.1876 lit. 19-Sep-3 Karlheinz Kaupp, Staufen #2104/R est:2000

TUTTLE, Charles Franklin (1841-1893) American
£1227 $2000 €1791 Blue boy (89x43cm-35x17in) 27-Sep-3 Thomaston Place, Thomaston #230

TUTTLE, Richard (1941-) American
£3800 $6042 €5510 Untitled 1975 (8x8cm-3x3in) paint wire sold with photograph and work by another hand. 11-Sep-3 Christie's, Kensington #205/R est:3000-4000
£15278 $27500 €22306 Untitled (19x21cm-7x8in) prov. 24-Apr-4 David Rago, Lambertville #256/R est:8000-12000
Prints
£1824 $2900 €2663 Sun (24x20cm-9x8in) s.i.d.63 woodcut. 12-Sep-3 Skinner, Boston #167/R
Sculpture
£2973 $5500 €4341 Fiction Fish 1 no 2 (19cm-7in) i.verso wood aluminium exec 1992 prov.exhib. 12-Feb-4 Sotheby's, New York #219/R est:3000-4000
£4698 $8409 €7000 Untitled (12x10x8cm-5x4x3in) acrylic wood glue nails sofa prov. 25-May-4 Dorotheum, Vienna #382/R est:7000-10000
£12570 $22500 €18352 Untitled - for artificial light (60x28x7cm-24x11x3in) mixed media polystyrene exec 1986 prov.exhib.lit. 13-May-4 Sotheby's, New York #189/R est:15000-20000
Works on paper
£787 $1337 €1125 Untitled (15x12cm-6x5in) biro W/C. 27-Nov-3 Lempertz, Koln #491/R
£839 $1427 €1200 Untitled (15x12cm-6x5in) W/C prov. 27-Nov-3 Lempertz, Koln #492/R
£1189 $2021 €1700 Before one and two No 16 (23x20cm-9x8in) s.i. i. verso col pen. 27-Nov-3 Lempertz, Koln #490/R est:3000

£1901	$3289	€2700	Composition (35x28cm-14x11in) s.d.1941 verso W/C ink diptych prov. 15-Dec-3 Charbonneaux, Paris #266 est:800
£2000	$3340	€2920	Firenze gold no 3 (29x42cm-11x17in) ink pencil graph paper prov. 22-Oct-3 Christie's, London #124/R est:2000-30000
£2297	$4250	€3354	Vienna Work 7 (14x22cm-6x9in) s.i.d.2/4/87 W/C gouache crayon card prov. 12-Feb-4 Sotheby's, New York #218/R est:3000-4000
£2432	$4500	€3551	Vienna Work 3 (14x22cm-6x9in) s.i.d.2/4/87 W/C gouache crayon card prov. 12-Feb-4 Sotheby's, New York #220/R est:3000-4000
£3297	$6000	€4814	Diptyque (42x35cm-17x14in) W/C gouache two sheets executed 1975 prov. 29-Jun-4 Sotheby's, New York #532/R est:8000-10000
£3514	$6500	€5130	Valentine's Day III (24x35cm-9x14in) s.i.d.6 Jan 83 verso W/C ruled paper prov. 12-Feb-4 Sotheby's, New York #213/R est:2000-3000
£4167	$7667	€6084	Old men and their garden (24x35cm-9x14in) s.i.d.82 verso W/C prov. 23-Jun-4 Koller, Zurich #3116/R est:3500-4500 (S.FR 9500)
£5988	$10000	€8742	Space in Finland 7-30 (21x21cm-8x8in) s.d.1988 verso W/C lacquer paintstick pencil glue two parts prov. 13-Nov-3 Sotheby's, New York #131/R est:6500-8500
£16760	$30000	€24470	Painting in Italy III (28x38cm-11x15in) pencil W/C coloured pencil four parts exec 1988 prov.exhib. 13-May-4 Sotheby's, New York #190/R est:20000-30000
£23952	$40000	€34970	Twisting works, no 3, 4, , 6 (36x28cm-14x11in) s.i.d.1971 i.verso ink pencil gouache four prov. 13-Nov-3 Sotheby's, New York #571/R est:20000-30000

TUTUNDJIAN, Léon (1905-1968) French/Armenian

£3333	$6133	€5000	Noyau (73x100cm-29x39in) s. 10-Jun-4 Camard, Paris #134/R est:4000-5000
£3741	$6697	€5500	Untitled (45x36cm-18x14in) s. paper on canvas. 21-Mar-4 Calmels Cohen, Paris #36/R est:6000-8000
£36254	$61631	€52931	Composition No. 103 (33x19cm-13x7in) s.i.d.1929 verso prov.exhib.lit. 5-Nov-3 AB Stockholms Auktionsverk #1116/R est:150000-200000 (S.KR 480000)

Works on paper

£265	$482	€400	La poire (30x20cm-12x8in) s.i. pen india ink prov. 15-Jun-4 Blanchet, Paris #180
£280	$467	€400	Composition (22x15cm-9x6in) s. ink dr exec.1927 prov. 29-Jun-3 Versailles Encheres #7
£400	$736	€600	Composition (24x18cm-9x7in) init. ink. 9-Jun-4 Le Roux & Morel, Paris #40
£633	$1165	€950	Composition (13x9cm-5x4in) init. 9-Jun-4 Le Roux & Morel, Paris #42
£867	$1595	€1300	Composition (24x17cm-9x7in) s.d.1928 ink. 9-Jun-4 Le Roux & Morel, Paris #38
£903	$1507	€1300	Untitled (17x22cm-7x9in) s.d.1926 Indian ink. 21-Oct-3 Artcurial Briest, Paris #116a/R est:1000-1200
£940	$1729	€1400	Composition (30x22cm-12x9in) s. ink. 24-Mar-4 Binoche, Paris #98/R
£944	$1605	€1350	Composition a la tangente (16x11cm-6x4in) mono. Indian ink exec.c.1926-1927 prov. 23-Nov-3 Cornette de St.Cyr, Paris #337/R
£1000	$1700	€1460	Abstract composition (20x15cm-8x6in) s.d.1960 mixed media collage. 9-Nov-3 Wright, Chicago #397 est:500-700
£1000	$1840	€1500	Composition (21x17cm-8x7in) s.d.1927 ink. 9-Jun-4 Le Roux & Morel, Paris #37/R est:500-600
£1100	$2024	€1650	Composition (25x18cm-10x7in) s.d.1928 ink. 9-Jun-4 Le Roux & Morel, Paris #39/R est:500-600
£1268	$2193	€1800	Statue dans un paysage (31x23cm-12x9in) s.d.1950 Indian ink. 14-Dec-3 Versailles Encheres #25 est:1000-1200
£1538	$2615	€2200	Composition au cercle rouge (33x43cm-13x17in) s.d.1927 ink W/C prov. 23-Nov-3 Cornette de St.Cyr, Paris #341/R est:600-800
£1608	$2734	€2300	A partir d'un point rouge (27x28cm-11x11in) s. Indian ink col ink prov. 23-Nov-3 Cornette de St.Cyr, Paris #340/R est:600-800
£1655	$2863	€2350	Composition (30x33cm-12x13in) s.d.1922 Indian ink wash. 14-Dec-3 Versailles Encheres #23/R est:1200-1500
£1757	$3320	€2600	Composition geometrique abstraite (22x16cm-9x6in) s.d.1928 Indian ink prov. 21-Feb-4 Cornette de St.Cyr, Paris #224/R est:2500-3000
£2267	$4171	€3400	Composition (28x20cm-11x8in) s.d.1927 ink. 9-Jun-4 Le Roux & Morel, Paris #41 est:500-600
£3217	$5469	€4600	Composition aux deux cercles (27x18cm-11x7in) s.d.1928 Indian ink prov. 23-Nov-3 Cornette de St.Cyr, Paris #338/R est:1500-2000
£3916	$6657	€5600	Composition au feuillage (26x33cm-10x13in) s.d.1927 ink W/C prov. 23-Nov-3 Cornette de St.Cyr, Paris #339/R est:600-800
£4336	$7371	€6200	Composition au cercle rouge (32x48cm-13x19in) s.d.1927 ink W/C prov. 23-Nov-3 Cornette de St.Cyr, Paris #342/R est:600-800

TUTUNOV, S A (1925-1999) Russian

£444	$800	€648	Kama river bank (21x34cm-8x13in) oil on cardboard. 24-Apr-4 Shishkin Gallery, Moscow #54/R
£447	$800	€653	At Metinsk Lake, midday (23x34cm-9x13in) cardboard painted 1955. 29-May-4 Shishkin Gallery, Moscow #64/R
£528	$950	€771	Kama river bank (24x35cm-9x14in) oil on cardboard. 24-Apr-4 Shishkin Gallery, Moscow #53/R
£531	$950	€775	Kama river (23x35cm-9x14in) cardboard painted 1951. 29-May-4 Shishkin Gallery, Moscow #67/R
£667	$1200	€974	Deep forest over the Kama River (18x35cm-7x14in) oil on cardboard. 24-Apr-4 Shishkin Gallery, Moscow #52/R est:2000-3000
£722	$1300	€1054	Evening at the landing stage, Ples (24x34cm-9x13in) oil on cardboard. 24-Apr-4 Shishkin Gallery, Moscow #55/R est:2000-3000
£833	$1500	€1216	Kama river (23x37cm-9x15in) oil on cardboard. 24-Apr-4 Shishkin Gallery, Moscow #51/R est:2000-3000
£894	$1600	€1305	Grey day (24x37cm-9x15in) cardboard painted 1955. 29-May-4 Shishkin Gallery, Moscow #65/R est:1500-2000
£1006	$1800	€1469	Ples (20x34cm-8x13in) cardboard painted 1952. 29-May-4 Shishkin Gallery, Moscow #63/R est:1500-2000
£1117	$2000	€1631	Sawing the firewood (23x27cm-9x11in) cardboard painted 1945. 29-May-4 Shishkin Gallery, Moscow #66/R est:1500-2000
£1222	$2200	€1784	Spring in Makarovka (46x69cm-18x27in) oil on cardboard. 24-Apr-4 Shishkin Gallery, Moscow #50/R est:5000-6000
£1229	$2200	€1794	Evening, Ples (19x34cm-7x13in) cardboard painted 1952. 29-May-4 Shishkin Gallery, Moscow #68/R est:1500-2000

TUXEN, Laurits (1853-1927) Danish

£328	$535	€479	Man wearing fur hat (35x27cm-14x11in) init.d.3-2-15. 27-Sep-3 Rasmussen, Havnen #2176/R (D.KR 3500)
£440	$758	€642	Interior sketch from Westminster Abbey (40x30cm-16x12in) 2-Dec-3 Kunsthallen, Copenhagen #508 (D.KR 4700)
£467	$738	€677	From the luxuriant Busch Garden in Pasadena, USA (46x39cm-18x15in) init.d.9-5-18. 2-Sep-3 Rasmussen, Copenhagen #1749/R (D.KR 5000)
£539	$1003	€787	Stormy seas with sea-nymphs (52x70cm-20x28in) i.verso. 2-Mar-4 Rasmussen, Copenhagen #1418/R (D.KR 6000)
£655	$1095	€956	Coronation scene (51x41cm-20x16in) init. 25-Oct-3 Rasmussen, Havnen #2210/R (D.KR 7000)
£656	$1128	€958	Bouquet of roses in glass vase on table (41x56cm-16x22in) init.d.23. 2-Dec-3 Kunsthallen, Copenhagen #584/R (D.KR 7000)
£756	$1308	€1104	Mythological scene with couple surprised by soldiers (31x34cm-12x13in) init.d.77 exhib. 9-Dec-3 Rasmussen, Copenhagen #1343/R (D.KR 8000)
£841	$1329	€1219	Coastal landscape with steep slopes (15x25cm-6x10in) init. 2-Sep-3 Rasmussen, Copenhagen #1758/R (D.KR 9000)
£945	$1635	€1380	Rough seas with sea nymph (43x62cm-17x24in) mono. 9-Dec-3 Rasmussen, Copenhagen #1452/R (D.KR 10000)
£992	$1776	€1448	Coastal landscape from Luksor (37x46cm-15x18in) s.i.d.20-2-14. 12-Jan-4 Rasmussen, Vejle #4/R (D.KR 10500)
£995	$1782	€1453	Copenhagen Harbour (29x38cm-11x15in) mono. panel. 10-May-4 Rasmussen, Vejle #380/R (D.KR 11000)
£1148	$1860	€1665	Seascape with foaming waves (30x40cm-12x16in) init.d.22/8 03. 4-Aug-3 Rasmussen, Vejle #19/R est:15000 (D.KR 12000)
£1215	$1920	€1762	Woman by fire (35x51cm-14x20in) init.d.23. 2-Sep-3 Rasmussen, Copenhagen #1775/R est:10000 (D.KR 13000)
£1253	$2294	€1829	From Greenland - icebergs in Disco Bay (39x46cm-15x18in) init.d.21 exhib. 9-Jun-4 Rasmussen, Copenhagen #1770/R est:8000-10000 (D.KR 14000)
£1264	$2363	€1845	Seascape with sailing ship on the horizon (42cm-17in circular) init.i.d.Nov.01 i.verso. 25-Feb-4 Museumsbygningen, Copenhagen #196/R est:5000 (D.KR 14000)
£1382	$2350	€2018	Coastal landscape with children at water's edge, Skagen (30x49cm-12x19in) init.d.22. 10-Nov-3 Rasmussen, Vejle #143/R est:20000-30000 (D.KR 15000)
£1402	$2215	€2033	From my garden near Rosenborg in Copenhagen (33x41cm-13x16in) init.d.2/5 13. 2-Sep-3 Rasmussen, Copenhagen #1755/R est:15000 (D.KR 15000)
£1538	$2754	€2245	View of the gardens near Rosenborg (38x45cm-15x18in) mono.d.6/6 10 panel lit. 10-May-4 Rasmussen, Vejle #98/R est:18000-20000 (D.KR 17000)
£2430	$3839	€3524	Coastal landscape from Brittany (24x47cm-9x19in) init.d.76. 2-Sep-3 Rasmussen, Copenhagen #1764/R est:20000 (D.KR 26000)
£2457	$4251	€3587	Bathers at Gammel Strand (20x28cm-8x11in) init.d.14 panel. 9-Dec-3 Rasmussen, Copenhagen #1453/R est:10000 (D.KR 26000)
£2647	$4578	€3865	Children and young fishermen on the beach at low tide, Brittany (35x44cm-14x17in) init.d.75 i.verso. 9-Dec-3 Rasmussen, Copenhagen #1270/R est:30000-40000 (D.KR 28000)
£2695	$5013	€3935	Seascape from Hojen, Skagen (50x61cm-20x24in) init.d.26/7 09. 2-Mar-4 Rasmussen, Copenhagen #1331/R est:30000 (D.KR 30000)
£4000	$7360	€5840	Miss Nina Tuxen in the garden of the artist's house at Skagen (74x53cm-29x21in) init. 23-Mar-4 Bonhams, New Bond Street #26/R est:5000-7000
£4476	$8192	€6535	Girl by pond (64x85cm-25x33in) s.d.1917. 9-Jun-4 Rasmussen, Copenhagen #1501/R est:50000-60000 (D.KR 50000)
£5198	$8993	€7589	Windy day in June, Skagen (46x64cm-18x25in) init.d.13/6 08. 9-Dec-3 Rasmussen, Copenhagen #1265/R est:60000 (D.KR 55000)
£7188	$13369	€10494	Bathing nymph (102x68cm-40x27in) init.d.12.6.10. 2-Mar-4 Rasmussen, Copenhagen #1271/R est:100000 (D.KR 80000)
£8953	$16383	€13071	The artist's daughter Nina in the garden at Skagen (73x53cm-29x21in) init. 9-Jun-4 Rasmussen, Copenhagen #1443/R est:100000-125000 (D.KR 100000)
£13084	$20673	€18972	Low tide at Portel on the French coast (66x89cm-26x35in) s.d.1888 exhib. 2-Sep-3 Rasmussen, Copenhagen #1518/R est:100000-150000 (D.KR 140000)
£18692	$29533	€27103	Young girl, Skagen Strand (95x120cm-37x47in) init. painted c.1912. 2-Sep-3 Rasmussen, Copenhagen #1516/R est:175000-200000 (D.KR 200000)

Works on paper

£492	$901	€718	Posing female nude (72x92cm-28x36in) init.d.911 chl crayon. 9-Jun-4 Rasmussen, Copenhagen #2037/R (D.KR 5500)
£1611	$2949	€2352	Birth of Venus (124x76cm-49x30in) init.d.11 chl crayon. 9-Jun-4 Rasmussen, Copenhagen #2036/R est:20000-25000 (D.KR 18000)

TUYMANS, Luc (1958-) Belgian

£14000	$25760	€20440	Reuntgen - X-Ray (40x30cm-16x12in) s.i.d.98 v paper on card on board prov.exhib. 24-Jun-4 Sotheby's, London #129/R est:10000-15000
£120000	$220800	€175200	Illegitimate VII (55x81cm-22x32in) s.d.97 verso acrylic prov.exhib. 24-Jun-4 Christie's, London #50/R est:50000-70000
£227545	$380000	€332216	Within (223x243cm-88x96in) painted 2001 prov.exhib.lit. 13-Nov-3 Phillips, New York #5/R est:150000-200000

Works on paper

£3067	$5000	€4478	Untitled (10x14cm-4x6in) s.d.86 gouache prov. 23-Sep-3 Christie's, Rockefeller NY #80/R est:4000-6000
£4667	$8540	€7000	Smoking (21x11cm-8x4in) s.i.d.1990 Indian ink brush. 4-Jun-4 Lempertz, Koln #497/R est:10000
£5500	$10010	€8030	Gemecties (40x30cm-16x12in) s.d.98 ink prov. 5-Feb-4 Christie's, London #229/R est:7000-9000
£7000	$12740	€10220	Untitled (46x37cm-18x15in) s.d.97 W/C prov. 5-Feb-4 Christie's, London #228/R est:7000-9000
£8500	$15640	€12410	Untitled (21x15cm-8x6in) s.d.97 gouache card prov.exhib. 24-Jun-4 Sotheby's, London #313/R est:5000-7000
£25000	$45500	€36500	Untitled (26x19cm-10x7in) s.d.81 gouache W/C pencil wallpaper prov. 5-Feb-4 Christie's, London #226/R est:25000-35000

TVEIT, Samuel Egilson (1866-1957) Norwegian

£409	$654	€593	Autumn sunshine (49x65cm-19x26in) s. 22-Sep-3 Blomqvist, Lysaker #1315 (N.KR 4800)
£537	$859	€779	Spring flowers (50x64cm-20x25in) s. 22-Sep-3 Blomqvist, Lysaker #1316/R (N.KR 6300)

TVETER, Kare (1922-) Norwegian

£275	$443	€402	Dark landscape (30x43cm-12x17in) s. panel. 25-Aug-3 Blomqvist, Lysaker #1330/R (N.KR 3200)
£852	$1363	€1235	Summer night (61x74cm-24x29in) s. 22-Sep-3 Blomqvist, Lysaker #1317/R (N.KR 10000)
£990	$1653	€1445	Moonlit night (51x61cm-20x24in) s. 20-Oct-3 Blomqvist, Lysaker #1336/R (N.KR 11500)
£3237	$5567	€4726	The land which is not - landscape from Svalbard (85x165cm-33x65in) s. i.verso. 8-Dec-3 Blomqvist, Oslo #565/R est:40000-60000 (N.KR 38000)

Works on paper

£327	$527	€477	Cold winter's day (27x36cm-11x14in) s. W/C. 25-Aug-3 Blomqvist, Lysaker #1333 (N.KR 3800)
£361	$582	€527	Landscape (27x38cm-11x15in) s. W/C. 25-Aug-3 Blomqvist, Lysaker #1331/R (N.KR 4200)
£448	$720	€654	Landscape (19x28cm-7x11in) s. W/C. 25-Aug-3 Blomqvist, Lysaker #1332 (N.KR 5200)
£1521	$2723	€2221	Winter landscape (53x75cm-21x30in) s. W/C. 22-Mar-4 Blomqvist, Oslo #635/R est:12000-14000 (N.KR 19000)
£1841	$3296	€2688	Mountain tops (53x75cm-21x30in) s. W/C. 22-Mar-4 Blomqvist, Oslo #636/R est:12000-14000 (N.KR 23000)

TVOROZHNIKOV, Ivan Ivanovich (1848-1919) Russian
£10500 $18795 €15330 Young peasant (90x67cm-35x26in) s. 26-May-4 Sotheby's, Olympia #381/R est:4000-6000

TWACHTMAN, John Henry (1853-1902) American
£30726 $55000 €44860 Road scene, Cincinnati (13x24cm-5x9in) s.i.d.78 prov. 6-May-4 Shannon's, Milford #110/R est:50000-75000
£34324 $63500 €51486 Niagara Falls (58x48cm-23x19in) s.d.79 prov.exhib. 14-Jul-4 American Auctioneer #490236/R est:20000-30000
£125000 $220000 €182500 Hayrick (56x76cm-22x30in) s. painted c.1890-1900 prov.exhib.lit. 19-May-4 Sotheby's, New York #23/R est:250000-350000
£139535 $240000 €203721 Gloucester harbour (34x56cm-13x22in) s. panel prov.exhib. 4-Dec-3 Christie's, Rockefeller NY #31/R est:100000-150000
Works on paper
£2072 $3750 €3025 Landscape (20x28cm-8x11in) W/C. 16-Apr-4 Du Mouchelle, Detroit #2127/R est:1500-2500

TWARDZIK, Henryk (1900-) American
£377 $600 €550 Fall afternoon in Dogtown (51x61cm-20x24in) s.d.1936. 12-Sep-3 Skinner, Boston #500/R

TWELLS, Arthur H (1921-) British
£280 $482 €409 A Mayo bog (25x30cm-10x12in) s. 3-Dec-3 John Ross, Belfast #75
£280 $482 €409 Still water, Lough Fee, Connemara (20x30cm-8x12in) s. 3-Dec-3 John Ross, Belfast #177
£280 $482 €409 Flooded meadow, Donegal (25x30cm-10x12in) s. 3-Dec-3 John Ross, Belfast #180
£380 $669 €555 Sheep farmer under stormy skies (36x42cm-14x17in) s. board. 18-May-4 Bonhams, Knightsbridge #104/R
£600 $1116 €876 Feeding chickens, Donegal (50x71cm-20x28in) s. board. 3-Mar-4 John Ross, Belfast #132
£750 $1245 €1095 Salmon fishing, River Lennon, Donegal (50x71cm-20x28in) s. 1-Oct-3 John Ross, Belfast #255
£800 $1464 €1168 Ladywell Park, Co. West Meath (61x122cm-24x48in) s. 2-Jun-4 John Ross, Belfast #129

TWINING, Yvonne (1907-) American
£598 $950 €873 Winter landscape with farmhouse (41x51cm-16x20in) s. masonite double-sided. 13-Sep-3 Weschler, Washington #770/R

TWOMBLY, Cy (1928-) American
£5588 $9500 €8158 Leo Castelli Gallery announcement design (40x34cm-16x13in) s.i.d.1976 oil stick black white gelatin silver print. 21-Nov-3 Swann Galleries, New York #209/R est:8000-12000
£65000 $108550 €94900 Untitled (23x25cm-9x10in) oil col pencil exec c.1961-63 prov. 21-Oct-3 Sotheby's, London #379/R est:22000-25000
£113772 $190000 €166107 Untitled (70x88cm-28x35in) s.d.jan 1970 verso oil wax crayon prov. 13-Nov-3 Sotheby's, New York #229/R est:100000-150000
£173184 $310000 €252849 Untitled (76x102cm-30x40in) s.d.Feb 69 verso oil white crayon paper prov. 13-May-4 Sotheby's, New York #168/R est:220000-280000
£1452514 $2600000 €2120670 Untitled - Bolsena (201x240cm-79x94in) oil based house paint wax crayon lead pencil prov.exhib.lit. 12-May-4 Sotheby's, New York #16/R est:2200000-2800000
Prints
£1892 $3386 €2800 Natural history I (76x55cm-30x22in) s. num.5/98 offset lithograph. 4-May-4 Calmels Cohen, Paris #117/R est:3000-4000
£2206 $3750 €3221 Untitled (76x59cm-30x23in) init. col lithograph collotype. 31-Oct-3 Sotheby's, New York #800/R
£2365 $4470 €3500 Jeux olympiques de Sarajevo (82x57cm-32x22in) s.num.22/150 col etching. 21-Feb-4 Cornette de St.Cyr, Paris #139/R est:3500-4000
£3800 $6916 €5548 Untitled (70x87cm-28x34in) init.d.1971 num.43/100 verso col offset lithograph. 1-Jul-4 Sotheby's, London #356/R est:1200-1500
£8824 $15000 €12883 Roman notes (87x70cm-34x28in) s. offset lithograph. 31-Oct-3 Sotheby's, New York #799/R
£8889 $16000 €12978 From Roman notes (34x27cm-13x11in) col lithograph. 24-Apr-4 David Rago, Lambertville #557/R est:6000-8000
£10734 $19000 €15672 Roman notes III (87x70cm-34x28in) s.d.1970 num.48/100 col offset lithograph. 28-Apr-4 Christie's, Rockefeller NY #435/R est:10000-15000
£21469 $38000 €31345 Natural history part I mushrooms (76x56cm-30x22in) init.num.93/98 col lithograph collage set of ten. 28-Apr-4 Christie's, Rockefeller NY #436/R est:20000-30000
£24000 $41280 €35040 Roman notes (87x70cm-34x28in) s.d.1970 verso num.85/100 col offset lithograph set of 6. 4-Dec-3 Sotheby's, London #260/R est:18000-22000
£42373 $75000 €61865 Roman notes (87x70cm-34x28in) s.d.1970 num.85/100 col offset lithograph set of six. 28-Apr-4 Christie's, Rockefeller NY #434/R est:70000-90000
Sculpture
£179641 $300000 €262276 Rome (127x14x14cm-50x6x6in) s. st.sig. num.4/4 painted synthetic resin exec 1977 prov.lit. 11-Nov-3 Christie's, Rockefeller NY #60/R est:300000-400000
Works on paper
£6690 $11708 €9500 Study for woodland (30x36cm-12x14in) d.1965 pen. 16-Dec-3 Finarte Semenzato, Milan #291/R est:8800-9200
£18824 $32000 €27483 Leo Castelli Gallery (57x45cm-22x18in) s.d.Nov 30 1968 pencil. 21-Nov-3 Swann Galleries, New York #210/R est:12000-18000
£28000 $50960 €40880 Untitled (30x36cm-12x14in) s.d.57 pencil col pencil wax crayon prov. 5-Feb-4 Sotheby's, London #42/R est:30000-40000
£156425 $280000 €228381 14 Papers (58x57cm-23x22in) s.i.d.83 gouache W/C graphite felt pen two parts joined prov. 12-May-4 Christie's, Rockefeller NY #192/R est:100000-150000
£371258 $620000 €542037 Untitled - Roma (140x70cm-55x28in) s.d.1972 verso gouache crayon graphite prov.exhib. 11-Nov-3 Christie's, Rockefeller NY #36/R est:300000-400000
£778443 $1300000 €1136527 Untitled - Rome (135x150cm-53x59in) s.d.1961 lead pencil wax crayon oil house hold paint prov.exhib. 12-Nov-3 Sotheby's, New York #21/R est:1200000-1800000

TWOPENY, Susen (19th C) British
Works on paper
£360 $598 €526 Edinburgh (16x23cm-6x9in) s. W/C. 1-Oct-3 Sotheby's, Olympia #3/R

TWORKOV, Jack (1900-1982) American
£3593 $6000 €5246 Expansion and contraction II (67x198cm-26x78in) s.d.80 i.verso acrylic prov. 7-Oct-3 Sotheby's, New York #356 est:8000-12000
£26946 $45000 €39341 Figure P-H (140x69cm-55x27in) prov.exhib. 13-Nov-3 Sotheby's, New York #171/R est:20000-30000
£32934 $55000 €48084 Counters (232x103cm-91x41in) s.i.d.62 verso prov. 12-Nov-3 Christie's, Rockefeller NY #319/R est:30000-40000
£85890 $140000 €125399 Day's end (152x193cm-60x76in) s.i.d.58-9 verso prov.exhib.lit. 23-Sep-3 Christie's, Rockefeller NY #21/R est:30000-50000
Works on paper
£299 $500 €437 Untitled (43x35cm-17x14in) init.d.60 graphite prov. 11-Nov-3 Christie's, Rockefeller NY #178/R
£1647 $2750 €2405 Seated nude (63x48cm-25x19in) init.d.54 chl exhib. 7-Oct-3 Sotheby's, New York #347 est:800-1200

TYLEE, Marion E (1900-1980) New Zealander
£1264 $2060 €1845 Kakariki and kerereu (60x23cm-24x9in) s. board pair. 23-Sep-3 Peter Webb, Auckland #133/R (NZ.D 3500)

TYLER, Bayard Henry (1855-1931) American
£1129 $2100 €1648 A winter evening (50x40cm-20x16in) s. 5-Mar-4 Skinner, Boston #489/R est:800-1200
£1882 $3500 €2748 Spring landscape, Hudson River and palisades, blossoming tree (51x61cm-20x24in) s. 3-Mar-4 Alderfer's, Hatfield #367/R est:600-800

TYLER, J G (1855-1931) American
£3039 $5500 €4437 Moonlit seascape with schooner (76x64cm-30x25in) s. 3-Apr-4 Nadeau, Windsor #243/R est:4000-6000

TYLER, James Gale (1855-1931) American
£300 $555 €438 Sailing ships at sea (38x51cm-15x20in) s. 13-Feb-4 Keys, Aylsham #638
£503 $800 €734 Moonlight sail (26x35cm-10x14in) s. 12-Sep-3 Skinner, Boston #289/R
£652 $1050 €952 Sunset cruise (20x25cm-8x10in) s. board. 20-Aug-3 James Julia, Fairfield #516/R
£807 $1300 €1178 Moonlight sail (51x76cm-20x30in) s. 20-Aug-3 James Julia, Fairfield #515/R
£894 $1600 €1305 Shoreline seascape (56x76cm-22x30in) s. 16-May-4 CRN Auctions, Cambridge #25/R
£1061 $1900 €1549 Ship at sea, at night (76x64cm-30x25in) s. 16-May-4 CRN Auctions, Cambridge #24/R
£1129 $2100 €1648 Sailing off Greenwich (43x76cm-17x30in) s. 7-Mar-4 William Jenack, New York #81 est:3000-5000
£1145 $1900 €1672 Bound in - Clipper Ship at sea (56x46cm-22x18in) s. i.verso. 4-Oct-3 Neal Auction Company, New Orleans #387/R est:2500-3500
£1366 $2200 €1994 Seascape with tall ship (56x46cm-22x18in) s. prov. 20-Aug-3 James Julia, Fairfield #517/R est:2000-3000
£1620 $2900 €2365 Sailing ship at moonlight (41x30cm-16x12in) s. 11-Jan-4 William Jenack, New York #269 est:1000-1500
£1747 $2900 €2551 Rocky coastline with sailboat (48x61cm-19x24in) s. prov. 4-Oct-3 South Bay, Long Island #158
£1818 $3200 €2654 Portrait of a ship in moonlight (71x51cm-28x20in) s. 21-May-4 Pook & Pook, Downington #125/R est:3000-4000
£1868 $3400 €2727 Nina, Pinta, and Santa Maria (241x152cm-95x60in) s.d.1893 canvas on board. 19-Jun-4 Jackson's, Cedar Falls #16/R est:2000-3000
£2374 $3750 €3466 Brig passing a tug under nighttime sky (71x102cm-28x40in) s. 25-Jul-3 Eldred, East Dennis #438/R est:3000-4000
£2374 $4250 €3466 Running free in the moonlight (76x56cm-30x22in) s. 16-Mar-4 Bonhams & Butterfields, San Francisco #6159/R est:3000-5000
£2570 $4600 €4314 Moonlit seascape with ship and lighthouse (53x76cm-21x30in) s. 20-Mar-4 Pook & Pook, Downington #543/R est:2000-3000
£3073 $5500 €4487 Full sail (97x76cm-38x30in) s. 6-May-4 Shannon's, Milford #256/R est:2500-3500
£3552 $6500 €5186 Fishing vessels off a lighthouse by moonlight (51x76cm-20x30in) s. 3-Jun-4 Christie's, Rockefeller NY #716/R est:2000-3000
£39773 $70000 €58069 Yacht race (76x107cm-30x42in) s. indis.i.d.94 stretcher prov. 19-May-4 Sotheby's, New York #62/R est:70000-90000
Works on paper
£193 $350 €282 Three-masted ship at twilight (15x28cm-6x11in) s. 2-Apr-4 Eldred, East Dennis #678

TYLER, William R (1825-1896) American
£4190 $7500 €6117 Expansive river landscape with cows watering (56x97cm-22x38in) s. 14-May-4 Skinner, Boston #93/R est:4500-5500

TYNDALE, Thomas Nicholson (1858-1936) British
Works on paper
£260 $465 €380 Shepherd and his flock in a snowy landscape (16x25cm-6x10in) s. W/C. 25-May-4 Bonhams, Knightsbridge #217
£350 $546 €508 Lady before mediaeval cottage, summer blossom beyond (30x20cm-12x8in) s. W/C exec.c.1920. 22-Sep-2 Desmond Judd, Cranbrook #814
£400 $624 €580 Lady before mediaeval cottage, summer blossom beyond (30x20cm-12x8in) s. W/C exec.c.1920. 22-Sep-2 Desmond Judd, Cranbrook #813
£460 $837 €672 Old cottages in Shartfield, Frensham (22x32cm-9x13in) s. W/C. 29-Jun-4 Anderson & Garland, Newcastle #244
£650 $1118 €949 Sussex cottage (18x12cm-7x5in) s. pencil W/C. 3-Dec-3 Christie's, Kensington #83/R
£750 $1290 €1095 Little Comberton, Worcester (25x19cm-10x7in) s. W/C. 3-Dec-3 Christie's, Kensington #79/R

TYNDALE, Walter (1855-1943) British
Works on paper
£450 $806 €657 View of a Venetian canal (34x24cm-13x9in) s. W/C. 25-May-4 Bonhams, Knightsbridge #12/R

£1000 $1840 €1460 Gate of Souk el Trouk, Tunisia (25x35cm-10x14in) s. pencil W/C exhib. 25-Mar-4 Christie's, Kensington #63/R est:300-500
£2113 $3655 €3000 Peasants in Rome (35x60cm-14x24in) s. W/C card. 11-Dec-3 Christie's, Rome #1/R est:1000-1500

TYNDALL, Peter (20th C) Australian
£4959 $9174 €7240 Detail, a person looks at a work of art, someone looks at something (153x152cm-60x60in) s. i.d.1984 verso oil canvas insulated wire prov.exhib. 10-Mar-4 Deutscher-Menzies, Melbourne #137/R est:12000-16000 (A.D 12000)

TYNELL, Marta (1865-1930) Swedish
£538 $926 €785 Paris (11x19cm-4x7in) mono.d.1893 panel. 3-Dec-3 AB Stockholms Auktionsverk #2301/R (S.KR 7000)

TYRAHN, Georg (1860-1917) German
£542 $856 €780 Young girl by lake. s. board. 6-Sep-3 Schopman, Hamburg #707/R

TYSHLER, Aleksander (1898-1980) Russian
£70000 $119000 €102200 Theatre woman (75x75cm-30x30in) s.d.1971. 19-Nov-3 Sotheby's, London #231/R est:80000-120000
Works on paper
£3333 $6000 €4866 Portrait of a woman (56x43cm-22x17in) s.d.69 felt pen. 23-Apr-4 Sotheby's, New York #122/R est:6000-8000
£3333 $6000 €4866 Still life with flowers (66x50cm-26x20in) s.i.d.1963 s.i.verso mixed media. 23-Apr-4 Sotheby's, New York #123/R est:6000-8000

TYSON, Carroll (1878-1956) American
£3201 $5250 €4641 Shoreline with cliff (64x76cm-25x30in) s. 2-Jun-3 Grogan, Boston #634/R
£3395 $5500 €4923 Somes Sound, Maine (58x72cm-23x28in) prov. 8-Aug-3 Barridorf, Portland #180/R est:3000-5000
£4070 $7000 €5942 Somes Sound from Fernalde Point (74x91cm-29x36in) painted c.1925. 7-Dec-3 Treadway Gallery, Cincinnati #556/R est:3000-5000

TYSON, Keith (1969-) British
£8000 $13360 €11680 Can't think what to do so we'll do a portrait of Schumacher for you (152x121cm-60x48in) i.d.30th June 2003 prov. 22-Oct-3 Christie's, London #126/R est:8000-12000
Photographs
£8380 $15000 €12235 Studio wall drawing, the edge of things no 20 isometric chain (152x122cm-60x48in) s.d.2001 verso digital print acrylic paper prov. 14-May-4 Phillips, New York #328/R est:8000-12000
Works on paper
£13000 $23920 €18980 Studio wall drawing - lecture on catastrophe theory to a dead mouse (152x122cm-60x48in) s.i.d.16.01.2001 mixed media prov.exhib.lit. 24-Jun-4 Sotheby's, London #126/R est:8000-12000

TYSON, Rowell (1926-) British
£480 $768 €701 Landscape under a crescent moon (71x92cm-28x36in) s.d.1952. 16-Sep-3 Bonhams, Knightsbridge #25

TYSZBLAT, Michel (1936-) French
£733 $1349 €1100 Composition (130x97cm-51x38in) s. painted 1972. 11-Jun-4 Pierre Berge, Paris #42/R
£1544 $2732 €2300 Eh oui c'est encore moi (92x73cm-36x29in) s. 29-Apr-4 Claude Aguttes, Neuilly #165/R est:2500-2700

TYTGAT, Edgard (1879-1957) Belgian
£2365 $4162 €3500 Eric Wansart with puppets (40x60cm-16x24in) s. 24-May-4 Bernaerts, Antwerp #705/R est:3600-4000
£4333 $7930 €6500 La danseuse deprimee (50x61cm-20x24in) s.d.1945 i.verso. 7-Jun-4 Palais de Beaux Arts, Brussels #307/R est:7000-8700
£10490 $17832 €15000 Scenes de la vie du Christ (46x90cm-18x35in) s.d.1939 canvas laid down. 1-Dec-3 Palais de Beaux Arts, Brussels #320/R est:15000-20000
£11888 $20210 €17000 L'attente (81x65cm-32x26in) s.d.1941 s.i.verso exhib.lit. 1-Dec-3 Palais de Beaux Arts, Brussels #318/R est:17500-30000
£12587 $21650 €18000 L'enfant a l'oiseau (66x51cm-26x20in) s.i.d.1923 s.i.d.verso exhib.lit. 2-Dec-3 Sotheby's, Amsterdam #69/R est:20000-25000
£14583 $24354 €21000 Aveugle et printemps (66x82cm-26x32in) s.d.1924 exhib.lit. 21-Oct-3 Campo & Campo, Antwerp #296/R est:14000-20000
£15068 $25616 €22000 Vue de la Place Royale (74x93cm-29x37in) s. 10-Nov-3 Horta, Bruxelles #149/R
Works on paper
£417 $679 €600 Figure bleue. s. gouache. 23-Sep-3 Galerie Moderne, Brussels #833/R
£448 $829 €650 Projet de decor de theatre (22x30cm-9x12in) s.d.1954 Indian ink. 16-Feb-4 Horta, Bruxelles #292
£1449 $2377 €2000 La derniere toilette (30x42cm-12x17in) s.i.d.1951 ink. 27-May-3 Sotheby's, Amsterdam #475/R est:2000-3000
£2000 $3660 €3000 Projet pour Noel sur la place (34x45cm-13x18in) W/C. 7-Jun-4 Palais de Beaux Arts, Brussels #309/R est:2000-3000

TYTGAT, Louis (1841-1918) Belgian
£350 $584 €500 Homme barbu lisant un journal (56x47cm-22x19in) s.d.1875. 7-Oct-3 Palais de Beaux Arts, Brussels #590

TZARA, Tristan (1896-1963) French
Prints
£20333 $36397 €30500 Untitled. engraving album exec.1918. 15-May-4 Renaud, Paris #390/R

TZEITLIN, G I (1911-) Russian
£1522 $2800 €2222 Playing chess (50x40cm-20x16in) painted 1949. 27-Mar-4 Shishkin Gallery, Moscow #68/R est:5000-6000

TZYPLAKOV, V G (1915-1986) Russian
£1111 $2000 €1622 Oka River (35x50cm-14x20in) oil on plywood. 24-Apr-4 Shishkin Gallery, Moscow #43/R est:2000-3000

UBAC, Raoul (1910-1985) Belgian
£5102 $9133 €7500 Foret apres la pluie II (24x43cm-9x17in) s. i.d.1947 verso exhib. 21-Mar-4 Calmels Cohen, Paris #32/R est:8000-10000
Sculpture
£2267 $4080 €3400 Untitled (12x5cm-5x2in) slate double-sided prov.lit. 25-Apr-4 Versailles Encheres #90 est:2000-3000
Works on paper
£1611 $2980 €2400 Composition (45x62cm-18x24in) s. W/C Indian ink. 13-Mar-4 De Vuyst, Lokeren #327/R est:2200-3000
£1867 $3397 €2800 Bouquet of tulips (75x55cm-30x22in) mono.d.44 ink prov. 30-Jun-4 Calmels Cohen, Paris #51/R est:3000-4000
£3867 $7076 €5800 Automne (48x64cm-19x25in) mono. gouache exec. 1951. 7-Jun-4 Palais de Beaux Arts, Brussels #198/R est:3500-4500
£5000 $9050 €7300 Composition (51x66cm-20x26in) s.d.1956 gouache. 1-Apr-4 Christie's, Kensington #210/R est:2000-3000

UBAGHS, Jean (1852-?) Belgian
£13000 $21710 €18980 Oriental woman playing the mandolin (152x100cm-60x39in) s. 14-Oct-3 Sotheby's, London #55/R est:8000-12000

UBEDA, Augustin (1925-) Spanish
£764 $1245 €1100 Grand cadeau (27x36cm-11x14in) s. s.i.verso. 23-Sep-3 Durán, Madrid #153/R
£1338 $2315 €1900 Femme au coq (42x50cm-17x20in) s. 13-Dec-3 Touati, Paris #172/R est:1200
£1399 $2406 €2000 Composition (54x65cm-21x26in) s. 3-Dec-3 Tajan, Paris #403 est:900-1200
£1399 $2406 €2000 Composition au poisson (54x65cm-21x26in) s. 3-Dec-3 Tajan, Paris #404 est:900-1200
£1412 $2500 €2062 Modernist view of children's toys (64x79cm-25x31in) s. 1-May-4 Thomaston Place, Thomaston #819/R
£1620 $2802 €2300 Fruits (54x65cm-21x26in) s. prov. 13-Dec-3 Touati, Paris #174/R est:1800-2000
£1901 $3289 €2700 Le bougeoir (54x65cm-21x26in) s. 13-Dec-3 Touati, Paris #171/R est:2200
£2007 $3472 €2850 Nature morte fond rouge (54x65cm-21x26in) s. prov. 13-Dec-3 Touati, Paris #173/R est:2000-2500
£2230 $3924 €3300 Still life in blue (49x64cm-19x25in) s. painted c.1955. 18-May-4 Segre, Madrid #106/R est:2500
£2292 $3781 €3300 Deaf (54x65cm-21x26in) s. s.i.verso. 2-Jul-3 Ansorena, Madrid #883/R
£2533 $4661 €3800 Composition (54x66cm-21x26in) s. prov. 8-Jun-4 Artcurial Briest, Paris #169/R est:3000-4000
£2684 $4993 €4000 Nature morte aux fruits (50x65cm-20x26in) s. prov. 2-Mar-4 Artcurial Briest, Paris #235 est:1400-1800
£2778 $4417 €4000 Un padrino (54x47cm-21x19in) s. s.i.verso. 29-Apr-3 Durán, Madrid #131/R est:4000
£2837 $4596 €4000 Los reyes (50x65cm-20x26in) s. 20-May-3 Ansorena, Madrid #316/R est:3000
£3288 $5589 €4800 Taureaux dans la ville (60x81cm-24x32in) s. 9-Nov-3 Eric Pillon, Calais #271/R
£3873 $6197 €5500 Oriental woman (60x81cm-24x32in) s. painted c.1958. 16-Sep-3 Segre, Madrid #115/R
£4755 $7941 €6800 Retrato de mujer con abanico (64x81cm-25x32in) s. s.verso prov.exhib. 24-Jun-3 Segre, Madrid #164/R est:6800
£5172 $9310 €7500 Still life with candle holder (81x100cm-32x39in) s. 26-Jan-4 Ansorena, Madrid #902/R est:6500
Works on paper
£458 $801 €650 Lovers (29x19cm-11x7in) s. gouache. 16-Dec-3 Segre, Madrid #255/R

UBEDA, Rafael (1932-) Spanish
£2329 $3959 €3400 Blue violin player (50x73cm-20x29in) s.d.1977 sid.verso. 4-Nov-3 Ansorena, Madrid #905/R est:3000

UBELESSKI, Alexandre (1649-1718) French
Works on paper
£1761 $3081 €2500 Un berger jouant de la flute sur le bord d'une fleuve (11x18cm-4x7in) pen grey ink wash prov. 17-Dec-3 Christie's, Paris #37/R est:1000-1500

UBERFELDT, Jan Braet van (1807-1894) Dutch
£1944 $3072 €2800 Woman grape picker (44x36cm-17x14in) s.d.1860 lit. 19-Sep-3 Schloss Ahlden, Ahlden #1472/R est:2800

UBERTALLI, Romolo (1871-1928) Italian
£2553 $4264 €3600 Landscape with figures (45x75cm-18x30in) s. 20-Oct-3 Sant Agostino, Torino #262/R est:250-3500

UBERTI, Dino (1885-1949) Italian
£400 $736 €600 Bench in the park (39x29cm-15x11in) s.d.1948 board. 14-Jun-4 Sant Agostino, Torino #151/R
£952 $1705 €1400 Roses (60x50cm-24x20in) s.d.1936 board. 22-Mar-4 Sant Agostino, Torino #204/R

UCHERMANN, Karl (1855-1940) Norwegian

£691	$1147	€1002	Cottage in Telemark (42x62cm-17x24in) s. 16-Jun-3 Blomqvist, Lysaker #1250/R (N.KR 8000)
£2402	$4299	€3507	Woman holding dog (59x47cm-23x19in) s. 22-Mar-4 Blomqvist, Oslo #349/R est:20000-25000 (N.KR 30000)
£3262	$5708	€4763	Puppy and sparrow (40x32cm-16x13in) s. 16-Dec-3 Grev Wedels Plass, Oslo #376/R est:20000 (N.KR 38000)
£20068	$33514	€29299	Cupboard love - bird and puppy by food bowl (46x54cm-18x21in) s.d.04. 13-Oct-3 Blomqvist, Oslo #297/R est:20000-25000 (N.KR 235000)

UCLES, Josep (1952-) Spanish

£590	$974	€850	Mountain dreams (146x114cm-57x45in) s.d.1988 s.i.d.verso. 2-Jul-3 Ansorena, Madrid #916/R

UDALTSOVA, Nadezhda (1886-1961) Russian

£9091	$15182	€13000	Self portrait (80x64cm-31x25in) s. 9-Oct-3 Michael Zeller, Lindau #780 est:3000
£25000	$42500	€36500	Still life summer (89x99cm-35x39in) s.d.1953 verso. 19-Nov-3 Sotheby's, London #206/R est:25000-35000
Works on paper			
£3198	$5500	€4669	Composition (30x23cm-12x9in) s. gouache pencil exec.c.1916. 7-Dec-3 Treadway Gallery, Cincinnati #644/R est:6000-8000

UDEN, Lucas van (1595-1672) Flemish

£5286	$8987	€7718	Woodland hunt (29x42cm-11x17in) s. bears i. panel. 5-Nov-3 Dobiaschofsky, Bern #1011/R est:8000 (S.FR 12000)
£5369	$9879	€8000	Wooded river landscape with shepherd and shepherdess and flock (59x84cm-23x33in) 24-Mar-4 Dorotheum, Vienna #367/R est:8000-12000
£9655	$16028	€14000	Flemish river landscape with view of town (41x59cm-16x23in) panel. 1-Oct-3 Dorotheum, Vienna #97/R est:12000-16000
£42000	$72660	€61320	Winter landscape with hunters (41x65cm-16x26in) s. prov.exhib. 11-Dec-3 Sotheby's, London #49/R est:20000-30000

UDEN, Lucas van (attrib) (1595-1672) Flemish

£1058	$2000	€1545	Flemish landscape with figures (36x48cm-14x19in) panel. 21-Feb-4 Jeffery Burchard, Florida #28/R
Works on paper			
£650	$1170	€949	Landscape with trees along a path and church in the distance (8x45cm-3x18in) bears i.verso black chk prov. 20-Apr-4 Sotheby's, Olympia #86/R

UDVARDY, Flora N (20th C) Hungarian

£409	$733	€597	Still life with fruit (58x73cm-23x29in) s. 12-May-4 Dobiaschofsky, Bern #1035/R (S.FR 950)

UECKER, Gunther (1930-) German

£2927	$4800	€4273	Anonymous (29x21cm-11x8in) s.d.75 three acrylic one pencil ultraphan foil four prov.lit. 28-May-3 Sotheby's, Amsterdam #36/R est:5000-7000
£23077	$39231	€33000	Moving field II (87x87cm-34x34in) s.d.64 verso oil nails panel exhib. 27-Nov-3 Lempertz, Koln #494/R est:30000
Sculpture			
£1007	$1652	€1400	Nail (178cm-70in) st.sig. steel. 4-Jun-3 Ketterer, Hamburg #934/R
£1007	$1802	€1500	Nail (178cm-70in) st.sig. steel. 25-May-4 Dorotheum, Vienna #381/R est:1500-2000
£2400	$4416	€3600	Aggressive object (30x30cm-12x12in) s.d.75 nails graphite canvas on panel one of 30. 12-Jun-4 Villa Grisebach, Berlin #853/R est:1200-1500
£2800	$5124	€4200	Untitled (99x32x14cm-39x13x6in) s.i.d.mai 1976 s.i. verso nails pencil gauze panel. 4-Jun-4 Lempertz, Koln #507/R est:3000-4000
£4895	$8420	€7000	Current (70x50cm-28x20in) s.i.d.94 nails chipboard. 4-Dec-3 Van Ham, Cologne #522/R est:5500
£7746	$13401	€11000	Field (40x30cm-16x12in) s.i.d.97 verso acrylic on nails prov. 13-Dec-3 Lempertz, Koln #363/R est:7000
£8000	$14720	€12000	Bird (39x32x32cm-15x13x13in) s.d.63 nails canvas on wood silver bronze metal prov.exhib.lit. 8-Jun-4 Sotheby's, Amsterdam #95/R est:6000-8000
£9146	$15000	€13353	Gegenlaufige diagonalreihung - counter rotating diagonally arranged (22x21x5cm-9x8x2in) s.i.d.65 verso nails oil canvas on wood prov.exhib.lit. 28-May-3 Sotheby's, Amsterdam #27/R est:10000-12000
£9790	$16839	€14000	Nagelrelief (30x30x10cm-12x12x4in) s.i.d.1968 verso nails canvas on wood prov.exhib.lit. 2-Dec-3 Sotheby's, Amsterdam #163/R est:10000-15000
£11333	$20287	€17000	Nail cushion (38x38x4cm-15x15x2in) oil nail relief canvas on panel prov. 15-May-4 Van Ham, Cologne #982/R est:2000
£18182	$31273	€26000	Greenbox III (82x82x10cm-32x32x4in) s.i. nails spray lacquer plywood on wood-box with perspex prov. 5-Dec-3 Ketterer, Munich #150/R est:20000-30000
£38462	$66154	€55000	Hommage a fontana III - gray phantom (175x117x10cm-69x46x4in) s.i.d.62 verso nails canvas on wood silverpaint lighting system. 2-Dec-3 Sotheby's, Amsterdam #165/R est:45000-65000
Works on paper			
£667	$1220	€1000	Untitled (65x50cm-26x20in) s.d.62 W/C on print. 4-Jun-4 Lempertz, Koln #603/R
£800	$1480	€1168	Untitled construction (16x31cm-6x12in) mixed media. 13-Jul-4 Bonhams, Knightsbridge #141
£1067	$1952	€1600	Untitled (86x61cm-34x24in) s.d.95 s.d.1995 stretcher ash glue graphite board. 4-Jun-4 Lempertz, Koln #502/R est:1800
£1067	$1963	€1600	Untitled (22x19cm-9x7in) s.d. Indian ink brush. 11-Jun-4 Hauswedell & Nolte, Hamburg #1572/R est:1200
£1127	$1972	€1600	Leipziger blatter (86x61cm-34x24in) s. collage chl prov. 18-Dec-3 Cornette de St.Cyr, Paris #46/R est:1200-1500
£1748	$2972	€2500	Bed rails (78x106cm-31x42in) s.i.d.1970 pencil prov. 27-Nov-3 Lempertz, Koln #497/R est:4000-4500
£2561	$4200	€3739	New York (17x12cm-7x5in) s.i.d.65 verso nail oil panel prov. 28-May-3 Sotheby's, Amsterdam #31/R est:5000-7000
£6643	$11294	€9500	Disc (69cm-27in circular) s.i.d.89 verso nails ash chk glue cotton on canvas lit. 27-Nov-3 Lempertz, Koln #495/R est:10000
£37931	$63345	€55000	Field (200x200cm-79x79in) s.i.d.1995 verso nails white latex on canvas. 13-Nov-3 Neumeister, Munich #649/R est:50000-70000

UELLIGER, Karl (1920-1993) Swiss

£538	$899	€785	First day in February (65x51cm-26x20in) s.i.d.Februar 73 acrylic. 24-Oct-3 Hans Widmer, St Gallen #69/R (S.FR 1200)
£897	$1498	€1310	Thought collector (70x86cm-28x34in) i.d.78 acrylic board. 24-Oct-3 Hans Widmer, St Gallen #4/R est:1800-3500 (S.FR 2000)
£1390	$2322	€2029	Cloud sun singer (36x31cm-14x12in) mono.i. bears d. acrylic scratch window glass. 24-Oct-3 Hans Widmer, St Gallen #71/R est:1500-3500 (S.FR 3100)

UFER, Walter (1876-1936) American

£7065	$13000	€10315	Spring blossoms (27x30cm-11x12in) s. 8-Jun-4 Bonhams & Butterfields, San Francisco #4127/R est:7000-10000
£11176	$19000	€16317	Taos Canyon, first snow (12x16cm-5x6in) s. canvas on canvas prov. 18-Nov-3 John Moran, Pasadena #117d est:15000-20000
£14706	$27500	€21471	New Mexican well (25x30cm-10x12in) s. s.i.verso canvas on board prov. 24-Jul-4 Coeur d'Alene, Hayden #238/R est:10000-20000
£17663	$32500	€25788	Indian boy in a cradle (35x27cm-14x11in) s. canvasboard prov. 8-Jun-4 Bonhams & Butterfields, San Francisco #4125/R est:25000-30000
Works on paper			
£932	$1500	€1351	Vanity Fair 1911 the Armour Calendar (56x36cm-22x14in) gouache. 22-Aug-3 Altermann Galleries, Santa Fe #191

UGALDE, Juan (1958-) Spanish

£458	$732	€650	Dusk (20x15cm-8x6in) s.d.1995 oil collage paper. 16-Sep-3 Segre, Madrid #248/R
£2162	$3805	€3200	Scene II (99x69cm-39x27in) s.d.1991 oil photograph paper. 18-May-4 Segre, Madrid #155/R est:3000
£2267	$4103	€3400	Rocks (54x60cm-21x24in) s.d.1998 verso oil collage prov.exhib. 30-Mar-4 Segre, Madrid #164/R est:1800

UGHI, Ludovico (18th C) Italian

Prints			
£6667	$12133	€10000	Plan of Venice (134x180cm-53x71in) eau forte. 4-Jul-4 Finarte, Venice #4/R est:4000-5000

UGLOW, Alan (20th C) ?

£389	$700	€568	Untitled, no 9 (30x22cm-12x9in) oil chk prov. 24-Apr-4 David Rago, Lambertville #116/R

UGYUK, Charlie (1931-) North American

Sculpture			
£1351	$2297	€1972	Falcon perched on a rock (36cm-14in) s. mottled green soapstone. 3-Nov-3 Waddingtons, Toronto #392/R est:3000-5000 (C.D 3000)
£2027	$3446	€2959	Falcon flying to its nest of eggs (29cm-11in) s. mottled dark soapstone. 3-Nov-3 Waddingtons, Toronto #396/R est:5000-7000 (C.D 4500)
£2703	$4595	€3946	Falcon perched on a rock (43cm-17in) s. marbled dark green serpentine. 3-Nov-3 Waddingtons, Toronto #391/R est:5000-7000 (C.D 6000)
£4054	$6892	€5919	Falcon holding a lemming, while another lemming peers out of it's burrow (51cm-20in) mottled green soapstone. 3-Nov-3 Waddingtons, Toronto #388/R est:7000-9000 (C.D 9000)
£4054	$6892	€5919	Devil with tusks holding a worm creature (48cm-19in) s. mottled green soapstone. 3-Nov-3 Waddingtons, Toronto #395/R est:5000-7000 (C.D 9000)

UHDE, Fritz von (1848-1911) German

£2416	$4518	€3600	Dutch woman (30x23cm-12x9in) s.d.1882 prov. 28-Feb-4 Bolland & Marotz, Bremen #297/R est:2200
£3241	$5413	€4700	Girl with pram in garden (26x21cm-10x8in) bears sig. canvas on board prov. 15-Nov-3 Lempertz, Koln #1708/R est:3000
£4138	$6910	€6000	The walk (24x41cm-9x16in) s. 15-Nov-3 Lempertz, Koln #1709/R est:5000
£8392	$14266	€12000	Girl reading in garden (64x54cm-25x21in) s. board on panel. 29-Nov-3 Villa Grisebach, Berlin #118/R est:12000-15000
£10667	$19413	€16000	Difficult journey (37x39cm-15x15in) s. board. 30-Jun-4 Neumeister, Munich #715/R est:1800
£35000	$63700	€51100	Shepherdess on Dachau heath (68x89cm-27x35in) s. prov.exhib.lit. 15-Jun-4 Sotheby's, London #34/R est:15000-20000
£48000	$87360	€70080	Dutch seamstresses in the sewing room (60x48cm-24x19in) s. prov.exhib.lit. 15-Jun-4 Sotheby's, London #33/R est:20000-30000

UHL, Emil (1864-?) Belgian

£845	$1352	€1200	Oriental bazar (30x49cm-12x19in) s. lit. 19-Sep-3 Karlheinz Kaupp, Staufen #1978/R
£2333	$4223	€3500	Street scene in Cairo (30x49cm-12x19in) s. panel. 1-Apr-4 Van Ham, Cologne #1673 est:3600

UHLE, Albert Bernard (1847-1930) American

£5866	$10500	€8564	Portrait of Abraham Lincoln (81x66cm-32x26in) s. prov. 20-Mar-4 Selkirks, St. Louis #150/R est:6000-8000

UHLIG, Max (1937-) German

£521	$870	€750	Untitled (21x30cm-8x12in) s.d. 24-Oct-3 Ketterer, Hamburg #1117/R
£600	$1104	€900	Landscape (29x65cm-11x26in) s.d.73 cardboard. 12-Jun-4 Villa Grisebach, Berlin #856/R
£2133	$3840	€3200	Landscape formations (63x202cm-25x80in) s.d. verso. 24-Apr-4 Dr Lehr, Berlin #476/R est:4000
£2267	$4057	€3400	Mont Ventoux (120x180cm-47x71in) s.i.d.April 1992 verso. 15-May-4 Van Ham, Cologne #993/R est:5000
£2378	$4042	€3400	Bush (100x151cm-39x59in) s.d.77 s.i.d. verso cotton. 27-Nov-3 Lempertz, Koln #500/R est:4500
Works on paper			
£333	$600	€500	Untitled - landscape formations (24x74cm-9x29in) s.d. W/C. 24-Apr-4 Dr Lehr, Berlin #477/R
£400	$716	€600	Landscape formation (28x72cm-11x28in) s.d.26.VII.88 W/C. 15-May-4 Bassenge, Berlin #7162/R

£451 $754 €650 Untitled - landscape formation (30x70cm-12x28in) s.d.17.VIII.78 W/C. 25-Oct-3 Dr Lehr, Berlin #514
£467 $854 €700 Untitled - landscape (31x79cm-12x31in) s.d.83 W/C. 4-Jun-4 Lempertz, Koln #508/R
£467 $854 €700 Untitled - landscape (35x75cm-14x30in) s.d.86 W/C. 4-Jun-4 Lempertz, Koln #509/R
£559 $951 €800 Untitled - figure (76x50cm-30x20in) s.d.84 W/C. 27-Nov-3 Lempertz, Koln #503/R

UHLIK, Eduard (1865-1952) Russian
£800 $1440 €1200 Durnstein (50x62cm-20x24in) s. board. 21-Apr-4 Dorotheum, Vienna #19/R

UHLMAN, Fred (1901-1985) British
£700 $1204 €1022 Still life with Greek vase (28x40cm-11x16in) s. board prov. 3-Dec-3 Christie's, Kensington #709/R
£850 $1564 €1275 Winter landscape (76x107cm-30x42in) s.d.1959. 23-Jun-4 Byrne's, Chester #644/R
£900 $1638 €1314 Welsh landscape (61x91cm-24x36in) s. 1-Jul-4 Christie's, Kensington #320/R
£950 $1672 €1387 Cottages and red sky (59x90cm-23x35in) s. painted c.1970 prov. 19-May-4 Sotheby's, Olympia #240/R
£1000 $1760 €1460 Still life with Greek figures (31x43cm-12x17in) s. board painted c.1956 prov. 19-May-4 Sotheby's, Olympia #253/R est:1000-1500
£1100 $1870 €1606 Red church (48x58cm-19x23in) s. 1-Dec-3 Bonhams, Bath #42/R est:600-800
£1200 $2220 €1752 Winter (25x30cm-10x12in) s. board. 11-Feb-4 Sotheby's, Olympia #214/R est:1200-1800
£1300 $2301 €1898 Early snow (60x90cm-24x35in) s.d.58. 27-Apr-4 Bonhams, Knightsbridge #38/R est:1200-1800
£1400 $2408 €2044 Coastal landscape with farm (24x35cm-9x14in) s.d.35 board. 2-Dec-3 Bonhams, New Bond Street #145/R est:800-1200
£1500 $2385 €2190 Lighthouse (44x53cm-17x21in) board prov. 10-Sep-3 Sotheby's, Olympia #244/R est:1500-2000
£1500 $2580 €2190 Night scene (39x49cm-15x19in) s. board exhib. 2-Dec-3 Bonhams, New Bond Street #144/R est:1000-1500
£1600 $2816 €2336 Sky over cottages (59x90cm-23x35in) s. painted c.1970 prov. 19-May-4 Sotheby's, Olympia #241/R est:800-1200
£2200 $3740 €3212 Sicily islands (28x41cm-11x16in) board prov. 26-Nov-3 Sotheby's, Olympia #129/R est:2000-3000
£4800 $8160 €7008 New York (61x91cm-24x36in) s.d.59. 26-Nov-3 Sotheby's, Olympia #101/R est:5000-7000

UHLMANN, Hans (1900-1975) German
Sculpture
£3873 $6701 €5500 Female figures (27cm-11in) s. brown pat.bronze Cast.HNoack Berlin. 13-Dec-3 Lempertz, Koln #364/R est:5000
Works on paper
£467 $835 €700 Untitled (48x19cm-19x7in) s.d. Indian ink W/C. 15-May-4 Bassenge, Berlin #7163/R
£530 $864 €800 Seated female nude (43x34cm-17x13in) s.d.52 Indian ink. 31-Jan-3 Altus, Berlin #730/R
£629 $1070 €900 Untitled (51x37cm-20x15in) s.d.49 gouache. 29-Nov-3 Villa Grisebach, Berlin #929/R est:1100-1200
£2533 $4661 €3800 Untitled (148x99cm-58x39in) s.d.1958 chk. 12-Jun-4 Villa Grisebach, Berlin #342/R est:4000-6000

UHRDIN, Sam (1886-1964) Swedish
£500 $860 €730 Two sisters in national costume (92x72cm-36x28in) s.d.1939. 7-Dec-3 Uppsala Auktionskammare, Uppsala #172/R (S.KR 6500)
£597 $1033 €872 Reading in the light of the open fire (73x92cm-29x36in) s.d.59. 15-Dec-3 Lilla Bukowskis, Stockholm #677 (S.KR 7600)
£620 $1036 €905 Interior scene with young woman by open fire (80x64cm-31x25in) s.d.40. 12-Oct-3 Uppsala Auktionskammare, Uppsala #125 (S.KR 8000)
£739 $1323 €1079 Lace-making by the open fire (73x92cm-29x36in) s.d.59. 26-May-4 AB Stockholms Auktionsverk #2307/R (S.KR 10000)

UHRE, Arnt (1954-) Danish
£271 $486 €396 Composition with reclining woman (104x134cm-41x53in) s.d.89. 10-May-4 Rasmussen, Vejle #761/R (D.KR 3000)

UHRY, Ghislain (1932-) ?
£369 $661 €550 Composition (73x60cm-29x24in) s.d.1955. 27-May-4 Christie's, Paris #141/R

UHTHOFF, Ina D D (1889-1971) Canadian
£260 $476 €380 Rocky Mountain tops (35x51cm-14x20in) s. board prov. 1-Jun-4 Hodgins, Calgary #165/R (C.D 650)

UITZ, Bela (1887-1972) Hungarian
Works on paper
£1054 $1908 €1539 Picking fruit (33x47cm-13x19in) ink. 16-Apr-4 Mu Terem Galeria, Budapest #11/R (H.F 400000)
£2871 $4967 €4192 Young girl (45x28cm-18x11in) Indian ink. 12-Dec-3 Kieselbach, Budapest #174/R (H.F 1100000)

UJVARY, Ignac (1880-1927) Hungarian
£1000 $1790 €1460 Country farm (60x70cm-24x28in) s. board. 18-Mar-4 Christie's, Kensington #514/R est:1000-1500
£11000 $20020 €16060 The harvesters (101x174cm-40x69in) s. prov.exhib. 15-Jun-4 Sotheby's, London #46/R est:8000-12000

ULFIG, Willi (1910-) German
Works on paper
£556 $928 €800 Blossom (48x66cm-19x26in) s.d. W/C. 24-Oct-3 Ketterer, Hamburg #1118/R

ULFT, Jacob van der (1627-1689) Dutch
Works on paper
£1007 $1852 €1500 Caprice architectural (14x19cm-6x7in) pen wash. 24-Mar-4 Claude Boisgirard, Paris #39/R est:1500-1800
£1622 $2854 €2400 View of San Stefano Rotondo, Rome (12x21cm-5x8in) pen brown ink wash black chk exhib. 19-May-4 Sotheby's, Amsterdam #108/R est:3000-4000
£2432 $4281 €3600 Roman ruin (13x23cm-5x9in) pen brown ink wash black chk prov.exhib.lit. 19-May-4 Sotheby's, Amsterdam #109/R est:4500-6000
£2600 $4498 €3796 Extensive river landscape with figures. Landscape with castle on a hill (17x17cm-7x7in) s.d.1686 black chk pen brown ink wash inscribed circles pair. 12-Dec-3 Christie's, Kensington #523/R est:1500-2000

ULFT, Jacob van der (attrib) (1627-1689) Dutch
Works on paper
£417 $679 €600 St Peter's cathedral (12x20cm-5x8in) brush over chk. 25-Sep-3 Dr Fritz Nagel, Stuttgart #1174/R

ULIBARRI GARCIA, Blanca de (1946-) Spanish
£739 $1279 €1050 John Paul II (33x91cm-13x36in) s.d.2003. 15-Dec-3 Ansorena, Madrid #356/R

ULISSE (1957-) Italian
£302 $559 €450 Nedlewomen (40x60cm-16x24in) s. board painted 1999. 13-Mar-4 Meeting Art, Vercelli #201
£467 $859 €700 Landscape with bridge (70x50cm-28x20in) s. s.i.verso board painted 2002. 12-Jun-4 Meeting Art, Vercelli #577/R
£470 $869 €700 Chess victory (70x50cm-28x20in) s. i.verso board. 13-Mar-4 Meeting Art, Vercelli #504

ULLBERG, Lloyd (1904-1996) American
Photographs
£1389 $2500 €2028 Man in a top hat (25x20cm-10x8in) gelatin silver print lit. 22-Apr-4 Phillips, New York #43/R est:3000-5000

ULLIK, Hugo (1838-1881) Czechoslovakian
£1094 $1817 €1597 Stones at water (32x51cm-13x20in) canvas on board. 4-Oct-3 Dorotheum, Prague #9/R est:50000-80000 (C.KR 50000)
£3913 $7278 €5713 Country building (43x56cm-17x22in) s.d.1868. 6-Mar-4 Dorotheum, Prague #37/R est:80000-120000 (C.KR 190000)

ULLMAN, Josef (1870-1922) Czechoslovakian
£569 $945 €831 Village under Brdy Mountains (14x24cm-6x9in) s. board. 4-Oct-3 Dorotheum, Prague #69/R est:8000-12000 (C.KR 26000)
£832 $1381 €1215 Summer landscape with river (50x65cm-20x26in) s.d.1920 board. 4-Oct-3 Dorotheum, Prague #60/R est:26000-40000 (C.KR 38000)
£875 $1453 €1278 Harvest (49x68cm-19x27in) s.d.1920 board. 4-Oct-3 Dorotheum, Prague #59/R est:26000-40000 (C.KR 40000)

ULLMAN, Micha (1939-) Israeli
Sculpture
£2235 $4000 €3263 Sand book (10x37x25cm-4x15x10in) init.num.6/8 steel sand. 18-Mar-4 Sotheby's, New York #46/R est:4000-6000

ULLMANN, Jozef (1833-1922) Hungarian
£679 $1215 €991 Landscape with river (48x59cm-19x23in) s. 10-May-4 Rasmussen, Vejle #463/R (D.KR 7500)

ULLMANN, Robert (1903-1966) Austrian
Sculpture
£2027 $3831 €3000 Nu assis (53cm-21in) s.d.1940 brown Meissen biscuit. 17-Feb-4 Vanderkindere, Brussels #164 est:3000-4000

ULLMANN, Rudolf Franz (1889-1973) Austrian
£316 $557 €474 Alpine landscape (47x68cm-19x27in) s. 22-May-4 Dorotheum, Prague #32/R est:15000-23000 (C.KR 15000)

ULLMANN, T (20th C) Austrian?
Sculpture
£967 $1750 €1412 Figure of native (43cm-17in) bronze. 16-Apr-4 Du Mouchelle, Detroit #2110/R est:2500-3000

ULLMANN, Theodore (?) ?
Sculpture
£1165 $1980 €1700 Pilote de courses (41x12x12cm-16x5x5in) s. black pat bronze sold with base. 5-Nov-3 Tajan, Paris #20/R

ULLOA BURGOS (20th C) Venezuelan?
£581 $970 €848 Seascape (50x60cm-20x24in) s. 19-Oct-3 Subastas Odalys, Caracas #95/R

ULLOA, Alberto (20th C) Venezuelan?
£363 $625 €530 Peasant man (50x40cm-20x16in) s. acrylic painted 1999. 7-Dec-3 Subastas Odalys, Caracas #44/R

£883 $1440 €1289 Cow (40x50cm-16x20in) s. acrylic painted 1999. 28-Sep-3 Subastas Odalys, Caracas #19/R

ULLULAQ, Judas (1937-1998) North American
Sculpture
£2703 $4595 €3946 Shaman holding a spirit (36cm-14in) s. marbled dark green soapstone antler. 3-Nov-3 Waddingtons, Toronto #399/R est:2500-3000 (C.D 6000)
£6306 $10721 €9207 Dancing and defecating musk ox with horns (46cm-18in) marbled dark green soapstone. 3-Nov-3 Waddingtons, Toronto #401/R est:12000-16000 (C.D 14000)
£6306 $10721 €9207 Inuit skull collector with teeth, spear, knife and rope (48cm-19in) s. mottled dark soapstone sinew. 3-Nov-3 Waddingtons, Toronto #403/R est:8000-12000 (C.D 14000)

ULNITZ, E C (1856-1933) Danish
£541 $849 €790 Still life of pink roses and lilacs (45x38cm-18x15in) s.d.1904. 30-Aug-3 Rasmussen, Havnen #2284 (D.KR 5800)

ULNITZ, Emil C (1856-1933) Danish
£1000 $1850 €1460 Summer flowers in a grey vase on polished table (32x24cm-13x9in) s.d1919. 14-Jul-4 Christie's, Kensington #1192/R est:1000-1500

ULRICH, Hans Caspar (1880-1950) Swiss
£776 $1389 €1133 Mountains (65x75cm-26x30in) i.d.1907 verso. 12-May-4 Dobiaschofsky, Bern #1036/R (S.FR 1800)

ULRICH, Hermann (1904-1961) Austrian
Works on paper
£379 $694 €550 Attersee (66x74cm-26x29in) s.d.17.7.47 gouache. 27-Jan-4 Dorotheum, Vienna #125/R

ULRICH, Johann (attrib) (1798-1877) Swiss
£433 $775 €632 Woodland study (48x69cm-19x27in) canvas on panel. 22-Mar-4 Philippe Schuler, Zurich #4364 (S.FR 1000)

ULRICH, Kjell (1942-) Danish
£271 $500 €396 Composition (62x52cm-24x20in) s. 15-Mar-4 Rasmussen, Vejle #618 (D.KR 3000)

ULRICH, Wilhelm (1905-1977) Austrian
Works on paper
£268 $494 €400 Ober-Plank am Kamp (47x65cm-19x26in) s.i.d.65 W/C. 26-Mar-4 Dorotheum, Vienna #353
£470 $864 €700 Vienna from Nussberg (55x76cm-22x30in) s.i.d.1968 W/C. 26-Mar-4 Dorotheum, Vienna #323/R

ULRICHS, Timm (1940-) German
Sculpture
£3333 $6133 €5000 Chair with shadow (90cm-35in) lacquered wood exec. 1969-80. 12-Jun-4 Villa Grisebach, Berlin #437/R est:5000-7000

ULTVEDT, Per Olof (1927-) Finnish
Sculpture
£2175 $3916 €3176 Black summer (61x61cm-24x24in) s.verso wall object. 26-Apr-4 Bukowskis, Stockholm #566/R est:40000-50000 (S.KR 30000)

ULVING, Even (1863-1952) Norwegian
£417 $679 €600 Summer landscape (48x68cm-19x27in) s. 29-Sep-3 Sotheby's, Amsterdam #289/R
£894 $1646 €1341 Still life of roses (56x84cm-22x33in) s. 14-Jun-4 Blomqvist, Lysaker #1416/R (N.KR 11000)
£1193 $2051 €1742 Summer evening near Aasgaardstrand (36x56cm-14x22in) s. i.stretcher. 8-Dec-3 Blomqvist, Oslo #481/R est:15000-18000 (N.KR 14000)
£1879 $3137 €2743 Woman washing clothes in yard, Voll in Romsdalen (43x60cm-17x24in) s. i.stretcher. 13-Oct-3 Blomqvist, Oslo #285/R est:20000-25000 (N.KR 22000)
£1958 $3504 €2859 Coastal landscape, possibly Helgeland (45x65cm-18x26in) s. canvas on panel. 25-May-4 Grev Wedels Plass, Oslo #55/R est:20000-30000 (N.KR 24000)
£2733 $4564 €3990 Winter morning from Kristiania fjord (64x100cm-25x39in) s. i.stretcher. 13-Oct-3 Blomqvist, Oslo #294/R est:30000-40000 (N.KR 32000)
£3407 $5860 €4974 Small girl visiting the workshop (77x100cm-30x39in) s. 8-Dec-3 Blomqvist, Oslo #473/R est:50000-60000 (N.KR 40000)

UMBEHR, Otto (1902-1980) German
Photographs
£2098 $3566 €3000 Untitled (24x18cm-9x7in) s.i.d. verso silver gelatin. 27-Nov-3 Villa Grisebach, Berlin #1436/R est:3000-4000
£2098 $3566 €3000 Black and white in Philadelphia (30x21cm-12x8in) s.i.d. verso lit.exhib. 27-Nov-3 Villa Grisebach, Berlin #1439/R est:3000-4000
£2174 $3565 €3000 Untitled (30x22cm-12x9in) i. verso vintage bromide silver. 30-May-3 Villa Grisebach, Berlin #1390/R est:3000-4000

UMBRIAN SCHOOL, Italian
£6623 $12053 €10000 Madonna and Child (72x54cm-28x21in) board. 16-Jun-4 Christie's, Rome #271/R est:10000-15000

UMBRIAN SCHOOL (14th C) Italian
Sculpture
£25000 $42500 €36500 Madonna and Child (114cm-45in) wood exhib. 29-Oct-3 Sotheby's, London #37/R est:30000-40000

UMBRIAN SCHOOL (15th C) Italian
£9155 $16021 €13000 La Vierge a l'Enfant entre Saint Jean Baptiste et Saint Etienne (35x22cm-14x9in) panel. 18-Dec-3 Tajan, Paris #1/R est:13000-15000

UMBRIAN SCHOOL (16th C) Italian
£6993 $12028 €10000 Saint Constance (154x106cm-61x42in) 2-Dec-3 Sotheby's, Milan #100/R est:12000-16000

UMGELTER, Hermann Ludwig (1891-1962) German
£263 $484 €400 Autumn landscape on Swabian Alb (69x86cm-27x34in) s. 24-Jun-4 Dr Fritz Nagel, Stuttgart #767/R
£461 $847 €700 Woodland stream near Busnau (75x60cm-30x24in) s. 24-Jun-4 Dr Fritz Nagel, Stuttgart #770/R
£526 $968 €800 Feuerbach valley (55x46cm-22x18in) s. 24-Jun-4 Dr Fritz Nagel, Stuttgart #768/R
£669 $1070 €950 Schwarzwald landscape (28x41cm-11x16in) s. board. 19-Sep-3 Sigalas, Stuttgart #354/R
£724 $1332 €1100 Autumn forest clearing (76x80cm-30x31in) s. board. 24-Jun-4 Dr Fritz Nagel, Stuttgart #769/R
£1111 $1833 €1600 Sunny wood (100x100cm-39x39in) s. 3-Jul-3 Dr Fritz Nagel, Stuttgart #525/R est:800
£1127 $1949 €1600 Spring in Botnang 1940 (60x76cm-24x30in) s. 11-Dec-3 Dr Fritz Nagel, Stuttgart #547/R est:700

UMLAUF, Charles (1911-1994) American
Sculpture
£1486 $2750 €2170 Longhorn steer (53x51cm-21x20in) incised sig.base dark brown pat bronze. 15-Jul-4 Sotheby's, New York #86/R est:2000-3000
£1737 $2900 €2536 John the Baptist (41x25x20cm-16x10x8in) stoneware. 18-Oct-3 David Dike, Dallas #159/R est:2000-4000
£2059 $3500 €3006 Seated figures (67cm-26in) i. Portuguese rose marble sold with pedestal. 29-Oct-3 Christie's, Los Angeles #60/R est:5000-7000
£2059 $3500 €3006 Nude torso (81cm-32in) i. Portuguese rose marble sold with wooden pedestal. 29-Oct-3 Christie's, Los Angeles #61/R est:5000-7000

UNBEREIT, Paul (1884-1937) German/Austrian
£300 $471 €435 At rest in pasture (38x47cm-15x19in) s. 28-Aug-3 Christie's, Kensington #113/R
£458 $760 €650 Weidling landscape (23x32cm-9x13in) s. i. verso board. 16-Jun-3 Dorotheum, Vienna #19/R
£596 $1091 €900 Farmstead in Schwallenbach, Wachau (25x35cm-10x14in) s. i.d.Oktober 1904 verso board. 8-Apr-4 Dorotheum, Vienna #11/R
£704 $1218 €1000 Village landscape (17x26cm-7x10in) s. board. 10-Dec-3 Dorotheum, Vienna #178
£1007 $1862 €1500 Birch trees by pond (31x26cm-12x10in) s. i. verso board. 9-Mar-4 Dorotheum, Vienna #5/R est:1800-2200

UNCETA Y LOPEZ, Marcelino de (1835-1905) Spanish
£347 $566 €500 Little dog (11x10cm-4x4in) s. board. 23-Sep-3 Durán, Madrid #1/R
£903 $1472 €1300 Toreadors (13x11cm-5x4in) s. cardboard. 23-Sep-3 Durán, Madrid #21/R
£1250 $2037 €1800 Bull (47x61cm-19x24in) s. board. 16-Jul-3 Durán, Madrid #112/R est:1800
£1776 $3215 €2700 Soldier (32x15cm-13x6in) s. board. 14-Apr-4 Ansorena, Madrid #104/R est:2500
£4965 $8291 €7000 French cavalry (18x28cm-7x11in) s. board. 20-Oct-3 Durán, Madrid #173/R
£9028 $14715 €13000 Berber battle (73x50cm-29x20in) s. paper on canvas en grisaille. 23-Sep-3 Durán, Madrid #199/R est:6000
Works on paper
£395 $714 €600 Head of horse (27x21cm-11x8in) pencil dr. 14-Apr-4 Ansorena, Madrid #389/R
£448 $744 €650 Monserrat sacked by the French (14x21cm-6x8in) s. wash ink. 1-Oct-3 Ansorena, Madrid #494/R
£1087 $1783 €1500 En formacion (23x35cm-9x14in) s. gouache. 27-May-3 Durán, Madrid #99/R est:1500
£2000 $3580 €2920 Alphonso King of Spain (20x32cm-8x13in) s.d.1884. 26-May-4 Sotheby's, Olympia #288/R est:2000-3000

UNCINI, Giuseppe (1929-) Italian
£676 $1189 €1000 Untitled (70x100cm-28x39in) s.d.1970 tempera paper. 24-May-4 Christie's, Milan #40
Sculpture
£18667 $34347 €28000 Reinforced concrete (68x44cm-27x17in) s.i.d.1960 verso prov. 14-Jun-4 Porro, Milan #31/R est:25000-27000
£33557 $60067 €50000 Reinforced concrete (87x122x10cm-34x48x4in) s.i.d.1960 verso iron concrete prov. 25-May-4 Sotheby's, Milan #282/R est:30000-40000
£35000 $58450 €51100 Reinforced concrete (153x96x3cm-60x38x1in) s.d.1962v. iron concrete prov. 20-Oct-3 Sotheby's, London #26/R est:32000
Works on paper
£759 $1267 €1100 Untitled (28x19cm-11x7in) s.d.2000 mixed media. 17-Nov-3 Sant Agostino, Torino #56/R
£878 $1546 €1300 Untitled (70x100cm-28x39in) s.d.1975 mixed media collage. 24-May-4 Christie's, Milan #42/R
£1351 $2378 €2000 Untitled (34x34cm-13x13in) assemblage on cardboard. 22-May-4 Galleria Pananti, Florence #338/R est:2000-2200
£2685 $4805 €4000 Untitled (47x65cm-19x26in) s.d.59 W/C pencil wire card prov. 25-May-4 Sotheby's, Milan #146/R est:1500

UNDERHILL, F (19th C) British
£1109 $1984 €1619 Man with crow (66x90cm-26x35in) i.verso. 26-May-4 AB Stockholms Auktionsverk #2363/R est:12000-15000 (S.KR 15000)

UNDERHILL, Frederick Thomas (fl.1868-1896) British			
£18000	$30600	€26280	On the sands (102x127cm-40x50in) s. exhib. 27-Nov-3 Sotheby's, London #386/R est:20000-30000
Works on paper			
£500	$850	€730	Tasting the broth (29x20cm-11x8in) s. W/C. 26-Nov-3 Hamptons Fine Art, Godalming #71/R
UNDERWOOD, Léon (1890-1975) British			
£7600	$12920	€11096	Reclining woman (51x76cm-20x30in) s.d.29. 26-Nov-3 Sotheby's, Olympia #142/R est:3000-5000
Sculpture			
£1100	$1870	€1606	Dance of Substance and Shadow (26x23x2cm-10x9x1in) s.d.52 num. II/VII bronze prov.exhib.lit. 26-Nov-3 Sotheby's, Olympia #146/R est:1200-1800
£1600	$2720	€2336	Jekyll and Hyde (12cm-5in) i. num.I/VII bronze wooden base exec.1937 prov.lit. 26-Nov-3 Sotheby's, Olympia #143/R est:800-1200
£1600	$2720	€2336	Daniel (18cm-7in) s.d.62 bronze wooden base prov.exhib.lit. 26-Nov-3 Sotheby's, Olympia #147/R est:1000-1500
£1800	$3060	€2628	Annunciation (13cm-5in) bronze exec.1955 prov.exhib.lit. 26-Nov-3 Sotheby's, Olympia #145/R est:1200-1800
£3200	$5440	€4672	Creator (21cm-8in) s. num.1/4 terracotta exec. 1937 prov.exhib.lit. 26-Nov-3 Sotheby's, Olympia #144/R est:1000-1500
£20000	$36600	€29200	Flux, the runner (54cm-21in) s.d.24 num.VI/VII pat bronze lit. 2-Jun-4 Sotheby's, London #54/R est:20000-30000
Works on paper			
£280	$518	€409	Icelandic girl and baby (28x18cm-11x7in) pencil. 11-Mar-4 Christie's, Kensington #172
£3800	$6574	€5548	Charterhouse Square, London (54x76cm-21x30in) s.d.39 W/C. 11-Dec-3 Lyon & Turnbull, Edinburgh #68/R est:2500-3500
UNG, Per (1933-) Norwegian			
Sculpture			
£1895	$3487	€2767	Reclining pregnant female nude (20x55x23cm-8x22x9in) s. brown pat.bronze sold with plywood base. 29-Mar-4 Rasmussen, Copenhagen #471/R est:20000 (D.KR 21000)
UNGALAQ, Natar (1959-) North American			
Sculpture			
£2432	$4135	€3551	Inuit man leading his dying father away (30cm-12in) s. mottled grey soapstone. 3-Nov-3 Waddingtons, Toronto #121/R est:3500-4500 (C.D 5400)
UNGER, Carl (1915-1995) German?			
£11111	$18889	€16000	Attersee (91x95cm-36x37in) mono.d.75 lit. 28-Oct-3 Wiener Kunst Auktionen, Vienna #227/R est:15000-35000
UNGER, Wolfgang Heinz (1929-) German			
£270	$496	€410	Lakeside cafe (39x29cm-15x11in) s. 25-Jun-4 Michael Zeller, Lindau #518/R
£426	$711	€600	Lake Geneva (49x98cm-19x39in) s. s.i. verso. 16-Oct-3 Dorotheum, Salzburg #719/R
£733	$1349	€1100	Venice (50x120cm-20x47in) s. jute. 9-Jun-4 Dorotheum, Salzburg #652/R
UNGERER, Tomi (1931-) ?			
Works on paper			
£559	$951	€800	Reclining female nude (52x35cm-20x14in) s.i.d. col chk over Indian ink pencil board. 21-Nov-3 Reiss & Sohn, Konigstein #640/R
£611	$1113	€892	Girl at window (44x29cm-17x11in) s.i.d. pencil W/C. 17-Jun-4 Kornfeld, Bern #801 (S.FR 1400)
£699	$1272	€1021	Kussnacht (21x29cm-8x11in) s.i.d.1974 pencil w/C. 17-Jun-4 Kornfeld, Bern #800 est:750 (S.FR 1600)
UNGERMANN, Arne (20th C) Danish			
£436	$698	€632	Mot-Bok (23x32cm-9x13in) s.i. w/. 17-Sep-3 Kunsthallen, Copenhagen #295/R (D.KR 4600)
Works on paper			
£455	$728	€660	Thriller (100x67cm-39x26in) s.d.49 pastel. 17-Sep-3 Kunsthallen, Copenhagen #299 (D.KR 4800)
UNGERN, Ragnar (1885-1955) Finnish			
£507	$811	€720	Forest (40x30cm-16x12in) s.d.1912. 18-Sep-3 Hagelstam, Helsinki #1020
£2533	$4535	€3800	Summer's day on the jetty, from Aabo skerries (41x31cm-16x12in) s.d.1953 board. 15-May-4 Hagelstam, Helsinki #139/R est:3500
UNGERS, Sybille (1960-) Irish			
Works on paper			
£1119	$1902	€1600	Geometric studies (31x24cm-12x9in) s.d.1991 pastel pair. 18-Nov-3 Whyte's, Dublin #85/R
UNGEWITTER, Hugo (1869-c.1944) German			
£2027	$3628	€3000	Herding animals in the Steppes (80x109cm-31x43in) s.d.1927 lit. 8-May-4 Schloss Ahlden, Ahlden #786/R est:3200
£10738	$19758	€16000	Galopping Cossacks (70x106cm-28x42in) s.i.d.1934 lit. 25-Mar-4 Karlheinz Kaupp, Staufen #2782/R est:1800
£23810	$42619	€35000	Rider from the Steppes with dogs (80x130cm-31x51in) s.d.1938. 17-Mar-4 Neumeister, Munich #642/R est:2500
UNOLD, Max (1885-1964) German			
£3200	$5728	€4800	Home time (58x69cm-23x27in) s. prov.lit. 14-May-4 Ketterer, Munich #81/R est:3500-4500
UNRUH, Curt von (1894-?) German			
£282	$487	€400	Village landscape (40x75cm-16x30in) mono. 10-Dec-3 Hugo Ruef, Munich #2513
UNSELD, Albert (1879-?) German			
£333	$600	€500	Building site (73x100cm-29x39in) s.d.1926 panel. 26-Apr-4 Rieber, Stuttgart #885/R
UNSWORTH, Ken (1931-) Australian			
Sculpture			
£4198	$7641	€6129	Suspended stone circle 1978 (52x38cm-20x15in) mild steel rod pebbles black thread prov.exhib. 16-Jun-4 Deutscher-Menzies, Melbourne #6/R est:9000-14000 (A.D 11000)
UNSWORTH, Peter (1937-) British			
£500	$895	€730	Leaving the Dinosaur Park (119x119cm-47x47in) painted c.1978. 18-Mar-4 Christie's, Kensington #697/R
UNTERBERGER, Franz Richard (1838-1902) Belgian			
£440	$700	€638	Italian lake scene (51x81cm-20x32in) s.d.1863. 12-Sep-3 Aspire, Cleveland #36
£3125	$5313	€4500	Procession in Southern Italy (32x30cm-13x12in) s. panel. 28-Oct-3 Christie's, Amsterdam #29/R est:4000-6000
£4225	$7310	€6000	Naples. Gulf of Naples (14x20cm-6x8in) s.i. panel two. 13-Dec-3 Lempertz, Koln #261/R est:6000
£4500	$7650	€6570	At a Tyrol lake-side (52x76cm-20x30in) s. 26-Nov-3 Hamptons Fine Art, Godalming #207/R est:4500-6000
£8889	$16000	€12978	Bay of Naples (53x76cm-21x30in) s. 20-Apr-4 Arthur James, Florida #79/R est:15000-20000
£17000	$31110	€24820	Italian coastal landscape with a group of figures (61x112cm-24x44in) s. prov. 8-Jul-4 Duke & Son, Dorchester #222/R
£18182	$30364	€26000	Street in Pompei (71x59cm-28x23in) s. 29-Jun-3 Eric Pillon, Calais #16/R
£20408	$36531	€30000	Tradesmen on Castellamare beach on the Gulf of Sorrento at night (73x120cm-29x47in) s. i. verso. 17-Mar-4 Neumeister, Munich #643/R est:14000
£56376	$99785	€84000	Palermo (85x155cm-33x61in) s. prov.lit. 28-Apr-4 Wiener Kunst Auktionen, Vienna #20/R est:40000-60000
UNTERBERGER, Franz Richard (attrib) (1838-1902) Belgian			
£1700	$3145	€2482	Fjord landscape (56x86cm-22x34in) bears sig. bears sig.i.verso. 14-Jul-4 Sotheby's, Olympia #157/R est:2000-3000
UNTERBERGER, Ignaz (1748-1797) Austrian			
£7000	$11900	€10220	Portrait of Wenzel Anton, Furst von Kaunitz, resting his right hand on an open book (33x28cm-13x11in) 29-Oct-3 Christie's, London #49/R est:6000-8000
UNTERLUGGAUER, Michael (1953-) Austrian			
Works on paper			
£951	$1664	€1350	Bride's song, Quo Vadis (70x50cm-28x20in) s.i.d.02 verso mixed media collage canvas. 19-Dec-3 Dorotheum, Vienna #391/R
UNTORO, Ugo (1970-) Indonesian			
£725	$1123	€1059	Bapak Kangen Anak (79x99cm-31x39in) s.d.2000 s.i.d.verso. 6-Oct-2 Sotheby's, Singapore #181/R (S.D 2000)
£1634	$2958	€2386	Komposisi merah (145x125cm-57x49in) s.i.d.1994. 4-Apr-4 Sotheby's, Singapore #186/R est:5000-7000 (S.D 5000)
UNWIN, Thomas (1782-1857) British?			
£400	$668	€580	Garland Beauty (80x66cm-31x26in) s.d.1852 verso. 17-Jun-3 Rosebery Fine Art, London #583/R
UPHOFF, Carl Emil (1885-1971) German			
£839	$1443	€1200	Evening in the Hamme marshes (61x78cm-24x31in) s. fibreboard. 5-Dec-3 Bolland & Marotz, Bremen #430/R
UPHOFF, Fritz (1890-1966) German			
£294	$550	€429	On the moor (38x48cm-15x19in) s. masonite. 25-Feb-4 Doyle, New York #29/R
£347	$566	€500	River landscape (50x63cm-20x25in) s. board. 27-Sep-3 Dr Fritz Nagel, Stuttgart #9387/R
£350	$594	€500	Heathland (65x85cm-26x33in) s. i. verso panel. 21-Nov-3 Reiss & Sohn, Konigstein #33/R
£979	$1684	€1400	Beautiful autumn evening at moor canal (50x62cm-20x24in) s. board. 5-Dec-3 Bolland & Marotz, Bremen #428/R
UPPER ITALIAN SCHOOL, 16th C			
£12414	$20607	€18000	Virgin and Child with Infant St John the Baptist (62x54cm-24x21in) panel prov. 1-Oct-3 Dorotheum, Vienna #279/R est:6000-10000
£16107	$29638	€24000	Holy Family (54x36cm-21x14in) panel prov. 24-Mar-4 Dorotheum, Vienna #45/R est:9000-12000
UPPER RHINE SCHOOL, 15th C			
£12937	$21605	€18500	Adoration of the Three Kings (80x58cm-31x23in) panel. 9-Oct-3 Michael Zeller, Lindau #502/R est:18500
£17241	$28793	€25000	Taking Christ prisoner (86x51cm-34x20in) panel prov. 15-Nov-3 Lempertz, Koln #1112/R est:25000-30000
£18341	$33380	€26778	Adoration of the Magi (51x34cm-20x13in) tempera panel exec. c.1480-90 exhib. 16-Jun-4 Fischer, Luzern #1001/R est:35000-40000 (S.FR 42000)

UPRKA, Joza (1861-?) Czechoslovakian
£1094 $1817 €1597 Girl with kerchiep (29x59cm-11x23in) mono.d.16 panel. 4-Oct-3 Dorotheum, Prague #25/R est:50000-75000 (C.KR 50000)
Works on paper
£253 $400 €369 Workers in a field (13x13cm-5x5in) s. W/C. 7-Sep-3 Treadway Gallery, Cincinnati #569/R

UPSON, Tony (20th C) ?
£185 $300 €268 View of an early Rolls-Royce (152x102cm-60x40in) acrylic. 1-Aug-3 Bonhams & Butterfields, San Francisco #823/R
£259 $420 €376 Rolls-Royce, Spirit of ecstasy mascot (366x310cm-144x122in) acrylic on board. 1-Aug-3 Bonhams & Butterfields, San Francisco #822/R
£370 $600 €537 Rolls-Royce in front of a villa (122x81cm-48x32in) acrylic. 1-Aug-3 Bonhams & Butterfields, San Francisco #824/R
£432 $700 €626 Study of early Roll-Royce in front of a villa (152x102cm-60x40in) acrylic. 1-Aug-3 Bonhams & Butterfields, San Francisco #827/R
£556 $900 €806 Study of a team Bentley with a Spitfire above (122x81cm-48x32in) acrylic. 1-Aug-3 Bonhams & Butterfields, San Francisco #828/R est:500-800
£1049 $1700 €1521 4.5 litre Blower Bentley (366x310cm-144x122in) acrylic on board. 1-Aug-3 Bonhams & Butterfields, San Francisco #826/R est:800-1000
£1111 $1800 €1611 Two Rolls-Royce powered spitfires crossing the English Channel (366x310cm-144x122in) acrylic on board. 1-Aug-3 Bonhams & Butterfields, San Francisco #825/R est:800-1000

UPTON, Florence K (?-1922) British
£6000 $11100 €8760 Portrait of Mrs Patrick Campbell (34x28cm-13x11in) board. 14-Jul-4 Sotheby's, Olympia #128/R est:1500-2500

UPTON, Roger (20th C) British
Works on paper
£1100 $1936 €1606 A Hobby. A male Goshawk. An immature Goshawk. A Raptor (41x33cm-16x13in) s. W/C htd four. 18-May-4 Woolley & Wallis, Salisbury #259/R est:300-500

UPWARD, Peter (1932-1984) Australian
£407 $728 €594 Green and pink abstract (28x28cm-11x11in) s.verso round. 4-May-4 Sotheby's, Melbourne #230 (A.D 1000)
£407 $728 €594 Brown and green abstract (28x28cm-11x11in) s.d.1972 verso round. 4-May-4 Sotheby's, Melbourne #231 (A.D 1000)
£7582 $12283 €11070 Elan vital (122x92cm-48x36in) s.i.verso oil mixed media board prov. 30-Jul-3 Goodman, Sydney #56/R est:3000-4000 (A.D 18500)
Works on paper
£2664 $4209 €3889 Untitled (73x53cm-29x21in) s.d.61 synthetic polymer board prov.exhib. 2-Sep-3 Deutscher-Menzies, Melbourne #112/R est:3500-5500 (A.D 6500)

URACH, Albrecht Furst von (1903-1969) German
£377 $675 €550 Still life of tulips (53x43cm-21x17in) s. masonite. 14-May-4 Eldred, East Dennis #767/R

URANJUMA, Luluna (20th C) Australian
Works on paper
£1255 $2246 €1832 Wonger Dog dreamings (29x47cm-11x19in) natural earth pigments bark exec 1960 prov. 25-May-4 Lawson Menzies, Sydney #279/R est:3000-5000 (A.D 3200)

URANOVSKY, Meyer (1939-) South African
£862 $1440 €1259 Nude woman (119x85cm-47x33in) s.d.1987 s.verso. 20-Oct-3 Stephan Welz, Johannesburg #370/R est:8000-12000 (SA.R 10000)

URBACH, Josef (1889-1973) German
£20667 $36993 €31000 Landscape with yellow house (63x41cm-25x16in) s. double-sided prov.exhib. 14-May-4 Ketterer, Munich #83/R est:4000-6000

URBAHN, Otto (19th C) German
£986 $1577 €1400 Four men in conversation around table (65x80cm-26x31in) s. 19-Sep-3 Karlheinz Kaupp, Staufen #2073/R

URBAIN, Alexandre (1875-1953) French
£396 $674 €578 Reclining female nude (27x41cm-11x16in) s.d.1927. 5-Nov-3 Dobiaschofsky, Bern #1014 (S.FR 900)

URBAN, Hermann (1866-1946) German
£268 $494 €400 Landscape with fields and trees (41x75cm-16x30in) s. 24-Mar-4 Hugo Ruef, Munich #1133
£272 $487 €400 Farmstead (53x63cm-21x25in) s. board. 18-Mar-4 Neumeister, Munich #2786/R
£272 $487 €400 Alpine landscape (53x63cm-21x25in) board. 18-Mar-4 Neumeister, Munich #2787
£336 $617 €500 Pre-alpine landscape in spring (54x64cm-21x25in) s. i. verso. 24-Mar-4 Hugo Ruef, Munich #1132/R
£1399 $2378 €2000 Southern coast (189x246cm-74x97in) s. 20-Nov-3 Van Ham, Cologne #1893/R est:1500

URBAN, Humberto (1936-) Mexican
£1264 $2150 €1845 Blue walls (100x120cm-39x47in) s.d.1992. 30-Oct-3 Louis Morton, Mexico #25/R est:17000-19000 (M.P 24000)

URBAN, Josef (1872-1933) American/Austrian
£1549 $2680 €2200 A good conversation (65x80cm-26x31in) s. 10-Dec-3 Dorotheum, Vienna #98/R est:1800-2000

URBANEK, Justyna (1955-) Norwegian/Polish
£500 $836 €730 Quo Vadis (99x136cm-39x54in) s. tempera sand gesso. 17-Nov-3 Blomqvist, Lysaker #1356 (N.KR 6000)

URBANOWICZ, Danuta (1932-) Polish
Works on paper
£353 $639 €530 Composition (38x34cm-15x13in) s. collage exec 2003. 4-Apr-4 Agra, Warsaw #24/R (P.Z 2500)

URBIETA, Jesus (1959-1977) Mexican
Sculpture
£11176 $19000 €16317 Carayoapa (52x29x13cm-20x11x5in) polychromed clay executed 1991 prov. 19-Nov-3 Sotheby's, New York #154/R est:10000-15000

URBINA, Luis (1937-) Nicaraguan
£207 $343 €300 Mutante (75x60cm-30x24in) s.d.1995. 12-Jun-3 Louis Morton, Mexico #91/R est:2500-3000 (M.P 3600)
£229 $381 €332 Mutante 2 (99x99cm-39x39in) s.d.1996. 12-Jun-3 Louis Morton, Mexico #107/R est:2500-3000 (M.P 4000)
Works on paper
£172 $286 €249 Abstract figure (120x90cm-47x35in) d.1997 mixed media canvas. 12-Jun-3 Louis Morton, Mexico #126 est:2800-3000 (M.P 3000)

URBINO, Carlo (16th C) Italian
Works on paper
£1400 $2422 €2044 Kneeling man looking up. Study of the same figure (11x10cm-4x4in) black white chk pair prov. 12-Dec-3 Christie's, Kensington #317/R est:500-700

URCULO (1938-2003) Spanish
£6711 $11879 €10000 La Communion Cosmica (160x130cm-63x51in) s.d.1970. 27-Apr-4 Campo, Vlaamse Kaai #605 est:2000-2500

URCULO, Eduardo (1938-2003) Spanish
£9655 $16124 €14000 Fruit at dawn (50x50cm-20x20in) s.d.80 s.i.d. verso. 17-Nov-3 Durán, Madrid #156/R est:6000
£15278 $25208 €22000 Great nude (115x115cm-45x45in) s.d.1976 s.i.d.verso. 2-Jul-3 Ansorena, Madrid #859/R
£15845 $27729 €22500 Figure (110x100cm-43x39in) s. acrylic. 16-Dec-3 Durán, Madrid #173/R est:9000
£17687 $32190 €26000 Claire's knee (100x95cm-39x37in) s.d.1970 prov. 3-Feb-4 Segre, Madrid #195/R est:18000
Works on paper
£839 $1401 €1200 Figure in landscape (24x31cm-9x12in) s.d.65 gouache. 30-Jun-3 Ansorena, Madrid #113/R
£1000 $1820 €1500 Ropa tendida al sol en Formentera (24x33cm-9x13in) s.d.1973 W/C ink wash. 29-Jun-4 Segre, Madrid #169/R est:900
£1083 $1993 €1581 Erotic scene with woman (100x70cm-39x28in) s.d.77 air brush. 29-Mar-4 Rasmussen, Copenhagen #330/R est:15000 (D.KR 12000)
£2361 $4014 €3400 Nude in the sun (35x26cm-14x10in) s.i.d.1973 W/C gouache ink prov. 28-Oct-3 Segre, Madrid #165/R est:1250
£4648 $7437 €6600 Dog in the field (68x98cm-27x39in) s.d.1982 pastel cardboard prov. 16-Sep-3 Segre, Madrid #146/R est:6600
£8333 $13583 €12000 Still life (113x110cm-44x43in) s.d.91 pastel. 23-Sep-3 Durán, Madrid #237/R est:12000

URDAL, Atle (1913-1988) Norwegian
£429 $751 €626 Figures (35x50cm-14x20in) s.d.1948 panel. 16-Dec-3 Grev Wedels Plass, Oslo #237/R (N.KR 5000)
£816 $1460 €1191 Composition (61x50cm-24x20in) s. panel. 25-May-4 Grev Wedels Plass, Oslo #98/R (N.KR 10000)
Works on paper
£238 $438 €347 From Tenerife (58x44cm-23x17in) s. gouache. 29-Mar-4 Blomqvist, Lysaker #1345 (N.KR 3000)

URDIN, Kiro (1945-) Yugoslavian
£738 $1307 €1100 Abstraction (77x51cm-30x20in) s.d.1994 cardboard. 27-Apr-4 Campo & Campo, Antwerp #226

UREN, J C (1845-1932) British
Works on paper
£750 $1365 €1095 Fisher folk in Mount's Bay (18x36cm-7x14in) s.d.1878 W/C. 15-Jun-4 David Lay, Penzance #362/R
£750 $1365 €1095 Fisher folk (18x36cm-7x14in) s.d.1878 W/C. 15-Jun-4 David Lay, Penzance #363
£1100 $1837 €1606 Shag Rock (46x71cm-18x28in) s. W/C. 14-Oct-3 David Lay, Penzance #631 est:400-450
£1100 $2035 €1606 Wreckers at work (25x43cm-10x17in) s. 10-Feb-4 David Lay, Penzance #232/R est:550-650
£1500 $2730 €2190 Fishing cove (23x43cm-9x17in) s. W/C. 15-Jun-4 David Lay, Penzance #223/R est:1000-1500
£1850 $3090 €2701 Porthgwarra Cove (25x38cm-10x15in) s. W/C. 14-Oct-3 David Lay, Penzance #60/R est:750-950

UREN, John C (1845-1932) British
Works on paper
£271 $453 €396 Seagulls on a rocky coast (27x46cm-11x18in) s. W/C. 17-Nov-3 Waddingtons, Toronto #49/R (C.D 600)
£294 $491 €429 Shipping off the coast of Cornwall (43x68cm-17x27in) s. W/C. 17-Nov-3 Waddingtons, Toronto #63/R (C.D 650)
£390 $663 €569 Coastal view, probably Cornwall (21x46cm-8x18in) s. W/C. 27-Nov-3 Greenslade Hunt, Taunton #963

£1400	$2576	€2044	Fishing boats in a calm off St Michaels' Mount. Fisherman on his boat (18x37cm-7x15in) s.d.1878 pencil W/C. 25-Mar-4 Christie's, Kensington #266/R est:500-700

URGELL Y INGLADA, Modesto (1839-1919) Spanish

£1477	$2746	€2200	Landscape with hut (26x35cm-10x14in) s. 2-Mar-4 Ansorena, Madrid #108/R est:2200
£12752	$23718	€19000	Night landscape (60x119cm-24x47in) s. 2-Mar-4 Ansorena, Madrid #61/R est:19000
Works on paper			
£828	$1374	€1200	View of village (20x32cm-8x13in) s. chl dr. 1-Oct-3 Ansorena, Madrid #478/R

URGELL, Ricardo (1874-1924) Spanish

£600	$1092	€900	Landscape (12x18cm-5x7in) s. board. 29-Jun-4 Segre, Madrid #76/R
£2055	$3493	€3000	Interior (35x27cm-14x11in) s.d.1912 board. 4-Nov-3 Ansorena, Madrid #64/R est:3000

URI, Aviva (1927-1989) Israeli

£3073	$5500	€4487	Untitled (73x60cm-29x24in) s.d.68 oil mixed media. 18-Mar-4 Sotheby's, New York #39/R est:5000-7000
£4432	$7800	€6471	Special agents (200x200cm-79x79in) s. oil mixed media painted c.1970 prov. 1-Jan-4 Ben-Ami, Tel Aviv #4374/R est:8000-12000

URIA MONZON, Antonio (1929-1996) Spanish

£5102	$9286	€7500	Maternity (100x100cm-39x39in) s. i.verso. 3-Feb-4 Segre, Madrid #159/R est:7000

URIARTE, Carlos (1910-) Argentinian

£1257	$2300	€1835	Fishing village (48x71cm-19x28in) tempera paper. 1-Jun-4 Arroyo, Buenos Aires #18
£2308	$4200	€3370	Spanish village (50x70cm-20x28in) s. tempera cardboard. 29-Jun-4 Arroyo, Buenos Aires #29/R est:2200
£3757	$6800	€5485	Figures (70x88cm-28x35in) 30-Mar-4 Arroyo, Buenos Aires #70
£3825	$7000	€5585	Two anglers (50x80cm-20x31in) 1-Jun-4 Arroyo, Buenos Aires #52
£3911	$7000	€5710	Composition with figures (60x95cm-24x37in) s. board. 4-May-4 Arroyo, Buenos Aires #28/R est:4200
Works on paper			
£1955	$3500	€2854	Parana coast (47x63cm-19x25in) s. W/C. 4-May-4 Arroyo, Buenos Aires #4/R est:1400
£3022	$5500	€4412	Fishermen (50x70cm-20x28in) s. mixed media. 29-Jun-4 Arroyo, Buenos Aires #5/R est:2000
£3094	$5600	€4517	Fishing village (48x68cm-19x27in) W/C. 30-Mar-4 Arroyo, Buenos Aires #18

URIBURU, Nicolas Garcia (1937-) Argentinian

£24590	$45000	€35901	Topa Topa (130x195cm-51x77in) 1-Jun-4 Arroyo, Buenos Aires #84

URK, Kees van (1895-1976) Dutch

£559	$934	€800	A family (46x38cm-18x15in) s. canvas on panel. 30-Jun-3 Sotheby's, Amsterdam #162/R

URLAUB, Georg Anton (1713-1759) German

£4138	$6869	€6000	Portrait of young man with curly hair (32x28cm-13x11in) lit.prov. 1-Oct-3 Dorotheum, Vienna #208/R est:4000-5000

URLAUB, Georg Carl (1749-1811) German

£1611	$2883	€2400	Portrait of Grafin Caroline zu Isenbug-Meerholz (43x33cm-17x13in) s.i.d.1795. 28-May-4 Altus, Berlin #599
£6291	$11450	€9500	Cavalry battles (22x28cm-9x11in) one s. both d.1798 panel two. 16-Jun-4 Hugo Ruef, Munich #883/R est:9500

URMANCHE, B I (1897-1990) Russian

£1397	$2500	€2040	Ala Tau (50x69cm-20x27in) cardboard painted 1947. 29-May-4 Shishkin Gallery, Moscow #40/R est:3000-4000
£1453	$2600	€2121	May (71x50cm-28x20in) cardboard painted 1947. 29-May-4 Shishkin Gallery, Moscow #41/R est:3000-4000

URQUHART, Tony (1934-) Canadian

£1135	$2111	€1657	Winter grove (45x101cm-18x40in) s.d.56 board prov. 2-Mar-4 Ritchie, Toronto #192/R est:3000-5000 (C.D 2825)
£1182	$1926	€1726	Child's landscape (86x98cm-34x39in) s.d.56 exhib. 23-Sep-3 Ritchie, Toronto #175/R est:3000-4000 (C.D 2600)
Works on paper			
£261	$486	€381	The Timothy icon, Timothy in the garden (19x16cm-7x6in) s.d.8/63 collage prov. 2-Mar-4 Ritchie, Toronto #191/R (C.D 650)

URRUCHI, Juan (1828-1892) Mexican

£14525	$26000	€21207	Bull scenes (24x33cm-9x13in) s.d.1862 pair. 26-May-4 Sotheby's, New York #75/R est:15000-20000

URRUCHUA, Demetrio (1902-1986) Argentinian

£6011	$11000	€8776	Black shawl (100x70cm-39x28in) 1-Jun-4 Arroyo, Buenos Aires #15

URSULA (1921-) German

£2254	$3899	€3200	Bird and summer palace (70x100cm-28x39in) s.d.1971 gold. 13-Dec-3 Lempertz, Koln #365/R est:2000
Works on paper			
£533	$976	€800	Spring trip (50x64cm-20x25in) s.i.d.1956-1969 W/C Indian ink. 4-Jun-4 Lempertz, Koln #511/R

URTA, Nicolas (1897-1959) South American

£2353	$4000	€3435	Autumn in Montevideo (99x100cm-39x39in) s. prov. 25-Nov-3 Galeria y Remates, Montevideo #50/R

URTEIL, Andreas (1933-1963) Austrian

Sculpture			
£1690	$2958	€2400	Rotating figure (44cm-17in) s.d.1961 num.VI dark pat bronze one of 1000 st.f.Venturi Arte. 19-Dec-3 Dorotheum, Vienna #248/R est:1900-2600

URTNOWSKI, Theodor (1881-?) ?

£833	$1508	€1250	Danzig (48x86cm-19x34in) s. 1-Apr-4 Van Ham, Cologne #167/R
£1585	$2885	€2314	Cityscape (48x86cm-19x34in) s. painted 1920. 20-Jun-4 Agra, Warsaw #55/R (P.Z 11000)

URUETA, Cordelia (1908-1995) Mexican

£1690	$3092	€2467	Window in the sun (50x40cm-20x16in) s.d.1985. 27-Jan-4 Louis Morton, Mexico #199/R est:16000-40000 (M.P 34000)

URY, Lesser (1861-1931) German

£2667	$4907	€4000	Portrait of a lady (75x50cm-30x20in) s. prov. 12-Jun-4 Villa Grisebach, Berlin #141/R est:5000-7000
£6395	$11000	€9337	Floral still life (50x35cm-20x14in) s. 3-Dec-3 Doyle, New York #120/R est:12000-18000
£8194	$12865	€11800	Figure sleeping on bench on sunny winter's day (33x49cm-13x19in) s.i.d.1887 oil tempera grisaille board. 30-Aug-3 Hans Stahl, Toestorf #61/R est:9000
£11409	$20993	€17000	Woman and horse drawn carriages in rainy Berlin boulevard (50x36cm-20x14in) s.d.11 chl. 26-Mar-4 Bolland & Marotz, Bremen #713a/R est:14000
£14685	$24965	€21000	Landscape (69x99cm-27x39in) s. prov. 29-Nov-3 Villa Grisebach, Berlin #121/R est:35000-45000
£20667	$38027	€31000	The blue mountain (79x96cm-31x38in) i.verso exec. c.1900-01 prov.lit. 12-Jun-4 Villa Grisebach, Berlin #142/R est:20000-30000
£20667	$38027	€31000	Promenade under the lime trees (31x24cm-12x9in) prov.lit. 12-Jun-4 Villa Grisebach, Berlin #151/R est:20000-30000
£25333	$45347	€38000	Tiergarten Avenue with monument (45x33cm-18x13in) s. 13-May-4 Neumeister, Munich #516/R est:38000-40000
£27972	$47552	€40000	Dutch canal with windmill (72x105cm-28x41in) s.d.1913 prov. 28-Nov-3 Villa Grisebach, Berlin #10/R est:30000-40000
£34965	$59441	€50000	Rainy street at night - Berlin (52x36cm-20x14in) s. prov. 28-Nov-3 Villa Grisebach, Berlin #13/R est:60000-80000
£36000	$64440	€54000	Walking in the rain (51x36cm-20x14in) s. 13-May-4 Neumeister, Munich #517/R est:30000-35000
£51333	$94453	€77000	Berlin street in autumn (44x39cm-17x15in) s. prov.exhib. 11-Jun-4 Villa Grisebach, Berlin #8/R est:60000-80000
£54667	$100587	€82000	Drosky, rainy mood (59x45cm-23x18in) s.d.1916 prov. 11-Jun-4 Villa Grisebach, Berlin #11/R est:40000-50000
Prints			
£2098	$3566	€3000	Woman hailing carriage (21x16cm-8x6in) s.i. drypoint. 29-Nov-3 Villa Grisebach, Berlin #687/R est:2500-3000
Works on paper			
£1259	$2140	€1800	Tying up corn (18x14cm-7x6in) s.d.82 brush pen. 29-Nov-3 Villa Grisebach, Berlin #685/R est:1800-2200
£2500	$4325	€3650	Abendstimmung am See (48x35cm-19x14in) pastel card prov. 11-Dec-3 Christie's, Kensington #94/R est:3000-4000
£2797	$4755	€4000	Dutch landscape with windmill (36x49cm-14x19in) s. pastel cardboard. 25-Nov-3 Christie's, Amsterdam #163/R est:9000-12000
£5333	$9813	€8000	Coastal sunset (34x48cm-13x19in) s. pastel cardboard exec. c.1912 prov.lit. 12-Jun-4 Villa Grisebach, Berlin #140/R est:8000-10000
£5333	$9813	€8000	Gentleman reading the newspaper in a cafe (50x31cm-20x12in) s. chl exec. c.1920. 12-Jun-4 Villa Grisebach, Berlin #149/R est:8000-10000
£5944	$10105	€8500	Morning mist (31x48cm-12x19in) s. W.C. 26-Nov-3 Dorotheum, Vienna #38/R est:5000-5500
£6993	$12028	€10000	View of tower Bridge, London (25x36cm-10x14in) s.i.d.1926 chl prov. 5-Dec-3 Ketterer, Munich #70/R est:10000-12000
£7500	$12525	€10950	Landscape (36x51cm-14x20in) s.d.1889 pastel prov. 21-Oct-3 Sotheby's, London #109/R est:8000-12000
£10490	$17832	€15000	Monte Baldo (50x36cm-20x14in) s.i.d.1891 pastel board. 29-Nov-3 Villa Grisebach, Berlin #119/R est:15000-20000
£12414	$20731	€18000	Havelsee with Scots pine (94x83cm-37x33in) i. pastel cardboard prov. 13-Nov-3 Neumeister, Munich #475/R est:15000-20000
£14118	$24000	€20612	View of figures on a bridge (50x37cm-20x15in) s.i.d.94 pastel gouache cardboard. 28-Oct-3 Sotheby's, New York #108/R est:18000-25000
£19580	$33287	€28000	Spring - trees by lake (52x37cm-20x15in) s.d.1903 pastel board. 29-Nov-3 Villa Grisebach, Berlin #122/R est:15000-20000
£46667	$85867	€70000	Unter den Linden (35x50cm-14x20in) s. pastel paintboard painted 1920s prov. 11-Jun-4 Villa Grisebach, Berlin #9/R est:70000-90000
£48000	$85920	€72000	In the cafe (50x35cm-20x14in) s.d.1910 pastel chk. 13-May-4 Neumeister, Munich #518/R est:45000-50000

USADEL, Max (?) German?

£403	$721	€600	River Rhine (63x83cm-25x33in) s.d.1906. 25-May-4 Durán, Madrid #172/R
£1208	$2247	€1800	View of Capri at sunset with ruins of temples in background (81x120cm-32x47in) s.i.d.1912. 5-Mar-4 Wendl, Rudolstadt #3995/R est:1400

USCHANOFF (?) ?

£408	$654	€580	Goshawk (100x70cm-39x28in) s. 18-Sep-3 Hagelstam, Helsinki #779/R

USELLINI, Gian Filippo (1903-1971) Italian

£1408	$2338	€2000	Carnival. The devil in a convent. Self-portrait (10x9cm-4x4in) s. card three. 11-Jun-3 Finarte Semenzato, Milan #512/R

Works on paper
£822 $1397 €1200 Mermaid (39x41cm-15x16in) s. mixed media exec.1971. 7-Nov-3 Galleria Rosenberg, Milan #72/R

USHER, Arland A (fl.1885-1893) British
£2148 $3801 €3200 At low tide (46x76cm-18x30in) s.i.verso exhib. 27-Apr-4 Whyte's, Dublin #125/R est:2000-3000

USLE, Juan (1953-) Spanish
£9000 $15030 €13140 Escoces (122x61cm-48x24in) s.i.d.93 verso acrylic prov.exhib. 22-Oct-3 Christie's, London #117/R est:8000-12000
Works on paper
£4027 $7450 €6000 Plates (61x45cm-24x18in) Mixed media canvas prov. 13-Mar-4 De Vuyst, Lokeren #513/R est:4500-5500

USSI, Stefano (1822-1901) Italian
£1192 $2170 €1800 Portrait of Doge (27x18cm-11x7in) i. board. 21-Jun-4 Pandolfini, Florence #73/R est:1800-2000
£35915 $62134 €51000 Campment around Cairo (45x82cm-18x32in) s.i.d.1874 prov. 11-Dec-3 Christie's, Rome #196/R est:25000-35000
Works on paper
£360 $590 €500 Portrait of Beduin (39x27cm-15x11in) W/C. 10-Jun-3 Pandolfini, Florence #111/R

USSING, Stephan (1868-1958) Danish
£270 $501 €394 Rosenborg Palace and garden (78x92cm-31x36in) s.d.1943. 2-Mar-4 Rasmussen, Copenhagen #1473 (D.KR 3000)
£359 $643 €524 The road to church, Nordby at Fanoe (43x52cm-17x20in) s.d.1925. 12-Jan-4 Rasmussen, Vejle #126/R (D.KR 3800)
£362 $648 €529 From Rosenborg Palace with road through garden (78x92cm-31x36in) s.d.1943. 10-May-4 Rasmussen, Vejle #477/R (D.KR 4000)

UTAGAWA, Toyoharu (1735-1814) Japanese
Prints
£2200 $4048 €3212 Perspective view of enjoying the evening cool by Eitaibashi at Fukagawa district (25x38cm-10x15in) s. print prov.lit. 8-Jun-4 Sotheby's, London #153/R est:1800-2200
£5500 $10120 €8030 Perspective view of the harbour in the eastern part of Holland (25x38cm-10x15in) s. print lit. 8-Jun-4 Sotheby's, London #154/R est:700-1000
Works on paper
£8696 $16000 €12696 Ten beauties of Edo (109x33cm-43x13in) s. col ink hanging scroll pair. 23-Mar-4 Christie's, Rockefeller NY #118/R est:20000-30000

UTAMARO (18th C) Japanese
Prints
£1734 $3190 €2600 Beauty. s. print. 11-Jun-4 Tajan, Paris #156/R est:2200-2500

UTAMARO II (fl.c.1804-1830) Japanese
Prints
£4000 $7360 €5840 Pictures of new pillows of marriage (37x25cm-15x10in) s. print one sheet from a triptych exec. late 1800's lit. 8-Jun-4 Sotheby's, London #273/R est:4000-5000

UTAMARO, Kitagawa (1753-1806) Japanese
£479 $815 €700 Oban of two women. s. 8-Nov-3 Dr Fritz Nagel, Stuttgart #2233/R
£479 $815 €700 Oban of young couple. s. seal. 8-Nov-3 Dr Fritz Nagel, Stuttgart #2234/R
Prints
£1748 $2972 €2500 Personnages de theatre (38x25cm-15x10in) s. col print exhib.lit. 25-Nov-3 Sotheby's, Paris #141/R est:3000-4000
£2000 $3680 €2920 The chatterbox and the naughty girl (38x25cm-15x10in) s. print exec. 1802 prov.lit. 8-Jun-4 Sotheby's, London #216/R est:2000-3000
£2400 $4416 €3504 Fushi of the Shizutamaya from the series Keisei Geisha Hana Awase (32x21cm-13x8in) s. print exec. early 1800's lit. 8-Jun-4 Sotheby's, London #197/R est:1500-2000
£2400 $4416 €3600 Celebres beautes d'Edo. col engraving. 9-Jun-4 Cornette de St.Cyr, Paris #10/R est:1500-2000
£2500 $4600 €3650 Hinazuru of the Chojiya parading with her shinzo and kamuro (38x25cm-15x10in) s.i. print exec. c.1794-95 lit. 8-Jun-4 Sotheby's, London #253/R est:2500-3500
£2657 $4517 €3800 Umegawa et Chubei (37x25cm-15x10in) s. col print lit. 25-Nov-3 Sotheby's, Paris #139/R est:4500-5500
£2657 $4517 €3800 Conversation (35x24cm-14x9in) s. col print exhib.lit. 25-Nov-3 Sotheby's, Paris #152/R est:4500-5500
£2797 $4755 €4000 Sechage des etoffes (37x25cm-15x10in) s. col print exhib.lit. 25-Nov-3 Sotheby's, Paris #151/R est:3000-4000
£2800 $5152 €4088 Geisha playing the Samisen from the series Edo Na Hana Musume Joruri (37x25cm-15x10in) s. print lit. 8-Jun-4 Sotheby's, London #198/R est:1800-2200
£3000 $5520 €4380 Act VI from the series Treasury of the forty-seven loyal retainers (37x25cm-15x10in) s. print exec. early 1800's prov.lit. 8-Jun-4 Sotheby's, London #210/R est:3000-4000
£3000 $5520 €4380 Act VIII from the series treasury of the forty-seven loyal retainers (37x24cm-15x9in) s. print exec. c.1800 lit. 8-Jun-4 Sotheby's, London #213/R est:3000-4000
£3000 $5520 €4380 Courtesan Yosooi of the Shoyoro (37x24cm-15x9in) s.i. print exec. c.1796 prov.lit. 8-Jun-4 Sotheby's, London #218/R est:3000-4000
£3200 $5888 €4672 March (34x15cm-13x6in) s. print exec. early 1800's lit. 8-Jun-4 Sotheby's, London #240/R est:2000-2500
£3400 $6256 €4964 The lovers Miuraya Agemaki and Yorozuya Sukeroku (36x26cm-14x10in) s. print exec. c.1798-99 lit. 8-Jun-4 Sotheby's, London #239/R est:2800-3200
£3636 $6182 €5200 Jeune femme avec cage (38x25cm-15x10in) s. col print prov.exhib.lit. 25-Nov-3 Sotheby's, Paris #146/R est:6000-7000
£3636 $6182 €5200 Maison (37x25cm-15x10in) col print prov.exhib.lit. 25-Nov-3 Sotheby's, Paris #148/R est:6000-7000
£3800 $6992 €5548 Yosooi and Matsumura of the Matsubaya (35x23cm-14x9in) s. print lit. 8-Jun-4 Sotheby's, London #209/R est:2000-3000
£4000 $7360 €5840 Woman threading a needle (37x25cm-15x10in) s. print exec. early 1800's lit. 8-Jun-4 Sotheby's, London #229/R est:4000-6000
£4545 $7727 €6500 Personnages de theatre (38x25cm-15x10in) s. col print exhib.lit. 25-Nov-3 Sotheby's, Paris #140/R est:7500-8500
£4545 $7727 €6500 Courtisanes (38x25cm-15x10in) s. col print lit. 25-Nov-3 Sotheby's, Paris #149/R est:7000-8000
£4545 $7727 €6500 Trois jeunes femmes (36x23cm-14x9in) col print exhib.lit. 25-Nov-3 Sotheby's, Paris #153/R est:7500-8500
£5500 $10120 €8030 The four accomplishments (38x25cm-15x10in) s. print three sheets from a pentaptych exec. early 1800's lit. 8-Jun-4 Sotheby's, London #241/R est:3500-5500
£6000 $11040 €8760 Woman emerging from a mosquito net, watched by her lover (39x26cm-15x10in) s. print exec. c.1799 lit. 8-Jun-4 Sotheby's, London #214/R est:5000-7000
£6200 $11408 €9052 Couple lying in front of a screen (26x38cm-10x15in) print exec. 1788 lit. 8-Jun-4 Sotheby's, London #255/R est:5200-5800
£6500 $11960 €9490 Woman with a battledore (38x26cm-15x10in) s.i. exec. early 1800's lit. 8-Jun-4 Sotheby's, London #228/R est:6000-7000
£6500 $11960 €9490 Fishing at Iwaya, Enoshima (37x25cm-15x10in) s. print triptych exec. c.1791 lit. 8-Jun-4 Sotheby's, London #234/R est:5000-6000
£7500 $13800 €10950 Madoka of the Tamaya (38x26cm-15x10in) s. print exec. early 1800's lit. 8-Jun-4 Sotheby's, London #205/R est:5000-7000
£7500 $13800 €10950 Women in the kitchen making rice cakes (33x70cm-13x28in) s. print three sheets exec. early 1800's prov.lit. 8-Jun-4 Sotheby's, London #243/R est:6000-8000
£8392 $14266 €12000 Teppo (38x26cm-15x10in) s. col print exhib.lit. 25-Nov-3 Sotheby's, Paris #144/R est:9000-12000
£9091 $15455 €13000 Deux jeunes femmes (38x26cm-15x10in) s. col print prov.exhib.lit. 25-Nov-3 Sotheby's, Paris #155/R est:12000-15000
£11000 $20240 €16060 Two women within an interior admiring a sweet rush (38x26cm-15x10in) s. print exec. c.1795 lit. 8-Jun-4 Sotheby's, London #206/R est:7000-9000
£12000 $22080 €17520 Image of Fugen (25x18cm-10x7in) s.d.1790 print folding album of 11 sheets lit. 8-Jun-4 Sotheby's, London #492/R est:12000-15000
£14000 $25760 €20440 The young Ebisu (25x18cm-10x7in) print folding album of 12 sheets exec. 1789 lit. 8-Jun-4 Sotheby's, London #493/R est:14000-18000
£14598 $24816 €20875 Deux jeunes femmes (36x24cm-14x9in) s. col print prov.exhib.lit. 25-Nov-3 Sotheby's, Paris #150/R est:24000-28000
£15000 $27600 €21900 Wakaume of the Tamaya in Edo-cho Itchome (37x25cm-15x10in) s. print exec. c.1793-4 lit. 8-Jun-4 Sotheby's, London #215/R est:15000-20000
£23496 $39944 €33600 Jeune femme frivole (37x24cm-15x9in) s. col print prov.exhib.lit. 25-Nov-3 Sotheby's, Paris #138/R est:40000-50000
£28000 $51520 €40880 A beauty painting her eyebrows (37x25cm-15x10in) s. print lit. 8-Jun-4 Sotheby's, London #254/R est:15000-20000
£31031 $52754 €44375 Bol de the (38x25cm-15x10in) s. col print prov.exhib.lit. 25-Nov-3 Sotheby's, Paris #157/R est:45000-55000
£46000 $84640 €67160 The Geisha Tatsumi Roko from the series of the renowned beauties (39x26cm-15x10in) s.i. print prov.lit. 8-Jun-4 Sotheby's, London #193/R est:20000-30000
£53000 $97520 €77380 Gifts of the ebb tide (27x19cm-11x7in) s. print folding album of 10 sheets exec. c.1789 lit. 8-Jun-4 Sotheby's, London #494/R est:24000-28000
£66000 $121440 €96360 Three beauties of Yoshiwara (39x26cm-15x10in) s. print prov.lit. 8-Jun-4 Sotheby's, London #224/R est:37000-40000
Works on paper
£89674 $165000 €130924 Man seducing a young woman (55x70cm-22x28in) s. col ink hanging scroll prov.exhib. 23-Mar-4 Christie's, Rockefeller NY #119/R est:100000-150000

UTECH, Joachim Christoph Ludwig (1889-1960) German
Sculpture
£1333 $2453 €2000 Girl wearing headscarf (26x20x20cm-10x8x8in) s.mono.d.1940 verso red granite. 10-Jun-4 Hauswedell & Nolte, Hamburg #708/R est:3000

UTH, Max (1863-1914) German
£1333 $2453 €2000 Mountain lake (70x70cm-28x28in) s. 12-Jun-4 Villa Grisebach, Berlin #158a/R est:2500-3500

UTKINA, Tatiana (1962-) Russian
£300 $528 €438 Young girl in an interior (80x65cm-31x26in) s. 18-May-4 Bonhams, Knightsbridge #107/R
Works on paper
£400 $716 €584 Morning (69x56cm-27x22in) s. 21-Mar-4 Lots Road Auctions, London #366

UTRECHT SCHOOL (17th C) Flemish
£6849 $11644 €10000 Orpheus charming the animals (115x153cm-45x60in) 4-Nov-3 Sotheby's, Amsterdam #45/R est:10000-15000
£24000 $43200 €35040 Young boy holding a pipe by candlelight (62x51cm-24x20in) prov. 22-Apr-4 Sotheby's, London #33/R est:15000-20000

UTRECHT, Adriaen van (attrib) (1599-1653) Flemish
£89404 $162715 €135000 Still life with basket of fruit and artichokes (66x50cm-26x20in) panel. 15-Jun-4 Claude Aguttes, Neuilly #15/R est:25000-30000

UTRECHT, Adriaen van (school) (1599-1653) Flemish
£5847 $10758 €8537 Still life of dead game and plate of fruit (112x146cm-44x57in) bears sig d.1643 prov. 14-Jun-4 Waddingtons, Toronto #258/R est:20000-30000 (C.D 14500)

UTRILLO, Maurice (1883-1955) French
£12227 $22253 €17851 Le Chateau de Chillon (48x61cm-19x24in) s. cardboard painted c.1916 prov. 18-Jun-4 Kornfeld, Bern #143/R est:30000 (S.FR 28000)
£16000 $29440 €23360 Fleurs (44x29cm-17x11in) s. board prov. 22-Jun-4 Sotheby's, London #257/R est:18000-25000
£20270 $37500 €29594 Faouet, Chapelle Sainte barbe (39x56cm-15x22in) s.d.1923 s.i.d.verso prov. 11-Feb-4 Sotheby's, New York #24/R est:30000-40000
£22535 $38986 €32000 Eglise sous la neige (61x50cm-24x20in) s.i.d.1922. 10-Dec-3 Ferri, Paris #97 est:40000-50000
£22624 $38462 €50000 Rue Corot a Montmartre (26x34cm-10x13in) s. cardboard prov. 25-Nov-3 Pierre Berge, Paris #6/R est:40000-50000
£23982 $40769 €53000 Lapin Agile (18x24cm-7x9in) s. cardboard prov.lit. 25-Nov-3 Pierre Berge, Paris #7/R est:25000-30000

£25000 $45500 €36500 La maison de Mimi Pinson a Montmartre (48x58cm-19x23in) s. board prov.lit. 3-Feb-4 Christie's, London #186/R est:25000-35000
£26333 $48453 €39500 Figures devant l'eglise (87x62cm-34x24in) s.d.1928 panel lit. 8-Jun-4 Artcurial Briest, Paris #149/R est:45000-60000
£28000 $51520 €40880 Montmartre - Le Moulin de la Galette (17x18cm-7x7in) s.i. paper on panel painted c.1937-38 prov.lit. 22-Jun-4 Sotheby's, London #272/R est:18000-25000
£32000 $58880 €46720 Rue de Mont Cenis (27x41cm-11x16in) s.i. prov. 22-Jun-4 Sotheby's, London #266/R est:25000-35000
£32000 $58880 €46720 La Belle Gabrielle et la rue Saint-Vincent a Montmartre (41x55cm-16x22in) s. oil gesso board on panel painted c.1910-1912 exhib. 23-Jun-4 Christie's, London #267/R est:25000-35000
£36313 $65000 €53017 Eglise de Murato - Corse (54x65cm-21x26in) s.i.d.1937 prov.lit. 6-May-4 Sotheby's, New York #465/R est:60000-80000
£38235 $65000 €55823 Eglise d'Ivry-Sur-Seine (64x50cm-25x20in) s.d.1922 lit. 5-Nov-3 Christie's, Rockefeller NY #283/R est:60000-80000
£42000 $77280 €61320 Eglise de Beaulieu (50x64cm-20x25in) s. painted c.1916 prov.lit. 22-Jun-4 Sotheby's, London #160/R est:40000-60000
£44118 $75000 €64412 Chapelle de buis (47x62cm-19x24in) s.d.1921 s.i.stretcher painted 1921 prov.exhib.lit. 6-Nov-3 Sotheby's, New York #164/R est:70000-90000
£46667 $85400 €70000 Le chateau de la Ferte-Milon, Aisne (55x74cm-22x29in) s. painted c.1939 prov.lit. 7-Jun-4 Artcurial Briest, Paris #45/R est:80000-100000
£49162 $88000 €71777 Eglise de Bessines (49x65cm-19x26in) s.d.1923 s.i.d.verso prov.lit. 5-May-4 Christie's, Rockefeller NY #287/R est:70000-90000
£49913 $91839 €74870 Paris, Rue des Gobelins (65x92cm-26x36in) s.d.1921 s.i.d.verso lit. 9-Jun-4 Tajan, Paris #45/R est:80000-100000
£50349 $86601 €72000 Rue a la Courneuve (50x61cm-20x24in) s. exhib.lit. 8-Dec-3 Artcurial Briest, Paris #30/R est:85000-125000
£54348 $89130 €75000 L'eglise de Saint-Bernard (38x46cm-15x18in) s.d.1924 lit. 31-May-3 Farsetti, Prato #727/R est:70000-90000
£55000 $101200 €80300 Grande rue a Groslay (41x66cm-16x26in) s. board on panel painted c.1933 prov.lit. 23-Jun-4 Christie's, London #269/R est:40000-60000
£55944 $95105 €80000 Caserme Valez a Alencon (45x61cm-18x24in) s. cardboard exhib.lit. 29-Nov-3 Farsetti, Prato #499/R est:80000-100000
£57353 $97500 €83735 Rue Saint-Rustique sous la neige (46x55cm-18x22in) s.i. painted c.1947 prov.lit. 6-Nov-3 Sotheby's, New York #323/R est:60000-80000
£58000 $106720 €84680 Moulin de la Galette a Montmartre (38x47cm-15x19in) s.i. painted c.1938 prov.lit. 22-Jun-4 Sotheby's, London #273/R est:40000-60000
£58000 $106720 €84680 Le moulin de la Galette sous la neige (46x55cm-18x22in) s. painted c.1938 prov.lit. 23-Jun-4 Christie's, London #151/R est:30000-40000
£58824 $100000 €85883 Cabaret du Lapin Agile (46x55cm-18x22in) s. prov. 5-Nov-3 Christie's, Rockefeller NY #274/R est:80000-100000
£59732 $106919 €89000 Eglise d'Amberieux-en-Dombes (62x50cm-24x20in) s.d.1928 s.i.d.verso exhib.lit. 29-May-4 Farsetti, Prato #513/R est:85000-95000
£60000 $110400 €87600 Carrefour a Sannois (60x81cm-24x32in) s. painted c.1936-37 prov.lit. 22-Jun-4 Sotheby's, London #263/R est:60000-80000
£61453 $110000 €89721 Square St Pierre a Montmartre (46x55cm-18x22in) s.i.d. prov. 6-May-4 Sotheby's, New York #410/R est:70000-90000
£63319 $115240 €92446 La maison de Berliox, Rue de Mont-Cenis a Montmartre (51x68cm-20x27in) s. cardboard on canvas painted c.1917 prov.exhib.lit. 18-Jun-4 Kornfeld, Bern #144/R est:150000 (S.FR 145000)
£70588 $120000 €103058 Le square Saint-Pierre a Montmartre (61x74cm-24x29in) s. painted c.1908 prov.exhib.lit. 5-Nov-3 Christie's, Rockefeller NY #260/R est:70000-90000
£78000 $143520 €113880 Ancien reservoir de Montmartre, Place Jean-Baptiste Clement (60x94cm-24x37in) s. board prov.exhib.lit. 23-Jun-4 Christie's, London #272/R est:90000-120000
£123529 $210000 €180352 Rue de Mont-Cenis (49x72cm-19x28in) s. i.stretcher painted c.1910 prov.lit. 6-Nov-3 Sotheby's, New York #174/R est:180000-220000
£125000 $227500 €182500 Le jardin de Luxembourg (60x73cm-24x29in) s.d.1925 prov.lit. 3-Feb-4 Christie's, London #259/R est:60000-80000
£153363 $274520 €223910 Vue de Corte (60x81cm-24x32in) s. painted 1912 prov.lit. 25-May-4 Bukowskis, Stockholm #364a/R est:1500000-1600000 (S.KR 2075000)
£179577 $310669 €255000 Rue de l'Abreuvoir a Montmartre (50x75cm-20x30in) s. panel prov.exhib.lit. 12-Dec-3 Piasa, Paris #22/R est:150000-200000

Prints
£1836 $3250 €2681 Pour le bal de L.A.A.A. (116x71cm-46x28in) col lithograph. 30-Apr-4 Sotheby's, New York #266/R est:4000-6000
£3240 $5800 €4730 Moulin de la gallette (23x30cm-9x12in) s. color lithograph. 6-May-4 Swann Galleries, New York #593/R est:5000-8000

Works on paper
£2416 $4325 €3600 Bouquet de fleurs (10x9cm-4x4in) s. col crayon graphite. 26-May-4 Christie's, Paris #33/R est:2400-2800
£5634 $9746 €8000 Maison a Montmartre (27x20cm-11x8in) s. W/C gouache. 9-Dec-3 Chambelland & Giafferi, Paris #113/R est:8000-9000
£9500 $17480 €13870 Sacre Coeur de Montmartre (29x38cm-11x15in) s.i.d.1935 col crayon pencil prov.lit. 22-Jun-4 Sotheby's, London #530/R est:10000-15000
£10915 $18120 €15500 Montmartre sous la neige (23x31cm-9x12in) s.i. gouache. 13-Jun-3 Renaud, Paris #45/R est:24000
£11892 $22000 €17362 Chateau de Jonchere a Anse (36x53cm-14x21in) s.d.1929 gouache paper on card. 11-Feb-4 Sotheby's, New York #29/R est:15000-20000
£14706 $25000 €21471 Montmartre (17x10cm-7x4in) s. gouache W/C prov. 6-Nov-3 Sotheby's, New York #321/R est:15000-20000
£15909 $28000 €23227 Rue de Versailles (51x64cm-20x25in) s. d.1919 verso gouache board prov. 23-May-4 Hindman, Chicago #952/R est:35000-55000
£16216 $30000 €23675 Sainte-Anne, femmes (37x46cm-15x18in) s.d.1925 gouache paper on card prov. 11-Feb-4 Sotheby's, New York #62/R est:35000-45000
£16279 $28000 €23767 Rue de Versailles (51x64cm-20x25in) s.d.1919 verso gouache board. 7-Dec-3 Hindman, Chicago #802/R est:35000-55000
£17318 $31000 €25284 Paris, Montmartre, rue de Mont Cenis, L'ancienne Masion Berlioz (27x36cm-11x14in) s.d.1923 gouache over pencil prov.exhib.lit. 5-May-4 Christie's, Rockefeller NY #150/R est:20000-30000
£17877 $32000 €26100 Eglise de Chapaizes - Saone et Loire (41x27cm-16x11in) s.i. gouache W/C prov. 5-May-4 Christie's, Rockefeller NY #155/R est:40000-60000
£20805 $37242 €31000 Rue a Pontoise (31x48cm-12x19in) s. gouache card lit. 29-May-4 Farsetti, Prato #514/R est:20000-25000
£23529 $40000 €34352 Ouvrieres (25x37cm-10x15in) s.d.1922 W/C gouache. 6-Nov-3 Sotheby's, New York #193/R est:35000-45000
£23743 $42500 €34665 Montmartre (48x63cm-19x25in) s.i. W/C gouache pencil card prov. 6-May-4 Sotheby's, New York #445/R est:30000-40000
£25000 $46000 €36500 Sacre Coeur de Montmartre (48x62cm-19x24in) s.i.d.1937 gouache paper on board prov.exhib.lit. 22-Jun-4 Sotheby's, London #527/R est:25000-35000
£25140 $45000 €36704 Rue de Norvins a Montmartre (48x63cm-19x25in) s.i. gouache over pencil exec c.1936 prov.lit. 5-May-4 Christie's, Rockefeller NY #145/R est:50000-70000
£30000 $55200 €43800 Moulin de la Galette (34x51cm-13x20in) s.i.d.1934 gouache prov.lit. 22-Jun-4 Sotheby's, London #531/R est:30000-40000
£36000 $65520 €52560 Carrefour a Montmartre (33x51cm-13x20in) s.i.d.1932 gouache oil paper on canvas lit. 4-Feb-4 Sotheby's, London #444/R est:30000-40000

UTSUMIYA, Isao (1945-) Japanese
£680 $1218 €1000 RA O 1973 (130x62cm-51x24in) s.d.73 acrylic. 19-Mar-4 Millon & Associes, Paris #182/R

UTTECH, Tom (1942-) American
£667 $1200 €974 Windigoostigwan Lake Outlet (46x61cm-18x24in) s.d.1-22-86 verso masonite exhib. 26-Jan-4 Schrager Galleries, Milwaukee #1382
£2186 $4000 €3192 Moose at the Kitchen Island (41x48cm-16x19in) masonite. 10-Jul-4 Hindman, Chicago #538/R est:200-400

UTTER, Andre (1886-1948) French
£2778 $4639 €4000 Nature morte - still life with guitar (92x73cm-36x29in) s. s.i. verso. 25-Oct-3 Dr Lehr, Berlin #519/R est:3000

UTTER, Bror (1913-1933) American
£2096 $3500 €3060 Untitled (71x76cm-28x30in) 18-Oct-3 David Dike, Dallas #144/R est:4000-6000

UTZ, Thornton (1915-) American
Works on paper
£4790 $8000 €6993 Lovelies lounging around the pool provide a motel's best advertising (81x74cm-32x29in) s. gouache. 15-Nov-3 Illustration House, New York #108/R est:7000-10000

UTZON, Lin (1946-) Danish
£845 $1411 €1234 Heaven and ocean (150x200cm-59x79in) s.d.8/89. 7-Oct-3 Rasmussen, Copenhagen #283/R (D.KR 9000)

UUTINEN, Marianna (1961-) Finnish
£1538 $2723 €2245 Untitled (90x72cm-35x28in) s.d.1993 mixed media canvas prov. 27-Apr-4 AB Stockholms Auktionsverk #1013/R est:15000-20000 (S.KR 21000)
Works on paper
£586 $1037 €856 Untitled (33x24cm-13x9in) s.d.1995 mixed media canvas. 27-Apr-4 AB Stockholms Auktionsverk #1014/R (S.KR 8000)

UVA, Cesare (1824-1886) Italian
£1667 $3067 €2500 Back from the fields (31x22cm-12x9in) s. tempera card. 10-Jun-4 Christie's, Rome #42/R est:2600-2900
£2632 $4842 €4000 View of Sorrento (37x57cm-15x22in) s. tempera. 22-Jun-4 Sotheby's, Milan #158/R est:4000-5000

UWINS, Thomas (1782-1857) British
£1500 $2370 €2190 Portrait of a beauty (78x64cm-31x25in) d.1852 s.verso oval. 7-Sep-3 Lots Road Auctions, London #364 est:1200-1800

UWINS, Thomas (attrib) (1782-1857) British
£1467 $2655 €2200 Allegory of spring (40x30cm-16x12in) oval. 1-Apr-4 Van Ham, Cologne #1678/R est:2200

UYTENBOGAART, Isaac (1767-1831) Dutch
Works on paper
£600 $1074 €900 Landscape with travelling peasants and wagons (17x24cm-7x9in) s.d.1801 verso chk wash. 13-May-4 Bassenge, Berlin #5506/R

UYTEWAEL, Joachim (style) (1566-1638) Dutch
£86667 $158600 €130000 Diana and Callistus (52x60cm-20x24in) prov.exhib.lit. 1-Jun-4 Sotheby's, Milan #76/R est:10000-15000

UYTEWAEL, Pieter (1596-1660) Dutch
£15541 $27351 €23000 Venus and Adonis with Cupid (22x34cm-9x13in) copper prov. 22-May-4 Lempertz, Koln #1171/R est:25000-30000

UYTTENBROECK, Moses van (1590-1648) Dutch
£3087 $5526 €4600 Paysage bucolique avec berger et troupeau (26x41cm-10x16in) panel. 25-May-4 Palais de Beaux Arts, Brussels #84/R est:5000-7000
£4636 $8437 €7000 Rustic scene (45x56cm-18x22in) panel prov. 16-Jun-4 Dorotheum, Vienna #53/R est:4000-6000
Works on paper
£1900 $3287 €2774 Group of children enacting the Triumph of Silenus (15x25cm-6x10in) indis.sig.i. red chk pen brown ink grey wash. 12-Dec-3 Christie's, Kensington #517/R est:1500-2000

UZELAC, Milivoy (1897-1950) Yugoslavian
£2138 $3549 €3100 Femmes au mouchoir blanc (97x130cm-38x51in) s. 1-Oct-3 Millon & Associes, Paris #63/R

UZIEMBLO, Henryk (1879-1949) Polish
£415 $768 €606 Landscape (14x22cm-6x9in) 14-Mar-4 Agra, Warsaw #33/R (P.Z 3000)

VA, Barry le (1941-) American
Works on paper
£1067 $1952 €1600 Accumulated vision (60x48cm-24x19in) s.d.1976 biro ink on pencil. 4-Jun-4 Lempertz, Koln #278/R est:1800

£4444 $8000 €6488 Studies-intersecting circles series, opposite walls (35x42cm-14x17in) s.i.d.1970 pen black ink col crayon prov. 24-Apr-4 David Rago, Lambertville #225/R est:2000-3000

VAA, Dyre (1903-1980) Norwegian
Sculpture
£2575 $4506 €3760 Kvitebjorn - King Valemon (51cm-20in) s. bronze. 16-Dec-3 Grev Wedels Plass, Oslo #336/R est:40000-50000 (N.KR 30000)

VAAMONDE, Joaquin (1872-1900) Spanish
£4326 $7009 €6100 Portrait of a woman (55x46cm-22x18in) s.d.1891 s.verso. 20-May-3 Ansorena, Madrid #111/R est:2100
Works on paper
£1233 $2096 €1800 Lady with umbrella (34x24cm-13x9in) s.d.1892 gouache. 4-Nov-3 Ansorena, Madrid #289/R est:1800
£1342 $2510 €2000 Lady (35x25cm-14x10in) s.d.1892 W/C. 24-Feb-4 Durán, Madrid #177/R est:1800

VAARBERG, Johannes Christoffel (1825-1871) Dutch
£3667 $6600 €5500 Art lovers (57x47cm-22x19in) s.d.57 panel prov. 21-Apr-4 Christie's, Amsterdam #13/R est:7000-9000

VAARDT, Jan van der (1647-1721) Dutch
£3843 $6880 €5611 Italianate landscape with figures (99x96cm-39x38in) s.d.1715. 28-May-4 Uppsala Auktionskammare, Uppsala #44/R est:40000-50000 (S.KR 52000)
Works on paper
£1300 $2379 €1898 View of Millbank, London, with Westminster Abbey and Lambeth Palace in the distance (20x29cm-8x11in) i. black chk pen ink. 6-Jul-4 Christie's, London #176/R est:1500-2000

VAARULA, Olavi (1927-1989) Finnish
£676 $1209 €1000 View from the north I (66x45cm-26x18in) s.d.1969. 8-May-4 Bukowskis, Helsinki #266/R
Works on paper
£479 $766 €680 Landscape with animals (47x40cm-19x16in) s.d.1989 mixed media. 18-Sep-3 Hagelstam, Helsinki #1026/R
£590 $986 €850 Joy (33x37cm-13x15in) s.d.1927 gouache. 23-Oct-3 Hagelstam, Helsinki #957/R
£638 $1186 €950 On the beach (23x30cm-9x12in) s.d.1986 mixed media. 7-Mar-4 Bukowskis, Helsinki #463/R

VACATKO, Ludvik (1873-1956) Austrian
£412 $766 €602 Horse at caravan (31x28cm-12x11in) s. board. 6-Mar-4 Dorotheum, Prague #52 est:10000-15000 (C.KR 20000)

VACCA, Luigi (1778-1854) Italian
Works on paper
£278 $472 €400 From 'The Fiances' (18x25cm-7x10in) s.d.1834 W/C. 1-Nov-3 Meeting Art, Vercelli #411

VACCARO, Andrea (c.1598-1670) Italian
£3688 $6159 €5200 Sant'Agata a tre quarti di figura (61x48cm-24x19in) prov. 18-Jun-3 Christie's, Rome #369 est:2000-3000
£7222 $13000 €10544 Mary Magdalene (102x76cm-40x30in) init. prov. 23-Jan-4 Christie's, Rockefeller NY #199/R est:12000-18000
£12000 $21960 €17520 Saint John the Baptist (100x74cm-39x29in) prov. 9-Jul-4 Christie's, Kensington #151/R est:3000-5000
£13121 $21911 €18500 Christ captured (152x115cm-60x45in) mono. lit. 23-Jun-3 Finarte Semenzato, Rome #170/R
£47682 $86781 €72000 Pasce oves meas (76x103cm-30x41in) init. 16-Jun-4 Christie's, Rome #500/R est:25000-30000

VACCARO, Andrea (attrib) (c.1598-1670) Italian
£4491 $7500 €6557 Portrait of a woman (45x34cm-18x13in) 7-Oct-3 Sotheby's, New York #37/R est:10000-12000
£5035 $8408 €7200 Magdalene repenting (90x74cm-35x29in) oval. 30-Jun-3 Ansorena, Madrid #362/R

VACCARO, Bon Giovanni (attrib) (19th C) Italian
Sculpture
£3147 $5413 €4500 Three shoe makers (37cm-15in) painted terracotta. 4-Dec-3 Christie's, Milan #449/R est:2000-3000

VACCARO, Domenico Antonio (1680-1750) Italian
£7092 $11844 €10000 Sacra Famiglia impartisce il collare a Santa Teresa d'Avila (127x99cm-50x39in) 18-Jun-3 Christie's, Rome #431/R est:12000-15000

VACCARO, Nicola (c.1634-1709) Italian
£21986 $36716 €31000 Three putti with goat and garland of flowers (95x130cm-37x51in) attrib to Nicollo Malinconico. 18-Jun-3 Christie's, Rome #436/R est:15000-18000

VACCARO, Vincenzo (1858-1929) Italian
£1342 $2497 €2000 Interior with figures (41x53cm-16x21in) s. pair. 8-Mar-4 Bernaerts, Antwerp #97/R est:2000-2400

VACCHI, Sergio (1925-) Italian
£690 $1152 €1000 Cupola and phone (50x70cm-20x28in) s. tempera paper. 13-Nov-3 Finarte Semenzato, Rome #113
£839 $1427 €1200 Monn landscape (35x50cm-14x20in) s.i.d.1967 verso. 24-Nov-3 Christie's, Milan #94
£1033 $1901 €1550 Adam tree in Italy (80x60cm-31x24in) s.d.1965. 12-Jun-4 Meeting Art, Vercelli #204/R est:750
£1067 $1963 €1600 Praying (50x70cm-20x28in) s.d.1962 cardboard prov. 8-Jun-4 Finarte Semenzato, Milan #283/R est:1000-1500
£2333 $4200 €3500 Thoughtful eagle (80x60cm-31x24in) s.d.1964 s.i.d.verso. 22-Apr-4 Finarte Semenzato, Rome #227/R est:1200-1400
£2703 $4757 €4000 Study for Galileo (90x70cm-35x28in) s.d.1967. 19-May-4 Il Ponte, Milan #1115 est:1200-1400
£3867 $6960 €5800 Leaving Italy (140x200cm-55x79in) s.d.1965 s.i.d.verso exhib. 22-Apr-4 Finarte Semenzato, Rome #228/R est:3500-4000

VACHAL, Josef (1884-1969) Czechoslovakian
£675 $1188 €1013 Landscape (30x30cm-12x12in) s.d.1914. 22-May-4 Dorotheum, Prague #120/R est:30000-45000 (C.KR 32000)
£1094 $1817 €1597 Landscape with church (34x50cm-13x20in) s. board on panel. 4-Oct-3 Dorotheum, Prague #19/R est:50000-80000 (C.KR 50000)
£1266 $2227 €1899 Village green (50x70cm-20x28in) s. cardboard. 22-May-4 Dorotheum, Prague #75/R est:50000-75000 (C.KR 60000)

VACHER, Charles (1818-1883) British
Works on paper
£360 $659 €526 Asouan, the ancient Syene, from the south (27x76cm-11x30in) s.i.d.1859 W/C. 27-Jan-4 Bonhams, Knightsbridge #21/R

VADASZ, Endre (1901-1944) Hungarian
Works on paper
£2271 $4020 €3316 Flower market (60x50cm-24x20in) s. mixed media. 28-Apr-4 Kieselbach, Budapest #35/R (H.F 850000)

VADDER, Frans de (1862-1935) Belgian
£336 $601 €500 Vue d'un bois (70x50cm-28x20in) s. 25-May-4 Campo & Campo, Antwerp #73
£350 $601 €500 Couple de fermiers (36x26cm-14x10in) s. panel. 2-Dec-3 Campo & Campo, Antwerp #113

VADDER, Lodewyk de (1605-1655) Flemish
£6500 $11245 €9490 Wooded landscape with travellers on a path (62x76cm-24x30in) prov. 12-Dec-3 Christie's, Kensington #14/R est:7000-10000

VADDER, Lodewyk de (attrib) (1605-1655) Flemish
£1854 $3375 €2800 Landscape with travellers (41x60cm-16x24in) 15-Jun-4 Claude Aguttes, Neuilly #28/R est:4000
£6500 $11245 €9490 River landscape with fisherman, a town beyond (40x63cm-16x25in) panel. 12-Dec-3 Christie's, Kensington #24/R est:2000-3000

VADILLO, Francisco (20th C) Spanish?
£262 $450 €383 Nude (35x46cm-14x18in) s. panel. 7-Dec-3 Subastas Odalys, Caracas #147
£336 $625 €491 Nude (33x41cm-13x16in) s. painted 1979. 14-Mar-4 Subastas Odalys, Caracas #30/R
£355 $550 €518 Nude (30x60cm-12x24in) s. painted 1992. 3-Nov-2 Subastas Odalys, Caracas #105/R
£433 $780 €632 Golf courses (30x60cm-12x24in) painted 1990. 25-Apr-4 Subastas Odalys, Caracas #95
£524 $875 €765 Composition (70x60cm-28x24in) s. painted 1972. 13-Jul-3 Subastas Odalys, Caracas #100/R
£664 $1060 €969 Avila (38x76cm-15x30in) s. 16-Mar-3 Subastas Odalys, Caracas #85
£848 $1560 €1238 Avila (50x100cm-20x39in) s. painted 1985. 28-Mar-4 Subastas Odalys, Caracas #106
£907 $1560 €1324 Country Club (50x100cm-20x39in) s. painted 1991. 7-Dec-3 Subastas Odalys, Caracas #25/R
£909 $1435 €1327 Avila (50x100cm-20x39in) s. 27-Apr-3 Subastas Odalys, Caracas #17
£956 $1720 €1396 Avila (61x102cm-24x40in) s. painted 1981. 25-Apr-4 Subastas Odalys, Caracas #42/R
£1288 $2345 €1932 Avila (61x120cm-24x47in) s. painted 1980. 21-Jun-4 Subastas Odalys, Caracas #155
£2850 $4560 €4161 Avila seen from the Country Club (60x92cm-24x36in) s. painted 1984. 21-Sep-3 Subastas Odalys, Caracas #95/R
£7444 $12655 €10868 Dusk (76x102cm-30x40in) s. painted 1974. 23-Nov-3 Subastas Odalys, Caracas #139/R

VAEL, Albert (1914-1981) Belgian?
£369 $687 €550 Composition with men's heads (108x85cm-43x33in) 8-Mar-4 Bernaerts, Antwerp #836

VAELTL, Otto (1885-1977) German
£6452 $11613 €9420 The Holy Family (132x115cm-52x45in) i. verso after van Dyck. 24-Apr-4 Rasmussen, Havnen #2209/R est:10000-15000 (D.KR 72000)

VAEREN-GOUGH, S V (19/20th C) ?
Sculpture
£5000 $8350 €7300 Young girl (48cm-19in) s. bronze marble. 14-Oct-3 Sotheby's, Olympia #36/R est:3000-4000

VAERENBERGH, Georges van (19/20th C) Belgian
Sculpture
£1800 $3276 €2628 Figure of a pierrot musclan (68cm-27in) s. gilt bronze marble. 29-Jun-4 Bonhams, Knightsbridge #298/R est:1800-2500

VAES, Walter (1882-1958) Belgian
£1489 $2487 €2100 Still life of pears (22x41cm-9x16in) init. canvas on board. 20-Oct-3 Glerum, Amsterdam #222/R est:1000-1500
£2333 $4200 €3500 Red flowers in a vase (27x22cm-11x9in) s. 20-Apr-4 Sotheby's, Amsterdam #80/R est:2000-3000
£2333 $4293 €3500 Hortensias (62x50cm-24x20in) s. i.verso. 9-Jun-4 Christie's, Amsterdam #95/R est:2500-3500
£4196 $7217 €6000 Bouquet de fleurs avec ange (50x40cm-20x16in) s. 2-Dec-3 Sotheby's, Amsterdam #32/R est:2000-3000

VAFFLARD, Pierre Antoine (1777-C.1840) French
£3200 $5888 €4800 Les petits ramoneurs (89x73cm-35x29in) 9-Jun-4 Oger, Dumont, Paris #40/R est:5000

VAGAGGINI, Memo (1892-1955) Italian
£2158 $3540 €3000 Poggio di Pratolino (48x60cm-19x24in) s. i.verso. 10-Jun-3 Pandolfini, Florence #224/R est:1300-1400

VAGH WEINMANN, Elemer (1906-) Hungarian
£333 $597 €500 Landscape (53x65cm-21x26in) s. painted 1970. 17-May-4 Chayette & Cheval, Paris #162
£347 $638 €520 Budapest (64x53cm-25x21in) s. 8-Jun-4 Livinec, Gaudcheau & Jezequel, Rennes #131
£414 $691 €600 Scene de rue animee (60x73cm-24x29in) s.verso. 11-Nov-3 Lesieur & Le Bars, Le Havre #110
£1167 $2100 €1750 Autumn in Paris (65x81cm-26x32in) s. 24-Apr-4 Cornette de St.Cyr, Paris #412 est:2500

VAGH WEINMANN, Maurice (1899-1986) Hungarian
£552 $921 €800 Village covered in snow (60x73cm-24x29in) s.d.1959. 11-Nov-3 Lesieur & Le Bars, Le Havre #111
£738 $1366 €1100 Le chemin de campagne (60x73cm-24x29in) s. 15-Mar-4 Claude Boisgirard, Paris #117

VAGH WEINMANN, Nandor (1897-1978) Hungarian
£1126 $2049 €1700 Deux garcons avec un chien (72x91cm-28x36in) s. 16-Jun-4 Claude Boisgirard, Paris #161/R est:1300-1500

VAGLIERI, Tino (1929-2000) Italian
£533 $981 €800 Town walker (60x50cm-24x20in) s. s.i.d.1993 verso. 12-Jun-4 Meeting Art, Vercelli #684/R
£556 $878 €800 Figure moving (50x60cm-20x24in) painted 1997. 6-Sep-3 Meeting Art, Vercelli #523
£599 $994 €850 Camminatore nella cittas (60x50cm-24x20in) s. s.i.d.1993 verso. 14-Jun-3 Meeting Art, Vercelli #205/R
£816 $1461 €1200 Figure (30x50cm-12x20in) s.d.1958 s.i.d.verso board. 16-Mar-4 Finarte Semenzato, Milan #266/R
£1678 $3003 €2500 For a delivery (92x79cm-36x31in) s.d.65 s.d.verso exhib. 25-May-4 Sotheby's, Milan #3/R est:3000
£1701 $3044 €2500 Dragged man (70x79cm-28x31in) s.d.58 s.i.d.verso prov. 16-Mar-4 Finarte Semenzato, Milan #268/R est:700
£2177 $3897 €3200 Study of head (90x70cm-35x28in) s.d.57 s.i.d.verso prov. 16-Mar-4 Finarte Semenzato, Milan #267/R est:700

VAGNETTI, Gianni (1898-1956) Italian
£331 $603 €500 Herrings (23x40cm-9x16in) s.d.45 masonite. 21-Jun-4 Pandolfini, Florence #467
£567 $1043 €850 Woman (60x47cm-24x19in) s. 11-Jun-4 Farsetti, Prato #444/R
£596 $1085 €900 Profile of woman (46x36cm-18x14in) s. board. 17-Jun-4 Galleria Pananti, Florence #536/R
£870 $1426 €1200 Night (30x36cm-12x14in) 27-May-3 Il Ponte, Milan #888
£942 $1545 €1300 Still life with figs (33x30cm-13x12in) 27-May-3 Il Ponte, Milan #910
£1014 $1664 €1400 Wedding celebration (39x63cm-15x25in) s.d.1943 i.verso. 27-May-3 Il Ponte, Milan #903
£7194 $11799 €10000 Roman woman (149x88cm-59x35in) s. lit. 10-Jun-3 Pandolfini, Florence #380/R est:12000-15000
Works on paper
£278 $506 €420 Red fish with seascape (25x26cm-10x10in) s. mixed media. 17-Jun-4 Galleria Pananti, Florence #522/R
£497 $904 €750 Female nude (35x46cm-14x18in) s. W/C. 17-Jun-4 Galleria Pananti, Florence #521/R

VAGO, Alexander (1887-?) Hungarian/American
£444 $800 €648 Elegant woman with a fan (97x69cm-38x27in) i. 24-Jan-4 Skinner, Boston #478
£2446 $4500 €3571 Village scene (89x127cm-35x50in) 11-Jun-4 Du Mouchelle, Detroit #2024/R est:4500-5500

VAGO, Sandor (1887-?) American
£1099 $2000 €1649 Portrait of a seated gentleman in formal attire with a monocle (102x76cm-40x30in) s. 16-Jun-4 Wolf's, New York #487190/R est:4000-6000

VAGO, Valentino (1931-) Italian
£764 $1207 €1100 M85 (92x73cm-36x29in) painted 1969. 6-Sep-3 Meeting Art, Vercelli #568
£845 $1403 €1200 MA.60 (100x70cm-39x28in) s.i. verso. 14-Jun-3 Meeting Art, Vercelli #110/R
£1200 $2208 €1800 Untitled (80x65cm-31x26in) s.verso. 14-Jun-4 Sant Agostino, Torino #393/R est:1000-1400

VAHEY, Brian (20th C) Irish
£867 $1569 €1300 October apples II (49x102cm-19x40in) s.i.verso board. 30-Mar-4 De Veres Art Auctions, Dublin #193/R

VAIL, Eugene Laurent (attrib) (1857-1934) American/French
£570 $1050 €850 Reunion de buveurs sur la place d'un village. Scene de mariage (16x12cm-6x5in) panel pair. 26-Mar-4 Piasa, Paris #75

VAILLANT, Wallerant (1623-1677) Dutch
Works on paper
£1096 $1863 €1600 Portrait de Marie Anne d'Autriche (58x45cm-23x18in) i.verso crayon chk. 6-Nov-3 Tajan, Paris #38/R

VAINIO, Armas (1923-2003) Finnish
£368 $615 €530 Flowers in jug (55x40cm-22x16in) s/d/1989. 26-Oct-3 Bukowskis, Helsinki #519/R
£389 $649 €560 River (41x60cm-16x24in) s.d.91. 26-Oct-3 Bukowskis, Helsinki #518/R
£436 $811 €650 Winter evening (45x55cm-18x22in) s.d.1989. 7-Mar-4 Bukowskis, Helsinki #464/R
£503 $926 €750 Pot and fungus (51x60cm-20x24in) s.d.1986. 25-Mar-4 Hagelstam, Helsinki #1028

VAISANEN, Hannu (1951-) Finnish
£608 $1089 €900 Story of fish (46x55cm-18x22in) s.d.2001 verso. 8-May-4 Bukowskis, Helsinki #283/R
£676 $1209 €1000 Kaspar Hauser (116x81cm-46x32in) s.d.82. 8-May-4 Bukowskis, Helsinki #297/R
Works on paper
£676 $1209 €1000 Composition - stulen maane (67x97cm-26x38in) s.d.83 gouache. 8-May-4 Bukowskis, Helsinki #306/R

VAISMAN, Meyer (1960-) American
Works on paper
£1297 $2400 €1894 Painting without context (181x130cm-71x51in) laminated process inks canvas exec 1986 exhib. 13-Jul-4 Christie's, Rockefeller NY #83/R est:3000-5000
£19553 $35000 €28547 Oral History (230x279cm-91x110in) processed inks canvas exec 1988 prov.exhib.lit. 13-May-4 Sotheby's, New York #473/R est:12000-15000

VAISOT, Mellou (19th C) ?
Works on paper
£220 $405 €321 Scene in the fish market, Galata, Constantinople (23x33cm-9x13in) s.i.d.Jan 1877 pencil. 25-Mar-4 Christie's, Kensington #56

VAJDA, Zsigmond (1860-1931) Hungarian
£783 $1355 €1143 In Pink (61x80cm-24x31in) s. 12-Dec-3 Kieselbach, Budapest #135/R (H.F 300000)

VAKHRAMEEV, A I (1874-1926) Russian
Works on paper
£611 $1100 €892 Listening to the music, people houses (28x39cm-11x15in) pastel pencil. 24-Apr-4 Shishkin Gallery, Moscow #1/R est:3000-4000

VAL, Valentine Synave Nicolaud (1870-1943) Belgian
£3000 $5520 €4380 Roses (91x31cm-36x12in) one s.d.89 pair. 25-Mar-4 Christie's, Kensington #88/R est:2000-3000

VALADE, Jean (attrib) (1709-1787) French
Works on paper
£2273 $4000 €3319 Portrait of a lady with a pink bow (48x38cm-19x15in) pastel paper on canvas. 18-May-4 Bonhams & Butterfields, San Francisco #43/R est:3000-5000

VALADIE, Jean Baptiste (1933-) French
£400 $692 €584 Pierrot family (65x50cm-26x20in) s. s.i.d.66. 9-Dec-3 Rosebery Fine Art, London #574/R
£704 $1218 €1000 My fair lady (73x60cm-29x24in) 10-Dec-3 Millon & Associes, Paris #315/R
£775 $1340 €1100 Fillette au bois (65x50cm-26x20in) s.d.1967. 10-Dec-3 Rossini, Paris #114
£986 $1706 €1400 Soeurs jumelles aux colombes (100x81cm-39x32in) 10-Dec-3 Millon & Associes, Paris #316/R
£1689 $3193 €2500 Le championnat (50x100cm-20x39in) s. s.i.verso. 21-Feb-4 Cornette de St.Cyr, Paris #225 est:2500-3000

VALADIER, Giuseppe (1762-1839) Italian
Works on paper
£68966 $115172 €100000 Rome, view of the Campidoglio (26x44cm-10x17in) s. pen ink W/C. 12-Nov-3 Sotheby's, Milan #176/R est:15000-20000

VALADIER, Luigi (1726-1785) Italian
Works on paper
£246 $450 €359 Design for an altar (27x13cm-11x5in) pen black ink gray wash. 29-Jan-4 Swann Galleries, New York #129/R

VALADON, Suzanne (1865-1938) French
£4225 $7310 €6000 Composition a la branche d'arbre (54x43cm-21x17in) mono. cardboard on canvas. 9-Dec-3 Artcurial Briest, Paris #135/R est:6000-8000
£10695 $20000 €15615 Deux roses dans un verre (28x24cm-11x9in) s.d.1933 panel prov.exhib.lit. 25-Feb-4 Christie's, Rockefeller NY #54/R est:10000-15000

£14000 $23380 €20440 Nature morte aux lapins (65x54cm-26x21in) s.d.1927 prov.exhib.lit. 21-Oct-3 Sotheby's, London #145/R est:15000-20000
£16107 $28510 €24000 Nu assis au bord de l'eau (60x73cm-24x29in) s.d.1929 prov.lit. 27-Apr-4 Artcurial Briest, Paris #161/R est:15000-20000
£20979 $36084 €30000 Nu debout a la draperie (81x65cm-32x26in) s.d.1924 prov.lit. 2-Dec-3 Calmels Cohen, Paris #48/R est:10000-50000
£26000 $46540 €39000 Roses dans un verre (46x33cm-18x13in) d.1936 exhib. 16-May-4 Osenat, Fontainebleau #118/R est:30000-40000
£28188 $49893 €42000 Autoportrait (72x57cm-28x22in) s.d.1911 prov.lit. 27-Apr-4 Artcurial Briest, Paris #160/R est:15000-20000
£35294 $60000 €51529 Femme allongee sur un canape (65x93cm-26x37in) s. painted c.1917-1918 prov.exhib.lit. 5-Nov-3 Christie's, Rockefeller NY #363/R est:30000-40000

Works on paper
£861 $1575 €1300 Maurice Utrillo enfant, nu, jouant a la balle (28x33cm-11x13in) s.d.94 chl drawing. 7-Apr-4 Piasa, Paris #40 est:1000-1200
£1235 $2100 €1803 Seated female nude (28x23cm-11x9in) s.d.1921 mixed media dr. 7-Nov-3 Selkirks, St. Louis #660 est:2500-3500
£1750 $2800 €2555 Nu assise (22x20cm-9x8in) s. pencil exec.c.1895. 18-Sep-3 Swann Galleries, New York #669/R est:2000-3000
£2973 $5500 €4341 Nu s'epongeant le dos (14x14cm-6x6in) s. chl prov.exhib. 12-Feb-4 Sotheby's, New York #9/R est:1500-2500
£3497 $5944 €5000 Femme a sa toilette (25x36cm-10x14in) s. W/C over pencil chl. 26-Nov-3 Dorotheum, Vienna #17/R est:4800-5500
£4000 $7160 €6000 Etude de nu feminin (9x29cm-4x11in) chl crayon graphite. 16-May-4 Osenat, Fontainebleau #52/R est:2000-3000
£4375 $7306 €6300 Nu assis (30x38cm-12x15in) s.d.1904 red chk col chk. 21-Oct-3 Christie's, Paris #94/R est:2000-3000
£4564 $8169 €6800 Nu assis sur un divan (18x21cm-7x8in) s. chl prov.lit. 26-May-4 Christie's, Paris #26/R est:3000-4000
£5500 $9185 €8030 Femme au tub (29x26cm-11x10in) s.d.1909 pastel chl. 21-Oct-3 Sotheby's, London #117/R est:6000-8000
£10830 $19928 €15812 Female model in erotic posture (48x61cm-19x24in) s.d.1908 pastel chk prov. 29-Mar-4 Rasmussen, Copenhagen #146/R est:40000-50000 (D.KR 120000)
£16216 $30000 €23675 Nature morte au compotier (61x50cm-24x20in) s.d.1920 prov.exhib.lit. 11-Feb-4 Sotheby's, New York #66/R est:25000-35000

VALAIN, Chris (20th C) French?
£267 $477 €400 Scene de rue animee (32x24cm-13x9in) s. cardboard. 16-May-4 Thierry & Lannon, Brest #233

Works on paper
£728 $1362 €1100 Grande Grue a Gourin (50x61cm-20x24in) s. pastel. 24-Jul-4 Thierry & Lannon, Brest #304
£1033 $1850 €1550 Jour de marche a Gourin (48x60cm-19x24in) s. pastel. 16-May-4 Thierry & Lannon, Brest #232/R est:1200-1500
£1197 $2095 €1700 Rue animee a Gourin (48x60cm-19x24in) s. pastel. 21-Dec-3 Thierry & Lannon, Brest #268 est:1000-1200

VALAND, Norvald (1897-1943) Norwegian
£358 $572 €519 Haymaking (47x52cm-19x20in) s. panel. 22-Sep-3 Blomqvist, Lysaker #1323 (N.KR 4200)

VALBERT, F (?) ?
£1050 $1943 €1533 First snow (58x78cm-23x31in) s. 14-Jul-4 Bonhams, Chester #431 est:300-500

VALCK, Adriaen de (attrib) (1622-?) Dutch
£1538 $2615 €2200 Still life with bust, books an small figure of Cupid (95x83cm-37x33in) 20-Nov-3 Van Ham, Cologne #1427a/R est:2000

VALCKERT, Werner van den (1585-c.1655) Dutch
£56075 $88598 €81309 Galathea and Neptune (108x80cm-43x31in) s. one d.1619 panel pair exhib. 2-Sep-3 Rasmussen, Copenhagen #1593/R est:600000-800000 (D.KR 600000)

VALDES, Diego de (20th C) Spanish
£658 $1191 €1000 Memorial (100x81cm-39x32in) s. board. 14-Apr-4 Ansorena, Madrid #256/R

VALDES, Manuel (1942-) Spanish
£67039 $120000 €97877 Caballero (198x157cm-78x62in) s. num.4 verso oil mixed media collage prov. 13-May-4 Sotheby's, New York #445/R est:40000-60000

VALDES, Montse (20th C) Spanish
Works on paper
£658 $1211 €1000 Nude study (66x46cm-26x18in) s. chl. 22-Jun-4 De Veres Art Auctions, Dublin #225/R

VALDEZ, Marino (1951-) Argentinian
£738 $1366 €1100 Clown and red striped zebra (53x48cm-21x19in) s.d.2000 acrylic. 9-Mar-4 Dorotheum, Vienna #244/R

VALDIECK, J (?) ?
£407 $729 €594 Portrait of female nude seated (90x63cm-35x25in) i.verso. 10-May-4 Rasmussen, Vejle #400/R (D.KR 4500)

VALDIVIESO, Antonio (1918-2000) Spanish
£1879 $3495 €2800 Still life with pomegranates (46x67cm-18x26in) s. 2-Mar-4 Ansorena, Madrid #12/R est:1200

VALDIVIESO, Raul (1931-) Chilean
Sculpture
£14706 $25000 €21471 Male torso (71x46x16cm-28x18x6in) i.d.76 black granite prov.lit. 19-Nov-3 Sotheby's, New York #26/R est:10000-15000

VALE, Florence Gertrude (1909-) Canadian
£298 $474 €435 Blue tea cozy (30x25cm-12x10in) s.d.54 s.i.d.54 verso on canvasboard. 15-Sep-3 Ritchie, Toronto #100/R (C.D 650)

Works on paper
£299 $476 €437 Pyramid of roses (11x16cm-4x6in) s.d.65 ink exhib. 15-Sep-3 Ritchie, Toronto #103/R (C.D 650)

VALE, R (?) ?
£3500 $5950 €5110 Ships of the allied Navy coming to anchor (58x75cm-23x30in) 19-Nov-3 Christie's, Kensington #438a/R est:4000-6000

VALENCIA, Francisco (1936-) Spanish
£448 $807 €650 Arcade in the Alhambra, Granada (97x130cm-38x51in) s. s.i.d.1990 verso. 26-Jan-4 Durán, Madrid #645/R
£448 $807 €650 Flowers and fruit (70x90cm-28x35in) s. s.i.d.1990 verso. 26-Jan-4 Durán, Madrid #699/R
£759 $1366 €1100 Smokers (132x184cm-52x72in) 26-Jan-4 Durán, Madrid #644/R

VALENCIA, Manuel (1856-1935) American
£409 $650 €597 Impressionistic California landscape with blue wildflowers and fisherman (51x41cm-20x16in) s. panel. 5-May-3 O'Gallerie, Oregon #841/R
£568 $1000 €829 Winter shadows (30x46cm-12x18in) s. 23-May-4 Bonhams & Butterfields, Los Angeles #7019/R
£838 $1500 €1223 River valley (30x46cm-12x18in) s. 21-Mar-4 Bonhams & Butterfields, Los Angeles #7327/R est:2000-3000
£1033 $1900 €1508 Waterfall in Yellowstone (50x41cm-20x16in) s.d.1924 prov. 8-Jun-4 Bonhams & Butterfields, San Francisco #4214/R
£1389 $2500 €2028 Road to Mount Tamalpais (30x45cm-12x18in) s. prov. 25-Apr-4 Bonhams & Butterfields, San Francisco #5507/R est:2000-3000
£1445 $2500 €2110 California Oaks with grazing cattle (51x76cm-20x30in) s. prov. 10-Dec-3 Bonhams & Butterfields, San Francisco #6178/R est:3000-5000
£1494 $2750 €2181 Old California (50x91cm-20x36in) s. prov. 8-Jun-4 Bonhams & Butterfields, San Francisco #4226/R est:4000-6000
£1589 $2750 €2320 Moonlight - near Pescadero Beach, California (51x76cm-20x30in) s. i.stretcher. 10-Dec-3 Bonhams & Butterfields, San Francisco #6173/R est:2500-3500
£1766 $3250 €2578 View of the coast with two figures on a path (55x71cm-22x28in) st.sig. canvas on board prov. 8-Jun-4 Bonhams & Butterfields, San Francisco #4213/R est:3000-5000
£2310 $4250 €3373 Wildflowers in the hills (40x61cm-16x24in) s. prov. 8-Jun-4 Bonhams & Butterfields, San Francisco #4187/R est:3000-5000

VALENCIA, Manuel (attrib) (1856-1935) American
£380 $700 €555 Cottages by a river with blooming wildflowers (30x46cm-12x18in) bears sig. or possibly by Ramona. 28-Mar-4 Bonhams & Butterfields, San Francisco #2746

VALENCIA, Pedro de (1902-1971) Spanish
£1846 $3267 €2750 Lady with gloves (72x60cm-28x24in) s.d.1950. 27-Apr-4 Durán, Madrid #88/R est:2500

Works on paper
£282 $493 €400 Boy with dove (17x11cm-7x4in) s. W/C ink wash. 16-Dec-3 Segre, Madrid #253/R
£435 $713 €600 Female nude (31x24cm-12x9in) s.d.1932 drawing. 27-May-3 Durán, Madrid #62/R

VALENCIA, Ramona (20th C) American
£670 $1200 €978 Flowering sandy hillside (23x30cm-9x12in) s. board. 16-Mar-4 Matthew's, Oregon #90/R

VALENCIAN SCHOOL (15th C) Spanish
£8219 $13973 €12000 Arma Christi (70x52cm-28x20in) tempera gold board. 9-Nov-3 Finarte, Venice #141/R est:10000-12000

VALENCIAN SCHOOL (16th C) Spanish
£6711 $12483 €10000 Entombment (98x123cm-39x48in) board. 2-Mar-4 Ansorena, Madrid #269/R est:10000

VALENCIAN SCHOOL (17th C) Spanish
£10000 $18000 €14600 Saint Stephen (98x77cm-39x30in) 21-Apr-4 Christie's, London #61/R est:7000-10000

VALENCIAN SCHOOL (19th C) Spanish
£5556 $10000 €8112 Flowers in a woven basket on a carved stone ledge (38x46cm-15x18in) 22-Jan-4 Sotheby's, New York #234/R est:10000-15000

VALENCIENNES, Pierre Henri de (attrib) (1750-1819) French
£6757 $11622 €9865 Classic landscape with figures (43x65cm-17x26in) s.d.1811 oil paper. 8-Dec-3 Philippe Schuler, Zurich #3439/R est:6000-8000 (S.FR 15000)
£6897 $11448 €10000 Falls near Tivoli (64x50cm-25x20in) prov. 1-Oct-3 Dorotheum, Vienna #80/R est:12000-15000
£23743 $42500 €34665 Mountainous Italianate landscape (73x100cm-29x39in) 27-May-4 Sotheby's, New York #77/R est:12000-15000
£30000 $54900 €43800 Landscape with Belisarius and view of Istanbul (43x65cm-17x26in) 8-Jul-4 Sotheby's, London #339/R est:8000-12000
£154930 $271126 €220000 Vue du tombeau de Jacques Rousseau a Ermenonville. Paysage classique (117x170cm-46x67in) pair. 18-Dec-3 Tajan, Paris #48/R est:40000-60000

VALENKAMPH, Theodor Victor Carl (1868-1924) American
£247 $400 €361 Landscape with fox running after fowl (16x20cm-6x8in) s. 31-Jul-3 Eldred, East Dennis #1204/R
£466 $750 €680 Homeward bound (61x71cm-24x28in) s. 21-Aug-3 Doyle, New York #50/R

£566 $900 €826 Clipper ship in choppy seas (81x69cm-32x27in) s. prov. 13-Sep-3 Selkirks, St. Louis #65
£883 $1500 €1289 Moonlight sail (31x46cm-12x18in) s. 21-Nov-3 Skinner, Boston #305/R est:1800-2200
£1242 $2000 €1813 Ship in rough seas (46x61cm-18x24in) s. 20-Aug-3 James Julia, Fairfield #716/R est:1200-1600
£1421 $2600 €2132 Schooner under sail in a calm sea with overcast skies (46x61cm-18x24in) s.d.1909. 29-Jul-4 Eldred, East Dennis #183/R est:800-1200

VALENSI, Henry (1883-1960) French
£3873 $6701 €5500 Fugue en jaune (82x101cm-32x40in) s.i.d.1948 exhib.lit. 9-Dec-3 Artcurial Briest, Paris #258/R est:6000-8000
£19575 $33865 €28580 Constantinople (65x81cm-26x32in) s.d.1914. 12-Dec-3 Kieselbach, Budapest #63/R (H.F 7500000)
Works on paper
£355 $592 €500 Femmes dans la casbah (32x23cm-13x9in) s.d.1920 col crayon. 19-Oct-3 Rabourdin & Choppin de Janvry, Paris #94/R
£490 $832 €700 Boxe (21x22cm-8x9in) s.i.d.1932 W/C graphite. 28-Nov-3 Drouot Estimations, Paris #182

VALENTA, Ludwig (1882-1943) Austrian
£560 $1003 €818 Evening meal (21x15cm-8x6in) s. panel. 12-May-4 Dobiaschofsky, Bern #1037/R (S.FR 1300)

VALENTI, Italo (1912-1995) Italian
£493 $818 €700 Still life (11x9cm-4x4in) s.verso canvas on cardboard lit. 13-Jun-3 Farsetti, Prato #563/R
£498 $846 €727 Flowers (28x23cm-11x9in) s. tempera. 25-Nov-3 Germann, Zurich #917 (S.FR 1100)
£1096 $2018 €1600 Castelfranco (22x27cm-9x11in) s.d.1968 verso. 23-Jun-4 Koller, Zurich #3095/R est:2000-3000 (S.FR 2500)
£1096 $2018 €1600 Oleggio IV (22x27cm-9x11in) s. s.i.verso. 23-Jun-4 Koller, Zurich #3096/R est:2000-3000 (S.FR 2500)
£1226 $1987 €1790 Liuto blu (18x24cm-7x9in) s.d.1969 verso exhib. 24-May-3 Burkhard, Luzern #77/R est:4000-6000 (S.FR 2600)
£1226 $1987 €1790 Liuto nero (18x24cm-7x9in) s. s.d.1969 verso exhib. 24-May-3 Burkhard, Luzern #90/R est:4000-6000 (S.FR 2600)
£1226 $1987 €1790 Liuti (18x24cm-7x9in) s.i.d.1970 verso. 24-May-3 Burkhard, Luzern #91/R est:4000-6000 (S.FR 2600)
£1351 $2324 €1972 Le crapau (25x29cm-10x11in) s. canvas on board painted 1954 prov.lit. 8-Dec-3 Philippe Schuler, Zurich #3456/R est:3000-5000 (S.FR 3000)
£1472 $2635 €2149 Abstract composition (38x46cm-15x18in) s.d.1959 s.i.d. verso. 22-Mar-4 Philippe Schuler, Zurich #4460/R est:3000-5000 (S.FR 3400)
£1538 $2615 €2200 Untitled (40x50cm-16x20in) s. s.d.1958 verso prov. two. 25-Nov-3 Sotheby's, Milan #159 est:2000-3000
£2172 $3627 €3171 Fiesta (22x27cm-9x11in) s.i.d.1968 verso pavatex on canvas prov.lit. 24-Jun-3 Germann, Zurich #126/R est:4500-5000 (S.FR 4800)
£2941 $5000 €4294 Formes (30x40cm-12x16in) s. lit.prov. 25-Nov-3 Germann, Zurich #10/R est:5000-7000 (S.FR 6500)
£3057 $5624 €4463 Composition (64x74cm-25x29in) s.d.1963 masonite on panel lit. 8-Jun-4 Germann, Zurich #107/R est:8000-10000 (S.FR 7000)
£3147 $5350 €4500 Untitled (72x73cm-28x29in) s.d.1966 verso. 25-Nov-3 Sotheby's, Milan #165/R est:2000-3000
£3394 $5769 €4955 Fields (73x72cm-29x28in) s. s.i.d.1967 verso prov. 22-Nov-3 Burkhard, Luzern #57/R est:8000-10000 (S.FR 7500)
£3521 $6092 €5000 Acrobats (45x62cm-18x24in) s. paper on cardboard. 15-Dec-3 Ansorena, Madrid #336/R est:5000
Works on paper
£498 $846 €727 Composition (42x49cm-17x19in) s. chl. 22-Nov-3 Burkhard, Luzern #43/R (S.FR 1100)
£660 $1070 €964 Composition (40x26cm-16x10in) s. W/C. 24-May-3 Burkhard, Luzern #78/R (S.FR 1400)
£814 $1385 €1188 Composition (26x33cm-10x13in) s. W/C exec. 1966 prov. 22-Nov-3 Burkhard, Luzern #36/R (S.FR 1800)
£1086 $1846 €1586 Incantation (22x18cm-9x7in) s. collage gouache cardboard on board exec. 1989 prov.exhib. 22-Nov-3 Burkhard, Luzern #58/R (S.FR 2400)
£1147 $1915 €1663 Composition (24x24cm-9x9in) s.d.1966 Indian ink brush bodycol. 19-Jun-3 Kornfeld, Bern #1017 est:1500 (S.FR 2500)
£1267 $2116 €1850 Lune (12x11cm-5x4in) s. s.i.d.1975 verso collage panel board lit. 24-Jun-3 Germann, Zurich #125/R est:3000-4000 (S.FR 2800)
£1310 $2410 €1913 Moulin (25x31cm-10x12in) s. i.d. verso collage paper on panel prov. 8-Jun-4 Germann, Zurich #92/R est:3000-4000 (S.FR 3000)
£1310 $2410 €1913 Tierce (35x43cm-14x17in) s. collage on aquatint prov.lit. 8-Jun-4 Germann, Zurich #108/R est:3500-4500 (S.FR 3000)
£1538 $2569 €2245 Mesure (16x8cm-6x3in) s. s.i.d.1970-73 verso collage panel prov.lit. 24-Jun-3 Germann, Zurich #124/R est:3500-4000 (S.FR 3400)
£1629 $2720 €2378 Euridice! (47x46cm-19x18in) s.i.d.1962 verso collage panel on pavatex prov.lit. 24-Jun-3 Germann, Zurich #127/R est:4500-5500 (S.FR 3600)
£2632 $4842 €3843 Cerf volant (27x27cm-11x11in) s. collage board. 23-Jun-4 Koller, Zurich #3093/R est:6000-9000 (S.FR 6000)

VALENTIEN, Anna Marie (1862-1947) American
£852 $1500 €1244 California landscape (41x51cm-16x20in) s. board painted c.1920. 23-May-4 Treadway Gallery, Cincinnati #499/R est:800-1200

VALENTIN, François (1738-1805) ?
Works on paper
£599 $1036 €850 Academie d'homme assis une jambe repliee (27x35cm-11x14in) sanguine. 12-Dec-3 Renaud, Paris #55
£704 $1218 €1000 Etude de femme en buste (33x36cm-13x14in) black crayon white chk. 12-Dec-3 Renaud, Paris #57 est:1000
£1761 $3046 €2500 Un ange portant une palme. Homme assis dans un taverne (44x52cm-17x20in) sanguine white chk double-sided. 12-Dec-3 Renaud, Paris #56/R est:2000

VALENTIN, Josef (1811-1895) German
£331 $606 €500 Portrait of young woman in 17th Century dress (79x64cm-31x25in) i. verso. 7-Apr-4 Dorotheum, Salzburg #80/R

VALENTIN, Marcelle (1906-1992) French
£333 $610 €500 Nature morte au mais (41x31cm-16x12in) s. cardboard. 4-Jun-4 Rieunier, Paris #90/R
£333 $610 €500 Nature morte aux poireaux (46x55cm-18x22in) s. cardboard. 4-Jun-4 Rieunier, Paris #91/R
Works on paper
£267 $488 €400 Ambiance gare (25x18cm-10x7in) s.verso i. 4-Jun-4 Rieunier, Paris #118/R
£267 $488 €400 Jeux (33x25cm-13x10in) s.i. gouache. 4-Jun-4 Rieunier, Paris #121/R
£267 $488 €400 Rayonnement (31x40cm-12x16in) s. i.verso gouache. 4-Jun-4 Rieunier, Paris #106/R
£267 $488 €400 Elan d'ondes (41x33cm-16x13in) s. i.verso gouache. 4-Jun-4 Rieunier, Paris #107/R
£267 $488 €400 Composition en eventail (33x33cm-13x13in) s. i.verso gouache. 4-Jun-4 Rieunier, Paris #110/R
£267 $488 €400 Rythme vertical (33x25cm-13x10in) s.verso i. 4-Jun-4 Rieunier, Paris #112/R
£300 $549 €450 Rythmes en courbes (33x41cm-13x16in) s. i.verso gouache. 4-Jun-4 Rieunier, Paris #108/R
£300 $549 €450 Composition musicale (36x46cm-14x18in) s. i.verso gouache. 4-Jun-4 Rieunier, Paris #109/R
£300 $549 €450 Noeud de developpement (25x32cm-10x13in) s.i. gouache double-sided. 4-Jun-4 Rieunier, Paris #119/R
£300 $549 €450 Envol (33x41cm-13x16in) s.i. gouache. 4-Jun-4 Rieunier, Paris #136/R
£333 $610 €500 Composition spatiale (31x40cm-12x16in) s. i.verso gouache. 4-Jun-4 Rieunier, Paris #111/R
£333 $610 €500 Jeux d'opposes (16x21cm-6x8in) s.i. gouache. 4-Jun-4 Rieunier, Paris #135/R
£333 $610 €500 Cadences (41x33cm-16x13in) s.i. gouache. 4-Jun-4 Rieunier, Paris #139/R
£407 $744 €610 Composition verticale (20x25cm-8x10in) s.i. pastel. 4-Jun-4 Rieunier, Paris #132/R
£433 $793 €650 Arabesque (32x25cm-13x10in) s.i. gouache. 4-Jun-4 Rieunier, Paris #127/R
£667 $1220 €1000 Tourbillon (32x41cm-13x16in) s.i. pastel. 4-Jun-4 Rieunier, Paris #140/R
£2667 $4880 €4000 Danse (33x25cm-13x10in) s.i. gouache. 4-Jun-4 Rieunier, Paris #124/R

VALENTINE-DAINES, Sherree (1956-) British
£2000 $3600 €2920 Cherry Blossom (62x122cm-24x48in) s. 20-Jan-4 Bonhams, Knightsbridge #295/R est:1200-1800

VALENTINI, Luigi (1920-) Italian
£284 $474 €400 Summer in the Stubai valley (50x70cm-20x28in) s. s.i.d.20.Juli 1945 verso. 16-Oct-3 Dorotheum, Salzburg #711/R

VALENTINI, Walter (1912-1995) Italian
Works on paper
£1329 $2259 €1900 Traces (60x45cm-24x18in) s.i. mixed media assemblage board. 26-Nov-3 Pandolfini, Florence #147/R est:2000-2200

VALENTINO, Gian Domenico (fl.1661-1681) Italian
£5594 $9343 €8000 Kitchen interior (46x65cm-18x26in) 7-Oct-3 Pandolfini, Florence #593/R est:8000-10000
£13000 $23400 €18980 Kitchen still life with various cooking utensil, suit of armour, pots and pans (96x134cm-38x53in) init.d. 20-Apr-4 Sotheby's, Olympia #336/R est:8000-10000
£19463 $35812 €29000 Kitchen interior (95x133cm-37x52in) prov.exhib.lit. 24-Mar-4 Finarte Semenzato, Rome #104/R est:35000

VALENTINO, Gian Domenico (attrib) (17th C) Italian
£1059 $1928 €1600 Nature morte aux utensiles de cuisine (48x64cm-19x25in) 21-Jun-4 Tajan, Paris #28 est:1000-1200

VALERA, Victor (1927-) Venezuelan
£652 $1200 €978 Untitled (60x45cm-24x18in) s. painted 1972. 27-Jun-4 Subastas Odalys, Caracas #3
Sculpture
£2431 $4375 €3549 Square with comparted circle (78x75x40cm-31x30x16in) painted iron exec.1982. 25-Apr-4 Subastas Odalys, Caracas #54/R

VALERE-BERNARD, Francois Marius (1859-1936) French
£4344 $7211 €6342 Virtue and vice (73x48cm-29x19in) s. 4-Oct-3 Kieselbach, Budapest #162/R (H.F 1600000)

VALERI, Auguste Pravot (1857-1930) French
£420 $777 €613 Shepherdess with her flock (46x38cm-18x15in) 16-Feb-4 Bonhams, Bath #25

VALERIO, Theodore (1819-1879) French
Works on paper
£533 $965 €800 Barques et voiliers sur la greve (22x30cm-9x12in) W/C. 30-Mar-4 Rossini, Paris #1065/R

VALERIO, Theodore (attrib) (1819-1879) French
Works on paper
£863 $1381 €1200 Greek soldier (48x29cm-19x11in) W/C blk crayon. 16-May-3 Tajan, Paris #186

VALERO, Salvador (20th C) South American
£247 $445 €361 Judah's death (80x60cm-31x24in) s. 25-Apr-4 Subastas Odalys, Caracas #76

£335 $560 €489 Players and cocks (64x54cm-25x21in) s. 19-Oct-3 Subastas Odalys, Caracas #42/R
£467 $780 €682 The three Magi on the Andes (67x84cm-26x33in) s. panel painted 1966. 19-Oct-3 Subastas Odalys, Caracas #83/R

VALERY, Paul (1871-1945) French
Works on paper
£400 $736 €600 Homme assis, accoude d'un air reveur (17x13cm-7x5in) s. pen wash exhib. 9-Jun-4 Piasa, Paris #250
£500 $920 €750 Portrait en buste de Jean Pozzi (22x14cm-9x6in) s.i.d.mai 1926 crayon W/C exhib. 9-Jun-4 Piasa, Paris #247
£1000 $1840 €1500 La Seine a Paris, vue du quai (19x30cm-7x12in) wash crayon htd white gouache. 9-Jun-4 Piasa, Paris #245 est:1500-2000
£1533 $2821 €2300 Untitled (11x18cm-4x7in) s.i. W/C gouache. 9-Jun-4 Piasa, Paris #248/R est:2000-3000

VALES, Edmond (1918-2001) ?
Works on paper
£567 $948 €800 View of Meknes (31x48cm-12x19in) s.i. gouache. 19-Oct-3 Rabourdin & Choppin de Janvry, Paris #101/R
£634 $1096 €900 Homme au burnous (47x40cm-19x16in) s. sanguine crayon. 15-Dec-3 Gros & Delettrez, Paris #331
£638 $1066 €900 Femme voilee portant couffin (47x30cm-19x12in) s. gouache. 19-Oct-3 Rabourdin & Choppin de Janvry, Paris #54/R
£780 $1303 €1100 Cafe a Meknes (47x62cm-19x24in) s. gouache. 19-Oct-3 Rabourdin & Choppin de Janvry, Paris #153/R

VALETTE, Adolphe (1861-1942) French
£900 $1530 €1314 Le pont Neuf. Le statue de Henri IV au Pont Neuf (17x25cm-7x10in) cardboard pair. 6-Nov-3 Christie's, Kensington #843/R
£1100 $1892 €1606 Building and canal, dusk (16x24cm-6x9in) board prov. 3-Dec-3 Christie's, Kensington #614 est:300-400
£14500 $23200 €21170 Bailey Bridge (33x41cm-13x16in) exhib. 16-Sep-3 Capes Dunn, Manchester #718/R
Works on paper
£300 $549 €438 French landscape (20x28cm-8x11in) W/C drawing. 6-Apr-4 Capes Dunn, Manchester #800/R
£1550 $2821 €2263 Spanish hilltop town. Puerto de Pollensa (26x36cm-10x14in) both s. W/C pair. 15-Jun-4 Bonhams, Knightsbridge #110/R est:500-800

VALETTE, Pierre Adolphe (1876-1942) French
£520 $920 €759 Farm in the mountains (30x42cm-12x17in) s. indis i. exhib. 28-Apr-4 Peter Wilson, Nantwich #25
£620 $1135 €905 The Hirders, depicting snow covered road with figures in foreground (44x54cm-17x21in) i. verso. 6-Jul-4 Peter Wilson, Nantwich #31/R
£1500 $2655 €2190 Salles rural landscape with figure in the foreground (28x36cm-11x14in) s.d.7 Nov 38. 28-Apr-4 Peter Wilson, Nantwich #10 est:150-300
£1650 $2921 €2409 Monsold, village landscape (24x31cm-9x12in) s.i.d.14 June 1939. 28-Apr-4 Peter Wilson, Nantwich #28
Works on paper
£520 $962 €759 Portrait of the artist's mother (25x19cm-10x7in) indis.i. d.22 Nov 14 pencil drawing. 14-Jul-4 Bonhams, Chester #356
£1000 $1770 €1460 Salles, landscape with village (26x35cm-10x14in) W/C. 28-Apr-4 Peter Wilson, Nantwich #119 est:250-300
£1050 $1859 €1533 Village in the mountains (28x38cm-11x15in) W/C. 28-Apr-4 Peter Wilson, Nantwich #121 est:200-300
£1500 $2655 €2190 Lake District (27x38cm-11x15in) s. W/C. 28-Apr-4 Peter Wilson, Nantwich #117 est:200-250

VALETTE, René (19/20th C) French
Works on paper
£433 $776 €650 Chiens et cheval au relais (24x35cm-9x14in) w.c. 12-May-4 Coutau Begarie, Paris #174/R

VALINOTTI, Domenico (1889-1962) Italian
£408 $731 €600 Landscape (29x35cm-11x14in) s.d.1925 board. 22-Mar-4 Sant Agostino, Torino #540/R
£680 $1218 €1000 At the river (29x35cm-11x14in) s.d.1925 board. 22-Mar-4 Sant Agostino, Torino #366/R
£826 $1512 €1206 Taking a nap on the beach (48x60cm-19x24in) s.d.1927. 4-Jun-4 Zofingen, Switzerland #2536 (S.FR 1900)
£833 $1417 €1200 Mower (41x64cm-16x25in) s.d.1954 masonite. 1-Nov-3 Meeting Art, Vercelli #186/R
£933 $1717 €1400 Landscape in Piedmonte (40x60cm-16x24in) s.d.1942 cardboard. 14-Jun-4 Sant Agostino, Torino #424/R
£1342 $2376 €2000 Village church (60x50cm-24x20in) s.d.1959. 1-May-4 Meeting Art, Vercelli #446 est:2000

VALK, Hendrik Jacobus (1897-1986) Dutch
£445 $757 €650 Epos 570, Black Forest (40x25cm-16x10in) s.d.1964 board. 5-Nov-3 Vendue Huis, Gravenhage #518
£1800 $3312 €2700 Roosjes in een fles (41x22cm-16x9in) init.d.64 s.i.d. verso board prov. 8-Jun-4 Sotheby's, Amsterdam #217/R est:2200-2800
£2667 $4907 €4000 Herfst (50x34cm-20x13in) init.d.66 s.i.d.verso cardboard on board prov. 8-Jun-4 Sotheby's, Amsterdam #216/R est:3000-4000

VALK, Hendrik de (fl.1693-1717) Dutch
£2703 $4757 €4000 Interior with a family before a notary making a contract (38x32cm-15x13in) s. 18-May-4 Sotheby's, Amsterdam #7/R est:4000-6000
£12000 $21960 €17520 Tavern interior with a merry company drinking and smoking (41x49cm-16x19in) 6-Jul-4 Sotheby's, Olympia #538/R est:8000-12000

VALK, Maurits van der (1857-1935) Dutch
Works on paper
£278 $453 €400 Forest landscape (45x59cm-18x23in) s.d.25 black chk. 29-Sep-3 Sotheby's, Amsterdam #157/R
£420 $722 €600 View of a canal (35x56cm-14x22in) s. black chk. 7-Dec-3 Sotheby's, Amsterdam #660/R
£521 $849 €750 View of a landscape (26x43cm-10x17in) s. pastel. 29-Sep-3 Sotheby's, Amsterdam #156/R

VALKEAPAA, Nils Aslak (20th C) Finnish?
£570 $1050 €850 Silloin aurinko oli aina luonamme (103x133cm-41x52in) s.d.1975. 25-Mar-4 Hagelstam, Helsinki #997/R

VALKENBORCH, Frederick van (attrib) (1570-1623) Flemish
£15789 $29053 €24000 Paradise (75x108cm-30x43in) panel. 24-Jun-4 Dr Fritz Nagel, Stuttgart #580/R est:18000

VALKENBORCH, Gillis van (c.1570-1622) Flemish
Works on paper
£253 $456 €380 Rural houses. Map with dams (18x25cm-7x10in) pen brush pencil ink double-sided. 21-Apr-4 Finarte Semenzato, Milan #540/R

VALKENBORCH, Gillis van (circle) (c.1570-1622) Flemish
£24000 $42960 €36000 Tower of Babel (112x165cm-44x65in) prov. 17-May-4 Christie's, Amsterdam #65/R est:15000-20000

VALKENBORCH, Lucas van (circle) (1535-1597) Italian
£22000 $39600 €32120 Extensive river landscape with the Parable of the Tentants and the vineyard owner (40x119cm-16x47in) mono.i.d.1594 panel exhib. 21-Apr-4 Christie's, London #19/R est:8000-12000

VALKENBORCH, Martin van (1535-1612) Flemish
£100000 $173000 €146000 Extensive river landscape with peasants haymaking , a view of Arenberg Castle beyond (21x29cm-8x11in) mono. panel prov.exhib.lit. 10-Dec-3 Christie's, London #13/R est:120000-180000
£161111 $290000 €235222 Tower of Babel (69x98cm-27x39in) panel lit. 22-Jan-4 Sotheby's, New York #218/R est:40000-60000

VALKENBORCH, Martin van (circle) (1535-1612) Flemish
£5369 $9879 €8000 Mountainous landscape with town near river (31x37cm-12x15in) panel. 24-Mar-4 Dorotheum, Vienna #146/R est:6000-10000

VALKENBURG, Dirk (attrib) (1675-1727) Dutch
£16447 $30263 €25000 Dead game in landscape (95x66cm-37x26in) one bears sig pair. 25-Jun-4 Piasa, Paris #28/R est:25000-30000

VALKENBURG, Hendrik (1826-1896) Dutch
£1736 $2829 €2500 Spinster (73x56cm-29x22in) s. 29-Sep-3 Sotheby's, Amsterdam #42/R
£3200 $5760 €4800 By the cradle (52x66cm-20x26in) s.d.1871. 20-Apr-4 Sotheby's, Amsterdam #126/R est:5000-7000
£5346 $8500 €7805 Minding baby (40x50cm-16x20in) s. 12-Sep-3 Skinner, Boston #233/R est:15000
£7237 $13316 €11000 Apentheater: the circus is coming (64x50cm-25x20in) s. 22-Jun-4 Christie's, Amsterdam #153/R est:3000-5000
Works on paper
£405 $750 €591 Cottage interior (69x86cm-27x34in) s. W/C. 18-Jul-4 Bonhams & Butterfields, Los Angeles #7015/R
£3000 $5460 €4380 Young woman sewing by a window (35x46cm-14x18in) s.d.79 pencil W/C htd white. 5-Feb-4 Mellors & Kirk, Nottingham #491/R est:3000-4000

VALLANCE, William Fleming (1827-1904) British
Works on paper
£280 $515 €409 At low tide (17x25cm-7x10in) init. W/C. 10-Jun-4 Lyon & Turnbull, Edinburgh #91

VALLARINO, Vincent (1929-) ?
Photographs
£4520 $8000 €6599 Luxembourg woods, no 2 (70x100cm-28x39in) s.i.d.1974 num.5/25 verso photo printed later. 28-Apr-4 Sotheby's, New York #254/R est:5000-7000

VALLAYER-COSTER, Anne (1744-1818) French
Works on paper
£5442 $9741 €8000 Pivoines (21x34cm-8x13in) s. black chk pen grey ink wash four. 18-Mar-4 Christie's, Paris #145/R est:8000-12000

VALLAYER-MOUTET, Pauline (19th C) French
£2416 $4494 €3600 Interior with spinners (54x76cm-21x30in) s. 8-Mar-4 Bernaerts, Antwerp #102/R est:4000-5000

VALLE, Rosina Becker do (20th C) Brazilian
£359 $575 €524 Galosna floresta (56x33cm-22x13in) s.i.d.1968. 20-Sep-3 Sloans & Kenyon, Bethesda #1039/R

VALLEE, Étienne Maxime (19th C) French
£336 $594 €500 Femme assise a l'oree d'un bois (32x40cm-13x16in) s. panel. 30-Apr-4 Tajan, Paris #176
£1379 $2303 €2000 Cour de ferme avec basse-cour aupres de la mare (65x92cm-26x36in) s.d.79. 16-Nov-3 Muizon & Le Coent, Paris #53/R

£1586 $2649 €2300 Pecheur en bord d'etang (65x92cm-26x36in) s. 17-Nov-3 Tajan, Paris #157/R est:2000-3000
£1733 $3172 €2600 Vaches a la mare (31x44cm-12x17in) s. panel. 6-Jun-4 Osenat, Fontainebleau #221/R est:1500-2000
£1812 $2971 €2500 Foret de Fontainebleau (50x65cm-20x26in) s. 11-May-3 Osenat, Fontainebleau #141/R est:2500-2800
£3986 $6536 €5500 Clairieres en foret (65x54cm-26x21in) s. pair. 11-May-3 Osenat, Fontainebleau #142 est:6000-6500

VALLEE, Étienne Maxime (attrib) (19th C) French
£294 $500 €429 Fishing boats on rough sea (55x100cm-22x39in) s.d.75. 19-Nov-3 Fischer, Luzern #2329/R (S.FR 650)

VALLEE, Ludovic (1864-1939) French
£231 $425 €337 Still life (48x36cm-19x14in) s. canvas on board. 26-Jun-4 Sloans & Kenyon, Bethesda #1068/R
£738 $1307 €1100 Elegante et fiacre devant le Louvre (41x27cm-16x11in) s. 30-Apr-4 Tajan, Paris #203
£800 $1456 €1200 Nature morte aux pommes (27x35cm-11x14in) s. 4-Jul-4 Eric Pillon, Calais #141/R
£1197 $2071 €1700 Nature morte a la pipe (47x61cm-19x24in) s. 10-Dec-3 Claude Boisgirard, Paris #27 est:1200-1800
£7383 $13215 €11000 Promenade au jardin public (106x87cm-42x34in) s. 25-May-4 Chambelland & Giafferi, Paris #111/R est:3000-4000

VALLELY, John B (1941-) British
£1733 $3137 €2600 Spiral staircase (24x17cm-9x7in) board prov. 31-Mar-4 James Adam, Dublin #73/R est:2000-3000
£3500 $5740 €5110 Fivemusicians (35x28cm-14x11in) mono. board. 4-Jun-3 John Ross, Belfast #35 est:4500
£4200 $7518 €6132 Bullet thrower 2 (17x25cm-7x10in) init. canvasboard prov. 14-May-4 Christie's, Kensington #420/R est:2500-3000
£4400 $7216 €6424 Playing the flute (30x35cm-12x14in) mono. 4-Jun-3 John Ross, Belfast #115 est:3750
£4500 $7650 €6570 Two violinists, abstract (41x51cm-16x20in) mono. prov. 5-Nov-3 John Nicholson, Haslemere #532/R est:2500-3000
£4800 $7968 €7008 Playing the pipes (50x71cm-20x28in) mono. 1-Oct-3 John Ross, Belfast #31 est:5500-6000
£5750 $9775 €8395 Four musicians, abstract (36x46cm-14x18in) s. prov. 5-Nov-3 John Nicholson, Haslemere #531/R est:2500-3000
£7042 $12183 €10000 Wedding of Diarmuid and Grainne (61x91cm-24x36in) init. s.i.verso. 10-Dec-3 Bonhams & James Adam, Dublin #128/R est:9000-10000
£7095 $13409 €10500 Hurlers (36x30cm-14x12in) s. 17-Feb-4 Whyte's, Dublin #107/R est:3500-4500
£7383 $13067 €11000 Bullet thrower (41x51cm-16x20in) s. 27-Apr-4 Whyte's, Dublin #178/R est:6000-8000
£8108 $15324 €12000 Musicians (51x76cm-20x30in) init. 17-Feb-4 Whyte's, Dublin #106/R est:8000-10000
£9722 $15847 €14000 Three musicians (101x122cm-40x48in) init. prov. 24-Sep-3 James Adam, Dublin #67/R est:15000-20000
Works on paper
£1000 $1720 €1460 Musicians (38x53cm-15x21in) s. mixed media. 3-Dec-3 John Ross, Belfast #63 est:600-800
£1100 $1826 €1606 Interior with figure (25x38cm-10x15in) s. mixed media. 1-Oct-3 John Ross, Belfast #16 est:800-1000
£1450 $2654 €2117 Calf in the auction ring (40x28cm-16x11in) s. pen ink. 2-Jun-4 John Ross, Belfast #181 est:1500-1800

VALLES, Lorenzo (1830-1910) Spanish
£405 $648 €575 Portrait of Mr Zanit (70x55cm-28x22in) s.i. 16-Sep-3 Segre, Madrid #78/R
£4698 $8785 €7000 Admiring paintings (28x42cm-11x17in) s. board. 24-Feb-4 Durán, Madrid #239/R est:7000

VALLET, Edouard (1876-1929) Swiss
£226 $391 €330 Couvent italien (55x33cm-22x13in) painted 1905. 12-Dec-3 Galerie du Rhone, Sion #597 (S.FR 500)
£4525 $7828 €6607 Paysage de Saint-Leonard (26x34cm-10x13in) s. cardboard exhib. 12-Dec-3 Galerie du Rhone, Sion #670/R est:20000-30000 (S.FR 10000)
£5240 $9380 €7650 Paysage (41x29cm-16x11in) s.d.1904. 26-May-4 Sotheby's, Zurich #41/R est:15000-20000 (S.FR 12000)
£10000 $18300 €14600 Marche (46x35cm-18x14in) s.d.03 i.verso. 7-Jun-4 Christie's, Zurich #28/R est:12000-15000 (S.FR 23000)
£10435 $19096 €15235 Jeune fille aux lilas (73x81cm-29x32in) s.d.07 prov. 7-Jun-4 Christie's, Zurich #30/R est:15000-25000 (S.FR 24000)
£11304 $20687 €16504 Jeune Valaisanne (33x22cm-13x9in) s.d.1922 prov. 4-Jun-4 Zofingen, Switzerland #2977/R est:12000 (S.FR 26000)
£13913 $25461 €20313 Spring landscape (54x65cm-21x26in) s.d.1926 prov. 7-Jun-4 Christie's, Zurich #29/R est:20000-30000 (S.FR 32000)
£45652 $83543 €66652 La tonelle (90x105cm-35x41in) s.d.1908 prov.exhib. 7-Jun-4 Christie's, Zurich #33/R est:30000-50000 (S.FR 105000)
Prints
£2752 $4596 €3990 Trois filles (35x38cm-14x15in) mono.d.1914 etching burin copper lit. 21-Jun-3 Galerie du Rhone, Sion #276/R est:5000-7000 (S.FR 6000)
Works on paper
£383 $659 €559 Peasants in a field in a country landscape (18x27cm-7x11in) s. pastel chk. 8-Dec-3 Philippe Schuler, Zurich #3240 (S.FR 850)
£568 $1045 €829 Portrait of man with hat (47x30cm-19x12in) s.d. chl wash. 14-Jun-4 Philippe Schuler, Zurich #4170/R (S.FR 1300)
£10870 $19891 €15870 Woman from Walliser winding wool (52x42cm-20x17in) s.d.1909 pastel board. 7-Jun-4 Christie's, Zurich #27/R est:25000-35000 (S.FR 25000)

VALLEY, J J la (1858-1930) American
£894 $1600 €1305 Early autumn (76x56cm-30x22in) 7-May-4 Douglas, South Deerfield #31

VALLGREN, Ville (1855-1940) French
Sculpture
£1067 $1909 €1600 The rose girl (26cm-10in) s.d.1919 pat terracotta. 15-May-4 Hagelstam, Helsinki #20/R est:1500
£1181 $1972 €1700 Dancer (31cm-12in) s. plaster. 26-Oct-3 Bukowskis, Helsinki #276/R est:500
£2517 $4280 €3600 Dragonflies (22cm-9in) s.i.d.1903 bronze. 29-Nov-3 Bukowskis, Helsinki #4/R est:2500-3000
£2517 $4280 €3600 Nude dancer (19cm-7in) s.d.1930 bronze. 29-Nov-3 Bukowskis, Helsinki #10/R est:1800-2000
£4196 $7133 €6000 The well known dancer (46cm-18in) s. pat.plaster. 29-Nov-3 Bukowskis, Helsinki #12/R est:2000-2500

VALLIN, Jacques Antoine (1760-1831) French
£3169 $5546 €4500 Portrait de jeune femme en Hebe (82x65cm-32x26in) 17-Dec-3 Piasa, Paris #95/R est:5000-7000
£9211 $16947 €14000 Venus et Adonis (97x77cm-38x30in) prov.lit. 23-Jun-4 Sotheby's, Paris #51/R est:15000-20000
£13158 $24211 €20000 Renaud et Armide (97x77cm-38x30in) prov.lit. 23-Jun-4 Sotheby's, Paris #52/R est:15000-20000
£16779 $29698 €25000 Young woman with flowers in her hair (44x33cm-17x13in) 2-May-4 Finarte, Venice #77/R est:29000-35000
£19718 $34113 €28000 Chasse de Diane (109x149cm-43x59in) exhib. 10-Dec-3 Beaussant & Lefèvre, Paris #53/R est:18000-22000

VALLIN, Jacques Antoine (attrib) (1760-1831) French
£961 $1720 €1403 Woman and cupid (22x16cm-9x6in) 26-May-4 AB Stockholms Auktionsverk #2577/R (S.KR 13000)
£1007 $1852 €1500 Scene de bacchanale (37x31cm-15x12in) 24-Mar-4 Tajan, Paris #118 est:1500-2000

VALLMAN, Uno (1913-) Swedish
£382 $615 €558 Wooded landscape (46x38cm-18x15in) s.d.1946. 25-Aug-3 Lilla Bukowskis, Stockholm #641 (S.KR 5000)
£492 $801 €718 Landscape with reindeer (81x61cm-32x24in) s.d.1956 panel. 29-Sep-3 Lilla Bukowskis, Stockholm #371 (S.KR 6400)
£612 $985 €894 Coastal walk with rocks (45x37cm-18x15in) s.d.1949 panel. 25-Aug-3 Lilla Bukowskis, Stockholm #99 (S.KR 8000)
£692 $1274 €1038 Composition with fish (54x73cm-21x29in) s.d.1961. 14-Jun-4 Lilla Bukowskis, Stockholm #112/R (S.KR 9500)
£702 $1257 €1025 Southern harbour town (54x77cm-21x30in) s.d.1967. 28-May-4 Uppsala Auktionskammare, Uppsala #349 (S.KR 9500)
£2697 $4962 €4046 Town view (123x75cm-48x30in) s.d.49 panel. 14-Jun-4 Lilla Bukowskis, Stockholm #201 est:12000-15000 (S.KR 37000)

VALLMITJANA, Abel (1909-1974) Spanish
£878 $1546 €1300 Figure 3 (70x50cm-28x20in) s.d.1957 s.i.verso prov. 18-May-4 Segre, Madrid #280/R

VALLMITJANA, Venancio (1850-1915) Spanish
Sculpture
£1135 $1838 €1600 Nino tumbado (12x24cm-5x9in) s. terracotta. 20-May-3 Ansorena, Madrid #815/R est:1200

VALLORZ, Paolo (1931-) Italian
£1549 $2572 €2200 Sunflowers (22x33cm-9x13in) painted 1972 lit. 11-Jun-3 Finarte Semenzato, Milan #516/R

VALLOTTON, Felix (1865-1925) Swiss
£12670 $21158 €18498 Femme nue de dos (61x50cm-24x20in) s.d.1909 lit. 24-Jun-3 Germann, Zurich #58/R est:20000-25000 (S.FR 28000)
£18502 $31454 €27013 Nature morte, tulipes perroquet dans une cruche verte (55x46cm-22x18in) st.sig.d.22 prov.exhib.lit. 7-Nov-3 Dobiaschofsky, Bern #109/R est:70000 (S.FR 42000)
£19565 $35804 €28565 Portrait decoratif de Fedor Dostoievski (78x58cm-31x23in) s.i.d.1902 board prov.exhib.lit. 7-Jun-4 Christie's, Zurich #55/R est:50000-70000 (S.FR 45000)
£27815 $50901 €42000 Sept pommes jaunes sur une serviette (38x55cm-15x22in) s.d.11 prov.lit. 7-Apr-4 Doutrebente, Paris #47/R est:20000-25000
£28000 $50960 €40880 Femme nue couchee (114x146cm-45x57in) s.d.13 prov.exhib.lit. 3-Feb-4 Christie's, London #290/R est:25000-35000
£30172 $55517 €44051 Souvenir des Etincelles (30x51cm-12x20in) s.i.d. 26-Mar-4 Koller, Zurich #518/R est:70000-90000 (S.FR 70000)
£34783 $63652 €50783 Deux femmes au bain (38x55cm-15x22in) st.sig. prov.lit. 7-Jun-4 Christie's, Zurich #53/R est:80000-120000 (S.FR 80000)
£36199 $62624 €52851 Jeune femme drapee dans une echarpe (80x65cm-31x26in) s. lit. 9-Dec-3 Sotheby's, Zurich #68/R est:45000-65000 (S.FR 80000)
£39130 $71609 €57130 Automne a Romanel (30x46cm-12x18in) s.d.03 board prov.exhib.lit. 7-Jun-4 Christie's, Zurich #64/R est:100000-120000 (S.FR 90000)
£43103 $77155 €62930 Pivoines (81x65cm-32x26in) s.d. prov.exhib. 17-May-4 Beurret, Zurich #37/R est:100000-150000 (S.FR 100000)
£43478 $79565 €63478 Oeillets et livre de comptes (50x65cm-20x26in) st.sig.d.25 prov.lit. 7-Jun-4 Christie's, Zurich #57/R est:120000-150000 (S.FR 100000)
£44843 $73094 €65471 Bords de Seine a Tournedos (65x81cm-26x32in) s.d.20 prov.lit. 29-Sep-3 Christie's, Zurich #37/R est:120000-150000 (S.FR 100000)
£51570 $84058 €75292 Pommes et vase marocain (65x81cm-26x32in) s.d.14 prov.lit. 29-Sep-3 Christie's, Zurich #48/R est:70000-90000 (S.FR 115000)
£52402 $93799 €76507 Prunes et capucines (46x55cm-18x22in) s.d.1911 prov.lit. 26-May-4 Sotheby's, Zurich #28/R est:120000-160000 (S.FR 120000)
£53812 $87713 €78566 Tulipes doubles jaunes sur un tabouret de paille (54x65cm-21x26in) s.d.23 prov.exhib.lit. 29-Sep-3 Christie's, Zurich #49/R est:60000-80000 (S.FR 120000)
£58824 $101765 €85883 Poissonniere en cuivre (53x64cm-21x25in) s.d.1910 lit. 9-Dec-3 Sotheby's, Zurich #38/R est:80000-120000 (S.FR 130000)
£73913 $135261 €107913 La Dent d'Oche, l'apres-midi (24x40cm-9x16in) board prov.exhib.lit. 7-Jun-4 Christie's, Zurich #66/R est:150000-200000 (S.FR 170000)
£132450 $242384 €200000 Un sentier entre deux buissons (88x82cm-35x32in) s.d.23 prov.lit. 7-Apr-4 Doutrebente, Paris #45/R est:120000-150000
£225166 $412053 €340000 Les bords de la Risle (54x81cm-21x32in) s.d.24 prov.lit. 7-Apr-4 Doutrebente, Paris #46/R est:100000-120000
£344371 $630199 €520000 Environs de Cagnes le soir (81x64cm-32x25in) s.d.24 prov.lit. 7-Apr-4 Doutrebente, Paris #44/R est:150000-180000
£670000 $1219400 €978200 Misia a sa coiffeuse (36x29cm-14x11in) s.d.98 prov.exhib.lit. 3-Feb-4 Sotheby's, London #47/R est:350000-500000

Prints

£1676	$3000	€2447	Le bon marche (20x26cm-8x10in) s. woodcut. 6-May-4 Swann Galleries, New York #344/R est:4000-6000
£1765	$3000	€2577	Les cygnes (14x18cm-6x7in) s. woodcut. 6-Nov-3 Swann Galleries, New York #451/R est:4000-6000
£1788	$3200	€2610	Le couplet patriotique (18x27cm-7x11in) s. woodcut. 6-May-4 Swann Galleries, New York #345/R est:2500-3500
£2183	$3974	€3187	L'eclat. s. woodcut. 17-Jun-4 Kornfeld, Bern #816/R est:6000 (S.FR 5000)
£2412	$4439	€3522	L'eclat (18x22cm-7x9in) s. num.51 woodcut. 23-Jun-4 Koller, Zurich #3302 est:4800-6000 (S.FR 5500)
£2752	$4596	€3990	L'eclat. s.i. woodcut. 19-Jun-3 Kornfeld, Bern #1028 est:5000 (S.FR 6000)
£2817	$4873	€4000	Le bon marche (20x26cm-8x10in) s. woodcut. 11-Dec-3 Piasa, Paris #165/R
£3303	$5516	€4789	Le mensonge. woodcut. 19-Jun-3 Kornfeld, Bern #1027 est:7500 (S.FR 7200)
£4585	$8345	€6694	L'irreparable. s.i. woodcut. 17-Jun-4 Kornfeld, Bern #815/R est:10000 (S.FR 10500)
£5677	$10162	€8288	Le bain (25x31cm-10x12in) st.mono. woodcut one of 10 lit. 26-May-4 Sotheby's, Zurich #84/R est:8000-12000 (S.FR 13000)
£13575	$23484	€19820	La paresse (18x22cm-7x9in) mono.i. num.132 woodcut one of 180. 9-Dec-3 Sotheby's, Zurich #28/R est:18000-25000 (S.FR 30000)

Works on paper

£500	$915	€750	Female nude (27x17cm-11x7in) mono. graphite dr. 3-Jun-4 E & Eve, Paris #17
£942	$1535	€1375	Standing male nude (62x47cm-24x19in) mono. chl. 29-Sep-3 Christie's, Zurich #36/R est:2000-3000 (S.FR 2100)
£1076	$1754	€1571	Two female nude studies (16x28cm-6x11in) mono. pencil. 29-Sep-3 Christie's, Zurich #34/R est:2000-3000 (S.FR 2400)
£1794	$2924	€2619	Figure study for 'Orphee depece' (31x23cm-12x9in) mono.i. pencil lit. 29-Sep-3 Christie's, Zurich #33/R est:2000-3000 (S.FR 4000)
£1810	$3241	€2643	Nu couche, james repliees (16x32cm-6x13in) mono. pencil prov. 14-May-4 Dobiaschofsky, Bern #122/R est:2600 (S.FR 4200)
£1973	$3216	€2881	Figure study for 'Andromede debout et Persee' (25x19cm-10x7in) mono.i. pencil lit. 29-Sep-3 Christie's, Zurich #32/R est:2000-3000 (S.FR 4400)
£4348	$7957	€6348	Arches in Bern (23x31cm-9x12in) mono.i.d.08 pencil prov.exhib. 7-Jun-4 Christie's, Zurich #59/R est:10000-12000 (S.FR 10000)
£13575	$23484	€19820	Nature morte, une grappe de raisin et des feuilles (28x34cm-11x13in) st.sig. d.1925 gouache board lit. 9-Dec-3 Sotheby's, Zurich #49/R est:50000-70000 (S.FR 30000)
£26201	$47686	€38253	Nature morte aux trois mandarines et un brin de mimosa (24x31cm-9x12in) s.d.24 W/C cardboard prov. 18-Jun-4 Kornfeld, Bern #146/R est:65000 (S.FR 60000)

VALLOU DE VILLENEUVE, Julien (19th C) French?

Photographs

£6644	$11095	€9500	Etude de nu (12x16cm-5x6in) salt print exec.c.1854 lit. 10-Oct-3 Tajan, Paris #99/R est:8000-10000

VALLS, Xavier (1923-) Spanish

Works on paper

£1014	$1814	€1500	Nature morte au verre (64x49cm-25x19in) mono. W/C. 4-May-4 Calmels Cohen, Paris #212 est:600-800
£1149	$2056	€1700	Nature morte aux figues (64x49cm-25x19in) mono. W/C. 4-May-4 Calmels Cohen, Paris #214 est:600-800

VALMIER, Georges (1885-1937) French

Works on paper

£2254	$3899	€3200	Paysage cubiste (18x24cm-7x9in) s.d.1922 crayon dr prov.lit. 9-Dec-3 Artcurial Briest, Paris #226b/R est:2500-3000
£3846	$6615	€5500	Composition au poisson (25x29cm-10x11in) s.d.1931 gouache. 4-Dec-3 Piasa, Paris #100/R est:5000-7000
£4333	$7973	€6500	Figure (26x12cm-10x5in) s. gouache lit. 8-Jun-4 Artcurial Briest, Paris #100/R est:8000-12000
£6301	$10712	€9200	Composition au poisson (23x28cm-9x11in) s. gouache collage. 9-Nov-3 Eric Pillon, Calais #254/R
£10000	$18401	€15000	Jeune fille assise (28x18cm-11x7in) s.d.1924 gouache prov.lit. 8-Jun-4 Artcurial Briest, Paris #101/R est:10000-12000
£24648	$43134	€35000	Composition cubiste (17x9cm-7x4in) W/C gouache collage paper on cardboard. 18-Dec-3 Tajan, Paris #29/R est:15000-18000

VALORE, Lucie (1878-1965) Swiss

£528	$877	€750	Portrait presume de Maurice utrillo (55x46cm-22x18in) s. s.d.verso prov. 16-Jun-3 E & Eve, Paris #91

VALTAT, Louis (1869-1952) French

£1500	$2715	€2190	Facade de l'eglise, effet de lumiere (26x35cm-10x14in) init. prov. 1-Apr-4 Christie's, Kensington #36/R est:2000-3000
£1549	$2711	€2200	Nature morte aux livres et au collier de perles (20x27cm-8x11in) s. isorel prov. 16-Dec-3 Claude Aguttes, Neuilly #27/R est:5000-7000
£1800	$3312	€2628	Jeune femme au chignon (12x11cm-5x4in) init. painted 1920 lit. 24-Mar-4 Sotheby's, Olympia #58/R est:2000-2500
£3000	$5430	€4500	Summer river landscape in France (30x37cm-12x15in) i. lit. 1-Apr-4 Frank Peege, Freiburg #1157/R est:4500
£3691	$6534	€5500	Still life of flowers (25x21cm-10x8in) mono. board. 30-Apr-4 Dr Fritz Nagel, Stuttgart #953/R est:7000
£3893	$6968	€5800	La truite (27x41cm-11x16in) mono. panel. 25-May-4 Chambelland & Giafferi, Paris #53/R est:3500-4000
£4000	$6920	€5840	Nature morte aux peches (17x27cm-7x11in) st.init. board painted c.1940. 11-Dec-3 Christie's, Kensington #57/R est:4000-6000
£4324	$8000	€6313	Tomatoes (15x25cm-6x10in) init. cardboard on panel. 12-Feb-4 Sotheby's, New York #5/R est:3000-5000
£4400	$7348	€6424	Vache a la Campagne (27x41cm-11x16in) s. prov. 22-Oct-3 Sotheby's, Olympia #113/R est:3500-4000
£4500	$7515	€6570	Pot de primeveres (18x14cm-7x6in) init. canvasboard painted 1916 lit. 21-Oct-3 Sotheby's, London #132/R est:5000-7000
£4706	$8000	€6871	Vase de fleurs, peonies (38x33cm-15x13in) studio st. 19-Nov-3 Bonhams & Butterfields, San Francisco #126/R
£5946	$11000	€8681	Nature morte (15x25cm-6x10in) st.init. panel prov. 11-Feb-4 Sotheby's, New York #11/R est:8000-12000
£7000	$12670	€10220	Fleurs dans un vase (35x26cm-14x10in) s. 1-Apr-4 Christie's, Kensington #39/R est:8000-12000
£7143	$13000	€10429	Femme au coffre (21x20cm-8x8in) init. painted 1928. 29-Jun-4 Sotheby's, New York #350/R est:7000-9000
£7394	$12792	€10500	Paysage a la barriere (45x37cm-18x15in) s. 12-Dec-3 Renaud, Paris #158/R est:10000
£7568	$14000	€11049	Femme assise (51x61cm-20x24in) init. W/C oil pastel paper on panel exec.1903 prov. 11-Feb-4 Sotheby's, New York #14/R est:15000-20000
£7639	$12758	€11000	Champs de ble devant la mer (39x47cm-15x19in) mono. canvas on panel lit. 21-Oct-3 Artcurial Briest, Paris #177/R est:12000-15000
£7895	$14526	€12000	Les tulipes (27x33cm-11x13in) s. 28-Jun-4 Rossini, Paris #74/R est:8000-10000
£7975	$13000	€11644	Rose au vase vert (34x25cm-13x10in) init. paper on panel prov.lit. 25-Sep-3 Christie's, Rockefeller NY #532/R est:5000-7000
£8054	$14980	€12000	L'oree du bois (30x21cm-12x8in) st.sig. exhib. 7-Mar-4 Lesieur & Le Bars, Le Havre #136/R
£9000	$16560	€13140	Bois de Boulogne (26x34cm-10x13in) st.init. canvas on cradled panel painted c.1935 prov. 22-Jun-4 Sotheby's, London #135/R est:8000-12000
£9412	$16000	€13742	Juliette juin a la collerette de dentelle (91x73cm-36x29in) s. i.verso painted c.1930. 6-Nov-3 Sotheby's, New York #157/R est:20000-30000
£10000	$17000	€14600	Roseraie (38x55cm-15x22in) s. 6-Nov-3 Sotheby's, New York #176/R est:18000-25000
£10490	$18042	€15000	Femme a la robe blanche (23x26cm-9x10in) st.mono. panel prov.lit. 8-Dec-3 Artcurial Briest, Paris #14/R est:15000-20000
£10588	$18000	€15458	Paysage - Les collettes a Cagnes (27x41cm-11x16in) init. painted c.1907. 6-Nov-3 Sotheby's, New York #181/R est:18000-25000
£11000	$20020	€16060	Barques au bois de Boulogne (34x54cm-13x21in) s. panel painted 1920 prov.lit. 4-Feb-4 Sotheby's, London #238/R est:8000-12000
£11409	$20423	€17000	Champs de ble (24x33cm-9x13in) s. canvas on panel painted c.1908. 25-May-4 Chambelland & Giafferi, Paris #54/R est:10000-12000
£11765	$20000	€17177	Tulipes et anemones (55x46cm-22x18in) s. 19-Nov-3 Bonhams & Butterfields, San Francisco #125/R
£12000	$20040	€17520	La Terrassa du cafe devant le cirque de Rouen (28x36cm-11x14in) init. board prov. 22-Oct-3 Bonhams, New Bond Street #21/R est:12000-18000
£12324	$21320	€17500	Les roches rouges (65x81cm-26x32in) s. painted c.1900. 10-Dec-3 Remi Ader, Paris #62/R est:12000-15000
£12324	$21320	€17500	Les roches rouges (65x81cm-26x32in) s. painted c.1900. 10-Dec-3 Neret-Minet, Paris #62/R est:12000-15000
£12385	$20683	€17958	Roseraie - jardin des roses (38x55cm-15x22in) s. i. stretcher. 19-Jun-3 Kornfeld, Bern #1032/R est:25000 (S.FR 27000)
£13081	$22500	€19098	Vase de fleurs (61x46cm-24x18in) init. prov. 3-Dec-3 Doyle, New York #40/R est:40000-60000
£14706	$25000	€21471	Personnages au bord de la riviere (43x49cm-17x19in) st.init. paper on canvas painted 1895 prov.lit. 6-Nov-3 Sotheby's, New York #182/R est:30000-40000
£15000	$27600	€21900	Corbeille de fruits (35x46cm-14x18in) init. painted c.1908 prov. 22-Jun-4 Sotheby's, London #255/R est:8000-12000
£16760	$30000	€24470	Portrait of a woman (81x65cm-32x26in) init. 5-May-4 Christie's, Rockefeller NY #334/R est:25000-35000
£16760	$30000	€24470	Calanque (66x81cm-26x32in) s. painted c.1907. 6-May-4 Sotheby's, New York #275/R est:25000-35000
£17568	$32500	€25649	Bol de peches (38x46cm-15x18in) init. prov. 11-Feb-4 Sotheby's, New York #34/R est:10000-15000
£18000	$33120	€26280	Bouquet of flowers on orange cloth (43x30cm-17x12in) s. painted c.1940 prov. 22-Jun-4 Sotheby's, London #256/R est:20000-30000
£18156	$32500	€26508	Immortelles au petit au vase de crystal (37x25cm-15x10in) s. painted c.1930 prov. 6-May-4 Sotheby's, New York #287/R est:12000-15000
£19118	$32500	€27912	Tulipes (55x38cm-22x15in) painted c.1930 prov. 6-Nov-3 Sotheby's, New York #183/R est:40000-60000
£19118	$32500	€27912	Jeune femme et son modele (55x46cm-22x18in) init. painted c.1899 prov.lit. 6-Nov-3 Sotheby's, New York #357/R est:15000-20000
£19463	$36201	€29000	Paysage du midi (38x50cm-15x20in) s.d.1897 verso. 7-Mar-4 Lesieur & Le Bars, Le Havre #135/R
£19463	$35617	€29000	Still life with a pot of flowers (46x55cm-18x22in) s. 7-Jul-4 Artcurial Briest, Paris #96/R est:25000-35000
£20667	$37820	€31000	Les choux rouges (50x61cm-20x24in) s. lit. 6-Jun-4 Anaf, Lyon #497/R est:20000-22000
£22346	$40000	€32625	Barriere du pre en Normandie (46x38cm-18x15in) s. painted c.1920. 6-May-4 Sotheby's, New York #419/R est:20000-25000
£22346	$40000	€32625	Normandie, la moisson en bord de mer (34x41cm-13x16in) init. canvasboard painted c.1910. 6-May-4 Sotheby's, New York #422/R est:15000-20000
£23000	$42320	€33580	Vase bleu, tulipes (46x38cm-18x15in) s. painted 1939 prov.lit. 23-Jun-4 Christie's, London #131/R est:18000-24000
£23529	$40000	€34352	Femme assise (73x92cm-29x36in) s. prov. 5-Nov-3 Christie's, Rockefeller NY #290/R est:50000-70000
£24648	$39683	€35000	Vase de fleurs (55x46cm-22x18in) s. painted 1920 lit. 22-Aug-3 Deauville, France #90/R est:35000-40000
£26761	$43353	€38000	Clairiere pres d'un verger en fleurs (64x81cm-25x32in) mono.d.1905 prov.lit. 5-Aug-3 Tajan, Paris #8/R est:40000-60000
£26846	$48054	€40000	Mimosas dans un pot vert, anemones dans un vase (47x61cm-19x24in) init. painted 1903 prov.lit. 26-May-4 Christie's, Paris #16/R est:22000-28000
£27815	$50623	€42000	Vase de fleurs (55x38cm-22x15in) s. painted c.1930 lit. 15-Jun-4 Blanchet, Paris #165/R est:30000-40000
£31016	$58000	€45283	Fleurs (46x55cm-18x22in) init. prov. 25-Feb-4 Christie's, Rockefeller NY #59/R est:30000-40000
£32000	$58880	€46720	Bouquets d'anemones (38x55cm-15x22in) s. painted c.1940 prov. 22-Jun-4 Sotheby's, London #164/R est:25000-30000
£32215	$59920	€48000	Pot de fleurs (46x55cm-18x22in) s. 2-Mar-4 Artcurial Briest, Paris #131/R est:25000-35000
£36000	$66240	€52560	Bouquet de glaieuls (81x65cm-32x26in) s. painted c.1940 prov. 22-Jun-4 Sotheby's, London #251/R est:30000-40000
£36313	$65000	€53017	Vase d'anemones et jonquilles (46x38cm-18x15in) s. prov. 5-May-4 Christie's, Rockefeller NY #336/R est:35000-45000
£38000	$69160	€55480	Rochers rouges (81x101cm-32x40in) s. prov.exhib. 3-Feb-4 Christie's, London #170/R est:40000-60000
£38411	$69907	€58000	Bouquet de fleurs dans un vase (54x73cm-21x29in) s. prov. 18-Jun-4 Piasa, Paris #23/R est:50000-60000
£38667	$69987	€58000	Bouquet de fleurs dans un vase rose (50x61cm-20x24in) s. 30-Mar-4 Gioffredo, Nice #118/R
£42000	$76440	€61320	Paysage d'ete a arromanches (86x123cm-34x48in) s. painted c.1910 prov. 4-Feb-4 Sotheby's, London #239/R est:45000-55000
£47486	$85000	€69330	Falaises (65x81cm-26x32in) init. painted 1905 prov. 6-May-4 Sotheby's, New York #273/R est:40000-60000
£52000	$94640	€75920	Grand bouquet a la cruche verte (100x81cm-39x32in) s. painted c.1922 prov.exhib.lit. 4-Feb-4 Sotheby's, London #243/R est:50000-70000
£52941	$90000	€77294	Trois vases de fleurs (72x92cm-28x36in) s. painted 1935 prov.lit. 5-Nov-3 Christie's, Rockefeller NY #280/R est:70000-90000
£65000	$119600	€94900	Bords de mer a Agay (81x100cm-32x39in) s. painted c.1904-1905 prov.exhib. 23-Jun-4 Christie's, London #130/R est:40000-60000

£70000 $128800 €102200 Femme au renard (100x80cm-39x31in) s.d.1902 prov. 23-Jun-4 Christie's, London #185/R est:40000-60000

£82353 $140000 €120235 Les baigneuses (131x162cm-52x64in) s. painted c.1906 prov. 5-Nov-3 Christie's, Rockefeller NY #247/R est:140000-180000

£117318 $210000 €171284 Au bord de la mer (65x81cm-26x32in) s. painted c.1906 prov. 6-May-4 Sotheby's, New York #290/R est:60000-80000

Works on paper

£245 $421 €350 Jean Valtat dessinant (27x32cm-11x13in) bears st.mono. chl. 3-Dec-3 Tajan, Paris #29/R

£350 $602 €500 Harlem (12x19cm-5x7in) bears st.mono. W/C. 3-Dec-3 Tajan, Paris #25/R

£698 $1200 €1019 Rue de village Catalan (31x24cm-12x9in) init. W/C pencil executed c.1895. 3-Dec-3 Doyle, New York #38/R est:1500-2500

£767 $1411 €1150 Jeune fille a la natte (26x19cm-10x7in) bears st.mono. W/C. 14-Jun-4 Tajan, Paris #33/R

£1399 $2378 €2000 Depart en barque (25x33cm-10x13in) st.init. W/C graphite. 28-Nov-3 Drouot Estimations, Paris #187

£1476 $2746 €2200 Prats de mollo, Catalogne (24x32cm-9x13in) mono. W/C pencil exec.c.1895. 2-Mar-4 Artcurial Briest, Paris #29/R est:1800-2500

£2162 $4000 €3157 Bassin d'Arachon (24x32cm-9x13in) W/C blk ink tan paper two prov.exhib. 12-Feb-4 Sotheby's, New York #20/R est:3000-5000

£3041 $5443 €4500 Filette et sa peluche (65x50cm-26x20in) s. chl sanguine htd gouache. 5-May-4 Coutau Begarie, Paris #48k est:4500-5000

£4605 $8474 €7000 Paveurs (52x67cm-20x26in) init. pastel. 23-Jun-4 Rieunier, Paris #43/R est:4000-5000

£5000 $7950 €7250 Suzanne Valtat et son fils, Jean (26x20cm-10x8in) init. W/C chk executed c.1910. 11-Sep-3 Christie's, Kensington #8/R est:4000-6000

VALTAT, Louis (attrib) (1869-1952) French

Works on paper

£375 $656 €548 Place de la Fontaine, Paris. mono. W/C. 18-Dec-3 John Nicholson, Haslemere #1109

VALTER, Frederick E (1850-1930) British

£650 $1203 €949 Sheep in a landscape (20x24cm-8x9in) s. 10-Feb-4 Bonhams, Knightsbridge #41/R

£650 $1203 €949 Sheep in an evening landscape (25x30cm-10x12in) s.d.1898. 10-Feb-4 Bonhams, Knightsbridge #55/R

Works on paper

£320 $582 €467 Cattle and calf at rest (31x21cm-12x8in) s.d.1890 W/C. 15-Jun-4 Bonhams, Leeds #38

£400 $740 €584 Close of the day (25x35cm-10x14in) s. i. verso W/C. 14-Jul-4 Bonhams, Chester #481

£550 $1001 €803 Hens in a farmyard. Cockerel and hen by a water pump (13x18cm-5x7in) one s.d.1909 one s.d.09 pencil W/C two. 1-Jul-4 Christie's, Kensington #469/R

VALTER, Henry (fl.1854-1864) British

£1020 $1827 €1500 Shipwreck on evening beach (18x27cm-7x11in) s. i. verso panel. 17-Mar-4 Neumeister, Munich #644/R est:1600

VALTIER, Gerard (20th C) French

£1361 $2435 €2000 Sous la Guinguette (60x73cm-24x29in) 21-Mar-4 Teitgen, Nancy #89

VALTON, C (?) ?

Sculpture

£1477 $2761 €2200 Cerf au brame (54x46cm-21x18in) i. green brown pat bronze. 1-Mar-4 Coutau Begarie, Paris #239/R est:2200-2800

VALTON, Charles (1851-1918) French

£490 $817 €700 Enfant a cheval (38x46cm-15x18in) s.d.1899. 25-Jun-3 Digard, Paris #51

Sculpture

£919 $1700 €1342 Wounded tiger (28x46cm-11x18in) s. bronze. 16-Jan-4 Aspire, Cleveland #221/R est:1000-1500

£1050 $1890 €1533 Bulldog straining on a chain (36cm-14in) s. brown pat. bronze. 21-Apr-4 Cheffins, Cambridge #631/R est:800-1200

£1300 $2210 €1898 Wolf stalking footprints in the snow (33x57cm-13x22in) pat bronze marble. 28-Oct-3 Sotheby's, London #119/R

£1800 $3060 €2628 Preludes d'amour (38x55cm-15x22in) s.st.f.Vollet pat bronze. 28-Oct-3 Sotheby's, London #165/R

£2000 $3640 €3000 Lionne et ses petits (27x51cm-11x20in) s. pat bronze. 4-Jul-4 Eric Pillon, Calais #13/R

£2484 $4000 €3627 Lioness and her cubs (56x91cm-22x36in) i. bronze. 14-Jan-4 Christie's, Rockefeller NY #330/R est:3000-5000

VANAISE, Gustaaf (1854-1902) Belgian

£347 $552 €500 Jeune femme de profil (46x35cm-18x14in) s. panel. 9-Sep-3 Palais de Beaux Arts, Brussels #285

£4670 $8500 €6818 Portrait of a young boy (171x94cm-67x37in) s.d.1879 prov. 29-Jun-4 Sotheby's, New York #84/R est:3000-5000

VANDENBERG, Philippe (1952-) Belgian?

£1733 $3103 €2600 Pas d'ombre au paradis, le voyage (150x200cm-59x79in) s.i.d.1989-1996-1997. 15-May-4 De Vuyst, Lokeren #600/R est:3000-4000

VANDENBRANDEN, Guy (1926-) Belgian

£282 $487 €400 Composition (90x90cm-35x35in) s.d.1980 verso. 9-Dec-3 Campo, Vlaamse Kaai #481

£317 $548 €450 Composition (125x90cm-49x35in) s.d.1977 verso panel. 9-Dec-3 Campo, Vlaamse Kaai #482

£333 $600 €500 Abstract composition (56x37cm-22x15in) s.d.68 oil paper. 26-Apr-4 Bernaerts, Antwerp #549/R

£336 $594 €500 Composition (90x90cm-35x35in) s.d.1981 verso. 27-Apr-4 Campo, Vlaamse Kaai #644

£369 $653 €550 Composition (90x70cm-35x28in) s.d.1972 verso panel. 27-Apr-4 Campo, Vlaamse Kaai #643

£382 $638 €550 Composition (125x125cm-49x49in) s.d.1972 verso panel. 21-Oct-3 Campo, Vlaamse Kaai #612

£417 $696 €600 Composition (180x180cm-71x71in) s.d.1975 verso panel. 21-Oct-3 Campo, Vlaamse Kaai #611

£537 $950 €800 Composition (125x125cm-49x49in) s.d.1970 verso panel. 27-Apr-4 Campo, Vlaamse Kaai #645

£764 $1276 €1100 Composition (125x125cm-49x49in) s.d.1977 verso panel. 21-Oct-3 Campo, Vlaamse Kaai #613/R

£5072 $8319 €7000 Untitled (113x86cm-44x34in) s.d.1957 verso. 27-May-3 Sotheby's, Amsterdam #367/R est:7000-10000

Works on paper

£278 $464 €400 Composition (45x35cm-18x14in) s.d.1971 gouache. 21-Oct-3 Campo, Vlaamse Kaai #615

VANDERBANK, John (1694-1739) British

£5587 $10000 €8157 Portrait of Jacob Tonson (127x101cm-50x40in) 27-May-4 Sotheby's, New York #211/R est:10000-15000

Works on paper

£19000 $34960 €27740 Gentleman on a horse by a training post (23x16cm-9x6in) i.verso pen ink wash over pencil. 26-Mar-4 Sotheby's, London #98/R est:2000-3000

VANDERBANK, John (attrib) (1694-1739) British

£2400 $4296 €3504 Portrait of a gentleman in armour (74x53cm-29x21in) 27-May-4 Christie's, Kensington #43/R est:800-1200

VANDERCAM, Serge (1924-) Danish

£1342 $2483 €2000 Le coupe-feu (146x114cm-57x45in) s.d.59 verso. 13-Mar-4 De Vuyst, Lokeren #332/R est:2000-2500

£1477 $2732 €2200 Composition (64x50cm-25x20in) s. s.d.64 verso prov. 13-Mar-4 De Vuyst, Lokeren #333/R est:1500-1700

Works on paper

£270 $476 €400 Composition (65x47cm-26x19in) s. ink. 18-May-4 Galerie Moderne, Brussels #286/R

VANDERCAMMEN, Edmond (1901-1980) Belgian

£2200 $3938 €3300 Les ombres (54x72cm-21x28in) s. panel. 15-May-4 De Vuyst, Lokeren #574/R est:3000-4000

Works on paper

£490 $832 €700 Deux chevaux au paturage (22x30cm-9x12in) s. gouache. 1-Dec-3 Palais de Beaux Arts, Brussels #143/R

£1399 $2378 €2000 L'amazone (48x63cm-19x25in) s.d.28 gouache. 1-Dec-3 Palais de Beaux Arts, Brussels #144/R est:2000-3000

VANDERLICK, Armand (1897-1985) Belgian

£490 $817 €700 Walker with dog (15x19cm-6x7in) mono. board. 11-Oct-3 De Vuyst, Lokeren #362

£1184 $2179 €1800 Woman wearing a green blouse (85x55cm-33x22in) s.d.71. 22-Jun-4 Christie's, Amsterdam #498/R est:2000-3000

£1748 $2972 €2500 L'enfant au beret marine (50x35cm-20x14in) s.d.47. 1-Dec-3 Palais de Beaux Arts, Brussels #332/R est:2500-3500

£1974 $3632 €3000 Dame au chapeau de paille (50x70cm-20x28in) s. s.i. on stretcher exhib. 22-Jun-4 Christie's, Amsterdam #500/R est:2000-3000

£3026 $5568 €4600 At the beach house (59x64cm-23x25in) s.d.55 exhib. 22-Jun-4 Christie's, Amsterdam #496/R est:2000-3000

£3472 $5799 €5000 Nature morte aux coquillages (90x110cm-35x43in) s. 21-Oct-3 Campo, Vlaamse Kaai #620/R est:4000-6000

£4577 $7919 €6500 Still life with red flowers (95x140cm-37x55in) s. lit. 13-Dec-3 De Vuyst, Lokeren #505/R est:7500-9000

£6164 $10479 €9000 Cabines a la Mer du Nord (88x109cm-35x43in) s. 10-Nov-3 Horta, Bruxelles #65/R

Works on paper

£270 $511 €400 Vase de fleurs (52x35cm-20x14in) s. W/C. 17-Feb-4 Vanderkindere, Brussels #34

£374 $670 €550 Le chasseur (28x36cm-11x14in) s. gouache W/C. 16-Mar-4 Vanderkindere, Brussels #298

£439 $830 €650 L'homme au chapeau (54x73cm-21x29in) s. W/C. 17-Feb-4 Vanderkindere, Brussels #52

£590 $986 €850 Femme a la fenetre (27x36cm-11x14in) s. gouache. 21-Oct-3 Campo & Campo, Antwerp #314/R

£604 $1117 €900 Small boy on the beach (46x31cm-18x12in) s. W/C. 13-Mar-4 De Vuyst, Lokeren #337

£625 $1044 €900 Jeune femme a la mer (53x71cm-21x28in) s. gouache. 21-Oct-3 Campo, Vlaamse Kaai #621

VANDERLYN, John (attrib) (1775-1852) American

Works on paper

£250 $433 €365 Two studies of a hand (48x31cm-19x12in) col chk prov. 12-Dec-3 Christie's, Kensington #573/R

VANDERPANT, John (1884-1939) Canadian

Photographs

£1808 $3200 €2640 Angles in black and white (46x35cm-18x14in) s.i. gelatin silver print. 27-Apr-4 Christie's, Rockefeller NY #37/R est:4000-6000

VANDERSTEEN, Germain (1925-) French

£1119 $1924 €1600 L'oiseau empereur (65x54cm-26x21in) s. s.i.verso panel. 3-Dec-3 Tajan, Paris #177/R est:700-800

£1189 $2045 €1700 En familles, les aristochats (91x73cm-36x29in) s. s.i.d.1972 verso. 3-Dec-3 Tajan, Paris #176/R est:800-1000

£1200 $2160 €1800 Feu d'artifice (54x65cm-21x26in) s.verso exhib. 26-Apr-4 Tajan, Paris #286/R est:1800-2000

Works on paper
£334 $600 €500 L'oiseau de paradis (26x20cm-10x8in) s. W/C. 26-Apr-4 Tajan, Paris #291
£367 $660 €550 Les soques (35x26cm-14x10in) s. gouache. 26-Apr-4 Tajan, Paris #289/R
£420 $722 €600 Oiseau de paradis (24x18cm-9x7in) s. gouache. 3-Dec-3 Tajan, Paris #179
£466 $840 €700 Fleurs au vase jaune (65x50cm-26x20in) s. gouache. 26-Apr-4 Tajan, Paris #275
£466 $840 €700 L'oiseau marguerite (65x50cm-26x20in) s. gouache. 26-Apr-4 Tajan, Paris #287/R
£600 $1080 €900 Chat fantastique (65x50cm-26x20in) s. crayon. 26-Apr-4 Tajan, Paris #288/R
£629 $1083 €900 Oiseau (69x50cm-27x20in) s. gouache. 3-Dec-3 Tajan, Paris #178

VANDEVERDONCK, Franz (19th C) Belgian
£700 $1099 €1015 Sheep and ducks in a field (18x24cm-7x9in) s.d.1863 i.verso panel. 28-Aug-3 Christie's, Kensington #115/R

VANDREST, Frans (?) ?
£680 $1218 €1000 Village (80x120cm-31x47in) s. 22-Mar-4 Durán, Madrid #630/R

VANELLI, Carlo (19/20th C) Italian
Sculpture
£6630 $12000 €9680 Figure of Napoleon on horseback (69cm-27in) i. bronze. 30-Mar-4 Sotheby's, New York #559/R est:7000-9000

VANGELLI, Antonio (1917-) Italian
£248 $462 €370 Two figures (40x30cm-16x12in) s. s.i.d.1956 verso. 4-Mar-4 Babuino, Rome #130
£403 $749 €600 Two women (70x50cm-28x20in) s.verso prov. 4-Mar-4 Babuino, Rome #8
£436 $811 €650 Man and ants (50x40cm-20x16in) s. 4-Mar-4 Babuino, Rome #19
£604 $1123 €900 Three figures (70x50cm-28x20in) s. s.verso oil dye. 4-Mar-4 Babuino, Rome #414

VANGI, Giuliano (1931-) Italian
£979 $1664 €1400 Young woman (100x70cm-39x28in) s. mixed media paper. 29-Nov-3 Arnold, Frankfurt #538/R est:1800
£1800 $3312 €2700 Figure (70x50cm-28x20in) s.d.80 tempera ink paper on cardboard. 11-Jun-4 Farsetti, Prato #376/R est:1900-2200
£2754 $4516 €3800 Seated man (137x74cm-54x29in) s.d.1970 oil mixed media. 27-May-3 Sotheby's, Milan #149 est:1000-1500

VANHOVE, Jo (1902-1956) Belgian
£1014 $1814 €1500 Les barques de peche (60x80cm-24x31in) s. painted c.1938. 10-May-4 Horta, Bruxelles #377/R est:1000-1200

VANKA, Maximilian (1889-1963) Croatian
Works on paper
£652 $1200 €952 Blue vase with flowers (41x30cm-16x12in) s. pastel. 11-Jun-4 David Rago, Lambertville #125/R est:900-1200

VANMOUR, Jan Baptiste (1671-1737) Flemish
£93407 $170000 €136374 Hunting party of Sultan Ahmed III (150x225cm-59x89in) prov.lit. 17-Jun-4 Christie's, Rockefeller NY #71/R est:100000-150000

VANNETTI, Angelo (20th C) Italian
£496 $829 €700 Canal in Venice (26x36cm-10x14in) s.verso board. 14-Oct-3 Finarte Semenzato, Milan #80/R

VANNETTI, Angiolo (19/20th C) Italian
Sculpture
£2873 $5200 €4195 Roman Charioteer with three rearing horses (41x53x38cm-16x21x15in) bears sig gilt bronze. 3-Apr-4 Neal Auction Company, New Orleans #33/R est:2000-3000

VANNI, Francesco (c.1563-1610) Italian
Works on paper
£700 $1211 €1022 Kneeling priest and two acolytes (13x15cm-5x6in) i. red chk prov. 12-Dec-3 Christie's, Kensington #325/R
£9500 $17385 €13870 Sheet of seven studies of the head of a young child (20x24cm-8x9in) red blk chk. 8-Jul-4 Sotheby's, London #48/R est:4500-6000

VANNI, Sam (1908-1992) Finnish
£878 $1572 €1300 Still life of flowers (81x65cm-32x26in) s.d.41. 8-May-4 Bukowskis, Helsinki #244/R
£878 $1572 €1300 Autumn day (60x81cm-24x32in) s.d.42. 8-May-4 Bukowskis, Helsinki #249/R
£4545 $7727 €6500 Composition (145x145cm-57x57in) s.d.87. 29-Nov-3 Bukowskis, Helsinki #297/R est:7000-10000
£16216 $29027 €24000 Chiavi d'oro - the golden keys (130x81cm-51x32in) s.d.59 exhib. 8-May-4 Bukowskis, Helsinki #263/R est:10000-13000
Works on paper
£1007 $1852 €1500 Composition (80x56cm-31x22in) s.d.1974 gouache. 25-Mar-4 Hagelstam, Helsinki #926/R est:1500
£1486 $2661 €2200 Composition (72x61cm-28x24in) s.d.85 gouache. 8-May-4 Bukowskis, Helsinki #302/R est:2000-2500
£3776 $6420 €5400 Composition (78x56cm-31x22in) s.d.56 gouache. 29-Nov-3 Bukowskis, Helsinki #307/R est:3000-4000

VANNINI, Ottavio (1585-1643) Italian
£27817 $46176 €39500 Eliezer et Rebecca (127x166cm-50x65in) prov.lit. 10-Jun-3 Renaud, Paris #12/R est:12000-15000

VANNUCCI, Pietro (circle) (1445-1523) Italian
£9500 $17385 €13870 Nativity (58x44cm-23x17in) canvas on panel prov. 9-Jul-4 Christie's, Kensington #191/R est:4000-6000
£40000 $73200 €58400 Portrait of a man in a black coat and cap (51x37cm-20x15in) fresco prov.lit. 7-Jul-4 Christie's, London #2/R est:20000-30000

VANNUCCI, Pietro (style) (1445-1523) Italian
£10000 $18000 €14600 Faith, Hope and Charity (152x166cm-60x65in) panel arched top prov. 21-Apr-4 Christie's, London #69/R est:10000-15000
£13000 $22490 €18980 Holy Family (88x88cm-35x35in) i.verso panel round prov. 11-Dec-3 Sotheby's, London #175/R est:8000-12000

VANNUTELLI, Cristina (19/20th C) Italian
£694 $1146 €1000 Italian town on mountain side (18x32cm-7x13in) s. panel. 2-Jul-3 Neumeister, Munich #804/R

VANNUTELLI, Scipione (1834-1894) Italian
£986 $1706 €1400 Lady (13x12cm-5x5in) s.d.1880 board. 11-Dec-3 Christie's, Rome #60/R
Works on paper
£355 $635 €518 Herder with staff (34x24cm-13x9in) s. W/C. 28-May-4 Uppsala Auktionskammare, Uppsala #124 (S.KR 4800)

VANNUTELLI, Scipione (attrib) (1834-1894) Italian
£2113 $3655 €3000 Turists at the Forum (62x50cm-24x20in) d.95. 10-Dec-3 Finarte Semenzato, Rome #271/R est:3000-4000

VANOTTI, Amalie (1853-?) German
£280 $467 €400 Old harbour of Constance on the Bodensee (50x41cm-20x16in) s. canvas on board. 28-Jun-3 Bolland & Marotz, Bremen #742/R

VANTONGERLOO, Georges (1886-1965) Belgian
£13656 $23216 €19938 Portrait of young woman (69x59cm-27x23in) s.d.1916. 5-Nov-3 Dobiaschofsky, Bern #1019/R est:5000 (S.FR 31000)
£47000 $85540 €68620 No.94 - etendue fermee (62x54cm-24x21in) s. i.d.1936 verso panel prov.exhib.lit. 4-Feb-4 Sotheby's, London #287/R est:30000-40000

VANTORE, Mogens (1895-1977) Danish
£305 $548 €445 Still life of flowers (65x67cm-26x26in) s. 24-Apr-4 Rasmussen, Havnen #2074/R (D.KR 3400)
£366 $667 €534 Still life of tulips in jug (69x52cm-27x20in) s. 7-Feb-4 Rasmussen, Havnen #4054/R (D.KR 4000)

VANZO, Julio (1901-?) Argentinian
£1676 $3000 €2447 Vase of flowers (50x40cm-20x16in) s.d.37 cardboard. 4-May-4 Arroyo, Buenos Aires #41/R est:2900
£2308 $4200 €3370 Flowers (50x69cm-20x27in) s.d.42 cardboard. 29-Jun-4 Arroyo, Buenos Aires #99/R est:2800

VAQUERO TURCIOS, Joaquin (1933-) Spanish
£833 $1417 €1200 Abstract (57x72cm-22x28in) s. acrylic paper. 28-Oct-3 Segre, Madrid #173

VARDA, Janco (20th C) ?
Works on paper
£600 $1110 €876 Derby (38x54cm-15x21in) s. mixed media. 15-Jan-4 Christie's, Kensington #1030

VARDANEGA, Gregorio (1923-) Argentinian
Sculpture
£4577 $7919 €6500 Variations chromatiques (80x80x17cm-31x31x7in) s.i.d.1967-1972 verso illuminated relief. 14-Dec-3 Rabourdin & Choppin de Janvry, Paris #91/R est:6500-8000
£5986 $10356 €8500 Espaces chromatiques (60x60x40cm-24x24x16in) s.i.d.1965-1968 verso programmed illuminated box prov. 14-Dec-3 Rabourdin & Choppin de Janvry, Paris #100/R est:9000-10000

VAREJAO, Adriana (1964-) Brazilian
£15294 $26000 €22329 A Chinesa - Chinese person (120x100cm-47x39in) s.i.d.1992 verso prov.exhib.lit. 18-Nov-3 Christie's, Rockefeller NY #11/R est:18000-22000

VARELA Y SARTORIO, Eulogio (1868-1955) Spanish
Works on paper
£405 $714 €600 Tide (26x38cm-10x15in) s.d.1935 gouache. 18-May-4 Segre, Madrid #33/R

VARELA, Abigail (1948-) Venezuelan
Sculpture
£11111 $20000 €16222 Traveller (83x65x55cm-33x26x22in) s. num.1/6 bronze. 25-Apr-4 Subastas Odalys, Caracas #63/R est:18000

VARENDE, Jean de la (1887-1959) French
Works on paper
£467 $859 €700 Tete de femme de profil, portant une couronne d'epines (29x24cm-11x9in) i.d.26 janvier MCMXVI W/C pen crayon. 9-Jun-4 Piasa, Paris #128
£467 $859 €700 Vase de fleurs (30x24cm-12x9in) gouache. 9-Jun-4 Piasa, Paris #129

VARESE, Giacomo (1892-?) Italian
£3356 $6174 €5000 Ligurian coast (52x90cm-20x35in) s.i.d.88. 25-Mar-4 Dr Fritz Nagel, Stuttgart #772/R est:1700

VARGA, Ferenc (1908-) Hungarian
£468 $767 €650 Still life of flowers (70x59cm-28x23in) s. 4-Jun-3 Ketterer, Hamburg #106/R

VARGA, Istvan (1895-1978) Hungarian
£1140 $1893 €1664 Still life of apples and pears (70x60cm-28x24in) s. 4-Oct-3 Kieselbach, Budapest #33/R (H.F 420000)
£1159 $2098 €1692 Storm clouds above a village (46x37cm-18x15in) s. 16-Apr-4 Mu Terem Galeria, Budapest #132/R (H.F 440000)
£1449 $2623 €2116 Green still life with sunflower (70x55cm-28x22in) s. s.stretcher. 16-Apr-4 Mu Terem Galeria, Budapest #187/R (H.F 550000)

VARGAS RUIZ, Guillermo (1910-1990) Spanish
£1042 $1656 €1500 En el hipodromo con autorretrato (22x35cm-9x14in) s. 29-Apr-3 Durán, Madrid #92/R est:1100
Works on paper
£423 $731 €600 Composition (15x22cm-6x9in) dr. 15-Dec-3 Ansorena, Madrid #223/R

VARGAS, Alberto (1896-1983) American
Works on paper
£3356 $6007 €5000 Untitled (25x20cm-10x8in) s. gouache crayon. 27-May-4 Sotheby's, Paris #139/R est:5000-7000
£10286 $18000 €15018 Vargas girl - what show are you watching (76x51cm-30x20in) s. W/C pencil illus board exec May 1961. 17-Dec-3 Christie's, Rockefeller NY #56/R est:20000-30000
£11429 $20000 €16686 Vargas Girl - I'm a little tired this evening (50x76cm-20x30in) s. W/C pencil ills board exec 1963. 17-Dec-3 Christie's, Rockefeller NY #170/R est:20000-30000
£13408 $24000 €19576 Seated woman with three hearts on foil (46x51cm-18x20in) s. W/C. 15-May-4 Illustration House, New York #122/R est:22000-30000
£16000 $28000 €23360 Vargas - What I asked you was how I liked my asp (76x51cm-30x20in) s. W/C pencil exec May 1969. 17-Dec-3 Christie's, Rockefeller NY #89/R est:20000-30000
£16000 $28000 €23360 Vargas Girl - Now both you and my hairdresser know for sure Mr Brighton (76x51cm-30x20in) s. W/C pencil ills board exec May 1964. 17-Dec-3 Christie's, Rockefeller NY #110/R est:20000-30000
£16000 $28000 €23360 Vargas Girl - If we don't go to bed Santa will never arrive (73x51cm-29x20in) s. W/C pencil ills board exec Dec 1964. 17-Dec-3 Christie's, Rockefeller NY #171/R est:20000-30000
£16000 $28000 €23360 Vargas Girl - I believe in black pride. (51x76cm-20x30in) s. W/C pencil ills board exec 1970. 17-Dec-3 Christie's, Rockefeller NY #250/R est:20000-30000
£18286 $32000 €26698 Vargas Girl (51x76cm-20x30in) s. W/C pencil ills board exec Dec 1967. 17-Dec-3 Christie's, Rockefeller NY #155/R est:25000-35000
£19022 $35000 €27772 World War II (61x97cm-24x38in) s. W/C pencil on board prov. 23-Mar-4 Arthur James, Florida #92/R est:35000-45000
£20000 $35000 €29200 Vargas Girl - Darling how about supplying a little shade (51x76cm-20x30in) s. W/C pencil ills board exec June 1971. 17-Dec-3 Christie's, Rockefeller NY #212/R est:25000-35000
£21714 $38000 €31702 Vargas Girl (51x77cm-20x30in) s. W/C pencil ills board exec Feb 1962. 17-Dec-3 Christie's, Rockefeller NY #156/R est:25000-35000
£21714 $38000 €31702 Vargas Girl - I don't like being treated as an object (76x51cm-30x20in) s. W/C pencil ills board exec 1970. 17-Dec-3 Christie's, Rockefeller NY #225/R est:25000-35000
£24000 $42000 €35040 This gang's going on a picnic this afternoon (76x51cm-30x20in) s. W/C pencil ills board exec Jan 1967. 17-Dec-3 Christie's, Rockefeller NY #109/R est:20000-30000
£24000 $42000 €35040 Vargas Girl - I never go out with married men so will you please come in (76x51cm-30x20in) s. W/C pencil ills board exec Feb 1966. 17-Dec-3 Christie's, Rockefeller NY #182/R est:25000-35000
£28571 $50000 €41714 Vargas Girl - Please don't peek until I finish dressing (76x51cm-30x20in) s. W/C pencil ills board exec Sept 1962. 17-Dec-3 Christie's, Rockefeller NY #90/R est:25000-35000
£34286 $60000 €50058 Vargas Girl - Trick or treat (76x51cm-30x20in) s. W/C pencil ills board exec Oct 1967. 17-Dec-3 Christie's, Rockefeller NY #183/R est:25000-35000

VARGAS, Luis de (1502-1568) Spanish
£3333 $6000 €4866 Betrayal of Christ (68x110cm-27x43in) panel transferred to canvas prov. 23-Jan-4 Christie's, Rockefeller NY #105/R est:5000-7000

VARGAS, Mario (20th C) Spanish?
Works on paper
£278 $464 €400 Le cadran solaire (65x55cm-26x22in) s. mixed media panel. 26-Oct-3 Feletin, Province #173

VARI, Sophie (1940-) Greek
Sculpture
£1216 $2299 €1800 Soiree du dimanche (24x33x10cm-9x13x4in) s.num.3/6 gilt pat bronze. 21-Feb-4 Cornette de St.Cyr, Paris #418/R est:2000-3000

VARIN, Eugene (19th C) French
Photographs
£3846 $6423 €5500 Sp. (17x13cm-7x5in) salt print exec.c.1853. 10-Oct-3 Beaussant & Lefèvre, Paris #32/R est:1000-1200

VARIOLA, Angelo (1906-) Italian
£979 $1684 €1400 Landscape with tree and vineyards (60x40cm-24x16in) s. painted 1977. 3-Dec-3 Stadion, Trieste #963/R

VARISCO, Grazia (1937-) Italian
Sculpture
£2733 $5029 €4100 Transparent (76x76cm-30x30in) s.verso net magnet painted wood exec.1960. 8-Jun-4 Finarte Semenzato, Milan #286/R est:1200-1500

VARLA, Felix (1903-) French
£993 $1808 €1500 L'essayage (54x65cm-21x26in) 16-Jun-4 Claude Boisgirard, Paris #165/R est:1500
£1408 $2437 €2000 Vendanges (54x65cm-21x26in) s. 14-Dec-3 Eric Pillon, Calais #227/R
Works on paper
£423 $731 €600 Jeune paysan (32x17cm-13x7in) gouache paper on canvas. 14-Dec-3 Eric Pillon, Calais #228/R

VARLESE, Giovanni (19th C) Italian
Sculpture
£967 $1750 €1412 Fisher boy (71cm-28in) s. bronze. 18-Apr-4 Jeffery Burchard, Florida #25/R

VARLEY, Cornelius (1781-1873) British
Works on paper
£500 $835 €730 Study of the sea and sky (12x38cm-5x15in) pencil. 16-Oct-3 Christie's, Kensington #26/R
£750 $1275 €1095 Shepherd and sheep in a wooded landscape (21x30cm-8x12in) blk white chk buff paper prov.exhib. 20-Nov-3 Christie's, London #65/R
£750 $1275 €1095 Study of a timber-framed gabled farmhouse (28x36cm-11x14in) pencil W/C prov. 20-Nov-3 Christie's, London #67/R
£2400 $4008 €3504 Study of a house in Dolgelly, north Wales (17x25cm-7x10in) init.i.d.1802 pencil W/C. 16-Oct-3 Christie's, Kensington #54/R est:600-800
£3400 $6256 €4964 Hilly landscape (17x25cm-7x10in) W/C over pencil. 26-Mar-4 Sotheby's, London #111/R est:1200-1800

VARLEY, Frederick Horsman (1881-1969) Canadian/British
£5691 $10187 €8309 Portrait of Dr John Goldie (61x50cm-24x20in) s. prov.lit. 27-May-4 Heffel, Vancouver #72/R est:15000-18000 (C.D 14000)
£8929 $15357 €13036 Autumn woods at Doon (30x37cm-12x15in) s. canvasboard prov. 2-Dec-3 Joyner Waddington, Toronto #87/R est:20000-30000 (C.D 20000)
£12613 $21441 €18415 Calm weather, Georgian Bay (22x27cm-9x11in) s. s.i. verso panel prov. 18-Nov-3 Sotheby's, Toronto #150/R est:12000-15000 (C.D 28000)
£13514 $22973 €19730 Belfountain (30x38cm-12x15in) s. i.d.1948 verso double sided prov. 27-Nov-3 Heffel, Vancouver #126/R est:20000-25000 (C.D 30000)
£42793 $72748 €62478 Lake Garibaldi, BC (30x38cm-12x15in) s. i.d.1928 verso panel. 18-Nov-3 Sotheby's, Toronto #152/R est:25000-35000 (C.D 95000)
Works on paper
£1423 $2547 €2078 Double nude, arms raised (42x28cm-17x11in) i.d.c.1930 verso chl prov.exhib.lit. 27-May-4 Heffel, Vancouver #74/R est:1500-2500 (C.D 3500)
£2027 $3446 €2959 John climbing a tree (120x56cm-47x22in) s. chl prov. 18-Nov-3 Sotheby's, Toronto #167/R est:7000-10000 (C.D 4500)
£2902 $4991 €4237 Gatineau Hills, Blue Sea Lake (19x28cm-7x11in) st.sig. W/C painted c.1958 prov. 2-Dec-3 Joyner Waddington, Toronto #156/R est:8000-10000 (C.D 6500)
£6306 $10721 €9207 Robin (43x39cm-17x15in) s. chl. prov.exhib. 18-Nov-3 Sotheby's, Toronto #169/R est:10000-12000 (C.D 14000)
£7317 $13098 €10683 Arctic landscape with figures (23x29cm-9x11in) s. W/C prov. 31-May-4 Sotheby's, Toronto #61/R est:6000-8000 (C.D 18000)

VARLEY, J (1778-1842) British
Works on paper
£800 $1280 €1160 River landscape with figures and castle (13x21cm-5x8in) s. 17-Sep-3 James Thompson, Kirby Lonsdale #107
£6200 $11222 €9052 Snowdon (26x66cm-10x26in) W/C. 15-Apr-4 Hobbs Parker, Ashford #682/R est:4000-6000

VARLEY, John (1778-1842) British
£660 $1221 €964 Welsh valley landscape with Snowdon in the distance (14x21cm-6x8in) W/C. 14-Jul-4 Bonhams, Chester #455
£750 $1373 €1095 Extensive classical landscape with sheep (41x104cm-16x41in) s. 7-Apr-4 Gardiner & Houlgate, Bath #123/R
£780 $1427 €1139 View on the River Wye with Hereford Cathedral in the distance (18x25cm-7x10in) s. 7-Apr-4 Gardiner & Houlgate, Bath #128/R
£4500 $8280 €6570 Extensive river landscape on the Thames (50x78cm-20x31in) 26-Mar-4 Sotheby's, London #54/R est:5000-7000
£5120 $8500 €7475 Figures on the bank of the river Thames (37x47cm-15x19in) prov. 30-Sep-3 Christie's, Rockefeller NY #345/R est:6000-8000
Works on paper
£260 $468 €380 Country cottage (29x23cm-11x9in) pencil prov. 21-Jan-4 Sotheby's, Olympia #112/R
£260 $476 €380 Open landscape with lake and distant tower (13x30cm-5x12in) pencil W/C exhib. 28-Jul-4 Mallams, Oxford #102/R
£280 $529 €409 Hilly rural landscape with two figures walking beside cottages (31x20cm-12x8in) s. W/C. 17-Feb-4 Fellows & Sons, Birmingham #137/R
£311 $510 €451 Italian scene with castle and coast (19x29cm-7x11in) W/C paper on board prov. 5-Jun-3 Heffel, Vancouver #82 (C.D 700)

£360	$587	€522	Castle in a rural landscape (14x22cm-6x9in) s. W/C. 23-Sep-3 Bonhams, Knightsbridge #55/R
£380	$635	€555	Figures in a rural landscape (10x18cm-4x7in) W/C gum arabic. 14-Oct-3 Bonhams, Knightsbridge #165/R
£430	$804	€645	Figures on a land passing houses (25x36cm-10x14in) s.d.1838 W/C. 22-Jul-4 Gorringes, Lewes #2006/R
£450	$774	€657	Landscape with figures and sheep, river and mountain to background (10x18cm-4x7in) s. i.verso. 3-Dec-3 Neal & Fletcher, Woodbridge #340
£450	$828	€657	View of Mount Snowdon (14x21cm-6x8in) W/C prov. 22-Jun-4 Bonhams, Knightsbridge #155/R
£480	$893	€701	Estuary scene (10x15cm-4x6in) s.d.1827 pencil. 2-Mar-4 Bearnes, Exeter #365
£500	$790	€725	Figures beside a cornfield (24x20cm-9x8in) s.i.d.1806 verso W/C. 3-Sep-3 Bonhams, Bury St Edmunds #326
£580	$1067	€847	Figures on a track with distant lake (8x12cm-3x5in) s. W/C. 23-Jun-4 Bonhams, Bury St Edmunds #312/R
£650	$1196	€949	Sheep grazing before a hillside village on the coast (9x13cm-4x5in) W/C. 25-Mar-4 Christie's, Kensington #27/R
£850	$1462	€1241	Shepherds before a fortified headland (9x13cm-4x5in) s. brown ink W/C prov. 3-Dec-3 Christie's, Kensington #14/R
£900	$1422	€1305	Mountainous lakeland landscape with figures in a sailing boat (24x33cm-9x13in) s.d.1810 W/C. 4-Sep-3 Locke & England, Leamington Spa #135
£900	$1638	€1314	A fortified village by a river (9x12cm-4x5in) s. pencil W/C. 1-Jul-4 Christie's, Kensington #73/R
£950	$1758	€1387	River landscape (9x13cm-4x5in) s. W/C. 9-Mar-4 Bonhams, New Bond Street #61/R
£1000	$1670	€1460	Figures by a cottage (9x14cm-4x6in) pencil W/C. 16-Oct-3 Christie's, Kensington #39/R est:800-1200
£1000	$1850	€1460	Cuidad Rodrigo, Spain (38x65cm-15x26in) W/C prov.exhib. 9-Mar-4 Bonhams, New Bond Street #28/R est:1000-1500
£1000	$1850	€1460	York Minster (16x30cm-6x12in) s. W/C. 9-Mar-4 Bonhams, New Bond Street #56/R est:600-900
£1050	$1890	€1533	Sheep grazing by a cottage, a church in the distance (14x20cm-6x8in) W/C over pencil. 21-Jan-4 Sotheby's, Olympia #114/R est:800-1200
£1200	$2160	€1752	Lake scene, North Wales (18x38cm-7x15in) s. W/C prov. 21-Apr-4 Cheffins, Cambridge #451/R est:400-600
£1250	$2038	€1825	Mountainous landscape with figures (33x45cm-13x18in) S.D.1832 W. 24-Sep-3 Dreweatt Neate, Newbury #9/R est:700-900
£1300	$2171	€1898	Bolton Abbey, Yorkshire (13x20cm-5x8in) W/C. 12-Nov-3 Halls, Shrewsbury #284/R est:600-800
£1300	$2366	€1898	On the Rhine (24x33cm-9x13in) W/C htd white scratching out. 5-Feb-4 Mellors & Kirk, Nottingham #493/R est:100-1400
£1400	$2380	€2044	Near Bookham, Surrey (17x23cm-7x9in) W/C. 29-Oct-3 Bonhams, Chester #415 est:500-800
£1400	$2590	€2044	View of Bolton Abbey, Yorkshire (14x20cm-6x8in) W/C prov. 9-Mar-4 Bonhams, New Bond Street #57/R est:1500-2000
£1700	$2890	€2482	Carnavon Castle (11x26cm-4x10in) s. W/C. 29-Oct-3 Bonhams, Chester #309/R est:1000-1400
£1700	$2924	€2482	On the Wye (23x34cm-9x13in) pencil W/C prov. 3-Dec-3 Christie's, Kensington #11/R est:1000-1500
£1700	$3094	€2482	Noel Hebog from Lynn Dinas, near Bedgellest, North Wales (48x79cm-19x31in) s.i. W/C prov. 4-Feb-4 John Nicholson, Haslemere #68/R est:2000-3000
£1800	$3294	€2628	Kilchurn Castle, Loch Awe (25x35cm-10x14in) s. pencil W/C scratching out. 3-Jun-4 Christie's, London #136/R est:1200-1800
£1800	$3276	€2628	Figures and sheep on the shore of Lake Geneva (16x29cm-6x11in) W/C over pencil. 1-Jul-4 Sotheby's, London #179/R est:2000-3000
£2200	$4070	€3212	Figures with sheep by a lake, a castle on a hill beyond (34x46cm-13x18in) W/C over pencil htd stopping out. 10-Mar-4 Sotheby's, Olympia #37/R est:3600-5100
£2200	$4026	€3212	Bolton Abbey on the Wharfe, Yorkshire (21x29cm-8x11in) s.d.1824 pencil W/C prov. 3-Jun-4 Christie's, London #137/R est:700-1000
£2600	$4758	€3796	Thames from Richmond (13x25cm-5x10in) s. i.d.1834 verso pencil W/C scratching out prov. 3-Jun-4 Christie's, London #135/R est:1500-2000
£3500	$6405	€5110	View of Snowdon, North Wales (35x53cm-14x21in) s.d.1802 pencil W/C scratching out. 3-Jun-4 Christie's, London #147/R est:2500-3500
£3800	$7030	€5548	St Nicholas's Cathedral, Newcastle (48x39cm-19x15in) s.i.d.August 15 1808 W/C. 9-Mar-4 Bonhams, New Bond Street #71/R est:1500-2000
£4200	$7770	€6132	Thatched cottage (16x21cm-6x8in) s.d.1825 W/C prov. 9-Mar-4 Bonhams, New Bond Street #55/R est:1500-2500
£4200	$7686	€6132	View of Snowdon, Wales (14x21cm-6x8in) s. pencil W/C scratching out. 3-Jun-4 Christie's, London #134/R est:1200-1800
£5500	$10120	€8030	Llyn Padarn, Dolbadarn Castle and Pass of Llanberis, Snowdon beyond (57x80cm-22x31in) W/C. 8-Jun-4 Bonhams, New Bond Street #26/R est:4000-6000
£5600	$10192	€8176	Tegwin ferry with Snowdon in the distance from near Harlech, North Wales (26x48cm-10x19in) s. W/C over pencil htd scratching out exhib. 1-Jul-4 Sotheby's, London #205/R est:3000-4000
£6200	$11470	€9052	Dustanburgh Castle, Northumberland (33x53cm-13x21in) s.i.d.Sept 20 1808 sold with two similar by the same hand. 9-Mar-4 Bonhams, New Bond Street #22/R est:800-1200
£6500	$12025	€9490	North west view of Bamburgh Castle (31x63cm-12x25in) i. pencil wash sold with three similar by the same hand. 9-Mar-4 Bonhams, New Bond Street #20/R est:1200-1800
£6500	$11895	€9490	Near Dolgelly, North Wales (14x21cm-6x8in) s. pencil W/C gum arabic scratching out. 3-Jun-4 Christie's, London #133/R est:1200-1800
£6500	$11830	€9490	Cader Idris, North Wales (43x61cm-17x24in) s.d.1819 W/C over pencil htd scratching out prov.exhib. 1-Jul-4 Sotheby's, London #204/R est:6000-8000
£7000	$12810	€10220	Tintern Abbey, Wales (29x54cm-11x21in) s.d.1832 pencil W/C htd touches bodycol prov.exhib. 3-Jun-4 Christie's, London #131/R est:2500-3500
£7500	$13875	€10950	Conway Castle (29x55cm-11x22in) s. W/C over pencil sold with six other views by the same hand. 9-Mar-4 Bonhams, New Bond Street #21/R est:1200-1800
£7500	$13725	€10950	Conway Castle, Wales (14x21cm-6x8in) s. pencil W/C gum arabic scratching out. 3-Jun-4 Christie's, London #132/R est:1500-2000
£8500	$14450	€12410	View of Moel Hedog, near Beddgelert, North Wales (36x54cm-14x21in) s.d.1826 W/C exhib. 4-Nov-3 Bonhams, New Bond Street #41/R est:7000-10000
£9500	$16625	€13870	Traveller resting at the roadside (35x49cm-14x19in) s.d.1813 W/C prov. 16-Dec-3 Bonhams, New Bond Street #3/R est:6000-8000
£16000	$27200	€23360	Cader Idris, North Wales (29x39cm-11x15in) W/C over pencil. 27-Nov-3 Sotheby's, London #268/R est:2500-3500

VARLEY, John (attrib) (1778-1842) British

£850	$1496	€1241	St. Michael's Mount, Cornwall (58x74cm-23x29in) s.d.1833. 19-May-4 Christie's, Kensington #584/R

Works on paper

£480	$787	€701	Figures outside an inn, in a wooded summer landscape (10x13cm-4x5in) s. 29-May-3 Neales, Nottingham #711/R
£550	$935	€803	Pigs on a road with a lake and a ruin beyond (18x48cm-7x19in) W/C prov. 30-Oct-3 Duke & Son, Dorchester #62/R
£1300	$2171	€1898	Shepherd by a tree lined pond (27x42cm-11x17in) s.d.1805 pencil W/C. 16-Oct-3 Christie's, Kensington #29/R est:1000-1500

VARLEY, John (jnr) (1850-1933) British

£750	$1395	€1095	Japanese street (27x34cm-11x13in) s.d.91 panel. 4-Mar-4 Christie's, Kensington #576
£4000	$7480	€6000	Spring blossoms, Tokio (28x33cm-11x13in) s.d.91/92 panel sold with another similar. 20-Jul-4 Peter Francis, Wales #75/R est:300-500

Works on paper

£500	$895	€730	The approach to Cairo. Boats (21x36cm-8x14in) W/C two. 25-May-4 Bonhams, Knightsbridge #291/R
£600	$1002	€876	Arran mountains and Penmaen pool (18x25cm-7x10in) s.verso W/C pair. 12-Nov-3 Halls, Shrewsbury #260/R
£700	$1281	€1022	Arabs near desert ruins (26x37cm-10x15in) both s. W/C pencil pair. 8-Jul-4 Lawrence, Crewkerne #1524/R
£950	$1701	€1387	The pyramids at Giza. A desert town (17x37cm-7x15in) s. W/C pair. 25-May-4 Bonhams, Knightsbridge #290/R
£1700	$3009	€2482	Cataract on the Nile. Temple of Isis at Philae (35x52cm-14x20in) s.d.98 W/C pair. 27-Apr-4 Bonhams, New Bond Street #72/R est:1500-2500

VARLIN, Willy Guggenheim (1900-1977) Swiss

£31674	$54796	€46244	The dog Lapponio (162x132cm-64x52in) s. oil chl material hair. 9-Dec-3 Sotheby's, Zurich #118/R est:70000-90000 (S.FR 70000)
£41304	$75587	€60304	Asta (104x135cm-41x53in) s.i.d.1943 prov.exhib.lit. 7-Jun-4 Christie's, Zurich #129/R est:20000-30000 (S.FR 95000)

VARNA, Frank J (20th C) American?

£614	$1100	€896	Old mining area (41x51cm-16x20in) s. canvasboard. 21-Mar-4 Bonhams & Butterfields, Los Angeles #7313/R est:500-700

VARNALIS, Ioakim (1907-1986) Greek

£1000	$1750	€1460	View of Nafplio (61x45cm-24x18in) s. canvas on board. 16-Dec-3 Bonhams, New Bond Street #74/R est:800-1200

VARNI, Antonio (c.1840-1908) Italian

£3233	$5787	€4720	Girl collecting leaves (58x39cm-23x15in) s.d.1901 paper on board. 12-May-4 Dobiaschofsky, Bern #1040/R est:2800 (S.FR 7500)

VARNOLD, C B (fl.1871) British?

£4000	$6800	€5840	Harvesting the corn (76x128cm-30x50in) s.d.1871. 25-Nov-3 Christie's, London #113/R est:3000-5000

VARO, Remedios (1900-1963) Spanish

Works on paper

£1618	$2750	€2362	Happy Christmas (22x10cm-9x4in) s.i.verso collage prov. 9-Nov-3 Bonhams & Butterfields, Los Angeles #4131/R est:1000-1500
£94118	$160000	€137412	Caminos tortuosos (47x27cm-19x11in) s. gouache executed 1957 prov.exhib.lit. 19-Nov-3 Sotheby's, New York #9/R est:100000-150000

VAROTARI, Alessandro (1588-1648) Italian

£5517	$9159	€8000	Charity (117x99cm-46x39in) prov. 1-Oct-3 Dorotheum, Vienna #22/R est:7000-10000

VAROTARI, Alessandro (studio) (1588-1648) Italian

£7639	$12757	€11000	Saint Francis and the angels (92x104cm-36x41in) 22-Oct-3 Finarte Semenzato, Milan #56/R est:12000-15000

VAROUCHAS, Georgios (19th C) Greek

£8000	$13600	€11680	Madonna of the Veil (99x73cm-39x29in) s. 18-Nov-3 Sotheby's, London #81/R est:8000-12000

VARRONE, Johann (1832-1910) Austrian

£1042	$1771	€1500	Tepia near Bellinzona, Switzerland (31x54cm-12x21in) s. board. 28-Oct-3 Dorotheum, Vienna #249/R est:3000-4000
£4762	$8524	€6953	Landscape near Bellinzona with animals and figures (91x127cm-36x50in) s.d.1874. 22-Mar-4 Philippe Schuler, Zurich #4433/R est:6000-8000 (S.FR 11000)

Works on paper

£1172	$1946	€1700	Rothenturmstrasse in 1840 (24x35cm-9x14in) s.i. W/C. 30-Sep-3 Dorotheum, Vienna #294/R est:3400-4000

VARVARESSOS, Vicki (1949-) Australian

£1570	$2905	€2292	Woman, arms folded (122x134cm-48x53in) init.d.88 s.i.d.verso enamel on hardboard prov. 15-Mar-4 Sotheby's, Melbourne #4 est:3000-5000 (A.D 3800)
£1653	$3058	€2413	Woman standing (170x122cm-67x48in) init.d.89 s.i.d.verso enamel oil hardboard prov. 15-Mar-4 Sotheby's, Melbourne #9 est:3000-5000 (A.D 4000)
£1736	$3211	€2535	Woman and shadow (122x137cm-48x54in) init.d.89 s.i.d.1989 verso enamel oil hardboard. 15-Mar-4 Sotheby's, Melbourne #18 est:3000-5000 (A.D 4200)

VASALLI, S (19th C) Italian

£1000	$1660	€1460	Jovial model (63x52cm-25x20in) init. 1-Oct-3 Sotheby's, Olympia #229/R est:1000-2000

VASARELY, Victor (1908-1997) Hungarian

£1370	$2329	€2000	Composition (18x18cm-7x7in) s. panel. 9-Nov-3 Eric Pillon, Calais #268/R
£1745	$3088	€2600	Composition (50x50cm-20x20in) s. acrylic collage thin board. 28-Apr-4 Artcurial Briest, Paris #338 est:3000-4000
£2483	$4395	€3700	Composition (50x50cm-20x20in) s. acrylic collage thin board. 28-Apr-4 Artcurial Briest, Paris #339/R est:3000-4000
£3125	$5156	€4500	Tridum-Deta-B (35x35cm-14x14in) s. s.i.d.1968 verso oil wood. 2-Jul-3 Cornette de St.Cyr, Paris #199/R est:4000-5000

£3514	$6500	€5130	Kiu-siu (48x46cm-19x18in) s. s.i.d.1962 verso tempera board on panel prov. 13-Jul-4 Christie's, Rockefeller NY #11/R est:4000-6000
£3784	$7000	€5525	Rhombus - B (46x46cm-18x18in) s. s.i.d.1968 verso tempera board prov. 13-Jul-4 Christie's, Rockefeller NY #12/R est:5000-7000
£4348	$7130	€6000	Kara-nor (30x29cm-12x11in) s. s.i.d.1954 verso board prov. 27-May-3 Sotheby's, Milan #150/R est:6000-8000
£4605	$8474	€6723	Imatra (35x31cm-14x12in) s. paper prov. 23-Jun-4 Koller, Zurich #3097/R est:10000-14000 (S.FR 10500)
£5034	$9211	€7500	Torobor II (80x60cm-31x24in) s. i.d.1982 verso acrylic. 7-Jul-4 Artcurial Briest, Paris #363/R est:8000-10000
£5240	$9642	€7650	Cyclon (52x51cm-20x20in) s. s.i.d.1984 verso acrylic. 8-Jun-4 Germann, Zurich #136/R est:12000-16000 (S.FR 12000)
£5521	$9000	€8061	Tridim-KK (68x52cm-27x20in) s. s.i.d.1968 verso tempera board on panel prov. 23-Sep-3 Christie's, Rockefeller NY #114/R est:3000-5000
£6294	$10825	€9000	Sarlant (83x83cm-33x33in) s. s.i.d.1989 verso. 4-Dec-3 Van Ham, Cologne #530/R est:10000
£6294	$10700	€9000	Cassiopee (43x33cm-17x13in) s. cardboard prov. 25-Nov-3 Tajan, Paris #52/R est:6000-8000
£6419	$12132	€9500	Tseress-RV (64x60cm-25x24in) s.i.verso panel. 21-Feb-4 Cornette de St.Cyr, Paris #420/R est:10000-12000
£6762	$10955	€9873	Hat-Kub SP n.2686 (108x94cm-43x37in) s.i.verso acrylic prov. 30-Jul-3 Goodman, Sydney #184/R est:15000-25000 (A.D 16500)
£7000	$12110	€10220	Mimas (92x51cm-36x20in) s. s.i.d.1958 verso oil wood board prov. 11-Dec-3 Christie's, Kensington #228/R est:8000-12000
£7333	$13200	€11000	Fall (73x73cm-29x29in) s. s.i.d.1968-1984 acrylic lit. 25-Apr-4 Versailles Encheres #176 est:8000-10000
£7383	$13215	€11000	Citra (37x34cm-15x13in) s. s.i.d.1955-59 verso prov. 26-May-4 Christie's, Paris #87/R est:6000-8000
£7553	$12840	€11027	The flower girl (143x90cm-56x35in) s. prov.lit. 4-Nov-3 Bukowskis, Stockholm #283/R est:60000-80000 (S.KR 100000)
£8000	$13840	€11680	Ceros (91x91cm-36x36in) s.d.1980 acrylic. 9-Dec-3 Maynards, Vancouver #191 est:25000-30000 (C.D 18000)
£8054	$14416	€12000	Rhombus-C (78x78cm-31x31in) s. s.i.d.1968 verso acrylic board. 28-May-4 Farsetti, Prato #155/R est:8200-9200
£8392	$14434	€12000	Guimen (80x80cm-31x31in) s. s.i.d.1987 verso. 4-Dec-3 Van Ham, Cologne #531/R est:10000
£8725	$15443	€13000	Composition (37x37cm-15x15in) s.d.1955 oil collage thin board. 28-Apr-4 Artcurial Briest, Paris #337/R est:4000-6000
£8725	$16228	€13000	Bokk (195x120cm-77x47in) s. s.i.d.1987 verso acrylic. 3-Mar-4 Artcurial Briest, Paris #528/R est:8000-12000
£9155	$15197	€13000	Sis-Ris-BB (59x59cm-23x23in) s. s.i.d.1959-68 oil acrylic panel. 14-Jun-3 Meeting Art, Vercelli #117/R est:12000
£9184	$16439	€13500	Vega - Pauk - W (50x24cm-20x9in) s. s.i.d.1971 verso prov. 19-Mar-4 Millon & Associes, Paris #185/R est:3000-4000
£9420	$15449	€13000	Ta-Ret (71x67cm-28x26in) s.i.d.1958 verso board. 27-May-3 Sotheby's, Milan #201/R est:8000-10000
£9701	$16784	€14163	OND-GJ (44x44cm-17x17in) s.i. s.d.1968 verso board prov. 9-Dec-3 Peter Webb, Auckland #85/R est:10000-15000 (NZ.D 26000)
£9890	$18000	€14439	Kutt (80x80cm-31x31in) s. s.i.d.1977 verso acrylic panel prov. 29-Jun-4 Sotheby's, New York #489/R est:10000-15000
£10000	$18400	€14600	P 1032 URSA-1 (82x162cm-32x64in) s. s.i.d.1979 verso. acrylic prov. 24-Jun-4 Sotheby's, London #155/R est:10000-15000
£10135	$17838	€15000	Procion-Foin (53x35cm-21x14in) s. s.i.d.1969-72 verso paint collage board panel prov.lit. 18-May-4 Tajan, Paris #96/R est:15000-18000
£10403	$18621	€15500	Anczy (80x80cm-31x31in) s. s.i.verso painted 1989. 28-May-4 Farsetti, Prato #216/R est:14000-16000
£11189	$19021	€16000	Aquila (66x57cm-26x22in) s. s.i.d.1948 verso prov. 25-Nov-3 Tajan, Paris #51/R est:15000-18000
£11207	$20060	€16362	Planck (80x80cm-31x31in) s. i.d.1978 verso acrylic. 12-May-4 Dobiaschofsky, Bern #1041/R est:33000 (S.FR 26000)
£11722	$20747	€17114	Quata (73x67cm-29x26in) s. d.i.d.1957 verso acrylic panel. 27-Apr-4 AB Stockholms Auktionsverk #1195/R est:100000-120000 (S.KR 160000)
£11888	$20210	€17000	Vonal Atlo Igr (100x100cm-39x39in) s.i.d.1969. 20-Nov-3 Finarte Semenzato, Milan #192/R est:10000-12000
£12085	$20544	€17644	Lora (114x114cm-45x45in) s. s.i.d.1964 verso acrylic. 5-Nov-3 AB Stockholms Auktionsverk #1132/R est:100000-120000 (S.KR 160000)
£12238	$20804	€17500	Diam bleu (100x69cm-39x27in) s. s.i.d.1969 verso acrylic panel. 28-Nov-3 Farsetti, Prato #171/R est:17000-20000
£13000	$22490	€18980	Timor (140x100cm-55x39in) s. s.i.d.1978 verso acrylic. 11-Dec-3 Christie's, Kensington #265/R est:8000-12000
£13333	$23067	€19466	Stiva (180x180cm-71x71in) s.i.d.1980 acrylic. 9-Dec-3 Maynards, Vancouver #192 est:45000-60000 (C.D 30000)
£13416	$24148	€19587	Cenlik - composition (116x116cm-46x46in) s.i.d.1985 verso. 26-Apr-4 Bukowskis, Stockholm #253/R est:120000-130000 (S.KR 185000)
£14667	$26693	€22000	Alphar (100x52cm-39x20in) s. s.i.d.1957 versopaint. 29-Jun-4 Cornette de St.Cyr, Paris #43/R est:20000-30000
£14685	$24965	€21000	Menny (159x80cm-63x31in) s. s.i.d.1965 verso acrylic panel prov. 29-Nov-3 Villa Grisebach, Berlin #326/R est:18000-24000
£15500	$28210	€22630	Locmaria (45x36cm-18x14in) s. s.i.d.1952 verso board prov. 5-Feb-4 Christie's, London #129/R est:700-10000
£16000	$29440	€23360	Deudell (149x157cm-59x62in) s. s.i.d.1974/75 verso acrylic prov. 24-Jun-4 Sotheby's, London #151/R est:10000-15000
£16784	$28532	€24000	VEGA-EG-1-2 (120x120cm-47x47in) s.i.d.1968-1973 prov. 25-Nov-3 Tajan, Paris #53/R est:18000-20000
£17347	$31051	€25500	One - Cheyt (156x150cm-61x59in) s. s.d.1971 verso. 19-Mar-4 Millon & Associes, Paris #184/R est:12000-15000
£17964	$30000	€26227	Dell-dell (201x100cm-79x39in) s.i.d.1973/74 acrylic. 13-Nov-3 Sotheby's, New York #233/R est:15000-20000
£18000	$32760	€26280	E-Vert-Rouge (75x75cm-30x30in) s. s.i.d.1964 verso wood prov.lit. 5-Feb-4 Christie's, London #130/R est:12000-15000
£18121	$32436	€27000	Zichy 2 (121x121cm-48x48in) s. s.i.d.1984 verso. 30-May-4 Meeting Art, Vercelli #57 est:25000
£18881	$31531	€27000	STRI-KU13 (120x120cm-47x47in) s. s.i.d.1973 verso prov. 11-Oct-3 Cornette de St.Cyr, Paris #75/R est:25000-30000
£19000	$31730	€27740	Vela (184x161cm-72x63in) s.i.d.1974 verso prov. 22-Oct-3 Christie's, London #36/R est:15000-20000
£27076	$49819	€39531	Coleum-g.r. OP art composition (200x200cm-79x79in) s. s.i.d.1979 verso. 29-Mar-4 Rasmussen, Copenhagen #177/R est:300000-350000 (D.KR 300000)
£30000	$55200	€43800	VEGA-EG-1-2 (121x121cm-48x48in) s. s.i.d.1968-73 verso acrylic. 24-Jun-4 Sotheby's, London #156/R est:15000-20000
£46000	$76820	€67160	Zebras (101x112cm-40x44in) s. painted 1932-42 prov.exhib.lit. 21-Oct-3 Sotheby's, London #333/R est:20000-30000

Prints

£2260	$4000	€3300	Kanta orion blanc negative (107x102cm-42x40in) s.num.22/31 verso polystyrene col blocks resin. 28-Apr-4 Christie's, Rockefeller NY #439/R est:2500-3500
£2400	$4416	€3600	EG, yellow grey (100x100cm-39x39in) s.verso num.4/4 multiple exec.1973. 14-Jun-4 Sant Agostino, Torino #391/R est:1800-2200
£2400	$4416	€3600	Kanta Alom green blue (95x95cm-37x37in) s. num.1/4 luran exhib.lit. 8-Jun-4 Finarte Semenzato, Milan #357/R est:2500-2800

Sculpture

£946	$1665	€1400	Gestalt - P (38x23x5cm-15x9x2in) s. num.53/100 acrylic wood prov. 18-May-4 Tajan, Paris #95/R est:1800-2000
£988	$1700	€1442	NB21 (84cm-33in) s.i.num.36/50 laminated plastic. 7-Dec-3 Freeman, Philadelphia #98 est:1000-1500
£1047	$1800	€1529	Planetary folklore participations No 1 (51x51cm-20x20in) polystyrene steel exec.c.1969. 7-Dec-3 Treadway Gallery, Cincinnati #1001/R est:1500-2000
£1464	$2651	€2137	Kroa (27x27cm-11x11in) s.i.d.1968 metal. 1-Apr-4 Heffel, Vancouver #101/R est:1500-2000 (C.D 3500)
£1511	$2568	€2206	Optical composition (49x49cm-19x19in) s. glass plastic. 5-Nov-3 AB Stockholms Auktionsverk #1133/R est:20000-25000 (S.KR 20000)
£1596	$2666	€2330	Tsillag (53cm-21in) s.num.2/175 painted wood. 7-Oct-3 Rasmussen, Copenhagen #238/R est:18000 (D.KR 17000)
£1620	$2835	€2300	Ter-G2 (15x12x3cm-6x5x1in) s. painted wood. 18-Dec-3 Cornette de St.Cyr, Paris #81/R est:2500-3000
£1685	$2982	€2460	Kezdi (143cm-56in) s.num.40/175 polychrome wood incl.black wood base. 27-Apr-4 AB Stockholms Auktionsverk #1154/R est:30000-35000 (S.KR 23000)
£5503	$9741	€8200	Kanta - Majus (100x105cm-39x41in) s. s.d.Decembre 1970 Basf polystrene metal support. 28-Apr-4 Artcurial Briest, Paris #340/R est:8000-10000
£12000	$22080	€18000	Multicolore (75x75x4cm-30x30x2in) s. s.i.d.1964 verso painted wood relief acrylic prov. 8-Jun-4 Artcurial Briest, Paris #268/R est:18000-22000

Works on paper

£333	$600	€500	Untitled (21x21cm-8x8in) gouache. 25-Apr-4 Daniel Herry, Beaune #128
£393	$679	€574	Tzikos (103x85cm-41x33in) s. collage. 15-Dec-3 Lilla Bukowskis, Stockholm #645 (S.KR 5000)
£636	$1145	€929	Dyok prositif (34x34cm-13x13in) s.verso mixed media panel exec.1967. 25-Apr-4 Subastas Odalys, Caracas #94/R
£897	$1497	€1300	Pantomime (28x18cm-11x7in) s. mixed media card. 13-Nov-3 Galleria Pace, Milan #111/R est:2000
£900	$1503	€1314	Composition (26x23cm-10x9in) s. collage sold with bound volume. 22-Oct-3 Bonhams, New Bond Street #97/R
£966	$1786	€1400	Deuton (32x30cm-13x12in) s.i.d.1966 verso gouache. 19-Jan-4 Horta, Bruxelles #400
£1389	$2319	€2000	Zebres, positif-negatif (32x23cm-13x9in) s. gouache collage. 25-Oct-3 Cornette de St.Cyr, Paris #832/R est:2200-2500
£1600	$2880	€2400	Fantomes (30x25cm-12x10in) s.d.1952 collage ink. 24-Apr-4 Cornette de St.Cyr, Paris #732/R est:2500-3000
£1800	$3276	€2628	Tridim (59x40cm-23x16in) s.i.d.1968 collage board prov. 4-Feb-4 Sotheby's, Olympia #198/R est:2000-3000
£1833	$3300	€2750	Composition geometrique (36x30cm-14x12in) s. collage cardboard. 24-Apr-4 Cornette de St.Cyr, Paris #731/R
£1875	$3094	€2700	Palota (36x36cm-14x14in) s. s.i.d.1990 verso collage. 2-Jul-3 Cornette de St.Cyr, Paris #200/R est:2500-3000
£2081	$3829	€3100	Koska-Dell (51x51cm-20x20in) i.d.1971 ink lead pencil felt pen col crayon. 29-Mar-4 Cornette de St.Cyr, Paris #27/R est:4000-5000
£2600	$4498	€3796	Guelbe (61x61cm-24x24in) s. s.i.d.1964-74 verso col card on card. 11-Dec-3 Christie's, Kensington #260/R est:3000-4000
£2685	$4805	€4000	Xico-A (37x28cm-15x11in) s. s.i.d.1972 verso collage gouache. 30-May-4 Eric Pillon, Calais #282/R
£2945	$4800	€4300	OETA (32x25cm-13x10in) s. s.i.d.1957 gouache board prov.exhib. 23-Sep-3 Christie's, Rockefeller NY #116/R est:2000-3000
£3221	$5895	€4800	Composition folklfore Planetaire - Dominante jaune (50x50cm-20x20in) s. collage decoupaqe board exec c.1985. 7-Jul-4 Artcurial Briest, Paris #362 est:5000-7000
£3333	$6133	€5000	Kiruna (37x26cm-15x10in) s. mixed media card. 12-Jun-4 Meeting Art, Vercelli #849/R est:2000
£3356	$6175	€5000	Gestalt (47x40cm-19x16in) s. collage. 29-Mar-4 Cornette de St.Cyr, Paris #28/R est:5000-6000
£3356	$6141	€5000	Composition folklore Planetaire - Dominante rouge (50x50cm-20x20in) s. collage decoupage board exec c.1985. 7-Jul-4 Artcurial Briest, Paris #361 est:5000-7000
£4430	$7929	€6600	Composition (40x40cm-16x16in) s.d.1955 gouache collage. 26-May-4 Christie's, Paris #86/R est:4500-6500
£4600	$8372	€6716	Tridim (36x36cm-14x14in) s.i.d.1967 verso collage board. 4-Feb-4 Sotheby's, Olympia #199/R est:2000-3000
£6000	$11040	€8760	Felemash (59x59cm-23x23in) s. s.i.verso gouache board prov. 24-Jun-4 Sotheby's, Olympia #508/R est:3000-4000
£7500	$13800	€10950	Vega-lila (36x36cm-14x14in) s. s.i.d.1968 verso gouache board prov. 24-Jun-4 Sotheby's, Olympia #509/R est:5000-7000

VASARI, Andrea (?) Italian

Works on paper

£820	$1419	€1197	Views in Venice and in Rome (27x37cm-11x15in) s. W/C pair. 9-Dec-3 Anderson & Garland, Newcastle #243

VASARI, Giorgio (1511-1574) Italian

£75000	$137250	€109500	Madonna and Child with Saint John the Baptist (69x48cm-27x19in) panel. 7-Jul-4 Christie's, London #82/R est:60000-80000

Works on paper

£4000	$7320	€5840	Christ appearing between the Madonna and St John the Baptist (31x24cm-12x9in) bears attrib pen ink double-sided prov. 8-Jul-4 Sotheby's, London #47/R est:4000-6000
£6000	$10980	€8760	Elaborate design for the decoration surrounding an apse and two chapels (41x55cm-16x22in) i. pen brown ink wash over traces blk chk stylus. 8-Jul-4 Sotheby's, London #42/R est:6000-8000
£28000	$51240	€40880	Resurrection with Saint Andrew, John the Baptist, Cosmas and Damian (27x19cm-11x7in) black chk pen ink wash prov. 6-Jul-4 Christie's, London #20/R est:30000-50000

VASARI, Giorgio (attrib) (1511-1574) Italian

£33333	$60000	€48666	Nativity with Adoration of the Shepherds (51x44cm-20x17in) slate. 22-Jan-4 Sotheby's, New York #18a/R est:60000-80000

Works on paper

£420	$722	€600	Crowning of Marien (28x26cm-11x10in) i.verso brown ink brown wash htd white black pencil. 5-Dec-3 Bolland & Marotz, Bremen #469/R

VASARRI, Emilio (19/20th C) Italian
£764 $1245 €1100 Girls resting in grass beside track (24x32cm-9x13in) s. panel. 25-Sep-3 Dr Fritz Nagel, Stuttgart #1436/R

VASCONCELLOS, J (20th C) ?
£611 $1040 €892 Portrait of Karen Blixen (100x80cm-39x31in) s,. 29-Nov-3 Rasmussen, Havnen #4055/R (D.KR 6500)

VASCONI, Franco (1920-) Italian
£333 $613 €500 Untitled (60x80cm-24x31in) s.d.1972 s.d.verso. 12-Jun-4 Meeting Art, Vercelli #764
£470 $869 €700 Horses (80x80cm-31x31in) s.d.1973. 13-Mar-4 Meeting Art, Vercelli #348

VASELLI, Jacob (17/18th C) ?
Works on paper
£612 $1096 €900 Paysage et vaches dans un paysage fluviale anime (20x29cm-8x11in) i. pen brown ink. 17-Mar-4 Tajan, Paris #25/R

VASI, Giuseppe (1710-1782) Italian
Prints
£3571 $6500 €5214 Prospetto del'Alma Citt'di Roma visto del Monte Giancolo (965x275cm-380x108in) etching twelve sheets paper on board exec 1745. 4-Feb-4 Christie's, Rockefeller NY #133/R est:4000-6000
Works on paper
£6897 $11517 €10000 View of Rome (20x32cm-8x13in) gouache vellum. 12-Nov-3 Sotheby's, Milan #166/R est:10000-15000

VASILIEV, Fyodor (attrib) (dl.1850-1873) Russian
£3000 $5520 €4380 Russian winter landscape (59x81cm-23x32in) 25-Mar-4 Christie's, Kensington #187/R est:1500-2000

VASILIEVA, Maria Ivanovna (1884-1957) Russian
£40000 $68000 €58400 Elegant lady taking tea by the seashore (62x50cm-24x20in) s.i. 19-Nov-3 Sotheby's, London #117/R est:6000-8000

VASILOVSKY, Sergei Ivanovich (1854-1917) Russian
£1744 $3000 €2546 Landscape with ducks (28x38cm-11x15in) s. board. 7-Dec-3 Grogan, Boston #33/R

VASNETSOV, Viktor Mikhaelovich (1848-1926) Russian
Works on paper
£4487 $7000 € Portrait of a saint (45x27cm-18x11in) s.cyrillic pencil W/C. 11-Apr-3 Christie's, Rockefeller NY #37/R est:10000-15000

VASQUEZ BRITO, Ramón (1927-) Venezuelan
£431 $720 €629 Guri (30x40cm-12x16in) s. painted 1968. 13-Jul-3 Subastas Odalys, Caracas #74
£656 $1095 €958 Untitled (46x65cm-18x26in) s. 13-Jul-3 Subastas Odalys, Caracas #40/R

VASQUEZ DEL RIO, Salvador (1907-1967) French
£285 $527 €416 La Suisse, Normande (54x65cm-21x26in) s. i.d.1965 verso board. 15-Jan-4 Christie's, Kensington #789

VASQUEZ DIAZ, Daniel (1882-1969) Spanish
Works on paper
£500 $910 €750 Paternidad (19x15cm-7x6in) ink pencil double-sided. 29-Jun-4 Segre, Madrid #288/R

VASQUEZ, Carlos (1869-1944) Spanish
£4138 $6869 €6000 Prisoner (107x107cm-42x42in) lit. 30-Sep-3 Ansorena, Madrid #91/R est:6000
£4483 $7441 €6500 Gypsy woman (100x132cm-39x52in) s.d.1937. 30-Sep-3 Ansorena, Madrid #90/R est:6000
Works on paper
£355 $592 €500 Gentleman (46x29cm-18x11in) s. gouache. 20-Oct-3 Durán, Madrid #7/R

VASQUEZ, Castor (?) ?
£253 $470 €369 Landscape (32x45cm-13x18in) s. 14-Mar-4 Subastas Odalys, Caracas #53
£255 $470 €383 Farm Mis Amores, La Victoria (50x70cm-20x28in) s. painted 1965. 27-Jun-4 Subastas Odalys, Caracas #56

VASS, Elemer (1887-1957) Hungarian
£802 $1419 €1171 Studio scene with a nude (64x54cm-25x21in) s.d.936 panel. 28-Apr-4 Kieselbach, Budapest #38/R (H.F 300000)
£869 $1442 €1269 Hillside (65x81cm-26x32in) s.d.937 verso board. 4-Oct-3 Kieselbach, Budapest #46/R (H.F 320000)
£949 $1717 €1386 Syringas (77x64cm-30x25in) s. 16-Apr-4 Mu Terem Galeria, Budapest #118/R (H.F 360000)
£1044 $1806 €1524 In sunlit grove (65x81cm-26x32in) s. board. 12-Dec-3 Kieselbach, Budapest #13/R (H.F 400000)

VASSALLO, Antonio Maria (attrib) (17th C) Italian
£8803 $14613 €12500 Le retour de David (165x230cm-65x91in) 11-Jun-3 Delorme & Bocage, Paris #3/R est:7000-9000
£9000 $15300 €13140 God naming the animals (136x99cm-54x39in) 30-Oct-3 Sotheby's, Olympia #117/R est:8000-12000

VASSE, Louis Claude (attrib) (1716-1772) French
Works on paper
£1769 $3166 €2600 Hercule se reposant sur un rocher de profil a gauche (23cm-9in circular) i.d.1767 red chk. 18-Mar-4 Christie's, Paris #102/R est:800-1200
£2041 $3653 €3000 Drawings of medals (22cm-9in circular) i.d. red chk four. 18-Mar-4 Christie's, Paris #110/R est:1200-1600

VASSELON, Alice (?) ?
£28000 $50960 €40880 Bouquet of field flowers in a pail (126x159cm-50x63in) s.d.1880. 17-Jun-4 Christie's, London #37/R est:30000-40000

VASSILAKIS, Takis (1925-) ?
Sculpture
£3846 $6423 €5500 Signal, serie 3 (199cm-78in) s.d.1974 num.82 electric lights socle. 11-Oct-3 Cornette de St.Cyr, Paris #80/R est:4500-5000

VASSILIEFF, Danila (1897-1958) Australian/Russian
£1525 $2593 €2227 Portrait of Mary Gill (41x33cm-16x13in) s. board prov. 24-Nov-3 Sotheby's, Melbourne #110/R est:4000-6000 (A.D 3600)

VASSILIEFF, Danila (attrib) (1897-1958) Australian/Russian
£1863 $3335 €2720 Boy fishing. 28-May-4 Lawson Menzies, Sydney #2116 (A.D 4750)

VASSILIEFF, Marie (1894-1955) Russian
£1126 $2049 €1700 Icone (16x13cm-6x5in) s.i.d.1953 verso panel. 15-Jun-4 Blanchet, Paris #171/R est:700-800
£5034 $8910 €7500 Figure maya (25x18cm-10x7in) s.i.d.1954 oil collage board. 27-Apr-4 Artcurial Briest, Paris #87 est:500-600
£8392 $14266 €12000 Portrait d'homme. s. painted c.1930. 28-Nov-3 Drouot Estimations, Paris #192/R est:12000-15000
£13000 $23270 €18980 Elegante by the sea (41x30cm-16x12in) s.d.1946. 26-May-4 Sotheby's, London #290/R est:15000-20000
£24503 $44596 €37000 Christ noir sur la croix (80x63cm-31x25in) s.i.d.1951 prov. 15-Jun-4 Blanchet, Paris #178/R est:6000-8000
£30000 $53700 €43800 Celebration, triple portrait (66x54cm-26x21in) s.i.d.1930. 26-May-4 Sotheby's, London #292/R est:30000-40000
Works on paper
£265 $482 €400 Composition aux visages (29x21cm-11x8in) s.i.d.1947 col crayon. 15-Jun-4 Blanchet, Paris #174/R
£364 $663 €550 Sculpture dans le jardin (24x31cm-9x12in) s.i.d.1950 W/C. 15-Jun-4 Blanchet, Paris #175/R
£397 $723 €600 Tete d'homme au pot de fleurs (22x13cm-9x5in) s.i. gouache. 15-Jun-4 Blanchet, Paris #173
£397 $723 €600 Le jardin (25x38cm-10x15in) s. W/C gouache. 15-Jun-4 Blanchet, Paris #176/R
£464 $844 €700 Le modele nu assis (30x22cm-12x9in) chl. 15-Jun-4 Blanchet, Paris #168
£464 $844 €700 Composition aux buveurs et aux musiciens (29x20cm-11x8in) grey crayon. 15-Jun-4 Blanchet, Paris #167/R
£530 $964 €800 Le modele nu debout (30x22cm-12x9in) chl. 15-Jun-4 Blanchet, Paris #169
£1476 $2613 €2200 Oiseau - coeur (22x22cm-9x9in) W/C gouache round exec c.1950. 27-Apr-4 Artcurial Briest, Paris #86 est:500-600
£2649 $4821 €4000 Portrait d'homme (30x23cm-12x9in) s.i.d.1947 W/C gouache. 15-Jun-4 Blanchet, Paris #177/R est:700-800
£4189 $7499 €6200 The proposal (25x30cm-10x12in) s.i.d.1950 gouache. 8-May-4 Bukowskis, Helsinki #438/R est:2200-2500
£6091 $10964 €8893 Woman (28x21cm-11x8in) s.i.d.1946 mixed media silver paper prov. 26-Apr-4 Bukowskis, Stockholm #240/R est:15000-18000 (S.KR 84000)

VASSILIEFF, Nicolai (1892-1970) American/Russian
£342 $550 €499 Fish on platter (61x86cm-24x34in) s.d.1945. 22-Feb-3 Bunte, Elgin #1210
£2152 $3400 €3142 Self portrait, artist holding a palette and brush (61x51cm-24x20in) s. exhib. 6-Sep-3 Brunk, Ashville #787
£6500 $11050 €9490 Village by moonlight (80x61cm-31x24in) s.d.1930. 19-Nov-3 Sotheby's, London #225/R est:4000-6000
£16667 $30000 €24334 Interior (72x91cm-28x36in) s. 23-Apr-4 Sotheby's, New York #46/R est:12000-18000
Works on paper
£2027 $3628 €3000 The model (35x50cm-14x20in) s. pencil prov. 8-May-4 Bukowskis, Helsinki #433/R est:500-800

VASSILIEV, Ivan (1930-) Russian
Works on paper
£270 $484 €400 The conflagration (20x33cm-8x13in) s. W/C. 8-May-4 Bukowskis, Helsinki #465/R

VASSILIKIOTIS, Aristotelis (1902-1972) Greek
£1500 $2685 €2190 Bazaar (47x54cm-19x21in) s. 11-May-4 Bonhams, New Bond Street #90/R est:1500-2000

VASSILIOU, Spyros (1902-1984) Greek
£2600 $4550 €3796 Brick wall with wild flowers (38x61cm-15x24in) canvas on board prov. 16-Dec-3 Bonhams, New Bond Street #122/R est:2000-3000
£3000 $5250 €4380 Artist with friend (33x55cm-13x22in) s.d.74 oil goldleaf collage prov. 16-Dec-3 Bonhams, New Bond Street #121/R est:3000-5000

£6000	$10740	€8760	View of Messolonghi (30x42cm-12x17in) s.d.68 tempera cardboard. 11-May-4 Bonhams, New Bond Street #91/R est:4000-6000
£9000	$15300	€13140	Evening glow (27x35cm-11x14in) s.d.86. 18-Nov-3 Sotheby's, London #64/R est:8000-12000
£10000	$17500	€14600	View of Athens (38x60cm-15x24in) s.d.66 oil paper on panel prov. 16-Dec-3 Bonhams, New Bond Street #105/R est:10000-15000
£10000	$17500	€14600	Dawn at the seaside (74x93cm-29x37in) s.d.82. 16-Dec-3 Bonhams, New Bond Street #111/R est:10000-15000
£11000	$19690	€16060	Athens (45x55cm-18x22in) s.d.80 oil paper goldleaf on canvas exhib. 10-May-4 Sotheby's, Olympia #60/R est:8000-12000
£20000	$34000	€29200	Acropolis, Athens (73x92cm-29x36in) s.d.76. 18-Nov-3 Sotheby's, London #74/R est:20000-30000
£20000	$35800	€29200	The family (73x54cm-29x21in) s.d.50-80 exhib. 11-May-4 Bonhams, New Bond Street #88/R est:15000-20000
£21000	$37590	€30660	Still life with musical instruments (73x92cm-29x36in) s.d.76 paper on canvas prov. 10-May-4 Sotheby's, Olympia #61/R est:10000-15000

VASTAGH, Geza (1866-1919) Hungarian

£2109	$3775	€3100	Lion couche (65x114cm-26x45in) s. 19-Mar-4 Millon & Associes, Paris #69/R est:1500-2000

VASTAGH, Gyorgy (elder) (1834-1922) Hungarian

£5344	$9460	€7802	Italian girl by the well (98x75cm-39x30in) s. 28-Apr-4 Kieselbach, Budapest #50/R (H.F 2000000)

VASZARY, Janos (1867-1939) Hungarian

£1229	$2176	€1794	Toledo (20x30cm-8x12in) s.i.d.1905 panel. 28-Apr-4 Kieselbach, Budapest #57/R (H.F 460000)
£2308	$3831	€3370	Lakeside with a boat (24x34cm-9x13in) 4-Oct-3 Kieselbach, Budapest #126/R (H.F 850000)
£5796	$10492	€8462	Kerchiefed woman (43x41cm-17x16in) s. 16-Apr-4 Mu Terem Galeria, Budapest #168/R (H.F 2200000)
£6786	$11740	€9908	Nude with blue background (50x39cm-20x15in) s. panel painted c.1920. 12-Dec-3 Kieselbach, Budapest #188/R (H.F 2600000)
£8144	$13520	€11890	Homewards (60x80cm-24x31in) s. 4-Oct-3 Kieselbach, Budapest #149/R (H.F 3000000)
£10440	$18061	€15242	Irises in green glass vase (51x33cm-20x13in) s. cardboard. 12-Dec-3 Kieselbach, Budapest #205/R (H.F 4000000)
£11875	$19000	€17338	View of Lemberg, Ukraine (56x69cm-22x27in) s.d.1915. 20-Sep-3 Sloans & Kenyon, Bethesda #1176/R est:7000-9000
£15660	$27092	€22864	Sunlit forest fringe (63x77cm-25x30in) s. 12-Dec-3 Kieselbach, Budapest #170/R (H.F 6000000)
£16289	$27040	€23782	Still life of roses (33x40cm-13x16in) cardboard painted c.1890. 4-Oct-3 Kieselbach, Budapest #90/R (H.F 6000000)
£22185	$38380	€32390	In the shadow (56x70cm-22x28in) s.d.06. 12-Dec-3 Kieselbach, Budapest #41/R (H.F 8500000)
£26722	$47298	€39014	Forest (70x80cm-28x31in) s. painted c.1907. 28-Apr-4 Kieselbach, Budapest #166/R (H.F 10000000)
£28982	$52458	€42314	Flower still life with Buddha sculpture (72x72cm-28x28in) s. 16-Apr-4 Mu Terem Galeria, Budapest #155/R (H.F 11000000)
£35000	$63700	€51100	Naples harbour (65x75cm-26x30in) s. 15-Jun-4 Sotheby's, London #70/R est:40000-60000
£36887	$66765	€53855	Seaside with parasols (42x62cm-17x24in) s. 16-Apr-4 Mu Terem Galeria, Budapest #137/R (H.F 14000000)
£39522	$71534	€57702	Boats in Pirano (32x49cm-13x19in) s. oil on card. 16-Apr-4 Mu Terem Galeria, Budapest #190/R (H.F 15000000)
£41760	$72245	€60970	Lady wearing a swiss cap (55x43cm-22x17in) s. 12-Dec-3 Kieselbach, Budapest #53/R (H.F 16000000)
Works on paper			
£814	$1352	€1188	Nude (20x25cm-8x10in) s. mixed media. 4-Oct-3 Kieselbach, Budapest #54/R (H.F 300000)
£1140	$1893	€1664	Port in San Remo with sailing boat (22x32cm-9x13in) s.d.937 col pencil. 4-Oct-3 Kieselbach, Budapest #1/R (H.F 420000)
£1436	$2483	€2097	On the beach (21x28cm-8x11in) s. col pencil. 12-Dec-3 Kieselbach, Budapest #120/R (H.F 550000)
£1493	$2479	€2180	Venice (16x24cm-6x9in) s.d.926 pastel. 4-Oct-3 Kieselbach, Budapest #94/R (H.F 550000)
£2138	$3784	€3121	Dream (65x50cm-26x20in) col chl exec. c.1930. 28-Apr-4 Kieselbach, Budapest #104/R (H.F 800000)
£2219	$3838	€3240	Rimini Beach (30x40cm-12x16in) s.d.1928 W/C. 12-Dec-3 Kieselbach, Budapest #4/R (H.F 850000)
£2480	$4290	€3621	Prisoners of war (43x60cm-17x24in) s. W/C. 12-Dec-3 Kieselbach, Budapest #167/R (H.F 950000)
£2715	$4507	€3964	On the beach (19x27cm-7x11in) s. col pencil. 4-Oct-3 Kieselbach, Budapest #142/R (H.F 1000000)
£3654	$6321	€5335	Alassio (39x49cm-15x19in) s. mixed media. 12-Dec-3 Kieselbach, Budapest #222/R (H.F 1400000)
£13050	$22577	€19053	Woman in hat (100x79cm-39x31in) pastel. 12-Dec-3 Kieselbach, Budapest #134/R (H.F 5000000)

VASZKO, Odon (1896-1945) Hungarian

£3132	$5418	€4573	Garden restaurant - Summer in the City Hall (62x85cm-24x33in) s. cardboard. 12-Dec-3 Kieselbach, Budapest #143/R (H.F 1200000)

VAUBOURGOIN, Thierry (1944-) French

£563	$975	€800	La lecon de piano (40x80cm-16x31in) 9-Dec-3 Chambelland & Giafferi, Paris #124

VAUCLEROY, Pierre de (1892-1969) Belgian

£4500	$7470	€6570	Reclining nude (80x65cm-31x26in) s.d.1925. 30-Sep-3 Sotheby's, London #257/R est:1500-2000

VAUDECHAMP, Joseph (1790-1866) French

£6044	$11000	€8824	Jean Baptiste Augustin (71x56cm-28x22in) s. prov. 7-Feb-4 Neal Auction Company, New Orleans #453/R est:12000-18000

VAUDOU, Gaston (1891-1957) French

£1293	$2315	€1888	Poires vertes et serviette (38x55cm-15x22in) s. i.d.1942 verso. 12-May-4 Dobiaschofsky, Bern #1043/R est:2600 (S.FR 3000)
Works on paper			
£352	$599	€514	Paris (32x49cm-13x19in) s. i. verso gouache two. 5-Nov-3 Dobiaschofsky, Bern #3773 (S.FR 800)

VAUGHAN, David Alfred (1891-?) American

£692	$1239	€1010	Fishing boats at Penzance (49x59cm-19x23in) painted c.1930. 12-May-4 Dunbar Sloane, Wellington #102/R est:750-2000 (NZ.D 2000)

VAUGHAN, Don (?) British?

£270	$483	€394	Landscape with fence in the foreground (38x60cm-15x24in) s. 16-Mar-4 Gildings, Market Harborough #465

VAUGHAN, Doris (1894-1975) British

£650	$1203	€949	Cornish Harbour (41x30cm-16x12in) prov. 11-Mar-4 Christie's, Kensington #214

VAUGHAN, Keith (1912-1974) British

£1650	$2954	€2409	Cornish street scene (30x41cm-12x16in) s.d.1949. 16-Mar-4 Lawrences, Bletchingley #1528/R est:1500-2000
£2200	$3674	€3212	Blue, white and black (20x23cm-8x9in) board painted c.1978 prov. 16-Oct-3 Christie's, Kensington #709/R est:600-800
£11000	$18700	€16060	Study for Laocoon (44x35cm-17x14in) s. board. 26-Nov-3 Sotheby's, Olympia #164/R est:3000-5000
£16800	$30576	€24528	Heath landscape (33x39cm-13x15in) studio st. board painted 1963 prov. 1-Jul-4 Christie's, Kensington #376/R est:6000-8000
£19000	$34770	€27740	Ruins of castle (25x46cm-10x18in) s. board prov. 2-Jun-4 Sotheby's, London #77/R est:10000-15000
£25000	$45750	€36500	Harbour with grey shore. Figure study (41x43cm-16x17in) board two prov. 4-Jun-4 Christie's, London #52/R est:8000-12000
£25000	$45500	€36500	Whitby Bay (42x52cm-17x20in) s. board. 15-Jun-4 Bonhams, New Bond Street #68/R est:5000-7000
£26000	$44200	€37960	Nude against a green background (84x63cm-33x25in) s.d.53 board prov.exhib. 21-Nov-3 Christie's, London #16/R est:20000-30000
£32000	$50880	€46720	Morvah (91x101cm-36x40in) s.i.d.1961 verso prov.exhib. 10-Sep-3 Sotheby's, Olympia #271/R est:10000-15000
Works on paper			
£250	$425	€365	Still life with jug (13x11cm-5x4in) studio st.verso pencil. 26-Nov-3 Sotheby's, Olympia #119/R
£280	$468	€409	Standing figure (28x20cm-11x8in) studio st.verso pencil. 16-Oct-3 Christie's, Kensington #568
£380	$703	€555	Figures in a landscape (11x16cm-4x6in) pencil. 11-Mar-4 Christie's, Kensington #181
£420	$777	€613	Crouching man at a nightclub (14x13cm-6x5in) pencil prov. 11-Mar-4 Christie's, Kensington #388
£500	$850	€730	Saint Paul's Church (24x17cm-9x7in) studio st.verso pencil pair. 26-Nov-3 Sotheby's, Olympia #118/R
£850	$1360	€1233	Landscape (16x40cm-6x16in) collage. 16-Sep-3 Bonhams, Knightsbridge #71/R
£850	$1547	€1241	Theseus II, study for the Festival of Britain (9x36cm-4x14in) mural pencil wash. 15-Jun-4 Bonhams, Knightsbridge #186/R
£900	$1431	€1314	Landscape with farm (23x34cm-9x13in) ink W/C prov. 10-Sep-3 Sotheby's, Olympia #289/R
£1100	$2002	€1606	Building a hut near the latrines (24x31cm-9x12in) s.d.41 pen brush black ink prov. 1-Jul-4 Christie's, Kensington #212/R est:800-1200
£1400	$2408	€2044	House in Cornwall (27x37cm-11x15in) blk ink wash W/C white pastel prov. 3-Dec-3 Sotheby's, London #55/R est:1500-2000
£1500	$2580	€2190	Prometheus (20x28cm-8x11in) s.d.42 pen blk ink red chk wash prov. 3-Dec-3 Sotheby's, London #30/R est:1500-2000
£2200	$3674	€3212	Abstract figure (39x28cm-15x11in) studio st. W/C brush black ink. 16-Oct-3 Christie's, Kensington #571/R est:1500-1800
£2500	$4400	€3650	Abstract composition (52x35cm-20x14in) init.d.18 Nov col crayons. 19-May-4 Sotheby's, Olympia #281/R est:2500-3500
£2600	$4420	€3796	Untitled (14x14cm-6x6in) studio st.verso crayon pastel. 26-Nov-3 Sotheby's, Olympia #162/R est:2000-3000
£3500	$6370	€5110	Miners (37x27cm-15x11in) s. pencil W/C bodycol brush blk ink chl chk exec 1952 prov. 1-Jul-4 Christie's, Kensington #213/R est:1500-2000
£5200	$8476	€7592	Oracle (19x28cm-7x11in) gouache. 24-Sep-3 Dreweatt Neate, Newbury #15/R est:300-500
£5500	$9185	€8030	Two figures (51x39cm-20x15in) W/C bodycol brush black ink. 16-Oct-3 Christie's, Kensington #567/R est:4000-6000
£7000	$13090	€10500	Study of head of man (28x18cm-11x7in) s.d.48 W/C. 21-Jul-4 John Nicholson, Haslemere #144/R est:2000-4000
£7500	$13200	€10950	Shepherd and flock (32x26cm-13x10in) s.d.1944 ink wash. 18-May-4 Woolley & Wallis, Salisbury #249/R est:400-600
£11000	$18920	€16060	Nissen (36x45cm-14x18in) s.d.1942 pen ink wash wax resist prov. 2-Dec-3 Bonhams, New Bond Street #83/R est:1500-2000
£11000	$20020	€16060	Two figures (52x42cm-20x17in) studio st. brush blk ink crayon exec c.1973. 1-Jul-4 Christie's, Kensington #210/R est:4000-6000
£11000	$20130	€16060	Landscape with miner (38x33cm-15x13in) s.verso gouache exec.1959. 28-Jul-4 Mallams, Oxford #272/R est:2000-3000
£13000	$22490	€18980	Boy with jug (46x30cm-18x12in) s.d.49 chl gouache prov. 11-Dec-3 Lyon & Turnbull, Edinburgh #77/R est:2000-3000
£13000	$23660	€18980	The sower (17x22cm-7x9in) s.d.1946 gouache ink prov. 15-Jun-4 Bonhams, New Bond Street #62/R est:4000-6000
£19000	$34770	€27740	Green pear figure (53x35cm-21x14in) s.d.1947 gouache crayon wax resist prov.exhib.lit. 4-Jun-4 Christie's, London #50/R est:10000-15000

VAUGHAN, Robert (20th C) British?

£809	$1400	€1181	Hunting scene (8x5cm-3x2in) 12-Dec-3 Du Mouchelle, Detroit #2292/R

VAUMOUSSE, Maurice (1876-1961) French

£927	$1687	€1400	La carriere (60x75cm-24x30in) 15-Jun-4 Blanchet, Paris #130/R

VAUTHIER, Pierre (1845-1916) French

£260	$434	€377	River landscape with a bridge and barges (12x20cm-5x8in) s. 17-Jun-3 Rosebery Fine Art, London #594/R
£347	$573	€500	Peniche a quai (38x56cm-15x22in) s. 3-Jul-3 Claude Aguttes, Neuilly #164
£382	$630	€550	Le ponton (55x38cm-22x15in) studio st.verso. 3-Jul-3 Claude Aguttes, Neuilly #163

£423 $739 €600 Fleuve (12x20cm-5x8in) s. board. 21-Dec-3 Thierry & Lannon, Brest #365
£921 $1695 €1400 Pont de Bir (24x55cm-9x22in) s.i. 22-Jun-4 Ribeyre & Baron, Paris #46
£1200 $1908 €1740 Theatre cocherie (46x38cm-18x15in) s. 11-Sep-3 Christie's, Kensington #113/R est:1200-1800
£1600 $2544 €2320 Barges a charleroi. Un Estuaire (38x55cm-15x22in) s.i. two. 11-Sep-3 Christie's, Kensington #114/R est:1500-2000
£1700 $2703 €2465 L'allee d'arbres. Bords de Seine (24x36cm-9x14in) atelier st. panel two. 11-Sep-3 Christie's, Kensington #115/R est:1000-1500
£2254 $3899 €3200 Quais, Paris (32x47cm-13x19in) s. 9-Dec-3 Artcurial Briest, Paris #128/R est:3500-4500
Works on paper
£543 $1000 €793 Vendor's stalls, Nanterre (18x28cm-7x11in) s.i.d. pencil W/C. 9-Jun-4 Doyle, New York #3082

VAUTHRIN, Ernest Germain (1878-1949) French
£658 $1230 €980 Goelette (14x18cm-6x7in) s.d.1922. 24-Feb-4 Thierry & Lannon, Brest #337/R

VAUTIER, Benjamin (elder) (1829-1898) German
£526 $879 €768 Roulottes (31x41cm-12x16in) s.d.1855 cardboard. 16-Nov-3 Koller, Geneva #1243/R (S.FR 1200)
£1086 $1846 €1586 Portrait study of young woman (24x22cm-9x9in) s.d.Januar 2 paper on panel. 19-Nov-3 Fischer, Luzern #1272/R est:2400-2600 (S.FR 2400)
£1940 $3472 €2832 Girl writing letter (27x22cm-11x9in) s. 13-May-4 Stuker, Bern #352/R est:6000-8000 (S.FR 4500)
£3524 $5991 €5145 Interior with family (45x37cm-18x15in) panel. 5-Nov-3 Dobiaschofsky, Bern #1020/R est:9500 (S.FR 8000)
£11086 $17738 €16186 Young woman knitting on verandah (43x31cm-17x12in) s. 19-Sep-3 Koller, Zurich #3077/R est:25000-30000 (S.FR 24500)
Works on paper
£495 $852 €723 Couple weeping together (36x30cm-14x12in) s.i. chk htd white. 8-Dec-3 Philippe Schuler, Zurich #4228/R (S.FR 1100)
£541 $930 €790 Seated peasant couple (40x36cm-16x14in) s.i. chk. 8-Dec-3 Philippe Schuler, Zurich #4229/R (S.FR 1200)

VAUTIER, Benjamin (elder-attrib) (1829-1898) German
£1057 $1797 €1543 Grandmother reading (34x27cm-13x11in) 5-Nov-3 Dobiaschofsky, Bern #1021/R est:1600 (S.FR 2400)

VAUTIER, Benjamin (younger) (1895-1974) Swiss
£550 $919 €798 Yachts in Lake Geneva harbour (50x61cm-20x24in) s. 23-Jun-3 Philippe Schuler, Zurich #3430 (S.FR 1200)
£789 $1318 €1152 Nature morte avec vase de fleurs (41x32cm-16x13in) s.d.1952 panel. 16-Nov-3 Koller, Geneva #1246 (S.FR 1800)
£1009 $1685 €1473 Nature morte aux fleurs (60x50cm-24x20in) s.d.1946. 16-Nov-3 Koller, Geneva #1244 est:3000-5000 (S.FR 2300)
£1053 $1758 €1537 Scene du rue (60x73cm-24x29in) s.d.1948. 16-Nov-3 Koller, Geneva #1245/R est:3000-5000 (S.FR 2400)
£1667 $2667 €2417 Horses in circus ring (54x72cm-21x28in) s.d.57. 15-May-3 Stuker, Bern #1555/R est:2500-3000 (S.FR 3500)
£3233 $5948 €4720 Park on shore of Lake Geneva (62x50cm-24x20in) s. prov. 26-Mar-4 Koller, Zurich #521/R est:4000-6000 (S.FR 7500)

VAUTIER, Carl (1860-?) Swiss
Works on paper
£1000 $1790 €1460 Portrait of a lady in a wide brimmed hat (78x63cm-31x25in) s. pastel oval. 25-May-4 Bonhams, Knightsbridge #67/R est:1000-1500

VAUTIER, Hans (1891-?) Swiss
£271 $462 €396 Locarno landscape (38x46cm-15x18in) s. i. stretcher. 18-Nov-3 Hans Widmer, St Gallen #1222 (S.FR 600)
£317 $538 €463 Autumn landscape in Unterengadin (61x46cm-24x18in) s. i.d.1939 verso. 28-Nov-3 Zofingen, Switzerland #3205 (S.FR 700)

VAUTIER, Otto (1863-1919) Swiss
£2431 $4060 €3525 La lecture (81x65cm-32x26in) s.d. prov. 21-Jun-3 Galerie du Rhone, Sion #459/R est:6000-8000 (S.FR 5300)
£4130 $7559 €6030 Femme aux chrysanthemes (58x46cm-23x18in) s.d.1906. 7-Jun-4 Christie's, Zurich #31/R est:6000-8000 (S.FR 9500)
Works on paper
£261 $477 €381 L'artiste peignant sous l'oeil de deux Saviesannes (27x16cm-11x6in) crayon exhib. 5-Jun-4 Galerie du Rhone, Sion #408 (S.FR 600)
£679 $1174 €991 Fillette a Saviese (57x41cm-22x16in) s. chl pastel. 12-Dec-3 Galerie du Rhone, Sion #598 (S.FR 1500)

VAUTRIN, Line (20th C) French
Sculpture
£3261 $6000 €4892 Cuff Dante (6x6x6cm-2x2x2in) st.init. gilt bronze exec.c.1945 prov.lit. 10-Jun-4 Phillips, New York #73/R est:7000-9000

VAUZELLE, Jean Lubin (1776-?) French
Works on paper
£408 $731 €600 Scene troubadour dans une eglise (27x19cm-11x7in) s. W/C black pencil. 19-Mar-4 Piasa, Paris #92

VAVRINA, Charles (1929-) American
£1899 $3000 €2773 Village entrance (56x61cm-22x24in) s. 27-Jul-3 Simpson's, Houston #245

VAWTER, Mary Howey Murray (1871-1950) American
Works on paper
£488 $800 €708 Indiana landscape (12x16cm-5x6in) s. pencil dr exec.c.1922. 7-Jun-3 Treadway Gallery, Cincinnati #1409

VAWTER, Will (1871-1941) American
£10989 $20000 €16044 Cabins in winter landscape (61x74cm-24x29in) s. prov. 15-Jun-4 John Moran, Pasadena #152 est:10000-15000

VAYREDA, Joaquin (1843-1894) Spanish
£1233 $2096 €1800 Landscape (18x23cm-7x9in) s. 4-Nov-3 Ansorena, Madrid #363/R est:1200
£2466 $4192 €3600 Beggars (44x35cm-17x14in) s.d.1887 cardboard oval. 4-Nov-3 Ansorena, Madrid #147/R est:1500

VAYSON, Paul (1842-1911) French
£370 $661 €540 Cattle and sheep grazing in meadow (24x33cm-9x13in) s. panel. 28-May-4 Uppsala Auktionskammare, Uppsala #236 (S.KR 5000)
£872 $1623 €1300 Scene de labour. Campement oriental (15x7cm-6x3in) i. panel two. 3-Mar-4 Ferri, Paris #387

VAZ, Oscar (1909-1987) Argentinian
£977 $1680 €1426 Winter morning (50x60cm-20x24in) s. paint. 3-Dec-3 Naón & Cia, Buenos Aires #151/R est:1500-2000
£1430 $2460 €2088 Street (30x40cm-12x16in) s. 3-Dec-3 Naón & Cia, Buenos Aires #99/R
£2279 $3920 €3327 Harbour (90x70cm-35x28in) s. s.i.verso. 3-Dec-3 Naón & Cia, Buenos Aires #143/R est:3500-4000
£3591 $6500 €5243 Little stream (60x70cm-24x28in) 30-Mar-4 Arroyo, Buenos Aires #64
£8197 $15000 €11968 Boats on the Mediterranean (50x60cm-20x24in) 1-Jun-4 Arroyo, Buenos Aires #54

VAZQUEZ DIAS, Daniel (1881-1969) Spanish
£8784 $15459 €13000 Peasant man with his horse (43x58cm-17x23in) s. 18-May-4 Segre, Madrid #93/R est:8400
£12081 $21383 €18000 Berta on the beach (66x50cm-26x20in) s. 27-Apr-4 Durán, Madrid #200/R est:15000
Works on paper
£599 $1048 €850 Boats in Nazareth (22x33cm-9x13in) pencil. 16-Dec-3 Segre, Madrid #252/R
£1056 $1827 €1500 Portrait (36x26cm-14x10in) s. pencil dr. 15-Dec-3 Ansorena, Madrid #185/R est:1500
£1645 $3026 €2500 Blind man (33x24cm-13x9in) s.i. dr. lit. 22-Jun-4 Durán, Madrid #139/R est:2000

VAZQUEZ, Dolores (19th C) Spanish
£2069 $3724 €3000 Plucking the turkey (105x85cm-41x33in) s.d.1889. 26-Jan-4 Ansorena, Madrid #236/R est:3000

VAZQUEZ, Gustavo (1943-) Uruguayan
£227 $400 €331 Abstract (24x33cm-9x13in) s.d.92 s.i.d.verso. 5-Jan-4 Galeria y Remates, Montevideo #1
£235 $400 €343 Blue abstract (91x72cm-36x28in) s.d.77. 25-Nov-3 Galeria y Remates, Montevideo #11/R
£259 $420 €376 Abstract (81x100cm-32x39in) s.verso. 29-Jul-3 Galeria y Remates, Montevideo #53
£1294 $2200 €1889 Abstract (90x150cm-35x59in) s.d.1989. 25-Nov-3 Galeria y Remates, Montevideo #91/R

VEAL, Hayward (1913-1968) Australian
£840 $1528 €1226 Rainy day, Sydney Harbour (38x45cm-15x18in) s.d.46 board prov. 16-Jun-4 Deutscher-Menzies, Melbourne #331/R est:1800-2600 (A.D 2200)
£884 $1476 €1282 Kincoppal (46x38cm-18x15in) s. 30-Jun-3 Australian Art Auctions, Sydney #116 (A.D 2200)

VEBER, Jean (1868-1928) French
£1733 $3137 €2600 Les culs de jatte (41x62cm-16x24in) s. panel. 5-Apr-4 Deburaux, Boulogne #88 est:1500-2000
£1867 $3379 €2800 Scene de menage (45x55cm-18x22in) s. panel. 5-Apr-4 Deburaux, Boulogne #87/R est:1500-2000
£2400 $4344 €3600 Le nain et la prisonniere (40x55cm-16x22in) s. panel. 5-Apr-4 Deburaux, Boulogne #89/R est:1500-2000

VECCHIA, Pietro della (1605-1678) Italian
Works on paper
£1973 $3532 €2900 Head of a man wearing a hat (17x21cm-7x8in) black crayon. 17-Mar-4 Tajan, Paris #16/R est:3000

VECENAJ, Yvan (1920-) Yugoslavian
£452 $783 €660 Recolte du bois (69x83cm-27x33in) s.d.1969. 12-Dec-3 Galerie du Rhone, Sion #142 (S.FR 1000)

VEDDER, Elihu (1836-1923) American
£1364 $2400 €1991 Pergola (20x33cm-8x13in) prov.exhib. 3-Jan-4 Collins, Maine #39/R est:2000-3000
£2000 $3600 €2920 Young reader (18x15cm-7x6in) mono.d.1864 panel prov. 24-Apr-4 Weschler, Washington #632/R est:3000-5000
£2045 $3600 €2986 Morning landscape (13x30cm-5x12in) s. panel prov.exhib. 3-Jan-4 Collins, Maine #40/R est:2000-3000
£2386 $4200 €3484 Sunset landscape (13x30cm-5x12in) s. prov.exhib. 3-Jan-4 Collins, Maine #38/R est:2000-3000
£2895 $5326 €4400 Portrait of woman (26x20cm-10x8in) s.i. board prov. 23-Jun-4 Finarte Semenzato, Rome #98/R est:1500-1800

Works on paper
£1796 $3000 €2622 Beached Boat (10x18cm-4x7in) s. W/C pencil crayon prov. 23-Oct-3 Shannon's, Milford #155/R est:2000-3000
£2065 $3800 €3015 Omar Khayyan, theologia (43x33cm-17x13in) i.verso black chk htd white pencil dr verso exhib. 10-Jun-4 Swann Galleries, New York #244/R est:2000-3000

VEDEL, Herman (1875-1948) Danish
£654 $1034 €948 View towards the artist's house in Tibirke Bakker (43x34cm-17x13in) i.stretcher prov. 3-Sep-3 Museumsbygningen, Copenhagen #251/R (D.KR 7000)

VEDELSBY, Poul (1892-?) Danish
£766 $1240 €1111 Interior scene with blanket draped over chair (54x40cm-21x16in) s.d.21 panel. 4-Aug-3 Rasmussen, Vejle #93/R (D.KR 8000)

VEDOVA, Emilio (1919-) Italian
£5944 $10105 €8500 Composition (70x50cm-28x20in) s.d.74 paper on canvas. 20-Nov-3 Finarte Semenzato, Milan #145/R est:8000-9000
£8389 $15520 €12500 Untitled (24x34cm-9x13in) s. paint paper painted 1994. 13-Mar-4 Meeting Art, Vercelli #122 est:5000
£11268 $19718 €16000 Study for 'Shot' (33x45cm-13x18in) oil tempera paper on canvas painted 1951. 16-Dec-3 Finarte Semenzato, Milan #318/R est:19000-22000
£11333 $20400 €17000 Moving space (23x35cm-9x14in) s.d.953 tempera paper on canvas prov. 22-Apr-4 Finarte Semenzato, Rome #347/R est:5500-6500
£12000 $22080 €18000 Situazioni (49x45cm-19x18in) s. s.i.d. verso canvas on panel. 11-Jun-4 Hauswedell & Nolte, Hamburg #1584/R est:15000
£12081 $21624 €18000 Untitled (48x68cm-19x27in) s.d.1987 paint paper. 30-May-4 Meeting Art, Vercelli #19/R est:10000
£12752 $22826 €19000 Spain today (26x50cm-10x20in) s.i.d.1961 tempera pastel collage cardboard prov.exhib. 25-May-4 Sotheby's, Milan #271/R est:15000-20000
£13986 $23776 €20000 Christmas evening in Treviso (37x47cm-15x19in) s. painted 1942. 29-Nov-3 Farsetti, Prato #476/R est:18000-20000
£26846 $48054 €40000 Study (24x33cm-9x13in) s.i.d.1951 verso prov. 25-May-4 Sotheby's, Milan #277/R est:20000-25000
£46980 $84094 €70000 Space 6 (100x70cm-39x28in) s.i.d.1956 verso tempera prov. 25-May-4 Sotheby's, Milan #278/R est:60000-80000
£76087 $124783 €105000 Second homage to Garcia Lorca (130x70cm-51x28in) s.i.d.1959 verso prov.exhib. 27-May-3 Sotheby's, Milan #276/R est:70000-90000
£120000 $200400 €175200 Ciclo varsavia no 2 (274x218cm-108x86in) s.i.d.1960 verso prov.exhib. 21-Oct-3 Christie's, London #21/R est:120000-160000
£139860 $237762 €200000 Cicle 61-5 (148x199cm-58x78in) s.i.d.61 verso prov.exhib.lit. 24-Nov-3 Christie's, Milan #341/R est:230000-260000
£185000 $340400 €270100 Dal ciclo della protesta 58 (145x190cm-57x75in) s.i.d.1958 prov.exhib. 24-Jun-4 Christie's, London #36/R est:100000-150000
Sculpture
£2759 $4607 €4000 Venice (18x22cm-7x9in) s.i. ceramic relief. 13-Nov-3 Finarte Semenzato, Rome #358/R est:1800-2400
£46154 $78462 €66000 Plurimo P 8 'I piedi sopra' (145x42x80cm-57x17x31in) i. iron wood prov.exhib.lit. 27-Nov-3 Lempertz, Koln #506/R est:30000-40000
Works on paper
£374 $670 €550 Several (21x30cm-8x12in) s.i. felt-tip pen paper on canvas. 16-Mar-4 Finarte Semenzato, Milan #271
£374 $670 €550 Several (19x30cm-7x12in) s.i. felt-tip pen paper on canvas. 16-Mar-4 Finarte Semenzato, Milan #270/R
£1133 $2051 €1700 Composition (10x15cm-4x6in) s. wax crayon cad on cardboard. 2-Apr-4 Farsetti, Prato #86/R est:1600-2000
£2174 $3565 €3000 Raking. Untitled (32x25cm-13x10in) i. s.i.d.1944 verso pencil W/C two. 27-May-3 Sotheby's, Milan #153/R est:2000-2400
£2207 $3686 €3200 Study for cathedral (21x15cm-8x6in) s.d.1951 verso ink card. 13-Nov-3 Finarte Semenzato, Rome #214/R est:1400-1800
£2958 $4910 €4200 Auguri dal Mio Labirinti (18x15cm-7x6in) pastel W/C. 14-Jun-3 Meeting Art, Vercelli #99/R est:3000
£3846 $6538 €5615 Untitled (38x53cm-15x21in) s.d.950 Indian ink W/C. 19-Nov-3 Fischer, Luzern #2570/R est:1300-1500 (S.FR 8500)
£4000 $7360 €6000 Composition (17x21cm-7x8in) s. s.i. verso Indian ink W/C bodycol. 11-Jun-4 Hauswedell & Nolte, Hamburg #1585/R est:3500
£4577 $7599 €6500 De America (50x35cm-20x14in) s.i.d.1970 mixed media. 14-Jun-3 Meeting Art, Vercelli #339/R est:5000
£5034 $9312 €7500 Composition (22x29cm-9x11in) s.d.1990 mixed media paper on canvas. 11-Mar-4 Galleria Pace, Milan #119/R est:8500-12000
£5245 $8916 €7500 Beyond (29x20cm-11x8in) s. collage paint prov. 20-Nov-3 Finarte Semenzato, Milan #111/R est:7500-8000

VEDOVA, Mario della (1958-) Italian
Sculpture
£5500 $9185 €8030 Golden quality (35x46cm-14x18in) s.i.d.2002 num.3/3 verso glazed ceramic. 20-Oct-3 Sotheby's, London #54/R est:4500-6500
Works on paper
£563 $986 €800 Christmas decorations (22x32cm-9x13in) mono.i. pencil. 16-Dec-3 Finarte Semenzato, Milan #230/R

VEDOVA-MAZZEI (20th C) Italian
Works on paper
£6338 $11092 €9000 Time without examples (158x158cm-62x62in) varnish plexiglass panel exec.2000. 16-Dec-3 Finarte Semenzato, Milan #252/R est:6600-7000

VEEGENS, Anna (1850-1942) Dutch
£280 $481 €400 Still life (37x46cm-15x18in) s. 8-Dec-3 Glerum, Amsterdam #60/R

VEEN, Otto van (1556-1629) Flemish
£3297 $6000 €4814 Christ victorious (50x40cm-20x16in) 17-Jun-4 Christie's, Rockefeller NY #4/R est:7000-10000
£3662 $6408 €5200 Nature fuyant vers la gauche avec deux amours sur la droite (12x10cm-5x4in) oil paper prov. 17-Dec-3 Christie's, Paris #20/R est:4000-6000
£6000 $9780 €8760 Scipio fighting at the Battle of Zama (73x106cm-29x42in) panel. 26-Sep-3 Christie's, Kensington #1/R est:2000-3000
Works on paper
£12000 $21960 €17520 Triumph of the Christ (27x39cm-11x15in) i. pen ink oil prov. 6-Jul-4 Christie's, London #161/R est:12000-18000
£12000 $21960 €17520 Triumph of the Word of God (27x39cm-11x15in) i. pen ink oil prov. 6-Jul-4 Christie's, London #162/R est:12000-18000

VEEN, Otto van (circle) (1556-1629) Flemish
£6500 $11050 €9490 Dives and Lazarus (73x102cm-29x40in) panel prov. 30-Oct-3 Sotheby's, Olympia #40/R est:5000-7000

VEEN, Rochus van (?-1706) Dutch
Works on paper
£541 $951 €800 Dead water rail (38x19cm-15x7in) bears sig. pen grey black ink col wash prov. 19-May-4 Sotheby's, Amsterdam #122/R
£1370 $2329 €2000 Bullfinch and beetle (15x19cm-6x7in) s.i.d.1672 verso pen black brown ink W/C. 4-Nov-3 Sotheby's, Amsterdam #145/R est:1000-1500
£2297 $4043 €3400 Caterpillar, crane fly and other insects (21x28cm-8x11in) s.i.d.1681 W/C prov.exhib.lit. 19-May-4 Sotheby's, Amsterdam #120/R est:1800-2200
£4054 $7135 €6000 Various insects by a fungus (20x30cm-8x12in) s.d.1681 W/C gouache black chk prov.exhib. 19-May-4 Sotheby's, Amsterdam #118/R est:2400-2800

VEEN, Stuyvesant van (1910-1977) American
Works on paper
£1796 $3250 €2622 Streetsweep (50x50cm-20x20in) i.verso gouache board prov. 31-Mar-4 Sotheby's, New York #34/R est:3000-4000

VEER, A (17th C) Dutch
£1538 $2646 €2245 Battle scene (58x81cm-23x32in) s. panel. 3-Dec-3 AB Stockholms Auktionsverk #2663/R est:25000-30000 (S.KR 20000)

VEER, Justus Pieter de (attrib) (1845-1921) Dutch
£496 $829 €700 Portrait of a lady (23x19cm-9x7in) panel prov. 20-Oct-3 Glerum, Amsterdam #191/R

VEEREN, Anna Maria van (1806-1890) Dutch
£789 $1429 €1200 Still life of fruit on a ledge (30x23cm-12x9in) init. panel. 19-Apr-4 Glerum, Amsterdam #21/R

VEGA DE SEOANE, Eduardo (1955-) Spanish
Works on paper
£694 $1104 €1000 Geist (150x190cm-59x75in) s.i.d.88 verso mixed media canvas. 29-Apr-3 Durán, Madrid #88/R
£764 $1215 €1100 Fin de semana en el campo (140x180cm-55x71in) s.i.d.89 verso mixed media canvas. 29-Apr-3 Durán, Madrid #89/R

VEGA FLORES, Jose Luis (20th C) Spanish
£870 $1426 €1200 Nude woman wearing a mask (81x147cm-32x58in) s. 27-May-3 Durán, Madrid #76/R

VEGA OSORIO, Jose (1945-) Spanish
£340 $619 €500 Gypsies (39x47cm-15x19in) s.d.1985 board. 3-Feb-4 Segre, Madrid #126/R
£458 $801 €650 Landscape (20x25cm-8x10in) s. board. 16-Dec-3 Durán, Madrid #1/R
£1510 $2763 €2250 Still life (82x97cm-32x38in) s. 12-Jul-4 Durán, Madrid #119/R est:1000
£1773 $2961 €2500 Toledo (82x97cm-32x38in) s. 23-Jun-3 Durán, Madrid #145/R est:2500

VEGA Y MARRUGAL, Jose de la (19th C) Spanish
£11594 $19014 €16000 Young girl with the chickens (44x35cm-17x14in) s.d.78. 27-May-3 Durán, Madrid #249/R est:10000

VEGA, Enrique (1953-) Spanish
£1267 $2318 €1900 Untitled (100x81cm-39x32in) s.verso prov. 7-Jun-4 Glerum, Amsterdam #255/R est:2000-4000

VEGA, Felix de la (1959-) Spanish
Works on paper
£345 $621 €500 Urban scene (80x61cm-31x24in) s. s.i.d.2002 verso mixed media board exhib. 26-Jan-4 Durán, Madrid #38/R
£448 $807 €650 Semi-naked painter (100x80cm-39x31in) s. s.i.d.2002 verso mixed media board exhib. 26-Jan-4 Durán, Madrid #37/R

VEILLAT, Just (1813-?) French
£1275 $2346 €1900 Couvee de perdrix (24x32cm-9x13in) s. panel. 26-Mar-4 Neret-Minet, Paris #38/R est:750

VEILLON, Auguste-Louis (1834-1890) Swiss
£390 $651 €566 Spring on the Bielersee (20x32cm-8x13in) s. board. 23-Jun-3 Philippe Schuler, Zurich #3433 (S.FR 850)
£517 $926 €755 Lake Geneva (21x41cm-8x16in) i. verso paper on board. 12-May-4 Dobiaschofsky, Bern #1045/R (S.FR 1200)
£1743 $2911 €2527 L'ile de Rhoda pres Caire (15x32cm-6x13in) s. board. 23-Jun-3 Philippe Schuler, Zurich #3432 est:1000-1400 (S.FR 3800)
£2703 $4649 €3946 Engstlensee (39x64cm-15x25in) s. 2-Dec-3 Koller, Zurich #3010a/R est:6000-9000 (S.FR 6000)
£2890 $4826 €4191 View of Grammont across Lake Geneva (33x50cm-13x20in) s. panel. 23-Jun-3 Philippe Schuler, Zurich #3431/R est:2000-2500 (S.FR 6300)

£3246 $5420 €4739 Lac de montagne (75x108cm-30x43in) s. 16-Nov-3 Koller, Geneva #1291/R est:5000-9000 (S.FR 7400)
£3394 $5871 €4955 En montagnes (116x175cm-46x69in) s. 9-Dec-3 Sotheby's, Zurich #17/R est:7000-9000 (S.FR 7500)
£5430 $9394 €7928 Au bord du lac (90x142cm-35x56in) s. 9-Dec-3 Sotheby's, Zurich #10/R est:5000-8000 (S.FR 12000)
Works on paper
£407 $692 €594 Two boys fishing in mountain lake (38x53cm-15x21in) s. W/C. 28-Nov-3 Zofingen, Switzerland #2492 (S.FR 900)

VEILLON, Auguste-Louis (attrib) (1834-1890) Swiss
£333 $533 €483 Vue d'Yvoire sur la cote de Savoie (32x46cm-13x18in) i. verso panel. 15-May-3 Stuker, Bern #1556/R (S.FR 700)

VEIMBERG, Joannes (1918-1982) German?
£1400 $2520 €2100 Bouquet de fleurs (128x80cm-50x31in) s. 20-Apr-4 Chenu & Scrive, Lyon #164/R est:1500-2000

VEISBERG, Vladimir Grigoryevich (1924-1985) Russian
£9444 $17000 €13788 Portrait of Olga Konik (53x47cm-21x19in) init.d.80 s.i.d.stretcher. 23-Apr-4 Sotheby's, New York #127/R est:15000-20000
Works on paper
£4200 $7518 €6132 Sleeping nude (33x48cm-13x19in) s.i. gouache. 26-May-4 Sotheby's, London #319/R est:3000-5000

VEITH, Eduard (1856-1925) Austrian
£690 $1145 €1000 Apothosis of art (42x55cm-17x22in) s.i.d.1907 oil sketch board. 30-Sep-3 Dorotheum, Vienna #369/R
Works on paper
£690 $1145 €1000 Altar, church in Prien (32x24cm-13x9in) s.i.d.25.August 1918 W/C. 30-Sep-3 Dorotheum, Vienna #382/R

VEITH, Franz Michael (1799-1846) Austrian
£1259 $2165 €1800 Bust portrait of a girl with pearl hairband from Augsburg (60x48cm-24x19in) s.d.1827. 5-Dec-3 Bolland & Marotz, Bremen #673/R est:2000

VEITH, Johann Philipp (1768-1837) German
Works on paper
£1233 $2096 €1800 River landscape (33x43cm-13x17in) s.d. WC pen. 4-Nov-3 Hartung & Hartung, Munich #3124/R est:1400

VEJRYCH, Rudolf (1882-1931) Czechoslovakian
£746 $1269 €1089 Bathing (104x90cm-41x35in) s. 29-Nov-3 Dorotheum, Prague #43/R est:30000-50000 (C.KR 34000)

VEKEMANS, Bruno (20th C) Belgian?
Works on paper
£833 $1392 €1200 Hermes (72x58cm-28x23in) s.d.1992 gouache pastel. 21-Oct-3 Campo & Campo, Antwerp #342/R est:1250-1750
£3125 $5219 €4500 Barmen (154x136cm-61x54in) s.d.1993 gouache. 21-Oct-3 Campo & Campo, Antwerp #343/R est:3500-4500

VEL, Gaston de (20th C) New Zealander
£357 $657 €521 Timber mill (59x75cm-23x30in) s.d.1968 canvasboard. 25-Mar-4 International Art Centre, Auckland #122/R (NZ.D 1000)
£362 $583 €529 Ham and bottle of beer (59x75cm-23x30in) s.d.1967. 20-Aug-3 Peter Webb, Auckland #2042/R (NZ.D 1000)
£362 $583 €529 Pineapples and wine bottles (60x75cm-24x30in) s.d.1967. 20-Aug-3 Peter Webb, Auckland #2043/R (NZ.D 1000)
£415 $743 €606 Oak Avenue, Hastings (74x59cm-29x23in) s.d.87. 12-May-4 Dunbar Sloane, Wellington #272 (NZ.D 1200)
£489 $831 €714 Zoclo, la catedral, Mexico (41x50cm-16x20in) s.d.1974. 27-Nov-3 International Art Centre, Auckland #132/R (NZ.D 1300)
£536 $986 €783 Date palms, Marrakesh Morocco (32x40cm-13x16in) s.d.1984. 25-Mar-4 International Art Centre, Auckland #158 (NZ.D 1500)
£543 $875 €793 Wine bottles and cakes (60x75cm-24x30in) s.d.1967. 20-Aug-3 Peter Webb, Auckland #2041/R (NZ.D 1500)
£658 $1118 €961 Crab apples and chrysanthemums (45x54cm-18x21in) s.d.1993. 27-Nov-3 International Art Centre, Auckland #136/R (NZ.D 1750)
Works on paper
£474 $815 €692 Tulips (52x43cm-20x17in) s. W/C. 7-Dec-3 International Art Centre, Auckland #280 (NZ.D 1275)

VELA ZANETTI, Jose (1913-1999) Spanish
£2656 $4250 €3878 Still life with pitcher and jug. s.d.59 board. 20-Sep-3 Harvey Clar, Oakland #1525
£5263 $9684 €8000 Day (48x61cm-19x24in) s.d.85 s.i.d.verso tempera. 22-Jun-4 Durán, Madrid #176/R est:6500
Works on paper
£3056 $5042 €4400 Warrior (68x99cm-27x39in) s. W/C. 2-Jul-3 Ansorena, Madrid #885/R
£10738 $19973 €16000 Still life (71x98cm-28x39in) mixed media cardboard on board. 2-Mar-4 Ansorena, Madrid #859/R est:16000

VELA, Vicente (1931-) Spanish
£387 $678 €550 Red light and evolution (32x41cm-13x16in) s.d.1968 s.i.d.verso. 16-Dec-3 Segre, Madrid #228/R
£694 $1146 €1000 Composition (50x64cm-20x25in) s.d.1972 s.i.d.verso. 2-Jul-3 Ansorena, Madrid #917/R

VELA, Vincenzo (1820-1891) Italian
Sculpture
£2765 $4700 €4037 Derniers jours de Napoleon (43cm-17in) s.d.1867 pat.bronze Cast Barbedienne. 10-Nov-3 Rasmussen, Vejle #1217/R est:25000-30000 (D.KR 30000)
£3953 $7075 €5771 Napoleon (45cm-18in) bronze gilt bronze green painted plinth prov. 15-May-4 Christie's, Sydney #255/R est:8000-12000 (A.D 10000)

VELARDE, Pablita (1918-) American
£1341 $2400 €1958 Mountain sheep dancer. Zuni Ho-o-te Kachina (30x25cm-12x10in) s. earth pigment on masonite two prov. 12-Jan-4 Christie's, Rockefeller NY #71/R est:2000-3000
Works on paper
£359 $600 €524 Navajo dancers (43x53cm-17x21in) gouache. 14-Nov-3 Du Mouchelle, Detroit #56/R
£1494 $2750 €2181 Roadrunners, group of there birds feeding in desert landscape (41x56cm-16x22in) s. gouache on board. 14-Jun-4 Bonhams & Butterfields, San Francisco #1116/R est:1500-2000

VELASCO (1960-) Italian
£933 $1717 €1400 Untitled (46x36cm-18x14in) s. tempera chl paper on canvas lit. 12-Jun-4 Meeting Art, Vercelli #261/R
£1034 $1728 €1500 Trees. Landscape in Valtellina (18x16cm-7x6in) s. tempera ink paper two. 13-Nov-3 Finarte Semenzato, Rome #123/R est:1400-1600
£1533 $2821 €2300 Town in 1913 (40x52cm-16x20in) s.i. tempera pastel paper on canvas painted 1994 lit. 12-Jun-4 Meeting Art, Vercelli #356/R est:1500
£2000 $3680 €3000 Plant (70x50cm-28x20in) s. oil collage. 12-Jun-4 Meeting Art, Vercelli #747/R est:3000
£2800 $5152 €4200 Hydrangea (30x40cm-12x16in) s. board painted 1992. 12-Jun-4 Meeting Art, Vercelli #964/R est:2000
£3221 $5960 €4800 Tree (60x50cm-24x20in) s. painted 1992 lit. 13-Mar-4 Meeting Art, Vercelli #266 est:3000
£4577 $8011 €6500 Beach (100x100cm-39x39in) s. s.i.d.2001 verso prov. 16-Dec-3 Finarte Semenzato, Milan #224/R est:4300-4700
£4930 $8627 €7000 Casbah (100x100cm-39x39in) s. s.i.d.2001 verso. 16-Dec-3 Finarte Semenzato, Milan #225/R est:4300-4700
£5369 $9611 €8000 By the wood (100x80cm-39x31in) s. 30-May-4 Meeting Art, Vercelli #45 est:5000
£5634 $9352 €8000 Vela (70x80cm-28x31in) s. s.i.d.1999 verso. 14-Jun-3 Meeting Art, Vercelli #60/R est:3000
£6667 $12267 €10000 Landscape (117x146cm-46x57in) s. painted 1995. 12-Jun-4 Meeting Art, Vercelli #635/R est:10000
Works on paper
£667 $1200 €1000 Morena (25x34cm-10x13in) s. W/C exec.1986 exhib. 22-Apr-4 Finarte Semenzato, Rome #118/R
£671 $1242 €1000 Untitled (31x44cm-12x17in) s.d.1994 chl paper on canvas lit. 13-Mar-4 Meeting Art, Vercelli #90
£733 $1349 €1100 Palm tree (68x50cm-27x20in) s. mixed media exec.1993 prov.exhib.lit. 14-Jun-4 Sant Agostino, Torino #266/R
£2483 $4594 €3700 Lymph (56x40cm-22x16in) s. mixed media paper on canvas. 13-Mar-4 Meeting Art, Vercelli #239 est:2000
£3221 $5960 €4800 Plants (100x70cm-39x28in) s. mixed media card. 13-Mar-4 Meeting Art, Vercelli #541 est:3000

VELASCO, Marco (1965-) Italian
Works on paper
£336 $621 €500 Obsession (100x150cm-39x59in) s.i.d.2000 verso mixed media on canvas. 13-Mar-4 Meeting Art, Vercelli #54
£352 $585 €500 Open me (120x120cm-47x47in) s.i.d.2002 applique canvas. 14-Jun-3 Meeting Art, Vercelli #243
£352 $585 €500 Amore Anemico (100x100cm-39x39in) s.i.d.2001 verso mixed media paper on canvas. 14-Jun-3 Meeting Art, Vercelli #338
£604 $1117 €900 Doors (150x100cm-59x39in) s.i.d.2002 mixed media on canvas. 13-Mar-4 Meeting Art, Vercelli #310

VELASCO, Rosario de (?) Spanish
£1103 $1832 €1600 Portrait of girl (46x38cm-18x15in) s. 30-Sep-3 Ansorena, Madrid #118/R est:1500
Works on paper
£621 $1030 €900 Lunch (42x61cm-17x24in) s. pastel. 1-Oct-3 Ansorena, Madrid #505/R

VELASQUEZ, Diego Rodriguez de Silva y (1599-1660) Spanish
£14000 $24220 €20440 Portrait of Prince Balthasar Carlos of Spain as a hunter (132x101cm-52x40in) prov.exhib.lit. 11-Dec-3 Sotheby's, London #190/R est:8000-12000

VELASQUEZ, Diego Rodriguez de Silva y (studio) (1599-1660) Spanish
£44444 $80000 €64888 Equestrian portrait of Balthasar Carlos (199x155cm-78x61in) prov. 22-Jan-4 Sotheby's, New York #282/R est:80000-120000

VELASQUEZ, Diego Rodriguez de Silva y (style) (1599-1660) Spanish
£12088 $22000 €17648 Self portrait wearing the badge of the Order of Santiago (58x43cm-23x17in) i. prov.exhib.lit. 17-Jun-4 Christie's, Rockefeller NY #66/R est:20000-30000
£53977 $95000 €78806 Philosopher heads (71x56cm-28x22in) pair. 19-May-4 Doyle, New York #6113/R est:8000-12000

VELAZQUEZ, Eugenio Lucas (1817-1870) Spanish
£2041 $3714 €3000 Luck (24x34cm-9x13in) s. 3-Feb-4 Segre, Madrid #54/R est:2000
£11972 $20711 €17000 Figures (92x73cm-36x29in) s. 15-Dec-3 Ansorena, Madrid #322/R est:15000
£14444 $26000 €21088 Bullfight (13x18cm-5x7in) oil on tin prov. 23-Jan-4 Christie's, Rockefeller NY #124/R est:8000-12000
£75000 $127500 €109500 Sleeping beauty (172x107cm-68x42in) bears sig.d. prov.exhib.lit. 18-Nov-3 Sotheby's, London #239/R

Works on paper
£448 $829 €650 Religious scene (18x25cm-7x10in) s. wash. 14-Jan-4 Castellana, Madrid #57/R
£496 $829 €700 Street scene (17x24cm-7x9in) s.d.1855 wash. 20-Oct-3 Durán, Madrid #3/R
£2305 $3849 €3250 Healers. Beauty of the jug (20x28cm-8x11in) s.d.1862 wash pair. 20-Oct-3 Durán, Madrid #131/R

VELDE, Adriaen van de (1636-1672) Dutch
£3803 $6807 €5400 Bergere et son garcon s'amusant a chevaucher une chevre (41x52cm-16x20in) s.d.1671. 11-Jan-4 Rouillac, Vendome #142
£3819 $6302 €5500 Bull and sheep in stable (26x21cm-10x8in) s. 3-Jul-3 Van Ham, Cologne #1026/R est:6000
£4167 $6875 €6000 Herding couple returning home with cattle (21x27cm-8x11in) s.d.1670 panel. 2-Jul-3 Neumeister, Munich #593/R est:6500
Works on paper
£4795 $8151 €7000 Shepherd couple and their animals resting under a tree by a pond (22x34cm-9x13in) s. brush grey wash over black chk prov. 4-Nov-3 Sotheby's, Amsterdam #59/R est:8000-12000
£22222 $40000 €32444 Standing male nude holding a staff (35x23cm-14x9in) bears i. red chk prov.exhib.lit. 21-Jan-4 Sotheby's, New York #71/R est:25000-35000

VELDE, Adriaen van de (attrib) (1636-1672) Dutch
£1518 $2535 €2216 Pastoral landscape (23x25cm-9x10in) panel. 17-Jun-3 Maynards, Vancouver #312 est:3000-4000 (C.D 3400)
£3691 $6792 €5500 Landscape with ruins and horsemen (37x57cm-15x22in) prov. 24-Mar-4 Dorotheum, Vienna #176/R est:3000-5000

VELDE, Bram van (1895-1981) Dutch
Works on paper
£7456 $13719 €10886 Composition (27x28cm-11x11in) s. gouache prov. 23-Jun-4 Koller, Zurich #3084/R est:7000-12000 (S.FR 17000)
£8784 $15723 €13000 Untitled (48x30cm-19x12in) gouache. 4-May-4 Calmels Cohen, Paris #163/R est:10000-15000
£10564 $18275 €15000 Composition (40x29cm-16x11in) s.verso W/C gouache cardboard. 9-Dec-3 Artcurial Briest, Paris #418/R est:10000-15000
£21477 $38443 €32000 Self-portrait (73x42cm-29x17in) s. gouache exhib.lit. 26-May-4 Christie's, Paris #98/R est:5000-7000

VELDE, Charles William Meredith van de (1818-1898) Dutch
Works on paper
£280 $476 €400 S Pietro Porto Venere in Genua (18x25cm-7x10in) s. W/C. 27-Nov-3 Bassenge, Berlin #5659

VELDE, Esaias van de (1587-1630) Dutch
£3233 $5787 €4720 On the attack (11x15cm-4x6in) s.d.162 panel. 13-May-4 Stuker, Bern #353/R est:10000-15000 (S.FR 7500)
£27586 $46069 €40000 Landscape with two riders before steep rocks (28x34cm-11x13in) s.d.1622 panel prov.lit. 15-Nov-3 Lempertz, Koln #1164/R est:25000-30000
£28000 $51240 €40880 Battle scene in open landscape (55x87cm-22x34in) s.d.1614 panel prov. 8-Jul-4 Sotheby's, London #115/R est:30000-50000
£30000 $54900 €43800 Landscape with travellers crossing bridge (28x34cm-11x13in) s.d.1622 panel prov.lit. 7-Jul-4 Sotheby's, London #4/R est:30000-40000
£70000 $121100 €102200 Wooded landscape with horsemen beside a river, ruined farm beyond (17x17cm-7x7in) s.d.1624 oak panel circular. 11-Dec-3 Sotheby's, London #64/R est:30000-50000
Prints
£3636 $6182 €5200 Skaters by windmill (8x18cm-3x7in) etching. 27-Nov-3 Bassenge, Berlin #5373/R est:3500
Works on paper
£5479 $9315 €8000 River landscape with boats by cottages, and mill behind (18x30cm-7x12in) indis.mono.i. black chk grey wash. 4-Nov-3 Sotheby's, Amsterdam #49/R est:3000-4000
£6111 $11000 €8922 Village on a river, figure in the foreground (12x22cm-5x9in) i. black chk pen brown ink W/C. 22-Jan-4 Christie's, Rockefeller NY #118/R est:5000-8000
£11486 $20216 €17000 Cavalry battle (19x28cm-7x11in) s.d.1627 black chk brown wash prov.exhib.lit. 19-May-4 Sotheby's, Amsterdam #59/R est:10000-15000

VELDE, Esaias van de (attrib) (1587-1630) Dutch
£6552 $10941 €9500 Looting in Dutch city (31x54cm-12x21in) i. verso panel. 9-Jul-3 Hugo Ruef, Munich #13/R est:3000

VELDE, Esaias van de (circle) (1587-1630) Dutch
£6667 $11933 €10000 Landscape with allegory on religious discord (59x103cm-23x41in) 17-May-4 Christie's, Amsterdam #97/R est:6000-8000

VELDE, Geer van (1898-c.1977) Dutch
£4184 $6988 €5900 Nature morte au verre, bouteille et lanterne sur une table (50x65cm-20x26in) s. init.verso. 19-Jun-3 Millon & Associes, Paris #261/R est:6000-7000
£6993 $11888 €10000 Untitled (80x50cm-31x20in) init. s.verso prov. 25-Nov-3 Christie's, Amsterdam #284/R est:15000-20000
£8278 $15066 €12500 Composition (21x37cm-8x15in) init. s.verso painted c.1947. 18-Jun-4 Charbonneaux, Paris #187/R est:8000-10000
£8392 $14434 €12000 Compositie (50x50cm-20x20in) init. s.verso painted 1971 prov.exhib. 2-Dec-3 Sotheby's, Amsterdam #96/R est:12000-15000
£10493 $18153 €14900 Personnage feminin dans un interieur (60x81cm-24x32in) mono. painted c.1939-1940. 14-Dec-3 Versailles Encheres #126/R est:18000-20000
£18310 $31676 €26000 Composition (33x46cm-13x18in) mono. painted c.1950 prov.lit. 14-Dec-3 Versailles Encheres #83/R est:25000-30000
£34899 $64214 €52000 Composition (145x133cm-57x52in) s. s.verso painted c.1960. 29-Mar-4 Cornette de St.Cyr, Paris #7/R est:50000-70000
£38462 $66154 €55000 Interieur exterieur (100x110cm-39x43in) init. s.i.d.50 verso prov.exhib. 2-Dec-3 Sotheby's, Amsterdam #121/R est:38000-45000
Works on paper
£652 $1070 €900 Untitled (21x22cm-8x9in) s. black chk. 27-May-3 Sotheby's, Amsterdam #530/R
£1329 $2259 €1900 Portrait of a lady (27x21cm-11x8in) init. W/C. 24-Nov-3 Glerum, Amsterdam #115/R est:2000-4000
£1722 $3134 €2600 Nature morte (24x29cm-9x11in) init. gouache. 18-Jun-4 Charbonneaux, Paris #121/R est:3000-3500
£1748 $2972 €2500 Composition (20x26cm-8x10in) init. pencil W/C. 25-Nov-3 Christie's, Amsterdam #283/R est:2500-3000
£1788 $3254 €2700 Nature morte (32x24cm-13x9in) init. gouache exec. c.1940. 18-Jun-4 Charbonneaux, Paris #120/R est:3000-3500
£1974 $3632 €3000 Composition (18x25cm-7x10in) mono. pastel exec c.1948. 28-Jun-4 Joron-Derem, Paris #227/R est:3000-3500
£2013 $3705 €3000 Composition (20x25cm-8x10in) mono. gouache. 24-Mar-4 Joron-Derem, Paris #124 est:3500-4000
£2174 $3565 €3000 Untitled (24x31cm-9x12in) s. gouache. 27-May-3 Sotheby's, Amsterdam #386/R est:3000-4000
£2349 $4322 €3500 Composition (19x26cm-7x10in) s. gouache exec c.1942. 24-Mar-4 Joron-Derem, Paris #120/R est:3500-4000
£2416 $4446 €3600 Composition (20x27cm-8x11in) mono. W/C exec c.1948. 24-Mar-4 Joron-Derem, Paris #125/R est:3500-4000
£2448 $4161 €3500 Untitled (16x20cm-6x8in) init. gouache. 25-Nov-3 Christie's, Amsterdam #287/R est:3500-5000
£2867 $4874 €4100 Composition (27x20cm-11x8in) init. W/C prov. 28-Nov-3 Blanchet, Paris #224/R est:4000-5000
£3125 $5156 €4500 Composition (30x30cm-12x12in) s. gouache prov.lit. 2-Jul-3 Cornette de St.Cyr, Paris #23/R est:4000-6000

VELDE, Henri van de (1896-1969) Dutch
£2349 $4346 €3500 Portrait of Van S B Slijper (35x27cm-14x11in) s. s.i.d.1930 verso panel. 15-Mar-4 Sotheby's, Amsterdam #529/R est:1500-2000

VELDE, Henry Clemens van de (1863-1957) Belgian
£4000 $7320 €6000 Portrait de la mere de l'artiste (46x70cm-18x28in) d.juin 88 prov.exhib. 7-Jun-4 Palais de Beaux Arts, Brussels #111/R est:6000-10000

VELDE, Jan Jansz van de (1620-1662) Dutch
£14000 $25620 €20440 Still life with glass of beer, pipe, tobacco, cards and brazier (14x12cm-6x5in) s. panel prov.exhib. 8-Jul-4 Sotheby's, London #145/R est:15000-20000
£111888 $192448 €160000 Still life with birch trees and haw (38x32cm-15x13in) s. 5-Dec-3 Bolland & Marotz, Bremen #498/R est:15000

VELDE, Jan van de II (c.1593-1641) Dutch
Prints
£4118 $7000 €6012 Star of kings (21x16cm-8x6in) etching. 31-Oct-3 Sotheby's, New York #180/R

VELDE, Pieter van de (1634-1687) Flemish
£3873 $6701 €5500 Navires a l'entree de ville hollandaise (45x59cm-18x23in) 15-Dec-3 Bailly Pommery, Paris #45/R est:8000-12000
£3974 $7232 €6000 Three master and other vessels off a port (50x58cm-20x23in) 16-Jun-4 Dorotheum, Vienna #93/R est:3000-5000
£5035 $8559 €7200 Dutch shipping off a rocky coastline with a fortified town beyond (87x125cm-34x49in) 26-Nov-3 James Adam, Dublin #2/R est:3000-4000
£6419 $11297 €9500 Dutch and English man-of-war. Two galleons, a merchantman and a rowing boat in the foreground (50x60cm-20x24in) s.d.1717 pair. 18-May-4 Sotheby's, Amsterdam #120/R est:8000-12000
£7534 $12808 €11000 View of a harbour with a galley and men-o-war and figures on a beach (83x119cm-33x47in) s.d.1703 prov. 4-Nov-3 Sotheby's, Amsterdam #65/R est:8000-12000
£9589 $16301 €14000 View of the roads of Antwerp with men-o-war in a gale (69x86cm-27x34in) s.indis.d. prov. 4-Nov-3 Sotheby's, Amsterdam #62/R est:5000-7000
£48276 $86897 €70000 View of Antwerp. View of harbour (69x86cm-27x34in) pair prov. 26-Jan-4 Ansorena, Madrid #55/R est:60000

VELDE, Pieter van de (attrib) (1634-1687) Flemish
£5034 $9262 €7500 La bataille de Lepante (76x111cm-30x44in) 24-Mar-4 Tajan, Paris #59/R est:5000-7000

VELDE, W van de (17/18th C) Dutch
Works on paper
£1724 $2879 €2500 Views of Corsica (41x58cm-16x23in) s. W/C pair. 11-Jul-3 Rabourdin & Choppin de Janvry, Paris #33/R

VELDE, Willem van de (17/18th C) Dutch
Works on paper
£260 $478 €380 Near Syracuse (17x25cm-7x10in) s. W/C htd white. 23-Jun-4 Bonhams, Bury St Edmunds #321

VELDE, Willem van de (attrib) (17/18th C) Dutch
£6040 $11114 €9000 Two battleships in storm (63x51cm-25x20in) canvas on panel. 26-Mar-4 Bolland & Marotz, Bremen #476/R est:9500
Works on paper
£350 $637 €511 Ships in a rough sea off the coast (18x25cm-7x10in) mono. 16-Jun-4 John Nicholson, Haslemere #656/R

VELDE, Willem van de (elder) (1611-1693) Dutch
Works on paper
£1806 $3250 €2637 Small boat in a calm sea with men rigging its sails (15x20cm-6x8in) s.d.1674 black lead wash two joined sheets prov. 21-Jan-4 Sotheby's, New York #73/R est:3000-4000
£10274 $17466 €15000 Man-of-war at sea, with rowing boat in the foreground (38x518cm-15x204in) s. pen brown ink vellum. 4-Nov-3 Sotheby's, Amsterdam #91/R est:18000-22000

VELDE, Willem van de (younger) (1633-1707) Dutch
£50000 $86500 €73000 An Indiaman in a gale off a rocky coast (58x74cm-23x29in) s.verso prov.exhib.lit. 11-Dec-3 Sotheby's, London #150/R est:20000-30000
£100000 $183000 €146000 Small craft in calm off the Dutch coast (14x20cm-6x8in) init. panel prov. 8-Jul-4 Sotheby's, London #121/R est:25000-35000
£280000 $512400 €408800 Galjoot and smalschip at anchor approached by a small kaag, and other vessels beyond (31x43cm-12x17in) init. panel prov.lit. 7-Jul-4 Christie's, London #55/R est:150000-200000
£310000 $536300 €452600 Calm - Dutch smalschips and a rowing boat in a light air (33x37cm-13x15in) mono. oak panel prov. 11-Dec-3 Sotheby's, London #71/R est:100000-150000
Works on paper
£433 $784 €650 Projet de plans de bateaux (26x42cm-10x17in) dr. 30-Mar-4 Campo & Campo, Antwerp #301/R
£700 $1211 €1022 Galleon (11x16cm-4x6in) brush grey wash over pencil. 9-Dec-3 Bonhams, Knightsbridge #8/R
£1049 $1804 €1500 Projet de plans de bateaux (28x40cm-11x16in) dr. 2-Dec-3 Campo & Campo, Antwerp #370/R est:3000-4000
£1300 $2379 €1898 English ship of 54 guns, possibly the Bristol (21x32cm-8x13in) i. black lead wash corners made up. 6-Jul-4 Christie's, London #179/R est:1000-1500
£2162 $3805 €3200 Eight ships on a choppy sea (22x32cm-9x13in) black chk two joined sheets. 19-May-4 Sotheby's, Amsterdam #69/R est:3500-4500
£4452 $7568 €6500 Man-of-war and other ships on a calm sea (15x19cm-6x7in) init. pen brown ink grey wash prov.exhib. 4-Nov-3 Sotheby's, Amsterdam #89/R est:4000-6000
£4730 $8324 €7000 Two frigates (24x19cm-9x7in) bears init. pen brown ink prov.lit. 19-May-4 Sotheby's, Amsterdam #68/R est:4500-6000

VELDE, Willem van de (younger-attrib) (1633-1707) Dutch
Works on paper
£1600 $2768 €2336 Ornamental design for the stern of a Dutch warship (31x42cm-12x17in) black chk prov. 9-Dec-3 Bonhams, Knightsbridge #10/R est:1200-1500
£2200 $3960 €3212 English men-of-war and rowing boats on a calm sea (16x20cm-6x8in) i. pen col ink grey wash black chk. 20-Apr-4 Sotheby's, Olympia #94/R est:700-900

VELDE, Willem van de (younger-style) (1633-1707) Dutch
£9667 $17593 €14500 Dutch ships in calm sea (79x117cm-31x46in) prov.exhib.lit. 29-Jun-4 Sotheby's, Paris #37/R est:10000-12000

VELDE, van de (17th C) Dutch
£1200 $2220 €1752 Artist visiting an Italian peasant family (62x85cm-24x33in) s.d.1850. 14-Jul-4 Bonhams, Chester #404/R est:1200-1600

VELDEN, Adrianus Dirk Blok van der (1913-1980) Dutch
£2268 $3924 €3311 Horses in meadow, winter (65x110cm-26x43in) s. 9-Dec-3 Rasmussen, Copenhagen #1592/R est:25000 (D.KR 24000)

VELDEN, Petrus van der (1837-1915) New Zealander/Dutch
£752 $1278 €1098 Edge of the beach (39x50cm-15x20in) s. board. 27-Nov-3 International Art Centre, Auckland #167/R (NZ.D 2000)
£1562 $2484 €2281 Evening light, Wellington Harbour (24x34cm-9x13in) canvas on board. 1-May-3 Dunbar Sloane, Wellington #17/R est:4500-7000 (NZ.D 4500)
£5208 $8281 €7604 Mount Rolleston and Otira Gorge. board. 1-May-3 Dunbar Sloane, Wellington #33/R est:25000-35000 (NZ.D 15000)
Works on paper
£418 $719 €610 Quayside street scene, Derdrecht, Holland (42x56cm-17x22in) s. pencil wash exec.1870. 7-Dec-3 International Art Centre, Auckland #230 (NZ.D 1125)

VELDHOEN, Aat (1934-) Dutch
£489 $841 €700 Still life with bread (70x100cm-28x39in) s. 7-Dec-3 Sotheby's, Amsterdam #793/R
£671 $1242 €1000 Self portrait (100x70cm-39x28in) s. 15-Mar-4 Sotheby's, Amsterdam #233/R est:1000-1500
£699 $1203 €1000 Boats on a lake (51x70cm-20x28in) s.d.74. 7-Dec-3 Sotheby's, Amsterdam #719
£1905 $3467 €2800 Flowergirl at Albert Cuyp market, Amsterdam (141x110cm-56x43in) s. acrylic. 3-Feb-4 Christie's, Amsterdam #332 est:600-800

VELDHUYZEN, Pieter (1806-1841) Dutch
£921 $1695 €1400 Admiring the artist at work (45x38cm-18x15in) s.d.1830. 22-Jun-4 Christie's, Amsterdam #19/R

VELGHE, Jean (1938-1999) Belgian
£690 $1276 €1000 Les amis de toujours (40x53cm-16x21in) s. 16-Feb-4 Horta, Bruxelles #68

VELICKOVIC, Vladimir (1935-) Yugoslavian
£1200 $2172 €1800 Exit (92x73cm-36x29in) s.i.d.1992 verso. 1-Apr-4 Credit Municipal, Paris #47 est:2000-2500
£2254 $3899 €3200 Saut (61x138cm-24x54in) s.d.1976 verso. 9-Dec-3 Artcurial Briest, Paris #561 est:3500-4000
£2381 $4262 €3500 Chute (73x60cm-29x24in) painted 1978 prov. 21-Mar-4 Calmels Cohen, Paris #151/R est:2000-2500
£3087 $5465 €4600 Profil (78x58cm-31x23in) s.d.1965 s.i.d.verso oil wash. 28-Apr-4 Artcurial Briest, Paris #404/R est:3000-4000
£3662 $6335 €5200 Saut (145x145cm-57x57in) s.i.d.1974 verso. 9-Dec-3 Artcurial Briest, Paris #560/R est:6000-8000
£3741 $6697 €5500 Ne (240x140cm-94x55in) s.d.1966 prov. 21-Mar-4 Calmels Cohen, Paris #152/R est:5000-7000
£4225 $7310 €6000 Homme qui court (200x146cm-79x57in) s. s.i.d.1976 verso. 9-Dec-3 Artcurial Briest, Paris #559/R est:6000-8000
Works on paper
£878 $1660 €1300 Paysage (29x64cm-11x25in) s.d.1999 mixed media cardboard. 21-Feb-4 Cornette de St.Cyr, Paris #422/R
£1824 $3266 €2700 Voyage (50x35cm-20x14in) s.d.1989 chl pastel oil collage. 4-May-4 Calmels Cohen, Paris #217/R est:2000-3000

VELLAN, Felice (1889-1976) Italian
£400 $736 €600 Balme (35x40cm-14x16in) s.d.1945 tempera card. 14-Jun-4 Sant Agostino, Torino #135/R
£414 $687 €600 Landscape (44x35cm-17x14in) s.d.1951 board. 1-Oct-3 Della Rocca, Turin #8/R
£442 $791 €650 Courmayeur (18x24cm-7x9in) s.d.1958. 22-Mar-4 Sant Agostino, Torino #161/R
£451 $767 €650 Landscape covered in snow (23x34cm-9x13in) s. board. 1-Nov-3 Meeting Art, Vercelli #61
£464 $844 €700 Rhodes (40x44cm-16x17in) s. cardboard painted 1940. 17-Jun-4 Finarte Semenzato, Milan #300
£467 $859 €700 Bridge in Favole (40x50cm-16x20in) s.d.1964 cardboard. 14-Jun-4 Sant Agostino, Torino #142/R
£503 $891 €750 By Caluso (27x35cm-11x14in) s.d.1961 board. 1-May-4 Meeting Art, Vercelli #454
£510 $913 €750 Mount Blanc (40x50cm-16x20in) s.i.d.1963 tempera. 22-Mar-4 Sant Agostino, Torino #171/R
£667 $1227 €1000 Sauze-d'Oulx (40x50cm-16x20in) s.d.1966 cardboard. 14-Jun-4 Sant Agostino, Torino #134/R
£671 $1188 €1000 Winter in Cormajore (31x36cm-12x14in) s. masonite painted 1944. 1-May-4 Meeting Art, Vercelli #29
£724 $1202 €1050 Landscape with bridge (50x60cm-20x24in) s.d. tempera cardboard. 1-Oct-3 Della Rocca, Turin #40/R
£769 $1285 €1100 Trees in Gressoney Valley (50x60cm-20x24in) s.d.1966 s.i.d.verso board. 26-Jun-3 Sant Agostino, Torino #129/R
£769 $1285 €1100 Gressoney Valley (40x50cm-16x20in) s.d.1965 canvas on board. 26-Jun-3 Sant Agostino, Torino #137/R
£780 $1303 €1100 Courtyard in Mazze' (40x50cm-16x20in) s.d.1963 masonite. 20-Oct-3 Sant Agostino, Torino #169/R
£800 $1472 €1200 Landscape in Tuscany (22x28cm-9x11in) s. cardboard prov. 14-Jun-4 Sant Agostino, Torino #138/R
£833 $1417 €1200 Spriong day in Mazze' (50x60cm-20x24in) s. s.i.d.1965 versolit. 1-Nov-3 Meeting Art, Vercelli #386
£839 $1401 €1200 Mazze', procession (17x23cm-7x9in) s.d.1959 cardboard. 26-Jun-3 Sant Agostino, Torino #139/R
£903 $1535 €1300 Gressoney Valley (40x50cm-16x20in) s.d.1965 board. 1-Nov-3 Meeting Art, Vercelli #230/R
£1206 $2013 €1700 Market by the lake (69x78cm-27x31in) s. tempera cardboard. 20-Oct-3 Sant Agostino, Torino #104/R est:1400
£1224 $2192 €1800 Susa valley (50x60cm-20x24in) s. i.d.1955 verso. 22-Mar-4 Sant Agostino, Torino #207/R est:2200
£1611 $2851 €2400 Beech in Salice d'Ulzio (50x60cm-20x24in) s.d.1944 board. 1-May-4 Meeting Art, Vercelli #51 est:2000
£2245 $4018 €3300 Party in Tirolo (100x70cm-39x28in) s.i.d.1951 tempera cardboard. 22-Mar-4 Sant Agostino, Torino #214/R est:3000
Works on paper
£333 $613 €500 Reading (33x26cm-13x10in) s.d.1920 mixed media card. 14-Jun-4 Sant Agostino, Torino #247/R
£347 $590 €500 Curtain (50x40cm-20x16in) s.d.1963 mixed media cardboard. 1-Nov-3 Meeting Art, Vercelli #226
£667 $1227 €1000 Rhodes (36x43cm-14x17in) s. mixed media card. 14-Jun-4 Sant Agostino, Torino #222/R
£694 $1181 €1000 Arma di Taggia (50x60cm-20x24in) s.i.d.1954 mixed media board. 1-Nov-3 Meeting Art, Vercelli #428/R
£733 $1349 €1100 On the Aufustus (46x42cm-18x17in) s.i.d.1936 mixed media card. 14-Jun-4 Sant Agostino, Torino #152/R
£733 $1349 €1100 Pool on the ferry (48x59cm-19x23in) s.i.d.1936 mixed media card. 14-Jun-4 Sant Agostino, Torino #330/R

VELLERT, Dirck (fl.1511-1544) Flemish
Prints
£4000 $7360 €5840 Temptation of Christ (11x7cm-4x3in) i.verso engraving sold with three other by different hand. 28-Jun-4 Bonhams, New Bond Street #67/R est:1000-1500

VELLUTINI, Pierre (20th C) French?
£292 $475 €420 Saint-Paul de Vence (46x55cm-18x22in) s. 29-Sep-3 Charbonneaux, Paris #288

VELSEN, Jacob Jansz van (?-1656) Dutch
£17731 $29610 €25000 Scene de concert dans un interieur Hollandais (37x49cm-15x19in) panel. 17-Oct-3 Tajan, Paris #65/R est:25000-30000

VELTEN, Maren (1924-) German
Works on paper
£287 $441 €450 Larkspur and sunflowers (48x38cm-19x15in) s. i. verso. 4-Sep-2 Schopman, Hamburg #175/R

VELTEN, Wilhelm (1847-1929) Russian
£1467 $2669 €2200 Camp (16x24cm-6x9in) s. panel. 30-Jun-4 Neumeister, Munich #727/R
£1467 $2669 €2200 At the blacksmiths (11x16cm-4x6in) s. panel. 30-Jun-4 Neumeister, Munich #728/R
£1538 $2615 €2200 Village blacksmith (16x24cm-6x9in) s. panel. 20-Nov-3 Van Ham, Cologne #1894/R est:2000
£1605 $2665 €2343 Departure of the hunt (16x24cm-6x9in) s. panel. 15-Jun-3 Agra, Warsaw #23/R est:10000 (P.Z 10000)
£1667 $2717 €2400 Riders talking to peasant outside farmstead (15x24cm-6x9in) s. panel. 24-Sep-3 Neumeister, Munich #589/R est:1800
£1793 $2994 €2600 On manoeuvres (14x21cm-6x8in) s. panel prov. 15-Nov-3 Lempertz, Koln #1710/R est:2700
£2038 $3750 €2975 Little girl with her pets (28x34cm-11x13in) s.i. panel. 27-Jun-4 Freeman, Philadelphia #38/R est:3000-5000
£2041 $3714 €3000 Travelers resting in a village (32x25cm-13x10in) s.i. panel. 3-Feb-4 Christie's, Amsterdam #113/R est:2500-3500
£2083 $3292 €3000 Horse market (16x24cm-6x9in) s. panel. 5-Sep-3 Wendl, Rudolstadt #3749/R est:3300
£2431 $4010 €3500 Sad discovery (36x30cm-14x12in) s.i. panel. 2-Jul-3 Neumeister, Munich #805/R est:3000
£2448 $4210 €3500 Departure of the fox hunters in front of Solitude Palace (16x24cm-6x9in) s. panel prov. 5-Dec-3 Ketterer, Munich #11/R est:4000-6000

£2869	$5250	€4189	Hunting morn (33x25cm-13x10in) s. panel. 10-Apr-4 Cobbs, Peterborough #64/R
£3067	$5581	€4600	Hunters outside Schloss Nymphenburg (14x23cm-6x9in) s. panel prov. 30-Jun-4 Neumeister, Munich #725/R est:4500
£3191	$5330	€4500	Horse drawn cart followed by riders (15x24cm-6x9in) s. panel. 21-Jun-3 Hans Stahl, Hamburg #13/R est:3800
£3632	$6500	€5303	At play (29x37cm-11x15in) s.i. panel prov. 14-May-4 Skinner, Boston #319/R est:4000-6000
£5500	$9845	€8030	Imperial hunting party (20x31cm-8x12in) s. 26-May-4 Sotheby's, London #86/R est:6000-8000
£6944	$11806	€10000	Amusing gesture (37x53cm-15x21in) s.i. panel. 28-Oct-3 Christie's, Amsterdam #198/R est:10000-15000

VELTHUYSEN, Henry van (1881-1954) Dutch

£685	$1164	€1000	Indian avenue (58x46cm-23x18in) s. maroufle. 5-Nov-3 Vendue Huis, Gravenhage #548
£748	$1339	€1100	Ehret die Frauen - woman at a temple gate (35x39cm-14x15in) s. s.i.verso panel. 16-Mar-4 Christie's, Amsterdam #45 est:600-800
£1020	$1827	€1500	Street scene (50x28cm-20x11in) s.d.32 canvas on panel. 16-Mar-4 Christie's, Amsterdam #96 est:1200-1600
£1020	$1827	€1500	Still life with tropical fruits (40x49cm-16x19in) s. canvas on board. 16-Mar-4 Christie's, Amsterdam #97 est:600-800

VELZEN, Johannes Petrus van (1816-1853) Dutch

£699	$1168	€1000	By the river (36x48cm-14x19in) s. 30-Jun-3 Sotheby's, Amsterdam #83

VEMREN, Hilde (1953-) Norwegian

£1223	$2190	€1786	Venetian vases (80x140cm-31x55in) s.d.99. 25-May-4 Grev Wedels Plass, Oslo #115/R est:15000-20000 (N.KR 15000)

VEMULLER, Hans (20th C) German?

£453	$825	€680	Skier (35x42cm-14x17in) s. 1-Jul-4 Weidler, Nurnberg #6507/R

VEN, Emanuel Ernest Gerardus van der (1866-1944) Dutch

£316	$572	€480	Still life of flowers in a pottery vase (60x48cm-24x19in) s. 19-Apr-4 Glerum, Amsterdam #150/R
£417	$679	€600	Flower still life (65x60cm-26x24in) s. 29-Sep-3 Sotheby's, Amsterdam #332

VEN, Emil (1902-1984) Hungarian?

£2939	$5203	€4291	Port (80x100cm-31x39in) s. 28-Apr-4 Kieselbach, Budapest #2/R (H.F 1100000)

VENAIN, R (19th C) French

£745	$1333	€1088	River landscape in summer (66x92cm-26x36in) s. 22-Mar-4 Philippe Schuler, Zurich #6200 (S.FR 1720)

VENARD, Claude (1913-1999) French

£235	$437	€350	Pont de chemin de fer (16x24cm-6x9in) st.sig. 3-Mar-4 Tajan, Paris #175
£279	$475	€407	Composition au fond bleu (75x75cm-30x30in) s. 21-Nov-3 Skinner, Boston #595/R
£438	$700	€639	Sailboat Abstraction (23x33cm-9x13in) s. 20-Sep-3 Bunte, Elgin #1264
£459	$850	€670	Deux mobiles (33x23cm-13x9in) s. prov. 15-Jul-4 Doyle, New York #81/R
£462	$850	€675	Still life with easel (33x33cm-13x13in) s. 25-Jun-4 Freeman, Philadelphia #304/R
£603	$958	€880	Untitled (75x75cm-30x30in) s. 29-Apr-3 Louis Morton, Mexico #100/R (M.P 10000)
£640	$1100	€934	Nude study (46x33cm-18x13in) s. prov. 7-Dec-3 Freeman, Philadelphia #64
£695	$1266	€1050	Notre Dame (73x60cm-29x24in) s. 18-Jun-4 Charbonneaux, Paris #178/R
£722	$1300	€1054	Les maisons (61x71cm-24x28in) s. 25-Jan-4 Bonhams & Butterfields, San Francisco #3622/R est:1000-2000
£809	$1400	€1181	Still life with goblet (64x53cm-25x21in) s. 15-Dec-3 Hindman, Chicago #12/R est:1600-1800
£882	$1500	€1288	Port (74x74cm-29x29in) s. i.on stretcher. 5-Nov-3 Doyle, New York #77/R est:1000-1500
£934	$1680	€1400	Le village (74x74cm-29x29in) s. 26-Apr-4 Tajan, Paris #197 est:1200-1500
£963	$1800	€1406	Nature morte (74x74cm-29x29in) s. 24-Feb-4 Arthur James, Florida #272
£1111	$1756	€1600	Paysage a la biche (100x100cm-39x39in) s. 25-Apr-3 Etude de Provence, Marseille #284 est:1600-1800
£1111	$1756	€1600	Paysage au Aloes (100x100cm-39x39in) s. 25-Apr-3 Etude de Provence, Marseille #285 est:1600-1800
£1196	$2200	€1746	Sailboats (58x74cm-23x29in) s. 25-Mar-4 Doyle, New York #70/R est:1000-1500
£1200	$2208	€1752	Interieur avec une ceramique de Picasso (24x33cm-9x13in) s. 24-Mar-4 Sotheby's, Olympia #131/R est:1500-2000
£1279	$2200	€1867	Inside Harbour No 1 (38x61cm-15x24in) s. prov. 7-Dec-3 Freeman, Philadelphia #65 est:800-1200
£1522	$2800	€2222	Still life (46x53cm-18x21in) s.d.57. 25-Mar-4 Doyle, New York #69/R est:800-1200
£1620	$2608	€2300	Nature morte (75x75cm-30x30in) s. 11-May-3 Versailles Encheres #159/R
£1944	$3247	€2800	Nature morte (80x99cm-31x39in) s.d.1959. 25-Oct-3 Cornette de St.Cyr, Paris #549 est:2500-3000
£2032	$3800	€2967	Nature morte avec carafe rouge (100x100cm-39x39in) s.d.56 i.verso prov. 25-Feb-4 Christie's, Rockefeller NY #117/R est:2000-3000
£2151	$4000	€3140	Still life with a compote with vase of flowers (75x75cm-30x30in) s. 3-Mar-4 Christie's, Rockefeller NY #63/R est:2000-3000
£2510	$4544	€3665	Les deux oranges (76x76cm-30x30in) s. i.verso prov. 1-Apr-4 Heffel, Vancouver #102/R est:4000-6000 (C.D 6000)
£2533	$4661	€3800	Bretagne (79x39cm-31x15in) s. prov. 9-Jun-4 Christie's, Amsterdam #128/R est:800-1200
£2600	$4342	€3796	Port d'Audierne (60x73cm-24x29in) s. prov. 22-Oct-3 Sotheby's, Olympia #174/R est:1800-2500
£2639	$4407	€3800	Nature morte aux cartes et a la mappemonde (100x100cm-39x39in) s. d.1957 verso. 25-Oct-3 Dianous, Marseille #375
£2639	$4407	€3800	Montmartre (100x100cm-39x39in) s. d.1957 verso. 25-Oct-3 Dianous, Marseille #425
£2762	$4750	€4033	Fruit and flowers (81x99cm-32x39in) s. i.verso prov. 7-Dec-3 Freeman, Philadelphia #61 est:2000-3000
£3000	$5010	€4380	Still life (60x120cm-24x47in) s. prov. 22-Oct-3 Sotheby's, Olympia #175/R est:3000-4000
£3333	$6133	€5000	Table chargee (100x100cm-39x39in) s. prov. 9-Jun-4 Christie's, Amsterdam #127/R est:2000-3000
£3472	$5799	€5000	Paysage de Provence (90x117cm-35x46in) s. 25-Oct-3 Dianous, Marseille #426
£3611	$6031	€5200	Nature morte sur fond rouge (92x73cm-36x29in) s. 25-Oct-3 Dianous, Marseille #374
£3667	$6747	€5500	Les deux pipes (38x46cm-15x18in) s. 9-Jun-4 Christie's, Amsterdam #129/R est:800-1200
£3800	$6346	€5548	Still life (75x75cm-30x30in) s. prov. 22-Oct-3 Sotheby's, Olympia #173/R est:2000-3000
£7487	$14000	€10931	Nature morte de musiquew (82x100cm-32x39in) s.d.51 prov. 25-Feb-4 Christie's, Rockefeller NY #101/R est:4000-6000

VENDERKOP, Johanna Croiset (?) ?

£389	$650	€568	Still life with wild flowers. s. 18-Oct-3 Harvey Clar, Oakland #1201

VENEMAN, Hans (1939-1991) Dutch

£486	$792	€700	Abstract composition (55x46cm-22x18in) s. acrylic. 29-Sep-3 Sotheby's, Amsterdam #352

VENET, Bernar (1941-) French

£1049	$1804	€1500	FIG 3 (40x27cm-16x11in) s.i.d.1966 verso canvas on panel. 4-Dec-3 Piasa, Paris #4/R est:1200-1800
£2937	$5052	€4200	FIG 120 (90x90cm-35x35in) s.d.1966 s.i.d.verso paint canvas. 4-Dec-3 Piasa, Paris #18/R est:1500-2000
£3636	$6255	€5200	Peinture industrielle (75x60cm-30x24in) paint folded cardboard wood panel painted c.1963. 4-Dec-3 Piasa, Paris #17/R est:4000-6000

Sculpture

£2533	$4661	€3800	Peinture industrielle (120x102cm-47x40in) s.i.d.1965 verso folded board acrylic prov. 9-Jun-4 Artcurial Briest, Paris #500/R est:4000-6000
£2667	$4906	€4000	Peinture industrielle (57x93cm-22x37in) s.i.d.1964 verso folded board acrylic prov. 9-Jun-4 Artcurial Briest, Paris #501 est:3000-4000
£5743	$10280	€8500	Ligne indetermine (11x21x22cm-4x8x9in) s.i.d.1998 steel. 4-May-4 Calmels Cohen, Paris #250/R est:5000-6000
£6643	$11094	€9500	Arc 109 (50x120cm-20x47in) I. black painted steel. 11-Oct-3 De Vuyst, Lokeren #505/R est:17000-20000
£8000	$14720	€12000	Ligne indeterminee (31x31x17cm-12x12x7in) s.d.20 89 painted steel prov. 9-Jun-4 Artcurial Briest, Paris #499/R est:8000-12000
£8535	$14509	€12461	Indeterminees (35x40x40cm-14x16x16in) s.d.0290 forge-iron on iron base prov. 5-Nov-3 AB Stockholms Auktionsverk #1110/R est:140000-160000 (S.KR 113000)
£10563	$18486	€15000	210,5 ARC x 5 (58x58cm-23x23in) i.base steel prov. 18-Dec-3 Cornette de St.Cyr, Paris #97/R est:12000-15000
£24476	$40874	€35000	Deux arcs de 214 (156x137cm-61x54in) i. steel. 11-Oct-3 De Vuyst, Lokeren #500/R
£50667	$93733	€76000	Arc (267x250x50cm-105x98x20in) i. iron exec.1995 prov.exhib. 18-Jul-4 Sotheby's, Paris #150/R est:60000-80000
£55866	$100000	€81564	Indeterminate line (112x128x81cm-44x50x32in) rolled steel prov.exhib. 12-May-4 Christie's, Rockefeller NY #416/R est:50000-70000

Works on paper

£420	$701	€600	Position of undetermined line (29x24cm-11x9in) s.d.1982 crayon collage prov. 29-Jun-3 Versailles Encheres #205
£695	$1266	€1050	Undetermined line (9x23cm-4x9in) mono.i.d.1980 chl prov. 16-Jun-4 Renaud, Paris #66/R
£1014	$1814	€1500	Ligne indeterminee (25x20cm-10x8in) mono.i.d.1990 ink collage. 4-May-4 Calmels Cohen, Paris #209 est:600-800
£1074	$1987	€1600	Ligne indeterminee (20x28cm-8x11in) s.i.d.1980 pencil collage. 13-Mar-4 De Vuyst, Lokeren #371/R est:1500-1700
£1099	$1945	€1605	Combinaison aleatoire de lignes indeterminees (22x33cm-9x13in) s.d.1992 collage mixed media. 27-Apr-4 AB Stockholms Auktionsverk #1231/R est:18000-20000 (S.KR 15000)
£1268	$2104	€1800	Stormer theory and Euler potentials (51x73cm-20x29in) s.d.68 collage board. 11-Jun-3 Finarte Semenzato, Milan #629/R
£1360	$2311	€1986	Randon combination of undetermined lines (23x34cm-9x13in) s.d.1991 mixed media. 5-Nov-3 AB Stockholms Auktionsverk #1112/R est:18000-20000 (S.KR 18000)
£1678	$3087	€2500	Reflex angle (125x92cm-49x36in) s.verso lead pencil. 24-Mar-4 Joron-Derem, Paris #180 est:4000-5000
£2133	$3883	€3200	Ligne indeterminee (28x39cm-11x15in) s. chl pastel oil collage prov. 29-Jun-4 Cornette de St.Cyr, Paris #128/R est:2000-3000
£2349	$4322	€3500	Three major arcs (96x126cm-38x50in) s.d.1979 verso collage lead pencil. 24-Mar-4 Joron-Derem, Paris #179/R est:5000-6000
£2417	$4109	€3529	Three undetermined lines (51x63cm-20x25in) s.d.78 collage oil paper prov. 5-Nov-3 AB Stockholms Auktionsverk #1113/R est:40000-50000 (S.KR 32000)
£10667	$19627	€16000	Ligne indeterminee (211x151cm-83x59in) s.i.d.1987 chl crayon collage prov. 8-Jun-4 Artcurial Briest, Paris #267/R est:15000-20000
£15493	$26803	€22000	Undetermined line (202x152cm-80x60in) s.i.d.87 pastel collage prov. 9-Dec-3 Artcurial Briest, Paris #395/R est:10000-14000

VENETIAN SCHOOL (14th C) Italian

£36667	$66733	€55000	Incoronation of the Virgin (28x14cm-11x6in) tempera gold board prov. 4-Jul-4 Finarte, Venice #49/R est:55000-65000

VENETIAN SCHOOL (15th/16th C) Italian

£18000	$32940	€26280	Venus and Mars in a river landscape with Vulcan labouring in his forge (32x25cm-13x10in) panel prov.lit. 7-Jul-4 Christie's, London #6/R est:10000-15000

VENETIAN SCHOOL (16th C) Italian
£6443 $11404 €9600 Portrait of gentleman (85x67cm-33x26in) d.1565. 28-Apr-4 Marc Kohn, Paris #135/R est:10000-12000
£6667 $12067 €10000 Holy Family with St John the Baptist (80x68cm-31x27in) panel. 1-Apr-4 Van Ham, Cologne #1253/R est:2200
£7877 $13390 €11500 Visit of the Magi (49x43cm-19x17in) mono.verso panel. 9-Nov-3 Finarte, Venice #56/R est:5000-6000
£9333 $16707 €14000 Holy Family with Saint Catherine (60x73cm-24x29in) board prov. 12-May-4 Stadion, Trieste #609/R est:10000-15000
£11000 $20130 €16060 Portrait of commander in landscape (32x26cm-13x10in) 8-Jul-4 Sotheby's, London #188/R est:3000-4000
£18750 $34500 €28500 Christ carrying the Cross (76x60cm-30x24in) board. 22-Jun-4 Finarte Semenzato, Rome #306/R est:30000-35000
£20979 $35035 €30000 Bust of Christ (29x23cm-11x9in) board. 24-Jun-3 Finarte Semenzato, Rome #611/R est:9000-10000
£26389 $47500 €38528 Study of a Dead Christ, head and shoulders (26x30cm-10x12in) oil paper on canvas. 21-Jan-4 Sotheby's, New York #22/R est:15000-20000
£27000 $48600 €39420 Madonna and Child with the infant Saint John the Baptist and patrican family as donors (102x136cm-40x54in) 21-Apr-4 Christie's, London #93/R est:10000-15000
£50000 $91500 €73000 Portrait of man in armour (58x44cm-23x17in) i.on stretcher prov.lit. 8-Jul-4 Sotheby's, London #194/R est:4000-6000
Prints
£20000 $35800 €30000 Christ between henchman and soldier (39x33cm-15x13in) woodcut. 13-May-4 Bassenge, Berlin #5331/R est:3500
Works on paper
£5200 $9516 €7592 Head of Vitellius (40x36cm-16x14in) blk chk htd white chk grey paper. 8-Jul-4 Sotheby's, London #27/R est:6000-8000
£8503 $15221 €12500 Un soldat agenouille tenant une epee dirigee vers le sol. Etude d'homme (33x25cm-13x10in) black chk double-sided prov.exhib. 18-Mar-4 Christie's, Paris #2/R est:4000-6000

VENETIAN SCHOOL (17th C) Italian
£4945 $9000 €7220 Family of Daruis before Alexander (86x126cm-34x50in) 29-Jun-4 Sotheby's, New York #16/R est:3000-4000
£5333 $9547 €8000 Juno (128x96cm-50x38in) 17-May-4 Finarte Semenzato, Rome #96/R est:10000-12000
£5705 $10497 €8500 St Catherine (73x96cm-29x38in) 25-Mar-4 Dr Fritz Nagel, Stuttgart #647/R est:1300
£6000 $10980 €8760 Narcissus and the Tiresias with a nymph (97x132cm-38x52in) 6-Jul-4 Sotheby's, Olympia #514/R est:6000-8000
£6376 $11732 €9500 Triumph of David (120x173cm-47x68in) prov. 24-Mar-4 Dorotheum, Vienna #9/R est:5000-7000
£10000 $17000 €14600 Bacchanalian scene before a classical palace (105x82cm-41x32in) 30-Oct-3 Sotheby's, Olympia #116/R est:6000-8000
£14000 $24220 €20440 Reclining Venus (100x150cm-39x59in) 10-Dec-3 Bonhams, New Bond Street #98/R est:10000-15000
Sculpture
£10000 $18300 €14600 Venus and Cupid (43cm-17in) bronze lit. 9-Jul-4 Sotheby's, London #68/R est:10000-15000

VENETIAN SCHOOL (17th/18th C) Italian
Sculpture
£5000 $8650 €7300 Woman, possibly represent a niobid (25cm-10in) light brown pat. marble base lit. 11-Dec-3 Christie's, London #44/R est:3000-4000

VENETIAN SCHOOL (18th C) Italian
£3352 $6000 €4894 Rsting on the Flight to Egypt (37x26cm-15x10in) canvas on board. 27-May-4 Sotheby's, New York #83/R est:6000-8000
£5082 $9300 €7420 Amnon and Tamar (152x222cm-60x87in) painted c.1700 exhib. 1-Feb-4 Ben-Ami, Tel Aviv #4632/R est:20000-30000
£5263 $9684 €8000 Joseph in prison (81x98cm-32x39in) 24-Jun-4 Dr Fritz Nagel, Stuttgart #642/R est:2000
£6500 $11050 €9490 Trompe l'oeil with a putto and a goat. Trompe l'oeil with putto and a lamb (110x140cm-43x55in) pair. 30-Oct-3 Sotheby's, Olympia #163/R est:4000-6000
£7830 $13546 €11432 Venetian detail (39x58cm-15x23in) 12-Dec-3 Kieselbach, Budapest #73/R (H.F 3000000)
£8000 $13840 €11680 Rebecca at the well (114x81cm-45x32in) 10-Dec-3 Bonhams, New Bond Street #119/R est:6000-8000
£8054 $14819 €12000 Minerva (35x26cm-14x10in) 25-Mar-4 Dr Fritz Nagel, Stuttgart #648/R est:15000
£9722 $15847 €14000 Maria with Jesus and St John the Baptist (74x56cm-29x22in) 25-Sep-3 Dr Fritz Nagel, Stuttgart #1214/R est:1400
£9859 $15873 €14000 Capriccio con rovine romane, ponte e chiesa sullo sfondo (70x98cm-28x39in) 8-May-3 Farsetti, Prato #599/R est:16000-18000
£10000 $17300 €14600 San Giorgio Maggiore, Venice (71x108cm-28x43in) prov. 10-Dec-3 Bonhams, New Bond Street #130/R est:10000-15000
£10067 $18523 €15000 Adoration of the Magi (126x156cm-50x61in) prov. 24-Mar-4 Dorotheum, Vienna #67/R est:15000-22000
£12000 $21960 €17520 The Bucintoro at the Molo (75x95cm-30x37in) 9-Jul-4 Christie's, Kensington #204/R est:5000-8000
£13000 $23790 €18980 Venice, view of the Piazzetta looking towards Santa Maria della Salute (54x79cm-21x31in) 6-Jul-4 Sotheby's, Olympia #605/R est:6000-8000
£13245 $24106 €20000 Venice, view of the Riva degli Schiavoni with the Ducal Palace (52x70cm-20x28in) prov. 16-Jun-4 Dorotheum, Vienna #28/R est:4000-6000
£19444 $35000 €28388 View of the Piazzetta and the Torre Dell Orologio (95x130cm-37x51in) 22-Jan-4 Sotheby's, New York #177/R est:30000-40000
£20000 $34600 €29200 Discovery of the cup in Benjamin's sack (121x160cm-48x63in) prov. 12-Dec-3 Christie's, Kensington #258/R est:8000-12000
£28000 $51240 €40880 Capriccios with figures (87x125cm-34x49in) pair. 8-Jul-4 Sotheby's, London #181/R est:30000-40000
£98361 $180000 €143607 Venice, the Piazza san Marco, at carnival time (116x143cm-46x56in) prov. 3-Jun-4 Christie's, Rockefeller NY #1211/R est:10000-15000

VENETIAN SCHOOL (19th C) Italian
£10791 $17698 €15000 Night scenes (32x50cm-13x20in) board pair. 4-Jun-3 Sotheby's, Milan #139/R est:15000-20000
£11409 $21221 €17000 Vue du pont du Rialto (60x95cm-24x37in) 8-Mar-4 Artcurial Briest, Paris #28/R est:12000-15000
£30000 $54900 €43800 Grand Canal, Venice, with a the Campo Santa Maria Zobenigo (58x86cm-23x34in) prov. 7-Jul-4 Bonhams, New Bond Street #137/R est:30000-50000
Sculpture
£13487 $24816 €20500 Moorish (188x48x48cm-74x19x19in) painted wood pair. 22-Jun-4 Finarte Semenzato, Rome #44/R est:32000-35000
£36620 $63352 €52000 Lion. Lioness (100cm-39in) gilt pewter pair. 13-Dec-3 Finarte, Venice #45/R est:98000-108000
Works on paper
£13103 $21883 €19000 Grand Canal (12x19cm-5x7in) gouache. 12-Nov-3 Sotheby's, Milan #136/R est:1000-2000

VENETIEN, Jean (1911-) ?
£533 $976 €800 River scene (62x52cm-24x20in) s. 7-Jun-4 Glerum, Amsterdam #92/R

VENETO SCHOOL (16th C) Italian
£5667 $10370 €8500 Baptism of Jesus (69x50cm-27x20in) board. 1-Jun-4 Sotheby's, Milan #128/R est:7000-10000
£6711 $12349 €10000 Nymph (117x87cm-46x34in) 29-Mar-4 Pandolfini, Florence #652/R est:12000
£10000 $18300 €15000 Supper in Emmaus (74x108cm-29x43in) board. 1-Jun-4 Sotheby's, Milan #123/R est:15000-20000

VENETO SCHOOL (16th/17th C) Italian
£25352 $44366 €36000 Gallant concert (125x203cm-49x80in) 17-Dec-3 Christie's, Rome #495/R est:25000-35000

VENETO SCHOOL (17th C) Italian
£4795 $7479 €7000 Portrait of man with white collar (50x40cm-20x16in) i.verso. 8-Apr-3 Il Ponte, Milan #35
£5594 $9622 €8000 Venus and Mars (58x170cm-23x67in) board painted c.1600. 2-Dec-3 Sotheby's, Milan #121/R est:8000-12000
£5616 $9548 €8200 Portrait of the Doge Francesco Morosini (77x60cm-30x24in) i. 9-Nov-3 Finarte, Venice #104/R est:7000-9000
£6040 $11114 €9000 Moses and the water from the rock (127x94cm-50x37in) 29-Mar-4 Pandolfini, Florence #781/R est:13000

VENETO SCHOOL (18th C) Italian
£5319 $8883 €7500 Portrait of lady (98x68cm-39x27in) 17-Jun-3 Finarte Semenzato, Milan #424/R
£12587 $21650 €18000 River landscape with bridge (43x63cm-17x25in) 2-Dec-3 Sotheby's, Milan #119/R est:10000-15000
£12667 $23180 €19000 Venice from the Grand Canal (45x73cm-18x29in) 1-Jun-4 Sotheby's, Milan #188/R est:15000-20000
£12950 $21237 €18000 Saint Mark's Square (45x72cm-18x28in) 4-Jun-3 Sotheby's, Milan #141/R est:18000-22000
£13333 $24400 €20000 Education of the VIrgin (102x88cm-40x35in) 1-Jun-4 Sotheby's, Milan #184/R est:6000-8000
£16000 $29280 €24000 Portrait of gentleman. Portrait of lady (72x59cm-28x23in) pair. 1-Jun-4 Sotheby's, Milan #185/R est:14000-18000
£19718 $31549 €28000 Landscapes with herds (142x109cm-56x43in) canvas on board set of 4. 20-Sep-3 Finarte, Venice #102/R est:40000
£45000 $76500 €65700 View of Bergamo (72x89cm-28x35in) 29-Oct-3 Christie's, London #99/R est:15000-20000
Sculpture
£10067 $18020 €15000 Water carriers (143cm-56in) polychrome wood pair. 26-May-4 Semenzato, Florence #75/R est:14000-16000

VENETO SCHOOL (18th/19th C) Italian
£22148 $40752 €33000 Landscape with buildings (168x225cm-66x89in) 27-Mar-4 Farsetti, Prato #345/R est:30000

VENETO SCHOOL (19th C) Italian
£9353 $15338 €13000 View of Venice (43x61cm-17x24in) 4-Jun-3 Sotheby's, Milan #89/R est:10000-15000
£13986 $24056 €20000 Capriccios (18x15cm-7x6in) pair. 2-Dec-3 Sotheby's, Milan #125/R est:12000-16000

VENETO-CRETAN SCHOOL (17th C) Italian
£4895 $8175 €7000 Annunciation (58x69cm-23x27in) board. 7-Oct-3 Pandolfini, Florence #546/R est:7000-9000

VENETO-DALMATIAN SCHOOL (16th C) Italian
£5369 $9879 €8000 Annunciation to the Virgin (70x82cm-28x32in) panel prov. 24-Mar-4 Dorotheum, Vienna #47/R est:8000-10000
£6643 $11427 €9500 Madonna and Child (92x124cm-36x49in) panel triptych. 8-Dec-3 Claude Aguttes, Neuilly #17/R est:6000

VENIER, Bruno (?) Argentinian?
£559 $1000 €816 Cock (57x44cm-22x17in) board. 11-May-4 Arroyo, Buenos Aires #101
£879 $1600 €1283 Figure with cock (84x38cm-33x15in) s. board. 5-Jul-4 Arroyo, Buenos Aires #49/R est:1500

VENNA, Lucio (1897-1974) Italian
£331 $603 €500 Flowers (70x50cm-28x20in) s. s.verso. 21-Jun-4 Pandolfini, Florence #185
£533 $981 €800 Seated man (60x50cm-24x20in) s. 11-Jun-4 Farsetti, Prato #508/R

VENNARD, Stanley (20th C) British?
£250 $430 €365 Killary harbour, County Mayo (30x40cm-12x16in) s.d.2003 verso board. 3-Dec-3 John Ross, Belfast #201

VENNE, Adolf van der (1828-1911) Austrian
£521 $828 €750 On the way to market (47x65cm-19x26in) s. 11-Sep-3 Weidler, Nurnberg #6506/R
£620 $1110 €905 Guarding the prisoners (33x42cm-13x17in) mono.d.862. 18-Mar-4 Christie's, Kensington #605/R
£1267 $2305 €1900 Gypsy camp in the Puszta (83x121cm-33x48in) s.d.896. 30-Jun-4 Neumeister, Munich #729/R
£2821 $4401 €4119 Horseman and horses on a riverside (103x125cm-41x49in) s.d.77. 30-Mar-3 Agra, Warsaw #21/R est:15000 (P.Z 18000)

VENNE, Adriaen Pietersz van de (1589-1662) Dutch
£10274 $17466 €15000 Beggar on his toes, with woman squatting. Woman on her toes with a man (27x22cm-11x9in) one indis.sig. i. panel pair. 4-Nov-3 Sotheby's, Amsterdam #80/R est:15000-20000
£17808 $30274 €26000 River landscape with figures on the bank near an inn, shipping beyond (21x41cm-8x16in) s. panel prov. 5-Nov-3 Christie's, Amsterdam #49/R est:18000-22000
£28767 $48904 €42000 Al-arm (39x30cm-15x12in) s.i.d.1632 en grisaille panel prov. 4-Nov-3 Sotheby's, Amsterdam #19/R est:25000-35000
£51370 $87329 €75000 Amorous peasant couple conversing (28x23cm-11x9in) s.d.1631 panel en grisaille prov.exhib. 4-Nov-3 Sotheby's, Amsterdam #12/R est:20000-30000
Works on paper
£759 $1267 €1100 Peasant couple fighting (24x32cm-9x13in) chk htd white prov. 15-Nov-3 Lempertz, Koln #1417/R
£4167 $7500 €6084 Quack dentist removing a tooth from a seated woman (11x14cm-4x6in) s. black chk pen brown ink grey wash pair. 22-Jan-4 Christie's, Rockefeller NY #123/R est:5000-7000
£11644 $19795 €17000 Marital roles (6x7cm-2x3in) i. pen black ink grey wash pair prov.lit. 4-Nov-3 Sotheby's, Amsterdam #38/R est:18000-22000
£20548 $34932 €30000 Scenes relating to marriage (5x7cm-2x3in) pen black brown ink grey wash pair prov. 4-Nov-3 Sotheby's, Amsterdam #37/R est:18000-22000
£54795 $93151 €80000 Interior of a circus tent, with performers (11x14cm-4x6in) s.d.1628 pen brown black ink grey wash prov.lit. 4-Nov-3 Sotheby's, Amsterdam #36/R est:60000-80000

VENNE, Francisc Vanden (?) ?
£267 $480 €400 Consiliarus (30x24cm-12x9in) s. 20-Apr-4 Galerie Moderne, Brussels #406

VENNE, Fritz van der (1873-1936) German
£2083 $3542 €3000 Returning from the bear hunt (16x21cm-6x8in) s.i. panel. 28-Oct-3 Christie's, Amsterdam #81/R est:3000-5000

VENNE, Paul van de (19/20th C) ?
£372 $654 €550 Marines (75x50cm-30x20in) s. panel set of 4. 18-May-4 Galerie Moderne, Brussels #263
£839 $1427 €1200 Le depart des pecheurs (50x75cm-20x30in) s. 18-Nov-3 Vanderkindere, Brussels #133

VENNE, Pieter van der (style) (?-1657) Dutch
£7383 $13215 €11000 Vase de fleurs sur une tablette en marbre (51x39cm-20x15in) panel. 25-May-4 Palais de Beaux Arts, Brussels #549/R est:8000-12000

VENNEMAN, Camille (1827-1868) Belgian
£10563 $18275 €15000 Le musicien ambulant (69x55cm-27x22in) s.d.1861 panel. 9-Dec-3 Campo, Vlaamse Kaai #485 est:15000-17000

VENNEMAN, Charles (1802-1875) Flemish
£403 $745 €600 Man looking through a window (14x13cm-6x5in) panel. 13-Mar-4 De Vuyst, Lokeren #372
£603 $1007 €850 Tavern scene with two figures (17x15cm-7x6in) s.d.1846 panel. 20-Oct-3 Bernaerts, Antwerp #123/R
£699 $1203 €1000 Feeding time (21x19cm-8x7in) s.d.1850 panel. 7-Dec-3 Sotheby's, Amsterdam #584/R
£1333 $2387 €2000 Vieux couple a l'auberge (27x21cm-11x8in) s. panel. 11-May-4 Vanderkindere, Brussels #102 est:1400-1800
£1399 $2378 €2000 La lecture de la lettre a l'auberge (27x21cm-11x8in) s. panel. 18-Nov-3 Vanderkindere, Brussels #46 est:2000-3000
£1600 $2928 €2400 La seduction (21x17cm-8x7in) s. panel. 7-Jun-4 Palais de Beaux Arts, Brussels #318/R est:1800-2400
£1748 $2972 €2500 Vieux couple au repas (24x20cm-9x8in) s. panel. 18-Nov-3 Vanderkindere, Brussels #10 est:2500-4000
£6667 $11933 €10000 Public house interior with card players (70x80cm-28x31in) s. 15-May-4 De Vuyst, Lokeren #529/R est:17000-19000
£20979 $35035 €30000 Jolly village gathering (69x56cm-27x22in) s.d.1858 panel. 11-Oct-3 De Vuyst, Lokeren #410/R

VENNEMAN, Charles (attrib) (1802-1875) Flemish
£655 $1094 €950 Le tastevin (27x21cm-11x8in) panel. 17-Nov-3 Bernaerts, Antwerp #2

VENNEMAN, Rosa (19th C) Belgian
£293 $525 €440 Landscape with cow (36x27cm-14x11in) s.d. s.i.verso. 15-May-4 De Vuyst, Lokeren #381
£570 $1021 €850 Vaches au repos (58x82cm-23x32in) s.d.1861. 25-May-4 Campo & Campo, Antwerp #327

VENTADOUR, Jean Nicolas (attrib) (1822-?) French
£368 $600 €537 Courting couple in 18th century dress (28x23cm-11x9in) bears sig.d.1854. 24-Sep-3 Doyle, New York #100

VENTH, Alois (1809-1868) German
£667 $1207 €1000 Portrait of a daughter of the Heinen family - Aachen (71x60cm-28x24in) s.d.1843. 1-Apr-4 Van Ham, Cologne #1684
£933 $1689 €1400 Portrait of the son of the Heinen family - Aachen (71x61cm-28x24in) s.d.1843. 1-Apr-4 Van Ham, Cologne #1682
£1067 $1931 €1600 Portrait of the oldest daughter of the Heinen family - Aachen (71x60cm-28x24in) s.d.1843. 1-Apr-4 Van Ham, Cologne #1683/R est:2000
£1267 $2293 €1900 Portrait of the youngest daughter of the Heinen family - Aachen (71x61cm-28x24in) s.d.1843. 1-Apr-4 Van Ham, Cologne #1685 est:2000

VENTNOR, Arthur (fl.1896-1926) British
£1200 $2148 €1752 Norwich Catheral (91x71cm-36x28in) 22-Mar-4 Bonhams & Brooks, Norfolk #227/R est:400-600

VENTO, Jose (1925-) Spanish
£690 $1152 €1000 Coffee pot (54x65cm-21x26in) s. 17-Nov-3 Durán, Madrid #232/R
£1319 $2151 €1900 Maternity (100x81cm-39x32in) s. 23-Sep-3 Durán, Madrid #219/R est:1600
£1338 $2342 €1900 Seated woman (100x65cm-39x26in) s. s.i.verso. 16-Dec-3 Durán, Madrid #202/R est:1700
£1897 $3167 €2750 Head of toreador (40x33cm-16x13in) s. s.i.verso. 17-Nov-3 Durán, Madrid #233/R est:1400
£2083 $3396 €3000 Nude (81x100cm-32x39in) s. 23-Sep-3 Durán, Madrid #218/R est:1600
Works on paper
£396 $737 €590 Still life (33x47cm-13x19in) s. gouache. 2-Mar-4 Ansorena, Madrid #818/R

VENTO, Vicente (20th C) Argentinian
£769 $1400 €1123 Carts (35x46cm-14x18in) s. cardboard. 5-Jul-4 Arroyo, Buenos Aires #65/R

VENTOSA, Josep (1897-1982) Spanish
£3356 $6275 €5000 Harvest (46x56cm-18x22in) s.d.57 s.i.verso. 24-Feb-4 Durán, Madrid #690/R est:800

VENTRILLON, Charles (20th C) ?
Works on paper
£253 $405 €369 Landscape (44x59cm-17x23in) W/C cardboard. 21-Sep-3 Subastas Odalys, Caracas #33
£259 $440 €378 Landscape in a village (43x58cm-17x23in) s. mixed media cardboard. 23-Nov-3 Subastas Odalys, Caracas #87

VENTRILLON, Gaston (1897-1982) French
£6338 $10965 €9000 Kasbah d'Asni (81x116cm-32x46in) s.i.d.1930. 15-Dec-3 Gros & Delettrez, Paris #54/R est:8000-10000

VENTURA DI MORO (15th C) Italian
£17000 $29410 €24820 Madonna and Child (139x65cm-55x26in) i. gold ground panel pointed top. 10-Dec-3 Christie's, London #80/R est:15000-20000

VENTURA MILLAN, Manuel (1923-1984) Spanish
£1510 $2824 €2250 Still life with garlic and sweetcorn (73x100cm-29x39in) s. 24-Feb-4 Durán, Madrid #187/R est:1500

VENTURI, L (19th C) Italian
£993 $1856 €1450 View from Venice (40x70cm-16x28in) s. 25-Feb-4 Kunsthallen, Copenhagen #499 (D.KR 11000)

VENTURI, Roberto (1846-1883) Italian
£6475 $10619 €9000 Good news (64x52cm-25x20in) s. 10-Jun-3 Pandolfini, Florence #98/R est:6000-8000

VENUS, Albert Franz (1842-1871) German
Works on paper
£538 $915 €770 Italian landscape (37x52cm-15x20in) s.d.66 i.d.verso W/C. 28-Nov-3 Wendl, Rudolstadt #4323/R

VENUS, August Leopold (1843-1886) German
Works on paper
£1049 $1752 €1500 Shepherd on donkey with flock outside farmstead (17x22cm-7x9in) s.i.d.1869 d. 16.August pencil. 10-Oct-3 Winterberg, Heidelberg #803/R est:1200
£6114 $11127 €8926 Hunters sitting up high in the forest (39x30cm-15x12in) s. pen bistre blue brush brown overworked exhib. 17-Jun-4 Kornfeld, Bern #78/R est:7500 (S.FR 14000)

VENUS, Franz Albert (1842-1871) German
Works on paper
£3319 $6040 €4846 Egaria Grove near Rome (30x48cm-12x19in) W/C over pen bistre dr over pencil prov.exhib. 17-Jun-4 Kornfeld, Bern #79/R est:5000 (S.FR 7600)

VENUSTI, Marcello (attrib) (c.1515-1579) Italian
£10000 $18000 €14600 Holy Family with Saint John the Baptist (58x43cm-23x17in) panel. 22-Apr-4 Sotheby's, London #53/R est:10000-15000
Works on paper
£1189 $2045 €1700 Etude de nu masculin, vu de dos (35x20cm-14x8in) i. sanguine prov. 3-Dec-3 Palais de Beaux Arts, Brussels #1285/R est:1000-1500

VERA SALES, Enrique (1886-1956) Spanish
£2200 $4048 €3212 Puente de San Martin, Toledo (68x59cm-27x23in) s.i.d.1930 i.verso board. 25-Mar-4 Christie's, Kensington #148/R est:2500-3500

£2394 $4142 €3400 Toledo street (50x30cm-20x12in) s. 15-Dec-3 Ansorena, Madrid #300/R est:2300

VERA, Cristino de (1931-) Spanish

£4189 $7373 €6200 Landscape in the Canaries (46x56cm-18x22in) s.i.d.1978 s.d.verso. 18-May-4 Segre, Madrid #296/R est:3000
£6250 $9938 €9000 Still life (29x38cm-11x15in) s.d.78. 29-Apr-3 Durán, Madrid #155/R est:9000
£7801 $12638 €11000 Calavera con cruz (100x70cm-39x28in) s.d.71. 20-May-3 Ansorena, Madrid #320/R est:7500
£8276 $13738 €12000 Still life (68x90cm-27x35in) s. 1-Oct-3 Ansorena, Madrid #574/R est:9000
£8511 $14213 €12000 Table and skull (100x75cm-39x30in) s.d.73 lit. 20-Oct-3 Durán, Madrid #232/R

VERAG, Lucienne (1914-1994) Belgian

£800 $1432 €1200 La voleuse (70x80cm-28x31in) s. 15-May-4 De Vuyst, Lokeren #382/R

VERAME, Jean (1939-) Belgian

Sculpture
£3986 $6657 €5700 Tibesti (200x197x50cm-79x78x20in) caisson lumineux bronze paint. 11-Oct-3 Cornette de St.Cyr, Paris #144/R est:6000-8000

VERBANCK, Geo (1881-1961) Belgian

Sculpture
£3467 $6205 €5200 Joy (52x36cm-20x14in) s. oak. 15-May-4 De Vuyst, Lokeren #383/R est:3300-3800

VERBECK, William Francis (1858-1933) American

Works on paper
£382 $650 €558 Tanky, an illustration from the little cat who journeyed to St. Ives (21x18cm-8x7in) s. graphite wash. 21-Nov-3 Skinner, Boston #94/R
£382 $650 €558 Tanky and the owl (24x20cm-9x8in) s. graphite wash. 21-Nov-3 Skinner, Boston #99
£382 $650 €558 On the boat (21x17cm-8x7in) s, graphite wash. 21-Nov-3 Skinner, Boston #100/R
£471 $800 €688 St. Ives, where numerous cats abide, and where Tank Tunk found a happy home (22x36cm-9x14in) s.i. mixed media collage. 21-Nov-3 Skinner, Boston #93/R

VERBEECK, Cornelis (1590-c.1635) Dutch

£10000 $18000 €14600 Dutch frigate in choppy waters and a man fishing on the shore (20x38cm-8x15in) init. panel prov. 21-Apr-4 Christie's, London #37/R est:6000-8000
£20000 $36600 €29200 Dutch shipping off rocky coast (15x29cm-6x11in) mono. panel prov. 8-Jul-4 Sotheby's, London #122/R est:20000-30000

VERBEECK, François Xavier Henri (1686-1755) Flemish

£1181 $1865 €1700 Elegant company making music in an interior (27x34cm-11x13in) panel. 2-Sep-3 Christie's, Amsterdam #90/R est:2500-3500

VERBEECK, Frans and Jan (attrib) (16/17th C) Flemish

£44295 $81946 €66000 La tentation de Saint Antoine (76x107cm-30x42in) panel on canvas. 15-Mar-4 Horta, Bruxelles #90/R est:75000-85000

VERBEECK, Henri Daniel (1817-1863) Flemish

£1958 $3329 €2800 Promeneurs dans un paysage (50x66cm-20x26in) panel. 1-Dec-3 Amberes, Antwerp #366

VERBEET, Gijsbertha (1838-1916) Dutch

£1467 $2625 €2200 Still life of various fruit (36x28cm-14x11in) s.d.1862 panel. 11-May-4 Vendu Notarishuis, Rotterdam #155/R est:1500-2000

VERBEKE, Pierre (1895-1962) Belgian

£302 $556 €450 Les reparateurs de toiles (70x70cm-28x28in) s. 23-Mar-4 Galerie Moderne, Brussels #314/R

VERBOECKHOVEN, Eugène (1798-1881) Belgian

£500 $895 €750 Chevre (21x22cm-8x9in) bears sig. oil paper on panel. 11-May-4 Vanderkindere, Brussels #138/R
£647 $1100 €945 Sheep and goat in a landscape (20x30cm-8x12in) s. panel. 31-Oct-3 North East Auctions, Portsmouth #1205
£829 $1500 €1210 Goats, lambs and chicken in landscape (36x25cm-14x10in) s. board. 2-Apr-4 Eldred, East Dennis #922/R est:2000-3000
£1173 $1900 €1713 Farmyard scene with sheep and chickens (41x53cm-16x21in) s. panel. 7-Aug-3 Eldred, East Dennis #141/R est:1000-2000
£1982 $3370 €2894 Cows and sheep in the country (71x91cm-28x36in) s.d.1855. 5-Nov-3 Dobiaschofsky, Bern #1023/R est:7000 (S.FR 4500)
£2013 $3705 €3000 Etude de moutons (23x27cm-9x11in) s.d.1853. 24-Mar-4 Claude Boisgirard, Paris #48/R est:3000-4000
£2186 $4000 €3192 Pastoral landscape with sheep grazing (36x46cm-14x18in) s.d.1861 panel. 5-Jun-4 Neal Auction Company, New Orleans #204/R est:8000-12000
£2400 $4392 €3600 Idyllic scene of shepherdesses and herd near edge of town (38x51cm-15x20in) s. 5-Jun-4 Arnold, Frankfurt #782/R est:4000
£2533 $4560 €3800 Sheep in a meadow (14x19cm-6x7in) s.d.1873 panel. 21-Apr-4 Christie's, Amsterdam #190/R est:3000-5000
£2708 $4469 €3900 Three sheep and hen in landscape (14x21cm-6x8in) s.d.1876 panel. 2-Jul-3 Neumeister, Munich #807/R est:3300
£2797 $4811 €4000 In the stable (17x18cm-7x7in) s.d.1875. 6-Dec-3 Quittenbaum, Hamburg #66/R est:4700
£3077 $5138 €4400 Sheep and a chicken in a landscape (20x22cm-8x9in) s.d.1874 panel. 11-Oct-3 De Vuyst, Lokeren #381/R est:4000-5000
£3819 $6302 €5500 Chickens, goat, lamb and sheep in hilly landscape (18x24cm-7x9in) s.d.1863 panel. 2-Jul-3 Neumeister, Munich #806/R est:3500
£4000 $7200 €6000 Awaiting their turn (20x25cm-8x10in) s.d.1849 panel. 21-Apr-4 Christie's, Amsterdam #203/R est:5000-7000
£4070 $7000 €5942 Sheeps and rabbit in stable (43x51cm-17x20in) s.d.1880. 2-Dec-3 Christie's, Rockefeller NY #44/R est:8000-12000
£5153 $8400 €7523 Moutons et poules dans un paysage (20x31cm-8x12in) s.d.1863. 17-Jul-3 Naón & Cia, Buenos Aires #71/R
£5333 $9653 €8000 Cattle in meadow (47x65cm-19x26in) s. panel. 1-Apr-4 Van Ham, Cologne #1688/R est:13000
£6993 $11888 €10000 Cattle in summer meadow (65x88cm-26x35in) s.d.1844. 20-Nov-3 Van Ham, Cologne #1897/R est:10000
£8333 $14167 €12000 La vache rouge et blanche se frottant la tete contre un morceau de bois (65x54cm-26x21in) s.d.1850 panel. 28-Oct-3 Christie's, Amsterdam #72/R est:15000-20000
£8667 $15860 €13000 Ane et chien au repos dans un paysage (60x56cm-24x22in) s.d.1852 panel. 7-Jun-4 Palais de Beaux Arts, Brussels #319/R est:12000-16000
£10500 $17535 €15330 Landscape with sheep by stall (75x98cm-30x39in) s.d.1854. 22-Jun-3 Wilkinson, Doncaster #274/R
£12000 $22200 €17520 Farm animals in pasture (49x63cm-19x25in) bears sig.d.1880 canvas on panel. 14-Jan-4 Lawrence, Crewkerne #1401/R est:12000-18000
£14000 $25760 €20440 Goats and a sheep beside a barn (20x31cm-8x12in) s.d.1863 i.verso panel. 23-Mar-4 Bonhams, New Bond Street #7/R est:15000-22000
£14118 $24000 €20612 Sheep and goats in a landscape (28x39cm-11x15in) s.d.1853 panel. 28-Oct-3 Sotheby's, New York #81/R est:15000-20000
£26667 $48000 €40000 At the gate (73x101cm-29x40in) s.d.1872 prov. 21-Apr-4 Christie's, Amsterdam #196/R est:40000-60000
£32000 $54400 €46720 Sheep in a stable interior (68x101cm-27x40in) s.d.1867 s.i.d.verso panel. 19-Nov-3 Bonhams, New Bond Street #7/R est:30000-50000
£32000 $57920 €48000 Herder driving cattle along alpine path (145x231cm-57x91in) s.d.1860 lit.prov. 1-Apr-4 Van Ham, Cologne #1686/R est:53000
Works on paper
£336 $614 €500 Vaches a l'abreuvoir. mono.d.1845 dr. 8-Jul-4 Campo, Vlaamse Kaai #284
£500 $860 €730 Cow grazing in open landscape (18x23cm-7x9in) s. pencil. 5-Dec-3 Keys, Aylsham #446/R
£1103 $2041 €1600 Head of a donkey (19x14cm-7x6in) s.d.66 mixed media oval. 19-Jan-4 Horta, Bruxelles #22 est:1000-1200

VERBOECKHOVEN, Eugène (attrib) (1798-1881) Belgian

£900 $1701 €1314 Sheep recumbent on a grassy bank (12x15cm-5x6in) indis.sig. panel. 18-Feb-4 Peter Wilson, Nantwich #42
£972 $1546 €1400 Cows in the meadow (70x58cm-28x23in) 15-Sep-3 Bernaerts, Antwerp #224/R
£1478 $2646 €2158 Pastoral landscape with cattle (58x82cm-23x32in) s.d.1856 canvas on panel. 25-May-4 Bukowskis, Stockholm #341/R est:20000-25000 (S.KR 20000)
£1831 $3204 €2600 Belier et agneau derriere cloture (50x61cm-20x24in) panel. 17-Dec-3 Piasa, Paris #38 est:2000-3000
£2603 $4425 €3800 Portrait of a Moor with turban (72x53cm-28x21in) 5-Nov-3 Vendue Huis, Gravenhage #75/R est:3000-4000

VERBOECKHOVEN, Eugène and VERWEE, Louis (19th C) Belgian

£2500 $3925 €3625 On the road to market (35x44cm-14x17in) s. panel. 28-Aug-3 Christie's, Kensington #88/R est:3000-5000

VERBOECKHOVEN, Eugène and VIGNE, Edouard de (19th C) Belgian

£6333 $11590 €9500 Paysage italien avec patres et troupeau (92x125cm-36x49in) 6-Jun-4 Osenat, Fontainebleau #58/R est:8000-10000

VERBOECKHOVEN, L (1802-1889) Belgian

£4362 $8114 €6500 Storm (20x27cm-8x11in) s. panel. 4-Mar-4 Auction Maastricht #1109/R est:6500-8000

VERBOECKHOVEN, Louis (1802-1889) Belgian

£1100 $1969 €1606 Dutch malschip running into the estuary (18x27cm-7x11in) s. board. 26-May-4 Christie's, Kensington #594/R est:800-1200
£1507 $2351 €2200 Seascape with boats and anglers (30x42cm-12x17in) s. board. 8-Apr-3 Il Ponte, Milan #595
£1586 $2649 €2300 Fishing boat off coast (16x22cm-6x9in) s. panel. 15-Nov-3 Lempertz, Koln #1711 est:2000
£1702 $2843 €2400 Retour des pecheurs (20x28cm-8x11in) s. cardboard on panel. 14-Oct-3 Vanderkindere, Brussels #77
£2031 $3250 €2965 Dutch harbour scene. s. board. 20-Sep-3 Harvey Clar, Oakland #1528a
£2222 $3511 €3200 Shipping in open water (16x20cm-6x8in) s. panel. 2-Sep-3 Christie's, Amsterdam #323/R est:1500-2000
£2416 $4446 €3600 Ships entering harbour (20x30cm-8x12in) s. panel. 25-Mar-4 Dr Fritz Nagel, Stuttgart #767/R est:4500
£2500 $4075 €3600 Seascape (18x24cm-7x9in) s. panel pair. 24-Sep-3 Neumeister, Munich #590/R est:4000
£2676 $4630 €3800 Seascape with sailing boats (16x20cm-6x8in) s. panel. 13-Dec-3 De Vuyst, Lokeren #421/R est:4000-5000
£3084 $5242 €4503 Seascape (19x27cm-7x11in) s. panel. 5-Nov-3 Dobiaschofsky, Bern #1024/R est:3600 (S.FR 7000)
£10490 $17832 €15000 Voiliers et pecheurs dans l'embouchure d'une riviere (50x75cm-20x30in) s. 1-Dec-3 Palais de Beaux Arts, Brussels #333/R est:12000-18000
£16107 $29638 €24000 Marine (50x73cm-20x29in) s. 23-Mar-4 Galerie Moderne, Brussels #344/R est:2000-4000

VERBOECKHOVEN, Louis (attrib) (1802-1889) Belgian

£961 $1768 €1403 Coastline with sailing boats and figures (22x28cm-9x11in) panel. 14-Jun-4 Philippe Schuler, Zurich #4334/R est:3500-4000 (S.FR 2200)

VERBOECKHOVEN, Louis II (1827-1884) Belgian

£2933 $5251 €4400 Seascape (16x20cm-6x8in) s. panel. 15-May-4 De Vuyst, Lokeren #531/R est:4400-5000

VERBOOM, Adriaen (1628-1670) Dutch

£6000 $10800 €8760 Wooded landscape with huntsmen on a path (98x138cm-39x54in) with sig.d.1672 prov. 21-Apr-4 Christie's, London #41/R est:6000-8000

VERBRUGGEN, Gaspar Pieter I (1635-1687) Flemish
£4225 $7394 €6000 Flowers in sculpted vase (48x91cm-19x36in) prov. 17-Dec-3 Christie's, Rome #445/R est:6000-8000
£7000 $12810 €10220 Bouquets of mixed flowers decorating a feigned stone cartouche, with butterflies (65x90cm-26x35in) s.d.1668 canvas on panel. 6-Jul-4 Sotheby's, Olympia #555/R est:7000-10000
£31724 $52662 €46000 Garland (127x93cm-50x37in) 30-Sep-3 Ansorena, Madrid #31/R est:46000
£42553 $68936 €60000 Garland of flowers (127x93cm-50x37in) 20-May-3 Ansorena, Madrid #90/R est:60000
£48951 $81748 €70000 Vase of flowers (57x47cm-22x19in) s. 30-Jun-3 Ansorena, Madrid #184/R est:70000

VERBRUGGEN, Gaspar Pieter II (1664-1730) Flemish
£4828 $8014 €7000 Still life of flowers with stone socle and garden vase (41x35cm-16x14in) i. 1-Oct-3 Dorotheum, Vienna #69/R est:7000-10000
£6040 $11114 €9000 Portrait of young woman as flora (51x61cm-20x24in) s. 25-Mar-4 Dr Fritz Nagel, Stuttgart #614/R est:17000
£7240 $12308 €10570 Roses, poppies, tulips and other flowers in glass vase (68x56cm-27x22in) s. 19-Nov-3 Fischer, Luzern #1049/R est:16000-20000 (S.FR 16000)
£8500 $14705 €12410 Lilies, tulips and other flowers in a glass vase with butterfly and beetle on a ledge (66x51cm-26x20in) 10-Dec-3 Bonhams, New Bond Street #86/R est:5000-7000
£8511 $13787 €12000 Young woman with flowers (52x61cm-20x24in) s. lit. 23-May-3 Karlheinz Kaupp, Staufen #1700/R est:12000
£16000 $28640 €24000 Vase of flowers with woman (100x129cm-39x51in) exhib.lit. 17-May-4 Finarte Semenzato, Rome #124/R est:28000-32000

VERBRUGGEN, Gaspar Pieter II (attrib) (1664-1730) Flemish
£1241 $2073 €1800 Nature morte avec sculpture (120x90cm-47x35in) 17-Nov-3 Bernaerts, Antwerp #143/R est:2000-3000
£3020 $5557 €4500 Nature morte au vase de fleurs (78x57cm-31x22in) 24-Mar-4 Tajan, Paris #49/R est:4500-5000
£5245 $9021 €7500 Vases de fleurs sur une tablette en marbre (90x70cm-35x28in) pair. 3-Dec-3 Palais de Beaux Arts, Brussels #1286/R est:7500-10000

VERBRUGGEN, Gaspar Pieter II (school) (1664-1730) Flemish
£16000 $28640 €24000 Still life of flowers and fruit with woman (96x111cm-38x44in) exhib.lit. 17-May-4 Finarte Semenzato, Rome #113/R est:25000-30000

VERBURGH, Dionys (1655-1722) Dutch
£4200 $7266 €6132 Extensive river landscape with figures on a track (47x63cm-19x25in) init. indis d. panel exhib. 10-Dec-3 Bonhams, New Bond Street #4/R est:5000-7000
£9375 $15469 €13500 Extensive landscape with towns on lake (88x125cm-35x49in) mono. panel. 3-Jul-3 Van Ham, Cologne #1028/R est:18000

VERBURGH, Dionys (attrib) (1655-1722) Dutch
£805 $1482 €1200 Man with dog and other figures by wood (17x23cm-7x9in) lit. 25-Mar-4 Karlheinz Kaupp, Staufen #2321/R
£2217 $3969 €3237 Italianate landscape (63x52cm-25x20in) bears mono. panel. 25-May-4 Bukowskis, Stockholm #461/R est:30000-40000 (S.KR 30000)

VERBURGH, Medard (1886-1957) Belgian
£1818 $3127 €2600 Bouquet fleuri (60x50cm-24x20in) s. 8-Dec-3 Horta, Bruxelles #133 est:2500-3500

VERBURGH, Rutger (1678-1746) Dutch
£7383 $13584 €11000 Peasants celebrating in village square (67x80cm-26x31in) s. 24-Mar-4 Dorotheum, Vienna #191/R est:9000-14000

VERBURGH, Rutger (attrib) (1678-1746) Dutch
£3474 $6218 €5072 Dutch town gate with figures (64x78cm-25x31in) 26-May-4 AB Stockholms Auktionsverk #2532/R est:30000-40000 (S.KR 47000)

VERBURGH, Rutger (circle) (1678-1746) Dutch
£6294 $10510 €9000 Rural fair (47x64cm-19x25in) lit. 7-Oct-3 Pandolfini, Florence #563/R est:7000-8000

VERBUYS, Arnold (c.1645-1729) Dutch
£1440 $2491 €2102 Portrait of a lady and a gentleman with a Negro servant beyond (36x29cm-14x11in) s. panel. 9-Dec-3 Sotheby's, Olympia #410/R est:1000-1500

VERCELLI, Giulio Romano (1871-1951) Italian
£500 $920 €750 Farm (25x36cm-10x14in) s. board painted 1927. 14-Jun-4 Sant Agostino, Torino #126/R
£500 $920 €750 Figures in the courtyard (25x36cm-10x14in) s. i.d.1927 verso board. 14-Jun-4 Sant Agostino, Torino #153/R
£559 $934 €800 Market (20x15cm-8x6in) s. cardboard prov. 26-Jun-3 Sant Agostino, Torino #111/R
£667 $1227 €1000 Cottages in the mountains (39x49cm-15x19in) s. s.i.d.1928 cardboard. 14-Jun-4 Sant Agostino, Torino #217/R
£872 $1544 €1300 Garden with figures (55x63cm-22x25in) s. cardboard. 1-May-4 Meeting Art, Vercelli #28
£909 $1518 €1300 Still life of fruit and flowers (53x63cm-21x25in) s. canvas on cardboard. 26-Jun-3 Sant Agostino, Torino #76/R

VERCRUYCE, Bernard (1949-) French
£1087 $1783 €1500 The tree of Noa (92x93cm-36x37in) 28-May-3 Coutau Begarie, Paris #159/R est:1800-2000

VERDAGUER, Josep (1923-) Spanish
£376 $650 €549 Sailing (61x74cm-24x29in) s. 13-Dec-3 Charlton Hall, Columbia #279/R

VERDASCO, Eduardo (1949-) Venezuelan
£800 $1448 €1200 Allegory of Religion (122x75cm-48x30in) s.d.1986 verso board prov. 30-Mar-4 Segre, Madrid #239/R

VERDE RUBIO, Ricardo (1876-1955) Spanish
£503 $941 €750 Landscape with peasant woman (37x62cm-15x24in) s. double-sided. 24-Feb-4 Durán, Madrid #684/R

VERDE, R (?) Spanish?
£1379 $2483 €2000 Courtyard (37x42cm-15x17in) s. board. 26-Jan-4 Durán, Madrid #701/R est:2000

VERDE, Vincent (20th C) Danish?
£364 $589 €528 Bull eyes (45x50cm-18x20in) s. i.verso. 4-Aug-3 Rasmussen, Vejle #677/R (D.KR 3800)

VERDEGEM, Jos (1897-1957) Belgian
£769 $1285 €1100 La femme a l'echarpe rouge (40x30cm-16x12in) s.d.1940-48 exhib. 11-Oct-3 De Vuyst, Lokeren #386
Works on paper
£528 $914 €750 Woman kneeling (34x26cm-13x10in) s. gouache. 13-Dec-3 De Vuyst, Lokeren #380
£733 $1313 €1100 Woman sitting. Woman weeping (26x35cm-10x14in) s.d.1947 W/C col chk two. 15-May-4 De Vuyst, Lokeren #387
£1141 $2111 €1700 Woman on a rug (48x35cm-19x14in) s. pastel exhib. 13-Mar-4 De Vuyst, Lokeren #376/R est:1500-2000
£2333 $4177 €3500 Geste (77x62cm-30x24in) s.i.d.1952 W/C exhib. W/C ink pastel exhib. 15-May-4 De Vuyst, Lokeren #578/R est:3500-4500
£2517 $4280 €3600 Vrouw in rieten zetel (89x63cm-35x25in) mixed media exhib. 1-Dec-3 Palais de Beaux Arts, Brussels #330/R est:1000-1200

VERDICKT, Gisleen (1883-1926) Belgian
£455 $759 €650 Paysage de campagne (95x85cm-37x33in) s. 7-Oct-3 Palais de Beaux Arts, Brussels #598

VERDIER, François (1651-1730) French
Works on paper
£328 $600 €479 Biblical scene with a ruler directing architects and builders (16x29cm-6x11in) brush gray wash black chk. 29-Jan-4 Swann Galleries, New York #209/R
£343 $583 €500 Jesus guerissant les paralytiques (26x43cm-10x17in) crayon chk. 6-Nov-3 Tajan, Paris #30

VERDIER, François (attrib) (1651-1730) French
Works on paper
£268 $502 €400 Untitled (30x17cm-12x7in) sanguine. 29-Feb-4 Osenat, Fontainebleau #230
£426 $711 €600 Mere et son enfant (25x17cm-10x7in) sanguine. 23-Jun-3 Ribeyre & Baron, Paris #4

VERDIER, Jean Louis (1849-1895) French
£2621 $4377 €3800 Le repas du chien (92x65cm-36x26in) s. 17-Nov-3 Tajan, Paris #109/R est:3000-4000

VERDIER, Jules Victor (1862-?) French
£2688 $5000 €3924 Odalisque (38x76cm-15x30in) s. 7-Mar-4 Treadway Gallery, Cincinnati #526/R est:4000-6000

VERDIER, Maurice (1919-) French
£417 $696 €600 Venise (38x46cm-15x18in) s. s.i.verso. 25-Oct-3 Cornette de St.Cyr, Paris #550
£423 $731 €600 Bouquet devant la fenetre (73x60cm-29x24in) s. 10-Dec-3 Rossini, Paris #115
£458 $792 €650 Vignes (33x41cm-13x16in) s. 10-Dec-3 Rossini, Paris #116

VERDIERE, Francois de (20th C) French
£1208 $2138 €1800 Bretagne bleue (100x81cm-39x32in) s. 29-Apr-4 Claude Aguttes, Neuilly #80 est:1600-1800

VERDILHAN, Andre (20th C) French
£313 $494 €450 Le pont des Arts a Paris s. 25-Apr-3 Etude de Provence, Marseille #318

VERDILHAN, Mathieu (1875-1928) French
£6711 $12483 €10000 Bateaux a quai (61x73cm-24x29in) s. 2-Mar-4 Artcurial Briest, Paris #140/R est:10000-12000
£17014 $28413 €24500 Troupeau a travers un hameau en Provence (60x81cm-24x32in) s. 25-Oct-3 Dianous, Marseille #430
Works on paper
£530 $964 €800 Peniche sur la Seine a Paris (22x27cm-9x11in) s. W/C gouache. 15-Jun-4 Blanchet, Paris #202/R
£1034 $1717 €1500 Buffet (15x20cm-6x8in) mono. pastel. 1-Oct-3 Millon & Associes, Paris #20

VERDUN, Raymond (1873-1954) French
£224 $375 €327 Paysage avec maison au Toit rouge (15x23cm-6x9in) s. board. 14-Nov-3 Aspire, Cleveland #45
£580 $951 €800 Vue sur le lac au sortir de la foret (39x56cm-15x22in) s.d.1911. 11-May-3 Osenat, Fontainebleau #217

£933 $1689 €1400 Rivage rocheux (73x100cm-29x39in) lit. 30-Mar-4 Rossini, Paris #1068/R
£1163 $2000 €1698 Coastal landscape (38x53cm-15x21in) s. 6-Dec-3 Pook & Pook, Downington #299 est:900-1200

VERDURA, Fulco (1898-1978) Italian
Works on paper
£2000 $3400 €2920 Etna (7x15cm-3x6in) s. pencil W/C bodycol prov. 6-Nov-3 Christie's, Kensington #1005/R est:400-600

VERDUSSEN, J P (1700-1763) Flemish
£3077 $5292 €4492 Landscape with palace, shepherd and riders (80x126cm-31x50in) s.d.46. 7-Dec-3 Uppsala Auktionskammare, Uppsala #38/R est:50000-60000 (S.KR 40000)

VERDUSSEN, Jan Peeter (1700-1763) Flemish
£10000 $18300 €14600 Winter landscape with numerous figures skating near a village (36x55cm-14x22in) s. indis d. 6-Jul-4 Sotheby's, Olympia #545/R est:6000-8000

VERDUSSEN, Jan Peeter (circle) (1700-1763) Flemish
£6000 $10800 €8760 Battle scene with village being sacked (43x57cm-17x22in) copper. 22-Apr-4 Sotheby's, London #96/R est:6000-8000

VERDYEN, Eugène (1836-1903) Belgian
£420 $701 €600 View of the beach (37x23cm-15x9in) s. paper on panel. 11-Oct-3 De Vuyst, Lokeren #387
Works on paper
£490 $832 €700 La lavandiere (53x38cm-21x15in) s. W/C. 1-Dec-3 Palais de Beaux Arts, Brussels #149/R
£2621 $4848 €3800 Jeune femme se preparant pour le bal masque (51x30cm-20x12in) s. mixed media. 16-Feb-4 Horta, Bruxelles #156 est:2000-3000

VERDYK, Gerard (1934-) Dutch
£909 $1564 €1300 Composition (100x140cm-39x55in) s.i. verso. 8-Dec-3 Glerum, Amsterdam #175/R
£1049 $1804 €1500 Composition (100x150cm-39x59in) s.d.62 verso. 8-Dec-3 Glerum, Amsterdam #179/R est:700-900

VEREECKE, Armand (1912-1990) Belgian
£336 $561 €480 L'interieur de l'artiste (50x66cm-20x26in) s. 13-Oct-3 Horta, Bruxelles #499
£336 $594 €500 Futuristic mirror image (80x100cm-31x39in) s. 27-Apr-4 Campo & Campo, Antwerp #266

VERELST, John (fl.1698-1734) Flemish
£5500 $9185 €8030 Portrait of a lady, in a pink bodice holding a sprig of orange blossom (28x101cm-11x40in) s.d.1713. 13-Nov-3 Christie's, Kensington #34/R est:5000-7000

VERELST, Pieter (c.1618-1668) Dutch
£900 $1665 €1314 Peasant seated in an interior at a table with a jug and a pipe (38x32cm-15x13in) 10-Feb-4 Bonhams, Knightsbridge #244/R

VERELST, Simon (1644-1721) Dutch
£3000 $5490 €4380 Still life of flowers (77x64cm-30x25in) prov. 9-Jul-4 Christie's, Kensington #63/R est:4000-6000
£9000 $16200 €13140 Roses, parrot, and other flowers in an urn with butterflies and a snail (74x62cm-29x24in) 23-Apr-4 Christie's, Kensington #112/R est:6000-8000
£15278 $27500 €22306 Still life of Irises, poppies, roses and other flowers in a vase on stone ledge (76x63cm-30x25in) s. prov. 22-Jan-4 Sotheby's, New York #139/R est:10000-15000
£27933 $50000 €40782 Portrait of Mary of Modena (128x102cm-50x40in) 27-May-4 Sotheby's, New York #220/R est:50000-70000
£28462 $48954 €41555 Still life of flowers in vase (76x60cm-30x24in) s. 2-Dec-3 Bukowskis, Stockholm #399/R est:300000-350000 (S.KR 370000)
£30172 $55517 €44051 Flowers (71x61cm-28x24in) prov.lit. 26-Mar-4 Koller, Zurich #3024/R est:70000-100000 (S.FR 70000)

VERELST, Simon (attrib) (1644-1721) Dutch
£3600 $6480 €5256 Still life with carnation, roses and other flowers in a vase (46x36cm-18x14in) bears sig. 20-Apr-4 Sotheby's, Olympia #297/R est:4000-6000

VERELST, Willem (?-c.1756) British
£5000 $8500 €7300 Portrait of a royal child, probably Princess Caroline Matilda (126x102cm-50x40in) s. indis d.1753 prov. 25-Nov-3 Christie's, London #25/R est:8000-12000

VERENDAEL, Nicolas van (1640-1691) Flemish
£30000 $51900 €43800 Garland of roses, peony and other flowers with a bumble bee and a butterfly (46x68cm-18x27in) prov.exhib. 10-Dec-3 Christie's, London #42/R est:25000-35000
£31469 $52552 €45000 Flowers (67x45cm-26x18in) board prov. 30-Jun-3 Ansorena, Madrid #183/R est:45000

VERENDAEL, Nicolas van (attrib) (1640-1691) Flemish
£6164 $10479 €9000 Tulips, roses and other flowers in a glass vase on a wooden ledge (46x36cm-18x14in) indis sig. prov.lit. 5-Nov-3 Christie's, Amsterdam #11/R est:10000-15000

VERENDAEL, Nicolas van (circle) (1640-1691) Flemish
£15000 $27450 €21900 Parrot tulips, roses and other flowers in a sculpted urn on a stone ledge (67x56cm-26x22in) 7-Jul-4 Christie's, London #39/R est:15000-25000

VERETSHCHAGIN, Piotr (1836-1886) Russian
£391892 $701487 €580000 View of the Kremlin in Moscow (54x90cm-21x35in) s.i. 8-May-4 Bukowskis, Helsinki #471/R est:50000-80000

VERETSHCHAGIN, Vassily Petrovich (attrib) (1835-1909) Russian
£107955 $190000 €157614 View of the Kremlin from the right bank of the Moscow River (41x76cm-16x30in) 18-May-4 Bonhams & Butterfields, San Francisco #87/R est:20000-30000

VERETSHCHAGIN, Vassily Vasilievich (1842-1904) Russian
£10500 $18795 €15330 Trophy of arms (132x118cm-52x46in) bears sig.d.1904. 26-May-4 Sotheby's, Olympia #384/R est:600-800
£85000 $144500 €127500 Winter view of the Kremlin (46x32cm-18x13in) s. s.i.d.1903 verso. 25-Nov-3 Christie's, London #134/R est:7000-8000
£216667 $390000 €316334 Cossack picket on the Danube (99x135cm-39x53in) s.d.1886 prov. 23-Apr-4 Sotheby's, New York #9/R est:400000-600000
Works on paper
£1330 $2381 €1942 Pastoral scene with bedouins (13x22cm-5x9in) s. sepia pencil. 26-May-4 AB Stockholms Auktionsverk #2468/R est:6000-8000 (S.KR 18000)
£1478 $2646 €2158 Priest and monk singing (21x25cm-8x10in) s. W/C. 26-May-4 AB Stockholms Auktionsverk #2469/R est:10000-15000 (S.KR 20000)
£2448 $4210 €3500 Rich Sultana in her living room with her son and servants (18x26cm-7x10in) i. W/C. 3-Dec-3 Neumeister, Munich #439/R est:2000

VERETSHCHAGIN, Vassily Vasilievich (attrib) (1842-1904) Russian
£2941 $5500 €4294 Sunrise, India (36x20cm-14x8in) panel on panel prov. 25-Feb-4 Doyle, New York #74/R est:800-1200

VERGA, Angelo (1933-) Italian
£333 $613 €500 Green sundial (70x80cm-28x31in) s.i.d.1976 verso. 12-Jun-4 Meeting Art, Vercelli #77

VERGARA, Carlos (1941-) Brazilian
£7326 $13407 €10989 Untitled (140x140cm-55x55in) s.d.1983 verso. 6-Jul-4 Bolsa de Arte, Rio de Janeiro #165/R (B.R 40000)

VERGE-SARRAT, Henri (1880-1966) French
Works on paper
£280 $476 €400 Le port, Collioure (24x32cm-9x13in) s.d.32 W/C. 1-Dec-3 Palais de Beaux Arts, Brussels #362

VERGEER, Jo (?) ?
£240 $400 €350 Still life of carnation and conk shell. s. 15-Nov-3 Harvey Clar, Oakland #1150

VERGES, Martin (1975-) Uruguayan
Works on paper
£259 $420 €376 Sketch for Vox Poupuli (50x70cm-20x28in) s.d.99 pastel. 29-Jul-3 Galeria y Remates, Montevideo #64/R

VERGNOLET, Tony (19th C) French
Works on paper
£2000 $3440 €2920 Design for an Algerian salon (16x87cm-6x34in) s.i. pencil W/C bodycol sold with 2 others by the same hand prov. 3-Dec-3 Christie's, Kensington #68/R est:800-1200

VERHAECHT, Tobias (attrib) (1561-1631) Flemish
Works on paper
£520 $952 €759 Fortified Harbour, a man driving a donkey in the foreground (22x33cm-9x13in) brown ink. 7-Apr-4 Woolley & Wallis, Salisbury #170/R
£946 $1665 €1400 Landscape with a bridge and building behind (16x22cm-6x9in) pen brown ink black ink prov.lit. 19-May-4 Sotheby's, Amsterdam #20/R
£1078 $1983 €1574 St Anthony in rocky landscape (20x26cm-8x10in) i. verso Indian ink. 26-Mar-4 Koller, Zurich #3074/R est:2500-3500 (S.FR 2500)

VERHAEGEN, Fernand (1884-1976) Belgian
£1189 $2021 €1700 Vue de village (33x41cm-13x16in) s. 18-Nov-3 Vanderkindere, Brussels #219 est:800-1000
£1310 $2424 €1900 Remorqueur sur la Seine devant Notre Dame (56x45cm-22x18in) s.d.1917. 19-Jan-4 Horta, Bruxelles #188/R est:2500-3500
£1379 $2552 €2000 Quai de Seine (55x45cm-22x18in) s.d.1917. 19-Jan-4 Horta, Bruxelles #189/R est:2500-3500
£2192 $3726 €3200 Marche de Sainte Rolende (60x70cm-24x28in) double-sided. 10-Nov-3 Horta, Bruxelles #43
£2797 $4671 €4000 Jardin sous la neige (60x50cm-24x20in) s. 13-Oct-3 Horta, Bruxelles #130/R est:4000-6000
£2933 $5397 €4400 Le grand rondo des Gilles de Binche (60x50cm-24x20in) s. painted c.1965. 14-Jun-4 Horta, Bruxelles #146/R est:4000-5000
£4828 $8931 €7000 Gilles (70x65cm-28x26in) s. 19-Jan-4 Horta, Bruxelles #187/R est:8000-10000
£4895 $8322 €7000 Doudou de Mons (78x124cm-31x49in) s. exhib. 18-Nov-3 Vanderkindere, Brussels #155/R est:7000-10000
£6333 $11590 €9500 La Pasqueye (106x86cm-42x34in) s. prov. 7-Jun-4 Palais de Beaux Arts, Brussels #115/R est:10000-15000

VERHAEREN, Alfred (1849-1924) Belgian
£598 $1100 €873 Impression of Japan (53x74cm-21x29in) s. panel. 25-Mar-4 Doyle, New York #71/R est:2000-3000

VERHAERT, Dirck (17th C) Dutch
£2200 $3960 €3212 Extensive river landscape with figures resting before ruins (24x32cm-9x13in) bears sig panel. 20-Apr-4 Sotheby's, Olympia #280/R est:1500-2000
£6897 $11448 €10000 Mountainous river landscape with tower and figures (33x42cm-13x17in) mono. panel prov. 1-Oct-3 Dorotheum, Vienna #186/R est:10000-14000

£60000 $109800 €87600 Rome, prospect of the Colosseum (196x277cm-77x109in) prov. 8-Jul-4 Sotheby's, London #178/R est:60000-80000

VERHAERT, Piet (1852-1908) Flemish
£455 $782 €650 Fermiere au travail dans un interieur (45x73cm-18x29in) s. 2-Dec-3 Campo & Campo, Antwerp #398
£490 $832 €700 Cuisine animee (28x32cm-11x13in) s.d.06 canvas on panel. 18-Nov-3 Vanderkindere, Brussels #223
£979 $1684 €1400 L'archiviste (28x25cm-11x10in) s.d.1888 panel. 2-Dec-3 Campo & Campo, Antwerp #399/R est:1500-2000

VERHAGEN, Pierre Jean Joseph (attrib) (1728-1811) Flemish
£1028 $1717 €1450 Moise sauve des eaux (79x63cm-31x25in) 14-Oct-3 Vanderkindere, Brussels #122

VERHAS, Frans (c.1827-1897) Belgian
£2113 $3655 €3000 Captain of the citizen guard in gala uniform (100x75cm-39x30in) s.d.1846 exhib.lit. 13-Dec-3 De Vuyst, Lokeren #382/R est:2500-3000
£13889 $25000 €20278 Tempting fruit (76x60cm-30x24in) s. panel. 23-Apr-4 Sotheby's, New York #112/R est:25000-35000
£34965 $58392 €50000 Elegant lady in front of a mirror (68x48cm-27x19in) s. panel. 11-Oct-3 De Vuyst, Lokeren #411/R

VERHAS, Jan Frans (1834-1896) Belgian
£769 $1285 €1100 Vue a Heist (27x36cm-11x14in) s. panel. 13-Oct-3 Horta, Bruxelles #196
£2535 $4386 €3600 Fillette aux fleurs (28x18cm-11x7in) s. panel. 10-Dec-3 Hotel des Ventes Mosan, Brussels #154/R est:1500-2000
£15436 $28557 €23000 Fillette quittant la plage (87x55cm-34x22in) s. 13-Mar-4 De Vuyst, Lokeren #421/R
£16000 $28640 €24000 Les jeunes artistes (90x145cm-35x57in) s.d.1894. 15-May-4 De Vuyst, Lokeren #434/R
£40000 $73600 €58400 Les petits artistes (57x92cm-22x36in) s. panel. 23-Mar-4 Bonhams, New Bond Street #11/R est:20000-30000
Works on paper
£709 $1184 €1000 Nymph in the water (70x57cm-28x22in) s. pastel. 20-Oct-3 Bernaerts, Antwerp #273/R

VERHAS, Theodor (1811-1872) German
£3200 $5728 €4800 High mountain landscape with wooden bridge (37x52cm-15x20in) s. paper on canvas. 13-May-4 Bassenge, Berlin #5679/R est:4500
Works on paper
£333 $613 €500 Bogenberg near Straubing (9x13cm-4x5in) pencil wash. 11-Jun-4 Hauswedell & Nolte, Hamburg #1078/R
£393 $715 €574 Castle ruins (72x57cm-28x22in) s. pen wash pencil htd white. 16-Jun-4 Fischer, Luzern #2614/R (S.FR 900)
£417 $696 €600 Stream in landscape (30x42cm-12x17in) s. W/C. 24-Oct-3 Ketterer, Hamburg #245/R

VERHEYDEN, D H (19th C) ?
£500 $790 €730 Columbian plantation. s. 7-Sep-3 Lots Road Auctions, London #335a

VERHEYDEN, François (1806-1889) Belgian
£872 $1614 €1300 Man offering flowers (10x8cm-4x3in) s.d.53 panel. 15-Mar-4 Sotheby's, Amsterdam #66/R est:300-500
£1690 $2924 €2400 L'arrestation du pere du famille (51x41cm-20x16in) s.d.1837. 9-Dec-3 Vanderkindere, Brussels #459/R est:2500-4000
£2717 $5000 €3967 Conspirators (43x36cm-17x14in) s. panel. 26-Jun-4 Susanin's, Chicago #6087/R est:4000-8000
£11888 $20448 €17000 Lettre d'amour (104x83cm-41x33in) s.d.1861. 2-Dec-3 Campo & Campo, Antwerp #400/R est:15000-20000
£17333 $31027 €26000 Genre scene (114x147cm-45x58in) s.indis.d. 17-May-4 Finarte Semenzato, Rome #90/R est:28000-32000

VERHEYDEN, Isidore (1848-1905) Belgian
£306 $548 €450 Vache au pre (14x16cm-6x6in) s. 16-Mar-4 Vanderkindere, Brussels #26
£352 $609 €500 Paysage brabancon (22x32cm-9x13in) s. 9-Dec-3 Campo, Vlaamse Kaai #489
£397 $723 €600 La basse-cour (30x40cm-12x16in) 15-Jun-4 Galerie Moderne, Brussels #209/R
£556 $883 €800 Orchard (51x32cm-20x13in) 15-Sep-3 Bernaerts, Antwerp #78
£600 $1074 €900 Sous-bois (29x34cm-11x13in) 15-May-4 De Vuyst, Lokeren #393/R
£759 $1403 €1100 Retour a la ferme au toit rouge (28x41cm-11x16in) s. 16-Feb-4 Horta, Bruxelles #461
£909 $1545 €1300 Les dunes (35x48cm-14x19in) s. panel. 1-Dec-3 Palais de Beaux Arts, Brussels #150/R
£927 $1687 €1400 Cour de ferme animee (38x71cm-15x28in) s. 15-Jun-4 Vanderkindere, Brussels #45
£1000 $1790 €1500 La voile blanche (28x40cm-11x16in) s. 11-May-4 Vanderkindere, Brussels #238/R est:1500-2000
£1325 $2411 €2000 Portrait de femme (110x80cm-43x31in) s. 15-Jun-4 Galerie Moderne, Brussels #345/R est:2000-3000
£1389 $2208 €2000 Sous-bois en hiver (104x74cm-41x29in) s. exhib. 9-Sep-3 Palais de Beaux Arts, Brussels #292/R est:450-550
£1736 $2899 €2500 Fermiere avec vache (80x90cm-31x35in) s. 21-Oct-3 Campo & Campo, Antwerp #344/R est:3000-5000
£3667 $6563 €5500 Sous-bois (134x85cm-53x33in) s. 15-May-4 De Vuyst, Lokeren #437/R est:7000-10000
£3733 $6683 €5600 Pecheur et vaches a l'etang (46x81cm-18x32in) s. 11-May-4 Vanderkindere, Brussels #212/R est:5000-7500

VERHEYDEN, Matthaeus (1700-1776) Dutch
Works on paper
£828 $1374 €1200 Time uncovering truth (39x28cm-15x11in) i. wash pen. 30-Sep-3 Dorotheum, Vienna #1/R

VERHEYEN, Bart (1963-) Belgian
£521 $870 €750 Precision (80x100cm-31x39in) s. acrylic. 21-Oct-3 Campo & Campo, Antwerp #346/R

VERHEYEN, Jan Hendrik (1778-1846) Dutch
£3000 $5400 €4500 Figures by the city wall of Utrecht, the Geertekerk in the distance (34x41cm-13x16in) s. panel prov. 21-Apr-4 Christie's, Amsterdam #35/R est:6000-8000
£28000 $50960 €42000 Figures in a quay n Dutch town, Figures on a square in a Dutch town (32x26cm-13x10in) s. panel pair. 1-Jul-4 Christie's, Amsterdam #716/R est:20000-30000

VERHEYEN, Jef (1932-1984) Belgian
£556 $928 €800 Paysage. 21-Oct-3 Campo, Vlaamse Kaai #622
£3049 $5000 €4452 Charlottelei (66x46cm-26x18in) s.i.d.1963 on stretcher prov.exhib. 28-May-3 Sotheby's, Amsterdam #61/R est:5000-7000
£4027 $7128 €6000 Bleu-noir (90x90cm-35x35in) s.verso panel. 27-Apr-4 Campo & Campo, Antwerp #268/R est:3000-5000

VERHEYEN, Robert Ferdinand (1877-1960) Dutch
£884 $1610 €1300 Chatting by an Amsterdam canal in winter (57x33cm-22x13in) s. 3-Feb-4 Christie's, Amsterdam #318 est:700-900

VERHOESEN, Albertus (1806-1881) Dutch
£933 $1671 €1400 Grazing cow (14x16cm-6x6in) s.indis.d. panel. 15-May-4 De Vuyst, Lokeren #395/R
£1056 $1827 €1500 Cow herd on the meadow (62x80cm-24x31in) s.d.1849 canvas on canvas. 12-Dec-3 Berlinghof, Heidelberg #1145/R est:1650
£1172 $1958 €1700 Poultry in the yard (22x26cm-9x10in) s.d.1876 panel. 11-Nov-3 Vendu Notarishuis, Rotterdam #72/R est:1500-2000
£1333 $2413 €2000 Poultry outside stable (31x43cm-12x17in) s.d.18 panel. 1-Apr-4 Van Ham, Cologne #1690/R est:2500
£1399 $2336 €2000 Head of a bull (80x62cm-31x24in) s. 30-Jun-3 Sotheby's, Amsterdam #116/R
£1418 $2369 €2000 Chiens au repos dans un paysage (14x19cm-6x7in) s.d.1879 panel. 19-Oct-3 St-Germain-en-Laye Encheres #13/R est:2000-2500
£1418 $2369 €2000 Coq, poules et paon dans un paysage (18x25cm-7x10in) s.d.1880 panel. 19-Oct-3 St-Germain-en-Laye Encheres #14/R est:3000-4000
£1447 $2620 €2200 Poultry in a landscape (23x19cm-9x7in) panel pair. 19-Apr-4 Glerum, Amsterdam #81/R est:2400-2600
£1507 $2562 €2200 Poultry (17x23cm-7x9in) s.d.1875 panel. 5-Nov-3 Vendue Huis, Gravenhage #83/R est:2000-3000
£1523 $2772 €2300 Poules et coq (19x23cm-7x9in) s.d.1875 panel. 19-Jun-4 St-Germain-en-Laye Encheres #36/R est:2200-2500
£1818 $3091 €2600 Poultry before old ruins (18x24cm-7x9in) s.d.1872 panel. 20-Nov-3 Van Ham, Cologne #1898/R est:2500
£1908 $3511 €2900 Cockerel's fight (23x31cm-9x12in) s.d.1869 panel. 28-Jun-4 Sotheby's, Amsterdam #35/R est:2000-3000
£2000 $3220 €2900 Cockerel, hens and chicks by a basket in a landscape (13x18cm-5x7in) s. indis d. 15-Aug-3 Keys, Aylsham #564/R est:500-700
£2042 $3533 €2900 Hen and chickens (17x24cm-7x9in) s.d.1873 panel. 13-Dec-3 De Vuyst, Lokeren #529/R est:3000-4000
£2083 $3479 €3000 Poultry in a landscape (12x10cm-5x4in) s.d.1858 panel. 21-Oct-3 Sotheby's, Amsterdam #15/R est:1000-2000
£2083 $3396 €3000 Cattle in a landscape. s.d.1846 panel. 29-Sep-3 Sotheby's, Amsterdam #53/R
£2096 $3815 €3060 Chickens roaming free (18x24cm-7x9in) s.d.1875 panel. 16-Jun-4 Fischer, Luzern #1112/R est:5000-7000 (S.FR 4800)
£2222 $3511 €3200 Hen and her chicks (23x30cm-9x12in) s.d.1865 panel. 2-Sep-3 Christie's, Amsterdam #154/R est:1000-1500
£2222 $3711 €3200 Chickens and a cockerel by a wall (31x25cm-12x10in) s.d.1857 panel. 21-Oct-3 Sotheby's, Amsterdam #18/R est:2000-3000
£2361 $4250 €3447 Peacocks among chickens (24x34cm-9x13in) s.d.1869. 21-Jan-4 Sotheby's, New York #239/R est:4000-6000
£2465 $3944 €3500 Two cows in meadow (10x12cm-4x5in) s.d.1861 panel lit. 19-Sep-3 Sigalas, Stuttgart #439/R est:3800
£2500 $4600 €3800 Peacocks, cockerels and chickens in a landscape near a ruined wall (22x31cm-9x12in) s.d.1869 panel. 28-Jun-4 Sotheby's, Amsterdam #36/R est:2000-3000
£2639 $4169 €3800 Cows in a panoramic polder landscape (23x65cm-9x26in) s.d.1839 panel. 2-Sep-3 Christie's, Amsterdam #164/R est:2500-3500
£3125 $5313 €4500 Poultry and a peacock by a ruin (13x17cm-5x7in) s. panel pair. 28-Oct-3 Christie's, Amsterdam #7/R est:4000-6000
£3800 $6992 €5548 Poultry beside a river (35x46cm-14x18in) s. 23-Mar-4 Bonhams, New Bond Street #8/R est:3000-4000
£4500 $8100 €6570 River landscape with chickens and ducks (17x23cm-7x9in) s.d.1876 panel pair. 20-Apr-4 Sotheby's, Olympia #389/R est:1500-2000
£5500 $9900 €8030 Landscape with peacocks and chickens (15x19cm-6x7in) s.d.1877 panel set of four. 20-Apr-4 Sotheby's, Olympia #390/R est:2000-4000

VERHOESEN, Albertus (attrib) (1806-1881) Dutch
£1103 $1843 €1600 Poultry in the yard (22x26cm-9x10in) panel. 11-Nov-3 Vendu Notarishuis, Rotterdam #73/R est:1000-1500

VERHOESEN, Johannes Marinus (1832-1898) Dutch
£594 $1010 €850 Paysage avec vaches a l'abreuvoir (23x32cm-9x13in) s. panel. 1-Dec-3 Palais de Beaux Arts, Brussels #383/R

VERHOEVEN, Jan (c.1600-1676) Flemish
£2778 $4389 €4000 Hunting still life with a sparrow, pigeon and woodpecker (55x61cm-22x24in) s. 2-Sep-3 Christie's, Amsterdam #89/R est:1200-1600

VERHOEVEN, Jan (1870-1941) Dutch
£529 $899 €772 Dancer (60x38cm-24x15in) s. 5-Nov-3 Dobiaschofsky, Bern #1025/R (S.FR 1200)
£2000 $3680 €3000 Wife and daughter of the artist - double portrait (71x100cm-28x39in) s. i. verso. 9-Jun-4 Dorotheum, Salzburg #557/R est:4800-6500

VERHOEVEN-BALL, Adrien Joseph (1824-1882) Belgian

£400	$668	€584	After the shoot (26x30cm-10x12in) panel. 11-Nov-3 Bonhams, Knightsbridge #86c/R
£1119	$1869	€1600	Fille au chapeau fleuri (26x21cm-10x8in) s.d.1876. 11-Oct-3 De Vuyst, Lokeren #389 est:1500-1700
£1695	$3000	€2475	Lesson by heart (69x56cm-27x22in) s. panel. 2-May-4 Grogan, Boston #54/R
£8000	$14720	€11680	Jordaens courting the daughter of Adam van Noordt (82x111cm-32x44in) s.i.d.1862 prov. 23-Mar-4 Bonhams, New Bond Street #2/R est:5000-7000

VERHOOG, Adrianus (1933-) Dutch

£461	$847	€700	Dreaming of Napoleon and Nietzsche (70x100cm-28x39in) s.d.69 acrylic. 22-Jun-4 Christie's, Amsterdam #589/R
£514	$873	€750	De val van Icarus II (68x68cm-27x27in) s.d.1970. 5-Nov-3 Vendue Huis, Gravenhage #455/R
£533	$976	€800	Three cheerful women (50x50cm-20x20in) s.d.1971 prov.exhib.lit. 7-Jun-4 Glerum, Amsterdam #213/R
£959	$1630	€1400	With Yasha in the garden (100x100cm-39x39in) s.d.1977. 5-Nov-3 Vendue Huis, Gravenhage #457

VERIN, Noel (1947-) French

£927	$1687	€1400	Marilyn (105x105cm-41x41in) s.d.VI/03 acrylic. 18-Jun-4 Charbonneaux, Paris #168/R

VERITY, Colin (?) ?

£541	$1000	€790	The Torrens running up the Channel (76x101cm-30x40in) s. 10-Feb-4 Christie's, Rockefeller NY #246/R

VERKADE, Jan (1868-1946) Dutch

£12414	$20731	€18000	The way to Gethsemani (23x32cm-9x13in) s. canvas on panel. 13-Nov-3 Neumeister, Munich #481/R est:2000-2500

VERKADE, Kees (1941-) Dutch

Sculpture

£1189	$2045	€1700	Marathonloopster (28cm-11in) s.d.81 num.5/6 bronze marble base. 2-Dec-3 Sotheby's, Amsterdam #285/R est:1500-2000
£1399	$2378	€2000	Surprise (38cm-15in) s.d.num.2/6 bronze incl bronze base conceived 1990. 25-Nov-3 Christie's, Amsterdam #139/R est:2500-3500
£2267	$4171	€3400	Johan Cruyff (23cm-9in) init.d.78 grey pat bronze conceived 1978 one of six. 9-Jun-4 Christie's, Amsterdam #273/R est:2000-3000
£4710	$7725	€6500	Two dancers (40cm-16in) num.1/6 i.d.94 bronze wooden base. 27-May-3 Sotheby's, Amsterdam #380/R est:7000-9000
£5944	$10105	€8500	L'equilibre (44cm-17in) init.d.num.1/6 bronze incl bronze base conceived 1978 lit. 25-Nov-3 Christie's, Amsterdam #140/R est:7000-9000
£6000	$11040	€9000	Hymne a l'amour (35cm-14in) s.d.83 num.4/6 brown pat. bronze one of six st.f.Cuvoi lit. 9-Jun-4 Christie's, Amsterdam #288/R est:5000-7000
£6333	$11653	€9500	L'entente totale (33x43cm-13x17in) s.d.95 num.I/IV brown pat bronze conceived 1995 one of six lit. 9-Jun-4 Christie's, Amsterdam #272/R est:8000-12000
£6333	$11653	€9500	Vrouw met Vogel (134cm-53in) i.d.1979 num.3/6 bronze. 8-Jun-4 Sotheby's, Amsterdam #23/R est:9000-12000
£7246	$11884	€10000	Male and female dancers (53cm-21in) num.1/6 i.d.94 bronze. 27-May-3 Sotheby's, Amsterdam #379/R est:7000-9000

Works on paper

£367	$671	€550	Ludmila (40x31cm-16x12in) s.i.d.1980 pen pencil. 7-Jun-4 Glerum, Amsterdam #231/R

VERKMAN, Leo (1924-) Russian

£805	$1426	€1200	Lenin and soldiers (81x73cm-32x29in) s.d.1949 lit. 1-May-4 Meeting Art, Vercelli #497

VERKOLJE, Nicolaes (1673-1746) Dutch

£961	$1748	€1403	Portrait of a woman wearing a blue jacket (38x32cm-15x13in) s.d.1709. 16-Jun-4 Fischer, Luzern #1056/R est:2400-2800 (S.FR 2200)

VERKOLJE, Nicolaes (attrib) (1673-1746) Dutch

£6790	$11000	€9913	Man playing cello beside woman at harpiscord with turkish rug (48x41cm-19x16in) indis.sig panel. 3-Aug-3 North East Auctions, Portsmouth #1716/R

VERLAT, Charles Michel Maria (1824-1890) Belgian

£966	$1612	€1400	Portrait d'une dame noble (115x92cm-45x36in) s.d.1847. 17-Nov-3 Bernaerts, Antwerp #9/R
£986	$1706	€1400	Renard et sa proie (28x36cm-11x14in) s.d.1860 wood. 9-Dec-3 Campo, Vlaamse Kaai #492/R
£1500	$2775	€2190	Hydrangeas, roses and other flowers around a balustrade (55x88cm-22x35in) s. panel. 15-Jan-4 Christie's, Kensington #1045/R est:1500-2500
£1806	$3015	€2600	Etude de singes (38x46cm-15x18in) s. 21-Oct-3 Campo, Vlaamse Kaai #622a/R est:1000-1500
£1900	$3154	€2774	Fido (55x45cm-22x18in) s.d.1874 panel. 1-Oct-3 Sotheby's, Olympia #208/R est:1500-2000
£2000	$3660	€3000	La lutte pour la chataigne (48x39cm-19x15in) s.d.1886 panel. 7-Jun-4 Palais de Beaux Arts, Brussels #117/R est:3000-5000
£2667	$4827	€4000	Gardien vigilant (53x43cm-21x17in) S. P. 30-Mar-4 Campo & Campo, Antwerp #339/R est:3000-4000

VERLAT, Charles Michel Maria (attrib) (1824-1890) Belgian

£1404	$2514	€2050	Camels resting (41x49cm-16x19in) s. 28-May-4 Uppsala Auktionskammare, Uppsala #116 est:6000-8000 (S.KR 19000)

VERLET, Raoul (1857-1923) French

Sculpture

£1399	$2378	€2000	Orphee et Cerbere (84cm-33in) brown pat bronze marble socle Cast Barbedienne. 27-Nov-3 Millon & Associes, Paris #92/R est:1500-2000
£4000	$7280	€6000	Orphee St Cerbere (99cm-39in) s.st.f. Barbedienne brown pat. bronze. 20-Jun-4 Wilkinson, Doncaster #19 est:4000-6000
£6800	$11764	€9928	Orpheus's sorrow (99cm-39in) s.st.f.F.Barbedienne brown pat bronze lit. 12-Dec-3 Sotheby's, London #257/R est:4000-6000
£13000	$23790	€18980	Douleur d'Orphee (126cm-50in) s.st.f.Barbedienne pat bronze lit. 9-Jul-4 Sotheby's, London #136/R est:10000-12000

VERLEUR, Andries (1876-1953) Dutch

£357	$650	€521	Flock with sheep on the heath (66x104cm-26x41in) s.d.1933. 19-Jun-4 Harvey Clar, Oakland #2183

VERLINDE, Claude (1927-) ?

£353	$600	€515	Two figures in surrealist village (64x53cm-25x21in) s.d.1959 masonite. 22-Nov-3 New Orleans Auction, New Orleans #683/R
£671	$1188	€1000	Soleil couchant (60x91cm-24x36in) s. 29-Apr-4 David Kahn, Paris #224/R

VERLING, Walter (1930-) Irish

£762	$1386	€1150	Ballinatray, Youghal, dawn (33x44cm-13x17in) s. canvasboard. 15-Jun-4 James Adam, Dublin #192/R

VERLON, Andre (1917-1993) Swiss

Works on paper

£452	$769	€660	Houses (45x65cm-18x26in) s.d. bears i. collage mixed media pavatex. 18-Nov-3 Hans Widmer, St Gallen #1223 (S.FR 1000)

VERMARE, Andre Cesar (1869-?) French

Sculpture

£1049	$1752	€1500	Homme de profil (44x27cm-17x11in) s.num.4 terracotta sold with a document. 13-Oct-3 Horta, Bruxelles #119 est:1000-1500

VERMEER OF DELFT, Jan (1632-1675) Dutch

£14500000	$26535000	€21170000	Young woman seated at virginals (25x20cm-10x8in) prov.exhib.lit. 7-Jul-4 Sotheby's, London #8/R

VERMEER OF HAARLEM, Jan (elder) (1628-1691) Dutch

£4225	$7310	€6000	Wooded landscape. Figures on woodland path (30x46cm-12x18in) panel two. 13-Dec-3 Lempertz, Koln #33/R est:4000

VERMEER OF HAARLEM, Jan (younger) (1656-1705) Dutch

Works on paper

£372	$654	€550	Sheep and lamb near a tree (13x18cm-5x7in) s.d.1687 black chk grey wash lit. 19-May-4 Sotheby's, Amsterdam #95/R
£690	$1152	€1000	Shepherd with sheep (15x24cm-6x9in) s.d.1687 chk prov. 15-Nov-3 Lempertz, Koln #1419/R
£7534	$12808	€11000	Mountainous river landscape with peasants and boats (21x35cm-8x14in) s.d.1686 i.verso black chk grey wash prov.exhib. 4-Nov-3 Sotheby's, Amsterdam #64/R est:5000-7000

VERMEER, Jan (after) (17th C) Dutch

£13000	$23790	€18980	View of Delft (61x74cm-24x29in) 6-Jul-4 Sotheby's, Olympia #478/R est:8000-12000

VERMEERSCH, Ivo Ambros (attrib) (1810-1852) Belgian

£699	$1189	€1000	Vue de ville, ou l'eglise de Bacarat. 18-Nov-3 Vanderkindere, Brussels #235

VERMEERSCH, Jose (1922-1997) Belgian

Sculpture

£2800	$5012	€4200	Sitting figure (24x19cm-9x7in) s.d.76 num.2/10 dark brown pat bronze. 15-May-4 De Vuyst, Lokeren #396/R est:2800-3000

VERMEHREN, Frederik (1822-1910) Danish

£809	$1504	€1181	Old peasant woman making dress for her grandchild (39x27cm-15x11in) s.d.1849. 2-Mar-4 Rasmussen, Copenhagen #1590/R (D.KR 9000)

VERMEHREN, Gustav (1863-1931) Danish

£323	$523	€472	Landscape with farm (31x38cm-12x15in) init.d.1913. 9-Aug-3 Hindemae, Ullerslev #95/R (D.KR 3400)
£1082	$2002	€1580	Cottage interior with sunshine coming through window (41x33cm-16x13in) s. 15-Mar-4 Rasmussen, Vejle #439/R est:10000-15000 (D.KR 12000)
£1121	$1772	€1625	Interior scene with figures, Hedeboe area (58x47cm-23x19in) s.indis.d. exhib. 2-Sep-3 Rasmussen, Copenhagen #1690/R est:6000-8000 (D.KR 12000)

VERMEHREN, Sophus (1866-1950) Danish

£369	$627	€539	Kitchen interior with seated woman (65x58cm-26x23in) s. 10-Nov-3 Rasmussen, Vejle #259/R (D.KR 4000)
£543	$972	€793	Woman peeling fruit (69x45cm-27x18in) s. 10-May-4 Rasmussen, Vejle #314/R (D.KR 6000)
£560	$930	€818	Interior, with mother and daughter (70x69cm-28x27in) s. 13-Jun-3 Jacobs & Hunt, Petersfield #249/R
£719	$1337	€1050	At the morning table - bouquet of flowers having been delivered (69x69cm-27x27in) s. 2-Mar-4 Rasmussen, Copenhagen #1646/R (D.KR 8000)
£1074	$1966	€1568	Serving breakfast (59x59cm-23x23in) s. 9-Jun-4 Rasmussen, Copenhagen #1994/R est:10000 (D.KR 12000)
£3581	$6553	€5228	Summer landscape with girls by white house (42x57cm-17x22in) s. prov. 9-Jun-4 Rasmussen, Copenhagen #1487/R est:40000-60000 (D.KR 40000)

VERMEHREN, Yelva (1880-1978) Danish
£341 $613 €498 Still life of roses in vase (32x34cm-13x13in) s. 24-Apr-4 Rasmussen, Havnen #2261 (D.KR 3800)

VERMEIR, Alfons (1905-1994) Belgian
£313 $522 €450 Les promeneurs (40x50cm-16x20in) s. panel. 21-Oct-3 Campo, Vlaamse Kaai #623
£333 $527 €480 Harbour of Antwerp (25x33cm-10x13in) s. cardboard. 2-Sep-3 Christie's, Amsterdam #418a
£333 $597 €500 Farm (41x50cm-16x20in) s. lit. 15-May-4 De Vuyst, Lokeren #398/R
£336 $621 €500 Figures in a forest landscape (38x48cm-15x19in) s. board. 15-Mar-4 Sotheby's, Amsterdam #155/R
£467 $845 €700 Paysage estival aux gerbes de ble (60x80cm-24x31in) s. 30-Mar-4 Campo, Vlaamse Kaai #218
£533 $955 €800 Landscape in Flanders (60x70cm-24x28in) s. 15-May-4 De Vuyst, Lokeren #397
£537 $993 €800 Evening in Schilde (50x65cm-20x26in) s. lit. 13-Mar-4 De Vuyst, Lokeren #378/R
£559 $934 €800 Potato pickers (50x60cm-20x24in) s. lit. 11-Oct-3 De Vuyst, Lokeren #390/R
£599 $1036 €850 Village under the snow (51x60cm-20x24in) s. panel. 13-Dec-3 De Vuyst, Lokeren #385
£1007 $1872 €1500 Street scene (70x80cm-28x31in) s. board. 4-Mar-4 Auction Maastricht #1111/R est:1200-1500
£1049 $1783 €1500 Landscape with farm and farmer (60x80cm-24x31in) s. 24-Nov-3 Glerum, Amsterdam #59/R est:1500-2000

VERMEIRE, Jules (1885-1977) Dutch
Sculpture
£1678 $2970 €2500 Jeune femme (40cm-16in) mono. stone. 27-Apr-4 Campo & Campo, Antwerp #271/R est:2600-3000
£2657 $4517 €3800 Head (28cm-11in) init. stone excl wooden base prov. 25-Nov-3 Christie's, Amsterdam #130/R est:4000-6000
£3147 $5350 €4500 Head (43cm-17in) bronze incl wooden base prov. 25-Nov-3 Christie's, Amsterdam #131/R est:5000-7000
Works on paper
£420 $713 €600 Two heads (43x56cm-17x22in) init. chl prov. 25-Nov-3 Christie's, Amsterdam #238/R

VERMEULEN, Andries (1763-1814) Dutch
£5137 $8733 €7500 Winter landscape with skaters on a frozen river (41x54cm-16x21in) s. 5-Nov-3 Christie's, Amsterdam #76/R est:8000-12000
£32000 $57600 €46720 Winter landscape with a frost fair and figures skating on a frozen river (41x70cm-16x28in) s. panel. 22-Apr-4 Sotheby's, London #90/R est:10000-15000
Works on paper
£833 $1500 €1216 Extensive landscape with herdsmen by a stream (23x33cm-9x13in) s. black chk W/C sold with two others similar. 22-Jan-4 Christie's, Rockefeller NY #244/R est:1500-2000

VERMEULEN, Andries (attrib) (1763-1814) Dutch
£800 $1264 €1160 Wooded landscape with figures and cattle (31x40cm-12x16in) s. panel. 24-Jul-3 Lawrence, Crewkerne #932/R

VERMEULEN, Eugene (?) ?
£5882 $10000 €8588 Fishing boats on a river by a village (47x57cm-19x22in) s.d.1832 panel. 29-Oct-3 Christie's, Rockefeller NY #1/R est:10000-15000

VERMEULEN, Marinus Cornelis Thomas (1868-1941) Dutch
£2632 $4842 €4000 Numerous figures on a frozen river (38x50cm-15x20in) s. panel. 22-Jun-4 Christie's, Amsterdam #10/R est:800-1200

VERMEULEN, Noel (1917-1989) Belgian
£268 $475 €400 Composition (86x112cm-34x44in) s. 27-Apr-4 Campo, Vlaamse Kaai #652

VERMEYLEN, Alphonse (1882-1939) Belgian
£276 $450 €403 Petit chantier (53x66cm-21x26in) s.i. panel. 27-Sep-3 Charlton Hall, Columbia #298/R

VERMI, Arturo (1929-1988) Italian
£1267 $2331 €1900 Diaries (120x100cm-47x39in) s.i.verso acrylic. 10-Jun-4 Galleria Pace, Milan #94/R est:3000
£2297 $4043 €3400 Moon (92x73cm-36x29in) painted c.1980. 22-May-4 Galleria Pananti, Florence #323/R est:3200-3500
Works on paper
£800 $1472 €1200 Untitled (100x80cm-39x31in) s.verso mixed media. 8-Jun-4 Finarte Semenzato, Milan #289/R
£1259 $2140 €1800 Diaries (70x100cm-28x39in) s.verso mixed media on canvas. 20-Nov-3 Finarte Semenzato, Milan #85/R est:1500-1800

VERNA, Germaine (1900-1975) French
£1374 $2500 €2006 House on the cliff at Orselina (97x130cm-38x51in) s. painted c.1955. 29-Jun-4 Sotheby's, New York #362/R est:3000-5000

VERNA, Jean Luc (20th C) French
Works on paper
£423 $731 €600 Centaure enceint (32x50cm-13x20in) s.d.95 pastel graphite dr. 9-Dec-3 Artcurial Briest, Paris #582
£423 $731 €600 Reine mere (32x50cm-13x20in) mono.d.95 graphite pastel dr. 9-Dec-3 Artcurial Briest, Paris #583

VERNAY, François (1821-1896) French
£1773 $2961 €2500 Paysage a l'etang (51x78cm-20x31in) s. 19-Oct-3 Anaf, Lyon #304/R est:3000-4000

VERNAY, Josephine (1861-?) Swiss
£699 $1272 €1021 Maid arranging her mistress's hair (57x43cm-22x17in) s.d.aout 1897. 16-Jun-4 Fischer, Luzern #2415/R (S.FR 1600)

VERNAZZA, Eduardo (1910-1991) ?
£235 $400 €343 Dance (70x96cm-28x38in) s. 25-Nov-3 Galeria y Remates, Montevideo #9
£241 $410 €352 Dance (31x41cm-12x16in) s. 20-Nov-3 Galeria y Remates, Montevideo #161/R
£324 $550 €473 Dance (76x89cm-30x35in) s. 25-Nov-3 Galeria y Remates, Montevideo #10/R
£549 $900 €802 Figures (120x80cm-47x31in) s. 3-Jun-3 Galeria y Remates, Montevideo #20
£1059 $1800 €1546 Candombe (50x70cm-20x28in) s.d.1972. 25-Nov-3 Galeria y Remates, Montevideo #115/R
£1412 $2400 €2062 Candombe (61x88cm-24x35in) s. 25-Nov-3 Galeria y Remates, Montevideo #114/R
Works on paper
£259 $420 €376 Market scene (62x71cm-24x28in) s. W/C board. 29-Jul-3 Galeria y Remates, Montevideo #136

VERNER, Elizabeth O'Neill (1884-1979) American
Works on paper
£11976 $20000 €17485 Hoeing the fields (48x30cm-19x12in) s. pastel. 23-Oct-3 Shannon's, Milford #30/R est:12000-18000

VERNER, F A (1836-1928) Canadian
Works on paper
£2400 $3984 €3504 Native Indians in a canoe (28x58cm-11x23in) s. 30-Sep-3 Andrew Smith, Winchester #107/R est:2000-3000

VERNER, Frederick Arthur (1836-1928) Canadian
£3091 $5038 €4513 Pastoral farm scene (61x94cm-24x37in) s.d.1902. 23-Sep-3 Ritchie, Toronto #79/R est:3000-4000 (C.D 6800)
£12195 $21829 €17805 Ojibway Indian encampment (69x69cm-27x27in) s.d.1874 prov. 31-May-4 Sotheby's, Toronto #82/R est:10000-15000 (C.D 30000)
Works on paper
£223 $373 €323 Figure walking past the cottage (16x23cm-6x9in) s.d.1896 W/C. 17-Jun-3 Pinneys, Montreal #156 (C.D 500)
£310 $500 €450 Untitled (32x64cm-13x25in) s. W/C on board. 24-Aug-3 Bonhams & Butterfields, Los Angeles #7038
£315 $536 €460 Picking flowers (36x30cm-14x12in) s.d.1874 W/C. 21-Nov-3 Walker's, Ottawa #97/R (C.D 700)
£333 $547 €486 Vessels alongside a dock (38x43cm-15x17in) s.d. W/C. 28-May-3 Maynards, Vancouver #62/R (C.D 750)
£362 $605 €529 Untitled - village at sunset (23x31cm-9x12in) s.d.1908 W/C. 17-Nov-3 Hodgins, Calgary #57/R (C.D 800)
£428 $727 €625 Figures on a forest path (33x51cm-13x20in) s.d.1900 W/C. 21-Nov-3 Walker's, Ottawa #98/R (C.D 950)
£450 $766 €657 Burnham Beeches (36x25cm-14x10in) s.d.1902 W/C prov. 23-Nov-3 Levis, Calgary #145/R (C.D 1000)
£480 $878 €701 Deer by a forest pool (32x49cm-13x19in) s.d.1897 W/C. 1-Jun-4 Joyner Waddington, Toronto #445 (C.D 1200)
£578 $959 €844 Untitled, walking home (11x22cm-4x9in) s. W/C exec.c.1897. 5-Oct-3 Levis, Calgary #121/R (C.D 1300)
£814 $1360 €1188 Hudson's Bay officials on rainy lake (24x46cm-9x18in) W/C. 17-Nov-3 Hodgins, Calgary #370 est:2500-3000 (C.D 1800)
£1081 $1838 €1578 November morning (35x52cm-14x20in) s.d.1898. 23-Nov-3 Levis, Calgary #144/R est:3000-3500 (C.D 2400)
£1120 $2050 €1635 Woodland stream at dusk (29x43cm-11x17in) s.d.1876 W/C. 1-Jun-4 Hodgins, Calgary #96/R est:1500-2000 (C.D 2800)
£1696 $2918 €2476 Advocate's Close, Edinburgh (71x41cm-28x16in) s.d.1882 W/C exhib.lit. 2-Dec-3 Joyner Waddington, Toronto #147/R est:3000-5000 (C.D 3800)
£2846 $5093 €4155 Wigwam, lake at the woods (27x53cm-11x21in) s.d.1898 i.verso W/C prov. 31-May-4 Sotheby's, Toronto #145/R est:8000-10000 (C.D 7000)
£4279 $7275 €6247 The Portage (31x62cm-12x24in) s.d.1902 s.i.verso W/C paper on paperboard prov. 23-Nov-3 Levis, Calgary #143/R est:6000-8000 (C.D 9500)
£5405 $9189 €7891 Algonquin Indians shooting the rapids, Muskoka (29x62cm-11x24in) s.d.1880 i.d.verso W/C prov. 18-Nov-3 Sotheby's, Toronto #172/R est:8000-10000 (C.D 12000)
£8108 $13784 €11838 Ojibway wigwams, Rainy River, Ontario (30x63cm-12x25in) s.d.1889 i.d.verso W/C board prov. 18-Nov-3 Sotheby's, Toronto #173/R est:12000-15000 (C.D 18000)
£8500 $13855 €12410 Indian camp (36x61cm-14x24in) s.d.1878 W/C prov. 25-Sep-3 Christie's, London #444/R est:6000-8000
£13000 $21190 €18980 Indian stalking a deer (36x61cm-14x24in) s.d.1876 W/C prov. 25-Sep-3 Christie's, London #443/R est:6000-8000

VERNET, Carle (1758-1836) French
£709 $1149 €1000 L'attaque (24x30cm-9x12in) s. panel prov.lit. 23-May-3 Karlheinz Kaupp, Staufen #1677/R
£36047 $62000 €52629 Lord Lowther's Busto with W Wheatley, up at Newmarket (51x62cm-20x24in) s.d.1815. 5-Dec-3 Christie's, Rockefeller NY #10/R est:30000-40000
£85333 $155307 €128000 Mamelouk tenant son cheval par la bride (64x82cm-25x32in) s. prov. 4-Jul-4 Eric Pillon, Calais #24/R
Works on paper
£428 $787 €650 Horse studies and oriental warrior (27x30cm-11x12in) s. pencil. 25-Jun-4 Michael Zeller, Lindau #802/R

VERNET, Carle (attrib) (1758-1836) French
£1800 $3060 €2628 Annunciation to the shepherds (37x45cm-15x18in) 31-Oct-3 Christie's, Kensington #90/R est:2000-3000
Works on paper
£1117 $1900 €1631 Les deux incroyables (32x33cm-13x13in) i. pen ink wash. 19-Nov-3 Bonhams & Butterfields, San Francisco #34/R

VERNET, Horace (1789-1863) French
£3624 $6487 €5400 Judith and Olophernes (162x131cm-64x52in) 26-May-4 Semenzato, Florence #221/R est:5000-6000
£8000 $14480 €12000 Portrait de bandit Napolitain (21x17cm-8x7in) mono. cardboard exhib. 30-Mar-4 Rossini, Paris #72/R est:4000-6000
£18881 $32476 €27000 Le soldat laboureur (55x46cm-22x18in) s. prov. 2-Dec-3 Sotheby's, Paris #18/R est:15000-20000
£41379 $75724 €60000 L'enlevement (92x73cm-36x29in) s.d.1833. 31-Jan-4 Osenat, Fontainebleau #613
£49645 $82908 €70000 Portrait de jeune africain en buste (53x45cm-21x18in) bears sig prov. 17-Oct-3 Renaud, Paris #53/R est:60000-80000
£109929 $183582 €155000 Depart pour la chasse aux Marais POntins (100x137cm-39x54in) s.i.d.1833 prov.exhib.lit. 17-Oct-3 Renaud, Paris #52/R est:120000-150000
Works on paper
£294 $505 €420 Portrait de Monsieur Brunet (22x15cm-9x6in) i. graphite wash W/C. 8-Dec-3 Christie's, Paris #10/R
£664 $1143 €950 Caricature d'Eugene Louis Lami a l'age de 16 ans, peignant (16x9cm-6x4in) s.i. brush brown ink brown wash. 2-Dec-3 Christie's, Paris #637/R
£2381 $4262 €3500 Scene de tabaille Napoleonienne (19x30cm-7x12in) i. pen black ink W/C. 19-Mar-4 Piasa, Paris #178/R est:2000

VERNET, Horace (attrib) (1789-1863) French
£1879 $3458 €2800 Soldier mourning dead comrades (67x76cm-26x30in) s. 25-Mar-4 Dr Fritz Nagel, Stuttgart #774/R est:2700
£3873 $6701 €5500 Portrait d'homme (75x62cm-30x24in) i. painted 1834. 12-Dec-3 Piasa, Paris #64/R est:4000-5000
Works on paper
£350 $627 €511 Study of two white horses (23x38cm-9x15in) s.d.1828 pencil white wash. 17-Mar-4 John Nicholson, Haslemere #662/R
£476 $852 €700 La chasse aux marais pontins (20x30cm-8x12in) i. black crayon. 22-Mar-4 Digard, Paris #50a
£800 $1448 €1200 Arab on horse (24x33cm-9x13in) i.d. W/C over pencil. 2-Apr-4 Winterberg, Heidelberg #568/R

VERNET, J (19th C) French
£1667 $3000 €2500 Looking out (26x16cm-10x6in) s. panel. 21-Apr-4 Christie's, Amsterdam #25/R est:3000-5000

VERNET, Jean (?) French?
£3261 $5967 €4761 Still life with a vase of roses in a river landscape (90x140cm-35x55in) s. prov. 4-Jun-4 Zofingen, Switzerland #2537/R est:12000 (S.FR 7500)

VERNET, Joseph (1714-1789) French
£7089 $12264 €10350 Mountain landscape with young couple fishing in lake (36x47cm-14x19in) s.d.1782. 9-Dec-3 Rasmussen, Copenhagen #1249/R est:20000-30000 (D.KR 75000)
£17361 $28993 €25000 Bad weather - sailing ship in difficulty (31x41cm-12x16in) s.d.1753 lit. 25-Oct-3 Bergmann, Erlangen #903/R est:13500
£30726 $55000 €44860 Banishment of Hagar and Ishmael (41x56cm-16x22in) s.d.1753 prov.exhib.lit. 27-May-4 Sotheby's, New York #96/R est:60000-80000
£34722 $57986 €50000 Stormy sea coast with figures (53x65cm-21x26in) s.d.1755. 24-Oct-3 Ketterer, Hamburg #39/R est:55000-65000
£55000 $95150 €80300 Rocky harbour by moonlight with a peasant couple conversing in the foreground (32x40cm-13x16in) prov. 10-Dec-3 Christie's, London #74/R est:30000-40000
£85000 $147050 €124100 Rocky coastal landscape with a fisherman talking to a peasant girl (32x40cm-13x16in) s.d.1770 prov.lit. 10-Dec-3 Christie's, London #73/R est:40000-60000
£236111 $425000 €344722 Landscape with bathers (90x135cm-35x53in) s.d.1777 prov.lit. 22-Jan-4 Sotheby's, New York #92/R est:200000-300000
£375000 $690000 €570000 Lancement d'un navire de guerre (96x160cm-38x63in) s.d.1781. 23-Jun-4 Rieunier, Paris #29/R est:300000-400000
Works on paper
£340 $609 €500 Village au bord de l'eau sur une falaise (14x18cm-6x7in) st.sig. pen brown ink. 17-Mar-4 Tajan, Paris #39
£420 $727 €613 Man rowing a boat. Men fishing in a boat. Boat on the shore (8x9cm-3x4in) i. black lead pen brown ink three in one mount. 12-Dec-3 Christie's, Kensington #445
£680 $1218 €1000 Vue de la muraille de Genes (19x28cm-7x11in) i. pen brown ink. 17-Mar-4 Maigret, Paris #32/R
£748 $1339 €1100 Un marin regardant vers le haut tenant un corde dans sa main droite (18x12cm-7x5in) black chk pen grey wash. 18-Mar-4 Christie's, Paris #271/R
£900 $1557 €1314 Peasant wearing a sheepskin coat (18x12cm-7x5in) i. black chk pen brown ink col wash. 12-Dec-3 Christie's, Kensington #446/R
£2517 $4505 €3700 Galeres et voilier dans un port. Scene de combat naval (15x42cm-6x17in) two. 17-Mar-4 Tajan, Paris #26/R est:4000
£3279 $6000 €4787 Landscape with figures among ruins of the Temple of Apollo (35x51cm-14x20in) i. pen black ink col wash pencil. 29-Jan-4 Swann Galleries, New York #226/R est:3000-5000
£6667 $12000 €9734 Bay of Naples with boats, Vesuvius beyond (27x40cm-11x16in) i. black chk pen brown ink wash. 22-Jan-4 Christie's, Rockefeller NY #107/R est:10000-15000

VERNET, Joseph (after) (1714-1789) French
£5000 $9000 €7300 Mediterranean harbour at sunset with stevedores on the quay (93x124cm-37x49in) 23-Apr-4 Christie's, Kensington #188/R est:5000-8000
£8824 $15000 €12883 Waterfalls near Tivoli (82x101cm-32x40in) 25-Nov-3 Christie's, Rockefeller NY #489/R est:2000-3000

VERNET, Joseph (attrib) (1714-1789) French
£498 $831 €727 Figures on a moonlit harbour (31x38cm-12x15in) panel. 17-Nov-3 Waddingtons, Toronto #224/R (C.D 1100)
£10490 $18042 €15000 Shipwreck (87x129cm-34x51in) s.d.1754 canvas on canvas. 5-Dec-3 Bolland & Marotz, Bremen #500/R est:22000
Works on paper
£1241 $2073 €1800 Italian fishermen talking (15x24cm-6x9in) i. pen over ochre wash prov. 15-Nov-3 Lempertz, Koln #1421 est:400

VERNET, Joseph (circle) (1714-1789) French
£3767 $6404 €5500 Lucky fishermen (54x79cm-21x31in) 4-Nov-3 Ansorena, Madrid #106/R est:5500
£17000 $31620 €24820 Morning. Evening (166x109cm-65x43in) pair. 4-Mar-4 Christie's, London #313/R est:10000-15000

VERNET, Joseph (style) (1714-1789) French
£6000 $10380 €8760 Mediterranean harbour scene with figures in Turkish dress (58x90cm-23x35in) canvas on board. 9-Dec-3 Sotheby's, Olympia #448/R est:5000-7000
£6000 $10980 €9000 View of harbour with boats and figures (55x80cm-22x31in) 1-Jun-4 Sotheby's, Milan #59/R est:3000-4000
£6471 $11000 €9448 Architectural capriccio (83x102cm-33x40in) 25-Nov-3 Christie's, Rockefeller NY #488/R est:1500-2000
£6600 $11418 €9636 Mediterranean harbour scene at dusk with figures on the shore (58x90cm-23x35in) canvas on board. 9-Dec-3 Sotheby's, Olympia #447/R est:5000-7000
£12500 $21250 €18250 Mediterranean harbour scene (55x78cm-22x31in) bears sig.d.1763. 30-Oct-3 Sotheby's, Olympia #161/R est:5000-7000
£12500 $21250 €18250 Southern harbour scene with figures loading a boat in the foreground (97x130cm-38x51in) 30-Oct-3 Sotheby's, Olympia #162/R est:7000-10000
£19000 $32870 €27740 Mediterranean harbour scenes at sunset (88x123cm-35x48in) pair prov. 11-Dec-3 Sotheby's, London #234/R est:15000-20000
£26000 $47580 €37960 Shipwreck upon Mediterranean coast (78x139cm-31x55in) bears sig. prov. 8-Jul-4 Sotheby's, London #343/R est:10000-15000

VERNET, Jules (1792-1843) French
Miniatures
£17450 $32107 €26000 La Marquise de Croy vetue d'une robe de soie noire a large col de dentelle blanche (11x9cm-4x4in) s. exec. c.1825-1830 oval gilt sculpted frame prov.lit. 26-Mar-4 Pierre Berge, Paris #95/R est:1500-2000
Works on paper
£1867 $3398 €2800 Jeune femme en robe de satin (7x5cm-3x2in) s.d.1828 oval. 30-Jun-4 Pierre Berge, Paris #92/R est:2500-3000

VERNET, Lionel (20th C) Haitian?
£492 $900 €718 Haitian wedding (51x40cm-20x16in) s.i. board. 3-Jun-4 Christie's, Rockefeller NY #1128/R

VERNEY, Sir John (1913-1993) British
Works on paper
£320 $531 €467 Spring in Castle Street (11x18cm-4x7in) s.d.74 pen ink W/C. 1-Oct-3 Woolley & Wallis, Salisbury #82/R

VERNIER, Émile Louis (1829-1887) French
£3500 $6545 €5110 Mediterranean fishing village (55x81cm-22x32in) s. 21-Jul-4 Lyon & Turnbull, Edinburgh #124/R est:3000-5000

VERNO, Camillo (1870-?) Italian
£2759 $4579 €4000 Contrasts (32x36cm-13x14in) s. s.d.1905 verso cardboard. 1-Oct-3 Della Rocca, Turin #92/R

VERNON, A (?) ?
£1200 $2004 €1752 The Sisters (89x69cm-35x27in) indis.s.d.1867. 8-Oct-3 Halls, Shrewsbury #99/R

VERNON, Emile (19/20th C) British
£8500 $15640 €12410 Summer beauty (62x51cm-24x20in) s. 23-Mar-4 Bonhams, New Bond Street #109/R est:8000-12000
£19000 $31160 €27740 Ready for the carnival (65x89cm-26x35in) s. 3-Jun-3 Fellows & Sons, Birmingham #83/R est:10000-15000
£26000 $45760 €37960 Half length portrait of a young blond beauty holding a puppy (52x63cm-20x25in) s.d.1915. 18-May-4 Fellows & Sons, Birmingham #108/R est:25000-35000
£33333 $60000 €48666 In the garden (76x50cm-30x20in) s.i.d.1910. 22-Apr-4 Christie's, Rockefeller NY #138/R est:60000-80000
£35294 $60000 €51529 Little kittens (65x54cm-26x21in) s.d.1919 prov. 29-Oct-3 Christie's, Rockefeller NY #120/R est:50000-70000

VERNON, Paul (1796-1875) French
£993 $1658 €1400 Pecheurs sur le bords de la riviere (20x27cm-8x11in) s.i. panel. 20-Jun-3 Drouot Estimations, Paris #73

VERNON, Walter (?) ?
Works on paper
£1136 $2000 €1659 Opening the gate. Fall. Surprise. Walking horse. Fall gallop (16x22cm-6x9in) s. W/C htd white set of five. 18-May-4 Sotheby's, New York #194/R est:2500-3500

VERNON, William H (1820-1909) British
£600 $1110 €876 Summer (29x24cm-11x9in) s. i. verso board. 14-Jul-4 Christie's, Kensington #823/R

VERNON, William H (attrib) (1820-1909) British
£1200 $2220 €1752 Caenarvon Castle, Wales (66x99cm-26x39in) 15-Jan-4 Christie's, Kensington #907/R est:700-1000

VEROMA, Pentti (1903-1979) Finnish
£1757 $3145 €2600 View from Aabo (77x52cm-30x20in) s.d.1948. 8-May-4 Bukowskis, Helsinki #143/R est:500-800

VERON (19th C) French
Sculpture
£1300 $2171 €1898 Innocence (45cm-18in) s. pat bronze. 15-Oct-3 Christie's, Kensington #296/R

VERON, Alexandre Paul Joseph (1773-1838) French
£1854 $3375 €2800 Fete villageoise (18x24cm-7x9in) panel. 15-Jun-4 Claude Aguttes, Neuilly #45/R est:4500
£7285 $13259 €11000 Scenes galants dans les parcs (25x35cm-10x14in) panel two. 21-Jun-4 Tajan, Paris #96/R est:6000-8000

VERON, Alexandre René (1826-1897) French
£600 $1098 €900 Voiliers sur la riviere (12x22cm-5x9in) s. panel. 6-Jun-4 Osenat, Fontainebleau #49
£634 $1052 €900 Jeune femme sur le chemin (32x19cm-13x7in) s. cardboard. 15-Jun-3 Peron, Melun #210
£780 $1303 €1100 Etang au crepuscule (14x22cm-6x9in) panel. 19-Oct-3 Daniel Herry, Beaune #41
£1000 $1790 €1500 Discussion aupres de la mare (33x54cm-13x21in) s.d.1883. 16-May-4 Thierry & Lannon, Brest #192/R est:1500-2000
£1400 $2240 €2030 Meeting in the village street (26x38cm-10x15in) s.d.1854. 18-Sep-3 Christie's, Kensington #9/R est:1200-1800
£1594 $2614 €2200 Paysan et son chien sous les pommiers. Bergere au bord de la riviere (13x8cm-5x3in) s. panel pair. 11-May-3 Osenat, Fontainebleau #155/R est:2600-3000
£3169 $5261 €4500 Regates (27x46cm-11x18in) s.d.1884. 15-Jun-3 Peron, Melun #205
£3497 $6014 €5000 Bords de l'Oise a Auvers-sur-Oise (39x54cm-15x21in) s.d.1856. 7-Dec-3 Osenat, Fontainebleau #86 est:5000-5500
£5072 $8319 €7000 Un dimanche au bord de la mer (44x75cm-17x30in) s.d.1873. 11-May-3 Osenat, Fontainebleau #156/R est:9000-10000
£5631 $9685 €8221 Landscape with stream, women washing and ducks (54x73cm-21x29in) s.d.1858. 8-Dec-3 Philippe Schuler, Zurich #3440/R est:8000-12000 (S.FR 12500)
£7692 $13231 €11000 Les cerisiers a Bonnieres (60x92cm-24x36in) s.d.1873. 7-Dec-3 Osenat, Fontainebleau #87 est:12000-13000
£8889 $16000 €12978 Lavandiere au bord de l'eau (54x74cm-21x29in) s.d.1858. 23-Apr-4 Sotheby's, New York #158/R est:14000-18000

VERON, Theodore (1821-1898) French
£1678 $3087 €2500 Scene from Macbeth (98x130cm-39x51in) s.d.68. 24-Mar-4 Il Ponte, Milan #583 est:3000-3500

VERONE (20th C) Swiss
£1719 $2871 €2510 Toutes griffes dehors (54x65cm-21x26in) s. acrylic. 24-Jun-3 Germann, Zurich #129/R est:4000-5000 (S.FR 3800)

VERONESE (16th C) Italian
Works on paper
£369 $650 €539 Putti (44x17cm-17x7in) pen brown ink. 19-May-4 Doyle, New York #6004/R

VERONESE (style) (16th C) Italian
£10989 $20000 €16044 Mystic marriage of Saint Catherine (255x152cm-100x60in) 17-Jun-4 Christie's, Rockefeller NY #41/R est:20000-30000

VERONESE SCHOOL (17th C) Italian
£6500 $11700 €9490 The Annunciation (23x29cm-9x11in) slate. 22-Apr-4 Sotheby's, London #66/R est:5000-7000
£7778 $14000 €11356 Capture of Samson (47x54cm-19x21in) oil on slate. 22-Jan-4 Sotheby's, New York #273/R est:12000-16000

VERONESE SCHOOL (18th C) Italian
£7042 $11690 €10000 Madonna and Child with Saint Dominique and Anthony (115x13cm-45x5in) 11-Jul-3 Finarte, Venice #545/R est:9000-11000

VERONESE, Paolo (after) (1528-1588) Italian
£6077 $11000 €8872 Finding of Moses (97x148cm-38x58in) 30-Mar-4 Christie's, Rockefeller NY #26/R est:7000-9000
£6901 $11939 €9800 Darius' family before Alexander (50x95cm-20x37in) 14-Dec-3 Finarte, Venice #99/R est:8000-9000

VERONESE, Paolo (attrib) (1528-1588) Italian
£37000 $66600 €54020 Knight and his page (93x74cm-37x29in) fragment lit. 21-Apr-4 Christie's, London #95/R est:10000-15000
Works on paper
£629 $1145 €950 Three women driving a man away with brooms and sticks (18x30cm-7x12in) ink pen. 16-Jun-4 Hugo Ruef, Munich #1122/R

VERONESE, Paolo (style) (1528-1588) Italian
£10717 $19183 €15647 The Finding of Moses (93x132cm-37x52in) 25-May-4 Bukowskis, Stockholm #431/R est:100000-125000 (S.KR 145000)

VERONESI, Luigi (1908-1998) Italian
£544 $974 €800 Composition (24x39cm-9x15in) s.d.64 s.i.d.verso pencil paper on board. 16-Mar-4 Finarte Semenzato, Milan #273/R
£1141 $2111 €1700 Geometry (35x25cm-14x10in) s.d.1978 tempera card. 13-Mar-4 Meeting Art, Vercelli #352 est:1500
£2685 $4805 €4000 Composition C 6 (50x40cm-20x16in) s.d.1994. 30-May-4 Meeting Art, Vercelli #42 est:4000
£2993 $5358 €4400 Composition (72x59cm-28x23in) s.d.1957 s.i.d.verso paper on canvas. 16-Mar-4 Finarte Semenzato, Milan #272/R est:550
£3221 $5766 €4800 Composition M5 (50x40cm-20x16in) s.d.95 s.i.d.verso. 28-May-4 Farsetti, Prato #348/R est:4500-5000
£4196 $7133 €6000 Composition SCIN13 (100x80cm-39x31in) s.d.91 acrylic. 24-Nov-3 Christie's, Milan #177/R est:5000-7000
£5705 $10211 €8500 Composition B6 (70x50cm-28x20in) s.d.68 s.i.d.verso canvas on board prov. 25-May-4 Sotheby's, Milan #156/R est:6000
£6000 $11040 €9000 Light 2 (50x70cm-20x28in) s. s.i.d.1953 verso prov.exhib. 14-Jun-4 Porro, Milan #26/R est:9000-11000
£6993 $11888 €10000 Organic 64 (48x69cm-19x27in) s.d.1964 canvas on board. 20-Nov-3 Finarte Semenzato, Milan #179/R est:10000-12000

VERREYT, Jacob Johan (1807-1872) Flemish
£806 $1484 €1177 Skaters and peasants on a frozen river (38x50cm-15x20in) panel. 14-Jun-4 Waddingtons, Toronto #41/R est:3000-5000 (C.D 2000)

VERRIER, Jean (?) ?
£6040 $10691 €9000 Fonderie (242x210cm-95x83in) s. prov. 27-Apr-4 Claude Aguttes, Neuilly #51/R

VERRIER, Maurice (1917-) French
£331 $600 €483 Tabletop still life (33x43cm-13x17in) s. board. 2-Apr-4 Freeman, Philadelphia #127

VERRIER, Max le (19/20th C) Belgian
Sculpture
£1000 $1840 €1500 Femme porteuse de plateau (50cm-20in) s. pat bronze blk marble base table lamp. 9-Jun-4 Beaussant & Lefèvre, Paris #242/R est:800-1000
£1100 $1980 €1606 Nude male hunter (51cm-20in) i. bronzed spelter stone base. 22-Apr-4 Christie's, Kensington #504/R est:700-900
£1469 $2497 €2100 Jeune homme au lion (56x59x22cm-22x23x9in) s. pat bronze marble socle. 27-Nov-3 Claude Aguttes, Neuilly #114/R est:1800-2000
£2222 $3711 €3200 Light (84cm-33in) i. pat.metal glass marble. 25-Oct-3 Auktionhaus Herr, Cologne #321/R est:2100-4200

VERROCCHI, Agostino (circle) (17th C) Italian
£6800 $11764 €9928 Fruit, cheese, bottle, glass on a marble ledge, with snail and butterfly (61x112cm-24x44in) 12-Dec-3 Christie's, Kensington #262/R est:7000-10000

VERRYCK, Theodor (1734-1786) Dutch
Works on paper
£400 $692 €584 River landscape with bridge and town beyond (24x32cm-9x13in) pen grey ink wash. 12-Dec-3 Christie's, Kensington #533
£2083 $3750 €3041 View of the Witte Vrowen Poort, Utrecht (26x40cm-10x16in) s. pen ink wash htd white prov.exhib. 21-Jan-4 Sotheby's, New York #134/R est:3000-4000

VERSCHAEREN, Theodoor (1874-1937) Belgian
£867 $1560 €1300 Young woman with fruit bowl (114x88cm-45x35in) s.d.1924. 26-Apr-4 Bernaerts, Antwerp #210/R
£867 $1560 €1300 Young couple at the table (100x90cm-39x35in) s. 26-Apr-4 Bernaerts, Antwerp #213/R
£966 $1612 €1400 Le mariage (116x84cm-46x33in) s.d.1928. 17-Nov-3 Bernaerts, Antwerp #359/R
£1200 $2160 €1800 At the opera (110x100cm-43x39in) s.d.1928. 26-Apr-4 Bernaerts, Antwerp #214/R est:1250-1500
£1333 $2400 €2000 Young girl playing the guitar with lover (96x97cm-38x38in) s.d.1936. 26-Apr-4 Bernaerts, Antwerp #212/R est:2000-3000
£1379 $2303 €2000 Le repas (123x100cm-48x39in) s.d.1928. 17-Nov-3 Bernaerts, Antwerp #357/R est:1000-1500
£1379 $2303 €2000 Fete de naissance (147x147cm-58x58in) s.d.1929. 17-Nov-3 Bernaerts, Antwerp #358/R est:1000-1500
£2069 $3455 €3000 Le critique. s.d.1929. 17-Nov-3 Bernaerts, Antwerp #360/R est:1000-1500
£2207 $3686 €3200 Les fiancailles (136x133cm-54x52in) s.d.1928. 17-Nov-3 Bernaerts, Antwerp #361/R est:1000-1500
£2400 $4320 €3600 Motherhood (135x108cm-53x43in) s.d.1928. 26-Apr-4 Bernaerts, Antwerp #215/R est:3000-4000

VERSCHAFFELT, Edouard (1874-1955) Belgian
£733 $1342 €1100 Nu vu de dos (47x35cm-19x14in) s. 7-Jun-4 Palais de Beaux Arts, Brussels #118/R
£1348 $2250 €1900 Marabout devant la mer (40x55cm-16x22in) s. 19-Oct-3 Rabourdin & Choppin de Janvry, Paris #152/R est:1500-2000
£1944 $3053 €2800 Portrait d'enfant (50x30cm-20x12in) s. 26-Aug-3 Galerie Moderne, Brussels #347/R est:2000-3000
£4000 $7240 €6000 L'heure du the (75x90cm-30x35in) s. 30-Mar-4 Palais de Beaux Arts, Brussels #735/R est:7000-9000
£4000 $7360 €6000 Scene de marche a Bou-Saada (41x30cm-16x12in) s. 14-Jun-4 Gros & Delettrez, Paris #477/R est:5000-7000
£6993 $12028 €10000 Roulage du grain (60x81cm-24x32in) s. 8-Dec-3 Tajan, Paris #337/R est:10000-12000
£10638 $17766 €15000 Le vieillard et l'enfant (101x84cm-40x33in) s. 16-Jun-3 Gros & Delettrez, Paris #431/R est:12000-15000
£12588 $21651 €18000 Jeune fille au foulard rouge (80x59cm-31x23in) s. 8-Dec-3 Tajan, Paris #338/R est:6000-8000

VERSCHININ, Ilja Jevgenivits (1859-1913) Russian
£2797 $4755 €4000 View of a harbour (40x27cm-16x11in) s. 29-Nov-3 Bukowskis, Helsinki #421/R est:4100-4300

VERSCHNEIDER, Jean (1872-1943) French
Sculpture
£1241 $2272 €1800 Le tambour (48cm-19in) s. brown pat bronze. 31-Jan-4 Osenat, Fontainebleau #603

£3591 $6500 €5243 Allegorical figure representing speed (74cm-29in) i. silvered bronze executed c.1925 prov. 30-Mar-4 Sotheby's, New York #184/R est:4000-6000

VERSCHUIER, Lieve (1630-1686) Dutch

£18000 $32940 €26280 Calm river scene with vessels (86x112cm-34x44in) s. prov.exhib.lit. 8-Jul-4 Sotheby's, London #120/R est:15000-20000

VERSCHURING, Hendrik (1627-1690) Dutch

Works on paper

£3889 $7000 €5678 Battle scene with trumpets blowing the retreat (36x45cm-14x18in) s.d.1662 pen grey ink wash prov. 22-Jan-4 Christie's, Rockefeller NY #122/R est:4000-6000

VERSCHUUR, Cornelius (19th C) Dutch

£822 $1397 €1200 Milking time (30x39cm-12x15in) s. 5-Nov-3 Vendue Huis, Gravenhage #236/R
£1049 $1751 €1500 Sheperdess with her flock (51x76cm-20x30in) s. 30-Jun-3 Sotheby's, Amsterdam #302

VERSCHUUR, Wouter (jnr) (1841-1936) Dutch

£1600 $2720 €2336 Horses and goat in a woodland (13x17cm-5x7in) s. panel. 29-Oct-3 Bonhams, Chester #486 est:1500-2000
£3500 $6545 €5250 Timber yard with men and horses at work (58x76cm-23x30in) s. 26-Jul-4 Bonhams, Bath #98/R est:3000-4000

VERSCHUUR, Wouter (snr) (1812-1874) Dutch

£1034 $1728 €1500 Paysan au travail au bord de l'eau (6x10cm-2x4in) panel. 17-Nov-3 Bernaerts, Antwerp #10 est:1000-1200
£4861 $8118 €7000 Horse in a stable (16x21cm-6x8in) s.d.1847 panel. 21-Oct-3 Sotheby's, Amsterdam #165/R est:10000-15000
£5000 $9200 €7500 Horses watering (20x28cm-8x11in) s.d.1846. 10-Jun-4 Christie's, Rome #128/R est:7000-10000
£9722 $16528 €14000 Grey in a stable (15x18cm-6x7in) s. panel painted oval prov. 28-Oct-3 Christie's, Amsterdam #45/R est:12000-16000
£10000 $18200 €15000 Tending to the horse (15x19cm-6x7in) s. panel. 1-Jul-4 Christie's, Amsterdam #715/R est:15000-20000
£17333 $31200 €26000 On the way (50x63cm-20x25in) s.d.1851 prov. 21-Apr-4 Christie's, Amsterdam #223/R est:30000-50000

VERSPRONCK, Jan (1597-1662) Dutch

£4444 $8000 €6488 Portrait of a gentleman of the Dicx family (82x68cm-32x27in) s.d.1637 prov.exhib.lit. 21-Jan-4 Sotheby's, New York #63/R est:8000-12000

VERSTER, Andrew (1937-) South African

£556 $944 €812 Swamp (90x120cm-35x47in) s.d.86 diptych. 4-Nov-3 Stephan Welz, Johannesburg #604/R est:7000-10000 (SA.R 6500)
£556 $944 €812 Untitled (147x156cm-58x61in) s.d.92 triptych exhib. 4-Nov-3 Stephan Welz, Johannesburg #695/R est:7000-10000 (SA.R 6500)

VERSTER, Floris (1861-1927) Dutch

£1944 $3247 €2800 Duinlandscap (24x37cm-9x15in) s.d.86 canvas on panel prov.exhib.lit. 21-Oct-3 Sotheby's, Amsterdam #94/R est:3000-5000
£3472 $5903 €5000 Zinnias in a vase (35x30cm-14x12in) init. prov. 28-Oct-3 Christie's, Amsterdam #175/R est:5000-7000
£3472 $5799 €5000 Three tin jugs (31x39cm-12x15in) s.d.04 oil on paper prov.exhib.lit. 21-Oct-3 Sotheby's, Amsterdam #88/R est:8000-12000
£5333 $9600 €8000 Flowers in a ginger jar (27x21cm-11x8in) s.d.10 panel prov.lit. 21-Apr-4 Christie's, Amsterdam #137/R est:8000-12000
£18056 $30694 €26000 Roses in a clay pot (35x30cm-14x12in) s.d.09 prov.lit. 28-Oct-3 Christie's, Amsterdam #186/R est:8000-12000
£18667 $33600 €28000 Twee dode roeken (24x53cm-9x21in) s.d.07 cardboard prov.exhib.lit. 21-Apr-4 Christie's, Amsterdam #125/R est:28000-38000

VERSTOCKT, Mark (1930-) Belgian

£417 $696 €600 Composition verticale (126x48cm-50x19in) s. d.1962 verso. 21-Oct-3 Campo & Campo, Antwerp #353/R

Works on paper

£745 $1244 €1050 Horizon (98x98cm-39x39in) s.d.09-92 verso graphite. 20-Oct-3 Bernaerts, Antwerp #243/R

VERSTRAETE, Eugene (19th C) Belgian

£520 $972 €780 Mountain and lakeside scene with figures (46x78cm-18x31in) s.i.d.1891. 22-Jul-4 Martel Maides, Guernsey #230/R

VERSTRAETE, Theodore (1850-1907) Belgian

£3239 $5604 €4600 Landscape with woman and cow (22x36cm-9x14in) s. s.i verso panel. 13-Dec-3 Lempertz, Koln #60/R est:2000

VERSTRAETEN, Edmond (1870-1956) Belgian

£336 $624 €500 Landscape (40x50cm-16x20in) mono. 8-Mar-4 Bernaerts, Antwerp #614/R
£493 $853 €700 Farm in the snow (27x36cm-11x14in) mono. prov. 13-Dec-3 De Vuyst, Lokeren #389
£537 $993 €800 Morning mist (26x35cm-10x14in) mono.d.1926. 13-Mar-4 De Vuyst, Lokeren #380
£764 $1276 €1100 Au verger (43x64cm-17x25in) s.d.1914. 21-Oct-3 Campo, Vlaamse Kaai #625
£915 $1584 €1300 Waasmunster farm in the snow (45x100cm-18x39in) mono. 13-Dec-3 De Vuyst, Lokeren #387/R
£979 $1635 €1400 River landscape with fisherman (35x100cm-14x39in) mono.d.1928. 11-Oct-3 De Vuyst, Lokeren #393/R
£1133 $2029 €1700 Snowy landscape (65x100cm-26x39in) mono.d.15. 15-May-4 De Vuyst, Lokeren #399/R est:1500-2000
£1241 $2073 €1800 Paysage estival anime d'une bergere a l'enfant (44x66cm-17x26in) 17-Nov-3 Bernaerts, Antwerp #338/R est:450-600
£2676 $4630 €3800 Fun on the ice in Waasmunster (45x100cm-18x39in) mono.d.1949. 13-Dec-3 De Vuyst, Lokeren #386/R est:1800-2200

VERSTRALEN, Anthonie (1594-1641) Dutch

£9459 $16649 €14000 River landscape with a ferry and figures resting in the foreground, farm beyond (29x35cm-11x14in) mono. panel. 18-May-4 Sotheby's, Amsterdam #105/R est:3000-4000

VERTANGEN, Daniel (1598-1684) Dutch

£2245 $4018 €3300 Dancing nymphs and satyrs by river (31x37cm-12x15in) s. panel. 17-Mar-4 Neumeister, Munich #385/R est:3000
£2600 $4680 €3796 Baptism of Christ (34x35cm-13x14in) mono. panel. 20-Apr-4 Sotheby's, Olympia #277/R est:1200-1800
£6000 $10980 €8760 Bacchanal (35x45cm-14x18in) s. panel. 7-Jul-4 Bonhams, New Bond Street #104/R est:6000-8000

VERTANGEN, Daniel (attrib) (1598-1684) Dutch

£750 $1200 €1095 A Bacchanalia with a Satyr and Nymphs in an extensive landscape (26x34cm-10x13in) panel. 21-Sep-3 Bonhams & Butterfields, San Francisco #2791/R est:1500-2000

VERTES, Marcel (1895-1961) French

£1796 $3000 €2622 In the boudoir (25x42cm-10x17in) s. masonite. 7-Oct-3 Sotheby's, New York #306 est:2000-3000
£1986 $3316 €2800 Au pays des pierrots, l'ensemble (89x146cm-35x57in) s. 19-Jun-3 Millon & Associes, Paris #249/R est:3000-4000
£1989 $3500 €2904 La vase Vallanris (61x74cm-24x29in) s. prov. 18-May-4 Arthur James, Florida #153 est:2000-3000
£2446 $4500 €3571 Ballerina (46x33cm-18x13in) s.d.1947 prov. 23-Mar-4 Arthur James, Florida #330/R est:3000-5000

Works on paper

£240 $400 €350 Woman with hat (39x26cm-15x10in) s. mixed media. 19-Oct-3 Bonhams & Butterfields, Los Angeles #7066
£242 $445 €353 Portrait of a woman (33x41cm-13x16in) s. pastel. 14-Jun-4 Waddingtons, Toronto #260/R (C.D 600)
£350 $595 €511 Pegasus (24x20cm-9x8in) s. chl W/C. 2-Nov-3 Lots Road Auctions, London #338
£389 $700 €568 By the open window (30x25cm-12x10in) s. W/C crayon. 20-Jan-4 Arthur James, Florida #126
£503 $805 €734 Woman with flower children and flower dog (48x64cm-19x25in) s. W/C graphite gouache. 20-Sep-3 Jeffery Burchard, Florida #76/R
£682 $1200 €996 Four ballet dancers (56x66cm-22x26in) s. mixed media. 21-May-4 North East Auctions, Portsmouth #1104/R
£920 $1500 €1343 Portrait de Colette (53x44cm-21x17in) s. W/C brush black ink paper on board prov.lit. 25-Sep-3 Christie's, Rockefeller NY #597/R est:3000-5000

VERTEVILLE, Christian de la (1949-) French

Works on paper

£694 $1090 €1000 Courses (15x22cm-6x9in) W/C. 29-Aug-3 Deauville, France #188

VERTEVILLE, Jean de (20th C) French

Works on paper

£632 $992 €910 Longchamp (16x20cm-6x8in) W/C. 29-Aug-3 Deauville, France #191

VERTIN, Petrus Gerardus (1819-1893) Dutch

£892 $1373 €1400 Canal in Amsterdam (26x35cm-10x14in) s. 4-Sep-2 Schopman, Hamburg #48/R
£1250 $2263 €1900 Figures in a ferry boat on the river in front of the city port (20x26cm-8x10in) s.d.1840 panel. 19-Apr-4 Glerum, Amsterdam #17/R est:2500-3500
£1262 $2335 €1843 Dutch town scene in winter (27x20cm-11x8in) s. 15-Mar-4 Rasmussen, Vejle #354/R est:3000 (D.KR 14000)
£2000 $3680 €2920 Dutch street scene (20x18cm-8x7in) s. panel. 25-Mar-4 Christie's, Kensington #163/R est:2500-3000
£2267 $4057 €3400 Old Dutch street with cart and many figures (22x17cm-9x7in) s. panel. 11-May-4 Vendu Notarishuis, Rotterdam #63/R est:3000-4000
£3000 $5400 €4500 Townsfolks in a Dutch street (15x20cm-6x8in) s.d.64 panel. 21-Apr-4 Christie's, Amsterdam #17/R est:5000-7000
£3333 $6000 €5000 Figures by a canal in a Dutch town (45x35cm-18x14in) s.d.88. 21-Apr-4 Christie's, Amsterdam #74/R est:5000-7000
£3467 $6275 €5200 Winter in the streets of The Hague (26x19cm-10x7in) s.d.47 panel. 1-Apr-4 Van Ham, Cologne #1691/R est:2800
£3472 $5903 €5000 Busy street in a Dutch town in winter (19x15cm-7x6in) s.d.67 panel. 28-Oct-3 Christie's, Amsterdam #96/R est:5000-7000
£3472 $5799 €5000 Villagers in the streets of a Dutch town (24x20cm-9x8in) s.d.57 panel. 21-Oct-3 Sotheby's, Amsterdam #13/R est:5000-7000
£3488 $6000 €5092 Villagers in a Dutch town (30x41cm-12x16in) s. panel. 7-Dec-3 Freeman, Philadelphia #19 est:3000-5000
£4000 $7200 €6000 Winter, sunlit street in a Dutch town (45x35cm-18x14in) s.indis.d.81. 21-Apr-4 Christie's, Amsterdam #213/R est:7000-9000
£4333 $7800 €6500 Jewish quarter, Amsterdam (19x15cm-7x6in) s.indis.d.68 panel. 21-Apr-4 Christie's, Amsterdam #7/R est:5000-7000
£4333 $7800 €6500 Canal in a Dutch town in summer (23x19cm-9x7in) s.d.82 panel. 21-Apr-4 Christie's, Amsterdam #63/R est:4000-6000
£5000 $9000 €7500 Figures by a church in a Dutch village (26x34cm-10x13in) s.d.67 panel. 21-Apr-4 Christie's, Amsterdam #1/R est:4000-6000
£5208 $8854 €7500 Roasting chestnuts - a Dutch town in winter (26x19cm-10x7in) s.d.83 panel. 28-Oct-3 Christie's, Amsterdam #2/R est:5000-7000
£5208 $8698 €7500 Snowy street scene (22x17cm-9x7in) s.d.82 panel prov. 21-Oct-3 Sotheby's, Amsterdam #52/R est:5000-7000
£5442 $9905 €8000 Townsfolk in a sunlit street (24x33cm-9x13in) s. panel. 3-Feb-4 Christie's, Amsterdam #73/R est:7000-9000
£5882 $10000 €8588 Street scene in winter with figures in the foreground (62x49cm-24x19in) s.i.d.80. 19-Nov-3 Bonhams & Butterfields, San Francisco #62/R
£7778 $14000 €11356 Villagers in a Dutch town (34x27cm-13x11in) s.d.65 panel. 22-Apr-4 Christie's, Rockefeller NY #18/R est:10000-15000

£9028 $15076 €13000 Busy street in a Dutch town (31x23cm-12x9in) s.d.50 panel. 21-Oct-3 Sotheby's, Amsterdam #45/R est:10000-15000
£13194 $22035 €19000 View of a canal with the Westerkerk in the background, Amsterdam (61x49cm-24x19in) s.d.81. 21-Oct-3 Sotheby's, Amsterdam #195/R est:15000-20000
£13889 $23194 €20000 Flirtation (58x46cm-23x18in) s.d.1830 panel prov. 21-Oct-3 Sotheby's, Amsterdam #189/R est:20000-30000

VERTUE, George (1684-1756) British
Works on paper
£6000 $10980 €8760 Portrait of Edmund, Duke of Buckingham, full-length in state dress (46x28cm-18x11in) s.i.d.1742 pencil W/C htd white gold vellum. 3-Jun-4 Christie's, London #47/R est:6000-8000

VERTUNNI, Achille (1826-1897) Italian
£400 $716 €600 Landscape at sunset with peasant woman (26x14cm-10x6in) s. board. 13-May-4 Babuino, Rome #259
£2717 $5000 €3967 Extensive landscape with village on a hillside overlooking a lake (67x95cm-26x37in) s. canvas on paperboard oval. 8-Jun-4 Auctions by the Bay, Alameda #1003/R
£3056 $5194 €4400 Pasture and ruins (42x71cm-17x28in) s. 1-Nov-3 Meeting Art, Vercelli #394/R est:1500

VERTUNNI, Achille (attrib) (1826-1897) Italian
£987 $1816 €1500 Countryside with herd and ruins (13x40cm-5x16in) i.on stretcher. 23-Jun-4 Finarte Semenzato, Rome #97/R est:1500-1800

VERUDA, Umberto (1868-1904) Italian
£1538 $2646 €2200 Portrait of man (70x53cm-28x21in) s. canvas on board lit. 3-Dec-3 Stadion, Trieste #1161/R est:2000-3000
£1678 $2887 €2400 Portrait of bearded man (46x39cm-18x15in) s. s.verso. 3-Dec-3 Stadion, Trieste #1165/R est:2500-3500
£1733 $3103 €2600 Portrait of Ugo Flumiani (59x40cm-23x16in) s.on stretcher. 12-May-4 Stadion, Trieste #782/R est:1800-2200
£7343 $12629 €10500 Awakening (115x76cm-45x30in) s. 3-Dec-3 Stadion, Trieste #1034/R est:10000-15000

VERVEER, Elchanon Leonardus (1826-1900) Dutch
£276 $500 €420 Portrait of a dog (33x25cm-13x10in) s. board. 19-Apr-4 Glerum, Amsterdam #99/R
£698 $1200 €1019 Beach with fisherman (46x61cm-18x24in) 6-Dec-3 South Bay, Long Island #179/R
£884 $1610 €1300 Mending nets (11x10cm-4x4in) s.d.79 panel. 3-Feb-4 Christie's, Amsterdam #142/R est:1000-1500
£2667 $4800 €4000 Playing with the baby (28x35cm-11x14in) s.d.71. 20-Apr-4 Sotheby's, Amsterdam #39/R est:4000-6000
£32000 $57600 €48000 Les voila, au bord de la mer (111x159cm-44x63in) s. prov. 21-Apr-4 Christie's, Amsterdam #218/R est:8000-12000
Works on paper
£315 $541 €450 Two girls gathering wood (23x17cm-9x7in) s. W/C. 8-Dec-3 Glerum, Amsterdam #20/R

VERVEER, Salomon Leonardus (1813-1876) Dutch
£1900 $3496 €2774 Barges on a river, Rotterdam (18x28cm-7x11in) 25-Mar-4 Christie's, Kensington #166/R est:2000-3000
£3333 $6000 €5000 Figures in the dunes near Scheveningen (18x27cm-7x11in) s.d.66 panel. 20-Apr-4 Sotheby's, Amsterdam #113/R est:5000-7000
£3896 $6974 €5688 Town on Dutch coast with figures and animals (91x152cm-36x60in) s. 22-Mar-4 Philippe Schuler, Zurich #4434/R est:12000-16000 (S.FR 9000)
Works on paper
£2778 $4639 €4000 Town view with figures by a canal (19x28cm-7x11in) s. W/C. 21-Oct-3 Sotheby's, Amsterdam #217/R est:4000-6000

VERVISCH, Jean (1896-1977) Belgian
£317 $555 €450 Marine (50x60cm-20x24in) s. cardboard. 16-Dec-3 Galerie Moderne, Brussels #663
£382 $638 €550 Maternite hivernale (64x47cm-25x19in) s. panel. 21-Oct-3 Galerie Moderne, Brussels #287/R
£451 $754 €650 Maternite hivernale (70x56cm-28x22in) s. 21-Oct-3 Galerie Moderne, Brussels #247/R
£946 $1693 €1400 Jeune femme sur fond de patineurs (50x60cm-20x24in) s. 10-May-4 Horta, Bruxelles #437/R
Works on paper
£385 $662 €550 Jeune femme nue (110x72cm-43x28in) s.i.d.1950 chl. 8-Dec-3 Horta, Bruxelles #353

VERVLOET, Augustine (1806-?) Belgian
£2703 $4757 €4000 Still life with flowers (46x38cm-18x15in) s.d.1870 panel. 24-May-4 Bernaerts, Antwerp #465/R est:2000-2500

VERVLOET, Frans (1795-1872) Dutch
£2639 $4143 €3800 Vue de Venise (22x26cm-9x10in) s.d.1853. 26-Aug-3 Galerie Moderne, Brussels #269/R est:3000-4000
£3310 $5726 €4700 Monk at his work (32x25cm-13x10in) s.i.d.1827. 13-Dec-3 De Vuyst, Lokeren #390/R est:1600-2000

VERVLOET, Victor (1829-1904) Belgian
£1208 $2235 €1800 Brugges by night (102x140cm-40x55in) s.i.d.1894. 13-Mar-4 De Vuyst, Lokeren #381/R est:1500-2000

VERWEE, Alfred Jacques (1838-1895) Belgian
£475 $850 €694 Barnyard animal scene (43x61cm-17x24in) s. 8-May-4 Susanin's, Chicago #6135/R
£709 $1341 €1050 Vache au bord de l'Escaut (40x32cm-16x13in) s. 17-Feb-4 Vanderkindere, Brussels #23
£1149 $2171 €1700 Cheval blanc (40x32cm-16x13in) s. 17-Feb-4 Vanderkindere, Brussels #24 est:1250-1750
£3121 $5211 €4400 Etalon prime (71x56cm-28x22in) s. 14-Oct-3 Vanderkindere, Brussels #115
£3221 $5960 €4800 Horses in the polder (43x60cm-17x24in) s. panel prov.exhib.lit. 13-Mar-4 De Vuyst, Lokeren #522/R est:4500-5000
£3262 $5448 €4600 Charrette a Knokke (50x60cm-20x24in) s.d.1889. 17-Jun-3 Galerie Moderne, Brussels #239/R est:2000-3000
£4459 $8428 €6600 Cheval et vaches au pre (105x135cm-41x53in) s.d.1889. 17-Feb-4 Vanderkindere, Brussels #44/R est:3500-8500

VERWEE, Charles Louis (?-1882) Belgian
£1342 $2483 €2000 In front of the mirror (49x37cm-19x15in) s. panel. 13-Mar-4 De Vuyst, Lokeren #382/R est:2400-2800

VERWEE, L P (1807-1877) Belgian
£1538 $2615 €2200 Moutons au paturage (17x25cm-7x10in) s. panel. 1-Dec-3 Palais de Beaux Arts, Brussels #336/R est:1500-2000

VERWEE, Louis Pierre (1807-1877) Belgian
£1477 $2717 €2200 Les moutons (24x32cm-9x13in) s. panel. 23-Mar-4 Galerie Moderne, Brussels #225/R est:1200-1600
£3600 $5724 €5220 Cattle grazing in a wooded landscape (62x76cm-24x30in) s.d.1843. 9-Sep-3 Bonhams, Knightsbridge #99/R est:2000-3000
£4138 $7655 €6000 Paysage d'hiver aux patineurs (50x68cm-20x27in) s. 13-Jan-4 Vanderkindere, Brussels #73 est:1500-2500
£5556 $9278 €8000 Herdsman with his cattle on a path (49x62cm-19x24in) s.d.40 panel. 21-Oct-3 Sotheby's, Amsterdam #35/R est:8000-12000

VERWER, Abraham de (?-1650) Dutch
£5500 $9130 €8030 Dutch warship at anchor in an estuary another small vessel nearby (52x74cm-20x29in) panel prov. 30-Sep-3 Sotheby's, London #258/R est:6000-8000
£7000 $12110 €10220 View of Vlissingen with shipping (53x73cm-21x29in) prov. 12-Dec-3 Christie's, Kensington #66/R est:8000-12000
Works on paper
£1712 $2911 €2500 Panoramic landscape with boats on a river, a town beyond (9x36cm-4x14in) bears sig.d.1636 pen brown ink col wash over black chk prov. 4-Nov-3 Sotheby's, Amsterdam #94/R est:3000-5000

VERWEY, Kees (1900-1995) Dutch
£1645 $3026 €2500 Vase with flowers (40x30cm-16x12in) s. s.i. verso prov. 28-Jun-4 Sotheby's, Amsterdam #251/R est:2500-3500
£2133 $3925 €3200 Still life with flowers (50x40cm-20x16in) s.d.1975. 8-Jun-4 Sotheby's, Amsterdam #238/R est:2500-3500
£2667 $4880 €4000 Spaarndam (34x38cm-13x15in) s.d.24 panel prov. 7-Jun-4 Glerum, Amsterdam #85/R est:4000-5000
£3200 $5888 €4800 Still life with flowers in a blue glass vase (80x70cm-31x28in) s.d.67 prov. 9-Jun-4 Christie's, Amsterdam #119/R est:4000-6000
Works on paper
£685 $1164 €1000 Still life (32x49cm-13x19in) s. W/C. 5-Nov-3 Vendue Huis, Gravenhage #220
£694 $1132 €1000 View of houses with palm trees (45x55cm-18x22in) s.indis.i.d.26 W/C. 29-Sep-3 Sotheby's, Amsterdam #344
£1497 $2724 €2200 Summer bouquet (21x27cm-8x11in) s.d.74 W/C prov. 3-Feb-4 Christie's, Amsterdam #611/R est:800-1200
£1538 $2646 €2200 Flowers in a glass vase (33x24cm-13x9in) s. W/C prov. 7-Dec-3 Sotheby's, Amsterdam #713/R
£1818 $3127 €2600 Still life with flowers (50x70cm-20x28in) s.d.77 W/C prov. 2-Dec-3 Sotheby's, Amsterdam #258/R est:2500-3000
£2667 $4907 €4000 Tuin te Haarlem (36x53cm-14x21in) s. W/C. 8-Jun-4 Sotheby's, Amsterdam #236/R est:4000-6000
£2797 $4811 €4000 Visser in Roeiboot (24x32cm-9x13in) s. W/C. 2-Dec-3 Sotheby's, Amsterdam #254/R est:3000-4000
£2899 $4754 €4000 Still life (46x62cm-18x24in) s.d.88 W/C. 27-May-3 Sotheby's, Amsterdam #496/R est:4000-6000

VESIN, Jaroslav Fr Julius (1859-1915) Bulgarian
£4698 $8315 €7000 Csar Nicholas II (42x62cm-17x24in) s. 28-Apr-4 Wiener Kunst Auktionen, Vienna #33/R est:7000-15000
£5369 $9503 €8000 After the hunt (50x75cm-20x30in) s. 28-Apr-4 Wiener Kunst Auktionen, Vienna #34/R est:8000-15000
£8824 $15000 €12883 Hunting Party (69x120cm-27x47in) s.i. 28-Oct-3 Sotheby's, New York #116/R est:15000-20000

VESPIGNANI, Renzo (1924-2001) Italian
£1655 $2764 €2400 Reclining female nude (72x102cm-28x40in) s.d.1972 oil mixed media paper on canvas. 17-Nov-3 Sant Agostino, Torino #91/R est:2000-2500
£1812 $3207 €2700 Amerique a Rome (60x46cm-24x18in) init.d.1944. 28-Apr-4 Charbonneaux, Paris #233/R est:1000-1200
£2941 $5500 €4294 Figure and car (71x99cm-28x39in) s.d.58 paper on canvas prov. 25-Feb-4 Christie's, Rockefeller NY #107/R est:6000-8000
£3655 $6104 €5300 Along the river (29x41cm-11x16in) s.d.1949 exhib. 13-Nov-3 Finarte Semenzato, Rome #309/R est:4500-5500
£4392 $7730 €6500 Portrait of woman with dog (100x64cm-39x25in) s.d.1960 paper on canvas prov.exhib. 24-May-4 Christie's, Milan #226/R est:7000-10000
£4392 $7730 €6500 Urban landscape (70x100cm-28x39in) s.d.1961 paper on canvas. 24-May-4 Christie's, Milan #225/R est:6000-8000
£4514 $7674 €6500 Composition (70x100cm-28x39in) s.d.1961 prov. 28-Oct-3 Il Ponte, Milan #243/R
Works on paper
£268 $475 €400 Jeune fille a la partition Chopin (37x24cm-15x9in) s.d.1945 Indian ink. 28-Apr-4 Charbonneaux, Paris #231
£268 $475 €400 Nu au corset de dos (42x24cm-17x9in) s.d.1946 Indian ink. 28-Apr-4 Charbonneaux, Paris #232
£302 $561 €450 Leaves (20x29cm-8x11in) s.i.d.1984 pencil. 4-Mar-4 Babuino, Rome #163
£1517 $2534 €2200 Roses (33x45cm-13x18in) s.d.1998 pastel W/C card. 13-Nov-3 Galleria Pace, Milan #119/R est:3300

£	$	€	Description
£1664	$2829	€2380	Nude (100x53cm-39x21in) s.d.1961 Chinese ink. 18-Nov-3 Babuino, Rome #137/R est:1500-1800
£2238	$3804	€3200	Reclining figure (72x100cm-28x39in) s.d.66 mixed media. 24-Nov-3 Christie's, Milan #27/R est:2500-3000
£2585	$4627	€3800	One and another (100x120cm-39x47in) s.i.d.1965 mixed media paper on canvas. 16-Mar-4 Finarte Semenzato, Milan #325/R est:4000
£4027	$7490	€6000	Suburbs (70x105cm-28x41in) s.d.1963 W/C Chinese ink card on canvas. 4-Mar-4 Babuino, Rome #397 est:3000-4000

VESSELOVSKII, Andrei (?) Russian

£748	$1362	€1100	Vladimir. s. 8-Feb-4 Lesieur & Le Bars, Le Havre #41/R

VESTER, Gesina (1857-1939) Dutch

£1184	$2179	€1800	Cattle on a path in a polder landscape (44x70cm-17x28in) s. 22-Jun-4 Christie's, Amsterdam #39/R est:2000-3000

VESTER, Willem (1824-1871) Dutch

£1375	$2200	€2008	Summer landscape with cows beside a stream (30x48cm-12x19in) s. 20-Sep-3 Pook & Pook, Downington #182/R est:1500-2500
£3472	$5799	€5000	Grazing cattle by the water (44x70cm-17x28in) s. prov. 21-Oct-3 Sotheby's, Amsterdam #65/R est:3000-5000
£3893	$7162	€5800	Paysage a la chaumiere (77x102cm-30x40in) s. 26-Mar-4 Daguerre, Paris #74/R est:6000-8000
£4000	$7240	€6000	Vaches en bordure de riviere (57x95cm-22x37in) s. 30-Mar-4 Campo, Vlaamse Kaai #221/R est:4000-5000
£4605	$8474	€7000	Extensive polder landscape in summer (58x95cm-23x37in) s. 22-Jun-4 Christie's, Amsterdam #14/R est:5000-7000
£5556	$9278	€8000	Extensive summer landscape with haying farmers (76x125cm-30x49in) s. 21-Oct-3 Sotheby's, Amsterdam #39/R est:10000-15000

VESTIER, Antoine (1740-1824) French

£2465	$4264	€3500	Portrait d'homme en habit rouge (41x33cm-16x13in) s.d.1776. 12-Dec-3 Libert, Castor, Paris #45/R est:3000-4000

VESTIER, Antoine (attrib) (1740-1824) French

£2616	$4500	€3819	Portrait of a gentleman, half length, holding a letter (74x61cm-29x24in) 7-Dec-3 Freeman, Philadelphia #12 est:3000-5000
£6615	$11378	€9658	Young lady wearing pink dress (54x44cm-21x17in) oval. 2-Dec-3 Bukowskis, Stockholm #418/R est:40000-45000 (S.KR 86000)
Miniatures			
£1007	$1852	€1500	Un homme de qualite en manteau gris-bleu, gilet or et perruque a rouleaux (4x3cm-2x1in) oval exec. c.1776 lit. 26-Mar-4 Pierre Berge, Paris #85/R est:600-800

VETCOUR, Fernand (1908-) Belgian

£662	$1205	€1000	Vue d'Espagne (42x53cm-17x21in) s. panel. 16-Jun-4 Hotel des Ventes Mosan, Brussels #239
£769	$1285	€1100	Les maisons blanches a Monteneau (60x80cm-24x31in) s. panel. 13-Oct-3 Horta, Bruxelles #345
£1088	$1948	€1600	En automne a Bourges, Ardennes (80x100cm-31x39in) s. panel. 17-Mar-4 Hotel des Ventes Mosan, Brussels #152 est:800-1000

VETTEN, Johannes (1827-1866) Dutch

Works on paper			
£283	$450	€413	Dressmaker working at a table (15x11cm-6x4in) s.d.1858 W/C. 13-Sep-3 Weschler, Washington #696/R

VETTENWINKEL, Hendrik (1809-1878) Dutch

£2028	$3387	€2900	Fisherwoman with children waiting for the boats (48x42cm-19x17in) s. 28-Jun-3 Bolland & Marotz, Bremen #749/R est:2200

VETTER, Charles (1858-1936) German

£2414	$4031	€3500	Park view, Botanical Gardens, Munich (55x67cm-22x26in) s.d.1921. 13-Nov-3 Neumeister, Munich #482/R est:2000-2200
£3819	$6493	€5500	Regentag in Munchen (60x53cm-24x21in) s.d.1917. 28-Oct-3 Christie's, Amsterdam #114/R est:8000-12000

VETTER, Jean (1820-1900) French

£3147	$5350	€4500	Portrait (81x65cm-32x26in) s. 27-Nov-3 Millon & Associes, Paris #162 est:4500-6500

VETTORI, Luigi (1901-?) Italian

£922	$1494	€1300	Paesaggio con case (47x64cm-19x25in) s. panel exhib. 22-May-3 Stadion, Trieste #294/R est:700-1000

VETTRIANO, Jack (1954-) British

£4000	$6920	€5840	Princess Street Gardens (40x51cm-16x20in) s. board. 11-Dec-3 Lyon & Turnbull, Edinburgh #100/R est:4000-6000
£4800	$8016	€7008	Moondancers (54x44cm-21x17in) s. canvasboard. 16-Oct-3 Bonhams, Edinburgh #61/R est:5000-7000
£5000	$8600	€7300	Venue 49 (31x25cm-12x10in) s. canvasboard. 4-Dec-3 Bonhams, Edinburgh #26a/R est:5000-7000
£9000	$14130	€13050	Edinburgh Castle from Princes Gardens (51x41cm-20x16in) s. 27-Aug-3 Sotheby's, London #1242/R est:6000-8000
£10000	$17300	€14600	Jive study (53x37cm-21x15in) s. board. 11-Dec-3 Lyon & Turnbull, Edinburgh #101/R est:5000-7000
£10800	$19764	€15768	And waiting still (29x24cm-11x9in) s. canvasboard exhib. 8-Apr-4 Bonhams, Edinburgh #45/R est:10000-15000
£11000	$17270	€15950	Restless natives (53x43cm-21x17in) s. canvasboard prov. 27-Aug-3 Sotheby's, London #1240/R est:3000-5000
£11000	$17270	€15950	Woman in a suit (48x37cm-19x15in) s. board. 27-Aug-3 Sotheby's, London #1241/R est:6000-8000
£14500	$23345	€21025	Ghosts of the past (30x25cm-12x10in) s. board prov. 21-Aug-3 Bonhams, Edinburgh #1153/R est:10000-15000
£15000	$23550	€21750	Confrontation (61x51cm-24x20in) s. canvasboard. 27-Aug-3 Sotheby's, London #1243/R est:15000-20000
£15000	$25800	€21900	And some they never do - Study (25x30cm-10x12in) s. painted 1994. 4-Dec-3 Bonhams, Edinburgh #25/R est:15000-20000
£15000	$26850	€21900	Model in black (61x51cm-24x20in) s. prov. 28-May-4 Lyon & Turnbull, Edinburgh #103/R est:10000-15000
£15500	$28055	€22630	Sailing boat (40x20cm-16x8in) s. board. 19-Apr-4 Sotheby's, London #181/R est:2000-3000
£16000	$28640	€23360	Model in a black hat (61x51cm-24x20in) s. prov. 28-May-4 Lyon & Turnbull, Edinburgh #95/R est:10000-15000
£19000	$32870	€27740	Model in black hat (61x51cm-24x20in) s. 11-Dec-3 Lyon & Turnbull, Edinburgh #40/R est:10000-15000
£24000	$43440	€35040	Breezy day (30x25cm-12x10in) s. board. 19-Apr-4 Sotheby's, London #179/R est:6000-8000
£27000	$42390	€39150	Candy stripe bodice (38x30cm-15x12in) s. i.verso canvasboard. 27-Aug-3 Sotheby's, London #1239/R est:10000-15000
£28000	$48440	€40880	Competition dancers, waiting in the wings (61x76cm-24x30in) s. board prov. 11-Dec-3 Lyon & Turnbull, Edinburgh #110/R est:20000-30000
£30000	$47100	€43500	Betrayal, first kiss (29x24cm-11x9in) s. prov. 27-Aug-3 Sotheby's, London #1245/R est:15000-20000
£30000	$53700	€43800	Study for yesterday's dreams. s. canvas on canvas. 28-May-4 Lyon & Turnbull, Edinburgh #96/R est:7000-10000
£32000	$50240	€46400	Red room (38x30cm-15x12in) s. i.verso. 27-Aug-3 Sotheby's, London #1237/R est:10000-15000
£32000	$50240	€46400	Married man (60x75cm-24x30in) prov. 27-Aug-3 Sotheby's, London #1244/R est:25000-35000
£32000	$55360	€46720	Midnight blue, study (25x30cm-10x12in) s. prov. 11-Dec-3 Lyon & Turnbull, Edinburgh #39/R est:15000-20000
£33000	$56760	€48180	Model by the easel (46x36cm-18x14in) s. prov. 4-Dec-3 Bonhams, Edinburgh #26/R est:15000-20000
£34000	$53380	€49300	Study for lunchtime lovers (30x25cm-12x10in) s. 27-Aug-3 Sotheby's, London #1238/R est:20000-30000
£34000	$60860	€49640	The sparkler (61x76cm-24x30in) s. board exhib. 28-May-4 Lyon & Turnbull, Edinburgh #101/R est:35000-45000
£42000	$67620	€60900	Dark, dark days (60x50cm-24x20in) s. 21-Aug-3 Bonhams, Edinburgh #1152/R est:20000-30000
£44000	$70840	€63800	Bathing party III (40x51cm-16x20in) s. board prov. 21-Aug-3 Bonhams, Edinburgh #1151/R est:18000-25000
£48000	$86880	€70080	Right time, right place (51x40cm-20x16in) s. 19-Apr-4 Sotheby's, London #171/R est:30000-40000
£48000	$85920	€70080	Heaven or hell, the sweetest choice (25x30cm-10x12in) s. 28-May-4 Lyon & Turnbull, Edinburgh #99/R est:15000-20000
£50000	$90500	€73000	Study for something in the air (38x30cm-15x12in) s. 19-Apr-4 Sotheby's, London #174/R est:20000-30000
£55000	$99550	€80300	Umbrella (30x25cm-12x10in) s. board. 19-Apr-4 Sotheby's, London #180/R est:8000-12000
£60000	$107400	€87600	Yesterday's dreams (38x30cm-15x12in) s. 28-May-4 Lyon & Turnbull, Edinburgh #98/R est:25000-35000
£62000	$112220	€90520	Study for, game on (30x25cm-12x10in) s. s.i.stretcher. 19-Apr-4 Sotheby's, London #172/R est:25000-35000
£62000	$112220	€90520	Study for suddenly one summer (36x25cm-14x10in) s. s.i.verso canvasboard. 19-Apr-4 Sotheby's, London #182/R est:15000-20000
£65000	$117650	€94900	In the heat of the night (61x76cm-24x30in) s. board. 19-Apr-4 Sotheby's, London #170/R est:30000-40000
£70000	$125300	€102200	Gentleman in waiting (50x61cm-20x24in) s. 28-May-4 Lyon & Turnbull, Edinburgh #94/R est:30000-40000
£75000	$117750	€108750	Study for the singing butler (38x30cm-15x12in) s. 27-Aug-3 Sotheby's, London #1246/R est:25000-30000
£75000	$134250	€109500	Strolling players (51x41cm-20x16in) s. 28-May-4 Lyon & Turnbull, Edinburgh #97 est:30000-40000
£82000	$141860	€119720	Embracing (76x61cm-30x24in) s. 11-Dec-3 Lyon & Turnbull, Edinburgh #38a/R est:40000-50000
£88000	$159280	€128480	Study for Edith and the kingpin (41x5cm-16x2in) s. 19-Apr-4 Sotheby's, London #175/R est:30000-40000
£90000	$161100	€131400	Bathers II (51x61cm-20x24in) s. prov. 28-May-4 Lyon & Turnbull, Edinburgh #100/R est:30000-50000
£95000	$171950	€138700	Queen of hearts (56x46cm-22x18in) s. prov. 19-Apr-4 Sotheby's, London #178/R est:30000-40000
£95000	$170050	€138700	In the heat of the day (81x71cm-32x28in) s. 28-May-4 Lyon & Turnbull, Edinburgh #93/R est:40000-60000
£100000	$179000	€146000	A kind of loving (71x91cm-28x36in) s. prov.lit. 28-May-4 Lyon & Turnbull, Edinburgh #104/R est:50000-70000
£125000	$226250	€182500	Incident on the promenade (71x81cm-28x32in) s. i.verso prov.exhib. 19-Apr-4 Sotheby's, London #176/R est:50000-70000
£140000	$253400	€204400	Assessors (81x71cm-32x28in) s. prov.lit. 19-Apr-4 Sotheby's, London #173/R est:50000-70000
£140000	$250600	€204400	Mad dogs (51x61cm-20x24in) s. prov. 28-May-4 Lyon & Turnbull, Edinburgh #93a est:40000-60000
£175000	$316750	€255500	Study for the administration of justice (40x46cm-16x18in) s. 19-Apr-4 Sotheby's, London #177/R est:25000-30000
£660000	$1194600	€963600	Singing butler (71x91cm-28x36in) s. exhib. 19-Apr-4 Sotheby's, London #169/R est:150000-200000
Works on paper			
£9500	$15295	€13775	Cheating hearts (51x41cm-20x16in) s. exhib. 21-Aug-3 Bonhams, Edinburgh #1157/R est:10000-15000

VEYRASSAT, Jules Jacques (1828-1893) French

£845	$1462	€1200	La moisson (7x14cm-3x6in) mono. panel. 10-Dec-3 Remi Ader, Paris #46/R
£845	$1462	€1200	La moisson (7x14cm-3x6in) mono. panel. 10-Dec-3 Neret-Minet, Paris #46/R
£2639	$4407	€3800	La fenaison (35x63cm-14x25in) s. panel. 22-Oct-3 Ribeyre & Baron, Paris #27 est:4800-6000
£2667	$4827	€4000	Attelage (24x32cm-9x13in) s. panel. 31-Mar-4 Sotheby's, Paris #100/R est:4000-6000
£2690	$4492	€3900	Deux chevaux de labours et paysans devant une ferme (38x49cm-15x19in) s. panel. 12-Nov-3 Chassaing Rivet, Toulouse #204
£3030	$5424	€4424	Peasants resting with horses under tree by water (30x38cm-12x15in) s. 22-Mar-4 Philippe Schuler, Zurich #4435/R est:4000-6000 (S.FR 7000)
£3467	$6344	€5200	Peintre a son chevalet (27x21cm-11x8in) s. 6-Jun-4 Osenat, Fontainebleau #110/R est:6000-6500
£3779	$6500	€5517	Coin de ferme Seine bo. (19x40cm-7x16in) 3-Dec-3 Naón & Cia, Buenos Aires #152/R
£4545	$7818	€6500	Le passage des chevaux (10x20cm-4x8in) s. panel. 7-Dec-3 Osenat, Fontainebleau #91 est:4500-5000
£4789	$7949	€6800	Chevaux a l'abreuvoir (21x33cm-8x13in) s. panel. 15-Jun-3 Peron, Melun #95
£4930	$8183	€7000	Retour du marche (35x48cm-14x19in) s. 15-Jun-3 Peron, Melun #97

£7092 $11489 €10000 Passage du bac (46x55cm-18x22in) s. 23-May-3 Sotheby's, Paris #36/R est:7000-9000
£7667 $14030 €11500 Scene de moisson (35x64cm-14x25in) s. panel. 6-Jun-4 Osenat, Fontainebleau #109/R est:12000-15000
£10000 $18300 €15000 Moisson (40x61cm-16x24in) s. 6-Jun-4 Osenat, Fontainebleau #108/R est:15000-18000
£11189 $19245 €16000 Le marche aux chevaux (32x58cm-13x23in) s. 7-Dec-3 Osenat, Fontainebleau #89/R est:15000-18000
Works on paper
£420 $722 €600 Scene champetre (15x23cm-6x9in) s. graphite. 7-Dec-3 Osenat, Fontainebleau #90

VEYRASSAT, Jules Jacques (attrib) (1828-1893) French
Works on paper
£282 $493 €400 Chevaux de trait (20x33cm-8x13in) i.verso Indian ink. 19-Dec-3 Delvaux, Paris #2

VEZIN, Charles (1858-1942) American
£800 $1440 €1168 February (30x40cm-12x16in) s. 21-Jan-4 Sotheby's, Olympia #516/R

VEZIN, Frederik (1859-?) American
£411 $736 €600 New York (30x40cm-12x16in) s.i.d.1906 board. 22-Mar-4 Philippe Schuler, Zurich #6202 (S.FR 950)
£467 $835 €700 Seascape in the early evening (18x24cm-7x9in) s. i.verso chipboard. 14-May-4 Von Zezschwitz, Munich #45/R

VEZZETTI, Tina Massera (?) ?
£320 $582 €480 Gifts of glorious sunshine (51x71cm-20x28in) s. 17-Jun-4 Gorringes, Worthing #712/R

VEZZOLI, Francesco (1971-) Italian
Photographs
£9497 $17000 €13866 Garbo cries (60x51cm-24x20in) col laser print canvas mesh metallic embroidery prov. 14-May-4 Phillips, New York #171/R est:10000-15000
Prints
£16000 $26720 €23360 Veruschka will be here soon (50x41cm-20x16in) col laser print on canvas metallic embroidery exec.2001 prov. 20-Oct-3 Sotheby's, London #51/R est:15000

VIAGGIO, Salvatore (1933-) Italian
£235 $436 €350 Small landscape (39x94cm-15x37in) s.i.d.1968 verso. 4-Mar-4 Babuino, Rome #445

VIALE, Patrick (1952-) Irish
£658 $1211 €1000 Garden table (59x59cm-23x23in) s. board. 22-Jun-4 De Veres Art Auctions, Dublin #174/R

VIALET, Laurent (1967-) French
£291 $545 €440 Marine a Kersiney Plouhinec (38x55cm-15x22in) s. 24-Jul-4 Thierry & Lannon, Brest #299
£298 $557 €450 Pont-Croix, effet de lumiere (50x61cm-20x24in) s. 24-Jul-4 Thierry & Lannon, Brest #298
£352 $616 €500 Locronan, le bourg (27x35cm-11x14in) s. 21-Dec-3 Thierry & Lannon, Brest #417
£364 $681 €550 Contre-jour sur le port d'Audierne (55x46cm-22x18in) s. 24-Jul-4 Thierry & Lannon, Brest #300/R

VIALLAT, Claude (1936-) French
£1141 $2020 €1700 Untitled (59x55cm-23x22in) acrylic tissue painted c.1960. 28-Apr-4 Artcurial Briest, Paris #386/R est:1800-2200
£1745 $3211 €2600 Numero 122 (185x92cm-73x36in) peinture cloth. 28-Mar-4 Anaf, Lyon #270/R est:2500-3000
£2215 $4075 €3300 Untitled (82x101cm-32x40in) acrylic tissue painted 2001. 24-Mar-4 Joron-Derem, Paris #147/R est:3800-4000
£2685 $4940 €4000 Numero 130 (170x290cm-67x114in) peinture canvas cover. 28-Mar-4 Anaf, Lyon #271/R est:4000-6000
£3356 $6175 €5000 Untitled (200x100cm-79x39in) dye acrylic prov. painted c.1988. 29-Mar-4 Cornette de St.Cyr, Paris #40/R est:5000-6000
£3521 $6092 €5000 Untitled (115x165cm-45x65in) acrylic painted 1981 prov. 9-Dec-3 Artcurial Briest, Paris #573/R est:5000-6000
£4000 $7240 €5840 Sans titre (171x169cm-67x67in) s.d.67 acrylic on two hinged pieces of tarpaulin. 1-Apr-4 Christie's, Kensington #222/R est:5000-7000
£4533 $8160 €6800 Bleu de methylene (290x182cm-114x72in) acrylic cloth. 20-Apr-4 Chenu & Scrive, Lyon #165/R est:5000-7000
£5034 $9262 €7500 Untitled (292x309cm-115x122in) painted 19891. 24-Mar-4 Joron-Derem, Paris #150/R est:10000-12000
£5369 $9879 €8000 Untitled (290x228cm-114x90in) acrylic canvas book painted 1989. 24-Mar-4 Joron-Derem, Paris #146/R est:10000-12000
Works on paper
£249 $430 €350 Empreinte (21x30cm-8x12in) s.d.1968 ink. 9-Dec-3 Artcurial Briest, Paris #392
£1409 $2593 €2100 Untitled (100x70cm-39x28in) gouache exec 1981. 24-Mar-4 Joron-Derem, Paris #149/R est:1800-2000

VIALOV, Konstantin (1900-1976) Russian
Works on paper
£4545 $7727 €6500 Costume sketch for Stenka Razine (37x26cm-15x10in) W/C ink pencil. 26-Nov-3 Dorotheum, Vienna #37/R est:6500-8000

VIANDEN, Heinrich (1814-1899) American
£1833 $3300 €2676 Moonlight landscape. s. 26-Jan-4 Schrager Galleries, Milwaukee #1373

VIANDIER, Richard (1858-1949) Belgian
£367 $664 €550 Lisiere de bois en automne (52x61cm-20x24in) s. 30-Mar-4 Palais de Beaux Arts, Brussels #736
£385 $642 €550 Lisiere de bois en automne (52x61cm-20x24in) s. 7-Oct-3 Palais de Beaux Arts, Brussels #600

VIANELLI, Achille (1803-1894) Italian
Works on paper
£909 $1564 €1300 Oratorio a Bitonto (30x23cm-12x9in) s.d.1851 crayon ink wash. 5-Dec-3 Gros & Delettrez, Paris #32
£1408 $2338 €2000 Interno del Duomo di Monreale (25x35cm-10x14in) s.d.1858 W/C monochrome cardboard exhib.lit. 11-Jun-3 Christie's, Rome #239/R est:2300-2800
£1549 $2572 €2200 Veduta di Napoli (25x35cm-10x14in) W/C cardboard. 11-Jun-3 Christie's, Rome #67/R est:1300-1800
£1613 $3000 €2355 S Gennaro a Pozzuoli. Capuccini di Pozzuoli (22x32cm-9x13in) s.d.1839 sepia W/C two. 5-Mar-4 Skinner, Boston #230/R est:3000-5000
£1958 $3329 €2800 Torretta di Chiaja near Naples (12x18cm-5x7in) s.i.d.1835 pen brush over pencil htd white. 27-Nov-3 Bassenge, Berlin #5662/R est:1600
£3226 $6000 €4710 Piazza d'Amalfi (22x38cm-9x15in) s.i.d.1839 sepia W/C. 5-Mar-4 Skinner, Boston #248/R est:1500-2500

VIANELLO, Cesare (19th C) Italian
£2466 $4192 €3600 The art collector (53x64cm-21x25in) s. 5-Nov-3 Vendue Huis, Gravenhage #99/R est:2000-3000
£3147 $5350 €4500 Idyllic family (48x68cm-19x27in) s. 28-Nov-3 Wiener Kunst Auktionen, Vienna #435/R est:3000-6000
£7285 $13258 €11000 Venetian flower seller (63x82cm-25x32in) s. 21-Jun-4 Dorotheum, Vienna #8/R est:7000-8000

VIANI, Alberto (1906-1989) Italian
Works on paper
£897 $1497 €1300 Nude (50x35cm-20x14in) s.d.950 pencil prov. 13-Nov-3 Finarte Semenzato, Rome #212/R est:1000-1200

VIANI, Antonio Maria (c.1555-1620) Italian
Works on paper
£1800 $3240 €2628 Draped male figure, standing, pointing to the left (35x24cm-14x9in) black chk htd white chk. 20-Apr-4 Sotheby's, Olympia #8/R est:2000-3000

VIANI, Lorenzo (1882-1936) Italian
£1892 $3330 €2800 Cain's sons (41x29cm-16x11in) tempera Chinese ink paper. 22-May-4 Galleria Pananti, Florence #434/R est:3500-4000
£8392 $14266 €12000 Viareggio prison (60x49cm-24x19in) s.d.1903 board prov. 24-Nov-3 Christie's, Milan #168/R est:7000-10000
£12838 $22595 €19000 Nude (96x65cm-38x26in) s. cardboard painted c.1915. 22-May-4 Galleria Pananti, Florence #532/R est:22000-26000
£13333 $24533 €20000 Huts (59x84cm-23x33in) s.d.1932 board. 11-Jun-4 Farsetti, Prato #584/R est:20000-25000
£14138 $23610 €20500 Annibalone the philosopher (86x63cm-34x25in) s. cardboard painted 1920 exhib. 17-Nov-3 Sant Agostino, Torino #265/R est:20000-25000
Works on paper
£400 $720 €600 Figures (31x20cm-12x8in) s. ink W/C exhib. 22-Apr-4 Finarte Semenzato, Rome #79/R
£530 $964 €800 Viareggio (18x23cm-7x9in) s. ink exhib. 21-Jun-4 Pandolfini, Florence #324
£538 $915 €770 Portrait (28x20cm-11x8in) s.verso ink. 18-Nov-3 Babuino, Rome #4/R
£563 $1025 €850 Painter's study (24x17cm-9x7in) ink. 17-Jun-4 Galleria Pananti, Florence #444/R
£671 $1248 €1000 Man in profile (18x13cm-7x5in) s. s.verso pastel. 4-Mar-4 Babuino, Rome #68
£972 $1536 €1400 Poors' Inn (24x31cm-9x12in) pencil dr exec.1934. 6-Sep-3 Meeting Art, Vercelli #634
£979 $1664 €1400 Untitled (61x28cm-24x11in) s. pastel cardboard. 25-Nov-3 Sotheby's, Milan #47/R
£2098 $3566 €3000 Man with hat (34x42cm-13x17in) s. W/C ink prov. 24-Nov-3 Christie's, Milan #25/R est:2000-3000
£6835 $11209 €9500 Family (93x75cm-37x30in) s. chl card. 10-Jun-3 Pandolfini, Florence #353/R est:10500-11500

VIARD, Georges (fl.1831-1848) French
£1467 $2684 €2200 Fishing boat and two-master on the harbour exit (45x65cm-18x26in) s. canvas on canvas. 5-Jun-4 Arnold, Frankfurt #783/R est:1600

VIAVANT, George L (1872-1925) American
Works on paper
£1279 $2200 €1867 Snipe. s. pencil W/C bodycol htd white. 5-Dec-3 Christie's, Rockefeller NY #89/R est:1000-1500
£2410 $4000 €3519 Still life of a bass (48x28cm-19x11in) s.d.1913 W/C. 4-Oct-3 Neal Auction Company, New Orleans #1070/R est:2200-2400
£2410 $4000 €3519 Still life of a squirrel (64x43cm-25x17in) s.d.1918 W/C. 4-Oct-3 Neal Auction Company, New Orleans #1071/R est:2500-3500
£4419 $7600 €6452 Mallard duck (58x43cm-23x17in) s.d.1924 W/C oval. 6-Dec-3 Neal Auction Company, New Orleans #566/R est:5000-7000

VIBERT, Alexandre (?-1909) French
Sculpture
£1655 $3029 €2400 L'Empereur Napoleon 1er (36cm-14in) s. brown pat bronze marble socle. 31-Jan-4 Osenat, Fontainebleau #602

VIBERT, Jean Georges (1840-1902) French
£700 $1099 €1015 Little flower picker (18x11cm-7x4in) s. board. 28-Aug-3 Christie's, Kensington #63/R
£3315 $6000 €4840 Le missionaire (36x26cm-14x10in) s.d.68 panel. 30-Mar-4 Christie's, Rockefeller NY #82/R est:8000-12000
£16667 $30000 €24334 At the corrida (24x38cm-9x15in) s.d.75 panel prov. 23-Apr-4 Sotheby's, New York #91/R est:30000-40000
Works on paper
£588 $982 €858 Arab in an interior (36x21cm-14x8in) s. W/C. 17-Nov-3 Waddingtons, Toronto #191/R (C.D 1300)

VIBORG, A L (19th C) Scandinavian
£656 $1207 €984 From Djurgarden (35x53cm-14x21in) s.d.1887. 14-Jun-4 Lilla Bukowskis, Stockholm #65/R (S.KR 9000)

VICAJI, Dorothy (fl.1915-1930) British
£320 $573 €467 Portrait of Enid de Winter wearing dress and jacet in green (111x85cm-44x33in) s.d.1938. 16-Mar-4 Bonhams, Oxford #70

VICENTE GIL, Victoriano de (20th C) South American
£791 $1250 €1155 Salty (63x87cm-25x34in) s. painted 1917. 27-Apr-3 Subastas Odalys, Caracas #76
£1198 $2060 €1749 Break (45x65cm-18x26in) s. painted 1926. 7-Dec-3 Subastas Odalys, Caracas #4/R
£2581 $4000 €3768 Landscape (53x78cm-21x31in) s. painted 1991. 29-Sep-2 Subastas Odalys, Caracas #82/R

VICENTE, Eduardo (1909-1968) Spanish
£493 $863 €700 Landscape (22x25cm-9x10in) s.i. cardboard. 16-Dec-3 Segre, Madrid #259/R
£612 $1096 €900 Around Madrid (46x38cm-18x15in) s. canvas on cardboard. 22-Mar-4 Durán, Madrid #564/R
£1348 $2250 €1900 Bulls at pasture (90x70cm-35x28in) 20-Oct-3 Durán, Madrid #102/R
£1831 $2930 €2600 Village celebrations (50x61cm-20x24in) 16-Sep-3 Segre, Madrid #308/R est:2000
Works on paper
£374 $670 €550 Shepherd by the river (63x49cm-25x19in) s. W/C. 22-Mar-4 Durán, Madrid #563/R
£390 $651 €550 Figura caminando (50x84cm-20x33in) s. W/C. 23-Jun-3 Durán, Madrid #770/R
£510 $913 €750 Rural scene (66x50cm-26x20in) s. W/C. 22-Mar-4 Durán, Madrid #5/R
£629 $1051 €900 Crossing the bridge (64x51cm-25x20in) s. W/C. 30-Jun-3 Ansorena, Madrid #1/R
£769 $1285 €1100 View of Madrid (64x51cm-25x20in) s. W/C. 30-Jun-3 Ansorena, Madrid #2/R

VICENZINO, Giuseppe (17/18th C) Italian
£13245 $24106 €20000 Basket with flowers (89x119cm-35x47in) 15-Jun-4 Claude Aguttes, Neuilly #13/R est:18000-22000
£49655 $82924 €72000 Still life with peaches, grapes, carnations and roses (94x118cm-37x46in) 15-Nov-3 Porro, Milan #216/R est:40000

VICENZINO, Giuseppe (attrib) (17/18th C) Italian
£12000 $20400 €17520 Carnation, roses and other flowers above a carved stone. Roses, tulips and other flowers on step (45x37cm-18x15in) pair. 29-Oct-3 Bonhams, New Bond Street #80/R est:3000-5000

VICHI, F (19th C) Italian
Sculpture
£2335 $4250 €3409 Mother and child (61cm-24in) marble. 20-Jun-4 Bonhams & Butterfields, Los Angeles #5213/R est:3000-4000
£3681 $6000 €5374 Sheperdess with lamb (91cm-36in) s. marble. 24-Sep-3 Doyle, New York #441/R est:12000-18000

VICHI, Ferdinando (19th C) Italian
Sculpture
£988 $1700 €1442 Bust of Apollo (33cm-13in) i. white Cararra marble. 7-Dec-3 Hindman, Chicago #404/R est:1200-1800
£1063 $1700 €1552 Young girl (51cm-20in) s. marble. 20-Sep-3 Nadeau, Windsor #229/R
£1163 $2000 €1698 Adoration (58x33x36cm-23x13x14in) s.verso marble marble base. 6-Dec-3 Neal Auction Company, New Orleans #129/R est:2500-3500
£2462 $4234 €3595 The shy girl (62cm-24in) s.i. white marble. 3-Dec-3 AB Stockholms Auktionsverk #2647/R est:30000-35000 (S.KR 32000)
£15000 $25500 €21900 Allegory of Italy (101cm-40in) s. marble. 28-Oct-3 Sotheby's, London #87/R
£15663 $26000 €22868 Bacchante (221x46x53cm-87x18x21in) s.i.base carrara marble inc carved marble pedestal. 4-Oct-3 Neal Auction Company, New Orleans #313/R est:25000-35000

VICKERS, Alfred (19th C) British
£320 $534 €467 Figures in a landscape (37x52cm-15x20in) s. 20-Oct-3 Bonhams, Bath #174
£450 $824 €657 Coastal landscape (20x41cm-8x16in) s. 8-Jul-4 Duke & Son, Dorchester #245/R
£475 $860 €694 Study of a woodland road with figures on horseback and cattle watering (23x36cm-9x14in) s.d.1861. 1-Apr-4 Biddle & Webb, Birmingham #893
£530 $917 €774 White Lion Inn (39x59cm-15x23in) s. 9-Dec-3 Bristol Auction Rooms #451/R
£600 $1080 €876 Landscape with distant view of the Isle of Wight (18x23cm-7x9in) 21-Jan-4 Sotheby's, Olympia #362/R
£1250 $2338 €1875 Figures in a landscape with a windmill (44x73cm-17x29in) 26-Jul-4 Bonhams, Bath #55/R est:1500-2000
£1278 $2300 €1866 Ship in distress on the high seas (43x61cm-17x24in) s.d.1861 prov. 24-Apr-4 Weschler, Washington #545/R est:1200-1800
£1300 $2379 €1898 River landscape with figures and a windmill (19x38cm-7x15in) panel. 7-Apr-4 Woolley & Wallis, Salisbury #298/R est:1000-1500
£1700 $3145 €2482 Salmon traps on the river Tamar (33x58cm-13x23in) s.d.1856. 11-Mar-4 Ewbank, Send #446/R est:1750-2500
Works on paper
£260 $434 €380 Babbling brook (23x30cm-9x12in) s.d.1832 pencil W/C. 16-Oct-3 Christie's, Kensington #58/R

VICKERS, Alfred (attrib) (19th C) British
£700 $1253 €1022 Figures crossing a bridge in a rocky river landscape (26x36cm-10x14in) 27-May-4 Christie's, Kensington #172/R
Works on paper
£550 $1001 €803 Yarmouth, Isle of Wight (13x23cm-5x9in) W/C. 4-Feb-4 John Nicholson, Haslemere #50/R

VICKERS, Alfred (snr) (1786-1868) British
£500 $925 €730 Rocky river landscape (26x36cm-10x14in) 9-Mar-4 Bonhams, Knightsbridge #144/R
£550 $985 €803 Figures and cattle beside a lake (26x36cm-10x14in) 11-May-4 Bonhams, Knightsbridge #157/R
£720 $1339 €1051 Ely Cathedral, on the Ouse (20x30cm-8x12in) panel. 4-Mar-4 Christie's, Kensington #516/R
£730 $1358 €1066 Cattle watering by a church in a river landscape (43x74cm-17x29in) s. 4-Mar-4 Christie's, Kensington #514/R
£825 $1378 €1205 Rocky country landscape with river and encampment (27x38cm-11x15in) s. board. 7-Oct-3 Bonhams, Knightsbridge #136/R
£1000 $1670 €1460 Ely Cathedral on the Ouse (28x38cm-11x15in) panel. 19-Jun-3 Mallams, Cheltenham #188/R est:1000-1500
£1800 $3006 €2628 Figures on heath (15x28cm-6x11in) s. board pair. 16-Oct-3 Lawrence, Crewkerne #734/R
£1900 $3496 €2774 Fall of the Derwent, near Matlock, Derbyshire (25x39cm-10x15in) s. s.d.1853 verso. 8-Jun-4 Bonhams, Knightsbridge #191/R est:1200-1800

VICKERS, Alfred (snr-attrib) (1786-1868) British
£360 $666 €526 Cattle in a river landscape (13x21cm-5x8in) indis.i.verso board. 13-Jan-4 Bonhams, Knightsbridge #54/R
£800 $1360 €1168 River landscape with fishing boats approaching a town (25x35cm-10x14in) 19-Nov-3 Tennants, Leyburn #1102/R
£1300 $2457 €1898 Close encounter off the harbour mouth (46x81cm-18x32in) with sig.d.1876. 19-Feb-4 Christie's, Kensington #103/R est:800-1200

VICKERS, Alfred Gomersal (1810-1837) British
Works on paper
£1600 $2720 €2336 Winter Palace at St Petersburg, Russia (13x21cm-5x8in) pencil W/C. 20-Nov-3 Christie's, London #121/R est:1500-2000
£3100 $5735 €4526 Winter palace at St. Petersburg, Russia (21x37cm-8x15in) i. pencil W/C. 15-Jan-4 Christie's, Kensington #1067/R est:1500-2500

VICKERS, Alfred Gomersal (attrib) (1810-1837) British
£800 $1472 €1168 Figures by a church with woodland (48x61cm-19x24in) panel. 23-Mar-4 Rosebery Fine Art, London #986

VICKERS, Alfred H (fl.1853-1907) British
£250 $433 €365 Old Hampton Bridge (20x30cm-8x12in) s. i.stretcher verso. 10-Dec-3 Bonhams, Bury St Edmunds #576/R
£260 $432 €380 Continental coastal scene (20x31cm-8x12in) s. 1-Oct-3 Woolley & Wallis, Salisbury #182/R
£278 $500 €406 Number 3 landscape in the night (18x25cm-7x10in) s. s.i.verso panel. 20-Jan-4 Arthur James, Florida #688
£300 $498 €438 Figure on a country path with ruined castle (31x26cm-12x10in) s. 1-Oct-3 Woolley & Wallis, Salisbury #181/R
£340 $636 €510 Estuary with town and castle beyond (20x30cm-8x12in) s.d.1894. 22-Jul-4 Gorringes, Lewes #1779/R
£360 $612 €526 Thatched cottages in a landscape (20x30cm-8x12in) s. 29-Oct-3 Bonhams, Chester #479
£420 $794 €613 Village street scene with church beyond (19x29cm-7x11in) s. 18-Feb-4 Peter Wilson, Nantwich #43
£550 $935 €803 Tow path by a bridge. River landscape with cottages (32x38cm-13x15in) s.d.1891 pair. 26-Nov-3 Hamptons Fine Art, Godalming #228
£600 $996 €876 River landscape with figures on a path and vessels and houses beyond (41x64cm-16x25in) s.d.1880. 1-Oct-3 Woolley & Wallis, Salisbury #183/R
£600 $996 €876 Figures near a cottage in an open landscape (41x64cm-16x25in) s. 1-Oct-3 Woolley & Wallis, Salisbury #184/R
£600 $1020 €876 Coastal scene with figures on a patch (20x30cm-8x12in) s. 19-Nov-3 Tennants, Leyburn #1037
£600 $1002 €876 On the Grand canal, Venice (20x41cm-8x16in) d.06. 27-Jun-3 Bigwood, Stratford on Avon #324
£620 $1097 €905 Sherwood Forest (20x30cm-8x12in) s. 27-Apr-4 Henry Adams, Chichester #684
£700 $1190 €1022 Figures on riverside path (20x41cm-8x16in) s. 18-Nov-3 Sotheby's, Olympia #34/R
£1000 $1870 €1460 Eaton College from the Thames (19x29cm-7x11in) s. 26-Feb-4 Lane, Penzance #187 est:1000-1200
£1200 $1896 €1740 An industrial coastal town (30x61cm-12x24in) s. 4-Sep-3 Christie's, Kensington #110/R est:1500-2000
£1200 $2220 €1752 Windmill on the banks of an estuary. Estuary scene (30x61cm-12x24in) s. one d.1897 pair. 10-Feb-4 Bonhams, Knightsbridge #79/R est:1200-1800
£4800 $8160 €7008 Sandown Bay. On the Medina, Newport, Isle of Wight (28x44cm-11x17in) i. pair. 25-Nov-3 Christie's, London #112/R est:4000-6000

VICKERS, Alfred H (attrib) (fl.1853-1907) British
£260 $442 €380 On the way home (20x30cm-8x12in) s. 6-Nov-3 Christie's, Kensington #795
£280 $510 €409 Country scene with farmhouse and figures on a path (18x38cm-7x15in) 3-Feb-4 Gorringes, Bexhill #948

VICKERS, Charles (19th C) British
£520 $931 €759 Haymakers outside an inn (76x127cm-30x50in) s. 25-May-4 Sworder & Son, Bishops Stortford #407

VICKERS, Henry Harold (1851-1919) British
£400 $732 €584 On the old London coach road in Stratford on Avon, Warwickshire, England (21x15cm-8x6in) s.d.1914 board. 1-Jun-4 Joyner Waddington, Toronto #377/R (C.D 1000)

VICKERS, W (19th C) British?
£875 $1400 €1278 Vast landscape with figures and cottage (46x79cm-18x31in) s.d.1860. 20-Sep-3 Bunte, Elgin #1417 est:1000-1500

VICKERY, Charles (1913-1998) American
£353 $650 €515 Skies and the sea (71x97cm-28x38in) s. i.stretcher. 25-Mar-4 Doyle, New York #72/R
£625 $1000 €913 Light of dawn (71x97cm-28x38in) s. painted c.1930. 17-May-3 Bunte, Elgin #1253 est:1500-2500
£1198 $2000 €1749 Seascape (89x107cm-35x42in) 14-Nov-3 Du Mouchelle, Detroit #2110/R est:1500-2000

VICKERY, Robert (20th C) American
Works on paper
£1087 $2000 €1587 Head of a man. Profile of a man (25x18cm-10x7in) s. pen ink two. 10-Jun-4 Swann Galleries, New York #246/R est:2000-3000

VICKLETI, W E (20th C) Hungarian
£829 $1500 €1210 City market (61x91cm-24x36in) s. 3-Apr-4 Charlton Hall, Columbia #108/R est:1200-1800

VICTOR IV (1929-1986) Dutch
£1986 $3713 €2900 The sun (44x105cm-17x41in) polychrome painted wooden planks. 25-Feb-4 Kunsthallen, Copenhagen #26/R est:25000 (D.KR 22000)
£3043 $4991 €4200 Untitled (152x70cm-60x28in) s.d.1965 panel. 27-May-3 Sotheby's, Amsterdam #555/R est:2000-3000

VICTORIA, Salvador (1929-1994) Spanish
£1250 $2125 €1800 Great illusion (65x54cm-26x21in) s.d.1968 s.i.d.verso oil collage board. 28-Oct-3 Segre, Madrid #195/R est:1800
£3310 $5792 €4700 Untitled (81x65cm-32x26in) s. s.i.d.61 verso. 16-Dec-3 Segre, Madrid #140/R est:3900

VICTORIAN SCHOOL (19th C) British
Sculpture
£5271 $8750 €7696 Shepherd Boy (173x33x33cm-68x13x13in) marble inc blk gold marble pedestal gilt moulding. 4-Oct-3 Neal Auction Company, New Orleans #395/R est:7500-10000

VICTORS, Jacobus (1640-1705) Dutch
£25000 $45000 €36500 Still life of two courting doves, partridge and her chicks and a further dove perched on a jar (60x74cm-24x29in) 20-Apr-4 Sotheby's, Olympia #302/R est:6000-8000

VICTORS, Jacobus (attrib) (1640-1705) Dutch
£15248 $25465 €21500 Animals (64x76cm-25x30in) pair. 23-Jun-3 Finarte Semenzato, Rome #164/R

VICTORS, Jan (1620-1676) Dutch
£4310 $7931 €6293 At the dentist (45x35cm-18x14in) panel prov. 26-Mar-4 Koller, Zurich #3030/R est:12000-18000 (S.FR 10000)
£13699 $23288 €20000 Peasants making merry and a wagon halting outside an inn (85x109cm-33x43in) s. 5-Nov-3 Christie's, Amsterdam #44/R est:20000-30000
£20000 $34000 €29200 Moses striking the rock (105x135cm-41x53in) prov.lit. 29-Oct-3 Christie's, London #24/R est:20000-30000

VICTORYNS, Anthonie (attrib) (1612-1655) Flemish
£1100 $2057 €1606 Peasants smoking and drinking in a tavern. Peasants in a tavern (13x20cm-5x8in) panel pair. 27-Feb-4 Christie's, Kensington #86/R est:1000-1500
£3688 $6159 €5200 Scene d'interieur d'auberge (40x55cm-16x22in) bears another indis.sig. 17-Oct-3 Tajan, Paris #75/R est:5000-6000
£4000 $6920 €5840 Interior with boors eating and drinking (23x35cm-9x14in) panel. 12-Dec-3 Christie's, Kensington #23/R est:2000-3000
£6738 $11252 €9500 La pedicure (24x31cm-9x12in) bears sig. panel. 17-Oct-3 Tajan, Paris #74/R est:5000-7000

VIDA, Gabor (1937-) Hungarian
£1931 $3225 €2800 At the tailors (40x49cm-16x19in) s. panel. 9-Jul-3 Hugo Ruef, Munich #231/R est:3500

VIDAL (?) French
Sculpture
£2300 $3634 €3358 Study of a bull (30cm-12in) s. green pat bronze rounded rec. base. 27-Apr-3 Wilkinson, Doncaster #17

VIDAL, Couce (20th C) American
£318 $550 €464 Ship in Haiti (61x76cm-24x30in) s. i.verso. 10-Dec-3 Alderfer's, Hatfield #387

VIDAL, Francisco (fl.1867-1889) Spanish?
£379 $683 €550 Fishing vessels (16x25cm-6x10in) s. board. 26-Jan-4 Durán, Madrid #228/R
£417 $679 €600 Vessel in the Mediterranean (15x21cm-6x8in) s. 23-Sep-3 Durán, Madrid #167/R
£1042 $1698 €1500 Royal Navy cutter (14x21cm-6x8in) s. board. 23-Sep-3 Durán, Madrid #168/R
£2083 $3396 €3000 Vessel sailing off Mahon (21x30cm-8x12in) s. board. 23-Sep-3 Durán, Madrid #169/R est:1600
£2241 $3743 €3250 The Dobhran (27x45cm-11x18in) s.i. board. 17-Nov-3 Durán, Madrid #200/R est:1700
£3793 $6334 €5500 Boat in Mahon harbour (27x43cm-11x17in) s.d.1878. 17-Nov-3 Durán, Madrid #207/R
£5000 $8350 €7250 The Ignacio Fuster (48x68cm-19x27in) s.d.1879. 17-Nov-3 Durán, Madrid #208/R est:6500
£10417 $16979 €15000 Vessel Hernan Cortes (48x69cm-19x27in) s. i.verso. 23-Sep-3 Durán, Madrid #170/R est:11000

VIDAL, Gustave (?) ?
£352 $609 €500 Paysage aux falaises, Corse (46x55cm-18x22in) s. isorel. 10-Dec-3 Rossini, Paris #119
£500 $800 €730 Moulin en Provence (117x231cm-46x91in) s. 18-May-3 Auctions by the Bay, Alameda #1023/R
£549 $884 €780 Paysage de Provence (38x46cm-15x18in) s. 11-May-3 Versailles Encheres #161
£577 $930 €820 Paysage de Provence (46x55cm-18x22in) s. 11-May-3 Versailles Encheres #160
£1736 $2743 €2500 Les guardians. s. 25-Apr-3 Etude de Provence, Marseille #296 est:2500-3000

VIDAL, Louis (1754-1807) French
£3911 $7000 €5710 Still life of fruit and flowers in landscape (60x74cm-24x29in) canvas on panel. 27-May-4 Sotheby's, New York #72/R est:8000-12000
£7586 $12668 €10695 Nature morte de fleurs et fruits sur un entablement (55x69cm-22x27in) s.d.1805 panel. 17-Oct-3 Tajan, Paris #116/R est:7000-10000
Works on paper
£6579 $12105 €10000 Nature morte aux fleurs et nid (70x50cm-28x20in) s. gouache. 24-Jun-4 Tajan, Paris #80/R est:4000-6000

VIDAL, Louis (1831-1892) French
Sculpture
£896 $1497 €1300 Le cerf (54x38x17cm-21x15x7in) s. brown pat bronze lit. 17-Nov-3 Tajan, Paris #34/R est:1000-1200

VIDAL, Margarita Hahn (1919-) American
£1852 $3000 €2685 Zinnias (76x61cm-30x24in) 23-May-3 Altermann Galleries, Santa Fe #208

VIDAL, Miguel Angel (1928-) Argentinian
£2235 $4000 €3263 Light space (100x100cm-39x39in) s.d.1985 verso acrylic. 4-May-4 Arroyo, Buenos Aires #64/R est:3800

VIDAL, Vincent (1811-1887) French
£371 $676 €542 River landscape (12x21cm-5x8in) s. d.24 juin 1880 verso panel. 16-Jun-4 Fischer, Luzern #2418/R (S.FR 850)

VIDALES, Juan Martin de (1930-2000) Spanish
Works on paper
£414 $691 €600 Composition X-1 (100x70cm-39x28in) s.d.66 sid.verso mixed media on canvas exhib. 17-Nov-3 Durán, Madrid #60/R

VIEGENER, Eberhard (1890-1969) German
£655 $1212 €950 Farmstead near Schleswig (41x63cm-16x25in) mono.d.53 s.i.d.1953 verso board. 14-Feb-4 Hans Stahl, Hamburg #104/R
£769 $1323 €1100 Farmstead near Schleswig (41x63cm-16x25in) mono.d.53 s.i.d.verso cardboard. 6-Dec-3 Hans Stahl, Toestorf #93/R
£1399 $2378 €2000 Hohen Tauern - Gastein (52x74cm-20x29in) mono. s.i.d.1961 verso masonite. 26-Nov-3 Lempertz, Koln #1015/R est:2200
£6643 $11294 €9500 Pot, plate, tumbler and dice (23x41cm-9x16in) mono.d.48 s.i.d. verso panel prov. 26-Nov-3 Lempertz, Koln #1014/R est:7000-8000
£7692 $13077 €11000 Peasant drinking (35x24cm-14x9in) s.d.1925 s.i. verso panel prov. 26-Nov-3 Lempertz, Koln #1012/R est:8000-10000
£9091 $15455 €13000 Shepherd with lamb (35x25cm-14x10in) s.d.1927 s.i. verso panel prov.lit. 26-Nov-3 Lempertz, Koln #1013/R est:10000-12000

VIEGERS, Bernardus Petrus (1886-1947) Dutch
£283 $516 €425 Bridge over the canal (39x49cm-15x19in) s. 30-Jun-4 Vendue Huis, Gravenhage #339
£890 $1514 €1300 Farm in hilly landscape (48x59cm-19x23in) s. board. 5-Nov-3 Vendue Huis, Gravenhage #212/R
£987 $1816 €1500 Streetscene at night (54x44cm-21x17in) s. 28-Jun-4 Sotheby's, Amsterdam #131/R est:1500-2000
£1118 $2058 €1700 Figures near a drawbridge in winter (40x49cm-16x19in) s. 28-Jun-4 Sotheby's, Amsterdam #154/R est:1500-2000
£1119 $1924 €1600 View of Dordrecht (30x60cm-12x24in) s. 8-Dec-3 Glerum, Amsterdam #124/R est:1200-1500
£1224 $2229 €1800 Windmills in a polder landscape (50x70cm-20x28in) s. 3-Feb-4 Christie's, Amsterdam #210/R est:1500-2000
£1497 $2724 €2200 View of the Hoofdtoren, Hoorn (50x60cm-20x24in) s. 3-Feb-4 Christie's, Amsterdam #350/R est:1500-2000
£1678 $2803 €2400 Moored boats (40x80cm-16x31in) s. 30-Jun-3 Sotheby's, Amsterdam #256/R
£1769 $3219 €2600 Inner harbour at Elburg (50x70cm-20x28in) s. 3-Feb-4 Christie's, Amsterdam #363/R est:2000-3000
£1815 $3086 €2650 Polder landscape with mills at the ditch (48x68cm-19x27in) s. lit. 5-Nov-3 Vendue Huis, Gravenhage #213 est:3000-4000

£2603 $4425 €3800 Bulb field (39x49cm-15x19in) s. 5-Nov-3 Vendue Huis, Gravenhage #240a est:1000-1400
£2857 $5200 €4200 Ladies in the Vuurbaaistraat, Scheveningen (40x49cm-16x19in) s. 3-Feb-4 Christie's, Amsterdam #388/R est:1500-2000
Works on paper
£274 $466 €400 Town view (28x45cm-11x18in) s. pastel. 5-Nov-3 Vendue Huis, Gravenhage #211/R
£308 $524 €450 View of Dordrecht (28x45cm-11x18in) s. pastel. 5-Nov-3 Vendue Huis, Gravenhage #214/R

VIEGERS, Bernardus Petrus (attrib) (1886-1947) Dutch
£987 $1816 €1500 View of Nijmegen (64x100cm-25x39in) 28-Jun-4 Sotheby's, Amsterdam #153/R est:1500-2000

VIEGINGER, Eberhard (1890-1967) German
Works on paper
£347 $566 €500 Shepherd in hilly landscape (45x59cm-18x23in) chl. 26-Sep-3 Bolland & Marotz, Bremen #694

VIEHBECK, Karl Ludwig Friedrich (1769-1827) Austrian
Works on paper
£486 $792 €700 Kloster Georgenberg near Schwaz, Tyrol (24x30cm-9x12in) i. verso pen W/C. 26-Sep-3 Venator & Hansten, Koln #947/R

VIEILLEVOYE, Barthelemy Josef (1788-1855) Belgian
£2657 $4571 €3800 Portrait d'homme assis devant sa bibliotheque (42x49cm-17x19in) s.d.1826. 2-Dec-3 Sotheby's, Paris #67/R est:4000-6000

VIEIRA DA SILVA, Maria Elena (1908-1992) French/Portuguese
£24306 $40591 €35000 Sans titre (37x45cm-15x18in) s.d.53 paper on canvas prov.exhib.lit. 21-Oct-3 Artcurial Briest, Paris #384/R est:20000-25000
£25503 $45651 €38000 Angle des boules (52x32cm-20x13in) s.d.57 tempera prov.exhib.lit. 26-May-4 Christie's, Paris #74/R est:25000-35000
£114094 $209933 €170000 Amerique (97x130cm-38x51in) s.d.1953 lit. 29-Mar-4 Cornette de St.Cyr, Paris #5/R est:180000-220000
£120000 $218400 €175200 Les grilles en emeute (60x81cm-24x32in) s.d.39 lit. 6-Feb-4 Sotheby's, London #155/R est:60000-80000
£120000 $218400 €175200 Place Ocre (97x130cm-38x51in) s.d.54 prov.exhib.lit. 5-Feb-4 Sotheby's, London #33/R est:80000-120000
£120667 $217200 €181000 Atelier (50x61cm-20x24in) s.d.1948 prov.lit. 25-Apr-4 Versailles Encheres #113 est:200000-250000
£131004 $241048 €191266 Hiver a Lisbonne (129x162cm-51x64in) s.d.1958 prov.exhib.lit. 8-Jun-4 Germann, Zurich #34/R est:250000-350000 (S.FR 300000)
Works on paper
£3474 $5906 €5072 Modern picture (11x17cm-4x7in) s.d.48 collage exhib. 4-Nov-3 Bukowskis, Stockholm #274/R est:30000-35000 (S.KR 46000)
£6395 $11000 €9337 Composition (26x26cm-10x10in) s.d.46 ink chl. 3-Dec-3 Doyle, New York #55/R est:6000-8000
£6500 $11960 €9490 Rio (25x20cm-10x8in) s.d.46 ink pencil lit. 24-Jun-4 Sotheby's, London #189/R est:6000-8000
£11000 $20020 €16060 Untitled (13x19cm-5x7in) s.d.49 W/C ink. 5-Feb-4 Christie's, London #119/R est:7000-9000
£14085 $24648 €20000 Paysage (27x21cm-11x8in) s.d.1961 gouache prov. 18-Dec-3 Cornette de St.Cyr, Paris #66/R est:22000-25000
£15116 $26000 €22069 Buissous (36x50cm-14x20in) s.d.67 gouache prov.exhib. 3-Dec-3 Doyle, New York #54/R est:14000-18000

VIEN, Joseph Marie (1716-1809) French
£5634 $9746 €8000 Agar presentee a Abraham par Sarah (27x38cm-11x15in) 15-Dec-3 Bailly Pommery, Paris #71/R est:2000-3000
£13158 $24211 €20000 Academie d'homme (98x132cm-39x52in) prov.lit. 24-Jun-4 Christie's, Paris #111/R est:20000-30000
£251701 $450544 €370000 Femme sortant des bains (95x68cm-37x27in) s.d.1763 prov.exhib.lit. 19-Mar-4 Beaussant & Lefèvre, Paris #74/R est:80000-90000
Works on paper
£616 $1048 €900 Bacchanal (10x42cm-4x17in) s.d.1759 pen ink. 6-Nov-3 Tajan, Paris #62
£1293 $2314 €1900 Virgile lisant l'Eneide a Auguste et Livie ou Tu Marcellus Eris (38x27cm-15x11in) pen grey ink col wash htd white. 18-Mar-4 Christie's, Paris #37/R est:800-1200
£15646 $28007 €23000 Une eglise avec un groupe de batiments, Rome (16x22cm-6x9in) black chk prov. 18-Mar-4 Christie's, Paris #33/R est:3000-5000

VIEN, Joseph Marie (attrib) (1716-1809) French
£1167 $2112 €1750 Scene antique (46x68cm-18x27in) 30-Mar-4 Millon & Associes, Paris #29 est:2000-3000

VIENNESE SCHOOL (18th C) Austrian
£12171 $22395 €18500 Landscape with herdsmen and washerwomen (54x63cm-21x25in) pair. 24-Jun-4 Dr Fritz Nagel, Stuttgart #670/R est:7000

VIENNOT, Claude Marie Rose Leopold (19/20th C) French
£320 $576 €480 Still life with pomegranate (23x33cm-9x13in) s. panel. 26-Apr-4 Rieber, Stuttgart #1228/R

VIERA, Conny (20th C) Venezuelan?
Photographs
£2071 $3375 €3024 Untitled (25x30cm-10x12in) s. black/white photograph. 28-Sep-3 Subastas Odalys, Caracas #85

VIERA, Petrona (1895-1960) Uruguayan?
£1217 $2300 €1777 Nude (18x14cm-7x6in) s. cardboard prov. 22-Feb-4 Galeria y Remates, Montevideo #63/R est:3500
£1587 $3000 €2317 Ibiscus flowers and apples (33x27cm-13x11in) s. cardboard prov. 22-Feb-4 Galeria y Remates, Montevideo #64/R est:3000
£2540 $4800 €3708 Dusk on the beach (19x24cm-7x9in) s. cardboard prov. 22-Feb-4 Galeria y Remates, Montevideo #61/R est:6000
£3228 $6100 €4713 Malvin Beach (14x18cm-6x7in) s. prov. 22-Feb-4 Galeria y Remates, Montevideo #62/R est:4800
£10294 $17500 €15029 Punta del Este (77x72cm-30x28in) s. 25-Nov-3 Galeria y Remates, Montevideo #157/R

VIERIN, Emmanuel (1869-1954) Belgian
£709 $1341 €1050 Marais (60x90cm-24x35in) s.d.90. 17-Feb-4 Vanderkindere, Brussels #104

VIERLING, Antoine (c.1842-?) French
£8609 $15669 €13000 Danseuse gitane aux castagnettes (94x59cm-37x23in) s. 19-Jun-4 Binoche, Orleans #42 est:4500-6000

VIERTHALER, Ludwig (1875-?) German
Sculpture
£2448 $4087 €3500 Dancer (59cm-23in) i. gilded bronze. 28-Jun-3 Bolland & Marotz, Bremen #299/R est:3800

VIETINGHOFF, Egon Alexis von (1903-1994) German
£195 $349 €285 Still life of flowers (55x46cm-22x18in) s. canvas on masonite. 22-Mar-4 Philippe Schuler, Zurich #6055 (S.FR 450)
£264 $449 €385 Still life with onions (38x46cm-15x18in) s. i. verso canvas on panel. 5-Nov-3 Dobiaschofsky, Bern #1209/R (S.FR 600)
£286 $487 €418 Still life with pears and walnuts (24x41cm-9x16in) s. i. verso canvas on panel. 5-Nov-3 Dobiaschofsky, Bern #1031/R (S.FR 650)
£303 $542 €442 Still life of fruit (33x41cm-13x16in) s.d. double-sided. 22-Mar-4 Philippe Schuler, Zurich #6056 (S.FR 700)

VIETOR, Frank (1919-) American
Works on paper
£305 $500 €442 Ducks in flight (10x14cm-4x6in) s. W/C gouache exec.c.1970. 7-Jun-3 Treadway Gallery, Cincinnati #1433
£457 $750 €663 Train on a stone bridge (7x12cm-3x5in) s. W/C gouache exec.c.1970. 7-Jun-3 Treadway Gallery, Cincinnati #1434
£518 $850 €751 Train with city in the distance (7x12cm-3x5in) s. W/C gouache exec.c.1970. 7-Jun-3 Treadway Gallery, Cincinnati #1435
£518 $850 €751 Train in winter (7x12cm-3x5in) s. W/C gouache exec.c.1970. 7-Jun-3 Treadway Gallery, Cincinnati #1436
£610 $1000 €885 Train on a wooden bridge (7x12cm-3x5in) s. W/C gouache exec.c.1970. 7-Jun-3 Treadway Gallery, Cincinnati #1437

VIETTI, Nicola (1945-) French
£268 $497 €400 Man from Marseille (40x30cm-16x12in) s. 13-Mar-4 Meeting Art, Vercelli #228
£352 $585 €500 Sul Divano (40x80cm-16x31in) s. 14-Jun-3 Meeting Art, Vercelli #180
£423 $701 €600 Passeggiata sul Lungomare (60x120cm-24x47in) s. 14-Jun-3 Meeting Art, Vercelli #394
£467 $859 €700 Shop (80x140cm-31x55in) s. s.verso. 12-Jun-4 Meeting Art, Vercelli #948/R
£470 $869 €700 Getting ready for a bath (70x90cm-28x35in) s. 13-Mar-4 Meeting Art, Vercelli #485

VIGAS, Oswaldo (1926-) Venezuelan
£1698 $3125 €2547 Offer (41x31cm-16x12in) s. canvas on masonite painted 1978. 27-Jun-4 Subastas Odalys, Caracas #89
£2695 $4500 €3935 Painful (90x70cm-35x28in) s. painted 1991. 13-Jul-3 Subastas Odalys, Caracas #44/R
£2805 $5105 €4208 Untitled (35x81cm-14x32in) s. painted 1963. 21-Jun-4 Subastas Odalys, Caracas #12/R
£6255 $11510 €9383 Always together (90x70cm-35x28in) s. painted 1997. 27-Jun-4 Subastas Odalys, Caracas #74 est:14000
£8014 $14585 €12021 Always together (90x70cm-35x28in) s. painted 1997. 21-Jun-4 Subastas Odalys, Caracas #43/R est:14000
Works on paper
£526 $905 €768 Untitled (27x21cm-11x8in) s. col ink exec.1997. 7-Dec-3 Subastas Odalys, Caracas #94/R
£667 $1200 €974 Untitled (60x47cm-24x19in) s. mixed media exec.1985. 25-Apr-4 Subastas Odalys, Caracas #49/R
£848 $1560 €1238 Untitled (66x50cm-26x20in) s. gouache paper on board exec.1976. 28-Mar-4 Subastas Odalys, Caracas #3/R
£5015 $8375 €7322 Shapes (107x80cm-42x31in) s. gouache card on panel exec.1956. 19-Oct-3 Subastas Odalys, Caracas #35/R est:9500

VIGE, Jens (1864-1912) Danish
£1500 $2579 €2190 Self-portrait (86x71cm-34x28in) s.d.1905 exhib. 3-Dec-3 Museumsbygningen, Copenhagen #214/R est:6000-8000 (D.KR 16000)

VIGEE-LEBRUN, Marie Louise Elisabeth (1755-1842) French
£10417 $17396 €15000 Portrait presume du Comte de Brie (73x61cm-29x24in) exhib.lit. 22-Oct-3 Ribeyre & Baron, Paris #5/R est:15000-20000
£31579 $58106 €48000 Portrait de Victoire de Bavilliers (66x54cm-26x21in) s.d.1777 oval prov. 24-Jun-4 Tajan, Paris #62/R est:40000-50000
£40141 $70246 €57000 Allegorie de la poesie (80x65cm-31x26in) s. prov.exhib.lit. 19-Dec-3 Delvaux, Paris #115/R est:40000-50000
£144737 $266316 €220000 Portrait de la pRincesse Caroline de Liechtenstein (65x54cm-26x21in) oval prov.exhib.lit. 24-Jun-4 Christie's, Paris #106/R est:60000-80000

VIGEE-LEBRUN, Marie Louise Elisabeth (attrib) (1755-1842) French
Works on paper
£2013 $3705 €3000 Portrait de dame au bonnet de dentelle (41x33cm-16x13in) bears sig. pastel oval. 24-Mar-4 Tajan, Paris #138/R est:3500-4000

VIGELAND, Gustav (1869-1943) Norwegian
Sculpture
£32520 $59512 €47479 The small child (48x22x15cm-19x9x6in) s. bronze exec.1911 lit. 7-Jun-4 Blomqvist, Oslo #391/R est:600000-700000 (N.KR 400000)

VIGH, Bertolan (1890-1946) Hungarian
£433 $780 €650 Soldier with woman (60x80cm-24x31in) s. 26-Apr-4 Rieber, Stuttgart #942/R

VIGIL, Luis Rodriguez (20th C) Spanish
£414 $691 €600 Boys (115x145cm-45x57in) s. 17-Nov-3 Durán, Madrid #65/R

VIGNAL, Pierre (1855-1925) French
Works on paper
£400 $716 €600 Terrasse a la Villa d'Este (37x55cm-15x22in) graphite W/C. 11-May-4 Christie's, Paris #143/R

VIGNE, Edouard de (1808-1866) Belgian
£1875 $2981 €2700 Paysage anime (35x48cm-14x19in) s. panel. 9-Sep-3 Vanderkindere, Brussels #57
£3121 $5211 €4400 Paysage au pont anime (42x62cm-17x24in) s. panel. 17-Jun-3 Vanderkindere, Brussels #412/R est:4000-6000

VIGNERON, Pierre Roch (1789-1872) French
£1800 $3330 €2628 Portrait of a lady arranging roses (46x38cm-18x15in) s.d.1836. 14-Jul-4 Sotheby's, Olympia #139/R est:2000-3000
Works on paper
£1761 $2923 €2500 Les amusements de l'enfance (34x49cm-13x19in) s.d.1860 W/C. 13-Jun-3 Renaud, Paris #36/R est:2000-3000

VIGNET, Henri (1857-1920) French
£496 $829 €700 Bridge over river (49x39cm-19x15in) s. 17-Oct-3 Behringer, Furth #1570/R

VIGNOLES, Andre (1920-) French
£326 $600 €476 Bouquet clair (66x46cm-26x18in) s. prov. 9-Jun-4 Doyle, New York #3086
£345 $617 €504 Still life with poppies in white jug (46x38cm-18x15in) s.d.68. 12-May-4 Dobiaschofsky, Bern #1048 (S.FR 800)
£380 $669 €555 La route de Bles (16x46cm-6x18in) s.d.59. 19-May-4 Dreweatt Neate, Newbury #73/R
£471 $800 €688 Still life with flowers (61x48cm-24x19in) s.d.59 prov. 22-Nov-3 Jackson's, Cedar Falls #394/R
£516 $950 €753 La pivoine (53x46cm-21x18in) s. prov. 9-Jun-4 Doyle, New York #3085
£802 $1500 €1171 Le debut du printemps (81x99cm-32x39in) s. s.i.verso prov. 25-Feb-4 Doyle, New York #93/R est:1200-1800
£1100 $2035 €1606 Fleurs de printemps (56x33cm-22x13in) s.d.57. 9-Mar-4 Gorringes, Lewes #2062
£1100 $2024 €1606 Nature morte aux oignons (65x100cm-26x39in) s. 24-Mar-4 Sotheby's, Olympia #62/R est:700-900
£1711 $3200 €2498 Sous-bois (49x73cm-19x29in) s.d.59 prov. 25-Feb-4 Christie's, Rockefeller NY #103/R est:2000-3000
£2032 $3800 €2967 Nature morte (48x65cm-19x26in) s.d.58. 25-Feb-4 Christie's, Rockefeller NY #100/R est:2500-3500

VIGNON, Charlotte (1639-?) French
£16667 $26500 €24500 Still life with fruit (53x41cm-21x16in) 23-Mar-3 Mercier & Cie, Lille #152/R est:27000-30000

VIGNON, Claude (1593-1670) French
£39474 $72632 €60000 Vocation de Saint-Pierre (98x76cm-39x30in) s. panel prov.lit. 24-Jun-4 Christie's, Paris #34/R est:30000-50000
£73239 $128169 €104000 Saint Matthieu (103x145cm-41x57in) 17-Dec-3 Piasa, Paris #71/R est:10000-15000
Works on paper
£291 $500 €425 Study of an old man (20x18cm-8x7in) W/C pencil. 7-Dec-3 Susanin's, Chicago #6021/R

VIGNON, Claude (style) (1593-1670) French
£7500 $12750 €10950 Allegory of wealth (105x92cm-41x36in) 30-Oct-3 Sotheby's, Olympia #113/R est:3000-5000

VIGNON, Philippe (attrib) (1638-1701) French
£3586 $6634 €5200 Portraits de femmes de qualite (41x32cm-16x13in) pair. 13-Feb-4 Rossini, Paris #10/R

VIGNON, Victor Alfred Paul (1847-1909) French
£1118 $2058 €1700 Overlooking rooftops: a study (23x45cm-9x18in) s. canvas on plywood. 22-Jun-4 Christie's, Amsterdam #221/R est:700-900
£1549 $2711 €2200 Le chemin de Chauny a Noroy sur Ourcq (15x27cm-6x11in) s. 16-Dec-3 Claude Aguttes, Neuilly #119/R est:2000-3000
£2600 $4784 €3900 Champs vallonnes (46x55cm-18x22in) s. 14-Jun-4 Tajan, Paris #10/R est:3000-4500
£4698 $8409 €7000 Rue du village (38x46cm-15x18in) s. prov. 26-May-4 Christie's, Paris #2/R est:1000-1500
£5503 $10126 €8200 Paysage de printemps (49x65cm-19x26in) s. 24-Mar-4 Binoche, Paris #81/R est:5000-7000
Works on paper
£2518 $4330 €3600 La Seine a Paris (23x32cm-9x13in) s. pastel. 3-Dec-3 Tajan, Paris #13 est:4000-5000

VIGNY, Sylvain (1902-1970) French
£268 $499 €400 La procession (65x81cm-26x32in) s. 3-Mar-4 Ferri, Paris #154
£268 $499 €400 Bouquet de fleurs (49x69cm-19x27in) s.d.52. 3-Mar-4 Ferri, Paris #156
£278 $464 €400 Portrait de jeune femme (73x60cm-29x24in) s. prov. 21-Oct-3 Artcurial Briest, Paris #23
£336 $625 €500 Portrait de femme (63x45cm-25x18in) s. oil paper on canvas. 2-Mar-4 Artcurial Briest, Paris #228
£403 $749 €600 Le joueur de mandoline (73x60cm-29x24in) s. 3-Mar-4 Ferri, Paris #157
£470 $869 €700 In the garden (42x59cm-17x23in) s. paper on board. 9-Mar-4 Dorotheum, Vienna #120
£537 $999 €800 Groupe de personnages dont un a la mandoline (81x100cm-32x39in) s. 3-Mar-4 Ferri, Paris #155
£537 $999 €800 Personnages sur un quai (45x91cm-18x36in) s. paper. 3-Mar-4 Ferri, Paris #158
£800 $1432 €1200 Self-portrait (81x65cm-32x26in) s. 17-May-4 Chayette & Cheval, Paris #205/R
Works on paper
£302 $559 €450 Le peintre et ses modeles (47x64cm-19x25in) s. W/C gouache. 15-Mar-4 Blanchet, Paris #124/R

VIGON, Louis Jacques (1897-1985) French
£621 $1030 €900 Laveuses (54x73cm-21x29in) s. 1-Oct-3 Millon & Associes, Paris #73

VIGOT, Jacques (20th C) French?
£280 $476 €400 Dernier etage (61x50cm-24x20in) s. 29-Nov-3 Neret-Minet, Paris #133/R
£294 $499 €420 La vie de chateau (50x40cm-20x16in) s. 29-Nov-3 Neret-Minet, Paris #225/R

VIGUIER, Fortune (19th C) French
£867 $1560 €1300 Landscape with cloud formations (7x23cm-3x9in) s. panel. 26-Apr-4 Rieber, Stuttgart #1112/R
£1400 $2520 €2100 Landscape with pond and figures (10x17cm-4x7in) s. panel. 26-Apr-4 Rieber, Stuttgart #1111/R est:1600

VIGUIER, Urbain Jean (19th C) French
£309 $574 €460 Portrait of a lady (24x19cm-9x7in) s.d.1868. 8-Mar-4 Bernaerts, Antwerp #266/R

VIIRILA, Reino (1901-) Finnish
£347 $580 €500 Tammelan Puistokatu (50x61cm-20x24in) s/d/56. 26-Oct-3 Bukowskis, Helsinki #521/R

VIKAS, Karl (1875-1934) Austrian
£264 $425 €385 Colourful landscape with hardwood trees in autumn (58x79cm-23x31in) s. 24-Feb-3 O'Gallerie, Oregon #836/R

VIKATOS, Spyros (1878-1960) Greek
£750 $1313 €1095 Still life with fruit (23x27cm-9x11in) s. hardboard. 16-Dec-3 Bonhams, New Bond Street #71/R

VIKE, Harald (1906-1987) Australian/Norwegian
£366 $575 €531 Landscape (59x69cm-23x27in) s.d.64 board. 26-Aug-3 Lawson Menzies, Sydney #40 est:1000-2000 (A.D 900)
£650 $1021 €943 Football game (61x49cm-24x19in) s. board. 26-Aug-3 Lawson Menzies, Sydney #337 est:400-600 (A.D 1600)

VIKHAGEN, Havard (1952-) Norwegian
£3407 $5860 €4974 Composition (60x87cm-24x34in) init. 8-Dec-3 Blomqvist, Oslo #578/R est:35000-40000 (N.KR 40000)
£3757 $6275 €5485 Thistles (116x165cm-46x65in) init. painted 1996-97 exhib.lit. 13-Oct-3 Blomqvist, Oslo #325/R est:50000-70000 (N.KR 44000)

VIKSTEN, Hans (1926-1987) Swedish
£308 $529 €450 Walk of life (55x46cm-22x18in) s.d.75. 7-Dec-3 Uppsala Auktionskammare, Uppsala #257 (S.KR 4000)
£363 $653 €530 Evening bird (46x55cm-18x22in) s.d.69. 26-Apr-4 Bukowskis, Stockholm #615/R (S.KR 5000)
£673 $1083 €983 The rope-dancer (100x65cm-39x26in) s.d.64 sold with letter. 25-Aug-3 Lilla Bukowskis, Stockholm #528 (S.KR 8800)
Works on paper
£468 $796 €683 The rescue (71x55cm-28x22in) s.d.67 mixed media. 4-Nov-3 Bukowskis, Stockholm #537/R (S.KR 6200)

VILA CANELLAS, Josep M (1914-) Spanish
£1748 $2920 €2500 Aaiguafreda hills (65x82cm-26x32in) s.d.42 s.i.d.verso. 30-Jun-3 Ansorena, Madrid #431/R

VILA FUDIO, Justo (1926-) Spanish
£414 $745 €600 Horizon (81x118cm-32x46in) s.d.73. 26-Jan-4 Durán, Madrid #20/R

VILA PUIG, Juan (1890-1963) Spanish
£724 $1332 €1100 Hay stacks (16x20cm-6x8in) s. board. 22-Jun-4 Durán, Madrid #66/R

VILA Y PRADES, Julio (1873-1930) Spanish
£352 $609 €500 Waterfall (33x25cm-13x10in) s. cardboard en grisaille. 15-Dec-3 Ansorena, Madrid #261/R
£699 $1168 €1000 Retarto de caballero (62x53cm-24x21in) s.i. canvas on board. 24-Jun-3 Segre, Madrid #85/R
£800 $1480 €1168 Boy with oranges (72x57cm-28x22in) s.i. prov. 10-Mar-4 Sotheby's, Olympia #298/R
£862 $1431 €1250 Seascape in Mar del Plata (13x22cm-5x9in) cardboard. 1-Oct-3 Ansorena, Madrid #732/R
£1342 $2510 €2000 Emptying the jug (24x15cm-9x6in) s.i. board. 24-Feb-4 Durán, Madrid #182/R est:2000
£1655 $2748 €2400 Woman (66x48cm-26x19in) s. 30-Sep-3 Ansorena, Madrid #106/R est:2400
£2128 $3447 €3000 Aldeana (66x48cm-26x19in) s. 20-May-3 Ansorena, Madrid #180/R est:3000
£2477 $4260 €3616 Spring (95x70cm-37x28in) s. board. 3-Dec-3 Naón & Cia, Buenos Aires #57/R est:2500-3000
£7237 $13316 €11000 Spring (96x70cm-38x28in) s. board. 22-Jun-4 Durán, Madrid #157/R est:9500
£9929 $16582 €14000 Valencian woman with cocks (140x75cm-55x30in) s. 20-Oct-3 Durán, Madrid #231/R
£15000 $25500 €21900 On the beach (37x46cm-15x18in) s. board prov. 18-Nov-3 Sotheby's, London #228/R
Works on paper
£915 $1602 €1300 Sharing lunch (44x40cm-17x16in) s. gouache. 16-Dec-3 Durán, Madrid #85/R

VILA, Gustavo (1939-) Spanish
£500 $905 €750 Autumn landscape (58x77cm-23x30in) s. 30-Mar-4 Segre, Madrid #365/R

VILADECANS, Joan Pere (1948-) Spanish
£311 $516 €454 The knot (100x79cm-39x31in) acrylic collage. 2-Oct-3 Heffel, Vancouver #45 (C.D 700)
£1733 $3137 €2600 Peninsula (102x72cm-40x28in) s.d.1982 oil mixed media paper on board prov.exhib.lit. 30-Mar-4 Segre, Madrid #168/R est:1600

VILADOMAT, Domingo (19/20th C) Spanish
Works on paper
£276 $458 €400 Landscape (48x67cm-19x26in) s. dr. 1-Oct-3 Ansorena, Madrid #491/R
£282 $487 €400 Landscape (48x67cm-19x26in) s. dr. 15-Dec-3 Ansorena, Madrid #220/R

VILADRICH, Miguel (1887-1956) Spanish
£5801 $10500 €8469 Miguelito (42x45cm-17x18in) board. 30-Mar-4 Arroyo, Buenos Aires #76

VILAIN, Walter (1938-) Belgian
Works on paper
£347 $580 €500 Composition (70x104cm-28x41in) s. mixed media. 21-Oct-3 Campo, Vlaamse Kaai #1188

VILALLONGA, Jesus Carlos de (1927-) Canadian
£248 $421 €362 Don Quijote y Sancho (60x50cm-24x20in) s.d.1959 i.verso board prov. 23-Nov-3 Levis, Calgary #146/R (C.D 550)
£273 $445 €399 La mort du Renne, Canada (30x41cm-12x16in) s.d.58 acrylic on masonite. 23-Sep-3 Ritchie, Toronto #188 (C.D 600)
£273 $445 €399 Head (30x41cm-12x16in) s.d.77 acrylic on masonite. 23-Sep-3 Ritchie, Toronto #189/R (C.D 600)
£293 $497 €428 Head of a young woman (30x41cm-12x16in) s. board prov. 21-Nov-3 Walker's, Ottawa #108/R (C.D 650)
£341 $556 €498 El trio (41x61cm-16x24in) s.d.61 acrylic on masonite. 23-Sep-3 Ritchie, Toronto #187/R (C.D 750)
£467 $849 €700 Mujer y su alma (51x41cm-20x16in) s.d.1982 oil acrylic panel. 29-Jun-4 Segre, Madrid #167/R
£676 $1149 €987 Chevalier and angels of inspiration (50x40cm-20x16in) s.i.d.1979 verso board prov. 27-Nov-3 Heffel, Vancouver #73/R (C.D 1500)
£721 $1225 €1053 Sombrero Papel (61x40cm-24x16in) s.d.59 prov. 18-Nov-3 Sotheby's, Toronto #15/R (C.D 1600)
£1689 $2872 €2466 Dreamers (51x41cm-20x16in) s.d.76 masonite prov. 18-Nov-3 Sotheby's, Toronto #73/R est:2500-3000 (C.D 3750)
£1802 $3063 €2631 Foret des amoureux I (76x102cm-30x40in) s.i.d.76 i.verso acrylic masonite prov. 18-Nov-3 Sotheby's, Toronto #127/R est:2500-3000 (C.D 4000)

VILATO, Javier (1921-2000) French
£1293 $2352 €1900 Blue portrait (52x38cm-20x15in) s.d.44 cardboard. 3-Feb-4 Segre, Madrid #155/R est:1800
£2013 $3745 €3000 Seated woman (92x73cm-36x29in) s.d.44. 2-Mar-4 Ansorena, Madrid #37/R est:3000
£2083 $3479 €3000 Jeune femme attablee (92x65cm-36x26in) s. d.V-55 Vi-55 verso prov. 21-Oct-3 Artcurial Briest, Paris #22 est:1000-1200
£2727 $4555 €3900 Paris (46x55cm-18x22in) s. d.iX-57 verso. 24-Jun-3 Segre, Madrid #172/R est:3900
£2937 $4905 €4200 Portrait of woman (52x38cm-20x15in) s.d.44. 30-Jun-3 Ansorena, Madrid #335/R est:4200
Works on paper
£352 $609 €500 Taureau (24x18cm-9x7in) s.d.1941 col crayon dr. 14-Dec-3 Eric Pillon, Calais #249/R

VILCHIS, Fernando (20th C) South American
£363 $627 €530 Untitled (125x100cm-49x39in) s.d.1994 oil sand masonite. 9-Dec-3 Louis Morton, Mexico #136/R est:10000-12000 (M.P 7000)

VILHUNEN, Risto (1945-) Finnish
£486 $812 €700 Winter landscape (43x67cm-17x26in) s.d.2000. 23-Oct-3 Hagelstam, Helsinki #941

VILLA, Edoardo (1920-) South African
Sculpture
£1293 $2159 €1888 Torso (34cm-13in) s.d.1968 num.3/6 bronze. 20-Oct-3 Stephan Welz, Johannesburg #406/R est:7000-10000 (SA.R 15000)

VILLA, Émile (19th C) French
£2500 $4625 €3650 Feeding time (59x45cm-23x18in) s. 14-Jul-4 Sotheby's, Olympia #254/R est:2500-3500

VILLA, Hernando (1881-1952) American
£815 $1500 €1190 Nativity (102x76cm-40x30in) s. 13-Jun-4 Bonhams & Butterfields, Los Angeles #7011/R est:800-1200
£879 $1600 €1283 The Enchanted Cove (61x102cm-24x40in) s.d.1918. 15-Jun-4 John Moran, Pasadena #71 est:2500-3500
£1720 $3250 €2511 Sailing vessel/coastal - Pirates Cove (51x61cm-20x24in) s.d.41 i. verso canvasboard. 17-Feb-4 John Moran, Pasadena #73/R est:2500-3500
Works on paper
£291 $550 €425 Courtyard (35x27cm-14x11in) W/C col pencil chl. 22-Feb-4 Bonhams & Butterfields, Los Angeles #7010
£467 $850 €682 The sailor (58x41cm-23x16in) s.d.32 mixed media chl crayon board prov. 15-Jun-4 John Moran, Pasadena #79a
£847 $1600 €1237 The Navajo (61x46cm-24x18in) s. chl prov. 17-Feb-4 John Moran, Pasadena #109/R est:1000-1500

VILLA, Miguel (1901-1988) Spanish
£1408 $2437 €2000 The San Diego (22x27cm-9x11in) s.i.d.1983 verso. 15-Dec-3 Ansorena, Madrid #946/R est:2000
£6207 $10303 €9000 Landscape with cattle (80x138cm-31x54in) s. 30-Sep-3 Ansorena, Madrid #81/R est:9000
£7718 $14356 €11500 Still life with fish and pomegranates (46x55cm-18x22in) s. 2-Mar-4 Ansorena, Madrid #76/R est:11500
£9155 $15838 €13000 Palm trees (65x81cm-26x32in) s.d.1980 verso. 15-Dec-3 Ansorena, Madrid #965/R est:13000
£11620 $20335 €16500 Village in Segur (50x61cm-20x24in) s.i.d.1934 verso prov. 16-Dec-3 Segre, Madrid #106/R est:16500

VILLACRES, Cesar A (1880-?) Ecuadorian
£256 $450 €374 Paris street scene (41x51cm-16x20in) s. 23-May-4 William Jenack, New York #124

VILLALBA, Dario (1939-) Spanish
£1000 $1810 €1500 Coast II (37x34cm-15x13in) s.d.1989 acrylic collage canvas on board prov. 30-Mar-4 Segre, Madrid #181/R est:1200
£1067 $1931 €1600 Coast I (37x35cm-15x14in) s.d.1989 oil collage canvas on board prov. 30-Mar-4 Segre, Madrid #180/R
£2027 $3568 €3000 Signs, bust and geometry (100x72cm-39x28in) s.d.1968 s.i.verso acrylic exhib.lit. 18-May-4 Segre, Madrid #215/R est:3000

VILLALON, Jesus (20th C) Venezuelan?
£258 $400 €377 Avila (80x120cm-31x47in) s. 3-Nov-2 Subastas Odalys, Caracas #29
£524 $875 €765 Valley (130x195cm-51x77in) s. painted 1993. 19-Oct-3 Subastas Odalys, Caracas #137

VILLALPANDO, Cristobal (1649-1714) Mexican
£16471 $28000 €24048 Judith (84x56cm-33x22in) s. 19-Nov-3 Sotheby's, New York #67/R est:20000-30000

VILLALTA MARZI, Esteban (1956-) Italian
£369 $683 €550 Where your heart leads you (50x70cm-20x28in) s.i.d.1995 verso acrylic. 13-Mar-4 Meeting Art, Vercelli #23
£563 $935 €800 Clik (65x80cm-26x31in) s.d.1991 acrylic. 14-Jun-3 Meeting Art, Vercelli #36/R

VILLAMIL, P (?) ?
£2300 $4186 €3358 Young beauty with a basket of roses on the Amalfi coast (63x51cm-25x20in) s. 16-Jun-4 Christie's, Kensington #120/R est:2500-3500

VILLANI, Enrico (1928-) Italian
£467 $859 €700 Presences (50x60cm-20x24in) s.d.1976. 12-Jun-4 Meeting Art, Vercelli #362

VILLANI, Gennaro (1885-1948) Italian
£317 $548 €450 Seascape with boats (23x31cm-9x12in) s. cardboard. 10-Dec-3 Finarte Semenzato, Rome #235/R
£1056 $1754 €1500 Scorcio di Parigi (30x32cm-12x13in) s. board prov. 11-Jun-3 Christie's, Rome #220/R est:1700-1900
£1268 $2104 €1800 Self Portrait at the Moulin Rouge (23x33cm-9x13in) s. board exhib.lit. 11-Jun-3 Christie's, Rome #221/R est:2000-2500

VILLANIS, E (19th C) French
Sculpture
£1056 $1754 €1500 Buste (62cm-24in) s. pat bronze. 10-Jun-3 Adjug'art, Brest #13a/R
£1172 $1958 €1700 Deborah, Oriental a la lyre (63cm-25in) medaille pat bronze. 12-Nov-3 Chassaing Rivet, Toulouse #132
£1329 $2219 €1900 Sibylle (52cm-20in) bronze. 7-Oct-3 Sotheby's, Amsterdam #183/R est:1500-2000
£1748 $3007 €2500 Bust Cendrillon (54cm-21in) bronze lit. 4-Dec-3 Vendue Huis, Gravenhage #1
£1800 $3006 €2628 Mignon (57cm-22in) s. pat bronze. 15-Oct-3 Christie's, Kensington #295/R
£2201 $3500 €3213 Esmerelda (56cm-22in) i. bronze. 23-Mar-3 Auctions by the Bay, Alameda #817/R
£2400 $4344 €3504 Walkyrie (28cm-11in) s. bronze marble base. 30-Mar-4 Keys, Aylsham #401/R
£2600 $4342 €3796 Diana (57cm-22in) s. pat bronze. 15-Oct-3 Christie's, Kensington #293/R

VILLANIS, Emmanuele (1880-1920) Italian
Sculpture
£924 $1700 €1349 Dancer (36cm-14in) s.i. bronze. 27-Jun-4 Hindman, Chicago #889/R est:1000-1500
£1067 $1920 €1600 Fille de Boheme (45cm-18in) i. brown pat.bronze. 24-Apr-4 Quittenbaum, Munich #146/R est:1800
£1081 $2000 €1578 Esmeralda (58cm-23in) i. base pat bronze st.f.Garanti. 15-Jul-4 Sotheby's, New York #123/R est:2000-3000
£1119 $1902 €1600 Saida (49cm-19in) s.i. pat bronze. 28-Nov-3 Drouot Estimations, Paris #25 est:1200-1500
£1216 $2177 €1800 Femme (45cm-18in) s. pat bronze. 5-May-4 Claude Boisgirard, Paris #46/R est:1800-2000
£1267 $2331 €1900 Femme a la branche de pommier (139x89cm-55x35in) s. pat bronze. 9-Jun-4 Beaussant & Lefèvre, Paris #235/R est:1800-2000
£1300 $2210 €1898 Moe (27cm-11in) i. bronze. 25-Nov-3 Sotheby's, Olympia #61/R est:800-1200
£1319 $2400 €1926 Lalla Roukh (66cm-26in) s. gilt brown pat bronze. 19-Jun-4 Jackson's, Cedar Falls #122/R est:2000-3000
£1350 $2525 €1971 Sapho, playing a lyre (56cm-22in) s.num.655 bronze st.f.Societe des Bronzes. 24-Feb-4 Sotheby's, Olympia #96/R est:1500-2000
£1600 $2928 €2336 Dalila, bust of a maiden (42cm-17in) i. bronze. 3-Jun-4 Sotheby's, Olympia #121/R est:1500-2000
£1700 $3043 €2482 Miarka (76cm-30in) s. dark pat.bronze. 25-May-4 Bukowskis, Stockholm #313/R est:12000-15000 (S.KR 23000)
£1722 $3134 €2600 Cendrillon (60cm-24in) s.i. brown pat. bronze incl. marble base. 16-Jun-4 Hotel des Ventes Mosan, Brussels #189 est:350-450
£1958 $3270 €2800 La captive. s. brown pat bronze. 24-Jun-3 Millon & Associes, Paris #12/R est:2500-3000
£2000 $3180 €2920 Sibylle (60cm-24in) s.i. bronze. 9-Sep-3 Sotheby's, Olympia #160/R est:2000-2200
£2100 $3927 €3066 Mignon, bust of a young girl (56cm-22in) s.i.num.117 bronze exec.c.1900. 24-Feb-4 Sotheby's, Olympia #98/R est:2000-2500
£2200 $4004 €3212 Bohemienne, lady figure (55cm-22in) s.i. brown pat. bronze. 5-Feb-4 Mellors & Kirk, Nottingham #667/R est:1500-2000
£2700 $5049 €3942 Galatee, bust of a maiden (50cm-20in) s. bronze exec.c.1900. 24-Feb-4 Sotheby's, Olympia #97/R est:1500-2000
£2727 $4555 €3900 Bust of Lucretia (70cm-28in) s.i. bronze Cast.Societe des Bronzes de Paris. 9-Oct-3 Michael Zeller, Lindau #957/R est:2500
£2781 $5062 €4200 Melody (75cm-30in) s.i. green pat bronze. 19-Jun-4 Quittenbaum, Hamburg #155/R est:4200
£3500 $6405 €5110 Figure of a nude reclining on an artist palette (40cm-16in) s. bronze. 3-Jun-4 Sotheby's, Olympia #120/R est:2000-3000
£3800 $6840 €5548 Bohemian musician (70cm-28in) s.i. brown pat bronze. 21-Apr-4 Sotheby's, London #132/R est:3500-5500
£4706 $8000 €6871 Walkyrie (80cm-31in) s. pat bronze. 28-Oct-3 Christie's, Rockefeller NY #107/R
£7343 $12483 €10500 Secret (85cm-33in) s. pat bronze onyx base. 25-Nov-3 Millon & Associes, Paris #8/R est:12000-15000

VILLAPAREDES, Esteban (1933-) Venezuelan
£380 $600 €555 Untitled (34x48cm-13x19in) s. cardboard. 1-Dec-2 Subastas Odalys, Caracas #10/R
£547 $875 €799 Face (34x41cm-13x16in) s. masonite. 21-Sep-3 Subastas Odalys, Caracas #25
£1146 $2085 €1719 Maternity (91x61cm-36x24in) s. masonite painted 1970. 21-Jun-4 Subastas Odalys, Caracas #6/R
£1463 $2310 €2136 Lady of the cat (60x80cm-24x31in) s. cardboard. 27-Apr-3 Subastas Odalys, Caracas #14
Works on paper
£421 $665 €615 Untitled (32x48cm-13x19in) s. mixed media panel. 1-Dec-2 Subastas Odalys, Caracas #76/R
£449 $835 €656 Untitled (51x41cm-20x16in) s. mixed media on canvas. 14-Mar-4 Subastas Odalys, Caracas #59/R

VILLAR, Isabel (1934-) Spanish
£1831 $3168 €2600 Gentlemen (97x120cm-38x47in) 15-Dec-3 Ansorena, Madrid #953/R est:3300

VILLAR, Jesus (1930-) Spanish
£586 $1055 €850 Peasant family (80x110cm-31x43in) s. 26-Jan-4 Ansorena, Madrid #263/R
£652 $1070 €900 Still life (65x100cm-26x39in) s. 27-May-3 Durán, Madrid #742/R
£1552 $2793 €2250 Peasant family (131x80cm-52x31in) s. 26-Jan-4 Durán, Madrid #71/R

VILLAR, Rafael del (19/20th C) Spanish?
£1224 $2229 €1800 Still life of flowers (70x52cm-28x20in) s.d.1894. 3-Feb-4 Segre, Madrid #46/R est:1200

VILLAS, Patrick (20th C) Belgian?
Sculpture
£2703 $4838 €4000 Panthers (26x101x30cm-10x40x12in) pat bronze Cast Art Casting exec.1999 pair. 10-May-4 Amberes, Antwerp #576/R

VILLE, Vickers de (1856-1925) British
£300 $555 €438 Figures beneath a windmill (13x23cm-5x9in) s. panel. 10-Feb-4 David Lay, Penzance #58
£377 $652 €550 Landscape with woman by bridge (30x25cm-12x10in) s.d.1894. 15-Dec-3 Lilla Bukowskis, Stockholm #1144 (S.KR 4800)
£692 $1100 €1010 Port Haven Bay (15x23cm-6x9in) s. 14-Sep-3 Susanin's, Chicago #6162/R

VILLEBRANCHE, Michel (1823-?) French?
Works on paper
£282 $468 €400 La Canada, village Mexicain, route de Mexico a Queretaro (11x24cm-4x9in) s. ink htd white exec.c.1850. 15-Jun-3 Muizon & Le Coent, Paris #9

VILLEGAS Y CORDERO, Jose (1848-1922) Spanish
£1310 $2359 €1900 Procession (27x16cm-11x6in) s. board. 26-Jan-4 Durán, Madrid #130/R est:1900
£3873 $6701 €5500 Still life of fruit and flowers (49x60cm-19x24in) s. 15-Dec-3 Ansorena, Madrid #26/R est:5500
£10000 $18400 €14600 After the feast (98x48cm-39x19in) s.indis.i.d.1892. 25-Mar-4 Christie's, Kensington #160/R est:10000-15000
£10145 $16638 €14000 Meditabunda (71x40cm-28x16in) s. lit. 27-May-3 Durán, Madrid #264/R est:10000

VILLEGAS, Armando (1928-) Peruvian
£467 $859 €700 Guerrero azul (80x60cm-31x24in) s. s.d.89 verso prov. 9-Jun-4 Artcurial Briest, Paris #446
£7263 $13000 €10604 Construction (124x109cm-49x43in) s.d.1958 s.i.d.1958 verso prov.exhib. 16-May-4 Wright, Chicago #239/R est:10000-15000

VILLEGLE, Jacques de la (1926-) French
Works on paper
£288 $472 €400 Marcadet 17 (16x12cm-6x5in) s.d.77 collage. 6-Jun-3 David Kahn, Paris #35
£387 $670 €550 Untitled (11x18cm-4x7in) s. torn posters. 9-Dec-3 Artcurial Briest, Paris #396
£417 $696 €600 Sans titre (51x22cm-20x9in) torn poster panel exec.c.1965. 25-Oct-3 Cornette de St.Cyr, Paris #355/R
£528 $913 €750 Untitled (11x18cm-4x7in) s. torn posters. 9-Dec-3 Artcurial Briest, Paris #397
£704 $1218 €1000 Alain Bashung (18x14cm-7x6in) s. i.d.1998 verso torn poster on canvas. 14-Dec-3 Versailles Encheres #175/R
£976 $1600 €1425 Affiche lacere Quai Bourden (9x9cm-4x4in) s. paper collage on canvas exec.1960 prov. 28-May-3 Sotheby's, Amsterdam #93/R est:1000-1500
£979 $1635 €1400 Reveillon (24x33cm-9x13in) s.d.66 s.i.verso decollage. 25-Jun-3 Digard, Paris #121/R
£1216 $2177 €1800 Untitled (30x20cm-12x8in) s. torn posters on canvas. 4-May-4 Calmels Cohen, Paris #255 est:1500-2000
£1341 $2200 €1958 Affiche lacere Rue de la Douane (10x6cm-4x2in) s. paper collage on canvas exec.1959 prov. 28-May-3 Sotheby's, Amsterdam #95/R est:3000-5000
£1951 $3200 €2848 Affiche lacere Phillipe Biennale (10x13cm-4x5in) s. paper collage on canvas exec.1961. 28-May-3 Sotheby's, Amsterdam #92/R est:2000-3000
£2098 $3608 €3000 Rue de Bretonvilliers (46x33cm-18x13in) s.d.65 s.i.d.verso poster on canvas. 4-Dec-3 Piasa, Paris #26/R est:1000-1500
£2439 $4000 €3561 Affiche lacere Paris (26x25cm-10x10in) s.d.77 i.d.77 verso paper collage on canvas prov. 28-May-3 Sotheby's, Amsterdam #82/R est:4000-6000
£2797 $4671 €4000 Aveneu Victoria (65x92cm-26x36in) s.d.65 i.verso decollage canvas. 25-Jun-3 Digard, Paris #115/R est:6000-9000
£3067 $5520 €4600 Boulevard de la villette (73x60cm-29x24in) i.d.1986 verso torn posters on canvas. 24-Apr-4 Cornette de St.Cyr, Paris #736 est:3500-4000
£3200 $5760 €4800 Germano (24x17cm-9x7in) s.i.d.64 verso torn posters on canvas. 24-Apr-4 Cornette de St.Cyr, Paris #737 est:1800-2000
£4600 $8372 €6716 Rue cuvier (53x42cm-21x17in) decollage board prov.exhib. 6-Feb-4 Sotheby's, London #217/R est:4000-6000
£4895 $8322 €7000 Pillage et matracage sont les deux mamelles du pouvoir (100x90cm-39x35in) s.i.d.1979 decollage board prov. 25-Nov-3 Sotheby's, Milan #154/R est:7000-9000
£5556 $9167 €8000 Rue du temple (100x81cm-39x32in) s.d. i.d.12 avril 1970 verso. 2-Jul-3 Cornette de St.Cyr, Paris #60/R est:8000-10000
£8053 $14818 €12000 L - Che - Rue Cuvier (53x42cm-21x17in) torn posters on board exec 1969 prov.exhib.lit. 29-Mar-4 Cornette de St.Cyr, Paris #64/R est:10000-12000
£9028 $14264 €13000 Gaite-Montparnasse (250x217cm-98x85in) s.i.d.1987 verso torn posters on canvas prov.exhib.lit. 27-Apr-3 Versailles Encheres #94
£9459 $16648 €14000 Place Edmond Michelet (171x133cm-67x52in) s. i.d.1986 verso torn posters on canvas prov. 18-May-4 Tajan, Paris #75/R est:15000-18000
£10403 $19141 €15500 Concerts (130x80cm-51x31in) s.i.d.5 juillet 1982 verso torn poster on canvas. 28-Mar-4 Anaf, Lyon #188/R est:1000-12000
£17333 $32067 €26000 158, Rue de Tolbiac (157x105cm-62x41in) s.d.62 s.i.d.verso decollage on canvas prov. 18-Jul-4 Sotheby's, Paris #249/R est:15000-20000
£41259 $68902 €59000 Rue de la Biche, Saint Denis (240x306cm-94x120in) s.i.d.septembre 1963 verso torn poster canvas prov.exhib.lit. 11-Oct-3 Cornette de St.Cyr, Paris #17/R est:30000-40000

VILLEMSENS, Jean Blaise (1806-1859) French
£470 $879 €700 Young soldier (46x38cm-18x15in) s.d.1834. 27-Feb-4 Altus, Berlin #451/R

VILLENEUVE, Arthur (1910-1990) Canadian
£1220 $2183 €1781 Levis (77x103cm-30x41in) s.i.d.9.61 verso. 31-May-4 Sotheby's, Toronto #y/R est:4000-5000 (C.D 3000)

VILLENEUVE, Cecile (1824-1901) French

Miniatures

£2500 $4475 €3650 Young girl, in lace bordered white dress. Marie de Polignac (3cm-1in) s.d.1855 two. 25-May-4 Christie's, London #169/R est:2500-3500

£14000 $25060 €20440 Vicomtesse Geoffroy de Ruille, in black dress, pink roses pined on her dress (10cm-4in) s.i.d.1872 ormolu easel frame. 25-May-4 Christie's, London #166/R est:2500-3500

VILLEON, Emmanuel de la (1858-1944) French

£300 $552 €450 Les transats (8x13cm-3x5in) init. paper two sheets painted c.1927 prov.lit. 9-Jun-4 Beaussant & Lefèvre, Paris #177/R

£769 $1323 €1100 La mare de Gucutteville (13x26cm-5x10in) s. cardboard prov.lit. 3-Dec-3 Beaussant & Lefèvre, Paris #54/R

£872 $1614 €1300 Pesselieres vu de la source (27x19cm-11x7in) s. i.verso paper on canvas. 14-Mar-4 St-Germain-en-Laye Encheres #94/R

£940 $1729 €1400 Saint Denis (33x59cm-13x23in) s.d. wood lit. 24-Mar-4 Joron-Derem, Paris #71

£979 $1684 €1400 La fontaine de Diane dans le parc (47x38cm-19x15in) panel. 7-Dec-3 Osenat, Fontainebleau #206

£1233 $2096 €1800 Promenade dans les acacias en fleurs (35x27cm-14x11in) s. panel. 9-Nov-3 Eric Pillon, Calais #68/R

£1258 $2290 €1900 Le pont des cascades (32x41cm-13x16in) s. i.verso panel exhib. 15-Jun-4 Blanchet, Paris #128/R est:1000-1200

£1600 $2880 €2400 Saint Brieuc des Iffs (46x38cm-18x15in) s. painted c.1907 lit. 26-Apr-4 Tajan, Paris #117/R est:2500-3500

£1879 $3026 €2800 Chemin en foret et sous-bois (41x22cm-16x9in) one s.d.1895 panel pair. 23-Feb-3 St-Germain-en-Laye Encheres #86/R est:2800-3000

£2448 $4210 €3500 Bouquet de fleurs sur une table (60x46cm-24x18in) s. 3-Dec-3 Tajan, Paris #369/R est:3000-3500

£2945 $4800 €4300 Le village sous la neige (81x99cm-32x39in) s.d.96. 25-Sep-3 Christie's, Rockefeller NY #518/R est:4000-6000

£4667 $8587 €7000 Jardin fleuri (82x100cm-32x39in) s. exec. 1916 lit. 8-Jun-4 Artcurial Briest, Paris #139/R est:7000-8000

£6154 $10585 €8800 Moulin de Hollande (110x220cm-43x87in) 3-Dec-3 Tajan, Paris #368/R est:8000-10000

Works on paper

£233 $420 €350 Sous-bois (46x27cm-18x11in) s. W/C lit. 26-Apr-4 Tajan, Paris #13

£233 $420 €350 Le manon au bois (65x50cm-26x20in) s. pastel lit. 26-Apr-4 Tajan, Paris #14

£235 $416 €350 Sous-bois (45x26cm-18x10in) mono. lead pencil col crayon paper on canvas lit. 27-Apr-4 Artcurial Briest, Paris #3

£278 $464 €400 Etude d'un arbre et petales de fleurs (46x61cm-18x24in) s.d.1897 col crayons lit. 21-Oct-3 Artcurial Briest, Paris #164

£403 $737 €600 Robardic, Le Patre (54x73cm-21x29in) s. pastel paper on canvas exec c.1895-1900 lit. 7-Jul-4 Artcurial Briest, Paris #40

£430 $783 €650 Sous-bois (45x26cm-18x10in) mono. col crayon paper on canvas lit. 19-Jun-4 St-Germain-en-Laye Encheres #190/R

VILLERET, François Etienne (1800-1866) French

Works on paper

£300 $498 €438 Figures at the west door of a church (30x23cm-12x9in) s. W/C htd bodycol. 1-Oct-3 George Kidner, Lymington #144/R

£496 $829 €700 Maisons gothiques dans le vieux Sens (6x9cm-2x4in) s. W/C. 20-Jun-3 Drouot Estimations, Paris #53

VILLERS, Adolphe de (19th C) French

£1418 $2369 €2000 Bord de l'etang (28x44cm-11x17in) s. panel. 19-Jun-3 Millon & Associes, Paris #145 est:1000-1500

VILLEVALDE, Bogdan Pavlovich (1818-1903) Russian

£90000 $153000 €131400 Russian soldiers rewarding the gypsy singers (43x32cm-17x13in) s.d.1886. 19-Nov-3 Sotheby's, London #29/R est:15000-20000

£121795 $190000 € Life Guard Lancer regiment and Guard Horse Grenadier regiment at rest (100x95cm-39x37in) s.cyrillic d.1849. 11-Apr-3 Christie's, Rockefeller NY #10/R est:90000-110000

VILLEVALDE, Count Alexander Bogdanovich (1857-?) Russian

£45946 $82243 €68000 Having a break (49x40cm-19x16in) s.d.1899. 8-May-4 Bukowskis, Helsinki #427/R est:5000-8000

VILLEVIELLE, Léon (1826-1863) French

£600 $1086 €900 Prairie aux environs de Paris (30x42cm-12x17in) s. cardboard on panel painted c.1851 lit. 30-Mar-4 Rossini, Paris #1080/R

£867 $1569 €1300 Bords de Seine avec des vaches (18x27cm-7x11in) s. panel painted c.1860 lit. 30-Mar-4 Rossini, Paris #1081

VILLIERS, Prosper Hyacinthe (1816-1879) French

Works on paper

£479 $828 €680 Constantinople vue des hauteurs (15x11cm-6x4in) s. W/C black crayon. 12-Dec-3 Renaud, Paris #99

VILLINGER, Karl (1902-) Swiss?

£286 $457 €415 Bar pianist (93x74cm-37x29in) 15-May-3 Stuker, Bern #1562 (S.FR 600)

£371 $683 €542 Interior with still life (91x72cm-36x28in) i.d. verso. 14-Jun-4 Philippe Schuler, Zurich #5756 (S.FR 850)

VILLODAS DE LA TORRE, Ricardo de (1846-1904) Spanish

Works on paper

£411 $699 €600 Pieta' (59x83cm-23x33in) s. chl dr. 4-Nov-3 Ansorena, Madrid #185/R

VILLON, Eugène (1879-?) French

Works on paper

£1733 $3120 €2600 Ile Barbe (75x109cm-30x43in) W/C. 24-Apr-4 Hotel des Ventes de Vienne, Vienne #193

£2113 $3655 €3000 Musiciens pres de la fontaine (56x40cm-22x16in) s.d.1923 W/C exhib.lit. 15-Dec-3 Gros & Delettrez, Paris #342/R est:2500-3500

VILLON, Eugène (attrib) (1879-?) French

Works on paper

£280 $496 €409 Boats at anchor (12x19cm-5x7in) W/C. 27-Apr-4 Bonhams, Knightsbridge #126/R

VILLON, Jacques (1875-1963) French

£559 $951 €800 Palette (51x43cm-20x17in) s.d.58 masonite. 18-Nov-3 Sotheby's, Paris #22/R

£1389 $2292 €2000 Treport (19x24cm-7x9in) s.d.26 cardboard on canvas. 3-Jul-3 Piasa, Paris #16/R est:1500-2000

£2083 $3437 €3000 La bouteille brune (24x19cm-9x7in) s.d.24. 3-Jul-3 Piasa, Paris #9/R est:2000-3000

£2222 $3667 €3200 Portrait de Madame Olga Burel (73x60cm-29x24in) s.d.63. 3-Jul-3 Piasa, Paris #40/R est:6000-8000

£2431 $4010 €3500 Portrait (35x27cm-14x11in) s.d.1909 cardboard. 3-Jul-3 Piasa, Paris #2/R est:1500-2000

£2431 $4010 €3500 Les vingts ans fiers (24x33cm-9x13in) s. panel. 3-Jul-3 Piasa, Paris #28/R est:1500-2000

£2639 $4354 €3800 Femme a genoux (55x46cm-22x18in) s.d.29 lit. 3-Jul-3 Piasa, Paris #26/R est:2500-3000

£2778 $4583 €4000 Le bras de platre (33x24cm-13x9in) s. painted c.1925. 3-Jul-3 Piasa, Paris #13/R est:1500-2000

£2917 $4813 €4200 Petite femme de revue (35x24cm-14x9in) s.d.29. 3-Jul-3 Piasa, Paris #27/R est:1500-2000

£2917 $4813 €4200 Sans titre (46x38cm-18x15in) s.d.32. 3-Jul-3 Piasa, Paris #33/R est:1500-2000

£3056 $5042 €4400 Le nu gris (35x27cm-14x11in) s.d.30. 3-Jul-3 Piasa, Paris #31/R est:1500-2000

£3125 $5156 €4500 Misere (73x60cm-29x24in) s. s.i.d.46 verso. 3-Jul-3 Piasa, Paris #37/R est:2000-3000

£3333 $5500 €4800 Sur la boite au lait (22x16cm-9x6in) s.d.1912 panel. 3-Jul-3 Piasa, Paris #3/R est:1500-2000

£3611 $5958 €5200 Le peintre nu (61x50cm-24x20in) s.d.30. 3-Jul-3 Piasa, Paris #30/R est:2000-3000

£3819 $6302 €5500 Fillette etendue (46x61cm-18x24in) s.d.29. 3-Jul-3 Piasa, Paris #23/R est:3000-4000

£4167 $6875 €6000 Le torse (127x65cm-50x26in) s. 3-Jul-3 Piasa, Paris #6/R est:8000-10000

£4167 $6875 €6000 Mythologie (22x27cm-9x11in) s.d.28 panel. 3-Jul-3 Piasa, Paris #20/R est:1500-2000

£4236 $6990 €6100 Yvonel (41x33cm-16x13in) s.d.27. 3-Jul-3 Piasa, Paris #17/R est:3500-4000

£4306 $7104 €6200 Tete de lapin (14x18cm-6x7in) s.d.33. 3-Jul-3 Piasa, Paris #34/R est:1500-2000

£4363 $8115 €6500 Le boeuf expirant (27x35cm-11x14in) s.d.44 s.verso prov. 2-Mar-4 Artcurial Briest, Paris #231/R est:4000-6000

£4514 $7448 €6500 Le saut a la corde (18x14cm-7x6in) s.d.27 panel. 3-Jul-3 Piasa, Paris #18/R est:2000-3000

£4722 $7792 €6800 La pipe (35x27cm-14x11in) s.d.24 cardboard on canvas. 3-Jul-3 Piasa, Paris #11/R est:2000-3000

£4722 $7792 €6800 Les vacances (42x61cm-17x24in) s.d.28. 3-Jul-3 Piasa, Paris #19/R est:5000-6000

£4792 $7906 €6900 Spheres (46x50cm-18x20in) s.d.29. 3-Jul-3 Piasa, Paris #24/R est:2000-3000

£5208 $8594 €7500 Paresse (33x41cm-13x16in) s.d.25. 3-Jul-3 Piasa, Paris #12/R est:2500-3000

£5208 $8594 €7500 Femme au foulard rouge (55x33cm-22x13in) s.d.62 s.i.verso exhib. 3-Jul-3 Piasa, Paris #39/R est:2000-3000

£5556 $9167 €8000 Pythagore (46x33cm-18x13in) s. 3-Jul-3 Piasa, Paris #38/R est:1500-2000

£5556 $9167 €8000 Un peintre (46x55cm-18x22in) s.d.24. 3-Jul-3 Piasa, Paris #10/R est:5000-6000

£5556 $9167 €8000 La blouse bleue (55x46cm-22x18in) exhib. 3-Jul-3 Piasa, Paris #21/R est:5000-6000

£6250 $10313 €9000 L'avion fantome (22x35cm-9x14in) s.d.29 panel. 3-Jul-3 Piasa, Paris #22/R est:2000-3000

£6389 $10542 €9200 La faute (55x38cm-22x15in) s.d.09. 3-Jul-3 Piasa, Paris #1/R est:6000-8000

£6471 $11000 €9448 Untitled - portrait d'homme (41x33cm-16x13in) s. 9-Nov-3 Wright, Chicago #102 est:7000-9000

£6944 $11458 €10000 Homme lisant (81x65cm-32x26in) s.d.26. 3-Jul-3 Piasa, Paris #14/R est:10000-15000

£6944 $11458 €10000 Le repos (60x73cm-24x29in) s.d.29. 3-Jul-3 Piasa, Paris #25/R est:5000-6000

£7292 $12031 €10500 Rue des renardieres (46x33cm-18x13in) s.d.1913 wood. 3-Jul-3 Piasa, Paris #5/R est:5000-6000

£7483 $13395 €11000 La Loire a Beaugency (38x55cm-15x22in) s.d.59 s.i.d.verso. 21-Mar-4 Calmels Cohen, Paris #160/R est:12000-15000

£7639 $12604 €11000 La dame du coiffeur (33x22cm-13x9in) s. 3-Jul-3 Piasa, Paris #36/R est:3000-4000

£7986 $13177 €11500 Les grands arbres (27x22cm-11x9in) s.d.26 panel on canvas. 3-Jul-3 Piasa, Paris #15/R est:3000-4000

£9333 $17173 €14000 Nature morte a la statuette (32x23cm-13x9in) s.d.35 prov.exhib.lit. 8-Jun-4 Artcurial Briest, Paris #180/R est:8000-12000

£9722 $16042 €14000 Boite au lait (22x17cm-9x7in) s.d.12 wood exhib. 3-Jul-3 Piasa, Paris #4/R est:2000-3000

£9859 $16366 €14000 Nu assis (14x27cm-6x11in) s.d.38. 13-Jun-3 Renaud, Paris #49/R est:10000

£10764 $17760 €15500 Les sculptures (81x116cm-32x46in) s.d.23. 3-Jul-3 Piasa, Paris #7/R est:10000-15000

£13889 $22917 €20000 Ciel et terre (60x73cm-24x29in) s.d.30. 3-Jul-3 Piasa, Paris #29/R est:5000-6000

£14118 $24000 €20612 Etude pour le portrait de Robert Azarias (41x33cm-16x13in) s. s.i.verso painted c.1945 prov.exhib. 6-Nov-3 Sotheby's, New York #373/R est:20000-30000

£14931 $24635 €21500 Coquillage (73x92cm-29x36in) s.d.32. 3-Jul-3 Piasa, Paris #32/R est:18000-22000

£15363	$27500	€22430	Paysage aux grands arbres (55x65cm-22x26in) s. s.d.45 verso prov.exhib. 6-May-4 Sotheby's, New York #408/R est:20000-30000
£18051	$33213	€26354	Coin de Vendanges (38x55cm-15x22in) s. s.d.44 verso. 29-Mar-4 Rasmussen, Copenhagen #25/R est:150000-200000 (D.KR 200000)
£18750	$30937	€27000	Le perroquet (49x26cm-19x10in) s.d.23 exhib.lit. 3-Jul-3 Piasa, Paris #8/R est:15000-20000
£25000	$41250	€36000	Paysage (54x81cm-21x32in) s.d.34 exhib. 3-Jul-3 Piasa, Paris #35/R est:15000-20000
£642458	$1150000	€937989	Acrobate (100x72cm-39x28in) init. s.verso painted 1913 prov.exhib.lit. 6-May-4 Sotheby's, New York #116/R est:500000-700000

Prints

£1676	$3000	€2447	En visite (30x40cm-12x16in) s. drypoint. 6-May-4 Swann Galleries, New York #599 est:2500-3500
£1676	$3000	€2447	Renee a bicyclette (40x30cm-16x12in) s.num.14/50 drypoint aquatint. 6-May-4 Swann Galleries, New York #604/R est:2500-3500
£1977	$3500	€2886	La loge (28x21cm-11x8in) s.num.49/200 col aquatint after Pierre Auguste Renoir. 30-Apr-4 Sotheby's, New York #270/R est:2500-3500
£2000	$3400	€2920	Londres (36x52cm-14x20in) bears two sig. num.179/200 col etching aquatint after Luce. 6-Nov-3 Swann Galleries, New York #741/R est:3000-5000
£2118	$3600	€3092	La tasse de the (48x44cm-19x17in) bears another sig.num.32/200 col aquatint after Metzinger. 6-Nov-3 Swann Galleries, New York #742/R est:2500-3500
£2158	$3540	€3000	Les roses (38x49cm-15x19in) s.i. col aquatint etching after van Gogh. 4-Jun-3 Ketterer, Hamburg #952/R est:4000-4500
£2162	$4000	€3157	Les roses (38x50cm-15x20in) s.num.131 of 200 col aquatint after Vincent van Gogh. 12-Feb-4 Christie's, Rockefeller NY #414/R est:5000-7000
£2235	$4000	€3263	La Parisienne, tournee a droite (47x34cm-19x13in) s. etching aquatint. 6-May-4 Swann Galleries, New York #596/R est:3500-5000
£2432	$4500	€3551	Le potin (42x58cm-17x23in) s.i.num.52 olive etching aquatint prov. 12-Feb-4 Christie's, Rockefeller NY #416/R est:5000-7000
£2844	$4750	€4124	Table d'echecs. mono. etching. 19-Jun-3 Kornfeld, Bern #1035 est:6000 (S.FR 6200)
£2905	$5201	€4300	Maggie Berck. lithograph. 5-May-4 Coutau Begarie, Paris #12/R est:2000-2500
£2941	$5000	€4294	Femme a la cruche (47x31cm-19x12in) col aquatint. 31-Oct-3 Sotheby's, New York #485/R
£3000	$5460	€4380	Les Saltimbanques (59x42cm-23x17in) aquatint. 30-Jun-4 Christie's, London #314/R est:2500-3500
£3020	$5648	€4500	Baudelaire au socle. s.i. num.15/50 eau forte. 1-Mar-4 Artcurial Briest, Paris #204 est:4000-5000
£3294	$5600	€4809	Le petite equilibriste (22x16cm-9x6in) s.i. drypoint. 6-Nov-3 Swann Galleries, New York #739/R est:4000-6000
£3481	$6265	€5082	Maternite (65x42cm-26x17in) bears sig.num.8/50 col aquatint after Picasso. 26-Apr-4 Bukowskis, Stockholm #440/R est:20000-25000 (S.KR 48000)
£3562	$6055	€5200	Nevers a Paris. s. aquatint drypoint. 6-Nov-3 Piasa, Paris #183/R
£3688	$6159	€5200	Nature morte (37x19cm-15x7in) bears sig.num.7/200 col aquatint vellum after Picasso. 19-Oct-3 Anaf, Lyon #226/R est:4000-5000
£3800	$6536	€5548	Devant un guignoi (40x30cm-16x12in) s.i. drypoint aquatint prov. 2-Dec-3 Christie's, London #326/R est:4000-6000
£3955	$7000	€5774	Le port de la Rochelle (44x59cm-17x23in) s. Villon and Signac i.d.11 Mars 1925 col aquaint after P Signac. 28-Apr-4 Christie's, Rockefeller NY #239/R est:3000-5000
£4000	$7360	€6000	Table d'echecs (20x16cm-8x6in) s.mono. etching. 10-Jun-4 Hauswedell & Nolte, Hamburg #717/R est:7500
£4412	$7500	€6442	Olympia (40x58cm-16x23in) col aquatint after Manet. 31-Oct-3 Sotheby's, New York #484/R
£5587	$10000	€8157	La femme au chien colley (51x39cm-20x15in) s.num.21/50 drypoint. 6-May-4 Swann Galleries, New York #600/R est:8000-12000
£6215	$11000	€9074	Olympia (40x58cm-16x23in) s.d.1929 num.8/25 hand colour aquatint after Edouard Manet. 30-Apr-4 Sotheby's, New York #269/R est:7000-9000
£6301	$10712	€9200	Gaby chaise longue. s. drypoint. 6-Nov-3 Piasa, Paris #184/R
£7059	$12000	€10306	Partie de Jacquet (53x69cm-21x27in) s. etching aquatint exec.1903. 4-Nov-3 Christie's, Rockefeller NY #215/R est:15000-20000
£7500	$13650	€10950	Odalisque sur la terrasse (63x72cm-25x28in) num.53/200 col aquatint sig. by and after Matisse. 1-Jul-4 Sotheby's, London #203/R est:4000-6000
£9396	$17570	€14000	Untitled. drypoint aquatint album. 1-Mar-4 Artcurial Briest, Paris #187 est:7000-8000
£10000	$16600	€14600	Odalisque sur la terrasse (48x60cm-19x24in) s.num.87/200 col aquatint after Henri Matisse. 6-Oct-3 Sotheby's, London #98/R est:3000-4000
£11409	$21335	€17000	Untitled. s. eauforte aquatint album. 1-Mar-4 Artcurial Briest, Paris #192/R est:6000-7000
£13423	$25101	€20000	Untitled. s. col print album. 1-Mar-4 Artcurial Briest, Paris #191 est:5000-6000
£14765	$27611	€22000	Untitled. s. drypoint eau forte album. 1-Mar-4 Artcurial Briest, Paris #185/R est:6000-7000
£14765	$27611	€22000	Untitled. s. aquatint album. 1-Mar-4 Artcurial Briest, Paris #186/R est:6000-7000
£18079	$32000	€26395	Yvonne D de face (56x41cm-22x16in) s.num.7/28 drypoint. 28-Apr-4 Christie's, Rockefeller NY #249/R est:40000-50000

Works on paper

£278	$458	€400	Chanteur de cours (20x13cm-8x5in) s.d.97 W/C. 3-Jul-3 Piasa, Paris #42
£278	$458	€400	Tete de femme (27x21cm-11x8in) s. Indian ink exec.c.1935. 3-Jul-3 Piasa, Paris #73
£278	$458	€400	Composition (26x21cm-10x8in) s.d.58 red ink. 3-Jul-3 Piasa, Paris #92
£280	$476	€400	Portrait d'homme (15x11cm-6x4in) s. ballpoint pen double-sided prov. 23-Nov-3 Cornette de St.Cyr, Paris #347
£292	$481	€420	Fillette assise dans un tub (24x18cm-9x7in) s. black crayon. 3-Jul-3 Piasa, Paris #52
£313	$516	€450	Etude d'homme (20x12cm-8x5in) s.d.97 Indian ink. 3-Jul-3 Piasa, Paris #43
£313	$516	€450	L'eleve de la gandara (20x15cm-8x6in) s. black crayon tracing paper. 3-Jul-3 Piasa, Paris #65
£313	$516	€450	Le long du parc (23x31cm-9x12in) s. Indian ink. 3-Jul-3 Piasa, Paris #91
£382	$630	€550	Personnages assis (16x21cm-6x8in) s. Indian ink. 3-Jul-3 Piasa, Paris #67
£382	$630	€550	Etude de femme (17x12cm-7x5in) s. Indian ink exec.c.1930. 3-Jul-3 Piasa, Paris #68
£382	$630	€550	Etude de nus (14x12cm-6x5in) s. ink bistre exec.c.1930. 3-Jul-3 Piasa, Paris #69
£417	$688	€600	Elegantes (46x36cm-18x14in) s. black crayon Indian ink exec.c.1900. 3-Jul-3 Piasa, Paris #47/R
£417	$688	€600	Etude d'homme (25x16cm-10x6in) mono. Indian ink exec.c.1935. 3-Jul-3 Piasa, Paris #78
£417	$688	€600	Haute ecole (13x19cm-5x7in) s. Indian ink exec.c.1950. 3-Jul-3 Piasa, Paris #90
£417	$696	€600	Dans l'atelier (19x19cm-7x7in) s. Indian ink over pencil study verso. 24-Oct-3 Ketterer, Hamburg #1132/R
£451	$745	€650	La bonne aventure (31x27cm-12x11in) s. Indian ink tracing paper. 3-Jul-3 Piasa, Paris #70
£451	$745	€650	Les vendanges (20x27cm-8x11in) s.d.40 Indian ink. 3-Jul-3 Piasa, Paris #80
£486	$802	€700	Nu allonge (16x22cm-6x9in) s. Indian ink newspaper exec.c.1935. 3-Jul-3 Piasa, Paris #77
£486	$802	€700	Le petit atelier de mecanique (14x21cm-6x8in) s. Indian ink. 3-Jul-3 Piasa, Paris #84
£490	$832	€700	Personnage bras leve (41x14cm-16x6in) pen W/C paper on canvas prov. 23-Nov-3 Cornette de St.Cyr, Paris #345/R
£521	$859	€750	Le petit breton (39x19cm-15x7in) s.i.d.1914 chl tracing paper. 3-Jul-3 Piasa, Paris #56
£521	$859	€750	Paresse (46x35cm-18x14in) s. black crayon tracing paper. 3-Jul-3 Piasa, Paris #93
£535	$1000	€781	Group of standing figures. Seated Moroccan man (20x13cm-8x5in) s. one d.95 W/C pair. 24-Feb-4 Arthur James, Florida #14
£556	$917	€800	Nu assis (10x13cm-4x5in) s.i. Indian ink exec.c.1930. 3-Jul-3 Piasa, Paris #66
£556	$917	€800	Insouciance (21x27cm-8x11in) s.d.32 Indian ink. 3-Jul-3 Piasa, Paris #72
£556	$917	€800	Portrait d'Anne Dariel (35x30cm-14x12in) s. Indian ink. 3-Jul-3 Piasa, Paris #82
£590	$974	€850	Portrait d'homme (24x18cm-9x7in) s. Indian ink exec.c.1938. 3-Jul-3 Piasa, Paris #79
£625	$1031	€900	Baudelaire (22x14cm-9x6in) s. Indian ink. 3-Jul-3 Piasa, Paris #61
£634	$1097	€900	Eclaireuses (25x20cm-10x8in) s.d.38 Chinese ink dr crayon. 9-Dec-3 Artcurial Briest, Paris #204
£660	$1089	€950	Nu debout (49x34cm-19x13in) s.d.1911 Indian ink wash. 3-Jul-3 Piasa, Paris #55/R
£764	$1260	€1100	Zut, encore un chien de police (55x44cm-22x17in) s.i.d.16 juillet 93 chl. 3-Jul-3 Piasa, Paris #41/R
£764	$1260	€1100	Le cheval (9x14cm-4x6in) s. black crayon dr. 3-Jul-3 Piasa, Paris #64
£799	$1318	€1150	Etude de personnage (17x12cm-7x5in) s.d.17 Indian ink. 3-Jul-3 Piasa, Paris #58
£833	$1375	€1200	Personnages (50x32cm-20x13in) mono. Indian ink wash exec.c.1910. 3-Jul-3 Piasa, Paris #53/R
£901	$1550	€1315	Bicycle rider (72x21cm-28x8in) s. Indian ink w/C. 2-Dec-3 Koller, Zurich #3062/R est:2000-3000 (S.FR 2000)
£903	$1490	€1300	Buste de Baudelaire (23x20cm-9x8in) s. Indian ink. 3-Jul-3 Piasa, Paris #62
£903	$1490	€1300	Cour de ferme (38x57cm-15x22in) s.d.53 Indian ink. 3-Jul-3 Piasa, Paris #87/R
£1042	$1719	€1500	Madame de Bernay (26x23cm-10x9in) mono. Indian ink. 3-Jul-3 Piasa, Paris #81/R est:600-800
£1111	$1833	€1600	Tete de lapin (13x19cm-5x7in) s.d.40 Indian ink. 3-Jul-3 Piasa, Paris #83 est:1000-1500
£1146	$1891	€1650	Les bucoliques (37x57cm-15x22in) s. Indian ink. 3-Jul-3 Piasa, Paris #86/R est:300-400
£1163	$2000	€1698	Vieille femme assise (19x12cm-7x5in) W/C chl pencil executed c.1900 prov. 3-Dec-3 Doyle, New York #140/R est:1200-1800
£1181	$1948	€1700	Portrait d'homme (33x25cm-13x10in) s. Indian ink exec.c.1935. 3-Jul-3 Piasa, Paris #75 est:300-400
£1250	$2063	€1800	Les blanchisseuses (35x26cm-14x10in) s. gouache chl. 3-Jul-3 Piasa, Paris #50/R est:1500-2000
£1319	$2177	€1900	Modele assis (28x44cm-11x17in) s. Indian ink. 3-Jul-3 Piasa, Paris #57/R est:600-800
£1667	$3000	€2500	Femme emmitouflee (74x51cm-29x20in) s.d.01 W/C ink. 26-Apr-4 Tajan, Paris #18/R est:1200-1500
£1736	$2865	€2500	Etude pour le portrait de Felix Barre (14x10cm-6x4in) mono. chl. 3-Jul-3 Piasa, Paris #54
£1875	$3094	€2700	Dans les grands bars (44x56cm-17x22in) s.d.08 Indian ink. 3-Jul-3 Piasa, Paris #51/R est:2000-3000
£1944	$3208	€2800	Le grand dessinateur assis (29x23cm-11x9in) s. red ink. 3-Jul-3 Piasa, Paris #76 est:200-300
£2083	$3437	€3000	Portrait de Colette Carre (27x20cm-11x8in) Indian ink. 3-Jul-3 Piasa, Paris #89 est:100-200
£2222	$3667	€3200	La table d'echecs (21x17cm-8x7in) mono. black crayon. 3-Jul-3 Piasa, Paris #59 est:200-300
£2431	$4010	€3500	Composition (65x50cm-26x20in) s. blue ink. 3-Jul-3 Piasa, Paris #88/R est:400-500
£2778	$4583	€4000	Etude pour Baudelaire (23x15cm-9x6in) s. black crayon. 3-Jul-3 Piasa, Paris #63 est:200-300
£3226	$6000	€4710	Justes noces (32x22cm-13x9in) s. gouache. 2-Mar-4 Swann Galleries, New York #667/R est:8000-12000
£3472	$5729	€5000	Portrait d'acteur, Felix Barre (21x16cm-8x6in) s.d.13 black crayon tracing paper. 3-Jul-3 Piasa, Paris #71/R est:1500-2000
£7639	$12604	€11000	Jeu (20x15cm-8x6in) s. blue Indian ink. 3-Jul-3 Piasa, Paris #60 est:200-300
£7778	$12833	€11200	Portrait de Marcel Duchamp (47x35cm-19x14in) s. Indian ink dr tracing paper exec.c.1950. 3-Jul-3 Piasa, Paris #85/R est:3000-4000
£16447	$30263	€25000	Au cafe (40x29cm-16x11in) s.d.98 gouache. 23-Jun-4 Maigret, Paris #10/R est:2000-2500

VILLORESI, Franco (1920-1975) Italian

£690	$1152	€1000	Mask and secretary (70x58cm-28x23in) s. i.d.1969 verso. 13-Nov-3 Finarte Semenzato, Rome #245
£800	$1448	€1200	Workers (84x79cm-33x31in) s. s.i.d.1950 verso. 2-Apr-4 Farsetti, Prato #131/R
£861	$1567	€1300	Industrial suburbs (50x70cm-20x28in) s. 17-Jun-4 Galleria Pananti, Florence #561/R
£861	$1567	€1300	Industrial suburbs (50x70cm-20x28in) s.d.1956. 17-Jun-4 Galleria Pananti, Florence #560/R
£1000	$1700	€1430	Suburbs (30x40cm-12x16in) s. 18-Nov-3 Babuino, Rome #495/R
£1342	$2497	€2000	Workmen (50x100cm-20x39in) s. s.d.1955 verso. 4-Mar-4 Babuino, Rome #12

VILOMARA, Mauricio (1847-1930) Spanish

Works on paper

£1164	$1979	€1700	Decorations (32x47cm-13x19in) s.d.92 gouache lit. 4-Nov-3 Ansorena, Madrid #288/R est:1100

VIMAR, Auguste (1851-1916) French
£1000 $1840 €1500 La chasse au Faucon (28x23cm-11x9in) s.i.d.1885. 14-Jun-4 Gros & Delettrez, Paris #517 est:1500-2000

VIMARD, Jacques (1942-) French
£604 $1111 €900 Intervention (162x195cm-64x77in) s.d.1968 diptych exhib. 24-Mar-4 Joron-Derem, Paris #153

VIMENET, Jean (20th C) French?
£265 $482 €400 Composition (27x35cm-11x14in) s.d.63. 18-Jun-4 Piasa, Paris #170
£298 $542 €450 Composition (65x50cm-26x20in) s.d.62. 18-Jun-4 Piasa, Paris #169
£1655 $3062 €2400 Toits sous la neige (100x81cm-39x32in) s.d.51. 16-Feb-4 Giraudeau, Tours #110

VIN, Paul van der (1823-1887) Belgian
£578 $1035 €850 Cheval blanc (36x30cm-14x12in) s.d.80 panel. 16-Mar-4 Vanderkindere, Brussels #6/R
£2400 $4344 €3600 Promenade en carrosse (35x49cm-14x19in) s. 30-Mar-4 Palais de Beaux Arts, Brussels #718 est:1500-2000
£2400 $4296 €3600 Annual market (48x70cm-19x28in) s. 15-May-4 De Vuyst, Lokeren #346/R est:2800-3300
£2517 $4330 €3600 La malle postale (37x50cm-15x20in) s. 8-Dec-3 Horta, Bruxelles #181/R est:3500-5000

VINAY, Jean (1907-1978) French
£890 $1514 €1300 La demeure familiale en hiver (46x61cm-18x24in) s.d.1941 isorel. 8-Nov-3 Gerard, Besancon #119

VINCELET, Victor (?-1871) French
£336 $571 €480 Nature morte aux fruits (44x71cm-17x28in) s. 24-Nov-3 Boscher, Cherbourg #805/R

VINCENT (?) ?
£898 $1500 €1311 La Mammouth a maree basse Zee (43x64cm-17x25in) 17-Oct-3 Du Mouchelle, Detroit #2009/R est:1500-1800
£1600 $2864 €2400 Maison sous la neige (55x38cm-22x15in) s.d.1985. 16-May-4 Feletin, Province #84

VINCENT, François Andre (1746-1816) French
Works on paper
£2676 $4630 €3800 Portrait of a woman sitting with her hands clasped (26x18cm-10x7in) i. sanguine. 10-Dec-3 Piasa, Paris #55/R est:2000-3000

VINCENT, George (1796-c.1831) British
£360 $655 €526 Cattle watering at woodland pool (23x28cm-9x11in) 5-Feb-4 Biddle & Webb, Birmingham #848
£1500 $2760 €2190 Chiswick Reach (8x11cm-3x4in) 11-Jun-4 Keys, Aylsham #604/R est:700-900

VINCENT, George (attrib) (1796-c.1831) British
£1330 $2381 €1942 Landscape with shepherd and sheep (50x60cm-20x24in) mono. 28-May-4 Uppsala Auktionskammare, Uppsala #107/R est:8000-10000 (S.KR 18000)

VINCENT, Harry A (1864-1931) American
£2260 $4000 €3300 Fishing boat at dock (28x36cm-11x14in) s. board. 2-May-4 Grogan, Boston #68/R
£2542 $4500 €3711 Fisherman in his shack (36x28cm-14x11in) s. board. 2-May-4 Grogan, Boston #69/R

VINCENT, M R (20th C) ?
Sculpture
£1284 $2298 €1900 Tete d'asiatique, Vietnamien. s.d.1931 gilt pat bronze. 10-May-4 Horta, Bruxelles #146 est:1000-1500

VINCENTIS, Francesco de (19/20th C) Italian
£1714 $3153 €2502 The art dealer (41x35cm-16x14in) s. board. 9-Jun-4 Walker's, Ottawa #329/R est:1500-2500 (C.D 4250)

VINCENZINA, Giuseppe (18th C) Italian
£8451 $14620 €12000 Bouquets (73x98cm-29x39in) 15-Dec-3 Bailly Pommery, Paris #66/R est:12000-14000
£14084 $24648 €20000 Nature morte de fleurs (61x88cm-24x35in) 18-Dec-3 Tajan, Paris #8/R est:6000-8000

VINCHE, Lionel (1936-) Belgian
£270 $476 €400 Mine Velasquez (150x100cm-59x39in) s.d.69. 18-May-4 Galerie Moderne, Brussels #303/R
£403 $713 €600 Un veterinaire apprenant l'anglais (97x130cm-38x51in) s. 27-Apr-4 Campo, Vlaamse Kaai #655
£533 $976 €800 Pour passer l'apres-midi (73x92cm-29x36in) s.d.96 paper on canvas. 7-Jun-4 Palais de Beaux Arts, Brussels #394
£590 $986 €850 Le grand oiseau sur la manche (140x100cm-55x39in) s. d.1988-89 verso. 21-Oct-3 Campo, Vlaamse Kaai #1190
£600 $1098 €900 Le depart des hirondelles (85x112cm-33x44in) s.d.92 verso cardboard. 7-Jun-4 Palais de Beaux Arts, Brussels #402
£733 $1342 €1100 En souvenir de Corneille et Maurice (71x90cm-28x35in) s.d.96 paper on canvas. 7-Jun-4 Palais de Beaux Arts, Brussels #397/R
£743 $1308 €1100 Histoire libre (95x85cm-37x33in) s. 18-May-4 Galerie Moderne, Brussels #306/R
£1467 $2684 €2200 Prunes et verre (114x146cm-45x57in) s.d.91 verso. 7-Jun-4 Palais de Beaux Arts, Brussels #401/R est:600-800
Works on paper
£278 $464 €400 Expression de colere (40x54cm-16x21in) s.d.1979 mixed media. 21-Oct-3 Campo & Campo, Antwerp #355
£293 $537 €440 Oiseau et fruit (73x100cm-29x39in) s.d.93 gouache. 7-Jun-4 Palais de Beaux Arts, Brussels #395
£533 $976 €800 Oiseau et citrons verts (73x100cm-29x39in) s.d.93 gouache. 7-Jun-4 Palais de Beaux Arts, Brussels #396

VINCIATA, Joseph Wallace King (1911-1996) American
£248 $400 €362 The noble man (33x58cm-13x23in) s. i.verso triptych prov. 21-Aug-3 Doyle, New York #51/R

VINCK, Franz (1827-1903) Belgian
£4483 $8293 €6500 Les confidentes (82x63cm-32x25in) s. 16-Feb-4 Horta, Bruxelles #198/R est:3500-5000

VINCKEBOONS, David (1576-1629) Flemish
£15000 $27450 €21900 Mountainous river landscape (59x89cm-23x35in) panel prov.exhib. 8-Jul-4 Sotheby's, London #236/R est:15000-20000
£23077 $38538 €33000 Ambush (44x67cm-17x26in) board prov. 30-Jun-3 Ansorena, Madrid #186/R
£50336 $90101 €75000 Fete villageoise avec a l'arriere-plan la ville d'Anvers (103x186cm-41x73in) bears mono. panel painted with studio prov. 25-May-4 Palais de Beaux Arts, Brussels #541/R est:82000-112000

VINCKEBOONS, David (circle) (1576-1629) Flemish
£179577 $314261 €255000 Kermesse d'Hoboken (45x69cm-18x27in) copper. 19-Dec-3 Pierre Berge, Paris #55/R est:90000-120000

VINCOTTE, Thomas (1850-1925) Belgian
Sculpture
£2797 $4671 €4000 Andromeda (73cm-29in) s. marble. 7-Oct-3 Sotheby's, Amsterdam #218/R est:4000-6000

VINDEVOGEL, Flore (1866-1938) Belgian
£1507 $2562 €2200 Bouquet campagnard (80x80cm-31x31in) s. 10-Nov-3 Horta, Bruxelles #69 est:2500-3000

VINDFELDT, Ejnar (1905-1953) Danish
£2865 $5243 €4183 Puppies playing in farmyard (41x53cm-16x21in) s.d.42-43 exhib. 9-Jun-4 Rasmussen, Copenhagen #1651/R est:25000 (D.KR 32000)
£4492 $8356 €6558 Gundog and her puppies (40x48cm-16x19in) s. 2-Mar-4 Rasmussen, Copenhagen #1602/R est:25000 (D.KR 50000)
£5000 $8500 €7300 Happy family (34x43cm-13x17in) s.d.44. 27-Nov-3 Christie's, Kensington #399/R est:4000-6000
Works on paper
£378 $654 €552 Small puppy (26x22cm-10x9in) s.d.47 pencil W/C. 9-Dec-3 Rasmussen, Copenhagen #1647/R (D.KR 4000)

VINE OF COLCHESTER, J (1809-1867) British
£1150 $2024 €1679 Hereford bull in a landscape (49x60cm-19x24in) s. 18-May-4 Woolley & Wallis, Salisbury #170/R est:600-800

VINE OF COLCHESTER, John (1809-1867) British
£3073 $5500 €4487 Holderness cattle in a landscape (61x99cm-24x39in) s. 8-Jan-4 James Julia, Fairfield #499/R est:6000-8000

VINEA, Francesco (1845-1902) Italian
£995 $1692 €1453 La Tarantella (22x13cm-9x5in) mono. panel. 28-Nov-3 Zofingen, Switzerland #2699/R est:2800 (S.FR 2200)
£3693 $6500 €5392 Serenade (32x41cm-13x16in) s. panel. 18-May-4 Bonhams & Butterfields, San Francisco #56/R est:6000-8000
£17931 $29945 €26000 Women on the roofs (15x25cm-6x10in) s.d.1877 board. 12-Nov-3 Sotheby's, Milan #144/R est:20000-30000
Works on paper
£933 $1689 €1400 Mosquetaire and cardinal (36x54cm-14x21in) s.d.1879 W/C. 30-Mar-4 Babuino, Rome #359/R
£1122 $2009 €1650 Interior (27x22cm-11x9in) s.d.1891 W/C. 22-Mar-4 Sant Agostino, Torino #268/R est:2000

VINES, Hernando (1904-1993) Spanish
£2535 $4056 €3600 Landscape (27x35cm-11x14in) s. 16-Sep-3 Segre, Madrid #309/R
£2817 $4873 €4000 Landscape (38x46cm-15x18in) s. 15-Dec-3 Ansorena, Madrid #982/R
£3082 $5240 €4500 Woman reading (32x42cm-13x17in) 4-Nov-3 Ansorena, Madrid #932/R est:4000
£3333 $5500 €4800 Still life (22x40cm-9x16in) s. 2-Jul-3 Ansorena, Madrid #849/R
£4027 $7490 €6000 Man reading (46x38cm-18x15in) s. 2-Mar-4 Ansorena, Madrid #862/R est:4800
£7383 $13732 €11000 La fenetre ouverte (55x46cm-22x18in) s.d.31. 2-Mar-4 Artcurial Briest, Paris #202/R est:2000-3000
£16667 $30667 €25000 L'atelier de l'artiste (100x81cm-39x32in) s.d.30. 8-Jun-4 Artcurial Briest, Paris #167/R est:25000-30000
£17000 $31280 €24820 La dessinatrice (73x92cm-29x36in) s.d.28. 24-Mar-4 Sotheby's, Olympia #124/R est:15000-20000
£21831 $37768 €31000 Village (54x65cm-21x26in) s. 15-Dec-3 Ansorena, Madrid #979/R est:23000

Works on paper

£805	$1442	€1200	Woman (31x23cm-12x9in) s. W/C. 25-May-4 Durán, Madrid #136/R
£1224	$2229	€1800	Landscape near Port Blanc (22x25cm-9x10in) s. W/C prov. 3-Feb-4 Segre, Madrid #140/R est:1200
£1538	$2569	€2200	Figures in the park (49x33cm-19x13in) s.d.30 W/C. 30-Jun-3 Ansorena, Madrid #41/R
£1711	$3147	€2600	Seascape in the South of France (39x55cm-15x22in) s. W/C. 22-Jun-4 Durán, Madrid #583/R est:2600

VINEZ, P (19th C) ?

£2344	$3750	€3422	Flirtatious cavaliers (33x41cm-13x16in) s. panel. 19-Sep-3 Freeman, Philadelphia #146/R est:500-800

VINIT, Pierre (1870-?) French

£897	$1497	€1300	Scene de marche sur la place de l'eglise (45x65cm-18x26in) s. 16-Nov-3 Muizon & Le Coent, Paris #37/R

VINKELES, Reinier (1741-1816) Dutch

Works on paper

£4795	$8151	€7000	View of the church at Passy, near Paris (18x24cm-7x9in) s.d.1770 bears i.verso pen black ink grey wash. 4-Nov-3 Sotheby's, Amsterdam #112/R est:4000-6000

VINNE, Vincent Jansz van der (1736-1811) Dutch

£1500	$2550	€2190	Winter landscape with skaters on a frozen river (21x29cm-8x11in) s. panel prov. 30-Oct-3 Sotheby's, Olympia #88/R est:3000-5000

VINNE, Vincent Laurensz van der (17/18th C) Dutch

£30000	$51900	€43800	Vanitas still life with a globe, hourglass and skull, musical instruments on a draped table (64x82cm-25x32in) s.d.1656 prov. 10-Dec-3 Christie's, London #34/R est:30000-50000

VINNEN, Carl (1863-1922) German

£664	$1129	€950	Mountain landscape, in the region of the Weyerberg (37x49cm-15x19in) i. panel lit. 28-Nov-3 Schloss Ahlden, Ahlden #717/R
£1329	$2285	€1900	Landscape with sand dunes (35x50cm-14x20in) mono.d.3 Juli 1915 cardboard. 6-Dec-3 Hans Stahl, Toestorf #94/R est:2000
£1854	$3375	€2800	Sand dunes (34x46cm-13x18in) d.1915 panel. 18-Jun-4 Bolland & Marotz, Bremen #400/R est:1200
£1958	$3368	€2800	Warehouse at the harbour (38x46cm-15x18in) i.d.1908 board. 5-Dec-3 Bolland & Marotz, Bremen #431/R est:3100

VINNEN, Carl (attrib) (1863-1922) German

£772	$1420	€1150	Moorland canal with jetty (52x62cm-20x24in) s. canvas on panel. 26-Mar-4 Bolland & Marotz, Bremen #378/R

VINOGRADOV, Sergei Arsenevich (1869-1938) Russian

£5369	$9933	€8000	Scene de campagne (48x39cm-19x15in) s.d.1889. 15-Mar-4 Claude Boisgirard, Paris #120/R est:3000-4000
£13000	$23270	€18980	Sunrise over a Russian village (32x49cm-13x19in) s. board. 26-May-4 Sotheby's, Olympia #432/R est:3000-4000
£19000	$32300	€27740	Watching the steam train (35x44cm-14x17in) s. 19-Nov-3 Sotheby's, London #69/R est:15000-20000

VINOGRADOV, Sergei Arsenevich (attrib) (1869-1938) Russian

Works on paper

£269	$500	€393	Landscape with monastery (18x23cm-7x9in) W/C. 7-Mar-4 William Jenack, New York #283

VINZIO, Giulio Cesare (1881-1940) Italian

£563	$975	€800	Sunset (40x28cm-16x11in) s. s.i.verso board. 9-Dec-3 Finarte Semenzato, Milan #28/R
£872	$1562	€1300	Landscape in Maremma (40x50cm-16x20in) s. board. 25-May-4 Finarte Semenzato, Milan #38/R est:1200-1400

VIOGEL, J J (19th C) ?

Works on paper

£7042	$12183	€10000	View of the City of Rio Janeiro taken from the Convent of St Theresa (40x68cm-16x27in) s.d.1832 W/C Indian ink. 14-Dec-3 St-Germain-en-Laye Encheres #31/R est:2500-3000

VIOLA, Domenicho (?-1696) Italian

£4800	$8592	€7200	Saint Peter's denial (78x102cm-31x40in) init. 13-May-4 Babuino, Rome #122/R est:6000-8000

VIOLA, Giovanni Battista (1576-1662) Italian

£83333	$150000	€121666	Extensive river landscape with a ferry. Mountainous landscape with a hunt (121x173cm-48x68in) pair. prov.exhib.lit. 23-Jan-4 Christie's, Rockefeller NY #170/R est:200000-300000

VIOLA, Giuseppe (1933-) Italian

£500	$920	€750	Santa Margherita Ligure (50x60cm-20x24in) s. 12-Jun-4 Meeting Art, Vercelli #291/R
£599	$994	€850	St Moritz (30x40cm-12x16in) s. i.verso panel. 14-Jun-3 Meeting Art, Vercelli #191/R
£604	$1117	€900	Angler with net (60x40cm-24x16in) s. masonite painted 1994. 13-Mar-4 Meeting Art, Vercelli #487
£915	$1520	€1300	Campagna Bergamasca (35x50cm-14x20in) s. s.i.d.1980 verso. 14-Jun-3 Meeting Art, Vercelli #420/R
£1000	$1840	€1500	Amalfi coast (100x100cm-39x39in) s. s.verso. 12-Jun-4 Meeting Art, Vercelli #965/R est:1500
£1056	$1754	€1500	Donna con rete da pesca (60x40cm-24x16in) s. s.i.d.1994 verso masonite. 14-Jun-3 Meeting Art, Vercelli #390/R est:1500
£1056	$1754	€1500	Venditrice di Castagne (60x40cm-24x16in) s. i.d.1994 verso panel. 14-Jun-3 Meeting Art, Vercelli #609/R est:1500
£1761	$2923	€2500	Fruit seller (100x70cm-39x28in) s. i.verso painted 1982. 14-Jun-3 Meeting Art, Vercelli #703/R est:2500

VIOLA, Manuel (1919-1987) Spanish

£347	$590	€500	Red and black abstraction (14x22cm-6x9in) s.verso. 28-Oct-3 Segre, Madrid #264/R
£423	$739	€600	Abstract (31x24cm-12x9in) s. acrylic paper. 16-Dec-3 Segre, Madrid #227/R
£458	$801	€650	Composition (21x28cm-8x11in) s. board. 16-Dec-3 Durán, Madrid #2/R
£467	$849	€700	Untitled (27x21cm-11x8in) s. panel. 29-Jun-4 Segre, Madrid #255/R
£500	$910	€750	Abstraccion azul (39x30cm-15x12in) s. panel. 29-Jun-4 Segre, Madrid #253/R
£517	$864	€750	Composition (23x23cm-9x9in) s. board. 17-Nov-3 Durán, Madrid #79/R
£521	$885	€750	Blue abstraction (22x17cm-9x7in) s. board. 28-Oct-3 Segre, Madrid #261/R
£559	$1029	€850	Untitled (53x41cm-21x16in) s. s.d.1962 verso cardboard. 22-Jun-4 Christie's, Amsterdam #349/R
£559	$1029	€850	Composition in blue and white (25x20cm-10x8in) s. board. 22-Jun-4 Durán, Madrid #86/R
£671	$1188	€1000	Composition (27x22cm-11x9in) s. board. 27-Apr-4 Durán, Madrid #7/R
£680	$1238	€1000	Untitled (27x35cm-11x14in) painted 1968 prov. 3-Feb-4 Segre, Madrid #322/R
£704	$1232	€1000	Composition (24x19cm-9x7in) s. acrylic board. 16-Dec-3 Durán, Madrid #42/R
£738	$1307	€1100	Composition (27x22cm-11x9in) s. board. 27-Apr-4 Durán, Madrid #8/R
£805	$1426	€1200	Composition (27x22cm-11x9in) s. board. 27-Apr-4 Durán, Madrid #18/R
£1007	$1782	€1500	Composition in black and yellow (45x37cm-18x15in) s. board. 27-Apr-4 Durán, Madrid #602/R est:800
£1007	$1782	€1500	Composition (27x22cm-11x9in) s. board. 27-Apr-4 Durán, Madrid #672/R
£1088	$1981	€1600	Abstract (46x38cm-18x15in) s. board. 3-Feb-4 Segre, Madrid #320/R
£1096	$1863	€1600	Untitled (50x40cm-20x16in) s. board. 4-Nov-3 Ansorena, Madrid #941/R est:1400
£1127	$1972	€1600	Cock fight (58x47cm-23x19in) s. acrylic board. 16-Dec-3 Durán, Madrid #122/R
£1127	$1972	€1600	Composition (46x37cm-18x15in) s. board. 16-Dec-3 Durán, Madrid #582/R
£1181	$1877	€1700	Composition (50x40cm-20x16in) s. masonite. 29-Apr-3 Durán, Madrid #48/R est:800
£1206	$1953	€1700	Pelea de gallos (40x32cm-16x13in) s. masonite. 20-May-3 Ansorena, Madrid #270/R est:700
£1379	$2290	€2000	Cock fight (55x46cm-22x18in). 1-Oct-3 Ansorena, Madrid #561/R est:2000
£1379	$2303	€2000	Untitled (63x63cm-25x25in) s. acrylic board. 11-Nov-3 Castellana, Madrid #84/R est:1500
£1389	$2361	€2000	Red abstraction (44x36cm-17x14in) s. board. 28-Oct-3 Segre, Madrid #262/R est:800
£1418	$2369	€2000	Composition (37x52cm-15x20in) s. board exhib. 20-Oct-3 Durán, Madrid #56/R
£1480	$2724	€2250	Composition (70x51cm-28x20in) s. paper. 22-Jun-4 Durán, Madrid #122/R est:1800
£1507	$2562	€2200	Wind (76x48cm-30x19in) s. board. 4-Nov-3 Ansorena, Madrid #944/R est:1800
£1507	$2562	€2200	View (49x75cm-19x30in) s. board. 4-Nov-3 Ansorena, Madrid #943/R est:1800
£1655	$2748	€2400	Sestruction (68x52cm-27x20in) s. board. 1-Oct-3 Ansorena, Madrid #585/R est:2000
£1702	$2757	€2400	Arlequin (60x49cm-24x19in) s. masonite. 20-May-3 Ansorena, Madrid #299/R est:1500
£1712	$2911	€2500	Untitled (73x53cm-29x21in) s. 4-Nov-3 Ansorena, Madrid #936/R est:2500
£1736	$2865	€2500	Untitled (44x62cm-17x24in) s. paper. 2-Jul-3 Ansorena, Madrid #934b/R
£1910	$3113	€2750	Composition (92x72cm-36x28in) s. 23-Sep-3 Durán, Madrid #50/R
£2222	$3667	€3200	Composition (47x65cm-19x26in) s. board. 2-Jul-3 Ansorena, Madrid #934a/R
£2257	$3679	€3250	Arlequin with cock (62x50cm-24x20in) s. board. 23-Sep-3 Durán, Madrid #226/R est:2500
£2432	$4281	€3600	Cocks fighting (46x38cm-18x15in) s. board. 18-May-4 Segre, Madrid #255/R est:1000
£2632	$4842	€4000	Leika (92x72cm-36x28in) s. 22-Jun-4 Durán, Madrid #138/R est:3000
£2797	$4671	€4000	Untitled (54x65cm-21x26in) s.d.1954. 24-Jun-3 Segre, Madrid #118/R est:4000
£4027	$7530	€6000	Mystery children (110x60cm-43x24in) s. exhib.lit. 24-Feb-4 Durán, Madrid #82/R est:4000
£4225	$7394	€6000	Composition (124x90cm-49x35in) s. acrylic board. 16-Dec-3 Durán, Madrid #203/R
£4698	$8785	€7000	On the time wings (89x146cm-35x57in) s. 24-Feb-4 Durán, Madrid #236/R est:6000
£4762	$8524	€7000	Composition (90x170cm-35x67in) s. prov. 22-Mar-4 Durán, Madrid #225/R est:7000
£4828	$8690	€7000	Unseizable (150x100cm-59x39in) s. exhib.lit. 26-Jan-4 Durán, Madrid #218/R est:6000
£4934	$9079	€7500	Cocks fighting (90x75cm-35x30in) s. board exhib. 22-Jun-4 Durán, Madrid #140/R est:6000
£5034	$8909	€7500	Midday (150x75cm-59x30in) s. exhib. 27-Apr-4 Durán, Madrid #100/R est:7000
£5208	$8490	€7500	Composition (100x250cm-39x98in) s. 23-Sep-3 Durán, Madrid #224/R est:5500
£5556	$9056	€8000	At night (150x70cm-59x28in) s. lit. 23-Sep-3 Durán, Madrid #225/R est:7500
£6250	$10313	€9000	Homage to Caravaggio (146x95cm-57x37in) lit. 2-Jul-3 Ansorena, Madrid #876b/R

£7895 $14289 €12000 Untitled (100x250cm-39x98in) s. 14-Apr-4 Ansorena, Madrid #269/R est:12000
£9929 $16085 €14000 Nevermore (131x97cm-52x38in) s.d.59 s.i.d.verso. 20-May-3 Ansorena, Madrid #317/R est:8400

VIOLLET LE DUC, Victor (1848-1901) French
Works on paper
£543 $1000 €793 Interior lamp - possibly for the Paris Opera (33x25cm-13x10in) mono. W/C over pencil htd white gouache prov. 26-Jun-4 Sloans & Kenyon, Bethesda #1022/R

VIOLLIER, Auguste Constantin (1854-1908) Swiss
£11111 $20000 €16222 Traveller's rest (88x122cm-35x48in) s.d.1882 prov. 22-Apr-4 Christie's, Rockefeller NY #147/R est:15000-20000

VIOLLIER, Henri Francois Gabriel (1750-1829) Swiss
Miniatures
£55000 $99000 €80300 Empress Maria Feodorovna and her six eldest children. i.d.1788 verso gold mount blue glass 7 in 1 gold frame oval prov. 22-Apr-4 Bonhams, New Bond Street #80/R est:30000-40000

VIOLLIER, Jean (1896-1985) Swiss
£1549 $2572 €2200 Objets et star, Marlene, ou nature morte a la caisse (101x82cm-40x32in) s.d.1938. 16-Jun-3 E & Eve, Paris #83/R

VIONOJA, Veikko (1909-2001) Finnish
£292 $487 €420 Girl (46x38cm-18x15in) s. 23-Oct-3 Hagelstam, Helsinki #912/R
£903 $1508 €1300 Spring by the sea (33x29cm-13x11in) s. 26-Oct-3 Bukowskis, Helsinki #523/R
£1056 $1690 €1500 Field (45x60cm-18x24in) s.d.1947. 18-Sep-3 Hagelstam, Helsinki #760/R est:1800
£1056 $1690 €1500 Huts (59x71cm-23x28in) s. exhib. 18-Sep-3 Hagelstam, Helsinki #761 est:1800
£1333 $2387 €2000 Still life of red potted plant (54x46cm-21x18in) i. 15-May-4 Hagelstam, Helsinki #197/R est:1800
£1745 $3246 €2600 The window (73x54cm-29x21in) s.d.66. 7-Mar-4 Bukowskis, Helsinki #466/R est:2200
£2254 $3606 €3200 Farm buildings (65x80cm-26x31in) s.d.57. 21-Sep-3 Bukowskis, Helsinki #486/R est:3500
£2533 $4535 €3800 River landscape (89x130cm-35x51in) s.d.1971 exhib. 15-May-4 Hagelstam, Helsinki #196/R est:4000
£3497 $5944 €5000 Midsummer Night (80x105cm-31x41in) s.d.59 exhib.lit. 29-Nov-3 Bukowskis, Helsinki #198/R est:5000-7000

VIRGIN, Mary (19th C) Danish?
£358 $655 €523 Still life of flowers in vase with parrot and snail (37x28cm-15x11in) i.stretcher. 9-Jun-4 Rasmussen, Copenhagen #1857/R (D.KR 4000)

VIRNICH, Thomas (1957-) German
£629 $1070 €900 Untitled (73x50cm-29x20in) s.d.1995 acrylic varnish on col photo. 27-Nov-3 Lempertz, Koln #509/R

VIRTANEN, Antti Into (20th C) Finnish
£366 $586 €520 Early spring in Jokikulma (35x45cm-14x18in) s.d.1991. 18-Sep-3 Hagelstam, Helsinki #883/R
£366 $586 €520 Evening dusk (24x40cm-9x16in) s.d.1988. 18-Sep-3 Hagelstam, Helsinki #884/R
£366 $586 €520 View of backyard (32x24cm-13x9in) s.d.1991. 18-Sep-3 Hagelstam, Helsinki #885/R
£394 $631 €560 Boy fishing (60x50cm-24x20in) s.d.1991. 18-Sep-3 Hagelstam, Helsinki #881

VIRTUE, John (1947-) British
£800 $1456 €1168 Landscape No 353 (30x41cm-12x16in) s.i.d.1997 verso. 1-Jul-4 Christie's, Kensington #375/R
£2400 $4296 €3504 Landscape, no 307 (183x244cm-72x96in) s.i.d.1966 verso prov. 16-Mar-4 Bonhams, New Bond Street #104/R est:2000-3000
Works on paper
£1892 $3500 €2762 Landscape 134 (79x127cm-31x50in) s.i.d.1990-1991 verso mixed media paper on wood prov. 12-Feb-4 Sotheby's, New York #310/R est:5000-7000

VIRY, Paul Alphonse (19th C) French
£979 $1635 €1400 Still life with musical instruments (70x112cm-28x44in) s.d.1893. 30-Jun-3 Ansorena, Madrid #395/R

VISANTI, Lyyli (1893-1971) Finnish
£336 $617 €500 Still life (37x41cm-15x16in) s. 25-Mar-4 Hagelstam, Helsinki #800

VISAT, Georges (?) ?
Prints
£5650 $10000 €8249 Aleko (47x52cm-19x20in) s.num.100/300 col lithograph after Marc Chagall. 30-Apr-4 Sotheby's, New York #82/R est:5000-7000

VISBY, Frederick Mayer (1839-1926) Danish
£1106 $1880 €1615 The first spring greeting (95x74cm-37x29in) s.d.1864 exhib. 10-Nov-3 Rasmussen, Vejle #370/R est:15000 (D.KR 12000)
£4726 $8176 €6900 Riders on mountain road, possibly in the West Indies (44x60cm-17x24in) s. 9-Dec-3 Rasmussen, Copenhagen #1503/R est:75000 (D.KR 50000)

VISCA, Rodolfo (1939-) Uruguayan
£414 $691 €600 Composition (17x35cm-7x14in) s. cardboard. 11-Nov-3 Castellana, Madrid #17/R
£414 $691 €600 Untitled (17x35cm-7x14in) s. cardboard. 11-Nov-3 Castellana, Madrid #43a/R
£483 $806 €700 Untitled (24x34cm-9x13in) s. 11-Nov-3 Castellana, Madrid #212/R
£483 $806 €700 Untitled (26x42cm-10x17in) s. cardboard. 11-Nov-3 Castellana, Madrid #221/R
Works on paper
£345 $576 €500 Untitled (10x24cm-4x9in) s. mixed media. 11-Nov-3 Castellana, Madrid #46/R

VISCH, Henk (1950-) Dutch
Sculpture
£16667 $30667 €25000 Heading North (204cm-80in) bronze cast 1998. 8-Jun-4 Sotheby's, Amsterdam #155/R est:15000-20000

VISCHER, August (1821-1898) German
£397 $723 €600 Portrait of the painter Kupetzky (84x67cm-33x26in) i.verso. 18-Jun-4 Bolland & Marotz, Bremen #789/R
£699 $1168 €1000 Portrait of Kupetzky (84x67cm-33x26in) i. verso. 28-Jun-3 Bolland & Marotz, Bremen #750/R

VISCHER, Emmanuel Rudolf (1901-1936) Swiss
£517 $926 €755 Spanish village (37x46cm-15x18in) s.d.28. 12-May-4 Dobiaschofsky, Bern #1050/R (S.FR 1200)

VISCHER, Hans (attrib) (1489-1550) German
Sculpture
£1149 $2056 €1700 Separation of Romulus and Remus (22x16cm-9x6in) bronze relief. 6-May-4 Michael Zeller, Lindau #2102/R est:1200

VISCHER, Jeronymus (attrib) (fl.1580-1620) Swiss
Works on paper
£1577 $2712 €2302 Two soldiers bearing the coat of arms for Altkirch in Alsace (34x25cm-13x10in) pen. 8-Dec-3 Philippe Schuler, Zurich #4231/R est:4000-5000 (S.FR 3500)

VISCONTI (?) ?
£2930 $5187 €4395 Portrait of a woman (62x47cm-24x19in) 27-Apr-4 Bolsa de Arte, Rio de Janeiro #30/R (B.R 16000)

VISCONTI MERINO, Julio (1921-) Spanish
Works on paper
£387 $678 €550 Village (47x68cm-19x27in) s. W/C. 16-Dec-3 Durán, Madrid #6/R

VISCONTI, Antonio (19th C) Italian?
£632 $1132 €923 Still life with urn (68x48cm-27x19in) s.d.84. 15-May-4 Christie's, Sydney #347/R (A.D 1600)

VISCONTI, E (?) Italian
£1702 $2843 €2400 Naples Bay with Vesuvius (58x96cm-23x38in) s. 14-Oct-3 Finarte Semenzato, Milan #61/R est:2500

VISCONTI, F (?) ?
£1329 $2219 €1900 Woodcutter resting (66x86cm-26x34in) s.d.74 panel. 27-Jun-3 Doutrebente, Paris #51/R est:1000-1200

VISEUX, Claude (1927-) French
£423 $680 €600 Facies (74x60cm-29x24in) s.d.1961 s.i.d.verso. 11-May-3 Versailles Encheres #267
Sculpture
£2098 $3566 €3000 Colonne (99cm-39in) s.d.LXXI steel. 18-Nov-3 Pierre Berge, Paris #26/R est:1000-1500
£2238 $3804 €3200 Tabouret (66cm-26in) polished metal. 30-Nov-3 Anaf, Lyon #208/R est:3000-3200
Works on paper
£302 $553 €450 Untitled (65x51cm-26x20in) s.d.56 mixed media. 7-Jul-4 Artcurial Briest, Paris #364
£769 $1285 €1100 Composition (96x159cm-38x63in) s. mixed media panel. 29-Jun-3 Versailles Encheres #40/R
£1141 $2088 €1700 Peridimiens (96x130cm-38x51in) s.d.60 s.i.d. verso mixed media canvas prov. 7-Jul-4 Artcurial Briest, Paris #365 est:1200-1500

VISKI, Janos (1891-1965) Hungarian
£267 $491 €400 At the well (50x70cm-20x28in) s. 9-Jun-4 Bukowskis, Helsinki #628/R
£278 $464 €400 Horses drinking (33x44cm-13x17in) s. lit. 25-Oct-3 Bergmann, Erlangen #967/R
£348 $550 €508 Horse-drawn wagons with horses galloping at full speed (61x79cm-24x31in) s. 6-Sep-3 Brunk, Ashville #617
£547 $989 €820 Wild horses (70x100cm-28x39in) s. 3-Apr-4 Hans Stahl, Hamburg #119/R
£567 $948 €800 Herding horses (70x100cm-28x39in) s. 14-Oct-3 Dorotheum, Vienna #107/R
£754 $1350 €1101 Sleighs with horses (36x24cm-14x9in) painted c.1930. 9-Jan-4 Du Mouchelle, Detroit #2176/R
£775 $1340 €1100 Animals watering (60x80cm-24x31in) s. 9-Dec-3 Pandolfini, Florence #371/R

VISO, Nicola (18th C) Italian

£	$	€	Details
£6711	$12349	€10000	Theseus picking up father's sword (127x154cm-50x61in) s. prov. 24-Mar-4 Dorotheum, Vienna #89/R est:12000-16000
£14184	$23688	€20000	Stag hunting. Back from hunting (43x65cm-17x26in) pair. 18-Oct-3 Meeting Art, Vercelli #460/R est:20000

VISO, Nicola (attrib) (18th C) Italian

£	$	€	Details
£1800	$3060	€2628	Jacob blessing Ephraim (38x48cm-15x19in) 29-Oct-3 Bonhams, New Bond Street #113/R est:2000-3000
£5369	$9880	€8000	Galeres dans un estuaire domine par des ruines antiques (75x128cm-30x50in) 24-Mar-4 Tajan, Paris #35/R est:5000-6000
£15000	$27450	€21900	Capriccio of an Italianate landscape with figures amongst temple ruins (101x127cm-40x50in) 7-Jul-4 Bonhams, New Bond Street #46/R est:5000-7000

VISPRE, Francis Xavier (c.1730-1790) French/British

£	$	€	Details
£2013	$3604	€3000	Raisins, pommes et coupe de peches sur un entablement (39x42cm-15x17in) 25-May-4 Palais de Beaux Arts, Brussels #553/R est:3300-5000

VISSCHER, Cornelis de (1619-1662) Dutch

Works on paper

£	$	€	Details
£16901	$29577	€24000	Portrait d'une femme en buste portant une coiffe (20x18cm-8x7in) s.i.d.1658 graphite vellum prov. 17-Dec-3 Christie's, Paris #28/R est:15000-20000

VISSER, Carel (1928-) Dutch

Sculpture

£	$	€	Details
£1000	$1840	€1500	Untitled (24x49cm-9x19in) welded oxidised iron wooden base exec. 1969 unique prov. 9-Jun-4 Christie's, Amsterdam #296/R est:4000-6000
£2448	$4161	€3500	Untitled (31x33cm-12x13in) welded iron exec c.1950-55 prov. 25-Nov-3 Christie's, Amsterdam #152/R est:4000-6000
£4895	$8322	€7000	Family (45x130cm-18x51in) welded iron exec c.1950-55 prov. 25-Nov-3 Christie's, Amsterdam #150/R est:3500-5500

Works on paper

£	$	€	Details
£839	$1401	€1200	Indian summer (71x80cm-28x31in) collage. 30-Jun-3 Sotheby's, Amsterdam #454/R
£1748	$2972	€2500	De boom (70x100cm-28x39in) s.d.89 graphite. 25-Nov-3 Christie's, Amsterdam #320/R est:2500-3500
£2667	$4907	€4000	Woman on one shoe (148x139cm-58x55in) s.i.d.2000 graphite collage cardboard. 9-Jun-4 Christie's, Amsterdam #370/R est:4000-6000

VISSER, Jan (1879-1961) Dutch

£	$	€	Details
£525	$876	€750	Arum lily (80x66cm-31x26in) s.i.d.34. 30-Jun-3 Sotheby's, Amsterdam #346/R

VISSER, Tjipke (1876-1955) Dutch

Sculpture

£	$	€	Details
£2657	$4517	€3800	Baboe mit kind (29cm-11in) mono. bronze incl wooden base conceived 1909 lit. 25-Nov-3 Christie's, Amsterdam #128/R est:2000-3000

VITA, Miguel de (1923-2001) South American

£	$	€	Details
£732	$1200	€1069	Seascape (65x81cm-26x32in) s. 3-Jun-3 Galeria y Remates, Montevideo #57
£824	$1400	€1203	Harbour (73x92cm-29x36in) s. 25-Nov-3 Galeria y Remates, Montevideo #12/R
£1051	$1850	€1534	Farm (73x79cm-29x31in) s. 5-Jan-4 Galeria y Remates, Montevideo #121/R est:2000-2500

VITAL, Edgar (1883-?) Swiss

£	$	€	Details
£181	$308	€264	Engadin carnations (74x60cm-29x24in) s.d.1964 s.i.d. verso. 18-Nov-3 Hans Widmer, St Gallen #1224 (S.FR 400)
£995	$1722	€1453	Autumn colours (46x55cm-18x22in) s.d.1952 panel lit. 9-Dec-3 Sotheby's, Zurich #77/R est:2000-3000 (S.FR 2200)

VITAL, Not (1948-) American

Sculpture

£	$	€	Details
£1216	$2250	€1775	Untitled (343cm-135in) hydrocal horns 2 parts exec 1988 prov. 12-Feb-4 Sotheby's, New York #238/R est:1500-2500
£1564	$2800	€2283	Binoculars (13x13cm-5x5in) s. num.7/12 prov. 16-May-4 Wright, Chicago #467/R est:700-900

Works on paper

£	$	€	Details
£209	$350	€305	Study of abreast (43x36cm-17x14in) s.d.1986 oilstick graphite. 19-Oct-3 Bonhams & Butterfields, Los Angeles #7090

VITAL-CORNU, Charles (1851-1927) French

Sculpture

£	$	€	Details
£1972	$3451	€2800	Le sommeil (30cm-12in) s.st.f.Susse brown pat bronze bas-relief exhib.lit. 17-Dec-3 Rabourdin & Choppin de Janvry, Paris #128/R est:3000-3500

VITALE, Carlo (1902-1996) Italian

£	$	€	Details
£1007	$1782	€1500	Ligurie - chemin de village (55x40cm-22x16in) s.d.69 panel. 27-Apr-4 Artcurial Briest, Paris #242 est:1500-2000
£1678	$2970	€2500	Ligurie - bateaux dans un port (60x70cm-24x28in) s.d.65. 27-Apr-4 Artcurial Briest, Paris #239/R est:1500-2000

VITALE, Filippo (1585-c.1650) Italian

£	$	€	Details
£4610	$7699	€6500	Sacred Family with San Giovannino and Sant'Anna (180x129cm-71x51in) 18-Jun-3 Christie's, Rome #343/R est:7000-9000

VITALE, Filippo (attrib) (1585-c.1650) Italian

£	$	€	Details
£2517	$4330	€3600	Saint Nicola of Bari (126x95cm-50x37in) 2-Dec-3 Sotheby's, Milan #21/R est:4000-6000

VITALE, Massimo (1944-) Italian

Photographs

£	$	€	Details
£2994	$5000	€4371	Marina di Massa (150x201cm-59x79in) num.2/9 chromogenic col print prov. 16-Oct-3 Phillips, New York #70/R est:10000-15000
£5389	$9000	€7868	Picnic allee 2 (119x150cm-47x59in) num.5/9 chromogenic col print prov. 16-Oct-3 Phillips, New York #71/R est:10000-15000
£5988	$10000	€8742	New Vecchino (150x201cm-59x79in) num.7/9 chromogenic col print. 16-Oct-3 Phillips, New York #69/R est:10000-15000

Prints

£	$	€	Details
£6287	$10500	€9179	Picnic allee (119x150cm-47x59in) num.7/9 chromogenic col print. 16-Oct-3 Phillips, New York #72/R est:10000-15000

VITALI, Alberto (1898-1974) Italian

£	$	€	Details
£403	$713	€600	Shepherds (43x53cm-17x21in) s. board lit. 1-May-4 Meeting Art, Vercelli #445

VITALI, Edouardo (19th C) Italian

Works on paper

£	$	€	Details
£472	$750	€689	Young man and woman with fishing nets (53x38cm-21x15in) s. W/C. 10-Sep-3 Alderfer's, Hatfield #279

VITALIS, Macario (1898-1990) Philippino

£	$	€	Details
£352	$609	€500	Le village (45x37cm-18x15in) s.d.59 cardboard. 13-Dec-3 Touati, Paris #183
£352	$609	€500	Deux femmes (41x33cm-16x13in) 13-Dec-3 Touati, Paris #185
£387	$670	€550	Le bonnet (27x22cm-11x9in) s.d.58. 13-Dec-3 Touati, Paris #176/R
£704	$1218	€1000	Mere et enfant (55x33cm-22x13in) s.d.54. 13-Dec-3 Touati, Paris #177/R
£704	$1218	€1000	La place du village (42x82cm-17x32in) s.d.47 panel. 13-Dec-3 Touati, Paris #178
£739	$1279	€1050	Printemps (50x63cm-20x25in) s.d.68 verso. 13-Dec-3 Touati, Paris #180/R
£800	$1440	€1200	Au bal (60x81cm-24x32in) s.d.50. 26-Apr-4 Tajan, Paris #204
£1092	$1888	€1550	La marchande de poissons (73x50cm-29x20in) s.d.51 cardboard. 13-Dec-3 Touati, Paris #175/R

VITI, Eugenio (1881-1952) Italian

£	$	€	Details
£2817	$4676	€4000	Still life with game (39x50cm-15x20in) s. board. 11-Jun-3 Christie's, Rome #233/R est:4300-4800
£2817	$4676	€4000	Donna in interno (42x33cm-17x13in) s. wood. 11-Jun-3 Christie's, Rome #234/R est:4200-4500

VITI, Timoteo (attrib) (1469-1523) Italian

Works on paper

£	$	€	Details
£2800	$5124	€4088	Woman seen from behind turned to the right (28x12cm-11x5in) pen ink corner make up prov. 6-Jul-4 Christie's, London #5/R est:3000-5000

VITIELLO, Ciro (20th C) Italian

£	$	€	Details
£2000	$3580	€3000	La Salute, Venice (45x55cm-18x22in) s.i.verso board. 12-May-4 Stadion, Trieste #778/R est:1500-2000

VITO, Camillo de (19th C) Italian

Works on paper

£	$	€	Details
£987	$1816	€1500	Pozzuoli Cave (27x35cm-11x14in) s. gouache pair. 22-Jun-4 Sotheby's, Milan #146/R est:1500-2000
£1171	$2014	€1710	The eruption of Cenere in 1810 (28x41cm-11x16in) s. gouache. 8-Dec-3 Philippe Schuler, Zurich #4233/R est:1500-2000 (S.FR 2600)

VITO, Camillo de (attrib) (19th C) Italian

£	$	€	Details
£2715	$4344	€3964	Eruption of Vesuvius (45x65cm-18x26in) gouache. 19-Sep-3 Koller, Zurich #3068/R est:5000-7000 (S.FR 6000)

Works on paper

£	$	€	Details
£1659	$3020	€2422	Grotta Blu a Capri (45x65cm-18x26in) gouache. 16-Jun-4 Fischer, Luzern #2615/R est:4000-5000 (S.FR 3800)

VITO, Michele de (19th C) Italian

£	$	€	Details
£282	$487	€400	Naples (20x25cm-8x10in) s.i. tempera paper. 11-Dec-3 Christie's, Rome #36

VITO, Nicola de (19th C) Italian

Works on paper

£	$	€	Details
£2676	$4630	€3800	Pipes player. Pulcinella. Peasant woman. Childminder. (26x17cm-10x7in) s. W/C set of 4 two in each frame. 10-Dec-3 Finarte Semenzato, Rome #145/R est:4000-5000

VITRINGA, Wigerus (1657-1721) Dutch

£	$	€	Details
£1867	$3341	€2800	Seascape (45x63cm-18x25in) board. 12-May-4 Finarte Semenzato, Milan #26/R est:2500-3000
£8392	$14266	€12000	Fishermen fishing at Cap Circeo (71x97cm-28x38in) mono. lit. 28-Nov-3 Schloss Ahlden, Ahlden #1377/R est:12500

Works on paper
£6849 $11644 €10000 Various ships and rowing boat on an estuary (12x18cm-5x7in) init. brush black ink grey wash over black chk prov. 4-Nov-3 Sotheby's, Amsterdam #92/R est:7000-9000

VITTORINI, Umberto (1890-1970) Italian
£430 $783 €650 Landscape (37x48cm-15x19in) s. board. 17-Jun-4 Galleria Pananti, Florence #113/R
£1007 $1802 €1500 Still life (66x48cm-26x19in) i.d.1938 verso board prov. 25-May-4 Finarte Semenzato, Milan #137/R est:1200-1400

VITY, Antonio de (1901-) Italian
£404 $650 €590 Paris street scene (61x122cm-24x48in) s. 17-Aug-3 Jeffery Burchard, Florida #102

VIUDES, Vincente (1916-) Spanish?
Works on paper
£395 $726 €600 Study for theatre setting (43x57cm-17x22in) s. gouache. 22-Jun-4 Durán, Madrid #1145

VIUSA, Manuel (1918-) Spanish
£348 $650 €508 Still life, fruit (38x56cm-15x22in) s. inid.d.1957 verso prov. 24-Feb-4 Arthur James, Florida #154
£455 $850 €664 Girl arranging flowers (99x51cm-39x20in) s. prov. 24-Feb-4 Arthur James, Florida #157

VIVANCOS, Miguel Garcia (1895-1972) Spanish
£1067 $1920 €1600 Fete foraine au port (49x60cm-19x24in) s.d.1959 s.i.d.verso. 26-Apr-4 Tajan, Paris #378/R est:700-800

VIVARINI, Alvise (c.1445-c.1503) Italian
£35000 $64050 €51100 Portrait of a gentleman in a black coat and cap (28x22cm-11x9in) marouflaged panel prov.exhib.lit. 7-Jul-4 Christie's, London #8/R est:15000-25000
£42553 $71064 €60000 Madonna and sleeping baby (60x42cm-24x17in) panel. 18-Jun-3 Christie's, Rome #461/R est:40000-60000

VIVES LLULL, Juan (1901-) Spanish
£1141 $2042 €1700 Landscape in Minorca (34x41cm-13x16in) s. cardboard. 25-May-4 Durán, Madrid #685/R est:1500

VIVES MARISTANY (19th C) Spanish
£646 $1176 €950 Beach with sailing boats (18x48cm-7x19in) s. board. 3-Feb-4 Segre, Madrid #45/R

VIVES-ATSARA, Jose (1919-1988) Mexican
£671 $1248 €1000 Mountains in Majorca (81x100cm-32x39in) s.i.d.1946 verso. 2-Mar-4 Ansorena, Madrid #137/R
£932 $1500 €1351 Old street in Mexico (25x30cm-10x12in) board. 22-Aug-3 Altermann Galleries, Santa Fe #183

VIVIAN, A (19th C) Italian
£1900 $3401 €2774 Grand Canal, Venice (48x74cm-19x29in) s. 17-Mar-4 Bonhams, Chester #319 est:300-500

VIVIAN, Calthea (1857-1943) American
£1494 $2750 €2181 The harbour, homeward bound (33x154cm-13x61in) s. paper on board triptych prov. 8-Jun-4 Bonhams & Butterfields, San Francisco #4252/R est:4000-6000

VIVIAN, George (1798-1873) British
£8000 $13600 €11680 Rialto Bridge and Grand Canal, Venice, with figures and gondolas (60x105cm-24x41in) s. 26-Nov-3 Mervyn Carey, Tenterden #170/R

VIVIAN, J (19th C) British
£450 $765 €657 North Italian lake scene with figures beside cottages (35x41cm-14x16in) 19-Nov-3 Tennants, Leyburn #1083
£2800 $5012 €4088 Bacino, Venice (51x76cm-20x30in) s. 27-May-4 Christie's, Kensington #254/R est:2500-3500
£15000 $25500 €21900 Barges and gondolas (76x127cm-30x50in) s. 19-Nov-3 Christie's, Kensington #611/R

VIVIANI, Cesare (19/20th C) Italian
Sculpture
£7647 $13000 €11165 Bathing nymph (43cm-17in) s. marble. 28-Oct-3 Christie's, Rockefeller NY #176/R

VIVIANI, Giuseppe (1898-1965) Italian
£2349 $4205 €3500 Dancer (105x55cm-41x22in) s. exhib. 25-May-4 Sotheby's, Milan #129/R est:6000

VIVIANI, J (?) Italian
£13500 $24975 €19710 View of Venice (58x104cm-23x41in) indis.sig. 9-Mar-4 Bonhams, Knightsbridge #283/R est:2000-3000

VIVIANI, Raoul (1883-1965) Italian
£347 $590 €500 Landscape with figures (40x50cm-16x20in) s. 1-Nov-3 Meeting Art, Vercelli #105
Works on paper
£685 $1068 €1000 Around Viggiu' (47x47cm-19x19in) mixed media card. 8-Apr-3 Il Ponte, Milan #529

VIVIEN, Jules (19/20th C) French
£2059 $3500 €3006 Ombues Mount (97x147cm-38x58in) s.d.1927. 25-Nov-3 Galeria y Remates, Montevideo #189/R

VIVIEN, Narcisse (19th C) French
£333 $607 €500 Foire dans la foret (26x35cm-10x14in) 30-Jun-4 Delvaux, Paris #3

VIVIN, Louis (1861-1936) French
£1560 $2606 €2200 Pecheur au clair de lune (50x70cm-20x28in) 15-Oct-3 Neret-Minet, Paris #19/R
£2032 $3800 €2967 Notre-Dame (65x55cm-26x22in) s. 25-Feb-4 Christie's, Rockefeller NY #4/R est:5000-7000
£2406 $4500 €3513 Scene de rue (60x81cm-24x32in) s. 25-Feb-4 Christie's, Rockefeller NY #5/R est:4000-6000
£2941 $5500 €4294 Interior of church (65x54cm-26x21in) s. prov.exhib. 25-Feb-4 Christie's, Rockefeller NY #3/R est:3000-5000
£8451 $14028 €12000 Paris, quai de l'Horloge (73x100cm-29x39in) s. exhib. 11-Jun-3 Delorme & Bocage, Paris #25 est:10000-12000

VIVO, Andres (20th C) Uruguayan
£423 $800 €618 Dusk in Montevideo harbour (60x80cm-24x31in) s. 22-Feb-4 Galeria y Remates, Montevideo #136/R

VIVO, Tommaso de (1790-1884) Italian
£3028 $5239 €4300 Spinning, allegory of Summer (63x49cm-25x19in) 14-Dec-3 Finarte, Venice #32/R est:3000-3500

VIVOT, Lea (1952-) Canadian/Czech
Sculpture
£1116 $1920 €1629 Lover's Bench (21cm-8in) s.i.d.74 bronze. 2-Dec-3 Joyner Waddington, Toronto #215/R est:3000-4000 (C.D 2500)

VIZKELETY, Emerich (1819-1895) Hungarian
£363 $668 €530 Arab merchants offering their wares (50x44cm-20x17in) s. canvas on masonite. 14-Jun-4 Waddingtons, Toronto #310/R est:700-900 (C.D 900)

VIZKELETY, W Eta (20th C) Hungarian
£447 $800 €653 Shucking corn (61x91cm-24x36in) s. 20-Mar-4 Sloans & Kenyon, Bethesda #1164/R

VLADIMIROFF, Ivan Alexeievitch (1869-1947) Russian
£330 $600 €482 Monastery (18x30cm-7x12in) board. 8-Feb-4 William Jenack, New York #16
£1081 $1935 €1600 Floral splendour (30x37cm-12x15in) board. 8-May-4 Bukowskis, Helsinki #457/R est:1300-1500

VLADIMIRSKY, Boris Eremeievich (1878-1950) Russian
£1528 $2597 €2200 Woman in boat reading (22x33cm-9x13in) s.cyrillic d.1914 canvas on board. 28-Oct-3 Dorotheum, Vienna #86/R est:2200-2500

VLAMINCK, Jan de (1810-?) Belgian
£300 $541 €438 Feeding the birds (25x32cm-10x13in) s.indis.d. panel. 26-Jan-4 Lilla Bukowskis, Stockholm #79 (S.KR 4000)

VLAMINCK, Maurice de (1876-1958) French
£10695 $20000 €15615 Paysage sous la neige (19x25cm-7x10in) s.s.verso board prov. 25-Feb-4 Christie's, Rockefeller NY #34/R est:22000-28000
£12500 $20875 €18250 Vase de fleurs (46x33cm-18x13in) s. 21-Oct-3 Sotheby's, London #39/R est:12000-15000
£12931 $23147 €18879 L'auberge (45x54cm-18x21in) s. 12-May-4 Dobiaschofsky, Bern #1052/R est:40000 (S.FR 30000)
£12941 $22000 €18894 Nature morte - pain et pichet (54x73cm-21x29in) s.d.Sept.42. 6-Nov-3 Sotheby's, New York #361/R est:25000-35000
£13986 $23357 €20000 Nature morte au pain et au vin (54x73cm-21x29in) s.d.42. 25-Jun-3 Digard, Paris #97/R est:25000-30000
£14706 $25000 €21471 Bords de riviere (46x56cm-18x22in) s. prov.exhib. 6-Nov-3 Sotheby's, New York #334/R est:30000-40000
£14865 $26608 €22000 Rue de village (33x41cm-13x16in) s. 5-May-4 Coutau Begarie, Paris #57/R est:25000-30000
£15278 $25514 €22000 Les Tas de Pois, pointe de Penhir, Bretagne (65x82cm-26x32in) s. painted c.1948 prov. 21-Oct-3 Christie's, Paris #197/R est:25000-35000
£15493 $27113 €22000 Bouquet de fleurs bleues (46x23cm-18x9in) s. prov. 16-Dec-3 Claude Aguttes, Neuilly #28/R est:18000-22000
£17000 $31280 €24820 Maisons dans les champs (33x41cm-13x16in) s. 22-Jun-4 Sotheby's, London #306/R est:16000-18000
£17568 $32500 €25649 Paysage avec arbre (66x81cm-26x32in) prov. 11-Feb-4 Sotheby's, New York #65/R est:30000-40000
£17606 $30810 €25000 Bouquet de fleurs rouges (46x23cm-18x9in) s. prov. 16-Dec-3 Claude Aguttes, Neuilly #29/R est:18000-22000
£19128 $34238 €28500 Paysage de neige (38x46cm-15x18in) s. 25-May-4 Chambelland & Giafferi, Paris #50/R est:15000-20000
£19173 $33552 €27225 Bouquet de fleurs dans un pichet (55x38cm-22x15in) s. prov.lit. 18-Dec-3 Tajan, Paris #49/R est:30000-35000
£19463 $35812 €29000 Degel en foret (60x73cm-24x29in) s. 26-Mar-4 Neret-Minet, Paris #14/R est:30000-35000
£19632 $32000 €28663 Nature morte avec vase de fleurs (46x33cm-18x13in) s. prov.lit. 25-Sep-3 Christie's, Rockefeller NY #535/R est:30000-40000
£20270 $37500 €29594 Fleurs dans un vase (55x46cm-22x18in) s. prov. 11-Feb-4 Sotheby's, New York #38/R est:20000-30000
£20280 $34881 €29000 Bouquet (61x50cm-24x20in) s. lit. 8-Dec-3 Artcurial Briest, Paris #69/R est:35000-40000

£20542	$35949	€29170	Silhouette dans un village (46x61cm-18x24in) s. i.verso prov.lit. 18-Dec-3 Tajan, Paris #50/R est:30000-50000
£20548	$34932	€30000	Paysage (38x46cm-15x18in) s. prov.lit. 9-Nov-3 Versailles Encheres #23/R est:30000-35000
£22000	$40040	€32120	La mare (65x92cm-26x36in) s. prov. 3-Feb-4 Christie's, London #262/R est:20000-30000
£22000	$40480	€32120	Bouquet de fleurs (65x50cm-26x20in) s. prov. 23-Jun-4 Christie's, London #156/R est:20000-30000
£22222	$37111	€32000	Bouquet de fleurs au vase brun (55x38cm-22x15in) s. painted c.1939-1940 prov. 21-Oct-3 Christie's, Paris #193/R est:25000-35000
£22346	$40000	€32625	Ferme (28x35cm-11x14in) s. 6-May-4 Sotheby's, New York #439/R est:20000-30000
£22378	$38042	€32000	Bouquet de fleurs (61x50cm-24x20in) s. prov. 26-Nov-3 Lempertz, Koln #1016/R est:35000-40000
£22378	$38042	€32000	Gros temps (55x65cm-22x26in) s. 28-Nov-3 Drouot Estimations, Paris #204/R est:30000-40000
£22535	$38986	€32000	Femme au bord de chemin (50x61cm-20x24in) s. 14-Dec-3 Eric Pillon, Calais #97/R
£22917	$38271	€33000	Bouquet de fleurs au vase blanc (55x38cm-22x15in) s. painted c.1939-1940 prov. 21-Oct-3 Christie's, Paris #192/R est:30000-50000
£23281	$40742	€33060	Fleurs dan sun pichet (55x38cm-22x15in) s. prov.lit. 18-Dec-3 Tajan, Paris #48/R est:30000-40000
£23529	$40000	€34352	Vase de fleurs (55x46cm-22x18in) s. 5-Nov-3 Christie's, Rockefeller NY #273/R est:40000-60000
£24476	$41608	€35000	Bouquet de fleurs (55x46cm-22x18in) s. 1-Dec-3 Camard, Paris #46/R est:45000-60000
£25000	$41750	€36000	Environs de Bourth (60x72cm-24x28in) s. painted c.1950 prov. 21-Oct-3 Christie's, Paris #196/R est:30000-50000
£26351	$47169	€39000	Village street (38x46cm-15x18in) s. i.d.1956 verso prov.lit. 8-May-4 Schloss Ahlden, Ahlden #835/R est:28000
£26389	$44069	€38000	Paysage de Beauce (60x73cm-24x29in) s. painted c.1952-1953 prov. 21-Oct-3 Christie's, Paris #191/R est:25000-35000
£26471	$45000	€38648	Rue de village (50x61cm-20x24in) s. painted c.1911 prov. 5-Nov-3 Christie's, Rockefeller NY #281/R est:40000-60000
£26471	$45000	€38648	Vase de fleurs (55x38cm-22x15in) s. 5-Nov-3 Christie's, Rockefeller NY #282/R est:35000-45000
£26471	$45000	€38648	Bouquet of flowers (61x50cm-24x20in) s. 5-Nov-3 Christie's, Rockefeller NY #365/R est:60000-80000
£26552	$48590	€38500	Route de campagne (37x46cm-15x18in) s. peinture. 1-Feb-4 Robin & Fattori, Granville #2
£26573	$45175	€38000	Paysage a la maison grise (54x65cm-21x26in) s. prov.exhib. 26-Nov-3 Dorotheum, Vienna #48/R est:38000-50000
£27465	$47514	€39000	Rue de village (65x81cm-26x32in) s. 9-Dec-3 Chambelland & Giafferi, Paris #114/R est:45000-50000
£27778	$46389	€40000	Nature morte avec le manuscrit du Portrait avant deces (60x81cm-24x32in) s. s.i.verso painted c.1942 prov.exhib. 21-Oct-3 Christie's, Paris #194/R est:40000-60000
£28169	$48732	€40000	Marine par gros temps (65x81cm-26x32in) s. painted c.1930. 10-Dec-3 Remi Ader, Paris #64/R est:40000-50000
£28169	$48732	€40000	Marine par gros temps (65x81cm-26x32in) s. painted c.1930. 10-Dec-3 Neret-Minet, Paris #64/R est:40000-50000
£28333	$51567	€42500	Auberge en bord de route (46x55cm-18x22in) s. lit. 4-Jul-4 Eric Pillon, Calais #108/R
£29050	$52000	€42413	Landscape (66x81cm-26x32in) s. prov. 5-May-4 Christie's, Rockefeller NY #338/R est:40000-60000
£29412	$50000	€42942	Verger sous la tempete (65x81cm-26x32in) s. prov. 5-Nov-3 Christie's, Rockefeller NY #297/R est:50000-70000
£29530	$52859	€44000	Vase de fleurs (55x46cm-22x18in) s. prov. 26-May-4 Christie's, Paris #30/R est:40000-60000
£30000	$55201	€45000	Deux paysannes devant une ferme (66x81cm-26x32in) s. exhib.lit. 9-Jun-4 Tajan, Paris #52/R est:50000-70000
£30000	$55200	€43800	Bouquet de fleurs (61x50cm-24x20in) s. prov. 23-Jun-4 Christie's, London #226/R est:35000-45000
£31788	$58172	€48000	Village (55x65cm-22x26in) s. 9-Apr-4 Bailly Pommery, Paris #87/R est:25000-30000
£32395	$56043	€46000	Paysage de neige (60x73cm-24x29in) s. lit. 9-Dec-3 Artcurial Briest, Paris #180/R est:45000-60000
£32400	$59616	€48600	Rue de village sous la neige (52x65cm-20x26in) s. 9-Jun-4 Beaussant & Lefèvre, Paris #225/R est:40000-50000
£35135	$61838	€52000	Vase de fleurs (55x46cm-22x18in) s. painted c.1920. 18-May-4 Segre, Madrid #298/R est:48000
£35294	$60000	€51529	Paysage a la Mairie (65x81cm-26x32in) s. 6-Nov-3 Sotheby's, New York #194/R est:70000-90000
£35294	$60000	€51529	Maisons en hiver (54x73cm-21x29in) s. prov. 5-Nov-3 Christie's, Rockefeller NY #166/R est:50000-70000
£36364	$62545	€52000	Paysage (46x55cm-18x22in) s. painted c.1912 prov. 2-Dec-3 Sotheby's, Amsterdam #85/R est:50000-70000
£38000	$69920	€55480	Maisons au bord de la route (54x65cm-21x26in) s. prov. 22-Jun-4 Sotheby's, London #307/R est:40000-60000
£38288	$65856	€55900	Flowers in vase (54x38cm-21x15in) s. prov. 2-Dec-3 Koller, Zurich #3053/R est:120000-180000 (S.FR 85000)
£40000	$72800	€58400	Le village de Mindrais (65x81cm-26x32in) s. 3-Feb-4 Christie's, London #269/R est:40000-60000
£40000	$72800	€58400	Nature morte aux fruits (81x116cm-32x46in) s. prov.exhib. 3-Feb-4 Christie's, London #289/R est:50000-70000
£40503	$72500	€59134	Maison dans la campagne (60x73cm-24x29in) s. painted c.1912 prov. 6-May-4 Sotheby's, New York #283/R est:80000-120000
£45000	$82800	€65700	La Tamise a Westminster (56x76cm-22x30in) s. painted c.1910-1912. 23-Jun-4 Christie's, London #157/R est:50000-70000
£45852	$83450	€66944	Eglise sous la neige (81x100cm-32x39in) s. painted c.1925 prov.lit. 18-Jun-4 Kornfeld, Bern #148/R est:50000 (S.FR 105000)
£48000	$88320	€70080	Personnage sur un chemin enneige (65x81cm-26x32in) s. exhib. 23-Jun-4 Christie's, London #270/R est:50000-70000
£48951	$84196	€70000	Bouquet de fleurs (73x60cm-29x24in) s. lit. 8-Dec-3 Artcurial Briest, Paris #32/R est:80000-100000
£51471	$87500	€75148	Paysage en hiver, Beauce (61x74cm-24x29in) s. prov.exhib. 6-Nov-3 Sotheby's, New York #358/R est:60000-80000
£52447	$90209	€75000	Route sous la neige (81x100cm-32x39in) s. prov.exhib. 8-Dec-3 Artcurial Briest, Paris #29/R est:60000-80000
£58824	$100000	€85883	Village enneige (73x92cm-29x36in) s. prov. 5-Nov-3 Christie's, Rockefeller NY #359/R est:80000-120000
£63063	$108468	€92072	Flowers in blue vase (73x59cm-29x23in) s. 2-Dec-3 Koller, Zurich #3078/R est:60000-90000 (S.FR 140000)
£70588	$120000	€103058	Village en Provence (54x65cm-21x26in) s.d.1914 prov. 5-Nov-3 Christie's, Rockefeller NY #261/R est:120000-160000
£80986	$141725	€115000	Vins, liqueurs (73x92cm-29x36in) s. prov.exhib. 18-Dec-3 Tajan, Paris #33/R est:120000-150000
£82781	$150662	€125000	Le pont de Chatou (46x58cm-18x23in) s. prov. 18-Jun-4 Piasa, Paris #27/R est:60000-80000
£85000	$154700	€124100	Nature morte au corbeille de fruits (72x92cm-28x36in) s. painted 1918 prov. 3-Feb-4 Christie's, London #155/R est:40000-60000
£94118	$160000	€137412	Toits d'un Village (55x55cm-22x22in) s. prov. 6-Nov-3 Sotheby's, New York #188/R est:90000-120000
£117318	$210000	€171284	Vase de fleurs et fruits (81x65cm-32x26in) s. painted 1910 prov.lit. 6-May-4 Sotheby's, New York #276/R est:80000-120000
£140000	$233800	€204400	Village au pied de la colline (60x73cm-24x29in) s. painted c.1912 prov. 21-Oct-3 Sotheby's, London #42/R est:60000-80000
£140000	$254800	€204400	Le pont a Chatou (39x46cm-15x18in) s. painted c.1907 prov. 3-Feb-4 Christie's, London #171/R est:150000-250000
£150000	$274500	€219000	La Seine a Chatou (73x92cm-29x36in) s. painted 1908 prov.exhib. 2-Feb-4 Christie's, London #26/R est:140000-180000
£150000	$276000	€219000	La Seine a Chatou (59x80cm-23x31in) s. painted 1908 prov.exhib.lit. 23-Jun-4 Christie's, London #153/R est:150000-250000
£284916	$510000	€415977	Vase aux bourgeons (53x44cm-21x17in) s. painted 1907 prov.exhib. 6-May-4 Sotheby's, New York #279/R est:400000-600000
Sculpture			
£3191	$5170	€4500	Fruit bowl with grapes and vines (36x16cm-14x6in) s. polychrome faience. 24-May-3 Martinot & Savignat, Pontoise #139/R est:4500-6000
Works on paper			
£1399	$2406	€2000	Small city street with trees, Valmondois (34x43cm-13x17in) s. pen Indian ink cardboard. 5-Dec-3 Ketterer, Munich #32/R est:6000-8000
£2098	$3608	€3000	Paysanne dans un champ pres d'un village (18x24cm-7x9in) s. Indian ink. 3-Dec-3 Tajan, Paris #35/R est:3000-4000
£2761	$4500	€4031	Bord de la riviere (42x47cm-17x19in) s. W/C pen Indian ink prov. 25-Sep-3 Christie's, Rockefeller NY #504/R est:5000-7000
£3125	$5219	€4500	La route (25x32cm-10x13in) s.i. ink wash india ink prov. 21-Oct-3 Christie's, Paris #78/R est:5000-7000
£3226	$6000	€4710	Les champs (20x34cm-8x13in) s. W/C. 2-Mar-4 Swann Galleries, New York #673/R est:8000-12000
£5070	$8772	€7200	Maison au bord de la riviere (30x36cm-12x14in) s. W/C gouache. 14-Dec-3 Eric Pillon, Calais #126/R
£6667	$12267	€10000	Village road (44x54cm-17x21in) s. gouache W/C. 8-Jun-4 Sotheby's, Amsterdam #63/R est:12000-15000
£6952	$13000	€10150	Rue dan sle village (47x58cm-19x23in) s. W/C brush Indi aink gouache prov. 25-Feb-4 Christie's, Rockefeller NY #42/R est:12000-16000
£6993	$11888	€10000	Landscape (50x64cm-20x25in) s. gouache. 29-Nov-3 Farsetti, Prato #496/R est:10000-15000
£7718	$14279	€11500	Petit chemin borde d'arbres (25x35cm-10x14in) s. W/C gouache lit. 14-Mar-4 Eric Pillon, Calais #105/R
£7746	$13401	€11000	Maisons en bord de chemin (46x55cm-18x22in) s. W/C gouache. 12-Dec-3 Piasa, Paris #125/R est:12000-15000
£8278	$15149	€12500	Le village (45x54cm-18x21in) s. W/C. 9-Apr-4 Claude Aguttes, Neuilly #86/R est:15000-18000
£8333	$13917	€12000	Maisons au bord d'un etang (38x45cm-15x18in) s. W/C gouache pencil prov. 21-Oct-3 Christie's, Paris #77/R est:6000-8000
£8500	$15640	€12410	L'arbre au bord de l'eau (43x54cm-17x21in) s. W/C gouache ink. 24-Mar-4 Sotheby's, Olympia #9/R est:8000-10000
£8824	$15000	€12883	Nature morte (35x57cm-14x22in) s. pen ink prov. 6-Nov-3 Sotheby's, New York #278/R est:12000-18000
£9000	$16380	€13140	Personnages sur une route de village (46x54cm-18x21in) s. W/C gouache brush ink. 4-Feb-4 Sotheby's, London #408/R est:8000-12000
£9000	$16560	€13140	Scene de village (49x59cm-19x23in) s. gouache W/C pen ink exec c.1925 prov. 24-Jun-4 Christie's, London #358/R est:10000-15000
£10000	$18300	€14600	Rue de village (40x31cm-16x12in) s. W/C. 4-Jun-4 Zofingen, Switzerland #2538/R est:20000 (S.FR 23000)
£11765	$22000	€17177	Maisons dans la rue (37x51cm-15x20in) s. gouache W/C over ink paper on board prov. 25-Feb-4 Christie's, Rockefeller NY #53/R est:14000-18000
£12217	$21136	€17837	Village sous la neige (44x53cm-17x21in) gouache prov. 12-Dec-3 Galerie du Rhone, Sion #200/R est:25000-35000 (S.FR 27000)
£12766	$20681	€18000	Les bords de l'Oise (44x60cm-17x24in) s. W/C. 24-May-3 Martinot & Savignat, Pontoise #172/R est:20000-22000
£13514	$25000	€19730	Paysage (46x55cm-18x22in) s. W/C gouache prov. 11-Feb-4 Sotheby's, New York #32/R est:18000-25000
£13986	$24056	€20000	Le perche (44x54cm-17x21in) s. gouache ink prov.exhib. 2-Dec-3 Sotheby's, Amsterdam #91/R est:20000-30000
£14085	$24366	€20000	Arbres au bord d'un sentier (36x44cm-14x17in) s. gouache. 12-Dec-3 Piasa, Paris #17/R est:15000-20000

VLASSELAER, Julien (1907-1982) Belgian

Works on paper			
£442	$791	€650	Le joueur d'harmonica (48x38cm-19x15in) s.d.27 chl. 16-Mar-4 Vanderkindere, Brussels #391

VLECK, Natalie van (1901-1981) American

£257	$475	€375	Tropical landscape (41x51cm-16x20in) s.d.1930. 13-Mar-4 DeFina, Austinburg #918/R
£459	$850	€670	Spring landscape (64x76cm-25x30in) s.d.1929. 13-Mar-4 DeFina, Austinburg #506/R

VLEUGHELS, Nicolas (1668-1737) French

£7047	$13178	€10500	Christ entering Jerusalem (26x20cm-10x8in) init.d.MDCCXVI board. 25-Feb-4 Porro, Milan #47/R est:8500
£7500	$13500	€10950	Artist in his studio (25x32cm-10x13in) init.d.1730 prov. 23-Apr-4 Christie's, Kensington #170/R est:7000-10000

VLIEGENER, Eberhard (?) Belgian?

£1042	$1740	€1500	Moisson et vue sur Soest (53x99cm-21x39in) mono. panel. 21-Oct-3 Campo, Vlaamse Kaai #626 est:1800-2200

VLIEGER, Simon de (1600-1653) Dutch

£36486	$64216	€54000	Estuary scene with a rocky coastline on the left and fishermen on the shore (36x53cm-14x21in) bears sig panel prov. 18-May-4 Sotheby's, Amsterdam #24/R est:50000-70000
Works on paper			
£3243	$5708	€4800	Women and a man. Two boats. Dog scratching. Women and child (16x10cm-6x4in) s. black chk four sheets prov.exhib. 19-May-4 Sotheby's, Amsterdam #64/R est:6000-8000

VLIEGER, Simon de (attrib) (1600-1653) Dutch
Works on paper
£400 $716 €600 Extensive river landscape with figures (11x20cm-4x8in) pen wash. 13-May-4 Bassenge, Berlin #5336/R
£878 $1546 €1300 Wooded river landscape with view of a church in the background (9x20cm-4x8in) bears init. black chk grey wash prov.exhib. 19-May-4 Sotheby's, Amsterdam #56/R

VLIET, Hendrik Cornelisz van der (1611-1675) Dutch
£1810 $2896 €2643 Church interior (28x22cm-11x9in) panel. 19-Sep-3 Koller, Zurich #3035/R est:6000-9000 (S.FR 4000)
£12222 $22000 €17844 Qude kerk in Delft with a grave digger in the foreground (45x36cm-18x14in) s.i.d.1661 prov. 23-Jan-4 Christie's, Rockefeller NY #146/R est:12000-18000

VLIET, Wout van (20th C) Dutch?
£1250 $1975 €1800 Christel (43x28cm-17x11in) mono.d.1974 board prov. 2-Sep-3 Christie's, Amsterdam #452/R est:1000-1500

VLIST, Leendert van der (1894-1962) Dutch
£362 $655 €550 Still life of pottery and tin (34x71cm-13x28in) s. 19-Apr-4 Glerum, Amsterdam #160/R
£789 $1429 €1200 Groenoord in winter (20x29cm-8x11in) canvas on panel prov. 19-Apr-4 Glerum, Amsterdam #239/R
£1135 $1895 €1600 Flower market in Amsterdam with mint tower (40x60cm-16x24in) s. 20-Oct-3 Glerum, Amsterdam #133/R est:700-900
Works on paper
£395 $726 €600 A view in Veere (73x50cm-29x20in) s. W/C htd white. 22-Jun-4 Christie's, Amsterdam #268/R

VOBECKY, Frantisek (1902-) Czechoslovakian
£8317 $13806 €12143 Interior (62x93cm-24x37in) s. 4-Oct-3 Dorotheum, Prague #116/R est:200000-300000 (C.KR 380000)

VOELLMY, Fritz (1863-?) Swiss
£948 $1697 €1384 Village by water (62x99cm-24x39in) s. pastel board. 13-May-4 Stuker, Bern #358 est:800-1200 (S.FR 2200)
£1552 $2778 €2266 Summer evening on Sylt (70x100cm-28x39in) s. pastel board. 13-May-4 Stuker, Bern #357 est:800-1200 (S.FR 3600)
£7328 $13116 €10699 Meadows (43x65cm-17x26in) s. 13-May-4 Stuker, Bern #359 est:600-800 (S.FR 17000)

VOERMAN, Jan (jnr) (1890-1976) Dutch
£1579 $2858 €2400 Apples on a branch (37x22cm-15x9in) s.d.58 canvas on panel. 19-Apr-4 Glerum, Amsterdam #281/R est:1500-2500
£1769 $3219 €2600 Pink roese (19x15cm-7x6in) s.d.64 canvas on cardboard. 3-Feb-4 Christie's, Amsterdam #284/R est:2000-2500
£3147 $5412 €4500 Quince (39x63cm-15x25in) s.d.63. 7-Dec-3 Sotheby's, Amsterdam #682/R

VOERMAN, Jan (snr) (1857-1941) Dutch
£544 $990 €800 Peeling potatoes (20x33cm-8x13in) init. canvas on panel. 3-Feb-4 Christie's, Amsterdam #200
£658 $1191 €1000 View of village canal with boats (28x41cm-11x16in) s. 19-Apr-4 Glerum, Amsterdam #264/R
Works on paper
£6944 $11806 €10000 Cows resting along the banks of the river Ussel (36x52cm-14x20in) init. W/C pastel htd white. 28-Oct-3 Christie's, Amsterdam #164/R est:5000-7000

VOET, Jacob Ferdinand (1639-c.1700) Flemish
£4930 $8627 €7000 Portrait of Vittorio Amedeo II (73x58cm-29x23in) oval. 17-Dec-3 Christie's, Rome #460/R est:7000-10000
£6000 $10980 €8760 Portrait of a gentleman in a black coat and white lace jobot (71x51cm-28x20in) 7-Jul-4 Bonhams, New Bond Street #105/R est:6000-8000
£30385 $52262 €44362 Soror Flavia Viginia - Aetatis Suae XVII (74x61cm-29x24in) s.i. 2-Dec-3 Bukowskis, Stockholm #357/R est:50000-60000 (S.KR 395000)

VOET, Jacob Ferdinand (attrib) (1639-c.1700) Flemish
£4800 $8304 €7008 Portrait of Hortense Mancini, Duchess of Mazarin (73x61cm-29x24in) painted oval. 10-Dec-3 Bonhams, New Bond Street #18/R est:4000-6000

VOET, Jacob Ferdinand (circle) (1639-c.1700) Flemish
£19000 $32870 €27740 Portrait of a gentleman, in a gold embroidered coat (74x61cm-29x24in) 12-Dec-3 Christie's, Kensington #203/R est:6000-8000

VOET, Karel Borchaert (1670-1743) German
£100000 $183000 €146000 Still lives of flowers on marble pedestal (113x86cm-44x34in) pair. 7-Jul-4 Sotheby's, London #13/R est:60000-80000

VOGEL VON VOGELSTEIN, Carl Christian (1788-1868) German
£2041 $3653 €3000 Woman's portrait (77x61cm-30x24in) s.i.d.1862. 17-Mar-4 Neumeister, Munich #649/R est:3500
£2431 $4059 €3500 Woman's portrait - probably Maria van Sachsen (77x61cm-30x24in) s.i.d. 24-Oct-3 Ketterer, Hamburg #117/R est:4000-5000

VOGEL, Bernhard (1961-) Austrian
Works on paper
£940 $1738 €1400 Jerusalem (37x57cm-15x22in) s.d.3/97 W/C. 9-Mar-4 Dorotheum, Vienna #260/R
£1197 $2095 €1700 Thumersbach near Zell am See (38x49cm-15x19in) s.d.93 W/C. 19-Dec-3 Dorotheum, Vienna #386/R est:1000-1300

VOGEL, Christian Leberecht (1759-1816) German
Works on paper
£1399 $2378 €2000 Artist's sons looking at book (25x32cm-10x13in) pencil W/C oval. 27-Nov-3 Bassenge, Berlin #5527/R est:2800

VOGEL, Cornelis Jan de (1824-1879) Flemish
£1299 $2325 €1897 House by river - near Dordrecht (60x80cm-24x31in) s.i. 22-Mar-4 Philippe Schuler, Zurich #4436/R est:4000-5000 (S.FR 3000)

VOGEL, Donald S (1917-) American
£1271 $2300 €1856 Portrait of a young girl with flowers (102x76cm-40x30in) s. 14-Apr-4 Dallas Auction Gallery, Dallas #262/R est:1000-1500

VOGEL, J G (1828-1915) Dutch
£478 $775 €693 Dutch town scene with figures at market (70x80cm-28x31in) s. i.verso. 4-Aug-3 Rasmussen, Vejle #436/R (D.KR 5000)

VOGEL, Leendert de (1910-) Dutch
£292 $461 €420 View of a town with a river (62x82cm-24x32in) s. 5-Sep-3 Wendl, Rudolstadt #3752/R

VOGEL, Nicolaas Cornelis (1787-1871) Dutch
£1500 $2385 €2190 Figures before an inn in a landscape (30x38cm-12x15in) s. panel prov. 9-Sep-3 Bonhams, Knightsbridge #101/R est:1000-1500

VOGEL, Susan Kaiser (20th C) American
Works on paper
£486 $900 €710 Point concepcion bookend (133x123cm-52x48in) pastel chalk blocks plexiglass case exec 1979-80 prov. 12-Feb-4 Sotheby's, New York #301/R

VOGEL, Werner (1889-?) German
£350 $539 €550 Farmstead in the Eifel (30x38cm-12x15in) s. 4-Sep-2 Schopman, Hamburg #116/R

VOGEL, Willy (1910-1987) German
£350 $601 €500 Worpswede farmstead (38x50cm-15x20in) s. panel. 4-Dec-3 Schopman, Hamburg #757/R

VOGEL-JORGENSEN, Age (1888-1964) Danish
£284 $455 €412 Still life of jug (43x38cm-17x15in) init.d.19 panel. 17-Sep-3 Kunsthallen, Copenhagen #231 (D.KR 3000)

VOGELAER, Karel van (style) (1653-1695) Dutch
£6000 $10380 €8760 Still life of roses, carnation and other flowers in an urn on a stone ledge (93x72cm-37x28in) 9-Dec-3 Sotheby's, Olympia #407/R est:3000-4000

VOGELER, Heinrich (1872-1942) German
£6944 $11319 €10000 Two clergymen conversing in Italian Park (16x24cm-6x9in) s.d.1893 panel. 26-Sep-3 Bolland & Marotz, Bremen #399/R est:6500
Works on paper
£667 $1227 €1000 Spring wind (20x18cm-8x7in) mono.i. Indian ink. 10-Jun-4 Hauswedell & Nolte, Hamburg #724/R

VOGELS, Guillaume (1836-1896) Belgian
£340 $609 €500 Village sous la neige (32x28cm-13x11in) s. canvas on panel. 16-Mar-4 Vanderkindere, Brussels #93
£603 $1007 €850 Ruelle animee sous la neige (31x23cm-12x9in) s. canvas on panel. 17-Jun-3 Vanderkindere, Brussels #15
£987 $1786 €1500 Village sous la neige (18x24cm-7x9in) s. panel. 19-Apr-4 Horta, Bruxelles #459 est:800-1000

VOGELSANG, Christian Rudolf (1824-1911) Danish
£302 $541 €441 Boy paddling wearing a rucksack (39x28cm-15x11in) init.d.77. 12-Jan-4 Rasmussen, Vejle #353/R (D.KR 3200)
£421 $682 €610 Fisherman with his dog on the beach (53x68cm-21x27in) s.d.1887. 4-Aug-3 Rasmussen, Vejle #10/R (D.KR 4400)

VOGLER, Hermann (1859-?) German
£274 $466 €400 Watchman (86x70cm-34x28in) s. 8-Nov-3 Geble, Radolfzell #807/R
£789 $1453 €1200 Elegant company (55x47cm-22x19in) s. 28-Jun-4 Sotheby's, Amsterdam #26/R

VOGLER, Paul (1852-1904) French
£294 $509 €429 Paysage enneige au crepuscule (26x42cm-10x17in) s. panel prov. 12-Dec-3 Galerie du Rhone, Sion #99/R (S.FR 650)
£695 $1273 €1050 Seine a Vetheuil (61x73cm-24x29in) s. 7-Apr-4 Piasa, Paris #49
£927 $1697 €1400 Peniche sur la Seine (59x72cm-23x28in) s. 7-Apr-4 Piasa, Paris #48

VOGT, Fritz G (19th C) American
Works on paper
£7059 $12000 €10306 Old homestead of Peter van Wie (53x69cm-21x27in) s. pencil prov. 31-Oct-3 North East Auctions, Portsmouth #1772 est:12000-18000

VOGT, Louis Charles (1864-?) American

Works on paper

£1138 $1900 €1661 South Street at the foot of Wall Street (23x30cm-9x12in) s. W/C. 23-Oct-3 Shannon's, Milford #53/R est:2500-3500

£1189 $2200 €1736 Wet day in Yokohama, Japan (15x23cm-6x9in) s. W/C over pencil exhib. 10-Mar-4 Doyle, New York #52/R

VOGUET, Léon (1879-?) French

£1724 $2879 €2500 Le modele, nu, assis (100x80cm-39x31in) s. 14-Nov-3 Claude Boisgirard, Paris #30/R est:1000-1200

VOIGHT, Harold (1939-) South African

£2586 $4319 €3776 Bushveld fire (52x96cm-20x38in) s.d.76. 20-Oct-3 Stephan Welz, Johannesburg #368/R est:9000-12000 (SA.R 30000)

VOIGT, Bruno (1912-1989) German

£4514 $7538 €6500 Beer improves strength (60x50cm-24x20in) mono.i.d. s.i.d. verso panel. 25-Oct-3 Dr Lehr, Berlin #522/R est:5000

£5867 $10501 €8800 Seduction (100x75cm-39x30in) mono.d. s.i.d. verso masonite. 14-May-4 Ketterer, Munich #86/R est:7500-8500

Works on paper

£933 $1717 €1400 Self portrait (51x35cm-20x14in) mono.d.1934 W/C pen ink over pencil. 12-Jun-4 Villa Grisebach, Berlin #660/R est:700-900

£1300 $2366 €1898 Drei personen auf der strasse (51x36cm-20x14in) mono. pen ink W/C chl. 21-Jun-4 Bonhams, New Bond Street #15/R est:1000-1500

£1400 $2506 €2100 The Fuhrer's birthday (48x36cm-19x14in) mono.d. i. verso W/C Indian ink prov. 14-May-4 Ketterer, Munich #85/R est:1200-1500

VOIGT, David (1944-) Australian

£370 $670 €540 Stratus two (190x152cm-75x60in) s.d.1978 verso acrylic canvas stainless steel. 30-Mar-4 Lawson Menzies, Sydney #93/R est:1000-2000 (A.D 900)

£617 $1117 €901 Solar day (150x180cm-59x71in) s.d.1977 verso exhib. 30-Mar-4 Lawson Menzies, Sydney #92/R est:1000-2000 (A.D 1500)

VOIGT, Franz Wilhelm (1867-?) German

£396 $650 €578 Zeppelin in a hangar with wooden scaffolding (46x56cm-18x22in) s.d.1923 prov. 31-May-3 Brunk, Ashville #222/R

VOIGT, Otto Eduard (19th C) German

Works on paper

£1284 $2259 €1900 Studies of cherry blossoms and roses (40x27cm-16x11in) s. gouache. 22-May-4 Lempertz, Koln #1470/R est:1600

£1284 $2259 €1900 Roses (41x27cm-16x11in) s.d.93 gouache. 22-May-4 Lempertz, Koln #1471/R est:1600

VOILLE, Jean (1744-1796) French

£12000 $21960 €17520 Portrait of lady wearing a blue satin dress (74x59cm-29x23in) s.d.1790. 6-Jul-4 Sotheby's, Olympia #578/R est:3000-5000

VOINESCO, Georges (?) French

Works on paper

£372 $580 €550 Portrait de Paul Leautaud (30x38cm-12x15in) s. crayon dr. 25-Mar-3 Brissoneau, France #93/R

£439 $685 €650 Portrait de Colette (29x39cm-11x15in) s. pastel. 25-Mar-3 Brissoneau, France #94/R

VOINOV, Sviatoslav Vladimirovich (1890-1920) Russian

£14000 $23800 €21000 View of Feropontov Monastery (59x84cm-23x33in) s.d.1918. 25-Nov-3 Christie's, London #216/R est:15000-20000

VOIRIN, Leon-Joseph (1833-1887) French

£2533 $4636 €3800 Bouquet de fleurs (73x59cm-29x23in) s. 6-Jun-4 Osenat, Fontainebleau #77/R est:4000-4500

£2733 $5002 €4100 Bouquet de fleurs (65x54cm-26x21in) s. 6-Jun-4 Osenat, Fontainebleau #76/R est:4000-4500

£8000 $13760 €11680 Promenade en caleche sur les grands boulevards (45x85cm-18x33in) s. 3-Dec-3 Christie's, London #38/R est:10000-15000

VOIRIOT, Guillaume (1713-1799) French

£6713 $11413 €9600 Portrait d'un architecte (101x83cm-40x33in) prov. 1-Dec-3 Rieunier, Paris #9/R est:9000-12000

VOIRIOT, Guillaume (attrib) (1713-1799) French

£2797 $4811 €4000 Portrait de Jean-Jacques Rousseau (53x42cm-21x17in) 8-Dec-3 Cornette de St.Cyr, Paris #51/R est:1500-2000

Works on paper

£23776 $40895 €34000 Un jeune turc assis appuye sur une pierre. Un turc assis portant un turban (55x42cm-22x17in) i. blk white chk grey paper two prov. 2-Dec-3 Christie's, Paris #504/R est:8000-12000

£29371 $50517 €42000 Un guerrier turc barbu tenant un sabre. Un turc portant un turban orne d'un croissant de lune (55x41cm-22x16in) i. blk white chk grey paper two prov. 2-Dec-3 Christie's, Paris #503/R est:8000-12000

VOIS, Arie de (1631-1680) Flemish

£16000 $28800 €23360 Portrait of a gentleman, wearing classical armour (13x10cm-5x4in) mono. copper oval. 22-Apr-4 Sotheby's, London #39/R est:10000-15000

Works on paper

£2027 $3568 €3000 Man in a hat, reading (14x13cm-6x5in) mono. black chk vellum. 19-May-4 Sotheby's, Amsterdam #62/R est:2200-2800

VOISIN, Charles (19th C) French

£2324 $3858 €3300 Les Juifs de l'Est reconnaissants (41x59cm-16x23in) s.d.1878. 13-Jun-3 Renaud, Paris #37/R est:3000-4000

VOIT, Robert (1889-1963) Austrian

£769 $1323 €1100 Bunch of flowers in glass jug (65x80cm-26x31in) s. board. 4-Dec-3 Dorotheum, Graz #43/R

VOKOS, Nicolaos (1861-1902) Greek

£14000 $23800 €20440 Still life with fish and jug (64x91cm-25x36in) s. 18-Nov-3 Sotheby's, London #88/R est:8000-12000

VOLA, Joseph (19th C) Belgian

£748 $1362 €1100 Old watermill (55x80cm-22x31in) s.d.1874. 3-Feb-4 Christie's, Amsterdam #112/R est:1200-1600

VOLAIRE, Pierre Jacques (1729-1802) French

£26000 $44980 €37960 Mediterranean port by moonlight with fishermen pulling in their nets (66x83cm-26x33in) s. prov. 11-Dec-3 Sotheby's, London #37/R est:30000-40000

£40000 $69200 €58400 Mediterranean bay with merchantman unloading and seamen playing cards (65x98cm-26x39in) s. prov. 11-Dec-3 Sotheby's, London #38/R est:30000-40000

£46053 $84737 €70000 Scene de peche. Scene de naufrage (47x67cm-19x26in) s.i.d.1770 pair. 23-Jun-4 Sotheby's, Paris #26/R est:60000-80000

VOLANEK, Raimund (20th C) Austrian

£300 $537 €450 Still life of fruit (46x59cm-18x23in) s. 13-May-4 Dorotheum, Linz #453/R

£559 $934 €800 Le rabbin a l'etude (20x15cm-8x6in) s. panel. 25-Jun-3 Rabourdin & Choppin de Janvry, Paris #89

VOLANG, Jean (1921-) Vietnamese

£1634 $2958 €2386 Dog on chair (100x75cm-39x30in) s.i. canvas on board. 4-Apr-4 Sotheby's, Singapore #91/R est:6000-8000 (S.D 5000)

£2133 $3819 €3200 Party in Hong Kong (90x142cm-35x56in) s. painted c.1948. 17-May-4 Marie & Robert, Paris #61 est:3000-4000

VOLCKAERT, Piet (1902-1973) Belgian

£276 $510 €400 Le depart de la ferme (40x50cm-16x20in) s. 13-Jan-4 Vanderkindere, Brussels #88

£276 $510 €400 Peniche dans la brume (56x71cm-22x28in) s. 16-Feb-4 Horta, Bruxelles #281

£284 $474 €400 Rue de Bruxelles animee (50x60cm-20x24in) s. 14-Oct-3 Vanderkindere, Brussels #112

£317 $548 €450 Chantier a Forest (40x50cm-16x20in) s. 9-Dec-3 Vanderkindere, Brussels #71

£486 $763 €700 Foret (40x30cm-16x12in) s. panel. 26-Aug-3 Galerie Moderne, Brussels #283

£507 $958 €750 Marche animee Place de la Chapelle (32x40cm-13x16in) s. 17-Feb-4 Vanderkindere, Brussels #119

£524 $892 €750 Plage animee (60x70cm-24x28in) s. 18-Nov-3 Vanderkindere, Brussels #176

£699 $1203 €1000 Le carrousel (40x50cm-16x20in) s. 8-Dec-3 Horta, Bruxelles #5

VOLDER, Joost de (attrib) (17th C) Dutch

£4133 $7399 €6200 Wooded landscape with sportsman on a path and figures by a farm (40x55cm-16x22in) panel oval. 17-May-4 Christie's, Amsterdam #8/R est:3000-5000

VOLEA, Joanes (16/17th C) Italian

Works on paper

£3061 $5480 €4500 Place animee (9x13cm-4x5in) s. pen brown ink vellum. 19-Mar-4 Piasa, Paris #21/R est:1500-2000

VOLK, Douglas (1856-1935) American

£2514 $4500 €3670 Children in the dunes (53x71cm-21x28in) s.i.d.1904 canvas on metal sold with two others by the same hand. 26-May-4 Doyle, New York #52/R est:2000-3000

VOLKEL, Reinhold (19/20th C) Austrian

Works on paper

£1103 $1832 €1600 Flower market in square (19x22cm-7x9in) s. w/C. 30-Sep-3 Dorotheum, Vienna #319/R est:1000-1200

VOLKER, Karl (1889-1962) German

£36913 $66074 €55000 The yellow mask (113x77cm-44x30in) mono. board lit.exhib. 25-May-4 Karl & Faber, Munich #566/R est:70000-80000

Works on paper

£467 $840 €700 Children with cat (43x34cm-17x13in) s.d. Indian ink brush pen. 24-Apr-4 Dr Lehr, Berlin #483/R

VOLKER, Wilhelm (19th C) Swiss

£413 $756 €603 The river fairy (33x24cm-13x9in) s.d.1856 panel. 4-Jun-4 Zofingen, Switzerland #2370 (S.FR 950)

VOLKERS, Emil (1831-1905) German

£560 $1046 €818 Portrait of a horse (24x32cm-9x13in) s.d.1902 panel. 25-Feb-4 Kunsthallen, Copenhagen #544 (D.KR 6200)

£704 $1218 €1000 Saddled brown horse (24x32cm-9x13in) s.d.1899. 11-Dec-3 Dr Fritz Nagel, Stuttgart #553/R
£851 $1379 €1200 Horse drawn sleigh in snowy winter landscape (25x36cm-10x14in) s. lit. 23-May-3 Karlheinz Kaupp, Staufen #1939
£1399 $2378 €2000 La charge de la cavalerie lors de la guerre de 1870 (36x65cm-14x26in) s. oil paper. 18-Nov-3 Vanderkindere, Brussels #62 est:1200-1800
£1736 $2726 €2500 Horse portrait (40x51cm-16x20in) s.d.1895 lit. 30-Aug-3 Hans Stahl, Toestorf #31/R est:2600
£1793 $3317 €2600 Horse portrait (23x32cm-9x13in) s.d.1894 panel. 14-Feb-4 Hans Stahl, Hamburg #105/R est:2000
£1824 $3266 €2700 Brown horse in stable (44x59cm-17x23in) s.d.Sept.1860 lit. 8-May-4 Schloss Ahlden, Ahlden #740/R est:2900
£2095 $3749 €3100 Brown horse in field (45x55cm-18x22in) s.d.1856 lit. 8-May-4 Schloss Ahlden, Ahlden #739/R est:3500
£2200 $3982 €3300 Horse portrait (23x32cm-9x13in) s.d.1902 panel. 3-Apr-4 Hans Stahl, Hamburg #120/R est:2200
£3700 $6179 €5402 Runaway carriage (51x100cm-20x39in) s.d.74. 12-Nov-3 Sotheby's, Olympia #148/R est:2500-3500
£5461 $9120 €7700 Horse portraits (24x32cm-9x13in) s. d.97 98 panel pair. 21-Jun-3 Hans Stahl, Hamburg #32/R est:7500

VOLKERS, Karl (1868-1944) German
£753 $1281 €1100 Black horse in landscape (34x45cm-13x18in) s. lit. 6-Nov-3 Allgauer, Kempten #3630/R est:900
£1259 $2140 €1800 Racehorse (60x72cm-24x28in) s.d.1894. 20-Nov-3 Van Ham, Cologne #1900/R est:1400

VOLKERT, Edward Charles (1871-1935) American
£2746 $4750 €4009 Oxen and a haywagon by a barn with man bailing hay (23x30cm-9x12in) s. board prov. 10-Dec-3 Bonhams & Butterfields, San Francisco #6028/R est:3000-5000
Works on paper
£449 $750 €656 Passing on the country lane (23x30cm-9x12in) s. gouache. 19-Oct-3 William Jenack, New York #366

VOLKHART, Max (1848-1935) German
£2200 $4048 €3212 His master's voice (57x39cm-22x15in) s.d.07. 25-Mar-4 Christie's, Kensington #193/R est:2000-3000

VOLKHART, Wilhelm (1815-1876) German
£473 $818 €691 Portrait of gentleman, possibly Henrik Rung (32x27cm-13x11in) s.indis.d. 9-Dec-3 Rasmussen, Copenhagen #1380/R (D.KR 5000)

VOLKMANN, Hans Richard von (1860-1927) German
£500 $830 €725 Spring landscape (53x71cm-21x28in) s. prov. 13-Jun-3 Zofingen, Switzerland #2539/R (S.FR 1100)
£738 $1373 €1100 Evening landscape with path leading up into the woods (44x63cm-17x25in) mono.d.1900 i.verso canvas on board. 5-Mar-4 Wendl, Rudolstadt #4002/R
£833 $1317 €1200 Hilly landscape (33x54cm-13x21in) s.d.1923 canvas on board. 5-Sep-3 Wendl, Rudolstadt #3754/R
£839 $1443 €1200 Early summer landscape (52x41cm-20x16in) s.d.1887 s.i. verso. 8-Dec-3 Bloss, Merzhausen #827/R
£845 $1462 €1200 Eifel Landscape (52x64cm-20x25in) s. 12-Dec-3 Berlinghof, Heidelberg #1146/R est:1300
£1067 $1941 €1600 View across the fields towards a town (55x75cm-22x30in) s.d.1919. 1-Jul-4 Van Ham, Cologne #1652 est:800
£1410 $2396 €2059 Summer landscape with trees (90x150cm-35x59in) s.d.1910. 5-Nov-3 Dobiaschofsky, Bern #1034/R est:5000 (S.FR 3200)
£2083 $3437 €3000 Summer landscape (55x75cm-22x30in) s.d.1923. 5-Jul-3 Geble, Radolfzell #489/R est:2800
Works on paper
£451 $713 €650 Hilly summer landscape (40x56cm-16x22in) mono.d.1907 W/C. 5-Sep-3 Wendl, Rudolstadt #3755/R
£470 $874 €700 Summer landscape with a village in the distance (29x43cm-11x17in) mono.d.1923 W/C. 5-Mar-4 Wendl, Rudolstadt #4003/R
£590 $933 €850 Pesant woman on field track (19x27cm-7x11in) s.d.92 W/C lit. 19-Sep-3 Schloss Ahlden, Ahlden #1500/R

VOLKMAR, Charles (1841-1914) American
£1389 $2500 €2028 Cattle watering (41x76cm-16x30in) s.d.72. 24-Apr-4 Weschler, Washington #625/R est:1000-1500

VOLKOV, Alexandre (1886-1957) Russian
£1296 $2085 €1892 Memory of St Petersburg (94x64cm-37x25in) s. verso oil on glass. 20-Aug-3 James Julia, Fairfield #1211/R est:2000-4000
£1517 $2534 €2200 Abstract composition (62x48cm-24x19in) s. Cyrillic d.1920. 13-Nov-3 Neumeister, Munich #444/R est:2000-2500

VOLKOV, Efim Efimovich (1844-1920) Russian
£1399 $2406 €2000 Evening landscape with water (32x23cm-13x9in) s.d.87. 5-Dec-3 Michael Zeller, Lindau #824/R est:850
£4336 $7371 €6200 Mountain landscape (34x51cm-13x20in) s. 29-Nov-3 Bukowskis, Helsinki #406/R est:1500-1800

VOLL, Christoph (1897-1939) German
Sculpture
£1264 $2325 €1845 Zu Pferde mit Schwierigkeit (25cm-10in) s. pat.bronze. 29-Mar-4 Rasmussen, Copenhagen #476/R est:20000 (D.KR 14000)
£1354 $2491 €1977 Madchenakt (46cm-18in) s. green pat.bronze ex.1926 lit. 29-Mar-4 Rasmussen, Copenhagen #477/R est:15000-20000 (D.KR 15000)

VOLLAK, Alexander (?) German?
£267 $485 €400 Hunting (70x80cm-28x31in) s. 1-Jul-4 Weidler, Nurnberg #6540

VOLLERDT, Johann Christian (1708-1769) German
£2395 $4000 €3497 Travellers in an extensive river landscape with castle (29x38cm-11x15in) panel. 7-Oct-3 Sotheby's, New York #65/R est:6000-8000
£2500 $4475 €3650 Figures in a classical capriccio landscape (13x20cm-5x8in) s. panel pair. 22-Mar-4 Bonhams & Brooks, Norfolk #281/R est:3000-5000
£3125 $5094 €4500 Peasants resting by classical ruins (23x28cm-9x11in) s. panel. 24-Sep-3 Neumeister, Munich #375/R est:4500
£5760 $9965 €8410 Landscape with travelers on a road near a village. s.d.1764. 9-Dec-3 Sotheby's, Olympia #439/R est:3000-5000
£6250 $10313 €9000 Italian landscape with hunters (49x61cm-19x24in) one of pair. 3-Jul-3 Dr Fritz Nagel, Stuttgart #469/R est:3000
£6250 $10313 €9000 Landscape with waterfall (49x61cm-19x24in) one of pair. 3-Jul-3 Dr Fritz Nagel, Stuttgart #470/R est:3000
£8333 $15000 €12166 Mountainous winter landscape with hunters in the foreground (22x28cm-9x11in) copper. 23-Jan-4 Christie's, Rockefeller NY #140/R est:20000-30000
£8389 $15436 €12500 Extensive wooded river landscape (62x77cm-24x30in) 24-Mar-4 Dorotheum, Vienna #263/R est:13000-16000
£8966 $14883 €13000 Winter landscape with skaters on frozen lake (40x58cm-16x23in) s.d.1762. 1-Oct-3 Dorotheum, Vienna #249/R est:15000-18000
£13636 $23182 €19500 Ideal Rhine landscape (61x76cm-24x30in) s.d.1755. 20-Nov-3 Van Ham, Cologne #1434/R est:10000
£30000 $54900 €43800 Rhenish landscape (27x38cm-11x15in) two s.d.1757 panel set of four. 7-Jul-4 Bonhams, New Bond Street #95/R est:25000-35000

VOLLERDT, Johann Christian (attrib) (1708-1769) German
£4636 $8437 €7000 River landscape with castle and travellers (29x39cm-11x15in) indis.sig.d.1756 panel. 16-Jun-4 Dorotheum, Vienna #168/R est:7000-10000

VOLLET, Henri Émile (1861-1945) French
£306 $548 €450 Pecheur breton isole sur un rocher au milieu d'un aber (47x61cm-19x24in) s. board. 21-Mar-4 Muizon & Le Coent, Paris #48
£324 $531 €450 Still life with apples (31x40cm-12x16in) s. card. 10-Jun-3 Pandolfini, Florence #252
£442 $791 €650 Lavandieres bretonnes au bord d'une riviere (46x55cm-18x22in) s. board. 21-Mar-4 Muizon & Le Coent, Paris #47
£719 $1180 €1000 Femme Bretonne de Pont Aven devant une chaumiere (33x46cm-13x18in) s. 3-Jun-3 Livinec, Gaudcheau & Jezequel, Rennes #65/R
£733 $1313 €1100 Lavandieres a Quimperle au bord de l'Ellee (46x55cm-18x22in) s. panel. 16-May-4 Thierry & Lannon, Brest #194/R
£1950 $3257 €2847 Breton port (44x53cm-17x21in) s. board. 14-Oct-3 Bearnes, Exeter #314/R est:400-600
£4558 $8159 €6700 Envol des colombes (38x55cm-15x22in) s.i.d.1903 panel. 21-Mar-4 St-Germain-en-Laye Encheres #133/R est:6000-6500

VOLLET, Jean (20th C) French
£355 $574 €500 Paysage en bord de riviere (60x81cm-24x32in) 24-May-3 Martinot & Savignat, Pontoise #167

VOLLEVENS, Johannes (17/18th C) Dutch
Works on paper
£616 $1048 €900 Study of a young woman as Diana (24x21cm-9x8in) black white chk. 4-Nov-3 Sotheby's, Amsterdam #155/R

VOLLEVENS, Johannes (elder) (1649-1728) Dutch
£5333 $9547 €8000 Portrait of Councilor Casper Fagel (68x53cm-27x21in) prov. 17-May-4 Glerum, Amsterdam #42/R est:6000-8000

VOLLMAR, Ludwig (1842-1884) German
£521 $870 €750 Interior with rococco couple playing music (25x20cm-10x8in) s. panel lit. 25-Oct-3 Bergmann, Erlangen #954/R

VOLLMBERG, Max (1882-?) German
£417 $679 €600 Outdoor singing (90x114cm-35x45in) s.d.1910 s.d.08 verso double-sided. 24-Sep-3 Neumeister, Munich #593/R

VOLLON, Alexis (1865-1945) French
£6000 $11040 €8760 Le Pont des Arcs, Paris (61x72cm-24x28in) s. 25-Mar-4 Christie's, Kensington #35/R est:6000-8000
Works on paper
£1733 $3120 €2600 Harbour of Dunkerque (31x47cm-12x19in) s. indis i. black chk htd white. 20-Apr-4 Sotheby's, Amsterdam #94/R est:3000-5000

VOLLON, Alexis (attrib) (1865-1945) French
£1974 $3632 €3000 Seine with Notre Dame in Paris (28x36cm-11x14in) s. 24-Jun-4 Dr Fritz Nagel, Stuttgart #771/R est:3800

VOLLON, Antoine (1833-1900) French
£226 $355 €330 Nature morte aux huitres et aux crevettes (20x26cm-8x10in) s. 26-Aug-3 Iegor de Saint Hippolyte, Montreal #150 (C.D 500)
£596 $1085 €900 Still life with jug and pearl necklace (25x33cm-10x13in) s. 16-Jun-4 Hugo Ruef, Munich #1104
£1268 $2104 €1800 Ferme au grand chene (57x71cm-22x28in) s. lit. 15-Jun-3 Peron, Melun #104a
£1324 $2250 €1933 Still life with mussels, a jug and a glass of wine (56x47cm-22x19in) s. 19-Nov-3 Bonhams & Butterfields, San Francisco #114/R
£1774 $3175 €2590 Still life of fruit (55x70cm-22x28in) s. 25-May-4 Bukowskis, Stockholm #382/R est:20000-25000 (S.KR 24000)
£2400 $4440 €3504 Chickens and ducks feeding (112x168cm-44x66in) s. 10-Mar-4 Sotheby's, Olympia #277/R est:2000-3000
£3000 $5550 €4380 Still life of plums with a pewter, jug and glass (61x75cm-24x30in) s. 10-Mar-4 Sotheby's, Olympia #290/R est:2000-3000
£3571 $6500 €5214 Still life with peaches, grapes and pitcher (66x79cm-26x31in) s. prov. 29-Jun-4 Sotheby's, New York #97/R est:5000-7000
£4348 $7000 €6348 Still life with grapes, peaches and a brass kettle (54x65cm-21x26in) s. 14-Jan-4 Christie's, Rockefeller NY #20/R est:7000-9000
£4348 $7000 €6348 Still life with grapes, pears and a brass pot (54x65cm-21x26in) s. 14-Jan-4 Christie's, Rockefeller NY #22/R est:7000-9000

Works on paper

£352	$585	€500	Arbres le soir (6x11cm-2x4in) mono. pastel dr htd W/C. 15-Jun-3 Peron, Melun #46
£387	$643	€550	Promenade en sous-bois (13x9cm-5x4in) mono. chl dr. 15-Jun-3 Peron, Melun #27
£423	$701	€600	Etude de pied (11x8cm-4x3in) mono. chl dr htd W/C. 15-Jun-3 Peron, Melun #44
£493	$818	€700	Deux vaches (6x11cm-2x4in) s. chl W/C. 15-Jun-3 Peron, Melun #15
£634	$1052	€900	Petit ane (16x18cm-6x7in) st.sig. wax crayon pastel htd gouache. 15-Jun-3 Peron, Melun #30
£704	$1169	€1000	Hameau (15x20cm-6x8in) sts.ig. chl pastel W/C. 15-Jun-3 Peron, Melun #43
£845	$1403	€1200	Cheval attele (7x11cm-3x4in) s. chl W/C dr. 15-Jun-3 Peron, Melun #22
£845	$1403	€1200	Paysanne au panier (1x7cm-0x3in) s. W/C dr. 15-Jun-3 Peron, Melun #23
£845	$1403	€1200	Vaches au pre (12x21cm-5x8in) st.sig. pastel W/C gouache dr. 15-Jun-3 Peron, Melun #25

VOLLON, Antoine (attrib) (1833-1900) French

£267	$485	€400	Still life with carafe and book (47x38cm-19x15in) 1-Jul-4 Neumeister, Munich #2942

VOLLWEIDER, Johann Jakob (1834-1891) German

£297	$550	€434	Alpine scene (30x41cm-12x16in) s. board. 18-Jul-4 William Jenack, New York #318

VOLMAR, Georg (1770-1831) German

£1733	$3172	€2600	Arcadian landscape (45x56cm-18x22in) s. 5-Jun-4 Arnold, Frankfurt #786/R est:800

VOLMAR, Georg (attrib) (1770-1831) German

£262	$477	€383	River landscape with wooden bridge (24x32cm-9x13in) panel. 16-Jun-4 Fischer, Luzern #2419/R (S.FR 600)

VOLMAR, Joseph Simon (1796-1865) Swiss

£571	$914	€828	Deer in wood (36x28cm-14x11in) s.d.182. 15-May-3 Stuker, Bern #1569 (S.FR 1200)
Works on paper			
£667	$1193	€1000	Chevaux (18x23cm-7x9in) s. wash. 16-May-4 Feletin, Province #114

VOLMAR, Theodor (1847-?) Swiss

£1638	$2932	€2391	Officers on Ostermundigenberg (108x72cm-43x28in) s. 14-May-4 Dobiaschofsky, Bern #35/R est:4000 (S.FR 3800)

VOLMER, Robert (1951-) Dutch

£313	$494	€450	Countryside 2 (40x40cm-16x16in) s.d.2001. 26-Apr-3 Auction Maastricht #159/R

VOLOCHINE, Maximilien (1877-1932) ?

Works on paper			
£3800	$6460	€5700	Landscapes (18x26cm-7x10in) one s.d.1918 one mono.d.12 W/C pair. 25-Nov-3 Christie's, London #223/R est:1500-2500

VOLPATO, Giovanni (1733-1803) Italian

Works on paper			
£3022	$4955	€4200	Veduta del Sepolcro di Cecilia Metella (37x53cm-15x21in) s.i. W/C Indian ink gouache. 4-Jun-3 Ketterer, Hamburg #109/R est:4000-5000
£10563	$18486	€15000	Vue des salles du Vatican (52x73cm-20x29in) s.i. W/C wash over engraving. 16-Dec-3 Christie's, Paris #273/R est:5000-7000

VOLPE, Alessandro la (1820-1887) Italian

£3057	$5563	€4463	View of Capri (44x71cm-17x28in) s. 16-Jun-4 Fischer, Luzern #1110/R est:8000-12000 (S.FR 7000)
£5556	$9444	€8000	View of Pompei (113x67cm-44x26in) s.d.1864. 29-Oct-3 Il Ponte, Milan #530/R
£7639	$12986	€11000	View on Palazzo d'Anna and the bay of Naples, the Vesuvius in the distance (44x73cm-17x29in) s.d.85. 28-Oct-3 Christie's, Amsterdam #26/R est:4000-6000
£17000	$30600	€24820	View over the Bay of Naples towards Vesuvius (79x119cm-31x47in) s. 21-Jan-4 Sotheby's, Olympia #420/R est:8000-12000
Works on paper			
£1528	$2490	€2200	Italian street scene (27x20cm-11x8in) s. W/C over pencil. 25-Sep-3 Dr Fritz Nagel, Stuttgart #1175/R est:2500

VOLPE, Angiolo (1943-) Italian

£310	$518	€450	Still life with seafood (50x60cm-20x24in) s. on canvas on cardboard. 14-Nov-3 Farsetti, Prato #424

VOLPE, Tommaso della (1883-1967) Italian

£1379	$2290	€2000	Vase with dahlias (95x105cm-37x41in) s.d.28. 1-Oct-3 Della Rocca, Turin #101/R est:2000-2500

VOLPE, Vincenzo (1855-1929) Italian

£1408	$2437	€2000	Lady in interior (81x54cm-32x21in) s. 11-Dec-3 Christie's, Rome #115/R est:2500-4000
£1700	$2720	€2465	Ritratto di una donna (89x58cm-35x23in) s. 18-Sep-3 Christie's, Kensington #67/R est:1200-1800

VOLPI, Alfredo (1896-1988) Brazilian

£6593	$11670	€9890	Abstract with flags (33x24cm-13x9in) s.verso tempera. 27-Apr-4 Bolsa de Arte, Rio de Janeiro #109/R (B.R 36000)
£10623	$18802	€15935	Composition with circular shapes (24x48cm-9x19in) s.verso tempera. 27-Apr-4 Bolsa de Arte, Rio de Janeiro #108/R (B.R 58000)
£12912	$23629	€19368	Abstract (72x36cm-28x14in) s.verso tempera. 6-Jul-4 Bolsa de Arte, Rio de Janeiro #167/R (B.R 70500)

VOLPINI, Renato (1934-) Italian

£805	$1442	€1200	Untitled (72x99cm-28x39in) s.d.60. 25-May-4 Sotheby's, Milan #107

VOLSCHENK, Jan E A (1853-1936) South African

£314	$562	€458	Rocks and sea, Riversdale coast (18x32cm-7x13in) s.d.1922 s.i.d. verso. 31-May-4 Stephan Welz, Johannesburg #246 (SA.R 3800)
£437	$791	€638	Ghwarriebome in die Klein Karroo (16x31cm-6x12in) s. i.verso canvasboard. 30-Mar-4 Stephan Welz, Johannesburg #464 est:4000-6000 (SA.R 5200)
£726	$1235	€1060	Where peace reigns at eventide (22x33cm-9x13in) s.d.1926 s.i.d.verso. 4-Nov-3 Stephan Welz, Johannesburg #607 est:5000-8000 (SA.R 8500)
£784	$1404	€1145	Bywoners dwelling (18x33cm-7x13in) s.d.1911 s.i.d.verso. 31-May-4 Stephan Welz, Johannesburg #140 (SA.R 9500)
£850	$1505	€1241	Mountains in Traduow's Pass, Swellendam (53x71cm-21x28in) s.d.1918 verso. 27-Apr-4 Bonhams, New Bond Street #94/R
£1404	$2513	€2050	Mountain peak, Riversdale (21x23cm-8x9in) s.d.1918 s.i.d. verso. 31-May-4 Stephan Welz, Johannesburg #533/R est:7000-10000 (SA.R 17000)
£2521	$4563	€3681	Mountains in morning light, Swellendam (45x99cm-18x39in) s.d.1918 s.i.d.verso. 30-Mar-4 Stephan Welz, Johannesburg #459/R est:20000-30000 (SA.R 30000)

VOLTEN, Andre (1925-2002) Dutch

£3892	$6500	€5682	Composition nr 7 (101x131cm-40x52in) s. i.d.1955 verso. 7-Oct-3 Sotheby's, New York #319 est:500-700
Sculpture			
£5333	$9813	€8000	Composition (72x150x36cm-28x59x14in) welded iron blk pat. exec. c.1960-62 unique prov. 9-Jun-4 Christie's, Amsterdam #297/R est:3000-5000

VOLTI (1915-1990) French

Works on paper			
£629	$1070	€900	Modele allonge (44x56cm-17x22in) s.d.1959 graphite. 18-Nov-3 Pierre Berge, Paris #54/R

VOLTI, Antoniucci (1915-1990) French

Sculpture			
£2118	$3600	€3092	Femme mue accroupie (13x23cm-5x9in) i. brown black pat. bronze prov. 22-Nov-3 Jackson's, Cedar Falls #383/R est:5000-7500
£2649	$4954	€4000	Victoire (14cm-6in) num.6/8 brown pat. bronze Cast Godard. 24-Jul-4 Thierry & Lannon, Brest #25/R est:4000-6000
£2667	$4827	€4000	Belle indonesienne (58x17x23cm-23x7x9in) s. num.2/2 sandstone. 1-Apr-4 Credit Municipal, Paris #106/R est:3000-3500
£2797	$4671	€4000	Victoire (14cm-6in) s.d.1988 num.6/8 prov. 7-Oct-3 Livinec, Gaudcheau & Jezequel, Rennes #165/R
£3423	$6298	€5100	Femma assise penchee (16x13x12cm-6x5x5in) s. num.8/8 blk pat bronze Cast f.Susse Paris. 29-Mar-4 Lombrail & Teucquam, Paris #86/R
£3490	$6421	€5200	Femma assise a demi couchee (20x15x22cm-8x6x9in) s.base num.7/8 blk pat bronze. 29-Mar-4 Lombrail & Teucquam, Paris #85/R
£3636	$6182	€5200	Femme allongee (29x17cm-11x7in) s. terracotta. 28-Nov-3 Drouot Estimations, Paris #207/R est:3000-3500
£3667	$6637	€5500	Nu assis sur ses talons (28x17x9cm-11x7x4in) s. num.1/6 green pat bronze st.f.Godard. 1-Apr-4 Credit Municipal, Paris #107 est:2500-3000
£3706	$6301	€5300	Femme assise penchee (16x13x12cm-6x5x5in) s.st.f.Susse num.8/8 pat bronze. 21-Nov-3 Lombrail & Teucquam, Paris #86/R
£3893	$6968	€5800	Nu assis (23x26cm-9x10in) s. num.1/8 terracotta. 30-May-4 Eric Pillon, Calais #62/R
£4133	$7481	€6200	Souvenir (39x29x20cm-15x11x8in) s. num.3/3 terracotta prov. 1-Apr-4 Credit Municipal, Paris #103/R est:2500-3000
£4267	$7723	€6400	Bonheur (37x11x6cm-15x4x2in) s. num.0/6 green pat bronze Cast Capelli. 1-Apr-4 Credit Municipal, Paris #104 est:3000-4000
£4306	$7190	€6200	Les deux Muses (36x20x4cm-14x8x2in) brown pat bronze marble socle Cast Godard. 23-Oct-3 Credit Municipal, Paris #117/R est:2500-3500
£4336	$7371	€6200	Femme assise (20x15x22cm-8x6x9in) s.st.f.Godard num.7/8 pat bronze. 21-Nov-3 Lombrail & Teucquam, Paris #85/R est:6000-7000
£4577	$7919	€6500	Femme assise (19cm-7in) s. terracotta. 14-Dec-3 Eric Pillon, Calais #178/R
£4667	$8447	€7000	Nu allonge sur le cote (7x18x9cm-3x7x4in) s. num.3/3 terracotta prov. 1-Apr-4 Credit Municipal, Paris #102 est:800-1000
£4667	$8447	€7000	Nu assis (26x16x17cm-10x6x7in) s. num.1/6 green pat bronze st.f.Susse. 1-Apr-4 Credit Municipal, Paris #108/R est:3000-3500
£5986	$10356	€8500	Jeune femme, un bras replie dans le dos (55cm-22in) s. num.5/8 black pat bronze cire perdue. 14-Dec-3 Rabourdin & Choppin de Janvry, Paris #59/R est:9000-10000
£6533	$11695	€9800	Nu de face reposant sur le dos (27x40cm-11x16in) s. terracotta. 16-May-4 Thierry & Lannon, Brest #21 est:10000-12000
£7000	$12670	€10500	Modele assis (19x16x12cm-7x6x5in) s. num.2/6 blk pat bronze st.f.Susses Freres. 1-Apr-4 Credit Municipal, Paris #105 est:2500-3000
£7042	$11338	€10000	Litchie (63x22x13cm-25x9x5in) s. num.1/6 pat bronze Cast Susse. 22-Aug-3 Deauville, France #100/R est:15000-18000
£7343	$12483	€10500	Seated woman (21cm-8in) s. num.HC 1/2 blue blk pat bronze Cast Delval. 1-Dec-3 Camard, Paris #100/R est:9000-10000
£9790	$16643	€14000	Nu allonge, accoude (25x60cm-10x24in) s. terracotta pat. 28-Nov-3 Blanchet, Paris #159/R est:10000-12000
£9912	$16850	€14472	Crouching bather (25x45cm-10x18in) s. num.5/6 Cast.Valsuani-Bacneux. 5-Nov-3 Dobiaschofsky, Bern #2469/R est:16000 (S.FR 22500)
£10490	$17517	€15000	Circee (44cm-17in) s. num.2/8 blue pat bronze Cast Delval. 25-Jun-3 Blanchet, Paris #68/R est:20000
£11189	$19021	€16000	Femme assise (31cm-12in) s.st.f.Clementi pat bronze. 18-Nov-3 Sotheby's, Paris #120/R est:15000-20000
£11739	$21483	€17139	Nu incline (20x50x30cm-8x20x12in) s. num.6/6 brown black green pat bronze prov. 5-Jun-4 Galerie du Rhone, Sion #572/R est:10000-15000 (S.FR 27000)
£14085	$22676	€20000	Carleen (47x23x40cm-19x9x16in) s. num.1/4 pat bronze Cast Susse. 22-Aug-3 Deauville, France #107/R est:25000-30000

£15493 $27113 €22000 Nue enroulee sur elle-meme (27x47cm-11x19in) varnished terracotta. 21-Dec-3 Thierry & Lannon, Brest #45/R est:20000-23000
£20775 $33447 €29500 Anita (55x52x32cm-22x20x13in) s. num.1/4 pat bronze Cast Susse lit. 22-Aug-3 Deauville, France #98/R est:30000-40000
£26389 $43014 €38000 Recueillement (50x50x47cm-20x20x19in) blue pat bronze Cast Godard. 21-Jul-3 Lesieur & Le Bars, Le Havre #65

Works on paper
£346 $629 €505 Untitled - nude (65x49cm-26x19in) s. i.d.1977 verso sanguine dr. prov. 1-Jul-4 Heffel, Vancouver #33/R (C.D 850)
£694 $1160 €1000 Nu accroupi (31x23cm-12x9in) s. sanguine. 23-Oct-3 Credit Municipal, Paris #51
£1092 $1987 €1594 Nu assis de dos (65x50cm-26x20in) s. red chk. 16-Jun-4 Fischer, Luzern #2681/R est:2500-3500 (S.FR 2500)
£1408 $2437 €2000 Nu allonge (46x62cm-18x24in) s. sanguine. 14-Dec-3 Rabourdin & Choppin de Janvry, Paris #61/R est:2000-2500
£1444 $2498 €2050 Nu allonge sur le dos (47x63cm-19x25in) s. sanguine. 14-Dec-3 Eric Pillon, Calais #183/R
£2113 $3655 €3000 Nu assis de dos (53x40cm-21x16in) s. sanguine. 14-Dec-3 Eric Pillon, Calais #177/R
£3380 $5848 €4800 Nu assis de dos (63x49cm-25x19in) s. sanguine. 14-Dec-3 Eric Pillon, Calais #180/R

VOLTZ, Friedrich (1817-1886) German
£347 $566 €500 Cow and calves (26x36cm-10x14in) s.d.3/37 board. 25-Sep-3 Dr Fritz Nagel, Stuttgart #1431/R
£510 $913 €750 Three deer in barn (13x18cm-5x7in) s. panel. 18-Mar-4 Neumeister, Munich #2790/R
£655 $1192 €956 Standing cow (30x43cm-12x17in) mono. canvas on cardboard. 16-Jun-4 Fischer, Luzern #2421/R (S.FR 1500)
£1385 $2548 €2078 Landscape with sheep (29x38cm-11x15in) s. panel. 14-Jun-4 Lilla Bukowskis, Stockholm #341/R est:15000-18000 (S.KR 19000)
£1987 $3616 €3000 Cows at the water's edge (34x71cm-13x28in) s. panel. 16-Jun-4 Hugo Ruef, Munich #1105/R est:2000
£3378 $5946 €5000 Cattle in meadow (47x42cm-19x17in) s. 21-May-4 Mehlis, Plauen #15195/R est:5000
£3819 $6302 €5500 Cows in alpine pasture (47x51cm-19x20in) s.d.1842. 2-Jul-3 Neumeister, Munich #810/R est:3500
£4367 $7948 €6376 Cows on the edge of Lake Starnberg, near Bernried (21x45cm-8x18in) s.d.1890 panel. 16-Jun-4 Fischer, Luzern #1209/R est:8000-10000 (S.FR 10000)
£11333 $20400 €17000 Returning home from hay harvest (73x60cm-29x24in) s.d.1889 canvas on panel lit. 22-Apr-4 Allgauer, Kempten #3755/R est:15000

Works on paper
£317 $567 €450 Bringing the cattle down from the mountain pastures (85x73cm-33x29in) s.d.12/42 mixed media paper on board. 8-Jan-4 Allgauer, Kempten #2295/R
£336 $617 €500 Torbole - Lake Garda (34x43cm-13x17in) i.d.8/9 pencil. 26-Mar-4 Venator & Hansten, Koln #1660
£1127 $1949 €1600 Girl with cattle at ford (22x23cm-9x9in) s.d.1865 pencil. 13-Dec-3 Lempertz, Koln #61/R est:800

VOLTZ, Ludwig (1825-1911) German
£268 $494 €400 Deer in forest clearing (92x75cm-36x30in) s. 24-Mar-4 Hugo Ruef, Munich #1139
£367 $667 €550 Fallow deer at the lakeside (2x51cm-1x20in) s. panel. 1-Jul-4 Van Ham, Cologne #1653
£1533 $2760 €2300 Fox killing duck (73x60cm-29x24in) s. lit. 22-Apr-4 Allgauer, Kempten #3756/R est:1100
£3357 $5706 €4800 Arabian horse (56x69cm-22x27in) s. 20-Nov-3 Van Ham, Cologne #1902/R est:4000

VOLTZ, Ludwig (attrib) (1825-1911) German
£272 $487 €400 Landscape (9x23cm-4x9in) i.d.1895 verso panel. 18-Mar-4 Neumeister, Munich #2792/R

VOLZ, Herman (1904-1990) American
£1406 $2250 €2053 Portrait of John Wilson (310x231cm-122x91in) s. i.d.1935 verso plywood. 18-May-3 Auctions by the Bay, Alameda #1160/R

VOLZ, Hermann (1814-1894) German
£903 $1490 €1300 Travelling sculptor in tavern (43x36cm-17x14in) s.d.1884. 3-Jul-3 Van Ham, Cologne #1492

VOLZ, Wolfgang (1948-) German
Photographs
£2754 $4516 €3800 Wrapped Reichstage, Berlin (80x100cm-31x39in) s.i. col photo. 30-May-3 Villa Grisebach, Berlin #1394/R est:1500-2000
£2754 $4516 €3800 Wrapped Reichstage, Berlin (80x100cm-31x39in) s.i. col photo. 30-May-3 Villa Grisebach, Berlin #1395/R est:1500-2000

VONCK, Jacobus (?-1773) Dutch
£20548 $34932 €30000 Still lifes with vase, birds, flowers, urn, shells and fruit (85x68cm-33x27in) s.d.1760 pair prov.exhib.lit. 4-Nov-3 Sotheby's, Amsterdam #98/R est:25000-35000

VONLANTHEN, Louis (1889-1937) Swiss
£374 $637 €546 Peacock on wall (96x36cm-38x14in) s. 5-Nov-3 Dobiaschofsky, Bern #1036/R (S.FR 850)

VONNOH, Bessie Potter (1872-1955) American
Sculpture
£3906 $6250 €5703 Good night (23cm-9in) s. num.25 Cast Roman Bronze Works bronze. 20-Sep-3 Jeffery Burchard, Florida #30/R
£4706 $8000 €6871 Girl dancing (33cm-13in) s. brown pat. bronze st.f.Roman executed c.1900. 22-Nov-3 Jackson's, Cedar Falls #70/R est:6000-8000
£5660 $9000 €8264 Good night (23cm-9in) s.i. bronze. 12-Sep-3 Skinner, Boston #340/R est:8000
£9730 $18000 €14206 Mother and child (20cm-8in) s.d.1902 indis.num. brown pat bronze prov. 11-Mar-4 Christie's, Rockefeller NY #32/R est:10000-15000

VONNOH, Robert (1858-1933) American
£331 $600 €483 Landscape with house (10x13cm-4x5in) board. 16-Apr-4 Du Mouchelle, Detroit #2144/R
£3714 $6500 €5422 Lakeside landscape (23x33cm-9x13in) s. panel prov. 19-Dec-3 Sotheby's, New York #1070/R est:6000-8000
£5294 $9000 €7729 Portrait of a young woman, possibly the artist's wife (61x51cm-24x20in) s. 21-Nov-3 Eldred, East Dennis #824/R est:6000-9000
£7910 $14000 €11549 The fagot gatherer, Grez (45x35cm-18x14in) s. 28-Apr-4 Christie's, Los Angeles #59/R est:4000-6000
£10465 $18000 €15279 American autumn (62x75cm-24x30in) s. i.stretcher prov. 3-Dec-3 Doyle, New York #229/R est:20000-30000

VONNOT-VIOLLET, Yvonne (1883-1936) French?
£400 $724 €600 Marine au coucher du soleil (75x100cm-30x39in) s. 30-Mar-4 Palais de Beaux Arts, Brussels #740
£753 $1281 €1100 Etang du chateau au crepuscule (45x55cm-18x22in) s.d.1924. 10-Nov-3 Horta, Bruxelles #510
£1329 $2259 €1900 Plage au coucher du soleil (41x77cm-16x30in) s.d.1921. 1-Dec-3 Palais de Beaux Arts, Brussels #337/R est:1800-2400

VONTILLIUS, Jeppe (1915-1994) Danish
£361 $675 €527 Gravel pit (22x37cm-9x15in) init. exhib. 25-Feb-4 Museumsbygningen, Copenhagen #38/R (D.KR 4000)
£379 $709 €553 Green and brown landscape (24x34cm-9x13in) init. s.d.67 stretcher. 25-Feb-4 Museumsbygningen, Copenhagen #37/R (D.KR 4200)
£379 $607 €553 Landscape (23x34cm-9x13in) init. masonite. 22-Sep-3 Rasmussen, Vejle #595/R (D.KR 4000)
£406 $759 €593 Field and edge of wood. init.d.1956 exhib. 25-Feb-4 Museumsbygningen, Copenhagen #39/R (D.KR 4500)
£433 $736 €632 Seated woman (45x30cm-18x12in) init. panel. 29-Nov-3 Rasmussen, Havnen #4020/R (D.KR 4600)
£616 $986 €893 Gravel heaps (66x87cm-26x34in) init. exhib. 17-Sep-3 Kunsthallen, Copenhagen #249/R (D.KR 6500)
£753 $1279 €1099 Interior scene with seated woman (81x54cm-32x21in) init. 26-Nov-3 Kunsthallen, Copenhagen #309/R (D.KR 8000)
£905 $1620 €1321 Woman seated on stool by table (62x126cm-24x50in) s.d.1953. 10-May-4 Rasmussen, Vejle #650/R (D.KR 10000)

VOOGD, Hendrik (1766-1839) Dutch
£3082 $5240 €4500 Extensive Italianate landscape at dusk with a shepherd sleeping beside a bull and cow (57x71cm-22x28in) s.d.1822. 5-Nov-3 Christie's, Amsterdam #75/R est:2000-3000
£12329 $20959 €18000 View of the Valley of Ariccia, with cows in the foreground (99x134cm-39x53in) s.d.1817 prov. 4-Nov-3 Sotheby's, Amsterdam #133/R est:20000-30000
£15000 $25950 €21900 View of the Roman Campagna with cattle grazing and storm approaching (64x87cm-25x34in) 11-Dec-3 Sotheby's, London #39/R est:15000-20000

Works on paper
£573 $986 €820 Chutes d'eau (15x24cm-6x9in) s.i.d.1792 graphite pen ink wash. 8-Dec-3 Christie's, Paris #20/R
£1216 $2141 €1800 Colosseum, with figures and cattle in the foreground (52x67cm-20x26in) pen black ink black chk prov.exhib.lit. 19-May-4 Sotheby's, Amsterdam #328/R est:1800-2200

VOORDECKER, Henri (1779-1861) Belgian
£1267 $2267 €1900 Winter landscape with figures (42x53cm-17x21in) s.d.1814. 11-May-4 Vendu Notarishuis, Rotterdam #48 est:2000-3000

VOORDEN, August Willem van (1881-1921) Dutch
£839 $1401 €1200 Harbour scene (31x40cm-12x16in) s. 30-Jun-3 Sotheby's, Amsterdam #155/R
£3333 $5667 €4800 Harbour activities, Rotterdam (20x32cm-8x13in) s. panel. 28-Oct-3 Christie's, Amsterdam #158/R est:4000-6000

Works on paper
£486 $768 €700 Busy quay (26x18cm-10x7in) s.d.1904 black chk W/C bodycol. 2-Sep-3 Christie's, Amsterdam #327

VOORHOUT, Johannes (1647-1723) Dutch
Works on paper
£340 $609 €500 La mort d'Abel (39x34cm-15x13in) s. black chk pen brown ink wash prov. 18-Mar-4 Christie's, Paris #328
£612 $979 €850 Allegorie dans un encadrement rocaille (30x25cm-12x10in) i. sanguine pen brown ink brown wash. 16-May-3 Tajan, Paris #76/R

VOORHOUT, Johannes (attrib) (1647-1723) Dutch
£1342 $2470 €2000 Portrait d'une jeune fille en Sainte Agnes (59x47cm-23x19in) 26-Mar-4 Piasa, Paris #20 est:2000-3000

VOORN, Gerard van der (?) Dutch
£650 $1190 €949 Dutch canal scene (88x75cm-35x30in) s. panel. 6-Apr-4 Bonhams, Knightsbridge #95/R

VOORST, Frieda van (1949-) Dutch
Works on paper
£590 $933 €850 Profile (100x100cm-39x39in) s.d.2003 egg distemper. 26-Apr-3 Auction Maastricht #12/R
£833 $1317 €1200 Femme (100x100cm-39x39in) s.d.2003 egg distemper. 26-Apr-3 Auction Maastricht #11/R

VOORT, Cornelis van der (1576-1624) Flemish
£12000 $21960 €17520 Portrait of gentleman. Portrait of lady (98x74cm-39x29in) i.d.1609 panel pair prov. 8-Jul-4 Sotheby's, London #265/R est:12000-18000

VOORT, Cornelis van der (circle) (1576-1624) Flemish
£5200 $8840 €7592 Portrait of a young girl holding a basket of cherries and a rattle (93x65cm-37x26in) i.d.1600 panel prov. 31-Oct-3 Christie's, Kensington #13/R est:5000-8000

VOORZAAT, Theo (1938-) Dutch
£490 $832 €700 Fisherman, house and ball (4x6cm-2x2in) s.d.75 board. 24-Nov-3 Glerum, Amsterdam #270/R
£594 $1010 €850 De Zweth (12x15cm-5x6in) s.d.76 board. 24-Nov-3 Glerum, Amsterdam #267/R

VORDEMBERGE, Friedrich (1897-1980) German
£909 $1564 €1300 Chestnuts in a yellow vase (80x61cm-31x24in) s. 4-Dec-3 Van Ham, Cologne #538/R
Works on paper
£420 $713 €600 Southern park landscape (71x54cm-28x21in) s. W/C. 26-Nov-3 Lempertz, Koln #1022/R
£524 $892 €750 Orange twig (72x52cm-28x20in) s.i.d.1975 W/C. 26-Nov-3 Lempertz, Koln #1023/R

VORDEMBERGE-GILDEWART, Friedrich (1899-1963) German
£90909 $154545 €130000 K No. 56 (60x80cm-24x31in) s.d.studio st. painted 1930 prov.exhib.lit. 25-Nov-3 Christie's, Amsterdam #198/R est:60000-80000
£115385 $196154 €165000 Composition No. 110A (80x102cm-31x40in) painted c.1938 prov.exhib.lit. 25-Nov-3 Christie's, Amsterdam #199/R est:60000-80000
Prints
£1834 $3338 €2678 Composition in black and red (27x20cm-11x8in) s.i.d. lithograph. 17-Jun-4 Kornfeld, Bern #822 est:750 (S.FR 4200)

VORDERMAYER, Ludwig (1868-?) German
Sculpture
£2000 $3640 €3000 Warrior stood by his horse (56cm-22in) s.d.1905 bronze. 20-Jun-4 Wilkinson, Doncaster #159 est:1800-2600

VORDERMAYER, Rupert (1843-1884) German
£317 $567 €450 Portrait of Doctor Geis (25x19cm-10x7in) s.i.d.1875 panel. 8-Jan-4 Allgauer, Kempten #2561/R
£317 $567 €450 Portrait of a girl (25x20cm-10x8in) panel. 8-Jan-4 Allgauer, Kempten #2562/R

VOROBIOVA, Nadejda (1924-) Russian
£300 $546 €438 Winter fun (35x50cm-14x20in) s. board painted 1966. 20-Jun-4 Lots Road Auctions, London #363/R

VOROS, Geza (1897-1957) Hungarian
£474 $858 €692 Flower still life (33x25cm-13x10in) s. 16-Apr-4 Mu Terem Galeria, Budapest #117/R (H.F 180000)
£1317 $2384 €1923 Spring flowers (75x60cm-30x24in) s. 16-Apr-4 Mu Terem Galeria, Budapest #153/R (H.F 500000)
£1827 $3161 €2667 Still life of flowers (57x66cm-22x26in) s. tempera. 12-Dec-3 Kieselbach, Budapest #33/R (H.F 700000)
£2371 $4292 €3462 Landscape with sunflowers (60x76cm-24x30in) s. 16-Apr-4 Mu Terem Galeria, Budapest #121/R (H.F 900000)
£2539 $4493 €3707 Nude with a veil (57x19cm-22x7in) s. painted c.1933. 28-Apr-4 Kieselbach, Budapest #116/R (H.F 950000)
£3915 $6773 €5716 Still life with oranges and a Buddha sculpture (100x60cm-39x24in) s.d.37. 12-Dec-3 Kieselbach, Budapest #190/R (H.F 1500000)
£3915 $6773 €5716 Still life with sunflowers and dahlias (100x74cm-39x29in) s.d.38. 12-Dec-3 Kieselbach, Budapest #155/R (H.F 1500000)
£6413 $11352 €9363 Woman reading (88x66cm-35x26in) s. 28-Apr-4 Kieselbach, Budapest #135/R (H.F 2400000)
£7377 $13353 €10770 Spring flowers with Buddha sculpture (117x88cm-46x35in) s. 16-Apr-4 Mu Terem Galeria, Budapest #54/R (H.F 2800000)
£9230 $15322 €13476 Nude in the studio (72x50cm-28x20in) tempera painted c.1930. 4-Oct-3 Kieselbach, Budapest #70/R (H.F 3400000)
Works on paper
£1436 $2483 €2097 Self portrait (49x43cm-19x17in) s. mixed media. 12-Dec-3 Kieselbach, Budapest #42/R (H.F 550000)

VORSTER, Gordon (1924-1988) South African
£276 $461 €403 Moremi forest number 2 (63x97cm-25x38in) s. 20-Oct-3 Stephan Welz, Johannesburg #605 est:3500-5000 (SA.R 3200)
£302 $504 €441 Extensive landscape (82x100cm-32x39in) s. board. 20-Oct-3 Stephan Welz, Johannesburg #606 est:3500-5000 (SA.R 3500)
£328 $547 €479 Moremi forest number 1 (68x98cm-27x39in) s. 20-Oct-3 Stephan Welz, Johannesburg #604 est:3500-5000 (SA.R 3800)
£345 $576 €504 Wildebeest in a landscape (41x61cm-16x24in) s. canvas on board. 20-Oct-3 Stephan Welz, Johannesburg #420 est:5000-7000 (SA.R 4000)
£362 $605 €529 Wildebeest in a landscape (36x62cm-14x24in) s. canvas on board. 20-Oct-3 Stephan Welz, Johannesburg #810 est:2000-4000 (SA.R 4200)
£733 $1224 €1070 Wildebeest and buck in a landscape (70x85cm-28x33in) s. board. 20-Oct-3 Stephan Welz, Johannesburg #603 est:3500-5000 (SA.R 8500)
£862 $1440 €1259 Wildebeest and zebra (89x119cm-35x47in) s. board. 20-Oct-3 Stephan Welz, Johannesburg #798 est:3000-4000 (SA.R 10000)
£1034 $1728 €1510 Zebras (27x37cm-11x15in) s. canvas on board. 20-Oct-3 Stephan Welz, Johannesburg #787 est:2500-3500 (SA.R 12000)
£1239 $2217 €1809 Burnt grass (69x89cm-27x35in) s. 31-May-4 Stephan Welz, Johannesburg #492/R est:5000-8000 (SA.R 15000)
Works on paper
£276 $461 €403 Sable antelope and wilderbeest in an extensive landscape (60x90cm-24x35in) s. mixed media paper on board. 20-Oct-3 Stephan Welz, Johannesburg #602 est:3500-5000 (SA.R 3200)
£314 $562 €458 Herd of zebra, impala and wildebeest in a bush landscape (66x96cm-26x38in) s. mixed media. 31-May-4 Stephan Welz, Johannesburg #227 (SA.R 3800)
£362 $605 €529 Zebra in a landscape (32x47cm-13x19in) s. W/C. 20-Oct-3 Stephan Welz, Johannesburg #669 est:1200-1600 (SA.R 4200)

VOS, Alda (1935-) Belgian
£467 $840 €700 Young women reading (120x98cm-47x39in) s.d.1978. 26-Apr-4 Bernaerts, Antwerp #1028/R

VOS, Cornelis de (1585-1651) Flemish
£1538 $2569 €2200 Salome presents the head of John the Baptist to Herodias (51x77cm-20x30in) bears sig. panel prov. 30-Jun-3 Sotheby's, Amsterdam #21/R
£12931 $23793 €18879 Diogenes on the search (144x212cm-57x83in) mono. 26-Mar-4 Koller, Zurich #3036/R est:40000-60000 (S.FR 30000)
£19444 $35000 €28388 Portrait of nobleman and three children (136x110cm-54x43in) prov.exhib.lit. 22-Jan-4 Sotheby's, New York #7/R est:40000-60000
£22517 $41205 €34000 Portrait of elegant woman with son (122x155cm-48x61in) panel painted with studio. 7-Apr-4 Dorotheum, Salzburg #75/R est:34000-38000
£30667 $55813 €46000 Portrait of Francois de Boisschot, Count of Erps, aged nine years (115x85cm-45x33in) i. 1-Jul-4 Van Ham, Cologne #1175/R est:15000

VOS, Daniel de (1568-1605) Flemish
£12000 $21600 €17520 Saint Eustace. Saint Arsenius (147x190cm-58x75in) i. pair prov. 20-Apr-4 Sotheby's, Olympia #248/R est:10000-15000

VOS, Hubert (1855-1935) American
£455 $800 €664 Portrait of a man leaning on a carved wood and leather chair (127x76cm-50x30in) s.d.1916. 21-May-4 North East Auctions, Portsmouth #887/R

VOS, Jan de (15/17th C) Dutch/Flemish
£201342 $374497 €300000 Deposition (110x73cm-43x29in) board prov.lit. 2-Mar-4 Ansorena, Madrid #279/R est:300000

VOS, Lucas de (20th C) ?
£250 $393 €365 Bruges, from the river (48x58cm-19x23in) s.i.d.1923. 10-Dec-2 Bamfords, Derby #778/R

VOS, Maria (1824-1906) Dutch
£2133 $3840 €3200 Quince pears on a silver plate with glass bottle and tankard (76x56cm-30x22in) s. prov. 21-Apr-4 Christie's, Amsterdam #80/R est:3000-5000
£2500 $4175 €3600 Kitchen still life with vegetables and sardines (29x24cm-11x9in) s. panel. 21-Oct-3 Sotheby's, Amsterdam #167/R est:2000-3000
Works on paper
£1042 $1646 €1500 Wine bottle, coconuts and oranges on a ledge (53x35cm-21x14in) s.d.1880 pencil W/C htd white. 2-Sep-3 Christie's, Amsterdam #151 est:700-900

VOS, Martin de (1532-1603) Flemish
£6207 $10303 €9000 Animals boarding Noah's Ark (46x52cm-18x20in) i. prov. 1-Oct-3 Dorotheum, Vienna #140/R est:9000-12000
Works on paper
£2400 $4392 €3504 Asia seated on a camel and holding an incense burner (27x19cm-11x7in) i. black chk pen ink wash. 6-Jul-4 Christie's, London #158/R est:1500-2000
£10855 $19974 €16500 Adam et Eve chasses du Paradis (23x20cm-9x8in) i. pen ink wash. 25-Jun-4 Rossini, Paris #11/R est:4500-5500

VOS, Martin de (attrib) (1532-1603) Flemish
£19463 $35812 €29000 Apollon et les 9 muses, entoure de naiades (72x116cm-28x46in) panel. 26-Mar-4 Pierre Berge, Paris #22/R est:30000-40000

VOS, Martin de (circle) (1532-1603) Flemish
£13000 $23790 €18980 Adoration of the Magi (150x183cm-59x72in) prov. 8-Jul-4 Sotheby's, London #247/R est:8000-12000

VOS, Martin de (studio) (1532-1603) Flemish
£8451 $14789 €12000 Allegory of the Five Senses (63x67cm-25x26in) board. 17-Dec-3 Christie's, Rome #496/R est:15000-20000

VOS, Martin de (style) (1532-1603) Flemish
£5405 $9514 €8000 Angel and Tobias regaled by his parents (76x109cm-30x43in) panel. 18-May-4 Sotheby's, Amsterdam #36/R est:8000-10000

VOS, Paul de (1596-1678) Flemish
£2980 $5424 €4500 Bear hunt (81x100cm-32x39in) 16-Jun-4 Dorotheum, Vienna #317/R est:5000-7000

VOS, Paul de (attrib) (1596-1678) Flemish
£3667 $6563 €5500 An eagle stealing a rabbit from hounds (122x187cm-48x74in) 14-May-4 Behringer, Furth #1696/R est:8500
£9091 $15455 €13000 Dog pack attacking two wolves in extensive wooded landscape (157x282cm-62x111in) 20-Nov-3 Dorotheum, Salzburg #92/R est:12000-18000
£9091 $15455 €13000 Dog pack chasing deer in extensive river landscape (157x282cm-62x111in) 20-Nov-3 Dorotheum, Salzburg #91/R est:12000-18000
£17219 $31338 €26000 Still life with fruit, vegetables, shot game, boy and a cat (116x149cm-46x59in) 16-Jun-4 Dorotheum, Vienna #65/R est:25000-35000

VOS, Paul de (circle) (1596-1678) Flemish
£8609 $15755 €13000 Peacock and cockerel fighting (121x171cm-48x67in) 7-Apr-4 Dorotheum, Salzburg #72/R est:13000-15000

VOS, Simon de (1603-1676) Flemish
£1268 $2218 €1800 Jugement de Midas (36x52cm-14x20in) panel. 17-Dec-3 Piasa, Paris #3 est:1500-2000

VOS, Simon de (attrib) (1603-1676) Flemish
£1056 $1849 €1500 Le jugement de Salomon (53x72cm-21x28in) panel. 18-Dec-3 Tajan, Paris #80 est:1500-2000
£3312 $6027 €5000 L'adoration des Mages (63x48cm-25x19in) copper. 21-Jun-4 Tajan, Paris #63 est:2000-3000

VOS, Thomas Andreas (1887-1948) Dutch
Sculpture
£2937 $5052 €4200 Dancer (35cm-14in) pat bronze. 5-Dec-3 Bolland & Marotz, Bremen #1120/R est:2200

VOS, Vincent de (1829-1875) Belgian
£486 $812 €700 Chien a l'etable (31x40cm-12x16in) s. 21-Oct-3 Campo & Campo, Antwerp #105
£497 $900 €726 Two favourite dogs (9x12cm-4x5in) s. panel. 30-Mar-4 Bonhams & Butterfields, San Francisco #94/R
£544 $974 €800 Chasse a la souris (20x26cm-8x10in) s. panel. 19-Mar-4 Millon & Associes, Paris #5/R
£578 $1035 €850 Chiens savants sont fatigues (14x21cm-6x8in) s. panel. 19-Mar-4 Millon & Associes, Paris #7/R
£578 $1035 €850 Chasse a la souris (14x21cm-6x8in) s. 19-Mar-4 Millon & Associes, Paris #8
£612 $1096 €900 Singe et chien en costume d'apparat (21x27cm-8x11in) s. 19-Mar-4 Millon & Associes, Paris #9/R
£683 $1100 €997 Unwelcome visitor (28x38cm-11x15in) s. panel. 20-Aug-3 James Julia, Fairfield #1050/R
£748 $1339 €1100 Batille pour une souris (22x29cm-9x11in) s. 19-Mar-4 Millon & Associes, Paris #6/R
£789 $1429 €1200 Two terriers on a red cushion (15x24cm-6x9in) s. panel. 19-Apr-4 Glerum, Amsterdam #285/R
£884 $1583 €1300 Stinge savant et son chien (17x23cm-7x9in) bears trace sig. panel. 19-Mar-4 Millon & Associes, Paris #10
£1241 $2297 €1800 Chiens chassant dans une ecurie (18x24cm-7x9in) s. panel. 16-Feb-4 Horta, Bruxelles #90 est:1200-1500
£1250 $2088 €1800 Two dogs (18x24cm-7x9in) s.d. panel. 24-Oct-3 Ketterer, Hamburg #118/R est:2000-2500
£1701 $3044 €2500 Apres le dejeuner. Une Surprise (18x24cm-7x9in) s. panel pair. 19-Mar-4 Millon & Associes, Paris #3/R est:1500-1800
£2411 $4027 €3400 Two King Charles spaniels on a cushion (43x54cm-17x21in) s. panel. 20-Oct-3 Glerum, Amsterdam #33/R est:4000-6000
£2449 $4384 €3600 Un bon repos (52x71cm-20x28in) s.d.1871. 19-Mar-4 Millon & Associes, Paris #4/R est:3000-5000
£2700 $4914 €3942 Dispute (27x36cm-11x14in) s. board. 3-Feb-4 Sworder & Son, Bishops Stortford #298/R est:1200-1500

VOSBERG, Heinrich (1833-1891) German
£3846 $6538 €5500 Pond in evening (104x155cm-41x61in) s.d.1888. 24-Nov-3 Dorotheum, Vienna #35/R est:5500-6000

VOSCHER, Leopold Heinrich (1830-1877) Austrian
£1325 $2424 €2000 Alpine pasture (24x30cm-9x12in) s. 8-Apr-4 Dorotheum, Vienna #36/R est:2500-3000
£1361 $2435 €2000 Wetterhorn near Grindelwald (71x194cm-28x76in) s.d.1868. 17-Mar-4 Neumeister, Munich #648/R est:2000
£2778 $4528 €4000 Southern mountain lake (79x97cm-31x38in) s.i. 24-Sep-3 Neumeister, Munich #591/R est:2500

VOSS, Frank B (1880-1953) American
£550 $952 €803 Study of a hunter in a stable (25x33cm-10x13in) s.d.1924. 9-Dec-3 Clarke Gammon, Guildford #47/R
£3352 $6000 €4894 Saint-James in landscape (44x56cm-17x22in) s.d.1924 prov. 27-May-4 Sotheby's, New York #292/R est:6000-8000

VOSS, Jan (1936-) German
£2587 $4399 €3700 Good morning Mr Mouse (80x120cm-31x47in) s.d.87 acrylic chk Indian ink paper collage prov. 27-Nov-3 Lempertz, Koln #513/R est:4000-5000
£3318 $5308 €4811 Ca, par example (65x50cm-26x20in) s. paper on canvas prov. 17-Sep-3 Kunsthallen, Copenhagen #33/R est:30000 (D.KR 35000)
£3600 $6552 €5256 Untitled (114x160cm-45x63in) s.d.79 prov.exhib. 4-Feb-4 Sotheby's, Olympia #223/R est:3000-4000
£3800 $6992 €5548 Untitled (141x113cm-56x44in) s.d.63 oil paper on canvas. 24-Jun-4 Sotheby's, Olympia #525/R est:4000-6000
£4545 $7727 €6500 Untitled (114x162cm-45x64in) s.d.91 i. verso oil canvas collage. 27-Nov-3 Lempertz, Koln #511/R est:7000-8000
£5333 $9813 €8000 Untitled (97x130cm-38x51in) s.d.57. 12-Jun-4 Villa Grisebach, Berlin #359/R est:8000-10000
£6498 $11957 €9487 Composition with many figures (195x113cm-77x44in) s.d.1963 paper on canvas. 29-Mar-4 Rasmussen, Copenhagen #158/R est:40000 (D.KR 72000)
Works on paper
£407 $680 €594 Untitled (45x45cm-18x18in) s.d.1973 gouache. 24-Jun-3 Germann, Zurich #1076 (S.FR 900)
£1678 $2803 €2400 Composition (100x73cm-39x29in) s.d.1962 mixed media on canvas prov. 29-Jun-3 Versailles Encheres #174/R
£3497 $5839 €5000 Dabeigewesen (99x130cm-39x51in) s.d.1963 mixed media on canvas prov.exhib. 29-Jun-3 Versailles Encheres #175/R

VOSS, Karl (1825-1896) German
Sculpture
£8333 $15000 €12166 Figure of Rebekah at the well (171cm-67in) s.i.d.1865 white marble pedestal. 23-Apr-4 Christie's, Rockefeller NY #173/R est:8000-12000

VOSS, Willy (1939-) Danish
£734 $1263 €1050 Winter scene with suburban houses (15x22cm-6x9in) oil collage. 6-Dec-3 Hans Stahl, Toestorf #124/R

VOSSEN, Andre van der (1893-1963) Dutch
Works on paper
£340 $619 €500 Austerite (50x32cm-20x13in) s. collage sold with another by same hand prov. 3-Feb-4 Christie's, Amsterdam #615
£461 $847 €700 Realities nouvelles (48x63cm-19x25in) mono. collage. 22-Jun-4 Christie's, Amsterdam #342/R
£510 $929 €750 Composition (50x32cm-20x13in) s. collage sold with another by same hand prov. 3-Feb-4 Christie's, Amsterdam #613
£658 $1211 €1000 Paysage (24x10cm-9x4in) mono. s.i. on mount collage two prov. 22-Jun-4 Christie's, Amsterdam #343/R
£680 $1238 €1000 Composition (50x32cm-20x13in) s. collage sold with another by same hand. 3-Feb-4 Christie's, Amsterdam #614 est:600-800

VOSTELL, Wolf (1932-1998) German
Sculpture
£2013 $3705 €3000 Zyklus Catalyad NR22 (41x29x11cm-16x11x4in) s.d.1973 photograph lead pencil felt pen in painted wooded box. 29-Mar-4 Cornette de St.Cyr, Paris #92/R est:3000-4000
£3497 $5944 €5000 For Christo (79x119x11cm-31x47x4in) s.i.d.87 glass panel print. 29-Nov-3 Villa Grisebach, Berlin #332/R est:5000-7000
Works on paper
£915 $1602 €1300 Archangeloi (70x100cm-28x39in) s.i.d.1981 pastel chl. 18-Dec-3 Cornette de St.Cyr, Paris #87/R est:1500-2000
£1544 $2732 €2300 Untitled (32x45cm-13x18in) s.d. dictation machine newspaper tempera prov. 30-Apr-4 Dr Fritz Nagel, Stuttgart #964/R est:2500
£1678 $2853 €2400 Endogene depression II - Version Nice (68x98cm-27x39in) s.i.d.86 graphite varnish chks acrylic board. 27-Nov-3 Lempertz, Koln #515/R est:3000
£1818 $3091 €2600 Untitled (73x102cm-29x40in) s.d.86 cement acrylic chk Indian ink board. 27-Nov-3 Lempertz, Koln #514/R est:2800
£3200 $5856 €4800 Cologne cathedral (76x100cm-30x39in) s.d.85 concrete panel. 4-Jun-4 Lempertz, Koln #522/R est:5000

VOUET, Simon (circle) (1590-1649) French
£32895 $60527 €50000 Jeune gitane et son enfant (111x91cm-44x36in) 24-Jun-4 Tajan, Paris #34/R est:10000-12000

VOUET, Simon (style) (1590-1649) French
£21111 $38000 €30822 Crucifixion with the Virgin and Saint John the Evangelist (42x28cm-17x11in) copper. 23-Jan-4 Christie's, Rockefeller NY #182/R est:25000-35000

VOUGUET, Leon (20th C) French?
Works on paper
£1119 $1924 €1600 Nu debout (130x90cm-51x35in) crayon sanguine. 5-Dec-3 Gros & Delettrez, Paris #38 est:600-1000

VOULKOS, Peter (1924-2002) American
Sculpture
£8333 $15000 €12166 Untitled (137cm-54in) cement incl. base. 25-Apr-4 Bonhams & Butterfields, San Francisco #5645/R est:1500-2500

VOULLEMIER, Anne Nicole (1796-1886) French
£2535 $4437 €3600 Jeune mere veillant sur son enfant endormi (49x38cm-19x15in) s. 18-Dec-3 Tajan, Paris #44/R est:4000-6000

VOURLOUMIS, Andreas (1910-) Greek
Works on paper
£2000 $3580 €2920 Tsakalof street from my terrace (28x37cm-11x15in) init.d.48 W/C. 10-May-4 Sotheby's, Olympia #128/R est:2000-3000

VOWE, Paul Gerhart (1874-?) German
£331 $603 €500 Portrait of a woman (48x39cm-19x15in) s. 16-Jun-4 Hugo Ruef, Munich #1106/R

VOYET, Jacques (1927-) French
£275 $500 €402 Still life of flowers (81x99cm-32x39in) s. 19-Jun-4 Jackson's, Cedar Falls #265/R
£685 $1164 €1000 Still life (33x41cm-13x16in) s. panel. 9-Nov-3 Eric Pillon, Calais #181/R
£856 $1455 €1250 Fillette aux bas blancs (41x33cm-16x13in) s. panel. 9-Nov-3 Eric Pillon, Calais #179/R
£1351 $2419 €2000 Nu aux bas blancs (46x55cm-18x22in) s. panel. 10-May-4 Giraudeau, Tours #193

VOYET, Maxime (1896-1985) French
£828 $1531 €1200 Jardin de fleurs (46x65cm-18x26in) s. panel. 16-Feb-4 Giraudeau, Tours #89
£1047 $1875 €1550 Barques et pecheur (33x46cm-13x18in) s. masonite. 10-May-4 Giraudeau, Tours #191

VRANCX, Sebastian (1573-1647) Flemish
£18310 $32042 €26000 Militaires attaquant un interieur de paysans (34x47cm-13x19in) panel painted with studio. 16-Dec-3 Artcurial Briest, Paris #208/R est:20000-25000
£38776 $61653 €57000 Autumn (51x66cm-20x26in) panel. 23-Mar-3 Mercier & Cie, Lille #182/R est:60000-65000

VRANCX, Sebastian (circle) (1573-1647) Flemish
£10000 $18300 €14600 Winter landscape with figures skating on a frozen canal (80x115cm-31x45in) 7-Jul-4 Bonhams, New Bond Street #5/R est:10000-15000

£24000 $43200 €35040 Village street with peasants playing cards in the foreground, supper at Emmaus beyond (52x67cm-20x26in) panel prov. 21-Apr-4 Christie's, London #22/R est:12000-18000

VRANCX, Sebastian (studio) (1573-1647) Flemish
£38000 $69540 €55480 Elegant company promenading outside palace (77x117cm-30x46in) prov. 8-Jul-4 Sotheby's, London #102/R est:25000-35000
£50000 $90000 €73000 Four seasons, spring, summer, autumn and winter (121x138cm-48x54in) different sizes. 23-Jan-4 Christie's, Rockefeller NY #125/R est:80000-120000

VRBOVA, Miloslava (1909-1991) Czechoslovakian
£280 $467 €400 Four ballet dancers (29x23cm-11x9in) s. board. 27-Jun-3 Michael Zeller, Lindau #697
£280 $502 €409 Seated ballet dancer wearing tutu (30x40cm-12x16in) s. panel. 12-May-4 Dobiaschofsky, Bern #3994 (S.FR 650)
£292 $461 €420 Three ballerinas (66x99cm-26x39in) acrylic board. 6-Sep-3 Arnold, Frankfurt #720/R
£313 $564 €470 Ballerina with flowers (41x30cm-16x12in) s. panel. 26-Apr-4 Rieber, Stuttgart #907/R
£350 $584 €500 Ballerina in tutu (22x28cm-9x11in) s. board. 27-Jun-3 Michael Zeller, Lindau #699/R
£396 $674 €578 Young ballet dancer on stage (47x33cm-19x13in) s. panel. 5-Nov-3 Dobiaschofsky, Bern #1038/R (S.FR 900)
£400 $720 €600 Seven ballerinas (36x41cm-14x16in) s. panel. 26-Apr-4 Rieber, Stuttgart #908/R
£423 $676 €600 Ballerina (60x50cm-24x20in) s. panel. 18-Sep-3 Rieber, Stuttgart #1129
£559 $934 €800 Old street in Prague in the winter (38x28cm-15x11in) s. board. 27-Jun-3 Michael Zeller, Lindau #703/R
£652 $1193 €952 Ballerina tying up her ballet shoes (40x30cm-16x12in) s. board. 4-Jun-4 Zofingen, Switzerland #2539 (S.FR 1500)
£739 $1353 €1079 Ballerina (30x40cm-12x16in) s. board. 4-Jun-4 Zofingen, Switzerland #2540 (S.FR 1700)
£800 $1440 €1200 Ballerina tying ballet shoes (80x60cm-31x24in) s. panel lit. 22-Apr-4 Allgauer, Kempten #3757/R

VREDENBURGH, C L van (fl.1880s) ?
£1892 $3500 €2762 Saint Bernard (46x38cm-18x15in) s. board. 10-Feb-4 Doyle, New York #165/R est:1500-2500

VREEDENBURGH, Cornelis (1880-1946) Dutch
£694 $1132 €1000 Small house near the waterside (25x33cm-10x13in) s. panel. 29-Sep-3 Sotheby's, Amsterdam #191/R
£987 $1816 €1500 Laren in winter (24x40cm-9x16in) s. panel. 22-Jun-4 Christie's, Amsterdam #95/R est:1200-1600
£1000 $1700 €1460 Stream running through a water meadow (33x41cm-13x16in) s.d.1904. 6-Nov-3 Christie's, Kensington #778/R est:1200-1800
£1579 $2905 €2400 Cows in a summer meadow (29x60cm-11x24in) s.d.1930 board. 22-Jun-4 Christie's, Amsterdam #319/R est:1800-2200
£2917 $4608 €4200 Sunday drive (15x24cm-6x9in) s. panel. 2-Sep-3 Christie's, Amsterdam #269/R est:4000-6000
£2961 $5447 €4500 Washing day at a farm (24x48cm-9x19in) s.d.08 panel. 22-Jun-4 Christie's, Amsterdam #98/R est:3000-4000
£3667 $6600 €5500 Peasant woman on a path along a canal (38x61cm-15x24in) s.d.07. 20-Apr-4 Sotheby's, Amsterdam #107/R est:4000-6000
£4167 $6958 €6000 Polder landscape (48x69cm-19x27in) s.d.1935 canvas on panel. 21-Oct-3 Sotheby's, Amsterdam #107/R est:4000-6000
£6333 $11400 €9500 Town scene with children at play Haarlem (38x45cm-15x18in) s.d.1930 board. 20-Apr-4 Sotheby's, Amsterdam #119/R est:7000-9000
£19444 $33056 €28000 Royal Palace and the Nieuwe Kerk on the Dam, Amsterdam (61x91cm-24x36in) s.d.1927 prov. 28-Oct-3 Christie's, Amsterdam #155/R est:30000-50000
£20000 $36000 €30000 View of Amsterdam with the St. Nicolaas Church (83x128cm-33x50in) s. 20-Apr-4 Sotheby's, Amsterdam #197/R est:30000-50000
£25333 $45600 €38000 View of the Montelbaanstoren and the Oudeschans, Amsterdam (80x100cm-31x39in) s.d.1925. 21-Apr-4 Christie's, Amsterdam #162/R est:20000-30000
Works on paper
£489 $817 €700 Boat on a lake (47x65cm-19x26in) s.d. W/C. 30-Jun-3 Sotheby's, Amsterdam #370/R
£872 $1605 €1300 Gooi avenue (26x49cm-10x19in) s.d.1933 W/C. 29-Mar-4 Glerum, Amsterdam #171

VREELAND, Francis William van (1879-1954) American
£625 $1100 €913 Mother and Child (46x61cm-18x24in) prov. 23-May-4 Hindman, Chicago #28/R

VREESE, Godefroid (1861-1941) Belgian
Sculpture
£2500 $3975 €3600 Retour du marche sur un ane (56x52cm-22x20in) s.i. medaille pat bronze. 15-Sep-3 Horta, Bruxelles #168/R est:2200-2800

VREESWYK, Jos van (1948-) Dutch
Works on paper
£490 $832 €700 Revealing the senses (21x30cm-8x12in) s.i.verso mixed media panel. 24-Nov-3 Glerum, Amsterdam #269/R

VREL, Jacob (17th C) Dutch
£57432 $101081 €85000 Interior with a woman sleeping near a fireplace with cat and dog (57x47cm-22x19in) panel prov.exhib.lit. 18-May-4 Sotheby's, Amsterdam #14/R est:25000-35000

VREUGDENHIL, Johannes (1904-1969) Dutch
£594 $1022 €850 Communication (90x125cm-35x49in) s. d.66 verso. 8-Dec-3 Glerum, Amsterdam #182/R

VRIES, Adriaen de (studio) (c.1550-1626) Dutch
Sculpture
£36000 $62280 €52560 Dancing faun (61cm-24in) bronze marble socle lit. 12-Dec-3 Sotheby's, London #193/R est:40000-60000

VRIES, Corstiaan de (1936-) Dutch
Works on paper
£408 $731 €600 Lady with Indonesian landscape (40x70cm-16x28in) pastel col crayons. 16-Mar-4 Christie's, Amsterdam #131/R

VRIES, Dirck de (16/17th C) Dutch
£26510 $46923 €39500 Ball in Venetian palace (112x160cm-44x63in) exhib.lit. 2-May-4 Finarte, Venice #16/R est:40000-50000

VRIES, Emanuel de (1816-1875) Dutch
£709 $1184 €1000 Sailing ships on the river (40x54cm-16x21in) s.indis.d. panel. 20-Oct-3 Glerum, Amsterdam #34

VRIES, Henriette de (1886-1942) Dutch
£816 $1486 €1200 Nassaukade, Amsterdam (51x41cm-20x16in) s. 3-Feb-4 Christie's, Amsterdam #327 est:1200-1600
Works on paper
£312 $509 €450 View of the Leidse Bosje, Amsterdam (36x46cm-14x18in) s. W/C. 29-Sep-3 Sotheby's, Amsterdam #158/R

VRIES, Herman de (1931-) Dutch
£1829 $3000 €2670 Untitled (21x14cm-8x6in) s.d.1961 verso oil glasspearls wood prov. 28-May-3 Sotheby's, Amsterdam #53/R est:3000-4000
Sculpture
£1707 $2800 €2492 V72-55 (38x42cm-15x17in) s.i.verso white wood prov. 28-May-3 Sotheby's, Amsterdam #58/R est:2000-3000

VRIES, Hubert de (1899-1979) Belgian
£372 $665 €550 Port de peche (109x109cm-43x43in) 10-May-4 Amberes, Antwerp #259
£382 $638 €550 Bateaux a Anvers (56x38cm-22x15in) s. s.verso. 21-Oct-3 Campo & Campo, Antwerp #109
£400 $724 €600 Manege a la kermesse (70x70cm-28x28in) s.d.1965 verso. 30-Mar-4 Campo & Campo, Antwerp #83
£724 $1332 €1100 At the fair (50x60cm-20x24in) s. 22-Jun-4 Christie's, Amsterdam #505/R

VRIES, Jan Feytsz de (17th C) Dutch
£21000 $36330 €30660 Naval engagement between Dutch and English ships. panel. 11-Dec-3 Sotheby's, London #142/R est:15000-20000

VRIES, Jochum Aebrechtsz de (fl.1628-1670) Dutch
£4795 $8151 €7000 Dutch whaling ships off a rocky coast in polar waters (49x93cm-19x37in) init. panel prov.lit. 5-Nov-3 Christie's, Amsterdam #19/R est:6000-8000

VRIES, Joseph Cohen de (1804-1853) Dutch
£1267 $2154 €1850 Interior of kitchen (33x39cm-13x15in) s.d.1840 panel. 1-Dec-3 Koller, Zurich #6491/R est:2000-3000 (S.FR 2800)

VRIES, Paul Vredeman de (1567-c.1630) Flemish
£16000 $28800 €23360 Elegant figures in a sumptuous interior (69x102cm-27x40in) s.d.1612 panel prov. 21-Apr-4 Christie's, London #11/R est:7000-10000

VRIES, Regina de (1913-1985) Swiss
Sculpture
£1357 $2267 €1981 Chant oriental (92cm-36in) nickled bronze granite socle. 24-Jun-3 Germann, Zurich #144/R est:2000-4000 (S.FR 3000)
£1900 $3174 €2774 Untitled (96x130x25cm-38x51x10in) iron. 24-Jun-3 Germann, Zurich #143/R est:2000-4000 (S.FR 4200)

VRIES, Roelof van (1631-1681) Dutch
£2411 $4026 €3520 Mill by a river (38x51cm-15x20in) panel. 17-Jun-3 Maynards, Vancouver #313 est:6000-8000 (C.D 5400)
£2667 $4773 €4000 Tavern by the water with a landing stage (46x62cm-18x24in) panel prov. 17-May-4 Glerum, Amsterdam #7/R est:5000-7000
£3000 $5490 €4380 Wooded river landscape with a mill and a cavalier giving alms to a beggar (64x48cm-25x19in) s. panel. 6-Jul-4 Sotheby's, Olympia #462/R est:3000-4000
£9655 $16028 €14000 Wooded river landscape with angler on bridge (63x78cm-25x31in) s. prov.exhib. 1-Oct-3 Dorotheum, Vienna #182/R est:12000-18000

VRIES, Roelof van (attrib) (1631-1681) Dutch
£2715 $4615 €3964 Peasant smoking pipe under oak tree (41x32cm-16x13in) mono. panel prov. 19-Nov-3 Fischer, Luzern #1013/R est:6000-9000 (S.FR 6000)
£2991 $4725 €4337 Landscape with two wanderers resting by river (48x65cm-19x26in) init. panel prov. 2-Sep-3 Rasmussen, Copenhagen #1596/R est:15000-25000 (D.KR 32000)
£3000 $5490 €4380 River landscape with travellers (29x40cm-11x16in) mono. panel oval prov. 9-Jul-4 Christie's, Kensington #76/R est:3000-5000

VRIES, de (style) (16/18th C) Dutch
£5800 $10208 €8468 Figures in a cathedral interior (57x45cm-22x18in) panel. 18-May-4 Woolley & Wallis, Salisbury #111/R est:2500-3500

VROILYNCK, Ghislain (?-1635) Dutch
£11111 $20000 €16222 Miracle of the prophet Elisha (107x151cm-42x59in) s.d.1624 panel prov. 22-Jan-4 Sotheby's, New York #42/R est:30000-50000

VROLYK, Adrianus Jacobus (1834-1862) Dutch

£890	$1514	€1300	Canal scene (18x23cm-7x9in) s.d.59 panel. 5-Nov-3 Vendue Huis, Gravenhage #68/R
£2657	$4517	€3800	Fishing boat on beach (26x35cm-10x14in) s. panel. 24-Nov-3 Dorotheum, Vienna #80/R est:3400-4000
£4000	$7200	€6000	Busy market in a Dutch town (35x49cm-14x19in) s. panel. 20-Apr-4 Sotheby's, Amsterdam #9/R est:7000-10000

VROLYK, Jan (1845-1894) Dutch

£544	$990	€800	In de schaduw, rest under a tree (39x32cm-15x13in) s. s.i.verso panel. 3-Feb-4 Christie's, Amsterdam #129

VROMANS, Pieter Pietersz (1612-?) Dutch

£866	$1550	€1264	Blind Tobias (43x54cm-17x21in) s. i. verso panel. 22-Mar-4 Philippe Schuler, Zurich #4437/R (S.FR 2000)

VROOM, Hendrik Cornelisz (1566-1640) Dutch

Works on paper			
£8904	$15137	€13000	Beach scene at Scheveningen. Shipping off a coast by a Dutch town (18x30cm-7x12in) pen brown ink wash double-sided prov.exhib. 4-Nov-3 Sotheby's, Amsterdam #95/R est:8000-12000

VU CAO DAM (1908-2000) Vietnamese

£2257	$3769	€3295	Divinity (55x46cm-22x18in) s.d.1984 verso prov. 12-Oct-3 Sotheby's, Singapore #89/R est:6000-8000 (S.D 6500)
£2451	$4436	€3578	Le cavalier (50x61cm-20x24in) s.d.1971 s.i.d.verso. 4-Apr-4 Sotheby's, Singapore #46/R est:5000-7000 (S.D 7500)
£3125	$5219	€4563	Man and Horse (27x37cm-11x15in) s.d.67 s.i.verso prov. 12-Oct-3 Sotheby's, Singapore #90/R est:4000-6000 (S.D 9000)
£3475	$5803	€5074	Rendez-vous - the meeting (54x65cm-21x26in) s.d.64 prov. 26-Oct-3 Christie's, Hong Kong #37/R est:50000-80000 (HK.D 45000)
£3595	$6507	€5249	Church (54x73cm-21x29in) s. painted c.1950. 4-Apr-4 Sotheby's, Singapore #77/R est:10000-12000 (S.D 11000)
£3757	$6500	€5485	La rencontre (64x76cm-25x30in) 12-Dec-3 Du Mouchelle, Detroit #2018/R est:1500-2500
£4086	$6538	€5966	Boy with rice bowl (22x18cm-9x7in) s. oil silk. 18-May-3 Sotheby's, Singapore #108/R est:6000-8000 (S.D 11400)
£4979	$8962	€7269	Maternite - motherhood (62x51cm-24x20in) s.d.73 s.i.d.verso. 25-Apr-4 Christie's, Hong Kong #530/R est:40000-55000 (HK.D 70000)
£6178	$10317	€9020	Le coq - the rooster (82x66cm-32x26in) s.d.64 prov. 26-Oct-3 Christie's, Hong Kong #38/R est:80000-100000 (HK.D 80000)
£7417	$13574	€11200	Spring (92x73cm-36x29in) s.d.68. 9-Apr-4 Bailly Pommery, Paris #101/R est:7000-10000
£7722	$12896	€11274	La rencontre - the meeting (61x46cm-24x18in) s.d.1978 prov. 26-Oct-3 Christie's, Hong Kong #39/R est:80000-100000 (HK.D 100000)
£8172	$13075	€11931	Man with fighting cockerel (56x45cm-22x18in) s. 18-May-3 Sotheby's, Singapore #98/R est:18000-25000 (S.D 22800)
£9028	$15076	€13181	Cockfight (60x73cm-24x29in) s.d.56 board. 12-Oct-3 Sotheby's, Singapore #91/R est:7000-9000 (S.D 26000)
£9804	$17745	€14314	Maternite - maternity (73x50cm-29x20in) s.d.57 board. 4-Apr-4 Sotheby's, Singapore #48/R est:20000-25000 (S.D 30000)
£10345	$17276	€15000	Maternite (72x50cm-28x20in) s.i.d.57 silk. 14-Nov-3 Piasa, Paris #311/R est:10000-12000
£11232	$17409	€16399	Lovers (55x46cm-22x18in) s. silk on canvas. 6-Oct-2 Sotheby's, Singapore #97/R est:8000-12000 (S.D 31000)
£15972	$26674	€23319	Mother and child (81x65cm-32x26in) s.d.63. 12-Oct-3 Sotheby's, Singapore #87/R est:6000-8000 (S.D 46000)
Sculpture			
£9804	$17745	€14314	Kneeling woman (27x21cm-11x8in) s.i. terracotta executed 1940-45 prov.exhib.lit. 4-Apr-4 Sotheby's, Singapore #74/R est:30000-35000 (S.D 30000)
Works on paper			
£1449	$2246	€2116	Cockerel (65x49cm-26x19in) s.d.1963 mixed media. 6-Oct-2 Sotheby's, Singapore #110/R est:4000-6000 (S.D 4000)
£3819	$6378	€5576	Vietnamese couple (33x24cm-13x9in) s. mixed media silk on panel exec c.1953-1955. 12-Oct-3 Sotheby's, Singapore #88/R est:8000-12000 (S.D 11000)
£7190	$13013	€10497	Young Vietnamese lady (34x24cm-13x9in) s. ink gouache silk on paper executed c.1940. 4-Apr-4 Sotheby's, Singapore #63/R est:22000-28000 (S.D 22000)
£9272	$16967	€14000	Portrait de jeune femme de trois-quarts a gauche (38x27cm-15x11in) s. gouache. 7-Apr-4 Piasa, Paris #161/R est:4000-5000
£26144	$47320	€38170	Portrait of a Vietnamese Mandarin (147x72cm-58x28in) s. ink gouache on silk executed 1945-46 prov.lit. 4-Apr-4 Sotheby's, Singapore #55/R est:60000-80000 (S.D 80000)
£31046	$56193	€45327	Lady in blue (64x45cm-25x18in) s. gouache ink on silk executed c.1938. 4-Apr-4 Sotheby's, Singapore #73/R est:70000-90000 (S.D 95000)

VUGHT, Reinoud van (1960-) Dutch

£567	$1037	€850	Abstract composition (150x210cm-59x83in) s.d.1995 verso acrylic. 7-Jun-4 Glerum, Amsterdam #233/R
£1200	$2208	€1800	Still life with roses and fire (19x24cm-7x9in) s.d.1998 verso acrylic triptych. 8-Jun-4 Sotheby's, Amsterdam #168/R est:2000-3000

VUILLARD (1868-1940) French

Prints			
£2901	$5221	€4235	A traverse champs (26x34cm-10x13in) lithograph lit. 26-Apr-4 Bukowskis, Stockholm #462/R est:50000-60000 (S.KR 40000)

VUILLARD, Edouard (1868-1940) French

£11189	$19021	€16000	Arbres et Feuillages (20x11cm-8x4in) st. cardboard painted c.1900 prov.lit. 25-Nov-3 Christie's, Amsterdam #178a/R est:15000-20000
£24454	$44507	€35703	Paysage a l'Etang-la-Ville (21x29cm-8x11in) s. cardboard painted c.1900 prov. 18-Jun-4 Kornfeld, Bern #150/R est:50000 (S.FR 56000)
£27933	$50000	€40782	Jeune file se coiffant (11x20cm-4x8in) st.init. cardboard painted c.1891 prov.exhib.lit. 6-May-4 Sotheby's, New York #202/R est:10000-15000
£32123	$57500	€46900	Portrait d'Ambroise Vollard (36x51cm-14x20in) st.sig. board on cradled panel painted c.1900-01 prov.exhib.lit. 6-May-4 Sotheby's, New York #207/R est:60000-80000
£40000	$72800	€58400	Femme dans l'atelier (32x37cm-13x15in) s. board painted c.1915 prov.exhib.lit. 3-Feb-4 Christie's, London #143/R est:50000-70000
£40000	$73600	€58400	Au restaurant (49x49cm-19x19in) st.sig. board painted c.1897-1899 prov.exhib.lit. 23-Jun-4 Christie's, London #124/R est:45000-65000
£48000	$87360	€70080	Roussel a la meche noire (34x23cm-13x9in) st.sig. oil pastel chl board exec.c.1890 prov.lit. 4-Feb-4 Sotheby's, London #421/R est:40000-60000
£54423	$97417	€80000	Dans son boudoir, dans le salon des Etincelles (65x54cm-26x21in) s. paper on canvas painted 1902 prov. 21-Mar-4 Calmels Cohen, Paris #171/R est:100000-150000
£60000	$100200	€87600	Fridette faton et le bonze (88x69cm-35x27in) s. painted 1927-28 prov.lit. 21-Oct-3 Sotheby's, London #32/R est:60000-80000
£64706	$110000	€94471	La salle Clarac au Louvre, etude 1 (98x113cm-39x44in) st.sig. peinture a la colle chl paper on canvas prov.lit. 5-Nov-3 Christie's, Rockefeller NY #228/R est:150000-200000
£83799	$150000	€122347	Marie au jardin (27x35cm-11x14in) st.sig. painted c.1893 prov.lit. 5-May-4 Christie's, Rockefeller NY #254/R est:150000-200000
£85000	$149600	€124100	Madame Hessel, la main sur la hanche (29x22cm-11x9in) init. board prov.lit. 19-May-4 Dreweatt Neate, Newbury #87/R est:50000-70000
£90000	$165600	€131400	Marthe Mellot (22x14cm-9x6in) init. painted c.1891-1892 prov. 23-Jun-4 Christie's, London #123/R est:60000-80000
£100000	$170000	€146000	Femme avec les sourcils noirs (76x62cm-30x24in) st. board painted c.1910 prov.exhib.lit. 6-Nov-3 Sotheby's, New York #129/R est:120000-180000
£103497	$175944	€148000	Femmes et enfant au jardin (25x43cm-10x17in) s. cardboard lit. 26-Nov-3 Daguerre, Paris #76/R est:100000-110000
£156425	$280000	€228381	Demoiselle en rouge (36x24cm-14x9in) s. canvas on panel painted 1893 prov.exhib.lit. 5-May-4 Sotheby's, New York #21/R est:150000-200000
£391061	$700000	€570949	La mere de Vuillard en profil (33x38cm-13x15in) st.sig. canvas on board painted c.1898 prov.exhib.lit. 5-May-4 Sotheby's, New York #23/R est:700000-900000
£391061	$700000	€570949	Enfant a table (48x62cm-19x24in) s. cardboard on panel prov.exhib.lit. 6-May-4 Sotheby's, New York #127/R est:800000-1200000
Prints			
£1695	$3000	€2475	L'Atre (35x27cm-14x11in) col lithograph edition of 100. 28-Apr-4 Christie's, Rockefeller NY #250/R est:4000-6000
£1765	$3000	€2577	Avenue (45x33cm-18x13in) col lithograph. 31-Oct-3 Sotheby's, New York #487/R
£2215	$3920	€3300	Interieur aux cinq poses. lithograph exec.c.1893. 29-Apr-4 Piasa, Paris #331/R est:4000-5000
£2250	$3600	€3285	Couverture de l'album, paysages et interieurs (51x40cm-20x16in) s. col lithograph edition of 100. 18-Sep-3 Swann Galleries, New York #678/R est:2500-3500
£2333	$4293	€3500	Interieur a la suspension (35x28cm-14x11in) lithograph exec.1899. 10-Jun-4 Piasa, Paris #211
£2533	$4661	€3800	Interieur aux tentures roses (34x27cm-13x11in) lithograph exec.1899. 10-Jun-4 Piasa, Paris #212
£2533	$4535	€3800	Le jardin devant l'atelier (63x48cm-25x19in) s. col lithograph. 15-May-4 Bassenge, Berlin #7183/R est:4000
£2941	$5000	€4294	Interieur aux teintures roses (39x31cm-15x12in) col lithograph. 31-Oct-3 Sotheby's, New York #489/R
£3000	$5460	€4380	La partie de dames (35x28cm-14x11in) lithograph. 30-Jun-4 Christie's, London #323/R est:3000-5000
£3128	$5600	€4567	L'atre (34x27cm-13x11in) color lithograph. 6-May-4 Swann Galleries, New York #348/R est:7000-10000
£3562	$6055	€5200	Interior in pink. col lithograph. 6-Nov-3 Piasa, Paris #198/R
£4118	$7000	€6012	Interior (36x29cm-14x11in) s. col lithograph exec.1899. 4-Nov-3 Christie's, Rockefeller NY #217/R est:7000-9000
£5333	$9813	€8000	Jeux d'enfants (26x43cm-10x17in) s. col lithograph exec.1897. 10-Jun-4 Piasa, Paris #210
£5400	$9936	€7884	La patisserie (38x29cm-15x11in) s. lithograph. 28-Jun-4 Bonhams, New Bond Street #286/R est:6000-8000
£6333	$11653	€9500	Interieur aux tentures roses (34x27cm-13x11in) lithograph exec.1899. 10-Jun-4 Piasa, Paris #213/R
£7647	$13000	€11165	Interieur a la suspension (38x30cm-15x12in) col lithograph. 31-Oct-3 Sotheby's, New York #488/R
£8235	$14000	€12023	Patisserie (40x31cm-16x12in) col lithograph. 31-Oct-3 Sotheby's, New York #490/R
£10959	$18630	€16000	Cuisiniere. lithograph. 6-Nov-3 Piasa, Paris #200/R
Works on paper			
£1100	$2024	€1606	Etude pour la comedie classique (19x11cm-7x4in) init. pencil executed 1912-13. 24-Mar-4 Sotheby's, Olympia #13/R est:1000-1500
£1100	$2024	€1606	Madame Hessel dans sa Chambe aux clayes (17x11cm-7x4in) init. pencil executed c.1912-13. 24-Mar-4 Sotheby's, Olympia #15/R est:800-1000
£1316	$2421	€1921	Two dancers (17x28cm-7x11in) st.sig. wash ink prov. 23-Jun-4 Koller, Zurich #3110 est:3000-5000 (S.FR 3000)
£1400	$2338	€2044	Branchage (23x31cm-9x12in) st.init. pastel prov. 22-Oct-3 Sotheby's, Olympia #13/R est:1500-2000
£1400	$2338	€2044	Landscape (27x27cm-11x11in) st.init. chl prov. 22-Oct-3 Sotheby's, Olympia #14/R est:1500-2000
£1422	$2375	€2062	Les deux joueurs (15x9cm-6x4in) st.mono. crayon exec.c.1920 prov. 21-Jun-3 Galerie du Rhone, Sion #511/R est:3500-4500 (S.FR 3100)
£1500	$2505	€2190	Window (27x24cm-11x9in) st.init. chl prov. 22-Oct-3 Sotheby's, Olympia #4/R est:1500-2000
£1800	$3312	€2628	Ernest Coquelin Cadet dans la Role de Leridon (31x23cm-12x9in) init. brush ink executed 1890. 24-Mar-4 Sotheby's, Olympia #20/R est:2000-3000
£1900	$3496	€2774	La rencontre (31x23cm-12x9in) init. brush ink executed 1893 prov. 24-Mar-4 Sotheby's, Olympia #21/R est:1500-2000
£2000	$3680	€2920	Etude pour les perruches (17x9cm-7x4in) init. pencil col crayon. 24-Mar-4 Sotheby's, Olympia #14/R est:1200-1500
£3113	$5665	€4700	Nu assis dans un fauteuil (48x35cm-19x14in) chl exec. c.1905 prov. 15-Jun-4 Blanchet, Paris #142/R est:4000-5000
£3846	$6423	€5500	Visage de jeune femme rousse (35x28cm-14x11in) st.sig. pastel exec.c.1928 lit. 30-Jun-3 Artcurial Briest, Paris #724/R est:6000-8000
£4800	$8016	€7008	Two nude academics (61x33cm-24x13in) st.sig. chl two. 22-Oct-3 Sotheby's, Olympia #11/R est:3000-4000
£5405	$9297	€7891	Femme en robe rouge (24x14cm-9x6in) st.sig. pastel board. 2-Dec-3 Koller, Zurich #3061/R est:12000-18000 (S.FR 12000)
£7718	$14356	€11500	Bord de mer ou enfant jouant dans les dunes (25x32cm-10x13in) s. pastel prov.lit. 2-Mar-4 Artcurial Briest, Paris #19/R est:12000-15000
£8042	$13832	€11500	Chemin dans un sous-bois (29x23cm-11x9in) mono. pastel. 3-Dec-3 Tajan, Paris #22/R est:10000-12000
£10204	$18265	€15000	Irene Montanet assise dans un fauteuil, regardant vers la gauche (42x32cm-17x13in) s.i. pastel prov.lit. 18-Mar-4 Christie's, Paris #185/R est:18000-22000
£10884	$19483	€16000	Le bassin du chateau des Clayes avec une statue en marbre (21x25cm-8x10in) s. pastel prov.lit. 18-Mar-4 Christie's, Paris #186/R est:10000-15000

£12000 $22080 €17520 Femme en robe rouge (24x14cm-9x6in) st.init. col crayon. 22-Jun-4 Sotheby's, London #421/R est:6000-8000
£12925 $23136 €19000 Deux figures assises sur les marches d'une maison (15x13cm-6x5in) s. pastel. 18-Mar-4 Christie's, Paris #187/R est:6000-8000
£13100 $23843 €19126 Maree basse (24x33cm-9x13in) st.sig. pastel exec. c.1909. 18-Jun-4 Kornfeld, Bern #149/R est:35000 (S.FR 30000)
£15000 $27600 €21900 Mme Vuillard et sa belle-fille a la Closerie des Genets (25x32cm-10x13in) s. pastel buff paper exec 1921-1922 prov.exhib.lit. 24-Jun-4 Christie's, London #344/R est:16000-20000
£15493 $26803 €22000 Esquisse pour portrait de Jane Renouardt (31x25cm-12x10in) pastel prov. 9-Dec-3 Artcurial Briest, Paris #86/R est:15000-20000
£17500 $32200 €25550 La maison dans la dune (65x49cm-26x19in) st.sig. peinture a la colle paper on canvas painted 1909 prov.lit. 23-Jun-4 Christie's, London #125/R est:18000-24000
£18000 $32580 €26280 Bouquet de roses (20x14cm-8x6in) st.init. pastel. 1-Apr-4 Christie's, Kensington #27/R est:8000-12000
£22000 $40260 €33000 Les pivoines aux clayes (31x24cm-12x9in) st.mono. pastel exec. c.1930-1938 prov.lit. 7-Jun-4 Artcurial Briest, Paris #18/R est:25000-35000
£24000 $43680 €35040 Jeune femme assis sous l'arbre dans le parc (26x32cm-10x13in) s. pastel exec c.1907 prov.exhib.lit. 5-Feb-4 Christie's, London #323/R est:25000-35000
£28571 $51143 €42000 Lucien Rosengart dans son usine a Levallois (32x25cm-13x10in) pastel prov.exhib.lit. 18-Mar-4 Christie's, Paris #184/R est:22000-30000
£53073 $95000 €77487 Maison bretonne, Saint-jacut (50x65cm-20x26in) st.sig. peinture a la colle paper on board on canvas prov.lit. 5-May-4 Christie's, Rockefeller NY #234/R est:70000-100000
£54422 $97415 €80000 Place Vintimille (181x50cm-71x20in) pastel prov.lit. 19-Mar-4 Millon & Associes, Paris #80/R est:80000-120000
£72626 $130000 €106034 Square Berlioz (45x76cm-18x30in) st.sig. peinture a la colle canvas on cradled panel prov.lit. 5-May-4 Christie's, Rockefeller NY #250/R est:180000-220000
£446927 $800000 €652513 Aux Pavillons a Cricqueboeuf, devant la maison (212x80cm-83x31in) s.d.1913 peinture a la colle prov.exhib.lit. 4-May-4 Christie's, Rockefeller NY #15/R est:800000-1200000

VUILLARD, Edouard (attrib) (1868-1940) French
£1061 $1900 €1549 Flowers in a basket (30x46cm-12x18in) board. 8-May-4 Susanin's, Chicago #6084/R est:1500-2400

VUILLEFROY, Felix Dominique de (1841-1910) French
£688 $1129 €950 Hautes herbes (50x60cm-20x24in) s. 11-May-3 Osenat, Fontainebleau #177

VUILLEFROY, Felix Dominique de (attrib) (1841-1910) French
£295 $490 €428 Cows on river shore (17x24cm-7x9in) s. panel. 13-Jun-3 Zofingen, Switzerland #2541 (S.FR 650)

VUILLERMET, Charles François (1849-1918) Swiss
£243 $450 €355 Continental portrait of a lady (71x58cm-28x23in) s. 14-Jul-4 Dallas Auction Gallery, Dallas #319/R
£702 $1172 €1025 Vue prise de Chardonne le matin (44x37cm-17x15in) s. 16-Nov-3 Koller, Geneva #1206/R (S.FR 1600)
£905 $1448 €1312 Esplanade in Lausanne (25x41cm-10x16in) s. panel. 15-May-3 Stuker, Bern #1571/R (S.FR 1900)

VUKMANOVIC, Stefan (1924-1995) Yugoslavian
£173 $310 €253 Thaw in Zagreb (77x102cm-30x40in) s.i. 22-Mar-4 Philippe Schuler, Zurich #6205 (S.FR 400)
Works on paper
£310 $518 €450 Wernick Street, Munich Schwabing (60x80cm-24x31in) s.i. mixed media. 10-Jul-3 Allgauer, Kempten #2774/R
£414 $691 €600 Masked figures (88x78cm-35x31in) s. i. verso mixed media. 10-Jul-3 Allgauer, Kempten #2773/R

VULLIAMY, Gerard (1909-) French
£567 $1020 €850 Composition (26x35cm-10x14in) s. painted 1954. 24-Apr-4 Cornette de St.Cyr, Paris #738
£900 $1620 €1350 Garde-freinet (38x46cm-15x18in) s.d.1963 s.i.d.verso prov. 25-Apr-4 Versailles Encheres #59
£3000 $5400 €4500 Composition (146x97cm-57x38in) s.d.1957 prov.exhib. 25-Apr-4 Versailles Encheres #42 est:4000-5000
Works on paper
£544 $975 €800 Untitled (23x32cm-9x13in) s.d.34 lead pencil drawing. 21-Mar-4 Calmels Cohen, Paris #70
£612 $1096 €900 Untitled (21x27cm-8x11in) mono. ink exec 1940. 21-Mar-4 Calmels Cohen, Paris #69/R

VUORI, Antti (1935-) Finnish
£268 $499 €400 Cosmic vehicle (50x63cm-20x25in) s.d.66. 7-Mar-4 Bukowskis, Helsinki #471/R

VUORI, Ilmari (1898-1975) Finnish
£347 $580 €500 Hogland (53x60cm-21x24in) s.d.1920. 23-Oct-3 Hagelstam, Helsinki #986

VUORI, Kaarlo (1863-1914) Finnish
£1342 $2470 €2000 Girl (45x31cm-18x12in) s.d.1897. 25-Mar-4 Hagelstam, Helsinki #1084 est:2500

VUUREN, Jan van (1871-1941) Dutch
Works on paper
£264 $473 €385 Window with a vase of flowers (41x33cm-16x13in) s.d.1990 gouache over pencil. 31-May-4 Stephan Welz, Johannesburg #171 (SA.R 3200)

VYARD, L (?) ?
£1056 $1827 €1500 Normandy coast (35x65cm-14x26in) s. 10-Dec-3 Castellana, Madrid #188/R est:200
£1408 $2437 €2000 Normandy harbour (35x65cm-14x26in) s. 10-Dec-3 Castellana, Madrid #181/R est:200

VYARET, Auguste (19th C) French
£705 $1198 €1029 River landscape. Cows in river (10x17cm-4x7in) s. panel pair. 5-Nov-3 Dobiaschofsky, Bern #1041/R (S.FR 1600)

VYSOTSKY, Konstantin Semionovich (1864-1938) Russian
£8000 $14320 €11680 Transporting the elk (63x100cm-25x39in) s. prov. 26-May-4 Sotheby's, London #75/R est:5000-7000

VYTLACIL, Vaclav (1892-1984) American
£380 $700 €555 Figure composition (89x61cm-35x24in) s.d.1953 paper. 10-Jun-4 Swann Galleries, New York #247/R
£1006 $1600 €1469 Girl with cat (83x55cm-33x22in) s.d.1946 i.d.December 1946 verso tempera masonite. 13-Sep-3 Weschler, Washington #794/R est:1500-2500
£6395 $11000 €9337 Abstracted hens (70x90cm-28x35in) painted c.1920 prov. 3-Dec-3 Doyle, New York #245/R est:6000-8000
Works on paper
£209 $375 €305 Abstracted harbour (46x61cm-18x24in) s.d.1969 pastel. 20-Mar-4 Rachel Davis, Shaker Heights #687/R
£351 $650 €512 Composition with instrument (38x30cm-15x12in) chl exec.c.1925. 13-Mar-4 Susanin's, Chicago #6054/R

VYZANTIOS, Konstantinos (1924-) Greek
£5500 $9350 €8030 Red abstract (97x146cm-38x57in) s.d.61 prov. 18-Nov-3 Sotheby's, London #108/R est:3000-5000

VYZANTIOS, Pericles (1893-1972) Greek
£10500 $18375 €15330 At the exhibition (50x74cm-20x29in) s. exhib. 16-Dec-3 Bonhams, New Bond Street #77/R est:8000-12000

W F E (?) ?
£400 $728 €584 Favourite hunter of Marie Louisa Chalon, wife of Major General Thomas Chalon (66x91cm-26x36in) mono. 4-Feb-4 John Nicholson, Haslemere #118

W H W (?) ?
Sculpture
£1400 $2506 €2044 Spanish dancer (29cm-11in) mono. chromed metal ebonised wood. 13-May-4 Christie's, Kensington #374/R est:900-1200

WAAGEN (19th C) German
Sculpture
£1208 $2259 €1800 Levrette (29cm-11in) brown pat bronze marble socle. 1-Mar-4 Coutau Begarie, Paris #235/R est:1800-2000

WAAGEN, Adalbert (1833-1898) German
£333 $557 €480 Dillingen (13x21cm-5x8in) s.d.94 board. 22-Oct-3 Neumeister, Munich #777
£833 $1358 €1200 Obersee near Berchtesgaden with Teufelshorn (80x74cm-31x29in) s.d.1877 canvas on panel. 24-Sep-3 Neumeister, Munich #596/R
£1275 $2346 €1900 Alpine landscape in autumn (72x92cm-28x36in) s. bears i. lit. 25-Mar-4 Karlheinz Kaupp, Staufen #2791/R est:1200
£3357 $5773 €4800 Girl going up to mountain pasture with cattle (88x116cm-35x46in) s.d.1870. 4-Dec-3 Neumeister, Munich #2864/R est:1000

WAAGEN, Adalbert (attrib) (1833-1898) German
£450 $824 €657 Extensive landscape (44x63cm-17x25in) bears i.verso. 6-Apr-4 Bonhams, Knightsbridge #73/R

WAAGEN, Arthur (19th C) French
Sculpture
£3169 $5261 €4500 Return from the hunt (89cm-35in) s. brown pat. bronze. 11-Jun-3 Sotheby's, Amsterdam #301 est:5000-6000
£6577 $12102 €9800 Chasse kabyle (92x72x34cm-36x28x13in) i. brown pat bronze. 29-Mar-4 Rieunier, Paris #94/R est:8000-10000
£9000 $15300 €13140 Kabyle au retour de la chasse (90x75cm-35x30in) s. pat bronze. 28-Oct-3 Sotheby's, London #102/R

WAAGENES, Trygve (?) Norwegian
£304 $527 €444 Fishing station, Lofoten (73x92cm-29x36in) s. panel. 13-Dec-3 Blomqvist, Lysaker #1392/R (N.KR 3500)

WAAGSTEIN, Joen (1879-1949) Danish
£1083 $1993 €1581 View of coastal cliffs, Faroe Islands (51x75cm-20x30in) s. 29-Mar-4 Rasmussen, Copenhagen #264 est:6000-8000 (D.KR 12000)
£1173 $2159 €1713 Fjord landscape, Faroe Islands (45x73cm-18x29in) init. 29-Mar-4 Rasmussen, Copenhagen #256 est:6000-8000 (D.KR 13000)
£1264 $2325 €1845 Coastal landscape near Thorshavn (77x105cm-30x41in) s.d.1934. 29-Mar-4 Rasmussen, Copenhagen #250/R est:8000-12000 (D.KR 14000)

WAAL, Cornelis de (1881-1946) Dutch
£455 $773 €650 Amsterdam harbour (80x120cm-31x47in) s. 28-Nov-3 Wendl, Rudolstadt #3954/R

WAAY, Nicolaas van der (1855-1936) Dutch
£2740 $4658 €4000 Woman in white dress (40x32cm-16x13in) s. 5-Nov-3 Vendue Huis, Gravenhage #120/R est:4000-6000

£13333 $24000 €20000 Quiet moment (134x57cm-53x22in) s. exhib. 20-Apr-4 Sotheby's, Amsterdam #229/R est:15000-20000
£14667 $26400 €22000 In the courtyard on a sunny afternoon (80x60cm-31x24in) s. 21-Apr-4 Christie's, Amsterdam #120/R est:10000-15000
Works on paper
£1351 $2378 €2000 Elegant interior with maid taking glasses out of a vitrine (80x60cm-31x24in) black chk prov.exhib. 19-May-4 Sotheby's, Amsterdam #359/R est:2000-3000
£1769 $3219 €2600 Jonge vrouw in empiretoilet, portrait of a young lady (78x59cm-31x23in) s. pencil W/C. 3-Feb-4 Christie's, Amsterdam #167/R est:2000-3000
£4333 $7800 €6500 An elegant lady (60x34cm-24x13in) s. W/C. 20-Apr-4 Sotheby's, Amsterdam #143/R est:4000-6000
£21711 $39296 €33000 Concert interval in the garden of the concert buildings (45x69cm-18x27in) s. W/C. 19-Apr-4 Glerum, Amsterdam #188/R est:13000-16000

WABEL (19th C) ?
Works on paper
£1888 $3153 €2700 Portrait of small girl wearing white dress with blue sash (68x56cm-27x22in) s.d.76 pastel oval. 9-Oct-3 Michael Zeller, Lindau #787/R est:1400

WABEL, Henry (1889-1981) Swiss
£407 $692 €594 Still life with blue vase (61x46cm-24x18in) s.d.54. 18-Nov-3 Hans Widmer, St Gallen #1225 (S.FR 900)
£452 $756 €660 Still life of fruit (33x41cm-13x16in) s.d.1955. 24-Jun-3 Germann, Zurich #1077 (S.FR 1000)
£452 $769 €660 Interior with table (50x40cm-20x16in) s.d.36. 28-Nov-3 Zofingen, Switzerland #3207 (S.FR 1000)
£658 $1178 €961 Interior with still life (61x46cm-24x18in) s.d. 22-Mar-4 Philippe Schuler, Zurich #4365 (S.FR 1520)
£995 $1692 €1453 Paris (50x61cm-20x24in) s. 25-Nov-3 Germann, Zurich #922/R est:2000-2500 (S.FR 2200)

WACHSMAN, Bedrich (1871-1944) Czechoslovakian
£535 $996 €781 Diana hunting (37x57cm-15x22in) i.d.1923 panel. 6-Mar-4 Dorotheum, Prague #72/R est:26000-38000 (C.KR 26000)
£3913 $7278 €5713 Shipbuilding yard in Triest (20x25cm-8x10in) s. wood. 6-Mar-4 Dorotheum, Prague #16/R est:50000-75000 (C.KR 190000)
Works on paper
£306 $509 €447 Summer afternoon (35x25cm-14x10in) s.d.1930 pastel. 4-Oct-3 Dorotheum, Prague #178/R est:10000-15000 (C.KR 14000)

WACHSMUTH, Maximilian (1859-1912) German
£313 $522 €450 Woodcutter and girl in conversation at table (49x55cm-19x22in) s. 22-Oct-3 Neumeister, Munich #778/R
£417 $663 €600 Interior (20x24cm-8x9in) s. panel. 11-Sep-3 Weidler, Nurnberg #366
£1222 $2200 €1784 Courting couples in domestic interior (44x37cm-17x15in) s. panel pair prov. 24-Apr-4 Weschler, Washington #570/R est:3000-5000
£1600 $2912 €2400 Musical moment (71x88cm-28x35in) s. 30-Jun-4 Neumeister, Munich #739/R

WACHTEL, Elmer (1864-1929) American
£2310 $4250 €3373 Canyon landscape (34x45cm-13x18in) mono. canvasboard prov. 8-Jun-4 Bonhams & Butterfields, San Francisco #4244/R est:7000-10000
£2793 $5000 €4190 Sierra landscape (81x61cm-32x24in) 16-May-4 Abell, Los Angeles #513
£3235 $5500 €4723 Foothill landscape (36x28cm-14x11in) s. canvasboard. 18-Nov-3 John Moran, Pasadena #21 est:5000-7500
£4412 $7500 €6442 Landscape (46x36cm-18x14in) s. s.d.1926 verso prov. 18-Nov-3 John Moran, Pasadena #132a est:5000-7000
£5780 $10000 €8439 Santa Barbara coast (41x61cm-16x24in) i.verso prov. 10-Dec-3 Bonhams & Butterfields, San Francisco #6255/R est:5000-7000
£5820 $11000 €8497 Flowers in California landscape (30x43cm-12x17in) 17-Feb-4 John Moran, Pasadena #45/R est:9000-12000
£17647 $30000 €25765 Santa Anita (51x66cm-20x26in) mono. i.verso prov. 18-Nov-3 John Moran, Pasadena #27 est:20000-30000
£20381 $37500 €29756 Snowy solitude (76x101cm-30x40in) s. prov.exhib. 8-Jun-4 Bonhams & Butterfields, San Francisco #4327/R est:25000-35000
£21676 $37500 €31647 Dawn (61x91cm-24x36in) s. 10-Dec-3 Bonhams & Butterfields, San Francisco #6220/R est:25000-35000
£31746 $60000 €46349 Stream in Santa Anita Canyon (71x61cm-28x24in) mono. prov. 17-Feb-4 John Moran, Pasadena #33/R est:25000-35000
£38462 $70000 €56155 Santa Anita Canyon (61x76cm-24x30in) mono. prov. 15-Jun-4 John Moran, Pasadena #66 est:30000-50000
Works on paper
£944 $1500 €1378 Open pasture (22x27cm-9x11in) s.d.98 W/C. 12-Sep-3 Skinner, Boston #421/R
£2500 $4250 €3650 Summer landscape (20x30cm-8x12in) s. W/C. 18-Nov-3 John Moran, Pasadena #173 est:2000-3000
£2747 $5000 €4011 Spanish style house in eucalyptus landscape (38x25cm-15x10in) s. W/C. 15-Jun-4 John Moran, Pasadena #24a est:6000-8000
£3297 $6000 €4814 San Gabriel Valley ranch house (23x41cm-9x16in) mono. W/C. 15-Jun-4 John Moran, Pasadena #24 est:6000-8000

WACHTEL, Marion K (1876-1954) American
£1902 $3500 €2777 Eucalyptus landscape (18x13cm-7x5in) s. oil paperboard. 8-Jun-4 Auctions by the Bay, Alameda #1093/R
£2335 $4250 €3409 Santa Barbara Canyon (28x41cm-11x16in) s. canvasboard. 29-Jun-4 Sotheby's, New York #253/R est:4000-6000
£4891 $9000 €7141 Point Lobos (34x46cm-13x18in) s. prov. 8-Jun-4 Bonhams & Butterfields, San Francisco #4236/R est:10000-15000
£5491 $9500 €8017 Stream and trees (43x34cm-17x13in) s. canvas on board. 10-Dec-3 Bonhams & Butterfields, San Francisco #6200/R est:12000-16000
£13736 $25000 €20055 The rushing stream (51x66cm-20x26in) i.verso prov. 15-Jun-4 John Moran, Pasadena #51 est:25000-35000
£15896 $27500 €23208 Mountain lake in the Sierras (41x51cm-16x20in) canvas laid down. 10-Dec-3 Bonhams & Butterfields, San Francisco #6199/R est:20000-30000
Works on paper
£397 $700 €580 Family portrait (30x25cm-12x10in) s. W/C. 23-May-4 Bonhams & Butterfields, Los Angeles #7025/R
£934 $1700 €1364 Portrait of a Lady. s. exec 1896. 7-Feb-4 Harvey Clar, Oakland #1593
£978 $1800 €1428 Flower vendor (19x16cm-7x6in) s. pencil W/C prov. 27-Jun-4 Bonhams & Butterfields, San Francisco #3831/R est:3000-5000
£4070 $7000 €5942 California landscape (23x30cm-9x12in) s. W/C prov. 7-Dec-3 Freeman, Philadelphia #121 est:3000-5000
£18519 $35000 €27038 San Gabriel Valley (46x61cm-18x24in) W/C. 17-Feb-4 John Moran, Pasadena #63/R est:2000-3000

WACHTEL, Wilhelm (1875-1942) German
£552 $1000 €806 The Chalutza, a woman pioneer (63x50cm-25x20in) s. painted 1920's. 1-Apr-4 Ben-Ami, Tel Aviv #4688/R

WACHTER, Emil (1921-) German
Works on paper
£322 $570 €480 Bird (29x15cm-11x6in) s.d. chk Indian ink brush. 30-Apr-4 Dr Fritz Nagel, Stuttgart #490/R
£369 $653 €550 Still life with flower (34x27cm-13x11in) s.d. W/C. 30-Apr-4 Dr Fritz Nagel, Stuttgart #489/R

WACHTER, Georg (attrib) (1809-1863) German
£350 $594 €500 Christ on the cross with Jerusalem beyond (45x35cm-18x14in) i. verso. 20-Nov-3 Dorotheum, Salzburg #168/R

WACHTER, Lou (19th C) German?
£413 $756 €603 Summer mountainous landscape with ruins (30x36cm-12x14in) i.stretcher. 4-Jun-4 Zofingen, Switzerland #2373 (S.FR 950)

WACHTER, Paula von (1860-1944) German
£1184 $2179 €1800 Woman reading (120x100cm-47x39in) s.d.98 i.verso. 25-Jun-4 Michael Zeller, Lindau #580/R

WACHTMEISTER, Rosina (20th C) German?
Works on paper
£403 $713 €600 Birds in open cage (66x45cm-26x18in) s.d. verso tempera acrylic collage board. 30-Apr-4 Dr Fritz Nagel, Stuttgart #492/R
£417 $679 €600 Flautist (65x50cm-26x20in) s.d.1992 mixed media collage tempera board. 27-Sep-3 Dr Fritz Nagel, Stuttgart #9401/R
£694 $1132 €1000 White dove in landscape (65x50cm-26x20in) s.d. mixed media collage tempera board. 27-Sep-3 Dr Fritz Nagel, Stuttgart #9400/R

WACHWEGER, Thomas (1943-) German
£671 $1235 €1000 Travel companion (223x160cm-88x63in) s.i.d. verso acrylic paper on cotton. 26-Mar-4 Ketterer, Hamburg #683/R

WACKER, Rudolf (1893-1939) Austrian
£27778 $47222 €40000 Bodensee landscape (59x44cm-23x17in) mono.d.28 s.i.d.26.IX,28 verso panel lit. 28-Oct-3 Wiener Kunst Auktionen, Vienna #107/R est:50000-100000
£30201 $53456 €45000 Bodensee landscape (50x65cm-20x26in) mono.d.31 i. verso board. 28-Apr-4 Wiener Kunst Auktionen, Vienna #118/R est:55000-80000
£40268 $72081 €60000 Still life with angel, gourd and picture of Punch and Judy (77x55cm-30x22in) s. lit. 27-May-4 Hassfurther, Vienna #74/R est:80000-120000
Prints
£2797 $4755 €4000 Self portrait (64x47cm-25x19in) s. lithograph. 25-Nov-3 Hassfurther, Vienna #82/R est:3000-3500
Works on paper
£855 $1574 €1300 Male nude (42x31cm-17x12in) mono.d.12 chl htd white. 22-Jun-4 Wiener Kunst Auktionen, Vienna #43/R
£1316 $2421 €2000 Self portrait (42x29cm-17x11in) s.d.1919 pencil. 22-Jun-4 Wiener Kunst Auktionen, Vienna #40/R est:2000
£1538 $2615 €2200 Reclining nude (42x29cm-17x11in) mono.d.32 black chk. 25-Nov-3 Hassfurther, Vienna #79/R est:2500-3000
£1645 $3026 €2500 Two nudes viewed from behind (51x36cm-20x14in) mono.d.22 pencil. 22-Jun-4 Wiener Kunst Auktionen, Vienna #41/R est:2500
£2098 $3566 €3000 Reclining nude (38x25cm-15x10in) mono.d.34 black chk. 25-Nov-3 Hassfurther, Vienna #78/R est:3000-3500
£2098 $3566 €3000 Elderly person crouching (33x24cm-13x9in) mono.d.24 black chk transparent paper lit. 25-Nov-3 Hassfurther, Vienna #80/R est:3000-4000
£2098 $3566 €3000 Landscape (24x33cm-9x13in) mono.d.24 chl transparent paper. 25-Nov-3 Hassfurther, Vienna #81/R est:3000-3500
£2308 $3923 €3300 Female nude supporting herself (42x29cm-17x11in) mono. black chk transparent paper lit. 25-Nov-3 Hassfurther, Vienna #75/R est:2800-3800
£2797 $4755 €4000 Back of nude standing in front of stove pipe (50x35cm-20x14in) mono. black chk transparent paper lit. 25-Nov-3 Hassfurther, Vienna #76/R est:3000-3500
£2797 $4755 €4000 Parish church (43x34cm-17x13in) mono.d.22 chl. 25-Nov-3 Hassfurther, Vienna #77/R est:3000-3500
£3356 $6007 €5000 Female nude (48x32cm-19x13in) mono.d.34 ochre. 25-May-4 Dorotheum, Vienna #183/R est:5000-5500

WACKERLE, Joseph (1880-1959) German
Sculpture
£2069 $3455 €3000 Bell ringer (88cm-35in) pat.bronze. 9-Jul-3 Hugo Ruef, Munich #1848/R est:4500
£3311 $6026 €5000 Bacchus (82cm-32in) s.d.1923 bronze. 16-Jun-4 Hugo Ruef, Munich #1767/R est:900

WADDELL, Lillian (20th C) American
£301 $550 €452 Still life with exotic vase and plumbs (61x74cm-24x29in) s.d.1939 verso. 31-Jul-4 Sloans & Kenyon, Bethesda #278/R

WADDELL, Peter (20th C) New Zealander
£290 $493 €423 Reclining male beneath an image of the Virgin Mary (70x100cm-28x39in) s.d.1986. 4-Nov-3 Peter Webb, Auckland #184/R (NZ.D 800)

WADDINGTON, Frank (20th C) British
£320 $573 €467 Douglas harbour scene (37x51cm-15x20in) s. i.stretcher. 17-Mar-4 Bonhams, Chester #253

WADDINGTON, Phillip J (20th C) New Zealander
£362 $587 €525 An Arawa chieftainess (14x19cm-6x7in) s.d.1974 panel. 31-Jul-3 International Art Centre, Auckland #134/R est:1400-1800 (NZ.D 1000)

WADE, Ben (19th C) American
£471 $800 €688 Daisy, a stallion (25x41cm-10x16in) s. 21-Nov-3 Eldred, East Dennis #228

WADE, David (20th C) American
£7487 $14000 €10931 Peak of the rut (76x122cm-30x48in) s. 24-Jul-4 Coeur d'Alene, Hayden #90/R est:15000-25000

WADE, George Edward (1853-1933) British
Sculpture
£1800 $3006 €2628 Grenadier Guard (57cm-22in) s.i. dark brown pat. bronze on wood plinth. 14-Oct-3 Sotheby's, Olympia #43/R est:2000-3000

WADE, Jonathan (1960-) British
£350 $557 €511 Mother earth (29x46cm-11x18in) s. board. 10-Sep-3 Sotheby's, Olympia #258/R
£450 $774 €657 Happy land (28x60cm-11x24in) s. board. 3-Dec-3 Christie's, Kensington #728/R
£450 $765 €657 Murder of Banquo (66x97cm-26x38in) s. board. 26-Nov-3 Sotheby's, Olympia #184/R
£450 $810 €657 God's country (61x78cm-24x31in) s. i.verso board. 21-Apr-4 Tennants, Leyburn #1236
£550 $946 €803 Just off the Falls Road, west Belfast (19x28cm-7x11in) s. board. 3-Dec-3 Christie's, Kensington #725/R
£550 $1023 €803 After the honeymoon (60x81cm-24x32in) s. board. 4-Mar-4 Christie's, Kensington #235/R
£580 $986 €847 Music, hounds on a hillside (17x24cm-7x9in) s. i.verso board. 19-Nov-3 Tennants, Leyburn #1276/R
£600 $1002 €876 Lonely cloud (36x25cm-14x10in) s. board. 16-Oct-3 Christie's, Kensington #620/R
£600 $1110 €876 Survival of the fittest (60x38cm-24x15in) s. s.i.verso board. 11-Feb-4 Sotheby's, Olympia #231/R
£650 $1203 €949 Reunion (21x27cm-8x11in) s. i.verso board. 11-Mar-4 Christie's, Kensington #202/R
£800 $1272 €1168 High tide (45x60cm-18x24in) s. board. 10-Sep-3 Sotheby's, Olympia #240/R
£1400 $2520 €2044 Journey's end (61x77cm-24x30in) s. i.verso board. 21-Apr-4 Tennants, Leyburn #1235/R est:700-900
£1420 $2414 €2073 Crofting (29x86cm-11x34in) s. board. 19-Nov-3 Tennants, Leyburn #1270/R est:700-900
£2100 $3927 €3150 The shooting lunch (28x82cm-11x32in) s. board. 22-Jul-4 Tennants, Leyburn #930/R est:700-900
Works on paper
£350 $585 €511 Morning (25x35cm-10x14in) s. s.i.verso pen black ink W/C bodycol. 16-Oct-3 Christie's, Kensington #621/R
£500 $925 €730 Saturday afternoon (25x35cm-10x14in) s. s.i.verso pen ink W/C gouache oil. 11-Feb-4 Sotheby's, Olympia #212/R

WADE, Jonathan (1941-1973) Irish
£1958 $3329 €2800 Ringsend skyline (61x74cm-24x29in) s. board prov. 18-Nov-3 Whyte's, Dublin #77/R est:2000-3000
£2394 $3831 €3400 Panic (76x51cm-30x20in) s.d.1968 prov.exhib. 16-Sep-3 Whyte's, Dublin #189/R est:2000-3000
£2535 $4056 €3600 Industrial landscape (61x91cm-24x36in) s. 16-Sep-3 Whyte's, Dublin #190/R est:2000-3000

WADE, Thomas (1828-1891) British
Works on paper
£400 $720 €584 North Hill, Clovelly (67x50cm-26x20in) s.d.1883 W/C over pencil. 22-Apr-4 Lawrence, Crewkerne #797

WADELTON, David (1955-) Australian
£1138 $1787 €1661 Starless (152x101cm-60x40in) s.i.d.1988 verso prov. 27-Aug-3 Christie's, Sydney #613/R est:4000-6000 (A.D 2800)
£1229 $1942 €1794 How soon is now? (131x177cm-52x70in) s.i.d.1991 verso pencil exhib. 2-Sep-3 Deutscher-Menzies, Melbourne #6/R est:4500-6000 (A.D 3000)
£2542 $4322 €3711 Cyber shift (122x183cm-48x72in) s.verso exhib. 24-Nov-3 Sotheby's, Melbourne #36/R est:5000-7000 (A.D 6000)

WADHAM, William Joseph (1863-1950) Australian
Works on paper
£250 $408 €365 Aberdaron village (28x43cm-11x17in) s. W/C. 27-Sep-3 Rogers Jones, Clwyd #23
£270 $491 €394 River landscape with figures fishing (48x74cm-19x29in) W/C. 4-Feb-4 Brightwells, Leominster #1011

WADSWORTH, Edward (1889-1949) British
Prints
£2500 $4600 €3650 Street singers (14x11cm-6x4in) s. woodcut executed c.1914. 29-Mar-4 Bonhams, New Bond Street #274/R est:1500-2000
£4000 $7360 €5840 Interior (11x73cm-4x29in) s.d.1917 woodcut. 29-Mar-4 Bonhams, New Bond Street #275/R est:1500-2000
£4600 $8464 €6716 Minesweepers in port (55x13cm-22x5in) s.d.1918 woodcut. 29-Mar-4 Bonhams, New Bond Street #276/R est:3000-5000
Works on paper
£360 $623 €526 Sulphuric acid, from Achievements of an Industry (10x18cm-4x7in) i.verso pen black ink prov. 9-Dec-3 Rosebery Fine Art, London #711
£450 $851 €657 Introduction, from Aspects of Industry (40x53cm-16x21in) i. verso pen prov. 17-Feb-4 Rosebery Fine Art, London #486
£900 $1683 €1350 Aspects of an industry (40x53cm-16x21in) gouache pastel. 22-Jul-4 Dominic Winter, Swindon #348
£1050 $1817 €1533 Sulphuric acid, from Achievements in Industry (21x38cm-8x15in) i. gouache prov. 9-Dec-3 Rosebery Fine Art, London #717 est:1000-2000
£1500 $2640 €2190 Quayside (42x26cm-17x10in) s.d.1924 pencil. 19-May-4 Sotheby's, Olympia #89/R est:1500-2000
£1800 $2862 €2628 Measured tread (28x31cm-11x12in) ink gouache. 10-Sep-3 Sotheby's, Olympia #293/R est:2000-4000
£6500 $12025 €9490 WW1 Shipping being camouflaged (11x14cm-4x6in) s.d.1918 pen in, W/C. 10-Mar-4 Sotheby's, Olympia #114/R est:400-600
£16000 $29120 €23360 Dazzle ships in Liverpool Docks (13x18cm-5x7in) pencil gouache. 15-Jun-4 Bonhams, New Bond Street #24/R est:5000-7000

WAEL, Cornelis de (1592-1667) Flemish
£6500 $11700 €9490 Courtyard scene with soldiers returning from battle (71x46cm-28x18in) prov. 20-Apr-4 Sotheby's, Olympia #335/R est:3000-4000
£7800 $13494 €11388 Naval battle between Turks and Christians (44x71cm-17x28in) 9-Dec-3 Sotheby's, Olympia #364/R est:6000-8000
£28000 $51240 €40880 Troops maneuvering in an extensive landscape (129x194cm-51x76in) prov.lit. 7-Jul-4 Christie's, London #84/R est:25000-35000
£28369 $45957 €40000 Campamento con soldados descansando (78x115cm-31x45in) prov. 20-May-3 Ansorena, Madrid #94a/R est:40000
£29655 $54862 €43000 Marchands de chevaux turcs au portes d'une vile en Italie (165x204cm-65x80in) 13-Feb-4 Rossini, Paris #11/R est:9000-10000

WAEL, Cornelis de (attrib) (1592-1667) Flemish
£3133 $5609 €4700 Columbus' arrival (80x130cm-31x51in) 13-May-4 Babuino, Rome #95/R est:4000-6000
£7586 $12593 €11000 Naval battle (77x124cm-30x49in) prov. 1-Oct-3 Dorotheum, Vienna #38/R est:10000-15000

WAENERBERG, Thorsten (1846-1917) Finnish
£1208 $2247 €1800 The manor house (21x35cm-8x14in) s.d.24/8 1900. 7-Mar-4 Bukowskis, Helsinki #474/R est:2000
£1351 $2419 €2000 Nokia river (19x35cm-7x14in) s.d.1876 canvas on board. 8-May-4 Bukowskis, Helsinki #142/R est:2000-2500
£2027 $3628 €3000 Fishermen at sea (22x30cm-9x12in) s.d.1891 canvas on board. 8-May-4 Bukowskis, Helsinki #178/R est:3000-3500
£2041 $3714 €3000 Large stones on beach (37x26cm-15x10in) s.d.15.8.1905. 8-Feb-4 Bukowskis, Helsinki #481/R est:1500
£2533 $4535 €3800 Seascape with sailing boats on stormy seas (24x36cm-9x14in) s.d.1885 panel. 15-May-4 Hagelstam, Helsinki #120/R est:4000
£2817 $4873 €4000 At sea (23x37cm-9x15in) canvas on panel. 13-Dec-3 Hagelstam, Helsinki #98/R est:3000
£4000 $7160 €6000 Sailing in evening (44x72cm-17x28in) s.d.1876. 15-May-4 Hagelstam, Helsinki #119/R est:6000
£4196 $7133 €6000 Waiting to go out - boats on beach (48x38cm-19x15in) s.d.23.1.1890. 29-Nov-3 Bukowskis, Helsinki #162/R est:6000-8000

WAENTIG, Walter (1881-1962) German
£1611 $2962 €2400 Constance (58x82cm-23x32in) s.d.1934 lit. 27-Mar-4 Geble, Radolfzell #769/R

WAERHERT, Arthur de (1881-1944) Belgian
£671 $1242 €1000 Landscape with sheep (53x73cm-21x29in) s. panel. 13-Mar-4 De Vuyst, Lokeren #119
£833 $1358 €1200 Sheep and goat in a landscape (33x46cm-13x18in) s. panel. 29-Sep-3 Sotheby's, Amsterdam #50/R
£1049 $1783 €1500 Moutons au paturage (56x67cm-22x26in) s. panel. 1-Dec-3 Palais de Beaux Arts, Brussels #242/R est:1500-2000

WAGEMAEKERS, Victor (1876-1953) Belgian
£246 $450 €359 Le meuse a la voir, landscape (23x30cm-9x12in) s. panel. 10-Apr-4 Auctions by the Bay, Alameda #1532/R
£364 $663 €550 Etang en foret (45x55cm-18x22in) s. 15-Jun-4 Vanderkindere, Brussels #152
£372 $665 €550 Etang en automne (80x100cm-31x39in) s. 10-May-4 Horta, Bruxelles #439
£604 $1117 €900 The watermill (45x55cm-18x22in) s. 13-Mar-4 De Vuyst, Lokeren #390
£612 $1096 €900 Chemin en foret (45x60cm-18x24in) s. 16-Mar-4 Vanderkindere, Brussels #16
£638 $1180 €950 Cows near the watermill (50x60cm-20x24in) s. 13-Mar-4 De Vuyst, Lokeren #389
£664 $1129 €950 Cour de ferme en fleurs (54x65cm-21x26in) s. 18-Nov-3 Vanderkindere, Brussels #89
£769 $1308 €1100 Fermiere et ses chevres, devant la ferme (50x89cm-20x35in) s. 18-Nov-3 Vanderkindere, Brussels #207
£3642 $6629 €5500 Canard dans la campagne (100x150cm-39x59in) s. 15-Jun-4 Galerie Moderne, Brussels #174/R est:3000-5000
Works on paper
£276 $500 €420 Pont a Bruges (34x46cm-13x18in) s. W/C. 19-Apr-4 Horta, Bruxelles #312

WAGEMAKER, Jaap (1906-1972) Dutch
Works on paper
£839 $1443 €1200 African style (75x61cm-30x24in) s.d.1956 gouache cardboard prov. 4-Dec-3 Van Ham, Cologne #539/R
£4348 $7130 €6000 Slate and shells (50x61cm-20x24in) s.d.66 s.i.d.66 verso mixed media panel lit. 27-May-3 Sotheby's, Amsterdam #431/R est:3500-4500
£4545 $7818 €6500 Gesloten vorm in de ruimte (136x57cm-54x22in) s.d.61 s.i.d.verso mixed media prov.exhib.lit. 2-Dec-3 Sotheby's, Amsterdam #120/R est:8000-12000
£6667 $12267 €10000 Witte ruimte II (115x125cm-45x49in) s. s.d.61 stretcher i. verso mixed media canvas lit. 8-Jun-4 Sotheby's, Amsterdam #75/R est:7000-9000

WAGEMAN, Thomas Charles (attrib) (1787-1863) British
£1000 $1820 €1460 Portrait of Edward Henry Howard (9x33cm-4x13in) i. board. 21-Jun-4 Christie's, London #192/R est:2000-3000

WAGEMANS, Maurice (1877-1927) Belgian
£382 $607 €550 Portrait de la soeur de l'artiste (55x44cm-22x17in) s. paper laid down exhib. 9-Sep-3 Palais de Beaux Arts, Brussels #291
£470 $869 €700 Rochers (40x60cm-16x24in) s. 15-Mar-4 Horta, Bruxelles #277
£733 $1327 €1100 Vue de l'Escaut (34x55cm-13x22in) s. wood. 30-Mar-4 Campo, Vlaamse Kaai #225/R
£833 $1392 €1200 Vue sur la Seine a Paris (26x44cm-10x17in) s. panel exhib. 21-Oct-3 Campo & Campo, Antwerp #357
£855 $1548 €1300 Nue de dos (60x40cm-24x16in) s. 19-Apr-4 Horta, Bruxelles #26
£1259 $2165 €1800 Depart de regate a Ostende (59x69cm-23x27in) s. 8-Dec-3 Horta, Bruxelles #45 est:1000-1500
£1333 $2413 €2000 Plage avec ramasseurs de coquillages (37x46cm-15x18in) mono. wood. 30-Mar-4 Campo, Vlaamse Kaai #224/R est:1200-1400
£3546 $5922 €5000 Nu couche (150x80cm-59x31in) s.d.1910. 14-Oct-3 Vanderkindere, Brussels #100/R
Works on paper
£1467 $2625 €2200 Beach scene (44x56cm-17x22in) s. W/C. 15-May-4 De Vuyst, Lokeren #401/R est:2200-2600

WAGEMANS, Pieter Johannes Alexander (1879-1955) Dutch
£400 $716 €600 Harbour view (49x79cm-19x31in) s. 11-May-4 Vendu Notarishuis, Rotterdam #16/R

WAGENBAUER, Max Josef (1774-1829) German
£6376 $11732 €9500 Herder resting with animals by stream (39x33cm-15x13in) s. i. verso panel. 24-Mar-4 Hugo Ruef, Munich #886 est:9500
Works on paper
£320 $573 €480 Mountain village (17x24cm-7x9in) s. chk. 13-May-4 Bassenge, Berlin #5680/R

WAGENBAUER, Max Josef (attrib) (1774-1829) German
Works on paper
£349 $642 €520 Resting cattle with herder (24x21cm-9x8in) W/C. 25-Mar-4 Dr Fritz Nagel, Stuttgart #507/R

WAGENSCHOEN, Franz Xaver (1726-1790) Austrian
£5517 $9159 €8000 Bacchanal, allegory of summer (76x95cm-30x37in) 1-Oct-3 Dorotheum, Vienna #276/R est:7000-12000
Works on paper
£464 $850 €677 Beauty and time, Venus crowned by cupid while time sleeps (22x28cm-9x11in) s. black chk. 29-Jan-4 Swann Galleries, New York #301/R

WAGHENAER, Lucas Janszoon (16th C) Dutch
Prints
£2500 $4675 €3650 Bristol Channel (37x52cm-15x20in) engraving. 26-Feb-4 Bruton Knowles, Cheltenham #24/R est:1200-1500

WAGNER, Albert (19th C) German?
£2083 $3542 €3000 Jager mit buchse (18x14cm-7x6in) s.i. panel. 28-Oct-3 Christie's, Amsterdam #93/R est:3000-5000

WAGNER, Alexander von (1838-1919) Hungarian
£4615 $7661 €6738 Antiquity shop (70x45cm-28x18in) s. 4-Oct-3 Kieselbach, Budapest #140/R (H.F 1700000)

WAGNER, Alexander von (attrib) (1838-1919) Hungarian
£1389 $2361 €2000 Portrait of a Bedouin (61x49cm-24x19in) mono.d.188. 28-Oct-3 Dorotheum, Vienna #195/R est:2500-3000

WAGNER, Carl (1796-1857) German
Works on paper
£533 $960 €800 Innsbruck (27x37cm-11x15in) i.d. W/C on pencil. 24-Apr-4 Reiss & Sohn, Konigstein #5574/R
£608 $1070 €900 In the Tyrolean Alps (21x19cm-8x7in) s.i. pen wash prov.lit. 22-May-4 Lempertz, Koln #1472

WAGNER, Cornelis (1870-1956) German
£364 $607 €520 Boats at sea (33x47cm-13x19in) s. 28-Jun-3 Bolland & Marotz, Bremen #751/R
£500 $905 €750 Lower Rhine in early spring (32x45cm-13x18in) mono.d.15 board. 1-Apr-4 Van Ham, Cologne #1696

WAGNER, Ferdinand (19/20th C) German
£3125 $4938 €4500 Neapolitan woman (120x72cm-47x28in) s. lit. 19-Sep-3 Schloss Ahlden, Ahlden #1476/R est:4800
Works on paper
£383 $700 €559 Got a bite! (41x41cm-16x16in) s.d.1950 W/C. 5-Jun-4 Treadway Gallery, Cincinnati #692/R

WAGNER, Ferdinand (jnr) (1847-1927) German
£2303 $4168 €3500 Allegory of the four seasons (170x200cm-67x79in) s. four-panels. 19-Apr-4 Glerum, Amsterdam #290/R est:3500-4500
£24324 $43541 €36000 Party group with mandolin player (120x171cm-47x67in) s. lit. 8-May-4 Schloss Ahlden, Ahlden #711/R est:38000

WAGNER, Fred (1864-1940) American
£10063 $16000 €14692 Winter scene with mill buildings along stream and waterfall (74x91cm-29x36in) s. 10-Sep-3 Alderfer's, Hatfield #394/R est:10000-12000
Works on paper
£279 $450 €407 Washington flower carts (15x18cm-6x7in) s. WC gouache. 20-Aug-3 James Julia, Fairfield #1651/R

WAGNER, Fritz (20th C) German
£560 $1042 €818 Old man smoking a pipe (23x17cm-9x7in) s. 2-Mar-4 Bristol Auction Rooms #313/R
£1000 $1790 €1500 The connoisseur (24x18cm-9x7in) s. prov. 14-May-4 Ketterer, Munich #109/R est:2000-2500
£1600 $2912 €2400 Monk tasting wine (45x40cm-18x16in) s.i. 30-Jun-4 Neumeister, Munich #742/R
£1769 $3166 €2600 Card game (65x80cm-26x31in) s.i. 17-Mar-4 Neumeister, Munich #652/R est:3000
£1933 $3461 €2900 Meal time (40x50cm-16x20in) s.i. prov. 14-May-4 Ketterer, Munich #102/R est:2500-3000
£2657 $4571 €3800 Three men smoking and reading together in a Dutch living room (45x40cm-18x16in) s.i. 3-Dec-3 Neumeister, Munich #790/R est:4000
£3121 $5055 €4400 Young woman reading at table, man smoking pipe (70x60cm-28x24in) s. lit. 23-May-3 Karlheinz Kaupp, Staufen #2019/R est:2000
£3333 $5967 €5000 Card players (65x80cm-26x31in) s.i. prov. 14-May-4 Ketterer, Munich #110/R est:4000-5000
£3493 $6148 €5100 Scene in drinking hole (72x66cm-28x26in) s.i. prov. 22-May-4 Galerie Gloggner, Luzern #111 est:3000-3500 (S.FR 8000)
£4000 $6880 €5840 Important document (60x70cm-24x28in) s.i. 4-Dec-3 Christie's, Kensington #171/R est:4000-6000
£4167 $6792 €6000 Dutch tavern (65x80cm-26x31in) s.i. 25-Sep-3 Dr Fritz Nagel, Stuttgart #1434/R est:2500
£4861 $7924 €7000 Four men preparing document (65x80cm-26x31in) s.i. 24-Sep-3 Neumeister, Munich #597/R est:4000
£5000 $9000 €7300 Discussing the voyage (60x50cm-24x20in) s. 22-Apr-4 Christie's, Rockefeller NY #34/R est:12000-18000
£5442 $9741 €8000 Men in Dutch tavern (80x100cm-31x39in) s. 17-Mar-4 Neumeister, Munich #653/R est:2500
£5594 $9622 €8000 Group of men studying a map in a Dutch living room (66x82cm-26x32in) s.i. 3-Dec-3 Neumeister, Munich #792/R est:1000
£6250 $10625 €9000 Frohliche Herrenrunde - enjoying the delicacies (80x100cm-31x39in) s. 28-Oct-3 Christie's, Amsterdam #25/R est:7000-9000
£14118 $24000 €20612 Next voyage (95x120cm-37x47in) s.i. 29-Oct-3 Christie's, Rockefeller NY #31/R est:20000-30000

WAGNER, Fritz (1896-1939) German
£4000 $7200 €6000 Musical interlude (71x86cm-28x34in) s.i. 20-Apr-4 Sotheby's, Amsterdam #71/R est:6000-8000
£4667 $8400 €7000 In the wine cellar (40x55cm-16x22in) s.i. 20-Apr-4 Sotheby's, Amsterdam #69/R est:3000-5000
£5333 $9600 €8000 Contract (66x80cm-26x31in) s.i. 20-Apr-4 Sotheby's, Amsterdam #56/R est:5000-7000

WAGNER, Hans (1885-?) Swiss
£235 $400 €343 Italian landscape (36x58cm-14x23in) s. 22-Nov-3 Jackson's, Cedar Falls #17/R
£322 $593 €480 Dutch harbour (70x100cm-28x39in) s. 27-Mar-4 Dannenberg, Berlin #643/R
£1060 $1939 €1600 Southern shore (71x100cm-28x39in) s. 8-Apr-4 Dorotheum, Vienna #145/R est:1800-2000

WAGNER, Hans Johann (1866-1940) Austrian
£450 $851 €657 Fishermen unloading at the quayside (69x105cm-27x41in) s. 19-Feb-4 Christie's, Kensington #132/R

WAGNER, Hansjorg (20th C) German?
£302 $556 €450 Returning home (70x80cm-28x31in) s. 27-Mar-4 Sigalas, Stuttgart #320/R

WAGNER, Jacob (1852-1896) American
£413 $689 €599 Paysage au bord du lac (35x55cm-14x22in) s. 21-Jun-3 Galerie du Rhone, Sion #94/R (S.FR 900)

WAGNER, Johan Georg (1744-1767) German
Works on paper
£312 $511 €430 Rocky landscape in the style of Salvator rosa (21x15cm-8x6in) s. brush over pencil. 30-May-3 Bassenge, Berlin #7813

WAGNER, Johann (19th C) German
£1267 $2318 €1900 Canal with fishing boats (90x124cm-35x49in) s. 5-Jun-4 Arnold, Frankfurt #788/R est:1000

WAGNER, Josef (?) ?
£288 $522 €420 Winter scene (68x55cm-27x22in) s. 31-Mar-4 Goodman, Sydney #437/R (A.D 700)

WAGNER, K (?) ?
£828 $1382 €1200 Black Forest landscape with stream (60x80cm-24x31in) s. 15-Nov-3 Lempertz, Koln #1714 est:1300
£2083 $3292 €3000 Lively southern street (73x101cm-29x40in) s. 6-Sep-3 Arnold, Frankfurt #721/R est:800

WAGNER, Karl (19/20th C) Austrian/German
£972 $1536 €1400 Gulf of Naples (72x100cm-28x39in) s. 6-Sep-3 Schopman, Hamburg #708/R
£1084 $1810 €1550 Italian coast road on spring day (74x100cm-29x39in) s. 27-Jun-3 Michael Zeller, Lindau #707/R est:1200
£1188 $1900 €1734 Italian road scene (69x107cm-27x42in) init. 20-Sep-3 Sloans & Kenyon, Bethesda #1171/R est:2500-2750
£1736 $2760 €2500 Dutch harbour (52x79cm-20x31in) s. 13-Sep-3 Quittenbaum, Hamburg #31/R est:2000

WAGNER, Karl Theodor (1856-1921) Austrian
£1067 $1931 €1600 Harbour of Belgian seaside town (50x81cm-20x32in) s. 1-Apr-4 Van Ham, Cologne #1698/R est:1400
£1267 $2293 €1900 Belgian seaside town (74x100cm-29x39in) s. 1-Apr-4 Van Ham, Cologne #1700/R est:1800
£3067 $5551 €4600 Southern Italian coast near Sorrento (74x100cm-29x39in) s. 1-Apr-4 Van Ham, Cologne #1699/R est:1200

WAGNER, Max (1956-) German
Sculpture
£1879 $3326 €2800 Gymnast (49cm-19in) dark pat.bronze exhib. 30-Apr-4 Dr Fritz Nagel, Stuttgart #972/R est:2800

WAGNER, Melanie von (attrib) (1866-?) German
£257 $475 €375 Shoreline amusement (91x71cm-36x28in) s.verso. 12-Mar-4 Jackson's, Cedar Falls #782/R

WAGNER, Michel (1883-1965) German
£455 $759 €650 Ballerinas (86x62cm-34x24in) s. s.i. stretcher. 10-Oct-3 Winterberg, Heidelberg #2094/R
Works on paper
£307 $555 €460 Ballerina tying shoes (58x47cm-23x19in) s. gouache. 2-Apr-4 Winterberg, Heidelberg #1712
£433 $789 €650 The dancing lesson (49x61cm-19x24in) s. mixed media lit. 3-Jul-4 Geble, Radolfzell #432/R

WAGNER, Olga (19th C) Danish
£2113 $3507 €3000 Dachsund (23x23cm-9x9in) s.d.1885. 16-Jun-3 Dorotheum, Vienna #29/R est:2000-2300

WAGNER, Otto Erich (1895-1975) Austrian
Works on paper
£486 $792 €700 Woman sitting (42x19cm-17x7in) pencil. 23-Sep-3 Wiener Kunst Auktionen, Vienna #65/R

WAGNER, Paul Hermann (1852-?) German
£2055 $3493 €3000 Boy playing flute and sitting on bench with girl (75x54cm-30x21in) s.i. lit. 6-Nov-3 Allgauer, Kempten #3631/R est:2500

WAGNER, Sigmund von (1759-1835) Swiss
Works on paper
£560 $1003 €818 Greek villa (26x22cm-10x9in) s.i.d.1802 bister W/C. 13-May-4 Stuker, Bern #9204/R (S.FR 1300)

WAGNER, Willem George (1814-1855) Dutch
£2837 $4738 €4000 View of Schevening beach with moored fishing vessels (29x40cm-11x16in) s.d.53 panel. 20-Oct-3 Glerum, Amsterdam #12/R est:1000-1200

WAGNER-DEINES, Johann (1803-1880) German
£903 $1426 €1300 Romantic winter landscape (45x76cm-18x30in) mono. 5-Sep-3 Wendl, Rudolstadt #3760/R

WAGNER-HOHENBERG, Josef (1870-1939) German
£5172 $9569 €7500 Consultation with notary (70x100cm-28x39in) s. lit. 13-Feb-4 Auktionhaus Georg Rehm, Augsburg #8180/R est:3500

WAGREZ, Jacques Clement (1846-1908) French
£10000 $18000 €14600 Cupid (140x104cm-55x41in) s. prov. 23-Apr-4 Sotheby's, New York #206/R est:15000-20000

WAGSTAFF, Samuel (19th C) British
£600 $996 €876 Scarborough North Bay with pier from Scalby Mills (50x68cm-20x27in) s.i. on stretcher. 6-Oct-3 David Duggleby, Scarborough #225/R

WAGULA, Hans (1894-1964) Austrian
Works on paper
£364 $667 €550 Projet d'Affiche (48x37cm-19x15in) s. W/C gouache. 7-Apr-4 Piasa, Paris #159

WAHL, Alicja (1932-) Polish
Works on paper
£254 $460 €371 Composition (80x71cm-31x28in) s.d.1994 gouache pastel. 4-Apr-4 Agra, Warsaw #53/R (P.Z 1800)

WAHL, Irene (20th C) Canadian
Works on paper
£294 $491 €429 Nana's garden (34x52cm-13x20in) s.i. W/C. 17-Nov-3 Hodgins, Calgary #19/R (C.D 650)
£400 $732 €584 Forest (36x53cm-14x21in) s. W/C. 1-Jun-4 Hodgins, Calgary #276/R (C.D 1000)

WAHLBERG, Alfred (1834-1906) Swedish
£430 $701 €628 Moonlit boat trip (10x13cm-4x5in) s.d.64. 29-Sep-3 Lilla Bukowskis, Stockholm #372 (S.KR 5600)
£503 $870 €734 Wooded landscape with figure walking (27x40cm-11x16in) s. 15-Dec-3 Lilla Bukowskis, Stockholm #817 (S.KR 6400)
£517 $926 €755 Harbour entrance with sailing boats (21x15cm-8x6in) panel. 26-May-4 AB Stockholms Auktionsverk #2216/R (S.KR 7000)
£707 $1223 €1032 Night fishing in moonlight (63x89cm-25x35in) s.d.1870. 15-Dec-3 Lilla Bukowskis, Stockholm #736 (S.KR 9000)
£1256 $2249 €1834 Coastal landscape - Le Havre (31x44cm-12x17in) s.d.13.8.68. 26-May-4 AB Stockholms Auktionsverk #2169/R est:12000-15000 (S.KR 17000)
£1421 $2316 €2075 Summer landscape (73x100cm-29x39in) s. 29-Sep-3 Lilla Bukowskis, Stockholm #560 est:20000-25000 (S.KR 18500)
£1458 $2682 €2187 Landscape from Auvers (33x45cm-13x18in) s.i.d.8 nov 1891 exhib. 14-Jun-4 Lilla Bukowskis, Stockholm #693/R est:8000-12000 (S.KR 20000)
£2069 $3704 €3021 Field landscape from Garny, Normandy (33x43cm-13x17in) s.d.10/7 93. 26-May-4 AB Stockholms Auktionsverk #2155/R est:18000-20000 (S.KR 28000)
£2231 $3837 €3257 Fishing village (43x73cm-17x29in) s. 3-Dec-3 AB Stockholms Auktionsverk #2253/R est:30000-40000 (S.KR 29000)
£3022 $5500 €4412 Coastal village by moonlight (63x94cm-25x37in) s.d.1887. 29-Jun-4 Sotheby's, New York #135/R est:10000-15000
£4615 $7938 €6738 Landscape with waterfall surrounded by forest and mountains in background (79x102cm-31x40in) s.d.1857-63 prov.exhib.lit. 2-Dec-3 Bukowskis, Stockholm #191/R est:25000-30000 (S.KR 60000)

WAHLBERG, Ulf (1938-) Swedish
£654 $1125 €955 Still life II (50x61cm-20x24in) exhib. 7-Dec-3 Uppsala Auktionskammare, Uppsala #290/R (S.KR 8500)
£3297 $5835 €4814 Wrecked car (100x80cm-39x31in) s.d.70-71. 27-Apr-4 AB Stockholms Auktionsverk #1011/R est:40000-50000 (S.KR 45000)

WAHLBERGSON, Erik (1808-1865) Swedish
£1256 $2249 €1834 Mary Magdalene in contemplation (47x39cm-19x15in) s.d.1850 prov.lit. 26-May-4 AB Stockholms Auktionsverk #2334/R est:8000-10000 (S.KR 17000)

WAHLBOM, Carl (1810-1858) Swedish
£2809 $5027 €4101 Figures and horses on the Roman Campagna (49x62cm-19x24in) s.i.d.1854. 25-May-4 Bukowskis, Stockholm #162/R est:25000-30000 (S.KR 38000)

WAHLE, Friedrich (1863-1927) German
£671 $1235 €1000 Bird handler (32x34cm-13x13in) s. board. 24-Mar-4 Hugo Ruef, Munich #1141
£1399 $2336 €2000 Family matters (39x28cm-15x11in) s. cardboard. 26-Jun-3 Sant Agostino, Torino #280/R est:2000-2500

WAHLQVIST, Ehrnfried (1814-1895) Swedish
£615 $1058 €898 View of Stockholm (33x50cm-13x20in) init.d.1871. 3-Dec-3 AB Stockholms Auktionsverk #2507/R (S.KR 8000)
£1077 $1852 €1572 View of Stockholm (49x69cm-19x27in) 7-Dec-3 Uppsala Auktionskammare, Uppsala #125/R (S.KR 14000)
£1109 $1984 €1619 Albano near Brunnsvik (38x59cm-15x23in) s/d/1859. 26-May-4 AB Stockholms Auktionsverk #2165/R est:12000-15000 (S.KR 15000)

WAHLROOS, Dora (1870-1947) Finnish
£669 $1157 €950 Garden (49x37cm-19x15in) s. 13-Dec-3 Hagelstam, Helsinki #162/R
£2222 $3711 €3200 The letter (78x58cm-31x23in) s.d.1896. 23-Oct-3 Hagelstam, Helsinki #879/R est:800

WAHLSTROM, Charlotte (1849-1924) Swedish
£407 $728 €594 Moonlight (78x54cm-31x21in) s. 26-May-4 AB Stockholms Auktionsverk #2342/R (S.KR 5500)
£614 $1002 €896 View towards Skalderviken (32x40cm-13x16in) s. canvas on panel. 29-Sep-3 Lilla Bukowskis, Stockholm #469 (S.KR 8000)
£1077 $1852 €1572 Summer landscape with flowering heather, Nordland (41x56cm-16x22in) s. exhib. 3-Dec-3 AB Stockholms Auktionsverk #2379/R (S.KR 14000)
£1996 $3572 €2914 Apple tree in blossom (54x73cm-21x29in) s. 25-May-4 Bukowskis, Stockholm #2/R est:12000-15000 (S.KR 27000)

WAHYUNI, Erica Hestu (1971-) Javanese
£2065 $3303 €3015 Picnic. 18-May-3 Sotheby's, Singapore #197/R est:2000-3000 (S.D 5760)
£2536 $3931 €3703 Barong candy (90x120cm-35x47in) s.d.99 acrylic. 6-Oct-2 Sotheby's, Singapore #185/R est:2000-3000 (S.D 7000)
£5556 $10056 €8112 Safari in China (100x145cm-39x57in) s.d.2003. 4-Apr-4 Sotheby's, Singapore #198/R est:2000-3000 (S.D 17000)

WAILAND, Friedrich (1821-1904) Austrian
Works on paper
£403 $741 €600 Young woman with white collar (5x4cm-2x2in) s. W/C ivory oval. 26-Mar-4 Dorotheum, Vienna #362/R

WAILLY, Charles de (1729-1798) French
Works on paper
£690 $1152 €1000 Church interior with procession (25x18cm-10x7in) W/C prov. 15-Nov-3 Lempertz, Koln #1432/R

£4422 $7915 €6500 Ambrogio Spinola conduit a l'Immortalite par Minerve. Etude pour un plafond (31x24cm-12x9in) pen grey ink wash W/C oval. 18-Mar-4 Christie's, Paris #274/R est:2500-3500

WAIN, Louis (1860-1939) British

£1100 $1760 €1606 Seated cat in a landscape (20x13cm-8x5in) s. W/C htd white. 18-Sep-3 Goldings, Lincolnshire #803/R est:600-900

Works on paper

£320 $512 €467 Our committee meeting (10x18cm-4x7in) s. ink. 18-Sep-3 Goldings, Lincolnshire #804/R
£320 $512 €467 At last (13x18cm-5x7in) s.i. ink bodycol. 18-Sep-3 Goldings, Lincolnshire #805/R
£370 $688 €540 Those with feelings wondrous kind, can love with kittens ever bind (25x30cm-10x12in) s. i.verso pen ink Press Club paper. 7-Mar-4 Lots Road Auctions, London #360
£400 $740 €584 Smiling cat (11x18cm-4x7in) s.i. pencil drawing. 14-Jul-4 Bonhams, Chester #506
£400 $732 €584 Bulldog of 1890 (48x38cm-19x15in) s.i. red chk. 6-Jul-4 Bearnes, Exeter #447/R
£420 $722 €613 Kitten (5cm-2in circular) s. pen dr. 3-Dec-3 Andrew Hartley, Ilkley #1079
£420 $773 €613 Naughty dog (38x28cm-15x11in) s. monochrome bodycol. 8-Jun-4 Bonhams, New Bond Street #141b
£420 $764 €613 A cautious glance (23x16cm-9x6in) s. red chk. 1-Jul-4 Christie's, Kensington #495/R
£500 $910 €730 Blue Siamese (21x21cm-8x8in) s.i. black ink exhib. 1-Jul-4 Christie's, Kensington #504/R
£520 $952 €759 Smiling cat (14x10cm-6x4in) s. grey brushpoint drawing over pencil. 8-Jul-4 Lawrence, Crewkerne #1563
£550 $1001 €803 A lizard, a grecos, and a tortoise met and danced (20x28cm-8x11in) s.i. pencil black ink htd white two. 1-Jul-4 Christie's, Kensington #506/R
£640 $1062 €934 There's nothing like a good cook (33x23cm-13x9in) s.d.23/9/02 ink. 30-Sep-3 Andrew Smith, Winchester #74/R
£700 $1274 €1022 Tis said A cat may look at a king, in this case it looks at a Queen (23x18cm-9x7in) s.i. black ink W/C htd white. 1-Jul-4 Christie's, Kensington #496/R
£706 $1200 €1031 Baking (21x16cm-8x6in) s. pen ink prov. 21-Nov-3 Skinner, Boston #115/R est:1800-2200
£750 $1275 €1095 Portraits of cats (14x14cm-6x6in) s. ink colour wash drawings circular pair. 6-Nov-3 Hobbs Parker, Ashford #683/R
£750 $1365 €1095 Head of a cat (18x15cm-7x6in) s. pencil. 16-Jun-4 Andrew Hartley, Ilkley #1013
£750 $1365 €1095 Dear me. Visitors coming and I've lost my comb and brush (38x27cm-15x11in) s.i. black ink two. 1-Jul-4 Christie's, Kensington #493/R
£780 $1459 €1170 Please mum, cook has made a fine art Christmas pudding for a surprise (16x26cm-6x10in) s.i. W/C bodycol. 26-Jul-4 Bonhams, Bath #25/R
£833 $1500 €1216 Cake Walk (34x50cm-13x20in) s. W/C ink. 24-Apr-4 Weschler, Washington #554/R est:2000-3000
£900 $1503 €1314 Fisherman (23x18cm-9x7in) s. red chk. 22-Oct-3 Cheffins, Cambridge #490
£1000 $1830 €1460 Letter (43x31cm-17x12in) s. red chk drawing. 6-Jul-4 Bearnes, Exeter #450/R est:600-800
£1100 $1837 €1606 Seated tabby cat licking her kitten (13x18cm-5x7in) s. pen ink wash prov. 14-Oct-3 Canterbury Auctions, UK #145/R est:600-800
£1300 $2171 €1898 Cleaning and goodnight (24x60cm-9x24in) s. pencil. 22-Oct-3 Cheffins, Cambridge #466/R est:300-400
£1400 $2562 €2044 Reflecting cat (45x34cm-18x13in) s.i. red chk. 6-Jul-4 Bearnes, Exeter #448/R est:800-1200
£1400 $2548 €2044 A balancing act (45x31cm-18x12in) s. pencil bodycol. 1-Jul-4 Christie's, Kensington #502/R est:600-800
£1500 $2580 €2190 A hasty retreat (28x49cm-11x19in) s. W/C bodycol. 4-Dec-3 Mellors & Kirk, Nottingham #834/R est:1500-2000
£1600 $2672 €2336 Study of crows (33x51cm-13x20in) s. W/C. 15-Oct-3 Brightwells, Leominster #945/R est:400-600
£1600 $2928 €2336 This way to the up-to-date year 1902 (51x39cm-20x15in) s. pencil ink. 8-Jul-4 Sotheby's, London #385/R est:1000-1500
£1600 $2912 €2336 Grooming. Looking pretty (30x23cm-12x9in) s. pencil black ink pair. 1-Jul-4 Christie's, Kensington #494/R est:600-800
£1700 $2839 €2482 Morning and playtime (24x60cm-9x24in) s. pencil. 22-Oct-3 Cheffins, Cambridge #465/R est:300-400
£1765 $3000 €2577 My first speech and powder puff (17x28cm-7x11in) s.i. pen ink prov. 21-Nov-3 Skinner, Boston #116/R est:2200-2800
£1846 $3250 €2695 Colonial produce (43x34cm-17x13in) s. i.verso pen ink wash prov. 18-May-4 Bonhams & Butterfields, San Francisco #173/R est:3000-5000
£1912 $3250 €2792 Mr. Intellectual (18x29cm-7x11in) s. pen ink prov. 21-Nov-3 Skinner, Boston #117/R est:2200-2800
£2000 $3640 €2920 Pussies at the well (19x36cm-7x14in) s. pen ink htd white prov. 1-Jul-4 Mellors & Kirk, Nottingham #759/R est:1000-1500
£2131 $3750 €3111 Lady Dainty (42x30cm-17x12in) s.i. pencil col wash htd white prov. 18-May-4 Bonhams & Butterfields, San Francisco #175/R est:4000-6000
£2273 $4000 €3319 Ginger cat (22x17cm-9x7in) s. col chk prov. 18-May-4 Bonhams & Butterfields, San Francisco #174/R est:3000-5000
£2400 $4128 €3504 Cranes in an exotic garden (26x37cm-10x15in) s. W/C bodycol. 3-Dec-3 Christie's, Kensington #269/R est:1500-2000
£2400 $4416 €3504 Milk please (36x30cm-14x12in) red chk. 8-Jun-4 Bonhams, New Bond Street #142/R est:1000-1500
£2500 $4175 €3650 Wet land (33x22cm-13x9in) s. pen ink wash. 22-Oct-3 Cheffins, Cambridge #492/R est:500-600
£2800 $5180 €4088 Time for a snooze (19x18cm-7x7in) s. red chk prov. 9-Mar-4 Bonhams, New Bond Street #141/R est:2000-3000
£2800 $5096 €4088 Simple Simon (28x23cm-11x9in) s. W/C. 16-Jun-4 Andrew Hartley, Ilkley #1012/R est:2500-3500
£2900 $4843 €4234 The crash, with cats scattered by a motor car (30x51cm-12x20in) s. pen ink. 15-Oct-3 Brightwells, Leominster #946/R est:500-800
£3000 $5550 €4380 Cats playing on the ice (27x38cm-11x15in) s. pen ink. 9-Mar-4 Bonhams, New Bond Street #142/R est:2000-4000
£3000 $5400 €4380 Fiddler playing to dancing rats (41x29cm-16x11in) s. W/C. 23-Apr-4 Charterhouse, Sherborne #680/R
£3000 $5520 €4380 Pirate's treasure (30x51cm-12x20in) s. W/C bodycol. 8-Jun-4 Bonhams, New Bond Street #144/R est:3000-5000
£3125 $5500 €4563 Road race (49x76cm-19x30in) s. pen ink. 18-May-4 Bonhams & Butterfields, San Francisco #172/R est:6000-8000
£3200 $5440 €4672 Pianist (23x17cm-9x7in) s. crayon prov. 4-Nov-3 Bonhams, New Bond Street #156/R est:1200-1800
£3200 $5888 €4672 Pretty pussy (27x30cm-11x12in) s. red chk. 8-Jun-4 Bonhams, New Bond Street #141a est:800-1200
£3600 $6012 €5256 Chairman speaks (17x22cm-7x9in) s. 22-Oct-3 Cheffins, Cambridge #491 est:400-500
£3800 $6840 €5548 Reluctant bather (41x32cm-16x13in) s. W/C. 22-Apr-4 Lawrence, Crewkerne #799/R est:500-800
£4000 $7200 €5840 Smokers (31x58cm-12x23in) s. W/C. 23-Apr-4 Charterhouse, Sherborne #681/R
£4000 $7360 €5840 Cat fishing (27x21cm-11x8in) s. W/C bodycol. 8-Jun-4 Bonhams, New Bond Street #145/R est:2500-3500
£4200 $7770 €6132 There was an old pussy who lived in a shoe (32x51cm-13x20in) s. pen ink prov. 9-Mar-4 Bonhams, New Bond Street #143/R est:2500-3500
£4200 $7560 €6132 Miss catty is a ratty (27x35cm-11x14in) W/C. 23-Apr-4 Charterhouse, Sherborne #659/R
£4500 $8190 €6570 Three's company (25x49cm-10x19in) s. pencil black ink W/C bodycol. 1-Jul-4 Christie's, Kensington #497/R est:3000-5000
£4800 $8736 €7008 The football players (31x48cm-12x19in) s.i. pencil W/C bodycol. 1-Jul-4 Christie's, Kensington #503/R est:3000-5000
£5000 $9300 €7300 Caught in the act (19x27cm-7x11in) s. W/C. 2-Mar-4 Bamfords, Derby #418/R est:1500-2000

WAIN, Louis (attrib) (1860-1939) British

Works on paper

£440 $801 €642 Portrait of a black cat (23x10cm-9x4in) gouache. 15-Jun-4 Canterbury Auctions, UK #136/R

WAINBURRANGA, Paddy Fordham (c.1938-) Australian

Works on paper

£784 $1404 €1145 Borlung (128x40cm-50x16in) natural earth pigments bark exec 1985 prov. 25-May-4 Lawson Menzies, Sydney #272/R (A.D 2000)
£863 $1544 €1260 Borlung (138x43cm-54x17in) natural earth pigments bark exec c.1985 prov. 25-May-4 Lawson Menzies, Sydney #273/R (A.D 2200)
£2479 $4215 €3619 Mimi man and mimi woman with bagy 1997 (237x132cm-93x52in) synthetic polymer paint on Belgian linen prov. 29-Oct-3 Lawson Menzies, Sydney #57/R est:4000-5000 (A.D 6000)

WAINEWRIGHT, T F (19th C) British

Works on paper

£280 $448 €409 Sheep in a landscape (25x48cm-10x19in) s.d.1865. 15-May-3 Mitchells, Cockermouth #1061

WAINEWRIGHT, Thomas Francis (19th C) British

Works on paper

£375 $700 €563 Cattle watering in a river landscape (41x71cm-16x28in) s.d.82 pencil W/C. 25-Jul-4 Bonhams & Butterfields, San Francisco #6013/R
£380 $646 €555 Sheep and lambs on a riverside bank (23x48cm-9x19in) s.d.1865 W/C. 18-Nov-3 Bonhams, Leeds #61/R
£460 $768 €672 Cows in a stream (24x45cm-9x18in) bears mono. d.November 1883 verso W/C. 20-Oct-3 Bonhams, Bath #75
£1250 $2300 €1825 Sheep at pasture. Cattle by a river (11x18cm-4x7in) s.d.1884 W/C pair. 24-Mar-4 Hamptons Fine Art, Godalming #259/R
£1500 $2550 €2190 Cattle resting in a meadow by a river (38x76cm-15x30in) s.i.d.1863 W/C. 26-Nov-3 Hamptons Fine Art, Godalming #54/R est:1500-1800

WAINIO, Carol (1955-) Canadian

£200 $366 €292 Reading tower (83x140cm-33x55in) acrylic painted 2000 prov. 1-Jun-4 Joyner Waddington, Toronto #417 (C.D 500)
£200 $366 €292 Les tres riches heures (83x140cm-33x55in) acrylic painted 2000 prov. 1-Jun-4 Joyner Waddington, Toronto #416 (C.D 500)

WAINWRIGHT, Albert (1862-1943) British

Works on paper

£400 $668 €584 Salome (22x18cm-9x7in) mono. pen ink W/C. 11-Oct-3 Shapes, Edinburgh #316

WAINWRIGHT, George (?) British?

£260 $478 €380 Fishing boats at low tide (16x31cm-6x12in) board. 8-Jun-4 Bonhams, Knowle #356

WAINWRIGHT, John (19th C) British

£3889 $7000 €5678 Still life with fruit and goldfish in a bowl on a ledge (43x33cm-17x13in) s.d.1859 panel prov. 22-Apr-4 Christie's, Rockefeller NY #82/R est:10000-15000

WAINWRIGHT, William John (1855-1931) British

£270 $505 €394 Portrait of a bearded monk (26x19cm-10x7in) s. board. 24-Feb-4 Bonhams, Knowle #72
£950 $1587 €1387 Portrait of a young man wearing a powdered wig and a tricorn hat (19x27cm-7x11in) s.d.1888. 7-Oct-3 Fellows & Sons, Birmingham #416/R

Works on paper

£1000 $1700 €1460 Cavalier playing a guitar (38x27cm-15x11in) s. W/C. 25-Nov-3 Bonhams, Knowle #187/R est:1000-1500
£1550 $2573 €2263 Long scores make short lives (76x53cm-30x21in) s.d.1886 W/C. 3-Oct-3 Mallams, Oxford #87/R est:1000-1200
£1850 $3145 €2701 Daughter of the house (38x28cm-15x11in) W/C. 1-Dec-3 Bonhams, Bath #71/R est:1000-1500
£7000 $12740 €10220 Portrait of the artist as Rubens (76x61cm-30x24in) s.d.1914 pencil W/C htd white. 5-Feb-4 Mellors & Kirk, Nottingham #503/R est:3000-4000

WAINWRIGHT, William John (attrib) (1855-1931) British

£270 $500 €394 An old man with a hat and stick (34x24cm-13x9in) 16-Feb-4 Bonhams, Bath #81

WAITE, Edward Wilkins (fl.1878-1927) British
£1350 $2120 €1958 Rustic female gathering faggots in a silver birch wood (36x30cm-14x12in) s. 15-Dec-2 Desmond Judd, Cranbrook #863
£3900 $7098 €5694 Cottage garden (29x44cm-11x17in) s. 3-Feb-4 Sworder & Son, Bishops Stortford #297/R est:3000-5000
£4000 $7080 €5840 Fishing by a quiet river (31x46cm-12x18in) s.d.1895. 27-Apr-4 Bonhams, Knowle #121 est:2000-3000
£7000 $11410 €10220 Mapledurham Mill (51x76cm-20x30in) 24-Sep-3 Dreweatt Neate, Newbury #167/R est:6000-8000
£7200 $12024 €10512 Sussex roadside (51x74cm-20x29in) s. prov. 14-Oct-3 Bearnes, Exeter #378/R est:5000-7000
£12000 $21840 €17520 Fishing. s.d.1892 prov. 1-Jul-4 Sotheby's, London #357/R est:10000-15000
£14500 $26680 €21170 At Peaslake (91x127cm-36x50in) s.d.1897. 11-Jun-4 Christie's, London #116/R est:12000-18000

WAITE, Emily Burling (1887-1962) American
£538 $1000 €785 In the orchard, portrait of a little girl (56x45cm-22x18in) s. 5-Mar-4 Skinner, Boston #372/R

WAITE, George (20th C) American?
£241 $400 €352 Abstract (117x135cm-46x53in) s. 4-Oct-3 Susanin's, Chicago #5074/R

WAITE, Harold (19/20th C) British
Works on paper
£350 $564 €508 Irish landscape with geese before a cottage (28x38cm-11x15in) s. W/C. 15-Aug-3 Keys, Aylsham #489

WAITE, James Clarke (1832-1921) British
£3600 $6120 €5256 Sick man reclining on a chaise longue with a nurse behind (90x72cm-35x28in) 6-Nov-3 Ambrose, Loughton #46/R est:1000-1500
£4464 $7679 €6517 Game of cards (77x66cm-30x26in) s. prov. 2-Dec-3 Ritchie, Toronto #54/R est:10000-15000 (C.D 10000)

WAITE, Robert Thorne (1842-1935) British
£800 $1336 €1168 Bristol valley (25x53cm-10x21in) 21-Oct-3 Gorringes, Lewes #2037
£2300 $3841 €3358 Harvesters in an open landscape. 21-Oct-3 Gorringes, Lewes #2038/R est:2000-2500
Works on paper
£260 $476 €380 Figures at a stream, cattle and a farm in the distance (23x34cm-9x13in) s. W/C scratching out. 6-Jul-4 Bearnes, Exeter #426
£360 $659 €526 Gatherers on the shore at low tide (24x42cm-9x17in) s. W/C pencil. 8-Jul-4 Lawrence, Crewkerne #1529
£380 $703 €555 Deal and Dover Road (18x33cm-7x13in) s. bears i.verso W/C. 10-Feb-4 David Lay, Penzance #136/R
£410 $763 €599 Gathering cockles (25x42cm-10x17in) s. W/C. 2-Mar-4 Bristol Auction Rooms #341
£420 $722 €613 Harvesters on a riverbank (15x25cm-6x10in) s. 2-Dec-3 Gorringes, Lewes #2313/R
£500 $860 €730 On the Sussex Downs, above Lancing (35x52cm-14x20in) pencil W/C. 3-Dec-3 Christie's, Kensington #114/R
£550 $1029 €825 Heather gatherers (33x51cm-13x20in) s. W/C. 22-Jul-4 Gorringes, Lewes #2008/R
£1000 $1840 €1460 On the Downs (33x51cm-13x20in) W/C. 8-Jun-4 Bonhams, New Bond Street #107/R est:1000-1500
£1500 $2760 €2190 Resting by the bay (34x51cm-13x20in) W/C prov. 8-Jun-4 Bonhams, New Bond Street #106/R est:2000-3000
£1600 $2720 €2336 Haymakers returning home (27x38cm-11x15in) s. W/C. 4-Nov-3 Bonhams, New Bond Street #103/R est:1200-1800
£2200 $4004 €3212 Harvest time. Making posy (27x19cm-11x7in) init. one indis sig. pencil W/C htd white pair. 1-Jul-4 Mellors & Kirk, Nottingham #673/R est:1000-1500
£3000 $5490 €4380 Haymaking (36x55cm-14x22in) s. W/C htd scratching out. 8-Jul-4 Lawrence, Crewkerne #1528/R est:1500-2000

WAITT, Richard (18th C) British
£2500 $4250 €3650 Portrait of a gentleman wearing a blue coat (73x58cm-29x23in) s. 27-Nov-3 Sotheby's, London #131/R est:3000-5000

WAKE, John Cheltenham (fl.1858-1875) British
£900 $1503 €1314 After the banquet (60x90cm-24x35in) s.d.1875 panel. 16-Oct-3 Lyon & Turnbull, Edinburgh #96
£1900 $3097 €2774 Fisherfolk and smacks on the beach before Mont San Michelle (85x125cm-33x49in) s.d.1871. 23-Sep-3 Anderson & Garland, Newcastle #370/R est:500-800

WAKEHAM, Duane (1937-) American
£273 $500 €399 Ridge, evening (132x127cm-52x50in) 10-Jul-4 Hindman, Chicago #544/R

WAKELIN, Roland Shakespeare (1887-1971) Australian
£360 $612 €526 Botanical gardens, Sydney (22x20cm-9x8in) s.d.54 artist board prov. 24-Nov-3 Sotheby's, Melbourne #237 (A.D 850)
£574 $906 €838 Studio nude (62x37cm-24x15in) board prov. 2-Sep-3 Deutscher-Menzies, Melbourne #301/R est:2000-3000 (A.D 1400)
£621 $968 €900 Still life with apples (52x44cm-20x17in) s.d.44 board. 1-Aug-2 Joel, Victoria #275 est:3000-5000 (A.D 1800)
£813 $1276 €1179 Street corner (26x33cm-10x13in) s. board. 26-Aug-3 Christie's, Sydney #383 est:2000-3000 (A.D 2000)
£936 $1591 €1367 Still life (52x42cm-20x17in) s.d.66 paper on composition board. 26-Nov-3 Deutscher-Menzies, Melbourne #255/R est:2500-3500 (A.D 2200)
£984 $1554 €1437 Nude (38x28cm-15x11in) s.d.47 board. 2-Sep-3 Deutscher-Menzies, Melbourne #284/R est:3000-5000 (A.D 2400)
£1025 $1660 €1497 Still life (37x32cm-15x13in) s. board. 30-Jul-3 Goodman, Sydney #98/R (A.D 2500)
£1787 $3038 €2609 Banana trees (25x41cm-10x16in) board. 25-Nov-3 Christie's, Melbourne #203/R est:3000-4000 (A.D 4200)
£1951 $3493 €2848 Still life with marigolds (40x30cm-16x12in) s.d.1940 composition board exhib. 4-May-4 Sotheby's, Melbourne #219/R est:5000-8000 (A.D 4800)
£3192 $5426 €4660 Archway at Golders Green, London (25x35cm-10x14in) s.d.1924 i.d.verso canvas on board prov. 26-Nov-3 Deutscher-Menzies, Melbourne #86/R est:8000-12000 (A.D 7500)
£3279 $5180 €4787 Woman reading in interior (75x62cm-30x24in) s.d.1945 canvas on board. 2-Sep-3 Deutscher-Menzies, Melbourne #143/R est:10000-14000 (A.D 8000)
£3814 $6483 €5568 Berry's Bay (29x39cm-11x15in) s.d.32 prov. 24-Nov-3 Sotheby's, Melbourne #196/R est:9000-12000 (A.D 9000)
£4065 $6382 €5894 Richmond, New South Wales (34x45cm-13x18in) s.d.47 canvas on board prov. 26-Aug-3 Christie's, Sydney #218/R est:10000-15000 (A.D 10000)
£11064 $18809 €16153 Window (50x37cm-20x15in) s.d.30 board prov. 26-Nov-3 Deutscher-Menzies, Melbourne #87/R est:16000-20000 (A.D 26000)

WAKHEVITCH, Georges (1907-1984) French
£265 $482 €400 Jeune homme accroupi (54x45cm-21x18in) s.d.1931 cardboard. 15-Jun-4 Rossini, Paris #139
£372 $654 €550 Composition abstraite (54x73cm-21x29in) s.d.75. 19-May-4 Camard, Paris #116

WAKSVIK, Skule (1927-) Norwegian
Sculpture
£1448 $2491 €2114 Polar bear (51x73x24cm-20x29x9in) s.d.19W83 bronze. 8-Dec-3 Blomqvist, Oslo #528/R est:18000-22000 (N.KR 17000)
£2215 $3809 €3234 Two elks (58x46x64cm-23x18x25in) s.d.19W93 num.3-6 bronze. 8-Dec-3 Blomqvist, Oslo #526/R est:30000-40000 (N.KR 26000)

WAL, Baroness Leontine de (19th C) Belgian
£3836 $6521 €5600 Composition aux fleurs et au perroquet (147x123cm-58x48in) s.d.1851 oval. 10-Nov-3 Horta, Bruxelles #173 est:3500-5500

WALBOURN, Ernest (1872-1927) British
£300 $552 €438 Evening on the Arun, Sussex (26x42cm-10x17in) mono. panel. 8-Jun-4 Bonhams, Knightsbridge #128/R
£480 $893 €701 Wixford (30x41cm-12x16in) s.d.98. 4-Mar-4 Christie's, Kensington #489/R
£814 $1400 €1188 Cottage landscape with figures (43x33cm-17x13in) s.d.1893. 7-Dec-3 Susanin's, Chicago #6068/R est:500-800
£950 $1663 €1387 Girl on a path and a shepherd driving sheep by a pond and cottage (28x38cm-11x15in) s. 18-Dec-3 John Nicholson, Haslemere #1191
£1198 $2000 €1749 English country landscape (25x30cm-10x12in) s. panel. 16-Nov-3 Simpson's, Houston #278/R
£1750 $2800 €2555 Figures in field harvesting (41x61cm-16x24in) s.d.98. 17-May-3 Bunte, Elgin #1223 est:2000-3000
£1850 $2923 €2683 Mother and daughter before rustic mill feeding ducks (61x51cm-24x20in) s. 17-Nov-2 Desmond Judd, Cranbrook #910
£1900 $3363 €2774 Figures and ducks by a village pond (51x76cm-20x30in) init.i. board. 27-Apr-4 Bonhams, Knowle #108 est:2000-3000
£2400 $4368 €3504 By the mill (48x61cm-19x24in) s. 16-Jun-4 Bonhams, New Bond Street #47/R est:2500-3500
£2800 $4676 €4088 Cottage garden (69x51cm-27x20in) s. 13-Nov-3 Christie's, Kensington #275/R est:3000-5000
£3295 $5800 €4811 Untitled garden scene (51x76cm-20x30in) s. 23-May-4 Hindman, Chicago #34/R est:3000-5000
£4200 $7224 €6132 Lady in a garden feeding pigeons and doves (61x43cm-24x17in) s. board. 2-Dec-3 Gorringes, Lewes #2382/R est:1500-2000
£5600 $8904 €8120 Extensive river landscape with girl feeding birds by a river (39x59cm-15x23in) s. 9-Sep-3 Bonhams, Knightsbridge #176/R est:2000-3000
£6000 $11040 €8760 Returning home, haytime, near Bury, Sussex (61x91cm-24x36in) s. 23-Mar-4 Bonhams, New Bond Street #120/R est:4000-6000
£7600 $13604 €11096 Feeding the chicks (51x76cm-20x30in) s. 17-Mar-4 Bonhams, Chester #306/R est:3000-4000
£12000 $18840 €17400 Home before dark. Flower pickers in a cottage garden (51x76cm-20x30in) s. pair. 28-Aug-3 Christie's, Kensington #158/R est:2500-3500

WALBOURN, Ernest (attrib) (1872-1927) British
£300 $537 €438 Girl feeding ducks (35x50cm-14x20in) 17-May-4 David Duggleby, Scarborough #667/R
£543 $1000 €793 The mill (79x53cm-31x21in) bears sig. 26-Jun-4 Selkirks, St. Louis #411
£1892 $3500 €2762 New Broxbourne, Hertfordshire (61x91cm-24x36in) indis.s. 15-Jul-4 Sotheby's, New York #33/R est:1000-1500

WALCH, Charles (1896-1948) French
£1049 $1804 €1500 Bouquet de fleurs dans un paysage (23x32cm-9x13in) s. panel. 5-Dec-3 Chochon-Barre & Allardi, Paris #153/R est:1000-1200
£3154 $5836 €4700 Femme penchant la tete (65x54cm-26x21in) s. i.d.1948 verso. 15-Mar-4 Blanchet, Paris #129/R est:2500-3000
Sculpture
£884 $1583 €1300 Femme nue allongee (17x32x5cm-7x13x2in) s. stone. 17-Mar-4 Tajan, Paris #11 est:500-600
Works on paper
£514 $950 €750 Soleil de mars (46x61cm-18x24in) s. gouache. 17-Jan-4 New Orleans Auction, New Orleans #523/R est:800-1200
£559 $934 €800 Le vase vert (46x36cm-18x14in) s. gouache. 25-Jun-3 Maigret, Paris #25
£1544 $2856 €2300 La corbeille a ouvrage (46x37cm-18x15in) s. gouache exec.c.1945-1946. 15-Mar-4 Blanchet, Paris #130/R est:1200-1500

WALCH, Paul Johann (1881-1958) German
£276 $461 €400 Landscape with stream (25x32cm-10x13in) s. panel. 9-Jul-3 Hugo Ruef, Munich #238
£347 $566 €500 Still life with chrysanthemums (70x60cm-28x24in) s.i. 24-Sep-3 Neumeister, Munich #598/R
£764 $1276 €1100 Summer mountain landscape (90x80cm-35x31in) s.i. 22-Oct-3 Neumeister, Munich #779/R

WALCH, Thomas (1867-1843) Austrian
£1867 $3397 €2800 Walker in the mountains playing a fiddle (30x36cm-12x14in) s. panel. 1-Jul-4 Van Ham, Cologne #1656/R est:500
£2517 $4204 €3600 Tyrolean mountain peasants praying in the evening (49x69cm-19x27in) s. canvas on panel. 27-Jun-3 Michael Zeller, Lindau #708/R est:400

WALCKIERS, Gustave (1831-1891) Belgian
£11888 $20210 €17000 La Grand Place de Bruxelles animee (100x80cm-39x31in) s. 18-Nov-3 Vanderkindere, Brussels #4/R est:7500-10000

WALCOT, William (1874-1943) British
Works on paper
£460 $731 €672 Figures on a London Street (23x20cm-9x8in) s. W/C. 9-Sep-3 Gorringes, Lewes #1880/R
£480 $883 €701 Victoria and Albert Museum, London (60x67cm-24x26in) W/C bodydcl. 23-Mar-4 Rosebery Fine Art, London #737/R
£1550 $2449 €2248 Marylebone Road (14x22cm-6x9in) i. W/C bodycol prov. 3-Sep-3 Bonhams, Bury St Edmunds #374 est:800-1200
£2000 $3340 €2920 Mansion house (23x15cm-9x6in) pencil W/C. 16-Oct-3 Christie's, Kensington #159/R est:800-1200
£2000 $3680 €2920 View across St Mark's Square, Venice (30x23cm-12x9in) s. W/C. 22-Jun-4 Bonhams, Knightsbridge #59/R est:800-1200

WALCOTT, Harry Mills (1870-1944) American
£8140 $14000 €11884 Waiting for the show (27x35cm-11x14in) i.stretcher prov. 3-Dec-3 Doyle, New York #231/R est:10000-15000

WALDBERG, Isabelle (1917-) French?
Sculpture
£1600 $2880 €2400 Couple de danseurs (51cm-20in) s. num.1/3 pat bronze. 24-Apr-4 Cornette de St.Cyr, Paris #739 est:3000-4000
£1767 $3180 €2650 Falaise (37x12x10cm-15x5x4in) s. num.1/8 pat bronze Cast Barelier exec.1973 lit. 25-Apr-4 Versailles Encheres #210 est:3000-4000
£1908 $3511 €2900 Sommet (32x12x19cm-13x5x7in) s. num.1/8 pat bronze Cast Barelier lit. 27-Jun-4 Versailles Encheres #155/R est:4000-5000
£2465 $4264 €3500 Haut de chose (88x50x38cm-35x20x15in) num.1/8 bronze exec. c.1950 cire perdue st.f. Clementi lit. 10-Dec-3 Claude Boisgirard, Paris #39 est:3500-4000

WALDE, Alfons (1891-1958) Austrian
£4027 $7208 €6000 Sight (19x18cm-7x7in) oil mixed media cardboard. 27-May-4 Hassfurther, Vienna #25/R est:5000-7000
£4698 $8409 €7000 Summer evening (17x23cm-7x9in) oil tempera cardboard. 27-May-4 Hassfurther, Vienna #24/R est:6000-9000
£4698 $8409 €7000 Corpse, self seer (29x22cm-11x9in) oil mixed media cardboard. 27-May-4 Hassfurther, Vienna #26/R est:4000-6000
£4895 $8322 €7000 Nude in the snow (18x13cm-7x5in) paper. 28-Nov-3 Wiener Kunst Auktionen, Vienna #550/R est:7000-15000
£7639 $12069 €11000 Two peasants (18x14cm-7x6in) s. oil W/C pencil board on panel lit. 19-Sep-3 Schloss Ahlden, Ahlden #1649/R est:11000
£8054 $14416 €12000 Kitzbuhel, Frauen Church, Andreas Church (15x22cm-6x9in) i.verso tempera oil board. 27-May-4 Hassfurther, Vienna #21/R est:12000-16000
£8392 $14266 €12000 Dancer (32x25cm-13x10in) tempera prov. 26-Nov-3 Dorotheum, Vienna #32/R est:7000-10000
£8392 $14266 €12000 Farmhouse in Pichlach in front of the Wilden Kaiser (15x22cm-6x9in) oil tempera paper. 25-Nov-3 Hassfurther, Vienna #10/R est:15000-20000
£9060 $16218 €13500 Half nude in front of the mirror (22x14cm-9x6in) i.verso tempera oil board. 27-May-4 Hassfurther, Vienna #19/R est:10000-16000
£10638 $17766 €15000 Snow queen (32x24cm-13x9in) tempera prov. 14-Oct-3 Dorotheum, Vienna #62/R est:13000-17000
£12270 $20000 €17914 Austrian mountain scene (56x69cm-22x27in) s. board. 28-Sep-3 Simpson's, Houston #350/R
£15385 $26154 €22000 Bathers in Schwarzsee (26x18cm-10x7in) board prov. 26-Nov-3 Dorotheum, Vienna #159/R est:14000-18000
£18792 $33638 €28000 Forest clearing (26x28cm-10x11in) indis.mono. cardboard lit. 27-May-4 Hassfurther, Vienna #27/R est:25000-30000
£33557 $60067 €50000 Wayside shrine covered in snow in Tyrol (45x56cm-18x22in) s. cardboard. 27-May-4 Hassfurther, Vienna #17/R est:40000-60000
£38000 $63460 €55480 Einsamer Berghof (33x52cm-13x20in) s. board. 22-Oct-3 Bonhams, New Bond Street #13/R est:30000-40000
£40268 $72081 €60000 Solitary house (70x49cm-28x19in) s. cardboard lit. 27-May-4 Hassfurther, Vienna #20/R est:60000-100000
£45455 $77273 €65000 Spring in Tyrol (63x50cm-25x20in) s. board. 25-Nov-3 Hassfurther, Vienna #5/R est:70000-90000
£48951 $83217 €70000 Going to church (28x23cm-11x9in) s. board prov. 26-Nov-3 Dorotheum, Vienna #47/R est:40000-55000
£48951 $83217 €70000 Going to church (29x31cm-11x12in) s. board. 28-Nov-3 Wiener Kunst Auktionen, Vienna #546/R est:50000-100000
£55944 $95105 €80000 Solitary dwelling (41x58cm-16x23in) s. board. 25-Nov-3 Hassfurther, Vienna #4/R est:90000-120000
£60403 $108121 €90000 Spring in the mountains (42x67cm-17x26in) s. board prov. 25-May-4 Dorotheum, Vienna #39/R est:90000-120000
£63758 $114128 €95000 Churchgoing (45x52cm-18x20in) s. cardboard lit. 27-May-4 Hassfurther, Vienna #16/R est:80000-120000
£69444 $118056 €100000 Mountain hamlet (48x69cm-19x27in) s. board lit. 28-Oct-3 Wiener Kunst Auktionen, Vienna #126/R est:70000-150000
£80420 $136713 €115000 New snow, Kitzbuhler Horn (69x54cm-27x21in) s. board lit. 25-Nov-3 Hassfurther, Vienna #2/R est:80000-120000
£80420 $136713 €115000 Alpine meadow in the snow (55x61cm-22x24in) s. board. 28-Nov-3 Wiener Kunst Auktionen, Vienna #553/R est:70000-150000
£87248 $156175 €130000 Solitary mountain farm (33x53cm-13x21in) s. cardboard lit. 27-May-4 Hassfurther, Vienna #28/R est:80000-120000
£93960 $166309 €140000 Alpine meadow in March (45x52cm-18x20in) s. board. 28-Apr-4 Wiener Kunst Auktionen, Vienna #1208/R est:120000-250000
£97222 $165278 €140000 Village street in the Tyrol (59x49cm-23x19in) s. board. 28-Oct-3 Wiener Kunst Auktionen, Vienna #120/R est:50000-200000
£107383 $192215 €160000 Mountain person with dog (49x70cm-19x28in) s. board prov. 25-May-4 Dorotheum, Vienna #50/R est:140000-180000
£174825 $297203 €250000 Ascent of the skier (42x67cm-17x26in) s. board. 25-Nov-3 Hassfurther, Vienna #1/R est:120000-150000
Works on paper
£2083 $3542 €3000 Bathers by Schwarzsee (18x12cm-7x5in) pencil. 28-Oct-3 Wiener Kunst Auktionen, Vienna #121/R est:3000-10000
£2083 $3542 €3000 Reclining figures (22x28cm-9x11in) pencil. 28-Oct-3 Wiener Kunst Auktionen, Vienna #122/R est:3000-10000
£2222 $3622 €3200 Erotic scene (10x14cm-4x6in) mono. pencil. 23-Sep-3 Wiener Kunst Auktionen, Vienna #62/R est:1500-3000
£4027 $7208 €6000 Erotic (18x13cm-7x5in) mixed media cardboard. 27-May-4 Hassfurther, Vienna #23/R est:5000-7000
£5208 $8854 €7500 Nude (24x17cm-9x7in) mixed media. 28-Oct-3 Wiener Kunst Auktionen, Vienna #124/R est:7000-12000
£5594 $9510 €8000 Nude from behind (25x12cm-10x5in) mixed media board. 28-Nov-3 Wiener Kunst Auktionen, Vienna #551/R est:6000-10000
£6040 $10812 €9000 Detailed study of a Tyrolean village (15x13cm-6x5in) s. mixed media. 27-May-4 Hassfurther, Vienna #20a est:6000-8000
£8054 $14255 €12000 Church in Kitzbuhl (14x11cm-6x4in) mixed media. 28-Apr-4 Wiener Kunst Auktionen, Vienna #109/R est:7000-15000
£8725 $15443 €13000 Female nude (21x26cm-8x10in) W/C. 28-Apr-4 Wiener Kunst Auktionen, Vienna #110/R est:7000-15000
£9790 $16643 €14000 Variete - wrestling match (23x29cm-9x11in) pencil tempera prov. 26-Nov-3 Dorotheum, Vienna #39/R est:8000-12000
£11409 $20423 €17000 Female dancer (32x15cm-13x6in) mixed media. 27-May-4 Hassfurther, Vienna #24a est:12000-16000
£13287 $22587 €19000 Spring awakening (20x22cm-8x9in) mixed media. 25-Nov-3 Hassfurther, Vienna #9/R est:18000-22000
£17361 $29514 €25000 Nude (42x28cm-17x11in) mono. mixed media. 28-Oct-3 Wiener Kunst Auktionen, Vienna #125/R est:15000-25000

WALDE, Martin (1957-) Austrian
Works on paper
£345 $631 €500 Untitled (52x54cm-20x21in) mixed media. 27-Jan-4 Dorotheum, Vienna #244/R

WALDEGG, Franz (1888-?) Austrian
£333 $600 €500 River meadows in lower Germany in evening light (86x120cm-34x47in) s. 26-Apr-4 Rieber, Stuttgart #1029/R

WALDEN, Kari (1941-) Finnish
£811 $1451 €1200 Ode in red (120x90cm-47x35in) s.d.85. 8-May-4 Bukowskis, Helsinki #269/R

WALDEN, Lionel (1861-1933) American
£1667 $3000 €2434 Spring in the Canyon (25x35cm-10x14in) s. panel. 25-Apr-4 Bonhams & Butterfields, San Francisco #5508/R est:1000-1500
£2317 $3800 €3360 Coastal landscape with boats on shore and distant mountain (25x36cm-10x14in) s. panel prov. 31-May-3 Brunk, Ashville #33/R est:800-1500
£2699 $4750 €3941 Sandy beach under a full moon (25x36cm-10x14in) s. board. 23-May-4 Bonhams & Butterfields, San Francisco #6605/R
£3354 $5500 €4863 Rocky coastal scene (38x56cm-15x22in) s.i. prov. 31-May-3 Brunk, Ashville #424/R est:1000-2000

WALDENBURG, Alfred von (1847-1915) German
£629 $1070 €900 Field workers on path (62x49cm-24x19in) lit. 28-Nov-3 Schloss Ahlden, Ahlden #1480/R

WALDMAN, Max (20th C) American?
Photographs
£1693 $3200 €2472 Natalia Makarova, American Ballet Theatre (35x41cm-14x16in) s.num.11/25 gelatin silver print. 17-Feb-4 Christie's, Rockefeller NY #233/R est:2000-3000

WALDMULLER, Ferdinand (1816-1885) Austrian
£972 $1585 €1400 Two nuns conversing in cloisters (42x34cm-17x13in) s.d.856 panel. 26-Sep-3 Bolland & Marotz, Bremen #629/R est:1300
£6040 $10812 €9000 Extensive Donau landscape with shepherds and flock (47x60cm-19x24in) s.d.1840. 27-May-4 Dorotheum, Vienna #145/R est:5000-6000
£21552 $39655 €31466 Portrait of Graf Czernin von Chudenice in cadet uniform (26x20cm-10x8in) s.d.1833 panel. 26-Mar-4 Koller, Zurich #3086/R est:20000-30000 (S.FR 50000)

WALDMULLER, Ferdinand Georg (1793-1865) Austrian
£5245 $8916 €7500 Rocks with trees (21x31cm-8x12in) i.verso paper on canvas. 28-Nov-3 Wiener Kunst Auktionen, Vienna #427/R est:3000-10000
£5766 $10725 €8418 Man portrait (36x29cm-14x11in) s.d.844 board. 6-Mar-4 Dorotheum, Prague #31/R est:150000-250000 (C.KR 280000)
£7383 $13215 €11000 Old woman with lace bonnet (26x21cm-10x8in) s.d.1857 panel. 27-May-4 Dorotheum, Vienna #110/R est:10000-15000
£15972 $26354 €23000 Portrait of Professor Karl Damian von Schroff (29x23cm-11x9in) panel lit. 2-Jul-3 Neumeister, Munich #814/R est:18000
£31469 $53497 €45000 Young woman wearing white derss (27x22cm-11x9in) s.d.1835 panel prov. 24-Nov-3 Dorotheum, Vienna #66/R est:26000-34000
£131944 $224306 €190000 Newborn baby (47x59cm-19x23in) s.d.1864 panel lit. 28-Oct-3 Wiener Kunst Auktionen, Vienna #27/R est:150000-350000
Works on paper
£2200 $3938 €3300 Portrait of Franz Jauner (33x26cm-13x10in) s. pencil. 13-May-4 Bassenge, Berlin #5682/R est:2800

WALDO, Benjamin (19th C) American
£264 $420 €385 Portrait of Anna Maria Daughaday (69x58cm-27x23in) s. canvas on board. 12-Sep-3 Aspire, Cleveland #38

WALDO, Samuel Lovett (1783-1861) American
£2581 $4750 €3768 Portrait of Mrs C F Lindsley (127x101cm-50x40in) s.i.d.1844 verso prov. 8-Jun-4 Bonhams & Butterfields, San Francisco #4001/R est:3000-5000

WALDO, Samuel Lovett (attrib) (1783-1861) American
£471 $800 €688 Portrait of a gentleman (76x61cm-30x24in) panel prov. 1-Nov-3 Skinner, Boston #252

WALDO, Samuel Lovett and JEWETT, William (19th C) American
£1000 $1820 €1460 American pre civil War portrait of a gentleman (104x81cm-41x32in) s.d.1837 panel. 15-Jun-4 Capes Dunn, Manchester #761/R

WALDORP, Antonie (1803-1866) Dutch
£3020 $5527 €4500 Marine (39x52cm-15x20in) s. panel. 8-Jul-4 Campo, Vlaamse Kaai #294 est:5000-6000
£4514 $7132 €6500 Busy shipping lane (43x55cm-17x22in) s. 2-Sep-3 Christie's, Amsterdam #322/R est:4000-6000
£6376 $11413 €9500 Sailing ship with figures in front of the coast (36x57cm-14x22in) s. panel. 27-May-4 Dorotheum, Vienna #12/R est:3000-3500
Works on paper
£694 $1132 €1000 Fishing boats (22x30cm-9x12in) s. W/C pencil. 26-Sep-3 Bolland & Marotz, Bremen #630/R

WALDORP, Antonie (attrib) (1803-1866) Dutch
£1081 $2000 €1578 Town scene (74x86cm-29x34in) bears sig. 18-Jul-4 Bonhams & Butterfields, Los Angeles #7011/R est:2500-3500

WALE, John Porter (1860-1920) British
Works on paper
£400 $692 €584 View of a cottage garden in bloom, mountain in the distance (35x26cm-14x10in) s. W/C gouache. 10-Dec-3 Rupert Toovey, Partridge Green #102/R
£480 $830 €701 Landscape with thatched cottage and garden in bloom (33x24cm-13x9in) s. W/C gouache. 10-Dec-3 Rupert Toovey, Partridge Green #103/R
£500 $815 €730 Summer flowers (24x45cm-9x18in) s. W/C htd white. 25-Sep-3 Mellors & Kirk, Nottingham #145/R
£1000 $1640 €1460 Still life of michaelmas daisies and mixed flowers in a green vase (33x23cm-13x9in) s. W/C bodycol htd white. 29-May-3 Neales, Nottingham #738/R est:600-800

WALES, Orlando G (fl.1906-1935) American
£253 $400 €369 Breaking waves on rocky coast (69x76cm-27x30in) s. 6-Sep-3 Brunk, Ashville #626

WALISZEWSKI, Zygmunt (1897-1936) Polish
Works on paper
£3596 $6653 €5250 Figures dancing (59x78cm-23x31in) W/C. 14-Mar-4 Agra, Warsaw #70/R (P.Z 26000)

WALKA, Molly Rogers (c.1945-) Australian
Works on paper
£813 $1285 €1187 Untitled (106x75cm-42x30in) i.verso synthetic polymer paint prov. 28-Jul-3 Sotheby's, Paddington #495/R est:2000-3000 (A.D 2000)

WALKER, Albert (1900-1984) British
£420 $760 €613 Stack yard (30x40cm-12x16in) s.d.1954 board exhib. 30-Mar-4 David Duggleby, Scarborough #152/R

WALKER, Aldo (1938-2000) Swiss
£1321 $2140 €1929 Untitled (75x60cm-30x24in) acrylic prov. 24-May-3 Burkhard, Luzern #180/R est:1500-2000 (S.FR 2800)
£1629 $2720 €2378 Untitled (160x112cm-63x44in) s.d.1985 verso acrylic. 24-Jun-3 Germann, Zurich #153/R est:3000-4000 (S.FR 3600)

WALKER, Bernard Eyre (1886-?) British
Works on paper
£300 $537 €438 Devils staircase Glencoe (29x45cm-11x18in) s.d.1937 W/C. 17-Mar-4 James Thompson, Kirby Lonsdale #33/R
£360 $662 €526 Cuillins, Skye (35x52cm-14x20in) s.d.1939 W/C. 25-Mar-4 Bonhams, Edinburgh #341

WALKER, Charles J (fl.1860-1870) British
£1500 $2745 €2190 Sunny day on Hampstead Heath (30x51cm-12x20in) s.i. stretcher. 8-Apr-4 Christie's, Kensington #79/R est:1500-2000

WALKER, Claude (1862-?) British
£424 $720 €619 Richmond Hill (24x35cm-9x14in) s.d.1920 board. 24-Nov-3 Sotheby's, Melbourne #313 (A.D 1000)

WALKER, Dame Ethel (1861-1951) British
£900 $1611 €1314 Mother and child. Coastal landscape (35x27cm-14x11in) s.verso double-sided board. 14-May-4 Christie's, Kensington #503/R
£1000 $1720 €1460 Memories of Jamaica (76x63cm-30x25in) s.i.verso. 3-Dec-3 Christie's, Kensington #417/R est:1000-1500
£1300 $2288 €1898 Portrait of a young girl (76x63cm-30x25in) s. 19-May-4 Sotheby's, Olympia #108/R est:800-1200
£1500 $2580 €2190 Contre jour (51x61cm-20x24in) prov. 3-Dec-3 Christie's, Kensington #523/R est:1500-2000
£1600 $2752 €2336 Seapiece, afternoon (63x77cm-25x30in) s.verso. 3-Dec-3 Christie's, Kensington #516/R est:1500-2000
£1800 $2862 €2628 Spray of flowers in a ware jug on a table (60x76cm-24x30in) 18-Mar-3 Anderson & Garland, Newcastle #417/R est:1500-2500
£1800 $3114 €2628 Farm scene with distant hill (38x48cm-15x19in) s. 11-Dec-3 Scarborough Perry Fine Arts, Hove #660
£2100 $3318 €3045 Handler with herd of horse watering by a ford (64x81cm-25x32in) s.verso. 27-Jul-3 Desmond Judd, Cranbrook #1032
Works on paper
£320 $512 €464 Tiger lilies (22x20cm-9x8in) s. gouache prov. 16-Sep-3 Bonhams, Knightsbridge #30
£3000 $5430 €4380 Tiger lilies (23x21cm-9x8in) s. gouache prov. 19-Apr-4 Sotheby's, London #89/R est:1500-2000

WALKER, David Bond (1891-1977) Irish
£300 $498 €438 Church by the trees (30x45cm-12x18in) s. 1-Oct-3 John Ross, Belfast #237
£480 $874 €701 Irish landscape (34x50cm-13x20in) s. 1-Jul-4 Mellors & Kirk, Nottingham #857
£550 $1023 €803 Trassie Bridge, Bryansford, Co. Down (73x73cm-29x29in) s. 3-Mar-4 John Ross, Belfast #91
£600 $1032 €876 Irish cottages (40x50cm-16x20in) s. board. 3-Dec-3 John Ross, Belfast #139
£600 $1032 €876 Landscape by County Down coast (40x50cm-16x20in) s. 3-Dec-3 John Ross, Belfast #209
£600 $1032 €876 Near Castlewellan (20x25cm-8x10in) mono. board. 3-Dec-3 John Ross, Belfast #231

WALKER, E D (?) British
£1650 $2855 €2409 Royal yacht Britannia docking at Maryport harbour with crowd (48x74cm-19x29in) s. 11-Dec-3 Mitchells, Cockermouth #925/R est:800-1200

WALKER, Eric Lionel (20th C) British
Works on paper
£550 $1029 €825 Saint-Ouens Bay, Jersey (53x72cm-21x28in) s. W/C. 22-Jul-4 Martel Maides, Guernsey #188/R

WALKER, Frances (1930-) British
£800 $1488 €1168 Rocky coastal landscape (68x107cm-27x42in) s. board. 4-Mar-4 Christie's, Kensington #205/R

WALKER, Frederick (1840-1875) British
Works on paper
£1000 $1820 €1460 The little farm boy (20x14cm-8x6in) pencil W/C bodycol. 1-Jul-4 Christie's, Kensington #171/R est:700-900
£58000 $98600 €84680 Bouquet (65x53cm-26x21in) init.d.1865 pencil W/C bodycol gum arabic scratching out. 26-Nov-3 Christie's, London #34/R est:30000-50000

WALKER, Frederick (attrib) (1840-1875) British
Works on paper
£700 $1141 €1022 Croydon cow boy (20x13cm-8x5in) W/C. 23-Sep-3 Anderson & Garland, Newcastle #264/R

WALKER, G (?) ?
£920 $1500 €1343 Woman crossing a stream (51x76cm-20x30in) s. 28-Sep-3 Simpson's, Houston #387/R

WALKER, Horatio (1858-1938) Canadian
£3636 $5927 €5309 La traite du soir (61x46cm-24x18in) init.i. canvas on board prov. 23-Sep-3 Ritchie, Toronto #74/R est:8000-12000 (C.D 8000)
Works on paper
£968 $1781 €1413 The thresher (50x35cm-20x14in) s.d.1900 black chk. 9-Jun-4 Walker's, Ottawa #60/R est:3000-4000 (C.D 2400)
£1875 $3225 €2738 Magnolias. Tree Study (54x44cm-21x17in) first s.indis.d. first W/C second chl pencil two. 2-Dec-3 Joyner Waddington, Toronto #353/R est:1500-2000 (C.D 4200)

WALKER, Inez Nathaniel (1911-1990) American
Works on paper
£1444 $2600 €2108 Brown face with hat (46x30cm-18x12in) crayon pencil. 24-Apr-4 Slotin Folk Art, Buford #432/R est:1000-2000

WALKER, James (19th C) British
£12353 $21000 €18035 Vista al popocatepetl e iztaccihuatl (36x46cm-14x18in) painted c.1888. 19-Nov-3 Sotheby's, New York #78/R est:12000-18000

WALKER, James Alexander (1841-1898) British
£1258 $2000 €1837 French dragoons (51x66cm-20x26in) s. 10-Sep-3 Alderfer's, Hatfield #269/R est:1500-2000

WALKER, James Crampton (20th C) Irish
£972 $1585 €1400 Connemara landscape (38x51cm-15x20in) s. prov. 23-Sep-3 De Veres Art Auctions, Dublin #194

WALKER, James William (1831-1898) British
Works on paper
£300 $483 €435 Hay barges on the bure at Aylsham (23x38cm-9x15in) s. W/C. 15-Aug-3 Keys, Aylsham #657/R

WALKER, John (1939-) British
£1695 $2881 €2475 Canoe (213x168cm-84x66in) s.d.1988 verso exhib. 24-Nov-3 Sotheby's, Melbourne #70/R est:4000-6000 (A.D 4000)
£1800 $3276 €2628 No 7 Open form and Shield (213x167cm-84x66in) s.i.d.1986 verso prov. 4-Feb-4 Sotheby's, Olympia #211/R est:1500-2000

WALKER, John Crampton (1890-1942) Irish
£1806 $2943 €2600 County Kerry landscape (58x73cm-23x29in) s. board. 24-Sep-3 James Adam, Dublin #92/R est:2500-3000
£1901 $3289 €2700 West of Ireland bog scene with turf reeks. Cattle grazin (38x48cm-15x19in) double-sided. 10-Dec-3 Bonhams & James Adam, Dublin #99/R est:3000-5000

WALKER, John Eaton (fl.1855-1866) British
£600 $1038 €876 Mountain Spring (71x58cm-28x23in) s.d.1863 oval. 11-Dec-3 Neales, Nottingham #644/R

WALKER, John Hanson (1844-1933) British
£1118 $1756 €1632 Portrait of young woman (46x36cm-18x14in) s. 30-Aug-3 Rasmussen, Havnen #2022/R est:12000-15000 (D.KR 12000)
£3800 $6004 €5510 Country lass (67x56cm-26x22in) s. i.verso exhib. 4-Sep-3 Christie's, Kensington #262/R est:4000-6000

WALKER, John Law (1899-1965) American
£4076 $7500 €5951 La vie parisienne (121x113cm-48x44in) s. 8-Jun-4 Bonhams & Butterfields, San Francisco #4359/R est:7000-9000

WALKER, John Rawson (1796-1873) British
Works on paper
£340 $609 €496 Romantic landscape (33x24cm-13x9in) s.d.1865 sepia wash. 18-Mar-4 Neales, Nottingham #708

WALKER, John Rawson (attrib) (1796-1873) British
£660 $1142 €964 Figures picnicking in a summer river landscape (36x58cm-14x23in) 11-Dec-3 Neales, Nottingham #669/R

WALKER, John Robert (1957-) Australian
£732 $1149 €1061 Standing nude (152x101cm-60x40in) s.i.verso. 26-Aug-3 Christie's, Sydney #267/R est:1800-2500 (A.D 1800)
£5668 $9126 €8275 Mirramina I (274x244cm-108x96in) s.d.1987 i.verso. 13-Oct-3 Joel, Victoria #407/R est:5000-6000 (A.D 14000)

WALKER, Kara (1969-) American
£23743 $42500 €34665 Uncle Remus spins a yarn (122x137cm-48x54in) s.i.d.95 overlap s.i.d.1994-5 stretcher cut outs prov. 13-May-4 Sotheby's, New York #355/R est:20000-30000
Works on paper
£4121 $7500 €6017 Eliza revised (46x30cm-18x12in) ink wash prov.exhib. 29-Jun-4 Sotheby's, New York #627/R est:4000-6000

WALKER, Marian (19th C) British
Works on paper
£250 $415 €365 Two young children by a pillar with a landscape beyond (55x39cm-22x15in) s.d.1836 W/C htd white. 1-Oct-3 Woolley & Wallis, Salisbury #168/R

WALKER, Marion (19/20th C) British
£290 $522 €423 Burn. s.d.1909. 22-Apr-4 Bonhams, Edinburgh #350

WALKER, R (1607-1658) British
£700 $1190 €1022 Archer, thought to be the society of St. George, in a wooded landscape (69x51cm-27x20in) s. 6-Nov-3 Christie's, Kensington #745/R

WALKER, Stuart (20th C) American?
Works on paper
£1471 $2500 €2148 Untitled, (36x25cm-14x10in) s.d.32 W/C prov. 1-Nov-3 Santa Fe Art, Santa Fe #143/R est:3000-5000

WALKER, T (19th C) ?
£650 $1105 €949 Extensive river landscape with figure on a path approaching cottages (76x127cm-30x50in) indis.sig. 19-Nov-3 Tennants, Leyburn #1101

WALKER, Thomas Bond (19th C) British?
£1000 $1810 €1500 Sailing boat on river Lagan, Belfast (25x37cm-10x15in) s. board. 31-Mar-4 James Adam, Dublin #145/R est:1000-2000

WALKER, Thornton (?) ?
£2234 $3798 €3262 Landscape - Lake Daylesford, Autumn (122x137cm-48x54in) s.d.92-93 verso prov.exhib. 26-Nov-3 Deutscher-Menzies, Melbourne #203/R est:6000-9000 (A.D 5250)
Works on paper
£468 $796 €683 White house - Cadaques (26x22cm-10x9in) init.d.95 W/C ink prov. 26-Nov-3 Deutscher-Menzies, Melbourne #266/R (A.D 1100)

WALKER, William Aiken (1838-1921) American
£497 $800 €726 Cotton picker (23x13cm-9x5in) board. 20-Aug-3 James Julia, Fairfield #82/R
£1033 $1900 €1508 Cotton picker (5x10cm-2x4in) mono. panel. 28-Mar-4 Carlsen Gallery, Greenville #566/R
£1829 $3000 €2652 View of ruins of rock structure and distant mountains (30x18cm-12x7in) s. i.verso artist board painted c.1880. 31-May-3 Brunk, Ashville #146/R est:5000-10000
£3867 $7000 €5646 Cabin on wash day (15x30cm-6x12in) board. 2-Apr-4 Douglas, South Deerfield #37
£4348 $8000 €6348 Old cotton picker (21x10cm-8x4in) s. board. 27-Jun-4 Freeman, Philadelphia #95/R est:5000-8000
£4396 $8000 €6418 In the cotton field (21x11cm-8x4in) s. board. 29-Jun-4 Sotheby's, New York #198/R est:5000-7000
£5723 $9500 €8356 Cabin Scene (15x30cm-6x12in) board. 4-Oct-3 Neal Auction Company, New Orleans #363/R est:9000-12000
£6858 $12550 €10287 Log cabin with tilting chimney, seated woman in doorway (13x28cm-5x11in) s. board. 7-Jun-4 Everard, Savannah #476354/R est:8000-12000
£7527 $14000 €10989 A cotton picker's cabin (15x31cm-6x12in) s. board. 5-Mar-4 Skinner, Boston #306/R est:5000-7000
£8242 $15000 €12033 Southern shanty (15x30cm-6x12in) s. board. 29-Jun-4 Sotheby's, New York #196/R est:10000-15000
£8383 $14000 €12239 Cotton pickers (31x15cm-12x6in) init. board pair. 9-Oct-3 Christie's, Rockefeller NY #11/R est:10000-15000
£9016 $16500 €13524 Log cabin with a woman seated in the doorway (23x30cm-9x12in) i.verso board. 7-Jun-4 Everard, Savannah #476435/R est:8000-12000
£10056 $18000 €14682 Cabin scene with live oak (23x30cm-9x12in) s. board prov. 6-May-4 Shannon's, Milford #16/R est:8000-12000
£10180 $17000 €14863 In the cotton fields (61x16cm-24x6in) init. board pair. 9-Oct-3 Christie's, Rockefeller NY #13/R est:8000-12000
£13408 $24000 €19576 Cabin scene with children, animals and cotton field (23x30cm-9x12in) s. board prov. 6-May-4 Shannon's, Milford #15/R est:9000-12000
£13636 $24000 €19909 Southern cabin scene with figures (13x30cm-5x12in) s. board. 22-May-4 Pook & Pook, Downington #697/R est:9000-12000
£14024 $23000 €20335 Still life of bluefish hanging from a nail (46x30cm-18x12in) s. i.verso artist board prov. 31-May-3 Brunk, Ashville #145/R est:5000-10000
£14205 $25000 €20739 Sugar cane cutting (15x30cm-6x12in) s. board prov. 19-May-4 Sotheby's, New York #85/R est:10000-15000
£14634 $24000 €21219 Still life of sheepshead fish hanging from a nail (46x30cm-18x12in) s. i.verso artist board painted c.1860 prov. 31-May-3 Brunk, Ashville #144/R est:5000-10000
£19886 $35000 €29034 Cotton field (15x30cm-6x12in) s. board prov. 19-May-4 Sotheby's, New York #84/R est:10000-15000
£162162 $300000 €236757 Noon day pause in the cotton field (36x61cm-14x24in) init. 11-Mar-4 Christie's, Rockefeller NY #17/R est:30000-50000
Works on paper
£3750 $6750 €5475 Cabin scene (23x30cm-9x12in) i.verso mixed media board. 20-Apr-4 Bunch, West Chester #162/R est:6000-8000

WALKER, William Aiken (attrib) (1838-1921) American
Works on paper
£419 $750 €612 African Americans. W/C collage four in one frame. 8-Jan-4 James Julia, Fairfield #801/R
£699 $1300 €1021 Nature morte. Game birds (61x41cm-24x16in) pastel pair. 7-Mar-4 William Jenack, New York #419 est:500-800

WALKER, Winifred (?) British
£250 $448 €365 Flowers in a vase on a ledge (51x76cm-20x30in) s. s.i.verso. 18-Mar-4 Christie's, Kensington #712/R

WALKOWITZ, Abraham (1878-1965) American/Russian
£407 $750 €594 Street scene, market day (25x28cm-10x11in) s. prov. 25-Jun-4 Freeman, Philadelphia #196/R
£659 $1100 €962 Flowers in blue jug. s. canvasboard. 18-Oct-3 Harvey Clar, Oakland #1274
£1176 $2000 €1717 Untitled - cityscape (58x48cm-23x19in) s.d.1910. 9-Nov-3 Wright, Chicago #142 est:2500-3500
£2235 $4000 €3263 Floral still life (61x46cm-24x18in) s. canvasboard prov. 14-May-4 Skinner, Boston #356/R est:3000-5000
£5308 $9500 €7750 My Paris studio (58x79cm-23x31in) s.i.d.1931 prov. 14-May-4 Skinner, Boston #358/R est:10000-20000
Works on paper
£265 $450 €387 Houses through the trees (25x33cm-10x13in) s. W/C chl card on board. 5-Nov-3 Doyle, New York #78/R
£279 $500 €407 Isadora Duncan (18x8cm-7x3in) s. ink W/C prov. 16-May-4 Wright, Chicago #123/R
£326 $600 €476 Study of Isadora Duncan (15x5cm-6x2in) s. W/C ink sold with two others one frame prov. 25-Jun-4 Freeman, Philadelphia #49/R
£335 $600 €489 Isadora Duncan (46x30cm-18x12in) s. chl. 16-May-4 Wright, Chicago #110/R
£391 $700 €571 Isadora Duncan (51x33cm-20x13in) s. pastel. 16-May-4 Wright, Chicago #111/R
£391 $700 €571 Isadora Duncan (48x30cm-19x12in) s. pastel. 16-May-4 Wright, Chicago #113/R
£391 $700 €571 Isadora Duncan (51x33cm-20x13in) s. chl pastel. 16-May-4 Wright, Chicago #115/R
£419 $750 €612 Isadora Duncan (51x33cm-20x13in) s. chl pastel. 16-May-4 Wright, Chicago #112/R
£419 $750 €612 Isadora Duncan (48x33cm-19x13in) s.chl pastel. 16-May-4 Wright, Chicago #114/R
£426 $750 €622 Figure (33x20cm-13x8in) s. ink W/C exec.c.1910. 23-May-4 Treadway Gallery, Cincinnati #701/R
£435 $800 €635 Rocky cliffs and sea (41x56cm-16x22in) s. W/C. 10-Jun-4 Swann Galleries, New York #249/R
£447 $800 €653 Leaves (36x28cm-14x11in) s.d.1904 pastel crayon. 16-May-4 Wright, Chicago #125/R
£471 $800 €688 Isadora Duncan (23x18cm-9x7in) s. graphite ink prov. 9-Nov-3 Wright, Chicago #116
£516 $950 €753 Isadora in green (36x20cm-14x8in) s. W/C. 25-Mar-4 Doyle, New York #74/R
£588 $1000 €858 Iasdora Ducan (25x18cm-10x7in) s. ink W/C exhib. 9-Nov-3 Wright, Chicago #118 est:500-700
£591 $1100 €863 Landscape (36x51cm-14x20in) s. W/C. 7-Mar-4 William Jenack, New York #146 est:1200-1600
£647 $1100 €945 Abstraction (30x20cm-12x8in) s.d.1912 ink. 9-Nov-3 Wright, Chicago #121 est:1000-1500
£652 $1200 €952 Isadora Duncan (15x5cm-6x2in) s. W/C pen ink three. 10-Jun-4 Swann Galleries, New York #251/R
£700 $1288 €1050 Isodora Duncan (25x20cm-10x8in) s.d.1909 W/C Indian ink over pencil. 10-Jun-4 Hauswedell & Nolte, Hamburg #727/R
£838 $1500 €1223 Isadora Duncan (35x21cm-14x8in) s.i. W/C prov. 14-May-4 Skinner, Boston #357/R est:800-1200
£872 $1500 €1273 Vase of flowers (46x38cm-18x15in) s. gouache pencil prov. 3-Dec-3 Doyle, New York #301/R est:2000-3000
£1235 $2100 €1803 Rooftops (38x46cm-15x18in) s. W/C. 9-Nov-3 Wright, Chicago #130 est:800-1200
£1413 $2600 €2063 Isadora Duncan (15x8cm-6x3in) init. W/C pen ink exec. c.1920 four. 10-Jun-4 Swann Galleries, New York #252/R est:1500-2500
£1739 $3200 €2539 Abstraction (46x33cm-18x13in) s. pencil card. 10-Jun-4 Swann Galleries, New York #248/R est:700-1000
£2072 $3750 €3025 Isadora Duncan (35x21cm-14x8in) s. ink W/C pair. 31-Mar-4 Sotheby's, New York #152/R est:1200-1600

WALL, Jeff (1946-) Canadian
Photographs
£35928 $60000 €52455 Diagonal composition (50x56cm-20x22in) num.2/4 cibachrome transparency fluorescent light case prov. 13-Nov-3 Sotheby's, New York #491/R est:40000-60000
Sculpture
£107784 $180000 €157365 Sunken area (234x290x26cm-92x114x10in) color photograph transparency in lightbox executed 1996 prov.exhib. 13-Nov-3 Phillips, New York #13/R est:150000-200000

WALL, William Archibald (1828-1875) British/American
£330 $518 €479 On the Thames near Ckenham (36x36cm-14x14in) init.verso painted c.1860. 15-Dec-2 Desmond Judd, Cranbrook #835

WALL, William Guy (1792-c.1864) American/Irish
£950 $1700 €1387 Hudson river scene (30x46cm-12x18in) s. 8-Jan-4 James Julia, Fairfield #892/R est:1500-2000
£1514 $2800 €2210 Afternoon outing (28x41cm-11x16in) board. 18-Jan-4 Carlsen Gallery, Greenville #432/R

WALL, William Guy (after) (1792-c.1864) American/Irish
Prints
£3243 $6000 €4735 New York, from Governors Island (35x53cm-14x21in) hand coloring aquatint. 15-Jan-4 Sotheby's, New York #142/R est:6000-8000

WALLA, August (1936-2001) Austrian
Works on paper
£533 $981 €800 Sozialistische Schwestern (32x40cm-13x16in) i. col crayon ball pen stamp prov. 9-Jun-4 Artcurial Briest, Paris #364/R
£629 $1070 €900 Grave! Deadman lives! Jesus 1 God! Chist! (29x42cm-11x17in) i. verso feltpen col pen board prov. 26-Nov-3 Dorotheum, Vienna #322/R
£1329 $2259 €1900 Jesus! (42x29cm-17x11in) i. verso col pen board. 26-Nov-3 Dorotheum, Vienna #323/R est:1200-1800
£1399 $2378 €2000 In love! Sun roses! We love each other. (30x40cm-12x16in) i. verso pencil feltpen board prov. 26-Nov-3 Dorotheum, Vienna #321/R est:1200-1800
£1477 $2643 €2200 German Yiddish; Yiddish German (21x28cm-8x11in) pencil W/C biro prov. 25-May-4 Dorotheum, Vienna #312/R est:1500-2500

WALLA, Erich (1947-) Austrian
Works on paper
£345 $631 €500 Dreaming girl in poetry garden (60x44cm-24x17in) s.d.1987/1990 mixed media board. 27-Jan-4 Dorotheum, Vienna #230/R

WALLACE, David A (20th C) American?
Works on paper
£333 $600 €486 The man with the plow (51x61cm-20x24in) s.d.41 s.i.d.verso W/C. 23-Jan-4 Freeman, Philadelphia #17/R

WALLACE, Ethel A (1885-1968) American
£1630 $3000 €2380 Still life of mixed flowers in a vase (76x63cm-30x25in) canvas laid down. 27-Jun-4 Freeman, Philadelphia #155/R est:3000-5000

WALLACE, H Frank (1881-1962) British
Works on paper
£300 $510 €438 Hinds on a moor (21x33cm-8x13in) s. W/C bodycol. 27-Nov-3 Christie's, Kensington #193/R
£380 $680 €555 The clearing in the wood (19x28cm-7x11in) s. bodycol. 25-May-4 Bonhams, Knightsbridge #23/R
£650 $1105 €949 Stag and hinds in a lowland landscape (34x49cm-13x19in) s. bodycol. 27-Nov-3 Christie's, Kensington #190/R
£750 $1380 €1095 Angling at upper Torrish Pool, Helmsdale (38x53cm-15x21in) s. bodycol on board prov. 10-Jun-4 Christie's, Kensington #231/R
£900 $1530 €1314 Feeding on the lowlands (34x49cm-13x19in) s. bodycol. 27-Nov-3 Christie's, Kensington #191/R
£950 $1615 €1387 Tail of the pool, the River Findhorn (32x49cm-13x19in) s. W/C bodycol prov. 27-Nov-3 Christie's, Kensington #192/R
£1300 $2210 €1898 Something's moved them meoble (34x48cm-13x19in) s. W/C bodycol prov. 27-Nov-3 Christie's, Kensington #194/R est:600-800

WALLACE, Harry Draper (1892-1977) Canadian
£1440 $2635 €2102 Painted gables (35x42cm-14x17in) s. verso board prov. 1-Jun-4 Joyner Waddington, Toronto #384/R est:2500-3000 (C.D 3600)

WALLACE, Henry (?) British
£1300 $2366 €1898 Wilford ferry. John Edwards cottage at Wilford (14x27cm-6x11in) mono.d.79 pair. 5-Feb-4 Mellors & Kirk, Nottingham #589/R est:600-1000

WALLACE, James (1872-1911) British
£337 $550 €492 River with anglers (25x38cm-10x15in) s. 28-Sep-3 Simpson's, Houston #215/R
£380 $669 €555 Faggot gatherers (41x61cm-16x24in) s. 19-May-4 Christie's, Kensington #534/R
£800 $1488 €1168 Roses in a sevres vase (49x39cm-19x15in) s.d.1916 painted oval exhib. 4-Mar-4 Christie's, Kensington #178/R
£2000 $3400 €2920 Coastal scene with three children in a small boat (51x68cm-20x27in) s.indis.d.1910. 19-Nov-3 Tennants, Leyburn #1029/R est:500-700

WALLACE, John (1841-1905) British
£811 $1500 €1184 Artist's studio (79x58cm-31x23in) s. board. 13-Mar-4 Susanin's, Chicago #6115/R est:2000-4000
£2550 $4590 €3723 Cullercoats Bay with figures on the shore (41x66cm-16x26in) s.d. 1891 i.verso. 24-Apr-4 Tamlyn, Bridgwater #142/R

WALLACE, Marjorie (1925-) British
Works on paper
£410 $697 €599 Seated boy on a beach (62x47cm-24x19in) s. pastel gouache. 4-Nov-3 Stephan Welz, Johannesburg #658 est:3000-5000 (SA.R 4800)

WALLACE-CRABBE, Robin (1938-) Australian
£407 $638 €590 Blinman (213x157cm-84x62in) s.i.verso painted c.1971 exhib.lit. 27-Aug-3 Christie's, Sydney #728/R (A.D 1000)

WALLAERT, Pierre Joseph (1753-1812) French
£6250 $11500 €9500 Naufrage par gros temps (98x137cm-39x54in) s.d.1786 prov. 24-Jun-4 Christie's, Paris #110/R est:15000-20000

WALLANDER, Alf (1862-1914) Swedish
£1538 $2646 €2245 Interior scene with girl sleeping (41x31cm-16x12in) s. 2-Dec-3 Bukowskis, Stockholm #81/R est:12000-15000 (S.KR 20000)
Works on paper
£4000 $6880 €5840 The flower market (84x118cm-33x46in) s.d.95 pastel. 2-Dec-3 Bukowskis, Stockholm #87/R est:25000-30000 (S.KR 52000)

WALLANDER, Gerda (1860-1926) Swedish
£1552 $2778 €2266 View from Slottsbacken towards the National Museum (54x81cm-21x32in) s. 26-May-4 AB Stockholms Auktionsverk #2161/R est:8000-10000 (S.KR 21000)

WALLANDER, Josef Wilhelm (1821-1888) Swedish
£5322 $9525 €7770 Ulla Winblad and Mollberg at Djurgarden (34x42cm-13x17in) s.d.1859 i.verso. 26-May-4 AB Stockholms Auktionsverk #2121/R est:20000-25000 (S.KR 72000)
£6652 $11907 €9712 Weaving woollen cloth - interior with couples dancing (74x97cm-29x38in) s.d.1881 prov.lit. 26-May-4 AB Stockholms Auktionsverk #2123/R est:100000-125000 (S.KR 90000)

WALLAS, Lee (20th C) American
£227 $400 €331 Playing cards (76x91cm-30x36in) s. masonite. 22-May-4 Selkirks, St. Louis #670/R
£265 $450 €387 The juggler (117x81cm-46x32in) s. board. 7-Nov-3 Selkirks, St. Louis #564/R

WALLAT, Paul (1879-?) German
£397 $723 €600 View of Rostock (70x80cm-28x31in) s. 18-Jun-4 Bolland & Marotz, Bremen #841/R

WALLBURG, Egon (19th C) ?
Works on paper
£775 $1340 €1100 Rural scene. Gallant scene (23x33cm-9x13in) one s.d.941 one s.d.942 W/C two. 9-Dec-3 Pandolfini, Florence #322/R

WALLCOTT, Augustus (?) American?
£290 $458 €420 Peaceful bay off a river (28x8cm-11x3in) s. 2-Apr-3 Woodwards, Cork #16

WALLEN, Gustaf Teodor (1860-1948) Swedish
Works on paper
£2217 $3969 €3237 Greenery outside farmhouse, Vitemole (24x32cm-9x13in) s.i. W/C. 26-May-4 AB Stockholms Auktionsverk #2096/R est:8000-10000 (S.KR 30000)

WALLER, Alice E (1884-1973) British
Works on paper
£350 $595 €511 View of Brecqhou from Sark (27x44cm-11x17in) s. W/C. 25-Nov-3 Martel Maides, Guernsey #193

WALLER, Frank (1842-1923) American
£1491 $2400 €2177 Tombs in a desert landscape (30x66cm-12x26in) s.d.74 canvas on board. 14-Jan-4 Christie's, Rockefeller NY #39/R est:2000-3000

WALLER, Margaret Mary (1916-1997) British
Works on paper
£380 $646 €555 La Seigneurie gardens, Sark (25x35cm-10x14in) s. W/C. 25-Nov-3 Martel Maides, Guernsey #192

WALLER, Mary Lemon (?-1931) British
£2700 $5049 €4050 Little girl with a pet rabbit (94x66cm-37x26in) s.d.1877 possibly exhib. 26-Jul-4 Bonhams, Bath #96/R est:2000-3000
£3889 $7000 €5678 Portrait of Elizabeth Cavendish and her son Tyrell (98x74cm-39x29in) s.d.1880. 21-Jan-4 Sotheby's, New York #206/R est:10000-15000
£4000 $6800 €5840 Portrait of Molly, daughter of the late Sir Arthur Pease, in a riding habit (121x86cm-48x34in) s.d.1902 exhib. 25-Nov-3 Christie's, London #129/R est:5000-8000

WALLER, Richard (1811-1882) British
£500 $910 €730 Portrait of a lady (76x63cm-30x25in) s.d.1878. 3-Feb-4 Sworder & Son, Bishops Stortford #291/R

WALLER, Samuel Edmund (1850-1903) British
£3593 $6000 €5246 Wide wide world (102x152cm-40x60in) s.d.1899. 7-Oct-3 Sotheby's, New York #97 est:8000-12000

WALLERT, Axel (1890-1962) Swedish
£537 $983 €784 Portrait of Mrs Margaret Hellstrom (35x32cm-14x13in) s.d.37 i.verso. 9-Jun-4 Rasmussen, Copenhagen #1997/R (D.KR 6000)
£1700 $3043 €2482 Landscape from Strandvagen, Stockholm (56x46cm-22x18in) s.d.1939. 25-May-4 Bukowskis, Stockholm #15/R est:20000-25000 (S.KR 23000)
£3172 $5393 €4631 The Queen of Paintings (46x55cm-18x22in) s.d.1923. 5-Nov-3 AB Stockholms Auktionsverk #774/R est:40000-50000 (S.KR 42000)
£3178 $5689 €4640 Cafe interior (38x46cm-15x18in) s. 25-May-4 Bukowskis, Stockholm #45/R est:40000-50000 (S.KR 43000)

WALLERT, Dieter (1935-1988) German
£455 $782 €650 Sunset (68x131cm-27x52in) s.d.64 verso. 5-Dec-3 Bolland & Marotz, Bremen #875/R

WALLET, Albert-Charles (1852-1918) French
£467 $854 €700 River course with sheep and houses (69x89cm-27x35in) s. canvas on canvas. 5-Jun-4 Arnold, Frankfurt #789/R

WALLET, Taf (1902-2000) Belgian
£336 $561 €480 Un jardin a St Idesbald (55x33cm-22x13in) s. 7-Oct-3 Palais de Beaux Arts, Brussels #602
£352 $609 €500 Still life with flowers (75x51cm-30x20in) s. 13-Dec-3 De Vuyst, Lokeren #397
£367 $656 €550 Nieuport (30x40cm-12x16in) s.d.1962 panel. 16-May-4 MonsAntic, Maisieres #483
£451 $754 €650 Poissons (50x65cm-20x26in) s. 21-Oct-3 Campo & Campo, Antwerp #358/R
£500 $895 €750 Bouquet a la rose jaune (100x80cm-39x31in) s.d.1967. 16-May-4 MonsAntic, Maisieres #482
£521 $870 €750 Still life with pheasant and apples (63x80cm-25x31in) s. panel. 21-Oct-3 Campo & Campo, Antwerp #359
£537 $950 €800 Nature morte aux fleurs (60x40cm-24x16in) s. 27-Apr-4 Campo & Campo, Antwerp #275/R
£594 $1010 €850 Port de peche anime (30x39cm-12x15in) s.d.XXXIII panel. 18-Nov-3 Vanderkindere, Brussels #96
£621 $1148 €900 Ostendaises sur fond mauve (40x50cm-16x20in) s. s.i.verso. 19-Jan-4 Horta, Bruxelles #441
£690 $1276 €1000 Legumes (47x47cm-19x19in) s.d.27 s.i.d.verso 1927. 19-Jan-4 Horta, Bruxelles #442
£769 $1308 €1100 Cabine blanche (20x36cm-8x14in) s. panel. 18-Nov-3 Galerie Moderne, Brussels #831/R
£1600 $2864 €2400 Nature morte aux brochets (100x125cm-39x49in) s.d.43. 11-May-4 Vanderkindere, Brussels #108 est:2500-3500
£1812 $3352 €2700 Plage (40x80cm-16x31in) s. s.d.1971. 13-Mar-4 De Vuyst, Lokeren #393/R est:2700-3000
£1837 $3288 €2700 Le depart des crevettiers (65x92cm-26x36in) s. s.i.d.1956 verso. 16-Mar-4 Vanderkindere, Brussels #65 est:3000-4000
£2153 $3423 €3100 Bouquet (85x65cm-33x26in) s. 9-Sep-3 Vanderkindere, Brussels #543
£2162 $3870 €3200 L'aieule (120x100cm-47x39in) s.d.29. 10-May-4 Horta, Bruxelles #70 est:3500-4500
£2297 $4112 €3400 Caleche en bord de mer (85x65cm-33x26in) s. 10-May-4 Horta, Bruxelles #71 est:2000-3000
£3776 $6495 €5400 Les parasols sur la plage (70x100cm-28x39in) s. 8-Dec-3 Horta, Bruxelles #48 est:1800-2200
£4795 $8151 €7000 Transats et parasols (131x81cm-52x32in) s. 10-Nov-3 Horta, Bruxelles #126/R
£9441 $16049 €13500 Le jongleur (150x89cm-59x35in) s.i.d.1927 s.d.verso. 18-Nov-3 Vanderkindere, Brussels #100/R est:10000-15000
Works on paper
£579 $1072 €840 Baigneurs a la mer du Nord (20x31cm-8x12in) s. gouache. 16-Feb-4 Horta, Bruxelles #316
£608 $1089 €900 Cabines a la Panne (69x48cm-27x19in) s. chl. 10-May-4 Horta, Bruxelles #73
£1667 $2650 €2400 Les pecheurs de crevettes a maree basse (39x57cm-15x22in) s.i.d.76 W/C. 15-Sep-3 Horta, Bruxelles #51 est:1800-2200

WALLGREN, Otto (attrib) (1795-1857) Swedish
£702 $1257 €1025 Oritya being abducted by Boreas (63x75cm-25x30in) 28-May-4 Uppsala Auktionskammare, Uppsala #83/R (S.KR 9500)

WALLIM, Dario (20th C) Italian?
£867 $1551 €1300 Cliffs with bathers (58x66cm-23x26in) s. i.verso. 12-May-4 Stadion, Trieste #754/R est:800-1200

WALLIN, Carl E (1879-?) American
£759 $1200 €1108 Siren (56x41cm-22x16in) s.d.1934 board. 7-Sep-3 Treadway Gallery, Cincinnati #674/R est:1500-2000

WALLIN, Ellis (1888-1972) Swedish
£595 $1070 €893 The long steps (117x81cm-46x32in) s.d.42. 25-Apr-4 Goteborg Auktionsverk, Sweden #338/R (S.KR 8200)

WALLINGER, Mark (1959-) British
£14000 $25480 €20440 Mr A Brown (110x110cm-43x43in) s.verso i.stretcher linen prov.lit. 6-Feb-4 Sotheby's, London #115/R est:8000-12000

WALLIS, Alfred (1855-1942) British
£4200 $7770 €6132 Two vessels at sea at night (9x14cm-4x6in) housepaint on board. 14-Jan-4 Lawrence, Crewkerne #1444/R est:2500-4000
£10500 $19110 €15330 Sailing ship and lighthouse (10x17cm-4x7in) oil pencil board prov. 15-Jun-4 Bonhams, New Bond Street #51/R est:300-5000
£15500 $28675 €22630 Schooner nearing a lighthouse (22x32cm-9x13in) housepaint pencil on board. 14-Jan-4 Lawrence, Crewkerne #1445/R est:6000-9000
£16000 $29120 €23360 Tug and lighthouse (14x27cm-6x11in) s. oil pencil board prov. 15-Jun-4 Bonhams, New Bond Street #50/R est:5000-7000
Works on paper
£800 $1456 €1168 St. Ives gaff-rigged fishing boat. Terrace of houses (25x38cm-10x15in) pencil double-sided. 15-Jun-4 David Lay, Penzance #267/R
£1500 $2730 €2190 Fishing boat. Fishing boat and lighthouse (23x38cm-9x15in) pencil double-sided. 15-Jun-4 David Lay, Penzance #266 est:2000-2500
£1800 $3276 €2628 Houses and trees (23x38cm-9x15in) pencil htd blue crayon. 15-Jun-4 David Lay, Penzance #265/R est:2000-2500
£2400 $4128 €3504 Two boats and a lighthouse. Ship and lighthouse (25x39cm-10x15in) pencil double-sided exhib. 3-Dec-3 Christie's, Kensington #699/R est:2000-3000
£4000 $7280 €5840 Three boats (23x36cm-9x14in) pencil double-sided prov. 15-Jun-4 Bonhams, New Bond Street #52/R est:2500-3000
£28000 $51240 €40880 Fish and trawlers (22x44cm-9x17in) s. pencil oil on card. 4-Jun-4 Christie's, London #51/R est:10000-15000

WALLIS, George Augustus (1770-1847) British
£722 $1192 €1040 Idyllic landscape with rocks (36x85cm-14x33in) mono. panel. 3-Jul-3 Dr Fritz Nagel, Stuttgart #526/R

WALLIS, Henry (1830-1916) British
£5138 $9198 €7501 Young girl with flowers (34x50cm-13x20in) board prov. 15-May-4 Christie's, Sydney #62/R est:15000-25000 (A.D 13000)

WALLIS, Joshua (1789-1862) British
Works on paper
£1464 $2401 €2020 Mountainous landscape with sheperd and animals (58x90cm-23x35in) W/C. 1-Jun-3 Babuino, Rome #350/R

WALLIS, Joshua (attrib) (1789-1862) British
Works on paper
£900 $1647 €1314 Snow covered landscape with walkers (66x99cm-26x39in) W/C. 6-Apr-4 Bristol Auction Rooms #419/R

WALLMANN, Peter (1957-) Danish
£383 $620 €555 My house in the mountains (120x98cm-47x39in) s.verso. 4-Aug-3 Rasmussen, Vejle #672/R (D.KR 4000)

WALLNER, Thure (1888-1965) Swedish
£517 $926 €755 Midsummer in the skerries (61x50cm-24x20in) s.d.1910. 26-May-4 AB Stockholms Auktionsverk #2163/R (S.KR 7000)
£601 $1081 €877 Scared crows (41x33cm-16x13in) s. panel. 26-Jan-4 Lilla Bukowskis, Stockholm #744 (S.KR 8000)
£615 $1058 €898 Fox in summer meadow (33x41cm-13x16in) s. panel. 3-Dec-3 AB Stockholms Auktionsverk #2284/R (S.KR 8000)
£653 $1064 €953 Blue tits (24x32cm-9x13in) s. panel. 29-Sep-3 Lilla Bukowskis, Stockholm #607 (S.KR 8500)
£656 $1207 €984 Great titmouse (21x27cm-8x11in) s. panel. 14-Jun-4 Lilla Bukowskis, Stockholm #320 (S.KR 9000)
£956 $1539 €1396 Jay (50x73cm-20x29in) s. 25-Aug-3 Lilla Bukowskis, Stockholm #107 (S.KR 12500)
£1035 $1852 €1511 Eagle owl in twilight landscape (89x84cm-35x33in) s. 25-May-4 Bukowskis, Stockholm #180/R (S.KR 14000)
£1109 $1984 €1619 Winter landscape with pheasants (38x46cm-15x18in) s. panel. 26-May-4 AB Stockholms Auktionsverk #2287/R est:10000-12000 (S.KR 15000)
£1231 $2117 €1797 Chaffinch (36x27cm-14x11in) s. panel. 3-Dec-3 AB Stockholms Auktionsverk #2318/R est:18000-20000 (S.KR 16000)
£1385 $2382 €2022 Fox in pine forest (46x60cm-18x24in) s. 2-Dec-3 Bukowskis, Stockholm #54/R est:12000-15000 (S.KR 18000)
£1462 $2514 €2135 Male chaffinch among spring flowers (35x27cm-14x11in) s. panel. 3-Dec-3 AB Stockholms Auktionsverk #2369/R est:8000-10000 (S.KR 19000)
£2069 $3704 €3021 Wooded landscape with greyhen and young (73x81cm-29x32in) s. 26-May-4 AB Stockholms Auktionsverk #2095/R est:40000-50000 (S.KR 28000)
£2217 $3969 €3237 Wooded landscape with fox (74x92cm-29x36in) s,. 25-May-4 Bukowskis, Stockholm #176/R est:25000-30000 (S.KR 30000)
£4065 $7276 €5935 Bullfinches (27x35cm-11x14in) s. panel painted 1948. 25-May-4 Bukowskis, Stockholm #91/R est:15000-18000 (S.KR 55000)
£4287 $7673 €6259 Horned eagle-owl and crows (85x120cm-33x47in) s.d.1911. 25-May-4 Bukowskis, Stockholm #174/R est:30000-35000 (S.KR 58000)
£4804 $8599 €7014 Summer landscape with cat (81x87cm-32x34in) s.d.1916. 25-May-4 Bukowskis, Stockholm #225/R est:50000-60000 (S.KR 65000)

WALLS, Paul (20th C) British?
£700 $1281 €1022 Dramatic sky over Lough Swilly, Co. Donegal (35x45cm-14x18in) s. board. 2-Jun-4 John Ross, Belfast #197

WALLS, William (1860-1942) British
£486 $900 €710 Head of an otterhound (30x36cm-12x14in) s. canvas on board prov. 10-Feb-4 Doyle, New York #162/R
£2162 $4000 €3157 Fox terrier in landscape (41x51cm-16x20in) s.i.d.1905. 10-Feb-4 Doyle, New York #187/R est:1800-2400
£3000 $4710 €4350 Safe shelter (46x61cm-18x24in) s. 27-Aug-3 Sotheby's, London #1011/R est:3000-5000
Works on paper
£2400 $4008 €3504 Lion Study. pencil sold with large collection. 16-Oct-3 Lyon & Turnbull, Edinburgh #40 est:300-500

WALLWORK, Richard (1882-1955) British
£513 $948 €749 Workshop (28x36cm-11x14in) s. board. 9-Mar-4 Watson's, Christchurch #27 est:2000-3000 (NZ.D 1400)
£1397 $2613 €2040 Nude in garden (35x28cm-14x11in) s. 24-Feb-4 Peter Webb, Auckland #38/R est:1500-2000 (NZ.D 3800)

WALMSLEY, James Ulric (1860-1954) British

£320 $534 €467 Sheep on the Moors (23x41cm-9x16in) s. 10-Oct-3 Richardson & Smith, Whitby #80

£520 $941 €759 Stormy coastal scene with vessels (28x43cm-11x17in) s.d.1911. 15-Apr-4 Richardson & Smith, Whitby #83/R

£1500 $2505 €2190 Robin Hood's Bay, towards Ravenscar (58x84cm-23x33in) s. 10-Oct-3 Richardson & Smith, Whitby #100/R est:1500-2000

Works on paper

£300 $477 €435 Harbour basin with abbey and St. Mary Church (19x25cm-7x10in) s. W/C. 9-Sep-3 David Duggleby, Scarborough #103

£300 $477 €435 Robin Hood's Bay from the south (18x28cm-7x11in) W/C. 9-Sep-3 David Duggleby, Scarborough #174

£380 $688 €555 Stoupe Brow (19x26cm-7x10in) s. W/C. 30-Mar-4 David Duggleby, Scarborough #4/R

£600 $1086 €876 View over Robin Hoods Bay (19x27cm-7x11in) s. W/C. 30-Mar-4 David Duggleby, Scarborough #34/R

WALMSLEY, Thomas (1763-1806) British

£9000 $16110 €13140 An artist sketching a ruined church in a landscape (65x82cm-26x32in) s.d.1798 prov.lit. 13-May-4 Sotheby's, London #1/R est:4000-6000

Works on paper

£1100 $1969 €1606 Ruined abbey (31x49cm-12x19in) W/C bodycol. 14-May-4 Christie's, London #26/R est:1200-1800

£1800 $3222 €2628 View near Kenmare, Co Kerry (45x57cm-18x22in) i. i.verso bodycol prov. 14-May-4 Christie's, London #59/R est:2000-3000

WALMSLEY, Thomas (attrib) (1763-1806) British

Works on paper

£9396 $16819 €14000 Lower lake Killarney, looking west (41x61cm-16x24in) bodycol. 26-May-4 James Adam, Dublin #10/R est:2000-3000

WALRAVEN, Ilja (1959-) Dutch

Works on paper

£333 $527 €480 Doggy VIII (65x47cm-26x19in) s.d.2001 mixed media on canvas. 26-Apr-3 Auction Maastricht #123/R

WALRAVEN, Jan (1827-?) Dutch

£1100 $1826 €1606 Feeding the rabbits (61x51cm-24x20in) s. 1-Oct-3 Sotheby's, Olympia #213/R est:1200-1800

£1626 $2911 €2374 Preparing dinner (47x37cm-19x15in) s. panel. 4-May-4 Ritchie, Toronto #67/R est:4000-6000 (C.D 4000)

£2200 $3938 €3212 Perilous situation (61x51cm-24x20in) s. 18-Mar-4 Christie's, Kensington #604/R est:1000-1500

WALRAVEN, Jan (attrib) (1827-?) Dutch

£1223 $2250 €1786 The protected (71x48cm-28x19in) indis.mono.i.verso. 9-Jun-4 Doyle, New York #3088 est:1800-2400

WALSCAPELLE, Jacob van (style) (1644-1727) Dutch

£5000 $9000 €7300 Rose, a poppy, delphiniums and other flower in a glass vase on a stone ledge, butterfly and beetle (33x44cm-13x17in) 21-Apr-4 Bonhams, New Bond Street #7/R est:5000-7000

WALSER, Karl (1877-1943) Swiss

£280 $439 €409 Farmyard with woman feeding chickens (40x51cm-16x20in) s. 30-Aug-3 Rasmussen, Havnen #2179 (D.KR 3000)

£3497 $6014 €5000 Karneval (61x90cm-24x35in) mono.d.1938. 2-Dec-3 Hauswedell & Nolte, Hamburg #672/R est.6000

£54348 $99457 €79348 Lady with dog (56x45cm-22x18in) panel prov.exhib.lit. 7-Jun-4 Christie's, Zurich #34/R est:60000-80000 (S.FR 125000)

WALSETH, Niels (1914-2001) Danish

£271 $500 €396 Young Italian women in a loggia (70x100cm-28x39in) s. 15-Mar-4 Rasmussen, Vejle #26 (D.KR 3000)

WALSH, Alfred Wilson (1859-1916) New Zealander

Works on paper

£658 $1118 €961 Milford Sound (31x49cm-12x19in) s. W/C. 27-Nov-3 International Art Centre, Auckland #109/R (NZ.D 1750)

£1316 $2237 €1921 The Dock, Wellington harbour (36x25cm-14x10in) s.d.1910 W/C. 27-Nov-3 International Art Centre, Auckland #105/R est:4000-6000 (NZ.D 3500)

WALSH, Dan (1960-) American

£1200 $2208 €1800 Notice (92x92cm-36x36in) s.d.1996 i. verso acrylic prov. 9-Jun-4 Artcurial Briest, Paris #562/R est:2000-2500

WALSH, Edward J (1756-1832) British

£1093 $2000 €1596 View of Quebec from Point Levi (41x51cm-16x20in) s.i.d.1832 board. 6-Jun-4 Skinner, Boston #223/R est:2000-4000

WALSH, Elizabeth (?) British

Works on paper

£260 $432 €380 Starlings (38x48cm-15x19in) s.d. W/C. 2-Oct-3 Mitchells, Cockermouth #847

WALSH, George (?) Irish?

Works on paper

£480 $878 €701 Street seller (50x33cm-20x13in) s. mixed media. 2-Jun-4 John Ross, Belfast #74

WALSH, John (?) New Zealander?

£1182 $1855 €1714 Time space traveller (28x41cm-11x16in) board. 27-Aug-3 Dunbar Sloane, Wellington #73/R est:2000-3000 (NZ.D 3250)

£1636 $2569 €2372 Untitled, Tiki (82x118cm-32x46in) s. board. 27-Aug-3 Dunbar Sloane, Wellington #45/R est:6000-10000 (NZ.D 4500)

£1636 $2569 €2372 Taniwha (23x118cm-9x46in) board. 27-Aug-3 Dunbar Sloane, Wellington #52/R est:4000-7000 (NZ.D 4500)

£1786 $3286 €2608 Kupe and his companion survey the planet Tukurua, Sirius (39x38cm-15x15in) s.d.1999 board. 25-Mar-4 International Art Centre, Auckland #1/R est:3500-5500 (NZ.D 5000)

WALSH, John Stanley (1907-) Canadian

Works on paper

£223 $373 €323 McGill Grounds (37x43cm-15x17in) s. W/C prov. 17-Jun-3 Pinneys, Montreal #160 (C.D 500)

WALSH, Mike (20th C) ?

Prints

£2870 $4879 €4190 Last disaster, the funeral of Andy Warhol (218x183cm-86x72in) silkscreen canvas. 4-Nov-3 Bukowskis, Stockholm #637/R est:15000-18000 (S.KR 38000)

WALSH, Phillip (1843-1914) New Zealander/Irish

Works on paper

£906 $1458 €1323 St. John's College (14x23cm-6x9in) s.d.1874 W/C. 20-Aug-3 Dunbar Sloane, Auckland #66/R est:2500-3500 (NZ.D 2500)

WALSHAW, James William (19th C) British

Works on paper

£300 $531 €438 Rural scenes with figures and children (22x34cm-9x13in) s. W/C pair. 28-Apr-4 Peter Wilson, Nantwich #135

WALSHE, Lorcan (1952-) Irish

£1119 $1902 €1600 Masks (42x48cm-17x19in) s.d.1986 board. 18-Nov-3 Whyte's, Dublin #83/R est:2000-3000

WALT DISNEY STUDIOS (20th C) American

£894 $1600 €1305 Ferdinand and matador in arena (18x23cm-7x9in) handpainted celluloid. 14-May-4 Skinner, Boston #417/R est:1000-1500

WALTENSPERGER, Charles (1870-1931) American

£438 $700 €639 Man with a staff (79x64cm-31x25in) 19-Sep-3 Du Mouchelle, Detroit #2276/R

£442 $800 €645 Portrait of a young girl (36x30cm-14x12in) 16-Apr-4 Du Mouchelle, Detroit #1049/R

£563 $900 €822 Portrait of a girl (30x23cm-12x9in) oak panel. 19-Sep-3 Du Mouchelle, Detroit #2277/R

£950 $1634 €1387 Old wharfs, Portland Maine, USA (46x66cm-18x26in) s. s.i.verso prov. 2-Dec-3 Sotheby's, London #122/R

£1012 $1750 €1478 Untitled, lady reading in an interior (51x41cm-20x16in) 12-Dec-3 Du Mouchelle, Detroit #2004/R est:1500-2000

£1511 $2750 €2206 Sunset in the harbour (74x93cm-29x37in) indis sig. 29-Jun-4 Sotheby's, New York #217/R est:3000-5000

WALTER, Christian J (1872-1938) American

£2285 $4250 €3336 The lone tree (55x67cm-22x26in) s. 5-Mar-4 Skinner, Boston #449/R est:4000-6000

WALTER, Franz Erhard (20th C) American

Works on paper

£1333 $2400 €1946 Untitled Innenbau (12x8cm-5x3in) one s.d.1968/71 ink W/C one s.d.1969-73 graphite double-side 2. 24-Apr-4 David Rago, Lambertville #467/R est:100-200

WALTER, H (19th C) German

£929 $1700 €1394 Battleship The Evening Gun at anchor (61x81cm-24x32in) s. 29-Jul-4 Eldred, East Dennis #298/R est:2000-3000

WALTER, Johan Ernst Christian (1799-1860) Danish

£972 $1624 €1400 Enjoying the ice by the city walls (35x49cm-14x19in) s.d.1851 lit. 25-Oct-3 Bergmann, Erlangen #918/R

WALTER, Joseph (1783-1856) British

£3500 $6265 €5110 Paddle-steamer and other shipping on the River Avon at Pill, near Bristol (41x56cm-16x22in) s. prov. 26-May-4 Christie's, Kensington #581/R est:4000-6000

WALTER, Karl (1868-?) German

£241 $450 €352 Bather by a stream (64x53cm-25x21in) 25-Feb-4 Doyle, New York #28/R

WALTER, Martha (1875-1976) American

£353 $650 €515 Two peasant women in extreme foreground (20x15cm-8x6in) s.verso panel. 9-Jun-4 Alderfer's, Hatfield #442/R

£1272 $2200 €1857 Laughing baby (19x13cm-7x5in) s. s.i.verso board. 13-Dec-3 Weschler, Washington #554 est:1000-1500

£1301 $2250 €1899 Souka at Tripoli North Africa (20x25cm-8x10in) board. 10-Dec-3 Alderfer's, Hatfield #353/R est:2500-3000
£1437 $2400 €2098 Alice Roullier (66x53cm-26x21in) s.i. painted c.1915 prov.lit. 7-Oct-3 Sotheby's, New York #218 est:4000-6000
£1875 $3000 €2738 Half-length portrait of a seated woman holding a book (81x46cm-32x18in) s. 20-Sep-3 Pook & Pook, Downington #261/R est:7500-8500
£2096 $3500 €3060 Still life with roses (33x41cm-13x16in) canvasboard prov. 23-Oct-3 Shannon's, Milford #171/R est:3000-5000
£2358 $3750 €3443 Still life with pink and white roses in blue vase on black drape (66x53cm-26x21in) s. 10-Sep-3 Alderfer's, Hatfield #454/R est:5000-7000
£2581 $4750 €3768 Portrait of old woman wearing head scarf and blue dress, holding baby in yellow dress (66x53cm-26x21in) sig. i.verso. 9-Jun-4 Alderfer's, Hatfield #441/R est:5000-7000
£2938 $4700 €4289 The Mosque-Tunis (23x23cm-9x9in) s. board. 20-Sep-3 Pook & Pook, Downington #253/R est:3000-4000
£4324 $8000 €6313 Townsmen (41x51cm-16x20in) s. indis.i.verso board. 11-Mar-4 Christie's, Rockefeller NY #65/R est:8000-12000
£5028 $9000 €7341 Italian woman (99x74cm-39x29in) estate st.stretcher prov. 26-May-4 Doyle, New York #89/R est:5000-7000
£7186 $12000 €10492 Summer afternoon in the Luxembourg garden (22x27cm-9x11in) s. board prov. 9-Oct-3 Christie's, Rockefeller NY #59/R est:12000-18000
£45455 $80000 €66364 Gloucester beach (36x46cm-14x18in) s. prov. 18-May-4 Christie's, Rockefeller NY #97/R est:40000-60000
£68182 $120000 €99546 Portrait of Elizabeth Chapman (122x102cm-48x40in) s. prov. 18-May-4 Christie's, Rockefeller NY #98/R est:70000-100000
Works on paper
£2844 $4750 €4152 High tide at Bass Rocks (25x28cm-10x11in) s. s.i.verso W/C prov. 23-Oct-3 Shannon's, Milford #13/R est:3000-5000
£3294 $5500 €4809 In the Murillo Gardens (20x23cm-8x9in) s. i.verso W/C prov. 23-Oct-3 Shannon's, Milford #14/R est:3000-5000
£3593 $6000 €5246 Gloucester Harbour (23x30cm-9x12in) W/C prov. 23-Oct-3 Shannon's, Milford #15/R est:5000-7000

WALTER, Otto (1853-1904) Austrian
£237 $425 €346 Girl in barn taking milk to kitten (13x10cm-5x4in) s. panel. 29-May-4 Brunk, Ashville #480a/R

WALTER, T (19/20th C) ?
£940 $1729 €1400 Forest clearing with faggot gatherer (69x55cm-27x22in) s. 25-Mar-4 Karlheinz Kaupp, Staufen #2793/R

WALTERS, Curt (1958-) American
£353 $600 €515 Schnebly Hill, Sedona (20x25cm-8x10in) s. s.i.verso masonite prov. 21-Nov-3 Skinner, Boston #331/R
£1553 $2500 €2252 Artist and patron's pathways (16x16cm-6x6in) 22-Aug-3 Altermann Galleries, Santa Fe #148
£3571 $6500 €5214 New Mexico quintessence (102x76cm-40x30in) s. painted c.1990 prov. 29-Jun-4 Sotheby's, New York #256/R est:4000-6000
£4469 $8000 €6525 Zion sunrise (97x145cm-38x57in) 15-May-4 Altermann Galleries, Santa Fe #180/R
£4706 $8000 €6871 Regeneration (91x91cm-36x36in) 1-Nov-3 Altermann Galleries, Santa Fe #186
£8380 $15000 €12235 Autumn's premiere (76x61cm-30x24in) 15-May-4 Altermann Galleries, Santa Fe #181/R
£17059 $29000 €24906 Brilliant soliloquy of winter (122x122cm-48x48in) s. i.verso prov. 1-Nov-3 Santa Fe Art, Santa Fe #97/R est:40000-50000

WALTERS, Evan (1893-1951) British
£300 $501 €438 Portrait of a young man (51x41cm-20x16in) s. 21-Oct-3 Peter Francis, Wales #21
£850 $1420 €1241 Crucifixion scene (41x51cm-16x20in) s.d.1909. 21-Oct-3 Peter Francis, Wales #18/R

WALTERS, George Stanfield (1838-1924) British
£300 $501 €438 Fishing boats off the coast (20x30cm-8x12in) s. board. 10-Jul-3 Gorringes, Worthing #786
£2197 $3800 €3208 Harbour scene (51x76cm-20x30in) s. 13-Dec-3 Charlton Hall, Columbia #78/R est:2000-4000
£3000 $5550 €4380 Port Enyon Bay, South Wales. Off the Yorkshire coast (20x31cm-8x12in) s. pair. 14-Jul-4 Sotheby's, Olympia #73/R est:2000-3000
Works on paper
£320 $512 €467 Quayside scene with figure in rowing boat at sunset (31x49cm-12x19in) s. W/C. 20-Sep-3 Lacy Scott, Bury St.Edmunds #428/R
£323 $594 €472 Mumbles Head, Swansea Bay (23x34cm-9x13in) s. W/C. 14-Jun-4 Waddingtons, Toronto #85/R (C.D 800)
£360 $576 €526 Quayside scene with rowing boats and seagulls hovering (31x49cm-12x19in) s. W/C htd. 20-Sep-3 Lacy Scott, Bury St.Edmunds #429/R
£563 $957 €822 Dordrecht on the Maas (33x51cm-13x20in) s. i.verso W/C prov. 23-Nov-3 Levis, Calgary #219/R (C.D 1250)
£650 $1196 €949 On the Noord, Holland (25x40cm-10x16in) s. W/C htd white. 29-Mar-4 Bonhams, Bath #19/R
£750 $1253 €1095 Liverpool Docks (32x50cm-13x20in) s.d. W/C. 22-Oct-3 Wingetts, Wrexham #342/R
£750 $1403 €1095 At Gillingham on the Medway. Traders on the Scheldt, Holland (24x39cm-9x15in) s.i. pencil W/C pair. 22-Jul-4 Tennants, Leyburn #649
£800 $1280 €1168 Off the Bligh - mouth of the Thames. Ramsgate trawler off the Nore. (32x50cm-13x20in) W/C pair. 17-Sep-3 Bonhams, Brooks & Langlois, Jersey #92/R
£900 $1530 €1314 Thames near Sonning (55x67cm-22x26in) s. 26-Nov-3 Hamptons Fine Art, Godalming #84

WALTERS, Gordon (1919-1995) New Zealander
£17293 $29398 €25248 Untitled - blue koru (50x50cm-20x20in) acrylic painted c.1970 prov. 26-Nov-3 Dunbar Sloane, Wellington #23/R est:40000-50000 (NZ.D 46000)
Prints
£2679 $4848 €3911 Tama (69x49cm-27x19in) s.i.d.1977 screenprint. 30-Mar-4 Peter Webb, Auckland #1/R est:4000-6000 (NZ.D 7500)

WALTERS, Miles (1774-1849) British
£3072 $5500 €4485 Ship David of Bristol, off Flatholm Island (46x76cm-18x30in) s. 16-Mar-4 Bonhams & Butterfields, San Francisco #6119/R est:6000-8000

WALTERS, Samuel (1811-1882) British
£5500 $9460 €8030 Barque Trinidad close reefed in a gale (59x89cm-23x35in) lit. 2-Dec-3 Sotheby's, London #143/R est:6000-8000
£6250 $11375 €9125 Man-of-war at anchor, figures in a small rowing boat and other boats in evening sun set (43x36cm-17x14in) s. panel. 4-Feb-4 John Nicholson, Haslemere #152/R est:5000-6000
£9000 $15480 €13140 Brig Spheroid Hove to of the south foreland (59x89cm-23x35in) lit. 2-Dec-3 Sotheby's, London #139/R est:10000-15000
£9000 $15480 €13140 Iron barque Merle inward bound off Dover (59x89cm-23x35in) s.d.1866 lit. 2-Dec-3 Sotheby's, London #142/R est:10000-15000
£13500 $23220 €19710 Barque Naparima outward bound off Deal (72x110cm-28x43in) s.d.1855 lit. 2-Dec-3 Sotheby's, London #141/R est:15000-25000
£20000 $34000 €29200 American Confederate raider Alabama (31x52cm-12x20in) s.d.1863. 19-Nov-3 Christie's, Kensington #455/R
£21622 $40000 €31568 Auxiliary schooner, Ceres, in Norwegian waters (51x81cm-20x32in) s. prov.lit. 10-Feb-4 Christie's, Rockefeller NY #197/R est:40000-60000
£30000 $51600 €43800 Barque Montrose outward bound off Margate (58x89cm-23x35in) s.d.1866 lit. 2-Dec-3 Sotheby's, London #140/R est:10000-15000
£35135 $65000 €51297 Confederate blockade runner CSS Colonel Lamb at sea (49x74cm-19x29in) s. prov. 10-Feb-4 Christie's, Rockefeller NY #191/R est:15000-25000

WALTHARD, Johann Jakob Friedrich (1818-1870) Swiss
£724 $1158 €1057 The children Johann Ludwig, Walter and Mina Schnell in garden (51x61cm-20x24in) s.d. verso. 16-Sep-3 Philippe Schuler, Zurich #3261 est:1500-2000 (S.FR 1600)

WALTHER, Franz-Erhard (1939-) German
Sculpture
£1067 $1952 €1600 Book (49x39x12cm-19x15x5in) linen prov. 4-Jun-4 Lempertz, Koln #526/R est:2000
£1399 $2378 €2000 Wall song (151x22x31cm-59x9x12in) wooden box cotton. 27-Nov-3 Lempertz, Koln #521/R est:2500
£1733 $3172 €2600 Vest (68x70x40cm-27x28x16in) linien foam prov. 4-Jun-4 Lempertz, Koln #524/R est:3000
£1748 $2972 €2500 Dialog (102x62x26cm-40x24x10in) material sold with W/C s.i.d.83. 27-Nov-3 Lempertz, Koln #520/R est:1500
£1812 $2971 €2500 Wall song (151x22x31cm-59x9x12in) wooden box col canvas one of 43 exec.1990. 27-May-3 Sotheby's, Amsterdam #459/R est:2500-3000

WALTHER, Gustav (1828-1904) German
£1037 $1700 €1504 Portrait of a woman in a black dress (117x81cm-46x32in) s.d.1872. 31-May-3 Brunk, Ashville #647/R est:1500-3000

WALTHER, Karl (1905-1981) German
£699 $1168 €1000 City in winter with snow, coach and few people (60x73cm-24x29in) s.d.29. 27-Jun-3 Altus, Berlin #589/R
£993 $1808 €1500 Street scene in Kaufinger with a view of the Karlstor (130x90cm-51x35in) s.d.1941. 19-Jun-4 Quittenbaum, Hamburg #60/R est:1500

WALTMANN, Harry Franklin (1871-1951) American
£444 $769 €648 Stars and stripes in Port (41x33cm-16x13in) s.d.1912 board. 9-Dec-3 Pinneys, Montreal #67 (C.D 1000)

WALTON, Allan (1892-?) British
£2000 $3700 €2920 Storm at Lowestoft (51x56cm-20x22in) s. 11-Mar-4 Christie's, Kensington #90/R est:600-800

WALTON, Constance (1865-1960) British
Works on paper
£450 $805 €657 Short break (53x38cm-21x15in) s. W/C. 26-May-4 Sotheby's, Olympia #116/R
£2500 $4525 €3650 Still life of dahlias (60x55cm-24x22in) s. W/C exhib. 19-Apr-4 Sotheby's, London #51/R est:3000-4000

WALTON, Edward Arthur (1860-1922) British
£4500 $8145 €6570 Lincolnshire landscape (41x61cm-16x24in) s.d.1889. 19-Apr-4 Sotheby's, London #46/R est:5000-7000
Works on paper
£5000 $7850 €7250 Pastoral (38x57cm-15x22in) s.d.1884 W/C prov. 27-Aug-3 Sotheby's, London #1021/R est:2500-3500

WALTON, Elijah (1832-1880) British
Works on paper
£280 $468 €409 Mountainous lake landscape (24x34cm-9x13in) s.i.d.1858 pencil W/C. 16-Oct-3 Christie's, Kensington #112/R
£550 $974 €803 Evening , the Nile (33x46cm-13x18in) i.d.1876 verso W/C. 29-Apr-4 Gorringes, Lewes #2310

WALTON, Frank (1840-1928) British
£440 $814 €642 Duck on a Surrey pond (75x62cm-30x24in) i. stretcher. 16-Feb-4 Bonhams, Bath #51
£900 $1503 €1314 Milking time (114x84cm-45x33in) s. s.i.stretcher. 13-Nov-3 Christie's, Kensington #177/R

WALTON, Henry (1804-1865) American
Works on paper
£22727 $40000 €33181 View of Geneva College, taken from South Road, 1837 (24x43cm-9x17in) i. W/C pen ink. 18-May-4 Sotheby's, New York #188/R est:10000-20000

WALTON, Henry (1746-1813) British
£1300 $2327 €1898 Portrait of a gentleman, Edward Bridgeman (23x18cm-9x7in) copper oval. 22-Mar-4 Bonhams & Brooks, Norfolk #270/R est:1500-2500
£140000 $254800 €204400 Hunt breakfast at Mr Palmer's House (90x124cm-35x49in) prov.exhib.lit. 1-Jul-4 Sotheby's, London #19/R est:100000-150000

WALTON, John (20th C) British
£2200 $3982 €3212 Market Scene (76x99cm-30x39in) s.d.1947. 17-Apr-4 Dickins, Middle Claydon #53

WALTON, Joseph (c.1810-1879) British
£2000 $3180 €2900 Children fishing off the brigg (45x76cm-18x30in) s.d.1866. 9-Sep-3 David Duggleby, Scarborough #371/R est:2000-3000

WALTON, Richard Guy (20th C) American
£401 $750 €585 Desert landscape with cactus (41x51cm-16x20in) s. canvasboard. 29-Feb-4 Bonhams & Butterfields, San Francisco #4553

WALTON, T J (?) American?
£1243 $2300 €1815 Laws (61x91cm-24x36in) s. 15-Feb-4 Outer Cape Auctions, Provincetown #43/R
£1307 $2300 €1908 Pear (102x86cm-40x34in) s. 3-Jan-4 Outer Cape Auctions, Provincetown #77a/R

WALTOS, Jacek (1938-) Polish
£897 $1497 €1300 Belated remorse (101x120cm-40x47in) s.i.d.1992 verso. 16-Nov-3 Agra, Warsaw #90/R

WALZ, Theodor (1892-1972) German
£366 $586 €520 Passau (68x100cm-27x39in) s. 18-Sep-3 Rieber, Stuttgart #1008/R

WAMBINY, Henry (c.1934-) Australian
Works on paper
£1804 $3229 €2634 Woorreringy - Ord River (91x122cm-36x48in) natural earth pigments linen exec 1994. 25-May-4 Lawson Menzies, Sydney #158/R est:7000-9000 (A.D 4600)

WAMPS, Bernard Joseph (1689-1750) French
£1600 $2864 €2400 Adoration of the Shepherds (125x97cm-49x38in) s.d.1731 arched top. 17-May-4 Christie's, Amsterdam #47/R est:3000-4000

WAN QINGLI (1945-) Chinese
Works on paper
£372 $654 €550 Hongshan in Wuhan (68x46cm-27x18in) s. seals Indian ink col hanging scroll. 21-May-4 Dr Fritz Nagel, Stuttgart #1120/R

WAN SHOUQI (1603-1652) Chinese
Works on paper
£1565 $2817 €2285 Bodhidharma (104x50cm-41x20in) s. ink hanging scroll. 25-Apr-4 Christie's, Hong Kong #360/R est:25000-30000 (HK.D 22000)
£2703 $4757 €4000 Garden festival (35x301cm-14x119in) s.d.1674 Indian ink col silk handscroll prov. 21-May-4 Dr Fritz Nagel, Stuttgart #1144/R est:1500

WANAMBI, Dundiwuy (1936-1996) Australian
Works on paper
£400 $688 €584 Kangaroo, snakes and birds (43x18cm-17x7in) ochre pigment. 2-Dec-3 Sotheby's, Olympia #361/R

WANBERG, Mary (19th C) Swedish
£2328 $4260 €3399 Allegorical scene of the Four Seasons (190x286cm-75x113in) s.d.1886-1892 four piece screen. 9-Jun-4 Rasmussen, Copenhagen #2002/R est:30000 (D.KR 26000)

WANDEL, Sigurd (1875-1947) Danish
£361 $675 €527 Woman and child in garden (93x100cm-37x39in) init.d.14 prov. 25-Feb-4 Museumsbygningen, Copenhagen #7 (D.KR 4000)

WANDESFORDE, Juan B (1817-1902) American
£11765 $20000 €17177 Western mountainous landscape with lake (91x152cm-36x60in) s.d.1886. 20-Nov-3 Auctions by the Bay, Alameda #1073/R

WANDS, Alfred James (1902-) American
£262 $450 €383 Mountain landscape (30x41cm-12x16in) s. canvasboard painted c.1970. 7-Dec-3 Treadway Gallery, Cincinnati #581/R

WANDSCHEER, Marie (1856-1936) Dutch
£278 $453 €400 Papavers - poppies (24x33cm-9x13in) s. board. 29-Sep-3 Sotheby's, Amsterdam #137
£347 $565 €500 Flower still life (22x28cm-9x11in) s. panel. 29-Sep-3 Sotheby's, Amsterdam #132
£347 $565 €500 Mushrooms (31x41cm-12x16in) s. canvas on panel. 29-Sep-3 Sotheby's, Amsterdam #135/R
£451 $736 €650 Portrait of Henriette Thuere with a doll (41x31cm-16x12in) s. 29-Sep-3 Sotheby's, Amsterdam #139/R
£625 $1018 €900 A little girl (23x32cm-9x13in) s.d.1902 board. 29-Sep-3 Sotheby's, Amsterdam #138/R

WANE, Harold (?-1900) British
£300 $519 €438 Harbour scene with fishing vessels and town beyond (43x81cm-17x32in) 11-Dec-3 Mitchells, Cockermouth #934

WANE, Richard (1852-1904) British
£250 $433 €365 Couple with chickens in a fishing village (29x49cm-11x19in) s. 9-Dec-3 Bonhams, Oxford #100
£420 $701 €613 Fishermans wife (20x13cm-8x5in) s. panel. 20-Jun-3 Chrystals Auctions, Isle of Man #260
£500 $835 €730 Douglas Bay (41x66cm-16x26in) s.i.verso. 20-Jun-3 Chrystals Auctions, Isle of Man #247
£500 $835 €730 Fishing boats in open sea (51x76cm-20x30in) s. 11-Nov-3 Bonhams, Knightsbridge #208/R
£620 $1073 €905 Fisherfolk on the seafront at a stormy sunset (39x65cm-15x26in) s. 9-Dec-3 Bonhams, Oxford #106
£780 $1264 €1139 Manx coast, with a figure on the shore (45x90cm-18x35in) s. 8-Aug-3 Jacobs & Hunt, Petersfield #184/R
£1300 $2418 €1898 Approaching storm (41x66cm-16x26in) s. 4-Mar-4 Christie's, Kensington #550/R est:700-800
Works on paper
£780 $1396 €1139 Douglas Bay. Manx view, thought to be Port St Mary (18x42cm-7x17in) both s. W/C pair. 17-Mar-4 Bonhams, Chester #252
£1500 $2775 €2190 Cottage garden in summer (60x89cm-24x35in) s. W/C. 9-Mar-4 Bonhams, New Bond Street #140/R est:1500-2000
£3400 $6188 €4964 Anglesey bay (69x129cm-27x51in) s. W/C htd white. 5-Feb-4 Mellors & Kirk, Nottingham #502/R est:2000-3000

WANG DU (1959-) ?
Sculpture
£8667 $16033 €13000 Tom Cruise (55x119x83cm-22x47x33in) init. painted resin newspapers exec.2000 one of 6 prov.lit. 18-Jul-4 Sotheby's, Paris #282/R est:8000-12000

WANG DUO (1592-1652) Chinese
Works on paper
£5690 $10242 €8307 Winter forest (112x49cm-44x19in) s.i.d.1650 ink hanging scroll silk. 25-Apr-4 Christie's, Hong Kong #358/R est:50000-70000 (HK.D 80000)

WANG ERSHUI (1870-1948) Chinese
Works on paper
£1892 $3330 €2800 Houses in the mountains by water (113x41cm-44x16in) i.d.1914 Indian ink col hanging scroll. 21-May-4 Dr Fritz Nagel, Stuttgart #1216/R est:500

WANG FENGYUAN (16th C) Chinese
Works on paper
£8535 $15363 €12461 Fishing alone in winter (138x61cm-54x24in) s.i. ink col hanging scroll silk prov. 25-Apr-4 Christie's, Hong Kong #325/R est:150000-200000 (HK.D 120000)

WANG FU (1362-1416) Chinese
Works on paper
£664 $1143 €950 Portrait of a young woman under a plum tree (146x49cm-57x19in) s.i.d.1896 ink col silk hanging scroll. 5-Dec-3 Lempertz, Koln #243

WANG GAI (c.1645-1705) Chinese
Works on paper
£46332 $77375 €67645 Viewing plum blossoms (30x469cm-12x185in) s.i.d.1692 ink col handscroll. 27-Oct-3 Sotheby's, Hong Kong #323/R est:600000-700000 (HK.D 600000)

WANG GUANGYI (1954-) Chinese
£29872 $53770 €43613 Mexx. Gillette. PEPSI (75x59cm-30x23in) sold with 2 lithograph prints. 25-Apr-4 Christie's, Hong Kong #735/R est:160000-260000 (HK.D 420000)

WANG JIAN (1598-1677) Chinese
Works on paper
£9246 $16643 €13499 Landscape (39x28cm-15x11in) s.i. ink hanging scroll after Wang Meng. 25-Apr-4 Christie's, Hong Kong #399/R est:40000-60000 (HK.D 130000)

WANG JIANZHANG (fl.c.1625-1650) Chinese
Works on paper
£18533 $30950 €27058 Thatched cottage in spring drizzle (81x31cm-32x12in) s. ink. 26-Oct-3 Christie's, Hong Kong #454/R (HK.D 240000)

WANG JIPING (1961-) Chinese
Works on paper
£338 $605 €500 L'oiseau en sous bois (73x71cm-29x28in) s. ink wash. 5-May-4 Coutau Begarie, Paris #120
£541 $968 €800 Le perroquet (135x54cm-53x21in) s. ink wash. 5-May-4 Coutau Begarie, Paris #119/R

WANG JIQIAN (1907-) Chinese
Works on paper
£2317 $3869 €3383 Landscape (39x56cm-15x22in) s.d.1971 ink col hanging scroll. 27-Oct-3 Sotheby's, Hong Kong #384/R est:30000-40000 (HK.D 30000)
£4748 $8500 €6932 Snowy in the moonlight (69x86cm-27x34in) s.d.1984 ink hanging scroll. 10-May-4 Bonhams & Butterfields, San Francisco #4400/R

WANG KEPING (1949-) Chinese
Sculpture
£3556 $6401 €5192 Couple (40cm-16in) s. Hom oak wood. 25-Apr-4 Christie's, Hong Kong #758/R est:38000-48000 (HK.D 50000)

WANG RONG (20th C) Chinese
Works on paper
£743 $1308 €1100 Lotus flowers (104x28cm-41x11in) s.i. seals Indian ink paper hanging scroll. 21-May-4 Dr Fritz Nagel, Stuttgart #1221/R

WANG SU (1794-1877) Chinese
Works on paper
£853 $1536 €1245 Vegetables (20x120cm-8x47in) s.i. ink col scroll. 25-Apr-4 Christie's, Hong Kong #407/R est:15000-20000 (HK.D 12000)

WANG WU (1632-1690) Chinese
Works on paper
£1955 $3500 €2854 Narcissus and rock (100x58cm-39x23in) s.d.1683 hanging ink. 10-May-4 Bonhams & Butterfields, San Francisco #4386/R

WANG WUXIE (1936-) Chinese
Works on paper
£1900 $3401 €2774 Seclusion (102x184cm-40x72in) s.d.1975 ink prov. 6-May-4 Sotheby's, London #178/R est:2000-4000
£2600 $4654 €3796 Gazing in solitude (82x155cm-32x61in) s.d.1974 col ink prov. 6-May-4 Sotheby's, London #179/R est:2000-3000

WANG XUETAO (1903-1982) Chinese
Works on paper
£1707 $3073 €2492 Kingfisher (136x19cm-54x7in) s.i.d.1961 ink col hanging scroll. 25-Apr-4 Christie's, Hong Kong #142/R est:20000-30000 (HK.D 24000)

WANG YONGQIANG (1945-) Chinese
£8170 $14788 €11928 Treaty (150x109cm-59x43in) s.d.2003. 3-Apr-4 Glerum, Singapore #87/R est:27000-32000 (S.D 25000)

WANG YONGYU (18th C) Chinese
Works on paper
£6800 $11696 €9928 Two crane wading in a river (178x95cm-70x37in) s. ink col. 4-Dec-3 Christie's, Kensington #250 est:1000-1500

WANG YOUZHENG (1941-) Chinese
Works on paper
£324 $571 €480 Girl in garden (83x51cm-33x20in) s.i. seals Indian ink col. 21-May-4 Dr Fritz Nagel, Stuttgart #1207/R
£608 $1070 €900 Girl writing in garden (137x68cm-54x27in) s.i.d.1988 seals Indian ink col. 21-May-4 Dr Fritz Nagel, Stuttgart #1210/R
£743 $1308 €1100 Boy in fur outfit (69x45cm-27x18in) s.i. seal Indian ink col hanging scroll. 21-May-4 Dr Fritz Nagel, Stuttgart #1208/R

WANG YUANQI (1642-1715) Chinese
Works on paper
£4267 $7681 €6230 Landscape (39x26cm-15x10in) s. ink hanging scroll after the Mi Style. 25-Apr-4 Christie's, Hong Kong #398/R est:40000-50000 (HK.D 60000)
£32432 $54162 €47351 Landscape after ancient master (87x45cm-34x18in) s.i.d.1701 ink hanging scroll. 27-Oct-3 Sotheby's, Hong Kong #319/R est:200000-300000 (HK.D 420000)

WANG YUANXUN (1728-1807) Chinese
Works on paper
£6564 $10961 €9583 Village scene (91x118cm-36x46in) s. ink col silk. 26-Oct-3 Christie's, Hong Kong #450/R (HK.D 85000)

WANG YUN (attrib) (1652-c.1735) Chinese
Works on paper
£894 $1600 €1305 Fenghou tu (248x127cm-98x50in) with sig. ink hanging scroll. 10-May-4 Bonhams & Butterfields, San Francisco #4385/R

WANG YUNHE (1939-) Chinese
£5690 $10242 €8307 Magnificent cityscape (73x92cm-29x36in) s.d.2000 lit. 25-Apr-4 Christie's, Hong Kong #750/R est:90000-110000 (HK.D 80000)
Works on paper
£3556 $6401 €5192 Cityscape (78x109cm-31x43in) s.d.99 W/C. 25-Apr-4 Christie's, Hong Kong #763/R est:60000-80000 (HK.D 50000)

WANG ZHEN (1866-1938) Chinese
Works on paper
£1158 $1934 €1691 Mushroom and turnip, calligraphy (20x32cm-8x13in) s.i. ink col hanging scrolls set of two. 26-Oct-3 Christie's, Hong Kong #277/R est:15000-20000 (HK.D 15000)
£3707 $6190 €5412 Delivering coal in the snow (133x33cm-52x13in) s.i.d.1919 ink col hanging scroll. 27-Oct-3 Sotheby's, Hong Kong #332/R est:30000-50000 (HK.D 48000)
£6046 $10882 €8827 Autumn blossoms (138x69cm-54x27in) s.i.d.1923 ink col hanging scroll. 26-Apr-4 Sotheby's, Hong Kong #653/R est:40000-60000 (HK.D 85000)
£20077 $33529 €29312 Bodhidharma (173x96cm-68x38in) s.i. ink col hanging scroll. 26-Oct-3 Christie's, Hong Kong #275/R est:70000-90000 (HK.D 260000)
£53343 $96017 €77881 Birds of the four seasons (248x61cm-98x24in) s.i.d.1916 ink col hanging scroll set of four. 25-Apr-4 Christie's, Hong Kong #75/R est:300000-400000 (HK.D 750000)

WANG ZHEN HAI (19th C) Chinese
Works on paper
£1300 $2379 €1898 Still life (41x46cm-16x18in) s. W/C two. 7-Apr-4 Sotheby's, Olympia #339/R est:500-600

WANG ZIHUI (1616-?) Chinese
Works on paper
£6178 $10317 €9020 Landscape (44x340cm-17x134in) s.i. ink col on silk after MI FU. 26-Oct-3 Christie's, Hong Kong #451/R (HK.D 80000)

WANG ZIWU (1936-) Chinese
Works on paper
£1900 $3496 €2774 Eagle (138x68cm-54x27in) s. ink hanging scroll. 8-Jun-4 Bonhams, New Bond Street #63/R est:1000-1500

WANG, Albert Edward (1864-1930) Danish
£336 $527 €491 Female model (31x16cm-12x6in) s.d.87 panel. 30-Aug-3 Rasmussen, Havnen #2080 (D.KR 3600)
£358 $645 €523 View of Paris (13x20cm-5x8in) init.i.d.89. 24-Apr-4 Rasmussen, Havnen #2041 (D.KR 4000)
£448 $806 €654 Morning on the coast of Oresund (43x57cm-17x22in) init. 24-Apr-4 Rasmussen, Havnen #2138 (D.KR 5000)

WANG, Ian (20th C) Australian?
£412 $745 €602 Buildings No.16 (112x122cm-44x48in) s.d.93. 30-Mar-4 Lawson Menzies, Sydney #182/R est:500-700 (A.D 1000)

WANGENSTEN, Wilhelm (1884-1962) Norwegian
£270 $466 €394 From Skaatoy (46x54cm-18x21in) s. 13-Dec-3 Blomqvist, Lysaker #1394 (N.KR 3100)

WANIEK, Henryk (20th C) Polish
Works on paper
£275 $457 €402 Mountain scene (48x59cm-19x23in) W/C exec. 1989. 2-Oct-3 Agra, Warsaw #42/R (P.Z 1800)
£306 $508 €447 Anubi (48x62cm-19x24in) chk exec. 1984. 2-Oct-3 Agra, Warsaw #41/R (P.Z 2000)

WANING, Cornelis Anthony van (1861-1929) Dutch
£428 $787 €650 View of a Dutch harbour (35x50cm-14x20in) s. 22-Jun-4 Christie's, Amsterdam #282/R
£800 $1448 €1200 Seaside town (60x100cm-24x39in) s. lit. 3-Apr-4 Badum, Bamberg #137/R
£993 $1658 €1400 City view (52x63cm-20x25in) s. 20-Oct-3 Glerum, Amsterdam #137/R
£6667 $12000 €10000 View of Het Zieken, The Hague (110x150cm-43x59in) s. 20-Apr-4 Sotheby's, Amsterdam #118/R est:10000-15000

WANKE, Alice (1873-1936) Austrian
Works on paper
£280 $507 €420 Dancing in the meadow (28x21cm-11x8in) Indian ink W/C col pen over pencil. 2-Apr-4 Winterberg, Heidelberg #661/R

WANKIE, Wladyslaw (c.1860-1925) Polish
£6421 $10658 €9375 On the terrace (61x78cm-24x31in) s. painted c.1886-1888. 15-Jun-3 Agra, Warsaw #9/R est:35000 (P.Z 40000)

WANKLYN, Joan (20th C) British
£250 $448 €365 The chestnut pony Rugshot of Felbridge and the skewbald Flamenco of Felbridge in paddock (36x51cm-14x20in) s.i.verso. 11-Jan-4 Desmond Judd, Cranbrook #715

WANLESS, Harry (snr) (1873-1933) British
£300 $549 €438 Brixham harbour (23x25cm-9x10in) s. i.verso. 7-Apr-4 Andrew Hartley, Ilkley #1129
Works on paper
£340 $626 €496 Fishing fleet leaving Scarborough (23x33cm-9x13in) s. W/C. 23-Mar-4 Anderson & Garland, Newcastle #248
£360 $612 €526 Herring fleet in Scarborough harbour (22x30cm-9x12in) s. W/C. 1-Dec-3 David Duggleby, Scarborough #283/R
£400 $704 €584 Harbour scene (23x25cm-9x10in) s. W/C. 30-Dec-3 British Auctioneer #799

WANN, Harry (20th C) Australian
£453 $819 €661 Boatsman daughter. board. 1-Apr-4 Joel, Victoria #84 (A.D 1100)

WANN, Michael (20th C) Irish?
Works on paper
£600 $1080 €900 Roadside tree II (43x38cm-17x15in) s.d.2004 carbon ink canvas. 20-Apr-4 James Adam, Dublin #167/R
£810 $1417 €1150 Tall tree 2 (75x35cm-30x14in) s. carbon ink triptych. 16-Dec-3 James Adam, Dublin #214/R
£833 $1308 €1200 Tall tree I (25x35cm-10x14in) s.d.2003 mixed media triptych. 26-Aug-3 James Adam, Dublin #230/R est:1200-1500
£1268 $2218 €1800 Woodland three (35x75cm-14x30in) s.d.2003 carbon ink triptych. 16-Dec-3 James Adam, Dublin #215/R est:1400-1800

WANTE, Paul (?) ?
£839 $1427 €1200 Dock a Anvers (54x70cm-21x28in) 1-Dec-3 Amberes, Antwerp #369

WAPLINGTON, Paul (1938-) British
£520 $972 €759 Slums at Shirebrook (120x120cm-47x47in) s. i.verso. 24-Feb-4 Bonhams, Knowle #132

WAPPMANNSBERGER, Bartholomaus (?) German
£890 $1514 €1300 Rimsting on the Chiemsee (29x39cm-11x15in) s. 5-Nov-3 Hugo Ruef, Munich #1172

WARB, Nicolaas (1906-1957) Dutch
Works on paper
£1467 $2699 €2200 Untitled (10x14cm-4x6in) studio st. i.d.49 52 verso gouache three. 8-Jun-4 Sotheby's, Amsterdam #252/R est:2500-3500

WARD OF HULL, John (1798-1849) British
£2500 $4250 €3650 Paddle steamer Vivid off the East coast (61x91cm-24x36in) s.i. 19-Nov-3 Christie's, Kensington #462/R est:2500-3000
£7500 $12000 €10950 Stoneferry (16x23cm-6x9in) s.i. panel. 16-Sep-3 Bonhams, New Bond Street #61/R est:4000-6000
£9000 $17010 €13140 British man of war leaving harbour (25x35cm-10x14in) s. panel. 23-Feb-4 David Duggleby, Scarborough #660/R est:8000-12000
£15500 $24800 €22630 HMS Britannia at anchor with the fleet (32x51cm-13x20in) s. prov.exhib.lit. 16-Sep-3 Bonhams, New Bond Street #28/R est:20000-30000

WARD, Bradley (20th C) British
£280 $468 €409 Riverside view of Gawsworth Hall, Macclesfield (46x75cm-18x30in) s.d.1976 verso. 9-Jul-3 Peter Wilson, Nantwich #36

WARD, Charles (19/20th C) British
£695 $1300 €1043 California landscape (30x41cm-12x16in) s. prov. 25-Jul-4 Bonhams & Butterfields, San Francisco #6078/R est:500-700

WARD, Cyril (1863-1935) British
Works on paper
£400 $740 €584 On the coast of Pembrokeshire (38x61cm-15x24in) s. W/C. 10-Feb-4 David Lay, Penzance #242
£427 $700 €619 Woodland landscape with view to open field (76x64cm-30x25in) s. W/C prov. 31-May-3 Brunk, Ashville #535/R
£865 $1548 €1263 Stream through the harbour, Anglesey (34x47cm-13x19in) s. W/C. 11-May-4 Watson's, Christchurch #28/R (NZ.D 2500)

WARD, Edgar Melville (1839-1915) American
£307 $550 €448 Courtyard study (43x36cm-17x14in) s.d.1875. 21-Mar-4 Jeffery Burchard, Florida #85/R
£8696 $16000 €12696 Fierte Paternelle (91x118cm-36x46in) s.d.1878 prov.exhib. 8-Jun-4 Bonhams & Butterfields, San Francisco #4006/R est:8000-12000

WARD, Edmund F (1892-1991) American
£1324 $2250 €1933 Thundering herd (61x91cm-24x36in) s.d.23 prov. 1-Nov-3 Santa Fe Art, Santa Fe #39/R est:2500-3500

WARD, Edward Matthew (1816-1879) British
£500 $835 €730 Young Jessica from Moore's poem (25x20cm-10x8in) s.i.verso oval. 13-Nov-3 Christie's, Kensington #309/R
£850 $1352 €1241 Young Jessica from Moor's Poems (25x20cm-10x8in) s.i.verso oval. 9-Sep-3 Gorringes, Lewes #2099/R
£950 $1758 €1387 Discussing the plans (39x41cm-15x16in) s. 13-Jan-4 Bonhams, Knightsbridge #172/R
£5000 $8500 €7300 La toilette des morts (78x65cm-31x26in) s.d.1862 exhib. 27-Nov-3 Sotheby's, London #333/R est:5000-7000
£6111 $11000 €8922 La toilette des morts (78x65cm-31x26in) s.d.1862 exhib. 22-Apr-4 Christie's, Rockefeller NY #78/R est:10000-15000
Works on paper
£652 $1193 €952 Melancholy reading (33x25cm-13x10in) s.d.1863 gouache oval. 4-Jun-4 Zofingen, Switzerland #2372/R (S.FR 1500)

WARD, Edward Norton (1928-) American
£301 $550 €439 Maroon Creek Aspens (51x41cm-20x16in) s. 10-Apr-4 Auctions by the Bay, Alameda #1575/R

WARD, Everett Stoutenburgh (1911-1994) American
£311 $500 €454 Fly fishing at the waterfall (53x76cm-21x30in) prov. 20-Aug-3 James Julia, Fairfield #273/R
£435 $700 €635 Fish on, a perfect day (61x81cm-24x32in) prov. 20-Aug-3 James Julia, Fairfield #272/R
£1366 $2200 €1994 Successful catch (43x30cm-17x12in) monochrome board prov. 20-Aug-3 James Julia, Fairfield #275/R est:500-1000
Works on paper
£217 $350 €317 Scaring the egrets (43x69cm-17x27in) s. chl graphite board prov. 20-Aug-3 James Julia, Fairfield #277/R

WARD, Harold Morse (1889-1973) American
£406 $650 €593 Silver Lake. s. board. 20-Sep-3 Harvey Clar, Oakland #1326
£753 $1400 €1099 California coastal view (40x50cm-16x20in) s.d.35. 5-Mar-4 Skinner, Boston #560/R est:1000-1500

WARD, James (1769-1859) British
£450 $806 €657 Wooded landscape (12x9cm-5x4in) oil paper on panel sketch. 27-May-4 Christie's, Kensington #113/R
£750 $1223 €1095 Study of a white fox terrier. Study of a fox terrier with brown ears (14x19cm-6x7in) two. 24-Sep-3 Dreweatt Neate, Newbury #83
£800 $1472 €1168 Bull and a hound (65x93cm-26x37in) 10-Jun-4 Christie's, Kensington #100
£929 $1700 €1394 A shorthorn heifer (33x46cm-13x18in) paper on panel. 9-Jul-4 Du Mouchelle, Detroit #2005/R est:1800-2800
£1500 $2640 €2190 Longhorn cow in a landscape with St Donat's Castle (60x75cm-24x30in) bears sig. 18-May-4 Woolley & Wallis, Salisbury #164/R est:2000-3000
£6000 $10560 €8760 Longhorn bull in a landscape (44x60cm-17x24in) s. prov. 18-May-4 Woolley & Wallis, Salisbury #158/R est:2000-3000
£6652 $11907 €9712 Summer landscape (61x76cm-24x30in) s. 26-May-4 AB Stockholms Auktionsverk #2413/R est:60000-80000 (S.KR 90000)
£10000 $17000 €14600 Portrait of an ox in a landscape with a figure and two oxen in the distance (33x43cm-13x17in) s. i.verso board prov. 25-Nov-3 Christie's, London #89/R est:7000-10000
£27933 $50000 €40782 Disobedience in danger. Disobedience detected (71x91cm-28x36in) pair prov.lit. 27-May-4 Sotheby's, New York #264/R est:50000-70000
Works on paper
£213 $350 €309 Artist's mother (13x10cm-5x4in) init.i. graphite. 2-Jun-3 Grogan, Boston #641c/R
£213 $350 €309 The ribble (25x38cm-10x15in) init.i. graphite. 2-Jun-3 Grogan, Boston #641d/R
£260 $434 €380 Study of a dilapidated thatched barn (25x36cm-10x14in) mono.i. pencil monochrome wash. 12-Nov-3 Halls, Shrewsbury #252
£650 $1105 €949 Tintern Abbey (20x37cm-8x15in) init.i. pencil prov. 4-Nov-3 Bonhams, New Bond Street #40/R
£732 $1200 €1061 Brahmin bull (33x25cm-13x10in) init. W/C. 2-Jun-3 Grogan, Boston #641b/R
£900 $1647 €1314 Study of a chestnut stallion (22x27cm-9x11in) init.d.1826 pencil W/C. 7-Apr-4 Woolley & Wallis, Salisbury #80/R
£1800 $3060 €2628 Landscape and sky study (12x18cm-5x7in) s.i. pencil W/C prov. 20-Nov-3 Christie's, London #64/R est:1500-2000
£2600 $4758 €3796 Devil's Bridge, North Wales (51x33cm-20x13in) mono.i.d.1807 pencil two joined sheets prov. 3-Jun-4 Christie's, London #119/R est:1800-2500

WARD, James (attrib) (19th C) British
£600 $1056 €876 Sketch of two cows looking over a rail fence (23x30cm-9x12in) 18-May-4 Woolley & Wallis, Salisbury #173/R
£680 $1258 €993 Portrait of Edward Thompson (75x60cm-30x24in) 14-Jan-4 Lawrence, Crewkerne #1393

WARD, James Charles (fl.1830-1859) British
£520 $946 €759 Black grapes, plums, a peach and a bird's nest on a wooden ledge (25x31cm-10x12in) indis.s.d.1867. 29-Jun-4 Bonhams, Knowle #97
£1500 $2745 €2190 Still life of a basket of fruit and dead game on a ledge (61x50cm-24x20in) s.i.d.1840. 6-Apr-4 Bonhams, Knightsbridge #177/R est:2000-3000

WARD, John (1917-) British
£750 $1253 €1095 Hyacinths in a jar (30x25cm-12x10in) s.d.1971. 16-Oct-3 Christie's, Kensington #367/R
£1600 $2816 €2336 Wild flowers (25x30cm-10x12in) board prov. 18-May-4 Woolley & Wallis, Salisbury #37/R est:1000-1500
£2600 $4576 €3796 Road to Provence (28x37cm-11x15in) s. board prov. 18-May-4 Woolley & Wallis, Salisbury #92/R est:600-800
Works on paper
£360 $612 €526 The Forum, Rome (30x40cm-12x16in) s. pencil pen ink exec.c.1978. 26-Nov-3 Sotheby's, Olympia #106/R
£450 $774 €657 Grand Canal, Venice (19x21cm-7x8in) s.d.1953 W/C pen black ink col chk. 3-Dec-3 Christie's, Kensington #482
£700 $1169 €1022 Boxing day (23x32cm-9x13in) s.d.1975 pencil W/C exhib. 16-Oct-3 Christie's, Kensington #334/R
£800 $1408 €1168 Chillingham wild cattle (32x47cm-13x19in) ink wash. 18-May-4 Woolley & Wallis, Salisbury #136/R
£840 $1571 €1226 Jessica (63x47cm-25x19in) s. W/C prov. 24-Feb-4 Bonhams, Knowle #133
£2100 $3696 €3066 Naples. Pavement cafe (47x63cm-19x25in) ink wash two. 18-May-4 Woolley & Wallis, Salisbury #135/R est:300-500

WARD, Leslie Moffat (1888-?) British
Works on paper
£420 $701 €613 Castle Street, Worcester (29x20cm-11x8in) s. pencil W/C. 16-Oct-3 Christie's, Kensington #202

WARD, Lynd (1905-1985) American
Works on paper
£1198 $2000 €1749 Mammoths and other extinct animals in sweeping landscape (41x76cm-16x30in) s. gouache sold with copy of the story. 15-Nov-3 Illustration House, New York #81/R est:3000-6000

WARD, Martin Theodore (1799-1874) British
£450 $828 €657 Poacher's lunch (18x27cm-7x11in) s. 10-Jun-4 Christie's, Kensington #248/R
£500 $850 €730 Deer stalker's companion (29x36cm-11x14in) init. 27-Nov-3 Christie's, Kensington #417/R
£914 $1444 €1334 Dog with catch (24x32cm-9x13in) s. 24-Jul-3 Louis Morton, Mexico #101/R (M.P 15000)
£1000 $1720 €1460 Terrier with a rabbit (41x50cm-16x20in) s. indis d. board. 3-Dec-3 Bonhams, Knightsbridge #76a est:1000-1500
£1100 $1870 €1606 Stable friends (30x31cm-12x12in) init. board. 19-Nov-3 Sotheby's, Olympia #30/R est:800-1200
£3600 $6552 €5256 Farmyard animals before a stable (72x91cm-28x36in) s.d.1820. 3-Feb-4 Sworder & Son, Bishops Stortford #255/R est:3000-4000

WARD, Sir Leslie (1851-1922) British
Works on paper
£2300 $4163 €3358 Mr Gilbert Jordan in running shorts, spikes and blazer (36x24cm-14x9in) W/C. 19-Apr-4 Bonhams, Chester #723 est:1200-1800
£3200 $5344 €4672 Portrait of Lord Shaughnessy (45x30cm-18x12in) s. bodycol. 14-Oct-3 Bonhams, New Bond Street #238a est:400-600
£3600 $6228 €5256 Very Rev'd Armitage Robinson, Dean of Westminster 1905 (36x26cm-14x10in) s. W/C htd white. 9-Dec-3 Bonhams, Oxford #55/R est:300-500
£6500 $10855 €9490 Caricature of an Asian Indian Prince (35x24cm-14x9in) s. W/C. 14-Oct-3 Bonhams, New Bond Street #238/R est:500-800

WARD, Velox (1901-1994) American
£2844 $4750 €4152 Couple on wagon (46x61cm-18x24in) masonite. 18-Oct-3 David Dike, Dallas #79/R est:6000-8000

WARD, Vernon (1905-1985) British
£300 $483 €438 View of Lake Windemere (35x45cm-14x18in) s. canvasboard. 12-Aug-3 Bonhams, Ipswich #236
£400 $732 €584 Flying ducks landing on still waters at sunset (38x48cm-15x19in) s.d.47. 28-Jan-4 Mallams, Oxford #503
£500 $835 €730 Still life with roses (46x34cm-18x13in) s. canvasboard. 16-Oct-3 Christie's, Kensington #366/R
£500 $925 €730 Morning walk (32x40cm-13x16in) board. 13-Jan-4 Bonhams, Knightsbridge #283/R
£600 $1110 €876 Soldiers at dusk (38x51cm-15x20in) s.d.41 b. 11-Mar-4 Christie's, Kensington #44/R
£700 $1169 €1022 Green pasture. Highwater (30x35cm-12x14in) s. canvasboard pair. 16-Oct-3 Christie's, Kensington #424/R
£750 $1253 €1095 Cattle in a meadow (61x91cm-24x36in) s.d.1924. 16-Oct-3 Christie's, Kensington #415/R
£760 $1398 €1110 Yellow and white flowers in a copper lustre jug (50x60cm-20x24in) s.d.46. 23-Mar-4 Anderson & Garland, Newcastle #328
£860 $1600 €1256 Island to Blakeney (36x51cm-14x20in) 6-Mar-4 Page, Batavia #23
£1300 $2093 €1885 Swans in a lake under tree blossom (28x38cm-11x15in) s. board. 13-Aug-3 Andrew Hartley, Ilkley #821/R est:800-1200
Works on paper
£550 $875 €803 Butterflies and flowers (54x37cm-21x15in) s. mixed media. 10-Sep-3 Sotheby's, Olympia #226/R

WARD, William (jnr) (?-1935) American
£222 $408 €324 Fishermen of Brittany (40x50cm-16x20in) s. s.i.verso. 9-Jun-4 Walker's, Ottawa #373/R (C.D 550)
£457 $850 €667 Harbour scene (30x41cm-12x16in) s. board. 3-Mar-4 Alderfer's, Hatfield #375/R
£782 $1400 €1142 Harbour scene in Normandy (71x97cm-28x38in) s. 16-Mar-4 Bonhams & Butterfields, San Francisco #6151/R est:600-800

WARD, William H (fl.1850-1882) British
£2600 $4108 €3770 At the riverbank (35x25cm-14x10in) s.d.1884. 4-Sep-3 Christie's, Kensington #268/R est:800-1200

WARDELL, Dorothy Wilma (1910-) Canadian?
£294 $491 €429 Entering the church, winter (30x40cm-12x16in) s. 17-Nov-3 Hodgins, Calgary #386 (C.D 650)

WARDEN, William (1908-1982) British
£300 $531 €438 St Ives (46x60cm-18x24in) board. 27-Apr-4 Bonhams, Knightsbridge #284/R
£380 $684 €555 Leeds and Liverpool Canal (72x92cm-28x36in) board. 20-Jan-4 Bonhams, Knightsbridge #22/R
£420 $756 €613 Still life with tea pot (62x84cm-24x33in) board. 20-Jan-4 Bonhams, Knightsbridge #16/R

WARDI, Rafael (1928-) Finnish
£1067 $1909 €1600 Still life (82x65cm-32x26in) s. 15-May-4 Hagelstam, Helsinki #216/R est:2000
£1333 $2387 €2000 Composition (65x50cm-26x20in) s. 15-May-4 Hagelstam, Helsinki #218/R est:2500
£1757 $3145 €2600 Etruscan still life (33x46cm-13x18in) s. 8-May-4 Bukowskis, Helsinki #315/R est:1500-2000
£2000 $3580 €3000 Evening sunshine (50x60cm-20x24in) s/ board. 15-May-4 Hagelstam, Helsinki #217/R est:2500
£2517 $4280 €3600 View from Munksnaas (101x73cm-40x29in) s. 29-Nov-3 Bukowskis, Helsinki #274/R est:2500-3000
£2676 $4630 €3800 In front of the mirror (60x81cm-24x32in) s. 13-Dec-3 Hagelstam, Helsinki #185/R est:3500
£3108 $5564 €4600 Still life (53x45cm-21x18in) s. 8-May-4 Bukowskis, Helsinki #294/R est:2000-2300
£4895 $8322 €7000 In the forest (74x89cm-29x35in) s.d.1973 exhib. 29-Nov-3 Bukowskis, Helsinki #305/R est:7000-8000
£5594 $9510 €8000 Before sunset (60x81cm-24x32in) s. 29-Nov-3 Bukowskis, Helsinki #309/R est:4000-5000
£7770 $13909 €11500 Still life of Chinese bowls (73x185cm-29x73in) s. exhib. 8-May-4 Bukowskis, Helsinki #255/R est:13000-16000

WARDLE, Arthur (1864-1947) British
£1100 $1980 €1606 Safe for now (35x45cm-14x18in) s. 22-Apr-4 Mellors & Kirk, Nottingham #1129/R est:800-1000
£1200 $2196 €1752 View of a leopard (23x38cm-9x15in) s. board. 28-Jul-4 Bonhams, Knightsbridge #155/R est:1200-1800
£1450 $2364 €2117 Gordon settlers (28x20cm-11x8in) s. canvas on board. 26-Sep-3 Dee Atkinson & Harrison, Driffield #524/R est:700-900
£1600 $2992 €2336 Champion Jetsam Bowdler, prize black cocker spaniel (30x47cm-12x19in) s.i.d.1906 board. 22-Jul-4 Tennants, Leyburn #882/R est:1000-1500
£5000 $9000 €7300 Spaniels by a stream (46x62cm-18x24in) s. 21-Jan-4 Sotheby's, New York #229/R est:10000-15000
£7027 $13000 €10259 Fox terrier with hare (41x38cm-16x15in) s.i.d.1900 canvas on board prov.exhib. 10-Feb-4 Doyle, New York #241/R est:3000-5000
£8649 $16000 €12628 English setters. Pointers (56x36cm-22x14in) s. two. 10-Feb-4 Doyle, New York #244/R est:25000-35000
£9189 $17000 €13416 Late for the train (91x71cm-36x28in) s.d.1897. 10-Feb-4 Doyle, New York #250/R est:15000-25000
£9500 $17290 €13870 Serving the guns (39x60cm-15x24in) s. 1-Jul-4 Mellors & Kirk, Nottingham #813/R est:6000-7000
£14000 $25200 €20440 Mischief in quadruplet (35x45cm-14x18in) s. 22-Apr-4 Mellors & Kirk, Nottingham #1127/R est:2500-3000
£14000 $25200 €20440 Empty plate (35x45cm-14x18in) s. 22-Apr-4 Mellors & Kirk, Nottingham #1128/R est:2500-3000
£17680 $32000 €25813 Three terriers (66x84cm-26x33in) s. 30-Mar-4 Bonhams & Butterfields, San Francisco #90/R est:25000-35000
£23256 $40000 €33954 Jack Russell terries at a rabbit hole (96x72cm-38x28in) s.d.86 prov. 5-Dec-3 Christie's, Rockefeller NY #53/R est:25000-35000
£38000 $66880 €55480 Gordon setters (46x61cm-18x24in) s. 21-May-4 Christie's, London #43/R est:18000-25000
Works on paper
£300 $546 €438 Study of a parrot (24x19cm-9x7in) s.i. pencil W/C bodycol. 1-Jul-4 Christie's, Kensington #286/R
£300 $552 €438 Leopard lying on a branch (30x46cm-12x18in) s. pastel. 24-Jun-4 Olivers, Sudbury #117/R
£450 $792 €657 Study of a pine martin (22x28cm-9x11in) s.i. pastel chl. 19-May-4 Christie's, Kensington #630/R
£550 $935 €803 Two cocker spaniels (22x16cm-9x6in) col chk prov. 27-Nov-3 Christie's, Kensington #423/R
£550 $1012 €803 Water buffalo (35x50cm-14x20in) s. pastel. 29-Mar-4 Bonhams, Bath #32/R
£700 $1169 €1022 Mounted Red Indian hunting buffalo (25x36cm-10x14in) s. W/C. 8-Oct-3 Christie's, Kensington #939/R
£6000 $10560 €8760 Two Scottish Deerhounds. Two Great Danes (45x30cm-18x12in) s. col chks col paper prov. two. 21-May-4 Christie's, London #14/R est:4000-6000
£10000 $17600 €14600 Two Wire-haired Fox Terriers. Two Cairn Terriers (45x30cm-18x12in) s. col chks col paper two prov. 21-May-4 Christie's, London #15/R est:4000-6000
£24000 $42240 €35040 Spaniels with a cock pheasant (60x50cm-24x20in) s. pencil W/C htd. bodycol buff col paper. 21-May-4 Christie's, London #42/R est:10000-15000

WARDLEWORTH, J L (19th C) British
£300 $519 €438 Female nude reclining in a bed of roses (18x41cm-7x16in) panel. 11-Dec-3 Mitchells, Cockermouth #946

WAREN, Matti (1891-1955) Finnish
£410 $684 €590 Aura Bridge in Aabo (50x60cm-20x24in) s.i.d.1926 exhib. 26-Oct-3 Bukowskis, Helsinki #531/R

WARFEL, Floretta (1916-) American
£240 $400 €350 Adam and Eve (74x112cm-29x44in) paint ink cloth prov. 15-Nov-3 Slotin Folk Art, Buford #636/R

WARFFEMIUS, Piet (1956-) Dutch
£667 $1227 €1000 Untitled (130x139cm-51x55in) s. 9-Jun-4 Christie's, Amsterdam #394/R

WARGH, Carl (1938-) Finnish
£833 $1392 €1200 Park (80x67cm-31x26in) s. 23-Oct-3 Hagelstam, Helsinki #856

WARHOL, Andy (1928-1987) American
£2053 $3736 €3100 Flash, green gun (53x53cm-21x21in) s. silkscreen exec. 1968 one of 200. 15-Jun-4 James Adam, Dublin #54/R est:1500-2000
£12000 $21840 €17520 Commitee 2000 (51x41cm-20x16in) st.i. num.PA 12.010 verso acrylic silkscreen ink prov. 6-Feb-4 Sotheby's, London #229/R est:10000-15000
£13473 $22500 €19671 Commitee 2000 (51x41cm-20x16in) estate st.i. acrylic silkscreen ink prov. 13-Nov-3 Sotheby's, New York #306/R est:20000-30000
£14970 $25000 €21856 Total eleven dollars 95/GE (56x41cm-22x16in) estate st. acrylic silkscreen ink prov.exhib. 13-Nov-3 Sotheby's, New York #270/R est:25000-35000
£16667 $26333 €24000 Dollar (89x56cm-35x22in) screenprint. 6-Sep-3 Meeting Art, Vercelli #615 est:20000
£17450 $32107 €26000 Committee 2000 (51x41cm-20x16in) i. st.s.verso acrylic serigraph painted 1982 prov. 24-Mar-4 Joron-Derem, Paris #143/R est:35000-40000
£18315 $32418 €26740 Chocolate bunny (51x41cm-20x16in) acrylic serigraph painted 1982. 27-Apr-4 AB Stockholms Auktionsverk #1214/R est:350000-400000 (S.KR 250000)
£20000 $36400 €30000 Studio 54 (23x39cm-9x15in) s.i. acrylic serigraphic ink exec.1978 prov. 29-Jun-4 Cornette de St.Cyr, Paris #118/R est:30000-40000
£20958 $35000 €30599 Flowers (13x13cm-5x5in) s.overlap acrylic silkscreen ink prov. 13-Nov-3 Sotheby's, New York #210/R est:25000-35000
£22000 $36740 €32120 Roll over mouse (28x35cm-11x14in) i. s.d.83 overlap acrylic silkscreen ink prov. 21-Oct-3 Sotheby's, London #420/R est:12000-15000

£22455	$37500	€32784	Toy apple (36x28cm-14x11in) estate st. acrylic silkscreen ink painted c.1983 prov. 13-Nov-3 Sotheby's, New York #268/R est:25000-35000
£24000	$40080	€35040	Shadow (35x28cm-14x11in) acrylic silkscreen ink painted 1978 prov. 21-Oct-3 Sotheby's, London #435/R est:12000-18000
£26000	$43420	€37960	Avanti Car (14x34cm-6x13in) s.d.62 verso acrylic silkscreen ink exec 1962. 21-Oct-3 Sotheby's, London #358/R est:30000-40000
£26000	$47320	€37960	Heart (35x28cm-14x11in) s.i.d.79 overlap acrylic silkscreen ink prov. 6-Feb-4 Sotheby's, London #221/R est:12000-15000
£26946	$45000	€39341	Flower (51x41cm-20x16in) estate st. acrylic pencil silkscreen ink painted c.1985 prov. 13-Nov-3 Sotheby's, New York #274/R est:20000-30000
£27933	$50000	€40782	Campbell's chicken noodle soup box (36x36cm-14x14in) s.d.86 overlap acrylic silkscreen inks prov. 13-May-4 Sotheby's, New York #214/R est:40000-60000
£30000	$55200	€43800	Knives (51x41cm-20x16in) acrylic silkscreen ink painted c.1981-2 prov.exhib. 24-Jun-4 Sotheby's, London #269/R est:30000-40000
£30726	$55000	€44860	Campbell's onion mushroom soup box (36x36cm-14x14in) s.d.86 overlap acrylic silkscreen inks prov. 13-May-4 Sotheby's, New York #235/R est:40000-60000
£32000	$58880	€46720	Mobilgas (56x56cm-22x22in) s.i.d.85 overlap acrylic silkscreen ink prov. 24-Jun-4 Sotheby's, London #268/R est:15000-20000
£32934	$55000	€48084	Puma sneaker (60x80cm-24x31in) acrylic prov. 13-Nov-3 Sotheby's, New York #278a/R est:30000-40000
£40000	$66800	€58400	Lifesavers (56x56cm-22x22in) i. s.d.85 overlap acrylic silkscreen ink prov.exhib. 21-Oct-3 Sotheby's, London #438/R est:30000-40000
£41916	$70000	€61197	Campbell's soup, tomato (51x41cm-20x16in) s.d.85 overlap acrylic prov. 13-Nov-3 Sotheby's, New York #271a/R est:80000-120000
£41916	$70000	€61197	VIP ticket (66x36cm-26x14in) estate st. acrylic silkscreen ink painted c.1978 prov.exhib. 13-Nov-3 Sotheby's, New York #299/R est:30000-40000
£53073	$95000	€77487	Knives (51x81cm-20x32in) acrylic silkscreen inks exec 1981-82 prov.exhib. 13-May-4 Sotheby's, New York #223/R est:60000-80000
£53892	$90000	€78682	Flowers (20x20cm-8x8in) s.i.overlap acrylic silkscreen ink prov. 13-Nov-3 Sotheby's, New York #198/R est:50000-70000
£56886	$95000	€83054	Campbell's onion mushroom soup box (51x51cm-20x20in) estate st. acrylic silkscreen ink prov.lit. 13-Nov-3 Sotheby's, New York #278/R est:50000-70000
£63758	$117315	€95000	Flowers (36x36cm-14x14in) s.d.1964 verso acrylic ink serigraph. 29-Mar-4 Cornette de St.Cyr, Paris #9/R est:100000-120000
£70000	$127400	€102200	Joseph Beuys (51x40cm-20x16in) s. synthetic polymer paint silkscreen canvas exec c.1983 prov. 5-Feb-4 Christie's, London #189/R est:50000-70000
£83832	$140000	€122395	Untitled - flowers (36x36cm-14x14in) s.d.64 acrylic silkscreen on canvas prov. 14-Nov-3 Phillips, New York #157/R est:100000-150000
£89385	$160000	€130502	Mao (30x25cm-12x10in) s.d.73 overlap acrylic silkscreen inks prov. 13-May-4 Sotheby's, New York #162/R est:180000-250000
£100000	$184000	€146000	Ladies and gentlemen (127x101cm-50x40in) s.d.75 overlap acrylic silkscreen ink on canvass prov.exhib. 23-Jun-4 Sotheby's, London #33/R est:120000-150000
£117318	$210000	€171284	Detail of the Last Supper - Be somebody with a body (127x152cm-50x60in) acrylic exec 1985-86 prov.exhib.lit. 12-May-4 Sotheby's, New York #48/R est:300000-400000
£117318	$210000	€171284	Flowers (36x36cm-14x14in) s.d.64 overlap acrylic silkscreen inks prov. 13-May-4 Sotheby's, New York #161/R est:120000-180000
£119760	$200000	€174850	Pair of white Jackies (102x41cm-40x16in) estate st. acrylic silkscreen ink two parts prov. 13-Nov-3 Sotheby's, New York #209/R est:250000-350000
£140000	$254800	€204400	Knives (178x127cm-70x50in) acrylic silkscreen ink painted c.1981-82 prov.exhib. 5-Feb-4 Sotheby's, London #25/R est:150000-200000
£140000	$254800	€204400	Ladies and Gentlemen (127x101cm-50x40in) s.d.75 overlap acrylic silkscreen ink prov.exhib. 5-Feb-4 Sotheby's, London #52/R est:120000-150000
£150000	$273000	€219000	Portrait of Gilbert and George (101x101cm-40x40in) st.sig. acrylic silkscreen ink two parts painted 1975 prov. 5-Feb-4 Sotheby's, London #23/R est:120000-150000
£223333	$410933	€335000	Children paintings, apple (28x35cm-11x14in) s.d.83 verso acrylic serigraph prov.exhib.lit. 8-Jun-4 Artcurial Briest, Paris #238/R est:28000-33000
£223464	$400000	€326257	Mao (66x56cm-26x22in) acrylic silkscreen ink painted c.1972-74 prov. 12-May-4 Sotheby's, New York #17/R est:350000-450000
£245509	$410000	€358443	Campbell's soup (182x152cm-72x60in) s.d.1985 overlap acrylic silkscreen ink prov. 13-Nov-3 Sotheby's, New York #275/R est:280000-350000
£251497	$420000	€367186	Gold Jackie (51x41cm-20x16in) s.on overlap acrylic silkscreen ink canvas prov.exhib. 12-Nov-3 Sotheby's, New York #40/R est:300000-400000
£260000	$478400	€379600	Four Marilyns - reversal series (91x71cm-36x28in) i.overlap acrylic silkscreen ink on canvas painted 1979-86. 23-Jun-4 Sotheby's, London #14/R est:220000-280000
£279330	$500000	€407822	Four multicoloured Marylins - Reversal series (92x71cm-36x28in) s.d.79/86 overlap acrylic silkscreen inks prov.exhib. 13-May-4 Sotheby's, New York #212/R est:450000-550000
£287425	$480000	€419641	Two white Mona Lisas (67x102cm-26x40in) acrylic silkscreen ink painted 1980 prov. 12-Nov-3 Sotheby's, New York #27/R est:400000-600000
£480000	$873600	€700800	Self-Portrait (57x57cm-22x22in) s.i.overlap acrylic silkscreen ink painted 1967 prov.exhib.lit. 5-Feb-4 Sotheby's, London #21/R est:450000-550000
£642458	$1150000	€937989	Self-portrait (102x102cm-40x40in) acrylic silkscreen ink exec 1986 prov. 12-May-4 Sotheby's, New York #4/R est:1000000-1500000
£800000	$1472000	€1168000	Little electric chair (56x71cm-22x28in) s.d.64 acrylic silkscreen ink on canvas prov.exhib.lit. 23-Jun-4 Sotheby's, London #15/R est:700000-900000
£958084	$1600000	€1398803	Last supper (101x101cm-40x40in) acrylic silkscreen ink on canvas executed 1986 prov.exhib. 12-Nov-3 Sotheby's, New York #30/R est:1200000-1800000
£1452514	$2600000	€2120670	Last Supper (230x640cm-91x252in) acrylic painted 1986 prov.exhib.lit. 12-May-4 Sotheby's, New York #42/R est:2500000-3500000
Photographs			
£5000	$9250	€7300	Muhammad Ali (9x7cm-4x3in) polaroid. 13-Jul-4 Bonhams, Knightsbridge #147/R est:5000-7000
£6207	$9931	€9000	Mick Jagger (11x8cm-4x3in) polaroid exec 1975. 13-Mar-3 Galleria Pace, Milan #101/R est:11000-14000
£8889	$16000	€12978	Untitled (70x54cm-28x21in) s.verso 4 stitched gelatin silver print prov. 23-Apr-4 Phillips, New York #12/R est:14000-18000
£8982	$15000	€13114	Milton Berle stitched photo (70x80cm-28x31in) s.d.86 gelatin silver print string 6 attached parts prov. 13-Nov-3 Sotheby's, New York #281/R est:10000-15000
Prints			
£1730	$3200	€2526	Mao (102x75cm-40x30in) s. col screenprint. 12-Feb-4 Christie's, Rockefeller NY #252/R est:2000-3000
£1757	$3250	€2565	Jackie III (102x74cm-40x29in) silkscreen. 15-Jul-4 Sotheby's, New York #104/R est:2000-3000
£1765	$3000	€2577	Karen Kain (101x81cm-40x32in) s. col screenprint. 31-Oct-3 Sotheby's, New York #824/R
£1765	$3000	€2577	Flash - November 22 (53x53cm-21x21in) s.verso colour screenprint. 21-Nov-3 Swann Galleries, New York #218/R est:2000-3000
£1765	$3000	€2577	Paloma Picasso (104x75cm-41x30in) s.i. col screenprint. 21-Nov-3 Swann Galleries, New York #222/R est:1800-2200
£1795	$3250	€2621	From Flowers (104x75cm-41x30in) init. s.i.num.7/50 verso hand col silkscreen. 19-Apr-4 Bonhams & Butterfields, San Francisco #317/R est:2500-3500
£1800	$3312	€2628	Sam (35x25cm-14x10in) s.i. num.PM06.0071 verso offset lithograph exec.c.1954 lit. 24-Jun-4 Sotheby's, Olympia #485/R est:2000-3000
£1882	$3200	€2748	Ten cherubs (22x28cm-9x11in) s. offset lithograph hand coloring W/C. 21-Nov-3 Swann Galleries, New York #217/R est:1500-2500
£1946	$3250	€2841	Marilyn 7 x 7, invitation (18x18cm-7x7in) s. col silkscreen from signed edition of 150. 21-Oct-3 Bonhams & Butterfields, San Francisco #1454/R
£1955	$3500	€2854	Edward Kennedy (102x82cm-40x32in) s.num.16/50 col silkscreen diamond dust board. 4-May-4 Doyle, New York #278/R est:2500-3500
£2000	$3440	€2920	Electric chair (90x121cm-35x48in) s.verso num.A.P XV/50 pink yellow screenprint. 2-Dec-3 Christie's, London #241 est:1500-2000
£2000	$3680	€3000	Grapes (102x76cm-40x30in) s.num.41/50 screenprint exec 1979. 8-Jun-4 Sotheby's, Amsterdam #330/R est:2500-3500
£2000	$3640	€2920	Commitee 2000 (76x51cm-30x20in) s.num.21/200 col silkscreen board. 1-Jul-4 Sotheby's, London #495/R est:2000-3000
£2000	$3680	€3000	Paloma Picasso (103x69cm-41x27in) s.d.1975 verso col serigraph one of 168. 12-Jun-4 Villa Grisebach, Berlin #867/R est:1800-2400
£2098	$3566	€3000	Queen Margrethe (100x80cm-39x31in) s.num.TP17/30 screenprint lit. 27-Nov-3 Millon & Associes, Paris #250/R est:2500-3000
£2133	$3840	€3200	Fiesta pig (54x77cm-21x30in) s. num.131/200 col serigraph. 24-Apr-4 Cornette de St.Cyr, Paris #311/R est:3000
£2175	$3916	€3263	Frolunda hockey player (100x80cm-39x31in) s.num.91/100 col silkscreen lit. 25-Apr-4 Goteborg Auktionsverk, Sweden #312/R est:25000 (S.KR 30000)
£2177	$3897	€3200	Ladies and gentlemen (100x70cm-39x28in) s. serigraph exec.1975. 16-Mar-4 Finarte Semenzato, Milan #281/R est:2000
£2197	$3800	€3208	From ladies and gentleman (111x73cm-44x29in) s.d.1975 verso screenprint one of 125 prov. 10-Dec-3 Phillips, New York #493/R est:3000-4000
£2200	$4048	€3212	Pink Marilyn (17x17cm-7x7in) col silkscreen card edition of 500 prov.exhib. 24-Jun-4 Sotheby's, Olympia #478/R est:1000-1200
£2200	$4004	€3212	After the party (55x76cm-22x30in) s.num.482/1000 col silkscreen. 1-Jul-4 Sotheby's, London #497/R est:2500-3000
£2206	$3750	€3221	Campbell's soup (61x43cm-24x17in) s. col screenprint. 31-Oct-3 Sotheby's, New York #804/R
£2210	$4000	€3227	Fiesta pig (54x77cm-21x30in) s.i.num.1/5 col silkscreen. 19-Apr-4 Bonhams & Butterfields, San Francisco #318/R est:2500-3500
£2235	$3800	€3263	Gee (24x20cm-9x8in) offset lithograph prov. 4-Nov-3 Christie's, Rockefeller NY #355/R est:3000-5000
£2238	$3804	€3200	Neuschwanstein (85x60cm-33x24in) s. num.81/100 col serigraph. 27-Nov-3 Lempertz, Koln #522/R est:3500
£2245	$3750	€3278	Sidewalk (74x107cm-29x42in) s.num.240/250 col silkscreen. 21-Oct-3 Bonhams & Butterfields, San Francisco #1458/R
£2282	$4085	€3400	Mao (102x75cm-40x30in) s. col silkscreen on wallpaper. 25-May-4 Dorotheum, Vienna #90/R est:3400-3600
£2346	$4200	€3425	After the party (55x77cm-22x30in) s.num.24/1000 color screenprint. 6-May-4 Swann Galleries, New York #612/R est:2500-3500
£2400	$3984	€3504	Mao (101x76cm-40x30in) s. col silkscreen edition of 100. 6-Oct-3 Sotheby's, London #363/R est:2000-2500
£2400	$4296	€3600	Cologne Cathedral (99x80cm-39x31in) s.i. col silkscreen diamond dust board. 15-May-4 Van Ham, Cologne #1021 est:4000
£2400	$4368	€3504	Cow (116x76cm-46x30in) estate st.verso col screenprint. 30-Jun-4 Christie's, Kensington #168/R est:1500-2500
£2400	$4368	€3504	Cow (116x75cm-46x30in) estate st.verso col screenprint. 30-Jun-4 Christie's, Kensington #167/R est:1500-2500
£2446	$4500	€3571	Details of Renaissance paintings (81x112cm-32x44in) s.num. silkscreen prov. 10-Jun-4 Phillips, New York #571/R est:3500-4500
£2447	$4209	€3500	Queen Beatrix (100x80cm-39x31in) s.num.17/30 col silkscreen. 3-Dec-3 Sotheby's, Amsterdam #408/R est:5000-7000
£2500	$4000	€3650	Plains Indian shield (61x61cm-24x24in) s.num.222/250 col screenprint board. 18-Sep-3 Swann Galleries, New York #680/R est:2000-3000
£2545	$4250	€3716	Letter to the world, the kick (92x92cm-36x36in) s.i.num.12/25 col silkscreen. 21-Oct-3 Bonhams & Butterfields, San Francisco #1459/R
£2600	$4472	€3796	Geronimo, from cowboys and Indians (91x91cm-36x36in) s. num.201/250 col screenprint. 2-Dec-3 Christie's, London #359/R est:2500-3500
£2600	$4732	€3796	Mao (101x75cm-40x30in) s. col screenprint wallpaper. 30-Jun-4 Christie's, Kensington #159/R est:1500-2000
£2621	$4377	€3800	Flower (58x58cm-23x23in) print one of 300. 13-Nov-3 Galleria Pace, Milan #131/R est:3500
£2647	$4500	€3865	Marilyn (31x31cm-12x12in) s. col screenprint. 31-Oct-3 Sotheby's, New York #829/R
£2667	$4773	€4000	Cologne Cathedral (100x80cm-39x31in) s. silkscreen diamond dust board. 15-May-4 Van Ham, Cologne #1020/R est:4000
£2715	$4615	€3964	Details of renaissance paintings - Leonardo da Vinci, The Annunciation (81x111cm-32x44in) s. col serigraph prov.lit. 25-Nov-3 Germann, Zurich #655/R est:5500-6000 (S.FR 6000)
£2717	$5000	€3967	Kiss (32x20cm-13x8in) s.i. screenprint Plexiglas prov. 10-Jun-4 Phillips, New York #573/R est:3000-4000
£2761	$4500	€4031	Fiesta Pig (55x78cm-22x31in) s. num.PP5/5 col screenprint Arches exec 1979. 24-Sep-3 Christie's, Rockefeller NY #419/R est:2000-3000
£2800	$4816	€4088	Mother and child, from cowboys and Indians (91x91cm-36x36in) s.i. col screenprint. 2-Dec-3 Christie's, London #357/R est:2500-3500
£2805	$4769	€4095	Dollar sign (50x39cm-20x15in) s. num.7/15 silkscreen exec. 1982 prov.lit. 22-Nov-3 Burkhard, Luzern #149/R est:6000-8000 (S.FR 6200)
£2994	$5000	€4371	Grapes (102x76cm-40x30in) s.num.13/50 col silkscreen. 21-Oct-3 Bonhams & Butterfields, San Francisco #1451/R
£3000	$5160	€4380	Cowboys and Indians, northwest coast mask (91x91cm-36x36in) s.i.num.21/36 col silkscreen board. 4-Dec-3 Sotheby's, London #266/R est:3000-5000
£3000	$5160	€4380	Tomato-beef noodle o's (89x58cm-35x23in) s.i.verso col screenprint. 2-Dec-3 Christie's, London #340/R est:2500-3500
£3000	$5460	€4380	Chicken Noodle (89x59cm-35x23in) s.num.28/250 verso col screenprint. 30-Jun-4 Christie's, Kensington #62/R est:1800-2200
£3038	$5500	€4435	Sitting Bull (92x92cm-36x36in) estate st.verso col silkscreen board. 19-Apr-4 Bonhams & Butterfields, San Francisco #320/R est:4500-6500
£3107	$5500	€4536	Kimiko (91x91cm-36x36in) s.num.240/250 col screenprint. 28-Apr-4 Christie's, Rockefeller NY #451/R est:3000-4000
£3125	$5094	€4500	Joseph Beuys (112x76cm-44x30in) s.i. col serigraph. 27-Sep-3 Dr Fritz Nagel, Stuttgart #9659/R est:6000
£3200	$5824	€4672	Myths, Santa Claus (97x97cm-38x38in) s.num.178/2000 col silkscreen diamond dust board. 1-Jul-4 Sotheby's, London #473/R est:3000-5000
£3235	$5500	€4723	Joseph Beuys (101x81cm-40x32in) s. col screenprint. 31-Oct-3 Sotheby's, New York #826/R
£3275	$6026	€4782	Karen Kain (100x80cm-39x31in) s. col serigraph diamond dust. 8-Jun-4 Germann, Zurich #653/R est:4000-6000 (S.FR 7500)
£3315	$6000	€4840	Grapes (102x76cm-40x30in) s.num.13/50 col silkscreen. 19-Apr-4 Bonhams & Butterfields, San Francisco #319/R est:6000-7000
£3497	$5944	€5000	Campbell's Soup II - Oyster Stew Soup (89x58cm-35x23in) s.i. col silkscreen. 26-Nov-3 Dorotheum, Vienna #216/R est:2800-3000
£3497	$6014	€5000	In her sweet little alice blue shoes (7x12cm-3x5in) s.i. W/C offset lithograph. 3-Dec-3 Hauswedell & Nolte, Hamburg #1044/R est:5000
£3500	$5810	€5110	After the party (55x78cm-22x31in) s.num.172/1000 col silkscreen. 6-Oct-3 Sotheby's, London #328/R est:1500-2000

£3500	$6370	€5110	Joseph Beuys (112x76cm-44x30in) screenprint. 30-Jun-4 Christie's, London #333/R est:2500-3500
£3500	$6405	€5110	Self portrait (58x58cm-23x23in) s.d.1966 num.47/300 screenprint silver coated paper. 3-Jun-4 Christie's, Kensington #519/R est:1400-1600
£3500	$6370	€5110	Campbell's Soup I, Green Pea (89x58cm-35x23in) s.num.138/250 verso col silkscreen. 1-Jul-4 Sotheby's, London #447/R est:2500-3500
£3500	$6370	€5110	Skulls (77x102cm-30x40in) s.i. col silkscreen. 1-Jul-4 Sotheby's, London #477/R est:3500-4500
£3529	$6000	€5152	Onion (81x47cm-32x19in) s. col screenprint. 31-Oct-3 Sotheby's, New York #815/R
£3529	$6000	€5152	Space fruit (76x101cm-30x40in) s. col screenprint pair. 31-Oct-3 Sotheby's, New York #823/R
£3529	$6000	€5152	Ingrid Bergman (97x97cm-38x38in) s. col screenprint. 31-Oct-3 Sotheby's, New York #830/R
£3529	$6000	€5152	Flowers (92x92cm-36x36in) s.verso col screenprint exec.1970. 4-Nov-3 Christie's, Rockefeller NY #365/R est:5000-6000
£3529	$6000	€5152	Flowers (92x92cm-36x36in) s.verso col screenprint exec.1970. 4-Nov-3 Christie's, Rockefeller NY #366/R est:5000-7000
£3533	$6500	€5158	Untitled, 12 (76x56cm-30x22in) col screenprint edition of 100 prov. 10-Jun-4 Phillips, New York #570/R est:2000-2500
£3625	$6163	€5293	From - Flowers (91x91cm-36x36in) s.num.114/250 col silkscreen lit. 4-Nov-3 Bukowskis, Stockholm #474/R est:50000-60000 (S.KR 48000)
£3672	$6500	€5361	Jacqeline Kennedy I (52x43cm-20x17in) signature verso num.VIII silver screenprint. 30-Apr-4 Sotheby's, New York #510/R est:4000-6000
£3800	$6802	€5700	Campbell's pepper pot soup (81x48cm-32x19in) s. verso col silkscreen. 15-May-4 Dr Sturies, Dusseldorf #216/R
£3800	$6916	€5548	Reigning queens, Queen Margrethe II (100x80cm-39x31in) s.num.36/40 col silkscreen board. 1-Jul-4 Sotheby's, London #465/R est:2500-3500
£3800	$6916	€5548	Mao (91x91cm-36x36in) s.num.35/250 verso col silkscreen. 1-Jul-4 Sotheby's, London #461/R est:2000-3000
£3800	$6916	€5548	Scotch Broth (89x58cm-35x23in) s.verso col screenprint. 30-Jun-4 Christie's, Kensington #63/R est:3500-4000
£3804	$7000	€5554	Mammy (97x97cm-38x38in) s. num.62/200 serigraph. 26-Jun-4 Susanin's, Chicago #6079/R est:6000-10000
£3804	$7000	€5554	Dollar sign (48x38cm-19x15in) s. num.10/60 silkscreen. 26-Jun-4 Susanin's, Chicago #6080/R est:4000-6000
£3810	$6743	€5563	Jackie II (61x76cm-24x30in) st.sig.num.XVII verso silkscreen lit. 27-Apr-4 AB Stockholms Auktionsverk #1365/R est:30000-35000 (S.KR 52000)
£3824	$6500	€5583	Joseph Beuys (101x81cm-40x32in) s. col screenprint. 31-Oct-3 Sotheby's, New York #828/R
£3824	$6500	€5583	Black bean (89x59cm-35x23in) s.verso col screenprint exec.1968. 4-Nov-3 Christie's, Rockefeller NY #362/R est:4000-6000
£3927	$6677	€5733	Mao (91x91cm-36x36in) s.num.126/250 col silkscreen lit. 4-Nov-3 Bukowskis, Stockholm #475/R est:50000-70000 (S.KR 52000)
£3944	$6586	€5758	Queen Margrethe II - from series Reigning queens (100x80cm-39x31in) s.num.4/30 trial proof serigraph prov.lit. 7-Oct-3 Rasmussen, Copenhagen #421/R est:30000-50000 (D.KR 42000)
£3964	$7095	€5787	Marx brothers (101x81cm-40x32in) s. num.186/200 col screenprint exec 1980. 31-May-4 Stephan Welz, Johannesburg #444/R est:60000-90000 (SA.R 48000)
£3988	$6500	€5822	Flowers (59x59cm-23x23in) s.d.1964 col offset lithograph. 24-Sep-3 Christie's, Rockefeller NY #414/R est:3000-5000
£4000	$6640	€5840	Mao (91x91cm-36x36in) s.num.241/250n verso col screenprint. 6-Oct-3 Sotheby's, London #321/R est:4500-5500
£4000	$6640	€5840	ADS Paramount (97x97cm-38x38in) s.num.128/190 col silkscreen board. 6-Oct-3 Sotheby's, London #359/R est:3500-4000
£4000	$7280	€5840	Reigning queens, Queen Margrethe II (100x80cm-39x31in) s.num.32/40 col silkscreen board. 1-Jul-4 Sotheby's, London #463/R est:2000-3000
£4005	$7250	€5847	Jacqueline Kennedy II (61x76cm-24x30in) s.num.150/200 col silkscreen. 19-Apr-4 Bonhams & Butterfields, San Francisco #316/R est:7000-9000
£4027	$7128	€6000	Flash - November 22 1962-1968 (52x52cm-20x20in) s. num.108/200 col serigraph lit. 28-Apr-4 Artcurial Briest, Paris #349/R est:8000-10000
£4118	$7000	€6012	Flowers (56x56cm-22x22in) s. offset lithograph. 31-Oct-3 Sotheby's, New York #805/R
£4118	$7000	€6012	Joseph Beuys (101x81cm-40x32in) s. col screenprint. 31-Oct-3 Sotheby's, New York #827/R
£4118	$7000	€6012	Paramount (96x96cm-38x38in) s. col screenprint. 31-Oct-3 Sotheby's, New York #831/R
£4154	$7145	€6065	Goethe (96x96cm-38x38in) s.num.8/100 col silkscreen. 7-Dec-3 Uppsala Auktionskammare, Uppsala #349/R est:30000-40000 (S.KR 54000)
£4200	$7644	€6132	Mao (91x91cm-36x36in) screenprint. 30-Jun-4 Christie's, London #324/R est:2000-3000
£4333	$7973	€6500	Electric chair (91x121cm-36x48in) s. num.004/250 col serigraph exec.1971. 8-Jun-4 Finarte Semenzato, Milan #295/R est:2000-3000
£4336	$7241	€6200	Portrait de Mao Tse Toung (91x91cm-36x36in) s.verso num.78/250 screenprint lit. 25-Jun-3 Digard, Paris #123/R est:2000-2500
£4472	$7020	€6484	Flowers (55x55cm-22x22in) s.d.1964 col screenprint. 26-Aug-3 Christie's, Sydney #251/R est:9000-12000 (A.D 11000)
£4500	$7740	€6570	Beetle (96x96cm-38x38in) s.num.A.P 29/30 col screenprint. 2-Dec-3 Christie's, London #355/R est:3000-5000
£4500	$8190	€6570	Campbell's Soup I, Pepper Pot (89x58cm-35x23in) s.num.149/250 verso col silkscreen. 1-Jul-4 Sotheby's, London #445/R est:2500-3500
£4500	$8190	€6570	Campbell's Soup I, Black Bean (89x58cm-35x23in) s.num.138/250 verso col silkscreen. 1-Jul-4 Sotheby's, London #446/R est:2500-3500
£4500	$8190	€6570	Reigning queens, Queen Margrethe II (100x80cm-39x31in) s.num.32/40 col silkscreen board. 1-Jul-4 Sotheby's, London #464/R est:2000-3000
£4545	$7818	€6500	Flowers (91x91cm-36x36in) s.verso num.135/250 silkscreen exec. 1970. 4-Dec-3 Van Ham, Cologne #547/R est:5000
£4700	$8554	€6862	Details of Renaissance paintings (81x112cm-32x44in) s.num.7/36 col silkscreen two. 1-Jul-4 Sotheby's, London #492/R est:3000-4000
£4706	$8000	€6871	Vegetable (81x47cm-32x19in) s. col screenprint pair. 31-Oct-3 Sotheby's, New York #816/R
£4790	$8000	€6993	Brooklyn Bridge (98x101cm-39x40in) s.num.58/200 col silkscreen. 21-Oct-3 Bonhams & Butterfields, San Francisco #1456/R
£4800	$8736	€7008	The nun (96x96cm-38x38in) s. screenprint. 30-Jun-4 Christie's, London #339/R est:3000-5000
£4802	$8500	€7011	Green pea (89x58cm-35x23in) s. num.44/250 verso col screenprint. 30-Apr-4 Sotheby's, New York #516/R est:6000-8000
£4895	$8420	€7000	Cologne Cathedral (100x80cm-39x31in) s. silkscreen one of 80 exec. 1985. 4-Dec-3 Van Ham, Cologne #546/R est:8500
£4909	$8346	€7167	Teddy Roosevelt - from Series Cowboys and Indians (91x91cm-36x36in) s.num.34/36 col silkscreen lit. 5-Nov-3 AB Stockholms Auktionsverk #1300/R est:50000-60000 (S.KR 65000)
£4985	$8474	€7278	Flower (56x56cm-22x22in) s.col offset lithograph lit. 4-Nov-3 Bukowskis, Stockholm #473/R est:30000-35000 (S.KR 66000)
£5000	$8300	€7300	Reigning queens, Queen Elizabeth II of the United Kingdom (100x80cm-39x31in) s.num.16/40 col silkscreen board. 6-Oct-3 Sotheby's, London #308/R est:3000-4000
£5000	$8300	€7300	Mao (91x91cm-36x36in) s.verso col screenprint edition of 250. 6-Oct-3 Sotheby's, London #322/R est:4500-5500
£5000	$8300	€7300	General Custer (91x91cm-36x36in) s.num.16/36 col silkscreen board. 6-Oct-3 Sotheby's, London #353/R est:4000-6000
£5000	$8300	€7300	Ingrid Bergman, the nun (37x37cm-15x15in) s.num.248/250 col silkscreen board. 6-Oct-3 Sotheby's, London #360/R est:5000-5500
£5000	$8500	€7300	Cow (116x75cm-46x30in) s. col screenprint. 31-Oct-3 Sotheby's, New York #806/R
£5000	$8500	€7300	Mao (91x91cm-36x36in) s. col screenprint. 31-Oct-3 Sotheby's, New York #820/R
£5000	$8500	€7300	Green pea (81x47cm-32x19in) s. col screenprint. 31-Oct-3 Sotheby's, New York #817/R
£5000	$8600	€7300	Flowers (91x91cm-36x36in) s.num.113/250 verso col silkscreen. 4-Dec-3 Sotheby's, London #261/R est:5000-6000
£5000	$8600	€7300	Flowers (91x91cm-36x36in) s.num.113/250 verso col silkscreen. 4-Dec-3 Sotheby's, London #262/R est:5000-6000
£5000	$8600	€7300	Flowers (91x91cm-36x36in) s.num.113/250 verso col silkscreen. 4-Dec-3 Sotheby's, London #264/R est:5000-6000
£5000	$8600	€7300	Flowers (91x91cm-36x36in) s.num.113/250 verso col silkscreen. 4-Dec-3 Sotheby's, London #265/R est:5000-6000
£5000	$8600	€7300	Campbell's soup II, chicken 'n dumplings (89x58cm-35x23in) s.i.verso col silkscreen. 4-Dec-3 Sotheby's, London #269/R est:3000-4000
£5000	$8600	€7300	Jacqueline Kennedy III (100x76cm-39x30in) with sig.num.154/200 silver black screenprint. 2-Dec-3 Christie's, London #336/R est:2500-3500
£5000	$8600	€7300	Queen Elizabeth II (100x80cm-39x31in) s.i. col screenprint. 2-Dec-3 Christie's, London #352/R est:3000-5000
£5000	$8950	€7500	Cologne Cathedral (100x80cm-39x31in) s. silkscreen board. 15-May-4 Van Ham, Cologne #1019/R est:8500
£5000	$9100	€7300	Queen Elizabeth II (100x80cm-39x31in) s. screenprint. 30-Jun-4 Christie's, London #341/R est:5000-7000
£5000	$9100	€7300	Campbell's Soup I, Vegetable (89x58cm-35x23in) s.num.138/250 verso col silkscreen. 1-Jul-4 Sotheby's, London #449/R est:2500-3500
£5085	$9000	€7424	Flowers (56x56cm-22x22in) s.d.1964 col offset lithograph edition of 300. 28-Apr-4 Christie's, Rockefeller NY #441/R est:4000-6000
£5085	$9000	€7424	Jacqueline Kennedy II (61x76cm-24x30in) st.sig. verso num.VIII violet screenprint. 30-Apr-4 Sotheby's, New York #511/R est:6000-8000
£5135	$9500	€7497	Miguel Bose (56x78cm-22x31in) si.d.83 black fibre tip pen col silkscreen prov.lit. 12-Feb-4 Sotheby's, New York #258/R est:7000-9000
£5200	$9464	€7592	Reigning queens, Queen Elizabeth II (100x80cm-39x31in) s.num.21/40 col screenprint board. 1-Jul-4 Sotheby's, London #468/R est:3000-4000
£5215	$8500	€7614	Jackie III (101x76cm-40x30in) st.sig.i. col screenprint wove paper exec 1966. 24-Sep-3 Christie's, Rockefeller NY #415/R est:4000-6000
£5439	$9845	€7941	Lifesavers (96x96cm-38x38in) s.num.3/5 silkscreen board exec. 1985 prov. 1-Apr-4 Heffel, Vancouver #108/R est:8000-12000 (C.D 13000)
£5500	$10010	€8030	Marilyn (91x91cm-36x36in) s.num.132/250 col silkscreen. 1-Jul-4 Sotheby's, London #443 est:2500-3000
£5500	$10010	€8030	Campbell's Soup I, Chicken Noodle (89x58cm-35x23in) s.num.138/250 verso col silkscreen. 1-Jul-4 Sotheby's, London #448/R est:2500-3500
£5500	$10010	€8030	Reigning queens, Queen Elizabeth II (100x80cm-39x31in) s.num.17/40 col silkscreen board. 1-Jul-4 Sotheby's, London #466/R est:5000-7000
£5500	$10010	€8030	Reigning queens, Queen Elizabeth II (100x80cm-39x31in) s.i.num.7/10 col silkscreen board. 1-Jul-4 Sotheby's, London #469/R est:3000-4000
£5500	$10010	€8030	Reigning queens, Queen Elizabeth II (100x80cm-39x31in) s.i.num.7/10 col silkscreen board. 1-Jul-4 Sotheby's, London #470/R est:3000-4000
£5500	$10010	€8030	Madonna and self portrait with skeleton's arm (81x102cm-32x40in) estate st.verso col silkscreen board after Munch. 1-Jul-4 Sotheby's, London #499/R est:4000-5000
£5525	$10000	€8067	Mother and child (92x92cm-36x36in) s.num.5/36 col silkscreen board. 19-Apr-4 Bonhams & Butterfields, San Francisco #322/R est:6000-8000
£5588	$9500	€8158	Cooking pot (15x11cm-6x4in) st.sig. photoengraving. 31-Oct-3 Sotheby's, New York #803/R
£5588	$9500	€8158	Jacqueline Kennedy II (102x76cm-40x30in) s. col screenprint exec.1966. 4-Nov-3 Christie's, Rockefeller NY #358/R est:5000-7000
£5594	$9622	€8000	Cologne Cathedral (100x80cm-39x31in) s. silkscreen one of 80 exec.1985. 4-Dec-3 Van Ham, Cologne #545/R est:8500
£5650	$10000	€8249	Flowers (56x56cm-22x22in) s.d.1964 offset lithograph. 30-Apr-4 Sotheby's, New York #507/R est:5000-7000
£5650	$10000	€8249	Mobil (95x95cm-37x37in) s. num.25/190 col screenprint. 30-Apr-4 Sotheby's, New York #522/R est:6000-8000
£5655	$9444	€8200	Mao (91x91cm-36x36in) s.verso num.165/250 col serigraph lit. 13-Nov-3 Finarte Semenzato, Rome #47/R est:3000-4000
£5800	$9628	€8468	Mao (91x91cm-36x36in) s.num.112/250 verso col silkscreen. 6-Oct-3 Sotheby's, London #325/R est:5000-7000
£5800	$9628	€8468	Dollar (50x40cm-20x16in) s.num.20/60 col silkscreen board. 6-Oct-3 Sotheby's, London #358/R est:6000-8000
£5800	$10556	€8468	Endangered species, bighorn ram (97x97cm-38x38in) s.i.num.12/30 col silkscreen board. 1-Jul-4 Sotheby's, London #475/R est:6000-8000
£5882	$10000	€8588	Flowers (91x91cm-36x36in) s. col screenprint. 31-Oct-3 Sotheby's, New York #819/R
£5882	$10000	€8588	Mao (91x91cm-36x36in) s. col screenprint. 31-Oct-3 Sotheby's, New York #822/R
£5882	$10000	€8588	Flowers (59x59cm-23x23in) s.d.1964 offset lithograph. 4-Nov-3 Christie's, Rockefeller NY #356/R est:4000-6000
£5882	$10000	€8588	Flowers (92x92cm-36x36in) s.verso col screenprint exec.1970. 4-Nov-3 Christie's, Rockefeller NY #367/R est:5000-7000
£5882	$10000	€8588	Flowers (92x92cm-36x36in) s.verso col screenprint exec.1970. 4-Nov-3 Christie's, Rockefeller NY #364/R est:5000-7000
£5882	$10000	€8588	Us dollar (50x40cm-20x16in) s. num.3/3 col screenprint exec.1982. 4-Nov-3 Christie's, Rockefeller NY #372/R est:4000-6000
£5932	$10085	€8661	Mick Jagger (110x73cm-43x29in) s. colour screen print edn 112/250. 24-Nov-3 Sotheby's, Melbourne #285/R est:14000-18000 (A.D 14000)
£6000	$9960	€8760	Jackie I (51x44cm-20x17in) s.num.142/200 verso silver silkscreen. 6-Oct-3 Sotheby's, London #307/R est:2000-3000
£6000	$9960	€8760	Campbell's soup I, cream of mushroom (89x58cm-35x23in) s.num.138/250 verso col silkscreen edition of 250. 6-Oct-3 Sotheby's, London #310/R est:2000-2500
£6000	$9960	€8760	Flowers (91x91cm-36x36in) s.verso col silkscreen edition of 250. 6-Oct-3 Sotheby's, London #316/R est:5000-6000
£6000	$9960	€8760	Flowers (91x91cm-36x36in) s.verso col silkscreen edition of 250. 6-Oct-3 Sotheby's, London #318/R est:5000-6000
£6000	$9960	€8760	Mao (91x91cm-36x36in) s.verso col silkscreen edition of 250. 6-Oct-3 Sotheby's, London #324/R est:4500-5500
£6000	$9960	€8760	Turtle (80x100cm-31x39in) s.num.15/250 col silkscreen board. 6-Oct-3 Sotheby's, London #327/R est:2000-3000
£6000	$10920	€8760	Mao (91x91cm-36x36in) s.num.35/250 verso col silkscreen. 1-Jul-4 Sotheby's, London #452/R est:6000-8000
£6000	$10920	€8760	Alfred Hitchcock (52x41cm-20x16in) estate st.verso col silkscreen. 1-Jul-4 Sotheby's, London #453/R est:6000-8000
£6091	$10964	€8893	From - Mick Jagger (110x74cm-43x29in) s.num.85/200 col silkscreen lit. 26-Apr-4 Bukowskis, Stockholm #449/R est:60000-80000 (S.KR 84000)

£6200	$11284	€9052	Untitled butterflies (32x45cm-13x18in) num.PM 14.00/76 offset lithograph W/C paper exec c.1955 prov. 4-Feb-4 Sotheby's, Olympia #24/R est:3000-4000
£6200	$11284	€9052	General Custer (91x91cm-36x36in) s.num.16/36 col silkscreen board. 1-Jul-4 Sotheby's, London #484/R est:4000-6000
£6215	$11000	€9074	Dollar (50x40cm-20x16in) s. num.21/60 screenprint. 30-Apr-4 Sotheby's, New York #518/R est:6000-8000
£6224	$10394	€9336	Mick Jagger red lips (111x73cm-44x29in) s. num.121/250 col screenprint lit. 27-Oct-3 Goodman, Sydney #12/R est:6000-8000 (A.D 15000)
£6381	$11487	€9316	From - Details of renaissance paintings - Sandro Bottelli, birth of Venus (63x94cm-25x37in) s.num.48/70 col silkscreen lit. 26-Apr-4 Bukowskis, Stockholm #452/R est:60000-80000 (S.KR 88000)
£6471	$11000	€9448	Mick Jagger (110x74cm-43x29in) s.num.53/250 silkscreen signed by Mick Jagger. 20-Nov-3 Auctions by the Bay, Alameda #1133/R
£6500	$10790	€9490	Mao (91x91cm-36x36in) s.verso col screenprint edition of 250. 6-Oct-3 Sotheby's, London #323/R est:4500-5500
£6500	$11960	€9490	La Grande Passion (102x101cm-40x40in) estate st.num.UP 26.04 verso silkscreen board. 24-Jun-4 Sotheby's, Olympia #611/R est:4000-6000
£6667	$12200	€10000	Joseph Beuys (101x81cm-40x32in) s. col serigraph feltpen board. 4-Jun-4 Lempertz, Koln #529/R est:4000
£6748	$11000	€9852	Mick Jagger (110x74cm-43x29in) s. num.61/250 col screenprint Arches exec 1975. 24-Sep-3 Christie's, Rockefeller NY #418/R est:4000-6000
£6780	$12000	€9899	Lenin (100x75cm-39x30in) s. num.25/120 col screenprint. 30-Apr-4 Sotheby's, New York #524/R est:14000-18000
£6800	$12376	€9928	Mao (57x44cm-22x17in) st. num.A117.0310 verso silkscreen ink exec.c.1978 prov. 6-Feb-4 Sotheby's, London #225/R est:6000-8000
£6800	$12376	€9928	Mao (91x91cm-36x36in) s.num.35/250 verso col silkscreen. 1-Jul-4 Sotheby's, London #456/R est:4000-5000
£6800	$12376	€9928	Mao (91x91cm-36x36in) s.num.35/250 verso col silkscreen. 1-Jul-4 Sotheby's, London #457/R est:4000-5000
£6800	$12376	€9928	Reigning queens, Queen Elizabeth II (100x80cm-39x31in) s.num.TP8/30 col silkscreen board. 1-Jul-4 Sotheby's, London #467/R est:7000-9000
£6889	$12400	€10058	From - Mick Jagger (110x74cm-43x29in) s.num.105/250 col silkscreen lit. 26-Apr-4 Bukowskis, Stockholm #451/R est:80000-100000 (S.KR 95000)
£6960	$12319	€10162	Mao Tse Tung (91x91cm-36x36in) s.num.2/50 verso sol silkscreen prov.lit. 27-Apr-4 AB Stockholms Auktionsverk #1366/R est:70000-90000 (S.KR 95000)
£7000	$11620	€10220	Flowers (91x91cm-36x36in) s.verso col silkscreen edition of 250. 6-Oct-3 Sotheby's, London #315/R est:5000-6000
£7000	$11620	€10220	Flowers (94x94cm-37x37in) s.verso col silkscreen edition of 250. 6-Oct-3 Sotheby's, London #317/R est:5000-6000
£7000	$11620	€10220	Myths, the witch (97x97cm-38x38in) s.num.21/30 col silkscreen diamond dust board. 6-Oct-3 Sotheby's, London #361/R est:5000-7000
£7000	$12740	€10220	Grande Passion (101x101cm-40x40in) num.UP26.05 verso col silkscreen exec 1984. 4-Feb-4 Sotheby's, Olympia #148/R est:5000-7000
£7000	$12740	€10220	Aretha Franklin and Keith Richards (46x52cm-18x20in) st. num.45.23 verso silkscreen board prov. 6-Feb-4 Sotheby's, London #238/R est:7000-10000
£7000	$12740	€10220	Giant Panda (96x96cm-38x38in) s. screenprint. 30-Jun-4 Christie's, London #336/R est:7000-10000
£7000	$12740	€10220	Bighorn ram (96x96cm-38x38in) s. screenprint. 30-Jun-4 Christie's, London #337/R est:7000-10000
£7000	$12740	€10220	Turtle (81x102cm-32x40in) s.num.5/10 col silkscreen board. 1-Jul-4 Sotheby's, London #476/R est:4000-5000
£7000	$12740	€10220	Shoes (102x151cm-40x59in) s.num.3/60 col silkscreen diamond dust. 1-Jul-4 Sotheby's, London #480/R est:7000-9000
£7200	$13104	€10512	Mao (91x91cm-36x36in) s.num.35/250 verso col silkscreen. 1-Jul-4 Sotheby's, London #458/R est:4000-5000
£7345	$13000	€10724	Mao (91x91cm-36x36in) s.num.184/250 verso col screenprint. 28-Apr-4 Christie's, Rockefeller NY #444/R est:8000-10000
£7345	$13000	€10724	Shoes (102x151cm-40x59in) s.i.verso screenprint diamond dust. 30-Apr-4 Sotheby's, New York #517/R est:8000-12000
£7345	$13000	€10724	African elephant (96x96cm-38x38in) s.i. col screenprint. 30-Apr-4 Sotheby's, New York #519/R est:5000-7000
£7500	$12450	€10950	Endangered species, pine barrens tree frog (97x97cm-38x38in) s.num.4/30 verso col silkscreen board. 6-Oct-3 Sotheby's, London #356/R est:5000-6000
£7500	$13650	€10950	Mao (91x91cm-36x36in) screenprint. 30-Jun-4 Christie's, London #325/R est:7000-10000
£7500	$13575	€10950	Love (76x56cm-30x22in) num.121-VT010 screenprint executed 1983. 1-Apr-4 Christie's, Kensington #289/R est:5000-7000
£7500	$13650	€10950	Herself (96x96cm-38x38in) s. screenprint. 30-Jun-4 Christie's, London #338/R est:4000-6000
£7500	$13800	€10950	Halston advertising campaign - Woman's wear (76x102cm-30x40in) s. num.A126.009 silkscreen print exec 1982 prov. 24-Jun-4 Sotheby's, London #260/R est:10000-12000
£7609	$14000	€11109	Shadow (97x97cm-38x38in) s.num.62/200 serigraph glitter. 26-Jun-4 Susanin's, Chicago #6078/R est:8000-10000
£7647	$13000	€11165	Kiku (50x66cm-20x26in) s. col screenprint exec.1983 set of 3. 4-Nov-3 Christie's, Rockefeller NY #373/R est:7000-9000
£7800	$13416	€11388	Goethe (96x96cm-38x38in) s.num.31/100 col silkscreen board. 4-Dec-3 Sotheby's, London #267/R est:4000-5000
£7800	$14196	€11388	Endangered species, pine barrens tree frog (97x97cm-38x38in) s.i.num.2/30 col silkscreen board. 1-Jul-4 Sotheby's, London #474/R est:6000-7000
£7800	$14196	€11388	Shoes (102x151cm-40x59in) s.num.3/60 col silkscreen diamond dust. 1-Jul-4 Sotheby's, London #482/R est:7000-9000
£7821	$14000	€11419	Pine barrens tree frog (97x97cm-38x38in) s.i.num.3/3 col screenprint prov. 4-May-4 Doyle, New York #279/R est:9000-12000
£7821	$14000	€11419	Reversal cow (114x89cm-45x35in) st.d.1978 num.VP 48.11 verso silkscreen prov.lit. 14-May-4 Phillips, New York #211/R est:12000-18000
£7977	$14358	€11646	From - Mick Jagger (110x74cm-43x29in) s.num.191/250 col silkscreen lit. 26-Apr-4 Bukowskis, Stockholm #450/R est:80000-100000 (S.KR 110000)
£8000	$13280	€11680	Flowers (91x91cm-36x36in) s.verso col silkscreen edition of 250. 6-Oct-3 Sotheby's, London #319/R est:5000-6000
£8000	$13760	€11680	Red Lenin (100x75cm-39x30in) col silkscreen. 4-Dec-3 Sotheby's, London #272/R est:7000-9000
£8053	$14818	€12000	Slash Marilyn (58x45cm-23x18in) serigraph paper exec 1978 prov. 29-Mar-4 Cornette de St.Cyr, Paris #60/R est:10000-15000
£8200	$14924	€11972	Liz (59x59cm-23x23in) s.d.1964 col offset lithograph. 1-Jul-4 Sotheby's, London #440/R est:4000-6000
£8200	$14924	€11972	Mao (91x91cm-36x36in) s.num.35/250 verso col silkscreen. 1-Jul-4 Sotheby's, London #454/R est:5000-6000
£8383	$14000	€12239	Dollar, 9 (102x81cm-40x32in) s.i.num.2/10 col silkscreen. 21-Oct-3 Bonhams & Butterfields, San Francisco #1455/R
£8425	$14912	€12301	Mick Jagger (110x74cm-43x29in) s.num.119/250 col silkscreen lit. 27-Apr-4 AB Stockholms Auktionsverk #1367/R est:100000-125000 (S.KR 115000)
£8475	$15000	€12374	Mao (91x91cm-36x36in) s.i.num.213/250 verso col screenprint. 28-Apr-4 Christie's, Rockefeller NY #445/R est:8000-10000
£8475	$15000	€12374	Liz (56x56cm-22x22in) s.d.1965 offset lithograph. 30-Apr-4 Sotheby's, New York #509/R est:8000-12000
£8500	$14110	€12410	Mao (91x91cm-36x36in) s.num.219/250 verso col silkscreen. 6-Oct-3 Sotheby's, London #326/R est:5000-7000
£8500	$14110	€12410	Shoes (102x151cm-40x59in) s.num.7/10 verso col silkscreen diamond dust. 6-Oct-3 Sotheby's, London #339/R est:6000-8000
£8500	$14110	€12410	Shoes (102x151cm-40x59in) s.num.7/10 verso col silkscreen diamond dust. 6-Oct-3 Sotheby's, London #340/R est:6000-8000
£8500	$14620	€12410	Skulls (76x102cm-30x40in) s.num.7/50 col screenprint set of four. 2-Dec-3 Christie's, London #348/R est:6000-8000
£8500	$15470	€12410	Kiku (50x66cm-20x26in) s.num.24/30 col screenprint set of three. 1-Jul-4 Sotheby's, London #483/R est:7000-8000
£8649	$16000	€12628	Mao (91x91cm-36x36in) s.num.76/250 verso col screenprint. 12-Feb-4 Christie's, Rockefeller NY #251/R est:5000-7000
£8667	$15947	€13000	Maddona and self portrait (81x101cm-32x40in) col serigraph on Lenox Museum board exec 1984 prov. 9-Jun-4 Artcurial Briest, Paris #492/R est:10000-12000
£8725	$16054	€13000	Mick Jagger (102x73cm-40x29in) s. col serigraph prov. 26-Mar-4 Ketterer, Hamburg #684/R est:9000-11000
£8725	$16054	€13000	Mick Jagger (106x70cm-42x28in) s.i. col serigraph prov. 26-Mar-4 Ketterer, Hamburg #685/R est:9000-11000
£8800	$16016	€12848	Mao (91x91cm-36x36in) s.num.35/250 verso col silkscreen. 1-Jul-4 Sotheby's, London #460/R est:4000-5000
£8824	$15000	€12883	Mao (91x91cm-36x36in) s. col screenprint. 31-Oct-3 Sotheby's, New York #821/R
£8824	$15000	€12883	Skulls (76x102cm-30x40in) s. col screenprint exec.1976 set of 4. 4-Nov-3 Christie's, Rockefeller NY #369/R est:12000-16000
£8939	$16000	€13051	Liz (53x53cm-21x21in) s.d.1966 offset lithograph. 6-May-4 Swann Galleries, New York #611/R est:5000-8000
£9000	$14940	€13140	Mao (91x91cm-36x36in) s.num.181/250 verso col silkscreen. 6-Oct-3 Sotheby's, London #320/R est:6000-7000
£9000	$14940	€13140	Shoes (102x151cm-40x59in) s.num.7/10 verso silkscreen diamond dust. 6-Oct-3 Sotheby's, London #338/R est:6000-8000
£9000	$15480	€13140	Van Heusen (96x96cm-38x38in) s.i. col screenprint. 2-Dec-3 Christie's, London #353/R est:5000-7000
£9000	$16380	€13140	Mao (81x81cm-32x32in) s.num.23/50 col silkscreen. 1-Jul-4 Sotheby's, London #472/R est:5000-7000
£9052	$15116	€13216	Grace Kelly (101x81cm-40x32in) s.num.70/225 col silkscreen. 20-Oct-3 Stephan Welz, Johannesburg #232/R est:50000-70000 (SA.R 105000)
£9412	$16000	€13742	Marilyn (91x91cm-36x36in) s. col screenprint. 31-Oct-3 Sotheby's, New York #810/R
£9412	$16000	€13742	Flash (53x53cm-21x21in) col screenprint set of 11. 31-Oct-3 Sotheby's, New York #812/R
£9500	$16340	€13870	Mick Jagger (110x74cm-43x29in) s.num.9/50 col silkscreen signed by Mick Jagger. 4-Dec-3 Sotheby's, London #271/R est:7000-9000
£9500	$16340	€13870	Mao (92x92cm-36x36in) s.verso num.241/250 col screenprint. 2-Dec-3 Christie's, London #338/R est:5000-7000
£9581	$16000	€13988	Muhammad Ali (114x89cm-45x35in) estate st. screenprint Curtis rag paper prov. 13-Nov-3 Sotheby's, New York #305/R est:15000-20000
£9722	$16042	€14000	Four dollar signs (101x81cm-40x32in) s.num.4/35 col screenprint. 2-Jul-3 Cornette de St.Cyr, Paris #97/R est:18000-20000
£9800	$17836	€14308	Mao (91x91cm-36x36in) s.num.35/250 verso col silkscreen. 1-Jul-4 Sotheby's, London #455/R est:5000-7000
£10000	$16600	€14600	Endangered species, bighorn ram (97x97cm-38x38in) s.num.7/30 verso col silkscreen board. 6-Oct-3 Sotheby's, London #365/R est:5000-7000
£10000	$17000	€14600	Marilyn (91x91cm-36x36in) s. col screenprint. 31-Oct-3 Sotheby's, New York #808/R
£10000	$17000	€14600	Tomato (81x47cm-32x19in) s. col screenprint. 31-Oct-3 Sotheby's, New York #818/R
£10000	$17000	€14600	Marilyn (91x91cm-36x36in) s.verso col screenprint exec.1967. 4-Nov-3 Christie's, Rockefeller NY #360/R est:15000-20000
£10000	$17000	€14600	Hammer and sickle (77x102cm-30x40in) s. col screenprint exec.1977 set of 4. 4-Nov-3 Christie's, Rockefeller NY #370/R est:12000-16000
£10000	$18200	€14600	Halston advertising campaign, women's accessories (76x102cm-30x40in) s. num.A128.009 verso silkscreen col paper collage board prov. 6-Feb-4 Sotheby's, London #235/R est:10000-12000
£10000	$18200	€14600	Mao (91x91cm-36x36in) s.num.35/250 verso col silkscreen. 1-Jul-4 Sotheby's, London #451/R est:6000-8000
£10000	$18200	€14600	Shoes (102x151cm-40x59in) s.num.3/60 col silkscreen diamond dust. 1-Jul-4 Sotheby's, London #481/R est:7000-9000
£10169	$18000	€14847	Pine barrens tree frog (96x96cm-38x38in) s. num.89/150 col screenprint. 30-Apr-4 Sotheby's, New York #520/R est:5000-7000
£10500	$17430	€15330	Shoes (102x151cm-40x59in) s.num.7/10 verso col silkscreen diamond dust. 6-Oct-3 Sotheby's, London #337/R est:6000-8000
£10500	$17430	€15330	Mick Jagger (110x74cm-43x29in) s.num.2/250 col silkscreen signed by Mick Jagger. 6-Oct-3 Sotheby's, London #348/R est:7000-10000
£10738	$19758	€16000	Dollar (102x81cm-40x32in) s.num.8/60 serigraph on lenon Museum Board exec 1982 lit. 29-Mar-4 Cornette de St.Cyr, Paris #61/R est:18000-20000
£10800	$19656	€16200	Dollar (102x81cm-40x32in) s. num.11/60 serigraph lit. 29-Jun-4 Cornette de St.Cyr, Paris #123/R est:16000-18000
£11000	$18920	€16060	Mao (92x92cm-36x36in) s.verso num.241/250 col screenprint. 2-Dec-3 Christie's, London #339/R est:5000-7000
£11000	$20020	€16060	Mao (91x91cm-36x36in) s.num.35/250 verso col silkscreen. 1-Jul-4 Sotheby's, London #459/R est:4000-5000
£11000	$20020	€16060	ADS 1985, Van Heusen, Ronald Reagan (97x96cm-38x38in) s.num.20/30 col silkscreen. 1-Jul-4 Sotheby's, London #485/R est:3000-4000
£11017	$18729	€16085	Mao (89x89cm-35x35in) silkscreen print edn 201/250 exec 1972. 24-Nov-3 Sotheby's, Melbourne #280/R est:15000-20000 (A.D 26000)
£11176	$19000	€16317	Marilyn (91x91cm-36x36in) s. col screenprint. 31-Oct-3 Sotheby's, New York #811/R
£11268	$19718	€16000	Quadrant (101x81cm-40x32in) s. num.8/60 col serigraph lenox board lit. 18-Dec-3 Cornette de St.Cyr, Paris #136/R est:18000-20000
£11500	$20930	€16790	Shoes (102x151cm-40x59in) s.num.3/60 col silkscreen diamond dust. 1-Jul-4 Sotheby's, London #479/R est:8000-10000
£11500	$20930	€16790	Mick Jagger (110x74cm-43x29in) s.num.60/250 col silkscreen sig. by Mick Jagger. 1-Jul-4 Sotheby's, London #486/R est:6000-8000
£11765	$20000	€17177	Campbell's soup (225x143cm-89x56in) st.sig. num.16/20 felt applique banner. 4-Nov-3 Christie's, Rockefeller NY #357/R est:10000-15000
£11888	$20448	€17000	Hermann Hesse C (101x101cm-40x40in) silkscreen exec. 1984. 4-Dec-3 Van Ham, Cologne #543/R est:17000
£11957	$19609	€16500	Summer arts in the park (61x46cm-24x18in) screenprint. 30-May-3 Farsetti, Prato #233/R
£12000	$19920	€17520	Endangered species, bald eagle (97x97cm-38x38in) s.num.7/30 verso col silkscreen board. 6-Oct-3 Sotheby's, London #355/R est:8000-10000
£12000	$20640	€17520	Beethoven (102x102cm-40x40in) s.verso col screenprint. 2-Dec-3 Christie's, London #358/R est:6000-8000
£12000	$21840	€17520	Daisy (96x96cm-38x38in) st. num.UP 21.32 verso silkscreen board exec.c.1982 prov. 6-Feb-4 Sotheby's, London #257/R est:15000-20000
£12000	$21840	€17520	Shoes (102x151cm-40x59in) s.num.3/60 col silkscreen diamond dust. 1-Jul-4 Sotheby's, London #478/R est:8000-10000
£12085	$20544	€17644	Mick Jagger (110x74cm-43x29in) s.num.85/250 also s. by Mick Jagger silkscreen lit. 5-Nov-3 AB Stockholms Auktionsverk #1299/R est:50000-60000 (S.KR 160000)

£12328	$22190	€17999	Candybox (25x36cm-10x14in) s. silkscreen synthetic polymer paint diamond dust prov. 26-Apr-4 Bukowskis, Stockholm #474/R est:70000-80000 (S.KR 170000)
£13000	$21580	€18980	Shoes (102x151cm-40x59in) s.num.7/10 verso col silkscreen diamond dust. 6-Oct-3 Sotheby's, London #336/R est:6000-8000
£13000	$22360	€18980	Beethoven (102x102cm-40x40in) s.verso col screenprint. 2-Dec-3 Christie's, London #356/R est:6000-8000
£13000	$23660	€18980	Marilyn Monroe (91x91cm-36x36in) screenprint. 30-Jun-4 Christie's, London #326/R est:15000-25000
£13966	$25000	€20390	Scream - After Munch (102x81cm-40x32in) unique screenprint on Lenox Museum Board exec 1984 lit. 13-May-4 Sotheby's, New York #248/R est:15000-20000
£14000	$25480	€20440	Liza Minnelli (96x96cm-38x38in) num.A233.009 verso screenprint exec 1978 lit. 5-Feb-4 Christie's, London #188/R est:10000-15000
£14000	$25480	€20440	Camouflage (97x97cm-38x38in) s.num.19/80 verso col screenprint board set of eight. 1-Jul-4 Sotheby's, London #488/R est:15000-20000
£14094	$26074	€21000	Pointsettias (78x55cm-31x22in) screenprint. 13-Mar-4 Meeting Art, Vercelli #98 est:15000
£14118	$24000	€20612	Marilyn (91x91cm-36x36in) s. col screenprint. 31-Oct-3 Sotheby's, New York #807/R
£14970	$25000	€21856	Vesuvius (80x100cm-31x39in) s. silkscreen on paper board executed 1985 prov. 14-Nov-3 Phillips, New York #155/R est:30000-40000
£15000	$24900	€21900	Myths, the shadow (97x97cm-38x38in) s.num.4/200 col silkscreen. 6-Oct-3 Sotheby's, London #306/R est:4000-6000
£15000	$24900	€21900	Marilyn (97x97cm-38x38in) s.num.196/250 col silkscreen. 6-Oct-3 Sotheby's, London #364/R est:10000-15000
£15278	$25208	€22000	Train, toy painting (28x35cm-11x14in) estate st.num.20-161 verso acrylic ink screenprint canvas. 2-Jul-3 Cornette de St.Cyr, Paris #88/R est:22000-25000
£15278	$25208	€22000	Casey, toy painting (35x28cm-14x11in) estate st.num.104-0210 verso acrylic ink screenprint canvas. 2-Jul-3 Cornette de St.Cyr, Paris #89/R est:22000-25000
£16000	$27520	€23360	Marylin (91x91cm-36x36in) s.verso num.106/250 col screenprint. 2-Dec-3 Christie's, London #337/R est:10000-12000
£16467	$27500	€24042	Self portrait (31x23cm-12x9in) s.d.67 silkscreen ink prov. 13-Nov-3 Sotheby's, New York #211/R est:25000-35000
£16667	$27500	€24000	Electric chair (45x60cm-18x24in) estate st.num.47-30 verso screenprint. 2-Jul-3 Cornette de St.Cyr, Paris #80/R est:25000-35000
£16783	$28028	€24000	Dollar, quadrant (101x81cm-40x32in) s.num.40/60 col screenprint board lit. 11-Oct-3 Cornette de St.Cyr, Paris #121/R est:15000-18000
£17000	$31280	€24820	Michael Jackson (80x59cm-31x23in) num.115/215 verso silkscreen ink exec 1984 prov. 24-Jun-4 Sotheby's, London #261/R est:18000-25000
£17361	$28646	€25000	Flowers (20x20cm-8x8in) s.d.1964 verso acrylic ink screenprint canvas. 2-Jul-3 Cornette de St.Cyr, Paris #79/R est:15000-20000
£17372	$29532	€25363	Three portraits of Ingrid Bergman (96x96cm-38x38in) s.num.80/250 col silkscreen portfolio of three lit. 4-Nov-3 Bukowskis, Stockholm #477/R est:140000-160000 (S.KR 230000)
£17964	$30000	€26227	Mickey Mouse (97x97cm-38x38in) s.i.num.17/30 col silkscreen. 21-Oct-3 Bonhams & Butterfields, San Francisco #1453/R
£18000	$29880	€26280	The scream (102x81cm-40x32in) artist st.verso col silkscreen board after Edvard Munch. 6-Oct-3 Sotheby's, London #347/R est:10000-12000
£18362	$32500	€26809	Rebel without a cause (96x96cm-38x38in) s.i. col screenprint. 30-Apr-4 Sotheby's, New York #523/R est:15000-20000
£19000	$32680	€27740	Ingrid Bergman (96x96cm-38x38in) s.i. col screenprint set of three. 2-Dec-3 Christie's, London #354/R est:12000-16000
£19553	$35000	€28547	Daisy (102x152cm-40x60in) estate st.num.UP21.56 verso screenprint board prov. 14-May-4 Phillips, New York #216/R est:40000-60000
£20667	$37820	€31000	Marilyn (91x92cm-36x36in) mono.d.67 col serigraph board. 4-Jun-4 Lempertz, Koln #528/R est:20000-25000
£21469	$38000	€31345	Mickey Mouse (97x97cm-38x38in) s.num.66/200 col screenprint diamond dust board. 28-Apr-4 Christie's, Rockefeller NY #452/R est:30000-40000
£22353	$38000	€32635	Marilyn (92x92cm-36x36in) s.verso col screenprint exec.1967. 4-Nov-3 Christie's, Rockefeller NY #359/R est:18000-22000
£22624	$35520	€33031	Flowers (20x20cm-8x8in) s.i.verso synthetic polymer serigraph. 26-Aug-3 Iegor de Saint Hippolyte, Montreal #151 (C.D 50000)
£22941	$39000	€33494	Campbell's soup II (89x59cm-35x23in) s.verso col screenprint exec.1969 set of 10. 4-Nov-3 Christie's, Rockefeller NY #363/R est:15000-20000
£23952	$40000	€34970	Marilyn (55x39cm-22x15in) estate st. screenprint exec.c.1979 prov. 13-Nov-3 Sotheby's, New York #277/R est:30000-40000
£25000	$42500	€36500	Rebel without cause (96x96cm-38x38in) s. col screenprint. 31-Oct-3 Sotheby's, New York #832/R
£25424	$45000	€37119	Cowboys and Indians (91x91cm-36x36in) s.num.26/250 col screenprint set of 10. 28-Apr-4 Christie's, Rockefeller NY #453/R est:30000-40000
£26000	$43420	€37960	Querelle (100x100cm-39x39in) st.num.93.004 verso silkscreen ink newspaper collage board prov. 22-Oct-3 Christie's, London #54/R est:15000-20000
£26471	$45000	€38648	Cowboys and Indians (91x91cm-36x36in) s.i. col screenprint exec.1986 set of 10. 4-Nov-3 Christie's, Rockefeller NY #376/R est:30000-40000
£26836	$47500	€39181	Marilyn (92x92cm-36x36in) s.num.193/250 col screenprint. 30-Apr-4 Sotheby's, New York #512/R est:40000-60000
£26836	$47500	€39181	Marilyn (91x91cm-36x36in) s.num.161/250 verso col screenprint. 30-Apr-4 Sotheby's, New York #514/R est:18000-22000
£30000	$50100	€43800	Beatles (81x102cm-32x40in) st. num.115.022 silkscreen ink col paper collage exec 1980 lit. 21-Oct-3 Sotheby's, London #357/R est:20000-30000
£32000	$58240	€46720	Marilyn (91x91cm-36x36in) s.num.104/250 verso col silkscreen. 1-Jul-4 Sotheby's, London #441/R est:20000-25000
£32353	$55000	€47235	Marilyn (91x92cm-36x36in) s. col screenprint. 31-Oct-3 Sotheby's, New York #809/R
£32768	$58000	€47841	Jews of the twentieth century (102x81cm-40x32in) s.num.81/200 col screenprint board. 28-Apr-4 Christie's, Rockefeller NY #449/R est:30000-40000
£33898	$60000	€49491	Marilyn (91x91cm-36x36in) init.num.2/250 verso col screenprint. 28-Apr-4 Christie's, Rockefeller NY #443/R est:35000-45000
£34667	$63787	€52000	Fashion (51x81cm-20x32in) serigraph acrylic on canvas exec.1983 prov. 14-Jun-4 Porro, Milan #48/R est:55000-65000
£35294	$60000	€51529	Campbell's soup (89x58cm-35x23in) col screenprint set of 10. 31-Oct-3 Sotheby's, New York #814/R
£36000	$60120	€52560	Shoes (102x152cm-40x60in) st. num.099E VT.031 verso silkscreen print diamond dust exec 1980. 21-Oct-3 Sotheby's, London #360/R est:15000-20000
£40000	$72800	€58400	Portraits of Jews of the twentieth century (109x85cm-43x33in) s.num.25/200 col silkscreen ten portfolio. 1-Jul-4 Sotheby's, London #462/R est:30000-40000
£41000	$74620	€59860	Details of Renaissance paintings (64x94cm-25x37in) s.num.12/18 col silkscreen set of 4. 1-Jul-4 Sotheby's, London #491/R est:28000-32000
£42000	$69720	€61320	Campbell's soup II (89x58cm-35x23in) s.num.131/250 verso col silkscreen series of ten. 6-Oct-3 Sotheby's, London #312/R est:35000-45000
£47059	$80000	€68706	Campbell's soup (89x58cm-35x23in) col screenprint set of 10. 31-Oct-3 Sotheby's, New York #813/R
£47059	$80000	€68706	Marilyn Monroe (91x91cm-36x36in) s.verso col screenprint exec.1967. 4-Nov-3 Christie's, Rockefeller NY #361/R est:28000-32000
£56000	$92960	€81760	Portraits of Jews of the twentieth century (102x81cm-40x32in) s.num.21/25 col silkscreen board ten portfolio box. 6-Oct-3 Sotheby's, London #357/R est:30000-40000
£56497	$100000	€82486	Marilyn (91x91cm-36x36in) s. num.171/250 verso col screenprint. 30-Apr-4 Sotheby's, New York #513/R est:60000-80000
£60000	$100200	€87600	Portrait of Joseph Beuys (132x102cm-52x40in) screenprint synthetic fibre prov. 22-Oct-3 Christie's, London #56/R est:60000-80000
£67797	$120000	€98984	Ads (96x96cm-38x38in) s.i. col screenprints portfolio. 30-Apr-4 Sotheby's, New York #521/R est:90000-120000
£76471	$130000	€111648	Mick Jagger (110x73cm-43x29in) s. col screenprint set of 10. 31-Oct-3 Sotheby's, New York #825/R
£85000	$141950	€124100	A la recherche du shoe perdu. 17 hand col W/C lithograph exec.c.1955 eighteen lit. 22-Oct-3 Christie's, London #57/R est:60000-80000
£124000	$225680	€181040	Mick Jagger (111x74cm-44x29in) s.num.141/250 col silkscreen sig. by Mick Jagger set of 10. 1-Jul-4 Sotheby's, London #487/R est:70000-90000
£380000	$691600	€554800	Marilyn Monroe (92x92cm-36x36in) set of ten screenprints lit. 4-Feb-4 Christie's, London #5/R est:200000-300000
Sculpture			
£36313	$65000	€53017	Brillo box (44x44x36cm-17x17x14in) synthetic polymer silkscreen inks wood exec 1968 prov. 13-May-4 Sotheby's, New York #153/R est:50000-70000
£50000	$92000	€73000	Brillo box (44x44x36cm-17x17x14in) synthetic polymer silkscreen on wood executed 1968 prov. 25-Jun-4 Christie's, London #195/R est:35000-45000
£105000	$175350	€153300	Campbell's Chicken Noodle Soup Box (103x98x32cm-41x39x13in) s.d.86 overlap acrylic silkscreen ink canvas construction prov. 21-Oct-3 Sotheby's, London #430/R est:75000-95000
£420000	$772800	€613200	Ten brillo boxes (43x43x36cm-17x17x14in) num.A134 042 synthetic polymer silkscreen on wood in 10 parts. 24-Jun-4 Christie's, London #40/R est:350000-450000
Works on paper			
£1130	$2000	€1650	Perfume bottle (24x16cm-9x6in) estate st. ink exec.c.1953. 2-May-4 Bonhams & Butterfields, Los Angeles #3044/R est:4000-6000
£1200	$2184	€1752	Campbell's Soup can (19x13cm-7x5in) s. printed base title-page. 30-Jun-4 Christie's, Kensington #74/R est:1500-2000
£1200	$2184	€1752	Campbell's Soup can (21x13cm-8x5in) s. printed base title-page. 30-Jun-4 Christie's, Kensington #75/R est:1500-2000
£1300	$2392	€1898	Gift, pyramid, the philosophy of Andy Warhol (2x13cm-1x5in) s.i. felt tip pen exec.c.1950. 24-Jun-4 Sotheby's, Olympia #610/R est:1500-2000
£1700	$3094	€2482	Campbells soup can (21x13cm-8x5in) s.i.d.1950 felt tip pen on printed page. 4-Feb-4 Sotheby's, Olympia #153/R est:1500-2000
£1892	$3500	€2762	Untitled - Stalks of willow tails and branch with berries (36x25cm-14x10in) ink gouache exec c.1952-55 prov. 12-Feb-4 Sotheby's, New York #128/R est:3000-4000
£2703	$5000	€3946	Kyoto, Japan (44x37cm-17x15in) s.i.d.1956 pen ink W/C prov.lit. 13-Jul-4 Christie's, Rockefeller NY #2/R est:1000-1500
£3514	$6500	€5130	Party (30x25cm-12x10in) s. blotted line pencil ink collage paper on board prov.exhib. 13-Jul-4 Christie's, Rockefeller NY #1/R est:7000-9000
£3529	$6000	€5152	Campbell's duck soup (19x13cm-7x5in) s.d.1975 felt tip pen. 21-Nov-3 Swann Galleries, New York #220/R est:4000-6000
£4790	$8000	€6993	Reclining cat and kitten (43x35cm-17x14in) ink exec.c.1954 prov. 7-Oct-3 Sotheby's, New York #410/R est:8000-12000
£4908	$8000	€7166	Barbara Feldon (25x22cm-10x9in) st.verso acetate fabric col paper prov.lit. 23-Sep-3 Christie's, Rockefeller NY #97/R est:5000-7000
£5587	$10000	€8157	Cowboys and Indians, Buffalo Nickel (80x60cm-31x24in) estate st. synthetic polymer paint prov. 14-May-4 Phillips, New York #212/R est:12000-18000
£7186	$12000	€10492	Christmas Wreath (57x36cm-22x14in) ink W/C exec c.1957 prov. 12-Nov-3 Christie's, Rockefeller NY #333/R est:15000-20000
£7821	$14000	€11419	Spotted dog (81x61cm-32x24in) pencil HMP paper exec 1983 prov. 13-May-4 Sotheby's, New York #215/R est:18000-25000
£7975	$13000	€11644	Barbara Feldon (27x22cm-11x9in) st.verso acetate fabric col paper prov.lit. 23-Sep-3 Christie's, Rockefeller NY #96/R est:6000-8000
£9500	$17480	€13870	Still life with butterfly (37x29cm-15x11in) st. verso ink aniline dye exec c.1952 prov. 24-Jun-4 Sotheby's, London #249/R est:8000-12000
£9581	$16000	€13988	Physiological Diagram (80x59cm-31x23in) ink exec 1985-1986 prov.exhib. 12-Nov-3 Christie's, Rockefeller NY #422/R est:20000-30000
£9816	$16000	€14331	Flowers (20x20cm-8x8in) s.d.67 verso synthetic polymer silkscreen ink exec.c.1967 prov. 23-Sep-3 Christie's, Rockefeller NY #101/R est:15000-20000
£9816	$16000	€14331	Nicky Weymouth (122x96cm-48x38in) st.verso synthetic polymer silkscreen ink prov. 23-Sep-3 Christie's, Rockefeller NY #127/R est:22000-28000
£10000	$18400	€14600	Fish (20x25cm-8x10in) estate st. synthetic polymer silkscreen ink on canvas. 25-Jun-4 Christie's, London #186/R est:8000-12000
£10000	$18400	€14600	Cecil Beaton (58x37cm-23x15in) s.i. ink W/C silver card collage exec c.1957 prov. 24-Jun-4 Sotheby's, London #245/R est:10000-15000
£11173	$20000	€16313	John Gotti (80x61cm-31x24in) synthetic polymer silkscreen inks col paper on paper prov. 12-May-4 Christie's, Rockefeller NY #216/R est:25000-35000
£11976	$20000	€17485	Space ship (60x80cm-24x31in) estate st. pencil exec.c.1983 prov.exhib. 13-Nov-3 Sotheby's, New York #269/R est:20000-30000
£13966	$25000	€20390	Flowers (36x37cm-14x15in) s.d.1964 verso silkscreen inks coloured paper. 13-May-4 Sotheby's, New York #152/R est:12000-18000
£14724	$24000	€21497	Are you different (51x41cm-20x16in) st.verso synthetic polymer silkscreen ink canvas prov.exhib. 23-Sep-3 Christie's, Rockefeller NY #130/R est:30000-40000
£14724	$24000	€21497	Motorcycle with sidecar (20x25cm-8x10in) s.d.83 verso synthetic polymer silkscreen ink canvas prov. 23-Sep-3 Christie's, Rockefeller NY #131/R est:15000-20000
£15862	$26490	€23000	Portrait of Franz Beckenbauer (80x60cm-31x24in) graphite. 13-Nov-3 Neumeister, Munich #656/R est:27000-28000
£18000	$32760	€26280	Fishes (29x36cm-11x14in) estate st.num.verso synthetic polymer paint silkscreen canvas 2. 30-Jun-4 Christie's, Kensington #156/R est:20000-30000
£18405	$30000	€26871	Aeroplane (30x36cm-12x14in) s.d.83 verso synthetic polymer silkscreen ink prov. 23-Sep-3 Christie's, Rockefeller NY #133/R est:18000-25000
£19553	$35000	€28547	Hearts - Four (35x35cm-14x14in) synthetic polymer paint diamond dust silkscreen inks prov.exhib. 13-May-4 Sotheby's, New York #247/R est:25000-35000
£20670	$37000	€30178	Toy painting, moon explorer (36x28cm-14x11in) s.d.83 overlap synthetic polymer paint silkscreen canvas. 14-May-4 Phillips, New York #214/R est:25000-35000
£21229	$38000	€30994	Flowers (13x13cm-5x5in) s.i.d.64 synthetic polymer silkscreen inks canvas prov. 12-May-4 Christie's, Rockefeller NY #139/R est:40000-60000
£21229	$38000	€30994	Toy painting, clockwork panda drummer (36x28cm-14x11in) s.d.83 overlap synthetic polymer paint silkscreen canvas prov. 14-May-4 Phillips, New York #213/R est:25000-35000
£24000	$43680	€35040	Divine Sarah. Diva. Diseuse. Soubrette (22x28cm-9x11in) ink four sheets exec 1953 prov.exhib. 5-Feb-4 Christie's, London #172/R est:5000-8000
£25150	$42000	€36719	Kareem Abdul Jabar (101x101cm-40x40in) synthetic polymer silkscreen inks exec 1977 prov. 12-Nov-3 Christie's, Rockefeller NY #424/R est:40000-60000
£27933	$50000	€40782	Hammer and sickle still lifes (68x102cm-27x40in) graphite on TH Saunders paper 2 parts exec 1977 prov.exhib. 13-May-4 Sotheby's, New York #224/R est:50000-70000
£28000	$50960	€40880	Clockwork Panda Drummer (35x28cm-14x11in) s.d.83 synthetic polymer paint silkscreen inks canvas prov. 5-Feb-4 Christie's, London #175/R est:15000-18000
£28743	$48000	€41965	Flowers (13x13cm-5x5in) s.i.d.64 synthetic polymer silkscreen inks prov. 12-Nov-3 Christie's, Rockefeller NY #401/R est:30000-40000

£29050 $52000 €42413 Campbell's Chicken Soup box (51x51cm-20x20in) synthetic polymer silkscreen inks canvas painted 1986 prov. 12-May-4 Christie's, Rockefeller NY #172/R est:60000-80000
£29940 $50000 €43712 Repent and Sin No More ! (51x41cm-20x16in) synthetic polymer silkscreen ink painted 1985-6 prov.exhib. 12-Nov-3 Christie's, Rockefeller NY #370/R est:20000-30000
£30000 $50100 €43800 Heaven and hell are just one breath away, positive and negative (51x41cm-20x16in) st.num. synthetic polymer paint silkscreen ink canvas pair prov. 22-Oct-3 Christie's, London #58/R est:30000-40000
£30000 $55200 €43800 Robot (25x20cm-10x8in) s.d.83 verso synthetic polymer silkscreen ink canvas. 25-Jun-4 Christie's, London #187/R est:15000-20000
£32402 $58000 €47307 Flowers (20x20cm-8x8in) init.d.64 overlap synthetic polymer silkscreen inks canvas prov. 12-May-4 Christie's, Rockefeller NY #171/R est:50000-70000
£33000 $60720 €48180 Campbell's onion soup box (51x51cm-20x20in) s.d.86 synthetic polymer silkscreen on canvas prov. 25-Jun-4 Christie's, London #190/R est:30000-40000
£35000 $64400 €51100 Gun (40x50cm-16x20in) estate st. synthetic polymer silkscreen ink on canvas prov. 25-Jun-4 Christie's, London #185/R est:35000-55000
£35000 $64400 €51100 Muratti (102x101cm-40x40in) s.d.1984 overlap synthetic polymer silkscreen on canvas prov. 25-Jun-4 Christie's, London #191/R est:35000-45000
£41916 $70000 €61197 Portrait of a Woman (74x58cm-29x23in) graphite exec 1962 prov.exhib. 12-Nov-3 Christie's, Rockefeller NY #335/R est:40000-60000
£42000 $70140 €61320 Hamburgers, positive and negative (41x51cm-16x20in) st.overlap synthetic polymer paint silkscreen ink pair prov. 22-Oct-3 Christie's, London #59/R est:30000-40000
£42000 $76440 €61320 VW beetle (41x50cm-16x20in) synthetic polymer paint silkscreen ink executed 1969-70. 4-Feb-4 Christie's, London #2/R est:40000-60000
£60000 $100200 €87600 James Dean (74x58cm-29x23in) pencil paper collage exec 1960 prov.exhib. 21-Oct-3 Sotheby's, London #437/R est:12000-18000
£65868 $110000 €96167 Pia (102x102cm-40x40in) s.i.d.83 synthetic polymer silkscreen inks prov. 12-Nov-3 Christie's, Rockefeller NY #366/R est:70000-90000
£70000 $128800 €102200 Portrait of Baroness von Thyssen (102x102cm-40x40in) s. synthetic polymer silkscreen on canvas executed 1973. 25-Jun-4 Christie's, London #201/R est:50000-70000
£75000 $136500 €109500 Flowers (36x36cm-14x14in) s.d.64 synthetic polymer paint silkscreen inks canvas prov. 5-Feb-4 Christie's, London #177/R est:70000-90000
£81006 $145000 €118269 Mao (30x25cm-12x10in) s.d.1973 overlap synthetic polymer silkscreen inks canvas prov. 12-May-4 Christie's, Rockefeller NY #188/R est:140000-180000
£89820 $150000 €131137 Alexander the Great (102x102cm-40x40in) synthetic polymer silkscreen inks exec 1982 prov. 12-Nov-3 Christie's, Rockefeller NY #403/R est:100000-150000
£94972 $170000 €138659 Diamond Dust shoes (127x107cm-50x42in) synthetic polymer silkscreen inks diamond dust canvas prov.exhib. 12-May-4 Christie's, Rockefeller NY #189/R est:150000-200000
£110000 $202400 €160600 Mao (30x26cm-12x10in) s.d.73 overlap synthetic polymer silkscreen ink on canvas prov. 24-Jun-4 Christie's, London #5/R est:80000-120000
£117318 $210000 €171284 Beatle boots - negative (203x183cm-80x72in) synthetic polymer silkscreen on canvas. 13-May-4 Phillips, New York #27/R est:200000-300000
£119760 $200000 €174850 Ladies and Gentlemen (127x102cm-50x40in) s.d.75 synthetic polymer silkscreen inks canvas prov.exhib.lit. 12-Nov-3 Christie's, Rockefeller NY #372/R est:200000-300000
£122905 $220000 €179441 Golden Monkey (58x43cm-23x17in) gold leaf gold trim collage over blotted blk ink prov.exhib.lit. 13-May-4 Sotheby's, New York #142/R est:120000-180000
£134078 $240000 €195754 Pink Marilyn - Reversal (46x36cm-18x14in) s.d.86 overlap synthetic polymer silkscreen inks canvas prov. 12-May-4 Christie's, Rockefeller NY #195/R est:200000-300000
£139665 $250000 €203911 Diamond dust shadow (198x127cm-78x50in) synthetic polymer silkscreen crushed glass silkscreen on canvas. 13-May-4 Phillips, New York #30/R est:300000-400000
£140000 $257600 €204400 Flowers (60x60cm-24x24in) synthetic polymer silkscreen ink on canvas executed 1964 prov. 24-Jun-4 Christie's, London #24/R est:150000-200000
£145000 $266800 €211700 One multicolored Marilyn (46x36cm-18x14in) s.d.79/86 overlap synthetic polymer silkscreen on canvas prov. 25-Jun-4 Christie's, London #202/R est:90000-120000
£145251 $260000 €212066 Russell Means (127x107cm-50x42in) s.d.1976 verso synthetic polymer silkscreen inks prov. 12-May-4 Christie's, Rockefeller NY #169/R est:250000-350000
£209581 $350000 €305988 Self-Portrait (56x56cm-22x22in) st.sig. synthetic polymer silkscreen inks prov. 12-Nov-3 Christie's, Rockefeller NY #381/R est:350000-450000
£280000 $515200 €408800 Jackie (51x41cm-20x16in) estate st. gold synthetic polymer silkscreen ink on canvas. 24-Jun-4 Christie's, London #7/R est:200000-300000
£284916 $510000 €415977 Four Marilyns (91x71cm-36x28in) st.sig. synthetic polymer executed 1979-86 pencil. 13-May-4 Phillips, New York #21/R est:400000-600000
£296089 $530000 €432290 S and H Green Stamps (41x57cm-16x22in) s.d.62 verso synthetic polymer paint rubber stamped prov.exhib.li. 13-May-4 Sotheby's, New York #146/R est:150000-200000
£301676 $540000 €440447 Two multicoloured Marilyns (46x71cm-18x28in) synthetic polymer silkscreen inks canvas prov.exhib.lit. 12-May-4 Christie's, Rockefeller NY #170/R est:400000-600000
£311377 $520000 €454610 Myths - Mickey Mouse (152x152cm-60x60in) s.d.1981 synthetic polymer silkscreen inks prov. 11-Nov-3 Christie's, Rockefeller NY #68/R est:500000-700000
£340000 $625600 €496400 Dollar sign (229x178cm-90x70in) estate st. synthetic polymer silkscreen ink on canvas prov.exhib. 24-Jun-4 Christie's, London #44/R est:240000-300000
£391061 $700000 €570949 Crosses (228x178cm-90x70in) s.d.82 verso synthetic polymer silkscreen on canvas prov.exhib.lit. 13-May-4 Phillips, New York #28/R est:500000-700000
£395210 $660000 €577007 Woman in Blue - After Matisse (132x107cm-52x42in) st.sig. synthetic polymer silkscreen inks painted 1985 prov.lit. 12-Nov-3 Christie's, Rockefeller NY #368/R est:300000-500000
£450000 $828000 €657000 Camouflage last supper (101x101cm-40x40in) with sig. on overlap synthetic polymer silkscreen ink on canvas. 24-Jun-4 Christie's, London #25/R est:500000-700000
£598802 $1000000 €874251 Self-Portrait (102x102cm-40x40in) s.d.86 synthetic polymer silkscreen inks prov.exhib. 11-Nov-3 Christie's, Rockefeller NY #47/R est:100000-1500000
£748503 $1250000 €1092814 Self-Portrait (51x41cm-20x16in) synthetic polymer silkscreen inks canvas painted 1964 prov.lit. 11-Nov-3 Christie's, Rockefeller NY #40/R est:700000-900000
£1005587 $1800000 €1468157 Campbell's soup can - Clam Chowder Manhatten style (51x41cm-20x16in) s.i.d.1962 stretcher casein pencil canvas prov.exhib.lit. 12-May-4 Sotheby's, New York #9/R est:1500000-2000000
£1197605 $2000000 €1748503 Details of the last supper (287x580cm-113x228in) silkscreen acrylic on canvas executed 1986. 12-Nov-3 Sotheby's, New York #37/R est:1500000-2000000
£1197605 $2000000 €1748503 Oxidation painting (199x553cm-78x218in) mixed media copper metallic paint on canvas executed 1978 prov. 12-Nov-3 Sotheby's, New York #41/R est:2200000-2800000
£1675978 $3000000 €2446928 Single Elvis (208x99cm-82x39in) silkscreen ink acrylic canvas exec 1963 prov.lit. 11-May-4 Christie's, Rockefeller NY #46/R est:2500000-3500000
£3351956 $6000000 €4893856 Large flowers (208x411cm-82x162in) synthetic polymer silkscreen inks canvas exec 1964 prov.exhib.lit. 11-May-4 Christie's, Rockefeller NY #31/R est:6500000-8500000
£3463687 $6200000 €5056983 Self portrait (183x183cm-72x72in) synthetic polymer silkscreen inks graphite canvas exec 1967 prov. 11-May-4 Christie's, Rockefeller NY #11/R est:6000000-8000000

WARIN, Jean III (attrib) (1604-1672) French

Sculpture
£11268 $19718 €16000 Louis XIV (49cm-19in) terracotta lit. 16-Dec-3 Christie's, Paris #313/R est:15000-25000

WARING, Henry Franks (fl.1900-1928) British

Works on paper
£300 $537 €438 On the Kennett (25x33cm-10x13in) s. W/C. 21-Mar-4 Lots Road Auctions, London #340
£360 $623 €526 Embankment, London in the snow (33x47cm-13x19in) s. 9-Dec-3 Bristol Auction Rooms #411

WARING, William Henry (19/20th C) British

£520 $952 €759 Fisherman on the River Llugwy, Betws-y-Coed, North Wales (60x95cm-24x37in) s.i.verso. 27-Jan-4 Bristol Auction Rooms #644/R
£2800 $5208 €4088 Haymaking (46x67cm-18x26in) s.d.16. 4-Mar-4 Christie's, Kensington #456/R est:1000-1500

WARKOV, Esther (1941-) Canadian

£413 $748 €603 Man from the Ritz III (91x94cm-36x37in) prov. 18-Apr-4 Levis, Calgary #320/R est:1500-2000 (C.D 1000)

WARLAND, Charles (19th C) Belgian

£1064 $1777 €1500 Landscape with watermill (110x130cm-43x51in) s. 20-Oct-3 Bernaerts, Antwerp #487a/R est:1250-1500

WARLAPINNI, Freda (1934-) Australian

Works on paper
£1277 $2209 €1864 Untitled (102x80cm-40x31in) i.d.1998 verso natural pigment binder canvas prov. 10-Dec-3 Shapiro, Sydney #183/R est:3500-5000 (A.D 3000)
£1362 $2356 €1989 Untitled (88x70cm-35x28in) natural pigment binder exec.c.1996 prov. 10-Dec-3 Shapiro, Sydney #180/R est:3000-5000 (A.D 3200)
£1804 $3229 €2634 Jilamirra (64x97cm-25x38in) natural earth pigments linen exec 2000 prov. 25-May-4 Lawson Menzies, Sydney #245/R est:5000-7000 (A.D 4600)
£2846 $4496 €4127 Untitled (99x67cm-39x26in) earth pigments linen prov. 28-Jul-3 Sotheby's, Paddington #422/R est:2500-3500 (A.D 7000)

WARLING, Elisabeth (1858-1915) Swedish

£1462 $2514 €2135 Old woman knitting in meadow (62x51cm-24x20in) s. 3-Dec-3 AB Stockholms Auktionsverk #2419/R est:20000-25000 (S.KR 19000)

WARMAN, Oliver Byrne (1932-) British

£330 $535 €482 Farm buildings in Italian landscape (36x25cm-14x10in) s.verso. 26-Jan-3 Desmond Judd, Cranbrook #914

WARMAN, W (?) British

Works on paper
£260 $434 €380 Charles I and his family (44x36cm-17x14in) s. W/C. 21-Oct-3 Bruton Knowles, Cheltenham #387

WARMAN, William (fl.1912-1919) British

Works on paper
£290 $508 €423 Interior scene with Charles I and children kneeling alongside (43x36cm-17x14in) s. W/C. 19-Dec-3 Mallams, Oxford #160/R

WARMINGTON, E A (19th C) British

Works on paper
£265 $425 €387 Mountain lake with figures (30x61cm-12x24in) s. W/C. 21-Sep-3 Grogan, Boston #54/R

WARMINGTON, Ebeneezer A (1830-1903) British

Works on paper
£280 $456 €409 Landscape with cattle crossing a bridge (23x47cm-9x19in) s.d.1896 W/C. 24-Sep-3 Dreweatt Neate, Newbury #5/R
£360 $659 €526 Elter Water and Langdale Pikes, mountainous lakeland landscape (32x63cm-13x25in) s. W/C. 28-Jan-4 Wintertons, Lichfield #355
£540 $999 €788 Welsh river landscapes (21x46cm-8x18in) s.d.93 W/C pair. 14-Jul-4 Bonhams, Chester #330
£560 $980 €818 River scene with angler (36x48cm-14x19in) s.d.1889 W/C. 19-Dec-3 Mallams, Oxford #89/R

WARNE-BROWN, Alfred J (fl.1890-1900) British
£217 $400 €317 Looking out to sea (25x36cm-10x14in) s. panel. 26-Jun-4 Sloans & Kenyon, Bethesda #1072/R
£560 $1025 €818 Country girl, sheep and ducks in an orchard (61x91cm-24x36in) s. 6-Jul-4 Bearnes, Exeter #519/R

WARNER, Everett L (1877-1963) American
£525 $950 €767 Untitled - industrial scene (30x41cm-12x16in) s. masonite. 3-Apr-4 David Rago, Lambertville #107/R
£1130 $2000 €1650 Snowy slope (29x40cm-11x16in) s. board. 28-Apr-4 Christie's, Los Angeles #43/R est:2500-3500
£4286 $7500 €6258 Street in Paris (24x33cm-9x13in) s.d.03 canvas on board. 19-Dec-3 Sotheby's, New York #1074/R est:6000-8000

WARNER, Nell Walker (1891-1970) American
£994 $1800 €1451 New England street scenes (20x25cm-8x10in) s. i.verso canvasboard pair. 31-Mar-4 Sotheby's, New York #109/R est:2000-3000
£994 $1800 €1451 Beached and spring in the mountains (20x25cm-8x10in) s. one acrylic canvas on board one canvasboard pair. 31-Mar-4 Sotheby's, New York #110/R est:2000-3000
£2312 $4000 €3376 Still life with flowers in a blue vase (41x76cm-16x30in) s. prov. 10-Dec-3 Bonhams & Butterfields, San Francisco #6275/R est:5000-7000
£2941 $5000 €4294 Laguna shore (41x51cm-16x20in) s. i.verso prov. 18-Nov-3 John Moran, Pasadena #153 est:3000-4000
£3529 $6000 €5152 Eucalyptus landscape (91x122cm-36x48in) s. board prov. 18-Nov-3 John Moran, Pasadena #105 est:7000-9000
£3533 $6500 €5158 Houses in Chavez Ravine, Los Angeles (35x45cm-14x18in) s. 8-Jun-4 Bonhams & Butterfields, San Francisco #4316/R est:3000-5000
£3911 $7000 €5867 Tranquillity (86x102cm-34x40in) s. 16-May-4 Abell, Los Angeles #28/R
£4118 $7000 €6012 Floral still life (76x66cm-30x26in) s. prov. 18-Nov-3 John Moran, Pasadena #45 est:5500-7500

WAROQUIER, Henry de (1881-1970) French
£567 $948 €800 Femme assise (27x35cm-11x14in) s. init.verso. 19-Jun-3 Millon & Associes, Paris #237/R
£604 $1081 €900 Roses rouges sur fond jaune (46x38cm-18x15in) s. bears init.i.verso. 25-May-4 Chambelland & Giafferi, Paris #96/R
£1067 $1963 €1600 Place animee, Maroc (50x65cm-20x26in) s. 14-Jun-4 Gros & Delettrez, Paris #238/R est:1000-1500
£2170 $3515 €3168 Entrevaux - Provence (46x55cm-18x22in) s.i. i. verso. 24-May-3 Burkhard, Luzern #36/R est:5000-6000 (S.FR 4600)
Works on paper
£270 $500 €394 Study of a woman with her eyes closed (43x28cm-17x11in) s.d.1916 sepia ink prov. 12-Feb-4 Sotheby's, New York #67/R
£272 $487 €400 Christ a la couronne d'epines (27x21cm-11x8in) s.d.1936 W/C wash. 19-Mar-4 Oger, Dumont, Paris #23
£300 $537 €450 Chaumiere bretonne (25x36cm-10x14in) i. sanguine wash. 16-May-4 Thierry & Lannon, Brest #39
£372 $702 €550 Un homme (31x23cm-12x9in) s.d.1916 and 1920 mixed media. 17-Feb-4 Galerie Moderne, Brussels #157/R
£461 $847 €700 Femme nue assise (41x28cm-16x11in) s.d.1934 crayon. 22-Jun-4 Ribeyre & Baron, Paris #68/R
£769 $1308 €1100 Danseurs du feu, Burlesques (36x40cm-14x16in) s.i. ball point pen pastel graphite 4 joined sheets. 27-Nov-3 Millon & Associes, Paris #67/R
£1469 $2497 €2100 Vue de Capri (34x47cm-13x19in) s.i. W/C ink graphite paper on cardboard. 28-Nov-3 Blanchet, Paris #96/R est:2300-2600

WARRABADALUMBA, Jabarrgwa (1896-?) Australian
Works on paper
£488 $771 €712 Untitled (38x59cm-15x23in) i.verso earth pigments eucalyptus bark exec.c.1968. 28-Jul-3 Sotheby's, Paddington #447/R (A.D 1200)
£2236 $3533 €3265 Untitled (37x26cm-15x10in) earth pigments composition board three prov. 28-Jul-3 Sotheby's, Paddington #239/R est:4000-6000 (A.D 5500)

WARRAMALA, Alex (20th C) Australian
Sculpture
£1240 $2107 €1810 Lorrkon burial pool (230cm-91in) painted ironbark prov. 29-Oct-3 Lawson Menzies, Sydney #75/R est:4000-5000 (A.D 3000)

WARRE, Sir Henry James (1819-1898) British
Works on paper
£326 $554 €476 Waitemata harbour near Auckland N.Z (23x49cm-9x19in) s.i.d.1860 ink wash. 4-Nov-3 Peter Webb, Auckland #241 (NZ.D 900)

WARREN, Alan (1919-1991) Australian
£405 $652 €591 Mountains across the bay (48x67cm-19x26in) s.d.60 board. 13-Oct-3 Joel, Victoria #388 est:1200-1500 (A.D 1000)

WARREN, Barbara (1925-) Irish?
£507 $932 €770 The Mall, Westport (22x29cm-9x11in) s. canvasboard prov. 22-Jun-4 De Veres Art Auctions, Dublin #245/R
£789 $1453 €1200 Female nude study (26x13cm-10x5in) s.i.d.1950 verso canvasboard. 22-Jun-4 De Veres Art Auctions, Dublin #29/R
£1000 $1660 €1460 Setting sail one morning (50x61cm-20x24in) s. 1-Oct-3 John Ross, Belfast #71 est:900-1200
£1736 $2830 €2500 Achill (61x87cm-24x34in) s. board prov. 23-Sep-3 De Veres Art Auctions, Dublin #148/R est:1500-2000
£2819 $4989 €4200 Setting sail one morning. Unfinish landscape (51x61cm-20x24in) s. double-sided prov.exhib. 27-Apr-4 Whyte's, Dublin #16/R est:2000-3000

WARREN, Bonomi Edward (19th C) British
Works on paper
£290 $499 €423 Woodland scene with children picking daffodils in the foreground and cottages (49x38cm-19x15in) s.d.1892 W/C. 5-Dec-3 ELR Auctions, Sheffield #684/R
£550 $1012 €803 Picking poppies in a wheatfield (32x48cm-13x19in) s.d.1893 pencil W/C bodycol. 25-Mar-4 Christie's, Kensington #159
£4000 $7320 €5840 Summer landscape with figures haymaking. Two girls returning from haymaking (80x132cm-31x52in) s.d.1836-37 W/C pair. 28-Jul-4 Hampton & Littlewood, Exeter #597 est:4000-4500

WARREN, C (?) ?
£6522 $12000 €9522 Moonlit road (76x53cm-30x21in) s. 26-Jun-4 Susanin's, Chicago #6070/R est:400-600

WARREN, Charles Wyatt (1908-) British
£280 $510 €409 Cottage near Snowdon (23x54cm-9x21in) s. board. 21-Jun-4 Bonhams, Bath #354
£300 $531 €438 Llyn Mymbyr and the Snowdon Range (94x54cm-37x21in) s. board. 28-Apr-4 Peter Wilson, Nantwich #85
£300 $555 €438 Welsh coast (23x53cm-9x21in) s. s.i. verso board. 14-Jul-4 Bonhams, Chester #348
£340 $578 €496 Yr Aran from Hafod Lwyfog (18x34cm-7x13in) s. board. 29-Oct-3 Bonhams, Chester #378
£360 $587 €526 Llyn Cwm Bychan (23x53cm-9x21in) s. board. 27-Sep-3 Rogers Jones, Clwyd #84
£360 $648 €526 Snowdonia landscape with cottages and birches (23x53cm-9x21in) s. board. 24-Apr-4 Rogers Jones, Clwyd #146
£360 $655 €526 Snowdonia (40x50cm-16x20in) s. board. 21-Jun-4 Bonhams, Bath #356
£360 $666 €526 Road near Snowdon (23x53cm-9x21in) s. board. 14-Jul-4 Bonhams, Chester #349
£420 $756 €613 Lake scene in Snowdonia (23x53cm-9x21in) s. board. 24-Apr-4 Rogers Jones, Clwyd #147
£440 $717 €642 Snowdon from Llyn Padarn under snow (23x53cm-9x21in) s. board. 27-Sep-3 Rogers Jones, Clwyd #83
£800 $1440 €1168 Porth Colmon (23x53cm-9x21in) s. 24-Apr-4 Rogers Jones, Clwyd #161

WARREN, Edmund George (1834-1909) British
Works on paper
£2300 $3818 €3358 Harvest time (43x63cm-17x25in) s. W/C. 1-Oct-3 Sotheby's, Olympia #71/R est:600-800

WARREN, Edward Vance (20th C) American
Works on paper
£206 $350 €301 Brooklyn Navy yard (44x56cm-17x22in) W/C. 21-Nov-3 Skinner, Boston #555/R

WARREN, Emily (1869-1956) Canadian
Works on paper
£386 $603 €560 Afternoon activity on a town lane (36x46cm-14x18in) s. W/C. 26-Mar-3 Walker's, Ottawa #468/R est:700-1000 (C.D 900)

WARREN, H Clifford (fl.1860-1885) British
Works on paper
£260 $434 €380 Returning home (16x25cm-6x10in) s.d.1885 pencil W/C. 16-Oct-3 Christie's, Kensington #188/R
£460 $851 €672 Hare on a forest path (50x35cm-20x14in) s.d.1865 W/C bodycol. 16-Feb-4 Bonhams, Bath #152

WARREN, Harold Broadfield (1859-1934) American
£1000 $1610 €1450 Harvesting by the coast (56x91cm-22x36in) s.d.1895. 15-Aug-3 Keys, Aylsham #735 est:1000-1250

WARREN, Henry (1794-1879) British
£500 $915 €730 Lady in a garden, holding a fan (41x30cm-16x12in) s. 27-Jan-4 Gorringes, Lewes #1714

WARREN, Melvin C (1920-1995) American
£2941 $5000 €4294 Horse and houses (28x41cm-11x16in) 1-Nov-3 Altermann Galleries, Santa Fe #134
Sculpture
£994 $1600 €1441 Alamo mission bell (25x20x28cm-10x8x11in) bronze. 22-Aug-3 Altermann Galleries, Santa Fe #22

WARREN, Nesta (20th C) British?
£260 $426 €380 Still life study of spring flowers in a vase (43x53cm-17x21in) s. 3-Jun-3 Fellows & Sons, Birmingham #47/R
Works on paper
£405 $750 €591 Dot, an English springer spaniel (38x33cm-15x13in) s.i. pastel sandpaper. 10-Feb-4 Doyle, New York #172/R

WARRILLOW, David Ross (1956-) British
£380 $695 €555 Wilton St. Glasgow (9x10cm-4x4in) s. i.verso board. 8-Apr-4 Bonhams, Edinburgh #27

WARSHAW, Howard (1920-1977) American
Works on paper
£714 $1300 €1042 Still life with animals skulls (83x200cm-33x79in) s.d.46 chl pastel paper on canvas. 29-Jun-4 Sotheby's, New York #512/R est:1000-1500

WARSHAWSKY, Abel George (1883-1962) American

£541 $1000 €790 Seated Nubian woman with beads (53x38cm-21x15in) s. panel. 13-Mar-4 DeFina, Austinburg #546/R
£1333 $2427 €2000 Portrait of a Sioux Indian (29x27cm-11x11in) s. panel. 1-Jul-4 Van Ham, Cologne #1657/R est:1200
£2060 $3750 €3008 Carmel cove (61x76cm-24x30in) s. 15-Jun-4 John Moran, Pasadena #112 est:4500-6500
£2373 $4200 €3465 Summer morning, Avenue General le Clerc, Paris (38x45cm-15x18in) s.i.d.48 verso board prov. 28-Apr-4 Christie's, Los Angeles #62/R est:3000-5000
£2568 $4750 €3749 Catalan village (46x56cm-18x22in) s. i.d.Feb 1931 verso gessoed panel. 10-Mar-4 Doyle, New York #53/R est:1500-2500
£2762 $4750 €4033 Along the canal (45x55cm-18x22in) s.d.20 canvas on masonite prov. 3-Dec-3 Doyle, New York #287/R est:3000-5000
£7692 $14000 €11230 Woman seated in flower garden (64x81cm-25x32in) s. 15-Jun-4 John Moran, Pasadena #82 est:8000-10000
£17442 $30000 €25465 Place de L'opera, Paris in spring (80x65cm-31x26in) s. prov. 3-Dec-3 Doyle, New York #191/R est:40000-60000

WARSHAWSKY, Alexander (1887-1945) American

£313 $497 €450 Still life with red vase (61x50cm-24x20in) s. 9-Sep-3 Vanderkindere, Brussels #83

WARSINSKI, Richard (1937-1996) Norwegian/Polish

Works on paper
£732 $1346 €1069 Figure (54x41cm-21x16in) s. mixed media. 10-Jun-4 Grev Wedels Plass, Oslo #113/R (N.KR 9000)
£1025 $1711 €1497 Composition with figures and animals (85x65cm-33x26in) s. mixed media. 13-Oct-3 Blomqvist, Oslo #377/R (N.KR 12000)
£1281 $2139 €1870 Composition with figure seated (117x96cm-46x38in) init. mixed media. 13-Oct-3 Blomqvist, Oslo #381/R est:18000-22000 (N.KR 15000)

WARTENA, Froukje (1855-1933) Dutch

Works on paper
£391 $700 €571 Cooking on the hearth (25x20cm-10x8in) s.d.07 pastel. 20-Mar-4 Sloans & Kenyon, Bethesda #320/R

WARUN, Kurun (20th C) Australian?

£329 $596 €480 Bleeding heart land. acrylic. 1-Apr-4 Joel, Victoria #251 (A.D 800)

WARZECHA, Marian (1930-) Polish

Works on paper
£636 $1150 €954 1964/80 (35x84cm-14x33in) s.d.1964/80 collage paper on canvas. 4-Apr-4 Agra, Warsaw #26/R (P.Z 4500)

WASASTJERNA, Torsten (1863-1924) Finnish

£563 $901 €800 Stream in landscape (24x33cm-9x13in) s. 18-Sep-3 Hagelstam, Helsinki #941/R
£1533 $2745 €2300 Boy fishing (26x37cm-10x15in) s. 15-May-4 Hagelstam, Helsinki #129/R est:1800
£2162 $3870 €3200 Evening in July (40x56cm-16x22in) s. 8-May-4 Bukowskis, Helsinki #100/R est:2500-3000
£6800 $12172 €10200 Girl in flower meadow (65x46cm-26x18in) s. painted c.1893. 15-May-4 Hagelstam, Helsinki #128/R est:10000

WASEM, C (20th C) Swiss

Prints
£2203 $3744 €3216 Planeyse Aviation, Grand Meeting d'Aviation (103x68cm-41x27in) i. col lithograph. 5-Nov-3 Dobiaschofsky, Bern #2323/R est:6500 (S.FR 5000)

WASHBOURN, Enga (20th C) New Zealander

Works on paper
£382 $607 €558 Looking along the beach Collingwood (29x37cm-11x15in) s. W/C. 1-May-3 Dunbar Sloane, Wellington #749 est:500-800 (NZ.D 1100)

WASHBURN, Mary Nightingale (1861-1932) American

Works on paper
£192 $350 €280 Beached dinghies (25x36cm-10x14in) s.d.1890 W/C. 19-Jun-4 Jackson's, Cedar Falls #272/R

WASHINGTON, Elizabeth Fisher (1871-1953) American

£1630 $3000 €2380 Near Springfield (63x76cm-25x30in) s. indis.i. exhib. 27-Jun-4 Freeman, Philadelphia #201/R est:4000-6000
£7386 $13000 €10784 Farm in the snow, winter landscape (51x61cm-20x24in) s.i. 21-May-4 Pook & Pook, Downington #190/R est:10000-15000
£10692 $17000 €15610 Roadside mill buildings (81x91cm-32x36in) s. 10-Sep-3 Alderfer's, Hatfield #387/R est:18000-22000
Works on paper
£318 $550 €464 Landscape with cathedral (36x30cm-14x12in) s. pastel. 10-Dec-3 Alderfer's, Hatfield #483

WASHINGTON, Georges (1827-1910) French

£3239 $5604 €4600 Halte de la caravane (31x49cm-12x19in) s. panel. 15-Dec-3 Gros & Delettrez, Paris #473/R est:4500-6000
£5960 $10907 €9000 Halte de cavaliers (27x47cm-11x19in) s. 9-Apr-4 Claude Aguttes, Neuilly #121/R est:7000-8000
Works on paper
£274 $465 €400 Chasse au faucon (18x24cm-7x9in) crayon. 6-Nov-3 Tajan, Paris #244
£667 $1227 €1000 Bivouac des touaregs (16x22cm-6x9in) mono.d.57 pastel. 9-Jun-4 Le Roux & Morel, Paris #20
£1800 $3222 €2700 Bedouin praying (34x49cm-13x19in) s. W/C oil lit. 14-May-4 Schloss Ahlden, Ahlden #2806/R est:2300

WASHINGTON, Georges (attrib) (1827-1910) French

£1049 $1752 €1500 Etude de cavaliers Arabes (12x15cm-5x6in) bears st.init. canvas on panel. 27-Jun-3 Calmels Cohen, Paris #15 est:1000-1200

WASIELEWSKI, Wilhelm von (1878-1956) German

£268 $491 €400 Female nude standing under trees (38x17cm-15x7in) s.d.1923 lit. 8-Jul-4 Allgauer, Kempten #2267/R

WASILEWSKI, Czeslaw (1875-1946) Polish

£1567 $2445 €2288 On a journey (32x50cm-13x20in) s. painted c.1930. 30-Mar-3 Agra, Warsaw #34/R est:8000 (P.Z 10000)
£1600 $2512 €2320 Troika ride (49x80cm-19x31in) s. 28-Aug-3 Christie's, Kensington #84/R est:800-1200
£1875 $2963 €2700 Horse-drawn sleigh with hunters and dogs (50x80cm-20x31in) s.d.1927, 5-Sep-3 Wendl, Rudolstadt #3761/R est:2200
£1986 $3316 €2800 Hunt (67x106cm-26x42in) s. canvas on board. 14-Oct-3 Dorotheum, Vienna #84/R est:2800-3500

WASKE, Erich (1889-?) German

£738 $1366 €1100 Sailing boat in the evening (58x48cm-23x19in) s. oil mixed media board. 9-Mar-4 Dorotheum, Vienna #126/R
£915 $1602 €1300 View from Naples (81x46cm-32x18in) s. 19-Dec-3 Dorotheum, Vienna #318/R
£1042 $1740 €1500 Woman by sea (53x79cm-21x31in) s. paper on masonite. 24-Oct-3 Ketterer, Hamburg #574/R est:1500-2000
£1389 $2319 €2000 Southern fantasy (80x120cm-31x47in) s. s.i. verso masonite. 24-Oct-3 Ketterer, Hamburg #573/R est:2000-3000
£1408 $2465 €2000 Fisherboys (46x56cm-18x22in) s. board. 19-Dec-3 Dorotheum, Vienna #319/R est:2000-2400

WASLEY, Frank (1848-1934) British

£480 $816 €701 Low tide, fishing boats off a shore (61x107cm-24x42in) s. 27-Nov-3 Greenslade Hunt, Taunton #1009/R
£595 $1100 €869 Ships in harbor at sawn (51x76cm-20x30in) s. 15-Jul-4 Doyle, New York #83/R est:1000-1500
£800 $1480 €1168 Waiting for the tide (41x60cm-16x24in) s. s.i.verso. 15-Jan-4 Christie's, Kensington #938/R
£800 $1448 €1168 Coastal scene, sunset (39x53cm-15x21in) s.d.1881. 30-Mar-4 David Duggleby, Scarborough #173/R
£980 $1813 €1431 Gondolas on the Grand Canal, Venice (44x59cm-17x23in) s. 14-Jul-4 Bonhams, Chester #433/R
£1050 $1880 €1533 Fisherfolk on the shore (56x96cm-22x38in) s. 17-Mar-4 Bonhams, Chester #340/R est:800-1200
£1150 $2082 €1679 Landing the catch in the Humber estuary (60x105cm-24x41in) s.d.87. 30-Mar-4 David Duggleby, Scarborough #40/R est:1000-1500
£1400 $2618 €2044 Fishing boats off a coastline at sunset (35x51cm-14x20in) s. 22-Jul-4 Tennants, Leyburn #809 est:1000-1500
£2300 $3910 €3358 Fishing boats, Gorleston (61x46cm-24x18in) s. sold with a photo. 19-Nov-3 Tennants, Leyburn #1023/R est:2000-2500
Works on paper
£400 $728 €584 Grand Canal Venice, with figures and boats (35x53cm-14x21in) s. W/C. 15-Jun-4 Bonhams, Oxford #49
£600 $1092 €876 Venice, lagoon with figures and boats (35x53cm-14x21in) s. W/C. 15-Jun-4 Bonhams, Oxford #41
£740 $1177 €1073 Figures at the cliff foot, bear Whitby (18x27cm-7x11in) s. W/C. 9-Sep-3 David Duggleby, Scarborough #2/R
£900 $1530 €1314 Wreck off the coast (28x45cm-11x18in) s. W/C. 25-Nov-3 Bonhams, Knightsbridge #49/R

WASMER, Erich (1915-1972) Swiss

£3524 $5991 €5145 All joy will be forever (55x46cm-22x18in) s.i.d.1937 stretcher. 7-Nov-3 Dobiaschofsky, Bern #224/R est:3500 (S.FR 8000)

WASSE, Arthur (19th C) British

£530 $964 €800 Castle tower in autumn, evening (95x75cm-37x30in) s. 18-Jun-4 Bolland & Marotz, Bremen #792

WASSERSTEIN, Julius (20th C) ?

£1359 $2500 €1984 Untitled (112x69cm-44x27in) s.verso. 27-Jun-4 Bonhams & Butterfields, San Francisco #3846/R est:1000-1500

WASSON, George Savery (1855-1926) American

£806 $1500 €1177 A fantasy view at Chateau de Chillon (40x66cm-16x26in) s.d.1876. 5-Mar-4 Skinner, Boston #304/R est:1000-1500

WASTEL, J (?) ?

£1324 $2250 €1933 Venice en fete from the lagoon (74x58cm-29x23in) s. 11-Nov-3 Lincoln, Orange #458

WATANABE, Kazan (1793-1841) Japanese

Prints
£2400 $4416 €3504 Surimono (21x19cm-8x7in) s. i. print exec. 1829. 8-Jun-4 Sotheby's, London #467/R est:1000-1500
Works on paper
£489 $900 €714 Weasel catching fish under the half moon (126x29cm-50x11in) s. ink hanging scroll. 23-Mar-4 Christie's, Rockefeller NY #109
£1739 $3200 €2539 Peach blossoms (41x16cm-16x6in) s.d.1836 col ink silver mica fan. 23-Mar-4 Christie's, Rockefeller NY #110/R est:1000-1500
£1739 $3200 €2539 Fisherman (28x18cm-11x7in) s.d.1832 col ink hanging scroll two prov.exhib. 23-Mar-4 Christie's, Rockefeller NY #111/R est:2500-3000

WATANABE, Kazan (attrib) (1793-1841) Japanese
Works on paper
£1522 $2800 €2222 Female horse trainer (49x16cm-19x6in) s. ink fan mounted on hanging scroll. 23-Mar-4 Christie's, Rockefeller NY #108/R est:1000-1500

WATELET, Charles Joseph (1867-1954) Belgian
£280 $518 €409 Portrait of a lady (50x35cm-20x14in) s. oval. 9-Mar-4 Bonhams, Knightsbridge #139/R
£552 $993 €800 Elegante a la robe verte (100x75cm-39x30in) s.d.1897. 20-Jan-4 Galerie Moderne, Brussels #293/R
£674 $1125 €950 Modele (43x33cm-17x13in) s. canvas on cardboard. 14-Oct-3 Vanderkindere, Brussels #21
£1284 $2298 €1900 Delassement (75x50cm-30x20in) s.d.1905. 10-May-4 Horta, Bruxelles #93 est:1800-2200
£1389 $2208 €2000 Rythme (62x82cm-24x32in) s. 9-Sep-3 Vanderkindere, Brussels #97

WATELET, Charles Joseph (attrib) (1867-1954) Belgian
£1944 $3247 €2800 Femme en robe de bal (220x110cm-87x43in) 21-Oct-3 Galerie Moderne, Brussels #374 est:1000-1500

WATELET, Louis Étienne (1780-1866) French
£633 $1165 €950 Walkers in an extensive landscape (32x40cm-13x16in) s.d.1818. 11-Jun-4 Wendl, Rudolstadt #4410/R
£2715 $4697 €3964 Troupeau traversant un pont de bois (33x46cm-13x18in) s. prov. 12-Dec-3 Galerie du Rhone, Sion #186/R est:4000-6000 (S.FR 6000)

WATELIN, Louis (1838-1907) French
£493 $863 €700 Maison en bord de riviere (30x37cm-12x15in) s. canvas on panel. 19-Dec-3 Delvaux, Paris #15
£550 $1018 €803 Market Stall (26x33cm-10x13in) s. board. 10-Mar-4 Sotheby's, Olympia #254/R
£1053 $1937 €1600 Vache a la mare (40x55cm-16x22in) s. 25-Jun-4 Millon & Associes, Paris #76 est:1200-1500
£1329 $2259 €1900 Vaches a la mare (40x55cm-16x22in) s. 27-Nov-3 Millon & Associes, Paris #10 est:1000-1200
£1479 $2455 €2100 Vachere (27x20cm-11x8in) s.i. panel. 15-Jun-3 Peron, Melun #160

WATERFORD, Louisa Marchioness of (1818-1891) British
Works on paper
£280 $482 €409 Portrait of a boy, by a greyhound (18x12cm-7x5in) W/C. 3-Dec-3 Christie's, Kensington #206/R
£550 $913 €803 Vanitas (25x12cm-10x5in) s.d.1889 W/C. 1-Oct-3 Woolley & Wallis, Salisbury #161/R
£700 $1288 €1022 The good samaritan (44x29cm-17x11in) W/C. 27-Mar-4 Thos Mawer, Lincoln #176/R
£1300 $2171 €1898 Children on bench (16x22cm-6x9in) mono. W/C. 12-Nov-3 Sotheby's, Olympia #116/R est:600-800

WATERHOUSE, Alfred (1830-1905) British
£1399 $2378 €2000 Sunday afternoon stroll (66x102cm-26x40in) mono.d.1901 lit. 28-Nov-3 Schloss Ahlden, Ahlden #1528/R est:1600

WATERHOUSE, John William (1849-1917) British
£1111 $1833 €1600 Portrait of young beauty (46x36cm-18x14in) 3-Jul-3 Van Ham, Cologne #1493/R est:1800
£69364 $120000 €101271 Sleep and his half brother death (72x92cm-28x36in) s. prov.exhib.lit. 11-Dec-3 Sotheby's, New York #71/R est:100000-150000
Works on paper
£7000 $12810 €10220 Studies for Flora and the Zephyrs (72x44cm-28x17in) chl double-sided prov. 3-Jun-4 Christie's, London #174/R est:6000-8000
£13000 $22100 €18980 Study for The Mermaid, half-length, and sutdy of a kneeling girl from the waist (49x44cm-19x17in) blk chk htd white recto blk brown red chk verso double-sided prov. 20-Nov-3 Christie's, London #137/R est:15000-20000

WATERHOUSE, Ralph (20th C) British
Works on paper
£700 $1260 €1022 Mouse in the reeds (24x17cm-9x7in) s. W/C. 21-Jan-4 James Thompson, Kirby Lonsdale #118

WATERLOO, Anthonie (1609-1690) Flemish
£8000 $14320 €12000 Country house Oudaen on the Vect with fishermen on the tow-path (60x48cm-24x19in) s. 17-May-4 Glerum, Amsterdam #19/R est:15000-20000
Works on paper
£500 $865 €730 Rocky landscape with figures crossing a bridge (28x20cm-11x8in) pen brown ink wash prov. 12-Dec-3 Christie's, Kensington #522/R
£690 $1152 €1000 Riverside farmstead in trees (28x27cm-11x11in) chk wash prov. 15-Nov-3 Lempertz, Koln #1433/R

WATERLOO, Anthonie (attrib) (1609-1690) Flemish
Works on paper
£1049 $1783 €1500 Woodland (27x22cm-11x9in) chk Indian ink brush. 27-Nov-3 Bassenge, Berlin #5381/R est:1800

WATERLOO, Joannes Petrus (1790-1870) Dutch
£638 $1180 €950 Landscape with peasants (29x38cm-11x15in) s.d.1817 panel. 15-Mar-4 Sotheby's, Amsterdam #77/R est:800-1200

WATERLOW, Sir Ernest Albert (1850-1919) British
£460 $768 €672 Study of a grey horse and wooden cart (23x25cm-9x10in) board prov. 14-Oct-3 Bearnes, Exeter #409/R
£580 $1067 €847 Thunder clouds, Reigate Heath (24x18cm-9x7in) s. panel prov. 8-Jun-4 Holloways, Banbury #269/R
£600 $1116 €876 Early spring, near Trefriw, North Wales (51x76cm-20x30in) s. i.verso. 4-Mar-4 Christie's, Kensington #477/R
£750 $1185 €1088 Early spring near Trefriw, North Wales, sheep and cattle in a river landscape (49x74cm-19x29in) s.d.1879. 2-Sep-3 Bonhams, Oxford #107
Works on paper
£400 $664 €584 Easedale Tarn (15x37cm-6x15in) init.d.14 W/C. 1-Oct-3 Sotheby's, Olympia #142/R est:400-600
£750 $1290 €1095 At the foot of Rydal Water (18x38cm-7x15in) s.d.91 W/C pair. 3-Dec-3 Cheffins, Cambridge #557

WATERLOW, Sir Ernest Albert (attrib) (1850-1919) British
£280 $512 €409 Feeding the chickens (25x36cm-10x14in) board. 7-Apr-4 Dreweatt Neate, Newbury #132

WATERMAN, Grace F (19/20th C) American
£221 $400 €323 Landscape with cows (46x61cm-18x24in) s.d.1911 verso. 3-Apr-4 Outer Cape Auctions, Provincetown #55/R

WATERMAN, Marcus (1834-1914) American
£2095 $3750 €3059 On the road to Fez (30x51cm-12x20in) s. prov. 14-May-4 Skinner, Boston #142/R est:4000-6000
£4255 $7106 €6000 Meeting by the fountain (51x40cm-20x16in) s. 19-Oct-3 Rabourdin & Choppin de Janvry, Paris #89/R est:7000-9000
£4255 $7106 €6000 Hommes en bleu (51x40cm-20x16in) s.d.1887. 19-Oct-3 Rabourdin & Choppin de Janvry, Paris #88/R est:7000-9000

WATERS, Billie (1896-1979) British
£420 $701 €613 Olive, grey and black (33x51cm-13x20in) s.verso board. 16-Oct-3 Christie's, Kensington #599

WATERS, George W (1832-1912) American
£2235 $4000 €3263 Brook in autumn (41x18cm-16x7in) init.d.78. 6-May-4 Shannon's, Milford #233/R est:3000-5000
£3911 $7000 €5710 Arnot Mill on Newtown Creek, Elmira, New York (17x28cm-7x11in) s.d.1876 prov.exhib. 6-May-4 Shannon's, Milford #109/R est:5000-7000
£7263 $13000 €10604 Winter light (51x81cm-20x32in) s. prov. 6-May-4 Shannon's, Milford #57/R est:6000-8000

WATERS, Maynard (1938-) Australian
£412 $745 €602 Charters Towers (69x86cm-27x34in) s. 31-Mar-4 Goodman, Sydney #457/R (A.D 1000)
£617 $1118 €901 Goulburn houses (103x157cm-41x62in) s. 31-Mar-4 Goodman, Sydney #456 (A.D 1500)
£823 $1490 €1202 Other side of town (91x122cm-36x48in) s.i.verso. 31-Mar-4 Goodman, Sydney #454/R (A.D 2000)
Works on paper
£1107 $1793 €1616 Slopes of Balmain (31x51cm-12x20in) s. mixed media canvas. 30-Jul-3 Goodman, Sydney #121/R (A.D 2700)

WATERS, Owen (?) British
£260 $476 €380 Rural landscape (61x74cm-24x29in) s. board. 27-Jul-4 Gorringes, Bexhill #934
£280 $507 €409 Norfolk landscape (28x38cm-11x15in) s. 16-Apr-4 Keys, Aylsham #638
£340 $585 €496 The mill farm, Norfolk (28x36cm-11x14in) s. 5-Dec-3 Keys, Aylsham #579
£1300 $2405 €1898 Mills on the Yare from Burgh Castle (56x89cm-22x35in) s. 13-Feb-4 Keys, Aylsham #633 est:1000-1200
Works on paper
£580 $1073 €847 Summer in Norfolk (38x48cm-15x19in) s. W/C. 13-Feb-4 Keys, Aylsham #634/R

WATERS, Susan (1823-1900) American
£11628 $20000 €16977 Pastoral landscape with twelve eves and lambs and sheep dog. s. 6-Dec-3 Pook & Pook, Downington #215/R est:15000-25000

WATERS, W R (19th C) British
£1325 $2200 €1935 Portrait of a child in red velvet dress, seated in a landscape holding a hoop (91x71cm-36x28in) s.d.1862. 4-Oct-3 Skinner, Boston #169/R est:800-1200

WATERWORTH, Anna (?) Irish?
£658 $1211 €1000 Lizard and tree (41x51cm-16x20in) s. 22-Jun-4 De Veres Art Auctions, Dublin #82/R

WATKINS, Carleton E (1829-1916) American
Photographs
£1695 $3000 €2475 Upper Valley, from Eagle Point Trail, Yosemite (39x54cm-15x21in) albumen print prov.exhib. 28-Apr-4 Sotheby's, New York #68/R est:5000-8000
£2841 $5000 €4148 Cathedral Rocks, Yosemite (40x52cm-16x20in) albumen print executed c.1866. 20-May-4 Swann Galleries, New York #229/R est:5000-6000
£3182 $5600 €4646 Dead giant (39x53cm-15x21in) albumen print. 20-May-4 Swann Galleries, New York #230/R est:4000-5000
£3955 $7000 €5774 Glacier Point, from Eagle Point Trail, Yosemite (54x39cm-21x15in) albumen print prov.exhib. 28-Apr-4 Sotheby's, New York #69/R est:5000-8000
£4802 $8500 €7011 View down the valley from the ferry bend, Yosemite (38x54cm-15x21in) albumen print prov.exhib. 28-Apr-4 Sotheby's, New York #62/R est:5000-8000
£5650 $10000 €8249 El Capitan 3600 feet, view from the foot of the Yosemite Valley (38x53cm-15x21in) albumen print prov.exhib. 28-Apr-4 Sotheby's, New York #64/R est:8000-12000

£7345 $13000 €10724 Domes, from Union Point, Yosemite (38x54cm-15x21in) albumen print prov.exhib. 28-Apr-4 Sotheby's, New York #61/R est:15000-25000
£7345 $13000 €10724 Cathedral rocks and spires, 2660 ft, Yosemite (38x54cm-15x21in) albumen print prov.exhib. 28-Apr-4 Sotheby's, New York #72/R est:5000-8000
£7910 $14000 €11549 Three Brothers 4480 ft, Yosemite (38x55cm-15x22in) albumen print prov.exhib. 28-Apr-4 Sotheby's, New York #60/R est:12000-18000
£7910 $14000 €11549 Pohono, the Bridal Veil Fall 940 ft, Yosemite (54x38cm-21x15in) albumen print prov.exhib. 28-Apr-4 Sotheby's, New York #63/R est:12000-18000
£10169 $18000 €14847 North Dome, from Camp Grove, Yosemite (39x54cm-15x21in) albumen print prov.exhib. 28-Apr-4 Sotheby's, New York #66/R est:5000-8000
£10180 $17000 €14863 Mirror view of the North Dome, Yosemite (40x52cm-16x20in) i.d.1870 verso num.57v. albumen print exec.1865-1866 prov.lit. 17-Oct-3 Phillips, New York #3/R est:10000-15000
£10734 $19000 €15672 Yosemite Falls, 2634 feet, front view, Yosemite (40x54cm-16x21in) albumen print prov.exhib. 28-Apr-4 Sotheby's, New York #73/R est:5000-8000
£11299 $20000 €16497 View from Inspiration Point, Yosemite (39x54cm-15x21in) albumen print prov.exhib. 28-Apr-4 Sotheby's, New York #74/R est:5000-8000
£11299 $20000 €16497 Yosemite new series views (38x55cm-15x22in) albumen print four prov.exhib.lit. 28-Apr-4 Sotheby's, New York #75/R est:7000-10000
£11299 $20000 €16497 Yosemite new series views (38x55cm-15x22in) albumen print five prov.exhib. 28-Apr-4 Sotheby's, New York #76/R est:6000-9000
£13559 $24000 €19796 Mirror Lake, Yosemite (54x39cm-21x15in) albumen print prov.exhib.lit. 28-Apr-4 Sotheby's, New York #50/R est:40000-60000
£13559 $24000 €19796 Winter on the Domes, Yosemite (38x55cm-15x22in) albumen print prov.exhib. 28-Apr-4 Sotheby's, New York #70/R est:5000-8000
£14689 $26000 €21446 Upper Yosemite Falls, 1600 ft, view from Eagle Point Trail, Yosemite (54x39cm-21x15in) albumen print prov.exhib. 28-Apr-4 Sotheby's, New York #67/R est:8000-12000
£14689 $26000 €21446 Pompompasos, the Three Brothers, Yosemite (55x38cm-22x15in) albumen print prov.exhib. 28-Apr-4 Sotheby's, New York #71/R est:5000-8000
£15819 $28000 €23096 Yosemite Valley, from Big Oak Flat Road (39x54cm-15x21in) albumen print prov.exhib. 28-Apr-4 Sotheby's, New York #57/R est:20000-30000
£21469 $38000 €31345 Mirror view of upper Yosemite Fall, 1600 feet (54x38cm-21x15in) albumen print prov.exhib. 28-Apr-4 Sotheby's, New York #65/R est:10000-15000
£23729 $42000 €34644 Half Dome, Vernal and Nevada Falls, from Glacier Point, Yosemite (39x54cm-15x21in) albumen print prov.exhib. 28-Apr-4 Sotheby's, New York #59/R est:20000-30000
£24859 $44000 €36294 Cathedral rocks and spires, Yosemite (38x55cm-15x22in) albumen print prov.exhib. 28-Apr-4 Sotheby's, New York #45/R est:30000-50000
£24859 $44000 €36294 El Capitan 3600 ft, Yosemite (54x38cm-21x15in) albumen print prov.exhib. 28-Apr-4 Sotheby's, New York #56/R est:20000-30000
£28249 $50000 €41244 Bridal Veil, from the Black Spring, Yosemite (37x52cm-15x20in) albumen print prov.exhib. 28-Apr-4 Sotheby's, New York #48/R est:50000-80000
£31073 $55000 €45367 Cathedral Spires 2200 ft, Yosemite (54x37cm-21x15in) albumen print prov.exhib. 28-Apr-4 Sotheby's, New York #54/R est:30000-50000
£31073 $55000 €45367 Vernal and Nevada Falls, from Glacier Point, Yosemite (37x54cm-15x21in) albumen print prov.exhib. 28-Apr-4 Sotheby's, New York #55/R est:30000-50000
£39548 $70000 €57740 On the road to Yosemite Falls 2634 ft, Yosemite (55x40cm-22x16in) albumen print prov.exhib. 28-Apr-4 Sotheby's, New York #44/R est:30000-50000
£42373 $75000 €61865 Vernal Fall 300 ft, Yosemite (37x54cm-15x21in) albumen print prov.exhib. 28-Apr-4 Sotheby's, New York #46/R est:50000-80000
£42373 $75000 €61865 Half Dome, from Glacier Point, Yosemite (40x54cm-16x21in) albumen print prov.exhib.lit. 28-Apr-4 Sotheby's, New York #53/R est:100000-150000
£48023 $85000 €70114 Yosemite Valley, from Big Oak Flat Road (38x54cm-15x21in) albumen print prov.exhib. 28-Apr-4 Sotheby's, New York #52/R est:50000-80000
£48023 $85000 €70114 Washington Column 208 ft, Yosemite (53x39cm-21x15in) albumen print prov.exhib. 28-Apr-4 Sotheby's, New York #58/R est:15000-25000
£56818 $100000 €82954 Yosemite Valley (19x29cm-7x11in) i. photograph album. 20-May-4 Swann Galleries, New York #231/R
£90395 $160000 €131977 Yosemite Falls, from Glacier Pont, Yosemite (39x54cm-15x21in) albumen print prov.exhib.lit. 28-Apr-4 Sotheby's, New York #49/R est:100000-150000
£129944 $230000 €189718 Yosemite Falls, view from the bottom, Yosemite (54x38cm-21x15in) albumen print prov.exhib.lit. 28-Apr-4 Sotheby's, New York #51/R est:100000-150000
£152542 $270000 €222711 Agassiz rock and the Yosemite falls, from Union Point (54x39cm-21x15in) albumen print prov.exhib.lit. 28-Apr-4 Sotheby's, New York #47/R est:100000-150000

WATKINS, Denys (1945-) New Zealander
£500 $905 €730 Longevity (50x66cm-20x26in) s.i. s.d.1998 verso acrylic on paper. 30-Mar-4 Peter Webb, Auckland #190/R est:2000-3000 (NZ.D 1400)
£1316 $2237 €1921 El nino - the child (91x97cm-36x38in) s.d.1995 acrylic. 27-Nov-3 International Art Centre, Auckland #11/R est:4000-6000 (NZ.D 3500)

Works on paper
£344 $585 €502 Re-entry (30x76cm-12x30in) s. s.i.d.1984 verso W/C. 4-Nov-3 Peter Webb, Auckland #86/R (NZ.D 950)
£362 $583 €529 El Paso (56x75cm-22x30in) s. pastel ink W/C. 12-Aug-3 Peter Webb, Auckland #62 (NZ.D 1000)
£1087 $1761 €1576 Loaves and fishes (64x102cm-25x40in) s. W/C. 31-Jul-3 International Art Centre, Auckland #5/R est:3000-5000 (NZ.D 3000)

WATKINS, Dick (1937-) Australian
£3086 $5586 €4506 Nudes October (170x123cm-67x48in) s. i.d.10.81. 30-Mar-4 Lawson Menzies, Sydney #123 est:3500-5500 (A.D 7500)
£5761 $10428 €8411 Wizard of Oz (173x243cm-68x96in) s.i.verso. 30-Mar-4 Lawson Menzies, Sydney #199/R est:7000-9000 (A.D 14000)

Works on paper
£247 $447 €361 Untitled 5 (33x48cm-13x19in) init.d.78 W/C. 30-Mar-4 Lawson Menzies, Sydney #25 (A.D 600)
£329 $596 €480 Untitled (49x33cm-19x13in) s.d.78 ink. 30-Mar-4 Lawson Menzies, Sydney #380 (A.D 800)
£576 $1043 €841 Untitled 4 (33x48cm-13x19in) init.d.78 W/C. 30-Mar-4 Lawson Menzies, Sydney #103/R est:400-800 (A.D 1400)
£617 $1117 €901 Untitled II (54x74cm-21x29in) init.d.79 synthetic polymer W/C. 30-Mar-4 Lawson Menzies, Sydney #411 est:500-900 (A.D 1500)
£741 $1341 €1082 Untitled I (54x74cm-21x29in) init.d.79 synthetic polymer W/C. 30-Mar-4 Lawson Menzies, Sydney #504 est:500-900 (A.D 1800)
£2254 $3562 €3291 Gattieres (125x167cm-49x66in) s.d.76 s.i.d.1976 verso synthetic polymer prov. 2-Sep-3 Deutscher-Menzies, Melbourne #113/R est:6500-9500 (A.D 5500)

WATKINS, Hy (19th C) British
£699 $1250 €1021 Auctioning of the farm. s. 8-Jan-4 James Julia, Fairfield #574/R

WATKINS, John Samuel (1886-1942) Australian
£553 $940 €807 Resignation (90x39cm-35x15in) s. prov. 25-Nov-3 Christie's, Melbourne #223/R (A.D 1300)

Works on paper
£344 $554 €502 Farmer and his draught horse (24x33cm-9x13in) s.d.10 gouache W/C. 25-Aug-3 Sotheby's, Paddington #423 (A.D 850)
£414 $646 €600 Boy and dog (22x29cm-9x11in) s. W/C. 1-Aug-2 Joel, Victoria #331 est:1200-1500 (A.D 1200)

WATKINS, Philip (20th C) Australian
£723 $1230 €1056 Commission (122x122cm-48x48in) s.d.1997 on stretcher. 25-Nov-3 Christie's, Melbourne #295/R (A.D 1700)

WATKINS, Richard John (1937-) Australian
Works on paper
£269 $497 €393 Untitled (35x53cm-14x21in) init.d.87 synthetic polymer. 15-Mar-4 Sotheby's, Melbourne #201/R (A.D 650)
£331 $612 €483 Untitled (35x53cm-14x21in) init.d.87 synthetic polymer. 15-Mar-4 Sotheby's, Melbourne #191 (A.D 800)
£2686 $4969 €3922 Dark rhythm (167x243cm-66x96in) s. i.d.1989 verso synthetic polymer prov.exhib. 10-Mar-4 Deutscher-Menzies, Melbourne #190/R est:7000-9000 (A.D 6500)

WATKINS, Susan (19th C) British
£1402 $2300 €2033 Recordo di Ana Capri (25x36cm-10x14in) s.i.d.1906 i.verso prov. 31-May-3 Brunk, Ashville #21/R est:500-1000

WATKISS, Gill (1938-) British
£290 $502 €423 After the service, chapel leavers (35x39cm-14x15in) s.d.1976 board. 11-Dec-3 Lane, Penzance #214/R
£320 $582 €467 Towednack Church (18x28cm-7x11in) s.d.96 i.verso board. 15-Jun-4 David Lay, Penzance #606
£350 $585 €511 Good day out (30x33cm-12x13in) s. i.verso board. 14-Oct-3 David Lay, Penzance #286
£420 $764 €613 Out walking (15x25cm-6x10in) s. board. 15-Jun-4 David Lay, Penzance #607
£500 $865 €730 A stroll by a stream, Newbridge, Penzance (39x38cm-15x15in) s.d.1975 board. 11-Dec-3 Lane, Penzance #216
£600 $1038 €876 Carnkie Men's Institute (36x41cm-14x16in) s. board. 11-Dec-3 Lane, Penzance #180/R
£620 $1073 €905 The unwilling helper (35x47cm-14x19in) s.d.1989 board. 11-Dec-3 Lane, Penzance #215/R
£1200 $2244 €1752 Lane to Carne Gloose (41x41cm-16x16in) s.i.d.03 verso board. 26-Feb-4 Lane, Penzance #195/R est:900-1200
£1250 $2163 €1825 Winter evening, Penlee Park Gates (44x53cm-17x21in) s.d.1993 board. 11-Dec-3 Lane, Penzance #40/R est:600-800

WATKISS, Reg (20th C) British
£250 $463 €365 Inshore, near Land's End (33x58cm-13x23in) s. acrylic. 10-Feb-4 David Lay, Penzance #265
£250 $455 €365 Landscape near St. Just (18x43cm-7x17in) s. i.verso acrylic. 15-Jun-4 David Lay, Penzance #482
£280 $510 €409 Field near Sancreed (41x76cm-16x30in) s. acrylic. 15-Jun-4 David Lay, Penzance #483
£350 $585 €511 North coast fields (46x76cm-18x30in) s.d.1968 i.verso. 14-Oct-3 David Lay, Penzance #572

WATMOUGH, Amos (fl.1884-1885) British
£460 $837 €672 Cattle and hens in a barn (36x43cm-14x17in) s.d.1903. 15-Jun-4 Bonhams, Leeds #122
£1400 $2380 €2044 Waiting for orders (60x90cm-24x35in) s.d.1883 i.verso. 1-Dec-3 Bonhams, Bath #113/R est:1500-2000

WATROUS, Harry W (1857-1940) American
£894 $1600 €1305 Colonial gentleman (20x13cm-8x5in) s. panel prov. 26-May-4 Doyle, New York #82/R est:1000-1500
£1278 $2300 €1866 Still life with Asian jar and ancient glass (23x20cm-9x8in) s. canvasboard. 24-Apr-4 Weschler, Washington #604/R est:2000-3000
£2023 $3500 €2954 Old Saint (84x56cm-33x22in) s. prov. 10-Dec-3 Bonhams & Butterfields, San Francisco #6022/R est:7000-10000
£3315 $6000 €4840 Silver duck (53x41cm-21x16in) s. painted c.1925 prov.exhib. 31-Mar-4 Sotheby's, New York #4/R est:6000-8000
£4121 $7500 €6017 Jar (54x46cm-21x18in) s. prov. 29-Jun-4 Sotheby's, New York #298/R est:7000-10000
£4144 $7500 €6050 Still life with golded flowers (69x46cm-27x18in) s. painted c.1925-1930 prov. 31-Mar-4 Sotheby's, New York #3/R est:6000-8000
£5495 $10000 €8023 Still life (77x91cm-30x36in) s. painted c.1925-30 prov. 29-Jun-4 Sotheby's, New York #297/R est:12000-18000

WATSON, Albert (1942-) American
Photographs
£2096 $3500 €3060 Gabrielle Reece, Vivienne Westwood, comedie Francaise, Paris (60x50cm-24x20in) s.i.d.1989 photo. 17-Oct-3 Sotheby's, New York #291/R est:5000-7000

WATSON, Alfred S (19/20th C) British
Works on paper
£380 $646 €555 Half timbered Tudor building with landscaped gardens (27x44cm-11x17in) s.d.1912 pencil W/C. 19-Nov-3 Tennants, Leyburn #984

WATSON, C (19th C) British
£1700 $3111 €2482 Milking time, mother and daughter with collie walking cattle along a track (69x90cm-27x35in) s. indis.d.1900. 28-Jan-4 Wintertons, Lichfield #371 est:1500-2500

WATSON, Charles H R (20th C) American?
Works on paper
£453 $810 €661 Highland cattle grazing (41x25cm-16x10in) s.d.1913 W/C pair. 11-May-4 Roland's, New York #473287/R

WATSON, Constance Stella (fl.1928) British
Works on paper
£1300 $2210 €1898 Still life with white roses in a plant pot (59x49cm-23x19in) s. W/C. 8-Nov-3 Shapes, Edinburgh #415/R est:1000-1500

WATSON, Donald (20th C) British
Works on paper
£320 $544 €467 Swans in marshland (26x31cm-10x12in) s.d.1974 W/C. 1-Dec-3 David Duggleby, Scarborough #226
£600 $1122 €876 Goosanders in April on the Nith (15x23cm-6x9in) s.d.1950 gouache. 25-Feb-4 Mallams, Oxford #187/R

WATSON, Dora (fl.1888-1924) British
£380 $635 €555 Returning from the front (33x47cm-13x19in) s. board. 27-Oct-3 Robin Fenner, Tavistock #1017

WATSON, George (1767-1837) British
£1400 $2338 €2044 On the Conway (41x61cm-16x24in) s. 13-Nov-3 Christie's, Kensington #183/R est:800-1200
£7500 $13800 €10950 Portrait of Captain Robert Dudgeon, standing by a column, wearing uniform (234x150cm-92x59in) prov. 26-Mar-4 Sotheby's, London #29/R est:8000-12000

WATSON, George (attrib) (1767-1837) British
£2800 $5040 €4088 Portrait of a boy, seated three-quarter length, holding a sheet of paper (76x62cm-30x24in) 21-Apr-4 Christie's, Kensington #391/R est:2000-3000

WATSON, Harry (1871-1936) British
£85000 $144500 €124100 Garden party (71x91cm-28x36in) s. prov. 27-Nov-3 Sotheby's, London #34/R est:80000-120000

WATSON, Homer Ransford (1855-1936) Canadian
£1351 $2297 €1972 Spring morning, Doon (36x62cm-14x24in) s. prov. 27-Nov-3 Heffel, Vancouver #149/R est:3500-4500 (C.D 3000)
£3348 $5759 €4888 Gleam after the shower (45x60cm-18x24in) s. canvas on panel. 2-Dec-3 Joyner Waddington, Toronto #186/R est:6000-8000 (C.D 7500)
£10714 $18429 €15642 Oak trees and cattle - towards evening (55x75cm-22x30in) s. painted 1893 prov.exhib.lit. 2-Dec-3 Joyner Waddington, Toronto #89/R est:15000-20000 (C.D 24000)

WATSON, Howard Noel (1929-) American
Works on paper
£231 $425 €337 Figures in boat on lake with rocky islets (25x36cm-10x14in) s. W/C. 9-Jun-4 Alderfer's, Hatfield #537

WATSON, Izett (fl.1870s-1900) Australian
£2632 $4237 €3843 Paper boys in the black lane off Collins Street, Melbourne (49x39cm-19x15in) painted c.1890. 13-Oct-3 Joel, Victoria #402 est:1500-2000 (A.D 6500)

WATSON, J Fletcher (?) British
Works on paper
£850 $1522 €1241 View of Morston, Norfolk (30x44cm-12x17in) s. W/C. 20-Mar-4 Lacy Scott, Bury St.Edmunds #458/R

WATSON, J N (20th C) American
£1384 $2200 €2021 California landscapes (35x46cm-14x18in) paper pair. 12-Sep-3 Skinner, Boston #416/R

WATSON, James (19/20th C) British
£740 $1177 €1073 Runswick Bay (22x30cm-9x12in) s. board. 9-Sep-3 David Duggleby, Scarborough #318
£850 $1352 €1233 Lady Palmer's cottage, Runswick Bay. View from her garden (29x45cm-11x18in) s. board pair. 9-Sep-3 David Duggleby, Scarborough #364/R
£1050 $1691 €1533 Coastal view, two fishermen and boat on beach with village to background (30x61cm-12x24in) s.d.04. 12-Aug-3 Canterbury Auctions, UK #169/R est:500-700

WATSON, John Dawson (1832-1892) British
£1600 $2720 €2336 Rest from chores (25x17cm-10x7in) mono.d.1856 panel. 19-Nov-3 Bonhams, New Bond Street #26/R est:1200-1800
£1695 $2881 €2475 Village cobbler (34x28cm-13x11in) mono. bears i.verso artist board. 24-Nov-3 Sotheby's, Melbourne #325/R est:4000-6000 (A.D 4000)
£3800 $6346 €5548 Morning, Loch Eck, Argyleshire (33x47cm-13x19in) s.d.1874 s.i.verso. 13-Nov-3 Christie's, Kensington #198/R est:2000-3000
£35000 $64400 €51100 Yeoman's wedding (122x214cm-48x84in) s.d.1879 exhib. 23-Mar-4 Bonhams, New Bond Street #75/R est:10000-15000
Works on paper
£556 $917 €800 Portrait of young girl with summer hat (33x26cm-13x10in) mono.d.1857 W/C. 3-Jul-3 Van Ham, Cologne #1494/R
£3500 $6370 €5110 Princess Tennyson (15x13cm-6x5in) mono.d.1858 pen ink. 1-Jul-4 Sotheby's, London #283/R est:2000-3000

WATSON, Judy (1959-) Australian
Works on paper
£1406 $2630 €2109 Janpanpa jukurrpa, native edible fungus dreaming (91x46cm-36x18in) i.verso synthetic polymer linen exec.1995 prov. 21-Jul-4 Shapiro, Sydney #106/R est:4000-6000 (A.D 3600)
£2128 $3617 €3107 Column (249x23cm-98x9in) s.i.d.97 verso pigment pastel canvas prov. 25-Nov-3 Christie's, Melbourne #88/R est:5000-7000 (A.D 5000)

WATSON, Lizzie May (19th C) British?
£1339 $2464 €1955 Loves offering (79x48cm-31x19in) s. 25-Mar-4 International Art Centre, Auckland #164/R est:1000-2000 (NZ.D 3750)

WATSON, Maggie Napangardi (1925-) Australian
Works on paper
£8627 $15443 €12595 KarlanguDigging stick dreaming (152x76cm-60x30in) synthetic polymer paint canvas exec 1997 prov. 25-May-4 Lawson Menzies, Sydney #42/R est:30000-40000 (A.D 22000)

WATSON, N Cameron (1955-) American
£220 $375 €321 Waiting for Bonnie (30x41cm-12x16in) s. board. 9-Nov-3 Outer Cape Auctions, Provincetown #68/R

WATSON, Robert (fl.1877-1920) British
£950 $1587 €1387 Guardian (50x75cm-20x30in) s.d.1890. 16-Oct-3 Bonhams, Edinburgh #200/R
£1800 $3222 €2628 Highland sheep (51x76cm-20x30in) s.d.1908. 26-May-4 Sotheby's, Olympia #114/R est:2000-3000
£1900 $3477 €2774 Highland cattle in a misty glen (59x90cm-23x35in) s.d.1904. 8-Jul-4 Lawrence, Crewkerne #1639/R est:1500-2000
£2000 $3320 €2920 Highland sheep (23x33cm-9x13in) s.d.1863. 1-Oct-3 Sotheby's, Olympia #44/R est:1000-1500
£2778 $4528 €4000 Return of the flock (77x127cm-30x50in) s.d.1902. 23-Sep-3 Galerie Moderne, Brussels #874/R est:3000-4000
£3000 $5580 €4380 Shepherd with his flock in a highland landscape (92x71cm-36x28in) s.d.1903. 4-Mar-4 Christie's, Kensington #26/R est:2000-3000
£3200 $5728 €4672 Highland cattle watering. Landscape with sheep (51x76cm-20x30in) s.d.1906 pair. 26-May-4 Sotheby's, Olympia #113/R est:3000-5000
£3500 $6300 €5110 Sheep and their lambs. Drovers with highland cattle (35x27cm-14x11in) s.d.1908 pair. 21-Apr-4 Tennants, Leyburn #1114/R est:3500-4500
£4000 $7440 €5840 Guarding the flock (61x91cm-24x36in) s.d.1889. 4-Mar-4 Christie's, Kensington #27/R est:4000-6000
£4100 $7339 €5986 Highland cattle on the side of the loch (61x91cm-24x36in) s.d.1913. 17-Mar-4 Bonhams, Chester #314/R est:2000-3000
£4299 $7179 €6277 Highland sheep (72x92cm-28x36in) s.d.1902 prov. 17-Nov-3 Waddingtons, Toronto #147/R est:4000-6000 (C.D 9500)
£4400 $7876 €6424 Sheep on a hillside. Highland cattle by a stream (41x61cm-16x24in) s. indis.d.1918 pair. 17-Mar-4 Bonhams, Chester #313/R est:2000-3000
£4600 $7820 €6716 Highland landscape with ewes and lambs. Highland cattle in a glen (61x91cm-24x36in) s. one d.1889 pair. 19-Nov-3 Tennants, Leyburn #1079/R est:4000-6000
£5000 $9300 €7300 Cattle fording a mill stream (76x127cm-30x50in) s. 4-Mar-4 Christie's, Kensington #25/R est:5000-8000
£5500 $10285 €8250 Sheep in a landscape. Cattle in a landscape (51x71cm-20x28in) s.d.1883 pair prov. 22-Jul-4 Tennants, Leyburn #823a/R est:4000-6000
£6500 $11700 €9490 Highland rovers, Highland cattle and their calves in a Scottish glen (91x71cm-36x28in) s.i.d.1908. 21-Apr-4 Tennants, Leyburn #1115/R est:3500-4500
£8500 $15300 €12410 Ewes and lambs beside a loch. Highland cattle and calves beside stream (61x91cm-24x36in) s.d.1900 pair. 21-Apr-4 Tennants, Leyburn #1116/R est:7000-9000

WATSON, Robert (1923-) American
£389 $650 €568 Lighthouse (96x66cm-38x26in) s.d.52 exhib. 26-Oct-3 Bonhams & Butterfields, San Francisco #6583/R

WATSON, Robert (1865-1916) British
£1046 $1893 €1527 Highland cattle (50x78cm-20x31in) s.d.1902 prov. 1-Apr-4 Heffel, Vancouver #109/R est:3000-4000 (C.D 2500)

WATSON, Robert Browning (20th C) New Zealander
£779 $1254 €1137 The wharf at Collingwood (50x60cm-20x24in) s. board. 20-Aug-3 Peter Webb, Auckland #2077 (NZ.D 2150)

WATSON, Ross (1962-) Australian
£813 $1455 €1187 Doorway, Mykonos (58x94cm-23x37in) s.d.1991 board. 10-May-4 Joel, Victoria #270 est:2000-3000 (A.D 2000)

WATSON, Samuel (1818-1867) Irish
£897 $1659 €1300 Cow boy (42x33cm-17x13in) s.d.1843 verso. 11-Feb-4 Woodwards, Cork #2/R
£100000 $179000 €146000 Scene at Donnybrook Fair (104x161cm-41x63in) i. i.d.1842 on stretcher exhib.lit. 13-May-4 Sotheby's, London #51/R est:100000-150000

WATSON, Sidney (19/20th C) British
£2699 $4750 €3941 Extensive mountainous landscape with highland cattle (46x61cm-18x24in) s.d.1901. 18-May-4 Bonhams & Butterfields, San Francisco #161/R est:3000-5000

WATSON, Sonja (20th C) Irish?
£263 $484 €400 The forty-foot, Sandycove (21x34cm-8x13in) canvasboard. 22-Jun-4 De Veres Art Auctions, Dublin #236/R

WATSON, Sydney A (19th C) British
£5800 $10440 €8468 Loch Long, Argyllshire (41x61cm-16x24in) s.d.1910 i.verso prov. 21-Apr-4 Tennants, Leyburn #1117/R est:3000-4000

WATSON, Thomas J (1847-1912) British
Works on paper
£250 $425 €365 Norwegian hay harvest (29x49cm-11x19in) s.d.1904 pencil W/C. 19-Nov-3 Tennants, Leyburn #967

WATSON, W R C (fl.1890-1898) British
£3200 $5824 €4800 Sheep in mountain landscape (36x46cm-14x18in) s.d.07. 30-Jun-4 Neumeister, Munich #745/R est:2000

WATSON, Walter J (1879-?) British
£1000 $1700 €1460 Morning, Bolton Abbey (38x61cm-15x24in) s. 11-Nov-3 Lincoln, Orange #478
£1324 $2250 €1933 Bolton Abbey (38x58cm-15x23in) s. 11-Nov-3 Lincoln, Orange #479
£1450 $2683 €2117 Raby, Cheshire (31x47cm-12x19in) s.d.1900 s.i. verso. 14-Jul-4 Bonhams, Chester #319/R est:1500-2000
£3000 $4680 €4380 Highland landscape with fast flowing brook, sheep and gorse in the foreground (41x61cm-16x24in) s.d.1907. 28-Mar-3 Bigwood, Stratford on Avon #400/R est:3000-4000
£4829 $8500 €7050 On the Lledr, North Wales (41x66cm-16x26in) s.d.1927 s.i.verso. 18-May-4 Bonhams & Butterfields, San Francisco #160/R est:3000-5000
£6000 $10980 €8760 By the Machno, North Wales (40x65cm-16x26in) s. s.i.verso. 8-Apr-4 Bonhams, Edinburgh #179 est:4000-6000
£6400 $10688 €9344 Lledr valley (41x66cm-16x26in) s.d. s.i.verso prov. 13-Nov-3 Christie's, Kensington #189/R est:2000-3000
£11500 $20585 €16790 Bolton Abbey, morning and afternoon (41x61cm-16x24in) s.d.1902 s.i.d.verso pair. 27-May-4 Christie's, Kensington #161/R est:5000-7000

WATSON, William (19/20th C) British
£950 $1758 €1387 Mother and child beside a stile (36x46cm-14x18in) s. 9-Mar-4 Gorringes, Lewes #2168
£1049 $1783 €1500 Sheep on high ground (34x49cm-13x19in) s.d.1892 one of pair. 24-Nov-3 Dorotheum, Vienna #194/R est:3000-3500
£5000 $7850 €7250 Hunting party (71x107cm-28x42in) s.d.1858 prov. 27-Aug-3 Sotheby's, London #1003/R est:6000-8000

WATSON, William (jnr) (?-1921) British
£2500 $4600 €3650 Sheep on the Welsh hills (46x68cm-18x27in) s.d.1879 prov. 10-Jun-4 Christie's, Kensington #226/R est:2500-3500
£3291 $5200 €4805 Sheep in hilly landscape, distant ocean (61x91cm-24x36in) s. canvas on masonite. 6-Sep-3 Brunk, Ashville #637
£5200 $9672 €7592 Highland cattle in a loch landscape (122x97cm-48x38in) s.d.1907. 4-Mar-4 Christie's, Kensington #28/R est:3500-4500

WATSON, William (jnr-attrib) (?-1921) British
£2000 $3240 €2920 Sheep at a loch side (33x49cm-13x19in) i.verso. 30-Jul-3 Hamptons Fine Art, Godalming #199/R est:2000-3000

WATSON, William Henry (19/20th C) British
£5000 $9050 €7300 West highlanders (82x107cm-32x42in) s.d.1891-92. 19-Apr-4 Sotheby's, London #32/R est:5000-7000

WATSON, William Peter (?-1932) British
£3593 $6000 €5246 Glan Goil. Lock Eck (30x23cm-12x9in) s. panel pair prov. 23-Oct-3 Shannon's, Milford #243/R est:5000-7000

WATSON, William R (20th C) American
£1229 $2200 €1794 Snow covered farm (51x61cm-20x24in) s. painted c.1940. 16-Mar-4 Matthew's, Oregon #27/R est:1200-1800

WATSON, William R C (fl.1890-1898) British
£1500 $2355 €2175 Cattle watering (33x48cm-13x19in) s. 27-Aug-3 Sotheby's, London #974/R est:1500-2000

WATT, Alison (1965-) British
£2800 $4676 €4088 Self portrait with binoculars (101x46cm-40x18in) s. 16-Oct-3 Christie's, Kensington #575/R est:3000-5000

WATT, Elizabeth Mary (fl.1922-1940) British
£980 $1823 €1431 Mixed roses in a vase (42x32cm-17x13in) s. board. 6-Mar-4 Shapes, Edinburgh #424/R

WATT, Frances (20th C) British
£380 $608 €555 Robbers in a bank (51x61cm-20x24in) s.d.1962 board. 15-May-3 Bonhams, Edinburgh #386

WATT, George Fiddes (1873-1960) British
£600 $948 €870 Portrait of Mr Pryor seated in a black suit, holding a notebook and pen (112x86cm-44x34in) s.d.1912 exhib. 4-Sep-3 Christie's, Kensington #68/R

WATT, James (?) British?
£300 $540 €438 Landscape in Perthshire (38x85cm-15x33in) s. board. 20-Jan-4 Bonhams, Knightsbridge #300/R

WATTEAU (style) (18/19th C) French
£5467 $9949 €8200 Fete galante (65x53cm-26x21in) 5-Jul-4 Marc Kohn, Paris #58/R est:8000-9000

WATTEAU DE LILLE, Louis Joseph (1731-1798) French
£16084 $26860 €23000 Accord de mariage (53x68cm-21x27in) s.d.1795 panel prov.exhib.lit. 30-Jun-3 Bailly Pommery, Paris #64/R
Works on paper
£272 $487 €400 Jeune femme debout portant un costume (26x18cm-10x7in) i. blk crayon. 17-Mar-4 Tajan, Paris #54

WATTEAU DE LILLE, Louis Joseph (attrib) (1731-1798) French
Works on paper
£979 $1684 €1400 Jeune fille en buste embrassant un oiseau (14x11cm-6x4in) lead pencil pen brown ink brown wash. 2-Dec-3 Christie's, Paris #510/R est:500-700

WATTEAU, Jean Antoine (after) (1684-1721) French
£5592 $10289 €8500 Bergers (55x78cm-22x31in) prov.lit. 24-Jun-4 Christie's, Paris #127/R est:6000-8000

WATTEAU, Jean Antoine (attrib) (1684-1721) French
£4310 $7716 €6293 Soldiers resting (28x36cm-11x14in) 12-May-4 Dobiaschofsky, Bern #1055/R est:6000 (S.FR 10000)

WATTENWYL, Peter von (1942-) Swiss
Works on paper
£431 $772 €629 At midday (48x38cm-19x15in) s.d.76 Indian ink col pen. 12-May-4 Dobiaschofsky, Bern #2164/R (S.FR 1000)

WATTIER, Charles Émile (1800-1868) French
£1900 $3040 €2755 La lecon de chant (24x33cm-9x13in) s. panel. 18-Sep-3 Christie's, Kensington #139/R est:1200-1800

WATTS, David (?) British
£260 $476 €380 Loch Katrine (50x75cm-20x30in) s.i. 1-Jun-4 Hodgins, Calgary #348/R (C.D 650)
£420 $769 €613 The Narrows, Kyles of Bute (50x75cm-20x30in) s.i. 1-Jun-4 Hodgins, Calgary #349/R (C.D 1050)

WATTS, Frederick William (1800-1862) British
£1500 $2550 €2190 Water mill by a river (53x66cm-21x26in) 26-Nov-3 Hamptons Fine Art, Godalming #152/R est:1500-2000
£1988 $3200 €2902 View of Shorewell, Isle of Wight (57x74cm-22x29in) i. prov. 14-Jan-4 Christie's, Rockefeller NY #65/R est:2000-3000
£3000 $4740 €4350 Figures in a boat by a Suffolk cottage (51x72cm-20x28in) 4-Sep-3 Christie's, Kensington #133/R est:4000-6000
£3000 $5580 €4380 Drover with cattle watering in a extensive landscape (51x76cm-20x30in) 4-Mar-4 Christie's, Kensington #494/R est:4000-6000
£3727 $6000 €5441 Cottage in a wooded landscape (55x76cm-22x30in) 14-Jan-4 Christie's, Rockefeller NY #66/R est:2000-3000
£4000 $6680 €5840 Watermill (61x91cm-24x36in) 13-Nov-3 Christie's, Kensington #112/R est:5000-8000
£5500 $8690 €7975 Barges on a river in a sunlit landscape (98x127cm-39x50in) 4-Sep-3 Christie's, Kensington #132/R est:5000-8000
£13966 $25000 €20390 Wooded landscape with cattle and cottage (107x145cm-42x57in) 27-May-4 Sotheby's, New York #281/R est:30000-40000
£16173 $30081 €23613 English landscape with angler by lock, Suffolk (56x83cm-22x33in) 2-Mar-4 Rasmussen, Copenhagen #1640/R est:50000 (D.KR 180000)

WATTS, George Frederick (1817-1904) British
£4000 $7280 €5840 Daphne (53x30cm-21x12in) 16-Jun-4 Bonhams, New Bond Street #28/R est:4000-6000
£4000 $7280 €5840 Portrait of a lady (66x53cm-26x21in) prov. 1-Jul-4 Sotheby's, London #296/R est:4000-6000
£4000 $7280 €5840 Portrait of the Countess Somers (44x38cm-17x15in) panel prov.exhib. 1-Jul-4 Sotheby's, London #296a/R est:4000-6000
£22000 $40040 €32120 Miss Georgina Treherne (48x67cm-19x26in) prov.exhib. 1-Jul-4 Sotheby's, London #297/R est:12000-18000
£26000 $47320 €37960 Petraia (31x65cm-12x26in) prov.exhib.lit. 1-Jul-4 Sotheby's, London #292/R est:15000-20000
£50000 $92000 €73000 When Poverty comes in at the door, Love flies out at the window (53x66cm-21x26in) s.i. prov.exhib.lit. 9-Jun-4 Christie's, London #30/R est:60000-80000
£55336 $99051 €80791 Olympus on Ida - The Judgement of Paris (147x102cm-58x40in) s.d.1885 prov.exhib.lit. 15-May-4 Christie's, Sydney #82/R est:140000-180000 (A.D 140000)
£60000 $109200 €87600 Paulo and Francesca (45x35cm-18x14in) panel prov.lit. 1-Jul-4 Sotheby's, London #294/R est:20000-30000
Works on paper
£2300 $4186 €3358 Ellen Terry at the piano (31x22cm-12x9in) i. pencil prov. 1-Jul-4 Sotheby's, London #302/R est:2000-3000
£4000 $7280 €5840 Ellen Terry asleep (22x32cm-9x13in) i. pencil prov.exhib. 1-Jul-4 Sotheby's, London #301/R est:2000-3000
£4200 $7644 €6132 Portrait of Ellen Terry. Portrait of a lady, possibly Julia Jackson (11x11cm-4x4in) one i. pencil three prov.exhib. 1-Jul-4 Sotheby's, London #300/R est:2000-3000
£6000 $10920 €8760 Portrait of the artist's wife Mary (63x52cm-25x20in) col chks prov. 1-Jul-4 Sotheby's, London #295/R est:5000-7000

WATTS, James T (1853-1930) British
£370 $681 €540 Dutch barges (51x63cm-20x25in) s. 23-Mar-4 Rosebery Fine Art, London #798/R
Works on paper
£450 $806 €657 Gypsy girl with donkey gathering wood at a small encampment (25x36cm-10x14in) s. 17-Mar-4 John Nicholson, Haslemere #685/R
£480 $802 €701 Woodland path (24x35cm-9x14in) s. W/C. 14-Oct-3 Bonhams, Knightsbridge #54/R
£500 $800 €730 Moonrise in the Ashdown Forest (14x10cm-6x4in) W/C. 16-Sep-3 Lawrences, Bletchingley #1815
£600 $1104 €876 Evening in a village (34x27cm-13x11in) s. W/C. 23-Mar-4 Bonhams, Knightsbridge #182/R
£620 $1122 €905 Untitled - after the spring rain (24x42cm-9x17in) s. W/C. 18-Apr-4 Levis, Calgary #219/R est:2000-2500 (C.D 1500)

£700 $1288 €1022 Lake side birch trees (30x38cm-12x15in) s. W/C. 8-Jun-4 Gorringes, Lewes #2008
£800 $1464 €1168 Evening glow in the woods (18x25cm-7x10in) s. i. verso W/C prov. 3-Jun-4 Christie's, London #29/R
£1000 $1830 €1460 Two figures with a jester in a wood (51x74cm-20x29in) s. W/C. 8-Jul-4 Lawrence, Crewkerne #1547/R est:1000-1500
£1050 $1701 €1523 Whitby (36x60cm-14x24in) s. W/C. 30-Jul-3 Hamptons Fine Art, Godalming #79/R est:800-1200

WATTS, William Clothier (1869-1961) American
£335 $550 €486 Landscape (53x76cm-21x30in) s. board painted c.1925. 7-Jun-3 Treadway Gallery, Cincinnati #1359
Works on paper
£706 $1200 €1031 Yacht Stor-Ella at sea (21x17cm-8x7in) s. i.d.May 15 1936 verso W/C prov. 18-Nov-3 John Moran, Pasadena #127a

WAUD, Alfred Rudolf (1828-1891) American
£2732 $5000 €4098 Shipping in a harbour (36x46cm-14x18in) s. 29-Jul-4 Eldred, East Dennis #289/R est:5000-10000
Works on paper
£2695 $4500 €3935 5th Corp Army of the Potomac (13x36cm-5x14in) init. gouache en grisaille. 23-Oct-3 Shannon's, Milford #123/R est:3000-5000

WAUER, William (1866-1962) German
£489 $817 €690 Dance (58x49cm-23x19in) s. tempera panel. 17-Oct-3 Behringer, Furth #1495/R
£496 $829 €700 All around (60x48cm-24x19in) s.d.60. 17-Oct-3 Behringer, Furth #1492/R
£496 $829 €700 Games (68x47cm-27x19in) s.d.60 tempera panel. 17-Oct-3 Behringer, Furth #1493/R
£692 $1191 €990 Monte Santo (49x69cm-19x27in) s.d.60 i. verso board. 5-Dec-3 Michael Zeller, Lindau #909/R
£12006 $20770 €17529 Non stop (61x54cm-24x21in) s.verso fibreboard painted 1930. 12-Dec-3 Kieselbach, Budapest #29/R (H.F 4600000)
£16289 $27040 €23782 Colour, fight (70x56cm-28x22in) s. 4-Oct-3 Kieselbach, Budapest #159/R (H.F 6000000)
£17646 $29293 €25763 Nell Walden (66x46cm-26x18in) s. cardboard. 4-Oct-3 Kieselbach, Budapest #55/R (H.F 6500000)
£23076 $38306 €33691 The winner (56x97cm-22x38in) s. panel. 4-Oct-3 Kieselbach, Budapest #87/R (H.F 8500000)
Sculpture
£1600 $2880 €2400 Nell Walden (15x16x17cm-6x6x7in) s.i. bronze Cast.W. Fussel, Berlin bronze. 24-Apr-4 Dr Lehr, Berlin #488/R est:2400

WAUGH, Coulton (1896-1973) American
£435 $700 €635 Storm king and snow (64x76cm-25x30in) s. painted c.1969. 22-Feb-3 Bunte, Elgin #1214

WAUGH, Frederick J (1861-1940) American
£270 $500 €394 Breakers (30x41cm-12x16in) s. board. 17-Jul-4 Outer Cape Auctions, Provincetown #73/R
£1136 $2000 €1659 Roaring Forties (13x18cm-5x7in) s. board prov. 3-Jan-4 Collins, Maine #29/R est:1200-1600
£1138 $1900 €1661 Study on board ship (30x41cm-12x16in) s. canvasboard. 19-Oct-3 William Jenack, New York #287 est:1000-1500
£1221 $2100 €1783 Art Deco design with figure (33x25cm-13x10in) mono. card. 7-Dec-3 Freeman, Philadelphia #180 est:2000-3000
£2235 $4000 €3263 Afternoon glow (14x18cm-6x7in) s. masonite prov. 6-May-4 Shannon's, Milford #137/R est:4000-6000
£2793 $5000 €4078 Niagara Falls (30x41cm-12x16in) s. board prov. 6-May-4 Shannon's, Milford #201/R est:3000-5000
£3352 $6000 €4894 Sunlight through the clouds (61x91cm-24x36in) s.d.1896 prov. 6-May-4 Shannon's, Milford #164/R est:8000-12000
£3523 $6200 €5144 Surf (28x38cm-11x15in) s. i.d.1908 verso prov. 3-Jan-4 Collins, Maine #28/R est:2500-3500
£3800 $6460 €5548 Morning light on breaking surf (63x76cm-25x30in) s. board. 4-Nov-3 Bonhams, New Bond Street #140/R est:4000-6000
£4706 $8000 €6871 Still life (36x46cm-14x18in) s. board. 29-Oct-3 Christie's, Los Angeles #14/R est:8000-12000
£5114 $9000 €7466 Saint Ives, Cornwall, England (64x76cm-25x30in) s.d.1906 prov. 3-Jan-4 Collins, Maine #27/R est:7000-9000
£5975 $9500 €8724 Seascape with waves crashing on rocks, dark clouds in sky (64x76cm-25x30in) s. 10-Sep-3 Alderfer's, Hatfield #301/R est:7000-9000
£7263 $13000 €10604 Lingering day (64x76cm-25x30in) s. canvasboard. 14-May-4 Skinner, Boston #229/R est:10000-15000
£8242 $15000 €12033 After the storm (76x102cm-30x40in) s. 29-Jun-4 Sotheby's, New York #231/R est:15000-20000
£10857 $19000 €15851 Edge of the reef (110x123cm-43x48in) s. 19-Dec-3 Sotheby's, New York #1121/R est:12000-18000
Works on paper
£279 $475 €407 French coastline (52x72cm-20x28in) s.i.d.1893 W/C gouache. 21-Nov-3 Skinner, Boston #311/R

WAUGH, Samuel Bell (1814-1885) American
£233 $375 €340 Portrait of lady (56x48cm-22x19in) s.d.1844. 22-Feb-3 Bunte, Elgin #1256a
£248 $400 €362 Portrait of child with wings (51x38cm-20x15in) s.d.1852 oval. 22-Feb-3 Bunte, Elgin #1268a
£295 $475 €431 Portrait of lady (61x51cm-24x20in) s.d.1870 oval. 22-Feb-3 Bunte, Elgin #1268b
£299 $550 €437 Portrait of Amy Sarah Waugh (43x36cm-17x14in) s.i.verso oval. 25-Jun-4 Freeman, Philadelphia #160/R
£444 $800 €648 Portrait of a young woman (61x51cm-24x20in) s. oval. 25-Apr-4 Hindman, Chicago #1595/R
£500 $900 €730 Portrait of a child (51x51cm-20x20in) s. circular. 25-Apr-4 Hindman, Chicago #1601/R est:1500-2500
£516 $950 €753 Portrait of a young child (51x41cm-20x16in) s. 27-Jun-4 Hindman, Chicago #863/R est:600-800
Works on paper
£417 $750 €609 Belvevere torso - Vatican (43x33cm-17x13in) s.i.d.1830-35 red conte pencil. 25-Apr-4 Hindman, Chicago #1603/R

WAUTERS, Camille (1856-1919) Belgian
£769 $1285 €1100 Coucher de soleil sur l'Escaut (46x70cm-18x28in) s. 13-Oct-3 Horta, Bruxelles #365

WAUTERS, Charles Augustin (1811-1869) Belgian
£1761 $3046 €2500 Young shepherd and is dog in a cave, with pig herd outside (50x61cm-20x24in) s.d.1849 panel. 10-Dec-3 Hugo Ruef, Munich #2521/R est:2500

WAUTERS, Constant (1826-1853) Belgian
£1931 $3225 €2800 Interior scene (50x40cm-20x16in) panel. 11-Nov-3 Vendu Notarishuis, Rotterdam #173/R est:3000-5000

WAUTERS, Émile Charles (1846-1933) Belgian
£757 $1400 €1105 Horseman at dusk near a castle (53x71cm-21x28in) bears mono. 17-Jul-4 New Orleans Auction, New Orleans #172/R est:1500-2000
Works on paper
£369 $683 €550 Young woman in evening dress (60x49cm-24x19in) s. pastel. 13-Mar-4 De Vuyst, Lokeren #397

WAUTERS, Jef (1927-) Belgian
£282 $468 €400 Hierarchie (55x46cm-22x18in) mono. oil collage. 14-Jun-3 Meeting Art, Vercelli #144
£400 $724 €600 La Sainte-Vierge et l'Enfant Jesus (42x33cm-17x13in) s. 30-Mar-4 Campo, Vlaamse Kaai #228

WAXSCHLUNGER, Johann Paul (c.1660-1724) German
£3793 $6334 €5500 Still life with flowers and fruit (81x102cm-32x40in) mono. 15-Nov-3 Lempertz, Koln #1174/R est:7500

WAY, Andrew John Henry (1826-1888) American
£4749 $8500 €6934 Peaches (30x46cm-12x18in) s.d.1873 prov. 26-May-4 Doyle, New York #10/R est:5000-7000
£7821 $14000 €11419 Still life with fruit and ewer (61x51cm-24x20in) s.d.1880 prov. 6-May-4 Shannon's, Milford #33/R est:8000-12000

WAY, Charles Jones (1834-1919) British
£405 $648 €587 Shoreline (17x27cm-7x11in) s. 15-May-3 Stuker, Bern #1573/R (S.FR 850)
£2800 $4759 €4088 Paysage Suisse (51x76cm-20x30in) s.d.1878 prov. 21-Nov-3 Walker's, Ottawa #84/R est:7000-9000 (C.D 6215)
Works on paper
£255 $433 €372 The Eiger (34x49cm-13x19in) s.i. W/C. 21-Nov-3 Walker's, Ottawa #83/R (C.D 565)
£281 $523 €410 Santa Maria della Salute (24x37cm-9x15in) s. W/C. 2-Mar-4 Ritchie, Toronto #64/R (C.D 700)
£300 $555 €438 Mountains landscape with path near the Matterhorn (23x15cm-9x6in) s.i. W/C. 14-Jan-4 Brightwells, Leominster #900
£560 $1042 €818 Torquay with Torre Abbey Sands (32x42cm-13x17in) s.d.1876 W/C scratching out. 2-Mar-4 Bearnes, Exeter #333/R

WAY, Johan Vilhelm Carl (1792-1873) Swedish
Miniatures
£1100 $1969 €1606 Young lady in lace bordered black dress, red cashmere shawl (6cm-2in) s.d.1820 gilt metal frame rectangular. 25-May-4 Christie's, London #165/R est:800-1200

WAY, Thomas Robert (1862-1913) British
£1900 $3515 €2774 On the Grand Boulevards, Paris (8x13cm-3x5in) s.d.1885. 14-Jan-4 Lawrence, Crewkerne #1427/R est:800-1200

WAYCOTT, Hedley (1865-1938) American
£301 $475 €439 Autumn landscape (36x51cm-14x20in) s. panel. 6-Apr-3 William Jenack, New York #270
£426 $775 €622 Impressionist landscape haystack (58x74cm-23x29in) s.d.32. 1-Jul-4 Dan Ripley, Indianapolis #149
£471 $800 €688 Marshes (28x38cm-11x15in) s. board. 21-Nov-3 Skinner, Boston #458/R

WAYMAN, Norbury L (19/20th C) American
Works on paper
£5294 $9000 €7729 Aerial panorama of the Louisiana Purchase Exposition of 1904 (274x91cm-108x36in) mixed media pencil W/C. 7-Nov-3 Selkirks, St. Louis #567/R est:6500-7500

WEARE, John (20th C) American
£820 $1500 €1230 River north rooftops (61x66cm-24x26in) 10-Jul-4 Hindman, Chicago #550/R est:300-500

WEATHERHEAD, William Harris (1843-1903) British
£1200 $2220 €1752 Passing the time (24x35cm-9x14in) 11-Feb-4 Cheffins, Cambridge #422 est:700-1000
Works on paper
£1152 $1878 €1682 Kitchen interior with woman (58x36cm-23x14in) s. W/C. 29-Sep-3 Lilla Bukowskis, Stockholm #804 est:4000-5000 (S.KR 15000)
£2000 $3340 €2920 Devonshire girl (66x40cm-26x16in) s.d.1884 W/C exhib. 26-Jun-3 Greenslade Hunt, Taunton #477/R est:1500-2500
£2000 $3460 €2920 When the boats are out (36x51cm-14x20in) s. W/C prov. 9-Dec-3 Maynards, Vancouver #139 est:5000-6000 (C.D 4500)

£2200 $4026 €3300 Momentous letter (60x38cm-24x15in) s. W/C. 27-Jul-4 Henry Adams, Chichester #410/R est:3000-5000
£8000 $14400 €11680 Fisherman's cottage with mother and child beside sunlit window (47x63cm-19x25in) s.d.1886 W/C gouache htd white. 21-Apr-4 Tennants, Leyburn #1012/R est:6000-7000

WEATHERHILL, Sarah Ellen (fl.1858-1868) British
Works on paper
£750 $1358 €1095 Black Nab, Whitby (23x33cm-9x13in) W/C. 15-Apr-4 Richardson & Smith, Whitby #131/R
£1000 $1810 €1460 On the rocks (23x33cm-9x13in) s. W/C. 15-Apr-4 Richardson & Smith, Whitby #103/R est:1000-1500

WEATHERILL, George (1810-1890) British
Works on paper
£320 $534 €467 Waterloo Cottages, Ruswarp (10x15cm-4x6in) i.verso W/C. 10-Oct-3 Richardson & Smith, Whitby #87
£320 $563 €467 Robin Hood's Bay (20x23cm-8x9in) init. pencil. 20-May-4 Richardson & Smith, Whitby #663
£600 $1002 €876 Ship ashore in the early morning light, Whitby (10x18cm-4x7in) s. W/C. 10-Oct-3 Richardson & Smith, Whitby #198/R
£600 $1122 €900 Castleton Rigg, North Yorkshire (25x41cm-10x16in) s. W/C. 22-Jul-4 Gorringes, Lewes #2035
£800 $1272 €1160 Goathland moor near Whitby (13x22cm-5x9in) s.i.d.1885 W/C. 9-Sep-3 David Duggleby, Scarborough #126
£800 $1448 €1168 Figure and beached vessel towards Whitby (13x18cm-5x7in) W/C. 15-Apr-4 Richardson & Smith, Whitby #99/R
£1200 $2172 €1752 Looking north to Whitby Piers (8x13cm-3x5in) W/C. 30-Mar-4 David Duggleby, Scarborough #90/R est:1200-1500
£1500 $2385 €2175 Eskdale cottages, milking in the foreground (13x19cm-5x7in) s. W/C. 9-Sep-3 David Duggleby, Scarborough #113/R est:1500-2000
£1500 $2640 €2190 Beach at Saltwick (18x25cm-7x10in) W/C. 20-May-4 Richardson & Smith, Whitby #681
£1800 $2862 €2610 Whitby abbey (14x24cm-6x9in) s. W/C. 9-Sep-3 David Duggleby, Scarborough #129 est:1500-2000
£1800 $3006 €2628 Figures at Saltwick looking seaward with Whitby Abbey (13x20cm-5x8in) W/C. 10-Oct-3 Richardson & Smith, Whitby #65/R est:300-400
£1900 $3173 €2774 Shipping off Whitby (10x20cm-4x8in) s. W/C. 14-Oct-3 David Lay, Penzance #280/R est:800-1200
£2200 $3960 €3212 Coastal landscape with Whitby Abbey (13x21cm-5x8in) s. W/C. 21-Jan-4 James Thompson, Kirby Lonsdale #100
£2250 $3578 €3263 Horses and cart with boats on beach near Whitby (12x21cm-5x8in) s. W/C. 9-Sep-3 David Duggleby, Scarborough #125 est:1500-2000
£2400 $4248 €3504 Rocky coastal scene with figures (10x15cm-4x6in) s. W/C. 28-Apr-4 George Kidner, Lymington #201/R est:2000-2500
£3000 $5430 €4380 Whitby from Stakesby Fields (25x36cm-10x14in) W/C. 15-Apr-4 Richardson & Smith, Whitby #120/R est:3000-5000
£3700 $6401 €5402 Height of the Storm, Whitby, Yorkshire (13x20cm-5x8in) s. W/C bodycol. 11-Dec-3 Neales, Nottingham #525/R est:700-800
£3800 $6992 €5548 Moonlight scene at Whitby Bay with shipping and Abbey (8x13cm-3x5in) s. W/C. 12-Jun-4 Dickins, Middle Claydon #50
£4000 $7480 €5840 Shipping off the coast of Whitby (12x20cm-5x8in) s. W/C over pencil. 20-Jul-4 Sworder & Son, Bishops Stortford #650/R est:600-800
£4450 $7076 €6453 Robin Hood's Bay, unloading on the beach (9x14cm-4x6in) W/C. 9-Sep-3 David Duggleby, Scarborough #31/R est:3000-4000
£4600 $7912 €6716 Whitby Harbour (14x24cm-6x9in) W/C two. 2-Dec-3 Sotheby's, London #33/R est:1500-2000
£5400 $9774 €7884 Whitby harbour (14x25cm-6x10in) s. W/C. 30-Mar-4 David Duggleby, Scarborough #100/R est:4000-5000
£5500 $10175 €8030 Busy port (13x20cm-5x8in) s. W/C. 10-Feb-4 David Lay, Penzance #490/R est:800-1200
£7400 $13542 €10804 Ferry boat in harbour (36x53cm-14x21in) s. W/C. 27-Jan-4 Gorringes, Lewes #1701 est:800-1200

WEATHERILL, George (attrib) (1810-1890) British
Works on paper
£500 $905 €730 Beached vessel and figures on Whitby Sands, towards Abbey (10x15cm-4x6in) W/C. 15-Apr-4 Richardson & Smith, Whitby #82/R
£1600 $2928 €2336 Abbey Ruins (23x36cm-9x14in) W/C. 27-Jan-4 Gorringes, Lewes #1702 est:500-800
£1850 $3349 €2701 Coastal scene with vessels and figures (20x36cm-8x14in) W/C. 15-Apr-4 Richardson & Smith, Whitby #117/R est:2000-3000
£2200 $4004 €3212 Steam engine pulling loaded wagons through the Industrial North (24x49cm-9x19in) s. pencil W/C htd white. 1-Jul-4 Christie's, Kensington #431/R est:600-800

WEATHERILL, Mary (1834-1913) British
Works on paper
£300 $561 €450 From Swarth house (20x36cm-8x14in) init. W/C. 22-Jul-4 Gorringes, Lewes #2034
£460 $833 €672 Charlbury, Oxfordshire (11x17cm-4x7in) mono. by Richard i.d.Aug 14th 1896. 30-Mar-4 David Duggleby, Scarborough #94/R
£600 $1086 €876 Lockwood Beck before the reservoir (13x17cm-5x7in) s. W/C. 30-Mar-4 David Duggleby, Scarborough #156/R
£750 $1350 €1095 North Yorkshire Moors with Captain Cook monument in distance (46x73cm-18x29in) s.d.1902 pencil W/C htd white. 21-Apr-4 Tennants, Leyburn #941
£1200 $1908 €1740 Sandsend cottages on the front with figures and stormy seas (18x27cm-7x11in) init. W/C scratching out. 9-Sep-3 David Duggleby, Scarborough #4/R est:1200-1800
£2400 $4296 €3504 Whitby harbour (16x37cm-6x15in) s. W/C. 26-May-4 Sotheby's, Olympia #101/R est:2000-3000

WEATHERILL, Richard (1844-1913) British
£350 $616 €511 Cattle by Whitby Abbey (13x18cm-5x7in) init. board. 20-May-4 Richardson & Smith, Whitby #684
£600 $1074 €876 View of Whitby (9x12cm-4x5in) s. board. 7-Jan-4 George Kidner, Lymington #201
£1250 $1988 €1825 Off Whitby Harbour (14x25cm-6x10in) s.d.1872 verso. 18-Mar-3 Anderson & Garland, Newcastle #161j/R est:600-800
Works on paper
£800 $1336 €1168 Shipping off Whitby, the abbey in the distance (13x23cm-5x9in) s. W/C. 14-Oct-3 David Lay, Penzance #281/R
£1550 $2465 €2248 Off Whitby Harbour - beached sailing vessel (15x25cm-6x10in) s.d.1872 W/C. 9-Sep-3 David Duggleby, Scarborough #117 est:2000-3000
£5400 $8586 €7830 Harbour and West Cliff Whitby (24x36cm-9x14in) s. W/C. 9-Sep-3 David Duggleby, Scarborough #101/R est:5000-7000
£5600 $8904 €8120 Overlooking Whitby Harbour towards Tate Hill Sands and abbey (24x36cm-9x14in) s. W/C. 9-Sep-3 David Duggleby, Scarborough #102/R est:5000-7000

WEATHERSTONE, Alfred C (fl.1888-1929) British
Works on paper
£1028 $1624 €1491 Roman girls on terrace at the Mediterranean (51x80cm-20x31in) s. W/C. 2-Sep-3 Rasmussen, Copenhagen #1971/R (D.KR 11000)
£1400 $2576 €2044 Allegory of freedom (49x79cm-19x31in) s. pencil W/C. 25-Mar-4 Christie's, Kensington #219/R est:1500-2000

WEAVER, Harold Buck (1889-1961) American
£4945 $9000 €7220 Cloud patterns (86x91cm-34x36in) s. i.verso masonite prov. 15-Jun-4 John Moran, Pasadena #125 est:4000-6000
£6044 $11000 €8824 Shadows at Jeddito, Arizona (64x76cm-25x30in) s.d.44 i.verso prov. 15-Jun-4 John Moran, Pasadena #124 est:3000-5000

WEAVER, Herbert Parsons (1872-1945) British
Works on paper
£252 $464 €368 Town by the river (25x35cm-10x14in) s.d.1930 W/C. 14-Jun-4 Waddingtons, Toronto #51/R (C.D 625)
£260 $434 €380 Old houses, Lisieux, Normandy (28x15cm-11x6in) s.d.1926 W/C. 16-Oct-3 Mallams, Cheltenham #235/R

WEAVER, Jay (?-1960) American
£270 $500 €394 Irish setter (38x53cm-15x21in) s. 16-Jan-4 Aspire, Cleveland #77/R

WEAVER, Louise (1966-) Australian
Works on paper
£325 $511 €475 Treasure pond (66x51cm-26x20in) init.i.d.91 silk thread W/C. 27-Aug-3 Christie's, Sydney #577 (A.D 800)

WEAVER, Peter Malcolm (1927-) British
Works on paper
£320 $563 €467 Museum landscape (42x58cm-17x23in) s.d.1994 W/C. 18-May-4 Woolley & Wallis, Salisbury #296/R

WEAVER, Robert (20th C) American
£535 $1000 €781 Highway overpass with circus poster below (36x23cm-14x9in) s. hardboard. 26-Feb-4 Illustration House, New York #195
Works on paper
£1257 $2200 €1835 Illustration to Ian Fleming's On her Majesty's Secret Service Part 2 (51x38cm-20x15in) gouache acrylic illus board exec April 1963 exhib. 17-Dec-3 Christie's, Rockefeller NY #71/R est:3000-4000

WEAVER, T (1774-1843) British
£5200 $8632 €7592 Miranda, 6 year old cow (55x67cm-22x26in) s.d.1822. 1-Oct-3 Woolley & Wallis, Salisbury #323/R est:1500-2500

WEAVER, Thomas (1774-1843) British
£2600 $4758 €3796 Portrait of a boy on a donkey in a park with terrier (56x69cm-22x27in) s.i.d.1833. 28-Jan-4 Dreweatt Neate, Newbury #58/R est:3000-5000
£3700 $6993 €5402 Study of a pointer in an English parkland setting (41x56cm-16x22in) s.d.1806. 19-Feb-4 Rendalls, Ashburton #1607
£6400 $11264 €9344 Prize cow in a landscape (59x73cm-23x29in) init.d.1807. 18-May-4 Woolley & Wallis, Salisbury #156/R est:4000-6000
£42000 $73920 €61320 Mr Jeremiah Whitehead, Mr Cawlishaw and Mr Yates coursing in a landscape (107x153cm-42x60in) s.d.1818 prov.lit. 21-May-4 Christie's, London #79/R est:20000-30000

WEBB, Archibald (jnr) (fl.1886-1892) British
Works on paper
£300 $510 €438 Lock with boats and windmill (46x68cm-18x27in) s.d.1890 W/C. 6-Nov-3 Ambrose, Loughton #157/R

WEBB, Archibald (jnr-attrib) (fl.1886-1892) British
£3000 $4890 €4380 Smalschips nearing a Dutch port (49x75cm-19x30in) with sig. 25-Sep-3 Mellors & Kirk, Nottingham #750/R est:3000-3500

WEBB, Ben (20th C) New Zealander
Works on paper
£277 $496 €404 Portrait - Untitled (75x57cm-30x22in) chl. 11-May-4 Peter Webb, Auckland #195/R (NZ.D 800)

WEBB, Byron (fl.1846-1866) British
£3073 $5500 €4487 Racing scene (43x65cm-17x26in) bears sig.indis d.185. 6-May-4 Doyle, New York #6/R est:5000-7000

WEBB, Charles Meer (1830-1895) British

£401	$750	€585	Woman with flowers in interior (36x28cm-14x11in) s.d.1860. 29-Feb-4 Grogan, Boston #8/R
£3497	$5944	€5000	Money lender (54x60cm-21x24in) s. 22-Nov-3 Arnold, Frankfurt #709/R est:2400
£10000	$16700	€14500	Profiteer (60x73cm-24x29in) s.d.1887 prov. 15-Nov-3 Lempertz, Koln #1716/R est:8000-10000
£10000	$18000	€15000	Poacher's arrest (75x104cm-30x41in) s.d.1888. 21-Apr-4 Christie's, Amsterdam #179/R est:7000-9000

WEBB, George Alfred John (1861-?) Australian/British

£894	$1601	€1305	Bullock Team (60x103cm-24x41in) s. 10-May-4 Joel, Victoria #313 est:2500-3500 (A.D 2200)

WEBB, Henry (?) British

Works on paper

£400	$680	€584	Cottages at Grinley with two figures in foreground (23x33cm-9x13in) W/C. 5-Nov-3 Brightwells, Leominster #1073

WEBB, James (1825-1895) British

£300	$555	€438	Landscape with heather (13x23cm-5x9in) s. panel. 10-Mar-4 Sotheby's, Olympia #203/R
£540	$950	€788	On the coast, Devonshire (19x12cm-7x5in) s. i. verso artist board. 18-May-4 Fellows & Sons, Birmingham #102/R
£600	$1074	€876	On the Dutch coast (13x21cm-5x8in) s. i.verso. 26-May-4 Christie's, Kensington #694/R
£756	$1300	€1104	Fisherman in the storm (30x41cm-12x16in) s.d.1976. 7-Dec-3 Susanin's, Chicago #6090/R est:1500-2000
£1100	$2035	€1606	Coming storm (36x61cm-14x24in) s.i.d.1876 verso prov.exhib. 15-Jan-4 Christie's, Kensington #940/R est:1000-1500
£1600	$2672	€2336	River landscape with a view of a town (24x32cm-9x13in) s.i. verso panel. 21-Oct-3 Sworder & Son, Bishops Stortford #309/R est:1500-2000
£1900	$3040	€2774	Scheveningen (36x61cm-14x24in) 16-Sep-3 Bonhams, New Bond Street #62/R est:2500-3500
£2250	$3600	€3285	Stormy seascape (61x107cm-24x42in) s. 20-Sep-3 Nadeau, Windsor #146/R
£2800	$4676	€4088	Near Bala, north Wales (61x91cm-24x36in) s.d.1877 s.i.d.verso. 13-Nov-3 Christie's, Kensington #179/R est:3000-5000
£2933	$5309	€4400	Dutch coast with sailing boats and resting figures (51x76cm-20x30in) s.d. mono.d. verso. 2-Apr-4 Winterberg, Heidelberg #575/R est:2200
£3104	$5557	€4532	Dutch fishing vessels off the coast of Scotland (71x91cm-28x36in) s. 26-May-4 AB Stockholms Auktionsverk #2393/R est:20000-25000 (S.KR 42000)
£3500	$6510	€5110	Givet, France (36x61cm-14x24in) s.d.79 s.i.d.1879 verso prov. 4-Mar-4 Christie's, Kensington #573/R est:3000-5000
£4000	$7480	€6000	Carthagena (60x104cm-24x41in) s.i. 26-Jul-4 Bonhams, Bath #100/R est:5000-7000
£4000	$6360	€5800	Fortress (76x127cm-30x50in) s. 9-Sep-3 Bonhams, Knightsbridge #232/R est:2000-3000
£5249	$9500	€7664	Panoramic city view (61x91cm-24x36in) s.d.1877-78. 3-Apr-4 Neal Auction Company, New Orleans #140/R est:10000-15000
£6000	$10020	€8760	Heidelberg (76x107cm-30x42in) s.d.1878. 13-Nov-3 Christie's, Kensington #339/R est:5000-7000
£6500	$11050	€9490	Ferry (95x87cm-37x34in) s. 27-Nov-3 Sotheby's, London #396/R est:5000-7000
£12000	$21840	€17520	Fisherfolk on the coast of Holland (89x51cm-35x20in) s. 5-Feb-4 Mellors & Kirk, Nottingham #550/R est:10000-15000
£18000	$30600	€26280	Unloading the catch (62x102cm-24x40in) s. 27-Nov-3 Sotheby's, London #395/R est:10000-15000

Works on paper

£500	$850	€730	Near Beddgelert, North Wales (20x25cm-8x10in) s.i.d.1876 pencil W/C. 4-Nov-3 Rowley Fine Art, Newmarket #371/R

WEBB, Kenneth (1927-) British

£290	$455	€421	Still life with a vase of flowers (20x16cm-8x6in) acrylic on card. 27-Aug-3 Mallams, Oxford #630
£450	$765	€657	Mumbles (23x36cm-9x14in) mono. board. 5-Nov-3 John Nicholson, Haslemere #562
£750	$1395	€1095	Portrait of a young girl (61x40cm-24x16in) s. 3-Mar-4 John Ross, Belfast #15
£800	$1464	€1168	Stroll by the harbour (61x43cm-24x17in) board. 2-Jun-4 John Ross, Belfast #211
£900	$1422	€1305	Horse and cart passing Alton Mill, Suffolk (40x61cm-16x24in) s. lit. 3-Sep-3 Bonhams, Bury St Edmunds #413
£1408	$2437	€2000	Coastal landscape (51x61cm-20x24in) s. 10-Dec-3 Bonhams & James Adam, Dublin #155/R est:1200-1800
£1477	$2613	€2200	The Mumbles (25x38cm-10x15in) init. board painted c.1949-1952. 27-Apr-4 Whyte's, Dublin #21/R est:1800-2200
£1711	$3147	€2600	West of Ireland, coastal landscape with thatched cottages (40x51cm-16x20in) s. canvasboard. 22-Jun-4 De Veres Art Auctions, Dublin #255 est:2000-3000
£1900	$3477	€2774	Downings, Donegal (35x76cm-14x30in) s.d.May 1968 verso. 2-Jun-4 John Ross, Belfast #130 est:1800-2000
£2200	$3476	€3190	Susanna and the Elders (40x60cm-16x24in) s. lit. 3-Sep-3 Bonhams, Bury St Edmunds #414/R est:1800-2500
£2200	$4114	€3300	Turf shed (38x58cm-15x23in) s.d.61. 21-Jul-4 John Nicholson, Haslemere #122 est:1800-2000
£3087	$5464	€4600	Poppies in a landscape (39x48cm-15x19in) s. painted c.1960. 27-Apr-4 Whyte's, Dublin #83/R est:4000-6000
£3217	$5469	€4600	The old mill (41x61cm-16x24in) s. 18-Nov-3 Whyte's, Dublin #100/R est:4000-5000
£3239	$5183	€4600	Dawn of spring (61x51cm-24x20in) s. prov. 16-Sep-3 Whyte's, Dublin #128/R est:3000-4000
£3356	$5940	€5000	Carrickfergus Castle and quay, County Antrim (41x102cm-16x40in) s. exhib. 27-Apr-4 Whyte's, Dublin #107/R est:5000-7000
£3357	$5706	€4800	Cottages, Atlantic Drive, Donegal (41x61cm-16x24in) s. i.verso. 18-Nov-3 Whyte's, Dublin #35/R est:4000-6000
£3378	$6385	€5000	Farm buildings, near Ballynahinch, County Down (38x91cm-15x36in) s. 17-Feb-4 Whyte's, Dublin #178/R est:4000-6000
£3500	$6510	€5110	Atlantic drive, Donegal (40x101cm-16x40in) s. 3-Mar-4 John Ross, Belfast #67 est:2500-3500
£3636	$6182	€5200	Cottage interior (51x61cm-20x24in) s.d.1968 i.verso. 18-Nov-3 Whyte's, Dublin #104/R est:5000-7000
£3916	$6657	€5600	Ballywater, County Down (38x91cm-15x36in) s. exhib. 18-Nov-3 Whyte's, Dublin #37/R est:4000-6000
£4161	$7365	€6200	Donegal mosaic (41x60cm-16x24in) s.d.1961 i.verso canvas on board exhib. 27-Apr-4 Whyte's, Dublin #15/R est:4000-6000
£4225	$6761	€6000	Four Courts, Dublin (41x102cm-16x40in) s. prov. 16-Sep-3 Whyte's, Dublin #123/R est:5000-7000
£4300	$7396	€6278	Mount Cashel from Errelough, Connemara (40x101cm-16x40in) s. 3-Dec-3 John Ross, Belfast #136 est:2500-3000
£4430	$7840	€6600	Sunset reflections (36x91cm-14x36in) s. i.verso prov. 27-Apr-4 Whyte's, Dublin #198/R est:4000-6000
£4730	$8939	€7000	Spanish gate, Galway (90x38cm-35x15in) s. i.on stretcher. 17-Feb-4 Whyte's, Dublin #68/R est:5000-7000
£4755	$8084	€6800	Farm buildings, Ards Peninsular - Five Roads End (38x91cm-15x36in) s. 18-Nov-3 Whyte's, Dublin #171/R est:4000-6000
£6690	$10704	€9500	Spring morning (51x91cm-20x36in) s. 16-Sep-3 Whyte's, Dublin #209/R est:7000-9000

Works on paper

£1000	$1660	€1460	Coal house (35x53cm-14x21in) s. mixed media. 1-Oct-3 John Ross, Belfast #230 est:800-1000
£1400	$2324	€2044	Snow scene (50x30cm-20x12in) s.d.59 mixed media. 1-Oct-3 John Ross, Belfast #136 est:700-800
£1831	$2930	€2600	Blanket bog, Connemara (36x53cm-14x21in) s. W/C. 16-Sep-3 Whyte's, Dublin #145/R est:3000-4000
£2162	$4086	€3200	Long walk, Galway, from the Claddagh (38x56cm-15x22in) s. W/C gouache. 17-Feb-4 Whyte's, Dublin #180/R est:3000-4000
£2162	$4086	€3200	Cottages, Atlantic Drive, County Donegal (38x53cm-15x21in) s. i.d.1984 verso W/C gouache. 17-Feb-4 Whyte's, Dublin #240/R est:2000-3000
£3087	$5464	€4600	Snow scene (50x28cm-20x11in) s.d.1959 gouache board prov. 27-Apr-4 Whyte's, Dublin #4/R est:3000-5000
£3826	$6771	€5700	Buttermilk Lane, with St Nicholas Church in the distance, Galway (56x39cm-22x15in) s. W/C gouache artist board. 27-Apr-4 Whyte's, Dublin #195/R est:3000-5000
£5068	$9578	€7500	Connemara Garden, poppies and daisies (56x76cm-22x30in) s. W/C gouache pastel. 17-Feb-4 Whyte's, Dublin #241/R est:4000-5000

WEBB, Marilyn (20th C) New Zealander

Works on paper

£284	$525	€415	Still water and summer snow from being in the Maniototo (24x32cm-9x13in) s.i.d.2001 W/C. 13-Jul-4 Watson's, Christchurch #5/R (NZ.D 800)

WEBB, Susan (20th C) Irish?

Works on paper

£319	$502	€460	Reclining nude (32x48cm-13x19in) s.d.94 pastel. 26-Aug-3 James Adam, Dublin #44/R

WEBB, Thomas (20th C) American

£1497	$2500	€2186	Romantic couple by firelight (84x102cm-33x40in) s. exec.c.1930. 15-Nov-3 Illustration House, New York #125/R est:2400-3200

WEBB, W B (?) ?

£731	$1257	€1067	After the storm (50x68cm-20x27in) bears sig. 7-Dec-3 Uppsala Auktionskammare, Uppsala #115/R (S.KR 9500)

WEBB, William (1790-1856) British

£900	$1656	€1314	Chestnut hunter in a stable (63x75cm-25x30in) s.d.1829. 10-Jun-4 Christie's, Kensington #74/R
£1500	$2490	€2190	Bay hunter in a landscape (76x21cm-30x8in) 1-Oct-3 Woolley & Wallis, Salisbury #215/R est:800-1200
£1800	$3060	€2628	Bright bay in a landscape (76x91cm-30x36in) 27-Nov-3 Christie's, Kensington #81/R est:2000-3000
£16758	$30500	€24467	John Myyton and his hounds (91x112cm-36x44in) 7-Feb-4 Sloans & Kenyon, Bethesda #1284/R est:25000-30000

WEBB, William (fl.1855-1873) British

£3793	$6334	€5500	Harbour with fishing boats (76x127cm-30x50in) s. 9-Jul-3 Hugo Ruef, Munich #239/R est:4500

WEBB, William Edward (1862-1903) British

£1600	$2960	€2336	Peel herring boat (24x19cm-9x7in) s. indis.d. 14-Jul-4 Bonhams, Chester #352/R est:1200-1600
£2000	$3340	€2920	Port St Mary, Isle of Man (41x21cm-16x8in) s. i.verso. 8-Oct-3 Christie's, Kensington #748/R est:800-1200
£2000	$3440	€2920	Unloading the catch (51x76cm-20x30in) s. 5-Dec-3 Chrystals Auctions, Isle of Man #246/R est:2200-3200
£2800	$5012	€4088	Low tide in an Isle of Man Harbour (36x25cm-14x10in) s. 26-May-4 Christie's, Kensington #718/R est:2000-3000
£3000	$5550	€4380	Peel harbour, Isle of Man (54x95cm-21x37in) s.i. 10-Feb-4 Bonhams, Knightsbridge #105/R est:3000-5000
£5000	$9000	€7300	Isle of man harbour (31x61cm-12x24in) s. 21-Jan-4 Sotheby's, Olympia #368/R est:1000-1500
£5300	$9805	€7738	Near the Mousehold, Cornish Coast (39x59cm-15x23in) s. s.i. verso. 14-Jul-4 Bonhams, Chester #351/R est:2500-3500
£5600	$8960	€8176	Unloading fishing boats on Manx coast (41x61cm-16x24in) s. s.i.verso. 16-Sep-3 Bonhams, New Bond Street #27/R est:2000-3000
£5800	$9976	€8468	Harbour scene (61x91cm-24x36in) s.d.1892. 2-Dec-3 Sotheby's, London #41/R est:1500-2000
£6182	$9705	€8964	Harbour scene, possibly Peel (54x95cm-21x37in) s. 27-Aug-3 Dunbar Sloane, Wellington #86/R est:9000-12000 (NZ.D 17000)
£6200	$11594	€9052	Harbour with boats, shipping and figures (53x94cm-21x37in) s. prov. 27-Feb-4 Thomson, Roddick & Medcalf, Carlisle #250
£6500	$10400	€9490	Fishing fleet at Peel, Isle of Man, beached at low tide (76x127cm-30x50in) s. 16-Sep-3 Bonhams, New Bond Street #33/R est:4000-6000
£6500	$11050	€9490	Mersey, Liverpool (40x60cm-16x24in) 1-Dec-3 Bonhams, Bath #145/R est:2000-3000
£6600	$11220	€9636	Busy harbour, possibly Peel (40x60cm-16x24in) s. 1-Dec-3 Bonhams, Bath #146/R est:2000-3000
£7000	$11200	€10220	Peel Castle, Isle of Man (41x61cm-16x24in) s. s.i.verso. 16-Sep-3 Bonhams, New Bond Street #26/R est:2000-3000
£7000	$12530	€10220	Fishing boats in the harbour at Dordrecht with sunset (76x127cm-30x50in) s. 26-May-4 Christie's, Kensington #716/R est:5000-8000
£7600	$12692	€11096	At Peel Isle of Man. Peel fishing boats unloading the catch (36x61cm-14x24in) s. pair. 20-Jun-3 Chrystals Auctions, Isle of Man #240b est:6000-7500

£13000 $22360 €18980 Manx miracle and peel fishing boats in harbour (76x127cm-30x50in) s. 5-Dec-3 Chrystals Auctions, Isle of Man #255 est:10000-15000
Works on paper
£2300 $3956 €3358 Unloading the catch (33x23cm-13x9in) s. W/C. 5-Dec-3 Chrystals Auctions, Isle of Man #257 est:1000-1500

WEBB, William Edward (attrib) (1862-1903) British
£290 $458 €421 Fishing smacks entering a port (30x36cm-12x14in) init. wood panel. 17-Nov-2 Desmond Judd, Cranbrook #889
£1400 $2590 €2044 Wreck of the Nable, Isle of Man (76x128cm-30x50in) bears sig. i.verso. 10-Mar-4 Sotheby's, Olympia #201/R est:1000-1500

WEBBE, William J (fl.1853-1878) British
Works on paper
£350 $644 €511 Donkeys and a camel resting at the wayside (42x30cm-17x12in) s. pencil W/C htd white. 25-Mar-4 Christie's, Kensington #68/R

WEBBER, O S (19th C) American
£2273 $4000 €3319 Seascape with a sloop sailing off of a light ship (51x76cm-20x30in) s. 22-May-4 Pook & Pook, Downington #544/R est:1500-2000

WEBBER, R (?) British?
£600 $1092 €876 Figures in a country market. after Stanhope Forbes. 4-Feb-4 John Nicholson, Haslemere #169

WEBBER, Wesley (1841-1914) American
£559 $1000 €816 Ships in a harbour. Ship at dusk (51x76cm-20x30in) s. pair. 16-Mar-4 Bonhams & Butterfields, San Francisco #6137/R
£659 $1100 €962 Ship on the seas (38x61cm-15x24in) d.1904. 17-Oct-3 Du Mouchelle, Detroit #42/R
£692 $1100 €1010 Moonlight sail (92x66cm-36x26in) s. 12-Sep-3 Skinner, Boston #301/R
£753 $1400 €1099 Maine inlet with seated figures conversing (30x56cm-12x22in) s. 6-Mar-4 North East Auctions, Portsmouth #229
£755 $1200 €1102 Open pasture (19x33cm-7x13in) s. 12-Sep-3 Skinner, Boston #269/R
£838 $1500 €1223 Still life with fruit (26x35cm-10x14in) s. 14-May-4 Skinner, Boston #98/R est:2500-3500
£1006 $1600 €1469 Storm tossed shore (41x66cm-16x26in) s.d.78. 12-Sep-3 Skinner, Boston #295/R
£1196 $2200 €1746 By the river at dusk (33x61cm-13x24in) s.d.83. 25-Jun-4 Freeman, Philadelphia #270/R est:1500-2500
£1221 $2100 €1783 Cattle watering, a town in the distance (36x61cm-14x24in) s. 7-Dec-3 Freeman, Philadelphia #112 est:1500-2500
£1816 $3250 €2651 Untitled (30x50cm-12x20in) 9-Jan-4 Du Mouchelle, Detroit #2005/R est:2000-3500
£2160 $3500 €3132 Ocean sunset (41x61cm-16x24in) 8-Aug-3 Barridorf, Portland #148/R est:2500-3500
£2469 $4000 €3580 Sunlit coastal cliffs and sea (36x51cm-14x20in) s. 8-Aug-3 Barridorf, Portland #56/R est:5000-7000
£2825 $5000 €4125 Busy shore (38x61cm-15x24in) s.d.1875. 2-May-4 Grogan, Boston #30/R
£4088 $6500 €5968 Minot's light (77x102cm-30x40in) s. 12-Sep-3 Skinner, Boston #290/R est:12000

WEBBER, Wesley (attrib) (1841-1914) American
£1202 $2200 €1803 Sloop near a lighthouse (43x71cm-17x28in) 29-Jul-4 Eldred, East Dennis #291/R est:1200-1400

WEBER, Adolf (1925-) Swiss
£318 $528 €461 Little tree in snow (67x40cm-26x16in) s.d.1985. 13-Jun-3 Zofingen, Switzerland #3069 (S.FR 700)
£1727 $2867 €2504 Artist's family in garden (81x100cm-32x39in) s. 13-Jun-3 Zofingen, Switzerland #3068/R est:2000 (S.FR 3800)

WEBER, Alfred (1859-1936) Swiss
£270 $432 €394 Swiss mountain scene with figures. 17-May-3 Hogben, Folkstone #177
£552 $921 €800 Une bonne nouvelle (24x14cm-9x6in) s. panel. 12-Nov-3 Chassaing Rivet, Toulouse #99
Works on paper
£612 $1096 €900 Un perroquet derobant sa dignite a un cardinal (33x25cm-13x10in) s. W/C black pencil. 19-Mar-4 Piasa, Paris #195

WEBER, Alfred Charles (1862-1922) French
£1333 $2400 €1946 Moment's diversion (46x37cm-18x15in) s. panel prov. 21-Jan-4 Sotheby's, New York #252/R est:4000-6000
£1840 $3000 €2686 Game of chess (97x117cm-38x46in) s. panel. 24-Sep-3 Doyle, New York #92/R est:2000-3000
£14500 $24940 €21170 La vieille chanson (60x75cm-24x30in) s. panel. 3-Dec-3 Christie's, London #76/R est:10000-15000

WEBER, Andreas Paul (1893-1980) German
Works on paper
£327 $591 €490 In conversation (18x16cm-7x6in) s. Indian ink feltpen pencil. 2-Apr-4 Winterberg, Heidelberg #1726/R
£347 $580 €500 Transitoriness of painting (24x30cm-9x12in) s. i. verso Indian ink board. 25-Oct-3 Dr Lehr, Berlin #527/R
£347 $580 €500 Death and the devil - chess game (8x15cm-3x6in) Indian ink. 24-Oct-3 Ketterer, Hamburg #1143/R
£347 $580 €500 Bird - the speaker (18x13cm-7x5in) s.mono. Indian ink. 24-Oct-3 Ketterer, Hamburg #1144/R
£360 $652 €540 Successful hunt (43x52cm-17x20in) s. Indian ink sketch verso. 2-Apr-4 Winterberg, Heidelberg #1724
£417 $696 €600 The correction (30x21cm-12x8in) Indian ink. 24-Oct-3 Ketterer, Hamburg #1142/R
£521 $870 €750 Genius and the little spirits (25x36cm-10x14in) mono.i. Indian ink. 24-Oct-3 Ketterer, Hamburg #577/R
£590 $986 €850 Escapee (26x48cm-10x19in) s.mono.i.d. Indian ink. 24-Oct-3 Ketterer, Hamburg #578/R
£867 $1560 €1300 May bowl (46x57cm-18x22in) s. 24-Apr-4 Dr Lehr, Berlin #490/R
£1049 $1783 €1500 Skaters (34x48cm-13x19in) s. Indian ink chk graphite. 29-Nov-3 Villa Grisebach, Berlin #943/R est:1500-1800

WEBER, Anton (1833-1909) German
£552 $922 €800 Chope, bouteille, verre de vin, hareng et pipe (34x46cm-13x18in) s. 17-Nov-3 Tajan, Paris #98

WEBER, August (1817-1873) German
£694 $1160 €1000 Moonlit river landscape (38x46cm-15x18in) s.d. prov. 24-Oct-3 Ketterer, Hamburg #119/R

WEBER, August (1888-1957) Swiss
£260 $465 €380 Mountain pasture with crocus (66x55cm-26x22in) s. 22-Mar-4 Philippe Schuler, Zurich #6061 (S.FR 600)

WEBER, Bruce (1946-) American
Photographs
£2395 $4000 €3497 George Upper Sarnac Lake (58x48cm-23x19in) s.i.d.1983 verso num.7/15 gelatin silver print prov. 17-Oct-3 Phillips, New York #253/R est:4000-6000
£2797 $4755 €4000 On the rooftop of the Shangri La, Santa Monica (42x34cm-17x13in) s.i. num.2/15 verso gelatin silver. 28-Nov-3 Bassenge, Berlin #4498/R est:4000

WEBER, C Phillip (1849-1921) American
£943 $1500 €1377 Moonlit pond. Transporting hay along a river (25x20cm-10x8in) s. pair prov. 13-Sep-3 Weschler, Washington #732/R est:1000-1500

WEBER, Carl (1850-1921) American
£1135 $2100 €1657 Bavaria (51x79cm-20x31in) s. 18-Jan-4 Carlsen Gallery, Greenville #167/R
£1136 $2000 €1659 Summer evening, Cranbury Lake, New Jersey (58x89cm-23x35in) s.d.1874. 23-May-4 Treadway Gallery, Cincinnati #534/R est:3000-5000
£1522 $2800 €2222 Sheep in a landscape (43x56cm-17x22in) s. 27-Jun-4 Freeman, Philadelphia #98/R est:2000-3000
£2907 $5000 €4244 Willow Creek Park, Philadelphia (56x91cm-22x36in) s. 7-Dec-3 Freeman, Philadelphia #106 est:4000-6000
£6077 $11000 €8872 Covered wagon and cattle in a landscape (51x91cm-20x36in) s. prov. 31-Mar-4 Sotheby's, New York #91/R est:4000-6000
Works on paper
£229 $375 €332 Pastoral landscape with grazing sheep (51x74cm-20x29in) s. W/C. 4-Jun-3 Alderfer's, Hatfield #415/R
£284 $475 €415 Herder with flock of sheep (38x69cm-15x27in) s. W/C. 20-Jun-3 Freeman, Philadelphia #72/R
£284 $475 €415 Cows in a landscape (46x70cm-18x28in) s. W/C. 16-Nov-3 Bonhams & Butterfields, Los Angeles #7041/R
£295 $550 €431 Landscape with grazing sheep (25x41cm-10x16in) s. W/C. 3-Mar-4 Alderfer's, Hatfield #307
£346 $550 €505 Figures walking in pastoral landscape (30x61cm-12x24in) s. W/C. 10-Sep-3 Alderfer's, Hatfield #392/R
£363 $650 €530 Landscape with figures in a boat next to a river (36x69cm-14x27in) W/C. 10-Jan-4 Pook & Pook, Downington #154/R
£373 $600 €545 Springtime flock (43x64cm-17x25in) s. W/C. 20-Aug-3 James Julia, Fairfield #1640/R
£377 $600 €550 Landscape with figures walking along lakeside road (30x61cm-12x24in) s. W/C. 10-Sep-3 Alderfer's, Hatfield #393/R
£389 $650 €568 Sheep by a brook in a landscape (43x69cm-17x27in) s. W/C. 20-Jun-3 Freeman, Philadelphia #66/R
£407 $650 €594 Landscape with river (30x48cm-12x19in) s. 20-Sep-3 Pook & Pook, Downington #480/R
£469 $750 €685 Coastal landscape (30x48cm-12x19in) s. W/C. 20-Sep-3 Pook & Pook, Downington #479/R
£509 $850 €743 Boats at dusk (41x64cm-16x25in) s. W/C. 20-Jun-3 Freeman, Philadelphia #26/R
£543 $1000 €793 Boats in an estuary (30x61cm-12x24in) s. W/C. 25-Jun-4 Freeman, Philadelphia #86/R
£625 $1000 €913 Spring landscape with flock of sheep and cottages (58x89cm-23x35in) s. W/C. 20-Sep-3 Pook & Pook, Downington #197/R
£643 $1150 €939 Sheep under apple trees (51x86cm-20x34in) s. W/C. 8-Jan-4 James Julia, Fairfield #832/R est:1200-1800
£758 $1250 €1099 Apple blossoms, with sheep in a landscape (36x66cm-14x26in) s. W/C. 7-Jul-3 Schrager Galleries, Milwaukee #1440
£1395 $2400 €2037 Pasture at evening, Delaware County, Pennsylvania (46x71cm-18x28in) s. W/C. 6-Dec-3 Pook & Pook, Downington #124/R est:1000-1500

WEBER, Evarist Adam (1887-?) German
£2098 $3503 €3000 Fishermen pulling boat onto shore (80x242cm-31x95in) s.d.19 i. verso triptych. 9-Oct-3 Michael Zeller, Lindau #793/R est:3000

WEBER, Fred W (1890-?) American
£353 $650 €515 Late fall landscape with buildings (41x51cm-16x20in) s.d.41 canvasboard. 9-Jun-4 Alderfer's, Hatfield #541
£538 $1000 €785 Farm buildings with rolling hills (30x41cm-12x16in) s.d.52 board. 3-Mar-4 Alderfer's, Hatfield #436 est:200-300

WEBER, Hugo (1918-1971) Swiss
Works on paper
£339 $577 €495 Untitled (31x44cm-12x17in) s.d.58 ink col clk. 22-Nov-3 Burkhard, Luzern #19/R (S.FR 750)
£830 $1527 €1212 Untitled (56x76cm-22x30in) s.d.1954 Indian ink brush prov. 8-Jun-4 Germann, Zurich #75/R (S.FR 1900)

£1448 $2462 €2114 Untitled (50x65cm-20x26in) s.d.50 gouache. 22-Nov-3 Burkhard, Luzern #14/R est:2000-2400 (S.FR 3200)
£1448 $2462 €2114 Untitled (50x65cm-20x26in) s.d.1957 gouache varnish. 22-Nov-3 Burkhard, Luzern #20/R est:2400-2800 (S.FR 3200)

WEBER, Ilse (1908-1984) Swiss
Works on paper
£1226 $1987 €1790 Untitled (33x24cm-13x9in) s.d. W/C pencil col pen prov. 24-May-3 Burkhard, Luzern #35/R est:2500-3000 (S.FR 2600)
£1321 $2140 €1929 Coffee (22x34cm-9x13in) s.d.78 W/C prov. 24-May-3 Burkhard, Luzern #34/R est:2500-3000 (S.FR 2800)

WEBER, J (?) ?
Prints
£2802 $5155 €4091 Hallwyler See with Schloss Brestenberg (41x133cm-16x52in) s.i. col etching. 26-Mar-4 Koller, Zurich #3323/R est:5000-7000 (S.FR 6500)

WEBER, Jean (19th C) French?
£6207 $10366 €9000 Adam et Eve (55x90cm-22x35in) s. 17-Nov-3 Delorme & Bocage, Paris #128/R est:6000-8000

WEBER, Johann (fl.1840s) Austrian
Works on paper
£268 $494 €400 Romantic landscape with ruins (18x24cm-7x9in) s.d.1844 gouache. 26-Mar-4 Dorotheum, Vienna #199/R

WEBER, Kurt (1893-1964) Austrian
£2416 $4325 €3600 Black white grey composition (63x54cm-25x21in) 25-May-4 Dorotheum, Vienna #200/R est:3600-4500
Works on paper
£333 $600 €500 Hilmteichschloss in Graz (42x58cm-17x23in) pencil W/C. 22-Apr-4 Dorotheum, Graz #75/R
£872 $1562 €1300 Untitled (42x30cm-17x12in) W/C Indian ink. 27-May-4 Dorotheum, Graz #114/R

WEBER, Maria (19th C) German
£13889 $23611 €20000 In the dressing room (73x133cm-29x52in) s. 28-Oct-3 Christie's, Amsterdam #69/R est:6000-8000

WEBER, Max (1881-1961) American
£4624 $8000 €6751 Winter twilight (76x102cm-30x40in) s. exhib. 15-Dec-3 Hindman, Chicago #7/R est:8000-12000
£14205 $25000 €20739 Woman with bird (51x64cm-20x25in) s.d.50 prov.exhib. 19-May-4 Sotheby's, New York #171/R est:15000-25000
£14371 $24000 €20982 The comb (76x61cm-30x24in) s.d.1952 prov.exhib. 9-Oct-3 Christie's, Rockefeller NY #112/R est:15000-25000
£17188 $27500 €25094 Reading the scroll (64x76cm-25x30in) s.d.1937. 20-Sep-3 Bunte, Elgin #1266 est:20000-30000
£227273 $400000 €331819 Imaginary portrait of a woman (91x61cm-36x24in) s.d.1913 prov.exhib.lit. 19-May-4 Sotheby's, New York #136/R est:400000-600000
Prints
£1622 $3000 €2368 New York (24x17cm-9x7in) s. hand col lithograph edition of 50. 12-Feb-4 Christie's, Rockefeller NY #288/R est:2000-3000
Sculpture
£2826 $5200 €4126 Untitled (13cm-5in) i.d.1916 num.1/3 bronze. 10-Jun-4 Swann Galleries, New York #253/R est:1500-2500
Works on paper
£262 $450 €383 Woman in blue (15x10cm-6x4in) s.d.49 W/C. 2-Dec-3 Christie's, Rockefeller NY #98/R
£559 $950 €816 Still life vase with flowers (33x23cm-13x9in) s. W/C paper on board exhib. 5-Nov-3 Doyle, New York #79/R
£625 $1000 €913 Female figure study (11x13cm-4x5in) s.d.1943 brush ink wash card. 18-Sep-3 Swann Galleries, New York #682/R
£1188 $1900 €1734 Interior scene with seated women (13x11cm-5x4in) s. W/C gouache card. 18-Sep-3 Swann Galleries, New York #683/R est:2000-3000
£2874 $4800 €4196 Still life (37x39cm-15x15in) pastel W/C pencil prov. 9-Oct-3 Christie's, Rockefeller NY #108/R est:6000-8000
£3167 $5290 €4624 Waiting (60x44cm-24x17in) s.i.d.1957 W/C gouache prov. 17-Nov-3 Waddingtons, Toronto #20/R est:6000-8000 (C.D 7000)
£9890 $18000 €14439 Spring (49x33cm-19x13in) s.d.1918 pastel paper on board prov.exhib. 29-Jun-4 Sotheby's, New York #319/R est:15000-20000

WEBER, Mili (1891-1978) Swiss
Works on paper
£591 $981 €857 Children visiting the Christ child (16x13cm-6x5in) mono. i. verso W/C. 13-Jun-3 Zofingen, Switzerland #3070/R (S.FR 1300)
£661 $1123 €965 Children's portraits (17x17cm-7x7in) mono. i. verso W/C three. 5-Nov-3 Dobiaschofsky, Bern #3786 (S.FR 1500)

WEBER, Otis S (19th C) American
£806 $1500 €1177 Grand Menan (61x91cm-24x36in) s.d.1878 i.verso. 6-Mar-4 Harvey Clar, Oakland #1582
£872 $1500 €1273 Owls Head Lighthouse with Penobscott natives (30x51cm-12x20in) s. 7-Dec-3 Grogan, Boston #54
Works on paper
£35294 $60000 €51529 Distant ships (36x52cm-14x20in) s. W/C. 21-Nov-3 Skinner, Boston #312/R est:800-1200

WEBER, Otto (1832-1888) German
£533 $971 €800 Cows by water trough in mountain pasture (40x63cm-16x25in) s. 30-Jun-4 Neumeister, Munich #746/R
Works on paper
£4800 $8160 €7008 Changing pastures (49x72cm-19x28in) s. pencil W/C. 19-Nov-3 Tennants, Leyburn #996/R est:1200-1400

WEBER, Paul (1823-1916) American/German
£274 $466 €400 Mountain landscape (45x30cm-18x12in) 5-Nov-3 Hugo Ruef, Munich #1176
£336 $617 €500 Shepherd (49x32cm-19x13in) s. 25-Mar-4 Dr Fritz Nagel, Stuttgart #776/R
£385 $662 €550 Cows on river flats (27x32cm-11x13in) s. 4-Dec-3 Neumeister, Munich #2868
£451 $745 €650 Woodland path (30x21cm-12x8in) s. i.d.1912 verso canvas on board. 3-Jul-3 Neumeister, Munich #2935
£604 $1111 €900 Stream in winter (18x24cm-7x9in) board. 24-Mar-4 Hugo Ruef, Munich #1142
£761 $1400 €1111 Rural landscape with figures by a pond (18x23cm-7x9in) s. oil paperboard. 8-Jun-4 Auctions by the Bay, Alameda #1015/R
£765 $1300 €1117 As the sun sets - snowy churchyard (47x40cm-19x16in) s.d.1884. 21-Nov-3 Skinner, Boston #212/R est:1000-1500
£940 $1729 €1400 Peasant woman with cow (39x54cm-15x21in) s. 26-Mar-4 Ketterer, Hamburg #221/R
£1905 $3410 €2800 Inn valley (35x45cm-14x18in) s. 17-Mar-4 Neumeister, Munich #658/R est:1500
£2431 $3962 €3500 Cows on village track (37x55cm-15x22in) s. 24-Sep-3 Neumeister, Munich #599/R est:2800
£4977 $8312 €7266 Shepherd and flock in an extensive landscape (91x138cm-36x54in) s. 17-Nov-3 Waddingtons, Toronto #13/R est:12000-14000 (C.D 11000)
£28409 $50000 €41477 Cascading waterfall (122x102cm-48x40in) s.d.1856 prov. 19-May-4 Sotheby's, New York #96/R est:40000-60000
Works on paper
£251 $450 €422 Old Swedes Church, Wicaco, Philadelphia (20x28cm-8x11in) i. W/C. 20-Mar-4 Pook & Pook, Downington #554/R
£403 $741 €600 Woodland path in summer with flowers (11x18cm-4x7in) st.sig. W/C on pencil board. 26-Mar-4 Venator & Hansten, Koln #1663

WEBER, Roland (20th C) ?
£386 $641 €560 Provence street (28x33cm-11x13in) s. masonite. 13-Jun-3 Zofingen, Switzerland #3071 (S.FR 850)

WEBER, Rudolf (1872-?) Austrian
£462 $837 €675 Dutch port (59x79cm-23x31in) s. board. 30-Mar-4 Stephan Welz, Johannesburg #410 est:4000-6000 (SA.R 5500)
£805 $1498 €1200 Lakeside scene with villas and hills, Lake Garda (60x80cm-24x31in) s. 5-Mar-4 Wendl, Rudolstadt #4012/R
£1014 $1814 €1500 Lake Como (39x59cm-15x23in) s. board. 6-May-4 Michael Zeller, Lindau #934/R est:1500

WEBER, Theodore (1838-1907) French
£1385 $2382 €1980 Men unloading boat on beach (36x56cm-14x22in) mono. 5-Dec-3 Michael Zeller, Lindau #828/R est:1500
£1477 $2600 €2156 Arrival at Boulogne (33x56cm-13x22in) s. 23-May-4 Hindman, Chicago #30/R est:2000-3000
£1600 $2720 €2336 Off to the fishing grounds (33x55cm-13x22in) s. 19-Nov-3 Bonhams, New Bond Street #123/R est:1500-2000
£2800 $4480 €4088 Unloading the catch (34x55cm-13x22in) s. 16-Sep-3 Bonhams, New Bond Street #40/R est:3000-5000
£2867 $4931 €4100 Gros temps, Treport (17x25cm-7x10in) s. panel. 5-Dec-3 Chochon-Barre & Allardi, Paris #155/R est:2500-3000
£2886 $5166 €4300 Retour de peche dans un port du Nord (33x55cm-13x22in) s. 25-May-4 Chambelland & Giafferi, Paris #113/R est:1500-2000

WEBER, Werner (1892-1977) Swiss
£317 $529 €463 Black grapes on tin plate with wine glass (28x33cm-11x13in) lit. 24-Jun-3 Germann, Zurich #1078 (S.FR 700)
£339 $567 €495 Pink rose in glass (27x22cm-11x9in) lit. 24-Jun-3 Germann, Zurich #1079 (S.FR 750)
£407 $692 €594 Ceramic pot, book, cigar and match (27x35cm-11x14in) s. 19-Nov-3 Fischer, Luzern #2339/R (S.FR 900)
£428 $736 €625 Still life (35x28cm-14x11in) s.d.1943. 8-Dec-3 Philippe Schuler, Zurich #3362 (S.FR 950)
£995 $1662 €1453 Black grapes (33x46cm-13x18in) s.d.1934. 24-Jun-3 Germann, Zurich #1080 est:700-900 (S.FR 2200)
£1322 $2247 €1930 White roses in vase (38x46cm-15x18in) s. lit. 7-Nov-3 Dobiaschofsky, Bern #217/R est:2200 (S.FR 3000)
£1584 $2740 €2313 Still life with books, shell and jug (39x55cm-15x22in) s. 9-Dec-3 Sotheby's, Zurich #30/R est:3500-4500 (S.FR 3500)

WEBER-FULOP, Elisabeth (1883-?) Hungarian
£284 $474 €400 Interior (87x74cm-34x29in) s. board. 14-Oct-3 Dorotheum, Vienna #25/R

WEBER-WIEN, Manfred (20th C) Austrian
Works on paper
£308 $524 €450 Claus Peymann (42x30cm-17x12in) s.i.d. mixed media on photo. 5-Nov-3 Dorotheum, Vienna #43/R

WEBSKY, Wolfgang von (1895-1992) German
£514 $873 €750 Model resting (39x51cm-15x20in) mono.d.1984 s.i. verso panel lit. 6-Nov-3 Allgauer, Kempten #3635/R
£1233 $2096 €1800 Still life - flowers in vase on table (50x60cm-20x24in) mono.d.74 canvas on board. 6-Nov-3 Allgauer, Kempten #3637/R est:2500
£1781 $3027 €2600 Still life - flowers in glass vase (68x52cm-27x20in) s.d.58 panel. 6-Nov-3 Allgauer, Kempten #3636/R est:3900
£1781 $3027 €2600 Wood (80x60cm-31x24in) mono.d.1979 s. verso. 6-Nov-3 Allgauer, Kempten #3638/R est:3900

Works on paper
£608 $1089 €900 Hilly landscape in the Allgau with village (35x47cm-14x19in) s. W/C. 6-May-4 Michael Zeller, Lindau #935/R

WEBSTER, A G (1852-1916) British
£633 $1146 €950 Portrait de jeune femme (41x32cm-16x13in) s. 30-Mar-4 Gioffredo, Nice #103/R

WEBSTER, Charles (19th C) British
£550 $935 €803 Fishing boats in the morning mist (1x102cm-0x40in) s. 1-Dec-3 Bonhams, Bath #110/R

WEBSTER, G (19th C) British
£1100 $2024 €1606 London from Hampstead Heath, with gypsy encampment and donkeys (31x41cm-12x16in) indis.sig. i.verso. 26-Mar-4 ELR Auctions, Sheffield #338 est:600-800

WEBSTER, George (19th C) British
£6500 $12285 €9490 Thames at Deptford (43x53cm-17x21in) indis.s. prov. 17-Feb-4 Bonhams, New Bond Street #14/R est:4000-6000
£7000 $12880 €10220 Frigate at anchor amidst local craft, including a doble, on the Medway (72x91cm-28x36in) s. 11-Jun-4 Christie's, London #64/R est:8000-12000
£8000 $15120 €11680 Two-decker signalling her departure from Portsmouth (46x61cm-18x24in) 17-Feb-4 Bonhams, New Bond Street #13/R est:4000-6000
£13000 $20800 €18980 Frigate and smaller craft ahead of squall. Heading out to sea (30x41cm-12x16in) s. pair. 16-Sep-3 Bonhams, New Bond Street #13/R est:5000-8000

WEBSTER, John C (1941-) Canadian
Works on paper
£560 $1025 €818 Sand Point, School House, Ontario (32x49cm-13x19in) s. W/C. 1-Jun-4 Joyner Waddington, Toronto #326/R (C.D 1400)

WEBSTER, R Wellesley (19/20th C) British
Works on paper
£320 $586 €467 Venice, boats before the Riva Degli Schiavoni (27x45cm-11x18in) s. W/C. 7-Apr-4 Bonhams, Bury St Edmunds #380
£320 $586 €467 Venice, looking towards St. Marks Square with boats in the foreground (22x48cm-9x19in) s. W/C. 7-Apr-4 Bonhams, Bury St Edmunds #381
£380 $711 €555 Farm girl with two calves on a country lane beside a lake, mountains beyond (49x90cm-19x35in) s.d.98 pencil W/C. 22-Jul-4 Tennants, Leyburn #772

WEBSTER, Stokely (1912-) American
£3073 $5500 €4487 Park bench and cafe (41x51cm-16x20in) s.d.84 canvasboard. 8-Jan-4 Doyle, New York #46/R est:1200-1800
£3073 $5500 €4487 Street scene with subway kiosk (56x71cm-22x28in) s. 8-Jan-4 Doyle, New York #47/R est:1200-1800

WEBSTER, Thomas (1800-1886) British
£500 $900 €730 Still life of summer flowers in a blue vase upon a marble topped table (76x63cm-30x25in) s. panel. 21-Apr-4 Tennants, Leyburn #1244
£520 $931 €759 Still life of summer flowers in a vase (89x69cm-35x27in) s. panel. 17-Mar-4 Bonhams, Chester #305
£600 $978 €876 Still life with flowers and fruit on a ledge (71x91cm-28x36in) s. panel. 24-Sep-3 Dreweatt Neate, Newbury #142/R
£620 $1147 €905 Flowers in a vase on a ledge (90x70cm-35x28in) s. panel. 14-Jul-4 Bonhams, Chester #522
£650 $1170 €949 Still life of flowers with plums and grapes. Still life of flowers with plums and damsons (41x31cm-16x12in) s. panel pair. 21-Apr-4 Tennants, Leyburn #1245
£650 $1216 €975 Still life of assorted flowers and fruit (76x63cm-30x25in) s. panel. 22-Jul-4 Tennants, Leyburn #885
£820 $1304 €1197 Young friends, three children with a nest of chicks (43x79cm-17x31in) i. 9-Sep-3 Bamfords, Derby #1160/R
£1000 $1580 €1450 Sickness and Health (16x28cm-6x11in) mono. board painted arch. 4-Sep-3 Christie's, Kensington #244/R est:1200-1800
£3800 $6004 €5510 Letter (30x25cm-12x10in) mono. panel. 4-Sep-3 Christie's, Kensington #270/R est:2000-3000

WEBSTER, Walter Ernest (1878-1959) British
£400 $716 €584 Boudoir scene with Rae Dorian, actress and model (50x70cm-20x28in) 11-May-4 Bonhams, Knightsbridge #121/R
£1500 $2700 €2190 Portrait of a young girl seated, wearing a green and cream dress (76x63cm-30x25in) s. 21-Apr-4 Tennants, Leyburn #1088 est:1000-1500

WECKE, Hans von (20th C) German
£232 $425 €339 City scene (41x30cm-16x12in) s.d.1952 board. 5-Jun-4 Treadway Gallery, Cincinnati #702/R

WECKER, R (19th C) ?
£1322 $2340 €1930 Dogs at play (40x53cm-16x21in) s.d.1891. 3-May-4 Lawson Menzies, Sydney #386 est:4000-6000 (A.D 3200)

WECKESSER, August (1821-1899) Swiss
£991 $1705 €1447 Mary and Joseph with baby Jesus (81x47cm-32x19in) s.d.1858. 8-Dec-3 Philippe Schuler, Zurich #3363/R (S.FR 2200)
£1747 $3179 €2551 Cineto Romano (60x45cm-24x18in) s.i. 16-Jun-4 Fischer, Luzern #1296/R est:4000-6000 (S.FR 4000)
£5298 $9642 €8000 Peasant on a mule in the midst of resting girls (115x165cm-45x65in) s.i.d.1868. 16-Jun-4 Hugo Ruef, Munich #1108/R est:2500

WECKMAN, Jan Kenneth (1946-) Finnish
Works on paper
£324 $581 €480 Letters (90x62cm-35x24in) s. mixed media. 8-May-4 Bukowskis, Helsinki #252/R
£490 $832 €700 From Pictora Piesis (90x66cm-35x26in) s. mixed media. 29-Nov-3 Bukowskis, Helsinki #277/R

WEDDERSPOON, Richard Gibson (1889-1976) American
£1744 $3000 €2546 Figure on a beach amongst palm trees, Florida (41x51cm-16x20in) s. prov. 7-Dec-3 Freeman, Philadelphia #190 est:3000-5000

WEDEL, Nils (1897-1967) Swedish
£659 $1167 €962 Still life of fruit (31x53cm-12x21in) s. 27-Apr-4 AB Stockholms Auktionsverk #719/R (S.KR 9000)
£940 $1757 €1400 Black and white (65x56cm-26x22in) s.d.50 i. verso panel. 28-Feb-4 Bolland & Marotz, Bremen #311/R
£1026 $1815 €1498 Still life composition (84x68cm-33x27in) s. 27-Apr-4 AB Stockholms Auktionsverk #673/R (S.KR 14000)
£2103 $3785 €3070 Abstract composition - Durstamd dag (96x131cm-38x52in) s. exhib. 26-Apr-4 Bukowskis, Stockholm #201/R est:25000-30000 (S.KR 29000)
£2341 $3980 €3418 Figures (122x98cm-48x39in) s. 4-Nov-3 Bukowskis, Stockholm #227/R est:20000-25000 (S.KR 31000)
£2683 $4830 €3917 Couple in landscape (74x55cm-29x22in) s.d.17. 26-Apr-4 Bukowskis, Stockholm #112/R est:60000-80000 (S.KR 37000)
£5801 $10442 €8469 The morning toilet (110x145cm-43x57in) s.d.26 exhib. 26-Apr-4 Bukowskis, Stockholm #111/R est:80000-100000 (S.KR 80000)
Works on paper
£508 $914 €762 Mother and baby (57x41cm-22x16in) s. pastel. 25-Apr-4 Goteborg Auktionsverk, Sweden #404/R (S.KR 7000)

WEDEPOHL, Theodor (1863-1923) British
£440 $700 €642 Icelandic landscape, with distant stream and snow packed mountains (69x48cm-27x19in) s. panel. 5-May-3 O'Gallerie, Oregon #856/R

WEDGE, H G (1957-) Australian
Works on paper
£3049 $4817 €4452 Make'n waves (91x121cm-36x48in) s.d.96 synthetic polymer paint canvas prov.exhib. 28-Jul-3 Sotheby's, Paddington #192/R est:4000-6000 (A.D 7500)

WEDGE, Harry (20th C) Australian
Works on paper
£352 $657 €528 Untitled (35x49cm-14x19in) s.d.98 synthetic polymer. 21-Jul-4 Shapiro, Sydney #133a/R (A.D 900)

WEDGEBURY, David (20th C) American
£286 $500 €418 Charlie Chaplin (46x46cm-18x18in) s.i. painted c.1970. 17-Dec-3 Christie's, Rockefeller NY #229/R
£457 $800 €667 Bunny Slot Machine (91x84cm-36x33in) s. painted c.1970. 17-Dec-3 Christie's, Rockefeller NY #235/R
£686 $1200 €1002 Blackjack Bunny (91x122cm-36x48in) s. painted c.1970. 17-Dec-3 Christie's, Rockefeller NY #236/R est:800-1200
£857 $1500 €1251 Ace of Spades Bunny (91x122cm-36x48in) s. painted c.1970. 17-Dec-3 Christie's, Rockefeller NY #230/R est:800-1200
£1200 $2100 €1752 Heads and Tails (91x122cm-36x48in) s. painted 1970. 17-Dec-3 Christie's, Rockefeller NY #238/R est:800-1200

WEDIG, Gotthardt de (attrib) (1583-1641) German
£10345 $17172 €15000 Still life with fish, lemon, olives and goblet (39x49cm-15x19in) 1-Oct-3 Dorotheum, Vienna #231/R est:14000-18000

WEE SHOO LEONG (1958-) Singaporean
£1242 $2248 €1813 Water pipe with cups (39x63cm-15x25in) s.d.93 s.i.d.verso. 4-Apr-4 Sotheby's, Singapore #122/R est:3800-4800 (S.D 3800)

WEED, Alice (20th C) American
£231 $375 €337 Harbour scene with cottages (30x41cm-12x16in) s. panel. 31-Jul-3 Eldred, East Dennis #240

WEEDEN, Maria Howard (1847-1905) American
Works on paper
£5682 $10000 €8296 Older black woman wearing kerchief. Older black man with moustache and beard (23x18cm-9x7in) both s. first i. W/C card pair. 3-Jan-4 Brunk, Ashville #444/R est:3000-6000

WEEDON, Augustus Walford (1838-1908) British
Works on paper
£1100 $1837 €1606 River in the highlands (64x91cm-25x36in) s.d.1890 W/C. 12-Nov-3 Halls, Shrewsbury #272/R est:1000-1500
£1100 $2024 €1606 Closing day, Ben Slioch, Loch Maree (34x54cm-13x21in) s.d.1873 W/C. 8-Jun-4 Bonhams, New Bond Street #121/R est:1200-1800

WEEGEE (1899-1968) American
Photographs
£1695 $3000 €2475 Dressing room at a New Orleans burly-que (24x34cm-9x13in) st.verso photo prov.lit. 27-Apr-4 Sotheby's, New York #13/R est:2000-3000
£1796 $3000 €2622 Equestrian (12x17cm-5x7in) i.verso gelatin silver print exec.1956 prov. 17-Oct-3 Phillips, New York #248/R est:2500-3500
£1796 $3000 €2622 In the foyer of the Metropolitan Opera House (26x34cm-10x13in) silver print. 21-Oct-3 Swann Galleries, New York #208/R est:2000-3000
£1796 $3000 €2622 Frank Pape, arrested for homicide November 10 (27x33cm-11x13in) st.verso gelatin silver print lit. 20-Oct-3 Christie's, Rockefeller NY #137/R est:3500-4500
£2011 $3800 €2936 Self portrait with celebrity mannequin heads (23x20cm-9x8in) ferrotype silver print. 17-Feb-4 Swann Galleries, New York #79/R est:3000-5000

£2029	$3328	€2800	Marilyn Monroe (23x19cm-9x7in) i. vintage silver gelatin lit. 30-May-3 Villa Grisebach, Berlin #1403/R est:1500-2000
£2133	$3819	€3200	Anthony Esposito (34x27cm-13x11in) i.verso silver print lit. 13-May-4 Le Mouel, Paris #145/R est:2800-3500
£2267	$4057	€3400	Heat spell (34x26cm-13x10in) i.verso silver print lit. 13-May-4 Le Mouel, Paris #146/R est:2800-3500
£2542	$4500	€3711	Drunk tank, 1950s (14x19cm-6x7in) gelatin silver print. 27-Apr-4 Christie's, Rockefeller NY #209/R est:7000-9000
£2994	$5000	€4371	Easter Sunday in Harlem (34x27cm-13x11in) silver print. 21-Oct-3 Swann Galleries, New York #205/R est:2500-3500
£3222	$5800	€4704	Eyes (25x21cm-10x8in) gelatin silver print prov. 23-Apr-4 Phillips, New York #229/R est:3000-5000
£3889	$7000	€5678	Accident, 42nd Street and 3rd Avenue (23x18cm-9x7in) gelatin silver print. 23-Apr-4 Phillips, New York #83/R est:4000-6000
£13559	$24000	€19796	Denver, Hot Tamales (33x26cm-13x10in) s.i. photo exec.c.1940 prov. 27-Apr-4 Sotheby's, New York #14/R est:4000-6000

WEEKES, Henry (jnr) (?-c.1910) British

£2800	$5180	€4088	Landscape at sunrise with shepherd boy sat on the ground (53x94cm-21x37in) s. canvas on canvas. 9-Mar-4 Capes Dunn, Manchester #713/R
£4651	$8000	€6790	Hound (50x66cm-20x26in) s. prov. 5-Dec-3 Christie's, Rockefeller NY #52/R est:6000-8000

WEEKES, William (fl.1864-1904) British

£297	$550	€434	Black and tan dachshund (15x23cm-6x9in) s. board. 10-Feb-4 Doyle, New York #138/R
£300	$531	€438	Bacon nightmare (20x15cm-8x6in) s. board. 29-Apr-4 Gorringes, Lewes #2346
£541	$1000	€790	Smooth fox terrier (15x23cm-6x9in) s. board. 10-Feb-4 Doyle, New York #137/R
£1800	$3330	€2628	Top hat (20x30cm-8x12in) s. board. 14-Jul-4 Sotheby's, Olympia #136/R est:1000-2000
£2000	$3680	€2920	The critics (46x31cm-18x12in) s. 23-Mar-4 Bonhams, New Bond Street #118/R est:2000-3000
£2100	$3318	€3066	Apple picker takes a tumble (67x44cm-26x17in) s. 2-Sep-3 Gildings, Market Harborough #434/R est:3000-5000
£2100	$3507	€3066	Unwelcome guests (30x61cm-12x24in) s. 13-Nov-3 Christie's, Kensington #227/R est:2000-3000
£2100	$3885	€3066	Friendly warning (28x18cm-11x7in) s. panel. 14-Jul-4 Bonhams, Chester #505/R est:1500-2000
£2700	$4590	€3942	Guile beyond stupidity (20x29cm-8x11in) s. board. 19-Nov-3 Bonhams, New Bond Street #108/R est:2000-3000
£3100	$5270	€4526	Foul play (20x29cm-8x11in) s. board. 19-Nov-3 Bonhams, New Bond Street #109/R est:2000-3000
£3500	$5845	€5110	Darby and Joan (28x19cm-11x7in) s. panel. 13-Nov-3 Christie's, Kensington #228/R est:4000-6000
£3500	$5845	€5110	Guest for dinner (36x27cm-14x11in) s. panel. 12-Nov-3 Sotheby's, Olympia #83/R est:3000-5000
£4400	$7348	€6424	Farmyard friends (33x22cm-13x9in) s. s.i.verso. 12-Nov-3 Sotheby's, Olympia #84/R est:3000-5000

WEEKS, Edwin Lord (1849-1903) American

£3200	$5440	€4672	Portrait of Sir Sayajir Rao, the 11th Maharaja Gaekwar of Baroda (36x24cm-14x9in) s.i. board. 4-Nov-3 Bonhams, New Bond Street #59/R est:2000-3000
£3395	$5500	€4923	Grainfield (27x36cm-11x14in) s.d.1874 i.on stretcher prov. 8-Aug-3 Barridorf, Portland #106/R est:5000-7000
£3892	$6500	€5682	Tanjier (48x25cm-19x10in) s.i.d.1876 canvas on masonite prov. 23-Oct-3 Shannon's, Milford #174/R est:3000-5000
£4630	$7500	€6714	Lane at Penne de pre (27x36cm-11x14in) s.d. prov. 8-Aug-3 Barridorf, Portland #105/R est:5000-7000
£11173	$20000	€16313	By the river at Ahmedabad, India (51x76cm-20x30in) s. prov. 20-Mar-4 Sloans & Kenyon, Bethesda #1209/R est:25000-35000
£12941	$22000	€18894	Birdhouse and Market-Ahmedabad, India (49x33cm-19x13in) s.i. painted c.1887-1892 prov.exhib. 29-Oct-3 Christie's, Rockefeller NY #162/R est:20000-30000
£23611	$42500	€34472	Feeding the sacred pigeons, Jaipur (46x56cm-18x22in) s.i. i.d.verso prov.exhib.lit. 23-Apr-4 Sotheby's, New York #92/R est:40000-60000
£24000	$39120	€35040	Street scene in North West India, probably Udaipur (46x30cm-18x12in) s. prov.lit. 24-Sep-3 Christie's, London #86/R est:12000-18000
£31944	$57500	€46638	Blue tiled mosque at Delhi, India (55x46cm-22x18in) s. prov.exhib. 23-Apr-4 Sotheby's, New York #93/R est:60000-80000
£100000	$182000	€146000	An open-air restaurant, Lahore (157x246cm-62x97in) s.d. painted c.1889 prov.exhib.lit. 17-Jun-4 Christie's, London #123/R est:100000-150000
Works on paper			
£2778	$4500	€4056	Craftsman selling cases by a real wood building (91x69cm-36x27in) s. pastel. 2-Aug-3 Neal Auction Company, New Orleans #200/R est:6000-9000

WEEKS, James (1922-1998) American

£4706	$8000	€6871	Lakeside (37x48cm-15x19in) init.d.63 board prov.,. 9-Nov-3 Bonhams & Butterfields, Los Angeles #4047/R
£10180	$17000	€14863	Gardens on a Hill (168x142cm-66x56in) s.d.66-79 verso acrylic prov.exhib. 12-Nov-3 Christie's, Rockefeller NY #419/R est:5000-7000
£13235	$22500	€19323	Two children with a ball (105x89cm-41x35in) init.d.63 i.verso prov. 9-Nov-3 Bonhams & Butterfields, Los Angeles #4048/R
£14124	$25000	€20621	Bocce ball no 2 (229x178cm-90x70in) init.d.87 s.i.d.verso acrylic. 2-May-4 Bonhams & Butterfields, Los Angeles #3074/R est:15000-20000
Works on paper			
£3676	$6250	€5367	Interior of Diebenkorn's studio (56x66cm-22x26in) s.d.1967 verso W/C tempera paper on board prov. 9-Nov-3 Bonhams & Butterfields, Los Angeles #4051/R est:2500-3500

WEEKS, John (1888-1965) New Zealander

£714	$1314	€1042	Still life (25x19cm-10x7in) s.d.1954 panel. 25-Mar-4 International Art Centre, Auckland #109/R (NZ.D 2000)
£996	$1614	€1444	Rural landscape (24x33cm-9x13in) s. board. 31-Jul-3 International Art Centre, Auckland #81/R est:2000-3000 (NZ.D 2750)
£2098	$3818	€3063	Nude female figure studies (31x36cm-12x14in) s. canvasboard. 29-Jun-4 Peter Webb, Auckland #64/R est:8000-12000 (NZ.D 6000)
£3249	$5296	€4744	Farm buildings (28x34cm-11x13in) s. board. 23-Sep-3 Peter Webb, Auckland #101/R est:12000-15000 (NZ.D 9000)
£5072	$8167	€7405	Market place (30x44cm-12x17in) s. board. 20-Aug-3 Peter Webb, Auckland #2038/R est:10000-13000 (NZ.D 14000)
£5415	$8827	€7906	Memory of a dream (24x35cm-9x14in) s. canvas on board. 23-Sep-3 Peter Webb, Auckland #99/R est:15000-20000 (NZ.D 15000)
£7463	$12910	€10896	Patterned landscape (38x48cm-15x19in) s. board. 9-Dec-3 Peter Webb, Auckland #65/R est:20000-30000 (NZ.D 20000)
Works on paper			
£346	$619	€505	Corte, Corsica (30x21cm-12x8in) s.d.1928 pen sepia wash. 11-May-4 Peter Webb, Auckland #134/R est:1200-1800 (NZ.D 1000)
£940	$1598	€1372	Tagendaft, Morocco (23x30cm-9x12in) s. pastel. 27-Nov-3 International Art Centre, Auckland #137/R (NZ.D 2500)
£1119	$1937	€1634	White mosque (22x45cm-9x18in) W/C. 9-Dec-3 Peter Webb, Auckland #148/R est:3000-5000 (NZ.D 3000)
£1178	$1908	€1708	Nice (35x25cm-14x10in) pastel. 31-Jul-3 International Art Centre, Auckland #127/R est:2500-3500 (NZ.D 3250)
£1306	$2259	€1907	Road through the Waitakeres (25x34cm-10x13in) s.d.1920 W/C. 9-Dec-3 Peter Webb, Auckland #149/R est:3000-5000 (NZ.D 3500)
£1567	$2711	€2288	St Tropez (11x18cm-4x7in) s. W/C exec.c.1926. 9-Dec-3 Peter Webb, Auckland #147/R est:3000-5000 (NZ.D 4200)
£1993	$3228	€2890	French bridge (40x49cm-16x19in) s. gouache. 31-Jul-3 International Art Centre, Auckland #29/R est:6500-8500 (NZ.D 5500)
£8271	$14060	€12076	Abstract (48x63cm-19x25in) s mixed media. 27-Nov-3 International Art Centre, Auckland #68/R est:25000-35000 (NZ.D 22000)

WEELE, Herman Johannes van der (1852-1930) Dutch

£280	$467	€400	Peasants returning from the fields (18x24cm-7x9in) s. 28-Jun-3 Bolland & Marotz, Bremen #754
£385	$662	€550	Cows (30x23cm-12x9in) s. 8-Dec-3 Glerum, Amsterdam #37/R
£390	$651	€550	Flock of sheep (35x50cm-14x20in) s. 20-Oct-3 Glerum, Amsterdam #87/R
£843	$1400	€1222	Bull and cart (46x69cm-18x27in) 13-Jun-3 Douglas, South Deerfield #3
Works on paper			
£280	$467	€400	Foolish Jack (25x40cm-10x16in) s. W/C. 30-Jun-3 Sotheby's, Amsterdam #186/R
£333	$600	€486	Feeding the sheep (28x41cm-11x16in) s. W/C. 23-Jan-4 Freeman, Philadelphia #70/R
£822	$1397	€1200	Chevre (57x33cm-22x13in) s. W/C gouache. 6-Nov-3 Sotheby's, Paris #136/R

WEENIX, Jan (1640-1719) Dutch

£4459	$7982	€6600	Hunting still life (120x93cm-47x37in) s.d.1697 lit. 8-May-4 Sebok, Bamberg #1753/R
£5556	$10000	€8112	Mother with daughter, holding a puppy in her lap, with a monkey on the floor (71x66cm-28x26in) 26-Jan-4 Schrager Galleries, Milwaukee #1355
£10000	$17300	€14600	Architectural Capriccio with a young lady asleep beside a basket of fruit (91x79cm-36x31in) i.verso prov. 11-Dec-3 Sotheby's, London #156/R est:10000-15000
£27778	$50000	€40556	Boy seated on a terrace with his pet monkey and a turkey, still life of flower in sculpted urn (112x77cm-44x30in) 22-Jan-4 Sotheby's, New York #196/R est:50000-80000

WEENIX, Jan (attrib) (1640-1719) Dutch

£4861	$7924	€7000	Still life of hunting trophies by wicker basket (73x60cm-29x24in) 25-Sep-3 Dr Fritz Nagel, Stuttgart #1259/R est:7000

WEENIX, Jan Baptist (1621-1663) Dutch

£4167	$6875	€6000	Southern landscape with shepherds resting (55x58cm-22x23in) s. 2-Jul-3 Neumeister, Munich #596/R est:7000
Works on paper			
£4000	$7320	€5840	Landscape with a carriage by a tree (22x15cm-9x6in) i. red chk pen ink framing lines. 6-Jul-4 Christie's, London #180/R est:3000-5000

WEENIX, Jan Baptist (attrib) (1621-1663) Dutch

£1192	$2170	€1800	Un chien devant sa niche (64x77cm-25x30in) 21-Jun-4 Tajan, Paris #48 est:2000-2500
£1322	$2247	€1930	Childhood of Zeus on Crete (35x51cm-14x20in) bears sig. 5-Nov-3 Dobiaschofsky, Bern #1045/R est:6000 (S.FR 3000)

WEERS, Richard (20th C) American

£241	$450	€352	Rural farm landscape (36x74cm-14x29in) s. painted c.1975. 25-Feb-4 Dallas Auction Gallery, Dallas #529/R

WEERT, Anna de (1867-1950) Belgian

£17333	$31027	€26000	Rose garden (51x51cm-20x20in) s. s.i.d.1924 verso exhib. 15-May-4 De Vuyst, Lokeren #461/R

WEGELIN, Émile (1875-1962) French

£407	$750	€594	Landscape with figure and cattle (25x41cm-10x16in) s. board. 25-Jun-4 Freeman, Philadelphia #144/R

WEGENER, Gerda (1885-1940) Danish

£327	$517	€474	View of a Moroccan landscape (24x32cm-9x13in) s.i. exhib. 2-Sep-3 Rasmussen, Copenhagen #2008/R (D.KR 3500)
£792	$1244	€1156	Still life of flowers (65x54cm-26x21in) s.i.d.1922. 30-Aug-3 Rasmussen, Havnen #4240 (D.KR 8500)
Works on paper			
£421	$682	€610	L'amour (47x32cm-19x13in) s.d.1919 W/C. 4-Aug-3 Rasmussen, Vejle #443/R (D.KR 4400)
£1527	$2841	€2229	Five North African children with newspaper (65x46cm-26x18in) s.i. W/C. 2-Mar-4 Rasmussen, Copenhagen #1680/R est:20000 (D.KR 17000)
£2647	$4578	€3865	Dark haired girl wearing turquoise blouse seated on sofa (74x57cm-29x22in) s. pencil W/C. 9-Dec-3 Rasmussen, Copenhagen #1761/R est:30000 (D.KR 28000)
£3472	$5660	€5000	Spanish woman (63x37cm-25x15in) s.d.1910 W/C pencil gouache. 26-Sep-3 Bolland & Marotz, Bremen #819/R est:6300

WEGERER, Julius (1886-1960) Austrian
£604 $1081 €900 Winter landscape with dead mountain goat (47x73cm-19x29in) s.d.1923. 27-May-4 Dorotheum, Graz #71/R
£640 $1100 €934 Expansive mountain landscape (66x97cm-26x38in) s.d.1922. 7-Dec-3 Treadway Gallery, Cincinnati #492/R

WEGERT, Friedrich Martin (1895-?) German
£320 $589 €480 Triumphal procession through the temple grounds (54x79cm-21x31in) s. 11-Jun-4 Wendl, Rudolstadt #4413/R

WEGMAN, William (1942-) American
Photographs
£1413 $2600 €2063 Rangeley, Maine (51x48cm-20x19in) photo edition of 75 prov. 10-Jun-4 Phillips, New York #531/R est:2500-3500
£2200 $3740 €3212 Orange block (10x10cm-4x4in) s.i.d,1995 num.1/12 chromogenic print. 18-Nov-3 Christie's, Kensington #255/R est:1500-2000
£2349 $4323 €3500 Harmless snake (61x50cm-24x20in) s.i.verso polaroid exec 1981 prov.exhib. 29-Mar-4 Cornette de St.Cyr, Paris #97/R est:3000-4000
£2395 $4000 €3497 Collars (61x51cm-24x20in) with sig.i.d.1990 polaroid print. 21-Oct-3 Swann Galleries, New York #339/R est:4000-6000
£2542 $4500 €3711 Tableau (71x55cm-28x22in) s.i.d.1988 col Polaroid print prov. 28-Apr-4 Sotheby's, New York #255/R est:5000-7000
£2994 $5000 €4371 Reading two books (32x27cm-13x11in) s.d.1972 num.90 verso photo. 17-Oct-3 Sotheby's, New York #293/R est:6000-9000
£3200 $5440 €4672 Green block on the nose (71x53cm-28x21in) s.i.d.1994 polaroid polacolor II. 18-Nov-3 Christie's, Kensington #256/R est:1500-2000
£3390 $6000 €4949 Red cube cub (11x11cm-4x4in) s.i.d.1995 num.1/12 verso chromogenic print prov. 27-Apr-4 Sotheby's, New York #41/R est:700-1000
£7910 $14000 €11549 Wedding (76x56cm-30x22in) s.i.d.1991 col Polaroid print prov. 27-Apr-4 Sotheby's, New York #42/R est:4000-6000

WEGMANN, Bertha (1847-1926) Danish
£824 $1500 €1203 Portrait of seated woman (61x47cm-24x19in) panel. 7-Feb-4 Rasmussen, Havnen #2030/R (D.KR 9000)
£1074 $1966 €1568 Appleblossom in spring (50x49cm-20x19in) init. exhib. 7-Jun-4 Museumsbygningen, Copenhagen #162/R est:8000-12000 (D.KR 12000)
£10821 $20018 €15799 Two friends having tea in the artist's studio (133x189cm-52x74in) s.d.1885-1925. 15-Mar-4 Rasmussen, Vejle #62/R est:200000-300000 (D.KR 120000)

WEGMANN, Carl (1902-) Swiss
Works on paper
£346 $620 €505 Untitled (49x62cm-19x24in) mono.d. wax canvas. 22-Mar-4 Philippe Schuler, Zurich #4367 (S.FR 800)

WEGMANN, Karl Jakob (1928-) Swiss
£452 $769 €660 Untitled (53x70cm-21x28in) mono. oil collage cardboard on canvas exhib. 22-Nov-3 Burkhard, Luzern #227/R (S.FR 1000)
£676 $1162 €987 Form rhythms (81x100cm-32x39in) mono. d.1974 verso stretcher. 8-Dec-3 Philippe Schuler, Zurich #3364 (S.FR 1500)

WEGNER, Erich (1899-1980) German
£2533 $4535 €3800 Woman with newspaper (32x23cm-13x9in) s. s.i.d. verso tempera chk study verso prov. 14-May-4 Ketterer, Munich #89/R est:3800-4400
Works on paper
£600 $1080 €900 Shipwrecked IV (22x20cm-9x8in) i. verso W/C on chk. 24-Apr-4 Dr Lehr, Berlin #492/R
£667 $1227 €1000 At the old docks (41x66cm-16x26in) s. s.i.verso wax crayon board. 12-Jun-4 Villa Grisebach, Berlin #868/R

WEGUELIN, John Reinhard (1849-1927) British
Works on paper
£360 $644 €526 Mermaid (25x36cm-10x14in) s.d.1911 W/C. 17-Mar-4 Bonhams, Chester #288

WEHLE, Heinrich Theodor (1778-1805) German
Works on paper
£850 $1530 €1241 View of the outskirts of a wood, with distant mountains (25x19cm-10x7in) bears i.mount black chk. 20-Apr-4 Sotheby's, Olympia #176/R

WEHMAS, Einari (1898-1955) Finnish
£531 $966 €780 Evening light (40x46cm-16x18in) s.d.47. 8-Feb-4 Bukowskis, Helsinki #483/R

WEHN, Randolf (1911-) German
£486 $792 €700 Venice (81x70cm-32x28in) s.i. 25-Sep-3 Neumeister, Munich #2898

WEHNERT, Edward Henry (1813-1868) British
Works on paper
£400 $724 €584 Beach scene at Bouley Bay Jersey (24x33cm-9x13in) s. W/C. 1-Apr-4 Martel Maides, Guernsey #215/R

WEHRINGER, Herbert (1926-) German
£302 $556 €450 Woman washing in town river (27x37cm-11x15in) s. panel. 26-Mar-4 Auktionhaus Georg Rehm, Augsburg #8194/R
£302 $556 €450 Morning on the Dachauer Moos (20x25cm-8x10in) s.i. panel. 26-Mar-4 Auktionhaus Georg Rehm, Augsburg #8195/R
£379 $633 €550 Autumn landscape (25x20cm-10x8in) s.i. panel. 10-Jul-3 Allgauer, Kempten #2777/R
£379 $633 €550 Walk in moonlit winter landscape (25x21cm-10x8in) s.i. panel. 10-Jul-3 Allgauer, Kempten #2778/R
£403 $636 €580 Hunter with dog on track (12x26cm-5x10in) s.i. i. verso panel. 19-Sep-3 Schloss Ahlden, Ahlden #1594/R

WEHRLE, John (20th C) American
£317 $600 €463 Clear, from the series of wildlife in urban setting (148x213cm-58x84in) 22-Feb-4 Bonhams & Butterfields, Los Angeles #7057

WEI RONG (1963-) Chinese
£10669 $19203 €15577 Musicians (81x65cm-32x26in) s.d.2001 lit. 25-Apr-4 Christie's, Hong Kong #736/R est:100000-120000 (HK.D 150000)
£29344 $49004 €42842 Fragrance of the battlefield (137x203cm-54x80in) oil on linen painted 2002. 26-Oct-3 Christie's, Hong Kong #102/R est:250000-350000 (HK.D 380000)
Works on paper
£6950 $11606 €10147 Enjoying opera (56x42cm-22x17in) s.d.2003 mixed media. 26-Oct-3 Christie's, Hong Kong #103/R est:30000-40000 (HK.D 90000)

WEIBEL, Jakob Samuel (1771-1846) Swiss
Works on paper
£699 $1286 €1021 Schloss Liebegg (23x33cm-9x13in) s.d. W/C. 14-Jun-4 Philippe Schuler, Zurich #4384/R (S.FR 1600)

WEIBOLD, Hans (1902-1984) Austrian
£350 $594 €500 Bunch of flowers in Gmunden jug (58x43cm-23x17in) s. panel. 27-Nov-3 Dorotheum, Linz #466/R
Works on paper
£280 $476 €400 Bunch of flowers in a vase (49x31cm-19x12in) s.d.1980 W/C. 27-Nov-3 Dorotheum, Linz #558/R

WEICHBERGER, Eduard (1843-1913) German
£633 $1165 €950 View towards Niederburg (47x67cm-19x26in) s.d.1908. 11-Jun-4 Wendl, Rudolstadt #4415/R
£851 $1345 €1200 Sunny wood (115x155cm-45x61in) s. 25-Jul-3 Altus, Berlin #614/R
Works on paper
£315 $535 €450 Landscape with village in distance (17x28cm-7x11in) s.d.1902 W/C. 28-Nov-3 Wendl, Rudolstadt #4334/R

WEICHBERGER, Philipp (20th C) German?
£315 $541 €450 Composition (80x100cm-31x39in) s.d.63. 5-Dec-3 Bolland & Marotz, Bremen #878

WEIDE, F W (19th C) ?
£935 $1477 €1356 Ship's portrait of Tritton (46x67cm-18x26in) s. 2-Sep-3 Rasmussen, Copenhagen #1628/R (D.KR 10000)

WEIDEMANN, Jakob (1923-2001) Norwegian
£430 $719 €628 House and trees (36x41cm-14x16in) s. 20-Oct-3 Blomqvist, Lysaker #1343/R (N.KR 5000)
£834 $1393 €1218 Portal in the garden (45x37cm-18x15in) s. panel. 17-Nov-3 Blomqvist, Lysaker #1362 (N.KR 10000)
£1045 $1912 €1526 Composition (23x30cm-9x12in) s. panel. 2-Feb-4 Blomqvist, Lysaker #1318/R est:6000-8000 (N.KR 13000)
£1193 $2051 €1742 Winter's day (22x37cm-9x15in) s.d.61 i.verso panel exhib. 8-Dec-3 Blomqvist, Oslo #551/R est:10000-12000 (N.KR 14000)
£1549 $2587 €2262 Composition (45x31cm-18x12in) s. panel. 20-Oct-3 Blomqvist, Lysaker #1345/R est:18000-22000 (N.KR 18000)
£1690 $2823 €2467 Figure composition (27x22cm-11x9in) s.d.49 masonite. 7-Oct-3 Rasmussen, Copenhagen #111/R est:20000-25000 (D.KR 18000)
£1789 $3273 €2612 Figure (55x46cm-22x18in) s.d.50 panel. 7-Jun-4 Blomqvist, Oslo #414/R est:30000-40000 (N.KR 22000)
£2065 $3449 €3015 Composition (45x31cm-18x12in) s. panel. 20-Oct-3 Blomqvist, Lysaker #1344/R est:18000-22000 (N.KR 24000)
£2114 $3868 €3086 Portrait of Kari Opdal (47x38cm-19x15in) s.d.43. 7-Jun-4 Blomqvist, Oslo #417/R est:20000-25000 (N.KR 26000)
£2135 $3565 €3117 From the window (60x50cm-24x20in) s.d.65 i.stretcher tempera lit. 13-Oct-3 Blomqvist, Oslo #319/R est:40000-50000 (N.KR 25000)
£2882 $5159 €4208 The first green bits (70x70cm-28x28in) s.indis.d.92 s.i.d.1992 verso. 22-Mar-4 Blomqvist, Oslo #627/R est:35000-45000 (N.KR 36000)
£4065 $7480 €5935 Fleurs des Champs (50x61cm-20x24in) s.d.69 s.i.d. verso exhib. 10-Jun-4 Grev Wedels Plass, Oslo #242/R est:30000-40000 (N.KR 50000)
£6388 $10988 €9326 Composition (100x81cm-39x32in) s. panel painted c.1947-48 lit. 8-Dec-3 Blomqvist, Oslo #549/R est:70000-90000 (N.KR 75000)
£6504 $11902 €9496 Spring (130x130cm-51x51in) s.d.92 i.d. verso. 7-Jun-4 Blomqvist, Oslo #443/R est:100000-120000 (N.KR 80000)
£13714 $23588 €20022 The baroness and Gilbert Lapp (118x122cm-46x48in) s. i.verso panel painted c.1946-47 lit. 8-Dec-3 Blomqvist, Oslo #544/R est:100000-150000 (N.KR 161000)
£18699 $34220 €27301 Composition (86x160cm-34x63in) s.d.69-70 exhib.lit. 7-Jun-4 Blomqvist, Oslo #435/R est:160000-180000 (N.KR 230000)
£23850 $41022 €34821 Autumn (112x98cm-44x39in) s.d.65 i.d.verso exhib.lit. 8-Dec-3 Blomqvist, Oslo #555/R est:250000-275000 (N.KR 280000)
£36627 $62998 €53475 The gloomy man (122x275cm-48x108in) s. panel painted c.1943 lit. 8-Dec-3 Blomqvist, Oslo #535/R est:350000 (N.KR 430000)
Works on paper
£317 $584 €463 Composition (35x45cm-14x18in) s. W/C. 29-Mar-4 Blomqvist, Lysaker #1349 (N.KR 4000)
£732 $1346 €1069 Female nude (33x24cm-13x9in) s.d.56 pencil oil panel. 10-Jun-4 Grev Wedels Plass, Oslo #241/R (N.KR 9000)

WEIDEMANN, Magnus (1880-?) German
£347 $549 €500 Romantic lake landscape (80x63cm-31x25in) s.d.1913. 6-Sep-3 Schopman, Hamburg #776/R
£490 $842 €700 Dune landscape (60x86cm-24x34in) mono.d.1925 tempera. 5-Dec-3 Bolland & Marotz, Bremen #780/R

£562 $955 €820 Schleswig Holstein spring landscape (27x36cm-11x14in) mono.d.1919 board. 8-Nov-3 Hans Stahl, Toestorf #88/R
£705 $1247 €1050 Mist and sun (47x64cm-19x25in) s.d.1929 board i. verso. 28-Apr-4 Schopman, Hamburg #655/R
£1528 $2399 €2200 Peasant ploughing (65x80cm-26x31in) mono.d.1923. 30-Aug-3 Hans Stahl, Toestorf #94/R est:2200

WEIDENBACHER, Georg (1905-) German
£274 $427 €400 Canal landscape (63x48cm-25x19in) s.d.42 i. verso board. 10-Apr-3 Weidler, Nurnberg #7085

WEIDINGER, Franz Xaver (1890-1972) Austrian
£403 $745 €600 Isolated farmstead (70x90cm-28x35in) tempera panel. 9-Mar-4 Dorotheum, Vienna #73/R
£470 $869 €700 Landscape (43x55cm-17x22in) board. 9-Mar-4 Dorotheum, Vienna #124/R
£470 $869 €700 Salzkammergut landscape (81x100cm-32x39in) tempera panel. 9-Mar-4 Dorotheum, Vienna #128/R
£537 $993 €800 Bathers (62x58cm-24x23in) oil tempera panel. 9-Mar-4 Dorotheum, Vienna #58/R
Works on paper
£300 $552 €450 Summer landscape (13x17cm-5x7in) s. W/C. 9-Jun-4 Dorotheum, Salzburg #813/R
£390 $651 €550 Evening near Thalheim (14x17cm-6x7in) s. W/C. 16-Oct-3 Dorotheum, Salzburg #944/R

WEIDLICH, Kunz (1878-1940) German
£612 $1096 €900 Inspecting the troops (39x54cm-15x21in) s.i.d. board lit. 20-Mar-4 Bergmann, Erlangen #1114

WEIDMANN, Ulrich (1840-1892) Swiss
£391 $716 €571 Vue de Valere et de la Vallee du Rhone (60x85cm-24x33in) s. 5-Jun-4 Galerie du Rhone, Sion #232/R (S.FR 900)
£1422 $2546 €2076 Landscape with fortress (90x125cm-35x49in) s. 14-May-4 Dobiaschofsky, Bern #70/R est:4500 (S.FR 3300)

WEIDNER, Joseph (1801-1870) Austrian
£563 $935 €800 Princess Marie Liechtenstein (40x33cm-16x13in) s.d.1860. 16-Jun-3 Dorotheum, Vienna #58/R

WEIDNER, Willem Frederik (1817-1850) Dutch
£699 $1203 €1000 Still life with flowers in a vase on a ledge (34x25cm-13x10in) s.d.1849 panel. 7-Dec-3 Sotheby's, Amsterdam #608/R

WEIE, Edvard (1879-1943) Danish
£284 $508 €415 Portrait of gentleman (35x30cm-14x12in) 12-Jan-4 Rasmussen, Vejle #626 (D.KR 3000)
£845 $1411 €1234 Interior scene with woman seated (39x32cm-15x13in) init. lit. 7-Oct-3 Rasmussen, Copenhagen #327/R (D.KR 9000)
£1264 $2363 €1845 The artist in his studio (94x79cm-37x31in) init. pr/. 25-Feb-4 Museumsbygningen, Copenhagen #92/R est:15000-18000 (D.KR 14000)
£1805 $3321 €2635 Interior scene with two figures by lamplight (70x82cm-28x32in) init. s.d.1912 stretcher prov. 29-Mar-4 Rasmussen, Copenhagen #512/R est:20000 (D.KR 20000)
£1878 $3136 €2742 Interior scene with woman reading (60x74cm-24x29in) painted c.1905 prov. 7-Oct-3 Rasmussen, Copenhagen #328/R est:20000-25000 (D.KR 20000)
£3286 $5488 €4798 Aladdin's wonderful cave (45x55cm-18x22in) i.stretcher prov.lit. 7-Oct-3 Rasmussen, Copenhagen #148/R est:40000-50000 (D.KR 35000)
£4874 $9114 €7116 Figure composition (84x74cm-33x29in) 25-Feb-4 Kunsthallen, Copenhagen #273/R est:50000 (D.KR 54000)
£8057 $12891 €11683 Romantic fantasy (51x60cm-20x24in) painted c.1920-22 prov. 17-Sep-3 Kunsthallen, Copenhagen #72/R est:75000 (D.KR 85000)
£8075 $13485 €11790 Landscape (74x67cm-29x26in) with sig.verso prov. 7-Oct-3 Rasmussen, Copenhagen #145/R est:80000-100000 (D.KR 86000)

WEIGHT, Carel (1908-1997) British
£350 $630 €511 Two women in a landscape (36x13cm-14x5in) s. board. 20-Jan-4 Bonhams, Knightsbridge #107a
£400 $720 €584 Piano top (23x27cm-9x11in) board. 20-Jan-4 Bonhams, Knightsbridge #107
£700 $1309 €1050 Man on a path (60x14cm-24x6in) s. board. 26-Jul-4 Bonhams, Bath #43/R
£800 $1440 €1168 Two figures at the cross (30x20cm-12x8in) board. 20-Jan-4 Bonhams, Knightsbridge #134/R
£850 $1530 €1241 Two figures walking through the allotment (20x23cm-8x9in) s. board. 20-Jan-4 Bonhams, Knightsbridge #132/R
£1200 $2244 €1752 Clay pits in Cornwall (51x45cm-20x18in) s. 24-Feb-4 Bonhams, Knowle #122 est:500-800
£1200 $2124 €1752 Portrait of Mrs Joyce E Doo (63x51cm-25x20in) prov. 27-Apr-4 Bonhams, Knightsbridge #219/R est:1200-1800
£1200 $2184 €1752 Irish landscape (28x24cm-11x9in) s. board painted 1961. 1-Jul-4 Christie's, Kensington #290/R est:1000-1500
£1250 $2038 €1813 Blue jeans (61x28cm-24x11in) s. 23-Sep-3 Bonhams, Leeds #165/R est:1400-1600
£1300 $2340 €1898 Bellman (51x20cm-20x8in) s. board prov. 20-Jan-4 Bonhams, Knightsbridge #112/R est:1000-1500
£1300 $2067 €1898 Turn in the road (28x36cm-11x14in) s. board. 10-Sep-3 Sotheby's, Olympia #208/R est:800-1200
£1300 $2366 €1898 Weir (35x46cm-14x18in) s. painted 1953 prov. 1-Jul-4 Christie's, Kensington #296/R est:1000-1500
£1400 $2520 €2044 Figure on a country lane (30x25cm-12x10in) s. board. 20-Jan-4 Bonhams, Knightsbridge #137/R est:600-800
£1400 $2618 €2100 Figures on a beach (18x43cm-7x17in) s. board. 22-Jul-4 Gorringes, Lewes #1982/R est:600-800
£1600 $2880 €2336 View of the rooftops (20x25cm-8x10in) board. 20-Jan-4 Bonhams, Knightsbridge #131/R est:400-600
£1700 $3145 €2482 West Dean 1987 (33x39cm-13x15in) s. board prov. 11-Mar-4 Christie's, Kensington #271/R est:1000-1500
£1700 $3009 €2482 Orchard (34x52cm-13x20in) s. 27-Apr-4 Bonhams, Knightsbridge #3/R est:800-1200
£1700 $3094 €2482 Garden (41x50cm-16x20in) s. board prov. 1-Jul-4 Christie's, Kensington #294/R est:1500-2000
£3000 $5100 €4380 Autumn, windy day (64x62cm-25x24in) s. board. 26-Nov-3 Hamptons Fine Art, Godalming #210/R est:3000-4000
£3500 $6545 €5250 Woman in a garden (91x122cm-36x48in) s. 26-Jul-4 Bonhams, Bath #42/R est:3000-4000
£3600 $6012 €5256 Woman running (91x71cm-36x28in) s. 16-Oct-3 Christie's, Kensington #617/R est:3000-5000
£4200 $7518 €6132 With Uncle Joe to Richmond (38x68cm-15x27in) 14-May-4 Christie's, Kensington #551/R est:4000-6000
£4400 $7744 €6424 The playboy of the western world (37x32cm-15x13in) s. board prov. 18-May-4 Woolley & Wallis, Salisbury #3/R est:4000-6000
£5800 $9976 €8468 Study for the Battersea Park, tragedy 1974 (61x50cm-24x20in) s. prov.exhib. 2-Dec-3 Bonhams, New Bond Street #143/R est:3000-4000
£11000 $20350 €16060 Double portrait (122x61cm-48x24in) s. 11-Feb-4 Sotheby's, Olympia #175/R est:5000-7000
£50000 $91500 €73000 Crossing the road, West Brompton Station (122x244cm-48x96in) s. board prov.exhib. 2-Jun-4 Sotheby's, London #79/R est:50000-70000
Works on paper
£250 $463 €365 Man with his dog walking in the pouring rain (25x17cm-10x7in) s.i. pencil W/C. 16-Feb-4 Bonhams, Bath #64
£380 $684 €555 Two figures on a windy day (27x20cm-11x8in) s. W/C crayon. 20-Jan-4 Bonhams, Knightsbridge #109a
£800 $1288 €1160 Shipyard workers (23x28cm-9x11in) s. pastel. 15-Aug-3 Keys, Aylsham #499/R

WEIGLIN, Anne (1945-) Norwegian
£254 $467 €371 Flowers (64x81cm-25x32in) s. 29-Mar-4 Blomqvist, Lysaker #1354 (N.KR 3200)

WEIJAND, Jacob Gerrit (1886-1960) Dutch
£3618 $6658 €5500 Pasage de Bergen (60x80cm-24x31in) s.d.28. 22-Jun-4 Christie's, Amsterdam #459/R est:2000-3000

WEIKERT, Georg (1745-1799) Austrian
£6711 $12349 €10000 Alleged portraits of three children of the princely Esterhazy family (79x136cm-31x54in) s.d.1771 verso prov. 24-Mar-4 Dorotheum, Vienna #238/R est:12000-16000

WEIL, Lucien (1902-1963) French
£355 $574 €500 Nature morte (27x46cm-11x18in) s. 24-May-3 Martinot & Savignat, Pontoise #192

WEIL, Otto (1884-1929) German
£730 $1306 €1080 Young gypsy girl (43x35cm-17x14in) s.d.16 lit. 8-May-4 Dawo, Saarbrucken #221/R
£845 $1512 €1250 Peasant ploughing in pre-Alpine landscape (65x80cm-26x31in) s. lit. 8-May-4 Dawo, Saarbrucken #220/R
Works on paper
£270 $484 €400 Women by canal in Italian town (43x32cm-17x13in) s. gouache lit. 8-May-4 Dawo, Saarbrucken #232/R

WEIL, Roberto (20th C) Venezuelan?
Works on paper
£253 $400 €369 President's dreams (22x28cm-9x11in) Chinese ink exec.2002. 17-Nov-2 Subastas Odalys, Caracas #139/R

WEILAND, Johannes (1856-1909) Dutch
£355 $592 €500 Tedious drudgery (36x25cm-14x10in) s.d.91 panel. 20-Oct-3 Glerum, Amsterdam #59
£600 $1092 €876 Dutch riverside town (64x97cm-25x38in) s. 15-Jun-4 Rosebery Fine Art, London #511
£1802 $3063 €2631 Preparing the meal (65x53cm-26x21in) s. prov. 21-Nov-3 Walker's, Ottawa #201/R est:2000-3000 (C.D 4000)
£2500 $4000 €3650 Interior scene with mother and baby (66x56cm-26x22in) s. panel prov. 20-Sep-3 Bunte, Elgin #1448 est:2000-3000
£4200 $7854 €6132 Preparing the meal (48x38cm-19x15in) s.d. 23-Jul-4 Tring Auctions, Tring #293/R est:4000-5000

WEILER, Max (1910-2001) Austrian
£8392 $14266 €12000 Autumn evening with tree (46x30cm-18x12in) s.i.d. egg tempera. 28-Nov-3 Wiener Kunst Auktionen, Vienna #629/R est:7000-15000
£9396 $16631 €14000 Like a flower (86x61cm-34x24in) mono. egg tempera. 28-Apr-4 Wiener Kunst Auktionen, Vienna #223/R est:11000-15000
£10738 $19007 €16000 The sun has set (40x60cm-16x24in) s.i.d. verso egg tempera. 28-Apr-4 Wiener Kunst Auktionen, Vienna #226/R est:15000-20000
£12752 $22570 €19000 Moon goddess and moon (56x80cm-22x31in) s.i.d.1955 egg tempera. 28-Apr-4 Wiener Kunst Auktionen, Vienna #224/R est:13000-18000
£26846 $47517 €40000 Woodland (100x70cm-39x28in) s.d. s.i. stretcher egg tempera. 28-Apr-4 Wiener Kunst Auktionen, Vienna #258/R est:25000-40000
£69444 $118056 €100000 Composition 2 (110x130cm-43x51in) mono. oil egg tempera exhib.lit. 28-Oct-3 Wiener Kunst Auktionen, Vienna #240/R est:50000-150000
£83893 $148490 €125000 Steep slope (200x120cm-79x47in) s.d. s.i.d. verso egg tempera prov.lit. 28-Apr-4 Wiener Kunst Auktionen, Vienna #290/R est:100000-200000
Works on paper
£2817 $4930 €4000 Untitled (35x32cm-14x13in) s.d.89 pen ink chk. 19-Dec-3 Dorotheum, Vienna #354/R est:4000-6000

WEILUC (1873-1947) French
Prints
£4336 $7371 €6200 Frou frou (134x113cm-53x44in) s.d.1900 lithograph. 18-Nov-3 Sotheby's, Paris #4/R est:7000-10000

WEINBERG, Emilie Sievert (1882-1958) American
£284 $475 €415 Still life with apple. s. 18-Oct-3 Harvey Clar, Oakland #1225

WEINBERG, Justus Fredrik (1770-1832) Swedish
Works on paper
£538 $926 €785 Large waterfall at Elf-Carleby (38x55cm-15x22in) s.d.1804 W/C. 3-Dec-3 AB Stockholms Auktionsverk #2342/R (S.KR 7000)
£850 $1521 €1241 Pastoral landscape with fishermen (27x38cm-11x15in) s.d.1792 W/C. 26-May-4 AB Stockholms Auktionsverk #2134/R (S.KR 11500)

WEINDORF, Paul Friedrich (1887-1965) American
£221 $400 €323 Riverside scene (36x46cm-14x18in) s.i.verso board. 3-Apr-4 Charlton Hall, Columbia #556/R

WEINER, Lawrence (1942-) American
£5389 $9000 €7868 Morgenrood (32x24cm-13x9in) init.d.89 num. consecutively acrylic ink 10. 13-Nov-3 Sotheby's, New York #573/R est:10000-15000
£14525 $26000 €21207 A bit plus a bit until a pot is full cat num 59, for Toba. wall painting prov. 14-May-4 Phillips, New York #240/R est:25000-35000
Works on paper
£1200 $2184 €1752 Pennies (27x20cm-11x8in) s.i.d.93 ink gouache marker pen prov. 4-Feb-4 Sotheby's, Olympia #10/R est:800-1200
£1678 $2803 €2400 Set up in order to be blown down (48x61cm-19x24in) s.i.d.1988 crayon W/C. 11-Oct-3 Cornette de St.Cyr, Paris #141/R est:2500-3000
£11976 $20000 €17485 Coals and stones and a large wooden box to contain them (59x84cm-23x33in) s.i.d.1988 W/C black ink pencil lit. 13-Nov-3 Sotheby's, New York #572/R est:15000-20000

WEINER, Louis (20th C) American?
Works on paper
£265 $450 €387 Old Mexican adobe (36x43cm-14x17in) s.d.29 W/C prov. 1-Nov-3 Santa Fe Art, Santa Fe #240/R

WEINER, Rosalie Roos (?-1982) American
Works on paper
£249 $450 €364 New Orleans junior league revue (23x33cm-9x13in) init. W/C. 3-Apr-4 Neal Auction Company, New Orleans #920

WEINGAERTNER, Hans (1896-1970) American/German
£8242 $15000 €12033 Self portrait - lenses (41x35cm-16x14in) s. painted c.1957 prov.exhib.lit. 29-Jun-4 Sotheby's, New York #323/R est:3000-5000

WEINGART, Joachim (1895-1942) Polish
£330 $624 €482 Portrait study (64x53cm-25x21in) s.i.d.1930 oil paper on board. 19-Feb-4 Christie's, Kensington #260
£750 $1418 €1095 Bath time (56x44cm-22x17in) s.d.16 oil paper on board. 19-Feb-4 Christie's, Kensington #258/R
£900 $1701 €1314 Motherly love (65x53cm-26x21in) s. 19-Feb-4 Christie's, Kensington #259
£1389 $2320 €2000 Portrait de jeune femme (65x54cm-26x21in) s. 21-Oct-3 Artcurial Briest, Paris #304/R est:2000-2500
£3500 $6160 €5110 Female nude (81x65cm-32x26in) s. pair. 19-May-4 Christie's, Kensington #726/R est:200-300
Works on paper
£255 $450 €372 Couple (56x45cm-22x18in) s. pastel mixed media exec.c.1920. 1-Jan-4 Ben-Ami, Tel Aviv #4361/R
£695 $1266 €1050 Maternite (63x48cm-25x19in) s. pastel. 16-Jun-4 Claude Boisgirard, Paris #170
£1342 $2456 €2000 Nu assis et personnage (64x49cm-25x19in) s. chl sanguine oil paper double-sided. 7-Jul-4 Artcurial Briest, Paris #126 est:2000-2200
£2013 $3725 €3000 Nature morte au compotier (64x49cm-25x19in) s. gouache. 15-Mar-4 Blanchet, Paris #115/R est:2500-3000

WEINGARTNER, Pedro (1853-1929) Brazilian
£7143 $13071 €10715 Interior (38x29cm-15x11in) s.i.d.1884. 6-Jul-4 Bolsa de Arte, Rio de Janeiro #116/R (B.R 39000)

WEINMAN, Adolph Alexander (1870-1952) American
Sculpture
£1497 $2500 €2186 Untitled (46cm-18in) Bronze exec. 1901. 17-Oct-3 Du Mouchelle, Detroit #2123/R est:500-800

WEINRICH, Agnes (?-1946) American
£1882 $3200 €2748 Seated woman (66x51cm-26x20in) s. 30-Oct-3 Phillips, New York #94/R est:3000-4000
Works on paper
£216 $400 €315 Landscape (20x30cm-8x12in) s. W/C. 17-Jul-4 Outer Cape Auctions, Provincetown #107/R
£432 $800 €631 Boy in chair reading (25x18cm-10x7in) s. 17-Jul-4 Outer Cape Auctions, Provincetown #71/R

WEINSHEIMER, H W (20th C) American
£274 $450 €400 Winter landscape with snow covered town (56x71cm-22x28in) 4-Jun-3 Alderfer's, Hatfield #381/R

WEINSTEIN, Gal (1970-) Israeli
Works on paper
£3911 $7000 €5710 Soul blade (33x33cm-13x13in) s.d.2003 col cotton carton ten. 18-Mar-4 Sotheby's, New York #74/R est:5000-7000

WEIR, Barbara (20th C) Australian
£1867 $3118 €2801 Grass seed (120x90cm-47x35in) i.verso. 27-Oct-3 Goodman, Sydney #52/R est:3000-5000 (A.D 4500)
Works on paper
£2266 $4237 €3399 Grass seed (122x122cm-48x48in) i.d.2003 verso synthetic polymer linen prov. 21-Jul-4 Shapiro, Sydney #82/R est:5000-7000 (A.D 5800)
£2941 $5265 €4294 My mother's country (192x124cm-76x49in) synthetic polymer paint linen exec 1998 prov. 25-May-4 Lawson Menzies, Sydney #224/R est:8000-10000 (A.D 7500)

WEIR, J Alden (1852-1919) American
£221 $400 €323 Still life of flowers in mug (41x51cm-16x20in) 2-Apr-4 Douglas, South Deerfield #39
£4491 $7500 €6557 Summer at Windham (30x23cm-12x9in) s. board prov. 9-Oct-3 Christie's, Rockefeller NY #31/R est:6000-8000
£9040 $16000 €13198 Lady with a mandolin (116x76cm-46x30in) prov.exhib. 28-Apr-4 Christie's, Los Angeles #37/R est:18000-22000
£11176 $19000 €16317 Summer day (30x61cm-12x24in) s.d.1897 board. 21-Nov-3 Skinner, Boston #481/R est:30000-50000
£17365 $29000 €25353 Belt of Wood (38x66cm-15x26in) s.d.88 panel prov. 23-Oct-3 Shannon's, Milford #153/R est:25000-35000
Works on paper
£1183 $2200 €1727 New England Village (23x34cm-9x13in) s. pencil W/C prov. 3-Mar-4 Christie's, Rockefeller NY #25/R est:2500-3500
£5988 $10000 €8742 The inlet, Isle of Man (20x33cm-8x13in) s. indis.i. pastel prov. 23-Oct-3 Shannon's, Milford #40/R est:10000-15000

WEIR, John Ferguson (1841-1926) American
£5714 $10000 €8342 West Point (31x51cm-12x20in) s.d.73 panel. 19-Dec-3 Sotheby's, New York #1091/R est:7000-10000

WEIR, John Ferguson (attrib) (1841-1926) American
£1573 $2500 €2297 White mountains (36x44cm-14x17in) init. 12-Sep-3 Skinner, Boston #276/R

WEIR, Linda (20th C) British
£250 $468 €365 Pedn Olva from Westcott Quay (24x33cm-9x13in) init.d.2003 board. 26-Feb-4 Lane, Penzance #32
£260 $450 €380 Misty harbour, St Ives (28x33cm-11x13in) s. i.verso board. 11-Dec-3 Lane, Penzance #63
£270 $451 €394 St. Ives with gerbera (36x41cm-14x16in) init.d.2003 board. 14-Oct-3 David Lay, Penzance #158
£280 $524 €409 St Ives harbour and fishermen (48x68cm-19x27in) init.d.03 board. 26-Feb-4 Lane, Penzance #5/R
£280 $524 €409 St Ives with rough sea (18x40cm-7x16in) init.d.2003 board. 26-Feb-4 Lane, Penzance #39
£420 $769 €613 St Ives, fishing boat WH97 at anchor (28x33cm-11x13in) init.d.03. 3-Jun-4 Lane, Penzance #105/R
Works on paper
£260 $476 €380 Harbour Master's house from Smeaton's pier St Ives (28x39cm-11x15in) init.d.2001. 3-Jun-4 Lane, Penzance #3

WEIR, Robert W (1803-1889) American
£3352 $6000 €4894 Fort on the Hudson (15x25cm-6x10in) s.d.1860 board. 6-May-4 Shannon's, Milford #21/R est:6000-8000

WEIROTTER, Franz Edmund (1730-1771) Austrian
£3642 $6629 €5500 Coastal landscape with castle and ships. Wooded river landscape (9x13cm-4x5in) oil paper on cardboard pair. 16-Jun-4 Dorotheum, Vienna #163/R est:5000-7000

WEIS, Johann Martin II (attrib) (1738-?) French
Works on paper
£298 $542 €450 Two noblemen and a countess with a greyhound (10x7cm-4x3in) i. pencil pen sepia. 16-Jun-4 Hugo Ruef, Munich #1186/R

WEISBUCH, Claude (1927-) French
£467 $835 €700 Tete d'homme (41x33cm-16x13in) s. 17-May-4 Chayette & Cheval, Paris #203
£1268 $2041 €1800 Untitled (50x61cm-20x24in) s. s.d.1960 verso. 11-May-3 Versailles Encheres #163/R
£1329 $2219 €1900 Repas (73x92cm-29x36in) s.d.1958. 25-Jun-3 Blanchet, Paris #109/R
£1477 $2643 €2200 Femme a sa toilette (91x73cm-36x29in) s. painted 1961. 30-May-4 Eric Pillon, Calais #267/R
£1958 $3329 €2800 Les amours des notables (73x92cm-29x36in) s. s.i.verso. 28-Nov-3 Blanchet, Paris #172/R est:3000-4000
£1986 $3377 €2900 Vieux clown rose (116x90cm-46x35in) s. 9-Nov-3 Eric Pillon, Calais #262/R
£2292 $3827 €3300 Course (54x65cm-21x26in) s. s.verso acrylic. 21-Oct-3 Campo & Campo, Antwerp #360/R est:2000-4000
£2333 $4247 €3500 Don Quichotte et Sancho Panza (46x55cm-18x22in) s. panel. 4-Jul-4 Eric Pillon, Calais #282/R
£2740 $4658 €4000 Exode des pitres (195x130cm-77x51in) s. i. verso painted 1961. 9-Nov-3 Eric Pillon, Calais #256/R
£3087 $5526 €4600 Buveur (75x93cm-30x37in) s. 30-May-4 Eric Pillon, Calais #268/R
£3691 $6607 €5500 Arlequin (116x89cm-46x35in) s. 30-May-4 Eric Pillon, Calais #263/R
£3889 $6494 €5600 Cavalier (89x116cm-35x46in) s. 25-Oct-3 Cornette de St.Cyr, Paris #466/R est:5000-6000
Works on paper
£369 $676 €550 Nu de dos (54x44cm-21x17in) s. blue pastel prov. 7-Jul-4 Artcurial Briest, Paris #65
£662 $1205 €1000 Le cavalier de cirque (53x75cm-21x30in) s. chl htd white. 18-Jun-4 Piasa, Paris #183

WEISBUCH, Paul (20th C) French
£420 $713 €600 Cavalier (26x22cm-10x9in) s. s.d.1959 verso. 23-Nov-3 Cornette de St.Cyr, Paris #631

WEISENBORN, Rudolph (1882-1974) American
£941 $1600 €1374 No.47 abstraction (94x69cm-37x27in) s.d.1937 tempera on board. 9-Nov-3 Wright, Chicago #237 est:2000-3000
Works on paper
£471 $800 €688 Construction (86x58cm-34x23in) s.d.1966 casein on board. 9-Nov-3 Wright, Chicago #245

WEISENBURG, George W (20th C) American
£262 $450 €383 Forest interior (51x41cm-20x16in) s. canvas laid down painted c.1925. 7-Dec-3 Treadway Gallery, Cincinnati #532/R
£403 $750 €588 Forest interior (41x51cm-16x20in) s. painted c.1925. 7-Mar-4 Treadway Gallery, Cincinnati #590/R

WEISGERBER, Albert (1878-1915) German
£1408 $2338 €2000 Standing female nude (95x51cm-37x20in) s.d.02. 12-Jun-3 Dorotheum, Graz #78/R
£1579 $2905 €2400 Man getting into a coach (60x80cm-24x31in) mono. 26-Jun-4 C & K, Leipzig #801/R est:1600
£13667 $25010 €20500 Judas kiss (65x79cm-26x31in) prov.exhib. 5-Jun-4 Lempertz, Koln #1021/R est:10000-12000

WEISGERBER, Carl (1891-1968) German
£333 $597 €500 Hibou sur une branche (103x89cm-41x35in) s. 11-May-4 Vanderkindere, Brussels #80
£350 $594 €500 Fox and dead jay (47x65cm-19x26in) s. tempera. 26-Nov-3 Lempertz, Koln #1025/R
£447 $808 €670 March snows in the Eifel (60x80cm-24x31in) s. 1-Apr-4 Van Ham, Cologne #1704/R
£470 $864 €700 Pheasants by wood (40x41cm-16x16in) s. 27-Mar-4 Geble, Radolfzell #770/R
£559 $951 €800 Park scene (36x24cm-14x9in) s. board lit. 28-Nov-3 Schloss Ahlden, Ahlden #1605/R
£1037 $1919 €1514 Winter landscape with a boar (60x81cm-24x32in) 14-Mar-4 Agra, Warsaw #44/R (P.Z 7500)

WEISHAUPT, Victor (1848-1925) German
£634 $1096 €900 Meadow landscape (73x60cm-29x24in) s. 10-Dec-3 Hugo Ruef, Munich #2522/R

WEISMAN, William H (1840-1922) American
£265 $450 €387 Sloop approaching a lighthouse in rough seas (33x25cm-13x10in) s. board. 21-Nov-3 Eldred, East Dennis #578/R
£1139 $1800 €1663 Coming through the notch (74x91cm-29x36in) s. 7-Sep-3 Treadway Gallery, Cincinnati #561/R est:2000-4000

WEISS, Bartholomaus Ignaz (c.1740-1814) German
Works on paper
£406 $650 €593 Nativity (23x28cm-9x11in) s.d.1814 brown ink sepia over pencil. 20-Sep-3 Sloans & Kenyon, Bethesda #1002/R

WEISS, Carl (1860-1931) German
£336 $628 €500 Inner courtyard (42x49cm-17x19in) s. board. 24-Feb-4 Dorotheum, Vienna #144/R
£464 $848 €700 Steps (47x35cm-19x14in) s. board. 8-Apr-4 Dorotheum, Vienna #185/R
£470 $879 €700 Capo d'Istria harbour (36x51cm-14x20in) s.i. verso canvas on board. 24-Feb-4 Dorotheum, Vienna #57/R
£556 $944 €800 Walk in spring landscape (34x49cm-13x19in) s. board. 28-Oct-3 Dorotheum, Vienna #261/R
£590 $1003 €850 Walk in the Wachau (36x48cm-14x19in) s. board. 28-Oct-3 Dorotheum, Vienna #96/R
£704 $1218 €1000 Inner courtyard in Wachau (49x35cm-19x14in) s. board. 10-Dec-3 Dorotheum, Vienna #40/R
Works on paper
£268 $494 €400 Schloss Durnstein/Donau (28x21cm-11x8in) s. W/C. 26-Mar-4 Dorotheum, Vienna #320/R
£268 $494 €400 Figures beneath trees in park (21x28cm-8x11in) s. W/C. 26-Mar-4 Dorotheum, Vienna #326/R
£345 $572 €500 Main square in Steyr (21x29cm-8x11in) s. W/C. 30-Sep-3 Dorotheum, Vienna #313/R
£403 $741 €600 Venice, Grand Canal (37x49cm-15x19in) s. mixed media board. 26-Mar-4 Dorotheum, Vienna #325/R

WEISS, David (1946-) Swiss
£814 $1360 €1188 Untitled (14x19cm-6x7in) oil chk. 24-Jun-3 Germann, Zurich #1085 est:1500-2000 (S.FR 1800)

WEISS, Emil Rudolf (1875-1942) German
£556 $917 €800 Flowers in vase (81x71cm-32x28in) s. 5-Jul-3 Geble, Radolfzell #490/R
£1250 $2088 €1800 Summer flowers (105x70cm-41x28in) s.d. 25-Oct-3 Dr Lehr, Berlin #538/R est:2700
£1342 $2376 €2000 Still life with tulips (82x58cm-32x23in) s.d. 30-Apr-4 Dr Fritz Nagel, Stuttgart #937/R est:2000
£1933 $3499 €2900 Old charmer (45x48cm-18x19in) s. 1-Apr-4 Van Ham, Cologne #1705/R est:2100
£2500 $4075 €3600 Lichtenthal Avenue in Baden Baden (50x59cm-20x23in) s.d.1905. 27-Sep-3 Dr Fritz Nagel, Stuttgart #9648/R est:4500

WEISS, Franz (1903-1982) German
Works on paper
£352 $630 €500 Two doves next to a flowerpot (47x43cm-19x17in) s. mixed media panel lit. 8-Jan-4 Allgauer, Kempten #2576/R
£403 $721 €600 St Christopher (59x41cm-23x16in) mono.d.1951 W/C. 27-May-4 Dorotheum, Graz #115/R

WEISS, Georges (1861-?) French
£1400 $2590 €2044 Afternoon's work (18x13cm-7x5in) s.d.84 panel. 14-Jul-4 Christie's, Kensington #882/R est:800-1200
£1453 $2500 €2121 Catnap (32x24cm-13x9in) s.d.90 panel. 3-Dec-3 Doyle, New York #116/R est:3000-5000

WEISS, Hugh (1925-) American
£221 $400 €323 Composition with figures (36x25cm-14x10in) i.verso board. 2-Apr-4 Freeman, Philadelphia #121

WEISS, Jose (1859-1919) British
£300 $537 €438 On the river at dusk (16x27cm-6x11in) s. panel. 26-May-4 Christie's, Kensington #696/R
£350 $648 €511 Woodland path (35x51cm-14x20in) s. 15-Jan-4 Christie's, Kensington #797/R
£640 $1171 €934 Spring in Essex (50x75cm-20x30in) s. canvas on board prov. 1-Jun-4 Hodgins, Calgary #393/R (C.D 1600)
£1486 $2750 €2170 Before the rain (51x76cm-20x30in) s. 15-Jul-4 Sotheby's, New York #39/R est:1000-1500
£1536 $2750 €2243 Cattle near a pool, evening (21x27cm-8x11in) s. i.verso panel. 6-May-4 Doyle, New York #40/R est:2000-3000
£2016 $3710 €2943 Sunlit river (71x122cm-28x48in) s. 14-Jun-4 Waddingtons, Toronto #126/R est:2500-3500 (C.D 5000)
£2149 $3589 €3138 Passing storm over a river landscape (40x61cm-16x24in) s. 17-Nov-3 Waddingtons, Toronto #115/R est:3000-5000 (C.D 4750)

WEISS, Joseph Andreas (1814-1887) German
Works on paper
£664 $1143 €950 Fish market in Antwerpen (34x28cm-13x11in) s.i.verso W/C. 3-Dec-3 Neumeister, Munich #447/R

WEISS, Lee (20th C) American?
Works on paper
£222 $400 €324 Lake Edge Weeds (66x102cm-26x40in) s.d.83 W/C. 26-Apr-4 Schrager Galleries, Milwaukee #1421/R
£240 $425 €350 Branches (66x102cm-26x40in) s. W/C. 1-May-4 Susanin's, Chicago #5053/R
£355 $650 €518 March first (66x102cm-26x40in) W/C. 10-Jul-4 Hindman, Chicago #552/R

WEISS, Oscar (1882-1965) Swiss
£339 $577 €495 House with garden. Empty grotto (46x60cm-18x24in) s.i. panel double-sided. 1-Dec-3 Koller, Zurich #6547 (S.FR 750)

WEISS, Paul Emil (1888-1977) Swiss
£1403 $2385 €2048 Winter evening in the mountains - Prattigau (70x100cm-28x39in) s.i. verso. 28-Nov-3 Zofingen, Switzerland #3214/R est:3500 (S.FR 3100)

WEISS, Rosie (1958-) Australian
£372 $688 €543 Recurrent (183x213cm-72x84in) s.d.89 verso exhib. 15-Mar-4 Sotheby's, Melbourne #158 est:400-600 (A.D 900)

WEISS, Rudolf Johann (1846-1933) Swiss
£271 $462 €396 House on Bielersee canal (51x75cm-20x30in) s.d.1920. 19-Nov-3 Fischer, Luzern #2344 (S.FR 600)
£1897 $3395 €2770 Bielersee (66x95cm-26x37in) s.d.1895 i. verso. 14-May-4 Dobiaschofsky, Bern #36/R est:4500 (S.FR 4400)

WEISS, Rudolph (1869-?) Czechoslovakian
£1812 $2971 €2500 Paturage sous un grand ciel (40x61cm-16x24in) s.d.85 panel. 11-May-3 Osenat, Fontainebleau #190 est:2800-3000

WEISS, Wojciech (1875-1950) Polish
£1766 $2931 €2578 Summer landscape with red rooftops (50x65cm-20x26in) s. painted c.1930. 15-Jun-3 Agra, Warsaw #21/R est:11000 (P.Z 11000)
£4702 $7335 €6865 Vase of colourful flowers (62x47cm-24x19in) s. cardboard painted c.1935. 30-Mar-3 Agra, Warsaw #11/R est:30000 (P.Z 30000)

WEISSBERG, Léon (1893-?) Polish
£4362 $8070 €6500 Maisons de banlieue (60x73cm-24x29in) s. 15-Mar-4 Claude Boisgirard, Paris #122/R est:4000-5000

WEISSBORT, George (20th C) British
£280 $451 €406 English rural harvesting scene (25x36cm-10x14in) s. painted c.1920-1930. 23-Feb-3 Desmond Judd, Cranbrook #1074

WEISSBROD, Johann Baptiste (1834-1912) Swiss
£519 $930 €758 Basel (19x46cm-7x18in) s.d.1895. 22-Mar-4 Philippe Schuler, Zurich #4438 (S.FR 1200)

WEISSENBRUCH, J H (1824-1903) Dutch
£1722 $2807 €2600 Depart au marche (18x28cm-7x11in) s. panel. 1-Feb-3 Dubee & Berron, Vernou en Sologne #22

WEISSENBRUCH, Jan Hendrik (1824-1903) Dutch

£1000	$1800	€1500	Barn interior (30x43cm-12x17in) s. canvas on panel. 21-Apr-4 Christie's, Amsterdam #93/R est:1500-2000
£1053	$1937	€1600	A figure passing a windmill (13x10cm-5x4in) s. canvas on panel. 22-Jun-4 Christie's, Amsterdam #159/R est:1200-1600
£1267	$2116	€1850	Haywagon in a rural landscape (20x27cm-8x11in) s. prov. 17-Nov-3 Waddingtons, Toronto #165/R est:6000-8000 (C.D 2800)
£2000	$3600	€3000	Farmhouse in a polder landscape (19x34cm-7x13in) s. 20-Apr-4 Sotheby's, Amsterdam #111/R est:3000-5000
£2431	$4059	€3500	Summer landscape (23x36cm-9x14in) s. panel prov. 21-Oct-3 Sotheby's, Amsterdam #96/R est:3000-5000
£8667	$15600	€13000	Farmhouses on the waterfront (20x38cm-8x15in) s. canvas on panel prov. 20-Apr-4 Sotheby's, Amsterdam #212/R est:10000-15000
£9028	$15347	€13000	Winter's Day (37x28cm-15x11in) s. 28-Oct-3 Christie's, Amsterdam #141/R est:5000-7000
£9333	$16800	€14000	Fisherman in a polder landscape (16x18cm-6x7in) s. panel. 21-Apr-4 Christie's, Amsterdam #84/R est:4000-6000
£10417	$17396	€15000	View of Haarlem (25x36cm-10x14in) s. panel prov.lit. 21-Oct-3 Sotheby's, Amsterdam #251/R est:14000-18000
£13194	$22035	€19000	Windmill in the dunes (29x37cm-11x15in) s.d.95 panel. 21-Oct-3 Sotheby's, Amsterdam #99/R est:8000-12000
£18000	$32400	€27000	On the tow path along the river Amstel (45x31cm-18x12in) s. i.verso. 20-Apr-4 Sotheby's, Amsterdam #201/R est:12000-18000
Works on paper			
£1118	$2058	€1700	Landscape with a windmill, towards twilight (12x19cm-5x7in) s. W/C. 28-Jun-4 Sotheby's, Amsterdam #29/R est:1200-1600
£1233	$2096	€1800	Polder landscape (19x25cm-7x10in) W/C prov. 5-Nov-3 Vendue Huis, Gravenhage #104/R est:300-400
£1579	$2858	€2400	Pipe smoking man at the backdoor of a house (35x23cm-14x9in) s. W/C. 19-Apr-4 Glerum, Amsterdam #119/R est:2500-3500
£2778	$4722	€4000	Figures on a village path, Noorden (33x24cm-13x9in) s. pencil blk chk W/C htd white exhib. 28-Oct-3 Christie's, Amsterdam #140/R est:5000-7000
£3667	$6600	€5500	Bomschuit on the beach (19x31cm-7x12in) s. W/C. 20-Apr-4 Sotheby's, Amsterdam #100/R est:6000-8000
£12000	$21600	€18000	Figures on a country road, church in the distance (30x53cm-12x21in) s. W/C. 20-Apr-4 Sotheby's, Amsterdam #223/R est:10000-15000
£19149	$31979	€27000	Mill in a polder landscape (22x33cm-9x13in) s. W/C. 20-Oct-3 Glerum, Amsterdam #70/R est:6500-7500

WEISSENBRUCH, Jan Hendrik (attrib) (1824-1903) Dutch

£2585	$4705	€3800	In de weide, cows in a polder landscape (12x23cm-5x9in) with sig. oil paper on panel. 3-Feb-4 Christie's, Amsterdam #141 est:1000-1500

WEISSENBRUCH, Willem (1864-1941) Dutch

£362	$655	€550	Polder landscape with a mill and a church in the distance (14x19cm-6x7in) s. panel. 19-Apr-4 Glerum, Amsterdam #103/R
£1579	$2905	€2400	Ringvaart: sailing down the river (32x40cm-13x16in) s. panel. 22-Jun-4 Christie's, Amsterdam #160/R est:2000-3000
Works on paper			
£525	$902	€750	Polder landscape with windmill (17x26cm-7x10in) s. W/C. 7-Dec-3 Sotheby's, Amsterdam #592/R

WEISSENDT, Edouard (1822-1893) French

Works on paper			
£1549	$2572	€2200	Vue de la rade et de la ville de Montevideo sur le Rio de La Plata (40x68cm-16x27in) W/C. 15-Jun-3 Muizon & Le Coent, Paris #7

WEISSMANN, Franz (1914-) Brazilian

Sculpture			
£6960	$12736	€10440	Square in three dimensions (112x121cm-44x48in) painted steel exec. c.1985. 6-Jul-4 Bolsa de Arte, Rio de Janeiro #173/R (B.R 38000)
£11355	$20099	€17033	Column (250x63x63cm-98x25x25in) painted steel. 27-Apr-4 Bolsa de Arte, Rio de Janeiro #100/R (B.R 62000)

WEISZ, Adolphe (1838-?) French/Hungarian

£42000	$72240	€61320	L'odalisque (70x101cm-28x40in) s. 3-Dec-3 Christie's, London #101/R est:30000-40000

WEISZ, Karl (1839-1914) German

£950	$1700	€1387	Reclining beauty under lamplight (74x99cm-29x39in) 7-May-4 Sloans & Kenyon, Bethesda #1647/R est:1200-1800

WEITZ, Jakob (1888-1970) German

£350	$594	€500	Karden an der Mosel (60x70cm-24x28in) s. 20-Nov-3 Van Ham, Cologne #1906
£483	$806	€700	Large marina, Capri (51x73cm-20x29in) s.i. i.verso oil gouache board on fibreboard exhib. 13-Nov-3 Neumeister, Munich #486/R

WEIXLGARTNER, Eduard (1816-1873) Hungarian/Austrian

Works on paper			
£267	$491	€400	Etude de Molchus Moldriterus Linn et Canis Crocuta Eral (22x30cm-9x12in) i.verso blk crayon W/C. 11-Jun-4 Maigret, Paris #24/R

WEL, Jean van (1906-1990) Belgian

£690	$1276	€1000	Champ de course (38x46cm-15x18in) s. 19-Jan-4 Horta, Bruxelles #385
Works on paper			
£315	$535	€450	Paddock. s. W/C. 18-Nov-3 Galerie Moderne, Brussels #736

WELBURN, Irene (fl.1936-1940) British

£320	$582	€467	Kingston Row Locks, Birmingham (61x92cm-24x36in) board. 15-Jun-4 Bonhams, Knightsbridge #98/R
£700	$1309	€1050	Three young ladies with two red setters and another dog (61x91cm-24x36in) s. board. 22-Jul-4 Tennants, Leyburn #902

WELCH, Ludmilla P (1867-1925) American

£270	$500	€394	Impressionistic landscape (22x25cm-9x10in) s. board. 18-Jan-4 Bonhams & Butterfields, Los Angeles #7011/R
£297	$475	€434	California Hills. s.d.1907. 20-Sep-3 Harvey Clar, Oakland #1324
£1902	$3500	€2777	Cattle beneath Mount Tamalpais (30x45cm-12x18in) s. prov. 8-Jun-4 Bonhams & Butterfields, San Francisco #4185/R est:3000-5000
£1902	$3500	€2777	Old ranch, Santa Barbara (24x45cm-9x18in) s. 8-Jun-4 Bonhams & Butterfields, San Francisco #4258/R est:3000-5000
£2059	$3500	€3006	Cows watering in ranch (10x18cm-4x7in) s. canvas on canvas. 18-Nov-3 John Moran, Pasadena #117 est:2000-3000
£2168	$3750	€3165	Marin coastal landscape. Coastal fog (27x45cm-11x18in) one d.July 17 first canvas laid down second board. 10-Dec-3 Bonhams & Butterfields, San Francisco #6180/R est:3000-5000
£2624	$4750	€3831	Robin Hood, a Cocker spaniel (29x25cm-11x10in) s.i.d.1903 board. 30-Mar-4 Bonhams & Butterfields, San Francisco #103/R est:3000-5000

WELCH, Nugent (1881-1970) New Zealander

£347	$552	€507	Fishing boat, Island Bay, Wellington (23x33cm-9x13in) s.d.1905 board. 1-May-3 Dunbar Sloane, Wellington #126 est:500-1000 (NZ.D 1000)
£461	$816	€673	Harbour scene (30x35cm-12x14in) s. board. 28-Apr-4 Dunbar Sloane, Auckland #48/R est:1000-3000 (NZ.D 1300)
Works on paper			
£543	$875	€793	Coastal landscape (48x65cm-19x26in) s. W/C. 12-Aug-3 Peter Webb, Auckland #33/R (NZ.D 1500)

WELCH, Rosemary Sarah (1946-) British

Works on paper			
£380	$680	€555	Cooling stream, New Forest (46x65cm-18x26in) s. pastel. 17-Mar-4 Rupert Toovey, Partridge Green #49/R
£500	$895	€730	New forest ponies (49x68cm-19x27in) s.i. pastel. 17-Mar-4 Rupert Toovey, Partridge Green #46/R

WELCH, Thaddeus (1844-1919) American

£1176	$2000	€1717	Deer in mountain river landscape (51x91cm-20x36in) s.indis.d.1904 canvas on canvas prov. 18-Nov-3 John Moran, Pasadena #180 est:3000-5000
£2260	$4000	€3300	Bolinas Bay (50x91cm-20x36in) s. 28-Apr-4 Christie's, Los Angeles #5/R est:5000-7000
£2838	$5250	€4257	Billy, aged 6 years (48x74cm-19x29in) s.i.d.89. 14-Jul-4 American Auctioneer #490313/R est:3000-5000
£4348	$8000	€6348	Summer afternoon, Sleepy Hollow, Marin County (40x61cm-16x24in) s.d.11 i. stretcher. 8-Jun-4 Bonhams & Butterfields, San Francisco #4186/R est:7000-10000
£5587	$10000	€8157	Haying, possibly a Marin County view (62x86cm-24x34in) s. 14-May-4 Skinner, Boston #82/R est:10000-15000

WELLENS, Charles (1889-1958) Belgian

£1049	$1752	€1500	Fen (57x149cm-22x59in) s. 11-Oct-3 De Vuyst, Lokeren #403/R est:2000-2500
£1184	$2143	€1800	Coucher de soleil sur le marais (77x128cm-30x50in) s. 19-Apr-4 Horta, Bruxelles #40 est:1200-1500

WELLER, Simona (1940-) Italian

Works on paper			
£1342	$2497	€2000	In the storm (50x70cm-20x28in) s.i.d.1981 verso mixed media collage board. 4-Mar-4 Babuino, Rome #46 est:1000-1500
£3087	$5742	€4600	Untitled (115x156cm-45x61in) s.d.1972 mixed media on canvas. 4-Mar-4 Babuino, Rome #45

WELLER, Theodor Leopold (1802-1880) German

£5000	$9100	€7300	Girl selling ducks (43x35cm-17x14in) s.d.1835 prov. 15-Jun-4 Sotheby's, London #20/R est:5000-7000

WELLERSHAUS, Paul (1887-1976) German

£417	$679	€600	Artist's house (60x80cm-24x31in) s. masonite. 27-Sep-3 Dr Fritz Nagel, Stuttgart #9403/R
£694	$1146	€1000	Landscape with village houses (74x100cm-29x39in) s. 3-Jul-3 Van Ham, Cologne #1498/R

WELLESLEY, Gerard E (fl.1890s) British

£372	$654	€550	Study of a gentleman wearing a turban (70x54cm-28x21in) s.d.1899-90. 19-May-4 James Adam, Dublin #3/R

WELLINGTON, Hubert Lindsay (1879-1967) British

£300	$531	€438	Cotswold corn (25x36cm-10x14in) panel. 29-Apr-4 Gorringes, Lewes #2410

WELLIVER, Neil (1929-) American

£5556	$9000	€8056	To escourt (61x61cm-24x24in) s. i.verso prov. 8-Aug-3 Barridorf, Portland #230/R est:9000-12000
Prints			
£1421	$2600	€2075	Greer's bag (102x102cm-40x40in) num.79/144 screenprint. 10-Jul-4 Hindman, Chicago #554/R est:1000-1500

WELLS, A V (?) ?

£941	$1750	€1374	Pointers (46x71cm-18x28in) 6-Mar-4 Page, Batavia #130

WELLS, Dennis G (1881-1973) British
£1700 $3094 €2482 Prelude (32x24cm-13x9in) s. s.i.verso panel. 5-Feb-4 Mellors & Kirk, Nottingham #577/R est:700-900
£2600 $4732 €3796 Still life with oriental porcelain (63x75cm-25x30in) s.d.29. 1-Jul-4 Christie's, Kensington #132/R est:800-1200
Works on paper
£260 $458 €380 The Strand (37x56cm-15x22in) s. pen ink W/C. 21-May-4 Bracketts, Tunbridge Wells #257/R
£260 $458 €380 Horseguards Parade (38x56cm-15x22in) s.d.69 W/C pen ink. 21-May-4 Bracketts, Tunbridge Wells #258/R

WELLS, George (fl.1842-1888) British
£900 $1548 €1314 Milkmaid (26x21cm-10x8in) s. 4-Dec-3 Bonhams, Edinburgh #56/R

WELLS, John (1907-2000) British
£1000 $1850 €1460 Monoprint I (23x18cm-9x7in) oil on paper. 10-Feb-4 David Lay, Penzance #454 est:300-400
£1450 $2683 €2117 Monoprint II (18x23cm-7x9in) oil on paper. 10-Feb-4 David Lay, Penzance #453 est:300-400
£16000 $29280 €23360 Construction (122x76cm-48x30in) s.i.d.1960 oil pencil board exhib. 2-Jun-4 Sotheby's, London #100/R est:12000-18000
Works on paper
£900 $1503 €1314 Two forms (22x18cm-9x7in) s.d.1958 pen brush black ink. 16-Oct-3 Christie's, Kensington #664/R
£1800 $3366 €2628 Untitled, abstract (19x23cm-7x9in) s.d.1965 mixed media card. 26-Feb-4 Lane, Penzance #140/R est:2000-3000
£2000 $3640 €2920 Untitled (24x34cm-9x13in) s.i.d.1974 pencil yellow crayon prov. 1-Jul-4 Christie's, Kensington #382/R est:1000-1500

WELLS, Madeline Rachel (fl.1909-1940) British
£2400 $4440 €3504 Riders to the sea (122x183cm-48x72in) s. tempera. 11-Feb-4 Sotheby's, Olympia #165/R est:1000-1500

WELLS, Reginald Fairfax (1877-?) British
Sculpture
£2400 $4080 €3504 Peasant woman and child (58cm-23in) s. pat bronze lit. 28-Oct-3 Sotheby's, London #206/R

WELLS, William (1842-1880) British
£1200 $2112 €1752 Nocturne Stirling (23x33cm-9x13in) indis.s. 19-May-4 James Thompson, Kirby Lonsdale #124

WELLS, William Frederick (1762-1836) British
£13500 $24300 €20250 Two women conversing over a gate, with chickens to side and sheep beyond (63x60cm-25x24in) s. 21-Apr-4 Wingetts, Wrexham #302 est:600-800

WELLS, William Page Atkinson (1871-1923) British
£2000 $3580 €2920 The picnic (34x44cm-13x17in) s. 28-May-4 Lyon & Turnbull, Edinburgh #62/R est:2000-3000
£5000 $9050 €7300 Farm house at Balnacrink in Colby, Isle of Man (71x102cm-28x40in) s. 19-Apr-4 Sotheby's, London #95/R est:5000-7000
Works on paper
£2400 $4344 €3504 Scything (35x30cm-14x12in) s. W/C scratching out. 19-Apr-4 Sotheby's, London #96/R est:2000-3000

WELTE, Gottlieb (1745-1790) German
£1572 $2500 €2295 Two women with laundry and child stop to talk to a shepherd (64x76cm-25x30in) s. 5-May-3 O'Gallerie, Oregon #839/R est:5000-7000
£6711 $12349 €10000 Loves at edge of forest (32x24cm-13x9in) s. panel one of pair. 24-Mar-4 Dorotheum, Vienna #240/R est:8000-12000
£6711 $12349 €10000 Huntsman resting in forest, mistress sleeping alongside (32x24cm-13x9in) s. panel one of pair. 24-Mar-4 Dorotheum, Vienna #241/R est:8000-12000
£7692 $13231 €11000 Musician and a shepherdess. Young woman and a shepherd (33x25cm-13x10in) first s.d.1770 second s. panel pair. 2-Dec-3 Christie's, Paris #714/R est:10000-15000

WELTI, Albert (1862-1912) Swiss
£881 $1498 €1286 Portrait of young man (15x17cm-6x7in) s.d.1884 verso board prov. 5-Nov-3 Dobiaschofsky, Bern #1048/R (S.FR 2000)

WELVAERT, Ernest (1880-1946) Belgian
£367 $656 €550 Landscape (19x24cm-7x9in) panel exhib. 15-May-4 De Vuyst, Lokeren #404
£17785 $31480 €26500 Mere et enfant (100x120cm-39x47in) s. 27-Apr-4 Campo, Vlaamse Kaai #657/R est:12000-16000
£34965 $58392 €50000 Picking flowers by the lake of Daknam (86x101cm-34x40in) s.d.1909. 11-Oct-3 De Vuyst, Lokeren #434/R

WELZ, Jean (1900-1975) South African
£1652 $2956 €2412 Still life of flowers (57x41cm-22x16in) s. indis.d. s.i.verso board. 31-May-4 Stephan Welz, Johannesburg #515/R est:20000-30000 (SA.R 20000)
£2064 $3695 €3013 Dream landscape (29x40cm-11x16in) s.d.50 board. 31-May-4 Stephan Welz, Johannesburg #495/R est:12000-18000 (SA.R 25000)
£6193 $11086 €9042 Bathers and the bridge (65x90cm-26x35in) s.d.1954 lit. 31-May-4 Stephan Welz, Johannesburg #488/R est:80000-100000 (SA.R 75000)
£7265 $12350 €10607 Still life with pomegranates, apples and grapes (29x39cm-11x15in) s.d.49 canvasboard exhib. 4-Nov-3 Stephan Welz, Johannesburg #707/R est:40000-60000 (SA.R 85000)
Works on paper
£248 $443 €362 Rietkuil Plaas, oorsprong van die Gamka rivier (42x68cm-17x27in) s.d.57 i. verso pen brush ink. 31-May-4 Stephan Welz, Johannesburg #112 (SA.R 3000)
£336 $608 €491 Nude study of a girl (59x46cm-23x18in) s.d.53 chl. 30-Mar-4 Stephan Welz, Johannesburg #485 est:3000-5000 (SA.R 4000)

WEMAIRE, Pierre (1913-) Belgian
£550 $880 €803 Coq (65x81cm-26x32in) s. s.i.d.Aout 59 verso prov. 16-Sep-3 Rosebery Fine Art, London #456
£941 $1599 €1374 Dudu (65x50cm-26x20in) s.d.59. 26-Nov-3 Kunsthallen, Copenhagen #154/R (D.KR 10000)
£2222 $3511 €3200 Intimite dans la foule (100x81cm-39x32in) s.d.1993 oil acrylic prov. 27-Apr-3 Versailles Encheres #4 est:2500-3000
£9333 $16800 €14000 Rapt (160x288cm-63x113in) s.d.1967 s.i.d.verso exhib. 25-Apr-4 Versailles Encheres #203 est:10000-12000
Works on paper
£378 $677 €552 Composition (25x40cm-10x16in) init.d.oct 68 W/C. 12-Jan-4 Rasmussen, Vejle #519 (D.KR 4000)

WEN BOREN (1502-1575) Chinese
Works on paper
£5500 $9185 €8030 Figures in mountainous river landscapes (33x31cm-13x12in) ink col set of 10. 14-Nov-3 Christie's, Kensington #248/R est:6000-8000

WEN ZHENGMING (1470-1559) Chinese
Works on paper
£6046 $10882 €8827 Travelling amidst snowy mountains (129x32cm-51x13in) s.i. ink col hanging scroll prov. 25-Apr-4 Christie's, Hong Kong #342/R est:60000-80000 (HK.D 85000)
£8535 $15363 €12461 Visiting a friend (111x41cm-44x16in) s. ink col scroll gold paper prov. 25-Apr-4 Christie's, Hong Kong #324/R est:45000-60000 (HK.D 120000)
£12091 $21764 €17653 Streams amongst verdant hills (27x418cm-11x165in) s.i. ink col handscroll. 25-Apr-4 Christie's, Hong Kong #346/R est:150000-230000 (HK.D 170000)
£18492 $33286 €26998 Landscape and calligraphy (25x94cm-10x37in) s. ink col handscroll two. 25-Apr-4 Christie's, Hong Kong #331/R est:150000-200000 (HK.D 260000)
£39118 $70413 €57112 Farewell at Huqiu (28x128cm-11x50in) s.d.1548 ink col handscroll sillk. 25-Apr-4 Christie's, Hong Kong #365/R est:600000-800000 (HK.D 550000)

WEN ZHENGMING (attrib) (1470-1559) Chinese
Works on paper
£2934 $4900 €4284 Landscape of the immortals (25x143cm-10x56in) s. ink on silk. 26-Oct-3 Christie's, Hong Kong #430/R (HK.D 38000)

WENBAN, Sion Longley (1848-1897) American
£382 $603 €550 Farm on the banks of a river (46x83cm-18x33in) s. 5-Sep-3 Wendl, Rudolstadt #3764/R

WENBAUM, Albert (c.1880-1943) French/Russian
£662 $1205 €1000 Rabbins et femme (81x64cm-32x25in) s.d.1930. 15-Jun-4 Rossini, Paris #76
Works on paper
£530 $964 €800 Water seller (53x38cm-21x15in) s.d.1932 gouache. 15-Jun-4 Rossini, Paris #77
£563 $1025 €850 Rabbins (22x31cm-9x12in) s. W/C gouache. 15-Jun-4 Rossini, Paris #79
£655 $1094 €950 Vue de Salers (40x54cm-16x21in) s.i.d.1930 W/C gouache. 17-Nov-3 Claude Boisgirard, Paris #101
£662 $1205 €1000 Une rue de banlieue (41x53cm-16x21in) s.d.1936 gouache. 16-Jun-4 Claude Boisgirard, Paris #168/R
£662 $1205 €1000 Rue Blanqui (41x53cm-16x21in) s.d.1936 gouache. 16-Jun-4 Claude Boisgirard, Paris #169/R
£690 $1152 €1000 Fleurs (48x39cm-19x15in) s.d.1931 W/C c. 17-Nov-3 Claude Boisgirard, Paris #102/R est:1000-1200
£1325 $2411 €2000 Still life with bouquet of flowers (49x37cm-19x15in) s.i.indis.d. gouache. 15-Jun-4 Rossini, Paris #78 est:400-700

WENCKE, Sophie (1874-1963) German
£280 $481 €400 Bank of Weser at sunset (40x50cm-16x20in) s. 5-Dec-3 Bolland & Marotz, Bremen #444/R
£867 $1560 €1300 Moorland canal (47x65cm-19x26in) s. 24-Apr-4 Reiss & Sohn, Konigstein #5379/R

WENCKER, Joseph (1848-1919) ?
£1475 $2700 €2154 Harem scene with two figures reclining (43x61cm-17x24in) s. 10-Apr-4 Brunk, Ashville #464/R est:1500-3000

WENDELIN, Martta (1893-1986) Finnish
£1544 $2840 €2300 Helsingfors (46x39cm-18x15in) s. 25-Mar-4 Hagelstam, Helsinki #834 est:500
Works on paper
£1215 $2030 €1750 The skiing trip. By the open fire (24x20cm-9x8in) one s. gouache two book illustrations. 26-Oct-3 Bukowskis, Helsinki #533/R est:500
£1667 $2783 €2400 The excursion (27x23cm-11x9in) s. gouache book illustration. 26-Oct-3 Bukowskis, Helsinki #534/R est:350

WENDISCH, Trakia (1958-) German
Sculpture
£5944 $10105 €8500 Grazie VII (170cm-67in) i. green pat.bronze exhib. 27-Nov-3 Lempertz, Koln #526/R est:6000

WENDLBERGER, Wenzel Hermann (1882-?) German
£423 $676 €600 Roses and forget me nots in ceramic vase (56x42cm-22x17in) s. lit. 19-Sep-3 Karlheinz Kaupp, Staufen #2041

£629 $1051 €900 Dahlias (65x55cm-26x22in) s. 9-Oct-3 Michael Zeller, Lindau #795/R
£1081 $1967 €1578 Still life with flowers in a vase on a draped table (72x55cm-28x22in) s. 20-Jun-4 Agra, Warsaw #56/R (P.Z 7500)
£1418 $2538 €2070 Southern harbour with figures (55x73cm-22x29in) s. 12-Jan-4 Rasmussen, Vejle #416/R est:18000-20000 (D.KR 15000)

WENDLER, Friedrich Moritz (1814-1872) German
£1798 $3326 €2625 Man with his gun dog in a river landscape (22x18cm-9x7in) 14-Mar-4 Agra, Warsaw #32/R (P.Z 13000)

WENDLING, Carl (1851-1914) German
£1732 $3100 €2529 Teatime (63x92cm-25x36in) s. 22-Mar-4 Philippe Schuler, Zurich #4439/R est:4000-6000 (S.FR 4000)

WENDLING, Gustav (1862-?) German
£1141 $2134 €1700 Dutch coast with fishing boats (100x128cm-39x50in) s. 24-Feb-4 Dorotheum, Vienna #138/R est:1800-2000

WENDT, William (1865-1946) American
£18824 $32000 €27483 California Valley (41x61cm-16x24in) s. prov. 29-Oct-3 Christie's, Los Angeles #56/R est:30000-50000
£19841 $37500 €28968 Owens Valley farm (61x76cm-24x30in) s. prov. 17-Feb-4 John Moran, Pasadena #70b/R est:40000-60000
£21739 $40000 €31739 Evening solitude (50x81cm-20x32in) s. prov. 8-Jun-4 Bonhams & Butterfields, San Francisco #4276/R est:40000-60000
£21739 $40000 €31739 Green hills (41x51cm-16x20in) s.d.1916 prov. 8-Jun-4 Bonhams & Butterfields, San Francisco #4304/R est:25000-35000
£22487 $42500 €32831 Oak trees in atmospheric landscape (41x61cm-16x24in) s. prov. 17-Feb-4 John Moran, Pasadena #77a/R est:25000-35000
£27456 $47500 €40086 New Corn (63x76cm-25x30in) s.d.1920 prov.exhib.lit. 10-Dec-3 Bonhams & Butterfields, San Francisco #6244/R est:50000-70000
£38043 $70000 €55543 A trickle of road (63x76cm-25x30in) s. i. stretcher exhib.lit. 8-Jun-4 Bonhams & Butterfields, San Francisco #4299/R est:50000-70000
£39548 $70000 €57740 Santa Ana River (50x91cm-20x36in) s.d.1919 prov.exhib.lit. 28-Apr-4 Christie's, Los Angeles #41/R est:70000-90000

WENGENROTH, Stow (1906-1978) American
Prints
£3315 $6000 €4840 Manhattan gateway (24x46cm-9x18in) s.i. lithograph. 19-Apr-4 Bonhams & Butterfields, San Francisco #63/R est:3000-5000
Works on paper
£843 $1400 €1231 Dunes and pines (36x58cm-14x23in) dry brush prov. 4-Oct-3 South Bay, Long Island #66
£1304 $2400 €1904 Dune road (33x58cm-13x23in) brush ink board exec. c.1949 sold with lithograph. 10-Jun-4 Swann Galleries, New York #254/R est:2500-3500
£2346 $3800 €3402 Pink and white carnation (41x30cm-16x12in) s. W/C. 8-Aug-3 Barridorf, Portland #210/R est:3000-5000

WENGLEIN, Joseph (1845-1919) German
£552 $1021 €800 Landscape with pond and cows (27x44cm-11x17in) mono. panel. 12-Feb-4 Weidler, Nurnberg #362/R
£604 $1111 €900 Three cows grazing (21x40cm-8x16in) s. canvas on board. 24-Mar-4 Hugo Ruef, Munich #1145
£764 $1245 €1100 Cow in meadow. s.d.68. 24-Sep-3 Neumeister, Munich #600/R
£816 $1461 €1200 Storm gathering over lake landscape (22x31cm-9x12in) s. board. 17-Mar-4 Neumeister, Munich #660
£1806 $2979 €2600 View over alpine meadow of Wetterstein mountains (38x54cm-15x21in) i. board. 2-Jul-3 Neumeister, Munich #817/R est:3000
£1867 $3397 €2800 Peasant farmstead by stream (24x33cm-9x13in) s.d.91 panel. 30-Jun-4 Neumeister, Munich #749/R est:2200
£2098 $3608 €3000 Scene de chasse dans un paysage d'automne (27x45cm-11x18in) s.d.80 panel. 5-Dec-3 Chochon-Barre & Allardi, Paris #12/R est:3000-3500
£2632 $4842 €4000 Moorland with evening sky (48x71cm-19x28in) s. 24-Jun-4 Dr Fritz Nagel, Stuttgart #775/R est:6000
£3472 $5729 €5000 Landscape with lake and mountains (44x61cm-17x24in) s. 2-Jul-3 Neumeister, Munich #816/R est:5000
£3846 $6615 €5500 Cows drinking from a pond (23x45cm-9x18in) s. panel. 3-Dec-3 Neumeister, Munich #799/R est:6000
£4200 $7644 €6300 Autumn landscape with ducks (70x90cm-28x35in) s.i. prov. 30-Jun-4 Neumeister, Munich #748/R est:4000
£5455 $9382 €7800 Autumnal landscape with young girl walking by a stream (27x35cm-11x14in) s.d.86 panel. 3-Dec-3 Neumeister, Munich #800/R est:2500
£6040 $11114 €9000 Isar valley (73x125cm-29x49in) s.d.84. 25-Mar-4 Dr Fritz Nagel, Stuttgart #777/R est:12000
Works on paper
£327 $584 €480 Trees on lakeshore (19x40cm-7x16in) s.i.d.87 pencil htd white. 17-Mar-4 Neumeister, Munich #321
£629 $1051 €900 Landscape with trees. Shore of the River Inn (20x20cm-8x8in) s.i. pencil chl htd white two. 10-Oct-3 Winterberg, Heidelberg #823
£1056 $1827 €1500 Upper Bavarian moorland in late autumn (40x60cm-16x24in) s. chk chl. 13-Dec-3 Lempertz, Koln #62/R est:1000

WENGLEIN, Joseph (attrib) (1845-1919) German
£411 $699 €600 Landscape with stream (26x38cm-10x15in) board. 5-Nov-3 Hugo Ruef, Munich #1177
£680 $1218 €1000 Hilly landscape (25x47cm-10x19in) i.d.84 canvas on board. 17-Mar-4 Neumeister, Munich #661
£800 $1456 €1200 Approaching thunderstorm (22x45cm-9x18in) 1-Jul-4 Van Ham, Cologne #1663

WENIG, H (20th C) ?
£1200 $2220 €1752 Harlequin (103x68cm-41x27in) s.d.39. 14-Jul-4 Christie's, Kensington #1248/R est:1200-1800

WENIG, Josef (1885-1939) Czechoslovakian
Works on paper
£316 $557 €474 Fairytale Queen with a rose (42x40cm-17x16in) s.d.1917 W/C. 22-May-4 Dorotheum, Prague #191/R est:8000-12000 (C.KR 15000)

WENING, Rudolf (1893-1970) Swiss
Sculpture
£9200 $15916 €13432 Bust of a girl (46cm-18in) s. white marble wood base. 12-Dec-3 Sotheby's, London #244/R est:4000-6000

WENK, Albert (1863-1934) German
£6597 $10424 €9500 Gulf of Naples (115x112cm-45x44in) s. 6-Sep-3 Schopman, Hamburg #709/R est:3000

WENNERBERG, Brynolf (1823-1894) Swedish
£379 $633 €550 Village in hilly landscape (32x36cm-13x14in) mono. bears i. verso canvas on panel. 10-Jul-3 Allgauer, Kempten #2783/R
£897 $1497 €1300 Standing female nued (33x25cm-13x10in) mono. board lit. 10-Jul-3 Allgauer, Kempten #2782/R
£3243 $5805 €4800 Woman's portrait (62x46cm-24x18in) mono. board lit. 8-May-4 Schloss Ahlden, Ahlden #806/R est:2700
Works on paper
£1400 $2408 €2044 Before the party (63x48cm-25x19in) init. pencil chl gouache. 4-Dec-3 Christie's, Kensington #155/R est:1000-1500

WENNERBERG, Gunnar (1863-1914) Swedish
£1077 $1852 €1572 Lady with parasol by Lake Garda (43x65cm-17x26in) s. 3-Dec-3 AB Stockholms Auktionsverk #2357/R (S.KR 14000)

WENNERWALD, Emil (1859-1934) Danish
£281 $458 €410 Landscape from Silkeborg Islands (47x70cm-19x28in) s.d.1910. 27-Sep-3 Rasmussen, Havnen #2106 (D.KR 3000)
£300 $500 €438 Coastal landscape, North Sjaelland (43x61cm-17x24in) s. 25-Oct-3 Rasmussen, Havnen #2055/R (D.KR 3200)
£340 $619 €500 Path along the coast (47x67cm-19x26in) s. 3-Feb-4 Segre, Madrid #114/R
£349 $650 €510 Lakeside (62x86cm-24x34in) s.d.1919. 5-Mar-4 Skinner, Boston #498/R
£356 $613 €520 Amalia - Portrait of young Italian woman (47x26cm-19x10in) s.d.07. 3-Dec-3 Museumsbygningen, Copenhagen #153 (D.KR 3800)
£376 $677 €549 Italian village scene (56x45cm-22x18in) s.d.1923. 24-Apr-4 Rasmussen, Havnen #2123 (D.KR 4200)
£376 $677 €549 View of bay with boats (56x60cm-22x24in) s.d.1898. 24-Apr-4 Rasmussen, Havnen #2272 (D.KR 4200)
£394 $642 €575 Summer's day by woodland lake (78x102cm-31x40in) s. 27-Sep-3 Rasmussen, Havnen #2125 (D.KR 4200)
£402 $651 €583 Evening at Ry station (76x100cm-30x39in) s. 4-Aug-3 Rasmussen, Vejle #309/R (D.KR 4200)
£513 $805 €749 Landscape from Silkeborg Islands (66x83cm-26x33in) s.d.1910. 30-Aug-3 Rasmussen, Havnen #2000 (D.KR 5500)
£568 $1000 €829 Untitled landscape (38x53cm-15x21in) s. 23-May-4 Hindman, Chicago #15/R
£588 $1053 €858 Landscape from Knud Lake in Ry (55x92cm-22x36in) s.d.1904. 10-May-4 Rasmussen, Vejle #129/R (D.KR 6500)
£1192 $2170 €1800 Sunny autumn forest (83x65cm-33x26in) s. 21-Jun-4 Dorotheum, Vienna #308/R est:2200-2600
£1513 $2617 €2209 Landscape (79x87cm-31x34in) s.d.1918. 14-Dec-3 Agra, Warsaw #41/R est:5000 (P.Z 10000)
£1552 $2778 €2266 Climbing plants on terrace with view of sea (52x69cm-20x27in) s.d.1913. 13-May-4 Stuker, Bern #373/R est:1000-1500 (S.FR 3600)
£2000 $3440 €2920 Italian hilltop town (47x68cm-19x27in) s.indis.d. 4-Dec-3 Christie's, Kensington #69/R est:2000-3000

WENNERWALD, Finn (1896-?) Danish
£546 $1000 €797 Edge of the pond (46x66cm-18x26in) s. painted c.1930. 5-Jun-4 Treadway Gallery, Cincinnati #556/R est:1400-1800

WENNING, Ype (1879-1959) Dutch
£278 $453 €400 View of the Amsterdam Port, Haaelem (17x26cm-7x10in) s. panel. 29-Sep-3 Sotheby's, Amsterdam #119/R
£380 $695 €555 Dutch, rural cottage with figure in garden (17x28cm-7x11in) s. board. 6-Jul-4 Peter Wilson, Nantwich #3/R
£578 $1052 €850 Peasants woman in a farmyard (50x60cm-20x24in) s. 3-Feb-4 Christie's, Amsterdam #253
£1027 $1747 €1500 Interior scene with man and woman seated (57x77cm-22x30in) s. 5-Nov-3 Vendue Huis, Gravenhage #224/R est:1400-1800
£1250 $1975 €1800 Sandpit in the dunes (60x100cm-24x39in) s. 2-Sep-3 Christie's, Amsterdam #272/R est:1500-2000

WENTCHER, Julius (c.1888-1962) ?
Works on paper
£374 $670 €550 Balinese beauties (41x29cm-16x11in) s.i.d.1934 W/C. 16-Mar-4 Christie's, Amsterdam #107

WENTORF, Carl (1863-1914) Danish
£376 $677 €549 Portrait of Professor C E Aagaard (28x23cm-11x9in) s.verso. 24-Apr-4 Rasmussen, Havnen #2353 (D.KR 4200)
£1869 $2953 €2710 The sisters Kirsten, Mette and Karen Clauson-Kaas (105x138cm-41x54in) 2-Sep-3 Rasmussen, Copenhagen #1719/R est:25000-30000 (D.KR 20000)

WENTSCHER, Julius (1842-1918) German
£350 $594 €500 Extensive landscape (73x97cm-29x38in) s.d.1909. 20-Nov-3 Van Ham, Cologne #1907

WENTSCHER, Tina (1887-1974) Australian
Sculpture
£1055 $1973 €1583 Andor (44x40x39cm-17x16x15in) painted plaster together with a W/C by the same hand exhib. 20-Jul-4 Goodman, Sydney #36/R est:3000-5000 (A.D 2700)
£1191 $2228 €1787 Balinese woman wearing red head cloth (23x18x15cm-9x7x6in) wax polychrome exec.c.1931 prov.exhib. 20-Jul-4 Goodman, Sydney #32/R est:1200-1800 (A.D 3050)

WENTWORTH, Daniel F (1850-1934) American
£924 $1700 €1349 Winter sunset landscape with a running brook (30x41cm-12x16in) s. board. 9-Jun-4 Alderfer's, Hatfield #443/R est:1000-1500
£1195 $1900 €1745 Winter farm view (56x76cm-22x30in) s. s.d.1921 verso. 12-Sep-3 Skinner, Boston #455/R
Works on paper
£329 $550 €480 Farmhouse with mountains in the distance (28x43cm-11x17in) init.d.Aug 4/1882 W/C paper on board. 18-Jun-3 Doyle, New York #82/R

WENTZEL, F C (17th C) Flemish
£2797 $4755 €4000 L'hallali du loup (93x128cm-37x50in) 20-Nov-3 Millon & Associes, Paris #183/R

WENTZEL, Gustav (1859-1927) Norwegian
£400 $692 €584 Spring landscape (28x36cm-11x14in) s. panel. 13-Dec-3 Blomqvist, Lysaker #1401/R (N.KR 4600)
£602 $1006 €879 By the shore (38x70cm-15x28in) s. 20-Oct-3 Blomqvist, Lysaker #1347/R (N.KR 7000)
£626 $1045 €914 Portrait of Carl Sebastian Wentzel (37x31cm-15x12in) s.verso panel. 17-Nov-3 Blomqvist, Lysaker #1367 (N.KR 7500)
£647 $1036 €938 October snow (29x13cm-11x5in) s. panel. 22-Sep-3 Blomqvist, Lysaker #1329/R (N.KR 7600)
£1363 $2344 €1990 Girl at window (26x33cm-10x13in) s. panel. 8-Dec-3 Blomqvist, Oslo #466/R est:18000-22000 (N.KR 16000)
£2896 $4981 €4228 Ski track in winter landscape (40x66cm-16x26in) s. 8-Dec-3 Blomqvist, Oslo #400/R est:25000-30000 (N.KR 34000)
£3915 $7008 €5716 Man and horse (60x78cm-24x31in) s.d.99. 25-May-4 Grev Wedels Plass, Oslo #36/R est:30000-40000 (N.KR 48000)
£5444 $9745 €7948 Norwegian mountain valley in winter sunshine (60x80cm-24x31in) s. 22-Mar-4 Blomqvist, Oslo #303/R est:35000-40000 (N.KR 68000)
£5500 $10010 €8030 In the farmyard (73x104cm-29x41in) s.d.90. 15-Jun-4 Sotheby's, London #366/R est:5000-7000

WENZEL, Edward August (1895-1971) German
£1879 $3477 €2800 Praying hands (80x100cm-31x39in) s.d.1933. 9-Mar-4 Dorotheum, Vienna #48/R est:3000-4000

WENZEL, Karlheinz (1932-) German
£313 $522 €450 Deer in autumnal mountain landscape (79x114cm-31x45in) s. 25-Oct-3 Bergmann, Erlangen #985/R

WENZEL, Peter Johann (attrib) (1745-1829) German
£748 $1339 €1100 Adam and Eve in the Garden of Eden (32x50cm-13x20in) lit. 20-Mar-4 Bergmann, Erlangen #1052

WENZELL, Albert Beck (1864-1917) American
Works on paper
£2395 $4000 €3497 Knight in 17th Century costume kneeling before a seated lady (119x114cm-47x45in) s.d.97 pastel. 27-Oct-3 Schrager Galleries, Milwaukee #1189/R
£9581 $16000 €13988 Crowd awaiting the start of a performance (56x97cm-22x38in) s.d.1894 gouache prov. 15-Nov-3 Illustration House, New York #29/R est:10000-15000

WERDEHAUSEN, Hans (1910-1977) German
£1000 $1790 €1500 Technical shapes (60x85cm-24x33in) i. verso. 15-May-4 Van Ham, Cologne #1025/R est:1000

WEREFKIN, Marianne von (1870-1938) Russian
£3247 $5812 €4741 Storm over lake. s. i. verso. 22-Mar-4 Philippe Schuler, Zurich #4071/R est:800-1000 (S.FR 7500)
Works on paper
£5667 $10370 €8500 The Holy Land (35x26cm-14x10in) mono.i. gouache Indian ink col chk. 5-Jun-4 Lempertz, Koln #1023/R est:6000-7000

WERENSKIOLD, Dagfinn (1892-1977) Norwegian
£258 $431 €377 Rapids (64x79cm-25x31in) s. panel. 20-Oct-3 Blomqvist, Lysaker #1348 (N.KR 3000)
£439 $733 €641 Man and horse on country road (100x130cm-39x51in) s. exhib. 20-Oct-3 Blomqvist, Lysaker #1349/R (N.KR 5100)
£488 $898 €712 Garden flowers (46x55cm-18x22in) init.d.1953 panel. 10-Jun-4 Grev Wedels Plass, Oslo #243/R (N.KR 6000)

WERENSKIOLD, Erik Theodor (1855-1938) Norwegian
£2276 $4166 €3323 Boy on horseback (69x87cm-27x34in) mono. 7-Jun-4 Blomqvist, Oslo #378/R est:25000-30000 (N.KR 28000)
£3252 $5984 €4748 Factory buildings at Lysaker (80x65cm-31x26in) init.d.07 s.i.stretcher exhib. 10-Jun-4 Grev Wedels Plass, Oslo #244/R est:40000-60000 (N.KR 40000)
£8967 $14974 €13092 Autumn landscape from Lysaker (98x87cm-39x34in) mono. 13-Oct-3 Blomqvist, Oslo #292/R est:80000-120000 (N.KR 105000)

WERFF, Adriaen van der (1659-1722) Dutch
£33784 $59459 €50000 Vanitas, a boy in a windoe blowing bubbles (29x22cm-11x9in) panel. 18-May-4 Sotheby's, Amsterdam #8/R est:30000-40000
£52000 $89960 €75920 Portrait of a lady wearing a black dress and cap (72x54cm-28x21in) s.d.1679 i.verso panel. 10-Dec-3 Bonhams, New Bond Street #6/R est:5000-8000

WERFF, Adriaen van der (after) (1659-1722) Dutch
£4698 $8691 €7000 Rest on flight to Egypt (36x29cm-14x11in) bears sig panel. 15-Mar-4 Sotheby's, Amsterdam #36/R est:3000-5000

WERFF, Adriaen van der (attrib) (1659-1722) Dutch
£1316 $2421 €2000 The atoning Magdalena (37x27cm-15x11in) panel. 26-Jun-4 Karrenbauer, Konstanz #1767/R est:1800

WERFF, Pieter van der (attrib) (1665-1722) Dutch
£1528 $2521 €2200 Sleeping Venus with satyr (45x40cm-18x16in) 3-Jul-3 Van Ham, Cologne #1030/R est:3000

WERGELAND, Oscar (1844-1910) Norwegian
£601 $1052 €877 The banquet (36x27cm-14x11in) s. 16-Dec-3 Grev Wedels Plass, Oslo #245/R (N.KR 7000)
£3018 $5402 €4406 King Sverre's procession across Voss mountains (64x90cm-25x35in) s.i.d.74. 25-May-4 Grev Wedels Plass, Oslo #58/R est:30000-40000 (N.KR 37000)

WERGELL, Carl (?) British?
£360 $655 €526 Study of a shepherd and his flock before a copse of trees (25x38cm-10x15in) s. 5-Feb-4 Biddle & Webb, Birmingham #770

WERKMAN, Hendrik Nicolaas (1882-1945) Dutch
Prints
£4710 $7725 €6500 Metro, Martinet 29-15 (65x50cm-26x20in) print prov.exhib. 27-May-3 Sotheby's, Amsterdam #624/R est:3500-4500
£6159 $10101 €8500 Composition, Martinet 42-84 (64x50cm-25x20in) d.1942 print sjablone prov.exhib. 27-May-3 Sotheby's, Amsterdam #626/R est:9000-13000
£13333 $24533 €20000 Vier ruiters in landschap - landscape with four riders (43x56cm-17x22in) d.1944 inkroll print stencil exhib. 9-Jun-4 Christie's, Amsterdam #252/R est:19000-24000
£54348 $89130 €75000 Legends (51x34cm-20x13in) s. num.19/20 print sjablone ten. 27-May-3 Sotheby's, Amsterdam #625/R est:40000-60000
£69931 $120282 €100000 Chassidische legenden (52x34cm-20x13in) s.num. hand printed stenciled templates 20 two portfolios. 3-Dec-3 Sotheby's, Amsterdam #411/R est:100000-120000

WERLEN, Ludwig (1884-1928) Swiss
£952 $1705 €1390 Fusilier of the 130 Artillery Battalion (43x37cm-17x15in) s.d.1914. 22-Mar-4 Philippe Schuler, Zurich #6062 (S.FR 2200)
£1739 $3183 €2539 Maisons dans la plaine du Rhone (45x60cm-18x24in) s.d.1919 prov. 5-Jun-4 Galerie du Rhone, Sion #556/R est:4000-6000 (S.FR 4000)
£2982 $4979 €4324 Weisshorn (40x60cm-16x24in) s. i.verso prov. 21-Jun-3 Galerie du Rhone, Sion #483/R est:5000-7000 (S.FR 6500)
Works on paper
£862 $1543 €1259 Farmstead in Wallis (19x24cm-7x9in) s. W/C. 14-May-4 Dobiaschofsky, Bern #162/R est:2600 (S.FR 2000)
£1086 $1846 €1586 Portrait of man wearing hat (50x49cm-20x19in) s. pastel. 28-Nov-3 Zofingen, Switzerland #3218 est:3000 (S.FR 2400)

WERNEKINCK, Sigismund (1872-1921) German
Sculpture
£987 $1815 €1500 Venus (58cm-23in) s. white marble incl. green base exec. c.1910. 22-Jun-4 Sotheby's, Amsterdam #240/R est:1000-1500

WERNER, Adolf (1827-1904) German
£306 $504 €440 Cattle market in small town (36x58cm-14x23in) s. 3-Jul-3 Van Ham, Cologne #1499
£738 $1373 €1100 Successful hunt (48x39cm-19x15in) s. 6-Mar-4 Arnold, Frankfurt #910/R
£5245 $8916 €7500 Fruit picking, Gleichenberg in Steiermark (73x95cm-29x37in) s. i. verso. 24-Nov-3 Dorotheum, Vienna #120/R est:5000-7000

WERNER, Anton Alexander von (1843-1915) German
Works on paper
£284 $460 €400 Soldier sitting on ground pulling on boots (39x49cm-15x19in) mono.d.1872 chl prov.lit. 23-May-3 Karlheinz Kaupp, Staufen #1874
£284 $460 €400 Uniformed figure (48x30cm-19x12in) mono.d.1879 chl col pen prov.lit. 23-May-3 Karlheinz Kaupp, Staufen #1901
£284 $460 €400 Capt z van Spring (48x31cm-19x12in) mono.i.d.1906 chl ochre htd white prov.lit. 23-May-3 Karlheinz Kaupp, Staufen #1910/R
£1781 $3027 €2600 Heringsdorf (36x25cm-14x10in) mono.i.d.1877 W/C. 4-Nov-3 Hartung & Hartung, Munich #3134/R est:1200

WERNER, Carl (1808-1894) German
£1472 $2635 €2149 Italian coast with figures (34x52cm-13x20in) s. canvas on board. 22-Mar-4 Philippe Schuler, Zurich #4440/R est:4000-6000 (S.FR 3400)
£3012 $5000 €4398 Fountain Hall in the Zisa, Palermo (64x51cm-25x20in) s.d.1878 i.verso. 4-Oct-3 Neal Auction Company, New Orleans #261/R est:6000-8000
£3147 $5350 €4500 Market in Rome (39x45cm-15x18in) s.d.1838. 24-Nov-3 Dorotheum, Vienna #127/R est:4000-4500
Works on paper
£679 $1086 €991 Landscape near Palermo (25x23cm-10x9in) s.d.1839 W/C. 19-Sep-3 Koller, Zurich #3133 est:1000-1500 (S.FR 1500)
£2069 $3455 €3000 Egyptian oasis (27x39cm-11x15in) s.d.1871 W/C. 15-Nov-3 Lempertz, Koln #1567/R est:3000

WERNER, Carl (attrib) (1808-1894) German
£1467 $2655 €2200 Cairo coffee house (28x40cm-11x16in) i. verso lit. 3-Apr-4 Badum, Bamberg #118/R est:2000

WERNER, Dietrich W (1948-) Canadian/German
£300 $549 €438 Meeting in paradise (75x75cm-30x30in) s.i.d.1986 acrylic. 1-Jun-4 Hodgins, Calgary #310/R (C.D 750)

WERNER, Gosta (1909-1989) Swedish
£353 $612 €515 Still life of sculpture and lemon with blue background (92x65cm-36x26in) s. 15-Dec-3 Lilla Bukowskis, Stockholm #723 (S.KR 4500)

WERNER, Heinrich Ferdinand (1867-1928) German
£3867 $7076 €5800 Christmas interior (50x38cm-20x15in) mono. i.d.1909. 5-Jun-4 Arnold, Frankfurt #792/R est:300

WERNER, Heinrich Ferdinand (attrib) (1867-1928) German
£1333 $2413 €2000 Castle interior (35x45cm-14x18in) 3-Apr-4 Badum, Bamberg #91/R est:2000

WERNER, Hermann (1816-1905) German
£1500 $2775 €2190 Talmud discussion (26x31cm-10x12in) s. board. 14-Jul-4 Sotheby's, Olympia #180/R est:1000-1500
£4545 $8000 €6636 Nap time (41x34cm-16x13in) s.d.77. 18-May-4 Bonhams & Butterfields, San Francisco #98/R est:8000-12000

WERNER, Hilding (1880-1944) Swedish
£614 $1002 €896 Sunset (47x78cm-19x31in) s.d.1925. 29-Sep-3 Lilla Bukowskis, Stockholm #197 (S.KR 8000)
£614 $1002 €896 Summer evening (46x72cm-18x28in) s. 29-Sep-3 Lilla Bukowskis, Stockholm #198 (S.KR 8000)
£3692 $6351 €5390 Landscape with Kils church (92x195cm-36x77in) s. 2-Dec-3 Bukowskis, Stockholm #35/R est:50000-60000 (S.KR 48000)

WERNER, Jacques Christophe (1798-1856) French
Works on paper
£1034 $1728 €1500 Deux chimpanzes (28x21cm-11x8in) s.d.1839 W/C black crayon. 13-Nov-3 Binoche, Paris #113 est:800

WERNER, Max (1879-?) German?
£280 $496 €409 Fishing boats, Copenhagen (50x60cm-20x24in) s. board. 27-Apr-4 Bonhams, Knightsbridge #174
£1500 $2385 €2175 Venetian canal (60x48cm-24x19in) board on panel. 11-Sep-3 Christie's, Kensington #24/R est:2000-3000

WERNER, Reinhold (1842-1922) German
£309 $574 €460 Interior scene with elderly woman reading at a table (38x50cm-15x20in) s. canvas on panel. 5-Mar-4 Wendl, Rudolstadt #4014/R

WERNER, Simon (20th C) American
£222 $400 €324 Still life of peonies and cherries (63x46cm-25x18in) s.i. 24-Apr-4 Weschler, Washington #603/R

WERNER, Theodor (1886-1969) German
£867 $1551 €1300 Falling/climbing (79x89cm-31x35in) mono.d.44 i. verso panel. 15-May-4 Van Ham, Cologne #1026/R est:4000
£1875 $3131 €2700 Still life with red roses (33x36cm-13x14in) s.d. board. 25-Oct-3 Dr Lehr, Berlin #539/R est:2500
£4861 $8118 €7000 Composition 50/1953 (70x100cm-28x39in) s.d. s.i.d. verso board prov.exhib. 24-Oct-3 Ketterer, Hamburg #580/R est:7000-9000
£14765 $26430 €22000 Composition "XXVII" (82x116cm-32x46in) s.d. exhib. 25-May-4 Karl & Faber, Munich #576/R est:22000-25000
Works on paper
£276 $461 €400 Untitled (11x16cm-4x6in) mono.d.1954 i.verso mixed media board. 13-Nov-3 Neumeister, Munich #661/R
£280 $501 €420 Signs and lines (91x14cm-36x6in) mono.d.54 mixed media board. 15-May-4 Van Ham, Cologne #1038
£315 $565 €470 Composition "M.2/57" (11x16cm-4x6in) mono.d.57 pastel pencil exhib. 25-May-4 Karl & Faber, Munich #578
£1333 $2387 €2000 Untitled (72x50cm-28x20in) s.d. pencil oil. 15-May-4 Bassenge, Berlin #7199/R est:2000
£2867 $5131 €4300 Improvisation (79x89cm-31x35in) s. oil gouache pencil. 15-May-4 Van Ham, Cologne #1027/R est:4000
£6207 $10366 €9000 Legend (99x80cm-39x31in) s.i.d.1946 verso mixed media prov. 13-Nov-3 Neumeister, Munich #658/R est:4000-5000

WERNER, Willibald (20th C) German
£1061 $1867 €1549 Street under snow (68x97cm-27x38in) s. 23-May-4 Agra, Warsaw #31/R (P.Z 7500)

WERSTUK, Dan (1949-) Canadian
Works on paper
£491 $845 €717 Muskoka Bay at sunset (50x37cm-20x15in) s. pastel. 2-Dec-3 Joyner Waddington, Toronto #380/R (C.D 1100)

WERTHEIM, Heinrich (1875-1945) Austrian
Works on paper
£345 $572 €500 Salzburg (39x59cm-15x23in) s. W/C. 30-Sep-3 Dorotheum, Vienna #340/R

WERTHEIMER, Gustave (1847-1904) Austrian
£1736 $2760 €2500 Lune blanche sur Louxor (112x152cm-44x60in) s. 9-Sep-3 Vanderkindere, Brussels #58

WERTHEIMER, Sam (20th C) American
Works on paper
£543 $1000 €793 Modernist cityscape (30x23cm-12x9in) s.d.1936 chl. 10-Jun-4 Swann Galleries, New York #255/R

WERTMULLER, Adolf Ulrik (attrib) (1751-1811) Swedish
£3077 $5292 €4492 Portrait of young boy, possibly Crown Prince Louis Charles of France (46x38cm-18x15in) painted c.1790. 3-Dec-3 AB Stockholms Auktionsverk #2333/R est:50000-60000 (S.KR 40000)

WERY, Émile Auguste (1868-1935) French
Works on paper
£559 $962 €800 Port breton (20x29cm-8x11in) s. gouache cardboard. 7-Dec-3 Livinec, Gaudcheau & Jezequel, Rennes #22

WERY, Fernand (1886-1964) Belgian
£1867 $3416 €2800 Le jeune paysan (60x50cm-24x20in) s. exhib. 7-Jun-4 Palais de Beaux Arts, Brussels #322/R est:2000-3000
£2621 $4848 €3800 La Place Ste Croix sous la neige (80x60cm-31x24in) s. 13-Jan-4 Vanderkindere, Brussels #100/R est:3000-4000

WERY, Pierre Nicolas (1770-1827) French
£671 $1235 €1000 Promeneurs pres d'une ferme fortifiee dominant la riviere (14x18cm-6x7in) s. panel. 26-Mar-4 Piasa, Paris #64

WESCOTT, Paul (1904-1970) American
£518 $850 €751 Grand Manan Island, off Maine (51x61cm-20x24in) 4-Jun-3 Alderfer's, Hatfield #402
£976 $1600 €1415 Harbour scene with sailboats (20x30cm-8x12in) s. 4-Jun-3 Alderfer's, Hatfield #400/R est:800-1200
£2591 $4250 €3757 Boatyard (46x71cm-18x28in) s. 4-Jun-3 Alderfer's, Hatfield #398/R est:2000-3000

WESEMANN, Alfred (1874-?) Austrian
£8000 $14560 €11680 Stork and pink flamingos (112x169cm-44x67in) s.d.1909 prov. 15-Jun-4 Sotheby's, London #87/R est:6000-8000

WESLEY, John (1928-) American
£5215 $8500 €7614 Good night (76x56cm-30x22in) s.i.d.1997 acrylic prov. 23-Sep-3 Christie's, Rockefeller NY #62/R est:5000-7000
£17333 $31720 €26000 Untitled (137x102cm-54x40in) s.d.1991 verso acrylic. 4-Jun-4 Lempertz, Koln #531/R est:30000
Works on paper
£4396 $8000 €6418 B'S ladder (56x66cm-22x26in) s.i.d.1973-74 gouache pencil prov. 29-Jun-4 Sotheby's, New York #534/R est:4000-6000
£4945 $9000 €7220 B'S front door (56x66cm-22x26in) s.i.d.1973-74 gouache pencil prov. 29-Jun-4 Sotheby's, New York #537/R est:3000-5000

WESLEY, Paul (20th C) American
£587 $1050 €857 Catskill stream (51x66cm-20x26in) s. i.verso. 20-Mar-4 Selkirks, St. Louis #164 est:300-500

WESLY, Fernand (1894-1983) Belgian
£282 $487 €400 La plage a Knokke Le Zoute (38x48cm-15x19in) s.d.1979 panel. 9-Dec-3 Campo, Vlaamse Kaai #507

WESSEL, Gerd (1938-) German
£253 $395 €400 In the country (77x110cm-30x43in) s.d.74 panel. 18-Oct-2 Von Zezschwitz, Munich #106/R

WESSEL, Wilhelm (1904-1971) German
£1259 $2165 €1800 Untitled (59x47cm-23x19in) s.d. i. verso oil Indian ink spatula sand collage canvas on board. 5-Dec-3 Ketterer, Munich #320/R est:1500-2000
£1958 $3368 €2800 Untitled (98x79cm-39x31in) s.d. oil Indian ink spatula canvas on board. 5-Dec-3 Ketterer, Munich #319/R est:2500-3000

WESSELINGH, J P van (19th C) Dutch
£1000 $1800 €1500 Landscape with children fishing (38x52cm-15x20in) s. 26-Apr-4 Rieber, Stuttgart #1128/R est:250

WESSELMANN, Tom (1931-) American
£1197 $2095 €1700 Smoking cigarette (17x15cm-7x6in) s.i.d.1998 liquitex board prov. 18-Dec-3 Cornette de St.Cyr, Paris #61/R est:2000-3000
£3374 $5500 €4926 Cigarette (23x20cm-9x8in) s.d.98 acrylic pencil paper collaged on paper two prov. 23-Sep-3 Christie's, Rockefeller NY #95/R est:3000-5000
£5333 $9760 €8000 Still life (13x18cm-5x7in) s.i.d.11/20 s.i.d.1974 verso liquitex collage masonite prov. 4-Jun-4 Lempertz, Koln #532/R est:6000
£6704 $12000 €9788 Study for embossed penis - Seascape (16x17cm-6x7in) s.i.d.78-8 prov. 12-May-4 Christie's, Rockefeller NY #136/R est:15000-20000
£7343 $12262 €10500 Nude no 35 (9x22cm-4x9in) s.d. liquitex graphite. 11-Oct-3 Cornette de St.Cyr, Paris #110/R est:10000-12000
£11377 $19000 €16610 Study for seascape nude (22x26cm-9x10in) s.d.78 overlap i.d.1978 stretcher acrylic pencil prov. 13-Nov-3 Sotheby's, New York #304/R est:25000-33300
£13889 $22083 €20000 Double study for bedrom painting (28x41cm-11x16in) s. 9-Sep-3 Vanderkindere, Brussels #198/R
£14000 $25340 €20440 Study of seascape prick (20x20cm-8x8in) s.d.69 i.d.on stretcher prov. 1-Apr-4 Christie's, Kensington #290/R est:8000-12000
£15951 $26000 €23288 Study for bedroom painting no 19 (20x25cm-8x10in) s.d.69 prov. 23-Sep-3 Christie's, Rockefeller NY #134/R est:7000-9000

£16760	$30000	€24470	Monica relaxing on robe - Variation no 5 (74x155cm-29x61in) s.i.d.89 verso enamel laser-cut steel prov. 13-May-4 Sotheby's, New York #246/R est:30000-40000
£19000	$31730	€27740	Study for bedroom foot (17x15cm-7x6in) s.d.79 i.d.1979 stretcher. 21-Oct-3 Sotheby's, London #359/R est:8000-12000
£22000	$40480	€32120	Study for bedroom face with purple pillow (19x24cm-7x9in) s.i.d.84 prov. 24-Jun-4 Sotheby's, London #267/R est:12000-18000
£22346	$40000	€32625	Compote with fruit - Colour Variant 1 (152x129cm-60x51in) s.i.d.1988 verso enamel on laser-cut steel exec 1988 prov. 13-May-4 Sotheby's, New York #216/R est:40000-60000
£23334	$42934	€35000	Double study for bedroom 22 (28x41cm-11x16in) s.d.1969 prov.exhib. 8-Jun-4 Artcurial Briest, Paris #231/R est:30000-40000
£23952	$40000	€34970	Monica sitting in hat and beads, colour variant no 3 (50x41cm-20x16in) s.i.d.1989 verso enamel laser cut steel prov. 13-Nov-3 Sotheby's, New York #293/R est:25000-35000
£32292	$53281	€46500	Study for smoker no 7, mouth no 21 (31x31cm-12x12in) i.d.1971 verso prov. 2-Jul-3 Cornette de St.Cyr, Paris #13/R est:40000-50000
£38000	$69160	€55480	Bedroom brunette doodle (160x185cm-63x73in) s.i.d.88 and 1984/8 verso enamel cut-out aluminium prov. 6-Feb-4 Sotheby's, London #222/R est:25000-35000
£44218	$79150	€65000	Study for nude collage edition (20x25cm-8x10in) s.d.70 prov. 19-Mar-4 Millon & Associes, Paris #193/R est:8000-10000
£47904	$80000	€69940	Study for Cynthia nude (43x57cm-17x22in) s.d.81 overlap prov. 13-Nov-3 Sotheby's, New York #296/R est:30000-40000
£49000	$88690	€71540	Bedroom blond doodle with photo (159x184cm-63x72in) s.i.d.85 enamel on cut aluminium. 1-Apr-4 Christie's, Kensington #291/R est:20000-30000
£80838	$135000	€118023	Still life no.7 (61x43cm-24x17in) s.d.62 s.i.d.verso oil paper cardboard collage panel prov. 12-Nov-3 Christie's, Rockefeller NY #338/R est:70000-90000
£173653	$290000	€253533	Seascape no.7 (183x162cm-72x64in) s.d.65 s.i.d.stretcher acrylic prov.exhib.lit. 12-Nov-3 Christie's, Rockefeller NY #327/R est:300000-400000
£201117	$360000	€293631	32 year old on the beach (122x165cm-48x65in) s.d.97 s.i.d.overlap prov. 12-May-4 Christie's, Rockefeller NY #187/R est:200000-300000
£208333	$343750	€300000	Study for bedroom painting no 8 (118x132cm-46x52in) s.d.1967-68 i.d.verso prov. 2-Jul-3 Cornette de St.Cyr, Paris #14/R est:250000-350000
£275449	$460000	€402156	Smoker no 6 - previously titled Mouth no 20 (107x169cm-42x67in) s.i.d.1967-69 shaped canvas prov.exhib. 11-Nov-3 Christie's, Rockefeller NY #65/R est:300000-400000
£329341	$550000	€480838	Great American Nude No 68 (163x170cm-64x67in) acrylic painted 1965 prov.exhib. 11-Nov-3 Christie's, Rockefeller NY #42/R est:550000-750000
Prints			
£1800	$3312	€2628	Cynthia in the bedroom (68x84cm-27x33in) s.num.10/100 col silkscreen paper. 24-Jun-4 Sotheby's, Olympia #481/R est:2000-3000
£1977	$3500	€2886	Monica in robe with Motherwell (110x147cm-43x58in) s. num.17/80 screenprint. 30-Apr-4 Sotheby's, New York #532/R est:4000-6000
£2059	$3500	€3006	Bedroom face (42x60cm-17x24in) s. col aquatint. 31-Oct-3 Sotheby's, New York #833/R
£2065	$3800	€3015	Nude with bouquet and stockings (113x203cm-44x80in) s.num.12 serigraph prov. 10-Jun-4 Phillips, New York #591/R est:4000-6000
£2353	$4000	€3435	Monica with tulips (91x114cm-36x45in) s. col screenprint. 31-Oct-3 Sotheby's, New York #838/R
£2365	$4234	€3500	Bedroom face (57x76cm-22x30in) s. num.53/75 col aquatint E.1977. 4-May-4 Calmels Cohen, Paris #119/R est:2000-2200
£2401	$4250	€3505	Monica sitting with Mondrian (129x94cm-51x37in) s. num.81/100 col screenprint. 30-Apr-4 Sotheby's, New York #530/R est:4000-6000
£2500	$4550	€3650	New bedroom blonde doodle (59x66cm-23x26in) s.num.62/100 col screenprint. 1-Jul-4 Sotheby's, London #500/R est:2500-3500
£2657	$4571	€3800	Great American nude (75x60cm-30x24in) s. col offset lithograph. 3-Dec-3 Hauswedell & Nolte, Hamburg #1048/R est:3800
£2715	$4534	€3964	Bedroom blonde (106x124cm-42x49in) s. col serigraph. 24-Jun-3 Germann, Zurich #635/R est:5500-6000 (S.FR 6000)
£2717	$5000	€3967	Still life with Lichtenstein (108x152cm-43x60in) s.num. serigraph prov. 10-Jun-4 Phillips, New York #593/R est:3000-4000
£2775	$4800	€4052	Blonde Vivienne (102x102cm-40x40in) s. mixografia one of 50 prov. 10-Dec-3 Phillips, New York #587/R est:3500-4500
£2824	$4800	€4123	Steel drawing (58x18cm-23x7in) st.sig. laser cut steel multiple enamel exec.1986. 4-Nov-3 Christie's, Rockefeller NY #378/R est:2500-3500
£2825	$5000	€4125	Nude (61x75cm-24x30in) s. num.146/200 col screenprint. 30-Apr-4 Sotheby's, New York #527/R est:2500-3500
£2953	$5463	€4400	Mixed bouquet with leger (128x137cm-50x54in) s. num.4/12 col print. 13-Mar-4 De Vuyst, Lokeren #400/R est:3500-4000
£3041	$5351	€4500	Monica with Robert Motherwell (100x146cm-39x57in) s. num.XIX/XX col serigraph exec 1994. 18-May-4 Tajan, Paris #172/R est:4500-5000
£3107	$5500	€4536	Brown nude banner (150x198cm-59x78in) s. num.1/30 brown black felt banner. 30-Apr-4 Sotheby's, New York #528/R est:5000-7000
£3529	$6000	€5152	Bedroom blonde (147x171cm-58x67in) s. col screenprint. 31-Oct-3 Sotheby's, New York #837/R
£3672	$6500	€5361	Still life with Liz (119x115cm-47x45in) s. num.39/30 col screenprint. 30-Apr-4 Sotheby's, New York #531/R est:3000-5000
£3700	$6734	€5402	Lulu (52x64cm-20x25in) s.num.VII/XXV col lithograph. 1-Jul-4 Sotheby's, London #501/R est:2000-3000
£3824	$6500	€5583	Big blonde with choker (122x173cm-48x68in) s. col screenprint. 31-Oct-3 Sotheby's, New York #836/R
£3824	$6500	€5583	Nude painting print (61x65cm-24x26in) s. stencil oil exec.1980. 31-Oct-3 Sotheby's, New York #835/R
£4706	$8000	€6871	Steel drawing (19x34cm-7x13in) s. laser cut steel enamel exec.1989 lit. 31-Oct-3 Sotheby's, New York #839/R
£4802	$8500	€7011	Blonde Vivienne (78cm-31in circular) s. num.49/50 mixografia print. 30-Apr-4 Sotheby's, New York #533/R est:3500-4500
£5500	$9130	€8030	Bedroom blonde. s.num.11/75 col silkscreen. 6-Oct-3 Sotheby's, London #366/R est:2500-3000
£5500	$10010	€8030	Nude (89x65cm-35x26in) s.d.80 num.43/100 pencil etching aquatint prov. 4-Feb-4 Sotheby's, Olympia #107/R est:1500-2000
£9412	$16000	€13742	Bedroom (25x28cm-10x11in) s.d.1978 pochoir liquitex set of 5. 31-Oct-3 Sotheby's, New York #834/R
Works on paper			
£764	$1276	€1100	Smoking cigarette in ashtray (28x20cm-11x8in) s.d.00 liquitex collage on Bristol board. 21-Oct-3 Artcurial Briest, Paris #549
£1049	$1752	€1500	Smoking cigarette (15x15cm-6x6in) s.d.1998 i.verso liquitex card. 29-Jun-3 Versailles Encheres #170/R
£1133	$2040	€1700	Smoking cigarette (17x13cm-7x5in) s.d.1984 liquitex cardboard. 24-Apr-4 Cornette de St.Cyr, Paris #740/R est:1500-2000
£1133	$2040	€1700	Smoking cigarette (21x17cm-8x7in) s.d.1999 liquitex cardboard. 24-Apr-4 Cornette de St.Cyr, Paris #742/R est:2000
£1333	$2400	€2000	Smoking cigarette in ashtray (19x20cm-7x8in) s.d.1999 liquitex cardboard. 24-Apr-4 Cornette de St.Cyr, Paris #743/R est:2000
£1333	$2400	€2000	Smoking cigarette in ashtray (20x16cm-8x6in) s.d.1999 liquitex cardboard. 24-Apr-4 Cornette de St.Cyr, Paris #741/R est:2000
£1667	$3033	€2500	Seascape (25x28cm-10x11in) s.d.1978 liquitex graphite lit. 29-Jun-4 Cornette de St.Cyr, Paris #117/R est:3000-4000
£1711	$3147	€2600	Smoking cigarette (19x18cm-7x7in) s. liquitex collage. 24-Jun-4 Credit Municipal, Paris #26 est:1200-1500
£1901	$3327	€2700	Untitled (28x25cm-11x10in) s.d.79 pencil W/C card. 16-Dec-3 Finarte Semenzato, Milan #72/R est:1300-1500
£1974	$3632	€3000	Smoking cigarette (18x15cm-7x6in) s. liquitex collage. 24-Jun-4 Credit Municipal, Paris #25 est:1500
£2231	$3837	€3257	Bedroom (11x21cm-4x8in) s.i. d.1974 verso collage prov. 7-Dec-3 Uppsala Auktionskammare, Uppsala #352/R est:18000-20000 (S.KR 29000)
£2588	$4400	€3778	T.V dinner (35x42cm-14x17in) s.d.1963 pencil. 21-Nov-3 Swann Galleries, New York #231/R est:3000-5000
£2958	$4910	€4200	Nude (12x17cm-5x7in) s.d.1969 W/C pencil collage. 11-Jun-3 Finarte Semenzato, Milan #630/R
£3294	$5600	€4809	Smoker (21x28cm-8x11in) s.i.d.1975 col pencil. 21-Nov-3 Swann Galleries, New York #233/R est:4000-6000
£4670	$8500	€6818	Woman in repose (11x15cm-4x6in) s.d.83 pencil col crayon. 29-Jun-4 Sotheby's, New York #545/R est:2500-3500
£5689	$9500	€8306	Nude with stockings (9x225cm-4x89in) s.d.81 W/C pencil card. 7-Oct-3 Sotheby's, New York #412 est:7000-10000
£6200	$10726	€9052	Study for yellow cabin by lake (21x24cm-8x9in) s.d.66 pencil liquitex. 11-Dec-3 Christie's, Kensington #202/R est:4000-6000
£6319	$11500	€9226	Nude (27x29cm-11x11in) s.d.85 liquitex over pencil. 29-Jun-4 Sotheby's, New York #564/R est:5000-7000
£6333	$11527	€9500	Seascape (25x28cm-10x11in) s.d.1978 liquitex graphite lit. 29-Jun-4 Cornette de St.Cyr, Paris #116/R est:8000-10000
£6787	$11538	€9909	Reclining nude (27x36cm-11x14in) s.d.1984 gouache. 22-Nov-3 Burkhard, Luzern #144/R est:15000-18000 (S.FR 15000)
£7143	$13000	€10429	Study for bedroom (30x23cm-12x9in) init.d.63 pencil. 29-Jun-4 Sotheby's, New York #469/R est:8000-12000
£7343	$12262	€10500	Embossed nude (29x38cm-11x15in) s.d.65 pencil liquitex. 11-Oct-3 De Vuyst, Lokeren #481/R est:10000-12000
£7627	$13500	€11135	Still life collage (13x18cm-5x7in) s.i.d.1974 mixed media acrylic collage on canvas. 30-Apr-4 Sotheby's, New York #529/R est:3000-4000
£7917	$13062	€11400	Nude no 101 (10x23cm-4x9in) s.d. liquitex graphite. 2-Jul-3 Cornette de St.Cyr, Paris #12/R est:6000-8000
£8000	$13840	€11680	Study for fruit bowl and tulips (18x23cm-7x9in) s. incorrectly dated 66 pencil liquitex. 11-Dec-3 Christie's, Kensington #193/R est:4000-6000
£8163	$14612	€12000	Nude collage edition (15x22cm-6x9in) s.i.d.1970 mixed media panel. 19-Mar-4 Millon & Associes, Paris #194/R est:2000-3000
£8500	$13515	€12325	Untitled (21x29cm-8x11in) s.d.67 liquitex. 11-Sep-3 Christie's, Kensington #170/R est:5000-7000
£8939	$16000	€13051	Nude in bathtub (27x29cm-11x11in) s.d.1964 pencil prov. 13-May-4 Sotheby's, New York #157/R est:8000-12000
£9581	$16000	€13988	Nude (11x12cm-4x5in) s.d.67 pencil felt tip pen W/C prov. 13-Nov-3 Sotheby's, New York #212/R est:10000-15000
£9581	$16000	€13988	Study for seascape no 26 (16x23cm-6x9in) s.i. ballpoint pen prov. 13-Nov-3 Sotheby's, New York #215/R est:10000-15000
£10056	$18000	€14682	Study for still life num 16 (24x42cm-9x17in) graphite col pencil vellum prov. 13-May-4 Phillips, New York #219/R est:10000-15000
£11976	$20000	€17485	Drawing for open ended nude (8x16cm-3x6in) s.d.70 pencil paperboard prov. 13-Nov-3 Sotheby's, New York #213/R est:5000-7000
£12324	$21567	€17500	Embossed nude no 21 (29x38cm-11x15in) s.d.1965 liquitex lead pencil lit. 18-Dec-3 Cornette de St.Cyr, Paris #133/R est:15000-20000
£12712	$22500	€18560	Study for bedroom face (33x37cm-13x15in) s.d.85 liquitex board. 2-May-4 Bonhams & Butterfields, Los Angeles #3045/R est:20000-25000
£13000	$23660	€18980	Embossed nude with still life (29x36cm-11x14in) s.i.d.67 prov. 6-Feb-4 Sotheby's, London #139/R est:8000-10000
£13966	$25000	€20390	Drawing for Great American Nude cut out (33x43cm-13x17in) s.d.71 pencil shaped paper board prov. 13-May-4 Sotheby's, New York #158/R est:15000-20000
£13966	$25000	€20390	Open ended nude no 163 (9x23cm-4x9in) s.d.1987 pencil liquitex ragboard prov. 13-May-4 Sotheby's, New York #231/R est:15000-20000
£14525	$26000	€21207	Study for Seascape 8 (22x13cm-9x5in) s.d.66 i.verso liquitex graphite prov. 12-May-4 Christie's, Rockefeller NY #137/R est:15000-20000
£14970	$25000	€21856	Study for reclining stocking nude (30x40cm-12x16in) s.d.82 pencil liquitex board on board prov. 13-Nov-3 Sotheby's, New York #272/R est:10000-15000
£14970	$25000	€21856	Open ended nude (9x23cm-4x9in) s.d.78 liquitex pencil paperboard prov. 13-Nov-3 Sotheby's, New York #297/R est:12000-18000
£15000	$26720	€23360	Smoker (19x20cm-7x8in) s.d.76 W/C pencil prov. 22-Oct-3 Christie's, London #52/R est:8000-10000
£16760	$30000	€24470	Study for Great American Nude (20x22cm-8x9in) s.d.66 i.verso liquitex graphite prov. 12-May-4 Christie's, Rockefeller NY #135/R est:25000-35000
£18121	$33342	€27000	Erotic nude drawing (21x22cm-8x9in) s. liquitex lead pencil cut paper exec 1967-1974. 29-Mar-4 Cornette de St.Cyr, Paris #54/R est:30000-40000
£19162	$32000	€27977	Study for Still life no.20 (44x57cm-17x22in) s.d.65 W/C graphite prov. 12-Nov-3 Christie's, Rockefeller NY #334/R est:20000-30000
£20280	$33867	€29000	Still life with petunias (56x67cm-22x26in) s.d.1986 liquitex prov. 29-Jun-3 Versailles Encheres #169/R
£21000	$38640	€30660	Bedroom collage (11x22cm-4x9in) s. i.d.1974 verso liquitex fabric card collage canvas on masonite. 24-Jun-4 Sotheby's, London #266/R est:6000-8000
£23313	$38000	€34037	Open-ended nudes (10x23cm-4x9in) s. one d.80 three d.82 s.i.verso liquitex pencil board four. 23-Sep-3 Christie's, Rockefeller NY #135/R est:18000-22000
£24000	$43680	€35040	Study for smoker (24x27cm-9x11in) s.d.74 pencil liquitex card prov. 6-Feb-4 Sotheby's, London #140/R est:12000-15000
£25000	$45500	€36500	Bedroom blonde with green wallpaper (151x177cm-59x70in) s.d.85 liquitex card prov. 6-Feb-4 Sotheby's, London #253/R est:15000-20000
£25449	$42500	€37156	Drawing for great American nude no 78 (20x24cm-8x9in) s. s.i.d.1966 and 77 verso pencil liquitex paperboard. 13-Nov-3 Sotheby's, New York #273/R est:10000-15000
£26000	$47320	€37960	Untitled (49x53cm-19x21in) s.d.94 d.1992-94 verso liquitex pencil card prov. 6-Feb-4 Sotheby's, London #240/R est:10000-15000
£26536	$47500	€38743	Study for the Great American Nude 57 (23x30cm-9x12in) s.d.64 W/C liquitex prov. 13-May-4 Sotheby's, New York #159/R est:30000-40000
£44910	$75000	€65569	Marie on my Bed (102x152cm-40x60in) Liquitex graphite exec 1982 prov. 12-Nov-3 Christie's, Rockefeller NY #371/R est:40000-60000
£51429	$90000	€75086	Study for the Great American Nude (28x41cm-11x16in) s.d.66 i.verso liquitex pencil prov.lit. 17-Dec-3 Christie's, Rockefeller NY #202/R est:40000-60000
£161677	$270000	€236048	Great American nude no.93 (153x159cm-60x63in) s.i.d.1967-69 liquitex shaped canvas prov.exhib.lit. 12-Nov-3 Sotheby's, New York #29/R est:300000-400000
£212291	$380000	€309945	Great American nude (121x165cm-48x65in) s.d.63 s.i.d.verso liquitex enamel printed paper collage prov. 11-May-4 Christie's, Rockefeller NY #66/R est:400000-600000

WESSMAN, Bjorn (1949-) Swedish

£689	$1240	€1006	Layer VII (57x57cm-22x22in) s.d.2002 verso. 26-Apr-4 Bukowskis, Stockholm #507/R (S.KR 9500)

£1462 $2514 €2135 Midnight (190x151cm-75x59in) s.d.1988 verso diptych. 7-Dec-3 Uppsala Auktionskammare, Uppsala #295/R est:8000-10000 (S.KR 19000)

WESSON, Edward (1910-1983) British

£243 $450 €355 Study of west highland terrier (30x25cm-12x10in) s. masonite prov. 10-Feb-4 Doyle, New York #140/R
£400 $636 €584 Thatched cottage (36x41cm-14x16in) s. board. 12-Sep-3 Gardiner & Houlgate, Bath #210/R
£850 $1547 €1241 Rolling countryside (46x61cm-18x24in) s. board. 1-Jul-4 Christie's, Kensington #115/R
£1200 $2040 €1752 Heavy light, Shoreham Old Church (39x50cm-15x20in) s. panel sold with two W/C's and an oil by different hands. 26-Nov-3 Hamptons Fine Art, Godalming #198/R est:800-1200

Works on paper
£260 $476 €380 Wylie Church (35x52cm-14x20in) s.i. W/C. 7-Apr-4 Woolley & Wallis, Salisbury #68/R
£310 $490 €450 The cross, Chester (21x29cm-8x11in) s. pen black ink W/C. 24-Jul-3 Lawrence, Crewkerne #878
£380 $600 €551 Chanctonbury ring from Ashington in the South Downs (24x35cm-9x14in) s.i.verso W/C. 2-Sep-3 Bonhams, Knowle #280
£400 $648 €584 Near Stoke Hill (32x49cm-13x19in) s. W/C. 27-Jan-3 Bristol Auction Rooms #455
£400 $740 €584 Willows at Ripley (32x49cm-13x19in) s. W/C. 14-Jul-4 Bonhams, Chester #472
£420 $781 €613 The pond, autumn (31x47cm-12x19in) s. W/C. 2-Mar-4 Bearnes, Exeter #374
£420 $756 €613 Landscape, trees against the sky (33x51cm-13x20in) s. pencil W/C. 22-Apr-4 Lawrence, Crewkerne #810
£450 $716 €657 Saint Albans, Wood Street (28x38cm-11x15in) s.d.46 W/C. 12-Sep-3 Gardiner & Houlgate, Bath #74/R
£450 $774 €657 River landscape with bridge and buildings (30x48cm-12x19in) s. W/C. 5-Dec-3 Keys, Aylsham #451
£500 $810 €725 Charing, Kent (32x47cm-13x19in) s. pen ink W/C lit. 30-Jul-3 Hamptons Fine Art, Godalming #147
£580 $1061 €847 Surrey Lane (32x45cm-13x18in) s. W/C. 28-Jan-4 Henry Adams, Chichester #236
£600 $1110 €876 Ludgate Hill and Staple Inn, Holborn (30x23cm-12x9in) s. W/C ink pair. 9-Mar-4 Gorringes, Lewes #2090
£640 $1190 €934 Glencoe from Loch Leven (31x49cm-12x19in) s. W/C. 2-Mar-4 Bearnes, Exeter #344/R
£650 $1203 €949 Church and Tudor shop front (56x38cm-22x15in) s. W/C pair. 9-Mar-4 Gorringes, Lewes #2088
£650 $1151 €949 Clement Danes. Tower Bridge (21x29cm-8x11in) s. pen ink wash pair. 28-Apr-4 George Kidner, Lymington #195
£650 $1196 €949 Village street scene with figures by houses (18x26cm-7x10in) s. W/C. 11-Jun-4 Keys, Aylsham #479/R
£680 $1251 €993 Blakeney and Cley (13x19cm-5x7in) s. W/C. 11-Jun-4 Keys, Aylsham #478
£720 $1339 €1051 Hedgerow under snow (31x49cm-12x19in) s. W/C. 2-Mar-4 Bearnes, Exeter #375
£750 $1388 €1095 March sur Loing (20x28cm-8x11in) s. W/C pen ink sold with a similar scene. 9-Mar-4 Gorringes, Lewes #2085
£750 $1380 €1095 Surrey farm (34x46cm-13x18in) s. W/C exhib. 24-Mar-4 Hamptons Fine Art, Godalming #238
£750 $1365 €1095 Gibralter. Ships at sea (25x32cm-10x13in) s. i.d.1945 W/C two. 1-Jul-4 Christie's, Kensington #117/R
£780 $1451 €1139 At West Mersea, Essex, estuary scene (31x59cm-12x23in) s. W/C prov. 2-Mar-4 Bearnes, Exeter #373
£820 $1410 €1197 Norfolk mill (33x48cm-13x19in) s. W/C. 5-Dec-3 Keys, Aylsham #452/R
£850 $1445 €1241 Roses in a bowl (30x46cm-12x18in) s.d.63 W/C sold with another by the same hand. 26-Nov-3 Hamptons Fine Art, Godalming #68
£850 $1556 €1241 Roses in a vase (23x33cm-9x13in) s. W/C pencil. 7-Apr-4 Woolley & Wallis, Salisbury #70/R
£880 $1593 €1285 Surrey village (33x51cm-13x20in) s. W/C. 2-Apr-4 Bracketts, Tunbridge Wells #395/R
£900 $1656 €1314 By a canal in a Dutch town (38x56cm-15x22in) s.d.54 W/C. 24-Mar-4 Hamptons Fine Art, Godalming #237
£900 $1584 €1314 French townscape with river and church (36x53cm-14x21in) s.indis.d. W/C. 21-May-4 Bracketts, Tunbridge Wells #248/R
£950 $1739 €1387 View from St Aubins of St Helier, Jersey (33x48cm-13x19in) s. 27-Jan-4 Gorringes, Lewes #1562
£1100 $2013 €1606 In the Estuary (32x49cm-13x19in) s. W/C. 7-Apr-4 Woolley & Wallis, Salisbury #66/R est:250-350
£1100 $1980 €1606 Boats at Mudeford (32x49cm-13x19in) s. W/C. 24-Apr-4 Windibank, Dorking #331 est:850-1000
£1200 $2040 €1752 St Nicholas (28x41cm-11x16in) s. W/C sold with another by the same hand. 26-Nov-3 Hamptons Fine Art, Godalming #94/R est:300-500
£1200 $2184 €1752 Oak tree. The windmill (32x50cm-13x20in) s. W/C two. 1-Jul-4 Christie's, Kensington #116/R est:700-1000
£1300 $2236 €1898 Jack and Jill Mills at Clayton (23x68cm-9x27in) s.d.91 W/C pen black ink prov. 3-Dec-3 Christie's, Kensington #483/R est:300-500
£1400 $2562 €2044 Thurne Marshes, Norfolk (25x33cm-10x13in) s. W/C. 7-Apr-4 Woolley & Wallis, Salisbury #65/R est:200-300
£1400 $2562 €2044 Winter trees (44x64cm-17x25in) s. W/C exhib. 7-Apr-4 Woolley & Wallis, Salisbury #69/R est:300-500
£1700 $2890 €2482 Guildford Cathedral from the river (38x55cm-15x22in) s. W/C sold with two others by the same hand. 26-Nov-3 Hamptons Fine Art, Godalming #52 est:600-1000
£1750 $2835 €2538 Kleats shore, Kilmorey. Tine mines near Camborne. Compton Chamberlain, Wiltshire (33x51cm-13x20in) s. W/C set of four. 30-Jul-3 Hamptons Fine Art, Godalming #78/R est:1500-1800
£2000 $3660 €2920 A Norfolk Harbour, Wells-next-the Sea (31x49cm-12x19in) s. W/C. 7-Apr-4 Woolley & Wallis, Salisbury #64/R est:300-500
£2000 $3660 €2920 Blackeney, Norfolk (31x49cm-12x19in) s. W/C. 7-Apr-4 Woolley & Wallis, Salisbury #67/R est:300-500

WESSON, Robert (19/20th C) American

£1080 $1900 €1577 Landscape of maple sugaring scene, team of oxen with the farmer (61x76cm-24x30in) s. 3-Jan-4 Cobbs, Peterborough #184/R

WESSON, Robert Shaw (1907-1967) American

£1129 $2100 €1648 Maine winter woodland scene (50x60cm-20x24in) s. i.verso. 5-Mar-4 Skinner, Boston #490/R est:500-700

WEST, Benjamin (1738-1820) British/American

£3846 $7000 €5615 Portrait of John J Sedley (91x71cm-36x28in) s.d.1802 prov.exhib. 29-Jun-4 Sotheby's, New York #180/R est:6000-8000
£4500 $8280 €6570 Christ showing a little child as the Emblem of Heven (69x50cm-27x20in) s. board prov.exhib.lit. 26-Mar-4 Sotheby's, London #49/R est:5000-7000
£22222 $40000 €32444 First interview of Telemachus with Calypso (102x143cm-40x56in) s.d.1801 prov.exhib.lit. 23-Jan-4 Christie's, Rockefeller NY #139/R est:20000-30000

WEST, David (1868-1936) British

£950 $1587 €1387 Below the Klondyke (23x30cm-9x12in) 21-Oct-3 Gorringes, Lewes #2203
£1300 $2171 €1898 Lossiemouth (23x30cm-9x12in) 21-Oct-3 Gorringes, Lewes #2202/R

Works on paper
£650 $1164 €949 Small boats off the coast (28x38cm-11x15in) s. W/C. 5-May-4 John Nicholson, Haslemere #391
£800 $1288 €1160 River bend (19x27cm-7x11in) s. W/C. 21-Aug-3 Bonhams, Edinburgh #1156
£1000 $1830 €1460 Klondyke (22x32cm-9x13in) s.i. W/C. 8-Apr-4 Bonhams, Edinburgh #135 est:1000-1500
£1500 $2685 €2190 Coastal landscape (33x51cm-13x20in) s. W/C. 26-May-4 Sotheby's, Olympia #160/R est:800-1200
£1750 $3203 €2555 Seatoun, Lossiemouth (22x32cm-9x13in) s. W/C. 8-Apr-4 Bonhams, Edinburgh #117 est:1500-2000
£1800 $3348 €2628 View of the mountains between Garve and Acnasheen, Rosshire (48x74cm-19x29in) s. pencil W/C scratching out. 4-Mar-4 Christie's, Kensington #224/R est:2000-3000

WEST, Douglas (20th C) British

£260 $478 €390 Fleet Street (48x38cm-19x15in) s. 24-Jun-4 Ewbank, Send #552

WEST, Edgar (fl.1857-1889) British

Works on paper
£700 $1204 €1022 Unloading the day's catch (54x76cm-21x30in) s.i. W/C bodycol. 2-Dec-3 Sotheby's, London #37/R
£1200 $2004 €1752 Girls on the shore in a stormy seascape (56x74cm-22x29in) s. W/C. 10-Oct-3 Richardson & Smith, Whitby #59 est:1200-1500

WEST, Edward E (19th C) European

Works on paper
£620 $980 €899 Sailing craft on calm waters (38x58cm-15x23in) s. W/C. 27-Jul-3 Desmond Judd, Cranbrook #1079

WEST, Francis Robert (c.1749-1809) Irish

Works on paper
£7500 $13425 €10950 Figures sewing in an interior (37x43cm-15x17in) col chk. 14-May-4 Christie's, London #113/R est:7000-10000

WEST, Franz (1947-) Austrian

Sculpture
£6000 $10020 €8760 Homemades (40x61x53cm-16x24x21in) paper waste steel pedestal edition 4 of 10 prov.exhib.lit. 22-Oct-3 Christie's, London #135/R est:6000-8000
£7383 $13215 €11000 Article (29x51cm-11x20in) board gauze plaster wire dispersion prov. 25-May-4 Dorotheum, Vienna #97/R est:12000-16000
£7692 $13077 €11000 Untitled (26x50x11cm-10x20x4in) diespersion plaster gauze wire plastic prov. 26-Nov-3 Dorotheum, Vienna #77/R est:11000-15000
£8084 $13500 €11803 Franfurt (140x70x40cm-55x28x16in) enamel iron paper mache television wooden stool executed 1993. 14-Nov-3 Phillips, New York #185/R est:15000-20000
£15642 $28000 €22837 Passtuck maske (33x69x36cm-13x27x14in) acrylic plaster prov. 14-May-4 Phillips, New York #177/R est:25000-35000
£22826 $42000 €33326 Untitled. metal linen welded foam mirror edition of 50 five parts prov. 10-Jun-4 Phillips, New York #441/R est:4000-6000

Works on paper
£629 $1070 €900 Firmament (10x15cm-4x6in) biro feltpen invitation. 26-Nov-3 Dorotheum, Vienna #289/R
£1208 $2235 €1800 Untitled (8x13cm-3x5in) s.d.73 pencil. 9-Mar-4 Dorotheum, Vienna #170/R est:1000-1200
£2238 $3804 €3200 Untitled (33x25cm-13x10in) s.d.76 gouache on illustration prov. 26-Nov-3 Dorotheum, Vienna #78/R est:3200-4000
£3472 $5903 €5000 Untitled (28x20cm-11x8in) s.d.79 mixed media collage newspaper. 28-Oct-3 Wiener Kunst Auktionen, Vienna #287/R est:5000-8000
£4362 $7721 €6500 Untitled (43x48cm-17x19in) s. collage mixed media board. 28-Apr-4 Wiener Kunst Auktionen, Vienna #287/R est:6500-10000
£4545 $7727 €6500 Composition with figure (73x36cm-29x14in) s.i.d.82 mixed media on newspaper prov. 26-Nov-3 Dorotheum, Vienna #96/R est:5000-7000
£6711 $12013 €10000 Erich, script (30x38cm-12x15in) s.d.80 gauze dispersion sand board prov. 25-May-4 Dorotheum, Vienna #109/R est:6000-9000
£14667 $26253 €22000 Composition (63x122cm-25x48in) s.d. collage fibreboard metal photos emulsion prov. 14-May-4 Ketterer, Munich #267/R est:19000-24000

WEST, Gerhard (1922-) German

£280 $481 €400 View towards Sullberg (43x75cm-17x30in) s.d.1984. 6-Dec-3 Quittenbaum, Hamburg #174/R

WEST, Joseph (1882-?) British

Works on paper
£310 $570 €465 Sheringham (23x28cm-9x11in) s. W/C. 26-Mar-4 Tring Auctions, Tring #339/R

WEST, Lee (19th C) American
£2432 $4500 €3551 Street scene with horse and carriage (25x36cm-10x14in) s.d.1888 tin plate. 13-Mar-4 DeFina, Austinburg #784/R est:1500-2500

WEST, Myrtice (1923-) American
£240 $400 €350 Adam and Eve (66x81cm-26x32in) acrylic prov. 15-Nov-3 Slotin Folk Art, Buford #342/R

WEST, Raphael Lamar (1769-1850) British
£450 $752 €657 Christ (91x71cm-36x28in) i.d.1779 verso. 13-Nov-3 Christie's, Kensington #250/R

WEST, Richard Whately (1848-1905) British
£370 $677 €540 Sunrise, Alassio (15x21cm-6x8in) s. i.d.1896 verso board. 6-Apr-4 Bristol Auction Rooms #472
£600 $1098 €876 The old Mill, Bramshott (25x33cm-10x13in) 28-Jul-4 Mallams, Oxford #373/R
Works on paper
£260 $426 €380 Irish landscape (17x25cm-7x10in) s.d.1925 W/C. 4-Jun-3 John Ross, Belfast #188

WEST, Richard William (1887-?) British
£420 $781 €613 Venice (33x23cm-13x9in) s. i.verso board. 4-Mar-4 Christie's, Kensington #171/R

WEST, Samuel (19th C) British
£740 $1347 €1080 Portrait of a lady in a black dress holding a fan (140x110cm-55x43in) s.d.1860. 29-Jun-4 Bonhams, Knowle #68

WEST, Temple (?) ?
£5521 $9000 €8061 Ship, Landseer (61x91cm-24x36in) sold with photos. 27-Sep-3 Thomaston Place, Thomaston #215

WESTALL, John (19th C) British
£500 $865 €730 Lake scenes with figures (17x38cm-7x15in) s. pair. 9-Dec-3 Bristol Auction Rooms #441

WESTALL, John (attrib) (19th C) British
£680 $1251 €993 Fishermen in an upland river landscape (20x40cm-8x16in) s. pair. 29-Mar-4 Bonhams, Bath #64/R

WESTALL, Richard (1765-1836) British
£1988 $3500 €2902 Venus and Cupid in an idyllic landscape (54x43cm-21x17in) 18-May-4 Bonhams & Butterfields, San Francisco #145/R est:3000-5000
£2600 $4836 €3796 Mary, Queen of Scots, taking her leave of Sir Arthur Melville, on her way to execution (30x38cm-12x15in) 4-Mar-4 Christie's, Kensington #3/R est:3000-5000

WESTALL, Richard (attrib) (1765-1836) British
Works on paper
£300 $552 €438 At the end of the service (32x22cm-13x9in) pencil W/C. 25-Mar-4 Christie's, Kensington #223

WESTALL, William (1781-1850) British
Works on paper
£550 $1001 €803 Carlisle from the road to Richerby, Cumbria (8x15cm-3x6in) pencil W/C scratching out. 1-Jul-4 Christie's, Kensington #79/R
£1100 $1793 €1606 Entrance to the cave at Elephanta, Bombay (20x28cm-8x11in) pencil W/C prov.exhib.lit. 24-Sep-3 Christie's, London #45/R est:1200-1800

WESTBROEK, Willem (1918-) Dutch
£2667 $4773 €4000 Dancer (74x85cm-29x33in) s.d.59. 11-May-4 Vendu Notarishuis, Rotterdam #125/R est:4000-5000

WESTBROOK, Elizabeth (fl.1861-1886) British
£1700 $3094 €2482 Le ruban d'or (44x34cm-17x13in) init.d.1872. 15-Jun-4 Rosebery Fine Art, London #555/R est:500-700

WESTCHILOFF, Constantin (1877-1945) Russian
£1676 $2900 €2447 Forest landscape (51x66cm-20x26in) s. board. 13-Dec-3 Sloans & Kenyon, Bethesda #786/R est:5000-7000
£4444 $8000 €6488 Winter landscape, Chomonix (36x28cm-14x11in) s.i. board prov. 23-Apr-4 Sotheby's, New York #34/R est:8000-12000
£4444 $8000 €6488 Pine tree in the snow (36x28cm-14x11in) s. canvas on board prov. 23-Apr-4 Sotheby's, New York #35/R est:8000-12000
£5282 $8768 €7500 Neige (54x64cm-21x25in) s. 10-Jun-3 Renaud, Paris #37 est:600-800
£5500 $9845 €8030 Seascape (20x23cm-8x9in) s. board. 26-May-4 Sotheby's, Olympia #414/R est:2000-3000
£6875 $11000 €10038 Winter landscape (91x74cm-36x29in) s. 20-Sep-3 Sloans & Kenyon, Bethesda #1178/R est:7000-9000
£8092 $14000 €11814 Luminist seascape (53x74cm-21x29in) s. prov. 13-Dec-3 Sloans & Kenyon, Bethesda #802/R est:15000-20000
£9066 $16500 €13236 Winter in Chamonix (84x71cm-33x28in) s. 7-Feb-4 Sloans & Kenyon, Bethesda #1279/R est:7000-9000
£9497 $17000 €13866 Marine seascape (56x71cm-22x28in) s.i. 7-May-4 Sloans & Kenyon, Bethesda #1655/R est:9000-12000
£9581 $16000 €13988 Winter sunset (82x103cm-32x41in) s. 21-Oct-3 Christie's, Rockefeller NY #109 est:8000-12000
£11000 $19690 €16060 Old forge (71x91cm-28x36in) s.i. 26-May-4 Sotheby's, London #109/R est:9000-12000
£11538 $18000 € Russian scene (51x64cm-20x25in) s. 11-Apr-3 Christie's, Rockefeller NY #27/R est:10000-15000
£13889 $25000 €20278 Sunlight breaking the waves (46x54cm-18x21in) s. prov. 23-Apr-4 Sotheby's, New York #31/R est:12000-18000
£14000 $23800 €20440 Golden Autumn (53x71cm-21x28in) s. board. 19-Nov-3 Sotheby's, London #94/R est:5000-7000
£14000 $23800 €20440 Winter sun in the mountains (54x65cm-21x26in) s. 19-Nov-3 Sotheby's, London #96/R est:6000-8000
£16667 $30000 €24334 Coastal scene (56x66cm-22x26in) s. prov. 23-Apr-4 Sotheby's, New York #32/R est:12000-18000
£16667 $30000 €24334 Winter landscape with golden sunlight (63x76cm-25x30in) s. prov. 23-Apr-4 Sotheby's, New York #36/R est:12000-18000
£17000 $30430 €24820 Waves breaking on the rocks (56x73cm-22x29in) s. 26-May-4 Sotheby's, London #261/R est:12000-18000
£18000 $32220 €26280 Coastal scene (66x81cm-26x32in) s. 26-May-4 Sotheby's, London #260/R est:12000-15000
£22000 $39380 €32120 Tree in the snow (91x71cm-36x28in) s. 26-May-4 Sotheby's, London #108/R est:12000-18000
£22000 $39380 €32120 Waves on the sea shore (75x92cm-30x36in) s. 26-May-4 Sotheby's, London #259/R est:8000-12000
£22000 $39380 €32120 Sunset over the ocean (54x65cm-21x26in) s. 26-May-4 Sotheby's, London #258/R est:6000-8000
£158906 $284442 €232003 The first meeting (182x310cm-72x122in) s.d.1911 lit. 25-May-4 Bukowskis, Stockholm #385/R est:500000-600000 (S.KR 2150000)

WESTCOTT, Carol Whorf (20th C) American
£588 $1000 €858 Truro to Provincetown (56x71cm-22x28in) s. 9-Nov-3 Outer Cape Auctions, Provincetown #99/R

WESTCOTT, Philip (1815-1878) British
£930 $1683 €1358 Near Yarmouth (57x91cm-22x36in) s.d.1875 prov. 18-Apr-4 Levis, Calgary #220/R est:1000-1200 (C.D 2250)

WESTENDORP-OSIECK, Betsy (1880-1968) Dutch
£1067 $1941 €1600 Drinking from a bowl (90x70cm-35x28in) s.d.1905. 1-Jul-4 Christie's, Amsterdam #450/R est:1000-1500
£1538 $2569 €2200 Still life with wine and bread on a table (72x85cm-28x33in) s. exhib. 30-Jun-3 Sotheby's, Amsterdam #373/R

WESTERBEEK, Cornelis (1844-1903) Dutch
£325 $553 €475 Landscape with cows at the water (20x13cm-8x5in) s. panel. 5-Nov-3 Vendue Huis, Gravenhage #145
£490 $842 €700 Two cows near a ditch (40x50cm-16x20in) s.d.1880. 8-Dec-3 Glerum, Amsterdam #10/R
£1047 $1800 €1529 Shepherdess and her flock (58x99cm-23x39in) s.d.99. 7-Dec-3 Freeman, Philadelphia #15 est:1500-2500
£1184 $2179 €1800 Homeward bound (60x101cm-24x40in) s.d.90. 22-Jun-4 Christie's, Amsterdam #280/R est:2000-3000
£1293 $2352 €1900 Autumn, cows by the waterside (20x31cm-8x12in) s. panel. 3-Feb-4 Christie's, Amsterdam #226 est:1200-1600
£5191 $9500 €7579 Shepherd and his flock (64x192cm-25x76in) s. 3-Jun-4 Christie's, Rockefeller NY #675/R est:3000-5000

WESTERBEEK, Cornelis (jnr) (1873-1917) Dutch
£1736 $2743 €2500 Guiding the flock home (68x98cm-27x39in) s. 2-Sep-3 Christie's, Amsterdam #271 est:2500-3500

WESTERFROLKE, Paul (1886-1975) German
£333 $607 €500 Landscape in Westphalia (54x69cm-21x27in) s.d.1922. 1-Jul-4 Van Ham, Cologne #1665

WESTERHOLM, Victor (1860-1919) Finnish
£543 $1000 €793 Spring landscape with pathway and river in distance (20x15cm-8x6in) s. panel. 25-Jun-4 Freeman, Philadelphia #344/R
£3497 $5944 €5000 Coastal landscape (24x36cm-9x14in) s.d.96 canvas on board. 29-Nov-3 Bukowskis, Helsinki #186/R est:5000-6000
£3521 $6092 €5000 Vallinkoski rapids in winter (13x21cm-5x8in) s.d.1914 panel lit. 13-Dec-3 Hagelstam, Helsinki #97/R est:6000
£6667 $11933 €10000 Coastal landscape, Pepparskar (20x31cm-8x12in) s.d.1919 exhib.lit. 15-May-4 Hagelstam, Helsinki #117/R
£9091 $15455 €13000 Dutch barn (37x55cm-15x22in) s.i.d.1879 exhib.prov. 29-Nov-3 Bukowskis, Helsinki #25a/R est:14000-16000
£9459 $16932 €14000 View from Billnaas (66x45cm-26x18in) s.d.1917 exhib.lit. 8-May-4 Bukowskis, Helsinki #103/R est:14000-16000
£10000 $17900 €15000 Dutch landscape (37x52cm-15x20in) s.d.1879 exhib.lit. 15-May-4 Hagelstam, Helsinki #118/R est:15000
£31469 $53497 €45000 Winter landscape from Hayskyvaara in Karelen (58x116cm-23x46in) s.d.1909 exhib.lit. 29-Nov-3 Bukowskis, Helsinki #125/R est:40000-50000

WESTERIK, Jacobus (1924-) Dutch
Works on paper
£476 $867 €700 Grootvader en kind - grandfather and child (25x24cm-10x9in) s.i.d.1960 ink. 3-Feb-4 Christie's, Amsterdam #592
£724 $1332 €1100 Cherries (8x11cm-3x4in) init.i.d.97 ink chk W/C two. 22-Jun-4 Christie's, Amsterdam #339/R
£1119 $1924 €1600 Untitled (18x16cm-7x6in) s.d.1974 W/C ink pastel. 2-Dec-3 Sotheby's, Amsterdam #357/R est:1200-1800
£2000 $3680 €3000 La Belgique (10x19cm-4x7in) s.i.d.1974 blk ink pastel W/C prov. 9-Jun-4 Christie's, Amsterdam #183/R est:3000-5000
£2857 $5200 €4200 Plantverschijning buiten (11x11cm-4x4in) s.d.71 pen W/C. 3-Feb-4 Christie's, Amsterdam #595/R est:1200-1600
£2937 $5052 €4200 Man in rolstoel (21x19cm-8x7in) s.d.1973 W/C pastel ink pencil. 2-Dec-3 Sotheby's, Amsterdam #356/R est:1200-1800
£2937 $5052 €4200 Soldaat (11x11cm-4x4in) s.d.1963 W/C ink two in one frame. 2-Dec-3 Sotheby's, Amsterdam #358/R est:1500-2000
£3265 $5943 €4800 Losegeraaki Zweeftuig (13x16cm-5x6in) s.d.1971 pen W/C. 3-Feb-4 Christie's, Amsterdam #587/R est:1200-1600
£5782 $10524 €8500 De oude dierentuin 2 (12x23cm-5x9in) s.i.d.1964 pen W/C. 3-Feb-4 Christie's, Amsterdam #586/R est:1500-2000
£12925 $23524 €19000 Sprookjesfiguur bij gras (21x15cm-8x6in) s.d.1971 pen W/C. 3-Feb-4 Christie's, Amsterdam #591/R est:1500-2000

WESTERLING, Erik (1819-1857) Swedish
£1077 $1852 €1572 View of Gustavsberg (70x100cm-28x39in) s.i.d.1857. 3-Dec-3 AB Stockholms Auktionsverk #2390/R (S.KR 14000)

WESTERLUND, Mia (20th C) American?
Works on paper
£278 $500 €406 Drawing IV (23x29cm-9x11in) graphite prov. 24-Apr-4 David Rago, Lambertville #521/R
£333 $600 €486 Drawing III (23x28cm-9x11in) graphite prov. 24-Apr-4 David Rago, Lambertville #243/R

WESTERMAN, Gerard (1880-1971) Dutch
£733 $1335 €1100 Amazone (63x63cm-25x25in) s. 1-Jul-4 Christie's, Amsterdam #444 est:300-500
£1000 $1820 €1500 Gecostumeerd feest - Fancy dress party (70x141cm-28x56in) s. oil on plywood. 1-Jul-4 Christie's, Amsterdam #447/R est:3000-5000

WESTERN, Barry Thomas (20th C) New Zealander?
£634 $1008 €926 Enamel tea pot and crock on bench (56x70cm-22x28in) s. acrylic on board. 9-Sep-3 Watson's, Christchurch #56 (NZ.D 1750)

WESTEROP, Wilhelm (20th C) German
£306 $483 €440 Horse in stable (36x45cm-14x18in) s.d.1932 i. stretcher. 6-Sep-3 Schopman, Hamburg #799/R
£403 $749 €600 Decorated horse (30x39cm-12x15in) bears sig.i. 6-Mar-4 Arnold, Frankfurt #911/R

WESTFELT-EGGERTZ, Ingeborg (1855-1936) Swedish
£2462 $4234 €3595 Family life at Skagen beach (32x47cm-13x19in) s.d.juli 1914 panel. 3-Dec-3 AB Stockholms Auktionsverk #2297/R est:20000-25000 (S.KR 32000)

WESTHUIZEN, Pieter van der (1931-) South African
Works on paper
£299 $509 €437 Three cottages (47x60cm-19x24in) s.d.79 conte. 4-Nov-3 Stephan Welz, Johannesburg #360 est:1500-2000 (SA.R 3500)
£359 $610 €524 Landscape with small houses (45x55cm-18x22in) s.d.75 mixed media. 4-Nov-3 Stephan Welz, Johannesburg #634 est:2500-4000 (SA.R 4200)
£410 $697 €599 Extensive landscape with figures and a windmill (44x55cm-17x22in) s. mixed media. 4-Nov-3 Stephan Welz, Johannesburg #635 est:2500-4000 (SA.R 4800)
£470 $799 €686 Portrait of an African woman (50x36cm-20x14in) s.d.75 pastel. 4-Nov-3 Stephan Welz, Johannesburg #340 est:1800-2400 (SA.R 5500)
£470 $799 €686 Four green trees (47x60cm-19x24in) s.d.78 mixed media. 4-Nov-3 Stephan Welz, Johannesburg #628 est:3000-5000 (SA.R 5500)
£684 $1162 €999 Farmstead (49x63cm-19x25in) s.d.79 mixed media. 4-Nov-3 Stephan Welz, Johannesburg #636 est:3000-5000 (SA.R 8000)

WESTIN, Fredrik (1782-1862) Swedish
£6154 $10585 €8985 Portrait of Baroness Eva Sofia Reuterskiold (112x88cm-44x35in) s.d.1834 prov.exhib.lit. 3-Dec-3 AB Stockholms Auktionsverk #2468/R est:100000-150000 (S.KR 80000)

WESTIN, Fredrik (attrib) (1782-1862) Swedish
£1308 $2249 €1910 Portrait of gentleman Portrait of lady (75x60cm-30x24in) pair. 3-Dec-3 AB Stockholms Auktionsverk #2465/R est:15000-20000 (S.KR 17000)

WESTMAN, Edvard (1865-1917) Swedish
£1183 $2117 €1727 Hohenzollern on Stockholm's river (31x40cm-12x16in) s.i.d.Aug 08 panel. 26-May-4 AB Stockholms Auktionsverk #2206/R est:10000-12000 (S.KR 16000)
£3243 $5805 €4800 The harbour in Copenhagen (21x32cm-8x13in) s.i.d.88. 8-May-4 Bukowskis, Helsinki #101/R est:4000-5000
£4000 $7160 €6000 Children on shore, landscape from Aaland (41x32cm-16x13in) s.d.1886 panel. 15-May-4 Hagelstam, Helsinki #80/R est:6500
£4399 $7610 €6423 Hay harvest (80x115cm-31x45in) indis.sig. 15-Dec-3 Lilla Bukowskis, Stockholm #430/R est:12000-15000 (S.KR 56000)
£4730 $8466 €7000 Summer day at Aaland (30x45cm-12x18in) s.d.91. 8-May-4 Bukowskis, Helsinki #85/R est:7000-8000
£6643 $11294 €9500 Evening glow over Aabo (24x33cm-9x13in) s.i.d.94 board. 29-Nov-3 Bukowskis, Helsinki #182/R est:6000-8000

WESTON, Brett (1911-1993) American
Photographs
£1693 $3200 €2472 Dune, Oceano (19x24cm-7x9in) gelatin silver print executed 1960. 17-Feb-4 Christie's, Rockefeller NY #70/R est:3000-4000
£1796 $3000 €2622 Beech forest, Netherlands (27x31cm-11x12in) with sig.d.1971 silver print. 21-Oct-3 Swann Galleries, New York #318/R est:1800-2200
£2011 $3800 €2936 Dune, Baja, California (19x24cm-7x9in) gelatin silver print executed c.1967. 17-Feb-4 Christie's, Rockefeller NY #68/R est:3000-4000
£2171 $3800 €3170 Nude in Pool, Carmel Valley, California (31x27cm-12x11in) gelatin silver print exec c.1986 lit. 17-Dec-3 Christie's, Rockefeller NY #279/R est:3000-5000
£2275 $3800 €3322 New York (20x24cm-8x9in) s.d.37 gelatin silver print exhib.lit. 16-Oct-3 Phillips, New York #111/R est:4000-6000
£2373 $4200 €3465 Oceano, California (19x24cm-7x9in) s.i.d.1957 gelatin silver print. 27-Apr-4 Christie's, Rockefeller NY #14/R est:4000-6000
£2395 $4000 €3497 Sundown, Garrapata beach (39x48cm-15x19in) s.d.1965 photo printed later. 17-Oct-3 Sotheby's, New York #180/R est:5000-7000
£2400 $4200 €3504 Nude in Pool, Carmel Valley, California (30x27cm-12x11in) gelatin silver print exec c.1986 lit. 17-Dec-3 Christie's, Rockefeller NY #281/R est:3000-5000
£2994 $5000 €4371 Underwater nude (49x39cm-19x15in) s.d.1979 photo prov. 17-Oct-3 Sotheby's, New York #120/R est:3000-5000
£2994 $5000 €4371 Dune (46x36cm-18x14in) s.d.1934 gelatin silver print lit. 16-Oct-3 Phillips, New York #131/R est:4000-6000
£3293 $5500 €4808 Mendenhall glacier (40x46cm-16x18in) s. photo exec.1973 printed later. 17-Oct-3 Sotheby's, New York #122/R est:8000-12000
£3593 $6000 €5246 Alaska (27x34cm-11x13in) s. i.d.1960 verso gelatin silver print printed c.1970-80 prov. 20-Oct-3 Christie's, Rockefeller NY #185/R est:6000-8000
£3892 $6500 €5682 Garapata beach (40x50cm-16x20in) s.d.1954 gelatin silver print printed c.1970 prov.lit. 20-Oct-3 Christie's, Rockefeller NY #183/R est:7000-9000
£3955 $7000 €5774 Garrapata Beach (19x24cm-7x9in) s.d.1952 s.i.d.1952 num.ga51 verso photo. 28-Apr-4 Sotheby's, New York #91/R est:7000-10000
£9040 $16000 €13198 Dune with mountains (19x24cm-7x9in) s.d.1939 photo. 28-Apr-4 Sotheby's, New York #90/R est:15000-25000

WESTON, Brett and Edward (20th C) American
Photographs
£2540 $4800 €3708 Nude (24x19cm-9x7in) s.i.d. silver print. 17-Feb-4 Swann Galleries, New York #45/R est:3500-4500

WESTON, David (1935-) British
£310 $555 €453 Midnight Express (38x48cm-15x19in) s.d.71. 6-Jan-4 Gildings, Market Harborough #415/R

WESTON, Edward (1886-1958) American
Photographs
£1977 $3500 €2886 E Town, New Mexico (19x24cm-7x9in) num.34A 33 gelatin silver print. 27-Apr-4 Christie's, Rockefeller NY #306/R est:4000-6000
£2381 $4500 €3476 Nude (18x24cm-7x9in) s.i.d.1936 num.237 gelatin silver print. 17-Feb-4 Christie's, Rockefeller NY #97/R est:2000-3000
£3955 $7000 €5774 Portrait of a male nude (24x19cm-9x7in) s.d.1922 platinum print. 28-Apr-4 Sotheby's, New York #170/R est:10000-15000
£4790 $8000 €6993 Church at E Town, New Mexico (19x24cm-7x9in) s.d.1933 num.20-50 i.verso gelatin silver print printed c.1935. 20-Oct-3 Christie's, Rockefeller NY #260/R est:9000-12000
£4830 $8500 €7052 Cypress, Point Lobos (24x19cm-9x7in) init. silver print. 20-May-4 Swann Galleries, New York #337/R est:8000-12000
£5085 $9000 €7424 Kelp (19x24cm-7x9in) init.d.1930 s.i.d.verso photo lit. 28-Apr-4 Sotheby's, New York #147/R est:10000-15000
£5085 $9000 €7424 Fragment, burned piano, Louisiana, 1941 (24x19cm-9x7in) init.d.1941 s.i.verso gelatin silver print prov.lit. 27-Apr-4 Christie's, Rockefeller NY #97/R est:7000-9000
£5389 $9000 €7868 Xenia (9x11cm-4x4in) s.d.1933 i.verso num.2/50 gelatin silver print board prov. 17-Oct-3 Phillips, New York #217/R est:10000-15000
£5650 $10000 €8249 Cypress, Point Lobos (24x19cm-9x7in) s.d.1930 num.5/50 gelatin silver print lit. 27-Apr-4 Christie's, Rockefeller NY #304/R est:10000-15000
£5988 $10000 €8742 Nude study (24x19cm-9x7in) s.d.1914 verso platinum print prov. 17-Oct-3 Sotheby's, New York #177/R est:10000-15000
£6349 $12000 €9270 Cypress, Pebble Beach (19x24cm-7x9in) silver print. 17-Feb-4 Swann Galleries, New York #56/R est:10000-15000
£6780 $12000 €9899 Pepper, 1930 (24x19cm-9x7in) gelatin silver print prov.lit. 27-Apr-4 Christie's, Rockefeller NY #305/R est:15000-20000
£6886 $11500 €10054 Xenia (9x11cm-4x4in) s.d.i.verso 1933 num.2/50 prov. 17-Oct-3 Phillips, New York #218/R est:10000-15000
£7784 $13000 €11365 Nude, Doris (9x12cm-4x5in) s.d.1933 num.1/50 d.num.104N verso gelatin silver print prov. 20-Oct-3 Christie's, Rockefeller NY #259/R est:15000-20000
£8383 $14000 €12239 Portrait of a woman (42x30cm-17x12in) s. photo. 17-Oct-3 Sotheby's, New York #178/R est:10000-15000
£8982 $15000 €13114 Stone crop and cypress, Point Lobos (19x24cm-7x9in) init.d.1941 s.i.d.num.verso photo sold with postcards prov.lit. 17-Oct-3 Sotheby's, New York #138/R est:6000-8000
£9281 $15500 €13550 Xenia (11x9cm-4x4in) s.d.1933 i.verso num.2/50 gelatin silver print board prov.lit. 17-Oct-3 Phillips, New York #216/R est:10000-15000
£12429 $22000 €18146 D H Lawrence (24x19cm-9x7in) s.i.d.1924 i.verso photo card. 28-Apr-4 Sotheby's, New York #175/R est:8000-12000
£14000 $24640 €20440 Nude, Charis (9x12cm-4x5in) s.i. gelatin silver print lit. 19-May-4 Christie's, London #183/R est:1000-15000
£14970 $25000 €21856 Clouds (19x24cm-7x9in) s. gelatin silver print paper on board exec.1936 prov.lit. 17-Oct-3 Phillips, New York #6/R est:25000-35000
£21111 $38000 €30822 Rag doll and sombrerito (24x19cm-9x7in) s.d.1925 gelatin silver print prov.lit. 23-Apr-4 Phillips, New York #32/R est:30000-50000
£25989 $46000 €37944 White radish (24x19cm-9x7in) s.i.d.1933 num. 3-50 and 56V verso photo prov. 27-Apr-4 Sotheby's, New York #18/R est:20000-30000
£26000 $47840 €39000 Nude, Oceano (18x24cm-7x9in) mono.d. i.d. verso silver gelatin board lit.exhib. 10-Jun-4 Villa Grisebach, Berlin #1332/R est:20000-25000
£27778 $50000 €40556 Nude study (24x19cm-9x7in) gelatin silver print prov. 22-Apr-4 Phillips, New York #41/R est:60000-80000
£28249 $50000 €41244 Dunes, oceano, 1934 (19x24cm-7x9in) s.d. i.verso gelatin silver print executed c.1940 lit. 27-Apr-4 Christie's, Rockefeller NY #89/R est:40000-60000
£39548 $70000 €57740 Nude on sand, Oceano, 1936 (19x24cm-7x9in) s.d.verso gelatin silver print executed 1940. 27-Apr-4 Christie's, Rockefeller NY #90/R est:70000-90000
£42373 $75000 €61865 Bananas (24x19cm-9x7in) init.d.1930 num.7/50 gelatin silver print lit. 27-Apr-4 Christie's, Rockefeller NY #303/R est:30000-40000
£48023 $85000 €70114 Charis, Santa Monica, 1935 (19x25cm-7x10in) s.d. gelatin silver print executed c.1940 lit. 27-Apr-4 Christie's, Rockefeller NY #95/R est:50000-70000
£50299 $84000 €73437 Tina Modotti (24x19cm-9x7in) s.i.d.1921 i.verso platinum print prov.lit. 17-Oct-3 Sotheby's, New York #134/R est:30000-50000
£50847 $90000 €74237 Dunes, Oceano (19x24cm-7x9in) s.d.1936 num.58SO verso photo prov.lit. 27-Apr-4 Sotheby's, New York #17/R est:40000-60000
£56497 $100000 €82486 Pepper, 3P (24x19cm-9x7in) s.d.1929 i.d.Jan 1930 verso photo card prov.lit. 28-Apr-4 Sotheby's, New York #144/R est:70000-100000
£62147 $110000 €90735 Pepper no.30, 1930 (42x19cm-17x7in) s.d. num.25/50 gelatin silver print executed c.1940. 27-Apr-4 Christie's, Rockefeller NY #91/R est:70000-90000
£84746 $150000 €123729 Dunes, Oceano (19x24cm-7x9in) s.d.1936 num.47SO verso photo prov.lit. 27-Apr-4 Sotheby's, New York #15/R est:50000-80000
£89820 $150000 €131137 Nude on sand, Oceano (19x24cm-7x9in) s.d.1936 num.232N verso photo prov.lit. 17-Oct-3 Sotheby's, New York #139/R est:100000-200000
£112994 $200000 €164971 Shells (23x18cm-9x7in) s.d.1927 num.18/50 i.d.1927 verso photo lit. 28-Apr-4 Sotheby's, New York #173/R est:150000-250000
£129944 $230000 €189718 Nude on sand, Oceano (19x24cm-7x9in) s.i.d.1936 num.237N verso photo prov.lit. 27-Apr-4 Sotheby's, New York #16/R est:100000-150000
£146893 $260000 €214464 Breast (19x24cm-7x9in) s.i.d.1922 i.num.35 verso platinum print prov.lit. 27-Apr-4 Sotheby's, New York #20/R est:150000-250000
£245509 $410000 €358443 Two shells (24x17cm-9x7in) s.d.1927 photo card prov.lit. 17-Oct-3 Sotheby's, New York #145/R est:200000-300000
Works on paper
£350 $627 €511 Landscape with trees (32x50cm-13x20in) s. W/C. 17-Mar-4 James Thompson, Kirby Lonsdale #246

WESTON, Harold (1894-1972) American
£645 $1200 €942 After lunch (41x56cm-16x22in) s. s.i.d.1974 verso. 3-Mar-4 Christie's, Rockefeller NY #53/R

WESTON, William Percy (1879-1967) Canadian
£1267 $2191 €1850 Near Keremeos (30x38cm-12x15in) s.d.45 panel. 9-Dec-3 Maynards, Vancouver #197 est:4000-6000 (C.D 2850)
£1524 $2728 €2225 Mountains, Howe Sound (30x38cm-12x15in) s.d.1929 s.i.d.verso panel prov. 27-May-4 Heffel, Vancouver #91/R est:4000-6000 (C.D 3750)
£1778 $2916 €2596 The Three Sisters, Fernie, BC (33x41cm-13x16in) s.d.45 panel. 28-May-3 Maynards, Vancouver #130/R est:4000-6000 (C.D 4000)
£2642 $4730 €3857 Rainy day near Seaside Park, Howe Sound (24x33cm-9x13in) s. s.i.d.1928 panel prov. 27-May-4 Heffel, Vancouver #43/R est:4500-6500 (C.D 6500)
£3252 $5821 €4748 Limestone mountain, Caithness, near Fernie (40x50cm-16x20in) s.d.1964 s.i.d.verso canvasboard prov. 27-May-4 Heffel, Vancouver #103/R est:4500-6500 (C.D 8000)
£3252 $5821 €4748 Atlin, B C (69x81cm-27x32in) s. s.i.d.1956 verso prov. 31-May-4 Sotheby's, Toronto #124/R est:12000-15000 (C.D 8000)
£8222 $13484 €12004 Gulf Islands (51x61cm-20x24in) s.d.1929 panel. 28-May-3 Maynards, Vancouver #92/R est:25000-30000 (C.D 18500)
£12195 $21829 €17805 Beach pattern, Copper Cove, BC (81x94cm-32x37in) s.d.1953 s.i.verso prov.exhib.lit. 27-May-4 Heffel, Vancouver #146/R est:35000-45000 (C.D 30000)
£12195 $21829 €17805 Abandoned gravel pit (91x101cm-36x40in) s. s.i.verso painted 1937 prov.exhib.lit. 27-May-4 Heffel, Vancouver #150/R est:35000-45000 (C.D 30000)
£13223 $23934 €19306 Lonely church, Spences Bridge (69x81cm-27x32in) s. s.i.verso prov. 18-Apr-4 Levis, Calgary #118/R est:20000-25000 (C.D 32000)
Works on paper
£264 $473 €385 Looking down into Horseshoe Bay (29x44cm-11x17in) i.d.1940 s.i.verso chl prov. 27-May-4 Heffel, Vancouver #149 (C.D 650)

WESTPFAHL, Conrad (1891-1976) German
Works on paper
£267 $477 €400 Untitled (16x24cm-6x9in) s.d.64 W/C col pen biro. 15-May-4 Van Ham, Cologne #1034
£839 $1443 €1200 Untitled (56x44cm-22x17in) s.d.1966 mixed media W/C gouache chk. 4-Dec-3 Van Ham, Cologne #562/R
£1034 $1728 €1500 Untitled (50x69cm-20x27in) s.d.1962 mixed media board. 13-Nov-3 Neumeister, Munich #665/R est:2500-2800
£1034 $1728 €1500 Rhodos (50x66cm-20x26in) s.i.d.1965 mixed media. 13-Nov-3 Neumeister, Munich #666/R est:2500-2800
£1049 $1804 €1500 Composition (56x75cm-22x30in) s.d.1963 mixed media chk gouache W/C. 4-Dec-3 Van Ham, Cologne #561/R est:1500

WESTPHAL, Otto (1878-?) German
£629 $1083 €900 Summer coastal landscape with waterlillies (75x85cm-30x33in) s. 5-Dec-3 Bolland & Marotz, Bremen #783/R

WESTPHALIAN SCHOOL (15th C) German
£5743 $10108 €8500 Christ on the cross (60x35cm-24x14in) panel prov. 22-May-4 Lempertz, Koln #1109/R est:10000

WESTPHALIAN SCHOOL (16th C) German
£20000 $36000 €29200 Descent from the Cross (136x134cm-54x53in) d.1515 panel prov. 21-Apr-4 Christie's, London #53/R est:20000-30000

WESTRUP, E Kate (fl.1910-1927) British
£550 $1018 €803 Mare and foal (25x33cm-10x13in) s. i.verso board. 10-Feb-4 David Lay, Penzance #497/R
£550 $1018 €803 Mare and foal (25x33cm-10x13in) s. i.verso board. 10-Feb-4 David Lay, Penzance #498

WESTWOOD, Bryan Wyndham (1930-2000) Australian
£412 $745 €602 Landscape. init. 31-Mar-4 Goodman, Sydney #335 (A.D 1000)
£621 $968 €900 French countryside (47x58cm-19x23in) s. board. 1-Aug-2 Joel, Victoria #235 est:2000-2500 (A.D 1800)
£650 $1021 €943 Hillside (30x28cm-12x11in) init. cardboard prov.exhib. 26-Aug-3 Christie's, Sydney #300 est:1500-2500 (A.D 1600)
£653 $1202 €953 Karen's back (39x39cm-15x15in) canvasboard prov. 29-Mar-4 Goodman, Sydney #217/R (A.D 1600)
£661 $1124 €965 Shell on cabinet (48x38cm-19x15in) s. i.verso board. 29-Oct-3 Lawson Menzies, Sydney #130/R est:1800-2500 (A.D 1600)
£810 $1304 €1183 Self Portrait (68x46cm-27x18in) init. 25-Aug-3 Sotheby's, Paddington #396/R (A.D 2000)
£1070 $1937 €1562 Small nude 1980 (38x28cm-15x11in) oil on card exhib. 30-Mar-4 Lawson Menzies, Sydney #100/R est:1500-2500 (A.D 2600)
£1207 $1883 €1750 Weighing in (135x74cm-53x29in) init. 1-Aug-2 Joel, Victoria #288 est:2000-3000 (A.D 3500)
£1317 $2384 €1923 House on a cliff (60x45cm-24x18in) s. board. 31-Mar-4 Goodman, Sydney #380/R est:2000-2500 (A.D 3200)
£1878 $3455 €2742 Study for a fence (24x29cm-9x11in) board. 29-Mar-4 Goodman, Sydney #222/R est:800-1000 (A.D 4600)
£2376 $4396 €3469 Centennial Park, Sydney (61x61cm-24x24in) board prov. 10-Mar-4 Deutscher-Menzies, Melbourne #347/R est:2500-3500 (A.D 5750)
£2642 $4148 €3831 Apples in a box (89x89cm-35x35in) init. canvas on board prov.exhib. 26-Aug-3 Christie's, Sydney #257/R est:3000-4000 (A.D 6500)
£3320 $5544 €4980 Still life (137x91cm-54x36in) init. 27-Oct-3 Goodman, Sydney #102/R est:8000-12000 (A.D 8000)
£3906 $7305 €5859 Young girl (106x106cm-42x42in) 20-Jul-4 Goodman, Sydney #72/R est:10000-15000 (A.D 10000)
£7143 $13143 €10429 Jindabyne evening no 1 (156x156cm-61x61in) prov. 29-Mar-4 Goodman, Sydney #76/R est:6000-8000 (A.D 17500)
£15447 $24252 €22398 Morning, Paddington (134x157cm-53x62in) init. board prov.exhib. 27-Aug-3 Christie's, Sydney #614/R est:7000-10000 (A.D 38000)

WET, Jacob Jacobsz de (1640-1697) Dutch
£1690 $2924 €2400 Allegorie de l'abondance (81x58cm-32x23in) s. 10-Dec-3 Maigret, Paris #64 est:1500-2000

WET, Jacob Jacobsz de (attrib) (1640-1697) Dutch
£1848 $3307 €2698 Scene from The history of Queen Tamiris (70x137cm-28x54in) panel. 25-May-4 Bukowskis, Stockholm #468/R est:30000-35000 (S.KR 25000)
£2923 $5028 €4268 Crowning scene (73x137cm-29x54in) 2-Dec-3 Bukowskis, Stockholm #358/R est:40000-50000 (S.KR 38000)

WET, Jacob de (1610-1671) Dutch
£995 $1692 €1453 Paul and Barnabas in Lystra (60x84cm-24x33in) panel. 19-Nov-3 Fischer, Luzern #1012/R est:3000-4000 (S.FR 2200)
£3221 $5928 €4800 River landscape with finding of Moses (62x53cm-24x21in) bears sig. 25-Mar-4 Dr Fritz Nagel, Stuttgart #627/R est:5500
£3793 $6334 €5500 Joseph, Egyptian king, with father and brother (60x84cm-24x33in) s. panel prov.lit. 15-Nov-3 Lempertz, Koln #1177/R est:6000
£5822 $9897 €8500 Israelites worship the Golden Calf (59x81cm-23x32in) panel. 4-Nov-3 Sotheby's, Amsterdam #114/R est:6000-8000
£8000 $14640 €11680 Meeting of David and Abigail (51x66cm-20x26in) bears sig panel. 6-Jul-4 Sotheby's, Olympia #434/R est:5000-7000

WETERING DE ROOY, Johann Embrosius van de (1877-1972) Dutch
£284 $474 €400 River landscape with boat and distant village (39x54cm-15x21in) s. 21-Jun-3 Hans Stahl, Hamburg #35/R
£341 $613 €498 Harbour view with figures and boats (41x46cm-16x18in) s. 24-Apr-4 Rasmussen, Havnen #2089/R (D.KR 3800)
£594 $992 €850 View of a village (26x34cm-10x13in) s. panel. 30-Jun-3 Sotheby's, Amsterdam #88
£2639 $4169 €3800 Harbour entrance (38x65cm-15x26in) s. s.on stretcher. 2-Sep-3 Christie's, Amsterdam #332/R est:1000-1500
Works on paper
£479 $815 €700 Peasant woman by wood mountain (32x46cm-13x18in) s. W/C. 5-Nov-3 Vendue Huis, Gravenhage #225/R

WETHERBEE, George Faulkner (1851-1920) American
£1504 $2556 €2196 Coastal scene with nymph (49x75cm-19x30in) s. 27-Nov-3 International Art Centre, Auckland #190/R est:4500-6500 (NZ.D 4000)

WETHERILL, Elisha Kent Kane (1874-1929) American
£1530 $2800 €2234 Approaching New York (76x114cm-30x45in) s. 31-Jan-4 South Bay, Long Island #141

WETLI, Hugo (1916-1972) Swiss
£1810 $3241 €2643 Winter in Emmental (60x70cm-24x28in) s.d.70 i. stretcher. 14-May-4 Dobiaschofsky, Bern #256/R est:2600 (S.FR 4200)

WETTERLING, Alexander Clemens (1796-1858) Swedish
Works on paper
£423 $728 €618 Soldiers defending the town Zinckhoffen on 29 Aug 1796 (39x58cm-15x23in) s. wash. 7-Dec-3 Uppsala Auktionskammare, Uppsala #78/R (S.KR 5500)
£769 $1323 €1123 The Battle at Duna 9 July 1701 (44x55cm-17x22in) s. wash. 7-Dec-3 Uppsala Auktionskammare, Uppsala #67/R (S.KR 10000)

WETZEL, Christoph (1947-) German
£1103 $1843 €1600 Reading room (166x216cm-65x85in) s.d.88. 15-Nov-3 Von Zezschwitz, Munich #191/R est:1800

WETZEL, Johann Jakob (1781-1834) Swiss
Works on paper
£338 $581 €493 Lake Como with view towards Palazzo al Ulmo (19x28cm-7x11in) s. pen wash. 8-Dec-3 Philippe Schuler, Zurich #4239/R (S.FR 750)
£6422 $10725 €9312 Palazzo Gallio near Gravedona on Lake Como (79x104cm-31x41in) s.d.1832 W/C paper on canvas. 23-Jun-3 Philippe Schuler, Zurich #3926/R est:5000-7000 (S.FR 14000)

WEURLANDER, Fridolf (1851-1900) Finnish
£973 $1810 €1450 Beached boat (13x25cm-5x10in) s. 7-Mar-4 Bukowskis, Helsinki #479/R

WEWERKA, Stefan (1928-) German
Works on paper
£490 $832 €700 Sketch for chair (30x54cm-12x21in) s.i.d.Marz 1973 W/C Indian ink board. 27-Nov-3 Lempertz, Koln #528/R

WEX, Adalbert (1867-1932) German
£547 $989 €820 Murnau moor with Benedict wall (65x70cm-26x28in) s. i. verso. 3-Apr-4 Hans Stahl, Hamburg #126/R

WEXLER, Jacob (1912-) Israeli
£856 $1600 €1250 Jew praying in the Synagogue (60x51cm-24x20in) s.d.1954 s.verso. 1-Mar-4 Ben-Ami, Tel Aviv #4661/R est:1500-2000
£929 $1700 €1356 Prayers in Ha ari Synagogue in Zaffed (60x45cm-24x18in) s.d.1954. 1-Feb-4 Ben-Ami, Tel Aviv #4395/R est:1500-2000

WEY, Alois (1891-1985) Swiss
Works on paper
£724 $1231 €1057 Palace with flag (45x49cm-18x19in) s. col pen Indian ink gold silver. 18-Nov-3 Hans Widmer, St Gallen #1256 est:1500-2800 (S.FR 1600)
£724 $1231 €1057 Palace (49x47cm-19x19in) s. col pen Indian ink gold silver. 18-Nov-3 Hans Widmer, St Gallen #1261 est:1500-2800 (S.FR 1600)

WEYDE, Julius (1822-1860) German
£2000 $3600 €3000 Happy family (85x69cm-33x27in) s.d.1856. 20-Apr-4 Sotheby's, Amsterdam #65/R est:2000-4000

WEYDEN, Goswyn van der (1465-1538) Flemish
£65000 $118950 €94900 Virgin and Child with Saint Catherine of Alexandria and Saint Margaret of Antioch (72x64cm-28x25in) panel prov.exhib.lit. 7-Jul-4 Christie's, London #18/R est:60000-80000

WEYDEN, Harry van der (1868-?) American
£400 $732 €584 Foreshore by moonlight (30x38cm-12x15in) s. board. 8-Jul-4 Duke & Son, Dorchester #267/R
£496 $829 €700 Landscape (18x24cm-7x9in) s. panel. 14-Oct-3 Dorotheum, Vienna #31/R
£800 $1464 €1168 Pinnacle Rock near Old Harry Point, Studland, Dorset (18x23cm-7x9in) s.i.verso board. 8-Jul-4 Duke & Son, Dorchester #266
£6800 $11560 €9928 View of Poole Harbour from Ballard Down (76x132cm-30x52in) s.d.1930 exhib. 30-Oct-3 Duke & Son, Dorchester #209/R est:3000-5000

WEYDEN, Rogier van der (circle) (1399-1464) Flemish
£190000 $323000 €277400 Virgin and child (29x18cm-11x7in) i. panel. 29-Oct-3 Christie's, London #9/R est:8000-12000

WEYDEN, Rogier van der (studio) (1399-1464) Flemish
£39474 $72632 €60000 Madonna and Child (34x26cm-13x10in) panel prov. 24-Jun-4 Christie's, Paris #37/R est:60000-80000

WEYDEN, Rogier van der (style) (1399-1464) Flemish
£8333 $15000 €12166 Holy Family in a landscape (60x42cm-24x17in) panel shaped top prov.exhib. 23-Jan-4 Christie's, Rockefeller NY #161/R est:8000-12000

WEYE-HANSEN, Stig (1946-) Danish
£347 $565 €507 Training by a hand shy angel (63x80cm-25x31in) mono. 27-Sep-3 Rasmussen, Havnen #4030 (D.KR 3700)

WEYER, Gabriel (1576-1632) German
Works on paper
£265 $482 €400 Romantic scene (14x19cm-6x7in) pen wash htd white. 18-Jun-4 Bolland & Marotz, Bremen #476/R

WEYER, Omer van de (1910-) Dutch
£7246 $11884 €10000 La rixe (65x80cm-26x31in) s. mono.d.1930 verso. 27-May-3 Sotheby's, Amsterdam #343/R est:12000-15000

WEYL, Hans (20th C) German
Works on paper
£503 $936 €750 Portrait of young woman in blue dress (114x66cm-45x26in) s. pastel. 6-Mar-4 Arnold, Frankfurt #912/R

WEYL, Max (1837-1914) American/German
£511 $950 €746 Rocky pasture with grazing cow (23x30cm-9x12in) s. 5-Mar-4 Skinner, Boston #444/R
£811 $1500 €1184 Peonies in a glass pitcher (64x41cm-25x16in) s.d.81. 10-Mar-4 Doyle, New York #54/R est:800-1200
£815 $1500 €1190 Country landscape (69x89cm-27x35in) s. canvas on panel. 26-Jun-4 Sloans & Kenyon, Bethesda #1087/R est:1000-1500
£1258 $2000 €1837 Landscape with pastures and pond (38x53cm-15x21in) s. 13-Sep-3 Weschler, Washington #724/R est:2000-3000
£1285 $2300 €1876 Landscape with cottage (28x41cm-11x16in) s.indis.d. 7-May-4 Sloans & Kenyon, Bethesda #1683/R est:1000-1200
£1359 $2500 €1984 Landscape with birches (41x56cm-16x22in) s. painted 1912. 13-Jun-4 William Jenack, New York #256 est:1000-1500
£1630 $3000 €2380 Rock Creek landscape (58x84cm-23x33in) painted 1902. 13-Jun-4 William Jenack, New York #255 est:2000-3000
£2374 $4250 €3466 Cows along a stream (46x66cm-18x26in) s. 7-May-4 Sloans & Kenyon, Bethesda #1690/R est:3000-4000
£5866 $10500 €8564 Potomac marshlands (51x76cm-20x30in) s. 20-Mar-4 Sloans & Kenyon, Bethesda #1199/R est:3500-4500

WEYMOUTH, George A (1936-) American
Works on paper
£5307 $9500 €7748 Snowdrops (53x74cm-21x29in) s. 8-Jan-4 James Julia, Fairfield #44/R est:2000-4000

WEYNS, Jan Harm (1864-1945) Dutch
£379 $633 €550 Gateway to Elburg (43x30cm-17x12in) s. board. 11-Nov-3 Vendu Notarishuis, Rotterdam #35/R
£428 $787 €650 Zonnige dag Noordwijk Binnen (50x61cm-20x24in) s. s.i. verso i. stretcher. 28-Jun-4 Sotheby's, Amsterdam #68/R
£544 $990 €800 Village in winter with a bridge over a stream (50x70cm-20x28in) s. 3-Feb-4 Christie's, Amsterdam #182
£638 $1180 €950 Farm in a summer landscape (40x50cm-16x20in) s. 15-Mar-4 Sotheby's, Amsterdam #172/R est:1000-1500
£961 $1768 €1403 Flower market (41x60cm-16x24in) s. 14-Jun-4 Philippe Schuler, Zurich #4345/R est:2000-2500 (S.FR 2200)

WEYRINGER, Johann (1949-) Austrian
Works on paper
£1418 $2369 €2000 Spinxlike she invites you to tea (76x56cm-30x22in) s.i.d.1984 W/C. 16-Oct-3 Dorotheum, Salzburg #942/R est:1600-2400
£1467 $2699 €2200 Triviale in Trivium (77x57cm-30x22in) s.i.d.1986 W/C mixed media. 9-Jun-4 Dorotheum, Salzburg #802/R est:1800-2400

WEYSSER, Karl (1833-1904) German
£1733 $3120 €2600 Baden Baden (56x39cm-22x15in) s.d.1884 canvas on board. 26-Apr-4 Rieber, Stuttgart #1184/R est:980
£2535 $4386 €3600 Timber framed house with outside steps (31x21cm-12x8in) s. lit. 13-Dec-3 Lempertz, Koln #63/R est:3000
£2535 $4386 €3600 View from courtyard of No 6 of St Stephanskirche. lit. 13-Dec-3 Lempertz, Koln #64/R est:3000
£3497 $6014 €5000 Village scene with family going for a stroll (35x27cm-14x11in) 3-Dec-3 Neumeister, Munich #801a/R est:3880
£6294 $10510 €9000 Town Hall in the Rue de la Mairie, Scherweiler (40x32cm-16x13in) s. 10-Oct-3 Winterberg, Heidelberg #825/R est:8500

WEYTS, Carolus (1828-1875) Belgian
£5063 $8000 €7392 Mr Ludwig of Warren, passing Dover Castle (61x79cm-24x31in) s. 25-Jul-3 Eldred, East Dennis #283c est:10000-12000

WEYTS, Petrus Cornelius (1799-1855) Flemish
£1500 $2835 €2190 Alacrity of Dover (42x58cm-17x23in) s.i.d.1838 glass. 17-Feb-4 Bonhams, New Bond Street #1/R est:800-1200

WHAITE, Henry Clarence (1828-1912) British
£800 $1432 €1168 Aber waterfall - Never ending (120x69cm-47x27in) i. canvas on panel. 11-May-4 Bonhams, Knightsbridge #141/R
£1027 $1900 €1499 Oyster dredgers coming ashore, an approaching storm (61x91cm-24x36in) s.d.1864. 10-Mar-4 Doyle, New York #55/R est:3000-5000
Works on paper
£260 $424 €380 Craggy moorland scene with distant lake and two figures and sheep (13x18cm-5x7in) s.indis.d. W/C. 27-Sep-3 Rogers Jones, Clwyd #27

WHAITE, James (19th C) British
£350 $637 €511 Dordtrecht (36x53cm-14x21in) s. 15-Jun-4 David Lay, Penzance #309
£400 $736 €584 Highland river with waterfall in the foreground (50x65cm-20x26in) s.d.1877. 29-Mar-4 Bonhams, Bath #77/R
Works on paper
£223 $373 €323 Cattle watering in a stream (41x51cm-16x20in) s. W/C. 17-Jun-3 Pinneys, Montreal #89 (C.D 500)
£360 $648 €526 Shorescape at Deganwy with numerous cockle gatherers (28x43cm-11x17in) s. W/C. 24-Apr-4 Rogers Jones, Clwyd #133
£400 $748 €584 Welford, Gloucestershire (29x48cm-11x19in) s. i.verso pencil W/C. 22-Jul-4 Tennants, Leyburn #740
£790 $1344 €1153 Caniston lake (60x94cm-24x37in) s.d.1875 W/C. 29-Oct-3 Louis Morton, Mexico #47/R est:20000-25000 (M.P 15000)

WHALE, R (19th C) British
£1350 $2457 €1971 Sketching lesson (91x96cm-36x38in) s. 29-Jun-4 Bonhams, Knowle #75 est:1500-2000

WHALE, R R (1805-1887) Canadian
£3200 $5440 €4672 Topsail schooner in the estuary at Bideford (61x88cm-24x35in) s. 19-Nov-3 Christie's, Kensington #459/R est:1500-2000

WHALE, Robert Heard (1857-1906) Canadian
£915 $1638 €1336 River landscape with figures and dog (71x58cm-28x23in) prov. 31-May-4 Sotheby's, Toronto #22/R est:3000-4000 (C.D 2250)
£1120 $2050 €1635 Figures by a river (40x60cm-16x24in) s. 1-Jun-4 Joyner Waddington, Toronto #266/R est:3000-4000 (C.D 2800)

WHALE, Robert Reginald (1805-1887) Canadian
£315 $536 €460 Jemina Whale, sister of Robert Whale (41x36cm-16x14in) bears name d.1844 i.verso canvas on board. 23-Nov-3 Levis, Calgary #147/R (C.D 700)
£1800 $3294 €2628 Cattle by a stream (71x57cm-28x22in) s. 1-Jun-4 Joyner Waddington, Toronto #196/R est:3500-4500 (C.D 4500)
£3252 $5821 €4748 Deer in forest interior (72x58cm-28x23in) s. prov. 31-May-4 Sotheby's, Toronto #21/R est:6000-8000 (C.D 8000)
£3659 $6549 €5342 Portrait of the artist's daughter, Bessie Whale (75x56cm-30x22in) i.verso canvas on masonite prov.exhib. 31-May-4 Sotheby's, Toronto #20/R est:10000-12000 (C.D 9000)

WHALLEY, John (20th C) American
Works on paper
£1657 $3000 €2486 Still life with watering can (99x147cm-39x58in) graphite. 16-Apr-4 American Auctioneer #424/R est:8000-10000

WHANKI, Kim (1913-1974) Korean
£23529 $40000 €34352 Abstract composition (124x104cm-49x41in) s. 4-Nov-3 Bonhams & Butterfields, San Francisco #3184/R est:40000-60000
£43478 $80000 €63478 Morning star (86x54cm-34x21in) s.d.1966 i.verso. 23-Mar-4 Christie's, Rockefeller NY #353/R est:30000-40000
£46196 $85000 €67446 Untitled (48x6cm-19x2in) s. i.verso. 23-Mar-4 Christie's, Rockefeller NY #354/R est:25000-30000

WHATLEY, Henry (1824-1901) British
£720 $1310 €1051 Lynmouth quay (50x75cm-20x30in) s. 21-Jun-4 Bonhams, Bath #403/R
Works on paper
£300 $549 €438 Portrait of a young woman (34x24cm-13x9in) s. W/C oval. 6-Jul-4 Peter Wilson, Nantwich #54/R

£3263 $5874 €4895 Victorian lady (66x103cm-26x41in) s.d.98 W/C htd white. 25-Apr-4 Goteborg Auktionsverk, Sweden #231/R est:40000 (S.KR 45000)

WHATLEY, Julia (20th C) British
£340 $598 €496 A corner of the bazaar II (19x26cm-7x10in) init. board. 18-May-4 Woolley & Wallis, Salisbury #139/R

WHEALE, Ivan Trevor (?) Canadian
£1700 $3111 €2482 After the storm (55x120cm-22x47in) s. painted 1988 prov. 1-Jun-4 Joyner Waddington, Toronto #240/R est:3000-5000 (C.D 4250)

WHEATLEY, Francis (1747-1801) British
£3352 $6000 €4894 Royal Navy Master and Commander, probably Commander David Mackay (46x36cm-18x14in) panel painted c.1781 prov. 18-Mar-4 Richard Opfer, Timonium #88/R est:7000-8000
£13000 $22490 €18980 Ploughman and his team by a wood (155x216cm-61x85in) s.d.1795 prov.lit. 10-Dec-3 Bonhams, New Bond Street #15/R est:4000-6000

WHEATLEY, Francis (attrib) (1747-1801) British
£280 $482 €409 In harvest moon (17x20cm-7x8in) panel prov. 7-Dec-3 Lots Road Auctions, London #359
Works on paper
£1700 $3145 €2482 Country scene with milkmaids (17x25cm-7x10in) s. over pencil. 10-Mar-4 Sotheby's, Olympia #125/R est:800-1200

WHEELER, Alfred (1852-1932) British
£560 $1008 €818 Study of the head of three fox hounds (25x41cm-10x16in) s.d.1899 board. 20-Apr-4 Canterbury Auctions, UK #114/R
£1000 $1830 €1460 Waiting outside the gates, a coach and four with driver up (44x80cm-17x31in) s. 6-Jul-4 Bearnes, Exeter #498/R est:1000-1500
£1700 $2890 €2482 Chestnut hunter in a stable (56x68cm-22x27in) init. 27-Nov-3 Christie's, Kensington #96/R est:1800-2200
£1800 $3186 €2628 Hunting scenes (44x60cm-17x24in) s. set of three. 28-Apr-4 Peter Wilson, Nantwich #62 est:1800-2000
£2400 $4392 €3504 Huntsman and hounds in a landscape (58x75cm-23x30in) s.i. 6-Apr-4 Bonhams, Knightsbridge #187/R est:500-800
£2600 $4706 €3796 Ormonde with Fred Archer up (35x46cm-14x18in) s.i. 31-Mar-4 Bonhams, Knightsbridge #73/R est:2000-3000
£3000 $5100 €4380 Jack Russell, terrier and spaniel, two king Charles spaniel (11x15cm-4x6in) init. board five in one frame. 27-Nov-3 Sotheby's, London #362/R est:3000-5000
£3200 $5984 €4672 Study of three foxhounds (30x45cm-12x18in) s. 22-Jul-4 Tennants, Leyburn #881/R est:600-800
£4000 $6880 €5840 Donovan. Ormonde (30x36cm-12x14in) s.i. pair. 3-Dec-3 Bonhams, Knightsbridge #140/R est:4000-6000

WHEELER, Charles Arthur (1881-1977) Australian
£372 $639 €543 Misty landscape (28x38cm-11x15in) s. board. 7-Dec-3 International Art Centre, Auckland #445 (NZ.D 1000)
£380 $623 €555 View from the Bogong Hotel, looking from Ryders, Australia (28x36cm-11x14in) i. 29-May-3 Neales, Nottingham #819
£407 $728 €594 In the Taieri Valley (29x39cm-11x15in) s. board. 10-May-4 Joel, Victoria #239 est:1000-1500 (A.D 1000)
£445 $717 €650 Bush track (27x39cm-11x15in) s. board. 13-Oct-3 Joel, Victoria #422 est:800-1200 (A.D 1100)
£552 $861 €800 Afternoon in the garden (44x60cm-17x24in) s. 1-Aug-2 Joel, Victoria #259 est:1000-1500 (A.D 1600)
£21186 $36017 €30932 Portrait of a young woman at a table (85x100cm-33x39in) s. prov. 24-Nov-3 Sotheby's, Melbourne #48/R est:50000-60000 (A.D 50000)
Works on paper
£414 $703 €604 A summers day (20x27cm-8x11in) s. W/C. 27-Nov-3 International Art Centre, Auckland #191/R (NZ.D 1100)

WHEELER, Clifton (1883-1953) American
£1209 $2200 €1765 Roadside rest (36x43cm-14x17in) 7-Feb-4 Dan Ripley, Indianapolis #11
£1266 $2000 €1848 Snowy Brown County landscape (51x61cm-20x24in) s. canvasboard. 7-Sep-3 Treadway Gallery, Cincinnati #671/R est:2000-3000
£3611 $6500 €5272 First snow (61x81cm-24x32in) s.d.52 masonite exhib. 24-Apr-4 Weschler, Washington #598/R est:3000-5000

WHEELER, Colin V (20th C) New Zealander
£451 $718 €658 Cromwell graveyard (60x55cm-24x22in) s.d.1985 board. 1-May-3 Dunbar Sloane, Wellington #88 est:1000-2000 (NZ.D 1300)
£532 $984 €777 Banks of the Pareora and Mt. Nimrod, South Canterbury (40x50cm-16x20in) s. board. 13-Jul-4 Watson's, Christchurch #87/R est:1500-2500 (NZ.D 1500)
£564 $959 €823 Rural scene with alps in the background (60x47cm-24x19in) s. board. 26-Nov-3 Dunbar Sloane, Wellington #582 est:700-1500 (NZ.D 1500)
£616 $979 €899 Harbour street from Overbridge (26x56cm-10x22in) s. board. 9-Sep-3 Watson's, Christchurch #54 (NZ.D 1700)
£652 $1037 €952 Humber street yards, Oamaru (22x48cm-9x19in) s. board. 9-Sep-3 Watson's, Christchurch #14 (NZ.D 1800)
£705 $1304 €1029 Canterbury landscape (33x43cm-13x17in) s. board. 9-Mar-4 Watson's, Christchurch #4 est:2500-3500 (NZ.D 1925)
£1250 $2300 €1825 Bakery (60x53cm-24x21in) s.d.1998 canvasboard. 25-Mar-4 International Art Centre, Auckland #115/R est:3500-5000 (NZ.D 3500)
£1315 $2354 €1920 Woolshed, Pouerua Station, Bay of Island (57x46cm-22x18in) s. board. 12-May-4 Dunbar Sloane, Wellington #188 est:2000-4000 (NZ.D 3800)
£1857 $3417 €2711 All Day Bay near Oamaru (48x126cm-19x50in) s.d.1987 board. 25-Mar-4 International Art Centre, Auckland #124/R est:3500-4500 (NZ.D 5200)
£3261 $5250 €4761 Country Township (67x90cm-26x35in) s.d.1958 board. 20-Aug-3 Peter Webb, Auckland #2037/R est:4000-6000 (NZ.D 9000)
Works on paper
£297 $512 €434 Sycamores (29x36cm-11x14in) s.d.1994 W/C. 7-Dec-3 International Art Centre, Auckland #234 (NZ.D 800)
£1353 $2301 €1975 Otago farm (36x48cm-14x19in) s.d.1967 W/C. 27-Nov-3 International Art Centre, Auckland #170/R est:2000-3000 (NZ.D 3600)

WHEELER, Hughlette (1901-1954) American
Sculpture
£1279 $2200 €1867 Sweet Briar (32cm-13in) i. pat bronze. 2-Dec-3 Christie's, Rockefeller NY #70/R est:2000-3000

WHEELER, J A (1821-1903) British
£1875 $3000 €2738 Untitled (64x86cm-25x34in) painted 1814. 19-Sep-3 Du Mouchelle, Detroit #2095/R est:1500-2000

WHEELER, Jessica Hilda (1879-1940) British
£440 $792 €642 Study of lion and lioness (51x71cm-20x28in) init. 20-Apr-4 Canterbury Auctions, UK #115/R

WHEELER, John Arnold (1821-1903) British
£375 $671 €548 Ormonde - a bay racehorse with jockey Fred Archer mounted (20x25cm-8x10in) s.d.1886 panel. 28-May-4 Bigwood, Stratford on Avon #362
£800 $1480 €1168 Jack Russell (30x35cm-12x14in) 14-Jul-4 Sotheby's, Olympia #64/R
£850 $1564 €1241 Hunted fox (35x30cm-14x12in) s. 10-Jun-4 Christie's, Kensington #49/R
£1243 $2250 €1815 Cocker amongst reeds (18x15cm-7x6in) i.verso board. 30-Mar-4 Bonhams & Butterfields, San Francisco #79/R est:1100-1500
£1400 $2590 €2044 Ladas with jockey up (34x43cm-13x17in) s.i. board. 10-Mar-4 Sotheby's, Olympia #185/R est:1500-2000
£1500 $2550 €2190 Study of hounds (25x45cm-10x18in) s. 19-Nov-3 Sotheby's, Olympia #41/R est:500-700
£1600 $2992 €2336 Huntsman on horseback with foxhounds approaching a stone wall (30x91cm-12x36in) s.i. 22-Jul-4 Tennants, Leyburn #879/R est:1000-1500
£1657 $3000 €2419 Full cry (46x61cm-18x24in) s.i. prov. 30-Mar-4 Christie's, Rockefeller NY #47/R est:4000-6000
£1892 $3500 €2762 Jack Russell terrier (28x36cm-11x14in) s. board. 10-Feb-4 Doyle, New York #269/R est:3000-5000
£2200 $3740 €3212 Huntsman and hounds (37x46cm-15x18in) s. board. 19-Nov-3 Sotheby's, Olympia #40/R est:1500-2000
£2273 $3864 €3319 Fox hounds (23x37cm-9x15in) s. board. 29-Oct-3 Lawson Menzies, Sydney #257/R est:6000-8000 (A.D 5500)
£2432 $4500 €3551 Four hounds (33x46cm-13x18in) s. board. 10-Feb-4 Doyle, New York #156/R est:4000-6000
£2950 $4897 €4307 Portrait of a smooth and wire haired terrier (20x33cm-8x13in) s. pair. 6-Oct-3 David Duggleby, Scarborough #211/R est:3000-4000
£3099 $5269 €4525 Favourite terriers (24x47cm-9x19in) s. board. 29-Oct-3 Lawson Menzies, Sydney #258/R est:7000-9000 (A.D 7500)
£3200 $5344 €4640 Dark chestnut hunter in a loose box (64x76cm-25x30in) s.d.1869. 22-Jun-3 Desmond Judd, Cranbrook #1021
£13514 $25000 €19730 The racehorse, Kilmarty, in stable. Racehorse, St Vincent (61x76cm-24x30in) s. one bears d. two. 10-Feb-4 Doyle, New York #233/R est:15000-25000

WHEELER, Muriel (1888-1979) British
£260 $447 €380 Spring fantasy (46x56cm-18x22in) s.i.d.1940 on stretcher exhib. 2-Dec-3 Bonhams, Ipswich #226

WHEELER, Pete (20th C) New Zealander
£525 $835 €767 14 minutes, 59 secs (120x120cm-47x47in) s. 9-Sep-3 Watson's, Christchurch #64 (NZ.D 1450)

WHEELER, Walter Herbert (1878-1960) British
£600 $1092 €876 Terrier in an oak tree. board. 3-Feb-4 Lawrences, Bletchingley #1603/R
£1200 $2040 €1752 Two terriers (23x29cm-9x11in) s.d.1903 board. 27-Nov-3 Christie's, Kensington #303/R est:800-1200

WHEELWRIGHT, Roland (1870-1955) British
£300 $549 €438 Plough horse (23x13cm-9x5in) s. panel. 8-Apr-4 Christie's, Kensington #145
£4200 $7812 €6132 Exploring the pool (51x61cm-20x24in) indis sig. 4-Mar-4 Christie's, Kensington #646/R est:2000-4000
£7000 $11900 €10220 Exploring pool (57x80cm-22x31in) s. 21-Nov-3 Christie's, London #127/R est:2500-3500

WHEELWRIGHT, W H (19th C) British
£800 $1472 €1168 Heather Bell, in a stable (51x61cm-20x24in) s.d.1874 panel. 10-Jun-4 Christie's, Kensington #77/R
£6400 $10880 €9344 Groom preparing a carriage outside stables. Carriage waiting at the steps of a house (58x82cm-23x32in) s.d.1878-79 pair. 27-Nov-3 Christie's, Kensington #110/R est:7000-10000

WHELAN, Leo (1892-1956) British
£10000 $17900 €14600 Kitchen interior. Interior study (63x53cm-25x21in) s. double-sided. 14-May-4 Christie's, London #161/R est:6000-8000

WHERRA, Jack (1924-) Australian
Sculpture
£1301 $2055 €1899 Untitled, shield with figures and animals (77cm-30in) earth pigments synthetic polymer paint hardwood exec.c.1965. 28-Jul-3 Sotheby's, Paddington #43/R est:1000-1500 (A.D 3200)

WHICKER, Frederick John Hayes (1901-) British
£450 $752 €657 Linotype room (99x114cm-39x45in) s. 14-Oct-3 David Lay, Penzance #523/R

WHINNEN, George (1891-1950) Australian

£267	$486	€390	Nuriootpa (28x35cm-11x14in) s. i.verso canvas on board. 16-Jun-4 Deutscher-Menzies, Melbourne #593/R (A.D 700)
£407	$728	€594	Rose study (61x55cm-24x22in) s. 10-May-4 Joel, Victoria #406 (A.D 1000)

WHIPPLE, Charles Ayer (1859-1928) American

£3825	$7000	€5585	Portrait of General Nelson Appleton Miles (163x86cm-64x34in) s.d.1895 prov. 5-Jun-4 Neal Auction Company, New Orleans #317/R est:1000-1500

WHISHAW, Anthony (1930-) British

£350	$637	€511	From Las Meninas I (25x60cm-10x24in) init. acrylic collage board painted 1984. 1-Jul-4 Christie's, Kensington #372/R
£350	$637	€511	After Las Meninas II (27x59cm-11x23in) init. board painted 1984/7. 1-Jul-4 Christie's, Kensington #373/R
£450	$819	€657	Mata Dero (35x66cm-14x26in) init.i. acrylic collage board. 1-Jul-4 Christie's, Kensington #374/R
£850	$1522	€1241	Crucifixion (176x148cm-69x58in) s.i. verso. 14-May-4 Christie's, Kensington #635/R
Works on paper			
£1000	$1860	€1460	Memory bank (31x62cm-12x24in) acrylic mixed media on board. 8-Mar-4 Christie's, London #18

WHISSON, Kenneth Ronald (1927-) Australian

£5469	$10227	€8204	Earth and concrete (68x99cm-27x39in) i.verso board. 20-Jul-4 Goodman, Sydney #63/R est:14000-18000 (A.D 14000)
£9836	$15541	€14361	Trees and structures (90x120cm-35x47in) s.i.d.26/1/87 verso oil gesso synthetic polymer paint prov.exhib. 2-Sep-3 Deutscher-Menzies, Melbourne #25/R est:25000-35000 (A.D 24000)
£17021	$28936	€24851	Circus III brown and red and yellow horses (99x119cm-39x47in) i.d.83 prov. 25-Nov-3 Christie's, Melbourne #23/R est:35000-45000 (A.D 40000)
Works on paper			
£287	$453	€419	Ringmaster and dromedary (50x59cm-20x23in) s.d.1997 pen prov. 2-Sep-3 Deutscher-Menzies, Melbourne #218/R (A.D 700)
£537	$994	€784	Landscape with horses and animals (49x62cm-19x24in) pencil ink prov. 15-Mar-4 Sotheby's, Melbourne #206 est:800-1200 (A.D 1300)
£1157	$2048	€1689	Untitled, drawing with dogs (49x68cm-19x27in) pastel prov. 3-May-4 Christie's, Melbourne #248/R est:2000-3000 (A.D 2800)

WHISTLER, James Abbott McNeill (1834-1903) American

Prints			
£1765	$3000	€2577	Nocturne (17x23cm-7x9in) s. etching. 31-Oct-3 Sotheby's, New York #49/R
£1765	$3000	€2577	Staircase (17x16cm-7x6in) s. lithograph. 31-Oct-3 Sotheby's, New York #77/R
£1765	$3000	€2577	Fruitiere (31x20cm-12x8in) lithograph. 31-Oct-3 Sotheby's, New York #99/R
£1765	$3000	€2577	St Giles-in-the-Fields (22x14cm-9x6in) mono. lithograph. 31-Oct-3 Sotheby's, New York #118/R
£1788	$3200	€2610	Confidences in the garden (21x16cm-8x6in) lithograph. 6-May-4 Swann Galleries, New York #375/R est:1500-2500
£1796	$3000	€2622	The music room (13x20cm-5x8in) etching. 25-Oct-3 Du Mouchelle, Detroit #3280/R est:700-1100
£1808	$3200	€2640	Bibi Lalouette (23x15cm-9x6in) etching. 30-Apr-4 Sotheby's, New York #34 est:3000-4000
£1912	$3250	€2792	Evening. lithograph. 31-Oct-3 Sotheby's, New York #111/R
£2000	$3400	€2920	Tatting (13x8cm-5x3in) etching. 6-Nov-3 Swann Galleries, New York #470/R est:3500-5000
£2000	$3400	€2920	The Adam and Eve, Old Chelsea (18x30cm-7x12in) etching. 6-Nov-3 Swann Galleries, New York #473/R est:2500-3500
£2059	$3500	€3006	Little court (12x17cm-5x7in) s. etching. 31-Oct-3 Sotheby's, New York #53
£2096	$3500	€3060	Limehouse (18x25cm-7x10in) etching. 11-Nov-3 Doyle, New York #411/R est:3000-4000
£2206	$3750	€3221	Barber's (17x24cm-7x9in) s. etching. 31-Oct-3 Sotheby's, New York #57/R
£2206	$3750	€3221	Tilbury (8x17cm-3x7in) s. etching. 31-Oct-3 Sotheby's, New York #63/R
£2206	$3750	€3221	Garden porch (21x16cm-8x6in) s. lithograph. 31-Oct-3 Sotheby's, New York #89/R
£2353	$4000	€3435	Little lagoon (22x15cm-9x6in) etching. 31-Oct-3 Sotheby's, New York #25/R
£2373	$4200	€3465	Lime burner (25x17cm-10x7in) etching. 30-Apr-4 Sotheby's, New York #33/R est:3000-4000
£2432	$4500	€3551	The duet (23x15cm-9x6in) black white lithograph. 12-Mar-4 Du Mouchelle, Detroit #2134/R est:2500-3000
£2500	$4250	€3650	Doorway and vine (23x17cm-9x7in) etching. 31-Oct-3 Sotheby's, New York #34/R
£2500	$4250	€3650	Wheelwright's. etching. 31-Oct-3 Sotheby's, New York #54
£2500	$4575	€3650	Harbour workers smoking pipes (27x20cm-11x8in) s.d.1860 etching. 28-Jan-4 Dreweatt Neate, Newbury #161/R est:600-800
£2647	$4500	€3865	Upright Venice (25x18cm-10x7in) s. etching. 31-Oct-3 Sotheby's, New York #42/R
£2647	$4500	€3865	Garden (30x23cm-12x9in) etching. 31-Oct-3 Sotheby's, New York #46/R
£2647	$4500	€3865	Cutler Street (17x13cm-7x5in) s. etching. 31-Oct-3 Sotheby's, New York #60/R
£2794	$4750	€4079	Forge (25x18cm-10x7in) lithograph. 31-Oct-3 Sotheby's, New York #96/R
£2905	$5200	€4241	Village sweet shop (8x12cm-3x5in) s.i. etching. 6-May-4 Swann Galleries, New York #372/R est:2500-3500
£3235	$5500	€4723	San Giorgio (21x30cm-8x12in) etching. 31-Oct-3 Sotheby's, New York #39/R
£3235	$5500	€4723	Lagoon at noon (13x20cm-5x8in) s. etching. 31-Oct-3 Sotheby's, New York #50/R
£3356	$6174	€5000	Rotherhite (27x20cm-11x8in) s.d. etching. 26-Mar-4 Ketterer, Hamburg #223/R est:1400-1600
£3412	$5800	€4982	Lime burner (25x17cm-10x7in) etching. 6-Nov-3 Swann Galleries, New York #463/R est:4000-6000
£3529	$6000	€5152	Weary (20x13cm-8x5in) drypoint. 31-Oct-3 Sotheby's, New York #17/R
£3529	$6000	€5152	Riva 1 (20x29cm-8x11in) etching. 31-Oct-3 Sotheby's, New York #32/R
£3529	$6000	€5152	Turkeys (20x13cm-8x5in) etching. 31-Oct-3 Sotheby's, New York #37/R
£3529	$6000	€5152	Fish shop (14x21cm-6x8in) s. etching. 31-Oct-3 Sotheby's, New York #56/R
£3529	$6000	€5152	Exeter Street (12x17cm-5x7in) s. etching. 31-Oct-3 Sotheby's, New York #59/R
£3529	$6000	€5152	Gants de suede (21x10cm-8x4in) s. lithograph. 31-Oct-3 Sotheby's, New York #74/R
£3529	$6000	€5152	Winged hat (18x17cm-7x7in) s. lithograph. 31-Oct-3 Sotheby's, New York #73/R
£3631	$6500	€5301	San Biagio (21x30cm-8x12in) s.i. etching. 6-May-4 Swann Galleries, New York #369/R est:4000-6000
£3824	$6500	€5583	Bibi Lalouette (23x15cm-9x6in) etching. 31-Oct-3 Sotheby's, New York #12/R
£3824	$6500	€5583	Riva 3 (20x30cm-8x12in) s. etching. 31-Oct-3 Sotheby's, New York #43/R
£3824	$6500	€5583	Mast (34x16cm-13x6in) s. etching drypoint. 31-Oct-3 Sotheby's, New York #205/R
£4118	$7000	€6012	Rotherhithe (27x20cm-11x8in) etching. 31-Oct-3 Sotheby's, New York #15/R
£4118	$7000	€6012	Beggars (30x21cm-12x8in) etching. 31-Oct-3 Sotheby's, New York #33/R
£4118	$7000	€6012	Little market place (13x18cm-5x7in) etching. 31-Oct-3 Sotheby's, New York #66/R
£4237	$7500	€6186	Thames. Kensington Gardens (27x20cm-11x8in) s. lithograph two. 30-Apr-4 Sotheby's, New York #37/R est:3500-4500
£4412	$7500	€6442	Long Venice (12x31cm-5x12in) s. etching. 31-Oct-3 Sotheby's, New York #48/R
£4412	$7500	€6442	Fish market (9x13cm-4x5in) s. etching. 31-Oct-3 Sotheby's, New York #64
£4412	$7500	€6442	Terrace (12x17cm-5x7in) s. etching. 31-Oct-3 Sotheby's, New York #78/R
£4469	$8000	€6525	La Salute, dawn (13x20cm-5x8in) s.i. etching drypoint. 6-May-4 Swann Galleries, New York #370/R est:5000-8000
£4706	$8000	€6871	Rialto (29x20cm-11x8in) s. etching. 31-Oct-3 Sotheby's, New York #47/R
£4706	$8000	€6871	Village sweet shop (82x122cm-32x48in) s. etching. 31-Oct-3 Sotheby's, New York #55/R
£4706	$8000	€6871	Doorway (9x13cm-4x5in) s. etching. 31-Oct-3 Sotheby's, New York #62/R
£4749	$8500	€6934	Duet (25x16cm-10x6in) lithograph. 6-May-4 Swann Galleries, New York #376/R est:8000-12000
£5000	$8500	€7300	Nocturne (15x22cm-6x9in) s. etching. 31-Oct-3 Sotheby's, New York #52/R
£5000	$8500	€7300	Rag shop (15x22cm-6x9in) s. etching. 31-Oct-3 Sotheby's, New York #58/R
£5000	$8500	€7300	Cafe Corazza (13x22cm-5x9in) etching. 31-Oct-3 Sotheby's, New York #79/R
£5294	$9000	€7729	Piazzetta, Venice (25x17cm-10x7in) etching. 31-Oct-3 Sotheby's, New York #28/R
£5587	$10000	€8157	Reading by lamplight (16x12cm-6x5in) s. with butterfly brown-black etching drypoint. 4-May-4 Doyle, New York #287/R est:3000-4000
£5882	$10000	€8588	Fishing boat (15x23cm-6x9in) s. etching. 31-Oct-3 Sotheby's, New York #45/R
£6471	$11000	€9448	Lime-burner (25x17cm-10x7in) etching. 31-Oct-3 Sotheby's, New York #10/R
£7059	$12000	€10306	Maude seated (15x11cm-6x4in) etching. 31-Oct-3 Sotheby's, New York #18/R
£7059	$12000	€10306	The Riva, no 2 (21x31cm-8x12in) butterfly sig.i. brown etching. 6-Nov-3 Swann Galleries, New York #476/R est:15000-20000
£7647	$13000	€11165	Ferry (24x30cm-9x12in) etching. 31-Oct-3 Sotheby's, New York #31/R
£7821	$14000	€11419	Palaces (25x35cm-10x14in) s.i. etching. 6-May-4 Swann Galleries, New York #368/R est:12000-18000
£8235	$14000	€12023	Miser (12x15cm-5x6in) drypoint. 31-Oct-3 Sotheby's, New York #16/R
£8475	$15000	€12374	Weary (20x13cm-8x5in) drypoint. 30-Apr-4 Sotheby's, New York #35/R est:8000-12000
£8824	$15000	€12883	San Biagio (21x30cm-8x12in) etching. 31-Oct-3 Sotheby's, New York #35/R
£8824	$15000	€12883	Limehouse (17x26cm-7x10in) lithograph. 6-Nov-3 Swann Galleries, New York #471/R est:12000-18000
£9412	$16000	€13742	Palaces (25x36cm-10x14in) etching. 31-Oct-3 Sotheby's, New York #26/R
£9412	$16000	€13742	Sisters (22x28cm-9x11in) lithograph. 31-Oct-3 Sotheby's, New York #100/R
£10588	$18000	€15458	Bridge (29x20cm-11x8in) etching. 31-Oct-3 Sotheby's, New York #41/R
£11765	$20000	€17177	Balcony (29x10cm-11x4in) s. etching. 31-Oct-3 Sotheby's, New York #44/R
£14706	$25000	€21471	Mill (16x24cm-6x9in) s. etching. 31-Oct-3 Sotheby's, New York #69/R
£16384	$29000	€23921	Pierrot (23x16cm-9x6in) etching. 30-Apr-4 Sotheby's, New York #36/R est:8000-12000
£20339	$36000	€29695	Early morning (17x26cm-7x10in) lithotint. 28-Apr-4 Christie's, Rockefeller NY #251/R est:6000-8000
£23529	$40000	€34352	Doorway (29x20cm-11x8in) etching. 31-Oct-3 Sotheby's, New York #27/R
£26471	$45000	€38648	Duet (29x22cm-11x9in) lithograph. 31-Oct-3 Sotheby's, New York #98/R
£30882	$52500	€45088	Nocturne (20x29cm-8x11in) etching. 31-Oct-3 Sotheby's, New York #24/R
£33824	$57500	€49383	Nocturne (17x25cm-7x10in) lithograph exec.1878. 31-Oct-3 Sotheby's, New York #20/R
Works on paper			
£925	$1600	€1351	Man seated at a desk (12x9cm-5x4in) pencil exec c.1860. 10-Dec-3 Bonhams & Butterfields, San Francisco #6051/R est:3000-5000
£12707	$23000	€18552	Souvenir of the gaiety (12x19cm-5x7in) chk pastel prov.exhib.lit. 31-Mar-4 Sotheby's, New York #36/R est:25000-35000
£26000	$47840	€37960	Street scene in Chelsea (15x10cm-6x4in) butterfly mono. pen ink. 23-Mar-4 Rosebery Fine Art, London #900/R est:3000-5000

WHISTLER, Rex (1905-1944) British

Works on paper

£280	$445	€409	Plain bridge player (18x18cm-7x7in) i. pen ink. 10-Sep-3 Sotheby's, Olympia #16/R
£280	$445	€409	Plain cook (23x18cm-9x7in) i. pen ink. 10-Sep-3 Sotheby's, Olympia #19/R
£280	$445	€409	Plain puritan (23x18cm-9x7in) i. pen ink. 10-Sep-3 Sotheby's, Olympia #21/R
£280	$445	€409	Subaltern (12x12cm-5x5in) pen ink sold with a print. 10-Sep-3 Sotheby's, Olympia #30/R
£280	$445	€409	Gentleman with moustache (14x8cm-6x3in) pen ink sold with a print. 10-Sep-3 Sotheby's, Olympia #35/R
£280	$445	€409	Plain man (12x9cm-5x4in) pen ink sold with a print. 10-Sep-3 Sotheby's, Olympia #37/R
£320	$509	€467	Plain gangster (23x18cm-9x7in) i. pen ink. 10-Sep-3 Sotheby's, Olympia #36/R
£360	$572	€526	Plain person of private means (23x18cm-9x7in) i. pen ink. 10-Sep-3 Sotheby's, Olympia #15/R
£360	$572	€526	Plain house master (23x18cm-9x7in) i. pen ink. 10-Sep-3 Sotheby's, Olympia #18/R
£360	$572	€526	Plain pessimist (17x23cm-7x9in) i. pen ink sold with a print. 10-Sep-3 Sotheby's, Olympia #27/R
£400	$636	€584	Connoisseur (25x18cm-10x7in) i. pen ink sold with a print. 10-Sep-3 Sotheby's, Olympia #33/R
£420	$668	€613	Plain pugilist (22x18cm-9x7in) i. pen ink sold with a print. 10-Sep-3 Sotheby's, Olympia #28/R
£450	$716	€657	Society beauty (13x12cm-5x5in) pen ink sold with a print. 10-Sep-3 Sotheby's, Olympia #14/R
£500	$920	€730	Drawing for a paneled door (25x38cm-10x15in) i. indian ink W/C. 12-Jun-4 Finan Watkins & Co, Mere #51/R
£500	$920	€730	Semicircular room (25x38cm-10x15in) i. pencil W/C dr. 12-Jun-4 Finan Watkins & Co, Mere #52/R
£500	$920	€730	Arch with figures (25x38cm-10x15in) pencil sketch. 12-Jun-4 Finan Watkins & Co, Mere #53/R
£600	$954	€876	Stockbroker (15x20cm-6x8in) pen ink sold with a print. 10-Sep-3 Sotheby's, Olympia #23/R
£650	$1034	€949	Winter pump (21x16cm-8x6in) pencil ink W/C. 10-Sep-3 Sotheby's, Olympia #7/R
£650	$1034	€949	Plain lady golfer (23x18cm-9x7in) i. pen ink sold with a print. 10-Sep-3 Sotheby's, Olympia #26/R
£700	$1113	€1022	Dancing differences (11x14cm-4x6in) pen ink. 10-Sep-3 Sotheby's, Olympia #3/R
£700	$1113	€1022	Toff and tramp (12x14cm-5x6in) pen ink. 10-Sep-3 Sotheby's, Olympia #6/R
£775	$1426	€1132	General's dilemma (28x41cm-11x16in) i.verso Indian ink W/C dr. 12-Jun-4 Finan Watkins & Co, Mere #54/R
£800	$1272	€1168	Vote for Smith (13x16cm-5x6in) pen ink exhib. 10-Sep-3 Sotheby's, Olympia #4/R
£800	$1272	€1168	Border design (35x24cm-14x9in) pen ink sold with 2 others by same hand. 10-Sep-3 Sotheby's, Olympia #34/R
£850	$1352	€1241	Watch your step (28x19cm-11x7in) pen ink. 10-Sep-3 Sotheby's, Olympia #12/R
£900	$1431	€1314	Bees in the bonnet (23x16cm-9x6in) i. pen ink. 10-Sep-3 Sotheby's, Olympia #10/R
£950	$1511	€1387	Family car (12x15cm-5x6in) pen ink. 10-Sep-3 Sotheby's, Olympia #9/R
£980	$1666	€1431	Christmas card design, for Welsh Guards (18x15cm-7x6in) s. pen ink. 29-Oct-3 Bonhams, Chester #473
£1000	$1590	€1460	Worth getting up for (12x15cm-5x6in) pen ink exhib. 10-Sep-3 Sotheby's, Olympia #1/R est:400-600
£1100	$1749	€1606	The chap who (25x14cm-10x6in) i. pencil pen ink gouache lit. 10-Sep-3 Sotheby's, Olympia #44/R est:800-1200
£1200	$1908	€1752	Wisdom of age (25x16cm-10x6in) s.i. pen ink lit. 10-Sep-3 Sotheby's, Olympia #41/R est:600-800
£1300	$2067	€1898	Ordinary motorist and his girl friend (23x18cm-9x7in) one mono. i. pen ink 2 sold with another and a print. 10-Sep-3 Sotheby's, Olympia #29/R
£1300	$2067	€1898	Sailor and the nursemaid (23x16cm-9x6in) i. pencil pen ink lit. 10-Sep-3 Sotheby's, Olympia #42/R est:600-800
£1400	$2226	€2044	Counseller and defendant (31x20cm-12x8in) i. pen ink lit. 10-Sep-3 Sotheby's, Olympia #45/R est:600-800
£1600	$2544	€2336	Bookmaker and backer (30x19cm-12x7in) s. pen ink lit. 10-Sep-3 Sotheby's, Olympia #40/R est:600-800
£1700	$2703	€2482	Private view (12x18cm-5x7in) pen ink exhib. 10-Sep-3 Sotheby's, Olympia #2/R est:500-700
£1700	$2703	€2482	Tea in the garden (10x17cm-4x7in) pen ink exhib. 10-Sep-3 Sotheby's, Olympia #5/R est:300-500
£1800	$2862	€2628	Old man and nurse (31x20cm-12x8in) s.i. pen ink lit. 10-Sep-3 Sotheby's, Olympia #39/R est:600-800
£2300	$3657	€3358	Duke and Duchess (27x17cm-11x7in) s.i. pencil pen ink lit. 10-Sep-3 Sotheby's, Olympia #38/R est:800-1200
£2800	$4452	€4088	The racer (24x15cm-9x6in) s.i. pencil pen ink lit. 10-Sep-3 Sotheby's, Olympia #43/R est:800-1200

WHITAKER, Frederic (1891-1980) American

Works on paper

£500	$800	€730	Altar guardians (53x76cm-21x30in) s. W/C executed c.1955. 17-May-3 Bunte, Elgin #1271a
£813	$1300	€1187	Tools of trade (58x64cm-23x25in) s. W/C graphic. 17-May-3 Bunte, Elgin #1271 est:300-500
£860	$1600	€1256	Untitled (41x56cm-16x22in) W/C. 6-Mar-4 Page, Batavia #147
£1471	$2500	€2148	Birds of a feather (74x56cm-29x22in) s. W/C prov. 18-Nov-3 John Moran, Pasadena #129 est:1200-1800

WHITAKER, George (1834-1874) British

Works on paper

£600	$1020	€876	Burgh Island, south Devon (58x118cm-23x46in) s.d.1873 W/C. 1-Dec-3 Bonhams, Bath #79/R

WHITAKER, George William (1841-1916) American

£610	$1000	€885	Still life with fruit (28x36cm-11x14in) s.d. 7-Jun-3 Treadway Gallery, Cincinnati #1340
£950	$1700	€1387	Farm view (35x51cm-14x20in) s.d.90. 14-May-4 Skinner, Boston #79/R est:1800-2200
£1075	$2000	€1570	Harvest still life (83x102cm-33x40in) s. 5-Mar-4 Skinner, Boston #259/R est:1000-1500
£1902	$3500	€2777	Fruit still life (64x147cm-25x58in) s. 9-Jun-4 Alderfer's, Hatfield #384/R est:4000-6000

WHITAKER, George William (attrib) (1841-1916) American

£267	$500	€390	Still life with fruit (18x30cm-7x12in) canvas on board. 29-Feb-4 Grogan, Boston #49/R

WHITCOMBE, Thomas (1760-c.1824) British

£15135	$28000	€22097	East Indiaman, Rodney, in two positions off the English coast (71x122cm-28x48in) s.d.1788 prov. 10-Feb-4 Christie's, Rockefeller NY #163/R est:30000-50000
£20000	$36800	€29200	Merchantman and other vessels off Castle Cornet, Guernsey (91x141cm-36x56in) 11-Jun-4 Christie's, London #49/R est:20000-30000

WHITCOMBE, Thomas (attrib) (1760-c.1824) British

£3000	$4800	€4380	The West Indianman, Ruckers, in three positions at the Nore, Sheerness Fort beyond (61x91cm-24x36in) 16-Sep-3 Bonhams, New Bond Street #10/R est:3000-5000
£8500	$16065	€12410	Royal Navy frigate outward bound, under full sail passing the Needles (53x76cm-21x30in) 17-Feb-4 Bonhams, New Bond Street #61/R est:5000-8000

WHITE BEAD, Baida (20th C) American

£2310	$4250	€3373	Snake Dance (127x94cm-50x37in) 24-Jun-4 Sotheby's, New York #245/R est:2000-3000

WHITE, A Lois (1903-1984) New Zealander?

£1135	$2009	€1657	Three fish (27cm-11in circular) acrylic wood plaque. 28-Apr-4 Dunbar Sloane, Auckland #44/R est:1200-2500 (NZ.D 3200)
£11278	$19173	€16466	Weeping women (50x40cm-20x16in) s. board painted 1939 prov.exhib. 27-Nov-3 International Art Centre, Auckland #71/R est:35000-45000 (NZ.D 30000)

Works on paper

£435	$700	€635	Life study, head of a woman (35x25cm-14x10in) s.d.1927 pencil dr. prov. 12-Aug-3 Peter Webb, Auckland #103/R (NZ.D 1200)
£5000	$9050	€7300	Composition with lizards, ferns and snails (20x50cm-8x20in) varnished W/C executed c.1950 prov. 30-Mar-4 Peter Webb, Auckland #26/R est:8000-12000 (NZ.D 14000)

WHITE, Arthur (1865-1953) British

£450	$833	€675	Evening on the wharf, St Ives (53x18cm-21x7in) board. 14-Jul-4 Brightwells, Leominster #678/R
£600	$1092	€876	St Ives fishing fleet off the coast (38x64cm-15x25in) s. board. 15-Jun-4 Bonhams, Knightsbridge #16/R
£1850	$3145	€2701	Fishing craft waiting for the incoming tide St Ives (41x48cm-16x19in) 20-Nov-3 Mallams, Cheltenham #431/R est:100-200

Works on paper

£250	$455	€365	Low tide St. Ives Harbour (18x25cm-7x10in) s. W/C. 15-Jun-4 David Lay, Penzance #208
£400	$664	€584	Back Road West, St Ives, Cornwall (21x29cm-8x11in) s. W/C. 2-Oct-3 Lane, Penzance #58
£400	$664	€584	Waiting for the tide, St Ives (24x33cm-9x13in) W/C. 2-Oct-3 Lane, Penzance #156
£800	$1328	€1168	The Committee boat, St Ives Regatta (24x34cm-9x13in) s. W/C. 2-Oct-3 Lane, Penzance #5/R

WHITE, Charles (1918-1979) American

Prints

£4190	$7500	€6117	Solid as a rock (97x38cm-38x15in) s.d.1958 linocut. 4-May-4 Doyle, New York #288/R est:3000-4000
£6875	$11000	€10038	Frederick Douglass (57x43cm-22x17in) s.i.d.1951 lithograph. 18-Sep-3 Swann Galleries, New York #696/R est:3000-5000
£8287	$15000	€12099	Peace on earth (37x60cm-15x24in) s. linocut pair exec.c.1940. 19-Apr-4 Bonhams & Butterfields, San Francisco #67/R est:800-1200

Works on paper

£14130	$26000	€20630	Boy with an accordion (71x48cm-28x19in) s.d.1939 black chk board. 10-Jun-4 Swann Galleries, New York #256/R est:12000-18000
£16129	$30000	€23548	Study of a man singing (68x49cm-27x19in) s.d.1943 black chk pencil. 2-Mar-4 Swann Galleries, New York #689/R est:7000-10000

WHITE, Cheverton (?) British

Works on paper

£420	$777	€613	Figures before country cottage (25x36cm-10x14in) s.d.1883 W/C pair. 13-Feb-4 Keys, Aylsham #436/R

WHITE, Clarence Alfred Burke (?) British?

£500	$790	€730	Portrait of a lady wearing a pink and green bonnet and dress (112x86cm-44x34in) s. 4-Sep-3 Amersham Auction Rooms, UK #306

WHITE, Clarence H (1871-1925) American

Photographs

£3107	$5500	€4536	Mother and child (24x20cm-9x8in) platinum print executed c.1915. 27-Apr-4 Christie's, Rockefeller NY #21/R est:7000-9000

WHITE, Edith (1855-1946) American

£2335	$4250	€3409	Yellow roses and foliage on table top (23x36cm-9x14in) s. prov. 15-Jun-4 John Moran, Pasadena #21 est:1500-2000

WHITE, Edwin (1817-1877) American

£331	$600	€483	First New England thanksgiving (13x15cm-5x6in) s. oil paper on canvas. 16-Apr-4 James Julia, Fairfield #899/R
£1738	$3250	€2537	Early rustic interiors, sparsely furnished. one init. one s.i.d.1857 pair. 28-Feb-4 Thomaston Place, Thomaston #260/R

WHITE, Ethelbert (1891-1972) British

£360	$659	€526	River landscape with a cow grazing (60x73cm-24x29in) s. 7-Apr-4 Woolley & Wallis, Salisbury #192/R
£594	$950	€867	September Lplowing, warming camp (56x66cm-22x26in) s. 16-Sep-3 Maynards, Vancouver #375a est:2500-3500 (C.D 1300)
£750	$1350	€1095	Moonlit landscape, Surrey (30x40cm-12x16in) s. board prov. 20-Jan-4 Bonhams, Knightsbridge #224
£850	$1445	€1241	Bather (40x51cm-16x20in) s. 26-Nov-3 Sotheby's, Olympia #49/R
£900	$1611	€1314	Pastoral landscape (61x76cm-24x30in) s. 14-May-4 Christie's, Kensington #527/R
£900	$1611	€1314	Through the wood (54x65cm-21x26in) s. 14-May-4 Christie's, Kensington #528/R
£1000	$1820	€1460	Woodland, Arundel (53x63cm-21x25in) s. exhib. 1-Jul-4 Christie's, Kensington #98/R est:1000-1500
£1200	$2112	€1752	Pin mill (26x35cm-10x14in) s. board. 19-May-4 Sotheby's, Olympia #201/R est:1200-1800
£1700	$3060	€2482	September plowing, warning camp (53x64cm-21x25in) s. 22-Apr-4 Lawrence, Crewkerne #948/R est:1800-2500
£1700	$3111	€2482	Extensive river landscape with a mother and daughter, rowing boat beyond (81x101cm-32x40in) s. board. 7-Apr-4 Woolley & Wallis, Salisbury #191/R est:1000-1500
£1700	$3094	€2482	Farm at Goodward (61x76cm-24x30in) s. 1-Jul-4 Christie's, Kensington #97/R est:1200-1800
£2200	$3740	€3212	Hampstead lane (61x76cm-24x30in) s. i.verso. 26-Nov-3 Sotheby's, Olympia #48/R est:1000-1500

Works on paper

£320	$566	€467	Road through a country landscape (12x18cm-5x7in) s. W/C pencil. 27-Apr-4 Bonhams, Knightsbridge #240/R
£360	$666	€526	Farm landscape (25x33cm-10x13in) s. W/C. 10-Feb-4 David Lay, Penzance #409
£380	$684	€555	Winter landscape with a barn (26x35cm-10x14in) s.i. W/C pencil. 22-Apr-4 Lawrence, Crewkerne #812
£450	$819	€657	Fishing port in Majorca (37x44cm-15x17in) W/C htd. 19-Jun-4 Lacy Scott, Bury St.Edmunds #388/R
£480	$845	€701	Boats at Aldeburgh (33x46cm-13x18in) s. W/C. 18-May-4 Bonhams, Knightsbridge #67/R
£550	$990	€803	Autumn landscape (36x53cm-14x21in) s. W/C. 20-Jan-4 Bonhams, Knightsbridge #23/R
£850	$1530	€1241	Old Cart (30x38cm-12x15in) s. W/C. 20-Jan-4 Bonhams, Knightsbridge #7/R

WHITE, Fritz (1930-) American

Sculpture

£4037	$6500	€5854	When the buffalo are gone (64cm-25in) bronze edition of 12. 22-Aug-3 Altermann Galleries, Santa Fe #213

WHITE, George Francis (1808-1898) British

Works on paper

£500	$815	€730	Gangoutri, source of the Ganges (30x46cm-12x18in) init.i. pencil htd white scratching prov. 24-Sep-3 Christie's, London #42/R
£650	$1118	€949	Fort Monghir, on the Ganges, near Patna (26x40cm-10x16in) init.i.d.16th Feb 1842 pencil. 3-Dec-3 Christie's, Kensington #21/R
£650	$1118	€949	Ruins of a palace at Rajmahal, on the Ganges, near Patna (28x42cm-11x17in) init.i.d.1842 pencil. 3-Dec-3 Christie's, Kensington #24/R
£800	$1416	€1168	Ganges at Varanasi, India (17x27cm-7x11in) init.d.1878 W/C bodycol. 27-Apr-4 Bonhams, New Bond Street #35/R
£900	$1548	€1314	Old mosque near Rajmahal, on the Ganges, near Patna (25x41cm-10x16in) init.i.d.1st Feby/42 pencil. 3-Dec-3 Christie's, Kensington #22/R

WHITE, George Harlow (1817-1888) Canadian/British

Works on paper

£261	$486	€381	Durham Cathedral (29x50cm-11x20in) s.d.1881 W/C. 2-Mar-4 Ritchie, Toronto #47/R (C.D 650)

WHITE, Henry Cooke (1861-1952) American

£1242	$2000	€1813	Autumn-Lyme, Conn (30x41cm-12x16in) s. s.i. verso panel. 20-Aug-3 James Julia, Fairfield #1627/R est:1150-1750

WHITE, J Talmage (1833-1907) British

Works on paper

£500	$910	€750	An inconsolable peasant girl before ruins on the Italian coast (29x47cm-11x19in) s.d.1869 pencil W/C htd bodycol. 1-Jul-4 Christie's, Kensington #352/R

WHITE, John (1851-1933) British

£300	$474	€438	Cornish coastal village street scene, with distant shipping (44x34cm-17x13in) mono.d.1899. 23-Jul-3 Hampton & Littlewood, Exeter #430/R

Works on paper

£370	$677	€540	Hanging out the washing (17x52cm-7x20in) s. W/C. 8-Jul-4 Lawrence, Crewkerne #1556
£700	$1274	€1022	Estuary at low tide (25x36cm-10x14in) s. W/C. 5-Feb-4 Gorringes, Worthing #474/R
£1150	$2093	€1679	Light and shade, Miltoncombe, near Yelverton, Devon (27x45cm-11x18in) s. W/C bodycol. 21-Jun-4 Bonhams, Bath #462/R est:1200-1800
£1200	$2004	€1752	Young lady walking through a village (35x25cm-14x10in) s.i. pencil W/C bodycol. 8-Oct-3 Christie's, Kensington #1087 est:250-350
£1250	$2075	€1825	Shower of gold (37x26cm-15x10in) s. W/C. 1-Oct-3 Sotheby's, Olympia #155/R est:700-1000
£1300	$2340	€1898	Lane in Devon (28x45cm-11x18in) s. W/C. 21-Jan-4 Sotheby's, Olympia #233/R est:1000-2000
£1300	$2392	€1898	Early spring (25x35cm-10x14in) s. W/C. 8-Jun-4 Bonhams, New Bond Street #96/R est:1500-2000
£1450	$2465	€2117	Milkmaid on a coastal path (35x24cm-14x9in) s. W/C bodycol. 25-Nov-3 Bonhams, Knowle #185 est:200-300
£1500	$2490	€2190	Feeding ducklings before a thatched cottage (35x26cm-14x10in) s. W/C. 2-Oct-3 Lane, Penzance #220/R est:1500-1700
£1500	$2730	€2190	Keeping the geese at bay (36x53cm-14x21in) s. W/C bodycol. 15-Jun-4 David Lay, Penzance #343/R est:1500-2500
£1600	$2672	€2336	View of a coastline (24x35cm-9x14in) s.i. pencil W/C sold with another by the same hand. 8-Oct-3 Christie's, Kensington #1125 est:400-600
£2300	$4140	€3358	Music hath charms (53x36cm-21x14in) s. W/C exhib. 21-Jan-4 Sotheby's, Olympia #232/R est:800-1200
£2300	$4186	€3358	Making a clean sweep, Beer, East Devon (54x36cm-21x14in) s. i.verso W/C. 21-Jun-4 Bonhams, Bath #463/R est:800-1200

WHITE, Jonathan (1938-) New Zealander

£602	$1023	€879	Kapiti (69x99cm-27x39in) s.i.d.1973 board. 26-Nov-3 Dunbar Sloane, Wellington #148 est:500-1000 (NZ.D 1600)
£1444	$2354	€2108	South Island mountain landscape (85x74cm-33x29in) s. 23-Sep-3 Peter Webb, Auckland #149/R est:2500-4000 (NZ.D 4000)

WHITE, Larry (1946-) American?

£503	$891	€750	Nu au fauteuil (46x55cm-18x22in) s. 29-Apr-4 Claude Aguttes, Neuilly #108

WHITE, Miles (20th C) American

Works on paper

£479	$800	€695	Bye Bye Birdie, portrait of Chita Rivera (30x48cm-12x19in) pen ink W/C acrylic dr. 25-Jun-3 Butterfields, San Francisco #3597
£958	$1600	€1389	Shirley MacLaine (58x48cm-23x19in) s. pen ink W/C dr. 25-Jun-3 Butterfields, San Francisco #3592 est:2000-3000
£1497	$2500	€2171	Marlene Dietrich in Wild West Saloon. Characters in Japanese sequence (58x38cm-23x15in) pen ink W/C drs two. 25-Jun-3 Butterfields, San Francisco #3591 est:200-3000

WHITE, Minnie F (1891-1984) New Zealander

Works on paper

£362	$587	€525	Inner city view (30x40cm-12x16in) s. W/C. 31-Jul-3 International Art Centre, Auckland #86/R est:2000-3000 (NZ.D 1000)

WHITE, Minor (1908-1976) American

Photographs

£1799	$3400	€2627	Windowsill, daydreaming (29x23cm-11x9in) i.d. verso silver print. 17-Feb-4 Swann Galleries, New York #83/R est:4000-5000
£1916	$3200	€2797	Christmas ornament, Batavia, New York (33x20cm-13x8in) with sig. silver print. 21-Oct-3 Swann Galleries, New York #255/R est:3500-4500
£1916	$3200	€2797	Peeled paint, Rochester (31x23cm-12x9in) with sig.i.d.1959 silver print. 21-Oct-3 Swann Galleries, New York #256/R est:3000-4000
£2515	$4200	€3672	Long cloud over Henry Mountains, Utah (13x24cm-5x9in) s.i.d.1966 verso gelatin silver print prov.lit. 17-Oct-3 Phillips, New York #259/R est:4000-6000
£2646	$5000	€3863	Metal part, from Sequence: 'Sound of one hand clapping' (23x29cm-9x11in) silver print. 17-Feb-4 Swann Galleries, New York #89/R est:3500-4500
£2684	$4750	€3919	Equivalent (27x34cm-11x13in) studio st.i.d.1950 verso photo prov. 28-Apr-4 Sotheby's, New York #146/R est:4000-6000
£3390	$6000	€4949	Peeled paint, Rochester, 1959 (24x19cm-9x7in) init.d.1959 gelatin silver print prov. 27-Apr-4 Christie's, Rockefeller NY #298/R est:3000-5000
£3955	$7000	€5774	Bullet holes, Capitol Reef, Utah (21x34cm-8x13in) s.d.1961 i.verso photo printed 1962 prov. 28-Apr-4 Sotheby's, New York #145/R est:7000-10000
£5085	$9000	€7424	Sun in rock (26x33cm-10x13in) s.i.d.1948 gelatin silver print lit. 27-Apr-4 Christie's, Rockefeller NY #10/R est:4000-6000
£7345	$13000	€10724	Grand Tetons, Wyoming, 1959 (26x30cm-10x12in) s.i.d.1949 gelatin silver print lit. 27-Apr-4 Christie's, Rockefeller NY #9/R est:4000-6000

WHITE, Nona (1859-1937) American

Works on paper

£659	$1200	€962	Floral still life (36x53cm-14x21in) s. W/C prov. 15-Jun-4 John Moran, Pasadena #53a

WHITE, Orrin A (1883-1969) American

£588	$1000	€858	Landscape (20x25cm-8x10in) s. board prov. 18-Nov-3 John Moran, Pasadena #7
£882	$1500	€1288	Juan Ortega de Sollano no 31, San Miguel Allende, Goto (41x51cm-16x20in) s. board prov. 18-Nov-3 John Moran, Pasadena #166 est:2000-3000
£1099	$2000	€1605	Taxco Mexico (61x51cm-24x20in) s. 7-Feb-4 Auctions by the Day, Alameda #1607/R
£1324	$2250	€1933	Landscape (25x30cm-10x12in) s. board prov. 18-Nov-3 John Moran, Pasadena #17 est:2000-3000
£1765	$3000	€2577	Landscape (25x30cm-10x12in) s. board. 18-Nov-3 John Moran, Pasadena #24 est:2000-3000
£1879	$3250	€2743	Mexican street scene (46x61cm-18x24in) s. 10-Dec-3 Bonhams & Butterfields, San Francisco #6217/R est:3000-5000
£2381	$4500	€3476	Stream in High Sierras landscape (38x48cm-15x19in) canvas on masonite. 17-Feb-4 John Moran, Pasadena #149/R est:2000-3000
£2794	$4750	€4079	Arroyo Seco landscape (48x33cm-19x13in) s. board prov. 18-Nov-3 John Moran, Pasadena #143 est:4000-5500
£3107	$5500	€4536	California mountains (40x50cm-16x20in) s. board prov. 28-Apr-4 Christie's, Los Angeles #16/R est:4000-6000
£3529	$6000	€5152	Arroyo Seco landscape (51x61cm-20x24in) s. prov. 18-Nov-3 John Moran, Pasadena #28 est:5000-7000
£4121	$7500	€6017	California landscape (61x76cm-24x30in) s. prov. 15-Jun-4 John Moran, Pasadena #43 est:9000-12000
£4121	$7500	€6017	Pasadena landscape (51x61cm-20x24in) s. 15-Jun-4 John Moran, Pasadena #52 est:5000-7000
£4396	$8000	€6418	House in a Californian landscape (64x76cm-25x30in) s. prov. 15-Jun-4 John Moran, Pasadena #67 est:9000-12000

£5000 $8500 €7300 Eucalyptus Arroyo landscape (61x76cm-24x30in) s. prov. 18-Nov-3 John Moran, Pasadena #168 est:7000-9000
£5294 $9000 €7729 Eucalyptus coastal (61x76cm-24x30in) s. prov. 18-Nov-3 John Moran, Pasadena #39 est:7000-9000
£9524 $18000 €13905 Eucalyptus (64x76cm-25x30in) s. i. stretcher prov. 17-Feb-4 John Moran, Pasadena #143/R est:10000-15000
£16484 $30000 €24067 High Sierras landscape (102x76cm-40x30in) s. prov. 15-Jun-4 John Moran, Pasadena #106 est:20000-30000
£16815 $26400 €24550 California landscape (64x79cm-25x31in) 1-Sep-3 William A Smith, Plainfield #19/R
Works on paper
£529 $900 €772 Cabin in eucalyptus landscape (33x41cm-13x16in) s. graphite. 18-Nov-3 John Moran, Pasadena #182

WHITE, Ralph (1921-) American
£2096 $3500 €3060 Texas classic near Bastrop (81x122cm-32x48in) acrylic masonite. 18-Oct-3 David Dike, Dallas #214/R est:5000-10000

WHITE, Robin (1946-) New Zealander
£24823 $43936 €36242 Mana Railway Station (120x182cm-47x72in) s.d.1971. 28-Apr-4 Dunbar Sloane, Auckland #26/R est:90000-140000 (NZ.D 70000)
Works on paper
£543 $875 €793 Florence is ill (21x29cm-8x11in) s.i.d.1984 pencil dr. 20-Aug-3 Dunbar Sloane, Auckland #106 est:2000-4500 (NZ.D 1500)
£3214 $5914 €4692 Red barn, Lincoln (22x15cm-9x6in) pencil prov. 25-Mar-4 International Art Centre, Auckland #66/R est:7000-10000 (NZ.D 9000)
£3393 $6243 €4954 Harbour cone (22x15cm-9x6in) s.d.1973 pencil. 25-Mar-4 International Art Centre, Auckland #67/R est:7000-10000 (NZ.D 9500)

WHITE, Thomas Gilbert (1877-1939) American
£2174 $4000 €3174 Gunnislake Bridge on the River Tamar, Cornwall (35x53cm-14x21in) s.d.99 i. stretcher. 8-Jun-4 Bonhams & Butterfields, San Francisco #4018/R est:3000-5000

WHITE, Ursula (20th C) American
Works on paper
£649 $1200 €948 Two greyhounds. Yorkie. Resting Peke (28x41cm-11x16in) s.d. pastel paperboard three. 10-Feb-4 Doyle, New York #117/R

WHITE, Vera (1888-1966) American
£818 $1300 €1194 Southwest mission (38x30cm-15x12in) s. board painted c.1930. 10-Sep-3 Alderfer's, Hatfield #398/R

WHITE, Wilfred (19/20th C) British
£310 $567 €453 Cattle on a country road (70x90cm-28x35in) s. indis.d.1912. 8-Jul-4 Lawrence, Crewkerne #1653

WHITE, Willie (c.1905-) American
Works on paper
£240 $400 €350 Two birds, a horse and a cross (56x71cm-22x28in) marker posterboard prov. 15-Nov-3 Slotin Folk Art, Buford #526/R
£278 $500 €406 Three green animal figures (56x71cm-22x28in) marker posterboard. 24-Apr-4 Slotin Folk Art, Buford #599/R

WHITEHAND, Michael J (1941-) British
£400 $716 €584 Thermopylae leaving the anchorage at Foochow (20x30cm-8x12in) s. 26-May-4 Christie's, Kensington #480/R
£600 $1020 €876 Battle of Flamborough (61x91cm-24x36in) s. 19-Nov-3 Christie's, Kensington #589/R
£1400 $2408 €2044 Clipper ship Ariel preparing to leave the pool of London (76x101cm-30x40in) s.i.d.2001. 2-Dec-3 Sotheby's, London #136/R est:1500-2000
£1500 $2685 €2190 Closely fought duel Britannia and Candida 1933 (76x101cm-30x40in) s. 26-May-4 Christie's, Kensington #503/R est:2000-3000
£3000 $5370 €4380 Candida and Britannia powering to windward off Cowes (76x102cm-30x40in) s. 26-May-4 Christie's, Kensington #502/R est:3000-4000
£8197 $15000 €11968 Westward and Meteor racing in Studland Bay off the Old Harry Rocks (76x127cm-30x50in) s. 29-Jul-4 Christie's, Rockefeller NY #297/R est:8000-12000
£8743 $16000 €12765 Ailsa and Britannia racing at the Royal Clyde Yacht Club Regatta (76x101cm-30x40in) s. 29-Jul-4 Christie's, Rockefeller NY #296/R est:7000-10000

WHITEHEAD, Dorothy (20th C) Australian
£336 $601 €504 Hens in the orchard (26x32cm-10x13in) s. board. 17-May-4 Sotheby's, Melbourne #586 (A.D 850)

WHITEHEAD, Elizabeth (19th C) British
£400 $736 €584 River meadow with a punt (21x29cm-8x11in) s. 25-Mar-4 Locke & England, Leamington Spa #85/R
£650 $1118 €949 Floral still life (30x25cm-12x10in) s.d.1884. 7-Dec-3 Lots Road Auctions, London #352a
Works on paper
£300 $540 €438 Dordrecht (23x43cm-9x17in) s.i. W/C. 21-Jan-4 Sotheby's, Olympia #238/R
£360 $569 €522 Little butcher row, Coventry (28x19cm-11x7in) s.d. W/C. 4-Sep-3 Locke & England, Leamington Spa #145/R
£750 $1185 €1088 Okens Corner, Warwick (31x20cm-12x8in) s. W/C. 4-Sep-3 Locke & England, Leamington Spa #144/R

WHITEHEAD, Frederick (1853-1938) British
£350 $655 €511 Distant view of Poole harbour with cattle in foreground (20x30cm-8x12in) s. panel. 22-Jul-4 Tennants, Leyburn #843
£388 $694 €566 Lakeside meadow with cows (17x33cm-7x13in) s. 13-May-4 Stuker, Bern #378/R (S.FR 900)
£420 $693 €613 Distant view of the Clee Hills (23x38cm-9x15in) s. exhib. 1-Jul-3 Tayler & Fletcher, Cheltenham #3
£460 $782 €672 Creech Heath, Dorset (17x26cm-7x10in) s.d.1897 s.i.d.verso board. 25-Nov-3 Bonhams, Knowle #229
£1000 $1670 €1460 Cottage scene with figures in a panoramic landscape, possibly Dorset (48x36cm-19x14in) s. 28-Jun-3 Hogben, Folkstone #192 est:1000-1500
£1500 $2505 €2190 Bend on the Avon, Bredon Hill (50x75cm-20x30in) s. i.verso. 27-Jun-3 Bigwood, Stratford on Avon #304/R est:1500-2500
£1700 $2737 €2465 Broadland landscape with mallard in flight (48x74cm-19x29in) s. 15-Aug-3 Keys, Aylsham #701 est:300-400
£1700 $3060 €2482 Flower garden (30x46cm-12x18in) 21-Jan-4 Sotheby's, Olympia #353/R est:1500-2000
£2400 $4080 €3504 View down high west street, Dorchester, with horse and cart (18x28cm-7x11in) s. panel. 30-Oct-3 Duke & Son, Dorchester #208/R est:2000-3000
Works on paper
£700 $1232 €1022 Warwick - Leicester Hospital (33x42cm-13x17in) s.i.d.1927 bears i. verso W/C. 18-May-4 Fellows & Sons, Birmingham #227/R

WHITEHEAD, Isaac (1819-1881) Australian
£11915 $20255 €17396 Milford Sound, New Zealand (60x91cm-24x36in) s.d.1878 prov. 26-Nov-3 Deutscher-Menzies, Melbourne #32/R est:35000-45000 (A.D 28000)

WHITELEY, Brett (1939-1992) Australian
£1822 $2933 €2660 Church (30x37cm-12x15in) board painted c.1959. 25-Aug-3 Sotheby's, Paddington #452/R est:3000-5000 (A.D 4500)
£5285 $8297 €7663 Figure on a bicycle (69x100cm-27x39in) ink. 26-Aug-3 Christie's, Sydney #127/R est:8000-12000 (A.D 13000)
£7114 $11168 €10315 The orange, fruit dove in Clark Park (75x53cm-30x21in) s.num.14/30 col screenprint. 27-Aug-3 Christie's, Sydney #624/R est:5000-8000 (A.D 17500)
£13008 $23285 €18992 Study for The Olgas (73x53cm-29x21in) s.i.verso prov. 4-May-4 Sotheby's, Melbourne #18/R est:25000-35000 (A.D 32000)
£16529 $29256 €24132 Bathers (97x92cm-38x36in) s. board prov.exhib. 3-May-4 Christie's, Melbourne #12/R est:40000-60000 (A.D 40000)
£20243 $32591 €29555 Kardichi (71x74cm-28x29in) i. s.d.70 verso composition board prov. 25-Aug-3 Sotheby's, Paddington #189/R est:50000-70000 (A.D 50000)
£20661 $38223 €30165 Bathroom series (56x76cm-22x30in) s.i.d.1964 oil gouache card on board prov. 10-Mar-4 Deutscher-Menzies, Melbourne #88/R est:50000-70000 (A.D 50000)
£26423 $47297 €38578 Window - Lavender Bay (39x50cm-15x20in) s. prov. 4-May-4 Sotheby's, Melbourne #22/R est:50000-70000 (A.D 65000)
£50813 $90955 €74187 2pm - Light - Early (76x76cm-30x30in) s.i.d.2-9/1/84 mixed media paper on board prov. 4-May-4 Sotheby's, Melbourne #5/R est:120000-150000 (A.D 125000)
£53279 $84180 €77787 Nude and necklace (80x106cm-31x42in) s.d.78 oil mixed media canvas board prov. 2-Sep-3 Deutscher-Menzies, Melbourne #39/R est:130000-160000 (A.D 130000)
£55785 $103202 €81446 Window and sculpture (162x83cm-64x33in) s.i.d.8.7.75. 10-Mar-4 Deutscher-Menzies, Melbourne #26/R est:160000-220000 (A.D 135000)
£99174 $168595 €144794 Cheetah in Rillington Place (206x183cm-81x72in) s.i.d.1964 oil tempera crayon collage board prov.exhib.lit. 29-Oct-3 Lawson Menzies, Sydney #36/R est:240000-340000 (A.D 240000)
£136179 $213801 €197460 St Remy de Provence (163x122cm-64x48in) s.i.d.82-83 oil ink paper plaster on board prov.exhib.lit. 26-Aug-3 Christie's, Sydney #36/R est:400000-500000 (A.D 335000)
£276116 $433501 €400368 Arkie under the shower (173x112cm-68x44in) s. s.i.d.1986-87 verso board prov. 26-Aug-3 Christie's, Sydney #52/R est:800000-1200000 (A.D 679245)
£381679 $694657 €557251 Lavender Bay at dusk (122x152cm-48x60in) s. s.i.d.84 verso board prov.exhib. 16-Jun-4 Deutscher-Menzies, Melbourne #21/R est:800000-1000000 (A.D 1000000)
Photographs
£8085 $13745 €11804 The cat (84x82cm-33x32in) s.num.2/100 photo silkscreen prov. 25-Nov-3 Christie's, Melbourne #64/R est:12000-15000 (A.D 19000)
Prints
£1829 $2872 €2652 Back of the asylum, St Remy (26x39cm-10x15in) s.num.27/100 etching prov. 26-Aug-3 Christie's, Sydney #344/R est:3000-5000 (A.D 4500)
£1829 $2872 €2652 Hyena from Regent's Park Zoo series (96x67cm-38x26in) s.num.39/70 col screenprint. 27-Aug-3 Christie's, Sydney #790/R est:2500-3500 (A.D 4500)
£1859 $3291 €2714 View of the garden (74x53cm-29x21in) s.num.9/75 lithograph prov. 3-May-4 Christie's, Melbourne #400/R est:2000-3000 (A.D 4500)
£1885 $2978 €2752 Young baboon (50x49cm-20x19in) s.i. sugarlift aquatint. 2-Sep-3 Deutscher-Menzies, Melbourne #223/R est:2500-3000 (A.D 4600)
£1957 $3327 €2857 Flowers on the table (71x50cm-28x20in) s. num.36/75 lithograph exec 1977 lit. 26-Nov-3 Deutscher-Menzies, Melbourne #3/R est:5000-7500 (A.D 4600)
£2099 $3821 €3065 Moreton Bay Fig (60x49cm-24x19in) etching. 16-Jun-4 Deutscher-Menzies, Melbourne #213/R est:5500-7500 (A.D 5500)
£2245 $4131 €3278 Anna, woman on a bed (29x30cm-11x12in) s.i.num.24/40 etching lit. 29-Mar-4 Goodman, Sydney #164/R est:5000-7000 (A.D 5500)
£2295 $3718 €3351 Swinging monkey 1 - from Regents Park Zoo Series 1 (76x56cm-30x22in) s. num.54/70 col screenprint prov. 30-Jul-3 Goodman, Sydney #22/R est:3000-5000 (A.D 5600)
£2344 $4383 €3516 Mother and child (60x45cm-24x18in) s.num.46/60 etching lit. 20-Jul-4 Goodman, Sydney #66/R est:3000-5000 (A.D 6000)
£2664 $4209 €3889 Palm tree (81x59cm-32x23in) s.i. num.31/50 screenprint. 2-Sep-3 Deutscher-Menzies, Melbourne #222/R est:5500-7500 (A.D 6500)
£2686 $4969 €3922 Catherine 1984 (63x47cm-25x19in) s.num.23/30 handcol etching prov. 10-Mar-4 Deutscher-Menzies, Melbourne #4/R est:6500-9500 (A.D 6500)
£2686 $4969 €3922 Garden in Sanur, Bali (60x79cm-24x31in) s.num.66/100 screenprint offset lithograph prov. 10-Mar-4 Deutscher-Menzies, Melbourne #291/R est:7000-10000 (A.D 6500)
£2754 $4682 €4021 Moreton Bay Fig (60x49cm-24x19in) s. num.60/200 etching. 24-Nov-3 Sotheby's, Melbourne #148/R est:4500-5500 (A.D 6500)
£2846 $4467 €4127 Back I (95x61cm-37x24in) s.num.11/35 lithograph. 26-Aug-3 Christie's, Sydney #363/R est:7000-10000 (A.D 7000)
£2846 $4467 €4127 Palm tree III (81x60cm-32x24in) s.num.2/50 lithograph. 27-Aug-3 Christie's, Sydney #659/R est:5000-7000 (A.D 7000)
£2893 $5351 €4224 Startled owl 1984 (49x50cm-19x20in) s.num.7/30 sugarlift aquatint prov. 10-Mar-4 Deutscher-Menzies, Melbourne #5/R est:8000-12000 (A.D 7000)
£3049 $4786 €4421 Palm tree (81x59cm-32x23in) s.num.41/50 silkscreen. 27-Aug-3 Christie's, Sydney #626/R est:3000-5000 (A.D 7500)
£3068 $5308 €4479 Woman under the shower (40x48cm-16x19in) s.num.29/100 etching. 10-Dec-3 Shapiro, Sydney #65/R est:8000-12000 (A.D 7210)
£3099 $5733 €4525 Lindfield gardens (77x114cm-30x45in) s. num.68/80 col lithograph. 10-Mar-4 Deutscher-Menzies, Melbourne #178/R est:8000-12000 (A.D 7500)

£3404	$5787	€4970	Lindfield Gardens (77x114cm-30x45in) s. num.14/80 colour lithograph prov.lit. 26-Nov-3 Deutscher-Menzies, Melbourne #2/R est:9000-12000 (A.D 8000)
£3435	$6252	€5015	Divided unity 1974 (66x94cm-26x37in) s.i.d.1974 num.68/70 col screenprint. 16-Jun-4 Deutscher-Menzies, Melbourne #9/R est:6000-8000 (A.D 9000)
£3455	$5425	€5010	Divided unity (66x93cm-26x37in) s.i.num.13/70 silkscreen. 27-Aug-3 Christie's, Sydney #503/R est:6000-8000 (A.D 8500)
£3512	$6498	€5128	Towards sculpture no.4 (77x53cm-30x21in) s.num.32/50 lithograph. 10-Mar-4 Deutscher-Menzies, Melbourne #184/R est:8000-12000 (A.D 8500)
£3719	$6880	€5430	Fruit dove in Clark Park (74x53cm-29x21in) s.i. num.6/30 colour screenprint. 10-Mar-4 Deutscher-Menzies, Melbourne #176/R est:10000-15000 (A.D 9000)
£3926	$7262	€5732	Sydney Harbour (89x66cm-35x26in) s.num.20/100 screenprint prov. 10-Mar-4 Deutscher-Menzies, Melbourne #177/R est:10000-15000 (A.D 9500)
£4065	$6382	€5894	Vincene, an essay in opposites (211x91cm-83x36in) s.num.30 col etching collage. 26-Aug-3 Christie's, Sydney #338/R est:8000-12000 (A.D 10000)
£4065	$6382	€5894	Bird and wave (72x71cm-28x28in) s.num.27/60 screenprint collage. 27-Aug-3 Christie's, Sydney #625/R est:4000-6000 (A.D 10000)
£4065	$7276	€5935	Sydney harbour by night (30x30cm-12x12in) s. linocut rice paper exec 1981 prov.lit. 4-May-4 Sotheby's, Melbourne #193/R est:8000-12000 (A.D 10000)
£4132	$7645	€6033	Seagull (50x49cm-20x19in) s.num.28/30 sugarlift aquatint. 10-Mar-4 Deutscher-Menzies, Melbourne #175/R est:11000-15000 (A.D 10000)
£4472	$7020	€6484	Lavender Bay wharf (60x50cm-24x20in) s.num.36/90 etching. 26-Aug-3 Christie's, Sydney #293/R est:10000-12000 (A.D 11000)
£5285	$8297	€7663	Sydney harbour (90x65cm-35x26in) s.num.66/100 silkscreen prov. 26-Aug-3 Christie's, Sydney #146/R est:12000-16000 (A.D 13000)
£6147	$9713	€8975	Seagull (50x49cm-20x19in) s. num.2/30 sugarlift aquatint. 2-Sep-3 Deutscher-Menzies, Melbourne #221/R est:6000-8000 (A.D 15000)
£6301	$9892	€9136	Port villa (47x63cm-19x25in) s.i.num.15/50 hand col etching. 27-Aug-3 Christie's, Sydney #651/R est:3000-5000 (A.D 15500)
£7232	$12294	€10559	Sydney Harbour 1980 (121x80cm-48x31in) s. num.74/100 silkscreen prov. 29-Oct-3 Lawson Menzies, Sydney #81/R est:10000-15000 (A.D 17500)
£8264	$15289	€12065	Dove 1982 (110x79cm-43x31in) s.num.24/30 col etching. 10-Mar-4 Deutscher-Menzies, Melbourne #3/R est:15000-20000 (A.D 20000)
£8537	$15280	€12464	Cat (81x83cm-32x33in) s.i. offset lithograph prov. 4-May-4 Sotheby's, Melbourne #100/R est:12000-16000 (A.D 21000)
£8678	$14752	€12670	Cat 1980 (84x82cm-33x32in) s. offset lithograph. 29-Oct-3 Lawson Menzies, Sydney #1/R est:12000-16000 (A.D 21000)
£9016	$14246	€13163	Towards sculpture 5 (77x46cm-30x18in) s.i. lithograph. 2-Sep-3 Deutscher-Menzies, Melbourne #16/R est:12000-16000 (A.D 22000)
£9504	$17583	€13876	Arrival 1988 (70x88cm-28x35in) s.i.num.7/22 offset lithograph. 10-Mar-4 Deutscher-Menzies, Melbourne #2/R est:15000-20000 (A.D 23000)
£12146	$19555	€17733	Portrait of Rimbaud (100x85cm-39x33in) s.d.70 i. num.1 and 2 silkscreen print ink mixed media board pair. 25-Aug-3 Sotheby's, Paddington #220/R est:30000-50000 (A.D 30000)

Works on paper

£813	$1455	€1187	Two blokes (11x12cm-4x5in) ink prov. 4-May-4 Sotheby's, Melbourne #195 (A.D 2000)
£1220	$2183	€1781	Helena Rubinstein (20x15cm-8x6in) ink after Dobell prov. 4-May-4 Sotheby's, Melbourne #196 est:3000-5000 (A.D 3000)
£1241	$2197	€1812	Untitled (68x48cm-27x19in) s. chl. 28-Apr-4 Dunbar Sloane, Auckland #60/R est:5000-7000 (NZ.D 3500)
£1423	$2547	€2078	Head of a man (24x13cm-9x5in) bears studio st. ink prov. 4-May-4 Sotheby's, Melbourne #197 est:3000-5000 (A.D 3500)
£1626	$2911	€2374	Woman in a hat (17x11cm-7x4in) blue ink after Picasso prov. 4-May-4 Sotheby's, Melbourne #199/R est:3000-5000 (A.D 4000)
£2236	$4002	€3265	Lavender Bay (19x20cm-7x8in) ink prov. 4-May-4 Sotheby's, Melbourne #200/R est:5000-7000 (A.D 5500)
£2686	$4969	€3922	Blue nude 2 (24x33cm-9x13in) ink prov. 10-Mar-4 Deutscher-Menzies, Melbourne #90/R est:8000-12000 (A.D 6500)
£2686	$4969	€3922	Blue nude 3 (24x33cm-9x13in) ink prov. 10-Mar-4 Deutscher-Menzies, Melbourne #91/R est:8000-12000 (A.D 6500)
£2686	$4969	€3922	Blue nude 4 (24x34cm-9x13in) ink prov. 10-Mar-4 Deutscher-Menzies, Melbourne #92/R est:8000-12000 (A.D 6500)
£2686	$4969	€3922	Blue nude 5 (24x33cm-9x13in) ink prov. 10-Mar-4 Deutscher-Menzies, Melbourne #93/R est:8000-12000 (A.D 6500)
£2686	$4969	€3922	Blue nude 6 (24x33cm-9x13in) ink prov. 10-Mar-4 Deutscher-Menzies, Melbourne #94/R est:8000-12000 (A.D 6500)
£2686	$4969	€3922	Blue nude 7 (24x33cm-9x13in) ink prov. 10-Mar-4 Deutscher-Menzies, Melbourne #95/R est:8000-12000 (A.D 6500)
£2686	$4969	€3922	Blue nude 8 (24x33cm-9x13in) ink prov. 10-Mar-4 Deutscher-Menzies, Melbourne #96/R est:8000-12000 (A.D 6500)
£2686	$4969	€3922	Blue nude 9 (24x33cm-9x13in) ink prov. 10-Mar-4 Deutscher-Menzies, Melbourne #97/R est:8000-12000 (A.D 6500)
£2686	$4969	€3922	Blue nude 10 (24x33cm-9x13in) ink prov. 10-Mar-4 Deutscher-Menzies, Melbourne #98/R est:8000-12000 (A.D 6500)
£3099	$5733	€4525	Blue nude 1 (24x33cm-9x13in) ink prov. 10-Mar-4 Deutscher-Menzies, Melbourne #89/R est:8000-12000 (A.D 7500)
£3252	$5821	€4748	Flower in floral vase (28x15cm-11x6in) chl prov. 4-May-4 Sotheby's, Melbourne #194/R est:8000-12000 (A.D 8000)
£3306	$6116	€4827	Two women beside the sea (20x33cm-8x13in) i. pencil executed c.1978 prov. 10-Mar-4 Deutscher-Menzies, Melbourne #1/R est:6500-9500 (A.D 8000)
£4082	$7510	€5960	Study after Picasso's fisherman (73x63cm-29x25in) s.i.d.1968 chl crayon. 29-Mar-4 Goodman, Sydney #71/R est:10000-12000 (A.D 10000)
£4771	$8683	€6966	Dog (23x31cm-9x12in) s. ink. 16-Jun-4 Deutscher-Menzies, Melbourne #274/R est:5000-8000 (A.D 12500)
£4858	$7822	€7093	Blue girl - after Picasso via Saturday Evening Post (35x25cm-14x10in) s.i.verso crayon pastel prov. 25-Aug-3 Sotheby's, Paddington #312/R est:12000-15000 (A.D 12000)
£5344	$9725	€7802	Nude on big brass bed (86x62cm-34x24in) ink exhib. 16-Jun-4 Deutscher-Menzies, Melbourne #160/R est:15000-25000 (A.D 14000)
£6911	$10850	€10021	Hibiscus (56x66cm-22x26in) s.d.87 W/C col pencil. 26-Aug-3 Christie's, Sydney #131/R est:8000-12000 (A.D 17000)
£7317	$11488	€10610	Lovers (25x30cm-10x12in) mono. ink. 26-Aug-3 Christie's, Sydney #140/R est:18000-25000 (A.D 18000)
£7634	$13893	€11146	Gambella (71x61cm-28x24in) d.2/6/73 chl W/C on canvas prov.exhib. 16-Jun-4 Deutscher-Menzies, Melbourne #22/R est:20000-30000 (A.D 20000)
£8097	$13036	€11822	Lovers (29x56cm-11x22in) s.d.1984 ink ink wash collage prov. 25-Aug-3 Sotheby's, Paddington #151/R est:20000-30000 (A.D 20000)
£11382	$20374	€16618	Study for Bondi beach (56x69cm-22x27in) s.i.d.1983/85 studio st. brown ink pencil prov. 4-May-4 Sotheby's, Melbourne #198/R est:25000-35000 (A.D 28000)
£12195	$21829	€17805	Great Bower bird (33x30cm-13x12in) s.i.d.17/9/71 mixed media prov. 4-May-4 Sotheby's, Melbourne #202/R est:30000-50000 (A.D 30000)
£12595	$22924	€18389	Her (90x63cm-35x25in) ink prov. 16-Jun-4 Deutscher-Menzies, Melbourne #95/R est:30000-40000 (A.D 33000)
£12712	$21610	€18560	Untitled (75x99cm-30x39in) s.d.1966 i.verso ink chl paint ball-point pen. 24-Nov-3 Sotheby's, Melbourne #41/R est:30000-40000 (A.D 30000)
£13223	$23405	€19306	Torso, study for large white marble (94x62cm-37x24in) artist st.d.2/3/74 s.i.d.1974 verso ink pair. 3-May-4 Christie's, Melbourne #149/R est:32000-38000 (A.D 32000)
£14050	$25992	€20513	Footbridge and Pont Neuf (56x77cm-22x30in) d.9.6.89 brush ink on rice paper prov.exhib. 10-Mar-4 Deutscher-Menzies, Melbourne #79/R est:38000-45000 (A.D 34000)
£14634	$26195	€21366	Glass House mountains (75x99cm-30x39in) s.d.1975-79 pencil prov. 4-May-4 Sotheby's, Melbourne #24/R est:40000-60000 (A.D 36000)
£15319	$26043	€22366	Sketch for large Flame Tree, Port Vila (62x50cm-24x20in) s.i.d.83 ink gouache collage prov.exhib. 26-Nov-3 Deutscher-Menzies, Melbourne #41/R est:40000-50000 (A.D 36000)
£15447	$24252	€22398	River at Yass New South Wales (52x74cm-20x29in) s.i.d.1977 pencil prov.exhib. 26-Aug-3 Christie's, Sydney #38/R est:25000-30000 (A.D 38000)
£15702	$27793	€22925	Wren (102x74cm-40x29in) s.i.d.1979 ink prov. 3-May-4 Christie's, Melbourne #15/R est:30000-40000 (A.D 38000)
£16170	$27489	€23608	Orchids in front of palm tree print (100x75cm-39x30in) s.i.d.5 oct/75 pen ink. 25-Nov-3 Christie's, Melbourne #11/R est:25000-35000 (A.D 38000)
£20648	$33243	€30146	Hillside (37x40cm-15x16in) studio st. W/C gouache ink card prov. 25-Aug-3 Sotheby's, Paddington #175/R est:28000-38000 (A.D 51000)
£24681	$41957	€36034	Blue wren (68x84cm-27x33in) s.i.d.79 ink W/C acrylic collage. 25-Nov-3 Christie's, Melbourne #2/R est:30000-40000 (A.D 58000)
£25203	$39569	€36544	Looking down New South Head Road from a block of flats (51x64cm-20x25in) i.d.25/82 ink. 26-Aug-3 Christie's, Sydney #1/R est:30000-50000 (A.D 62000)
£27660	$47021	€40384	The river (198x168cm-78x66in) s. wool tapestry prov.exhib.lit. 25-Nov-3 Christie's, Melbourne #7/R est:65000-85000 (A.D 65000)
£29787	$50638	€43489	Afternoon on the I'Ile-St-Louis (58x76cm-23x30in) artist st. d.10/6/89 gouache collage exec 1989 prov.exhib.lit. 26-Nov-3 Deutscher-Menzies, Melbourne #34/R est:45000-55000 (A.D 70000)

WHITELEY, John William (fl.1882-1916) British

£360	$572	€522	Study of a standing male nude (75x45cm-30x18in) 9-Sep-3 Bonhams, Knightsbridge #194/R

WHITEMAN, Vera (20th C) New Zealander

£940	$1598	€1372	Hunting scene (28x39cm-11x15in) s. board. 27-Nov-3 International Art Centre, Auckland #114/R (NZ.D 2500)

WHITEREAD, Rachel (1953-) British

Sculpture

£1600	$2928	€2400	Switch (9x9x3cm-4x4x1in) mono.d.1994 plaster. 4-Jun-4 Lempertz, Koln #534/R est:3000
£234637	$420000	€342570	Untitled - 16 spaces. coloured resin 16 parts exec 1995 prov.exhib. 12-May-4 Sotheby's, New York #39/R est:400000-600000

Works on paper

£8939	$16000	€13051	Study for wax corridor (46x30cm-18x12in) s.d.92 correction fluid ink graph paper prov. 12-May-4 Christie's, Rockefeller NY #342/R est:18000-22000
£12291	$22000	€17945	Resin table and chair (34x22cm-13x9in) s.i.d.94 verso ink resin graph paper prov. 12-May-4 Christie's, Rockefeller NY #341/R est:18000-22000

WHITESIDE, Frank Reed (1866-1929) American

£535	$850	€781	Landscape with woods in springtime (28x36cm-11x14in) st.verso board. 10-Sep-3 Alderfer's, Hatfield #370/R
£915	$1500	€1327	Desert river (36x51cm-14x20in) 4-Jun-3 Alderfer's, Hatfield #279/R est:1800-2200
£1220	$2000	€1769	Zuni Territory New Mexico (36x51cm-14x20in) s. 4-Jun-3 Alderfer's, Hatfield #278/R est:1800-2200
£11765	$20000	€17177	Zuni pueblo scene (46x61cm-18x24in) s.d.1917 prov.lit. 1-Nov-3 Santa Fe Art, Santa Fe #223/R est:30000-40000

WHITFORD, Richard (19th C) British

£440	$805	€642	Manchester terrier (50x60cm-20x24in) s.d.1868. 1-Jun-4 Hodgins, Calgary #298/R (C.D 1100)
£980	$1725	€1431	Lincoln red cow and calf in a stable (34x44cm-13x17in) s.d.1882. 18-May-4 Woolley & Wallis, Salisbury #162/R
£2200	$3960	€3212	Carriage driver surveying the landscape (30x39cm-12x15in) s.d.1863. 21-Apr-4 Christie's, Kensington #18/R est:2000-3000
£3600	$6336	€5256	Devon bull, cow and calf in landscape (62x75cm-24x30in) s. 18-May-4 Woolley & Wallis, Salisbury #157/R est:2000-3000
£3700	$6512	€5402	Prize black bull in a landscape (48x59cm-19x23in) s.d.1888. 18-May-4 Woolley & Wallis, Salisbury #160/R est:1500-2500
£4200	$7392	€6132	Prize Devon cow in a landscape (49x65cm-19x26in) s.d.1873. 18-May-4 Woolley & Wallis, Salisbury #225/R est:1500-2500

WHITFORD, W (19th C) British

£2200	$4048	€3212	Cherry Blossom, Champion, Smithfield (46x61cm-18x24in) s.d.1884. 23-Mar-4 Rosebery Fine Art, London #853/R est:400-600

WHITING, Frederick (1874-1962) British

Works on paper

£350	$641	€511	Study of a Riding school (40x50cm-16x20in) s. W/C. 28-Jan-4 Henry Adams, Chichester #246

WHITNALL, Walter E (fl.1901-1910) British

Works on paper

£800	$1376	€1168	Beach scene (47x74cm-19x29in) s. W/C. 2-Dec-3 Sotheby's, London #82/R

WHITTAKER, James William (1828-1876) British

£486	$900	€710	River scene in North Wales (41x61cm-16x24in) s.d.1876. 17-Jul-4 New Orleans Auction, New Orleans #236/R

WHITTALL, Thomas (?) British
£250 $450 €365 Vale of Conway North Wales (23x33cm-9x13in) s. 24-Apr-4 Rogers Jones, Clwyd #179

WHITTENBURY, Ron (attrib) (fl.1920-1955) British?
£221 $400 €323 Italian village near Lake Como (41x48cm-16x19in) i.verso board. 3-Apr-4 Charlton Hall, Columbia #34

WHITTINGHAM, Bonnie (?-2000) American
£221 $400 €323 Boat and pier (15x58cm-6x23in) s. board prov. 3-Apr-4 Outer Cape Auctions, Provincetown #56/R
£227 $400 €331 Untitled Dories (8x20cm-3x8in) s. board. 3-Jan-4 Outer Cape Auctions, Provincetown #56/R

WHITTINGHAM, Bonnie (attrib) (?-2000) American
£230 $375 €336 Untitled (25x20cm-10x8in) indis sig. 19-Jul-3 Outer Cape Auctions, Provincetown #18/R

WHITTINGTON, William G (fl.1904-1914) British
Works on paper
£202 $371 €295 Sea reach no.331 (51x36cm-20x14in) s. s.i.verso W/C. 14-Jun-4 Waddingtons, Toronto #80/R (C.D 500)

WHITTLE, Thomas (19th C) British
£480 $859 €701 Landscape with windmill and lightning storm (45x60cm-18x24in) s.d.1887. 16-Mar-4 Bonhams, Oxford #61
£500 $935 €750 Highland lake scene (30x60cm-12x24in) s.d.1869. 26-Jul-4 Bonhams, Bath #71/R
£828 $1500 €1209 Faggot gatherer at sunset (25x36cm-10x14in) s.d.1875 prov. 18-Apr-4 Bonhams & Butterfields, Los Angeles #7050 est:2000-3000

WHITTLE, Thomas (jnr) (19th C) British
£520 $931 €759 Wooded hillside with sheep grazing and farmer resting (19x34cm-7x13in) s. indis.d. 17-Mar-4 Bonhams, Chester #361
£550 $897 €803 Pandy Mill Dolgellau (33x43cm-13x17in) s.d.1889. 25-Sep-3 Mellors & Kirk, Nottingham #760/R
£700 $1253 €1022 Repose of evening (20x30cm-8x12in) s.d.1873 board. 26-May-4 Sotheby's, Olympia #75/R

WHITTLESEA, Michael (1938-) British
£700 $1232 €1022 The end of the barn (51x51cm-20x20in) s.d.97 verso. 18-May-4 Woolley & Wallis, Salisbury #68/R
Works on paper
£600 $1056 €876 Winter evening (30x30cm-12x12in) W/C. 18-May-4 Woolley & Wallis, Salisbury #131/R

WHITTREDGE, Worthington (1820-1910) American
£1381 $2500 €2016 Third beach, Newport, Rhode Island (15x23cm-6x9in) s. 16-Apr-4 James Julia, Fairfield #616/R est:5000-7000
£1932 $3400 €2821 Newport, Rhode Island (23x38cm-9x15in) s. board prov. 3-Jan-4 Collins, Maine #41/R est:2500-3500
£3143 $5500 €4589 Whittredge's dog (36x28cm-14x11in) s. 19-Dec-3 Sotheby's, New York #1078/R est:3000-5000
£6587 $11000 €9617 Villa d'Esta, Tivoli (40x30cm-16x12in) s. 7-Oct-3 Sotheby's, New York #172 est:3000-5000
£16760 $30000 €24470 Gray day under the cliff (41x28cm-16x11in) s. 6-May-4 Shannon's, Milford #83/R est:15000-20000
£46512 $80000 €67908 Indian summer (47x39cm-19x15in) s. painted c.1870 prov. 4-Dec-3 Christie's, Rockefeller NY #43/R est:80000-120000

WHITTREDGE, Worthington (attrib) (1820-1910) American
Works on paper
£865 $1600 €1263 Forest landscape (61x41cm-24x16in) 13-Mar-4 DeFina, Austinburg #800/R est:800-1200

WHORF, John (1903-1959) American
£2459 $4500 €3590 Sailboats ashore at evening (48x48cm-19x19in) s. 5-Jun-4 Dan Ripley, Indianapolis #242
£5367 $9500 €7836 To autumn (28x20cm-11x8in) s. 2-May-4 Bonhams & Butterfields, San Francisco #1133/R est:2000-3000
£36932 $65000 €53921 Boats in the surf (74x91cm-29x36in) s. prov. 19-May-4 Sotheby's, New York #113/R est:18000-24000
Works on paper
£236 $375 €345 Farm (34x46cm-13x18in) s. W/C. 12-Sep-3 Skinner, Boston #426/R
£273 $500 €399 Summer (25x36cm-10x14in) s. W/C executed c.1930. 5-Jun-4 Treadway Gallery, Cincinnati #656/R
£412 $700 €602 Coastal Rocks (29x32cm-11x13in) s. W/C. 21-Nov-3 Skinner, Boston #566/R
£581 $1000 €848 Winter landscape with trees (36x50cm-14x20in) s. W/C. 2-Dec-3 Christie's, Rockefeller NY #82/R
£988 $1600 €1442 Western border town (14x28cm-6x11in) s. 31-Jul-3 Eldred, East Dennis #1193/R est:2000-3000
£1105 $1900 €1613 Horse and buggy on wintry road (36x53cm-14x21in) s. W/C. 7-Dec-3 Grogan, Boston #79
£1117 $2000 €1631 Fallen tree (38x51cm-15x20in) s. i.verso W/C prov. 6-May-4 Shannon's, Milford #180/R est:1200-1800
£1258 $2000 €1837 Bathers (54x37cm-21x15in) s. W/C. 12-Sep-3 Skinner, Boston #355/R
£1412 $2500 €2062 North African scene with figures working in a quarry (14x20cm-6x8in) bears sig.i. pencil W/C. 2-May-4 Bonhams & Butterfields, San Francisco #1163/R est:2500-3500
£1534 $2500 €2240 Ocean scene (36x48cm-14x19in) s. W/C. 19-Jul-3 Outer Cape Auctions, Provincetown #29/R
£1676 $3000 €2447 Mountain sunset (53x41cm-21x16in) s. s.i.verso W/C prov. 6-May-4 Shannon's, Milford #221/R est:2500-3500
£1747 $3250 €2551 The bather (49x39cm-19x15in) s. W/C. 5-Mar-4 Skinner, Boston #399/R est:3000-5000
£1902 $3100 €2777 Jolly sailor (61x76cm-24x30in) s. W/C. 19-Jul-3 Outer Cape Auctions, Provincetown #39/R
£2000 $3600 €2920 Bathing (41x56cm-16x22in) s. W/C prov. 25-Jan-4 Hindman, Chicago #1081/R est:1200-1600
£2000 $3600 €2920 Oil skins, ploughing out (36x53cm-14x21in) s. W/C prov. 25-Jan-4 Hindman, Chicago #1091/R est:1200-1800
£2151 $4000 €3140 Rocky coast (55x76cm-22x30in) s. i.verso W/C gouache. 5-Mar-4 Skinner, Boston #553/R est:3500-5500
£2210 $4000 €3227 At the bazaar (50x65cm-20x26in) s.d.25 W/C graphite. 31-Mar-4 Sotheby's, New York #143/R est:4000-6000
£2260 $4000 €3300 Rapids on a New England river (21x29cm-8x11in) s. pencil W/C. 2-May-4 Bonhams & Butterfields, San Francisco #1088/R est:2000-3000
£2260 $4000 €3300 Study of North African figures (13x19cm-5x7in) s. pencil W/C. 2-May-4 Bonhams & Butterfields, San Francisco #1164/R est:2000-3000
£2454 $4000 €3583 Landscape (41x56cm-16x22in) s. W/C. 19-Jul-3 Outer Cape Auctions, Provincetown #72/R
£2542 $4500 €3711 Still life with codfish and onions (15x22cm-6x9in) s.indis.i. pencil W/C. 2-May-4 Bonhams & Butterfields, San Francisco #1159/R est:2000-3000
£2556 $4600 €3732 Boats at twilight (56x74cm-22x29in) s. W/C prov. 25-Jan-4 Hindman, Chicago #1080/R est:1600-2200
£2793 $5000 €4078 Provincetown dunes (56x76cm-22x30in) s. W/C gouache. 14-May-4 Skinner, Boston #274/R est:7000-9000
£2844 $4750 €4152 Ducks taking fight (36x53cm-14x21in) s. W/C. 16-Nov-3 CRN Auctions, Cambridge #12/R
£3086 $5000 €4506 Blue Jay family (20x28cm-8x11in) s. 31-Jul-3 Eldred, East Dennis #994/R est:6000-8000
£3107 $5500 €4536 Two figures skiing downhill (16x22cm-6x9in) s. pencil W/C. 2-May-4 Bonhams & Butterfields, San Francisco #1181/R est:4000-6000
£3390 $6000 €4949 Nude bathers (56x38cm-22x15in) s. pencil W/C. 2-May-4 Bonhams & Butterfields, San Francisco #1069/R est:3000-5000
£3672 $6500 €5361 Cottage in snow (14x21cm-6x8in) s.i. W/C. 2-May-4 Bonhams & Butterfields, San Francisco #1145/R est:3000-5000
£4096 $7250 €5980 Portage, Quebec (15x15cm-6x6in) s. pencil W/C. 2-May-4 Bonhams & Butterfields, San Francisco #1171/R est:2000-3000
£4237 $7500 €6186 Spring at Hartwell Farm with a lady in the foreground (15x27cm-6x11in) s. W/C. 2-May-4 Bonhams & Butterfields, San Francisco #1126/R est:4000-6000
£4520 $8000 €6599 Pheasants in flight (15x22cm-6x9in) s. W/C. 2-May-4 Bonhams & Butterfields, San Francisco #1134/R est:2000-3000
£4601 $7500 €6717 Duck hunters. Beached boat in winter storm (36x53cm-14x21in) s.verso W/C double-sided. 19-Jul-3 Outer Cape Auctions, Provincetown #49/R
£5247 $8500 €7608 Fishing above the rapids, White River, Vermont (52x69cm-20x27in) s.i. W/C gouache. 8-Aug-3 Barridorf, Portland #250/R est:5000-7000
£5650 $10000 €8249 Men moving logs downstream (15x22cm-6x9in) s. pencil W/C. 2-May-4 Bonhams & Butterfields, San Francisco #1170/R est:6000-8000
£5882 $10000 €8588 Moonpath no 3 schooner Islander (56x74cm-22x29in) s. i.verso W/C exec.c.1950. 28-Nov-3 Thomaston Place, Thomaston #800
£5914 $11000 €8634 Harbour boats (19x25cm-7x10in) s. W/C gouache. 5-Mar-4 Skinner, Boston #538/R est:7000-9000
£5932 $10500 €8661 Cape Cod, windward tack (15x22cm-6x9in) s. pencil W/C. 2-May-4 Bonhams & Butterfields, San Francisco #1093/R est:6000-8000
£5932 $10500 €8661 Approaching the finish (15x22cm-6x9in) s. pencil W/C. 2-May-4 Bonhams & Butterfields, San Francisco #1100/R est:6000-8000
£5932 $10500 €8661 By the campfire (15x22cm-6x9in) s. pencil W/C. 2-May-4 Bonhams & Butterfields, San Francisco #1175/R est:2000-3000
£6215 $11000 €9074 Sunny day on the Province town shore (15x22cm-6x9in) s. pencil W/C. 2-May-4 Bonhams & Butterfields, San Francisco #1101/R est:4000-6000
£7627 $13500 €11135 Monday wash (22x30cm-9x12in) s. pencil W/C. 2-May-4 Bonhams & Butterfields, San Francisco #1178/R est:6000-8000
£8475 $15000 €12374 Trap boats at moonlight (22x30cm-9x12in) s. pencil W/C. 2-May-4 Bonhams & Butterfields, San Francisco #1089/R est:4000-6000
£9857 $17400 €14391 Siesta, self portrait (38x56cm-15x22in) s. pencil W/C prov. 2-May-4 Bonhams & Butterfields, San Francisco #1066/R est:8000-12000
£9877 $16000 €14322 Fishing in the rapids (51x71cm-20x28in) s. W/C gouache. 8-Aug-3 Barridorf, Portland #249/R est:5000-7000
£10686 $18915 €15602 Edge of the fast water (15x22cm-6x9in) s. pencil W/C prov. 2-May-4 Bonhams & Butterfields, San Francisco #1087/R est:7000-10000
£10686 $18915 €15602 On the shoreline (22x30cm-9x12in) s. pencil W/C. 2-May-4 Bonhams & Butterfields, San Francisco #1094/R est:6000-8000
£10686 $18915 €15602 Winter day, Quincy Market, Faneuil Hall, Boston (20x30cm-8x12in) s. pencil W/C prov. 2-May-4 Bonhams & Butterfields, San Francisco #1103/R est:10000-15000
£14557 $25750 €21253 Ballerinas (30x40cm-12x16in) s. pencil W/C. 2-May-4 Bonhams & Butterfields, San Francisco #1180/R est:7000-10000

WHORF, Nancy (20th C) American
£3235 $5500 €4723 The garden (91x122cm-36x48in) s. board painted c.1990. 9-Nov-3 Outer Cape Auctions, Provincetown #50/R

WHORF, Richard (20th C) American
£346 $550 €505 Thomas brothers great animals circus (23x51cm-9x20in) s. board. 23-Mar-3 Auctions by the Bay, Alameda #850/R

WHYATT, George (fl.1910-1923) British
Works on paper
£260 $476 €380 Tarrant Moncton, Dorset (15x25cm-6x10in) s. W/C. 28-Jul-4 Mallams, Oxford #214/R
£270 $494 €394 Storm coming on South Downs (15x23cm-6x9in) s. W/C. 28-Jul-4 Mallams, Oxford #216/R
£850 $1445 €1241 Village scene with figures and donkey. Shepherd and sheep in a landscape (34x53cm-13x21in) s. W/C pair. 19-Nov-3 Tennants, Leyburn #965

WHYDALE, Ernest Herbert (1886-1952) British
£300 $549 €438 Pentire Head North Cornwall (27x37cm-11x15in) s. s.i.verso. 3-Jun-4 Lane, Penzance #33
£720 $1346 €1051 Figure loading a horsedrawn cart with hay (6x10cm-2x4in) i.verso board. 25-Feb-4 Mallams, Oxford #393/R
£2050 $3526 €2993 The old cart shed (48x58cm-19x23in) s. 5-Dec-3 Keys, Aylsham #659/R est:300-400

WHYMPER, Josiah Wood (1813-1903) British
Works on paper
£500 $815 €730 Windmill above a wooded valley with figures (28x61cm-11x24in) s.d.1862 pencil W/C htd white. 25-Sep-3 Mellors & Kirk, Nottingham #699/R
£500 $865 €730 Rural landscape with cattle amongst trees. s.d.1850 W/C. 9-Dec-3 Lawrences, Bletchingley #1692
£700 $1288 €1022 Cader Idris (51x70cm-20x28in) s.d.84 pencil W/C. 25-Mar-4 Christie's, Kensington #142/R

WHYTE, Alice F (1880-1952) New Zealander
£326 $528 €473 Cornwall Park, kiosk (40x50cm-16x20in) s. board. 31-Jul-3 International Art Centre, Auckland #180/R (NZ.D 900)
£526 $895 €768 Northland Valley farm (31x42cm-12x17in) board. 27-Nov-3 International Art Centre, Auckland #65/R (NZ.D 1400)
£725 $1174 €1051 Daisies (51x40cm-20x16in) board. 31-Jul-3 International Art Centre, Auckland #110/R est:2000-3000 (NZ.D 2000)
Works on paper
£435 $704 €631 Boats tied up (29x40cm-11x16in) s. W/C. 31-Jul-3 International Art Centre, Auckland #28/R est:2000-3000 (NZ.D 1200)

WHYTE, Duncan McGregor (1866-1953) British
£300 $552 €438 River landscape (33x48cm-13x19in) s.d.51. 10-Jun-4 Lyon & Turnbull, Edinburgh #121
£920 $1536 €1343 Sewing bunny rabbit (79x107cm-31x42in) s. 23-Oct-3 Bonhams, Edinburgh #327
£3500 $6510 €5110 Green rabbit (77x107cm-30x42in) s. 4-Mar-4 Christie's, Kensington #161/R est:3000-5000

WHYTE, Peter (?) Canadian
£3054 $5101 €4459 Untitled - mountain peak (23x26cm-9x10in) s.d.1929. 17-Nov-3 Hodgins, Calgary #164/R est:3500-4500 (C.D 6750)

WIBERG, Harald (1908-1986) Swedish
£734 $1182 €1072 Harvest time with drying hurdles and crows (56x64cm-22x25in) s.d.1944 panel. 25-Aug-3 Lilla Bukowskis, Stockholm #971 (S.KR 9600)
£1139 $1971 €1663 Black-grouse in wooded landscape (46x55cm-18x22in) s.d.1951 panel. 15-Dec-3 Lilla Bukowskis, Stockholm #701 (S.KR 14500)
£2439 $4366 €3561 Sneaking cat (44x59cm-17x23in) s.d.1941. 25-May-4 Bukowskis, Stockholm #227/R est:18000-20000 (S.KR 33000)
Works on paper
£370 $661 €540 Saturday night with elks at Kalakershornet, Blekhem (26x39cm-10x15in) s. W/C. 28-May-4 Uppsala Auktionskammare, Uppsala #248 (S.KR 5000)
£615 $1058 €898 Flock of animals on town street (30x39cm-12x15in) s.d.1972 W/C. 7-Dec-3 Uppsala Auktionskammare, Uppsala #208 (S.KR 8000)
£731 $1257 €1067 Winter landscape with deer (32x39cm-13x15in) s.d.1980. 7-Dec-3 Uppsala Auktionskammare, Uppsala #207 (S.KR 9500)

WICART, Nicolaas (1748-1815) Dutch
Works on paper
£612 $1096 €900 Bateaux et barque de pecheurs sur une riviere (31x45cm-12x18in) s. pen black ink grey wash. 19-Mar-4 Piasa, Paris #64
£651 $1106 €950 View of Leksmond (26x37cm-10x15in) s.i.d.1770 pen black ink grey wash. 4-Nov-3 Sotheby's, Amsterdam #118/R
£1020 $1827 €1500 Barques de pecheurs aux abords d'un village (31x45cm-12x18in) s. pen black ink grey wash. 19-Mar-4 Piasa, Paris #62/R est:1000
£2365 $4162 €3500 Wooded river landscape with travellers (40x54cm-16x21in) s. pen black ink W/C. 19-May-4 Sotheby's, Amsterdam #269/R est:3000-4000

WICHERS, Hal (1893-1968) Dutch
£654 $1183 €955 Beach of Sumatra (33x25cm-13x10in) s.d.1955 board. 3-Apr-4 Glerum, Singapore #77/R (S.D 2000)

WICHERT, Ernst (1831-1902) German
£298 $483 €420 Hessen landscape with peasant couple (33x48cm-13x19in) s. board. 23-May-3 Altus, Berlin #605/R

WICHMANN, Georg (1876-1944) German?
£685 $1164 €1000 Snow capped mountains (67x95cm-26x37in) s.d.35 panel lit. 6-Nov-3 Allgauer, Kempten #3647/R

WICHT, John von (1888-1970) American/German
£652 $1200 €952 Mallorca (94x69cm-37x27in) s. painted c.1960. 10-Jun-4 Swann Galleries, New York #257/R
£750 $1200 €1095 Interlinked (51x61cm-20x24in) s. 20-Sep-3 Bunte, Elgin #1268
£2206 $3750 €3221 Untitled (74x30cm-29x12in) 9-Nov-3 Wright, Chicago #288 est:4000-5000
Works on paper
£529 $900 €772 Untitled (33x41cm-13x16in) s. W/C crayon prov. 9-Nov-3 Wright, Chicago #287
£4595 $8500 €6709 Untitled (58x74cm-23x29in) s. one board gouache exec.c.1940 four. 10-Mar-4 Doyle, New York #59/R est:2000-3000

WICKENBERG, Per (1812-1846) Swedish
£352 $566 €514 At the dressing table (34x22cm-13x9in) after Terborch. 25-Aug-3 Lilla Bukowskis, Stockholm #93 (S.KR 4600)
£923 $1588 €1348 Coastal landscape in winter (25x32cm-10x13in) s. 3-Dec-3 AB Stockholms Auktionsverk #2400/R (S.KR 12000)

WICKENBURG, Alfred (1885-1978) Austrian
£1645 $3026 €2500 Abstract study (22x36cm-9x14in) mono. board. 22-Jun-4 Wiener Kunst Auktionen, Vienna #349/R est:2500

WICKER, Gwen (fl.1940-1965) British
£280 $518 €409 Still life of wild flowers in a ceramic vase (50x41cm-20x16in) s. board. 14-Jul-4 Christie's, Kensington #986
£450 $752 €657 Pantry still life (66x81cm-26x32in) s. 14-Oct-3 David Lay, Penzance #522/R
£520 $946 €759 Tulips in the window (71x61cm-28x24in) s. board. 15-Jun-4 David Lay, Penzance #368/R

WICKERTSHEIMER, Wilhelm (1886-1968) German
£563 $1007 €822 Landscape (66x77cm-26x30in) s. 22-Mar-4 Philippe Schuler, Zurich #6207 (S.FR 1300)

WICKHAM, Julia M (fl.1935-1938) American
£1160 $2100 €1694 Path to Peconic (36x46cm-14x18in) canvas on panel. 3-Apr-4 South Bay, Long Island #124

WICKLER, Charles (20th C) American
Works on paper
£260 $475 €390 Why not a blue wall (56x76cm-22x30in) mixed media. 10-Jul-4 Hindman, Chicago #563/R

WICKSTROM, Martin (1957-) Swedish
Sculpture
£1208 $2054 €1764 First Lady (66x56cm-26x22in) init.d.90 verso varnished wood armature prov. 5-Nov-3 AB Stockholms Auktionsverk #1028/R est:10000-12000 (S.KR 16000)

WIDAYAT (1923-2002) Indonesian
£4348 $6739 €6348 Sekaten (46x95cm-18x37in) s.d.79. 6-Oct-2 Sotheby's, Singapore #156/R est:12000-15000 (S.D 12000)
£5556 $10056 €8112 Birds of Paradise (107x70cm-42x28in) s.d.70. 3-Apr-4 Glerum, Singapore #34/R est:12000-16000 (S.D 17000)
£8602 $13763 €12559 Flamboyan (100x120cm-39x47in) s.d.2001 s.i.d.2001 verso. 18-May-3 Sotheby's, Singapore #170/R est:18000-25000 (S.D 24000)
£19355 $30968 €28258 Pulang dari pasar (95x145cm-37x57in) s.d.89 s.i.d.89 verso lit. 18-May-3 Sotheby's, Singapore #160/R est:25000-35000 (S.D 54000)
£35562 $64011 €51921 Pertapa di hutan tropices - Meditation in tropical forest (145x195cm-57x77in) s.d.74. 25-Apr-4 Christie's, Hong Kong #574/R est:280000-380000 (HK.D 500000)
£65972 $110174 €96319 Bird's Paradise (150x195cm-59x77in) s.d.75. 12-Oct-3 Sotheby's, Singapore #145/R est:100000-120000 (S.D 190000)

WIDDAS, Ernest A (fl.1906-1923) British
£320 $586 €467 Summer day on the river (127x101cm-50x40in) s. 8-Jul-4 Lawrence, Crewkerne #1656

WIDDAS, Richard Dodd (1826-1885) British
£500 $945 €730 Changing horses (39x67cm-15x26in) s.d.1881 board. 19-Feb-4 Christie's, Kensington #331/R

WIDDAS, Richard Dodd (attrib) (1826-1885) British
£1796 $3000 €2622 Close finish (46x61cm-18x24in) 7-Oct-3 Sotheby's, New York #166 est:3000-5000

WIDER, Wilhelm (1818-1884) German
£7483 $13395 €11000 Meeting by water source (168x117cm-66x46in) s.i.d.57 canvas on panel. 17-Mar-4 Neumeister, Munich #663/R est:6000

WIDERBERG, Frans (1934-) Norwegian
£2981 $5128 €4352 Man on horseback in green room (90x54cm-35x21in) s. 8-Dec-3 Blomqvist, Oslo #580/R est:50000-70000 (N.KR 35000)
£8092 $13918 €11814 Couple (118x100cm-46x39in) s. i.d.1980 verso. 8-Dec-3 Blomqvist, Oslo #569/R est:100000-120000 (N.KR 95000)
Works on paper
£648 $1075 €940 Rider and star (25x17cm-10x7in) s. W/C. 16-Jun-3 Blomqvist, Lysaker #1267/R (N.KR 7500)
£6405 $11465 €9351 Horseman in the horizon (187x90cm-74x35in) init. gouache paper on canvas. 22-Mar-4 Blomqvist, Oslo #631/R est:55000-65000 (N.KR 80000)

WIDERBERG, Nico (1960-) Norwegian
Sculpture
£1533 $2453 €2223 Upwards (46cm-18in) s.num.4/10 bronze incl.socle. 22-Sep-3 Blomqvist, Lysaker #1335/R est:12000-15000 (N.KR 18000)
£1721 $2874 €2513 Figure on wheel (64cm-25in) s. bronze on stone socle. 20-Oct-3 Blomqvist, Lysaker #1356/R est:12000-15000 (N.KR 20000)
£2129 $3663 €3108 Cycle (72x21x21cm-28x8x8in) s.d.97 num.4/6 bronze on socle. 8-Dec-3 Blomqvist, Oslo #532/R est:25000-35000 (N.KR 25000)

WIDFORSS, Gunnar M (1879-1934) American
Works on paper
£815 $1500 €1190 Three masted sailing ship with other fishing boats in a harbour (17x25cm-7x10in) s.d.1910 pencil W/C prov.exhib. 8-Jun-4 Bonhams & Butterfields, San Francisco #4092/R est:2000-3000
£1359 $2500 €1984 View along a canal (43x29cm-17x11in) s.d.1911 pencil W/C prov.exhib. 8-Jun-4 Bonhams & Butterfields, San Francisco #4083/R est:3000-5000
£1445 $2500 €2110 Snow-covered mountain landscape (20x49cm-8x19in) s.d.1916 pencil W/C paper board prov.exhib. 10-Dec-3 Bonhams & Butterfields, San Francisco #6098/R est:3000-5000
£1902 $3500 €2777 Venezia (40x52cm-16x20in) s.i.d.1910 pencil W/C prov.exhib. 8-Jun-4 Bonhams & Butterfields, San Francisco #4080/R est:4000-6000

£1902	$3500	€2777	Ancient doorway (47x34cm-19x13in) s.d.1916 pencil W/C prov.exhib. 8-Jun-4 Bonhams & Butterfields, San Francisco #4081/R est:3000-5000
£1922	$3440	€2806	Mountain landscape (40x25cm-16x10in) s.d.1911 W/C. 26-May-4 AB Stockholms Auktionsverk #2202/R est:15000-20000 (S.KR 26000)
£2023	$3500	€2954	Old Archway opening to a village street (46x38cm-18x15in) s.d.1918 pencil W/C prov.exhib. 10-Dec-3 Bonhams & Butterfields, San Francisco #6074/R est:4000-6000
£2312	$4000	€3376	Storm approaching mountain peaks (22x16cm-9x6in) s.d.1921 pencil W/C prov. 10-Dec-3 Bonhams & Butterfields, San Francisco #6097/R est:3000-5000
£3297	$6000	€4814	Yosemite Valley landscape (20x15cm-8x6in) s.d.26 W/C prov. 15-Jun-4 John Moran, Pasadena #90b est:4000-6000
£4624	$8000	€6751	Sunlit trees (33x47cm-13x19in) s.d.1916 indis.i.verso W/C prov.exhib. 10-Dec-3 Bonhams & Butterfields, San Francisco #6099/R est:6000-8000
£14706	$25000	€21471	Canyon from the rim (13x21cm-5x8in) s. W/C. 18-Nov-3 John Moran, Pasadena #116d est:20000-30000

WIDGERY, F J (1861-1942) British

Works on paper

£300	$498	€438	Barren moorland scene with a stone monument in the foreground (25x36cm-10x14in) s. gouache. 2-Oct-3 Amersham Auction Rooms, UK #224
£340	$564	€496	Barren moorland scene with a rocky outcrop on the skyline (18x25cm-7x10in) s. gouache. 2-Oct-3 Amersham Auction Rooms, UK #223
£400	$728	€584	Coastal rocks (28x46cm-11x18in) s. bodycol. 15-Jun-4 David Lay, Penzance #234
£420	$785	€613	Dunkery Beacon, Exmoor (25x36cm-10x14in) s. W/C. 24-Feb-4 Tayler & Fletcher, Cheltenham #3
£1300	$2405	€1950	Cattle grazing overlooking woody bay (23x36cm-9x14in) s. W/C gouache. 15-Jul-4 Rendalls, Ashburton #1920
£1350	$2498	€2025	Sheep in moorland view (25x46cm-10x18in) s. gouache. 15-Jul-4 Rendalls, Ashburton #1921
£1400	$2590	€2100	Cattle grazing in Dartmoor stream (23x36cm-9x14in) s. W/C. 15-Jul-4 Rendalls, Ashburton #1918
£1900	$3515	€2774	West country coastal towns (28x18cm-11x7in) s. gouache pair. 9-Mar-4 Gorringes, Lewes #2302 est:450-550
£2050	$3793	€3075	Dusk at Arms Tor, Lydford (18x51cm-7x20in) s. W/C. 15-Jul-4 Rendalls, Ashburton #1922
£2300	$4255	€3450	Cattle grazing beside a Dartmoor stream (25x46cm-10x18in) s.d.1904 gouache. 15-Jul-4 Rendalls, Ashburton #1924

WIDGERY, Frederick John (1861-1942) British

£320	$586	€467	Moorland (24x33cm-9x13in) s. board. 6-Jul-4 Bearnes, Exeter #517/R
£600	$966	€870	Dartmoor hills, Cawsand Beacon from Woodbury Common (20x25cm-8x10in) s. 15-Aug-3 Keys, Aylsham #771
£750	$1253	€1095	Bedruthan Steps (26x76cm-10x30in) s. 12-Nov-3 Sotheby's, Olympia #126/R
£820	$1394	€1197	Summer landscape with trees and a pond (35x45cm-14x18in) s.d.1926. 29-Oct-3 Hampton & Littlewood, Exeter #595/R
£900	$1557	€1314	Woodbury Common, Devon (15x24cm-6x9in) s. panel. 11-Dec-3 Lane, Penzance #69
£1300	$2392	€1898	Bedruthan Steps, near Newquay (27x76cm-11x30in) s. 24-Mar-4 Hamptons Fine Art, Godalming #272/R
£3400	$6018	€4964	Flooded water meadows on the river Exe (36x74cm-14x29in) s. 28-Apr-4 Hampton & Littlewood, Exeter #555/R est:3000-4000

Works on paper

£252	$450	€368	Moorland landscape with sheep (25x35cm-10x14in) s.verso gouache prov. 14-May-4 Skinner, Boston #31/R
£260	$471	€380	Taw Marsh, Belston Torr (26x35cm-10x14in) gouache. 2-Apr-4 Bracketts, Tunbridge Wells #387/R
£268	$461	€391	The River Lyd (25x35cm-10x14in) s. i.verso W/C. 2-Dec-3 Ritchie, Toronto #29/R (C.D 600)
£280	$510	€409	Kynance Cove, Cornwall (24x34cm-9x13in) s. W/C gouache. 21-Jun-4 Bonhams, Bath #386a
£280	$518	€409	Moorland scene (37x48cm-15x19in) s. W/C. 16-Jul-4 Charterhouse, Sherborne #504/R
£310	$567	€453	Summer coastal scene (23x32cm-9x13in) s. gouache. 28-Jul-4 Hampton & Littlewood, Exeter #580/R
£350	$616	€511	Highland landscape with cattle (25x34cm-10x13in) gouache. 21-May-4 Bracketts, Tunbridge Wells #265/R
£380	$654	€555	Moorland scene (28x46cm-11x18in) s. gouache. 2-Dec-3 Sworder & Son, Bishops Stortford #491/R
£380	$692	€555	North Cornish coast near Newquay (24x34cm-9x13in) s. W/C gouache. 21-Jun-4 Bonhams, Bath #381a
£380	$692	€555	Cornish coast near Perranporth (25x35cm-10x14in) s. W/C gouache. 21-Jun-4 Bonhams, Bath #383a/R
£380	$695	€555	Moorland landscape with distant hills (36x53cm-14x21in) s. W/C bodycol. 8-Jul-4 Duke & Son, Dorchester #69
£400	$640	€584	Doone Valley, Devon (19x18cm-7x7in) s. 16-Sep-3 Holloways, Banbury #256
£400	$716	€584	Cornish Coast (17x27cm-7x11in) s. gouache. 16-Mar-4 Bearnes, Exeter #387
£400	$728	€584	Waves crashing against the headland (28x46cm-11x18in) s. pencil W/C bodycol. 1-Jul-4 Christie's, Kensington #329/R
£420	$764	€613	Bude (25x35cm-10x14in) s. 21-Jun-4 Bonhams, Bath #383
£420	$756	€613	Cornish beach at low tide (45x69cm-18x27in) s. W/C. 22-Apr-4 Charles Ross, Woburn #258
£430	$731	€628	Dartmoor landscape (24x35cm-9x14in) W/C. 19-Nov-3 James Thompson, Kirby Lonsdale #22
£450	$828	€657	Landscape with pathway, Scots pine onto open common (53x18cm-21x7in) s. W/C. 26-Mar-4 Bigwood, Stratford on Avon #296
£460	$768	€672	Great Hound Tor, west Hey Tor (18x27cm-7x11in) s. gouache. 14-Oct-3 Bearnes, Exeter #335/R
£460	$842	€672	Fristral Bay, Newquay (25x34cm-10x13in) s. gouache. 6-Jul-4 Bearnes, Exeter #439/R
£460	$842	€672	Maer Lake, Bude (25x35cm-10x14in) s. gouache. 6-Jul-4 Bearnes, Exeter #440/R
£520	$936	€759	River landscape (28x45cm-11x18in) s. W/C. 21-Jan-4 Sotheby's, Olympia #222/R
£580	$1061	€847	Mullion Cove (24x35cm-9x14in) s. bodycol. 27-Jan-4 Bonhams, Knightsbridge #333/R
£600	$1002	€876	Doone Valley (18x28cm-7x11in) s. gouache. 17-Oct-3 Keys, Aylsham #479
£600	$1002	€876	Near Perranporth, north Cornwall (29x39cm-11x15in) s. bodycol. 13-Nov-3 Christie's, Kensington #181/R
£600	$1002	€876	Moors near Wild Tor, Dartmoor (18x53cm-7x21in) s.d.1903 W/C bodycol. 26-Jun-3 Greenslade Hunt, Taunton #493
£600	$1062	€876	Dunkery Beacon, Exmoor (25x35cm-10x14in) s. gouache. 28-Apr-4 Hampton & Littlewood, Exeter #507
£630	$1071	€920	Steperton Tor, Dartmoor (28x45cm-11x18in) s. i.verso W/C bodycol. 27-Nov-3 Greenslade Hunt, Taunton #974
£630	$1071	€920	The Doone Valley, Exmoor (28x45cm-11x18in) s. i.verso W/C bodycol. 27-Nov-3 Greenslade Hunt, Taunton #975
£650	$1086	€949	Near Lee Bay (28x36cm-11x14in) s. gouache. 17-Oct-3 Keys, Aylsham #480/R
£650	$1118	€949	Wood Bay, West Lynton. Dunkerry Beacon (18x27cm-7x11in) s. W/C pair. 2-Dec-3 Sworder & Son, Bishops Stortford #468a/R
£680	$1176	€993	Near Haytor, Dartmoor (43x58cm-17x23in) s.i. gouache. 9-Dec-3 Bearnes, Exeter #806
£700	$1239	€1022	Estuary of the Gunnell Newquay (39x100cm-15x39in) W/C bodycol. 28-Apr-4 Peter Wilson, Nantwich #162
£724	$1209	€1057	Fur Tor, Dartmoor (19x54cm-7x21in) s.i. W/C. 17-Nov-3 Waddingtons, Toronto #54/R (C.D 1600)
£740	$1376	€1080	Dunkery Beacon, Exmoor (24x34cm-9x13in) s. W/C. 2-Mar-4 Bearnes, Exeter #317/R
£750	$1215	€1088	On a beach (25x37cm-10x15in) s. gouache. 30-Jul-3 Hamptons Fine Art, Godalming #140
£769	$1285	€1123	Cattle grazing on the moors (35x53cm-14x21in) s. gouache. 17-Nov-3 Waddingtons, Toronto #52/R (C.D 1700)
£800	$1456	€1168	Trebarwith Sands, Cornwall (25x45cm-10x18in) s. W/C gouache. 21-Jun-4 Bonhams, Bath #384/R
£800	$1456	€1168	Coast at Bude (28x79cm-11x31in) s.i. W/C bodycol. 21-Jun-4 Bonhams, Bath #385/R
£850	$1590	€1275	Sandy walk down the bay (25x33cm-10x13in) s. W/C. 21-Jul-4 John Nicholson, Haslemere #41
£880	$1558	€1285	Exe Estuary and Exmouth from Turl (18x54cm-7x21in) s. W/C bodycol. 28-Apr-4 Hampton & Littlewood, Exeter #528/R
£880	$1602	€1285	Doone Valley, Exmoor (49x74cm-19x29in) s.i. gouache. 15-Jun-4 Bonhams, Oxford #55
£900	$1665	€1314	Dartmoor (33x50cm-13x20in) s. W/C. 16-Feb-4 Bonhams, Bath #82
£950	$1710	€1387	Bunkery Beacon, Exmoor (51x76cm-20x30in) s.i. W/C. 21-Jan-4 Sotheby's, Olympia #220/R est:800-1200
£1000	$1660	€1460	Slopes of Cawsand Beacon (20x29cm-8x11in) s. W/C. 1-Oct-3 George Kidner, Lymington #147/R est:1200-1500
£1000	$1860	€1460	Hey Tor, Dartmoor (28x77cm-11x30in) s. gouache. 2-Mar-4 Bearnes, Exeter #315/R est:300-500
£1050	$1785	€1533	Views of Woody Bay, near Linton (35x53cm-14x21in) s. gouache pair. 4-Nov-3 Holloways, Banbury #494 est:400-600
£1300	$2379	€1898	Teignmouth from the West (27x18cm-11x7in) s.i. gouache. 6-Jul-4 Bearnes, Exeter #438/R est:1200-1500
£1450	$2654	€2117	Source of the Dart. Dartmoor (36x54cm-14x21in) s.i. bodycol. 27-Jan-4 Bonhams, Knightsbridge #206/R est:800-1200
£1500	$2745	€2190	Burgh Island, Bigbury Bay, Devon (44x60cm-17x24in) s. W/C bodycol. 27-Jan-4 Bonhams, Knightsbridge #161/R est:1500-2000
£1600	$2800	€2336	Steperton Tor, Dartmoor. Hey Tor, Dartmoor (25x36cm-10x14in) s. bodycol pair. 16-Dec-3 Capes Dunn, Manchester #744/R
£1680	$3125	€2453	Dartmoor (28x77cm-11x30in) s. W/C. 2-Mar-4 Bearnes, Exeter #316/R est:500-700
£1900	$3458	€2774	Pond beneath Dartmoor Tors (45x60cm-18x24in) s. W/C bodycol. 21-Jun-4 Bonhams, Bath #386/R est:700-900
£2000	$3660	€2920	Teignmouth town from the east (27x18cm-11x7in) s.i. gouache. 6-Jul-4 Bearnes, Exeter #437/R est:1200-1500
£2300	$3910	€3358	Near Belston Tors, Dartmoor (51x76cm-20x30in) s. W/C bodycol. 1-Dec-3 Bonhams, Bath #59/R est:2000-3000
£2400	$4464	€3504	Belstone, Dartmoor (43x59cm-17x23in) s. gouache. 2-Mar-4 Bearnes, Exeter #319/R est:500-700

WIDGERY, W (1822-1893) British

Works on paper

£260	$465	€380	View on Dartmoor, Devon (32x50cm-13x20in) s. W/C. 25-May-4 Sworder & Son, Bishops Stortford #378/R
£380	$635	€555	Rural scene (48x30cm-19x12in) s. W/C. 13-Nov-3 Rendalls, Ashburton #1997
£2000	$3260	€2920	Bridge over river (71x46cm-28x18in) s. W/C. 17-Jul-3 Rendalls, Ashburton #1773

WIDGERY, William (1822-1893) British

£380	$692	€555	Woodland stream (49x34cm-19x13in) s. W/C. 3-Feb-4 Sworder & Son, Bishops Stortford #278
£400	$636	€584	Holy Street Mill at Chagford (91x71cm-36x28in) s.d.1870. 12-Sep-3 Gardiner & Houlgate, Bath #174/R
£480	$864	€701	Figures on a bridge in a mountainous river landscape (33x41cm-13x16in) s. 20-Apr-4 Clarke Gammon, Guildford #25
£700	$1281	€1022	After Landseer, the Blacksmiths (75x62cm-30x24in) s.i.d.1854. 6-Apr-4 Bonhams, Knightsbridge #168/R
£740	$1236	€1080	Drovers with cattle (48x58cm-19x23in) s. 17-Oct-3 Keys, Aylsham #771
£850	$1590	€1241	River landscape with sheep by a waterfall (24x29cm-9x11in) s. two. 26-Feb-4 Locke & England, Leamington Spa #91/R
£1150	$2105	€1679	North Devon coastal landscape. Rocky coastal scene (29x44cm-11x17in) both s. pair. 6-Jul-4 Bearnes, Exeter #527 est:400-600
£1600	$2672	€2336	Stream through a wooded landscape (104x70cm-41x28in) s. 7-Oct-3 Bonhams, Knightsbridge #162/R est:1000-1500
£2500	$4250	€3650	River view on the edge of Dartmoor (61x110cm-24x43in) s. 1-Dec-3 Bonhams, Bath #102/R est:1200-1800
£2840	$4600	€4146	On the Upper Dart, England (76x127cm-30x50in) s. 2-Aug-3 Neal Auction Company, New Orleans #233/R est:4000-6000
£4400	$7480	€6424	Extensive Dartmoor landscape with Brentor in the distance (74x148cm-29x58in) s.d.1870. 29-Oct-3 Hampton & Littlewood, Exeter #596/R est:2500-3000

Works on paper

£270	$500	€394	Cattle watering in a woodland stream (46x29cm-18x11in) s. W/C. 16-Feb-4 Bonhams, Bath #165
£300	$558	€438	Windy Post Cross, Whitchurch Common, Dartmoor (23x112cm-9x44in) s. W/C. 2-Mar-4 Bearnes, Exeter #318
£320	$582	€467	Moorland torrent (44x71cm-17x28in) s. W/C. 21-Jun-4 Bonhams, Bath #381
£400	$632	€584	Stream on Dartmoor (28x73cm-11x29in) s. W/C. 5-Sep-3 Honiton Galleries, Honiton #30/R
£430	$718	€628	Lyford Gorge (41x23cm-16x9in) s. W/C. 13-Nov-3 Rendalls, Ashburton #1983

£440	$818	€642	Woodland stream (74x23cm-29x9in) s. W/C. 2-Mar-4 Bearnes, Exeter #313
£446	$768	€651	Passing shower on the moor (23x74cm-9x29in) s. W/C prov. 2-Dec-3 Ritchie, Toronto #28/R (C.D 1000)
£480	$802	€701	Devon creek (27x49cm-11x19in) s. W/C. 20-Oct-3 Bonhams, Bath #128
£680	$1265	€993	Dartmoor pool (22x111cm-9x44in) s. W/C bodycol. 2-Mar-4 Bearnes, Exeter #309/R
£700	$1162	€1022	Summer sunset on Dartmoor (43x69cm-17x27in) s. W/C gouache. 1-Oct-3 Sotheby's, Olympia #137/R
£2000	$3340	€2920	Bridge over river (71x46cm-28x18in) s. W/C. 13-Nov-3 Rendalls, Ashburton #1987
£3100	$5735	€4650	Figure working at Sheeps Tor (46x71cm-18x28in) s. W/C. 15-Jul-4 Rendalls, Ashburton #1923

WIDHOPFF, D O (1867-1933) French

£690	$1152	€1000	Elegante a l'eventail rouge (146x68cm-57x27in) s. 17-Nov-3 Claude Boisgirard, Paris #103
£1192	$2170	€1800	Paysage aux sapins (73x60cm-29x24in) s.d.1927. 16-Jun-4 Claude Boisgirard, Paris #172/R est:2000-3000
£1457	$2652	€2200	Garden in bloom (81x60cm-32x24in) s. 19-Jun-4 St-Germain-en-Laye Encheres #191/R est:500
£1523	$2772	€2300	Femme au chat siamois (81x65cm-32x26in) s.d.1920. 16-Jun-4 Claude Boisgirard, Paris #174/R est:2000-2500
£2759	$4607	€4000	L'heure de the (76x106cm-30x42in) s. panel. 17-Nov-3 Claude Boisgirard, Paris #104/R est:3000-4000
£3691	$6829	€5500	Le Vallon (66x94cm-26x37in) s. 15-Mar-4 Claude Boisgirard, Paris #123 est:2000-2500
£3691	$6829	€5500	La mare jaune (75x103cm-30x41in) s. 15-Mar-4 Claude Boisgirard, Paris #124/R est:2000-2500
£4967	$9040	€7500	Paysage de Touraine (69x93cm-27x37in) s. 16-Jun-4 Claude Boisgirard, Paris #173/R est:3500-4000
£6291	$11450	€9500	Nature morte aux personnages en faience (69x91cm-27x36in) s.d.1926 cardboard. 16-Jun-4 Claude Boisgirard, Paris #171/R est:4000-4500

WIDMAN, Bruno (1930-) Uruguayan

£240	$400	€350	Moons (50x70cm-20x28in) s.d.94 s.i.d.verso. 7-Oct-3 Galeria y Remates, Montevideo #73
£376	$700	€549	Los veccinos (16x21cm-6x8in) s.d.75 s.i.verso board. 5-Mar-4 Skinner, Boston #347/R
£435	$800	€635	Work (60x70cm-24x28in) s.d.73. 22-Jun-4 Galeria y Remates, Montevideo #150/R
£767	$1350	€1120	Travel (80x81cm-31x32in) s. s.i.verso. 5-Jan-4 Galeria y Remates, Montevideo #16/R
£1529	$2600	€2232	Clock (73x100cm-29x39in) s.d.94. 25-Nov-3 Galeria y Remates, Montevideo #82/R

WIDNMANN, Julius (1865-1930) German

£296	$550	€432	Untitled (38x61cm-15x24in) 6-Mar-4 Page, Batavia #17

WIDOFF, Anders (1953-) Swedish

£680	$1156	€993	Bricklayers (136x140cm-54x55in) s.d.77. 4-Nov-3 Bukowskis, Stockholm #535/R (S.KR 9000)

WIE, Gustav (19th C) German

£336	$571	€480	Prussian troops in a winter landscape (28x23cm-11x9in) s.d.1881 lit. 28-Nov-3 Schloss Ahlden, Ahlden #1458/R

WIECHMANN, Julius (1894-?) German

£308	$529	€440	Two women (130x77cm-51x30in) s.d.53. 5-Dec-3 Bolland & Marotz, Bremen #879/R
£420	$722	€600	Composition (130x77cm-51x30in) 5-Dec-3 Bolland & Marotz, Bremen #882/R

WIED, Gustav (1858-1914) Danish

Works on paper

£2336	$3692	€3387	Self-portrait of the author Gustav Wied (49x75cm-19x30in) gouache. 3-Sep-3 Museumsbygningen, Copenhagen #249/R est:5000 (D.KR 25000)

WIEDEN, Ludwig (1869-?) Austrian

£272	$487	€400	View from Doges Palace (24x20cm-9x8in) copy after Amerling. 17-Mar-4 Dorotheum, Vienna #11

WIEDENHOFER, Oskar (1889-?) Austrian

£7000	$12600	€10220	Bathsheba (152x122cm-60x48in) mono.d.1914. 21-Jan-4 Sotheby's, Olympia #494/R est:7000-9000

WIEDERKEHR, Gido (1941-) Swiss

£568	$1045	€829	Untitled (120x120cm-47x47in) s.d.1988 verso acrylic. 8-Jun-4 Germann, Zurich #895 (S.FR 1300)

WIEDUWIL, Franz O (19/20th C) German

£461	$847	€700	Winter woodland landscape with a stream (60x80cm-24x31in) s.i.d.1913. 25-Jun-4 Michael Zeller, Lindau #591/R

WIEGAND, Charmion von (1899-1983) American

Works on paper

£659	$1200	€962	Untitled (31x25cm-12x10in) s.i.d.1959 gouache prov. 29-Jun-4 Sotheby's, New York #461/R est:2000-3000

WIEGAND, Gustave (1870-1957) American

£435	$700	€635	Pickering house (64x76cm-25x30in) s. i. verso. 20-Aug-3 James Julia, Fairfield #1384/R
£449	$750	€656	Autumnal landscape (64x76cm-25x30in) s. 19-Oct-3 William Jenack, New York #245
£552	$1000	€806	Glorious autumn at lake Sunapee, N H (74x86cm-29x34in) s. 16-Apr-4 James Julia, Fairfield #532/R est:3000-4000
£569	$950	€831	Winter sketch (23x30cm-9x12in) s.i. canvasboard. 16-Nov-3 William Jenack, New York #393
£598	$1100	€873	Peonies (64x76cm-25x30in) s. 25-Mar-4 Doyle, New York #76/R est:2000-3000
£692	$1100	€1010	Sunrise (25x35cm-10x14in) s. canvas on board. 12-Sep-3 Skinner, Boston #423/R
£699	$1250	€1021	From the Dolomites (76x91cm-30x36in) s. i.verso. 8-Jan-4 James Julia, Fairfield #764d/R
£872	$1500	€1273	Twilight (25x30cm-10x12in) s. board. 3-Dec-3 Doyle, New York #202/R est:2500-3500
£883	$1500	€1289	Late autumn landscape, sunrise (23x31cm-9x12in) s. board. 21-Nov-3 Skinner, Boston #443/R est:2500-3500
£901	$1532	€1315	Summertime (41x30cm-16x12in) s. 21-Nov-3 Walker's, Ottawa #274/R est:3000-3500 (C.D 2000)
£914	$1700	€1334	Dusk (24x40cm-9x16in) s. board. 5-Mar-4 Skinner, Boston #446/R est:2500-3500
£988	$1600	€1442	Fall landscape (74x86cm-29x34in) s. 31-Jul-3 Eldred, East Dennis #875/R est:1000-2000
£1241	$2073	€1800	Hudson River landscape (51x41cm-20x16in) s. prov. 15-Nov-3 Lempertz, Koln #1720/R est:2000
£1258	$2000	€1837	Cottage by pond (43x61cm-17x24in) s. 12-Sep-3 Skinner, Boston #264/R
£1757	$3250	€2565	November glow. s. 13-Mar-4 DeFina, Austinburg #722/R est:1500-2500
£2095	$3750	€3059	Apple blossoms (36x51cm-14x20in) s. 26-May-4 Doyle, New York #76/R est:3000-5000
£2500	$4250	€3650	Snowy landscape with brook in foreground and distant mountains (51x76cm-20x30in) s. 8-Nov-3 Van Blarcom, South Natick #123/R est:2000-3000

WIEGAND, Martin (1867-?) German

£483	$806	€700	Knight with horse (101x80cm-40x31in) s.d.34 panel. 9-Jul-3 Hugo Ruef, Munich #243/R

WIEGANDT, Bernhard (1851-1918) German

£1736	$2830	€2500	Iguazu waterfall, Brazil (97x87cm-38x34in) s.d.1878 i. stretcher. 24-Sep-3 Neumeister, Munich #601/R est:4500

WIEGELE, Franz (1887-1944) Austrian

£4196	$7133	€6000	Woman on balcony (69x29cm-27x11in) i.d.1906. 25-Nov-3 Hassfurther, Vienna #86/R est:5000-7000

Works on paper

£704	$1232	€1000	Head of a girl (34x29cm-13x11in) pencil. 19-Dec-3 Dorotheum, Vienna #113/R

WIEGERS, Jan (1893-1959) Dutch

£3158	$5811	€4800	Flower still life (60x50cm-24x20in) init. s.d.1956 verso. 28-Jun-4 Sotheby's, Amsterdam #254/R est:2500-3500
£4000	$7320	€6000	Portrait of a lady (79x61cm-31x24in) s. 7-Jun-4 Glerum, Amsterdam #135 est:4000-6000
£4333	$7973	€6500	Landschap Veluwe - landscape (61x51cm-24x20in) s.d.41 prov. 9-Jun-4 Christie's, Amsterdam #199/R est:8000-12000
£7692	$13077	€11000	Summer flowers in a jug (70x55cm-28x22in) canvas on board. 25-Nov-3 Christie's, Amsterdam #165/R est:7000-9000

Works on paper

£278	$453	€400	View of the dunes (32x43cm-13x17in) s. ink prov. 29-Sep-3 Sotheby's, Amsterdam #279/R
£336	$571	€480	View of a village in the Swiss Alps (23x29cm-9x11in) s.indis.d. pastel. 24-Nov-3 Glerum, Amsterdam #61/R
£350	$594	€500	Mountain landscape in summer, Ticino (36x48cm-14x19in) s.d.47 pastel. 24-Nov-3 Glerum, Amsterdam #63/R
£699	$1189	€1000	Frauenkirch (25x18cm-10x7in) s.d.36 Indian ink W/C. 24-Nov-3 Glerum, Amsterdam #637/R

WIEGERSMA, Hendrik (1891-1969) Dutch

£972	$1536	€1400	Portrait of the writer Antoon Coolen (131x91cm-52x36in) init. s.i.d.1959 verso. 2-Sep-3 Christie's, Amsterdam #374/R est:1200-1600

WIEGHARDT, Paul (1897-1969) German

£284	$500	€415	Untitled (30x33cm-12x13in) init. painted c.1950. 23-May-4 Treadway Gallery, Cincinnati #764/R

WIEGHORST, Olaf (1899-1988) American

£1912	$3250	€2792	Boot hill (28x36cm-11x14in) s. board prov.lit. 1-Nov-3 Santa Fe Art, Santa Fe #232/R est:4000-6000
£2429	$4250	€3546	Cowboy on horseback (51x57cm-20x22in) canvas on panel. 19-Dec-3 Sotheby's, New York #1136/R est:5000-10000
£5682	$10000	€8296	River rider (61x51cm-24x20in) s. i.stretcher prov. 19-May-4 Sotheby's, New York #209/R est:15000-25000
£7647	$13000	€11165	Sioux warrior (25x20cm-10x8in) s. i.verso panel prov.lit. 1-Nov-3 Santa Fe Art, Santa Fe #105/R est:8000-10000
£9091	$17000	€13273	Montana cowboy (61x64cm-24x25in) s. 24-Jul-4 Coeur d'Alene, Hayden #246/R est:20000-30000
£11765	$20000	€17177	Challenge (64x76cm-25x30in) 1-Nov-3 Altermann Galleries, Santa Fe #70
£12353	$21000	€18035	Stolen stock (61x76cm-24x30in) 1-Nov-3 Altermann Galleries, Santa Fe #69
£13235	$22500	€19323	Wagon boss (46x56cm-18x22in) s. lit. 1-Nov-3 Santa Fe Art, Santa Fe #175/R est:20000-25000

Works on paper

£621	$1000	€900	Indian portrait (23x15cm-9x6in) W/C. 22-Aug-3 Altermann Galleries, Santa Fe #9
£1235	$2000	€1791	Cowboy's best friend (27x22cm-11x9in) s. W/C. 8-Aug-3 Barridorf, Portland #256/R est:2000-3000
£1553	$2500	€2267	Cowboy and horse in snow (33x25cm-13x10in) s. W/C. 20-Aug-3 James Julia, Fairfield #1600/R est:1500-2500

£2235 $3800 €3263 Cowboy and horse resting at the base of a tree (18x13cm-7x5in) pen ink W/C. 1-Nov-3 Altermann Galleries, Santa Fe #67
£2941 $5000 €4294 Bucking bronco (36x28cm-14x11in) s. pen ink prov.lit. 1-Nov-3 Santa Fe Art, Santa Fe #5/R est:2000-3000
£2941 $5500 €4294 Cowboy with pack horse. Buffalo greeting (18x18cm-7x7in) s. mixed media pair prov. 24-Jul-4 Coeur d'Alene, Hayden #105/R est:4000-6000
£2941 $5500 €4294 Fancy quirt (28x23cm-11x9in) s. mixed media prov. 24-Jul-4 Coeur d'Alene, Hayden #110/R est:4000-6000
£3088 $5250 €4508 Mexican cowboy (25x20cm-10x8in) s.i. W/C ink prov.lit. 1-Nov-3 Santa Fe Art, Santa Fe #6/R est:7000-10000
£3209 $6000 €4685 Northern plains warrior (28x23cm-11x9in) s. mixed media prov. 24-Jul-4 Coeur d'Alene, Hayden #109/R est:2000-3000
£3235 $5500 €4723 Roping cowboy (30x25cm-12x10in) W/C. 1-Nov-3 Altermann Galleries, Santa Fe #66
£3476 $6500 €5075 Bandito (30x25cm-12x10in) s. mixed media prov. 24-Jul-4 Coeur d'Alene, Hayden #107/R est:4000-6000
£4011 $7500 €5856 Indian on horseback. Portrait of an Indian. Indian on horseback dragging Travois. Slippery pavement (28x20cm-11x8in) s. pen ink chl set of four prov. 24-Jul-4 Coeur d'Alene, Hayden #261/R est:4000-8000
£4545 $8500 €6636 Cowboy (28x23cm-11x9in) s. mixed media prov. 24-Jul-4 Coeur d'Alene, Hayden #263/R est:4000-6000
£6952 $13000 €10150 Snowstorm cowboy (23x23cm-9x9in) s. W/C. 24-Jul-4 Coeur d'Alene, Hayden #269/R est:4000-6000
£8021 $15000 €11711 Charge (28x23cm-11x9in) s. mixed media. 24-Jul-4 Coeur d'Alene, Hayden #19/R est:6000-9000

WIEGMAN, Matthieu (1886-1971) Dutch
£526 $968 €800 Portrait of a young woman (72x60cm-28x24in) s. s.d.1939 on stretcher. 22-Jun-4 Christie's, Amsterdam #435/R
£1645 $3026 €2500 Still life with dahlias and sunflowers (76x60cm-30x24in) s. plywood. 22-Jun-4 Christie's, Amsterdam #479/R est:2500-3500
£1748 $2919 €2500 Religious scene (45x37cm-18x15in) s. prov. 30-Jun-3 Sotheby's, Amsterdam #439/R
£1974 $3632 €3000 A view in Chartres (36x38cm-14x15in) s. 22-Jun-4 Christie's, Amsterdam #552/R est:1200-1600
£2041 $3714 €3000 Still life with tulips and lemons (73x60cm-29x24in) s. 3-Feb-4 Christie's, Amsterdam #442 est:2000-3000
£2105 $3874 €3200 Bloemen - Flowers (46x38cm-18x15in) s. i.d.1962 on stretcher. 22-Jun-4 Christie's, Amsterdam #490/R est:1500-2000
£2133 $3925 €3200 Village (73x60cm-29x24in) s. prov. 9-Jun-4 Christie's, Amsterdam #13/R est:3000-4000
£2174 $3565 €3000 Still life of flowers (117x96cm-46x38in) s. 27-May-3 Sotheby's, Amsterdam #482/R est:3000-5000
£2667 $4907 €4000 Still life with fruit (55x45cm-22x18in) s. board. 8-Jun-4 Sotheby's, Amsterdam #194/R est:4000-6000
£2685 $4966 €4000 Still life with apples (54x65cm-21x26in) s. canvas on board. 15-Mar-4 Sotheby's, Amsterdam #186/R est:1500-2000
£7971 $13072 €11000 Still life with chair (130x97cm-51x38in) s. prov. 27-May-3 Sotheby's, Amsterdam #304/R est:8000-12000
Works on paper
£764 $1245 €1100 View of the bridge, Ville Franche (38x49cm-15x19in) s.i.d.1960 verso W/C. 29-Sep-3 Sotheby's, Amsterdam #227/R
£769 $1284 €1100 View of the Drome, France (25x31cm-10x12in) s. W/C. 30-Jun-3 Sotheby's, Amsterdam #348/R
£805 $1490 €1200 Forest landscape (44x36cm-17x14in) s. gouache. 15-Mar-4 Sotheby's, Amsterdam #192/R est:750-850

WIEGMAN, Petrus Jacobus Maria (1930-) Dutch
£280 $467 €400 View of a landscape (49x60cm-19x24in) s. cardboard. 30-Jun-3 Sotheby's, Amsterdam #480/R

WIEGMAN, Piet (1885-1963) Dutch
£9333 $17173 €14000 View of Thorn with a goat (98x125cm-39x49in) init. painted 1925 prov. 9-Jun-4 Christie's, Amsterdam #195/R est:7000-9000

WIEGMANN, Alfred (?) German
£265 $482 €400 Farm house in early spring (36x45cm-14x18in) s. board. 18-Jun-4 Bolland & Marotz, Bremen #417
£282 $451 €400 Autumn landscape with stream (76x66cm-30x26in) s. 18-Sep-3 Rieber, Stuttgart #931

WIEGMANN, Marie Elisabeth (1826-1893) German
£1042 $1719 €1500 Portrait of Frau Carl vom Rath (112x96cm-44x38in) s.d.1866 prov. 3-Jul-3 Van Ham, Cologne #1502/R est:1500

WIEHL, Hermann (20th C) German
£5667 $10257 €8500 Winter landscape with Black Forest farmstead (50x75cm-20x30in) mono. panel lit. 1-Apr-4 Frank Peege, Freiburg #1199/R est:8000
£6000 $10860 €9000 Boats near Hemmenhofen (50x60cm-20x24in) s. board lit. 1-Apr-4 Frank Peege, Freiburg #1200/R est:8500

WIELAND, Hans Beat (1867-1945) Swiss
£431 $772 €629 Lake Thun in autumn (53x64cm-21x25in) s.d.1934 i. verso. 13-May-4 Stuker, Bern #384 (S.FR 1000)
£826 $1379 €1198 Niederried on the Brienzersee (54x64cm-21x25in) s. 23-Jun-3 Philippe Schuler, Zurich #3437 (S.FR 1800)
£1176 $2035 €1717 Brienz in autumn (71x58cm-28x23in) s. s.i.d.1932 verso. 9-Dec-3 Sotheby's, Zurich #78/R est:2000-3000 (S.FR 2600)
£1719 $2975 €2510 Winter morning at Schwarzmonch (57x71cm-22x28in) s.d.1944 s.i.d.1944 verso. 9-Dec-3 Sotheby's, Zurich #96/R est:2500-3500 (S.FR 3800)
Works on paper
£325 $543 €475 Snow covered peak (51x36cm-20x14in) s. W/C. 8-Oct-3 Andrew Hartley, Ilkley #1061

WIELAND, Joyce (1931-) Canadian
£388 $668 €566 Two figures (20x22cm-8x9in) 2-Dec-3 Joyner Waddington, Toronto #523 (C.D 870)
£3125 $5375 €4563 Ann's Moon (82x95cm-32x37in) s.d.86 prov. 2-Dec-3 Joyner Waddington, Toronto #217/R est:8000-10000 (C.D 7000)
Works on paper
£268 $461 €391 Couple (29x45cm-11x18in) chl. 2-Dec-3 Joyner Waddington, Toronto #482 (C.D 600)
£357 $614 €521 She speaks about reason (25x25cm-10x10in) s.d.79 col pencils. 2-Dec-3 Joyner Waddington, Toronto #473 (C.D 800)

WIELEN, Genevieve van der (1954-) Belgian
£1020 $1806 €1520 L'artiste et son modele (82x100cm-32x39in) mono. 29-Apr-4 Claude Aguttes, Neuilly #260 est:1500-1800

WIEMKEN, Walter Kurt (1907-1940) Swiss
£9955 $17222 €14534 The photograph (61x74cm-24x29in) canvas on masonite prov.exhib.lit. 9-Dec-3 Sotheby's, Zurich #121/R est:22000-28000 (S.FR 22000)
£34783 $63652 €50783 The mystery of the Sphinx, I (116x81cm-46x32in) prov.exhib.lit. 7-Jun-4 Christie's, Zurich #128/R est:25000-35000 (S.FR 80000)

WIENER, Alfred (1877-1958) German
£403 $741 €600 Sunny Berlin courtyard (49x60cm-19x24in) s.d.15 board. 26-Mar-4 Bolland & Marotz, Bremen #649/R

WIERINGA, Harmen Willems (attrib) (17th C) Dutch
£700 $1295 €1022 Portrait of an officer in an interior (55x38cm-22x15in) panel. 9-Mar-4 Bonhams, Knightsbridge #173/R

WIERINGEN, Cornelis Claesz van (1580-1633) Dutch
£26950 $45007 €38000 View of Vlissingen harbour (64x95cm-25x37in) mono. board. 23-Jun-3 Finarte Semenzato, Rome #163/R

WIERINGER, Hans (1949-) Austrian
Works on paper
£2639 $4301 €3800 Loving couple (59x79cm-23x31in) s.indis.d. mixed media. 23-Sep-3 Wiener Kunst Auktionen, Vienna #163/R est:2000-4000

WIERIX, Hieronymus (c.1533-1619) Flemish
Prints
£2000 $3580 €3000 Melancolia I (24x19cm-9x7in) copperplate after Durer. 13-May-4 Bassenge, Berlin #5343/R est:1800

WIERIX, Johan (attrib) (c.1549-c.1615) Flemish
Works on paper
£1701 $3044 €2500 Portrait de Daniel L'Hermite (14x11cm-6x4in) i.d.1600 pen brown ink vellum. 18-Mar-4 Christie's, Paris #315/R est:1000-1500

WIERS, Margaret (?) British?
£650 $1190 €949 Group of spaniels with their owner in a garden (55x80cm-22x31in) s. 28-Jul-4 Bonhams, Knightsbridge #185

WIERTZ, Joub (1893-1966) Dutch
£486 $792 €700 Horse rider (100x80cm-39x31in) s.d.1928. 29-Sep-3 Sotheby's, Amsterdam #235/R

WIERUSZ-KOWALSKI, Alfred von (1849-1915) Polish
£7343 $12483 €10500 Horse and sleigh (27x40cm-11x16in) s. canvas on board. 29-Nov-3 Bukowskis, Helsinki #392/R est:2000-3000
£10807 $19669 €15778 Man horse riding in the water (21x48cm-8x19in) s. painted 1880-1890. 20-Jun-4 Agra, Warsaw #57/R (P.Z 75000)
£20173 $36715 €29453 Landscape with horse and cart (47x64cm-19x25in) s. painted 1890. 20-Jun-4 Agra, Warsaw #58/R (P.Z 140000)
£22472 $37303 €32809 Attack of the wolves (49x71cm-19x28in) s. painted c.1900. 15-Jun-3 Agra, Warsaw #5/R est:140000 (P.Z 140000)
£25682 $42632 €37496 Hunters in the bullrushes (44x56cm-17x22in) s. painted c.1890. 15-Jun-3 Agra, Warsaw #4/R est:140000 (P.Z 160000)
£26846 $49396 €40000 Winter landscape (78x99cm-31x39in) s. canvas on masonite prov.lit. 25-Mar-4 Karlheinz Kaupp, Staufen #2801/R est:29000
£28289 $49788 €41302 Arabian figures in courtyard (47x62cm-19x24in) painted 1903. 23-May-4 Agra, Warsaw #4/R (P.Z 200000)
£28409 $50000 €41477 Joy ride (80x107cm-31x42in) s. 18-May-4 Bonhams & Butterfields, San Francisco #91/R est:6000-8000
£28744 $49728 €41966 Three horsemen on a mountain trail (57x49cm-22x19in) s. painted 1880-1885. 14-Dec-3 Agra, Warsaw #16/R est:190000 (P.Z 190000)
£32000 $58240 €46720 The welcoming party (45x59cm-18x23in) s. prov. 15-Jun-4 Sotheby's, London #39/R est:20000-30000
£36775 $64724 €53692 Cart on rural path (78x100cm-31x39in) 23-May-4 Agra, Warsaw #2/R (P.Z 260000)
£59002 $102073 €86143 Wolf attack (51x85cm-20x33in) s. painted c.1885-1890. 14-Dec-3 Agra, Warsaw #18/R est:390000 (P.Z 390000)

WIESCHEBRINK, Franz (1818-1884) German
£7200 $11952 €10512 Love letter (85x71cm-33x28in) s. 1-Oct-3 Sotheby's, Olympia #216/R est:3000-4000

WIESLER, Adolf (1878-?) Austrian
£528 $877 €750 Autumnal slope (65x54cm-26x21in) s.d.1922 board. 12-Jun-3 Dorotheum, Graz #80/R

WIESMANN, Theo (1912-) Swiss
£260 $465 €380 Water lilies (38x60cm-15x24in) canvas on masonite. 22-Mar-4 Philippe Schuler, Zurich #6064 (S.FR 600)

WIETHASE, Edgard (1881-1965) Belgian

£320	$586	€467	Tete d'enfant (34x25cm-13x10in) s.d.1921 oil on card. 8-Apr-4 Christie's, Kensington #52
£347	$580	€500	Chevaux dans la prairie (27x41cm-11x16in) s. panel. 21-Oct-3 Campo, Vlaamse Kaai #629
£423	$731	€600	Still life. Portrait (30x37cm-12x15in) s.d.1956 panel double-sided. 13-Dec-3 De Vuyst, Lokeren #399

WIGAND, Albert (1890-1978) German

£2667	$4800	€4000	Poppitz in Dresden (33x43cm-13x17in) s. i. verso canvas on board. 24-Apr-4 Dr Lehr, Berlin #497/R est:5000
£3333	$6000	€5000	Untitled (47x31cm-19x12in) s. oil tempera panel. 24-Apr-4 Dr Lehr, Berlin #498/R est:5000
Works on paper			
£267	$480	€400	Untitled (10x14cm-4x6in) s.d. verso collage mixed media board. 24-Apr-4 Dr Lehr, Berlin #503
£333	$600	€500	Commence-fini (10x16cm-4x6in) s.i.d.1.62/12.69 verso collage gouache board. 24-Apr-4 Dr Lehr, Berlin #504/R
£382	$638	€550	Untitled (17x11cm-7x4in) s.i.d. verso collage board silver paper. 25-Oct-3 Dr Lehr, Berlin #545/R
£417	$696	€600	Untitled (18x10cm-7x4in) s. collage Indian ink board. 25-Oct-3 Dr Lehr, Berlin #544/R
£590	$986	€850	Stotteritz Christmas (14x21cm-6x8in) s.i.d. collage over mixed media. 25-Oct-3 Dr Lehr, Berlin #543/R
£800	$1464	€1200	Dresden, Frauenkirche (25x35cm-10x14in) s. bodycol pastel chk on pencil. 5-Jun-4 Lempertz, Koln #1024/R

WIGAND, Balthasar (1771-1846) Austrian

Works on paper			
£690	$1152	€1000	Vues de Vienne (27x37cm-11x15in) s.d.1832 gouache trompe-l'oeil. 17-Nov-3 Delorme & Bocage, Paris #73/R
£2667	$4800	€3894	Trompe-l'oeil with seventeen drawings of Viennese monuments (27x38cm-11x15in) s.i.d.MDCCCXXXII pen brown ink bodycol. 22-Jan-4 Christie's, Rockefeller NY #153/R est:4000-6000
£4500	$8190	€6570	Vienna from the Galizienberg (9x9cm-4x4in) s.i. W/C gouache. 15-Jun-4 Sotheby's, London #2/R est:5000-7000
£5705	$10497	€8500	Wieden (11x18cm-4x7in) s.i. pen Indian ink W/C painted with studio. 26-Mar-4 Dorotheum, Vienna #189/R est:4000-5000
£6040	$10691	€9000	Curtys (13x22cm-5x9in) s.i. gouache prov. 28-Apr-4 Wiener Kunst Auktionen, Vienna #24/R est:7000-15000
£11000	$18920	€16060	Battle scenes (24x35cm-9x14in) three s. W/C gouache four. 4-Dec-3 Christie's, Kensington #206/R est:6000-8000

WIGDAHL, Anders Guttormsen (1830-1914) Norwegian

£627	$1129	€915	Landscape near Dusseldorf, man by rapids (45x71cm-18x28in) s.d.1876. 24-Apr-4 Rasmussen, Havnen #2078/R (D.KR 7000)

WIGDEHL, Michaloff (1856-1921) Norwegian

£449	$745	€651	Nunatakprofil (57x57cm-22x22in) s. i.verso. 16-Jun-3 Blomqvist, Lysaker #1272 (N.KR 5200)

WIGERT, Hans (1932-) Swedish

£474	$763	€692	Tree (62x56cm-24x22in) s. s.d.60 verso. 25-Aug-3 Lilla Bukowskis, Stockholm #144 (S.KR 6200)
£659	$1167	€962	The wolf (54x54cm-21x21in) s.i.d.1982 verso exhib. 27-Apr-4 AB Stockholms Auktionsverk #1027/R (S.KR 9000)
£879	$1556	€1283	The track in the snow (60x73cm-24x29in) s.i.d.1973 verso. 27-Apr-4 AB Stockholms Auktionsverk #1026/R (S.KR 12000)
£1392	$2464	€2032	Neckan (55x46cm-22x18in) s.i.d.1966 verso exhib. 27-Apr-4 AB Stockholms Auktionsverk #1025/R est:10000-12000 (S.KR 19000)
£2175	$3916	€3176	Sand Island (87x115cm-34x45in) s.i.d.1979 verso. 26-Apr-4 Bukowskis, Stockholm #502/R est:20000 30000 (S.KR 30000)
£3077	$5446	€4492	At the photographer - Lillan and me (116x88cm-46x35in) s.i.d.1966 verso exhib. 27-Apr-4 AB Stockholms Auktionsverk #1028/R est:25000-30000 (S.KR 42000)

WIGFULL, W Edward (?) ?

£280	$484	€409	Aboard ship during a 19th century naval battle (55x35cm-22x14in) board. 11-Dec-3 Lane, Penzance #67

WIGG, Charles Mayes (1889-1969) British

Works on paper			
£300	$555	€438	Oulton Broad (25x36cm-10x14in) s. W/C. 13-Feb-4 Keys, Aylsham #577
£300	$552	€438	Norfolk wheeries (14x20cm-6x8in) W/C. 11-Jun-4 Keys, Aylsham #583
£380	$703	€555	Cromer (23x33cm-9x13in) W/C. 13-Feb-4 Keys, Aylsham #575/R
£400	$740	€584	Norfolk wherry (23x33cm-9x13in) s. W/C. 13-Feb-4 Keys, Aylsham #576
£420	$777	€613	Horning ferry (33x51cm-13x20in) s. W/C. 13-Feb-4 Keys, Aylsham #572
£480	$869	€701	Hickling, back water behind Pleasure Boat Inn (25x36cm-10x14in) s. i.verso W/C. 16-Apr-4 Keys, Aylsham #651/R
£600	$1002	€876	Wherry (30x38cm-12x15in) s. W/C. 17-Oct-3 Keys, Aylsham #660

WIGGERS, Dirk (1866-1933) Dutch

£1678	$2887	€2400	View of Cairo by night (51x81cm-20x32in) s. maroufle. 8-Dec-3 Glerum, Amsterdam #119/R est:2000-2500
£2483	$4593	€3600	Vue de Kairouan, le soir (54x82cm-21x32in) s. canvas on panel. 16-Feb-4 Horta, Bruxelles #152/R est:4000-6000
Works on paper			
£294	$505	€420	View of Cairo (34x46cm-13x18in) s.d.1920 pastel. 8-Dec-3 Glerum, Amsterdam #118/R

WIGGERS, Karel (1916-1989) Dutch

£340	$619	€500	Damesportret - portrait of a lady (50x49cm-20x19in) s.d.70 s.i.verso plywood. 3-Feb-4 Christie's, Amsterdam #546/R
£4110	$6986	€6000	Card player (68x78cm-27x31in) s.d.67 board. 5-Nov-3 Vendue Huis, Gravenhage #448/R est:4000-6000
£4110	$6986	€6000	Boy with ornament (68x58cm-27x23in) s. panel. 5-Nov-3 Vendue Huis, Gravenhage #449/R est:4000-6000
£4895	$8420	€7000	Woman with necklace (84x64cm-33x25in) s.d.63 s.i.d.verso. 2-Dec-3 Sotheby's, Amsterdam #263/R est:5000-7000
£14667	$26840	€22000	A child on the Queen's birthday (63x59cm-25x23in) s. panel. 7-Jun-4 Glerum, Amsterdam #338/R est:5000-7000

WIGGIN, John (19th C) British

£436	$772	€650	Hiver a Ixelles (70x90cm-28x35in) s. panel. 27-Apr-4 Campo & Campo, Antwerp #278/R

WIGGINS, Carleton (1848-1932) American

£297	$525	€434	Roat at North Hadley, Mass (25x33cm-10x13in) s. 2-May-4 Van Blarcom, South Natick #74
£1062	$1900	€1551	Mountain landscape (23x41cm-9x16in) s. canvas on board prov. 6-May-4 Shannon's, Milford #245/R est:2000-3000
£1087	$2000	€1587	Shepherd with his flock on the dunes (39x52cm-15x20in) s. prov. 8-Jun-4 Bonhams & Butterfields, San Francisco #4037/R est:3000-5000
£1235	$2000	€1791	In the harbour (23x18cm-9x7in) s. board. 26-Jul-3 Thomaston Place, Thomaston #136/R
£1728	$2800	€2506	Crossing the dunes, evening (33x48cm-13x19in) i. 8-Aug-3 Barridorf, Portland #143/R est:1500-2500
£11765	$20000	€17177	Daybreak (30x51cm-12x20in) s.d.1897 prov. 30-Oct-3 Phillips, New York #50/R est:20000-25000

WIGGINS, Guy A (1920-) American

£1605	$2600	€2343	Autumn days (20x25cm-8x10in) s. i.d.1951 verso academy board. 26-Jul-3 Thomaston Place, Thomaston #29/R

WIGGINS, Guy Carleton (1883-1962) American

£2557	$4500	€3733	Spring in Essex (64x74cm-25x29in) s.i. 21-May-4 Pook & Pook, Downington #347/R est:6000-8000
£2989	$5500	€4364	Golden days (40x50cm-16x20in) s.i. 8-Jun-4 Bonhams & Butterfields, San Francisco #4038/R est:3000-5000
£3145	$5000	€4592	Up country (41x51cm-16x20in) s. i.verso canvasboard. 9-Sep-3 Arthur James, Florida #107
£3591	$6500	€5243	Harbor scene (23x33cm-9x13in) canvasboard. 16-Apr-4 Du Mouchelle, Detroit #2073/R est:4000-6000
£3779	$6500	€5517	Georgia landscape (51x61cm-20x24in) s. i.d.1939 verso. 7-Dec-3 Freeman, Philadelphia #125 est:6000-8000
£3892	$6500	€5682	Cornwall, England (25x20cm-10x8in) s. board prov. 9-Oct-3 Christie's, Rockefeller NY #56/R est:4000-6000
£5587	$10000	€8157	At the Plaza (23x30cm-9x12in) s. canvasboard exhib. 26-May-4 Doyle, New York #139/R est:15000-25000
£8125	$13000	€11863	Shining harbour (66x61cm-26x24in) s.i. 21-Sep-3 William Jenack, New York #244 est:15000-20000
£9202	$15000	€13435	European village (41x51cm-16x20in) s. 28-Sep-3 Simpson's, Houston #390/R
£10484	$19290	€15307	White Mantle (18x23cm-7x9in) s. i.verso. 14-Jun-4 Waddingtons, Toronto #22/R est:10000-15000 (C.D 26000)
£10494	$17000	€15321	Harbour scene probably near Old Lyme, Connecticut (30x25cm-12x10in) s. 31-Jul-3 Eldred, East Dennis #992/R est:20000-30000
£11976	$20000	€17485	Washington Square Park in winter (30x41cm-12x16in) s. canvasboard. 9-Oct-3 Christie's, Rockefeller NY #72/R est:15000-25000
£14118	$24000	€20612	Fifth Avenue in winter (30x23cm-12x9in) board. 31-Oct-3 North East Auctions, Portsmouth #1881 est:20000-30000
£15528	$25000	€22671	New York winter (30x41cm-12x16in) s.d.48. 20-Aug-3 James Julia, Fairfield #1272/R est:27500-32500
£16022	$29000	€23392	New York in the snow (30x23cm-12x9in) s. canvasboard prov. 31-Mar-4 Sotheby's, New York #128/R est:10000-15000
£18466	$32500	€26960	Winter in Washington Square (41x51cm-16x20in) s.i. s.d.1936 verso prov. 19-May-4 Sotheby's, New York #189/R est:30000-50000
£18863	$31500	€27540	Winter in Central Park (58x74cm-23x29in) s. s.i.verso. 23-Oct-3 Shannon's, Milford #50/R est:35000-45000
£22099	$40000	€32265	Midtown, winter (41x30cm-16x12in) s. s.i.d.1936 verso canvasboard. 31-Mar-4 Sotheby's, New York #127/R est:20000-30000
£26163	$45000	€38198	Winter at the Plaza (51x61cm-20x24in) s. s.i.verso prov. 3-Dec-3 Sotheby's, New York #166/R est:30000-50000
£27027	$50000	€39459	Subtreasury, winter (41x30cm-16x12in) s. s.i.d.1936 verso prov. 11-Mar-4 Christie's, Rockefeller NY #59/R est:40000-60000
£27616	$47500	€40319	Fifth Avenue at 55TH Street (30x41cm-12x16in) s. s.i.verso canvasboard prov. 3-Dec-3 Sotheby's, New York #165/R est:30000-50000
£28743	$48000	€41965	Snow storm on Fifth Avenue (41x30cm-16x12in) s. canvasboard. 9-Oct-3 Christie's, Rockefeller NY #51/R est:25000-35000
£34091	$60000	€49773	Morning on the East river (63x76cm-25x30in) s. s.i.d.1947 verso prov. 18-May-4 Christie's, Rockefeller NY #78/R est:60000-80000
£35227	$62000	€51431	Park Avenue, winter (41x31cm-16x12in) s. s.i.verso painted 1936. 18-May-4 Christie's, Rockefeller NY #107/R est:30000-50000
£36932	$65000	€53921	Wall street, winter (41x30cm-16x12in) s. s.i.verso painted 1936. 18-May-4 Christie's, Rockefeller NY #106/R est:40000-60000
£42614	$75000	€62216	New York Avenue (72x59cm-28x23in) s. s.i.d.1939 verso prov. 18-May-4 Christie's, Rockefeller NY #104/R est:50000-70000
£46961	$85000	€68563	Broadway at night (41x30cm-16x12in) s. s.i.verso masonite prov. 31-Mar-4 Sotheby's, New York #129/R est:10000-15000
£58140	$100000	€84884	Public Library, New York (63x76cm-25x30in) s. s.i.verso prov. 3-Dec-3 Sotheby's, New York #167/R est:50000-70000
£66860	$115000	€97616	Winter's evening, New York (63x76cm-25x30in) s. s.i.d.1960 verso prov. 3-Dec-3 Sotheby's, New York #168/R est:50000-70000
Works on paper			
£1038	$1900	€1515	Waiting for a fare in New York. s. W/C. 31-Jan-4 South Bay, Long Island #171

WIGGINS, Kim Douglas (1960-) American

£1056	$1700	€1542	Confrontation (51x41cm-20x16in) 22-Aug-3 Altermann Galleries, Santa Fe #200
£1988	$3200	€2902	Sacrifice (61x51cm-24x20in) 22-Aug-3 Altermann Galleries, Santa Fe #198

£5587 $10000 €8157 Coronado's Quest (102x152cm-40x60in) 15-May-4 Altermann Galleries, Santa Fe #143/R

WIGGLI, Oskar (1927-) Swiss
Works on paper
£642 $1072 €931 Sculpture sketches (32x50cm-13x20in) s.d.6.5.61 Indian ink wash. 19-Jun-3 Kornfeld, Bern #1049 (S.FR 1400)

WIGLE, Archie Palmer (20th C) American
£375 $600 €548 Landscape (28x36cm-11x14in) board. 19-Sep-3 Du Mouchelle, Detroit #2455/R

WIGMANA, Gerard (1673-1741) Dutch
£2838 $5166 €4143 Joseph accused before Pottiphar (71x54cm-28x21in) s. panel. 16-Jun-4 Fischer, Luzern #1044/R est:8000-12000 (S.FR 6500)

WIGSTEAD, Henry (1793-?) British
Works on paper
£1000 $1670 €1460 Caricature of a Jewish merchant (13x9cm-5x4in) W/C. 14-Oct-3 Bonhams, New Bond Street #122/R est:1000-1500

WIIG-HANSEN, Svend (1922-1997) Danish
£7220 $13285 €10541 Torso - large figure composition (180x135cm-71x53in) init.d.58 s.d.1958 verso exhib.prov. 29-Mar-4 Rasmussen, Copenhagen #135/R est:75000-100000 (D.KR 80000)
Sculpture
£1805 $3321 €2635 Seated woman with her arms out-stretched (22cm-9in) init.num.3/6 pat.bronze. 29-Mar-4 Rasmussen, Copenhagen #319/R est:10000 (D.KR 20000)
£2708 $4982 €3954 Seated woman with long hair (29cm-11in) pat.bronze. 29-Mar-4 Rasmussen, Copenhagen #320/R est:15000-20000 (D.KR 30000)
Works on paper
£284 $455 €412 Study of heads (50x65cm-20x26in) s.i.d.93 crayon. 17-Sep-3 Kunsthallen, Copenhagen #127 (D.KR 3000)
£284 $455 €412 Roman fantasies (32x42cm-13x17in) s.i.d.1960 Indian ink exhib.lit. 17-Sep-3 Kunsthallen, Copenhagen #128 (D.KR 3000)

WIIK, Maria (1853-1928) Finnish
£3521 $5634 €5000 Coastal cliffs (23x38cm-9x15in) s. 21-Sep-3 Bukowskis, Helsinki #489/R est:5000
£6197 $10721 €8800 Portrait of Anna Wiik (40x35cm-16x14in) s.d.1873 canvas on board lit. 13-Dec-3 Hagelstam, Helsinki #71/R est:8500
£43333 $77567 €65000 A look at the artist's studio (31x24cm-12x9in) s. panel lit. 15-May-4 Hagelstam, Helsinki #100/R est:65000
£62937 $106993 €90000 Nordic spring - blond girl looking through green leaves (26x35cm-10x14in) s.d.95 lit. 29-Nov-3 Bukowskis, Helsinki #59/R est:100000-120000
Works on paper
£699 $1189 €1000 Boy (46x29cm-18x11in) s. chl. 29-Nov-3 Bukowskis, Helsinki #211/R
£1056 $1827 €1500 Mealtime (18x28cm-7x11in) s. pencil. 13-Dec-3 Hagelstam, Helsinki #75/R est:1000
£1127 $1949 €1600 Lake landscape (13x20cm-5x8in) s. W/C. 13-Dec-3 Hagelstam, Helsinki #74/R est:1500
£1757 $3145 €2600 By the window (57x40cm-22x16in) pastel. 8-May-4 Bukowskis, Helsinki #50/R est:2500-2800
£2535 $4386 €3600 Girl and boy (24x32cm-9x13in) s. W/C. 13-Dec-3 Hagelstam, Helsinki #73/R est:2000
£2973 $5322 €4400 Flowers (12x17cm-5x7in) s. W/C. 8-May-4 Bukowskis, Helsinki #168/R est:2000-2300
£3706 $6301 €5300 Self-portrait (54x39cm-21x15in) s. mixed media. 29-Nov-3 Bukowskis, Helsinki #210/R est:1500-2000
£6197 $10721 €8800 Iris (43x34cm-17x13in) s. gouache. 13-Dec-3 Hagelstam, Helsinki #72/R est:4000
£11888 $20210 €17000 Kirsti (24x24cm-9x9in) s.d.21 pastel lit. 29-Nov-3 Bukowskis, Helsinki #209/R est:4500-5000

WIINBLAD, Bjorn (1918-) Danish
Works on paper
£344 $558 €499 Female figure (230x120cm-91x47in) s. gouache paper on canvas. 4-Aug-3 Rasmussen, Vejle #633/R (D.KR 3600)
£409 $654 €593 Musicians (17x19cm-7x7in) s. Indian ink. 22-Sep-3 Blomqvist, Lysaker #1336 (N.KR 4800)

WIJNBERG, Nicolaas (1918-) Dutch
Works on paper
£274 $466 €400 Woman reading (36x23cm-14x9in) s.d.44 pastel. 5-Nov-3 Vendue Huis, Gravenhage #486/R

WIJNGAERDT, Piet van (1873-1964) Dutch
£235 $435 €350 Keukenstuk (59x79cm-23x31in) s. s.i.verso. 15-Mar-4 Sotheby's, Amsterdam #144
£294 $499 €420 Cloud study, Amstelveenseweg, Amsterdam (37x47cm-15x19in) s. i.verso canvas on panel. 24-Nov-3 Glerum, Amsterdam #15/R
£544 $990 €800 Poinsettia's (80x68cm-31x27in) s. s.i.verso. 3-Feb-4 Christie's, Amsterdam #449
£559 $934 €800 Luxury of flowers (80x60cm-31x24in) s.verso. 10-Oct-3 Vendue Huis, Gravenhage #812
£638 $1129 €950 Rhododendron and azalea in vase (78x68cm-31x27in) s. i. verso. 28-Apr-4 Schopman, Hamburg #592/R
£658 $1211 €1000 Chrysanthemums (89x69cm-35x27in) s. s.i. verso. 28-Jun-4 Sotheby's, Amsterdam #253/R
£658 $1211 €1000 Landschap met Boerenwagen (70x80cm-28x31in) s. s.i.d.1957 verso. 28-Jun-4 Sotheby's, Amsterdam #197/R
£685 $1164 €1000 Gladioli (78x68cm-31x27in) s. s.d.59 verso. 5-Nov-3 Vendue Huis, Gravenhage #345
£789 $1453 €1200 Landscape in Brabant (50x60cm-20x24in) s. s.i.verso prov. 22-Jun-4 Christie's, Amsterdam #553/R
£800 $1464 €1200 Roses in a glass vase (80x69cm-31x27in) s. 7-Jun-4 Glerum, Amsterdam #102/R
£800 $1464 €1200 Amaryllis and Guelder rose (80x70cm-31x28in) s. s.i.verso. 7-Jun-4 Glerum, Amsterdam #130/R
£884 $1610 €1300 Poinsettia's (78x67cm-31x26in) s. s.i.verso. 3-Feb-4 Christie's, Amsterdam #435/R est:1300-1500
£909 $1545 €1300 Red roses in a glass (60x90cm-24x35in) s. 24-Nov-3 Glerum, Amsterdam #132/R
£979 $1635 €1400 Profusion of chrysanthemums (80x70cm-31x28in) s.d.1957 s.i.verso. 30-Jun-3 Sotheby's, Amsterdam #261
£987 $1816 €1500 Tulpen (93x76cm-37x30in) s. s.i. verso. 28-Jun-4 Sotheby's, Amsterdam #171/R est:1000-1500
£1088 $1981 €1600 Tulpen - tulips (68x78cm-27x31in) s. s.i.verso. 3-Feb-4 Christie's, Amsterdam #443 est:600-800
£1119 $1924 €1600 Amaryllis met boeken en kruik (106x88cm-42x35in) s. s.i.verso. 2-Dec-3 Sotheby's, Amsterdam #237/R est:1000-1500
£3333 $6133 €5000 Drie boeren - three farmers (109x140cm-43x55in) s. s.i.verso painted c.1922 prov.lit. 9-Jun-4 Christie's, Amsterdam #5/R est:5000-7000
£3357 $5773 €4800 Boerenerf (109x150cm-43x59in) s. s.i.verso. 2-Dec-3 Sotheby's, Amsterdam #241/R est:4000-6000
Works on paper
£280 $467 €400 Farmhouse in a winter landscape (28x35cm-11x14in) s. pastel black chk. 30-Jun-3 Sotheby's, Amsterdam #202
£280 $467 €400 The hay harvest (34x44cm-13x17in) s.i.d.57 pastel. 30-Jun-3 Sotheby's, Amsterdam #262/R
£282 $519 €420 Man with hat sitting at a table (64x54cm-25x21in) s.i.d.35 pastel. 29-Mar-4 Glerum, Amsterdam #67
£1184 $2179 €1800 Farmyard with pollarded willows (34x28cm-13x11in) s. chl pastel two. 22-Jun-4 Christie's, Amsterdam #556/R est:800-1200

WIJNVELD, Barend (1820-1902) Dutch
£496 $829 €700 Old woman reading (75x61cm-30x24in) s. lit. 20-Oct-3 Glerum, Amsterdam #49
£789 $1429 €1200 Interior of an abbey with a monk and dog (33x27cm-13x11in) panel. 19-Apr-4 Glerum, Amsterdam #87/R

WIKSTROM, Bror Anders (1854-1909) American/Swedish
£4368 $7250 €6377 Sailing ship on Lake Pontchartrain (53x76cm-21x30in) s.d.1885 prov. 4-Oct-3 Neal Auction Company, New Orleans #579/R est:5000-7000

WILBAULT, Nicolas (1686-1763) French
£1343 $2457 €1961 Young noble lady holding an architectural drawing (134x74cm-53x29in) s.indis.i. 9-Jun-4 Rasmussen, Copenhagen #1593/R est:25000 (D.KR 15000)

WILBAUT, Jacques (1729-1816) French
£6111 $11000 €8922 Portrait of a lady seated, wearing a black dress (81x64cm-32x25in) s.d.9 prov. 23-Jan-4 Christie's, Rockefeller NY #114/R est:6000-8000

WILBERG, Christian (1839-1882) German
£979 $1664 €1400 Charlottenburg castle park (61x46cm-24x18in) s. canvas on board. 27-Nov-3 Bassenge, Berlin #5668/R
£1192 $2170 €1800 View of S M della Salute (30x52cm-12x20in) s. panel. 21-Jun-4 Dorotheum, Vienna #22/R est:1800-2400

WILCOX, Leslie A (1904-) British
£480 $782 €701 Steamer on a choppy sea (61x81cm-24x32in) s. board. 24-Sep-3 Dreweatt Neate, Newbury #95/R
£1550 $2511 €2248 Dawn return (51x76cm-20x30in) s. exhib. 30-Jul-3 Hamptons Fine Art, Godalming #204 est:300-500
Works on paper
£280 $476 €409 On the Thames near Blackfriars Bridge (51x77cm-20x30in) W/C. 26-Nov-3 Hamptons Fine Art, Godalming #57
£335 $600 €489 Battleships (43x74cm-17x29in) s. W/C. 8-May-4 Susanin's, Chicago #6034/R

WILCOX, William H (1831-?) American
£723 $1150 €1056 Mill beside a mountain stream (76x64cm-30x25in) s.d.1865. 13-Sep-3 Selkirks, St. Louis #67

WILD, Charles (1781-1835) British
£600 $1110 €876 Old St. Pauls Penance of Jane Shore (102x76cm-40x30in) 9-Mar-4 Peter Francis, Wales #23

WILD, Frank Percy (1861-1950) British
£4000 $7200 €5840 Little Miss Mischief (127x102cm-50x40in) s.i.verso prov. 21-Jan-4 Sotheby's, Olympia #301/R est:4000-6000
£6800 $11560 €9928 Picking berries (53x74cm-21x29in) s. 27-Nov-3 Sotheby's, London #412/R est:8000-12000
£12000 $20400 €17520 Patience (92x61cm-36x24in) s. 27-Nov-3 Sotheby's, London #415/R est:10000-15000

WILDA, Charles (1854-1907) Austrian
£9000 $16560 €13140 Furtive cigarette (69x42cm-27x17in) s.d.1906. 25-Mar-4 Christie's, Kensington #221/R est:8000-12000
£12000 $21840 €17520 Mosque (36x23cm-14x9in) s. panel. 17-Jun-4 Christie's, London #127/R est:12000-16000
£18000 $32760 €26280 Water carriers (58x40cm-23x16in) s.d.1836 panel. 17-Jun-4 Christie's, London #113/R est:18000-25000
Works on paper
£3800 $6916 €5548 Carpet weaver (19x25cm-7x10in) s.d.1900 W/C. 17-Jun-4 Christie's, London #117/R est:3000-4000

WILDA, Hans Gottfried (1862-1911) Austrian
Works on paper
£364 $604 €528 Horse and carriage in front of Viennese Karlskirche (20x28cm-8x11in) s.d.1889 W/C. 13-Jun-3 Zofingen, Switzerland #2544/R (S.FR 800)
£638 $1129 €950 Kaiser Franz Joseph I von Osterreich (33x23cm-13x9in) s.d.1888 W/C. 29-Apr-4 Dorotheum, Vienna #78/R

WILDE, Alexander (1855-1929) Danish
£400 $680 €584 Barge in a tree lined loch with figures (58x74cm-23x29in) s.d.1905. 5-Nov-3 John Nicholson, Haslemere #577

WILDE, Auguste de (1819-1886) Belgian
£933 $1699 €1400 Young couple whispering cute things to each other, watched by an elderly mother (50x43cm-20x17in) s.d.1853 panel. 1-Jul-4 Van Ham, Cologne #1667/R
£2550 $4718 €3800 Copper kettle (48x38cm-19x15in) s. 13-Mar-4 De Vuyst, Lokeren #120/R est:2800-3500
£3061 $5571 €4500 Les arlesiennes (98x121cm-39x48in) s.d.1882. 3-Feb-4 Christie's, Amsterdam #84/R est:4000-6000

WILDE, Charles (19th C) British
£250 $450 €365 Clifton near Nottingham (30x46cm-12x18in) s. 22-Apr-4 Mellors & Kirk, Nottingham #1147
£300 $552 €450 Near Sherwood, with shepherd and his flock (30x45cm-12x18in) s. 25-Jun-4 Bigwood, Stratford on Avon #282/R
£650 $1170 €949 Rural scene with figures and sheep in the foreground (51x76cm-20x30in) s. 21-Apr-4 Tennants, Leyburn #1136
£800 $1336 €1168 On the bank of a tranquil river (36x53cm-14x21in) s.d.85. 13-Nov-3 Christie's, Kensington #158/R
£1300 $2158 €1898 Gamekeeper (51x77cm-20x30in) s.d.82 init.indis.i.verso. 1-Oct-3 Sotheby's, Olympia #67/R est:1000-1500

WILDE, Elizabeth M (fl.1897-1938) British
£700 $1295 €1022 Cornish harbour (41x51cm-16x20in) init. 11-Mar-4 Christie's, Kensington #72/R

WILDE, John (1919-) American
£4545 $8000 €6636 Wilde house (28x41cm-11x16in) init. s.i.d.1952 verso board. 23-May-4 Treadway Gallery, Cincinnati #645/R est:4000-6000

WILDE, Samuel de (attrib) (1748-1832) British
£4000 $6680 €5840 Portrait of an actor in the character of an army officer (67x53cm-26x21in) lit. 14-Oct-3 Sotheby's, London #432/R est:4000-6000

WILDE, William (1826-1901) British
Works on paper
£265 $485 €400 View of the French countryside (11x24cm-4x9in) s.i. W/C. 9-Apr-4 Bailly Pommery, Paris #14

WILDEMANN, Heinrich (1904-1964) German
£1007 $1782 €1500 Untitled (65x80cm-26x31in) mono.d. s.d.stretcher oil sand canvas. 30-Apr-4 Dr Fritz Nagel, Stuttgart #966/R est:1500

WILDENRADT, J P (1861-1904) Danish
£357 $608 €521 Coastal landscape (27x39cm-11x15in) s.i.d.1898 exhib. 29-Nov-3 Rasmussen, Havnen #2063 (D.KR 3800)

WILDENS, Jan (1586-1653) Flemish
£21277 $34468 €30000 Landscape with shepherds and sheep (85x130cm-33x51in) s. 20-May-3 Ansorena, Madrid #102/R est:30000
Works on paper
£4054 $7135 €6000 Landscape with castle behind a cornfield (15x20cm-6x8in) pen brown ink W/C black chk prov.lit. 19-May-4 Sotheby's, Amsterdam #41/R est:2200-2800

WILDENS, Jan and WOUTERS, Frans (attrib) (17th C) Flemish
£5944 $9927 €8500 Jacob et Rachel (32x39cm-13x15in) copper. 27-Jun-3 Millon & Associes, Paris #5/R est:5000-7000

WILDER, Andre (1871-1965) French
£765 $1300 €1117 Cathedral at Reims (91x71cm-36x28in) s.d.1911 board. 22-Nov-3 New Orleans Auction, New Orleans #680/R est:1200-1800
£1000 $1790 €1500 Falaises a Camaret soiree orageuse (60x73cm-24x29in) s. 16-May-4 Thierry & Lannon, Brest #196/R est:1500-2000
£1127 $1972 €1600 Bruges, le pont Tournant (65x81cm-26x32in) s.d.1909 i.verso. 19-Dec-3 Delvaux, Paris #27/R est:1500-2000
£5235 $9685 €7800 Voiliers rouges (60x81cm-24x32in) s.d.1907. 14-Mar-4 St-Germain-en-Laye Encheres #110/R est:10000

WILDER, Andre (attrib) (1871-1965) French
£1342 $2497 €2000 Le peintre a la pipe (50x65cm-20x26in) mono. 3-Mar-4 Ferri, Paris #202 est:600-800

WILDER, Hans (19th C) Austrian
Works on paper
£383 $700 €559 Carriages along path (23x46cm-9x18in) s. W/C executed c.1880. 5-Jun-4 Treadway Gallery, Cincinnati #580/R

WILDHAGEN, Fritz (1878-1956) German
£2797 $4755 €4000 March day on Pechsee (103x127cm-41x50in) s. exhib. 29-Nov-3 Villa Grisebach, Berlin #110/R est:4000-5000

WILDING, Ludwig (1927-) German
Sculpture
£2262 $3846 €3303 Stereo object (120x120x15cm-47x47x6in) kinetic object wooden box exec. 1976. 22-Nov-3 Burkhard, Luzern #165/R est:4000-6000 (S.FR 5000)

WILDING, Robert Thornton (20th C) British
Works on paper
£181 $302 €264 Shepherd and flock in a village lane (21x15cm-8x6in) s. W/C. 17-Nov-3 Waddingtons, Toronto #40/R (C.D 400)
£400 $724 €584 Cockington village (18x28cm-7x11in) s. W/C. 16-Apr-4 Keys, Aylsham #47

WILDMAN, John R (fl.1823-1839) British
£11000 $19690 €16060 Portrait of Niccolo Paganini (76x63cm-30x25in) s. prov. 11-May-4 Sotheby's, Olympia #563/R est:6000-8000

WILDT, Adolfo (1868-1931) Italian
Sculpture
£16667 $27833 €24000 Kind soul, strong attitude (40x56x37cm-16x22x15in) bronze. 23-Oct-3 Finarte Semenzato, Milan #37/R est:20000
£18919 $33297 €28000 Virgin (34cm-13in) s.i. marble. 19-May-4 Il Ponte, Milan #1064 est:18000-20000
Works on paper
£1667 $2983 €2500 Nativity (14x15cm-6x6in) s. pencil. 12-May-4 Stadion, Trieste #632/R est:1000-1500

WILDT, Sylvester (20th C) ?
£300 $489 €438 An artist's studio (27x34cm-11x13in) s.d.1930. 28-Sep-3 Hindemae, Ullerslev #21/R (D.KR 3200)

WILES, Gladys (1890-1984) American
£602 $1000 €879 Still life with bowl of fruit, flowers and statue (64x76cm-25x30in) s. 4-Oct-3 South Bay, Long Island #65

WILES, Irving Ramsey (1861-1948) American
£7910 $14000 €11549 Portrait of Mrs Lousie Carleton Putram (68x53cm-27x21in) s.d.1902 prov. 28-Apr-4 Christie's, Los Angeles #39/R est:15000-25000
£12707 $23000 €18552 Portrait of Mrs Edward W Redfield (91x71cm-36x28in) s.i.verso painted c.1920. 31-Mar-4 Sotheby's, New York #57/R est:8000-12000
£15909 $28000 €23227 Before the storm, Peconic Bay, Long Island (13x22cm-5x9in) s. s.i.d.1924 verso panel prov. 18-May-4 Christie's, Rockefeller NY #70/R est:20000-30000
£18466 $32500 €26960 Still life with lustware and peaches (51x41cm-20x16in) s.d.1888 prov.lit. 19-May-4 Sotheby's, New York #37/R est:20000-30000
£73864 $130000 €107841 Storybook (36x31cm-14x12in) s.d.1917 prov.exhib. 18-May-4 Christie's, Rockefeller NY #42/R est:80000-120000
£220930 $380000 €322558 Corner table (51x66cm-20x26in) s.d.1886 exhib. 4-Dec-3 Christie's, Rockefeller NY #33/R est:100000-150000
Works on paper
£18466 $32500 €26960 In the park (28x36cm-11x14in) s.d.1887 s.i.verso W/C. 19-May-4 Sotheby's, New York #3/R est:12000-18000

WILES, Irving Ramsey (attrib) (1861-1948) American
£1125 $1800 €1643 At the piano (66x41cm-26x16in) 19-Sep-3 Freeman, Philadelphia #182/R est:2000-3000

WILES, Lemuel (1826-1905) American
£5435 $10000 €7935 Cattle watering at a bend in the river (54x106cm-21x42in) s. prov. 8-Jun-4 Bonhams & Butterfields, San Francisco #4021/R est:12000-18000
£8380 $15000 €12235 Activities on the Hudson River (6x11cm-2x4in) board on panel. 6-May-4 Shannon's, Milford #117/R est:10000-15000

WILES, Lucy Mary (1920-) South African
£318 $548 €464 Wooded river landscape (80x120cm-31x47in) s. board. 3-Dec-3 Stephan Welz, Johannesburg #40 est:3000-5000 (SA.R 3500)
£364 $626 €531 Still life of delphiniums in a jug (59x49cm-23x19in) s. 3-Dec-3 Stephan Welz, Johannesburg #39 est:2500-3500 (SA.R 4000)

WILES, Walter G (1875-1966) South African
£655 $1127 €956 Road through a forest (60x90cm-24x35in) s. board. 3-Dec-3 Stephan Welz, Johannesburg #37 est:5000-8000 (SA.R 7200)
£682 $1174 €996 Lagoon landscape with cottage (50x75cm-20x30in) s. board. 3-Dec-3 Stephan Welz, Johannesburg #38 est:4000-6000 (SA.R 7500)
Works on paper
£437 $791 €638 Sunset, Knysna (38x54cm-15x21in) s. pastel. 30-Mar-4 Stephan Welz, Johannesburg #187 est:1500-2000 (SA.R 5200)
£454 $813 €663 Fishermen on the shore with boats (25x37cm-10x15in) s. pastel. 31-May-4 Stephan Welz, Johannesburg #251 (SA.R 5500)

WILEY, William T (1937-) American
£1099 $2000 €1605 Devil in the woods with his shadow (109x163cm-43x64in) s.d.93 acrylic chl. 29-Jun-4 Sotheby's, New York #610/R est:3000-4000
£2198 $4000 €3209 Parable of the blind (127x194cm-50x76in) init.d.94 s.i.d.verso acrylic pencil. 29-Jun-4 Sotheby's, New York #604/R est:5000-7000
Works on paper
£1236 $2250 €1805 Say mould reek west (36x25cm-14x10in) mono.i.d.1972 pen ink W/C. 29-Jun-4 Sotheby's, New York #540/R est:3000-5000
£3107 $5500 €4536 Ballsigh Sea doublet (62x46cm-24x18in) s.i.d.1972 W/C pen ink sold with two companions. 2-May-4 Bonhams & Butterfields, Los Angeles #3075/R est:3000-5000

WILHELM, Paul (1886-1965) German

£2133	$3840	€3200	Garden in autumn (40x50cm-16x20in) s. 24-Apr-4 Dr Lehr, Berlin #512/R est:4000
£3104	$5183	€4500	Femme et enfant devant une paillote dans les Iles Samoa (71x56cm-28x22in) s.i. 17-Nov-3 Tajan, Paris #181/R est:5000-7000
£3467	$6240	€5200	Houses on Lossnitz (55x75cm-22x30in) s. 24-Apr-4 Dr Lehr, Berlin #511/R est:4000
£4167	$6958	€6000	Garden with larkspur (96x75cm-38x30in) s. s. verso. 25-Oct-3 Dr Lehr, Berlin #547/R est:6000
Works on paper			
£467	$840	€700	Dresden garden (32x50cm-13x20in) s. W/C on pencil. 24-Apr-4 Dr Lehr, Berlin #513/R
£667	$1200	€1000	Pink gladioli (43x31cm-17x12in) s. W/C on pencil. 24-Apr-4 Dr Lehr, Berlin #514/R

WILHELM, Theo (1912-) German

£839	$1401	€1200	Composition (45x35cm-18x14in) s.d.1954 lit. 11-Oct-3 Hans Stahl, Hamburg #131/R

WILHELMS, Alexander (1886-1972) Finnish

£286	$520	€420	Sailing in moonlight (30x47cm-12x19in) s.d.1951. 8-Feb-4 Bukowskis, Helsinki #484/R
£423	$676	€600	At sea (106x132cm-42x52in) s.d.1926-38. 18-Sep-3 Hagelstam, Helsinki #996
£625	$1044	€900	Full sails ahead (81x96cm-32x38in) s.d.1938. 26-Oct-3 Bukowskis, Helsinki #537/R

WILHELMS, Carl (1889-1953) Finnish

£3104	$5557	€4532	A smoke on the beach (60x30cm-24x12in) 26-May-4 AB Stockholms Auktionsverk #2292/R est:25000-30000 (S.KR 42000)

WILHELMSON, Carl (1866-1928) Swedish

£525	$966	€788	Study (12x26cm-5x10in) panel. 14-Jun-4 Lilla Bukowskis, Stockholm #977 (S.KR 7200)
£1348	$2481	€2022	Mode seated in yellow armchair (49x36cm-19x14in) s.d.1926 panel. 14-Jun-4 Lilla Bukowskis, Stockholm #811 est:15000-20000 (S.KR 18500)
£1382	$2253	€2018	Evening (25x35cm-10x14in) s. panel lit. 29-Sep-3 Lilla Bukowskis, Stockholm #692 est:25000-30000 (S.KR 18000)
£1478	$2646	€2158	Old man in landscape (120x75cm-47x30in) s. 28-May-4 Uppsala Auktionskammare, Uppsala #163/R est:20000-25000 (S.KR 20000)
£1846	$3175	€2695	Landscape from Lapland (36x68cm-14x27in) s.d.1918 exhib.lit. 2-Dec-3 Bukowskis, Stockholm #26/R est:30000-40000 (S.KR 24000)
£2217	$3969	€3237	Summer evening in Fiskebackskil (24x35cm-9x14in) s. panel. 26-May-4 AB Stockholms Auktionsverk #2114/R est:30000-35000 (S.KR 30000)
£2217	$3969	€3237	Quinto Alvarez (35x25cm-14x10in) s.d.1920 panel exhib. 25-May-4 Bukowskis, Stockholm #167/R est:30000-35000 (S.KR 30000)
£4582	$8203	€6690	Woman with green hat (48x26cm-19x10in) s. canvas on panel study. 25-May-4 Bukowskis, Stockholm #166/R est:50000-60000 (S.KR 62000)
£6231	$10717	€9097	The water carrier (53x32cm-21x13in) s. exhib.lit. 2-Dec-3 Bukowskis, Stockholm #25/R est:50000-60000 (S.KR 81000)
£8462	$14554	€12355	Evening landscape (38x45cm-15x18in) s.d.1919 prov.exhib.lit. 2-Dec-3 Bukowskis, Stockholm #28/R est:80000-100000 (S.KR 110000)
£12692	$21831	€18530	After sunset (36x45cm-14x18in) s. exhib.lit. 2-Dec-3 Bukowskis, Stockholm #27/R est:80000-100000 (S.KR 165000)
£22173	$39690	€32373	Girls in summer (79x70cm-31x28in) s. 26-May-4 AB Stockholms Auktionsverk #2194/R est:275000-300000 (S.KR 300000)
Works on paper			
£276	$451	€403	Study of man (18x11cm-7x4in) s. W/C double-sided. 29-Sep-3 Lilla Bukowskis, Stockholm #293 (S.KR 3600)
£393	$679	€574	Female figure (35x26cm-14x10in) s. W/C sketch. 15-Dec-3 Lilla Bukowskis, Stockholm #99 (S.KR 5000)
£394	$724	€591	English coast (32x23cm-13x9in) s. W/C. 14-Jun-4 Lilla Bukowskis, Stockholm #93 (S.KR 5400)
£3692	$6351	€5390	Avenue with building by water (30x25cm-12x10in) s.d.87 W/C htd white. 3-Dec-3 AB Stockholms Auktionsverk #2291/R est:30000-35000 (S.KR 48000)

WILHJELM, Johannes (1868-1938) Danish

£627	$1147	€915	Seagulls over the sea (47x62cm-19x24in) init. prov. 9-Jun-4 Rasmussen, Copenhagen #1811/R (D.KR 7000)
£748	$1181	€1085	Venetian canal view (51x66cm-20x26in) init.d.29. 2-Sep-3 Rasmussen, Copenhagen #1665/R (D.KR 8000)
£1072	$1683	€1565	Summer's day on the beach, two young girls seated (64x82cm-25x32in) s. 30-Aug-3 Rasmussen, Havnen #2093/R (D.KR 11500)

WILICH, F C (19th C) ?

£1056	$1827	€1500	View through rocky gateway (33x55cm-13x22in) s.d.1869 panel. 10-Dec-3 Dorotheum, Vienna #173/R est:1300-1500

WILKE, Paul Ernst (1894-1972) German

£320	$579	€480	Fishing boats in harbour (30x24cm-12x9in) s. board. 3-Apr-4 Hans Stahl, Hamburg #130/R
£364	$663	€550	After the storm (60x50cm-24x20in) s.d.68 i.d.verso board. 18-Jun-4 Bolland & Marotz, Bremen #422/R
£384	$699	€580	Landscape with house (49x60cm-19x24in) s. i.d.1963 verso board. 18-Jun-4 Bolland & Marotz, Bremen #421/R
£420	$722	€600	Landscape near Worpswede (30x40cm-12x16in) s. i.d.1965 verso fibreboard. 5-Dec-3 Bolland & Marotz, Bremen #451/R
£559	$962	€800	Danish harbour (40x57cm-16x22in) s. i.d.1958 verso fibreboard. 5-Dec-3 Bolland & Marotz, Bremen #452/R
£604	$1111	€900	Harbour with boats loading (32x49cm-13x19in) s. i. verso board. 26-Mar-4 Bolland & Marotz, Bremen #386/R
£800	$1472	€1200	Two fishing boats on the river Hamme in an extensive landscape (40x60cm-16x24in) s.i. cardboard painted c.1940. 11-Jun-4 Wendl, Rudolstadt #4420/R
£909	$1564	€1300	On the Weser near Brake (60x80cm-24x31in) s. i.d.1952 verso fibreboard. 5-Dec-3 Bolland & Marotz, Bremen #447/R
£1042	$1698	€1500	Cutter in Dorum harbour (60x80cm-24x31in) s. id.1968 verso. 26-Sep-3 Bolland & Marotz, Bremen #424/R est:1300
£1119	$1924	€1600	Cutter in Norderney harbour (50x40cm-20x16in) s. fibreboard. 5-Dec-3 Bolland & Marotz, Bremen #450/R est:1300
£1325	$2411	€2000	Harbour scene with boats (71x100cm-28x39in) s.d.40. 18-Jun-4 Bolland & Marotz, Bremen #418/R est:2500
£1806	$2943	€2600	Cutter in Norderney harbour (70x100cm-28x39in) s.d.1928. 26-Sep-3 Bolland & Marotz, Bremen #422/R est:2300
£1806	$2943	€2600	Bremerhaven lighthouse (60x80cm-24x31in) s. i.d.1971 verso panel. 26-Sep-3 Bolland & Marotz, Bremen #423/R est:1500
£2168	$3729	€3100	Wremen harbour (70x100cm-28x39in) s. i.d.1943 verso. 5-Dec-3 Bolland & Marotz, Bremen #446/R est:2100
£2185	$3977	€3300	Boats in Norderney harbour (90x131cm-35x52in) s. 18-Jun-4 Bolland & Marotz, Bremen #420/R est:2400
£2384	$4339	€3600	Ditzum harbour (90x125cm-35x49in) s.d.1951. 18-Jun-4 Bolland & Marotz, Bremen #419/R est:2500

WILKE, Viktor (1941-) German

£1329	$2259	€1900	The Stadtschloss in Berlin (30x40cm-12x16in) s. panel. 28-Nov-3 Schloss Ahlden, Ahlden #1547/R est:1800

WILKERSON, Jerry (20th C) American

£324	$550	€473	Candles (23x18cm-9x7in) s.d.1996 verso acrylic wood. 7-Nov-3 Selkirks, St. Louis #570/R

WILKIE, Sir David (1785-1841) British

£600	$1032	€876	Figures conversing in a kitchen interior (28x23cm-11x9in) 5-Dec-3 Keys, Aylsham #640/R
£17000	$27370	€24650	Card players (23x30cm-9x12in) 21-Aug-3 Bonhams, Edinburgh #1121/R est:8000-12000
£320000	$544000	€467200	Spanish girl (67x56cm-26x22in) s.i.d.1828 prov.exhib.lit. 26-Nov-3 Christie's, London #9/R est:250000-350000
Works on paper			
£480	$826	€701	Portrait of Gustavus Adolphus, King of Sweden (18x9cm-7x4in) pencil W/C buff paper. 4-Dec-3 Bonhams, Edinburgh #62/R
£620	$1066	€905	Studies for a carnival (9x20cm-4x8in) ink prov. 4-Dec-3 Bonhams, Edinburgh #59/R
£850	$1369	€1233	Study for village school (9x17cm-4x7in) pen ink prov. 21-Aug-3 Bonhams, Edinburgh #1018/R
£980	$1686	€1431	Studies of hands (12x21cm-5x8in) pencil chk. 4-Dec-3 Bonhams, Edinburgh #60/R
£1150	$1978	€1679	Soldiers at Holyrood (13x17cm-5x7in) s.i.d.1822 pencil buff paper prov. 4-Dec-3 Bonhams, Edinburgh #61/R est:800-1200
£1300	$2236	€1898	Island in Loch Lomond (22x32cm-9x13in) i.d.August 28th 1817 chks. 4-Dec-3 Bonhams, Edinburgh #64/R est:800-1200
£2000	$3440	€2920	View across Edinburgh to the Lomond Hills (17x24cm-7x9in) i. pencil chk exec c.1817. 4-Dec-3 Bonhams, Edinburgh #58/R est:600-800
£2000	$3440	€2920	Sir Willoughby Gordon lifting the lid of a boiling pot (11x15cm-4x6in) init.i.d.october 182 ink. 4-Dec-3 Bonhams, Edinburgh #63/R est:600-800
£5500	$9350	€8030	Portrait of Julia Emily Gordon, wearing an African fez, in a garden (22x16cm-9x6in) i. pencil pen brown ink blue chk W/C htd white prov. 30-Oct-3 Christie's, London #5/R est:3000-5000

WILKIE, Ulfert (20th C) American

Works on paper			
£240	$400	€350	Untitled (28x48cm-11x19in) s. pen. 25-Oct-3 Rachel Davis, Shaker Heights #659/R

WILKIN, Frank W (c.1800-1842) British

Works on paper			
£820	$1533	€1197	Head of a donkey (61x46cm-24x18in) s.d.1834 chl col chk pair. 21-Jul-4 Bonhams, New Bond Street #151/R
£2100	$3864	€3066	Portrait of The Hon Charles Ewan Law Esq (74x62cm-29x24in) s.d.1823 i.verso black white col chk. 23-Jun-4 Cheffins, Cambridge #459/R est:1500-2500

WILKINS, George (attrib) (19th C) British

£400	$748	€584	Derbyshire Peak landscape, cattle grazing in foreground (100x60cm-39x24in) 25-Feb-4 British Auctioneer #178/R

WILKINS, Robert (attrib) (1740-1790) British

£994	$1800	€1451	Fighting the storm (51x61cm-20x24in) 3-Apr-4 Neal Auction Company, New Orleans #143/R est:2500-3500

WILKINSON, Arthur (?) Australian

Works on paper			
£360	$648	€526	Feeding the ducks. Sheep in the lowlands (24x34cm-9x13in) s. pencil W/C htd white two. 22-Apr-4 Mellors & Kirk, Nottingham #1055
£400	$632	€580	River landscape (25x74cm-10x29in) s. W/C bodycol pair. 3-Sep-3 Bonhams, Bury St Edmunds #340
£420	$764	€613	Village pond (34x50cm-13x20in) s. pencil W/C htd white. 5-Feb-4 Mellors & Kirk, Nottingham #475/R
£500	$910	€730	Cottage garden (26x36cm-10x14in) s. W/C htd white. 5-Feb-4 Mellors & Kirk, Nottingham #476/R
£620	$1153	€905	Sannox Bay, Aaran (48x74cm-19x29in) s.i. W/C. 2-Mar-4 Bearnes, Exeter #326/R

WILKINSON, Arthur Stanley (c.1860-c.1930) British

Works on paper			
£276	$450	€403	Cottage by a stream (25x36cm-10x14in) s. W/C. 17-Jul-3 Doyle, New York #53/R
£340	$626	€496	Road home, Devon (33x50cm-13x20in) s. W/C prov. 23-Jun-4 Cheffins, Cambridge #468/R
£349	$600	€510	Cottage with thatched roof (25x36cm-10x14in) s. W/C. 7-Dec-3 Grogan, Boston #11/R

WILKINSON, E (19/20th C) British

Works on paper

£1119	$1902	€1600	The Fultala at sea (61x98cm-24x39in) s. gouache. 18-Nov-3 Cambi, Genoa #396/R est:1800-2000

WILKINSON, H W (19th C) British

£720	$1138	€1051	Pigs and horses in a stable (91cm-36in circular) s. after John Frederick Herring. 3-Sep-3 Bonhams, Bury St Edmunds #447/R

WILKINSON, Henry (19/20th C) British

£560	$935	€818	Springer spaniels flushing a pheasant (49x65cm-19x26in) s. 9-Jul-3 Peter Wilson, Nantwich #60

WILKINSON, Norman (1878-1971) British

£500	$865	€730	Low water salmon waiting to run (61x46cm-24x18in) s. prov. 11-Dec-3 Lyon & Turnbull, Edinburgh #64/R
£500	$865	€730	Salmon pool, river Moidart, Argyll (46x61cm-18x24in) s. board. 11-Dec-3 Lyon & Turnbull, Edinburgh #65/R
£650	$1047	€943	Rock pool, Knockando, River Spey (34x44cm-13x17in) s. canvasboard. 21-Aug-3 Bonhams, Edinburgh #1150
£750	$1388	€1095	Avon at Ibbsley (46x61cm-18x24in) s. prov. 11-Feb-4 Sotheby's, Olympia #146/R
£900	$1530	€1314	Battle of the Yellow Sea (32x55cm-13x22in) s. pair en grisaille. 19-Nov-3 Christie's, Kensington #698/R
£900	$1620	€1314	Yachts in sunlight (42x71cm-17x28in) s. board. 21-Jan-4 Sotheby's, Olympia #382/R est:1000-1500
£1100	$1936	€1606	Game on the beach at Seagrove Bay, Isle of Wight (61x81cm-24x32in) s. 19-May-4 Christie's, Kensington #571/R est:700-900
£1700	$3043	€2482	Booth Line's steamer Ambrose II on her maiden voyage 1903 (84x112cm-33x44in) s.d.1903. 26-May-4 Christie's, Kensington #551/R est:2000-3000
£1800	$3222	€2628	Cruising in the Mediterranean off Gibraltar (46x61cm-18x24in) s. 26-May-4 Christie's, Kensington #742/R est:1800-2500
£2800	$4452	€4088	The 1951 exhibition from Shell Mex House (56x96cm-22x38in) s. 10-Sep-3 Sotheby's, Olympia #91/R est:2000-3000
£2800	$5012	€4088	Convoy (66x91cm-26x36in) s. exhib. 26-May-4 Christie's, Kensington #735/R est:3000-4000
£3000	$5370	€4380	Barges and tugs on the Thames before St Paul's Cathedral (61x81cm-24x32in) s. 26-May-4 Christie's, Kensington #743/R est:1200-1800
£5400	$8964	€7884	Setting out, Inchenor, Sussex (43x58cm-17x23in) s. 3-Oct-3 Mallams, Oxford #253/R est:3000-4000
£6000	$9960	€8760	Gravesend (43x58cm-17x23in) s. 3-Oct-3 Mallams, Oxford #252/R est:3000-4000
£6000	$9960	€8760	Poole harbour, Dorset (43x58cm-17x23in) s. 3-Oct-3 Mallams, Oxford #254/R est:3000-4000

Works on paper

£320	$550	€467	Fishing on the Sligahan Burn, Isle of Skye (18x24cm-7x9in) s. pencil W/C. 4-Dec-3 Mellors & Kirk, Nottingham #830
£480	$845	€701	Last of the Spanish Armada (105x105cm-41x41in) s. bears i. verso W/C. 18-May-4 Fellows & Sons, Birmingham #226/R
£720	$1267	€1051	View overlooking Jerusalem and Bethlehem (65x99cm-26x39in) s.i. pencil W/C. 19-May-4 Sotheby's, Olympia #86/R
£1600	$2560	€2336	Coronation review of the fleet at Spithead on 16th August 1902 (33x59cm-13x23in) s.d.02 W/C htd white. 16-Sep-3 Bonhams, New Bond Street #22/R est:1500-2000

WILKINSON, Rev Joseph (19th C) British

Works on paper

£340	$588	€496	Cockermouth Castle (23x36cm-9x14in) i.mount pencil W/C. 11-Dec-3 Mitchells, Cockermouth #910/R

WILKINSON, Thomas Harrison (1847-1929) Canadian

Works on paper

£260	$476	€380	Rider on a forest road (45x32cm-18x13in) s. W/C. 1-Jun-4 Hodgins, Calgary #338/R (C.D 650)

WILKON, Jozef (20th C) Polish

Works on paper

£348	$602	€508	Peacock and fishes (30x42cm-12x17in) s. ink pen wash W/C gouache pastel. 10-Dec-3 Agra, Warsaw #38/R (P.Z 2300)
£414	$691	€600	Spacer, man walking dog in forest (97x88cm-38x35in) s. gouache ink pastel board painted 1970's. 16-Nov-3 Agra, Warsaw #91/R
£828	$1382	€1200	Spacer (69x49cm-27x19in) s.d.74 gouache pastel. 16-Nov-3 Agra, Warsaw #69/R
£917	$1523	€1339	Concert (67x46cm-26x18in) gouache. 2-Oct-3 Agra, Warsaw #17/R est:2000 (P.Z 6000)

WILKS, Maurice C (1910-1984) British

£250	$415	€365	Co. Antrim farmhouses (25x33cm-10x13in) 1-Oct-3 John Ross, Belfast #103
£450	$774	€657	Female portrait (50x40cm-20x16in) s.d.December 1957 verso. 3-Dec-3 John Ross, Belfast #244
£650	$1079	€949	Dun River, Co. Antrim (25x33cm-10x13in) s. 1-Oct-3 John Ross, Belfast #29
£750	$1275	€1095	Mill at Groenekan, Holland (19x24cm-7x9in) s. 29-Oct-3 Edgar Horn, Eastbourne #362
£850	$1411	€1241	Snow topped mountains (20x25cm-8x10in) s. board. 1-Oct-3 John Ross, Belfast #210
£1100	$1804	€1606	River Dun (25x35cm-10x14in) s. board. 4-Jun-3 John Ross, Belfast #92
£1100	$2002	€1606	Sunlit mountain lake scene (30x41cm-12x16in) s. 29-Jun-4 Bonhams, Knowle #82 est:600-800
£1141	$2042	€1700	Green reflections (44x54cm-17x21in) s. 26-May-4 James Adam, Dublin #159/R est:4000-5000
£1200	$2232	€1752	Calm morning, Lough Inagh, Galway (40x50cm-16x20in) s. 3-Mar-4 John Ross, Belfast #239 est:1400-1500
£1300	$2236	€1898	Near Clifden, Connemara (36x46cm-14x18in) s. 2-Dec-3 Gorringes, Lewes #2254/R est:600-800
£1300	$2236	€1898	Rosemary (76x63cm-30x25in) s.d.1956 verso. 3-Dec-3 John Ross, Belfast #29 est:1200-1500
£1300	$2379	€1898	Connemara Lough (35x45cm-14x18in) s. 2-Jun-4 John Ross, Belfast #217 est:1400-1600
£1350	$2322	€1971	Mamm Turk-Hills, Connemara, from Kylemore Lakes (25x30cm-10x12in) s. board. 3-Dec-3 John Ross, Belfast #55 est:1200-1400
£1389	$2264	€2000	Landscape, Connemara (33x43cm-13x17in) s. 23-Sep-3 De Veres Art Auctions, Dublin #239 est:2000-3000
£1400	$2408	€2044	River Dun, County Antrim (33x40cm-13x16in) s. board. 3-Dec-3 John Ross, Belfast #131 est:1400-1500
£1471	$2500	€2148	At Rossglass Co. Down (25x41cm-10x16in) s. prov. 22-Nov-3 Jackson's, Cedar Falls #18/R est:2000-3000
£1500	$2685	€2190	Solitude (35x46cm-14x18in) s. i.verso. 14-May-4 Christie's, Kensington #350/R est:1500-2000
£1600	$2624	€2336	Female nude study (61x50cm-24x20in) 4-Jun-3 John Ross, Belfast #166 est:1800
£1600	$2896	€2400	Ballyconneely, Connemara (33x44cm-13x17in) s. 31-Mar-4 James Adam, Dublin #55/R est:2000-3000
£1600	$2896	€2400	Winter, Lough Kylemore, Connemara (34x44cm-13x17in) s.i.verso prov. 31-Mar-4 James Adam, Dublin #112/R est:2500-3500
£1600	$2720	€2336	Winter, Lough Kylemore, Connemara (35x45cm-14x18in) s. 29-Oct-3 Edgar Horn, Eastbourne #363 est:500-700
£1600	$2928	€2336	Connemara Lough (50x61cm-20x24in) s. 2-Jun-4 John Ross, Belfast #118 est:1800-2000
£1650	$2838	€2409	Breaking seas, Ballintoy (40x50cm-16x20in) s. 3-Dec-3 John Ross, Belfast #12 est:1200-1400
£1650	$3069	€2409	Snow in Glendun, Co. Antrim (45x35cm-18x14in) s. 3-Mar-4 John Ross, Belfast #87 est:1400-1600
£1748	$2972	€2500	Ballet study (41x51cm-16x20in) s. cab. 18-Nov-3 Whyte's, Dublin #232/R est:2000-3000
£1757	$3320	€2600	North Channel (38x51cm-15x20in) s. prov. 17-Feb-4 Whyte's, Dublin #131/R est:3000-4000
£1800	$3222	€2628	Beach at White Pork Bay, Co Antrim (30x35cm-12x14in) s. canvas on board. 14-May-4 Christie's, Kensington #359/R est:2000-3000
£2000	$3580	€2920	Connemara landscape near Roundstone (18x23cm-7x9in) s. s.i.verso canvasboard. 14-May-4 Christie's, Kensington #349/R est:800-1200
£2013	$3564	€3000	Salmon pool, Glendun, County Antrim (33x41cm-13x16in) s. 27-Apr-4 Whyte's, Dublin #201/R est:3000-4000
£2083	$3396	€3000	Muckish mountains from Cresslough (40x50cm-16x20in) s. 24-Sep-3 James Adam, Dublin #83/R est:3000-5000
£2200	$3674	€3212	Summer evening, Rockport, Cushendaan, Co. Antrim (28x34cm-11x13in) s. canvasboard. 16-Oct-3 Bonhams, Edinburgh #141 est:1000-1500
£2200	$4092	€3212	Snow at Orra, Glendun, Co. Antrim (45x56cm-18x22in) s. 3-Mar-4 John Ross, Belfast #159 est:2000-2500
£2254	$3606	€3200	Reflections, Dun River, County Antrim (36x46cm-14x18in) s. i.verso exhib. 16-Sep-3 Whyte's, Dublin #152/R est:2500-3500
£2300	$4255	€3358	Summer afternoon, Dun River, Cushendun, Co Antrim (51x61cm-20x24in) s. i. verso. 14-Jul-4 Bonhams, Chester #467/R est:2000-3000
£2365	$4470	€3500	Blue hills (28x41cm-11x16in) canvasboard. 17-Feb-4 Whyte's, Dublin #167/R est:2000-3000
£2394	$3831	€3400	Sunlit wood, Cushendun, County Atrim (30x36cm-12x14in) s. canvasboard prov. 16-Sep-3 Whyte's, Dublin #153/R est:3000-4000
£2400	$4008	€3504	Creggan Bawn, Co Mayo (46x61cm-18x24in) s. i.verso. 16-Oct-3 Christie's, Kensington #475/R est:1500-2000
£2458	$4400	€4127	Coastal scene (41x51cm-16x20in) s. i.verso. 20-Mar-4 Pook & Pook, Downington #592/R est:2500-4500
£2550	$4514	€3800	Breaking seas, Ballinatoy (41x51cm-16x20in) s. i.verso. 27-Apr-4 Whyte's, Dublin #203/R est:3500-4500
£2600	$4680	€3796	County Down landscape, Bally Na Hinch (29x34cm-11x13in) s. board. 23-Jan-4 British Auctioneer #624/R est:1000-1500
£2700	$4644	€3942	Sunlit lane, Cushendun (30x35cm-12x14in) s. board. 3-Dec-3 John Ross, Belfast #111 est:1800-2000
£2703	$5108	€4000	Mountains landscape with cottages (41x51cm-16x20in) s. 17-Feb-4 Whyte's, Dublin #128/R est:4000-5000
£2800	$5208	€4088	Slieve Meelmore, Mourne Mountains (40x50cm-16x20in) s. 3-Mar-4 John Ross, Belfast #161 est:2500-2800
£2800	$5012	€4088	Across Dublin Bay from Redrock, Co Dublin (35x47cm-14x19in) s. 14-May-4 Christie's, Kensington #358/R est:3000-4000
£2817	$4507	€4000	Near Castlewellan, County Down (41x51cm-16x20in) s. i.verso exhib. 16-Sep-3 Whyte's, Dublin #155/R est:4000-6000
£2823	$5194	€4122	At Ballyconneely, Connemara (51x61cm-20x24in) s. i.verso prov. 14-Jun-4 Waddingtons, Toronto #175/R est:6000-8000 (C.D 7000)
£2838	$5364	€4200	Stormy seas, Antrim coast (41x51cm-16x20in) s. 17-Feb-4 Whyte's, Dublin #129/R est:3000-4000
£2958	$4732	€4200	Twilight, Inagh Valley, Connemara (61x91cm-24x36in) s. i.verso prov. 16-Sep-3 Whyte's, Dublin #148/R est:4000-6000
£3000	$4920	€4380	Bog and mountains (40x50cm-16x20in) s. 4-Jun-3 John Ross, Belfast #154
£3000	$5370	€4380	Ross's Coast, Co Donegal (46x61cm-18x24in) s. prov. 14-May-4 Christie's, Kensington #352/R est:3000-5000
£3100	$5332	€4526	Across Strangford to Scrabo (35x45cm-14x18in) s. canvas on board. 3-Dec-3 John Ross, Belfast #124 est:2500-2800
£3125	$5313	€4563	Lake Cadmlough (51x61cm-20x24in) s. i.verso prov. 6-Nov-3 Heffel, Vancouver #116/R est:6000-8000 (C.D 7000)
£3200	$5248	€4672	Summer in the Glens (40x50cm-16x20in) s. 4-Jun-3 John Ross, Belfast #113
£3310	$5726	€4700	Ballington village (51x61cm-20x24in) s. prov. 10-Dec-3 Bonhams & James Adam, Dublin #75/R est:4500-6000
£3400	$6154	€4964	Down landscape, Vallynanimch (28x33cm-11x13in) s. i.verso. 16-Apr-4 Keys, Aylsham #805/R est:2500-3500
£3500	$6020	€5110	Irish cottages (40x50cm-16x20in) s. 3-Dec-3 John Ross, Belfast #215 est:2500-3500
£3500	$6405	€5110	Coastal view of County Antrim (51x61cm-20x24in) s. 9-Jul-4 Dreweatt Neate, Newbury #426/R est:1500-2000
£3600	$5976	€5256	Errigal Range Co. Donnegal (54x71cm-21x28in) s. i.verso prov. 1-Oct-3 Woolley & Wallis, Salisbury #195/R est:3000-5000
£3611	$5886	€5200	Near Ballyconneely, Connemara (40x49cm-16x19in) s. i.verso. 24-Sep-3 James Adam, Dublin #98/R est:3000-5000
£3800	$7030	€5548	Near Killory, Connemara (41x51cm-16x20in) s. 13-Feb-4 Bracketts, Tunbridge Wells #715/R est:600-1000
£4196	$7133	€6000	Sunlight and shadow, Crolly, County Donegal (46x56cm-18x22in) s. i.verso prov. 18-Nov-3 Whyte's, Dublin #41/R est:4000-6000
£4200	$6888	€6132	Evening light (30x35cm-12x14in) s. board. 4-Jun-3 John Ross, Belfast #61
£4392	$8301	€6500	Figures on the strand, County Donegal (46x56cm-18x22in) s. 17-Feb-4 Whyte's, Dublin #134/R est:5000-7000
£4400	$7964	€6600	Galway reflections, Roundstone, Connemara (45x90cm-18x35in) s. 31-Mar-4 James Adam, Dublin #121/R est:6000-8000

£4600	$7360	€6716	On the Mayo Coast (45x61cm-18x24in) s. 16-Sep-3 Rosebery Fine Art, London #649/R est:2000-3000
£4605	$8474	€7000	Saving the turf, above Letterfrack, County Galway (51x76cm-20x30in) s.i.verso. 22-Jun-4 De Veres Art Auctions, Dublin #57/R est:6000-8000
£4889	$8116	€7138	Near Letterfrack, Renvyle, Connemara (49x53cm-19x21in) 2-Oct-3 Heffel, Vancouver #47 (C.D 11000)
£4895	$8322	€7000	Showery day, Co. Donegal (38x51cm-15x20in) s. i.verso. 25-Nov-3 De Veres Art Auctions, Dublin #13/R est:5000-7000
£5500	$10010	€8030	At Mulrany, Co Mayo (51x69cm-20x27in) s. i.stretcher. 29-Jun-4 Bonhams, Knowle #84 est:1500-2500
£6500	$10400	€9490	At the Bloody Foreland, County Donegal (45x61cm-18x24in) s. 16-Sep-3 Rosebery Fine Art, London #650/R est:2000-3000
£6711	$12013	€10000	On the Kerry Coast, Kenmare (40x50cm-16x20in) s. i. verso. 31-May-4 Hamilton Osborne King, Dublin #156/R est:10000-15000
£8392	$14266	€12000	Winter cushendun, Co. Antrim (45x55cm-18x22in) s. i.verso prov. 25-Nov-3 De Veres Art Auctions, Dublin #44/R est:10000-15000
£16000	$28640	€23360	Misty morning (51x61cm-20x24in) s. 13-May-4 Sotheby's, London #91/R est:8000-12000
£17606	$28169	€25000	Women of Donegal (51x66cm-20x26in) s. i.verso prov.lit. 16-Sep-3 Whyte's, Dublin #108/R est:15000-20000
Works on paper			
£280	$512	€409	Thatched cottage, Donegal (12x17cm-5x7in) s. W/C. 2-Jun-4 John Ross, Belfast #20
£300	$492	€438	Near Dundrum (12x17cm-5x7in) s. W/C. 4-Jun-3 John Ross, Belfast #170
£300	$549	€438	Strangford Lough, Co. Down (12x17cm-5x7in) s. W/C. 2-Jun-4 John Ross, Belfast #21
£338	$592	€480	Dock land study (24x32cm-9x13in) s.i.verso W/C. 16-Dec-3 James Adam, Dublin #47/R
£400	$732	€584	Portrait of a young girl (45x35cm-18x14in) s. mixed media. 2-Jun-4 John Ross, Belfast #223
£550	$946	€803	Cottage in the glens (23x28cm-9x11in) s. W/C. 3-Dec-3 John Ross, Belfast #88
£550	$1007	€803	Rowing boats at Cushendun (25x35cm-10x14in) s. W/C. 2-Jun-4 John Ross, Belfast #54
£560	$1025	€818	Dull weather, Loch Tulla (26x37cm-10x15in) s. W/C. 8-Apr-4 Bonhams, Edinburgh #28
£600	$1032	€876	Murlough Bay, County Antrim (25x35cm-10x14in) s. W/C. 3-Dec-3 John Ross, Belfast #4
£650	$1209	€949	Cottages, Donegal (22x30cm-9x12in) W/C. 3-Mar-4 John Ross, Belfast #2
£650	$1209	€949	River Dun, Co. Antrim (25x38cm-10x15in) s. W/C. 3-Mar-4 John Ross, Belfast #26
£650	$1190	€949	Thatched cottages, Donegal (25x35cm-10x14in) s. W/C. 2-Jun-4 John Ross, Belfast #2
£700	$1239	€1022	Garron point from Torr Head Road (25x36cm-10x14in) s. W/C prov. 27-Apr-4 Bonhams, Knightsbridge #13/R
£700	$1253	€1022	Glen Head, Columkille (26x37cm-10x15in) s. pencil W/C prov. 14-May-4 Christie's, Kensington #357/R
£769	$1308	€1100	Silvey Morn, Downings, County Donegal (24x34cm-9x13in) s. i.verso W/C over pencil. 18-Nov-3 Whyte's, Dublin #20/R
£800	$1464	€1168	Roses (25x20cm-10x8in) s. W/C set of three. 2-Jun-4 John Ross, Belfast #117
£1000	$1800	€1460	Glenarm, Antrim (28x37cm-11x15in) s. W/C. 23-Jan-4 British Auctioneer #580/R est:700-1000
£1000	$1810	€1500	Cushendun Bay and Garran Point from Torr Head, Co Antrim (26x36cm-10x14in) s. W/C. 31-Mar-4 James Adam, Dublin #143/R est:1500-2500
£1119	$1902	€1600	Large clipper in a harbour (28x38cm-11x15in) s. W/C. 18-Nov-3 Mealy's, Castlecomer #1423/R est:1200-1800
£1150	$1955	€1679	Irish Coastal Scene (26x36cm-10x14in) s. 19-Nov-3 James Thompson, Kirby Lonsdale #181
£2600	$4472	€3796	Near Marble Hill, Donegal (45x55cm-18x22in) s. W/C. 3-Dec-3 John Ross, Belfast #145 est:2800-3000

WILKS, Maxwell (1944-) Australian

£340	$568	€496	Goat Island - Sydney Harbour (51x61cm-20x24in) s.d.74. 21-Oct-3 Bonhams, Knightsbridge #12/R
£340	$568	€496	Sydney Harbour bridge from the rocks (51x66cm-20x26in) s.d.74. 21-Oct-3 Bonhams, Knightsbridge #13/R

WILL, J (19th C) ?

£2143	$3837	€3129	Coastal promenade (32x55cm-13x22in) s.i.d.avril 93. 26-May-4 AB Stockholms Auktionsverk #2419/R est:12000-15000 (S.KR 29000)

WILLAERT, Arthur (1875-1942) Belgian

£292	$464	€420	L'eglise a Wenduine (16x22cm-6x9in) s. 15-Sep-3 Horta, Bruxelles #1

WILLAERT, Ferdinand (1861-1938) Belgian

£503	$931	€750	Arcade a Tanger (26x32cm-10x13in) s. 15-Mar-4 Horta, Bruxelles #27
£845	$1462	€1200	Street with figures (46x38cm-18x15in) s. 15-Dec-3 Bernaerts, Antwerp #237/R
£2823	$5194	€4122	Quiet reflections, Ghent (129x98cm-51x39in) s. 14-Jun-4 Waddingtons, Toronto #43/R est:8000-10000 (C.D 7000)

WILLAERTS, Abraham (1603-1669) Dutch

£19719	$34508	€28000	Navires Hollandais pres d'une cote rocheuse (50x74cm-20x29in) mono.indis.d.16 panel. 18-Dec-3 Tajan, Paris #27/R est:20000-30000

WILLAERTS, Adam (1577-1669) Dutch

Works on paper			
£21918	$37260	€32000	Fisherfolk hauling their boat onto the shore, shipping behind (17x27cm-7x11in) init.d.1623 pen brown ink W/C over black chk exhib. 4-Nov-3 Sotheby's, Amsterdam #96/R est:40000-60000

WILLAERTS, Isaac (1620-1693) Dutch

£18000	$32940	€26280	Coastal landscape with boats and figures (45x73cm-18x29in) s.d.1662 panel. 8-Jul-4 Sotheby's, London #116/R est:20000-30000
£19079	$35105	€29000	Riviere d'une petite ville en Hollande avec des promeneurs (91x131cm-36x52in) mono. panel prov. 25-Jun-4 Rossini, Paris #39/R est:18000-22000

WILLAERTS, Isaac (attrib) (1620-1693) Dutch

£4362	$8027	€6500	Admiral on horseback by coast (23x32cm-9x13in) copper. 24-Mar-4 Dorotheum, Vienna #101/R est:6000-9000

WILLARD, William (1818-1904) American

£226	$400	€330	Portrait of William Morris Hunt (61x51cm-24x20in) prov.exhib. 27-Apr-4 Doyle, New York #11a

WILLE, August von (1829-1887) German

£1800	$3096	€2628	Monastic meal (49x37cm-19x15in) s. panel. 4-Dec-3 Christie's, Kensington #110/R est:2000-3000

WILLE, Clara von (1838-1883) German

£629	$1051	€900	Portrait of hunting dog (42x38cm-17x15in) s. 9-Oct-3 Michael Zeller, Lindau #802/R

WILLE, Fritz von (1860-1941) German

£267	$488	€400	Portrait of a man with beard in profile (43x36cm-17x14in) s. 5-Jun-4 Arnold, Frankfurt #795/R
£915	$1584	€1300	Village church in autumn (16x24cm-6x9in) s.indis.i. 10-Dec-3 Christie's, Amsterdam #211
£1000	$1810	€1500	Schleiden (32x45cm-13x18in) s.i.d.12.12.2. 1-Apr-4 Van Ham, Cologne #1710/R est:1500
£1133	$2051	€1700	Lansape (30x45cm-12x18in) s. 2-Apr-4 Dr Fritz Nagel, Leipzig #3948/R est:500
£1586	$2934	€2300	Autumn wood with stream (105x80cm-41x31in) s.d.92. 12-Feb-4 Weidler, Nurnberg #312/R est:2520
£1806	$2979	€2600	Wooded summer landscape near Kerpen (40x50cm-16x20in) mono.d.21.7.23. 3-Jul-3 Van Ham, Cologne #1508/R est:3500
£1867	$3397	€2800	October day in the Eifel (60x80cm-24x31in) s. 30-Jun-4 Neumeister, Munich #751/R est:800
£1944	$3208	€2800	Oedland near Reifferschied (39x46cm-15x18in) s. i. stretcher. 3-Jul-3 Van Ham, Cologne #1506/R est:3500
£2027	$3568	€3000	Eiffel landscape (50x60cm-20x24in) s.d.7.6.12 canvas on panel. 22-May-4 Lempertz, Koln #1629/R est:3000
£2098	$3566	€3000	Maar in the Eifel (49x58cm-19x23in) s.i. 20-Nov-3 Van Ham, Cologne #1917/R est:3500
£2267	$4103	€3400	Last snow (40x49cm-16x19in) s.d.27.4.03 canvas on board. 1-Apr-4 Van Ham, Cologne #1708/R est:1900
£2432	$4281	€3600	Eiffel landscape (50x60cm-20x24in) s. 22-May-4 Lempertz, Koln #1628/R est:4000
£2740	$4959	€4110	Moonlight in Alken an der Mosel (100x80cm-39x31in) s. panel. 1-Apr-4 Van Ham, Cologne #1709/R est:5000
£3125	$5156	€4500	Heathland in bloom on Meerfelder Maar, Eifel (41x50cm-16x20in) s. 3-Jul-3 Van Ham, Cologne #1507/R est:5500

WILLE, Johann Georg (1715-1808) German

Works on paper			
£439	$773	€650	Four women round table by candlelight (16x10cm-6x4in) s. prov. 22-May-4 Lempertz, Koln #1381
£1408	$2437	€2000	Enfant dans un paysage rocheux (20x29cm-8x11in) pen brown ink brown wash. 10-Dec-3 Piasa, Paris #53/R est:1200-1500
£2667	$4800	€3894	Ruins of the castle of Montfort Lamaury (24x35cm-9x14in) s.i.d.1779 brown chk prov. 22-Jan-4 Christie's, Rockefeller NY #108/R est:2000-3000

WILLE, Johann Georg (attrib) (1715-1808) German

Works on paper			
£1027	$1747	€1500	Portrait of Joseph Parrocel (24x20cm-9x8in) sanguine oval. 5-Nov-3 Beaussant & Lefèvre, Paris #12/R

WILLE, Pierre-Alexandre (1748-1821) French

Works on paper			
£921	$1695	€1400	Portrait de femme coiffe d'un bonnet (30x27cm-12x11in) s. sanguine. 25-Jun-4 Rossini, Paris #21/R
£1118	$2058	€1700	Portrait de jeune fille en buste coiffee d'un bonnet (36x28cm-14x11in) s.d.1773 sanguine. 25-Jun-4 Rossini, Paris #22/R est:1500-2200
£1500	$2700	€2190	Wooded landscape with young couple fishing (19x25cm-7x10in) s. pen brown ink col wash prov. 20-Apr-4 Sotheby's, Olympia #127/R est:1500-2000
£1667	$3000	€2434	Children being scolded, by a thatched house (17x22cm-7x9in) s.d.1796 black chk pen black ink W/C. 22-Jan-4 Christie's, Rockefeller NY #249/R est:3000-5000
£3618	$6658	€5500	Etude de jeune garcon debout. s.d.1770 sanguine. 25-Jun-4 Doutrebente, Paris #1/R est:2500-3000

WILLE, Pierre-Alexandre (attrib) (1748-1821) French

Works on paper			
£2657	$4571	€3800	Portrait de Claire Josephe Hippolyte Liris de la Tude (41x33cm-16x13in) blk white blue chk htd white prov. 2-Dec-3 Christie's, Paris #508/R est:5000-7000

WILLEBORD, T (fl.1657) Flemish

£2500	$4325	€3650	Raspberries in a porcelain tazza, other fruit and glass on a table (73x92cm-29x36in) s.d.1657. 12-Dec-3 Christie's, Kensington #87/R est:3000-5000

WILLEBRANT, James (1950-) Australian

£339	$576	€509	Room with a view (60x75cm-24x30in) s.i.verso acrylic canvas on board. 28-Oct-3 Goodman, Sydney #263 (A.D 820)
£615	$996	€898	End of season detail (58x76cm-23x30in) s. s.i.d.86 verso acrylic. 30-Jul-3 Goodman, Sydney #54/R (A.D 1500)
£996	$1663	€1494	Rhino race (94x117cm-37x46in) s.d.74 i.verso acrylic. 27-Oct-3 Goodman, Sydney #243/R (A.D 2400)
£2245	$4131	€3278	First ball of the day (120x180cm-47x71in) s. acrylic. 29-Mar-4 Goodman, Sydney #165/R est:4000-6000 (A.D 5500)

WILLEMESE, Hank (1915-1980) Dutch
£222 $400 €324 Still life of bottles (89x117cm-35x46in) s.d.60. 23-Jan-4 Freeman, Philadelphia #209/R
£240 $400 €350 Figure composition (91x46cm-36x18in) indis.sig. s.verso. 20-Jun-3 Freeman, Philadelphia #129/R
£249 $450 €364 Autumn trees (183x117cm-72x46in) s. s.i.d.1964 verso. 2-Apr-4 Freeman, Philadelphia #190
£278 $500 €406 Landscape (140x259cm-55x102in) s.d.64. 23-Jan-4 Freeman, Philadelphia #256/R
£306 $550 €447 Destruction (127x107cm-50x42in) s.d.68 s.i.d.verso. 23-Jan-4 Freeman, Philadelphia #201/R
£329 $550 €480 Barge at Amsterdam (89x99cm-35x39in) s. s.i.verso. 20-Jun-3 Freeman, Philadelphia #184/R
£333 $600 €486 Woods (89x117cm-35x46in) init.d.61 s.indis.i.verso. 23-Jan-4 Freeman, Philadelphia #137/R
£333 $600 €486 Building construction (99x127cm-39x50in) s.d.59. 23-Jan-4 Freeman, Philadelphia #261/R
£417 $750 €609 Abstract (157x180cm-62x71in) s.d.67. 23-Jan-4 Freeman, Philadelphia #130/R
£872 $1500 €1273 Studio still life (107x127cm-42x50in) s.d.60 s.verso prov. 7-Dec-3 Freeman, Philadelphia #74 est:700-1000
£884 $1600 €1291 Ship in port (137x142cm-54x56in) s.d.57. 2-Apr-4 Freeman, Philadelphia #125
£1056 $1900 €1542 Saint Maarten, children's holiday (109x119cm-43x47in) s.d.62. 23-Jan-4 Freeman, Philadelphia #259/R est:300-500

WILLEMS, Florent (1823-1905) Belgian
£694 $1181 €1000 Boy and dog (28x23cm-11x9in) s.d.1843 board. 28-Oct-3 Segre, Madrid #64/R
£1528 $2399 €2200 Le songe (57x43cm-22x17in) s. panel. 26-Aug-3 Galerie Moderne, Brussels #243/R est:3000-5000
£1816 $3250 €2651 Proposition (48x51cm-19x20in) s. panel. 20-Mar-4 Sloans & Kenyon, Bethesda #1187/R est:4000-6000
£4056 $6895 €5800 Jeune femme au chapeau et aux fleurs (137x99cm-54x39in) s. 24-Nov-3 Boscher, Cherbourg #758/R est:2000-3000
£4200 $7644 €6132 Feeding the new arrivals (55x20cm-22x8in) s. panel. 16-Jun-4 Christie's, Kensington #163/R est:3000-5000
£5882 $10000 €8588 Elegant lady with her dog in an interior (46x37cm-18x15in) s. panel. 29-Oct-3 Christie's, Rockefeller NY #138/R est:10000-15000
£5986 $10356 €8500 Jeune fille etudiant une partition (65x47cm-26x19in) s. panel. 10-Dec-3 Remi Ader, Paris #41/R est:6000-8000
£5986 $10356 €8500 Jeune fille etudiant une partition (65x47cm-26x19in) s. panel. 10-Dec-3 Neret-Minet, Paris #41/R est:6000-8000

WILLEMS, L (?) ?
£1676 $3000 €2447 Take a rest madam (64x48cm-25x19in) bears sig panel. 21-Mar-4 Bonhams & Butterfields, Los Angeles #7370/R est:2000-3000

WILLEMS, Yvonne (20th C) Belgian
£493 $853 €700 Still life of flowers, fruit and grisaille (109x48cm-43x19in) s. 15-Dec-3 Bernaerts, Antwerp #11/R

WILLEMSENS, Abraham (fl.1627-1672) Flemish?
£15000 $25500 €21900 Courtyyard of a country inn with peasnats eating and drinking (67x82cm-26x32in) 29-Oct-3 Christie's, London #11/R est:7000-10000

WILLERS, Ernst (1803-1880) German
£795 $1446 €1200 Landscape with a lake (13x25cm-5x10in) s.i.d.1873 verso panel. 18-Jun-4 Bolland & Marotz, Bremen #794/R
£4667 $8493 €7000 Aqueduct in the countryside near Rome (37x62cm-15x24in) s.d.1839 panel. 1-Jul-4 Van Ham, Cologne #1669/R est:1800

WILLERS, Margarete (1883-?) German
£1933 $3461 €2900 Still life of flowers (56x40cm-22x16in) mono.d. 15-May-4 Dr Sturies, Dusseldorf #218/R

WILLETO, Charlie (1906-1964) American
Sculpture
£2389 $4300 €3488 Navajo buffalo spirit figure (48x10cm-19x4in) carved painted wood. 24-Apr-4 Slotin Folk Art, Buford #295/R est:3000-5000

WILLETT, Arthur (c.1857-1918) British
Works on paper
£260 $476 €390 River landscape (58x46cm-23x18in) s. W/C. 28-Jul-4 Mallams, Oxford #247
£280 $524 €409 In full cry (12x51cm-5x20in) s. W/C bodycol. 24-Feb-4 Bonhams, Knowle #38
£380 $711 €555 Going home (11x44cm-4x17in) s. W/C. 24-Feb-4 Bonhams, Knowle #37
£380 $699 €555 Wintry day, Bagshot (34x49cm-13x19in) s. W/C bodycol. 23-Mar-4 Bonhams, Knightsbridge #162/R
£600 $1056 €876 Fox hunting scenes - Persuit across the stream. Woodland interior (45x13cm-18x5in) both s. W/C htd white pair. 18-May-4 Fellows & Sons, Birmingham #172/R
£750 $1373 €1095 Meet. Tally Ho (22x50cm-9x20in) s. W/C htd white pair. 28-Jul-4 Bonhams, Knightsbridge #83/R
£1100 $1870 €1606 Huntsman and hounds in a meadow, with sheep and stream (55x38cm-22x15in) s. i.d.mount pencil W/C. 19-Nov-3 Tennants, Leyburn #906/R est:600-800

WILLETTE, Adolphe (1857-1926) French
Works on paper
£650 $1196 €949 Countess and the painter (30x21cm-12x8in) s.i. ink W/C pair. 8-Jun-4 Bonhams, Knightsbridge #21/R
£1667 $3050 €2500 Amour de mariage (42x67cm-17x26in) s.d.1922 W/C gouache. 6-Jun-4 Osenat, Fontainebleau #90 est:2500-3000

WILLEY, Chief (1889-1980) American
£276 $500 €403 Coconut trees (41x51cm-16x20in) s.d.1976 masonite. 3-Apr-4 Neal Auction Company, New Orleans #909
£383 $650 €559 Last sleigh ride (41x51cm-16x20in) s.d.1976 acrylic on masonite. 22-Nov-3 New Orleans Auction, New Orleans #1260

WILLIAMS OF PLYMOUTH, William (1808-1895) British
£700 $1260 €1022 Teign from Shaldon (19x29cm-7x11in) s.i. s.i.verso board. 22-Apr-4 Mellors & Kirk, Nottingham #1110/R
£900 $1638 €1314 Figure on a wooden bridge over a Devon river (29x47cm-11x19in) s. board. 21-Jun-4 Bonhams, Bath #464/R
£3911 $7000 €5710 Near Bolton, Lancashire (66x102cm-26x40in) s. prov. 6-May-4 Shannon's, Milford #192/R est:6000-8000

WILLIAMS, Albert (1922-) British
£270 $451 €394 Gladioli in a Chinese vase (78x53cm-31x21in) s. 20-Oct-3 Bonhams, Bath #40
£360 $601 €526 Still life of hollyhocks, delphiniums and summer flowers in a basket (60x50cm-24x20in) s. board. 11-Nov-3 Bonhams, Ipswich #222
£400 $688 €584 Still life of flowers in Chinese vase (23x28cm-9x11in) s.d.38 board. 3-Dec-3 Andrew Hartley, Ilkley #1170
£1250 $2088 €1825 Still life study of mixed summer flowers in Chinese jar on ledge (58x48cm-23x19in) s. 17-Oct-3 Keys, Aylsham #717 est:1250-1500
£1600 $2672 €2336 Still life of spring and summer flowers (41x51cm-16x20in) s. 21-Oct-3 Bonhams, Knightsbridge #145/R est:1500-2000

WILLIAMS, Alexander (1846-1930) British
£424 $750 €619 Landscape (25x46cm-10x18in) s. canvasboard. 1-May-4 Harvey Clar, Oakland #1359
£537 $988 €800 Shore scene with cattle beyond (29x45cm-11x18in) s. 23-Mar-4 Mealy's, Castlecomer #1134
£600 $1104 €876 Irish landscape (36x61cm-14x24in) s. 8-Jun-4 Gorringes, Lewes #2175
£700 $1204 €1022 Irish thatched cottage (25x45cm-10x18in) s. board. 3-Dec-3 John Ross, Belfast #234
£820 $1369 €1197 Fishermen by the shore of a Lough, mist covered hills beyond (18x34cm-7x13in) s. board sold with a companion. 26-Jun-3 Greenslade Hunt, Taunton #528/R
£1259 $2140 €1800 Moorland (20x38cm-8x15in) s. panel prov. 18-Nov-3 Whyte's, Dublin #110/R est:1800-2200
£1333 $2413 €2000 Cottage in mountain landscape (24x43cm-9x17in) s. board. 31-Mar-4 James Adam, Dublin #58a/R est:2500-3000
£1408 $2437 €2000 Lake and mountain landscapes (17x34cm-7x13in) s. board pair. 10-Dec-3 Bonhams & James Adam, Dublin #51/R est:2000-2500
£1800 $2934 €2628 Middle Lake, Killarney. Rain coming from Ross Castle, Killarneyq (26x46cm-10x18in) one s. i.verso one s. board two. 24-Sep-3 Dreweatt Neate, Newbury #101/R est:400-600
£3356 $5940 €5000 Middle Lake, Killarney. Rain coming on from Ross Castle, Killarney (25x44cm-10x17in) s. i.verso one panel one canvas on board pair prov.exhib. 27-Apr-4 Whyte's, Dublin #209/R est:5000-7000
Works on paper
£282 $505 €420 At Arklow (18x35cm-7x14in) s. W/C. 26-May-4 James Adam, Dublin #178/R
£329 $605 €500 Lough Conn, County Mayo (27x46cm-11x18in) s.i. W/C. 22-Jun-4 Mealy's, Castlecomer #131/R
£329 $605 €500 Middle Lake, Killarney (25x43cm-10x17in) s.indis.i. W/C. 22-Jun-4 Mealy's, Castlecomer #132/R
£367 $664 €550 Lower lake, Killarney (28x47cm-11x19in) s.i. W/C. 30-Mar-4 De Veres Art Auctions, Dublin #248
£369 $661 €550 Cottage (25x45cm-10x18in) W/C. 26-May-4 James Adam, Dublin #181/R
£380 $635 €555 Brioka Owemore river (24x41cm-9x16in) s. W/C. 22-Oct-3 Wingetts, Wrexham #363
£400 $756 €584 Irish moorland landscape (29x65cm-11x26in) s. W/C. 23-Feb-4 David Duggleby, Scarborough #701/R
£400 $724 €600 Glendalough, Recess, Connemara (26x46cm-10x18in) s.i. W/C. 30-Mar-4 De Veres Art Auctions, Dublin #249
£470 $841 €700 Blackwater, near Dromana, Co. Cork (25x46cm-10x18in) s. W/C. 26-May-4 James Adam, Dublin #176/R
£600 $1092 €876 Glendalough recess Connemara. Lower Lake Killarney (25x45cm-10x18in) s.i. pencil W/C pair. 5-Feb-4 Mellors & Kirk, Nottingham #485
£704 $1218 €1000 Muckross lake, Killarney (23x44cm-9x17in) s. W/C. 10-Dec-3 Bonhams & James Adam, Dublin #33/R

WILLIAMS, Alfred Walter (1824-1905) British
£300 $549 €450 Langdale (17x25cm-7x10in) init.d.1873 card. 27-Jul-4 Henry Adams, Chichester #454
£550 $985 €803 On the Surrey hills (23x30cm-9x12in) init.d.1895 i.stretcher. 27-May-4 Christie's, Kensington #141/R
£872 $1500 €1273 Lake in the Tyrol (74x100cm-29x39in) s.d.1878. 3-Dec-3 Doyle, New York #95/R est:3000-5000
£1000 $1860 €1460 Returning home with the flock (15x22cm-6x9in) init.d.1861. 4-Mar-4 Christie's, Kensington #450/R est:800-1200

WILLIAMS, C (?) ?
£1500 $2700 €2190 River scene (71x92cm-28x36in) s. 21-Jan-4 Sotheby's, Olympia #386/R est:500-700

WILLIAMS, Caroline Marsh (1945-) Australian
£325 $511 €471 Back wall (91x122cm-36x48in) init. oil pencil prov. 27-Aug-3 Christie's, Sydney #679 (A.D 800)

WILLIAMS, Charles (1965-) British/American
£400 $708 €584 Dark artist (122x76cm-48x30in) 27-Apr-4 Bonhams, Knightsbridge #122/R
£1200 $2160 €1752 Malcolm Sings (92x82cm-36x32in) 20-Jan-4 Bonhams, Knightsbridge #266/R est:500-700
£1500 $2505 €2190 George, green man and trainset (41x46cm-16x18in) init. 16-Oct-3 Christie's, Kensington #618/R est:1000-2000

£1500 $2505 €2190 Girl with remote (41x46cm-16x18in) init. 16-Oct-3 Christie's, Kensington #619/R est:1000-2000

WILLIAMS, Charles R (20th C) American
£500 $850 €730 Desert landscape (61x76cm-24x30in) s. prov. 18-Nov-3 John Moran, Pasadena #175

WILLIAMS, Charles Truett (1918-1966) American
Sculpture
£1676 $3000 €2447 Untitled. metal. 13-May-4 Dallas Auction Gallery, Dallas #275b/R est:3000-6000

WILLIAMS, Chester (1790-1850) American
£428 $787 €650 Harbour (46x71cm-18x28in) s.d.79. 22-Jun-4 De Veres Art Auctions, Dublin #232/R
£533 $965 €800 Abstract (63x43cm-25x17in) s. board. 30-Mar-4 De Veres Art Auctions, Dublin #56/R
£920 $1500 €1343 Walk through the country side (25x38cm-10x15in) s. 28-Sep-3 Simpson's, Houston #373/R

WILLIAMS, Christopher David (1873-1934) British
£460 $837 €672 Barmouth, bridge over the estuary (44x59cm-17x23in) 21-Jun-4 Bonhams, Bath #359
£480 $816 €701 Haverfordwest (30x40cm-12x16in) s. canvas on board. 18-Nov-3 Sotheby's, Olympia #176/R
£1300 $2236 €1898 Woman on a beach (30x46cm-12x18in) board. 2-Dec-3 Peter Francis, Wales #50/R est:250-350

WILLIAMS, Colin (1935-) Canadian
£226 $378 €330 Untitled - farming in the foothills (60x75cm-24x30in) 17-Nov-3 Hodgins, Calgary #347/R (C.D 500)
£249 $416 €364 Untitled - fields in harvest (60x75cm-24x30in) s. 17-Nov-3 Hodgins, Calgary #399/R (C.D 550)

WILLIAMS, E C (1807-1881) British
£500 $835 €730 Landscape with figures and cattle in the foreground (41x51cm-16x20in) s. 8-Oct-3 Andrew Hartley, Ilkley #1135

WILLIAMS, Edward (1782-1855) British
£1400 $2646 €2044 Moonlit ferry (48x69cm-19x27in) init. 19-Feb-4 Christie's, Kensington #120/R est:400-600
£1450 $2465 €2117 Country scene with figures on a pathway (23x30cm-9x12in) panel. 19-Nov-3 James Thompson, Kirby Lonsdale #214
£1500 $2505 €2190 Cattle on a barge in a moonlit landscape. Cattle and sheep in moonlight (23x35cm-9x14in) init. panel pair. 13-Nov-3 Christie's, Kensington #74/R est:1000-1500
£1550 $2775 €2263 Boys fishing by a stream (63x76cm-25x30in) prov. 27-May-4 Christie's, Kensington #146/R est:2000-3000
£1800 $3060 €2628 Village scene with figures, dog and poultry (35x30cm-14x12in) board. 19-Nov-3 James Thompson, Kirby Lonsdale #213
£1850 $3330 €2701 Country scene with water carrier child, dog and cottage (45x25cm-18x10in) panel. 21-Jan-4 James Thompson, Kirby Lonsdale #152/R
£1900 $3420 €2774 Gypsy encampment (38x59cm-15x23in) 21-Jan-4 James Thompson, Kirby Lonsdale #151/R
£2000 $3600 €2920 Travelers on a country road (43x62cm-17x24in) 21-Jan-4 James Thompson, Kirby Lonsdale #150/R
£2200 $3938 €3212 River Yare, near Norwich (41x53cm-16x21in) prov. 27-May-4 Christie's, Kensington #148/R est:3000-5000
£2700 $4779 €3942 Wooded landscape with figures and cattle (21x29cm-8x11in) init. panel. 27-Apr-4 Henry Adams, Chichester #735/R est:3000-4000
£3500 $6265 €5110 Figures in a river landscape, with harvesters beyond. Figures by a pond (30x40cm-12x16in) panel pair. 27-May-4 Christie's, Kensington #138/R est:4000-6000

WILLIAMS, Edward (attrib) (1782-1855) British
£700 $1106 €1015 Quiet pool (17x15cm-7x6in) panel. 7-Sep-3 Lots Road Auctions, London #337
£1200 $2148 €1752 Gypsy camp (38x58cm-15x23in) s. i.verso. 27-May-4 Christie's, Kensington #140/R est:1200-1800
£1800 $3060 €2628 Crossing the stream. Wayside chat (30x40cm-12x16in) panel pair. 19-Nov-3 Bonhams, New Bond Street #21/R est:2000-3000

WILLIAMS, Edward Charles (1807-1881) British
£621 $1000 €907 Noon day rest (30x40cm-12x16in) panel prov. 14-Jan-4 Christie's, Rockefeller NY #52/R est:2000-3000
£1500 $2505 €2190 Figures by a cottage (30x41cm-12x16in) init. prov. 13-Nov-3 Christie's, Kensington #79/R est:1500-2000
£1800 $3240 €2628 Fisherman on the riverbank, water mill and cattle beyond (62x75cm-24x30in) 21-Jan-4 Sotheby's, Olympia #333/R est:800-1200
£3000 $5550 €4380 Cattle watering (61x51cm-24x20in) s.d.1847. 13-Jan-4 Bonhams, Knightsbridge #249/R est:3000-4000
£6500 $11050 €9490 Meeting. Path from the village church, Isle of Wight (30x23cm-12x9in) panel pair. 25-Nov-3 Christie's, London #111/R est:3000-5000
£13000 $23920 €18980 Gypsy encampment in a wooded landscape (76x127cm-30x50in) indis sig.d.1850. 11-Jun-4 Christie's, London #131/R est:10000-15000

WILLIAMS, Edward Charles (attrib) (1807-1881) British
£248 $439 €362 Fishing in the mill stream (34x44cm-13x17in) panel. 3-May-4 Lawson Menzies, Sydney #395 (A.D 600)
£400 $648 €580 Wooded river landscape with a shepherd in a field (23x28cm-9x11in) panel. 30-Jul-3 Hamptons Fine Art, Godalming #277
£900 $1647 €1314 Extensive landscape with figures in a clearing, woodland beyond (28x38cm-11x15in) panel. 6-Apr-4 Bonhams, Knightsbridge #70/R
£5322 $9525 €7770 View of a broken bridge near Venice (56x67cm-22x26in) prov. 28-May-4 Uppsala Auktionskammare, Uppsala #24/R est:25000-30000 (S.KR 72000)

WILLIAMS, Edward K (1870-?) American
£1508 $2700 €2202 Landscape with view of mountains from clearing (36x43cm-14x17in) s. 29-May-4 Brunk, Ashville #539/R
Works on paper
£307 $550 €448 Landscape (41x36cm-16x14in) s. W/C. 11-Jan-4 William Jenack, New York #286

WILLIAMS, Ellen (1790-?) British
£872 $1544 €1300 Young woman with a water pitcher leaning by a well (25x17cm-10x7in) panel prov. 27-Apr-4 Whyte's, Dublin #121/R

WILLIAMS, Evelyn (1929-) British
£500 $835 €730 Sleeping figure (50x40cm-20x16in) 21-Oct-3 Bonhams, Knightsbridge #154/R

WILLIAMS, Florence White (?-1953) American
£1163 $2000 €1698 Back yards, Saugatuck (61x86cm-24x34in) s. i.verso painted c.1935. 7-Dec-3 Treadway Gallery, Cincinnati #542/R est:2500-3500
£1374 $2500 €2006 Boothbay Harbour, Maine (69x69cm-27x27in) s. i.stretcher. 7-Feb-4 Harvey Clar, Oakland #1577

WILLIAMS, Frederick Ballard (1871-1956) American
£435 $800 €635 Trio (25x23cm-10x9in) s. prov. 25-Mar-4 Doyle, New York #80/R
£462 $850 €675 Old stone wall (30x41cm-12x16in) s. board. 25-Mar-4 Doyle, New York #78/R
£508 $950 €742 Blue Ridge Mountains, Virginia (46x75cm-18x30in) s. 26-Feb-4 Skinner, Bolton #610/R
£1033 $1900 €1508 In the garden (41x61cm-16x24in) s. 25-Mar-4 Doyle, New York #79/R est:1200-1800
£1223 $2250 €1786 L'heure joyeuse (64x76cm-25x30in) s. 8-Jun-4 Bonhams & Butterfields, San Francisco #4072/R est:3000-5000
£1445 $2500 €2110 Arcadian Vista (53x102cm-21x40in) s. prov. 10-Dec-3 Bonhams & Butterfields, San Francisco #6021/R est:3000-5000

WILLIAMS, Frederick Ronald (1927-1982) Australian
£828 $1291 €1201 Portrait (30x22cm-12x9in) s. oil on paper. 1-Aug-2 Joel, Victoria #335 est:1000-2000 (A.D 2400)
£17073 $26805 €24756 Bayswater landscape (52x69cm-20x27in) s. board painted c.1958 prov. 26-Aug-3 Christie's, Sydney #37/R est:35000-45000 (A.D 42000)
£26860 $47541 €39216 Snowy mountains (45x59cm-18x23in) s.d.72 acrylic board prov. 3-May-4 Christie's, Melbourne #43/R est:45000-55000 (A.D 65000)
£41322 $73140 €60330 Werribee gorge (96x106cm-38x42in) s. prov.exhib. 3-May-4 Christie's, Melbourne #90/R est:100000-140000 (A.D 100000)
£41985 $76412 €61298 Hanging Rock (85x95cm-33x37in) d. 16-Jun-4 Deutscher-Menzies, Melbourne #71/R est:130000-160000 (A.D 110000)
£59426 $93893 €86762 Blackwood wattle (101x101cm-40x40in) s. prov. 2-Sep-3 Deutscher-Menzies, Melbourne #46/R est:160000-200000 (A.D 145000)
£59574 $101277 €86978 St Andrews - the botanist's garden (101x101cm-40x40in) s. prov.lit. 25-Nov-3 Christie's, Melbourne #38/R est:150000-200000 (A.D 140000)
£61983 $109711 €90495 Cottlesbridge landscape with derelict car (101x101cm-40x40in) s. painted c.1975 prov. 3-May-4 Christie's, Melbourne #29/R est:160000-180000 (A.D 150000)
£63524 $100369 €92745 Wedderburn (101x75cm-40x30in) s. prov. 2-Sep-3 Deutscher-Menzies, Melbourne #36/R est:140000-180000 (A.D 155000)
£70539 $117801 €105809 Acacias (107x96cm-42x38in) s. painted 1976. 27-Oct-3 Goodman, Sydney #84/R est:120000-160000 (A.D 170000)
£85106 $144681 €124255 The botanist's garden (106x96cm-42x38in) s. i.d.1976 verso prov. 25-Nov-3 Christie's, Melbourne #70/R est:200000-250000 (A.D 200000)
£154472 $242520 €223984 Upwey landscape (136x151cm-54x59in) s. painted c.1965-66 prov.exhib.lit. 27-Aug-3 Christie's, Sydney #565/R est:350000-450000 (A.D 380000)
£172065 $277024 €251215 Lysterfield II (152x122cm-60x48in) s. painted July 1974 prov.exhib.lit. 25-Aug-3 Sotheby's, Paddington #162/R est:350000-400000 (A.D 425000)
Works on paper
£420 $764 €613 Portrait of Doug Hall (12x15cm-5x6in) s. ball point pen. 16-Jun-4 Deutscher-Menzies, Melbourne #405/R est:600-900 (A.D 1100)
£681 $1157 €994 Nude (26x14cm-10x6in) init. pen ink exec c.1945. 26-Nov-3 Deutscher-Menzies, Melbourne #233/R (A.D 1600)
£1025 $1660 €1497 English church (21x29cm-8x11in) s. W/C gouache. 30-Jul-3 Goodman, Sydney #169/R (A.D 2500)
£2273 $4022 €3319 Figure in Lilydale landscape (29x39cm-11x15in) s. W/C gouache prov. 3-May-4 Christie's, Melbourne #314/R est:6000-8000 (A.D 5500)
£8097 $13036 €11822 Hillside (34x52cm-13x20in) s. gouache prov. 25-Aug-3 Sotheby's, Paddington #143/R est:20000-30000 (A.D 20000)
£9322 $15847 €13610 Landcape, Upwey (52x68cm-20x27in) s. gouache paper on board prov. 24-Nov-3 Sotheby's, Melbourne #29/R est:20000-30000 (A.D 22000)
£9917 $18347 €14479 Glasshouse Mountain II 1971 (33x75cm-13x30in) s. synthetic polymer gouache prov.exhib. 10-Mar-4 Deutscher-Menzies, Melbourne #70/R est:26000-34000 (A.D 24000)
£10246 $16598 €14959 North East River, Flinders Island (57x74cm-22x29in) s. gouache prov. 30-Jul-3 Goodman, Sydney #29/R est:25000-30000 (A.D 25000)
£10569 $18919 €15431 Landscape (47x73cm-19x29in) s. gouache painted c.1965 prov. 4-May-4 Sotheby's, Melbourne #7/R est:25000-30000 (A.D 26000)
£11064 $18809 €16153 Water birds and Lily pads, Botanic Gardens Lake VII (52x77cm-20x30in) s. gouache exec 1970 prov.exhib. 26-Nov-3 Deutscher-Menzies, Melbourne #33/R est:26000-32000 (A.D 26000)
£11570 $21405 €16892 Gum trees in a landscape, Lysterfield (55x75cm-22x30in) s. gouache executed c.1966 prov. 10-Mar-4 Deutscher-Menzies, Melbourne #117/R est:30000-40000 (A.D 28000)
£12397 $21942 €18100 Avenel landscape (55x75cm-22x30in) s. gouache. 3-May-4 Christie's, Melbourne #104/R est:40000-55000 (A.D 30000)
£13008 $20423 €18862 Landscape, Bushfire series (55x75cm-22x30in) s. gouache prov. 26-Aug-3 Christie's, Sydney #11/R est:24000-28000 (A.D 32000)
£14634 $26195 €21366 Water pond in a landscape (55x74cm-22x29in) s. gouache exec 1966 prov. 4-May-4 Sotheby's, Melbourne #36/R est:28000-38000 (A.D 36000)

WILLIAMS, Geoff (20th C) British
£2336 $4181 €3411 Still life - Narcissus (51x68cm-20x27in) s.d.92 board. 11-May-4 Watson's, Christchurch #68/R est:9000-15000 (NZ.D 6750)

WILLIAMS, Geoff (20th C) New Zealander

£4511	$7669	€6586	Hot n' spicy (60x90cm-24x35in) s. board. 27-Nov-3 International Art Centre, Auckland #44/R est:12000-14000 (NZ.D 12000)

Works on paper

£634	$1027	€919	Nude on couch (28x52cm-11x20in) s.d.1994 pencil. 31-Jul-3 International Art Centre, Auckland #96/R est:1400-1800 (NZ.D 1750)

WILLIAMS, George (1920-1985) British

£830	$1510	€1212	Poisson rouge (33x53cm-13x21in) s.d.74 paper. 16-Jun-4 Fischer, Luzern #1164/R (S.FR 1900)

WILLIAMS, George (20th C) American

Sculpture

£2156	$3600	€3148	Statue of Liberty (48x15x8cm-19x6x3in) paint wood prov. 15-Nov-3 Slotin Folk Art, Buford #286/R est:1000-2000

WILLIAMS, George Augustus (1814-1901) British

£600	$948	€870	Sunset over the coast (41x66cm-16x26in) mono. 4-Sep-3 Christie's, Kensington #190/R
£1400	$2408	€2044	The road to the mill (16x22cm-6x9in) mono.i.d.1855 panel. 4-Dec-3 Mellors & Kirk, Nottingham #937/R est:400-600
£1700	$2754	€2465	Morning on the common. Showery day (36x61cm-14x24in) mono. pair. 30-Jul-3 Hamptons Fine Art, Godalming #201/R est:1500-2000
£2000	$3580	€2920	On the ice, sunset (34x70cm-13x28in) mono. prov. 7-Jan-4 George Kidner, Lymington #215/R est:2000-3000
£3600	$6624	€5256	Village inn (41x51cm-16x20in) mono. 11-Jun-4 Christie's, London #138/R est:4000-6000
£4500	$8325	€6570	Cutting the reeds (42x62cm-17x24in) mono. 14-Jul-4 Sotheby's, Olympia #82/R est:2000-3000
£4800	$8640	€7008	River landscape with a mother and children, a dog, a sailing boat and a horse (46x71cm-18x28in) s.d.1864. 21-Apr-4 Tennants, Leyburn #1160/R est1500-2000
£6500	$11245	€9490	Bend in the river at dusk (81x127cm-32x50in) s.d. s.d.1859 stretcher. 10-Dec-3 Bonhams, Bury St Edmunds #595/R est:5000-8000

WILLIAMS, Glynn (1939-) British

£600	$1002	€876	Gun salute (30x41cm-12x16in) s. board. 16-Oct-3 Christie's, Kensington #433/R

WILLIAMS, Graham (19th C) British

£230	$425	€336	A steady breeze (91x58cm-36x23in) s. 16-Jan-4 Aspire, Cleveland #37/R
£300	$501	€438	Loch Morlich (61x91cm-24x36in) s. 17-Oct-3 Keys, Aylsham #728
£360	$680	€526	Loch scene (50x74cm-20x29in) s. 23-Feb-4 David Duggleby, Scarborough #616/R
£550	$1023	€803	Scotland for ever, sundown o'er Glen Affric, Inverness (61x91cm-24x36in) s. i.verso. 4-Mar-4 Christie's, Kensington #151/R

WILLIAMS, H Perry (fl.1841-1857) British

Works on paper

£600	$1098	€876	Pony and trap beneath Welsh castle, with sea in distance (43x69cm-17x27in) W/C. 31-Jan-4 Nigel Ward, Hereford #1381/R

WILLIAMS, Harry (19th C) British

£330	$591	€482	Cornish harbour (45x75cm-18x30in) s.d.1876. 22-Mar-4 Bearnes, Exeter #238/R
£740	$1206	€1080	Holiday makers and bathing machines at King Edwards's Bay, Tynemouth (48x67cm-19x26in) s.d.1843. 23-Sep-3 Anderson & Garland, Newcastle #372/R

WILLIAMS, Henry (1807-1886) British

£284	$491	€415	River landscape (22x28cm-9x11in) s.d.1882 panel. 9-Dec-3 Rasmussen, Copenhagen #1698/R (D.KR 3000)
£4577	$8011	€6500	Les batteuses de ble (57x81cm-22x32in) s.i. 16-Dec-3 Claude Aguttes, Neuilly #89/R est:5000-7000

WILLIAMS, Hugh Grecian (1773-1829) British

Works on paper

£800	$1432	€1168	View towards Naupactus (20x30cm-8x12in) pen ink wash bodycol. 10-May-4 Sotheby's, Olympia #142/R
£850	$1420	€1241	Ruined abbey (38x49cm-15x19in) s. pencil W/C. 16-Oct-3 Christie's, Kensington #27/R
£850	$1573	€1241	Windsor Castle with women collecting kindling watched by deer (32x48cm-13x19in) W/C prov. 11-Feb-4 Cheffins, Cambridge #387/R
£1700	$3128	€2482	Edinburgh from the Pentland Hills (37x52cm-15x20in) pencil grey ink W/C prov. 25-Mar-4 Christie's, Kensington #185/R est:1500-2500
£1950	$3647	€2925	Kenmore, Loch Tay. Bridge of Douglas near Inverary (23x31cm-9x12in) s. one d.1805 one d.1802 pencil W/C pair. 26-Jul-4 Bonhams, Bath #6/R est:800-1000

WILLIAMS, Jacqueline (1962-) British

£270	$500	€394	Playing the guitar (44x59cm-17x23in) init. board prov. 13-Jul-4 Rosebery Fine Art, London #624
£400	$728	€584	Beach scene, Sennem Cove (21x39cm-8x15in) init. board. 21-Jun-4 Bonhams, Bath #432
£600	$942	€870	Garden table laid for tea (61x46cm-24x18in) 28-Aug-3 Christie's, Kensington #331/R
£840	$1478	€1226	Roses and garden table (51x26cm-20x10in) init. board. 18-May-4 Woolley & Wallis, Salisbury #82/R
£1200	$2112	€1752	Painting in the garden (57x29cm-22x11in) init. board. 18-May-4 Woolley & Wallis, Salisbury #36/R est:250-350

WILLIAMS, James Francis (1785-1846) British

£1600	$2864	€2336	Castle Tioram, Moidart (37x50cm-15x20in) s.d.1830 s.i.d.verso. 26-May-4 Sotheby's, Olympia #27/R est:1500-2000

WILLIAMS, John W (fl.1900-1920) British

Works on paper

£400	$724	€584	Whitby Harbour towards the abbey (15x25cm-6x10in) s. W/C. 15-Apr-4 Richardson & Smith, Whitby #134/R
£440	$796	€642	Henrietta Street, Whitby (15x25cm-6x10in) s. W/C. 15-Apr-4 Richardson & Smith, Whitby #138
£560	$890	€818	Darnholm, Goathland (23x34cm-9x13in) s. W/C. 9-Sep-3 David Duggleby, Scarborough #7
£660	$1049	€964	Whitby Harbour (23x43cm-9x17in) s. W/C. 9-Sep-3 David Duggleby, Scarborough #48
£660	$1195	€964	Low tide in Whitby harbour (24x16cm-9x6in) s. W/C. 30-Mar-4 David Duggleby, Scarborough #60/R

WILLIAMS, Jon (1946-) Canadian

Works on paper

£226	$378	€330	Native portrait (60x45cm-24x18in) s.d.1974 pastel. 17-Nov-3 Hodgins, Calgary #35/R (C.D 500)
£280	$512	€409	Many mules (68x50cm-27x20in) s. W/C prov. 1-Jun-4 Hodgins, Calgary #169/R (C.D 700)

WILLIAMS, Keith Shaw (1906-1951) American

Works on paper

£741	$1200	€1074	Portrait of Andrew Winter (63x48cm-25x19in) chl. 8-Aug-3 Barridorf, Portland #174/R est:600-900

WILLIAMS, Kyffin (1918-) British

£4200	$7644	€6132	Mr Thomas, Cemlyn (21x15cm-8x6in) init. panel. 21-Jun-4 Bonhams, Bath #372/R est:1500-2000
£5000	$8500	€7300	Scuola Grande di San Marco, Venice (29x19cm-11x7in) init. board prov. 18-Nov-3 Sotheby's, Olympia #65/R est:2000-3000
£5000	$9100	€7300	Portrait of Dom John Roberts (60x50cm-24x20in) init. painted c.1957. 21-Jun-4 Bonhams, Bath #374/R est:2500-3500
£6600	$11220	€9636	Gwen (60x49cm-24x19in) init. i.on stretcher lit. 29-Oct-3 Bonhams, Chester #374/R est:4000-6000
£12500	$22750	€18250	Cloud over Moelwyn Mawr, from Lian Ffestiniog (76x127cm-30x50in) init. 21-Jun-4 Bonhams, Bath #376/R est:10000-15000
£14500	$23635	€21170	Caernarfonshire mountain path with Rivals in the distance (48x74cm-19x29in) init. 27-Sep-3 Rogers Jones, Clwyd #95/R
£14500	$26100	€21170	Snowdon partly snowcapped and Crib Goch (25x58cm-10x23in) init. prov. 24-Apr-4 Rogers Jones, Clwyd #184/R
£15000	$25500	€21900	Eryri, Snowdon (76x127cm-30x50in) painted 1960 set of 4 prov.lit. 18-Nov-3 Sotheby's, Olympia #194/R est:10000-15000
£15000	$25500	€21900	Hill farmers (51x51cm-20x20in) init. prov. 18-Nov-3 Sotheby's, Olympia #211/R est:7000-10000
£15500	$27745	€22630	Sea at llanddwyn (51x112cm-20x44in) init. prov. 14-May-4 Christie's, Kensington #603/R est:6000-8000
£16000	$28800	€23360	Hendre Selar Cwm Ystradllyn (58x51cm-23x20in) init.i. prov. 24-Apr-4 Rogers Jones, Clwyd #157/R
£16500	$30030	€24090	Redwarf Bay, Anglesey (50x75cm-20x30in) s. 21-Jun-4 Bonhams, Bath #379/R est:8000-10000
£17000	$30600	€24820	Snow in Cwm Pennant (76x61cm-30x24in) s. i.verso prov. 24-Apr-4 Rogers Jones, Clwyd #159/R
£17500	$32375	€25550	Rhoscryman (61x61cm-24x24in) init. prov. 11-Mar-4 Christie's, Kensington #249/R est:8000-12000
£18000	$30060	€26280	Hill farmer no 1 (61x51cm-24x20in) 16-Oct-3 Christie's, Kensington #634/R est:8000-12000
£18000	$33300	€26280	Evening Talysarn (61x61cm-24x24in) init. prov. 11-Mar-4 Christie's, Kensington #255/R est:10000-15000
£18500	$33855	€27010	Harbourmaster's cottage (49x75cm-19x30in) init. 6-Jul-4 Bearnes, Exeter #474/R est:4000-6000

Works on paper

£460	$750	€672	Farm horse (10x18cm-4x7in) init. pencil dr. 27-Sep-3 Rogers Jones, Clwyd #45
£800	$1304	€1168	Study of a ram (15x28cm-6x11in) init. pastel colourwash. 27-Sep-3 Rogers Jones, Clwyd #10
£900	$1467	€1314	Study of Barbary sheep (38x48cm-15x19in) init. colourwash. 27-Sep-3 Rogers Jones, Clwyd #42
£950	$1615	€1387	Fresian bull (25x36cm-10x14in) s.i.verso ink. 18-Nov-3 Sotheby's, Olympia #69/R
£1000	$1700	€1460	Welsh pony (11x14cm-4x6in) init. pencil wash. 18-Nov-3 Sotheby's, Olympia #210/R est:1000-1500
£1300	$2210	€1898	Penrhyn Isaf, near Abafraw, Anglesey (31x49cm-12x19in) init. i.verso W/C. 29-Oct-3 Bonhams, Chester #375/R est:1000-1500
£1350	$2457	€1971	Nant Peris (37x49cm-15x19in) init. ink wash. 21-Jun-4 Bonhams, Bath #371 est:400-600
£1500	$2505	€2190	Figure in a village street (25x36cm-10x14in) W/C. 21-Oct-3 Peter Francis, Wales #46/R est:600-800
£1600	$2608	€2336	Two Indian gamecock (48x36cm-19x14in) init. pencil colourwash. 27-Sep-3 Rogers Jones, Clwyd #30/R
£1600	$2720	€2336	Landscape with cottages (34x47cm-13x19in) init. pencil wash. 18-Nov-3 Sotheby's, Olympia #70/R est:800-1200
£1600	$2928	€2336	Barbary sheep (22x29cm-9x11in) mono.i. W/C pencil. 6-Jul-4 Peter Wilson, Nantwich #91/R est:1250-1500
£2000	$3640	€2920	Nant Ffrancon Pass, Snowdonia (34x48cm-13x19in) init. pen ink wash. 21-Jun-4 Bonhams, Bath #375/R est:1000-1200
£2000	$3640	€2920	Welsh black bull (29x44cm-11x17in) init. ink W/C. 21-Jun-4 Bonhams, Bath #378/R est:1000-1500
£2100	$3507	€3066	Hillside cottages (25x36cm-10x14in) init. W/C. 21-Oct-3 Peter Francis, Wales #45/R est:700-900
£2100	$3822	€3066	Horse riders in a Patagonian village (24x33cm-9x13in) init. pen ink W/C wash. 21-Jun-4 Bonhams, Bath #377 est:2500-3500
£2200	$3740	€3212	Fedw Fawr (21x40cm-8x16in) init. pencil W/C. 26-Nov-3 Sotheby's, Olympia #105/R est:800-1200
£2300	$4209	€3358	Study of a bird of prey (34x44cm-13x17in) mono. ink wash. 6-Jul-4 Peter Wilson, Nantwich #90/R est:1800-2200
£2500	$4550	€3650	Cottages in a North Wales landscape (36x55cm-14x22in) init. pen ink monochrome wash. 21-Jun-4 Bonhams, Bath #373/R est:1000-1500
£2500	$4425	€3650	Study of a badger (25x34cm-10x13in) mono. ink wash. 28-Apr-4 Peter Wilson, Nantwich #202 est:1800-2000
£2600	$4576	€3796	Welsh ponies (35x47cm-14x19in) init. pencil W/C prov. 19-May-4 Sotheby's, Olympia #269/R est:1500-2000

£2750 $4950 €4015 Sunset over The Rivals with cottages in the foreground (25x33cm-10x13in) init. 24-Apr-4 Rogers Jones, Clwyd #130/R
£3100 $5673 €4526 Port Meirion Village, North Wales (22x30cm-9x12in) mono. pencil over W/C. 6-Jul-4 Peter Wilson, Nantwich #61/R est:3000-4000
£3500 $6300 €5110 John Jones and Mot Nant Peris, farmer and dog (18x25cm-7x10in) init. 24-Apr-4 Rogers Jones, Clwyd #135
£3500 $6195 €5110 Welsh village (31x48cm-12x19in) mono. W/C pencil. 28-Apr-4 Peter Wilson, Nantwich #170 est:2000-2500

WILLIAMS, Lucy Gwendolen (1870-1955) British
Sculpture
£3360 $6014 €4906 Queen of dreams (20cm-8in) bronze green marble base prov. 15-May-4 Christie's, Sydney #256/R est:5000-7000 (A.D 8500)

WILLIAMS, Margaret Lindsay (?-1960) British
£520 $972 €780 Violet Barlow, nee Dinwall, wife of Sir Robert Barlow (70x75cm-28x30in) s.d.1902. 26-Jul-4 Bonhams, Bath #52/R

WILLIAMS, Mervyn (1940-) New Zealander?
£2797 $5091 €4084 Poles apart (80x67cm-31x26in) i. s.d.1996 verso acrylic. 29-Jun-4 Peter Webb, Auckland #139/R est:7000-9000 (NZ.D 8000)
£5435 $8750 €7935 God of fire (163x136cm-64x54in) s.i.d.1993 verso. 20-Aug-3 Dunbar Sloane, Auckland #54/R est:10000-15000 (NZ.D 15000)
Works on paper
£316 $543 €461 Blue, green abstract (76x57cm-30x22in) s.d.1986 W/C. 7-Dec-3 International Art Centre, Auckland #264/R (NZ.D 850)

WILLIAMS, Micah (1782-1837) American
£2830 $4500 €4132 Woman with floral embroidered shawl and beaded necklace (76x64cm-30x25in) 10-Sep-3 Sotheby's, New York #164/R est:3000-6000
Works on paper
£9290 $17000 €13563 Portrait of a man (61x46cm-24x18in) s.stretcher pastel. 6-Jun-4 Skinner, Boston #267 est:600-800
£11950 $19000 €17447 Woman holding a book and wearing a lace hat (66x56cm-26x22in) pastel exec.c.1830. 10-Sep-3 Sotheby's, New York #167/R est:4000-6000

WILLIAMS, Neil (1934-) American
£1216 $2250 €1775 Grey flannel dwarf (183x183cm-72x72in) acrylic resin paint canvas painted 1965 prov. 12-Feb-4 Sotheby's, New York #107/R est:3000-5000

WILLIAMS, P V and PIMENOV, Y I (20th C) Russian
Works on paper
£531 $950 €775 Political caricature (34x27cm-13x11in) ink gouache exec.1920's. 29-May-4 Shishkin Gallery, Moscow #5/R

WILLIAMS, Pauline Bliss (1888-?) American
£348 $550 €508 Sunset, Gloucester Harbour (30x36cm-12x14in) s.d.1932 board. 7-Sep-3 Treadway Gallery, Cincinnati #612/R

WILLIAMS, Penry (1798-1885) British
£800 $1408 €1168 Longhorn bull (25x36cm-10x14in) sketch. 18-May-4 Woolley & Wallis, Salisbury #219/R
£1049 $1804 €1500 Les passeurs sur fond de paysage montagneux (75x125cm-30x49in) s.d.1874. 8-Dec-3 Horta, Bruxelles #390 est:2000-3000
£1850 $3460 €2701 Portrait of a young lady in a yellow dress (8x6cm-3x2in) 25-Feb-4 Mallams, Oxford #257/R est:300-400
£4700 $7426 €6815 Peasants in the Campagna (31x76cm-12x30in) s.d.1853. 24-Jul-3 Lawrence, Crewkerne #947/R est:2500-3500
£6000 $10200 €8760 Travellers in the Roman Campagna (31x77cm-12x30in) s.d.1853. 19-Nov-3 Bonhams, New Bond Street #20/R est:6000-8000

WILLIAMS, Simon (20th C) New Zealander
£532 $941 €777 Sailing boats on Hauraki Gulf (60x70cm-24x28in) s. 28-Apr-4 Dunbar Sloane, Auckland #96 (NZ.D 1500)
£709 $1255 €1035 Sailing boats and Rangitoto (39x49cm-15x19in) s. board. 28-Apr-4 Dunbar Sloane, Auckland #97/R (NZ.D 2000)

WILLIAMS, Sue (1954-) American
£1359 $2500 €1984 Dreaming (46x40cm-18x16in) oil paper. 10-Jun-4 Phillips, New York #436/R
£6145 $11000 €8972 Green and blue with fuzzy pads (38x46cm-15x18in) s.i.d.1997 verso acrylic prov. 14-May-4 Phillips, New York #137/R est:12000-18000
£7500 $13650 €10950 No Brain (122x107cm-48x42in) s.i.d.1989 verso acrylic paper on canvas. 4-Feb-4 Sotheby's, Olympia #212/R est:5000-7000
£8380 $15000 €12235 Busy plain, itchy back (38x46cm-15x18in) s.i.d.1997 verso acrylic oil prov. 14-May-4 Phillips, New York #142/R est:15000-20000
£8982 $15000 €13114 Purple, no face on someone (39x46cm-15x18in) s.i.d.1996 verso acrylic prov. 14-Nov-3 Phillips, New York #101/R est:15000-20000
£17877 $32000 €26100 National feet (188x208cm-74x82in) s.i.d.1998 verso oil acrylic prov. 14-May-4 Phillips, New York #106/R est:25000-35000
£19162 $32000 €27977 Cute outfit (122x147cm-48x58in) s.i.d.98 verso oil acrylic on canvas prov. 14-Nov-3 Phillips, New York #105/R est:20000-30000
£23952 $40000 €34970 Pile Up (244x274cm-96x108in) painted 1999 prov.exhib. 12-Nov-3 Christie's, Rockefeller NY #516/R est:25000-35000
Works on paper
£867 $1551 €1300 Sketch collage (46x33cm-18x13in) photo ink. 12-May-4 Chochon-Barre & Allardi, Paris #121/R
£933 $1671 €1400 Feeling of satisfaction (41x53cm-16x21in) ink. 12-May-4 Chochon-Barre & Allardi, Paris #120

WILLIAMS, Terrick (1860-1936) British
£373 $600 €545 Forest interior (33x28cm-13x11in) s. board. 20-Aug-3 James Julia, Fairfield #1081/R
£880 $1602 €1285 Arab gateway (25x41cm-10x16in) board. 16-Jun-4 Andrew Hartley, Ilkley #1067
£1550 $2744 €2263 Sunny street, Pont Aven, Brittany (25x35cm-10x14in) s.d.98 s.i.d.verso. 27-Apr-4 Bonhams, Knowle #96 est:500-800
£1800 $3330 €2628 Breton market (28x41cm-11x16in) s. board. 10-Feb-4 David Lay, Penzance #473/R est:1800-2400
£4200 $7686 €6132 Numerous boats in a harbour with figures (30x48cm-12x19in) s. 27-Jan-4 Rogers Jones, Clwyd #107/R
£4400 $7040 €6424 Unloading the catch (30x46cm-12x18in) s.d.98. 16-Sep-3 Bonhams, New Bond Street #77/R est:5000-8000
£4706 $8000 €6871 Morning sun, Concarneau (36x46cm-14x18in) s. board prov. 19-Nov-3 Bonhams & Butterfields, San Francisco #150/R
£5000 $8350 €7300 Grey morning (25x35cm-10x14in) s. s.i.d.1906 verso. 16-Oct-3 Christie's, Kensington #406/R est:3000-5000
£9000 $14670 €13140 Notre Dame, Paris, with boats and numerous figures (58x48cm-23x19in) s. i.verso. 27-Sep-3 Rogers Jones, Clwyd #123/R
£11290 $20774 €16483 Lincoln (61x91cm-24x36in) s. s.i.verso pencil. 14-Jun-4 Waddingtons, Toronto #167/R est:10000-15000 (C.D 28000)
Works on paper
£1300 $2236 €1898 St. Tropez (21x28cm-8x11in) pastel prov. 2-Dec-3 Bonhams, New Bond Street #4/R est:1000-1500
£1800 $3312 €2628 L'arena de L'opera, Paris (10x13cm-4x5in) s. i.verso W/C. 11-Jun-4 Keys, Aylsham #428/R est:600-800

WILLIAMS, Virgil (1830-1886) American
£403 $750 €588 Spinning yarn (33x23cm-13x9in) s.i.d.1870 panel. 3-Mar-4 Christie's, Rockefeller NY #4/R
£2310 $4250 €3373 Cow and woman carrying hay on a country road (27x38cm-11x15in) s.d.69 prov. 8-Jun-4 Bonhams & Butterfields, San Francisco #4224/R est:4000-6000

WILLIAMS, W (19th C) British
£4000 $7400 €5840 Landscapes with figures (20x25cm-8x10in) init. pair. 12-Feb-4 Andrew Hartley, Ilkley #855/R est:1200-1800

WILLIAMS, Walter (attrib) (19th C) British
£250 $395 €365 Figure on a rocky beach (11x14cm-4x6in) panel. 6-Sep-3 Shapes, Edinburgh #326
£280 $448 €409 Scene in Borrowdale, Cumberland (51x76cm-20x30in) indis.sig. i.verso. 16-Sep-3 Capes Dunn, Manchester #771

WILLIAMS, Walter (1835-1906) British
£600 $954 €876 Lady beside a waterfall in a wooded valley (64x85cm-25x33in) s.d.1876. 9-Sep-3 Sworder & Son, Bishops Stortford #390/R
£700 $1302 €1022 Figures in a lake landscape (12x18cm-5x7in) init.d.77. 4-Mar-4 Christie's, Kensington #507/R
£991 $1774 €1447 Near Cookham, Bucks (20x35cm-8x14in) mono. 31-May-4 Stephan Welz, Johannesburg #34 (SA.R 12000)
£1300 $2171 €1898 Mountain mist, North Wales (24x38cm-9x15in) init. 13-Nov-3 Christie's, Kensington #195/R est:1000-1500
£1600 $2960 €2336 Haymaking (18x33cm-7x13in) 13-Jan-4 Bonhams, Knightsbridge #187/R est:1000-1500
£2800 $4480 €4088 Children with catch by river in a landscape (30x61cm-12x24in) s. 21-Sep-3 Desmond Judd, Cranbrook #1122
£3300 $5346 €4818 Country folk conversing in open river landscape, mountains beyond (51x76cm-20x30in) s. 25-May-3 Desmond Judd, Cranbrook #1062/R
£5000 $9200 €7300 Harvesters at rest (61x107cm-24x42in) s.i. 11-Jun-4 Christie's, London #168/R est:6000-10000
£5500 $10120 €8030 Cutting hay (61x108cm-24x43in) s. prov. 11-Jun-4 Christie's, London #169/R est:6000-10000
£7500 $13800 €10950 On the Stour (62x106cm-24x42in) s. 11-Jun-4 Christie's, London #167/R est:6000-10000
£8000 $12640 €11600 Harvesting. Sheep grazing, Barnes, Surrey (22x25cm-9x10in) init. i.on stretcher pair. 4-Sep-3 Christie's, Kensington #124/R est:2000-3000

WILLIAMS, Walter (fl.1841-1876) British
£300 $474 €435 On the Otter near St. Mary Ottery (20x30cm-8x12in) s. s.i.verso board. 4-Sep-3 Christie's, Kensington #145/R
£5000 $9300 €7300 Borrowdale, Cumbria (61x107cm-24x42in) s.d.1859. 4-Mar-4 Christie's, Kensington #438/R est:5000-8000
Works on paper
£360 $598 €526 Halden Moor, estuary of the Exe (28x23cm-11x9in) s.i. W/C. 2-Oct-3 Neales, Nottingham #635/R

WILLIAMS, Walter Heath (19th C) British
£700 $1162 €1022 Fishing boats in a swell off a jetty (76x126cm-30x50in) s. 1-Oct-3 Woolley & Wallis, Salisbury #288/R
£1800 $3006 €2628 Boys fishing by a stream (46x66cm-18x26in) 13-Nov-3 Christie's, Kensington #115/R est:2000-3000
£1900 $3401 €2774 Fishermen by a lake at dusk (28x41cm-11x16in) s. 27-May-4 Christie's, Kensington #144/R est:1000-1500
£2000 $3580 €2920 Figures in a wooded landscape, coastal view beyond (20x15cm-8x6in) init.d.1881. 27-May-4 Christie's, Kensington #143/R est:800-1200
£2800 $5012 €4088 Children by a pond in a wooded landscape with cattle beyond (67x102cm-26x40in) with sig. 27-May-4 Christie's, Kensington #137/R est:3000-5000

WILLIAMS, Walter Heath (attrib) (19th C) British
£900 $1503 €1314 Woodland river landscape (46x61cm-18x24in) bears sig. 12-Nov-3 Sotheby's, Olympia #45/R

WILLIAMS, Warren (1863-1918) British
£1050 $1670 €1533 Nevin Bay (26x37cm-10x15in) s.i. 18-Mar-3 Anderson & Garland, Newcastle #333/R est:200-300
Works on paper
£600 $1092 €876 Solitude-Lyn Idwal and the Devil's Kitchen above Llyn Owen (35x51cm-14x20in) s.i. W/C. 15-Jun-4 Rosebery Fine Art, London #601
£700 $1141 €1022 North Wales river scene with fishermen (30x20cm-12x8in) s. W/C. 27-Sep-3 Rogers Jones, Clwyd #71

£700 $1253 €1022 Coastal landscape with two small female figures with baskets (18x33cm-7x13in) s. W/C. 13-May-4 Mitchells, Cockermouth #1053/R
£750 $1350 €1095 Rushing river with mill and fishermen (33x53cm-13x21in) s. W/C. 24-Apr-4 Rogers Jones, Clwyd #118
£750 $1328 €1095 In the Conway valley (28x36cm-11x14in) s. W/C. 28-Apr-4 Halls, Shrewsbury #479/R
£925 $1508 €1351 Crafnant lake with cottage and woman on a path (30x20cm-12x8in) s. W/C. 27-Sep-3 Rogers Jones, Clwyd #72
£1000 $1810 €1500 Conway Bay, Wales (34x52cm-13x20in) s. W/C. 3-Apr-4 Hans Stahl, Hamburg #132/R est:300
£1300 $2119 €1898 Anglesey coastalscape near Moelfre with boats and figures (25x36cm-10x14in) s. W/C. 27-Sep-3 Rogers Jones, Clwyd #68/R
£1300 $2119 €1898 Anglesey coastalscape with fishermen and boats (25x36cm-10x14in) s. W/C. 27-Sep-3 Rogers Jones, Clwyd #70
£1300 $2210 €1898 Conway River from above Benansh (33x51cm-13x20in) s. i.verso W/C. 29-Oct-3 Bonhams, Chester #316 est:1200-1600
£1350 $2295 €1971 Coastal landscape in North Wales, with two girls gathering flowers (28x42cm-11x17in) s. W/C. 29-Oct-3 Bonhams, Chester #321 est:1000-1500
£1400 $2282 €2044 Gwynant Valley with sheep on the river bank (25x36cm-10x14in) s. W/C. 27-Sep-3 Rogers Jones, Clwyd #67/R
£1400 $2226 €2044 Llyn Idwal, Devil's Kitchen, Snowdonia (60x40cm-24x16in) s. 30-Apr-3 Peter Wilson, Nantwich #105/R est:1500-2000
£1400 $2590 €2044 Evening on the Conway. Llyn Dinas (23x34cm-9x13in) both s W/C pair. 14-Jul-4 Bonhams, Chester #311/R est:1500-2000
£1450 $2639 €2117 Llynogwen (46x60cm-18x24in) s. W/C htd white. 29-Jun-4 Bonhams, Knowle #59 est:300-400
£1900 $3135 €2774 Estuary scenes with fisherman by dinghy, and beached fishing lock (25x43cm-10x17in) s. W/C pair. 3-Jul-3 Biddle & Webb, Birmingham #895
£2400 $4080 €3504 Conway estuary from Bryn Nockyn Farm above Conway castle (74x103cm-29x41in) s.i. W/C. 29-Oct-3 Bonhams, Chester #357/R est:3000-5000
£3900 $6825 €5694 Nevin Bay, N Wales. Conway Castle, N Wales (33x51cm-13x20in) s.i. W/C pair. 16-Dec-3 Capes Dunn, Manchester #770/R

WILLIAMS, Wheeler (1897-1972) American
Sculpture
£5882 $10000 €8588 Pegasus (94cm-37in) i.d.1946 pat bronze pair. 25-Nov-3 Christie's, Rockefeller NY #193/R est:15000-25000
£42614 $75000 €62216 Four seasons (104cm-41in) i.d.1934 alabstone four prov. 19-May-4 Sotheby's, New York #159/R est:50000-70000

WILLIAMS, William (attrib) (18th C) British
£3500 $6440 €5110 Portrait of a gentleman, standing in a landscape (75x62cm-30x24in) 26-Mar-4 Sotheby's, London #23/R est:4000-6000

WILLIAMS, William (attrib) (fl.1758-1797) British
£50000 $92000 €73000 Group portrait of the Rev Thomas Eyre, his sister Frances and her husband Major Robert Sherwood, Oxf (98x122cm-39x48in) prov. 9-Jun-4 Christie's, London #9/R est:60000-80000

WILLIAMS, William (1727-1791) American
Works on paper
£440 $800 €642 Study of a planter (42x26cm-17x10in) s.i. red chk paper on paper. 4-Feb-4 Christie's, Rockefeller NY #129/R

WILLIAMS, Willmotte (1916-) Australian
£296 $531 €432 Terrace House, Paddington (38x45cm-15x18in) s. s.i.verso board. 15-May-4 Christie's, Sydney #135 (A.D 750)

WILLIAMS-LYOUNS, Herbert (1863-1933) British
Works on paper
£800 $1472 €1168 Gulf of Corinth (57x86cm-22x34in) pencil W/C. 25-Mar-4 Christie's, Kensington #50/R

WILLIAMSON, Frederick (c.1835-1900) British
Works on paper
£460 $823 €672 Rural scene with sheep by a wooden gate (10x13cm-4x5in) s.d.1809 W/C. 6-May-4 Amersham Auction Rooms, UK #292
£600 $1092 €876 Sheep grazing on the Sussex Downs (30x47cm-12x19in) s.d.1861 pencil W/C bodycol gum arabic. 1-Jul-4 Christie's, Kensington #111/R
£700 $1204 €1022 Cattle and sheep resting on a hillside (18x29cm-7x11in) s. pencil W/C. 3-Dec-3 Christie's, Kensington #123/R
£900 $1647 €1350 Sheep grazing (31x52cm-12x20in) s. W/C. 27-Jul-4 Henry Adams, Chichester #401/R
£920 $1647 €1343 Sheep resting amongst heather and gorse (15x22cm-6x9in) s.d.1866 W/C htd gouache. 17-Mar-4 Rupert Toovey, Partridge Green #150/R
£1800 $2934 €2628 Rural scene with sheep resting under tree and grazing sheep and haystacks (20x36cm-8x14in) s.d.1866 W/C. 27-Sep-3 Rogers Jones, Clwyd #114/R

WILLIAMSON, Harold (1898-1972) British
£280 $468 €409 Albert Square, Manchester (62x75cm-24x30in) s. 24-Jun-3 Bonhams, Chester #923

WILLIAMSON, Harold Sandys (1892-1978) British
£450 $833 €657 Albert Square, Manchester (63x76cm-25x30in) s. 15-Jan-4 Christie's, Kensington #1016/R

WILLIAMSON, J (?) ?
Works on paper
£360 $590 €526 Belfast docks (38x63cm-15x25in) s. W/C. 4-Jun-3 John Ross, Belfast #256

WILLIAMSON, John (1826-1885) American
£989 $1800 €1444 Ruins at sunset (22x30cm-9x12in) mono. board prov. 29-Jun-4 Sotheby's, New York #202/R est:3000-5000
£3911 $7000 €5710 Mountain landscape (18x28cm-7x11in) indis.sig. 6-May-4 Shannon's, Milford #12/R est:5000-7000

WILLIAMSON, Philip J (?) British?
Works on paper
£380 $707 €555 Peters Hill, Belfast (40x58cm-16x23in) s. W/C. 3-Mar-4 John Ross, Belfast #240

WILLIAMSON, Samuel (1792-1840) British
£280 $515 €409 Sunset (14x25cm-6x10in) i.d.1812 board. 23-Mar-4 Rosebery Fine Art, London #971

WILLIAMSON, William Henry (1820-1883) British
£450 $806 €657 Lugger heading out to sea (25x46cm-10x18in) s.d.1879. 26-May-4 Christie's, Kensington #717/R
£591 $1058 €863 Vessel by coast in rough seas (25x46cm-10x18in) s.d.1880. 26-May-4 AB Stockholms Auktionsverk #2387/R (S.KR 8000)
£600 $1020 €876 Fishermen (39x55cm-15x22in) 19-Nov-3 Christie's, Kensington #538/R
£600 $1020 €876 Figures in a fishing boat at sunset. Fishing boats off a coastline (20x41cm-8x16in) s.d.1897 pair. 19-Nov-3 Tennants, Leyburn #1020
£1100 $1870 €1606 Fishing and other boats off the coast, buildings to the quayside (30x61cm-12x24in) s.d.1871. 5-Nov-3 John Nicholson, Haslemere #653 est:1000-1500
£3800 $6840 €5548 Return of the fishing fleet, a storm clearing (73x124cm-29x49in) s.d.1859. 22-Apr-4 Mellors & Kirk, Nottingham #114/R est:2500-3500

WILLICH, Caesar (1825-1886) German
£1745 $3211 €2600 Musician from Savoie (102x72cm-40x28in) s.d.1855. 24-Mar-4 Hugo Ruef, Munich #1149/R est:1500

WILLIGEN, Claes Jansz van der (1630-1676) Dutch
£800 $1432 €1200 Rhine landscape with herdsmen on a sandy path (68x57cm-27x22in) bears sig. panel. 17-May-4 Glerum, Amsterdam #5/R

WILLIGEN, N H van der (19th C) Dutch
£1379 $2303 €2000 Wooded mountain landscape with herder and cows (76x102cm-30x40in) s.d.1862. 11-Nov-3 Vendu Notarishuis, Rotterdam #88/R est:2000-2500

WILLIKENS, Ben (1939-) German
£2667 $4907 €4000 Door 1 (150x160cm-59x63in) s.i.d.1977 acrylic pencil panel lit. 12-Jun-4 Villa Grisebach, Berlin #411/R est:4000-6000
Works on paper
£667 $1220 €1000 Building I door (56x41cm-22x16in) s.d.78 i. verso pencil spray board. 4-Jun-4 Lempertz, Koln #536/R

WILLINK, Carel (1900-1979) Dutch
£3867 $7115 €5800 Boerderij met boom (48x34cm-19x13in) s.d.1918 lit. 8-Jun-4 Sotheby's, Amsterdam #227/R est:6000-8000
£12587 $21399 €18000 Preparatory study for the Hermit - selfportrait (27x23cm-11x9in) s.d.38 lit. 25-Nov-3 Christie's, Amsterdam #182/R est:18000-22000
Works on paper
£1689 $2973 €2500 Standing Javanese woman (65x45cm-26x18in) i.d.7 jan 1922 chl prov.exhib. 19-May-4 Sotheby's, Amsterdam #383/R est:3000-4000
£2838 $4995 €4200 Seated nude (81x45cm-32x18in) s.d.4 Dec 26 pencil lit. 19-May-4 Sotheby's, Amsterdam #382/R est:2200-2800
£3200 $5888 €4800 Anteaters in landscape (48x64cm-19x25in) s.d.58 blk white chk. 8-Jun-4 Sotheby's, Amsterdam #231/R est:4000-6000

WILLIOT, P (19th C) Dutch?
£2238 $3804 €3200 Paysage d'hiver avec patineurs (71x60cm-28x24in) s.d.86. 1-Dec-3 Palais de Beaux Arts, Brussels #339/R est:3000-4000

WILLIS, A V (19th C) British?
£753 $1400 €1099 Travellers on a road (68x55cm-27x22in) s.d.1882. 5-Mar-4 Skinner, Boston #251/R est:1000-1500

WILLIS, E B (19/20th C) New Zealander
Works on paper
£3804 $6163 €5516 Panorama of Auckland and Rangitoto (47x73cm-19x29in) s.i.d.1903 W/C. 31-Jul-3 International Art Centre, Auckland #42/R est:18000-26000 (NZ.D 10500)

WILLIS, Fritz (20th C) American?
£4362 $7809 €6500 The breakfast (61x46cm-24x18in) s. painted c.1950. 27-May-4 Sotheby's, Paris #141/R est:1500-2000
Works on paper
£1377 $2300 €2010 Happiness machine (64x33cm-25x13in) s. gouache. 15-Nov-3 Illustration House, New York #139/R est:2000-3000

WILLIS, Henry Brittan (1810-1884) British
£900 $1503 €1314 Midday heat, shepherd and flock resting beneath the shade of a tree (59x49cm-23x19in) s.d.1847 oval. 11-Jul-3 Jacobs & Hunt, Petersfield #276/R
£1750 $2923 €2555 Gypsy family and donkey in a wooded encampment (30x41cm-12x16in) s.indis.d.1864. 16-Nov-3 Desmond Judd, Cranbrook #1066
£2552 $4721 €3700 Group of cattle, figures and house in rural setting (61x48cm-24x19in) s.d.1853. 11-Feb-4 Woodwards, Cork #16/R est:2000-3000
Works on paper
£260 $465 €380 Plough horse (23x37cm-9x15in) s. W/C scratching out. 22-Mar-4 Bonhams & Brooks, Norfolk #123/R

WILLIS, J B (?) British
Works on paper
£2000 $3320 €2920 Cattle resting by a pool (38x58cm-15x23in) s.d.56-57 W/C bodycol htd white. 2-Oct-3 Neales, Nottingham #639/R est:2000-3000

WILLIS, John Christopher Temple (1900-1969) British
Works on paper
£950 $1720 €1387 Morston church, Norfolk. Sheep Bridge, Blakeney, Norfolk (23x33cm-9x13in) s. W/C pair. 16-Apr-4 Keys, Aylsham #479/R

WILLIS, Joseph R (1876-?) American
£4853 $8250 €7085 Desert scene with Indian riders (61x152cm-24x60in) s.d.1926 prov. 1-Nov-3 Santa Fe Art, Santa Fe #227/R est:20000-25000

WILLIS, Luster (1913-) American
£299 $500 €437 Couple talking (41x51cm-16x20in) tempera paper prov. 15-Nov-3 Slotin Folk Art, Buford #471/R
£329 $550 €480 Eric Clapton (79x94cm-31x37in) tempera ink posterboard. 15-Nov-3 Slotin Folk Art, Buford #470/R
£329 $550 €480 Father time with lady on box (56x71cm-22x28in) paint glitter poster prov. 15-Nov-3 Slotin Folk Art, Buford #472/R

WILLIS, Thomas (1850-1912) American
£874 $1600 €1311 The sailboat Punkam (30x41cm-12x16in) s. 29-Jul-4 Eldred, East Dennis #186/R est:500-700
£1189 $2200 €1736 US M Frank and Helen McAvoy in coastal waters (51x93cm-20x37in) s.d.1910 silk velour. 10-Feb-4 Christie's, Rockefeller NY #30/R est:3000-5000
£1189 $2200 €1736 The Naiad in calm waters (51x92cm-20x36in) s. silk thread cotton. 10-Feb-4 Christie's, Rockefeller NY #31/R est:3000-5000
£2270 $4200 €3314 The schooner Alert of the New York Yacht Club (56x91cm-22x36in) silk velour. 10-Feb-4 Christie's, Rockefeller NY #32/R est:5000-7000
£6024 $10000 €8795 Arkadia and Underwriter (53x46cm-21x18in) init.i. canvas applied silk velour prov. 4-Oct-3 Neal Auction Company, New Orleans #362/R est:12000-18000

WILLIS, Thornton (1936-) American
£476 $843 €695 Brown house, green field (76x57cm-30x22in) s.d.81 verso oil paper. 27-Apr-4 AB Stockholms Auktionsverk #1213/R (S.KR 6500)
£1040 $1800 €1518 Wall (213x183cm-84x72in) s. acrylic prov. 15-Dec-3 Hindman, Chicago #118/R est:1500-2000
£1566 $2600 €2286 Stripes (257x178cm-101x70in) s.i.d.69 verso. 4-Oct-3 Neal Auction Company, New Orleans #1148/R est:1500-2500

WILLIS, Wesley (1963-) American
Works on paper
£240 $400 €350 Chicago skyline (71x104cm-28x41in) marker paper on poster prov. 15-Nov-3 Slotin Folk Art, Buford #498/R

WILLIS-PRYCE, G (19th C) British
£280 $468 €409 Wynstone Leys, on the Wye, near Monmouth (30x46cm-12x18in) s. 15-Oct-3 Brightwells, Leominster #881
£380 $695 €555 River landscape with church and hills to distance (39x59cm-15x23in) s. 28-Jan-4 Wintertons, Lichfield #380

WILLISON, George (1741-1797) British
£2500 $4250 €3650 Portrait of a gentleman wearing a brown coat (71x61cm-28x24in) 27-Nov-3 Sotheby's, London #148/R est:3000-4000

WILLMANN, Michael Lukas (attrib) (1630-1706) Austrian
£679 $1154 €991 Ascension of Saint Magdalena (41x34cm-16x13in) canvas on panel prov. 19-Nov-3 Fischer, Luzern #2348/R (S.FR 1500)
Works on paper
£1067 $1920 €1600 Dragon with prisoners of Kadmos (20x26cm-8x10in) i. wash Indian ink brush on chk. 24-Apr-4 Reiss & Sohn, Konigstein #5450/R est:1400

WILLOTT, N Fowler (?) ?
Works on paper
£420 $668 €613 Zuitohan, Dutch river scene with barges and mills (36x54cm-14x21in) s.i. W/C. 9-Sep-3 Bamfords, Derby #1085/R

WILLROIDER, Josef (1838-1915) Austrian
£1233 $2096 €1800 Pre alpine landscape with peasants in fields (24x28cm-9x11in) s. board. 5-Nov-3 Hugo Ruef, Munich #1182/R est:800
£1316 $2421 €2000 Landscape on Lake Starnberger (17x32cm-7x13in) s. cardboard prov. 25-Jun-4 Michael Zeller, Lindau #537/R
£1538 $2615 €2200 Landscape with figures (16x25cm-6x10in) s. canvas on board. 24-Nov-3 Dorotheum, Vienna #178/R est:2800-3200
£1611 $3012 €2400 Autumn landscape (26x34cm-10x13in) s. panel. 28-Feb-4 Quittenbaum, Hamburg #22/R est:2000
£1958 $3270 €2800 Interior wit h cat (32x46cm-13x18in) s. 10-Oct-3 Winterberg, Heidelberg #829/R est:3600
£2649 $4821 €4000 River landscape (25x35cm-10x14in) s. cardboard. 16-Jun-4 Hugo Ruef, Munich #1115/R est:2000
£9692 $16476 €14150 Maria Worth by Worthersee (42x70cm-17x28in) s. 5-Nov-3 Dobiaschofsky, Bern #1056/R est:7000 (S.FR 22000)
Works on paper
£1181 $1972 €1700 River Inn at Rosenheim (19x27cm-7x11in) s. W/C. 25-Oct-3 Bergmann, Erlangen #926/R

WILLROIDER, Ludwig (1845-1910) German
£596 $1085 €900 Meadow landscape (25x37cm-10x15in) s. cardboard. 16-Jun-4 Hugo Ruef, Munich #1114/R
£903 $1508 €1300 Autumn landscape (21x32cm-8x13in) s. canvas on board lit. 25-Oct-3 Bergmann, Erlangen #961/R
£1119 $1902 €1600 Italian landscape study (29x23cm-11x9in) s. board. 19-Nov-3 Dorotheum, Klagenfurt #38 est:1000
£1259 $2165 €1800 Country landscape with trees and farmhouse (46x58cm-18x23in) s. 3-Dec-3 Neumeister, Munich #803/R est:2000
£2083 $3396 €3000 Dutch coast with windmill (35x58cm-14x23in) s.i.d.1872 panel. 25-Sep-3 Dr Fritz Nagel, Stuttgart #1435/R est:3900
£2517 $4280 €3600 On the Gunz (28x41cm-11x16in) bears sig. i. verso board. 24-Nov-3 Dorotheum, Vienna #92/R est:4000-5000
£4698 $8409 €7000 Dutch harbour landscape (44x75cm-17x30in) s.i.d.1873. 27-May-4 Dorotheum, Vienna #166/R est:8000-9000
£7986 $13337 €11500 Extensive Bavarian landscape with lake (55x75cm-22x30in) s. lit. 25-Oct-3 Bergmann, Erlangen #925/R
Works on paper
£839 $1502 €1250 Quarry near Ebersberg (26x35cm-10x14in) s.i.d.79 chl. 25-May-4 Karl & Faber, Munich #153/R

WILLS, William Gorman (attrib) (1828-1891) British
£320 $592 €467 Portrait of a lady, believed to be Isabella Renny (47x40cm-19x16in) i.verso oval. 9-Mar-4 Bonhams, Knightsbridge #296/R

WILLSHER, Brian (1930-) British
Sculpture
£950 $1757 €1387 Untitled (74cm-29in) s.i.d.1995 Brazilian mahogany. 11-Feb-4 Sotheby's, Olympia #242/R est:800-1200
£1000 $1590 €1460 White city (99x101cm-39x40in) painted wood. 10-Sep-3 Sotheby's, Olympia #326/R est:700-1000
£1300 $2210 €1898 A propos (91cm-36in) s.i. wood. 26-Nov-3 Sotheby's, Olympia #141/R est:700-900
£1500 $2775 €2190 Untitled (111cm-44in) s.d.1999 mahogany. 11-Feb-4 Sotheby's, Olympia #241/R est:800-1200

WILLSHER-MARTEL, Joan (1925-) Canadian
£241 $448 €352 Athabaska (96x96cm-38x38in) s.d.58 exhib. 2-Mar-4 Ritchie, Toronto #185/R (C.D 600)

WILLSON, James Mallory (1890-1943) American
£1899 $3000 €2773 Genre scene of black boy playing with cards and other figures (48x74cm-19x29in) s. 8-Sep-3 Winter Associates, Plainville #100

WILLUMS, Olaf Abrahamsen (1886-1967) Norwegian
£516 $831 €753 Boy at the cheese farm (71x82cm-28x32in) s. 25-Aug-3 Blomqvist, Lysaker #1364/R (N.KR 6000)

WILLUMSEN, J F (1863-1958) Danish
£3033 $4853 €4398 Michelle Bouret wearing red dress (45x33cm-18x13in) init.d.1927. 17-Sep-3 Kunsthallen, Copenhagen #70/R est:12000 (D.KR 32000)
£8531 $13649 €12370 Portrait of Michelle Bourret (24x35cm-9x14in) init.d.1927. 17-Sep-3 Kunsthallen, Copenhagen #63/R est:12000 (D.KR 90000)
Works on paper
£627 $1129 €915 Kokotte (30x23cm-12x9in) init. pencil. 24-Apr-4 Rasmussen, Havnen #4110/R (D.KR 7000)

WILLUMSEN, Jens Ferdinand (1863-1958) Danish
£4253 $7613 €6209 The artist's Muse dancing in landscape (38x46cm-15x18in) init.d.1932. 12-Jan-4 Rasmussen, Vejle #489/R est:40000-50000 (D.KR 45000)
£4593 $7441 €6660 Two women in forest (46x71cm-18x28in) 4-Aug-3 Rasmussen, Vejle #557/R est:20000-25000 (D.KR 48000)
£5263 $8526 €7631 Woodland glade, autumn (55x66cm-22x26in) init.d.18 sept.1903. 4-Aug-3 Rasmussen, Vejle #558/R est:20000-30000 (D.KR 55000)
£6606 $11825 €9645 Avenue with plane trees, Fontainebleau (92x74cm-36x29in) mono.d.1932 lit. 10-May-4 Rasmussen, Vejle #586/R est:75000-100000 (D.KR 73000)
£35681 $59587 €52094 Mountain tops with snow and clouds - study for Sun over southern mountains (98x208cm-39x82in) s.d.1901 stretcher canvas on canvas prov.lit. 7-Oct-3 Rasmussen, Copenhagen #134/R est:500000 (D.KR 380000)

WILMARTH, Christopher (1943-1987) American
Sculpture
£2361 $4250 €3447 Table (8x8x6cm-3x3x2in) s.num.9/30 glass wood. 24-Apr-4 David Rago, Lambertville #293/R est:600-1200
£47904 $80000 €69940 Untitled, drawing (43x43x2cm-17x17x1in) glass etched glass steel wire prov.exhib. 13-Nov-3 Sotheby's, New York #128/R est:12000-18000
£47904 $80000 €69940 Third stray (89x70x10cm-35x28x4in) s.i.d.1977 verso glass iron prov.exhib. 13-Nov-3 Sotheby's, New York #150/R est:40000-60000
Works on paper
£8649 $16000 €12628 Study for Panoply's Angel (31x31cm-12x12in) init.d.73 i.verso pencil tracing paper round prov.exhib. 12-Feb-4 Sotheby's, New York #203/R est:3000-5000

WILMER, John Riley (fl.1905-1926) British
Works on paper
£3915 $6773 €5716 Girl with a guardian angel (30x23cm-12x9in) s.d.1918 W/C. 12-Dec-3 Kieselbach, Budapest #171/R (H.F 1500000)

WILMOVSKY, Charles (1885-1974) American
£723 $1200 €1056 Tree lined path, Southern landscape (41x51cm-16x20in) s. 4-Oct-3 Neal Auction Company, New Orleans #595/R

WILMS, Joseph (1814-1892) German
£2371 $4244 €3462 Still life with pineapple and punch bowl (55x72cm-22x28in) s.i.d.1840. 12-May-4 Dobiaschofsky, Bern #1067/R est:8000 (S.FR 5500)

WILS, Jan (1600-1660) Dutch
£993 $1827 €1450 Portrait of seated woman (115x90cm-45x35in) s. 29-Mar-4 Rasmussen, Copenhagen #513/R (D.KR 11000)

WILS, Wilhelm (1880-1960) Danish
£280 $515 €409 Winter landscape (35x49cm-14x19in) s.d.05 prov. 29-Mar-4 Rasmussen, Copenhagen #490 (D.KR 3100)
£289 $454 €422 Still life of fruit (65x81cm-26x32in) s. 30-Aug-3 Rasmussen, Havnen #4357/R (D.KR 3100)
£722 $1329 €1054 Portrait of woman (91x65cm-36x26in) s.d.20. 29-Mar-4 Rasmussen, Copenhagen #515/R (D.KR 8000)
£1627 $2635 €2359 Portrait of woman with dark hair and red dress (108x80cm-43x31in) s.d.15. 4-Aug-3 Rasmussen, Vejle #631/R est:5000 (D.KR 17000)

WILSON, Alan Dent (1923-) American?
£202 $371 €295 Backyards, West Toronto (30x40cm-12x16in) s. s.i.d.1965-1966 verso board. 9-Jun-4 Walker's, Ottawa #71/R (C.D 500)

WILSON, Andrew (attrib) (1780-1848) British
£800 $1464 €1168 Sleaford church, Lincolnshire (20x18cm-8x7in) board. 7-Apr-4 Andrew Hartley, Ilkley #1077/R

WILSON, Anna (20th C) American
£3439 $6500 €5021 Portrait of Carol Lombard and her dog (112x86cm-44x34in) s.d.1935 prov. 17-Feb-4 John Moran, Pasadena #185/R est:2000-3000

WILSON, Arthur (fl.1873-1878) British
Works on paper
£420 $785 €630 View of the Thames at night with Waterloo Bridge and Shot Tower (27x37cm-11x15in) s. W/C htd bodycol. 22-Jul-4 Dominic Winter, Swindon #114/R

WILSON, Avray (20th C) ?
£446 $768 €651 Configuration, grey and black (35x92cm-14x36in) s.d.57 prov. 2-Dec-3 Ritchie, Toronto #80/R (C.D 1000)
£670 $1152 €978 Composition red, yellow, green (76x56cm-30x22in) s.d.57 masonite prov. 2-Dec-3 Ritchie, Toronto #79/R (C.D 1500)

WILSON, Benjamin (1721-1788) British
£5000 $8350 €7300 Portrait of a gentleman, in a brown coat holding a cane (122x97cm-48x38in) canvas on board oval. 13-Nov-3 Christie's, Kensington #30/R est:5000-8000

WILSON, Benjamin (attrib) (1721-1788) British
£3200 $5728 €4672 Portrait of Sir William Gleadowe Newcomen and the honorable Thomas Newcom (77x64cm-30x25in) 27-May-4 Christie's, Kensington #60/R est:1000-1500

WILSON, Bryan (1927-) American
Works on paper
£1337 $2500 €2006 Aleutian geese (153x183cm-60x72in) init.d.65 casein prov. 25-Jul-4 Bonhams & Butterfields, San Francisco #6147/R est:600-800

WILSON, C E (1854-1941) British
Works on paper
£2800 $5292 €4088 Pet lamb (36x23cm-14x9in) s. W/C. 19-Feb-4 Grant, Worcester #413/R est:400-600

WILSON, Charles Edward (1854-1941) British
Works on paper
£600 $1110 €876 Woodland pond (48x32cm-19x13in) s. W/C. 9-Mar-4 Bonhams, New Bond Street #124/R
£1400 $2590 €2044 Hayfield (25x37cm-10x15in) s. W/C. 9-Mar-4 Bonhams, New Bond Street #123/R est:1000-1500
£1500 $2685 €2190 On the River Wey (26x35cm-10x14in) s. W/C. 26-May-4 Sotheby's, Olympia #163/R est:1500-2000
£1900 $3173 €2774 After school (24x32cm-9x13in) s. W/C. 22-Oct-3 Cheffins, Cambridge #508 est:800-1200
£4000 $7400 €5840 Playing marbles (25x37cm-10x15in) s. W/C. 9-Mar-4 Bonhams, New Bond Street #120/R est:4000-6000
£4000 $7400 €5840 Young girl fetching water (29x21cm-11x8in) s. W/C. 9-Mar-4 Bonhams, New Bond Street #121/R est:3000-5000
£5700 $10203 €8322 Mischief (39x28cm-15x11in) s. W/C. 17-Mar-4 Bonhams, Chester #283/R est:2000-3000
£5800 $9860 €8468 In time of war (20x13cm-8x5in) s.d.1900 W/C. 4-Nov-3 Bonhams, New Bond Street #139/R est:6000-8000
£6000 $11100 €8760 Golden days (21x31cm-8x12in) s. W/C. 14-Jul-4 Sotheby's, Olympia #104/R est:4000-6000
£6000 $11100 €8760 Between school hours (20cm-8in circular) s. pencil W/C. 14-Jul-4 Sotheby's, Olympia #106/R est:4000-6000
£6200 $11408 €9052 Farmer's boy (25x18cm-10x7in) s. W/C. 8-Jun-4 Bonhams, New Bond Street #104/R est:5000-8000
£9600 $15840 €14016 Young girl and kitten playing with a ball of wool before a doorway (38x28cm-15x11in) s. W/C. 3-Jul-3 Biddle & Webb, Birmingham #950/R

WILSON, Charles Edward (attrib) (1854-1941) British
Works on paper
£300 $555 €438 Two children by a stream fishing for tiddlers (33x26cm-13x10in) s. W/C htd white. 11-Mar-4 Morphets, Harrogate #331/R

WILSON, Chris (1959-) British
Works on paper
£500 $860 €730 Interior, Rathfarnham Castle, Dublin (56x81cm-22x32in) s.d.88 mixed media. 3-Dec-3 John Ross, Belfast #109
£1007 $1782 €1500 Standing nude (74x53cm-29x21in) s.i.d.1981 col pencil artist board. 27-Apr-4 Whyte's, Dublin #158/R est:1800-2200

WILSON, Clive (?) British?
£280 $482 €409 Native procession (152x152cm-60x60in) s.d.78. 3-Dec-3 John Ross, Belfast #175

WILSON, Donald Roller (1938-) American
£2825 $5000 €4125 Little Miss Rockwell and Mr Pooh. s.d.May 22 1972. 1-May-4 Thomaston Place, Thomaston #815/R
£4420 $8000 €6453 Don's shoe went right up (25x38cm-10x15in) board. 16-Apr-4 American Auctioneer #427/R est:3000-5000

WILSON, Dora Lynell (1883-1946) Australian
£293 $548 €440 Archway (34x25cm-13x10in) s. board. 21-Jul-4 Goodman, Sydney #175 (A.D 750)
£810 $1304 €1183 Churches, Collins Street (49x39cm-19x15in) s. canvas on board painted c.1935. 13-Oct-3 Joel, Victoria #403 est:2000-3000 (A.D 2000)
£1445 $2703 €2168 Piazza Firenze (39x32cm-15x13in) s. board. 21-Jul-4 Goodman, Sydney #188 est:1500-2500 (A.D 3700)
£1626 $2911 €2374 Princes Bridge (29x39cm-11x15in) s. canvas on board painted c.1930. 10-May-4 Joel, Victoria #257 est:1500-2500 (A.D 4000)
£2273 $4022 €3319 From the treasury looking across Spring Street to Collins Street (36x39cm-14x15in) s. board. 3-May-4 Christie's, Melbourne #398 est:1500-2000 (A.D 5500)
Works on paper
£455 $773 €664 Paris les bouquinistes - secondhand booksellers. Cottage (38x38cm-15x15in) s. W/C double-sided executed c.1938. 29-Oct-3 Lawson Menzies, Sydney #105/R est:800-1000 (A.D 1100)
£488 $873 €712 Yellow rose (46x42cm-18x17in) s. pastel. 10-May-4 Joel, Victoria #357 (A.D 1200)
£1379 $2152 €2000 Dappled sunlight (36x26cm-14x10in) s. pastel. 1-Aug-2 Joel, Victoria #189 est:3000-4000 (A.D 4000)

WILSON, Edward Adrian (1872-1912) British
Works on paper
£1900 $3097 €2774 Goshawk's nest (18x12cm-7x5in) i.verso W/C sold with two drs by the same artist prov. 25-Sep-3 Christie's, London #404 est:1000-1500
£2500 $3874 €3650 Discovery at Hut Point (14x22cm-6x9in) W/C. 25-Sep-2 Christie's, London #301/R est:3000-5000
£2600 $4238 €3796 Slopes of Mount Erebus (13x22cm-5x9in) W/C. 24-Sep-3 Christie's, London #328/R est:2000-3000
£4000 $6520 €5840 Discovery Expedition, farthest south ever reached (19x27cm-7x11in) s.d.1905 W/C. 24-Sep-3 Christie's, London #329/R est:2000-3000
£8000 $13040 €11680 Emperor penguin rookery, Cape Crozier (25x38cm-10x15in) s. W/C prov. 25-Sep-3 Christie's, London #406/R est:3000-5000

WILSON, Eric (1911-1947) Australian
£4453 $7170 €6501 Street corner, Montmatre, Paris (30x39cm-12x15in) s. 13-Oct-3 Joel, Victoria #252/R est:20000-25000 (A.D 11000)

WILSON, Francis (1876-1957) British
£450 $720 €657 Little cowherd (51x61cm-20x24in) s. 15-May-3 Bonhams, Edinburgh #321

WILSON, Frank Avray (1914-) British
£450 $806 €657 Composition, red blue and green (46x35cm-18x14in) s.d.61 verso masonite prov. 14-May-4 Christie's, Kensington #631/R
£750 $1388 €1095 Miniature no.51 abstract composition (25x17cm-10x7in) init. board. 10-Mar-4 Cheffins, Cambridge #107/R
£1300 $2405 €1898 Miniature no.65 abstract composition (25x20cm-10x8in) init. board. 10-Mar-4 Cheffins, Cambridge #106/R est:250-350
£1400 $2590 €2044 Miniature no.45 abstract composition (25x17cm-10x7in) init. board. 10-Mar-4 Cheffins, Cambridge #105/R est:250-350
£1400 $2590 €2044 Miniature no.40 abstract composition (25x17cm-10x7in) init. 10-Mar-4 Cheffins, Cambridge #108/R est:250-350
£2300 $3910 €3358 Abstract (76x199cm-30x78in) 26-Nov-3 Hamptons Fine Art, Godalming #227/R est:2500-3500

WILSON, Gahan (1930-) American
Works on paper
£743 $1300 €1085 Three images of Sherlock Holmes (37x31cm-15x12in) s.verso pen ink coated paper exec 1959. 17-Dec-3 Christie's, Rockefeller NY #24/R
£743 $1300 €1085 Harvey, you come down here this instant (51x38cm-20x15in) s. ink W/C paper on ills board exec 1963. 17-Dec-3 Christie's, Rockefeller NY #175/R
£1257 $2200 €1835 Looks like the end of civilisation as they know it (38x32cm-15x13in) s. ink W/C varnish paper on illus board exec Aug 1958 exhib. 17-Dec-3 Christie's, Rockefeller NY #49/R est:1000-1500

WILSON, Gus (?) American
Sculpture
£1242 $2000 €1813 Seagull (48cm-19in) painted carved wood. 20-Aug-3 James Julia, Fairfield #24/R est:4000-6000

WILSON, Harry Mitton (fl.1901-1926) British
£265 $477 €387 Ploughman and team in rolling country landscape (20x29cm-8x11in) panel. 20-Apr-4 Rowley Fine Art, Newmarket #396/R

£320 $502 €464 Haystack in pasture before a summer landscape (51x61cm-20x24in) s. 28-Aug-3 Christie's, Kensington #335
£2000 $3660 €2920 Children skating in a winter landscape (35x62cm-14x24in) 28-Jan-4 Hampton & Littlewood, Exeter #414/R est:2000-2500
£2500 $4575 €3650 An afternoon nap (35x60cm-14x24in) 28-Jan-4 Hampton & Littlewood, Exeter #413/R est:2000-2500

WILSON, Henry (1864-1934) British
Works on paper
£250 $440 €365 Stained glass window design for St Marys Church, Weymouth (33cm-13in circular) W/C gouache. 19-May-4 Hampton & Littlewood, Exeter #612/R

WILSON, Hugh Cameron (1885-?) British
£1000 $1770 €1460 Portrait of a lady in profile wearing a red hat (54x44cm-21x17in) s. 27-Apr-4 Bonhams, Knightsbridge #144/R est:800-1200

WILSON, J (?) British
£378 $654 €552 Three master off a rocky coast (20x30cm-8x12in) s. panel. 9-Dec-3 Rasmussen, Copenhagen #1469/R (D.KR 4000)
£1900 $3230 €2774 Shoreline study with figures and boats (46x61cm-18x24in) i.mount. 6-Nov-3 Biddle & Webb, Birmingham #911/R est:1500-2000

WILSON, James Perry (1889-1976) American
£494 $800 €716 New England landscape, spring (26x36cm-10x14in) s.d.1934 canvasboard. 8-Aug-3 Barridorf, Portland #297/R
£926 $1500 €1343 Whitehead, Monhegan (20x25cm-8x10in) s.d.1929 panel. 8-Aug-3 Barridorf, Portland #296/R est:1200-1800

WILSON, Jane (1924-) American
£1730 $3200 €2526 Rain on Avenue B (36x36cm-14x14in) s. prov. 13-Jul-4 Christie's, Rockefeller NY #61/R est:400-600

WILSON, John (1774-1855) British
£420 $714 €613 Ships on squally seas (30x48cm-12x19in) 30-Oct-3 Bracketts, Tunbridge Wells #1104/R
£650 $1229 €949 Merchantmen's graveyard (63x99cm-25x39in) 19-Feb-4 Christie's, Kensington #101
£2500 $4725 €3650 Becalmed off the coast (29x37cm-11x15in) s.d.1841. 17-Feb-4 Bonhams, New Bond Street #39/R est:2000-3000
Prints
£4570 $8500 €6672 Mother and child (35x30cm-14x12in) s.i.d.1956 lithograph. 2-Mar-4 Swann Galleries, New York #691/R est:1500-2500

WILSON, John (attrib) (1774-1855) British
£550 $935 €803 Fisherman's cottage, on the Fifeshire coast (30x40cm-12x16in) board. 19-Nov-3 Tennants, Leyburn #1051

WILSON, John James (1818-1875) British
£700 $1253 €1022 Fishing boats unloading on the shore (25x44cm-10x17in) s. canvas on canvas. 17-May-4 David Duggleby, Scarborough #622/R
£1000 $1620 €1450 On a coast (48x79cm-19x31in) init. 30-Jul-3 Hamptons Fine Art, Godalming #253/R est:900-1200
£1200 $2208 €1752 Shipping off a pier (49x79cm-19x31in) init. 8-Jun-4 Bonhams, Knightsbridge #279/R est:1200-1800
£1500 $2835 €2190 Unloading the catch (30x49cm-12x19in) s. board. 17-Feb-4 Bonhams, New Bond Street #35/R est:1500-2000
£3400 $5372 €4964 St Valery-sur-Somme, fishing boats off a coastal village (37x75cm-15x30in) 23-Jul-3 Hampton & Littlewood, Exeter #444/R est:1000-1500
£3600 $6120 €5256 Figures and fishing boats on a coast line. Figures unloading the catch (30x50cm-12x20in) s. pair. 19-Nov-3 Tennants, Leyburn #1052/R est:1200-1800
£3800 $6346 €5548 Figures before a cottage, near Hemingstone (28x49cm-11x19in) 13-Nov-3 Christie's, Kensington #124/R est:2000-3000
£6000 $10200 €8760 Greenwich, the departure of the Belgian steamer (83x91cm-33x36in) s. i.verso. 27-Nov-3 Sotheby's, London #383/R est:4000-6000

WILSON, John James (attrib) (1818-1875) British
£900 $1665 €1314 Harbour mouth with fishing boats in fresh breeze off the shore (61x89cm-24x35in) s. 11-Mar-4 Morphets, Harrogate #281/R

WILSON, L W (19/20th C) New Zealander
Works on paper
£1811 $3350 €2644 Clinton River, Lake te Anau (32x67cm-13x26in) s.i. W/C. 9-Mar-4 Watson's, Christchurch #47 est:12500-15000 (NZ.D 4940)

WILSON, Lawrence W (1859-c.1920) New Zealander
£364 $571 €528 New Zealand coastal scene (26x43cm-10x17in) s. board. 27-Aug-3 Dunbar Sloane, Wellington #129 (NZ.D 1000)
£3759 $6391 €5488 Entrance to Milford Sound (55x88cm-22x35in) s.i. prov. 27-Nov-3 International Art Centre, Auckland #101/R est:10000-15000 (NZ.D 10000)
£3759 $6391 €5488 West wing of Manapouri (53x86cm-21x34in) 27-Nov-3 International Art Centre, Auckland #102/R est:10000-15000 (NZ.D 10000)
Works on paper
£286 $517 €418 Road Ossen Park, Wellington (30x27cm-12x11in) s. W/C. 4-Apr-4 International Art Centre, Auckland #231/R (NZ.D 800)
£441 $825 €644 Wet jacket Arm, Dusky Sound (25x35cm-10x14in) s.i. W/C. 24-Feb-4 Peter Webb, Auckland #64/R (NZ.D 1200)
£827 $1406 €1207 Lake Te Anau (18x34cm-7x13in) s.d.1892 W/C. 27-Nov-3 International Art Centre, Auckland #123/R (NZ.D 2200)

WILSON, Margaret E (1890-?) British
£250 $418 €365 Floral still life (62x98cm-24x39in) s. 12-Oct-3 Lots Road Auctions, London #352
£300 $552 €450 Fishing vessels in a river estuary (41x48cm-16x19in) s. 24-Jun-4 Ewbank, Send #591/R
£330 $551 €482 Floral still life (60x114cm-24x45in) s. 12-Oct-3 Lots Road Auctions, London #351

WILSON, Marion Henderson (1869-1956) British
Sculpture
£3900 $6981 €5694 Cupid's heads amid stylized foliage (67cm-26in) mono. brass wall sconce. 6-May-4 Bonhams, Edinburgh #228/R est:800-1200

WILSON, Mary Georgina Wade (fl.1882-1936) British
Works on paper
£360 $601 €526 Garden path (49x39cm-19x15in) init. pastel. 13-Nov-3 Bonhams, Edinburgh #345

WILSON, Matthew Henry (1814-1892) American
£583 $950 €845 Portrait of a bearded gentleman (66x56cm-26x22in) s.d.1879. 19-Jul-3 New Orleans Auction, New Orleans #906/R

WILSON, Nicholas (1947-) American
Works on paper
£852 $1500 €1244 Appaloosa (79x104cm-31x41in) s.d.74 mixed media board. 23-May-4 Bonhams & Butterfields, San Francisco #6619/R

WILSON, Norman (20th C) British
£348 $550 €508 Figure on a country path with animals (61x91cm-24x36in) s. 7-Sep-3 Treadway Gallery, Cincinnati #540/R

WILSON, Oscar (1867-1930) British
Works on paper
£294 $550 €429 Young fashionable woman making friends with squirrel (33x23cm-13x9in) s. W/C exec.c.1900. 26-Feb-4 Illustration House, New York #199

WILSON, P MacGregor (c.1855-1928) British
£320 $573 €467 On the coast of Scotland (29x49cm-11x19in) s. 17-Mar-4 Bonhams, Chester #370
£420 $727 €613 Cottage interior scene with a young girl reading in a kitchen (58x38cm-23x15in) s. 11-Dec-3 Scarborough Perry Fine Arts, Hove #652
£600 $1074 €876 Church interior. Village arch (35x25cm-14x10in) s. pair. 26-May-4 Sotheby's, Olympia #203/R
Works on paper
£250 $465 €365 Coastal scene with fishing vessels and fishermen mending nets in foreground (30x50cm-12x20in) s.d.1902 W/C. 4-Mar-4 Clevedon Sale Rooms #151

WILSON, Patten (1868-?) British
£972 $1585 €1400 Debarquement St Pol de Leon (65x81cm-26x32in) s. 18-Jul-3 Feletin, Province #91

WILSON, Paul (20th C) British
£250 $415 €365 Souvenir of a journey (76x61cm-30x24in) s.d.1995 verso. 1-Oct-3 John Ross, Belfast #120

WILSON, Richard (1714-1782) British
£12500 $23000 €18250 Lake Avernus with figures in the foreground and the Temple of Apollo beyond (40x52cm-16x20in) s.i. 26-Mar-4 Sotheby's, London #59/R est:8000-12000
£34000 $62560 €49640 Figures in a landscape with ruins (119x170cm-47x67in) 11-Jun-4 Christie's, London #39/R est:15000-25000
£50000 $85000 €73000 View of the Castel Gandolfo and Lake Albano (75x99cm-30x39in) mono.i. prov.exhib.lit. 25-Nov-3 Christie's, London #61/R est:50000-80000
£88000 $161920 €128480 Rome from the Villa Madama. St. Peter's and the Vatican from the Janiculum (69x131cm-27x52in) pair prov.lit. 26-Mar-4 Sotheby's, London #52/R est:50000-70000
Works on paper
£1100 $2013 €1606 Burdock leaves (18x22cm-7x9in) blk white chk grey paper pencil study verso prov. 3-Jun-4 Christie's, London #57/R est:1200-1800
£1700 $2890 €2482 Classical landscape (20x22cm-8x9in) mono.d.1754 pen brown ink prov.exhib.lit. 20-Nov-3 Christie's, London #10/R est:1500-2000
£2400 $4392 €3504 Italian landscape with figures on a path and a town beyond (17x21cm-7x8in) pencil chk stump htd white pink paper prov.exhib.lit. 3-Jun-4 Christie's, London #58/R est:2500-3500

WILSON, Richard (after) (1714-1782) British
£3779 $6500 €5517 Falls of Tivoli (117x175cm-46x69in) i.verso on stretcher canvas on panel. 6-Dec-3 Neal Auction Company, New Orleans #444/R est:3000-5000

WILSON, Richard (attrib) (1714-1782) British
£567 $1043 €850 Group of people at a view point in the mountains, monastery in background (38x31cm-15x12in) 11-Jun-4 Wendl, Rudolstadt #3942/R
£2320 $4200 €3387 Figures on a riverbank in an extensive Italianate landscape (27cm-11in circular) prov. 30-Mar-4 Christie's, Rockefeller NY #33/R est:2000-3000
£2400 $4368 €3504 Portrait of a gentleman, possibly Richard Myddelton in a red coat (75x61cm-30x24in) lit. 21-Jun-4 Christie's, London #106/R est:3000-5000

WILSON, Robert (1941-) American
Works on paper
£650 $1183 €949 Untitled (28x55cm-11x22in) s.d.82 pencil two. 4-Feb-4 Sotheby's, Olympia #193/R

WILSON, Robert (1963-) British
Works on paper
£545 $927 €780 Oiseaux et poissons (31x22cm-12x9in) s. Indian ink prov. 23-Nov-3 Cornette de St.Cyr, Paris #351
£594 $1010 €850 Oiseaux et poissons (18x22cm-7x9in) s. Indian ink wash prov. 23-Nov-3 Cornette de St.Cyr, Paris #352

WILSON, Ronald York (1907-1984) Canadian
£803 $1494 €1172 Gondola (39x29cm-15x11in) s. panel prov. 2-Mar-4 Ritchie, Toronto #191a/R est:700-900 (C.D 2000)
£1120 $2050 €1635 Moroccan conversation piece (90x75cm-35x30in) s. 1-Jun-4 Joyner Waddington, Toronto #407 est:1800-2200 (C.D 2800)
Works on paper
£313 $538 €457 Knossos (49x62cm-19x24in) s. gouache prov. 2-Dec-3 Joyner Waddington, Toronto #400 (C.D 700)
£720 $1318 €1051 Montmartre at night (120x57cm-47x22in) s. board mixed media prov. 1-Jun-4 Joyner Waddington, Toronto #419/R est:1800-2200 (C.D 1800)

WILSON, Ross (1959-) British
£1958 $3329 €2800 Long dog (36x51cm-14x20in) s.i. board. 18-Nov-3 Whyte's, Dublin #72/R est:3000-4000
Works on paper
£400 $656 €584 Pig (12x12cm-5x5in) mono. mixed media. 4-Jun-3 John Ross, Belfast #81
£450 $747 €657 Wookey Hill Fish (23x33cm-9x13in) mono.d.25/12/87 verso pastel. 1-Oct-3 John Ross, Belfast #164
£450 $837 €657 James Joyce (20x15cm-8x6in) s.d.Nov 78 pencil W/C wash. 3-Mar-4 John Ross, Belfast #183
£500 $915 €730 Study towards a northern man head (28x20cm-11x8in) s.d.96 mixed media. 2-Jun-4 John Ross, Belfast #76
£580 $951 €847 Ballycraigy tulip II (25x35cm-10x14in) s.d.1985 chl. 4-Jun-3 John Ross, Belfast #163
£625 $1019 €900 Thick foliage (61x87cm-24x34in) chl. 23-Sep-3 De Veres Art Auctions, Dublin #306
£1700 $3043 €2482 Man with Hambletonian Mount Stewart (68x83cm-27x33in) s. pencil chl bodycol prov. 14-May-4 Christie's, Kensington #421/R est:400-600
£1950 $3198 €2847 Hare (76x106cm-30x42in) s. mixed media. 4-Jun-3 John Ross, Belfast #127a est:1400
£3108 $5874 €4600 Angelwatch (81x55cm-32x22in) mono. pencil wax crayon. 17-Feb-4 Whyte's, Dublin #197/R est:1500-2000

WILSON, Scottie (1891-1972) British
£2381 $4262 €3500 Untitled (54x38cm-21x15in) s. black col ink. 21-Mar-4 Calmels Cohen, Paris #11/R est:3500-4000
Works on paper
£300 $501 €438 Tree, birds and flowers (36x26cm-14x10in) s. ink pastel. 16-Oct-3 Bonhams, Edinburgh #37
£350 $648 €511 Abstract butterfly (25x17cm-10x7in) s. pencil W/C bodycol. 11-Mar-4 Christie's, Kensington #299
£380 $680 €555 Heads (36x28cm-14x11in) pencil. 5-May-4 British Auctioneer #807
£400 $680 €584 Shoal of fish (37x28cm-15x11in) s. W/C. 26-Nov-3 Sotheby's, Olympia #116/R
£586 $1060 €856 Untitled (12x32cm-5x13in) s. col pencil ink prov. 1-Apr-4 Heffel, Vancouver #110/R (C.D 1400)
£680 $1244 €993 Fishes (63x50cm-25x20in) s. pastel. 8-Apr-4 Bonhams, Edinburgh #20
£711 $1287 €1038 Untitled (24x17cm-9x7in) s. col pencil prov. 1-Apr-4 Heffel, Vancouver #111/R (C.D 1700)
£789 $1453 €1200 Untitled (34x28cm-13x11in) s. col crayon ink. 28-Jun-4 Joron-Derem, Paris #143/R
£1760 $3046 €2500 Composition (35x25cm-14x10in) s. Chinese ink col crayon prov. 9-Dec-3 Artcurial Briest, Paris #475/R est:2500-3000

WILSON, Sol (1896-1974) American/Polish
£297 $550 €434 Boats on beach (28x20cm-11x8in) s. board. 15-Feb-4 Outer Cape Auctions, Provincetown #60a/R
£455 $800 €664 Sunday, Brooklyn (61x46cm-24x18in) s. 3-Jan-4 Outer Cape Auctions, Provincetown #93/R
£1051 $1650 €1534 Brooklyn Bridge (61x46cm-24x18in) s. 20-Apr-3 Outer Cape Auctions, Provincetown #70/R

WILSON, Tim (20th C) New Zealander
£435 $800 €635 See me (107x183cm-42x72in) s.i.d.2003 verso prov. 10-Jun-4 Phillips, New York #482/R
£483 $831 €705 Coastal sunset (40x40cm-16x16in) s. 7-Dec-3 International Art Centre, Auckland #376 (NZ.D 1300)
£632 $1087 €923 Lake scene (29x39cm-11x15in) s.d.1996. 7-Dec-3 International Art Centre, Auckland #366/R (NZ.D 1700)
£743 $1279 €1085 Wanganui River (23x49cm-9x19in) s. canvasboard. 7-Dec-3 International Art Centre, Auckland #245/R (NZ.D 2000)

WILSON, William (1905-1972) British
£250 $448 €365 Loch Venacher (51x61cm-20x24in) s. 13-May-4 Mitchells, Cockermouth #1081
Works on paper
£380 $699 €555 The harbour (27x33cm-11x13in) pencil W/C. 10-Jun-4 Lyon & Turnbull, Edinburgh #54
£400 $736 €584 Segovia (33x46cm-13x18in) s.i.d.1932 pen ink sepia. 10-Jun-4 Lyon & Turnbull, Edinburgh #52
£420 $773 €613 San Francesco, Assisi (35x40cm-14x16in) s.i. pen ink sepia. 10-Jun-4 Lyon & Turnbull, Edinburgh #50
£1300 $2249 €1898 Olive trees, San Gimignano (45x60cm-18x24in) s.d.1952 pencil W/C exhib. 11-Dec-3 Lyon & Turnbull, Edinburgh #8/R est:800-1200
£3800 $6802 €5548 Menton (47x62cm-19x24in) s. pen ink W/C. 28-May-4 Lyon & Turnbull, Edinburgh #1/R est:1500-2000

WILSON, William Heath (1849-1927) British
£820 $1296 €1189 Arno below Florence (12x20cm-5x8in) i.verso panel sold with etching. 3-Sep-3 Bonhams, Bury St Edmunds #454

WILT, Hans (1867-1917) Austrian
£1319 $2151 €1900 Scicilian mountain track (36x51cm-14x20in) s.d.1894 canvas on board. 24-Sep-3 Neumeister, Munich #604/R est:1000

WILT, Pieter Cent van der (1908-1976) Dutch
£748 $1362 €1100 Cattle in a polder landscape (95x140cm-37x55in) s. 3-Feb-4 Christie's, Amsterdam #192/R est:1000-1500

WILT, Thomas van der (1659-1733) Dutch
£1800 $3060 €2628 Portrait of a gentleman wearing a brown silk robe. Portrait of a lady in a red velvet dress (48x39cm-19x15in) d.1762 pair prov. 31-Oct-3 Christie's, Kensington #68/R est:1500-2500
£3425 $5822 €5000 Annunciation (64x46cm-25x18in) panel. 4-Nov-3 Sotheby's, Amsterdam #110/R est:6000-8000
£13000 $22100 €18980 Elegant company playing tric-trac around a table in an interior (69x60cm-27x24in) 29-Oct-3 Christie's, London #21/R est:10000-15000

WIMBUSH, Henry B (fl.1881-1904) British
£600 $978 €876 Broddick Bay, Isle of Arran (50x76cm-20x30in) s. 26-Sep-3 Bigwood, Stratford on Avon #396
Works on paper
£400 $732 €584 Mediterranean coastal view, probably France or Italy (54x76cm-21x30in) s. W/C. 27-Jan-4 Holloways, Banbury #348
£500 $920 €730 River rapids (57x79cm-22x31in) s. W/C. 23-Mar-4 Bonhams, Knightsbridge #44/R
£1120 $2094 €1635 Church beside highland loch (46x58cm-18x23in) s. W/C. 23-Jul-4 Tring Auctions, Tring #268/R est:600-800
£1500 $2745 €2190 Brissago, Lake Maggiori (52x83cm-20x33in) s. W/C. 8-Apr-4 Bonhams, Edinburgh #177 est:800-1200
£1600 $2944 €2336 Figures by a bridge at Granada, Spain (43x51cm-17x20in) s. pencil W/C. 25-Mar-4 Christie's, Kensington #93/R est:500-700
£3100 $5704 €4526 West country coastal scene (56x76cm-22x30in) s.d.1890 W/C. 26-Mar-4 Tring Auctions, Tring #350/R est:1200-1500

WIMMER, Franz (1892-1974) Austrian
Works on paper
£533 $955 €800 Midday (24x24cm-9x9in) mono.d.1916 chl board lit. 14-May-4 Ketterer, Munich #91/R

WIMMER, Hans (1907-1992) German
Sculpture
£2098 $3608 €3000 Reclining model (12x25x7cm-5x10x3in) mono. bronze. 2-Dec-3 Hauswedell & Nolte, Hamburg #675/R est:3000
£5035 $8559 €7200 Girl walking - little mourner (27cm-11in) brown pat.bronze prov. 29-Nov-3 Villa Grisebach, Berlin #297/R est:5000-7000

WIMMER, Konrad (1844-1905) German
£733 $1335 €1100 Covered wagon approaching a frozen lake in the moonlight (58x89cm-23x35in) s. 1-Jul-4 Van Ham, Cologne #1670/R
£1905 $3410 €2800 Enjoying the ice (27x50cm-11x20in) s.i.d.75. 17-Mar-4 Neumeister, Munich #665/R est:4500

WIMMER, Paula (1886-1971) German
£284 $474 €400 Veduta di Stoccarda (47x68cm-19x27in) s. 21-Jun-3 Stadion, Trieste #2/R
£1133 $2029 €1700 Nymphenburger Park in autumn (40x65cm-16x26in) s.d. 13-May-4 Neumeister, Munich #522/R est:700-800

WIMMER, Rudolf (1849-1915) German
£5986 $10356 €8500 Retriever resting after a successful day shooting (200x150cm-79x59in) s.i. 10-Dec-3 Christie's, Amsterdam #810/R est:8000-12000

WIMPERIS, Edmund Morison (1835-1900) British
£250 $448 €365 Reed gatherers (58x89cm-23x35in) mono. 28-May-4 Tring Auctions, Tring #404
£360 $666 €526 Rushing river (61x91cm-24x36in) mono. 10-Feb-4 Bonhams, Knightsbridge #132/R
£420 $735 €613 Sheep resting in a polder landscape (33x51cm-13x20in) init. 19-Dec-3 Mallams, Oxford #224/R
£500 $795 €730 Folding sheep (17x25cm-7x10in) init.d.86. 18-Mar-3 Anderson & Garland, Newcastle #370/R
£1600 $2560 €2336 On the Swail, Yorks (49x57cm-19x22in) 17-Sep-3 Bonhams, Brooks & Langlois, Jersey #60/R est:1500-2000
Works on paper
£280 $468 €409 Arundel Castle (23x34cm-9x13in) init. W/C. 14-Oct-3 Bonhams, Knightsbridge #7/R
£300 $489 €438 North Wales landscape with river, cattle and drover (30x48cm-12x19in) init. W/C. 27-Sep-3 Rogers Jones, Clwyd #38
£300 $555 €438 River scene with windmill (15x22cm-6x9in) init.d.June/91 W/C prov. 10-Mar-4 Sotheby's, Olympia #150/R
£315 $536 €460 Rough heath (37x51cm-15x20in) s.d.1885 i.verso W/C exhib. 21-Nov-3 Walker's, Ottawa #260/R (C.D 700)
£350 $648 €511 Cattle in a valley (22x34cm-9x13in) init.d.1900 W/C. 10-Mar-4 Sotheby's, Olympia #151/R
£450 $720 €657 Farm by the river landscape with sheep (36x48cm-14x19in) mono. W/C. 18-Sep-3 Goldings, Lincolnshire #744/R
£650 $1196 €949 Cottages at Bosham (9x13cm-4x5in) init.d.93 W/C. 24-Mar-4 Hamptons Fine Art, Godalming #247/R

£700 $1204 €1022 Approaching storm (34x61cm-13x24in) init.d.1864 pencil W/C. 3-Dec-3 Christie's, Kensington #120/R
£900 $1665 €1314 Figures by a river (24x34cm-9x13in) init.d.1900 W/C. 10-Mar-4 Sotheby's, Olympia #146/R est:600-800
£1650 $3086 €2409 River Llugwy, North Wales (18x26cm-7x10in) init.d.73 W/C. 25-Feb-4 Mallams, Oxford #203/R est:800-1000

WIMPERIS, Jenny (1838-1927) ?
Works on paper
£1540 $2479 €2248 View of Southern Alps (65x122cm-26x48in) s.d.1919 W/C. 20-Aug-3 Dunbar Sloane, Auckland #93/R est:4000-6000 (NZ.D 4250)

WINANCE, Jean (1911-) Belgian
£612 $1096 €900 Nu feminin (80x70cm-31x28in) s. 17-Mar-4 Hotel des Ventes Mosan, Brussels #146

WINANS, Theodore Fonville (1911-1992) American
Photographs
£2892 $4800 €4222 Dixie Belles (41x51cm-16x20in) s.d.1938 num.037A 38/50 verso silver gelatin photograph. 4-Oct-3 Neal Auction Company, New Orleans #1109/R est:5000-7000

WINANS, Walter (1852-1920) British
Sculpture
£1243 $2200 €1815 Figure of a woman (29cm-11in) s.i.d.1904 brown pat bronze. 2-May-4 Bonhams & Butterfields, San Francisco #1518/R est:1500-2000

WINBERG, Iwan (fl.1830-1846) Russian
Miniatures
£5500 $9515 €8030 Russian nobleman holding scroll (13x19cm-5x7in) s. cast gilt-bronze frame. 9-Dec-3 Christie's, London #248/R est:600-800
£11000 $19030 €16060 Hekena Bibikov seated half length (10cm-4in) s. ormolu frame oval prov. 9-Dec-3 Christie's, London #242/R est:4000-6000
£14000 $24220 €20440 Prince Fedor Petrovich Uvarov in red coat (10x8cm-4x3in) s. cast gilt-bronze frame. 9-Dec-3 Christie's, London #247/R est:800-1200

WINBERG, Iwan (attrib) (fl.1830-1846) Russian
Miniatures
£2200 $3938 €3212 Grand Duke Constantine Nikolaevich of Russia (5cm-2in) gilt metal frame prov. 25-May-4 Christie's, London #117/R est:800-1200

WINCH, John (1944-) Australian
Works on paper
£586 $1096 €879 Spanish landscape (101x80cm-40x31in) s. mixed media board. 20-Jul-4 Goodman, Sydney #65/R (A.D 1500)

WINCHELL, Elizabeth Burt (attrib) (1890-1959) American
£500 $850 €730 Sheep in Central Park, New York. Cow resting under a tree (15x20cm-6x8in) s. one i.verso board pair prov. 18-Nov-3 John Moran, Pasadena #1

WINCK, Johann Amandus (1748-1817) German
£6507 $11062 €9500 Mouse with hazelnuts and fruit. Mouse with walnuts, blossom and pears (15x20cm-6x8in) mono. panel pair prov. 4-Nov-3 Sotheby's, Amsterdam #96/R est:7000-9000
£6667 $12000 €9734 Still life of fruit and nuts with a wine glass resting on a ledge (28x37cm-11x15in) s.d.1809 panel. 22-Jan-4 Sotheby's, New York #203/R est:12000-15000

WINCK, Johann Christian Thomas (1738-1797) German
£2778 $4583 €4000 Moses and the snake (33x24cm-13x9in) canvas on board. 2-Jul-3 Neumeister, Munich #598/R est:4000
£3125 $5156 €4500 Moses getting water out of the rock (33x24cm-13x9in) canvas on board. 2-Jul-3 Neumeister, Munich #597/R est:4500
£7000 $12110 €10220 Christ and the woman from Samaria. Noli me Tangere (32x25cm-13x10in) first s.d.10 Nov/Ao 1763 panel pair. 11-Dec-3 Sotheby's, London #201/R est:8000-12000

WINCK, Willibald (1867-1932) German
£1554 $2782 €2300 Riding through the woods (40x51cm-16x20in) s. lit. 8-May-4 Schloss Ahlden, Ahlden #708/R est:1800

WIND, Gerhard (1928-1994) German
£600 $1074 €900 Figuration K.F. XXX (75x60cm-30x24in) s.i.d.VI 65 verso. 15-May-4 Van Ham, Cologne #1035
£1000 $1790 €1500 Figuration KF. IV (50x60cm-20x24in) s.i.d.V.57 verso. 15-May-4 Van Ham, Cologne #1036/R est:800

WINDER, Berthold (1833-1888) Austrian
£574 $959 €810 Thurm Luginsland in Nurnberg (31x24cm-12x9in) s.d.1859. 17-Oct-3 Behringer, Furth #1532/R

WINDER, Daniel H (fl.1880-1920) British
£420 $672 €613 Teignbrook, Kyle of Bute, Scotland (36x61cm-14x24in) s.d.1897 i.stretcher. 16-Sep-3 Capes Dunn, Manchester #783/R
£500 $885 €730 Figure on a riverbank (56x41cm-22x16in) s.d.1905. 28-Apr-4 Halls, Shrewsbury #522

WINDHAGER, Franz (1879-1959) Austrian
£591 $1100 €863 The tasting (55x45cm-22x18in) s. masonite. 5-Mar-4 Skinner, Boston #530/R

WINDLE, J (19th C) British?
£6200 $10912 €9052 Shorthorn cow in a landscape with a Firefly locomotive and farmhouse (70x89cm-28x35in) s.d.1852. 18-May-4 Woolley & Wallis, Salisbury #222/R est:4000-6000

WINDMAIER, Anton (1840-1896) German
£1224 $2192 €1800 Children with sledge in village street in winter (51x41cm-20x16in) s.d.89. 17-Mar-4 Neumeister, Munich #664/R est:1500
£1955 $3500 €2854 Sunset over a snowy landscape (28x38cm-11x15in) s.indis.d. board. 7-May-4 Sloans & Kenyon, Bethesda #1651/R est:3000-5000

WINDNER, Isabella (20th C) German
£403 $741 €600 Still life of fruit (42x56cm-17x22in) s.d.1921 board. 24-Mar-4 Hugo Ruef, Munich #1151

WINDRED, E H (?) ?
£380 $684 €555 Portrait of a racing pigeon, Lightning (36x46cm-14x18in) s. 24-Apr-4 Tamlyn, Bridgwater #146/R

WINDT, Chris van der (1877-1952) Dutch
£921 $1667 €1400 Summer landscape with farm (30x22cm-12x9in) s. canvas on panel. 19-Apr-4 Glerum, Amsterdam #132/R
£1053 $1905 €1600 Back of houses (31x24cm-12x9in) s. canvas on panel. 19-Apr-4 Glerum, Amsterdam #144/R est:700-900
£1600 $2944 €2400 Gladioli (25x26cm-10x10in) s. canvas on masonite. 9-Jun-4 Dorotheum, Salzburg #633/R est:1000-1400
£1611 $2948 €2400 Old houses along the banks of a stream (25x34cm-10x13in) s. 9-Jul-4 Dawo, Saarbrucken #61/R est:2400
£2303 $4168 €3500 Chrysanthemums in a vase (52x70cm-20x28in) s.d.1929. 19-Apr-4 Glerum, Amsterdam #143/R est:1000-1200
£2500 $4525 €3800 Snow covered houses in Leidschendam (40x50cm-16x20in) s. 19-Apr-4 Glerum, Amsterdam #135/R est:2500-3500
£3819 $6493 €5500 Wine bottle, oysters and fruit on a draped table (53x72cm-21x28in) s.d.1928. 28-Oct-3 Christie's, Amsterdam #150/R est:3000-5000
Works on paper
£625 $1131 €950 Rainy street scene with figures (23x34cm-9x13in) s. W/C. 19-Apr-4 Glerum, Amsterdam #142
£2368 $4287 €3600 Reewijk farm (30x40cm-12x16in) s. i.d.1929 verso. 19-Apr-4 Glerum, Amsterdam #136/R est:3000-4000
£2500 $4525 €3800 Farmer's wife working in front of a dwelling (36x54cm-14x21in) s. W/C. 19-Apr-4 Glerum, Amsterdam #141/R est:3000-4000
£2961 $5359 €4500 Farmer in the yard of a farm in a polder landscape (35x54cm-14x21in) s. W/C. 19-Apr-4 Glerum, Amsterdam #137/R est:2700-3000
£4000 $7200 €6000 Farmhouse along a stream (32x54cm-13x21in) s. W/C htd white. 21-Apr-4 Christie's, Amsterdam #163/R est:6000-8000
£4667 $8400 €7000 Peasant at work in his vegetable garden (29x48cm-11x19in) s.d.1908 W/C htd white. 20-Apr-4 Sotheby's, Amsterdam #140/R est:7000-9000

WINDT, Gerard Carl Lodewyk (1868-1949) Dutch
£263 $476 €400 View of the River Vecht (24x35cm-9x14in) s. panel. 19-Apr-4 Glerum, Amsterdam #254

WINDT, Philip Pieter (attrib) (1847-1921) Dutch
£3297 $6000 €4946 Sunset beach scene with boats and figures (79x104cm-31x41in) s. wood. 19-Jun-4 Jeffery Burchard, Florida #116

WINFIELD, Rodney (20th C) American
Works on paper
£1193 $2100 €1742 Man is a lonely city (46x61cm-18x24in) W/C gesso exhib. 22-May-4 Selkirks, St. Louis #678/R est:1200-1500

WINGATE, Sir James Lawton (1846-1924) British
£360 $666 €526 Horse and cart on a country track (27x22cm-11x9in) indis.s. board. 14-Jul-4 Bonhams, Chester #419
£400 $720 €584 Sunset (34x52cm-13x20in) s. canvas on panel. 22-Apr-4 Bonhams, Edinburgh #368
£450 $752 €657 Shepherd (35x25cm-14x10in) s. 13-Nov-3 Bonhams, Edinburgh #300a
£500 $915 €730 Cattle beneath trees (48x43cm-19x17in) s. 27-Jan-4 Gorringes, Lewes #1678
£500 $930 €730 Sunlit lane (30x23cm-12x9in) s. board prov. 4-Mar-4 Christie's, Kensington #141
£520 $868 €759 Fishing fleet, Kilbrannian Sound (31x41cm-12x16in) s. 16-Oct-3 Bonhams, Edinburgh #221
£600 $1032 €876 Country lane at Muthill (36x25cm-14x10in) s. 2-Dec-3 Gorringes, Lewes #2504
£620 $1035 €905 Beneath apple blossom (40x50cm-16x20in) s. 16-Oct-3 Bonhams, Edinburgh #120
£887 $1632 €1295 From a garden in late autumn (77x63cm-30x25in) s. 14-Jun-4 Waddingtons, Toronto #190/R est:3000-5000 (C.D 2200)

WINGE, Hanna (1838-1896) Swedish
£559 $951 €800 Young girl with basket of vegetables (60x44cm-24x17in) s.d.1859. 29-Nov-3 Bukowskis, Helsinki #388/R

WINGE, Sigurd (1909-1970) Norwegian
£870 $1504 €1270 Icon (35x55cm-14x22in) s. enamel. 13-Dec-3 Blomqvist, Lysaker #1407 (N.KR 10000)

WINGFIELD, James Digman (attrib) (1809-1872) British
£451 $726 €658 The artist's studio (16x20cm-6x8in) panel. 25-Aug-3 Lilla Bukowskis, Stockholm #625 (S.KR 5900)
£700 $1253 €1022 Crowning the victor (53x49cm-21x19in) s. panel. 18-Mar-4 Christie's, Kensington #464/R

£1800 $3330 €2628 Cavaliers in a wooded avenue, a country house beyond (91x71cm-36x28in) 14-Jul-4 Christie's, Kensington #801a/R est:2000-3000

WINGHE, Joos van (studio) (1544-1603) Flemish
£13000 $22100 €18980 Samson and Delilah (97x124cm-38x49in) panel. 30-Oct-3 Sotheby's, Olympia #41/R est:4000-6000

WINIARKSI, Ryszard (20th C) Polish
£223 $384 €326 Chance in game (41x33cm-16x13in) s. acrylic pencil painted 1999. 4-Dec-3 Agra, Warsaw #48/R (P.Z 1500)
£229 $381 €334 Third game (17x13cm-7x5in) acrylic painted 1999. 2-Oct-3 Agra, Warsaw #69/R (P.Z 1500)
£254 $406 €371 Geometric shape (41x33cm-16x13in) acrylic. 17-Sep-3 Agra, Warsaw #4/R (P.Z 1600)
£398 $660 €581 Chance in game for one (25x25cm-10x10in) acrylic pencil painted 1984. 2-Oct-3 Agra, Warsaw #7/R (P.Z 2600)
£1379 $2303 €2000 Chance in game for one (49x49cm-19x19in) s.i.d.90 acrylic pencil board. 16-Nov-3 Agra, Warsaw #35/R est:1000
£2828 $4722 €4100 Chance in game (100x100cm-39x39in) s.i.d.90 verso acrylic pencil. 16-Nov-3 Agra, Warsaw #97/R est:2000
£3107 $5624 €4536 Area 164 (100x100cm-39x39in) s.d.1973 acrylic. 4-Apr-4 Agra, Warsaw #38/R (P.Z 22000)

WINKFIELD, Frederick A (fl.1873-1920) British
£4865 $9000 €7103 Below London Bridge, Old Billingsgate fish market on the right (46x76cm-18x30in) s. prov. 10-Feb-4 Christie's, Rockefeller NY #240/R est:7000-9000

WINKLER, Carl von (1860-1911) ?
Works on paper
£500 $905 €750 Baltic coast with fishing nets and beach (24x35cm-9x14in) s.i. W/C gouache. 3-Apr-4 Hans Stahl, Hamburg #133

WINKLER, Herbert (1949-) ?
£700 $1211 €1022 Ohne titel (49x37cm-19x15in) s.d.02 acrylic paper sold with another by the same artist. 11-Dec-3 Christie's, Kensington #263/R

WINN, Alice Collingbourne (20th C) American
£249 $450 €364 La Porte Indiana (23x25cm-9x10in) s. 18-Apr-4 Jeffery Burchard, Florida #231/R

WINN, Betty (1915-) American
£479 $800 €699 Pyracantha (66x56cm-26x22in) masonite. 18-Oct-3 David Dike, Dallas #85/R

WINN, James (1949-) American
£1749 $3200 €2554 Pasture no.2 (43x97cm-17x38in) acrylic on paper. 10-Jul-4 Hindman, Chicago #576/R est:500-700

WINNEWISSER, Rolf (1949-) Swiss
£1086 $1846 €1586 Untitled (146x221cm-57x87in) s.d.1984 acrylic. 25-Nov-3 Germann, Zurich #85/R est:1200-1500 (S.FR 2400)

WINOGRAND, Garry (1928-1984) American
Photographs
£1667 $3000 €2434 Untitled (22x33cm-9x13in) s.i.verso num.25/80 gelatin silver print prov.lit. 23-Apr-4 Phillips, New York #67/R est:2000-3000
£1778 $3200 €2596 Metropolitan Opera (28x34cm-11x13in) gelatin silver print prov. 23-Apr-4 Phillips, New York #176/R est:3000-5000
£2156 $3600 €3148 Untitled, woman with shopping bag (22x33cm-9x13in) s. num.55/80 verso gelatin silver print exec. c.1970 prov.lit. 17-Oct-3 Phillips, New York #174/R est:3000-5000
£2260 $4000 €3300 World's fair, New York City, 1964 (22x33cm-9x13in) s.num.16/75 gelatin silver print lit. 27-Apr-4 Christie's, Rockefeller NY #343/R est:5000-7000
£2333 $4200 €3406 Boxer (22x33cm-9x13in) num.35 gelatin silver print prov. 23-Apr-4 Phillips, New York #151/R est:3000-5000
£2667 $4800 €3894 Untitled (16x24cm-6x9in) i.num.9 gelatin silver print prov. 23-Apr-4 Phillips, New York #152/R est:5000-7000
£2874 $4800 €4196 Dallas, Texas (22x33cm-9x13in) s.i.d.1964 verso gelatin silver print lit. 16-Oct-3 Phillips, New York #177/R est:4000-6000
£3114 $5200 €4546 New York City (22x33cm-9x13in) s. num.77/80 verso gelatin silver print exec. c.1967 prov.lit. 17-Oct-3 Phillips, New York #173/R est:5000-7000
£3611 $6500 €5272 New Mexico (22x33cm-9x13in) gelatin silver print prov.lit. 23-Apr-4 Phillips, New York #47/R est:6000-8000
£3955 $7000 €5774 Staten Island Ferry, New York, 1971 (22x33cm-9x13in) s.num.16/75 gelatin silver print lit. 27-Apr-4 Christie's, Rockefeller NY #344/R est:4000-6000
£4192 $7000 €6120 World's Fair, New York City (22x33cm-9x13in) s.num.33/80 verso gelatin silver print exec.1964 lit. 20-Oct-3 Christie's, Rockefeller NY #196/R est:7000-9000
£4192 $7000 €6120 Los Angeles (22x33cm-9x13in) s.verso gelatin silver print exhib.lit. 16-Oct-3 Phillips, New York #176/R est:4000-6000
£4520 $8000 €6599 Selected images (22x32cm-9x13in) one s.i. one bears another sig.verso photo 2 printed later prov. 28-Apr-4 Sotheby's, New York #161/R est:5000-7000
£4671 $7800 €6820 World's Fair, New York City (22x33cm-9x13in) s. num.14/20 gelatin silver print exec.1964 prov.lit. 17-Oct-3 Phillips, New York #56/R est:6000-8000
£5367 $9500 €7836 Selected images (22x34cm-9x13in) estate st. one d.1957 and d.1967 photo 2 printed later prov. 28-Apr-4 Sotheby's, New York #165/R est:5000-7000
£5367 $9500 €7836 New Mexico, 1957 (22x33cm-9x13in) s.num.16/75 gelatin silver print lit. 27-Apr-4 Christie's, Rockefeller NY #163/R est:5000-7000
£5556 $10000 €8112 Circle line statue of Liberty Ferry, New York (22x33cm-9x13in) gelatin silver print l. 23-Apr-4 Phillips, New York #198/R est:3000-5000
£6667 $12000 €9734 New York City (22x32cm-9x13in) s.num.1/2 verso gelatin silver print lit. 23-Apr-4 Phillips, New York #87/R est:6000-8000
£7186 $12000 €10492 London (34x22cm-13x9in) s.i. gelatin silver print lit. 16-Oct-3 Phillips, New York #173/R est:6000-8000
£25989 $46000 €37944 Fifteen photographs (22x33cm-9x13in) s.num.36/75 photo exec.1952-73 printed 1974 fifteen folio. 28-Apr-4 Sotheby's, New York #230/R est:30000-50000
£32934 $55000 €48084 Women are beautiful (22x33cm-9x13in) s.num.66/80 verso gelatin silver print 85 folio clamshell box. 20-Oct-3 Christie's, Rockefeller NY #198/R est:30000-40000

WINSLOW, Earle Bartrom (1884-1969) American
£353 $600 €515 Untitled - Woodstock (43x53cm-17x21in) s. 9-Nov-3 Wright, Chicago #131

WINSLOW, Helen (20th C) American
£405 $750 €591 Floral still life with irises and apples (56x51cm-22x20in) s. 18-Jan-4 Bonhams & Butterfields, Los Angeles #7027/R
£811 $1500 €1184 California coast. s.i. 14-Jul-4 Dallas Auction Gallery, Dallas #381/R est:1000-1500

WINSLOW, John (20th C) American
£273 $500 €399 In the studio II (173x173cm-68x68in) 10-Jul-4 Hindman, Chicago #577/R

WINSLOW, Lasse (1911-) Danish?
£322 $516 €470 Interior scene with female nude standing (93x45cm-37x18in) s.d.1948. 22-Sep-3 Rasmussen, Vejle #624/R (D.KR 3400)

WINSON, Annie (19th C) American
£298 $525 €435 The Shoshone camp (91x61cm-36x24in) s. 20-May-4 American Auctioneer #475029/R

WINSTANLEY, Hamlet (1698-1756) British
£2000 $3720 €2920 Portrait of a lady, seated in a landscape (127x100cm-50x39in) s.d.1732. 4-Mar-4 Christie's, Kensington #324/R est:1500-2000

WINSTANLEY, Henry (19th C) British
£360 $659 €526 Woodland scene with sheep and cottages (61x91cm-24x36in) s.d.89. 27-Jan-4 Holloways, Banbury #372

WINT, Peter de (1784-1849) British
£550 $985 €803 View of Litchfield from the fens (15x28cm-6x11in) indis sig. 13-May-4 Grant, Worcester #388/R
£1100 $1837 €1606 Turf gatherers, Chat Moss (20x30cm-8x12in) 21-Oct-3 Gorringes, Lewes #2182
Works on paper
£280 $512 €409 View on the river Lowther, Westmoreland (16x27cm-6x11in) i.verso col chk prov. 27-Jan-4 Holloways, Banbury #333
£280 $512 €409 Sheep and cattle grazing by a clump of trees. Cattle and vegetation (16x23cm-6x9in) col chk double-sided prov. 27-Jan-4 Holloways, Banbury #334/R
£320 $586 €467 Ox drawn cart with a drover (7x11cm-3x4in) black chk prov. 27-Jan-4 Holloways, Banbury #335
£650 $1196 €949 The post. The well (15x11cm-6x4in) pencil W/C prov. pair. 25-Mar-4 Christie's, Kensington #25
£850 $1556 €1241 Gloucester Cathedral (18x30cm-7x12in) W/C prov. 7-Apr-4 Woolley & Wallis, Salisbury #118/R
£900 $1683 €1314 Harvesting, Leatherhead (29x41cm-11x16in) i. pencil W/C exec. 1824. 22-Jul-4 Tennants, Leyburn #641
£1000 $1720 €1460 Dolbadon Castle, N Wales (28x43cm-11x17in) W/C. 2-Dec-3 Gorringes, Lewes #2480/R est:1000-1500
£1200 $2040 €1752 Harrow on the Hill from Stanmore (9x33cm-4x13in) W/C over pencil. 27-Nov-3 Sotheby's, London #299/R est:1000-1500
£1800 $3312 €2628 View of Westminster from Battersea (13x24cm-5x9in) W/C over pencil htd scratching out prov.exhib. 26-Mar-4 Sotheby's, London #113/R est:2000-3000
£2500 $4550 €3650 Lincolnshire stackyard (15x31cm-6x12in) W/C over pencil. 1-Jul-4 Sotheby's, London #220/R est:3000-4000
£2600 $4758 €3796 Shepherd and flock on a bridge, near Newark (18x26cm-7x10in) pencil W/C prov. 3-Jun-4 Christie's, London #127/R est:2500-3500
£2800 $5096 €4088 Horses drinking at a pool (23x32cm-9x13in) W/C over pencil. 1-Jul-4 Sotheby's, London #217/R est:3000-4000
£2973 $5500 €4460 Boats on the Thames (18x30cm-7x12in) pencil W/C prov. 14-Jul-4 American Auctioneer #490477/R est:1000-1500
£3200 $5888 €4672 Old Putney (19x29cm-7x11in) W/C. 8-Jun-4 Bonhams, New Bond Street #24/R est:2500-3500
£3300 $6072 €4818 Carting corn (20x36cm-8x14in) W/C prov. 8-Jun-4 Bonhams, New Bond Street #23/R est:3000-5000
£3400 $6222 €4964 Farmer's return (22x32cm-9x13in) pencil W/C prov. 3-Jun-4 Christie's, London #128/R est:2500-3500
£3400 $6358 €4964 Returning from market (30x25cm-12x10in) W/C prov. 22-Jul-4 Tennants, Leyburn #642 est:600-900
£4200 $7770 €6132 Harvesters at work (26x51cm-10x20in) W/C prov. 9-Mar-4 Bonhams, New Bond Street #36/R est:3000-5000
£4500 $7650 €6570 View of Ludlow Castle (23x31cm-9x12in) pencil W/C. 20-Nov-3 Christie's, London #60/R est:2000-3000
£4800 $8784 €7008 Stacking Barley, Lincolnshire (55x88cm-22x35in) pencil W/C gum arabic htd white scratching out prov.exhib.lit. 3-Jun-4 Christie's, London #125/R est:5000-7000
£5000 $9150 €7300 Bristol Cathedral from the South (18x33cm-7x13in) pencil W/C prov.lit. 3-Jun-4 Christie's, London #130/R est:5000-8000
£9000 $16470 €13140 View over Tetford from the Bluestone Heath Road, Lincolnshire (15x65cm-6x26in) pencil W/C two joined sheets. 3-Jun-4 Christie's, London #126/R est:10000-15000
£11000 $18700 €16060 Hasting from the East Cliff (37x54cm-15x21in) W/C exhib. 4-Nov-3 Bonhams, New Bond Street #37/R est:6000-8000
£11000 $18700 €16060 View of Bolton Abbey, Yorkshire (47x83cm-19x33in) i.verso pencil W/C scratching out prov.exhib. 20-Nov-3 Christie's, London #81/R est:12000-18000
£28571 $51143 €42000 Holkar Sands, Lancashire (48x71cm-19x28in) W/C htd gouache. 17-Mar-4 Maigret, Paris #20/R est:3000-4000

WINT, Peter de (attrib) (1784-1849) British
Works on paper
£250 $455 €365 A church in an extensive landscape (13x36cm-5x14in) pencil W/C. 1-Jul-4 Christie's, Kensington #70/R
£400 $740 €584 Dovecot, Derbyshire (46x69cm-18x27in) W/C. 13-Feb-4 Keys, Aylsham #468/R

£450	$788	€657	Lone figure in a cornfield overlooking a valley (18x28cm-7x11in) W/C. 18-Dec-3 John Nicholson, Haslemere #1035/R
£450	$788	€657	Evening landscape with a lone figure walking on a path beside a pond (23x30cm-9x12in) W/C. 18-Dec-3 John Nicholson, Haslemere #1036/R
£480	$787	€701	Cottages and pool, in a wooded landscape (10x13cm-4x5in) pencil sepia wash. 29-May-3 Neales, Nottingham #712/R

WINTEGHEM, Clothilde van (?) Belgian

£304	$535	€450	Still life with bouquet of white roses (38x58cm-15x23in) s. 24-May-4 Bernaerts, Antwerp #472/R

WINTER, Alice Beach (1877-c.1970) American

£598	$1100	€873	Pink flowers (41x76cm-16x30in) s. 25-Jun-4 Freeman, Philadelphia #323/R

WINTER, Andrew (1893-1958) American

£1235	$2000	€1791	Monhegan surf (20x25cm-8x10in) s. canvasboard prov. 8-Aug-3 Barridorf, Portland #193/R est:900-1200
£1728	$2800	€2506	Blue seas (30x61cm-12x24in) s. masonite prov. 8-Aug-3 Barridorf, Portland #195/R est:3000-5000
£2778	$4500	€4028	Hurricane Edna (46x61cm-18x24in) s. canvasboard prov. 8-Aug-3 Barridorf, Portland #184/R est:4000-6000
£3210	$5200	€4655	Drydock, Monhegan (20x25cm-8x10in) s.d.28 board. 8-Aug-3 Barridorf, Portland #302/R est:3000-5000
£3704	$6000	€5371	Low tide (61x91cm-24x36in) s. board prov. 8-Aug-3 Barridorf, Portland #183/R est:6000-9000
£4938	$8000	€7160	Fishing boats (30x46cm-12x18in) s. 8-Aug-3 Barridorf, Portland #194/R est:4000-6000
£5525	$10000	€8067	Lighthouse and coast guard station (20x30cm-8x12in) s. s.i.d.1939 verso canvasboard prov. 31-Mar-4 Sotheby's, New York #29/R est:2000-4000
£8025	$13000	€11636	Mohegan thaw (30x46cm-12x18in) s.d.24 board. 8-Aug-3 Barridorf, Portland #173/R est:9000-12000
£8333	$15500	€12166	Monhegan Harbour in winter (51x61cm-20x24in) s. board. 6-Mar-4 North East Auctions, Portsmouth #541/R est:8000-12000
£13580	$22000	€19691	Lekking house from Monhegan harbor (46x61cm-18x24in) s. board. 8-Aug-3 Barridorf, Portland #200/R est:12000-18000
£17059	$29000	€24906	Winter evening, Monhegan (74x99cm-29x39in) s.d.31 exhib. 31-Oct-3 North East Auctions, Portsmouth #1883 est:18000-24000

WINTER, Bernhard (1871-1964) German

£364	$607	€520	Family portrait (102x126cm-40x50in) s.i.d.1930. 28-Jun-3 Bolland & Marotz, Bremen #1056

WINTER, Charles Allan (1869-1942) American

£252	$450	€368	Portrait of a young woman (56x43cm-22x17in) s. 8-Jan-4 James Julia, Fairfield #1170/R

WINTER, Eugene (1918-1980) Dutch

£724	$1332	€1100	The Westerkirk, Amsterdam (113x57cm-44x22in) s. 22-Jun-4 Christie's, Amsterdam #486/R

WINTER, Fritz (1905-1976) German

£594	$1022	€850	White markings on dark background (25x18cm-10x7in) s.d. oil over pencil. 5-Dec-3 Ketterer, Munich #336/R
£1200	$2208	€1800	The red sheets (18x25cm-7x10in) s.i.d.64 paper. 12-Jun-4 Villa Grisebach, Berlin #870/R est:1800-2000
£1200	$2208	€1800	Untitled (18x25cm-7x10in) s.d.64 oil bodycol chl. 12-Jun-4 Villa Grisebach, Berlin #871/R est:1800-2000
£1329	$2259	€1900	Untitled (46x60cm-18x24in) s.i. oil over serigraph. 29-Nov-3 Villa Grisebach, Berlin #946/R est:1400-1800
£1667	$3067	€2500	Figure with a bird's head (44x28cm-17x11in) mono.d.29 paper prov. 12-Jun-4 Villa Grisebach, Berlin #336/R est:3000-4000
£2000	$3680	€3000	Composition (49x64cm-19x25in) s.d.55 oil over col serigraph. 12-Jun-4 Villa Grisebach, Berlin #405/R est:3000-4000
£2064	$3447	€2993	Composition (49x70cm-19x28in) s.d.53 oil W/C frottage carpenter's pencil collage. 19-Jun-3 Kornfeld, Bern #1053/R est:5000 (S.FR 4500)
£2168	$3685	€3100	Untitled (17x24cm-7x9in) s.d.60. 27-Nov-3 Lempertz, Koln #534/R est:3000
£2238	$3804	€3200	Untitled (50x65cm-20x26in) mono.d.31 board prov. 27-Nov-3 Lempertz, Koln #532/R est:3500
£2282	$4085	€3400	Composition with red (18x24cm-7x9in) s.d.60. 25-May-4 Karl & Faber, Munich #585/R est:3000
£2308	$3923	€3300	Composition (61x43cm-24x17in) s.d.71 oil gouache board. 29-Nov-3 Villa Grisebach, Berlin #280/R est:3000-4000
£2550	$4693	€3800	Composition with grey and red (13x16cm-5x6in) s.d. paper. 26-Mar-4 Ketterer, Hamburg #695/R est:2500-3000
£2685	$4940	€4000	Composition (49x69cm-19x27in) s.d. acrylic W/C col chk board panel. 26-Mar-4 Ketterer, Hamburg #693/R est:4000-4500
£3067	$5643	€4600	Untitled (18x19cm-7x7in) s.d.59 oil acrylic paper. 12-Jun-4 Villa Grisebach, Berlin #869/R est:2000-3000
£3497	$5944	€5000	Composition (50x70cm-20x28in) s.d.53 oil gouache board. 29-Nov-3 Villa Grisebach, Berlin #281/R est:5000-7000
£3846	$6538	€5500	Building up (50x70cm-20x28in) s.d.2 s.i.d.52 verso oil pastel chk board prov.exhib. 27-Nov-3 Lempertz, Koln #533/R est:7000-8000
£5245	$9021	€7500	Two rhythms (50x65cm-20x26in) s.d. s.i.d. verso oil tempera board prov. 5-Dec-3 Ketterer, Munich #307/R est:7000-9000
£6376	$11732	€9500	Untitled (49x63cm-19x25in) tempera oil wax prov. 26-Mar-4 Ketterer, Hamburg #692/R est:9000-12000
£6993	$11888	€10000	First snow (70x50cm-28x20in) mono.d.56. 29-Nov-3 Bassenge, Berlin #7036/R est:15000
£7667	$14107	€11500	Lightness (50x70cm-20x28in) s.d.1951 paper. 12-Jun-4 Villa Grisebach, Berlin #337/R est:9000-11000
£7746	$13401	€11000	Composition in red and black I (65x51cm-26x20in) s.d.32 paper on canvas lit.exhib. 13-Dec-3 Lempertz, Koln #194/R est:5000
£8333	$15250	€12500	Untitled (50x70cm-20x28in) s.d.50 board. 4-Jun-4 Lempertz, Koln #538/R est:6000-7000
£10839	$18427	€15500	Excited (70x80cm-28x31in) mono.d.57 s.i.d.1957 verso prov. 27-Nov-3 Lempertz, Koln #530/R est:8000
£13287	$22587	€19000	Construction blue-red (90x80cm-35x31in) s.d.69 s.i.d. verso prov. 27-Nov-3 Lempertz, Koln #531/R est:20000-22000
£14000	$25620	€21000	Transmission (70x104cm-28x41in) s.d.52 s.i.d. verso prov.lit. 4-Jun-4 Lempertz, Koln #537/R est:18000-22000
£15333	$27447	€23000	Horizontal light and dark blue (130x97cm-51x38in) s.d. s.i.d. verso. 15-May-4 Dr Sturies, Dusseldorf #219/R
£23239	$40204	€33000	Between black (90x80cm-35x31in) s.d.67 s.i.d.67 verso lit. 13-Dec-3 Lempertz, Koln #195/R est:7000-8000
£27972	$47552	€40000	The oracle (97x130cm-38x51in) s.d.58 s.i.d. verso prov. 28-Nov-3 Villa Grisebach, Berlin #85/R est:40000-50000

Works on paper

£252	$413	€350	Composition (21x20cm-8x8in) mono. feltpen. 4-Jun-3 Ketterer, Hamburg #991/R
£252	$413	€350	Composition (20x28cm-8x11in) mono.i.d. feltpen. 4-Jun-3 Ketterer, Hamburg #992/R
£268	$494	€400	Composition (20x18cm-8x7in) mono.i.d. feltpen. 26-Mar-4 Ketterer, Hamburg #1215/R
£1138	$1900	€1661	Abstract (61x46cm-24x18in) mixed media. 19-Jun-3 Shelley, Hendersonville #982
£1972	$3411	€2800	Abstract composition (25x18cm-10x7in) s.d.64 mixed media. 13-Dec-3 Lempertz, Koln #196/R est:1000
£2886	$5310	€4300	Untitled (50x70cm-20x28in) s.i.d. pastel chk. 26-Mar-4 Ketterer, Hamburg #694/R est:4000-6000
£3000	$5520	€4380	Sich losendes grun uber rot (49x69cm-19x27in) s.d.53 s.i.d.53 verso gouache wash card prov.lit. 24-Jun-4 Sotheby's, Olympia #565/R est:3000-4000
£3221	$5702	€4800	Untitled (61x43cm-24x17in) s.d. W/C gouache Indian ink prov. 30-Apr-4 Dr Fritz Nagel, Stuttgart #967/R est:3000
£3819	$6378	€5500	Untitled (61x40cm-24x16in) s.d. gouache. 24-Oct-3 Ketterer, Hamburg #581/R est:6000-7000

WINTER, Fritz (attrib) (1905-1976) German

£1667	$3033	€2500	Abstract composition (59x39cm-23x15in) paper. 3-Jul-4 Badum, Bamberg #24/R est:3000

WINTER, Georg (1899-1955) German

£300	$537	€450	Portrait of Michael Schoberth in the studio (104x68cm-41x27in) s.d.1938. 14-May-4 Behringer, Furth #1539

WINTER, Hans (19th C) Austrian

£1816	$3250	€2651	Rabbis at prayer (18x13cm-7x5in) s. panel pair. 18-Mar-4 Sotheby's, New York #260/R est:3000-5000
£3103	$5586	€4500	Religious scene (27x34cm-11x13in) s. 21-Jan-4 Tajan, Paris #145/R est:6000-8000

WINTER, Janus de (1882-1951) Dutch

Works on paper

£646	$1176	€950	Kolibri (100x50cm-39x20in) s. pastel. 3-Feb-4 Christie's, Amsterdam #513

WINTER, Konrad (1963-) Austrian

£284	$474	€400	Untitled (95x120cm-37x47in) mono.d.90. 16-Oct-3 Dorotheum, Salzburg #788/R

WINTER, Pharaon de (1849-1924) French

£260	$416	€380	Still life with bowl of fruit and a flagon (44x31cm-17x12in) s. board. 16-Sep-3 Rosebery Fine Art, London #500/R

WINTER, Robert A (1953-) American

£1615	$2600	€2358	Got-yah (22x28cm-9x11in) 22-Aug-3 Altermann Galleries, Santa Fe #125
£1765	$3000	€2577	Taos (46x61cm-18x24in) 1-Nov-3 Altermann Galleries, Santa Fe #105

WINTER, William Arthur (1909-1986) Canadian

£194	$311	€283	Children in a field (30x41cm-12x16in) s. board. 16-Sep-3 Maynards, Vancouver #386 (C.D 425)
£217	$393	€317	Untitled - getting ready for the beach (25x20cm-10x8in) s. canvasboard prov. 18-Apr-4 Levis, Calgary #604/R (C.D 525)
£240	$439	€350	Northern kid (25x20cm-10x8in) s. canvasboard prov. 1-Jun-4 Joyner Waddington, Toronto #448 (C.D 600)
£250	$408	€365	At the table (27x37cm-11x15in) board. 23-Sep-3 Ritchie, Toronto #127/R (C.D 550)
£289	$524	€422	Children with cat (20x25cm-8x10in) s. i.verso canvasboard prov. 18-Apr-4 Levis, Calgary #605/R (C.D 700)
£446	$768	€651	Children in the forum (29x49cm-11x19in) s. canvasboard prov. 2-Dec-3 Joyner Waddington, Toronto #287/R (C.D 1000)
£560	$1025	€818	Young mother and child (49x40cm-19x16in) s. board prov. 1-Jun-4 Joyner Waddington, Toronto #420 (C.D 1400)
£640	$1171	€934	Artist (65x40cm-26x16in) board prov. 1-Jun-4 Joyner Waddington, Toronto #288/R (C.D 1600)
£714	$1229	€1042	Autumn streets (30x40cm-12x16in) s. canvasboard. 2-Dec-3 Joyner Waddington, Toronto #251/R (C.D 1600)
£1200	$2196	€1752	Just married (54x42cm-21x17in) s. board. 1-Jun-4 Joyner Waddington, Toronto #106/R est:3000-4000 (C.D 3000)
£1200	$2196	€1752	Red wagon (30x40cm-12x16in) s. canvasboard. 1-Jun-4 Joyner Waddington, Toronto #529 est:1500-1800 (C.D 3000)

WINTER, William Tatton (1855-1928) British

Works on paper

£250	$458	€365	Extensive open landscape with a figure walking along a windswept path (26x37cm-10x15in) s. W/C. 28-Jan-4 Dreweatt Neate, Newbury #37
£260	$486	€380	Sailing vessels moored at a quay (5x8cm-2x3in) s. W/C. 25-Feb-4 Mallams, Oxford #335
£270	$459	€394	Koudekerke - Dutch town scene (24x34cm-9x13in) s. i.verso W/C. 29-Oct-3 Bonhams, Chester #405
£280	$484	€409	Windmill (20x31cm-8x12in) s.d.1914 W/C. 10-Dec-3 Bonhams, Bury St Edmunds #517
£289	$512	€422	French town scene (24x34cm-9x13in) s.d.1911 W/C. 3-May-4 Lawson Menzies, Sydney #398 (A.D 700)
£300	$558	€438	Sunbury on Thames (24x34cm-9x13in) s.i.d.May 1912 W/C. 2-Mar-4 Bearnes, Exeter #338/R

£360 $652 €526 Extensive heathland scene with grouse shooters (28x51cm-11x20in) s.d.1902 W/C. 30-Mar-4 Rogers Jones, Clwyd #116/R
£420 $756 €613 Mill at Eve (33x25cm-13x10in) s. W/C sold with painting by Rose Champion. 22-Apr-4 Lawrence, Crewkerne #805
£440 $788 €642 Ploughman and his team (28x58cm-11x23in) s. W/C. 7-May-4 Mallams, Oxford #210/R
£480 $898 €701 Figures on a country lane approaching the outskirts of a village (34x44cm-13x17in) s. pencil W/C htd white prov. 22-Jul-4 Tennants, Leyburn #756
£600 $1104 €876 Feeding the geese (19x43cm-7x17in) s.d.98 pencil W/C. 25-Mar-4 Christie's, Kensington #144/R
£722 $1177 €1054 Bruges (24x34cm-9x13in) s.d.1911 W/C. 23-Sep-3 Peter Webb, Auckland #166/R (NZ.D 2000)

WINTERBOTTOM, Austin (fl.1887-1906) British
£1000 $1670 €1460 Winter woodland (88x223cm-35x88in) s. 7-Oct-3 Fellows & Sons, Birmingham #405/R est:1000-1500

WINTERHALTER, Franz Xavier (1806-1873) German
£7042 $12183 €10000 Portrait de femme (130x98cm-51x39in) s.d.1844. 12-Dec-3 Piasa, Paris #68/R est:10000-15000
£29412 $50000 €42942 Princess Marie Woronzoff (65x54cm-26x21in) s.i.d.1853 prov.exhib.lit. 28-Oct-3 Sotheby's, New York #56/R est:60000-80000
£65000 $118300 €94900 Portrait of Count Paul Andeievich Shouvaloff (91x72cm-36x28in) s.i.d.1860 oval prov.lit. 17-Jun-4 Christie's, London #65/R est:20000-30000
Works on paper
£433 $797 €650 Portrait of four children (12x16cm-5x6in) W/C oval. 12-Jun-4 Karlheinz Kaupp, Staufen #1223/R
£467 $859 €700 Portrait of a young woman (14x11cm-6x4in) mixed media oval. 12-Jun-4 Karlheinz Kaupp, Staufen #1222/R
£1200 $2076 €1752 Portrait of a seated lady, her hands folded on her lap (34x26cm-13x10in) s. black lead grey wash. 12-Dec-3 Christie's, Kensington #568/R est:600-800
£9170 $16690 €13388 Half-length portrait of Crown Princess Victoria of Prussia, later Kaiserin Friedrich (31x27cm-12x11in) s.d.1855 W/C prov.exhib. 17-Jun-4 Kornfeld, Bern #81/R est:10000 (S.FR 21000)

WINTERHALTER, Franz Xavier (after) (1806-1873) German
£5500 $9350 €8030 Queen Victoria (57x45cm-22x18in) 25-Nov-3 Christie's, London #156/R est:4000-6000

WINTERHALTER, Franz Xavier (attrib) (1806-1873) German
£800 $1480 €1168 Spanish beauty (67x56cm-26x22in) s.d.1867. 15-Jan-4 Christie's, Kensington #743/R
£3333 $5500 €4800 Portrait of woman with rose in hair (81x60cm-32x24in) i.d.1864 oval. 2-Jul-3 Neumeister, Munich #822/R est:4500

WINTERHALTER, Hermann (1808-1891) German
£4500 $7200 €6525 Portrait of a lady holding a fan (124x103cm-49x41in) s.d.1857. 18-Sep-3 Christie's, Kensington #173/R est:5000-7000

WINTERHALTER, Joseph (younger) (1743-1807) Austrian
Works on paper
£3691 $6792 €5500 Adoration of the lamb by angels (17x19cm-7x7in) wash pen. 26-Mar-4 Dorotheum, Vienna #56/R est:600-800

WINTERLIN, Anton (1805-1894) Swiss
£541 $930 €790 View of Lake Thun and the Rothorn (26x36cm-10x14in) mono. panel. 8-Dec-3 Philippe Schuler, Zurich #3365/R (S.FR 1200)
£2172 $3692 €3171 Rotteln ruins near Lorrach (60x81cm-24x32in) mono.d.1856 i. verso. 28-Nov-3 Zofingen, Switzerland #2493/R est:6500 (S.FR 4800)
£4783 $8752 €6983 Landscape in the Berner Oberland (57x76cm-22x30in) s.d.1860. 4-Jun-4 Zofingen, Switzerland #2375/R est:9500 (S.FR 11000)
£9649 $17754 €14088 Landscape in Berner Oberland (52x78cm-20x31in) s.indis.d. 23-Jun-4 Koller, Zurich #3001/R est:7500-10000 (S.FR 22000)
Works on paper
£1322 $2247 €1930 Wooded landscape with peasants looking at lake (42x59cm-17x23in) s.d.1858 W/C. 7-Nov-3 Dobiaschofsky, Bern #7/R est:5000 (S.FR 3000)

WINTERS, Terry (1949-) American
Prints
£1765 $3000 €2577 Marginalia (122x81cm-48x32in) init. col lithograph. 31-Oct-3 Sotheby's, New York #840/R
Works on paper
£1923 $3500 €2808 Schema 52 (30x21cm-12x8in) gouache oil graphite executed 1985-86 prov.exhib. 29-Jun-4 Sotheby's, New York #563/R est:1000-1500
£2703 $5000 €3946 Meshworks II (50x71cm-20x28in) init.i. pencil exec 2000 prov. 12-Feb-4 Sotheby's, New York #237/R est:5000-6000
£6145 $11000 €8972 Botanical subject (66x48cm-26x19in) chl crayon exec 1981 prov.exhib. 13-May-4 Sotheby's, New York #465/R est:8000-12000

WINTERSBERGER, Lambert Maria (1941-) German
£1074 $1976 €1600 Self portrait (130x85cm-51x33in) s.d.1982 1 prov.exhib. 26-Mar-4 Ketterer, Hamburg #698/R est:1800-2400
£3467 $6379 €5200 Wounds (170x200cm-67x79in) s.i.d.68 verso acrylic. 12-Jun-4 Villa Grisebach, Berlin #410/R est:3500-4500

WINTERSCHEIT, Karl (1927-) Polish
£268 $494 €400 Small town in the evening (20x16cm-8x6in) s. panel. 27-Mar-4 L & B, Essen #225/R

WINTERSCHMIDT, Christian Gottlob (1755-1809) German
Works on paper
£940 $1729 €1400 Dutch scenes (25x19cm-10x7in) s. mixed media two. 24-Mar-4 Hugo Ruef, Munich #1202/R

WINTHER, Frederick Julius August (1853-1916) Danish
£284 $455 €415 Fox out hunting (80x57cm-31x22in) s.d.1895 exhib. 22-Sep-3 Rasmussen, Vejle #474 (D.KR 3000)
£17958 $31068 €26219 The calm lake at Dyrehaven, summer (88x138cm-35x54in) s.d.1908 exhib. 9-Dec-3 Rasmussen, Copenhagen #1437/R est:50000-75000 (D.KR 190000)

WINTHER, Richard (1926-) Danish
£531 $849 €770 Composition (80x66cm-31x26in) s.d.1960-67-71. 17-Sep-3 Kunsthallen, Copenhagen #130 (D.KR 5600)

WINTOUR, John Crawford (1825-1882) British
£720 $1202 €1051 Path to the well (44x33cm-17x13in) s. board. 19-Jun-3 Bonhams, Edinburgh #389
£1800 $3114 €2628 Helping hand (37x29cm-15x11in) init.d.58 board. 11-Dec-3 Lyon & Turnbull, Edinburgh #57/R est:1500-2000

WINTTER, Joseph Georg (1751-1789) German
Works on paper
£280 $476 €400 Deer under large tree (23x30cm-9x12in) s.d. Indian ink brush over pencil sold with two others. 21-Nov-3 Reiss & Sohn, Konigstein #150
£811 $1427 €1200 Elegant deer hunters on horseback (29x47cm-11x19in) pen wash prov. 22-May-4 Lempertz, Koln #1383/R

WINTZ, Guillaume (1823-1899) French
£909 $1563 €1300 Sheep in a landscape (74x101cm-29x40in) s. 7-Dec-3 Sotheby's, Amsterdam #616/R

WINTZ, Raymond (1884-?) French
£952 $1514 €1400 Bretonnes devant la chapelle (33x41cm-13x16in) s. 18-Mar-3 Adjug'art, Brest #130
£1268 $2218 €1800 Barques sous voiles (41x33cm-16x13in) s. 21-Dec-3 Thierry & Lannon, Brest #367 est:600-800
£1955 $3500 €2854 Port en Bretagne Ecole Francaise (81x99cm-32x39in) s. 10-Jan-4 Auctions by the Bay, Alameda #523/R
£2394 $4190 €3400 Port Bigouden (54x65cm-21x26in) s. 21-Dec-3 Thierry & Lannon, Brest #212/R est:2500-3000

WIPPEL, Antoni (1868-1939) Polish
£990 $1743 €1485 Landscape in North Africa (77x57cm-30x22in) s. 23-May-4 Agra, Warsaw #37/R (P.Z 7000)

WIPPELL, E G (fl.1925) British
£6500 $12285 €9490 Proud procession (46x61cm-18x24in) s. pair. 19-Feb-4 Christie's, Kensington #343/R est:2000-4000

WIRE, Melville Thomas (1877-1966) American
£838 $1500 €1223 Golden field (20x25cm-8x10in) s. painted c.1920. 16-Mar-4 Matthew's, Oregon #103/R est:1500-1800

WIRGMAN, Charles (1832-1891) British
Works on paper
£3800 $5890 €5548 Tea party (20x28cm-8x11in) s. W/C. 26-Sep-2 Christie's, London #101/R est:3000-5000

WIRGMAN, Charles A (1864-1922) British
Works on paper
£500 $850 €730 Lake Chuzenji, Honshu, Japan (23x42cm-9x17in) s.i.d.1900 W/C. 4-Nov-3 Bonhams, New Bond Street #14

WIRSUM, Karl (20th C) American
Works on paper
£818 $1300 €1194 Overall blue feeling. Contrasting glasses (36x28cm-14x11in) one s.d.Nov 15 1965 mixed media pair. 14-Sep-3 Susanin's, Chicago #6128/R est:1500-2000

WIRTANEN, Kaapo (1886-1959) Finnish
£336 $617 €500 Cottage (53x64cm-21x25in) s.d.1931. 25-Mar-4 Hagelstam, Helsinki #871
£349 $642 €520 Town (55x65cm-22x26in) s.d.1923. 25-Mar-4 Hagelstam, Helsinki #895
£676 $1209 €1000 Sheep (47x56cm-19x22in) s.d.1944. 8-May-4 Bukowskis, Helsinki #171/R

WIRZ, Johann (attrib) (1640-c.1709) Swiss
Works on paper
£1379 $2303 €2000 Slumbering Cupid watched by Psyche (22x26cm-9x10in) i.d.1707 ochre wash prov. 15-Nov-3 Lempertz, Koln #1435/R est:800

WIRZ, Johann Jacob (1694-1773) Swiss
Works on paper
£1921 $3497 €2805 Portrait of Joh Casparus Meyerus, half-length towards right (32x21cm-13x8in) s.i.d.52 pen ink brush wash prov. 17-Jun-4 Kornfeld, Bern #82/R est:2000 (S.FR 4400)

WISCHNIOWSKY, Josef (1856-1926) Austrian
£400 $732 €584 Interior with bewigged gentleman watching a canary eating cherries (8x7cm-3x3in) s. panel. 6-Apr-4 Bonhams, Knightsbridge #87/R

WISELBERG, Fanny (20th C) Canadian
£811 $1378 €1184 Italian landscape (37x48cm-15x19in) s. prov. 23-Nov-3 Levis, Calgary #148/R est:2000-2500 (C.D 1800)
Works on paper
£536 $921 €783 Portrait of a woman resting (54x46cm-21x18in) s.i. chl. 2-Dec-3 Joyner Waddington, Toronto #118/R (C.D 1200)

WISELBERG, Rose (1908-1992) Canadian
£811 $1378 €1184 View of Seminary, at Water Ave., Westmount Que (44x60cm-17x24in) s. s.i.verso paperboard prov. 23-Nov-3 Levis, Calgary #149/R est:2000-2500 (C.D 1800)
£1040 $1903 €1518 Harbour, Montreal (45x60cm-18x24in) s.i.d.1948 board prov. 1-Jun-4 Joyner Waddington, Toronto #155/R est:3000-4000 (C.D 2600)
£1351 $2297 €1972 Fantasy (50x66cm-20x26in) s.d.1959 board prov. 27-Nov-3 Heffel, Vancouver #131 est:3500-4500 (C.D 3000)

WISINGER-FLORIAN, Olga (1844-1926) Austrian
£1818 $3036 €2600 Still life of flowers with berries (43x43cm-17x17in) 9-Oct-3 Michael Zeller, Lindau #803/R est:1500
£3819 $6035 €5500 Still life of flowers (16x21cm-6x8in) s. canvas on board lit. 19-Sep-3 Schloss Ahlden, Ahlden #1648/R est:5500
£4305 $7877 €6500 Evening (8x13cm-3x5in) mono. board. 8-Apr-4 Dorotheum, Vienna #141/R est:3000-3600
£10490 $17832 €15000 Tavern garden in November (34x37cm-13x15in) s. board. 24-Nov-3 Dorotheum, Vienna #90/R est:15000-20000
£15000 $27300 €21900 A spray of wild flowers (18x27cm-7x11in) s. panel. 15-Jun-4 Sotheby's, London #9/R est:4000-6000
£18182 $30909 €26000 Path along stream (36x27cm-14x11in) s. board. 24-Nov-3 Dorotheum, Vienna #140/R est:15000-18000
£37000 $67340 €54020 Roses and pansies in a basket (67x54cm-26x21in) s. panel. 15-Jun-4 Sotheby's, London #52/R est:10000-15000
£48611 $82639 €70000 Country scene with children playing (46x67cm-18x26in) s. panel. 28-Oct-3 Wiener Kunst Auktionen, Vienna #53/R est:80000-130000

WISKOVSKY, Eugen (1888-1964) Czechoslovakian
Photographs
£2667 $4800 €3894 Insulator with the spring II (38x29cm-15x11in) silkscreen i.d.1935 verso gelatin silver print. 22-Apr-4 Phillips, New York #36/R est:3000-5000

WISLICENUS, Hermann (1825-1899) German
Works on paper
£493 $789 €700 Portrait of Julius Schnorr von Carolsfeld (54x45cm-21x18in) mono.d.1868 pencil lit. 19-Sep-3 Karlheinz Kaupp, Staufen #2027/R

WISLICENUS, Lilli (1872-1939) German
Sculpture
£1656 $3013 €2500 Female nude standing, with chained hands and a headband (68cm-27in) s. bronze incl. stone base. 16-Jun-4 Hugo Ruef, Munich #1768/R est:800
£2069 $3455 €3000 Standing female nude (68cm-27in) s. pat.bronze stone socle. 9-Jul-3 Hugo Ruef, Munich #1849/R est:500

WISLICENUS, Max (1861-1957) German
£302 $541 €450 Destroy bridge in Warsaw (42x52cm-17x20in) s.d.1915. 25-May-4 Karl & Faber, Munich #587/R

WISSANT, Charles (19th C) French
Works on paper
£452 $724 €660 French landscape (15x22cm-6x9in) W/C. 19-Sep-3 Koller, Zurich #3107/R (S.FR 1000)

WISSE, Jan (1955-) Dutch
£486 $768 €700 Femme au chapeau Picasso (58x48cm-23x19in) s.d.1998 verso panel on aluminium. 26-Apr-3 Auction Maastricht #179/R

WISSELINGH, Johannes Pieter van (1812-1899) Dutch
£3200 $5824 €4672 Skaters in a Dutch winter landscape (43x66cm-17x26in) init.d.1838. 16-Jun-4 Christie's, Kensington #181/R est:3000-5000
£10417 $17396 €15000 Peasants on a country road near Rhenen (105x160cm-41x63in) s. 21-Oct-3 Sotheby's, Amsterdam #55/R est:7000-10000

WISSING, Willem (1653-1687) Dutch
£4500 $8370 €6570 Portrait of John, Baron Cutts of Gowran (76x63cm-30x25in) s. prov.exhib. 4-Mar-4 Christie's, Kensington #288/R est:2500-3500

WISTERNIGG, Franz (19th C) ?
£455 $773 €650 Winter landscape (70x100cm-28x39in) s. 27-Nov-3 Dorotheum, Linz #483/R

WISZNIEWSKI, Adrian (1958-) ?
Works on paper
£360 $601 €526 Sailor and girl (21x30cm-8x12in) W/C. 16-Oct-3 Lyon & Turnbull, Edinburgh #17

WIT, Jacob de (1695-1754) Dutch
£10135 $17838 €15000 Allegory of the hunt (148x101cm-58x40in) bears sig en grisaille shaped painted with studio. 18-May-4 Sotheby's, Amsterdam #116/R est:18000-25000
£22346 $40000 €32625 Allegory of the hunt in a trompe-l'oeil niche (146x118cm-57x46in) en grisaille prov. 27-May-4 Sotheby's, New York #41/R est:25000-35000
Works on paper
£993 $1818 €1500 Putti. pen ink htd white gouache. 9-Apr-4 Bailly Pommery, Paris #7/R est:1200-1500
£1486 $2616 €2200 Four evangelists (12x25cm-5x10in) pen wash htd white prov. 22-May-4 Lempertz, Koln #1385/R est:2200
£3000 $5490 €4380 Putti with garlands of flowers within a fictive roundel (15cm-6in circular) pen ink wash over black chk pair. 7-Jul-4 Bonhams, Knightsbridge #61/R est:1000-1500

WIT, Prosper Joseph de (c.1862-c.1951) Belgian
£308 $514 €440 Chemin ensoleille (27x36cm-11x14in) s. panel. 13-Oct-3 Horta, Bruxelles #107
£320 $573 €480 Grain sheaves (24x33cm-9x13in) s. board. 15-May-4 De Vuyst, Lokeren #110
£664 $1143 €950 Vue sur un village (69x114cm-27x45in) s. 2-Dec-3 Campo & Campo, Antwerp #118/R
£1119 $1869 €1600 Borde de riviere en automne (80x110cm-31x43in) s. 13-Oct-3 Horta, Bruxelles #106 est:1500-2000
£2238 $3737 €3200 Riviere bordee de saules en hiver (80x70cm-31x28in) s. 13-Oct-3 Horta, Bruxelles #105 est:2800-3200
£3147 $5413 €4500 La lavoir (80x100cm-31x39in) s. 2-Dec-3 Campo & Campo, Antwerp #117/R est:3500-4000

WITDOECK, Petrus Josephus (1803-1840) Flemish
£900 $1530 €1314 Hound in a kennel (38x46cm-15x18in) s. 27-Nov-3 Christie's, Kensington #373/R

WITHALM (Foryod) Hungarian
£4267 $7851 €6400 Jeune Orientale dansant (100x68cm-39x27in) s. 14-Jun-4 Gros & Delettrez, Paris #429/R est:6000-8000

WITHERINGTON, William Frederick (1785-1865) British
£500 $835 €730 Figures picknicking (38x58cm-15x23in) s.d.1866. 17-Oct-3 Keys, Aylsham #731
£1600 $2944 €2336 Harvester's repast (63x76cm-25x30in) s.d.1859. 8-Jun-4 Bonhams, Knightsbridge #199/R est:1500-2000
£8500 $15300 €12410 Harvesting, near Derwentwater, Cumberland (69x97cm-27x38in) s.d.1854 exhib. 21-Jan-4 Sotheby's, Olympia #279/R est:6000-8000
£14000 $25760 €20440 Midday rest (87x115cm-34x45in) s. indis d. s.i.verso prov. 11-Jun-4 Christie's, London #132/R est:8000-12000

WITHERINGTON, William Frederick (attrib) (1785-1865) British
£800 $1488 €1168 Figures boarding a ferry (21x28cm-8x11in) board. 4-Mar-4 Christie's, Kensington #408/R

WITHERS, Alfred (1856-1932) American
£400 $732 €584 Extensive river landscape, with figure in a boat (60x120cm-24x47in) s. 6-Apr-4 Bonhams, Knightsbridge #72/R

WITHERS, Augusta Innes (fl.1829-1865) British
Works on paper
£720 $1318 €1051 Still life with a bird's nest and flowers on a ledge (26x39cm-10x15in) s.d.1843 W/C. 7-Apr-4 Woolley & Wallis, Salisbury #76/R
£3000 $5550 €4380 Agave americana variegata (75x50cm-30x20in) s.i. pencil pen ink W/C. 15-Jul-4 Bonhams, New Bond Street #46/R est:3000-5000

WITHERS, Walter (1854-1914) Australian
£4962 $9031 €7245 Road and cottage, Eltham (24x35cm-9x14in) s. panel. 16-Jun-4 Deutscher-Menzies, Melbourne #170/R est:15000-20000 (A.D 13000)
£7660 $13021 €11184 Eltham (22x20cm-9x8in) panel prov. 26-Nov-3 Deutscher-Menzies, Melbourne #128/R est:8000-12000 (A.D 18000)
£8264 $14628 €12065 Coming storm, winter (30x50cm-12x20in) s. painted c.1898 prov.exhib. 3-May-4 Christie's, Melbourne #98/R est:20000-30000 (A.D 20000)
Works on paper
£2869 $4533 €4189 Cowes beach and ferry (28x47cm-11x19in) s.d.13 W/C prov. 2-Sep-3 Deutscher-Menzies, Melbourne #298/R est:3000-5000 (A.D 7000)
£60728 $97774 €88663 Farmhouse, Heidelberg (75x101cm-30x40in) s. 13-Oct-3 Joel, Victoria #330/R est:80000-120000 (A.D 150000)

WITHERS, Walter (attrib) (1854-1914) Australian
£372 $688 €543 Broken fence (18x18cm-7x7in) panel. 10-Mar-4 Deutscher-Menzies, Melbourne #520/R (A.D 900)

WITHERSPOON, Mary Eleanor (1906-1999) American
Works on paper
£389 $650 €568 Landscape (25x36cm-10x14in) pastel. 18-Oct-3 David Dike, Dallas #150/R

WITHOOS, Alida (1660-1715) Dutch
Works on paper
£1689 $2973 €2500 Barrenwort (41x26cm-16x10in) s. W/C bodycol black chk prov. 19-May-4 Sotheby's, Amsterdam #132/R est:2200-2800
£1757 $3092 €2600 Study of a plant, possibly a danewort (37x23cm-15x9in) s. W/C gouache black chk prov.exhib.lit. 19-May-4 Sotheby's, Amsterdam #131/R est:2500-3500
£1892 $3330 €2800 Persian buttercups (34x22cm-13x9in) s. W/C gouache black chk. 19-May-4 Sotheby's, Amsterdam #134/R est:3500-4500
£3649 $6422 €5400 Wild rose (36x26cm-14x10in) s. W/C gouache black chk prov.exhib. 19-May-4 Sotheby's, Amsterdam #128/R est:3500-4500
£3716 $6541 €5500 Columbine (34x22cm-13x9in) s. W/C gouache black chk. 19-May-4 Sotheby's, Amsterdam #129/R est:3000-4000

WITHOOS, Matthias (1627-1703) Dutch
£8523 $15000 €12444 Garden views (67x55cm-26x22in) pair. 19-May-4 Doyle, New York #6079/R est:8000-12000

WITHOOS, Pieter (1654-1693) Dutch
Works on paper
£778 $1400 €1136 Geese, ducks and other birds on a pond with distant houses (29x41cm-11x16in) s.d.1678 bodycol on board. 22-Jan-4 Christie's, Rockefeller NY #255/R
£1014 $1784 €1500 Young herring gull (17x22cm-7x9in) init. pen black ink W/C gouache. 19-May-4 Sotheby's, Amsterdam #121/R est:1800-2200
£3041 $5351 €4500 Butterflies and mosquitos (23x33cm-9x13in) init. W/C gouache. 19-May-4 Sotheby's, Amsterdam #126/R est:2500-3000
£10811 $19027 €16000 Studies of moths and a dragonfly (23x17cm-9x7in) s. pen black ink W/C gouache. 19-May-4 Sotheby's, Amsterdam #127/R est:2200-2800

WITJENS, Jacques Stephen (1881-1956) Dutch
£773 $1400 €1129 Landscape in Balcarce (24x25cm-9x10in) canvas on cardboard. 30-Mar-4 Arroyo, Buenos Aires #33
£1050 $1900 €1533 Poor people (13x18cm-5x7in) canvas on cardboard. 30-Mar-4 Arroyo, Buenos Aires #38
£1492 $2700 €2178 Balcarce (18x24cm-7x9in) canvas on cardboard. 30-Mar-4 Arroyo, Buenos Aires #37
£1530 $2800 €2234 Stable (17x23cm-7x9in) cardboard. 1-Jun-4 Arroyo, Buenos Aires #38
£1758 $3200 €2567 Landscape (17x24cm-7x9in) s. cardboard on canvas. 29-Jun-4 Arroyo, Buenos Aires #22/R est:1400
£1955 $3500 €2854 Dutch canal (20x28cm-8x11in) s. board. 4-May-4 Arroyo, Buenos Aires #27/R est:1700
£2123 $3800 €3100 View of Kager Lagoon (15x18cm-6x7in) cardboard. 11-May-4 Arroyo, Buenos Aires #102
£2473 $4500 €3611 Canal (27x34cm-11x13in) s. board. 29-Jun-4 Arroyo, Buenos Aires #3/R est:2500
£2486 $4500 €3630 Figures in landscape (40x50cm-16x20in) canvas on cardboard. 30-Mar-4 Arroyo, Buenos Aires #102
£2541 $4600 €3710 Run (13x18cm-5x7in) canvas on cardboard. 30-Mar-4 Arroyo, Buenos Aires #39
£3591 $6500 €5243 Sender (72x60cm-28x24in) board. 30-Mar-4 Arroyo, Buenos Aires #98
£3631 $6500 €5301 By the canal (26x36cm-10x14in) s. s.d.1925 verso. 4-May-4 Arroyo, Buenos Aires #40/R est:2400
£3631 $6500 €5301 On the beach (24x30cm-9x12in) s. canvas on board. 4-May-4 Arroyo, Buenos Aires #105/R est:2600
£3846 $7000 €5615 Waiting for the catch (39x47cm-15x19in) s. 29-Jun-4 Arroyo, Buenos Aires #89/R est:5000
£3934 $7200 €5744 Beached boat (50x60cm-20x24in) board. 1-Jun-4 Arroyo, Buenos Aires #94
£4505 $8200 €6577 Mills (60x80cm-24x31in) s. 5-Jul-4 Arroyo, Buenos Aires #100/R est:6800
£5028 $9000 €7341 House by the canal (45x55cm-18x22in) s. 4-May-4 Arroyo, Buenos Aires #102/R est:3500
£5464 $10000 €7977 Beach and lighthouse (40x50cm-16x20in) board. 1-Jun-4 Arroyo, Buenos Aires #57
£6983 $12500 €10195 Bell tower in Katwijk (15x20cm-6x8in) s. s.i.verso cardboard. 4-May-4 Arroyo, Buenos Aires #98/R est:2500

WITJENS, Willem (1884-1962) Dutch
£395 $714 €600 Still life of flowers in front of a window (65x76cm-26x30in) s. 19-Apr-4 Glerum, Amsterdam #145/R
£428 $787 €650 A panoramic view of the countryside in Kent (30x40cm-12x16in) i.verso canvas on board prov. 22-Jun-4 Christie's, Amsterdam #296/R
£493 $893 €750 Ditch at the back of farm (60x80cm-24x31in) s. 19-Apr-4 Glerum, Amsterdam #234/R
Works on paper
£532 $888 €750 Old watermill of Oele (31x48cm-12x19in) s.d.1931 W/C. 20-Oct-3 Glerum, Amsterdam #168

WITKAMP, Ernest Sigismund (1854-1897) Dutch
£933 $1671 €1400 Study of a young lady (40x31cm-16x12in) s.d.1897 panel. 11-May-4 Vendu Notarishuis, Rotterdam #271/R
Works on paper
£414 $691 €600 Portrait of a man (29x24cm-11x9in) s. W/C. 11-Nov-3 Vendu Notarishuis, Rotterdam #15/R

WITKIEWICZ, Stanislaw (1851-1915) Polish
Works on paper
£3852 $6395 €5624 Portrait of a man (61x46cm-24x18in) s.d.1930 pastel. 15-Jun-3 Agra, Warsaw #11/R est:16000 (P.Z 24000)

WITKIEWICZ, Stanislaw Ignacy (1885-1939) Polish
Works on paper
£2351 $3668 €3432 Portrait of a young girl (67x49cm-26x19in) pastel. 30-Mar-3 Agra, Warsaw #23/R est:15000 (P.Z 15000)
£2408 $3997 €3516 Portrait of a child, Tomasza Domaniewskiego (60x46cm-24x18in) s.d.1924 pastel. 15-Jun-3 Agra, Warsaw #16/R est:18000 (P.Z 15000)
£2594 $4720 €3787 Portrait of Kobiety (67x51cm-26x20in) s.d.8/V 1917 pastel. 20-Jun-4 Agra, Warsaw #59/R (P.Z 18000)
£3328 $5758 €4859 Portrait of a male. s.i.d.1931 pastel lit. 14-Dec-3 Agra, Warsaw #78/R est:18500 (P.Z 22000)
£3918 $6113 €5720 Portrait of a man (64x48cm-25x19in) s.d.May 1929 pastel. 30-Mar-3 Agra, Warsaw #16/R est:18000 (P.Z 25000)
£4219 $7045 €6160 Portrait of Jana Leszczynskiego (66x48cm-26x19in) s. pastel exec.c.1930. 19-Oct-3 Agra, Warsaw #15/R est:20000 (P.Z 27000)
£4375 $7306 €6388 Portrait of a woman (59x47cm-23x19in) s.d.1930 pastel. 19-Oct-3 Agra, Warsaw #14/R est:20000 (P.Z 28000)

WITKIN, Joel Peter (1939-) American
Photographs
£1695 $3000 €2475 Art Deco lamp, New Mexico (37x37cm-15x15in) s.i.d.1986 num.4/15 toned photo. 28-Apr-4 Sotheby's, New York #252/R est:5000-8000
£1796 $3000 €2622 Woman breastfeeding eel (71x70cm-28x28in) s.i.d.verso gelatin silver print lit. 16-Oct-3 Phillips, New York #247/R est:5000-7000
£2147 $3800 €3135 Leda, Los Angelers, 1986 (27x37cm-11x15in) s.i.d.1986 gelatin silver print lit. 27-Apr-4 Christie's, Rockefeller NY #339/R est:3000-5000
£2238 $3737 €3200 John Herring, PWA posed as Flova with lover and mother, New Mexico (92x102cm-36x40in) s.i.d.verso black white photo edition of 15 lit. 11-Oct-3 Cornette de St.Cyr, Paris #162/R est:3000-4000
£2994 $5000 €4371 Sanitarium (37x37cm-15x15in) s.i.d.verso gelatin silver print lit. 16-Oct-3 Phillips, New York #244/R est:8000-12000
£7345 $13000 €10724 Harvest, Philadelphia (37x37cm-15x15in) s.i.d.1984 num.6/15 toned photo. 28-Apr-4 Sotheby's, New York #253/R est:8000-10000

WITKOWSKI, Karl (1860-1910) American
£5291 $10000 €7725 Portrait of a woman wearing a lace shawl holding a book (76x64cm-30x25in) s.d.1885. 21-Feb-4 Brunk, Ashville #192/R est:4000-8000

WITKOWSKI, Romuald Kamil (1876-1950) Polish
£1176 $2175 €1717 Still life with fruit (21x30cm-8x12in) 14-Mar-4 Agra, Warsaw #69/R (P.Z 8500)

WITSEN, Willem (1860-1923) Dutch
Works on paper
£1892 $3330 €2800 View of the Kromme Waal, Amsterdam (13x23cm-5x9in) bears i.verso chl exhib.lit. 19-May-4 Sotheby's, Amsterdam #351/R est:900-1200
£2162 $3805 €3200 View of the Binnenkant, Amsterdam (13x23cm-5x9in) bears i.verso chl exhib.lit. 19-May-4 Sotheby's, Amsterdam #353/R est:900-1200
£28000 $50400 €42000 Joden Houttuinen (54x64cm-21x25in) s. black chk W/C htd white prov.exhib. 21-Apr-4 Christie's, Amsterdam #119/R est:15000-20000

WITT, Antony de (1876-1967) Italian
£1418 $2369 €2000 Tuscan village with houses (55x75cm-22x30in) painted 1960 exhib.lit. 20-Oct-3 Sant Agostino, Torino #124/R est:1000-1400
£1479 $2558 €2100 Red hat (57x42cm-22x17in) s.d.1896. 10-Dec-3 Finarte Semenzato, Rome #208/R est:2300-2500

WITT, Graham (19th C) ?
£331 $572 €483 River landscape by Tigre, Buenos Aires (32x38cm-13x15in) with sig.verso. 9-Dec-3 Rasmussen, Copenhagen #1518 (D.KR 3500)

WITTE, Adrien de (1850-1935) Belgian
£496 $829 €700 Le pont de la Cannet (33x46cm-13x18in) s. indis.i.verso. 15-Oct-3 Hotel des Ventes Mosan, Brussels #132
Works on paper
£1944 $3247 €2800 Letter (52x35cm-20x14in) s.d.1881 W/C. 21-Oct-3 Sotheby's, Amsterdam #26/R est:1500-2000

WITTE, Emanuel de (1617-1692) Dutch
£90000 $155700 €131400 Interior of a church with two gentlemen conversing in the foreground (56x43cm-22x17in) panel prov. 10-Dec-3 Christie's, London #31/R est:70000-100000

WITTE, Gaspar de (1624-1681) Flemish
£3000 $5190 €4380 Italianate river landscape with ruins and herdsmen on a path (12x27cm-5x11in) s. panel. 12-Dec-3 Christie's, Kensington #106/R est:2000-3000

WITTE-LENOIR, Heinz (1880-1961) German?
£759 $1403 €1100 Paris Montparnasse (40x50cm-16x20in) s. board. 14-Feb-4 Hans Stahl, Hamburg #109/R

WITTEL, Gaspar van (1653-1736) Dutch
£60000 $109800 €87600 Rome, view of the Tiber with Ponte Rotto (23x44cm-9x17in) prov. 7-Jul-4 Sotheby's, London #61/R est:60000-80000
£340000 $622200 €496400 Venice, Saint Giorgio Maggiore. Venice, Saint Michele Island (20x91cm-8x36in) s. pair prov. 7-Jul-4 Sotheby's, London #60/R est:200000-300000
£777778 $1400000 €1135556 View of Lake Maggiore with Isola Bella (50x99cm-20x39in) s.d.1715 prov. 22-Jan-4 Sotheby's, New York #76/R est:150000-200000
Works on paper
£1093 $2000 €1596 Wooded landscape (21x28cm-8x11in) pen brown ink wash. 29-Jan-4 Swann Galleries, New York #178/R est:3000-5000
£1093 $2000 €1596 Wooded landscape with rolling hills (21x27cm-8x11in) pen brown ink wash. 29-Jan-4 Swann Galleries, New York #179/R est:3000-5000
£6000 $10980 €8760 Landscape with figure walking towards a temple (27x41cm-11x16in) black chk pen ink wash W/C bodycol htd white prov. 6-Jul-4 Christie's, London #90/R est:6000-8000
£14444 $26000 €21088 View of Urbino from San Donato, with a study of a cathedral dome (28x82cm-11x32in) black chk pen brown ink grey wash prov. 22-Jan-4 Christie's, Rockefeller NY #60/R est:15000-20000
£21000 $38430 €30660 View of the Roman Campagna. Partial view of the Palace of Caprarola (24x37cm-9x15in) i. verso pen brown ink over blk chk double-sided. 8-Jul-4 Sotheby's, London #92/R est:7000-9000
£28169 $49296 €40000 Un paysage avec une ville fortifiee sur une colline, un estuaire dans le (15x19cm-6x7in) fond. 17-Dec-3 Christie's, Paris #19/R est:15000-20000

WITTEL, Gaspar van (attrib) (1653-1736) Dutch
£8235 $14000 €12023 Italian town with boats moored on the riverbank with elegant figures and peasants (20x36cm-8x14in) 19-Nov-3 Bonhams & Butterfields, San Francisco #13/R

WITTEL, Gaspar van (circle) (1653-1736) Dutch
£18000 $32400 €26280 Venice, view of the Riva Degli Schiavoni with the Palazzo Ducale (50x108cm-20x43in) init.verso. 22-Apr-4 Sotheby's, London #122/R est:15000-20000

WITTEL, Gaspar van (style) (1653-1736) Dutch
£15493 $26803 €22000 Florence (65x88cm-26x35in) i. 11-Dec-3 Dr Fritz Nagel, Stuttgart #497/R est:12000
£28000 $51240 €40880 View of Vaprio d'Adda (58x111cm-23x44in) 8-Jul-4 Sotheby's, London #176/R est:20000-30000

WITTERSTATTER, Paul (20th C) ?
£600 $1092 €900 View of Nierstadt-am-Rhein (57x80cm-22x31in) s. 1-Jul-4 Van Ham, Cologne #1671

WITTING, Gustavo (1827-?) Italian
Works on paper
£450 $752 €657 River Arno, Florence (19x32cm-7x13in) s.d.1850 W/C. 14-Oct-3 Bonhams, Knightsbridge #49/R

WITTKAMP, Arnold (1827-1900) Dutch
£323 $600 €472 Crossroads (61x102cm-24x40in) s. painted c.1870. 7-Mar-4 Treadway Gallery, Cincinnati #521/R

WITTKAMP, Johann Bernhard (1820-1885) German
£671 $1242 €1000 Pious maiden (54x43cm-21x17in) s. 15-Mar-4 Sotheby's, Amsterdam #111 est:800-1200

WITTON, Frederick (20th C) American
£396 $650 €574 Number one in the fog, harbour scene (51x61cm-20x24in) s. 4-Jun-3 Alderfer's, Hatfield #282/R

WITZ, Dan (20th C) American
Works on paper
£213 $375 €311 Fist (32x22cm-13x9in) s.d.1983 verso mixed media on canvas. 23-May-4 Bonhams & Butterfields, Los Angeles #7081/R

WIX, Henry Otto (1866-1922) American
Works on paper
£925 $1600 €1351 Yosemite Falls (69x48cm-27x19in) s. pencil W/C. 10-Dec-3 Bonhams & Butterfields, San Francisco #6186/R est:2500-3500
£925 $1600 €1351 Half Dome in the morning, Yosemite (52x74cm-20x29in) s. pencil W/C. 10-Dec-3 Bonhams & Butterfields, San Francisco #6185/R est:2500-3500

WJUSCHIN, Alexander (1835-1904) Russian?
£1408 $2338 €2000 Sailing ship in storm (25x31cm-10x12in) s.cyrillic da.1857. 16-Jun-3 Dorotheum, Vienna #142/R est:2200-2500

WLCEK, Franz (20th C) Austrian
Works on paper
£2098 $3566 €3000 Donau meadow (45x65cm-18x26in) mono.d.73 mixed media. 26-Nov-3 Dorotheum, Vienna #230/R est:2000-3000

WLERICK, Robert (1882-1944) French
Sculpture
£2568 $4519 €3800 Portrait de Corbin (33cm-13in) s. num.3/10 pat bronze marble base. 18-May-4 Christie's, Paris #45/R est:2500-3500
£3586 $5953 €5200 Buste de Therese (56cm-22in) s. black pat bronze prov.exhib.lit. 2-Oct-3 Sotheby's, Paris #148/R est:6000
£3716 $6652 €5500 Buste feminin (58cm-23in) s. num.5/10 bronze Cast Thinot. 4-May-4 Calmels Cohen, Paris #223/R est:3000-4000
£9310 $15455 €13500 Lulu Lapalue (77cm-30in) s.st.f.Valsuani brown pat bronze prov.lit. 2-Oct-3 Sotheby's, Paris #145/R est:15000
£17241 $28621 €25000 Rolande (84cm-33in) s. num.8/10 brown pat bronze prov.exhib.lit. 2-Oct-3 Sotheby's, Paris #144/R est:15000

WOAKES, Maude (19/20th C) British
Works on paper
£280 $468 €409 Elegant couple (26x19cm-10x7in) s.d.1892 W/C. 12-Nov-3 Sotheby's, Olympia #118/R

WOBRING, Franz (1862-?) German
£1887 $3509 €2755 Girl with pink cheeks and high necked blouse. Portrait of lady (66x47cm-26x19in) s. double-sided. 2-Mar-4 Rasmussen, Copenhagen #1622/R est:20000 (D.KR 21000)

WOCHER, Marquard (1760-1830) Swiss
Works on paper
£474 $849 €692 Home of the hermit Sanct Immer (15x20cm-6x8in) s. W/C pen. 13-May-4 Stuker, Bern #9208/R (S.FR 1100)
£867 $1560 €1300 Ruins of Gothic church (19x26cm-7x10in) bears sig. Indian ink brush on pencil. 24-Apr-4 Reiss & Sohn, Konigstein #5578/R

WODZINOWSKY, Wincenty (1866-1940) Polish
£2874 $4973 €4196 Village pathway (47x67cm-19x26in) s.d.94. 14-Dec-3 Agra, Warsaw #26/R est:18000 (P.Z 19000)

WOELFLE, Arthur William (1873-1936) American
£245 $450 €358 Floral still life (20x25cm-8x10in) s. board. 25-Jun-4 Freeman, Philadelphia #227/R

WOERFFEL, Abraham C F (19/20th C) ?
Sculpture
£1325 $2411 €2000 Departure (28cm-11in) i. pat bronze exec. c.1900. 18-Jun-4 Bolland & Marotz, Bremen #1065/R est:900

WOESTIJNE, G van de (1881-1947) Belgian
£1348 $2250 €1900 Vue de Bruges (81x101cm-32x40in) s.indis.d.27 cardboard. 17-Jun-3 Vanderkindere, Brussels #178 est:700-1000

WOESTIJNE, Gustave van de (1881-1947) Belgian
£34965 $59441 €50000 Portrait de jeune femme assise (120x90cm-47x35in) s. 1-Dec-3 Palais de Beaux Arts, Brussels #134/R est:50000-75000
Works on paper
£43357 $73706 €62000 Jeune femme au torse nu (108x67cm-43x26in) s. mixed media canvas exhib. 1-Dec-3 Palais de Beaux Arts, Brussels #142/R est:62000-87000

WOESTIJNE, Maxime van de (1911-2000) Belgian
£658 $1211 €1000 Still life with apples and pears (41x62cm-16x24in) s.d.1949. 22-Jun-4 Palais de Beaux Arts, Brussels #320/R
£2857 $5200 €4200 Les contours de la Vie (50x40cm-20x16in) s.d.1969 s.i.d.verso board. 3-Feb-4 Christie's, Amsterdam #570/R est:2000-3000
Works on paper
£433 $784 €650 Figure (32x22cm-13x9in) s.d.1982 gouache. 30-Mar-4 Campo, Vlaamse Kaai #180
£467 $835 €700 Composition I (44x54cm-17x21in) s.d.1975 gouache. 15-May-4 De Vuyst, Lokeren #347
£1119 $1902 €1600 Paysage surrealiste (31x26cm-12x10in) s.d.1973 gouache exhib. 1-Dec-3 Palais de Beaux Arts, Brussels #129 est:700-1000

WOHL, Mildred (20th C) American
£1104 $1800 €1601 Suddenly black II (119x91cm-47x36in) s.i.verso masonite. 19-Jul-3 New Orleans Auction, New Orleans #987/R est:1200-1800

WOHLBERG, Alfred (fl.1880-1920) American
£480 $850 €701 Extensive landscape under clouds (25x41cm-10x16in) s. board. 2-May-4 Bonhams & Butterfields, San Francisco #1050/R

WOHLERS, Julius (1867-1953) German
£1793 $3317 €2600 Wood (54x40cm-21x16in) 14-Feb-4 Hans Stahl, Hamburg #170/R est:1900

WOHLGEMUTH, Daniel (1876-1967) German
£333 $603 €500 Italian landscape near Terracina (50x64cm-20x25in) s. canvas on board. 1-Apr-4 Van Ham, Cologne #1712/R
£464 $844 €700 Harbour scene (42x53cm-17x21in) s. 18-Jun-4 Bolland & Marotz, Bremen #795/R

WOHLK, Ernst (1894-1977) German?
Works on paper
£472 $789 €680 Death's head (24x33cm-9x13in) s.d. gouache. 24-Oct-3 Ketterer, Hamburg #1168/R

WOHLRAB, Hans (1905-1978) Austrian
£352 $609 €500 Hands holding a tankard (40x50cm-16x20in) s.d.47 fibreboard. 10-Dec-3 Hugo Ruef, Munich #2524

WOHNER, Louis (1888-1958) German
£470 $860 €700 Meadow flowers in a vase (66x56cm-26x22in) s. 8-Jul-4 Allgauer, Kempten #2288/R
£704 $1261 €1000 Farmhouse in a winter landscape (65x86cm-26x34in) s. lit. 8-Jan-4 Allgauer, Kempten #2587/R
£1033 $1870 €1550 Chiemsee with Fraueninsel (51x66cm-20x26in) 3-Apr-4 Badum, Bamberg #47/R est:180056

WOICESKE, Ronau William (1887-1953) American
£1000 $1600 €1460 Mountain landscape with house (51x61cm-20x24in) s. 21-Sep-3 Grogan, Boston #43/R

WOITSCH, Emmy (attrib) (1894-1981) Austrian
Works on paper
£333 $597 €500 Corn maiden (18x24cm-7x9in) W/C. 13-May-4 Dorotheum, Linz #549

WOJCIECHOWSKY, Agatha (1896-1986) American?
Works on paper
£1437 $2400 €2098 Untitled (37x27cm-15x11in) s. W/C executed 1964 prov. 11-Nov-3 Christie's, Rockefeller NY #186/R est:200-300

WOJTKIEWICZ, Dennis (20th C) American
£205 $375 €308 Reflections (132x91cm-52x36in) 10-Jul-4 Hindman, Chicago #579/R

£301 $550 €452 Still life in Portage II (74x109cm-29x43in) oil on paper. 10-Jul-4 Hindman, Chicago #579a/R

WOLCHONOK, Louis (1898-1973) American
£291 $520 €425 Posing in the artists studio (127x91cm-50x36in) s. 8-Jan-4 James Julia, Fairfield #1081/R

WOLCK, Nikolaus (1887-1950) German
£333 $523 €480 Apple blossom (55x40cm-22x16in) s.d.37 board. 30-Aug-3 Hans Stahl, Toestorf #97
£1806 $2835 €2600 Colourful flower garden (95x89cm-37x35in) s.d.38. 30-Aug-3 Hans Stahl, Toestorf #98/R est:2500
Works on paper
£766 $1240 €1111 The artist's house by Aabenraa fjord (36x37cm-14x15in) s.i.d.1933 gouache. 4-Aug-3 Rasmussen, Vejle #667/R (D.KR 8000)

WOLCK, Preben (1925-2000) Danish
£303 $485 €442 Autumn (75x120cm-30x47in) s. d.1977 verso. 22-Sep-3 Rasmussen, Vejle #636/R (D.KR 3200)
£322 $516 €470 Winter (75x120cm-30x47in) s. d.1977 verso. 22-Sep-3 Rasmussen, Vejle #634/R (D.KR 3400)
£397 $711 €580 We have often seen that (80x100cm-31x39in) s. d.1967-68 verso. 12-Jan-4 Rasmussen, Vejle #611 (D.KR 4200)

WOLCOTT, Harold C (20th C) American
£441 $700 €644 Artist's studio (61x51cm-24x20in) s. canvas on board. 12-Sep-3 Skinner, Boston #353/R

WOLD, Roar (1926-1990) Norwegian
£1382 $2529 €2018 Composition (58x100cm-23x39in) s. d.1961 verso panel. 7-Jun-4 Blomqvist, Oslo #432/R est:20000-25000 (N.KR 17000)
£3042 $5446 €4441 Composition (120x160cm-47x63in) s. exhib. 22-Mar-4 Blomqvist, Oslo #625/R est:25000-35000 (N.KR 38000)
Works on paper
£285 $525 €416 Southern landscape (107x78cm-42x31in) s. W/C. 29-Mar-4 Blomqvist, Lysaker #1362 (N.KR 3600)

WOLD-TORNE, Oluf (1867-1919) Norwegian
£2927 $5356 €4273 In the sunshine, Sandoen (95x114cm-37x45in) s. exhib. 7-Jun-4 Blomqvist, Oslo #379/R est:40000-60000 (N.KR 36000)
Works on paper
£2146 $3755 €3133 Decorative fantasy figures (60x46cm-24x18in) s. two i.d.1910 verso W/C seven. 16-Dec-3 Grev Wedels Plass, Oslo #125/R est:30000-50000 (N.KR 25000)

WOLDE, Paul (1885-?) German?
£625 $994 €900 Hamburg harbour (75x100cm-30x39in) s. 13-Sep-3 Quittenbaum, Hamburg #64/R

WOLF (?) ?
Sculpture
£1100 $1870 €1606 Boar (30x46cm-12x18in) with sig.d.1876 brown pat. bronze. 27-Nov-3 Christie's, Kensington #283/R est:1000-1500

WOLF, Albert (1863-?) German
£351 $639 €530 Summer landscape in the Black Forest (75x52cm-30x20in) s.d.1914. 17-Jun-4 Frank Peege, Freiburg #1173/R

WOLF, August (1842-1915) German
£881 $1498 €1286 Rowers returning home (155x109cm-61x43in) 5-Nov-3 Dobiaschofsky, Bern #1060/R (S.FR 2000)

WOLF, Caspar (1735-1798) Swiss
£8734 $15895 €12752 Un pont sur l'Aar, au pied de la Montagne de Grimsel (30x20cm-12x8in) W/C on pencil. 17-Jun-4 Kornfeld, Bern #122/R est:15000 (S.FR 20000)
£17937 $29238 €26188 Lauenental waterfalls in early spring (52x72cm-20x28in) s. lit. 29-Sep-3 Christie's, Zurich #1/R est:25000-35000 (S.FR 40000)
£19651 $35764 €28690 Rocky landscape (17x27cm-7x11in) s. panel exhib. 17-Jun-4 Kornfeld, Bern #119/R est:30000 (S.FR 45000)
Works on paper
£7860 $14306 €11476 Landscape with riding party resting (37x53cm-15x21in) sepia brush wash on pencil. 17-Jun-4 Kornfeld, Bern #120 est:20000 (S.FR 18000)

WOLF, Caspar (attrib) (1735-1798) Swiss
£1972 $3451 €2800 Personnages sur le bord de falaise (22x29cm-9x11in) canvas on panel. 17-Dec-3 Piasa, Paris #43/R est:3000-5000
£7391 $13526 €10791 Le Cervin (76x104cm-30x41in) prov. 5-Jun-4 Galerie du Rhone, Sion #526/R est:8000-10000 (S.FR 17000)
Works on paper
£3287 $5587 €4700 Chute d'eau sur le Wasserberg dans le canton de Schwitz (34x23cm-13x9in) i. verso W/C gouache Indian ink gold board. 21-Nov-3 Reiss & Sohn, Konigstein #153/R est:2500

WOLF, Franz Xaver (1896-1989) Austrian
£1200 $2004 €1752 Still life of flowers with orange lily (50x40cm-20x16in) s. panel. 12-Nov-3 Sotheby's, Olympia #233/R est:1000-1500
£2654 $4750 €3875 Gentleman reading in his library (50x40cm-20x16in) s.i. panel. 6-May-4 Doyle, New York #61/R est:4000-6000
£5500 $10010 €8030 Anemones and lilies with other wild alpine flowers and butterflies (65x50cm-26x20in) s. panel. 15-Jun-4 Sotheby's, London #17/R est:4000-6000
£6000 $10920 €8760 Morning-glory, daisies, wild roses and pansies in a vase (64x50cm-25x20in) s. panel. 15-Jun-4 Sotheby's, London #18/R est:4000-6000

WOLF, Galen R (1889-1976) American
£370 $700 €540 Figures in church interior (28x23cm-11x9in) s. masonite. 17-Feb-4 John Moran, Pasadena #23/R

WOLF, Georg (1882-1962) German
£265 $482 €400 Young boy with a horse (56x70cm-22x28in) s. 18-Jun-4 Bolland & Marotz, Bremen #847/R
£278 $439 €400 Carthorse (50x60cm-20x24in) s. lit. 19-Sep-3 Schloss Ahlden, Ahlden #1560/R
£300 $543 €450 Peasant in field with horse cart (18x24cm-7x9in) s. panel. 1-Apr-4 Van Ham, Cologne #1714
£313 $509 €450 Bush in bloom (36x48cm-14x19in) s. board. 26-Sep-3 Bolland & Marotz, Bremen #703/R
£533 $971 €800 Farmers and their horses entering a village (40x50cm-16x20in) s. panel. 1-Jul-4 Van Ham, Cologne #1672
£533 $971 €800 Two farmers with four horses (37x51cm-15x20in) s. board. 1-Jul-4 Van Ham, Cologne #1673
£533 $971 €800 Portrait of a harnessed carthorse (60x70cm-24x28in) s. 1-Jul-4 Van Ham, Cologne #1674
£559 $934 €800 Peasant with horses walking home along lower Rhine (32x46cm-13x18in) s. 28-Jun-3 Bolland & Marotz, Bremen #817/R
£628 $1087 €917 Cattle in meadow (65x90cm-26x35in) s. 15-Dec-3 Lilla Bukowskis, Stockholm #506 (S.KR 8000)
£694 $1146 €1000 Portrait of two cows by summer wood (76x100cm-30x39in) 3-Jul-3 Van Ham, Cologne #1514
£1301 $2212 €1900 Thekla and Pascha (32x42cm-13x17in) i. canvas on panel. 8-Nov-3 Hans Stahl, Toestorf #18 est:700
£2053 $3736 €3100 Shepherd boy with two cows under a tree by the river (80x100cm-31x39in) s.d.1912. 19-Jun-4 Bergmann, Erlangen #837 est:2500

WOLF, J (19th C) German?
£2778 $4583 €4000 Mother and daughter in interior (53x47cm-21x19in) s. 3-Jul-3 Van Ham, Cologne #1512 est:1400

WOLF, Joseph (1820-1899) German
Works on paper
£380 $646 €555 Study of a long-eared owl on a wall, with butterflies (61x48cm-24x19in) s.d.Dec 1872 pencil chl wash prov. 19-Nov-3 Tennants, Leyburn #914
£500 $860 €730 Unwanted intruder (25x37cm-10x15in) W/C prov. 3-Dec-3 Christie's, Kensington #150

WOLF, Ludwig (1776-1832) German
Works on paper
£923 $1588 €1348 Turkish warriors (34x45cm-13x18in) s.i.d.1832 W/C. 3-Dec-3 AB Stockholms Auktionsverk #2629/R (S.KR 12000)

WOLF, Max (19/20th C) German
£545 $911 €780 On the Neckar (50x36cm-20x14in) board. 10-Oct-3 Winterberg, Heidelberg #831

WOLF, Rudolf Robert (1877-1940) German
£692 $1239 €1010 Interesting reading (59x49cm-23x19in) s. 12-May-4 Dunbar Sloane, Wellington #104/R est:3000-5000 (NZ.D 2000)

WOLFAERTS, Artus (1581-c.1641) Flemish
£9000 $15570 €13140 Saint Jerome in his study (64x49cm-25x19in) panel prov. 9-Dec-3 Sotheby's, Olympia #308/R est:4000-6000
£13000 $23790 €18980 Saint James the Greater (105x90cm-41x35in) 8-Jul-4 Sotheby's, London #253/R est:8000-12000
£21053 $38737 €32000 Adoration of the Magi (118x170cm-46x67in) prov. 24-Jun-4 Tajan, Paris #12/R est:18000-20000
£41899 $75000 €61173 Saint Andrew (116x91cm-46x36in) i. prov.lit. 27-May-4 Sotheby's, New York #15/R est:80000-120000

WOLFE, Ada (1878-1945) American
£1319 $2400 €1926 Tea time (102x76cm-40x30in) s. 19-Jun-4 Jackson's, Cedar Falls #171/R est:2500-3500

WOLFE, Byron B (1904-1973) American
£1429 $2300 €2086 Dawn raid for pony soldier horses (20x23cm-8x9in) 22-Aug-3 Altermann Galleries, Santa Fe #102
Works on paper
£497 $800 €726 Sign of spring (8x10cm-3x4in) W/C. 22-Aug-3 Altermann Galleries, Santa Fe #105
£932 $1500 €1361 Palo Duro Canyon, General MacKenzie's scout (11x16cm-4x6in) W/C. 22-Aug-3 Altermann Galleries, Santa Fe #101
£1801 $2900 €2629 Trouble on a rope (16x20cm-6x8in) W/C. 22-Aug-3 Altermann Galleries, Santa Fe #104

WOLFE, Edward (1897-1982) British
£300 $519 €438 Abstract composition (36x46cm-14x18in) board. 9-Dec-3 Rosebery Fine Art, London #620/R
£1300 $2288 €1898 Abstract (51x66cm-20x26in) board painted c.1940 prov. 19-May-4 Sotheby's, Olympia #282/R est:1000-1500
£1800 $3096 €2628 Thassos, Greece (41x51cm-16x20in) s. s.i.d.1963 verso canvas on board. 3-Dec-3 Christie's, Kensington #466/R est:2000-3000
£2700 $4320 €3942 Mermaid (167x106cm-66x42in) s.d.1950. 19-May-3 Bruton Knowles, Cheltenham #249/R est:1500-2000
£4200 $7770 €6132 Still life of flowers (51x35cm-20x14in) s.i. 11-Feb-4 Sotheby's, Olympia #157/R est:2500-3500
£6500 $11440 €9490 Mermaid (168x107cm-66x42in) s. 19-May-4 Sotheby's, Olympia #215/R est:4000-6000

Works on paper
£400 $724 €584 Coastal landscape at Portmeirion (47x56cm-19x22in) s. W/C. 2-Apr-4 Moore Allen & Innocent, Cirencester #726
£400 $724 €584 Eve seated with apple. Head study of a girl (33x24cm-13x9in) s. i.verso double-sided. 2-Apr-4 Moore Allen & Innocent, Cirencester #728/R
£480 $869 €701 Portrait of a girl (53x41cm-21x16in) s.d.1st July 1955 black pen. 2-Apr-4 Moore Allen & Innocent, Cirencester #724/R
£600 $1032 €876 Fishing boats on the beach (30x46cm-12x18in) s. pen black ink W/C. 3-Dec-3 Christie's, Kensington #693/R

WOLFE, George (1834-1890) British
Works on paper
£600 $1104 €876 Heidelberg. Statdt and Schloss, Heidelberg (36x53cm-14x21in) s.i.d.1862 pencil W/C pair. 25-Mar-4 Christie's, Kensington #104/R
£600 $1104 €876 Sandsend (18x27cm-7x11in) i. W/C. 22-Jun-4 Bonhams, Knightsbridge #45/R
£750 $1373 €1095 Yarmouth (16x52cm-6x20in) W/C htd white pair. 8-Jul-4 Lawrence, Crewkerne #1546/R
£3000 $5490 €4380 Coastal scenes with figures and shipping (22x31cm-9x12in) s. one d.1855 W/C pair. 6-Apr-4 Bristol Auction Rooms #477/R est:1000-1500

WOLFE, Steve (1955-) American
£14525 $26000 €21207 Untitled, revolver (39x38cm-15x15in) oil enamel lithograph modeling paste board prov.exhib. 12-May-4 Christie's, Rockefeller NY #319/R est:20000-30000
Sculpture
£1267 $2267 €1900 Andy Warhol diaries. wood trompe-l'oeil lacquer. 12-May-4 Chochon-Barre & Allardi, Paris #101 est:150-200

WOLFF, Cornelis de (1889-1963) Dutch
£280 $467 €400 Farmhouses in a landscape (50x60cm-20x24in) s. 30-Jun-3 Sotheby's, Amsterdam #339

WOLFF, Emil (1802-1879) German
Sculpture
£8077 $13892 €11792 Boy draped in skin from beast of prey (99cm-39in) s.i. marble. 7-Dec-3 Uppsala Auktionskammare, Uppsala #355/R est:25000-30000 (S.KR 105000)
£8200 $15006 €11972 Bust of man (81cm-32in) s. marble lit. 9-Jul-4 Sotheby's, London #104/R est:3000-5000

WOLFF, Eugen (1873-1937) German
£280 $502 €409 Interior (80x64cm-31x25in) s.d.1920. 13-May-4 Stuker, Bern #838/R (S.FR 650)
£430 $783 €650 Woodland scene in autumn (100x76cm-39x30in) s. 18-Jun-4 Bolland & Marotz, Bremen #796/R
£1533 $2760 €2300 Oven room in Filseck Castle (81x54cm-32x21in) s.d.1929. 26-Apr-4 Rieber, Stuttgart #1217/R est:1380

WOLFF, Gustav H (1863-1935) American/German
£436 $750 €637 Farm in winter (30x41cm-12x16in) s.d.1905. 6-Dec-3 Selkirks, St. Louis #180/R
Sculpture
£3846 $6538 €5500 Reclining horse (31x49x41cm-12x19x16in) black pat.artificial stone prov.exhib.lit. 26-Nov-3 Lempertz, Koln #1026/R est:7500

WOLFF, Hermann (1841-?) German
£537 $983 €800 Young shepherds with cows in the mountains (25x37cm-10x15in) s. 8-Jul-4 Allgauer, Kempten #2294/R

WOLFF, Jose (1884-1964) Belgian
£303 $561 €440 Ferme en Ardennes (34x41cm-13x16in) s. 19-Jan-4 Horta, Bruxelles #273
£331 $603 €500 Vue de vallee (33x43cm-13x17in) s. panel. 16-Jun-4 Hotel des Ventes Mosan, Brussels #206
£340 $569 €480 Sous-bois en automne (38x46cm-15x18in) s. panel. 15-Oct-3 Hotel des Ventes Mosan, Brussels #216
£352 $609 €500 Vue de Bruges (27x36cm-11x14in) s. oil paper. 10-Dec-3 Hotel des Ventes Mosan, Brussels #245
£608 $1089 €900 Chemin en automne (82x60cm-32x24in) s. 10-May-4 Horta, Bruxelles #26
£634 $1096 €900 Paysages (30x41cm-12x16in) s.i. one d.1951 verso pair. 10-Dec-3 Hotel des Ventes Mosan, Brussels #217
£878 $1572 €1300 Cours d'eau en automne (50x70cm-20x28in) s. 10-May-4 Horta, Bruxelles #25

WOLFF, Karoly (1869-?) Hungarian
£1268 $2028 €1800 Reclining female nude (67x110cm-26x43in) s. lit. 19-Sep-3 Karlheinz Kaupp, Staufen #2118/R est:1800
£3000 $5460 €4380 Reclining nude (67x110cm-26x43in) s. 16-Jun-4 Christie's, Kensington #264/R est:3000-5000

WOLFF, Richard (1880-?) Austrian
Works on paper
£390 $632 €550 Dolomiti innevate (41x53cm-16x21in) s. mixed media board. 22-May-3 Stadion, Trieste #263/R

WOLFF, Robert Jay (1905-1977) American
Works on paper
£471 $800 €688 Untitled (23x33cm-9x13in) s.d.1936 W/C ink. 9-Nov-3 Wright, Chicago #304

WOLFF, Willy (1905-) German
£9790 $16643 €14000 Teresa V.K. (122x94cm-48x37in) s.d.19 6 9 s.d.Aug-Sept 1969 verso panel exhib. 29-Nov-3 Villa Grisebach, Berlin #335/R est:8000-10000

WOLFGANG, Alexander (1894-1970) German
£338 $605 €500 Woodland pond with punt (37x59cm-15x23in) s. tempera on board. 6-May-4 Michael Zeller, Lindau #942
£533 $960 €800 Outdoor festival (48x39cm-19x15in) s. panel double-sided. 24-Apr-4 Dr Lehr, Berlin #515/R

WOLFHAGEN, Ernst (1907-1992) German
£903 $1508 €1300 Man with dancer (96x49cm-38x19in) mono.d. 25-Oct-3 Dr Lehr, Berlin #551/R

WOLFLE, Franz Xavier (1887-1972) German
£313 $509 €450 Peasant with pipe (23x20cm-9x8in) s. panel. 25-Sep-3 Neumeister, Munich #2905/R
£621 $1148 €900 Peasant with pipe (13x18cm-5x7in) s. panel. 13-Feb-4 Auktionhaus Georg Rehm, Augsburg #8197
£908 $1570 €1326 Portrait of a man smoking (24x20cm-9x8in) s. panel painted c.1930. 14-Dec-3 Agra, Warsaw #56/R est:4000 (P.Z 6000)
£2000 $3660 €2920 Tyrolean characters (18x14cm-7x6in) s. panel set of four. 8-Apr-4 Christie's, Kensington #64/R est:2000-3000

WOLFLI, Adolf (1864-1930) Swiss
Works on paper
£3095 $4952 €4488 Design (21x28cm-8x11in) i. verso pencil col pen. 15-May-3 Stuker, Bern #1585/R est:6000-8000 (S.FR 6500)
£3500 $6370 €5110 Untitled (47x30cm-19x12in) s.d.1926 i.verso col pencil pastel. 4-Feb-4 Sotheby's, Olympia #194/R est:4000-6000
£4977 $8312 €7266 Composition (34x25cm-13x10in) col chk i. verso lit. 24-Jun-3 Germann, Zurich #47/R est:10000-15000 (S.FR 11000)
£6193 $10342 €8980 Rudolf (33x22cm-13x9in) i. col pen pencil. 19-Jun-3 Kornfeld, Bern #1054/R est:12500 (S.FR 13500)
£6769 $12319 €9883 Five flowers (47x31cm-19x12in) col pen. 17-Jun-4 Kornfeld, Bern #827/R est:10000 (S.FR 15500)
£16143 $26314 €23569 Holy Centtenaaia (50x76cm-20x30in) s.i. pencil col pen prov. 29-Sep-3 Christie's, Zurich #85/R est:40000-60000 (S.FR 36000)
£30568 $56245 €44629 Page from Book No 13 (100x72cm-39x28in) s.d.1915 pencil on newspaper exhib.lit. 8-Jun-4 Germann, Zurich #37/R est:30000-35000 (S.FR 70000)

WOLFRAM, F (19th C) Austrian
£1042 $1771 €1500 Children sitting on rocking horse (110x91cm-43x36in) s.d.1846. 28-Oct-3 Dorotheum, Vienna #11/R est:3000-3500

WOLFS, Hubert (1899-1937) Belgian
£600 $1074 €900 Night spider (40x50cm-16x20in) s. panel. 15-May-4 De Vuyst, Lokeren #409

WOLFSEN, Aleijda (1648-1690) Dutch
£2262 $3914 €3303 Jeune homme au perroquet (42x32cm-17x13in) s. panel prov. 12-Dec-3 Galerie du Rhone, Sion #163/R est:7000-9000 (S.FR 5000)

WOLFSFELD, Erich (19/20th C) ?
£280 $504 €409 Man with white horse (38x56cm-15x22in) s. paper. 20-Jan-4 Bonhams, Knightsbridge #91

WOLFSON, Alan (1948-) American
Sculpture
£3087 $5526 €4600 Terminal diner (37x52x52cm-15x20x20in) diorama mixed media electrics plexiglass box exec. 1990 prov. 27-May-4 Sotheby's, Paris #253/R est:3000-4000

WOLFTHORN, Julie (1868-?) ?
£2303 $4168 €3500 An interior with blossoming magnolia in a vase (130x100cm-51x39in) s. 19-Apr-4 Glerum, Amsterdam #305/R est:3500-4500

WOLGERS, Dan (1955-) Swedish
Photographs
£2637 $4668 €3850 Here is the end of the public road I (29x49cm-11x19in) s.d.1995 num.46/75 verso cibachrome exhib.prov. 27-Apr-4 AB Stockholms Auktionsverk #922/R est:25000-30000 (S.KR 36000)
Sculpture
£2039 $3467 €2977 From the year 1991 light cocoons now comes butterflies (38cm-15in) s.d.1998 lightbulbs wood exhib.lit. 5-Nov-3 AB Stockholms Auktionsverk #1029/R est:25000-30000 (S.KR 27000)
£6007 $10633 €8770 Globe of the world (33cm-13in) s.d.1997 clear glass globe metal wood base exhib.lit. 27-Apr-4 AB Stockholms Auktionsverk #1012/R est:40000-50000 (S.KR 82000)
£8791 $15560 €12835 He's lost an ear (25cm-10in) object toy dog executed 1993 exhib.lit. 27-Apr-4 AB Stockholms Auktionsverk #969/R est:100000-125000 (S.KR 120000)

WOLKERS, Jan (1925-) Dutch
Works on paper
£1133 $2085 €1700 Untitled (43x80cm-17x31in) s.d.1962 verso mixed media plywood. 9-Jun-4 Christie's, Amsterdam #189/R est:1500-2000

WOLKONSKY, Prince Piotr (c.1901-) Russian
£3000 $5370 €4380 View of St. Tropez (60x73cm-24x29in) s.d.1927. 26-May-4 Sotheby's, Olympia #428/R est:3000-4000
£15493 $26803 €22000 Mosquee de Tlemcen (65x81cm-26x32in) s.d.1924. 15-Dec-3 Gros & Delettrez, Paris #55/R est:8000-10000

WOLLASTON, John (jnr) (fl.1738-1775) British
£3100 $5704 €4526 Portrait of Lady Nellie Montrose (34x26cm-13x10in) painted c.1780. 11-Jun-4 Keys, Aylsham #487/R est:2000-3000

WOLLEN, William Barns (1857-1936) British
£300 $531 €438 Royalist (51x36cm-20x14in) s.d.1905. 28-Apr-4 Halls, Shrewsbury #496

WOLLHEIM, Gert (1894-1974) American/German
Sculpture
£1119 $1924 €1600 Bust of Hasso Wollheim (49cm-19in) pat bronze st.f.Gladenbeck. 5-Dec-3 Bolland & Marotz, Bremen #1121 est:1600
Works on paper
£3667 $6563 €5500 The rainy day hindered the bathers (26x34cm-10x13in) bears sig. i. pen W/C. 15-May-4 Bassenge, Berlin #7206/R est:2800
£4545 $7727 €6500 Girl walking (34x26cm-13x10in) s.d.1921 Indian ink brush W/C. 26-Nov-3 Lempertz, Koln #1027/R est:5000-6000
£5667 $10143 €8500 Kabarel (34x26cm-13x10in) s.i.d. Indian ink brush gouache opaque white gold silver prov. 14-May-4 Ketterer, Munich #214/R est:8000-10000

WOLMANS, Jacques (1919-1991) Belgian
£414 $766 €600 Port Breton (40x50cm-16x20in) s. panel. 19-Jan-4 Horta, Bruxelles #326
£448 $829 €650 Maison au bord de phare (40x50cm-16x20in) s. 19-Jan-4 Horta, Bruxelles #327
£493 $893 €750 Ete Breton (50x60cm-20x24in) s.i.verso. 19-Apr-4 Horta, Bruxelles #253
£559 $1012 €850 Paysage de Bretagne (40x50cm-16x20in) s.i.verso. 19-Apr-4 Horta, Bruxelles #252

WOLMARK, Alfred (1877-1961) British
£250 $463 €365 Chamonix (30x40cm-12x16in) board. 11-Mar-4 Christie's, Kensington #105
£600 $1092 €876 Still life with tulips (46x35cm-18x14in) indis.s. 1-Jul-4 Christie's, Kensington #141/R
£1200 $2040 €1752 Extensive landscape with children, possibly South Wales (33x41cm-13x16in) s.d.1932 i.verso board. 18-Nov-3 Bonhams, Leeds #122/R est:500-700
£1250 $2025 €1813 Alpine village with cars (41x30cm-16x12in) canvasboard. 30-Jul-3 Hamptons Fine Art, Godalming #161/R est:1500-2000
£1800 $3096 €2628 Cow in a farmyard (33x40cm-13x16in) s.d.32 board. 3-Dec-3 Christie's, Kensington #507/R est:2000-3000
£3000 $5190 €4380 Still life (53x43cm-21x17in) mono.d.1924-35 panel. 11-Dec-3 Lyon & Turnbull, Edinburgh #112/R est:3000-4000
£3073 $5500 €4487 Self portrait with Van Gogh's self portrait (58x48cm-23x19in) d.1941 panel exhib. 18-Mar-4 Sotheby's, New York #111/R est:5000-7000
£3500 $6475 €5110 Woman in white (76x64cm-30x25in) s. 11-Mar-4 Christie's, Kensington #17/R est:4000-6000
£3800 $7030 €5548 Alpine village with cars (40x30cm-16x12in) i.verso cardboard prov. 11-Mar-4 Christie's, Kensington #102/R est:1500-2000
£6704 $12000 €9788 Cubist self portrait (98x67cm-39x26in) s. panel painted c.1916. 18-Mar-4 Sotheby's, New York #110/R est:12000-15000
Works on paper
£550 $919 €803 Studies of female nudes (72x54cm-28x21in) s.indis.i. chl pair. 16-Oct-3 Christie's, Kensington #174/R
£2200 $3652 €3212 Nude study (68x37cm-27x15in) s. blk chk. 30-Sep-3 Sotheby's, London #3 est:300-400

WOLPERDING, Friedrich Ernst (1815-1888) German
£414 $691 €600 Hilly landscape (50x70cm-20x28in) s.d.1843. 9-Jul-3 Hugo Ruef, Munich #245

WOLS, Wolfgang (1913-1951) German
Works on paper
£6466 $11573 €9440 Untitled (22x14cm-9x6in) s. W/C pastel. 12-May-4 Dobiaschofsky, Bern #1069/R est:15000 (S.FR 15000)
£7500 $13800 €10950 Monstres obsedants (29x23cm-11x9in) s. ink W/C exec c.1940-41 prov.exhib. 24-Jun-4 Sotheby's, London #217/R est:5000-7000
£18182 $30909 €26000 Untitled (12x8cm-5x3in) s. W/C Indian ink pen paper on board prov. 28-Nov-3 Villa Grisebach, Berlin #80/R est:20000-25000
£21000 $38220 €30660 Untitled (28x31cm-11x12in) s. W/C ink paper on board prov. 5-Feb-4 Christie's, London #121/R est:10000-15000

WOLSELEY, Garnet (1884-1967) British
£1100 $1969 €1606 Docks (25x30cm-10x12in) s. panel. 16-Mar-4 Bonhams, New Bond Street #3/R est:1000-1500
£2000 $3580 €2920 Looking out to sea (35x30cm-14x12in) s. 16-Mar-4 Bonhams, New Bond Street #4/R est:2000-3000
£17692 $30431 €25830 Girl playing with toys (115x140cm-45x55in) s. 3-Dec-3 AB Stockholms Auktionsverk #2591/R est:125000-150000 (S.KR 230000)

WOLSELEY, John Walter (1938-) Australian/British
£6911 $10850 €10021 Concerning the making of steel (122x380cm-48x150in) s.d.1993.94. 27-Aug-3 Christie's, Sydney #571/R est:18000-25000 (A.D 17000)
Works on paper
£264 $414 €383 Sheet steel making drawing IV (77x57cm-30x22in) s.d.93 pencil pastel W/C prov. 27-Aug-3 Christie's, Sydney #635 (A.D 650)
£325 $511 €471 Sketch and map of Port Hedland (57x67cm-22x26in) s.d.7.12.93 pencil W/C prov. 27-Aug-3 Christie's, Sydney #553/R (A.D 800)
£345 $542 €500 Sheet steel making drawing I (71x51cm-28x20in) s.d.23.11.93 pencil pastel W/C prov. 27-Aug-3 Christie's, Sydney #672a (A.D 850)
£772 $1212 €1119 Study for Mount Whaleback (60x89cm-24x35in) s.d.1.12.93 pastel W/C prov. 27-Aug-3 Christie's, Sydney #639 est:1200-1800 (A.D 1900)
£1951 $3063 €2829 Design painting for, concerning the making of steel (55x122cm-22x48in) s.d.Nov 15/93 pencil W/C pastel prov. 27-Aug-3 Christie's, Sydney #615 est:2000-3000 (A.D 4800)
£4959 $9174 €7240 Two weeks at Emily Gap - a survey (199x199cm-78x78in) s.d.July 3.17.1979 s.i.verso mixed media varnished paper on canvas. 15-Mar-4 Sotheby's, Melbourne #61/R est:8000-12000 (A.D 12000)
£6098 $9573 €8842 Marra Mamba (118x163cm-46x64in) s.i.d.93 pastel photo paper canvas mail bag prov. 27-Aug-3 Christie's, Sydney #628/R est:8000-12000 (A.D 15000)

WOLSFELD, Erich (20th C) British
Works on paper
£900 $1620 €1314 Three Donkeys (57x76cm-22x30in) s. W/C. 20-Jan-4 Bonhams, Knightsbridge #97

WOLSTENHOLME, Dean (jnr-attrib) (1798-1883) British
£351 $650 €512 Setter in landscape (8x10cm-3x4in) panel. 10-Feb-4 Doyle, New York #216/R

WOLSTENHOLME, Dean (snr) (1757-1837) British
£1429 $2600 €2086 Mail coach. Hull coach (41x61cm-16x24in) s.i. verso pair. 4-Feb-4 Christie's, Rockefeller NY #27/R est:2000-3000
£3200 $5856 €4672 Huntsmen, whippers in and hounds at covetside (55x78cm-22x31in) 28-Jul-4 Bonhams, Knightsbridge #95/R est:2000-3000
£4800 $8832 €7008 Market cart (36x46cm-14x18in) s. i.verso. 23-Mar-4 Bonhams, New Bond Street #38/R est:2000-3000
£7500 $12900 €10950 Essex hunt (64x77cm-25x30in) 3-Dec-3 Bonhams, Knightsbridge #166/R est:8000-12000

WOLTER, Hendrik Jan (1873-1952) Dutch
£349 $601 €500 White boat (15x26cm-6x10in) studio st. verso board. 7-Dec-3 Sotheby's, Amsterdam #701
£526 $968 €800 Rocky coast (40x32cm-16x13in) s. 22-Jun-4 Christie's, Amsterdam #466/R
£533 $976 €800 Canal, bridge and church in Venice (22x26cm-9x10in) i.d.1931 verso board. 7-Jun-4 Glerum, Amsterdam #56/R
£725 $1188 €1000 Rome (26x21cm-10x8in) s. studio st. verso board. 27-May-3 Sotheby's, Amsterdam #503/R est:1000-1500
£1067 $1952 €1600 Grand Canal, Venice (22x28cm-9x11in) i.d.1931 verso board. 7-Jun-4 Glerum, Amsterdam #63/R est:650-750
£1111 $1756 €1600 Sunset over San Gimignano (150x185cm-59x73in) s. exhib.lit. 2-Sep-3 Christie's, Amsterdam #381 est:3000-5000
£1200 $2196 €1800 View of Enkhuizen (21x27cm-8x11in) s. panel. 7-Jun-4 Glerum, Amsterdam #66/R est:800-1200
£1342 $2483 €2000 Farmer at work (71x56cm-28x22in) s. 15-Mar-4 Sotheby's, Amsterdam #214/R est:2000-3000
£1382 $2474 €2018 Oude Brik, Whitby (35x45cm-14x18in) s.i. panel. 4-May-4 Ritchie, Toronto #68/R est:2000-3000 (C.D 3400)
£1736 $2743 €2500 Pont Neuf, Paris (21x26cm-8x10in) s. s.i.verso plywood. 2-Sep-3 Christie's, Amsterdam #398 est:1500-2000
£2000 $3680 €3000 View of the city of London (21x26cm-8x10in) plywood. 9-Jun-4 Christie's, Amsterdam #58/R est:3000-5000
£2174 $3565 €3000 Inner harbour, Amsterdam (35x43cm-14x17in) studio st. verso board. 27-May-3 Sotheby's, Amsterdam #495/R est:3000-4000
£2667 $4880 €4000 Harbour scene (45x54cm-18x21in) 7-Jun-4 Glerum, Amsterdam #65/R est:20000-25000
£2722 $5008 €3974 Showery day, Paris (45x36cm-18x14in) s. prov. 9-Jun-4 Walker's, Ottawa #302/R est:3000-5000 (C.D 6750)
£3043 $4991 €4200 Ducdalf, Enkhuizen (35x44cm-14x17in) s. s.i.verso board prov. 27-May-3 Sotheby's, Amsterdam #497/R est:3000-4000
£5333 $9813 €8000 Motrico, a man and two children (180x104cm-71x41in) s.i.d.1935. 9-Jun-4 Christie's, Amsterdam #237/R est:8000-12000
£6389 $10094 €9200 Schepen en dekschuiten op het Ij in Amsterdam - ships and barges on the Ij, Amsterdam (55x65cm-22x26in) s. lit. 2-Sep-3 Christie's, Amsterdam #346/R est:4000-6000
£11888 $20448 €17000 Harbour of Polperro (65x81cm-26x32in) s.d.1911. 2-Dec-3 Sotheby's, Amsterdam #10/R est:12000-15000
Works on paper
£420 $722 €600 Harbour of Camogli (86x55cm-34x22in) ink black chk exhib. 7-Dec-3 Sotheby's, Amsterdam #695
£7895 $14289 €12000 Needlewoman in the Willebrordstraat in Amsterdam (60x75cm-24x30in) s. pastel. 19-Apr-4 Glerum, Amsterdam #256/R est:12000-16000

WOLTERS, Eugène (1844-1905) Belgian
£319 $508 €460 Bateaux de peche au clair de lune (31x24cm-12x9in) s.d.1893 verso panel. 9-Sep-3 Palais de Beaux Arts, Brussels #293
£556 $928 €800 Paysage (48x72cm-19x28in) s.d.1869. 21-Oct-3 Campo, Vlaamse Kaai #632
£1250 $2088 €1800 Le petit pecheur (69x97cm-27x38in) s.d.1869. 21-Oct-3 Campo, Vlaamse Kaai #631 est:1750-2000
£2516 $4679 €3673 Seascape with fishing boats in high seas (86x101cm-34x40in) s.d.1886. 2-Mar-4 Rasmussen, Copenhagen #1453/R est:25000 (D.KR 28000)

WOLTERS, Georg (1866-1943) German
£278 $458 €400 Flying pheasant in wood (64x50cm-25x20in) s. 3-Jul-3 Van Ham, Cologne #1515
£600 $1086 €900 Hamburg harbour (80x120cm-31x47in) s. 1-Apr-4 Van Ham, Cologne #1714a/R

WOLTON, Alan (1934-) American
£1044 $1900 €1524 Soft day, Colorado (71x76cm-28x30in) s. painted c.1990. 29-Jun-4 Sotheby's, New York #262/R est:2500-3500
£1511 $2750 €2206 Pacific coast camp, California (102x92cm-40x36in) s. painted c.1990. 29-Jun-4 Sotheby's, New York #261/R est:2500-3500

WOLTZE, Berthold (1829-1896) German

£1965	$3576	€2869	An unwelcome departure (66x79cm-26x31in) s. 16-Jun-4 Fischer, Luzern #1217/R est:5000-7000 (S.FR 4500)

WOLVECAMP, Theo (1925-1992) Dutch

£3000	$5520	€4500	Mask (40x30cm-16x12in) s. exec.1963 prov.lit. 9-Jun-4 Christie's, Amsterdam #337/R est:4500-5500
£3147	$5350	€4500	Head (24x30cm-9x12in) s.verso painted c.1958. 25-Nov-3 Christie's, Amsterdam #256/R est:3000-5000
£3192	$5331	€4660	Figure composition (50x40cm-20x16in) s. painted c.1965. 7-Oct-3 Rasmussen, Copenhagen #18/R est:15000 (D.KR 34000)
£3333	$6133	€5000	Abstract composition (91x60cm-36x24in) s.d.68 verso prov. 9-Jun-4 Christie's, Amsterdam #323/R est:6000-8000
£4667	$8587	€7000	Untitled (100x70cm-39x28in) s. verso. 8-Jun-4 Sotheby's, Amsterdam #265/R est:6000-8000
£5245	$9021	€7500	Untitled (60x57cm-24x22in) s. s.d.72 verso panel. 2-Dec-3 Sotheby's, Amsterdam #152/R est:7000-9000
£5333	$9813	€8000	Untitled (206x150cm-81x59in) studio st. verso. 8-Jun-4 Sotheby's, Amsterdam #269/R est:8000-12000
£9000	$16560	€13140	Untitled (129x109cm-51x43in) s.d.57 verso. 24-Jun-4 Sotheby's, Olympia #556/R est:5000-7000
Works on paper			
£400	$732	€600	Monster with sight (22x30cm-9x12in) mixed media green paper. 7-Jun-4 Glerum, Amsterdam #410/R
£894	$1519	€1305	Composition (24x31cm-9x12in) s. W/C. 26-Nov-3 Kunsthallen, Copenhagen #113/R (D.KR 9500)

WOLVENS, Henri Victor (1896-1977) Belgian

£769	$1308	€1100	Le commissionnaire (42x32cm-17x13in) s.d.1936. 1-Dec-3 Palais de Beaux Arts, Brussels #151
£931	$1722	€1350	Le champ de ble (16x26cm-6x10in) s. panel. 13-Jan-4 Vanderkindere, Brussels #10
£987	$1816	€1500	Paysage (65x100cm-26x39in) s. 28-Jun-4 Joron-Derem, Paris #130/R est:5000-6000
£1277	$2132	€1800	Petite fille assise (23x17cm-9x7in) s. panel prov. 14-Oct-3 Vanderkindere, Brussels #95
£1533	$2806	€2300	La dique (16x26cm-6x10in) s. panel. 7-Jun-4 Palais de Beaux Arts, Brussels #80/R est:1000-1200
£2378	$4042	€3400	La mansarde (50x60cm-20x24in) s.d.1936 exhib. 1-Dec-3 Palais de Beaux Arts, Brussels #154/R est:2000-3000
£2517	$4280	€3600	Ruelle animee donnant sur la mer (60x40cm-24x16in) s.d.1963. 18-Nov-3 Vanderkindere, Brussels #157 est:1000-1500
£2797	$4755	€4000	La mer (40x60cm-16x24in) s.d.1964. 18-Nov-3 Vanderkindere, Brussels #143 est:1000-1500
£3169	$5482	€4500	Breakwater, Brise-Lames (40x50cm-16x20in) s.d.1958 panel. 13-Dec-3 De Vuyst, Lokeren #571/R est:5000-6000
£3497	$5839	€5000	Fishermen along the Seine (54x64cm-21x25in) s.i.1934 lit. 11-Oct-3 De Vuyst, Lokeren #545/R est:6000-7000
£3497	$5944	€5000	Terrasse animee (43x63cm-17x25in) s. cardboard. 18-Nov-3 Vanderkindere, Brussels #165/R est:3000-4500
£5634	$9746	€8000	Apres la seance (80x120cm-31x47in) s.d.1950 lit. 13-Dec-3 De Vuyst, Lokeren #570/R est:8000-10000
£6338	$10965	€9000	Mushrooms on a table (84x95cm-33x37in) s.d.1942. 13-Dec-3 De Vuyst, Lokeren #491/R est:7000-9000
£9790	$16350	€14000	Terrace (50x70cm-20x28in) s.d.1964. 11-Oct-3 De Vuyst, Lokeren #473/R est:13000-15000
£17333	$31027	€26000	Breakfast table (100x150cm-39x59in) s.d.1970. 15-May-4 De Vuyst, Lokeren #501/R
£20280	$33867	€29000	At Marie Siska (100x150cm-39x59in) s.d.1961 i.verso lit. 11-Oct-3 De Vuyst, Lokeren #469/R

WOMBILL, William (19th C) European

£700	$1260	€1022	Dapple grey horse in a stable (49x60cm-19x24in) s. 23-Jan-4 British Auctioneer #578/R

WONAEAMIRRI, Pedro (1977-) Australian

Works on paper			
£2148	$4018	€3222	Pwoja, pukumani body paint design (124x72cm-49x28in) earth pigments linen prov. 26-Jul-4 Sotheby's, Melbourne #60/R est:5000-7000 (A.D 5500)
£2148	$4018	€3222	Pwoja, pukumani body paint design (126x71cm-50x28in) earth pigments linen prov. 26-Jul-4 Sotheby's, Melbourne #61/R est:5000-7000 (A.D 5500)

WONDER, Pieter Christoffel (1780-1852) Dutch

£5106	$8528	€7200	Dressing for the evening (31x27cm-12x11in) s. panel. 20-Oct-3 Glerum, Amsterdam #5/R est:6000-7000

WONG, Su-en (1973-) American

£1359	$2500	€1984	Sunkissed yellow (71x122cm-28x48in) s.i.d.2002 verso acrylic col pencil panel prov. 10-Jun-4 Phillips, New York #474/R est:3000-4000
£1630	$3000	€2380	Yellow highlighter (48x76cm-19x30in) s.i.d.2002 verso acrylic col pencil panel prov. 10-Jun-4 Phillips, New York #477/R est:2000-3000
£13966	$25000	€20390	Butter and egg - yellow painting with girl in red gloves (193x178cm-76x70in) s.i.d.2000 overlap acrylic col pencil linen prov.exhib. 13-May-4 Sotheby's, New York #323/R est:25000-35000

WONNACOTT, William (attrib) (1841-1878) British

Works on paper			
£1700	$2839	€2482	View of Mount Kanchenjunga from Darjeeling (44x64cm-17x25in) W/C over pencil htd bodycol. 14-Oct-3 Sotheby's, London #152/R est:1000-1500

WONNER, Paul (1920-) American

£1250	$2250	€1825	Untitled (61x86cm-24x34in) bears sig.verso. 25-Apr-4 Bonhams & Butterfields, San Francisco #5658/R est:1000-1500
£3390	$6000	€4949	The waiter (25x21cm-10x8in) board. 2-May-4 Bonhams & Butterfields, Los Angeles #3071/R est:3000-5000
£128492	$230000	€187598	Boy and girl in garden (137x84cm-54x33in) s. painted 1959 prov. 13-May-4 Sotheby's, New York #149/R est:80000-120000
Works on paper			
£278	$500	€406	Untitled (45x58cm-18x23in) s. mixed media. 25-Apr-4 Bonhams & Butterfields, San Francisco #5657/R
£722	$1300	€1054	The moon, sick and dying (45x36cm-18x14in) s. casein chl pencil exec.1973-1974. 25-Apr-4 Bonhams & Butterfields, San Francisco #5656/R est:1000-1500
£1163	$2000	€1698	Landscape (42x35cm-17x14in) s. W/C prov. 3-Dec-3 Doyle, New York #36/R est:2500-3500
£1279	$2200	€1867	Book, beaker and peach (58x46cm-23x18in) s.i. pencil W/C prov. 3-Dec-3 Doyle, New York #32/R est:1500-2500
£1286	$2250	€1878	Ruins at noon (35x43cm-14x17in) s. W/C gouache. 19-Dec-3 Sotheby's, New York #1148/R est:2500-3500
£1714	$3000	€2502	Sodom burning (35x43cm-14x17in) s. W/C gouache. 19-Dec-3 Sotheby's, New York #1147/R est:2500-3500
£2361	$4250	€3447	Figure and plants (127x101cm-50x40in) s.i.verso mixed media canvas. 25-Apr-4 Bonhams & Butterfields, San Francisco #5659/R est:3000-5000
£2429	$4250	€3546	Petunias (43x35cm-17x14in) s. W/C over pencil prov. 19-Dec-3 Sotheby's, New York #1153/R est:2500-3500

WONTNER, William Clarke (1857-1930) British

£13636	$24000	€19909	Portrait of a woman with rosy cheeks and marbled background (61x51cm-24x20in) s.d.1916. 1-Jan-4 Quinn's, Falls Church #228/R
£27000	$49680	€39420	Turban (63x53cm-25x21in) s.d.1925 prov.exhib. 11-Jun-4 Christie's, London #159/R est:20000-30000

WOO, Catherine (1966-) Australian

Works on paper			
£661	$1223	€965	Bloodline II (342x81cm-135x32in) s.d.98 mixed media tree resin copper pigment prov.exhib. 15-Mar-4 Sotheby's, Melbourne #138 est:1800-2500 (A.D 1600)

WOO, Jade Fon (1911-1983) American

Works on paper			
£307	$550	€448	Tug and tower, view of Coit Tower from the San Francisco Bay (38x56cm-15x22in) s. W/C. 8-May-4 Auctions by the Bay, Alameda #543/R
£1720	$3250	€2511	In the Arroyo - Running horses (53x74cm-21x29in) W/C prov. 17-Feb-4 John Moran, Pasadena #78/R est:2500-3500

WOOD, Agnes (20th C) New Zealander

£725	$1167	€1059	Woman with symbols II (91x66cm-36x26in) s. s.i.d.1998 verso. 12-Aug-3 Peter Webb, Auckland #159 (NZ.D 2000)

WOOD, Alan (1935-) British/Canadian

£386	$691	€564	Forest falls (59x105cm-23x41in) s.i.d.1987 verso acrylic collage prov. 6-May-4 Heffel, Vancouver #147/R (C.D 950)

WOOD, Albert Victor Ormsby (1904-1977) Irish

£280	$448	€409	Wood black stockings no.2 (46x11cm-18x4in) mono. tempera. 19-May-3 Bruton Knowles, Cheltenham #147

WOOD, Catherine M (attrib) (fl.1880-1929) British

£1562	$2750	€2281	Still life with books (25x46cm-10x18in) bears sig. 18-May-4 Bonhams & Butterfields, San Francisco #167/R est:3000-5000

WOOD, Charles Clatworthy (19th C) British

Works on paper			
£9500	$17005	€13870	HMS Collingwood 80 guns in the bay of Valparaiso (38x53cm-15x21in) s.i.d.1847 brown ink W/C. 26-May-4 Christie's, Kensington #398/R est:3000-5000

WOOD, Charles Erskine Scott (1852-1944) American

£5090	$8500	€7431	Still life with fruit and wine (28x56cm-11x22in) s. prov. 27-Oct-3 O'Gallerie, Oregon #801/R est:9000-12000

WOOD, Charles R (fl.1899-1929) British

Works on paper			
£320	$522	€467	Ferry on the river Dee at Farndon (39x54cm-15x21in) s.d.06 W/C. 23-Sep-3 Bonhams, Chester #827

WOOD, Christopher (1901-1930) British

£16000	$25440	€23360	French street scene with figures and a car before the Gianton Cafe (36x45cm-14x18in) prov. 18-Mar-3 Anderson & Garland, Newcastle #499/R est:4000-6000
£22000	$37400	€32120	Wooden bridge on the Seine (38x46cm-15x18in) board painted 1924 prov.exhib.lit. 21-Nov-3 Christie's, London #14/R est:20000-30000
£45000	$76500	€65700	Church and market Brittany (57x82cm-22x32in) board painted 1930 prov.exhib.lit. 21-Nov-3 Christie's, London #13/R est:50000-80000
£50000	$86000	€73000	Flowers in a white pot (38x46cm-15x18in) board prov.lit. 3-Dec-3 Sotheby's, London #28/R est:50000-70000
£50000	$91500	€73000	Still life (19x24cm-7x9in) board prov.lit. 2-Jun-4 Sotheby's, London #61/R est:30000-40000
Works on paper			
£600	$1110	€876	Mother and child (33x23cm-13x9in) pencil prov. 11-Mar-4 Christie's, Kensington #48/R
£1100	$2035	€1606	Brittany (34x42cm-13x17in) pencil prov.exhib. 10-Mar-4 Sotheby's, Olympia #112/R est:1000-1500
£1445	$2703	€2168	Streetscape, probably St Ives (30x47cm-12x19in) pencil prov. 20-Jul-4 Goodman, Sydney #46/R est:1200-1800 (A.D 3700)
£1800	$2826	€2610	Breton fishing village (32x40cm-13x16in) pencil prov.exhib. 28-Aug-3 Christie's, Kensington #497/R est:2000-4000
£1900	$3458	€2774	Garden in the south of France (23x33cm-9x13in) pen ink lit. 15-Jun-4 Bonhams, New Bond Street #53/R est:1500-2000
£1900	$3458	€2774	Two women (30x23cm-12x9in) crayon prov. 15-Jun-4 Bonhams, New Bond Street #54/R est:1000-1500

£2188 $4091 €3282 Portrait drawing (51x35cm-20x14in) s.i. pencil prov. 20-Jul-4 Goodman, Sydney #44/R est:2000-3000 (A.D 5600)
£3000 $5550 €4380 Three Graces (31x23cm-12x9in) i. pencil prov. 10-Mar-4 Sotheby's, Olympia #107/R est:2200-2900
£3000 $5550 €4380 Wine shop, Rome (24x32cm-9x13in) i.verso red white chk prov. 11-Mar-4 Christie's, Kensington #100/R est:1000-2000
£3320 $6209 €4980 Paris street (27x37cm-11x15in) W/C black ink pencil prov. 20-Jul-4 Goodman, Sydney #49/R est:4000-6000 (A.D 8500)
£3400 $6290 €4964 Nude studies (47x31cm-19x12in) red crayon chl. 11-Feb-4 Sotheby's, Olympia #97/R est:2000-3000
£3500 $6370 €5110 Two female nudes in a bedroom interior (47x61cm-19x24in) pen brown ink prov. 1-Jul-4 Christie's, Kensington #5/R est:4000-6000
£5000 $8950 €7300 Seated girl (32x23cm-13x9in) pencil pastel. 16-Mar-4 Bonhams, New Bond Street #35/R est:2000-3000
£5000 $8950 €7300 Two figures dancing, from the series The Dancers (58x46cm-23x18in) chl sanguine chalk prov. 4-May-4 Gorringes, Bexhill #1412/R est:5000-7000

WOOD, Donald (1930-) British
£650 $1177 €949 Whitehall shipyard (38x58cm-15x23in) 15-Apr-4 Richardson & Smith, Whitby #153
£700 $1190 €1022 Four horses grazing beneath the shade of a tree (45x91cm-18x36in) s. 19-Nov-3 Tennants, Leyburn #1188/R
Works on paper
£250 $455 €365 Portrait of a lady (48x38cm-19x15in) s.d.1936 pastel. 4-Feb-4 John Nicholson, Haslemere #55

WOOD, Eleanor Stuart (fl.1876-1910) British
£950 $1710 €1387 Still life of grapes, oranges, a lemon and other fruits upon a table (39x54cm-15x21in) s.d.1893. 22-Apr-4 Lawrence, Crewkerne #918/R
£1500 $2730 €2190 In Parham Woods, Sussex (102x124cm-40x49in) i. 15-Jun-4 Capes Dunn, Manchester #759/R

WOOD, Emmie Stewart (fl.1888-1910) British
£2800 $5180 €4088 Castel Gandolofo. Lake Albano (30x46cm-12x18in) s. pair. 14-Jul-4 Sotheby's, Olympia #137/R est:3000-5000

WOOD, Frank Watson (1862-1953) British
£2700 $4887 €3942 Herring fleet at sunset (124x74cm-49x29in) s.d.1902. 19-Apr-4 British Auctioneer #500/R
Works on paper
£300 $501 €438 HMS Furious (17x28cm-7x11in) s.i.d.1939 W/C. 13-Nov-3 Bonhams, Edinburgh #317
£375 $638 €548 Royal yacht (28x36cm-11x14in) s.d.1904. 5-Nov-3 John Nicholson, Haslemere #481
£420 $752 €613 Figures in a pony and trap in a summer garden (34x56cm-13x22in) s.d.1920 W/C. 16-Mar-4 Bonhams, Oxford #18
£440 $810 €642 HMS St Jean D'Arce, Lisbon (29x43cm-11x17in) s.i.d.1908 W/C. 23-Mar-4 Rosebery Fine Art, London #763/R
£520 $941 €759 Sunrise off Berwick (10x10cm-4x4in) s.d.1914 W/C. 19-Apr-4 British Auctioneer #487
£640 $1101 €934 Harbour scenes (36x25cm-14x10in) s.d.1900 W/C pair. 3-Dec-3 Andrew Hartley, Ilkley #1026
£650 $1190 €949 Cruiser squadron at sea (45x78cm-18x31in) s.d.1908 W/C htd white. 27-Jan-4 Bonhams, Knightsbridge #168/R
£680 $1136 €993 Destroyer in a sea loch (13x37cm-5x15in) s.d.1927 W/C pair. 16-Oct-3 Bonhams, Edinburgh #170
£700 $1295 €1022 First Battle Squadron (33x73cm-13x29in) s.i.d.1910 W/C. 14-Jul-4 Sotheby's, Olympia #133/R
£720 $1318 €1051 HMS Queen Elizabeth entering Portsmouth Harbour (34x52cm-13x20in) s.i.d.1935 W/C htd white. 8-Apr-4 Bonhams, Edinburgh #92
£800 $1472 €1168 Evening mail Royal Boder Bridge, Berwick (25x36cm-10x14in) s.d.1938 W/C. 28-Jun-4 British Auctioneer #379/R
£900 $1629 €1314 Three masted vessel moored at Carr Rock (36x25cm-14x10in) s.d.1900 W/C. 19-Apr-4 British Auctioneer #490/R
£950 $1739 €1387 Evening on the forth, HMS Nelson (37x52cm-15x20in) s.i.d.Oct 1936 W/C. 8-Apr-4 Bonhams, Edinburgh #143/R
£1050 $1922 €1533 Berwick-upon-Tweed (25x36cm-10x14in) s.d.48 W/C. 8-Apr-4 Bonhams, Edinburgh #86 est:400-600
£1200 $2064 €1752 Harbour scene with shipping (25x36cm-10x14in) s.d.1900 W/C. 3-Dec-3 Andrew Hartley, Ilkley #1025
£1200 $2172 €1752 Berwick Bridge and the Tweed Ferry (23x36cm-9x14in) s.d.1913 W/C. 19-Apr-4 British Auctioneer #488/R
£1300 $2080 €1898 HMS Hood, Invergordon (13x36cm-5x14in) s.i.d.1927 W/C htd white. 16-Sep-3 Bonhams, New Bond Street #2/R est:600-800
£1400 $2240 €2044 Panorama of upper reaches of Portsmouth Harbour (15x68cm-6x27in) s.d.1909 W/C. 16-Sep-3 Bonhams, New Bond Street #25/R est:1000-1500
£1500 $2715 €2190 Fishing boats tied at Carr Rock, Berwick light beyond (36x25cm-14x10in) s.d.1900 W/C. 19-Apr-4 British Auctioneer #489/R
£1850 $2960 €2701 Drake's island, with Plymouth across the Sound, as seen from Mount Edgecumbe (34x74cm-13x29in) s.d.1907 W/C. 16-Sep-3 Bonhams, New Bond Street #23/R est:2000-3000
£1900 $3230 €2774 Old Bridge, Berwick-on-Tweed (44x61cm-17x24in) s.d.1884 W/C. 4-Nov-3 Bonhams, New Bond Street #128/R est:1000-1500
£2900 $5249 €4234 Busy scene unloading boats at Carr Rock (25x36cm-10x14in) s.d.1900 W/C. 19-Apr-4 British Auctioneer #491/R

WOOD, George Bacon (jnr) (1832-1910) American
£2381 $4500 €3476 Horse and carriage scene (30x61cm-12x24in) s.d.1872 i. stretcher. 22-Feb-4 Skinner, Boston #332/R est:2000-4000

WOOD, Grant (1892-1942) American
£10588 $18000 €15458 Quetzal in flight (79x89cm-31x35in) s. oil on fiberboard prov. 22-Nov-3 Jackson's, Cedar Falls #64/R est:17000-25000
Prints
£1730 $3200 €2526 March (23x30cm-9x12in) s. lithograph edition of 250. 12-Feb-4 Christie's, Rockefeller NY #291/R est:3000-5000
£1734 $3000 €2532 In the spring (24x31cm-9x12in) s. lithograph prov. 13-Dec-3 Weschler, Washington #667 est:2000-3000
£2059 $3500 €3006 March (23x28cm-9x11in) s. lithograph. 7-Nov-3 Selkirks, St. Louis #574/R est:2500-3500
£2147 $3500 €3135 January (30x41cm-12x16in) s. lithograph from edition of 250 GCM wove paper. 24-Sep-3 Christie's, Rockefeller NY #39/R est:2500-3500
£2147 $3800 €3135 July Fifteenth (23x30cm-9x12in) s. lithograph edition of 250. 28-Apr-4 Christie's, Rockefeller NY #252/R est:4000-6000
£2151 $4000 €3140 In the spring (23x30cm-9x12in) s. lithograph. 2-Mar-4 Swann Galleries, New York #694/R est:3000-5000
£2258 $4200 €3297 Seed time and harvest (19x31cm-7x12in) s.d.1937 lithograph. 2-Mar-4 Swann Galleries, New York #692/R est:3000-5000
£2570 $4600 €3752 In the spring (23x30cm-9x12in) s. lithograph. 6-May-4 Swann Galleries, New York #614/R est:3000-5000
£2682 $4800 €3916 July Fifteenth (23x30cm-9x12in) s. lithograph. 6-May-4 Swann Galleries, New York #613/R est:3000-5000
£2692 $4900 €3930 Approaching storm (30x23cm-12x9in) s. lithograph. 19-Jun-4 Jackson's, Cedar Falls #188/R est:4500-5500
£2903 $5400 €4238 Approaching storm (30x22cm-12x9in) s. lithograph. 2-Mar-4 Swann Galleries, New York #695/R est:3000-5000
£3824 $6500 €5583 March (22x30cm-9x12in) s. lithograph. 31-Oct-3 Sotheby's, New York #210/R

WOOD, Harold (1918-) British
£400 $740 €584 Abstract painting of two heads (70x80cm-28x31in) s. board. 16-Jul-4 Charterhouse, Sherborne #473/R
£480 $874 €701 Copse at sunset (33x41cm-13x16in) s. indis.d. board. 15-Jun-4 Bonhams, Knightsbridge #39/R
£493 $908 €750 Boy and girl (51x66cm-20x26in) s.d.1970 board prov. 22-Jun-4 De Veres Art Auctions, Dublin #83/R

WOOD, Harry E (1879-1951) American
£269 $500 €393 Haystacks at sunset (46x61cm-18x24in) s.d.27 board prov. 6-Mar-4 Dan Ripley, Indianapolis #268
£363 $675 €530 Sunrise fishing (51x36cm-20x14in) s. canvasboard prov. 6-Mar-4 Dan Ripley, Indianapolis #271
£417 $775 €609 Tippecanoe lake (41x48cm-16x19in) s.d.1929 prov. 6-Mar-4 Dan Ripley, Indianapolis #262
£430 $800 €628 Summer landscape with cottage (25x36cm-10x14in) s.indis.d.1930 or '36 canvasboard. 6-Mar-4 Dan Ripley, Indianapolis #270
£430 $800 €628 Downtown Indy Hoosier Salon (53x76cm-21x30in) s. prov. 6-Mar-4 Dan Ripley, Indianapolis #273
£618 $1150 €902 Tippecanoe lake, possibly, with rowboats and dock (48x58cm-19x23in) canvasboard. 6-Mar-4 Dan Ripley, Indianapolis #264
£726 $1350 €1060 Tippecanoe lake, possibly, with orange canoe and children (38x48cm-15x19in) s. prov. 6-Mar-4 Dan Ripley, Indianapolis #263

WOOD, J (19th C) British
£2200 $3960 €3212 Portrait of George, aged 12 (48x68cm-19x27in) s. 21-Jan-4 Sotheby's, Olympia #327/R est:800-1200

WOOD, Jimmy (c.1957-) Australian
£392 $702 €572 Ceremonial Ground (106x42cm-42x17in) exec 1985 prov. 25-May-4 Lawson Menzies, Sydney #275/R (A.D 1000)
Works on paper
£305 $482 €442 Male and female mimih spirits (122x59cm-48x23in) earth pigments eucalyptus bark prov. 28-Jul-3 Sotheby's, Paddington #523 (A.D 750)
£386 $610 €560 Female mimih spirit (95x60cm-37x24in) earth pigments eucalyptus bark prov. 28-Jul-3 Sotheby's, Paddington #524 (A.D 950)

WOOD, John (1801-1870) British
£15363 $27500 €22430 Portrait of three children in landscape with dog (155x143cm-61x56in) 27-May-4 Sotheby's, New York #280/R est:25000-35000

WOOD, Karl E (1944-1990) Canadian
£249 $416 €364 Bow river (45x60cm-18x24in) s.i. board. 17-Nov-3 Hodgins, Calgary #86/R (C.D 550)

WOOD, Lawson (1878-1957) British
Works on paper
£360 $659 €526 Kippers (25x38cm-10x15in) s.d.14 W/C. 8-Jul-4 Duke & Son, Dorchester #147
£460 $754 €672 Trials of a sportsmen (37x25cm-15x10in) s.d.14 i.verso W/C pencil. 3-Jun-3 Fellows & Sons, Birmingham #92/R
£480 $898 €701 One in the eye, monkeys at a coconut shy (40x30cm-16x12in) W/C. 26-Feb-4 Lane, Penzance #62
£480 $864 €701 An apparition (23x11cm-9x4in) s.d.1901 s.i.d.verso W/C. 22-Apr-4 Mellors & Kirk, Nottingham #987/R
£700 $1204 €1022 In the mine (49x35cm-19x14in) s. brush black ink pastel bodycol. 3-Dec-3 Christie's, Kensington #460/R

WOOD, Lewis John (1813-1901) British
£725 $1305 €1088 Street scene with church, France (62x46cm-24x18in) s.d.1868. 25-Apr-4 Goteborg Auktionsverk, Sweden #227/R (S.KR 10000)
£993 $1818 €1500 Market in town square (31x41cm-12x16in) s.d.1863. 7-Apr-4 Dorotheum, Salzburg #115/R est:2200-3000
£1389 $2361 €2000 Rouen, Rue de la Grande Horloge near the cathedral (30x22cm-12x9in) s.d.1866 panel. 28-Oct-3 Dorotheum, Vienna #237/R est:2200-2400

WOOD, Lewis John (attrib) (1813-1901) British
Works on paper
£419 $750 €612 Cathedral (25x36cm-10x14in) W/C. 8-May-4 Susanin's, Chicago #6026/R

WOOD, Lewis Pinhorn (fl.1870-1897) British
Works on paper
£480 $802 €701 Arrival of a steamer at the Old Kew Bridge (21x34cm-8x13in) s. W/C htd white. 14-Oct-3 Bearnes, Exeter #327/R

WOOD, Molly Wheeler (20th C) American
£690 $1250 €1007 Still life with poppies (66x41cm-26x16in) s. 16-Apr-4 James Julia, Fairfield #866/R est:1400-1800

WOOD, Ogden (1851-1912) American
£1744 $3000 €2546 Cattle resting in landscape (108x154cm-43x61in) s. 2-Dec-3 Christie's, Rockefeller NY #69/R est:4000-6000

WOOD, Peter M (1914-1982) British
£460 $842 €672 Boats at Mevagissey (59x89cm-23x35in) s. board. 6-Jul-4 Bearnes, Exeter #475/R
£550 $1012 €803 Clipper ship Torrens on the Thames estuary (70x91cm-28x36in) s. 8-Jun-4 Bonhams, Knightsbridge #243/R

WOOD, Robert E (1926-1979) American
£1786 $3250 €2608 June morning (46x66cm-18x26in) s. i.verso prov. 15-Jun-4 John Moran, Pasadena #27a est:2500-3500
£2335 $4250 €3409 Luminescent seascape (46x61cm-18x24in) s.d.56 i.verso prov. 15-Jun-4 John Moran, Pasadena #27 est:3000-4000

WOOD, Robert Sydney Rendle (1894-?) British
£300 $540 €438 Coastal view, possibly Ballygally, Co Antrim (38x51cm-15x20in) s. board. 20-Jan-4 Bonhams, Knightsbridge #105

WOOD, Robert W (1889-1979) American
£235 $400 €343 In repose (51x61cm-20x24in) s. i.verso prov. 18-Nov-3 John Moran, Pasadena #185
£615 $1100 €898 Laguna shores (36x46cm-14x18in) s.i.d.1973 s.verso. 26-May-4 Doyle, New York #120/R
£1099 $2000 €1605 Luminescent seascape (41x51cm-16x20in) s. i.verso prov. 15-Jun-4 John Moran, Pasadena #182 est:2500-3500
£1257 $2250 €1835 Heavy surf (51x102cm-20x40in) s.i. 26-May-4 Doyle, New York #119/R est:3000-5000
£1324 $2250 €1933 Teton Peaks (46x61cm-18x24in) s. i.verso masonite exhib. 18-Nov-3 John Moran, Pasadena #184 est:3000-5000
£1720 $3250 €2511 Seascape (61x122cm-24x48in) s. 22-Feb-4 Bonhams & Butterfields, Los Angeles #7018 est:2500-3500
£1875 $3000 €2738 Mount Ranier (64x76cm-25x30in) s. painted c.1930. 17-May-3 Bunte, Elgin #1264 est:3000-5000
£2174 $4000 €3174 Afternoon rays (61x91cm-24x36in) s.d.57. 8-Jun-4 Bonhams & Butterfields, San Francisco #4347/R est:5000-7000
£2516 $4000 €3673 Portrait of Mount Baldy, California (64x76cm-25x30in) s. 10-Sep-3 Alderfer's, Hatfield #309/R est:3000-5000
£2616 $4500 €3819 Summer in Colorado (64x76cm-25x30in) s. i.stretcher painted c.1930. 7-Dec-3 Treadway Gallery, Cincinnati #562/R est:2500-4500
£2647 $4500 €3865 River in a mountain landscape (64x76cm-25x30in) s. canvas on canvas. 18-Nov-3 John Moran, Pasadena #163 est:5000-7000
£2910 $5500 €4249 Barn in landscape (64x76cm-25x30in) s.d.45 i. verso prov. 17-Feb-4 John Moran, Pasadena #70/R est:3000-5000
£3571 $6500 €5214 Blue bonnets, Texas (30x41cm-12x16in) s. i.verso. 15-Jun-4 John Moran, Pasadena #157 est:7000-9000
£4121 $7500 €6017 The road home (61x91cm-24x36in) s. i.verso. 15-Jun-4 John Moran, Pasadena #172 est:3000-5000
£4233 $8000 €6180 Laguna Beach - Crystal Cove (64x76cm-25x30in) s.d.44 prov. 17-Feb-4 John Moran, Pasadena #105 est:6000-8000
£4865 $9000 €7103 Texas hill country (64x76cm-25x30in) s. 17-Jan-4 New Orleans Auction, New Orleans #740/R est:10000-15000
£5026 $9500 €7338 Carmel - coastal landscape (64x76cm-25x30in) i.d.46 verso. 17-Feb-4 John Moran, Pasadena #26/R est:7500-9500
£9249 $16000 €13504 Floral Path (61x91cm-24x36in) s. i.verso prov. 10-Dec-3 Bonhams & Butterfields, San Francisco #6047/R est:10000-15000
£9412 $16000 €13742 Bluebonnet field (51x62cm-20x24in) s. canvasboard prov. 21-Nov-3 Skinner, Boston #453/R est:7000-9000
£10778 $18000 €15736 Texas wildflowers (61x91cm-24x36in) 18-Oct-3 David Dike, Dallas #165/R est:14000-18000

WOOD, Robert William (1901-1977) American
£1163 $2000 €1698 Landscape with distant mountains (64x76cm-25x30in) s. 7-Dec-3 Hindman, Chicago #765/R est:2000-3000

WOOD, Thomas Waterman (1823-1903) American
£9783 $18000 €14283 Visit from the landlord (76x50cm-30x20in) s.d.1885 prov. 8-Jun-4 Bonhams & Butterfields, San Francisco #4005/R est:12000-15000
£12346 $20000 €17902 Feeding time (26x39cm-10x15in) s.d.1885. 8-Aug-3 Barridorf, Portland #123/R est:20000-30000

WOOD, Vernon (1923-1995) American
£870 $1600 €1270 Impressionist autumn landscape (76x61cm-30x24in) s.d.58 board. 9-Jun-4 Alderfer's, Hatfield #546 est:800-1200

WOOD, Watson (1900-1985) British
Works on paper
£750 $1380 €1095 Lindisfarne (25x36cm-10x14in) s. W/C. 28-Jun-4 British Auctioneer #376/R

WOOD, William (1769-1810) British
Miniatures
£1200 $2040 €1752 Gentleman with blue coat and tied cravat (7cm-3in) gilt frame oval. 18-Nov-3 Bonhams, New Bond Street #104/R est:1200-1500
£3800 $6992 €5548 Harriet Beachcroft wearing white dress (8cm-3in) set in red leather travelling case prov. 24-Jun-4 Bonhams, New Bond Street #136/R est:2000-3000
£4500 $8100 €6570 Portraits of Sir William Beaumarris Rush and Lady Rush (9cm-4in) s.i.d.Sept 1st 1750 verso ormolu frame oval pair exhib.lit. 22-Apr-4 Bonhams, New Bond Street #115/R est:5000-7000
£4600 $8464 €6716 Mrs Beachcroft, wearing white dress (8cm-3in) s.verso set in red leather travelling case prov.lit. 24-Jun-4 Bonhams, New Bond Street #137/R est:1000-1500
£4800 $8832 €7008 Colonel Matthew Beachcroft wearing a blue coat (8cm-3in) s. gold frame set in red leather case prov.lit. 24-Jun-4 Bonhams, New Bond Street #134/R est:2000-3000
£6500 $11960 €9490 Husband and wife (7cm-3in) s. pair prov. 24-Jun-4 Bonhams, New Bond Street #138/R est:3000-5000
£7500 $13800 €10950 Elizabeth Seward, wearing a white dress (8cm-3in) s. gold frame set in red leather case prov.lit. 24-Jun-4 Bonhams, New Bond Street #133/R est:3000-5000
£8500 $15640 €12410 Lady of the Beachcroft family, wearing white dress (8cm-3in) s.verso gold frame set in red leather case. 24-Jun-4 Bonhams, New Bond Street #135/R est:2500-3500
£9730 $18000 €14206 Portrait of a lady (8x5cm-3x2in) exec.c.1790 oval. 12-Mar-4 Du Mouchelle, Detroit #2030/R est:1000-2000

WOOD, William (1960-) American
£707 $1300 €1061 Untitled (38x28cm-15x11in) s.d.1997 verso oil paper prov. 10-Jun-4 Phillips, New York #671/R est:1500-2000
£751 $1300 €1096 Untitled (38x29cm-15x11in) paper prov. 10-Dec-3 Phillips, New York #595/R
£1189 $2200 €1736 Untitled (38x29cm-15x11in) paper sold with companion painting prov. 13-Jul-4 Christie's, Rockefeller NY #95/R est:1500-2000

WOOD, William John (1877-1954) Canadian
£1964 $3379 €2867 At the beach (44x36cm-17x14in) s.d.1932 canvas on board lit. 2-Dec-3 Joyner Waddington, Toronto #295/R est:4000-5000 (C.D 4400)

WOOD, William Reuben Clark (1875-1915) American
£377 $600 €550 Maryland woodland clearing, autumn (56x71cm-22x28in) s.d.1910 prov. 13-Sep-3 Weschler, Washington #737/R
£802 $1300 €1171 Sunset gleam, Barnstable, Cape Cod (20x26cm-8x10in) s. 31-Jul-3 Eldred, East Dennis #1201/R

WOOD, William Thomas (1877-1958) British
£280 $476 €409 Springtime flowers (41x30cm-16x12in) s.d.1949. 30-Oct-3 Duke & Son, Dorchester #221
Works on paper
£350 $585 €511 Shadows on the snow (26x38cm-10x15in) s. W/C. 14-Oct-3 Bonhams, Knightsbridge #178/R

WOODBURY, Charles (1864-1940) American
£223 $400 €326 Seascape (20x25cm-8x10in) 14-May-4 Skinner, Boston #281a/R
£479 $800 €699 Off the Florida coast (41x46cm-16x18in) s.stretcher. 16-Nov-3 CRN Auctions, Cambridge #6/R
£699 $1300 €1021 Rolling hills (30x43cm-12x17in) s. canvasboard. 5-Mar-4 Skinner, Boston #457/R est:1200-1800
£726 $1300 €1060 Storm (20x25cm-8x10in) s. board. 16-May-4 CRN Auctions, Cambridge #36/R
£806 $1500 €1177 The whirlpool (43x53cm-17x21in) s.i. 5-Mar-4 Skinner, Boston #561/R est:2000-3000
£860 $1600 €1256 Ocean view (25x35cm-10x14in) canvasboard. 5-Mar-4 Skinner, Boston #577/R est:2000-4000
£1049 $1700 €1521 Seascape (25x36cm-10x14in) board prov. 8-Aug-3 Barridorf, Portland #300/R est:1200-1800
£1173 $2100 €1713 Rough waters (51x68cm-20x27in) 14-May-4 Skinner, Boston #250/R est:3000-5000
£1505 $2800 €2197 Rolling sea (26x35cm-10x14in) canvasboard. 5-Mar-4 Skinner, Boston #563/R est:2000-4000
£1613 $3000 €2355 Ogunquit Ledges (73x91cm-29x36in) init.i.verso. 5-Mar-4 Skinner, Boston #565/R est:6000-8000
£2540 $4750 €3708 Shoreline with clamshacks (61x76cm-24x30in) 29-Feb-4 Grogan, Boston #68/R
£3955 $7000 €5774 Autumn landscape (17x21cm-7x8in) s. sold with a companion and one by another hand. 2-May-4 Bonhams & Butterfields, San Francisco #1120/R est:600-800
£6471 $11000 €9448 Violent sea (74x91cm-29x36in) s. i.verso. 21-Nov-3 Skinner, Boston #580/R est:8000-12000

WOODBURY, R F (?) American?
Works on paper
£1111 $1800 €1622 Dartmouth College (18x30cm-7x12in) init.i. crayon sold with lithograph. 1-Aug-3 North East Auctions, Portsmouth #409/R

WOODCOCK, Hartwell L (1852-1929) American
Works on paper
£324 $550 €473 Seascape with fishing boats (33x48cm-13x19in) s.d.1897 W/C. 21-Nov-3 Eldred, East Dennis #582
£391 $700 €571 Caribbean beachscape (48x34cm-19x13in) s.d.1927 W/C paperboard. 14-May-4 Skinner, Boston #255/R

WOODCOCK, Keith (20th C) British
£250 $458 €365 Study of a Gauntlet Mark 1 bi-plane from number 19 Squadron (51x60cm-20x24in) s. 2-Jun-4 Dickinson, Davy & Markham, Brigg #944

WOODFORD, David (1938-) British
£320 $522 €467 Snowdonia scene with snowy mountain tops (13x23cm-5x9in) s. board. 27-Sep-3 Rogers Jones, Clwyd #99
£650 $1216 €949 Pen Maen and Aran Fawddwy from Craig Conarch (35x28cm-14x11in) s. 25-Feb-4 Mallams, Oxford #218
£950 $1710 €1387 Landscape, Llyn Gwynant and Yr Aran (23x28cm-9x11in) s. 24-Apr-4 Rogers Jones, Clwyd #177

WOODFORDE, Samuel (1763-1817) British
Works on paper
£700 $1288 €1022 Convent at grotta Ferrata (25x37cm-10x15in) s. W/C pencil. 8-Jun-4 Bonhams, New Bond Street #49/R

WOODFORDE, Samuel (attrib) (1763-1817) British

£660	$1042	€950	Cleopatra at the feet of Caesar (43x36cm-17x14in) metal. 6-Sep-3 Arnold, Frankfurt #727/R

WOODHOUSE, Frederick (jnr) (1847-1927) Australian

£936	$1591	€1367	Horse in a stable (46x61cm-18x24in) s.d.1875. 26-Nov-3 Deutscher-Menzies, Melbourne #225/R (A.D 2200)

WOODHOUSE, Frederick (snr) (1820-1909) Australian

£7647	$13459	€11165	Cardinal Wiseman with rider William Rutland and owner Benjamin Warby (40x53cm-16x21in) s.d.1858. 19-May-4 Sotheby's, Melbourne #385/R est:20000-30000 (A.D 19500)

WOODHOUSE, Herbert (1855-c.1920) Australian

Works on paper

£843	$1534	€1231	The Race. d.1888 mixed media. 1-Jul-4 Joel, Victoria #325 (A.D 2200)

WOODHOUSE, W (1857-1939) British

Works on paper

£880	$1496	€1285	Dapple grey stallion with work harness, in stable interior (23x33cm-9x13in) s. W/C. 31-Oct-3 Moore Allen & Innocent, Cirencester #447
£980	$1666	€1431	Black stallion in stable interior with collie resting below manger (24x33cm-9x13in) s. W/C. 31-Oct-3 Moore Allen & Innocent, Cirencester #448
£1050	$1785	€1533	Two work horses in stable interior (24x35cm-9x14in) s. W/C. 31-Oct-3 Moore Allen & Innocent, Cirencester #449 est:500-800
£1050	$1785	€1533	Two farm horses in a stable interior at manger (24x34cm-9x13in) s. W/C. 31-Oct-3 Moore Allen & Innocent, Cirencester #450/R est:500-800

WOODHOUSE, William (1857-1939) British

£447	$800	€653	Quail trophy (10x12cm-4x5in) 9-Jan-4 Du Mouchelle, Detroit #2011/R
£3038	$5500	€4435	Spaniel with a mallard (51x40cm-20x16in) s. 30-Mar-4 Bonhams & Butterfields, San Francisco #75/R est:6000-8000
£3591	$6500	€5243	Spaniel with a pheasant (54x43cm-21x17in) s. 30-Mar-4 Bonhams & Butterfields, San Francisco #76/R est:8000-12000
£4972	$9000	€7259	Spaniel with a woodcock (51x40cm-20x16in) s. 30-Mar-4 Bonhams & Butterfields, San Francisco #74/R est:10000-15000
£5000	$7850	€7250	Springer spaniel and a widgeon (60x46cm-24x18in) s. 27-Aug-3 Sotheby's, London #993/R est:5000-7000
£5525	$10000	€8067	Setter with game (61x45cm-24x18in) s. 30-Mar-4 Bonhams & Butterfields, San Francisco #78/R est:12000-15000

Works on paper

£400	$748	€600	Shot peasant with gundog looking on (34x27cm-13x11in) s. W/C. 22-Jul-4 Dominic Winter, Swindon #116/R
£480	$816	€701	Springtime Heysham Rocks (31x35cm-12x14in) s. 19-Nov-3 James Thompson, Kirby Lonsdale #54
£880	$1602	€1285	Two bay horses in a stable (23x33cm-9x13in) s. W/C. 15-Jun-4 Bonhams, Leeds #18
£900	$1530	€1314	Shore scene with sandpipers (34x52cm-13x20in) s. W/C. 19-Nov-3 James Thompson, Kirby Lonsdale #78
£1350	$2417	€1971	Shire horse (23x33cm-9x13in) s. W/C. 17-Mar-4 James Thompson, Kirby Lonsdale #51
£1400	$2506	€2044	Two stable horses (24x34cm-9x13in) s. W/C. 17-Mar-4 James Thompson, Kirby Lonsdale #50/R
£2600	$4680	€3796	Spring lambs, a study of sheep beside a haystack (26x36cm-10x14in) s. pencil W/C htd white. 21-Apr-4 Tennants, Leyburn #1030/R est:1500-1700

WOODHOUSE, William (attrib) (1857-1939) British

Works on paper

£350	$655	€511	Young boy standing beside a sunlit wall holding a pair of scissors (25x19cm-10x7in) pencil W/C. 22-Jul-4 Tennants, Leyburn #717

WOODINGTON, Walter (1916-) British

£300	$528	€438	Provence (25x35cm-10x14in) init. board. 18-May-4 Bonhams, Knightsbridge #54

WOODLOCK, David (1842-1929) British

£350	$627	€511	Resting in the wood (23x15cm-9x6in) oil paper. 18-Mar-4 Christie's, Kensington #438/R
£400	$688	€584	Unloading the skate, Onchan (20x28cm-8x11in) s. board. 5-Dec-3 Chrystals Auctions, Isle of Man #285

Works on paper

£270	$473	€394	Figures by a thatched cottage (25x18cm-10x7in) s. W/C. 16-Dec-3 Gorringes, Bexhill #1163
£300	$567	€438	Feeding the calves, with a lady beside a thatched cottage (21x15cm-8x6in) s. W/C. 18-Feb-4 Peter Wilson, Nantwich #71
£360	$644	€526	Venetian ladies with parasol passing before a doorway of the Doges Palace (27x21cm-11x8in) s. W/C. 17-Mar-4 Bonhams, Chester #231
£360	$655	€526	Woman feeding chickens outside a cottage (24x29cm-9x11in) s. W/C. 15-Jun-4 Bonhams, Oxford #25
£450	$806	€657	Lady seated at a cottage door (34x24cm-13x9in) s. W/C. 17-Mar-4 Bonhams, Chester #218
£520	$962	€759	School lane (25x17cm-10x7in) s. W/C sold with Conway Castle by Leyton Forbes two. 10-Mar-4 Sotheby's, Olympia #161/R
£540	$999	€788	Young maid at a cottage door (24x17cm-9x7in) s. W/C. 14-Jul-4 Bonhams, Chester #325
£580	$986	€847	Rhododendron gardens, Bidston (30x19cm-12x7in) s. W/C. 29-Oct-3 Bonhams, Chester #337
£750	$1403	€1095	Feeding the turkeys (25x17cm-10x7in) s. W/C bodycol. 20-Jul-4 Sworder & Son, Bishops Stortford #703/R
£750	$1365	€1095	Feeding the chickens (25x18cm-10x7in) s. pencil W/C. 1-Jul-4 Christie's, Kensington #199/R
£800	$1440	€1168	Two young ladies picking flowers beside a river (16x24cm-6x9in) s. W/C. 21-Apr-4 Tennants, Leyburn #1059
£860	$1462	€1256	Cottage at Welford-on-Avon (24x17cm-9x7in) s. W/C. 29-Oct-3 Bonhams, Chester #335
£960	$1718	€1402	Off to market (24x34cm-9x13in) s. W/C. 17-Mar-4 Bonhams, Chester #227/R
£1300	$2327	€1898	Venetian scene in the springtime (46x28cm-18x11in) s.d.April 23 94 W/C. 13-May-4 Grant, Worcester #356/R est:200-300
£1800	$3402	€2628	Young woman standing at a rose covered cottage door feeding birds (73x48cm-29x19in) s.d.97 W/C. 18-Feb-4 Peter Wilson, Nantwich #69
£2300	$4301	€3358	Goose girl (22x34cm-9x13in) s. W/C bodycol. 20-Jul-4 Sworder & Son, Bishops Stortford #705/R est:2000-3000
£2500	$4175	€3650	Dutch canal scene (36x51cm-14x20in) s. W/C. 20-Jun-3 Chrystals Auctions, Isle of Man #280 est:2200-2800

WOODMAN, Francesca (1958-1981) American

Photographs

£7186	$12000	€10492	Roma (19x19cm-7x7in) s.i. gelatin silver print exec.1977-1978 lit. 17-Oct-3 Phillips, New York #98/R est:15000-20000
£8982	$15000	€13114	Jill's mask (13x13cm-5x5in) s.i. num.verso photo. 17-Oct-3 Sotheby's, New York #276/R est:15000-25000
£41916	$70000	€61197	Self-deceit (8x8cm-3x3in) s.i.d.78 num.2 gelatin silver print five one of five prov.lit. 17-Oct-3 Phillips, New York #54/R est:70000-100000

WOODRING, Gaye (20th C) American

£349	$600	€510	Choir boy (46x51cm-18x20in) s. painted c.1940. 7-Dec-3 Treadway Gallery, Cincinnati #597/R

WOODROOFE, Louise (1892-1996) American

£269	$500	€393	Abstract composition (64x76cm-25x30in) painted c.1950. 7-Mar-4 Treadway Gallery, Cincinnati #727/R
£1111	$1800	€1611	Gloucester corner (51x60cm-20x24in) s. board prov. 8-Aug-3 Barridorf, Portland #315/R est:1500-2500
£2215	$3500	€3234	Market day (30x41cm-12x16in) s. canvas on board. 7-Sep-3 Treadway Gallery, Cincinnati #611/R est:1500-2500

Works on paper

£369	$650	€539	Abstract composition (38x28cm-15x11in) s. gouache exec.c.1950. 23-May-4 Treadway Gallery, Cincinnati #756/R

WOODROW, Bill (1948-) British

Sculpture

£824	$1500	€1203	Sink (37x40cm-15x16in) metal vase shaped cut assembled two parts. 29-Jun-4 Sotheby's, New York #621/R est:1500-2000
£1350	$2200	€1971	Untitled (165x114x61cm-65x45x24in) painted steel assemblage prov. 23-Sep-3 Christie's, Rockefeller NY #182/R est:4000-6000
£1700	$3145	€2482	Half life, half life (234cm-92in) painted metal conceived 1981. 11-Mar-4 Christie's, Kensington #364/R est:2000-3000

WOODROW, Joash (1926-) British

£11200	$20384	€16352	Three autumnal trees, Leeds (100x122cm-39x48in) board painted c.1980. 15-Jun-4 Bonhams, Leeds #39/R

WOODRUFF, Hale (1900-1980) American

Works on paper

£1657	$3000	€2419	Modern abstract (15x13cm-6x5in) s. W/C. 16-Apr-4 James Julia, Fairfield #714/R est:1000-2000

WOODRUFF, Leonard (19/20th C) American

£436	$750	€637	Grapes in a basket (48x76cm-19x30in) s. 7-Dec-3 Susanin's, Chicago #6060/R
£465	$800	€679	Peaches (48x76cm-19x30in) s. 7-Dec-3 Susanin's, Chicago #6007/R
£756	$1300	€1104	Pears (48x76cm-19x30in) s. 7-Dec-3 Susanin's, Chicago #6059/R est:600-1000

WOODRUFF, Porter (20th C) American

£361	$650	€527	Arab horse trainers (182x305cm-72x120in) board on panel four panel screen. 23-Apr-4 Weschler, Washington #124/R
£417	$750	€609	Caravan in the Tunisian desert (71x96cm-28x38in) s. 23-Apr-4 Weschler, Washington #123/R

Works on paper

£444	$800	€648	Street scene, Tunisia. Stormy coastal scene (61x48cm-24x19in) s. i. gouache two. 23-Apr-4 Weschler, Washington #118/R

WOODS, Henry (1846-1921) British

£260	$481	€380	Church of the Gesuati, Venice (28x17cm-11x7in) panel. 15-Jan-4 Christie's, Kensington #960
£750	$1185	€1088	On the terrace of a Venetian villa (29x38cm-11x15in) panel. 4-Sep-3 Christie's, Kensington #213/R
£1200	$1992	€1752	Interior of St Peter Martyr, Murano Venice (59x50cm-23x20in) s.i.d.1915 bears i.stretcher. 1-Oct-3 Sotheby's, Olympia #130/R est:1200-1800
£2600	$4654	€3796	Washerwoman in an alpine courtyard (61x46cm-24x18in) s.d.1909. 17-Mar-4 Bonhams, Chester #397/R est:2500-3500
£2800	$4424	€4060	Venetian beauty (48x30cm-19x12in) s.d.1906 canvasboard. 4-Sep-3 Christie's, Kensington #212/R est:1000-1500
£11000	$20240	€16060	Fruit sellers from the Islands, Venice (56x48cm-22x19in) s.i.d.1903 exhib. 26-Mar-4 Sotheby's, London #82/R est:5000-7000
£17369	$31090	€25359	By the canal, Venice (93x52cm-37x20in) s.i.d.1890 prov. 25-May-4 Bukowskis, Stockholm #353/R est:125000-150000 (S.KR 235000)

Works on paper

£600	$1098	€876	Pool of London (26x36cm-10x14in) both s. W/C pair. 6-Jul-4 Bearnes, Exeter #405

WOODS, Henry (attrib) (1846-1921) British
£400 $632 €580 Venetian backwater (28x41cm-11x16in) 4-Sep-3 Christie's, Kensington #214/R

WOODS, Padraic (1893-1991) Irish
£278 $453 €400 Northern seascape (61x75cm-24x30in) s. 23-Sep-3 De Veres Art Auctions, Dublin #277
£350 $602 €511 Port-na-Blagh (63x76cm-25x30in) s. 3-Dec-3 John Ross, Belfast #65
£1338 $2141 €1900 Loading turf, Dunfanaghy, County Donegal (36x44cm-14x17in) s. 16-Sep-3 Whyte's, Dublin #154/R est:2000-3000

WOODS, Sidney (19th C) British
£815 $1500 €1190 Sea nymph (33x18cm-13x7in) s. panel. 26-Jun-4 Susanin's, Chicago #6092/R est:1500-2500

WOODSIDE, John Archibald (snr) (1781-1852) American
Works on paper
£1395 $2400 €2037 Portrait of two allegorical figures in a wooded landscape (33x28cm-13x11in) s. 6-Dec-3 Pook & Pook, Downington #289a est:1500-2000

WOODVILLE, Richard Caton (jnr) (1856-1927) British
Works on paper
£2200 $4048 €3212 Regimental studies (26x17cm-10x7in) init.d.1894-1895 pencil W/C twelve in four frames prov. 25-Mar-4 Christie's, Kensington #268/R est:1500-2500

WOODWARD, Ellsworth (1861-1939) American
£6024 $10000 €8795 Newcomb Chapel (38x28cm-15x11in) s. board prov. 4-Oct-3 Neal Auction Company, New Orleans #561/R est:10000-15000

WOODWARD, Mabel (1877-1945) American
£559 $1000 €816 Rocky coastline with distant sailing ship (41x51cm-16x20in) s. 14-May-4 Skinner, Boston #248/R
£782 $1400 €1142 Snowy landscape (38x48cm-15x19in) s. masonite. 14-May-4 Skinner, Boston #226/R est:600-800
£2841 $5000 €4148 Beach scene with bathers strolling (15x18cm-6x7in) prov. 3-Jan-4 Cobbs, Peterborough #24/R
£4070 $7000 €5942 Rockport Harbour (25x33cm-10x13in) s. canvas on board. 7-Dec-3 Freeman, Philadelphia #126 est:4000-6000
£5864 $9500 €8503 Sweeping, Venice (46x36cm-18x14in) s. 8-Aug-3 Barridorf, Portland #112/R est:6000-9000
£7485 $12500 €10928 At the beach (25x33cm-10x13in) prov. 23-Oct-3 Shannon's, Milford #52/R est:12000-18000
£11976 $20000 €17485 Woman in a garden (33x25cm-13x10in) s. canvas on board. 23-Oct-3 Shannon's, Milford #137/R est:20000-30000
Works on paper
£335 $600 €489 Grass covered dunes (33x48cm-13x19in) s. W/C. 8-Jan-4 James Julia, Fairfield #1545/R
£879 $1600 €1283 Woman in white dress gathering pink roses (33x20cm-13x8in) s. W/C. 15-Jun-4 John Moran, Pasadena #88b est:1000-2000

WOODWARD, Margaret (1938-) Australian
£412 $745 €602 Reaching along the table (21x47cm-8x19in) i.verso oil flax canvas on hardboard. 31-Mar-4 Goodman, Sydney #449/R (A.D 1000)

WOODWARD, Neil (1947-) Canadian
£482 $896 €704 Early morning on the West Coast (26x102cm-10x40in) s. s.i.d.2001 verso acrylic board. 4-Mar-4 Heffel, Vancouver #50/R (C.D 1200)
£1577 $2680 €2302 A day seized and well spent (57x86cm-22x34in) s. s.i.d.2003 verso acrylic board. 27-Nov-3 Heffel, Vancouver #71/R est:2500-3500 (C.D 3500)

WOODWARD, Stanley W (1890-1970) American
£353 $600 €515 Rocky shore scene (41x51cm-16x20in) s. board. 21-Nov-3 Eldred, East Dennis #871/R
£566 $900 €826 Portland light (30x40cm-12x16in) s. i.verso canvas on board. 12-Sep-3 Skinner, Boston #485/R
£588 $1000 €858 Whale cove (63x76cm-25x30in) s. i.verso prov. 21-Nov-3 Skinner, Boston #549/R est:2000-4000
£1243 $2200 €1815 White caps in the Caribbean (41x51cm-16x20in) s. prov. 2-May-4 Grogan, Boston #33/R
£1647 $2800 €2405 Moon magic (76x91cm-30x36in) s. prov. 21-Nov-3 Skinner, Boston #548/R est:2000-4000
£1946 $3250 €2841 Ledges off Monhegan, Maine (76x101cm-30x40in) s. s.i.stretcher prov. 7-Oct-3 Sotheby's, New York #195 est:2000-3000
Works on paper
£469 $750 €685 St Augustine lighthouse (30x23cm-12x9in) s. i.verso W/C. 20-Sep-3 Jeffery Burchard, Florida #65/R

WOODWARD, Thomas (1801-1852) British
£685 $1068 €1000 Bird (36x36cm-14x14in) s.d.1819. 8-Apr-3 Il Ponte, Milan #615
£5500 $9350 €8030 Chestnut and gray in an extensive river landscape (47x61cm-19x24in) mono.d.1823. 25-Nov-3 Christie's, London #98/R est:4000-6000

WOODWARD, Thomas (attrib) (1801-1852) British
£480 $869 €701 Portrait of a grey hunter in a landscape (17x22cm-7x9in) 31-Mar-4 Bonhams, Knightsbridge #77/R

WOODWARD, William (1859-1939) American
£12222 $22000 €17844 Three tenement brick and timber cottage just off Esplanade Ave, LA (23x33cm-9x13in) init. s.i.d.1890 verso panel prov. 24-Apr-4 Collins, Maine #3/R est:5000-7000
£15060 $25000 €21988 Lotus Fountain, Newcomb Chapel (48x38cm-19x15in) s.d.08 canvasboard. 4-Oct-3 Neal Auction Company, New Orleans #560/R est:25000-35000
£18889 $34000 €27578 Haunted house, French Quarter, New Orleans (36x25cm-14x10in) s. oil crayon board prov. 24-Apr-4 Collins, Maine #2/R est:6000-8000
£45082 $82500 €65820 Oyster Wharf Biloxi (56x71cm-22x28in) s.d.25. 5-Jun-4 Neal Auction Company, New Orleans #388/R est:20000-30000
£46667 $84000 €68134 Cabildo and St Louis Cathedral, French Quarter, New Orleans (71x56cm-28x22in) s.d.14 oil crayon board prov.exhib. 24-Apr-4 Collins, Maine #1/R est:15000-20000
£75301 $125000 €109939 Ursuline Convent, New Orleans (56x71cm-22x28in) s.d.02 Rafaelli oil crayon board. 4-Oct-3 Neal Auction Company, New Orleans #536/R est:25000-35000
Works on paper
£588 $1000 €858 Three Graces (33x23cm-13x9in) s. conte crayon graphite. 22-Nov-3 New Orleans Auction, New Orleans #1072/R est:1200-1800

WOODWARD-SMITH, Sydney (1904-1972) Australian
£409 $650 €597 Valley in spring (25x36cm-10x14in) s. 12-Sep-3 Skinner, Boston #418/R

WOOG, Madeleine (1892-1929) Swiss
£352 $599 €514 Still life with flowers in jug and book (73x60cm-29x24in) s. 5-Nov-3 Dobiaschofsky, Bern #3800 (S.FR 800)

WOOL, Christopher (1955-) American
£3892 $6500 €5682 Untitled (102x67cm-40x26in) alkyd on rice paper painted c.1990 prov. 14-Nov-3 Phillips, New York #81/R est:8000-12000
£5028 $9000 €7341 Untitled (188x94cm-74x37in) s.d.1990 verso alkyd paper prov. 12-May-4 Christie's, Rockefeller NY #333/R est:8000-12000
£7975 $13000 €11644 Untitled, R27 (188x95cm-74x37in) st.sig. alkyd rice paper prov.exhib. 23-Sep-3 Christie's, Rockefeller NY #148/R est:12000-18000
£14970 $25000 €21856 Untitled (122x81cm-48x32in) s.d.87 alkyd acrylic on aluminum prov. 14-Nov-3 Phillips, New York #132/R est:20000-30000
£16760 $30000 €24470 Untitled D 66 (168x120cm-66x47in) alkyd gouache rice paper painted 1998 prov. 13-May-4 Sotheby's, New York #399/R est:10000-15000
£16760 $30000 €24470 Untitled (183x122cm-72x48in) s.i.d.87 verso alkyd flashe aluminum prov. 14-May-4 Phillips, New York #180/R est:25000-35000
£23464 $42000 €34257 Untitled, P62 (183x122cm-72x48in) s.i.d.1988 verso alkyd flashe aluminum prov. 14-May-4 Phillips, New York #181/R est:25000-35000
£38000 $69920 €55480 Untitled (119x152cm-47x60in) enamel on canvas painted 1998 prov. 25-Jun-4 Christie's, London #229/R est:20000-30000
£40419 $67500 €59012 Untitled, run dog run (89x61cm-35x24in) s.d.1990 verso alkyd paper prov. 13-Nov-3 Sotheby's, New York #464/R est:70000-90000
£41916 $70000 €61197 Run (61x41cm-24x16in) s.d.1990 verso enamel on aluminium prov. 12-Nov-3 Christie's, Rockefeller NY #562/R est:80000-120000
£46089 $82500 €67290 Untitled - S64 (91x61cm-36x24in) s.i.d.1990 verso alkyd aluminium prov. 13-May-4 Sotheby's, New York #326/R est:60000-80000
£221557 $370000 €323473 Untitled (244x183cm-96x72in) enamel on aluminum painted 1990 prov.exhib.lit. 13-Nov-3 Phillips, New York #14/R est:200000-300000
£335196 $600000 €489386 Untitled P III (244x183cm-96x72in) alkyd acrylic aluminium painted 1988 prov. 13-May-4 Sotheby's, New York #400/R est:40000-60000
£418994 $750000 €611731 Untitled (274x183cm-108x72in) s.d.1990 i.verso enamel aluminum in five parts. 13-May-4 Phillips, New York #20/R est:500000-700000
Prints
£2065 $3800 €3015 Untitled (95x62cm-37x24in) s.d.1989 verso monoprint prov. 10-Jun-4 Phillips, New York #464/R est:3000-4000
Works on paper
£8696 $16000 €12696 Untitled, noir sur noir (183x122cm-72x48in) s.d.1986 verso alkyd aluminum prov. 10-Jun-4 Phillips, New York #408/R est:10000-15000

WOOLCOCK, Marjorie (1898-1965) Australian
£328 $518 €479 Flowers (51x45cm-20x18in) s. 2-Sep-3 Deutscher-Menzies, Melbourne #373/R (A.D 800)

WOOLCOTT, Sina (20th C) New Zealander
Works on paper
£443 $785 €647 Forest gleam (53x73cm-21x29in) s.d.1962. 28-Apr-4 Dunbar Sloane, Auckland #98 (NZ.D 1250)

WOOLLASTON, Leslie A (1900-1976) British
£500 $900 €730 Hampton Court Bridge (44x64cm-17x25in) s. 20-Jan-4 Bonhams, Knightsbridge #181/R

WOOLLASTON, Sir Mountford Tosswill (1910-1998) New Zealander
£945 $1484 €1370 Bayley's Hill (26x36cm-10x14in) s.d.1967 oil stick ink. 27-Aug-3 Dunbar Sloane, Wellington #125 (NZ.D 2600)
£2256 $3835 €3294 Seated figure (47x37cm-19x15in) s. board. 27-Nov-3 International Art Centre, Auckland #61/R est:12000-16000 (NZ.D 6000)
£3249 $5296 €4744 Riwaka cemetery (43x47cm-17x19in) board prov. 23-Sep-3 Peter Webb, Auckland #87/R est:8000-10000 (NZ.D 9000)
£7143 $12929 €10429 Greymouth, sea and piece (44x52cm-17x20in) s.i. si.d.1965 verso board prov. 30-Mar-4 Peter Webb, Auckland #44/R est:15000-25000 (NZ.D 20000)
£8333 $13250 €12166 Mt. Arthur, from Moutere, Nelson (40x47cm-16x19in) s. board painted c.1940. 9-Sep-3 Watson's, Christchurch #40 (NZ.D 23000)
£8741 $15909 €12762 Otira 2 (59x44cm-23x17in) s. i.verso board. 29-Jun-4 Peter Webb, Auckland #73/R est:35000-45000 (NZ.D 25000)
£19930 $36273 €29098 Nelson Plains (88x118cm-35x46in) s.d.1987 board. 29-Jun-4 Peter Webb, Auckland #66/R est:60000-80000 (NZ.D 57000)
Works on paper
£409 $703 €597 Portrait of a girl (35x26cm-14x10in) s. W/C. 7-Dec-3 International Art Centre, Auckland #236/R (NZ.D 1100)
£451 $767 €658 Landscape (26x37cm-10x15in) s. ink. 26-Nov-3 Dunbar Sloane, Wellington #92 est:1300-1500 (NZ.D 1200)
£507 $817 €740 Study of a male figurehead (31x24cm-12x9in) s.d.1980 pencil. 12-Aug-3 Peter Webb, Auckland #243 (NZ.D 1400)
£893 $1616 €1304 Portrait of Jeremy Claasen (34x27cm-13x11in) s. W/C. 30-Mar-4 Peter Webb, Auckland #161/R est:2500-3500 (NZ.D 2500)

£909 $1427 €1318 Double portrait (36x26cm-14x10in) s.d.1962 W/C. 27-Aug-3 Dunbar Sloane, Wellington #16 (NZ.D 2500)
£984 $1554 €1437 Portrait of two boy's heads (25x35cm-10x14in) s.d.Nov 4 1963 W/C prov. 2-Sep-3 Deutscher-Menzies, Melbourne #140/R est:2000-3000 (A.D 2400)
£1065 $1683 €1555 Mouteka (25x36cm-10x14in) W/C prov. 2-Sep-3 Deutscher-Menzies, Melbourne #139/R est:2000-3000 (A.D 2600)
£1159 $1878 €1681 Tasman Bay - the big blue (22x29cm-9x11in) s.d.1990 W/C. 31-Jul-3 International Art Centre, Auckland #3/R est:2400-2800 (NZ.D 3200)
£1179 $2133 €1721 In the Takaka Valley (26x36cm-10x14in) s. ink. 30-Mar-4 Peter Webb, Auckland #10/R est:2500-3500 (NZ.D 3300)
£1222 $2077 €1784 Auckland harbour from Devonport (30x20cm-12x8in) s. W/C prov. 27-Nov-3 International Art Centre, Auckland #12/R est:2700-3600 (NZ.D 3250)
£1471 $2632 €2148 Portrait of a friend (29x22cm-11x9in) s.d.80 W/C. 12-May-4 Dunbar Sloane, Wellington #44/R est:5000-7000 (NZ.D 4250)
£1625 $2648 €2373 Bayley's Hill, Taranaki (30x38cm-12x15in) W/C. 23-Sep-3 Peter Webb, Auckland #118/R est:4000-6000 (NZ.D 4500)
£1625 $2648 €2373 Seated male figure (30x22cm-12x9in) s.d.1980 W/C. 23-Sep-3 Peter Webb, Auckland #121/R est:2500-4000 (NZ.D 4500)
£1679 $2905 €2451 Grey river (27x36cm-11x14in) s.d.1961 W/C. 9-Dec-3 Peter Webb, Auckland #23/R est:4000-6000 (NZ.D 4500)
£1875 $3450 €2738 Tasman Bay (26x36cm-10x14in) s. W/C prov. 25-Mar-4 International Art Centre, Auckland #6/R est:3800-5500 (NZ.D 5250)
£1903 $3407 €2778 North Canterbury (31x38cm-12x15in) i.d.1966 W/C. 12-May-4 Dunbar Sloane, Wellington #43/R est:3500-5500 (NZ.D 5500)

WOOLLATT, Edgar (1871-1931) British
£260 $486 €390 Head and shoulders portrait of a man in a red sleeveless jacket and scarf (45x35cm-18x14in) s. 22-Jul-4 Dominic Winter, Swindon #174/R

WOOLLEN, Cress (19/20th C) British
Works on paper
£700 $1190 €1022 Portrait of an elegant lady (52x44cm-20x17in) s. W/C. 25-Nov-3 Bonhams, Knightsbridge #56/R

WOOLLETT, Henry A (19th C) British
£1300 $2210 €1898 Dark brown hunter with two hounds in a landscape, with Brindle church, Lancashire beyond (35x46cm-14x18in) s.d.1859. 27-Nov-3 Christie's, Kensington #91/R est:1000-1500

WOOLLETT, Henry Charles (fl.1851-1872) British
£280 $501 €409 Donkey and cockerel (23x30cm-9x12in) s. 11-May-4 Bonhams, Ipswich #310
£366 $656 €534 Two horses by farmstead (23x30cm-9x12in) s. 12-May-4 Dobiaschofsky, Bern #1070/R (S.FR 850)
£980 $1754 €1431 Cattle, sheep and farmers on a highland path. Farmer and cattle on a path (51x92cm-20x36in) s. pair. 17-Mar-4 Bonhams, Chester #357

WOOLMER, Alfred Joseph (1805-1892) British
£600 $1086 €876 Young girl paddling by a woodland stream (86x74cm-34x29in) 16-Apr-4 Keys, Aylsham #740/R
£894 $1600 €1305 Gypsy fortune teller (84x65cm-33x26in) s. 6-May-4 Doyle, New York #21/R est:3000-5000
£1518 $2611 €2216 Come into the garden Maud (30x22cm-12x9in) board prov.exhib. 2-Dec-3 Ritchie, Toronto #47/R est:2000-3000 (C.D 3400)
£2800 $5012 €4088 Young lady reading at a lectern (33x30cm-13x12in) s.d.1826 panel. 22-Mar-4 Bonhams & Brooks, Norfolk #268/R est:800-1200

WOOLMER, Alfred Joseph (attrib) (1805-1892) British
£580 $1044 €847 Three ladies by a lake (56x44cm-22x17in) 21-Jan-4 Sotheby's, Olympia #273/R

WOOLNER, Thomas (1825-1892) British
£3889 $7000 €5678 Triumph of love (93x70cm-37x28in) 21-Jan-4 Sotheby's, New York #2223/R est:4000-6000
Sculpture
£18000 $31140 €26280 Thetis imploring Zeus, Achilles shouting and Thetis rousing Achilles (45x74cm-18x29in) glazed plaster reliefs three in one frame exhib.lit. 12-Dec-3 Sotheby's, London #231/R est:15000-20000

WOOLNOTH, Charles (1815-1906) British
Works on paper
£250 $400 €365 Mountain landscape with brook (18x38cm-7x15in) s. W/C. 20-Sep-3 Sloans & Kenyon, Bethesda #138/R
£260 $471 €380 River gorge with mountains rising in background (45x34cm-18x13in) s. W/C htd white. 2-Apr-4 Moore Allen & Innocent, Cirencester #749
£780 $1232 €1131 On the Luss Road, near Loch Lomond (49x76cm-19x30in) i.verso W/C. 24-Jul-3 Dominic Winter, Swindon #81/R
£1200 $2040 €1752 On the Luss Road, near Loch Lomond (51x79cm-20x31in) indis.i. pencil W/C bodycol gum arabic. 30-Oct-3 Christie's, London #74/R est:1500-2000

WOOLRYCH, F Humphry W (1868-1941) American/Australian
£326 $600 €489 Oaks (38x36cm-15x14in) s. s.i.verso board. 26-Jun-4 Selkirks, St. Louis #134
Works on paper
£346 $620 €505 Seated holy man holding a book in red (38x53cm-15x21in) s.d.1888 W/C. 11-May-4 Roland's, New York #473262/R

WOOLSEY, Clarence (20th C) American
Sculpture
£8383 $14000 €12239 Three bears figures (150x74cm-59x29in) bottlecap three. 15-Nov-3 Slotin Folk Art, Buford #144/R est:10000-15000

WOOTTON, Frank (1911-1998) British
£550 $875 €803 Oil rig (55x64cm-22x25in) s. 10-Sep-3 Sotheby's, Olympia #268/R
£800 $1272 €1168 Imam reza (59x71cm-23x28in) s. 10-Sep-3 Sotheby's, Olympia #269/R
£800 $1416 €1168 Household Cavalry, Buckingham Palace (55x55cm-22x22in) s. 2-May-4 Lots Road Auctions, London #350
£800 $1432 €1168 Alfriston Church and River Cuckmere (58x74cm-23x29in) s. 4-May-4 Gorringes, Bexhill #1308/R
£1100 $1749 €1606 British might, fueling at Abadan (59x66cm-23x26in) s. i.d.July 4th/46 verso. 10-Sep-3 Sotheby's, Olympia #270/R est:500-700
£1700 $3111 €2482 Looking across the Cuckmere Valley (51x61cm-20x24in) s. 27-Jan-4 Gorringes, Lewes #1657/R est:800-1200
£2200 $4114 €3300 Winter sunshine, Bo-Peep Farm (51x61cm-20x24in) s. board. 22-Jul-4 Gorringes, Lewes #1797/R est:1200-1600
£6000 $10980 €8760 Start (39x54cm-15x21in) s. 28-Jul-4 Bonhams, Knightsbridge #121/R est:6000-8000

WOOTTON, John (c.1682-1764) British
£15000 $25050 €21900 Grey hunter with a groom (124x100cm-49x39in) 14-Oct-3 Sotheby's, London #430/R est:6000-8000
£60000 $103800 €87600 3rd Duke of Devonshire's racehorse, Scamp with a jockey in yellow and blue livery (84x116cm-33x46in) prov. 10-Dec-3 Bonhams, New Bond Street #29/R est:50000-80000
£85000 $144500 €124100 Hunting scene showing the release of the hounds, in a wooded landscape (22x107cm-9x42in) prov. 25-Nov-3 Christie's, London #85/R est:50000-80000

WOOTTON, John (circle) (c.1682-1764) British
£6800 $11968 €9928 Landscape with a bay hunter held by a groom, gentleman and greyhounds (61x73cm-24x29in) 18-May-4 Woolley & Wallis, Salisbury #98/R est:2000-3000
£26000 $47840 €37960 Racehorses and their jockeys returning to the stables (49x112cm-19x44in) 26-Mar-4 Sotheby's, London #42/R est:5000-7000

WOPFNER, Joseph (1843-1927) Austrian
£336 $617 €500 Lake jetty (28x43cm-11x17in) mono. 24-Mar-4 Hugo Ruef, Munich #1154
£2721 $4871 €4000 Fishing boat on stormy sea (31x51cm-12x20in) s. panel lit. 20-Mar-4 Bergmann, Erlangen #1103 est:4000
£2937 $5052 €4200 Woman making hay (7x11cm-3x4in) s. panel. 5-Dec-3 Bolland & Marotz, Bremen #685/R est:1000
£4218 $7550 €6200 Hay harvesting near Munich (29x66cm-11x26in) s.i.d.79. 17-Mar-4 Neumeister, Munich #670/R est:6000
£4507 $7797 €6400 Fisherman's battle (12x15cm-5x6in) s. panel. 13-Dec-3 Lempertz, Koln #264 est:1000
£4895 $8420 €7000 Collecting the day's catch (7x11cm-3x4in) s. cardboard on panel. 3-Dec-3 Neumeister, Munich #808/R est:2000
£5034 $9011 €7400 Chiemsee fishermen (15x20cm-6x8in) s. panel. 17-Mar-4 Neumeister, Munich #671/R est:3500
£6122 $10959 €9000 Procession on Chiemsee (10x19cm-4x7in) s. panel. 17-Mar-4 Neumeister, Munich #669/R est:6000
£6294 $10825 €9000 Preparing to go to the rescue (45x36cm-18x14in) s.i. panel. 3-Dec-3 Neumeister, Munich #807/R est:3000
£9333 $16987 €14000 Flower garden on Fraueninsel (29x26cm-11x10in) s.d.1914 canvas on board. 30-Jun-4 Neumeister, Munich #759/R est:8000
£13333 $24267 €20000 Fishermen at jetty (30x41cm-12x16in) s. panel lit. 30-Jun-4 Neumeister, Munich #758/R est:8000

WORDEN, Willard E (1868-1946) American
£300 $500 €438 Wildflowers of California (38x50cm-15x20in) s.i. oil photographic base. 26-Oct-3 Bonhams & Butterfields, San Francisco #6508/R
£479 $800 €699 Mount Tamalpais with poppies in the foreground (51x38cm-20x15in) s.i. oil photographic base. 26-Oct-3 Bonhams & Butterfields, San Francisco #6509/R

WORES, Theodore (1859-1939) American
£3261 $6000 €4761 Japanese garden (16x21cm-6x8in) s. panel prov. 8-Jun-4 Bonhams & Butterfields, San Francisco #4248/R est:6000-8000
£6593 $12000 €9626 Summer landscape (41x48cm-16x19in) s. 15-Jun-4 John Moran, Pasadena #42 est:9000-12000
£8696 $16000 €12696 Lotus flowers (35x9cm-14x4in) s. i.verso panel. 8-Jun-4 Bonhams & Butterfields, San Francisco #4206/R est:4000-6000
£10405 $18000 €15191 View of a Samoan Village (95x73cm-37x29in) s.i. canvas laid down. 10-Dec-3 Bonhams & Butterfields, San Francisco #6249/R est:20000-30000
£73446 $130000 €107231 Sunshine and cherry blossom, Nogeyama, Yokohama (40x50cm-16x20in) s.i.d.1893 rosewood prov.exhib.lit. 28-Apr-4 Christie's, Los Angeles #53/R est:100000-150000
Works on paper
£569 $950 €831 Afternoon stroll, Yokohama (23x32cm-9x13in) s.i.d.1886 W/C. 26-Oct-3 Bonhams & Butterfields, San Francisco #6499/R

WORK, Maud Estelle (1883-1943) American
£419 $700 €612 Bluebonnets (43x61cm-17x24in) canvasboard. 18-Oct-3 David Dike, Dallas #200/R

WORKMAN, Mark (1960-) American
Works on paper
£190 $350 €277 Tree branch by moonlight (28x43cm-11x17in) s.d.01 pastel. 25-Jun-4 Freeman, Philadelphia #84/R

WORLIDGE, Thomas (attrib) (1700-1766) British
£889 $1600 €1298 Portrait of a man with beard (71x58cm-28x23in) indis sig. 21-Jan-4 Doyle, New York #120/R est:3000-4000

WORMS, Jules (1832-1924) French
£7059 $12000 €10306 Spanish courtyard with horse and figures (51x62cm-20x24in) s. canvas on board. 19-Nov-3 Bonhams & Butterfields, San Francisco #108/R
£11765 $20000 €17177 Connoisseur (46x27cm-18x11in) s. prov. 28-Oct-3 Sotheby's, New York #166/R est:20000-30000

WORMS, Roger (1907-1980) French
£559 $951 €800 Personnage dans un paysage boise avec etang (65x92cm-26x36in) s. 1-Dec-3 Palais de Beaux Arts, Brussels #384/R
£1477 $2732 €2200 Barques et bateaux (65x81cm-26x32in) s. 14-Mar-4 Eric Pillon, Calais #185/R

WORN, Walter (1901-1963) German
Works on paper
£382 $623 €550 Figures in room (44x32cm-17x13in) pastel. 27-Sep-3 Dr Fritz Nagel, Stuttgart #9407/R
£1477 $2613 €2200 Seated nude (53x44cm-21x17in) mono.d. pastel prov.exhib.lit. 30-Apr-4 Dr Fritz Nagel, Stuttgart #942/R est:1900

WORNDLE, Edmund von (1827-1906) Austrian
£1667 $2833 €2400 Mountain landscape with figures (59x57cm-23x22in) s. 28-Oct-3 Dorotheum, Vienna #19/R est:2200-2600

WOROSCHILOFF, C (19/20th C) ?
£7042 $12183 €10000 Winter journey (37x57cm-15x22in) s. 13-Dec-3 Hagelstam, Helsinki #32/R est:2500

WORP, Willem van der (1803-1878) Belgian
£483 $806 €700 Polder with cows watering (37x58cm-15x23in) s. 11-Nov-3 Vendu Notarishuis, Rotterdam #86

WORRELL, Abraham Bruiningh van (1787-?) Dutch
£6534 $10650 €9540 Figures by entrance (71x91cm-28x36in) s.d.1833. 17-Jul-3 Naón & Cia, Buenos Aires #6/R

WORSDALE, James (?-1767) British
£9722 $16528 €14000 Portrait of young lady (127x102cm-50x40in) s.d.1725. 28-Oct-3 Mealy's, Castlecomer #477

WORSEL, Troels (1950-) Danish
£941 $1599 €1374 Composition (150x100cm-59x39in) s.d.1975 verso. 26-Nov-3 Kunsthallen, Copenhagen #163/R (D.KR 10000)

WORSEY, Thomas (1829-1875) British
£2000 $3180 €2920 Still life study of flowers (41x30cm-16x12in) s.d.1853 prov. 9-Sep-3 Peter Francis, Wales #11/R est:1000-1500
£2600 $4420 €3796 Still life of crocuses and other flowers on a mossy bank (54x46cm-21x18in) s.d.1858. 19-Nov-3 Bonhams, New Bond Street #106/R est:1200-1800
£4200 $7140 €6132 Still life of bird's nest and flowers on a mossy bank (36x28cm-14x11in) s.d.1861 pair. 19-Nov-3 Bonhams, New Bond Street #105/R est:2500-3500

WORSFOLD, Deborah (1959-) Canadian
Works on paper
£226 $378 €330 Pink Fuji (120x120cm-47x47in) s.i.d.2001 mixed media. 17-Nov-3 Hodgins, Calgary #327/R (C.D 500)

WORSLEY, C N (c.1850-1923) New Zealander
Works on paper
£2198 $4066 €3209 Cecil and Water Peaks, Queenstown (36x54cm-14x21in) s. W/C. 9-Mar-4 Watson's, Christchurch #20 est:6000-12000 (NZ.D 6000)
£2422 $4336 €3536 Ruanui Station (30x54cm-12x21in) s. W/C executed c.1875. 12-May-4 Dunbar Sloane, Wellington #50/R est:3500-5000 (NZ.D 7000)

WORSLEY, Charles N (c.1850-1923) New Zealander
Works on paper
£326 $554 €476 Mouth of the Hutt River, Wellington (25x45cm-10x18in) s. W/C. 4-Nov-3 Peter Webb, Auckland #247/R (NZ.D 900)
£376 $639 €549 Coastal albatross (36x51cm-14x20in) s. W/C. 27-Nov-3 International Art Centre, Auckland #146/R (NZ.D 1000)
£429 $789 €626 Hilltop village, Europe (34x24cm-13x9in) s. W/C. 25-Mar-4 International Art Centre, Auckland #161/R (NZ.D 1200)
£500 $915 €730 Young Nicks Head, Poverty Bay, Giborne, New Zealand (25x18cm-10x7in) s. W/C exhib. 27-Jan-4 Bonhams, Knightsbridge #11/R
£502 $863 €733 Mt Codd and Tasman Glacier from Birch Hill (24x44cm-9x17in) s. W/C. 7-Dec-3 International Art Centre, Auckland #307/R (NZ.D 1350)
£725 $1174 €1051 Lake Como, Italy (25x35cm-10x14in) s. W/C. 31-Jul-3 International Art Centre, Auckland #117/R est:2000-3000 (NZ.D 2000)

WORTEL, Ans (1929-1996) Dutch
£2098 $3503 €3000 Out of recollection (125x86cm-49x34in) s.d.71 s.i.d.71 verso sold with book. 30-Jun-3 Sotheby's, Amsterdam #447/R

WORTHMAN, Harry (20th C) American
£240 $400 €350 Mexico City (20x41cm-8x16in) canvasboard. 18-Oct-3 David Dike, Dallas #291/R

WOSTRY, Carlo (1865-1943) Italian
£280 $467 €400 Church interior in Hollywood (43x30cm-17x12in) s. cardboard. 10-Oct-3 Stadion, Trieste #400
£1267 $2267 €1900 Barcola harbour (40x40cm-16x16in) s. board. 12-May-4 Stadion, Trieste #680/R est:1500-2000
£3098 $5050 €4523 Portrait of young woman (61x50cm-24x20in) s.i.d.1909. 17-Jul-3 Naón & Cia, Buenos Aires #55/R
Works on paper
£336 $561 €480 Saying hello in the park (21x28cm-8x11in) s. mixed media cardboard. 10-Oct-3 Stadion, Trieste #398/R

WOTRUBA, Fritz (1907-1975) Austrian
£16779 $29698 €25000 Three figures (150x116cm-59x46in) s.mono. tempera Indian ink squared paper lit. 28-Apr-4 Wiener Kunst Auktionen, Vienna #217/R est:10000-15000
Sculpture
£1000 $1800 €1500 Small seated figure (21x13x20cm-8x5x8in) s. black brown pat. 21-Apr-4 Dorotheum, Vienna #160/R est:1200-1700
£1056 $1827 €1500 Head (15cm-6in) st.sig.i. brown pat.bronze. 13-Dec-3 Lempertz, Koln #367/R est:1000
£1538 $2615 €2200 Small sitting figure (21cm-8in) s. num.32 pat bronze lit. 28-Nov-3 Wiener Kunst Auktionen, Vienna #602/R est:1500-2500
£1600 $2944 €2400 Small standing figure (21cm-8in) s.verso st.f.venturi Arte black brown pat bronze one of 1000. 12-Jun-4 Villa Grisebach, Berlin #873/R est:1000-1500
£3147 $5350 €4500 Reclining item (26x10cm-10x4in) s.d.1962 gold brown pat.bronze. 26-Nov-3 Dorotheum, Vienna #207/R est:3000-4000
£4577 $7919 €6500 Small torso (19cm-7in) st.sig. brown pat.bronze prov. 13-Dec-3 Lempertz, Koln #368/R est:5000
£6643 $11294 €9500 Relief with six figures (16x27x3cm-6x11x1in) mono. black brown pat.bronze prov. 26-Nov-3 Dorotheum, Vienna #66/R est:6000-9000
£12081 $21383 €18000 Small standing figure - 'The Needle' (33cm-13in) dark pat.bronze lit.prov. 28-Apr-4 Wiener Kunst Auktionen, Vienna #208/R est:15000-20000
£18792 $33638 €28000 Small reclining figure (22x53x280cm-9x21x110in) mono.i. black brown pat.bronze. 25-May-4 Dorotheum, Vienna #61/R est:28000-36000
£27778 $47222 €40000 Seated figure (102x77x171cm-40x30x67in) limestone lit. 28-Oct-3 Wiener Kunst Auktionen, Vienna #221/R est:30000-100000
Works on paper
£940 $1738 €1400 Seated figures (30x21cm-12x8in) pencil. 9-Mar-4 Dorotheum, Vienna #81/R
£987 $1816 €1500 Erda appears (34x48cm-13x19in) s.i. W/C pencil. 22-Jun-4 Wiener Kunst Auktionen, Vienna #309/R est:2000
£1023 $1800 €1494 Three standing figures (41x30cm-16x12in) s. ink W/C exhib. 22-May-4 Selkirks, St. Louis #812/R est:1800-2400
£1208 $2235 €1800 Composition (30x40cm-12x16in) pencil W/C gouache. 9-Mar-4 Dorotheum, Vienna #156/R est:1600-2400
£1420 $2500 €2073 Reclining figure (30x43cm-12x17in) s.d.1959 W/C ink prov. 22-May-4 Selkirks, St. Louis #811/R est:1200-1600
£1678 $2853 €2400 Two standing figures (42x30cm-17x12in) s.d.1954 W/C. 29-Nov-3 Villa Grisebach, Berlin #952/R est:2000-3000
£3147 $5350 €4500 Sketch (29x42cm-11x17in) s.d.1964 pen Indian ink W/C prov. 26-Nov-3 Dorotheum, Vienna #210/R est:3200-5000
£7240 $12308 €10570 Standing boy (40x30cm-16x12in) s.d.1929 pencil W/C lit. 25-Nov-3 Germann, Zurich #83/R est:7000-9000 (S.FR 16000)

WOU, Claes Claesz (1592-1665) Dutch
£4828 $8014 €7000 Naval battle between Dutch three-master and Spanish warship (60x84cm-24x33in) s. panel lit. 1-Oct-3 Dorotheum, Vienna #96/R est:8000-12000
£7263 $13000 €10604 Ships on stormy sea (49x84cm-19x33in) s. panel. 27-May-4 Sotheby's, New York #63a/R est:8000-12000

WOULFART, Marius (1905-) French
£289 $500 €422 Les boeufs (46x55cm-18x22in) s. masonite. 13-Dec-3 Weschler, Washington #513

WOUTERMAERTENS, Constant (1823-1867) Belgian
£897 $1614 €1300 Paysage avec chasseurs, cascade et chateau (70x100cm-28x39in) mono. 20-Jan-4 Galerie Moderne, Brussels #324/R

WOUTERMAERTENS, Edouard (1819-1897) Belgian

£690	$1234	€1007	Paturage des Flandres (59x100cm-23x39in) s. i.d.1881 verso. 12-May-4 Dobiaschofsky, Bern #1071/R est:3000 (S.FR 1600)
£738	$1366	€1100	Troupeau de moutons (22x33cm-9x13in) mono. panel. 15-Mar-4 Horta, Bruxelles #30
£839	$1427	€1200	The hunting party (50x69cm-20x27in) s. 29-Nov-3 Bukowskis, Helsinki #371/R
£872	$1597	€1300	Berger et son troupeau dans un paysage (60x80cm-24x31in) s. 8-Jul-4 Campo, Vlaamse Kaai #302
£937	$1491	€1350	Moutons au pre (29x44cm-11x17in) s. panel. 9-Sep-3 Vanderkindere, Brussels #17/R

WOUTERS, Frans (1614-1659) Flemish

£3691	$6607	€5500	Le repos de Diane (44x57cm-17x22in) panel. 25-May-4 Palais de Beaux Arts, Brussels #93/R est:6000-8000
£5479	$9315	€8000	Resting during the Flight to Egypt (26x44cm-10x17in) board. 4-Nov-3 Ansorena, Madrid #34/R est:8000
£10067	$18523	€15000	Satyr watching nymph sleeping in wooded landscape (36x40cm-14x16in) 24-Mar-4 Dorotheum, Vienna #117/R est:15000-18000
£16000	$27680	€23360	Cloelia and her companions escaping from the Etruscans (56x78cm-22x31in) prov. 11-Dec-3 Sotheby's, London #131/R est:15000-20000
£50336	$92617	€75000	Judgement of Paris (46x65cm-18x26in) copper. 24-Mar-4 Dorotheum, Vienna #205/R est:30000-40000

WOUTERS, Rik (1882-1916) Belgian

Sculpture

£6993	$11888	€10000	Masque de Madame Giroux (26cm-10in) terracotta wood socle. 1-Dec-3 Palais de Beaux Arts, Brussels #342/R est:10500-12500
£34965	$58392	€50000	Contemplation (45x52cm-18x20in) s.d.1911 plaster wood base exhib.lit. 11-Oct-3 De Vuyst, Lokeren #443/R est:14000-20000

Works on paper

£350	$594	€500	Sketches after Old Master pictures (17x22cm-7x9in) i. col crayons. 25-Nov-3 Christie's, Amsterdam #218/R
£921	$1695	€1400	View of Amersfoort (8x12cm-3x5in) blk chk. 28-Jun-4 Sotheby's, Amsterdam #268/R
£1528	$2551	€2200	Nel se reposant a table (25x36cm-10x14in) st.verso col dr. 21-Oct-3 Campo, Vlaamse Kaai #633/R est:1500-2000
£2448	$4161	€3500	La toilette (18x14cm-7x6in) indis.i. pencil lit. 25-Nov-3 Christie's, Amsterdam #212/R est:3500-4500
£7534	$12808	€11000	Femme ecrivant (46x32cm-18x13in) i.d.1915 Chinese ink wash dr. 10-Nov-3 Horta, Bruxelles #194/R
£9091	$15455	€13000	Nel seated at a table (30x23cm-12x9in) s. bl ink. 25-Nov-3 Christie's, Amsterdam #232/R est:12000-16000

WOUTERS, Rik (attrib) (1882-1916) Belgian

Works on paper

£3034	$5614	€4400	Esquisse de l'allee rose A (32x39cm-13x15in) i.verso W/C. 13-Jan-4 Vanderkindere, Brussels #165/R est:2500-4000

WOUTERS, Wilhelmus Hendrikus Marie (1887-1957) Dutch

£5594	$9622	€8000	Volendam (73x118cm-29x46in) i.verso. 2-Dec-3 Sotheby's, Amsterdam #3/R est:4000-6000

WOUW, Anton van (1862-1945) South African

Sculpture

£3716	$6652	€5425	Laughing Basuto (29cm-11in) s.d.1936 bronze f.G Massa Roma. 31-May-4 Stephan Welz, Johannesburg #577/R est:40000-60000 (SA.R 45000)
£4132	$7314	€6033	Skapu player (30cm-12in) s.d.1907 bronze. 3-May-4 Lawson Menzies, Sydney #8 est:10000-15000 (A.D 10000)
£7461	$12833	€10893	Lehman, the postman (44cm-17in) s.d.1901 brown pat bronze lit. 3-Dec-3 Stephan Welz, Johannesburg #36/R est:35000-45000 (SA.R 82000)

WOUWERMAN (17th C) Dutch

£2411	$4027	€3400	La halte des cavaliers. Les trophees de chasse (30x40cm-12x16in) s. panel pair. 17-Jun-3 Galerie Moderne, Brussels #402/R est:2000-2400

WOUWERMAN, Jan (1629-1666) Dutch

£1087	$2000	€1631	Untitled (38x51cm-15x20in) panel. 28-Mar-4 Carlsen Gallery, Greenville #398/R

WOUWERMAN, Jan (attrib) (1629-1666) Dutch

£2703	$4757	€4000	Dune landscape with a traveler and two donkeys on a path, city in the distance (33x45cm-13x18in) mono. panel. 18-May-4 Sotheby's, Amsterdam #83/R est:4000-6000
£3356	$6174	€5000	Landscape with trees (49x66cm-19x26in) panel. 27-Mar-4 Geble, Radolfzell #774/R est:5000

WOUWERMAN, Philips (1619-1668) Dutch

£61453	$110000	€89721	Halt at the gypsy camp (36x42cm-14x17in) mono. panel prov.exhib.lit. 27-May-4 Sotheby's, New York #23/R est:70000-90000
£100000	$183000	€146000	Cavalier holding a dappled grey horse (28x29cm-11x11in) mono. panel prov.lit. 7-Jul-4 Sotheby's, London #5/R est:40000-60000

WOUWERMAN, Philips (attrib) (1619-1668) Dutch

£280	$515	€420	Two horses in a stable (23x23cm-9x9in) indis.s. 11-Jun-4 Wendl, Rudolstadt #4426/R
£878	$1572	€1300	Landscape with three riders and a stream (24x33cm-9x13in) mono.verso panel. 7-May-4 Paul Kieffer, Pforzhiem #8196
£3380	$5442	€4800	Landscape with figures and riders outside tavern (50x61cm-20x24in) or circle. 22-Aug-3 Altus, Berlin #546/R est:4800
£22973	$40432	€34000	Cavalry battle scene with soldiers fighting on a bridge near burning ruins (92x136cm-36x54in) mono. prov.lit. 18-May-4 Sotheby's, Amsterdam #23/R est:15000-20000

WOUWERMAN, Philips (school) (1619-1668) Dutch

£7333	$13127	€11000	Genre scene (48x74cm-19x29in) board. 17-May-4 Finarte Semenzato, Rome #36/R est:10000-12000

WOUWERMAN, Philips (style) (1619-1668) Dutch

£2897	$4837	€4200	Horses bathing (31x37cm-12x15in) 12-Nov-3 Sotheby's, Milan #114/R est:3000-5000

WOUWERMAN, Pieter (1623-1682) Dutch

£3706	$6301	€5300	Falcon hunt (44x55cm-17x22in) bears mono. 20-Nov-3 Van Ham, Cologne #1440/R est:3500
£7077	$12172	€10332	Battle scene (50x68cm-20x27in) mono. panel. 3-Dec-3 AB Stockholms Auktionsverk #2664/R est:75000-100000 (S.KR 92000)
£8276	$13738	€12000	Horseman resting in mountainous landscape (37x30cm-15x12in) mono. panel prov. 1-Oct-3 Dorotheum, Vienna #203/R est:12000-16000

WRAGE, Hans (1921-) German

£1319	$2085	€1900	Bridge (40x50cm-16x20in) s.d.2000. 6-Sep-3 Schopman, Hamburg #777/R est:1700

WRAY, F Douglas (fl.1920-1951) British

£2200	$3586	€3212	Circe (39x56cm-15x22in) s.i.verso. 25-Sep-3 Mellors & Kirk, Nottingham #783/R est:1000-1400

WRBA, Georg (1872-1939) German

Sculpture

£1646	$2567	€2600	Europa on bull (29x27x8cm-11x11x3in) s.i. bronze Cast.Cosmas Leyrer, Munchen. 18-Oct-2 Von Zezschwitz, Munich #17/R est:2500

WRETMAN, Fredrik (1953-) Swedish?

£1133	$1926	€1654	Composition (60x230cm-24x91in) s.d.84 verso. 5-Nov-3 AB Stockholms Auktionsverk #1051/R est:20000-25000 (S.KR 15000)

WRIGHT OF DERBY, Joseph (1734-1797) British

£8000	$14720	€11680	Portrait of gentleman, wearing a brown coat and a white stock (74x61cm-29x24in) painted oval. 26-Mar-4 Sotheby's, London #18/R est:10000-15000
£12000	$22080	€17520	Portrait of a lady, wearing a blue dress with silk cloak (65x53cm-26x21in) 26-Mar-4 Sotheby's, London #24/R est:8000-12000
£12500	$23000	€18250	View of Hight Tor, Matlock, Derbyshire (62x82cm-24x32in) prov. 11-Jun-4 Christie's, London #44/R est:7000-10000
£19000	$32300	€27740	Vesuvius in eruption seen from Posillipo (58x74cm-23x29in) 27-Nov-3 Sotheby's, London #186/R est:20000-30000
£22000	$37400	€32120	Portrait of John Heath of Derby wearing a blue coat (76x65cm-30x26in) prov.exhib.lit. 25-Nov-3 Christie's, London #32/R est:20000-30000
£23333	$42000	€34066	Portrait of a young girl in a white dress (41x33cm-16x13in) prov. 23-Jan-4 Christie's, Rockefeller NY #78/R est:10000-15000
£28000	$51240	€40880	Portrait of the Hon Caroline Curzon (43x38cm-17x15in) prov.exhib.lit. 8-Jul-4 Sotheby's, London #228/R est:15000-25000

WRIGHT OF DERBY, Joseph (attrib) (1734-1797) British

£1000	$1790	€1460	Moonlit landscape, castle on the hillside (15x20cm-6x8in) panel. 5-May-4 John Nicholson, Haslemere #525/R est:500-750
£1600	$2864	€2336	Portrait of Rev Thomas Alleyne (76x63cm-30x25in) painted oval. 22-Mar-4 Bonhams & Brooks, Norfolk #320/R est:2000-3000
£2000	$3320	€2920	Portrait of a gentleman, with white stock and brown coat (74x61cm-29x24in) 3-Oct-3 Mallams, Oxford #228/R est:2000-3000

Works on paper

£2800	$4760	€4088	River Derwent, near Matlock, Derbyshire (25x32cm-10x13in) pencil W/C grum arabic prov.exhib. 20-Nov-3 Christie's, London #6/R est:1500-2000

WRIGHT OF DERBY, Joseph (circle) (1734-1797) British

£38000	$64600	€55480	Portrait of the late J Strutt, at a desk with a book and letters (127x102cm-50x40in) 19-Nov-3 Tennants, Leyburn #1143/R est:4000-6000

WRIGHT, Alice Morgan (1881-1975) American

Sculpture

£2446	$4500	€3571	Dancing figure (28cm-11in) s.d.1915 brown pat. bronze. 23-Jun-4 Doyle, New York #5086/R est:600-800

WRIGHT, Cory Bernice (1868-1948) American

£472	$750	€689	Still life with crabapples blossoms, Chinese sandals and vase (51x71cm-20x28in) s.d.34. 23-Mar-3 Auctions by the Bay, Alameda #859

WRIGHT, Don (20th C) American
£216 $350 €315 On night, Louisiana Bayou (46x36cm-18x14in) s.i.d.95. 2-Aug-3 Neal Auction Company, New Orleans #554

WRIGHT, Ethel (fl.1887-1900) British
£350 $602 €511 Summer flowers in a green jug (60x50cm-24x20in) s. board. 4-Dec-3 Mellors & Kirk, Nottingham #949

WRIGHT, Ferdinand von (1822-1906) Finnish
£1056 $1827 €1500 Portrait of a boy, Bohuslan (19x16cm-7x6in) i.verso cardboard. 13-Dec-3 Hagelstam, Helsinki #115/R est:1800
£8042 $13671 €11500 Waxwing and a pair of bullfinches (35x28cm-14x11in) s.d.03. 29-Nov-3 Bukowskis, Helsinki #212/R est:13000-15000
£8451 $14620 €12000 Croft by edge of lake (35x46cm-14x18in) s.d.1878. 13-Dec-3 Hagelstam, Helsinki #112/R est:10000
£14865 $26608 €22000 Bullfinches (25x21cm-10x8in) s.d.1876. 8-May-4 Bukowskis, Helsinki #148/R est:10000-14000
£54054 $96757 €80000 Capercaillies (62x72cm-24x28in) s.d.1870 exhib.lit. 8-May-4 Bukowskis, Helsinki #211/R est:80000-90000

WRIGHT, Francis Welsh (20th C) American
£1913 $3500 €2870 Untitled (396x178cm-156x70in) s. gold leaf fiberboard folding screen exec.c.1948 prov. 6-Jun-4 Wright, Chicago #193/R est:5000-7000

WRIGHT, Frank (1860-1923) New Zealander
Works on paper
£362 $587 €525 Waiting for the tide (24x37cm-9x15in) s. W/C. 31-Jul-3 International Art Centre, Auckland #131/R est:1500-2500 (NZ.D 1000)
£699 $1273 €1021 Maori figures on riverbank (24x36cm-9x14in) s. W/C. 29-Jun-4 Peter Webb, Auckland #158/R est:2000-3000 (NZ.D 2000)

WRIGHT, Frank (1932-) American
£829 $1500 €1210 The studio (74x91cm-29x36in) 16-Apr-4 American Auctioneer #431/R est:3000-5000

WRIGHT, Frank Lloyd (19/20th C) American
Works on paper
£1022 $1900 €1492 Plans of concrete works (61x91cm-24x36in) s. red black ink blue pencil. 7-Mar-4 Treadway Gallery, Cincinnati #412/R est:700-900

WRIGHT, G (19/20th C) British
£879 $1600 €1283 Fishing boats in rough seas (61x64cm-24x25in) s. 8-Feb-4 William Jenack, New York #266 est:1600

WRIGHT, George (1860-1942) British
£420 $714 €613 Bay horse (41x56cm-16x22in) s. 19-Nov-3 Sotheby's, Olympia #64/R
£650 $1216 €975 Driving rain (30x45cm-12x18in) s. monochrome oil. 26-Jul-4 Bonhams, Bath #92/R
£900 $1620 €1314 The elopement (51x41cm-20x16in) s. 21-Apr-4 Tennants, Leyburn #1184
£900 $1647 €1314 The gift, bay hunter in a stable (38x53cm-15x21in) s. 28-Jul-4 Mallams, Oxford #350
£1050 $1964 €1575 Huntsman making way for a motor car (30x46cm-12x18in) s. monochrome oil. 26-Jul-4 Bonhams, Bath #91/R
£1125 $1800 €1643 Toast to a safe return (36x30cm-14x12in) painted 1886. 19-Sep-3 Du Mouchelle, Detroit #2142/R est:1500-2500
£2200 $4004 €3212 Romanies and horses (41x30cm-16x12in) s. grisaille. 1-Jul-4 Mellors & Kirk, Nottingham #823/R est:1500-2500
£2600 $4420 €3796 Hunt in full cry (20x30cm-8x12in) s. board. 30-Oct-3 Duke & Son, Dorchester #196/R est:500-1000
£2800 $5152 €4088 London and Exeter coach arriving at a staging inn (25x40cm-10x16in) s. 29-Mar-4 Bonhams, Bath #83/R est:2500-3500
£3000 $5100 €4380 Going over a ditch with a farmstead beyond (18x30cm-7x12in) s. 30-Oct-3 Duke & Son, Dorchester #197/R est:500-1000
£3200 $5312 €4672 Interior scene with three hounds and a terrier looking into fire embers (25x29cm-10x11in) s.d.89. 6-Oct-3 David Duggleby, Scarborough #210/R est:2000-4000
£3600 $6660 €5256 Chestnut hunter with three hounds in a stable yard (36x51cm-14x20in) s. 11-Mar-4 Duke & Son, Dorchester #150/R est:1000-2000
£3800 $6460 €5548 Water jump (20x33cm-8x13in) s.i.verso. 30-Oct-3 Duke & Son, Dorchester #195/R est:500-1000
£3900 $6630 €5694 Passing sportsmen on the road, autumn (30x60cm-12x24in) s. 1-Dec-3 Bonhams, Bath #128/R est:3000-5000
£4200 $7224 €6132 Changing horses (38x60cm-15x24in) s. 4-Dec-3 Mellors & Kirk, Nottingham #938/R est:700-1100
£4400 $8096 €6424 Before the meet (34x51cm-13x20in) s. 24-Mar-4 Hamptons Fine Art, Godalming #310
£5500 $9350 €8030 Passing a hunt on the road, spring (30x60cm-12x24in) s. 1-Dec-3 Bonhams, Bath #127/R est:3000-5000
£7500 $13800 €10950 Refreshments outside the King's Arms (35x51cm-14x20in) s. 10-Jun-4 Christie's, Kensington #131/R est:6000-8000
£8140 $14000 €11884 Hunt scene (53x91cm-21x36in) s. 6-Dec-3 Pook & Pook, Downington #376/R est:7000-9000
£11173 $20000 €16313 Horses being groomed in courtyard (55x91cm-22x36in) s. 27-May-4 Sotheby's, New York #293/R est:8000-12000

WRIGHT, George (attrib) (1860-1942) British
£610 $1019 €891 Fishing boats (51x94cm-20x37in) 17-Oct-3 Keys, Aylsham #786/R

WRIGHT, Gilbert Scott (1880-1958) British
£3867 $7000 €5646 Taking the horse to market (41x60cm-16x24in) s. 30-Mar-4 Christie's, Rockefeller NY #49/R est:4000-6000
£4624 $8000 €6751 Figures and dogs fox hunting (61x91cm-24x36in) s. 10-Dec-3 Boos Gallery, Michigan #515/R est:10000-12000
£10000 $17200 €14600 Assignation with a huntsman (50x37cm-20x15in) s. 3-Dec-3 Bonhams, Knightsbridge #142/R est:10000-15000

WRIGHT, Helen (1956-) Australian
Works on paper
£682 $1261 €996 Underwater (113x76cm-44x30in) pastel prov. 15-Mar-4 Sotheby's, Melbourne #115 est:300-500 (A.D 1650)

WRIGHT, James (?-1947) British
Works on paper
£600 $1002 €876 Girls picnicking by the lochside (50x60cm-20x24in) s. W/C. 16-Oct-3 Lyon & Turnbull, Edinburgh #8

WRIGHT, Jefferson (attrib) (1798-1846) American
£3038 $4800 €4435 Portrait of Lydia and Mason (69x56cm-27x22in) pair. 6-Sep-3 Brunk, Ashville #781

WRIGHT, John (1745-1820) British
Miniatures
£1300 $2210 €1898 Lady, full face (7cm-3in) oval. 18-Nov-3 Bonhams, New Bond Street #161/R est:1200-1500
£5200 $9360 €7592 Georgina, Countess Bathurst (8cm-3in) s.verso pearl gold frame oval exhib. 22-Apr-4 Bonhams, New Bond Street #125/R est:3000-5000
£13000 $23400 €18980 Henry Paget, 1st Marquess of Anglesey (8cm-3in) gold frame oval exhib.lit. 22-Apr-4 Bonhams, New Bond Street #122/R est:6000-8000

WRIGHT, John Masey (1777-1866) British
Works on paper
£350 $606 €511 Artist's studio (18x23cm-7x9in) W/C. 12-Dec-3 Halls, Shrewsbury #628

WRIGHT, John Michael (1617-1694) British
£20500 $37310 €29930 Portrait of Mr Thomas Sydserff (125x99cm-49x39in) prov.exhib.lit. 1-Jul-4 Sotheby's, London #109 est:18000-24000
£45000 $76500 €65700 Portrait of Lady Catherine Dormer in a pink dress with jewels and pearl necklace (127x104cm-50x41in) s.d.1659 prov. 25-Nov-3 Christie's, London #8/R est:25000-35000

WRIGHT, John Michael (attrib) (1617-1694) British
£2500 $4250 €3650 Portrait of Thomas Johnson of Olney and Witham with a hound at his side. Portrait of Ann Johnson (102x84cm-40x33in) pair. 30-Oct-3 Duke & Son, Dorchester #171/R est:2000-4000

WRIGHT, John Michael (studio) (1617-1694) British
£5500 $9350 €8030 Portrait of Margaret Countess of Wemyss (124x98cm-49x39in) prov. 27-Nov-3 Sotheby's, London #124/R est:4000-6000

WRIGHT, Joseph (fl.1880-1927) British
£1554 $2750 €2269 Portrait of a woman (30x23cm-12x9in) indis.i.d.17 stretcher. 27-Apr-4 Doyle, New York #32 est:1500-2500

WRIGHT, Maggie (20th C) Australian?
£600 $1080 €900 Interval at the opera (59x49cm-23x19in) s. 20-Apr-4 James Adam, Dublin #113/R

WRIGHT, Magnus von (1805-1868) Finnish
£5986 $10356 €8500 View towards the sea, landscape from Haiko (30x42cm-12x17in) i.verso lit. 13-Dec-3 Hagelstam, Helsinki #111/R est:10000
£9155 $15838 €13000 Arrival of the sailing ship, view from Haiko (29x40cm-11x16in) s.d.1862 i.verso lit. 13-Dec-3 Hagelstam, Helsinki #110/R est:17000
£22448 $38161 €32100 Coastal landscape from Hainalax (60x89cm-24x35in) s.d.1861 lit. 29-Nov-3 Bukowskis, Helsinki #221/R est:35000-45000
Works on paper
£436 $803 €650 Sheep (13x24cm-5x9in) s. pen. 25-Mar-4 Hagelstam, Helsinki #1074

WRIGHT, Margaret Isobel (1884-1957) British
Works on paper
£550 $935 €803 Brother and sister (63x51cm-25x20in) s.d.1914 W/C. 26-Nov-3 Hamptons Fine Art, Godalming #49

WRIGHT, Michael (20th C) British
Works on paper
£525 $850 €761 Automotive (51x38cm-20x15in) s. gouache. 1-Aug-3 Bonhams & Butterfields, San Francisco #820/R
£900 $1638 €1314 Phantom at Cap Martin (59x51cm-23x20in) s. mixed media. 19-Jun-4 Bonhams, New Bond Street #32/R est:1200-1500
£900 $1656 €1314 Bentley in the Alps (69x55cm-27x22in) s. mixed media. 25-Jun-4 Bonhams, New Bond Street #289

WRIGHT, Nelson (20th C) British
£550 $974 €803 Tan and white cows grazing by trees (44x59cm-17x23in) s. 28-Apr-4 Peter Wilson, Nantwich #59

WRIGHT, R Stephens (1903-) American
£341 $600 €498 Landscape (48x61cm-19x24in) s. 23-May-4 Hindman, Chicago #160/R

WRIGHT, Richard Henry (1857-1930) British
Works on paper
£766 $1410 €1118 Italian coastal views with castles (35x50cm-14x20in) one s.d.1910 one d.1898 W/C three. 9-Jun-4 Walker's, Ottawa #359/R est:900-1200 (C.D 1900)

WRIGHT, Robert Murdoch (fl.1889-1902) British
Works on paper
£540 $972 €788 Glimpse of the Nile. Waiting for the procession (24x52cm-9x20in) s. i.verso W/C pair. 21-Jan-4 Sotheby's, Olympia #219/R

WRIGHT, Robert W (fl.1880-1900) British
£2000 $3720 €2920 Children in a cottage interior (36x30cm-14x12in) s. panel. 4-Mar-4 Christie's, Kensington #631/R est:2500-3500
£2300 $4117 €3358 Village scene with figures (44x75cm-17x30in) s.d.1886. 16-Mar-4 Bonhams, Leeds #636/R est:2500-3500
£3000 $5100 €4380 Cooking apples by the fireside. Secret letter (26x20cm-10x8in) s. one d.1877 one d.1879 panel pair. 19-Nov-3 Bonhams, New Bond Street #25/R est:3000-5000
£4800 $8160 €7008 Mending the violin. Picture book (25x20cm-10x8in) s.d.1887 panel pair. 19-Nov-3 Tennants, Leyburn #1240/R est:3000-5000
£39011 $71000 €56956 Village green (102x64cm-40x25in) s.d.1885 prov. 19-Jun-4 Jackson's, Cedar Falls #42/R est:20000-25000

WRIGHT, Rufus (1832-?) American
£2795 $4500 €4081 Portrait of captain and assistant surgeon James Cooper McKee (76x64cm-30x25in) i.verso. 20-Aug-3 James Julia, Fairfield #50/R est:8000-10000

WRIGHT, Thomas (1792-1849) British
Miniatures
£5500 $9515 €8030 Prince Mikhail Volkonskii (12cm-5in) s.d.1836 oval. 9-Dec-3 Christie's, London #251/R est:200-300

WRIGHT, Walter (1866-1933) New Zealander
£3080 $4989 €4466 Princess Wharf, Auckland (29x44cm-11x17in) s. 31-Jul-3 International Art Centre, Auckland #80/R est:5000-7000 (NZ.D 8500)
Works on paper
£297 $512 €434 Riverbed with cows (24x37cm-9x15in) s. W/C. 7-Dec-3 International Art Centre, Auckland #334/R (NZ.D 800)

WRIGHT, Wilhelm von (1810-1887) Finnish
Works on paper
£845 $1462 €1200 Hazel-hen - Tetrao bonasia, Linn (29x33cm-11x13in) s.d.1825 mixed media exhib. 13-Dec-3 Hagelstam, Helsinki #109/R
£2378 $4042 €3400 Black and white goose (28x30cm-11x12in) s. W/C. 29-Nov-3 Bukowskis, Helsinki #206/R est:3000-3500

WRINCH, Mary Evelyn (1877-1969) Canadian
£357 $614 €521 Capricorn Hotel, Amalfi, Italy (14x17cm-6x7in) s.d.14 board. 2-Dec-3 Joyner Waddington, Toronto #434 (C.D 800)
£578 $948 €844 White House (23x36cm-9x14in) s. board. 28-May-3 Maynards, Vancouver #1 (C.D 1300)
£720 $1318 €1051 Don River, York Mills (25x30cm-10x12in) s. board. 1-Jun-4 Joyner Waddington, Toronto #287/R est:1500-1800 (C.D 1800)
£1040 $1903 €1518 Beech trees, Belfountain, Caledon (25x30cm-10x12in) s. board. 1-Jun-4 Joyner Waddington, Toronto #343/R est:1500-1800 (C.D 2600)
£1071 $1843 €1564 Child with dog (17x14cm-7x6in) s. board. 2-Dec-3 Joyner Waddington, Toronto #258/R est:800-1200 (C.D 2400)
£1071 $1843 €1564 Tiger Lily Garden (19x23cm-7x9in) s. board sold with silkscreen print attrib to the artist two. 2-Dec-3 Joyner Waddington, Toronto #522 est:800-1200 (C.D 2400)
£1920 $3514 €2803 Tamagami (25x30cm-10x12in) s. board painted 1926. 1-Jun-4 Joyner Waddington, Toronto #459 est:800-1200 (C.D 4800)
£1964 $3379 €2867 Violets (21x34cm-8x13in) canvasboard. 2-Dec-3 Joyner Waddington, Toronto #329/R est:1000-1200 (C.D 4400)
Works on paper
£320 $586 €467 Temagami (24x22cm-9x9in) s.i. mixed media. 1-Jun-4 Joyner Waddington, Toronto #361/R (C.D 800)

WROBLEWSKI, Andrzej (1927-1957) Polish
£8616 $15595 €12579 Young child walking. oil tempera painted 1955. 4-Apr-4 Agra, Warsaw #13/R (P.Z 61000)
£19310 $32248 €28000 Portrait of a woman from side view (80x65cm-31x26in) s.i.verso painted 1956. 16-Nov-3 Agra, Warsaw #12/R est:10000
Works on paper
£438 $793 €639 Geometric abstract (16x23cm-6x9in) s. W/C pencil exec 1948. 4-Apr-4 Agra, Warsaw #48/R (P.Z 3100)

WROBLEWSKI, Constantin (1868-1939) Russian
£2027 $3628 €3000 Surf (47x67cm-19x26in) s.d.1904 i. verso lit. 8-May-4 Schloss Ahlden, Ahlden #767/R est:2800

WRZESZCZ, Eugeniusz (1851-1917) Polish
£2500 $4175 €3650 Summer field landscape (74x120cm-29x47in) s. 19-Oct-3 Agra, Warsaw #25/R est:11000 (P.Z 16000)

WSSEL DE GUIMBARDA, Manuel (1833-1907) Spanish
£1236 $2100 €1805 Elegant lady and her dog (28x18cm-11x7in) s.d.76 panel. 21-Nov-3 Skinner, Boston #153/R est:2800-3200
£3200 $5120 €4640 Spanish beauty (28x21cm-11x8in) s.d.81 panel. 18-Sep-3 Christie's, Kensington #121/R est:1500-2000
£6040 $10812 €9000 Waiting for the bull show (29x22cm-11x9in) s. board. 25-May-4 Durán, Madrid #193/R est:8000
£8451 $14789 €12000 Bull fight (29x22cm-11x9in) s.d.81 board. 16-Dec-3 Durán, Madrid #211/R est:12000
Works on paper
£3738 $5907 €5420 Spanish lady (71x50cm-28x20in) s.d.88 W/C pencil. 2-Sep-3 Rasmussen, Copenhagen #1705/R est:30000 (D.KR 40000)

WU CHANGSHUO (1844-1927) Chinese
Works on paper
£4633 $7737 €6764 Peaches (67x33cm-26x13in) s.i. ink col hanging scroll. 26-Oct-3 Christie's, Hong Kong #284/R est:40000-60000 (HK.D 60000)
£4633 $7737 €6764 Plum blossoms (41x169cm-16x67in) s.i.d.1902 ink handscroll. 26-Oct-3 Christie's, Hong Kong #286/R est:60000-80000 (HK.D 60000)
£6178 $10317 €9020 Grand waterfall (124x42cm-49x17in) s.i.d.1915 ink satin hanging scroll. 27-Oct-3 Sotheby's, Hong Kong #338/R est:80000-120000 (HK.D 80000)
£15647 $28165 €22845 Peony and rock (151x40cm-59x16in) s.i. ink col hanging scroll prov. 26-Apr-4 Sotheby's, Hong Kong #601/R est:150000-200000 (HK.D 220000)
£22760 $40967 €33230 Landscape (135x48cm-53x19in) s.i.d.1919 ink satin hanging scroll prov.exhib.lit. 26-Apr-4 Sotheby's, Hong Kong #581/R est:150000-200000 (HK.D 320000)
£27027 $45135 €39459 Flowers of the four seasons (101x27cm-40x11in) s.i.d.1890 ink col hanging scrolls set of four. 26-Oct-3 Christie's, Hong Kong #283/R est:180000-220000 (HK.D 350000)
£27027 $48649 €39459 Flower (137x41cm-54x16in) s.i.d.1917 ink col hanging scroll satin. 25-Apr-4 Christie's, Hong Kong #72/R est:100000-120000 (HK.D 380000)
£27027 $48649 €39459 Pomegrante (140x38cm-55x15in) s.i.d.1918 ink col hanging scroll. 25-Apr-4 Christie's, Hong Kong #73/R est:120000-150000 (HK.D 380000)
£28450 $51209 €41537 Prunus (137x67cm-54x26in) s.i.d.1917 ink col hanging scroll. 25-Apr-4 Christie's, Hong Kong #74/R est:150000-200000 (HK.D 400000)

WU DAYU (1903-1988) Chinese
£30888 $51583 €45096 Early morning in the park (54x39cm-21x15in) exhib.lit. 26-Oct-3 Christie's, Hong Kong #125/R est:400000-500000 (HK.D 400000)
£39118 $70413 €57112 Cat on the balcony (53x38cm-21x15in) exhib.lit. 25-Apr-4 Christie's, Hong Kong #707/R est:450000-550000 (HK.D 550000)

WU DE CHUN (20th C) Chinese
Sculpture
£2168 $3620 €3100 1/2 equals 1 (52x52x11cm-20x20x4in) s. welded iron sold with base exec.1993 prov.exhib. 29-Jun-3 Versailles Encheres #228/R est:3500-4500

WU GUANDAI (1862-1929) Chinese
£500 $865 €730 Untitled (137x54cm-54x21in) paint paper scroll. 11-Dec-3 Sotheby's, Olympia #521/R

WU GUANZHONG (1919-) Chinese
£37066 $61900 €54116 Spring (38x45cm-15x18in) s.d.91 exhib.lit. 26-Oct-3 Christie's, Hong Kong #136/R est:350000-450000 (HK.D 480000)
£53343 $96017 €77881 Ducks (29x39cm-11x15in) s.d.1976 s.i.d.verso board. 26-Apr-4 Sotheby's, Hong Kong #508/R est:350000-400000 (HK.D 750000)
£53343 $96017 €77881 Beidaihe (45x45cm-18x18in) s.d.1976 board prov. 26-Apr-4 Sotheby's, Hong Kong #512/R est:480000-600000 (HK.D 750000)
£73359 $122510 €107104 Pomegranate (35x42cm-14x17in) s.d.74 board exhib.lit. 26-Oct-3 Christie's, Hong Kong #135/R est:350000-450000 (HK.D 950000)
£104167 $173958 €152084 Small market in Indonesia (60x92cm-24x36in) s.d.94 s.i.d.verso exhib.lit. 12-Oct-3 Sotheby's, Singapore #199/R est:150000-220000 (S.D 300000)
£104167 $173958 €152084 Houses in Jiangnan (85x100cm-33x39in) s.d.2000 s.i.d.verso. 12-Oct-3 Sotheby's, Singapore #200/R est:180000-270000 (S.D 300000)
£115830 $193436 €169112 Large haul (46x61cm-18x24in) s.d.76 board lit. 26-Oct-3 Christie's, Hong Kong #134/R est:500000-700000 (HK.D 1500000)

Prints

£1797	$3253	€2624	Long, still day (70x140cm-28x55in) s.num.12/100 lithograph rice paper. 3-Apr-4 Glerum, Singapore #79/R est:3000-4000 (S.D 5500)

Works on paper

£4267	$7681	€6230	Sisters (36x27cm-14x11in) s.i.d.1961 W/C lit. 26-Apr-4 Sotheby's, Hong Kong #505/R est:60000-80000 (HK.D 60000)
£6757	$12162	€9865	Pasture in Xinjiang (28x48cm-11x19in) s.i.d.1981 col sketch prov.lit. 26-Apr-4 Sotheby's, Hong Kong #503/R est:90000-120000 (HK.D 95000)
£6757	$12162	€9865	Paddy field (25x35cm-10x14in) s.i.d.1959 W/C prov.lit. 26-Apr-4 Sotheby's, Hong Kong #504/R est:80000-100000 (HK.D 95000)
£7112	$12802	€10384	Zhou village (25x35cm-10x14in) s.i.d.1985 sketch lit. 26-Apr-4 Sotheby's, Hong Kong #502/R est:70000-90000 (HK.D 100000)
£7112	$12802	€10384	Hong Kong at night (36x27cm-14x11in) s.i.d.1986 ink col prov.lit. 26-Apr-4 Sotheby's, Hong Kong #509/R est:100000-150000 (HK.D 100000)
£8535	$15363	€12461	Mansion in Zhou village (25x35cm-10x14in) s.i.d.1985 sketch exhib.lit. 26-Apr-4 Sotheby's, Hong Kong #501/R est:65000-85000 (HK.D 120000)
£8535	$15363	€12461	Nude (30x45cm-12x18in) s.d.1990 sketch lit. 26-Apr-4 Sotheby's, Hong Kong #506/R est:50000-70000 (HK.D 120000)
£10039	$16764	€14657	Street in Mudanjiang (29x40cm-11x16in) s.i.d.1986 W/C scroll. 26-Oct-3 Christie's, Hong Kong #316/R est:70000-90000 (HK.D 130000)
£12802	$23044	€18691	Skyscrapers in Hong Kong (33x67cm-13x26in) s.i.d.1991 ink col exhib.lit. 26-Apr-4 Sotheby's, Hong Kong #510/R est:180000-250000 (HK.D 180000)
£13900	$23212	€20294	Opera figures (51x41cm-20x16in) s. ink col. 27-Oct-3 Sotheby's, Hong Kong #355/R est:80000-120000 (HK.D 180000)
£14225	$25605	€20769	Bamboo grove (47x44cm-19x17in) seal of artist ink col hanging scroll lit. 25-Apr-4 Christie's, Hong Kong #111/R est:200000-250000 (HK.D 200000)
£15647	$28165	€22845	Bridge (38x48cm-15x19in) ink col lit. 26-Apr-4 Sotheby's, Hong Kong #511/R est:120000-150000 (HK.D 220000)
£15647	$28165	€22845	Snowy spring (64x134cm-25x53in) ink col. 26-Apr-4 Sotheby's, Hong Kong #518/R est:220000-250000 (HK.D 220000)
£16988	$28371	€24802	Tak wan tea house (53x47cm-21x19in) s.i.d.1990 ink W/C exhib. 27-Oct-3 Sotheby's, Hong Kong #349/R est:100000-150000 (HK.D 220000)
£18492	$33286	€26998	Snow-clad mountains (48x44cm-19x17in) ink col. 26-Apr-4 Sotheby's, Hong Kong #517/R est:80000-120000 (HK.D 260000)
£20077	$33529	€29312	Manor (68x68cm-27x27in) s.i.d.1995 ink col. 27-Oct-3 Sotheby's, Hong Kong #352/R est:160000-200000 (HK.D 260000)
£22760	$40967	€33230	Wisteria (46x68cm-18x27in) d.1980 ink col. 26-Apr-4 Sotheby's, Hong Kong #513/R est:180000-220000 (HK.D 320000)
£22760	$40967	€33230	Sunrise at Mount Huang (136x67cm-54x26in) d.1986 ink col. 26-Apr-4 Sotheby's, Hong Kong #514/R est:300000-400000 (HK.D 320000)
£24710	$41266	€36077	Xishuangbanna, yunnan (34x46cm-13x18in) artist seal ink col exhib. 27-Oct-3 Sotheby's, Hong Kong #353/R est:120000-180000 (HK.D 320000)
£27027	$45135	€39459	Village in Jiangnan (69x85cm-27x33in) artist seal ink col. 27-Oct-3 Sotheby's, Hong Kong #350/R est:250000-350000 (HK.D 350000)
£29344	$49004	€42842	Landscape (89x95cm-35x37in) artist seal ink col scroll. 26-Oct-3 Christie's, Hong Kong #318/R est:400000-500000 (HK.D 380000)
£29872	$53770	€43613	Silkworm in a cocoon (34x48cm-13x19in) s.d.1980 ink col prov. 26-Apr-4 Sotheby's, Hong Kong #507/R est:150000-200000 (HK.D 420000)
£35562	$64011	€51921	Forest in Xishuangbanna (52x52cm-20x20in) ink col prov. 26-Apr-4 Sotheby's, Hong Kong #516/R est:180000-220000 (HK.D 500000)
£37066	$61900	€54116	Bamboo shoots in spring (67x67cm-26x26in) artist seal ink col. 27-Oct-3 Sotheby's, Hong Kong #347/R est:180000-250000 (HK.D 480000)
£39118	$70413	€57112	Home village (69x77cm-27x30in) seal of artist ink col scroll lit. 25-Apr-4 Christie's, Hong Kong #112/R est:400000-550000 (HK.D 550000)
£65637	$109614	€95830	Rock (95x126cm-37x50in) artist seal ink col exhib. 27-Oct-3 Sotheby's, Hong Kong #351/R est:550000-750000 (HK.D 850000)
£113798	$204836	€166145	Shidu (82x136cm-32x54in) ink col. 26-Apr-4 Sotheby's, Hong Kong #515/R est:600000-800000 (HK.D 1600000)
£193050	$322394	€281853	Zhoushan harbour at night (102x102cm-40x40in) artist seal ink col prov.exhib. 27-Oct-3 Sotheby's, Hong Kong #348/R est:800000-1500000 (HK.D 2500000)

WU GUANZHONG (attrib) (1919-) Chinese

Works on paper

£7432	$13081	€11000	Riverside village (67x67cm-26x26in) s. seal Indian ink col. 21-May-4 Dr Fritz Nagel, Stuttgart #1106/R est:2500

WU HUFAN (1894-1968) Chinese

Works on paper

£1565	$2817	€2285	Bamboo and rock (19x49cm-7x19in) s.i.d.1947 i.verso ink folding fan. 25-Apr-4 Christie's, Hong Kong #85/R est:25000-35000 (HK.D 22000)
£1991	$3585	€2907	Calligraphy in running script (106x52cm-42x20in) s. ink scroll. 25-Apr-4 Christie's, Hong Kong #16/R est:15000-20000 (HK.D 28000)
£5334	$9602	€7788	Living in the mountain (103x40cm-41x16in) s.i.d.1934 ink hanging scroll. 25-Apr-4 Christie's, Hong Kong #121/R est:80000-100000 (HK.D 75000)
£5405	$9027	€7891	Pines on the hills (21x26cm-8x10in) s.i.d.1953 ink. 27-Oct-3 Sotheby's, Hong Kong #264/R est:70000-90000 (HK.D 70000)
£9266	$15475	€13528	Landscape (60x97cm-24x38in) s.i. ink col. 27-Oct-3 Sotheby's, Hong Kong #265/R est:120000-180000 (HK.D 120000)
£9957	$17923	€14537	Pine and rock (95x35cm-37x14in) s.i.d.1943 ink col hanging scroll. 26-Apr-4 Sotheby's, Hong Kong #620/R est:50000-70000 (HK.D 140000)
£14225	$25605	€20769	Lotus (53x78cm-21x31in) s.i.d.1958 ink col hanging scroll. 26-Apr-4 Sotheby's, Hong Kong #617/R est:200000-250000 (HK.D 200000)
£21337	$38407	€31152	Waterfall (93x47cm-37x19in) s.i.d.1944 ink col hanging scroll exhib.lit. 26-Apr-4 Sotheby's, Hong Kong #626/R est:280000-350000 (HK.D 300000)

WU LIANG ZHI (16/17th C) Chinese

Works on paper

£8696	$16000	€12696	Composing poetry by moonlight (102x64cm-40x25in) s. ink wash silk. 24-Mar-4 Christie's, Rockefeller NY #21/R est:8000-12000

WU QINMU (1894-1953) Chinese

Works on paper

£10669	$19203	€15577	Scenes of Jiangnan (41x23cm-16x9in) s.i. ink col four. 26-Apr-4 Sotheby's, Hong Kong #618/R est:80000-100000 (HK.D 150000)

WU XINGQIAN (?) Chinese

Works on paper

£1477	$2732	€2200	Figures, cavalier et elephants. ink. 12-Mar-4 Piasa, Paris #300/R est:1500-2000

WU ZHEN (attrib) (1280-1354) Chinese

Works on paper

£4979	$8962	€7269	Fishermen (30x559cm-12x220in) s.i. ink handscroll silk. 25-Apr-4 Christie's, Hong Kong #309/R est:80000-100000 (HK.D 70000)

WU ZHENG (1876-1949) Chinese

Works on paper

£6401	$11522	€9345	Various subjects (25x30cm-10x12in) s. five d.1918 ink col album 12 leaves. 26-Apr-4 Sotheby's, Hong Kong #675/R est:45000-60000 (HK.D 90000)

WU ZUOREN (1908-1997) Chinese

£20077	$33529	€29312	Bathing beach (53x40cm-21x16in) s.i.d.1956 board lit. 26-Oct-3 Christie's, Hong Kong #139/R est:260000-360000 (HK.D 260000)

Works on paper

£4623	$8321	€6750	Goldfish (53x104cm-21x41in) s.d.1980 ink col scroll. 25-Apr-4 Christie's, Hong Kong #129/R est:60000-80000 (HK.D 65000)

WU ZUOREN and XIAO HUFANG (20th C) Chinese

Works on paper

£2647	$4500	€3865	Gold fish. Orchid (86x112cm-34x44in) s. one d.1982 ink col hanging scrolls pair. 4-Nov-3 Bonhams & Butterfields, San Francisco #3452/R est:2000-3000

WU ZUOREN and YU FEIAN (20th C) Chinese

Works on paper

£2134	$3841	€3116	Flower and bees. Goldfish (15x41cm-6x16in) s.i.d.1949 s.verso ink col folding fan double-sided. 25-Apr-4 Christie's, Hong Kong #83/R est:20000-30000 (HK.D 30000)

WUCHERER, Fritz (1873-1948) Swiss

£500	$900	€750	Evening woodland (55x80cm-22x31in) s. s.i. verso. 24-Apr-4 Reiss & Sohn, Konigstein #5380/R
£872	$1623	€1300	Barge (34x55cm-13x22in) s.i.d.1896 verso. 6-Mar-4 Arnold, Frankfurt #914/R
£1810	$3241	€2643	Frankfurt am Main (15x23cm-6x9in) s. panel. 13-May-4 Stuker, Bern #388 est:1000-1500 (S.FR 4200)

Works on paper

£371	$630	€530	Old stone bridge in Frankfurt (20x27cm-8x11in) s.d.9.VII.26 Indian ink board. 21-Nov-3 Reiss & Sohn, Konigstein #332/R

WUERMER, Carl (1900-1982) American

£5435	$10000	€7935	Houses in a valley (77x92cm-30x36in) s. prov. 27-Jun-4 Freeman, Philadelphia #116/R est:5000-8000

WUERPEL, Edmund H (1866-1958) American

£409	$650	€597	Dusk (34x42cm-13x17in) mono. s.i.d.1939-42 verso board. 12-Sep-3 Skinner, Boston #400/R
£457	$850	€667	Daybreak (20x13cm-8x5in) mono. board painted c.1910. 7-Mar-4 Treadway Gallery, Cincinnati #503/R
£488	$800	€708	Evening on the Mississippi river (30x20cm-12x8in) canvas on board exec.c.1915. 7-Jun-3 Treadway Gallery, Cincinnati #1384
£588	$1000	€858	Twilight lake landscape (46x36cm-18x14in) init. 7-Nov-3 Selkirks, St. Louis #579
£598	$1100	€873	Crepuscule (33x41cm-13x16in) init. masonite. 26-Jun-4 Selkirks, St. Louis #135/R
£698	$1200	€1019	Quiet pool (61x46cm-24x18in) mono. painted c.1934. 7-Dec-3 Treadway Gallery, Cincinnati #550/R
£1136	$2000	€1659	The pool, early evening (91x127cm-36x50in) mono. painted c.1921. 23-May-4 Treadway Gallery, Cincinnati #494/R est:3000-5000

WULFF, A M (?) ?

Sculpture

£1250	$2037	€1800	Cossack couple on horse (31cm-12in) s.cyrillic dark pat.bronze. 25-Sep-3 Dr Fritz Nagel, Stuttgart #1584/R est:1200

WULFING, Sulamith (1901-) German

Works on paper

£263 $473 €384 The prayer (23x18cm-9x7in) s.d.1955 W/C htd white. 26-Jan-4 Lilla Bukowskis, Stockholm #535 (S.KR 3500)
£590 $974 €850 Magnolias (27x21cm-11x8in) s.d.1936 pencil W/C. 2-Jul-3 Neumeister, Munich #506/R

WULULU, Jimmy (1936-) Australian

Sculpture

£1563 $2922 €2345 Hollow log coffin (179cm-70in) earth pigments hardwood prov. 26-Jul-4 Sotheby's, Melbourne #231/R est:4000-6000 (A.D 4000)
£1875 $3506 €2813 Hollow log coffin (228cm-90in) earth pigments hardwood prov. 26-Jul-4 Sotheby's, Melbourne #230/R est:5000-8000 (A.D 4800)

WULZ, Hugo (1937-) Austrian

£319 $533 €450 Love constellation (42x42cm-17x17in) s. oil acrylic. 16-Oct-3 Dorotheum, Salzburg #739/R

WUNDER, Wilhelm Ernst (1713-1787) Dutch

£5034 $9262 €7500 Still life with lobster, vegetables, butterfly and snail (40x49cm-16x19in) s. one of pair. 24-Mar-4 Dorotheum, Vienna #251/R est:10000-14000

WUNDERLICH, Albert (1876-1946) German

£476 $818 €680 Winter stream (38x53cm-15x21in) s.d.1917 i. verso board. 5-Dec-3 Michael Zeller, Lindau #830/R

WUNDERLICH, Edmund (1902-1985) Swiss

£366 $656 €534 Bondasca mountains (65x140cm-26x55in) s.d.64 i. verso. 13-May-4 Stuker, Bern #390 (S.FR 850)

WUNDERLICH, Paul (1927-) German

£571 $1010 €850 Brown torso (66x54cm-26x21in) s. verso acrylic painted 1967. 28-Apr-4 Artcurial Briest, Paris #468
£604 $1069 €900 Blue torso (66x54cm-26x21in) s.d.67 verso acrylic prov. 28-Apr-4 Artcurial Briest, Paris #469 est:1200-1500
£1511 $2568 €2206 Still life of fish (53x67cm-21x26in) s.d.73. 4-Nov-3 Bukowskis, Stockholm #615/R est:25000-30000 (S.KR 20000)
£1622 $2903 €2400 Woman with helmet-like hat (99x79cm-39x31in) s.d.91 acrylic. 8-May-4 Dawo, Saarbrucken #171/R est:2800
£2238 $3804 €3200 Untitled - figure (27x41cm-11x16in) s. i. verso prov. 27-Nov-3 Lempertz, Koln #535/R est:3000
£2400 $4344 €3504 Portrait en buste d'une jeune femme, apres Lucas Cranach (80x65cm-31x26in) s. s.i.d.90 verso. 1-Apr-4 Christie's, Kensington #254/R est:1000-1500
£2400 $4344 €3504 Sans tites (91x73cm-36x29in) s.d.63. 1-Apr-4 Christie's, Kensington #256/R est:1500-2000
£3667 $6710 €5500 Salomo II, 9. Look he's standing behind our wall (130x97cm-51x38in) s.d.69/70 prov.exhib. 4-Jun-4 Lempertz, Koln #541/R est:5500
£4225 $7310 €6000 Untitled (92x73cm-36x29in) s.d.69 acrylic lit. 13-Dec-3 Lempertz, Koln #197/R est:3000-3500
£5000 $9150 €7500 Salomo VII, 2-1 (160x130cm-63x51in) s.d.69/70 prov.exhib. 4-Jun-4 Lempertz, Koln #542/R est:7500

Sculpture

£1079 $1770 €1500 Chess game. wood pat.bronze. 4-Jun-3 Ketterer, Hamburg #997/R est:3000-3500
£1389 $2319 €2000 Crescent moon (117cm-46in) i. bronze marble socle. 25-Oct-3 Auktionhaus Herr, Cologne #323/R est:2200-4400
£1600 $2864 €2400 Nike (59cm-23in) brown green pat.bronze marble socle. 15-May-4 Van Ham, Cologne #1045/R est:2000
£6643 $11294 €9500 Woman (206cm-81in) s. acrylic spray pencil panel mahogany onyx exhib. 27-Nov-3 Lempertz, Koln #536/R est:9500
£6667 $12200 €10000 Chairman (135x45x25cm-53x18x10in) st.mono.d.68 brown gold pat.bronze prov.exhib. 4-Jun-4 Lempertz, Koln #540/R est:10000

Works on paper

£400 $724 €600 Jeune femme allongee (83x66cm-33x26in) s. gouache lead pencil. 1-Apr-4 Credit Municipal, Paris #26
£470 $832 €700 Joanna sur une chaise (88x72cm-35x28in) s.d.69 mixed media prov.exhib. 28-Apr-4 Artcurial Briest, Paris #471
£604 $1069 €900 Torse mit herz (86x69cm-34x27in) s.d.70 gouache prov.exhib. 28-Apr-4 Artcurial Briest, Paris #470/R est:1200-1500
£604 $1117 €900 Fleurs et lineaire (46x32cm-18x13in) s.d.1978 gouache sold with a book. 15-Mar-4 Horta, Bruxelles #232
£738 $1366 €1100 Fleur et lineaire (46x32cm-18x13in) s.d.1978 gouache sold with a book. 15-Mar-4 Horta, Bruxelles #231
£900 $1629 €1314 Sans titre (72x50cm-28x20in) s.d.15.9.90 pencil col chks. 1-Apr-4 Christie's, Kensington #255/R
£1467 $2684 €2200 Nude and door handle (73x55cm-29x22in) s.d.75 spray W/C. 4-Jun-4 Lempertz, Koln #544/R est:2500
£2400 $4344 €3504 Femme au chapeau (86x65cm-34x26in) s. s.i.d.91 verso pencil oil on canvas. 1-Apr-4 Christie's, Kensington #253/R est:1000-1500

WUNDERWALD, Gustav (1882-1945) German

Works on paper

£432 $708 €600 Boats on the Wannsee (15x24cm-6x9in) s. col pen pencil board. 4-Jun-3 Ketterer, Hamburg #1000/R
£719 $1180 €1000 Boats on lakeshore (15x24cm-6x9in) s. col pen pencil board. 4-Jun-3 Ketterer, Hamburg #999/R
£1000 $1840 €1500 Electricity pylons (46x36cm-18x14in) s. chk. 12-Jun-4 Villa Grisebach, Berlin #662/R est:1500-2000
£2667 $4907 €4000 Freight boat (39x54cm-15x21in) s. pencil brown paper exhib. 12-Jun-4 Villa Grisebach, Berlin #663/R est:2000-3000

WUNNENBERG, Walther (1818-1900) German

£369 $687 €550 Rhine landscape near Bingen (55x81cm-22x32in) s. 6-Mar-4 Arnold, Frankfurt #920/R
£839 $1427 €1200 Woodland with stream (22x25cm-9x10in) s. panel. 21-Nov-3 Reiss & Sohn, Konigstein #37/R est:1000
£1241 $2297 €1800 Rhine panorama near Roland's corner (39x60cm-15x24in) s. 14-Feb-4 Hans Stahl, Hamburg #110/R est:1400

WUNSCH, E (19th C) ?

£1182 $1962 €1714 Venice - Grand Canal (26x35cm-10x14in) s. board. 13-Jun-3 Zofingen, Switzerland #2384/R est:1200 (S.FR 2600)

WUNSCH, Marie (1862-1898) German

£1338 $2221 €1900 Small secret (27x18cm-11x7in) s. panel. 12-Jun-3 Dorotheum, Graz #81

WUNUWUN, Jack (1930-1990) Australian

Works on paper

£3711 $6939 €5567 Barritji, yam, murguruwal, dragonfly, and bunba, butterfly (145x79cm-57x31in) name.i.verso earth pigment eucalyptus bark exec.c.1978 prov. 26-Jul-4 Sotheby's, Melbourne #400/R est:5000-8000 (A.D 9500)

WUORILA-STENBERG, Henry (1949-) Finnish

£267 $491 €400 Dark composition (70x52cm-28x20in) s.d.1989 verso. 9-Jun-4 Bukowskis, Helsinki #579/R
£347 $638 €520 Light composition (70x52cm-28x20in) s.d.1989 verso. 9-Jun-4 Bukowskis, Helsinki #580/R

WURM, Erwin (1954-) Austrian

Sculpture

£3356 $5940 €5000 Untitled (58x87cm-23x34in) panel tin. 28-Apr-4 Wiener Kunst Auktionen, Vienna #310/R est:5000-9000

Works on paper

£946 $1665 €1400 Make your own F E Walther (21x30cm-8x12in) s.i.d.2001 felt pen wax crayon prov.lit. 18-May-4 Tajan, Paris #182/R est:1000-1200

WURRABADALAMBA, Meingara (20th C) Australian

Works on paper

£386 $606 €564 Connexion Island (42x73cm-17x29in) natural pigments bark. 27-Aug-3 Christie's, Sydney #775 (A.D 950)

WURRABADALAMBA, Nangwara (20th C) Australian

Works on paper

£732 $1149 €1069 Cutting cicatrices (43x73cm-17x29in) natural pigments bark. 27-Aug-3 Christie's, Sydney #773/R est:500-800 (A.D 1800)
£1057 $1659 €1543 Echidna and Dugong (44x73cm-17x29in) natural pigments bark. 27-Aug-3 Christie's, Sydney #777/R est:500-800 (A.D 2600)

WURRAMARA, Mangalala (20th C) Australian

Works on paper

£386 $606 €564 Untitled (61x39cm-24x15in) natural pigments bark. 27-Aug-3 Christie's, Sydney #772 (A.D 950)

WURRAMARA, Nadjalgala (20th C) Australian

Works on paper

£650 $1021 €949 South east wind (62x39cm-24x15in) natural pigments bark. 27-Aug-3 Christie's, Sydney #763 est:500-800 (A.D 1600)

WURSTER, Bruno Carlos (1939-) Swiss

Works on paper

£431 $772 €629 Untitled (110x90cm-43x35in) s.d.IX 1968 i. verso mixed media canvas. 12-May-4 Dobiaschofsky, Bern #1074/R (S.FR 1000)

WURTH, Xavier (1869-1933) Belgian

£600 $1074 €900 Paysage a la riviere (46x61cm-18x24in) s. 11-May-4 Vanderkindere, Brussels #6
£1181 $1877 €1700 Paysage d'automne anime (136x101cm-54x40in) s.d.1904. 9-Sep-3 Vanderkindere, Brussels #12

WURTZEN, Carl (1825-1880) Danish

£280 $439 €409 Landscape with woodland lake (26x39cm-10x15in) s. 30-Aug-3 Rasmussen, Havnen #2143 (D.KR 3000)

£305	$548	€445	Heather at Silkeborg Islands (30x41cm-12x16in) s. 24-Apr-4 Rasmussen, Havnen #2278 (D.KR 3400)
£321	$583	€469	Wooded landscape (31x51cm-12x20in) s. 7-Feb-4 Rasmussen, Havnen #2113 (D.KR 3500)
£374	$591	€542	Pipe smoking farmer enjoying the sunset (65x89cm-26x35in) s.d.1855. 2-Sep-3 Rasmussen, Copenhagen #1909/R (D.KR 4000)
£375	$611	€548	Autumn day in the woods (40x60cm-16x24in) s.d.1869. 27-Sep-3 Rasmussen, Havnen #2193 (D.KR 4000)
£586	$1084	€856	Wooded landscape with children walking (44x70cm-17x28in) s. 15-Mar-4 Rasmussen, Vejle #450/R (D.KR 6500)
£1028	$1624	€1491	Landscape from Maalov, children watching ducks from bridge (43x69cm-17x27in) s.d.1860. 2-Sep-3 Rasmussen, Copenhagen #1947/R (D.KR 11000)
£1882	$3387	€2748	Autumn landscape with harvesters (59x96cm-23x38in) s.d.1879. 24-Apr-4 Rasmussen, Havnen #2338/R est:8000-10000 (D.KR 21000)

WUST, Christoffel (1801-?) American

£2533	$4585	€3800	Sleeping kitchen maid (60x48cm-24x19in) s. panel. 1-Apr-4 Van Ham, Cologne #1715/R est:3800

WUST, Johann Heinrich (1741-1821) Swiss

£3664	$6558	€5349	Wooded river landscape with figures (44x59cm-17x23in) s.d.98. 13-May-4 Stuker, Bern #389/R est:4000-6000 (S.FR 8500)

WUTHRICH, Marianne (1931-) Swiss

Works on paper

£280	$502	€409	Doll (57x36cm-22x14in) s.d.75 W/C on pencil. 12-May-4 Dobiaschofsky, Bern #2178/R (S.FR 650)

WUTKY, Michael (1739-1823) Austrian

£11189	$19021	€16000	Cascata delle Marmore in Terni (95x63cm-37x25in) paper on board prov.lit. 20-Nov-3 Van Ham, Cologne #1441/R est:12000

WUTTKE, Carl (1849-1927) German

£400	$720	€600	Southern landscape with temple, palms and figures (33x21cm-13x8in) s. panel. 22-Apr-4 Weidler, Nurnberg #311/R
£423	$731	€600	Landscape near Tonadico, Valle di primero (23x32cm-9x13in) s.d.84 i.verso cardboard. 10-Dec-3 Hugo Ruef, Munich #2525/R
£473	$832	€700	Ante room of Church (31x22cm-12x9in) s. panel. 22-May-4 Lempertz, Koln #1631/R
£473	$832	€700	Church by sea with Etna beyond (37x29cm-15x11in) s. panel. 22-May-4 Lempertz, Koln #1630/R
£557	$1042	€830	Southern landscape with temple ruins, palms and figures (33x21cm-13x8in) s. panel. 27-Feb-4 Weidler, Nurnberg #8773/R
£634	$1096	€900	View of Torbole (35x24cm-14x9in) s.d.1894 i.verso cardboard. 10-Dec-3 Hugo Ruef, Munich #2526/R
£662	$1205	€1000	View of the Nile (25x37cm-10x15in) s.d.1902 cardboard. 16-Jun-4 Hugo Ruef, Munich #1118/R
£826	$1379	€1198	Landscape near Assuan (20x13cm-8x5in) s.i. panel. 23-Jun-3 Philippe Schuler, Zurich #3555/R est:1400-1800 (S.FR 1800)
£872	$1605	€1300	David Street in Jerusalem (20x13cm-8x5in) s. i. verso panel. 24-Mar-4 Hugo Ruef, Munich #1155/R
£1000	$1790	€1460	Abu Simbel. The Sphinx and the Pyramids (20x27cm-8x11in) s. one i. panel pair. 18-Mar-4 Christie's, Kensington #642/R est:1200-1800
£1181	$1948	€1700	Oriental street scene (20x28cm-8x11in) s. panel. 3-Jul-3 Neumeister, Munich #2945 est:250
£1202	$2116	€1755	Venice (20x13cm-8x5in) s. 23-May-4 Agra, Warsaw #25/R (P.Z 8500)
£1831	$3168	€2600	Oriental street (20x13cm-8x5in) s. board. 13-Dec-3 Lempertz, Koln #65/R est:2000

WYANT, Alexander H (1836-1892) American

£443	$700	€647	Path through the woods (20x13cm-8x5in) grisaille. 7-Sep-3 Treadway Gallery, Cincinnati #559/R
£682	$1200	€996	Study of tree (51x30cm-20x12in) s. prov.exhib. 3-Jan-4 Collins, Maine #37/R
£966	$1700	€1410	Poetic landscape (15x25cm-6x10in) s. prov. 3-Jan-4 Collins, Maine #33/R est:600-900
£995	$1662	€1453	Figure fishing in a summer landscape (21x36cm-8x14in) s. 17-Nov-3 Waddingtons, Toronto #12/R est:2000-3000 (C.D 2200)
£1176	$1965	€1717	Figure in a clearing (24x39cm-9x15in) s. 17-Nov-3 Waddingtons, Toronto #11/R est:2000-3000 (C.D 2600)
£1285	$2300	€1876	Mohawk Valley (10x18cm-4x7in) s. indis.d. panel prov. 20-Mar-4 Sloans & Kenyon, Bethesda #1197/R est:1500-2000
£1413	$2600	€2063	Quiet stream (41x30cm-16x12in) s. prov. 26-Jun-4 Sloans & Kenyon, Bethesda #1086/R est:1800-2200
£1471	$2500	€2148	Wyant's Rock (23x36cm-9x14in) s. prov. 21-Nov-3 Skinner, Boston #261/R est:5000-7000
£1887	$3000	€2755	Autumn trees (31x41cm-12x16in) s. 12-Sep-3 Skinner, Boston #279/R
£4706	$8000	€6871	Lake in the Adirondacks (30x51cm-12x20in) s. prov. 30-Oct-3 Phillips, New York #20/R est:8000-10000
£4938	$8000	€7160	Mountain mist (44x65cm-17x26in) s. 8-Aug-3 Barridorf, Portland #68/R est:4000-6000
£5389	$9000	€7868	Pastoral landscape (28x36cm-11x14in) s. board. 7-Oct-3 Sotheby's, New York #190 est:4000-6000
£9497	$17000	€13866	Evening landscape (30x46cm-12x18in) s. prov. 6-May-4 Shannon's, Milford #41/R est:6000-8000
£15988	$27500	€23342	River through the woods (46x61cm-18x24in) s.d.1865. 3-Dec-3 Sotheby's, New York #129/R est:12000-15000
£21802	$37500	€31831	Storm ahead (58x81cm-23x32in) s.d.1864. 3-Dec-3 Sotheby's, New York #128/R est:20000-30000

WYATT, Benjamin Dean (1775-1850) British

Works on paper

£900	$1656	€1314	Maresfield Park, East Sussex (32x51cm-13x20in) s.d.1816 W/C prov. 8-Jun-4 Bonhams, New Bond Street #45/R

WYATT, Irene (fl.1927-1939) British

£300	$501	€438	Good book (50x60cm-20x24in) s. 16-Oct-3 Lyon & Turnbull, Edinburgh #18

WYATT, Katharine Montagu (fl.1889-1929) British

Works on paper

£450	$819	€675	The yellow room at Holland House (48x37cm-19x15in) s.i. pencil W/C bodycol gum arabic. 1-Jul-4 Christie's, Kensington #260/R
£620	$1141	€905	Procession in Fuenterrabia, Spain (35x25cm-14x10in) s. W/C over pencil. 29-Mar-4 Bonhams, Bath #33/R

WYATT, Samuel (18th C) British

Works on paper

£1100	$1947	€1606	Town and citadel of Corinth (36x60cm-14x24in) i.verso W/C. 29-Apr-4 Christie's, Kensington #185/R est:1000-1500

WYATVILLE, Sir Jeffry (1766-1840) British

Works on paper

£3000	$5520	€4380	Design for entrance door of the Coffe Room at Windsor Castle (27x23cm-11x9in) i. W/C prov. 8-Jun-4 Bonhams, New Bond Street #43/R est:3000-5000

WYBURD, Francis John (1826-1893) British

£2372	$4245	€3463	Imogen (19x15cm-7x6in) mono. board prov. 15-May-4 Christie's, Sydney #142/R est:8000-12000 (A.D 6000)

WYCK, Jan (1640-1702) Dutch

£7000	$12110	€10220	Cavalry battle scene (39x55cm-15x22in) s. 11-Dec-3 Sotheby's, London #147/R est:6000-8000
£19444	$35000	€28388	Calvary skirmish by a river, fortress beyond (99x131cm-39x52in) s. 23-Jan-4 Christie's, Rockefeller NY #22/R est:50000-70000

WYCK, Jan (attrib) (1640-1702) Dutch

£3695	$6615	€5395	Harbour scene with figures (106x148cm-42x58in) 26-May-4 AB Stockholms Auktionsverk #2551/R est:60000-80000 (S.KR 50000)

WYCK, Thomas (1616-1677) Dutch

£483	$806	€700	Man with horse drinking from cistern (17x19cm-7x7in) bears i. Indian ink brush bister wash over ochre chk prov. 15-Nov-3 Lempertz, Koln #1440/R
£7534	$12808	€11000	Landscape with figures (53x70cm-21x28in) s. panel. 5-Nov-3 Beaussant & Lefèvre, Paris #33/R
£7692	$13231	€11000	Stopping at the inn (35x28cm-14x11in) mono. board. 2-Dec-3 Sotheby's, Milan #68/R est:7000-10000

WYCK, Thomas (attrib) (1616-1677) Dutch

£4730	$8324	€7000	Southern harbour scene with workmen unloading (43x52cm-17x20in) 18-May-4 Sotheby's, Amsterdam #19/R est:7000-9000
£5333	$9547	€8000	Study of the alchemist in his workshop (27x21cm-11x8in) panel. 15-May-4 Hagelstam, Helsinki #30/R est:7000
£6000	$11220	€9000	Travellers resting outside the walls of an Italian town (51x43cm-20x17in) s. panel prov. 20-Jul-4 Peter Francis, Wales #32/R est:5000-8000

Works on paper

£1712	$2911	€2500	Corner of a barn interior (28x20cm-11x8in) black chk col wash. 4-Nov-3 Sotheby's, Amsterdam #57/R est:2500-3500

WYCK, Thomas (circle) (1616-1677) Dutch

£5500	$10065	€8030	Mediterranean coastal view (48x65cm-19x26in) init. 9-Jul-4 Christie's, Kensington #28/R est:3000-5000

WYCKAERT, Maurice (1923-1996) Belgian

£733	$1342	€1100	Les maisons rouges (40x55cm-16x22in) s.d.49. 7-Jun-4 Palais de Beaux Arts, Brussels #200/R
£2282	$4039	€3400	Dialogue parisien (80x70cm-31x28in) s. 27-Apr-4 Campo, Vlaamse Kaai #662 est:2500-3000
£2657	$4438	€3800	Qui regarde qui (75x80cm-30x31in) s.d.1990 verso. 13-Oct-3 Horta, Bruxelles #199 est:3000-3500
£2953	$5463	€4400	Glorious day (60x49cm-24x19in) s. i.d.74 verso prov. 13-Mar-4 De Vuyst, Lokeren #404/R est:3500-4500
£3916	$6657	€5600	Le glaneur (160x140cm-63x55in) s. d.90 verso. 18-Nov-3 Vanderkindere, Brussels #175/R est:5000-6500
£4577	$7919	€6500	L'origine des choses (120x100cm-47x39in) s.d.1974 s.i.d.74. 13-Dec-3 De Vuyst, Lokeren #586/R est:7500-9000
£8000	$14640	€12000	D'un autre age (116x95cm-46x37in) s.d.71 verso prov. 7-Jun-4 Palais de Beaux Arts, Brussels #146/R est:10000-15000

Works on paper

£295	$546	€440	Landscape II (24x31cm-9x12in) s. wash exhib. 13-Mar-4 De Vuyst, Lokeren #407

£872 $1614 €1300 Aladdin's wonderful carpet (54x63cm-21x25in) s.d.75 gouache exhib. 13-Mar-4 De Vuyst, Lokeren #405/R
£872 $1614 €1300 Trou ou tache (54x63cm-21x25in) s.d.76 gouache exhib. 13-Mar-4 De Vuyst, Lokeren #406/R

WYCZOLKOWSKI, Léon (1852-1936) Polish

Works on paper
£2656 $4436 €3878 Trees (61x46cm-24x18in) s. pastel exec.c.1930. 19-Oct-3 Agra, Warsaw #23/R est:1000 (P.Z 17000)
£3631 $6281 €5301 Interior of a church (68x47cm-27x19in) s.d.1928 chk W/C sepia. 14-Dec-3 Agra, Warsaw #51/R est:9000 (P.Z 24000)
£3906 $6523 €5703 Woman in traditional dress (45x36cm-18x14in) s.d.1914 W/C. 19-Oct-3 Agra, Warsaw #16/R est:25000 (P.Z 25000)
£4539 $7852 €6627 Yellow flowers (33x45cm-13x18in) s. pastel exec. c.1910. 14-Dec-3 Agra, Warsaw #73/R est:30000 (P.Z 30000)
£7031 $11742 €10265 Still life with flowers and plant (51x77cm-20x30in) s.d.1914 W/C. 19-Oct-3 Agra, Warsaw #7/R est:40000 (P.Z 45000)
£10273 $17053 €14999 Autumn landscape (46x65cm-18x26in) s.d.1910 pastel W/C. 15-Jun-3 Agra, Warsaw #7/R est:60000 (P.Z 64000)

WYDEVELD, Arnoud (19th C) Dutch

£471 $800 €688 Still life with peaches (33x46cm-13x18in) s. 22-Nov-3 Jackson's, Cedar Falls #369/R
£539 $900 €787 Still life with fish (37x51cm-15x20in) s. i.verso board. 19-Oct-3 Bonhams & Butterfields, Los Angeles #7054
£2857 $5000 €4171 Still life with strawberries, peaches and bananas (51x38cm-20x15in) s. panel. 19-Dec-3 Sotheby's, New York #1075/R est:5000-7000
£2989 $5500 €4364 Still life with grapes, a peach and glass of wine on a ledge (25x20cm-10x8in) s. panel prov. 8-Jun-4 Bonhams & Butterfields, San Francisco #4014/R est:3000-5000

WYDOOGEN, N M (attrib) (19th C) Dutch

£3265 $5943 €4800 Winter, house by a frozen river at dusk (60x86cm-24x34in) with sig. 3-Feb-4 Christie's, Amsterdam #81/R est:3000-5000

WYETH, Andrew (1917-) American

£426136 $750000 €622159 Monday morning (30x41cm-12x16in) s. tempera panel painted 1955 prov.exhib.lit. 19-May-4 Sotheby's, New York #173/R est:400000-600000
Prints
£2095 $3750 €3059 Fog bell (69x48cm-27x19in) s. collotype edition of 250. 8-Jan-4 James Julia, Fairfield #504/R est:6000-8000
Works on paper
£1497 $2500 €2186 Liberty bearer (36x25cm-14x10in) i. pen ink prov. 7-Oct-3 Sotheby's, New York #245 est:3000-5000
£11892 $22000 €17362 Spring lambs (24x25cm-9x10in) s. pencil. 11-Mar-4 Christie's, Rockefeller NY #107/R est:6000-8000
£14535 $25000 €21221 Shore barrier (53x48cm-21x19in) s. blk ink wash scratching out card exec 1939 prov.exhib. 7-Dec-3 Freeman, Philadelphia #120 est:25000-40000
£17442 $30000 €25465 Portrait of Bishop John B Coburn (34x55cm-13x22in) s. gouache drybrush. 4-Dec-3 Christie's, Rockefeller NY #115/R est:30000-50000
£24709 $42500 €36075 Low tide (45x55cm-18x22in) s.i. W/C executed 1938 prov.exhib. 3-Dec-3 Sotheby's, New York #63/R est:40000-60000
£34591 $55000 €50503 Fog Horns (53x74cm-21x29in) W/C exec 1952. 25-Feb-3 Bunch, West Chester #482/R
£36932 $65000 €53921 Under the live oaks (46x56cm-18x22in) s. W/C exec 1937 prov. 19-May-4 Sotheby's, New York #178/R est:30000-50000
£48295 $85000 €70511 Deep woods (53x76cm-21x30in) s. W/C exec 1973 prov.exhib.lit. 19-May-4 Sotheby's, New York #192/R est:85000-100000
£48295 $85000 €70511 Attic (53x74cm-21x29in) s. W/C prov.exhib. 19-May-4 Sotheby's, New York #193/R est:35000-45000
£104651 $180000 €152790 Mending fences (56x76cm-22x30in) s. W/C executed 1960 prov.exhib. 3-Dec-3 Sotheby's, New York #71/R est:125000-175000
£153409 $270000 €223977 Moonrise (53x74cm-21x29in) s. W/C exec 1938. 19-May-4 Sotheby's, New York #177/R est:80000-120000

WYETH, Henriette (1907-1997) American

£1955 $3500 €2854 Portrait of Peter Hurd (51x36cm-20x14in) s. 8-Jan-4 James Julia, Fairfield #505/R est:2000-3000
£7784 $13000 €11365 Portrait of a young girl (51x46cm-20x18in) s. prov.exhib. 23-Oct-3 Shannon's, Milford #117/R est:8000-12000
£10588 $18000 €15458 Still life with bulto (25x36cm-10x14in) prov.lit. 1-Nov-3 Santa Fe Art, Santa Fe #75/R est:25000-35000

WYETH, James (1946-) American

£170455 $300000 €248864 Orca Bates (102x102cm-40x40in) s.i. panel painted 1990 prov.exhib.lit. 19-May-4 Sotheby's, New York #188/R est:300000-500000
Works on paper
£1497 $2500 €2186 Portrait of Arnold Schwartzenegger, study no 7 (116x91cm-46x36in) s. chl corrugated cardboard exec.c.1977. 7-Oct-3 Sotheby's, New York #349 est:2500-4000
£1648 $3000 €2406 Arnold Schwarzenegger flexing his biceps (117x91cm-46x36in) s. chl corrugated cardboard. 29-Jun-4 Sotheby's, New York #316/R est:2500-4000
£3086 $5000 €4475 Portrait of Jimmy Carter (25x30cm-10x12in) s.i. dr. 8-Aug-3 Barridorf, Portland #242/R est:6000-9000
£12784 $22500 €18665 Bollard (48x60cm-19x24in) s. W/C prov. 18-May-4 Sotheby's, New York #214/R est:8000-12000
£31977 $55000 €46686 Andy Warhol, profile, seted (41x34cm-16x13in) s. gouache W/C pencil paper on board prov.exhib. 4-Dec-3 Christie's, Rockefeller NY #116/R est:25000-35000

WYETH, Newell Convers (1882-1945) American

£31250 $55000 €45625 Carvers of the Sphinx (92x59cm-36x23in) s.i. canvas on board painted 1926 lit. 18-May-4 Christie's, Rockefeller NY #152/R est:70000-100000
£34884 $60000 €50931 Story of glass (69x63cm-27x25in) s. panel lit. 3-Dec-3 Sotheby's, New York #161/R est:60000-80000
£40698 $70000 €59419 Story of tin (69x63cm-27x25in) s. panel lit. 3-Dec-3 Sotheby's, New York #160/R est:70000-90000
£40698 $70000 €59419 Story of salt (69x63cm-27x25in) s. panel lit. 3-Dec-3 Sotheby's, New York #162/R est:70000-90000
£46023 $81000 €67194 He kept his gaze fixed as before and pointed (96x66cm-38x26in) s.d.05 prov.lit. 18-May-4 Christie's, Rockefeller NY #151/R est:80000-120000
£56818 $100000 €82954 Next to me was a girl who looked about eighteen (107x91cm-42x36in) s. painted c.1929 prov.exhib.lit. 19-May-4 Sotheby's, New York #204/R est:125000-175000
£58140 $100000 €84884 Story of furs (69x63cm-27x25in) s. i.verso panel lit. 3-Dec-3 Sotheby's, New York #159/R est:70000-90000
£58140 $100000 €84884 Duck hunt (64x130cm-25x51in) s. prov. 4-Dec-3 Christie's, Rockefeller NY #104/R est:120000-180000
£102273 $180000 €149319 Hiawatha fishing (94x68cm-37x27in) s. painted 1907 prov.lit. 18-May-4 Christie's, Rockefeller NY #56/R est:180000-240000

WYETH, Newell Convers (attrib) (1882-1945) American

£18634 $30000 €27206 Study for The Clippers (97x66cm-38x26in) 20-Aug-3 James Julia, Fairfield #590/R est:30000-40000

WYETH, Paul James Logan (1920-1983) British

£250 $455 €365 Portrait of a lady in a formal golden dress (91x71cm-36x28in) s.d.70. 1-Jul-4 Christie's, Kensington #179/R
£260 $481 €380 Still life with yellow roses (61x51cm-24x20in) board. 11-Mar-4 Christie's, Kensington #1/R
£300 $501 €438 Poix, France (15x25cm-6x10in) init. s.verso panel. 16-Oct-3 Christie's, Kensington #318
£300 $555 €438 Country landscape with horse grazing (46x91cm-18x36in) 11-Mar-4 Christie's, Kensington #146
£300 $546 €438 Apple orchard (46x61cm-18x24in) s. 1-Jul-4 Christie's, Kensington #163/R
£320 $582 €467 Carina and Pipi with the apple blossom (84x107cm-33x42in) s.d.67. 1-Jul-4 Christie's, Kensington #159/R
£420 $764 €613 St Germaindu Bel Air Lot (71x91cm-28x36in) s.d.79 s.i. verso board. 1-Jul-4 Christie's, Kensington #166/R
£650 $1203 €949 Apple blossom. Still life with yellow roses (61x51cm-24x20in) s.d.77 two. 11-Mar-4 Christie's, Kensington #141/R
£700 $1295 €1022 Portrait a lady (127x101cm-50x40in) s.d.70. 11-Mar-4 Christie's, Kensington #152/R
£700 $1295 €1022 Carola in the dining room (91x71cm-36x28in) s.d.63. 11-Mar-4 Christie's, Kensington #154/R
£800 $1456 €1168 Carina and Pipi in the Dining Room (110x91cm-43x36in) s.d.56 s.i. verso. 1-Jul-4 Christie's, Kensington #175/R
£800 $1456 €1168 Mrs Titula Wyeth, Carina and Carola in the studio (127x102cm-50x40in) s.d.58. 1-Jul-4 Christie's, Kensington #177/R
£850 $1573 €1241 Horse and cart in an orchard (63x76cm-25x30in) 11-Mar-4 Christie's, Kensington #157/R
£1000 $1850 €1460 Carina Wyeth in the artist studio (106x96cm-42x38in) s.d.78. 11-Mar-4 Christie's, Kensington #153/R est:1200-1800
£1000 $1820 €1460 Gideon and friends (151x181cm-59x71in) s.i. 1-Jul-4 Christie's, Kensington #185/R est:1000-1500
£1400 $2590 €2044 Danse Macabra (127x174cm-50x69in) s.d.72 s.i.verso. 11-Mar-4 Christie's, Kensington #161/R est:1500-2000
£1400 $2548 €2044 Early spring, Dordogne, France (185x145cm-73x57in) s.d.81. 1-Jul-4 Christie's, Kensington #168/R est:1500-2000
£1600 $2960 €2336 Self portrait with daughters. Carola Wyeth and toys (127x101cm-50x40in) s.d.57 i.verso two. 11-Mar-4 Christie's, Kensington #155/R est:1200-1800
£1700 $3145 €2482 Portobello Road fantasy (244x183cm-96x72in) 11-Mar-4 Christie's, Kensington #160/R est:2000-3000
Works on paper
£500 $910 €730 Portfolio of studies of family members including Carina, Carola and Gideon (58x41cm-23x16in) s.d. chl red chk. 1-Jul-4 Christie's, Kensington #174/R
£500 $910 €730 Collection of life drawings (52x43cm-20x17in) chl red chk. 1-Jul-4 Christie's, Kensington #169/R
£1200 $2184 €1752 Portfolio of portraits (76x54cm-30x21in) s.i.d. pencil chl red chk. 1-Jul-4 Christie's, Kensington #172/R est:600-800

WYGANT, Bob (1927-) American

£3352 $6000 €4894 Crossing in the Canyon (43x69cm-17x27in) acrylic board. 15-May-4 Altermann Galleries, Santa Fe #3/R

WYGRZYWALSKI, Feliks (1875-1944) Polish

£503 $931 €750 La priere (39x49cm-15x19in) s. panel. 15-Mar-4 Gros & Delettrez, Paris #124
£830 $1535 €1212 Young men rowing choppy sea with other boats (60x44cm-24x17in) d.1917. 14-Mar-4 Agra, Warsaw #34/R (P.Z 6000)
£867 $1577 €1300 Breakers at the seaside (45x80cm-18x31in) s. 1-Jul-4 Van Ham, Cologne #1676
£937 $1705 €1368 Rowing boat taking to sea (55x75cm-22x30in) s. painted 1939. 20-Jun-4 Agra, Warsaw #60/R (P.Z 6500)
£1172 $1957 €1711 Courting (35x50cm-14x20in) s. plywood. 19-Oct-3 Agra, Warsaw #46/R est:7000 (P.Z 7500)
£1200 $2172 €1800 Boys fishing off quay (32x22cm-13x9in) s.d.1912 panel. 1-Apr-4 Van Ham, Cologne #1716/R
£2000 $3600 €2920 Desert prayer (56x66cm-22x26in) s.i. 21-Jan-4 Sotheby's, Olympia #440/R est:2000-3000
£2821 $4401 €4119 Pirates (64x85cm-25x33in) s. painted c.1930. 30-Mar-3 Agra, Warsaw #20/R est:18000 (P.Z 18000)

£5000 $9000 €7500 Maharadja's entourage (59x79cm-23x31in) s. 21-Apr-4 Christie's, Amsterdam #44/R est:5000-7000

WYK, Hendrik Jan van (1911-) Dutch
£455 $782 €650 Basket with fruit, a butterfly and a beetle (20x23cm-8x9in) s. panel oval. 8-Dec-3 Glerum, Amsterdam #341/R

WYK, Henri van (1833-?) Dutch
£600 $1110 €876 Bord de riviere (19x24cm-7x9in) s. panel. 14-Jul-4 Christie's, Kensington #939/R
£1444 $2600 €2108 Boats moored at a dock (32x46cm-13x18in) s. 24-Apr-4 Weschler, Washington #564/R est:1500-2500
£1888 $3248 €2700 Cafe en Asie Mineure (35x65cm-14x26in) s. 8-Dec-3 Tajan, Paris #333/R est:2400-2600

WYLD, William (1806-1889) British
Works on paper
£563 $975 €800 Paysage cotier. Paysage de riviere (8x13cm-3x5in) one s. W/C pair. 10-Dec-3 Piasa, Paris #154
£800 $1480 €1168 Continental town landscape with a river boats and building, possibly Venice (13x18cm-5x7in) s. W/C. 11-Mar-4 Ewbank, Send #449
£900 $1656 €1314 Views of Paris from the Seine (18x26cm-7x10in) s. pencil W/C grey wash pair. 25-Mar-4 Christie's, Kensington #248/R
£1200 $2040 €1752 Piazza del Priori, Perugia (22x28cm-9x11in) s.i. W/C htd bodycol. 27-Nov-3 Sotheby's, London #280/R est:1200-1800
£2800 $5124 €4088 Flower market, Verona (23x33cm-9x13in) s.i. pencil W/C gum arabic htd white. 3-Jun-4 Christie's, London #159/R est:2000-3000
£4000 $6800 €5840 Doge's Palace, Venice (15x27cm-6x11in) s. W/C over pencil htd bodycol. 27-Nov-3 Sotheby's, London #279/R est:2000-3000
£4000 $7320 €5840 View of Naples (18x26cm-7x10in) s.i. pencil W/C htd bodycol scratching out prov. 3-Jun-4 Christie's, London #123/R est:1800-2500

WYLD, William (attrib) (1806-1889) British
£7500 $13650 €10950 Venetian regatta with numerous figures in fancy dress (43x61cm-17x24in) 16-Jun-4 John Nicholson, Haslemere #781/R est:2000-3000

WYLER, Otto (1887-1965) Swiss
£693 $1240 €1012 Park in St Cloud (66x81cm-26x32in) s.i.d.1929. 22-Mar-4 Philippe Schuler, Zurich #4368/R (S.FR 1600)

WYLIE, Kate (1877-1941) British
£600 $1050 €876 Roses (45x35cm-18x14in) s. 18-Dec-3 Bonhams, Edinburgh #310
£680 $1170 €993 Pink roses in a vase (29x22cm-11x9in) s. canvasboard. 4-Dec-3 Bonhams, Edinburgh #90
£850 $1488 €1241 Bowl of anemones and daisies (55x41cm-22x16in) s. 18-Dec-3 Bonhams, Edinburgh #326
£1100 $2013 €1606 Chines jug (45x50cm-18x20in) s. 8-Apr-4 Bonhams, Edinburgh #118 est:500-700
£2200 $4070 €3212 Stocks (46x61cm-18x24in) s. 11-Feb-4 Sotheby's, Olympia #170/R est:800-1200

WYLLER, Sverre (1953-) Norwegian
Works on paper
£680 $1156 €993 The NY Series - no.7 (35x45cm-14x18in) s.d.1993 verso collage acrylic panel prov.exhib.lit. 5-Nov-3 AB Stockholms Auktionsverk #1071/R (S.KR 9000)
£881 $1576 €1286 New York Series Number 2 (36x46cm-14x18in) s.i.d.1993 verso collage acrylic paper on panel. 22-Mar-4 Blomqvist, Oslo #626/R (N.KR 11000)

WYLLIE, Charles William (1853-1923) British
£600 $1002 €876 Entering port (23x33cm-9x13in) s. 14-Oct-3 Canterbury Auctions, UK #113/R
£5464 $10000 €7977 Shipping at dawn, Woolwich reach on the river Thames (46x81cm-18x32in) s. prov. 29-Jul-4 Christie's, Rockefeller NY #259/R est:12000-18000

WYLLIE, Harold (1880-?) British
Works on paper
£980 $1725 €1431 Warships in a harbour (36x58cm-14x23in) s.d.04 W/C. 21-May-4 Bracketts, Tunbridge Wells #259/R
£1950 $3432 €2847 Sailing ships in a harbour (32x55cm-13x22in) s.d.04 W/C. 21-May-4 Bracketts, Tunbridge Wells #260/R est:250-350

WYLLIE, W L (1851-1931) British
Works on paper
£1350 $2133 €1971 Cornish fishermen offshore (28x48cm-11x19in) s.d.1894. 23-Jul-3 Grant, Worcester #464 est:1000-1200

WYLLIE, William (?) British
Works on paper
£699 $1306 €1021 Plymouth Sound (26x41cm-10x16in) s.i. W/C. 24-Feb-4 Peter Webb, Auckland #182/R (NZ.D 1900)

WYLLIE, William Lionel (1851-1931) British
£800 $1432 €1168 Tugs and other shipping on the Thames (9x16cm-4x6in) card. 26-May-4 Christie's, Kensington #736/R
£1724 $2879 €2517 Pool of London (44x60cm-17x24in) s.d.1904 board. 20-Oct-3 Stephan Welz, Johannesburg #187/R est:5000-7000 (SA.R 20000)
£21000 $33600 €30660 Opening of Tower Bridge, 30th June 1894 (79x135cm-31x53in) 16-Sep-3 Bonhams, New Bond Street #50/R est:20000-30000
£22000 $37400 €32120 Landing fish at Ambleteuse (86x179cm-34x70in) s.d.1870 exhib. 19-Nov-3 Christie's, Kensington #591/R
£27000 $46440 €39420 L'entente Cordiale arrival of the French fleet in Cowes Roads (149x272cm-59x107in) s.d.1906 exhib. 2-Dec-3 Sotheby's, London #147/R est:30000-50000
£38000 $65360 €55480 Pushing down against the flood (122x214cm-48x84in) s.d.1902 exhib.lit. 2-Dec-3 Sotheby's, London #97/R est:30000-50000
Works on paper
£250 $398 €365 Portrait head and shoulders of a sailor (25x23cm-10x9in) s. W/C. 1-May-3 John Nicholson, Haslemere #653/R
£280 $512 €420 Thornycroft's shipyard (48x75cm-19x30in) s. W/C htd white. 27-Jul-4 Henry Adams, Chichester #392
£440 $700 €638 Antwerp Harbour (13x18cm-5x7in) s.i.d.1889 W/C. 9-Sep-3 David Duggleby, Scarborough #28
£460 $842 €672 Arrival of the Royal Yacht Victoria and Albert II (21x33cm-8x13in) W/C en grisaille. 27-Jan-4 Bonhams, Knightsbridge #293
£500 $915 €730 Ralholm and the Sogne Fjord (25x41cm-10x16in) s. W/C. 28-Jan-4 Mallams, Oxford #526/R
£500 $900 €730 Barges and other shipping in the Thames (25x35cm-10x14in) s.verso W/C. 22-Apr-4 Locke & England, Leamington Spa #86/R
£500 $885 €730 HMS Victory and other shipping outside Portsmouth Harbour (15x27cm-6x11in) s. W/C pencil. 27-Apr-4 Henry Adams, Chichester #617
£550 $935 €803 Thames barge and smaller craft offshore (18x39cm-7x15in) s. W/C. 25-Nov-3 Bonhams, Knightsbridge #59/R
£900 $1611 €1314 Bruinisse (12x41cm-5x16in) s.i. W/C. 26-May-4 Christie's, Kensington #461/R
£1000 $1800 €1460 Vlissingen from the canal (9x20cm-4x8in) s. W/C prov. 21-Apr-4 Cheffins, Cambridge #455/R est:400-500
£1000 $1770 €1460 Destroyers patrolling (25x41cm-10x16in) s.i. ink wash drawing. 28-Apr-4 Halls, Shrewsbury #477/R est:700-1000
£1100 $1991 €1606 First World War warship in harbour (23x33cm-9x13in) s.d.1910 W/C. 16-Apr-4 Keys, Aylsham #520/R est:1000-1500
£1100 $1969 €1606 Big-class yachts racing in Plymouth Sound (27x40cm-11x16in) s.i. pencil W/C. 26-May-4 Christie's, Kensington #496/R est:1200-1800
£2595 $4800 €3789 Bombardment of the Turkish Forts at Chanak during World War 1 (27x43cm-11x17in) s.i. pencil W/C. 10-Feb-4 Christie's, Rockefeller NY #137/R est:2000-3000
£3200 $5728 €4672 HMS Undaunted at Harwich (25x35cm-10x14in) pencil W/C scratching out. 26-May-4 Christie's, Kensington #460/R est:3500-4000
£3400 $6222 €4964 Woolwich Reach, tide time. s.i. W/C. 6-Jul-4 Bearnes, Exeter #409 est:500-700
£3500 $5950 €5110 Regatta at Kiel (26x476cm-10x187in) s.i.d.1912 pencil W/C. 19-Nov-3 Christie's, Kensington #427/R
£16000 $25600 €23360 Thames barges in the Pool of London racing down the river with the tide (67x95cm-26x37in) s. W/C htd white. 16-Sep-3 Bonhams, New Bond Street #79/R est:15000-20000

WYLLIE, William Lionel (attrib) (1851-1931) British
Works on paper
£360 $569 €522 View of the Royal Exchange, London (33x44cm-13x17in) pen ink wash dr card. 24-Jul-3 Dominic Winter, Swindon #84

WYLLIE, William Morison (fl.1852-1890) British
£1600 $2976 €2336 Harvesting (27x38cm-11x15in) s. panel. 4-Mar-4 Christie's, Kensington #497/R est:700-1000

WYMANS, Wilhelmus Lambertus (1888-1968) Dutch
£470 $874 €700 Harbour in Veere (30x40cm-12x16in) s.d. 4-Mar-4 Auction Maastricht #1060/R

WYMER, Reginald Augustus (19/20th C) British
Works on paper
£300 $555 €438 Fifth, Royal Irish Lancers (33x25cm-13x10in) s. W/C. 11-Mar-4 Duke & Son, Dorchester #121/R
£400 $668 €584 Uniforms of 4th Light Dragoons (36x54cm-14x21in) init.d.1886 W/C over pencil htd bodycol 12 on one sheet. 16-Oct-3 Lawrence, Crewkerne #640
£600 $996 €876 Coldstream Guards (20x11cm-8x4in) W/C three in one frame set of two. 1-Oct-3 Woolley & Wallis, Salisbury #169/R
£1620 $2592 €2300 Parade of the 5th Dragoon Guards (36x57cm-14x22in) s. W/C htd white prov. 22-Sep-3 Sotheby's, Amsterdam #307/R est:1000-1500

WYNANTS, Ernest (1878-1964) Belgian
Sculpture
£1842 $3389 €2800 Girl (42cm-17in) s. plaster. 28-Jun-4 Sotheby's, Amsterdam #293/R est:800-1200

WYNANTS, Jan (1630-1684) Dutch
£7000 $12110 €10220 Extensive wooded landscape with herdsman resting by a tree (45x37cm-18x15in) s. panel. 12-Dec-3 Christie's, Kensington #82/R est:6000-8000

WYNANTS, Jan and WYNTRACK, Dirck (17th C) Dutch
£49342 $90789 €75000 Pond with swans and ducks by farm (97x84cm-38x33in) prov.lit. 24-Jun-4 Christie's, Paris #28/R est:50000-70000

WYNANTSZ, August (1795-1848) Dutch
£819 $1466 €1196 Church at end of narrow street (17x15cm-7x6in) s.d.1840 panel. 12-May-4 Dobiaschofsky, Bern #1075/R est:3800 (S.FR 1900)
£1000 $1620 €1460 Figures on a Dutch street, near a church (20x16cm-8x6in) s.d.1824 panel. 30-Jul-3 Hamptons Fine Art, Godalming #247/R est:1000-1500
£4800 $8592 €7200 Vue de Gand anime (32x39cm-13x15in) s.d.1829 panel. 11-May-4 Vanderkindere, Brussels #149 est:5500-7500

WYNDHAM, Madeleine (fl.1896-1898) British
Works on paper
£2700 $4833 €3942 Ballad of Mr Rock (35x33cm-14x13in) indis sig. W/C bodycol set of three. 22-Mar-4 Bonhams & Brooks, Norfolk #103/R est:500-800

WYNDHAM, Richard (1896-1948) British
£1800 $3006 €2628 Cottages by a weir (64x76cm-25x30in) s. 16-Oct-3 Christie's, Kensington #468/R est:800-1200

WYNEN, Dominicus van (1661-?) Dutch
£16000 $27680 €23360 Scene of Witchcraft (122x93cm-48x37in) i. prov. 11-Dec-3 Sotheby's, London #198/R est:12000-18000

WYNFIELD, David Wilkie (1837-1887) British
£1800 $3222 €2628 Young king visits his fiancé (111x85cm-44x33in) i. 11-May-4 Bonhams, Knightsbridge #174/R est:2000-3000

WYNGAARD, Herman J (1922-) Dutch
£493 $883 €740 River landscape in the evening (59x89cm-23x35in) s. 11-May-4 Vendu Notarishuis, Rotterdam #169/R

WYNGAERDT, A J van (1808-1887) Dutch
£1399 $2336 €2000 Man in punt (17x29cm-7x11in) 11-Oct-3 Dr Fritz Nagel, Leipzig #3922/R est:1300

WYNGAERDT, Anthonie Jacobus van (1808-1887) Dutch
£500 $885 €730 Shepherd and his flock on a hill side (20x39cm-8x15in) mono.d. 29-Apr-4 Christie's, Kensington #169/R
£1933 $3480 €2900 Wood gatherers resting (18x15cm-7x6in) s.d.1855 panel. 20-Apr-4 Sotheby's, Amsterdam #4/R est:3000-5000
£2632 $4763 €4000 Summer landscape with shepherd and shepherdess resting with flock of sheep (23x35cm-9x14in) s. panel. 19-Apr-4 Glerum, Amsterdam #50/R est:1800-2200
£2917 $4871 €4200 Cows in a summer landscape (11x15cm-4x6in) s. panel. 21-Oct-3 Sotheby's, Amsterdam #21/R est:2000-3000
£5000 $9250 €7300 Harvesting the reeds (37x57cm-15x22in) s. 10-Mar-4 Sotheby's, Olympia #236/R est:4000-6000
£5903 $10035 €8500 Figures by a farmhouse on the heath (23x36cm-9x14in) s. panel. 28-Oct-3 Christie's, Amsterdam #17/R est:6000-8000
£6333 $11400 €9500 Cows in a meadow (23x36cm-9x14in) s. panel. 21-Apr-4 Christie's, Amsterdam #71/R est:6000-8000
Works on paper
£816 $1486 €1200 Peasant girl feeding a goat by a farm (19x32cm-7x13in) s. W/C htd white. 3-Feb-4 Christie's, Amsterdam #57 est:1500-2000

WYNGAERDT, Anthonie Jacobus van (attrib) (1808-1887) Dutch
£7500 $13800 €10950 Pastoral landscape (30x43cm-12x17in) panel. 25-Mar-4 Christie's, Kensington #171/R est:3000-5000

WYNGAERDT, Petrus Theodorus van (1816-1893) Dutch
£1333 $2400 €2000 Young poet (27x21cm-11x8in) s. panel. 20-Apr-4 Sotheby's, Amsterdam #21/R est:2000-3000

WYNN, Spencer (20th C) Canadian
£249 $416 €364 Inlet (28x35cm-11x14in) s.i.d.2001 board. 17-Nov-3 Hodgins, Calgary #40/R (C.D 550)
£813 $1455 €1187 Cascading glacier, Cariboo Mountain Rang, BC (61x91cm-24x36in) s.d.04 s.i.d. verso prov. 31-May-4 Sotheby's, Toronto #121/R est:3000-4000 (C.D 2000)

WYNNE, Bernard (20th C) American
£1955 $3500 €2933 Desert evening (61x86cm-24x34in) s. 16-May-4 Abell, Los Angeles #514/R

WYNNE, David (1926-) British
Sculpture
£5000 $8500 €7300 Melesande (32cm-13in) s.d.1950 bronze incl stone base. 18-Nov-3 Bonhams, Knightsbridge #216/R est:2000-4000

WYNNE-JONES, Nancy (1922-) British
£431 $702 €620 Outfarm (29x42cm-11x17in) acrylic prov.exhib. 23-Sep-3 De Veres Art Auctions, Dublin #137/R
£572 $1053 €870 Water lilies (42x30cm-17x12in) paper prov. 22-Jun-4 De Veres Art Auctions, Dublin #140/R
£1049 $1783 €1500 Bog with patch of light (28x41cm-11x16in) paper. 18-Nov-3 Whyte's, Dublin #62/R est:1500-2000
Works on paper
£500 $925 €730 Untitled 1963 (56x38cm-22x15in) s.d.1963 verso W/C. 11-Mar-4 Christie's, Kensington #376/R

WYNTER, Bryan (1915-1975) British
£2200 $3498 €3212 Abstract city (60x91cm-24x36in) s.d.49. 10-Sep-3 Sotheby's, Olympia #313/R est:2500-3500
£12000 $22200 €17520 Dark traverse (152x122cm-60x48in) s.i.d.1961 verso. 11-Feb-4 Sotheby's, Olympia #254/R est:5000-7000

WYNTRACK, Dirck (1625-1678) Dutch
£2747 $5000 €4011 Kitchen interior with boors smoking in the background (47x63cm-19x25in) panel. 4-Feb-4 Christie's, Rockefeller NY #63/R est:3000-5000

WYNTRACK, Dirck (attrib) (1625-1678) Dutch
£2933 $5280 €4400 Chiens attaquant des cygnes (23x34cm-9x13in) panel. 25-Apr-4 Chenu & Scrive, Lyon #53/R est:3000-4000

WYRSCH, Charles (1920-) Swiss
£568 $1033 €829 Head of a Spanish gentleman (41x33cm-16x13in) s. s.d.1971/1972/1973 verso. 16-Jun-4 Fischer, Luzern #2431/R (S.FR 1300)
£614 $1025 €896 Untitled (65x50cm-26x20in) s. s.d.1970 verso prov. 15-Nov-3 Galerie Gloggner, Luzern #110/R (S.FR 1400)
£877 $1465 €1280 Le poete (65x50cm-26x20in) s. s.i.d.1956-1957 verso prov. 15-Nov-3 Galerie Gloggner, Luzern #111/R (S.FR 2000)
Works on paper
£655 $1153 €956 Female nude (42x55cm-17x22in) s.d.Juli 1979 chl pastel chk prov. 22-May-4 Galerie Gloggner, Luzern #113/R (S.FR 1500)
£778 $1261 €1136 Nude (39x47cm-15x19in) s.d.1985 pastel chk chl. 24-May-3 Burkhard, Luzern #6/R (S.FR 1650)

WYRSCH, Johann Melchior (attrib) (1732-1798) Swiss
£1293 $2315 €1888 Madonna with sleeping child (47x38cm-19x15in) panel. 12-May-4 Dobiaschofsky, Bern #1076/R est:4000 (S.FR 3000)
£2098 $3503 €3000 Portrait of Franz Peter de Zeltner (87x73cm-34x29in) 7-Oct-3 Pandolfini, Florence #588/R est:4000-5000

WYSMULLER, Jan Hillebrand (1855-1925) Dutch
£382 $603 €550 Forest at Oosterbeek (36x60cm-14x24in) init.i. 2-Sep-3 Christie's, Amsterdam #279
£544 $990 €800 De groene wipbrug, green drawbridge in autumn (37x49cm-15x19in) s. canvas on board. 3-Feb-4 Christie's, Amsterdam #281
£658 $1211 €1000 Cows in a stable (36x59cm-14x23in) s. canvas on panel. 22-Jun-4 Christie's, Amsterdam #105/R
£1053 $1937 €1600 Houses along a river (41x60cm-16x24in) s. 22-Jun-4 Christie's, Amsterdam #309/R est:1200-1600
£1250 $1975 €1800 Fishing nets drying in a polder landscape (40x60cm-16x24in) s. 2-Sep-3 Christie's, Amsterdam #254/R est:1800-2000
£2639 $4169 €3800 Gathering shells at dusk (29x46cm-11x18in) s. panel. 2-Sep-3 Christie's, Amsterdam #252/R est:2500-3500

WYSPIANSKI, Stanislas (1869-1907) Polish
Works on paper
£3026 $5234 €4418 Roses (26x22cm-10x9in) mono.d.1904 W/C chk lit. 14-Dec-3 Agra, Warsaw #37/R est:15000 (P.Z 20000)
£9375 $15656 €13688 Portrait of a man with a hat (46x38cm-18x15in) s. pastel. 19-Oct-3 Agra, Warsaw #5/R est:35000 (P.Z 60000)
£15469 $25833 €22585 Portrait of Dagny Przybyszewskiej (27x40cm-11x16in) mono. pastel. 19-Oct-3 Agra, Warsaw #2/R est:35000 (P.Z 99000)
£24206 $41876 €35341 Portrait of Antoniego Kamienskiego (46x62cm-18x24in) mono.d.1900 pastel. 14-Dec-3 Agra, Warsaw #38/R est:145000 (P.Z 160000)

WYSS, Caspar (1762-1798) German
Works on paper
£948 $1697 €1384 Village in western Switzerland (28x41cm-11x16in) s.d.1790 W/C Indian ink. 14-May-4 Dobiaschofsky, Bern #19/R est:3000 (S.FR 2200)

WYSS, Johann Emanuel (1782-1837) Swiss
Works on paper
£1724 $3086 €2517 Landscapes (42x57cm-17x22in) s.d.1807 gouache pair. 13-May-4 Stuker, Bern #9442/R est:4500-6000 (S.FR 4000)

WYSS, Paul (1897-1984) Swiss
£733 $1312 €1070 Lake with sailing boats (60x100cm-24x39in) s.d.21. 13-May-4 Stuker, Bern #391 est:1200-1500 (S.FR 1700)

WYTSMAN, Juliette (1866-1925) Belgian
£1400 $2240 €2030 Arranging flowers (74x58cm-29x23in) indis.sig. 18-Sep-3 Christie's, Kensington #37/R est:1500-2000

£10000 $18200 €15000 Jardin fleuri (60x70cm-24x28in) s. 4-Jul-4 MonsAntic, Maisieres #491 est:18000-22000
£13986 $23776 €20000 Bruyere fleurie autour d'un etang (60x80cm-24x31in) s. 1-Dec-3 Palais de Beaux Arts, Brussels #147/R est:20000-30000

WYTSMAN, Rodolphe (1860-1927) Belgian
£1479 $2558 €2100 Verger en fleurs a Linkebeek (39x29cm-15x11in) s. i.verso. 9-Dec-3 Vanderkindere, Brussels #70 est:1000-1500
£1575 $2678 €2300 Meuse a Wepion (27x32cm-11x13in) s. panel. 10-Nov-3 Horta, Bruxelles #191
£1831 $3168 €2600 Dunes a Heyst (24x32cm-9x13in) s. i.d.1904 verso panel prov.lit. 13-Dec-3 De Vuyst, Lokeren #406/R est:2500-3500
£2432 $4597 €3600 Paysage avec canal et moulin a vent (44x66cm-17x26in) s. 17-Feb-4 Galerie Moderne, Brussels #234/R est:3000-4000
£3521 $6092 €5000 Landscape with farm (40x60cm-16x24in) s. lit. 13-Dec-3 De Vuyst, Lokeren #405/R est:4000-5000
£4667 $8493 €7000 View of Dordrecht (46x60cm-18x24in) s. 1-Jul-4 Van Ham, Cologne #1677/R est:7000
£4895 $8175 €7000 Summer in the Dordrecht surroundings (45x54cm-18x21in) s. s.i.verso panel lit. 11-Oct-3 De Vuyst, Lokeren #429/R est:7000-8000
£10067 $17819 €15000 Paysage ensoleille en Brabant. s. 27-Apr-4 Campo & Campo, Antwerp #281/R est:8000-12000
Works on paper
£822 $1397 €1200 Parc (44x59cm-17x23in) s. pastel. 10-Nov-3 Horta, Bruxelles #192
£2238 $3804 €3200 Vue de verger en automne (60x73cm-24x29in) s.d.04 pastel. 1-Dec-3 Palais de Beaux Arts, Brussels #156/R est:1800-2400

WYWIORSKY, Michal (1861-1926) Polish
£1268 $2104 €1800 Baltic coast at sunset (21x32cm-8x13in) s. board prov. 16-Jun-3 Dorotheum, Vienna #8/R est:2800-3000
£3181 $5885 €4644 Landscape with trees (52x68cm-20x27in) 14-Mar-4 Agra, Warsaw #25/R (P.Z 23000)
£4075 $6357 €5950 Winter landscape (70x101cm-28x40in) painted c.1900. 30-Mar-3 Agra, Warsaw #14/R est:20000 (P.Z 26000)
£5034 $9010 €7500 A winter evening (86x133cm-34x52in) s. 27-May-4 Dorotheum, Vienna #81/R est:6500-7500
£16973 $29873 €24781 Cart in the field (65x100cm-26x39in) 23-May-4 Agra, Warsaw #5/R (P.Z 120000)

XAUS COMPTE, Antonio (1932-) Spanish
£290 $475 €400 N1 - y N2 - E (147x230cm-58x91in) s.d.90 s.i.verso acrylic diptych. 27-May-3 Durán, Madrid #638/R

XAVERY, Franciscus (1740-?) Dutch
£4500 $7650 €6570 Italianate landscape with shepherd surprising nymphs bathing at a stream (33x46cm-13x18in) s. panel. 29-Oct-3 Bonhams, New Bond Street #127/R est:3000-5000
£10959 $18630 €16000 Wooded landscape with a shepherd playing a flute and another spinning (31x40cm-12x16in) s. panel prov. 4-Nov-3 Sotheby's, Amsterdam #103/R est:10000-15000
Works on paper
£1007 $1802 €1500 Scenes pastorales (19x29cm-7x11in) s. wash pair. 25-May-4 Palais de Beaux Arts, Brussels #363/R est:1200-1800

XAVERY, Jacob (after) (1736-1769) Dutch
£6711 $12013 €10000 Vase de fleurs sur un entablement (82x62cm-32x24in) 25-May-4 Palais de Beaux Arts, Brussels #557/R est:10000-15000

XCERON, Jean (1890-1967) American/Greek
£917 $1532 €1330 Le violon (38x46cm-15x18in) s.d.31. 23-Jun-3 Philippe Schuler, Zurich #3575/R (S.FR 2000)
£1470 $2500 €2146 Untitled (122x91cm-48x36in) s.i.d.1959 verso prov. 9-Nov-3 Bonhams & Butterfields, Los Angeles #4077/R est:3000-5000
Works on paper
£417 $750 €609 Circular (21x18cm-8x7in) s.d.1948 pen ink W/C. 22-Jan-4 Swann Galleries, New York #267
£503 $900 €734 Abstraction (28x20cm-11x8in) s. gouache. 16-May-4 Wright, Chicago #247/R

XENAKIS, Constantin (1931-) Egyptian
£313 $522 €450 Parcours (40x27cm-16x11in) s. s.i.d.1987 verso. 25-Oct-3 Cornette de St.Cyr, Paris #838/R
£400 $720 €600 Untitled (106x38cm-42x15in) s. W/C ink. 24-Apr-4 Cornette de St.Cyr, Paris #744/R
£420 $713 €600 Espace (65x92cm-26x36in) s. s.i.d.1960 verso. 18-Nov-3 Pierre Berge, Paris #45
£1733 $3120 €2600 Parade G (55x46cm-22x18in) s.i.d.1986 verso acrylic prov. 25-Apr-4 Versailles Encheres #36 est:2500-3000

XENAKIS, Cosmas (1925-1984) Greek
£2400 $4296 €3504 Girls (31x47cm-12x19in) s. acrylic paper exhib. 10-May-4 Sotheby's, Olympia #101/R est:1000-1500

XENOS, Nicholaos (1908-1984) Greek
£2000 $3580 €2920 View of the Acropolis (52x62cm-20x24in) s.d.1955 panel. 11-May-4 Bonhams, New Bond Street #12/R est:2000-3000
£5000 $8950 €7300 Vouliagmeni (60x100cm-24x39in) s. 10-May-4 Sotheby's, Olympia #122/R est:5000-7000

XI DEJIN (1923-1981) Chinese
£4000 $6680 €5840 Farmer and geese (39x51cm-15x20in) s.d.1956. 14-Nov-3 Christie's, Kensington #277/R est:4000-6000
Works on paper
£2000 $3340 €2920 Boy seated in street (53x37cm-21x15in) s.d.1957 W/C. 14-Nov-3 Christie's, Kensington #278/R est:2500-4000
£6178 $10317 €9020 Old houses (56x77cm-22x30in) s.d.1978 W/C. 27-Oct-3 Sotheby's, Hong Kong #363/R est:45000-60000 (HK.D 80000)

XI GANG (1746-1803) Chinese
Works on paper
£4979 $8962 €7269 Landscape (135x32cm-53x13in) s.i. ink hanging scroll. 25-Apr-4 Christie's, Hong Kong #409/R est:40000-50000 (HK.D 70000)

XIA LINGYI (19th C) Chinese
Works on paper
£372 $654 €550 Bamboo and rock (129x29cm-51x11in) s.i. seals hanging scroll. 21-May-4 Dr Fritz Nagel, Stuttgart #1211/R

XIANG SHENGMO (1597-1658) Chinese
Works on paper
£123552 $206332 €180386 Landscapes and poetry (22x25cm-9x10in) s. ink set of 10. 26-Oct-3 Christie's, Hong Kong #437/R (HK.D 1600000)

XIAO HONG (1966-) Oriental
£2614 $4732 €3816 Intellectual yuth no 4 (160x150cm-63x59in) s.d.2004. 3-Apr-4 Glerum, Singapore #56/R est:4000-6000 (S.D 8000)

XIAO HUA GAO (1955-) Chinese
£1437 $2400 €2098 Winter grove (86x91cm-34x36in) s. 11-Oct-3 Nadeau, Windsor #28/R est:4500-7500

XIAO SHUFANG (1911-) Chinese
Works on paper
£3912 $7041 €5712 Flowers (58x76cm-23x30in) s.d.1955 W/C prov. 26-Apr-4 Sotheby's, Hong Kong #548/R est:40000-60000 (HK.D 55000)

XIAO YUNCONG (1596-1673) Chinese
Works on paper
£77220 $128958 €112741 Lofty mountains (20x396cm-8x156in) s.i.d.1658 ink col handscroll. 27-Oct-3 Sotheby's, Hong Kong #321/R est:800000-1200000 (HK.D 1000000)

XIE CHUNYAN (1942-) Chinese
Works on paper
£1081 $1903 €1600 Animals and figures (136x34cm-54x13in) s.i. seals Indian ink col 4 hanging scrolls 1 calligraphy. 21-May-4 Dr Fritz Nagel, Stuttgart #1201/R est:600

XIE JIN (14/15th C) Chinese
Works on paper
£5405 $9027 €7891 Visiting a friend at the Western villa (129x42cm-51x17in) i.d. ink col. 26-Oct-3 Christie's, Hong Kong #433/R (HK.D 70000)

XIE SHICHEN (c.1487-1567) Chinese
Works on paper
£4979 $8962 €7269 Fishermen (28x175cm-11x69in) s.d.1535 ink col handscroll. 25-Apr-4 Christie's, Hong Kong #336/R est:80000-100000 (HK.D 70000)

XIE ZHIGUANG (1900-1976) Chinese
Works on paper
£608 $1070 €900 Red cherry blossom (67x33cm-26x13in) s.i. Indian ink col hanging scroll. 21-May-4 Dr Fritz Nagel, Stuttgart #1116/R

XIE ZHILIU (1910-1997) Chinese
Works on paper
£2239 $3740 €3269 Bamboo and peach blossom (19x44cm-7x17in) s.i.d.1975 i.verso ink col folding fan. 27-Oct-3 Sotheby's, Hong Kong #298/R est:20000-30000 (HK.D 29000)
£2703 $4514 €3946 Spring in Fuchun (18x50cm-7x20in) s.i.d.1956 i.verso ink col folding fan. 27-Oct-3 Sotheby's, Hong Kong #297/R est:35000-45000 (HK.D 35000)
£5690 $10242 €8307 Scholar (141x56cm-56x22in) s.i.d.1943 ink col scroll silk. 25-Apr-4 Christie's, Hong Kong #146/R est:38000-42000 (HK.D 80000)
£6564 $10961 €9583 Panoramic view (30x67cm-12x26in) s.i. ink col. 27-Oct-3 Sotheby's, Hong Kong #270/R est:40000-60000 (HK.D 85000)
£7336 $12251 €10711 Lotus (48x178cm-19x70in) s.d.1994 ink col scroll. 26-Oct-3 Christie's, Hong Kong #287/R est:60000-80000 (HK.D 95000)

£9246 $16643 €13499 Misty landscape (50x83cm-20x33in) s.i.d.1990 ink col lit. 26-Apr-4 Sotheby's, Hong Kong #667/R est:50000-70000 (HK.D 130000)
£9266 $15475 €13528 Boating in autumn (92x47cm-36x19in) s.i.d.1964 ink col hanging scroll exhib. 27-Oct-3 Sotheby's, Hong Kong #267/R est:120000-150000 (HK.D 120000)
£10000 $17000 €14600 Landscapes (61x81cm-24x32in) s. ink col twelve album. 4-Nov-3 Bonhams & Butterfields, San Francisco #3451/R est:7000-10000
£71124 $128023 €103841 Red lotus (133x96cm-52x38in) s.i.d.1963 ink col hanging scroll exhib.lit. 26-Apr-4 Sotheby's, Hong Kong #646/R est:220000-280000 (HK.D 1000000)

XIMENES, E (19/20th C) Italian
£1690 $2806 €2400 Capri scene (23x52cm-9x20in) s. 11-Jun-3 Christie's, Rome #26 est:800-1200

XIMENES, Ettore (1855-1926) Italian
£338 $595 €500 River landscape with buffaloes (50x40cm-20x16in) s.d.1914. 19-May-4 Il Ponte, Milan #700
£1800 $3312 €2628 Washerwomen at the edge of an italian lake (16x25cm-6x10in) s. panel. 25-Mar-4 Christie's, Kensington #132/R est:2000-3000

XU BEIHONG (1895-1953) Chinese
Works on paper
£5019 $8382 €7328 Pair of geese (34x45cm-13x18in) s.i.d.1934 ink col scroll. 26-Oct-3 Christie's, Hong Kong #271/R est:40000-50000 (HK.D 65000)
£6564 $10961 €9583 Cat (33x35cm-13x14in) s.d.1945 col ink prov. 27-Oct-3 Sotheby's, Hong Kong #306/R est:60000-80000 (HK.D 85000)
£6849 $11644 €10000 Resting water buffalo (58x56cm-23x22in) s. seals Indian ink hanging scroll prov. 7-Nov-3 Dr Fritz Nagel, Stuttgart #957/R est:8000
£7722 $12896 €11274 Magpie (82x34cm-32x13in) s.d.1945 ink col scroll. 26-Oct-3 Christie's, Hong Kong #272/R est:40000-60000 (HK.D 100000)
£7824 $14083 €11423 Magpie on a red leafed branch (57x30cm-22x12in) s.i.d.1943 ink col hanging scroll. 26-Apr-4 Sotheby's, Hong Kong #658/R est:70000-90000 (HK.D 110000)
£11583 $19344 €16911 Peach blossom with a magpie (68x46cm-27x18in) s.d.1948 ink col hanging scroll prov. 27-Oct-3 Sotheby's, Hong Kong #301/R est:150000-200000 (HK.D 150000)
£12802 $23044 €18691 Cockeral (67x27cm-26x11in) s.i.d.1942 ink col hanging scroll. 25-Apr-4 Christie's, Hong Kong #80/R est:100000-120000 (HK.D 180000)
£12802 $23044 €18691 Himalayas (40x61cm-16x24in) s.i.d.1940 ink col. 26-Apr-4 Sotheby's, Hong Kong #640/R est:150000-200000 (HK.D 180000)
£17070 $30725 €24922 Eagle (64x82cm-25x32in) s.i.d.1938 ink hanging scroll. 25-Apr-4 Christie's, Hong Kong #78/R est:150000-200000 (HK.D 240000)
£20077 $33529 €29312 Two horses (88x47cm-35x19in) s.d.1943 ink col scroll. 26-Oct-3 Christie's, Hong Kong #273/R est:250000-300000 (HK.D 260000)
£20077 $33529 €29312 Geese (50x61cm-20x24in) si.d.1931 ink col hanging scroll. 27-Oct-3 Sotheby's, Hong Kong #305/R est:180000-250000 (HK.D 260000)
£22760 $40967 €33230 Horse drinking water (72x35cm-28x14in) s.d.1948 ink col scroll. 25-Apr-4 Christie's, Hong Kong #79/R est:200000-250000 (HK.D 320000)
£23166 $38687 €33822 Eagle (90x48cm-35x19in) s.d.1944 ink col scroll. 26-Oct-3 Christie's, Hong Kong #274/R est:250000-300000 (HK.D 300000)

XU CAO (1899-1961) Chinese
Works on paper
£1158 $1934 €1691 Ladies of the river Xiang (19x52cm-7x20in) s.i.d.1928 ink col folding fan. 26-Oct-3 Christie's, Hong Kong #219/R est:15000-20000 (HK.D 15000)
£1931 $3224 €2819 Spring (18x49cm-7x19in) s.i. ink col folding fan. 26-Oct-3 Christie's, Hong Kong #215/R est:25000-35000 (HK.D 25000)

XU LINLU (1916-) Chinese
Works on paper
£411 $699 €600 Basket of fruit and red chrysanthemums (68x45cm-27x18in) s.i. Indian ink col hanging scroll. 7-Nov-3 Dr Fritz Nagel, Stuttgart #948/R
£445 $757 €650 Begonias and rocks (68x34cm-27x13in) s.i.d.1978 seals Indian ink col hanging scroll. 7-Nov-3 Dr Fritz Nagel, Stuttgart #959/R
£4623 $8321 €6750 Persimmon (68x69cm-27x27in) s.i. ink col scroll. 25-Apr-4 Christie's, Hong Kong #25/R est:40000-50000 (HK.D 65000)
£7112 $12802 €10384 Fish and lotus (136x59cm-54x23in) s.i. ink scroll. 25-Apr-4 Christie's, Hong Kong #24/R est:60000-80000 (HK.D 100000)

XU XI (1940-) Chinese
Works on paper
£445 $757 €650 Girl with goats (34x44cm-13x17in) s.i.d.1978 Indian ink col hanging scroll. 7-Nov-3 Dr Fritz Nagel, Stuttgart #951/R
£1507 $2562 €2200 Bamboo with junks on river (68x67cm-27x26in) s.d.1977 seals Indian ink col hanging scroll. 7-Nov-3 Dr Fritz Nagel, Stuttgart #972/R est:250

XUAREZ, Nicolas Rodriguez (1667-1734) Mexican
£2759 $4607 €4000 Saint Antoine de Padoue avec l'Enfant Jesus (77x57cm-30x22in) s.i. 16-Nov-3 Muizon & Le Coent, Paris #14/R

XUE KUN (19th C) Chinese
Works on paper
£1422 $2560 €2076 Flowers and calligraphy (86x50cm-34x20in) s. ink col hanging scroll. 25-Apr-4 Christie's, Hong Kong #442/R est:20000-30000 (HK.D 20000)

XUL SOLAR, Alejandro (1887-1963) Argentinian
£139665 $250000 €203911 Untitled (100x33cm-39x13in) s.d.1952 tempera paper. 4-May-4 Arroyo, Buenos Aires #90/R est:220000
Works on paper
£20000 $36800 €30000 Mansilla 2936 (14x19cm-6x7in) i. W/C prov.lit. 10-Jun-4 Christie's, Paris #10/R est:28000-36000

XURXO ALONSO (1956-) Argentinian
Works on paper
£582 $942 €820 Batalla no.4 punto rojo (69x100cm-27x39in) mixed media. 20-May-3 Ansorena, Madrid #289/R

XYLANDER, Wilhelm (1840-1913) Danish
£276 $470 €403 Landscape with stream (31x46cm-12x18in) s. 10-Nov-3 Rasmussen, Vejle #93/R (D.KR 3000)
£1589 $2893 €2400 Portsmouth harbour in moonlight (29x41cm-11x16in) s.d.1880 panel. 19-Jun-4 Hans Stahl, Hamburg #125/R est:2000
£2336 $4345 €3411 Sailing vessels at harbour entrance, night (53x64cm-21x25in) s. panel. 2-Mar-4 Rasmussen, Copenhagen #1443/R est:15000 (D.KR 26000)

YA'ARI, Sharon (1966-) Israeli
Photographs
£4749 $8500 €6934 Dunes (111x139cm-44x55in) c-print edition 1 of 3 exhib. 18-Mar-4 Sotheby's, New York #78/R est:5000-7000

YABLONSKY (20th C) Russian
£1400 $2506 €2044 Spring (95x150cm-37x59in) s. s.i.d.17.5.96 verso. 26-May-4 Sotheby's, Olympia #430/R est:1000-1500

YAGUE, Cesar (1948-) Spanish
£532 $862 €750 Procession (55x46cm-22x18in) s. canvas on panel. 20-May-3 Ansorena, Madrid #273/R

YAKOVLEV, Vladimir (1934-1998) Russian
£14000 $25060 €20440 Portrait of a boy (101x80cm-40x31in) s.d.79. 26-May-4 Sotheby's, London #317/R est:12000-18000
Works on paper
£2682 $4800 €3916 Flower (44x55cm-17x22in) gouache exec. 1970. 29-May-4 Shishkin Gallery, Moscow #34/R est:5000-7000

YALKARRIWUY, Banaumbur (1948-) Australian
Sculpture
£1020 $1825 €1489 Morning star pole (175cm-69in) feathers bush string wild bees wax pigments wood exec 1994 prov. 25-May-4 Lawson Menzies, Sydney #258/R est:3000-5000 (A.D 2600)

YAMAMOTO, Masao (?) Japanese?
£537 $999 €800 Le moulin rouge (52x44cm-20x17in) s. 3-Mar-4 Ferri, Paris #127

YAN BOLONG (1898-1954) Chinese
Works on paper
£946 $1665 €1400 Bird on Lotus stem (98x33cm-39x13in) s.i.d.1947 seals hanging scroll. 21-May-4 Dr Fritz Nagel, Stuttgart #1220/R
£2027 $3568 €3000 Two birds on bough (33x97cm-13x38in) s.i. seals Indian ink col hanging scroll prov. 21-May-4 Dr Fritz Nagel, Stuttgart #1126/R est:450
£2230 $3924 €3300 Two birds on camellia stem on rock (115x34cm-45x13in) s.i.d.1928 seal Indian ink col hanging scroll. 21-May-4 Dr Fritz Nagel, Stuttgart #1222/R est:450

YAN PEI MING (1960-) Chinese
£6597 $10885 €9500 Double tete (200x200cm-79x79in) s.d.1989 verso acrylic diptych prov. 2-Jul-3 Cornette de St.Cyr, Paris #180/R est:10000-12000
£12000 $21840 €18000 Paysage international (180x300cm-71x118in) s.i.d.97 verso acrylic. 29-Jun-4 Cornette de St.Cyr, Paris #141/R est:15000-20000
£15879 $27946 €23500 L'homme invisible (200x200cm-79x79in) s.i.d.1997 verso prov.exhib. 18-May-4 Tajan, Paris #146/R est:25000-30000
£25874 $43210 €37000 Portrait de timonnier no 3 (130x97cm-51x38in) s.i.d.1997 verso. 11-Oct-3 Cornette de St.Cyr, Paris #130/R est:15000-20000
£35417 $58437 €51000 Vermillon de chine no 3 (200x235cm-79x93in) s.verso prov.exhib. 2-Jul-3 Cornette de St.Cyr, Paris #181/R est:35000-45000

YAN SHENGSUN (1623-1702) Chinese
Works on paper
£9783 $18000 €14283 Feast of the immortals (206x380cm-81x150in) i. ink wash eight panel silk screen. 24-Mar-4 Christie's, Rockefeller NY #22/R est:12000-18000

YANAGI, Miwa (1967-) American?
Photographs
£1796 $3000 €2622 Untitled, elevator girl series (10x51cm-4x20in) c-print plexiglas edition of 20 prov. 13-Nov-3 Sotheby's, New York #477/R est:3000-4000
£8383 $14000 €12239 Elevator girl house B4 (90x109cm-35x43in) c-print plexiglas prov. 13-Nov-3 Sotheby's, New York #522/R est:8000-12000

YANCHAK, Elena Vatslovana (1918-1967) Russian
£323 $600 €472 Melon patch (36x48cm-14x19in) s.d.1953 board. 7-Mar-4 Treadway Gallery, Cincinnati #535/R

YANG CHIHONG (1947-) Taiwanese
Works on paper
£1390 $2321 €2029 Before the eruption (56x76cm-22x30in) s.d.85 mixed media prov. 26-Oct-3 Christie's, Hong Kong #155/R est:20000-30000 (HK.D 18000)

YANG FEIYUN (1954-) Chinese
£4748 $8500 €6932 Waking up from a nap (80x100cm-31x39in) s.d.1989.7 prov. 10-May-4 Bonhams & Butterfields, San Francisco #4411/R est:4000-6000

YANG HSIEN MIN (20th C) Chinese
Works on paper
£254 $425 €371 Spring moonlight (51x69cm-20x27in) s. W/C. 11-Oct-3 Nadeau, Windsor #83/R

YANG SHANSHEN (1913-) Chinese
Works on paper
£3089 $5158 €4510 Before the rain (52x68cm-20x27in) s.d.1986 ink col scroll. 26-Oct-3 Christie's, Hong Kong #254/R est:30000-40000 (HK.D 40000)
£6757 $12162 €9865 Egret (145x75cm-57x30in) s.d.1987 ink col hanging scroll. 25-Apr-4 Christie's, Hong Kong #61/R est:100000-120000 (HK.D 95000)
£15444 $25792 €22548 Pheasant (129x66cm-51x26in) s.i.d.1996 ink col hanging scroll. 26-Oct-3 Christie's, Hong Kong #350/R est:150000-200000 (HK.D 200000)

YANG SHANSHEN and ZHAO SHAOANG (20th C) Chinese
Works on paper
£853 $1536 €1245 Bamboo, plum blossom (92x30cm-36x12in) s.i.d.1967 ink scroll. 25-Apr-4 Christie's, Hong Kong #11/R est:12000-15000 (HK.D 12000)

YANG WENCONG (1597-1645) Chinese
Works on paper
£3912 $7041 €5712 Secluded cottage by the stream (167x58cm-66x23in) s.i.d.1640 ink hanging scroll. 25-Apr-4 Christie's, Hong Kong #343/R est:60000-80000 (HK.D 55000)

YANG YANWEN (1939-) Chinese
Works on paper
£207 $375 €302 Landscape (68x45cm-27x18in) s. ink wash. 6-Apr-4 Bonhams & Butterfields, San Francisco #6215/R

YANKARR, Boxer (c.1930-1995) Australian
Works on paper
£73171 $115610 €106830 Ngurrara canvas I (470x780cm-185x307in) synthetic polymer paint rubber cloth multi artists prov.exhib. 28-Jul-3 Sotheby's, Paddington #246/R est:300000-500000 (A.D 180000)

YANKEL, Jacques (1920-) French
£280 $510 €420 Composition (30x10cm-12x4in) s. painted c.1970. 5-Jul-4 Le Mouel, Paris #93
£324 $550 €473 Harbor scene (64x46cm-25x18in) s. prov. 5-Nov-3 Doyle, New York #81/R

YANN, Robert (1901-1994) French
£333 $597 €500 Le Pont Neuf (19x25cm-7x10in) s. isorel. 16-May-4 Thierry & Lannon, Brest #375
£1056 $1849 €1500 Port breton (33x40cm-13x16in) s. panel. 21-Dec-3 Thierry & Lannon, Brest #368 est:1300-1500
£1800 $3222 €2700 La balise de Brignogan (33x41cm-13x16in) s. 16-May-4 Thierry & Lannon, Brest #377/R est:1500-1800
£2000 $3580 €3000 Jour de pardon a Penhors (40x70cm-16x28in) s. panel. 16-May-4 Thierry & Lannon, Brest #197 est:3000-3500

YANNACOPOULOS, Konstantinos (1927-) Greek
£750 $1343 €1095 Still life of fruit (28x44cm-11x17in) s. board sold with another by same hand. 10-May-4 Sotheby's, Olympia #159/R

YAOUANC, Alain le (c.1940-) French
£604 $1124 €900 Composition (80x65cm-31x26in) s.d.79. 3-Mar-4 Artcurial Briest, Paris #486
£921 $1695 €1400 Figures au chien (150x72cm-59x28in) s.d.91 panel diptych. 24-Jun-4 Credit Municipal, Paris #56
Works on paper
£238 $426 €350 Untitled (65x48cm-26x19in) s.d.1974 collage prov. 21-Mar-4 Calmels Cohen, Paris #134/R
£329 $605 €500 Composition (97x130cm-38x51in) paper collage prov. 23-Jun-4 Maigret, Paris #34
£428 $787 €650 Composition aux colombes (29x21cm-11x8in) s.d.74 mixed media. 24-Jun-4 Credit Municipal, Paris #64
£921 $1695 €1400 Composition a la jeune femme (54x36cm-21x14in) s.d.78 mixed media. 24-Jun-4 Credit Municipal, Paris #55

YARBER, Robert (1948-) American
£2973 $5500 €4341 Valley (168x168cm-66x66in) s.d.82 i.verso. 12-Feb-4 Sotheby's, New York #284/R est:2000-4000

YARD, Sydney Janis (1855-1909) American
Works on paper
£556 $1000 €812 Pending storm over the oaks (12x17cm-5x7in) s. W/C. 25-Apr-4 Bonhams & Butterfields, San Francisco #5506/R
£598 $1100 €873 Landscape at sunset (25x38cm-10x15in) s. W/C. 26-Jun-4 Selkirks, St. Louis #117/R
£769 $1400 €1123 Cows in wooded pastoral scene (15x20cm-6x8in) s. W/C. 15-Jun-4 John Moran, Pasadena #17 est:1500-2000
£1467 $2700 €2142 Sunset landscape at water's edge (41x51cm-16x20in) s. W/C. 26-Jun-4 Selkirks, St. Louis #118/R est:1500-2000
£1720 $3250 €2511 Cattle in Calif landscape (23x28cm-9x11in) s. W/C. 17-Feb-4 John Moran, Pasadena #85a/R est:2500-3500
£2060 $3750 €3008 Cattle in California landscape (25x36cm-10x14in) s. W/C. 15-Jun-4 John Moran, Pasadena #87a est:2500-3500

YARDLEY, Bruce (1962-) British
£550 $880 €798 Reading in the drawing room (51x61cm-20x24in) s. 16-Sep-3 Bonhams, Knightsbridge #72/R

YARDLEY, John (1933-) British
£1000 $1570 €1450 Amongst the petunias (46x55cm-18x22in) s. 28-Aug-3 Christie's, Kensington #321/R est:500-700
Works on paper
£300 $531 €438 The American yacht, Dartmouth (33x23cm-13x9in) s. W/C. 28-Apr-4 Hales, Bovey Tracey #454
£320 $534 €467 Mevagissy (32x46cm-13x18in) s. pencil W/C. 16-Oct-3 Christie's, Kensington #282
£420 $743 €613 Venetian canal scene (30x41cm-12x16in) s. W/C pencil. 27-Apr-4 Bonhams, Knightsbridge #226/R
£480 $778 €696 An evening sail (25x36cm-10x14in) s. W/C. 30-Jul-3 Hamptons Fine Art, Godalming #81
£520 $842 €754 Shore view near the Butt and Oyster (32x41cm-13x16in) s. W/C. 30-Jul-3 Hamptons Fine Art, Godalming #82
£550 $891 €798 Maldon Foreshore (36x51cm-14x20in) s. W/C. 30-Jul-3 Hamptons Fine Art, Godalming #124
£600 $972 €870 Deck chairs by the west pier, Brighton (25x36cm-10x14in) s. W/C. 30-Jul-3 Hamptons Fine Art, Godalming #120/R

YARNOLD, George B (19th C) British
£380 $700 €555 Landscape with faggot gatherer (53x43cm-21x17in) s.d. 23-Jun-4 Doyle, New York #5077/R
£500 $885 €730 Salmon pool. An old stone bridge (48x48cm-19x19in) s. board arched top two. 28-Apr-4 Halls, Shrewsbury #524

YARNOLD, Joseph W (19th C) British
£340 $537 €493 Victorian fishing village with figures (38x51cm-15x20in) s. 27-Jul-3 Desmond Judd, Cranbrook #1108
£1700 $3162 €2482 Frmyard (76x127cm-30x50in) s.d.1888. 4-Mar-4 Christie's, Kensington #483/R est:1500-2000

YAROSHENKO, Nikolai Alexandrovich (1846-1898) Russian
£2200 $4070 €3212 Portrait of a bearded gentleman in a fur jacket (59x51cm-23x20in) board. 15-Jan-4 Christie's, Kensington #835/R est:400-600
£11824 $21166 €17500 An interior (32x41cm-13x16in) s. board. 8-May-4 Bukowskis, Helsinki #459/R est:5000-7000

YARWOOD, Thomas J (19/20th C) British
£300 $558 €438 Dane meadow, Shipbrook, Cheshire (25x35cm-10x14in) mono.d.1897. 4-Mar-4 Christie's, Kensington #491/R

YASHIMA, Gakutei (19th C) Japanese
Works on paper
£900 $1647 €1314 Three Surimono. W/C three from a set of five. 7-Apr-4 Sotheby's, Olympia #3/R

YASHIMA, Taro (1908-) American/Japanese
£438 $700 €639 Green field with buildings (71x76cm-28x30in) s.d.July 1952. 20-Sep-3 Sloans & Kenyon, Bethesda #983/R

YASUICHI, Awakawa (1907-1976) Japanese
Works on paper
£559 $962 €800 Daikoku creating charms from his hammer (33x44cm-13x17in) i. ink. 5-Dec-3 Lempertz, Koln #799/R

YASUNOBU, Kano (1613-1685) Japanese

Works on paper

£1189	$2045	€1700	Landscape with temple on a cliff overhang (103x39cm-41x15in) s. ink hanging scroll. 5-Dec-3 Lempertz, Koln #753/R est:1700

YATES, Cullen (1866-1945) American

£1381	$2500	€2016	Golden summer landscape (61x91cm-24x36in) s. 16-Apr-4 James Julia, Fairfield #734/R est:2750-3250
£2545	$4250	€3716	Forest Interior (41x51cm-16x20in) s. 23-Oct-3 Shannon's, Milford #66/R est:3000-5000

YATES, Fred (1922-) British

£245	$450	€358	St. Ives beach scene (46x84cm-18x33in) oil on paper. 11-Jun-4 David Rago, Lambertville #142/R
£258	$475	€377	Village north of England (30x46cm-12x18in) s. 11-Jun-4 David Rago, Lambertville #146/R
£280	$510	€409	Figures in a Cornish street (28x30cm-11x12in) s. board. 21-Jun-4 Bonhams, Bath #405
£290	$458	€423	Coastal rocky inlet (16x12cm-6x5in) s. 4-Sep-3 Bonhams, Cornwall #467
£300	$498	€438	Pendeen, Cornwall (10x14cm-4x6in) s. board. 2-Oct-3 Lane, Penzance #62
£326	$600	€476	Untitled - harbour scene (25x28cm-10x11in) s. masonite. 11-Jun-4 David Rago, Lambertville #154/R
£380	$654	€555	On the beach (30x46cm-12x18in) s. board. 3-Dec-3 Christie's, Kensington #748/R
£400	$688	€584	Brighton pier (30x61cm-12x24in) s. board. 3-Dec-3 Christie's, Kensington #743/R
£400	$688	€584	Cott valley (23x43cm-9x17in) s. i.verso board. 3-Dec-3 Christie's, Kensington #762
£420	$697	€613	The weighing machine (13x10cm-5x4in) s. i.verso canvasboard. 2-Oct-3 Lane, Penzance #265
£450	$774	€657	Greenhouse with rows of potted flowering plants (29x40cm-11x16in) s. hardboard. 4-Dec-3 Bonhams, Cornwall #451/R
£480	$826	€701	Still life with flowers (43x38cm-17x15in) board. 3-Dec-3 Christie's, Kensington #752/R
£500	$860	€730	Bouquet des fleurs (30x26cm-12x10in) s. board. 3-Dec-3 Christie's, Kensington #749/R
£500	$860	€730	Portrait of a boy (35x35cm-14x14in) s. board. 3-Dec-3 Christie's, Kensington #750/R
£500	$860	€730	Dancing figures (25x35cm-10x14in) s. board. 3-Dec-3 Christie's, Kensington #755/R
£520	$952	€759	Porthmeor, St Ives (20x22cm-8x9in) s. board. 3-Jun-4 Lane, Penzance #4
£550	$946	€803	Over the bridge (30x57cm-12x22in) s.d.68 s.i.verso board. 3-Dec-3 Christie's, Kensington #756/R
£580	$986	€847	Fory by river's edge with crowds of people and children on beach by wall (25x25cm-10x10in) s. panel. 31-Oct-3 Moore Allen & Innocent, Cirencester #886/R
£600	$1032	€876	Still life with orange jug (41x30cm-16x12in) s. 3-Dec-3 Christie's, Kensington #753/R
£740	$1280	€1080	The walk (30x9cm-12x4in) s. board. 11-Dec-3 Lane, Penzance #329
£750	$1290	€1095	At the ballet (30x35cm-12x14in) s. board. 3-Dec-3 Christie's, Kensington #742/R
£760	$1338	€1110	Up north, children in a village street (19x14cm-7x6in) board. 18-May-4 Woolley & Wallis, Salisbury #8/R
£800	$1440	€1168	Coastal Scene, France (38x46cm-15x18in) s. 20-Jan-4 Bonhams, Knightsbridge #247/R
£800	$1336	€1168	Vortex - the end of the world (76x113cm-30x44in) board. 14-Oct-3 Bearnes, Exeter #401/R
£840	$1327	€1226	Polruan Quay (45x35cm-18x14in) s. board. 4-Sep-3 Bonhams, Cornwall #468/R
£880	$1549	€1285	Cornish scene (61x122cm-24x48in) s. board. 19-May-4 Sotheby's, Olympia #243/R
£900	$1503	€1314	Daisies in an orange jug (25x20cm-10x8in) s. 16-Oct-3 Christie's, Kensington #677/R
£900	$1620	€1314	Kent Neptune House, Fowey, Cornwall (30x120cm-12x47in) s. board. 20-Jan-4 Bonhams, Knightsbridge #173/R
£920	$1711	€1343	Fore Street, Fowey (34x53cm-13x21in) s. board. 4-Mar-4 Bonhams, Cornwall #247
£950	$1587	€1387	Lady reclining on a chaise longue (25x40cm-10x16in) s. board. 16-Oct-3 Christie's, Kensington #605/R
£950	$1739	€1387	Fleurs de la Gartempe. s. 3-Jun-4 Lane, Penzance #267
£1000	$1670	€1460	Still life with thistles (35x30cm-14x12in) s. 16-Oct-3 Christie's, Kensington #675/R est:600-800
£1000	$1820	€1460	Morrab Gardens (25x30cm-10x12in) s. i.verso board. 15-Jun-4 David Lay, Penzance #398 est:400-600
£1100	$1837	€1606	Crowd (30x40cm-12x16in) s. board. 16-Oct-3 Christie's, Kensington #598/R est:500-700
£1100	$1837	€1606	Beach on Sunday morning (50x182cm-20x72in) s.d.67 board 1967. 14-Oct-3 Bearnes, Exeter #396/R est:1200-1800
£1150	$2093	€1679	St. Ives Harbour (38x57cm-15x22in) s. board. 21-Jun-4 Bonhams, Bath #404/R est:700-900
£1150	$2093	€1679	Cottages (53x91cm-21x36in) s.d.67 board. 15-Jun-4 David Lay, Penzance #163 est:800-1000
£1200	$2004	€1752	Figures playing near the pier (25x30cm-10x12in) s. 16-Oct-3 Christie's, Kensington #661/R est:300-500
£1200	$2004	€1752	Still life with flowers on a striped cloth (30x25cm-12x10in) s. 16-Oct-3 Christie's, Kensington #676/R est:600-800
£1250	$2075	€1825	Children before cottages (35x29cm-14x11in) s. board prov. 2-Oct-3 Lane, Penzance #166 est:1000-1500
£1300	$2171	€1898	Figures on the promenade (30x41cm-12x16in) s. 16-Oct-3 Christie's, Kensington #659/R est:500-700
£1400	$2408	€2044	Polkerris cannons (61x107cm-24x42in) s. board. 3-Dec-3 Christie's, Kensington #754/R est:1500-2000
£1600	$2656	€2336	Sunday in the park (35x29cm-14x11in) s. board prov. 2-Oct-3 Lane, Penzance #165/R est:1000-1500
£1700	$2992	€2482	Sennen beach (50x93cm-20x37in) s. board. 18-May-4 Bonhams, Knightsbridge #61/R est:800-1200
£1750	$3080	€2555	Flowers from Provence (87x59cm-34x23in) s. board. 18-May-4 Woolley & Wallis, Salisbury #194/R est:800-1200
£2000	$3700	€2920	Source of the Rhone (92x73cm-36x29in) 11-Feb-4 Sotheby's, Olympia #230/R est:2000-3000
£2000	$3660	€2920	Money Penny Lane (76x61cm-30x24in) s. 3-Jun-4 Lane, Penzance #70/R est:1500-1750
£2500	$4575	€3650	Marazion, the lily pond (51x66cm-20x26in) s.i. 3-Jun-4 Lane, Penzance #278 est:2500-3000
£2500	$4575	€3650	Figures in a Sennen cove (48x91cm-19x36in) board. 3-Jun-4 Lane, Penzance #315 est:2750-3000
£2700	$4914	€3942	Lamorna (109x89cm-43x35in) s. board. 15-Jun-4 David Lay, Penzance #690/R est:2000-3000
£2800	$5012	€4088	St Michael's Mount (38x71cm-15x28in) s. board. 14-May-4 Christie's, Kensington #624/R est:1500-2000
£2800	$4928	€4088	St Michael's Mount (61x76cm-24x30in) s. 18-May-4 Woolley & Wallis, Salisbury #15/R est:800-1200
£3000	$5550	€4380	Polperro Harbour (53x71cm-21x28in) s. board. 11-Mar-4 Christie's, Kensington #355/R est:2000-3000
£3400	$6222	€4964	Newlyn, cottages Tolcarne (29x91cm-11x36in) s. 3-Jun-4 Lane, Penzance #265/R est:1500-1800
£3500	$6405	€5110	Walk, St Ives (46x65cm-18x26in) s. board. 3-Jun-4 Lane, Penzance #266 est:1800-2000
£5500	$10010	€8030	Cottage garden (75x63cm-30x25in) s. board. 1-Jul-4 Christie's, Kensington #338/R est:2500-3500

Works on paper

£300	$546	€450	Tuscany (36x55cm-14x22in) s. W/C. 15-Jun-4 Rosebery Fine Art, London #583
£350	$585	€511	Worthing (18x25cm-7x10in) s.i. W/C. 14-Oct-3 David Lay, Penzance #59
£450	$774	€657	La riviere (74x55cm-29x22in) s.i. W/C. 3-Dec-3 Christie's, Kensington #771/R
£520	$900	€759	Cornish cottages (43x29cm-17x11in) s. ink conte paint. 11-Dec-3 Lane, Penzance #228
£550	$919	€803	Angels (49x46cm-19x18in) s. collage oil board. 16-Oct-3 Christie's, Kensington #600/R
£550	$919	€803	Playground (19x27cm-7x11in) s. W/C. 16-Oct-3 Christie's, Kensington #602/R
£1150	$1909	€1679	Bristol Cathedral (55x75cm-22x30in) s. W/C. 2-Oct-3 Lane, Penzance #20/R est:500-800

YATES, Frederic (1854-1919) British

£1250	$2088	€1825	Dennen (30x43cm-12x17in) s. board. 14-Oct-3 David Lay, Penzance #273 est:600-800

Works on paper

£550	$919	€803	St. Michael's Mount (53x76cm-21x30in) s. crayon. 14-Oct-3 David Lay, Penzance #574

YATES, Gideon (19th C) British

Works on paper

£450	$734	€657	New London Bridge (29x55cm-11x22in) W/C. 24-Sep-3 Christie's, London #20/R
£700	$1281	€1022	Lambeth Bridge (30x53cm-12x21in) s.d.1829 W/C. 27-Jan-4 Bonhams, Knightsbridge #198/R

YATES, Thomas (?-1796) British

£5405	$10000	€7891	Squadron of the White lying at anchor in Gibraltar Bay (46x76cm-18x30in) s.d.1792 prov. 10-Feb-4 Christie's, Rockefeller NY #161/R est:10000-15000

YATES, William Henry (1845-1934) American

£278	$450	€406	Still life with flower basket (25x33cm-10x13in) s. 31-Jul-3 Eldred, East Dennis #289/R

YATRIDES, Georges (1931-) American

£455	$800	€664	Composition around a Shaddock (71x48cm-28x19in) s.d.58 prov. 23-May-4 Hindman, Chicago #999/R

YAVNO, Max (1921-1985) American

Photographs

£1796	$3000	€2622	Muscle Beach (17x23cm-7x9in) gelatin silver print exec. c.1949 prov.lit. 17-Oct-3 Phillips, New York #225/R est:4000-6000
£1796	$3000	€2622	Powell Street, San Francisco (50x39cm-20x15in) s. gelatin silver print exec.1947 prov. 21-Oct-3 Bonhams & Butterfields, San Francisco #1597/R
£2222	$4200	€3244	The Heiress (49x39cm-19x15in) silver print. 17-Feb-4 Swann Galleries, New York #73/R est:3000-4000
£2844	$4750	€4152	Muscle beach (21x34cm-8x13in) s. i.verso photo exec.1949 printed later prov. 17-Oct-3 Sotheby's, New York #150/R est:3000-5000

YBANEZ, Miguel (20th C) ?

£921	$1695	€1400	Composition (100x100cm-39x39in) s.indis.d.1987 oil on sand. 22-Jun-4 Christie's, Amsterdam #338/R

YDEMA, Egnatius (1876-1937) Dutch

£559	$1029	€850	Trees in a polder landscape (25x34cm-10x13in) s. canvas on plywood two. 22-Jun-4 Christie's, Amsterdam #111/R

YE QIANYU (1907-) Chinese

Works on paper

£753	$1281	€1100	Mongolian dancer (67x45cm-26x18in) s.d.1964 seal Indian ink col hanging scroll. 7-Nov-3 Dr Fritz Nagel, Stuttgart #950/R

YEATES, George W (fl.1884-1931) Irish?

£1333	$2413	€2000	Ballycastle harbour, Co Antrim (27x35cm-11x14in) s.d.Sept 1945 and Sept 1922 canvas on board prov. 30-Mar-4 De Veres Art Auctions, Dublin #26/R est:2000-3000

YEATS, Anne (1919-2001) Irish

£1329	$2259	€1900	The scarecrow (38x46cm-15x18in) s. i.verso board prov. 18-Nov-3 Whyte's, Dublin #71/R est:1500-2000
£1351	$2554	€2000	Shawl (36x53cm-14x21in) board prov. 17-Feb-4 Whyte's, Dublin #34/R est:2000-3000
£1408	$2437	€2000	Garden with red flower (50x76cm-20x30in) s. exhib. 10-Dec-3 Bonhams & James Adam, Dublin #173/R est:1000-1500
£2027	$3831	€3000	Balloon face (46x41cm-18x16in) s. exhib. 17-Feb-4 Whyte's, Dublin #16/R est:3000-4000
£2153	$3380	€3100	Duck eggs on a yellow cloth (20x35cm-8x14in) s. board. 26-Aug-3 Thomas Adams, Dublin #3
Works on paper			
£300	$555	€438	Stones and pink sand (26x35cm-10x14in) s. mixed media. 11-Mar-4 Morphets, Harrogate #310
£315	$500	€460	Abstract (27x35cm-11x14in) s. mixed media. 12-Sep-3 Skinner, Boston #548/R

YEATS, Jack Butler (1871-1957) Irish/British

£15493	$24789	€22000	An Capallin Ban. Manuscript letter (9x11cm-4x4in) canvas on board with signed letter framed as one prov. 16-Sep-3 Whyte's, Dublin #62/R est:1500-2000
£26000	$46540	€37960	By Streedagh Strand (23x35cm-9x14in) s. panel prov.exhib.lit. 14-May-4 Christie's, London #157/R est:25000-35000
£31944	$52069	€46000	Sandhill near Tralee Bay (23x36cm-9x14in) s.i.verso panel prov.exhib.lit. 24-Sep-3 James Adam, Dublin #82/R est:35000-50000
£45000	$80550	€65700	Drama (23x35cm-9x14in) s. panel prov.exhib.lit. 13-May-4 Sotheby's, London #96/R est:30000-40000
£60000	$107400	€87600	Turf on the canal (46x61cm-18x24in) s. prov.exhib.lit. 13-May-4 Sotheby's, London #66/R est:60000-80000
£63063	$107207	€92072	The boat builder (22x35cm-9x14in) s. panel painted 1923 prov.exhib.lit. 27-Nov-3 Heffel, Vancouver #10/R est:125000-175000 (C.D 140000)
£63953	$110000	€93371	Jockey club, 1945 (36x46cm-14x18in) s. prov.exhib.lit. 3-Dec-3 Doyle, New York #129/R est:120000-180000
£77845	$130000	€113654	Mountain Path (36x46cm-14x18in) s. i.stretcher prov. 23-Oct-3 Shannon's, Milford #113/R est:150000-200000
£90090	$153153	€131531	The mail car, early morning (22x35cm-9x14in) s. panel painted 1920 prov.exhib.lit. 27-Nov-3 Heffel, Vancouver #9/R est:125000-175000 (C.D 200000)
£130000	$232700	€189800	Style (23x35cm-9x14in) s. board prov.lit. 13-May-4 Sotheby's, London #98/R est:100000-150000
£180000	$322200	€262800	Quiet harbour (46x61cm-18x24in) s. prov.exhib.lit. 13-May-4 Sotheby's, London #105/R est:120000-180000
£211268	$365493	€300000	Thraw bawn (61x91cm-24x36in) s. prov.exhib.lit. 10-Dec-3 Bonhams & James Adam, Dublin #64/R est:150000-200000
£218023	$375000	€318314	View (35x46cm-14x18in) s. i.verso masonite prov.lit. 3-Dec-3 Doyle, New York #128/R est:400000-600000
£300000	$537000	€438000	On to glory (46x61cm-18x24in) s. prov.exhib.lit. 13-May-4 Sotheby's, London #48/R est:300000-500000
£500000	$895000	€730000	Here she comes (61x91cm-24x36in) s. i.verso i. on stretcher prov.exhib.lit. 14-May-4 Christie's, London #45/R est:400000-600000
Works on paper			
£400	$664	€584	Steward (12x10cm-5x4in) pencil. 1-Oct-3 John Ross, Belfast #78
£921	$1695	€1400	The kelp gatherer. Landscape with cottages (13x9cm-5x4in) pencil wash double-sided. 22-Jun-4 De Veres Art Auctions, Dublin #85/R
£1477	$2613	€2200	Barrow man (6x10cm-2x4in) s.d.21 December 1955 pen blue ink. 27-Apr-4 Whyte's, Dublin #138/R est:800-1200
£1800	$3222	€2628	Law on Kingsbridge River (12x8cm-5x3in) i. pencil W/C prov. 14-May-4 Christie's, London #51/R est:2000-3000
£1800	$3222	€2628	Cottie Yeats, the artist's wife (12x8cm-5x3in) pencil prov. 14-May-4 Christie's, London #54/R est:2000-3000
£2200	$3938	€3212	Arthur Griffith, the United Irishman (12x8cm-5x3in) i. pencil W/C. 14-May-4 Christie's, London #52/R est:800-1200
£2533	$4585	€3800	Singer Greaser at Buffalo Bills (9x14cm-4x6in) init.i. pen ink prov. 31-Mar-4 James Adam, Dublin #61/R est:2000-3000
£2632	$4842	€4000	Valley Wood (13x9cm-5x4in) init. W/C prov.lit. 22-Jun-4 De Veres Art Auctions, Dublin #54/R est:2500-3500
£2657	$4517	€3800	Collegians (26x16cm-10x6in) s. pencil prov.lit. 25-Nov-3 De Veres Art Auctions, Dublin #192/R est:4000-6000
£2800	$5012	€4088	Illustration to A Moral Ballad of the Plague of Eyam (7x14cm-3x6in) s. s.i.d.1910 verso black ink. 14-May-4 Christie's, London #47/R est:1500-2000
£2800	$5012	€4088	St Alphonsus (77x47cm-30x19in) mono. W/C gouache over pencil prov.lit. 13-May-4 Sotheby's, London #9/R est:3000-5000
£3356	$5940	€5000	Apparitions (28x18cm-11x7in) mono. pen ink W/C prov.lit. 27-Apr-4 Whyte's, Dublin #139/R est:4000-6000
£4577	$7919	€6500	Lady Gregory (18x13cm-7x5in) i. pencil. 10-Dec-3 Bonhams & James Adam, Dublin #54/R est:3000-4000
£4577	$7919	€6500	George Moore as King of Ireland (30x25cm-12x10in) W/C prov.exhib. 10-Dec-3 Bonhams & James Adam, Dublin #58/R est:6000-8000
£5333	$9653	€8000	In a tombstone makers' garden (22x14cm-9x6in) s. W/C prov. 31-Mar-4 James Adam, Dublin #60/R est:5000-8000
£6000	$10740	€8760	In a Liverpool Christy Minstrels' show, singing The Irish Emigrant (32x47cm-13x19in) s. col chk prov.exhib.lit. 14-May-4 Christie's, London #153/R est:5000-7000
£7432	$14047	€11000	Illustration to Campeachy picture by John Manefield, 1908 (12x17cm-5x7in) s. pencil pen ink on card prov.lit. 17-Feb-4 Whyte's, Dublin #54/R est:10000-12000
£7500	$13425	€10950	The unruly horse (21x29cm-8x11in) s.d.1890 pen black ink W/C. 13-May-4 Sotheby's, London #11/R est:5000-7000
£7500	$13425	€10950	Group of four sketches for the Abbey Theatre (30x24cm-12x9in) i. pen black ink W/C four. 13-May-4 Sotheby's, London #55/R est:4000-6000
£8882	$16342	€13500	Self portrait (18x23cm-7x9in) init. pen. ink prov.lit. 22-Jun-4 De Veres Art Auctions, Dublin #12/R est:9000-12000
£12000	$21720	€18000	Horse fair of Ballinasloe (22x14cm-9x6in) s. Indian ink prov. 30-Mar-4 De Veres Art Auctions, Dublin #19/R est:8000-12000
£14000	$25060	€20440	The railway station (33x27cm-13x11in) s. i.verso black ink W/C bodycol exec.c.1921-25. 14-May-4 Christie's, London #152/R est:7000-10000
£15493	$26803	€22000	Illustrations for The Woman of Three Cows (11x16cm-4x6in) one s. one mono. pen ink W/C pair prov.exhib.lit. 10-Dec-3 Bonhams & James Adam, Dublin #77/R est:12000-15000
£17361	$28299	€25000	Through the woods (33x25cm-13x10in) s.d.1897 W/C prov.lit. 24-Sep-3 James Adam, Dublin #87/R est:20000-25000
£22667	$41027	€34000	Fully loaded side car (26x45cm-10x18in) s. W/C bodycol prov.lit. 30-Mar-4 De Veres Art Auctions, Dublin #50/R est:30000-40000
£25352	$43859	€36000	Pilot (21x14cm-8x6in) s. W/C pen ink exec.c.1902 prov.exhib.lit. 10-Dec-3 Bonhams & James Adam, Dublin #59/R est:20000-30000
£30000	$53700	€43800	Roulette (27x18cm-11x7in) s.i. black ink W/C. 14-May-4 Christie's, London #154/R est:30000-50000
£34000	$60860	€49640	The auction (24x34cm-9x13in) s.indis.d.97 W/C gouache prov.exhib.lit. 13-May-4 Sotheby's, London #56/R est:25000-35000

YEATS, John Butler (1839-1922) Irish

Works on paper

£350	$627	€511	Study of a man, bust-length (9x9cm-4x4in) pencil prov. 14-May-4 Christie's, London #56/R
£1200	$2112	€1752	Portrait of John S Taylor (21x16cm-8x6in) s.i.d.1904 pencil. 19-May-4 Sotheby's, Olympia #77/R est:1000-1500
£2400	$4296	€3504	The Loste Land (24x16cm-9x6in) i. pencil. 14-May-4 Christie's, London #55/R est:700-1000
£2700	$4833	€3942	Portrait of a man (34x23cm-13x9in) s.d.1905 pencil prov. 14-May-4 Christie's, London #57/R est:1000-1500

YECKLEY, Norman H (1914-) American

£1505	$2800	€2197	Verdugo Canyon (61x76cm-24x30in) s.d.1941. 7-Mar-4 Treadway Gallery, Cincinnati #615/R est:800-1200

YEE BON (1905-1995) Chinese

£1544	$2579	€2254	Flower still life (29x40cm-11x16in) s. board. 26-Oct-3 Christie's, Hong Kong #143/R est:35000-65000 (HK.D 20000)
£2780	$4642	€4059	Portrait of a village woman (34x44cm-13x17in) s. board. 26-Oct-3 Christie's, Hong Kong #142/R est:30000-60000 (HK.D 36000)

YEGOROV, Andrei (1878-1954) Russian

£486	$763	€700	Sunlit snowy landscape with peasant women and horse drawn sledge (25x34cm-10x13in) s. tempera gouache. 30-Aug-3 Hans Stahl, Toestorf #49/R
Works on paper			
£308	$529	€440	Farmer's sleigh in a winter woodland scene (18x24cm-7x9in) s. gouache. 3-Dec-3 Neumeister, Munich #387
£370	$676	€540	Horse-drawn sleigh in a landscape (23x31cm-9x12in) s. gouache. 4-Jun-4 Zofingen, Switzerland #2475 (S.FR 850)
£839	$1427	€1200	On the way to the well (26x43cm-10x17in) s. gouache. 29-Nov-3 Bukowskis, Helsinki #412/R
£900	$1611	€1314	Russian landscape with horse drawn sleigh (35x49cm-14x19in) s. gouache. 17-May-4 David Duggleby, Scarborough #673/R
£979	$1684	€1400	Winter landscape with farm wagon (33x46cm-13x18in) s. gouache. 3-Dec-3 Neumeister, Munich #386/R
£1014	$1814	€1500	The sleigh ride (23x32cm-9x13in) s. gouache. 8-May-4 Bukowskis, Helsinki #407/R est:1700-2000
£1216	$2177	€1800	On the way home (33x48cm-13x19in) s. gouache. 8-May-4 Bukowskis, Helsinki #406/R est:2000-2500
£1419	$2540	€2100	Sleigh ride (36x45cm-14x18in) s. gouache. 8-May-4 Bukowskis, Helsinki #404/R est:2500-3000
£2238	$3804	€3200	Sleigh ride (35x47cm-14x19in) s. gouache. 29-Nov-3 Bukowskis, Helsinki #399/R est:2400-2600
£2500	$4250	€3750	View of the shore line of Tallinn (32x64cm-13x25in) pencil gouache board. 25-Nov-3 Christie's, London #196/R est:2500-3500
£2600	$4420	€3796	View of the River Neva with Saint Isaac's Cathedral and the Admiralty (24x35cm-9x14in) s. gouache. 19-Nov-3 Sotheby's, London #86/R est:2000-3000

YELA CORRAL, Joaquin (20th C) Spanish

£276	$497	€400	Still life with lemons (81x100cm-32x39in) s. 26-Jan-4 Ansorena, Madrid #378/R

YELLAND, Raymond D (1848-1900) American

£982	$1700	€1434	Rocky Coast (22x30cm-9x12in) paper on board prov. 10-Dec-3 Bonhams & Butterfields, San Francisco #6175/R est:3000-5000
£1111	$2000	€1622	Near Dordrecht, Holland (35x61cm-14x24in) s. 25-Apr-4 Bonhams & Butterfields, San Francisco #5503/R est:2000-3000

£14946 $27500 €21821 The Golden Gate from the Piedmont Hills (35x55cm-14x22in) s. s.i.d.1899 verso prov. 8-Jun-4 Bonhams & Butterfields, San Francisco #4166/R est:10000-15000
£24457 $45000 €35707 Schooner approaching the coast at sunset (35x61cm-14x24in) s.d.1875 prov. 8-Jun-4 Bonhams & Butterfields, San Francisco #4165/R est:20000-30000

YELLAND, Raymond D (attrib) (1848-1900) American
£1223 $2250 €1835 The rocky California coast (40x76cm-16x30in) prov. 8-Jun-4 Bonhams & Butterfields, San Francisco #4211/R est:3000-5000

YELTSEVA, Dina (1965-) Russian
£275 $514 €413 Apple (25x30cm-10x12in) s. 21-Jul-4 John Nicholson, Haslemere #442/R
£336 $628 €500 Orange (25x30cm-10x12in) s. 24-Feb-4 Durán, Madrid #739/R
£336 $594 €500 Snowman (25x30cm-10x12in) s. 27-Apr-4 Durán, Madrid #729/R
£369 $661 €550 Fishing in winter (15x30cm-6x12in) s. 25-May-4 Durán, Madrid #736/R
£390 $651 €550 Autumn celebration (25x30cm-10x12in) s. 20-Oct-3 Durán, Madrid #723/R
£435 $713 €600 La Manzana (25x30cm-10x12in) s. 27-May-3 Durán, Madrid #786/R
£442 $791 €650 Russian winter (25x30cm-10x12in) s. 22-Mar-4 Durán, Madrid #709/R
£660 $1075 €950 Noah's arc (40x50cm-16x20in) s. 23-Sep-3 Durán, Madrid #676/R
£845 $1479 €1200 Fishermen in winter (25x30cm-10x12in) s. 16-Dec-3 Durán, Madrid #710/R

YEN PIN (?) Chinese
£539 $900 €787 Autumn Water (91x147cm-36x58in) s.d. 11-Oct-3 Nadeau, Windsor #1/R

YEN WEN LIANG (1893-1990) Chinese
£34139 $61451 €49843 Landscape by the riverside (58x73cm-23x29in) s. prov. 25-Apr-4 Christie's, Hong Kong #708/R est:240000-280000 (HK.D 480000)

YENCESSE, Hubert (1900-) French
Sculpture
£1800 $3006 €2628 Male torso (72cm-28in) s.i. bronze. 21-Oct-3 Bonhams, Knightsbridge #181/R est:1200-1500

YENIKEYEVA, Tatyana (1968-) Russian
£300 $525 €438 Before dancing lesson (24x35cm-9x14in) s. 17-Dec-3 John Nicholson, Haslemere #196/R
£300 $525 €438 Little flower girl (35x27cm-14x11in) s. 17-Dec-3 John Nicholson, Haslemere #197
£350 $613 €511 Girl with kittens (27x35cm-11x14in) s. 17-Dec-3 John Nicholson, Haslemere #57

YENS, Karl Julius Heinrich (1868-1945) American
£886 $1400 €1294 House in a California landscape (38x48cm-15x19in) board. 7-Sep-3 Treadway Gallery, Cincinnati #578/R
Works on paper
£1040 $1800 €1518 Artist sketching in Laguna Canyon (54x59cm-21x23in) s. pencil W/C. 10-Dec-3 Bonhams & Butterfields, San Francisco #6326/R est:2500-3500

YEO KIM SENG (1938-1994) Singaporean
£1268 $1966 €1851 River Thames at Battersea. Boats on the beach, Ibiza (40x56cm-16x22in) s. s.d.1979 verso one i.verso two. 6-Oct-2 Sotheby's, Singapore #85/R est:3000-4000 (S.D 3500)

YEOMANS, Peter (1930-) Australian
Works on paper
£537 $994 €784 Running out the pilot (84x193cm-33x76in) chl exhib. 15-Mar-4 Sotheby's, Melbourne #161 est:400-600 (A.D 1300)

YEOMANS, Thomas (19th C) British
£2813 $4500 €4107 Groomer (69x91cm-27x36in) painted 1844. 19-Sep-3 Du Mouchelle, Detroit #2141/R est:2500-3500

YEPES, Eduardo Diaz (1909-1979) Uruguayan
Sculpture
£1307 $2300 €1908 Genesis (40x15x10cm-16x6x4in) marble onyx. 5-Jan-4 Galeria y Remates, Montevideo #55/R est:3000-4000
£1875 $3300 €2738 Fight (46x35x34cm-18x14x13in) s. bronze. 5-Jan-4 Galeria y Remates, Montevideo #56/R est:3000-4000

YEPES, Tomas (1600-1674) Spanish
£80000 $138400 €116800 White roses in a lobed footed copper lustre mailica Manises vase on a ledge (90x70cm-35x28in) prov.lit. 10-Dec-3 Christie's, London #60/R est:80000-100000
£320000 $553600 €467200 Myrtle in a lobed footed polychrome majolica Manises vase on a draped ledge (90x70cm-35x28in) s.d.1663 prov.exhib.lit. 10-Dec-3 Christie's, London #59/R est:150000-200000

YERGER, John (20th C) American
£403 $750 €588 Still life with pear and strawberries (12x17cm-5x7in) s.d.93 board. 5-Mar-4 Skinner, Boston #363/R
£457 $850 €667 Oriental miniature vase (18x13cm-7x5in) s. panel. 5-Mar-4 Skinner, Boston #364/R
£484 $900 €707 Still life with pears and cherries (20x35cm-8x14in) s.d.93 board. 5-Mar-4 Skinner, Boston #362/R

YERKA, Jacek (1952-) Polish
Works on paper
£257 $445 €375 Bath in the jungle (11x14cm-4x6in) s.i.d.03 chk pencil. 10-Dec-3 Agra, Warsaw #43/R (P.Z 1700)
£908 $1570 €1326 Sundial (56x46cm-22x18in) s. pastel exec. 2000. 14-Dec-3 Agra, Warsaw #47/R est:6000 (P.Z 6000)
£908 $1570 €1326 Orange trees with clocks (46x58cm-18x23in) s. pastel exec. 2000. 14-Dec-3 Agra, Warsaw #48/R est:6000 (P.Z 6000)
£966 $1612 €1400 Bedroom scene in the middle of the forest (47x59cm-19x23in) s.d.03 pastel. 16-Nov-3 Agra, Warsaw #70/R
£1009 $1836 €1473 Garden jacuzzi (47x59cm-19x23in) s. pastel exec 2004. 20-Jun-4 Agra, Warsaw #61/R (P.Z 7000)
£1062 $1902 €1551 Niagara (59x47cm-23x19in) pastel exec.2004. 6-May-4 Agra, Warsaw #68/R (P.Z 7500)
£1073 $1943 €1567 Composition (59x47cm-23x19in) s.d.04 pastel. 4-Apr-4 Agra, Warsaw #84/R (P.Z 7600)
£1073 $1943 €1567 Landscape fantasy (46x58cm-18x23in) s.d.99 pastel. 4-Apr-4 Agra, Warsaw #85/R (P.Z 7600)
£1074 $1858 €1568 Peacefully travelling through the jungle (48x60cm-19x24in) s.d.03 pastel. 10-Dec-3 Agra, Warsaw #44/R (P.Z 7100)
£1081 $1967 €1578 Composition (45x61cm-18x24in) s. pastel exec 1997. 20-Jun-4 Agra, Warsaw #62/R (P.Z 7500)
£1310 $2188 €1900 Underwater train tin the shape of a fish (47x59cm-19x23in) s.d.03 pastel. 16-Nov-3 Agra, Warsaw #80/R est:1000
£1529 $2538 €2232 Untitled (46x59cm-18x23in) pastel cardboard exec.2002. 2-Oct-3 Agra, Warsaw #66/R est:10000 (P.Z 10000)
£2344 $3914 €3422 Lazienka (48x60cm-19x24in) s.d.03 pastel. 19-Oct-3 Agra, Warsaw #27/R est:6000 (P.Z 15000)

YERMOKHINA, Elena (20th C) Russian
£290 $475 €400 Still life with carrot and other vegetables (27x35cm-11x14in) s. 27-May-3 Durán, Madrid #787/R

YERMOLOV, Pavel (1971-) Russian
£350 $613 €511 Ancient Shelf (30x40cm-12x16in) s. 17-Dec-3 John Nicholson, Haslemere #42/R
£399 $651 €575 Still life (30x40cm-12x16in) s. 16-Jul-3 Durán, Madrid #660/R
£680 $1218 €1000 Still life with hunting items (38x55cm-15x22in) s. 22-Mar-4 Durán, Madrid #710/R

YETER, Hannefi (20th C) German
£420 $713 €600 Rest and pleasure - happiness and passion (119x119cm-47x47in) s.d.1989. 29-Nov-3 Arnold, Frankfurt #586/R

YEVGENI, I Rudov (1931-) Russian
£5866 $10500 €8564 Kolkhoz wedding (108x140cm-43x55in) painted 1952. 29-May-4 Shishkin Gallery, Moscow #62/R est:20000-30000

YEVONDE, Madame (1893-1975) British
Photographs
£3333 $6000 €4866 Portrait of an unidentified woman (34x27cm-13x11in) vivex colour print. 23-Apr-4 Phillips, New York #128/R est:4000-6000

YEWELL, George Henry (1830-1923) American
£3779 $6500 €5517 Bab Zuweyleh, Cairo, Egypt (30x25cm-12x10in) 3-Dec-3 Doyle, New York #183/R est:4000-6000

YGAN, Stanislav de Nagy (20th C) American
£349 $600 €510 French Quarter courtyard (20x25cm-8x10in) s. masonite. 6-Dec-3 Neal Auction Company, New Orleans #611
£814 $1400 €1188 Upper Bourbon Street (23x30cm-9x12in) masonite. 6-Dec-3 Neal Auction Company, New Orleans #612 est:600-800

YI HAUNG (1820-1898) Korean
Works on paper
£16304 $30000 €23804 Orchids and rocks (22x31cm-9x12in) s.i. ink on silk eight panel screen. 23-Mar-4 Christie's, Rockefeller NY #324/R est:30000-40000

YI INMUN (1745-1821) Korean
Works on paper
£10326 $19000 €15076 Landscape (69x45cm-27x18in) i. ink. 23-Mar-4 Christie's, Rockefeller NY #321/R est:20000-25000

YIP, Richard (1919-1981) American/Chinese

Works on paper

£297 $550 €434 River landscape with bridge (36x51cm-14x20in) s.i. W/C. 13-Mar-4 Auctions by the Bay, Alameda #432/R

£378 $700 €552 Rural landscape with farm (36x53cm-14x21in) s.i.d.78 W/C. 13-Mar-4 Auctions by the Bay, Alameda #399/R

YIRAWALA (c.1900-1976) Australian

Works on paper

£586 $1096 €879 Lorrkon ceremony kangaroo (79x33cm-31x13in) earth pigments eucalyptus bark exec.c.1960 prov. 26-Jul-4 Sotheby's, Melbourne #390/R (A.D 1500)

£977 $1826 €1466 Mullet (35x72cm-14x28in) bears name.i.verso earth pigment eucalyptus bark exec.c.1970 prov. 26-Jul-4 Sotheby's, Melbourne #393/R (A.D 2500)

£2148 $4018 €3222 Maraian messengers, spirit figures (76x34cm-30x13in) earth pigments eucalyptus bark exec.c.1969 prov. 26-Jul-4 Sotheby's, Melbourne #387/R est:7000-10000 (A.D 5500)

£2539 $4748 €3809 Maraian source of life for man and nature (66x44cm-26x17in) bears name.i. earth pigments eucalyptus bark exec.c.1968 prov. 26-Jul-4 Sotheby's, Melbourne #238/R est:12000-18000 (A.D 6500)

£2734 $5113 €4101 Lumahlumah's daughters (43x20cm-17x8in) bears name.d.1963 verso earth pigments eucalyptus bark prov. 26-Jul-4 Sotheby's, Melbourne #284/R est:7000-10000 (A.D 7000)

£3906 $7305 €5859 Copulating Mimih, Mimih increase ritual (46x18cm-18x7in) bears name.i.d.1962 earth pigments eucalyptus bark prov. 26-Jul-4 Sotheby's, Melbourne #35/R est:12000-18000 (A.D 10000)

£4297 $8035 €6446 Female black kangaroo (89x33cm-35x13in) bears name.i.d.1962 verso earth pigments eucalyptus bark prov. 26-Jul-4 Sotheby's, Melbourne #237/R est:15000-20000 (A.D 11000)

£4688 $8766 €7032 Lumahlumah's daughters (54x25cm-21x10in) earth pigments eucalyptus bark exec.c.1970 prov. 26-Jul-4 Sotheby's, Melbourne #36/R est:15000-20000 (A.D 12000)

£4878 $7707 €7073 Untitled (110x54cm-43x21in) earth pigments eucalyptus bark exec.c.1970 prov. 28-Jul-3 Sotheby's, Paddington #137/R est:12000-18000 (A.D 12000)

£5691 $8992 €8252 Sacred body designs (73x14cm-29x6in) earth pigments eucalyptus bark exec.c.1972 prov. 28-Jul-3 Sotheby's, Paddington #241/R est:10000-15000 (A.D 14000)

£6098 $9634 €8842 Frog and turtle (61x33cm-24x13in) earth pigments eucalyptus bark prov. 28-Jul-3 Sotheby's, Paddington #135/R est:12000-18000 (A.D 15000)

£7317 $11561 €10610 Last fight of Lumahlumah (94x49cm-37x19in) earth pigments eucalyptus bark exec.c.1970 prov. 28-Jul-3 Sotheby's, Paddington #136/R est:18000-25000 (A.D 18000)

£7422 $13879 €11133 Kundaagi, the red plains kangaroo (55x23cm-22x9in) name.i. d.1963 and 1964 verso earth pigments eucalyptus bark 2. 26-Jul-4 Sotheby's, Melbourne #236/R est:15000-20000 (A.D 19000)

£7724 $12203 €11200 Wind mimihs (32x27cm-13x11in) i.d.1971 verso earth pigments eucalyptus bark pair prov. 28-Jul-3 Sotheby's, Paddington #138/R est:15000-20000 (A.D 19000)

£9766 $18262 €14649 Mimih mourning (52x26cm-20x10in) earth pigments eucalyptus bark prov. 26-Jul-4 Sotheby's, Melbourne #34/R est:14000-18000 (A.D 25000)

£17073 $26976 €24756 Three mimih spirits (87x59cm-34x23in) earth pigments eucalyptus bark exec.c.1958 prov.lit. 28-Jul-3 Sotheby's, Paddington #82/R est:20000-30000 (A.D 42000)

YKELENSTAM, Hendrikus (1897-1993) Dutch

£680 $1238 €1000 Still life with green box, vase and a jug (38x31cm-15x12in) s.d.34. 3-Feb-4 Christie's, Amsterdam #512/R est:1000-1500

YKENS, Frans (1601-1693) Flemish

£8219 $13973 €12000 Virgin and Child with the young Saint John the Baptist, surrounded by a cartouche (73x56cm-29x22in) panel prov. 5-Nov-3 Christie's, Amsterdam #35/R est:12000-18000

£28671 $47881 €41000 Still life of flowers including roses, tulips and insects (62x40cm-24x16in) panel. 10-Oct-3 Winterberg, Heidelberg #415a/R est:12500

£44444 $80000 €64888 Still life of peaches, grapes, pomegranates, figs and wild strawberries in porcelain bowl. Still lif (41x54cm-16x21in) s. copper pair. 22-Jan-4 Sotheby's, New York #53/R est:80000-120000

YKENS, Frans (circle) (1601-1693) Flemish

£5000 $8650 €7300 Swag of grapes, other fruit and flowers over a ledge (64x77cm-25x30in) 12-Dec-3 Christie's, Kensington #70/R est:5000-7000

YLLANES, Alejindro Mario (1913-1960) Bolivian

£2446 $4500 €3669 Dance of the plow (137x193cm-54x76in) canvas on board painted 1940. 13-Jun-4 William Jenack, New York #155 est:5000-8000

£5242 $9750 €7653 Wirakhocha danzante (208x188cm-82x74in) s. oil on burlap. 7-Mar-4 William Jenack, New York #258 est:8000-12000

YNGVADOTTIR, Johanna Kristin (1953-1991) Icelandic

£1690 $2823 €2467 Waiting for spring (100x75cm-39x30in) s.d.88. 7-Oct-3 Rasmussen, Copenhagen #247/R est:18000-20000 (D.KR 18000)

YOAKUM, Joseph (1915-) American

Works on paper

£4444 $8000 €6488 Mt. Houseback in Rocky Knob Range. s.d.5/29/69 pen col pencil. 24-Apr-4 Slotin Folk Art, Buford #273/R est:6000-8000

YOCHIM, Louis Dunn (1909-) American

£682 $1200 €996 Untitled (102x76cm-40x30in) s. board painted c.1960. 23-May-4 Treadway Gallery, Cincinnati #766/R

YOCHIM, Maurice (1908-) American

£403 $750 €588 Between chores (51x61cm-20x24in) s. painted c.1940 exhib. 7-Mar-4 Treadway Gallery, Cincinnati #652/R

YODER, Susan Bankey (20th C) American

Works on paper

£640 $1100 €934 Winter scene of a buck and 2 doe in a clearing (325x91cm-128x36in) s.d.1991 W/C gouache. 6-Dec-3 Pook & Pook, Downington #101/R

YOLDJOGLOU, Georges (1933-) ?

£265 $450 €387 Fenetre sur les dunes (61x51cm-24x20in) s. 5-Nov-3 Doyle, New York #83/R

£265 $450 €387 Terasse sur Paris (46x56cm-18x22in) s. 5-Nov-3 Doyle, New York #84/R

£297 $550 €434 Le figaro en fleurs (91x74cm-36x29in) s. 15-Jul-4 Doyle, New York #86/R

£408 $750 €596 Les roses de trepied (56x46cm-22x18in) s. i.d.2001 stretcher. 23-Jun-4 Doyle, New York #5081/R

£432 $800 €631 Plage (61x74cm-24x29in) s. i.overlap. 10-Mar-4 Doyle, New York #56/R

£460 $750 €672 Fleurs et musique (51x61cm-20x24in) s. i.overlap. 17-Jul-3 Doyle, New York #55/R

£516 $950 €753 Fenetre fleurie sur le plage (61x51cm-24x20in) s. 9-Jun-4 Doyle, New York #3092

£543 $1000 €793 La cote d'opale en bord de mer (51x66cm-20x26in) s. i.d.2001 stretcher. 23-Jun-4 Doyle, New York #5078/R est:1800-2200

£670 $1200 €978 Bord de mer en fleurs (53x64cm-21x25in) s. i. stretcher. 8-Jan-4 Doyle, New York #48/R

£1902 $3500 €2777 Bord mer anime (38x46cm-15x18in) s. i.d.2002 stretcher. 25-Mar-4 Doyle, New York #82/R est:1800-2200

YON, Edmond (1836-1897) French

£966 $1786 €1400 Bord de riviere (38x28cm-15x11in) s. 16-Feb-4 Giraudeau, Tours #111

£3000 $5490 €4500 Pecheur dans sa barque (32x47cm-13x19in) s. 6-Jun-4 Osenat, Fontainebleau #71/R est:5500-6000

£5245 $9021 €7500 Village au bord de la riviere (44x70cm-17x28in) s. 7-Dec-3 Osenat, Fontainebleau #177 est:6000-6500

Works on paper

£543 $891 €750 Village pres de l'eau (18x27cm-7x11in) s. W/C. 11-May-3 Osenat, Fontainebleau #3

YON, Edmond (attrib) (1836-1897) French

£900 $1647 €1314 Sewing by the window (35x24cm-14x9in) s. 8-Apr-4 Christie's, Kensington #92/R

YONG JIN HAN (1934-) Chinese?

Sculpture

£2200 $3938 €3212 Stone (30x30x20cm-12x12x8in) two pieces of stone. 6-May-4 Sotheby's, London #88/R est:2300-3400

YONG RONG (?-1790) Chinese

Works on paper

£2134 $3841 €3116 Return from fishing (82x40cm-32x16in) i.d.1771 hanging scroll ink. 26-Apr-4 Christie's, Hong Kong #933/R est:40000-50000 (HK.D 30000)

£64011 $115220 €93456 Landscapes (23x65cm-9x26in) s.i. ink col fans pair. 26-Apr-4 Christie's, Hong Kong #962/R est:250000-300000 (HK.D 900000)

YONG, Joe de (1894-1975) American

Works on paper

£223 $400 €326 Prospector (30x41cm-12x16in) s. W/C gouache ink. 20-Mar-4 Selkirks, St. Louis #165

£337 $550 €492 Afternoon playtime (51x71cm-20x28in) s. gouache. 28-Sep-3 Bonhams & Butterfields, Los Angeles #7007 est:800-1200

£427 $700 €619 Home sweet home (8x10cm-3x4in) s.d. pen ink. 7-Jun-3 Treadway Gallery, Cincinnati #1472

YOO, Debra (20th C) American

£246 $450 €369 Still life with matisse book (99x117cm-39x46in) 10-Jul-4 Hindman, Chicago #581/R

YORKE, W H (19th C) British

£2622 $4378 €3828 Ship's portrait Mot Hermanos (50x78cm-20x31in) s.d.1883. 25-Oct-3 Rasmussen, Havnen #2609/R est:7000-10000 (D.KR 28000)

YORKE, William Gay (1817-1883) American
£15625 $25000 €22813 Ocean Queen (66x91cm-26x36in) s.i. prov. 21-Sep-3 Grogan, Boston #89/R

YORKE, William Henry (19th C) British
£1900 $3268 €2774 Three masted sailing ship at sea (48x58cm-19x23in) 5-Dec-3 Keys, Aylsham #606/R est:2000-3000

YORKE, William Hoard (fl.1858-1903) British
£2412 $4413 €3522 Ship's portrait of Solglyt (50x76cm-20x30in) s. 2-Feb-4 Blomqvist, Lysaker #1329 est:12000-15000 (N.KR 30000)
£2516 $4679 €3673 Ship's portrait of Anna of Fanoe (50x76cm-20x30in) s.d.1890. 2-Mar-4 Rasmussen, Copenhagen #1426/R est:30000 (D.KR 28000)
£3000 $5370 €4380 Pilot cutter running out to meet the Danish barquentine Moto Hermanos (50x76cm-20x30in) s.d.1889. 26-May-4 Christie's, Kensington #623/R est:3000-5000
£3500 $6020 €5110 Barque Ladstock inward bound for Liverpool, off the South Stack Lighthouse, Anglesey (51x77cm-20x30in) s. 2-Dec-3 Sotheby's, London #26/R est:4000-6000
£4500 $7740 €6570 Outward bound sailing ship Criccieth Castle passing point Lynas, Anglesey (61x92cm-24x36in) 2-Dec-3 Sotheby's, London #24/R est:5000-7000
£4969 $8000 €7255 Schooner, Estrella (51x76cm-20x30in) s. prov. 20-Aug-3 James Julia, Fairfield #695/R est:10000-20000

YORKE, William Hoard (attrib) (fl.1858-1903) British
£1400 $2240 €2044 Full-rigged ship Elphinston outward bound in the Channel (51x76cm-20x30in) 16-Sep-3 Bonhams, New Bond Street #53/R est:1500-2000

YORSTON, Fleur (20th C) New Zealander?
Works on paper
£278 $442 €406 Father (118x58cm-46x23in) s.i.d.Dec 94 mixed media tryptich. 1-May-3 Dunbar Sloane, Wellington #323 (NZ.D 800)

YOSHIDA, Hiroshi (1876-1950) Japanese
£306 $550 €447 Persian jar (43x33cm-17x13in) s.d.1964 canvas on panel. 23-Jan-4 Freeman, Philadelphia #119/R
Prints
£1503 $2750 €2194 Moraine Lake. s.i.d.1925 print. 6-Apr-4 Bonhams & Butterfields, San Francisco #3004/R est:1200-1800
£1776 $3250 €2593 Matterhorn - night (54x41cm-21x16in) s.i.d.1925 print. 6-Apr-4 Bonhams & Butterfields, San Francisco #3007/R est:2500-4000
£2000 $3580 €2920 Asahi (58x75cm-23x30in) s.i. woodblock. 6-May-4 Sotheby's, London #11/R est:2200-2800
£2186 $4000 €3192 Morning mist in Taj Mahal no.5 (41x55cm-16x22in) s.i.d.1932 print. 6-Apr-4 Bonhams & Butterfields, San Francisco #3063/R est:1800-2500
£2240 $4100 €3270 Matterhorn (54x42cm-21x17in) s.i.d.1925 print. 6-Apr-4 Bonhams & Butterfields, San Francisco #3006/R est:2000-3000
£2459 $4500 €3590 Fujiyama - Ten views of Fuji series (58x76cm-23x30in) s.i.d.1926 oversized print. 6-Apr-4 Bonhams & Butterfields, San Francisco #3020/R est:6000-8000
£2869 $5250 €4189 El captitan. s.d.1925 print. 6-Apr-4 Bonhams & Butterfields, San Francisco #3001 est:1500-2500
£4098 $7500 €5983 Mt. Rainier (40x53cm-16x21in) s.i.d.1925 print. 6-Apr-4 Bonhams & Butterfields, San Francisco #3003/R est:4000-6000
£7650 $14000 €11169 Kumoi cherry tree (58x74cm-23x29in) s.i.d.1926 oversized print. 6-Apr-4 Bonhams & Butterfields, San Francisco #3029/R est:20000-30000
Works on paper
£723 $1200 €1048 Landscape (33x48cm-13x19in) s. W/C. 14-Jun-3 Rachel Davis, Shaker Heights #145/R
£815 $1500 €1190 Two landscapes (23x34cm-9x13in) s. W/C two. 23-Mar-4 Christie's, Rockefeller NY #130/R est:1500-2000

YOSHIDA, M (20th C) Japanese
£884 $1600 €1291 Female nude (33x24cm-13x9in) s. panel. 18-Apr-4 Bonhams & Butterfields, Los Angeles #7090 est:500-700

YOSHIMITSU (19/20th C) Japanese
Sculpture
£1918 $3260 €2800 Archer (46cm-18in) s. verso bronze. 8-Nov-3 Dr Fritz Nagel, Stuttgart #1835/R est:800

YOSHIMURA, Fumio (1926-2002) Japanese
Sculpture
£1047 $1800 €1529 Onions (25x20cm-10x8in) s.i. base carved linden prov. 7-Dec-3 Freeman, Philadelphia #93 est:250-400
£1163 $2000 €1698 Tea bag (25x10cm-10x4in) s.d.84 base carved linden thread prov. 7-Dec-3 Freeman, Philadelphia #92 est:250-400
£1359 $2500 €1984 Bunch of five daffodils (48cm-19in) carved pine in a glass vase. 27-Jun-4 Freeman, Philadelphia #143/R est:3000-5000
£1686 $2900 €2462 Half grapefruit in a bowl and a juice carton with straw (28cm-11in) carved linden perspex case incl base exec 1982 prov. 7-Dec-3 Freeman, Philadelphia #87 est:600-1000
£1744 $3000 €2546 Peapod (41x107x5cm-16x42x2in) carved pine within box exec 1975 prov.exhib. 7-Dec-3 Freeman, Philadelphia #90 est:300-500
£1890 $3250 €2759 Pomegranates (18cm-7in) carved linden and penduke perspex case incl base prov.exhib. 7-Dec-3 Freeman, Philadelphia #88 est:600-1000
£1890 $3250 €2759 Eggs (43x64cm-17x25in) carved linden in perspex case exec 1981 prov.exhib. 7-Dec-3 Freeman, Philadelphia #94 est:600-1000
£2762 $4750 €4033 Bunch of five daffodils (53cm-21in) carved pine prov. 7-Dec-3 Freeman, Philadelphia #96 est:400-600
£3488 $6000 €5092 Artichoke (36x25x15cm-14x10x6in) s.d.82 base carved pine prov.exhib. 7-Dec-3 Freeman, Philadelphia #97 est:300-500

YOSHINOBU, Komai (fl.1765-1770) Japanese
Prints
£2500 $4600 €3650 Princess Onnasannomiya and kitten (26x19cm-10x7in) s. print unique lit. 8-Jun-4 Sotheby's, London #101/R est:2500-3000

YOSHITANI (19th C) Japanese
Sculpture
£4110 $6986 €6000 Sshakudo and shibuichi owl on tree trunk (30cm-12in) i. i. gilt silver glass. 8-Nov-3 Dr Fritz Nagel, Stuttgart #1847/R est:2800

YOSHITOSHI, Tsukioka (1839-1892) Japanese
Works on paper
£81522 $150000 €119022 Fujiwara no yasumasa playing the flute by moonlight (141x79cm-56x31in) s.d.1882 col ink black lacquer hanging scroll prov.exhib. 23-Mar-4 Christie's, Rockefeller NY #129/R est:50000-70000

YOST, Frederico (19th C) American
Works on paper
£211 $390 €308 Dragonflies flitting throughout a marsh (41x36cm-16x14in) s. W/C. 16-Jan-4 Aspire, Cleveland #153/R
£249 $460 €364 New York Philharmonic (51x43cm-20x17in) s.d.1967 W/C. 16-Jan-4 Aspire, Cleveland #152/R

YOUNG, Alexander (1865-1923) British
£400 $668 €584 Harvest time (31x46cm-12x18in) s. 23-Oct-3 Bonhams, Edinburgh #301
£500 $835 €730 Musselburgh harbour (31x46cm-12x18in) s. i.stretcher. 23-Oct-3 Bonhams, Edinburgh #300
£700 $1295 €1022 In the harbour (36x24cm-14x9in) s.d.87 board. 14-Jul-4 Sotheby's, Olympia #91/R
£750 $1253 €1095 Unloading the day's catch on a Scottish quayside. Mending the nets (43x61cm-17x24in) s. pair. 8-Oct-3 Christie's, Kensington #741/R
£1500 $2775 €2190 Fishing boat entering the harbour at St Andrews (48x74cm-19x29in) s. 12-Feb-4 Andrew Hartley, Ilkley #835/R est:1500-2000
£2200 $3938 €3212 Mending the nets (41x70cm-16x28in) s.d.88. 28-May-4 Lyon & Turnbull, Edinburgh #11/R est:2000-3000
£2222 $3778 €3200 Peasant woman with cows by woodland stream (35x56cm-14x22in) s.d. 28-Oct-3 Dorotheum, Vienna #100/R est:3200-3800
£4200 $7140 €6132 Sorting Fish, Pittenweem (51x76cm-20x30in) s. prov. 30-Oct-3 Christie's, London #101/R est:2500-3500
£4200 $7518 €6132 Unloading the catch, largo (41x67cm-16x26in) s.d.91. 28-May-4 Lyon & Turnbull, Edinburgh #9/R est:2000-3000

YOUNG, Charles Morris (1869-1964) American
£806 $1500 €1177 Winter stream (61x46cm-24x18in) s. 5-Mar-4 Skinner, Boston #496/R est:3000-5000
£813 $1455 €1187 Milford Sound (72x170cm-28x67in) s. board. 10-May-4 Joel, Victoria #328 est:1200-1800 (A.D 2000)
£2134 $3500 €3094 Early spring landscape (51x51cm-20x20in) s.i.d.1931 verso. 4-Jun-3 Alderfer's, Hatfield #378/R est:2500-3500
£2344 $3750 €3422 Seascape (38x46cm-15x18in) s.d.1924. 19-Sep-3 Freeman, Philadelphia #175/R est:1500-2500
£3261 $6000 €4761 Rocky shoreline with a sailing ship in the distance (63x76cm-25x30in) indis.s.i.d.1928. 27-Jun-4 Freeman, Philadelphia #190/R est:4000-6000

YOUNG, Chris (1963-) American
£988 $1650 €1442 See both sides (81x122cm-32x48in) s. 11-Oct-3 Nadeau, Windsor #153/R est:5000-7000

YOUNG, E Brown (19th C) American
£403 $750 €588 Mountainous landscape with figures (76x127cm-30x50in) s. 3-Mar-4 Alderfer's, Hatfield #308/R

YOUNG, Edward Drummond (?) British
Photographs
£18563 $31000 €27102 Portrait of Walter Sickert (47x35cm-19x14in) platinum print exec.c.1918 exhib. 17-Oct-3 Sotheby's, New York #192/R est:12000-18000

YOUNG, Florence Upson (1872-1964) American
£341 $550 €494 Still life with feathers (61x51cm-24x20in) s. 24-Aug-3 Bonhams & Butterfields, Los Angeles #7020
£404 $650 €586 Still life with roses (58x69cm-23x27in) s. 24-Aug-3 Bonhams & Butterfields, Los Angeles #7022
£482 $900 €723 Monterey cypress (63x76cm-25x30in) s. 25-Jul-4 Bonhams & Butterfields, San Francisco #6085/R

YOUNG, Harry Anthony de (1893-1956) American

Works on paper

£299 $500 €437 O'Henry house, San Antonio, Texas (28x23cm-11x9in) pencil. 18-Oct-3 David Dike, Dallas #57/R

YOUNG, Henry (1792-1861) American

Works on paper

£875 $1400 €1278 Two women flanking a monument enclosing script (41x30cm-16x12in) W/C ink. 20-Sep-3 Pook & Pook, Downington #445/R est:2000-4000

£1497 $2500 €2186 Birth certificate for Isaiah Wilon Moses 1849 (25x19cm-10x7in) W/C ink. 11-Nov-3 Christie's, Rockefeller NY #211/R est:800-1200

£3488 $6000 €5092 Birth certificate for Joseph Horner (25x18cm-10x7in) d.1841 W/C ink. 6-Dec-3 Pook & Pook, Downington #252/R est:2000-4000

YOUNG, Jean (1914-) British

£280 $468 €406 Men pruning an olive grove (51x61cm-20x24in) 22-Jun-3 Desmond Judd, Cranbrook #1036

YOUNG, John Tobias (fl.1811-1822) British

£5800 $9280 €8468 Figures in wooded countryside with view of Mount Orgueil Castle (33x53cm-13x21in) mahogany panel. 17-Sep-3 Bonhams, Brooks & Langlois, Jersey #84/R est:2000-3000

YOUNG, Mabel (1889-1974) Irish/British

£380 $627 €555 To the far off hills. mono. board i.d.1959 verso. 3-Jul-3 Biddle & Webb, Birmingham #799

£572 $1053 €870 Connemara (26x36cm-10x14in) canvasboard. 22-Jun-4 De Veres Art Auctions, Dublin #198

£1119 $1902 €1600 To the far off hills (13x15cm-5x6in) mono i.d.1959 verso board. 18-Nov-3 Whyte's, Dublin #1/R est:1000-1200

£1208 $2138 €1800 Bright day on Achill Sound (36x51cm-14x20in) s. 27-Apr-4 Whyte's, Dublin #206/R est:1500-2000

£1275 $2257 €1900 Scene in the Wicklow mountains (30x41cm-12x16in) s. 27-Apr-4 Whyte's, Dublin #205/R est:1500-2000

£1538 $2615 €2200 White lenten roses (46x36cm-18x14in) s. board. 18-Nov-3 Whyte's, Dublin #181/R est:1500-2000

£1678 $2853 €2400 Near Delphi, Connemara (36x41cm-14x16in) s.i. s.verso. 25-Nov-3 De Veres Art Auctions, Dublin #65/R est:2000-3000

YOUNG, Mabel I (fl.1896-1903) British

£300 $540 €438 Fruit woman (19x28cm-7x11in) board. 22-Apr-4 Lawrence, Crewkerne #924

YOUNG, Murat (1901-1973) American

Works on paper

£569 $950 €831 Blondie's hat purchase turns out to be a calamity (41x43cm-16x17in) s. pen ink. 15-Nov-3 Illustration House, New York #59/R

YOUNG, Oscar van (1906-) American

£2941 $5000 €4294 Chavez ravine, Los Angeles (46x61cm-18x24in) s.d.41 board double-sided prov. 18-Nov-3 John Moran, Pasadena #97a est:3000-5000

YOUNG, Peter Ford (1943-) American

£294 $500 €429 Untitled (201x140cm-79x55in) acrylic prov. 9-Nov-3 Wright, Chicago #405

£361 $650 €527 Drawing for a green paintings (16x16cm-6x6in) acrylic board prov. 24-Apr-4 David Rago, Lambertville #493/R

£1353 $2300 €1975 Number 2 (191x191cm-75x75in) acrylic prov. 7-Nov-3 Selkirks, St. Louis #583/R est:1500-2000

Works on paper

£1611 $2900 €2352 Untitled (15x18cm-6x7in) one s.d.1968 marking pen one acrylic paper two prov. 24-Apr-4 David Rago, Lambertville #491/R est:100-200

YOUNG, Purvis (1943-) American

£222 $400 €324 Woman's face with blue hair (122x66cm-48x26in) board. 24-Apr-4 Slotin Folk Art, Buford #454/R

£264 $475 €385 Larger crowd (33x76cm-13x30in) housepaint pen on paper prov. 24-Apr-4 Slotin Folk Art, Buford #455/R

£329 $550 €480 Horses and faces (130x119cm-51x47in) household paint board. 15-Nov-3 Slotin Folk Art, Buford #284/R

£333 $600 €486 White horses (81x66cm-32x26in) housepaint on posterboard. 24-Apr-4 Slotin Folk Art, Buford #456/R

£361 $650 €527 Warriors on horses (122x61cm-48x24in) housepaint scrap wood. 24-Apr-4 Slotin Folk Art, Buford #452/R

£417 $750 €609 Leaving the city (41x66cm-16x26in) board painted c.1996. 24-Apr-4 Slotin Folk Art, Buford #453/R

YOUNG, Robert Clouston (fl.1920s) British

Works on paper

£900 $1548 €1314 Yacht on the horizon (53x70cm-21x28in) s. W/C. 2-Dec-3 Sotheby's, London #104/R

YOUNG, William (19th C) British

Works on paper

£492 $797 €718 The Team Orange (38x55cm-15x22in) s.i.d.1923 W/C. 30-Jul-3 Goodman, Sydney #115/R (A.D 1200)

YOUNG, William Blamire (1862-1935) Australian

Works on paper

£310 $484 €450 New baby (17x16cm-7x6in) s. W/C. 1-Aug-2 Joel, Victoria #200 est:1000-2000 (A.D 900)

£325 $511 €471 The valley (12x22cm-5x9in) s. W/C. 26-Aug-3 Christie's, Sydney #361 (A.D 800)

£681 $1157 €994 View out to sea (15x31cm-6x12in) s. W/C. 26-Nov-3 Deutscher-Menzies, Melbourne #180/R (A.D 1600)

£3239 $5215 €4729 Doon of Hellas (74x109cm-29x43in) s. W/C. 13-Oct-3 Joel, Victoria #334/R est:6000-8000 (A.D 8000)

YOUNG, Yone (20th C) Canadian

Works on paper

£200 $366 €292 How to recognise a witch (44x49cm-17x19in) s.i. mixed media. 1-Jun-4 Hodgins, Calgary #67/R (C.D 500)

YOUNGBLOOD, William A (20th C) American

£347 $600 €507 Fishing boat at dock (86x119cm-34x47in) s.d.72 board. 13-Dec-3 Sloans & Kenyon, Bethesda #760/R

YOUNGERMAN, Jack (1926-) American

£924 $1700 €1349 Abstract composition (79x61cm-31x24in) s.d.1966 tempera paper. 10-Jun-4 Swann Galleries, New York #258/R est:1000-1500

Works on paper

£266 $425 €388 Abstract composition (53x25cm-21x10in) init. pen ink. 18-Sep-3 Swann Galleries, New York #699/R

YOUNGHUSBAND, Adele (1878-1969) New Zealander

£1534 $2501 €2240 Floral still life with fruit (59x43cm-23x17in) s.d.1958 plywood. 23-Sep-3 Peter Webb, Auckland #123/R est:2500-3500 (NZ.D 4250)

£3147 $5727 €4595 Beach houses (60x75cm-24x30in) s.d.1936 s.i.verso. 29-Jun-4 Peter Webb, Auckland #62/R est:9000-12000 (NZ.D 9000)

YOUNGMAN, Annie Mary (1859-1919) British

Works on paper

£340 $578 €496 Gloire de Dijon roses (40x30cm-16x12in) s. W/C. 25-Nov-3 Bonhams, Knightsbridge #18/R

YOUNGMAN, John Mallows (1817-1899) British

Works on paper

£290 $476 €423 Cottage and figures beside stream (56x43cm-22x17in) s. W/C. 6-Jun-3 Biddle & Webb, Birmingham #230

YOUON, Konstantin (1875-1958) Russian

£4027 $7450 €6000 Un jour d'ete (18x30cm-7x12in) s. canvas on cardboard. 15-Mar-4 Claude Boisgirard, Paris #126/R est:2500-3000

£118243 $211655 €175000 View from Moscow (53x71cm-21x28in) s. 8-May-4 Bukowskis, Helsinki #430/R est:20000-30000

Works on paper

£11000 $18700 €16500 Winter market by the Kremlin (25x29cm-10x11in) s. W/C card. 25-Nov-3 Christie's, London #148/R est:7000-10000

£11000 $18700 €16500 Market scene (23x18cm-9x7in) s. pencil W/C. 25-Nov-3 Christie's, London #149/R est:6000-8000

YOUON, Konstantin (attrib) (1875-1958) Russian

£1317 $2200 €1923 Winter scene with figures and sleds (48x71cm-19x28in) canvasboard. 16-Nov-3 William Jenack, New York #293 est:1000-1500

Works on paper

£3145 $5849 €4592 View of a Russian town in winter (38x48cm-15x19in) s. gouache. 2-Mar-4 Rasmussen, Copenhagen #1318/R est:10000 (D.KR 35000)

£10067 $18624 €15000 St Sergei von Radonezh monastery (24x31cm-9x12in) i. gouache. 9-Mar-4 Dorotheum, Vienna #68/R est:1500-2000

YOUQUA (19th C) Oriental

£6471 $11000 €9448 View of the Hongs at Canton (46x61cm-18x24in) prov. 1-Nov-3 Skinner, Boston #93/R est:10000-15000

YOURIEVITCH, Serge (20th C) French

Sculpture

£3500 $5950 €5110 Danseuse Nattova (39cm-15in) s.num.112 pat bronze. 28-Oct-3 Sotheby's, London #95/R

£3500 $5950 €5110 Danseuse Nattova (78cm-31in) st.sig. pat bronze marble plinth. 20-Nov-3 Sotheby's, Olympia #200/R est:2500-3500

YOVITS, Esther (1916-) American
£341 $600 €498 After snow (56x66cm-22x26in) s. painted c.1941. 23-May-4 Treadway Gallery, Cincinnati #665/R

YOWELL, Chris (20th C) Irish?
£318 $579 €480 Circus genus 7 (80x95cm-31x37in) mono. acrylic panel. 15-Jun-4 James Adam, Dublin #220/R

YPERMAN, L (19/20th C) ?
£1105 $1900 €1613 Red Dress (91x74cm-36x29in) s. 7-Dec-3 Freeman, Philadelphia #17 est:1000-1500

YPPEN, Grete (1917-) Austrian
£1316 $2421 €2000 Untitled (115x55cm-45x22in) 22-Jun-4 Wiener Kunst Auktionen, Vienna #447/R est:2000

YRAOLA, Ignacio (1928-) Spanish
Works on paper
£915 $1602 €1300 Red wall (51x43cm-20x17in) s.d.73 mixed media collage. 16-Dec-3 Durán, Madrid #95/R

YRISARRI, Mario (1933-) American
£333 $600 €486 Stern (82x68cm-32x27in) s.i.d.1967 verso. 24-Apr-4 David Rago, Lambertville #505/R
£778 $1400 €1136 Untitled (69x48cm-27x19in) s.d.1968 acrylic. 24-Apr-4 David Rago, Lambertville #202/R

YRURTIA, Rogelio (1879-1950) Argentinian
Sculpture
£18256 $31400 €26654 Head of fatality (58cm-23in) s. pat bronze marble base prov. 3-Dec-3 Naón & Cia, Buenos Aires #607/R est:15000-18000

YSENDYCK, Anton van (attrib) (1801-1875) Belgian
£29577 $51169 €42000 Les trois graces (82x65cm-32x26in) oval. 9-Dec-3 Vanderkindere, Brussels #5/R est:2000-3000

YSERN Y ALIE, Pedro (1876-1946) Spanish
£322 $537 €460 Bosque (24x14cm-9x6in) s. panel. 24-Jun-3 Segre, Madrid #280/R
£629 $1051 €900 Arboles (27x35cm-11x14in) s. board. 24-Jun-3 Segre, Madrid #281/R
£638 $1034 €900 Claro en el bosque (20x33cm-8x13in) s. board. 20-May-3 Segre, Madrid #109/R
£646 $1176 €950 Strolling in the park (35x27cm-14x11in) s. board. 3-Feb-4 Segre, Madrid #123/R
£664 $1109 €950 Marina (23x32cm-9x13in) s. panel. 24-Jun-3 Segre, Madrid #283/R
£816 $1461 €1200 Danseuse (60x47cm-24x19in) s. oval. 22-Mar-4 Durán, Madrid #121/R
£1119 $1869 €1600 Ballerinas (19x32cm-7x13in) s. board. 24-Jun-3 Segre, Madrid #282/R est:1500
£1842 $3334 €2800 Majorca landscape (55x66cm-22x26in) s. board. 14-Apr-4 Ansorena, Madrid #50/R est:2800
£1993 $3268 €2750 Landscape (64x80cm-25x31in) s. 27-May-3 Durán, Madrid #242/R est:2750
£2431 $3962 €3500 Folies-Bergeres, Paris (50x61cm-20x24in) s. 23-Sep-3 Durán, Madrid #209/R est:3250
£4366 $7554 €6200 Female nude (148x91cm-58x36in) s. 15-Dec-3 Ansorena, Madrid #333/R est:6200
£4930 $8528 €7000 Dance in the fields (65x81cm-26x32in) s. 15-Dec-3 Ansorena, Madrid #339/R est:6000
Works on paper
£798 $1300 €1165 Dancers (24x29cm-9x11in) s. mixed media. 28-Sep-3 Bonhams & Butterfields, Los Angeles #7025 est:2000-3000

YSSEL, Aart van den (1922-1983) Dutch
Sculpture
£1049 $1751 €1500 Man riding on horseback (24cm-9in) metal. 30-Jun-3 Sotheby's, Amsterdam #448/R
£3497 $6014 €5000 Rider (80cm-31in) brass. 8-Dec-3 Glerum, Amsterdam #270/R est:3000-5000

YTHJALL, Terje (1943-) Norwegian
£1707 $3124 €2492 Haaken A Christensen MA, listening to two painted figures on their way to something (54x54cm-21x21in) s.d.1983 exhib. 7-Jun-4 Blomqvist, Oslo #438/R est:20000 (N.KR 21000)
£2520 $4612 €3679 Transport, procession, the road to/ the road from? (80x110cm-31x43in) s.d.1991 exhib. 7-Jun-4 Blomqvist, Oslo #460/R est:30000-35000 (N.KR 31000)
£3672 $6132 €5361 The tight-ropers meeting (105x50cm-41x20in) s.d.1984 pair. 13-Oct-3 Blomqvist, Oslo #331/R est:35000-45000 (N.KR 43000)

YTURRALDE, Jose Maria (1942-) Spanish
£660 $1122 €950 Impossible shapes (55x46cm-22x18in) s.d.1971 acrylic board. 28-Oct-3 Segre, Madrid #207/R
£660 $1122 €950 Impossible shapes (55x46cm-22x18in) s.d.1971 acrylic board. 28-Oct-3 Segre, Madrid #206/R

YU CHENG-YAO (1898-1993) Chinese
Works on paper
£2793 $5000 €4078 Lnsdscape (69x45cm-27x18in) s.i. ink hanging scroll prov. 10-May-4 Bonhams & Butterfields, San Francisco #4406/R est:3500-5500
£9266 $15475 €13528 Dreamy mountains (120x59cm-47x23in) s. ink hanging scroll prov. 27-Oct-3 Sotheby's, Hong Kong #288/R est:120000-150000 (HK.D 120000)
£17781 $32006 €25960 Mountain peaks (109x51cm-43x20in) s. col ink exhib.lit. 25-Apr-4 Christie's, Hong Kong #730/R est:250000-300000 (HK.D 250000)
£32006 $57610 €46729 River gorge (120x59cm-47x23in) s. ink hanging scroll prov. 26-Apr-4 Sotheby's, Hong Kong #580/R est:120000-150000 (HK.D 450000)

YU FEIAN (1888-1959) Chinese
Works on paper
£4247 $7093 €6201 Peonies and bees (88x34cm-35x13in) s.i.d.1941 ink col hanging scroll. 26-Oct-3 Christie's, Hong Kong #203/R est:60000-80000 (HK.D 55000)
£15647 $28165 €22845 Horse riding (21x126cm-8x50in) s.i.d.1942 ink scroll. 25-Apr-4 Christie's, Hong Kong #141/R est:150000-200000 (HK.D 220000)
£15647 $28165 €22845 Peony and birds (87x34cm-34x13in) s.i.d.1940 ink col hanging scroll. 26-Apr-4 Sotheby's, Hong Kong #657/R est:100000-120000 (HK.D 220000)
£18492 $33286 €26998 Pine and pigeons (130x75cm-51x30in) s.d.1956 ink col exhib.lit. 26-Apr-4 Sotheby's, Hong Kong #612/R est:250000-350000 (HK.D 260000)
£20077 $33529 €29312 Lotus pond (103x53cm-41x21in) s.i.d.1944 ink col hanging scroll. 27-Oct-3 Sotheby's, Hong Kong #299/R est:250000-300000 (HK.D 260000)
£24893 $44808 €36344 Peony and birds (101x53cm-40x21in) s.i.d.1947 ink col hanging scroll exhib.lit. 26-Apr-4 Sotheby's, Hong Kong #613/R est:200000-300000 (HK.D 350000)
£27027 $48649 €39459 Morning glory and insects (100x22cm-39x9in) s.i.d.1930 ink col exhib.lit. 26-Apr-4 Sotheby's, Hong Kong #656/R est:180000-250000 (HK.D 380000)
£88803 $148301 €129652 Magnolia and two birds (133x68cm-52x27in) s. ink col exhib. 27-Oct-3 Sotheby's, Hong Kong #238/R est:650000-850000 (HK.D 1150000)

YU MING (1884-1935) Chinese
Works on paper
£7468 $13442 €10903 Portrait of a lady (129x32cm-51x13in) s.i.d.1935 ink col. 26-Apr-4 Sotheby's, Hong Kong #554/R est:40000-60000 (HK.D 105000)

YUAN JIANG (after) (c.1690-1724) Chinese
Works on paper
£14130 $26000 €20630 Paradies (187x376cm-74x148in) ink silk on board folding screen. 23-Mar-4 Sotheby's, New York #558/R est:20000-30000

YUAN SONGNIAN (1895-1966) Chinese
Works on paper
£2987 $5377 €4361 The bank at dawn (42x64cm-17x25in) s.i.d.1957 ink col hanging scroll. 26-Apr-4 Sotheby's, Hong Kong #568/R est:15000-25000 (HK.D 42000)

YUE ZHENWEN (1956-) Chinese
Works on paper
£4979 $8962 €7269 Autumn scene (47x508cm-19x200in) s.i.d.2003 ink col handscroll. 26-Apr-4 Sotheby's, Hong Kong #537/R est:40000-60000 (HK.D 70000)
£5792 $9672 €8456 Landscape (47x541cm-19x213in) s.i.d.2002 ink handscroll. 27-Oct-3 Sotheby's, Hong Kong #380/R est:40000-60000 (HK.D 75000)

YUN SHOUPING (1633-1690) Chinese
Works on paper
£2845 $5121 €4154 Bird and plum blossoms (116x49cm-46x19in) s.i. ink hanging scroll prov.lit. 25-Apr-4 Christie's, Hong Kong #440/R est:40000-50000 (HK.D 40000)
£20626 $37127 €30114 Bamboo grove (38x235cm-15x93in) s.i.d.1689 ink col handscroll. 26-Apr-4 Sotheby's, Hong Kong #693/R est:100000-200000 (HK.D 290000)

YUN XI (?-1758) Chinese
Works on paper
£42674 $76814 €62304 Landscapes (28x25cm-11x10in) ink col on silk album of twelve leaves. 26-Apr-4 Christie's, Hong Kong #930/R est:60000-80000 (HK.D 600000)

YUNIZAR (1971-) Chinese
£1307 $2366 €1908 Cerita baru (120x130cm-47x51in) s.d.1997. 4-Apr-4 Sotheby's, Singapore #183/R est:4000-6000 (S.D 4000)

YUNKERS, Adja (1900-) American
£472 $850 €689 White on red (24x30cm-9x12in) init.d.1970 acrylic collage canvasboard. 24-Apr-4 David Rago, Lambertville #565/R

YUNUPINGU, Luma Luma (1941-1985) Australian
Works on paper
£813 $1285 €1187 Mana the shark (57x146cm-22x57in) earth pigments eucalyptus bark exec.c.1982 prov. 28-Jul-3 Sotheby's, Paddington #331 (A.D 2000)

YUNUPINGU, Munggurraway (1907-1979) Australian
Sculpture
£5469 $10227 €8204 Laintjung (74cm-29in) earth pigments wood human hair resin feathers string prov. 26-Jul-4 Sotheby's, Melbourne #152/R est:12000-16000 (A.D 14000)
Works on paper
£625 $1169 €938 Untitled (96x49cm-38x19in) bears name.i.handprint verso earth pigments eucalyptus bark prov. 26-Jul-4 Sotheby's, Melbourne #530/R (A.D 1600)
£1875 $3506 €2813 Coming of fire (156x49cm-61x19in) earth pigments eucalyptus bark exec.c.1970 prov. 26-Jul-4 Sotheby's, Melbourne #531/R est:5000-8000 (A.D 4800)
£2148 $4018 €3222 The great fire (137x53cm-54x21in) earth pigments eucalyptus bark prov. 26-Jul-4 Sotheby's, Melbourne #155/R est:8000-12000 (A.D 5500)
£2927 $4624 €4244 Spider. Birimbirna. Untitled (41x20cm-16x8in) earth pigments eucalyptus bark exec.c.1960 three prov. 28-Jul-3 Sotheby's, Paddington #323/R est:3000-5000 (A.D 7200)
£3320 $6209 €4980 The flood (130x55cm-51x22in) earth pigments eucalyptus bark exec.c.1963 prov.exhib. 26-Jul-4 Sotheby's, Melbourne #156/R est:12000-18000 (A.D 8500)
£3906 $7305 €5859 Ceremonial and sacred grounds of the Gumatj (139x58cm-55x23in) earth pigments eucalyptus bark prov. 26-Jul-4 Sotheby's, Melbourne #157/R est:10000-15000 (A.D 10000)
£4878 $7707 €7073 Creation time ceremony (166x85cm-65x33in) earth pigments eucalyptus bark exec.c.1972 prov.exhib.lit. 28-Jul-3 Sotheby's, Paddington #254/R est:8000-12000 (A.D 12000)
£17154 $27104 €24873 Djulpan, the constellation of Orion and the Pleiades (157x61cm-62x24in) earth pigments eucalyptus bark exec.c.1958 prov. 28-Jul-3 Sotheby's, Paddington #85/R est:25000-35000 (A.D 42200)

YUSHO, Kaiho (1533-1615) Japanese
Works on paper
£19022 $35000 €27772 Birds and flowers, insects, landscapes, horse, daoist sage and interiors (153x356cm-60x140in) ink gold leaf pair of six panel screens. 23-Mar-4 Christie's, Rockefeller NY #66/R est:40000-60000

YUSKAVAGE, Lisa (1962-) American
£13966 $25000 €20390 Wee allergin (23x18cm-9x7in) s.i.d.1997 verso prov.exhib. 13-May-4 Sotheby's, New York #315/R est:25000-35000

YUZBASIYAN, Arto (1948-) Canadian
£536 $921 €783 Town Houses (45x60cm-18x24in) s. prov. 2-Dec-3 Joyner Waddington, Toronto #428 (C.D 1200)
£1802 $3063 €2631 Snow storm on King Street (66x81cm-26x32in) s. prov. 18-Nov-3 Sotheby's, Toronto #179/R est:5000-7000 (C.D 4000)
£3153 $5360 €4603 Queen St (66x86cm-26x34in) s. 18-Nov-3 Sotheby's, Toronto #40/R est:6000-8000 (C.D 7000)

YVARAL (1934-) French
£596 $996 €864 Diffraction polychrome (42x42cm-17x17in) s. s.i.d.1971 verso masonite prov. 23-Jun-3 Philippe Schuler, Zurich #8647 (S.FR 1300)
£611 $1125 €892 Carbone C (52x52cm-20x20in) s. s.i.d.1970 verso acrylic panel. 8-Jun-4 Germann, Zurich #897 (S.FR 1400)
£671 $1242 €1000 Dali digitalise (100x100cm-39x39in) s.d.1977. 15-Mar-4 Sotheby's, Amsterdam #229/R est:1000-1200
£2817 $4930 €4000 Horizon polyedrique (200x200cm-79x79in) s.i.d.1977 verso. 18-Dec-3 Cornette de St.Cyr, Paris #84/R est:4000-6000
Works on paper
£872 $1562 €1300 Paysage numerique, Place de la Concorde (46x75cm-18x30in) s.i.d.1984 verso mixed media paper on panel. 25-May-4 Chambelland & Giafferi, Paris #94/R

YVON, Adolphe (1817-1893) French
£9247 $15719 €13500 Allegorie des saisons (40x165cm-16x65in) s. set of three. 5-Nov-3 Rabourdin & Choppin de Janvry, Paris #77/R est:13000-15000
Works on paper
£967 $1750 €1412 Family (61x43cm-24x17in) s.d.1870 pencil gouache. 3-Apr-4 Neal Auction Company, New Orleans #68/R est:1500-2000

ZAALBERG, Hester Adriana Cornelia (1836-1909) Dutch
£1644 $2795 €2400 Dutch winter landscape with figures and buildings (18x26cm-7x10in) s. panel lit. 8-Nov-3 Hans Stahl, Toestorf #27/R est:2500
£2416 $4470 €3600 Winter landscape with skaters on the ice (60x80cm-24x31in) s.d.1867 panel. 15-Mar-4 Sotheby's, Amsterdam #75/R est:1800-2500

ZABALETA, Rafael (1907-1960) Spanish
£26056 $45077 €37000 Quesada Square (50x61cm-20x24in) s. 15-Dec-3 Ansorena, Madrid #31/R est:33000
£31469 $52552 €45000 Quesada Square (50x61cm-20x24in) s. 30-Jun-3 Ansorena, Madrid #358/R est:45000
£34507 $59697 €49000 Landscape in Quesada (49x61cm-19x24in) 15-Dec-3 Ansorena, Madrid #32/R est:39000
Works on paper
£552 $993 €800 Triumph Arch in Paris (33x27cm-13x11in) s.d.1949 pencil dr. 26-Jan-4 Ansorena, Madrid #336/R
£1233 $2096 €1800 Model (56x43cm-22x17in) s. ink dr. 4-Nov-3 Ansorena, Madrid #215/R est:1500

ZABALLA, Ana (1945-) Spanish
£455 $759 €650 ATZP (138x122cm-54x48in) s.i.d.1986 verso. 24-Jun-3 Segre, Madrid #155/R

ZABEHLITZKY, Alois (1883-1969) Austrian
£451 $713 €650 Still life with flowers (75x56cm-30x22in) s. canvas on board. 5-Sep-3 Wendl, Rudolstadt #3782/R
£6000 $9600 €8700 Flowers in a vase on a ledge (68x55cm-27x22in) s.d.1922 panel. 18-Sep-3 Christie's, Kensington #34/R est:4000-6000

ZABELLANA, Giovanni (15th C) Italian
Sculpture
£56376 $99785 €84000 Madonna and Child enthroned (118x57x20cm-46x22x8in) painted wood lit. 2-May-4 Finarte, Venice #72/R est:80000-90000

ZABOKLICKA-BUDZICHOWA, Maria (1924-1977) Polish
£616 $1048 €900 Behemot et Marguerite (81x64cm-32x25in) s.d.1975 prov. 4-Nov-3 Servarts Themis, Bruxelles #646

ZABOROV, Boris (1937-) ?
£3716 $6540 €5500 Couple de vieux (130x89cm-51x35in) mono.d.1982-3 acrylic photo on canvas prov. 18-May-4 Tajan, Paris #148/R est:6000-8000

ZABOTIN, Vladimir Lukianowitsch von (1884-1967) Russian
£2937 $4905 €4200 Young woman reclining on cushion (120x161cm-47x63in) s. 30-Jun-3 Bloss, Merzhausen #1997/R est:900

ZACH, Bruno (1891-?) Austrian
Sculpture
£1241 $2073 €1800 Girl with short skirt and bow in her hair (37cm-15in) i. col pat bronze marble base. 13-Nov-3 Neumeister, Munich #186/R est:1400-1600
£1525 $2776 €2227 Can can girl (48cm-19in) s. gilt bronze marble base. 4-Feb-4 John Nicholson, Haslemere #635 est:1500-2000
£1528 $2429 €2200 Dancer (41cm-16in) i. pat.bronze stone socle. 15-Sep-3 Dorotheum, Vienna #195/R est:1500-2000
£2098 $3566 €3000 Dancer (42cm-17in) pat.bronze stone socle lit. 25-Nov-3 Dorotheum, Vienna #359/R est:2200-3000
£2148 $3844 €3200 Indian on horseback (47x51cm-19x20in) mono. green pat.bronze Cast.Argentor-Vienna. 26-May-4 Dorotheum, Vienna #348/R est:1500-2000
£2200 $3938 €3212 Spring dancer (41cm-16in) s. pat bronze. 13-May-4 Christie's, Kensington #363/R est:2500-3500
£2222 $3533 €3200 Seated woman with cigarette and book (30cm-12in) i. green pat.bronze stone socle. 15-Sep-3 Dorotheum, Vienna #192/R est:2000-3000
£3261 $6000 €4892 Flapper (66cm-26in) i. black pat bronze marble base prov.lit. 27-Jun-4 Bonhams & Butterfields, Los Angeles #1271/R est:5000-7000
£4225 $7394 €6000 Le marchand d'esclave (70cm-28in) s. brown pat bronze marble base lit. 16-Dec-3 Claude Aguttes, Neuilly #73a/R est:6000-8000
£4348 $8000 €6522 Dancer (48cm-19in) i. pat bronze marble base. 27-Jun-4 Bonhams & Butterfields, Los Angeles #1269/R est:4000-6000
£8696 $16000 €13044 Cigarette girl (63cm-25in) i. pat bronze onyx base lit. 27-Jun-4 Bonhams & Butterfields, Los Angeles #1270/R est:6000-9000
£10500 $17850 €15330 Polo match (29x33cm-11x13in) s. Art Deco bronze marble base exec.c.1930. 19-Nov-3 Sotheby's, Olympia #161/R est:4000-6000

ZACH, Bruno (after) (1891-?) Austrian
Sculpture
£5495 $10000 €8243 Young woman with a cane (30cm-12in) i. brown black pat bronze exec. c.1920. 16-Jun-4 Sotheby's, New York #255/R est:5000-7000

ZACH, Ferdinand (1868-1956) Austrian
Works on paper
£345 $572 €500 Karlsplatz (34x24cm-13x9in) s. w/C. 30-Sep-3 Dorotheum, Vienna #312/R

ZACH, Karl (19/20th C) Austrian
£467 $840 €700 Church in Aggsbach Wachau (58x46cm-23x18in) 21-Apr-4 Dorotheum, Vienna #94/R
Works on paper
£400 $720 €600 Church in Grinzing with brewery (65x91cm-26x36in) s.d.1912 mixed media board. 21-Apr-4 Dorotheum, Vienna #77/R

ZACHARIAS, Otto (19/20th C) German?
£377 $640 €550 Still life with geraniums and apples (52x47cm-20x19in) s.d.40 board. 5-Nov-3 Hugo Ruef, Munich #1184

ZACHO, Christian (1843-1913) Danish
£293 $533 €428 Landscape near Frederiksvaerk (25x33cm-10x13in) init.d.90. 7-Feb-4 Rasmussen, Havnen #2076 (D.KR 3200)
£311 $567 €454 Where the river ends (22x30cm-9x12in) init. panel. 7-Feb-4 Rasmussen, Havnen #2077 (D.KR 3400)
£313 $573 €457 Chillon Palace by Lac Leman (27x35cm-11x14in) init.d.87. 9-Jun-4 Rasmussen, Copenhagen #1849 (D.KR 3500)
£356 $581 €520 Coastal landscape with slope (26x34cm-10x13in) init.d.10. 27-Sep-3 Rasmussen, Havnen #2226 (D.KR 3800)
£375 $645 €548 Evening by the sea (32x42cm-13x17in) s.d.1870 i.verso. 3-Dec-3 Museumsbygningen, Copenhagen #216 (D.KR 4000)
£421 $664 €610 Italian landscape (26x34cm-10x13in) init.d.09. 2-Sep-3 Rasmussen, Copenhagen #1884 (D.KR 4500)
£425 $761 €621 At sunset - Italian coastal landscape with woman (33x52cm-13x20in) init.d.91. 10-May-4 Rasmussen, Vejle #124/R (D.KR 4700)
£427 $777 €641 Winter landscape with sleigh ride (38x57cm-15x22in) s.d.1895. 19-Jun-4 Rasmussen, Havnen #2057/R (D.KR 4800)
£489 $832 €714 Summer's day in Dyrehaven (39x57cm-15x22in) s.d.1902. 29-Nov-3 Rasmussen, Havnen #2147/R (D.KR 5200)
£533 $971 €800 Spring idyll by house near fjord (34x54cm-13x21in) s.d.1886. 19-Jun-4 Rasmussen, Havnen #2106/R (D.KR 6000)
£550 $1018 €803 Woodland river (66x90cm-26x35in) s.d.1903. 13-Jan-4 Bonhams, Knightsbridge #314/R
£676 $1251 €987 Landscape from Dyrehaven with deer (39x57cm-15x22in) s.d.1902. 15-Mar-4 Rasmussen, Vejle #480/R (D.KR 7500)
£701 $1107 €1016 Hilly landscape with view towards fishing village (60x91cm-24x36in) s.d.1903. 2-Sep-3 Rasmussen, Copenhagen #1942 (D.KR 7500)
£764 $1207 €1100 Summer meadow landscape (18x29cm-7x11in) mono.d.1873. 6-Sep-3 Schopman, Hamburg #711/R
£812 $1501 €1186 Landscape with country road by the coast (36x54cm-14x21in) s.d.1910. 15-Mar-4 Rasmussen, Vejle #479/R (D.KR 9000)
£851 $1472 €1242 View over the Mediterranean (32x52cm-13x20in) init.d.85 prov. 9-Dec-3 Rasmussen, Copenhagen #1357/R (D.KR 9000)
£894 $1519 €1305 Italian landscape with view towards Castel Gandolpho (35x58cm-14x23in) init.i.d.1873. 29-Nov-3 Rasmussen, Havnen #2001/R (D.KR 9500)
£898 $1607 €1311 Landscape from Gudenaa near Silkeborg (40x61cm-16x24in) init.d.10 juli 1876. 12-Jan-4 Rasmussen, Vejle #70/R (D.KR 9500)
£945 $1635 €1380 View of town through trees by lake (29x51cm-11x20in) s.d.1885 prov. 9-Dec-3 Rasmussen, Copenhagen #1358/R (D.KR 10000)
£945 $1635 €1380 By a waterhole (32x40cm-13x16in) s. 9-Dec-3 Rasmussen, Copenhagen #1701/R (D.KR 10000)
£1078 $2005 €1574 Old garden gate at Sandviggaard, winter (75x112cm-30x44in) s.d.1900 exhib. 2-Mar-4 Rasmussen, Copenhagen #1656/R est:5000-7000 (D.KR 12000)
£1402 $2215 €2033 Wooded landscape with lake, sunny day in spring (52x79cm-20x31in) s.d.1898. 2-Sep-3 Rasmussen, Copenhagen #1661/R est:15000 (D.KR 15000)
£1500 $2444 €2190 Wooded landscape with lake (60x84cm-24x33in) s.d.1882. 27-Sep-3 Rasmussen, Havnen #2156/R est:4000-6000 (D.KR 16000)
£1797 $3342 €2624 Shore scene, Bramsnaesvig (117x174cm-46x69in) s.d.1911 exhib. 2-Mar-4 Rasmussen, Copenhagen #1234/R est:25000-35000 (D.KR 20000)
£1971 $3548 €2878 Landscape with cattle watering, boy fishing in background (60x72cm-24x28in) s.d.1899. 24-Apr-4 Rasmussen, Havnen #2220/R est:6000 (D.KR 22000)
£1987 $3616 €3000 Woodland pond at dusk (74x110cm-29x43in) s.d.1905. 19-Jun-4 Hans Stahl, Hamburg #126/R est:2800
£2930 $5069 €4278 Dyrehaven in spring (146x183cm-57x72in) s.d.1902 exhib. 9-Dec-3 Rasmussen, Copenhagen #1433/R est:25000 (D.KR 31000)
£6542 $10336 €9486 Helsingor - view from Marienlyst Park (108x126cm-43x50in) s.d.1907 exhib.prov. 2-Sep-3 Rasmussen, Copenhagen #1564/R est:75000 (D.KR 70000)
£19118 $32500 €27912 River landscape (189x232cm-74x91in) s.d.1885 exhib. 28-Oct-3 Sotheby's, New York #128/R est:25000-35000

ZACHRISSON, Axel (1884-1944) Swedish
£480 $860 €701 Northern summer's night (90x120cm-35x47in) s. 26-May-4 AB Stockholms Auktionsverk #2234/R (S.KR 6500)

ZACK (?) ?
Sculpture
£3695 $6615 €5395 Slave trader and female nude (68cm-27in) s. cold painted pat.bronze. 28-May-4 Uppsala Auktionskammare, Uppsala #400/R est:30000-40000 (S.KR 50000)

ZACK, Bruno (20th C) ?
Sculpture
£1800 $3006 €2628 Figure (33cm-13in) s. pat bronze. 15-Oct-3 Christie's, Kensington #665/R est:2000-3000
£3800 $6346 €5548 High kicker (48cm-19in) indis.sig. pat bronze. 15-Oct-3 Christie's, Kensington #663/R est:3000-4000

ZACK, Léon (1892-1980) Russian
£612 $973 €900 Untitled (65x54cm-26x21in) s.d. 21-Mar-3 Bailly Pommery, Paris #129
£889 $1600 €1298 Holy Family (64x46cm-25x18in) masonite. 24-Apr-4 Du Mouchelle, Detroit #3302/R est:300-500
£1690 $2924 €2400 Composition (45x55cm-18x22in) s.indis.d.6. 13-Dec-3 Martinot & Savignat, Pontoise #274/R est:2500-3000
£1736 $2899 €2500 Composition (65x92cm-26x36in) s.d.1978. 25-Oct-3 Cornette de St.Cyr, Paris #840/R est:2000-2500
£1806 $2979 €2600 Composition (60x72cm-24x28in) s.d.1968 lit. 2-Jul-3 Cornette de St.Cyr, Paris #18/R est:3000-3500
£1944 $3072 €2800 Composition (130x97cm-51x38in) s.d.1972 prov. 27-Apr-3 Versailles Encheres #12
£2715 $4969 €4100 Composition (72x91cm-28x36in) s.d.64. 7-Apr-4 Piasa, Paris #244/R est:2000-2500
£6333 $11400 €9500 Composition (162x114cm-64x45in) s.d.1978 exhib.lit. 25-Apr-4 Versailles Encheres #108 est:10000-15000
Works on paper
£336 $625 €500 Untitled (22x29cm-9x11in) s.d.1949 ink. 3-Mar-4 Tajan, Paris #213
£338 $639 €500 Tete d'homme (26x21cm-10x8in) s. chl wash. 17-Feb-4 Vanderkindere, Brussels #57
£594 $1010 €850 Composition (48x26cm-19x10in) s.d.51 W/C ink. 1-Dec-3 Camard, Paris #78

ZADEL (attrib) (?) ?
Works on paper
£2600 $4576 €3796 Tiger with glass eyes (40x54cm-16x21in) sand. 18-May-4 Woolley & Wallis, Salisbury #311/R est:150-250

ZADEMACK, Siegfried (1952-) German
£503 $891 €750 Testsprung (80x60cm-31x24in) s.d. i. verso. 30-Apr-4 Dr Fritz Nagel, Stuttgart #519/R
£503 $891 €750 Flirt (56x51cm-22x20in) s.d. i. verso. 30-Apr-4 Dr Fritz Nagel, Stuttgart #520/R
£833 $1392 €1200 The Beck's experience (59x48cm-23x19in) s.d. acrylic. 24-Oct-3 Ketterer, Hamburg #582/R
£1049 $1752 €1500 Circle of puppets (52x70cm-20x28in) s.d.1991. 28-Jun-3 Bolland & Marotz, Bremen #906/R est:2000
£1189 $1985 €1700 Dreamy female nude (62x42cm-24x17in) s.d.1001. 28-Jun-3 Bolland & Marotz, Bremen #905/R est:2200
£1678 $2803 €2400 Venus with puppets (70x50cm-28x20in) s.d.1991. 28-Jun-3 Bolland & Marotz, Bremen #904/R est:2400

ZADKINE, Ossip (1890-1967) French
£350 $594 €500 Composition sur une page de livre d'or (56x38cm-22x15in) mono.d.1956. 23-Nov-3 Cornette de St.Cyr, Paris #353/R
Sculpture
£3297 $6000 €4814 Pieta (33cm-13in) plaster painted black. 29-Jun-4 Sotheby's, New York #356/R est:1500-2000
£6667 $12267 €10000 Leda (41x54x17cm-16x21x7in) i.d.1920 num.2/6 f.Susse polished bronze cast 1966 exhib.lit. 8-Jun-4 Sotheby's, Amsterdam #71/R est:10000-15000
£9639 $16000 €14073 Le messager (58cm-23in) s. num.III blk pat bronze St.f.Bisceglia conceived 1937 lit. 2-Oct-3 Christie's, Tel Aviv #25/R est:20000-30000
£11905 $21310 €17500 Douce malancolie (31cm-12in) mono. num.3/5 brown pat bronze Cast Susse Paris prov.lit. 19-Mar-4 Millon & Associes, Paris #144/R est:18000-25000
£12000 $21840 €17520 Le second personnage or arlequin assis sur un violincello (32cm-13in) i.num.3/6 bronze st.f.Guss cast 1966 prov.lit. 4-Feb-4 Sotheby's, London #283/R est:8000-12000
£12676 $21930 €18000 Messager (58cm-23in) s.st.f.Bisceglia num.III pat bronze lit. 9-Dec-3 Artcurial Briest, Paris #231/R est:20000-25000
£13194 $20847 €19000 Intimate (50cm-20in) mono.d.49 num.4/4 polished bronze. 19-Sep-3 Schloss Ahlden, Ahlden #776/R est:18500
£15000 $27150 €21900 Le violoncelliste (43x20x25cm-17x8x10in) init.num.6/6 green pat bronze st.f.Modern Art lit. 1-Apr-4 Christie's, Kensington #80/R est:20000-30000
£15646 $28007 €23000 Untitled (31cm-12in) mono.num.4/10 brown green pat bronze Cast Susse Paris prov.lit. 19-Mar-4 Millon & Associes, Paris #145/R
£16000 $26720 €23360 Femme a la tete penchee (48cm-19in) i.num.1/5 bronze st.f.Susse cast 1960 prov.lit. 21-Oct-3 Sotheby's, London #95/R est:12000-16000
£18000 $32760 €26280 Tete de femme ou tete heroique (38cm-15in) s.num.2/4 bronze lit. 21-Jun-4 Bonhams, New Bond Street #44/R est:20000-30000
£18786 $32500 €27428 Adam and Eve (63x114x14cm-25x45x6in) with sig.d.1930 num.2/5 bronze st.f.Guss-Priessmann-Bauer prov. 13-Dec-3 Sotheby's, New York #574/R est:20000-30000
£20000 $31800 €29000 Homme assis (34cm-13in) green pat. bronze including base conceived 1925 lit. 11-Sep-3 Christie's, Kensington #111/R est:20000-30000
£21000 $38220 €30660 Femme assise au luth (43cm-17in) init. num.4/6 st.f.Susse brown pat bronze prov.exhib.lit. 3-Feb-4 Christie's, London #206/R est:25000-35000
£26667 $49067 €40000 Arlequin (78cm-31in) init. num.2/4 grey green pat bronze one of three exhib.lit. 9-Jun-4 Christie's, Amsterdam #277/R est:45000-60000
£52000 $94640 €75920 Acordeoniste (51cm-20in) i. bronze st.f.Susse conceived 1924 prov.lit. 4-Feb-4 Sotheby's, London #275/R est:50000-70000
Works on paper
£324 $613 €480 Labyrinthe (23x29cm-9x11in) mono. ink. 21-Feb-4 Cornette de St.Cyr, Paris #227
£467 $859 €700 Composition (32x24cm-13x9in) s.d.67 red biro pen. 8-Jun-4 Artcurial Briest, Paris #130/R
£490 $832 €700 Personnage (20x14cm-8x6in) s. Indian ink. 18-Nov-3 Pierre Berge, Paris #29
£596 $1091 €900 Tete d'homme (31x22cm-12x9in) mono. blue crayon. 7-Apr-4 Piasa, Paris #185
£671 $1188 €1000 Deux personnages (20x13cm-8x5in) mono. ink exec c.1963. 27-Apr-4 Artcurial Briest, Paris #88 est:700-900
£671 $1188 €1000 Etude pour le monument aux freres Van Gogh (20x13cm-8x5in) mono. Indian ink exhib. 27-Apr-4 Artcurial Briest, Paris #89
£828 $1515 €1250 Le guitariste (23x19cm-9x7in) s.d.1965 ink. 7-Apr-4 Doutrebente, Paris #72

£872	$1614	€1300	Personnage de profil (27x18cm-11x7in) init. pen Indian ink wash. 15-Mar-4 Blanchet, Paris #83
£1034	$1862	€1500	Couple (26x17cm-10x7in) mono. s.i.verso ink drawing. 25-Jan-4 Chayette & Cheval, Paris #132b est:1200-1500
£1215	$2030	€1750	Les musiciens (29x18cm-11x7in) mono. ink. 25-Oct-3 Cornette de St.Cyr, Paris #556 est:1200-1500
£1457	$2652	€2200	Nu assis (34x25cm-13x10in) s. chl. 15-Jun-4 Blanchet, Paris #149/R est:1500-2000
£1467	$2699	€2200	Composition (65x50cm-26x20in) s.d. Indian ink on pencil. 11-Jun-4 Hauswedell & Nolte, Hamburg #1606/R est:3000
£1565	$2801	€2300	Composition en carre (50x47cm-20x19in) s.d.66 red blk felt pen Japan paper prov.lit. 19-Mar-4 Millon & Associes, Paris #133/R est:2000-3000
£2041	$3653	€3000	Aller a Grand pas (21x28cm-8x11in) init. bears i. ink col crayons exec c.1963 prov.lit. 19-Mar-4 Millon & Associes, Paris #136/R est:3000-4000
£2857	$5114	€4200	Gros poulet (47x45cm-19x18in) init. pastel crayon exec c.1963 prov.lit. 19-Mar-4 Millon & Associes, Paris #134/R est:3000-4000
£3000	$5190	€4380	Study for Le demeure (75x53cm-30x21in) s.d.59 brush black ink paper on card prov. 11-Dec-3 Christie's, Kensington #162/R est:1200-1800
£3061	$5480	€4500	Couple a table (41x33cm-16x13in) init. lead pencil prov. 19-Mar-4 Millon & Associes, Paris #132/R est:5000-6000
£3800	$6992	€5700	Paysage Cezannien (34x24cm-13x9in) s.d.1919 W/C. 13-Jun-4 Lombrail & Teucquam, Paris #115/R
£4688	$7500	€6844	Scene du combat (66x50cm-26x20in) s.d.1939 gouache over pencil. 18-Sep-3 Swann Galleries, New York #701/R est:7000-10000
£4967	$9089	€7500	Man at the guitar (75x55cm-30x22in) s. blk crayon. 7-Apr-4 Piasa, Paris #187/R est:8000-10000
£5034	$9010	€7500	Chevaux et figures dans une ecurie (22x27cm-9x11in) s. gouache. 27-May-4 Christie's, Paris #119/R est:4000-6000
£5442	$9741	€8000	Heros de la Patrie (71x54cm-28x21in) s. ink lead pencil exec c.1946 prov.lit. 19-Mar-4 Millon & Associes, Paris #129/R est:8000-10000
£5500	$9515	€8030	Le musicien (61x39cm-24x15in) s. brush brown ink gouache. 11-Dec-3 Christie's, Kensington #88/R est:4000-6000
£6122	$10959	€9000	Autoportrait au regard (21x14cm-8x6in) s. blk ink exec c.1950 prov.lit. 19-Mar-4 Millon & Associes, Paris #128/R est:8000-10000
£6704	$12000	€9788	Deux figures et un enfant (72x46cm-28x18in) s.i.d.46 gouache India ink wash prov. 6-May-4 Sotheby's, New York #357/R est:8000-10000
£7000	$12740	€10220	La fenetre (45x60cm-18x24in) s.d.28 gouache pencil card prov. 4-Feb-4 Sotheby's, London #531/R est:8000-12000
£9396	$17195	€14000	Trois personnages (59x46cm-23x18in) s.d.55 gouache. 7-Jul-4 Artcurial Briest, Paris #72/R est:15000-20000
£9500	$17290	€13870	Homme dans un interieur (64x49cm-25x19in) s.d.29 gouache pencil prov. 4-Feb-4 Sotheby's, London #532/R est:10000-15000
£11268	$19493	€16000	Repos (60x50cm-24x20in) s.d.38 gouache. 9-Dec-3 Artcurial Briest, Paris #230/R est:15000-20000
£11667	$21000	€17034	Strange possession (48x61cm-19x24in) d.1946 gouache. 24-Apr-4 Du Mouchelle, Detroit #3304/R est:5000-8000
£12000	$21960	€18000	Figures in room (62x44cm-24x17in) s.d.22 gouache. 5-Jun-4 Lempertz, Koln #1027/R est:20000-22000
£12925	$23136	€19000	Couple blanc (65x48cm-26x19in) s.d.48 gouache prov.lit. 19-Mar-4 Millon & Associes, Paris #141/R est:15000-20000
£13253	$22000	€19349	Les musiciens (60x45cm-24x18in) s.d.1921 gouache W/C prov. 2-Oct-3 Christie's, Tel Aviv #51/R est:12000-16000
£13253	$22000	€19349	Couple (50x35cm-20x14in) s.d.1921 gouache W/C prov. 2-Oct-3 Christie's, Tel Aviv #52/R est:10000-15000
£17284	$28000	€25062	Man in a yellow hat with folk, glass and seashell (77x56cm-30x22in) s.d. gouache prov. 8-Aug-3 Barridorf, Portland #160/R est:10000-15000
£20834	$34793	€30000	Famille (65x45cm-26x18in) s.d.1962 i.verso gouache prov. 21-Oct-3 Artcurial Briest, Paris #96/R est:22000-25000
£27933	$50000	€40782	Personnage a l'escalier (71x53cm-28x21in) s.d.22 pastel pencil prov. 6-May-4 Sotheby's, New York #373/R est:25000-35000

ZADOR, Istvan (1882-?) Hungarian

£500	$880	€730	Still life of figurines and china on a polished table (51x55cm-20x22in) s. 19-May-4 Christie's, Kensington #728/R

ZADORECKI, M J (19th C) Austrian

£1034	$1728	€1500	Lady with sword (98x72cm-39x28in) s. 11-Nov-3 Vendu Notarishuis, Rotterdam #16 est:1000-1500
£1086	$1944	€1586	Madonna and Child and small boy (70x61cm-28x24in) s.i.d.1870 oval. 10-May-4 Rasmussen, Vejle #437/R est:6000-8000 (D.KR 12000)

ZAGANELLI, Bernardino (1470-1510) Italian

£118421	$217895	€180000	Madonna and Child with two angels (91x47cm-36x19in) panel prov. 24-Jun-4 Christie's, Paris #55/R est:60000-80000
£146479	$234366	€208000	Madonna and Child with Saint Rocco and Saint Sebastian (46x37cm-18x15in) board prov.lit. 21-Sep-3 Finarte, Venice #60/R est:200000-230000

ZAGO, Erma (1880-1942) Italian

£775	$1286	€1100	Roma, Piazza Navona (35x50cm-14x20in) s. wood. 11-Jun-3 Christie's, Rome #149/R
£979	$1635	€1400	Market in Venice (19x27cm-7x11in) s. board. 26-Jun-3 Sant Agostino, Torino #59/R
£1007	$1852	€1500	Grand Canal (18x26cm-7x10in) s. board. 24-Mar-4 Il Ponte, Milan #592/R est:2000-2200
£1007	$1852	€1500	Embarcadero in Venice (20x24cm-8x9in) s. board. 24-Mar-4 Il Ponte, Milan #608/R est:2200
£1042	$1771	€1500	Venetian market (19x27cm-7x11in) s. board lit. 1-Nov-3 Meeting Art, Vercelli #430/R est:1500
£1049	$1752	€1500	Gondola (19x27cm-7x11in) s. board. 26-Jun-3 Sant Agostino, Torino #58/R est:1600
£1064	$1777	€1500	Venetian scene (19x26cm-7x10in) s. board. 20-Oct-3 Sant Agostino, Torino #276/R est:1800
£1127	$1949	€1600	Venetian scene (17x25cm-7x10in) indis sig. board. 9-Dec-3 Finarte Semenzato, Milan #30/R est:800-1000
£1141	$2042	€1700	La Salute (19x26cm-7x10in) s. board prov. 25-May-4 Finarte Semenzato, Milan #160/R est:1200-1300
£1348	$2250	€1900	Boats in the lagoon (19x27cm-7x11in) s. board. 20-Oct-3 Sant Agostino, Torino #277/R est:1800
£2013	$3564	€3000	Venice (19x27cm-7x11in) s. board. 1-May-4 Meeting Art, Vercelli #332 est:2000
£2416	$4446	€3600	Venice (56x43cm-22x17in) s. board. 24-Mar-4 Il Ponte, Milan #538/R est:1800
£2465	$4092	€3500	Venezia, davanti alla chiesa. Venezia, sul ponticello (19x27cm-7x11in) s. wood two. 11-Jun-3 Christie's, Rome #135/R est:1800-2200
£2500	$4250	€3600	Saint Mark's Square (45x60cm-18x24in) s. board. 1-Nov-3 Meeting Art, Vercelli #235/R est:3000
£4161	$7656	€6200	Campiello, Venice (45x58cm-18x23in) s. board. 24-Mar-4 Il Ponte, Milan #577/R est:3000-3500

ZAGO, Luigi (1894-1952) Italian

£705	$1198	€1029	Palazzolo nevicato (50x60cm-20x24in) s. panel. 5-Nov-3 Dobiaschofsky, Bern #1064/R (S.FR 1600)
£797	$1307	€1100	Landscape around Biella (50x60cm-20x24in) s. cardboard exhib. 27-May-3 Finarte Semenzato, Milan #15/R

ZAHALKA, Anne (20th C) German?

Photographs

£2100	$3696	€3150	Cook, der kock, Michael Scjmidt, Architect (85x81cm-33x32in) s.verso cibachrome. 18-May-4 Bonhams, New Bond Street #517/R est:1500-2000

ZAHND, Johann (1854-1934) Swiss

£565	$1034	€825	View of the church in Schwarzenburg (33x55cm-13x22in) s.d.1909. 4-Jun-4 Zofingen, Switzerland #2997 (S.FR 1300)
£2333	$4223	€3500	Aquaduct near Rome (21x35cm-8x14in) s.d.91 canvas on board. 1-Apr-4 Van Ham, Cologne #1718/R est:2400
£3448	$6172	€5034	Herders in Roman Campagna (91x63cm-36x25in) s.d.84. 14-May-4 Dobiaschofsky, Bern #31/R est:2000 (S.FR 8000)
£7000	$12950	€10220	Figures on a country road with Rome in the distance (63x110cm-25x43in) s.d.1880. 9-Mar-4 Bonhams, Knightsbridge #272/R est:3000-5000

ZAHRTMANN, Kristian (1843-1917) Danish

£369	$627	€539	Peace (35x29cm-14x11in) mono.d.1914 grisaille. 10-Nov-3 Rasmussen, Vejle #238/R (D.KR 4000)
£374	$591	€542	Study for Nazareth (52x26cm-20x10in) prov. 2-Sep-3 Rasmussen, Copenhagen #1974/R (D.KR 4000)
£737	$1253	€1076	A proposal - fisherman and fishergirl (32x23cm-13x9in) prov.lit. 10-Nov-3 Rasmussen, Vejle #266/R (D.KR 8000)
£1297	$2400	€1894	Elderly peasant woman (41x30cm-16x12in) mono.d.1884 panel prov. 15-Jul-4 Sotheby's, New York #38/R est:1000-1500
£1343	$2457	€1961	Italian view from Civita d'Antonio (35x45cm-14x18in) mono.d.1902 prov.lit. 7-Jun-4 Museumsbygningen, Copenhagen #161/R est:10000-15000 (D.KR 15000)
£2363	$4088	€3450	Portrait of Mrs K - Interior scene with Mrs E Knudtzon (56x67cm-22x26in) mono.d.1894 exhib.prov. 9-Dec-3 Rasmussen, Copenhagen #1566/R est:20000-25000 (D.KR 25000)
£2804	$4430	€4066	Self portrait in lamplight (26x22cm-10x9in) mono.d.1914 prov. 2-Sep-3 Rasmussen, Copenhagen #1872/R est:10000-15000 (D.KR 30000)
£3871	$6581	€5652	Before breakfast in Civita d'Antino - with Poul Christensen and Anders Truelson (61x73cm-24x29in) mono.d.1911 lit.prov. 10-Nov-3 Rasmussen, Vejle #220/R est:40000-50000 (D.KR 42000)
£4253	$7358	€6209	Parthenon seen from the west (40x32cm-16x13in) mono.d.1884 panel exhib.prov. 9-Dec-3 Rasmussen, Copenhagen #1254/R est:30000-50000 (D.KR 45000)
£7637	$14205	€11150	Before breakfast in Civita d'Antino with Poul Christiansen and Anders Trulson (62x75cm-24x30in) mono.d.1911 exhib.prov. 2-Mar-4 Rasmussen, Copenhagen #1285/R est:85000 (D.KR 85000)

ZAINI (1926-1977) Indonesian

£2536	$3931	€3703	Self portrait (46x55cm-18x22in) s.d.65 sold with oils by KARTIKA, MULJADI three. 6-Oct-2 Sotheby's, Singapore #124/R est:7000-9000 (S.D 7000)

ZAINO, Salvador (20th C) Argentinian?

£1530	$2800	€2234	Poplar grove. Landscape (18x23cm-7x9in) board pair. 1-Jun-4 Arroyo, Buenos Aires #39

ZAIRIS, Emmanuel (1876-1948) Greek

£1467	$2625	€2200	Still life (26x34cm-10x13in) s. board. 13-May-4 Neumeister, Munich #525/R est:700-900

ZAIS, Gaetano (18th C) Italian

£9155	$14648	€13000	Mountainous landscape with stream. River landscape with ruins (41x54cm-16x21in) pair. 21-Sep-3 Finarte, Venice #15/R est:12500
£9859	$15775	€14000	River landscapes (41x54cm-16x21in) pair. 21-Sep-3 Finarte, Venice #14/R est:12500

ZAIS, Giuseppe (1709-1784) Italian

£4192	$7000	€6120	Wooded river landscape (79x107cm-31x42in) 16-Nov-3 William Jenack, New York #104 est:8000-12000
£15000	$27450	€21900	Rocky river landscape with figures resting beside the bank. Extensive landscape with peasants (52x70cm-20x28in) pair. 7-Jul-4 Bonhams, New Bond Street #26/R est:12000-18000

£20000 $34600 €29200 Pastoral landscape with a fisherman and other figures by a stream (66x91cm-26x36in) 11-Dec-3 Sotheby's, London #236/R est:20000-30000

ZAJAC, Jack (1929-) American

£529 $900 €772 Untitled (56x66cm-22x26in) s. s.d.1961 verso. 9-Nov-3 Bonhams & Butterfields, Los Angeles #4043/R

Sculpture

£867 $1500 €1266 Metamorphis Rome no 4 (28cm-11in) bronze prov. 15-Dec-3 Hindman, Chicago #78/R est:3000-5000

ZAJICEK, Carl Wenzel (1860-1923) Austrian

Works on paper

£738 $1358 €1100 Old Burgtheater in Vienna (11x17cm-4x7in) s. W/C. 26-Mar-4 Dorotheum, Vienna #267/R
£1042 $1698 €1500 Paradise garden (14x21cm-6x8in) s.d.897 W/C. 23-Sep-3 Wiener Kunst Auktionen, Vienna #37/R est:1500-2500
£1342 $2470 €2000 Hernalser line (11x16cm-4x6in) s. W/C paper on board. 26-Mar-4 Dorotheum, Vienna #287/R est:1400-1600
£1745 $3211 €2600 Fasszieherhaus (19x14cm-7x6in) s. W/C. 26-Mar-4 Dorotheum, Vienna #276/R est:1600-1800

ZAK, Eugène (1884-1926) Polish

£12081 $22470 €18000 Paysage (36x44cm-14x17in) s. painted c.1920 prov. 2-Mar-4 Artcurial Briest, Paris #194/R est:10000-12000
£12588 $21022 €18000 Paysage de l'Estaque (54x65cm-21x26in) s. 30-Jun-3 Artcurial Briest, Paris #734/R est:10000-15000
£13855 $23000 €20228 Pastorale (60x73cm-24x29in) s. 2-Oct-3 Christie's, Tel Aviv #23/R est:18000-24000

Works on paper

£7821 $14000 €11419 Child with doll (36x33cm-14x13in) s.d.08 pierre noire pen ink W/C gouache paper on board. 6-May-4 Doyle, New York #65/R est:3000-5000

ZAKANITCH, Robert (1935-) American

£471 $800 €688 Orange life (137x28cm-54x11in) s.i.verso. 9-Nov-3 Wright, Chicago #388

ZAKHAROV, Fiodor (1919-1994) Russian

£435 $713 €600 Still life with roses (60x50cm-24x20in) s. 27-May-3 Durán, Madrid #791/R

ZAKRSEWSKI, Wlodzimierz (1916-1992) Polish

£938 $1566 €1369 Street scene (55x69cm-22x27in) s.d.1964. 19-Oct-3 Agra, Warsaw #57/R est:6000 (P.Z 6000)
£2038 $3179 €2975 Suburb in Krakow (73x92cm-29x36in) s.d.1967. 30-Mar-3 Agra, Warsaw #26/R est:7000 (P.Z 13000)

ZAKRZEWSKI, Roman (20th C) Polish

£425 $761 €621 Seated woman (100x65cm-39x26in) acrylic painted 1989. 6-May-4 Agra, Warsaw #1/R (P.Z 3000)
£1062 $1902 €1551 Seated woman (130x80cm-51x31in) acrylic painted 1990. 6-May-4 Agra, Warsaw #16/R (P.Z 7500)

ZALCE, Alfredo (1908-2003) Mexican

£2371 $4031 €3462 Vase of flowers (50x40cm-20x16in) s.d.1985 paper. 30-Oct-3 Louis Morton, Mexico #93/R est:50000-80000 (M.P 45000)
£7376 $12540 €10769 Vase and watermelon (38x45cm-15x18in) s.d.1974 paper. 30-Oct-3 Louis Morton, Mexico #94/R est:80000-100000 (M.P 140000)

Works on paper

£542 $863 €791 Fishermen (85x53cm-33x21in) s.d.1979 ink. 29-Apr-3 Louis Morton, Mexico #130/R (M.P 9000)
£2143 $3750 €3129 Harvesting (50x34cm-20x13in) s.d.1986 W/C. 19-Dec-3 Sotheby's, New York #1169/R est:4000-5000

ZALDUMBIDE, Alberto (19/20th C) Spanish?

£2368 $4287 €3600 Basque man in landscape (99x99cm-39x39in) s.d.1935. 14-Apr-4 Ansorena, Madrid #68/R est:3600

ZAMACOIS Y ZABALA, Eduardo (1842-1871) Spanish

£19928 $32681 €27500 Jugando a las tabas (32x24cm-13x9in) s. panel. 27-May-3 Durán, Madrid #244/R est:18000

ZAMAZAL, Jaroslav (1900-1983) Czechoslovakian

£824 $1532 €1203 Girl nude (47x67cm-19x26in) s. board. 6-Mar-4 Dorotheum, Prague #131/R est:40000-60000 (C.KR 40000)

ZAMBEAUX, Eric (?) French?

Sculpture

£1399 $2406 €2000 Rhinoceros d'Africque (22x56cm-9x22in) num.2/8 green brown pat bronze Cast Barthelemy. 3-Dec-3 Coutau Begarie, Paris #242/R est:2200-2500

ZAMBRANO, Carmelo (20th C) Venezuelan?

£357 $560 €521 Surprise box (120x100cm-47x39in) s. painted 1993. 23-Nov-2 Subastas Odalys, Caracas #5

ZAMBRANO, Raul (20th C) Venezuelan?

£240 $400 €350 Boats in Pampatar Bay (50x60cm-20x24in) s. painted 1975. 19-Oct-3 Subastas Odalys, Caracas #102
£3043 $5600 €4443 Boats in Pampatar Bay (50x60cm-20x24in) s. painted 1975. 28-Mar-4 Subastas Odalys, Caracas #27/R

ZAMORA, Jose de (?) Spanish

£507 $892 €750 Seated lady (70x50cm-28x20in) s. card. 18-May-4 Segre, Madrid #31

Works on paper

£379 $630 €550 Balle poster (40x31cm-16x12in) s.i.d.1956 gouache. 1-Oct-3 Ansorena, Madrid #649/R

ZAMORANO, P (20th C) ?

£1303 $2163 €1850 Portrait de Tomiko Asabuki, Paris (100x100cm-39x39in) mono.i.d.1930 s.verso. 16-Jun-3 E & Eve, Paris #84/R

ZAMORANO, Ricardo (1922-) Spanish

£347 $552 €500 Two women (57x46cm-22x18in) s. paper. 29-Apr-3 Durán, Madrid #764/R
£2897 $4808 €4200 Waiting (100x85cm-39x33in) s. 1-Oct-3 Ansorena, Madrid #542/R est:600

ZAMPIGHI, Eugenio (1859-1944) Italian

£2174 $4000 €3174 Young girl pouring wine for an older woman (30x41cm-12x16in) s. 9-Jun-4 Alderfer's, Hatfield #345/R est:5000-7000
£5000 $8000 €7250 Toast to youth (44x58cm-17x23in) s. 18-Sep-3 Christie's, Kensington #70/R est:6000-8000
£5600 $9688 €8176 Playmates (24x34cm-9x13in) s. 9-Dec-3 Anderson & Garland, Newcastle #482/R est:3000-5000
£6000 $10380 €8760 Pets (24x34cm-9x13in) s. 9-Dec-3 Anderson & Garland, Newcastle #483/R est:3000-5000
£7000 $12530 €10220 Feeding the baby (57x77cm-22x30in) s. 26-May-4 Sotheby's, Olympia #291/R est:8000-12000
£8523 $15000 €12444 Happiness at the hearth (56x76cm-22x30in) s. 18-May-4 Bonhams & Butterfields, San Francisco #57/R est:10000-15000
£11000 $19800 €16060 New born nephew. Fresh cherries (25x35cm-10x14in) s. pair. 21-Jan-4 Sotheby's, Olympia #455/R est:4000-6000
£12000 $20400 €17520 Storytime, elderly couple telling a story to two children (76x55cm-30x22in) s.i. 19-Nov-3 Tennants, Leyburn #1255/R est:8000-12000
£12941 $22000 €18894 Playtime with grandpa (56x77cm-22x30in) s. 29-Oct-3 Christie's, Rockefeller NY #231/R est:18000-25000
£16000 $27200 €23360 Grandma's helping hand (56x77cm-22x30in) s. 19-Nov-3 Bonhams, New Bond Street #87/R est:12000-18000
£17647 $30000 €25765 The most welcome visitor (75x105cm-30x41in) s. 29-Oct-3 Christie's, Rockefeller NY #230/R est:30000-40000
£19444 $35000 €28388 Happy family (56x77cm-22x30in) s. 23-Apr-4 Sotheby's, New York #181/R est:18000-25000
£20000 $34000 €29200 In concert (56x77cm-22x30in) s. 19-Nov-3 Bonhams & Butterfields, San Francisco #47/R
£22353 $38000 €32635 Playing with baby (74x105cm-29x41in) s. 29-Oct-3 Christie's, Rockefeller NY #232/R est:40000-60000
£24706 $42000 €36071 Baby's first kiss (51x66cm-20x26in) s. 29-Oct-3 Christie's, Rockefeller NY #236/R est:30000-40000

Works on paper

£400 $728 €584 An idle conversation by a Venetian canal (38x28cm-15x11in) pencil W/C. 1-Jul-4 Christie's, Kensington #418/R
£850 $1573 €1241 Interesting story (36x53cm-14x21in) s. W/C prov. 14-Jul-4 Sotheby's, Olympia #205/R
£2326 $4000 €3396 Muscial accompaniment (53x33cm-21x13in) s. W/C. 7-Dec-3 Freeman, Philadelphia #24 est:2000-3000

ZANANITCH, Robert S (20th C) American

£757 $1400 €1105 Butter beans (83x209cm-33x82in) s.i.d.84 acrylic exhib. 3 sheets of joined paper exhib. 12-Feb-4 Sotheby's, New York #297/R est:800-1200

ZANAROFF, Prudent Pohl (1885-1966) French

£658 $1211 €1000 Moret sur Loing (43x62cm-17x24in) s. wood exec 1930. 28-Jun-4 Joron-Derem, Paris #123

ZANCANARO, Tono (1906-1985) Italian

Works on paper

£1267 $2280 €1900 Seascape and two faces (52x55cm-20x22in) mixed media cardboard. 22-Apr-4 Finarte Semenzato, Rome #367/R est:2500-3000
£1667 $3000 €2500 Seascape and three faces (68x96cm-27x38in) s. mixed media cardboard exec.1966. 22-Apr-4 Finarte Semenzato, Rome #368/R est:3000-3500

ZANCHI, Antonio (1631-1722) Italian

£15556 $28000 €22712 Death of Seneca (127x173cm-50x68in) prov.lit. 23-Jan-4 Christie's, Rockefeller NY #7/R est:15000-20000

ZANCHI, Antonio (attrib) (1631-1722) Italian

£2817 $4930 €4000 Madonna and Child (97x60cm-38x24in) 17-Dec-3 Christie's, Rome #387/R est:4000-6000

ZANCO, Nereo (1897-1969) Italian
£265 $482 €400 Portrait of girl with fruit (50x40cm-20x16in) s.d.1948 exhib. 21-Jun-4 Pandolfini, Florence #190/R

ZANDER, Heinz (1939-) German
£867 $1560 €1300 Only draw what you see! (70x30cm-28x12in) mono.d. s.i. verso panel. 24-Apr-4 Dr Lehr, Berlin #519/R
£2292 $3827 €3300 House angel's dream and desire (80x99cm-31x39in) mono.d. s.i.d. verso. 25-Oct-3 Dr Lehr, Berlin #552/R est:3000
£3333 $5567 €4800 Galatea (90x100cm-35x39in) mono.d. s.i.d. verso. 25-Oct-3 Dr Lehr, Berlin #553/R est:3000
Works on paper
£280 $504 €420 Tristan and Isolde (44x60cm-17x24in) s.i.d. pencil board. 24-Apr-4 Dr Lehr, Berlin #525/R
£433 $780 €650 Niobe, daughter of Tantalos, wife of Amphion (42x59cm-17x23in) s.i.d. pencil board. 24-Apr-4 Dr Lehr, Berlin #524/R

ZANDER, Nils Gunnar (1944-) Australian
£496 $917 €724 Desert town no.11 (152x168cm-60x66in) s.d.91 oil mixed media. 15-Mar-4 Sotheby's, Melbourne #102 est:1000-2000 (A.D 1200)

ZANDLEVEN, J A (1868-1923) Dutch
£1293 $2352 €1900 Study of tree (38x30cm-15x12in) i. canvas on panel. 3-Feb-4 Christie's, Amsterdam #406/R est:1500-2000

ZANDLEVEN, Jan Adam (1868-1923) Dutch
£267 $488 €400 Lilac in a vase (40x31cm-16x12in) s.d.1901 exhib. 7-Jun-4 Glerum, Amsterdam #11/R
£403 $745 €600 Tree (38x29cm-15x11in) s.d.1915 canvas on board. 15-Mar-4 Sotheby's, Amsterdam #96/R
£556 $906 €800 Winter landscape (34x48cm-13x19in) s.d.1918. 29-Sep-3 Sotheby's, Amsterdam #185/R
£638 $1180 €950 Rhododendrons (35x50cm-14x20in) s.d.1909 canvas on board. 15-Mar-4 Sotheby's, Amsterdam #283/R est:750-800
£814 $1385 €1188 Country house with garden (54x68cm-21x27in) s. 1-Dec-3 Koller, Zurich #6577 est:2500-4000 (S.FR 1800)
£816 $1486 €1200 Trees (41x33cm-16x13in) s.d.1913 board. 3-Feb-4 Christie's, Amsterdam #407/R est:700-900
£816 $1486 €1200 Witte boom - white tree (42x33cm-17x13in) s.d.1914. 3-Feb-4 Christie's, Amsterdam #409 est:600-800
£979 $1635 €1400 Still life with Delft vase (40x50cm-16x20in) s.d.19 exhib. 30-Jun-3 Sotheby's, Amsterdam #362/R
£1020 $1857 €1500 Still life with flowers in a blue and white vase (34x42cm-13x17in) s.d.1920. 3-Feb-4 Christie's, Amsterdam #413/R est:800-1200
£1111 $1811 €1600 View of a landscape (50x33cm-20x13in) s.d.1914. 29-Sep-3 Sotheby's, Amsterdam #187/R
£1361 $2476 €2000 Trees in autumn (41x32cm-16x13in) s.d. 3-Feb-4 Christie's, Amsterdam #412 est:600-800
£1958 $3270 €2800 Still life with daffodils (39x31cm-15x12in) s.d.1912. 30-Jun-3 Sotheby's, Amsterdam #363/R
£2381 $4333 €3500 Bright winter's day (45x60cm-18x24in) s.d.1917. 3-Feb-4 Christie's, Amsterdam #411/R est:1200-1600
Works on paper
£278 $453 €400 Tree in a landscape (58x44cm-23x17in) s. black red chk htd white. 29-Sep-3 Sotheby's, Amsterdam #189/R

ZANDOMENEGHI, Federico (1841-1917) Italian
£47518 $79355 €67000 Parisian suburbs (41x32cm-16x13in) s.d.76 lit. 14-Oct-3 Finarte Semenzato, Milan #170/R est:60000
£97315 $181980 €145000 Vase and gloves (65x65cm-26x26in) s.d.1914 prov.exhib.lit. 25-Feb-4 Porro, Milan #36/R est:180000
£213333 $392533 €320000 At the balcony (65x54cm-26x21in) s. prov.exhib.lit. 8-Jun-4 Sotheby's, Milan #138/R est:300000-400000
Works on paper
£5775 $9990 €8200 Study of nude (42x25cm-17x10in) pencil. 9-Dec-3 Finarte Semenzato, Milan #74/R est:9000-10000
£24648 $42641 €35000 Head of girl (45x37cm-18x15in) s. pastel prov.lit. 10-Dec-3 Sotheby's, Milan #118/R est:20000-30000
£25352 $43859 €36000 Lucie (45x37cm-18x15in) s. pastel prov.lit. 10-Dec-3 Sotheby's, Milan #119/R est:20000-30000
£32886 $58866 €49000 Tete de femme (41x33cm-16x13in) s. pastel prov.lit. 25-May-4 Finarte Semenzato, Milan #190/R est:45000-55000

ZANDT, W van (19th C) American
£914 $1700 €1334 Portrait of a cow in barnyard with chickens (43x61cm-17x24in) s.d.93 board. 3-Mar-4 Alderfer's, Hatfield #306/R est:1000-1500

ZANETTI ZILLA, Vettore (1864-1946) Italian
£580 $951 €800 Along the Brenta (33x30cm-13x12in) init. board. 27-May-3 Il Ponte, Milan #934
£594 $1022 €850 Veneto landscape (16x21cm-6x8in) s.verso cardboard. 3-Dec-3 Stadion, Trieste #1053/R
£870 $1426 €1200 Landscape in the lagoon with boat (65x88cm-26x35in) s. init.verso board. 27-May-3 Il Ponte, Milan #950/R
£1467 $2625 €2200 Canal in Venice (35x27cm-14x11in) s. cardboard. 12-May-4 Stadion, Trieste #760/R est:2000-3000
£1736 $2951 €2500 Under Rialto Bridge (28x37cm-11x15in) s. cardboard. 1-Nov-3 Meeting Art, Vercelli #182/R est:2500
£1757 $3092 €2600 Houses in Burano (35x50cm-14x20in) init.d.1905 cardboard. 19-May-4 Il Ponte, Milan #679 est:1200-1500

ZANETTI, Antonio Maria (younger) (1706-1778) Italian
Works on paper
£333 $600 €486 Artist Zoboli (21x17cm-8x7in) i. ink prov. 21-Jan-4 Sotheby's, New York #49/R

ZANG, John J (19th C) American
£587 $1050 €857 Peasant girl with sheep travelling along a river path (36x30cm-14x12in) 15-May-4 Jeffery Burchard, Florida #132
£1397 $2500 €2040 Over the bridge in winter (30x46cm-12x18in) s. board prov. 6-May-4 Shannon's, Milford #195/R est:2500-3500
£2174 $3500 €3174 Alpine woodsmen (102x81cm-40x32in) s. 20-Aug-3 James Julia, Fairfield #1506/R est:3500-4500

ZANGRANDO, Giovanni (1869-1941) Italian
£284 $474 €400 Miramar Castle, Trieste (30x38cm-12x15in) s. cardboard. 20-Oct-3 Sant Agostino, Torino #171
£1258 $2290 €1900 Boats in Sistiana (38x48cm-15x19in) s. board. 18-Jun-4 Stadion, Trieste #115/R est:1200-1600
£1554 $2937 €2300 Reading in the wood (40x50cm-16x20in) s. board. 20-Feb-4 Stadion, Trieste #810/R est:1500
£2400 $4296 €3600 Seashores in Trieste (49x59cm-19x23in) s. 12-May-4 Stadion, Trieste #793/R est:2500-3500
Works on paper
£594 $993 €850 Thoghtful (144x82cm-57x32in) init. pencil dr. 10-Oct-3 Stadion, Trieste #503/R

ZANGRANDO, Miete (?) Italian
£390 $651 €550 Ciliegie (49x58cm-19x23in) s. plywood. 21-Jun-3 Stadion, Trieste #200/R

ZANGS, Herbert (1924-2003) German
£400 $716 €600 Blue windscreen wiper II (62x77cm-24x30in) s. tempera board. 13-May-4 Neumeister, Munich #802/R
£764 $1276 €1100 Windscreen wipers - rows of blue and white (67x62cm-26x24in) s. dispersion. 24-Oct-3 Ketterer, Hamburg #587/R
£1000 $1840 €1500 Untitled (14x78cm-6x31in) s.d.58 verso blk paint board. 8-Jun-4 Sotheby's, Amsterdam #109/R est:2000-3000
£1399 $2378 €2000 Untitled (72x16cm-28x6in) s. verso oil on board relief. 27-Nov-3 Lempertz, Koln #538/R est:2200
£1667 $2783 €2400 Drip painting (34x23cm-13x9in) s.d. acrylic oil gouache hessian. 24-Oct-3 Ketterer, Hamburg #586/R est:2500-3000
£4028 $6726 €5800 Untitled (218x126cm-86x50in) s. verso dispersion hessian. 24-Oct-3 Ketterer, Hamburg #585/R est:6000-7000
Sculpture
£1342 $2470 €2000 Untitled (100x57cm-39x22in) s.d.63 painted cloth string board prov. 26-Mar-4 Ketterer, Hamburg #705/R est:3600-4600
£5594 $9622 €8000 Untitled - knupfung (75x60cm-30x24in) s.d.52 verso tempera cork mixed media burlap on panel prov. 2-Dec-3 Sotheby's, Amsterdam #170/R est:6000-8000
Works on paper
£400 $720 €600 Composition (69x50cm-27x20in) s.d. W/C bodycol paper on board. 24-Apr-4 Reiss & Sohn, Konigstein #5880/R
£1342 $2470 €2000 Untitled (100x72cm-39x28in) s. collage dispersion packing paper board prov. 26-Mar-4 Ketterer, Hamburg #706/R est:2500-2700
£5944 $10224 €8500 Untitled - gratfaltung (94x78cm-37x31in) s.d.56 white painted paper on card prov. 2-Dec-3 Sotheby's, Amsterdam #172/R est:6000-8000

ZANGUIDI, Jacopo (1544-1574) Italian
£46980 $83154 €70000 Saint Peter and Saint Paul (22x8cm-9x3in) board. 27-Apr-4 Porro, Milan #313/R est:80000
Works on paper
£3537 $6332 €5200 Une gorgone conduisant une chimere, un homme jouant au violon (15x13cm-6x5in) i. black chk pen brown ink wash. 18-Mar-4 Christie's, Paris #54/R est:5000-7000
£4762 $8524 €7000 Deux etudes pour un homme assis dans un paysage. Pieta (12x20cm-5x8in) i. pen col ink red chk double-sided prov. 18-Mar-4 Christie's, Paris #53/R est:4000-6000
£6500 $11895 €9490 Christ in the garden of Gethsemane supported by two angels (20x20cm-8x8in) i. black chk pen ink htd white. 6-Jul-4 Christie's, London #26/R est:7000-10000

ZANIN, Angelo (1825-1862) Italian
£7194 $11799 €10000 Grand Canal with Rialto Bridge (37x42cm-15x17in) 4-Jun-3 Sotheby's, Milan #142/R est:10000-15000

ZANIN, Francesco (19th C) Italian
£5944 $10105 €8500 Ponte delle Parzienze on Barnaba Canal, Venice (64x50cm-25x20in) 24-Nov-3 Dorotheum, Vienna #10/R est:5000-7000
£26000 $44980 €37960 Piazzo San Marco, Venice (43x63cm-17x25in) s. 12-Dec-3 Christie's, Kensington #282/R est:12000-18000

ZANIN, Francesco (after) (19th C) Italian
£7200 $11448 €10512 St. Marks Square, Venice (43x64cm-17x25in) bears sig. overpainted print. 9-Sep-3 Gorringes, Lewes #1959/R est:200-250

ZANINI, Luigi (1893-1962) Italian
£12583 $22901 €19000 Landscape with river (130x148cm-51x58in) s.d.1929 board. 21-Jun-4 Pandolfini, Florence #164/R est:1200-1500

ZANINO DI PIETRO (circle) (15th C) Italian
£7042 $11268 €10000 Madonna and Child with angels and Saints (16x26cm-6x10in) tempera gold board. 21-Sep-3 Finarte, Venice #55/R est:4500

ZANK, Gerhard (1937-) Dutch
£552 $921 €800 Winter landscape with hunters (14x30cm-6x12in) panel. 11-Nov-3 Vendu Notarishuis, Rotterdam #648/R
£552 $921 €800 Hunters with their loot (14x30cm-6x12in) panel. 11-Nov-3 Vendu Notarishuis, Rotterdam #649

ZANTEN, Ek van (1933-) Dutch
Sculpture
£940 $1738 €1400 Rugby player (37cm-15in) i.num2 bronze. 15-Mar-4 Sotheby's, Amsterdam #348a/R est:1000-1500

ZANUTTO, Renzo (1909-1979) Italian
£533 $955 €800 Chased from the temple (45x40cm-18x16in) s. s.i.d.1940 verso cardboard. 12-May-4 Stadion, Trieste #825

ZAO-WOU-KI (1920-) Chinese
£420 $701 €600 Les voiliers (25x16cm-10x6in) s. 25-Jun-3 Rabourdin & Choppin de Janvry, Paris #130
£15385 $28000 €22462 Westminster Abbey (19x22cm-7x9in) s.d.51 s.i.d.51 verso masonite prov.exhib. 29-Jun-4 Sotheby's, New York #423/R est:10000-15000
£24419 $42000 €35652 I Juillet (38x46cm-15x18in) s. 7-Dec-3 Hindman, Chicago #843/R est:25000-30000
£24419 $42000 €35652 Aube VI (33x41cm-13x16in) s. 7-Dec-3 Hindman, Chicago #844/R est:25000-30000
£31690 $54824 €45000 Structures - 7.10.71 (54x65cm-21x26in) s. s. verso lit. 13-Dec-3 Lempertz, Koln #198/R est:20000-25000
£34507 $59697 €49000 Composition (54x65cm-21x26in) s. s.d.6 novembre 1982 verso. 12-Dec-3 Piasa, Paris #51/R est:37500-45000
£44737 $82316 €68000 Composition jaune pale (55x50cm-22x20in) s.i.d.63 verso prov. 22-Jun-4 Ribeyre & Baron, Paris #71/R est:25000-30000
£47058 $80000 €68705 Reindeer (94x114cm-37x45in) s. i.verso prov. 4-Nov-3 Bonhams & Butterfields, San Francisco #3458/R est:10000-15000
£50000 $80000 €73000 Sous bois dans la nuit (91x74cm-36x29in) s.d.1955. 20-Sep-3 Bunte, Elgin #1289 est:10000-15000
£53343 $96017 €77881 10.5.70 (46x55cm-18x22in) s. 25-Apr-4 Christie's, Hong Kong #722/R est:400000-500000 (HK.D 750000)
£54054 $90270 €78919 L'aube (55x46cm-22x18in) s.d.56 prov. 26-Oct-3 Christie's, Hong Kong #132/R est:500000-600000 (HK.D 700000)
£54545 $91091 €78000 Composition (81x90cm-32x35in) s. s.d.4 september 96 verso. 11-Oct-3 Cornette de St.Cyr, Paris #66/R est:70000-80000
£55556 $87778 €80000 Untitled (81x100cm-32x39in) s. s.d.96 verso prov. 27-Apr-3 Versailles Encheres #56
£55634 $96246 €79000 Sans titre (81x54cm-32x21in) s. s.d.22-1-71 verso prov. 14-Dec-3 Versailles Encheres #132/R est:90000-100000
£58042 $96930 €83000 Untitled (100x81cm-39x32in) s. s.d.81 verso lit. 29-Jun-3 Versailles Encheres #105/R
£59868 $110158 €91000 Composition (73x60cm-29x24in) s. s.d.1974 verso prov. 27-Jun-4 Versailles Encheres #70/R est:60000-70000
£62667 $112173 €94000 Composition (85x70cm-33x28in) s. d.76 verso prov.lit. 15-May-4 De Vuyst, Lokeren #505a/R
£64000 $117760 €93440 30-3-71 (105x95cm-41x37in) s. s.d.30.3.71 verso prov.lit. 24-Jun-4 Sotheby's, London #178/R est:40000-60000
£75419 $135000 €110112 Red still life (44x53cm-17x21in) s. painted 1951 prov.exhib. 13-May-4 Sotheby's, New York #119/R est:60000-80000
£119760 $200000 €174850 Sandscape (150x163cm-59x64in) s. s.d.15.5.77/11.3.80 verso prov. 13-Nov-3 Sotheby's, New York #236/R est:200000-250000
£125000 $227500 €182500 Deep water (50x100cm-20x39in) s.d.57 s.i.d.verso p. 4-Feb-4 Christie's, London #14/R est:35000-45000
£170697 $307255 €249218 Number 21-6-61 (73x60cm-29x24in) s. lit. 26-Apr-4 Sotheby's, Hong Kong #526/R est:1200000-1500000 (HK.D 2400000)
£197674 $340000 €288604 Composition (162x130cm-64x51in) s. s.d.Mai 1950 verso prov. 3-Dec-3 Doyle, New York #92/R est:150000-200000
£235294 $400000 €343529 23 April 1962 (368x287cm-145x113in) s. d.23.4.62 verso prov. 4-Nov-3 Bonhams & Butterfields, San Francisco #3461/R est:80000-120000
£248933 $448080 €363442 2.6.61 (73x116cm-29x46in) s. 25-Apr-4 Christie's, Hong Kong #721/R est:1600000-2000000 (HK.D 3500000)
£270270 $486486 €394594 Voie lactee (162x114cm-64x45in) s. prov.exhib.lit. 25-Apr-4 Christie's, Hong Kong #720/R est:2200000-3200000 (HK.D 3800000)
£293436 $490039 €428417 7.4.61 (195x114cm-77x45in) s. painted 1961. 26-Oct-3 Christie's, Hong Kong #133/R est:2000000-3000000 (HK.D 3800000)
Prints
£3057 $5563 €4463 Bain de soleil. Montagnes et soleil. s.s.i.d. col lithograph. 17-Jun-4 Kornfeld, Bern #830 est:2000 (S.FR 7000)
Sculpture
£5068 $9071 €7500 Untitled (38x42cm-15x17in) s.d.1996 painted ceramic. 4-May-4 Calmels Cohen, Paris #208/R est:3000-4000
Works on paper
£3944 $6823 €5600 Composition (25x18cm-10x7in) s.d.1970 prov. 14-Dec-3 Versailles Encheres #96/R est:4000-5000
£5035 $8559 €7200 Untitled (57x44cm-22x17in) s.d.89 Chinese ink. 21-Nov-3 Lombrail & Teucquam, Paris #162/R est:7600-10000
£5066 $8612 €7396 Abstract composition (18x13cm-7x5in) s.d.54 pen W/C. 5-Nov-3 Dobiaschofsky, Bern #1067/R est:7500 (S.FR 11500)
£5245 $8759 €7500 Composition (32x27cm-13x11in) s.d.1971 W/C prov. 29-Jun-3 Versailles Encheres #102/R
£5245 $8916 €7500 Untitled (57x44cm-22x17in) s.d.89 Chinese ink. 21-Nov-3 Lombrail & Teucquam, Paris #161/R est:7600-10000
£5667 $10200 €8500 Composition (21x17cm-8x7in) s.d.1960 ink wash prov. 25-Apr-4 Versailles Encheres #87 est:6000-8000
£5944 $9927 €8500 Composition (34x29cm-13x11in) s.d.1971 W/C. 29-Jun-3 Versailles Encheres #103/R
£5944 $9927 €8500 Composition (41x25cm-16x10in) s.d.1971 W/C prov.lit. 29-Jun-3 Versailles Encheres #101/R
£5986 $10356 €8500 Composition (22x29cm-9x11in) s. Indian ink. 14-Dec-3 Versailles Encheres #95/R est:6000-7000
£6622 $11853 €9800 Untitled (27x28cm-11x11in) s.d.76 W/C paper on canvas. 4-May-4 Calmels Cohen, Paris #206/R est:4000-5000
£6950 $11606 €10147 Still life (30x40cm-12x16in) s.d.51 ink dr. 26-Oct-3 Christie's, Hong Kong #160/R est:30000-40000 (HK.D 90000)
£7042 $12183 €10000 Composition (37x45cm-15x18in) s.d.1960 W/C prov. 14-Dec-3 Versailles Encheres #81/R est:6000-8000
£7200 $13248 €10512 Untitled (27x27cm-11x11in) s.d.80 ink paper on paperboard prov. 24-Jun-4 Sotheby's, Olympia #538/R est:3000-4000
£7986 $12618 €11500 Composition (28x38cm-11x15in) s.d.1987 W/C prov. 27-Apr-3 Versailles Encheres #55
£8667 $15947 €13000 Untitled (29x33cm-11x13in) s.d.59 ink. 8-Jun-4 Sotheby's, Amsterdam #132/R est:7000-9000
£8667 $15600 €13000 Naked trees (26x21cm-10x8in) s.d.1950 W/C. 25-Apr-4 Versailles Encheres #86 est:10000-12000
£8667 $15947 €13000 Composition (65x66cm-26x26in) s. india ink exec. 2003 prov. 11-Jun-4 Pierre Berge, Paris #85/R est:3000-5000
£8681 $13715 €12500 Composition (88x94cm-35x37in) s.d.1999 ink prov. 27-Apr-3 Versailles Encheres #54
£8741 $14598 €12500 Composition (28x28cm-11x11in) s.d.1976 W/C prov. 29-Jun-3 Versailles Encheres #100/R
£10000 $18400 €14600 Untitled (57x44cm-22x17in) s.d.89 ink. 24-Jun-4 Sotheby's, London #183/R est:6000-8000
£11000 $20020 €16060 Entre deux villes (22x27cm-9x11in) s.i.d.55 W/C ink prov. 5-Feb-4 Christie's, London #122/R est:8000-12000
£11409 $20195 €17000 Composition (87x65cm-34x26in) s.d.88 Indian ink ink wash. 28-Apr-4 Artcurial Briest, Paris #255/R est:8000-12000
£13423 $23758 €20000 Composition feuillages (87x65cm-34x26in) s.d.88 Indian ink ink wash. 28-Apr-4 Artcurial Briest, Paris #256/R est:8000-12000
£16438 $25808 €24000 Composition (102x102cm-40x40in) s. Chinese ink exec.1989. 20-Apr-3 Deauville, France #145/R est:10000-12000
£17000 $31280 €24820 Untitled (76x57cm-30x22in) s.d.68 ink W/C. 24-Jun-4 Sotheby's, London #175/R est:6000-80000
£22048 $39687 €32190 Abstract landscape (103x103cm-41x41in) s.d.81 ink. 25-Apr-4 Christie's, Hong Kong #755/R est:180000-260000 (HK.D 310000)
£22760 $40967 €33230 Abstract landscape (56x75cm-22x30in) s.d.74 W/C. 25-Apr-4 Christie's, Hong Kong #754/R est:100000-150000 (HK.D 320000)
£240000 $441600 €350400 Grand marche (81x100cm-32x39in) s.d.56 s.i.d.verso prov. 23-Jun-4 Sotheby's, London #28/R est:100000-150000

ZAPATA, Ernesto (20th C) American?
Works on paper
£257 $475 €375 Indian mother and child (61x46cm-24x18in) s. pastel. 13-Mar-4 Susanin's, Chicago #6067/R

ZAPATA, Pedro León (1929-) Venezuelan
Works on paper
£259 $410 €378 Golpistas ! (35x17cm-14x7in) Chinese ink card. 17-Nov-2 Subastas Odalys, Caracas #78
£261 $470 €381 Figures (35x64cm-14x25in) s. mixed media diptych. 25-Apr-4 Subastas Odalys, Caracas #123
£329 $520 €480 Those who are paid to walk are to be called walkers (35x17cm-14x7in) Chinese ink card. 17-Nov-2 Subastas Odalys, Caracas #10/R
£690 $1125 €1007 Chiguire. mixed media exec.2000. 20-Jul-3 Subastas Odalys, Caracas #50
£949 $1500 €1386 Not a step back (35x17cm-14x7in) graphite Chinese ink card. 17-Nov-2 Subastas Odalys, Caracas #93/R
£1013 $1600 €1479 Bow your ear to this caricature (35x16cm-14x6in) graphite Chinese ink card. 17-Nov-2 Subastas Odalys, Caracas #109/R
£1266 $2000 €1848 The first victim (35x16cm-14x6in) graphite Chinese ink card. 17-Nov-2 Subastas Odalys, Caracas #120/R

ZAPPELLONI, Andrea (1877-1961) Italian
£604 $1069 €900 Boats on Lake Maggiore (39x42cm-15x17in) s. board. 1-May-4 Meeting Art, Vercelli #165
£671 $1188 €1000 Laveno hill (40x50cm-16x20in) s. board. 1-May-4 Meeting Art, Vercelli #50
£1087 $1783 €1500 Chapel (40x50cm-16x20in) s.d.1918. 27-May-3 Finarte Semenzato, Milan #39/R
£1304 $2139 €1800 Chickens eating (63x50cm-25x20in) s. board. 27-May-3 Finarte Semenzato, Milan #100/R est:1800-2000
£1304 $2139 €1800 Little bridge with cypress (72x40cm-28x16in) s. 27-May-3 Finarte Semenzato, Milan #99/R est:1800-2000

ZAPPETTINI, Gianfranco (1939-) Italian
£867 $1595 €1300 Structures (90x90cm-35x35in) s.i.d.1972 verso acrylic. 12-Jun-4 Meeting Art, Vercelli #481/R

ZARATE, Luis (20th C) ?
£9484 $16122 €13847 Bat flight at night (116x153cm-46x60in) s.d.1987 exhib. 30-Oct-3 Louis Morton, Mexico #80/R est:200000-220000 (M.P 180000)

ZARB, Michelle (20th C) Canadian
£560 $1025 €818 Shareholder's meeting (90x120cm-35x47in) s. prov. 1-Jun-4 Hodgins, Calgary #179/R (C.D 1400)

ZARCO, Antonio (1930-) Spanish
£884 $1610 €1300 Fruit bowl (41x33cm-16x13in) s.d.1988 paper prov. 3-Feb-4 Segre, Madrid #315/R
£884 $1610 €1300 Fruit bowl I (41x33cm-16x13in) s.d.1988 paper prov. 3-Feb-4 Segre, Madrid #314/R

ZARINA, Anna (1907-1984) Belgian
£1600 $2896 €2400 Nu couche (116x130cm-46x51in) s. 30-Mar-4 Campo & Campo, Antwerp #370 est:650-750

ZARING, Louise E (c.1875-c.1945) American
£432 $800 €631 Chrysanthemums (56x43cm-22x17in) s. 18-Jan-4 Bonhams & Butterfields, Los Angeles #7004/R

ZARITSKY, Joseph (1891-1985) Israeli
£7263 $13000 €10604 Untitled (50x54cm-20x21in) s. 18-Mar-4 Sotheby's, New York #36/R est:12000-18000
£43373 $72000 €63325 Painting - Flowers (120x150cm-47x59in) s. painted 1955 prov.exhib.lit. 2-Oct-3 Christie's, Tel Aviv #82/R est:60000-80000
Works on paper
£5464 $10000 €7977 Street in Tel-Aviv (50x66cm-20x26in) W/C pencil prov.exhib.lit. 1-Jun-4 Ben-Ami, Tel Aviv #4840/R est:12000-15000
£6024 $10000 €8795 Tel Aviv. Still life by an open window (33x39cm-13x15in) s. W/C over pencil double-sided exhib. 2-Oct-3 Christie's, Tel Aviv #84/R est:6000-8000

ZARRAGA, Angel (1886-1946) Mexican
£7263 $13000 €10604 Maternite francaise avec enfant (41x13cm-16x5in) s.d.27 s.i.d.verso panel. 26-May-4 Sotheby's, New York #83/R est:10000-15000
£27465 $47514 €39000 Promeneurs pres de l'arbre aux oiseaux (81x65cm-32x26in) s. 14-Dec-3 Eric Pillon, Calais #260/R
£55866 $100000 €81564 Woman at well (114x145cm-45x57in) s. painted c.1915 prov.exhib.lit. 26-May-4 Sotheby's, New York #27/R est:100000-150000
£56667 $104267 €85000 Femmes a l afontaine (160x10cm-63x4in) s.d.1922 prov.lit. 10-Jun-4 Christie's, Paris #4/R est:80000-120000
Works on paper
£331 $603 €500 Visage de femme (18x12cm-7x5in) s.i. pen india ink exec. c.1920. 15-Jun-4 Blanchet, Paris #213
£1111 $1855 €1600 Etude pour l'adoration des bergers (40x34cm-16x13in) s.i. lead pencil. 21-Oct-3 Artcurial Briest, Paris #118/R est:1500-2000

ZARUBIN, Viktor Ivanovich (1866-1928) Russian
£5000 $8950 €7300 Russian village in winter (33x40cm-13x16in) s.d.1912 board. 26-May-4 Sotheby's, London #92/R est:5000-7000

ZATZKA, Hans (1859-1949) Austrian
£1275 $2257 €1900 Kaiser Karl I and Erzherzog Friedrich (83x49cm-33x19in) s. 29-Apr-4 Dorotheum, Vienna #101/R est:800-1000
£1310 $2424 €1900 The good shepherd (63x148cm-25x58in) s. 12-Feb-4 Weidler, Nurnberg #6552 est:2120
£2000 $3320 €2920 Love letter (39x25cm-15x10in) s. panel. 1-Oct-3 Sotheby's, Olympia #243/R est:2000-3000
£2500 $4500 €3650 In love (47x31cm-19x12in) s. s.i.verso panel prov. 21-Jan-4 Sotheby's, Olympia #459/R est:2500-3500
£2639 $4407 €3800 Ein suber traum (51x82cm-20x32in) s.i.verso. 21-Oct-3 Sotheby's, Amsterdam #77/R est:3000-5000
£3500 $6370 €5110 Summer flowers on a ledge, landscape beyond (77x63cm-30x25in) s. 16-Jun-4 Christie's, Kensington #56/R est:3000-5000
£4800 $8640 €7008 Love letter (58x36cm-23x14in) s. i.verso panel prov. 21-Jan-4 Sotheby's, Olympia #457/R est:3500-5000
£5034 $9010 €7500 Large still life with fruit and view of a landscape (71x100cm-28x39in) s. i.verso. 27-May-4 Dorotheum, Vienna #54/R est:7000-9000
£5800 $10440 €8468 Who goes there (61x37cm-24x15in) s. prov. 21-Jan-4 Sotheby's, Olympia #458/R est:3500-5000
£8725 $16054 €13000 Mythological scene on rivershore (57x80cm-22x31in) i. verso. 25-Mar-4 Dr Fritz Nagel, Stuttgart #778/R est:2400
£8939 $16000 €13051 Maidens by the sea (58x25cm-23x10in) s.i. two. 6-May-4 Doyle, New York #62/R est:7000-9000
£13000 $23660 €18980 Dancing beauty (105x68cm-41x27in) s. 15-Jun-4 Sotheby's, London #136/R est:10000-12000
£16000 $29120 €23360 Moonlight serenade (68x105cm-27x41in) s. 15-Jun-4 Sotheby's, London #135/R est:10000-15000
£17450 $31235 €26000 Blossom time (79x58cm-31x23in) i.verso. 27-May-4 Dorotheum, Vienna #52/R est:14000-18000
£19444 $35000 €28388 Sleeping beauty (82x130cm-32x51in) s. 22-Apr-4 Christie's, Rockefeller NY #49/R est:25000-35000

ZATZKA, Hans (attrib) (1859-1949) Austrian
£1192 $2170 €1800 Yearning (81x34cm-32x13in) s. 21-Jun-4 Dorotheum, Vienna #231/R est:1800-2000

ZAUGG, Hans (1894-1986) Swiss
£323 $579 €472 Geranium (33x27cm-13x11in) s. pavatex. 13-May-4 Stuker, Bern #846 (S.FR 750)

ZAVATTARI FAMILY (attrib) (15th C) Italian
£15000 $25500 €21900 Two Saints (100x28cm-39x11in) gold ground panel pair. 29-Oct-3 Christie's, London #88/R est:15000-20000

ZAVERDINOS, Dionissis (1954-) Greek
£2100 $3675 €3066 Abstract (50x70cm-20x28in) s. 16-Dec-3 Bonhams, New Bond Street #147/R est:2000-3000
£3000 $5370 €4380 Abstract composition (60x80cm-24x31in) s.d.03. 10-May-4 Sotheby's, Olympia #79/R est:3000-4000

ZAVROS, Michael (1974-) Australian
Works on paper
£1374 $2501 €2006 It is happening again (57x76cm-22x30in) init.d.03 chl exhib. 16-Jun-4 Deutscher-Menzies, Melbourne #184/R est:2000-3000 (A.D 3600)

ZAWADZINSKI, Czeslaw (19/20th C) Polish
£872 $1614 €1300 Beaulieu-sur-Mer (37x43cm-15x17in) s. canvas on cardboard. 15-Mar-4 Claude Boisgirard, Paris #129/R

ZAYON, Seymour (1930-) American
£203 $350 €296 Abstract work in black and white over newspaper stock listing (36x28cm-14x11in) s. oil pencil on board. 10-Dec-3 Alderfer's, Hatfield #490

ZBINDEN, Fritz (1896-1968) Swiss
£596 $996 €864 Spring landscape near Hirzel (64x81cm-25x32in) s.d.1957. 23-Jun-3 Philippe Schuler, Zurich #3438 (S.FR 1300)

ZDANEVICH, Kyril (1882-1970) Russian
£18000 $32760 €26280 Gubpolitprosvet (63x38cm-25x15in) oil collage prov. 21-Jun-4 Bonhams, New Bond Street #26/R est:20000-30000

ZDICHINEC, Bernhard (1883-1968) Austrian
£347 $566 €500 View of the Dachstein (86x78cm-34x31in) s. panel. 23-Sep-3 Wiener Kunst Auktionen, Vienna #31/R

ZDYBAL, Mariusz (1955-) Polish
£378 $654 €552 Charlotte Corday (81x65cm-32x26in) s.i. 10-Dec-3 Agra, Warsaw #47/R (P.Z 2500)

ZECCA, Antonello (1944-) Italian
Works on paper
£510 $929 €750 Milan, Piazza Scala (70x50cm-28x20in) s. W/C cardboard. 6-Feb-4 Galleria Rosenberg, Milan #143/R

ZECHYR, Othmar (1938-1996) Austrian
Works on paper
£448 $820 €650 Untitled (27x20cm-11x8in) s.d.1983 pencil oil chk. 27-Jan-4 Dorotheum, Vienna #234/R
£1645 $3026 €2500 Untitled (45x31cm-18x12in) s.d.1983 ink. 22-Jun-4 Wiener Kunst Auktionen, Vienna #429/R est:1000
£2069 $3703 €3021 Untitled (100x70cm-39x28in) s.d.Juli 1970 bodycol collage. 12-May-4 Dobiaschofsky, Bern #2223/R est:3000 (S.FR 4800)
£2098 $3566 €3000 Composition (115x90cm-45x35in) i.d.1971 pen Indian ink transparent paper. 26-Nov-3 Dorotheum, Vienna #271/R est:1900-2600

ZEE, Jan van der (1898-1988) Dutch
£3741 $6810 €5500 Farm houses in Groningen (50x70cm-20x28in) s.d.38 s.stretcher. 3-Feb-4 Christie's, Amsterdam #433/R est:3500-4500
£5594 $9510 €8000 Composition (60x80cm-24x31in) s. s.d.62 verso prov.exhib.lit. 25-Nov-3 Christie's, Amsterdam #285/R est:8000-12000

ZEEGERS, Harry (?) Dutch?
£604 $1117 €900 Farmhouse interior (100x77cm-39x30in) s. 10-Mar-4 James Adam, Dublin #6/R

ZEFIROV, Konstantin Klavdianovitch (1879-1960) Russian
£1133 $2085 €1700 Danse populaire (35x49cm-14x19in) s.d.1932 canvas on cardboard. 9-Jun-4 Oger, Dumont, Paris #82 est:1500-2000

ZEGALSKI, Lesnek Michal (20th C) Polish
£521 $896 €761 Man holding bull by horns, upside down (130x97cm-51x38in) s.d.90 i.verso. 4-Dec-3 Agra, Warsaw #15/R (P.Z 3500)

ZEGELAAR, Gerrit (attrib) (1719-1794) Dutch
Works on paper
£2568 $4519 €3800 Man resting on a bench (24x29cm-9x11in) black chk htd white prov. 19-May-4 Sotheby's, Amsterdam #263/R est:1000-1500

ZEGNARD, A (19th C) German?
Works on paper
£1216 $2177 €1800 Empire/Biedermeier room of Dr Dominik von Vivenot Vienna (23x45cm-9x18in) s.d.1837 W/C. 6-May-4 Michael Zeller, Lindau #949/R est:1500

ZEGRAY, Lucienne (20th C) Canadian
Works on paper
£225 $383 €329 McGill sous la neige (20x25cm-8x10in) s. pastel prov. 23-Nov-3 Levis, Calgary #151/R (C.D 500)
£407 $680 €594 During the carnival, Quebec (40x50cm-16x20in) s.i.d.2000 pastel. 17-Nov-3 Hodgins, Calgary #13/R (C.D 900)

ZEHBE, Philipp (19/20th C) German?
£521 $823 €750 Female rider on horseback at the edge of the sea (83x71cm-33x28in) s.d.14. 5-Sep-3 Wendl, Rudolstadt #3784/R

ZEHENDER, Johann Caspar (1742-1805) German
£5000 $8500 €7300 Panoramic view of Frankfurt am Main, with peasants bleaching linen (53x152cm-21x60in) init.d.1774 prov. 29-Oct-3 Christie's, London #52/R est:8000-12000

ZEHME, Werner (1859-?) German
£4000 $7160 €6000 By the oven (141x74cm-56x29in) s. 13-May-4 Neumeister, Munich #526/R est:5000-7000

ZEINE, Jacques Camille de (1884-?) Belgian
£350 $584 €500 Vaches a l'abreuvoir (23x30cm-9x12in) s. panel. 13-Oct-3 Horta, Bruxelles #472

ZEISS, Friedrich (19th C) German
Works on paper
£367 $667 €550 Southern coastal town with ruins (33x46cm-13x18in) s.d.1856 W/C. 30-Jun-4 Neumeister, Munich #436/R

ZEITBLOM, Bartholome (style) (c.1455-1522) German
£6993 $12028 €10000 Saint Nicolas of Myra (109x60cm-43x24in) i.verso panel prov.lit. 3-Dec-3 Neumeister, Munich #520a/R est:3000

ZELDIS, Malcah (1931-) American
£419 $700 €612 Couple in bedroom (61x91cm-24x36in) masonite board. 15-Nov-3 Slotin Folk Art, Buford #213/R
£889 $1600 €1298 Card game (36x46cm-14x18in) s.1977. 24-Apr-4 Slotin Folk Art, Buford #416/R est:1000-2000
£1278 $2300 €1866 Coney Island, Broadwalk (48x64cm-19x25in) d.1972. 24-Apr-4 Slotin Folk Art, Buford #415/R est:1000-3000
£5000 $9000 €7300 King and queen and their court (61x81cm-24x32in) d.1978 acrylic board. 24-Apr-4 Slotin Folk Art, Buford #414/R est.1000-3000
Works on paper
£333 $600 €486 Girl in a room (23x30cm-9x12in) gouache prov. 24-Apr-4 Slotin Folk Art, Buford #417/R

ZELENINE, Edouard (1938-) British
£1309 $2421 €1950 Composition (100x81cm-39x32in) s.d.1976. 15-Mar-4 Claude Boisgirard, Paris #130/R est:1000-1200
Works on paper
£596 $1085 €900 Composition aux deux violons (57x47cm-22x19in) s. gouache pastel. 16-Jun-4 Claude Boisgirard, Paris #176

ZELGER, Jakob Joseph (1812-1885) Swiss
£339 $577 €495 Herons in landscape (34x61cm-13x24in) s. 18-Nov-3 Hans Widmer, St Gallen #1234 (S.FR 750)
£824 $1500 €1203 Der matterhorn (112x91cm-44x36in) s. 29-Jun-4 Sotheby's, New York #128/R est:3000-5000
£1810 $3077 €2643 High Alpine landscape (47x63cm-19x25in) s.d.1860. 19-Nov-3 Fischer, Luzern #1254/R est:2600-4000 (S.FR 4000)
£2941 $5000 €4294 Mountain landscape with track (64x81cm-25x32in) s. 19-Nov-3 Fischer, Luzern #1253/R est:5500-6000 (S.FR 6500)

ZELGER, Jakob Joseph (attrib) (1812-1885) Swiss
Works on paper
£800 $1440 €1168 Swiss mountain lakeside town with figures in the foreground (16x22cm-6x9in) s. W/C pair. 23-Jan-4 British Auctioneer #507/R

ZELLENBERG, Franz Zeller von (1805-1876) Austrian
£352 $585 €500 Dead fox in extensive landscape (32x44cm-13x17in) s.d.1853. 16-Jun-3 Dorotheum, Vienna #230/R
Works on paper
£414 $687 €600 Railway crossing (42x92cm-17x36in) s. W/C. 30-Sep-3 Dorotheum, Vienna #263/R

ZELLER, Fred (1912-) French
£263 $484 €400 Vertiges sous le soleil couchant (29x38cm-11x15in) s. i.d.1989 verso paper on panel. 28-Jun-4 Joron-Derem, Paris #235
£296 $545 €450 Gourmandise (55x46cm-22x18in) s. s.verso. 24-Jun-4 Credit Municipal, Paris #60
£296 $545 €450 Belotte (73x60cm-29x24in) s. s.i.verso. 24-Jun-4 Credit Municipal, Paris #61
£302 $556 €450 Vergites sous le soleil couchant (29x38cm-11x15in) s. i.d.1989 verso paper on panel. 24-Mar-4 Joron-Derem, Paris #207
£350 $584 €500 Les deux femmes au parapluie (25x30cm-10x12in) s. panel. 29-Jun-3 Feletin, Province #124/R
£556 $928 €800 Deux baigneuses (60x81cm-24x32in) s. s.i.verso. 21-Oct-3 Artcurial Briest, Paris #348

ZELLER, Hans Arnold (1897-1983) Swiss
£353 $600 €515 View of Seealp valley (19x16cm-7x6in) s.d.1944 i.verso masonite. 1-Dec-3 Koller, Zurich #6533 (S.FR 780)
£1310 $2306 €1913 Late autumn - Santis (33x41cm-13x16in) s.d.1936 i.d.1936 verso board prov. 22-May-4 Galerie Gloggner, Luzern #114/R est:3800-4500 (S.FR 3000)
£1391 $2546 €2031 Santis landscape in early spring (33x41cm-13x16in) s.d.1942 i.d.1942 verso board. 7-Jun-4 Christie's, Zurich #109/R est:3000-5000 (S.FR 3200)
£1536 $2504 €2243 Alpine landscape (28x36cm-11x14in) s.d.1957 panel. 29-Sep-3 Lilla Bukowskis, Stockholm #630 est:10000-12000 (S.KR 20000)
£1794 $2996 €2619 Landscape near Heerbrugg (23x19cm-9x7in) s.d.1965 board. 24-Oct-3 Hans Widmer, St Gallen #45/R est:4000-7500 (S.FR 4000)
£1928 $3220 €2815 Landscape (30x30cm-12x12in) s.d.1944 i. stretcher board. 24-Oct-3 Hans Widmer, St Gallen #142/R est:4000-6500 (S.FR 4300)
£2018 $3370 €2946 Schwendi valley with Bogarten (35x27cm-14x11in) s.d.1943 i. verso pavatex. 24-Oct-3 Hans Widmer, St Gallen #143/R est:4000-6500 (S.FR 4500)
£3620 $6262 €5285 Sunny winter day in Appenzellerland, Santis (45x37cm-18x15in) s.d.1951 masonite. 9-Dec-3 Sotheby's, Zurich #100/R est:10000-14000 (S.FR 8000)
£4036 $6740 €5893 Santis and Altmann in morning sun (32x40cm-13x16in) s.d.1955 board. 24-Oct-3 Hans Widmer, St Gallen #108/R est:8000-12000 (S.FR 9000)
£4036 $6740 €5893 Landscape near Urnasch with view of Gamschopf (46x37cm-18x15in) s.d.1949 board. 24-Oct-3 Hans Widmer, St Gallen #110/R est:7000-14000 (S.FR 9000)
£4484 $7489 €6547 Santis and Altmann from Kellersegg (33x39cm-13x15in) s.d.1964 board. 24-Oct-3 Hans Widmer, St Gallen #109/R est:6000-11000 (S.FR 10000)
£7623 $12731 €11130 Ohrli and Santis in morning sun (33x41cm-13x16in) s.d.1964 pavatex. 24-Oct-3 Hans Widmer, St Gallen #144/R est:10000-14000 (S.FR 17000)
£10314 $17224 €15058 Valley, Urnasch (55x46cm-22x18in) s.d.1949 board. 24-Oct-3 Hans Widmer, St Gallen #44/R est:10000-18000 (S.FR 23000)
£11659 $19471 €17022 Appenzell girl wearing hat (41x32cm-16x13in) s.d.1968 pavatex. 24-Oct-3 Hans Widmer, St Gallen #43/R est:10000-16000 (S.FR 26000)

ZELLER, Johann Conrad (1807-1856) Swiss
Works on paper
£839 $1427 €1200 Capri after sunset (15x25cm-6x10in) s. W/C bodycol over pencil. 27-Nov-3 Bassenge, Berlin #5670/R

ZELLER, Magnus (1888-1972) German
Works on paper
£350 $594 €500 Landscape (48x27cm-19x11in) s. W/C. 29-Nov-3 Villa Grisebach, Berlin #693/R
£591 $981 €857 Autumnal street (42x30cm-17x12in) s.d.1945 w/C. 13-Jun-3 Zofingen, Switzerland #2548 (S.FR 1300)
£933 $1680 €1400 Snake and death's head (60x47cm-24x19in) s.d. W/C board. 24-Apr-4 Dr Lehr, Berlin #527/R

ZELMAN, Victor (1877-1960) Australian
£451 $718 €658 Spring is whisering (80x122cm-31x48in) s. 1-May-3 Dunbar Sloane, Wellington #482 est:300-500 (NZ.D 1300)
£529 $946 €772 Summer's day (34x43cm-13x17in) s. board. 10-May-4 Joel, Victoria #349 est:2000-3000 (A.D 1300)

ZELONI, Remo (20th C) Italian
£800 $1432 €1200 Date (30x40cm-12x16in) s. pair. 13-May-4 Babuino, Rome #491

ZELTER, Georges (1938-) French
£1818 $3091 €2600 Le bassin du Jardin du Luxembourg (65x92cm-26x36in) s. 27-Nov-3 Calmels Cohen, Paris #128/R est:1400-1600

ZEMP, Leodegar (1805-1878) Swiss
£437 $795 €638 Portrait of the building inspector Joseph Schneller (32x24cm-13x9in) s.i.d.1840 verso. 16-Jun-4 Fischer, Luzern #2434/R (S.FR 1000)

ZEN, Sergio (1936-) Italian
£333 $613 €500 Airy 17 (50x50cm-20x20in) s. s.i.d.2000 verso. 12-Jun-4 Meeting Art, Vercelli #439/R
£336 $621 €500 More inside than outside (50x50cm-20x20in) s. painted 2000. 13-Mar-4 Meeting Art, Vercelli #328

ZENDEL, Gabriel (1906-1992) French
£263 $484 €400 Still life with flowers on a tripod table (80x40cm-31x16in) s. 22-Jun-4 Christie's, Amsterdam #592/R
£329 $605 €500 Still life with apples in a basket (22x27cm-9x11in) s. 22-Jun-4 Christie's, Amsterdam #583/R

ZENDER, Rudolf (1901-1988) Swiss
£371 $631 €542 Sunset over freight harbour (24x32cm-9x13in) s. board. 18-Nov-3 Hans Widmer, St Gallen #1238 (S.FR 820)
£393 $723 €574 On the Seine, Paris (22x57cm-9x22in) s.d. canvas on board. 14-Jun-4 Philippe Schuler, Zurich #5757 (S.FR 900)
£413 $756 €603 Riverside town (38x46cm-15x18in) s. 4-Jun-4 Zofingen, Switzerland #3000 (S.FR 950)
£543 $907 €793 Dyke with lighthouse (26x34cm-10x13in) s.d.1955 board. 24-Jun-3 Germann, Zurich #1091 (S.FR 1200)
£606 $1085 €885 Early spring on the Thur (81x65cm-32x26in) s. 22-Mar-4 Philippe Schuler, Zurich #4369 (S.FR 1400)
£724 $1252 €1057 Seine prise II (22x56cm-9x22in) s.d.1964 board. 9-Dec-3 Sotheby's, Zurich #72/R est:1500-2000 (S.FR 1600)
£1267 $2027 €1850 On the Seine (60x73cm-24x29in) s. 16-Sep-3 Philippe Schuler, Zurich #3262/R est:2000-3000 (S.FR 2800)
£1351 $2324 €1972 On the banks of the Seine (130x97cm-51x38in) s.d.1965/68. 8-Dec-3 Philippe Schuler, Zurich #3367/R est:3000-3500 (S.FR 3000)
£1584 $2740 €2313 Harbour view, Paris (46x55cm-18x22in) s.d.1968. 9-Dec-3 Sotheby's, Zurich #61/R est:2500-3500 (S.FR 3500)
£3139 $5242 €4583 La Seine (88x129cm-35x51in) s.d.63 i. stretcher. 24-Oct-3 Hans Widmer, St Gallen #16/R est:2000-5500 (S.FR 7000)

ZENETZIS, Vasilis (1935-) Greek
£1000 $1700 €1460 View of the acropolis (40x50cm-16x20in) s. i.verso. 18-Nov-3 Sotheby's, London #141/R est:1000-1500
£1200 $2148 €1752 Acropolis (50x40cm-20x16in) s. s.i.d.1974 verso. 10-May-4 Sotheby's, Olympia #134/R est:800-1200
£2400 $4080 €3504 View of the acropolis from Plaka (40x50cm-16x20in) s. i.verso. 18-Nov-3 Sotheby's, London #142/R est:1000-1500
£2400 $4296 €3504 Acropolis (45x60cm-18x24in) s. s.i.verso. 10-May-4 Sotheby's, Olympia #135/R est:2000-3000
£3500 $6265 €5110 Plaka with the Acropolis beyond (70x100cm-28x39in) s. s.i.verso exhib. 10-May-4 Sotheby's, Olympia #136/R est:1200-1500

ZENNARO, Giorgio (1926-) Italian
Sculpture
£1295 $2124 €1800 Apertura eveniente (86x73x29cm-34x29x11in) s.i.d. plexiglas wooden socle. 4-Jun-3 Ketterer, Hamburg #1011/R est:3500-3800

ZENNSTROM, Petter (1945-) Swedish
£290 $522 €423 Untitled (81x61cm-32x24in) init.d.95 panel. 26-Apr-4 Bukowskis, Stockholm #600/R (S.KR 4000)

ZENO, Jorge (1956-) Puerto Rican
Works on paper
£645 $1200 €942 On the veranda (102x76cm-40x30in) s. W/C gouache executed c.1990. 7-Mar-4 Treadway Gallery, Cincinnati #658/R est:2500-3500

ZENONE, Vince (20th C) American
Works on paper
£1265 $2100 €1847 Raymond H Weill, Rare stamps shop on Royal Street (36x25cm-14x10in) s.d.71 W/C prov. 4-Oct-3 Neal Auction Company, New Orleans #538/R est:300-500

ZENS, Herwig (1943-) Austrian
£658 $1211 €1000 Untitled (100x100cm-39x39in) s. acrylic chl. 22-Jun-4 Wiener Kunst Auktionen, Vienna #441/R
£658 $1211 €1000 Apollo and Daphne (100x160cm-39x63in) s. acrylic diptych. 22-Jun-4 Wiener Kunst Auktionen, Vienna #443/R

ZEPHIRIN, Frantz (1963-) Haitian
£333 $597 €500 La protection maternelle (51x60cm-20x24in) s. 17-May-4 Rogeon, Paris #142b

ZEPPEL-SPERL, Robert (1944-) Austrian
£352 $563 €500 Still life (63x45cm-25x18in) s.i. W/C. 16-Sep-3 Dorotheum, Vienna #234
Works on paper
£336 $621 €500 Beautiful woman 3 (64x46cm-25x18in) s.i.d.1973/9 W/C. 9-Mar-4 Dorotheum, Vienna #177
£355 $592 €500 Untitled - from the series, Max Ernst (58x39cm-23x15in) i.d.79/10 mixed media. 14-Oct-3 Dorotheum, Vienna #234/R
£483 $883 €700 Feather crown (62x47cm-24x19in) s.d.1973/7 mixed media gold silver prov. 27-Jan-4 Dorotheum, Vienna #197/R
£600 $1080 €900 Goddess (63x46cm-25x18in) s.i.d.1970 W/C. 21-Apr-4 Dorotheum, Vienna #222/R
£658 $1211 €1000 Central person (65x47cm-26x19in) s.i.d.1973 W/C. 22-Jun-4 Wiener Kunst Auktionen, Vienna #336/R
£759 $1388 €1100 Land of mountains and rivers (124x88cm-49x35in) s.d.1983/3 mixed media prov. 27-Jan-4 Dorotheum, Vienna #232/R

ZERBE, Karl (1903-1972) American/German
£343 $550 €501 Shadow no.1 (152x102cm-60x40in) s.d.1960 acrylic. 17-May-3 Bunte, Elgin #1316

ZERFFI, Florence (1882-1962) British/South African
£325 $552 €475 Still life with a plant and fruit on a windowsill (60x50cm-24x20in) s.d.54. 4-Nov-3 Stephan Welz, Johannesburg #705 est:4000-6000 (SA.R 3800)

ZERILLI, Francesco (?-1837) Italian
Works on paper
£4333 $7973 €6500 View of catania (29x44cm-11x17in) gouache card. 10-Jun-4 Christie's, Rome #146/R est:4000-6000
£6333 $11653 €9500 Taormina, Sicily (30x44cm-12x17in) init. gouache card. 10-Jun-4 Christie's, Rome #145/R est:4000-6000

ZERMATI, J (20th C) Italian
£2119 $3878 €3200 Women and children in room (71x100cm-28x39in) s. 8-Apr-4 Dorotheum, Vienna #146/R est:2000-2400

ZEROLO, Martin (1928-) Spanish
£590 $974 €850 Still life (73x91cm-29x36in) s. si.d1990 verso. 2-Jul-3 Ansorena, Madrid #838/R

ZERRITSCH, Fritz (jnr) (1888-1985) Austrian
£355 $592 €500 Old mill in Mauerkirchen (40x32cm-16x13in) s. i. verso board. 16-Oct-3 Dorotheum, Salzburg #623/R

ZESATTI, Luis Armando (1967-) Latin American
£16201 $29000 €23653 Waking up (130x180cm-51x71in) s. acrylic painted 2001 prov. 26-May-4 Sotheby's, New York #147/R est:18000-22000

ZESHIN, Shibata (1807-1891) Japanese
£750 $1298 €1095 Rural scenes (46x26cm-18x10in) s. ink col handscroll wooden box. 11-Dec-3 Sotheby's, Olympia #24/R
Prints
£3947 $7145 €6000 Gourd (24x25cm-9x10in) s. Indian ink woodcut. 16-Apr-4 Dorotheum, Vienna #368/R est:4000-5000
Works on paper
£265 $482 €400 The good old man being looked after by sparrows (27x24cm-11x9in) s. dr. 19-Jun-4 Klefisch, Cologne #281/R
£265 $482 €400 Nautical equipment (17x24cm-7x9in) ink. 19-Jun-4 Klefisch, Cologne #282/R
£700 $1169 €1022 Festival flags with Mount Fuji in background (41x55cm-16x22in) s. ink col gold silk. 12-Nov-3 Christie's, London #57/R
£900 $1503 €1314 Frog (16x14cm-6x6in) s. lacquer. 12-Nov-3 Christie's, London #56/R
£1370 $2329 €2000 Cat with flowerpot (108x31cm-43x12in) s. seal Indian ink seal after Maruyama Kyo. 8-Nov-3 Dr Fritz Nagel, Stuttgart #1864/R est:1800

ZETSCHE, Eduard (1844-1927) Austrian
£6711 $12013 €10000 Old city on the Main (30x40cm-12x16in) s. bears d.1902 canvas on board exhib. 25-May-4 Dorotheum, Vienna #129/R est:6000-8000
Works on paper
£284 $460 €400 Village with castle ruins (10x16cm-4x6in) s.d.1897 W/C Indian ink. 23-May-3 Paul Kieffer, Pforzhiem #5810
£331 $603 €500 View of lake (28x30cm-11x12in) s.d.1902 W/C. 18-Jun-4 Stadion, Trieste #24
£503 $926 €750 Wine barrel in courtyard (12x18cm-5x7in) s. W/C sketch. 26-Mar-4 Dorotheum, Vienna #296/R
£872 $1605 €1300 Steps in Durnstein (23x17cm-9x7in) s.i. W/C paper on board. 26-Mar-4 Dorotheum, Vienna #305/R
£1611 $2964 €2400 Kalkofen near Sattelbach (23x15cm-9x6in) s.i.d.94 verso W/C paper on board. 26-Mar-4 Dorotheum, Vienna #304/R est:1600-2000

ZETTERBERG, Nisse (1910-1986) Swedish
£350 $644 €525 Two Mandarins (20x25cm-8x10in) mono.d.21 april 1977 panel. 14-Jun-4 Lilla Bukowskis, Stockholm #526 (S.KR 4800)
£453 $770 €661 Captain's farm (82x101cm-32x40in) init.d.35. 5-Nov-3 AB Stockholms Auktionsverk #861/R (S.KR 6000)

ZETTERSTROM, Mimmi (1843-1885) Swedish
£1923 $3308 €2808 Woman with parasol on beach, Jersey (81x59cm-32x23in) s.i.d.1881. 3-Dec-3 AB Stockholms Auktionsverk #2259/R est:30000-40000 (S.KR 25000)

ZETTERWALL, Eva H (1941-) Swedish
£834 $1501 €1218 Model (97x72cm-38x28in) s. 26-Apr-4 Bukowskis, Stockholm #594/R (S.KR 11500)

ZETTLER, Max (20th C) German
£336 $617 €500 Landscape near Hindelang (11x18cm-4x7in) s. i. verso board. 24-Mar-4 Hugo Ruef, Munich #1158

£738 $1358 €1100 Perlach market near Munich (18x10cm-7x4in) s. i. verso board. 24-Mar-4 Hugo Ruef, Munich #1159

ZEUTHEN, C O (1812-1890) Danish

£461 $783 €673 Church interior (55x42cm-22x17in) s.d.1844. 10-Nov-3 Rasmussen, Vejle #506/R (D.KR 5000)

ZEUTHEN, Christian Olavius (1812-1890) Danish

Works on paper

£306 $550 €447 Interior in the house of Lord Chamberlan O'Neill, Strandaede, Copenhagen (22x32cm-9x13in) s.d.1844 W/C pencil. 21-Jan-4 Sotheby's, New York #244/R

ZEUTHEN, Ernst (1880-1938) Danish

£451 $844 €658 Two fishing boats on green sea (79x102cm-31x40in) s.d.1936 exhib. 25-Feb-4 Museumsbygningen, Copenhagen #24 (D.KR 5000)
£587 $1079 €857 Mountain landscape from Lifjeldet, Norway 1930 (91x112cm-36x44in) s. double-sided lit. 29-Mar-4 Rasmussen, Copenhagen #491/R (D.KR 6500)
£677 $1245 €988 Field workers by the sea (66x78cm-26x31in) s. 29-Mar-4 Rasmussen, Copenhagen #572/R (D.KR 7500)
£724 $1296 €1057 Two fishing boats (79x102cm-31x40in) s.d.1936 exhib. 10-May-4 Rasmussen, Vejle #694/R (D.KR 8000)
£903 $1661 €1318 Still life of flowers (65x75cm-26x30in) s.d.1929. 29-Mar-4 Rasmussen, Copenhagen #566/R (D.KR 10000)
£1262 $2335 €1843 Vessel on fire off the coast (93x109cm-37x43in) s.d.1925. 15-Mar-4 Rasmussen, Vejle #670/R est:15000-20000 (D.KR 14000)
£1512 $2707 €2208 Sailing boats in evening glow (90x121cm-35x48in) s.d.1936 prov. 12-Jan-4 Rasmussen, Vejle #561/R est:6000 (D.KR 16000)

ZEVENBERGHEN, Georges van (1877-1968) Belgian

£263 $484 €400 Souvenir d'Espagne (40x32cm-16x13in) s.i.d.1918 verso. 22-Jun-4 Palais de Beaux Arts, Brussels #326

ZEYER, Erich (1903-1960) German

£267 $480 €400 White and brown horse in stable (60x70cm-24x28in) s. panel. 26-Apr-4 Rieber, Stuttgart #910/R
£289 $462 €410 Horse drawn cart (60x71cm-24x28in) s. 18-Sep-3 Rieber, Stuttgart #853
£350 $584 €500 Peasant ploughing (56x66cm-22x26in) s.d.46 board. 9-Oct-3 Michael Zeller, Lindau #810
£400 $720 €600 White and brown horse with peasant (70x60cm-28x24in) s. board. 26-Apr-4 Rieber, Stuttgart #911/R

ZEZZOS, Alessandro (1848-1914) Italian

£10000 $18200 €14600 Flirtation (83x54cm-33x21in) s. panel. 16-Jun-4 Bonhams, New Bond Street #78/R est:6000-8000
£20979 $35664 €30000 Little actress (66x46cm-26x18in) s.d.1884. 24-Nov-3 Dorotheum, Vienna #11/R est:4000-6000

Works on paper

£4027 $7208 €6000 Venetian lady at the window (67x54cm-26x21in) s. W/C. 27-May-4 Dorotheum, Vienna #65/R est:8000-10000

ZHABA, Alfons (1878-1942) Russian

£1831 $3039 €2600 Horses in snowstorm (36x70cm-14x28in) cyrillic d.1918. 16-Jun-3 Dorotheum, Vienna #144/R est:2600-2800

ZHANG BHU (?) Oriental

Works on paper

£7336 $12251 €10711 Blossoming flowers (68x138cm-27x54in) s.i. ink col scroll. 26-Oct-3 Christie's, Hong Kong #264/R est:100000-120000 (HK.D 95000)

ZHANG CHONG (16/17th C) Chinese

Works on paper

£4623 $8321 €6750 Lady with osmanthus flowers (80x52cm-31x20in) s.i.d.1641 ink col hanging scroll. 25-Apr-4 Christie's, Hong Kong #396/R est:40000-50000 (HK.D 65000)

ZHANG DAFENG (fl.1658-1673) Chinese

Works on paper

£2098 $3608 €3000 Old pine trees. Rocks and plants (35x26cm-14x10in) s. ink two lit. 5-Dec-3 Lempertz, Koln #258/R est:3000

ZHANG DAQIAN (1899-1983) Chinese

Works on paper

£3243 $5416 €4735 Cloudy mountain (20x52cm-8x20in) s.i. ink col folding fan. 26-Oct-3 Christie's, Hong Kong #325/R est:30000-40000 (HK.D 42000)
£3861 $6448 €5637 Hibiscus (79x32cm-31x13in) s.i.d.1948 ink col hanging scroll. 26-Oct-3 Christie's, Hong Kong #322/R est:25000-35000 (HK.D 50000)
£3861 $6448 €5637 Green landscape (18x49cm-7x19in) s.i.d.1947 ink col folding fan. 27-Oct-3 Sotheby's, Hong Kong #217/R est:50000-70000 (HK.D 50000)
£3912 $7041 €5712 Prunus (45x60cm-18x24in) s.i.d.1969 ink colscroll. 25-Apr-4 Christie's, Hong Kong #89/R est:25000-30000 (HK.D 55000)
£4190 $7500 €6117 Scholar under an autumn tree (82x41cm-32x16in) s.i.d.1948 ink hanging scroll. 10-May-4 Bonhams & Butterfields, San Francisco #4405/R est:7000-9000
£4247 $7093 €6201 Mushroom (52x40cm-20x16in) s.i.d.1965 ink cardboard prov. 27-Oct-3 Sotheby's, Hong Kong #219/R est:40000-50000 (HK.D 55000)
£4247 $7093 €6201 Wild mushroom (45x38cm-18x15in) s. i.verso ink col cardboard prov. 27-Oct-3 Sotheby's, Hong Kong #220/R est:40000-50000 (HK.D 55000)
£4633 $7737 €6764 Branch of plum blossoms (45x61cm-18x24in) s.i.d.1969 ink col cardboard. 27-Oct-3 Sotheby's, Hong Kong #227/R est:60000-80000 (HK.D 60000)
£4706 $8000 €6871 Boating to a shoreline retreat (99x76cm-39x30in) s.d.1959 ink monochrome board. 4-Nov-3 Bonhams & Butterfields, San Francisco #3457/R est:3000-5000
£5334 $9602 €7788 Self portrait (21x31cm-8x12in) i. ink. 26-Apr-4 Sotheby's, Hong Kong #649/R est:40000-60000 (HK.D 75000)
£5792 $9672 €8456 Persimmons (44x59cm-17x23in) s. ink col scroll. 26-Oct-3 Christie's, Hong Kong #227/R est:40000-60000 (HK.D 75000)
£5792 $9672 €8456 Rock and plum blossoms (90x40cm-35x16in) s.i.d.1976 ink col hanging scroll. 26-Oct-3 Christie's, Hong Kong #323/R est:30000-40000 (HK.D 75000)
£5792 $9672 €8456 Fisherman (25x43cm-10x17in) s.i.d.1966 ink prov. 27-Oct-3 Sotheby's, Hong Kong #232/R est:40000-60000 (HK.D 75000)
£7722 $12896 €11274 Self portrait (52x40cm-20x16in) s.i. ink scroll lit. 26-Oct-3 Christie's, Hong Kong #225/R est:40000-60000 (HK.D 100000)
£7722 $12896 €11274 Flowers (24x27cm-9x11in) s.i.d.1965 ink col scrolls set of two. 26-Oct-3 Christie's, Hong Kong #320a/R est:25000-35000 (HK.D 100000)
£7722 $12896 €11274 Chestnut (36x67cm-14x26in) s.d.1969 ink col prov. 27-Oct-3 Sotheby's, Hong Kong #229/R est:100000-150000 (HK.D 100000)
£8494 $14185 €12401 Landscape (37x45cm-15x18in) s.i.d.1964 ink col paperboard. 26-Oct-3 Christie's, Hong Kong #228/R est:50000-70000 (HK.D 110000)
£9246 $16643 €13499 Peony (126x66cm-50x26in) s.i. ink col hanging scroll. 25-Apr-4 Christie's, Hong Kong #17/R est:25000-30000 (HK.D 130000)
£9246 $16643 €13499 Scholar (105x38cm-41x15in) s.i.d.1933 ink col hanging scroll. 25-Apr-4 Christie's, Hong Kong #87/R est:80000-100000 (HK.D 130000)
£9412 $16000 €13742 Mountain trail and waterfall (130x114cm-51x45in) s.d.1959 ink col silk board. 4-Nov-3 Bonhams & Butterfields, San Francisco #3456/R est:4000-6000
£10669 $19203 €15577 Cherries and bamboo shoots (42x30cm-17x12in) s. ink col lit. 26-Apr-4 Sotheby's, Hong Kong #585/R est:80000-120000 (HK.D 150000)
£10811 $18054 €15784 Fish pond (40x89cm-16x35in) s.i.d.1977 ink col scroll. 26-Oct-3 Christie's, Hong Kong #224/R est:80000-100000 (HK.D 140000)
£10811 $18054 €15784 Pink lotus (46x53cm-18x21in) s.i.d.1973 ink col cardboard. 27-Oct-3 Sotheby's, Hong Kong #226/R est:70000-90000 (HK.D 140000)
£11583 $19344 €16911 Mount Pingfeng (107x60cm-42x24in) s.i.d.1947 ink col scroll. 26-Oct-3 Christie's, Hong Kong #327/R est:150000-180000 (HK.D 150000)
£12355 $20633 €18038 Bird on a branch (97x56cm-38x22in) s.i.d.1966 ink col hanging scroll prov. 27-Oct-3 Sotheby's, Hong Kong #224/R est:150000-200000 (HK.D 160000)
£13127 $21923 €19165 Lotus (48x99cm-19x39in) s.i.d.1980 ink col scroll. 26-Oct-3 Christie's, Hong Kong #223/R est:120000-150000 (HK.D 170000)
£13514 $24324 €19730 Spring haze in Sichuan (18x49cm-7x19in) s.i.d.1948 ink col fan. 26-Apr-4 Sotheby's, Hong Kong #670/R est:50000-70000 (HK.D 190000)
£13900 $23212 €20294 Plum blossoms (69x134cm-27x53in) s.i. ink col scroll. 26-Oct-3 Christie's, Hong Kong #222/R est:180000-200000 (HK.D 180000)
£13900 $23212 €20294 Landscape in the splashed ink style (60x45cm-24x18in) s.i. ink col paperboard. 26-Oct-3 Christie's, Hong Kong #229/R est:200000-250000 (HK.D 180000)
£14225 $25605 €20769 Lady beside lotus pond (116x49cm-46x19in) s.i. ink col scroll. 25-Apr-4 Christie's, Hong Kong #88/R est:60000-80000 (HK.D 200000)
£14225 $25605 €20769 Vegetables (89x33cm-35x13in) s.i.d.1950 ink col prov.exhib. 26-Apr-4 Sotheby's, Hong Kong #615/R est:120000-150000 (HK.D 200000)
£14225 $25605 €20769 Landscape (40x28cm-16x11in) s. ink pair prov. 26-Apr-4 Sotheby's, Hong Kong #650/R est:50000-70000 (HK.D 200000)
£15647 $28165 €22845 Scholar searching for flowers (76x41cm-30x16in) s.i.d.1966 ink scroll exhib.lit. 25-Apr-4 Christie's, Hong Kong #37/R est:150000-200000 (HK.D 220000)
£16988 $28371 €24802 Lady from the Southern Kingdom (95x43cm-37x17in) s.i.d.1944 ink col hanging scroll. 26-Oct-3 Christie's, Hong Kong #324/R est:150000-200000 (HK.D 220000)
£17070 $30725 €24922 Running stream in cave longmen (37x115cm-15x45in) s.i.d.1973 ink col scroll. 25-Apr-4 Christie's, Hong Kong #93/R est:250000-300000 (HK.D 240000)
£17070 $30725 €24922 Landscape (99x39cm-39x15in) s.i.d.1982 ink col hanging scroll lit. 26-Apr-4 Sotheby's, Hong Kong #669/R est:160000-200000 (HK.D 240000)
£17808 $30274 €26000 Landscape in blue and green (43x32cm-17x13in) s.d.1975 Indian ink col hanging scroll. 7-Nov-3 Dr Fritz Nagel, Stuttgart #946/R est:3800
£19915 $35846 €29076 Peony and butterfly (86x44cm-34x17in) s.i.d.1947 ink col hanging scroll. 26-Apr-4 Sotheby's, Hong Kong #616/R est:250000-350000 (HK.D 280000)
£21337 $38407 €31152 Seclusion (96x50cm-38x20in) s.i.d.1967 ink col hanging scroll exhib.lit. 26-Apr-4 Sotheby's, Hong Kong #666/R est:300000-500000 (HK.D 300000)
£21622 $36108 €31568 Diamond mountain (171x81cm-67x32in) s.i.d.1932 ink col hanging scroll. 26-Oct-3 Christie's, Hong Kong #221/R est:80000-100000 (HK.D 280000)
£21622 $36108 €31568 Lotus (69x135cm-27x53in) s.i.d.1967 ink scroll. 26-Oct-3 Christie's, Hong Kong #226/R est:220000-260000 (HK.D 280000)
£22760 $40967 €33230 Peony (62x96cm-24x38in) s.i. ink col scroll lit. 25-Apr-4 Christie's, Hong Kong #115/R est:200000-250000 (HK.D 320000)
£23166 $38687 €33822 Fragrance of lotus (48x108cm-19x43in) s.i.d.1980 ink col scroll. 26-Oct-3 Christie's, Hong Kong #326/R est:80000-120000 (HK.D 300000)
£23166 $38687 €33822 Dewy lotus (41x32cm-16x13in) s.i. ink col cardboard. 27-Oct-3 Sotheby's, Hong Kong #237/R est:150000-250000 (HK.D 300000)
£24710 $41266 €36077 On the mountain top (90x45cm-35x18in) s.i.d.1982 ink col scroll lit. 26-Oct-3 Christie's, Hong Kong #220/R est:200000-250000 (HK.D 320000)
£24710 $41266 €36077 Sailing (94x61cm-37x24in) s.d.1967 splashed ink col hanging scroll prov. 27-Oct-3 Sotheby's, Hong Kong #221/R est:180000-250000 (HK.D 320000)
£24893 $44808 €36344 Peach blossoms (16x94cm-6x37in) s.i. one d.1934 one d.1932 ink col handscroll pair. 25-Apr-4 Christie's, Hong Kong #28/R est:400000-600000 (HK.D 350000)
£24893 $44808 €36344 Greenslopes and winding torrents (118x65cm-46x26in) s.i.d.1960 ink col hanging scroll exhib.lit. 25-Apr-4 Christie's, Hong Kong #35/R est:400000-600000 (HK.D 350000)
£24893 $44808 €36344 Ancient house in the mountain (60x45cm-24x18in) s.i.d.1965 i.verso ink col scroll gold paper exhib.lit. 25-Apr-4 Christie's, Hong Kong #42/R est:400000-600000 (HK.D 350000)
£27027 $48649 €39459 Plantin leaves and cherry (135x68cm-53x27in) s.i.d.1963 ink col hanging scroll exhib.lit. 25-Apr-4 Christie's, Hong Kong #36/R est:250000-350000 (HK.D 380000)

£28450 $51209 €41537 White lotus (134x67cm-53x26in) s.i.d.1968 ink col hanging scroll wooden box. 25-Apr-4 Christie's, Hong Kong #29/R est:400000-500000 (HK.D 400000)
£28450 $51209 €41537 Flowers of prosperity (89x45cm-35x18in) s.i.d.1982 ink col scroll lit. 25-Apr-4 Christie's, Hong Kong #30/R est:450000-550000 (HK.D 400000)
£32006 $57610 €46729 Running stream across the mountain (93x42cm-37x17in) s.i. ink col scroll exhib.lit. 25-Apr-4 Christie's, Hong Kong #38/R est:500000-700000 (HK.D 450000)
£38610 $64479 €56371 Various subjects (27x36cm-11x14in) s. one d.1959 three d.1975 one d.1976 ink col 13 leaves album. 27-Oct-3 Sotheby's, Hong Kong #342/R est:400000-600000 (HK.D 500000)
£42674 $76814 €62304 Scent of lotus (135x67cm-53x26in) s.i.d.1963 ink col prov. 26-Apr-4 Sotheby's, Hong Kong #651/R est:400000-600000 (HK.D 600000)
£46230 $83215 €67496 Herding (76x49cm-30x19in) s.i.d.1946 ink col scroll. 25-Apr-4 Christie's, Hong Kong #116/R est:700000-900000 (HK.D 650000)
£50193 $83822 €73282 Lotus in the breeze (193x92cm-76x36in) s.i.d.1962 ink col hanging scroll. 27-Oct-3 Sotheby's, Hong Kong #225/R est:650000-800000 (HK.D 650000)
£56899 $102418 €83073 Ascending the mountain (183x94cm-72x37in) s.i.d.1963 ink col scroll exhib.lit. 25-Apr-4 Christie's, Hong Kong #40/R est:900000-1000000 (HK.D 800000)
£64011 $115220 €93456 Landscape in splash colour (62x97cm-24x38in) s.i.d.1966 ink col scroll. 25-Apr-4 Christie's, Hong Kong #18/R est:450000-550000 (HK.D 900000)
£64011 $115220 €93456 Bodhisattva (185x109cm-73x43in) i. ink col hanging scroll. 25-Apr-4 Christie's, Hong Kong #31/R est:1000000-1500000 (HK.D 900000)
£64011 $115220 €93456 Vimalakirti (185x109cm-73x43in) i. ink col hanging scroll. 25-Apr-4 Christie's, Hong Kong #32/R est:1000000-1500000 (HK.D 900000)
£71124 $128023 €103841 Guanyin (115x60cm-45x24in) s.i. ink col scroll. 25-Apr-4 Christie's, Hong Kong #90/R est:600000-800000 (HK.D 1000000)
£77220 $128958 €112741 Lost in thought (42x36cm-17x14in) s.i.d.1953 ink col cardboard. 27-Oct-3 Sotheby's, Hong Kong #236/R est:350000-450000 (HK.D 1000000)
£92461 $166430 €134993 Red lotus (137x68cm-54x27in) s.i.d.1942 ink col hanging scroll lit. 25-Apr-4 Christie's, Hong Kong #117/R est:500000-600000 (HK.D 1300000)
£92461 $166430 €134993 Lady of the Tang Dynasty (81x45cm-32x18in) s.i.d.1951 ink col lit. 26-Apr-4 Sotheby's, Hong Kong #662/R est:800000-1200000 (HK.D 1300000)
£111969 $186988 €163475 Lakeshore (53x106cm-21x42in) artist seal splashed ink col panel exec.c.1972 prov. 27-Oct-3 Sotheby's, Hong Kong #228/R est:500000-700000 (HK.D 1450000)
£163585 $294452 €238834 Composing poetry in a garden (95x51cm-37x20in) s.i.d.1953 ink col hanging scroll prov.exhib.lit. 26-Apr-4 Sotheby's, Hong Kong #588/R est:800000-1200000 (HK.D 2300000)
£170697 $307255 €249218 Playing the zither under cloudy trees (92x61cm-36x24in) s.i.d.1953 ink col scroll exhib.lit. 25-Apr-4 Christie's, Hong Kong #39/R est:2500000-3500000 (HK.D 2400000)
£227596 $409673 €332290 Viewing the waterfall (134x68cm-53x27in) s.i.d.1963 ink col scroll exhib.lit. 25-Apr-4 Christie's, Hong Kong #41/R est:3500000-4500000 (HK.D 3200000)
£248933 $448080 €363442 Self portrait with Saint Bernard (179x96cm-70x38in) i. ink col hanging scroll exhib.lit. 25-Apr-4 Christie's, Hong Kong #33/R est:2000000-3000000 (HK.D 3500000)
£270270 $486486 €394594 Blue and green landscape (58x111cm-23x44in) s.i.d.1981 ink col. 26-Apr-4 Sotheby's, Hong Kong #647/R est:2500000-3500000 (HK.D 3800000)

ZHANG DAQIAN and PU RU (20th C) Chinese

Works on paper
£4633 $7737 €6764 Boating (20x50cm-8x20in) s.i.d.1939 ink col folding fan. 27-Oct-3 Sotheby's, Hong Kong #239/R est:45000-60000 (HK.D 60000)

ZHANG DAZHUANG (1900-1980) Chinese

Works on paper
£2317 $3869 €3383 Cat and flower (127x58cm-50x23in) artist seal ink col hanging scroll. 27-Oct-3 Sotheby's, Hong Kong #310/R est:30000-50000 (HK.D 30000)

ZHANG DONGFENG (1958-) Chinese

£1307 $2366 €1908 Rocky mountain (50x60cm-20x24in) s. 3-Apr-4 Glerum, Singapore #80/R est:4000-5000 (S.D 4000)

ZHANG HONG TU (1943-) Chinese

£6178 $10317 €9020 Shen Zhou - Monet no.4 (244x66cm-96x26in) s. painted 1999 lit. 26-Oct-3 Christie's, Hong Kong #101/R est:100000-200000 (HK.D 80000)
£28450 $51209 €41537 Guo Xi's scroll of early spring, van Gogh (244x173cm-96x68in) s.d.1998 exhib.lit. 25-Apr-4 Christie's, Hong Kong #732/R est:150000-250000 (HK.D 400000)

ZHANG HUAN (1965-) Chinese

Photographs
£8982 $15000 €13114 To add one meter to an unknown mountain (103x154cm-41x61in) s.i.num.9/5 d.1995 verso cibachrome print prov. 12-Nov-3 Christie's, Rockefeller NY #555/R est:18000-22000

ZHANG JISU (c.1600-1676) Chinese

Works on paper
£37066 $61900 €54116 Landscape of Wangchuan (28x344cm-11x135in) i. ink col prov. 26-Oct-3 Christie's, Hong Kong #443/R est:150000-250000 (HK.D 480000)

ZHANG KUNYI (1895-1969) Chinese

Works on paper
£2703 $4514 €3946 Orchid (68x42cm-27x17in) s. ink col hanging scroll exhib. 27-Oct-3 Sotheby's, Hong Kong #257/R est:35000-50000 (HK.D 35000)
£5405 $9027 €7891 Ducks (134x57cm-53x22in) s.d.1939 ink col hanging scroll exhib. 27-Oct-3 Sotheby's, Hong Kong #256/R est:70000-90000 (HK.D 70000)

ZHANG RENZHI (1935-) Chinese

Works on paper
£372 $654 €550 Autumn in the mountains near Peking (69x66cm-27x26in) s.i.d.1977 Indian in col hanging scroll. 21-May-4 Dr Fritz Nagel, Stuttgart #1103/R

ZHANG RUITU (1576-1641) Chinese

Works on paper
£3475 $5803 €5074 Couple in running script calligraphy (108x27cm-43x11in) s. ink pair. 26-Oct-3 Christie's, Hong Kong #440/R (HK.D 45000)

ZHANG SHANZI (1882-1940) Chinese

Works on paper
£1200 $2208 €1752 Tigers (87x44cm-34x17in) s. ink hanging scroll. 8-Jun-4 Bonhams, New Bond Street #52 est:800-1200
£4979 $8962 €7269 Fruits and flowers (29x143cm-11x56in) s.i.d.1936 ink col. 26-Apr-4 Sotheby's, Hong Kong #652/R est:30000-50000 (HK.D 70000)
£10039 $16764 €14657 Tigers (161x79cm-63x31in) s.i.d.1930 ink col two panelled screen. 26-Oct-3 Christie's, Hong Kong #281/R est:100000-150000 (HK.D 130000)
£15647 $28165 €22845 Outing on horseback (120x44cm-47x17in) s.d.1933 ink col hanging scroll. 26-Apr-4 Sotheby's, Hong Kong #553/R est:40000-60000 (HK.D 220000)

ZHANG SHIYUAN (1898-1959) Chinese

Works on paper
£6757 $12162 €9865 Distant view of Wangyun studio (35x141cm-14x56in) s.i.d.1952 ink col handscroll. 26-Apr-4 Sotheby's, Hong Kong #674/R est:40000-60000 (HK.D 95000)

ZHANG WEN XIN (1926-) Chinese

£1198 $2000 €1749 Waiting (124x56cm-49x22in) s.d. 11-Oct-3 Nadeau, Windsor #31/R est:7500-10000

ZHANG XIAO GANG (1958-) Chinese

£12091 $21764 €17653 Recall from the past (71x54cm-28x21in) s.d.1989 oil paperboard. 25-Apr-4 Christie's, Hong Kong #768/R est:35000-50000 (HK.D 170000)
£17070 $30725 €24922 Boy. Two sisters. A family (130x110cm-51x43in) s. with two lithograph prints. 25-Apr-4 Christie's, Hong Kong #734/R est:150000-250000 (HK.D 240000)

ZHAO BO (1974-) Chinese

£980 $1775 €1431 The night (150x150cm-59x59in) s.d.2002 i.d.2002 verso. 3-Apr-4 Glerum, Singapore #62/R est:4000-6000 (S.D 3000)

ZHAO CHENG (1581-?) Chinese

Works on paper
£7824 $14083 €11423 Landscape (55x30cm-22x12in) s.i.d.1656 ink col gold hanging scroll silk after Zhao Bo Qu. 25-Apr-4 Christie's, Hong Kong #327/R est:60000-80000 (HK.D 110000)

ZHAO CHUNXIANG (1912-1991) Chinese

£3556 $6401 €5192 Tropical fishes (61x39cm-24x15in) acrylic ink painted c.1980 lit. 25-Apr-4 Christie's, Hong Kong #753/R est:35000-45000 (HK.D 50000)

ZHAO MENGFU (style) (1254-1322) Chinese

Works on paper
£8494 $14185 €12401 Scholar under pine tree (145x95cm-57x37in) s. ink col on silk. 26-Oct-3 Christie's, Hong Kong #439/R (HK.D 110000)

ZHAO SHAOANG (1905-1998) Chinese

Works on paper
£1699 $2837 €2481 Bird on a prunus tree (105x37cm-41x15in) s.i.d.1956 ink col scroll. 26-Oct-3 Christie's, Hong Kong #352/R est:25000-30000 (HK.D 22000)
£2008 $3353 €2932 Bamboo and cicada (91x29cm-36x11in) s.i.d.1945 ink col hanging scroll. 26-Oct-3 Christie's, Hong Kong #351/R est:30000-40000 (HK.D 26000)
£2276 $4097 €3323 Prunus (86x40cm-34x16in) s.i.d.1984 ink scroll. 25-Apr-4 Christie's, Hong Kong #62/R est:30000-40000 (HK.D 32000)
£2471 $4127 €3608 Flowers and insects (29x36cm-11x14in) s.i. one d.1946 one d.1939 ink col leaves 2. 26-Oct-3 Christie's, Hong Kong #354/R est:40000-60000 (HK.D 32000)
£2845 $5121 €4154 Flowers and mantis (128x41cm-50x16in) s.i. ink col scroll. 25-Apr-4 Christie's, Hong Kong #56/R est:40000-60000 (HK.D 40000)
£3556 $6401 €5192 Mantis and autumn leaves (69x40cm-27x16in) s.d.1957 ink col hanging scroll. 26-Apr-4 Sotheby's, Hong Kong #586/R est:40000-60000 (HK.D 50000)
£4267 $7681 €6230 Willow and cicada (86x39cm-34x15in) s.i.d.1948 ink col hanging scroll. 25-Apr-4 Christie's, Hong Kong #55/R est:50000-60000 (HK.D 60000)
£4633 $7737 €6764 Brood (106x39cm-42x15in) s.i.d.1944 ink col hanging scroll. 27-Oct-3 Sotheby's, Hong Kong #260/R est:60000-80000 (HK.D 60000)
£4979 $8962 €7269 Peach blossom and bird (55x84cm-22x33in) s.i.d.1946 ink col scroll. 25-Apr-4 Christie's, Hong Kong #59/R est:50000-70000 (HK.D 70000)
£5019 $8382 €7328 Flowers and bird (29x104cm-11x41in) s.d.1950 ink col scroll. 26-Oct-3 Christie's, Hong Kong #207/R est:40000-90000 (HK.D 65000)

£5405 $9514 €8000 Birds and insects (34cm-13in circular) s.i.d. Indian ink col pair hanging scrolls. 21-May-4 Dr Fritz Nagel, Stuttgart #1128/R est:3800
£8494 $14185 €12401 Fishing in the autumn (52x90cm-20x35in) s.i.d.1959 ink col scroll. 26-Oct-3 Christie's, Hong Kong #355/R est:80000-100000 (HK.D 110000)
£8535 $15363 €12461 Winter night (105x61cm-41x24in) s.i.d.1953 ink col hanging scroll. 26-Apr-4 Sotheby's, Hong Kong #562/R est:120000-160000 (HK.D 120000)
£10039 $16764 €14657 Birds on a willow tree (98x37cm-39x15in) s.i.d.1939 ink col hanging scroll. 26-Oct-3 Christie's, Hong Kong #206/R est:80000-100000 (HK.D 130000)
£15647 $28165 €22845 Blossoming flowers and the singing birds (60x106cm-24x42in) s. ink col scroll exhib. 25-Apr-4 Christie's, Hong Kong #57/R est:120000-150000 (HK.D 220000)
£16988 $28371 €24802 Mount Emei (140x47cm-55x19in) s.i.d.1944 ink col hanging scroll. 27-Oct-3 Sotheby's, Hong Kong #261/R est:100000-150000 (HK.D 220000)

ZHAO WANGYUN (1906-1977) Chinese
Works on paper
£685 $1164 €1000 Mountain landscape with girl and goats (78x40cm-31x16in) s. seal Indian ink col hanging scroll. 7-Nov-3 Dr Fritz Nagel, Stuttgart #971/R

ZHAO YONG (1289-c.1363) Chinese
Works on paper
£23166 $38687 €33822 Thoughts by the river (101x54cm-40x21in) s. ink col lit. 26-Oct-3 Christie's, Hong Kong #499/R (HK.D 300000)

ZHAO ZHENCHUAN (20th C) Chinese
Works on paper
£342 $582 €500 Village in the mountains (45x35cm-18x14in) s.d.1978 seal hanging scroll. 7-Nov-3 Dr Fritz Nagel, Stuttgart #966/R

ZHAO ZUO (fl.1603-1629) Chinese
Works on paper
£6757 $12162 €9865 Fishing (77x37cm-30x15in) s.i. ink col hanging scroll silk. 25-Apr-4 Christie's, Hong Kong #326/R est:50000-60000 (HK.D 95000)

ZHE SHENG HE (20th C) Chinese
£778 $1300 €1136 Wedding (178x112cm-70x44in) s.d. 11-Oct-3 Nadeau, Windsor #10/R

ZHENG BAICHONG (1945-) Chinese
Works on paper
£5405 $9027 €7891 Riding through the glacier (96x180cm-38x71in) s.i.d.2001 ink col scroll. 26-Oct-3 Christie's, Hong Kong #357/R est:70000-90000 (HK.D 70000)

ZHENG WUCHANG (1894-1952) Chinese
Works on paper
£1991 $3585 €2907 Various subjects (30x23cm-12x9in) s.i.d.1941 ink col scroll table screen painted with other artists. 25-Apr-4 Christie's, Hong Kong #148/R est:30000-50000 (HK.D 28000)
£46230 $83215 €67496 Landscape (129x63cm-51x25in) s.i.d.1947 ink col hanging scroll exhib.lit. 26-Apr-4 Sotheby's, Hong Kong #623/R est:80000-120000 (HK.D 650000)

ZHENG XIE (1693-1765) Chinese
Works on paper
£6950 $11606 €10147 Wine shop on mountain path (149x43cm-59x17in) i. ink. 26-Oct-3 Christie's, Hong Kong #461/R (HK.D 90000)
£46332 $77375 €67645 Bamboo and rock (177x45cm-70x18in) s.i. ink set of 4 lit. 26-Oct-3 Christie's, Hong Kong #463/R (HK.D 600000)

ZHENG ZHONG (16/17th C) Chinese
Works on paper
£4000 $6680 €5840 Lohan (248cm-98in) ink col on silk. 13-Nov-3 Sotheby's, Olympia #699/R est:5000-7000

ZHITNEV, Evgenii Petrovich (1809-1860) Russian
Works on paper
£4487 $7000 € Portrait of Anna Grigor'evna Engel'gardt. Portrait of Aleksandr Egorovich Engel'gardt (22x18cm-9x7in) one s. i. pencil W/C black ink two. 11-Apr-3 Christie's, Rockefeller NY #1/R est:7000-9000

ZHONG CHEN (1969-) Australian?
£7438 $12645 €10859 Flower drum IV 2002 (122x122cm-48x48in) s.d.2002 verso. 29-Oct-3 Lawson Menzies, Sydney #2/R est:7000-12000 (A.D 18000)
Works on paper
£3099 $5733 €4525 Romeo 2000 (83x83cm-33x33in) s.d.2000 verso synthetic polymer photoscan on canvas prov. 10-Mar-4 Deutscher-Menzies, Melbourne #157/R est:7000-9000 (A.D 7500)
£5785 $10702 €8446 Painting 2001 (127x167cm-50x66in) s.d.2001 verso synthetic polymer. 10-Mar-4 Deutscher-Menzies, Melbourne #8/R est:12000-15000 (A.D 14000)
£6612 $12231 €9654 Juliet III (117x117cm-46x46in) s.d.2000 digital scan synthetic polymer prov.exhib. 15-Mar-4 Sotheby's, Melbourne #6/R est:10000-15000 (A.D 16000)

ZHOU BICHU (1903-1995) Chinese
£15444 $25792 €22548 Landscape of Bali (100x76cm-39x30in) s.d.1953. 26-Oct-3 Christie's, Hong Kong #121/R est:220000-260000 (HK.D 200000)

ZHOU CHEN (c.1450-1535) Chinese
Works on paper
£5690 $10242 €8307 Winter landscape (81x9cm-32x4in) s.i. ink col hanging scroll prov. 25-Apr-4 Christie's, Hong Kong #330/R est:80000-120000 (HK.D 80000)

ZHOU JUN (1955-) Chinese
Works on paper
£1014 $1784 €1500 Bamboo and rocks (24x52cm-9x20in) s.i.d.1881 seal Indian ink col silk fan. 21-May-4 Dr Fritz Nagel, Stuttgart #1200/R est:150

ZHOU LIAN (19th C) Chinese
Works on paper
£350 $601 €500 Mountain landscape with huts and river (130x42cm-51x17in) s.i.d.1850 ink hanging scroll. 5-Dec-3 Lempertz, Koln #241

ZHOU SHUNCHANG (17th C) Chinese
Works on paper
£2489 $4481 €3634 Eagle (109x40cm-43x16in) s.d.1625 ink col hanging scroll. 25-Apr-4 Christie's, Hong Kong #328/R est:50000-60000 (HK.D 35000)

ZHOU SICONG (1939-) Chinese
Works on paper
£946 $1665 €1400 Yellow lotus blossoms (55x48cm-22x19in) s.d.1977 seal Indian ink col hanging scroll. 21-May-4 Dr Fritz Nagel, Stuttgart #1117/R
£1370 $2329 €2000 Girl with horse (68x45cm-27x18in) s.d.1977 Indian ink col hanging scroll. 7-Nov-3 Dr Fritz Nagel, Stuttgart #952/R est:350

ZHU DAOPING (1949-) Chinese
Works on paper
£2134 $3841 €3116 Landscapes (30x43cm-12x17in) s.i.d.1987 ink col leaves eight album. 25-Apr-4 Christie's, Hong Kong #98/R est:30000-40000 (HK.D 30000)
£2703 $4514 €3946 Boating in the spring (92x144cm-36x57in) s.d.2003 ink col scroll. 26-Oct-3 Christie's, Hong Kong #356/R est:30000-40000 (HK.D 35000)

ZHU DE-QUN (1922-) Chinese
£9246 $16643 €13499 Rhythm of colours (55x46cm-22x18in) s.d.84. 25-Apr-4 Christie's, Hong Kong #728/R est:60000-80000 (HK.D 130000)
£42471 $70927 €62008 Lumiere insinuante (195x129cm-77x51in) s.d.90. 26-Oct-3 Christie's, Hong Kong #131/R est:300000-400000 (HK.D 550000)
£61776 $103166 €90193 Amid thousand green spots, on red (97x130cm-38x51in) s. painted 1959 lit. 26-Oct-3 Christie's, Hong Kong #129/R est:450000-650000 (HK.D 800000)
£67568 $121622 €98649 Eclate nocturne (162x130cm-64x51in) s.d.94 exhib.lit. 25-Apr-4 Christie's, Hong Kong #727/R est:250000-350000 (HK.D 950000)
£199147 $358464 €290755 Transparence verticate (160x220cm-63x87in) s.d.98 exhib.lit. 25-Apr-4 Christie's, Hong Kong #726/R est:350000-450000 (HK.D 2800000)
Works on paper
£15647 $28165 €22845 No 15 (70x132cm-28x52in) s.d.98 Chinese ink. 25-Apr-4 Christie's, Hong Kong #756/R est:120000-160000 (HK.D 220000)

ZHU HENG (1916-) Chinese
Works on paper
£2008 $3353 €2932 Verdant mountains (130x48cm-51x19in) s.i. ink col hanging scroll. 26-Oct-3 Christie's, Hong Kong #359/R est:25000-35000 (HK.D 26000)

ZHU MEICHUN (1911-) Chinese
Works on paper
£2134 $3841 €3116 Lady (135x33cm-53x13in) s.i. ink col hanging scroll. 25-Apr-4 Christie's, Hong Kong #147/R est:18000-22000 (HK.D 30000)

ZHU QIZHAN (1892-1996) Chinese
Works on paper
£1014 $1784 €1500 Wine jug and chrysanthemums (68x44cm-27x17in) s.i.d.1984 seal Indian ink col. 21-May-4 Dr Fritz Nagel, Stuttgart #1133/R est:700
£3556 $6401 €5192 Chrysanthemum and rock (89x47cm-35x19in) s.i.d.1987 ink col scroll. 25-Apr-4 Christie's, Hong Kong #125/R est:50000-70000 (HK.D 50000)
£4979 $8962 €7269 Sunflowers (89x49cm-35x19in) s.i.d.1985 ink col prov. 26-Apr-4 Sotheby's, Hong Kong #587/R est:50000-70000 (HK.D 70000)
£12802 $23044 €18691 Summer landscape in rain (136x67cm-54x26in) s.i.d.1988 ink col scroll. 25-Apr-4 Christie's, Hong Kong #127/R est:180000-220000 (HK.D 180000)

ZHU SHENG (1618-c.1690) Chinese
Works on paper
£9957 $17923 €14537 Bamboo and rock (178x82cm-70x32in) s. ink hanging scroll silk. 25-Apr-4 Christie's, Hong Kong #417/R est:50000-70000 (HK.D 140000)

ZHU YUANZHI (1906-1963) Chinese
£32432 $54162 €47351 Frost in Central Park (51x63cm-20x25in) s. 27-Oct-3 Sotheby's, Hong Kong #367/R est:350000-500000 (HK.D 420000)
£61776 $103166 €90193 Cowboy (28x39cm-11x15in) s. prov.exhib. 27-Oct-3 Sotheby's, Hong Kong #366/R est:450000-550000 (HK.D 800000)

ZHURAVLEV, Firs Sergeevich (1836-1901) Russian
£41892 $74986 €62000 In the governor's office (40x64cm-16x25in) s.d.1888 exhib. 8-May-4 Bukowskis, Helsinki #469/R est:13000-20000

ZIAO JINZHONG (1937-) Chinese
Works on paper
£304 $535 €450 Bamboo stalks (68x113cm-27x44in) seal Indian ink col. 21-May-4 Dr Fritz Nagel, Stuttgart #1219/R

ZIC, Zivko (1924-) American
£316 $500 €461 Floral still life (30x23cm-12x9in) s. board. 7-Sep-3 Treadway Gallery, Cincinnati #648/R

ZICHY, Count Mihaly von (1827-1906) Hungarian
£3952 $7153 €5770 Next day (25x20cm-10x8in) s. oil on wood. 16-Apr-4 Mu Terem Galeria, Budapest #89/R (H.F 1500000)
Works on paper
£2081 $3828 €3100 Three village musicians (64x48cm-25x19in) s.i.d.10 Juni 1874 Indian ink brush pencil. 26-Mar-4 Venator & Hansten, Koln #1259/R est:2100

ZICK, Gustav (1809-1886) German
£436 $803 €650 Deer by wood (40x31cm-16x12in) s.d.1860 i. verso panel lit. 25-Mar-4 Karlheinz Kaupp, Staufen #2808/R

ZICK, Januarius (1730-1797) German
£3819 $6226 €5500 The Holy Family (64x52cm-25x20in) 25-Sep-3 Dr Fritz Nagel, Stuttgart #1270/R est:6500
£4895 $8322 €7000 Christ on the cross (43x24cm-17x9in) 20-Nov-3 Van Ham, Cologne #1443/R est:10000
£7047 $12967 €10500 La diseuse de bonne aventure (31x44cm-12x17in) s. panel. 24-Mar-4 Tajan, Paris #44/R est:4000-6000
£8333 $15000 €12166 Peasant loading firewood onto his mule (55x48cm-22x19in) panel oval. 23-Jan-4 Christie's, Rockefeller NY #150/R est:15000-20000
Miniatures
£1325 $2424 €2000 Portrait of old man (12x10cm-5x4in) s. tin. 7-Apr-4 Dorotheum, Salzburg #206/R est:2600-3000
Works on paper
£3378 $5946 €5000 Flight to Egypt (17x17cm-7x7in) s. pen brush wash htd white prov.lit.exhib. 22-May-4 Lempertz, Koln #1391/R est:6000

ZICK, Januarius (attrib) (1730-1797) German
£1200 $2172 €1800 Bearded prophet (21x15cm-8x6in) panel. 1-Apr-4 Van Ham, Cologne #1260/R est:2600
£2083 $3396 €3000 Ecce homo (69x48cm-27x19in) 25-Sep-3 Dr Fritz Nagel, Stuttgart #1271/R est:3500
£3356 $6175 €5000 Joseph et la femme de Putiphar. Suzanne et les vieillards. David et Sarah (59x73cm-23x29in) set of three. 24-Mar-4 Tajan, Paris #83 est:6000-8000
£11765 $20000 €17177 Satyr family (53x37cm-21x15in) 28-Nov-3 Zofingen, Switzerland #2495/R est:6000 (S.FR 26000)

ZICK, Johann (1702-1762) German
Works on paper
£805 $1482 €1200 Portrait study (32x28cm-13x11in) chl. 26-Mar-4 Ketterer, Hamburg #225/R

ZIEBLAND, Hermann (?) ?
£364 $604 €528 Nobleman with pipe and pewter tankard (63x37cm-25x15in) s.i. panel. 13-Jun-3 Zofingen, Switzerland #2549/R (S.FR 800)

ZIEBOLZ, Herbert (1903-1985) American?
£3667 $6563 €5500 Dancing figures (36x25cm-14x10in) s. i. verso panel. 13-May-4 Neumeister, Munich #806/R est:3000-3500

ZIEGELMUELLER, Martin (1935-) Swiss
£264 $449 €385 Seated female nude (52x39cm-20x15in) mono. panel. 5-Nov-3 Dobiaschofsky, Bern #3808 (S.FR 600)

ZIEGER, Hugo (1864-1932) German
£420 $722 €600 Small girl in a garden (45x30cm-18x12in) 5-Dec-3 Bolland & Marotz, Bremen #686/R
£638 $1173 €950 Else Baxmann aged 4 (64x47cm-25x19in) s. mixed media. 26-Mar-4 Bolland & Marotz, Bremen #613/R

ZIEGLER, Archibald (1903-) British
£400 $704 €584 View of the Seine, Paris (46x89cm-18x35in) s. board. 18-May-4 Bonhams, Knightsbridge #219/R

ZIEGLER, Eustace Paul (1881-1969) American
£5080 $9500 €7417 Raven flood totem (30x25cm-12x10in) s. canvasboard prov.exhib.lit. 24-Jul-4 Coeur d'Alene, Hayden #31/R est:8000-12000
£5080 $9500 €7417 Horse on a hill (25x20cm-10x8in) s. board prov. 24-Jul-4 Coeur d'Alene, Hayden #147/R est:6000-8000
£9091 $17000 €13273 King Island Eskimo (51x41cm-20x16in) s. canvasboard prov. 24-Jul-4 Coeur d'Alene, Hayden #231/R est:10000-20000
£13369 $25000 €19519 Pack train near Mt. McKinley (41x51cm-16x20in) s. canvasboard prov. 24-Jul-4 Coeur d'Alene, Hayden #230/R est:12000-20000
£22727 $42500 €33181 Three wise men (61x91cm-24x36in) s. prov. 24-Jul-4 Coeur d'Alene, Hayden #146/R est:30000-50000

ZIEGLER, F (19/20th C) ?
£2685 $5020 €4000 Montegriner returning home (85x130cm-33x51in) s. 24-Feb-4 Dorotheum, Vienna #52/R est:2000-2300

ZIEGLER, Frederick J (1886-?) ?
Sculpture
£1395 $2400 €2037 Centaur (56cm-22in) st.f.Valsuani i. green pat bronze. 2-Dec-3 Christie's, Rockefeller NY #71/R est:3000-5000

ZIEGLER, Henry Bryan (1793-1874) British
Works on paper
£246 $431 €350 Harvest (48x63cm-19x25in) s.d.1872 W/C. 17-Dec-3 Il Ponte, Milan #455

ZIEGLER, J (19th C) ?
£2800 $4956 €4088 English cemetery, Gamboa, Rio de Janeiro (36x48cm-14x19in) s.d.1824 board. 29-Apr-4 Christie's, Kensington #153/R est:2500-3500

ZIEGLER, L W (20th C) American
£540 $950 €788 Musical serenade (76x64cm-30x25in) mono. 22-May-4 Selkirks, St. Louis #686

ZIEGLER, Michael (1960-) Austrian
£567 $1043 €850 Still life with fruit (50x70cm-20x28in) s.d.89/90 verso acrylic. 9-Jun-4 Dorotheum, Salzburg #735/R

ZIEGLER, Nellie Evelyn (20th C) American
£867 $1500 €1266 Street in Rockport, Mass (63x76cm-25x30in) s. prov. 10-Dec-3 Bonhams & Butterfields, San Francisco #6037/R est:3000-5000

ZIEGLER, Rolf (1955-) Swiss
Works on paper
£346 $620 €505 Composition (88x68cm-35x27in) s.d. mixed media. 22-Mar-4 Philippe Schuler, Zurich #6067 (S.FR 800)

ZIEGLER, Theodor (1830-?) German
£709 $1121 €1000 Young woman wearing black dress (78x57cm-31x22in) s.d.74. 25-Jul-3 Altus, Berlin #569/R

ZIELASCO, Robert (1948-) Austrian
£350 $594 €500 Untitled (50x65cm-20x26in) s. canvas-collage. 27-Nov-3 Dorotheum, Linz #544/R
£667 $1200 €1000 Untitled (160x56cm-63x22in) s.d.91 mixed media collage. 21-Apr-4 Dorotheum, Vienna #331/R

ZIELER, Mogens (1905-1983) Danish
£1411 $2399 €2060 Interior scene with woman and cat on sofa (93x92cm-37x36in) s.d.48 panel. 29-Nov-3 Rasmussen, Havnen #4431/R est:8000-12000 (D.KR 15000)
£6769 $12455 €9883 With Chinese hat - the artist's wife and cat (135x85cm-53x33in) s.d.58 s.d.1958 stretcher. 29-Mar-4 Rasmussen, Copenhagen #15/R est:20000-25000 (D.KR 75000)

ZIELKE, Julius (1826-1907) German
Works on paper
£1584 $2692 €2313 Street in Rome (30x54cm-12x21in) s. W/C htd white. 19-Nov-3 Fischer, Luzern #2492/R est:4000-5000 (S.FR 3500)
£1584 $2692 €2313 Octavia's Hall in Rome - old fish market (30x54cm-12x21in) s. W/C htd white. 19-Nov-3 Fischer, Luzern #2493/R est:4000-5000 (S.FR 3500)

ZIEM, Felix (1821-1911) French

£521	$849	€750	La gondole et les voilieres (10x18cm-4x7in) s. i. verso board. 26-Sep-3 Bolland & Marotz, Bremen #632/R
£1133	$2051	€1700	Portrait presume de Madame Ziem (14x10cm-6x4in) indis.sig. studio st.verso peinture paper. 30-Mar-4 Rossini, Paris #332/R est:800-1500
£1500	$2760	€2190	Devant les jardins Francois (27x27cm-11x11in) s. panel prov.lit. 23-Mar-4 Bonhams, New Bond Street #100/R est:1000-1500
£1622	$3000	€2368	Coastal landscape with seated figure (33x66cm-13x26in) s. panel. 17-Jan-4 New Orleans Auction, New Orleans #502/R est:3500-5000
£1676	$3000	€2447	Scene of Bosphorus with St Sophia on the horizon (15x23cm-6x9in) s. panel prov. 20-Mar-4 Sloans & Kenyon, Bethesda #1184/R est:2000-4000
£1931	$3225	€2800	Embarcations de peche au rivage (13x28cm-5x11in) bears studio st. panel prov. 17-Nov-3 Tajan, Paris #69/R est:3000-5000
£2133	$3861	€3200	Rochers du Rove, pres Marseille (22x34cm-9x13in) s. cardboard on canvas painted c.1860 exhib.lit. 30-Mar-4 Rossini, Paris #331/R est:2000-3000
£2180	$3750	€3183	Fishing boats in the Bacino Venice (25x38cm-10x15in) s. panel. 3-Dec-3 Doyle, New York #93/R est:10000-15000
£2533	$4585	€3800	Poissonniere dans la halle de la croix (63x42cm-25x17in) s. lit. 30-Mar-4 Rossini, Paris #329/R est:4000-6000
£2667	$4827	€4000	Maison aux trois piliers, Turquie (33x27cm-13x11in) s. exhib.lit. 30-Mar-4 Rossini, Paris #321/R est:4000-7000
£3116	$5298	€4550	Gondole pres de rivage (21x16cm-8x6in) s. panel. 9-Nov-3 Eric Pillon, Calais #23/R
£3623	$5942	€5000	Venise, la lagune (28x39cm-11x15in) s. oil paper on canvas. 11-May-3 Osenat, Fontainebleau #157/R est:6000-7000
£3986	$6536	€5500	Entree en foret de Fontainebleau (42x60cm-17x24in) s. 11-May-3 Osenat, Fontainebleau #138 est:6000-7000
£4161	$7365	€6200	Villefranche (73x50cm-29x20in) s. panel. 27-Apr-4 Artcurial Briest, Paris #132/R est:4000-6000
£4299	$7179	€6277	The lagoon (26x34cm-10x13in) s. panel. 17-Nov-3 Waddingtons, Toronto #198/R est:3000-5000 (C.D 9500)
£4667	$8447	€7000	Le paon (42x31cm-17x12in) s. panel exhib.lit. 30-Mar-4 Rossini, Paris #322/R est:4000-6000
£4760	$8092	€6950	La Piazzetta inondee, Venise (32x45cm-13x18in) studio st.verso lit. 9-Nov-3 Eric Pillon, Calais #25/R
£4884	$8400	€7131	Environs de Venise (31x53cm-12x21in) s. paint board. 3-Dec-3 Naón & Cia, Buenos Aires #18/R
£5282	$9137	€7500	Lavandiere dans l'arriere Pays Nicois (49x35cm-19x14in) bears sig panel. 14-Dec-3 Eric Pillon, Calais #1a/R
£7143	$13000	€10429	View of Venice in sunset (61x50cm-24x20in) s. panel. 29-Jun-4 Sotheby's, New York #71/R est:10000-15000
£7183	$12427	€10200	Gondoles sur la lagune (36x66cm-14x26in) s. 14-Dec-3 Eric Pillon, Calais #1/R
£8000	$14480	€12000	Vue de Holland, les bords de la Meuse a Dordrecht (71x107cm-28x42in) s. lit. 30-Mar-4 Rossini, Paris #323/R est:12000-18000
£8099	$14011	€11500	Gondoles sur la lagune (45x55cm-18x22in) s. prov.lit. 15-Dec-3 Marc Kohn, Paris #81/R est:8000-10000
£8288	$13012	€12100	Gondole a Venise (43x64cm-17x25in) s. panel. 20-Apr-3 Deauville, France #76/R est:12000-15000
£9655	$16124	€14000	Gondoles sur la lagune (54x81cm-21x32in) s. panel lit. 17-Nov-3 Tajan, Paris #71/R est:15000-20000
£9667	$17497	€14500	Saint Marc, Venise (51x64cm-20x25in) st. panel painted c.1895 lit. 30-Mar-4 Rossini, Paris #320/R est:14000-18000
£9767	$16800	€14260	Venice (56x85cm-22x33in) s. paint. 3-Dec-3 Naón & Cia, Buenos Aires #22/R
£10000	$18000	€14600	La peche au large de Burano, Venice (53x85cm-21x33in) s. panel prov.lit. 22-Apr-4 Christie's, Rockefeller NY #226/R est:20000-30000
£10127	$16000	€14785	Venetian scene with fishermen (43x64cm-17x25in) s. 6-Sep-3 Brunk, Ashville #858
£10284	$17174	€14500	Le kiosque des eaux douces (74x93cm-29x37in) s. prov.lit. 19-Jun-3 Millon & Associes, Paris #128/R est:15000-20000
£11745	$20789	€17500	Kiosque des eaux douces (73x92cm-29x36in) s. prov.lit. 30-Apr-4 Tajan, Paris #104/R est:15000-20000
£14894	$24128	€21000	Bragoso et sandolo, langune a Venise (41x55cm-16x22in) s. panel lit. 23-May-3 Sotheby's, Paris #25/R est:12000-15000
£15141	$26496	€21500	Vue de Venise (44x71cm-17x28in) s. panel prov. 16-Dec-3 Claude Aguttes, Neuilly #87/R est:20000-25000
£16471	$28000	€24048	Gondolas on the lagoon, Venice (63x81cm-25x32in) s. prov.lit. 29-Oct-3 Christie's, Rockefeller NY #243/R est:30000-40000
£18751	$31313	€27000	Palais des Doges, Vue du Canal de la Grazzia (32x46cm-13x18in) s. panel lit. 21-Oct-3 Artcurial Briest, Paris #155/R est:12000-15000
£18792	$35141	€28000	Venice at sunset (70x109cm-28x43in) s. 28-Feb-4 Bolland & Marotz, Bremen #298/R est:22000
£19868	$36358	€30000	Grande voile a Venise (35x50cm-14x20in) s. panel. 7-Apr-4 Piasa, Paris #30/R est:15000-20000
£25157	$40000	€36729	Venetian view (83x114cm-33x45in) s. prov. 12-Sep-3 Skinner, Boston #313/R
£26389	$47500	€38528	Santa Maria della Salute at sunset (53x75cm-21x30in) s. panel. 23-Apr-4 Sotheby's, New York #101/R est:25000-35000
£37063	$63007	€53000	Vue de Venise (70x113cm-28x44in) s. 21-Nov-3 Lombrail & Teucquam, Paris #111 est:23000-30000
£50000	$87500	€71000	Vue du Grand Canal a Venise (74x107cm-29x42in) s. prov. 16-Dec-3 Claude Aguttes, Neuilly #86/R est:75000-80000

Works on paper

£294	$490	€420	Etude de bateaux et type Italien (22x30cm-9x12in) s. crayon. 29-Jun-3 Feletin, Province #134
£317	$548	€450	Personnages aux abords de fortifications a Naples (19x31cm-7x12in) s.i.d.18- 7 blk crayon. 10-Dec-3 Piasa, Paris #140
£544	$974	€800	Paysage (11x20cm-4x8in) s. W/C. 22-Mar-4 Digard, Paris #72/R
£933	$1689	€1400	La pourvoyeuse (18x12cm-7x5in) st. W/C exhib.lit. 30-Mar-4 Rossini, Paris #324/R
£1000	$1810	€1500	Fleurs (21x17cm-8x7in) st. W/C exec.c.1845-1846. 30-Mar-4 Rossini, Paris #326/R est:1500-2500
£1133	$2051	€1700	Gondole et voiliers au clair de lune (8x14cm-3x6in) st. W/C. 30-Mar-4 Rossini, Paris #325 est:300-500
£1329	$2219	€1900	Venise, bateau (8x15cm-3x6in) s. W/C. 29-Jun-3 Eric Pillon, Calais #8/R
£1644	$2795	€2400	Venise, bateau devant le jardin francais (8x15cm-3x6in) s. W/C. 9-Nov-3 Eric Pillon, Calais #6/R
£1645	$3026	€2500	Gondolier au large de Venise (25x34cm-10x13in) studio st. W/C. 23-Jun-4 Sotheby's, Paris #81/R est:2500-3500
£3200	$5856	€4672	Quay of a busy port at dawn (18x28cm-7x11in) s. black lead W/C prov.exhib. 6-Jul-4 Christie's, London #194/R est:4000-6000
£3750	$6713	€5475	Venice (26x36cm-10x14in) s. W/C. 13-May-4 Stuker, Bern #393/R est:12000-15000 (S.FR 8700)
£4636	$8437	€7000	La remontee des filets (31x48cm-12x19in) s.d.47 W/C. 18-Jun-4 Piasa, Paris #13/R est:6000-8000
£6122	$10959	€9000	Vue de la lagune a Martigues (16x30cm-6x12in) s. W/C gouache prov. 18-Mar-4 Christie's, Paris #175/R est:3000-5000

ZIEM, Felix (attrib) (1821-1911) French

£1875	$3000	€2738	Venetian water scene (36x66cm-14x26in) 19-Sep-3 Du Mouchelle, Detroit #2282/R est:5000-6000
£2838	$5166	€4143	On the water, Venice (15x24cm-6x9in) s. panel. 16-Jun-4 Fischer, Luzern #1109/R est:6500-7500 (S.FR 6500)

ZIEMSKI, Jan (1920-1988) Polish

£480	$869	€701	Two figures (48x48cm-19x19in) paper board. 4-Apr-4 Agra, Warsaw #75/R (P.Z 3400)
£480	$869	€701	Composition (53x48cm-21x19in) paper board painted 1950. 4-Apr-4 Agra, Warsaw #76/R (P.Z 3400)

Works on paper

£2381	$4095	€3476	Form II (103x62cm-41x24in) s.i.d.1959 verso mixed media. 4-Dec-3 Agra, Warsaw #31/R est:4000 (P.Z 16000)

ZIEMSKI, Rajmund (1930-) Polish

£1103	$1843	€1600	Landscape (99x80cm-39x31in) s.d.84 s.i.d.verso. 16-Nov-3 Agra, Warsaw #59/R est:1000

ZIER, Wolmer (1910-1990) Danish

£379	$607	€553	Breakers (68x95cm-27x37in) s. 22-Sep-3 Rasmussen, Vejle #702 (D.KR 4000)
£543	$972	€793	Breakers at Lokken (67x80cm-26x31in) s. 10-May-4 Rasmussen, Vejle #387/R (D.KR 6000)

ZIERCKE, Louis (1887-?) German

£341	$600	€498	Still life with chrysanthemums in an earthenware (91x66cm-36x26in) s.d.1923. 22-May-4 Harvey Clar, Oakland #2224

ZIERMANN, Carl (1850-1881) German

£1750	$3185	€2555	Umbrella salesman trying to entice the dog (64x53cm-25x21in) s. prov. 4-Feb-4 John Nicholson, Haslemere #156/R est:1500-2000

ZIESENIS, Johan Georg (1716-1776) Danish

£6199	$11407	€9235	La resurrection (74x66cm-29x26in) s.verso. 24-Mar-4 Tajan, Paris #75/R est:4000-6000

ZIESENIS, Johan Georg (attrib) (1716-1776) Danish

£2254	$3899	€3200	Portrait of a man (85x66cm-33x26in) 11-Dec-3 Dr Fritz Nagel, Stuttgart #482/R

ZIFFER, Sandor (1888-1962) Hungarian

£5973	$9914	€8721	Malomarok in Nagybanya (60x66cm-24x26in) s. 4-Oct-3 Kieselbach, Budapest #198/R (H.F 2200000)
£8958	$16214	€13079	Painter's garden (58x89cm-23x35in) s. 16-Apr-4 Mu Terem Galeria, Budapest #152/R (H.F 3400000)
£9230	$15322	€13476	Home of the artist with self portrait in the mirror (117x104cm-46x41in) s. 4-Oct-3 Kieselbach, Budapest #123/R (H.F 3400000)

ZIGAINA, Giuseppe (1924-) Italian

£4333	$7800	€6500	Peasant woman and hen (50x70cm-20x28in) s.d.56. 22-Apr-4 Finarte Semenzato, Rome #234/R est:2800-3400

Works on paper

£805	$1442	€1200	Starship (25x22cm-10x9in) s. gouache. 29-May-4 Farsetti, Prato #464/R
£2933	$5280	€4400	Mushrooms (50x70cm-20x28in) s.d.63 mixed media paper on canvas. 22-Apr-4 Finarte Semenzato, Rome #236/R est:2800-3400
£4200	$7518	€6300	Miners on strike (36x91cm-14x36in) s.d.49 chl paper on cardboard. 12-May-4 Stadion, Trieste #705/R est:2800-3800

ZIKARAS, Teisutis (1922-) Australian

Sculpture

£1721	$2770	€2513	Untitled (73cm-29in) s. bronze. 13-Oct-3 Joel, Victoria #327 est:3000-5000 (A.D 4250)

ZILLA, Vettore Zanetti (1866-1945) Italian

£1000	$1840	€1500	Mate's house in Sottomarina (49x70cm-19x28in) s.i. s.i.verso tempera card. 8-Jun-4 Sotheby's, Milan #56/R est:1500-2500

£3490 $6247 €5200 Glasses and mirror (57x103cm-22x41in) s.d.1927 board lit. 25-May-4 Finarte Semenzato, Milan #95/R est:5000-6000
£6040 $10812 €9000 Job (100x110cm-39x43in) s. painted 1932. 25-May-4 Finarte Semenzato, Milan #232/R est:8000-10000
£8725 $15617 €13000 Venetian coast (112x53cm-44x21in) s. s.i.d.1939 verso. 25-May-4 Finarte Semenzato, Milan #198/R est:10000-12000

ZILLE, Heinrich (1858-1929) German
Prints
£2000 $3660 €3000 Children singing (27x22cm-11x9in) s. lithograph. 5-Jun-4 Lempertz, Koln #1031/R est:2500
Works on paper
£268 $475 €400 Male nude (30x19cm-12x7in) st.sig. chl double-sided. 30-Apr-4 Dr Fritz Nagel, Stuttgart #522/R
£350 $601 €500 Man wearing hat (17x11cm-7x4in) chl. 4-Dec-3 Van Ham, Cologne #578/R
£420 $713 €600 Station manager (14x9cm-6x4in) chl. 29-Nov-3 Bassenge, Berlin #7054
£490 $832 €700 Woman seated at window (20x14cm-8x6in) chl. 29-Nov-3 Bassenge, Berlin #7057
£515 $912 €752 Study of a man with a melon (18x12cm-7x5in) chk col chk. 12-Jun-4 Falk & Falk, Zurich #1023/R (S.FR 1200)
£515 $912 €752 Cavalier with a lady (18x13cm-7x5in) chl prov. 12-Jun-4 Falk & Falk, Zurich #1024 (S.FR 1200)
£576 $944 €800 Berlin figures (10x17cm-4x7in) chl. 4-Jun-3 Ketterer, Hamburg #1013/R
£644 $1139 €940 Lady out for a stroll (18x10cm-7x4in) i. chl prov. 12-Jun-4 Falk & Falk, Zurich #1026 est:1200 (S.FR 1500)
£839 $1427 €1200 Berlin town hall tower (25x20cm-10x8in) col chk board. 29-Nov-3 Bassenge, Berlin #7050
£979 $1664 €1400 Maid doing errands (23x12cm-9x5in) chl. 29-Nov-3 Bassenge, Berlin #705/R
£1000 $1600 €1460 Man carrying flowers (16x10cm-6x4in) col crayon exec. c.1910. 16-Sep-3 Rosebery Fine Art, London #445/R est:1000-1500
£1000 $1790 €1500 Mother with baby and toddler (18x13cm-7x5in) chk. 15-May-4 Bassenge, Berlin #7216 est:1800
£1200 $2160 €1800 Young girl with hat (19x11cm-7x4in) st.sig. chl col chk. 26-Apr-4 Rieber, Stuttgart #4494/R
£1467 $2625 €2200 Girl wearing red dress and hat (17x8cm-7x3in) chk bodycol prov. 15-May-4 Bassenge, Berlin #7217/R est:1800
£1467 $2625 €2200 Bride-mobile (14x22cm-6x9in) Indian ink gouache. 15-May-4 Van Ham, Cologne #1053/R est:1800
£1467 $2699 €2200 Woman standing and facing left (14x6cm-6x2in) s. pen ink over pencil prov. 12-Jun-4 Villa Grisebach, Berlin #666/R est:700-900
£1467 $2699 €2200 Self portrait (17x12cm-7x5in) s.i.d.1919 pen ink. 12-Jun-4 Villa Grisebach, Berlin #667/R est:1400-1800
£1533 $2821 €2300 Fat Bertha (21x25cm-8x10in) mono. st.sig. chl chk. 10-Jun-4 Hauswedell & Nolte, Hamburg #731/R est:3000
£1538 $2615 €2200 Photo time in courtyard (31x21cm-12x8in) s. Indian ink chk. 29-Nov-3 Bassenge, Berlin #7060/R
£1667 $3067 €2500 Seduction (15x9cm-6x4in) s.d.1914 ink W/C pencil prov. 12-Jun-4 Villa Grisebach, Berlin #132/R est:2500-3500
£1818 $3091 €2600 Woman in cape (41x29cm-16x11in) chl. 29-Nov-3 Villa Grisebach, Berlin #695/R est:2000-3000
£2133 $3819 €3200 Berlin nanny leading two children by the hand (18x11cm-7x4in) mono. chk. 15-May-4 Bassenge, Berlin #7214/R est:1800
£3147 $5350 €4500 Self portrait at the easel (12x10cm-5x4in) Indian ink lit.exhib. 29-Nov-3 Villa Grisebach, Berlin #132/R est:4500-5500
£4000 $7320 €6000 Studies of children (29x39cm-11x15in) i. st.sig. verso col chk. 5-Jun-4 Lempertz, Koln #1029/R est:3000
£4667 $8587 €7000 Sweet burdens (29x24cm-11x9in) s.i.d.7/1926 pen W/C paper on card prov.lit. 12-Jun-4 Villa Grisebach, Berlin #129/R est:5000-7000
£5245 $8916 €7500 Meda Hippauf (26x25cm-10x10in) s. pen chk htd bodycol board. 29-Nov-3 Villa Grisebach, Berlin #136/R est:8000-10000
£5333 $9813 €8000 In a hurry (27x32cm-11x13in) s. col chk chl ink prov. 12-Jun-4 Villa Grisebach, Berlin #131/R est:10000-15000
£7692 $13077 €11000 Children with pram (28cm-11in) s. Indian ink w/C. 29-Nov-3 Villa Grisebach, Berlin #134/R est:7000-9000
£8000 $14720 €12000 Blow hard (26x22cm-10x9in) s. W/C ink col chk cardboard lit. 12-Jun-4 Villa Grisebach, Berlin #130/R est:12000-15000

ZILLEN, Johannes Wilhelm (1824-1870) Danish
£316 $591 €461 A goat (27x34cm-11x13in) init.d.25 aug 54. 25-Feb-4 Museumsbygningen, Copenhagen #205/R (D.KR 3500)
£451 $844 €658 Children playing (22x34cm-9x13in) mono. cardboard. 25-Feb-4 Kunsthallen, Copenhagen #492 (D.KR 5000)

ZILLER, Leopold (19th C) German
£1000 $1600 €1450 Venetian canal (24x35cm-9x14in) s. 18-Sep-3 Christie's, Kensington #83/R est:1200-1800
£1622 $3000 €2433 Ships before the Doge's Palace (53x81cm-21x32in) s. 17-Jul-4 Skinner, Boston #70/R est:3000-5000

ZILLER, W (19th C) ?
£1690 $2924 €2400 Caiques sur les bords du Bosphore (24x35cm-9x14in) s. 15-Dec-3 Gros & Delettrez, Paris #258/R est:2000-2500

ZIMMER, Bernd (1948-) German
£800 $1432 €1200 Tree stump (46x30cm-18x12in) s.i.d.84 verso. 15-May-4 Van Ham, Cologne #1051/R
£1549 $2680 €2200 Untitled - sea (61x85cm-24x33in) s.d.87 board. 13-Dec-3 Lempertz, Koln #373/R est:900
£2000 $3680 €3000 Untitled (72x92cm-28x36in) s.d. acrylic paper. 11-Jun-4 Hauswedell & Nolte, Hamburg #1611/R est:4000
£2098 $3608 €3000 Kampf zweier naturen (190x290cm-75x114in) acrylic prov. 3-Dec-3 Tajan, Paris #484/R est:3000-5000
£3930 $7231 €5738 Bei l'aquile (160x200cm-63x79in) s.i.d.1984 verso acrylic prov. 8-Jun-4 Germann, Zurich #73/R est:8000-12000 (S.FR 9000)
£4027 $7409 €6000 Cow (124x99cm-49x39in) s.d. acrylic chl packing paper. 26-Mar-4 Ketterer, Hamburg #717/R est:6000-7000
£4545 $7818 €6500 Untitled - autumn (161x200cm-63x79in) s.i.d. verso acrylic. 3-Dec-3 Hauswedell & Nolte, Hamburg #1071/R est:4000
£5634 $9746 €8000 Evening snowfall (100x120cm-39x47in) s.i.d.84/85 prov. 13-Dec-3 Lempertz, Koln #370/R est:3000
£7746 $13401 €11000 Misty sun (130x160cm-51x63in) s.i.d.82 verso cotton. 13-Dec-3 Lempertz, Koln #369/R est:3500
£9790 $16643 €14000 Evening (200x411cm-79x162in) s.i.d.81 verso acrylic. 29-Nov-3 Villa Grisebach, Berlin #400/R est:12000-15000
Works on paper
£490 $832 €700 Untitled - mountain (70x100cm-28x39in) s.d.84 gouache oil chk board. 27-Nov-3 Lempertz, Koln #542/R
£559 $951 €800 Untitled - mountain (69x99cm-27x39in) s.d.84 gouache oil chk board. 27-Nov-3 Lempertz, Koln #541/R
£759 $1267 €1100 Landscape (28x38cm-11x15in) s.d.1984 mixed media. 13-Nov-3 Neumeister, Munich #683/R
£1549 $2680 €2200 Untitled - red blue landscape (70x100cm-28x39in) s.d.82 gouache. 13-Dec-3 Lempertz, Koln #372/R est:900
£2113 $3655 €3000 Untitled - blue yellow landscape (70x100cm-28x39in) s.d.81 gouache board. 13-Dec-3 Lempertz, Koln #371/R est:900
£2345 $3916 €3400 City (69x99cm-27x39in) s.d.1984 mixed media board. 13-Nov-3 Neumeister, Munich #682/R est:2000-2200

ZIMMER, Ernst (1864-?) German
Works on paper
£288 $449 €420 Cavalry battle (40x66cm-16x26in) s.d.1924. 10-Apr-3 Weidler, Nurnberg #356/R

ZIMMER, H P (1936-1992) German
£347 $580 €500 Couple in love (54x40cm-21x16in) s.i.d. oil on col photo board. 24-Oct-3 Ketterer, Hamburg #1188/R

ZIMMER, Hans Peter (1936-1992) German
£2166 $3986 €3162 Figure composition (60x60cm-24x24in) 29-Mar-4 Rasmussen, Copenhagen #132a est:30000 (D.KR 24000)
£8000 $14720 €12000 Untitled (150x140cm-59x55in) s.verso prov. 9-Jun-4 Christie's, Amsterdam #304/R est:8000-12000

ZIMMER, Wilhelm Carl August (1853-1937) German
£1879 $3495 €2800 Portrait of Grand Duke Wilhelm Ernst of Sachsen-Weimar and Eisenach (189x106cm-74x42in) s.d.1901. 5-Mar-4 Wendl, Rudolstadt #4023/R est:2800
£11111 $18111 €16000 Winter of the pig bowling (72x109cm-28x43in) s.d.82. 24-Sep-3 Neumeister, Munich #605/R est:20000

ZIMMERMAN, Theodore (20th C) British
Works on paper
£800 $1304 €1168 Beautiful day at Le Touquet (21x28cm-8x11in) s.i. pastel prov. 23-Sep-3 Anderson & Garland, Newcastle #149/R
£820 $1509 €1197 At the hunt meeting, Ireland (23x29cm-9x11in) s.i. studio st. pastel. 23-Mar-4 Anderson & Garland, Newcastle #179/R
£900 $1638 €1314 Three girls paddling (16x21cm-6x8in) s.i. pastel. 29-Jun-4 Anderson & Garland, Newcastle #120/R
£960 $1526 €1402 Children and friends at Le touquet (15x24cm-6x9in) s.i. pastel. 18-Mar-3 Anderson & Garland, Newcastle #144/R
£1100 $1903 €1606 Madame Zimmerman et Louise sur la Plage dans Normandie (21x26cm-8x10in) s.i. pastel. 9-Dec-3 Anderson & Garland, Newcastle #277/R est:800-1200
£2200 $3960 €3212 A day to remember with the family at Le Touquet (22x39cm-9x15in) s.i. pastel prov. 21-Apr-4 Tennants, Leyburn #1000/R est:1400-1600
£2300 $3910 €3358 Lovely day on the beach at Le Touquet, France (17x22cm-7x9in) s.i. i.verso pastel prov. 19-Nov-3 Tennants, Leyburn #927/R est:800-1200
£2300 $4301 €3358 Beautiful summer day in Normandy (38x49cm-15x19in) s. pastel prov. 22-Jul-4 Tennants, Leyburn #693/R est:1400-1800

ZIMMERMAN, William (20th C) American
£929 $1700 €1356 Pheasants (46x81cm-18x32in) s. board painted c.1920. 5-Jun-4 Treadway Gallery, Cincinnati #646/R est:3500-4500

ZIMMERMANN, Albert (1809-1888) German
£1765 $2929 €2577 Landscape in the Alps with a torrential brook (31x52cm-12x20in) s. panel. 4-Oct-3 Kieselbach, Budapest #29/R (H.F 650000)
£1879 $3458 €2800 Farmstead with sheep grazing (60x80cm-24x31in) s. board. 24-Mar-4 Hugo Ruef, Munich #1156/R est:1800
£2013 $3765 €3000 Wetterhorn and Rosenlaui glacier (102x147cm-40x58in) s. 24-Feb-4 Dorotheum, Vienna #160/R est:2600-3000
£3356 $6275 €5000 Mountain torrent (106x50cm-42x20in) s. 24-Feb-4 Dorotheum, Vienna #125/R est:5500-6000
£3800 $6916 €5700 Villefranche-sur-mer near Nice (36x58cm-14x23in) s. i. verso panel. 30-Jun-4 Neumeister, Munich #760/R est:3000
£6376 $11413 €9500 Dolomite landscape with deer (113x148cm-44x58in) s. 27-May-4 Dorotheum, Vienna #132/R est:6500-7500

£7895 $14526 €12000 Upper Italian landscape with lake (49x60cm-19x24in) s. panel. 24-Jun-4 Dr Fritz Nagel, Stuttgart #776/R est:2000
£12000 $21600 €18000 Elegant ladies overlooking the bay of Naples, Italy (69x113cm-27x44in) s. 21-Apr-4 Christie's, Amsterdam #170/R est:10000-15000

ZIMMERMANN, Alfred (1854-1910) German
£490 $817 €700 Farmstead with figures (30x40cm-12x16in) s. board lit. 27-Jun-3 Auktionhaus Georg Rehm, Augsburg #8234/R

ZIMMERMANN, August Albert (1808-1888) German
£647 $1157 €945 Shepherd in southern mountain landscape (42x58cm-17x23in) s. panel. 12-May-4 Dobiaschofsky, Bern #1085/R est:2600 (S.FR 1500)
£855 $1574 €1300 Italian landscape in a summer's evening (13x18cm-5x7in) s. panel. 25-Jun-4 Michael Zeller, Lindau #541/R

ZIMMERMANN, Carl (1863-1930) German
£1268 $2193 €1800 Venturing out of the snowy forest (55x85cm-22x33in) s. 10-Dec-3 Christie's, Amsterdam #837/R est:1800-2400
£1408 $2437 €2000 Heading into the sunlit valley (75x56cm-30x22in) s. 10-Dec-3 Christie's, Amsterdam #838/R est:1500-2000

ZIMMERMANN, Clemens von (1788-1869) German
£1678 $3087 €2500 Koster Palazuola on Albanian lake (48x64cm-19x25in) s.d.1856 i. verso. 24-Mar-4 Hugo Ruef, Munich #1157/R est:2500

ZIMMERMANN, Ernst (1898-1966) German
£385 $654 €550 Awareness (65x48cm-26x19in) s. i.verso. 28-Nov-3 Wendl, Rudolstadt #4354/R

ZIMMERMANN, Ernst Karl Georg (1852-1901) German
£931 $1722 €1350 Monk drinking (50x36cm-20x14in) s. panel. 12-Feb-4 Weidler, Nurnberg #6578

ZIMMERMANN, Ernst Reinhard (1881-1939) German
£417 $676 €609 Bouquet of garden flowers (69x78cm-27x31in) s.d.1923. 9-Aug-3 Hindemae, Ullerslev #5/R (D.KR 4400)
£764 $1276 €1100 Roses (73x65cm-29x26in) s. canvas on board. 22-Oct-3 Neumeister, Munich #788/R

ZIMMERMANN, Friedrich (1823-1884) German
£261 $477 €381 Summer meadow landscape (35x63cm-14x25in) mono. 4-Jun-4 Zofingen, Switzerland #2377 (S.FR 600)

ZIMMERMANN, Mac (1912-1995) German
£1479 $2558 €2100 Artists in the morning (50x92cm-20x36in) s.d.67 s.i.d.1967 verso board exhib. 13-Dec-3 Lempertz, Koln #199/R est:800
£2183 $3493 €3100 The test (50x60cm-20x24in) s.d.1952 panel. 18-Sep-3 Rieber, Stuttgart #1191/R est:4950
Works on paper
£214 $400 €312 Modern composition (100x65cm-39x26in) s.d.51 mixed media board. 26-Feb-4 Skinner, Bolton #718/R
£883 $1500 €1289 Surreal works, divergierendes. Divertimento (71x99cm-28x39in) s.d.54 mixed media prov. two prov. 21-Nov-3 Skinner, Boston #600/R est:3000-5000

ZIMMERMANN, Reinhard Sebastian (1815-1893) German
£1996 $3572 €2914 Monks in the studio (40x60cm-16x24in) s. strengthened panel. 25-May-4 Bukowskis, Stockholm #365/R est:35000-40000 (S.KR 27000)
£4362 $7809 €6500 Kasper, Melchoir and Balthasar (62x77cm-24x30in) s. 27-May-4 Dorotheum, Vienna #142/R est:4000-5000

ZIMMERMANN, Richard (1820-1875) German
£900 $1620 €1314 Private chapel interior with a lady at prayer with a priest (43x56cm-17x22in) s.d.1875 panel. 21-Apr-4 Brightwells, Leominster #764

ZINCKE, Christian Friedrich (1683-1767) German
Miniatures
£1400 $2506 €2044 Gentleman in a blue velvet coat (5cm-2in) enamel on copper prov. 25-May-4 Christie's, London #8/R est:800-1200
£1517 $2534 €2200 Gentleman (4cm-2in) metal frame. 12-Nov-3 Sotheby's, Milan #1/R est:1700-2400
£1931 $3225 €2800 Joseph Addison (4cm-2in) exec.c.1720 oval. 12-Nov-3 Sotheby's, Milan #2/R est:1600-2000
£2000 $3320 €2920 Young gentleman wearing a blue coat (4cm-2in) enamel gold frame prov. 2-Oct-3 Sotheby's, Olympia #5/R est:1400-1800
£2200 $3938 €3212 Duchess of Kingstone in a black coat, elaborate bonnet (5cm-2in) enamel on copper. 25-May-4 Christie's, London #5/R est:700-900
£2600 $4654 €3796 Gentleman in a lilac velvet coat (5cm-2in) enamel on copper prov. 25-May-4 Christie's, London #6/R est:1000-1500
£5500 $9845 €8030 Young gentleman in heavily gold embroidered velvet coat (5cm-2in) enamel on copper prov. 25-May-4 Christie's, London #3/R est:1500-2500
£7000 $12600 €10220 Lady wearing a decollette leaf green dress (5cm-2in) enamel gilt metal mount oval exhib. 22-Apr-4 Bonhams, New Bond Street #42/R est:2500-3500
£11000 $19690 €16060 Portrait of Duchess in a blue dress (5cm-2in) enamel on copper. 22-Mar-4 Bonhams & Brooks, Norfolk #84/R est:3000-5000

ZINGG, Adrian (1734-1816) Swiss
Prints
£2098 $3503 €3000 Arcadian landscape with classical figures (44x61cm-17x24in) i. wash etching. 10-Oct-3 Winterberg, Heidelberg #525/R est:1950
Works on paper
£1088 $1948 €1600 Landscape with trees and figures by wayside memorial (19x31cm-7x12in) s.d.1785 pen wash. 17-Mar-4 Neumeister, Munich #277/R est:1900
£2620 $4769 €3825 River with bridge and travellers near Nossen (20x31cm-8x12in) s.i.d.1785 pen ink brush wash prov.exhib. 17-Jun-4 Kornfeld, Bern #84/R est:3000 (S.FR 6000)
£3931 $6565 €5700 River landscape with traveller and two pack horses (49x64cm-19x25in) s.d.1786 W/C grisaille. 15-Nov-3 Lempertz, Koln #1441/R est:6000
£4056 $6773 €5800 Landscape with Halsbrugge viaduct near Feyberg in Sachsen (48x64cm-19x25in) i. verso wash Indian ink brush pen. 10-Oct-3 Winterberg, Heidelberg #524/R est:6800
£7424 $13511 €10839 The Elbe in Switzerland with trees in the foreground (39x31cm-15x12in) pen bistre brush brown wash prov. 17-Jun-4 Kornfeld, Bern #83/R est:7500 (S.FR 17000)

ZINGG, Jules (1882-1942) French
£543 $1000 €793 Floral still life. s. 26-Jun-4 Susanin's, Chicago #6001/R est:2000-3000
£1818 $3091 €2600 Scene de labours (35x55cm-14x22in) s. cardboard. 28-Nov-3 Blanchet, Paris #92/R est:3000-4000
£2133 $3861 €3200 Vacher et troupeau a l'oree du bois (49x61cm-19x24in) s. panel. 3-Apr-4 Gerard, Besancon #82
£2431 $4059 €3500 Meule, Vexin (54x65cm-21x26in) s. 21-Oct-3 Artcurial Briest, Paris #211/R est:3500-4500
£2467 $4489 €3700 Fenaison (38x55cm-15x22in) s. panel. 4-Jul-4 Eric Pillon, Calais #283/R
£3022 $5500 €4412 Vallee du Rupt (54x81cm-21x32in) s. 29-Jun-4 Arroyo, Buenos Aires #47/R est:5500
£3867 $6921 €5800 La moisson (38x55cm-15x22in) s. 16-May-4 Thierry & Lannon, Brest #198/R est:5000-6000
£3956 $7200 €5776 Labour in the fields (54x73cm-21x29in) s. board. 29-Jun-4 Arroyo, Buenos Aires #48/R est:5500
£4437 $7764 €6300 Scene de moisson a Perros-Guirec (54x73cm-21x29in) panel. 16-Dec-3 Claude Aguttes, Neuilly #8/R est:4000-6000
£4667 $8493 €7000 Travaux des champs (73x100cm-29x39in) s. 4-Jul-4 Eric Pillon, Calais #286/R
£5894 $10727 €8900 Fenaison (38x55cm-15x22in) s. 19-Jun-4 St-Germain-en-Laye Encheres #151/R est:10000
£7746 $13556 €11000 Soleil couchant sur la riviere (60x81cm-24x32in) s. painted c.1925. 21-Dec-3 Thierry & Lannon, Brest #215/R est:10000-12000
£9000 $16110 €13500 Skieurs aux Rousses (50x73cm-20x29in) s. panel. 17-May-4 Chayette & Cheval, Paris #188/R est:8000-10000
£18310 $32042 €26000 Paradis terrestre (81x102cm-32x40in) s. painted c.1920. 21-Dec-3 Thierry & Lannon, Brest #216/R est:22000-24000
Works on paper
£500 $910 €750 Bateau sur le fleuve (22x35cm-9x14in) s. Chinese ink dr. 4-Jul-4 Eric Pillon, Calais #278/R
£596 $1085 €900 Marche en Auvergne (31x46cm-12x18in) s. ink. 19-Jun-4 Gerard, Besancon #11
£800 $1432 €1200 L'attelage (35x53cm-14x21in) W/C. 16-May-4 Osenat, Fontainebleau #58/R
£1033 $1881 €1550 Fenaisons (29x46cm-11x18in) s. W/C. 4-Jul-4 Eric Pillon, Calais #279/R
£1060 $1981 €1600 Bord de mer, les genets (21x32cm-8x13in) s. W/C. 24-Jul-4 Thierry & Lannon, Brest #86/R est:1800-2000
£1391 $2601 €2100 Fenaison (32x50cm-13x20in) s. W/C. 24-Jul-4 Thierry & Lannon, Brest #87/R est:2300-2500
£1549 $2711 €2200 Village anime aux toits de chaume. s.d.1917 W/C. 21-Dec-3 Thierry & Lannon, Brest #78/R est:2200-2500
£1589 $2972 €2400 Les bateaux (32x50cm-13x20in) s. W/C. 24-Jul-4 Thierry & Lannon, Brest #88/R est:2500-2800
£1620 $2835 €2300 Paysage a la gardienne de vache (31x24cm-12x9in) s.d.1917 W/C. 21-Dec-3 Thierry & Lannon, Brest #244 est:1500-1800
£1690 $2958 €2400 L'enterrement en bord de mer en Bretagne (25x44cm-10x17in) studio st. W/C htd gouache. 21-Dec-3 Thierry & Lannon, Brest #77/R est:2200-2500
£1831 $3204 €2600 Promenade (32x24cm-13x9in) studio st. W/C. 21-Dec-3 Thierry & Lannon, Brest #245/R est:1500-1800
£2042 $3574 €2900 Troupeau pres de la cote en Bretagne (48x32cm-19x13in) s. W/C exec c.1920. 21-Dec-3 Thierry & Lannon, Brest #79/R est:2200-2500
£2465 $4265 €3500 Aux champs (30x48cm-12x19in) s. W/C. 9-Dec-3 Artcurial Briest, Paris #263/R est:2500-3000
£2746 $4806 €3900 Danseuses sur la plage (48x63cm-19x25in) studio st. W/C. 21-Dec-3 Thierry & Lannon, Brest #76/R est:3800-4000
£3179 $5944 €4800 La voile rouge (27x47cm-11x19in) s. W/C. 24-Jul-4 Thierry & Lannon, Brest #89/R est:3000-3200

ZINGONI, Aurelio (1853-1922) Italian
£1500 $2490 €2190 Hungry chimney sweep (83x69cm-33x27in) s.d.1879. 1-Oct-3 Sotheby's, Olympia #218/R est:800-1200
£14085 $24366 €20000 Harvest (69x114cm-27x45in) s. 10-Dec-3 Sotheby's, Milan #90/R est:20000-30000

ZINGONI, Aurelio (attrib) (1853-1922) Italian
£4110 $6986 €6000 Still life with vegetables. Still life with wine bottle (63x51cm-25x20in) pair. 7-Nov-3 Farsetti, Prato #491 est:7500-8500

ZINHOBL, Karl (1921-) Austrian
£1200 $2208 €1800 Seated nude (62x50cm-24x20in) s.d.1958 tempera gouache. 9-Jun-4 Dorotheum, Salzburg #681/R est:2400-3000

ZINI, Umberto (1878-?) Italian
£879 $1600 €1283 Venice, Grand Canal (50x70cm-20x28in) s. 29-Jun-4 Arroyo, Buenos Aires #53/R est:1600
Works on paper
£292 $475 €420 View of Venice (32x19cm-13x7in) s. W/C. 23-Sep-3 Durán, Madrid #621/R

ZINKEISEN, Anna (1901-1976) British
£1300 $2210 €1898 Still life of orchids (63x75cm-25x30in) s. 26-Nov-3 Sotheby's, Olympia #127/R est:600-800
£1400 $2240 €2044 Portrait of Lady Dunn (183x84cm-72x33in) s.d.27th June 1961 verso. 16-Sep-3 Bonhams, Knowle #111/R est:1500-2000
£1400 $2338 €2044 Buxted Park (41x74cm-16x29in) s. 17-Oct-3 Keys, Aylsham #724
£2200 $3894 €3212 Portrait of Audrey (61x51cm-24x20in) s.d.1921. 27-Apr-4 Bonhams, Knightsbridge #137/R est:800-1200
£2800 $5096 €4088 Portrait of Julia Heseltine (91x71cm-36x28in) s. 1-Jul-4 Christie's, Kensington #36/R est:2000-3000

ZINKEISEN, Doris (1898-1991) British
£260 $491 €380 Down in the mouth (61x51cm-24x20in) prov. 17-Feb-4 Rosebery Fine Art, London #539
£500 $850 €730 Spanish dancer (40x30cm-16x12in) s. 1-Dec-3 Bonhams, Bath #47/R
£650 $1086 €949 Lady and gentleman in a horse drawn carriage (51x69cm-20x27in) s. 21-Oct-3 Bonhams, Knightsbridge #39/R
£700 $1113 €1022 New Forest ponies (51x101cm-20x40in) s. 10-Sep-3 Sotheby's, Olympia #212/R
£700 $1253 €1022 Summer carriage drive (51x57cm-20x22in) s. 14-May-4 Christie's, Kensington #494/R
£800 $1464 €1168 Riding Out (51x76cm-20x30in) s. 28-Jan-4 Dreweatt Neate, Newbury #113/R
£850 $1445 €1241 Alpine panorama (51x61cm-20x24in) s. 26-Nov-3 Sotheby's, Olympia #74/R
£1200 $2160 €1752 Lady on a white horse (44x54cm-17x21in) s. board. 20-Jan-4 Bonhams, Knightsbridge #55b est:1200-1800
£1800 $3240 €2628 Picnic (51x76cm-20x30in) s. 20-Jan-4 Bonhams, Knightsbridge #56/R est:2000-3000
£1820 $3130 €2657 Grand National (50x100cm-20x39in) s. 3-Dec-3 Stephan Welz, Johannesburg #7/R est:20000-30000 (SA.R 20000)
£1950 $3452 €2847 Haymaking (51x76cm-20x30in) s. 27-Apr-4 Bonhams, Knightsbridge #201/R est:2000-3000
£4600 $8096 €6716 Peggy Woffington on stage (60x49cm-24x19in) s. 19-May-4 Sotheby's, Olympia #192/R est:1500-2000

ZINNER, Robert (1904-) Austrian
£350 $601 €500 Early spring in the Morsbachalm/Donnersbacher Tauern (71x55cm-28x22in) s.d.1943 board. 4-Dec-3 Dorotheum, Graz #51/R
£483 $883 €700 High mountains (66x50cm-26x20in) s. panel prov. 27-Jan-4 Dorotheum, Vienna #71/R
£533 $981 €800 Spring in the mountains (100x121cm-39x48in) s. 9-Jun-4 Dorotheum, Salzburg #635/R
£563 $986 €800 Early spring in the mountains (50x66cm-20x26in) s. plywood. 19-Dec-3 Dorotheum, Vienna #87/R
£690 $1262 €1000 Alpine pasture in the Dolomites (63x78cm-25x31in) s. masonite prov. 27-Jan-4 Dorotheum, Vienna #65/R
£845 $1479 €1200 Hochtor-Nordwand (100x80cm-39x31in) cardboard. 19-Dec-3 Dorotheum, Vienna #83/R

ZINNOGGER, Leopold (1811-1872) Austrian
£2958 $5294 €4200 Still life with fruit in a silver bowl (52x42cm-20x17in) s. lit. 8-Jan-4 Allgauer, Kempten #2593/R est:2000

ZINOVIEW, Alexandre (19/20th C) ?
Works on paper
£362 $666 €550 Ode a l'amour (24x19cm-9x7in) s. W/C crayon gouache. 24-Jun-4 Credit Municipal, Paris #34

ZION, Ben (20th C) American?
£248 $400 €362 Bearded figure (38x18cm-15x7in) s. board. 22-Feb-3 Bunte, Elgin #1168

ZIRGES, Willy (1867-?) German
£310 $518 €450 Salome (76x70cm-30x28in) s. lit. 10-Jul-3 Allgauer, Kempten #2789/R

ZITARA, F (19/20th C) ?
£1181 $1972 €1700 Pecheurs dans la rade de Marseille. s. 25-Oct-3 Dianous, Marseille #410

ZITEK, Ladislaus (1886-1935) Czechoslovakian
£403 $742 €588 Petrin, mount of Prague (86x91cm-34x36in) s. 14-Jun-4 Waddingtons, Toronto #203/R est:1000-1500 (C.D 1000)

ZITKO, Otto (20th C) ?
£1879 $3477 €2800 Untitled (60x50cm-24x20in) mono.d.89 verso soot behind glass prov. 9-Mar-4 Dorotheum, Vienna #178/R est:2600-3600
£2013 $3725 €3000 Untitled (60x50cm-24x20in) mono.d.89 soot behind glass prov. 9-Mar-4 Dorotheum, Vienna #179/R est:2600-3600

ZITTER, Harry (20th C) American
£1397 $2500 €2040 East Side street scene (30x46cm-12x18in) s.d.44 i.stretcher. 26-May-4 Doyle, New York #134/R est:4000-6000

ZITZEWITZ, Augusta von (1880-1960) German
£892 $1373 €1400 Still life of flowers (65x80cm-26x31in) s.d.49. 4-Sep-2 Schopman, Hamburg #119/R

ZIVERI, Alberto (1908-1990) Italian
£3448 $5759 €5000 Seated nude (52x37cm-20x15in) s.d.1960. 17-Nov-3 Sant Agostino, Torino #280/R est:5000-6000
£6552 $10941 €9500 Abattoir (53x51cm-21x20in) s.d.1949 exhib.lit. 13-Nov-3 Finarte Semenzato, Rome #370/R est:1000-15000
£15172 $25338 €22000 Self-portrait on the phone (140x104cm-55x41in) exhib.lit. 17-Nov-3 Sant Agostino, Torino #243/R est:22000-26000
£20690 $34552 €30000 Danae (133x155cm-52x61in) s.d.1943 exhib.lit. 17-Nov-3 Sant Agostino, Torino #244/R est:30000-40000
Works on paper
£331 $553 €480 Church in Rome (25x34cm-10x13in) s. chl. 17-Nov-3 Sant Agostino, Torino #35/R

ZIVERI, Umberto (1891-1971) Italian
£503 $891 €750 Landscape in LOmbardy (55x45cm-22x18in) s. 1-May-4 Meeting Art, Vercelli #460

ZIWKOW, Andrej (20th C) ?
£306 $496 €444 Couple of boys bathing (73x92cm-29x36in) s,. 4-Aug-3 Rasmussen, Vejle #690 (D.KR 3200)

ZIX, Benjamin (1772-1811) French
£1500 $2775 €2190 Cavalry skirmish with a burning town beyond (51x66cm-20x26in) oil paper on board. 10-Feb-4 Bonhams, Knightsbridge #261/R est:1000-1500
Works on paper
£1769 $3166 €2600 Un homme tenant sa fille par la main saluant Dominique (16x19cm-6x7in) i. black chk pen brown ink wash. 18-Mar-4 Christie's, Paris #290/R est:1200-2000

ZMURKO, François (1859-1910) Polish
£7031 $11742 €10265 Head and shoulders of a blond lady (51x40cm-20x16in) s. cardboard painted c.1895. 19-Oct-3 Agra, Warsaw #8/R est:28000 (P.Z 45000)
£12039 $19984 €17577 Evening on the lake (100x200cm-39x79in) s.d.1894. 15-Jun-3 Agra, Warsaw #6/R est:75000 (P.Z 75000)
Works on paper
£2874 $4973 €4196 Seaside scene (21x50cm-8x20in) s. pastel cardboard exec. c.1893 lit. 14-Dec-3 Agra, Warsaw #25/R est:18000 (P.Z 19000)

ZO, Henri (1873-1933) French
£6490 $11812 €9800 La corrida (46x61cm-18x24in) s. 18-Jun-4 Piasa, Paris #139/R est:10000-12000
£11268 $19493 €16000 Entree des arenes (81x66cm-32x26in) s. 9-Dec-3 Artcurial Briest, Paris #92/R est:15000-20000

ZOBEL, Benjamin (1762-1831) German
£1700 $2890 €2482 Reclining leopard in a wooded landscape (43x58cm-17x23in) oil sand. 26-Nov-3 Mallams, Oxford #262/R est:300-500
£1750 $2975 €2555 Reclining tiger at the entrance to a cave (38x46cm-15x18in) s. oil sand. 26-Nov-3 Mallams, Oxford #263/R est:300-500
£2050 $3485 €2993 Reclining tiger in a cave (56x84cm-22x33in) oil sand. 26-Nov-3 Mallams, Oxford #264/R est:300-400

ZOBEL, Fernando (1924-1987) Spanish
£3871 $6194 €5652 Untitled (30x32cm-12x13in) s. canvas on board. 18-May-3 Sotheby's, Singapore #80/R est:10000-18000 (S.D 10800)
£4375 $7000 €6388 Untitled. s.d.1962. 20-Sep-3 Harvey Clar, Oakland #1541
£7042 $12324 €10000 Football 8 (60x60cm-24x24in) s. s.i.d.78 verso prov. 16-Dec-3 Segre, Madrid #135/R est:3000
£9589 $16301 €14000 Untitled (70x100cm-28x39in) s. s.d.59 verso. 4-Nov-3 Ansorena, Madrid #914/R est:12000
£9655 $17379 €14000 Composition (70x100cm-28x39in) s. s.d.59. 26-Jan-4 Ansorena, Madrid #896/R est:14000
£11184 $20243 €17000 Orange and green (100x81cm-39x32in) s. s.i.verso. 14-Apr-4 Ansorena, Madrid #271/R est:16000
£12418 $22477 €18130 Untitled (80x99cm-31x39in) s. 4-Apr-4 Sotheby's, Singapore #120/R est:20000-25000 (S.D 38000)
Works on paper
£1900 $3021 €2755 Pabellon- estufa de cristal (38x57cm-15x22in) s.i.d.1982 pen ink W/C set of five. 11-Sep-3 Christie's, Kensington #238/R est:500-700

ZOBERNIG, Heimo (1958-) ?
£3867 $7076 €5800 Untitled (100x100cm-39x39in) s.d.1988 verso. 4-Jun-4 Lempertz, Koln #553/R est:4500-5000

ZOBOLI, Giacomo (1682-1757) Italian
Works on paper
£472 $850 €689 Male nude from behind (43x28cm-17x11in) red chk htd white. 21-Jan-4 Doyle, New York #24

ZOBUS, Wilhelm (1831-1869) German
£1250 $2037 €1800 Gothic church by mountain lake (84x122cm-33x48in) s.d.1868. 25-Sep-3 Neumeister, Munich #2915/R est:1200

ZOCCHI, Carlo (1894-1965) Italian
£738 $1307 €1100 Autumnal landscape (15x27cm-6x11in) s. board. 1-May-4 Meeting Art, Vercelli #190

ZOCCHI, Emilio (1835-1913) Italian
Sculpture
£1622 $2903 €2400 Michelangelo (51cm-20in) s.i. white marble lit. 8-May-4 Schloss Ahlden, Ahlden #1067/R est:2400

ZOCCHI, Giuseppe (1711-1767) Italian
£20000 $34600 €29200 Meeting of Jephthah and his daughter (46x61cm-18x24in) two prov. 11-Dec-3 Sotheby's, London #202/R est:25000-35000
£450000 $778500 €657000 Florence, view of the Arno taken from the Porta a San Niccolo (57x87cm-22x34in) 11-Dec-3 Sotheby's, London #45/R est:300000-400000
£559441 $962238 €800000 View of the Arno, Florence from the Vagaloggia. The Arno, Florence from the Ponte Delle Grazie (60x84cm-24x33in) pair. 2-Dec-3 Christie's, Paris #718/R est:80000-120000
£1150000 $1989500 €1679000 Florence, view of the Piazza della Signoria and figures gathered round a puppet show (56x87cm-22x34in) prov.exhib.lit. 11-Dec-3 Sotheby's, London #44/R est:300000-400000
Works on paper
£2533 $4611 €3800 Quattro Capi Bridge in Rome (19x31cm-7x12in) pierre noire pen ink wash. 30-Jun-4 Pierre Berge, Paris #15/R est:3000-4000
£3716 $6541 €5500 View of the Colosseum from the Palatine (23x51cm-9x20in) black chk col wash two joined sheets prov. 19-May-4 Sotheby's, Amsterdam #173/R est:5500-6500

ZOCCHI, Giuseppe (attrib) (1711-1767) Italian
£1544 $2841 €2300 La Manne. Abraham et Melchisedech (44x58cm-17x23in) oval pair. 24-Mar-4 Tajan, Paris #26 est:3000-4000

ZOCCHI, Guglielmo (1874-?) Italian
£7561 $13081 €11039 Woman playing music in a colonnade (50x60cm-20x24in) s. 9-Dec-3 Rasmussen, Copenhagen #1567/R est:40000 (D.KR 80000)
£7778 $14000 €11356 Recital (70x110cm-28x43in) s. 22-Apr-4 Christie's, Rockefeller NY #243/R est:25000-35000
£15556 $28000 €22712 Cock fight (66x94cm-26x37in) s. prov. 22-Apr-4 Christie's, Rockefeller NY #242/R est:18000-25000
£27000 $49140 €39420 Vanity (43x103cm 17x41in) s. prov. 15-Jun-4 Sotheby's, London #207/R est:10000-15000
Works on paper
£7930 $13480 €11578 Happy childhood (49x34cm-19x13in) s.i. stretcher. 5-Nov-3 Dobiaschofsky, Bern #1069/R est:12000 (S.FR 18000)

ZOCHER, Johan David (1791-1870) Dutch
Works on paper
£1644 $2795 €2400 Design for a garden (31x38cm-12x15in) s.i.d.1856 pen brown ink W/C over black chk. 4-Nov-3 Sotheby's, Amsterdam #141/R est:2000-3000

ZOELLY, Paul (1896-1971) Swiss
£1135 $2089 €1657 Enthusiast (52x49cm-20x19in) s. acrylic. 8-Jun-4 Germann, Zurich #137/R est:2000-3000 (S.FR 2600)

ZOFF, Alfred (1852-1927) Austrian
£764 $1245 €1100 Fishing nets on beach (30x45cm-12x18in) mono. 24-Sep-3 Neumeister, Munich #609/R
£2685 $4805 €4000 Rocky landscape with mountain farmstead (29x45cm-11x18in) s. panel. 27-May-4 Dorotheum, Graz #76/R est:4000
£3333 $6000 €5000 Village near Wildon (26x41cm-10x16in) s. canvas on board. 22-Apr-4 Dorotheum, Graz #35/R est:3500
£4667 $8400 €7000 Windmill in Bruges (36x47cm-14x19in) s. i. verso canvas on board. 22-Apr-4 Dorotheum, Graz #34/R est:5500
£5594 $9510 €8000 Rio Maggiore near Cinque Terre (52x40cm-20x16in) s. i. verso. 24-Nov-3 Dorotheum, Vienna #150/R est:8000-10000
£6711 $12013 €10000 Farmstead near Graz (40x52cm-16x20in) s. canvas on board. 27-May-4 Dorotheum, Graz #80/R est:7000
£7692 $13077 €11230 Landscape by moonlight (66x101cm-26x40in) 1-Dec-3 Koller, Zurich #6487/R est:8000-12000 (S.FR 17000)
£8054 $14255 €12000 Garden (46x39cm-18x15in) s. i. verso board. 28-Apr-4 Wiener Kunst Auktionen, Vienna #61/R est:8000-12000
£8054 $14255 €12000 Village landscape near Krems (31x51cm-12x20in) s. board prov. 28-Apr-4 Wiener Kunst Auktionen, Vienna #62/R est:11000-22000
£11409 $20423 €17000 Market place of Nieuport (47x59cm-19x23in) s. i.verso. 27-May-4 Dorotheum, Vienna #224/R est:16000-18000
Works on paper
£2431 $3962 €3500 Steep coast (48x69cm-19x27in) s. pastel board. 23-Sep-3 Wiener Kunst Auktionen, Vienna #112/R est:2500-4000

ZOFFANY, Johann (1733-1810) British
£105000 $193200 €153300 Portrait of Miss Matilda Clevland in blue and white dress (56x44cm-22x17in) panel prov.exhib.lit. 9-Jun-4 Christie's, London #3/R est:50000-80000
£180000 $331200 €262800 The Misses Garrick by the Thames at Hampton (65x77cm-26x30in) prov.lit. 9-Jun-4 Christie's, London #4/R est:200000-300000

ZOFFANY, Johann (attrib) (1733-1810) British
£40000 $68000 €58400 Conversation piece with two ladies at a table (68x77cm-27x30in) 27-Nov-3 Sotheby's, London #6/R est:15000-20000

ZOFFANY, Johann (circle) (1733-1810) British
£27933 $50000 €40782 Portrait of the Sayer family (101x127cm-40x50in) prov.lit. 27-May-4 Sotheby's, New York #242/R est:50000-70000

ZOFFANY, Johann (style) (1733-1810) British
£6000 $10200 €8760 Portrait of George III, half length, wearing a gold and white jacket (62x48cm-24x19in) 29-Oct-3 Hampton & Littlewood, Exeter #565/R est:500-700

ZOFFOLI, Angelo (fl.1860-1910) Italian
£18056 $32500 €26362 Audience with the cardinal (60x100cm-24x39in) s.i. 23-Apr-4 Sotheby's, New York #123/R est:25000-35000

ZOFFOLI, Giacomo (18th C) Italian
Sculpture
£28000 $50400 €40880 Group of the Laocoon (44x32cm-17x13in) s. brown pat bronze after the Antique. 21-Apr-4 Sotheby's, London #42/R est:15000-20000

ZOFREA, Salvatore (1946-) Italian
£862 $1345 €1250 Anna (58x89cm-23x35in) s. 1-Aug-2 Joel, Victoria #319 est:2000-3000 (A.D 2500)
£1429 $2629 €2086 Figures in a landscape (70x90cm-28x35in) s. 29-Mar-4 Goodman, Sydney #214/R est:4000-6000 (A.D 3500)
£2049 $3320 €2992 St. Francis and the cheetah (91x152cm-36x60in) s. prov. 30-Jul-3 Goodman, Sydney #143/R est:5000-7000 (A.D 5000)
£3441 $5540 €5024 Circus (180x270cm-71x106in) s.d.87. 25-Aug-3 Sotheby's, Paddington #451/R est:7000-9000 (A.D 8500)

ZOGBAUM, Wilfrid M (1915-1965) American
Sculpture
£1285 $2300 €1876 Untitled (20x36cm-8x14in) s. welded steel stone prov. 20-Mar-4 Sloans & Kenyon, Bethesda #1131/R est:1000-1500

ZOGG, Ernst (1913-1981) Swiss
£633 $1077 €924 Bodeli (22cm-9in circular) s. i. verso tempera. 18-Nov-3 Hans Widmer, St Gallen #1262 (S.FR 1400)

ZOGMAYER, Leo (20th C) Austrian?
£1958 $3329 €2800 Two figures (115x155cm-45x61in) s.d.84 acrylic. 26-Nov-3 Dorotheum, Vienna #298/R est:3000-4000
Works on paper
£400 $736 €600 Bather (87x60cm-34x24in) s.d.84 gouache. 9-Jun-4 Dorotheum, Salzburg #705/R

ZOGRAFFOS, Constantinos (1883-1913) Greek
Works on paper
£2100 $3759 €3066 View of the Acropolis. View of the Parthenon. From the Acropolis (36x25cm-14x10in) s.d.1907 W/C three. 11-May-4 Bonhams, New Bond Street #15/R est:1200-1800

ZOHAR, Israel (1945-) ?
£1200 $2184 €1800 Portrait de Vera (54x65cm-21x26in) s. painted 1985. 4-Jul-4 Eric Pillon, Calais #164/R

ZOIA, Krukowskaja (1903-) Russian/Swedish
£270 $484 €400 From Tunisia (24x33cm-9x13in) s.d.1931 board. 8-May-4 Bukowskis, Helsinki #374/R

ZOLL, Kilian (1818-1860) Swedish
£541 $968 €800 Smoking on the sly (46x34cm-18x13in) s. 8-May-4 Bukowskis, Helsinki #381/R
£1035 $1852 €1511 Visiting the tailor (21x16cm-8x6in) s.d.1849 panel exhib. 26-May-4 AB Stockholms Auktionsverk #2175/R (S.KR 14000)

£1035	$1852	€1511	Girl with kitten (19x16cm-7x6in) s. exhib. 26-May-4 AB Stockholms Auktionsverk #2176/R (S.KR 14000)

ZOLLA, Venanzio (1880-1961) Italian

£345	$572	€500	Portrait of woman (48x38cm-19x15in) s. card. 1-Oct-3 Della Rocca, Turin #306/R
£408	$731	€600	Landscape with figures (15x16cm-6x6in) s.d.1924. 22-Mar-4 Sant Agostino, Torino #193/R
£503	$891	€750	Church interior with figures (44x31cm-17x12in) s. cardboard. 1-May-4 Meeting Art, Vercelli #259
£503	$891	€750	Interior (47x31cm-19x12in) s. cardboard. 1-May-4 Meeting Art, Vercelli #462
£537	$950	€800	Woman by river (32x46cm-13x18in) s. cardboard. 1-May-4 Meeting Art, Vercelli #34
£816	$1461	€1200	Cafe concert (30x40cm-12x16in) s. cardboard. 22-Mar-4 Sant Agostino, Torino #201/R
£979	$1635	€1400	London street (40x50cm-16x20in) s. cardboard. 26-Jun-3 Sant Agostino, Torino #55/R
£1007	$1782	€1500	Empty street in London (57x77cm-22x30in) s. cardboard painted 1956. 1-May-4 Meeting Art, Vercelli #355 est:1500
£1119	$1869	€1600	Landscape with figures in the snow (40x50cm-16x20in) s. cardboard. 26-Jun-3 Sant Agostino, Torino #53/R est:1800
£1172	$1946	€1700	Still life of fruit and bowls (50x57cm-20x22in) s. cardboard. 1-Oct-3 Della Rocca, Turin #45
£1241	$2061	€1800	Girl sewing (46x65cm-18x26in) s. card. 1-Oct-3 Della Rocca, Turin #252/R
£1268	$2193	€1800	The Po in winter (49x68cm-19x27in) s. cardboard. 9-Dec-3 Finarte Semenzato, Milan #8/R est:500-700
£1586	$2633	€2300	Venice (50x70cm-20x28in) s. board. 1-Oct-3 Della Rocca, Turin #293/R

ZOLNHOFER, Fritz (1896-1965) German

£544	$995	€810	Interior scene in the salon (40x30cm-16x12in) 9-Jul-4 Dawo, Saarbrucken #163/R
£1342	$2456	€2000	Country scene with houses (50x60cm-20x24in) mono. panel. 9-Jul-4 Dawo, Saarbrucken #169/R est:2200
£1678	$3070	€2500	Playing chess in a cafe (50x59cm-20x23in) s. board. 9-Jul-4 Dawo, Saarbrucken #154/R est:2800
Works on paper			
£369	$676	€550	Industrial landscape in the Saar region (29x46cm-11x18in) mono. W/C. 9-Jul-4 Dawo, Saarbrucken #170/R
£436	$798	€650	Shepherd huts and shepherds (37x29cm-15x11in) s. gouache. 9-Jul-4 Dawo, Saarbrucken #172/R
£503	$921	€750	Industrial landscape in the Saar region (42x30cm-17x12in) s. gouache. 9-Jul-4 Dawo, Saarbrucken #171/R

ZOMBORY, Lajos (1867-1933) Hungarian

£1449	$2623	€2116	Relaxing (58x72cm-23x28in) s. 16-Apr-4 Mu Terem Galeria, Budapest #143/R (H.F 550000)

ZOMMER, Richard Karlovich (1866-1939) Russian

£3400	$6290	€4964	Rest on the way (35x24cm-14x9in) s. 15-Jan-4 Christie's, Kensington #773/R est:500-700
£3500	$5950	€5110	Street traders in Samarkand (27x20cm-11x8in) s. canvas on board. 19-Nov-3 Sotheby's, London #49/R est:1500-2000
£16000	$28640	€23360	Caucasian caravan (47x68cm-19x27in) s. 26-May-4 Sotheby's, London #73/R est:10000-15000
£26000	$46540	€37960	Street scene in Samarkand (85x62cm-33x24in) s.i.d.1895. 26-May-4 Sotheby's, London #74/R est:8000-12000
Works on paper			
£4000	$6800	€5840	Solitary horseman (30x89cm-12x35in) s. W/C. 19-Nov-3 Sotheby's, London #51/R est:2500-3500

ZON, Jacob (1872-1932) Dutch

£578	$1052	€850	By the kitchen fire (22x31cm-9x12in) s. cardboard. 3-Feb-4 Christie's, Amsterdam #286
£839	$1443	€1200	Peat ship (28x36cm-11x14in) s. board. 8-Dec-3 Glerum, Amsterdam #74/R

ZONA, Antonio (1813-1892) Italian

£1528	$2597	€2200	Portrait of Elvira Bauer (62x50cm-24x20in) s. 29-Oct-3 Il Ponte, Milan #540

ZONARO, Fausto (1854-1929) Italian

£1250	$2000	€1825	Oriental vision (15x13cm-6x5in) s. panel. 21-Sep-3 Grogan, Boston #60/R
£3046	$5544	€4600	Port de Naples (17x28cm-7x11in) s.i.d.1889 verso panel. 15-Jun-4 Rossini, Paris #17/R est:2500-3500
£3125	$5000	€4563	Around Constantinople (28x43cm-11x17in) s. panel. 21-Sep-3 Grogan, Boston #41/R
£7551	$13516	€11100	Two oriental women blowing soap bubbles (45x37cm-18x15in) s. 17-Mar-4 Neumeister, Munich #676/R est:9000
£42000	$76440	€61320	The scribe (38x60cm-15x24in) s. 15-Jun-4 Sotheby's, London #147/R est:30000-40000
£185000	$314500	€270100	Boats, Constantinoples (55x97cm-22x38in) s. 18-Nov-3 Sotheby's, London #308/R

ZONGOLOPOULOS, George (1903-?) Greek

Sculpture			
£17000	$30430	€24820	The shoemaker of Psychiko (57cm-22in) init. brown pat bronze bakelite base. 11-May-4 Bonhams, New Bond Street #87/R est:10000-15000

ZOPF, Carl (1858-1944) German

£355	$592	€500	Hofgastein with Gaukogel and Fischlerkaar (100x77cm-39x30in) s.d.21 s.i. verso board. 14-Oct-3 Dorotheum, Vienna #68/R
£563	$975	€800	A sultry summer day (69x47cm-27x19in) s.d.23 i.verso cardboard. 10-Dec-3 Hugo Ruef, Munich #2528/R
Works on paper			
£313	$489	€457	Ladies beside window looking onto the street (46x35cm-18x14in) s. W/C gouache exec.c.1900. 30-Mar-3 Agra, Warsaw #52/R (P.Z 2000)

ZOPF, Julius (attrib) (1838-1897) Austrian

£280	$476	€400	Hut in Dachstain area (19x29cm-7x11in) 20-Nov-3 Dorotheum, Salzburg #150/R
£1854	$3375	€2800	Idyllic forest with wild deer at the stream (93x165cm-37x65in) 21-Jun-4 Dorotheum, Vienna #215/R est:1500-1800

ZOPPO, Rocco (?-1508) Italian

£27778	$50000	€40556	Madonna and Child with two angels (51x38cm-20x15in) panel prov.exhib.lit. 22-Jan-4 Sotheby's, New York #55/R est:80000-120000

ZORACH, Marguerite (1887-1968) American

£8750	$14000	€12775	Mountains (30x41cm-12x16in) panel prov. 21-Sep-3 Grogan, Boston #84/R
£11299	$20000	€16497	Magnificent rhubarb (76x91cm-30x36in) s. 1-May-4 Thomaston Place, Thomaston #60/R
Prints			
£1975	$3200	€2864	New England family (32x22cm-13x9in) s.i.d.1921 linocut. 8-Aug-3 Barridorf, Portland #18/R est:2000-3000
Works on paper			
£741	$1200	€1074	Head of a woman (45x33cm-18x13in) s. dr. 8-Aug-3 Barridorf, Portland #16/R est:1500-1800
£3395	$5500	€4923	Portrait of William Zorach (49x32cm-19x13in) s.d.1921 pencil dr. 8-Aug-3 Barridorf, Portland #9/R est:6000-9000
£18519	$30000	€26853	Dancers (41x31cm-16x12in) s. W/C. 8-Aug-3 Barridorf, Portland #1/R est:12000-18000

ZORACH, William (1887-1966) American

Prints			
£1505	$2800	€2197	Sailing (17x16cm-7x6in) s. i.verso woodcut prov. 5-Mar-4 Skinner, Boston #150/R est:3000-5000
£1852	$3000	€2685	Pegasus (11x12cm-4x5in) s.d.1917 linocut. 8-Aug-3 Barridorf, Portland #13/R est:600-900
£3086	$5000	€4475	Weirs (39x21cm-15x8in) s.i.d.1916 linocut. 8-Aug-3 Barridorf, Portland #15/R est:2000-3000
£3086	$5000	€4475	To a swimmer (25x14cm-10x6in) s.i.d.1916 linocut. 8-Aug-3 Barridorf, Portland #29/R est:2000-3000
£4012	$6500	€5817	Maine coast village (27x18cm-11x7in) s.i.d.1920 linocut. 8-Aug-3 Barridorf, Portland #23/R est:2000-3000
£19753	$32000	€28642	Mountain stream (28x36cm-11x14in) s.d.1916 linocut. 8-Aug-3 Barridorf, Portland #11/R est:9000-12000
Sculpture			
£1957	$3600	€2857	Head of Christ (30cm-12in) s.d.1941 num.2/5 green pat bronze Cast Roman. 10-Jun-4 Swann Galleries, New York #261/R est:3000-5000
£2446	$4500	€3571	Head of Choun (18cm-7in) s. num.2/6 gold pat bronze incl base. 27-Jun-4 Freeman, Philadelphia #145/R est:2500-4000
£3073	$5500	€4487	Embrace (44cm-17in) s. gold pat brown. 14-May-4 Skinner, Boston #363/R est:4000-6000
£3704	$6000	€5371	Leda (39cm-15in) bronze prov. 8-Aug-3 Barridorf, Portland #284/R est:3000-5000
£4070	$7000	€5942	Dance - Family Musical (23x23cm-9x9in) i.d.1930 bronze relief plaque edn of 8. 7-Dec-3 Freeman, Philadelphia #140 est:3000-5000
£4972	$9000	€7259	Mother and child (40x16cm-16x6in) s. aluminum relief mahogany plaque. 31-Mar-4 Sotheby's, New York #19/R est:1500-2500
£5679	$9200	€8235	Novation (46cm-18in) s. bronze prov. 8-Aug-3 Barridorf, Portland #283/R est:3000-5000
£7222	$13000	€10544	Seated cat (34cm-13in) s.base bronze prov. 24-Apr-4 Weschler, Washington #635/R est:6000-8000
Works on paper			
£299	$550	€437	Reclining figure (41x53cm-16x21in) s. pen ink. 10-Jun-4 Swann Galleries, New York #260/R
£412	$725	€602	Towered citadel (30x23cm-12x9in) s.d.1920 graphite. 24-May-4 Winter Associates, Plainville #216/R
£615	$1100	€898	Landscape (30x41cm-12x16in) s.d.1930 W/C. 8-May-4 Susanin's, Chicago #6070/R est:800-1200
£688	$1100	€1004	House and mountains (18x25cm-7x10in) s.d.1915 W/C. 21-Sep-3 Grogan, Boston #83/R
£756	$1300	€1104	House with dock, Panajachel, Guatamala (38x56cm-15x22in) s.d.March 1960 W/C. 3-Dec-3 Doyle, New York #298/R est:2500-3500
£988	$1600	€1433	Maine landscape (22x28cm-9x11in) s.i.d.1918 pencil dr. 8-Aug-3 Barridorf, Portland #3/R est:1200-1800
£1006	$1800	€1469	Fishboat in harbour (23x33cm-9x13in) s.d.1922 W/C pencil. 26-May-4 Doyle, New York #142/R est:3000-5000
£1235	$2000	€1791	Maine landscape with houses (22x28cm-9x11in) s.i.d.1918 pencil dr. 8-Aug-3 Barridorf, Portland #4/R est:1200-1800

£1389	$2500	€2028	Beach scene with sailboats (25x36cm-10x14in) s. W/C pencil rice paper laid down prov. 24-Apr-4 Weschler, Washington #634/R est:1000-2000
£1796	$3000	€2622	White house (40x58cm-16x23in) s. W/C prov. 7-Oct-3 Sotheby's, New York #203 est:3000-5000
£2059	$3500	€3006	Mountain stream (33x25cm-13x10in) s.d.1915 W/C. 9-Nov-3 Wright, Chicago #132 est:1500-2000
£2273	$4000	€3319	Beach in Popham (38x56cm-15x22in) s. W/C exhib. 3-Jan-4 Collins, Maine #26/R est:6000-8000
£2469	$4000	€3580	Yosemite trees (39x33cm-15x13in) s. W/C. 8-Aug-3 Barridorf, Portland #5/R est:9000-12000
£2469	$4000	€3580	Park (22x29cm-9x11in) mono. brush ink prov. 8-Aug-3 Barridorf, Portland #343/R est:4000-6000
£3086	$5000	€4475	Robinhood, Maine (39x56cm-15x22in) s.d.1926 W/C prov. 8-Aug-3 Barridorf, Portland #8/R est:6000-9000
£3704	$6000	€5371	Robinhood, Maine (46x56cm-18x22in) s.i.d.1925 W/C. 8-Aug-3 Barridorf, Portland #6/R est:6000-9000
£4324	$8000	€6313	Deserted ferry ship (39x58cm-15x23in) s.d.1941 s.verso W/C pencil. 11-Mar-4 Christie's, Rockefeller NY #93/R est:10000-15000
£4595	$8500	€6709	Quebec City (33x23cm-13x9in) s.d.1913 W/C pencil prov. 11-Mar-4 Christie's, Rockefeller NY #96/R est:5000-7000
£4790	$8000	€6993	Zorach house in Maine (38x56cm-15x22in) s.d.1927 W/C pencil. 11-Nov-3 Christie's, Rockefeller NY #187/R est:7000-9000
£5556	$9000	€8056	At the beach (39x57cm-15x22in) s.i.d.1954 W/C. 8-Aug-3 Barridorf, Portland #10/R est:6000-9000
£6486	$12000	€9470	Five trees in the distance (28x22cm-11x9in) s.d.1913 W/C pencil prov. 11-Mar-4 Christie's, Rockefeller NY #98/R est:10000-15000
£8025	$13000	€11636	Yosemite stream (39x33cm-15x13in) s.d.1920 W/C. 8-Aug-3 Barridorf, Portland #2/R est:9000-12000

ZORILLA DE SAN MARTIN, Jose Luis (1891-1975) Uruguayan

Prints

£3059	$5200	€4466	Montevideo carnival (195x118cm-77x46in) engraving. 25-Nov-3 Galeria y Remates, Montevideo #81

ZORIO, Gilberto (1944-) Italian

£3147	$5350	€4500	Untitled (81x102cm-32x40in) s.d.2000 tempera ink chl glue sand card. 24-Nov-3 Christie's, Milan #146/R est:4500-6500

Sculpture

£20134	$36040	€30000	Star (240x286cm-94x113in) s.d.82 verso leather painted wood prov. 25-May-4 Sotheby's, Milan #315/R est:30000-40000

Works on paper

£1419	$2540	€2100	Untitled (30x46cm-12x18in) s.d.90 mixed media. 4-May-4 Calmels Cohen, Paris #245/R est:2500-3000
£2083	$3292	€3000	Untitled (42x54cm-17x21in) s.d.1987 mixed media prov. 27-Apr-3 Versailles Encheres #110
£2536	$4159	€3500	Untitled (50x65cm-20x26in) s.d.74 Chinese ink ink. 27-May-3 Sotheby's, Milan #154 est:800-1000
£3846	$6538	€5500	Star (71x101cm-28x40in) s.d.91 s.d.verso mixed media paint cardboard. 25-Nov-3 Sotheby's, Milan #111/R est:5000-7000
£5405	$9514	€8000	Sieve (136x206cm-54x81in) s.d.81 mixed media cardboard on board prov. 24-May-4 Christie's, Milan #228/R est:9000-13000
£6400	$11776	€9344	Untitled (142x201cm-56x79in) s.d.89 volcanic sand iron filings resin paper nails prov. 24-Jun-4 Sotheby's, London #233/R est:6000-8000
£6400	$11776	€9344	Untitled (66x111cm-26x44in) s.d.1977 ball point pen oil leather collage on leather prov. 24-Jun-4 Sotheby's, London #234/R est:6000-8000
£7186	$12000	€10492	Untitled (70x99cm-28x39in) s. wax copper board prov. 13-Nov-3 Sotheby's, New York #561/R est:10000-15000
£15000	$27150	€21900	Untitled (242x229cm-95x90in) painted leather on wood executed 1985 prov.exhib. 1-Apr-4 Christie's, Kensington #235/R est:12000-15000
£37000	$61790	€54020	Stella. s.d.74 ball point pen leather board five prov. 21-Oct-3 Christie's, London #66/R est:40000-60000

ZORN, Anders (1860-1920) Swedish

£23651	$42336	€34530	Girl in wooded landscape (35x54cm-14x21in) prov. 28-May-4 Uppsala Auktionskammare, Uppsala #153/R est:250000-300000 (S.KR 320000)
£39542	$70780	€57731	Interior scene with seated lady - Mrs Bertha Berg (130x100cm-51x39in) s.d.1917 prov.exhib.lit. 26-May-4 AB Stockholms Auktionsverk #2203/R est:300000-400000 (S.KR 535000)
£180769	$310923	€263923	Bay in the skerries - light summer breeze (50x100cm-20x39in) s. painted 1889 exhib.prov. 3-Dec-3 AB Stockholms Auktionsverk #2276/R est:1200000-1500000 (S.KR 2350000)
£192308	$330769	€280770	By the fence - female nude in water (85x65cm-33x26in) s.d.1913 prov.lit. 2-Dec-3 Bukowskis, Stockholm #178/R est:2500000-3000000 (S.KR 2500000)
£247598	$443200	€361493	Unicorn - female nude in front of tapestry (125x90cm-49x35in) s.d.1906 prov.lit. 25-May-4 Bukowskis, Stockholm #188/R est:2500000-3000000 (S.KR 3350000)
£473077	$813692	€690692	Fetching water (119x89cm-47x35in) s.d.1907 prov.exhib.lit. 2-Dec-3 Bukowskis, Stockholm #173/R est:4500000-5000000 (S.KR 6150000)

Prints

£2077	$3572	€3032	Axel Herman Hagg III (39x26cm-15x10in) s. etching lit. 3-Dec-3 AB Stockholms Auktionsverk #2533/R est:20000-25000 (S.KR 27000)
£2217	$3969	€3237	Fishermen in St. Ives (28x20cm-11x8in) s. etching prov.lit. 25-May-4 Bukowskis, Stockholm #242a/R est:40000-45000 (S.KR 30000)
£2217	$3969	€3237	Girl smoking cigarette (16x12cm-6x5in) s. etching lit. 25-May-4 Bukowskis, Stockholm #243/R est:30000-35000 (S.KR 30000)
£2462	$4234	€3595	Axel Herman Hagg III (38x26cm-15x10in) s.i. etching lit. 2-Dec-3 Bukowskis, Stockholm #194/R est:40000-50000 (S.KR 32000)
£3308	$5689	€4830	Zorn and his wife (32x21cm-13x8in) s. etching. 2-Dec-3 Bukowskis, Stockholm #196/R est:30000-40000 (S.KR 43000)
£3326	$5953	€4856	Cheers (32x27cm-13x11in) s. one of 75 etching lit. 25-May-4 Bukowskis, Stockholm #246/R est:40000-45000 (S.KR 45000)
£3385	$5822	€4942	Omnibus (42x31cm-17x12in) s. etching lit. 2-Dec-3 Bukowskis, Stockholm #199/R est:30000-40000 (S.KR 44000)
£6154	$10585	€8985	Cousins (68x55cm-27x22in) s. etching one of c.40. 2-Dec-3 Bukowskis, Stockholm #193/R est:100000-125000 (S.KR 80000)

Sculpture

£5026	$8996	€7338	Gryvel - nude girl kneeling playing with an insect (8x11cm-3x4in) s. green pat.bronze Cast.Otto Meyer lit. 26-May-4 AB Stockholms Auktionsverk #2124/R est:50000-60000 (S.KR 68000)
£5174	$9261	€7554	Gustav Vasa (19cm-7in) green pat.bronze Cast Otto Meyer exec.c.1901-1902 lit. 26-May-4 AB Stockholms Auktionsverk #2125/R est:20000-25000 (S.KR 70000)
£9231	$15877	€13477	Alma I - nude girl standing (22cm-9in) s.d.1910 pat.bronze Cast.Meyer lit. 3-Dec-3 AB Stockholms Auktionsverk #2454/R est:60000-80000 (S.KR 120000)
£44615	$76738	€65138	Nude girl standing (104cm-41in) s.i.d.1911 pat.bronze fountain figure II lit. 3-Dec-3 AB Stockholms Auktionsverk #2453/R est:700000-900000 (S.KR 580000)

Works on paper

£2175	$3916	€3263	Portrait of woman (20x12cm-8x5in) i.verso pencil exec.c.1900 lit.prov. 25-Apr-4 Goteborg Auktionsverk, Sweden #201/R est:40000 (S.KR 30000)
£4702	$8558	€7100	Cousines (31x20cm-12x8in) s.i. pen wash htd white. 15-Jun-4 Rossini, Paris #24/R est:9000
£5174	$9261	€7554	Miss Dolly Redford (19x14cm-7x6in) s.i. W/C gold ground. 26-May-4 AB Stockholms Auktionsverk #2126/R est:80000-100000 (S.KR 70000)
£46154	$79385	€67385	Portrait of the young Henry Trevelyan (50x31cm-20x12in) s.d.87 W/C prov.lit. 3-Dec-3 AB Stockholms Auktionsverk #2317/R est:600000-800000 (S.KR 600000)
£83149	$148836	€121398	Indolence (40x27cm-16x11in) s.d.82 W/C lit. 25-May-4 Bukowskis, Stockholm #189/R est:1000000-1500000 (S.KR 1125000)

ZORNES, Milford (1908-) American

£3352	$6000	€4894	Halawa valley. Above Pukoo. To Mokio Point (57x77cm-22x30in) s. W/C set of three. 21-Mar-4 Bonhams & Butterfields, Los Angeles #7312/R est:2500-3500

Works on paper

£217	$400	€317	Sheet of my demonstration animals and figures (71x56cm-28x22in) i. W/C. 29-Mar-4 O'Gallerie, Oregon #691/R
£417	$750	€609	Old farmhouse with a storm approaching (38x55cm-15x22in) pencil W/C. 25-Apr-4 Bonhams & Butterfields, San Francisco #5551/R
£476	$900	€695	Evening 42 - ship in coastal (23x30cm-9x12in) init.d.42 i. verso mixed media panel prov. 17-Feb-4 John Moran, Pasadena #131/R
£476	$900	€695	Desert Storm (20x28cm-8x11in) init. verso W/C paper on board prov. 17-Feb-4 John Moran, Pasadena #136/R
£582	$1100	€850	Laguna Beach (20x28cm-8x11in) ini.d.48 i.d. verso W/C paper on board prov. 17-Feb-4 John Moran, Pasadena #93b/R
£635	$1200	€927	Rough seas at Point Arguello (30x41cm-12x16in) s.d.1949 s.i. verso W/C prov. 17-Feb-4 John Moran, Pasadena #94b/R
£741	$1400	€1082	The little lake (25x41cm-10x16in) s.d.1939 i.d. verso mixed media canvas on masonite. 17-Feb-4 John Moran, Pasadena #94a/R est:1000-1500
£899	$1700	€1313	Puddingstone Lake (43x53cm-17x21in) s.d.1948 s.i.d. verso prov. 17-Feb-4 John Moran, Pasadena #130/R est:1000-1500
£952	$1800	€1390	At La Jolla (20x28cm-8x11in) init.d.50 i.d. verso W/C prov. 17-Feb-4 John Moran, Pasadena #93a/R est:1000-1500
£1032	$1900	€1507	Mt. Carmel Cottonwoods, Texas River. Winter at Mt. Carmel (56x74cm-22x29in) s.d.68 W/C set of three. 28-Mar-4 Bonhams & Butterfields, San Francisco #2737 est:2500-3500
£1038	$1900	€1515	Rancho de Taos (53x74cm-21x29in) s.d.1920 i.verso W/C. 5-Jun-4 Treadway Gallery, Cincinnati #649/R est:2000-3000
£1236	$2250	€1805	Back Bay, Newport (56x79cm-22x31in) s. i.verso W/C. 15-Jun-4 John Moran, Pasadena #89 est:3000-4000
£1323	$2500	€1932	Utah landscape (38x58cm-15x23in) s.d.1949 i. verso prov. 17-Feb-4 John Moran, Pasadena #92b/R est:1000-2000
£1323	$2500	€1932	Untitled landscape of farm land (38x56cm-15x22in) s.d.Jan 1945 W/C prov. 17-Feb-4 John Moran, Pasadena #94/R est:1000-1500
£1323	$2500	€1932	Walls of Old Ft Lowell 1947 (38x56cm-15x22in) s.d.May 13, 1947 i.d. verso prov. 17-Feb-4 John Moran, Pasadena #134/R est:1000-2000
£1323	$2500	€1932	Joshua Tree Valley (38x56cm-15x22in) s.d.39 W/C prov. 17-Feb-4 John Moran, Pasadena #135/R est:1000-2000
£1359	$2500	€1984	Cannon beach, Oregon, seascape with Haystack Rock and figures (56x76cm-22x30in) s. i.verso W/C prov. 29-Mar-4 O'Gallerie, Oregon #118/R est:1000-1500
£1587	$3000	€2317	Puddingstone Lake 1939 (36x56cm-14x22in) s.d.1949 i.d. verso W/C. 17-Feb-4 John Moran, Pasadena #93/R est:1500-2500
£1618	$2750	€2362	Casita de Colena (20x30cm-8x12in) s.d.71 i.verso W/C prov. 18-Nov-3 John Moran, Pasadena #128 est:800-1200
£1720	$3250	€2511	Los Berros Creek. Mojave (28x38cm-11x15in) s.d.37 i. verso prov. two. 17-Feb-4 John Moran, Pasadena #133/R est:1000-2000
£1902	$3500	€2777	In Madrid. Island patterns. From Cabra Island , Puerto Rico (56x77cm-22x30in) s.d.71 W/C set of three. 27-Jun-4 Bonhams & Butterfields, San Francisco #3838/R est:2500-3500
£1923	$3500	€2808	Hawaii landscape, above Pukoo (56x76cm-22x30in) s.d.73 i.d.1973 verso W/C. 15-Jun-4 John Moran, Pasadena #86a est:3000-4500
£1923	$3500	€2808	Street scene (36x53cm-14x21in) s.d.54 W/C. 15-Jun-4 John Moran, Pasadena #136a est:2000-3000
£2060	$3750	€3008	Hawaii landscape, Halasw Valley (56x76cm-22x30in) s.d.73 i.d.1973 W/C. 15-Jun-4 John Moran, Pasadena #87 est:3000-4500
£2083	$3750	€3041	Bario de Los Camareros. Manzanillo Harbour. Rocky shore at Manzanillo (55x76cm-22x30in) two s.d.75 one s.d.73 s.i.verso pencil W/C three. 25-Apr-4 Bonhams & Butterfields, San Francisco #5549/R est:2500-3500
£2116	$4000	€3089	Avila Creek 1949 (36x53cm-14x21in) init.d.Dec 26, 1949 i.d. verso W/C prov. 17-Feb-4 John Moran, Pasadena #92a/R est:1500-2500

£2273 $4250 €3319 Sheep wagon, Idaho. Idaho farm. San Juan river at Four Corners (56x76cm-22x30in) s.d.74 s.i.verso one d.75 W/C set of three. 29-Feb-4 Bonhams & Butterfields, San Francisco #4555 est:2500-3500
£2273 $4250 €3410 Over the Arkansas. Cave falls. Back country (56x76cm-22x30in) s. one d.75 one d.73 one d.60 s.i.verso W/C set of three. 25-Jul-4 Bonhams & Butterfields, San Francisco #6109/R est:2500-3500
£3175 $6000 €4636 On Morro Rock 1950 (41x51cm-16x20in) s.d.1950 i.d. verso mixed media board prov. 17-Feb-4 John Moran, Pasadena #92/R est:2000-3000
£3243 $6000 €4735 Green river, Wyoming, evening on the Wabash, Indiana, Baronzer, Wyoming (56x76cm-22x30in) s. i.d.verso W/C paperboard. 18-Jul-4 Bonhams & Butterfields, Los Angeles #7053/R est:2500-3500
£3297 $6000 €4814 Hawaii landscape (56x76cm-22x30in) s.d.1973 i.d.verso W/C. 15-Jun-4 John Moran, Pasadena #86 est:3000-4500
£3804 $7000 €5554 Bridge at Sutter's Mill. Lakeside park. Stout Creek. Zion Canyon (55x76cm-22x30in) s. three d.74 one d.73 i. verso W/C four prov. 8-Jun-4 Bonhams & Butterfields, San Francisco #4382/R est:3500-4500
£3804 $7000 €5554 Canyon walls. Gold town. Rex Burg Butte. El Morro (55x76cm-22x30in) s. various dates 1971-75 W/C four. 8-Jun-4 Bonhams & Butterfields, San Francisco #4383/R est:3500-4500
£4118 $7000 €6012 Arbol Verdi (53x74cm-21x29in) s.d.37 W/C double-sided prov. 18-Nov-3 John Moran, Pasadena #89 est:2500-3500
£4143 $7500 €6049 Idaho Falls. Storm over the Tetons. In silver city, Idaho (57x76cm-22x30in) s. W/C set of three. 18-Apr-4 Bonhams & Butterfields, Los Angeles #7021 est:2500-3500
£4324 $8000 €6313 Fishermen's shacks at Manzanillo Quey Pilots Laguna Cayatlay, Manzanilla (57x77cm-22x30in) s. i.d.verso W/C paperboard. 18-Jul-4 Bonhams & Butterfields, Los Angeles #7052/R est:2500-3500
£4891 $9000 €7141 Mount San Jacinto. Evening sky. Ranch pond (54x74cm-21x29in) i. one d.59 one s.d.72 one s.d.66 W/C three. 8-Jun-4 Bonhams & Butterfields, San Francisco #4381/R est:3000-5000

ZORRILLA, Alfredo (1927-1990) Uruguayan
£366 $600 €534 Homage to Utrillo (43x54cm-17x21in) s.d.66 cardboard. 3-Jun-3 Galeria y Remates, Montevideo #58
£1080 $1750 €1566 Family portrait (38x46cm-15x18in) s.d.88 prov. 29-Jul-3 Galeria y Remates, Montevideo #61/R est:2000-3000
£2195 $3600 €3205 Tea time (89x99cm-35x39in) s.d.76 cardboard. 3-Jun-3 Galeria y Remates, Montevideo #105
£3069 $5800 €4481 Family (81x100cm-32x39in) s.d.88 s.i.d.verso. 22-Feb-4 Galeria y Remates, Montevideo #130/R est:7000
£3492 $6600 €5098 View from Mansa Beach (100x110cm-39x43in) s.i.d.1981 verso. 22-Feb-4 Galeria y Remates, Montevideo #131/R est:7000

ZOTL, Aloys (1803-1887) Swiss
Works on paper
£3401 $6088 €5000 Une etude de seiche (45x34cm-18x13in) s.d.19 Mai 1881 graphite W/C. 18-Mar-4 Christie's, Paris #200/R est:3000-5000
£3401 $6088 €5000 Deux etudes de seiches (45x34cm-18x13in) s.i.d.20 September 1881 graphite W/C. 18-Mar-4 Christie's, Paris #201/R est:3000-5000
£18120 $33704 €27000 Der choras simia mormon (28x37cm-11x15in) s.d.19 decembre 1836 W/C prov.lit. 8-Mar-4 Artcurial Briest, Paris #14/R est:20000

ZOU CHUANAN (1941-) Chinese
Works on paper
£3475 $5803 €5074 Bird standing on a fence (89x66cm-35x26in) s.i.d.2002 ink col scroll. 26-Oct-3 Christie's, Hong Kong #266/R est:50000-60000 (HK.D 45000)

ZOUBTCHENKO, Katia (1922-) ?
Works on paper
£420 $713 €600 Composition (65x50cm-26x20in) s. W/C. 28-Nov-3 Blanchet, Paris #234

ZOX, Larry (1936-) American
£1223 $2250 €1786 Anticosti (141x141cm-56x56in) acrylic prov. 8-Jun-4 Germann, Zurich #76/R est:2000-3000 (S.FR 2800)
Works on paper
£204 $375 €298 Scissors Jack series (28x33cm-11x13in) s.i.d.1965 ink. 25-Jun-4 Freeman, Philadelphia #81/R

ZOZULIN, Grigory Stepanovich (1893-1973) Russian
Works on paper
£1500 $2550 €2190 Set design with provincial Russian Church (34x47cm-13x19in) gouache card. 19-Nov-3 Sotheby's, London #185/R est:2000-3000

ZRZAVY, Jan (1890-1977) Czechoslovakian
Works on paper
£438 $727 €639 Yacht (10x15cm-4x6in) mono.d.64 pastel. 4-Oct-3 Dorotheum, Prague #294/R est:20000-30000 (C.KR 20000)
£527 $896 €769 Head of a woman II (15x9cm-6x4in) s. pencil. 29-Nov-3 Dorotheum, Prague #151/R est:15000-23000 (C.KR 24000)
£5906 $10394 €8859 Head (22x20cm-9x8in) init.i. pastel. 22-May-4 Dorotheum, Prague #229/R est:200000-350000 (C.KR 280000)

ZUANICH, Frank H (1890-1978) American
£221 $400 €323 Town square (46x56cm-18x22in) s.d.1963 board. 3-Apr-4 Harvey Clar, Oakland #1243

ZUBAR, R (20th C) Czechoslovakian
£1200 $2220 €1752 Reclining nude (75x104cm-30x41in) s. 10-Mar-4 Sotheby's, Olympia #308/R est:1200-1800

ZUBER, Henri (1844-1909) French
£528 $914 €750 Paysage, bord de riviere (32x46cm-13x18in) s. 12-Dec-3 Piasa, Paris #96
£629 $1151 €950 Vaches au paturage (50x65cm-20x26in) s. 7-Apr-4 Piasa, Paris #50
£662 $1212 €1000 Promenade, jeune femme en sous-bois au-dessus de la mer (46x33cm-18x13in) s. 7-Apr-4 Piasa, Paris #51
£1620 $2802 €2300 La cueillette des oranges (45x65cm-18x26in) s. 12-Dec-3 Piasa, Paris #97/R est:1000-1500
Works on paper
£333 $603 €500 Jardin du Luxembourg au Crepuscule (10x17cm-4x7in) st.mono. W/C black crayon. 30-Mar-4 Rossini, Paris #1092
£364 $667 €550 Port d'Antibes (24x36cm-9x14in) s. W/C. 7-Apr-4 Piasa, Paris #52
£367 $664 €550 Moulin Hollandais (30x45cm-12x18in) st.sig. W/C. 30-Mar-4 Rossini, Paris #1083
£467 $845 €700 Riviere au clair de lune (48x32cm-19x13in) st.sig.i. W/C black crayon sold with W/C by another hand. 30-Mar-4 Rossini, Paris #1088
£467 $845 €700 Paris quartiers pauvres sous la lune. Allee du Luxembourg au Crepuscule (14x10cm-6x4in) one bears mono. W/C two in one frame lit. 30-Mar-4 Rossini, Paris #1089
£467 $845 €700 Allee dans un parc (24x18cm-9x7in) st.mono. i.verso W/C two sheets. 30-Mar-4 Rossini, Paris #1094
£533 $965 €800 Allee au Luxembourg (12x20cm-5x8in) st.mono. W/C lit. 30-Mar-4 Rossini, Paris #1086
£600 $1086 €900 Au jardin du Luxembourg, Paris (34x24cm-13x9in) W/C. 30-Mar-4 Rossini, Paris #1085/R
£800 $1448 €1200 Ile, etude de ciel, prairie (12x19cm-5x7in) one bears st.mono. W/C pair. 30-Mar-4 Rossini, Paris #1095
£867 $1569 €1300 Cannes (35x49cm-14x19in) s. W/C. 30-Mar-4 Rossini, Paris #1084
£867 $1569 €1300 Couple de cavaliers Place de la Concorde. Chataigniers au soleil couchant (35x50cm-14x20in) st.sig. i.erso double-sided. 30-Mar-4 Rossini, Paris #1082/R
£1067 $1931 €1600 Deux vues du Luxembourg (18x13cm-7x5in) one bears st.mono. one bears studio st.verso W/C pair. 30-Mar-4 Rossini, Paris #1087 est:220-300

ZUBER, Jean (1943-) Swiss
£1042 $1740 €1500 L'oreille de Bouddha (130x160cm-51x63in) prov. 25-Oct-3 Cornette de St.Cyr, Paris #467 est:100-150

ZUBER, Max (20th C) Swiss?
£1310 $2410 €1913 Mother and child (33x23cm-13x9in) s. 14-Jun-4 Philippe Schuler, Zurich #4240/R est:3000-3500 (S.FR 3000)

ZUBER-BUHLER, Fritz (1822-1896) Swiss
£2483 $4445 €3700 Jeune femme tenant un livre (46x38cm-18x15in) s. 25-May-4 Chambelland & Giafferi, Paris #14/R est:1200-1500
£4706 $8000 €6871 Daydreams (74x61cm-29x24in) s. prov. 29-Oct-3 Christie's, Rockefeller NY #55/R est:10000-15000

ZUBIAURRE, Ramon de (1882-1969) Spanish
£408 $731 €600 Lady (9x12cm-4x5in) s. card. 22-Mar-4 Durán, Madrid #67/R
£18092 $33289 €27500 Working hard (75x90cm-30x35in) s.d.1934. 22-Jun-4 Durán, Madrid #214/R est:22500
Works on paper
£1267 $2305 €1900 Personages castellanos (32x26cm-13x10in) s. W/C. 29-Jun-4 Segre, Madrid #68/R est:1200

ZUBIAURRE, Valentin de (1879-1963) Spanish
£4113 $6870 €5800 Trois femmes attablees (105x87cm-41x34in) s. 15-Oct-3 Rabourdin & Choppin de Janvry, Paris #36/R est:5000-10000
£9103 $16386 €13200 Landscape (32x41cm-13x16in) s. 26-Jan-4 Ansorena, Madrid #204/R est:13200
£17241 $31034 €25000 The mayor (60x46cm-24x18in) s. 26-Jan-4 Ansorena, Madrid #214/R est:19300
£20000 $34000 €29200 On the balcony, Sepulveda (90x90cm-35x35in) s. prov.exhib. 18-Nov-3 Sotheby's, London #209/R
£39474 $72632 €60000 Fishermen in Ondarroa (85x100cm-33x39in) s. 22-Jun-4 Durán, Madrid #215/R est:37500

ZUCCA, Teresio (1926-) Italian
£278 $472 €400 Still life of fruit (50x70cm-20x28in) s. s.i.verso. 1-Nov-3 Meeting Art, Vercelli #369
£345 $572 €500 Yellow roses (30x40cm-12x16in) 1-Oct-3 Della Rocca, Turin #201/R

ZUCCARELLI, Francesco (1702-1788) Italian

£15000	$25500	€21900	Italianate river landscape with herdsman and woman fetching water (45x69cm-18x27in) 29-Oct-3 Christie's, London #95/R est:7000-10000
£33188	$60402	€48454	Wedding party and houses in a landscape (39x55cm-15x22in) prov. 16-Jun-4 Fischer, Luzern #1074/R est:40000-45000 (S.FR 76000)
£84507	$136056	€120000	Paesaggio con la fuga in Egitto (71x106cm-28x42in) 8-May-3 Farsetti, Prato #784/R est:130000-150000
£90000	$155700	€131400	Landscape with peasants and animals by a river with a fortified town on a ridge beyond (82x116cm-32x46in) prov. 10-Dec-3 Christie's, London #52/R est:100000-150000
£102013	$190765	€152000	Landscape with washerwomen. Landscape with cattle (70x113cm-28x44in) pair prov.exhib. 25-Feb-4 Porro, Milan #79/R est:130000
Works on paper			
£260	$475	€380	Arcadian landscape with a temple (15x23cm-6x9in) brush brown ink wash over pencil. 29-Jan-4 Swann Galleries, New York #125/R
£464	$844	€700	Procession in landscape (27x43cm-11x17in) sanguine pen ink W/C prov. 16-Jun-4 Christie's, Rome #466
£1639	$3000	€2393	Return of the Prodigal Son. Shepherdess with boy and their flock (36x46cm-14x18in) brush brown ink wash pair. 29-Jan-4 Swann Galleries, New York #126/R est:3000-5000
£1769	$3166	€2600	Un paysage avec des figures sous un arbre, un village a l'arrier-plan (27x42cm-11x17in) i. black chk pen brown ink col wash htd white. 18-Mar-4 Christie's, Paris #36/R est:3000-5000
£3741	$6697	€5500	Un paysage avec des bergers, une ville dans le lointain (27x43cm-11x17in) s. pen brown ink grey wash htd white prov. 18-Mar-4 Christie's, Paris #34/R est:5000-7000
£3741	$6697	€5500	Un paysage de montagne avec un troupeau, un village au fond (33x50cm-13x20in) pen brown ink grey wash htd white prov. 18-Mar-4 Christie's, Paris #35/R est:6000-8000
£4000	$7320	€5840	River landscape with buildings and a church on the far bank and two women (27x39cm-11x15in) col wash gouache over black chk two joined sheets. 7-Jul-4 Bonhams, Knightsbridge #56/R est:4000-6000

ZUCCARELLI, Francesco (attrib) (1702-1788) Italian

£6000	$10200	€8760	River landscape with a girl walking over a bridge, anglers beneath (37x47cm-15x19in) 31-Oct-3 Christie's, Kensington #143/R est:4000-6000
Works on paper			
£1000	$1830	€1460	Portrait of a girl, looking right (34x23cm-13x9in) black white chk. 6-Jul-4 Christie's, London #75/R est:1000-1500
£1448	$2462	€2114	Riders fighting (25x45cm-10x18in) brown ink wash. 28-Nov-3 Falk & Falk, Zurich #382/R est:4500 (S.FR 3200)

ZUCCARELLI, Francesco (circle) (1702-1788) Italian

£5369	$9879	€8000	Peasant family (62x84cm-24x33in) 24-Mar-4 Hugo Ruef, Munich #888/R est:3000
£28000	$51240	€42000	Landscape with waterfall. Landscape with stream (37x46cm-15x18in) pair. 1-Jun-4 Sotheby's, Milan #179/R est:10000-15000

ZUCCARELLI, Francesco (style) (1702-1788) Italian

£11500	$20700	€16790	Extensive landscape with figures fishing before a bridge. Landscape with fishermen and maids by pool (42x63cm-17x25in) pair. 20-Apr-4 Sotheby's, Olympia #394/R est:8000-10000

ZUCCARO, Federico (1540-1609) Italian

Works on paper			
£2800	$5124	€4088	Fra Stefano, procurator of the Camaldolites at Vallombrose, as Romuald (27x16cm-11x6in) i.d.1577 black red chk. 6-Jul-4 Christie's, London #18/R est:1500-2000
£3767	$6404	€5500	Xanthos buying Aesopus (27x44cm-11x17in) i. pen ink wash over crayon per. 6-Nov-3 Tajan, Paris #1/R
£4412	$7500	€6442	Study of the right hand side of the rule of the anti Christ (22x16cm-9x6in) i. pencil red chk two after Signorelli prov. 19-Nov-3 Bonhams & Butterfields, San Francisco #2/R
£5850	$9302	€8600	Saint Lawrence's martyrdom (25x18cm-10x7in) i.verso pen ink wash gouache. 21-Mar-3 Bailly Pommery, Paris #41
£9444	$17000	€13788	Apollo and the Muses on Parnassus (19x28cm-7x11in) pen brown ink. 22-Jan-4 Christie's, Rockefeller NY #14/R est:10000-15000
£10588	$18000	€15458	Study of celestial figures (20x27cm-8x11in) pencil red chk set of four after Correggio prov. 19-Nov-3 Bonhams & Butterfields, San Francisco #3/R
£10884	$19483	€16000	Vierge couronnee par deux anges tenant dans ses bras l'enfant Jesus (34x27cm-13x11in) pen brown ink blk crayon brown wash htd white gouache prov. 17-Mar-4 Tajan, Paris #8/R est:15000
£15294	$26000	€22329	Mystic marriage of St. Catherine (22x17cm-9x7in) i. pencil red chk set of four after Correggio. 19-Nov-3 Bonhams & Butterfields, San Francisco #4/R

ZUCCARO, Federico (attrib) (1540-1609) Italian

Works on paper			
£2500	$4500	€3650	Sant Angelo in Vado, Marches (20x20cm-8x8in) i. pen ink wash. 21-Jan-4 Sotheby's, New York #42/R est:2000-3000
£4965	$8291	€7000	Tete de jeune garcon (12x10cm-5x4in) pierre noire sanguine. 19-Oct-3 Anaf, Lyon #305/R est:7000-8000

ZUCCARO, Taddeo (1529-1566) Italian

Works on paper			
£8743	$16000	€12765	Adoration of the Shepherds (47x80cm-19x31in) pen brown ink wash card stock 2 sheets. 29-Jan-4 Swann Galleries, New York #15/R est:3000-5000

ZUCCHI, Antonio (1726-1795) Italian

£1700	$3060	€2482	Allegorical portraits (23x17cm-9x7in) panel oval pair. 21-Jan-4 Sotheby's, Olympia #31/R est:800-1200

ZUCCHI, Francesco (1570-1623) Italian

Works on paper			
£900	$1557	€1314	View of Terracina, with the monastery of Sant'Angelo to the right (9x15cm-4x6in) i. black chk pen brown ink grey wash prov. 12-Dec-3 Christie's, Kensington #388/R

ZUCCOLI, Oreste (1889-1980) Italian

£467	$845	€700	Woman (100x65cm-39x26in) s. 2-Apr-4 Farsetti, Prato #485

ZUCHORS, Walter (1870-?) Dutch

£1259	$2102	€1800	Elegant lady (60x47cm-24x19in) s.d.1902. 30-Jun-3 Sotheby's, Amsterdam #222/R

ZUCKER, Jakub (1900-1981) American/Polish

£482	$799	€704	Blond haired girl (35x27cm-14x11in) s. 15-Jun-3 Agra, Warsaw #45/R (P.Z 3000)
£963	$1599	€1406	Flowers in a basket (61x50cm-24x20in) s. 15-Jun-3 Agra, Warsaw #35/R est:6000 (P.Z 6000)

ZUCKER, Joe (1941-) American

£16760	$30000	€24470	Triassic Jurassic (244x610cm-96x240in) s.i.d.1/1/77 verso acrylic cotton rhoplex four parts prov.exhib. 13-May-4 Sotheby's, New York #470/R est:10000-20000
Works on paper			
£300	$546	€438	Boot (196x196cm-77x77in) s.i.d.5/5/88 stretcher mixed media rope wax. 4-Feb-4 Sotheby's, Olympia #242/R

ZUCKERMAN, S Scott (1951-) American

£328	$600	€479	Moose standing in a woodland, mid winter scene (28x20cm-11x8in) s. masonite. 10-Apr-4 Cobbs, Peterborough #193/R
£464	$850	€677	Red fox in the sunlight (38x51cm-15x20in) s. board. 10-Apr-4 Cobbs, Peterborough #195/R

ZUFFREY, Christiane (1920-) Swiss

£226	$391	€330	Panier de fleurs (33x46cm-13x18in) s. 12-Dec-3 Galerie du Rhone, Sion #602 (S.FR 500)
£409	$733	€597	Au village un jour d'hivers (20x47cm-8x19in) s.d.73 i. stretcher panel. 12-May-4 Dobiaschofsky, Bern #4013 (S.FR 950)
£588	$1018	€858	Pavillion rouge (11x19cm-4x7in) s. board. 12-Dec-3 Galerie du Rhone, Sion #601 (S.FR 1300)

ZUGEL, Heinrich von (1850-1941) German

£521	$859	€750	Dead bird (18x21cm-7x8in) lit. 2-Jul-3 Neumeister, Munich #833
£567	$1043	€850	Three hounds resting at the forest edge (27x20cm-11x8in) s.d.1883 panel. 12-Jun-4 Karlheinz Kaupp, Staufen #1227
£590	$974	€850	Sheepshearing (35x27cm-14x11in) s. board. 2-Jul-3 Neumeister, Munich #834
£1154	$1962	€1650	Pastoral landscape (70x100cm-28x39in) i.d.99 lit. 28-Nov-3 Schloss Ahlden, Ahlden #718/R est:1600
£1479	$2558	€2100	Two sheep (44x52cm-17x20in) s. 11-Dec-3 Dr Fritz Nagel, Stuttgart #554/R est:3800
£2685	$4805	€4000	Three sheep (14x23cm-6x9in) s. board. 27-May-4 Dorotheum, Vienna #130/R est:4000-6000
£3020	$5557	€4500	Young cattle in field (45x60cm-18x24in) s.d.11 lit. 25-Mar-4 Dr Fritz Nagel, Stuttgart #779/R est:5000
£3289	$6053	€5000	Shepherd letting flock out of pasture (54x80cm-21x31in) i. 24-Jun-4 Dr Fritz Nagel, Stuttgart #778/R est:12000
£3497	$5944	€5000	Horse and cart with peasant (47x70cm-19x28in) s.d.96. 29-Nov-3 Villa Grisebach, Berlin #114/R est:5000-7000
£3500	$5845	€5110	Cattle watering (60x80cm-24x31in) s.indis.d. 8-Oct-3 Christie's, Kensington #723/R est:4000-6000
£4895	$8322	€7000	Peasant with oxen in water (47x68cm-19x27in) s.d.22. 20-Nov-3 Van Ham, Cologne #1930/R est:8000
£5000	$8250	€7200	Two loaded donkeys (32x47cm-13x19in) s. board lit. 2-Jul-3 Neumeister, Munich #832/R est:300
£7746	$13401	€11000	Ford (25x43cm-10x17in) s.d.1908. 13-Dec-3 Lempertz, Koln #66/R est:6000
£10884	$19483	€16000	Three calves with herder (47x65cm-19x26in) s. lit. 17-Mar-4 Neumeister, Munich #678/R est:14000
£13889	$23611	€20000	Three cows with cowherd (47x65cm-19x26in) s. prov. 28-Oct-3 Christie's, Amsterdam #202/R est:20000-30000
£18367	$32878	€27000	Landscape (70x100cm-28x39in) s.d.1904 prov.lit. 17-Mar-4 Neumeister, Munich #677/R est:25000

£20979 $36084 €30000 Fruit garden in part sun with shepherdess with white headscarf and flock (60x80cm-24x31in) s. prov. 5-Dec-3 Ketterer, Munich #24/R est:30000-40000
Works on paper
£306 $504 €440 Flock of sheep (35x51cm-14x20in) s.i.d.8.Ockt 01 chl. 2-Jul-3 Neumeister, Munich #508

ZUGNO, Francesco (1709-1787) Italian
£8511 $14213 €12000 La cattura di Cristo (87x72cm-34x28in) s.d.1615 prov.lit. 17-Jun-3 Finarte Semenzato, Milan #652/R est:8000-12000

ZUHR, Hugo (1895-1971) Swedish
£413 $665 €603 Landscape (50x65cm-20x26in) s. prov. 25-Aug-3 Lilla Bukowskis, Stockholm #562 (S.KR 5400)
£476 $776 €695 Coastal landscape (46x61cm-18x24in) s. 29-Sep-3 Lilla Bukowskis, Stockholm #577 (S.KR 6200)
£480 $860 €701 Pine trees in the skerries (40x35cm-16x14in) s.d.17 verso. 28-May-4 Uppsala Auktionskammare, Uppsala #233/R (S.KR 6500)
£659 $1167 €962 Fishing boats in harbour (38x55cm-15x22in) mono. d.1960 verso. 27-Apr-4 AB Stockholms Auktionsverk #724/R (S.KR 9000)
£906 $1541 €1323 Farm in open landscape (38x55cm-15x22in) mono. d.1957 verso. 5-Nov-3 AB Stockholms Auktionsverk #737/R (S.KR 12000)
£1154 $1985 €1685 Landscape (80x100cm-31x39in) mono. 7-Dec-3 Uppsala Auktionskammare, Uppsala #261/R est:8000-10000 (S.KR 15000)
£1885 $3394 €2752 Coastal landscape (73x93cm-29x37in) mono. s.d.63 verso. 26-Apr-4 Bukowskis, Stockholm #193/R est:18000-20000 (S.KR 26000)
£2039 $3467 €2977 Bjornloka - wild flower (60x73cm-24x29in) mono. 4-Nov-3 Bukowskis, Stockholm #209/R est:18000-20000 (S.KR 27000)

ZUKOWSKI, S (?) ?
£1427 $2626 €2083 Interior scene with woman (78x106cm-31x42in) s. 29-Mar-4 Blomqvist, Lysaker #1366 est:3000-4000 (N.KR 18000)

ZULAWSKI, Marek (1908-) Polish
£350 $585 €511 Preparing nets (43x53cm-17x21in) s.d.1949. 14-Oct-3 David Lay, Penzance #206

ZULIANI, Giovanni (1836-1892) Italian
£5102 $9133 €7500 The day before the wedding (95x65cm-37x26in) s. exhib. 22-Mar-4 Sant Agostino, Torino #225/R est:6500-8500

ZULOAGA, Elisa Elvira (1900-1980) South American?
£882 $1500 €1288 Untitled (40x32cm-16x13in) s. 23-Nov-3 Subastas Odalys, Caracas #124/R

ZULOAGA, Ignacio (1870-1945) Spanish
£380000 $646000 €554800 Las Pasiones Street (202x296cm-80x117in) s.d.1904 prov.exhib.lit. 18-Nov-3 Sotheby's, London #210/R est:600000

ZULOW, Franz von (1883-1963) Austrian
£4698 $8315 €7000 Still life of flowers (74x60cm-29x24in) s.d.54 panel. 28-Apr-4 Wiener Kunst Auktionen, Vienna #74/R est:6000-10000
£5282 $9243 €7500 House with bench and well (25x34cm-10x13in) s.d.1924 board. 19-Dec-3 Dorotheum, Vienna #65/R est:7000-10000
£6376 $11795 €9500 Street (31x46cm-12x18in) s. board. 9-Mar-4 Dorotheum, Vienna #61/R est:8000-12000
£7692 $13077 €11000 Village with little church (25x35cm-10x14in) s. panel prov. 26-Nov-3 Dorotheum, Vienna #158/R est:10000-12000
£7718 $13815 €11500 Flowers in a vase (46x36cm-18x14in) s.d.29. 27-May-4 Hassfurther, Vienna #77/R est:9000-10000
£9732 $17419 €14500 Perchtoldsdorf (49x39cm-19x15in) s.d.1926. 27-May-4 Hassfurther, Vienna #76/R est:12000-16000
£12500 $21250 €18000 Gmunden (63x76cm-25x30in) s.d.33 board. 28-Oct-3 Wiener Kunst Auktionen, Vienna #106/R est:15000-30000
£16667 $28333 €24000 Village with trees (55x65cm-22x26in) s.d.31 panel. 28-Oct-3 Wiener Kunst Auktionen, Vienna #105/R est:18000-35000
£19444 $33056 €28000 Haugsdorf (38x48cm-15x19in) s.d.25 i. verso board lit. 28-Oct-3 Wiener Kunst Auktionen, Vienna #104/R est:10000-25000
Prints
£2148 $3844 €3200 Sievering (44x57cm-17x22in) s.i.d.1941. 25-May-4 Dorotheum, Vienna #205/R est:1600-1900
Works on paper
£352 $616 €500 Display duck (9x10cm-4x4in) s. pen ink W/C. 19-Dec-3 Dorotheum, Vienna #61/R
£417 $679 €600 City with moat (37x44cm-15x17in) s.d.1920 W/C. 23-Sep-3 Wiener Kunst Auktionen, Vienna #98/R
£709 $1184 €1000 Woman on horse (20x20cm-8x8in) s. Indian ink W/C. 14-Oct-3 Dorotheum, Vienna #132/R
£851 $1421 €1200 Man on horseback (25x24cm-10x9in) s. Indian ink W/C. 14-Oct-3 Dorotheum, Vienna #133/R
£1049 $1783 €1500 Still life of flowers (38x28cm-15x11in) s.d.1962 gouache. 20-Nov-3 Van Ham, Cologne #1931 est:500
£1133 $2040 €1700 Landscape in early spring with green houses and a tower (30x40cm-12x16in) s.d.31 W/C. 21-Apr-4 Dorotheum, Vienna #53/R est:1800-2600
£1184 $2179 €1800 Sausage stand (30x43cm-12x17in) s.d.53 mixed media. 22-Jun-4 Wiener Kunst Auktionen, Vienna #133/R est:1500
£1447 $2663 €2200 Adam and Eva (23x19cm-9x7in) s.d.50 W/C. 22-Jun-4 Wiener Kunst Auktionen, Vienna #131/R est:1500
£1467 $2699 €2200 Balinese fairytale scene (22x30cm-9x12in) s. Indian ink W/C paper on board. 9-Jun-4 Dorotheum, Salzburg #820/R est:1400-2000
£1560 $2606 €2200 Village street (36x50cm-14x20in) s.d.25 W/C Indian ink. 16-Oct-3 Dorotheum, Salzburg #948/R est:2200-3200
£1600 $2880 €2400 Landscape with small castle (30x42cm-12x17in) s.d.45 pencil W/C. 21-Apr-4 Dorotheum, Vienna #131/R est:2200-3000
£1645 $3026 €2500 Hirschbach (32x43cm-13x17in) s.d.55 mixed media. 22-Jun-4 Wiener Kunst Auktionen, Vienna #132/R est:2000
£1733 $3120 €2600 Houses in Muhlviertel (30x40cm-12x16in) s.d.31 W/C. 21-Apr-4 Dorotheum, Vienna #52/R est:2200-3000
£1748 $2972 €2500 Landscape (28x35cm-11x14in) s. mixed media. 28-Nov-3 Wiener Kunst Auktionen, Vienna #485/R est:3000-5000
£2083 $3396 €3000 Village landscape (29x39cm-11x15in) s. mixed media. 23-Sep-3 Wiener Kunst Auktionen, Vienna #99/R est:1500-3000
£2207 $4039 €3200 Landscape (34x48cm-13x19in) s.d.54 paste. 27-Jan-4 Dorotheum, Vienna #120/R est:2400-3400
£2937 $4993 €4200 Old brewery in Freistadt (45x60cm-18x24in) s. mixed media. 27-Nov-3 Dorotheum, Linz #546/R est:4500-6500
£3356 $5940 €5000 Finding of Moses (57x84cm-22x33in) s.d.1923 W/C Indian ink. 28-Apr-4 Wiener Kunst Auktionen, Vienna #75/R est:5000-10000

ZULOW, Marie von (1854-1930) German
Works on paper
£658 $1211 €1000 Large bunch of meadow flowers (56x69cm-22x27in) s.d.1917 mixed media oval. 22-Jun-4 Wiener Kunst Auktionen, Vienna #151/R

ZUMBUSCH, Ludwig von (1861-1927) German
£1538 $2569 €2200 Red Riding Hood and the wolf (32x45cm-13x18in) 28-Jun-3 Bolland & Marotz, Bremen #758/R est:2000
£2381 $4262 €3500 Little butterfly catchers (48x40cm-19x16in) s. board. 17-Mar-4 Neumeister, Munich #681/R est:3500

ZUMEL, Nelson (1928-) Spanish
£604 $1105 €900 Landscape (20x23cm-8x9in) s. board. 12-Jul-4 Durán, Madrid #6/R
£1007 $1782 €1500 Landscape (30x41cm-12x16in) s. board. 27-Apr-4 Durán, Madrid #1176/R est:300

ZUMKELLER, Luigi (19/20th C) Italian?
Works on paper
£288 $472 €400 Church of the Immacolata, Livorno (64x36cm-25x14in) s.d.1911 W/C. 10-Jun-3 Pandolfini, Florence #10/R

ZUMSANDE, Josef (1806-1865) German
Works on paper
£552 $916 €800 Portrait of girl wearing white dress (11x8cm-4x3in) s. W/C ivory. 30-Sep-3 Dorotheum, Vienna #393/R

ZUND, Robert (1827-1909) Swiss
£1310 $2384 €1913 The Jewish cemetery (30x34cm-12x13in) painted 1860 after Jacob van Ruisdael lit. 16-Jun-4 Fischer, Luzern #1277/R est:3000-4000 (S.FR 3000)
£2715 $4615 €3964 Ruysdael Monastery (30x34cm-12x13in) d.26.Juni 1860 lit. 19-Nov-3 Fischer, Luzern #1256/R est:7000-9000 (S.FR 6000)
£5727 $9736 €8361 Landscape near Winkel on the Vierwaldstattersee (14x18cm-6x7in) s. panel. 7-Nov-3 Dobiaschofsky, Bern #34/R est:15000 (S.FR 13000)
£5800 $10440 €8468 Cattle on lakeside path (36x51cm-14x20in) s.d.1859. 21-Jan-4 Sotheby's, Olympia #399/R est:4000-6000
£15284 $27817 €22315 On the banks of a lake, with rowing boat, cows at the water's edge (36x51cm-14x20in) s.d.1859. 16-Jun-4 Fischer, Luzern #1282/R est:35000-45000 (S.FR 35000)
£17467 $31266 €25502 Forest clearing (81x61cm-32x24in) s. 26-May-4 Sotheby's, Zurich #10/R est:40000-60000 (S.FR 40000)
£30435 $55696 €44435 Farm near Luzerne (40x51cm-16x20in) s. 7-Jun-4 Christie's, Zurich #6/R est:40000-60000 (S.FR 70000)
£40724 $69231 €59457 Reichenbach near Meiringen (61x81cm-24x32in) s. prov. 19-Nov-3 Fischer, Luzern #1259/R est:90000-120000 (S.FR 90000)
£43668 $79476 €63755 View towards Pilatus (74x99cm-29x39in) s. prov.exhib. 16-Jun-4 Fischer, Luzern #1283/R est:100000-120000 (S.FR 100000)
£47414 $84871 €69224 Woodland (77x103cm-30x41in) s. 17-May-4 Beurret, Zurich #36/R est:40000-60000 (S.FR 110000)
Works on paper
£271 $462 €396 Tree study (13x9cm-5x4in) s.d.1850 pencil. 19-Nov-3 Fischer, Luzern #2703 (S.FR 600)
£873 $1563 €1275 Group of trees (7x13cm-3x5in) s.i. pencil. 26-May-4 Sotheby's, Zurich #3/R est:2000-2500 (S.FR 2000)

ZUNIGA, Francisco (1913-1998) Costa Rican
Sculpture
£2162 $3676 €3157 Figure (15x10x11cm-6x4x4in) s.i.d.1975 bronze stone plynth. 23-Nov-3 Levis, Calgary #220/R est:3500-4000 (C.D 4800)
£6667 $12267 €10000 Mujeres Platicando (20x40x22cm-8x16x9in) s.i. bronze. 11-Jun-4 Hauswedell & Nolte, Hamburg #1613/R est:12000
£6977 $12000 €10186 Desnudo (28x28x20cm-11x11x8in) s.d.1974 num.XII/XXVIII gold brown pat. bronze prov.lit. 3-Dec-3 Doyle, New York #14/R est:12000-16000
£8286 $14335 €12098 Seated woman with shawl (34x35x39cm-13x14x15in) s.d.1971 num.IV/IV bronze. 9-Dec-3 Louis Morton, Mexico #119/R est:180000-220000 (M.P 160000)
£8824 $15000 €12883 Silvia agachada I (16x29x25cm-6x11x10in) sig.d.1967 num.V/VI brown pat. bronze lit. 19-Nov-3 Sotheby's, New York #131/R est:12000-18000

£8824	$15000	€12883	Silvia agachada (23cm-9in) s.d.1967 num.6/6 verso green brown pat. bronze prov.lit. 18-Nov-3 Christie's, Rockefeller NY #144/R est:15000-20000
£9322	$16126	€13610	Seated woman (49x40x30cm-19x16x12in) s.d.1971 num.III/IV bronze. 9-Dec-3 Louis Morton, Mexico #120/R est:190000-240000 (M.P 180000)
£9333	$17173	€14000	Silvia kneeling (24x31x27cm-9x12x11in) s.d.1967 num.V/VI pat bronze lit. 10-Jun-4 Christie's, Paris #28/R est:16000-20000
£11765	$20000	€17177	Mujer en la puerta (49x42x4cm-19x17x2in) inscribed sig.d.1970 num.111/111 brown pat. bronze relief lit. 19-Nov-3 Sotheby's, New York #101/R est:15000-20000
£13529	$23000	€19752	Mujer indigena (31x29x28cm-12x11x11in) sig.d.1978 num.III/VI green pat, bronze exhib.lit. 19-Nov-3 Sotheby's, New York #113/R est:22000-28000
£23529	$40000	€34352	Maternidad (33x25x23cm-13x10x9in) sig.d.77 num.IV/VI brown pat. bronze lit. 19-Nov-3 Sotheby's, New York #105/R est:18000-22000
£26536	$47500	€38743	Seated woman (48x48x48cm-19x19x19in) st.sig.d.1971 num.VI/VI bronze prov.lit. 26-May-4 Sotheby's, New York #87/R est:25000-35000
£39106	$70000	€57095	Silvia naked (29x38x38cm-11x15x15in) st.sig.d.1975 black marble prov.lit. 26-May-4 Sotheby's, New York #36/R est:50000-70000
£39106	$70000	€57095	Woman combing her hair (43x30x26cm-17x12x10in) st.sig.d.1974 black marble prov.lit. 26-May-4 Sotheby's, New York #99/R est:40000-50000
£53073	$95000	€77487	People chatting (42x49x40cm-17x19x16in) st.sig.d.1985 num.VI/VI pat bronze prov.lit. 26-May-4 Sotheby's, New York #100/R est:40000-60000
£64706	$110000	€94471	Mujer pensativa (42x22x36cm-17x9x14in) sig.d.1972 num.VI/VI green pat. bronze lit. 19-Nov-3 Sotheby's, New York #135/R est:25000-30000
£76471	$130000	€111648	Joven descansando (27x21x44cm-11x8x17in) i.d.1967 white onyx prov.lit. 19-Nov-3 Sotheby's, New York #20/R est:60000-80000
£195531	$350000	€285475	Evelia seated (140x78x78cm-55x31x31in) st.sig.d.1977 num.I/IV pat bronze prov.lit. 26-May-4 Sotheby's, New York #28/R est:175000-225000

Works on paper

£419	$750	€612	Person under serape (43x41cm-17x16in) s.d.63 chl bark paper. 8-May-4 Susanin's, Chicago #6102/R
£1486	$2750	€2170	Woman (69x48cm-27x19in) s.d.1977 pencil. 14-Jan-4 Dallas Auction Gallery, Dallas #119/R est:5000-8000
£1486	$2750	€2170	Reclining woman (48x69cm-19x27in) s. pastel. 14-Jan-4 Dallas Auction Gallery, Dallas #120/R est:5000-8000
£2335	$4250	€3409	Retrato de Nina (46x32cm-18x13in) s.d.45 pencil. 29-Jun-4 Sotheby's, New York #657/R est:4000-5000
£2429	$4250	€3546	Reclining nude (50x65cm-20x26in) init.d.1973 brown conte crayon. 19-Dec-3 Sotheby's, New York #1175/R est:4000-6000
£2794	$4750	€4079	Two women (48x61cm-19x24in) s.d.1954 W/C ink prov. 9-Nov-3 Bonhams & Butterfields, Los Angeles #4126/R est:5000-7000
£2825	$5000	€4125	Seated woman wearing a white camisa and yellow ribbon in her hair (55x60cm-22x24in) s.d.71 chl pastel white chk. 2-May-4 Bonhams & Butterfields, Los Angeles #3102/R est:4000-6000
£3022	$5500	€4412	Tres mujeres (44x39cm-17x15in) s.d.60 W/C. 29-Jun-4 Sotheby's, New York #661/R est:4000-5000
£3022	$5500	€4412	Crouching nude (50x61cm-20x24in) s.d.1962 ink pastel prov. 29-Jun-4 Sotheby's, New York #665/R est:4000-6000
£3429	$6000	€5006	Crouching woman (49x70cm-19x28in) s.d.1978 pastel. 19-Dec-3 Sotheby's, New York #1167/R est:8000-10000
£3631	$6500	€5301	Woman with fruit (48x66cm-19x26in) s.d.1973 pastel white chk prov. 6-May-4 Doyle, New York #131/R est:6000-8000
£3750	$6000	€5475	Mirando en el espejo (50x70cm-20x28in) s.d. chl chk. 18-Sep-3 Swann Galleries, New York #715/R est:4000-6000
£3867	$7076	€5800	Untitled - four women (50x62cm-20x24in) s.d.61 chk W/C. 5-Jun-4 Lempertz, Koln #1032/R est:4000
£4121	$7500	€6017	Mujer reclinada (64x50cm-25x20in) s.d.1968 chl W/C prov. 29-Jun-4 Sotheby's, New York #668/R est:7000-9000
£4190	$7500	€6117	Sleeping nude (50x65cm-20x26in) s.d.1973 brown conte chl prov. 6-May-4 Doyle, New York #102/R est:5000-7000
£4412	$7500	€6442	Dos mujeres sentadas - Two seated women (50x70cm-20x28in) s.d.1979 col chl pastel. 18-Nov-3 Christie's, Rockefeller NY #162/R est:4000-6000
£4571	$8000	€6674	Crouching nude (50x51cm-20x20in) s.d.1964 chl W/C prov. 19-Dec-3 Sotheby's, New York #1164/R est:8000-10000
£4706	$8000	€6871	Mujer sentada - Seated woman (65x50cm-26x20in) s.d.1971 chl pencil prov. 18-Nov-3 Christie's, Rockefeller NY #179/R est:8000-10000
£5220	$9500	€7621	Mujer desnuda (80x65cm-31x26in) init.d.1969 crayon chl prov. 29-Jun-4 Sotheby's, New York #663/R est:6000-8000
£5220	$9500	€7621	Estudio de silvia de perfil (65x50cm-26x20in) s. i.d.1969 verso pastel prov. 29-Jun-4 Sotheby's, New York #685/R est:7000-9000
£5587	$10000	€8157	Two women (65x50cm-26x20in) s.d.1970 pastel W/C. 26-May-4 Sotheby's, New York #97/R est:12000-18000
£6044	$11000	€8824	Desnudo reclinado (50x72cm-20x28in) s.d.1978 chl prov. 29-Jun-4 Sotheby's, New York #677/R est:7000-9000
£7647	$13000	€11165	Descansando (58x89cm-23x35in) s.d.1973 conte crayon prov. 19-Nov-3 Sotheby's, New York #111/R est:10000-15000
£19553	$35000	€28547	Peasant scenes (49x64cm-19x25in) s.d.1972 mixed media set of 3 prov. 26-May-4 Sotheby's, New York #166/R est:18000-22000
£26536	$47500	€38743	Virginia resting (48x63cm-19x25in) s.d.1974 pastelprov.lit. 26-May-4 Sotheby's, New York #98/R est:10000-15000

ZUNIGA, Francisco (attrib) (1913-1998) Costa Rican

Works on paper

£3261	$6000	€4761	Two women (48x64cm-19x25in) s.d.1966 W/C chl graphite. 26-Jun-4 Susanin's, Chicago #6100/R est:7000-9000

ZUPAN, Bruno (1939-) American

£625	$1000	€913	Still life with candles (84x84cm-33x33in) s. 19-Sep-3 Freeman, Philadelphia #176/R est:300-500

ZUPPINGER, Ernst Theodor (1875-1948) Swiss

£922	$1540	€1300	Mountain lake (80x60cm-31x24in) s.d.1910. 14-Oct-3 Dorotheum, Vienna #26/R

ZURBARAN, Francisco (1598-1664) Spanish

£200000	$366000	€292000	Saint Francis of Assisi in prayer (114x89cm-45x35in) painted with studio lit. 7-Jul-4 Christie's, London #75/R est:200000-300000

ZURBARAN, Francisco (circle) (1598-1664) Spanish

£6335	$10136	€9249	St Francis meditating (108x84cm-43x33in) 19-Sep-3 Koller, Zurich #3015/R est:15000-25000 (S.FR 14000)

ZURBARAN, Francisco (school) (1598-1664) Spanish

£7267	$13225	€10900	Virgin of the Rosary (44x33cm-17x13in) panel. 5-Jul-4 Marc Kohn, Paris #17/R est:10000-15000

ZURCHER, Frederik Willem (attrib) (1835-1894) Dutch

£500	$795	€730	Figures, horse and cart in a courtyard (36x41cm-14x16in) s. 9-Sep-3 Gorringes, Lewes #1927/R

ZURINI, K (20th C) American?

£305	$500	€442	Peacock (38x46cm-15x18in) indis.sig.d. board. 7-Jun-3 Treadway Gallery, Cincinnati #1496

ZURKINDEN, Irene (1909-1987) Swiss

£351	$586	€512	Portrait of Nelly Eggenberger Stocker (50x35cm-20x14in) s. board. 15-Nov-3 Galerie Gloggner, Luzern #115/R (S.FR 800)
£545	$905	€790	Portrait study (32x32cm-13x13in) s.d.Mai 1936 board. 13-Jun-3 Zofingen, Switzerland #3081 (S.FR 1200)
£2096	$3857	€3060	Rhine harbour in Basel (35x46cm-14x18in) s.d. 14-Jun-4 Philippe Schuler, Zurich #4241/R est:4000-5000 (S.FR 4800)
£3238	$5181	€4695	Parisian scene (46x38cm-18x15in) s. 15-May-3 Stuker, Bern #1596/R est:12000-14000 (S.FR 6800)
£3587	$5991	€5237	Self portrait (46x35cm-18x14in) s.d.68 board. 24-Oct-3 Hans Widmer, St Gallen #55/R est:7000-11000 (S.FR 8000)
£4367	$7817	€6376	Autoportrait en Italie (55x46cm-22x18in) s.d.1958. 26-May-4 Sotheby's, Zurich #124/R est:10000-14000 (S.FR 10000)

Works on paper

£352	$599	€514	Paris (55x36cm-22x14in) s. mixed media. 5-Nov-3 Dobiaschofsky, Bern #1072 (S.FR 800)
£362	$615	€529	Three ballet dancers (40x31cm-16x12in) s. pastel. 28-Nov-3 Zofingen, Switzerland #3233 (S.FR 800)
£413	$756	€603	Striptease (20x27cm-8x11in) st.sig. ink. 4-Jun-4 Zofingen, Switzerland #3004 (S.FR 950)
£450	$775	€657	Sur les toits de Paris (36x40cm-14x16in) s. pastel. 2-Dec-3 Koller, Zurich #3035 (S.FR 1000)
£478	$875	€698	La maitresse (20x15cm-8x6in) s. mixed media. 4-Jun-4 Zofingen, Switzerland #3005 (S.FR 1100)
£647	$1157	€945	Circus (23x31cm-9x12in) gouache. 14-May-4 Dobiaschofsky, Bern #259/R est:1900 (S.FR 1500)

ZURN, Jorg (circle) (c.1583-1635) Austrian

Sculpture

£13889	$23611	€20000	Angels (40cm-16in) wood prov.lit. two. 28-Oct-3 Wiener Kunst Auktionen, Vienna #179/R est:20000-40000

ZURN, Michael (17th C) Austrian

Sculpture

£11189	$19021	€16000	Angel (110cm-43in) wood. 20-Nov-3 Dorotheum, Salzburg #574/R est:28000-30000

ZURN, Unica (1916-1970) German

Works on paper

£21477	$38013	€32000	Untitled (29x21cm-11x8in) s. dr album. 29-Apr-4 Christie's, Paris #205/R est:40000-60000

ZURSTRASSEN, Yves (1956-) Belgian

£805	$1490	€1200	Composition (195x122cm-77x48in) s.d.90 verso. 13-Mar-4 De Vuyst, Lokeren #409

ZUSH (1946) Spanish

£9859	$17254	€14000	July III (146x145cm-57x57in) s.i.d.1973 verso exhib.lit. 16-Dec-3 Segre, Madrid #154/R est:9000

ZUSTERS, Jane (1951-) New Zealander?

£969	$1734	€1415	Paramour for Matisse (57x75cm-22x30in) s.i.d.1988 acrylic on paper. 11-May-4 Peter Webb, Auckland #123/R est:2500-3500 (NZ.D 2800)

Works on paper

£662	$1238	€967	Plication (57x75cm-22x30in) s.i.d.1987 acrylic mixed media paper. 24-Feb-4 Peter Webb, Auckland #37/R (NZ.D 1800)

ZUSTERS, Reinis (1918-1999) Australian

£352	$658	€528	Moored boats (44x60cm-17x24in) s. board. 25-Jul-4 Lawson Menzies, Sydney #94/R (A.D 900)
£375	$689	€548	Adventure in green (44x30cm-17x12in) 25-Jun-4 Lawson Menzies, Sydney #2206 (A.D 1000)

£412 $758 €602 Barefoot barnyard games (30x40cm-12x16in) s. board. 25-Jun-4 Lawson Menzies, Sydney #2204/R (A.D 1100)
£664 $1109 €996 Summer (59x75cm-23x30in) s.d.72 board. 27-Oct-3 Goodman, Sydney #249/R (A.D 1600)
£1393 $2257 €2034 Paddington scene (75x100cm-30x39in) s. board prov. 30-Jul-3 Goodman, Sydney #164/R est:1000-1500 (A.D 3400)
Works on paper
£311 $520 €467 Untitled (37x43cm-15x17in) s. pastel gouache. 27-Oct-3 Goodman, Sydney #240/R (A.D 750)

ZVEREV, Anatoli (1931-1986) Russian
£699 $1189 €1000 A church (66x47cm-26x19in) s.d.84 board. 29-Nov-3 Bukowskis, Helsinki #341/R
£979 $1664 €1400 A beauty (66x47cm-26x19in) s. board. 29-Nov-3 Bukowskis, Helsinki #346/R
£3000 $5100 €4380 Cockerel (50x68cm-20x27in) init.indis.d. board. 19-Nov-3 Sotheby's, London #241/R est:3000-5000
£3000 $5100 €4380 Fish (33x50cm-13x20in) init.d.80 board. 19-Nov-3 Sotheby's, London #242/R est:3000-5000
£21000 $37590 €30660 Pine trees, Nikolina gora, Rublevka Region (138x97cm-54x38in) s.d.1968 prov.exhib. 26-May-4 Sotheby's, London #315/R est:12000-18000
Works on paper
£323 $594 €472 Head of a man (56x39cm-22x15in) init.d.53 mixed media W/C. 14-Jun-4 Waddingtons, Toronto #350/R (C.D 800)
£662 $1205 €1000 Double autoportrait (68x49cm-27x19in) s. W/C. 16-Jun-4 Claude Boisgirard, Paris #179
£2500 $4475 €3650 Red flowers (54x39cm-21x15in) init.i. W/C gouache. 26-May-4 Sotheby's, Olympia #470/R est:2500-3000

ZWALM, Cor van der (?) Dutch?
£360 $644 €540 View of River Maas near Rotterdam with tugboat (59x99cm-23x39in) 11-May-4 Vendu Notarishuis, Rotterdam #673/R

ZWARA, John (20th C) American
£467 $850 €682 Autumn landscape (56x76cm-22x30in) s. 20-Jun-4 Charlton Hall, Columbia #569/R
Works on paper
£220 $350 €321 Shady landscape (23x33cm-9x13in) s.d.1934 gouache. 13-Sep-3 Weschler, Washington #765/R

ZWART, Arie (1903-1981) Dutch
£263 $484 €400 Cagnes sur Mer: a view of the harbour at Cagnes (50x75cm-20x30in) s. s.i.verso. 22-Jun-4 Christie's, Amsterdam #318/R
£276 $461 €400 Farm (24x34cm-9x13in) s. 11-Nov-3 Vendu Notarishuis, Rotterdam #133
£294 $505 €420 Village in the sunny south (60x70cm-24x28in) s. 8-Dec-3 Glerum, Amsterdam #377/R
£350 $594 €500 View of Rijnsburg near Leiden (40x60cm-16x24in) s. 24-Nov-3 Glerum, Amsterdam #49/R
£367 $667 €550 Farm interior in Hulsel (48x38cm-19x15in) s. 30-Jun-4 Vendue Huis, Gravenhage #514/R
£414 $691 €600 Village near Altea, Spain (38x48cm-15x19in) s. 11-Nov-3 Vendu Notarishuis, Rotterdam #49/R
£476 $867 €700 Birches in spring (70x61cm-28x24in) s. 3-Feb-4 Christie's, Amsterdam #271
£526 $968 €800 Flowers in a vase (70x60cm-28x24in) s. 22-Jun-4 Christie's, Amsterdam #172/R
£625 $1018 €900 Town view with figures on a bridge (50x40cm-20x16in) s. 29-Sep-3 Sotheby's, Amsterdam #164/R
£733 $1313 €1100 Outewater bridge (49x59cm-19x23in) s. 11-May-4 Vendu Notarishuis, Rotterdam #118/R
£952 $1733 €1400 Brem, flowering heathland by a pond (40x80cm-16x31in) s. i.on stretcher. 3-Feb-4 Christie's, Amsterdam #257 est:700-900
£1007 $1862 €1500 Oud Brabants interieur (50x40cm-20x16in) s.i.verso. 15-Mar-4 Sotheby's, Amsterdam #140/R est:800-1200
£1034 $1914 €1500 Winter im Giethoorn (60x70cm-24x28in) s. 13-Jan-4 Vanderkindere, Brussels #51 est:150-250
£1189 $2045 €1700 Winter landscape with willows (48x38cm-19x15in) s. 8-Dec-3 Glerum, Amsterdam #328/R est:250-350
£1379 $2303 €2000 North Giethoorn (48x39cm-19x15in) s. 11-Nov-3 Vendu Notarishuis, Rotterdam #33/R est:800-1000
£3401 $6190 €5000 Cows in a summer meadow (52x70cm-20x28in) s. 3-Feb-4 Christie's, Amsterdam #148/R est:5000-7000

ZWART, Willem de (1862-1931) Dutch
£1208 $2235 €1800 Still life with fish (38x50cm-15x20in) s. prov. 15-Mar-4 Sotheby's, Amsterdam #64/R est:1500-2000
£1259 $2102 €1800 Portrait of the wife of the artist (28x27cm-11x11in) init. canvas on board. 30-Jun-3 Sotheby's, Amsterdam #96
£1399 $2336 €2000 Farmhouse in a landscape (31x43cm-12x17in) s. 30-Jun-3 Sotheby's, Amsterdam #95
£1944 $3072 €2800 Landschap bij Loosduinen - cows in a meadow by Loosduinen (33x46cm-13x18in) s. panel. 2-Sep-3 Christie's, Amsterdam #213/R est:2500-3500
£3357 $5773 €4800 Landscape (24x36cm-9x14in) s. 8-Dec-3 Glerum, Amsterdam #47/R est:6000-8000
£4276 $7740 €6500 Houses in Santpoort (35x49cm-14x19in) s. canvas on panel prov.exhib. 19-Apr-4 Glerum, Amsterdam #198/R est:4000-6000
£8500 $15300 €12410 Figures on a beach (14x24cm-6x9in) s. panel. 22-Apr-4 Lawrence, Crewkerne #894/R est:1500-2000
£9028 $15076 €13000 Figures in a park (25x23cm-10x9in) init. panel prov. 21-Oct-3 Sotheby's, Amsterdam #93/R est:7000-9000
£11111 $17556 €16000 Summer. Farmhouse amongst trees (50x65cm-20x26in) s. pair. 2-Sep-3 Christie's, Amsterdam #214/R est:4000-6000
Works on paper
£315 $525 €450 A peacock (45x31cm-18x12in) init. black chk. 30-Jun-3 Sotheby's, Amsterdam #91
£559 $900 €816 Twilight pastoral (15x20cm-6x8in) s. W/C. 20-Aug-3 James Julia, Fairfield #1157/R
£680 $1238 €1000 Peaceful pastimes, lady embroidering. Lady making music (52x36cm-20x14in) s. black chk W/C htd white pair. 3-Feb-4 Christie's, Amsterdam #152 est:1000-1500
£2083 $3479 €3000 By the farm (27x27cm-11x11in) s. W/C. 21-Oct-3 Sotheby's, Amsterdam #132/R est:3000-5000

ZWEDEN, Johan van (1986-1975) Dutch
Works on paper
£490 $832 €700 Vase with flowers (54x41cm-21x16in) s.d.50 gouache. 24-Nov-3 Glerum, Amsterdam #6/R

ZWEIGBERGK, Bo Eison von (1897-1940) Swedish
£1284 $2183 €1875 The pier in Menton (46x55cm-18x22in) s.d.1933 panel. 5-Nov-3 AB Stockholms Auktionsverk #865/R est:12000-15000 (S.KR 17000)
£3927 $6677 €5733 Harbour scene (178x79cm-70x31in) s. painted c.1920. 4-Nov-3 Bukowskis, Stockholm #8a/R est:50000-60000 (S.KR 52000)
Works on paper
£3927 $6677 €5733 Indian on horseback (46x35cm-18x14in) s.d.21 mixed media exhib. 4-Nov-3 Bukowskis, Stockholm #50/R est:40000-50000 (S.KR 52000)

ZWENGAUER, Anton (elder) (1810-1884) German
£1608 $2686 €2300 Evening by the lake (107x147cm-42x58in) s. 11-Oct-3 De Vuyst, Lokeren #407 est:1500-1700

ZWENGAUER, Anton (younger) (1850-1928) German
£600 $1080 €900 Landscape (80x100cm-31x39in) i. verso. 22-Apr-4 Weidler, Nurnberg #6516/R

ZWERVER, Dolf (1932-) Dutch
£629 $1051 €900 A bird (16cm-6in circular) s. panel. 30-Jun-3 Sotheby's, Amsterdam #538
£1399 $2406 €2000 Maskarade (12x16cm-5x6in) s.d.68 canvas on board prov. 2-Dec-3 Sotheby's, Amsterdam #269/R est:2000-3000
£2937 $5052 €4200 Vogel (20x18cm-8x7in) s.d.77 canvas on board prov. 2-Dec-3 Sotheby's, Amsterdam #264/R est:4000-6000
£2937 $5052 €4200 De schilder (13x15cm-5x6in) canvas on board. 2-Dec-3 Sotheby's, Amsterdam #268/R est:4000-6000

ZWICKLE, Hubert von (1875-1947) Austrian
Works on paper
£300 $537 €450 Peasant women in traditional costume (89x89cm-35x35in) s. mixed media. 13-May-4 Dorotheum, Linz #620/R

ZWIERS, Piet (1907-1965) Dutch
£283 $516 €425 Two moored rowing boats (29x39cm-11x15in) s. 30-Jun-4 Vendue Huis, Gravenhage #393

ZWIETEN, Cornelis van (17th C) Dutch
£2282 $4199 €3400 Dutch dune landscape with church (45x56cm-18x22in) mono.d.1660 panel. 24-Mar-4 Dorotheum, Vienna #386/R est:3000-4500

ZWILLER, Marie Augustin (1850-1939) French
£1867 $3397 €2800 Jeune femme nue (46x38cm-18x15in) s. 29-Jun-4 Sotheby's, Paris #20/R est:1500-2000
£1892 $3386 €2800 Young woman sitting on chair (72x43cm-28x17in) i. 8-May-4 Dawo, Saarbrucken #75/R est:2800
£1946 $3601 €2900 Nu dans le parc pres du lac (33x24cm-13x9in) s. 14-Mar-4 Eric Pillon, Calais #69/R
£2162 $3870 €3200 Young woman sitting in front of mirror (65x54cm-26x21in) s. lit. 8-May-4 Dawo, Saarbrucken #72/R est:3200
Works on paper
£365 $653 €540 Portrait of woman from Alsace (40x31cm-16x12in) s. chl htd white. 8-May-4 Dawo, Saarbrucken #79/R

ZYGMUNT, Dobezycki (?) Polish
£347 $580 €500 Couple (42x32cm-17x13in) mono. 21-Oct-3 Campo, Vlaamse Kaai #1206

ZYL, Gerard Pietersz van (1607-1665) Dutch
£6757 $11892 €10000 Elegant company courting and making music in an interior (48x58cm-19x23in) prov. 18-May-4 Sotheby's, Amsterdam #115/R est:10000-15000

81802